1998

DIRECTORY OF CORPORATE AFFILIATIONS

This edition of *Directory of Corporate Affiliations: Master Index* was prepared by National Register Publishing's Database Publishing Group in collaboration with the Publications Systems Department.

Editorial:
Managing Editor: Christine Kerwin
Senior Editors: Brittany Hartman, Barbara J. Morse, John R. Platt
Associate Editors: Matthew Hanagan, Heather M. Lordi
Assistant Editors: Elizabeth Higgins, Kerri Nelen, Jason Rimmer

Research:
Director: Judy Redel
Senior Managing Editor: Lisa Weissbard
Senior Editor: Beverly A. Heath
Associate Editors: Barrett Barnes, Laura Naphor

Production:
Production & Training Director: Mark Van Orman
Senior Production Editor: Matthew O'Connell

Editorial Systems:
Vice President, Information Technology: John Roney
Director, Biographical & Reference Systems: Carter McWilliams
Manager, Reference & Biographic Systems: Helene Davis
Senior Programmers: Victoria Maurer, Sophia Pikulin

Vice President, Database Production: Dean Hollister
Senior Editorial Director: Thomas Bachmann
Senior Managing Editor: Patricia Flinsch-Rodriguez

1998

DIRECTORY OF CORPORATE AFFILIATIONS

VOLUME 2

MASTER INDEX

U.S. Public • U.S. Private • International

"WHO OWNS WHOM"

National Register Publishing
A Division of Reed Elsevier Inc.
New Providence, New Jersey

Published by National Register Publishing, a division of Reed Elsevier Inc.

Lou Andreozzi - Chief Operating Officer
Randy H. Mysel - Vice President, Publisher

Printed and bound in the United States of America.
International Standard Book Number:

Vol 2: 0-87217-216-3
Directory of Corporate Affiliations 5 Vol Library: 0-87217-217-1

Library of Congress Catalog Card Number: 67-22770

ISBN 0-87217-216-3

9 780872 172166

CONTENTS

VOLUME II

Preface vii

How to Use the *Directory of Corporate Affiliations* ix

Alphabetical Compendium of S.I.C. Codes 1

Numerical Compendium of S.I.C. Codes 13

Master S.I.C. Index 23

Master Personnel Index 503

THE DIRECTORY OF CORPORATE AFFILIATIONS

The *Directory of Corporate Affiliations* (DCA) is a logically organized business reference tool that covers major public and private businesses in the United States and throughout the world. The principle of organization for the set is geographical (by parent company) and hierarchical (by company reportage). Subsidiaries of a parent company, no matter where they are located, will be found in the same volume as the ultimate parent.

Entry criteria for the set are flexible. Generally speaking, domestic companies must demonstrate revenue in excess of $10 million, substantial assets/net worth, or a work force in excess of 300 persons. Non-U.S. based companies must demonstrate revenues in excess of $50 million.

SET ORGANIZATION AND CONTENT

A brief outline of the volumes and their components follows. Please note that every volume in the set, including this one, has a customized 'How-to-Use' guide for the benefit of the researcher. These include extensive listing and referencing examples that go into great detail.

Master Index, Volume I
— Master Company Name Index
— Master Brand Name Index
— Master Geographic Index, U.S.
— Master Geographic Index, Non-U.S.

Master Index, Volume II
— Master S.I.C. Index
— Master Corporate Responsibilities Index

U.S. Public Companies, Volume III
— Public Company Name Index
— Public Company Listings
— Public S.I.C. Index

U.S. Private Companies, Volume IV
— Private Company Name Index
— Private Company Listings
— Private S.I.C. Index

International Public and Private Companies, Volume V
— International Company Name Index
— International Company Listings
— International S.I.C. Index

CUMULATIVE ENTRY STATISTICS FOR THIS EDITION

These statistics show the sum of entry listings across all three volumes. Individual statistics are provided in each volume.

— 14,778 Ultimate parent companies.
— 47,366 U.S. located sub companies.
— 54,432 Non-U.S. located sub companies.
— 116,576 Total entry units listed.

— 27,617 Outside service firms.

COMPILATION

The *Directory of Corporate Affiliations* is compiled and updated from information supplied by the companies themselves, business publications, and annual reports. Each company is sent at least one listing mailer for updating prior to publication.

RELATED SERVICES

For information on the CD-ROM version of the directory, *Corporate Affiliations PLUS*, please call (800) 521-8110. Mailing lists compiled from information contained in the directory may be ordered from Rich Lukowski, Reed Elsevier Business Lists, 1350 East Touhy Avenue, Des Plaines, IL 60018; telephone (800) 323-4958, ext. 2340. Electronic database tapes of the directory in raw data format are available for lease. Please contact John Sonta, NRP Electronic Sales, 121 Chanlon Road, New Providence, NJ 07974; telephone (800) 521-8110, ext. 4698. The *Directory of Corporate Affiliations* is also available online through LEXIS-NEXIS and The Dialog Corporation. For LEXIS-NEXIS information please call (800) 227-4908. For more information on DIALOG please call (800) 334-2564.

Companies who wish to add or correct their listings can contact the editors by mailing to: National Register Publishing, DCA Editorial, 121 Chanlon Road, New Providence, NJ 07974, or calling (908) 464-6800.

In addition to keeping the information in our directories as up to date as possible, we are constantly trying to improve their design or add useful new features. Any comments or suggestions in this regard can be directed to the editors at the above address.

HOW TO USE THE DIRECTORY OF CORPORATE AFFILIATIONS

The *Directory of Corporate Affiliations* (DCA) presents extensive information on U.S. and foreign companies, both public and private. Entries include information on financials, personnel, outside service firms, and subsidiaries with an emphasis on hierarchy and reportage. Entry criteria for the set are flexible. Domestic companies generally show revenues in excess of $10 million, employee totals in excess of 300 persons, or substantial assets/net worth. Non-U.S. companies generally show revenue in excess of $50 million.

This user guide is divided into four parts.

— **Part A,** 'How to Locate a Company' gives referencing instructions and samples of indexes. It demonstrates many useful methods for getting the information you need from the DCA set at large.

— **Part B,** 'How to Locate an Executive' shows how to locate names of personnel listed throughout the DCA set.

— **Part C,** 'Sample Entries' shows the various data elements and listing style of a typical DCA company listing.

— **Part D,** 'Understanding Levels of Reportage' demonstrates how company reportage structures are simply and clearly presented throughout DCA.

PART A: HOW TO LOCATE A COMPANY

1. **If you know the name of the company, but do not know its nationality or ownership status:**

Look in the 'Master Index to Company Names' in volume one of the *Master Index*. This index will direct you to the correct volume of the set (i.e. International, Public, or Private) and the correct page listing therein.

AEMTLERHALLE AG—See Hurliman Holding AG; *Int'l*, pg. 643
AEON GROUP; *Int'l*, pg. 30
AEQUINTRON MEDICAL, INC.; *U.S. Public*, pg. 28
AER LINGUS; *Int'l*, pg. 31
AERACOM TECHNOLOGIES, PTE. LTD.—See Ssangyong Business Group; *Int'l*, pg. 1294
AERCO INTERNATIONAL INC.; *U.S. Private*, pg. 23

2. **If you do know a parent company's nationality and ownership status:**

You can turn directly to the company listings in the appropriate volume, all of which are alphabetized by the name of the parent company.

3. If you know the name of a subsidiary or division:

You can turn to the 'Master Index of Company Names' in the *Master Index* Volume I or the 'Index of Company Names' in the appropriate volume. In either place, the subsidiary entry will also show you the name of its ultimate parent and the volume and page of its listing.

JHK & ASSOCIATES, INC.—See Science Applications International Corp.; *U.S. Private*, pg. 986
JIB GROUP PLC—See Jardine Matheson Holdings Limited; *Int'l*, pg. 711
JII/SALES PROMOTION ASSOCIATES, INC.—See Jordan Industries, Inc.; *U.S. Private*, pg. 604
JIT-STAL AB—See Rautaruukki Oy; *Int'l*, pg. 1036
JJC SPECIALIST CORP.—See The Quick & Reilly Group Inc.; *U.S. Public*, pg. 1397

4. If you cannot find the company's name in the indexes:

It may mean that the company has been acquired or changed its name. To confirm this, try looking in the 'Mergers, Acquisitions and Name Changes' section at the front of the appropriate volume. If not successful, you can try the cumulative 'Mergers and Acquisitions' section in the *Master Index* Volume I. This shows such activity from as early as 1976.

Sample of 'Mergers, Acquisitions and Name Changes'

Friendly Ice Cream Corp.—acquired by Hershey Foods Corp.
Frigitronics, Inc.—acquired by Revlon, Inc.
Frontier Oil Corporation—acquired by Wainoco Oil Corporation
Furr Cafeterias, Inc.—acquired by Kmart Corp.
GAC Corp.—name changed to Avatar Holdings, Inc.

5. To locate companies in a given line of business:

Use the S.I.C. (Standard Industrial Classification) Index. There is one in each volume as well as in the *Master Index* Volume II. This index arranges companies by particular products and services, and is a useful prospecting tool. The index is preceded by two helpful compendia: one sorts the codes alphabetically by the name of the product or service, the other numerically by the code itself.

Sample of Alpha Compendium of S.I.C.s

Description	*SIC Code*
M	
Machinery, Electrical Equipment & Supplies, NEC	3699
Machinery, Special Industry	3559
Machines & Equipment, General Industry, NEC	3569
Magazine Publishing & Printing	2721
Magazines, Wholesale	5192
Magnesium & Alloys Bars, Rods, Shapes	3356
Magnesium Compounds	2819

Sample of Numeric Compendium of S.I.C.s

Code	*Title*
62	**SECURITY & COMMODITY BROKERS**
6211	Security Brokers, Dealers & Flotation Companies
6221	Commodity Contracts, Brokers & Dealers
6231	Security & Commodity Exchanges
6282	Investment Advice
6289	Services Allied With Exchange of Securities or Commodities, NEC

Both parent and sub companies are covered in this index; parent companies are printed in bold type, sub companies in regular typeface. The term "NEC" stands for "Not Elsewhere Classified". A sample of the S.I.C. Index is shown here:

3552—TEXTILE MACHINERY

APV GAULIN—APV PLC; *Int'l*, Pg. 19
AMERICAN BARMAG CO.; *U.S. Private*, pg. 51
THE AMERICAN GROUP; *U.S. Private*, pg. 56
AMERICAN SAHM CORPORATION—Georg Sahm GmbH & Co. KG Masschinenfabrik; *Int'l*, pg. 1177
AMERICAN SUESSEN—Spindelfabrik Suessen; *Int'l*, pg. 1292

6. **To locate a company via a particular brand or trade name:**

Look to the 'Brand Name Index' in the *Master Index* Volume I. Brand and trade names of products and services are indexed here showing the name of the company, its listing volume and page number.

JIFFY-GRO—Garden Products—Jiffy Products of America, Inc.; *Int'l*, pg. 714
JIFFY KIT—Automotive Products—Standard Motor Products, Inc.; *U.S. Public*, pg. 1556
JIFFY LUBE—Oil Change Facilities—Jiffy Lube International, Inc.; *U.S. Public*, pg. 1317
JIFFY MIRACLE PEAT—Garden Products—Jiffy Products of America, Inc.; *Int'l*, pg. 714
JIFFY-MIX—Garden Products—Jiffy Products of America, Inc.; *Int'l*, pg. 714
JIFFY POP—Popcorn—American Home Food Products; *U.S. Private*, pg. 530
JIFFY-POTS—Garden Products—Jiffy Products of America, Inc.; *Int'l*, pg. 714
JIFFY PREP—Paint Condition—Jones Blair Company; *U.S. Private*, pg. 602

7. **To locate a company in a given geographical area:**

Look to the 'Geographic Index' in the *Master Index* Volume I. Arranged in two parts — U.S. locations and non-U.S. locations — this index interfiles data from all three volumes of DCA, and shows the company's listing volume and page number.

CALIFORNIA
Los Angeles

A A CATER TRUCK MANUFACTURING COMPANY, INC., 750 E. Slauson Ave., 90011, pg. 1 PV
ABC Entertainment, 2040 Ave. of the Stars, 90067, pg. 528 PB
ABC/Watermark, Inc., 3575 Cahuenga Blvd. W, 90068 pg. 528 PB
ABN AMRO Bank, N.V. (Los Angeles), 300 S. Grand Ave., Ste. 1115, 90071-7519, pg. 10 IT
AAMES FINANCIAL CORPORATION, 3731 Wilshire Blvd., 10th Fl., 90010, pg. 16 PB

PB - *U.S. Public Companies Volume*
PV - *U.S. Private Companies Volume*
IT - *International Public & Private Companies Volume*

PART B: HOW TO LOCATE EXECUTIVES

Personnel are indexed in DCA by their title or area of activity. To find people in a given area or title such as Marketing, Sales, CEO, or Treasurer, use the 'Corporate Responsibilities Index' in the *Master Index* Volume II. This index lists personnel from every parent and subsidiary entry in the set by key areas of responsibility. Also included are their company name, listing volume, and page number.

Hancock, Edward R., Mktg. Dir.—Farnam Sealing Systems Division, Troy, MI; *U.S. Public*, pg. 411
Hancock, Jayne, V.P.-Sports Mktg.—DirecTV Inc., El Segundo, CA; *U.S. Public*, pg. 736
Hancock, John, V.P.-Sls. & Mktg.—Coburn Optical Industries Inc., Tulsa, OK; *U.S. Private*, pg. 249
Hancock, Larry, Mgr.-Mktg. & Opers.—Hayes Microcomputer Products, Inc., Norcross, GA; *U.S. Private*, pg. 517

PART C: BASIC COMPONENTS OF A DCA COMPANY LISTING

Following is an example of a typical parent company listing with tags to some of its basic components.

STANDARD MEDICAL GROUP ———— **Company Name**
560 River Rd. ———— **Company Address**
Richmond, VA 23219
Tel.: 804-223-3289 ———— **DE** ———— **Telecommunications Data & State of Incorporation**
Telex: 95421
Fax: 804-223-3290
E-Mail: info@standardmed.com ———— **Electronic Addresses**
Web Site: www.standardmed.com
Year Founded: 1967
SMG—(ASE) ———— **Ticker Symbol and Stock Exchanges**
Approx. Sls.: $16,000,000 ———— **Financial Information**
Assets: $24,000,000

Liabilities: $16,000,000
Net Worth: $8,000,000
Earnings: ($1,500,000)
Emp: 580 —————— **No. of Employees, Including Sub-entries**
Fiscal Year End: 12/31/97
Business Description:
Research Technology Company that —————— **Business Description**
Develops and Manufactures Medical
Products
Import Export
S.I.C.: 2833, 2834, 3841, 3844 —————— **Standard Industrial Classification codes**
Personnel:
John R. Callahan (Chm. Bd.) —————— **Key Personnel**
Cynthia I. Jenkins (Pres. & Chief Exec. Officer)
William E. Kirkpatrick (Exec. V.P.)
Albert N. Hackett (V.P.-Res. & Devel.)
Lawrence Woods (V.P.-Sls.)
Board of Directors:
John R. Callahan —————— **Members of the Board**
David C. Abel
William A. Scott
Carolyn H. Trunbull
Paul Underdahl

Legal Firm:
Scott, Morris & Tyler —————— **Name, Address & Phone of Outside Service Firm**
315 Fifth St.
Richmond, VA 23260
Tel.: 804-292-6521

Auditor:
DeCorva & Abbott
19 39th St.
Norfolk, VA 23502
Tel.: 804-466-2121

Following each parent company listing are the entries for each of that company's divisions, subsidiaries, affiliates, joint ventures, units etc. Though companies vary widely in their usage of these terms, some of the more common company designations can be defined as follows:

Affiliate A chartered business owned by the company at less than 50%.

Division An internal unit of a company, not incorporated.

Joint Venture A business in which two or more companies share responsibility and ownership.

Subsidiary A chartered business owned by the company at 50% or more.

PART D: UNDERSTANDING LEVELS OF REPORTAGE

Each sub-unit of the company will have a number in parentheses to the right of the company name. This number represents the level of reportage for that particular company. Any company with a level (1) reports directly to the parent company. Level (2) companies report to the level (1) company immediately above them. Level (3) companies report to the level (2) company immediately above them, etc.

Subsidiaries:

Brock Corporation (1) —— **Reports to parent company (Standard Medical Group)**
6060 Wall St.
Hartford, CT 06103
Tel: 203-251-6526 (100%) —— **Percent of Ownership**
Approx. Sls: 2,000,000
Emp.: 98
Mfr. of Pharmaceuticals
S.I.C.: 2834
J.M. McAleer (Pres.)
Michael F. Hamilton (Sr. V.P.-Res. & Devel.)

Subsidiary:

Clark Technology (2) —— **Reports to level 1 company above (Brock Corporation)**
601 Pulaski St.
Jackson, MS 39215
Tel: 601-848-4626 (100%)
Emp.: 850
Mfr. of Sutures and Other Surgical Products
S.I.C.: 3842
Steven Colaccino (Pres.)

Branch:

Clark Technology (3) —— **Reports to level 2 company above (Clark Technology)**
52 Main St.
Wayne, NJ 07435
Tel: 201-662-7654
Mfr. of Sutures
S.I.C. 3842

Cedar Laboratories (1) —— **Reports to parent company (Standard Medical Group)**
51 16th St.
Wilmington, MA 01887 (65%)
Tel: 508-223-1000
Emp.: 124
Research & Develop Antibiotics
S.I.C.: 2834
Melissa A. Newman (Chief Oper. Officer)

Non-U.S. Subsidiary:

Merieux Pharmaceuticals (1) —— **Subsidiary not located in the U.S. Reports to the parent company (Standard Medical Group)**
1421 rue Gourbet, 75755
Paris, Cedex 15, France
Tel: 42 73 10 08 (100%)
Approx Sls.: $1,500,000
Emp.: 118
Mfr. of Pharmaceuticals
S.I.C.: 2834
G. Bidaud (Pres.)

In addition to keeping the information in our directories as up to date as possible, we are constantly trying to improve their design and organization, or to add useful new features. Any comments or suggestions in this regard can be directed to: National Register Publishing, DCA Editorial, 121 Chanlon Road, New Providence, NJ 07974.

Request For Additional Companies Not Now Listed

Directory of Corporate Affiliations
National Register Publishing
121 Chanlon Road, New Providence, NJ 07974
908-464-6800

AS A CURRENT SUBSCRIBER to the *Directory of Corporate Affiliations*, are there companies not currently listed in the directory that you would like to see included? If so, please fill out the following and return to the above address.

Please type or print all information and return completed form.

Company or Institution Name

Address

City | State / Country | Zip

Phone | Fax

Company or Institution Name

Address

City | State / Country | Zip

Phone | Fax

ALPHABETICAL COMPENDIUM OF S.I.C. CODES

Standard Industrial Classification Manual, 1987, U.S. Government Office of Management and Budget; All codes for manufacturing unless otherwise stated.

A

Description	SIC Code
Abrasive Products	3291
Accessory & Specialty Stores, Women's	5632
Accident & Health Insurance	6321
Accounting Services	8721
Acetate, Cellulose	2821
Acetate, Synthetic	2869
Acetate Fibers	2823
Acids, Cool Tar	2865
Acids, Fatty	2899
Acids, Inorganic, Except Nitric & Phosphoric	2899
Acids, Organic	2869
Acids, Wholesale	5169
Acoustical Tile & Board	3296
Adhesive Tape, Cellophane	2672
Adhesives	2891
Advertising, NEC	7319
Advertising Agencies	7311
Advertising Representatives, Radio, Television & Publishers'	7313
Advertising Services, Outdoor	7312
Agricultural Chemicals	2879
Air Conditioners	3585
Air Conditioning Contractors	1711
Air Conditioning Equipment & Supplies, Wholesale	5075
Air Courier Services	4513
Air Purification Equipment	3564
Air Purifiers, Portable	3634
Air & Water Resource & Solid Waste Managament	9511
Aircraft	3721
Aircraft Lighting Fixtures	3647
Aircraft Parts & Equipment	3728
Aircraft Repair & Service	4581
Airplane Models, Toys & Hobby	3944
Airplane Rental & Leasing	7359
Airports	4581
Alarms, Security	3669
Alcohol, Non-Beverage	2869
Alcoholism, Residential Rehabilitation Centers	8361
Alcoholism, Residential Hospitals	8069
Alfalfa, Wholesale	5191
Alfalfa Farms	0139
Alfalfa Prepared as Feed	2048
Alkalies	2812
Alkaline Storage Batteries	3691
Alternators & Generator Testers	3825
Alternators, Motor Vehicle	3694
Alumina	2819
Aluminum Castings, Except Dye Casting	3365
Aluminum Dye Casting	3363
Aluminum Ingots, Primary Production	3334
Aluminum Ore Mining	1099
Aluminum Products Wholesale	5051
Aluminum Rolling & Drawing, NEC	3355
Aluminum Smelting & Refining, Secondary	3341
Ambulance Services, Air	4522
Ambulance Services, Road	4119
Amines	2869
Ammonia, Anhydrous	2873
Ammonium Compounds	2819
Ammonium Phosphate	2874
Ammunition & Component Parts, More Than 30mm	3483
Ammunition & Component Parts, Small Arms	3482
Amplifiers	3651
Amusement Centers & Parks	7996
Amusement Rides & Concessions Services	7999
Amusement Rides for Carnivals	3599
Analog Converters, Electronic	3825
Animal Shelters	0752
Animal Specialties	0279
Antennas, Communication	3663
Antennas, Receiving	3679
Antibiotics, Bulk	2833
Antibiotics, Packaged	2834
Apparel & Accessories, NEC	2389
Apparel & Accessory Stores, Misc.	5699
Appliance Cords	3699
Appliances, Electric Televisions & Radio Sets, Wholesale	5064
Appliances, Household, NEC	3639
Aquaculture	0273
Architectural Services	8712
Armature Rewinding Shops	7694
Armored Car Services	7381
Asbestos Products	3292
Asphalt Paving Mixtures & Blocks	2951
Associations, Civic, Social & Fraternal	8641
Atom Smashers	3699
Audio Equipment	3651
Automatic Merchandising Machine Operators	5962
Automobile & Home Supply Stores	5531
Automobile Services, Except Repair & Car Washes	7549
Automobiles, Dealers, New & Used	5511
Automobiles, Manufacturing	3711
Automotive Dealers, NEC	5599
Automotive Lighting	3447
Automotive Trimmings	2396

B

Description	SIC Code
Baby Foods, Canned	2032
Baby Formula	2023
Badminton Equipment	3949
Bag & Envelope Making Machinery	3554
Bagel Stores, Retail	5461
Bags, Plastic, Foil & Coated Paper	2673
Bags, Paper	2674
Bags, Textile	2393
Bags, Uncoated Paper & Multiwall	2674
Bakeries	5461
Bakery Products, Fresh	2051
Bakery Products, Frozen	2053
Bakery Products, Frozen, Wholesale	5142
Bakery Products, Wholesale	5149
Balances, Except Laboratory	3596
Balances, Except Laboratory, Wholesale	5046
Balances, Laboratory	3821
Balances, Wholesale	5049
Ball Bearings & Parts	3562
Ballpoint Pens	3951
Balls, Sports	3949
Banana Farms	0179
Bandages & Dressings	3842
Bandages, Wholesale	5122
Bands, Orchestras, Actors & Other Entertainers & Entertainment Groups	7929
Banjos & Parts	3931
Bank Holding Cos.	6712
Banks, National	6021
Banks, State	6022
Barbecue Sauce	2033
Barbecues, Grills	3631
Barber Shops	7231
Barite Mining	1479
Barium Compounds	2819
Barium Diagnostic Agents	2835
Barley Farms	0119
Barley, Wholesale	5153
Barometers	3829
Barrels, Stripping, Steel & Other Metal	3412
Barrels, Wood	2449
Bathing Suits, Girls', Children's & Infants'	2369
Bathing Suits, Men's & Boys'	2329
Bathing Suits, Women's, Misses' & Juniors'	2329
Bathroom Accessories, Vitreous China & Earthenware	3261
Bathroom Fixtures, Enameled Iron	3431
Bathroom Fixtures, Plastics	3088
Bathroom Scales	3596
Batteries, Primary Dry & Wet	3692
Batteries, Storage	3691
Battery Cable Wiring Sets	3694
Bauxite Mining	1099
Bauxite, Refined	2819
Beans, Grain & Field, Buying & Marketing	5153
Bearings, Ball and Roller	3562
Bearings, Motor Vehicle	3714
Beauty Shops	7231
Beauticians	7231
Beds & Springs, Retail	5712
Beds, Household, Metal	2514
Beds, Household, Wood	2511
Bedspreads	2392
Bedspreads, Wholesale	5023
Bedsprings, Assembled	2515
Bedsprings, Wholesale	5021
Beef Cattle, Except Feedlots	0212
Beef Cattle, Feedlots	0211
Beeper Communications Service	4812
Beer & Ale, Wholesale	5181
Beets (Sugar)	0133
Belting, Rubber & Plastics	3052
Belts	2387
Berry Farms	0171
Bicycles & Parts	3751
Bicycles & Parts, Retail	5941
Bicycles & Parts, Wholesale	5091
Billboard Advertising	7312
Billiard Equipment	3949
Billiards Equipment & Supplies, Wholesale	5091
Binoculars	3827
Biological Products, Except Diagnostic Substances	2836
Bird Food	2048
Biscuits	2051
Bits, Rock, Oil & Gas Fields	3533
Bituminous Coal Mining	1221
Bituminous Coal Strip Mining	1221
Blacktop Work, Contractors	1771
Blades, Knife & Razor	3421
Blades, Saw	3425
Blast Furnaces	3212
Bleaches, Hair	2844
Bleaches, Household	2842
Bleaches, Industrial	2819
Blenders, Electric	3634
Blinds, Venetian & Vertical	2591
Blood Banks	8099
Blood Pressure Apparatus	3841
Blouses, Girls', Children's & Infants'	2361
Blouses, Wholesale	5137
Blouses & Shirts, Women's, Misses' & Juniors'	2331
Blow Torches	3423
Blueprint, Paper & Equipment	3861
Blueprinting Equipment, Wholesale	5044
Blueprinting Service	7334
Boat Dealers	5551
Boats, Fiberglass	3732
Body Shops, Automotive	7532
Boilers, Industrial	3443
Boilers, Steam & Hot Water	3433
Boilers, Wholesale	5074
Bolts, Metal	3452
Bolts, Nuts, Rivets & Screws, Wholesale	5072
Bond & Mortgage Cos.	6162
Bone China	3262

Alphabetical S.I.C. Compendium-continued

Description	SIC Code
Book Clubs, Not Publishing	5961
Book Printing	2732
Book Publishing	2731
Book Stores, New Publications	5942
Book Stores, Used Publications	5932
Bookbinding	2789
Bookcases, Household, Metal	2514
Bookcases, Household, Wood	2511
Bookcases, Office, Except Wood	2522
Bookcases, Office, Wood	2521
Bookkeeping & Billing Services	8721
Books, Blank	2782
Books, Wholesale	5192
Boot & Shoe Cut Stock & Findings	3131
Boots, Dress & Casual, Men's	3143
Boots, Plastic or Rubber	3021
Boots, Women's	3144
Borax Mining	1474
Botanical Products	2833
Bottle Caps & Tops, Metal	3466
Bottle Caps & Tops, Plastic	3089
Bottle Corks and Covers	2499
Bottles, Glass	3221
Bottles, Plastic	3085
Bottles, Rubber	3069
Bottles, Vacuum	3429
Bottling Machinery	3565
Bow Ties, Men's & Boy's	2323
Bowling Alleys & Accessories	3949
Box Making Machines for Plastic Boxes	3554
Box Making Machines for Wooden Boxes	3553
Boxes, Corrugated & Solid Fiber	2653
Boxes, Folding Paperboard	2657
Boxes, Set-up Paperboard	2652
Boxes, Nailed & Lock Corner Wooden	2441
Boxes, Paperboard, Wholesale	5113
Boxes, Plastic	3089
Boxes, Wood, Wirebound	2449
Boxing Equipment	3949
Brackets, Iron & Steel	3429
Brackets, Wood	2431
Brads, Steel	3429
Brads, Wholesale	5072
Brake Drums	3714
Brake Fluid, Hydraulic	2992
Brake Lining, Pads, Asbestos	3292
Brake Lining, Rubber	3069
Brakes, Aircraft	3728
Brakes & Brake Parts, Automotive	3714
Bran, Except Rice	2041
Bran, Rice	2044
Brandy & Brandy Spirits	2084
Brandy & Spirits, Wholesale	5182
Brass Die Castings	3364
Brass Foundries	3366
Brass Goods, Plumbers	3432
Brass Goods, Plumbers, Wholesale	5074
Brass, Rolling & Drawing	3351
Brass Smelting & Refining, Secondary	3341
Brassieres, Girdles, etc.	2342
Breakfast Cereals	2043
Breakfast Cereals, Wholesale	5149
Breathing Systems	3829
Breweries	2082
Brewers Machinery	3556
Brick & Tile Dealers, Retail	5211
Brick, Common, Face	3251
Brick, Refractory	3297
Brick, Stone & Related Construction Materials, Wholesale	5032
Bricklaying Contractors	1741
Bridge Construction	1622
Briefcases	3161
Briquettes, Fuel	2999
Broadcast Equipment	3663
Broadcasting Stations, Radio	4832
Broadcasting Stations, Television	4833
Broiler, Fryer, & Roaster Chickens	0251
Brokers, Commodity	6221
Brokers, Insurance	6411
Brokers, Real Estate	6531
Brokers, Security	6211
Brokers, Shipping	4731
Bronze, Rolling & Drawing	3351
Bronze, Smelting & Refining, Secondary	3341
Brooms, Hand & Machine	3991
Broth, Except Seafood, Canned	2032
Brushes	3991
Building Equipment, Installation or Erection, NEC	1796
Business Associations	8611
Business Consulting Services, NEC	8748
Bulbs, Growing of	0181
Bulbs, Seeds, Nursery Stock, Retail	5261
Bulbs, Seeds, Nursery Stock, Wholesale	5191
Bulldozers, Construction	3531
Bulletin Boards	2499
Bullion, Precious Metals, Wholesale	5094
Buns, Bread	2051
Burglar Alarms	3669
Burlap, Jute	2299
Burlap, Wholesale	5199
Bus Charter Services, Local	4141
Bus Services, NEC	7389
Buses, Motor	3711
Buses, Wholesale	5012
Business Forms, Manifold	2761
Business Forms, Wholesale	5112
Business Management Services	8741
Butane Gas, Bottled, Retail	5984
Butane Gas, Natural, Production	1321
Butane Gas, Wholesale	5172
Butter	2021
Butter, Wholesale	5143
Buttons	3965
C	
Cabinets, Wood, for Televisions, Radios, Phonographs & Sewing Machines	2517
Cable, Fiber	2298
Cable, Steel, Insulated	3315
Cable, Uninsulated Wire	3496
Cable Television Equipment	3663
Cable Television Services	4841
Cafeterias	5812
Cake Mixes	2045
Calcium Carbide, Chloride & Hydrochloride	2819
Camera & Photographic Supply Stores	5946
Cameras, Still & Motion Picture	3861
Cameras, Television	3663
Campers, For Mounting on Trucks	3792
Campgrounds	7033
Camping Equipment, Retail	5941
Camping Equipment, Wholesale	5091
Camping Trailers	3792
Camshafts, Motor Vehicle	3714
Can Openers, Electric	3634
Can Openers, Except Electric	3423
Cane Sugar Refining	2062
Cans, Aluminum, Metal	3411
Canvas	2211
Canvas Bags	2393
Canvas Products, Except Bags	2394
Capacitors, Electronic	3675
Capacitors, Electronic, Wholesale	5065
Caps & Plugs, Attachment, Electric	3643
Capsules, Gelatin, Empty	2899
Car Leasing, Passenger	7515
Car Phones	3663
Car Washes	7542
Carbide	2819
Carbon Black	2895
Carbon Paper	3955
Carbon Products	3624
Cardboard	2631
Cardboard, Die-Cut, Coated	2675
Cardboard, Wholesale	5113
Cards, Greeting	2771
Cards, Index	2675
Carnival & Amusement Park Equipment, Wholesale	5087
Carnival Amusement Rides	3599
Carpentry Work	1751
Carpet Laying & Removal Service	1752
Carpet Stores, Retail	5713
Carpet Sweepers, Except Vacuum Cleaners	3589
Carpet & Upholstery Cleaning	7217
Carpet Yarn	2281
Carpets, Textile Fiber	2273
Carpets, Wholesale	5023
Carry-Out Restaurants	5812
Carts, Golf, Hand	3949
Carts, Grocery	3496
Carts, Restaurant	2599
Cash Grains	0119
Cash Registers	3578
Cash Registers, Wholesale	5044
Casino Hotels	7011
Caskets, Burial	3995
Caskets, Burial, Wholesale	5087
Cassette Tapes, Blank	3695
Catalog, Order Taking	5961
Catalog Showrooms	5399
Catalogs, Printing of Only	2759
Catalogs, Publishing	2741
Catfish Farms	0273
Cathode Ray Tubes	3671
Catsup	2033
Caulking Compounds	2891
Caulking Guns, Tool, Hand	3423
Caustic Soda, Potash	2812
Caustic Soda, Wholesale	5119
Ceilings, Acoustical	3296
Ceilings, Acoustical Installation	1742
Cellophane Adhesive Tape	2672
Cellos & Parts	3931
Cellular Radio Telephone	3663
Cellular Telephone Services	4812
Cellulose, Man-Made Fibers	2823
Cellulose Fibers	2821
Cement, Hydraulic, Portland	3241
Cemeteries	6553
Centrifuges, Industrial	3569
Centrifuges, Laboratory	3821
Ceramic Kilns	3567
Ceramic Tile	3253
Ceramic Tile, Wholesale	5032
Cesspool Cleaning	7699
Chainsaw Blades	3425
Chainsaws	3546
Chainsaws, Retail	5251
Chainsaws, Wholesale	5084
Chairs, Household, Not Upholstered	2511
Chairs, Office, Except Wood	2522
Chairs, Office, Wood	2521
Chairs, Upholstered	2512
Chairs, Wholesale	5021
Chamois Leather	3111
Chamois Leather, Wholesale	5199
Chandeliers, Commercial	3646
Chandeliers, Residential	3645
Change-Making Machines	3578
Charcoal, Activated	2819
Charcoal, Except Activated	2861
Charcoal, Wholesale	5199
Chart & Graph Design Services	7336
Chart & Graph Paper, Ruled	2782
Checkbooks	2782
Check-Writing Machines	3579
Cheese, Mail-Order, Retail	5961
Cheese Curls & Puffs	2096
Cheese Products	2022
Cheese Stores, Retail	5451
Cheesecloth	2211
Cheesecloth, Wholesale	5131
Cheese-Making Machines	3556
Chemical Bulk Stations & Terminals	5169
Chemicals, NEC	2899
Chewing Gum	2067
Chewing Gum, Wholesale	5145

Description	SIC Code
Chewing Tobacco	2131
Chewing Tobacco, Wholesale	5194
Chicken Production	0251
Child Care Centers	8351
Children's & Infants' Wear Stores	5641
Chili Con Carne, Canned	2032
Chili Pepper or Powder	2099
Chili Sauce	2033
Chimes, Electric	3699
Chimney Cleaning Service	7349
Chimney Construction & Maintenance	1741
China Closets	2511
China Tableware	3262
China, Wholesale	5023
Chisels	3423
Chlorine	2812
Chlorine, Compressed or Liquefied	2812
Chlorine, Wholesale	5169
Chocolate, Sweetened or Unsweetened	2066
Chlorine Bleach	2842
Chocolate Bars	2066
Chocolate Candy, Except Bars	2064
Chocolate Syrup	2066
Chow Mein, Chop Suey, Canned	2032
Chowders, Fish & Seafood, Canned	2091
Chowders, Fish & Seafood, Frozen	2092
Christmas Tree Growing	0811
Christmas Tree Lighting Sets	3699
Christmas Trees, Artificial	3999
Christmas Trees, Natural, Retail	5261
Christmas Trees, Wholesale	5199
Chromium Compounds	2819
Chromium Ore Mining	1061
Chromium Plating of Metals	3471
Chromium Refining	3339
Cider, Nonalcoholic	2099
Cider Presses	3556
Cigar Stores & Stands	5993
Cigarettes	2111
Cigarettes, Wholesale	5194
Cigars	2121
Cigars, Wholesale	5194
Circuit Boards	3672
Citizen's Band (CB) Radios	3663
Citric Acid	2869
Citrus Fruits	0174
Citrus Groves	0724
Clay Refractories	3255
Clays, Common, Quarrying	1459
Cleaning & Dying Plants, Except Rug	7216
Cleaning Preparations	2842
Cleansing Tissues	2676
Clock Radios	3651
Clock Repair	7631
Clocks, Except Timeclocks	3873
Clocks, Wholesale	5094
Clothes Dryers, Electric, Commercial	3582
Clothes Dryers, Electric, Household	3633
Clothes Dryers, Wood	2499
Clothing, Men's, Boys' NEC	2329
Clothing & Accessories, Women's, Children's, Infants', Wholesale	5137
Clothing & Accessory Stores, Men's & Boys'	5611
Clothing & Furnishings, Men's & Boys', Wholesale	5136
Clothing Stores, Women's	5621
Coal Mining, Anthracite	1231
Coal Mining, Bituminous, Surface	1221
Coal Mining, Bituminous, Underground	1222
Coal Mining Services	1241
Coal Products, NEC	2999
Coal Tar	2865
Coal Tar Products	5169
Coal, Wholesale	5052
Coating, Engraving & Allied Services, NEC	3479
Coating of Metals	3479
Coats, Girls', Children's, Infants'	2369
Coats, Women's, Misses', Juniors'	2339
Coats, Men's, Boys'	2311
Coaxial Cable, Nonferrous	3357
Coaxial Cable, Wholesale	5063
Cobalt Ore Mining	1061
Cocktails, Alcoholic	2085
Cocktails, Alcoholic, Premixed, Retail	5182
Cocoa, Powdered & Mix	2066
Codfish, Smoked, Dried, etc.	2091
Coffee, Instant	2095
Coffee Farms	0179
Coffee Makers, Electric	3634
Coffee Roasting	2095
Coffee Roasting & Grinding Machines	3556
Coffee Shops	5812
Coffee Stores, Retail	5499
Coils, Electronics	3677
Coils, Ignition	3694
Coils for Motors & Generators	3621
Coin-Operated Game Machines, Wholesale	5099
Coin-Operated Laundries	7215
Coin-Operated Machines, Selling Merchandise	5962
Coke Ovens	3212
Coke, Petroleum	2911
Cold Storage Locker Rental	4222
Cold Storage Warehousing	4222
Collection Agencies, Accounts	7322
Colognes	2844
Combination Utilities, NEC	4939
Combs, Plastics	3089
Comic Books Publishing	2721
Commercial Art & Graphic Design	7336
Commercial Equipment, Wholesale	5046
Communication Services, NEC	4899
Communications Equipment, Mobile & Microwave	3663
Communications Equipment, NEC	3669
Communications Equipment, Telephone & Telegraph	3661
Communications Equipment, Wholesale	5065
Communications Equipment Installation	1731
Compact Disc Players	3651
Compact Discs, Prerecorded, Except Video	3652
Compasses, Except Portable	3812
Compasses, Portable	3829
Compressors, Air & Gas, Industrial	3563
Compressors, Refrigeration	3585
Computer & Computer Software Stores	5734
Computer Consultants	7379
Computer Facilities Management Services	7376
Computer Forms	2761
Computer Hardware Rental	7377
Computer Logic Modules	3674
Computer Paper, Wholesale	5112
Computer Peripherals	3577
Computer Peripherals, Rental	7377
Computer Peripherals, Wholesale	5045
Computer Repair & Maintenance	7378
Computer Software	7372
Computer Software, Stores	5734
Computer Software, Tape & Disks, Blank	3685
Computer Software, Wholesale	5045
Computer Storage Units	3572
Computer Stores, Retail	5734
Computer Terminals	3575
Computer Terminals, Wholesale	5045
Computers, Electronic	3571
Concrete Block & Brick	3271
Concrete Block Laying	1741
Concrete & Cinder Block, Retail	5211
Concrete & Cinder Block, Wholesale	5032
Concrete Curing Compounds	2899
Concrete Mixers, Plants	3531
Concrete Products, Precast, Except Block & Brick	3272
Concrete, Ready-Mix	3273
Concrete Reinforcement Mesh	3496
Concrete Reinforcement Steel Bars	3449
Concrete Work, Except Paving	1771
Concrete Work, Paving	1611
Condensed Milk	2032
Condensers, Electronic	3675
Condensers, Electronic, Wholesale	5065
Condensers, Refrigeration	3585
Condensers, Steam	3443
Condensers for Motors & Generators	3629
Condensing Units, Air-Conditioning, Wholesale	5075
Condensing Units, Refrigeration, Wholesale	5078
Condominium Developers	1531
Conduits & Fittings, Electrical	3644
Conduits, Concrete	3272
Confectionery	2064
Confectionery Stores	5441
Confectionery, Wholesale	5145
Connectors, Electric Cord	3643
Connectors, Electronic	3678
Connectors, Electronic Wholesale	5065
Construction, Bridges, Tunnels	1622
Construction, Sand & Gravel	1442
Construction, Water, Sewer, Pipeline, Power Line	1623
Construction Equipment, Heavy Rental	7353
Construction Machinery, Except Mining	3531
Construction Material, Wholesale	5039
Construction Paper	2651
Consumer Finance Companies	6141
Contact Lenses	3851
Contact Lenses, Wholesale	5048
Containers, Wood, Nec	2449
Contractors, Family Houses	1521
Contractors, Industrial Buildings & Warehouses	1541
Contractors, Non-Residential Buildings	1542
Contractors, Residential Buildings	1522
Contractors, Special Trade	1799
Control Panels	3613
Control Transformers	3612
Control Valves	3492
Controls, Industrial	3625
Controls, Industrial, Wholesale	5084
Controls & Timing Devices	3824
Convection Ovens	3631
Convenience Food Stores	5411
Conveyor Belts	3496
Conveyor Systems, Industrial	3535
Conveyor Systems, Wholesale	5084
Cookie Stores	5461
Cookies	2052
Cookies, Wholesale	5149
Cooking Appliances	3634
Cooking Oils, Vegetable	2079
Cooking Oils, Wholesale	5149
Coolers, Drinking Fountain	3431
Copiers	3579
Copper Alloy Foundries	3366
Copper Chloride, Sulfate	2819
Copper Die-Castings	3364
Copper Ingots	3331
Copper Ore, Wholesale	5052
Copper Ore Mining	1021
Copper Rolling, Drawing, Extruding	3351
Copper Smelting	3331
Cord, Braided	2298
Cord Connectors, Electric	3643
Cord for Reinforcing Rubber Tires	2296
Cord Sets, Flexible	3357
Cordage & Twine	2298
Corduroys, Cotton	2211
Core Drills	3532
Cork, Wholesale	5085
Cork Products	2499
Corn, Wholesale	5153
Corn Chips, Wholesale	5145
Corn Chips & Snacks	2096
Corn Flakes	2043
Corn Oil	2046
Corn Pickers & Shellers	3523
Corn Popping Machines	3589
Corn Production	0115
Corn Starch	2046
Correctional Facilities, Private	8744
Correspondence Schools	8249
Cosmetics	2844

Alphabetical S.I.C. Compendium-continued

Description	SIC Code
Cosmetics, Wholesale	5122
Costume Jewelry	3961
Cottage Cheese	2026
Cotton, Finishers of Broad Woven Fabrics	2261
Cotton, Raw, Wholesale	5159
Cotton & Cottonseed Production	0131
Cotton Balers & Presses	3523
Cotton Fabric	2211
Cotton Ginning	0724
Cotton Ginning Machinery	3559
Cotton Piece Goods, Wholesale	5131
Cotton Thread	2284
Cotton Yarn	2281
Cotton Yarns, Wholesale	5199
Cottonseed Oil	2074
Cough Drops	2064
Cough Medicines	2834
Couplings, Hose	3429
Couplings, Pipe	3494
Courier Services, Air	4513
Courier Services, Except Air	4215
Crackers	2052
Crackers, Wholesale	5149
Craft & Hobby Sets	3944
Craft & Hobby Shops	5945
Craft Kits, Wholesale	5092
Cranes, Construction	3531
Cranes, Wholesale	5084
Crankshaft Assemblies	3714
Crowns & Closures, Metal	3466
Crayons	3952
Cream Substitutes	2023
Credit Card Service	7389
Credit Clearinghouses	7323
Credit Institutions, Misc. Business	6159
Credit Institutions, Short-Term Business, Except Agriculture	6153
Credit Unions, Federal	6061
Credit Unions, State	6062
Crepe Paper	2679
Crop Driers	3523
Crop Dusting	0721
Crop Planting, Cultivation & Protection Services	0721
Crop Preparation Services for Market, Except Cotton Ginning	0723
Crops, Food, Grown Under Cover	0182
Crucibles, Fire Clay	3255
Crucibles, Non-Clay	3297
Crude Oil, Wholesale	5172
Crude Oil Production	1311
Crude Petroleum Pipe Lines	4612
Crystals & Crystal Assemblies	3679
Cultured Pearl Production	0919
Cups, Foamed Plastic	3086
Cups, Paper	2656
Cups, Plastic, Except Foam	3089
Cured Meats	2011
Curio Shops	5947
Curlers, Hair	3965
Curling Irons, Electrical	3634
Current-Carrying Wiring Devices	3643
Curtains & Draperies, NEC	2391
Curtains & Fabrics, Lace	2258
Curtains, Wholesale	5023
Cylinders, Pump	3561
D	
Dairy Farms	0241
Dairy Product Stores	5451
Dairy Products, Except Dried or Canned, Wholesale	5143
Dairy Products Machinery & Equipment	3556
Dairy Products Machinery, Wholesale	5084
Data Base Information Retrieval Services	7375
Data Entry Services	7374
Data Processing Services	7374
Deciduous Tree Fruits Production	0175
Decoders, Computer	3577
Deep Sea Foreign Freight Transportation	4412
Deep Sea Foreign Passenger Transportation	4481
Dehumidifiers, Not Portable, Electric	3585
Dehumidifiers, Portable, Electric	3634
Dehydrated Fruits, Vegetables, Soups	2034
Dehydrating Equipment, Food	3556
Denims	2211
Dental Equipment	3843
Dental Equipment, Wholesale	5047
Deodorants, Non Personal	2842
Deodorants, Personal	2844
Department Stores, Retail	5311
Deposit Insurance	6399
Desalination Equipment	3559
Desalter Kits, Sea Water	2899
Desserts, Frozen, Except Bakery	2024
Desserts, Ready-to-Mix	2099
Detection Systems & Instruments	3812
Detective Agencies	7381
Detergents	2841
Detergents, Wholesale	5169
Developing & Printing, Commercial Motion Picture Film	7819
Developing & Printing, Home Movies	7384
Diamond Cutting & Polishing	3915
Diamond Mining, Industrial	1499
Diamonds, Gems, Wholesale	5094
Diamonds, Industrial & Natural, Wholesale	5085
Diapers, Cotton	2399
Diapers, Disposable	2676
Diapers, Wholesale	5137
Die-Casting Machines	3542
Die-Castings, Aluminum	3363
Die-Castings, Nonferrous, Except Aluminum	3634
Dies, Metalworking, Except Threading	3544
Dies, Thread Cutting	3545
Diesel Engines & Parts	3519
Diesel Engines & Parts, Wholesale	5084
Diet Workshops	7299
Dietary Supplements	2023
Digital Encoders	3663
Digital Test Equipment	3825
Dimension Stone	1411
Dining Room Furniture, Wood	2511
Dinners, Frozen & Packaged	2038
Dinners, Frozen, Wholesale	5142
Dinnerware, Plastic	3089
Diodes, Solid-State	3674
Diodes, Wholesale	5065
Direct Mail Advertising	7331
Direct Selling Establishments	5963
Directories, Printed, Not Published	2759
Directories, Publishing	2741
Dishes, Fine & Earthenware	3263
Dishes, Paper	2656
Dishes, Paper & Plastics, Wholesale	5113
Dishwashers, Commercial, Electric	3589
Dishwashers, Electric, Wholesale	5064
Dishwashers, Household, Electric	3639
Disinfecting & Pest Control Services	7342
Disk & Diskette Conversion Services	7379
Disk Drives, Computer	3572
Disk Drives, Wholesale	5045
Diskettes, Wholesale	5065
Dog & Cat Food	2047
Dog & Cat Food, Wholesale	5149
Dogs, Rental of, Protective	7381
Dolls	3942
Dolls, Wholesale	5092
Door Frames & Sash, Metal	3442
Door Frames & Sash, Wood	2431
Door Frames, Wholesale	5031
Door Locks & Lock Sets	3429
Door Opening & Closing Devices, Electrical	3699
Doors, Metal	3442
Doors, Wood	2431
Doughnut Shops, Retail	5461
Drafting Instruments	3829
Drafting Instruments, Wholesale	5049
Drafting Service	7389
Draperies & Fabrics, Cotton	2211
Draperies, Plastic	2391
Draperies, Silk & Man-made Fibers	2221
Draperies, Wholesale	5023
Drapery Rods, Fixture	2591
Dresses, Girls', Children's & Infants'	2361
Dresses, Womens', Misses' & Juniors'	2335
Dressing Tables	2511
Dressings, Surgical	3842
Dried Fruits & Vegetables	2034
Driers, Hand, Face & Hair, Electric	3634
Drill Bits, Metalworking	3545
Drill Bits, Wholesale	5084
Drill Bits, Woodworking	3423
Drilling Mud	2899
Drilling Mud, Wholesale	5169
Drinking Places (Alcoholic Beverages)	5813
Drug Stores, Retail	5912
Drugs, Wholesale	5122
Dry Cell Batteries	3692
Dry Cleaning	7215
Dry Ice	2813
Dry Ice, Wholesale	5169
Dryers, Laboratory	3821
Dryers, Laundry	3633
Drywall	1742
Duplicating Ink	2893
Duplicating Machines	3579
Duplicating Machines, Wholesale	5044
Durable Goods, NEC, Wholesale	5099
Dyes, Hair	2844
Dyes, Household	2899
Dyes, Synthetic	2865
Dyestuffs, Natural	2861
Dyestuffs, Wholesale	5169
Dynamite	2892
E	
Earth Moving Equipment Rental & Leasing	7353
Earth Moving, Contractors	1794
Earthenware	3263
Edge Act Corporations	6082
Editing Equipment, Motion Picture	3861
Egg Production	0252
Egg Substitutes	2015
Eggs, Wholesale	5144
Elastomers	2822
Electric Lamp Bulbs & Tubes	3641
Electric & Other Services Combined	4931
Electric Services	4911
Electric Wiring, Construction Wholesale	5063
Electrical Industrial Apparatus, NEC	3629
Electrical Work Contractors	1731
Electromedical & Electrotherapeutic Apparatus	3845
Electrometallurgical Products, Except Steel	3213
Electron Tubes	3671
Electronic Parts & Equipment, Wholesale	5065
Electronic Stores, Consumer, Radio & Television	5731
Elevator Installation	1796
Elevators, Grain Storage	4221
Elevators, Passenger & Freight	3534
Elevators, Wholesale	5084
Emergency Medical Centers, Freestanding	8011
Employment Agencies, General	7361
Enamel Tile	3253
Enamels	2851
Enamels, Wholesale	5198
Energy Measuring Equipment, Electrical	3825
Engine Repair, Automotive	7538
Engine Repair, Except Automotive	7699
Engineering Services	8711
Engines & Engine Parts, Aircraft	3724
Engines & Engine Parts, Automotive	3714
Engines, Internal Combustion, Except Aircraft & Non-Diesel Automotive	3519
Enlargers, Photographic	3861
Envelopes	2677
Envelopes, Wholesale	5112

Description	SIC Code
Epoxy Adhesives	2891
Epoxy Resins	2821
Equipment Rental & Leasing, NEC	7359
Erasers, Rubber	3069
Escalators	3534
Escrow Agents	6531
Esters	2869
Ethanol Industrial	2869
Ether	2869
Ethyl Acetate	2869
Ethyl Chloride	2869
Evaporated Milk	2023
Excavation & Foundation Work	1794
Exercise Cycles	3949
Exercising Machines	3949
Exhaust Systems & Parts, Aircraft	3724
Exhaust Systems & Parts, Motor Vehicle	3714
Explosives	2892
Extruded Shapes, Aluminum	3354
Extruded Shapes, Copper	3351
Extruded Shapes, Nonferrous, Except Copper & Aluminum	3356
Eyeglass Cases	3172
Eyeglasses, Lenses & Frames	3851
F	
Fabric, Nonwoven	2297
Fabric Shops, Retail	5949
Fabric Softeners	2842
Fabricated Metal Products, NEC	3499
Fabricated Pipe & Fabricated Pipe Fittings	3498
Fabricated Wire Products, Misc.	3469
Facial Tissues	2676
Facilities Support Management Services	8744
Facsimile Equipment	3661
Facsimile Transmission Services	4822
Factors of Commercial Paper	6153
Family Clothing Stores	5651
Family Services	8322
Fans, Electric, Household	3634
Fans, Except Household	3564
Fans, Industrial, Wholesale	5084
Farm Labor Contractors	0761
Farm Machinery & Equipment	3523
Farm Machinery & Equipment, Wholesale	5083
Farm Management Services	0762
Farm Production Warehousing & Storage	4221
Farm Supplies, Wholesale	5191
Farms, Primarily Crop	0191
Farms, Primarily Livestock	0291
Fasteners	3965
Fats & Oils, Animal & Marine	2077
Feed Grinders	3523
Feed Pre-mixes & Supplements	2048
Felt Tip Markers	3951
Fencing, Wire	3496
Fencing, Wood	2499
Ferries	4482
Fertilizers, Mixing Only	2875
Fertilizers, Nitrogenous	2873
Fertilizers, Phosphatic	2874
Fiber Cans, Tubes, Drums & Similar Products	2655
Fiber Optics Cable	3357
Fiber Optics Strands	3229
Fibers, Synthetic	2284
Field Crops, Except Cash Grains, Nec	0139
Filing Boxes, Paperboard	2652
Filing Folders	2675
Film, Movie, X-Ray, Still Camera	3861
Filters, Air for Furnaces	3564
Filters, Fluid, General	3569
Finance Leasing of Automobiles, Trucks, Machinery	6159
Financial Advice	6282
Financing of Automobiles, Furniture, Appliances	6141
Finfish, Catching	0912
Fire Alarm Apparatus	3669
Fire Extinguishers, Portable	3999
Fire Extinguishers, Wholesale	5099
First Aid Kits	3842
Fish, Canned	2091
Fish, Cured, Dried, Smoked	2091
Fish, Cured, Fresh, Wholesale	5146
Fish, Fresh & Frozen, Prepared	2092
Fish Food	2048
Fish Hatcheries	0921
Fish Sticks	2092
Fishing Lines, Nets	2298
Flags, Fabric	2399
Flagstones	3281
Flannels, Wool, Mohair	2231
Flares	2899
Flashlights	3648
Flashlights, Wholesale	5063
Flatware, Table	3914
Flavoring Concentrates, Extracts	2087
Flight Simulators	3699
Float Glass	3211
Floodlights	3648
Floor Coverings, Asphalted-Feltbase	3996
Floor Laying & Other Floor Work	1752
Floor Tile, Asphalt	3292
Floor Tile, Ceramic	3253
Floor Tile Stores	5713
Floor Waxes	2842
Floor Waxes & Polishes, Electric	3639
Florists, Retail	5992
Florists, Wholesale	5193
Flour, Blended	2041
Flour, Wholesale	5149
Flowers, Artificial Except Glass	3999
Flowers, Artificial Glass	3231
Flowers, Artificial, Retail	5999
Flowers, Artificial, Wholesale	5193
Flowers, Growing of	0181
Fluid Power Motors	3593
Fluid Power Pumps	3594
Fluid Power Valves & Fittings	3492
Fluorescent Lamps	3641
Fluorescent Lighting Fixtures, Commercial	3646
Fluorescent Lighting Fixtures, Residential	3645
Flush Valves	3432
Flying Instruction	8299
Foam Rubber	3069
Foam Rubber, Wholesale	5199
Foil, Aluminum	3353
Food Brokers	5141
Food, Mail-Order Retail	5961
Food Mixers, Household, Electric	3634
Food Preparation, NEC	2099
Food Processing Machinery	3556
Food Service, Institutional	5812
Food Stores, Misc.	5499
Food Warming Equipment, Commercial	3589
Food Warming Equipment, Commercial, Wholesale	5046
Foods, Frozen, Packaged, Wholesale	5142
Footwear, Men's	3143
Footwear, Women's	3144
Foreign Banks, Branches & Agencies	6081
Foreign Trade & International Banking Institutions	6082
Forest Nurseries & Forest Products	0831
Forestry Services	0851
Forgings, Iron & Steel	3462
Forgings, Nonferrous	3463
Forklift Trucks	3537
Forks, Garden	3423
Foundries, Gray & Ductile Iron	3321
Foundries, Malleable Iron	3322
Foundries, Nonferrous, Except Aluminum & Copper	3369
Foundries, Steel	3325
Foundries, Steel Investment	3324
Fountain Pens & Sets	3951
Flour Mill Machinery	3556
Flour Mills	2041
Freezers	3632
Freezers, Ice Cream, Commercial	3556
Freezers, Ice Cream, Household	3499
Freight Cars & Equipment	3743
Freight Forwarding	4731
Freight Packing & Crating	4783
Freight Trucking Terminals	4231
Frosting, Prepared	2099
Frozen Dinners, Packaged	2038
Frozen Fish, Packaged	2092
Frozen Fruits, Juices, Vegetables	2037
Frozen Vegetables, Juices, Fruits, Wholesale	5142
Fruit Stores	5431
Fruit Tree Production	0175
Fruits, Fresh, Wholesale	5148
Fuel Oil Dealers	5983
Fuel Pumps, Automotive	3714
Funeral Homes, Parlors	7261
Fur Goods	2371
Fur-Bearing Animals	0271
Furnaces, Industrial	3567
Furnaces, Warm Air	3585
Furnaces, Warm Air, Wholesale	5075
Furniture & Fixtures	2599
Furniture Rental & Leasing	7359
Furniture, Household, Glass & Plastic	2519
Furniture, Household, Metal	2514
Furniture, Household, Rattan, Wicker	2519
Furniture, Household, Upholstered	2512
Furniture, Household, Wood	2511
Furniture, Laboratory	3821
Furniture, Office, Metal	2522
Furniture, Office, Wood	2521
Furniture, Public Building & Related	2531
Furniture, Wholesale	5021
Furniture Stores	5712
Fuses	3613
Futures Dealers & Brokers	6221
G	
Games, Coin-Operated	3999
Games, Computer Software	7372
Games, Puzzles	3944
Garage Doors, Overhead, Metal	3442
Garage Doors, Overhead, Wood	2431
Garages, Automobile Parking	7521
Garages, Automotive Repair	7538
Garages, Prefabricated, Metal	3448
Garbage Collecting, Not Disposal	4212
Garbage Collecting & Disposal	4953
Garbage Containers, Metal	3469
Garbage Containers, Plastic	3089
Garbage Disposers, Commercial	3589
Garbage Disposers, Electric, Household	3639
Garden Handtools	3423
Garden Hose	3052
Garden Supplies & Tools, Retail	5261
Gas, Natural, Compressed	1623
Gas, Natural, Distribution	4924
Gas, Natural, Production	1311
Gas, Natural, Transmission & Distribution	4923
Gas, Natural, Transmission Only	4922
Gas & Other Services Combined	4932
Gas Masks	3842
Gas Turbines	3511
Gases, Industrial	2813
Gaskets	3053
Gaskets, Wholesale	5085
Gasoline, Natural, Production	1321
Gasoline & Oil, Retail	5541
Gauges, Machine Tool	3545
Gauges, Pressure, Temperature	3824
Gear Motors	3566
Gears, Motor Vehicle	3714
Gears, Motorcycle & Bicycle	3751
Gears, Steel	3462
Gears, Wholesale	5085
Geiger Counters	3829
Gelatin Dessert Preparations	2099

Alphabetical S.I.C. Compendium-continued

Description	SIC Code
Gem Stone Mining	1499
Gems, Preparation of for Setting	3915
General Stores, Retail	5399
Generators	3621
Generators, Aircraft & Motor Vehicle	3694
Gift Shops	5947
Gift Wrap Paper	2679
Gin, Alcoholic Beverage	2085
Ginger Ale, Bottled, Canned	2086
Glass, Flat, Colored	3211
Glass & Glazing Work	1793
Glass & Glassware, Pressed & Blown	3229
Glass Products, Made of Purchased Glass	3231
Globes, Geographical	3999
Gloves, Dress & Work	2381
Gloves, Leather	3151
Gloves, Rubber	3069
Goggles, Underwater, Safety	3851
Gold Ores Mining	1041
Government, General, NEC	9199
Granite, Crushed & Broken	1423
Grape Production	0172
Graphite Products	3624
Grave Markers, Vaults, Concrete	3272
Greeting Cards	2771
Grills for Outdoor Cooking	3631
Groceries, General Line, Wholesale	5141
Groceries & Related Products, Wholesale, NEC	5149
Guided Missle Propulsion Units & Propulsion Unit Parts	3764
Gum, Chemicals	2861
Guns, 30mm or Less	3484
Guns, More Than 30mm	3489
Guns, BB and Pellet	3484
Guns, Toy	3944
Gypsum Building Board	3275

H

Description	SIC Code
Hair Goods	3999
Hammers	3423
Handbags, Retail	5632
Handbags, Wholesale	5137
Handbags, Women's	3171
Handtools	3423
Handtools, Power Driven	3546
Hang Gliders	3721
Hardboard	2493
Hardboard, Wholesale	5031
Hardware, Wholesale	5072
Hardware Stores	5251
Harness Assemblies, Electronic	3679
Harvesting Machines	3523
Hatcheries, Fish	0921
Hatcheries, Poultry	0254
Hats	2353
Hazardous Waste Disposal Sites	4953
Headlights, Vehicular	3647
Headphones, Radio	3679
Health Food Stores	5499
Health Foods, Wholesale	5149
Health Insurance	6321
Health Lamps	3641
Health Practitioners, Offices & Clinics, NEC	8049
Health Programs, Public, Administration of	9431
Hearing Aids	3842
Hearing Aids, Retail	5999
Hearing Aids, Wholesale	5047
Heat Exchangers	3443
Heat Exchangers, Wholesale	5084
Heating & Air Conditioning Units, Combined	3585
Heating Units, Electric	3634
Heavy Construction, NEC	1629
Heavy Water	2819
Helicopters	3721
Helium	2813
Helmets, Athletic	3949
Help Supply Service	7363
Herbicides	2879
High Fidelity Equipment	3651
High Fidelity Equipment, Retail	5731
High Fidelity Equipment, Wholesale	5064
Highway & Street Construction	1611
Hinges	3429
Hobby Kits	3944
Hobby Stores	5945
Hog Production	0213
Hoists	3536
Hoists, Wholesale	5084
Holding Companies, Bank	6712
Holding Companies, Except Bank	6719
Home Construction, Single-Family	1521
Home Furnishing Stores, Misc.	5719
Home Furnishings, Wholesale	5023
Home Healthcare Services	8082
Horses & Other Equines Farms	0272
Hose Fittings & Assemblies	3492
Hose, Plastic or Rubber	3052
Hosiery, Ankle-Length	2252
Hosiery, Men's & Boys' Wholesale	5136
Hosiery, Women's & Children's Wholesale	5137
Hosiery, Women's Full Length & Knee High	2251
Hospital & Medical Service Plans	6324
Hospitals, Children's	8069
Hospitals, General	8062
Hospitals, Psychiatric	8063
Hospitals, Specialty	8069
Hospitals for Mentally Retarded	8051
Hot Tubs	2449
Hot Tubs, Retail	5999
Hot Tubs, Wholesale	5091
Hotels	7011
House Furnishings, Except Curtains & Draperies	2392
House-to-House Sales	5963
Household Appliance Stores	5722
Humidifiers, Dehumidifiers, Not Portable	3585
Humidifiers, Dehumidifiers, Portable	3634
Hunting, Trapping & Game	0971
Hydraulic Hose	3492
Hydraulic Pumps, Aircraft	3594
Hydraulic Turbines	3511
Hydraulic Valves	3492
Hydrochloric Acid	2819
Hydrogen	2813

I

Description	SIC Code
IV Transfusion Equipment	3841
Ice	2097
Ice Chests or Coolers, Except Insulated Foam Plastic	3429
Ice Chests or Coolers, Foam Plastics	3086
Ice Chests or Coolers, Plastics, not Insulated or Foam Plastic	3089
Ice Cream	2024
Ice Cream Stores	5451
Ice Cream, Wholesale	5143
Ice Skates	3949
Iced Tea, Bottled or Canned	2086
Ignition Apparatus	3694
Ignition Testing Equipment	3825
In Vitro & In Vivo Diagnostics	2835
Incinerator Operation	4953
Incinerators, Metal	3567
Industrial Chemicals, Wholesale	5169
Industrial Controls	3625
Industrial Machinery & Equipment, Wholesale	5084
Industrial Molds	3544
Industrial Patterns	3543
Industrial Supplies, Wholesale	5085
Ink	2893
Inner Tubes	3011
Inorganic Chemicals, NEC	2819
Insecticides	2879
Insecticides, Wholesale	5191
Inspection & Weighing Services for Motor Vehicle Transportation	4785
Instant Coffee	2095
Instruments & Apparatus, Medical Except Electromedical	3841
Instruments, Electrical Measurement	3825
Instruments, Musical	3931
Insulated Wire & Cable, Nonferrous	3357
Insulation Asbestos	3292
Insulation Materials, Plastic Foam	3086
Insulation Siding Board	2493
Insulation Work	1742
Insulin	2834
Insurance, Accident	6321
Insurance, Casualty	6331
Insurance, Health	6321
Insurance, Life	6311
Insurance, Surety	6351
Insurance, Title	6361
Insurance Brokers, Agents	6411
Insurance Carriers, NEC	6399
Investment Counselors	6282
Investment Firm	6211
Investment Funds, Closed-End	6726
Investment Funds, Open-End	6722
Investors, NEC	6799
Iron, Pig	3312
Iron, Pig, Wholesale	5051
Iron & Steel Scrap	5093
Iron Ore Mining	1011
Iron Ore Wholesale	5052
Irons, Electric, Household	3634
Irrigation Systems	4971

J

Description	SIC Code
Jackets, Girls', Children's, Infants'	2369
Jackets, Leather	2386
Jackets, Men's & Boys' Sport	2329
Jackets, Men's & Boys' Work	2326
Jackets, Not Tailored	2339
Jacks, Hydraulic	3569
Janitorial Service	7349
Jeans, Girls, Children's, Infants'	2369
Jeans, Men's & Boys'	2325
Jeans, Women's, Misses', Juniors'	2339
Jellies, Jams, Edible	2033
Jet Engines	3724
Jewelry	3911
Jewelry Findings & Materials	3915
Jewelry Repair	7631
Jewelry Stores, Costume	5632
Jewelry Stores, Not Costume	5944
Jewelry, Wholesale	5094
Job Counseling	8331
Juices, Fruit & Vegetable	2033

K

Description	SIC Code
Kaolin, Ground Treated	3295
Kaolin Mining	1455
Karate Instruction	7999
Kennels	0752
Ketone	2869
Ketchup	2033
Keys	3429
Kilns, Cement	3559
Kilns, Except Cement	3567
Kitchen Utensils, Metal Stamped/Pressed	3469
Kitchen Woodenware	2499
Kitchenware, Cast Aluminum	3365
Kitchenware, China	3262
Kitchenware, Earthenware	3263
Kitchenware, Plastic	3089
Kitchenware Stores	5719
Knit Fabrics, Warp	2258
Knit Fabrics, Weft	2257
Knit Fabrics, Wholesale	5131
Knit Outerwear Mills	2253
Knit Underwear & Nightwear Mills	2254
Knitting Machines	3552
Knitting Mills, NEC	2259

Description	SIC Code
Knitting Yarn	2281
Knitting Yarn Shops	5949
Knives, Kitchen & Table	3421
Knives, Surgical	3841
Kraft Liner Board	2631

L

Description	SIC Code
LP Gas Distribution, Retail	5984
LP Gas Production	1321
Labels, Cotton, Printed	2269
Labels, Printed	2759
Labels, Woven	2241
Laboratories, Commercial	8731
Laboratories, Medical & X-Ray	8071
Laboratories, Testing	8734
Laboratory Apparatus	3821
Lacquers	2851
Lacquers, Wholesale	5198
Ladders, Metal, Portable	3499
Ladders, Wood	2499
Laminated Cardboard	2675
Laminated Glass	3211
Laminated Plastics	3083
Lamp Light Bulbs	3641
Lamp Light Bulbs, Wholesale	5063
Lamps, Residential	3645
Landfill Sanitary	4953
Landscape Counseling & Planning	0781
Language Schools	8299
Lapidary Work	3915
Laser Diodes	3674
Laser Systems, Medical	3845
Laser Welding Equipment	3699
Launderers, Industrial	7218
Launderettes, Laundromats	7215
Laundry Equipment, Commercial	3582
Laundry Equipment, Household	3633
Laundry & Garment Services, NEC	7219
Laundry Services	7211
Law Offices	8111
Lawn & Garden Services	0782
Lawnmowers	3524
Laxatives	2834
Lead Ore Mining	1031
Lead Smelting & Refining, Primary	3339
Lead Smelting & Refining, Secondary	3341
Lead, Wholesale	5051
Leather Dyes & Stains	2865
Leather Finishing Agents	2843
Leather Goods, NEC	3199
Leather Goods, Personal Except Handbags & Purses	3172
Leather Tanning & Finishing	3111
Legal Services	8111
Lemonade	2086
Lenses, Ophthalmic	3851
Lenses, Optical	3827
Leotards, Girls', Children's & Infants'	2369
Leotards, Womens', Misses' & Juniors'	2339
Lessors of Railroad Property	6517
Lessors of Real Property, NEC	6519
Lettuce Farms	0161
Levels, Carpenters	3423
Libraries & Information Centers	8231
Licensing & Inspection of Misc. Commercial Sectors	9651
Lift Trucks	3537
Lift Trucks, Wholesale	5084
Lifts, Elevator	3534
Lighting Equipment	3648
Lighting Fixtures, Commercial	3646
Lighting Fixtures, Residential	3645
Lighting Fixtures, Vehicular	3647
Lignite Mining	1221
Limbs, Artificial	3842
Lime	3274
Lime Groves	0174
Limestone, Crushed & Broken	1422
Limestone, Wholesale	5032

Description	SIC Code
Linen Fabrics	2299
Linoleum	3996
Liquor, Packaged, Retail	5921
Liquors, Distilled & Blended	2085
Liquors, Wholesale	5182
Lithium	2819
Lithographic Plates	2796
Lithographic Printing	2752
Livestock, Buying & Marketing	5154
Livestock Services, Except Veterinary	0751
Loan Agents, Brokers	6163
Loan Companies, Small	6141
Loan Institutions	6159
Locker Rental, Except Cold Storage	7299
Lockers, Not Refrigerated	2542
Lockers, Refrigerated	3585
Locomotives	3743
Lodging Houses on Membership Basis	7041
Log Cabins, Prefabricated	2452
Logging Camps & Contractors	2411
Logs, Fireplace, Electric	3699
Logs, Fireplace, Gas	3433
Looseleaf Binders	2782
Looseleaf Binders, Wholesale	5112
Lotteries	7999
Lubricating Oils & Leases	2992
Lubricating Oils & Leases, Wholesale	5172
Lubrication Equipment	3569
Lubrication Systems, Aircraft	3724
Lubrication Systems & Parts, Automotive	3714
Lubrication Systems, Locomotive	3743
Luggage	3161
Luggage, Wholesale	5099
Lumber & Building Material Dealers, Retail	5211
Lumber, Frying, Stacking, Rough	2421
Lumber, Retail	5211
Lumber, Wholesale	5031
Luncheon Meat, Except Poultry	2011
Luncheon Meat, Poultry	2015
Lye, Household	2842

M

Description	SIC Code
Machinery, Electrical Equipment & Supplies, NEC	3699
Machinery, Special Industry	3559
Machines & Equipment, General Industry, NEC	3569
Magazine Publishing & Printing	2721
Magazines, Wholesale	5192
Magnesium & Alloys Bars, Rods, Shapes	3356
Magnesium Compounds	2819
Magnetic Recording Tape, Blank	3695
Magnetic Recording Tape , Prerecorded	3625
Magnetic Recording Tape, Wholesale	5065
Magnetic Storage Devices, Computer	3572
Magnets, Permanent, Ceramic or Ferrite	3264
Magnets, Permanent, Metal	3499
Mail Advertising Services	7331
Mail Order Houses	5961
Mailgram Services	4822
Mainframe Computers	3571
Malt, Barley, Rye, Wheat, etc.	2083
Malt, Wholesale	5149
Management Consulting Services	8742
Manifold Business Forms	2761
Manifold Business Forms, Wholesale	5112
Manila Folders	2675
Manufacturing Industries, NEC	3999
Maps, Publishing & Printing	2741
Margarine	2079
Margarine, Wholesale	5149
Marinas	4493
Marine Cargo Handling	4491
Marine Engines	3519
Marine Paints	2851
Marine Products Production, Misc.	0919
Marketing Consultants	8742
Marking Devices	3953
Marshmallows	2064

Description	SIC Code
Masking Tape	2672
Masonry, Stone Work	1741
Matches & Match Books	3999
Matches, Wholesale	5199
Materials Handling Equipment	3537
Materials Handling Equipment, Wholesale	5084
Mattresses, Innerspring, Box Spring, etc.	2515
Mattresses, Wholesale	5021
Mayonnaise	2035
Meat Markets	5421
Meat & Meat Products, Wholesale	5147
Meat Packing Plants	2011
Meat Products, Cooked, Cured	2013
Meat Products, Prepared	2013
Mechanical Power Transmission Equipment, NEC	3568
Medical Equipment, Renting, Leasing	7352
Medical Services Plans	6324
Medicinal Chemicals	2833
Melon Farms	0161
Membership Organizations, Professional	8621
Mental Hospitals	8063
Merchandising Stores, Misc. General	5399
Mercury Compounds, Medical	2833
Mercury Ore Mining	1099
Mercury Oxides, Inorganic	2819
Metal, Structural, Fabricated	3441
Metal Buildings	3448
Metal Buildings, Wholesale	5039
Metal Fasteners	3429
Metal Foil & Leaf	3497
Metal Heat Treating	3398
Metal Mining Services	1081
Metal Products, Primary, NEC	3399
Metal Stampings	3469
Metal Waste & Scrap, Wholesale	5093
Metal Work, Architectural & Ornamental	3446
Metal Work, Structural, NEC	3449
Metals Service Centers & Offices	5051
Metalworking Machinery, NEC	3549
Metalworking Tools & Machinery	3545
Metalworking Tools & Machinery, Wholesale	5084
Meters, Electric	3825
Meters, Gas, Liquid	3824
Methanol, Natural	2861
Methanol, Synthetic	2869
Methyl Alcohol	2861
Methyl Chloride	2869
Mexican Foods, Canned	2032
Mica Mining	1499
Mica Products	3299
Microcircuits Integrated	3674
Microcomputers	3571
Microfiche Readers	3861
Microscopes, Electron & Proton	3826
Microscopes, Except Electron & Proton	3827
Microwave Communication Equipment	3663
Microwave Components	3679
Microwave Ovens, Household	3631
Microwave Ovens Wholesale	5064
Milk, Bottled	2026
Milk, Concentrated & Condensed, Dried, Evaporated	2023
Milking Machines	3523
Mills, Hardwood Dimension & Flooring	2426
Millwork Products	2431
Millwork, Wholesale	5031
Mineral Products, Nonmetallic, NEC	3299
Mineral Water	2086
Minerals & Earths, Ground or Otherwise Treated	3295
Minerals, Nonmetallic, Except Fuels, Misc., NEC	1499
Minerals, Nonmetallic, Except Fuels, Services	1481
Mining, Chemical & Fertilizer Mineral, NEC	1479
Mining, Gold Ores	1041
Mining Machinery & Equipment	3532
Mining Machinery & Equipment, Wholesale	5082
Mirrors	3231
Mirrors, Optical	3827

Alphabetical S.I.C. Compendium-continued

Description	SIC Code
Missile Guidance Systems	3812
Missile Warheads	3483
Mixers, Concrete	3531
Mixers, Electric, Food	3556
Mobile Communications Equipment	3663
Mobile Homes, Except Recreational	2451
Mobile Homes, Recreational	3792
Mobile Homes, Retail	5271
Mobile Homes, Wholesale	5039
Modems	3661
Modems, Wholesale	5065
Moldings & Trim, Stamped, Metal Automotive	3465
Moldings & Trim, Stamped, Metal, Except Automotive	3442
Moldings, Plastic	3089
Moldings, Wood	2431
Monorail Systems	3536
Mortgage Brokers & Companies	6162
Mortgage Guarantee Insurance	6351
Morticians	7261
Motels	7011
Motion Picture Distribution	7822
Motion Picture Equipment	3861
Motion Picture Equipment, Wholesale	5043
Motion Picture Distribution, Services Allied	7829
Motion Picture Production, Services Allied	7819
Motion Picture Production & Distribution	7812
Motor Homes, Self-Contained	3711
Motor Vehicle Dealers, Used	5521
Motor Vehicle Distribution, Wholesale	5012
Motor Vehicle Parts	3714
Motor Vehicle Parts, Used Wholesale & Retail	5015
Motor Vehicle Supplies & New Parts, Wholesale	5013
Motorcycle Dealers	5571
Motorcycles & Parts	3751
Motorcycles & Parts, Wholesale	5012
Mufflers, Exhaust, Motor Vehicle	3714
Mufflers, Installation, Repair	7533
Museums & Art Galleries	8412
Music Sheet, Publishing	2741
Music Video Production	7812
Musical Instrument Stores	5736
Musical Instruments & Accessories	3931
Musical Instruments & Accessories, Wholesale	5099
Mutual Funds	6722
Mutual Funds, Agents	6211

N

Description	SIC Code
Nails	3315
Nails, Wholesale	5051
Napkins, Fabric	2392
Napkins, Paper & Sanitary	2676
Natural Gas, Liquid Production	1321
Natural Gas, Production	1311
Natural Gas Storage & Transmission	4922
Navigation Systems & Instruments	3812
Neckwear, Men's & Boys'	2323
Needles, Hand, Machine	3965
Needles, Hypodermic, Suture	3841
Needlework	2395
Needlework Stores	5949
Neon	2813
Neon Signs	3993
Neon Signs, Wholesale	5046
News Dealers & Newsstands	5994
News Ticker Services	7383
Newspaper Publishing	2711
Newspapers, Wholesale	5192
Newsprint	2621
Nickel & Alloy Products	3356
Nickel Ore Mining	1061
Nickel Refining, Primary	3339
Nitric Acid	2873
Nitrogen	2813
Nonclassifiable Establishments	9999
Nondurable Goods, Wholesale	5199
Nuclear Reactors	3443
Nursery Schools	8351
Nursery Stock, Production	0181
Nursery Stock, Retail	5261
Nursery Stock, Wholesale	5193
Nursing Homes, Intermediate Care	8052
Nursing Homes, Skilled Care	8051
Nuts, Candy Covered	2064
Nuts, Dehydrated, Dried, Salted, Roasted	2068
Nuts, Metal	3452
Nuts, Plastic	3089
Nylon Fabrics, Resins	2221
Nylon Fibers, Bristles, Threads	2824
Nylon Yarn, Spinning	2281
Nylon Yarn, Throwing	2282

O

Description	SIC Code
Oats, Oatmeal	2043
Oats, Wholesale	5153
Off-Highway Machinery	3536
Office Equipment, Wholesale	5049
Office Supplies, Wholesale	5112
Offset Printing	2752
Oil & Gas Field Exploration Services	1382
Oil & Gas Field Machinery & Equipment	3533
Oil & Gas Field Services, NEC	1389
Oil Royalty Traders	6792
Oil, Corn	2046
Oil, Cottonseed	2074
Oil Refining Machinery, Equipment, Wholesale	5084
Oil, Vegetable, Except Corn Oil	2079
Oils, Lubricating	2911
Oils, Sulfonated	2843
Oleo	2079
On-Line Database Information Retrieval	7375
Operators of Apartment Buildings	6513
Operators of Nonresidential Buildings	6512
Ophthalmic Goods	3851
Ophthalmic Goods, Wholesale	5048
Ophthalmic Instruments & Apparatus	3841
Optical Goods, Retail	5995
Optical Lens Machinery	3559
Optical Readers & Scanners	3577
Optical Test & Inspection Equipment	3827
Optometrists, Offices & Clinics	8042
Ordinance & Accessories, NEC	3489
Ore Crushing Machinery	3532
Organic Chemicals	2869
Organic Fibers	2824
Organic Pigments	2865
Ornamental Shrub & Tree Services	0783
Outboard Motors, Electric	3699
Outboard Motors, Except Electric	3519
Outboard Motors, Wholesale	5091
Oxygen, Compressed & Liquefied	2813

P

Description	SIC Code
Pacemakers	3845
Packaging Machinery	3565
Packing & Scaling Devices	3053
Padlocks	3429
Painting & Paper Hanging	1721
Paints	2851
Paints, Wholesale	5198
Pallets, Wooden	2653
Paper, Coated & Laminated, NEC	2672
Paper, Industrial & Personal Service, Wholesale	5113
Paper, Printing & Writing, Wholesale	5111
Paper & Paperboard, Die-cut	2675
Paper & Paperboard Products, Converted, NEC	2679
Paper Mills	2621
Paperboard Mills	2631
Parcel Delivery, Air	4513
Parcel Delivery, Except Air	4215
Parking Lots	7521
Parquet Flooring, Wood	2426
Particleboard	2493
Particleboard, Wholesale	5031
Partitians, Wood	2541
Pasta, Dry	2098
Patent Owners & Lessors	6794
Payroll Accounting Service	8721
Peanut Butter	2099
Pencils, Mechanical	3951
Pencils, Not Mechanical	3952
Pencils & Pens Wholesale	5112
Pens & Pen Parts	3951
Pension, Health & Welfare Funds	6371
Percale	2211
Perfumes	2844
Perfumes, Wholesale	5122
Periodicals, Publishing & Printing	2721
Periodicals, Wholesale	5192
Peripheral Equipment	3577
Peripheral Equipment, Wholesale	5045
Personal Services, NEC	7299
Pesticides	2879
Pesticides, Wholesale	5191
Pet Food, Dog & Cat	2047
Pet Food, Except Dog & Cat	2048
Pet Food Stores	5999
Pet Food, Wholesale	5149
Petroleum Brokers	5172
Petroleum Bulk Stations & Terminals, Wholesale	5171
Petroleum Gas Products &/or Distribution, Mixed or Liquified	4925
Petroleum Products, NEC	2999
Petroleum Refining	2911
Pharmaceuticals	2834
Pharmaceuticals, Wholesale	5122
Phonographs	3651
Phonographs, Wholesale	5046
Phosphate Rock	1475
Phosphates	2874
Phosphoric Acid	2874
Photocopy Machine	3861
Photocopy Machines, Wholesale	5044
Photocopy Service	7334
Photofinishing Laboratories	7384
Photographers & Photographic Studios	7221
Photographic Equipments & Supplies, Wholesale	5043
Physical Fitness Centers	7991
Pianos	3931
Pickles & Relishes	2035
Pigments, Inorganic	2816
Pigments, Organic	2865
Pins	3965
Pipe, Non-Ferrous	3356
Pipe, Sewer, Clay	3259
Pipe, Stainless Steel	3317
Pipe Lines, NEC	4619
Pipeline Construction	1623
Pizza, Frozen	2038
Pizzerias	5812
Plastering	1742
Plastic Coating of Metals	3479
Plastics, Bottle	3085
Plastics, Film, Coated, Laminated for Packaging	2671
Plastics, Film & Sheet Unsupported	3081
Plastics, Foam	3086
Plastics, Laminated, Except Packaging	3083
Plastics Materials, Wholesale	5162
Plastics, Pipe	3084
Plastics, Plumbing Fixtures	3088
Plastics Products, NEC	3089
Plastics, Resins	2821
Plastics, Resins Wholesale	5162
Plate Glass	3211
Plate Glass, Wholesale	5039
Platinum Ore Mining	1099
Plumbing Contractors	1711

Description	SIC Code
Plumbing Fixture Fittings & Trim	3432
Plumbing Fixtures, Vitreous China	3261
Plywood, Hardwood	2435
Plywood, Softwood	2436
Plywood, Wholesale	5031
Pneumatic Valves	3492
Polishes	2842
Polishes, Wholesale	5169
Polyester, Polypropylene, Polyvinyl Fabrics	2221
Polyester, Polypropylene, Polyvinyl Resins	2821
Polyester, Polypropylene, Polyvinyl Yarn	2281
Polyester Fibers, Threads	2284
Popcorn Farms	0119
Popcorn, Packaged, Except Popped	2099
Popcorn, Popped	2096
Popcorn, Wholesale	5145
Porcelain Cement, Household	2891
Porcelain Parts for Electrical & Electronic Use	3264
Portland Cement	3241
Potash Mining	1474
Potassium Chloride, Chlorate	2819
Potato Farms	0134
Potatoes, Fresh, Wholesale	5148
Pottery Products	3269
Poultry Feeds & Supplements	2048
Poultry, Processed	2015
Poultry Production	0259
Poultry Products, Wholesale	5144
Pre-Mixed Concrete, Wholesale	5032
Precious Metals & Stones, Wholesale	5094
Prefabricated Buildings, Metal	3448
Prefabricated Buildings, Wholesale	5039
Prefabricated Buildings, Wood	2452
Preschool Centers	8351
Presses, Hydraulic & Pneumatic	3542
Pressure Control Valves	3492
Pressure Gauges	3823
Pressure Sensitive Tape	2672
Pressure Sensitive Tape Wholesale	5113
Printed Circuit Boards	3672
Printing, Commercial, NEC	2759
Printers, Computer	3577
Printing, Lithographic & Off-Set	2752
Printing Gravure	2754
Printing Ink	2893
Printing Presses	3555
Printing Trade Machinery & Equipment, Wholesale	5084
Propane Production	1321
Protective Service, Guard	7381
Psychiatric Hospitals	8063
Public Finance, Taxation & Monetary Policy	9311
Public Relations Services	8743
Publishing, Book	2731
Publishing, Directory	2741
Publishing & Printing, Magazines	2721
Pulp Mills	2611
Pumps	3561
Pumps, Measuring & Dispensing	3586

R

Description	SIC Code
Racing, Including Track Operation	7948
Radar Systems	3812
Radio Stations	4832
Radioactive Waste, Disposal of	4953
Radios	3651
Railroad Cars & Locomotives, Equipment	3743
Railroad Equipment & Supplies, Wholesale	5088
Railroad Switching & Terminal Establishments	4013
Railroads, Commuter, Suburban	4111
Railroads, Line-Haul	4011
Rain Coats & Waterproof Outwear	2385
Ramie Fabrics	2299
Razor Blades	3421
Razors, Non-Electric	3421
Ready-Mix Concrete	3273
Real Estate Agents	6531
Real Estate Development	6552
Real Estate Investment Trusts	6798
Record & Prerecorded Tape Stores	5735
Records, Phonograph	3652
Rectifiers, Electronic Wholesale	5065
Rectifiers, Except Solid-State	3679
Rectifiers, Solid-State	3674
Refined Petroleum Pipe Lines	4613
Refineries, Petroleum	2911
Refractories, Clay	3255
Refractories, Non-Clay	3297
Refractory Material, Wholesale	5085
Refrigerated Warehouses	4222
Refrigeration Controls	3822
Refrigeration Machinery	3585
Refrigerators, Commercial, Wholesale	5078
Refrigerators, Household	3632
Refrigerators, Household, Wholesale	5064
Refuse Systems	4953
Regulation & Administration of Communication, Electric, Gas & Other Utilities	9631
Regulation of Agricultural Marketing & Commodities	9641
Relays	3625
Relays, Wholesale	5063
Rental of Automobiles	7514
Rental of Computers	7377
Rental of Equipment	7359
Rental of Motion Picture Films	7819
Rental of Railroad Cars	4741
Repair of Equipment	7699
Repair Shops, Air Conditioning	7623
Repair Shops, Automobile, NEC	7539
Repair Shops, Automotive Exhaust System	7533
Repair Shops, Automotive Transmission	7537
Repair Shops, Electrical & Electronic, NEC	7631
Repair Shops, Radio & Television	7622
Repair Shops, Refrigeration	7623
Research, Commercial Economic, Sociological & Educational	8732
Research & Development	8731
Research Organizations, Noncommercial	8733
Residential Care	8361
Resins	2821
Resins, Custom Compounding of Purchased Plastic	3087
Resistors, Electronic	3676
Resistors, Electronic, Wholesale	5065
Restaurants	5812
Retail Stores, Misc., NEC	5999
Ribbons, Inked	3955
Ribbons, Inked, Wholesale	5112
Rice Cleaning & Polishing	2044
Rice Production	0112
Rifles	3484
Rivets, Metal	3452
Road Construction	1611
Robes & Dressing Gowns	2384
Robots	3569
Rockets, Guided Missiles	3761
Rockets, Pyrotechnic	2899
Rolling Mill Machinery	3547
Rolling Mills	3212
Roofing Contractor, Siding, Sheet Metal Work	1761
Roofing Fabrics	2952
Roofing, Siding & Installation Materials, Wholesale	5033
Rooming & Boarding Houses	7021
Rotogravure Printing	2754
Rubber & Plastic Hose	3052
Rubber Goods, Molded, Extruded	3061
Rubber Goods, NEC	3069
Rubber, Synthetic	2822
Rugs	2273
Rugs, Wholesale	5023
Rust Removers	2842

S

Description	SIC Code
Saccharin	2869
Saddles & Parts	3199
Saddles, Motorcycle, Bicycle	3751
Safes & Vaults	3499
Safes & Vaults, Wholesale	5044
Safety Glass	3231
Safety Gloves	3842
Safety Pins	3965
Sailboats	3732
Sailboats, Wholesale	5091
Salad Dressings, Dry Mixes	2099
Salad Dressings, Except Dry Mixes	2035
Salad Oils	2079
Salads, Fresh	2099
Salmon, Smoked, etc.	2091
Salt	2899
Salt Mining	1479
Salt, Wholesale	5149
Sand, Industrial	1446
Sand & Gravel Dealers	5211
Sandpaper	3291
Sanitary Napkins	2676
Sanitary Services, NEC	4959
Sanitary Paper Food Containers	2656
Satellite Home Antennas	3679
Satellites, Communications	3663
Sauces, Tomato-Based	2033
Sauces, Vegetable Meat	2035
Sauces, Wholesale	5149
Sausages	2013
Savings & Loan, Federal	6035
Savings & Loan, State	6036
Saw Blades	3425
Saw Blades, Wholesale	5072
Sawmills	2421
Sawmills, Special Product, NEC	2429
Saws, Hand	3425
Saws, Power, Metal Cutting	3541
Saws, Power Woodworking	3553
Scaffolds, Metal	3446
Scaffolds, Wholesale	5082
Scaffolds, Wood	2499
Scales, Except Laboratory	3596
Scales, Except Laboratory, Wholesale	5046
Scales, Laboratory	3821
Schiffli Machine Embroideries	2397
School Buses	4151
School Photographers	7221
Schools & Camps, Sports	7999
Schools & Educational Services, NEC	8299
Schools for Handicapped	8211
Schools, Business & Secretarial	8244
Schools, Colleges, Universities & Professional	8221
Schools, Correspondence	8249
Schools, Dance	7911
Schools, Data Processing	8243
Schools, Elementary & Secondary	8211
Schools, Junior Colleges & Technical Institutes	8222
Schools, Riding	7999
Schools, Vocational & Correspondence	8249
Scissors, Electric	3634
Scissors, Hand	3421
Scotch Whiskey	2085
Scrap & Waste Materials, Wholesale	5093
Screening, Window, Plastic	3089
Screening, Window, Wire	3496
Screens, Door & Window, Metal Frame	3442
Screw Drivers	3423
Screw Machine Products	3451
Screws, Metal	3452
Seafood Products, Canned & Cured	2091
Seafood Products, Fresh & Frozen	2092
Sealants, Wholesale	5169
Sealing Compounds	2891
Search Systems & Instruments	3812
Seasonings	2035
Seatbelts, Automotive & Aircraft	2399

Alphabetical S.I.C. Compendium-continued

Description	*SIC Code*
Seatbelts, Automotive, Wholesale	5013
Seats, Automobile, Aircraft	2531
Security Dealers, Brokers	6211
Security Systems Services	7382
Semiconductor Devices	3674
Semiconductor Devices, Wholesale	5065
Service Establishment Equipment & Supplies, Except Motor Vehicle, Wholesale	5087
Service Stations, Gasoline	5541
Services, NEC	8999
Services Allied With Exchange of Securities or Commodities, NEC	6289
Servomotors	3621
Sewerage Systems	4959
Sewing Machines, Household	3639
Sewing Machines, Household, Wholesale	5064
Sewing Machines, Industrial	3559
Sewing Machines, Industrial, Wholesale	5084
Sewing Thread	2284
Shampoos, Hair	2844
Sheet Metal Work	3444
Shellfish	0913
Shelving, Not Wood	2542
Shelving, Wholesale	5046
Shelving, Wood	2541
Shingles, Asphalt, Tar	2952
Shingles, Wood	2429
Ship Building & Repairing	3731
Shirts, Men's & Boys', Except Work Shirts	2321
Shirts, Women's, Misses' & Juniors'	2337
Shoe Stores	5661
Shoes, Children's & Infants'	3149
Shoes, Men's	3143
Shoes, Wholesale	5139
Shoes, Women's	3144
Siding, Plastic	3089
Siding, Sheet Metal	3444
Signs & Advertising Displays	3993
Silver Mining	1044
Ski Wear	2329
Skids, Wooden	2448
Skis & Skiing Equipment	3949
Simulators, Training	3699
Slacks, Girls' & Children's	2369
Slacks, Men's & Boys'	2325
Slacks, Women's, Misses' & Juniors'	2339
Slippers, House	3142
Slot Machines	3999
Smoke Detectors	3669
Soaps & Cleaners	2841
Soft Drinks, Bottled or Canned	2086
Soft Drinks, Wholesale	5149
Software, Prepackaged	7372
Software, Systems Analysis, Custom	7371
Software, Wholesale	5045
Soil Preparation Services	0711
Solar Cells	3674
Solar Energy Collectors, Heaters	3433
Soldering Guns & Tools, Hand, Electric	3423
Solenoid Switches	3625
Solenoid Valves	3492
Solvents, Degreasing	2842
Solvents, Organic	2869
Sonar Systems	3812
Sound Recording Equipment	3861
Soup Mixes	2034
Soups, Canned, Except Fish & Seafood	2032
Soups, Canned, Fish & Seafood	2091
Soups, Frozen, Except Seafood	2038
Soups, Frozen, Fish & Seafood	2092
Sour Cream	2026
Soy Sauce	2035
Soybean Oil Mills	2075
Soybean Production	0116
Soybeans, Wholesale	5153
Space Capsules	3769
Space Vehicle Propulsion Units & Propulsion Unit Parts	3764
Space Vehicles	3761
Spaghetti Sauce	2033
Spaghetti, Dry	2098
Spectrometers	3829
Speed Changers, Industrial High Speed Drives	3566
Spices	2099
Spices, Wholesale	5149
Sponge Gathering	0919
Sporting Goods	3949
Sporting Goods, Retail	5941
Sporting & Recreational Goods & Supplies, Wholesale	5091
Sports Clubs & Promoters, Professional	7941
Sports & Recreation Clubs, Membership	7997
Stainless Steel	3312
Stamp Pads, Stamping Devices	3953
Staples, Steel	3315
Staples, Wire	3496
State Banks	6022
Stationery	2678
Stationery Stores	5943
Steam & Air-Conditioning Supply	4961
Steam Fittings	3494
Steam Fittings, Wholesale	5074
Steam Turbines	3511
Steel Bars, Sheet, Strip	3316
Steel Foundries	3312
Steel, Wholesale	5051
Sterilizers, Dental	3843
Sterilizers, Laboratory	3821
Sterilizers, Medical	3842
Stevedoring	4491
Stitching & Tucking, Pleating, Decorative & Novelty	2395
Stone, Crushed & Broken, NEC	1429
Stone Quarrying	3281
Storage Batteries	3691
Stoves, Commercial	3589
Stoves, Household, Cooking	3631
Stoves, Household Heating	3433
Strip Mining, Anthracite	1231
Strip Mining, Bituminous	1221
Structural Steel Erection	1791
Sugar, Granulated, Beet	2063
Sugar, Granulated, Cane	2061
Sugar, Wholesale	5149
Sugar Beet Production	0133
Sugar Cane Production	0133
Suitcases	3161
Suits & Overcoats, Men's & Boys'	2311
Sulfuric Acid	2819
Sunflower Farms	0119
Sunflower Seed Oil	2076
Sunglasses	3851
Supermarkets	5411
Surface Active Agents	2843
Surfboards	3949
Surgical Equipment, Wholesale	5047
Surgical Instruments	3841
Surveying Instruments	3829
Surveying Services	8713
Sweeteners, Synthetic	2869
Switchboard Apparatus	3613
Switches, Electric	3643
Switches, Electronic	3679
Switchgear	3613
Switchgear, Wholesale	5063
Synthesizers, Music	3931
Synthetic Fibers	2284
Systems Analysis & Design	7371
Systems Engineering	8748
T	
Tablets, Writing	2678
Tanks & Tank Components	3795
Tape, Audio Magnetic, Prerecorded	3652
Tape, Magnetic, Blank	3695
Tape, Masking	2672
Tape, Pressure Sensitive	2672
Tape, Pressure Sensitive, Wholesale	5113
Tape Distribution for Television	7822
Tape Recorders	3651
Tape Storage Units, Computer	3572
Tapes, Audio & Video Recording, Wholesale	5065
Tax Return Preparation	7291
Tea, Wholesale	5149
Tea Blending	2099
Telegraph Services	4822
Telephone Answering Machines	3661
Telephone Communication, Except Radio	4813
Telephone Equipment, Wholesale	5065
Telephones	3661
Telephones, Cellular, Radio	3663
Television Sets	3651
Television Stations	4833
Temperature Controls, Automatic	3822
Terminals, Computer	3575
Textile Goods, NEC	2299
Textile Machinery	3552
Textile Mills, Broadwoven	2211
Textile Mills, Narrow Woven	2241
Textile Products, Fabricated, NEC	2399
Textiles, Wholesale	5131
Theaters, Movie, Drive-In	7833
Theaters, Moving Picture	7832
Theatrical Producers & Services, Except Motion Picture	7922
Theme Parks	7996
Thermostats	3822
Tile, Acoustical	3296
Tile, Asphalt	3292
Tile, Ceramic & Clay	3253
Tile, Concrete	3272
Tile, Gypsum	3275
Tile, Terrazzo, Marble, Mosaic Contractors	1743
Tile, Vinyl Asbestos	3292
Timber Tracts	0811
Timeclocks, Time-stamps	3579
Timing Devices	3625
Tin Cans	3411
Tin Compounds	2819
Tin Ore Mining	1099
Tin Smelting & Refining	3341
Tire Retreading & Repair Shop	7534
Tires & Tubes, Wholesale	5014
Tires, Cushion or Solid Rubber	3011
Title Insurance	6361
Title Search Companies	6541
Tobacco Production	0132
Tobacco Stemming & Redrying	2141
Tobacco Stores & Stands	5993
Toilet Fixtures, Iron	3431
Toilet Fixtures, Plastics	3088
Toilet Fixtures, Vitreous China	3261
Toilet Tissue	2621
Toiletries	2844
Toiletries, Wholesale	5122
Tool Rental	7359
Tools, Cutting, NEC	3545
Tools, Drilling, Oil Wells, etc.	3533
Tools, Hand, Except Power Driven	3423
Tools, Hand, Power Driven	3546
Tools, Machine, Metal Cutting	3541
Tools, Machine, Metal Forming	3542
Tools, Power Driven & Hand, Wholesale	5251
Tour Operators	4725
Towing & Tugboat Services	4492
Toy Stores	5945
Toys, Except Dolls	3944
Toys, Dolls	3942
Toys, Stuffed	3942
Toys & Hobby Goods & Supplies, Wholesale	5092
Tractors, Industrial	3537
Tractors, Lawn & Garden	3524
Trading Companies	6799
Trailer & Recreational Vehicle Utility Rental	7519
Trailers, Boat	3799
Trailers, Farm	3523
Trailers, Industrial	3537
Trailers, Mobile Home, Recreational	3792

Description	SIC Code
Trailers, Travel, Camping	3792
Trains, Toy, & Equipment	3944
Transformers, Electric	3612
Transformers, Electric, Wholesale	5063
Transformers, Electronic	3677
Transformers, Electronic, Wholesale	5065
Transistors	3674
Transistors, Wholesale	5065
Translation Service	7389
Transmission Equipment, Motor Vehicle	3714
Transportation, Air, Nonscheduled	4522
Transportation, Air, Services, NEC	4512
Transportation, Arrangement of Freight & Cargo	4731
Transportation, Arrangement of Passenger	4729
Transportation, Deep Sea Freight, Domestic	4424
Transportation, Equipment & Supplies, Except Motor Vehicle, Wholesale	5088
Transportation, Great Lakes Freight	4432
Transportation, Intercity & Rural Bus	4131
Transportation, Local Passenger, NEC	4119
Transportation Equipment, NEC	3799
Transportation Services, NEC	4789
Travel Agencies	4724
Trophies, Metal	3499
Trophies, Silver, Nickel Silver, Pewter, Plated	3914
Trophies, Wholesale	5094
Trousers, Men's & Boys'	2325
Truck Beds & Bodies	3713
Truck Leasing	7513
Truck Trailers	3715
Truck Trailers, Wholesale	5012
Trucking, Except Local	4213
Trucking, Local	4212
Trucking, Local, with Storage	4214
Trucks, Off-Highway	3531
Trucks, Wholesale	5012
Trust Facilities, Nondeposit	6091
Trusts, Personal Investment, Management	6733
Tubes, Aluminum	3353
Tubes, Plastics	3082
Tubes, Seamless Steel	3317
Tubing, Glass	3229
Tubing, Metal	3317
Tubing, Metal, Wholesale	5051
Tuna Fish, Canned	2091
Tunnel Construction	1622
Turbine Generator Sets	3511
Turbines, Aircraft	3724
Turkeys, Processed	2015
Turkeys & Turkey Egg Products	0251
Turnstiles	3829
Turtles, Catching of	0919
Typesetting	2791
Typewriter Ribbons	3955
Typewriters	3579
Typewriters, Wholesale	5044

U

Description	SIC Code
Underwear, Men's & Boys'	2322
Ultraviolet Lamps	3641
Ultraviolet Sensors	3674
Umbrellas	3999
Underwear, Men's and Boys'	2322
Underwear, Men's and Boys', Wholesale	5136
Underwear, Women's, Misses', Children's, Infants'	2341
Underwear, Women's, Misses', Children's, Infants', Wholesale	5137
Uniform Supply Service	7213
Uranium Ore Mining	1094

V

Description	SIC Code
Vacuum Bottles	3429
Vacuum Brakes, Motor Vehicle	3714
Vacuum Brakes, Railway	3743
Vacuum Cleaner Hose	3052
Vacuum Cleaners, Electric, Household	3635
Vacuum Cleaners, Electric, Household, Wholesale	5064
Vacuum Cleaners, Electric, Industrial & Commercial	3589
Vacuum Cleaning Systems, Wholesale	5087
Vacuum Pumps, Except Laboratory	3563
Vacuum Pumps, Laboratory	3821
Vacuum Tubes	3671
Vacuum Tunnels	3443
Valves, Air Ventilating	3491
Valves, Automatic Control, Fluid Power	3492
Valves, Hard Rubber	3069
Valves, Hydraulic & Pneumatic	3492
Valves, PCV	3714
Valves, Plumbing & Heating	3494
Valves, Plumbing & Heating Wholesale	5074
Van Conversions	7532
Vanadium Ore Mining	1094
Vaporizers, Electric, Household	3634
Variety Stores	5331
Varnish Removers & Stains	2851
Varnishes	2851
Varnishes, Wholesale	5198
Veal	2011
Vegetable Farms	0161
Vegetable Juices	2033
Vegetable Oil Mills, Except Corn, Cottonseed & Soybean	2076
Vegetable Oils	2899
Vegetables, Canned	2033
Vegetables, Frozen	2037
Vegetables, Wholesale	5148
Vending Machines, Coin Operated	3581
Vending Machines, Rental	7359
Vending Machines, Wholesale	5046
Veneer, Hardwood Including Plywood	2435
Veneer, Softwood, Not Including Plywood	2436
Venetian Blinds	2591
Ventilating Fans, Electric, Household	3634
Veterinary Pharmaceutical Preparations	2834
Video Cameras	3651
Video Cassette Recorders, Players	3651
Video Game Machines	3944
Video Remote Control Devices	3651
Video Tape Production	7812
Video Tape Rental	7841
Vinegar	2099
Vineyards	0172
Vinyl Acetate	2869
Vinyl Asbestos Tile	3292
Vinyl Coated Fabrics	2295
Vinyl Fibers	2824
Vinyl Resins	2821
Vinyl Sheet & Film	3081
Vitamin Preparation	2834
Vitamins, Natural	2833
Vitamins, Wholesale	5122
Vocational Schools	8249
Voltage Regulators, Motor Vehicle	3694
Voltage Regulators, Transmission, Transformers	3612
Voltmeters	3825

W

Description	SIC Code
Wallboard, Gypsum	3275
Wallboard, Wholesale	5031
Wallboard, Wood Fiber	2493
Wallpaper	2679
Wallpaper, Wholesale	5198
Warehousing, Cold Storage	4222
Warehousing, General	4225
Warehousing & Storage, Special, NEC	4226
Warm Air Heating Equipment & Supplies, Wholesale	5075
Washers, Metal	3452
Washers, Plastics	3089
Washing Machines, Household, Electric	3633
Washing Machines, Household, Electric, Wholesale	5064
Waste Treatment Plants	4953
Wastepaper, Recycling, Wholesale	5093
Watch Crystals	3231
Watch Jewels	3915
Watches & Parts	3873
Watches & Parts, Wholesale	5094
Water Coolers, Electric	3585
Water Filters & Softeners	3589
Water Heaters, Electric, Wholesale	5064
Water Heaters, Except Electric, Wholesale	5074
Water Heaters, Household	3639
Water Purification & Softening Equipment, Household	3589
Water Quality Controls	3823
Water, Sewer Construction	1623
Water Softening Service	7389
Water Supply	4941
Water Transportation, Passenger, NEC	4489
Water Transporation Services, NEC	4499
Water Well Drilling	1781
Welding & Cutting Tools	3548
Welding & Cutting Tools, Wholesale	5084
Welding Repair	7692
Well Drilling, Oil Gas	1381
Well Drilling, Water	1781
Well Servicing Oil & Gas	1389
Wet Corn Milling	2041
Wet Corn Milling Products	5149
Wheat Production	0111
Wheat Products	2041
Wheat, Wholesale	5153
Wheel Balancing Equipment	3559
Wheel Chairs	3842
Wheelbarrows	3799
Wheels, Abrasive, Dental	3843
Wheels, Aircraft	3728
Wheels, Grinding, Abrasive	3291
Wheels, Motor Vehicle	3714
Wheels, Stamped Metal	3499
Whiskey, Scotch Whiskey	2085
Wicker Furniture	2519
Wigs	3999
Wigs, Wholesale	5199
Wind Tunnels	3443
Window Frames & Sash, Metal	3442
Window Frames & Sash, Wood	3431
Window Units	2431
Window Glass	3211
Window Glass, Wholesale	5039
Window Screens, Metal Frame	3442
Window Screens, Wood Frame	2331
Window Shades	2591
Windows & Doors, Wholesale	5031
Wines	2084
Wines, Wholesale	5182
Wire, Nonferrous	3357
Wire, Steel	3315
Wood Alcohol	2861
Wood Chips	2421
Wood Chips, Wholesale	5099
Wood Kitchen Cabinets	2434
Wood Members, Structural, NEC	2439
Wood Panels, Wholesale	5031
Wood Preserving	2491
Wood Production	0214
Wood Products	0214
Wood Products, Reconstituted	2493
Wood Stains	2851
Wooden Pallets	2448
Woodworking Machinery, Wholesale	5084
Woodworking Machines	3553
Wool Fabrics, Broad Woven	2231
Wool Fabrics, Narrow Woven	2241
Wool, Mineral	3296
Wool, Raw, Wholesale	5159
Wool Yarn	2282
Work Clothing, Men's & Boys'	2326
Wrecker Service	7549

Alphabetical S.I.C. Compendium-continued

Description	SIC Code
Wrecking of Buildings	1795
Wrenches	3423
X	
X-Ray Apparatus	3844
X-Ray Film	3861
X-Ray Machines & Parts, Wholesale	5047
Y	
Yard Goods, Stores	5949
Yard Goods, Wholesale	5131
Yarn, Spun	2281
Yarns, Wholesale	5199
Yeast	2099
Yeast, Wholesale	5149
Yogurt	2026
Yogurt, Frozen	2024
Yogurt, Wholesale	5143
Z	
Zinc Ore, Wholesale	5052
Zinc Ore Mining	1031
Zinc Pigments	2816
Zinc, Rolling, Drawing, Extruding	3341
Zippers	3965
Zippers, Wholesale	5131
Zirconium Bars, Strips, etc.	3356
Zirconium Ore Mining	1099

NUMERICAL COMPENDIUM OF S.I.C. CODES

* NEC Denotes a Business or Service Not Elsewhere Classified

Code	*Title*
01	**AGRICULTURAL PRODUCTION-CROPS**
0111	Wheat Production
0112	Rice Production
0115	Corn Production
0116	Soybean Production
0119	Cash Grains, NEC
0131	Cotton & Cottonseed Production
0132	Tobacco Production
0133	Sugarcane & Sugar Beet Production
0134	Irish Potato Production
0139	Field Crops, Except Cash Grains, NEC
0161	Vegetable & Melon Production
0171	Berry Farms
0172	Production of Grapes
0173	Production of Tree Nuts
0174	Citrus Fruits Production
0175	Deciduous Tree Fruits Production
0179	Production of Fruits & Tree Nuts, NEC
0181	Ornamental Floraculture & Nursery Products Production
0182	Food Crops Grown Under Cover
0191	General Farms, Primarily Crop
02	**AGRICULTURAL PRODUCTION-LIVESTOCK**
0211	Beef Cattle Feedlots
0212	Beef Cattle, Except Feedlots
0213	Hog Production
0214	Sheep & Goats Production
0219	General Livestock, Except Dairy & Poultry
0241	Dairy Farms
0251	Broiler, Fryer & Roaster Chickens
0252	Chicken Eggs Production
0253	Turkeys & Turkey Eggs Production
0254	Poultry Hatcheries Production
0259	Poultry & Eggs Production, NEC
0271	Fur-Bearing Animals & Rabbits
0272	Horses & Other Equines Farms
0273	Animal Aquaculture
0279	Animal Specialties, NEC
0291	General Farms, Primarily Livestock & Animal
07	**AGRICULTURAL SERVICES**
0711	Soil Preparation Services
0721	Crop Planting, Cultivating & Protection Services
0722	Crop Harvesting, Primarily by Machine
0723	Crop Preparation Services for Market
0724	Cotton Ginning
0751	Livestock Services, Except Veterinary
0752	Animal Specialty Services, Except Veterinary
0761	Farm Labor Contractors & Crew Leaders
0762	Farm Management Services
0781	Landscape Counseling & Planning
0782	Lawn & Garden Services
0783	Ornamental Shrub & Tree Services
08	**FORESTRY & FOREST PRODUCTS**
0811	Timber Tracts
0831	Forest Nurseries & Forest Products
0851	Forestry Services
09	**FISHING & HUNTING**
0912	Catching of Finfish
0913	Catching or Taking of Shellfish
0919	Miscellaneous Marine Products Production
0921	Fish Hatcheries & Preserves
0971	Hunting, Trapping & Game Propagation

Code	*Title*
10	**METAL MINING & RELATED SERVICES**
1011	Iron Ores Mining
1021	Copper Ores Mining
1031	Lead & Zinc Ores Mining
1041	Gold Ores Mining
1044	Silver Ores Mining
1061	Ferroalloy Ores Mining, Except Vanadium
1081	Metal Mining Services
1094	Uranium-Radium-Vanadium Ores
1099	Miscellaneous Metal Ores Mining, NEC
12	**COAL MINING**
1221	Surface Mining-Bituminous Coal & Lignite
1222	Underground Mining-Bituminous Coal
1231	Anthracite Mining
1241	Coal Mining Services
13	**OIL & GAS PRODUCTION**
1311	Crude Petroleum & Natural Gas
1321	Natural Gas Liquids
1381	Drilling Oil & Gas Wells
1382	Oil & Gas Field Exploration Services
1389	Oil & Gas Field Services, NEC
14	**NONMETALLIC MINERALS**
1411	Dimension Stone
1422	Crushed & Broken Limestone
1423	Crushed & Broken Granite
1429	Crushed & Broken Stone, NEC
1442	Construction Sand & Gravel
1446	Industrial Sand
1455	Kaolin & Ball Clay
1459	Clay, Ceramic & Refractory Minerals, NEC
1474	Potash, Soda & Borate Minerals
1475	Phosphate Rock
1479	Chemical & Fertilizer Mineral Mining, NEC
1481	Nonmetallic Minerals (Except Fuel) Services
1499	Miscellaneous Nonmetallic Minerals, Except Fuels
15	**BUILDING CONTRACTORS**
1521	General Contractors-Single Family Houses
1522	General Contractors, Other Than Single-Family Houses
1531	Operative Builders
1541	General Contractors-Industrial Buildings & Warehouses
1542	General Contractors-Non-Residential Buildings
16	**HEAVY CONSTRUCTION**
1611	Highway & Street Construction, Except Elevated Hwy.
1622	Bridge, Tunnel & Elevated Highway Construction
1623	Water, Sewer, Power Line, Pipeline & Communications Construction
1629	Heavy Construction, NEC
17	**SPECIAL TRADE CONTRACTORS**
1711	Plumbing, Heating & Air Conditioning Contractors
1721	Painting & Paper Hanging Contractors
1731	Electrical Work Contractors
1741	Masonry, Stone Setting & Other Stone Work
1742	Plastering, Drywall & Insulation Work Contractors
1743	Terrazzo, Tile, Marble & Mosaic Work Contractors
1751	Carpentry Work
1752	Floor Laying & Other Floor Work, NEC
1761	Roofing, Siding & Sheet Metal Work
1771	Concrete Work
1781	Water Well Drilling

Code	Title
1791	Structural Steel Erection
1793	Glass & Glazing Work
1794	Excavating & Foundation Work
1796	Installation or Erection of Building Equipment, NEC
20	**FOOD & RELATED PRODUCTS**
2011	Meat Packing Plants
2013	Sausage & Other Prepared Meats
2015	Poultry Slaughtering & Processing
2021	Creamery Butter
2022	Natural, Processed & Imitation Cheese
2023	Dry, Condensed & Evaporated Dairy Products
2024	Ice Cream & Frozen Desserts
2026	Fluid Milk
2032	Canned Specialties
2033	Canned Fruits, Vegetables, Preserves, James & Jellies
2034	Dried & Dehydrated Fruits, Vegetables & Soup Mixes
2035	Pickled Fruits & Vegetables, Salad Dressings,Vegetable Sauces & Seasonings
2037	Frozen Fruits, Fruit Juices & Vegetables
2038	Frozen Specialties, NEC
2041	Flour & Other Grain Mill Products
2043	Cereal Breakfast Foods
2044	Rice Milling
2045	Prepared Flour Mixes & Doughs
2046	Wet Corn Milling
2047	Dog & Cat Food
2048	Prepared Feeds for Livestock
2051	Bread & Bakery Products, Except Cookies & Crackers
2052	Cookies & Crackers
2053	Frozen Baking Products, Except Bread
2061	Cane Sugar, Except Refining
2062	Cane Sugar Refining
2063	Beet Sugar Manufacturing
2064	Candy & Confectionery Products
2066	Chocolate & Cocoa Products
2067	Chewing Gum
2068	Salted & Roasted Nuts & Seeds
2074	Cottonseed Oil Mills
2075	Soybean Oil Mills
2076	Vegetable Oil Mills, Except Corn, Cottonseed & Soybean
2077	Animal & Marine Fats & Oils
2079	Shortening, Margarine, Fats & Oils, NEC
2082	Malt Beverages
2083	Malt
2084	Wines, Brandy & Brandy Spirits
2085	Distilled & Blended Liquors
2086	Bottled & Canned Soft Drinks & Carbonated Waters
2087	Flavoring Extracts & Flavoring Syrups, NEC
2091	Canned & Cured Fish & Seafoods
2092	Prepared Fresh or Frozen Fish & Seafoods
2095	Roasted Coffee
2096	Potato Chips, Corn Chips & Similar Snacks
2097	Manufactured Ice
2098	Macaroni, Spaghetti, Vermicelli & Noodles
2099	Food Preparations, NEC
21	**TOBACCO PRODUCTS**
2111	Cigarettes
2121	Cigars
2131	Tobacco (Chewing & Smoking) & Snuff
2141	Tobacco Stemming & Redrying
22	**TEXTILES**
2211	Broad Woven Fabric Mills, Cotton
2221	Broad Woven Fabric Mills, Man-Made Fiber & Silk
2231	Broad Woven Fabric Mills, Wool
2241	Narrow Fabrics & Other Smallwares Mills
2251	Women's Full-Length & Knee-Length Hosiery
2252	Hosiery, NEC
2253	Knit Outerwear Mills
2254	Knit Underwear & Nightwear Mills
2257	Circular Knit Fabric Mills
2258	Lace & Warp Knit Fabric Mills
2259	Knitting Mills, NEC
2261	Finishers of Broad Woven Fabrics of Cotton
2262	Finishers of Broad Woven Fabrics, Man-Made Fiber & Silk
2269	Finishers of Textiles, NEC
2273	Carpets & Rugs
2281	Yarn Spinning Mills
2282	Yarn Throwing, Twisting & Winding Mills
2284	Thread Mills
2295	Coated Fabrics, Not Rubberized
2296	Tire Cord & Fabric
2297	Nonwoven Fabrics
2298	Cordage & Twine
2299	Textile Goods, NEC
23	**APPAREL & OTHER TEXTILE PRODUCTS**
2311	Men's & Boys' Suits, Coats & Overcoats
2321	Men's & Boys' Shirts, Except Work Shirts
2322	Men's & Boys' Underwear & Nightwear
2323	Men's & Boys' Neckwear
2325	Men's & Boys' Trousers & Slacks
2326	Men's & Boys' Work Clothing
2329	Men's & Boys' Clothing, NEC
2331	Women's, Misses' & Juniors' Blouses & Shirts
2335	Women's, Misses' & Juniors' Dresses
2337	Women's, Misses' & Juniors' Suits, Skirts & Coats
2339	Women's, Misses' & Juniors' Outerwear,NEC
2341	Women's, Misses', Children's & Infants' Underwear & Nightwear
2342	Brassieres, Girdles & Allied Garments
2353	Hats, Caps & Millinery
2361	Girls', Children's & Infants' Dresses, Blouses & Shirts
2369	Girls', Children's & Infants' Outerwear, NEC
2371	Fur Goods
2381	Dress & Work Gloves, Except Knit & Leather
2384	Robes & Dressing Gowns
2385	Raincoats & Waterproof Outerwear
2386	Leather & Sheep-Lined Clothing
2387	Apparel Belts
2389	Apparel & Accessories, NEC
2391	Curtains & Draperies, NEC
2392	Housefurnishings, Except Curtains & Draperies
2393	Textile Bags
2394	Canvas & Related Products
2395	Pleating, Tucking for the Trade, Decorative & Novelty Stitching
2396	Automotive Trimmings, Apparel Findings & Related Prods.
2397	Schiffli Machine Embroideries
2399	Fabricated Textile Products, NEC
24	**LUMBER & WOOD PRODUCTS**
2411	Logging Camps & Logging Contractors
2421	Sawmills & Planing Mills, General
2426	Hardwood Dimension & Flooring Mills
2429	Special Product Sawmills, NEC
2431	Millwork
2434	Wood Kitchen Cabinets

Code	Title
2435	Hardwood Veneer & Plywood
2436	Softwood Veneer & Plywood
2439	Structural Wood Members, NEC
2441	Nailed & Lock Corner Wooden Boxes & Shook
2448	Wood Pallets & Skids
2449	Wood Containers, NEC
2451	Mobile Homes
2452	Prefabricated Wood Buildings & Components
2491	Wood Preserving
2493	Reconstituted Wood Products
2499	Wood Products, NEC
25	**FURNITURE & FIXTURES**
2511	Wood Household Furniture, Except Upholstered
2512	Wood Household Furniture, Upholstered
2514	Metal Household Furniture
2515	Mattresses, Foundations & Convertible Beds
2517	Wood Television, Radio, Phonograph & Sewing Machine Cabinets
2519	Household Furniture, NEC
2521	Wood Office Furniture
2522	Metal office Furniture
2531	Public Building & Related Furniture
2541	Wood Partitions, Shelving & Fixtures
2542	Office & Store Fixtures & Shelving, Except Wood
2591	Drapery Hardward & Window Blinds & Shades
2599	Furniture & Fixtures, NEC
26	**PAPER & RELATED PRODUCTS**
2611	Pulp Mills
2621	Paper Mills
2631	Paperboard Mills
2652	Set-Up Paperboard Boxes
2653	Corrugated & Solid Fiber Boxes
2655	Fiber Cans, Tubes, Drums & Similar Products
2656	Sanitary Food Containers, Except Folding
2657	Folding Paperboard Boxes, Including Sanitary
2671	Coated & Laminated Paper & Plastic Film
2673	Plastics, Foil & Coated Paper Bags
2674	Uncoated Paper & Multiwall Bags
2675	Die-Cut Paper, Paperboard & Cardboard
2676	Sanitary Paper Products
2677	Envelopes
2678	Stationery, Tablets & Related Products
2679	Converted Paper & Paperboard Products, NEC
27	**PRINTING & PUBLISHING**
2711	Newspapers: Publishing, or Publishing & Printing
2721	Periodicals: Publishing, or Publishing & Printing
2731	Books: Publishing, or Publishing & Printing
2732	Book Printing
2741	Miscellaneous Publishing
2752	Commercial Printing, Lithographic
2754	Commercial Printing, Gravure
2759	Commercial Printing, NEC
2761	Manifold Business Forms
2771	Greeting Card Publishing & Printing
2782	Blankbooks, Loose Leaf Binders & Devices
2789	Bookbinding & Related Work
2791	Typesetting
2796	Platemaking & Related Services
28	**CHEMICALS & RELATED PRODUCTS**
2812	Alkalies & Chlorine
2813	Industrial Gases

Code	Title
2816	Inorganic Pigments
2819	Industrial Inorganic Chemicals, NEC
2821	Plastics Materials, Nonvulanizable Elastomers & Synthetic Resins
2822	Synthetic Rubber (Vulcanizable Elastomers)
2823	Cellulosic Man-Made Fibers
2824	Synthetic Organic Fibers Exept Cellulosic
2833	Medicinal Chemical & Botanical Products
2834	Pharmaceutical Preparations
2835	In Vitro & In Vivo Diagnostic Substances
2836	Biological Products, Except Diagnostic Substances
2841	Soap & Other Detergents, Except Specialty Cleaners
2842	Specialty Cleaning, Polishing & Sanitation Preparations
2843	Surface Active Agents, Finishing Agents & Sulfonated Oils & Assistants
2844	Perfumes, Cosmetics & Other Toilet Preparations
2851	Paints, Varnishes, Lacquers, Enamels & Allied Products
2861	Gum & Wood Chemicals
2865	Cyclic Organic Crudes & Intermediates, Organic Dyes & Pigments
2869	Industrial Organic Chemicals, NEC
2873	Nitrogenous Fertilizers
2874	Phosphatic Fertilizers
2875	Fertilizers, Mixing Only
2879	Pesticides & Agricultural Chemicals, NEC
2891	Adhesives & Sealants
2892	Explosives
2893	Printing Ink
2895	Carbon Black
2899	Chemicals & Chemical Preparations, NEC
29	**PETROLEUM & COAL PRODUCTS**
2911	Petroleum Refining
2951	Asphalt Paving Mixtures & Blocks
2952	Asphalt Felts & Coatings
2992	Lubricating Oils & Greases
2999	Products of Petroleum & Coal, NEC
30	**RUBBER & MISCELLANEOUS PLASTICS**
3011	Tires & Inner Tubes
3021	Rubber & Plastics Footwear
3052	Rubber & Plastics Hose & Belting
3053	Gaskets, Packing & Sealing Devices
3061	Molded, Extruded & Lathe-Cut Rubber Goods
3069	Fabricated Rubber Products, NEC
3081	Unsupported Plastics Film & Sheet
3082	Unsupported Plastics Profile Shapes
3083	Laminated Plastics, Plate, Sheet & Profile Shapes
3084	Plastic Pipe
3085	Plastic Bottles
3086	Plastic Foam Products
3087	Custom Compounding of Purchased Plastic Resins
3088	Plastic Plumbing Fixtures
3089	Plastic Products, NEC
31	**LEATHER & LEATHER PRODUCTS**
3111	Leather Tanning & Finishing
3131	Boot & Shoe Cut Stock & Findings
3142	House Slippers
3143	Men's Footwear, Except Athletic
3144	Women's Footwear, Except Athletic
3149	Footwear, Except Rubber, NEC
3151	Leather Gloves & Mittens
3161	Luggage
3171	Women's Handbags & Purses

Numerical S.I.C. Compendium—continued

Code	Title
3172	Personal Leather Goods, Except Women's Handbags & Purses
3199	Leather Goods, NEC
32	**STONE, CLAY & GLASS PRODUCTS**
3211	Flat Glass
3221	Glass Containers
3229	Pressed & Blown Glass & Glassware, NEC
3231	Glass Products, Made of Purchased Glass
3241	Cement, Hydraulic
3251	Brick & Structural Clay Tile
3253	Ceramic Wall & Floor Tile
3255	Clay Refractories
3259	Structural Clay Products, NEC
3261	Vitreous China Plumbing Fixtures, China & Earthenware Fittings & Bathroom Accessories
3262	Vitreous China Table & Kitchen Articles
3263	Fine Earthenware (Whiteware) Table & Kitchen Articles
3264	Porcelain Electrical Supplies
3269	Pottery Products, NEC
3271	Concrete Block & Brick
3272	Concrete Products, Except Block & Brick
3273	Ready-Mix Concrete
3275	Gypsum Products
3281	Cut Stone & Stone Products
3291	Abrasive Products
3292	Asbestos Products
3299	Nonmetallic Mineral Products, NEC
33	**PRIMARY METAL INDUSTRIES**
3312	Steel Works & Blast Furnaces
3313	Electromettalurgic Products, Except Steel
3315	Steel Wiredrawing, Steel Nails & Spikes
3316	Cold Rolled Steel Sheet, Strip & Bars
3317	Steel Pipe & Tubes
3321	Gray & Ductile Iron Foundries
3322	Malleable Iron Foundries
3324	Steel Investment Foundries
3325	Steel Foundries, NEC
3331	Primary Smelting & Refining of Copper
3334	Primary Production of Aluminum
3339	Primary Smelting & Refining of Nonferrous Metals, Except Copper & Aluminum
3341	Secondary Smelting & Refining of Nonferrous Metals
3351	Rolling, Drawing & Extruding of Copper
3353	Aluminum Sheet, Plate & Foil
3354	Aluminum Extruded Products
3355	Aluminum Rolling & Drawing, NEC
3356	Rolling, Drawing & Extruding of Nonferrous Metals, Except Copper & Aluminum
3357	Drawing & Insulating of Nonferrous Wire
3363	Aluminum Die-Castings
3364	Nonferrous Die-Castings, Except Aluminum
3365	Aluminum Foundries
3366	Copper Foundries
3369	Nonferrous Foundries, Except Aluminum & Copper
3398	Metal Heat Treating
3399	Primary Metal Products, NEC
34	**FABRICATED METAL PRODUCTS**
3411	Metal Cans
3412	Metal Shipping Barrels, Drums, Kegs & Pails
3421	Cutlery
3423	Hand & Edge Tools, Except Machine Tools & Hand Saws
3425	Hand Saws & Blades
3429	Hardware, NEC

Code	Title
3431	Enameled Iron & Metal Sanitary Ware
3432	Plumbing Fixture Fittings & Trim
3433	Heating Equipment, Except Electrical & Warm Air Furnaces
3441	Fabricated Structural Metal
3442	Metal Doors, Sash, Frames, Molding & Trim
3443	Fabricated Plate Work (Boiler Shops)
3444	Sheet Metal Work
3446	Architectural & Ornamental Metal Work
3448	Prefabricated Metal Buildings & Components
3449	Miscellaneous Structural Metal Work
3451	Screw Machine Products
3452	Bolts, Nuts, Screws, Rivets & Washers
3462	Iron & Steel Forgings
3463	Nonferrous Forgings
3465	Automotive Stampings
3466	Metal Crowns & Closures
3469	Metal Stampings, NEC
3471	Electroplating, Plating, Polishing, Anodizing & Coloring
3479	Coating, Engraving & Allied Services, NEC
3482	Small Arms Ammunition
3483	Ammunition, Except Small Arms, NEC
3484	Small Arms
3489	Ordnance & Accessories, NEC
3491	Industrial Valves
3492	Fluid Power Valves & Hose Fittings
3493	Steel Springs, Except Wire
3494	Valves & Pipe Fittings, NEC
3495	Wire Springs
3496	Miscellaneous Fabricated Wire Products
3497	Metal Foil & Leaf
3498	Fabricated Pipe & Fabricated Pipe Fittings
3499	Fabricated Metal Products, NEC
35	**INDUSTRIAL EQUIPMENT & MACHINERY**
3511	Steam, Gas & Hydraulic Turbines
3519	Internal Combustion Engines, NEC
3523	Farm Machinery & Equipment
3524	Lawn & Garden Tractors, Home Lawn & Garden Equipment
3531	Construction Machinery & Equipment
3532	Mining Machinery & Equipment, Except Oil & Gas Field Machinery Equipment
3533	Oil & Gas Field Machinery & Equipment
3534	Elevators & Moving Stairways
3535	Conveyors & Conveying Equipment
3536	Overhead Traveling Cranes, Hoists & Monorail Systems
3537	Industrial Trucks, Tractors, Trailers & Stackers
3541	Machine Tools, Metal Cutting Types
3542	Machine Tools, Metal Forming Types
3543	Industrial Patterns
3544	Special Dies, Tools, Die Sets, Jigs, Fixtures, Industrial Molds
3545	Cutting Tools, Machine Tool Accessories & Machinists Precision Measuring Devices
3546	Power Driven Hand Tools
3547	Rolling Mill Machinery & Equipment
3548	Electric & Gas Welding & Soldering Equipment
3549	Metalworking Machinery, NEC
3552	Textile Machinery
3553	Woodworking Machinery
3554	Paper Industries Machinery
3555	Printing Trades Machinery & Equipment
3556	Food Products Machinery
3559	Special Industry Machinery, NEC
3561	Pumps & Pumping Equipment
3562	Ball & Roller Bearings
3563	Air & Gas Compressors

Code	Title
3564	Industrial & Commercial Fans, Blowers & Air Purification Equipment
3565	Packaging Machinery
3566	Speed Changers, Industrial High Speed Drives & Gears
3567	Industrial Process Furnaces & Ovens
3568	Mechanical Power Transmission Equipment, NEC
3569	General Industrial Machinery & Equipment, NEC
3571	Electronic Computers
3572	Computer Storage Devices
3575	Computer Terminals
3577	Computer Peripheral Equipment, NEC
3578	Calculating & Accounting Machines, Except Electronic Computers
3579	Office Machines, NEC
3581	Automatic Vending Machines
3582	Commercial Laundry, Dry Cleaning & Pressing Machines
3585	Air Conditioning, Warm Air Heating Equipment & Commercial & Industrial Refrigeration Equipment
3586	Measuring & Dispensing Pumps
3589	Service Industry Machines, NEC
3592	Carburetors, Pistons, Piston Rings & Valves
3593	Fluid Power Cylinders & Actuators
3594	Fluid Power Pumps & Motors
3596	Scales & Balances, Except Laboratory
3599	Industrial & Commercial Machinery & Equipment, NEC
36	**ELECTRONIC & ELECTRIC EQUIPMENT**
3612	Power, Distribution & Specialty Transformers
3613	Switchgear & Switchboard Apparatus
3621	Motors & Generators
3624	Carbon & Graphite Products
3625	Relays & Industrial Controls
3629	Electrical Industrial Apparatus, NEC
3631	Household Cooking Equipment
3632	Household Refrigerators & Home & Farm Freezers
3633	Household Laundry Equipment
3634	Electric Housewares & Fans
3635	Household Vacuum Cleaners
3639	Household Appliances, NEC
3641	Electric Lamp Bulbs & Tubes
3643	Current-Carrying Wiring Devices
3644	Noncurrent-Carrying Wiring Devices
3645	Residential Electric Lighting Fixtures
3646	Commercial, Industrial & Institutional Electric Lighting Fixtures
3647	Vehicular Lighting Equipment
3648	Lighting Equipment, NEC
3651	Household Audio & Video Equipment
3652	Phonograph Records & Pre-Recorded Audio Tapes & Discs
3661	Telephone & Telegraph Apparatus
3663	Radio & TV Broadcasting & Communications Equipment
3669	Communications Equipment, NEC
3671	Electron Tubes
3672	Printed Circuit Boards
3674	Semiconductors & Related Devices
3675	Electronic Capacitors
3676	Electronic Resistors
3677	Electronic Coils, Transformers & Other Inductors
3678	Electronic Connectors
3679	Electronic Components, NEC
3691	Storage Batteries
3692	Primary Batteries, Dry & Wet
3694	Electrical Equipment for Internal Combustion Engines
3695	Magnetic & Optical Recording Media
3699	Electrical Machinery, Equipment & Supplies, NEC

Code	Title
37	**TRANSPORTATION EQUIPMENT**
3711	Motor Vehicles & Passenger Car Bodies
3713	Truck & Bus Bodies
3714	Motor Vehicle Parts & Accessories
3715	Truck Trailers
3716	Motor Homes
3721	Aircraft
3724	Aircraft Engines & Engine Parts
3728	Aircraft Parts & Auxiliary Equipment, NEC
3731	Ship Building & Repairing
3732	Boat Building & Repairing
3743	Railroad Equipment
3751	Motorcycles, Bicycles & Parts
3761	Guided Missiles & Space Vehicles
3764	Guided Missile & Space Vehicle Propulsion Units & Propulsion Unit Parts
3769	Guided Missile & Space Vehicle Parts & Auxiliary Equipment, NEC
3792	Travel Trailers & Campers
3795	Tanks & Tank Components
3799	Transportation Equipment, NEC
38	**INSTRUMENTS & RELATED PRODUCTS**
3812	Navigation, Guidance, Search & Detection Systems & Instruments
3821	Laboratory Apparatus & Furniture
3822	Automatic Controls for Regulating Residential & Commercial Environments & Appliances
3823	Industrial Instruments for Measurement, Display & Control of Process Variables & Related Products
3824	Totalizing Fluid Meters & Counting Devices
3825	Instruments for Measuring & Testing of Electricity & Electrical Signals
3826	Laboratory Analytical Instruments
3827	Optical Instruments & Lenses
3829	Measuring & Controlling Devices, NEC
3841	Surgical & Medical Instruments & Apparatus
3842	Orthopedic, Prosthetic & Surgical Supplies
3843	Dental Equipment & Supplies
3844	X-Ray Apparatus, Tubes & Equipment
3845	Electromedical & Electrotherapeutic Apparatus
3851	Opthalmic Goods
3861	Photographic Equipment & Supplies
3873	Watches, Clocks, & Clockwork Operated Devices & Parts
39	**MISCELLANEOUS MANUFACTURING**
3912	Jewelry, Precious Metal
3914	Silverware, Plated Ware & Stainless Steel Ware
3915	Jewelers Findings & Materials & Lapidary Work
3925	Minerals & Earths, Ground or Otherwise Treated
3926	Mineral Wool
3927	Nonclay Refractories
3931	Musical Instruments
3942	Dolls & Stuffed Toys
3944	Games, Toys & Children's Vehicles, Except Dolls & Bicycles
3951	Pens, Mechanical Pencils & Parts
3952	Lead Pencils, Crayons & Artists' Materials
3953	Marking Devices
3955	Carbon Paper & Inked Ribbons
3961	Costume Jewelry & Costume Novelties, Except Precious Metal
3965	Fasteners, Buttons, Needles & Pins
3991	Brooms & Brushes
3993	Signs & Advertising Displays
3995	Burial Caskets

Numerical S.I.C. Compendium—continued

Code	Title
3996	Linoleum, Asphalt-Feltbase & Other ard Surface Floor Coverings, NEC
3999	Manufacturing Industries, NEC
40	**RAILROAD TRANSPORTATION**
4011	Railroads, Line-Haul Operating
4013	Railroad Switching & Terminal Establishments
41	**LOCAL & INTERURBAN PASSENGER TRANSIT**
4111	Local & Suburban Transit
4119	Local Passenger Transportation, NEC
4121	Taxicabs
4131	Intercity & Rural Bus Transportation
4141	Local Bus Charter Service
4142	Bus Charter Service, Except Local
4151	School Buses
4173	Terminal & Passenger Transportation Service Facilities for Motor Vehicles
42	**TRUCKING & WAREHOUSING**
4212	Local Trucking Without Storage
4213	Trucking, Except Local
4214	Local Trucking With Storage
4215	Courier Services, Except by Air
4221	Farm Product Warehousing & Storage
4222	Refrigerated Warehousing & Storage
4225	General Warehousing & Storage
4226	Special Warehousing & Storage, NEC
4231	Terminal & Joint Terminal Maintenance Facilities for Motor Freight Transportation
43	**U.S. POSTAL SERVICE**
4311	U.S. Postal Service
44	**WATER TRANSPORTATION**
4412	Deep Sea Freight Transportation-Foreign
4424	Deep Sea Freight Transportation-Domestic
4432	Great Lakes Freight Transportation
4449	Freight Transportation-Water, NEC
4481	Passenger Transportation-Deep Sea
4482	Ferries
4489	Water Transportation-Passenger, NEC
4491	Marine Cargo Handling
4492	Towing & Tugboat Services
4493	Marinas
4499	Water Transportation Services, NEC
45	**AIR TRANSPORTATION**
4512	Air Transportation, Scheduled
4513	Air Courier Services
4522	Air Transportation, Non-Scheduled
4581	Airports, Flying Fields & Airport Terminal Services
46	**PIPELINES, EXCEPT GAS**
4612	Crude Petroleum Pipe Lines
4613	Refined Petroleum Pipe Lines
4619	Pipe Lines, NEC
47	**TRANSPORTATION SERVICES**
4724	Travel Agencies
4725	Tour Operators
4729	Arrangement of Passenger Transportation, NEC
4731	Arrangement of Transportation of Freight & Cargo
4741	Rental of Railroad Cars
4783	Packing & Crating
4785	Inspection & Weighing Services for Motor Vehicle Transportation
4789	Transportation Services, NEC
48	**COMMUNICATIONS**
4812	Radio Telephone Communications
4813	Telephone Communications, Except Radio Telephone
4822	Telegraph & Other Message Communications
4832	Radio Broadcasting Stations
4833	Television Broadcasting Stations
4841	Cable & Other Pay Television Services
4899	Communication Services, NEC
49	**ELECTRIC, GAS & SANITARY SERVICES**
4911	Electric Services
4922	Natural Gas Transmission
4923	Natural Gas Transmission & Distribution
4924	Natural Gas Distribution
4925	Mixed, Manufactured or Liquefied Petroleum Gas Production and/or Distribution
4931	Electric & Other Services Combined
4932	Gas & Other Services Combined
4939	Combination Utilities, NEC
4941	Water Supply
4952	Sewerage Systems
4953	Refuse Systems
4959	Sanitary Services, NEC
4961	Steam & Air-Conditioning Supply
4971	Irrigation Systems
50	**DURABLE WHOLESALE TRADE**
5012	Distribution of Automobiles & Other Motor Vehicles
5013	Motor Vehicle Supplies & New Parts
5014	Tires & Tubes
5015	Motor Vehicle Parts, Used
5021	Furniture
5023	Home Furnishings
5031	Lumber, Plywood, Millwork & Wood Panels
5033	Roofing, Siding & Insulation Materials
5039	Construction Materials, NEC
5043	Photographic Equipment & Supplies
5044	Office Equipment
5045	Computers & Computer Peripheral Equipment & Software
5046	Commercial Equipment
5047	Medical, Dental & Hospital Equipment & Supplies
5048	Opthalmic Goods
5049	Professional Equipment & Supplies
5051	Metals Service Centers & Offices
5052	Coal & Other Minerals & Ores
5063	Electrical Apparatus & Equipment
5064	Electrical Appliances, Television & Radio Sets
5065	Electronic Parts & Equipment
5072	Hardware
5074	Plumbing & Heating Equipment & Supplies
5075	Warm Air Heating & Air Conditioning Equipment
5078	Refrigeration Equipment & Supplies
5082	Construction & Mining Machinery & Equipment, Except Petroleum, Wholesale
5083	Farm & Garden Machinery & Equipment
5084	Industrial Machinery & Equipment
5085	Industrial Supplies
5087	Service Establishment Equipment & Supplies
5088	Transportation Equipment & Supplies, Except Motor Vehicles
5091	Sporting & Recreational Goods & Supplies
5092	Toys & Hobby Goods & Supplies

Code	Title
5093	Scrap & Waste Materials
5094	Jewelry, Watches, Precious Stones & Precious Metals, Wholesale
5099	Wholesale Durable Goods, NEC
51	**NONDURABLE WHOLESALE TRADE**
5111	Printing & Writing Paper
5112	Stationery & Office Supplies
5113	Industrial & Personal Service Paper
5122	Drugs, Drug Proprietaries & Sundries
5131	Piece Goods, Notions & Other Dry Goods
5136	Men's & Boys' Clothing & Furnishings
5137	Women's, Children's & Infants' Clothing & Accessories
5139	Footwear
5141	Groceries, General Line
5142	Packaged Frozen Foods
5143	Dairy Products, Except Dried or Canned
5144	Poultry & Poultry Products
5145	Confectionery
5146	Fish & Seafoods
5147	Meats & Meat Products
5148	Fresh Fruits & Vegetables
5149	Grocers & Related Products, NEC
5153	Grains & Field Beans-Buying & Marketing
5154	Livestock Buying & Marketing
5159	Farm Product Raw Materials Buying & Marketing, NEC
5162	Plastics Materials & Basic Forms & Shapes
5169	Chemicals & Allied Products, NEC
5171	Petroleum Bulk Stations & Terminals
5172	Petroleum & Petroleum Products, NEC-Except Bulk Stations & Terminals-Wholesale
5181	Beer & Ale
5182	Wines & Distilled Alcoholic Beverages
5191	Farm Supplies
5192	Books, Periodicals & Newspapers
5193	Flowers, Nursery Stock & Florists' Supplies-Wholesale
5194	Tobacco & Tobacco Products
5198	Paints, Varnishes & Supplies
5199	Nondurable Goods, NEC
52	**RETAIL BUILDING MATERIALS & GARDEN SUPPLIES**
5211	Lumber & Other Building Materials Dealers
5231	Paint, Glass & Wallpaper Stores
5251	Hardware Stores
5261	Retail Nurseries, Lawn & Garden Supply Stores
5271	Mobile Home Dealers
53	**RETAIL GENERAL MERCHANDISE STORES**
5311	Department Stores
5331	Variety Stores
5399	Miscellaneous General Merchandise Stores
54	**RETAIL FOOD STORES**
5411	Grocery Stores
5421	Meat & Fish Markets, Including Freezer Provisions
5441	Candy, Nut & Confectionary Stores
5451	Dairy Products Stores
5461	Retail Bakeries
5499	Miscellaneous Food Stores
55	**RETAIL AUTOMOTIVE DEALERS & SERVICE STATIONS**
5511	Motor Vehicle Dealers (New & Used Cars)
5521	Motor Vehicle Dealers (Used Cars Only)

Code	Title
5531	Auto & Home Supply Stores
5541	Gasoline Service Stations
5551	Boat Dealers
5561	Recreational Vehicle Dealers
5571	Motorcycle Dealers
5599	Automotive Dealers, NEC
56	**RETAIL APPAREL STORES**
5611	Men's & Boys' Clothing & Accessory Stores
5621	Women's Clothing Stores
5632	Women's Accessory & Specialty Stores
5641	Children's & Infants' Wear Stores
5651	Family Clothing Stores
5661	Shoe Stores
5699	Miscellaneous Apparel & Accessory Stores
57	**RETAIL FURNITURE & HOME FURNISHINGS**
5712	Furniture Stores
5713	Floor Covering Stores
5714	Drapery, Curtain & Upholstery Stores
5719	Miscellaneous Homefurnishing Stores
5722	Household Appliance Stores
5731	Radio, Television & Consumer Electronic Stores
5734	Computer & Computer Software Stores
5735	Record & Prerecorded Tape Stores
5736	Musical Instrument Stores
58	**DINING & DRINKING PLACES**
5812	Eating Places
5813	Drinking Places (Alcoholic Beverages)
59	**MISCELLANEOUS RETAIL**
5912	Drug Stores & Proprietary Stores
5921	Liquor Stores
5932	Used Merchandise Stores
5941	Sporting Goods & Bicycle Shops
5942	Book Stores
5943	Stationery Stores
5944	Jewelry Stores
5945	Hobby, Toy & Game Shops
5946	Camera & Photographic Supply Stores
5947	Gift, Novelty & Souvenir Shops
5948	Luggage & Leather Goods Stores
5949	Sewing, Needlework & Piece Goods Stores
5961	Catalog & Mail Order Houses
5962	Automatic Merchandising Machine Operators
5963	Direct Selling Establishments
5983	Fuel Oil Dealers
5984	Bottled or Bulk Liquefied Petroleum (LP) Gas Dealers
5989	Fuel Dealers, NEC
5992	Tobacco Stores & Stands
5994	News Dealers & Newsstands
5995	Optical Goods Stores
5999	Miscellaneous Retail Stores, NEC
60	**BANKS & BANKING SERVICES**
6011	Federal Reserve Banks
6019	Central Reserve Depository Institutions, NEC
6021	National Commercial Banks
6022	State Commercial Banks & Trust Companies
6029	Commercial Banks, NEC
6035	Savings Institutions, Federally Chartered
6036	Savings Institutions, Not Federally Chartered
6061	Credit Unions, Federally Chartered
6062	Credit Unions, Not Federally Chartered

Numerical S.I.C. Compendium—continued

Code	Title
6081	Branches & Agencies of Foreign Banks
6082	Foreign Trade & International Banking Institutions
6091	Nondeposit Trust Facilities
6099	Functions Related to Depository Banking, NEC
61	**NONDEPOSITORY FINANCIAL INSTITUTIONS**
6111	Federal & Federally Sponsored Credit Agencies
6141	Personal Credit Institutions
6153	Short-Term Business Credit Institutions, Except Agricultural
6159	Miscellaneous Business Credit Institutions
6162	Mortgage Bankers & Loan Correspondents
6163	Loan Brokers
62	**SECURITY & COMMODITY BROKERS**
6211	Security Brokers, Dealers & Flotation Companies
6221	Commodity Contracts Brokers & Dealers
6231	Security & Commodity Exchanges
6282	Investment Advice
6289	Services Allied With Exchange of Securities or Commodities, NEC
63	**INSURANCE CARRIERS**
6311	Life Insurance
6321	Accident & Health Insurance
6324	Hospital & Medical Service Plans
6331	Fire, Marine & Casualty Insurance
6351	Surety Insurance
6361	Title Insurance
6371	Pension, Health & Welfare Funds
6399	Insurance Carriers, NEC
64	**INSURANCE AGENTS, BROKERS & SERVICES**
6411	Insurance Agents, Brokers & Services
65	**REAL ESTATE**
6512	Operators of Nonresidential Buildings
6513	Operators of Apartment Buildings
6514	Operators of Dwellings Other Than Apartment Buildings
6515	Operators of Residential Mobile Home Sites
6517	Lessors of Railroad Property
6519	Lessors of Real Property, NEC
6531	Real Estate Agents & Managers
6541	Title Abstract Offices
6552	Land Subdividers & Developers, Except Cemeteries
6553	Cemetery Subdividers & Developers
67	**HOLDING & INVESTMENT OFFICES**
6712	Offices of Bank Holding Companies
6719	Offices of Holding Companies, NEC
6722	Management Investment Companies, Open-End
6726	Unit Investment Trusts, Face-Amount Certificate Offices, Closed-End Management Investment Offices
6732	Educational Religious & Charitable Trusts
6733	Trusts, Except Educational, Religious & Charitable
6792	Oil Royalty Traders
6794	Patent Owners & Lessors
6798	Real Estate Investment Trusts
6799	Investors, NEC
70	**HOTELS & LODGING PLACES**
7011	Hotels & Motels
7021	Rooming & Boarding Houses
7032	Sporting & Recreational Camps
7033	Recreational Vehicle Parks & Campsites
7041	Organization Hotels & Lodging Houses, Membership Basis

Code	Title
72	**PERSONAL SERVICES**
7211	Power Laundries, Family & Commercial
7212	Garment Pressing & Agents for Laundries & Dry Cleaners
7213	Linen Supply Services
7215	Coin-Operated Laundries & Dry Cleaning
7216	Dry Cleaning Plants, Except Rug Cleaning
7217	Carpet & Upholstery Cleaning
7218	Industrial Launderers
7219	Laundry & Garment Services, NEC
7221	Photographic Studios, Portrait
7231	Beauty Shops
7241	Barber Shops
7251	Shoe Repair Shops & Shoe Shine Parlors
7261	Funeral Service & Crematories
7291	Tax Return Preparation Services
7299	Miscellaneous Personal Services, NEC
73	**BUSINESS SERVICES**
7311	Advertising Agencies
7312	Outdoor Advertising Services
7313	Radio, Television & Publishers' Advertising Representatives
7319	Advertising, NEC
7322	Adjustment & Collection Services
7323	Credit Reporting Services
7331	Direct Mail Advertising Services
7334	Photocopy & Duplicating Service
7335	Commercial Photography
7336	Commercial Art & Graphic Design
7338	Secretarial & Court Reporting Services
7342	Disinfecting & Pest Control Services
7349	Building Cleaning & Maintenance Services, NEC
7352	Medical Equipment Rental & Leasing
7353	Heavy Construction Equipment Rental & Leasing
7359	Equipment Rental & Leasing, NEC
7361	Computer Programming Services
7372	Prepackaged Software
7373	Computer Integrated Systems Design
7374	Computer Processing & Processing & Data Preparation Services
7375	Information Retrieval Services
7376	Computer Facilities Management Services
7377	Computer Rental & Leasing
7378	Computer Maintenance & Repair
7379	Computer Related Services, NEC
7381	Detective, Guard & Armored Car Services
7382	Security Systems Services
7383	News Syndicates
7384	Photofinishing Laboratories
7389	Business Services, NEC
75	**AUTO REPAIR, SERVICES & PARKING**
7513	Truck Rental & Leasing, Without Drivers
7514	Passenger Car Rental
7515	Passenger Car Leasing
7519	Utility Trailer & Recreational Vehicle Rental
7521	Automobile Parking
7532	Top, Body, Upholstery Repair & Paint Shops
7533	Automotive Exhaust System Repair Shops
7534	Tire Retreading & Repair Shops
7536	Automotive Glass Replacement Shops
7537	Automotive Transmission Repair Shops
7538	General Automotive Repair Shops
7539	Automobile Repair Shops, NEC
7542	Car Washes
7549	Automobile Services, Except Repair & Washes

Code	Title
76	**MISCELLANEOUS REPAIR SERVICES**
7622	Radio & Television Repair Shops
7623	Refrigeration & Air Conditioning Service & Repair Shops
7629	Electrical & Electronic Repair Shops, NEC
7631	Watch, Clock & Jewelry Repair
7641	Reupholstery & Furniture Repair
7692	Welding Repair
7694	Armature Rewinding Shops
7699	Repair Shops & Related Services, NEC
78	**MOTION PICTURES**
7812	Motion Picture & Video Tape Production
7819	Services Allied to Motion Picture Production
7822	Motion Picture & Video Tape Distribution
7829	Services Allied to Motion Picture Distribution
7832	Motion Picture Theaters, Except Drive-In
7833	Drive-In Motion Picture Theaters
7841	Video Tape Rental
79	**AMUSEMENT & RECREATION**
7911	Dance Halls, Studios & Schools
7922	Theatrical Producers (Except Motion Picture) & Miscellaneous Theatrical Services
7929	Bands, Orchestras, Actors, & Other Entertainers & Entertainment Groups
7933	Bowling Alleys
7941	Professional Sports Clubs & Promoters
7948	Racing, Including Track Operation
7991	Physical Fitness Facilities
7992	Public Golf Courses
7993	Coin-Operated Amusement Devices
7996	Amusement Parks
7997	Membership Sports & Recreation Clubs
7999	Amusement & Recreation Services, NEC
80	**HEALTH SERVICES**
8011	Offices & Clinics of Doctors of Medicine
8021	Offices & Clinics of Dentists
8031	Offices & Clinics of Doctors of Osteopathy
8041	Offices & Clinics of Chiropractors
8042	Offices & Clinics of Optometrists
8043	Offices & Clinics of Podiatrists
8049	Offices & Clinics of Health Practitioners, NEC
8051	Skilled Nursing Care Facilities
8052	Intermediate Care Facilities
8059	Nursing & Personal Care Facilities, NEC
8062	General Medical & Surgical Hospitals
8063	Psychiatric Hospitals
8069	Specialty Hospitals, Except Psychiatric
8071	Medical Laboratories
8072	Dental Laboratories
8082	Home Health Care Services
8092	Kidney Dialysis Centers
8093	Specialty Outpatient Facilities, NEC
8099	Health & Allied Services, NEC
81	**LEGAL SERVICES**
8111	Legal Services
82	**EDUCATIONAL SERVICES**
8211	Elementary & Secondary Schools
8221	Colleges, Universities & Professional Schools
8222	Junior Colleges & Technical Institutes
8231	Libraries & Information Centers
8243	Data Processing Schools

Code	Title
8244	Business & Secretarial Schools
8249	Vocational Schools, NEC
8299	Schools & Educational Services, NEC
83	**SOCIAL SERVICES**
8322	Individual & Family Social Services
8331	Job Training & Vocational Rehabilitation Services
8351	Child Day Care Services
8361	Residential Care
8399	Social Services, NEC
84	**MUSEUMS & BOTANICAL OR ZOOLOGICAL GARDENS**
8412	Museums & Art Galleries
8422	Arboreta & Botanical Or Zoological Gardens
86	**MEMBERSHIP ORGANIZATIONS**
8611	Business Associations
8621	Professional Membership Organizations
8631	Labor Unions & Similar Labor Organizations
8641	Civic, Social & Fraternal Associations
8651	Political Organizations
8661	Religious Organizations
8699	Membership Organizations, NEC
87	**ENGINEERING & MANAGEMENT SERVICES**
8711	Engineering Services
8712	Architectural Services
8713	Surveying Services
8721	Accounting, Auditing & Bookkeeping Services
8731	Commercial, Physical & Biological Research
8732	Commercial, Economic, Sociological & Educational Research
8733	Noncommercial Research Organizations
8734	Testing Laboratories
8741	Management Services
8742	Management Consulting Services
8743	Public Relations Services
8744	Facilities Support Management Services
8748	Business Consulting Services, NEC
88	**PRIVATE HOUSEHOLDS**
8811	Private Households
89	**SERVICES, NEC**
8999	Services, NEC
91	**EXECUTIVE, LEGISLATIVE & GENERAL GOVERNMENT**
9111	Executive Offices
9121	Legislative Bodies
9131	Executive & Legislative Offices Combined
9199	General Government, NEC
92	**JUSTICE, PUBLIC ORDER & SAFETY**
9211	Courts
9221	Police Protection
9222	Legal Counsel & Prosecution
9223	Correctional Institutions
9224	Fire Protection
9229	Public Order & Safety, NEC
93	**PUBLIC FINANCE ADMINISTRATION**
9311	Public Finance, Taxation & Monetary Policy
94	**HUMAN RESOURCES ADMINISTRATION**
9411	Administration of Educational Programs
9431	Administration of Public Health Programs

Code	Title
9441	Administration of Social Manpower Programs
9451	Administration of Veterans' Affairs
95	**ENVIRONMENTAL QUALITY & HOUSING**
9511	Air & Water Resource & Solid Waste Management
9512	Land, Mineral, Wildlife & Forest Conservation
9531	Administration of Housing Programs
9532	Administration of Urban Planning & Community & Rural Development
96	**ECONOMIC PROGRAM ADMINISTRATION**
9611	Administration of General Economic Programs
9621	Regulation & Administration of Transportation Programs
9631	Regulation & Administration of Communication, Electric, Gas & Other Utilities

Code	Title
9641	Regulation of Agricultural Marketing & Commodities
9651	Regulation, Licensing & Inspection of Miscellaneous Commercial Sectors
9661	Space Research & Technology
97	**NATIONAL SECURITY & INTERNATIONAL AFFAIRS**
9711	National Security
9721	International Affairs
9999	Nonclassifiable Establishments

MASTER S.I.C. INDEX

0111 — WHEAT PRODUCTION

AZENIDA AGRICOLA PEROLLA S.R.L.—Allianz Aktiengesellschaft; *Int'l*, pg. 61
DELTIC TIMBER CORPORATION; *U.S. Public*, pg. 498
NORTHRUP KING CO.—Novartis AG; *Int'l*, pg. 974
OMNITRAX INC.—Broe Companies; *U.S. Private*, pg. 171
PIONEER HI-BRED INTERNATIONAL, INC.; *U.S. Public*, pg. 1298
SANDOZ SEEDS LTD.—Novartis AG; *Int'l*, pg. 972
TAYWOOD FARMS PTY. LTD.—Taylor Woodrow plc; *Int'l*, pg. 1360
YOSUBA FARMS—Maxxam Inc.; *U.S. Public*, pg. 1062

0112 — RICE PRODUCTION

ADM MILLING CO. - RICE DIVISION—Archer Daniels Midland Company (ADM); *U.S. Public*, pg. 128
DELTIC TIMBER CORPORATION; *U.S. Public*, pg. 498
EURYZA BV—CSM N.V.; *Int'l*, pg. 243
EURYZA INTERNATIONAL AG—CSM N.V.; *Int'l*, pg. 244
EURYZA REIS GMBH—CSM N.V.; *Int'l*, pg. 244
PRODUCERS RICE MILL INC.; *U.S. Private*, pg. 888
RING AROUND PRODUCTS, INC.—Occidental Petroleum Corporation; *U.S. Public*, pg. 1210
YOSUBA FARMS—Maxxam Inc.; *U.S. Public*, pg. 1062

0115 — CORN PRODUCTION

CARGILL SEED DIV.—Cargill; *U.S. Private*, pg. 210
CIBA SEEDS—Novartis AG; *Int'l*, pg. 973
DEKALB ARGENTINA, S.A.—Dekalb Genetics Corporation; *U.S. Public*, pg. 493
DEKALB CANADA INC.—Dekalb Genetics Corporation; *U.S. Public*, pg. 493
DEKALB GENETICS CORPORATION; *U.S. Public*, pg. 493
DELTA & PINE LAND COMPANY; *U.S. Public*, pg. 497
DELTIC TIMBER CORPORATION; *U.S. Public*, pg. 498
GARST SEED COMPANY—Zeneca Group Plc; *Int'l*, pg. 1524
GROUPE LIMAGRAIN; *Int'l*, pg. 566
INTERSTATE PAYCO SEED COMPANY; *U.S. Private*, pg. 573
LG SEEDS INC.—Groupe Limagrain; *Int'l*, pg. 566
LIMAGRAIN GENETICS CORP.—Groupe Limagrain; *Int'l*, pg. 566
MAICES HIBRIDOS Y SEMILLAS SA—Novartis AG; *Int'l*, pg. 983
NORTHRUP KING CO.—Novartis AG; *Int'l*, pg. 974
L.L. OLDS SEED COMPANY; *U.S. Private*, pg. 814
PIONEER HI-BRED INTERNATIONAL, INC.; *U.S. Public*, pg. 1298
ROGERS BROTHERS SEED COMPANY—Novartis AG; *Int'l*, pg. 974
SANDOZ SEEDS LTD.—Novartis AG; *Int'l*, pg. 972
SHISSLER SEED CO.—Groupe Limagrain; *Int'l*, pg. 566

0116 — SOYBEAN PRODUCTION

DEKALB GENETICS CORPORATION; *U.S. Public*, pg. 493
DELTA & PINE LAND COMPANY; *U.S. Public*, pg. 497
DELTIC TIMBER CORPORATION; *U.S. Public*, pg. 498
GARST SEED COMPANY—Zeneca Group Plc; *Int'l*, pg. 1524
JACOB HARTZ SEED COMPANY, INC.—Monsanto Company; *U.S. Public*, pg. 1125
LG SEEDS INC.—Groupe Limagrain; *Int'l*, pg. 566
NORTHRUP KING CO.—Novartis AG; *Int'l*, pg. 974
PIONEER HI-BRED INTERNATIONAL, INC.; *U.S. Public*, pg. 1298
RING AROUND PRODUCTS, INC.—Occidental Petroleum Corporation; *U.S. Public*, pg. 1210
SANDOZ SEEDS LTD.—Novartis AG; *Int'l*, pg. 972

0119 — CASH GRAINS, NEC

B&W CO-OP, INC.; *U.S. Private*, pg. 105
CONTINENTAL GRAIN COMPANY; *U.S. Private*, pg. 268
DEKALB ARGENTINA, S.A.—Dekalb Genetics Corporation; *U.S. Public*, pg. 493
DEKALB CANADA INC.—Dekalb Genetics Corporation; *U.S. Public*, pg. 493
DEKALB GENETICS CORPORATION; *U.S. Public*, pg. 493
GARST SEED COMPANY—Zeneca Group Plc; *Int'l*, pg. 1524
GROUPE LIMAGRAIN; *Int'l*, pg. 566
HILLESHOG MONO-HY INC.—Novartis AG; *Int'l*, pg. 973
MAINE POTATO GROWERS, INC.; *U.S. Private*, pg. 697
NORTHRUP KING CO.—Novartis AG; *Int'l*, pg. 974
OCEAN MIST FARMS CORP.; *U.S. Private*, pg. 811
OMNITRAX INC.—Broe Companies; *U.S. Private*, pg. 171
PIONEER HI-BRED INTERNATIONAL, INC.; *U.S. Public*, pg. 1298
ROGERS BROTHERS SEED COMPANY—Novartis AG; *Int'l*, pg. 974
SANDOZ SEEDS LTD.—Novartis AG; *Int'l*, pg. 972
SEMILLAS MERIEL—Pioneer Hi-Bred International, Inc.; *U.S. Public*, pg. 1299
SHISSLER SEED CO.—Groupe Limagrain; *Int'l*, pg. 566
TRIPLE F, INC.; *U.S. Private*, pg. 1104
ZWAAN UND CO. SAMENZUCHT G.M.B.H.—Novartis AG; *Int'l*, pg. 986

0131 — COTTON & COTTONSEED PRODUCTION

AMFAC, INC.—JMB Realty Corporation; *U.S. Private*, pg. 577
DELTA & PINE LAND COMPANY; *U.S. Public*, pg. 497
DELTIC TIMBER CORPORATION; *U.S. Public*, pg. 498
HARRIS FARMS, INC.; *U.S. Private*, pg. 505
ITOCHU COTTON, INC.—Itochu Corporation; *Int'l*, pg. 694
LONRHO PLC; *Int'l*, pg. 817
RING AROUND PRODUCTS, INC.—Occidental Petroleum Corporation; *U.S. Public*, pg. 1210

0132 — TOBACCO PRODUCTION

B.A.T INDUSTRIES P.L.C.; *Int'l*, pg. 110
GENERAL CIGAR HOLDINGS INC; *U.S. Public*, pg. 707
STANDARD COMMERCIAL CORPORATION; *U.S. Public*, pg. 1501

0133 — SUGARCANE & SUGAR BEET PRODUCTION

A & B-HAWAII, INC.—Alexander & Baldwin, Inc.; *U.S. Public*, pg. 39
ALEXANDER & BALDWIN, INC.; *U.S. Public*, pg. 39
AMFAC, INC.—JMB Realty Corporation; *U.S. Private*, pg. 577
C. BREWER & COMPANY, LIMITED—Buyco, Inc.; *U.S. Private*, pg. 190
HAWAIIAN COMMERCIAL & SUGAR CO.—Alexander & Baldwin, Inc.; *U.S. Public*, pg. 39
HILLESHOG AB—Novartis AG; *Int'l*, pg. 982
HILLESHOG SUGAR BEET SEED AB—Novartis AG; *Int'l*, pg. 982
S.A. INDUSTRIAS VOTORANTIM; *Int'l*, pg. 677
LONRHO PLC; *Int'l*, pg. 817
OLOKELE SUGAR CO., LIMITED—Buyco, Inc.; *U.S. Private*, pg. 191
PUNA SUGAR CO., LTD.—JMB Realty Corporation; *U.S. Private*, pg. 578
SANDOZ SEEDS LTD.—Novartis AG; *Int'l*, pg. 972

0134 — IRISH POTATO PRODUCTION

IDAHO SUPREME COMPANY; *U.S. Private*, pg. 557
MAGIC VALLEY FOODS, INC.; *U.S. Private*, pg. 695
MAINE POTATO GROWERS, INC.; *U.S. Private*, pg. 697
MCCAIN PRODUCE INC.—McCain Foods Limited; *Int'l*, pg. 850

0139 — FIELD CROPS, EXCEPT CASH GRAINS, NEC

GARST SEED COMPANY—Zeneca Group Plc; *Int'l*, pg. 1524
NK LAWN & GARDEN—Novartis AG; *Int'l*, pg. 974
NORTHRUP KING CO.—Novartis AG; *Int'l*, pg. 974
PIONEER HI-BRED INTERNATIONAL, INC.; *U.S. Public*, pg. 1298
SANDOZ SEEDS LTD.—Novartis AG; *Int'l*, pg. 972
TEJON RANCH COMPANY; *U.S. Public*, pg. 1566

0161 — VEGETABLE & MELON PRODUCTION

ALABAMA FARMERS CO-OP; *U.S. Private*, pg. 30
WM. BOLTHOUSE FARMS, INC.; *U.S. Private*, pg. 155
JOSEPH CAMPBELL COMPANY—Campbell Soup Company; *U.S. Public*, pg. 299
DEARDORFF-JACKSON COMPANY; *U.S. Private*, pg. 319
DOLE FOOD COMPANY, INC.; *U.S. Public*, pg. 515
A. DUDA & SONS INC.; *U.S. Private*, pg. 344
GEBRUDER DIPPE SAATZUCHT G.M.B.H.—Novartis AG; *Int'l*, pg. 982
HILLESHOG AB—Novartis AG; *Int'l*, pg. 982
HILLESHOG SKOGAR AB—Novartis AG; *Int'l*, pg. 982
L.O. JEFFS LTD.—Geest PLC; *Int'l*, pg. 542
NK LAWN & GARDEN—Novartis AG; *Int'l*, pg. 974
NORTHRUP KING SEMENTI S.P.A.—Novartis AG; *Int'l*, pg. 983
OCEAN MIST FARMS CORP.; *U.S. Private*, pg. 811
ROGERS N.K. SEED CO.—Novartis AG; *Int'l*, pg. 974
SEALED-SWEET GROWERS, INC.; *U.S. Private*, pg. 978
SPEEDLING INCORPORATED; *U.S. Private*, pg. 1024
VALLEY FARMS LIMITED—McCain Foods Limited; *Int'l*, pg. 850
YOSUBA FARMS—Maxxam Inc.; *U.S. Public*, pg. 1062
ZAADUNIE B.V.—Novartis AG; *Int'l*, pg. 986
ZWAAN UND CO. SAMENZUCHT G.M.B.H.—Novartis AG; *Int'l*, pg. 986

0171 — BERRY FARMS

DEARDORFF-JACKSON COMPANY; *U.S. Private*, pg. 319
MICHIGAN BLUEBERRY GROWERS ASSN.; *U.S. Private*, pg. 740
NORTHLAND CRANBERRIES, INC.; *U.S. Public*, pg. 1197
TOM WADE CO.; *U.S. Private*, pg. 1145

0172 — PRODUCTION OF GRAPES

BEAULIEU VINEYARD—Diageo Plc; *Int'l*, pg. 410
CALLAWAY VINEYARD & WINERY—Allied Domecq PLC; *Int'l*, pg. 63
THE FIRESTONE VINEYARD—Suntory Ltd.; *Int'l*, pg. 1321
E. & J. GALLO WINERY; *U.S. Private*, pg. 438
JEKEL VINEYARDS—Brown-Forman Corporation; *U.S. Public*, pg. 261
JULIANA VINEYARDS—Reunion Industries, Inc.; *U.S. Public*, pg. 1383
RACKE USA—A. Racke GmbH; *Int'l*, pg. 1083
TEJON RANCH COMPANY; *U.S. Public*, pg. 1566
THE WINE ALLIANCE—Allied Domecq PLC; *Int'l*, pg. 63

0173 — PRODUCTION OF TREE NUTS

HANCOCK PEANUT COMPANY—Morven Partners LP; *U.S. Private*, pg. 763
MACFARMS OF HAWAII, INC.—Campbell Soup Company; *U.S. Public*, pg. 299
MORVEN PARTNERS LP; *U.S. Private*, pg. 763
PLANTERS COMPANY—RJR Nabisco Holdings Corp.; *U.S. Public*, pg. 1355
STAHMANN FARMS, INC.; *U.S. Private*, pg. 1029

0174 — CITRUS FRUITS PRODUCTION

ALICO, INC.; *U.S. Public*, pg. 41
BENGUET MANAGEMENT CORPORATION—Benguet Corporation; *Int'l*, pg. 186
BOWEN BROTHERS FRUIT CO., INC.; *U.S. Private*, pg. 162
C&D GROVES—Cigna Corp.; *U.S. Public*, pg. 365
CONSOLIDATED-TOMOKA LAND CO.; *U.S. Public*, pg. 437

A. DUDA & SONS INC.; *U.S. Private*, pg. 344
GROVE DIVISION—Orange-Co., Inc.; *U.S. Public*, pg. 1229
HAINES CITY CITRUS GROWERS ASSOCIATION; *U.S. Private*, pg. 494
HELLER BROS. PACKING CORP.; *U.S. Private*, pg. 520
THE IRVINE COMPANY; *U.S. Private*, pg. 575
LAKE PLACID GROVES—Consolidated-Tomoka Land Co.; *U.S. Public*, pg. 437
ORANGE-CO., INC.; *U.S. Public*, pg. 1229
PARAMOUNT CITRUS ASSOCIATION—Roll International Corporation; *U.S. Private*, pg. 941
PARAMOUNT FARMING COMPANY—Roll International Corporation; *U.S. Private*, pg. 941
THE PROCTER & GAMBLE COMPANY; *U.S. Public*, pg. 1330
SEALED-SWEET GROWERS, INC.; *U.S. Private*, pg. 978
SILVER SPRINGS CITRUS CO-OP; *U.S. Private*, pg. 1000

0175 — DECIDUOUS TREE FRUITS PRODUCTION

BENGUET MANAGEMENT CORPORATION—Benguet Corporation; *Int'l*, pg. 186
HARRIS FARMS, INC.; *U.S. Private*, pg. 505
HARRY AND DAVID—Yamanouchi Pharmaceutical Co. Ltd.; *Int'l*, pg. 1518
PARAMOUNT FARMING COMPANY—Roll International Corporation; *U.S. Private*, pg. 941
SHAKLEE CORPORATION—Yamanouchi Pharmaceutical Co. Ltd.; *Int'l*, pg. 1518
TROUT-BLUE CHELIAU, INC.; *U.S. Private*, pg. 1105
WASHINGTON STATE APPLE COMMISSION; *U.S. Private*, pg. 1152

0179 — PRODUCTION OF FRUITS & TREE NUTS, NEC

A & B-HAWAII, INC.—Alexander & Baldwin, Inc.; *U.S. Public*, pg. 39
ALEXANDER & BALDWIN, INC.; *U.S. Public*, pg. 39
CHIQUITA BRANDS INTERNATIONAL, INC.; *U.S. Public*, pg. 349
DIAMOND WALNUT GROWERS, INC.—Sun Diamond Growers of California; *U.S. Private*, pg. 1051
DOLE FOOD COMPANY, INC.; *U.S. Public*, pg. 515
HAZELNUT GROWERS OF OREGON—Sun Diamond Growers of California; *U.S. Private*, pg. 1051
KILAUEA AGRONOMICS, INC.—Buyco, Inc.; *U.S. Private*, pg. 190
MAUI LAND & PINEAPPLE CO., INC.; *U.S. Public*, pg. 1060
MAUNA KEA AGRIBUSINESS CO., INC.—Buyco, Inc.; *U.S. Private*, pg. 190
MAUNA LOA MACADAMIA PARTNERS, L.P.; *U.S. Public*, pg. 1060
PHILIPPINE COCOA ESTATES CORPORATION—Benguet Corporation; *Int'l*, pg. 187
SUN DIAMOND GROWERS OF CALIFORNIA; *U.S. Private*, pg. 1051
SUPERIOR COFFEE & FOODS/HAWAII—Buyco, Inc.; *U.S. Private*, pg. 191
VALLEY FIG GROWERS—Sun Diamond Growers of California; *U.S. Private*, pg. 1051

0181 — ORNAMENTAL FLORICULTURE & NURSERY PRODUCTS PRODUCTION

ADVANCE SEED COMPANY—Groupe Limagrain; *Int'l*, pg. 566
AMERICAN NURSERY PRODUCTS, LLC; *U.S. Private*, pg. 59
ASGROW CANADA, LTD.—Pharmacia & Upjohn, Inc.; *Int'l*, pg. 1049
ASGROW DO BRASIL SEMENTES LTDA.—Pharmacia & Upjohn, Inc.; *Int'l*, pg. 1049
ASGROW FRANCE S.A.—Pharmacia & Upjohn, Inc.; *Int'l*, pg. 1049
ASGROW MEXICANA S.A. DE C.V.—Pharmacia & Upjohn, Inc.; *Int'l*, pg. 1049
ASGROW SEED COMPANY—Pharmacia & Upjohn, Inc.; *Int'l*, pg. 1048
BALL FLORAPLANT—Ball Horticultural Company; *U.S. Private*, pg. 112
BALL HORTICULTURAL COMPANY; *U.S. Private*, pg. 112
BARENBRUG HOLLAND BV; *Int'l*, pg. 166
BARENBRUG NORTHEAST—Barenbrug Holland BV; *Int'l*, pg. 167
BARENBRUG USA—Barenbrug Holland BV; *Int'l*, pg. 166
BOOKER PLC; *Int'l*, pg. 202
BURNSTAD BROTHERS, INC.; *U.S. Private*, pg. 187
W. ATLEE BURPEE CO.; *U.S. Private*, pg. 187
CARGILL LTD.—Cargill; *U.S. Private*, pg. 210
CIBA-GEIGY ARGENTINA S.A.I.C. Y F.—Novartis AG; *Int'l*, pg. 976
CIBA-GEIGY CANADA LTD.-HONEYWOOD RESEARCH FARM—Novartis AG; *Int'l*, pg. 976
CIBA-GEIGY HELLAS S.A.—Novartis AG; *Int'l*, pg. 977
CIBA-GEIGY KOREA LTD.—Novartis AG; *Int'l*, pg. 977
CIBA-GEIGY (MPL) LIMITED—Novartis AG; *Int'l*, pg. 978
CIBA-GEIGY QUIMICA S.A.—Novartis AG; *Int'l*, pg. 979
CIBA-GEIGY SERVICES A.G.—Novartis AG; *Int'l*, pg. 979
CIBA-GEIGY SERVICES AG-TECHNICAL ADVISORY OFFICE—Novartis AG; *Int'l*, pg. 979
CIBA HUNGARIA KFT.—Novartis AG; *Int'l*, pg. 980
CIBA SEEDS(CIBA-GEIGY CANADA LTD.)—Novartis AG; *Int'l*, pg. 976
COLOR SPOT NURSERY, INC.; *U.S. Private*, pg. 254
PAUL ECKE RANCH; *U.S. Private*, pg. 359
ESTEVAN DIVISION—MacMillan Bloedel Limited; *Int'l*, pg. 828
EVE RIVER DIVISION—MacMillan Bloedel Limited; *Int'l*, pg. 828
FERRY-MORSE SEED COMPANY—Groupe Limagrain; *Int'l*, pg. 566
FRANKLIN RIVER DIVISION—MacMillan Bloedel Limited; *Int'l*, pg. 828
FREDONIA SEED CO.—Novartis AG; *Int'l*, pg. 974
GEBRUDER DIPPE SAATZUCHT G.M.B.H.—Novartis AG; *Int'l*, pg. 982
GENERAL CIGAR HOLDINGS INC; *U.S. Public*, pg. 707
GREEN SEED CO.; *U.S. Private*, pg. 477
GROUPE LIMAGRAIN; *Int'l*, pg. 566
HILLESHOG AB—Novartis AG; *Int'l*, pg. 982
HILLESHOG SKOGAR AB—Novartis AG; *Int'l*, pg. 982
IMPERIAL NURSERIES INC.—General Cigar Holdings Inc; *U.S. Public*, pg. 707
JACKSON & PERKINS—Yamanouchi Pharmaceutical Co. Ltd.; *Int'l*, pg. 1518
KELSEY BAY DIV.—MacMillan Bloedel Limited; *Int'l*, pg. 828
LES GRAINES CAILLARD S.A.—Novartis AG; *Int'l*, pg. 983
LIMAGRAIN GENETICS CORP.—Groupe Limagrain; *Int'l*, pg. 566
MAICES HIBRIDOS Y SEMILLAS SA—Novartis AG; *Int'l*, pg. 983
MCHUTCHINSON DIV.—Novartis AG; *Int'l*, pg. 973
MID-WESTERN OF ALABAMA DIVISION—American Nursery Products, LLC; *U.S. Private*, pg. 60
MID-WESTERN NURSERY DIVISION—American Nursery Products, LLC; *U.S. Private*, pg. 60
MOCK SEED COMPANY—Seed Corporation of America; *U.S. Private*, pg. 981
MONROVIA NURSERY CO.; *U.S. Private*, pg. 757
NK LAWN & GARDEN—Novartis AG; *Int'l*, pg. 974
NORTHLAND EVERGREENS, INC.—American Nursery Products, LLC; *U.S. Private*, pg. 60
NORTHRUP KING PTY. LTD.—Novartis AG; *Int'l*, pg. 983
NORTHRUP KING SEEDS LTD.—Novartis AG; *Int'l*, pg. 983
NORTHRUP KING SEMENCES S.A.—Novartis AG; *Int'l*, pg. 983
NORTHRUP KING SEMENTI S.P.A.—Novartis AG; *Int'l*, pg. 983
NORTHRUP KING SEMILLAS S.A.—Novartis AG; *Int'l*, pg. 983
NORTHRUP KING Y COMPANIA, S.A. DE C.V.—Novartis AG; *Int'l*, pg. 983
NOVARTIS—Novartis AG; *Int'l*, pg. 972
NOVARTIS AG; *Int'l*, pg. 971
NOVARTIS SEEDS, INC.—Novartis AG; *Int'l*, pg. 974
O'S GOLD SEED CO.—Pharmacia & Upjohn, Inc.; *Int'l*, pg. 1048
L.L. OLDS SEED COMPANY; *U.S. Private*, pg. 814
PAN-AMERICAN SEED CO.—Ball Horticultural Company; *U.S. Private*, pg. 112
PEDIGREE SEED CO.—Novartis AG; *Int'l*, pg. 974
PETOSEED CO.—W. Atlee Burpee Co.; *U.S. Private*, pg. 188
PREMIER BRANDS, INC.—Premier CDN Enterprises Ltd.; *Int'l*, pg. 1068
PROCORDIA FOOD AB—Orkla A.S.A.; *Int'l*, pg. 1011
K.J. QUINN S. A.—Novartis AG; *Int'l*, pg. 984
ROUGH BROTHERS, INC.; *U.S. Private*, pg. 947
SAKATA SEED AMERICA, INC.—Sakata Seed Corporation; *Int'l*, pg. 1178
SAKATA SEED CORPORATION; *Int'l*, pg. 1178
SAKATA SEED DO BRASIL LTDA.—Sakata Seed Corporation; *Int'l*, pg. 1178
SAKATA SEED EUROPE B.V.—Sakata Seed Corporation; *Int'l*, pg. 1178
SANDOZ SEEDS LTD.—Novartis AG; *Int'l*, pg. 972
SCHWEIZERISCHE GENPSSENSCHAFT FUR GEMUSEBAU—Coop Switzerland; *Int'l*, pg. 330
THE SCOTTS COMPANY; *U.S. Public*, pg. 1446
SEED CORPORATION OF AMERICA; *U.S. Private*, pg. 981
SHAKLEE CORPORATION—Yamanouchi Pharmaceutical Co. Ltd.; *Int'l*, pg. 1518
SHISSLER SEED CO.—Groupe Limagrain; *Int'l*, pg. 566
SOCIEDADE AGRICOLA GERMINAL LTDA.—Novartis AG; *Int'l*, pg. 985
SPEEDLING INCORPORATED; *U.S. Private*, pg. 1024
SPEEDLING INCORPORATED—Speedling Incorporated; *U.S. Private*, pg. 1024
STOWE-PHARR MILLS, INC.; *U.S. Private*, pg. 1045
SUN BULB COMPANY, INC.; *U.S. Private*, pg. 1050
WETSEL SEED COMPANY—Southern States Cooperative, Inc.; *U.S. Private*, pg. 1017
ZAADUNIE B.V.—Novartis AG; *Int'l*, pg. 986
ZENECA AGROCHEMICALS AND SEEDS—Zeneca Group Plc; *Int'l*, pg. 1524
ZENECA GROUP PLC; *Int'l*, pg. 1524
ZWAAN UND CO. SAMENZUCHT G.M.B.H.—Novartis AG; *Int'l*, pg. 986

0182 — FOOD CROPS GROWN UNDER COVER

AMYCEL, INC.—Monterey Mushrooms, Inc.; *U.S. Private*, pg. 758
BOOKER PLC; *Int'l*, pg. 202
BRUINSMA SEEDS, B.V.—Pharmacia & Upjohn, Inc.; *Int'l*, pg. 1049
CAMPBELL SOUP COMPANY; *U.S. Public*, pg. 298
CAMPBELL USA—Campbell Soup Company; *U.S. Public*, pg. 299
CAMPBELL'S FRESH, INC.—Campbell Soup Company; *U.S. Public*, pg. 299
LEAVER MUSHROOMS CO. LIMITED—ConAgra, Inc.; *U.S. Public*, pg. 428
MONTEREY MUSHROOMS, INC.; *U.S. Private*, pg. 758
MYKORA OY—Kemira Oy; *Int'l*, pg. 728
QUINCY CORP.—Sylvan Inc.; *U.S. Public*, pg. 1545
ROYAL CHAMPIGNON—Groupe Saint Louis; *Int'l*, pg. 567
SYLVAN INC.; *U.S. Public*, pg. 1545
VALLEY FARMS LIMITED—McCain Foods Limited; *Int'l*, pg. 850

0191 — GENERAL FARMS, PRIMARILY CROP

AMANA FARMS, INC.—Amana Society, Inc.; *U.S. Private*, pg. 48
HARRIS FARMS, INC.; *U.S. Private*, pg. 505
HUNT OIL COMPANY; *U.S. Private*, pg. 548
THE IRVINE COMPANY; *U.S. Private*, pg. 575
LONRHO PLC; *Int'l*, pg. 817
THE NEWHALL LAND AND FARMING COMPANY; *U.S. Public*, pg. 1178
J.R. NORTON COMPANY; *U.S. Private*, pg. 807
REUNION INDUSTRIES, INC.; *U.S. Public*, pg. 1383
ROLL INTERNATIONAL CORPORATION; *U.S. Private*, pg. 941
J.R. SIMPLOT COMPANY; *U.S. Private*, pg. 1002

0211 — BEEF CATTLE FEEDLOTS

BARTLETT AND COMPANY; *U.S. Private*, pg. 118
CACTUS FEEDERS, INC.; *U.S. Private*, pg. 198
CARGILL; *U.S. Private*, pg. 210
CATTLE FEEDING DIV.—Continental Grain Company; *U.S. Private*, pg. 268
CONAGRA RED MEAT COMPANIES—ConAgra, Inc.; *U.S. Public*, pg. 427
CONTINENTAL GRAIN COMPANY; *U.S. Private*, pg. 268
FALLEY'S INC.—The Yucaipa Companies; *U.S. Private*, pg. 1202
FRIONA INDUSTRIES, L.P.; *U.S. Private*, pg. 429
GARNEY HOLDING COMPANY, INC.; *U.S. Private*, pg. 440
WM. HAUGHTON & CO. LTD.—Foster's Brewing Group Limited; *Int'l*, pg. 501
HOLSTEIN ASSOCIATION USA, INC.; *U.S. Private*, pg. 536
MONFORT, INC.—ConAgra, Inc.; *U.S. Public*, pg. 427
SCHAAKE CORPORATION; *U.S. Private*, pg. 969
SWISHER COUNTY CATTLE CO.—Friona Industries, L.P.; *U.S. Private*, pg. 429

0212 — BEEF CATTLE, EXCEPT FEEDLOTS

A BAR A RANCH—Cody Company; *U.S. Private*, pg. 249
ALICO, INC.; *U.S. Public*, pg. 41
AZENIDA AGRICOLA PEROLLA S.R.L.—Allianz Aktiengesellschaft; *Int'l*, pg. 61
CACTUS FEEDERS, INC.; *U.S. Private*, pg. 198
CODY COMPANY; *U.S. Private*, pg. 249
A. DUDA & SONS INC.; *U.S. Private*, pg. 344
HARRIS FARMS, INC.; *U.S. Private*, pg. 505
THE HONDO COMPANY—Lonrho plc; *Int'l*, pg. 818
HUNT OIL COMPANY; *U.S. Private*, pg. 548
LANE INDUSTRIES, INC.; *U.S. Private*, pg. 649
LINCOLN INDUSTRIES; *U.S. Private*, pg. 668
PETERSON FARMS; *U.S. Private*, pg. 857
TEJON RANCH COMPANY; *U.S. Public*, pg. 1566
UNITED STATES SUGAR CORPORATION; *U.S. Private*, pg. 1126

0213 — HOG PRODUCTION

BRECKLAND FARMS—J. Sainsbury plc; *Int'l*, pg. 1170
CARGILL ANIMAL NUTRITION DIV.—Cargill; *U.S. Private*, pg. 210
CARROLL'S FOODS, INC.; *U.S. Private*, pg. 215
CENTRAL STATES ENTERPRISES, INC.; *U.S. Private*, pg. 225
DEKALB GENETICS CORPORATION; *U.S. Public*, pg. 493
DEKALB SWINE BREEDERS, INC.—Dekalb Genetics Corporation; *U.S. Public*, pg. 493
MURPHY FAMILY FARMS; *U.S. Private*, pg. 768
TYSON FOODS, INC.; *U.S. Public*, pg. 1652
UNITED FEEDS, INC.; *U.S. Private*, pg. 1122

0214 — SHEEP & GOATS PRODUCTION

PRAKTIKER BAU- UND HEIMWERKEMARKT AG—Metro AG; *Int'l*, pg. 863
SLOCAN FOREST PRODUCTS LTD.; *Int'l*, pg. 1263
TAYWOOD FARMS PTY. LTD.—Taylor Woodrow plc; *Int'l*, pg. 1360
WOOL FILTERS INTL.—Fruit of the Loom, Inc.; *U.S. Public*, pg. 686

0219 — GENERAL LIVESTOCK, EXCEPT DAIRY & POULTRY

J.R. SIMPLOT COMPANY; *U.S. Private*, pg. 1002

0241 — DAIRY FARMS

AZENIDA AGRICOLA PEROLLA S.R.L.—Allianz Aktiengesellschaft; *Int'l*, pg. 61
COMPANIA PERUANA DE ALIMENTOS S.A.—Nestle S.A.; *Int'l*, pg. 920
DAIRY MART FARMS, INC.—Dairy Mart Convenience Stores, Inc.; *U.S. Public*, pg. 476
LAND O' LAKES—Land O'Lakes, Inc.; *U.S. Private*, pg. 646
TURNER HOLDING LLC—Turner Holding LLC; *U.S. Private*, pg. 1109

0251 — BROILER, FRYER, & ROASTER CHICKENS PRODUCTION

AVICOLA PILGRIM'S PRIDE DE MEXICO, S.A. DE C.V.—Pilgrim's Pride Corporation; *U.S. Public*, pg. 1296
BOOKER PLC; *Int'l*, pg. 202
CAGLE'S INC.; *U.S. Public*, pg. 291
CASE FARMS, INC.—Case Foods, Inc.; *U.S. Private*, pg. 218

CONTINENTAL GRAIN COMPANY; *U.S. Private*, pg. 268
EMPIRE KOSHER POULTRY, INC.; *U.S. Private*, pg. 374
GOLD'N PLUMP POULTRY—JFC Inc.; *U.S. Private*, pg. 577
JFC INC.; *U.S. Private*, pg. 577
K & L FEEDS—Empire Kosher Poultry, Inc.; *U.S. Private*, pg. 374
MATTERN HATCHERY—Empire Kosher Poultry, Inc.; *U.S. Private*, pg. 374
MOORLAND FOODS—Hillsdown Holdings Plc; *Int'l*, pg. 619
PERDUE FARMS INCORPORATED; *U.S. Private*, pg. 852
PETERSON FARMS; *U.S. Private*, pg. 857
PILGRIM'S PRIDE CORPORATION; *U.S. Public*, pg. 1296
ROSS BREEDERS, INC.—Hillsdown Holdings Plc; *Int'l*, pg. 619
SANDERSON FARMS FOODS DIV.—Sanderson Farms, Inc.; *U.S. Public*, pg. 1431
SANDERSON FARMS, INC.; *U.S. Public*, pg. 1430
SANDERSON FARMS PROCESSING DIV.—Sanderson Farms, Inc.; *U.S. Public*, pg. 1431
SANDERSON FARMS PRODUCTION DIV.—Sanderson Farms, Inc.; *U.S. Public*, pg. 1431
TYSON FOODS, INC.—Tyson Foods, Inc.; *U.S. Public*, pg. 1652
TYSON FOODS, INC.; *U.S. Public*, pg. 1652
UWAJIMA CANNING CO., LTD.—Meiji Seika Kaisha, Ltd.; *Int'l*, pg. 855
ZACKY FARMS, INC.; *U.S. Private*, pg. 1203

0252 — CHICKEN EGGS PRODUCTION

CWT FARMS INTERNATIONAL—Booker PLC; *Int'l*, pg. 202
CAL-MAINE FOODS, INC.; *U.S. Public*, pg. 292
CARGILL; *U.S. Private*, pg. 210
GOLD'N PLUMP POULTRY—JFC Inc.; *U.S. Private*, pg. 577
JFC INC.; *U.S. Private*, pg. 577
PILGRIM'S PRIDE CORPORATION; *U.S. Public*, pg. 1296
ROSE ACRE FARMS; *U.S. Private*, pg. 944

0253 — TURKEYS & TURKEY EGGS PRODUCTION

ARBOR ACRES FARM, INC.—Booker PLC; *Int'l*, pg. 202
BERNARD MATTHEWS PLC; *Int'l*, pg. 189
BOOKER PLC; *Int'l*, pg. 202
BRITISH UNITED TURKEYS LTD.—Merck & Co., Inc.; *U.S. Public*, pg. 1091
CARROLL'S FOODS, INC.; *U.S. Private*, pg. 215
CASE FARMS, INC.—Case Foods, Inc.; *U.S. Private*, pg. 218
MOORLAND FOODS—Hillsdown Holdings Plc; *Int'l*, pg. 619
NICHOLAS TURKEY BREEDING FARMS—Booker PLC; *Int'l*, pg. 202
PETERSON FARMS; *U.S. Private*, pg. 857
ROSS BREEDERS, INC.—Hillsdown Holdings Plc; *Int'l*, pg. 619
SHADY BROOK FARMS—Rocco Inc.; *U.S. Private*, pg. 937

0254 — POULTRY HATCHERIES PRODUCTION

ARBOR ACRES FARM, INC.—Booker PLC; *Int'l*, pg. 202
BERNARD MATTHEWS PLC; *Int'l*, pg. 189
CAL-MAINE FOODS, INC.; *U.S. Public*, pg. 292
GOLD'N PLUMP POULTRY—JFC Inc.; *U.S. Private*, pg. 577
GRESS FOODS INC.; *U.S. Private*, pg. 480
HUBBARD FARMS, INC.—Merck & Co., Inc.; *U.S. Public*, pg. 1092
JFC INC.; *U.S. Private*, pg. 577
KOUDIJS-WOUDA VOEDERS B.V.—Goodman Fielder Limited; *Int'l*, pg. 555
PERDUE FARMS INCORPORATED; *U.S. Private*, pg. 852
TATUM FARMS INT., INC.; *U.S. Private*, pg. 1069
TYSON FOODS, INC.—Tyson Foods, Inc.; *U.S. Public*, pg. 1652

0259 — POULTRY & EGGS PRODUCTION, NEC

PETERSON FARMS; *U.S. Private*, pg. 857

0271 — FUR-BEARING ANIMALS & RABBITS PRODUCTION

MARUHA CORPORATION; *Int'l*, pg. 845

0272 — HORSES & OTHER EQUINES FARMS

JACK KENT COOKE, INC.; *U.S. Private*, pg. 273
HARRIS FARMS, INC.; *U.S. Private*, pg. 505
INTERNATIONAL THOROUGHBRED BREEDERS, INC.; *U.S. Public*, pg. 908

0273 — ANIMAL AQUACULTURE

BALTEK CORPORATION; *U.S. Public*, pg. 171
BOOKER PLC; *Int'l*, pg. 202
CLEAR SPRINGS FOODS, INC.; *U.S. Private*, pg. 245
CONAGRA, INC.; *U.S. Public*, pg. 425
DELTA PRIDE CATFISH, INC.; *U.S. Private*, pg. 322
UNILEVER N.V.—Unilever Plc; *Int'l*, pg. 1434

0279 — ANIMAL SPECIALTIES, NEC

BAUSCH & LOMB INCORPORATED; *U.S. Public*, pg. 194
CHARLES RIVER CANADA, INC.—Bausch & Lomb Incorporated; *U.S. Public*, pg. 195
CHARLES RIVER ESPANA S.A.—Bausch & Lomb Incorporated; *U.S. Public*, pg. 195
CHARLES RIVER FRANCE S.A.—Bausch & Lomb Incorporated; *U.S. Public*, pg. 195
CHARLES RIVER ITALIA S.P.A.—Bausch & Lomb Incorporated; *U.S. Public*, pg. 195
CHARLES RIVER JAPAN, INC.—Bausch & Lomb Incorporated; *U.S. Public*, pg. 195
CHARLES RIVER U.K., LTD.—Bausch & Lomb Incorporated; *U.S. Public*, pg. 195
CHARLES RIVER WIGA G.M.B.H.—Bausch & Lomb Incorporated; *U.S. Public*, pg. 195
COVANCE RESEARCH PRODUCTS, INC.—Covance, Inc.; *U.S. Public*, pg. 454
DONG-SUH FOODS CORPORATION; *Int'l*, pg. 416
MARINE HARVEST MCCONNELL—Booker PLC; *Int'l*, pg. 202
SHAMROCK (GREAT BRITAIN) LTD.—Bausch & Lomb Incorporated; *U.S. Public*, pg. 196
TSI WASHINGTON LABORATORIES—Genzyme Corporation; *U.S. Public*, pg. 733

0291 — GENERAL FARMS, PRIMARILY LIVESTOCK & ANIMAL SPECIALTIES

AMANA FARMS, INC.—Amana Society, Inc.; *U.S. Private*, pg. 48
AYRSHIRE LAND COMPANY—Cyprus Amax Minerals Company; *U.S. Public*, pg. 471
EMPIRE LIVESTOCK MARKETING INC.—Dairylea Cooperative Inc.; *U.S. Private*, pg. 308
FARMERS UNION MARKETING & PROCESSING ASSOCIATION; *U.S. Private*, pg. 395
GOLDSBORO MILLING COMPANY; *U.S. Private*, pg. 462
LONRHO PLC; *Int'l*, pg. 817
NATIONAL FARMS INC.; *U.S. Private*, pg. 782
TEJON AGRICULTURAL CORP.—Tejon Ranch Company; *U.S. Public*, pg. 1566
TEJON RANCH COMPANY; *U.S. Public*, pg. 1566

0711 — SOIL PREPARATION SERVICES

AGRI TERMINAL CORPORATION—American Grain & Related Industries; *U.S. Private*, pg. 55
AGWAY AGRICULTURAL PRODUCTS (AAP)—Agway, Inc.; *U.S. Private*, pg. 27
AGWAY, INC.; *U.S. Private*, pg. 27
NICKERSON SEEDS LTD.—Royal Dutch/Shell Group of Companies; *Int'l*, pg. 1139
WESTERN ENVIRONMENTAL CONTRACTING, INC.—CalMat Co.; *U.S. Public*, pg. 296
WESTERN THERMAL SOILS CO.—CalMat Co.; *U.S. Public*, pg. 296

0721 — CROP PLANTING, CULTIVATING & PROTECTION SERVICES

AGWAY AGRICULTURAL PRODUCTS (AAP)—Agway, Inc.; *U.S. Private*, pg. 27
AGWAY, INC.; *U.S. Private*, pg. 27
CIBA-GEIGY PERUANA S.A.—Novartis AG; *Int'l*, pg. 978
CIBA-PILATUS AERIAL SPRAYING CO. LTD.—Oerlikon-Buhrle Holding AG; *Int'l*, pg. 998
EARLY CALIFORNIA FOODS—Erly Industries, Inc.; *U.S. Public*, pg. 591
FRESH WORLD—Empressa La Moderna SA de CV; *Int'l*, pg. 454
LEVER SOLOMONS LTD.—Unilever Plc; *Int'l*, pg. 1438
LYKES BROTHERS INC.; *U.S. Private*, pg. 682
MYCOGEN CORPORATION; *U.S. Public*, pg. 1142
MYCOGEN CROP PROTECTION—Mycogen Corporation; *U.S. Public*, pg. 1142
NICKERSON ZWAAN—Royal Dutch/Shell Group of Companies; *Int'l*, pg. 1135
PAMOL (NIGERIA) LTD.—Unilever Plc; *Int'l*, pg. 1438
PAMOL PLANTATIONS SDN. BHD.—Unilever Plc; *Int'l*, pg. 1438
PLANTATIONS LEVER AU ZAIRE S.A.R.L.—Unilever Plc; *Int'l*, pg. 1438
PLANTATIONS PAMOL DU CAMEROON LTD.—Unilever Plc; *Int'l*, pg. 1438

0722 — CROP HARVESTING, PRIMARILY BY MACHINE

GOLDEN GEM GROWERS INC.; *U.S. Private*, pg. 460
TEJON FARMING COMPANY—Tejon Ranch Company; *U.S. Public*, pg. 1566

0723 — CROP PREPARATION SERVICES FOR MARKET, EXCEPT COTTON GINNING

BEST FOODS SAUDI ARABIA CO. LTD.—Bestfoods; *U.S. Public*, pg. 225
CALIFORNIA FARM PRODUCTS—J.M. Smucker Company; *U.S. Public*, pg. 1480
CITRUS WORLD INC.; *U.S. Private*, pg. 241
COLLINGWOOD GRAIN, INC.—Archer Daniels Midland Company (ADM); *U.S. Public*, pg. 128
COOP SWITZERLAND; *Int'l*, pg. 329
COUNTRY PRODUCTS GROUP—Agway, Inc.; *U.S. Private*, pg. 27
DAIRY EXPORT CO., INC.—Darigold, Inc.; *U.S. Private*, pg. 311
DAVID MANUFACTURING COMPANY (DMC)—The GSI Group, Inc.; *U.S. Private*, pg. 436
DEARDORFF-JACKSON COMPANY; *U.S. Private*, pg. 319
DIAMOND WALNUT GROWERS, INC.—Sun Diamond Growers of California; *U.S. Private*, pg. 1051
A. DUDA & SONS INC.; *U.S. Private*, pg. 344
THE GSI GROUP, INC.; *U.S. Private*, pg. 436
GOLDEN GEM GROWERS INC.; *U.S. Private*, pg. 460
HAINES CITY CITRUS GROWERS ASSOCIATION; *U.S. Private*, pg. 494
HAZELNUT GROWERS OF OREGON—Sun Diamond Growers of California; *U.S. Private*, pg. 1051
HELLER BROS. PACKING CORP.; *U.S. Private*, pg. 520
LANGWOOD (PREPARED VEGETABLES) LIMITED—Avonmore Waterford Group plc; *Int'l*, pg. 102
MFA INCORPORATED; *U.S. Private*, pg. 686
MESA CITRUS GROWERS; *U.S. Private*, pg. 733
OCEANA FOODS—Cherry Central Cooperative; *U.S. Private*, pg. 234
PARAMOUNT CITRUS ASSOCIATION—Roll International Corporation; *U.S. Private*, pg. 941
PRODUCERS CO-OP ASSOCIATION, INC.; *U.S. Private*, pg. 888
PRODUCERS RICE MILL INC.; *U.S. Private*, pg. 888
RICELAND FOODS, INC.; *U.S. Private*, pg. 928
SF SERVICES; *U.S. Private*, pg. 956
THE SCOULAR COMPANY; *U.S. Private*, pg. 977
SEBASTIAN COTTON & GRAIN CORP.; *U.S. Private*, pg. 980
SHERLEY GRAIN COMPANY; *U.S. Private*, pg. 993
STONEVILLE PEDIGREED SEED CO.—Monsanto Company; *U.S. Public*, pg. 1124
SUN DIAMOND GROWERS OF CALIFORNIA; *U.S. Private*, pg. 1051
TRINIDAD/BENHAM CORP.; *U.S. Private*, pg. 1103
VALLEY FIG GROWERS—Sun Diamond Growers of California; *U.S. Private*, pg. 1051

0724 — COTTON GINNING

CALCOT, LTD.; *U.S. Private*, pg. 200
CHICKASHA COTTON OIL CO.—Tomen Corporation; *Int'l*, pg. 1395
WADE GIN CO.—Tom Wade Co.; *U.S. Private*, pg. 1146
TOM WADE CO.; *U.S. Private*, pg. 1145

0751 — LIVESTOCK SERVICES, EXCEPT VETERINARY

ABS GLOBAL INC.; *U.S. Private*, pg. 3
DALGETY AGRICULTURE, LIMITED—Dalgety Plc; *Int'l*, pg. 376
PIG IMPROVEMENT GROUP LTD.—Dalgety Plc; *Int'l*, pg. 376
QUINCY DESIGN & MANUFACTURING—Brunner Engineering & Manufacturing, Inc.; *U.S. Private*, pg. 176
SELECT SIRES, INC.; *U.S. Private*, pg. 982

0752 — ANIMAL SPECIALTY SERVICES, EXCEPT VETERINARY

CHARLES RIVER BREEDING LABS—Bausch & Lomb Incorporated; *U.S. Public*, pg. 194
CHARLES RIVER LABORATORIES, INC.—Bausch & Lomb Incorporated; *U.S. Public*, pg. 194

0762 — FARM MANAGEMENT SERVICES

FARMERS NATIONAL COMPANY—Metropolitan Life Insurance Co.; *U.S. Private*, pg. 738
GOLDEN GEM GROWERS INC.; *U.S. Private*, pg. 460
STANDARD CHARTERED ESTATE MANAGEMENT LIMITED—Standard Chartered Bank PLC; *Int'l*, pg. 1295
TEJON FARMING COMPANY—Tejon Ranch Company; *U.S. Public*, pg. 1566
TURNER FOODS CORPORATION—FPL Group, Inc.; *U.S. Public*, pg. 608

0781 — LANDSCAPE COUNSELING & PLANNING

AMLINGS FLOWERLAND; *U.S. Private*, pg. 66
ASPLUNDH TREE EXPERT CO.; *U.S. Private*, pg. 89
ENVIRONMENTAL INDUSTRIES, INC.; *U.S. Private*, pg. 378
GOODKIND & O'DEA, INC.—Dewberry & Davis; *U.S. Private*, pg. 329
ISS-INTERNATIONAL SERVICE SYSTEM A/S; *Int'l*, pg. 656
MITSUI NORIN CO., LTD.—Mitsui & Co., Ltd.; *Int'l*, pg. 878
MITSUI ROAD CO., LTD.—Mitsui & Co., Ltd.; *Int'l*, pg. 877
OBAYASHI CORPORATION; *Int'l*, pg. 995
ORKIN PLANTSCAPING—Rollins, Inc.; *U.S. Public*, pg. 1405
PETRICCA INDUSTRIES, INC.; *U.S. Private*, pg. 858
SMITH & HAWKEN—CML Group, Inc.; *U.S. Public*, pg. 279
STILES CORPORATION; *U.S. Private*, pg. 1043

0782 — LAWN & GARDEN SERVICES

AGRIBIOTECH, INC.; *U.S. Public*, pg. 28
CHEMI-TROL CHEMICAL CO.; *U.S. Public*, pg. 345
THE DAVEY TREE EXPERT COMPANY; *U.S. Private*, pg. 314
ENVIRONMENTAL INDUSTRIES, INC.; *U.S. Private*, pg. 378
LAWN DOCTOR INC.; *U.S. Private*, pg. 653
MAPCO NATURAL GAS LIQUIDS INC.—Mapco Inc.; *U.S. Public*, pg. 1042
OBAYASHI CORPORATION; *Int'l*, pg. 995
ORKIN EXTERMINATING CO., INC.—Rollins, Inc.; *U.S. Public*, pg. 1404
ORKIN LAWN CARE—Rollins, Inc.; *U.S. Public*, pg. 1405
RINGER CORPORATION; *U.S. Public*, pg. 1390
ROLLINS, INC.; *U.S. Public*, pg. 1404
THE SERVICEMASTER COMPANY; *U.S. Public*, pg. 1461

SPRING-GREEN LAWN CARE CORPORATION; *U.S. Private*, pg. 1027
TRIANGLE SERVICES, INC.; *U.S. Private*, pg. 1102
TRUGREEN-CHEMLAWN—The ServiceMaster Company; *U.S. Public*, pg. 1461

0783 — ORNAMENTAL SHRUB & TREE SERVICES

THE F.A. BARTLETT TREE EXPERT CO.; *U.S. Private*, pg. 119
CANADIAN SHADE TREE SERVICE, LTD.—The Davey Tree Expert Company; *U.S. Private*, pg. 314
THE DAVEY TREE EXPERT COMPANY; *U.S. Private*, pg. 314
ENVIRONMENTAL INDUSTRIES, INC.; *U.S. Private*, pg. 378
NORTHERN TREE SERVICE, INC.—ESELCO, Inc.; *U.S. Public*, pg. 592

0811 — TIMBER TRACTS

AVENOR, INC.; *Int'l*, pg. 101
BMC FORESTRY CORPORATION—Benguet Corporation; *Int'l*, pg. 186
BEAR ISLAND TIMBERLANDS COMPANY, L.P.—The Washington Post Company; *U.S. Public*, pg. 1743
BOXHOLMS SKOGAR AB/SKANSKA FORESTRY GROUP—Skanska AB; *Int'l*, pg. 1260
CANADIAN FOREST PRODUCTS LTD., CHETWYND DIVISION—Canfor Corporation; *Int'l*, pg. 260
CAPITAL DEVELOPMENT CO.; *U.S. Private*, pg. 205
CARTER HOLT HARVEY FORESTS LIMITED—International Paper Company; *U.S. Public*, pg. 905
CARTER HOLT HARVEY LIMITED—International Paper Company; *U.S. Public*, pg. 904
CAVENHAM FOREST INDUSTRIES INC.—Hanson PLC; *Int'l*, pg. 593
CAXTON FORESTS LIMITED—International Paper Company; *U.S. Public*, pg. 905
CRESCENT RESOURCES, INC.—Duke Energy Corporation; *U.S. Public*, pg. 534
CRESTBROOK FOREST INDUSTRIES LTD.; *Int'l*, pg. 348
DELTIC TIMBER CORPORATION; *U.S. Public*, pg. 498
DUKE ENERGY CORPORATION; *U.S. Public*, pg. 534
ENSO OYJ; *Int'l*, pg. 455
FORT JAMES CORPORATION; *U.S. Public*, pg. 670
FORT JAMES CORPORATION—Fort James Corporation; *U.S. Public*, pg. 672
FORT JAMES TIMBER CORP.—Fort James Corporation; *U.S. Public*, pg. 672
GEORGIA PACIFIC—Georgia-Pacific Corporation; *U.S. Public*, pg. 736
THE GLATFELTER PULP WOOD CO.—P.H. Glatfelter Company; *U.S. Public*, pg. 746
GREIF BROTHERS CORPORATION; *U.S. Public*, pg. 763
HILLESHOG FORESTRY AB—Novartis AG; *Int'l*, pg. 982
INTERNATIONAL FOREST SEED COMPANY—Novartis AG; *Int'l*, pg. 973
INTERNATIONAL PAPER COMPANY; *U.S. Public*, pg. 901
KARELIA PROCUREMENT AREA—Enso Oyj; *Int'l*, pg. 455
MENASHA CORPORATION; *U.S. Private*, pg. 731
METSA-SERLA CORPORATION; *Int'l*, pg. 863
MO OCH DOMSJO AB; *Int'l*, pg. 885
NORSKE SKOGINDUSTRIER A.S; *Int'l*, pg. 965
PCS PHOSPHATE - RALEIGH—Potash Corporation of Saskatchewan Inc.; *Int'l*, pg. 1064
THE PACIFIC LUMBER COMPANY—Maxxam Inc.; *U.S. Public*, pg. 1062
PLUM CREEK TIMBER CO., L.P.; *U.S. Public*, pg. 1311
POPE RESOURCES; *U.S. Public*, pg. 1317
PROCUREMENT AREA SOUTH OF FINLAND—Enso Oyj; *Int'l*, pg. 455
ROSEBURG RESOURCES CO.—RLC Industries Co.; *U.S. Private*, pg. 905
SAIMAA PROCUREMENT AREA—Enso Oyj; *Int'l*, pg. 455
ST. CROIX WATER POWER CO.—Georgia-Pacific Corporation; *U.S. Public*, pg. 736
ST. JOSEPH LAND & DEVELOPMENT COMPANY—St. Joe Corp.; *U.S. Public*, pg. 1427
SAVO PROCUREMENT AREA—Enso Oyj; *Int'l*, pg. 455
STORA FOREST AB—Stora Kopparbergs Bergslags AB; *Int'l*, pg. 1303
STORA KOPPARBERGS BERGSLAGS AB; *Int'l*, pg. 1302
SUNICAL LAND & LIVESTOCK DIVISION—The Hearst Corporation; *U.S. Private*, pg. 518
TEMPLE-INLAND FOREST PRODUCTS CORP.-FORESTS DIVISION—Temple-Inland Inc.; *U.S. Public*, pg. 1575
TENNECO PACKAGING—Tenneco Inc.; *U.S. Public*, pg. 1579
UPM-KYMMENE CORPORATION; *Int'l*, pg. 1427
UNION CAMP CORPORATION; *U.S. Public*, pg. 1665
UNION CAMP WOODLANDS DIV.—Union Camp Corporation; *U.S. Public*, pg. 1666
U.S. TIMBERLANDS COMPANY, L.P.; *U.S. Public*, pg. 1688
WEYERHAEUSER COMPANY; *U.S. Public*, pg. 1764
WEYERHAEUSER FOREST PRODUCTS COMPANY—Weyerhaeuser Company; *U.S. Public*, pg. 1764
WILLAMETTE INDUSTRIES, INC.; *U.S. Public*, pg. 1768
WILLAMETTE INDUSTRIES, INC.—Willamette Industries, Inc.; *U.S. Public*, pg. 1769

0831 — FOREST NURSERIES & GATHERING OF FOREST PRODUCTS

CARTER HOLT HARVEY LIMITED—International Paper Company; *U.S. Public*, pg. 904
COLOR SPOT NURSERY, INC.; *U.S. Private*, pg. 254
DOMAN INDUSTRIES LIMITED; *Int'l*, pg. 414
FLETCHER CHALLENGE CANADA LIMITED—Fletcher Challenge Limited; *Int'l*, pg. 495
FLETCHER CHALLENGE LIMITED; *Int'l*, pg. 494
FORT JAMES CORPORATION; *U.S. Public*, pg. 670
FORT JAMES CORPORATION—Fort James Corporation; *U.S. Public*, pg. 672
FORT JAMES TIMBER CORP.—Fort James Corporation; *U.S. Public*, pg. 672
GRAINES FRANCO-SUEDOISES S.A.—Novartis AG; *Int'l*, pg. 982
HAPPY HOLIDAY TREE FARMS—Color Spot Nursery, Inc.; *U.S. Private*, pg. 254
HILLESHOG FORESTRY AB—Novartis AG; *Int'l*, pg. 982
INTERNATIONAL FOREST SEED COMPANY—Novartis AG; *Int'l*, pg. 973
INTERNATIONAL PAPER COMPANY; *U.S. Public*, pg. 901
KARELIA PROCUREMENT AREA—Enso Oyj; *Int'l*, pg. 455
MOSINEE INDUSTRIAL FOREST DIVISION—Wausau-Mosinee Paper Corporation; *U.S. Public*, pg. 1747
NORAM FIELD SERVICES CORP.—Houston Industries Incorporated; *U.S. Public*, pg. 843
PROCUREMENT AREA SOUTH OF FINLAND—Enso Oyj; *Int'l*, pg. 455
SAIMAA PROCUREMENT AREA—Enso Oyj; *Int'l*, pg. 455
SAVO PROCUREMENT AREA—Enso Oyj; *Int'l*, pg. 455
SIME DARBY BERHAD; *Int'l*, pg. 1249
SIME DARBY COMMODITY TRADING & PLANTATIONS DIVISION—Sime Darby Berhad; *Int'l*, pg. 1250
TASMAN FORESTRY LIMITED—Fletcher Challenge Limited; *Int'l*, pg. 495
TEMPLE-INLAND FOREST PRODUCTS CORPORATION—Temple-Inland Inc.; *U.S. Public*, pg. 1575
TEMPLE-INLAND INC.; *U.S. Public*, pg. 1574
UNION CAMP CORPORATION; *U.S. Public*, pg. 1665
UNION CAMP WOODLANDS DIV.—Union Camp Corporation; *U.S. Public*, pg. 1666
WEYERHAEUSER FOREST PRODUCTS COMPANY—Weyerhaeuser Company; *U.S. Public*, pg. 1764

0851 — FORESTRY SERVICES

BAIGENT FOREST INDUSTRIES LIMITED—International Paper Company; *U.S. Public*, pg. 905
BORREGAARD SKOGER AS—Orkla A.S.A.; *Int'l*, pg. 1011
E.D. COLLIER & SON—Bateman Brothers Lumber Co., Inc.; *U.S. Private*, pg. 122
CONSOLIDATED-TOMOKA LAND CO.; *U.S. Public*, pg. 437
DAISHOWA PAPER MFG. CO., LTD.; *Int'l*, pg. 373
THE GLATFELTER PULP WOOD CO.—P.H. Glatfelter Company; *U.S. Public*, pg. 746
IP TIMBERLANDS, LTD.—International Paper Company; *U.S. Public*, pg. 904
T.L. JAMES & COMPANY; *U.S. Private*, pg. 580
KIMBERLY-CLARK, EVERETT—Kimberly-Clark Corporation; *U.S. Public*, pg. 958
MITSUI NORIN CO., LTD.—Mitsui & Co., Ltd.; *Int'l*, pg. 878
PLANTACIONES MESOPOTAMICAS—Corporacion MAPFRE, Compania Internacional de Reaseguros, S.A.; *Int'l*, pg. 333
PROPRIETORY PRODUCTS GROUP—Esco Corporation; *U.S. Private*, pg. 383
SORAK CO., LTD.—KOHAP Group; *Int'l*, pg. 743
STORA BILLERUD PAPER S.A.—Stora Kopparbergs Bergslags AB; *Int'l*, pg. 1302
STORA CELL AB—Stora Kopparbergs Bergslags AB; *Int'l*, pg. 1303
STORA FOREST AB—Stora Kopparbergs Bergslags AB; *Int'l*, pg. 1303
STORA KOPPARBERGS BERGSLAGS AB; *Int'l*, pg. 1302
STORA TIMBER AB—Stora Kopparbergs Bergslags AB; *Int'l*, pg. 1303
TASMAN CHILE S.A.—Fletcher Challenge Limited; *Int'l*, pg. 495
TEMPLE-INLAND FOREST PRODUCTS CORP.-FORESTS DIVISION—Temple-Inland Inc.; *U.S. Public*, pg. 1575

0912 — CATCHING OF FINFISH

ARCTIC ALASKA FISHERIES CORPORATION—Tyson Foods, Inc.; *U.S. Public*, pg. 1652
GOLDEN ALASKA SEAFOODS, INC.—Nichiro Corporation; *Int'l*, pg. 928
P.T. IRIAN MARINE PRODUCT DEVELOPMENT—Nissho Iwai Corporation; *Int'l*, pg. 948
MARINE CONSTRUCTION & DESIGN CO.; *U.S. Private*, pg. 703
NIPPON SUISAN KAISHA, LTD.; *Int'l*, pg. 940
TYSON FOODS, INC.; *U.S. Public*, pg. 1652
WILLAWA FISHING CO.—Marine Construction & Design Co.; *U.S. Private*, pg. 703
ZAPATA CORPORATION; *U.S. Public*, pg. 1789

0913 — CATCHING OR TAKING OF SHELLFISH

ARCTIC ALASKA FISHERIES CORPORATION—Tyson Foods, Inc.; *U.S. Public*, pg. 1652
BLUEPOINTS CO., INC.—The First Republic Corporation of America; *U.S. Public*, pg. 637
CONAGRA SHRIMP COMPANY—ConAgra, Inc.; *U.S. Public*, pg. 427
THE FIRST REPUBLIC CORPORATION OF AMERICA; *U.S. Public*, pg. 637
NIPPON SUISAN KAISHA, LTD.; *Int'l*, pg. 940
O'DONNELL-USEN FISHERIES CORP.—ConAgra, Inc.; *U.S. Public*, pg. 427
SEABOARD CORPORATION; *U.S. Public*, pg. 1448
SEABOARD FLOUR CORPORATION—Seaboard Corporation; *U.S. Public*, pg. 1449
TYSON FOODS, INC.; *U.S. Public*, pg. 1652

0919 — MISCELLANEOUS MARINE PRODUCTS PRODUCTION

MARUHA CORPORATION; *Int'l*, pg. 845
C. PLATH NORTH AMERICAN DIV.—Litton Industries, Inc.; *U.S. Public*, pg. 1002
QUAKER BRASIL, LTDA.—The Quaker Oats Company; *U.S. Public*, pg. 1348
TODD ENTERPRISES—Chem-Tainer Industries; *U.S. Private*, pg. 231

0921 — FISH HATCHERIES & PRESERVES

ACUICULTURA DE CEUTA, S.A.—Caja de Madrid Group; *Int'l*, pg. 252
CRUSTACEA CORPORATION—Baltek Corporation; *U.S. Public*, pg. 172

1011 — IRON ORES MINING

ARBED S.A.; *Int'l*, pg. 78
BERGBAUSTAHL GMBH—Fried. Krupp AG; *Int'l*, pg. 513
THE BROKEN HILL PROPRIETARY COMPANY LIMITED; *Int'l*, pg. 223
CAM—Imetal; *Int'l*, pg. 662
CLEVELAND-CLIFFS INC; *U.S. Public*, pg. 386
THE CLEVELAND-CLIFFS IRON COMPANY—Cleveland-Cliffs Inc; *U.S. Public*, pg. 386
DOMICILIO CONOCIDO HERCULES—Grupo Acerero del Norte S.A. de C.V. (GAN); *Int'l*, pg. 572
ESTA GESELLSCHAFT FUR EDELSTAHLVERARBEITUNG MBH—Fried. Krupp AG; *Int'l*, pg. 513
EVELETH MINES—Oglebay Norton Company; *U.S. Public*, pg. 1213
FALCONBRIDGE (JAPAN) LTD.—EdperBrascan Corporation; *Int'l*, pg. 434
GRAFITO SUPERIOR SA—Superior Graphite Co.; *U.S. Private*, pg. 1055
GRANGES INTERNATIONAL MINING—Electrolux, AB; *Int'l*, *pg. 439*
GRUPO ACERERO DEL NORTE S.A. DE C.V. (GAN); *Int'l*, *pg. 572*
HOESCH PLATINEN GMBH—Fried. Krupp AG; *Int'l*, pg. 512
HUTTENWERKE KRUPP MANNESMANN GMBH—Fried. Krupp AG; *Int'l*, pg. 512
IMETAL; *Int'l*, pg. 661
INLAND STEEL MINING CO.—Inland Steel Industries, Inc.; *U.S. Public*, pg. 879
IRON-ORE COMPANY OF CANADA—North Limited; *Int'l*, pg. 967
KRUPP HOESCH STAHL AG - DORTMUND—Fried. Krupp AG; *Int'l*, pg. 512
KRUPP SIGMA-STAHL GMBH—Fried. Krupp AG; *Int'l*, pg. 513
LAFARGE CONSTRUCTION MATERIALS—Lafarge S.A.; *Int'l*, pg. 788
LAMCO J.V. OPERATING CO.—Electrolux, AB; *Int'l*, pg. 443
LORMINES (SOCIETE DES MINES DE SACILOR)—Groupe Usinor; *Int'l*, pg. 571
MESABA-CLIFFS MINING CO.—NKK Corporation; *Int'l*, pg. 903
MINAS DA SERRA BERAL S.A.—Nissho Iwai Corporation; *Int'l*, pg. 948
OGLEBAY NORTON COMPANY; *U.S. Public*, pg. 1213
OUTOKUMPU OYJ; *Int'l*, pg. 1015
PICKANDS MATHER & CO. INTERNATIONAL—Cleveland-Cliffs Inc; *U.S. Public*, pg. 386
QUEBEC CARTIER MINING CO.—DoFasco, Inc.; *Int'l*, pg. 414
THE RTZ CORPORATION PLC—Rio Tinto PLC; *Int'l*, pg. 1118
USX CORPORATION; *U.S. Public*, pg. 1661
USINAS SIDERURGICAS DE MINAS GERAIS S.A.—Nissho Iwai Corporation; *Int'l*, pg. 949

1021 — COPPER ORES MINING

ALTA GOLD CO.; *U.S. Public*, pg. 58
ANDINA DIVISION—CODELCO Chile (Corporacion Nacional Del Cobre De Chile); *Int'l*, pg. 302
ASARCO INCORPORATED; *U.S. Public*, pg. 137
ATLAS CONSOLIDATED MINING & DEVELOPMENT CORPORATION; *Int'l*, pg. 95
BHP COPPER NORTH AMERICA—The Broken Hill Proprietary Company Limited; *Int'l*, pg. 224
BENGUET CORPORATION; *Int'l*, pg. 186
BRUNSWICK MINING & SMELTING CORP. LTD.—EdperBrascan Corporation; *Int'l*, pg. 434
CRA LIMITED—Rio Tinto PLC; *Int'l*, pg. 1119
CEBU MINING OPERATION—Atlas Consolidated Mining & Development Corporation; *Int'l*, pg. 95
CHINO MINES COMPANY—Phelps Dodge Corporation; *U.S. Public*, pg. 1287
CHUQUICAMATA DIVISION—CODELCO Chile (Corporacion Nacional Del Cobre De Chile); *Int'l*, pg. 302
COMINCO, LTD.; *Int'l*, pg. 307
COMPANIA MINERA DISPUTADA DE LAS CONDES S.S.—Exxon Corporation; *U.S. Public*, pg. 601
CONTINENTAL CATALINA, INC.—Continental Materials Corporation; *U.S. Public*, pg. 441
COPPER RANGE COMPANY—Metallgesellschaft AG; *Int'l*, pg. 862
CYPRUS AMAX MINERALS COMPANY; *U.S. Public*, pg. 470
CYPRUS BAGDAD COPPER CORPORATION—Cyprus Amax Minerals Company; *U.S. Public*, pg. 471
CYPRUS MIAMI MINING CORPORATION—Cyprus Amax Minerals Company; *U.S. Public*, pg. 471
CYPRUS MINES CORP.—Cyprus Amax Minerals Company; *U.S. Public*, pg. 471

CYPRUS SIERRITA—Cyprus Amax Minerals Company; U.S. Public, pg. 471
CYPRUS TOHONO CORPORATION—Cyprus Amax Minerals Company; U.S. Public, pg. 471
EMPRESAS FRISCO SA DE CV—Grupo Carso S.A. de C.V.; Int'l, pg. 572
FALCONBRIDGE (JAPAN) LTD.—EdperBrascan Corporation; Int'l, pg. 434
FALCONBRIDGE LIMITED—EdperBrascan Corporation; Int'l, pg. 433
FISHERY FOODS GMBH—Fishery Products International Ltd.; Int'l, pg. 492
FISHERY PRODUCTS INTERNATIONAL LTD.; Int'l, pg. 492
FISHERY PRODUCTS INTERNATIONAL USA—Fishery Products International Ltd.; Int'l, pg. 492
FREEPORT-MCMORAN COPPER & GOLD, INC.—Freeport-McMoRan Inc.; U.S. Public, pg. 680
FREEPORT-MCMORAN INC.; U.S. Public, pg. 680
P.T. FREEPORT INDONESIA CO.—Freeport-McMoRan Inc.; U.S. Public, pg. 681
THE GOLDFIELD CORPORATION; U.S. Public, pg. 750
GRUPO MEXICO S.A. DE C.V.—Asarco Incorporated; U.S. Public, pg. 138
HIGHLAND VALLEY COPPER—Cominco, Ltd.; Int'l, pg. 308
INCO LIMITED; Int'l, pg. 672
INDUSTRIAS PENOLES S.A. DE C.V.; Int'l, pg. 677
JAPAN ENERGY CORPORATION; Int'l, pg. 702
KENNECOTT HOLDINGS CORPORATION—Rio Tinto PLC; Int'l, pg. 1119
KENNECOTT UTAH COPPER CORPORATION—Rio Tinto PLC; Int'l, pg. 1119
THE LORDSBURG MINING COMPANY—The Goldfield Corporation; U.S. Public, pg. 750
MAGMA-ROBINSON MINING DISTRICT—The Broken Hill Proprietary Company Limited; Int'l, pg. 224
MAGMA-SAN MANUEL MINING DIVISION—The Broken Hill Proprietary Company Limited; Int'l, pg. 224
MAGMA-SUPERIOR MINING DIVISION—The Broken Hill Proprietary Company Limited; Int'l, pg. 224
MINERA OUTOKUMPU CHILE S.A.—Outokumpu Oyj; Int'l, pg. 1016
MINORCO—Anglo American Corporation of South Africa Limited; Int'l, pg. 77
MOUNT ISA MINES LTD.—M.I.M. Holdings Ltd.; Int'l, pg. 827
NORANDA INC.—EdperBrascan Corporation; Int'l, pg. 433
NORD PACIFIC LIMITED—Nord Resources Corporation; U.S. Public, pg. 1188
NORTH LIMITED; Int'l, pg. 967
OK TEDI MINING LIMITED—The Broken Hill Proprietary Company Limited; Int'l, pg. 228
OUTOKUMPU BASE METALS OY—Outokumpu Oyj; Int'l, pg. 1016
OUTOKUMPU MINES LTD.—Outokumpu Oyj; Int'l, pg. 1016
OUTOKUMPU MINING OY—Outokumpu Oyj; Int'l, pg. 1016
PALABORA MINING CO. LTD.—Rio Tinto PLC; Int'l, pg. 1119
PHELPS DODGE CORPORATION; U.S. Public, pg. 1286
PHELPS DODGE TYRONE—Phelps Dodge Corporation; U.S. Public, pg. 1287
PLACER DOME INC.; Int'l, pg. 1060
THE RTZ CORPORATION PLC—Rio Tinto PLC; Int'l, pg. 1118
RIO ALGOM LIMITED; Int'l, pg. 1118
RIO TINTO ZIMBABWE LIMITED—Rio Tinto PLC; Int'l, pg. 1119
ST. CLOUD MINING CO.—The Goldfield Corporation; U.S. Public, pg. 750
SOUTHERN PERU COPPER CORP.—Asarco Incorporated; U.S. Public, pg. 138
STANDARD METALS CORPORATION; U.S. Public, pg. 1502
SUNSHINE MINING AND REFINING COMPANY; U.S. Public, pg. 1536
SUNSHINE PRECIOUS METALS, INC.—Sunshine Mining And Refining Company; U.S. Public, pg. 1536
WESTMIN RESOURCES LTD.—EdperBrascan Corporation; Int'l, pg. 435

1031 — LEAD & ZINC ORES MINING

ALTA GOLD CO.; U.S. Public, pg. 58
ARMENONIC DEL ECUADOR, S.A.—Nissho Iwai Corporation; Int'l, pg. 949
THE BROKEN HILL PROPRIETARY COMPANY LIMITED; Int'l, pg. 223
CRA LIMITED—Rio Tinto PLC; Int'l, pg. 1119
CHILTEM GROUP SAM—Alpha Omikron Limited; Int'l, pg. 65
COMINCO ALASKA INCORPORATED—Cominco, Ltd.; Int'l, pg. 307
COMINCO AMERICAN INCORPORATED—Cominco, Ltd.; Int'l, pg. 308
COMINCO, LTD.; Int'l, pg. 307
THE DOE RUN COMPANY—Renco Group; U.S. Private, pg. 922
EMPRESAS FRISCO SA DE CV—Grupo Carso S.A. de C.V.; Int'l, pg. 572
FALCONBRIDGE LIMITED—EdperBrascan Corporation; Int'l, pg. 433
GRUPO MEXICO S.A. DE C.V.—Asarco Incorporated; U.S. Public, pg. 138
HECLA MINING COMPANY; U.S. Public, pg. 803
HERZOG COILEX GMBH—Fried. Krupp AG; Int'l, pg. 512
INDUSTRIAS PENOLES S.A. DE C.V.; Int'l, pg. 677
S.A. INDUSTRIAS VOTORANTIM; Int'l, pg. 677
JAPAN ENERGY CORPORATION; Int'l, pg. 702
KENNECOTT HOLDINGS CORPORATION—Rio Tinto PLC; Int'l, pg. 1119
LUCKY FRIDAY UNIT—Hecla Mining Company; U.S. Public, pg. 804
MONTANA TUNNELS MINING, INC.—Pegasus Gold Corporation; U.S. Public, pg. 1269
MOUNT ISA MINES LTD.—M.I.M. Holdings Ltd.; Int'l, pg. 827
NANISIVIK MINES LTD.—Royal Dutch/Shell Group of Companies; Int'l, pg. 1138
NORANDA INC.—EdperBrascan Corporation; Int'l, pg. 433
OUTOKUMPU BASE METALS OY—Outokumpu Oyj; Int'l, pg. 1016
OUTOKUMPU MINING OY—Outokumpu Oyj; Int'l, pg. 1016
PENARROYA ESPANA—Imetal; Int'l, pg. 662
PENARROYA METAL EUROPE—Imetal; Int'l, pg. 662
PHELPS DODGE CORPORATION; U.S. Public, pg. 1286
PREDIL-PERTUSOLA—Imetal; Int'l, pg. 662
THE RTZ CORPORATION PLC—Rio Tinto PLC; Int'l, pg. 1118
ST. CLOUD MINING CO.—The Goldfield Corporation; U.S. Public, pg. 750
SOCIETE MINIERE DE BOUGRINE S.A.—Metallgesellschaft AG; Int'l, pg. 862
STANDARD METALS CORPORATION; U.S. Public, pg. 1502
TARA MINES LIMITED—Outokumpu Oyj; Int'l, pg. 1016
WESTMIN RESOURCES LTD.—EdperBrascan Corporation; Int'l, pg. 435

1041 — GOLD ORES MINING

ADDWEST MINERALS, INC.; U.S. Private, pg. 17
ALTA GOLD CO.; U.S. Public, pg. 58
AMAX GOLD INC.—Cyprus Amax Minerals Company; U.S. Public, pg. 470
ARMENONIC DEL ECUADOR, S.A.—Nissho Iwai Corporation; Int'l, pg. 949
ASIA MINERALS CORP.—Royal Oak Mines Inc.; U.S. Public, pg. 1411
ATLAS CONSOLIDATED MINING & DEVELOPMENT CORPORATION; Int'l, pg. 95
BARRICK GOLD—Barrick Gold Corporation; Int'l, pg. 169
BARRICK GOLD CORPORATION; Int'l, pg. 168
BARRICK MINERALS (CANADA) INC.—Barrick Gold Corporation; Int'l, pg. 169
BASIN CREEK MINE—Pegasus Gold Corporation; U.S. Public, pg. 1269
BATTLE MOUNTAIN (AUSTRALIA) INC.—Battle Mountain Gold Company; U.S. Public, pg. 193
BATTLE MOUNTAIN GOLD COMPANY; U.S. Public, pg. 193
BEAL MOUNTAIN MINING INC.—Pegasus Gold Corporation; U.S. Public, pg. 1269
BENGUET CORPORATION; Int'l, pg. 186
BOLIDEN BERGSOE AB—Trelleborg AB; Int'l, pg. 1422
BOLIDEN MINERAL AB—Trelleborg AB; Int'l, pg. 1422
BOLIDEN WP-CONTECH AB—Trelleborg AB; Int'l, pg. 1422
CR BRIGGS CORPORATION—Canyon Resources Corporation; U.S. Public, pg. 302
CR KENDALL CORPORATION—Canyon Resources Corporation; U.S. Public, pg. 302
CALLAHAN MINING CORPORATION—Coeur D'Alene Mines Corporation; U.S. Public, pg. 394
CAMBIOR INC.; Int'l, pg. 253
CANYON RESOURCES CORPORATION; U.S. Public, pg. 301
CEBU MINING OPERATION—Atlas Consolidated Mining & Development Corporation; Int'l, pg. 95
COEUR D'ALENE MINES CORPORATION; U.S. Public, pg. 394
COEUR ROCHESTER, INC.—Coeur D'Alene Mines Corporation; U.S. Public, pg. 394
COMINCO AMERICAN RESOURCES INCORPORATED, BUCKHORN OPERATIONS—Cominco, Ltd.; Int'l, pg. 307
COMINCO, LTD.; Int'l, pg. 307
COMMERCE GROUP CORP.; U.S. Public, pg. 410
COMMERCE/SANSEB—Commerce Group Corp.; U.S. Public, pg. 410
COMMERCE/SANSEB JOINT VENTURE—Commerce Group Corp.; U.S. Public, pg. 410
COMPANIA MINERA MANTOS DE ORO—Placer Dome Inc.; Int'l, pg. 1060
COMPANIA NACIONAL DE MINERACAO—TVX Gold Inc.; Int'l, pg. 1345
CONSOLIDATED VISCOUNT RESOURCES LTD.; Int'l, pg. 326
CORPORACION INDUSTRIAL SANLUIS; Int'l, pg. 332
CROWN GOLD, INC.—Crown Central Petroleum Corporation; U.S. Public, pg. 462
DAKOTA MINING CORPORATION; U.S. Public, pg. 477
DAVY INTERNATIONAL, SAN FRANCISCO—Kvaerner a.s.a.; Int'l, pg. 774
ECHO BAY ALASKA INC.—Echo Bay Mines Ltd.; U.S. Public, pg. 562
ECHO BAY MINES LTD.; U.S. Public, pg. 561
ECHO BAY MINES-LUPIN OPERATIONS—Echo Bay Mines Ltd.; U.S. Public, pg. 562
ECHO BAY MINING COMPANY—Echo Bay Mines Ltd.; U.S. Public, pg. 562
EMPRESAS FRISCO SA DE CV—Grupo Carso S.A. de C.V.; Int'l, pg. 572
FMC GOLD CO.—FMC Corporation; U.S. Public, pg. 605
FREEPORT-MCMORAN COPPER & GOLD, INC.—Freeport-McMoRan Inc.; U.S. Public, pg. 680
FREEPORT-MCMORAN INC.; U.S. Public, pg. 680
P.T. FREEPORT INDONESIA CO.—Freeport-McMoRan Inc.; U.S. Public, pg. 681
GETCHELL GOLD CORP.; U.S. Public, pg. 740
GILT EDGE MINE—Dakota Mining Corporation; U.S. Public, pg. 477
GOLDCORP INC.—CSA Management Inc.; Int'l, pg. 243
GOLDEN REWARD MINE—CSA Management Inc.; Int'l, pg. 243
GOLDEN REWARD MINE—Dakota Mining Corporation; U.S. Public, pg. 477
GOLDSTRIKE MINE—Barrick Gold Corporation; Int'l, pg. 169
GRANNY SMITH JOINT VENTURE—Placer Dome Inc.; Int'l, pg. 1060
GREENS CREEK UNIT—Hecla Mining Company; U.S. Public, pg. 804
HECLA MINING COMPANY; U.S. Public, pg. 803
HIPPOCRENE HOLDINGS—Pegasus Gold Corporation; U.S. Public, pg. 1269
HOLT-MCDERMOTT MINE—Barrick Gold Corporation; Int'l, pg. 169
HOMESTAKE CANADA INC.—Homestake Mining Company; U.S. Public, pg. 833
HOMESTAKE MINING COMPANY; U.S. Public, pg. 832
INCO LIMITED; Int'l, pg. 672
JAPAN ENERGY CORPORATION; Int'l, pg. 702
KETTLE RIVER GOLD MINE, ECHO BAY MINERALS—Echo Bay Mines Ltd.; U.S. Public, pg. 562
KIDSTON GOLD MINES LIMITED—Placer Dome Inc.; Int'l, pg. 1060
KIENA GOLD MINES, LTD.—Placer Dome Inc.; Int'l, pg. 1060
KINROSS GOLD CORPORATION; Int'l, pg. 734
KLOOF GOLD MINING COMPANY LIMITED; Int'l, pg. 738
LONRHO PLC; Int'l, pg. 817
THE LORDSBURG MINING COMPANY—The Goldfield Corporation; U.S. Public, pg. 750
MAGMA-ROBINSON MINING DISTRICT—The Broken Hill Proprietary Company Limited; Int'l, pg. 224
MASBATE GOLD OPERATION—Atlas Consolidated Mining & Development Corporation; Int'l, pg. 95
MCCOY/COVE MINES—Echo Bay Mines Ltd.; U.S. Public, pg. 562
MERCUR MINE—Barrick Gold Corporation; Int'l, pg. 169
MINERA HECLA S.A. DE CV—Hecla Mining Company; U.S. Public, pg. 804
MINERA HISPANIOLA, S.A.—Canyon Resources Corporation; U.S. Public, pg. 302
MINERACAO SERRAS DO SUL LTDA.—Inco Limited; Int'l, pg. 673
MINERAL SAN SEBASTIAN S.A.—Commerce Group Corp.; U.S. Public, pg. 410
MINORCO—Anglo American Corporation of South Africa Limited; Int'l, pg. 77
MISIMA MINES PTY. LTD.—Placer Dome Inc.; Int'l, pg. 1060
MONTANA PARTICIPACOES LIMITADA—Montana Power Company; U.S. Public, pg. 1127
MONTANA TUNNELS MINING, INC.—Pegasus Gold Corporation; U.S. Public, pg. 1269
NEWHAWK GOLD MINES LTD.—Homestake Mining Company; U.S. Public, pg. 833
NEWMONT GOLD COMPANY—Newmont Mining Corporation; U.S. Public, pg. 1179
NEWMONT MINING CORPORATION; U.S. Public, pg. 1178
NORANDA INC.—EdperBrascan Corporation; Int'l, pg. 433
NORD PACIFIC LIMITED—Nord Resources Corporation; U.S. Public, pg. 1188
NORTH LIMITED; Int'l, pg. 967
OK TEDI MINING LIMITED—The Broken Hill Proprietary Company Limited; Int'l, pg. 228
OUTOKUMPU BASE METALS OY—Outokumpu Oyj; Int'l, pg. 1016
PACIFICORP; U.S. Public, pg. 1251
PEGASUS GOLD CORPORATION; U.S. Public, pg. 1269
PEGASUS MINERA DE CHILE LTDA—Pegasus Gold Corporation; U.S. Public, pg. 1269
PHELPS DODGE CORPORATION; U.S. Public, pg. 1286
PINSON MINE—Barrick Gold Corporation; Int'l, pg. 169
PIONEER GOLDFIELDS LIMITED—The Pioneer Group, Inc.; U.S. Public, pg. 1298
PLACER DOME INC.; Int'l, pg. 1060
PLACER PACIFIC LIMITED—Placer Dome Inc.; Int'l, pg. 1060
PORGERA JOINT VENTURE—Placer Dome Inc.; Int'l, pg. 1060
THE RTZ CORPORATION PLC—Rio Tinto PLC; Int'l, pg. 1118
RED LAKE MINE—CSA Management Inc.; Int'l, pg. 243
RIO TINTO ZIMBABWE LIMITED—Rio Tinto PLC; Int'l, pg. 1119
THE ROSEBUD MINING COMPANY, L.L.C.—Hecla Mining Company; U.S. Public, pg. 804
ROUND MOUNTAIN GOLD CORPORATION—Echo Bay Mines Ltd.; U.S. Public, pg. 562
ROUND MOUNTAIN GOLD CORPORATION—Homestake Mining Company; U.S. Public, pg. 833
ROYAL OAK MINES INC.; U.S. Public, pg. 1410
ST. CLOUD MINING CO.—The Goldfield Corporation; U.S. Public, pg. 750
SAN SEBASTIAN GOLD MINES, INC.—Commerce Group Corp.; U.S. Public, pg. 410
SIGMA MINES (QUEBEC) LTD.—Placer Dome Inc.; Int'l, pg. 1060
STANDARD METALS CORPORATION; U.S. Public, pg. 1502
STIBNITE MINE—Dakota Mining Corporation; U.S. Public, pg. 477
STROUD RESOURCES LTD.; Int'l, pg. 1304
SUMITOMO METAL MINING CO., LTD.; Int'l, pg. 1316
TVX GOLD INC.; Int'l, pg. 1345
TEBEREBIE GOLDFIELDS, LTD.—The Pioneer Group, Inc.; U.S. Public, pg. 1298
TRELLEBORG MINING & METALS DIV.—Trelleborg AB; Int'l, pg. 1422
VISTA GOLD CORP.; U.S. Public, pg. 1723
WESTMIN RESOURCES LTD.—EdperBrascan Corporation; Int'l, pg. 435
WHARF MINE—CSA Management Inc.; Int'l, pg. 243
WHARF RESOURCES LTD.—CSA Management Inc.; Int'l, pg. 243

WHEATON RIVER MINERALS LTD.; *Int'l*, pg. 1498
WORSLEY ALUMINA PTY. LTD.—Reynolds Metals Company; *U.S. Public*, pg. 1387
ZORTMAN MINING INC.—Pegasus Gold Corporation; *U.S. Public*, pg. 1269

1044 — SILVER ORES MINING

ADDWEST MINERALS, INC.; *U.S. Private*, pg. 17
ALTA GOLD CO.; *U.S. Public*, pg. 58
ARMENONIC DEL ECUADOR, S.A.—Nissho Iwai Corporation; *Int'l*, pg. 949
ATLAS CONSOLIDATED MINING & DEVELOPMENT CORPORATION; *Int'l*, pg. 95
BASIN CREEK MINE—Pegasus Gold Corporation; *U.S. Public*, pg. 1269
BEAL MOUNTAIN MINING INC.—Pegasus Gold Corporation; *U.S. Public*, pg. 1269
BRUNSWICK MINING & SMELTING CORP. LTD.—EdperBrascan Corporation; *Int'l*, pg. 434
CALLAHAN MINING CORPORATION—Coeur D'Alene Mines Corporation; *U.S. Public*, pg. 394
CEBU MINING OPERATION—Atlas Consolidated Mining & Development Corporation; *Int'l*, pg. 95
CHILTEM GROUP SAM—Alpha Omikron Limited; *Int'l*, pg. 65
COEUR D'ALENE MINES CORPORATION; *U.S. Public*, pg. 394
COEUR ROCHESTER, INC.—Coeur D'Alene Mines Corporation; *U.S. Public*, pg. 394
COMINCO AMERICAN RESOURCES INCORPORATED, BUCKHORN OPERATIONS—Cominco, Ltd.; *Int'l*, pg. 307
COMINCO, LTD.; *Int'l*, pg. 307
COMPANIA NACIONAL DE MINERACAO—TVX Gold Inc.; *Int'l*, pg. 1345
CONSOLIDATED VISCOUNT RESOURCES LTD.; *Int'l*, pg. 326
CONTINENTAL QUICKSILVER, INC.—Continental Materials Corporation; *U.S. Public*, pg. 441
CORPORACION INDUSTRIAL SANLUIS; *Int'l*, pg. 332
CYPRUS MINES CORP.—Cyprus Amax Minerals Company; *U.S. Public*, pg. 471
ECHO BAY MINES LTD.; *U.S. Public*, pg. 561
FMC GOLD CO.—FMC Corporation; *U.S. Public*, pg. 605
FREEPORT-MCMORAN INC.; *U.S. Public*, pg. 680
THE GOLDFIELD CORPORATION; *U.S. Public*, pg. 750
GREENS CREEK UNIT—Hecla Mining Company; *U.S. Public*, pg. 804
GROUSE CREEK UNIT—Hecla Mining Company; *U.S. Public*, pg. 804
HECLA MINING COMPANY; *U.S. Public*, pg. 803
THE LORDSBURG MINING COMPANY—The Goldfield Corporation; *U.S. Public*, pg. 750
LUCKY FRIDAY UNIT—Hecla Mining Company; *U.S. Public*, pg. 804
MASBATE GOLD OPERATION—Atlas Consolidated Mining & Development Corporation; *Int'l*, pg. 95
MCCOY/COVE MINES—Echo Bay Mines Ltd.; *U.S. Public*, pg. 562
MISIMA MINES PTY. LTD.—Placer Dome Inc.; *Int'l*, pg. 1060
MONTANA TUNNELS MINING, INC.—Pegasus Gold Corporation; *U.S. Public*, pg. 1269
NEWHAWK GOLD MINES LTD.—Homestake Mining Company; *U.S. Public*, pg. 833
PACIFICORP; *U.S. Public*, pg. 1251
PHELPS DODGE CORPORATION; *U.S. Public*, pg. 1286
PLACER DOME INC.; *Int'l*, pg. 1060
THE RTZ CORPORATION PLC—Rio Tinto PLC; *Int'l*, pg. 1118
ST. CLOUD MINING CO.—The Goldfield Corporation; *U.S. Public*, pg. 750
STANDARD METALS CORPORATION; *U.S. Public*, pg. 1502
SUNSHINE MINING AND REFINING COMPANY; *U.S. Public*, pg. 1536
SUNSHINE PRECIOUS METALS, INC.—Sunshine Mining And Refining Company; *U.S. Public*, pg. 1536
TVX GOLD INC.; *Int'l*, pg. 1345

1061 — FERROALLOY ORES MINING, EXCEPT VANADIUM

AMERICAN COPPER & NICKEL COMPANY, INC.—Inco Limited; *Int'l*, pg. 672
BENGUET CORPORATION; *Int'l*, pg. 186
THE BROKEN HILL PROPRIETARY COMPANY LIMITED; *Int'l*, pg. 223
COMPANIA MINERA AUTLAN S.A. DE C.V.; *Int'l*, pg. 324
CYPRUS AMAX MINERALS COMPANY; *U.S. Public*, pg. 470
CYPRUS BAGDAD COPPER CORPORATION—Cyprus Amax Minerals Company; *U.S. Public*, pg. 471
CYPRUS MINES CORP.—Cyprus Amax Minerals Company; *U.S. Public*, pg. 471
CYPRUS SIERRITA—Cyprus Amax Minerals Company; *U.S. Public*, pg. 471
ERAMET-SLN—Imetal; *Int'l*, pg. 661
FALCONBRIDGE (JAPAN) LTD.—EdperBrascan Corporation; *Int'l*, pg. 434
FALCONBRIDGE LIMITED—EdperBrascan Corporation; *Int'l*, pg. 433
FREEPORT-MCMORAN COPPER & GOLD, INC.—Freeport-McMoRan Inc.; *U.S. Public*, pg. 680
P.T. FREEPORT INDONESIA CO.—Freeport-McMoRan Inc.; *U.S. Public*, pg. 681
GROOTE EYLANDT MINING COMPANY—The Broken Hill Proprietary Company Limited; *Int'l*, pg. 224
HIGHLAND VALLEY COPPER—Cominco, Ltd.; *Int'l*, pg. 308
INCO LIMITED; *Int'l*, pg. 672
INCO LIMITED, MANITOBA DIVISION—Inco Limited; *Int'l*, pg. 672
INCO LIMITED, ONTARIO DIVISION—Inco Limited; *Int'l*, pg. 672
P.T. INTERNATIONAL NICKEL INDONESIA—Nissho Iwai Corporation; *Int'l*, pg. 947
IRON-ORE COMPANY OF CANADA—North Limited; *Int'l*, pg. 967
METALLURG, INC.; *U.S. Private*, pg. 735
MINORCO—Anglo American Corporation of South Africa Limited; *Int'l*, pg. 77
MOLYCORP, INC.—Unocal Corporation; *U.S. Public*, pg. 1698
OUTOKUMPU BASE METALS OY—Outokumpu Oyj; *Int'l*, pg. 1016
OUTOKUMPU MINES LTD.—Outokumpu Oyj; *Int'l*, pg. 1016
OUTOKUMPU MINING OY—Outokumpu Oyj; *Int'l*, pg. 1016
PLACER DOME INC.; *Int'l*, pg. 1060
RIO ALGOM LIMITED; *Int'l*, pg. 1118
RIO TINTO ZIMBABWE LIMITED—Rio Tinto PLC; *Int'l*, pg. 1119
RIO-TUBA NICKEL MINING CORP.—Nissho Iwai Corporation; *Int'l*, pg. 949
SACEM—Imetal; *Int'l*, pg. 662
SUDBURY DIVISION—EdperBrascan Corporation; *Int'l*, pg. 433
TIROLER MAGNESIT, A.G.—RGP Holding, Inc.; *U.S. Private*, pg. 904

1081 — METAL MINING SERVICES

ASARCO INCORPORATED; *U.S. Public*, pg. 137
AUSTRALIAN NATIONAL INDUSTRIES LIMITED; *Int'l*, pg. 100
BARRICK GOLD—Barrick Gold Corporation; *Int'l*, pg. 169
BENGUETCORP CANADA LTD.—Benguet Corporation; *Int'l*, pg. 187
BENGUETCORP. INTERNATIONAL LTD.—Benguet Corporation; *Int'l*, pg. 187
BENGUETCORP U.S.A., INC.—Benguet Corporation; *Int'l*, pg. 187
BERGBAUSTAHL GMBH—Fried. Krupp AG; *Int'l*, pg. 513
CARPENTARIA GOLD PTY. LTD.—M.I.M. Holdings Ltd.; *Int'l*, pg. 827
CERRO MATOSO—Royal Dutch/Shell Group of Companies; *Int'l*, pg. 1141
CLEVELAND-CLIFFS INC; *U.S. Public*, pg. 386
COEUR D'ALENE MINES CORPORATION; *U.S. Public*, pg. 394
COEUR EXPLORATIONS, INC.—Coeur D'Alene Mines Corporation; *U.S. Public*, pg. 394
COEUR INTERNATIONAL INC.—Coeur D'Alene Mines Corporation; *U.S. Public*, pg. 394
COMMERCE GROUP CORP.; *U.S. Public*, pg. 410
DCA OF WEST VIRGINIA, INC.—Lennar Corporation; *U.S. Public*, pg. 988
DEUTSCHE TIEFBOHR AG—Preussag AG; *Int'l*, pg. 1069
ESTA GESELLSCHAFT FUR EDELSTAHLVERARBEITUNG MBH—Fried. Krupp AG; *Int'l*, pg. 513
FALCONBRIDGE CHILE S.A.—EdperBrascan Corporation; *Int'l*, pg. 434
FALCONBRIDGE EXPLORATIONS—EdperBrascan Corporation; *Int'l*, pg. 433
FALCONBRIDGE EXPLORATIONS (ZIMBABWE)—EdperBrascan Corporation; *Int'l*, pg. 434
GRANT GEOPHYSICAL INC.; *U.S. Private*, pg. 470
HOESCH PLATINEN GMBH—Fried. Krupp AG; *Int'l*, pg. 512
HUTTENWERKE KRUPP MANNESMANN GMBH—Fried. Krupp AG; *Int'l*, pg. 512
KIEWIT MINING GROUP, INC.—Peter Kiewit Sons Inc.; *U.S. Private*, pg. 619
PETER KIEWIT SONS INC.; *U.S. Private*, pg. 619
KRUPP HOESCH STAHL AG - DORTMUND—Fried. Krupp AG; *Int'l*, pg. 512
KRUPP SIGMA-STAHL GMBH—Fried. Krupp AG; *Int'l*, pg. 513
METALLGESELLSCHAFT AG; *Int'l*, pg. 860
NEWHAWK GOLD MINES LTD.—Homestake Mining Company; *U.S. Public*, pg. 833
NEWMONT EXPLORATION LTD.—Newmont Mining Corporation; *U.S. Public*, pg. 1179
OMNIA MINERIOS LTDA.—Reynolds Metals Company; *U.S. Public*, pg. 1387
PRODUCTORES DE SEMILLAS S.A.—Novartis AG; *Int'l*, pg. 983
REUNION INDUSTRIES, INC.; *U.S. Public*, pg. 1383
RIAU TIN MINING—Royal Dutch/Shell Group of Companies; *Int'l*, pg. 1139
RIO ALGOM EXPLORATION, INC.—Rio Algom Limited; *Int'l*, pg. 1118
SANTA FE SHAFT DRILLING CO.—Kuwait Petroleum Corporation; *Int'l*, pg. 765
SHELL BRASIL SA (PETROLEO)—Royal Dutch/Shell Group of Companies; *Int'l*, pg. 1141
SLUIS & GROOT SEMILAS S.A.—Novartis AG; *Int'l*, pg. 985
SUMITOMO METAL MINING CO., LTD.; *Int'l*, pg. 1316
THAILAND SMELTING & REFINING, CO. LTD.—Royal Dutch/Shell Group of Companies; *Int'l*, pg. 1140
UNION PACIFIC CORPORATION; *U.S. Public*, pg. 1667
VALESUL ALUMINIO—Royal Dutch/Shell Group of Companies; *Int'l*, pg. 1142
A/S VAN SEVEREN & CO. LTD.—Norske Skogindustrier A.S; *Int'l*, pg. 965

1094 — URANIUM-RADIUM-VANADIUM ORES

COMURHEX—COGEMA - Compagnie Generale des Matieres Nucleaires; *Int'l*, pg. 305
CONTINENTAL URANIUM, INC.—Continental Materials Corporation; *U.S. Public*, pg. 441
COTTER CORP.—Unicom Corporation; *U.S. Public*, pg. 1664
FREEPORT-MCMORAN INC.; *U.S. Public*, pg. 680
FREEPORT-MCMORAN RESOURCE PARTNERS, LTD.—Freeport-McMoRan Inc.; *U.S. Public*, pg. 681
KENDRICK BAY MINING CO.—Standard Metals Corporation; *U.S. Public*, pg. 1502
NZU, INC.—New Mexico & Arizona Land Co.; *U.S. Public*, pg. 1172
NORTH LIMITED; *Int'l*, pg. 967
PINNACLE EXPLORATION, INC.—Coeur D'Alene Mines Corporation; *U.S. Public*, pg. 394
QUIVERA MINING COMPANY—Rio Algom Limited; *Int'l*, pg. 1118
RIO ALGOM LIMITED; *Int'l*, pg. 1118
RIO ALGOM MINING CORP.—Rio Algom Limited; *Int'l*, pg. 1118
ROSSING URANIUM LTD.—Rio Tinto PLC; *Int'l*, pg. 1119
STANDARD METALS CORPORATION; *U.S. Public*, pg. 1502
TENNECO URANIUM, INC.—Tenneco Inc.; *U.S. Public*, pg. 1579
TOTAL S.A.; *Int'l*, pg. 1408
URANERZ USA INC.—Preussag AG; *Int'l*, pg. 1070
URANERZBERGBAU GMBH—Preussag AG; *Int'l*, pg. 1070
URANIT GMBH—Veba AG; *Int'l*, pg. 1457

1099 — MISCELLANEOUS METAL ORES MINING, NEC

ALCAN ALUMINIO DO BRASIL S.A.—Alcan Aluminium Limited; *Int'l*, pg. 50
ALCAN JAMAICA CO.—Alcan Aluminium Limited; *Int'l*, pg. 51
ALCOA ALUMINIO S.A.—Aluminum Company of America; *U.S. Public*, pg. 61
ALCOA MINERACAO S.A.—Aluminum Company of America; *U.S. Public*, pg. 62
ALCOA MINERALS OF JAMAICA, INC.—Aluminum Company of America; *U.S. Public*, pg. 62
ALCOA OF AUSTRALIA LIMITED—Aluminum Company of America; *U.S. Public*, pg. 62
ALUMINUM COMPANY OF AMERICA; *U.S. Public*, pg. 60
ALUSUISSE-LONZA HOLDING LTD.; *Int'l*, pg. 66
ANGLESEY ALUMINIUM LIMITED—Maxxam Inc.; *U.S. Public*, pg. 1063
ANGLESEY ALUMINIUM LIMITED—Rio Tinto PLC; *Int'l*, pg. 1119
AROAIMA BAUXITE COMPANY LTD.—Reynolds Metals Company; *U.S. Public*, pg. 1386
AROAIMA MINING COMPANY LIMITED—Reynolds Metals Company; *U.S. Public*, pg. 1386
BASIC RESOURCES, INC.—Texas Utilities Company; *U.S. Public*, pg. 1587
BRASCAN BRAZIL—EdperBrascan Corporation; *Int'l*, pg. 435
THE BROKEN HILL PROPRIETARY COMPANY LIMITED; *Int'l*, pg. 223
BRUSH WELLMAN INC.; *U.S. Public*, pg. 266
CRA LIMITED—Rio Tinto PLC; *Int'l*, pg. 1119
COMALCO MINERALS & ALUMINA—Comalco Limited; *Int'l*, pg. 307
EASTERN SMELTING & REFINING CORPORATION; *U.S. Private*, pg. 357
HERZOG COILEX GMBH—Fried. Krupp AG; *Int'l*, pg. 512
IDEAL DOMINICANA, S.A.—Holderbank Financiere Glaris Ltd.; *Int'l*, pg. 628
INDIAN ALUMINIUM CO. LTD.—Alcan Aluminium Limited; *Int'l*, pg. 51
JOHORE MINING & STEVEDORING CO.—Alcan Aluminium Limited; *Int'l*, pg. 52
KOBE ALUMINA ASSOCIATES (AUSTRALIA) PTY. LTD.—Kobe Steel, Ltd.; *Int'l*, pg. 741
KOBE ALUMINA ASSOCIATES (AUSTRALIA) PTY. LTD.—Nissho Iwai Corporation; *Int'l*, pg. 946
KRONOS TITAN A/S—Contran Corporation; *U.S. Private*, pg. 271
KYANITE MINING CORPORATION; *U.S. Private*, pg. 638
LATAS DE ALUMINIO, S/A-LATASA—Reynolds Metals Company; *U.S. Public*, pg. 1387
LYKES BROTHERS INC.; *U.S. Private*, pg. 682
M.I.M. HOLDINGS LTD.; *Int'l*, pg. 827
MINERACAO RIO DO NORTE S.A.—Alcan Aluminium Limited; *Int'l*, pg. 52
MINORCO—Anglo American Corporation of South Africa Limited; *Int'l*, pg. 77
MOLYCORP, INC.—Unocal Corporation; *U.S. Public*, pg. 1698
NORD RUTILE CORP.—Nord Resources Corporation; *U.S. Public*, pg. 1188
PLACER DOME INC.; *Int'l*, pg. 1060
QIT-FER ET TITANE—Rio Tinto PLC; *Int'l*, pg. 1119
THE RTZ CORPORATION PLC—Rio Tinto PLC; *Int'l*, pg. 1118
RAYROCK YELLOWKNIFE RESOURCES INC.; *Int'l*, pg. 1089
SORAL - SOR-NORGE ALUMINUM A/S—Alusuisse-Lonza Holding Ltd.; *Int'l*, pg. 69
STANDARD METALS CORPORATION; *U.S. Public*, pg. 1502
SUNSHINE MINING AND REFINING COMPANY; *U.S. Public*, pg. 1536
SUNSHINE PRECIOUS METALS, INC.—Sunshine Mining And Refining Company; *U.S. Public*, pg. 1536
TALC DE LUZENAC S.A.—Rio Tinto PLC; *Int'l*, pg. 1119
TAYWOOD MINERALS INC.—Taylor Woodrow plc; *Int'l*, pg. 1359
TEJON RANCH COMPANY; *U.S. Public*, pg. 1566
UNOCAL CARBON & MINERALS—Unocal Corporation; *U.S. Public*, pg. 1698
VAW ALUMINUM AG—Viag AG; *Int'l*, pg. 1466
ZEMEX CORPORATION; *Int'l*, pg. 1523

1221 — SURFACE MINING-BITUMINOUS COAL & LIGNITE

ALLEGHENY PITTSBURGH COAL CO.—Allegheny Power System, Inc.; *U.S. Public*, pg. 42
ALLEGHENY POWER SYSTEM, INC.; *U.S. Public*, pg. 42
AMAX COAL COMPANY—Cyprus Amax Minerals Company; *U.S. Public*, pg. 470
AMERICAN ELECTRIC POWER COMPANY, INC.; *U.S. Public*, pg. 71
ARCH COAL, INC.—Ashland, Inc.; *U.S. Public*, pg. 139
ARCO COAL AUSTRALIA, INC.—Atlantic Richfield Company; *U.S. Public*, pg. 144
ARCO COAL COMPANY—Atlantic Richfield Company; *U.S. Public*, pg. 144
ASHLAND, INC.; *U.S. Public*, pg. 138
ATLANTIC RICHFIELD COMPANY; *U.S. Public*, pg. 144
AUSTEN & BUTTA—Royal Dutch/Shell Group of Companies; *Int'l*, pg. 1137
BNI COAL, LTD.—Minnesota Power; *U.S. Public*, pg. 1116
BP AMERICA INC.—The British Petroleum Company P.L.C.; *Int'l*, pg. 220
BALE OF KENTUCKY, INC.; *U.S. Private*, pg. 112
BEECH COAL COMPANY—Cyprus Amax Minerals Company; *U.S. Public*, pg. 471
BELLAIRE CORPORATION—NACCO Industries, Inc.; *U.S. Public*, pg. 1149
BERWIND CORPORATION; *U.S. Private*, pg. 138
BLUE CIRCLE SOUTHERN CEMENT LIMITED—Boral Limited; *Int'l*, pg. 203
CRA LIMITED—Rio Tinto PLC; *Int'l*, pg. 1119
CANNELTON INDUSTRIES, INC.—Cyprus Amax Minerals Company; *U.S. Public*, pg. 471
CAPE BRETON DEVELOPMENT CORPORATION; *Int'l*, pg. 265
CENTRAL OHIO COAL CO.—American Electric Power Company, Inc.; *U.S. Public*, pg. 73
CHARBONNAGES DE FRANCE; *Int'l*, pg. 280
CHARTER PLC; *Int'l*, pg. 280
THE COASTAL CORPORATION; *U.S. Public*, pg. 389
COGENTRIX INCORPORATED; *U.S. Private*, pg. 249
COLLINSVILLE COAL CO. PTY. LTD.—M.I.M. Holdings Ltd.; *Int'l*, pg. 827
CONESVILLE COAL PREPARATION CO.—American Electric Power Company, Inc.; *U.S. Public*, pg. 72
CONOCO INC.—Du Pont (E.I. Du Pont De Nemours & Co.); *U.S. Public*, pg. 531
CONSOL OF KENTUCKY, INC.—Du Pont (E.I. Du Pont De Nemours & Co.); *U.S. Public*, pg. 531
COSTAIN MINING LIMITED—Costain Group PLC; *Int'l*, pg. 336
THE COTEAU PROPERTIES CO.—NACCO Industries, Inc.; *U.S. Public*, pg. 1149
CROWN COAL & COKE CO. INC.; *U.S. Private*, pg. 292
CROWS NEST RESOURCES LIMITED—Royal Dutch/Shell Group of Companies; *Int'l*, pg. 1138
CYPRUS AMAX COAL CO.—Cyprus Amax Minerals Company; *U.S. Public*, pg. 470
CYPRUS AMAX MINERALS COMPANY; *U.S. Public*, pg. 470
CYPRUS CUMBERLAND COAL CORPORATION—Cyprus Amax Minerals Company; *U.S. Public*, pg. 471
CYPRUS KANAWHA CORPORATION—Cyprus Amax Minerals Company; *U.S. Public*, pg. 471
CYPRUS MOUNTAIN COALS CORPORATION—Cyprus Amax Minerals Company; *U.S. Public*, pg. 471
DRUMMOND COMPANY, INC.; *U.S. Private*, pg. 343
EASTERN ASSOCIATED COAL CORP.—Hanson PLC; *Int'l*, *pg. 594*
ELECTRIC FUEL CORP.—Florida Progress Corporation; *U.S. Public*, pg. 655
ESSO AUSTRALIA RESOURCES LTD.—Exxon Corporation; *U.S. Public*, pg. 602
EXXON COAL AUSTRALIA LTD.—Exxon Corporation; *U.S. Public*, pg. 602
THE FALKIRK MINING CO.—NACCO Industries, Inc.; *U.S. Public*, pg. 1149
FLORIDA PROGRESS CORPORATION; *U.S. Public*, pg. 655
FLUOR CORPORATION; *U.S. Public*, pg. 659
FORDING COAL LTD.—Canadian Pacific Limited; *Int'l*, pg. 259
FREEMAN ENERGY CORPORATION—General Dynamics Corporation; *U.S. Public*, pg. 709
GLENROCK COAL COMPANY—PacifiCorp; *U.S. Public*, pg. 1251
GREENE MANOR COAL CO.—PP&L Resources; *U.S. Public*, pg. 1244
HOUILLERES DE BASSIN DU CENTRE ET DU MIDI—Charbonnages de France; *Int'l*, pg. 280
HUGHES GROUP; *U.S. Private*, pg. 546
HULLERAS DEL NORTE, S.A. (HUNOSA); *Int'l*, pg. 639
INTERKOHLE BETEILIGUNGSGESELLSCHAFT MIT BESCHRANKTER HAFTUNG—Veba AG; *Int'l*, pg. 1456
INTERNATIONAL COLUMBIA RESOURCES CORPORATION—Exxon Corporation; *U.S. Public*, pg. 602
ISCOR; *Int'l*, pg. 688
JESSE BRANCH COAL CO.—Berwind Corporation; *U.S. Private*, pg. 139
K.I.M COAL CO.—Taylor Woodrow plc; *Int'l*, pg. 1359
KENNECOTT ENERGY AND COAL COMPANY—Rio Tinto PLC; *Int'l*, pg. 1119
KENT COAL MINING—Rochester & Pittsburgh Coal Company; *U.S. Public*, pg. 1395
KERR-MCGEE COAL CORP.—Kerr-McGee Corporation; *U.S. Public*, pg. 952
KERR-MCGEE CORPORATION; *U.S. Public*, pg. 952
KEYSTONE COAL MINING CORP.—Rochester & Pittsburgh Coal Company; *U.S. Public*, pg. 1395
KIEWIT MINING GROUP, INC.—Peter Kiewit Sons Inc.; *U.S. Private*, pg. 619
PETER KIEWIT SONS INC.; *U.S. Private*, pg. 619
KNIFE RIVER COAL MINING COMPANY—MDU Resources Group, Inc.; *U.S. Public*, pg. 1025
KYBER COAL CO.—Berwind Corporation; *U.S. Private*, pg. 138
LADY JANE COLLIERIES, INC.—PP&L Resources; *U.S. Public*, pg. 1244
LEE RANCH COAL COMPANY—Hanson PLC; *Int'l*, pg. 594
LODESTAR ENERGY INC.; *U.S. Private*, pg. 672
LOGAN & KANAWHA COAL CO.; *U.S. Private*, pg. 672
MDU RESOURCES GROUP, INC.; *U.S. Public*, pg. 1025
M.I.M. HOLDINGS LTD.; *Int'l*, pg. 827
MAPCO COAL INC.—Mapco Inc.; *U.S. Public*, pg. 1042
MAPCO INC.; *U.S. Public*, pg. 1042
A.T. MASSEY COAL COMPANY, INC.—Fluor Corporation; *U.S. Public*, pg. 660
MINNESOTA POWER; *U.S. Public*, pg. 1116
MONTANA POWER COMPANY; *U.S. Public*, pg. 1126
MORRISON KNUDSEN CORPORATION; *U.S. Public*, pg. 1133
MOTO, INC.; *U.S. Private*, pg. 764
NB COAL COMPANY LIMITED—New Brunswick Power Corporation; *Int'l*, pg. 923
NACCO INDUSTRIES, INC.; *U.S. Public*, pg. 1149
NATIONAL MINES CORP.—NKK Corporation; *Int'l*, pg. 903
NEWLANDS COAL PTY. LTD.—M.I.M. Holdings Ltd.; *Int'l*, pg. 827
NISSHO IWAI COAL DEVELOPMENT (CANADA) LTD.—Nissho Iwai Corporation; *Int'l*, pg. 948
THE NORTH AMERICAN COAL CORPORATION—NACCO Industries, Inc.; *U.S. Public*, pg. 1149
NORTHWESTERN RESOURCES COMPANY—Montana Power Company; *U.S. Public*, pg. 1127
PACIFICORP; *U.S. Public*, pg. 1251
PEABODY COAL CO.—Hanson PLC; *Int'l*, pg. 594
PEABODY HOLDING COMPANY, INC.—Hanson PLC; *Int'l*, pg. 594
PEABODY RESOURCES LIMITED—Hanson PLC; *Int'l*, pg. 594
PEABODY WESTERN COAL COMPANY—Hanson PLC; *Int'l*, pg. 594
PHILLIPS COAL COMPANY—Phillips Petroleum Company; *U.S. Public*, pg. 1291
PHILLIPS PETROLEUM COMPANY; *U.S. Public*, pg. 1290
THE PITTSTON COMPANY; *U.S. Public*, pg. 1305
PITTSTON MINERALS GROUP, INC.—The Pittston Company; *U.S. Public*, pg. 1305
POWDER RIVER COAL COMPANY—Hanson PLC; *Int'l*, pg. 594
THE RTZ CORPORATION PLC—Rio Tinto PLC; *Int'l*, pg. 1118
RAAB KARCHER FRANCE S.A.—Veba AG; *Int'l*, pg. 1458
REITZ COAL COMPANY—Berwind Corporation; *U.S. Private*, pg. 139
RESURRECTION MINING CO.—Newmont Mining Corporation; *U.S. Public*, pg. 1179
RIO ALGOM LIMITED; *Int'l*, pg. 1118
ROCHESTER & PITTSBURGH COAL COMPANY; *U.S. Public*, pg. 1395
SAARBERGWERKE AKTIENGESELLSCHAFT; *Int'l*, pg. 1166
THE SABINE MINING CO.—NACCO Industries, Inc.; *U.S. Public*, pg. 1149
SASOL MINING (PTY.) LTD.—Sasol Limited; *Int'l*, pg. 1197
SHELL COAL BOTSWANA—Royal Dutch/Shell Group of Companies; *Int'l*, pg. 1136
SHELL INTERNATIONALE PETROLEUM MIJ BV—Royal Dutch/Shell Group of Companies; *Int'l*, pg. 1135
SOUTHERN UTAH FUEL CO.—The Coastal Corporation; *U.S. Public*, pg. 390
SUNBELT MINING CO., INC.—Public Service Company of New Mexico; *U.S. Public*, pg. 1340
TECO COAL CORP.—TECO Energy, Inc.; *U.S. Public*, pg. 1565
TAYWOOD MINING INC.—Taylor Woodrow plc; *Int'l*, pg. 1359
TECO ENERGY, INC.; *U.S. Public*, pg. 1565
TOTAL S.A.; *Int'l*, pg. 1408
TRITON ENERGY LIMITED; *U.S. Public*, pg. 1640
UBE INDUSTRIES LTD.; *Int'l*, pg. 1426
UNITED EASTERN COAL SALES CORP.—Rochester & Pittsburgh Coal Company; *U.S. Public*, pg. 1395
USIBELLI COAL MINE, INC.; *U.S. Private*, pg. 1129
WESTAR GROUP LTD.; *Int'l*, pg. 1491
WESTCO COAL CO.—Rochester & Pittsburgh Coal Company; *U.S. Public*, pg. 1395
WESTERN ENERGY COMPANY—Montana Power Company; *U.S. Public*, pg. 1127
WESTERN SYNCOAL COMPANY—Montana Power Company; *U.S. Public*, pg. 1127
WESTMORELAND COAL CO.; *U.S. Public*, pg. 1761
WESTMORELAND RESOURCES, INC.—Westmoreland Coal Co.; *U.S. Public*, pg. 1761
WESTSHORE TERMINALS LTD.—Westar Group Ltd.; *Int'l*, pg. 1401
WINDSOR COAL CO.—American Electric Power Company, Inc.; *U.S. Public*, pg. 73

1222 — UNDERGROUND MINING-BITUMINOUS COAL

ACI RESOURCES LTD.—BTR plc; *Int'l*, pg. 128
ALLEGHENY POWER SYSTEM, INC.; *U.S. Public*, pg. 42
AMAX COAL COMPANY—Cyprus Amax Minerals Company; *U.S. Public*, pg. 470
AMERICAN ELECTRIC POWER COMPANY, INC.; *U.S. Public*, pg. 71
ARCH COAL, INC.—Ashland, Inc.; *U.S. Public*, pg. 139
ASHLAND, INC.; *U.S. Public*, pg. 138
BP AMERICA INC.—The British Petroleum Company P.L.C.; *Int'l*, pg. 220
BASIN RESOURCES—Montana Power Company; *U.S. Public*, pg. 1127
BERWIND CORPORATION; *U.S. Private*, pg. 138
BLAIR ATHOL COAL—BTR plc; *Int'l*, pg. 128
CRA LIMITED—Rio Tinto PLC; *Int'l*, pg. 1119
THE COASTAL CORPORATION; *U.S. Public*, pg. 389
COLUMBIA COAL GASIFICATION CORP.—Columbia Energy Group; *U.S. Public*, pg. 402
CONOCO INC.—Du Pont (E.I. Du Pont De Nemours & Co.); *U.S. Public*, pg. 531
CONSOL—Du Pont (E.I. Du Pont De Nemours & Co.); *U.S. Public*, pg. 531
CONSOL—RWE AG; *Int'l*, pg. 1081
CONSOLIDATED COAL CO.—Du Pont (E.I. Du Pont De Nemours & Co.); *U.S. Public*, pg. 531
CONSOLIDATION COAL CO., REND LAKE MINE—Du Pont (E.I. Du Pont De Nemours & Co.); *U.S. Public*, pg. 531
CROWN COAL & COKE CO. INC.; *U.S. Private*, pg. 292
CURRAGH COAL—BTR plc; *Int'l*, pg. 128
CYPRUS AMAX COAL CO.—Cyprus Amax Minerals Company; *U.S. Public*, pg. 470
CYPRUS AMAX MINERALS COMPANY; *U.S. Public*, pg. 470
CYPRUS EMERALD RESOURCES CORPORATION—Cyprus Amax Minerals Company; *U.S. Public*, pg. 471
CYPRUS EMPIRE CORPORATION—Cyprus Amax Minerals Company; *U.S. Public*, pg. 471
CYPRUS KANAWHA CORPORATION—Cyprus Amax Minerals Company; *U.S. Public*, pg. 471
CYPRUS PLATEAU MINING CORPORATION—Cyprus Amax Minerals Company; *U.S. Public*, pg. 471
CYPRUS SHOSHONE COAL CORPORATION—Cyprus Amax Minerals Company; *U.S. Public*, pg. 471
DAVIS MINING & MANUFACTURING; *U.S. Private*, pg. 315
DRUMMOND COMPANY, INC.; *U.S. Private*, pg. 343
EASTERN ASSOCIATED COAL CORP.—Hanson PLC; *Int'l*, *pg. 594*
FRANKLIN COAL—Zeigler Coal Holding Company; *U.S. Public*, pg. 1790
FREEMAN ENERGY CORPORATION—General Dynamics Corporation; *U.S. Public*, pg. 709
HELVETIA COAL CO.—Rochester & Pittsburgh Coal Company; *U.S. Public*, pg. 1395
HORIZON COAL SERVICES, INC.—Montana Power Company; *U.S. Public*, pg. 1127
KERR-MCGEE COAL CORP.—Kerr-McGee Corporation; *U.S. Public*, pg. 952
KERR-MCGEE CORPORATION; *U.S. Public*, pg. 952
KIEWIT MINING GROUP, INC.—Peter Kiewit Sons Inc.; *U.S. Private*, pg. 619
PETER KIEWIT SONS INC.; *U.S. Private*, pg. 619
LODESTAR ENERGY INC.; *U.S. Private*, pg. 672
LOGAN & KANAWHA COAL CO.; *U.S. Private*, pg. 672
MAPCO INC.; *U.S. Public*, pg. 1042
MITSUI MINING CO., LTD.—Mitsui & Co., Ltd.; *Int'l*, pg. 878
NATREF—Sasol Limited; *Int'l*, pg. 1197
OAKY CREEK COAL PTY. LTD.—M.I.M. Holdings Ltd.; *Int'l*, *pg. 827*
OLD BEN COAL CO.—Zeigler Coal Holding Company; *U.S. Public*, pg. 1790
PACIFICORP; *U.S. Public*, pg. 1251
PEABODY COAL CO.—Hanson PLC; *Int'l*, pg. 594
THE PITTSBURG & MIDWAY COAL MINING CO.—Chevron Corporation; *U.S. Public*, pg. 348
THE PITTSTON COMPANY; *U.S. Public*, pg. 1305
PITTSTON MINERALS GROUP, INC.—The Pittston Company; *U.S. Public*, pg. 1305
POWDER RIVER COAL COMPANY—Hanson PLC; *Int'l*, pg. 594
PREUSSAG ANTHRAZIT GMBH—Preussag AG; *Int'l*, pg. 1069
PYRO MINING CO.—Costain Group PLC; *Int'l*, pg. 337
THE RTZ CORPORATION PLC—Rio Tinto PLC; *Int'l*, pg. 1118
RWE-DEA AG—RWE AG; *Int'l*, pg. 1081
RHEINBRAUN AG—RWE AG; *Int'l*, pg. 1081
ROCHESTER & PITTSBURGH COAL COMPANY; *U.S. Public*, pg. 1395
SASOL MINING—Sasol Limited; *Int'l*, pg. 1197
SHAND MINING INC.—Charter plc; *Int'l*, pg. 281
SOUTHERN OHIO COAL CO.—American Electric Power Company, Inc.; *U.S. Public*, pg. 73
TECO COAL CORP.—TECO Energy, Inc.; *U.S. Public*, pg. 1565
TECO ENERGY, INC.; *U.S. Public*, pg. 1565
TRITON ENERGY LIMITED; *U.S. Public*, pg. 1640
USX CORPORATION; *U.S. Public*, pg. 1661
THE UNITED COMPANY; *U.S. Private*, pg. 1121
US STEEL MINING CO., INC.—USX Corporation; *U.S. Public*, pg. 1662
WALTER INDUSTRIES, INC.; *U.S. Public*, pg. 1736
ZEIGLER COAL HOLDING COMPANY; *U.S. Public*, pg. 1790

1231 — ANTHRACITE MINING

AMERICOAL SERVICES COMPANY—Zeigler Coal Holding Company; *U.S. Public*, pg. 1790
CHARBONNAGES DE FRANCE; *Int'l*, pg. 280
CONOCO INC.—Du Pont (E.I. Du Pont De Nemours & Co.); *U.S. Public*, pg. 531
HOUILLERES DE BASSIN DU CENTRE ET DU MIDI—Charbonnages de France; *Int'l*, pg. 280
HULLERAS DEL NORTE, S.A. (HUNOSA); *Int'l*, pg. 639
PHOENIX LAND COMPANY—Zeigler Coal Holding Company; *U.S. Public*, pg. 1790
READING ANTHRACITE CO.; *U.S. Private*, pg. 913
SMC MINING COMPANY—Zeigler Coal Holding Company; *U.S. Public*, pg. 1790
SHAND MINING INC.—Charter plc; *Int'l*, pg. 281
TOTAL S.A.; *Int'l*, pg. 1408
TRITON ENERGY LIMITED; *U.S. Public*, pg. 1640
WESTIM RESOURCES LTD.—EdperBrascan Corporation; *Int'l*, pg. 435

1241 — COAL MINING SERVICES

BADGER SERVICE CO.—Wisconsin Energy Corporation; *U.S. Public*, pg. 1773
BLACK HILLS CORPORATION; *U.S. Public*, pg. 235
CNG COAL CO.—Consolidated Natural Gas Company; *U.S. Public*, pg. 435
CHACO ENERGY CO.—Texas Utilities Company; *U.S. Public*, pg. 1587
CHARBONNAGES DE FRANCE; *Int'l*, pg. 280
COAL INDIA LIMITED; *Int'l*, pg. 298
FLUOR CORPORATION; *U.S. Public*, pg. 659
HOUILLERES DE BASSIN DU CENTRE ET DU MIDI—Charbonnages de France; *Int'l*, pg. 280
HULLERAS DEL NORTE, S.A. (HUNOSA); *Int'l*, pg. 639
KIEWIT MINING GROUP, INC.—Peter Kiewit Sons Inc.; *U.S. Private*, pg. 619
PETER KIEWIT SONS INC.; *U.S. Private*, pg. 619
LOGAN & KANAWHA COAL CO.; *U.S. Private*, pg. 672
M.I.M. HOLDINGS LTD.; *Int'l*, pg. 827
NISSHO IWAI COAL DEVELOPMENT (CANADA) LTD.—Nissho Iwai Corporation; *Int'l*, pg. 948
THE NORTH AMERICAN COAL CORPORATION—NACCO Industries, Inc.; *U.S. Public*, pg. 1149
SAARBERG-INTERPLAN GESELLSCHAFT FUER ROHSTOFF-, ENERGIE-UND INGENIEURTECHNIK MBH—Saarbergwerke Aktiengesellschaft; *Int'l*, pg. 1167
SANTA FE SHAFT DRILLING CO.—Kuwait Petroleum Corporation; *Int'l*, pg. 765
TENNECO COAL CO.—Tenneco Inc.; *U.S. Public*, pg. 1579
TENNECO SNG, INC.—Tenneco Inc.; *U.S. Public*, pg. 1579
TENNECO SYNFUELS CO.—Tenneco Inc.; *U.S. Public*, pg. 1578
TEXAS UTILITIES MINING CO.—Texas Utilities Company; *U.S. Public*, pg. 1588
WESTIM RESOURCES LTD.—EdperBrascan Corporation; *Int'l*, pg. 435
WYODAK RESOURCES DEVELOPMENT CORP.—Black Hills Corporation; *U.S. Public*, pg. 236

1311 — CRUDE PETROLEUM & NATURAL GAS

AGIP PETROLEUM CO., INC.—ENI S.p.A.; *Int'l*, pg. 428
AGIP PETROLI—ENI S.p.A.; *Int'l*, pg. 428
ANR PRODUCTION CO.—The Coastal Corporation; *U.S. Public*, pg. 389
APC OPERATING PARTNERSHIP, L.P.—Apache Corporation; *U.S. Public*, pg. 119
ABU DHABI GAS INDUSTRIES—Royal Dutch/Shell Group of Companies; *Int'l*, pg. 1140
ACTION OILFIELD SERVICES, INC.—Prima Energy Corporation; *U.S. Public*, pg. 1325
ADAMS RESOURCES & ENERGY, INC.; *U.S. Public*, pg. 18
ADAMS RESOURCES EXPLORATION CORP.—Adams Resources & Energy, Inc.; *U.S. Public*, pg. 19
AKER RAJ ASA; *Int'l*, pg. 41
ALASKA PIPELINE CO.—Seagull Energy Corporation; *U.S. Public*, pg. 1450
ALTANA EXPLORATION COMPANY—Montana Power Company; *U.S. Public*, pg. 1127
AMAX ENERGY, INC.—Cyprus Amax Minerals Company; *U.S. Public*, pg. 470
AMERAC ENERGY CORP.—Southern Mineral Corporation; *U.S. Public*, pg. 1490
AMERADA HESS CORPORATION; *U.S. Public*, pg. 65
AMERADA HESS NORGE A/S—Amerada Hess Corporation; *U.S. Public*, pg. 65
AMERADA HESS (U.K.) LTD.—Amerada Hess Corporation; *U.S. Public*, pg. 65
AMERICAN COMETRA, INC.—Groupe Bruxelles Lambert S.A.; *Int'l*, pg. 562
AMERICAN TRADING AND PRODUCTION CORPORATION; *U.S. Private*, pg. 63
AMOCO ABU DHABI EXPLORATION CO.—Amoco Corporation; *U.S. Public*, pg. 103
AMOCO ARGENTINA OIL CO.—Amoco Corporation; *U.S. Public*, pg. 102
AMOCO AUSTRALIA PETROLEUM COMPANY—Amoco Corporation; *U.S. Public*, pg. 102
AMOCO CANADA PETROLEUM COMPANY LTD.—Amoco Corporation; *U.S. Public*, pg. 103
AMOCO CANADA RESOURCES LTD.—Amoco Corporation; *U.S. Public*, pg. 103
AMOCO COLOMBIA PETROLEUM COMPANY—Amoco Corporation; *U.S. Public*, pg. 102
AMOCO CORPORATION; *U.S. Public*, pg. 101
AMOCO EGYPT OIL COMPANY—Amoco Corporation; *U.S. Public*, pg. 102
AMOCO ESPANA EXPLORATION CO.—Amoco Corporation; *U.S. Public*, pg. 102
AMOCO MADAGASCAR PETROLEUM COMPANY—Amoco Corporation; *U.S. Public*, pg. 102
AMOCO NETHERLANDS PETROLEUM CO.—Amoco Corporation; *U.S. Public*, pg. 102
AMOCO NORWAY OIL CO.—Amoco Corporation; *U.S. Public*, pg. 102
AMOCO OMAN PETROLEUM COMPANY—Amoco Corporation; *U.S. Public*, pg. 102
AMOCO PRODUCTION COMPANY—Amoco Corporation; *U.S. Public*, pg. 102
AMOCO RAS AL KHAIMAH OIL CO.—Amoco Corporation; *U.S. Public*, pg. 102
AMOCO SHARJAH OIL CO.—Amoco Corporation; *U.S. Public*, pg. 102
AMOCO TRINIDAD OIL CO.—Amoco Corporation; *U.S. Public*, pg. 103
AMOCO (U.K.) EXPLORATION COMPANY—Amoco Corporation; *U.S. Public*, pg. 102
AMOCO (U.K.) LTD.—Amoco Corporation; *U.S. Public*, pg. 103
ANADARKO ALGERIA CORPORATION—Anadarko Petroleum Corporation; *U.S. Public*, pg. 107
ANADARKO OIL & GAS COMPANY—Anadarko Petroleum Corporation; *U.S. Public*, pg. 107
ANADARKO PETROLEUM CORPORATION; *U.S. Public*, pg. 107
ANCHOR GASOLINE CORPORATION; *U.S. Private*, pg. 70
ANSCHUTZ CORPORATION; *U.S. Private*, pg. 75
THE ANSCHUTZ OVERSEAS CORP.—Anschutz Corporation; *U.S. Private*, pg. 75
APACHE CANADA LTD.—Apache Corporation; *U.S. Public*, pg. 119
APACHE CORPORATION; *U.S. Public*, pg. 119
APACHE INTERNATIONAL FINANCE, N.V.—Apache Corporation; *U.S. Public*, pg. 119
APACHE INTERNATIONAL, INC.—Apache Corporation; *U.S. Public*, pg. 119
APCO ARGENTINA INC.; *U.S. Public*, pg. 119
AQUILA ENERGY CORP.—UtiliCorp United Inc.; *U.S. Public*, pg. 1701
ARABIAN OIL COMPANY, LTD.; *Int'l*, pg. 78
ARCO ALASKA INC.—Atlantic Richfield Company; *U.S. Public*, pg. 144
ARCO BRITISH LIMITED—Atlantic Richfield Company; *U.S. Public*, pg. 144
ARCO DUBAI, INCORPORATED—Atlantic Richfield Company; *U.S. Public*, pg. 144
ARCO INTL. OIL & GAS CO.—Atlantic Richfield Company; *U.S. Public*, pg. 144
ARROW OILFIELD SERVICE COMPANY—Texas Pacific Group; *U.S. Private*, pg. 1078
ASHLAND OIL INTL. LTD.—Ashland, Inc.; *U.S. Public*, pg. 139
ASHLAND OIL (NIGERIA) CO., LTD.—Ashland, Inc.; *U.S. Public*, pg. 140
ATKINSON; *U.S. Public*, pg. 143
ATLANTIC RICHFIELD COMPANY; *U.S. Public*, pg. 144
BEB ERDGAS UND ERDOEL GMBH—Exxon Corporation; *U.S. Public*, pg. 601
BG PLC; *Int'l*, pg. 118
BG PLC EXPLORATION & PRODUCTION LTD.—BG Plc; *Int'l*, pg. 119
BHP PETROLEUM (AMERICAS) INC.—The Broken Hill Proprietary Company Limited; *Int'l*, pg. 225
BHP PETROLEUM (CANADA) INC.—The Broken Hill Proprietary Company Limited; *Int'l*, pg. 225
BHP PETROLEUM LTD.—The Broken Hill Proprietary Company Limited; *Int'l*, pg. 225
BHP PETROLEUM PTY LTD.—The Broken Hill Proprietary Company Limited; *Int'l*, pg. 225
BP AMERICA INC.—The British Petroleum Company P.L.C.; *Int'l*, pg. 220
BP EXPLORATION (ALASKA) INC.—The British Petroleum Company P.L.C.; *Int'l*, pg. 220
BP EXPLORATION COMPANY LIMITED—The British Petroleum Company P.L.C.; *Int'l*, pg. 220
BP INTERNATIONAL LTD.—The British Petroleum Company P.L.C.; *Int'l*, pg. 220
BAKER/MO SERVICES, INC.—Michael Baker Corporation; *U.S. Public*, pg. 168
BAKER/OTS INTERNATIONAL LTD.—Michael Baker Corporation; *U.S. Public*, pg. 168
BARNWELL OF CANADA LTD.—Barnwell Industries, Inc.; *U.S. Public*, pg. 191
BARRETT RESOURCES CORPORATION; *U.S. Public*, pg. 191
BASIN ELECTRIC POWER COOPERATIVE; *U.S. Private*, pg. 121
BAYOU STATE OIL CORPORATION; *U.S. Private*, pg. 125
BELDEN & BLAKE CORPORATION—Texas Pacific Group; *U.S. Private*, pg. 1078
BENTON OIL & GAS COMPANY; *U.S. Public*, pg. 212
BERRY PETROLEUM COMPANY; *U.S. Public*, pg. 223
BLACK WARRIOR METHANE CORP.—Walter Industries, Inc.; *U.S. Public*, pg. 1737
BLACK WARRIOR TRANSMISSION CORP.—Sonat Inc.; *U.S. Public*, pg. 1485
BLACK WARRIOR TRANSMISSION CORP.—Walter Industries, Inc.; *U.S. Public*, pg. 1737
THE BRITISH PETROLEUM COMPANY P.L.C.; *Int'l*, pg. 219
THE BROKEN HILL PROPRIETARY COMPANY LIMITED; *Int'l*, pg. 223
TOM BROWN, INC.; *U.S. Public*, pg. 262
TOM BROWN, INC.—Tom Brown, Inc.; *U.S. Public*, pg. 262
BRUNEI COLDGAS—Royal Dutch/Shell Group of Companies; *Int'l*, pg. 1139
BRUNEI LNG—Royal Dutch/Shell Group of Companies; *Int'l*, pg. 1139
BRUNEI SHELL PETROLEUM CO SDN BHD—Royal Dutch/Shell Group of Companies; *Int'l*, pg. 1139
BUM-A PETROLEUM CO., LTD.—Ssangyong Business Group; *Int'l*, pg. 1292
BURK ROYALTY CO.; *U.S. Private*, pg. 182
BURLINGTON RESOURCES INC.; *U.S. Public*, pg. 269
BUTCHER ENERGY—Butcher & Co., Inc.; *U.S. Private*, pg. 189
BUTTES DRILLING-C COMPANY—Reunion Industries, Inc.; *U.S. Public*, pg. 1383
CGAS, INC.—Enron Corp.; *U.S. Public*, pg. 585
CIG EXPLORATION, INC.—The Coastal Corporation; *U.S. Public*, pg. 390
CMS NOMECO—CMS Energy Corporation; *U.S. Public*, pg. 280
CNG PRODUCING CO.—Consolidated Natural Gas Company; *U.S. Public*, pg. 435
CABOT OIL & GAS CORPORATION; *U.S. Public*, pg. 289
CALLON OFFSHORE PRODUCTION—Callon Petroleum Company; *U.S. Public*, pg. 295
CALUMET FLORIDA, INC.—Plains Resources Inc.; *U.S. Public*, pg. 1308
CANADIAN-MONTANA GAS CO., LTD.—Montana Power Company; *U.S. Public*, pg. 1127
CANADIAN NATURAL RESOURCES LIMITED; *Int'l*, pg. 258
CANADIAN OCCIDENTAL PETROLEUM LTD.—Occidental Petroleum Corporation; *U.S. Public*, pg. 1210
CARSON WATER CO.—Southwest Gas Corporation; *U.S. Public*, pg. 1493
CASTLE ENERGY CORPORATION; *U.S. Public*, pg. 313
CAVENHAM FOREST INDUSTRIES INC.—Hanson PLC; *Int'l*, pg. 593
CELSIUS ENERGY COMPANY—Questar Corporation; *U.S. Public*, pg. 1352
CENTRICA PLC; *Int'l*, pg. 279
CHALLENGER MINERALS INC.—Global Marine Inc.; *U.S. Public*, pg. 748
CHEVRON CORPORATION; *U.S. Public*, pg. 347
CHEVRON SHALE OIL CO.—Chevron Corporation; *U.S. Public*, pg. 348
CHEVRON U.S.A. INC.—Chevron Corporation; *U.S. Public*, pg. 348
CHEVRON USA PRODUCTION CO.—Chevron Corporation; *U.S. Public*, pg. 348
CHIEFTAIN EXPLORATION (U.K.) LTD.—Chieftain International, Inc.; *Int'l*, pg. 284
CHIEFTAIN INTERNATIONAL, INC.; *Int'l*, pg. 284
CHIEFTAIN INTERNATIONAL NORTH SEA LIMITED—Chieftain International, Inc.; *Int'l*, pg. 284
CHIEFTAIN INTERNATIONAL (U.S.) INC.—Chieftain International, Inc.; *Int'l*, pg. 284
CHINESE PETROLEUM CORPORATION; *Int'l*, pg. 286
CLAM PETROLEUM CO.—USX Corporation; *U.S. Public*, pg. 1662
CLINTON GAS MARKETING—Enron Corp.; *U.S. Public*, pg. 585
THE CLINTON OIL COMPANY—Enron Corp.; *U.S. Public*, pg. 585
COASTAL (BERMUDA) PETROLEUM LIMITED—The Coastal Corporation; *U.S. Public*, pg. 390
THE COASTAL CORPORATION; *U.S. Public*, pg. 389
CODA ENERGY, INC.—Enron Corp.; *U.S. Public*, pg. 584
COHO ENERGY, INC.; *U.S. Public*, pg. 396
COLUMBIA ENERGY GROUP; *U.S. Public*, pg. 402
COLUMBIA NATURAL RESOURCES, INC.—Columbia Energy Group; *U.S. Public*, pg. 403
COMPAGNIE GENERALE DE GEOPHYSIQUE—CGG Group; *Int'l*, pg. 241
CONOCO NORWAY, INC.—Du Pont (E.I. Du Pont De Nemours & Co.); *U.S. Public*, pg. 531
CONSOLIDATED NATURAL GAS COMPANY; *U.S. Public*, pg. 435
CONSOLIDATED VISCOUNT RESOURCES LTD.; *Int'l*, pg. 326
COSCOL PETROLEUM CORP.—The Coastal Corporation; *U.S. Public*, pg. 390
CRAB RUN GAS CO.—Washington Gas Light Co.; *U.S. Public*, pg. 1740
CROWN NIGERIA, INC.—Crown Central Petroleum Corporation; *U.S. Public*, pg. 462
CRYSTAL EURASIA OIL CO.—Crystal Oil Company; *U.S. Public*, pg. 466
CRYSTAL EXPLORATION & PRODUCTION CO.—Crystal Oil Company; *U.S. Public*, pg. 466
CRYSTAL OIL COMPANY; *U.S. Public*, pg. 466
DSM ENERGIE B.V.—DSM N.V.; *Int'l*, pg. 353
DELHI PETROLEUM PTY. LTD.—Exxon Corporation; *U.S. Public*, pg. 601
DEMINEX ALBANIA PETROLEUM GMBH—Veba AG; *Int'l*, pg. 1461
DEMINEX ARGENTINA SA—Veba AG; *Int'l*, pg. 1461
DEMINEX (CANADA) LTD.—Veba AG; *Int'l*, pg. 1461
DEMINEX-DEUTSCHE GMBH—Veba AG; *Int'l*, pg. 1460
DEMINEX EGYPT—Veba AG; *Int'l*, pg. 1461
DEMINEX INDONESIA—Veba AG; *Int'l*, pg. 1461
DEMINEX MOSCOW OFFICE—Veba AG; *Int'l*, pg. 1461
DEMINEX NORGE AS—Veba AG; *Int'l*, pg. 1461
DEMINEX SYRIA GMBH—Veba AG; *Int'l*, pg. 1461
DEMINEX UK OIL AND GAS LTD.—Veba AG; *Int'l*, pg. 1461
DESCO CORPORATION; *U.S. Private*, pg. 326
DEUTSCHE SHELL AG—Royal Dutch/Shell Group of Companies; *Int'l*, pg. 1138
DEVON ENERGY CORPORATION; *U.S. Public*, pg. 503
DOMAIN ENERGY CORPORATION; *U.S. Public*, pg. 515
DOMAIN ENERGY FINANCE CORPORATION—Domain Energy Corporation; *U.S. Public*, pg. 516
DOMAIN ENERGY INTERNATIONAL CORPORATION—Domain Energy Corporation; *U.S. Public*, pg. 516
DOMAIN ENERGY PRODUCTION CORPORATION—Domain Energy Corporation; *U.S. Public*, pg. 516
DOMAIN ENERGY VENTURES CORPORATION—Domain Energy Corporation; *U.S. Public*, pg. 516
DOVER EXPLORATION COMPANY—Chesapeake Utilities Corporation; *U.S. Public*, pg. 347
DU PONT (E.I. DU PONT DE NEMOURS & CO.); *U.S. Public*, pg. 530
DUBAI PETROLEUM COMPANY—Du Pont (E.I. Du Pont De Nemours & Co.); *U.S. Public*, pg. 533
DUGAN PRODUCTION CORP.; *U.S. Private*, pg. 345
DURUM (AUSTRALIA) PTY. LTD.—Durum Energy Corp.; *Int'l*, pg. 422
DURUM ENERGY CORP.; *Int'l*, pg. 422
DURUM ENERGY CORP., SUCURSAL DEL PERU—Durum Energy Corp.; *Int'l*, pg. 422
DYAS B.V.—SHV Holdings N.V.; *Int'l*, pg. 1155
EEX CORPORATION; *U.S. Public*, pg. 542
ENI S.P.A.; *Int'l*, pg. 428
EAGLE MOUNTAIN ENERGY, INC.—Enron Corp.; *U.S. Public*, pg. 585
EASTERN AMERICAN ENERGY CORPORATION; *U.S. Private*, pg. 357
EASTERN PENNSYLVANIA EXPLORATION CO.—PECO Energy Company; *U.S. Public*, pg. 1268
EASTEX ENERGY INC.—El Paso Natural Gas Co.; *U.S. Public*, pg. 567
EASTEX GAS PRODUCTION CO.—El Paso Natural Gas Co.; *U.S. Public*, pg. 567
ELF AQUITAINE, INC.—Elf Aquitane; *Int'l*, pg. 445

ELF AQUITAINE NORGE A/S—Elf Aquitane; *Int'l*, pg. 445
ELF AQUITANE; *Int'l*, pg. 444
ELF CONGO—Elf Aquitane; *Int'l*, pg. 446
ELF GABON—Elf Aquitane; *Int'l*, pg. 446
ELF IDROCARBURI ITALIANA SPA—Elf Aquitane; *Int'l*, pg. 446
ELF NIGERIA—Elf Aquitane; *Int'l*, pg. 446
ELF PETROLAND—Elf Aquitane; *Int'l*, pg. 446
ELF PETROLEUM U.K.—Elf Aquitane; *Int'l*, pg. 446
ELF SEREPCA—Elf Aquitane; *Int'l*, pg. 446
ENERGEN CORPORATION; *U.S. Public*, pg. 581
ENERGEX CORP.—Eaton Vance Corp.; *U.S. Public*, pg. 559
ENERGIE BEHEER NEDERLAND B.V.—DSM N.V.; *Int'l*, pg. 353
ENERGY COMPANIES OF ONEOK—ONEOK Inc.; *U.S. Public*, pg. 1226
ENRON CORP.; *U.S. Public*, pg. 584
ENRON OIL & GAS CO.—Enron Corp.; *U.S. Public*, pg. 584
ENSCO MARINE CO.—Ensco International Incorporated (ENSCO); *U.S. Public*, pg. 585
ENSERCH CORPORATION—Texas Utilities Company; *U.S. Public*, pg. 1587
ENSERCH EXPLORATION (UK) LTD.—Texas Utilities Company; *U.S. Public*, pg. 1587
ENTRADA INDUSTRIES, INC.—Questar Corporation; *U.S. Public*, pg. 1352
EQUITABLE RESOURCES ENERGY COMPANY—Equitable Resources, Inc.; *U.S. Public*, pg. 589
EQUITABLE RESOURCES EXPLORATION DIVISION—Equitable Resources, Inc.; *U.S. Public*, pg. 589
EQUITY OIL COMPANY; *U.S. Public*, pg. 590
ESSO AUSTRALIA RESOURCES LTD.—Exxon Corporation; *U.S. Public*, pg. 602
ESSO EXPLORATION AND PRODUCTION UK LIMITED—Exxon Corporation; *U.S. Public*, pg. 602
ESSO MALAYSIA BERHAD—Exxon Corporation; *U.S. Public*, pg. 602
ESSO PRODUCTION MALAYSIA INC.—Exxon Corporation; *U.S. Public*, pg. 602
ESSO STANDARD THAILAND LTD.—Exxon Corporation; *U.S. Public*, pg. 602
EXPLORATION & PRODUCTION DIVISION—Mobil Oil Corporation; *U.S. Public*, pg. 1118
EXXON CHEMICAL LIMITED—Exxon Corporation; *U.S. Public*, pg. 602
EXXON COMPANY, U.S.A.—Exxon Corporation; *U.S. Public*, pg. 601
EXXON EXPLORATION COMPANY—Exxon Corporation; *U.S. Public*, pg. 601
EXXON YEMEN INC.—Exxon Corporation; *U.S. Public*, pg. 601
FIDELITY OIL CO.—MDU Resources Group, Inc.; *U.S. Public*, pg. 1025
FIDELITY OIL HOLDINGS, INC.—MDU Resources Group, Inc.; *U.S. Public*, pg. 1025
FINA EXPLORATION NORWAY, S.A. (FEN SA)—Petrofina S.A.; *Int'l*, pg. 1043
FINA, INC.—Petrofina S.A.; *Int'l*, pg. 1044
FINA REP S.P.R.L.—Petrofina S.A.; *Int'l*, pg. 1044
FLETCHER CHALLENGE PETROLEUM INC.—Fletcher Challenge Limited; *Int'l*, pg. 495
FLETCHER CHALLENGE PETROLEUM LIMITED—Fletcher Challenge Limited; *Int'l*, pg. 495
FLYING J. INC.; *U.S. Private*, pg. 415
FOREST OIL CORPORATION; *U.S. Public*, pg. 670
FOREST OIL OFFSHORE PRODUCTION OFFICE—Forest Oil Corporation; *U.S. Public*, pg. 670
FREEPORT-MCMORAN RESOURCE PARTNERS, LTD.—Freeport-McMoRan Inc.; *U.S. Public*, pg. 681
GARVEY INDUSTRIES, INC.; *U.S. Private*, pg. 440
GARY-WILLIAMS ENERGY CORPORATION; *U.S. Private*, pg. 440
GARY-WILLIAMS ENERGY CORPORATION—Gary-Williams Energy Corporation; *U.S. Private*, pg. 440
GAZ DE FRANCE; *Int'l*, pg. 541
GENERAL SEKIYU K.K.—Exxon Corporation; *U.S. Public*, pg. 602
GETTY GAS GATHERING, INC.—Texaco Inc.; *U.S. Public*, pg. 1583
GIANT EXPLORATION & PRODUCTION CO.—Giant Industries Inc.; *U.S. Public*, pg. 742
GIANT INDUSTRIES INC.; *U.S. Public*, pg. 741
GLOBAL MARINE INC.; *U.S. Public*, pg. 748
GREAT RIVER OIL & GAS CORP.—Georgia Gulf Corporation; *U.S. Public*, pg. 735
GULF CANADA RESOURCES LTD.; *Int'l*, pg. 577
GULF OF SUEZ PETROLEUM COMPANY—Amoco Corporation; *U.S. Public*, pg. 102
GULFMARK ENERGY INC.—Adams Resources & Energy, Inc.; *U.S. Public*, pg. 19
GULFSTAR ENERGY, INC.—Domain Energy Corporation; *U.S. Public*, pg. 510
HCO ENERGY LTD.—HarCor Energy, Inc.; *U.S. Public*, pg. 782
HDM, HOLLANDSCHE DELFSTOFFEN MAATSCHAPPIJ BV—Hollandsche Beton Groep NV; *Int'l*, pg. 630
HADSON CORPORATION—Apache Corporation; *U.S. Public*, pg. 119
HALLWOOD ENERGY PARTNERS, L.P.—The Hallwood Group Incorporated; *U.S. Public*, pg. 778
HARCOR ENERGY, INC.; *U.S. Public*, pg. 782
HARKEN ENERGY CORPORATION; *U.S. Public*, pg. 785
HARKEN EXPLORATION COMPANY—Harken Energy Corporation; *U.S. Public*, pg. 785
HARKEN RESOURCE MANAGEMENT COMPANY—Harken Energy Corporation; *U.S. Public*, pg. 785
HELMERICH & PAYNE, INC.; *U.S. Public*, pg. 808
HONDO OIL & GAS COMPANY—Lonrho plc; *Int'l*, pg. 818
HOWELL PETROLEUM CORP.—Howell Corporation; *U.S. Public*, pg. 844
J.M. HUBER CORPORATION; *U.S. Private*, pg. 544
HUMPHREYS MINERAL INDUSTRIES, INC.—Reunion Industries, Inc.; *U.S. Public*, pg. 1383
CAROLINE HUNT TRUST ESTATE; *U.S. Private*, pg. 548
HUNT OIL COMPANY; *U.S. Private*, pg. 548
HUSKY OIL INTL. LTD.—Husky Oil Ltd.; *Int'l*, pg. 640
HUSKY OIL LTD.; *Int'l*, pg. 640
HUSKY OIL OPERATIONS LTD.—Husky Oil Ltd.; *Int'l*, pg. 640
IGC ENERGY, INC.—Indiana Energy, Inc.; *U.S. Public*, pg. 875
IMPERIAL OIL LIMITED—Exxon Corporation; *U.S. Public*, pg. 602
INDUSTRIAL EQUITY LIMITED; *Int'l*, pg. 676
INEXCO OIL COMPANY—Burlington Resources Inc.; *U.S. Public*, pg. 269
INTERMOUNTAIN INDUSTRIES, INC.; *U.S. Private*, pg. 568
CIA. DE INVESTIGACION Y EXPLOTACIONES PETROLIFERAS, S.A. (CIEPSA)—Compania Espanola de Petroleos, S.A. (CEPSA); *Int'l*, pg. 323
JUPITER ENERGY CORP.—Jupiter Industries, Inc.; *U.S. Private*, pg. 602
JUSTISS OIL CO., INC.; *U.S. Private*, pg. 602
K N ENERGY, INC.; *U.S. Public*, pg. 937
KCS ENERGY INC.; *U.S. Public*, pg. 938
KCS MICHIGAN RESOURCES, INC.—KCS Energy Inc.; *U.S. Public*, pg. 939
KCS RESOURCES, INC.—KCS Energy Inc.; *U.S. Public*, pg. 939
KERR-MCGEE CORPORATION; *U.S. Public*, pg. 952
KERR-MCGEE OIL (U.K.) PLC—Kerr-McGee Corporation; *U.S. Public*, pg. 952
KERR-MCGEE PETROLEUM EXPLORATION & PRODUCTION DIVISION—Kerr-McGee Corporation; *U.S. Public*, pg. 952
KNOX OIL OF TEXAS INC.; *U.S. Private*, pg. 627
KOCH INDUSTRIES, INCORPORATED; *U.S. Private*, pg. 628
LL&E COLOMBIA, INC.—Burlington Resources Inc.; *U.S. Public*, pg. 269
LL&E EUROPE-AFRICA-MIDDLE EAST, INC.—Burlington Resources Inc.; *U.S. Public*, pg. 269
LL&E, INC.—Burlington Resources Inc.; *U.S. Public*, pg. 269
LL&E (NETHERLANDS), INC.—Burlington Resources Inc.; *U.S. Public*, pg. 269
LL&E NETHERLANDS PETROLEUM COMPANY—Burlington Resources Inc.; *U.S. Public*, pg. 269
LL&E (UK) INC.—Burlington Resources Inc.; *U.S. Public*, pg. 269
LACLEDE ENERGY RESOURCES, INC.—Laclede Gas Company; *U.S. Public*, pg. 974
LARIO OIL & GAS COMPANY; *U.S. Private*, pg. 651
LASMO AMERICA INC.—LASMO plc; *Int'l*, pg. 804
LASMO NORTH SEA PLC—LASMO plc; *Int'l*, pg. 804
LASMO PLC; *Int'l*, pg. 803
LLOYD PROPERTIES; *U.S. Private*, pg. 672
LOEWS CORPORATION; *U.S. Public*, pg. 1010
LOMAK OPERATING COMPANY—Lomak Petroleum Inc.; *U.S. Public*, pg. 1012
LOMAK PETROLEUM INC.; *U.S. Public*, pg. 1012
LOMAK PRODUCTION COMPANY—Lomak Petroleum Inc.; *U.S. Public*, pg. 1012
LONRHO PLC; *Int'l*, pg. 817
LOUIS DREYFUS NATURAL GAS CORP.—Louis Dreyfus Corporation; *U.S. Private*, pg. 342
THE LOUISIANA LAND AND EXPLORATION COMPANY—Burlington Resources Inc.; *U.S. Public*, pg. 269
MDU RESOURCES GROUP, INC.; *U.S. Public*, pg. 1025
MG REFINING & MARKETING, INC.—Metallgesellschaft AG; *Int'l*, pg. 862
MW PETROLEUM CORP.—Apache Corporation; *U.S. Public*, pg. 119
MWJR. PETROLEUM CORP.—Apache Corporation; *U.S. Public*, pg. 119
MAGELLAN PETROLEUM AUSTRALIA LTD.—Magellan Petroleum Corporation; *U.S. Public*, pg. 1037
MAGELLAN PETROLEUM CORPORATION; *U.S. Public*, pg. 1036
MAGUIRE OIL CO.; *U.S. Private*, pg. 696
MALAYSIA LNG—Royal Dutch/Shell Group of Companies; *Int'l*, pg. 1140
MAPCO INC.; *U.S. Public*, pg. 1042
MARATHON ASHLAND PETROLEUM LLC—Ashland, Inc.; *U.S. Public*, pg. 139
MARATHON ASHLAND PETROLEUM LLC—USX Corporation; *U.S. Public*, pg. 1662
MARATHON OIL U.K., LTD.—USX Corporation; *U.S. Public*, pg. 1662
MARATHON PETROLEUM INDONESIA, LTD.—USX Corporation; *U.S. Public*, pg. 1662
MARATHON PETROLEUM IRELAND, LTD.—USX Corporation; *U.S. Public*, pg. 1662
MARK RESOURCES INC.; *Int'l*, pg. 842
MARTIN EXPLORATION MANAGEMENT COMPANY; *U.S. Private*, pg. 709
MAXUS ENERGY CORPORATION—Y.P.F., S.A.; *Int'l*, pg. 1515
MAXUS SOUTHEAST SUMATRA—Y.P.F., S.A.; *Int'l*, pg. 1515
MAYNARD OIL CO.; *U.S. Public*, pg. 1064
MERIDIAN OIL HOLDING INC.—Burlington Resources Inc.; *U.S. Public*, pg. 269
MICHIGAN HOLDINGS, INC.—Bank of Montreal; *Int'l*, pg. 155
MINORCO—Anglo American Corporation of South Africa Limited; *Int'l*, pg. 77
MISSISSIPPI MARKETING, INC.—Callon Petroleum Company; *U.S. Public*, pg. 295
MITCHELL ENERGY & DEVELOPMENT CORP.; *U.S. Public*, pg. 1117
MOBIL CHEMICAL CANADA, LTD.—Mobil Oil Corporation; *U.S. Public*, pg. 1119
MOBIL EXPLORATION NORWAY, INC.—Mobil Oil Corporation; *U.S. Public*, pg. 1119
MOBIL NORTH SEA LIMITED—Mobil Oil Corporation; *U.S. Public*, pg. 1119
MOBIL OIL CANADA, LTD.—Mobil Oil Corporation; *U.S. Public*, pg. 1119
MOBIL OIL CORPORATION; *U.S. Public*, pg. 1118
MOBIL OIL SUDAN LIMITED—Mobil Oil Corporation; *U.S. Public*, pg. 1119
MOBIL PRODUCING NIGERIA—Mobil Oil Corporation; *U.S. Public*, pg. 1119
MOBILE OIL INDONESIA, INC.—Mobil Oil Corporation; *U.S. Public*, pg. 1119
MOBILE PRODUCING NETHERLANDS INCORPORATED—Mobil Oil Corporation; *U.S. Public*, pg. 1119
MONO POWER COMPANY—Edison International; *U.S. Public*, pg. 564
MONTANA POWER COMPANY; *U.S. Public*, pg. 1126
MOUNTAIN GAS REOURCES, INC.—Western Gas Resources, Inc.; *U.S. Public*, pg. 1758
MURPHY EXPLORATION & PRODUCTION CO.—Murphy Oil Corporation; *U.S. Public*, pg. 1142
MURPHY OIL CO., LTD.—Murphy Oil Corporation; *U.S. Public*, pg. 1142
MURPHY OIL CORPORATION; *U.S. Public*, pg. 1141
MURPHY PETROLEUM LTD.—Murphy Oil Corporation; *U.S. Public*, pg. 1142
NGC CORPORATION; *U.S. Public*, pg. 1146
NGO DEVELOPMENT CORPORATION—National Gas & Oil Company; *U.S. Public*, pg. 1157
NIC RESOURCES, INC.—Nissho Iwai Corporation; *Int'l*, pg. 948
NAGASCO, INC.—Apache Corporation; *U.S. Public*, pg. 119
NATIONAL ENERGY GROUP, INC.; *U.S. Public*, pg. 1156
NATIONAL GAS & OIL COMPANY; *U.S. Public*, pg. 1156
NATIONAL REFINERY LIMITED; *Int'l*, pg. 909
NEDERLANDSE AARDOLIE MAATSCHAPPIJ B.V.—Exxon Corporation; *U.S. Public*, pg. 603
NEDERLANDSE AARDOLIE MAATSCHAPPIJ B.V.—Royal Dutch/Shell Group of Companies; *Int'l*, pg. 1136
NEDERLANDSE GASUNIE N.V.—Royal Dutch/Shell Group of Companies; *Int'l*, pg. 1135
NESTE OY; *Int'l*, pg. 912
NESTE PETROLEUM A/S—Neste Oy; *Int'l*, pg. 915
NEW ENGLAND ENERGY, INC.—New England Electric System; *U.S. Public*, pg. 1171
NIPSCO EXPLORATION CO., INC.—NIPSCO Industries, Inc.; *U.S. Public*, pg. 1185
NIPSCO FUEL COMPANY, INC.—NIPSCO Industries, Inc.; *U.S. Public*, pg. 1185
NOBLE AFFILIATES, INC.; *U.S. Public*, pg. 1186
NORAM ENERGY CORP.—Houston Industries Incorporated; *U.S. Public*, pg. 843
NORCEN ENERGY RESOURCES LIMITED—EdperBrascan Corporation; *Int'l*, pg. 434
NORTH AMERICAN RESOURCES CO.—Montana Power Company; *U.S. Public*, pg. 1127
NORTH AMERICAN ROYALTIES, INC.; *U.S. Private*, pg. 803
NORTH CAROLINA NATURAL GAS CORPORATION; *U.S. Public*, pg. 1194
NORTH WEST SHELF DEVELOPMENT—Royal Dutch/Shell Group of Companies; *Int'l*, pg. 1137
NORTHROCK RESOURCES LTD.; *Int'l*, pg. 970
NUEVO ENERGY COMPANY; *U.S. Public*, pg. 1206
NUMAC ENERGY INC.; *Int'l*, pg. 990
OMI CORP.; *U.S. Public*, pg. 1208
OCCIDENTAL PERUANA, INC.—Occidental Petroleum Corporation; *U.S. Public*, pg. 1210
OCCIDENTAL PETROLEUM CORPORATION; *U.S. Public*, pg. 1210
OCEANEERING A/S—Oceaneering International, Inc.; *U.S. Public*, pg. 1211
OCEANEERING AUSTRALIA PTY. LTD.—Brambles Industries Limited; *Int'l*, pg. 211
OCEANEERING AUSTRALIA PTY. LTD.—Oceaneering International, Inc.; *U.S. Public*, pg. 1211
OCEANEERING INTERNATIONAL, INC.; *U.S. Public*, pg. 1211
OCEANEERING INTERVENTION ENGINEERING—Oceaneering International, Inc.; *U.S. Public*, pg. 1211
OCEANEERING MULTIFLEX—Oceaneering International, Inc.; *U.S. Public*, pg. 1211
OCEANEERING PRODUCTION SYSTEMS—Oceaneering International, Inc.; *U.S. Public*, pg. 1211
OFFSHORE & OVERSEAS PETROLEUM EXPLORATION DIVISION—Chinese Petroleum Corporation; *Int'l*, pg. 286
ONEOK INC.; *U.S. Public*, pg. 1226
ONEOK RESOURCES CO.—ONEOK Inc.; *U.S. Public*, pg. 1226
OPICOIL HOUSTON, INC.—Chinese Petroleum Corporation; *Int'l*, pg. 286
ORYX ENERGY; *U.S. Public*, pg. 1232
OVERLAND ENERGY, INC.—Yellow Corporation; *U.S. Public*, pg. 1788
OXBOW CORPORATION; *U.S. Private*, pg. 825
PNC LIFE INSURANCE COMPANY—PNC Bank Corp.; *U.S. Public*, pg. 1243
PSNC PRODUCTION CORP.—Public Service Company of North Carolina, Inc.; *U.S. Public*, pg. 1340
PACIFICORP; *U.S. Public*, pg. 1251
PAN CANADIAN ENERGY SERVICES—Canadian Pacific Limited; *Int'l*, pg. 259
PANACO, INC.; *U.S. Public*, pg. 1255
PATINA OIL & GAS CORP.; *U.S. Public*, pg. 1264
PEAKE ENERGY, INC.—Texas Pacific Group; *U.S. Private*, pg. 1078
PECO ENERGY COMPANY; *U.S. Public*, pg. 1268
THE PENINSULAR AND ORIENTAL STEAM NAVIGATION COMPANY; *Int'l*, pg. 1032
PENNZOIL COMPANY; *U.S. Public*, pg. 1272
PENNZOIL EXPLORATION & PRODUCTION CO.—Pennzoil Company; *U.S. Public*, pg. 1272
PETRO-CANADA; *Int'l*, pg. 1041
PETROBRAS INTERNACIONAL S.A. (BRASPETRO)—Petrobras - Petroleo Brasileiro S.A.; *Int'l*, pg. 1042

PETROBRAS - PETROLEO BRASILEIRO S.A.; *Int'l*, pg. 1041
PETROCORP EXPLORATION LIMITED—Fletcher Challenge Limited; *Int'l*, pg. 495
PETROFINA S.A.; *Int'l*, pg. 1043
PETROLEOS DE VENEZUELA S.A.; *Int'l*, pg. 1045
PETROLEOS MEXICANOS; *Int'l*, pg. 1046
PETROLEUM DEVELOPMENT CORPORATION; *U.S. Public*, pg. 1280
PHILADELPHIA DRILLING COMPANY—Cigna Corp.; *U.S. Public*, pg. 358
PHILADELPHIA FALCON DRILLING CORPORATION—Cigna Corp.; *U.S. Public*, pg. 358
PHILLIPS PETROLEUM CO. NORWAY—Phillips Petroleum Company; *U.S. Public*, pg. 1291
PHILLIPS PETROLEUM COMPANY; *U.S. Public*, pg. 1290
THE PHOENIX RESOURCE COMPANIES, INC.—Apache Corporation; *U.S. Public*, pg. 119
PIEDMONT INTERSTATE PIPELINE COMPANY—Piedmont Natural Gas Co., Inc.; *U.S. Public*, pg. 1295
PINNACLE EXPLORATION, INC.—Coeur D'Alene Mines Corporation; *U.S. Public*, pg. 394
PINNACLE GAS TREATING, INC.—Western Gas Resources, Inc.; *U.S. Public*, pg. 1758
PIONEER NATURAL RESOURCES CO.; *U.S. Public*, pg. 1299
PLAINS ILLINOIS, INC.—Plains Resources Inc.; *U.S. Public*, *pg. 1308*
PLAINS MARKETING & TRANSPORTATION—Plains Resources Inc.; *U.S. Public*, pg. 1308
PLAINS PETROLEUM COMPANY—Barrett Resources Corporation; *U.S. Public*, pg. 191
PLAINS PETROLEUM OPERATING CO.—Barrett Resources Corporation; *U.S. Public*, pg. 191
PLAINS RESOURCES INC.; *U.S. Public*, pg. 1307
POCO PETROLEUMS LTD.; *Int'l*, pg. 1061
POGO PRODUCING COMPANY; *U.S. Public*, pg. 1312
PRESIDIO EXPLORATION, INC.—Tom Brown, Inc.; *U.S. Public*, pg. 262
PREUSSAG ENERGIE GMBH—Preussag AG; *Int'l*, pg. 1069
PRIMA ENERGY CORPORATION; *U.S. Public*, pg. 1325
PRIMA NATURAL GAS MARKETING, INC.—Prima Energy Corporation; *U.S. Public*, pg. 1325
PRIMA OIL AND GAS COMPANY—Prima Energy Corporation; *U.S. Public*, pg. 1325
PUGET SOUND ENERGY, INC.; *U.S. Public*, pg. 1342
PYRO MINING CO.—Costain Group PLC; *Int'l*, pg. 337
QUESTAR CORPORATION; *U.S. Public*, pg. 1352
QUINTANA PETROLEUM CORP.; *U.S. Private*, pg. 901
RANGER OIL COMPANY—Ranger Oil Limited; *Int'l*, pg. 1086
RANGER OIL LIMITED; *Int'l*, pg. 1086
RENAISSANCE ENERGY LTD.; *Int'l*, pg. 1102
REPSOL EXPLORACION ALGERIE, S.A.—Repsol S.A.; *Int'l*, pg. 1105
REPSOL EXPLORATION ARGENTINA, S.A.—Repsol S.A.; *Int'l*, pg. 1105
REPSOL S.A.; *Int'l*, pg. 1104
REUNION ENERGY COMPANY—Reunion Industries, Inc.; *U.S. Public*, pg. 1383
REUNION INDUSTRIES, INC.; *U.S. Public*, pg. 1383
REUNION OPERATING COMPANY—Reunion Industries, Inc.; *U.S. Public*, pg. 1383
RIGEL ENERGY CORPORATION; *Int'l*, pg. 1117
RILEY NATURAL GAS—Petroleum Development Corporation; *U.S. Public*, pg. 1281
ROAN RESOURCES LTD—Montana Power Company; *U.S. Public*, pg. 1127
ROHOL-AUFSUCHUNGS—Royal Dutch/Shell Group of Companies; *Int'l*, pg. 1138
ROSEWOOD CORPORATION—Caroline Hunt Trust Estate; *U.S. Private*, pg. 548
ROYAL DUTCH/SHELL GROUP OF COMPANIES; *Int'l*, pg. 1135
ROYAL NEDLLOYD GROUP N.V.; *Int'l*, pg. 1143
RUHRGAS AKTIENGESELLSCHAFT; *Int'l*, pg. 1148
SEECO, INC.—Southwestern Energy Company; *U.S. Public*, *pg. 1494*
SHV HOLDINGS N.V.; *Int'l*, pg. 1154
SOCO HOLDINGS INC.—Snyder Oil Corporation; *U.S. Public*, pg. 1482
SOCO WATTENBERG CORPORATION—Snyder Oil Corporation; *U.S. Public*, pg. 1482
SAGA PETROLEUM ASA; *Int'l*, pg. 1169
SAMEDAN OIL OF CANADA, INC.—Noble Affiliates, Inc.; *U.S. Public*, pg. 1186
SANTA FE ENERGY RESOURCES, INC.; *U.S. Public*, pg. 1431
SANTA FE MINERALS INC.—Kuwait Petroleum Corporation; *Int'l*, pg. 765
SARAWAK SHELL—Royal Dutch/Shell Group of Companies; *Int'l*, pg. 1140
SASOL LIMITED; *Int'l*, pg. 1196
SASOL OIL—Sasol Limited; *Int'l*, pg. 1197
SAUDI ARABIAN TEXACO INC.—Texaco Inc.; *U.S. Public*, pg. 1583
SEAGULL ENERGY CORPORATION; *U.S. Public*, pg. 1450
SEAGULL ENERGY E & P, INC.—Seagull Energy Corporation; *U.S. Public*, pg. 1450
SENECA RESOURCES CORP.—National Fuel Gas Company; *U.S. Public*, pg. 1156
SHELL CANADA LTD.—Royal Dutch/Shell Group of Companies; *Int'l*, pg. 1138
SHELL DEVELOPMENT CO.—Royal Dutch/Shell Group of Companies; *Int'l*, pg. 1136
SHELL INTERNATIONAL PETROLEUM CO. LTD.—Royal Dutch/Shell Group of Companies; *Int'l*, pg. 1139
SHELL OIL COMPANY—Royal Dutch/Shell Group of Companies; *Int'l*, pg. 1136
SHELL OLIE-OG GASUDVINDING DANMARK—Royal Dutch/Shell Group of Companies; *Int'l*, pg. 1138
THE SHELL PETROLEUM DEVELOPMENT COMPANY OF NIGERIA LTD.—Royal Dutch/Shell Group of Companies; *Int'l*, pg. 1137
SHELL WEST EXPLORATION & PRODUCTION INC.—Royal Dutch/Shell Group of Companies; *Int'l*, pg. 1142
SHELL WINNING NV—Royal Dutch/Shell Group of Companies; *Int'l*, pg. 1140
SIERRA PACIFIC RESOURCES; *U.S. Public*, pg. 1470
SINOCHEM INTERNATIONAL PETROLEUM CO. LTD.; *Int'l*, pg. 1254
SNYDER OIL CORPORATION; *U.S. Public*, pg. 1481
SOLUS OCEANEERING (MALAYSIA) SDN. BHD.—Oceaneering International, Inc.; *U.S. Public*, pg. 1211
SONAT EXPLORATION COMPANY—Sonat Inc.; *U.S. Public*, pg. 1485
SONAT EXPLORATION GOM INC.—Sonat Inc.; *U.S. Public*, pg. 1485
SONAT INC.; *U.S. Public*, pg. 1484
SOUTH EAST ASIA PETROLEUM EXPLORATION CO., LTD.—Mitsui & Co., Ltd.; *Int'l*, pg. 877
SOUTHWESTERN ENERGY COMPANY; *U.S. Public*, pg. 1494
SOUTHWESTERN ENERGY PRODUCTION CO.—Southwestern Energy Company; *U.S. Public*, pg. 1494
SPIRIT ENERGY 76—Unocal Corporation; *U.S. Public*, pg. 1698
P.T. STANVAC INDONESIA—Exxon Corporation; *U.S. Public*, pg. 603
STATES, INC.; *U.S. Private*, pg. 1037
STATEX PETROLEUM, INC.—PS Group Holdings; *U.S. Public*, pg. 1245
STATOIL; *Int'l*, pg. 1297
STOCKER RESOURCES, INC.—Plains Resources Inc.; *U.S. Public*, pg. 1308
STONE & WEBSTER OIL COMPANY, INC.—Stone & Webster, Incorporated; *U.S. Public*, pg. 1519
SUN COMPANY, INC.; *U.S. Public*, pg. 1530
SUN INTERNATIONAL PRODUCTION COMPANY LIMITED—Sun Company, Inc.; *U.S. Public*, pg. 1530
SUNCOR EXPLORATION & PRODUCTION GROUP—Suncor Inc.; *Int'l*, pg. 1320
SUNCOR INC.; *Int'l*, pg. 1320
SUNCOR OIL SANDS GROUP—Suncor Inc.; *Int'l*, pg. 1320
SUNTERRA GAS GATHERING COMPANY—Public Service Company of New Mexico; *U.S. Public*, pg. 1340
SUNTERRA GAS PROCESSING COMPANY—Public Service Company of New Mexico; *U.S. Public*, pg. 1340
TPC CORPORATION—PacifiCorp; *U.S. Public*, pg. 1252
TAIWAN PETROLEUM EXPLORATION DIVISION—Chinese Petroleum Corporation; *Int'l*, pg. 286
TALISMAN ENERGY (U.K.) LIMITED—Talisman Energy Inc.; *Int'l*, pg. 1352
TARGET OILFIELD PIPE & SUPPLY COMPANY (TOPS)—Texas Pacific Group; *U.S. Private*, pg. 1078
TAURUS EXPLORATION, INC.—Energen Corporation; *U.S. Public*, pg. 581
TEJAS GAS CORPORATION—Royal Dutch/Shell Group of Companies; *Int'l*, pg. 1136
TENNECO COAL CONVERSION CO.—Tenneco Inc.; *U.S. Public*, pg. 1579
TENNECO COAL GASIFICATION CO.—Tenneco Inc.; *U.S. Public*, pg. 1579
TENNECO UNITED KINGDOM, INC.—Tenneco Inc.; *U.S. Public*, pg. 1580
TESORO PETROLEUM COMPANIES, INC.—Tesoro Petroleum Corporation; *U.S. Public*, pg. 1582
TESORO PETROLEUM CORPORATION; *U.S. Public*, pg. 1581
TEXACO INC.; *U.S. Public*, pg. 1582
TEXACO OVERSEAS PETROLEUM CO.—Texaco Inc.; *U.S. Public*, pg. 1583
THAI SHELL EXPLORATION & PRODUCTION, CO. LTD.—Royal Dutch/Shell Group of Companies; *Int'l*, pg. 1140
THOMASVILLE ENERGY CORPORATION—Snyder Oil Corporation; *U.S. Public*, pg. 1482
TIDELANDS OIL PRODUCTION CO.; *U.S. Private*, pg. 1084
TIPPERARY CORPORATION; *U.S. Public*, pg. 1618
TIPPERARY OIL & GAS CORP.—Tipperary Corporation; *U.S. Public*, pg. 1618
TOSCO CORPORATION; *U.S. Public*, pg. 1624
TOTAL EXPLOITATIE EN PRODUKTIE MAATSCHAPPIJ B.K. (TEPMA)—Total S.A.; *Int'l*, pg. 1409
TOTAL HOLDINGS (AUSTRALIA) PTY. LTD.—Total S.A.; *Int'l*, pg. 1409
TOTAL ITALIANA SRL.—Total S.A.; *Int'l*, pg. 1409
TOTAL OIL GREAT BRITAIN LTD.—Total S.A.; *Int'l*, pg. 1409
TOTAL OUTRE-MER—Total S.A.; *Int'l*, pg. 1409
TOTAL PETROLEUM CANADA LTD.—Total S.A.; *Int'l*, pg. 1409
TOTAL PETROLEUM, INC.—Ultramar Diamond Shamrock Corporation; *U.S. Public*, pg. 1663
TOTAL S.A.; *Int'l*, pg. 1408
TOTAL SOUTH AFRICA (PTY.) LTD.—Total S.A.; *Int'l*, pg. 1409
TRANSAMERICAN NATURAL GAS CORPORATION; *U.S. Private*, pg. 1096
TRANSCAPACITY, L.P.—Eastern Utilities Associates; *U.S. Public*, pg. 550
TRANSMONTAIGNE OIL COMPANY; *U.S. Public*, pg. 1631
TRITON ENERGY LIMITED; *U.S. Public*, pg. 1640
TRUE COMPANIES; *U.S. Private*, pg. 1107
USX CORPORATION; *U.S. Public*, pg. 1661
UNION ENERGY INC.—Westcoast Energy Inc.; *Int'l*, pg. 1492
UNION PACIFIC CORPORATION; *U.S. Public*, pg. 1667
UNION PACIFIC RESOURCES COMPANY (UPRC)—Union Pacific Corporation; *U.S. Public*, pg. 1668
UNION TEXAS PETROLEUM HOLDINGS; *U.S. Public*, pg. 1669
UNIT CORPORATION; *U.S. Public*, pg. 1672
UNIVERSAL RESOURCES CORPORATION—Questar Corporation; *U.S. Public*, pg. 1352
UNOCAL CANADA LIMITED—Unocal Corporation; *U.S. Public*, pg. 1698
UNOCAL CORPORATION; *U.S. Public*, pg. 1698
UNOCAL INDONESIA, LTD.—Unocal Corporation; *U.S. Public*, pg. 1698
UNOCAL NETHERLANDS—Unocal Corporation; *U.S. Public*, pg. 1698
UNOCAL THAILAND—Unocal Corporation; *U.S. Public*, pg. 1698
UPLAND RESOURCES, INC.—Westvaco Corporation; *U.S. Public*, pg. 1762
VANGUARD ENERGY CORP.; *U.S. Private*, pg. 1133
WAINOCO OIL & GAS COMPANY—Wainoco Oil Corporation; *U.S. Public*, pg. 1732
WAINOCO OIL CORPORATION; *U.S. Public*, pg. 1732
WAINOCO RESOURCES, INC.—Wainoco Oil Corporation; *U.S. Public*, pg. 1732
WARD LAKE DRILLING, INC.—Texas Pacific Group; *U.S. Private*, pg. 1078
WESTANA GATHERING COMPANY—Duke Energy Corporation; *U.S. Public*, pg. 535
WESTANA GATHERING COMPANY—Western Gas Resources, Inc.; *U.S. Public*, pg. 1759
WESTAR GROUP LTD.; *Int'l*, pg. 1491
WESTCOAST PETROLEUM LTD.—Westcoast Energy Inc.; *Int'l*, pg. 1492
WESTERN GAS RESOURCES CANADA, INC.—Western Gas Resources, Inc.; *U.S. Public*, pg. 1759
WESTERN GAS RESOURCES, INC.; *U.S. Public*, pg. 1758
WESTERN GAS RESOURCES STORAGE, INC.—Western Gas Resources, Inc.; *U.S. Public*, pg. 1759
WESTERN GAS RESOURCES-LOUISIANA, INC.—Western Gas Resources, Inc.; *U.S. Public*, pg. 1758
WESTERN GAS RESOURCES-OKLAHOMA, INC.—Western Gas Resources, Inc.; *U.S. Public*, pg. 1758
WESTERN GAS RESOURCES-TEXAS, INC.—Western Gas Resources, Inc.; *U.S. Public*, pg. 1759
WEXPRO COMPANY—Questar Corporation; *U.S. Public*, pg. 1352
WILCOX ENERGY COMPANY—Callon Petroleum Company; *U.S. Public*, pg. 295
WILSHIRE OIL CO. OF TEXAS; *U.S. Public*, pg. 1770
WINTERSHALL AG—BASF AG; *Int'l*, pg. 104
WINTERSHALL GAS GMBH—BASF AG; *Int'l*, pg. 105
THE WISER OIL COMPANY; *U.S. Public*, pg. 1773
WOODSIDE OFFSHORE PETROLEUM PTY. LTD.—Royal Dutch/Shell Group of Companies; *Int'l*, pg. 1137
WOODSIDE PETROLEUM LTD.—Royal Dutch/Shell Group of Companies; *Int'l*, pg. 1137
XEROX FINANCIAL SERVICES LIFE INSURANCE CO.—Xerox Corporation; *U.S. Public*, pg. 1785

1321 — NATURAL GAS LIQUIDS

ANR PRODUCTION CO.—The Coastal Corporation; *U.S. Public*, pg. 389
AMERICAN OIL & GAS CORPORATION—K N Energy, Inc.; *U.S. Public*, pg. 937
AMOCO CANADA PETROLEUM COMPANY LTD.—Amoco Corporation; *U.S. Public*, pg. 103
AMOCO CANADA RESOURCES LTD.—Amoco Corporation; *U.S. Public*, pg. 103
AMOCO CORPORATION; *U.S. Public*, pg. 101
AMOCO PRODUCTION COMPANY—Amoco Corporation; *U.S. Public*, pg. 102
AMOCO SHARJAH LPG CO.—Amoco Corporation; *U.S. Public*, pg. 102
ANADARKO PETROLEUM CORPORATION; *U.S. Public*, pg. 107
ANCHOR GASOLINE CORPORATION; *U.S. Private*, pg. 70
BP AMERICA INC.—The British Petroleum Company P.L.C.; *Int'l*, pg. 220
THE BRITISH PETROLEUM COMPANY P.L.C.; *Int'l*, pg. 219
CGC ENERGY, INC.—Cascade Natural Gas Corporation; *U.S. Public*, pg. 311
CGC RESOURCES, INC.—Cascade Natural Gas Corporation; *U.S. Public*, pg. 311
CHINESE PETROLEUM CORPORATION; *Int'l*, pg. 286
CLEAN ENERGY ENTERPRISE, INC.—Public Service Company of North Carolina, Inc.; *U.S. Public*, pg. 1340
THE COASTAL CORPORATION; *U.S. Public*, pg. 389
COLUMBIA ENERGY GROUP; *U.S. Public*, pg. 402
COLUMBIA NATURAL RESOURCES, INC.—Columbia Energy Group; *U.S. Public*, pg. 403
COLUMBIA PROPANE CORP.—Columbia Energy Group; *U.S. Public*, pg. 403
DUKE ENERGY INTERNATIONAL, L.L.C.—Duke Energy Corporation; *U.S. Public*, pg. 534
DYAS B.V.—SHV Holdings N.V.; *Int'l*, pg. 1155
ENI S.P.A.; *Int'l*, pg. 428
ENERGEN CORPORATION; *U.S. Public*, pg. 581
ENERGY COMPANIES OF ONEOK—ONEOK Inc.; *U.S. Public*, pg. 1226
ENRON CORP.; *U.S. Public*, pg. 584
ENSERCH CORPORATION—Texas Utilities Company; *U.S. Public*, pg. 1587
ENTERPRISE PRODUCTS COMPANY; *U.S. Private*, pg. 377
GREEN MOUNTAIN PROPANE GAS CO.—Green Mountain Power Corporation; *U.S. Public*, pg. 761
ICG PROPANE INC.—Petro-Canada; *Int'l*, pg. 1041
JUPITER INDUSTRIES, INC.; *U.S. Private*, pg. 602
KENTUCKY HYDROCARBON DIVISION—Equitable Resources, Inc.; *U.S. Public*, pg. 589
LL&E (UK) INC.—Burlington Resources Inc.; *U.S. Public*, pg. 269
THE LOUISIANA LAND AND EXPLORATION COMPANY—Burlington Resources Inc.; *U.S. Public*, pg. 269
MFA OIL COMPANY; *U.S. Private*, pg. 687
MAGELLAN PETROLEUM AUSTRALIA LTD.—Magellan Petroleum Corporation; *U.S. Public*, pg. 1037

MAGELLAN PETROLEUM CORPORATION; *U.S. Public*, pg. 1036
MAPCO INC.; *U.S. Public*, pg. 1042
MITCHELL ENERGY & DEVELOPMENT CORP.; *U.S. Public*, pg. 1117
MONTANA POWER COMPANY; *U.S. Public*, pg. 1126
MOUNTAIN GAS REOURCES, INC.—Western Gas Resources, Inc.; *U.S. Public*, pg. 1758
NATIONAL HELIUM CORPORATION—Duke Energy Corporation; *U.S. Public*, pg. 534
NEDERLANDSE GASUNIE N.V.—Royal Dutch/Shell Group of Companies; *Int'l*, pg. 1135
ONEOK INC.; *U.S. Public*, pg. 1226
ONEOK PRODUCTS CO.—ONEOK Inc.; *U.S. Public*, pg. 1226
PM TERMINALS, INC.—Petroleum Marketers, Inc.; *U.S. Private*, pg. 859
PSNC BLUE RIDGE CORP.—Public Service Company of North Carolina, Inc.; *U.S. Public*, pg. 1340
PENNZOIL COMPANY; *U.S. Public*, pg. 1272
PETRO-CANADA; *Int'l*, pg. 1041
PHILLIPS PETROLEUM COMPANY; *U.S. Public*, pg. 1290
PINNACLE GAS TREATING, INC.—Western Gas Resources, Inc.; *U.S. Public*, pg. 1758
RIGEL ENERGY CORPORATION; *Int'l*, pg. 1117
SHV HOLDINGS N.V.; *Int'l*, pg. 1154
SANTA FE MINERALS INC.—Kuwait Petroleum Corporation; *Int'l*, pg. 765
SHELL OFFSHORE—Royal Dutch/Shell Group of Companies; *Int'l*, pg. 1142
SONAT EXPLORATION COMPANY—Sonat Inc.; *U.S. Public*, pg. 1485
SONAT INC.; *U.S. Public*, pg. 1484
SUN COMPANY, INC.; *U.S. Public*, pg. 1530
SUN INTERNATIONAL PRODUCTION COMPANY LIMITED—Sun Company, Inc.; *U.S. Public*, pg. 1530
SUNCOR INC.; *Int'l*, pg. 1320
TAURUS EXPLORATION, INC.—Energen Corporation; *U.S. Public*, pg. 581
TECO COALBED METHANE, INC.—TECO Energy, Inc.; *U.S. Public*, pg. 1565
TECO ENERGY, INC.; *U.S. Public*, pg. 1565
VALERO ENERGY CORPORATION; *U.S. Public*, pg. 1704
WARREN PETROLEUM COMPANY—NGC Corporation; *U.S. Public*, pg. 1146
WESTANA GATHERING COMPANY—Duke Energy Corporation; *U.S. Public*, pg. 535
WESTANA GATHERING COMPANY—Western Gas Resources, Inc.; *U.S. Public*, pg. 1759
WESTAR GROUP LTD.; *Int'l*, pg. 1491
WESTERN GAS RESOURCES, INC.; *U.S. Public*, pg. 1758
WESTERN GAS RESOURCES-LOUISIANA, INC.—Western Gas Resources, Inc.; *U.S. Public*, pg. 1758
WESTERN GAS RESOURCES-OKLAHOMA, INC.—Western Gas Resources, Inc.; *U.S. Public*, pg. 1758
WESTERN GAS RESOURCES-TEXAS, INC.—Western Gas Resources, Inc.; *U.S. Public*, pg. 1759
Y.P.F., S.A.; *Int'l*, pg. 1515

1381 — DRILLING OIL & GAS WELLS

AKER RAJ ASA; *Int'l*, pg. 41
ALAMCO, INC.—Columbia Energy Group; *U.S. Public*, pg. 403
AMOCO CANADA RESOURCES LTD.—Amoco Corporation; *U.S. Public*, pg. 103
ANSCHUTZ CORPORATION; *U.S. Private*, pg. 75
APPLIED DRILLING TECHNOLOGY INC.—Global Marine Inc.; *U.S. Public*, pg. 748
ARAB DRILLING & WORKOVER COMPANY—Kuwait Petroleum Corporation; *Int'l*, pg. 765
ATKINSON; *U.S. Public*, pg. 143
ATWOOD OCEANICS AUSTRALIA PTY. LTD.—Atwood Oceanics, Inc.; *U.S. Public*, pg. 146
ATWOOD OCEANICS DRILLING CO.—Atwood Oceanics, Inc.; *U.S. Public*, pg. 146
ATWOOD OCEANICS, INC.; *U.S. Public*, pg. 146
AUSTRALIAN OIL & GAS CORPORATION LIMITED; *Int'l*, pg. 101
BJ SERVICES COMPANY; *U.S. Public*, pg. 161
BARNWELL INDUSTRIES, INC.; *U.S. Public*, pg. 190
BRITISH AMERICAN OFFSHORE LIMITED—Rowan Companies, Inc.; *U.S. Public*, pg. 1410
BRUNEI COLDGAS—Royal Dutch/Shell Group of Companies; *Int'l*, pg. 1139
BRUNEI LNG—Royal Dutch/Shell Group of Companies; *Int'l*, pg. 1139
BRUNEI SHELL PETROLEUM CO SDN BHD—Royal Dutch/Shell Group of Companies; *Int'l*, pg. 1139
BURNS DRILLING COMPANY—Harken Energy Corporation; *U.S. Public*, pg. 785
BUTCHER ENERGY—Butcher & Co., Inc.; *U.S. Private*, pg. 189
CALLON PETROLEUM COMPANY; *U.S. Public*, pg. 295
P.T. CALTEX PACIFIC INDONESIA—Chevron Corporation; *U.S. Public*, pg. 348
P.T. CALTEX PACIFIC INDONESIA—Texaco Inc.; *U.S. Public*, pg. 1585
CHEVRON CANADA LIMITED—Chevron Corporation; *U.S. Public*, pg. 348
CHEVRON CANADA RESOURCES LIMITED—Chevron Corporation; *U.S. Public*, pg. 348
CHEVRON OIL COMPANY OF NETHERLANDS—Chevron Corporation; *U.S. Public*, pg. 348
CHEVRON OVERSEAS PETROLEUM, INC.—Chevron Corporation; *U.S. Public*, pg. 348
CHEVRON PETROLEUM COMPANY OF COLOMBIA—Chevron Corporation; *U.S. Public*, pg. 348
CHEVRON STANDARD LIMITED—Chevron Corporation; *U.S. Public*, pg. 348
CHEVRON (U.K.) LTD.—Chevron Corporation; *U.S. Public*, pg. 348
CLEARWAYS DRILLING (M) SDN BHD—Atwood Oceanics, Inc.; *U.S. Public*, pg. 146
CLIFFS DRILLING COMPANY; *U.S. Public*, pg. 386
COLONIAL DRILLING & EXPLORATION CORPORATION—Colonial Oil Industries; *U.S. Private*, pg. 254
COMPAGNIE FRANCAISE DES PETROLES (ALGERIE) CFP (A)—Total S.A.; *Int'l*, pg. 1409
DCA OIL & GAS ONE, INC.—Lennar Corporation; *U.S. Public*, pg. 988
DEUTSCHE SHELL AG—Royal Dutch/Shell Group of Companies; *Int'l*, pg. 1138
DRY HOLE OIL & GAS CORPORATION—Torchmark Corporation; *U.S. Public*, pg. 1623
DUGAN PRODUCTION CORP.; *U.S. Private*, pg. 345
EAGLE OCEANICS, INC.—Atwood Oceanics, Inc.; *U.S. Public*, pg. 146
ELF AQUITANE; *Int'l*, pg. 444
ELF CONGO—Elf Aquitane; *Int'l*, pg. 446
ELF GABON—Elf Aquitane; *Int'l*, pg. 446
ELF PETROLAND—Elf Aquitane; *Int'l*, pg. 446
ELF SEREPCA—Elf Aquitane; *Int'l*, pg. 446
ENERGY COMPANIES OF ONEOK—ONEOK Inc.; *U.S. Public*, pg. 1226
ENSCO INTERNATIONAL INCORPORATED (ENSCO); *U.S. Public*, pg. 585
EXXON TRADING ASIA PACIFIC PRIVATE LIMITED—Exxon Corporation; *U.S. Public*, pg. 602
FINA, INC.—Petrofina S.A.; *Int'l*, pg. 1044
FINA PETROLEOS DE ANGOLA, S.A.R.L.—Petrofina S.A.; *Int'l*, pg. 1044
FORASOL S.A.; *Int'l*, pg. 496
FOREST OIL CORPORATION; *U.S. Public*, pg. 670
FORWEST INC.—Forasol S.A.; *Int'l*, pg. 496
GLOBAL MARINE DRILLING CO.—Global Marine Inc.; *U.S. Public*, pg. 748
GLOBAL MARINE INC.; *U.S. Public*, pg. 748
GROUNDWATER TECHNOLOGY GOVERNMENT SERVICES, INC.—Fluor Corporation; *U.S. Public*, pg. 660
HCO ENERGY LTD.—HarCor Energy, Inc.; *U.S. Public*, pg. 782
HDM, HOLLANDSCHE DELFSTOFFEN MAATSCHAPPIJ BV—Hollandsche Beton Groep NV; *Int'l*, pg. 630
HELMERICH & PAYNE, INC.; *U.S. Public*, pg. 808
HUSKY OIL INTL. LTD.—Husky Oil Ltd.; *Int'l*, pg. 640
HUSKY OIL LTD.; *Int'l*, pg. 640
HUSKY OIL OPERATIONS LTD.—Husky Oil Ltd.; *Int'l*, pg. 640
IP GAS SUPPLY CO.—Illinova Inc.; *U.S. Public*, pg. 869
INDUSTRIAL EQUITY LIMITED; *Int'l*, pg. 676
INTAKE WATER CO.—Tenneco Inc.; *U.S. Public*, pg. 1579
JUSTISS OIL CO., INC.; *U.S. Private*, pg. 602
KEPEC RESOURCES LIMITED—Empire Company Limited; *Int'l*, pg. 454
KEY ENERGY GROUP INC.; *U.S. Public*, pg. 953
KUWAIT DRILLING CO.—Kuwait Petroleum Corporation; *Int'l*, pg. 765
KUWAIT PETROLEUM CORPORATION; *Int'l*, pg. 764
LOMAK OPERATING COMPANY—Lomak Petroleum Inc.; *U.S. Public*, pg. 1012
LOMAK PETROLEUM INC.; *U.S. Public*, pg. 1012
MAGUIRE OIL CO.; *U.S. Private*, pg. 696
MARINE DRILLING COMPANIES, INC.; *U.S. Public*, pg. 1044
MCCULLOUGH, AN ATLAS WIRELINE SERVICES OPERATION—Litton Industries, Inc.; *U.S. Public*, pg. 1004
MITCHELL ENERGY & DEVELOPMENT CORP.; *U.S. Public*, pg. 1117
MOBIL OIL CANADA, LTD.—Mobil Oil Corporation; *U.S. Public*, pg. 1119
NABORS ALASKA DRILLING, INC.—Nabors Industries, Inc.; *U.S. Public*, pg. 1148
NABORS DRILLING INTERNATIONAL LIMITED—Nabors Industries, Inc.; *U.S. Public*, pg. 1148
NABORS DRILLING USA, INC.—Nabors Industries, Inc.; *U.S. Public*, pg. 1149
NABORS INDUSTRIES, INC.; *U.S. Public*, pg. 1148
NATIONAL ENERDRILL—KCS Energy Inc.; *U.S. Public*, pg. 939
NEDERLANDSE AARDOLIE MAATSCHAPPIJ B.V.—Exxon Corporation; *U.S. Public*, pg. 603
NEDERLANDSE AARDOLIE MAATSCHAPPIJ B.V.—Royal Dutch/Shell Group of Companies; *Int'l*, pg. 1136
NOBLE DRILLING CORPORATION; *U.S. Public*, pg. 1186
NOBLE DRILLING (WEST AFRICA) LTD.—Noble Drilling Corporation; *U.S. Public*, pg. 1187
NOBLE-NATIONAL JOINT VENTURE—Noble Drilling Corporation; *U.S. Public*, pg. 1186
NOBLE OFFSHORE CORPORATION—Noble Drilling Corporation; *U.S. Public*, pg. 1186
A/S NORSKE SHELL—Royal Dutch/Shell Group of Companies; *Int'l*, pg. 1139
NORTHROCK RESOURCES LTD.; *Int'l*, pg. 970
NUMAC ENERGY INC.; *Int'l*, pg. 990
OCCIDENTAL PETROLEUM CORPORATION; *U.S. Public*, pg. 1210
ONEOK INC.; *U.S. Public*, pg. 1226
PARKER DRILLING COMPANY; *U.S. Public*, pg. 1259
PATTERSON DRILLING CO.—Patterson Energy, Inc.; *U.S. Public*, pg. 1265
PATTERSON ENERGY, INC.; *U.S. Public*, pg. 1265
PEAK OILFIELD SERVICES COMPANY—Nabors Industries, Inc.; *U.S. Public*, pg. 1149
PERFORACIONES MARITIMAS PROTEXA S.A. DE C.V.—Grupo Protexa S.A. de C.V.; *Int'l*, pg. 576
PETRO-HUNT CORPORATION; *U.S. Private*, pg. 858
PETROBRAS INTERNACIONAL S.A. (BRASPETRO)—Petrobras - Petroleo Brasileiro S.A.; *Int'l*, pg. 1042
PETROBRAS - PETROLEO BRASILEIRO S.A.; *Int'l*, pg. 1041
PETROLEOS DE VENEZUELA S.A.; *Int'l*, pg. 1045
PETROLEOS MEXICANOS; *Int'l*, pg. 1046
PETROLEUM DEVELOPMENT CORPORATION; *U.S. Public*, pg. 1280
PHILLIPS GAS COMPANY—Phillips Petroleum Company; *U.S. Public*, pg. 1291
THE PHOENIX RESOURCE COMPANIES, INC.—Apache Corporation; *U.S. Public*, pg. 119
PRECISION DRILLING CORPORATION; *Int'l*, pg. 1066
PRIDE INTERNATIONAL, INC.; *U.S. Public*, pg. 1324
QATAR DRILLING CO.—Kuwait Petroleum Corporation; *Int'l*, pg. 765
R&B FALCON CORPORATION; *U.S. Public*, pg. 1354
RPC INCORPORATED; *U.S. Public*, pg. 1356
RANGER OIL LIMITED; *Int'l*, pg. 1086
READING & BATES CORPORATION—R&B Falcon Corporation; *U.S. Public*, pg. 1354
READING & BATES DRILLING CO.—R&B Falcon Corporation; *U.S. Public*, pg. 1354
REFINERIA PANAMA S.A.—Texaco Inc.; *U.S. Public*, pg. 1584
REFINERIA TEXACO DE HONDURAS, S.A.—Texaco Inc.; *U.S. Public*, pg. 1584
RIGS AND SPECIAL WELL SERVICES COORDINATION (GESEP)—Petrobras - Petroleo Brasileiro S.A.; *Int'l*, pg. 1042
ROWAN COMPANIES, INC.; *U.S. Public*, pg. 1409
ROWAN DRILLING CO., INC.-ALASKA DIV.—Rowan Companies, Inc.; *U.S. Public*, pg. 1410
ROWAN DRILLING (U.K.) LIMITED—Rowan Companies, Inc.; *U.S. Public*, pg. 1410
ROWEN DRILLING & AVIATION B.V.—Rowan Companies, Inc.; *U.S. Public*, pg. 1410
RUHRGAS AKTIENGESELLSCHAFT; *Int'l*, pg. 1148
SNC - AKER OFFSHORE INC. (AE)—Aker Raj Asa; *Int'l*, pg. 42
SAMEDAN OIL OF CANADA, INC.—Noble Affiliates, Inc.; *U.S. Public*, pg. 1186
SANTA FE DRILLING CO.—Kuwait Petroleum Corporation; *Int'l*, pg. 765
SANTA FE INTERNATIONAL CORPORATION—Kuwait Petroleum Corporation; *Int'l*, pg. 765
SANTA FE INTERNATIONAL SERVICES, INC.—Kuwait Petroleum Corporation; *Int'l*, pg. 765
SAW DRILLING, INC.—Stone & Webster, Incorporated; *U.S. Public*, pg. 1519
SCHLUMBERGER LIMITED; *U.S. Public*, pg. 1439
SCOPE ENERGY RESOURCES, INC.—Scope Industries; *U.S. Public*, pg. 1444
SCOPE INDUSTRIES; *U.S. Public*, pg. 1444
SEDNETH, SEA DRILLING NETHERLANDS BV—Hollandsche Beton Groep NV; *Int'l*, pg. 630
SHELL CANADA LTD.—Royal Dutch/Shell Group of Companies; *Int'l*, pg. 1138
SHELL FRANCAISE—Royal Dutch/Shell Group of Companies; *Int'l*, pg. 1138
SHELL INTERNATIONAL PETROLEUM CO. LTD.—Royal Dutch/Shell Group of Companies; *Int'l*, pg. 1139
SHELL (SWITZERLAND)—Royal Dutch/Shell Group of Companies; *Int'l*, pg. 1139
SHELL WINNING NV—Royal Dutch/Shell Group of Companies; *Int'l*, pg. 1140
SHIN NISHI NIHON—Royal Dutch/Shell Group of Companies; *Int'l*, pg. 1140
SOUTH SEAS DRILLING CO.—Kuwait Petroleum Corporation; *Int'l*, pg. 766
SWIFTDRILL, INC.—Atwood Oceanics, Inc.; *U.S. Public*, pg. 146
SYRIA SHELL PETROLEUM DEVELOPMENT BV—Royal Dutch/Shell Group of Companies; *Int'l*, pg. 1141
TECHNIP; *Int'l*, pg. 1360
TENNECO MINERALS CO.—Tenneco Inc.; *U.S. Public*, pg. 1579
TEXACO INC.; *U.S. Public*, pg. 1582
THAI SHELL EXPLORATION & PRODUCTION, CO. LTD.—Royal Dutch/Shell Group of Companies; *Int'l*, pg. 1140
TORCH ENERGY ADVISORS, INCORPORATED—Torchmark Corporation; *U.S. Public*, pg. 1623
TOTAL HOLDINGS (AUSTRALIA) PTY. LTD.—Total S.A.; *Int'l*, pg. 1409
TOTAL INDONESIE—Total S.A.; *Int'l*, pg. 1409
TOTAL MARINE EXPLOITATIE N.V.-TME—Total S.A.; *Int'l*, pg. 1409
TOTAL NORGE AS—Total S.A.; *Int'l*, pg. 1409
TOTAL OIL MARINE P.L.C.-TOM—Total S.A.; *Int'l*, pg. 1409
TOTAL S.A.; *Int'l*, pg. 1408
TRANSOCEAN OFFSHORE, INC.; *U.S. Public*, pg. 1631
UNION DRILLING DIVISION—Equitable Resources, Inc.; *U.S. Public*, pg. 590
WELL ENGINEERING AND TECHNOLOGY (GETEP)—Petrobras - Petroleo Brasileiro S.A.; *Int'l*, pg. 1042
WESTCOAST PETROLEUM LTD.—Westcoast Energy Inc.; *Int'l*, pg. 1492
WILSON BROTHERS DRILLING CO.—Burlington Resources Inc.; *U.S. Public*, pg. 269
RALPH C. WILSON ENTERPRISES; *U.S. Private*, pg. 1181
YALE E KEY, INC.—Key Energy Group Inc.; *U.S. Public*, pg. 953

1382 — OIL & GAS FIELD EXPLORATION SERVICES

AEC OIL & GAS—Alberta Energy Company, Ltd.; *Int'l*, pg. 48
ADAMS RESOURCES & ENERGY, INC.; *U.S. Public*, pg. 18
AERO SERVICE CORP.—Litton Industries, Inc.; *U.S. Public*, pg. 1003
ALAMCO-DELAWARE, INC.—Columbia Energy Group; *U.S. Public*, pg. 403
ALAMCO, INC.—Columbia Energy Group; *U.S. Public*, pg. 403
ALBERTA ENERGY COMPANY, LTD.; *Int'l*, pg. 48

ALTANA EXPLORATION COMPANY—Montana Power Company; U.S. Public, pg. 1127
AMERAC ENERGY CORP.—Southern Mineral Corporation; U.S. Public, pg. 1490
AMERADA HESS (U.K.) LTD.—Amerada Hess Corporation; U.S. Public, pg. 65
AMOCO ARGENTINA OIL CO.—Amoco Corporation; U.S. Public, pg. 102
ANSCHUTZ CORPORATION; U.S. Private, pg. 75
ATCO GROUP CO.; Int'l, pg. 95
ATWOOD OCEANICS AUSTRALIA PTY. LTD.—Atwood Oceanics, Inc.; U.S. Public, pg. 146
ATWOOD OCEANICS DRILLING CO.—Atwood Oceanics, Inc.; U.S. Public, pg. 146
ATWOOD OCEANICS, INC.; U.S. Public, pg. 146
BEB ERDGAS UND ERDOEL GMBH—Exxon Corporation; U.S. Public, pg. 601
BERRY PETROLEUM COMPANY; U.S. Public, pg. 223
BOLT GEOPHYSICAL CORPORATION—Bolt Technology Corporation; U.S. Public, pg. 244
BOLT TECHNOLOGY CORPORATION; U.S. Public, pg. 244
BROCK EXPLORATION CORPORATION—Key Production Company, Inc.; U.S. Public, pg. 953
TOM BROWN, INC.; U.S. Public, pg. 262
CGG AMERICAN SERVICES INC.—CGG Group; Int'l, pg. 241
CMS NOMECO—CMS Energy Corporation; U.S. Public, pg. 280
CABRE EXPLORATION LTD.; Int'l, pg. 247
CALLON PETROLEUM COMPANY; U.S. Public, pg. 295
P.T. CALTEX PACIFIC INDONESIA—Chevron Corporation; U.S. Public, pg. 348
P.T. CALTEX PACIFIC INDONESIA—Texaco Inc.; U.S. Public, pg. 1585
CELERON CORPORATION—The Goodyear Tire & Rubber Company; U.S. Public, pg. 753
CHAUVCO RESOURCES LTD.—Trimac Corporation; Int'l, pg. 1424
CHEVRON CANADA LIMITED—Chevron Corporation; U.S. Public, pg. 348
CHEVRON CANADA RESOURCES LIMITED—Chevron Corporation; U.S. Public, pg. 348
CHEVRON CORPORATION; U.S. Public, pg. 347
CHEVRON OIL COMPANY OF NETHERLANDS—Chevron Corporation; U.S. Public, pg. 348
CHEVRON OVERSEAS PETROLEUM, INC.—Chevron Corporation; U.S. Public, pg. 348
CHEVRON PETROLEUM COMPANY OF COLOMBIA—Chevron Corporation; U.S. Public, pg. 348
CHEVRON STANDARD LIMITED—Chevron Corporation; U.S. Public, pg. 348
CHEVRON (U.K.) LTD.—Chevron Corporation; U.S. Public, pg. 348
CHEVRON U.S.A. INC.—Chevron Corporation; U.S. Public, pg. 348
CHIEFTAIN DEVELOPMENT CO. LTD.—Alberta Energy Company, Ltd.; Int'l, pg. 49
CLEARWAYS DRILLING (M) SDN BHD—Atwood Oceanics, Inc.; U.S. Public, pg. 146
COASTAL OIL & GAS CORP.—The Coastal Corporation; U.S. Public, pg. 390
COLONIAL DRILLING & EXPLORATION CORPORATION—Colonial Oil Industries; U.S. Private, pg. 254
COMPAGNIE FRANCAISE DES PETROLES (ALGERIE) CFP (A)—Total S.A.; Int'l, pg. 1409
COMPAGNIE GENERALE DE GEOPHYSIQUE—CGG Group; Int'l, pg. 241
COMPRESSOR SYSTEMS, INC.—Pearson plc; Int'l, pg. 1027
CONOCO INC.—Du Pont (E.I. Du Pont De Nemours & Co.); U.S. Public, pg. 531
CONOCO NORWAY, INC.—Du Pont (E.I. Du Pont De Nemours & Co.); U.S. Public, pg. 531
CONOCO (UK) LTD.—Du Pont (E.I. Du Pont De Nemours & Co.); U.S. Public, pg. 531
CONTINENTAL NETHERLANDS OIL COMPANY—Du Pont (E.I. Du Pont De Nemours & Co.); U.S. Public, pg. 532
COORS ENERGY CO.—Adolph Coors Company; U.S. Public, pg. 446
DDD ENERGY—Seitel, Inc.; U.S. Public, pg. 1454
DATATEL, INC.—Seitel, Inc.; U.S. Public, pg. 1454
DAWSON GEOPHYSICAL COMPANY; U.S. Public, pg. 489
DELHI PETROLEUM PTY. LTD.—Exxon Corporation; U.S. Public, pg. 601
DELMARVA ENERGY COMPANY—Conectiv; U.S. Public, pg. 431
DELMARVA INDUSTRIES, INC.—Conectiv; U.S. Public, pg. 431
DEUTSCHE SHELL AG—Royal Dutch/Shell Group of Companies; Int'l, pg. 1138
DEVON ENERGY CORPORATION; U.S. Public, pg. 503
DOMINION ENERGY, INC.—Dominion Resources, Inc.; U.S. Public, pg. 516
DRESSER INDUSTRIES, INC.; U.S. Public, pg. 528
DRILLERS INC.—Grey Wolf, Inc.; U.S. Public, pg. 765
DUBAI PETROLEUM COMPANY—Du Pont (E.I. Du Pont De Nemours & Co.); U.S. Public, pg. 533
EVI, INC.; U.S. Public, pg. 547
EAGLE OCEANICS, INC.—Atwood Oceanics, Inc.; U.S. Public, pg. 146
EASTEX ENERGY INC.—El Paso Natural Gas Co.; U.S. Public, pg. 567
ELF AQUITAINE ANGOLA—Elf Aquitane; Int'l, pg. 444
ELF AQUITANE; Int'l, pg. 444
ELF EXPLORATION INC.—Elf Aquitane; Int'l, pg. 445
ELF IDROCARBURI ITALIANA SPA—Elf Aquitane; Int'l, pg. 446
ELF NIGERIA—Elf Aquitane; Int'l, pg. 446
ENERGY COMPANIES OF ONEOK—ONEOK Inc.; U.S. Public, pg. 1226
ENERGY WEST INC.; U.S. Public, pg. 581
ENERGY WEST RESOURCES—Energy West Inc.; U.S. Public, pg. 581
ENGLEKIRK & SABOL, INC.—Robert Englekirk, Inc.; U.S. Private, pg. 377
ENSCO INTERNATIONAL INCORPORATED (ENSCO); U.S. Public, pg. 585
EQUIPMENT LEASING LIMITED—Halliburton Company; U.S. Public, pg. 776
ESSO AUSTRALIA RESOURCES LTD.—Exxon Corporation; U.S. Public, pg. 602
ESSO EXPLORATION AND PRODUCTION UK LIMITED—Exxon Corporation; U.S. Public, pg. 602
ESSO PRODUCTION MALAYSIA INC.—Exxon Corporation; U.S. Public, pg. 602
EXPLORATION & PRODUCTION DIVISION—Mobil Oil Corporation; U.S. Public, pg. 1118
EXSOL, INC.—Seitel, Inc.; U.S. Public, pg. 1454
EXXON CORPORATION; U.S. Public, pg. 601
EXXON EXPLORATION COMPANY—Exxon Corporation; U.S. Public, pg. 601
EXXON YEMEN INC.—Exxon Corporation; U.S. Public, pg. 601
FAIRFIELD INDUSTRIES, INC.—Fairfield Maxwell Ltd.; U.S. Private, pg. 391
FINA EXPLORATION LTD.—Petrofina S.A.; Int'l, pg. 1044
FINA PETROLEOS DE ANGOLA, S.A.R.L.—Petrofina S.A.; Int'l, pg. 1044
FINA RESEARCH S.A.—Petrofina S.A.; Int'l, pg. 1043
FLETCHER CHALLENGE LIMITED; Int'l, pg. 494
FLETCHER CHALLENGE PETROLEUM INC.—Fletcher Challenge Limited; Int'l, pg. 495
FLETCHER CHALLENGE PETROLEUM LIMITED—Fletcher Challenge Limited; Int'l, pg. 495
FORASOL S.A.; Int'l, pg. 496
FORWEST INC.—Forasol S.A.; Int'l, pg. 496
FUGRO GROUP COMPANIES; U.S. Private, pg. 430
GCO MINERALS CO.—International Paper Company; U.S. Public, pg. 902
GSI DE MEXICO S.A. DE C.V.—Halliburton Company; U.S. Public, pg. 776
GEOREX INC.—CGG Group; Int'l, pg. 241
GEOSISMO S.A.—Halliburton Company; U.S. Public, pg. 777
GEOSOURCE CO. (CAYMAN) LTD.—Halliburton Company; U.S. Public, pg. 777
GEOSOURCE INDUSTRIA E COMMERCIO LTDA.—Halliburton Company; U.S. Public, pg. 777
GEOSOURCE INTERNATIONAL (NEDERLAND) B.V.—Halliburton Company; U.S. Public, pg. 777
GEOSOURCE NIGERIA LTD.—Halliburton Company; U.S. Public, pg. 777
GEOSOURCE S.A.R.L.—Halliburton Company; U.S. Public, pg. 777
GEOSOURCE U.K. LIMITED—Halliburton Company; U.S. Public, pg. 777
GREY WOLF, INC.; U.S. Public, pg. 765
HS RESOURCES; U.S. Public, pg. 772
HALLIBURTON SERVICES, LTD.—Halliburton Company; U.S. Public, pg. 777
HANNA HAMILTON HOLDINGS CO.—M.A. Hanna Company; U.S. Public, pg. 781
HARKEN ENERGY CORPORATION; U.S. Public, pg. 785
HELM RESOURCES INC.; U.S. Public, pg. 808
HOLLY PETROLEUM, INC.—Holly Corporation; U.S. Public, pg. 830
HUNT OIL COMPANY; U.S. Private, pg. 548
HUSKY OIL LTD.; Int'l, pg. 640
IMPERIAL OIL LIMITED—Exxon Corporation; U.S. Public, pg. 602
INDUSTRIAL EQUITY LIMITED; Int'l, pg. 676
INEXCO OIL COMPANY—Burlington Resources Inc.; U.S. Public, pg. 269
INSTITUTIONAL SERVICES, INC.—Snyder Oil Corporation; U.S. Public, pg. 1482
KENNEDY & MITCHELL, INC.—Harken Energy Corporation; U.S. Public, pg. 785
KEPEC RESOURCES LIMITED—Empire Company Limited; Int'l, pg. 454
KEY ENERGY GROUP INC.; U.S. Public, pg. 953
KEY PRODUCTION COMPANY, INC.; U.S. Public, pg. 953
KUWAIT FOREIGN PETROLEUM EXPLORATION CO. KSC—Kuwait Petroleum Corporation; Int'l, pg. 765
KUWAIT OIL COMPANY K.S.C.—Kuwait Petroleum Corporation; Int'l, pg. 765
KUWAIT PETROLEUM CORPORATION; Int'l, pg. 764
LGS ENERGY CORP.—Citizens Utilities Company; U.S. Public, pg. 380
LGS EXPLORATION, INC.—Citizens Utilities Company; U.S. Public, pg. 380
LL&E (UK) INC.—Burlington Resources Inc.; U.S. Public, pg. 269
L.S. HOLDING COMPANY—Cigna Corp.; U.S. Public, pg. 358
LASMO AMERICA INC.—LASMO plc; Int'l, pg. 804
LASMO PLC; Int'l, pg. 803
LOMAK OPERATING COMPANY—Lomak Petroleum Inc.; U.S. Public, pg. 1012
LOMAK PETROLEUM INC.; U.S. Public, pg. 1012
MAGUIRE OIL CO.; U.S. Private, pg. 696
MAPCO INC.; U.S. Public, pg. 1042
MARBLEHEAD ENERGY CORP.—Eaton Vance Corp.; U.S. Public, pg. 559
MAYNARD OIL CO.; U.S. Public, pg. 1064
MERIDIAN OIL HOLDING INC.—Burlington Resources Inc.; U.S. Public, pg. 269
THE MERIDIAN RESOURCE CORPORATION; U.S. Public, pg. 1095
MITSUBISHI OIL CO. LTD.; Int'l, pg. 876
MOBIL EXPLORATION NORWAY, INC.—Mobil Oil Corporation; U.S. Public, pg. 1119
MOBIL NORTH SEA LIMITED—Mobil Oil Corporation; U.S. Public, pg. 1119
MOBIL OIL CORPORATION; U.S. Public, pg. 1118
MOBIL PRODUCING NIGERIA—Mobil Oil Corporation; U.S. Public, pg. 1119
MOBILE OIL INDONESIA, INC.—Mobil Oil Corporation; U.S. Public, pg. 1119
MOBILE PRODUCING NETHERLANDS INCORPORATED—Mobil Oil Corporation; U.S. Public, pg. 1119
MORRISON NUCLEAR, INC.—Morrison Petroleums Ltd.; Int'l, pg. 895
MORRISON PETROLEUMS LTD.; Int'l, pg. 895
NEDDRILL NEDERLAND B.V.—Royal Nedlloyd Group N.V.; Int'l, pg. 1144
NEDLLOYD ENERGY B.V.—Royal Nedlloyd Group N.V.; Int'l, pg. 1144
NJR ENERGY SERVICES CORPORATION—New Jersey Resources Corporation; U.S. Public, pg. 1172
A/S NORSKE SHELL—Royal Dutch/Shell Group of Companies; Int'l, pg. 1139
OCCIDENTAL OIL & GAS CORPORATION—Occidental Petroleum Corporation; U.S. Public, pg. 1210
ONEOK INC.; U.S. Public, pg. 1226
ONEOK RESOURCES CO.—ONEOK Inc.; U.S. Public, pg. 1226
OPICOIL HOUSTON, INC.—Chinese Petroleum Corporation; Int'l, pg. 286
PACIFIC LIGHTING GAS DEVELOPMENT CO.—Pacific Enterprises; U.S. Public, pg. 1249
PATTERSON DRILLING CO.—Patterson Energy, Inc.; U.S. Public, pg. 1265
PATTERSON ENERGY, INC.; U.S. Public, pg. 1265
PETRO-CANADA; Int'l, pg. 1041
PETRO-HUNT CORPORATION; U.S. Private, pg. 858
PETROBRAS INTERNACIONAL S.A. (BRASPETRO)—Petrobras - Petroleo Brasileiro S.A.; Int'l, pg. 1042
PETROBRAS - PETROLEO BRASILEIRO S.A.; Int'l, pg. 1041
PETROCORP EXPLORATION LIMITED—Fletcher Challenge Limited; Int'l, pg. 495
PETROFIELDS EXPLORATION & DEVELOPMENT CO., INC.—Benguet Corporation; Int'l, pg. 187
PETROFINA S.A.; Int'l, pg. 1043
PETROLEOS DE VENEZUELA S.A.; Int'l, pg. 1045
PETROLEOS MEXICANOS; Int'l, pg. 1046
PETROLEUM DRILLING SERVICES COLUMBIA PTY., LTD.—Halliburton Company; U.S. Public, pg. 777
PETROLEUM INC.; U.S. Private, pg. 858
PLAZA RESOURCES COMPANY—Berkshire Hathaway Inc.; U.S. Public, pg. 220
POGO PRODUCING COMPANY, INTERNATIONAL DIVISION—Pogo Producing Company; U.S. Public, pg. 1313
POGO PRODUCING COMPANY, ONSHORE DIVISION—Pogo Producing Company; U.S. Public, pg. 1313
PRAKLA-SEISMOS AG—Schlumberger Limited; U.S. Public, pg. 1439
PRODUCTION MANAGEMENT COMPANIES, INC.; U.S. Private, pg. 888
QUINTANA PETROLEUM CORP.; U.S. Private, pg. 901
QUINTANA PETROLEUM SERVICES—Quintana Petroleum Corp.; U.S. Private, pg. 901
R.I. DEVELOPMENT & EXPLORATION CO.—Valley Resources, Inc.; U.S. Public, pg. 1706
RANGER OIL LIMITED; Int'l, pg. 1086
ROYAL DUTCH/SHELL GROUP OF COMPANIES; Int'l, pg. 1135
SNC - AKER OFFSHORE INC. (AE)—Aker Raj Asa; Int'l, pg. 42
SAGE ENERGY COMPANY; U.S. Public, pg. 1426
SANTA FE INTERNATIONAL CORPORATION—Kuwait Petroleum Corporation; Int'l, pg. 765
SASOL LIMITED; Int'l, pg. 1196
SCEPTRE RESOURCES LIMITED; Int'l, pg. 1203
SEITEL DATA CORP.—Seitel, Inc.; U.S. Public, pg. 1454
SEITEL GAS & ENERGY CORP.—Seitel, Inc.; U.S. Public, pg. 1454
SEITEL GEOPHYSICAL, INC. DBA EAGLE GEOPHYSICAL, INC.—Seitel, Inc.; U.S. Public, pg. 1454
SEITEL, INC.; U.S. Public, pg. 1454
SEITEL INTERNATIONAL, INC.—Seitel, Inc.; U.S. Public, pg. 1454
SEITEL OFFSHORE CORP.—Seitel, Inc.; U.S. Public, pg. 1454
SENSORE NEDERLAND B.V.—Halliburton Company; U.S. Public, pg. 777
SENSORE S.A.—Halliburton Company; U.S. Public, pg. 777
SHELL CANADA LTD.—Royal Dutch/Shell Group of Companies; Int'l, pg. 1138
SHELL D'EXPLORATION—Royal Dutch/Shell Group of Companies; Int'l, pg. 1137
SHELL FRANCAISE—Royal Dutch/Shell Group of Companies; Int'l, pg. 1138
SHELL INTERNATIONAL PETROLEUM CO. LTD.—Royal Dutch/Shell Group of Companies; Int'l, pg. 1139
SHELL IVOIRIENNE—Royal Dutch/Shell Group of Companies; Int'l, pg. 1137
SHELL TCHADIENNE—Royal Dutch/Shell Group of Companies; Int'l, pg. 1137
SHELL TUNISIENNE—Royal Dutch/Shell Group of Companies; Int'l, pg. 1137
SHELL WINNING NV—Royal Dutch/Shell Group of Companies; Int'l, pg. 1140
SHIN NISHI NIHON—Royal Dutch/Shell Group of Companies; Int'l, pg. 1140
SIMON-DIASOL—Simon Engineering plc; Int'l, pg. 1251
SIMON PETROLEUM TECHNOLOGY LTD.—Simon Engineering plc; Int'l, pg. 1251
SMITH INTERNATIONAL, INC.; U.S. Public, pg. 1478
SONAT EXPLORATION GOM INC.—Sonat Inc.; U.S. Public, pg. 1485
SOUTHERN MINERAL CORPORATION; U.S. Public, pg. 1490
P.T. STANVAC INDONESIA—Exxon Corporation; U.S. Public, pg. 603
SWENCO-WESTERN, INC.—Swift Energy Company; U.S. Public, pg. 1543
SWIFT ENERGY COMPANY; U.S. Public, pg. 1543

SWIFTDRILL, INC.—Atwood Oceanics, Inc.; U.S. Public, pg. 146
SYRIA SHELL PETROLEUM DEVELOPMENT BV—Royal Dutch/Shell Group of Companies; Int'l, pg. 1141
TALISMAN ENERGY (U.K.) LIMITED—Talisman Energy Inc.; Int'l, pg. 1352
TECHNIP; Int'l, pg. 1360
TENNECO UNITED KINGDOM, INC.—Tenneco Inc.; U.S. Public, pg. 1580
TESORO BOLIVIA PETROLEUM COMPANY—Tesoro Petroleum Corporation; U.S. Public, pg. 1582
TESORO PETROLEUM CORPORATION; U.S. Public, pg. 1581
TEXACO INC.; U.S. Public, pg. 1582
THAI SHELL EXPLORATION & PRODUCTION, CO. LTD.—Royal Dutch/Shell Group of Companies; Int'l, pg. 1140
TOTAL HOLDINGS (AUSTRALIA) PTY. LTD.—Total S.A.; Int'l, pg. 1409
TOTAL INDONESIE—Total S.A.; Int'l, pg. 1409
TOTAL MARINE EXPLOITATIE N.V.-TME—Total S.A.; Int'l, pg. 1409
TOTAL NORGE AS—Total S.A.; Int'l, pg. 1409
TOTAL OIL MARINE P.L.C.-TOM—Total S.A.; Int'l, pg. 1409
TOTAL PETROLEUM CANADA LTD.—Total S.A.; Int'l, pg. 1409
TOTAL S.A.; Int'l, pg. 1408
TRIANGLE GEOPHYSICAL CO.—Helm Resources Inc.; U.S. Public, pg. 808
TRITON COLUMBIA, INC.—Triton Energy Limited; U.S. Public, pg. 1640
TRITON ENERGY LIMITED; U.S. Public, pg. 1640
TRITON OIL CO. OF THAILAND (BANGKOK)—Triton Energy Limited; U.S. Public, pg. 1640
UNION PACIFIC RESOURCES COMPANY (UPRC)—Union Pacific Corporation; U.S. Public, pg. 1668
UNIT CORPORATION; U.S. Public, pg. 1672
VARCO INTERNATIONAL, INC.; U.S. Public, pg. 1709
VEBA OEL AG—Veba AG; Int'l, pg. 1460
VULCAN OIL & GAS COMPANY—Atrion Corporation; U.S. Public, pg. 146
WAHKIAKUM GAS CORPORATION—Boise Cascade Corporation; U.S. Public, pg. 243
WESTERN ATLAS INC.; U.S. Public, pg. 1757
WESTERN ATLAS INTERNATIONAL, INC.—Western Atlas Inc.; U.S. Public, pg. 1757
WESTERN GEOPHYSICAL—Western Atlas Inc.; U.S. Public, pg. 1757
WESTIM RESOURCES LTD.—EdperBrascan Corporation; Int'l, pg. 435
WILLIAMS FIELD SERVICES—The Williams Companies, Inc.; U.S. Public, pg. 1769
WILSHIRE OIL OF CANADA, LTD.—Wilshire Oil Co. of Texas; U.S. Public, pg. 1770
WINTERSHALL CANADA LTD.—BASF AG; Int'l, pg. 110
WINTERSHALL ERDGAS BETEILIGUNGS GMBH—BASF AG; Int'l, pg. 105
WINTERSHALL ERDGAS HANDELSHAUS GMBH—BASF AG; Int'l, pg. 105
WINTERSHALL NEDERLAND B.V.—BASF AG; Int'l, pg. 110
WINTERSHALL NOORDZEE B.V—BASF AG; Int'l, pg. 110
WINTERSHALL OIL AG—BASF AG; Int'l, pg. 110
WINTERSHALL PETROLEUM IBERIA S.A.—BASF AG; Int'l, pg. 110
THE WISER OIL COMPANY; U.S. Public, pg. 1773
WOODSIDE OFFSHORE PETROLEUM PTY. LTD.—Royal Dutch/Shell Group of Companies; Int'l, pg. 1137
WOODSIDE PETROLEUM LTD.—Royal Dutch/Shell Group of Companies; Int'l, pg. 1137
YALE E KEY, INC.—Key Energy Group Inc.; U.S. Public, pg. 953

1389 — OIL & GAS FIELD SERVICES, NEC

AKER RAJ ASA; Int'l, pg. 41
ALAMCO-DELAWARE, INC.—Columbia Energy Group; U.S. Public, pg. 403
ALBERTA ENERGY COMPANY, LTD.; Int'l, pg. 48
AMBAR, INC.—The Beacon Group; U.S. Private, pg. 126
ARROW OILFIELD SERVICE COMPANY—Texas Pacific Group; U.S. Private, pg. 1078
ATWOOD DEEP SEAS, LTD.—Cigna Corp.; U.S. Public, pg. 358
ATWOOD FALCON I, LTD.—Cigna Corp.; U.S. Public, pg. 358
BEB ERDGAS UND ERDOEL GMBH—Exxon Corporation; U.S. Public, pg. 601
BJ SERVICES COMPANY; U.S. Public, pg. 161
BJ-TITAN SERVICES COMPANY (PARTNERSHIP)—Baker Hughes Incorporated; U.S. Public, pg. 166
BPB INDUSTRIES PLC; Int'l, pg. 122
BAKER HUGHES DRILLING TECHNOLOGIES—Baker Hughes Incorporated; U.S. Public, pg. 166
BAKER HUGHES INCORPORATED; U.S. Public, pg. 165
BAKER/MO SERVICES, INC.—Michael Baker Corporation; U.S. Public, pg. 168
BAKER/OTS INTERNATIONAL LTD.—Michael Baker Corporation; U.S. Public, pg. 168
BAKER PETROLITE CORPORATION—Baker Hughes Incorporated; U.S. Public, pg. 166
BARBER INDUSTRIES INC.; Int'l, pg. 164
BARBER INDUSTRIES LTD.-SERVICE CENTER—Barber Industries Inc.; Int'l, pg. 164
BELDEN & BLAKE CORPORATION—Texas Pacific Group; U.S. Private, pg. 1078
BLACK HILLS CORPORATION; U.S. Public, pg. 235
D.H. BLATTNER & SONS, INC.; U.S. Private, pg. 148
JOHN BROWN E & C CORPORATE OFFICES (U.S.)—Kvaerner a.s.a.; Int'l, pg. 774
BURRO PIPELINE CORP.—Tipperary Corporation; U.S. Public, pg. 1618
CALTEX PETROLEUM CORPORATION—Chevron Corporation; U.S. Public, pg. 348
CALTEX PETROLEUM CORPORATION—Texaco Inc.; U.S. Public, pg. 1583
CAMCO INTERNATIONAL INC.; U.S. Public, pg. 297
CAMCO INTERNATIONAL INC.—Camco International Inc.; U.S. Public, pg. 298
CHEVRON CANADA LIMITED—Chevron Corporation; U.S. Public, pg. 348
CHEVRON CANADA RESOURCES LIMITED—Chevron Corporation; U.S. Public, pg. 348
CHEVRON OIL COMPANY OF NETHERLANDS—Chevron Corporation; U.S. Public, pg. 348
CHEVRON PETROLEUM COMPANY OF COLOMBIA—Chevron Corporation; U.S. Public, pg. 348
CHEVRON STANDARD LIMITED—Chevron Corporation; U.S. Public, pg. 348
CHEVRON (U.K.) LTD.—Chevron Corporation; U.S. Public, pg. 348
COMPANIA HALLIBOURTON DE CEMENTACION—Halliburton Company; U.S. Public, pg. 776
COMPUTALOG LTD.; Int'l, pg. 325
CONOCO—Du Pont (E.I. Du Pont De Nemours & Co.); U.S. Public, pg. 531
CORE LABORATORIES-CANADA LTD.—Litton Industries, Inc.; U.S. Public, pg. 1004
DELHI PETROLEUM PTY. LTD.—Exxon Corporation; U.S. Public, pg. 601
DIAMOND OFFSHORE DRILLING, INC.—Loews Corporation; U.S. Public, pg. 1011
DOWELL SCHLUMBERGER CANADA INC.—Schlumberger Limited; U.S. Public, pg. 1439
DOWNHOLE SEISMIC SERVICES—Litton Industries, Inc.; U.S. Public, pg. 1003
DRESSER INDUSTRIES, INC.; U.S. Public, pg. 528
EASTERN OIL WELL SERVICES—PrimeEnergy Corporation; U.S. Public, pg. 1329
EASTEX ENERGY INC.—El Paso Natural Gas Co.; U.S. Public, pg. 567
EBASCO SERVICES OF CANADA LIMITED—Texas Utilities Company; U.S. Public, pg. 1587
EDISON S.P.A.—Compart SpA; Int'l, pg. 324
ENERFLEX LEASING—Toromont Industries Ltd.; Int'l, pg. 1400
EXPLORATION COMPUTING LIMITED—Halliburton Company; U.S. Public, pg. 776
EXXON EXPLORATION COMPANY—Exxon Corporation; U.S. Public, pg. 601
FORASOL S.A.; Int'l, pg. 496
FORATEX INC.—Forasol S.A.; Int'l, pg. 496
FOREST OIL CORPORATION; U.S. Public, pg. 670
GO INTERNATIONAL DE ARGENTINA S.A.—Halliburton Company; U.S. Public, pg. 776
GO INTERNATIONAL DE VENEZUELA, S.A.—Halliburton Company; U.S. Public, pg. 776
GO INTERNATIONAL SERVICES ELECTRO-DIGITAL DE BRAZIL, LTDA.—Halliburton Company; U.S. Public, pg. 776
GO INTERNATIONAL SOUTH AMERICA, S.A.—Halliburton Company; U.S. Public, pg. 776
GO WELL SERVICES, INC.—Halliburton Company; U.S. Public, pg. 776
GEARHART AUSTRALIA LIMITED—Halliburton Company; U.S. Public, pg. 776
GEARHART FRANCE S.A.R.L.—Halliburton Company; U.S. Public, pg. 776
GEARHART GEO CONSULTANTS LIMITED—Halliburton Company; U.S. Public, pg. 776
GEARHART GEODATA SERVICES (OVERSEAS) LIMITED—Halliburton Company; U.S. Public, pg. 776
GEARHART (MALAYSIA) SDN. BHD.—Halliburton Company; U.S. Public, pg. 776
GEARHART M.E. HOLDINGS, INC.—Halliburton Company; U.S. Public, pg. 776
GEARHART MIDDLE EAST S.A.—Halliburton Company; U.S. Public, pg. 776
GEARHART NIGERIA LIMITED—Halliburton Company; U.S. Public, pg. 776
GEARHART TESEL LIMITED—Halliburton Company; U.S. Public, pg. 776
GEARHART WEST AFRICA S.A.—Halliburton Company; U.S. Public, pg. 776
GEARHART WIRELINE SERVICES, LTD.—Halliburton Company; U.S. Public, pg. 776
GEODESY (GEODES)—Petrobras - Petroleo Brasileiro S.A.; Int'l, pg. 1041
GEOREX INC.—CGG Group; Int'l, pg. 241
GLOBAL INDUSTRIES, LTD.; U.S. Public, pg. 748
GLOBAL PIPELINE SURVEYS—T.D. Williamson, Inc.; U.S. Private, pg. 1180
GOINBRAS INDUSTRIA E COMERCIA DO BRASIL, LTDA.—Halliburton Company; U.S. Public, pg. 777
HCW OIL INCOME FUND (DEVONIAN)—Cigna Corp.; U.S. Public, pg. 361
HALLIBURTON ARGENTINA S.A.—Halliburton Company; U.S. Public, pg. 777
HALLIBURTON COMPANY; U.S. Public, pg. 775
HALLIBURTON COMPANY GERMANY GMBH—Halliburton Company; U.S. Public, pg. 777
HALLIBURTON DE MEXICO S.A. DE C.V.—Halliburton Company; U.S. Public, pg. 777
HALLIBURTON ENERGY SERVICES—Halliburton Company; U.S. Public, pg. 776
HALLIBURTON ENERGY SERVICES, INC.—Halliburton Company; U.S. Public, pg. 776
HALLIBURTON ITALIANA S.P.A—Halliburton Company; U.S. Public, pg. 777
HALLIBURTON NIGERIA LTD.—Halliburton Company; U.S. Public, pg. 777
HALLIBURTON SERVICES, LTD.—Halliburton Company; U.S. Public, pg. 777
HALLIBURTON TRINIDAD LTD.—Halliburton Company; U.S. Public, pg. 777
HUSKY OIL LTD.; Int'l, pg. 640
ICO, INC.; U.S. Public, pg. 853
IDEMITSU KOSAN CO., LTD.; Int'l, pg. 659
INDIAN OIL CORPORATION LIMITED; Int'l, pg. 673
INTAIRDRIL LTD.—Pool Energy Services Co.; U.S. Public, pg. 1316
INTERNATIONAL SEA DRILLING LTD.—Pool Energy Services Co.; U.S. Public, pg. 1316
INTERNATIONAL WIRE LINE SERVICES, INC.—Halliburton Company; U.S. Public, pg. 777
KVAERNER INSTALLASJON A.S.—Kvaerner a.s.a.; Int'l, pg. 769
LARCOM INSURANCE COMPANY, LTD.—Pride International, Inc.; U.S. Public, pg. 1325
LIQUID ENERGY CORPORATION—Mitchell Energy & Development Corp.; U.S. Public, pg. 1117
LUBRICANTES Y TAMBORES DEL ECUADOR, C.A.—Texaco Inc.; U.S. Public, pg. 1584
M-I L.L.C.—Halliburton Company; U.S. Public, pg. 776
M-I L.L.C.—Smith International, Inc.; U.S. Public, pg. 1478
MARK RESOURCES INC.; Int'l, pg. 842
MATHESON GAS PRODUCTS, INC.—Nippon Sanso Corporation; Int'l, pg. 938
MESA OPERATING LIMITED PARTNERSHIP (MOLP)—Pioneer Natural Resources Co.; U.S. Public, pg. 1300
MILCHEM CANADA LTD.—Baker Hughes Incorporated; U.S. Public, pg. 167
MOBIL OIL CORPORATION; U.S. Public, pg. 1118
MOBIL OIL LIBERIA INCORPORATED—Mobil Oil Corporation; U.S. Public, pg. 1119
MOBIL OIL OY A.B.—Mobil Oil Corporation; U.S. Public, pg. 1119
MOBIL OIL SIERRA LEONE LIMITED—Mobil Oil Corporation; U.S. Public, pg. 1119
MOBIL OIL THAILAND LIMITED—Mobil Oil Corporation; U.S. Public, pg. 1119
NABORS INDUSTRIES, INC.; U.S. Public, pg. 1148
NANA REGIONAL CORPORATION, INC.; U.S. Private, pg. 774
NEWPARK RESOURCES, INC.; U.S. Public, pg. 1179
NOBLE OFFSHORE CORPORATION—Noble Drilling Corporation; U.S. Public, pg. 1186
NORTH AMERICAN SALT COMPANY—Harris Chemical Group, Inc.; U.S. Private, pg. 505
NOWSCO WELL SERVICE LTD.; Int'l, pg. 989
OCEANEERING A/S—Oceaneering International, Inc.; U.S. Public, pg. 1211
OCEANEERING AUSTRALIA PTY. LTD.—Brambles Industries Limited; Int'l, pg. 211
OCEANEERING AUSTRALIA PTY. LTD.—Oceaneering International, Inc.; U.S. Public, pg. 1211
OCEANEERING INTERNATIONAL, INC.; U.S. Public, pg. 1211
OCEANEERING INTERVENTION ENGINEERING—Oceaneering International, Inc.; U.S. Public, pg. 1211
OCEANEERING MULTIFLEX—Oceaneering International, Inc.; U.S. Public, pg. 1211
OCEANEERING PRODUCTION SYSTEMS—Oceaneering International, Inc.; U.S. Public, pg. 1211
OIL MOP, INC.—The Beacon Group; U.S. Private, pg. 126
OIL PATCH & INDUSTRIAL SERVICES, LTD.—ABB Asea Brown Boveri (Holding) Ltd.; Int'l, pg. 6
OREGON NATURAL GAS DEVELOPMENT CORP.—Northwest Natural Gas Company; U.S. Public, pg. 1200
OTIS ENGINEERING INTERNATIONAL—Halliburton Company; U.S. Public, pg. 777
OTIS INTERNATIONAL, LTD.—Halliburton Company; U.S. Public, pg. 777
OTIS NIGERIA, LTD.—Halliburton Company; U.S. Public, pg. 777
PAMCO DIVISION—Toromont Industries Ltd.; Int'l, pg. 1400
PETROCORP—Cigna Corp.; U.S. Public, pg. 358
PETROCORP EXPLORATION LIMITED—Fletcher Challenge Limited; Int'l, pg. 495
PETROLEUM AUTHORITY OF THAILAND; Int'l, pg. 1046
PETROLEUM DEVELOPMENT CORPORATION; U.S. Public, pg. 1280
PETROLEUM SUPPLY COMPANY—Pride International, Inc.; U.S. Public, pg. 1325
PETROLEUM WORLD—Cleveland Capital Holdings; U.S. Private, pg. 246
PETROLIAM NASIONAL BERHAD (PETRONAS); Int'l, pg. 1046
POOL ARABIA, LTD.—Pool Energy Services Co.; U.S. Public, pg. 1316
POOL ARCTIC ALASKA—Pool Energy Services Co.; U.S. Public, pg. 1316
POOL CALIFORNIA ENERGY SERVICES, INC.—Pool Energy Services Co.; U.S. Public, pg. 1316
POOL COMPANY—Pool Energy Services Co.; U.S. Public, pg. 1316
POOL COMPANY (TEXAS), INC.—Pool Energy Services Co.; U.S. Public, pg. 1316
POOL ENERGY SERVICES CO.; U.S. Public, pg. 1316
POOL INTERNATIONAL ARGENTINA S.A.—Pool Energy Services Co.; U.S. Public, pg. 1316
PRIDE INTERNATIONAL, LTD.—Pride International, Inc.; U.S. Public, pg. 1325
PRIDE OFFSHORE, INC.—Pride International, Inc.; U.S. Public, pg. 1325
PRIMEENERGY CORPORATION; U.S. Public, pg. 1328
PRIMEENERGY MANAGEMENT CORPORATION—PrimeEnergy Corporation; U.S. Public, pg. 1329
PRODUCTION MANAGEMENT COMPANIES, INC.; U.S. Private, pg. 888
PRODUCTION OPERATORS INC.—Camco International Inc.; U.S. Public, pg. 298
PRODUCTION OPERATORS, INC.—Camco International Inc.; U.S. Public, pg. 298
QUESTAR CORPORATION; U.S. Public, pg. 1352
RACAL ELECTRONICS PLC; Int'l, pg. 1082
REFINERIA PANAMA S.A.—Texaco Inc.; U.S. Public, pg. 1584
ROYAL NEDLLOYD GROUP N.V.; Int'l, pg. 1143

ROYSTON LABORATORIES—Chase Corporation; *U.S. Public*, pg. 337
SAFE PARTNERS AB—Celsius AB; *Int'l*, pg. 277
SAFE SERVICE AB—Celsius AB; *Int'l*, pg. 277
SAFE SERVICE LTD.—Celsius AB; *Int'l*, pg. 277
SCHLUMBERGER LIMITED; *U.S. Public*, pg. 1439
SCHLUMBERGER OILFIELD SERVICES—Schlumberger Limited; *U.S. Public*, pg. 1439
SERGAZ S.A. (SOCIETE DE SERVICE DU GAZODUC TRANST.)—ENI S.p.A.; *Int'l*, pg. 429
SERV-TECH, INC.; *U.S. Public*, pg. 1460
SERVICE & SUPPLY CO. OF WEST AFRICA—ABB Asea Brown Boveri (Holding) Ltd.; *Int'l*, pg. 6
SIGNAL HILL SERVICE CENTER—T.D. Williamson, Inc.; *U.S. Private*, pg. 1180
SIME DARBY BERHAD MALAYSIA REGION—Sime Darby Berhad; *Int'l*, pg. 1250
SMITH INTERNATIONAL, INC.; *U.S. Public*, pg. 1478
SOLOCO, INC.—Newpark Resources, Inc.; *U.S. Public*, pg. 1179
SOLUS OCEANEERING (MALAYSIA) SDN. BHD.—Oceaneering International, Inc.; *U.S. Public*, pg. 1211
SOUTHWEST OILFIELD CONSTRUCTION COMPANY—PrimeEnergy Corporation; *U.S. Public*, pg. 1329
SPERRY-SUN DRILLING SERVICES DIVISION—Dresser Industries, Inc.; *U.S. Public*, pg. 528
SUNDOWNER OFFSHORE SERVICES, INC.—Nabors Industries, Inc.; *U.S. Public*, pg. 1149
SUNRISE ENERGY SERVICES, INC.; *U.S. Private*, pg. 1053
TDW SERVICES, INC.—T.D. Williamson, Inc.; *U.S. Private*, pg. 1180
TESEL INTERNATIONAL SERVICES LIMITED—Halliburton Company; *U.S. Public*, pg. 777
TESEL OVERSEAS SERVICES LIMITED—Halliburton Company; *U.S. Public*, pg. 777
TESEL PLC—Halliburton Company; *U.S. Public*, pg. 777
TESEL SERVICES LIMITED—Halliburton Company; *U.S. Public*, pg. 777
TESEL WIRELINE SERVICES LIMITED—Halliburton Company; *U.S. Public*, pg. 777
TETRA TECHNOLOGIES; *U.S. Public*, pg. 1582
TIDEWATER COMPRESSION SERVICE, INC.—Tidewater Inc.; *U.S. Public*, pg. 1608
TIDEWATER PORT JACKSON MARINE PTY. LIMITED—Brambles Industries Limited; *Int'l*, pg. 211
TRANS MOUNTAIN PETROLEUMS LTD.—BC Gas Inc.; *Int'l*, pg. 114
TRANSOK, INC.—Royal Dutch/Shell Group of Companies; *Int'l*, pg. 1136
TRI-CAN PERFORATORS LIMITED—Halliburton Company; *U.S. Public*, pg. 777
TUBOSCOPE INCORPORATED; *U.S. Public*, pg. 1643
TUBOSCOPE VETCO (DEUTCHSLAND)—Tuboscope Incorporated; *U.S. Public*, pg. 1644
WEATHERFORD BIN HAMODAH—Weatherford Enterra Incorporated; *U.S. Public*, pg. 1750
WEATHERFORD ENTERRA INCORPORATED; *U.S. Public*, pg. 1749
WEATHERFORD OIL TOOL (PTE.) LTD.—Weatherford Enterra Incorporated; *U.S. Public*, pg. 1750
WEDGE DIA-LOG—Wedge Energy Group Inc.; *U.S. Private*, *pg. 1158*
WESTERN ATLAS INC.; *U.S. Public*, pg. 1757
WESTERN PRODUCTION COMPANY—Black Hills Corporation; *U.S. Public*, pg. 236
WICOR, INC.; *U.S. Public*, pg. 1767
T.D. WILLIAMSON (U.K.) LTD.—T.D. Williamson, Inc.; *U.S. Private*, pg. 1180
WINSCHERMANN BERLIN GMBH—Saarbergwerke Aktiengesellschaft; *Int'l*, pg. 1167

1411 — DIMENSION STONE

AMISTAD GATHERING CO.—Hanson PLC; *Int'l*, pg. 593
AUTUMN ROSE QUARRY, INC.—Rock of Ages Corporation; *U.S. Public*, pg. 1396
J.E. BAKER CO.; *U.S. Private*, pg. 112
BLUE CIRCLE SOUTHERN CEMENT LIMITED—Boral Limited; *Int'l*, pg. 203
CAROLINA QUARRIES, INC.—Rock of Ages Corporation; *U.S. Public*, pg. 1396
CHEMSTONE CORP.; *U.S. Private*, pg. 233
COLD SPRING GRANITE COMPANY; *U.S. Private*, pg. 250
EMPRESAS ICA SOCIEDAD CONTROLADORA S.A.C.V.; *Int'l*, pg. 454
L.G. EVERIST INC.; *U.S. Private*, pg. 386
THE GEORGIA MARBLE COMPANY; *U.S. Private*, pg. 448
GEORGIA STONE INDUSTRIES, INC.—New England Stone Industries, Inc.; *U.S. Private*, pg. 793
GIFFORD-HILL COMPANY—Hanson PLC; *Int'l*, pg. 593
IDEAL DOMINICANA, S.A.—Holderbank Financiere Glaris Ltd.; *Int'l*, pg. 628
KEYSTONE & CHILDS, INC.—Rock of Ages Corporation; *U.S. Public*, pg. 1396
MISSISSIPPI LIME CO.; *U.S. Private*, pg. 753
NEW ENGLAND STONE INDUSTRIES, INC.; *U.S. Private*, pg. 793
PENNSYLVANIA GRANITE CORP.—Rock of Ages Corporation; *U.S. Public*, pg. 1396
PLUESS-STAUFER AG; *Int'l*, pg. 1061
ROCK OF AGES CANADA, INC.—Rock of Ages Corporation; *U.S. Public*, pg. 1396
ROCK OF AGES CORPORATION; *U.S. Public*, pg. 1396
ZEIDLER & WIMMEL GMBH & CO.—Philipp Holzmann AG; *Int'l*, pg. 633

1422 — CRUSHED & BROKEN LIMESTONE

AMERICAN AGGREGATES CORP.—CSR Limited; *Int'l*, pg. 245
ARKANSAS LIME CO.—United States Lime & Minerals; *U.S. Public*, pg. 1685
ASH GROVE CEMENT COMPANY; *U.S. Private*, pg. 87
ASLAND S.A.—Lafarge S.A.; *Int'l*, pg. 790
BALE OF KENTUCKY, INC.; *U.S. Private*, pg. 112
BARRICK GOLD—Barrick Gold Corporation; *Int'l*, pg. 169
BLUE CIRCLE SOUTHERN CEMENT LIMITED—Boral Limited; *Int'l*, pg. 203
CSR AMERICA INC.—CSR Limited; *Int'l*, pg. 245
CASTLE CONCRETE CO.—Continental Materials Corporation; *U.S. Public*, pg. 441
CHINA HI-MENT CORP.—China Steel Corporation; *Int'l*, pg. 285
CIMENTS FRANCAIS; *Int'l*, pg. 292
CONTINENTAL MATERIALS CORPORATION; *U.S. Public*, *pg. 441*
CORSON LIME COMPANY—United States Lime & Minerals; *U.S. Public*, pg. 1685
DRAVO LIME COMPANY—Dravo Corporation; *U.S. Public*, pg. 527
FEATHERLITE BUILDING PRODUCTS OPERATION—Justin Industries, Inc.; *U.S. Public*, pg. 936
H.G. FENTON MATERIAL COMPANY; *U.S. Private*, pg. 400
FLORIDA CRUSHED STONE COMPANY; *U.S. Private*, pg. 414
FLORIDA ROCK INDUSTRIES, INC.; *U.S. Public*, pg. 655
THE GEORGIA MARBLE COMPANY; *U.S. Private*, pg. 448
A.P. GREEN INDUSTRIES, INC.; *U.S. Public*, pg. 761
HARPER BROS., INC.; *U.S. Private*, pg. 504
HAWAIIAN DREDGING & CONSTRUCTION COMPANY—Dillingham Construction Corporation; *U.S. Private*, pg. 333
HEMPT BROTHERS, INC.; *U.S. Private*, pg. 521
J.M. HUBER, CALCIUM CARBONATE DIVISION—J.M. Huber Corporation; *U.S. Private*, pg. 545
JUSTIN INDUSTRIES, INC.; *U.S. Public*, pg. 936
KETTLE FALLS LIMESTONE COMPANY—Boise Cascade Corporation; *U.S. Public*, pg. 243
LINEAR DYNAMICS INC.; *U.S. Private*, pg. 668
MARTIN MARIETTA AGGREGATES—Lockheed Martin Corporation; *U.S. Public*, pg. 1007
MARTIN MARIETTA MATERIALS, INC.—Lockheed Martin Corporation; *U.S. Public*, pg. 1007
MEDUSA MINERALS CO—Medusa Corporation; *U.S. Public*, pg. 1084
H.B. MELLOTT ESTATE, INC.; *U.S. Private*, pg. 730
MILLVILLE QUARRY INC.—Bardon Group PLC; *Int'l*, pg. 166
OMYA, INC.—Pluess-Staufer AG; *Int'l*, pg. 1061
PCS PHOSPHATE - RALEIGH—Potash Corporation of Saskatchewan Inc.; *Int'l*, pg. 1064
PIONEER INTERNATIONAL LTD.; *Int'l*, pg. 1058
PLUESS-STAUFER AG; *Int'l*, pg. 1061
PLUESS-STAUFER (CALIFORNIA), INC.—Pluess-Staufer AG; *Int'l*, pg. 1061
PLUESS-STAUFER INDUSTRIES, INC.—Pluess-Staufer AG; *Int'l*, pg. 1061
RESCO PRODUCTS, INC.; *U.S. Private*, pg. 924
SCANCEM AB; *Int'l*, pg. 1198
STABLER COMPANIES, INC.; *U.S. Private*, pg. 1028
TARMAC PLC; *Int'l*, pg. 1355
TEXAS LIME CO.—United States Lime & Minerals; *U.S. Public*, pg. 1685
UNION QUARRIES, INC.—Ash Grove Cement Company; *U.S. Private*, pg. 88
UNITED STATES LIME & MINERALS; *U.S. Public*, pg. 1684
VULCAN MATERIALS COMPANY; *U.S. Public*, pg. 1725
ZEIDLER & WIMMEL GMBH & CO.—Philipp Holzmann AG; *Int'l*, pg. 633

1423 — CRUSHED & BROKEN GRANITE

THE ARUNDEL CORPORATION—Florida Rock Industries, Inc.; *U.S. Public*, pg. 656
LOCKHEED MARTIN CORPORATION; *U.S. Public*, pg. 1006
MARTIN MARIETTA AGGREGATES—Lockheed Martin Corporation; *U.S. Public*, pg. 1007
MARTIN MARIETTA MATERIALS, INC.—Lockheed Martin Corporation; *U.S. Public*, pg. 1007
MARYLAND STONE INC.—Florida Rock Industries, Inc.; *U.S. Public*, pg. 656
TARMAC PLC; *Int'l*, pg. 1355
VULCAN MATERIALS COMPANY; *U.S. Public*, pg. 1725
VULCAN MATERIALS COMPANY-MIDEAST DIV.—Vulcan Materials Company; *U.S. Public*, pg. 1725

1429 — CRUSHED & BROKEN STONE, NEC

AMERICAN AGGREGATES CORP.—CSR Limited; *Int'l*, pg. 245
CSR AMERICA INC.—CSR Limited; *Int'l*, pg. 245
ELKEM TANA—Elkem ASA; *Int'l*, pg. 448
GSM—Ciments Francais; *Int'l*, pg. 292
MARTIN MARIETTA AGGREGATES—Lockheed Martin Corporation; *U.S. Public*, pg. 1007
MARTIN MARIETTA MATERIALS, INC.—Lockheed Martin Corporation; *U.S. Public*, pg. 1007
MEDUSA AGGREGATE CO.—Medusa Corporation; *U.S. Public*, pg. 1084
MEDUSA CORPORATION; *U.S. Public*, pg. 1084
NORRKOPINGS SAND AB—Scancem AB; *Int'l*, pg. 1200
SAND & GRUS AB JEHANDER—Scancem AB; *Int'l*, pg. 1200
VULCAN MATERIALS COMPANY; *U.S. Public*, pg. 1725
VULCAN MATERIALS COMPANY-MIDEAST DIV.—Vulcan Materials Company; *U.S. Public*, pg. 1725
ZEIDLER & WIMMEL GMBH & CO.—Philipp Holzmann AG; *Int'l*, pg. 633

1442 — CONSTRUCTION SAND & GRAVEL

APAC HOLDINGS, INC.—Ashland, Inc.; *U.S. Public*, pg. 139
ALLIED CONCRETE, INC.—CalMat Co.; *U.S. Public*, pg. 295
AMERICAN AGGREGATES CORP.—CSR Limited; *Int'l*, pg. 245
AMERON INTERNATIONAL CORPORATION; *U.S. Public*, pg. 98
THE ARUNDEL CORPORATION—Florida Rock Industries, Inc.; *U.S. Public*, pg. 656
AZUSA ROCK, INC.—CalMat Co.; *U.S. Public*, pg. 295
BERKS PRODUCTS CORPORATION; *U.S. Private*, pg. 136
BLUE CIRCLE AGGREGATES, INC.—Blue Circle Industries PLC; *Int'l*, pg. 198
BORAL LIMITED; *Int'l*, pg. 203
BORAL RESOURCES LTD.—Boral Limited; *Int'l*, pg. 203
BRAZOS POINT, INC.—Centex Corporation; *U.S. Public*, pg. 322
CSR AMERICA INC.—CSR Limited; *Int'l*, pg. 245
CX-GRUS—Scancem AB; *Int'l*, pg. 1200
THE CADMAN COMPANIES—Heidelberger Zement A.G.; *Int'l*, pg. 605
CALMAT CO.; *U.S. Public*, pg. 295
CALMAT CO. OF ARIZONA—CalMat Co.; *U.S. Public*, pg. 295
CALMAT OF CENTRAL CALIFORNIA—CalMat Co.; *U.S. Public*, pg. 295
CASTLE CONCRETE CO.—Continental Materials Corporation; *U.S. Public*, pg. 441
CENTRAL ALLIED ENTERPRISES; *U.S. Private*, pg. 222
CONTINENTAL MATERIALS CORPORATION; *U.S. Public*, *pg. 441*
DUFFERIN AGGREGATES—Holderbank Financiere Glaris Ltd.; *Int'l*, pg. 628
GIFFORD-HILL COMPANY—Hanson PLC; *Int'l*, pg. 593
GRAV & SCHAKT VASTERAS AB—Scancem AB; *Int'l*, pg. 1200
GREENHAM CONSTRUCTION MATERIALS LIMITED—Taylor Woodrow plc; *Int'l*, pg. 1358
HC&D DIV.—Ameron International Corporation; *U.S. Public*, *pg. 99*
HECK INDUSTRIES; *U.S. Private*, pg. 519
HIDDEN VALLEY COAL COMPANY—CalMat Co.; *U.S. Public*, pg. 296
K.F. JACOBSON CO.—R.B. Pamplin Corp.; *U.S. Private*, pg. 836
KIRST CONSTRUCTION CO., INC.—CalMat Co.; *U.S. Public*, pg. 296
KNIFE RIVER COAL MINING COMPANY—MDU Resources Group, Inc.; *U.S. Public*, pg. 1025
LAFARGE CONSTRUCTION MATERIALS—Lafarge S.A.; *Int'l*, pg. 788
EDWARD C. LEVY CO.; *U.S. Private*, pg. 664
LOUISIANA INDUSTRIES DIV.—Texas Industries, Inc.; *U.S. Public*, pg. 1585
MDU RESOURCES GROUP, INC.; *U.S. Public*, pg. 1025
MARTIN MARIETTA AGGREGATES—Lockheed Martin Corporation; *U.S. Public*, pg. 1007
MARTIN MARIETTA MATERIALS, INC.—Lockheed Martin Corporation; *U.S. Public*, pg. 1007
MARYLAND ROCK INDUSTRIES, INC.—Florida Rock Industries, Inc.; *U.S. Public*, pg. 656
MATERIAL SERVICE CORP.—General Dynamics Corporation; *U.S. Public*, pg. 709
NORRKOPINGS SAND AB—Scancem AB; *Int'l*, pg. 1200
POLIET—Saint-Gobain; *Int'l*, pg. 1177
REDLAND PLC; *Int'l*, pg. 1090
RINKER MATERIALS CORP.—CSR Limited; *Int'l*, pg. 246
RITCHIE CORPORATION; *U.S. Private*, pg. 933
ROGERS GROUP INC.; *U.S. Private*, pg. 939
ROSS ISLAND SAND & GRAVEL CO., INC.—R.B. Pamplin Corp.; *U.S. Private*, pg. 836
ST. LAWRENCE CEMENT INC.—Holderbank Financiere Glaris Ltd.; *Int'l*, pg. 628
SAND & GRUS AB JEHANDER—Scancem AB; *Int'l*, pg. 1200
SANGER ROCK AND SAND—CalMat Co.; *U.S. Public*, pg. 296
SCANCEM AB; *Int'l*, pg. 1198
SIMURA—Imetal; *Int'l*, pg. 662
JOSEF SKIPIOL STRASSENBAUSTOFFE GMBH & CO. KG—Philipp Holzmann AG; *Int'l*, pg. 633
SLOAN CANYON SAND CO.—CalMat Co.; *U.S. Public*, pg. 296
TEXAS INDUSTRIES, INC.; *U.S. Public*, pg. 1585
THORSTENBERG MATERIALS CO., INC.—Holderbank Financiere Glaris Ltd.; *Int'l*, pg. 628
TRIANGLE ROCKS PRODUCTS, INC.—CalMat Co.; *U.S. Public*, pg. 296
VULCAN MATERIALS COMPANY; *U.S. Public*, pg. 1725
WHIBCO, INC.; *U.S. Private*, pg. 1171
WINSTONE AGGREGATES LIMITED—Fletcher Challenge Limited; *Int'l*, pg. 495
YORK BUILDING PRODUCTS CO., INC.; *U.S. Private*, pg. 1196

1446 — INDUSTRIAL SAND

ACI MILLING PTY. LTD.—BTR plc; *Int'l*, pg. 128
BRADY PLANT—Oglebay Norton Company; *U.S. Public*, pg. 1213
GLASS ROCK PLANT—Oglebay Norton Company; *U.S. Public*, pg. 1213
ISCOR; *Int'l*, pg. 688
MILLWOOD PLANT—Oglebay Norton Company; *U.S. Public*, pg. 1213
OGLEBAY NORTON COMPANY; *U.S. Public*, pg. 1213
WHIBCO, INC.; *U.S. Private*, pg. 1171

1455 — KAOLIN & BALL CLAY

COLONIAL TERMINALS, INC.—Colonial Oil Industries; *U.S. Private*, pg. 254
COMALCO MINERALS & ALUMINA—Comalco Limited; *Int'l*, pg. 307
ENGLISH CHINA CLAYS PLC; *Int'l*, pg. 455
HECLA MINING COMPANY; *U.S. Public*, pg. 803
J.M. HUBER, CLAY DIV.—J.M. Huber Corporation; *U.S. Private*, pg. 545
KENTUCKY-TENNESSEE CLAY CO.—Hecla Mining Company; *U.S. Public*, pg. 804
PIEDMONT MINERALS—Thiele Kaolin Co.; *U.S. Private*, pg. 1081
THIELE KAOLIN CO.; *U.S. Private*, pg. 1081
R.T. VANDERBILT COMPANY, INC.; *U.S. Private*, pg. 1133

1459 — CLAY, CERAMIC & REFRACTORY MINERALS, NEC

AMCOL INTERNATIONAL CORP.; *U.S. Public*, pg. 63
APPLIED INDUSTRIAL MATERIALS CORPORATION—Walter Industries, Inc.; *U.S. Public*, pg. 1736
BENTONE-CHEMIE GMBH—Contran Corporation; *U.S. Private*, pg. 271
ECC INTERNATIONAL LTD.—English China Clays Plc; *Int'l*, *pg. 455*
ENGLISH CHINA CLAYS PLC; *Int'l*, pg. 455
THE FELDSPAR CORP.—Zemex Corporation; *Int'l*, pg. 1523
HECLA MINING COMPANY; *U.S. Public*, pg. 803
HEPWORTH REFRACTORIES LTD.—Hepworth Plc; *Int'l*, pg. 615
KENTUCKY-TENNESSEE CLAY CO.—Hecla Mining Company; *U.S. Public*, pg. 804
MONTANA MINERALS DEVELOPMENT CORP.—AMCOL International Corp.; *U.S. Public*, pg. 64
NANOCOR, INC.—AMCOL International Corp.; *U.S. Public*, pg. 64
OIL-DRI CORPORATION OF AMERICA; *U.S. Public*, pg. 1214
OIL-DRI CORPORATION OF GEORGIA—Oil-Dri Corporation of America; *U.S. Public*, pg. 1215
OIL-DRI PRODUCTION CO.—Oil-Dri Corporation of America; *U.S. Public*, pg. 1215
WESTERN AGGREGATES, INC.—Inco Limited; *Int'l*, pg. 672
ZEMEX CORPORATION; *Int'l*, pg. 1523

1474 — POTASH, SODA & BORATE MINERALS

ELF AQUITAINE, INC.—Elf Aquitane; *Int'l*, pg. 445
ENTREPRISE MINIERE ET CHIMIQUE; *Int'l*, pg. 458
FMC WYOMING CORP.—FMC Corporation; *U.S. Public*, pg. 605
HEPWORTH REFRACTORIES LTD.—Hepworth Plc; *Int'l*, pg. 615
IMC GLOBAL; *U.S. Public*, pg. 856
KALIUM CHEMICALS, LTD.—IMC Global; *U.S. Public*, pg. 856
MISSISSIPPI CHEMICAL CORPORATION; *U.S. Public*, pg. 1117
MISSISSIPPI POTASH. INC.—Mississippi Chemical Corporation; *U.S. Public*, pg. 1117
PCS PHOSPHATE - RALEIGH—Potash Corporation of Saskatchewan Inc.; *Int'l*, pg. 1064
POTASH CORPORATION OF SASKATCHEWAN INC.; *Int'l*, pg. 1064

1475 — PHOSPHATE ROCK

CF INDUSTRIES, INC.; *U.S. Private*, pg. 193
ELF AQUITAINE, INC.—Elf Aquitane; *Int'l*, pg. 445
FREEPORT-MCMORAN INC.; *U.S. Public*, pg. 680
FREEPORT-MCMORAN RESOURCE PARTNERS, LTD.—Freeport-McMoRan Inc.; *U.S. Public*, pg. 681
IMC GLOBAL; *U.S. Public*, pg. 856

1479 — CHEMICAL & FERTILIZER MINERAL MINING, NEC

ANTILLES INTERNATIONAL SALT COMPANY NV—Akzo Nobel N.V.; *Int'l*, pg. 44
H.J. BAKER & BRO., INC.; *U.S. Private*, pg. 112
BARYTINE DE CHAILLAC S.A.—Solvay S.A.; *Int'l*, pg. 1279
CANADIAN BRINE LTD.—Morton International Inc.; *U.S. Public*, pg. 1135
THE CANADIAN SALT CO. LTD.—Morton International Inc.; *U.S. Public*, pg. 1135
CARGILL; *U.S. Private*, pg. 210
CYPRUS AMAX MINERALS COMPANY; *U.S. Public*, pg. 470
DANSK SALT I/S—Akzo Nobel N.V.; *Int'l*, pg. 44
ELF AQUITAINE, INC.—Elf Aquitane; *Int'l*, pg. 445
ESSO MALAYSIA BERHAD—Exxon Corporation; *U.S. Public*, pg. 602
FMC CORP., LITHIUM DIVISION—FMC Corporation; *U.S. Public*, pg. 605
FREEPORT-MCMORAN INC.; *U.S. Public*, pg. 680
FREEPORT-MCMORAN RESOURCE PARTNERS, LTD.—Freeport-McMoRan Inc.; *U.S. Public*, pg. 681
GREEK SALT INDUSTRIAL COMMERCIAL EPE—Akzo Nobel N.V.; *Int'l*, pg. 44
GRUPO INDUSTRIAL CAMESA S.A. DE C.V.; *Int'l*, pg. 575
MORTON INTERNATIONAL INC.; *U.S. Public*, pg. 1134
NORDDEUTSCHE SALINEN GMBH—Akzo Nobel N.V.; *Int'l*, pg. 44
ORIENT MINING COMPANY—Boise Cascade Corporation; *U.S. Public*, pg. 243
PCS PHOSPHATE - RALEIGH—Potash Corporation of Saskatchewan Inc.; *Int'l*, pg. 1064
PENNZOIL COMPANY; *U.S. Public*, pg. 1272
PETROSUL INTERNATIONAL LTD.; *Int'l*, pg. 1046

1481 — NONMETALLIC MINERALS (EXCEPT FUEL) SERVICES

BENGUETCORP CANADA LTD.—Benguet Corporation; *Int'l*, pg. 187
BENGUETCORP. INTERNATIONAL LTD.—Benguet Corporation; *Int'l*, pg. 187
BENGUETCORP U.S.A., INC.—Benguet Corporation; *Int'l*, pg. 187
BOART LONGYEAR PTY. LTD.—Anglo American Corporation of South Africa Limited; *Int'l*, pg. 76
DAVY INTERNATIONAL, SAN FRANCISCO—Kvaerner a.s.a.; *Int'l*, pg. 774
GRANT GEOPHYSICAL INC.; *U.S. Private*, pg. 470
IDAHO ENERGY RESOURCES CO.—Idaho Power Company; *U.S. Public*, pg. 862
M.I.M. HOLDINGS LTD.; *Int'l*, pg. 827
RENISON GOLDFIELDS CONSOLIDATED LIMITED—Hanson PLC; *Int'l*, pg. 595

1499 — MISCELLANEOUS NONMETALLIC MINERALS, EXCEPT FUELS

ACMAT CORPORATION; *U.S. Public*, pg. 16
BPB INDUSTRIES PLC; *Int'l*, pg. 122
BRITISH GYPSUM LTD.—BPB Industries PLC; *Int'l*, pg. 122
CDM (PROPRIETARY) LIMITED—Anglo American Corporation of South Africa Limited; *Int'l*, pg. 77
CRA LIMITED—Rio Tinto PLC; *Int'l*, pg. 1119
CELITE CORPORATION—Alleghany Corporation; *U.S. Public*, pg. 42
CHEVRON CORPORATION; *U.S. Public*, pg. 347
CHRISTENSEN GULF SERVICES (PRIVATE) LIMITED—Saint-Gobain; *Int'l*, pg. 1174
CHRISTENSEN RODER ARGENTINA S.A.—Saint-Gobain; *Int'l*, pg. 1174
CHRISTENSEN RODER PRODUCTOS DIAMANTADOS LTDA.—Saint-Gobain; *Int'l*, pg. 1174
CHRISTENSEN SAUDI ARABIA LIMITED—Saint-Gobain; *Int'l*, pg. 1174
CYPRUS AMAX MINERALS COMPANY; *U.S. Public*, pg. 470
DE BEERS CONSOLIDATED MINES LIMITED—Anglo American Corporation of South Africa Limited; *Int'l*, pg. 76
EASTMAN CHRISTENSEN (CAMEROON) S.A.R.L.—Baker Hughes Incorporated; *U.S. Public*, pg. 167
EASTMAN CHRISTENSEN (CHINA) LIMITED—Baker Hughes Incorporated; *U.S. Public*, pg. 167
EASTMAN CHRISTENSEN DE ESPANA S.A.—Baker Hughes Incorporated; *U.S. Public*, pg. 167
L.G. EVERIST INC.; *U.S. Private*, pg. 386
FISONS WESTERN CORPORATION—Rhone-Poulenc S.A.; *Int'l*, pg. 1111
GARTENHILFE GES.M.B.H.—DSM N.V.; *Int'l*, pg. 356
GREFCO, INC.—RGP Holding, Inc.; *U.S. Private*, pg. 903
GYPSUM INDUSTRIES PLC.—BPB Industries PLC; *Int'l*, pg. 123
HARBORLITE CORPORATION—Alleghany Corporation; *U.S. Public*, pg. 42
HARPER BROS., INC.; *U.S. Private*, pg. 504
HEPWORTH REFRACTORIES LTD.—Hepworth Plc; *Int'l*, pg. 615
HUGHES GROUP; *U.S. Private*, pg. 546
L. ROBERT KIMBALL & ASSOCIATES; *U.S. Private*, pg. 619
LAFARGE CONSTRUCTION MATERIALS—Lafarge S.A.; *Int'l*, pg. 788
M.I.M. HOLDINGS LTD.; *Int'l*, pg. 827
MAPCO INC.; *U.S. Public*, pg. 1042
S.A. MINERACAO DE AMIANTO—Saint-Gobain; *Int'l*, pg. 1171
NYCO MINERALS—Canadian Pacific Limited; *Int'l*, pg. 259
NORD RESOURCES CORPORATION; *U.S. Public*, pg. 1188
OGLEBAY NORTON COMPANY; *U.S. Public*, pg. 1213
THE RTZ CORPORATION PLC—Rio Tinto PLC; *Int'l*, pg. 1118
RESCO PRODUCTS, INC.; *U.S. Private*, pg. 924
RIO TINTO ZIMBABWE LIMITED—Rio Tinto PLC; *Int'l*, pg. 1119
SAARBERG-INTERPLAN GESELLSCHAFT FUER ROHSTOFF-, ENERGIE-UND INGENIEURTECHNIK MBH—Saarbergwerke Aktiengesellschaft; *Int'l*, pg. 1167
SIBEKA—Union Miniere; *Int'l*, pg. 1442
TITANIA A/S—Contran Corporation; *U.S. Private*, pg. 271
R.T. VANDERBILT COMPANY, INC.; *U.S. Private*, pg. 1133
VULCAN MATERIALS COMPANY; *U.S. Public*, pg. 1725
WESTERN MINING CORPORATION HOLDINGS LIMITED; *Int'l*, pg. 1494
YESO PANAMERICANO, S.A. DE C.V.—USG Corporation; *U.S. Public*, pg. 1660
ZIEGLER CHEMICAL & MINERAL CORP.; *U.S. Private*, pg. 1205

1521 — GENERAL CONTRACTORS-SINGLE FAMILY HOUSES

AP TECHNOLOGY MANAGEMENT INC.—Adolfson & Peterson, Inc.; *U.S. Private*, pg. 18
J.R. ABBOTT CONSTRUCTION, INC.; *U.S. Private*, pg. 9
AMREP CORPORATION; *U.S. Public*, pg. 104
AMREP SOUTHWEST, INC.—AMREP Corporation; *U.S. Public*, pg. 104
AOKI CORPORATION; *Int'l*, pg. 78
AOKI CORPORATION—Aoki Corporation; *Int'l*, pg. 78
ARAPILES, S.A.—Vallehermoso, S.A.; *Int'l*, pg. 1447
ATLANTIC HOMES CORP.—The Great Atlantic Management Company; *U.S. Private*, pg. 473
AUSHERMAN CONSTRUCTION COMPANY; *U.S. Private*, pg. 99
BALFOUR BEATTY LIMITED—BICC plc; *Int'l*, pg. 120
BARRATT AMERICAN INC.—Barratt Developments Plc; *Int'l*, pg. 168
BARRATT BRISTOL—Barratt Developments Plc; *Int'l*, pg. 168
BARRATT CENTRAL—Barratt Developments Plc; *Int'l*, pg. 168
BARRATT CHESTER—Barratt Developments Plc; *Int'l*, pg. 168
BARRATT COMMERCIAL—Barratt Developments Plc; *Int'l*, pg. 168
BARRATT CONSTRUCTION—Barratt Developments Plc; *Int'l*, pg. 168
BARRATT DEVELOPMENTS PLC; *Int'l*, pg. 167
BARRATT EAST MIDLANDS—Barratt Developments Plc; *Int'l*, pg. 168
BARRATT LEEDS—Barratt Developments Plc; *Int'l*, pg. 168
BARRATT MANCHESTER—Barratt Developments Plc; *Int'l*, *pg. 168*
BARRATT NEWCASTLE—Barratt Developments Plc; *Int'l*, pg. 168
BARRATT NORTHERN—Barratt Developments Plc; *Int'l*, pg. 168
BARRATT SOUTH WALES—Barratt Developments Plc; *Int'l*, pg. 168
BARRATT SOUTHAMPTON—Barratt Developments Plc; *Int'l*, pg. 168
BARRATT WEST MIDLANDS—Barratt Developments Plc; *Int'l*, pg. 168
BARRATT WEST SCOTLAND—Barratt Developments Plc; *Int'l*, pg. 168
BARRATT YORK—Barratt Developments Plc; *Int'l*, pg. 168
BATI-SERVICE—Kaufman and Broad Home Corporation; *U.S. Public*, pg. 945
BEAZER GROUP PLC; *Int'l*, pg. 181
M.J. BROCK & SONS, INC.—The Ryland Group, Inc.; *U.S. Public*, pg. 1414
BROOKFIELD HOMES—Brookfield Properties Corporation; *Int'l*, pg. 228
BROOKFIELD HOMES LTD.—Brookfield Properties Corporation; *Int'l*, pg. 228
BURNSIDE CONSTRUCTION CO.; *U.S. Private*, pg. 187
BURNSTEAD CONSTRUCTION COMPANY; *U.S. Private*, pg. 187
A.B. CAIRNS LIMITED—Taylor Woodrow plc; *Int'l*, pg. 1359
CARLSBERG FINANCIAL CORP.; *U.S. Private*, pg. 211
CAVALIER HOMES, INC.; *U.S. Public*, pg. 318
CENTENNIAL HOMES INC.—Weyerhaeuser Company; *U.S. Public*, pg. 1764
CENTEX CORPORATION; *U.S. Public*, pg. 322
CENTEX REAL ESTATE CORP./CENTEX HOMES—Centex Corporation; *U.S. Public*, pg. 323
CENTEX-ROONEY CONSTRUCTION CO., INC.—Centex Corporation; *U.S. Public*, pg. 322
CENTRAL PARK SOUTH, INC.—Lennar Corporation; *U.S. Public*, pg. 987
CHIEF INDUSTRIES - HOUSING DIV.—Chief Industries, Inc.; *U.S. Private*, pg. 236
BARTLETT COCKE, INC.; *U.S. Private*, pg. 249
CONTINENTAL HOMES HOLDING CORP.; *U.S. Public*, pg. 440
CONTINENTAL HOMES, INC.—Continental Homes Holding Corp.; *U.S. Public*, pg. 440
COSCAN WATERWAYS, INC.—Brookfield Properties Corporation; *Int'l*, pg. 228
COUNTY & DISTRICT PROPERTIES LIMITED—Costain Group PLC; *Int'l*, pg. 337
COVENTRY HOMES OF COLORADO—Del Webb Corporation; *U.S. Public*, pg. 495
DCA SERVICES, INC.—Lennar Corporation; *U.S. Public*, pg. 988
DARSA GADITANA, S.A.—Telefonica de Espana, S.A.; *Int'l*, *pg. 1372*
DAWSON CONSTRUCTION CO., INC.; *U.S. Private*, pg. 316
DEL WEBB CALIFORNIA CORPORATION—Del Webb Corporation; *U.S. Public*, pg. 495
DESIGN SYSTEMS INC.—AGA AB; *Int'l*, pg. 13
DEVCO OF ORLANDO, INC.—Lennar Corporation; *U.S. Public*, pg. 988
DEVELOPMENT CORP. OF DELRAY, INC.—Lennar Corporation; *U.S. Public*, pg. 988
DOMINION HOMES; *U.S. Public*, pg. 516
DYNAMIC HOMES, INC.; *U.S. Public*, pg. 538
DYNAMIC HOMES OF DAKOTA—Dynamic Homes, Inc.; *U.S. Public*, pg. 539
ELDORADO AT SANTA FE—AMREP Corporation; *U.S. Public*, pg. 105
EMPRESAS ICA SOCIEDAD CONTROLADORA S.A.C.V.; *Int'l*, pg. 454
ENGLE HOMES, INC.; *U.S. Public*, pg. 583
FAIRCLOUGH HOMES LTD.—AMEC Plc; *Int'l*, pg. 16
FAIRMONT MORTGAGE, INC.—Del Webb Corporation; *U.S. Public*, pg. 495
FARNSWORTH HOMES—Farnsworth Companies; *U.S. Private*, pg. 397
FIRST FINANCIAL GROUP, INC.; *U.S. Private*, pg. 407
FOX RIDGE HOMES—NVR, Inc.; *U.S. Public*, pg. 1148
GA LTD.—Hollandsche Beton Groep NV; *Int'l*, pg. 630
THE GATE DEVELOPMENT CORP.—Lennar Corporation; *U.S. Public*, pg. 988
GENERAL HOMES CORPORATION; *U.S. Private*, pg. 444
GOSNELL BUILDERS—Pointe Group Ltd.; *U.S. Private*, pg. 873
GREAT PLAINS COMPANIES, INC.; *U.S. Private*, pg. 475
HARDAWAY CONSTRUCTION CORP. OF TENNESSEE, INC.; *U.S. Private*, pg. 501

HAWAIIAN DREDGING & CONSTRUCTION COMPANY—Dillingham Construction Corporation; *U.S. Private*, pg. 333
THE HERONHILL CORPORATION—Taylor Woodrow plc; *Int'l*, pg. 1359
HILLEN & ROOSEN B.V.—Philipp Holzmann AG; *Int'l*, pg. 633
HOCHTIEF AG; *Int'l*, pg. 623
HOCHTIEF LIMITED—Hochtief AG; *Int'l*, pg. 624
HOMES BY DAVE BROWN; *U.S. Private*, pg. 537
HOVNANIAN ENTERPRISES, INC.; *U.S. Public*, pg. 843
K. HOVNANIAN COMPANIES NORTHEAST, INC.—Hovnanian Enterprises, Inc.; *U.S. Public*, pg. 843
HUNT BUILDING CORPORATION; *U.S. Private*, pg. 548
IDEAL HOMES HOLDINGS PLC—Kvaerner a.s.a.; *Int'l*, pg. 773
IMBAU INDUSTRIELLES BAUEN GMBH—Philipp Holzmann AG; *Int'l*, pg. 633
INTERVAM B.V.—Hollandsche Beton Groep NV; *Int'l*, pg. 630
IRVINE APARTMENT COMMUNITIES INCORPORATED—The Irvine Company; *U.S. Private*, pg. 575
THE IRVINE COMPANY; *U.S. Private*, pg. 575
JM BYGGNADS OCH FASTIGHETS AB—Skanska AB; *Int'l*, *pg. 1260*
JOTSA, S.A. EMPRESSA CONSTRUCTOR—Philipp Holzmann AG; *Int'l*, pg. 634
JONATHAN JAMES LIMITED—Taylor Woodrow plc; *Int'l*, pg. 1358
C.G. JENSEN A/S—Skanska AB; *Int'l*, pg. 1261
KG CONSTRUCTION—Kumagai Gumi Co., Ltd.; *Int'l*, pg. 764
KG LAND NEW YORK CORPORATION—Kumagai Gumi Co., Ltd.; *Int'l*, pg. 764
KM CONSTRUCTION CO.—Kumagai Gumi Co., Ltd.; *Int'l*, pg. 764
KABUTO DECOM INC.; *Int'l*, pg. 721
KAUFMAN AND BROAD HOME CORPORATION; *U.S. Public*, pg. 944
KILLEARN CONSTRUCTION, INC.—Killearn Properties, Inc.; *U.S. Public*, pg. 956
KUMAGAI GUMI CO., LTD.; *Int'l*, pg. 763
LAING HOMES LTD.—John Laing PLC; *Int'l*, pg. 796
LARWIN COMPANY; *U.S. Private*, pg. 652
LEECH HOMES LIMITED—Hanson PLC; *Int'l*, pg. 593
LENNAR CORPORATION; *U.S. Public*, pg. 987
LENNAR HOMES OF ARIZONA, INC.—Lennar Corporation; *U.S. Public*, pg. 988
LENNAR HOMES INC.—Lennar Corporation; *U.S. Public*, pg. 988
LEVITT CORPORATION—Starrett HRH; *U.S. Private*, pg. 1035
LEXFORD RESIDENTIAL TRUST; *U.S. Public*, pg. 991
LINKOUS CONSTRUCTION COMPANY, INC.; *U.S. Private*, *pg. 669*
LOMBARD COMPANY; *U.S. Private*, pg. 673
THE LOUISIANA PURCHASE—AMREP Corporation; *U.S. Public*, pg. 105
LUCERNE LAKES GOLF COLONY INC.—Lennar Corporation; *U.S. Public*, pg. 988
LUCKY DEVELOPMENT CO. LTD.—LG Group; *Int'l*, pg. 779
M.A.P. BUILDERS INC.—Lennar Corporation; *U.S. Public*, pg. 988
M.D.C. HOLDINGS, INC.; *U.S. Public*, pg. 1025
MABON B.V.—Hollandsche Beton Groep NV; *Int'l*, pg. 630
MCLEAN HOMES NORTH EAST LTD.—Tarmac plc; *Int'l*, pg. 1355
MCLEAN HOMES NORTH LONDON LTD.—Tarmac plc; *Int'l*, pg. 1355
MCLEAN HOMES NORTHERN LIMITED—Tarmac plc; *Int'l*, *pg. 1355*
MICHAELS DEVELOPMENT GROUP, INC.; *U.S. Private*, pg. 740
MID-CORP, INC.—Forest City Enterprises, Inc.; *U.S. Public*, *pg. 669*
MITSUI HOME CO., LTD.—Mitsui & Co., Ltd.; *Int'l*, pg. 877
MONARCH CONSTRUCTION LTD.—Taylor Woodrow plc; *Int'l*, pg. 1359
MONARCH DEVELOPMENT CORPORATION—Taylor Woodrow plc; *Int'l*, pg. 1359
THE MONARCH GROUP—Taylor Woodrow plc; *Int'l*, pg. 1359
MONARCH HOMES INC.—George Wimpey PLC; *Int'l*, pg. 1510
MONTICELLO MANAGEMENT CO.; *U.S. Private*, pg. 759
HAROLD MOORE & ASSOCIATES, INC.; *U.S. Private*, pg. 759
MORRISON HOMES—George Wimpey PLC; *Int'l*, pg. 1510
NVR HOMES, INC.—NVR, Inc.; *U.S. Public*, pg. 1148
NVR, INC.; *U.S. Public*, pg. 1148
NEW MEXICO & ARIZONA LAND CO.; *U.S. Public*, pg. 1172
NITTSU REAL ESTATE CO., LTD.—Nippon Express Co., Ltd.; *Int'l*, pg. 934
NITTSU SHOJI CO., LTD.—Nippon Express Co., Ltd.; *Int'l*, pg. 934
NORD FRANCE S.A.—Philipp Holzmann AG; *Int'l*, pg. 634
OAK HILL WEST, INC.—Lennar Corporation; *U.S. Public*, pg. 988
OPTECH S.A.R.L.—Olympus Optical Co., Ltd.; *Int'l*, pg. 1005
PAR FOUR DEVELOPMENT CORP.—Lennar Corporation; *U.S. Public*, pg. 988
PAR ONE DEVELOPMENT CORP.—Lennar Corporation; *U.S. Public*, pg. 988
PAR TWO DEVELOPMENT CORP.—Lennar Corporation; *U.S. Public*, pg. 988
PARDEE CONSTRUCTION COMPANY—Weyerhaeuser Company; *U.S. Public*, pg. 1764
THE PENINSULAR AND ORIENTAL STEAM NAVIGATION COMPANY; *Int'l*, pg. 1032
PRUM-TURENWERK GMBH—Hochtief AG; *Int'l*, pg. 623
PULTE CORPORATION; *U.S. Public*, pg. 1344
PULTE GEORGIA DIVISION—Pulte Corporation; *U.S. Public*, pg. 1344
THE QUADRANT CORPORATION—Weyerhaeuser Company; *U.S. Public*, pg. 1764
RICHMOND AMERICAN HOMES OF CALIFORNIA, INC.—M.D.C. Holdings, Inc.; *U.S. Public*, pg. 1025
RICHMOND AMERICAN HOMES OF VIRGINIA, INC.—M.D.C. Holdings, Inc.; *U.S. Public*, pg. 1025
RICHMOND HOMES, INC. I—M.D.C. Holdings, Inc.; *U.S. Public*, pg. 1025
ROBINHOOD HOMES, INC.; *U.S. Private*, pg. 936
THE ROTTLUND COMPANY, INC.; *U.S. Public*, pg. 1406
THE RYLAND GROUP, INC.; *U.S. Public*, pg. 1414
F.J. SCIAME CONSTRUCTION CO. INC.; *U.S. Private*, pg. 975
SIMPLEX CONSTRUCTION CO. INC.—Simplex Industries, Inc.; *U.S. Private*, pg. 1001
SKANSKA AB; *Int'l*, pg. 1260
SKANSKA BOSTADER STOCKHOLM AB—Skanska AB; *Int'l*, pg. 1260
SKANSKA BYGG AB—Skanska AB; *Int'l*, pg. 1260
SKANSKA INTERNATIONAL BUILDING AB—Skanska AB; *Int'l*, pg. 1260
SKANSKA NORR AB—Skanska AB; *Int'l*, pg. 1260
SKANSKA OY—Skanska AB; *Int'l*, pg. 1261
SKANSKA STOCKHOLM MALARDALEN—Skanska AB; *Int'l*, pg. 1260
SKANSKA SYD—Skanska AB; *Int'l*, pg. 1260
SKANSKA VAST—Skanska AB; *Int'l*, pg. 1261
STANDARD PACIFIC-NO. CALIFORNIA—Standard Pacific Corp.; *U.S. Public*, pg. 1503
STANDARD PACIFIC OF SAN DIEGO—Standard Pacific Corp.; *U.S. Public*, pg. 1503
STANDARD-PACIFIC-TEXAS, INC.—Standard Pacific Corp.; *U.S. Public*, pg. 1504
STANDARD-PACIFIC-TEXAS—Standard Pacific Corp.; *U.S. Public*, pg. 1504
STANDARD PACIFIC VENTURA—Standard Pacific Corp.; *U.S. Public*, pg. 1504
STANPAC CORP—Standard Pacific Corp.; *U.S. Public*, pg. 1504
STANPAC PARTNERS—Standard Pacific Corp.; *U.S. Public*, pg. 1504
STARRETT HRH; *U.S. Private*, pg. 1035
STREIF AG—Hochtief AG; *Int'l*, pg. 623
SULLIVAN LONG & HAGERTY, INC.; *U.S. Private*, pg. 1050
SUN CITY LAS VEGAS—Del Webb Corporation; *U.S. Public*, pg. 495
SUN CITY PALM SPRINGS—Del Webb Corporation; *U.S. Public*, pg. 495
SUN CITY TUCSON—Del Webb Corporation; *U.S. Public*, pg. 495
SUN CITY WEST—Del Webb Corporation; *U.S. Public*, pg. 495
SUNBUILT HOMES, INC.—Centex Corporation; *U.S. Public*, *pg. 323*
TIC GROUP LTD.—Lennar Corporation; *U.S. Public*, pg. 989
TARMAC CANADA INC.—Tarmac plc; *Int'l*, pg. 1355
TARMAC HOMES MIDLANDS LTD.—Tarmac plc; *Int'l*, pg. 1355
TARMAC PLC; *Int'l*, pg. 1355
TAYLOR-MORLEY, INC.; *U.S. Private*, pg. 1071
TAYLOR WOODROW CONSTRUCTION CORP.—Taylor Woodrow plc; *Int'l*, pg. 1359
TAYLOR WOODROW HOMES BUILDERS PTY. LTD.—Taylor Woodrow plc; *Int'l*, pg. 1359
TAYLOR WOODROW HOMES CALIFORNIA LIMITED—Taylor Woodrow plc; *Int'l*, pg. 1359
TAYLOR WOODROW HOMES FLORIDA INC.—Taylor Woodrow plc; *Int'l*, pg. 1359
TAYLOR WOODROW INTERNATIONAL NZ LIMITED—Taylor Woodrow plc; *Int'l*, pg. 1359
TAYLOR WOODROW INTERNATIONAL PROJECTS LTD.—Taylor Woodrow plc; *Int'l*, pg. 1358
TAYLOR WOODROW PLC; *Int'l*, pg. 1358
TAYWOOD HOMES LTD.—Taylor Woodrow plc; *Int'l*, pg. 1359
TEAMWORK CONSTRUCTIONS PTY. LIMITED—Taylor Woodrow plc; *Int'l*, pg. 1360
TOLL BROTHERS, INC.; *U.S. Public*, pg. 1620
TOWNHOMES OF COUNTRY RUN, INC.—Lennar Corporation; *U.S. Public*, pg. 989
TRENDMAKER HOMES INC.—Weyerhaeuser Company; *U.S. Public*, pg. 1764
U.S. HOME CORPORATION; *U.S. Public*, pg. 1682
UNIVERSAL HOMES, INC.—Del Webb Corporation; *U.S. Public*, pg. 495
VALLEHERMOSO, S.A.; *Int'l*, pg. 1447
WALTER INDUSTRIES, INC.; *U.S. Public*, pg. 1736
WASHINGTON GAS ENERGY SYSTEMS, INC.—Washington Gas Light Co.; *U.S. Public*, pg. 1741
WASHINGTON GAS LIGHT CO.; *U.S. Public*, pg. 1740
WASHINGTON HOMES, INC. OF VIRGINIA—Washington Homes, Inc.; *U.S. Public*, pg. 1741
WATKINS ENGINEERS & CONSTRUCTORS, INC.—Dillingham Construction Corporation; *U.S. Private*, pg. 333
WESTMINSTER HOMES OF NORTH CAROLINA, INC.—Washington Homes, Inc.; *U.S. Public*, pg. 1741
WICK BUILDING SYSTEMS; *U.S. Private*, pg. 1174
WILSON CONNOLLY; *Int'l*, pg. 1510
GEORGE WIMPEY PLC; *Int'l*, pg. 1510
WIMPEY HOMES HOLDINGS LTD.—George Wimpey PLC; *Int'l*, pg. 1510
WINCHESTER HOMES, INC.—Weyerhaeuser Company; *U.S. Public*, pg. 1764

1522 — GENERAL CONTRACTORS-RESIDENTIAL BUILDINGS, OTHER THAN SINGLE-FAMILY

ARB INC.; *U.S. Private*, pg. 7
ADOLFSON & PETERSON, INC.; *U.S. Private*, pg. 17
AFFILIATED PUBLISHERS, INC.; *U.S. Private*, pg. 26
AMANA SOCIETY, INC.; *U.S. Private*, pg. 48
AOKI CORPORATION; *Int'l*, pg. 78
AOKI CORPORATION—Aoki Corporation; *Int'l*, pg. 78
APARTMENT SERVICE CO.; *U.S. Private*, pg. 77
ARAPILES, S.A.—Vallehermoso, S.A.; *Int'l*, pg. 1447
ATLANDIA DESIGN & FURNISHINGS, INC.—Mirage Resorts Incorporated; *U.S. Public*, pg. 1116
BARCLAY WHITE INCORPORATED; *U.S. Private*, pg. 115
BARRATT AMERICAN INC.—Barratt Developments Plc; *Int'l*, pg. 168
BARRATT BRISTOL—Barratt Developments Plc; *Int'l*, pg. 168
BARRATT CENTRAL—Barratt Developments Plc; *Int'l*, pg. 168
BARRATT CHESTER—Barratt Developments Plc; *Int'l*, pg. 168
BARRATT COMMERCIAL—Barratt Developments Plc; *Int'l*, pg. 168
BARRATT CONSTRUCTION—Barratt Developments Plc; *Int'l*, pg. 168
BARRATT DEVELOPMENTS PLC; *Int'l*, pg. 167
BARRATT EAST MIDLANDS—Barratt Developments Plc; *Int'l*, pg. 168
BARRATT LEEDS—Barratt Developments Plc; *Int'l*, pg. 168
BARRATT MANCHESTER—Barratt Developments Plc; *Int'l*, *pg. 168*
BARRATT NEWCASTLE—Barratt Developments Plc; *Int'l*, pg. 168
BARRATT NORTHERN—Barratt Developments Plc; *Int'l*, pg. 168
BARRATT SOUTH WALES—Barratt Developments Plc; *Int'l*, pg. 168
BARRATT SOUTHAMPTON—Barratt Developments Plc; *Int'l*, pg. 168
BARRATT WEST MIDLANDS—Barratt Developments Plc; *Int'l*, pg. 168
BARRATT WEST SCOTLAND—Barratt Developments Plc; *Int'l*, pg. 168
BARRATT YORK—Barratt Developments Plc; *Int'l*, pg. 168
BARTON MALOW ENTERPRISES, INC.; *U.S. Private*, pg. 120
BAUGH CONSTRUCTION COMPANY; *U.S. Private*, pg. 123
ROBERT E. BAYLEY CONSTRUCTION; *U.S. Private*, pg. 125
BEAZER GROUP PLC; *Int'l*, pg. 181
BECHTEL CIVIL, INC.—Bechtel Group, Inc.; *U.S. Private*, pg. 128
BECON CONSTRUCTION COMPANY, INC.—Bechtel Group, Inc.; *U.S. Private*, pg. 128
RAY BELL CONSTRUCTION CO. INC.; *U.S. Private*, pg. 131
BENCHMARK CONTRACTORS, INC.—Morley Builders; *U.S. Private*, pg. 761
DAVID BOLAND, INC.; *U.S. Private*, pg. 154
BOVIS URBAN RENEWAL LTD.—The Peninsular and Oriental Steam Navigation Company; *Int'l*, pg. 1032
BOYKIN MANAGEMENT CO.; *U.S. Private*, pg. 162
BRITISH AEROSPACE P.L.C.; *Int'l*, pg. 217
BROOKFIELD HOMES LTD.—Brookfield Properties Corporation; *Int'l*, pg. 228
BURNSIDE CONSTRUCTION CO.; *U.S. Private*, pg. 187
BURRISS CORP.; *U.S. Private*, pg. 188
CALPROP CORPORATION; *U.S. Public*, pg. 296
CAMBIUM CORPORATION—Forest City Enterprises, Inc.; *U.S. Public*, pg. 668
CANTON L.D. CORPORATION—Forest City Enterprises, Inc.; *U.S. Public*, pg. 668
THE P.J. CARLIN CONSTRUCTION COMPANY; *U.S. Private*, pg. 211
CARNIVAL HOTELS & CASINOS—Patriot American Hospitality, Inc.; *U.S. Public*, pg. 1265
THE CEDARWOOD CONSTRUCTION COMPANY; *U.S. Private*, pg. 221
CENTEX-ROONEY CONSTRUCTION CO., INC.—Centex Corporation; *U.S. Public*, pg. 322
CHRISTIANA COMMUNITY BUILDERS—Christiana Companies, Inc.; *U.S. Public*, pg. 352
COSCAN WASHINGTON, INC.—Brookfield Properties Corporation; *Int'l*, pg. 228
COSHOCTON L.D. CORP.—Forest City Enterprises, Inc.; *U.S. Public*, pg. 668
COSTAIN HOMES LIMITED—Costain Group PLC; *Int'l*, pg. 336
CRANE CONSTRUCTION CO.; *U.S. Private*, pg. 286
CUNNINGHAM-LIMP DEVELOPMENT CO.; *U.S. Private*, pg. 297
DCA OF GOLDEN GATE, INC.—Lennar Corporation; *U.S. Public*, pg. 988
DCA OF LAKE WORTH INC.—Lennar Corporation; *U.S. Public*, pg. 988
DCA SERVICES, INC.—Lennar Corporation; *U.S. Public*, pg. 988
DARSA GADITANA, S.A.—Telefonica de Espana, S.A.; *Int'l*, *pg. 1372*
DAVIDSON COSCAN PARTNERS—Brookfield Properties Corporation; *Int'l*, pg. 228
DAWSON CONSTRUCTION CO., INC.; *U.S. Private*, pg. 316
DEVELOPMENT CORP. OF DELRAY, INC.—Lennar Corporation; *U.S. Public*, pg. 988
DILLINGHAM CONSTRUCTION CORPORATION; *U.S. Private*, pg. 333
DILLINGHAM CONSTRUCTION N.A., INC.—Dillingham Construction Corporation; *U.S. Private*, pg. 333
DOMINION HOMES; *U.S. Public*, pg. 516
DYNAMIC HOMES, INC.; *U.S. Public*, pg. 538

DYNAMIC HOMES OF DAKOTA—Dynamic Homes, Inc.; U.S. Public, pg. 539
EL CONQUISTADOR DEVELOPMENT CORP.—Lennar Corporation; U.S. Public, pg. 988
ENGLE HOMES, INC.; U.S. Public, pg. 583
F.C. BURTON L.D. CORP.—Forest City Enterprises, Inc.; U.S. Public, pg. 668
F.C. PROPERTIES CO.—Forest City Enterprises, Inc.; U.S. Public, pg. 668
F.C.D. PARMA LIMITED DIVIDEND CORP.—Forest City Enterprises, Inc.; U.S. Public, pg. 668
FAIRMONT MORTGAGE, INC.—Del Webb Corporation; U.S. Public, pg. 495
FARNSWORTH HOMES—Farnsworth Companies; U.S. Private, pg. 397
FLETCHER HOMES LIMITED—Fletcher Challenge Limited; Int'l, pg. 495
FLUOR CORPORATION; U.S. Public, pg. 659
FOREST CITY ENTERPRISES, INC.; U.S. Public, pg. 667
FOREST CITY RESIDENTIAL DEVELOPMENT INC.—Forest City Enterprises, Inc.; U.S. Public, pg. 669
THE GATE DEVELOPMENT CORP.—Lennar Corporation; U.S. Public, pg. 988
GRUPO POSADAS S.A. DE C.V.; Int'l, pg. 576
GRUPO SITUR SA DE CV—Grupo Sidek, S.A. de C.V.; Int'l, pg. 576
HRH CONSTRUCTION CORP.—Starrett HRH; U.S. Private, pg. 1035
HANJIN SHIPPING COMPANY LTD.; Int'l, pg. 592
HARBOUR CONTRACTORS, INC.; U.S. Private, pg. 500
HARDAWAY CONSTRUCTION CORP. OF TENNESSEE, INC.; U.S. Private, pg. 501
HARKINS BUILDERS, INC.; U.S. Private, pg. 502
HASEKO (CALIFORNIA) INC.—Haseko Corporation; Int'l, pg. 600
HASEKO COMMUNITY INC.—Haseko Corporation; Int'l, pg. 600
HASEKO CORPORATION; Int'l, pg. 599
HASEKO (HAWAII) INC.—Haseko Corporation; Int'l, pg. 600
THE HASSINGER COMPANIES HOFFMAN HOMES; U.S. Private, pg. 510
HAWAIIAN DREDGING & CONSTRUCTION COMPANY—Dillingham Construction Corporation; U.S. Private, pg. 333
HOCHTIEF LIMITED—Hochtief AG; Int'l, pg. 624
JOHN HOLLAND GROUP PTY. LTD.; Int'l, pg. 630
HOLLANDSCHE BETON GROEP NV; Int'l, pg. 630
HOLLOWAY WHITE ALLOM LTD.—John Laing PLC; Int'l, pg. 796
HOMEWOOD CORPORATION; U.S. Private, pg. 537
HOVNANIAN ENTERPRISES, INC.; U.S. Public, pg. 843
K. HOVNANIAN COMPANIES NORTHEAST, INC.—Hovnanian Enterprises, Inc.; U.S. Public, pg. 843
HUNT BUILDING CORPORATION; U.S. Private, pg. 548
HYUNDAI ENGINEERING & CONSTRUCTION CO., LTD.—Hyundai Motor Company; Int'l, pg. 641
IMBAU INDUSTRIELLES BAUEN GMBH—Philipp Holzmann AG; Int'l, pg. 633
INTERBETON B.V.—Hollandsche Beton Groep NV; Int'l, pg. 630
INTERVAM B.V.—Hollandsche Beton Groep NV; Int'l, pg. 630
JM BYGGNADS OCH FASTIGHETS AB—Skanska AB; Int'l, pg. 1260
J. JARVIS & SONS P.L.C.—Jarvis Plc; Int'l, pg. 705
JARVIS PLC; Int'l, pg. 705
JENKINS & ASSOCIATES; U.S. Private, pg. 585
C.G. JENSEN A/S—Skanska AB; Int'l, pg. 1261
M.B. KAHN CONSTRUCTION CO., INC.; U.S. Private, pg. 604
KAUFMAN AND BROAD HOME CORPORATION; U.S. Public, pg. 944
KETTLER BROTHERS, INC.; U.S. Private, pg. 617
KILLEARN CONSTRUCTION, INC.—Killearn Properties, Inc.; U.S. Public, pg. 956
KJELLSTROM & LEE, INC.—Gilbane Building Company; U.S. Private, pg. 453
KRAUS-ANDERSON CONSTRUCTION COMPANY—Kraus-Anderson Incorporated; U.S. Private, pg. 635
LTB—Linbeck Construction Corp; U.S. Private, pg. 668
JOHN LAING CONSTRUCTION LTD.—John Laing PLC; Int'l, pg. 796
JOHN LAING INTERNATIONAL LTD.—John Laing PLC; Int'l, pg. 796
THE LAW COMPANY, INC.; U.S. Private, pg. 653
LEISURE RESORTS MANAGEMENT—Barratt Developments Plc; Int'l, pg. 168
LEXFORD RESIDENTIAL TRUST; U.S. Public, pg. 991
LINCOLN PROPERTY CO., NORTHERN CALIFORNIA—Lincoln Property Company; U.S. Private, pg. 668
LOMBARD COMPANY; U.S. Private, pg. 673
MABON B.V.—Hollandsche Beton Groep NV; Int'l, pg. 630
JAMES MCHUGH CONSTRUCTION CO.; U.S. Private, pg. 721
MCLEAN—Zero Corporation; U.S. Public, pg. 1791
MID ATLANTIC CONSTRUCTION, INC.—Rodgers Builders, Inc.; U.S. Private, pg. 939
H. MILLER & SONS, INC.—Lennar Corporation; U.S. Public, pg. 989
W.G. MILLS, INC.; U.S. Private, pg. 749
MONTICELLO MANAGEMENT CO.; U.S. Private, pg. 759
HAROLD MOORE & ASSOCIATES, INC.; U.S. Private, pg. 759
MORLEY BUILDERS; U.S. Private, pg. 761
MOZEL DEVELOPMENT CORP.; U.S. Private, pg. 765
NNG ENERGY SYSTEMS, INC.—Northwest Natural Gas Company; U.S. Public, pg. 1200
NVR, INC.; U.S. Public, pg. 1148
NEW MEXICO & ARIZONA LAND CO.; U.S. Public, pg. 1172
NITTSU REAL ESTATE CO., LTD.—Nippon Express Co., Ltd.; Int'l, pg. 934
NITTSU SHOJI CO., LTD.—Nippon Express Co., Ltd.; Int'l, pg. 934
NORBURY CONSTRUCTION CO.—The Rouse Company; U.S. Public, pg. 1409
OAK HILL WEST, INC.—Lennar Corporation; U.S. Public, pg. 988
O'NEIL INDUSTRIES INC.; U.S. Private, pg. 817
W.E. O'NEIL CONSTRUCTION COMPANY—O'Neil Industries Inc.; U.S. Private, pg. 817
ORCHARD PARADE HOLDINGS LIMITED; Int'l, pg. 1007
ORLEANS CORPORATION—FPA Corporation; U.S. Public, pg. 608
OXFORD REALTY FINANCIAL GROUP; U.S. Private, pg. 825
CHARLES PANKOW BUILDERS, LTD.; U.S. Private, pg. 836
PANTECH CONSTRUCTION CO.; U.S. Private, pg. 837
THE PENINSULAR AND ORIENTAL STEAM NAVIGATION COMPANY; Int'l, pg. 1032
PERFORMA ENTERTAINMENT REAL ESTATE, INC.; U.S. Private, pg. 853
PERINI BUILDING COMPANY-CENTRAL U.S. DIVISION—Perini Corporation; U.S. Public, pg. 1278
PERINI BUILDING CO., INC.-EASTERN U.S. DIVISION—Perini Corporation; U.S. Public, pg. 1278
PERINI BUILDING CO., INC. WESTERN U.S. DIVISION—Perini Corporation; U.S. Public, pg. 1278
PERINI CORPORATION; U.S. Public, pg. 1278
PRINCEVILLE CORPORATION; U.S. Private, pg. 885
PULTE CORPORATION; U.S. Public, pg. 1344
PULTE GEORGIA DIVISION—Pulte Corporation; U.S. Public, pg. 1344
REECE-CAMPBELL, INC.; U.S. Private, pg. 916
RENTENBACH ENGINEERING COMPANY; U.S. Private, pg. 923
RETIREMENT COMMUNITY SPECIALISTS, INC.; U.S. Private, pg. 925
RITTER BROS., INC.; U.S. Private, pg. 933
RODGERS BUILDERS, INC.; U.S. Private, pg. 939
RUSCON CORP.; U.S. Private, pg. 952
F.J. SCIAME CONSTRUCTION CO. INC.; U.S. Private, pg. 975
SCRUFARI CONSTRUCTION CO. INC.; U.S. Private, pg. 977
KENNETH M. SEATON ENTERPRISES—Family Inns of America, Inc.; U.S. Private, pg. 393
SHAPELL INDUSTRIES, INC.; U.S. Private, pg. 990
R.M. SHOEMAKER CO.; U.S. Private, pg. 996
SKANSKA AB; Int'l, pg. 1260
SKANSKA BOSTADER STOCKHOLM AB—Skanska AB; Int'l, pg. 1260
SKANSKA BYGG AB—Skanska AB; Int'l, pg. 1260
SKANSKA INTERNATIONAL BUILDING AB—Skanska AB; Int'l, pg. 1260
SKANSKA NORR AB—Skanska AB; Int'l, pg. 1260
SKANSKA OY—Skanska AB; Int'l, pg. 1261
SKANSKA STOCKHOLM MALARDALEN—Skanska AB; Int'l, pg. 1260
SKANSKA SYD—Skanska AB; Int'l, pg. 1260
SKANSKA (U.S.A.) INC.—Skanska AB; Int'l, pg. 1261
SKANSKA VAST—Skanska AB; Int'l, pg. 1261
GEORGE SOLLITT CONSTRUCTION; U.S. Private, pg. 1013
THE SPANOS COMPANIES; U.S. Private, pg. 1020
SSANGYONG BUSINESS GROUP; Int'l, pg. 1291
SSANGYONG ENGINEERING & CONSTRUCTION CO., LTD.—Ssangyong Business Group; Int'l, pg. 1291
STAHLBAU LAVIS OFFENBACH GMBH—Philipp Holzmann AG; Int'l, pg. 633
STARRETT HRH; U.S. Private, pg. 1035
STREIF AG—Hochtief AG; Int'l, pg. 623
SULLIVAN & COZART INC.; U.S. Private, pg. 1049
SULLIVAN LONG & HAGERTY, INC.; U.S. Private, pg. 1050
SUNDT CORP.; U.S. Private, pg. 1051
SUTHERLAND LUMBER CO.; U.S. Private, pg. 1057
SVERDRUP CORPORATION; U.S. Private, pg. 1057
TARMAC CONSTRUCTION INTL.—Tarmac plc; Int'l, pg. 1355
TAYLOR-MORLEY, INC.; U.S. Private, pg. 1071
TAYLOR WOODROW OF SAN FRANCISCO INC.—Taylor Woodrow plc; Int'l, pg. 1359
TAYLOR WOODROW PROPERTY CO. OF AMERICA INC.—Taylor Woodrow plc; Int'l, pg. 1359
TISHMAN REALTY & CONSTRUCTION CO., INC.; U.S. Private, pg. 1089
TOLL BROTHERS, INC.; U.S. Public, pg. 1020
TOWNHOMES OF COUNTRY RUN, INC.—Lennar Corporation; U.S. Public, pg. 989
TURNER CARIBE, INC.—The Turner Corporation; U.S. Public, pg. 1646
TURNER CONSTRUCTION COMPANY—The Turner Corporation; U.S. Public, pg. 1645
THE TURNER CORPORATION; U.S. Public, pg. 1645
TURNER INTERNATIONAL INDUSTRIES, INC.—The Turner Corporation; U.S. Public, pg. 1646
TURNER INTERNATIONAL U.K. LTD.—The Turner Corporation; U.S. Public, pg. 1646
UNIVERSAL CONSTRUCTION CO.—The Turner Corporation; U.S. Public, pg. 1646
VALLEHERMOSO, S.A.; Int'l, pg. 1447
WALBRIDGE ALDINGER COMPANY—Walbridge Aldinger Company; U.S. Private, pg. 1147
WARREN PROPERTIES; U.S. Private, pg. 1151
WATKINS ENGINEERS & CONSTRUCTORS, INC.—Dillingham Construction Corporation; U.S. Private, pg. 333
WICK BUILDING SYSTEMS; U.S. Private, pg. 1174
WIL-FREDS INC.; U.S. Private, pg. 1176
WILLIAMS COMPANY OF ORLANDO, INC.; U.S. Private, pg. 1177

1531 — OPERATIVE BUILDERS

ATLANTIC HOMES CORP.—The Great Atlantic Management Company; U.S. Private, pg. 473
BROOKFIELD HOMES LTD.—Brookfield Properties Corporation; Int'l, pg. 228
BUILDERS DEVELOPMENT INC.—Garvey Industries, Inc.; U.S. Private, pg. 440
BURNSIDE CONSTRUCTION CO.; U.S. Private, pg. 187
BURNSTEAD CONSTRUCTION COMPANY; U.S. Private, pg. 187
CALTON HOMES, INC.—Calton, Inc.; U.S. Public, pg. 296
CALTON, INC.; U.S. Public, pg. 296
CROSSMANN COMMUNITIES, INC.; U.S. Public, pg. 461
DEL WEBB CORPORATION; U.S. Public, pg. 494
DEVELOPMENT CORPORATION OF AMERICA—Lennar Corporation; U.S. Public, pg. 987
THE DONOHOE COMPANIES, INC.; U.S. Private, pg. 340
FIRST ATLANTIC BUILDING CORP.—Lennar Corporation; U.S. Public, pg. 988
THE FLATLEY COMPANY; U.S. Private, pg. 410
G.E. POWER SYSTEMS—General Electric Company; U.S. Public, pg. 711
GOSNELL BUILDERS—Pointe Group Ltd.; U.S. Private, pg. 873
THE GREAT ATLANTIC MANAGEMENT COMPANY; U.S. Private, pg. 473
GREATER CONSTRUCTION CORP.; U.S. Private, pg. 476
HOMEWOOD CORPORATION; U.S. Private, pg. 537
D.R. HORTON, INC.; U.S. Public, pg. 840
HOUSTON DIVISION—U.S. Home Corporation; U.S. Public, pg. 1683
THE IDI GROUP COMPANIES; U.S. Private, pg. 554
JACOBS INTERNATIONAL LIMITED, INC.—Jacobs Engineering Group Inc.; U.S. Public, pg. 922
KAJIMA CORPORATION; Int'l, pg. 721
KAJIMA U.S.A., INC.—Kajima Corporation; Int'l, pg. 722
KAUFMAN AND BROAD OF TEXAS, LTD.—Kaufman and Broad Home Corporation; U.S. Public, pg. 945
KETTLER BROTHERS, INC.; U.S. Private, pg. 617
KORMAN SERVICES, L.P.; U.S. Private, pg. 632
LTB—Linbeck Construction Corp; U.S. Private, pg. 668
JOHN LAING SERVICES LTD.—John Laing PLC; Int'l, pg. 796
LAING MANAGEMENT LTD.—John Laing PLC; Int'l, pg. 796
LANDSTAR DEVELOPMENT COMPANY; U.S. Private, pg. 649
LEISURE TECHNOLOGY, INC.; U.S. Private, pg. 659
LEISURE TECHNOLOGY, NEW JERSEY DIV.—Leisure Technology, Inc.; U.S. Private, pg. 659
LEWIS HOMES MANAGEMENT CORP.; U.S. Private, pg. 665
WILLIAM LYON COMPANY; U.S. Private, pg. 684
MILLER & SMITH, INC.; U.S. Private, pg. 746
MOUNTAIN OPERATIONS LAND DIVISION—U.S. Home Corporation; U.S. Public, pg. 1683
NEW FORTIS CORP.—Hovnanian Enterprises, Inc.; U.S. Public, pg. 843
NORTH FLORIDA DIV.—U.S. Home Corporation; U.S. Public, pg. 1683
O&Y PROPERTIES CORPORATION; Int'l, pg. 993
OHIO DIV.—U.S. Home Corporation; U.S. Public, pg. 1683
ORIOLE HOMES CORP.; U.S. Public, pg. 1230
OVERTON MOORE & ASSOCIATES; U.S. Private, pg. 823
OXFORD REALTY FINANCIAL GROUP; U.S. Private, pg. 825
PURCELL CO., INC.; U.S. Private, pg. 895
THE QUADRANT CORPORATION—Weyerhaeuser Company; U.S. Public, pg. 1764
RHOADES DEVELOPMENT; U.S. Private, pg. 927
ROCKEFELLER GROUP, INC.—Mitsubishi Estate Co., Ltd.; Int'l, pg. 873
THE ROUSE COMPANY; U.S. Public, pg. 1407
SAN ANTONIO DIV.—U.S. Home Corporation; U.S. Public, pg. 1683
F.J. SCIAME CONSTRUCTION CO. INC.; U.S. Private, pg. 975
SEKISUI CHEMICAL CO., LTD.; Int'l, pg. 1219
SELIGMAN & ASSOCIATES, INC.; U.S. Private, pg. 982
SHAPELL INDUSTRIES, INC.; U.S. Private, pg. 990
SHEA HOMES; U.S. Private, pg. 990
BERT L. SMOKLER & CO.—Lennar Corporation; U.S. Public, pg. 989
SOUTH FLORIDA LAND DIVISION—U.S. Home Corporation; U.S. Public, pg. 1683
SSANGYONG BUSINESS GROUP; Int'l, pg. 1291
SSANGYONG ENGINEERING & CONSTRUCTION CO., LTD.—Ssangyong Business Group; Int'l, pg. 1291
THOMPSON DIVISION—U.S. Home Corporation; U.S. Public, pg. 1683
TOP OF THE WORLD VENTURES, INC—Galesi Group; U.S. Private, pg. 438
THE VAN METRES COMPANIES; U.S. Private, pg. 1132
WARMINGTON HOMES; U.S. Private, pg. 1150
WASHINGTON HOMES, INC.; U.S. Public, pg. 1741
JOHN WIELAND HOMES INC.; U.S. Private, pg. 1175
JOHN WIELAND HOMES OF SOUTH CAROLINA, INC.—John Wieland Homes Inc.; U.S. Private, pg. 1175
JOHN WIELAND HOMES OF TENESSEE, INC.—John Wieland Homes Inc.; U.S. Private, pg. 1175

1541 — GENERAL CONTRACTORS-INDUSTRIAL BUILDINGS & WAREHOUSES

ABB C-E SERVICES—ABB Asea Brown Boveri (Holding) Ltd.; Int'l, pg. 3
ABB LUMMUS GLOBAL INC.—ABB Asea Brown Boveri (Holding) Ltd.; Int'l, pg. 4
ADP MARSHALL CONTRACTORS INC.—Fluor Corporation; U.S. Public, pg. 660
ARB INC.; U.S. Private, pg. 7
ABELL-HOWE COMPANY; U.S. Private, pg. 10

ABRAMS CONSTRUCTION, INC.—Abrams Industries, Inc.; *U.S. Public*, pg. 14
ABRAMS INDUSTRIES, INC.; *U.S. Public*, pg. 14
ADOLFSON & PETERSON, INC.; *U.S. Private*, pg. 17
AGROTECHNIP S.A.—Technip; *Int'l*, pg. 1360
J.S. ALBERICI CONSTRUCTION CO., INC.; *U.S. Private*, pg. 32
AMELCO, INC.—Amelco Corporation; *U.S. Public*, pg. 65
ARAPILES, S.A.—Vallehermoso, S.A.; *Int'l*, pg. 1447
ATKINSON; *U.S. Public*, pg. 143
ATKINSON INTERNATIONAL VENEZUELA—Atkinson; *U.S. Public*, pg. 143
ATLANTIC BUILDERS GROUP INC.; *U.S. Private*, pg. 95
THE AUCHTER COMPANY; *U.S. Private*, pg. 98
THE AUSTIN COMPANY; *U.S. Private*, pg. 99
BE & K, INC.; *U.S. Private*, pg. 106
BEC INC.; *U.S. Private*, pg. 106
BFC FRONTIER—BFC Construction Corporation; *Int'l*, pg. 118
BARCLAY WHITE INCORPORATED; *U.S. Private*, pg. 115
BARNHILL CONTRACTING COMPANY; *U.S. Private*, pg. 117
BARRATT CENTRAL—Barratt Developments Plc; *Int'l*, pg. 168
BARRATT COMMERCIAL—Barratt Developments Plc; *Int'l*, pg. 168
BARRATT DEVELOPMENTS PLC; *Int'l*, pg. 167
BARRATT EAST MIDLANDS—Barratt Developments Plc; *Int'l*, pg. 168
BARRATT LEEDS—Barratt Developments Plc; *Int'l*, pg. 168
BARRATT MANCHESTER—Barratt Developments Plc; *Int'l*, pg. 168
BARRATT NEWCASTLE—Barratt Developments Plc; *Int'l*, pg. 168
BARRATT NORTHERN—Barratt Developments Plc; *Int'l*, pg. 168
BARRATT SOUTH WALES—Barratt Developments Plc; *Int'l*, pg. 168
BARRATT SOUTHAMPTON—Barratt Developments Plc; *Int'l*, pg. 168
BARRATT SOUTHERN—Barratt Developments Plc; *Int'l*, pg. 168
BARRATT WEST SCOTLAND—Barratt Developments Plc; *Int'l*, pg. 168
BARRATT YORK—Barratt Developments Plc; *Int'l*, pg. 168
BARTLETT BRAINARD EACOTT, INC.; *U.S. Private*, pg. 118
BARTON-ASCHMAN ASSOCIATES, INC.—Parsons Corporation; *U.S. Private*, pg. 841
BARTON MALOW ENTERPRISES, INC.; *U.S. Private*, pg. 120
BATTEAST CONSTRUCTION COMPANY, INC.; *U.S. Private*, pg. 123
BAUGH CONSTRUCTION COMPANY; *U.S. Private*, pg. 123
BECHTEL CIVIL, INC.—Bechtel Group, Inc.; *U.S. Private*, pg. 128
BECHTEL LTD.—Bechtel Group, Inc.; *U.S. Private*, pg. 128
BECHTEL MINING & METALS—Bechtel Group, Inc.; *U.S. Private*, pg. 128
BECHTEL PETROLEUM & CHEMICAL—Bechtel Group, Inc.; *U.S. Private*, pg. 128
BECON CONSTRUCTION COMPANY, INC.—Bechtel Group, Inc.; *U.S. Private*, pg. 128
RAY BELL CONSTRUCTION CO. INC.; *U.S. Private*, pg. 131
BENCHMARK CONTRACTORS, INC.—Morley Builders; *U.S. Private*, pg. 761
BERNARDS BROTHERS, INC.; *U.S. Private*, pg. 136
WM. BLANCHARD CO.; *U.S. Private*, pg. 148
BORDEN INTERNATIONAL, INC.—Borden, Inc.; *U.S. Private*, pg. 158
BOVIS CONSTRUCTION GROUP—The Peninsular and Oriental Steam Navigation Company; *Int'l*, pg. 1032
BOVIS URBAN RENEWAL LTD.—The Peninsular and Oriental Steam Navigation Company; *Int'l*, pg. 1032
BRENCAL CONTRACTORS INC.—BEC Inc.; *U.S. Private*, pg. 106
FRANK BRISCOE CO. INC.; *U.S. Private*, pg. 169
BRITISH AEROSPACE P.L.C.; *Int'l*, pg. 217
BROWER COMPANY—Bay Industries Inc.; *U.S. Private*, pg. 124
BUCON, INC.—Butler Manufacturing Company; *U.S. Public*, pg. 271
BUTLER MANUFACTURING COMPANY; *U.S. Public*, pg. 271
CAMOSY, INC.; *U.S. Private*, pg. 203
CANADIAN MINI-WAREHOUSE PROPERTIES, LTD.—Public Storage, Inc.; *U.S. Public*, pg. 1341
CAPITAL DEVELOPMENT CO.; *U.S. Private*, pg. 205
CAPITAL FACTORS, INC.—Union Planters Corporation; *U.S. Public*, pg. 1669
CAPITOL CONSTRUCTION GROUP, INC.; *U.S. Private*, pg. 206
CARLTON, INC.—Maescher Industries, Inc.; *U.S. Private*, pg. 694
CENTEX CONSTRUCTION GROUP, INC.—Centex Corporation; *U.S. Public*, pg. 322
CENTEX CORPORATION; *U.S. Public*, pg. 322
CENTEX FORCUM-LANNOM, INC.—Centex Corporation; *U.S. Public*, pg. 322
F.H. CHASE, INC.; *U.S. Private*, pg. 230
LOUIS P. CIMINELLI CONSTRUCTION CO. INC.; *U.S. Private*, pg. 239
CINCINNATI UNITED CONTRACTORS; *U.S. Private*, pg. 240
CLARK CONSTRUCTION GROUP, INC.—Clark Enterprises, Inc.; *U.S. Private*, pg. 242
CLEANROOM TECHNOLOGY—Groupe Strafor Facom; *Int'l*, pg. 569
COMP-AIRE SYSTEMS INC.—BTR plc; *Int'l*, pg. 126
CONSTRUCTION COUNSELLORS, INC.; *U.S. Private*, pg. 266
CONSTRUTORA DUMEZ-GTM LTDA—Lyonnaise des Eaux S.A.; *Int'l*, pg. 823
CORPOREX COMPANIES, INC.; *U.S. Private*, pg. 276
CUNNINGHAM-LIMP DEVELOPMENT CO.; *U.S. Private*, pg. 297
DSS ENGINEERS, INC.—Stone & Webster, Incorporated; *U.S. Public*, pg. 1519
DAHLEM COMPANY, INC.; *U.S. Private*, pg. 306
THE DANIS COMPANIES; *U.S. Private*, pg. 310
DAWSON CONSTRUCTION CO., INC.; *U.S. Private*, pg. 316
DEGGENDORFER WERFT UND EISENBAU GMBH—MAN Aktiengesellschaft; *Int'l*, pg. 824
DEMARIA BUILDING CO. INC.; *U.S. Private*, pg. 323
DEUTSCHE INDUSTRIEANLAGENGESELLSCHAFT MBH—MAN Aktiengesellschaft; *Int'l*, pg. 824
DICK CORPORATION; *U.S. Private*, pg. 331
DILLINGHAM CONSTRUCTION CORPORATION; *U.S. Private*, pg. 333
DONLEY'S, INC.; *U.S. Private*, pg. 340
DOVER INDUSTRIES, INC.—Dover Corporation; *U.S. Public*, pg. 520
L.F. DRISCOLL CO.; *U.S. Private*, pg. 343
DUGAN & MEYERS CONSTRUCTION CO.—Dugan & Meyers Interests, Inc.; *U.S. Private*, pg. 345
DUMEZ-GTM—Lyonnaise des Eaux S.A.; *Int'l*, pg. 823
E.P.I.—Bouygues; *Int'l*, pg. 206
ETCD—Lyonnaise des Eaux S.A.; *Int'l*, pg. 823
EARL CONSTRUCTION COMPANY—Sundt Corp.; *U.S. Private*, pg. 1051
MARTIN K. EBY CONSTRUCTION COMPANY, INC.—Eby Corporation; *U.S. Private*, pg. 359
ELKINS CONSTRUCTORS, INC.; *U.S. Private*, pg. 372
EMPRESAS ICA SOCIEDAD CONTROLADORA S.A.C.V.; *Int'l*, pg. 454
A. EPSTEIN AND SONS, INTL., INC.; *U.S. Private*, pg. 379
A.J. ETKIN CONSTRUCTION CO.—Alex J. Etkin, Inc.; *U.S. Private*, pg. 384
F/N GROUP, INC.—American International Group, Inc.; *U.S. Public*, pg. 84
J.H. FINDORFF & SON, INC.; *U.S. Private*, pg. 405
FIRST FINANCIAL BUILDING CORPORATION; *U.S. Private*, pg. 407
FISCHBACH CORPORATION—American International Group, Inc.; *U.S. Public*, pg. 84
THE FLATLEY COMPANY; *U.S. Private*, pg. 410
THE FLETCHER CONSTRUCTION COMPANY LIMITED—Fletcher Challenge Limited; *Int'l*, pg. 495
FLETCHER PACIFIC CONSTRUCTION COMPANY LIMITED—Fletcher Challenge Limited; *Int'l*, pg. 495
FLUOR CONSTRUCTORS INTERNATIONAL, INC.—Fluor Corporation; *U.S. Public*, pg. 660
FLUOR CORPORATION; *U.S. Public*, pg. 659
FLUOR DANIEL WRIGHT LIMITED—Fluor Corporation; *U.S. Public*, pg. 660
4520 CORP., INC.—Blount International, Inc.; *U.S. Public*, pg. 239
FOSTER WHEELER BIMAS—Foster Wheeler Corporation; *U.S. Public*, pg. 677
FOSTER WHEELER CORPORATION; *U.S. Public*, pg. 676
THE FUSCO CORPORATION; *U.S. Private*, pg. 432
G.E. POWER SYSTEMS—General Electric Company; *U.S. Public*, pg. 711
GIP GEWERBE IM PARK GMBH—Philipp Holzmann AG; *Int'l*, pg. 632
GEUPEL DEMARS, INC.; *U.S. Private*, pg. 449
GIFFELS TECHNOLOGIES, INC.—Giffels Associates, Inc.; *U.S. Private*, pg. 452
GILBANE BUILDING COMPANY; *U.S. Private*, pg. 452
GLENROY CONSTRUCTION CO. INC.; *U.S. Private*, pg. 456
JAMES N. GRAY CONSTRUCTION CO., INC.; *U.S. Private*, pg. 472
GRAYCOR OPERATING COMPANIES; *U.S. Private*, pg. 472
HCBECK; *U.S. Private*, pg. 490
HNTB DESIGN & BUILD—HNTB Corporation; *U.S. Private*, pg. 492
HRH/ATLAS CONSTRUCTION INC.—Starrett HRH; *U.S. Private*, pg. 1035
C.F. HAGLIN & SONS; *U.S. Private*, pg. 493
FRANZ HANIEL & CIE, GMBH; *Int'l*, pg. 591
HARBERT CORPORATION; *U.S. Private*, pg. 500
HARBOUR CONTRACTORS, INC.; *U.S. Private*, pg. 500
HARDAWAY CONSTRUCTION CORP. OF TENNESSEE, INC.; *U.S. Private*, pg. 501
HARFORD SYSTEMS, INC.—Lab Products, Inc.; *U.S. Private*, pg. 641
HARKINS BUILDERS, INC.; *U.S. Private*, pg. 502
HARRISON CONSTRUCTION CORP.; *U.S. Private*, pg. 506
HARTUNG, KUHN, & CO., MASCHINENFABRIK GMBH—Fried. Krupp AG; *Int'l*, pg. 511
HAWAIIAN DREDGING & CONSTRUCTION COMPANY—Dillingham Construction Corporation; *U.S. Private*, pg. 333
PAUL HEMMER CONSTRUCTION COMPANY; *U.S. Private*, pg. 521
HENSEL PHELPS CONSTRUCTION CO.; *U.S. Private*, pg. 523
A.D. HERMAN CONSTRUCTION CO.—Starrett HRH; *U.S. Private*, pg. 1035
HICKORY CONSTRUCTION COMPANY; *U.S. Private*, pg. 525
HOCHTIEF LIMITED—Hochtief AG; *Int'l*, pg. 624
HOLLANDSCHE BETON GROEP NV; *Int'l*, pg. 630
HOMES & SON CONTRACTORS, INC.; *U.S. Private*, pg. 537
E.W. HOWELL COMPANY, INC.—Obayashi Corporation; *Int'l*, pg. 995
HUBER, HUNT & NICHOLS, INC.—The Hunt Corporation; *U.S. Private*, pg. 548
THE HUNT CORPORATION; *U.S. Private*, pg. 548
HY VEE WEITZ CONSTRUCTION, L.C.—The Weitz Company, Inc.; *U.S. Private*, pg. 1161
HYUNDAI ENGINEERING & CONSTRUCTION CO., LTD.—Hyundai Motor Company; *Int'l*, pg. 641
ICF KAISER ENGINEERS, INC.—ICF Kaiser International Inc.; *U.S. Public*, pg. 853
ICF KAISER INTERNATIONAL INC.; *U.S. Public*, pg. 852
IHC GROUP, INC.; *U.S. Private*, pg. 555
INDUSTRA SERVICE CORPORATION—American Eco Corporation; *Int'l*, pg. 74
INDUSTRIAL CONTRACTING OF FAIRMONT, INC.—Salem Group, Inc.; *U.S. Private*, pg. 961
INDUSTRIAL RESOURCES, INC.—Salem Group, Inc.; *U.S. Private*, pg. 961
INMAN CONSTRUCTION CORPORATION; *U.S. Private*, pg. 564
ISEMOTO CONTRACTING CO. LTD.; *U.S. Private*, pg. 575
THE JCM GROUP—Peck Jones Construction; *U.S. Private*, pg. 846
JE MERIT CONSTRUCTORS, INC.—Jacobs Engineering Group Inc.; *U.S. Public*, pg. 921
JGC CORPORATION; *Int'l*, pg. 697
JM BYGGNADS OCH FASTIGHETS AB—Skanska AB; *Int'l*, pg. 1260
JACOBS INTERNATIONAL LIMITED, INC.—Jacobs Engineering Group Inc.; *U.S. Public*, pg. 922
JACOBS MAINTENANCE, INC.—Jacobs Engineering Group Inc.; *U.S. Public*, pg. 921
JONATHAN JAMES LIMITED—Taylor Woodrow plc; *Int'l*, pg. 1358
J. JARVIS & SONS P.L.C.—Jarvis Plc; *Int'l*, pg. 705
JARVIS PLC; *Int'l*, pg. 705
C.G. JENSEN A/S—Skanska AB; *Int'l*, pg. 1261
JOFFKO INTERNATIONAL; *U.S. Private*, pg. 589
AL JOHNSON CONSTRUCTION CO.; *U.S. Private*, pg. 590
J.A. JONES, INC.—Philipp Holzmann AG; *Int'l*, pg. 633
KG LAND NEW YORK CORPORATION—Kumagai Gumi Co., Ltd.; *Int'l*, pg. 764
M.B. KAHN CONSTRUCTION CO., INC.; *U.S. Private*, pg. 604
KEATING BUILDING CORP.; *U.S. Private*, pg. 610
DANIEL J. KEATING CO.; *U.S. Private*, pg. 610
KELLER CONSTRUCTION COMPANY LTD.; *U.S. Private*, pg. 612
KELSEY CONSTRUCTION, INC.; *U.S. Private*, pg. 613
KEMMONS WILSON, INC.; *U.S. Private*, pg. 613
KIEWIT CONSTRUCTION GROUP, INC.—Peter Kiewit Sons Inc.; *U.S. Private*, pg. 619
PETER KIEWIT SONS INC.; *U.S. Private*, pg. 619
KILMEADEN FOODS LIMITED—Avonmore Waterford Group plc; *Int'l*, pg. 102
FRANZ KIRCHFELD GMBH & CO. KG—MAN Aktiengesellschaft; *Int'l*, pg. 824
KITCHELL CORPORATION; *U.S. Private*, pg. 624
KLOECKNER & CO. AG; *Int'l*, pg. 737
KLOECKNER INDUSTRIE-ANLAGEN GMBH—RWE AG; *Int'l*, pg. 1081
KOKOSING CONSTRUCTION COMPANY, INC.; *U.S. Private*, pg. 631
KRAUS-ANDERSON CONSTRUCTION COMPANY—Kraus-Anderson Incorporated; *U.S. Private*, pg. 635
KRUPP KOPPERS GMBH—Fried. Krupp AG; *Int'l*, pg. 511
KRUPP WILPUTTE CORP.—Fried. Krupp AG; *Int'l*, pg. 512
KUMAGAI GUMI CO., LTD.; *Int'l*, pg. 763
JOHN LAING INTERNATIONAL LTD.—John Laing PLC; *Int'l*, pg. 796
LAMB ENGINEERING & CONSTRUCTION CO.; *U.S. Private*, pg. 644
ROBERT E. LAMB, INC.; *U.S. Private*, pg. 644
LANDAU BUILDING CO.; *U.S. Private*, pg. 646
THE LATHROP COMPANY—The Turner Corporation; *U.S. Public*, pg. 1645
LAWSON MECHANICAL CONTRACTORS; *U.S. Private*, pg. 654
LEHRER MCGOVERN BOVIS INC.—The Peninsular and Oriental Steam Navigation Company; *Int'l*, pg. 1035
LIEBHERR-INDUSTRIEANLAGEN AG—Liebherr-International AG; *Int'l*, pg. 808
LIN & ROE COMPANY—Burns & Roe Enterprises, Inc.; *U.S. Private*, pg. 187
LINBECK CONSTRUCTION CORP; *U.S. Private*, pg. 667
LINKOUS CONSTRUCTION COMPANY, INC.; *U.S. Private*, pg. 669
LOMBARD COMPANY; *U.S. Private*, pg. 673
LUWA BAHNSON, INC.; *U.S. Private*, pg. 682
MAN GHH AUSTRALIA PTY. LTD.—MAN Aktiengesellschaft; *Int'l*, pg. 824
MAN GHH CORP.—MAN Aktiengesellschaft; *Int'l*, pg. 824
MAN GUTEHOFFNUNGSHUETTE AG—MAN Aktiengesellschaft; *Int'l*, pg. 824
MCDR, INC.; *U.S. Private*, pg. 686
MAESCHER INDUSTRIES, INC.; *U.S. Private*, pg. 694
MAINTENANCE BUILDING & SIGNAGE—Vaux Group Plc; *Int'l*, pg. 1454
MANHATTAN CONSTRUCTION COMPANY—Rooney Brothers Company; *U.S. Private*, pg. 943
MASTER BUILDERS INC.—Viag AG; *Int'l*, pg. 1465
MASTER BUILDERS TECHNOLOGIES LTD.—Viag AG; *Int'l*, pg. 1465
MATRIX BUILDING CO., INC.—Maescher Industries, Inc.; *U.S. Private*, pg. 694
MCCARTHY BROTHERS CO.—McCarthy Building Companies; *U.S. Private*, pg. 719
MCCARTHY BUILDING COMPANIES; *U.S. Private*, pg. 719
J.H. MCCORMICK, INC.; *U.S. Private*, pg. 720
MCCRORY CONSTRUCTION CO., INC.; *U.S. Private*, pg. 720
MECO ENGINEERING CO.—Meco Development Limited; *Int'l*, pg. 852
MECO HOLDINGS CO. LTD.—Meco Development Limited; *Int'l*, pg. 852
FRANK MESSER & SONS CONSTRUCTION CO.; *U.S. Private*, pg. 734
METRIC CONSTRUCTORS, INC.—Philipp Holzmann AG; *Int'l*, pg. 633

MID ATLANTIC CONSTRUCTION, INC.—Rodgers Builders, Inc.; *U.S. Private*, pg. 939
MILLER BUILDING CORP.; *U.S. Private*, pg. 746
W.G. MILLS, INC.; *U.S. Private*, pg. 749
MITSUI CONSTRUCTION CO., LTD.—Mitsui & Co., Ltd.; *Int'l*, pg. 877
MITSUI PRECON CO., LTD.—Mitsui & Co., Ltd.; *Int'l*, pg. 877
MONARCH CONSTRUCTION COMPANY; *U.S. Private*, pg. 757
MONTICELLO MANAGEMENT CO.; *U.S. Private*, pg. 759
MORAN COMPANY—American International Group, Inc.; *U.S. Public*, pg. 84
MORRISON KNUDSEN CORPORATION; *U.S. Public*, pg. 1133
M.A. MORTENSON COMPANY; *U.S. Private*, pg. 763
MOUNTAINEER RESOURCES, INC.—Salem Group, Inc.; *U.S. Private*, pg. 961
MUSKEGON CONSTRUCTION COMPANY—Owen-Ames-Kimball Co.; *U.S. Private*, pg. 824
MYRICK CONSTRUCTION INC.; *U.S. Private*, pg. 771
MYTON LIMITED—Taylor Woodrow plc; *Int'l*, pg. 1358
NC BUILDERS INC.—Nason and Cullen Group Incorporated; *U.S. Private*, pg. 775
NCC AB; *Int'l*, pg. 898
NCC CIVIL ENGINEERING—NCC AB; *Int'l*, pg. 899
NCC ESKILSTUNA—NCC AB; *Int'l*, pg. 899
NCC HUS—NCC AB; *Int'l*, pg. 899
NABHOLZ CONSTRUCTION CORP.; *U.S. Private*, pg. 772
NAKANO VINEGAR CO., LTD.; *Int'l*, pg. 904
NASON AND CULLEN GROUP INCORPORATED; *U.S. Private*, pg. 775
NESS HOLDING CO.; *U.S. Private*, pg. 791
NEWBERG PERINI—Perini Corporation; *U.S. Public*, pg. 1278
AL NEYER, INC.; *U.S. Private*, pg. 797
NIELSEN DILLINGHAM BUILDERS, INC.—Dillingham Construction Corporation; *U.S. Private*, pg. 333
NINTEMAN CONSTRUCTION COMPANY, INC.—Sundt Corp.; *U.S. Private*, pg. 1052
NISHIMATSU CONSTRUCTION CO., LTD.; *Int'l*, pg. 942
NORCAM CONSTRUCTION COMPANY—Ritter Bros., Inc.; *U.S. Private*, pg. 934
OBERLANDER RECYCLING TECHNIK GMBH—Fried. Krupp AG; *Int'l*, pg. 513
JOHN M. OLSON COMPANY; *U.S. Private*, pg. 815
O'NEIL INDUSTRIES INC.; *U.S. Private*, pg. 817
OPUS CORP.; *U.S. Private*, pg. 818
OPUS SOUTH CORPORATION; *U.S. Private*, pg. 818
OWEN-AMES-KIMBALL CO.; *U.S. Private*, pg. 823
OWEN-AMES-KIMBALL ENGINEERING, INC.—Owen-Ames-Kimball Co.; *U.S. Private*, pg. 824
PCL-BRAUN-SIMONS LTD.—Kuwait Petroleum Corporation; *Int'l*, pg. 765
PMI—Todd & Sargent, Inc.; *U.S. Private*, pg. 1089
PALA GROUP, INC.; *U.S. Private*, pg. 834
PALA INTERSTATE—Pala Group, Inc.; *U.S. Private*, pg. 834
PAYNE & KELLER COMPANY, INC.—Jacobs Engineering Group Inc.; *U.S. Public*, pg. 921
PECK JONES CONSTRUCTION; *U.S. Private*, pg. 846
THE PEPPER COMPANIES, INC.; *U.S. Private*, pg. 851
HARRY PEPPER & ASSOCIATES; *U.S. Private*, pg. 851
PEPPER-LAWSON—The Pepper Companies, Inc.; *U.S. Private*, pg. 851
PERFORMA ENTERTAINMENT REAL ESTATE, INC.; *U.S. Private*, pg. 853
PERFORMANCE CONTRACTORS INC.; *U.S. Private*, pg. 853
PERINI BUILDING COMPANY-CENTRAL U.S. DIVISION—Perini Corporation; *U.S. Public*, pg. 1278
PERINI BUILDING CO., INC.-EASTERN U.S. DIVISION—Perini Corporation; *U.S. Public*, pg. 1278
PERINI BUILDING CO., INC. WESTERN U.S. DIVISION—Perini Corporation; *U.S. Public*, pg. 1278
PERINI CORPORATION; *U.S. Public*, pg. 1278
PERINI MANAGEMENT SERVICES, INC.—Perini Corporation; *U.S. Public*, pg. 1278
PETERS CONSTRUCTION CORP.; *U.S. Private*, pg. 856
PINKERTON & LAWS INC.; *U.S. Private*, pg. 865
PIZZAGALLI CONSTRUCTION CO.; *U.S. Private*, pg. 868
POTTER-SHACKELFORD CONSTRUCTION CO.; *U.S. Private*, pg. 877
POWER CONTRACTING & ENGINEERING CORP.; *U.S. Private*, pg. 877
POWERS CONSTRUCTION CO., INC.; *U.S. Private*, pg. 878
PRICE WOODS, INC.—Joe E. Woods, Inc.; *U.S. Private*, pg. 1187
PRIMESOUTH, INC.—SCANA Corporation; *U.S. Public*, pg. 1436
PUBLIC STORAGE, INC.; *U.S. Public*, pg. 1340
RAGNAR BENSON, INC.—The Austin Company; *U.S. Private*, pg. 99
WILLIAM A. RANDOLPH, INC.; *U.S. Private*, pg. 909
RAYTHEON COMPANY; *U.S. Public*, pg. 1364
RENTENBACH ENGINEERING COMPANY; *U.S. Private*, pg. 923
RENTOKIL INITIAL PLC—Sophus Berendsen A/S; *Int'l*, pg. 1285
RICHTER & RATNER CONTRACTING CORPORATION; *U.S. Private*, pg. 930
RITTER BROS., INC.; *U.S. Private*, pg. 933
ROCKTON ASSOCIATES, INCORPORATED—Stone & Webster, Incorporated; *U.S. Public*, pg. 1519
RODGERS BUILDERS, INC.; *U.S. Private*, pg. 939
ROONEY BROTHERS COMPANY; *U.S. Private*, pg. 943
RUDOLPH AND SLETTEN, INC.; *U.S. Private*, pg. 950
RUDOLPH/LIBBE, INC.; *U.S. Private*, pg. 950
RUFFIN BUILDING SYSTEMS, INC.; *U.S. Private*, pg. 950
THE RUHLIN COMPANY; *U.S. Private*, pg. 951
RUSCON CORP.; *U.S. Private*, pg. 952
RYAN CONSTRUCTION COMPANY—Ryan Construction Company of Minnesota, Inc.; *U.S. Private*, pg. 953
SDL CONSTRUCTION—McCarthy Building Companies; *U.S. Private*, pg. 719
SNC-LAVALIN GROUP INC.; *Int'l*, pg. 1161
SADCO LTD.—Joffko International; *U.S. Private*, pg. 589
PT SAGITA DUMEZ—Lyonnaise des Eaux S.A.; *Int'l*, pg. 823
SALEM CORPORATION—Salem Group, Inc.; *U.S. Private*, pg. 961
SCHAL BOVIS INC.—The Peninsular and Oriental Steam Navigation Company; *Int'l*, pg. 1033
F.J. SCIAME CONSTRUCTION CO. INC.; *U.S. Private*, pg. 975
SCRUFARI CONSTRUCTION CO. INC.; *U.S. Private*, pg. 977
SEKTIONSBYGGARNA AB—Skanska AB; *Int'l*, pg. 1260
SELLEN CONSTRUCTION COMPANY; *U.S. Private*, pg. 982
SERVICE PRODUCTS BUILDINGS, INC.—The Turner Corporation; *U.S. Public*, pg. 1645
SHANGHAI MASTER BUILDERS CO., LTD.—Novartis AG; *Int'l*, pg. 985
R.M. SHOEMAKER CO.; *U.S. Private*, pg. 996
SHOLODGE, INC.; *U.S. Public*, pg. 1467
SHOOK NATIONAL CORPORATION; *U.S. Private*, pg. 996
SIMON ENGINEERING PLC; *Int'l*, pg. 1251
SIMON UNITED STATES HOLDINGS INC.—Simon Engineering plc; *Int'l*, pg. 1252
SKANSKA AB; *Int'l*, pg. 1260
SKANSKA BOSTADER STOCKHOLM AB—Skanska AB; *Int'l*, pg. 1260
SKANSKA BYGG AB—Skanska AB; *Int'l*, pg. 1260
SKANSKA INTERNATIONAL BUILDING AB—Skanska AB; *Int'l*, pg. 1260
SKANSKA LONDON—Skanska AB; *Int'l*, pg. 1261
SKANSKA NORR AB—Skanska AB; *Int'l*, pg. 1260
SKANSKA OY—Skanska AB; *Int'l*, pg. 1261
SKANSKA STOCKHOLM MALARDALEN—Skanska AB; *Int'l*, pg. 1260
SKANSKA SYD—Skanska AB; *Int'l*, pg. 1260
SKANSKA (U.S.A.) INC.—Skanska AB; *Int'l*, pg. 1261
SKANSKA VAST—Skanska AB; *Int'l*, pg. 1261
GEORGE SOLLITT CONSTRUCTION; *U.S. Private*, pg. 1013
SOUTHERN INSTRUMENTS, INC.—Jacobs Engineering Group Inc.; *U.S. Public*, pg. 921
SSANGYONG ENGINEERING & CONSTRUCTION CO., LTD.—Ssangyong Business Group; *Int'l*, pg. 1291
THE STELLAR GROUP INC.; *U.S. Private*, pg. 1040
STILES CORPORATION; *U.S. Private*, pg. 1043
STONE & WEBSTER CONSTRUCTION COMPANY, INC.—Stone & Webster, Incorporated; *U.S. Public*, pg. 1519
STONE & WEBSTER, INCORPORATED; *U.S. Public*, pg. 1519
STONE & WEBSTER OVERSEAS GROUP, INC.—Stone & Webster, Incorporated; *U.S. Public*, pg. 1519
STONE & WEBSTER WORLDWIDE, INC.—Stone & Webster, Incorporated; *U.S. Public*, pg. 1519
STORA PROJECT—NCC AB; *Int'l*, pg. 899
SUITT CONSTRUCTION COMPANY, INC.—BE & K, Inc.; *U.S. Private*, pg. 106
SULZER IMMOBILIEN AG—Sulzer Ltd.; *Int'l*, pg. 1306
SULZER INFRA DEUTSCHLAND GMBH.—Sulzer Ltd.; *Int'l*, pg. 1306
SULZER INFRA (UK)—Sulzer Ltd.; *Int'l*, pg. 1306
SUNDT CORP.; *U.S. Private*, pg. 1051
SUPER HOMES LTD.—John Laing PLC; *Int'l*, pg. 796
SUPERIOR INDUSTRIES OF NEBRASKA, INC.; *U.S. Private*, pg. 1055
SVEDALA INDUSTRI AB; *Int'l*, pg. 1323
SVERDRUP CORPORATION; *U.S. Private*, pg. 1057
SWINERTON INC.; *U.S. Private*, pg. 1059
TABC, INC.—Toyota Motor Corporation; *Int'l*, pg. 1412
TAISEI CORPORATION; *Int'l*, pg. 1347
TARLTON CORPORATION; *U.S. Private*, pg. 1069
TARMAC CONSTRUCTION INTL.—Tarmac plc; *Int'l*, pg. 1355
TAYLOR WOODROW CONSTRUCTION CORP.—Taylor Woodrow plc; *Int'l*, pg. 1359
TAYLOR WOODROW INDUSTRIAL ESTATES LTD.—Taylor Woodrow plc; *Int'l*, pg. 1358
TAYLOR WOODROW INTERNATIONAL NZ LIMITED—Taylor Woodrow plc; *Int'l*, pg. 1359
TAYLOR WOODROW INTERNATIONAL PROJECTS LTD.—Taylor Woodrow plc; *Int'l*, pg. 1358
TAYLOR WOODROW MANAGEMENT & ENGINEERING LIMITED—Taylor Woodrow plc; *Int'l*, pg. 1358
TAYLOR WOODROW OF GHANA LIMITED—Taylor Woodrow plc; *Int'l*, pg. 1360
TAYLOR WOODROW OF NIGERIA LIMITED—Taylor Woodrow plc, *Int'l*, pg. 1360
TAYLOR WOODROW PLC; *Int'l*, pg. 1358
TAYLOR WOODROW-TOWELL CO. (LLC)—Taylor Woodrow plc; *Int'l*, pg. 1360
TAYSEC CONSTRUCTION LTD.—Taylor Woodrow plc; *Int'l*, pg. 1360
TAYWOOD PLANT COMPANY LTD.—Taylor Woodrow plc; *Int'l*, pg. 1359
TEAMWORK CONSTRUCTIONS PTY. LIMITED—Taylor Woodrow plc; *Int'l*, pg. 1360
TEAMWORK MALAYSIA SENDIRIAN BERHAD—Taylor Woodrow plc; *Int'l*, pg. 1360
TEAMWORK SAUDI ARABIA LIMITED—Taylor Woodrow plc; *Int'l*, pg. 1360
TEAMWORK SENDIRIAN BERHAD—Taylor Woodrow plc; *Int'l*, pg. 1360
TECHNIP; *Int'l*, pg. 1360
TECHNIP UK LTD.—Technip; *Int'l*, pg. 1361
TECNOLOGIE PROGETTI LAVORI SPA—Technip; *Int'l*, pg. 1361
TEKKEN CORPORATION; *Int'l*, pg. 1362
TESCO CO., LTD.—Skylark Co., Ltd.; *Int'l*, pg. 1262
TETRA LAVAL FOOD—Tetra Laval Group; *Int'l*, pg. 1378
TETRA PAK—Tetra Laval Group; *Int'l*, pg. 1378
THOMPSON-STARRETT CONSTRUCTION COMPANY, INC.—Elgin National Industries, Inc.; *U.S. Private*, pg. 371
TISHMAN REALTY & CONSTRUCTION CO., INC.; *U.S. Private*, pg. 1089
TODD & SARGENT, INC.; *U.S. Private*, pg. 1089
CHAS. H. TOMPKINS CO.—Philipp Holzmann AG; *Int'l*, pg. 633
TORCON, INC.; *U.S. Private*, pg. 1092
TOSHIBA ENGINEERING & CONSTRUCTION CO., LTD.—Toshiba Corporation; *Int'l*, pg. 1404
TOYO ENGINEERING CORP.—Mitsui & Co., Ltd.; *Int'l*, pg. 878
TRAFALGAR HOUSE CONSTRUCTION INC.—Kvaerner a.s.a.; *Int'l*, pg. 774
TRIBBLE & STEPHENS CO.; *U.S. Private*, pg. 1102
TURNER CARIBE, INC.—The Turner Corporation; *U.S. Public*, pg. 1646
TURNER CONSTRUCTION COMPANY—The Turner Corporation; *U.S. Public*, pg. 1645
THE TURNER CORPORATION; *U.S. Public*, pg. 1645
TURNER INTERNATIONAL INDUSTRIES, INC.—The Turner Corporation; *U.S. Public*, pg. 1646
TURNER INTERNATIONAL U.K. LTD.—The Turner Corporation; *U.S. Public*, pg. 1646
UNDERGROUND CONSTRUCTION CO., INC.; *U.S. Private*, pg. 1116
UNIVERSAL CONSTRUCTION CO.—The Turner Corporation; *U.S. Public*, pg. 1646
UNIVERSAL CONSTRUCTION COMPANY, INC.; *U.S. Private*, pg. 1127
VALLEHERMOSO, S.A.; *Int'l*, pg. 1447
VULCAN CONSTRUCTION COMPANY—The Weitz Company, Inc.; *U.S. Private*, pg. 1161
WALBRIDGE ALDINGER COMPANY; *U.S. Private*, pg. 1146
WALSH CONSTRUCTION COMPANY—Atkinson; *U.S. Public*, pg. 143
WALSH CONSTRUCTION COMPANY (WEST)—Atkinson; *U.S. Public*, pg. 143
WARM BROTHERS CONSTRUCTION COMPANY; *U.S. Private*, pg. 1150
WATERFORD FOODS IRELAND LTD.—Avonmore Waterford Group plc; *Int'l*, pg. 102
WATERFORD FOODS LIMITED—Avonmore Waterford Group plc; *Int'l*, pg. 102
WATKINS ENGINEERS & CONSTRUCTORS, INC.—Dillingham Construction Corporation; *U.S. Private*, pg. 333
WEAVER CONSTRUCTION, LLC; *U.S. Private*, pg. 1156
WEHR CONSTRUCTORS INC.; *U.S. Private*, pg. 1159
THE WEITZ COMPANY, INC.; *U.S. Private*, pg. 1160
THE WEITZ COMPANY, INC.—The Weitz Company, Inc.; *U.S. Private*, pg. 1161
WEITZ-COHEN CONSTRUCTION CO.—The Weitz Company, Inc.; *U.S. Private*, pg. 1161
WHITTENBERG CONSTRUCTION CO.; *U.S. Private*, pg. 1174
WIL-FREDS INC.; *U.S. Private*, pg. 1176
F.A. WILHELM CONSTRUCTION CO., INC.; *U.S. Private*, pg. 1176
JOE E. WOODS, INC.; *U.S. Private*, pg. 1187
H.B. ZACHRY COMPANY—H.B. Zachry; *U.S. Private*, pg. 1203

1542 — GENERAL CONTRACTORS-NONRESIDENTIAL BUILDINGS, OTHER THAN INDUSTRIAL BUILDINGS & WAREHOUSES

ADP MARSHALL CONTRACTORS INC.—Fluor Corporation; *U.S. Public*, pg. 660
AMB DEVELOPMENT GROUP LLC; *U.S. Private*, pg. 6
AMEC BUILDING LTD.—AMEC Plc; *Int'l*, pg. 16
ARB INC.; *U.S. Private*, pg. 7
J.R. ABBOTT CONSTRUCTION, INC.; *U.S. Private*, pg. 9
ABRAMS CONSTRUCTION, INC.—Abrams Industries, Inc.; *U.S. Public*, pg. 14
ABRAMS INDUSTRIES, INC.; *U.S. Public*, pg. 14
ACOUSTI ENGINEERING CO. OF FLORIDA; *U.S. Private*, pg. 14
ADOLFSON & PETERSON, INC.; *U.S. Private*, pg. 17
J.S. ALBERICI CONSTRUCTION CO., INC.; *U.S. Private*, pg. 32
ALLIANCE CONSTRUCTION SOLUTIONS, INC.; *U.S. Private*, pg. 38
AMERICAN MEDICORP DEVELOPMENT CO.—Columbia/HCA Healthcare Corporation; *U.S. Public*, pg. 403
ASHLEY INTERNATIONAL & PASCHEN; *U.S. Private*, pg. 88
ATKINSON; *U.S. Public*, pg. 143
ATKINSON INTERNATIONAL VENEZUELA—Atkinson; *U.S. Public*, pg. 143
ATLANTIC BUILDERS GROUP INC.; *U.S. Private*, pg. 95
GEORGE W. AUCH CO.; *U.S. Private*, pg. 98
THE AUCHTER COMPANY; *U.S. Private*, pg. 98
AUSHERMAN CONSTRUCTION COMPANY; *U.S. Private*, pg. 99
THE AUSTIN COMPANY; *U.S. Private*, pg. 99
AUSTIN INDUSTRIES, INC.; *U.S. Private*, pg. 99
BEC INC.; *U.S. Private*, pg. 106
BAKER MELLON STUART CONSTRUCTION, INC.—Michael Baker Corporation; *U.S. Public*, pg. 168
BARCLAY WHITE INCORPORATED; *U.S. Private*, pg. 115
BARGER BUILDERS; *U.S. Private*, pg. 116
BARNHILL CONTRACTING COMPANY; *U.S. Private*, pg. 117
BARR & BARR, INC.; *U.S. Private*, pg. 117
BARRATT CENTRAL—Barratt Developments Plc; *Int'l*, pg. 168
BARRATT COMMERCIAL—Barratt Developments Plc; *Int'l*, pg. 168
BARRATT DEVELOPMENTS PLC; *Int'l*, pg. 167

BARRATT EAST MIDLANDS—Barratt Developments Plc; *Int'l*, pg. 168
BARRATT LEEDS—Barratt Developments Plc; *Int'l*, pg. 168
BARRATT MANCHESTER—Barratt Developments Plc; *Int'l*, pg. 168
BARRATT NORTHERN—Barratt Developments Plc; *Int'l*, pg. 168
BARRATT SOUTH WALES—Barratt Developments Plc; *Int'l*, pg. 168
BARRATT SOUTHAMPTON—Barratt Developments Plc; *Int'l*, pg. 168
BARRATT SOUTHERN—Barratt Developments Plc; *Int'l*, pg. 168
BARRATT WEST SCOTLAND—Barratt Developments Plc; *Int'l*, pg. 168
BARRATT YORK—Barratt Developments Plc; *Int'l*, pg. 168
BARTLETT BRAINARD EACOTT, INC.; *U.S. Private*, pg. 118
BARTON MALOW ENTERPRISES, INC.; *U.S. Private*, pg. 120
BATSON-COOK COMPANY; *U.S. Private*, pg. 123
BATTEAST CONSTRUCTION COMPANY, INC.; *U.S. Private*, pg. 123
BAUGH CONSTRUCTION COMPANY; *U.S. Private*, pg. 123
BECHTEL CIVIL, INC.—Bechtel Group, Inc.; *U.S. Private*, pg. 128
BECON CONSTRUCTION COMPANY, INC.—Bechtel Group, Inc.; *U.S. Private*, pg. 128
BEERS CONSTRUCTION COMPANY—Skanska AB; *Int'l*, pg. 1261
RAY BELL CONSTRUCTION CO. INC.; *U.S. Private*, pg. 131
BERNARDS BROTHERS, INC.; *U.S. Private*, pg. 136
WM. BLANCHARD CO.; *U.S. Private*, pg. 148
S. BOEG-THOMSEN A/S—Taylor Woodrow plc; *Int'l*, pg. 1359
BOVIS CONSTRUCTION GROUP—The Peninsular and Oriental Steam Navigation Company; *Int'l*, pg. 1032
BRENCAL CONTRACTORS INC.—BEC Inc.; *U.S. Private*, pg. 106
BRIDGES & COMPANY, INC.; *U.S. Private*, pg. 168
FRANK BRISCOE CO. INC.; *U.S. Private*, pg. 169
BRITISH AEROSPACE P.L.C.; *Int'l*, pg. 217
BROOKFIELD HOMES LTD.—Brookfield Properties Corporation; *Int'l*, pg. 228
BROWER COMPANY—Bay Industries Inc.; *U.S. Private*, pg. 124
BROWN & ROOT LTD.—Halliburton Company; *U.S. Public*, pg. 776
BUQUET & LE BLANC INC.; *U.S. Private*, pg. 181
BURNS & ROE ENTERPRISES, INC.; *U.S. Private*, pg. 187
BURNSIDE CONSTRUCTION CO.; *U.S. Private*, pg. 187
BURRISS CORP.; *U.S. Private*, pg. 188
BUTLER MANUFACTURING COMPANY; *U.S. Public*, pg. 271
CALUMET CONSTRUCTION CORPORATION; *U.S. Private*, pg. 201
CAMOSY, INC.; *U.S. Private*, pg. 203
CAPITAL DEVELOPMENT CO.; *U.S. Private*, pg. 205
CAPITOL CONSTRUCTION GROUP, INC.; *U.S. Private*, pg. 206
THE P.J. CARLIN CONSTRUCTION COMPANY; *U.S. Private*, pg. 211
THE CEDARWOOD CONSTRUCTION COMPANY; *U.S. Private*, pg. 221
CEGELEC—Alcatel Alsthom Compagnie Generale D'Electricite; *Int'l*, pg. 52
CENTEX CONSTRUCTION COMPANY—Centex Corporation; *U.S. Public*, pg. 322
CENTEX CONSTRUCTION GROUP, INC.—Centex Corporation; *U.S. Public*, pg. 322
CENTEX CORPORATION; *U.S. Public*, pg. 322
CENTEX FORCUM-LANNOM, INC.—Centex Corporation; *U.S. Public*, pg. 322
CENTEX-RODGERS CONSTRUCTION COMPANY—Centex Corporation; *U.S. Public*, pg. 322
CENTEX-ROONEY CONSTRUCTION CO., INC.—Centex Corporation; *U.S. Public*, pg. 322
CHAMPION, INC.; *U.S. Private*, pg. 228
CHARTER BUILDERS, INC.—John Mowlem & Company plc; *Int'l*, pg. 896
F.H. CHASE, INC.; *U.S. Private*, pg. 230
LOUIS P. CIMINELLI CONSTRUCTION CO. INC.; *U.S. Private*, pg. 239
CINCINNATI UNITED CONTRACTORS; *U.S. Private*, pg. 240
CLARK CONSTRUCTION GROUP, INC.—Clark Enterprises, Inc.; *U.S. Private*, pg. 242
BARTLETT COCKE, INC.; *U.S. Private*, pg. 249
CONGAREE CONSTRUCTION CO., INC.; *U.S. Private*, pg. 263
CONSTRUCTION COUNSELLORS, INC.; *U.S. Private*, pg. 266
CONSTRUTORA DUMEZ-GTM LTDA—Lyonnaise des Eaux S.A.; *Int'l*, pg. 823
CORPORACION MAPFRE, COMPANIA INTERNACIONAL DE REASEGUROS, S.A.; *Int'l*, pg. 332
CORPOREX COMPANIES, INC.; *U.S. Private*, pg. 276
COSTAIN CONSTRUCTION LIMITED—Costain Group PLC; *Int'l*, pg. 336
THE COURT COMPANY; *U.S. Private*, pg. 279
CRANE CONSTRUCTION CO.; *U.S. Private*, pg. 286
CUNNINGHAM-LIMP DEVELOPMENT CO.; *U.S. Private*, pg. 297
DKM PROPERTIES CORPORATION—The Dyson-Kissner-Moran Corporation; *U.S. Private*, pg. 351
DPR CONSTRUCTION, INC.; *U.S. Private*, pg. 305
DAHLEM COMPANY, INC.; *U.S. Private*, pg. 306
DAW TECHNOLOGIES, INC.; *U.S. Public*, pg. 489
DAWSON CONSTRUCTION CO., INC.; *U.S. Private*, pg. 316
DEMARIA BUILDING CO. INC.; *U.S. Private*, pg. 323
DICK CORPORATION; *U.S. Private*, pg. 331
J.D. DIFFENBAUGH, INC.; *U.S. Private*, pg. 332
DILLINGHAM CONSTRUCTION CORPORATION; *U.S. Private*, pg. 333
DILLINGHAM CONSTRUCTION N.A., INC.—Dillingham Construction Corporation; *U.S. Private*, pg. 333
DIMEO CONSTRUCTION COMPANY; *U.S. Private*, pg. 333
DONLEY'S, INC.; *U.S. Private*, pg. 340
THE DONOHOE COMPANIES, INC.; *U.S. Private*, pg. 340
DOUBLE AA BUILDERS, LTD.; *U.S. Private*, pg. 341
DRAKE CONSTRUCTION COMPANY—Dunn Industries Inc.; *U.S. Private*, pg. 347
L.F. DRISCOLL CO.; *U.S. Private*, pg. 343
DUGAN & MEYERS CONSTRUCTION CO.—Dugan & Meyers Interests, Inc.; *U.S. Private*, pg. 345
DUMEZ-GTM—Lyonnaise des Eaux S.A.; *Int'l*, pg. 823
DUNLAP & CO. INC.; *U.S. Private*, pg. 346
J.E. DUNN CONSTRUCTION CO.—Dunn Industries Inc.; *U.S. Private*, pg. 347
DYCKERHOFF & WIDMANN AG; *Int'l*, pg. 423
DYNAMIC HOMES, INC.; *U.S. Public*, pg. 538
ETCD—Lyonnaise des Eaux S.A.; *Int'l*, pg. 823
EARL CONSTRUCTION COMPANY—Sundt Corp.; *U.S. Private*, pg. 1051
MARTIN K. EBY CONSTRUCTION COMPANY, INC.—Eby Corporation; *U.S. Private*, pg. 359
ECKMAN CONSTRUCTION COMPANY; *U.S. Private*, pg. 359
EDWARDS & KELCEY CONSTRUCTION, INC.—Edwards and Kelcey, Inc.; *U.S. Private*, pg. 364
EDWARDS & KELCEY WIRELESS—Edwards and Kelcey, Inc.; *U.S. Private*, pg. 364
EGIZII ELECTRIC, INC.; *U.S. Private*, pg. 366
ELKINS CONSTRUCTORS, INC.; *U.S. Private*, pg. 372
ENSERCH CORPORATION—Texas Utilities Company; *U.S. Public*, pg. 1587
A.J. ETKIN CONSTRUCTION CO.—Alex J. Etkin, Inc.; *U.S. Private*, pg. 384
ALEX J. ETKIN, INC.; *U.S. Private*, pg. 384
FAIRMONT MORTGAGE, INC.—Del Webb Corporation; *U.S. Public*, pg. 495
FAIRVIEW CONSTRUCTION, INC; *U.S. Private*, pg. 392
FARNSWORTH HOMES—Farnsworth Companies; *U.S. Private*, pg. 397
FERNWAERMEVERBUND SAAR GMBH—Saarbergwerke Aktiengesellschaft; *Int'l*, pg. 1167
J.H. FINDORFF & SON, INC.; *U.S. Private*, pg. 405
FIRST FINANCIAL BUILDING CORPORATION; *U.S. Private*, pg. 407
FISCHBACH CORPORATION—American International Group, Inc.; *U.S. Public*, pg. 84
THE FLATLEY COMPANY; *U.S. Private*, pg. 410
FLORIDA PROGRESS CORPORATION; *U.S. Public*, pg. 655
FLUOR CORPORATION; *U.S. Public*, pg. 659
FLUOR DANIEL WILLIAMS BROTHERS—Fluor Corporation; *U.S. Public*, pg. 660
FLUOR DANIEL WRIGHT LIMITED—Fluor Corporation; *U.S. Public*, pg. 660
FORD DEVELOPMENT CORPORATION; *U.S. Private*, pg. 418
FOREST CITY COMMERCIAL CONSTRUCTION COMPANY, INC.—Forest City Enterprises, Inc.; *U.S. Public*, pg. 668
4520 CORP., INC.—Blount International, Inc.; *U.S. Public*, pg. 239
THE FUSCO CORPORATION; *U.S. Private*, pg. 432
GAILEY & ROBERTS LTD.—Unilever Plc; *Int'l*, pg. 1437
GARNEY HOLDING COMPANY, INC.; *U.S. Private*, pg. 440
GENCON SERVICES, INC.—George W. Auch Co.; *U.S. Private*, pg. 98
GEUPEL DEMARS, INC.; *U.S. Private*, pg. 449
GIANT CONSTRUCTION CO., INC.—Giant Food Inc.; *U.S. Public*, pg. 741
GIFFELS TECHNOLOGIES, INC.—Giffels Associates, Inc.; *U.S. Private*, pg. 452
GILBANE BUILDING COMPANY; *U.S. Private*, pg. 452
GLENROY CONSTRUCTION CO. INC.; *U.S. Private*, pg. 456
GOSNELL BUILDERS—Pointe Group Ltd.; *U.S. Private*, pg. 873
GRANGER CONSTRUCTION CO.; *U.S. Private*, pg. 469
GRANGES HEDLUND AB—Electrolux, AB; *Int'l*, pg. 439
GRAYCOR CONSTRUCTION COMPANY INC.—Graycor Operating Companies; *U.S. Private*, pg. 472
GRAYCOR OPERATING COMPANIES; *U.S. Private*, pg. 472
GREAT PLAINS COMPANIES, INC.; *U.S. Private*, pg. 475
HBE CORPORATION/DESIGN BUILD DIVISIONS; *U.S. Private*, pg. 489
HCBECK; *U.S. Private*, pg. 490
HNTB DESIGN & BUILD—HNTB Corporation; *U.S. Private*, pg. 492
HRH CONSTRUCTION CORP.—Starrett HRH; *U.S. Private*, pg. 1035
C.F. HAGLIN & SONS; *U.S. Private*, pg. 493
HARBOUR CONTRACTORS, INC.; *U.S. Private*, pg. 500
HARDIN CONSTRUCTION GROUP, INC.; *U.S. Private*, pg. 501
HARKINS BUILDERS, INC.; *U.S. Private*, pg. 502
HARRISON CONSTRUCTION CORP.; *U.S. Private*, pg. 506
HARTZ MOUNTAIN INDUSTRIES—The Hartz Mountain Corp.; *U.S. Private*, pg. 508
HASEKO (CALIFORNIA) INC.—Haseko Corporation; *Int'l*, pg. 600
HASEKO (HAWAII) INC.—Haseko Corporation; *Int'l*, pg. 600
HAWAIIAN DREDGING & CONSTRUCTION COMPANY—Dillingham Construction Corporation; *U.S. Private*, pg. 333
PAUL HEMMER CONSTRUCTION COMPANY; *U.S. Private*, pg. 521
JOSEPH J. HENDERSON & SON, INC.; *U.S. Private*, pg. 521
HENSEL PHELPS CONSTRUCTION CO.; *U.S. Private*, pg. 523
HICKORY CONSTRUCTION COMPANY; *U.S. Private*, pg. 525
HILLEN & ROOSEN B.V.—Philipp Holzmann AG; *Int'l*, pg. 633
HOCHTIEF LIMITED—Hochtief AG; *Int'l*, pg. 624
HOFFMAN CORPORATION; *U.S. Private*, pg. 532
HOLDER CORPORATION; *U.S. Private*, pg. 533
HOMES & SON CONTRACTORS, INC.; *U.S. Private*, pg. 537
E.W. HOWELL COMPANY, INC.—Obayashi Corporation; *Int'l*, pg. 995
HUGHES CONSTRUCTION, INC.; *U.S. Private*, pg. 546
ICF KAISER ENGINEERS, INC.—ICF Kaiser International Inc.; *U.S. Public*, pg. 853
ICF KAISER INTERNATIONAL INC.; *U.S. Public*, pg. 852
IHC GROUP, INC.; *U.S. Private*, pg. 555
IFFLAND KAVANAGH WATERBURY, PLLC—Edwards and Kelcey, Inc.; *U.S. Private*, pg. 364
IMBAU INDUSTRIELLES BAUEN GMBH—Philipp Holzmann AG; *Int'l*, pg. 633
INLAND CONCRETE CONSTRUCTORS—J.D. Diffenbaugh, Inc.; *U.S. Private*, pg. 332
INMAN CONSTRUCTION CORPORATION; *U.S. Private*, pg. 564
ISEMOTO CONTRACTING CO. LTD.; *U.S. Private*, pg. 575
JGC CORPORATION; *Int'l*, pg. 697
JM BYGGNADS OCH FASTIGHETS AB—Skanska AB; *Int'l*, pg. 1260
JACOBS ENGINEERING GROUP INC.; *U.S. Public*, pg. 921
J. JARVIS & SONS P.L.C.—Jarvis Plc; *Int'l*, pg. 705
JARVIS PLC; *Int'l*, pg. 705
JENKINS & ASSOCIATES; *U.S. Private*, pg. 585
C.G. JENSEN A/S—Skanska AB; *Int'l*, pg. 1261
G.E. JOHNSON CONSTRUCTION CO., INC.; *U.S. Private*, pg. 591
J.A. JONES, INC.—Philipp Holzmann AG; *Int'l*, pg. 633
M.B. KAHN CONSTRUCTION CO., INC.; *U.S. Private*, pg. 604
KAJIMA CORPORATION; *Int'l*, pg. 721
KAJIMA INTERNATIONAL, INC.—Kajima Corporation; *Int'l*, pg. 722
KAUFMAN AND BROAD DEVELOPPEMENT—Kaufman and Broad Home Corporation; *U.S. Public*, pg. 945
KEATING BUILDING CORP.; *U.S. Private*, pg. 610
DANIEL J. KEATING CO.; *U.S. Private*, pg. 610
KELLER CONSTRUCTION COMPANY LTD.; *U.S. Private*, pg. 612
KELSEY CONSTRUCTION, INC.; *U.S. Private*, pg. 613
KIEWIT CONSTRUCTION GROUP, INC.—Peter Kiewit Sons Inc.; *U.S. Private*, pg. 619
PETER KIEWIT SONS INC.; *U.S. Private*, pg. 619
KITCHELL CORPORATION; *U.S. Private*, pg. 624
KJELLSTROM & LEE, INC.—Gilbane Building Company; *U.S. Private*, pg. 453
KNUTSON CONSTRUCTION CO.; *U.S. Private*, pg. 627
KOKOSING CONSTRUCTION COMPANY, INC.; *U.S. Private*, pg. 631
KOLL CO.; *U.S. Private*, pg. 631
KVAERNER ROSENBERG A/S ROSENBERG VERFT—Kvaerner a.s.a.; *Int'l*, pg. 769
LTB—Linbeck Construction Corp; *U.S. Private*, pg. 668
LTB WARD CONSTRUCTORS, INC.—Dunn Industries Inc.; *U.S. Private*, pg. 347
ROBERT E. LAMB, INC.; *U.S. Private*, pg. 644
THE LATHROP COMPANY—The Turner Corporation; *U.S. Public*, pg. 1645
THE LAW COMPANY, INC.; *U.S. Private*, pg. 653
LEHRER MCGOVERN BOVIS INC.—The Peninsular and Oriental Steam Navigation Company; *Int'l*, pg. 1035
LENNAR COMMERCIAL PROPERTIES, INC.—Lennar Corporation; *U.S. Public*, pg. 988
LENNAR CORPORATION; *U.S. Public*, pg. 987
LIN & ROE COMPANY—Burns & Roe Enterprises, Inc.; *U.S. Private*, pg. 187
LINBECK CONSTRUCTION CORP; *U.S. Private*, pg. 667
LINCOLN PROPERTY CO., NORTHERN CALIFORNIA—Lincoln Property Company; *U.S. Private*, pg. 668
LINKOUS CONSTRUCTION COMPANY, INC.; *U.S. Private*, pg. 669
LOMBARD COMPANY; *U.S. Private*, pg. 673
LOOMIS BROTHERS, INC.; *U.S. Private*, pg. 675
T.A. LOVING COMPANY; *U.S. Private*, pg. 677
MCC GROUP, L.L.C.; *U.S. Private*, pg. 686
MCDR, INC.; *U.S. Private*, pg. 686
MPS CORPORATION; *U.S. Private*, pg. 687
MAESCHER INDUSTRIES, INC.; *U.S. Private*, pg. 694
MANHATTAN CONSTRUCTION COMPANY—Rooney Brothers Company; *U.S. Private*, pg. 943
MASHBURN CONSTRUCTION COMPANY; *U.S. Private*, pg. 711
MASTER BUILDERS INC.—Viag AG; *Int'l*, pg. 1465
MASTER BUILDERS TECHNOLOGIES LTD.—Viag AG; *Int'l*, pg. 1465
MATRIX BUILDING CO., INC.—Maescher Industries, Inc.; *U.S. Private*, pg. 694
MAY DESIGN & CONSTRUCTION CO.—The May Department Stores Company; *U.S. Public*, pg. 1064
MCCARTHY BROTHERS CO.—McCarthy Building Companies; *U.S. Private*, pg. 719
MCCARTHY BUILDING COMPANIES; *U.S. Private*, pg. 719
J.H. MCCORMICK, INC.; *U.S. Private*, pg. 720
MCCRORY CONSTRUCTION CO., INC.; *U.S. Private*, pg. 720
JAMES MCHUGH CONSTRUCTION CO.; *U.S. Private*, pg. 721
FRANK MESSER & SONS CONSTRUCTION CO.; *U.S. Private*, pg. 734
METRIC CONSTRUCTORS, INC.—Philipp Holzmann AG; *Int'l*, pg. 633

MID ATLANTIC CONSTRUCTION, INC.—Rodgers Builders, Inc.; *U.S. Private*, pg. 939
MILLER BUILDING CORP.; *U.S. Private*, pg. 746
H. MILLER & SONS, INC.—Lennar Corporation; *U.S. Public*, pg. 989
W.G. MILLS, INC.; *U.S. Private*, pg. 749
MING SURVEYORS, INC.—Hoffman Corporation; *U.S. Private*, pg. 532
THE MONAHAN COMPANY; *U.S. Private*, pg. 756
MONARCH CONSTRUCTION COMPANY; *U.S. Private*, pg. 757
MORLEY BUILDERS; *U.S. Private*, pg. 761
MORSE DIESEL INTERNATIONAL, INC.; *U.S. Private*, pg. 762
M.A. MORTENSON COMPANY; *U.S. Private*, pg. 763
JOHN MOWLEM & COMPANY PLC; *Int'l*, pg. 896
MOZEL DEVELOPMENT CORP.; *U.S. Private*, pg. 765
MULACH STEEL CORPORATION; *U.S. Private*, pg. 766
MUSKEGON CONSTRUCTION COMPANY—Owen-Ames-Kimball Co.; *U.S. Private*, pg. 824
MYRICK CONSTRUCTION INC.; *U.S. Private*, pg. 771
NC BUILDERS INC.—Nason and Cullen Group Incorporated; *U.S. Private*, pg. 775
NCC AB; *Int'l*, pg. 898
NCC ESKILSTUNA—NCC AB; *Int'l*, pg. 899
NABHOLZ CONSTRUCTION CORP.; *U.S. Private*, pg. 772
NAMKWANG ENGINEERING & CONSTRUCTION CO., LTD.—Ssangyong Business Group; *Int'l*, pg. 1291
NASON AND CULLEN GROUP INCORPORATED; *U.S. Private*, pg. 775
NEWBERG PERINI—Perini Corporation; *U.S. Public*, pg. 1278
AL NEYER, INC.; *U.S. Private*, pg. 797
NIELSEN DILLINGHAM BUILDERS, INC.—Dillingham Construction Corporation; *U.S. Private*, pg. 333
NINTEMAN CONSTRUCTION COMPANY, INC.—Sundt Corp.; *U.S. Private*, pg. 1052
NITTSU SHOJI CO., LTD.—Nippon Express Co., Ltd.; *Int'l*, pg. 934
NORD FRANCE S.A.—Philipp Holzmann AG; *Int'l*, pg. 634
JOHN M. OLSON COMPANY; *U.S. Private*, pg. 815
OLTMANS CONSTRUCTION COMPANY; *U.S. Private*, pg. 815
OMEGA ENVIRONMENTAL SERVICES—Omega Environmental Inc.; *U.S. Public*, pg. 1222
O'NEIL INDUSTRIES INC.; *U.S. Private*, pg. 817
OPUS CORP.; *U.S. Private*, pg. 818
OPUS SOUTH CORPORATION; *U.S. Private*, pg. 818
OWEN-AMES-KIMBALL CO.; *U.S. Private*, pg. 823
OWEN-AMES-KIMBALL ENGINEERING, INC.—Owen-Ames-Kimball Co.; *U.S. Private*, pg. 824
CHARLES PANKOW BUILDERS, LTD.; *U.S. Private*, pg. 836
PARLIAMENT COMPANY; *U.S. Private*, pg. 840
PATTEN-BEERS CONSTRUCTORS—Skanska AB; *Int'l*, pg. 1261
PECK JONES CONSTRUCTION; *U.S. Private*, pg. 846
THE PEPPER COMPANIES, INC.; *U.S. Private*, pg. 851
PEPPER-LAWSON—The Pepper Companies, Inc.; *U.S. Private*, pg. 851
PERINI BUILDING COMPANY-CENTRAL U.S. DIVISION—Perini Corporation; *U.S. Public*, pg. 1278
PERINI BUILDING CO., INC.-EASTERN U.S. DIVISION—Perini Corporation; *U.S. Public*, pg. 1278
PERINI BUILDING CO., INC. WESTERN U.S. DIVISION—Perini Corporation; *U.S. Public*, pg. 1278
PERINI CORPORATION; *U.S. Public*, pg. 1278
PERINI MANAGEMENT SERVICES, INC.—Perini Corporation; *U.S. Public*, pg. 1278
GERALD H. PHIPPS, INC.; *U.S. Private*, pg. 862
PINKERTON & LAWS INC.; *U.S. Private*, pg. 865
PIZZAGALLI CONSTRUCTION CO.; *U.S. Private*, pg. 868
POWER CONTRACTING & ENGINEERING CORP.; *U.S. Private*, pg. 877
POWERS CONSTRUCTION CO., INC.; *U.S. Private*, pg. 878
PRECISION ASBESTOS ABATEMENT COMPANY—Hoffman Corporation; *U.S. Private*, pg. 532
PRECISION CONSTRUCTION COMPANY—Hoffman Corporation; *U.S. Private*, pg. 532
RAGNAR BENSON, INC.—The Austin Company; *U.S. Private*, pg. 99
WILLIAM A. RANDOLPH, INC.; *U.S. Private*, pg. 909
REDLAND AGGREGATES LTD.—Redland PLC; *Int'l*, pg. 1090
REECE-CAMPBELL, INC.; *U.S. Private*, pg. 916
RENTENBACH ENGINEERING COMPANY; *U.S. Private*, pg. 923
RICHTER & RATNER CONTRACTING CORPORATION; *U.S. Private*, pg. 930
RODGERS BUILDERS, INC.; *U.S. Private*, pg. 939
ROONEY BROTHERS COMPANY; *U.S. Private*, pg. 943
RUDOLPH AND SLETTEN, INC.; *U.S. Private*, pg. 950
RUDOLPH/LIBBE, INC.; *U.S. Private*, pg. 950
THE RUHLIN COMPANY; *U.S. Private*, pg. 951
RUSCON CORP.; *U.S. Private*, pg. 952
H.J. RUSSELL & CO.; *U.S. Private*, pg. 952
RYAN CONSTRUCTION COMPANY—Ryan Construction Company of Minnesota, Inc.; *U.S. Private*, pg. 953
RYCO-ALBERICI, LTD.—J.S. Alberici Construction Co., Inc.; *U.S. Private*, pg. 32
SDL CONSTRUCTION—McCarthy Building Companies; *U.S. Private*, pg. 719
SNC-LAVALIN GROUP INC.; *Int'l*, pg. 1161
SADUC—Lyonnaise des Eaux S.A.; *Int'l*, pg. 823
SATO KOGYO CO., LTD.; *Int'l*, pg. 1197
SCHAL BOVIS INC.—The Peninsular and Oriental Steam Navigation Company; *Int'l*, pg. 1033
SCHUMACHER-DUGAN CONSTRUCTION; *U.S. Private*, pg. 973
F.J. SCIAME CONSTRUCTION CO. INC.; *U.S. Private*, pg. 975
SEKTIONSBYGGARNA AB—Skanska AB; *Int'l*, pg. 1260
SELLEN CONSTRUCTION COMPANY; *U.S. Private*, pg. 982
SHANGHAI MASTER BUILDERS CO., LTD.—Novartis AG; *Int'l*, pg. 985
SHIMIZU CORPORATION; *Int'l*, pg. 1233
R.M. SHOEMAKER CO.; *U.S. Private*, pg. 996
SHOLODGE, INC.; *U.S. Public*, pg. 1467
SHOOK NATIONAL CORPORATION; *U.S. Private*, pg. 996
SIOUX FALLS CONSTRUCTION COMPANY; *U.S. Private*, pg. 1003
SKANSKA AB; *Int'l*, pg. 1260
SKANSKA BOSTADER STOCKHOLM AB—Skanska AB; *Int'l*, pg. 1260
SKANSKA BYGG AB—Skanska AB; *Int'l*, pg. 1260
SKANSKA INTERNATIONAL BUILDING AB—Skanska AB; *Int'l*, pg. 1260
SKANSKA NORR AB—Skanska AB; *Int'l*, pg. 1260
SKANSKA OY—Skanska AB; *Int'l*, pg. 1261
SKANSKA STOCKHOLM MALARDALEN—Skanska AB; *Int'l*, pg. 1260
SKANSKA SYD—Skanska AB; *Int'l*, pg. 1260
SKANSKA (U.S.A.) INC.—Skanska AB; *Int'l*, pg. 1261
SKANSKA VAST—Skanska AB; *Int'l*, pg. 1261
SKYLINE CHILI, INC.; *U.S. Public*, pg. 1475
SMITHGROUP, INC.; *U.S. Private*, pg. 1010
SOCIETE GENERALE POUR LES TECHNIQUES NOUVELLES S.A. (SGN)—Technip; *Int'l*, pg. 1361
GEORGE SOLLITT CONSTRUCTION; *U.S. Private*, pg. 1013
SORDONI SKANSKA CONSTRUCTION CO.—Skanska AB; *Int'l*, pg. 1261
SPAGHETTI WAREHOUSE CONSTRUCTION—Spaghetti Warehouse, Inc.; *U.S. Public*, pg. 1495
THE SPANOS COMPANIES; *U.S. Private*, pg. 1020
SSANGYONG BUSINESS GROUP; *Int'l*, pg. 1291
SSANGYONG ENGINEERING & CONSTRUCTION CO., LTD.—Ssangyong Business Group; *Int'l*, pg. 1291
STARRETT HRH; *U.S. Private*, pg. 1035
THE STELLAR GROUP INC.; *U.S. Private*, pg. 1040
STILES CORPORATION; *U.S. Private*, pg. 1043
THE STONE BUILDING COMPANY—Dimeo Construction Company; *U.S. Private*, pg. 334
STORA PROJECT—NCC AB; *Int'l*, pg. 899
STREIF AG—Hochtief AG; *Int'l*, pg. 623
SUITT CONSTRUCTION COMPANY, INC.—BE & K, Inc.; *U.S. Private*, pg. 106
SULLIVAN & COZART INC.; *U.S. Private*, pg. 1049
SUNDT CORP.; *U.S. Private*, pg. 1051
SVERDRUP CORPORATION; *U.S. Private*, pg. 1057
SWINERTON INC.; *U.S. Private*, pg. 1059
TAISEI AMERICA CORP.—Taisei Corporation; *Int'l*, pg. 1347
TAISEI CORPORATION; *Int'l*, pg. 1347
TAYLOR WOODROW CONSTRUCTION CORP.—Taylor Woodrow plc; *Int'l*, pg. 1359
TAYLOR WOODROW PLC; *Int'l*, pg. 1358
TAYLOR WOODROW PROPERTY CO. OF AMERICA INC.—Taylor Woodrow plc; *Int'l*, pg. 1359
TECHNIP; *Int'l*, pg. 1360
TECHNIP UK LTD.—Technip; *Int'l*, pg. 1361
TECNOLOGIE PROGETTI LAVORI SPA—Technip; *Int'l*, pg. 1361
TEKKEN CORPORATION; *Int'l*, pg. 1362
TILBURY DOUGLAS PLC—Philipp Holzmann AG; *Int'l*, pg. 634
TOKYU CORPORATION; *Int'l*, pg. 1394
CHAS. H. TOMPKINS CO.—Philipp Holzmann AG; *Int'l*, pg. 633
TORCON, INC.; *U.S. Private*, pg. 1092
TRAVAUX CONSTRUCTION, INC.—Forest City Enterprises, Inc.; *U.S. Public*, pg. 670
TRAYLOR BROTHERS, INC.; *U.S. Private*, pg. 1098
TRIBBLE & STEPHENS CO.; *U.S. Private*, pg. 1102
TURNER CARIBE, INC.—The Turner Corporation; *U.S. Public*, pg. 1646
TURNER CONSTRUCTION COMPANY—The Turner Corporation; *U.S. Public*, pg. 1645
THE TURNER CORPORATION; *U.S. Public*, pg. 1645
TURNER INTERNATIONAL INDUSTRIES, INC.—The Turner Corporation; *U.S. Public*, pg. 1646
TURNER INTERNATIONAL U.K. LTD.—The Turner Corporation; *U.S. Public*, pg. 1646
TURNER STEINER INTERNATIONAL—The Turner Corporation; *U.S. Public*, pg. 1646
TUTOR-SALIBA CORPORATION; *U.S. Private*, pg. 1111
UNDERGROUND CONSTRUCTION CO., INC.; *U.S. Private*, pg. 1116
UNIVERSAL CONSTRUCTION CO.—The Turner Corporation; *U.S. Public*, pg. 1646
UNIVERSAL CONSTRUCTION COMPANY, INC.; *U.S. Private*, pg. 1127
WALBRIDGE ALDINGER COMPANY; *U.S. Private*, pg. 1146
WALBRIDGE ALDINGER COMPANY—Walbridge Aldinger Company; *U.S. Private*, pg. 1147
WALSH CONSTRUCTION COMPANY—Atkinson; *U.S. Public*, pg. 143
WALSH CONSTRUCTION CO. OF ILLINOIS—Walsh Group; *U.S. Private*, pg. 1148
WALSH CONSTRUCTION COMPANY (WEST)—Atkinson; *U.S. Public*, pg. 143
WARM BROTHERS CONSTRUCTION COMPANY; *U.S. Private*, pg. 1150
WARMINGTON HOMES; *U.S. Private*, pg. 1150
WATKINS ENGINEERS & CONSTRUCTORS, INC.—Dillingham Construction Corporation; *U.S. Private*, pg. 333
WEAVER CONSTRUCTION, LLC; *U.S. Private*, pg. 1156
WEHR CONSTRUCTORS INC.; *U.S. Private*, pg. 1159
WHITTENBERG CONSTRUCTION CO.; *U.S. Private*, pg. 1174
WIL-FREDS INC.; *U.S. Private*, pg. 1176
F.A. WILHELM CONSTRUCTION CO., INC.; *U.S. Private*, pg. 1176
WILLIAMS COMPANY OF ORLANDO, INC.; *U.S. Private*, pg. 1177
WITCHER CONSTRUCTION CO.; *U.S. Private*, pg. 1185
WITCHER CONSTRUCTION COMPANY—Dunn Industries Inc.; *U.S. Private*, pg. 347
JOE E. WOODS, INC.; *U.S. Private*, pg. 1187
WORLD TRADE CENTER—Taylor Woodrow plc; *Int'l*, pg. 1359
H.B. ZACHRY COMPANY—H.B. Zachry; *U.S. Private*, pg. 1203

1611 — HIGHWAY & STREET CONSTRUCTION, EXCEPT ELEVATED HIGHWAYS

A-E DIVISION—Central Allied Enterprises; *U.S. Private*, pg. 222
APAC/BALLENGER PAVING COMPANY, INC.—Ashland, Inc.; *U.S. Public*, pg. 139
APAC HOLDINGS, INC.—Ashland, Inc.; *U.S. Public*, pg. 139
ARC CONBLOC LIMITED—Hanson PLC; *Int'l*, pg. 592
AJAX PAVING INDUSTRIES INC.; *U.S. Private*, pg. 29
AMICK CONSTRUCTION LTD.; *U.S. Private*, pg. 66
ANDERSON BROTHERS CONSTRUCTION BRAINERD; *U.S. Private*, pg. 72
ARCON CONSTRUCTION CO., INC.; *U.S. Private*, pg. 80
ASHLAND, INC.; *U.S. Public*, pg. 138
ATKINSON CONSTRUCTION—Atkinson; *U.S. Public*, pg. 143
ATLAS STONE PRODUCTS LIMITED—Hanson PLC; *Int'l*, pg. 592
BFC CIVIL—BFC Construction Corporation; *Int'l*, pg. 118
BFC CONSTRUCTION CORPORATION; *Int'l*, pg. 118
BACCO CONSTRUCTION CO.; *U.S. Private*, pg. 109
BAKER MELLON STUART CONSTRUCTION, INC.—Michael Baker Corporation; *U.S. Public*, pg. 168
BARBER BROTHERS CONTRACTING COMPANY; *U.S. Private*, pg. 115
BARNHILL CONTRACTING COMPANY; *U.S. Private*, pg. 117
BASIC CONSTRUCTION COMPANY; *U.S. Private*, pg. 121
BECHTEL CIVIL, INC.—Bechtel Group, Inc.; *U.S. Private*, pg. 128
BECON CONSTRUCTION COMPANY, INC.—Bechtel Group, Inc.; *U.S. Private*, pg. 128
BITUMINOUS ROADWAYS, INC.; *U.S. Private*, pg. 146
BIZZACK INC.; *U.S. Private*, pg. 146
D.H. BLATTNER & SONS, INC.; *U.S. Private*, pg. 148
BORDER STATES PAVING, INC.; *U.S. Private*, pg. 160
DAVID A. BRAMBLE, INC.; *U.S. Private*, pg. 165
CAPITAL PAVING CO., INC.—Killearn Properties, Inc.; *U.S. Public*, pg. 956
CARDER, INC.; *U.S. Private*, pg. 208
JOHN CARLO INC.; *U.S. Private*, pg. 211
CENTRAL ALLIED ENTERPRISES; *U.S. Private*, pg. 222
CLARK CONSTRUCTION GROUP, INC.—Clark Enterprises, Inc.; *U.S. Private*, pg. 242
COSTAIN INTERNATIONAL LIMITED—Costain Group PLC; *Int'l*, pg. 336
J.B. COXWELL CONTRACT, INC.; *U.S. Private*, pg. 283
CROWDER CONSTRUCTION CO.; *U.S. Private*, pg. 291
CURRAN GROUP, INC.; *U.S. Private*, pg. 297
DEMIX CONSTRUCTION—Holderbank Financiere Glaris Ltd.; *Int'l*, pg. 629
DENTON ENTERPRISES INC.; *U.S. Private*, pg. 325
DEPEW DEVELOPMENT INC.; *U.S. Private*, pg. 326
DEVCON INTERNATIONAL CORP.; *U.S. Public*, pg. 502
DICKERSON CAROLINA, INC.—The Dickerson Group, Inc.; *U.S. Private*, pg. 331
THE DICKERSON GROUP, INC.; *U.S. Private*, pg. 331
DICKERSON, INC.—The Dickerson Group, Inc.; *U.S. Private*, pg. 331
DILLINGHAM CONSTRUCTION CORPORATION; *U.S. Private*, pg. 333
DOLPHIN CONSTRUCTION CO.—Texas Industries, Inc.; *U.S. Public*, pg. 1585
JAMES H. DREW CORP.—Medusa Corporation; *U.S. Public*, pg. 1084
DUFFERIN CONSTRUCTION—Holderbank Financiere Glaris Ltd.; *Int'l*, pg. 628
DUNN INVESTMENT CO.; *U.S. Private*, pg. 347
DYCKERHOFF & WIDMANN AG; *Int'l*, pg. 423
DYCKERHOFF & WIDMANN GESELLSCHAFT M.B.H.—Dyckerhoff & Widmann AG; *Int'l*, pg. 424
EMPRESAS ICA SOCIEDAD CONTROLADORA S.A.C.V.; *Int'l*, pg. 454
THE FLETCHER CONSTRUCTION COMPANY LIMITED—Fletcher Challenge Limited; *Int'l*, pg. 495
FREHNER CONSTRUCTION COMPANY, INC.; *U.S. Private*, pg. 426
GEORGE & LYNCH, INC.; *U.S. Private*, pg. 448
GILPATRICK CONSTRUCTION COMPANY, INC; *U.S. Private*, pg. 454
GILVIN-TERRILL INC.; *U.S. Private*, pg. 455
GOHMANN ASPHALT & CONSTRUCTION INC.; *U.S. Private*, pg. 459
GRANITE CONSTRUCTION INCORPORATED; *U.S. Public*, pg. 759
GREAT LAKES CONSTRUCTION CO.; *U.S. Private*, pg. 474
HWZ, HOLLANDSCHE WEGENBOUW ZANEN B.V.—Hollandsche Beton Groep NV; *Int'l*, pg. 630
HAINES KIBBLEHOUSE; *U.S. Private*, pg. 494
HALL CONTRACTING CORP.; *U.S. Private*, pg. 495
HARBERT CORPORATION; *U.S. Private*, pg. 500
HARPER BROS., INC.; *U.S. Private*, pg. 504
HAWAIIAN DREDGING & CONSTRUCTION COMPANY—Dillingham Construction Corporation; *U.S. Private*, pg. 333
HEMPT BROTHERS, INC.; *U.S. Private*, pg. 521
HENSEL PHELPS CONSTRUCTION CO.; *U.S. Private*, pg. 523
HERCULES GRANDLAGGNING AB—NCC AB; *Int'l*, pg. 899

HILLS MATERIALS CO.—Northwestern Engineering Co.; *U.S. Private*, pg. 806
HOCHTIEF AG; *Int'l*, pg. 623
HOLLANDSCHE BETON GROEP NV; *Int'l*, pg. 630
HUBBARD CONSTRUCTION CO.; *U.S. Private*, pg. 544
THE HUNT CORPORATION; *U.S. Private*, pg. 548
HUNTER CONTRACTING COMPANY; *U.S. Private*, pg. 549
HYCON, INC.—Pitt-Des Moines, Inc.; *U.S. Public*, pg. 1304
HYUNDAI ENGINEERING & CONSTRUCTION CO., LTD.—Hyundai Motor Company; *Int'l*, pg. 641
IA CONSTRUCTION CORP.; *U.S. Private*, pg. 552
ICOPAL A/S; *Int'l*, pg. 658
INTERBETON B.V.—Hollandsche Beton Groep NV; *Int'l*, pg. 630
AL JOHNSON CONSTRUCTION CO.; *U.S. Private*, pg. 590
LEGRAND JOHNSON CONSTRUCTION CO.; *U.S. Private*, pg. 591
J.A. JONES, INC.—Philipp Holzmann AG; *Int'l*, pg. 633
JOHN R. JURGENSEN CO.—Valley Asphalt Corporation; *U.S. Private*, pg. 1131
P.J. KEATING COMPANY; *U.S. Private*, pg. 610
KIEWIT CONSTRUCTION GROUP, INC.—Peter Kiewit Sons Inc.; *U.S. Private*, pg. 619
PETER KIEWIT SONS INC.; *U.S. Private*, pg. 619
KARL KOCH ERECTING CO. INC.—Skanska AB; *Int'l*, pg. 1261
KOKOSING CONSTRUCTION COMPANY, INC.; *U.S. Private*, pg. 631
KORMAN SERVICES, L.P.; *U.S. Private*, pg. 632
LA COMPAGNIE FOUNDATION LIMITEE—BFC Construction Corporation; *Int'l*, pg. 118
LAKESIDE INDUSTRIES; *U.S. Private*, pg. 644
THE LANE CONSTRUCTION CORP.; *U.S. Private*, pg. 649
C.J. LANGENFELDER & SON, INC.; *U.S. Private*, pg. 650
EDWARD C. LEVY CO.; *U.S. Private*, pg. 664
LINEAR DYNAMICS INC.; *U.S. Private*, pg. 668
T.A. LOVING COMPANY; *U.S. Private*, pg. 677
MEDUSA CORPORATION; *U.S. Public*, pg. 1084
METROPOLITAN ASPHALT, INC.—Peter A. Basile Sons Inc.; *U.S. Private*, pg. 121
MILESTONE CONTRACTORS INC.; *U.S. Private*, pg. 745
MITSUI ROAD CO., LTD.—Mitsui & Co., Ltd.; *Int'l*, pg. 877
MONTEREY CONSTRUCTION COMPANY—Atkinson; *U.S. Public*, pg. 143
MOUNTAIN STATES CONSTRUCTORS, INC.; *U.S. Private*, pg. 764
JOHN MOWLEM & COMPANY PLC; *Int'l*, pg. 896
NCC AB; *Int'l*, pg. 898
NCC ESKILSTUNA—NCC AB; *Int'l*, pg. 899
NORTHWESTERN ENGINEERING CO.; *U.S. Private*, pg. 806
EDMUND NUTTALL LTD.—Hollandsche Beton Groep NV; *Int'l*, pg. 630
ORLANDO PAVING COMPANY—Hubbard Construction Co.; *U.S. Private*, pg. 544
OVERSTREET PAVING COMPANY; *U.S. Private*, pg. 823
PARK CONSTRUCTION COMPANY; *U.S. Private*, pg. 839
PECKHAM INDUSTRIES, INC.; *U.S. Private*, pg. 846
PERINI BUILDING CO., INC. U.S. HEAVY DIVISION—Perini Corporation; *U.S. Public*, pg. 1278
PERINI BUILDING CO., INC. WESTERN U.S. DIVISION—Perini Corporation; *U.S. Public*, pg. 1278
PERINI MANAGEMENT SERVICES, INC.—Perini Corporation; *U.S. Public*, pg. 1278
PERINI-METROPOLITAN NEW YORK DIV.—Perini Corporation; *U.S. Public*, pg. 1278
PETRICCA INDUSTRIES, INC.; *U.S. Private*, pg. 858
PIKE INDUSTRIES INC.—CRH, plc; *Int'l*, pg. 242
QUEBEC & MARITIMES DIV. ST. LAWRENCE CEMENT—Holderbank Financiere Glaris Ltd.; *Int'l*, pg. 629
REA CONSTRUCTION CO.—Philipp Holzmann AG; *Int'l*, pg. 633
REDLAND AGGREGATES LTD.—Redland PLC; *Int'l*, pg. 1090
REDLAND PLC; *Int'l*, pg. 1090
RIETH-RILEY CONSTRUCTION CO. INC.; *U.S. Private*, pg. 930
RISSLER & MCMURRY COMPANY; *U.S. Private*, pg. 933
RITCHIE CORPORATION; *U.S. Private*, pg. 933
ROGERS GROUP INC.; *U.S. Private*, pg. 939
THE RUHLIN COMPANY; *U.S. Private*, pg. 951
ST. LAWRENCE CEMENT INC.—Holderbank Financiere Glaris Ltd.; *Int'l*, pg. 628
H.E. SARGENT, INC.; *U.S. Private*, pg. 966
SCHEID STRASSENBAUGESELLSCHAFT MBH—Philipp Holzmann AG; *Int'l*, pg. 633
SCHUMACHER-DUGAN CONSTRUCTION; *U.S. Private*, pg. 973
SHEPHERD CONSTRUCTION CO., INC.; *U.S. Private*, pg. 993
SIOUX FALLS CONSTRUCTION COMPANY; *U.S. Private*, pg. 1003
SKANSKA (U.S.A.) INC.—Skanska AB; *Int'l*, pg. 1261
SLATTERY ASSOCIATES INC.—Skanska AB; *Int'l*, pg. 1261
SOUTHERN PAVING CO.—LeGrand Johnson Construction Co.; *U.S. Private*, pg. 591
STABLER COMPANIES, INC.; *U.S. Private*, pg. 1028
STABLER CONSTRUCTION COMPANY—Stabler Companies, Inc.; *U.S. Private*, pg. 1028
STORA PROJECT—NCC AB; *Int'l*, pg. 899
SUNDT CORP.; *U.S. Private*, pg. 1051
SVERDRUP CORPORATION; *U.S. Private*, pg. 1057
TAISEI CORPORATION; *Int'l*, pg. 1347
TAISEI ROTEC CORP.—Taisei Corporation; *Int'l*, pg. 1347
TARMAC (ABU DHABI) LTD.—Tarmac plc; *Int'l*, pg. 1355
TARMAC CANADA INC.—Tarmac plc; *Int'l*, pg. 1355
TEERBAU GMBH—Ruetgers A.G.; *Int'l*, pg. 1148
A. TEICHERT & SON, INC.; *U.S. Private*, pg. 1072
THOMPSON-MCCULLY CO.; *U.S. Private*, pg. 1083
TILCON, INC.; *U.S. Private*, pg. 1086
TRAFALGAR HOUSE TECHNOLOGY LIMITED (MAPLE CROSS HOUSE)—Kvaerner a.s.a.; *Int'l*, pg. 774
TURNER INDUSTRIES; *U.S. Private*, pg. 1109
VALLEY ASPHALT CORPORATION; *U.S. Private*, pg. 1131
VIRGINIA PAVING CO.—The Lane Construction Corp.; *U.S. Private*, pg. 649
VULCAN MATERIALS COMPANY; *U.S. Public*, pg. 1725
WESTERN MOBILE INC.—Redland PLC; *Int'l*, pg. 1091
RALPH C. WILSON ENTERPRISES; *U.S. Private*, pg. 1181
WINDSOR SERVICE, INC.—Haines Kibblehouse; *U.S. Private*, pg. 494
H.B. ZACHRY COMPANY—H.B. Zachry; *U.S. Private*, pg. 1203

1622 — BRIDGE, TUNNEL & ELEVATED HIGHWAY CONSTRUCTION

AFFHOLDER, INC.—Insituform Technologies, Inc.; *U.S. Public*, pg. 881
AKER RAJ ASA; *Int'l*, pg. 41
ATKINSON; *U.S. Public*, pg. 143
ATKINSON CONSTRUCTION—Atkinson; *U.S. Public*, pg. 143
ATKINSON INTERNATIONAL VENEZUELA—Atkinson; *U.S. Public*, pg. 143
AUSTIN INDUSTRIES, INC.; *U.S. Private*, pg. 99
BFC CIVIL—BFC Construction Corporation; *Int'l*, pg. 118
BFC CONSTRUCTION CORPORATION; *Int'l*, pg. 118
BECON CONSTRUCTION COMPANY, INC.—Bechtel Group, Inc.; *U.S. Private*, pg. 128
RAY BELL CONSTRUCTION CO. INC.; *U.S. Private*, pg. 131
BELLAMY BROTHERS, INC.; *U.S. Private*, pg. 132
BETON-UND MONIERBAU GMBH—Preussag AG; *Int'l*, pg. 1069
D.H. BLATTNER & SONS, INC.; *U.S. Private*, pg. 148
BRITISH AEROSPACE P.L.C.; *Int'l*, pg. 217
CALUMET CONSTRUCTION CORPORATION; *U.S. Private*, pg. 201
CEMENTATION MINING LIMITED—Kvaerner a.s.a.; *Int'l*, pg. 772
COMPAGNIE GENERALE DES EAUX; *Int'l*, pg. 321
CONGAREE CONSTRUCTION CO., INC.; *U.S. Private*, pg. 263
CROWDER CONSTRUCTION CO.; *U.S. Private*, pg. 291
DEILMANN-HANIEL GMBH—Preussag AG; *Int'l*, pg. 1069
DEPEW DEVELOPMENT INC.; *U.S. Private*, pg. 326
DICKERSON, INC.—The Dickerson Group, Inc.; *U.S. Private*, pg. 331
DILLINGHAM CONSTRUCTION CORPORATION; *U.S. Private*, pg. 333
DUGAN & MEYERS CONSTRUCTION CO.—Dugan & Meyers Interests, Inc.; *U.S. Private*, pg. 345
MARTIN K. EBY CONSTRUCTION COMPANY, INC.—Eby Corporation; *U.S. Private*, pg. 359
EMPRESAS ICA SOCIEDAD CONTROLADORA S.A.C.V.; *Int'l*, pg. 454
ENGINEERED PRODUCTS, INC.; *U.S. Private*, pg. 376
EUROTUNNEL DEVELOPMENTS S.A.—The Eurotunnel Group; *Int'l*, pg. 466
THE EUROTUNNEL GROUP; *Int'l*, pg. 466
THE FLETCHER CONSTRUCTION COMPANY LIMITED—Fletcher Challenge Limited; *Int'l*, pg. 495
GAI CONSTRUCTION SERVICES, INC.—GAI Consultants, Inc.; *U.S. Private*, pg. 434
GAI CONSULTANTS, INC.—GAI Consultants, Inc.; *U.S. Private*, pg. 434
GEORGE & LYNCH, INC.; *U.S. Private*, pg. 448
GILVIN-TERRILL INC.; *U.S. Private*, pg. 455
GRANITE CONSTRUCTION INCORPORATED; *U.S. Public*, pg. 759
GRUPO MEXICANO DE DESARROLLO; *Int'l*, pg. 575
W.L. HAILEY & COMPANY, INC.; *U.S. Private*, pg. 494
HANOI RESIDENT REPRESENTATIVE OFFICE—Nishimatsu Construction Co., Ltd.; *Int'l*, pg. 942
HARBERT CORPORATION; *U.S. Private*, pg. 500
HAWAIIAN DREDGING & CONSTRUCTION COMPANY—Dillingham Construction Corporation; *U.S. Private*, pg. 333
HAWKER SIDDELEY CANADA INC.; *Int'l*, pg. 604
HOCHTIEF AG; *Int'l*, pg. 623
HOLLANDSCHE BETON GROEP NV; *Int'l*, pg. 630
HUGHES GROUP; *U.S. Private*, pg. 546
HYUNDAI ENGINEERING & CONSTRUCTION CO., LTD.—Hyundai Motor Company; *Int'l*, pg. 641
ICF KAISER ENGINEERS, INC.—ICF Kaiser International Inc.; *U.S. Public*, pg. 853
ICF KAISER INTERNATIONAL INC.; *U.S. Public*, pg. 852
IRVING F. JENSEN CO., INC.; *U.S. Private*, pg. 586
AL JOHNSON CONSTRUCTION CO.; *U.S. Private*, pg. 590
JOHNSON BROS. CORPORATION; *U.S. Private*, pg. 590
J.A. JONES, INC.—Philipp Holzmann AG; *Int'l*, pg. 633
KIEWIT CONSTRUCTION GROUP, INC.—Peter Kiewit Sons Inc.; *U.S. Private*, pg. 619
PETER KIEWIT SONS INC.; *U.S. Private*, pg. 619
KARL KOCH ERECTING CO. INC.—Skanska AB; *Int'l*, pg. 1261
KOKOSING CONSTRUCTION COMPANY, INC.; *U.S. Private*, pg. 631
LA COMPAGNIE FOUNDATION LIMITEE—BFC Construction Corporation; *Int'l*, pg. 118
THE LANE CONSTRUCTION CORP.; *U.S. Private*, pg. 649
C.J. LANGENFELDER & SON, INC.; *U.S. Private*, pg. 650
LARRYS, INC.; *U.S. Private*, pg. 652
LEE CONSTRUCTION CO.—National Engineering & Contracting Co.; *U.S. Private*, pg. 782
T.A. LOVING COMPANY; *U.S. Private*, pg. 677
JAMES MCHUGH CONSTRUCTION CO.; *U.S. Private*, pg. 721
MCKINNON BRIDGE CO.; *U.S. Private*, pg. 723
MISENER MARINE CONSTRUCTION; *U.S. Private*, pg. 752
MONTEREY CONSTRUCTION COMPANY—Atkinson; *U.S. Public*, pg. 143
MORRISON KNUDSEN CORPORATION; *U.S. Public*, pg. 1133
JOHN MOWLEM & COMPANY PLC; *Int'l*, pg. 896
C.C. MYERS, INC.; *U.S. Private*, pg. 770
NCC AB; *Int'l*, pg. 898
NCC ESKILSTUNA—NCC AB; *Int'l*, pg. 899
NAMKWANG ENGINEERING & CONSTRUCTION CO., LTD.—Ssangyong Business Group; *Int'l*, pg. 1291
NATIONAL ENGINEERING & CONTRACTING CO.; *U.S. Private*, pg. 782
NISHIMATSU CONSTRUCTION CO., LTD.; *Int'l*, pg. 942
NISHIMATSU - CORPRO CONSTRUCTION (M) SDN. BHD.—Nishimatsu Construction Co., Ltd.; *Int'l*, pg. 943
EDMUND NUTTALL LTD.—Hollandsche Beton Groep NV; *Int'l*, pg. 630
OBAYASHI CORPORATION; *Int'l*, pg. 995
OPTIMALGRUND BAUTRAGERGESELLSCHAFT MBH—Dyckerhoff & Widmann AG; *Int'l*, pg. 423
PARK CONSTRUCTION COMPANY; *U.S. Private*, pg. 839
PERINI CORPORATION; *U.S. Public*, pg. 1278
PERINI MANAGEMENT SERVICES, INC.—Perini Corporation; *U.S. Public*, pg. 1278
PERINI-METROPOLITAN NEW YORK DIV.—Perini Corporation; *U.S. Public*, pg. 1278
PITT-DES MOINES, INC.; *U.S. Public*, pg. 1304
RAYTHEON INFRASTRUCTURE INCORPORATED—Raytheon Company; *U.S. Public*, pg. 1366
REPUBLIC CONTRACTING CORP.; *U.S. Private*, pg. 923
SADE—Compagnie Generale Des Eaux; *Int'l*, pg. 321
SCHIAVONE CONSTRUCTION CO.; *U.S. Private*, pg. 970
SIOUX FALLS CONSTRUCTION COMPANY; *U.S. Private*, pg. 1003
SKANSKA (U.S.A.) INC.—Skanska AB; *Int'l*, pg. 1261
GEORGE SOLLITT CONSTRUCTION; *U.S. Private*, pg. 1013
SSANGYONG BUSINESS GROUP; *Int'l*, pg. 1291
SSANGYONG ENGINEERING & CONSTRUCTION CO., LTD.—Ssangyong Business Group; *Int'l*, pg. 1291
STORA PROJECT—NCC AB; *Int'l*, pg. 899
SUNDT CORP.; *U.S. Private*, pg. 1051
SVERDRUP CORPORATION; *U.S. Private*, pg. 1057
TIC; *U.S. Private*, pg. 1064
TAISEI CORPORATION; *Int'l*, pg. 1347
TAISEI ROTEC CORP.—Taisei Corporation; *Int'l*, pg. 1347
TARMAC CANADA INC.—Tarmac plc; *Int'l*, pg. 1355
TAYLOR WOODROW CONSTRUCTION (MIDLANDS) LTD.—Taylor Woodrow plc; *Int'l*, pg. 1358
TAYLOR WOODROW CONSTRUCTION (NORTHERN) LTD.—Taylor Woodrow plc; *Int'l*, pg. 1358
TEKKEN CORPORATION; *Int'l*, pg. 1362
TILCON, INC.; *U.S. Private*, pg. 1086
TRAFALGAR HOUSE TECHNOLOGY LIMITED (MAPLE CROSS HOUSE)—Kvaerner a.s.a.; *Int'l*, pg. 774
TRAYLOR BROTHERS, INC.; *U.S. Private*, pg. 1098
UNDERGROUND CONSTRUCTION CO., INC.; *U.S. Private*, pg. 1116
WALSH CONSTRUCTION COMPANY—Atkinson; *U.S. Public*, pg. 143
THE WHITING-TURNER CONTRACTING CO.; *U.S. Private*, pg. 1174
YANTIS CORPORATION; *U.S. Private*, pg. 1195
ZIMBABWE PROJECT OFFICE—Nishimatsu Construction Co., Ltd.; *Int'l*, pg. 943

1623 — WATER, SEWER, PIPELINE, COMMUNICATIONS & POWER LINE CONSTRUCTION

ARB INC.; *U.S. Private*, pg. 7
ABDULLA FOUAD CORPORATION LTD.—Abdulla Fouad Co. Ltd.; *Int'l*, pg. 502
ADVANCE MECHANICAL SYSTEMS, INC.; *U.S. Private*, pg. 18
AKER RAJ ASA; *Int'l*, pg. 41
AMERON INTERNATIONAL CORPORATION; *U.S. Public*, pg. 98
ANSALDO INDUSTRIA S.P.A.—IRI Istituto Ricostruzione Industriale; *Int'l*, pg. 653
APPLIED DIGITAL ACCESS; *U.S. Public*, pg. 122
ARCON CONSTRUCTION CO., INC.; *U.S. Private*, pg. 80
ASIA CABLE ENGINEERING CO., PTE. LTD. (ACECO)—The Furukawa Electric Co., Ltd.; *Int'l*, pg. 530
ATKINSON; *U.S. Public*, pg. 143
AWABED - SSANGYONG CONTRACTING CO.—Ssangyong Business Group; *Int'l*, pg. 1292
BFC CONSTRUCTION CORPORATION; *Int'l*, pg. 118
BFC UTILITIES—BFC Construction Corporation; *Int'l*, pg. 118
BFI CONSTRUCTORS—Browning-Ferris Industries, Inc.; *U.S. Public*, pg. 263
BANTREL INC.—BFC Construction Corporation; *Int'l*, pg. 118
BASIC CONSTRUCTION COMPANY; *U.S. Private*, pg. 121
BECHTEL CIVIL, INC.—Bechtel Group, Inc.; *U.S. Private*, pg. 128
BECHTEL GROUP, INC.; *U.S. Private*, pg. 128
BECHTEL LTD.—Bechtel Group, Inc.; *U.S. Private*, pg. 128
BECHTEL PETROLEUM & CHEMICAL—Bechtel Group, Inc.; *U.S. Private*, pg. 128
BECHTEL POWER CORPORATION—Bechtel Group, Inc.; *U.S. Private*, pg. 128
BECON CONSTRUCTION COMPANY, INC.—Bechtel Group, Inc.; *U.S. Private*, pg. 128
BRINK ELECTRIC CONSTRUCTION COMPANY; *U.S. Private*, pg. 169
BROKEN BOW GAS CO.—Energy West Inc.; *U.S. Public*, pg. 581
R.J. BROWN AMERICA, INC.—Kvaerner a.s.a.; *Int'l*, pg. 766
BURNUP & SIMS COMMUNICATIONS SERVICES—MasTec, Inc.; *U.S. Public*, pg. 1056
BURNUP & SIMS COMTEC, INC.—MasTec, Inc.; *U.S. Public*, pg. 1056

BURNUP & SIMS OF CALIFORNIA, INC.—MasTec, Inc.; *U.S. Public*, pg. 1056
BURNUP & SIMS OF TX—MasTec, Inc.; *U.S. Public*, pg. 1056
BURNUP & SIMS TELCOM, INC.—MasTec, Inc.; *U.S. Public*, pg. 1056
CALUMET CONSTRUCTION CORPORATION; *U.S. Private*, pg. 201
COLEJON CORPORATION; *U.S. Private*, pg. 251
COMMONWEALTH COMMUNICATIONS—RCN Corporation; *U.S. Public*, pg. 1354
COMMONWEALTH TELEPHONE ENTERPRISES, INC.; *U.S. Public*, pg. 415
COMMUNICATIONS SERVICES PTE. LTD.—Telefonaktiebolaget LM Ericsson; *Int'l*, pg. 1365
COMPAGNIE GENERALE DES EAUX; *Int'l*, pg. 321
CONGAREE CONSTRUCTION CO., INC.; *U.S. Private*, pg. 263
COSTAIN ENGINEERING & CONSTRUCTION LIMITED—Costain Group PLC; *Int'l*, pg. 336
MICHAEL CURRAN & ASSOCIATES; *U.S. Private*, pg. 297
DCA GENERAL CONTRACTORS, INC.—Lennar Corporation; *U.S. Public*, pg. 988
DEPEW DEVELOPMENT INC.; *U.S. Private*, pg. 326
THE DEVINEY COMPANY INC.—MasTec, Inc.; *U.S. Public*, pg. 1056
DILLINGHAM CONSTRUCTION CORPORATION; *U.S. Private*, pg. 333
DIVERSIFIED GROUP, INC.; *U.S. Private*, pg. 336
ER-ELECTRIC A/S—ABB Asea Brown Boveri (Holding) Ltd.; *Int'l*, pg. 3
ERE P DIVISION—Alcatel Alsthom Compagnie Generale D'Electricite; *Int'l*, pg. 52
MARTIN K. EBY CONSTRUCTION COMPANY, INC.—Eby Corporation; *U.S. Private*, pg. 359
ENVIROQ—Insituform Technologies, Inc.; *U.S. Public*, pg. 881
C.R. FEDRICK, INC.—Sundt Corp.; *U.S. Private*, pg. 1052
FITTON & PITTMAN, INC.—MasTec, Inc.; *U.S. Public*, pg. 1056
FLOWMOLE LIMITED—UTILX Corporation; *U.S. Public*, pg. 1701
FLUOR CORPORATION; *U.S. Public*, pg. 659
FURUKAWA SAUDI ARABIA, LTD. (FSA)—The Furukawa Electric Co., Ltd.; *Int'l*, pg. 531
GSI OF CALIFORNIA—Gulf States, Inc.; *U.S. Private*, pg. 487
GARNEY HOLDING COMPANY, INC.; *U.S. Private*, pg. 440
ROBERT GIBB & SONS, INC.; *U.S. Private*, pg. 451
THE GILBERT COMPANIES, INC.; *U.S. Private*, pg. 453
GRUPO TRIBASA S.A. DE C.V.; *Int'l*, pg. 577
GULF STATES, INC.; *U.S. Private*, pg. 487
W.L. HAILEY & COMPANY, INC.; *U.S. Private*, pg. 494
HALL CONTRACTING CORP.; *U.S. Private*, pg. 495
HARBERT CORPORATION; *U.S. Private*, pg. 500
HARRIS CONTRACTING CO.; *U.S. Private*, pg. 505
HAWAIIAN DREDGING & CONSTRUCTION COMPANY—Dillingham Construction Corporation; *U.S. Private*, pg. 333
HAWKER SIDDELEY CANADA INC.; *Int'l*, pg. 604
HAWKEYE CONSTRUCTION, INC.—MYR Group Inc.; *U.S. Public*, pg. 1029
HENKELS & MCCOY, INC.; *U.S. Private*, pg. 522
HICKORY CONSTRUCTION COMPANY; *U.S. Private*, pg. 525
HOCHTIEF AG; *Int'l*, pg. 623
HOOD CORPORATION—Lombardi Holdings Inc.; *U.S. Private*, pg. 673
HOUSATONIC CORPORATION—Yankee Energy System, Inc.; *U.S. Public*, pg. 1787
HUBBARD CONSTRUCTION CO.; *U.S. Private*, pg. 544
HYUNDAI ENGINEERING & CONSTRUCTION CO., LTD.—Hyundai Motor Company; *Int'l*, pg. 641
ICF KAISER ENGINEERS, INC.—ICF Kaiser International Inc.; *U.S. Public*, pg. 853
ICF KAISER INTERNATIONAL INC.; *U.S. Public*, pg. 852
IHC GROUP, INC.; *U.S. Private*, pg. 555
INGENIERA DE TELECOMUNICACIONES E INSTALACIONES S.A.—Telefonaktiebolaget LM Ericsson; *Int'l*, pg. 1368
INSITUFORM CENTRAL, INC.—Insituform Technologies, Inc.; *U.S. Public*, pg. 882
INSITUFORM DE PUERTO RICO, INC.—Insituform Technologies, Inc.; *U.S. Public*, pg. 882
INSITUFORM EAST, INC.—CERBCO, Inc.; *U.S. Public*, pg. 330
INSITUFORM MISSOURI, INC.—Insituform Technologies, Inc.; *U.S. Public*, pg. 882
INSITUFORM NORTH, INC.—Insituform Technologies, Inc.; *U.S. Public*, pg. 882
INSITUFORM PLAINS, INC.—Insituform Technologies, Inc.; *U.S. Public*, pg. 882
INSITUFORM ROCKIES, INC.—Insituform Technologies, Inc.; *U.S. Public*, pg. 882
INSITUFORM TECHNOLOGIES, INC.; *U.S. Public*, pg. 881
INSITUFORM TEXARK, INC.—Insituform Technologies, Inc.; *U.S. Public*, pg. 882
IROQUOIS GAS TRANSMISSION SYSTEM—Transcanada Pipelines Limited; *Int'l*, pg. 1417
IROQUOIS GAS TRANSMISSION SYSTEM—Yankee Energy System, Inc.; *U.S. Public*, pg. 1787
C.G. JENSEN A/S—Skanska AB; *Int'l*, pg. 1261
JOHNSON BROS. CORPORATION; *U.S. Private*, pg. 590
KENETECH CORP.; *U.S. Public*, pg. 950
KIEWIT CONSTRUCTION GROUP, INC.—Peter Kiewit Sons Inc.; *U.S. Private*, pg. 619
PETER KIEWIT SONS INC.; *U.S. Private*, pg. 619
KOKOSING CONSTRUCTION COMPANY, INC.; *U.S. Private*, pg. 631
LNG ENERGY, INC.—Southwest Gas Corporation; *U.S. Public*, pg. 1493
LAMB ENGINEERING & CONSTRUCTION CO.; *U.S. Private*, pg. 644
THE LANE CONSTRUCTION CORP.; *U.S. Private*, pg. 649
LARRYS, INC.; *U.S. Private*, pg. 652
LEE CONSTRUCTION CO.—National Engineering & Contracting Co.; *U.S. Private*, pg. 782
LUDVIGSEN & HERMANN A/S—Celsius AB; *Int'l*, pg. 278
MYR GROUP INC.; *U.S. Public*, pg. 1029
MAKO CONSTRUCTION CO.—Henkels & McCoy, Inc.; *U.S. Private*, pg. 522
MASTEC, INC.; *U.S. Public*, pg. 1055
MCDERMOTT INTERNATIONAL, INC.; *U.S. Public*, pg. 1067
MIDWEST MANAGEMENT (1987) LIMITED—Agra Inc.; *Int'l*, pg. 31
NCC AB; *Int'l*, pg. 898
NCC ESKILSTUNA—NCC AB; *Int'l*, pg. 899
NS PIPE TECHNOLOGY—Nippon Steel Corporation; *Int'l*, pg. 940
NATIONAL ENGINEERING & CONTRACTING CO.; *U.S. Private*, pg. 782
NISHIMATSU CONSTRUCTION CO., LTD.; *Int'l*, pg. 942
NORTHERN PIPELINE CONSTRUCTION CO.—Southwest Gas Corporation; *U.S. Public*, pg. 1493
OCEANEERING A/S—Oceaneering International, Inc.; *U.S. Public*, pg. 1211
OCEANEERING AUSTRALIA PTY. LTD.—Brambles Industries Limited; *Int'l*, pg. 211
OCEANEERING AUSTRALIA PTY. LTD.—Oceaneering International, Inc.; *U.S. Public*, pg. 1211
OCEANEERING INTERNATIONAL, INC.; *U.S. Public*, pg. 1211
OCEANEERING TECHNOLOGIES—Oceaneering International, Inc.; *U.S. Public*, pg. 1211
OVERSTREET PAVING COMPANY; *U.S. Private*, pg. 823
PCM CONSTRUCTION, INC.—Henkels & McCoy, Inc.; *U.S. Private*, pg. 522
PDM WATER—Pitt-Des Moines, Inc.; *U.S. Public*, pg. 1304
PACIFIC TELECOM CABLE, INC.—Cable and Wireless plc; *Int'l*, pg. 247
PACIFICORP; *U.S. Public*, pg. 1251
PACTEM SYSTEMS, INC.—Insituform Technologies, Inc.; *U.S. Public*, pg. 882
PATTON MANAGEMENT, INC.; *U.S. Private*, pg. 843
PERINI CORPORATION; *U.S. Public*, pg. 1278
PERINI MANAGEMENT SERVICES, INC.—Perini Corporation; *U.S. Public*, pg. 1278
PERINI-METROPOLITAN NEW YORK DIV.—Perini Corporation; *U.S. Public*, pg. 1278
PERRY ENGINEERING COMPANY, INC.; *U.S. Private*, pg. 854
PIRELLI JACOBSON, INC.—Pirelli S.p.A.; *Int'l*, pg. 1059
PIRELLI TRI-STATE INC.—Pirelli S.p.A.; *Int'l*, pg. 1059
THE RADOS COMPANIES; *U.S. Private*, pg. 907
REPUBLIC CONTRACTING CORP.; *U.S. Private*, pg. 923
ROCKWATER CO.—Halliburton Company; *U.S. Public*, pg. 776
SADE—Compagnie Generale Des Eaux; *Int'l*, pg. 321
SAIT-RADIOHOLLAND GROUP S.A.; *Int'l*, pg. 1151
SCOGAT S.A. (SOCIETE POUR LA CONSTRUCTION DU GAZODUC TRANST.)—ENI S.p.A.; *Int'l*, pg. 429
SANTA FE OFFSHORE CONSTRUCTION CO.—Kuwait Petroleum Corporation; *Int'l*, pg. 765
H.E. SARGENT, INC.; *U.S. Private*, pg. 966
SCHIAVONE CONSTRUCTION CO.; *U.S. Private*, pg. 970
SKANSKA OY—Skanska AB; *Int'l*, pg. 1261
SOLUS OCEANEERING (MALAYSIA) SDN. BHD.—Oceaneering International, Inc.; *U.S. Public*, pg. 1211
SSANGYONG DEVELOPMENTS PTE. LTD.—Ssangyong Business Group; *Int'l*, pg. 1292
SSANGYONG ENG. & CONST. (M) SDN. BHD.—Ssangyong Business Group; *Int'l*, pg. 1292
STET SOCIETA FINANZIARIA TELEFONICA—IRI Istituto Ricostruzione Industriale; *Int'l*, pg. 655
STORA PROJECT—NCC AB; *Int'l*, pg. 899
SUEDWESTDEUTSCHE ROHRLEITUNGSBAU GMBH—Hochtief AG; *Int'l*, pg. 623
O.C. SUMMERS LTD.—John Laing PLC; *Int'l*, pg. 796
SUNDT CORP.; *U.S. Private*, pg. 1051
SVERDRUP CORPORATION; *U.S. Private*, pg. 1057
SWINERTON INC.; *U.S. Private*, pg. 1059
TIC; *U.S. Private*, pg. 1064
TARLTON CORPORATION; *U.S. Private*, pg. 1069
TARMAC CANADA INC.—Tarmac plc; *Int'l*, pg. 1355
TEKKEN CORPORATION; *Int'l*, pg. 1362
TELEMONTAJE ERICSSON S.A. DE C.V.—Telefonaktiebolaget LM Ericsson; *Int'l*, pg. 1371
TURNER INDUSTRIES; *U.S. Private*, pg. 1109
UNDERGROUND CONSTRUCTION CO., INC.; *U.S. Private*, pg. 1116
UNITED PIPELINE SYSTEMS, INC—Insituform Technologies, Inc.; *U.S. Public*, pg. 882
UNITED SISTEMA DE TUBERIAS LTDA—Insituform Technologies, Inc.; *U.S. Public*, pg. 882
UTILITIES CONSTRUCTION CO., INC. OF SOUTH CAROLINA; *U.S. Private*, pg. 1130
UTILX CORPORATION; *U.S. Public*, pg. 1701
WESTOWER CORPORATION; *U.S. Public*, pg. 1762
WINTERS WELDING WORKS, INC.; *U.S. Private*, pg. 1183
WRIGHT & LOPEZ, INC.—Patton Management, Inc.; *U.S. Private*, pg. 843
YANTIS CORPORATION; *U.S. Private*, pg. 1195
H.B. ZACHRY COMPANY—H.B. Zachry; *U.S. Private*, pg. 1203

1629 — HEAVY CONSTRUCTION, NEC

ABB ENERGY VENTURES INC.—ABB Asea Brown Boveri (Holding) Ltd.; *Int'l*, pg. 4
ABB ENVIRONMENTAL SERVICES INC.—ABB Asea Brown Boveri (Holding) Ltd.; *Int'l*, pg. 4
ABB HYDRO POWER DIV.—ABB Asea Brown Boveri (Holding) Ltd.; *Int'l*, pg. 4
AMEC CIVIL ENGINEERING LTD.—AMEC Plc; *Int'l*, pg. 16
AMEC CONSTRUCTION LTD., INDUSTRIAL ENGINEERING DIV.—AMEC Plc; *Int'l*, pg. 16
AMEC CONSTRUCTION SCOTLAND LTD.—AMEC Plc; *Int'l*, pg. 16
AMEC CONSTRUCTION SERVICES LTD.—AMEC Plc; *Int'l*, pg. 16
AMEC DEVELOPMENT LTD.—AMEC Plc; *Int'l*, pg. 16
AMEC ENGINEERING LTD.-C.V. BUCHAN (CONCRETE) LTD.—AMEC Plc; *Int'l*, pg. 16
AMEC MINING LTD.—AMEC Plc; *Int'l*, pg. 16
AMEC PLC; *Int'l*, pg. 16
ARB INC.; *U.S. Private*, pg. 7
ACOUSTI ENGINEERING CO. OF FLORIDA; *U.S. Private*, pg. 14
AERIMPIANTI S.P.A.—IRI Istituto Ricostruzione Industriale; *Int'l*, pg. 653
AGRA FOUNDATIONS INC.—Agra Inc.; *Int'l*, pg. 31
AGRA FOUNDATIONS LIMITED—Agra Inc.; *Int'l*, pg. 30
AGRA INC.; *Int'l*, pg. 30
AGRA INC.—Agra Inc.; *Int'l*, pg. 30
AGRA MARINE CONSTRUCTION LIMITED—Agra Inc.; *Int'l*, pg. 30
AKER CONTRACTING A.S.—Aker Raj Asa; *Int'l*, pg. 41
AKER RAJ ASA; *Int'l*, pg. 41
AL OTAIBA-COSTAIN COMPANY—Costain Group PLC; *Int'l*, pg. 337
ALGERNON BLAIR INTERNATIONAL; *U.S. Private*, pg. 33
ALLIED INDUS., INC.—Halliburton Company; *U.S. Public*, pg. 775
ALLSPANN, ALLGEMEINE SPANNBETONGESELLSCHAFT M.B.H.—Dyckerhoff & Widmann AG; *Int'l*, pg. 424
AMBOY AGGREGATES—Great Lakes Dredge & Dock Co.; *U.S. Private*, pg. 474
AMERICAN ECOLOGY CORPORATION; *U.S. Public*, pg. 71
AMERICAN REFRACTORIES CO.—RGP Holding, Inc.; *U.S. Private*, pg. 903
AMICK CONSTRUCTION LTD.; *U.S. Private*, pg. 66
ANSALDO TRANSPORTI SPA—IRI Istituto Ricostruzione Industriale; *Int'l*, pg. 653
ATECSA—Dyckerhoff & Widmann AG; *Int'l*, pg. 424
ATKINSON; *U.S. Public*, pg. 143
ATKINSON CONSTRUCTION—Atkinson; *U.S. Public*, pg. 143
AVIATION CONSTRUCTORS, INC.—Cleveland Group, Inc.; *U.S. Private*, pg. 246
BFC BUILDINGS—BFC Construction Corporation; *Int'l*, pg. 118
BFC CIVIL—BFC Construction Corporation; *Int'l*, pg. 118
BFC CONSTRUCTION CORPORATION; *Int'l*, pg. 118
BFC INDUSTRIAL NICHOLLS-RADTKE—BFC Construction Corporation; *Int'l*, pg. 118
BFC PIPELINES—BFC Construction Corporation; *Int'l*, pg. 118
BHC COMPANY—Aquarion Company; *U.S. Public*, pg. 126
BABCOCK AFRICA (PTY) LTD.—Babcock International Group PLC; *Int'l*, pg. 131
BABCOCK & WILCOX CO.—McDermott International, Inc.; *U.S. Public*, pg. 1068
BABCOCK CONSTRUCTION LIMITED—Babcock International Group PLC; *Int'l*, pg. 130
BABCOCK ENERGY LIMITED—Babcock International Group PLC; *Int'l*, pg. 130
BABCOCK ENGINEERING CONTRACTORS (PTY) LTD—Babcock International Group PLC; *Int'l*, pg. 131
BABCOCK INTERNATIONAL GROUP PLC; *Int'l*, pg. 130
BABCOCK KING - WILKINSON LIMITED—Babcock International Group PLC; *Int'l*, pg. 131
N.G. BAILEY & CO. LTD.; *Int'l*, pg. 132
BAKER MELLON STUART CONSTRUCTION, INC.—Michael Baker Corporation; *U.S. Public*, pg. 168
MICHAEL BAKER CORPORATION; *U.S. Public*, pg. 168
BALLAST NEDAM NV; *Int'l*, pg. 133
BARNWELL INDUSTRIES, INC.; *U.S. Public*, pg. 190
BEAZER GROUP PLC; *Int'l*, pg. 181
BECHTEL CIVIL, INC.—Bechtel Group, Inc.; *U.S. Private*, pg. 128
BECHTEL GROUP, INC.; *U.S. Private*, pg. 128
BECHTEL LTD.—Bechtel Group, Inc.; *U.S. Private*, pg. 128
BECHTEL MINING & METALS—Bechtel Group, Inc.; *U.S. Private*, pg. 128
BECHTEL PETROLEUM & CHEMICAL—Bechtel Group, Inc.; *U.S. Private*, pg. 128
BECHTEL POWER CORPORATION—Bechtel Group, Inc.; *U.S. Private*, pg. 128
BECON CONSTRUCTION COMPANY, INC.—Bechtel Group, Inc.; *U.S. Private*, pg. 128
BELLAMY BROTHERS, INC.; *U.S. Private*, pg. 132
AB BINAB—NCC AB; *Int'l*, pg. 899
BLACK & VEATCH; *U.S. Private*, pg. 146
BOH BROS. CONSTRUCTION CO., LLC; *U.S. Private*, pg. 154
BOUYGUES; *Int'l*, pg. 206
BOVIS CONSTRUCTION LTD.—The Peninsular and Oriental Steam Navigation Company; *Int'l*, pg. 1032
BRINK ELECTRIC CONSTRUCTION COMPANY; *U.S. Private*, pg. 169
BRITISH AEROSPACE P.L.C.; *Int'l*, pg. 217
BROWN AND CALDWELL; *U.S. Private*, pg. 173
BROWN & ROOT DEVELOPMENT, INC.—Halliburton Company; *U.S. Public*, pg. 775
BROWN & ROOT INC.—Halliburton Company; *U.S. Public*, pg. 775
BROWN & ROOT INTERNATIONAL, INC.—Halliburton Company; *U.S. Public*, pg. 775
BROWN & ROOT U.S.A. INC.—Halliburton Company; *U.S. Public*, pg. 775
BRUCKNER GRUNDBAU GMBH—Hochtief AG; *Int'l*, pg. 623
BUFETE INDUSTRIAL S.A. DE C.V.; *Int'l*, pg. 232
CALUMET CONSTRUCTION CORPORATION; *U.S. Private*, pg. 201
CAPITAL DEVELOPMENT CO.; *U.S. Private*, pg. 205
CEGELEC—Alcatel Alsthom Compagnie Generale D'Electricite; *Int'l*, pg. 52
CENTURY FENCE COMPANY; *U.S. Private*, pg. 226

CHINA ECOTEK CORPORATION—China Steel Corporation; *Int'l*, pg. 285
CLARK CONSTRUCTION GROUP, INC.—Clark Enterprises, Inc.; *U.S. Private*, pg. 242
CLARKSON CONSTRUCTION COMPANIES; *U.S. Private*, pg. 244
CLEVELAND GROUP, INC.; *U.S. Private*, pg. 246
COCKERILL SAMBRE; *Int'l*, pg. 301
CONGAREE CONSTRUCTION CO., INC.; *U.S. Private*, pg. 263
CONSTRUCCIONES PITT-DES MOINES VENEZUELA, C.A.—Pitt-Des Moines, Inc.; *U.S. Public*, pg. 1304
CONSTRUCTORA ALMEX S.A.—Dyckerhoff & Widmann AG; *Int'l*, pg. 424
COSTAIN (AFRICA) LIMITED—Costain Group PLC; *Int'l*, pg. 337
COSTAIN INTERNATIONAL LIMITED—Costain Group PLC; *Int'l*, pg. 336
COSTAIN (WEST AFRICA) LTD.—Costain Group PLC; *Int'l*, pg. 337
COWIN & COMPANY, INC.; *U.S. Private*, pg. 280
CROWDER CONSTRUCTION CO.; *U.S. Private*, pg. 291
CROWLEY MARITIME CORPORATION; *U.S. Private*, pg. 292
CUNNINGHAM-LIMP DEVELOPMENT CO.; *U.S. Private*, pg. 297
DSI DYWIDAG-SYSTEMS INTERNATIONAL GMBH—Dyckerhoff & Widmann AG; *Int'l*, pg. 423
DAEWOO ENGINEERING COMPANY—Daewoo Corporation; *Int'l*, pg. 357
DAEWOO SHIPBUILDING & HEAVY MACHINERY, LTD.—Daewoo Corporation; *Int'l*, pg. 357
THE DANIS COMPANIES; *U.S. Private*, pg. 310
DANIS HEAVY CONSTRUCTION CO.—The Danis Companies; *U.S. Private*, pg. 310
DANSK INDUSTRI SYNDIKAT A/S; *Int'l*, pg. 381
DAVY DRAVO DIVISION—Kvaerner a.s.a.; *Int'l*, pg. 774
DEUTSCHE BAU-UND SIEDLUNGS-GESELLSCHAFT MBH—Hochtief AG; *Int'l*, pg. 623
DEVCON INTERNATIONAL CORP.; *U.S. Public*, pg. 502
DIETER HAFEMEISTER ERDBAU GMBH & CO.—Hochtief AG; *Int'l*, pg. 623
DILLINGHAM CONSTRUCTION CORPORATION; *U.S. Private*, pg. 333
DIVERSIFIED GROUP, INC.; *U.S. Private*, pg. 336
DUGAN & MEYERS CONSTRUCTION CO.—Dugan & Meyers Interests, Inc.; *U.S. Private*, pg. 345
DUKE/FLUOR DANIEL—Duke Energy Corporation; *U.S. Public*, pg. 535
DUKE/FLUOR DANIEL—Fluor Corporation; *U.S. Public*, pg. 660
DUMEZ-GTM—Lyonnaise des Eaux S.A.; *Int'l*, pg. 823
DYCKERHOFF & WIDMANN AG SUCURSAL BUENOS AIRES—Dyckerhoff & Widmann AG; *Int'l*, pg. 424
DYCKERHOFF & WIDMANN BAUGESELLSCHAFT MBH—Dyckerhoff & Widmann AG; *Int'l*, pg. 423
DYCKERHOFF & WIDMANN GESELLSCHAFT M.B.H.—Dyckerhoff & Widmann AG; *Int'l*, pg. 424
DYWIBEL N.V.—Dyckerhoff & Widmann AG; *Int'l*, pg. 424
DYWIDAG CAMEROUN S.A.R.L.—Dyckerhoff & Widmann AG; *Int'l*, pg. 424
DYWIDAG NIGERIA LTD.—Dyckerhoff & Widmann AG; *Int'l*, pg. 424
DYWIDAG-SYSTEMEN NEDERLAND B.V.—Dyckerhoff & Widmann AG; *Int'l*, pg. 424
DYWIDAG-SYSTEMS INTERNATIONAL FAR EAST, LTD.—Dyckerhoff & Widmann AG; *Int'l*, pg. 424
DYWIDAG SYSTEMS NORGE A/S—Dyckerhoff & Widmann AG; *Int'l*, pg. 424
DYWIT S.P.A.—Dyckerhoff & Widmann AG; *Int'l*, pg. 425
ETCD—Lyonnaise des Eaux S.A.; *Int'l*, pg. 823
EASTERN ENVIRONMENTAL SERVICES, INC.; *U.S. Public*, pg. 549
MARTIN K. EBY CONSTRUCTION COMPANY, INC.—Eby Corporation; *U.S. Private*, pg. 359
ENGINEERED CONSTRUCTION-SACRAMENTO—Pitt-Des Moines, Inc.; *U.S. Public*, pg. 1304
ENVIROMENTAL PRODUCTS INC.—The Will-Burt Company; *U.S. Private*, pg. 1177
ENVIROQ—Insituform Technologies, Inc.; *U.S. Public*, pg. 881
MARSHALL ERDMAN AND ASSOCIATES, INC.; *U.S. Private*, pg. 380
L.G. EVERIST INC.; *U.S. Private*, pg. 386
FABRICATION & OFFSHORE OPERATIONS—McDermott International, Inc.; *U.S. Public*, pg. 1068
C.R. FEDRICK, INC.—Sundt Corp.; *U.S. Private*, pg. 1052
J.H. FINDORFF & SON, INC.; *U.S. Private*, pg. 405
GEORG FISCHER DISA INC.—Dansk Industri Syndikat A/S; *Int'l*, pg. 382
FISH INTERNATIONAL CO.—KTI Fish; *U.S. Private*, pg. 604
FISK ELECTRIC COMPANY—AMEC Plc; *Int'l*, pg. 16
FLUOR CONSTRUCTORS INTERNATIONAL, INC.—Fluor Corporation; *U.S. Public*, pg. 660
FLUOR CORPORATION; *U.S. Public*, pg. 659
FLUOR DANIEL HOUSTON—Fluor Corporation; *U.S. Public*, pg. 660
FLUOR DANIEL WILLIAMS BROTHERS—Fluor Corporation; *U.S. Public*, pg. 660
FLUOR DANIEL WRIGHT LIMITED—Fluor Corporation; *U.S. Public*, pg. 660
FOSTER WHEELER CORPORATION; *U.S. Public*, pg. 676
FRAMATOME SA; *Int'l*, pg. 502
FRED WEBER, INC.; *U.S. Private*, pg. 424
FUGRO GROUP COMPANIES; *U.S. Private*, pg. 430
G.E. NUCLEAR ENERGY—General Electric Company; *U.S. Public*, pg. 711
G.F.C.—Bouygues; *Int'l*, pg. 206
GSI OF CALIFORNIA—Gulf States, Inc.; *U.S. Private*, pg. 487
G.T.F.C.—Bouygues; *Int'l*, pg. 206
GAICO—Parsons Corporation; *U.S. Private*, pg. 841
GARANTI-KOZA INSAAT—Hochtief AG; *Int'l*, pg. 624
GEORGE & LYNCH, INC.; *U.S. Private*, pg. 448
GESELLSCHAFT ZUR VERMITTLUNG VON BAUVERSICHERUNGEN MBH—Hochtief AG; *Int'l*, pg. 623
GIFFELS TECHNOLOGIES, INC.—Giffels Associates, Inc.; *U.S. Private*, pg. 452
GILVIN-TERRILL INC.; *U.S. Private*, pg. 455
GLOBAL INDUSTRIES, LTD.; *U.S. Public*, pg. 748
GOHMANN ASPHALT & CONSTRUCTION INC.; *U.S. Private*, pg. 459
GOODKIND & O'DEA, INC.—Dewberry & Davis; *U.S. Private*, pg. 329
GOWAN, INC.—EMCOR Group, Inc.; *U.S. Public*, pg. 572
GRANGER COMPANIES; *U.S. Private*, pg. 469
GRANITE CONSTRUCTION INCORPORATED; *U.S. Public*, pg. 759
GRAYCOR OPERATING COMPANIES; *U.S. Private*, pg. 472
GRAYSTONE CORPORATION—Northern States Power Company; *U.S. Public*, pg. 1195
GREAT LAKES DREDGE & DOCK CO.; *U.S. Private*, pg. 474
GRUPO MEXICANO DE DESARROLLO; *Int'l*, pg. 575
GRUPO PROTEXA S.A. DE C.V.; *Int'l*, pg. 576
GULF STATES, INC.; *U.S. Private*, pg. 487
HAM, HOLLANDSCHE AANNEMING MAATSCHAPPIJ B.V.—Hollandsche Beton Groep NV; *Int'l*, pg. 630
HCBECK; *U.S. Private*, pg. 490
HADEN MACLELLAN HOLDINGS PLC; *Int'l*, pg. 585
W.L. HAILEY & COMPANY, INC.; *U.S. Private*, pg. 494
HALL CONTRACTING CORP.; *U.S. Private*, pg. 495
HALLIBURTON COMPANY; *U.S. Public*, pg. 775
HALLIBURTON ENERGY SERVICES, INC.—Halliburton Company; *U.S. Public*, pg. 776
HANSEN MECHANICAL CONTRACTORS, INC.—EMCOR Group, Inc.; *U.S. Public*, pg. 572
HARBERT CORPORATION; *U.S. Private*, pg. 500
THE HARDAWAY COMPANY; *U.S. Private*, pg. 501
HARPER BROS., INC.; *U.S. Private*, pg. 504
HAWAIIAN DREDGING & CONSTRUCTION COMPANY—Dillingham Construction Corporation; *U.S. Private*, pg. 333
JOSEPH J. HENDERSON & SON, INC.; *U.S. Private*, pg. 521
HENSEL PHELPS CONSTRUCTION CO.; *U.S. Private*, pg. 523
HERCULES GRANDLAGGNING AB—NCC AB; *Int'l*, pg. 899
HOCHTIEF AG; *Int'l*, pg. 623
HOLTER GROUP—Australian National Industries Limited; *Int'l*, pg. 101
HUBBARD CONSTRUCTION CO.; *U.S. Private*, pg. 544
HUNTER CORP.; *U.S. Private*, pg. 549
HYUNDAI ENGINEERING & CONSTRUCTION CO., LTD.—Hyundai Motor Company; *Int'l*, pg. 641
IA CONSTRUCTION CORP.; *U.S. Private*, pg. 552
ICF KAISER ENGINEERS, INC.—ICF Kaiser International Inc.; *U.S. Public*, pg. 853
ICF KAISER INTERNATIONAL INC.; *U.S. Public*, pg. 852
IHC GROUP, INC.; *U.S. Private*, pg. 555
IMS INGENIEURGESELLSCHAFT MBH—Philipp Holzmann AG; *Int'l*, pg. 633
INGRAM PRODUCTION COMPANY—Ingram Industries Inc.; *U.S. Private*, pg. 563
ISEMOTO CONTRACTING CO. LTD.; *U.S. Private*, pg. 575
JACOBS ENGINEERING GROUP INC.; *U.S. Public*, pg. 921
JACOBS INTERNATIONAL LIMITED, INC.—Jacobs Engineering Group Inc.; *U.S. Public*, pg. 922
JALAL-COSTAIN W.L.L.—Costain Group PLC; *Int'l*, pg. 337
T.L. JAMES & COMPANY; *U.S. Private*, pg. 580
THE JAPAN STEEL WORKS, LTD.—Mitsui & Co., Ltd.; *Int'l*, pg. 878
AL JOHNSON CONSTRUCTION CO.; *U.S. Private*, pg. 590
JOHNSON BROS. CORPORATION; *U.S. Private*, pg. 590
J.A. JONES, INC.—Philipp Holzmann AG; *Int'l*, pg. 633
JUSTISS OIL CO., INC.; *U.S. Private*, pg. 602
KTI FISH; *U.S. Private*, pg. 604
M.B. KAHN CONSTRUCTION CO., INC.; *U.S. Private*, pg. 604
KAJIMA CORPORATION; *Int'l*, pg. 721
KAJIMA ENGINEERING AND CONSTRUCTION INC.—Kajima Corporation; *Int'l*, pg. 722
THE M.W. KELLOGG COMPANY—Dresser Industries, Inc.; *U.S. Public*, pg. 528
M.W. KELLOGG LIMITED—Dresser Industries, Inc.; *U.S. Public*, pg. 528
KESSER—Bouygues; *Int'l*, pg. 206
KIEWIT CONSTRUCTION GROUP, INC.—Peter Kiewit Sons Inc.; *U.S. Private*, pg. 619
PETER KIEWIT SONS INC.; *U.S. Private*, pg. 619
KINETICS TECHNOLOGY INTERNATIONAL BV—Mannesmann A.G.; *Int'l*, pg. 837
KLOCKNER INA INDUSTRIAL INSTALLATIONS, INC.—RWE AG; *Int'l*, pg. 1081
KLOECKNER IONON GMBH—Klockner-Werke AG; *Int'l*, pg. 737
KLOECKNER IONON OF AMERICA, INC.—Klockner-Werke AG; *Int'l*, pg. 737
KNIK CONSTRUCTION CO., INC.—Lynden Incorporated; *U.S. Private*, pg. 683
KNUTSON CONSTRUCTION CO.; *U.S. Private*, pg. 627
KOP-COAT—RPM, Inc.; *U.S. Public*, pg. 1357
KOREA HEAVY INDUSTRIES & CONSTRUCTION CO., LTD.; *Int'l*, pg. 758
KRAFTWERK SCHKOPAU GMBH—Veba AG; *Int'l*, pg. 1460
KVAERNER DAVY—Kvaerner a.s.a.; *Int'l*, pg. 774
KVAERNER INSTALLASJON A.S.—Kvaerner a.s.a.; *Int'l*, pg. 769
KVAERNER KIMEK A.S.—Kvaerner a.s.a.; *Int'l*, pg. 770
LG & E POWER SYSTEMS INC.—LG & E Energy Corp.; *U.S. Public*, pg. 970
LNG PROJECT & CONSTRUCTION DIVISION—Chinese Petroleum Corporation; *Int'l*, pg. 286
LA COMPAGNIE FOUNDATION LIMITEE—BFC Construction Corporation; *Int'l*, pg. 118
LAMB ENGINEERING & CONSTRUCTION CO.; *U.S. Private*, pg. 644
THE LANE CONSTRUCTION CORP.; *U.S. Private*, pg. 649
C.J. LANGENFELDER & SON, INC.; *U.S. Private*, pg. 650
LEE CONSTRUCTION CO.—National Engineering & Contracting Co.; *U.S. Private*, pg. 782
LEHNKERING MONTAN TRANSPORT AG—Metallgesellschaft AG; *Int'l*, pg. 862
LEHNKERING MONTAN TRANSPORT AG—Preussag AG; *Int'l*, pg. 1069
LEIGHTON ASIA—Hochtief AG; *Int'l*, pg. 624
LEIGHTON HOLDINGS LIMITED—Hochtief AG; *Int'l*, pg. 624
LIN & ROE COMPANY—Burns & Roe Enterprises, Inc.; *U.S. Private*, pg. 187
LOCKHEED AUSTIN DIVISION—Lockheed Martin Corporation; *U.S. Public*, pg. 1008
THE LOS ANGELES DEPARTMENT OF WATER AND POWER (DWP); *U.S. Private*, pg. 676
T.A. LOVING COMPANY; *U.S. Private*, pg. 677
LURGI AG—Metallgesellschaft AG; *Int'l*, pg. 861
LURGI ESPANOLA S.A.—Metallgesellschaft AG; *Int'l*, pg. 861
LYONNAISE DES EAUX S.A.; *Int'l*, pg. 822
MISR DYWIDAG—Dyckerhoff & Widmann AG; *Int'l*, pg. 425
MAESCHER INDUSTRIES, INC.; *U.S. Private*, pg. 694
MARSHALL ERDMAN & ASSOC., INC.—Marshall Erdman and Associates, Inc.; *U.S. Private*, pg. 380
MARUBENI CORPORATION; *Int'l*, pg. 844
MASSMAN CONSTRUCTION COMPANY; *U.S. Private*, pg. 713
MAXUM ENGINEERING ENTERPRISES LTD.—Agra Inc.; *Int'l*, pg. 31
MCDERMOTT INTERNATIONAL, INC.; *U.S. Public*, pg. 1067
MCDERMOTT SOUTHEAST ASIA PTY. LTD.—McDermott International, Inc.; *U.S. Public*, pg. 1068
JAMES MCHUGH CONSTRUCTION CO.; *U.S. Private*, pg. 721
MECANARBED DOMMELDANGE S.A.R.L.—Arbed S.A.; *Int'l*, pg. 80
METROPOLITANA MILANESE S.P.A.; *Int'l*, pg. 863
THE MEYNE COMPANY—Bulley & Andrews Company; *U.S. Private*, pg. 180
MIDWEST PIPELINE CONTRACTORS LTD.—Agra Inc.; *Int'l*, pg. 31
MINCO INTERNATIONAL AB—Trelleborg AB; *Int'l*, pg. 1423
MISENER MARINE CONSTRUCTION; *U.S. Private*, pg. 752
MITSUBISHI HEAVY INDUSTRIES LTD.; *Int'l*, pg. 873
MITSUI HARBOUR & URBAN CONSTRUCTION CO., LTD.—Mitsui & Co., Ltd.; *Int'l*, pg. 877
MIZUNO CORPORATION; *Int'l*, pg. 884
MONSANTO ENVIRO-CHEM. SYSTEMS, INC.—Monsanto Company; *U.S. Public*, pg. 1125
MONTEREY CONSTRUCTION COMPANY—Atkinson; *U.S. Public*, pg. 143
MONTEREY MECHANICAL COMPANY; *U.S. Private*, pg. 758
MORRISON KNUDSEN CORPORATION; *U.S. Public*, pg. 1133
M.A. MORTENSON COMPANY; *U.S. Private*, pg. 763
MOUNTAIN STATES CONSTRUCTORS, INC.; *U.S. Private*, pg. 764
JOHN MOWLEM & COMPANY PLC; *Int'l*, pg. 896
NB COAL COMPANY LIMITED—New Brunswick Power Corporation; *Int'l*, pg. 923
NCC AB; *Int'l*, pg. 898
NCC ESKILSTUNA—NCC AB; *Int'l*, pg. 899
NKK CORPORATION; *Int'l*, pg. 902
NKK CORPORATION-THAILAND—NKK Corporation; *Int'l*, pg. 903
NAMKWANG ENGINEERING & CONSTRUCTION CO., LTD.—Ssangyong Business Group; *Int'l*, pg. 1291
NATIONAL ENGINEERING & CONTRACTING CO.; *U.S. Private*, pg. 782
NESMA-COSTAIN PROCESS CO. LIMITED—Costain Group PLC; *Int'l*, pg. 337
NEW ENGLAND CRINC.—Wellman, Inc.; *U.S. Public*, pg. 1753
NORTH AMERICAN TRAILING CO.—Great Lakes Dredge & Dock Co.; *U.S. Private*, pg. 474
PCL-BRAUN-SIMONS LTD.—Kuwait Petroleum Corporation; *Int'l*, pg. 765
PDM WATER—Pitt-Des Moines, Inc.; *U.S. Public*, pg. 1304
PARSONS CONSTRUCTORS INC.—Parsons Corporation; *U.S. Private*, pg. 842
PECK JONES CONSTRUCTION; *U.S. Private*, pg. 846
HARRY PEPPER & ASSOCIATES; *U.S. Private*, pg. 851
PERINI BUILDING CO., INC. U.S. HEAVY DIVISION—Perini Corporation; *U.S. Public*, pg. 1278
PERINI BUILDING CO., INC. WESTERN U.S. DIVISION—Perini Corporation; *U.S. Public*, pg. 1278
PERINI CORPORATION; *U.S. Public*, pg. 1278
PERINI MANAGEMENT SERVICES, INC.—Perini Corporation; *U.S. Public*, pg. 1278
PERINI-METROPOLITAN NEW YORK DIV.—Perini Corporation; *U.S. Public*, pg. 1278
PETRO CHEM DEVELOPMENT COMPANY; *U.S. Private*, pg. 858
PETROCARBON DEVELOPMENTS INC.—Costain Group PLC; *Int'l*, pg. 337
PITT-DES MOINES, INC.; *U.S. Public*, pg. 1304
PIZZAGALLI CONSTRUCTION CO.; *U.S. Private*, pg. 868
POWERLINES CENTRAL AFRICA (PVT.)—ABB Asea Brown Boveri (Holding) Ltd.; *Int'l*, pg. 3
POWERLINES LTD.—ABB Asea Brown Boveri (Holding) Ltd.; *Int'l*, pg. 3
PRESS CONSTRUCTION LTD., UTILITIES DIV.—AMEC Plc; *Int'l*, pg. 16

PRESS OFFSHORE LTD.—AMEC Plc; *Int'l*, pg. 16
PROTENDIDOS DYWIDAG LTDA,—Dyckerhoff & Widmann AG; *Int'l*, pg. 425
WILLIAM A. RANDOLPH, INC.; *U.S. Private*, pg. 909
RAYTHEON ENGINEERS & CONSTRUCTORS—Raytheon Company; *U.S. Public*, pg. 1366
REPUBLIC CONTRACTING CORP.; *U.S. Private*, pg. 923
REYNOLDS METALS COMPANY-BELLWOOD—Reynolds Metals Company; *U.S. Public*, pg. 1385
RIETH-RILEY CONSTRUCTION CO. INC.; *U.S. Private*, pg. 930
RIGGS INDUSTRIES, INC.; *U.S. Private*, pg. 930
RITTER BROS., INC.; *U.S. Private*, pg. 933
ROANOKE VALLEY PLANT—LG & E Energy Corp.; *U.S. Public*, pg. 970
THE ROWE CORPORATION; *U.S. Private*, pg. 948
SABM, SOCIETE AFRICAINE DE BETON MANUFACTURE S.A.—Dyckerhoff & Widmann AG; *Int'l*, pg. 425
SADUC—Lyonnaise des Eaux S.A.; *Int'l*, pg. 823
SAMEIET AKER BRYGGE A/S—Aker Raj Asa; *Int'l*, pg. 41
H.E. SARGENT, INC.; *U.S. Private*, pg. 966
SAW CONSTRUCTION CORPORATION—Stone & Webster, Incorporated; *U.S. Public*, pg. 1519
SCHIAVONE CONSTRUCTION CO.; *U.S. Private*, pg. 970
SCORIA INCORPORATED—Northern States Power Company; *U.S. Public*, pg. 1195
JAMES SCOTT MECHANICAL & ELECTRICAL SERVICES LTD.—AMEC Plc; *Int'l*, pg. 16
SHOOK NATIONAL CORPORATION; *U.S. Private*, pg. 996
SIGAL CONSTRUCTION CORP.; *U.S. Private*, pg. 999
SIMON-CARVES AUSTRALIA—Simon Engineering plc; *Int'l*, *pg. 1252*
SIMON-CARVES LTD.—Simon Engineering plc; *Int'l*, pg. 1251
SIMON ENGINEERING PLC; *Int'l*, pg. 1251
SKANSKA AB; *Int'l*, pg. 1260
SKANSKA ANLAGGNING AB—Skanska AB; *Int'l*, pg. 1260
SKANSKA INTERNATIONAL CIVIL ENGINEERING AB—Skanska AB; *Int'l*, pg. 1260
SLATTERY ASSOCIATES INC.—Skanska AB; *Int'l*, pg. 1261
SMITH TECHNOLOGIES CORP.—Smith Environmental Technologies Corp.; *U.S. Public*, pg. 1478
GEORGE SOLLITT CONSTRUCTION; *U.S. Private*, pg. 1013
SOLOCO, INC.—Newpark Resources, Inc.; *U.S. Public*, pg. 1179
SOUTHERN OHIO FABRICATORS, INC.; *U.S. Private*, pg. 1017
SPRAYROQ, INC.—Insituform Technologies, Inc.; *U.S. Public*, pg. 882
SSANGYONG BUSINESS GROUP; *Int'l*, pg. 1291
SSANGYONG ENGINEERING & CONSTRUCTION CO., LTD.—Ssangyong Business Group; *Int'l*, pg. 1291
SSANGYONG RESOURCES DEVELOPMENT CO., LTD.—Ssangyong Business Group; *Int'l*, pg. 1291
SSANGYONG SINGAPORE PTE., LTD.—Ssangyong Business Group; *Int'l*, pg. 1291
STOCKTON COGEN (I), INC.—Air Products and Chemicals, Inc.; *U.S. Public*, pg. 31
STONE & WEBSTER, INCORPORATED; *U.S. Public*, pg. 1519
STORA PROJECT—NCC AB; *Int'l*, pg. 899
SULZER INFRA DEUTSCHLAND GMBH.—Sulzer Ltd.; *Int'l*, *pg. 1306*
SUMMIT-BEERS CONSTRUCTION COMPANY—Skanska AB; *Int'l*, pg. 1261
SUNDT CORP.; *U.S. Private*, pg. 1051
SWEDISH RAIL SYSTEM SRS—Scancem AB; *Int'l*, pg. 1199
SWINERTON INC.; *U.S. Private*, pg. 1059
TARLTON CORPORATION; *U.S. Private*, pg. 1069
TARMAC CANADA INC.—Tarmac plc; *Int'l*, pg. 1355
TARMAC CONSTRUCTION LIMITED—Tarmac plc; *Int'l*, pg. 1355
TARMAC CONSTRUCTION MAJOR PROJECTS LIMITED—Tarmac plc; *Int'l*, pg. 1355
TAYLOR WOODROW CONSTRUCTION (MIDLANDS) LTD.—Taylor Woodrow plc; *Int'l*, pg. 1358
TAYLOR WOODROW CONSTRUCTION (NORTHERN) LTD.—Taylor Woodrow plc; *Int'l*, pg. 1358
TAYLOR WOODROW CONSTRUCTION (SCOTLAND) LTD.—Taylor Woodrow plc; *Int'l*, pg. 1358
TECNIMONT SPA—Compart SpA; *Int'l*, pg. 324
TEKKEN CORPORATION; *Int'l*, pg. 1362
TILBURY DOUGLAS PLC—Philipp Holzmann AG; *Int'l*, pg. 634
TOBETON, SOCIETE TOGOLAISE DE BETON, S.A.—Dyckerhoff & Widmann AG; *Int'l*, pg. 425
TORCON, INC.; *U.S. Private*, pg. 1092
TOWNSEND & BOTTUM, INC.—Black & Veatch; *U.S. Private*, pg. 146
TRAFALGAR HOUSE CONSTRUCTION INC.—Kvaerner a.s.a.; *Int'l*, pg. 774
TRAYLOR BROTHERS, INC.; *U.S. Private*, pg. 1098
TRUMBULL CORPORATION/P.J. DICK, INC.; *U.S. Private*, *pg. 1107*
TUTOR-SALIBA CORPORATION; *U.S. Private*, pg. 1111
TYLER BERLIN GMBH—Franz Haniel & Cie, GmbH; *Int'l*, pg. 592
UNDERGROUND CONSTRUCTION CO., INC.; *U.S. Private*, pg. 1116
VARA INTERNATONAL—Calgon Carbon Corporation; *U.S. Public*, pg. 293
VOLT VIEWTECH, INC.—Volt Information Sciences, Inc.; *U.S. Public*, pg. 1724
VON ROLL AG DEPARTEMENT UMWELTTECHNIK—Von Roll AG; *Int'l*, pg. 1480
WALSH CONSTRUCTION COMPANY—Atkinson; *U.S. Public*, pg. 143
WATSON STEEL & CO. (CONSTRUCTIONAL ENGINEERS) LTD.—AMEC Plc; *Int'l*, pg. 16
WATSON STEEL & CO. (STEELWORK) LTD.—AMEC Plc; *Int'l*, pg. 16
WELLMAN, INC.; *U.S. Public*, pg. 1752
WESTMORELAND ENERGY, INC.—Westmoreland Coal Co.; *U.S. Public*, pg. 1761
WHEELABRATOR TECHNOLOGIES INC.—Waste Management, Inc.; *U.S. Public*, pg. 1745
WHESSOE PLC; *Int'l*, pg. 1498
WHESSOE PROJECTS LTD.—Whessoe Plc; *Int'l*, pg. 1498
THE WHITING-TURNER CONTRACTING CO.; *U.S. Private*, pg. 1174
WILLIAMS INTERNATIONAL INDUSTRIES, INC.; *U.S. Private*, pg. 1178
GEORGE WIMPEY INTERNATIONAL LTD.—George Wimpey PLC; *Int'l*, pg. 1510
YAHYA COSTAIN LLC—Costain Group PLC; *Int'l*, pg. 337
H.B. ZACHRY COMPANY—H.B. Zachry; *U.S. Private*, pg. 1203
ZURN INDUSTRIES, INC.; *U.S. Public*, pg. 1794

1711 — PLUMBING, HEATING & AIR CONDITIONING CONTRACTORS

ABI IMTECH NV—Internatio-Muller N.V.; *Int'l*, pg. 681
AC CORPORATION; *U.S. Private*, pg. 3
API GROUP INC.; *U.S. Private*, pg. 7
ACMAT CORPORATION; *U.S. Public*, pg. 16
ADVANCE MECHANICAL SYSTEMS, INC.; *U.S. Private*, pg. 18
J.F. AHERN CO.; *U.S. Private*, pg. 27
AIR CONDITIONING CO., INC.; *U.S. Private*, pg. 28
AIR ENGINEERING CO., INC.—Amelco Corporation; *U.S. Public*, pg. 65
AIRCO COMMERCIAL SERVICES, INC.—Airco Mechanical Inc.; *U.S. Private*, pg. 29
AIRCO MECHANICAL INC.; *U.S. Private*, pg. 29
AIRTROL, INC.; *U.S. Private*, pg. 29
AMELCO CORPORATION; *U.S. Public*, pg. 65
AMELCO, INC.—Amelco Corporation; *U.S. Public*, pg. 65
AMERICAN HOME SHIELD CORPORATION—The ServiceMaster Company; *U.S. Public*, pg. 1461
BG CHECO CONSTRUCTION—Alcatel Alsthom Compagnie Generale D'Electricite; *Int'l*, pg. 53
BALFOUR BEATTY LIMITED—BICC plc; *Int'l*, pg. 120
BARR ELECTRIC CORPORATION; *U.S. Private*, pg. 117
BAYSIDE FUEL OIL CORP.—Bayside Fuel Oil Depot Corp.; *U.S. Private*, pg. 125
BERKS PRODUCTS CORPORATION; *U.S. Private*, pg. 136
BEUTLER HEATING & AIR CONDITIONING INC.; *U.S. Private*, pg. 141
JOHN BOUCHARD & SONS COMPANY; *U.S. Private*, pg. 161
CFEM—Groupe Usinor; *Int'l*, pg. 571
CAL-AIR INC.; *U.S. Private*, pg. 199
THE ROBERT CARTER CORP.—United Dominion Industries, Ltd.; *U.S. Public*, pg. 1676
CHEMED CORPORATION; *U.S. Public*, pg. 343
CLEVELAND ELECTRIC CO.—Cleveland Group, Inc.; *U.S. Private*, pg. 246
CLEVELAND GROUP, INC.; *U.S. Private*, pg. 246
COLEJON CORPORATION; *U.S. Private*, pg. 251
CONTROLLED SYSTEMS OF WISCONSIN, INC.; *U.S. Private*, pg. 271
CORRIGAN BROS., INC.; *U.S. Private*, pg. 277
M.J. DALY & SONS, INC.; *U.S. Private*, pg. 309
JOHN W. DANFORTH CO.; *U.S. Private*, pg. 309
JOSEPH DAVIS, INC.; *U.S. Private*, pg. 315
DELCHESTER OIL CO. INC.—Heating Oil Partners L.P.; *U.S. Private*, pg. 518
DIMEO CONSTRUCTION COMPANY; *U.S. Private*, pg. 333
DOWNEY, INC.—K & G of Wisconsin, Inc.; *U.S. Private*, pg. 602
DUNLAP & CO. INC.; *U.S. Private*, pg. 346
EGAN COS.; *U.S. Private*, pg. 365
EGAN MECHANICAL CONTRACTORS INC.—Egan Cos.; *U.S. Private*, pg. 366
EGIZII ELECTRIC, INC.; *U.S. Private*, pg. 366
EMCOR GROUP, INC.; *U.S. Public*, pg. 571
ENERGY SYSTEMS INDUSTRIES, INC.; *U.S. Private*, pg. 376
ENVIRONMENTAL AIR SYSTEMS, INC.; *U.S. Private*, pg. 378
FIBREBOND CORPORATION; *U.S. Private*, pg. 402
FICON CORPORATION—American International Group, Inc.; *U.S. Public*, pg. 84
FIRE PROTECTION INDUSTRIES, INC.—Compagnie Generale Des Eaux; *Int'l*, pg. 321
FISCHBACH & MOORE INTERNATIONAL CORP.—American International Group, Inc.; *U.S. Public*, pg. 84
FISCHBACH CORPORATION—American International Group, Inc.; *U.S. Public*, pg. 84
GSI OF CALIFORNIA—Gulf States, Inc.; *U.S. Private*, pg. 487
GAYLE SUPPLY INC.—Hughes Supply, Inc.; *U.S. Public*, pg. 847
ROBERT GIBB & SONS, INC.; *U.S. Private*, pg. 451
S.I. GOLDMAN CO.; *U.S. Private*, pg. 461
JOHN E. GREEN CO.; *U.S. Private*, pg. 477
GRINNELL CORPORATION—Tyco International Ltd.; *U.S. Public*, pg. 1651
GROUP MAINTENANCE AMERICA CORP.; *U.S. Public*, pg. 766
GULF STATES, INC.; *U.S. Private*, pg. 487
HARLAN ELECTRIC CO.—MYR Group Inc.; *U.S. Public*, pg. 1029
HARPER MECHANICAL CORPORATION—Compagnie Generale Des Eaux; *Int'l*, pg. 322
HARRIS CONTRACTING CO.; *U.S. Private*, pg. 505
HEATING OIL PARTNERS L.P.; *U.S. Private*, pg. 518
HEIGHTS HEATING & COOLING; *U.S. Private*, pg. 519
J.C. HIGGINS CORP.—EMCOR Group, Inc.; *U.S. Public*, pg. 572
HONEYWELL INC.; *U.S. Public*, pg. 833
HUSSMANN CORP.—Whitman Corporation; *U.S. Public*, pg. 1766
INDUSTRIAL COMPONENTS GROUP—BTR plc; *Int'l*, pg. 127
INDUSTRIAL CONSTRUCTION, INC.; *U.S. Private*, pg. 560
INDUSTRIVENTILATION SVENSKA AB—Skanska AB; *Int'l*, *pg. 1261*
ITALIMPIANTI S.P.A.—IRI Istituto Ricostruzione Industriale; *Int'l*, pg. 654
JOHNSON CONTROLS, INC.; *U.S. Public*, pg. 932
JUPITER INDUSTRIES, INC.; *U.S. Private*, pg. 602
K & G OF WISCONSIN, INC.; *U.S. Private*, pg. 602
KAJIMA INTERNATIONAL, INC.—Kajima Corporation; *Int'l*, pg. 722
KATHABAR SYSTEMS EUROPE, ZOETERMEER—Internatio-Muller N.V.; *Int'l*, pg. 681
KUHLMAN, INC.; *U.S. Private*, pg. 636
KVAERNER ROSENBERG A.S.—Kvaerner a.s.a.; *Int'l*, pg. 769
LBI LUFTBEHANDLING AB—Skanska AB; *Int'l*, pg. 1261
LARRYS, INC.; *U.S. Private*, pg. 652
LAWSON MECHANICAL CONTRACTORS; *U.S. Private*, pg. 654
LIMBACH CO.—Compagnie Generale Des Eaux; *Int'l*, pg. 322
LIMBACH CONSTRUCTORS, INC.—Compagnie Generale Des Eaux; *Int'l*, pg. 322
LIMBACH HOLDINGS, INC.—Compagnie Generale Des Eaux; *Int'l*, pg. 321
LINDE REFRIGERATION LTD.—Linde AG; *Int'l*, pg. 811
MFRI INC.; *U.S. Public*, pg. 1026
MJN—Staveley Industries PLC; *Int'l*, pg. 1299
MPH INDUSTRIES—General Signal Corporation; *U.S. Public*, pg. 726
MASTERS INC.; *U.S. Private*, pg. 714
MECHANICAL HEAT & COLD, INC.—Compagnie Generale Des Eaux; *Int'l*, pg. 322
MIDWEST MECHANICAL CONTRACTORS INC.—MMC Corp.; *U.S. Private*, pg. 687
MOLLENBERG-BETZ INC.; *U.S. Private*, pg. 756
MONTEREY MECHANICAL COMPANY; *U.S. Private*, pg. 758
MORRISON, INC.; *U.S. Private*, pg. 762
NVR, INC.; *U.S. Public*, pg. 1148
NASHVILLE MACHINE CO. INC.; *U.S. Private*, pg. 774
NATKIN GROUP, INC.—American International Group, Inc.; *U.S. Public*, pg. 84
NEW MECH COMPANIES, INC.; *U.S. Private*, pg. 794
NORTHWESTERN INDUSTRIAL PIPING; *U.S. Private*, pg. 806
OSBY PARCA AB—Trelleborg AB; *Int'l*, pg. 1422
P & F INDUSTRIES, INC.; *U.S. Public*, pg. 1239
P.T. PANATA TAMA INTER INSTALASI INDONESIA—Internatio-Muller N.V.; *Int'l*, pg. 681
PENGUIN AIR CONDITIONING CORP.—EMCOR Group, Inc.; *U.S. Public*, pg. 572
PIEDMONT MECHANICAL, INC.; *U.S. Private*, pg. 865
PLANT CONSTRUCTION PLC—Haden Maclellan Holdings plc; *Int'l*, pg. 585
POWER PROCESS PIPING, INC.; *U.S. Private*, pg. 878
QUACKENBUSH CO. INC.; *U.S. Private*, pg. 897
R & G PLUMBING—Hughes Supply, Inc.; *U.S. Public*, pg. 847
RK MECHANICAL, INC.; *U.S. Private*, pg. 904
RIDDLEBERGER BROS.. INC.; *U.S. Private*, pg. 930
CHAS ROBERTS AIR CONDITIONING, INC.; *U.S. Private*, pg. 935
J.B. RODGERS MECHANICAL CONTRACTORS; *U.S. Private*, pg. 939
ROTO-ROOTER—Chemed Corporation; *U.S. Public*, pg. 344
H. SAND & CO., INC.—Skanska AB; *Int'l*, pg. 1261
SCOTTPOLAR CORPORATION—Toromont Industries Ltd.; *Int'l*, pg. 1400
SERVICE AMERICA SYSTEMS, INC.—Chemed Corporation; *U.S. Public*, pg. 344
THE SERVICEMASTER COMPANY; *U.S. Public*, pg. 1461
BENJAMIN F. SHAW CO.—Blount International, Inc.; *U.S. Public*, pg. 239
SHIN NIPPON AIR CONDITIONING ENGINEERING CO., LTD.—Mitsui & Co., Ltd.; *Int'l*, pg. 877
SKANSKA INSTALLATION AB—Skanska AB; *Int'l*, pg. 1260
SKANSKA (U.S.A.) INC.—Skanska AB; *Int'l*, pg. 1261
SOUTHEAST FIRE SPRINKLER COMPANY—S.I. Goldman Co.; *U.S. Private*, pg. 462
SOUTHLAND INDUSTRIES; *U.S. Private*, pg. 1018
SPARTAN OIL CORP.; *U.S. Private*, pg. 1021
TD INDUSTRIES INC.; *U.S. Private*, pg. 1063
TEMCO MECHANICAL MAINTENANCE—Temco Service Industries; *U.S. Public*, pg. 1574
TEMP-CONTROL MECHANICAL CORP.; *U.S. Private*, pg. 1075
TOROMONT PROCESS SYSTEMS INC.—Toromont Industries Ltd.; *Int'l*, pg. 1401
TOTAL WALTHER FEUERSCHUTZ GMBH—Tyco International Ltd.; *U.S. Public*, pg. 1651
TRELLEBORG BUILDING & DISTRIBUTION DIV.—Trelleborg AB; *Int'l*, pg. 1421
TRIANGLE SERVICES, INC.; *U.S. Private*, pg. 1102
UNIVERSITY MECHANICAL & ENGINEERING CONTRACTORS, INC.—EMCOR Group, Inc.; *U.S. Public*, pg. 572
VENTILIZATIONUNION AB—Trelleborg AB; *Int'l*, pg. 1422
ZURN INDUSTRIES, INC.; *U.S. Public*, pg. 1794

1721 — PAINTING & PAPER HANGING CONTRACTORS

BAYCOAT LIMITED—Stelco Inc.; *Int'l*, pg. 1299
HOLLOWAY WHITE ALLOM LTD.—John Laing PLC; *Int'l*, pg. 796
LAING TECHNOLOGY GROUP LTD.—John Laing PLC; *Int'l*, pg. 796
TRIANGLE SERVICES, INC.; *U.S. Private*, pg. 1102

1731 — ELECTRICAL WORK CONTRACTORS

AC CORPORATION; *U.S. Private*, pg. 3
ADT EUROPE—Tyco International Ltd.; *U.S. Public*, pg. 1649
ADT GREECE, S.A.—Tyco International Ltd.; *U.S. Public*, pg. 1649
ADT ITALIANA, S.P.A.—Tyco International Ltd.; *U.S. Public*, pg. 1649
ADT/PROEGUR, S.A.—Tyco International Ltd.; *U.S. Public*, pg. 1649
ADT SECURITY SYSTEMS—Tyco International Ltd.; *U.S. Public*, pg. 1649
AFA PROTECTIVE SYSTEMS, INC.; *U.S. Public*, pg. 5
API GROUP INC.; *U.S. Private*, pg. 7
ARI GROUP EUROPE—Tyco International Ltd.; *U.S. Public*, pg. 1650
ATA S.A.—Alcatel Alsthom Compagnie Generale D'Electricite; *Int'l*, pg. 53
AANNEMINGSBEDRIJF VAN OUDBROEKHUIZEN B.V., NIEUWEGLIN—Internatio-Muller N.V.; *Int'l*, pg. 681
ABRAMS INDUSTRIES, INC.; *U.S. Public*, pg. 14
ACMAT CORPORATION; *U.S. Public*, pg. 16
ALCATEL ALSTHOM COMPAGNIE GENERALE D'ELECTRICITE; *Int'l*, pg. 52
THE ALPINE GROUP, INC.; *U.S. Public*, pg. 58
AMELCO CORPORATION; *U.S. Public*, pg. 65
AMERICAN ELECTRIC CO., LTD.—Amelco Corporation; *U.S. Public*, pg. 65
AMERICAN SYSTEMS CORPORATION; *U.S. Private*, pg. 63
AMERICAN TECHNICAL SERVICES GROUP, INC.—Strategic Distribution Inc.; *U.S. Public*, pg. 1523
ANDERSON ELECTRIC, INC.; *U.S. Private*, pg. 72
ANSALDO TRANSPORTI SPA—IRI Istituto Ricostruzione Industriale; *Int'l*, pg. 653
APPLIED DIGITAL ACCESS; *U.S. Public*, pg. 122
ARKANSAS ELECTRIC COOPERATIVES INC.; *U.S. Private*, pg. 82
BG CHECO CONSTRUCTION—Alcatel Alsthom Compagnie Generale D'Electricite; *Int'l*, pg. 53
BICC PLC; *Int'l*, pg. 120
BT (WORLDWIDE) LTD.—British Telecommunications plc; *Int'l*, pg. 222
BABCOCK ELECTRICAL PROJECTS LTD—FKI Plc; *Int'l*, pg. 471
BABCOCK INDUSTRIAL CONTRACTORS (PTY) LTD.—FKI Plc; *Int'l*, pg. 474
N.G. BAILEY & CO. LTD.; *Int'l*, pg. 132
BALFOUR BEATTY LIMITED—BICC plc; *Int'l*, pg. 120
BARR ELECTRIC CORPORATION; *U.S. Private*, pg. 117
BERGELECTRIC CORPORATION; *U.S. Private*, pg. 135
BLOOM ELECTRIC SERVICES, INC.; *U.S. Private*, pg. 150
BLUMBERG COMMUNICATIONS INC.—Caribiner International, Inc.; *U.S. Public*, pg. 305
BRITISH ELECTRICAL REPAIRS LTD.—Delta plc; *Int'l*, pg. 390
BRYANT ELECTRIC COMPANY, INC.; *U.S. Private*, pg. 176
COMSIP AL A'ALI W.L.L.—Alcatel Alsthom Compagnie Generale D'Electricite; *Int'l*, pg. 53
COMSIP AUTOMATION BENELUX, S.A.—Alcatel Alsthom Compagnie Generale D'Electricite; *Int'l*, pg. 53
COMSIP CAM—Alcatel Alsthom Compagnie Generale D'Electricite; *Int'l*, pg. 53
COMSIP LTD.—Alcatel Alsthom Compagnie Generale D'Electricite; *Int'l*, pg. 53
COMSIP NEDERLAND B.V.—Alcatel Alsthom Compagnie Generale D'Electricite; *Int'l*, pg. 53
CABINAS TELEFONICAS, S.A. (CABITEL)—Telefonica de Espana, S.A.; *Int'l*, pg. 1371
CABLEVISION—Cablevision Systems Corporation; *U.S. Public*, pg. 288
CEGELEC—Alcatel Alsthom Compagnie Generale D'Electricite; *Int'l*, pg. 52
CEGELEC DE MEXICO—Alcatel Alsthom Compagnie Generale D'Electricite; *Int'l*, pg. 53
CEGELEC ENGENHARIA S.A.—Alcatel Alsthom Compagnie Generale D'Electricite; *Int'l*, pg. 53
CEGELEC ENTREPRISES, INC.—Alcatel Alsthom Compagnie Generale D'Electricite; *Int'l*, pg. 53
CEGELEC GMBH—Alcatel Alsthom Compagnie Generale D'Electricite; *Int'l*, pg. 53
CEGELEC (M) SDN BHD—Alcatel Alsthom Compagnie Generale D'Electricite; *Int'l*, pg. 53
CEITRONICS, INC.—Synergism, Inc.; *U.S. Private*, pg. 1060
CELEGEC AUTOMATION—Alcatel Alsthom Compagnie Generale D'Electricite; *Int'l*, pg. 53
CHRISTENSON ELECTRIC, INC.; *U.S. Private*, pg. 238
CITY COM B.V.—Internatio-Muller N.V.; *Int'l*, pg. 681
CLEVELAND ELECTRIC CO.—Cleveland Group, Inc.; *U.S. Private*, pg. 246
CLEVELAND GROUP, INC.; *U.S. Private*, pg. 246
COKEN COMPANY, INC.; *U.S. Private*, pg. 250
COLLINS ELECTRIC COMPANY, INC.; *U.S. Private*, pg. 253
COMMERCIAL LIGHT COMPANY; *U.S. Private*, pg. 258
COMSIP AUTOMACION S.A.—Alcatel Alsthom Compagnie Generale D'Electricite; *Int'l*, pg. 53
CONSTRUCCIONES INSTALACIONES BABCOCK S.A. DE C.V.—FKI Plc; *Int'l*, pg. 474
CONSTRUCTION MANAGEMENT SERVICE; *U.S. Private*, pg. 266
CUMMINGS INC.; *U.S. Private*, pg. 295
CUPERTINO ELECTRIC, INC.—Synergism, Inc.; *U.S. Private*, pg. 1060
D.W. CLOSE COMPANY—MYR Group Inc.; *U.S. Public*, pg. 1029
DAIDONE ELECTRICAL INC.; *U.S. Private*, pg. 307
DAVIS ELECTRICAL CONSTRUCTORS, INC.; *U.S. Private*, pg. 315
DELTA PLC; *Int'l*, pg. 389
DEUTSCHE TELEKOM AG; *Int'l*, pg. 407
DIVANE BROS. ELECTRIC CO.; *U.S. Private*, pg. 336
DYCOM INDUSTRIES, INC.; *U.S. Public*, pg. 538
DYNALECTRIC COMPANY—EMCOR Group, Inc.; *U.S. Public*, pg. 571
EIJ IMTECH N.V.—Internatio-Muller N.V.; *Int'l*, pg. 682
EPEX GROUP—Alcatel Alsthom Compagnie Generale D'Electricite; *Int'l*, pg. 52
ERE T DIVISION—Alcatel Alsthom Compagnie Generale D'Electricite; *Int'l*, pg. 52
EGIZII ELECTRIC, INC.; *U.S. Private*, pg. 366
ELECTRIC POWER EQUIPMENT CO.; *U.S. Private*, pg. 368
ELECTRIC PROTECTION SERVICES (EPS)—Tyco International Ltd.; *U.S. Public*, pg. 1650
ELECTRO PROTECTION SERVICES/CEPS—Tyco International Ltd.; *U.S. Public*, pg. 1650
EMCOR GROUP, INC.; *U.S. Public*, pg. 571
ENERGY SERVICES, INC.—Edison International; *U.S. Public*, pg. 564
ENTERPRISE GENERALE DE TELECOMMUNICATIONS—France Telecom; *Int'l*, pg. 503
ERICSSON NETWORK CONSTRUCTIONS AB—Telefonaktiebolaget LM Ericsson; *Int'l*, pg. 1363
ERIE COUNTY CABLEVISION—Blade Communications, Inc.; *U.S. Private*, pg. 147
ERMCO, INC.; *U.S. Private*, pg. 381
E.C. ERNST, INC.—The Philadelphia Bourse, Inc.; *U.S. Private*, pg. 861
FARNSWORTH HOMES—Farnsworth Companies; *U.S. Private*, pg. 397
FERGUSON ELECTRIC CONSTRUCTION CO., INC.; *U.S. Private*, pg. 401
FERRANTI AIR SYSTEMS LTD.—Datel Technologies Ltd.; *Int'l*, pg. 384
FIBER CABLE, INC.—Dycom Industries, Inc.; *U.S. Public*, pg. 538
FIBER OPTIC SERVICES, INC.—The Goldfield Corporation; *U.S. Public*, pg. 750
FICON CORPORATION—American International Group, Inc.; *U.S. Public*, pg. 84
FINSIEL—IRI Istituto Ricostruzione Industriale; *Int'l*, pg. 654
FISCHBACH & MOORE, INC.—American International Group, Inc.; *U.S. Public*, pg. 84
FISCHBACH & MOORE INTERNATIONAL CORP.—American International Group, Inc.; *U.S. Public*, pg. 84
FISCHBACH CORPORATION—American International Group, Inc.; *U.S. Public*, pg. 84
FISK ELECTRIC COMPANY—AMEC Plc; *Int'l*, pg. 16
FORE LINE SECURITY—Reeves Southeastern Corporation; *U.S. Private*, pg. 917
GSI OF CALIFORNIA—Gulf States, Inc.; *U.S. Private*, pg. 487
GTE SOUTH INCORPORATED—GTE Corporation; *U.S. Public*, pg. 697
GEREMIA ELECTRIC CO., INC.—ACMAT Corporation; *U.S. Public*, pg. 16
THE GILBERT COMPANIES, INC.; *U.S. Private*, pg. 453
THE GOLDFIELD CORPORATION; *U.S. Public*, pg. 750
GUARANTEE ELECTRICAL COMPANY; *U.S. Private*, pg. 485
GULF STATES, INC.; *U.S. Private*, pg. 487
HMI, HOLLANDSCHE MAATSCHAPPIJ INSTALLATIETECHNIEK BV—Hollandsche Beton Groep NV; *Int'l*, pg. 630
HALL & KAY FIRE—Staveley Industries PLC; *Int'l*, pg. 1298
HARLAN ELECTRIC CO.—MYR Group Inc.; *U.S. Public*, pg. 1029
HATZEL & BUEHLER, INC.—Construction Management Service; *U.S. Private*, pg. 266
HAUENSTEIN & BURMEISTER, INC.; *U.S. Private*, pg. 510
HAWKEYE CONSTRUCTION, INC.—MYR Group Inc.; *U.S. Public*, pg. 1029
EDD HELMS ELECTRICAL CONTRACTING; *U.S. Private*, pg. 520
HENDERSON ELECTRIC CO., INC.; *U.S. Private*, pg. 521
THE HITE COMPANY; *U.S. Private*, pg. 531
HOLEC PROJECTS B.V.—Royal Begemann Group; *Int'l*, pg. 1133
HOW GROUP LIMITED; *Int'l*, pg. 636
HUNTER CORP.; *U.S. Private*, pg. 549
HYRE ELECTRIC COMPANY OF INDIANA, INC.—EMCOR Group, Inc.; *U.S. Public*, pg. 572
IMTECH PROJECTS ZUIT B.V.—Internatio-Muller N.V.; *Int'l*, pg. 681
INTERACTIVE TELECARD SERVICES, INC. (ITS); *U.S. Private*, pg. 566
INTERNATIO-MULLER N.V.; *Int'l*, pg. 680
INTERSERVICIOS Y TECNOLOGIA S.A., BARCELONA—Internatio-Muller N.V.; *Int'l*, pg. 681
ITALTEL—Telecom Italia S.p.A.; *Int'l*, pg. 1363
JESCO—United Dominion Industries, Ltd.; *U.S. Public*, pg. 1676
JOSLYN CORPORATION—Danaher Corporation; *U.S. Public*, pg. 481
KLT TELECOM INC.—Kansas City Power & Light Company; *U.S. Public*, pg. 943
KNC (KOREA NETWORK CORPORATION)—KOHAP Group; *Int'l*, pg. 742
KELLEY ELECTRIC COMPANY—The Gilbert Companies, Inc.; *U.S. Private*, pg. 453
KELSO-BURNETT COMPANY; *U.S. Private*, pg. 613
KOHLER CONSTRUCTION COMPANY, INC.—Dycom Industries, Inc.; *U.S. Public*, pg. 538
LAKE ERIE ELECTRIC, INC.; *U.S. Private*, pg. 643
LAMINAIRE CORPORATION—Thermo-Mizer Environmental Corp.; *U.S. Public*, pg. 1596
LINDER & ASSOCIATES, INC.; *U.S. Private*, pg. 668
MG ELECTRIC POWER, INC.—Metallgesellschaft AG; *Int'l*, pg. 862
MJN—Staveley Industries PLC; *Int'l*, pg. 1299
MYR GROUP INC.; *U.S. Public*, pg. 1029
MAINTENANCE SERVICES GROUP—Namanco LLC; *U.S. Private*, pg. 773
MCCARTHY BAILEY LIMITED—N.G. Bailey & Co. Ltd.; *Int'l*, pg. 133
MILLER ELECTRIC COMPANY; *U.S. Private*, pg. 747
MITEL CORPORATION; *Int'l*, pg. 870
MITEL SEMICONDUCTOR—Mitel Corporation; *Int'l*, pg. 870
MOSS TELECOMMUNICATIONS SERVICES; *U.S. Private*, pg. 763
MUSKA ELECTRIC COMPANY; *U.S. Private*, pg. 768
NETTENBOUW B.V., AMERSFOORT—Internatio-Muller N.V.; *Int'l*, pg. 681
THE NEWTRON GROUP INC.; *U.S. Private*, pg. 797
NIGERLEC CONTRACTORS LTD.—Alcatel Alsthom Compagnie Generale D'Electricite; *Int'l*, pg. 53
PACIFICORP; *U.S. Public*, pg. 1251
PALMER ELECTRIC CO.; *U.S. Private*, pg. 834
P.T. PANATA TAMA INTER INSTALASI INDONESIA—Internatio-Muller N.V.; *Int'l*, pg. 681
PEIRCE-PHELPS, INC.; *U.S. Private*, pg. 847
PEOPLES ELECTRIC CONTRACTOR, INC.; *U.S. Private*, pg. 851
PHILIPPINE LONG DISTANCE TELEPHONE COMPANY; *Int'l*, pg. 1051
PILLAR ENGINEERING LTD.—Caradon Plc; *Int'l*, pg. 267
PLATEAU ELECTRIC CONSTRUCTION INC.—Amelco Corporation; *U.S. Public*, pg. 65
PRECISION POWER, INC.—United Illuminating Company; *U.S. Public*, pg. 1678
PROCESS PLANT CONTRACTING DIV.—FKI Plc; *Int'l*, pg. 472
PROGRAM WATER TECHNOLOGIES—Sloan Valve Company; *U.S. Private*, pg. 1006
QUINTRON SYSTEMS, INC.; *U.S. Private*, pg. 901
R&H AUSTRALIA PTY. LTD.—Internatio-Muller N.V.; *Int'l*, pg. 681
RFL ELECTRONICS, INC.; *U.S. Private*, pg. 903
THOMAS ROBINSON GROUP PLC—Brunel Holdings Plc; *Int'l*, pg. 231
ROMAN ELECTRIC COMPANY, INC.; *U.S. Private*, pg. 942
RONCO COMMUNICATIONS & ELECTRONICS INC.; *U.S. Private*, pg. 943
ROSENDIN ELECTRIC, INC.; *U.S. Private*, pg. 945
THE ROWE CORPORATION; *U.S. Private*, pg. 948
SECO INDUSTRIES, INC.—Serv-Tech, Inc.; *U.S. Public*, pg. 1460
STS, INC.—Dycom Industries, Inc.; *U.S. Public*, pg. 538
SASCO ELECTRIC—Sasco Group; *U.S. Private*, pg. 967
SASCO GROUP; *U.S. Private*, pg. 967
SASCO/VALLEY ELECTRIC—Sasco Group; *U.S. Private*, pg. 967
SENTROL CONTROLS GROUP—Berwind Corporation; *U.S. Private*, pg. 139
SERV-TECH EUROPE—Serv-Tech, Inc.; *U.S. Public*, pg. 1460
THE SERVICEMASTER COMPANY; *U.S. Public*, pg. 1461
SHARE TECHNOLOGIES - FAIRCHILD—Tel-Save Holdings, Inc.; *U.S. Public*, pg. 1568
JOHN SHELBOURNE & CO. LTD.—Costain Group PLC; *Int'l*, pg. 337
SHORROCK SECURITY LTD.—Sophus Berendsen A/S; *Int'l*, pg. 1285
SIMKO TICARET VE SANAYI A.S.—Siemens AG; *Int'l*, pg. 1248
SIRTI—Telecom Italia S.p.A.; *Int'l*, pg. 1362
SISSING ELEKTROTECHNIEK B.V.—Royal Begemann Group; *Int'l*, pg. 1133
SOUTH ATLANTIC TRI-CITY—Tri-City Electrical Contractors Inc.; *U.S. Private*, pg. 1100
SOUTHEAST POWER CORPORATION—The Goldfield Corporation; *U.S. Public*, pg. 750
SPIE BATIGNOLLES—AMEC Plc; *Int'l*, pg. 16
STEINY & COMPANY, INC.; *U.S. Private*, pg. 1039
STET INTERNATIONAL—Telecom Italia S.p.A.; *Int'l*, pg. 1363
STET SOCIETA FINANZIARIA TELEFONICA—IRI Istituto Ricostruzione Industriale; *Int'l*, pg. 655
STURGEON ELECTRIC COMPANY—MYR Group Inc.; *U.S. Public*, pg. 1029
SUPERIOR TELECOMMUNICATIONS—The Alpine Group, Inc.; *U.S. Public*, pg. 58
SUPERVISORY & INDUSTRIAL PROCESS CONTROL LIMITED—N.G. Bailey & Co. Ltd.; *Int'l*, pg. 133
SWITCHGEAR & INSTRUMENTATION LTD.—N.G. Bailey & Co. Ltd.; *Int'l*, pg. 133
TELECOM ITALIA S.P.A.; *Int'l*, pg. 1362
TELECOM ITALIA S.P.A.—Telecom Italia S.p.A.; *Int'l*, pg. 1363
TELEPORT COMMUNICATIONS GROUP; *U.S. Public*, pg. 1572
TELETTRA—Alcatel Alsthom Compagnie Generale D'Electricite; *Int'l*, pg. 55
TIE/COMMUNICATIONS, INC.; *U.S. Private*, pg. 1085
TOSHIBA TELECOMMUNICATION FIELD ENGINEERING CORPORATION—Toshiba Corporation; *Int'l*, pg. 1405
TRI-CITY ELECTRICAL CONTRACTORS INC.; *U.S. Private*, pg. 1100
TRI-STATE ARMATURE & ELECTRIC WORKS; *U.S. Private*, pg. 1100
TRIANGLE ELECTRIC COMPANY; *U.S. Private*, pg. 1102
TRIANGLE SERVICES, INC.; *U.S. Private*, pg. 1102
UTILITIES CONSTRUCTION CO., INC. OF SOUTH CAROLINA; *U.S. Private*, pg. 1130
VAN BUUREN-VAN SWAAY MARINE AIRCONDITIONING, ZOETERMEER—Internatio-Muller N.V.; *Int'l*, pg. 681
VAN SWAAY INTERNATIONAL CONTRACTING B.V.—Internatio-Muller N.V.; *Int'l*, pg. 681
VEREBUS ENGINEERING B.V., THE HAGUE—Internatio-Muller N.V.; *Int'l*, pg. 680
VOLTELCON—Volt Information Sciences, Inc.; *U.S. Public*, pg. 1724
WHS—Staveley Industries PLC; *Int'l*, pg. 1299
WEBB ELECTRIC CO.—Jervis B. Webb Company; *U.S. Private*, pg. 1156
JERVIS B. WEBB COMPANY; *U.S. Private*, pg. 1156
WEBB, MURRAY & ASSOCIATES; *U.S. Private*, pg. 1157
WELSBACH ELECTRIC CORP.—EMCOR Group, Inc.; *U.S. Public*, pg. 572

WESTGATE INC.; *U.S. Private*, pg. 1169
WESTSTAR ENGINEERING INC.—Amelco Corporation; *U.S. Public*, pg. 65
WINDEMULLER ELECTRIC INC.; *U.S. Private*, pg. 1182
WINSTAR COMMUNICATIONS; *U.S. Public*, pg. 1772

1741 — MASONRY, STONE SETTING & OTHER STONE WORK CONTRACTORS

ARC CONBLOC LIMITED—Hanson PLC; *Int'l*, pg. 592
ASHBY & HORNER LTD.—The Peninsular and Oriental Steam Navigation Company; *Int'l*, pg. 1032
ASHBY & HORNER MASONRY LTD.—The Peninsular and Oriental Steam Navigation Company; *Int'l*, pg. 1032
BATH & PORTLAND STONE LIMITED—Hanson PLC; *Int'l*, pg. 592
BORAL CONCRETE PRODUCTS PTY. LTD.—Boral Limited; *Int'l*, pg. 203
DBM HATCH, INC.; *U.S. Private*, pg. 300
HAWAIIAN DREDGING & CONSTRUCTION COMPANY—Dillingham Construction Corporation; *U.S. Private*, pg. 333
E.P. HENRY CORPORATION; *U.S. Private*, pg. 522
JESCO COMPANY—Al Johnson Construction Co.; *U.S. Private*, pg. 590
KARL KOCH ERECTING CO. INC.—Skanska AB; *Int'l*, pg. 1261
KVAERNER DORIS OFFSHORE CONCRETE A/S—Kvaerner a.s.a.; *Int'l*, pg. 766
LAFARGE CANADA INC.—Lafarge S.A.; *Int'l*, pg. 789
SKANSKA AB; *Int'l*, pg. 1260

1742 — PLASTERING, DRYWALL, ACOUSTICAL & INSULATION WORK CONTRACTORS

AC & S INC.—Irex Corporation; *U.S. Public*, pg. 913
ACOUSTI ENGINEERING CO. OF FLORIDA; *U.S. Private*, pg. 14
AIRTITE CONTRACTORS INC.; *U.S. Private*, pg. 29
ANCO INSULATIONS, INC.; *U.S. Private*, pg. 71
ANNING-JOHNSON COMPANY—Anson Industries, Inc.; *U.S. Private*, pg. 76
ANSON INDUSTRIES, INC.; *U.S. Private*, pg. 76
BORAL AUSTRALIAN GYPSUM LTD.—Boral Limited; *Int'l*, pg. 203
CEILING & PARTITIONS, INC.; *U.S. Private*, pg. 221
COURTAULDS AEROSPACE—Courtaulds plc; *Int'l*, pg. 338
DAVENPORT INSULATION, INC; *U.S. Private*, pg. 314
HAUENSTEIN & BURMEISTER, INC.; *U.S. Private*, pg. 510
HAWAIIAN DREDGING & CONSTRUCTION COMPANY—Dillingham Construction Corporation; *U.S. Private*, pg. 333
IREX CORPORATION; *U.S. Public*, pg. 913
JOHNSON ACOUSTICAL & SUPPLY CO.; *U.S. Private*, pg. 590
MADER CONSTRUCTION CORP; *U.S. Private*, pg. 693
NATIONAL SERVICE INDUSTRIES, INC.; *U.S. Public*, pg. 1160
NATIONAL THERMAL INSULATION—Transco Inc.; *U.S. Private*, pg. 1096
NORTH BROS. CO.—Performance Contracting Group; *U.S. Private*, pg. 853
PERFORMANCE CONTRACTING GROUP; *U.S. Private*, pg. 853
SUPERIOR INDUSTRIES OF NEBRASKA, INC.; *U.S. Private*, pg. 1055
TRANSCO PRODUCTS INC.—Transco Inc.; *U.S. Private*, pg. 1096
TRULINE TREETEX LIMITED—SAS Holdings Limited; *Int'l*, pg. 1152

1743 — TERRAZZO, TILE, MARBLE & MOSAIC WORK CONTRACTORS

NEW ENGLAND STONE INDUSTRIES, INC.; *U.S. Private*, pg. 793

1751 — CARPENTRY WORK

ASHBY & HORNER LTD.—The Peninsular and Oriental Steam Navigation Company; *Int'l*, pg. 1032
CARPENTRY & HARDWARE SERVICES—Harkins Builders, Inc.; *U.S. Private*, pg. 503
FRANZ HANIEL & CIE, GMBH; *Int'l*, pg. 591
LOZIER CORPORATION; *U.S. Private*, pg. 679
B.T. MANCINI CO., INC.; *U.S. Private*, pg. 699
SCHUCK & SONS CONSTRUCTION CO.; *U.S. Private*, pg. 973
TRIANGLE SERVICES, INC.; *U.S. Private*, pg. 1102

1752 — FLOOR LAYING & OTHER FLOOR WORK, NEC

ACMAT CORPORATION; *U.S. Public*, pg. 16
AIRTITE CONTRACTORS INC.; *U.S. Private*, pg. 29
CENTIMARK CORPORATION; *U.S. Private*, pg. 222
DOMCO INC.—Domco Inc.; *Int'l*, pg. 415
HOBOKEN WOOD FLOORING CORPORATION; *U.S. Private*, pg. 532
STONHARD, INC.—RPM, Inc.; *U.S. Public*, pg. 1358

1761 — ROOFING, SIDING & SHEET METAL WORK

ANNING-JOHNSON COMPANY—Anson Industries, Inc.; *U.S. Private*, pg. 76
ANSON INDUSTRIES, INC.; *U.S. Private*, pg. 76
ATLAS MANUFACTURING DIVISION—Upper Midwest Industries, Incorporated; *U.S. Private*, pg. 1129
BEACON SALES CORPORATION; *U.S. Private*, pg. 126
JOHN J. CAMPBELL CO., INC.; *U.S. Private*, pg. 204
CENTIMARK CORPORATION; *U.S. Private*, pg. 222
COMMERICAL ROOFERS INC.; *U.S. Private*, pg. 258
CORRIGAN BROS., INC.; *U.S. Private*, pg. 277
D.C. TAYLOR CO.; *U.S. Private*, pg. 300
M.J. DALY & SONS, INC.; *U.S. Private*, pg. 309
B.T. MANCINI CO., INC.; *U.S. Private*, pg. 699
AB MATAKI—Trelleborg AB; *Int'l*, pg. 1422
MATAKI HELTACKANDE TAK—Trelleborg AB; *Int'l*, pg. 1422
NORTH AMERICAN ROOFING SYSTEMS, INC.; *U.S. Private*, pg. 803
OWEN PACIFIC; *U.S. Private*, pg. 824
PACIFIC COAST BUILDING PRODUCTS INC.; *U.S. Private*, pg. 830
POLYTUIL S.A.—International Paper Company; *U.S. Public*, pg. 903
SENIOR COLMAN LIMITED—Senior Engineering Group, plc.; *Int'l*, pg. 1220
SENIOR CONSTRUCTION SERVICES LIMITED—Senior Engineering Group, plc.; *Int'l*, pg. 1220
SENIOR ENGINEERING GROUP, PLC.; *Int'l*, pg. 1220
SENIOR HARGREAVES LIMITED—Senior Engineering Group, plc.; *Int'l*, pg. 1221
SENIOR MODUCEL LIMITED—Senior Engineering Group, plc.; *Int'l*, pg. 1221
SENIOR PHOENIX RFS LIMITED—Senior Engineering Group, plc.; *Int'l*, pg. 1221
TIFT SA—Senior Engineering Group, plc.; *Int'l*, pg. 1223
D.C. TAYLOR CO.; *U.S. Private*, pg. 1070
WEISS SHEET METAL COMPANY; *U.S. Private*, pg. 1160
WESTERN PACIFIC ROOFING; *U.S. Private*, pg. 1168

1771 — CONCRETE WORK

ARB INC.; *U.S. Private*, pg. 7
BACCO CONSTRUCTION CO.; *U.S. Private*, pg. 109
BAKER CONCRETE CONSTRUCTION, INC.; *U.S. Private*, pg. 111
BANKHEAD ENTERPRISES INC.; *U.S. Private*, pg. 114
CALUMET CONSTRUCTION CORPORATION; *U.S. Private*, pg. 201
CECO CONCRETE CONSTRUCTION LLC—Pettibone Corporation; *U.S. Private*, pg. 859
DILLINGHAM CONSTRUCTION CORPORATION; *U.S. Private*, pg. 333
DONLEY'S, INC.; *U.S. Private*, pg. 340
DUGAN & MEYERS CONSTRUCTION CO.—Dugan & Meyers Interests, Inc.; *U.S. Private*, pg. 345
FORD DEVELOPMENT CORPORATION; *U.S. Private*, pg. 418
HAWAIIAN DREDGING & CONSTRUCTION COMPANY—Dillingham Construction Corporation; *U.S. Private*, pg. 333
INTREPID ENTERPRISES, INC.; *U.S. Private*, pg. 574
JESCO COMPANY—Al Johnson Construction Co.; *U.S. Private*, pg. 590
LINBECK CONSTRUCTION CORP; *U.S. Private*, pg. 667
MAESCHER INDUSTRIES, INC.; *U.S. Private*, pg. 694
MILLER & LONG CO. INC.; *U.S. Private*, pg. 746
THE MILLGARD CORP.; *U.S. Private*, pg. 748
MORLEY BUILDERS; *U.S. Private*, pg. 761
NORWEGIAN CONTRACTORS A/S—Aker Raj Asa; *Int'l*, pg. 42
RITCHIE CORPORATION; *U.S. Private*, pg. 933

1781 — WATER WELL DRILLING

BARNWELL INDUSTRIES, INC.; *U.S. Public*, pg. 190
CALENERGY CO.; *U.S. Public*, pg. 292
HYDRO GROUP, INC.; *U.S. Private*, pg. 552
LAYNE-WESTERN CO., INC.—Layne Christenson Co.; *U.S. Public*, pg. 981
THE MARLEY COOLING TOWER CO.—United Dominion Industries, Ltd.; *U.S. Public*, pg. 1676

1791 — STRUCTURAL STEEL ERECTION

ADDISON STEEL INC.; *U.S. Private*, pg. 17
AKER VERDAL A.S.—Aker Raj Asa; *Int'l*, pg. 42
ARIDO ABDICHTUNGS-GESELLSCHAFT—Dyckerhoff & Widmann AG; *Int'l*, pg. 423
ARNOLD STEEL COMPANY, INC.; *U.S. Private*, pg. 84
BELMONT INDUSTRIES, INC.—RGP Holding, Inc.; *U.S. Private*, pg. 903
THE BERLIN STEEL CONSTRUCTION COMPANY; *U.S. Private*, pg. 136
BROAD, VOGT & CONANT, INC.; *U.S. Private*, pg. 170
BROWN-MINNEAPOLIS TANK & FABRICATING CO.—ITEQ, Inc.; *U.S. Public*, pg. 914
CALUMET CONSTRUCTION CORPORATION; *U.S. Private*, pg. 201
CINCINNATI UNITED CONTRACTORS; *U.S. Private*, pg. 240
ELASTIC MATERIALS, INC.; *U.S. Private*, pg. 367
GEBAUER AG—Schindler Holding AG; *Int'l*, pg. 1204
HAVENS STEEL CO.; *U.S. Private*, pg. 510
HIGH INDUSTRIES, INC.; *U.S. Private*, pg. 528
HITACHI ZOSEN CORPORATION; *Int'l*, pg. 622
HUNTER CORP.; *U.S. Private*, pg. 549
IDEA ENGINEERING & FABRICATING; *U.S. Private*, pg. 557
KENAI LNG CORPORATION—Phillips Petroleum Company; *U.S. Public*, pg. 1291
LEBLANC COMMUNICATIONS, INC.; *U.S. Private*, pg. 656
MATRIX SERVICE COMPANY; *U.S. Public*, pg. 1057
NATIONAL ENGINEERING & CONTRACTING CO.; *U.S. Private*, pg. 782
NORWEGIAN CONTRACTORS A/S—Aker Raj Asa; *Int'l*, pg. 42
OMEGA ENVIRONMENTAL INC.; *U.S. Public*, pg. 1221
OVERHEAD CONVEYOR CO.; *U.S. Private*, pg. 822
PDM BRIDGE—Pitt-Des Moines, Inc.; *U.S. Public*, pg. 1305
PASCOE BUILDING SYSTEMS, INC.; *U.S. Private*, pg. 842
PITT-DES MOINES, INC.; *U.S. Public*, pg. 1304
RGP HOLDING, INC.; *U.S. Private*, pg. 903
RAPID INDUSTRIES, INC.; *U.S. Private*, pg. 910
RIGGS INDUSTRIES, INC.; *U.S. Private*, pg. 930
SCHUFF STEEL CO.; *U.S. Private*, pg. 973
SHELBY STEEL PROCESSING CO.—McClain Industries, Inc.; *U.S. Public*, pg. 1065
SKANSKA AB; *Int'l*, pg. 1260
SKANSKA STALTEKNIK AB—Skanska AB; *Int'l*, pg. 1261
SOUTHERN OHIO FABRICATORS, INC.; *U.S. Private*, pg. 1017
L.H. SOWLES COMPANY, INC.; *U.S. Private*, pg. 1019
STEEL MOULDS LTD.—Tarmac plc; *Int'l*, pg. 1355
STEEL TANK & FABRICATING CORP.—Kennedy Tank & Manufacturing Co., Inc.; *U.S. Private*, pg. 615
TURNER INDUSTRIES; *U.S. Private*, pg. 1109
VULCAN IRON WORKS, INC.; *U.S. Private*, pg. 1144
VYTAHY SCHINDLER A.S.—Schindler Holding AG; *Int'l*, pg. 1205
WILLIAMS STEEL ERECTION CO., INC.—Williams Industries, Inc.; *U.S. Public*, pg. 1770

1793 — GLASS & GLAZING WORK

APOGEE ENTERPRISES, INC.; *U.S. Public*, pg. 120
BENSON INDUSTRIES, INC.; *U.S. Private*, pg. 133
HARMON CONTRACT GLAZING, INC.—Apogee Enterprises, Inc.; *U.S. Public*, pg. 120
HARMON GLASS COMPANY—Apogee Enterprises, Inc.; *U.S. Public*, pg. 120
HARMON GLASS OF FLORIDA, INC.—Apogee Enterprises, Inc.; *U.S. Public*, pg. 120
HAWAIIAN DREDGING & CONSTRUCTION COMPANY—Dillingham Construction Corporation; *U.S. Private*, pg. 333
HOFFER'S INC.—The Churchill Companies; *U.S. Private*, pg. 239
INFORMATION PRODUCTS, INC.—Donnelly Corporation; *U.S. Public*, pg. 519
MODEL GLASS COMPANY; *U.S. Private*, pg. 754
PG VINYL WINDOWS/PG PROGLASS CONSTRUCTION; *U.S. Private*, pg. 826
WALTERS & WOLF; *U.S. Private*, pg. 1149

1794 — EXCAVATING & FOUNDATION WORK

DAVID A. BRAMBLE, INC.; *U.S. Private*, pg. 165
CALUMET CONSTRUCTION CORPORATION; *U.S. Private*, pg. 201
CARDER, INC.; *U.S. Private*, pg. 208
FORD DEVELOPMENT CORPORATION; *U.S. Private*, pg. 418
FRANKI GRUNDBAU GMBH—Philipp Holzmann AG; *Int'l*, pg. 632
GEO-CON, INC.—URS Corporation; *U.S. Public*, pg. 1657
HAINES KIBBLEHOUSE; *U.S. Private*, pg. 494
LEE CONSTRUCTION CO.—National Engineering & Contracting Co.; *U.S. Private*, pg. 782
MAESCHER INDUSTRIES, INC.; *U.S. Private*, pg. 694
MANESS INDUSTRIES, INC.; *U.S. Private*, pg. 699
THE MILLGARD CORP.; *U.S. Private*, pg. 748
MISENER MARINE CONSTRUCTION; *U.S. Private*, pg. 752
NATIONAL ENGINEERING & CONTRACTING CO.; *U.S. Private*, pg. 782
SKANSKA (U.S.A.) INC.—Skanska AB; *Int'l*, pg. 1261
TRUMBULL CORPORATION/P.J. DICK, INC.; *U.S. Private*, pg. 1107
TURNER INDUSTRIES; *U.S. Private*, pg. 1109
WOODWARD-CONSTRUCTORS—URS Corporation; *U.S. Public*, pg. 1657
R.S. YOUNG EXCAVATING, INC.; *U.S. Private*, pg. 1202

1795 — WRECKING & DEMOLITION WORK

AMERICAN ECO CORPORATION; *Int'l*, pg. 73
GRAYCOR BLASTING COMPANY INC.—Graycor Operating Companies; *U.S. Private*, pg. 472
GRAYCOR OPERATING COMPANIES; *U.S. Private*, pg. 472
HAINES KIBBLEHOUSE; *U.S. Private*, pg. 494
PENHALL INTERNATIONAL; *U.S. Private*, pg. 849
PHOENIX CONCRETE CUTTING—Penhall International; *U.S. Private*, pg. 849
MAYER POLLACK STEEL CORPORATION—The Pollock Corp.; *U.S. Private*, pg. 874
THE POLLOCK CORP.; *U.S. Private*, pg. 874
SEVENSON ENVIRONMENTAL SERVICES, INC.; *U.S. Public*, pg. 1462
WASTE STREAM TECHNOLOGY, INC.—Sevenson Environmental Services, Inc.; *U.S. Public*, pg. 1463

1796 — INSTALLATION OR ERECTION OF BUILDING EQUIPMENT, NEC

ARIZONA ELEVATOR, INC.—Dover Corporation; *U.S. Public*, pg. 521
ASHLEY INTERNATIONAL & PASCHEN; *U.S. Private*, pg. 88
AYCOCK, INC.; *U.S. Private*, pg. 103
BARTON MALOW ENTERPRISES, INC.; *U.S. Private*, pg. 120
BORAL ACROW LTD. (NEW ZEALAND)—Boral Limited; *Int'l*, pg. 203
CALUMET CONSTRUCTION CORPORATION; *U.S. Private*, pg. 201
CIRMA ENTERPRISE—Alcatel Alsthom Compagnie Generale D'Electricite; *Int'l*, pg. 53

COMPUTER POWER INCORPORATED; *U.S. Public*, pg. 421
DAIWA HOUSE INDUSTRY CO., LTD.; *Int'l*, pg. 374
DEARBORN FABRICATING & ENGINEERING CO.—Tomkins PLC; *Int'l*, pg. 1397
ENERGY SYSTEMS INDUSTRIES, INC.; *U.S. Private*, pg. 376
FERROSTAAL AKTIENGESELLSCHAFT—MAN Aktiengesellschaft; *Int'l*, pg. 824
FLUOR CORPORATION; *U.S. Public*, pg. 659
GEBAUER AG—Schindler Holding AG; *Int'l*, pg. 1204
GOWAN, INC.—EMCOR Group, Inc.; *U.S. Public*, pg. 572
HADEN DRYSYS GMBH—Haden Maclellan Holdings plc; *Int'l*, pg. 586
HADEN SCHWEITZER CANADA INC.—Haden Maclellan Holdings plc; *Int'l*, pg. 586
HADEN SCHWEITZER CORPORATION—Haden Maclellan Holdings plc; *Int'l*, pg. 586
HANKOOK OTIS ELEVATOR COMPANY—United Technologies Corporation; *U.S. Public*, pg. 1691
HANSEN MECHANICAL CONTRACTORS, INC.—EMCOR Group, Inc.; *U.S. Public*, pg. 572
HAWAIIAN DREDGING & CONSTRUCTION COMPANY—Dillingham Construction Corporation; *U.S. Private*, pg. 333
HAWAIIAN PACIFIC ELEVATOR COMPANY—Dover Corporation; *U.S. Public*, pg. 521
HENKELS & MCCOY, INC.; *U.S. Private*, pg. 522
HERITAGE AIR SYSTEMS, INC.—EMCOR Group, Inc.; *U.S. Public*, pg. 572
J.C. HIGGINS CORP.—EMCOR Group, Inc.; *U.S. Public*, pg. 572
HONEYWELL INC.; *U.S. Public*, pg. 833
HUNTER CORP.; *U.S. Private*, pg. 549
INDUSTRIAL CONTRACTING OF FAIRMONT, INC.—Salem Group, Inc.; *U.S. Private*, pg. 961
INDUSTRIAL RESOURCES, INC.—Salem Group, Inc.; *U.S. Private*, pg. 961
JARDINE MATHESON HOLDINGS LIMITED; *Int'l*, pg. 703
MAKO CONSTRUCTION CO.—Henkels & McCoy, Inc.; *U.S. Private*, pg. 522
MCHAL CORPORATION—Salem Group, Inc.; *U.S. Private*, pg. 961
MECO ENGINEERING CO.—Meco Development Limited; *Int'l*, pg. 852
MECO HOLDINGS CO. LTD.—Meco Development Limited; *Int'l*, pg. 852
MID AMERICAN ELEVATOR CO., INC.; *U.S. Private*, pg. 743
MONTGOMERY KONE INC.—Kone Corporation; *Int'l*, pg. 746
MOUNTAINEER RESOURCES, INC.—Salem Group, Inc.; *U.S. Private*, pg. 961
NASHVILLE MACHINE CO. INC.; *U.S. Private*, pg. 774
PACE MECHANICAL SERVICES, INC—EMCOR Group, Inc.; *U.S. Public*, pg. 572
PIEDMONT MECHANICAL, INC.; *U.S. Private*, pg. 865
POWER PROCESS PIPING, INC.; *U.S. Private*, pg. 878
RELIANCE ELEVATOR COMPANY; *U.S. Private*, pg. 921
SALEM CORPORATION—Salem Group, Inc.; *U.S. Private*, pg. 961
SALEM ELECTRIC COMPANY—Salem Group, Inc.; *U.S. Private*, pg. 961
SALEM ERECTORS—Salem Group, Inc.; *U.S. Private*, pg. 961
SALEM FURNACE CO.—Salem Group, Inc.; *U.S. Private*, pg. 961
SANDVIK PROCESS SYSTEMS GMBH—Sandvik AB; *Int'l*, pg. 1187
SCHINDLER LIFTS (HONG KONG) LTD.—Schindler Holding AG; *Int'l*, pg. 1205
SCHLEGEL RETROFIT CORPORATION—BTR plc; *Int'l*, pg. 128
TODD & SARGENT, INC.; *U.S. Private*, pg. 1089
TOMKINS INDUSTRIES INC.—Tomkins PLC; *Int'l*, pg. 1397
TOSHIBA ELEVATOR & ESCALATOR SERVICE CO., LTD.—Toshiba Corporation; *Int'l*, pg. 1404
TOSTEM CORPORATION; *Int'l*, pg. 1408
TRAUTMAN & SHREVE, INC.—EMCOR Group, Inc.; *U.S. Public*, pg. 572
U.S. ELEVATOR—Thyssen AG; *Int'l*, pg. 1387
VYTAHY SCHINDLER A.S.—Schindler Holding AG; *Int'l*, pg. 1205
WEST VIRGINIA ELECTRIC CORP.—Salem Group, Inc.; *U.S. Private*, pg. 962

1799 — SPECIAL TRADE CONTRACTORS, NEC

API GROUP INC.; *U.S. Private*, pg. 7
ARB INC.; *U.S. Private*, pg. 7
AMERICAN FENCE & SECURITY COMPANY; *U.S. Private*, pg. 54
AMERICAN TECHNICAL SERVICES GROUP, INC.—Strategic Distribution Inc.; *U.S. Public*, pg. 1523
AMERON INTERNATIONAL CORPORATION; *U.S. Public*, pg. 98
ANNING-JOHNSON COMPANY—Anson Industries, Inc.; *U.S. Private*, pg. 76
ANSON INDUSTRIES, INC.; *U.S. Private*, pg. 76
ANTHONY AND SYLVAN POOLS CORPORATION—Essef Corporation; *U.S. Public*, pg. 593
ASHBY & HORNER FURNISHINGS LTD.—The Peninsular and Oriental Steam Navigation Company; *Int'l*, pg. 1032
BPB INDUSTRIES PLC; *Int'l*, pg. 122
BAILEY FIRE PROTECTION—N.G. Bailey & Co. Ltd.; *Int'l*, pg. 133
N.G. BAILEY & CO. LTD.; *Int'l*, pg. 132
BARTON-MALOW RIGGING CO.—Barton Malow Enterprises, Inc.; *U.S. Private*, pg. 120
BLACK & EDGINGTON LTD.; *Int'l*, pg. 197
BLISS-SALEM, INC.; *U.S. Private*, pg. 149
BORAL ACROW LTD. (NEW ZEALAND)—Boral Limited; *Int'l*, pg. 203
BUTLER BUILDING SYSTEMS LTD.—Butler Manufacturing Company; *U.S. Public*, pg. 271
CABLE CONSTRUCTORS, INC.; *U.S. Private*, pg. 197
CANADIAN STEBBINS ENGINEERING & MFG. CO. LTD.—Stebbins Engineering & Mfg. Co.; *U.S. Private*, pg. 1037
CELSIUS AB; *Int'l*, pg. 276
CERAMIC COOLING TOWER CO.—Amsted Industries Incorporated; *U.S. Private*, pg. 68
CHEMPOWER, INC.—American Eco Corporation; *Int'l*, pg. 74
CONSTRUCTION SPECIALTIES, INC.; *U.S. Private*, pg. 266
JACK KENT COOKE, INC.; *U.S. Private*, pg. 273
CROWN FENCE CO.; *U.S. Private*, pg. 292
CURRAN GROUP, INC.; *U.S. Private*, pg. 297
DEI DIVISION—Alcatel Alsthom Compagnie Generale D'Electricite; *Int'l*, pg. 52
DMR GROUP, INC.—Fujitsu Limited; *Int'l*, pg. 527
DSI GROUP—Alcatel Alsthom Compagnie Generale D'Electricite; *Int'l*, pg. 52
JOHN W. DANFORTH CO.; *U.S. Private*, pg. 309
DEBORAH SERVICES—Sophus Berendsen A/S; *Int'l*, pg. 1285
DYCOM INDUSTRIES, INC.; *U.S. Public*, pg. 538
ENERGY SYSTEMS INDUSTRIES, INC.; *U.S. Private*, pg. 376
EVANS INDUSTRIES, INC.; *U.S. Private*, pg. 385
FIBER OPTIC SERVICES, INC.—The Goldfield Corporation; *U.S. Public*, pg. 750
GENERAL AQUATICS CORPORATION—Essef Corporation; *U.S. Public*, pg. 592
GLOBAL POWER COMPANY—American Eco Corporation; *Int'l*, pg. 74
JOHN E. GREEN CO.; *U.S. Private*, pg. 477
HAUENSTEIN & BURMEISTER, INC.; *U.S. Private*, pg. 510
HOW GROUP LIMITED; *Int'l*, pg. 636
JESCO—United Dominion Industries, Ltd.; *U.S. Public*, pg. 1676
JOHNSON ACOUSTICAL & SUPPLY CO.; *U.S. Private*, pg. 590
JOHNSON CONTROLS, INC.; *U.S. Public*, pg. 932
JUSTIN INDUSTRIES, INC.; *U.S. Public*, pg. 936
KENNEDY EQUIPMENT CO., INC.—Kennedy Tank & Manufacturing Co., Inc.; *U.S. Private*, pg. 614
KENNEDY TANK & MANUFACTURING CO., INC.; *U.S. Private*, pg. 614
KVAERNER ROSENBERG A.S.—Kvaerner a.s.a.; *Int'l*, pg. 769
MBT (AUSTRALIA) PTY. LTD.—Viag AG; *Int'l*, pg. 1465
MBT HOLDING, LTD.—Viag AG; *Int'l*, pg. 1465
MGS ENERGY SERVICES, INC.—Mobile Gas Service Corp.; *U.S. Public*, pg. 1120
MAIN BROTHERS OIL COMPANY, INC.; *U.S. Private*, pg. 697
MANESS INDUSTRIES, INC.; *U.S. Private*, pg. 699
MASTER BUILDERS INC.—Viag AG; *Int'l*, pg. 1465
MASTER BUILDERS TECHNOLOGIES LTD.—Viag AG; *Int'l*, pg. 1465
MCLAREN/HART ENVIRONMENTAL ENGINEERING COMPANY—Viag AG; *Int'l*, pg. 1465
MEYER INTERNATIONAL PLC; *Int'l*, pg. 864
MEYNADIER AG—Viag AG; *Int'l*, pg. 1465
MODERN BUILDING CLEANING INC.—Aramark Corp.; *U.S. Private*, pg. 79
NCC STORA PROJELET—NCC AB; *Int'l*, pg. 899
NATIONAL RESTORATION CONTRACTORS, INC.—The Western Group; *U.S. Private*, pg. 1165
NETTENBOUW B.V., AMERSFOORT—Internatio-Muller N.V.; *Int'l*, pg. 681
NORTHWEST FENCE PRODUCTS CO.—Carl Weissman & Sons, Inc.; *U.S. Private*, pg. 1160
OMEGA ENVIRONMENTAL INC.—Omega Environmental Inc.; *U.S. Public*, pg. 1222
OMEGA ENVIRONMENTAL SERVICES—Omega Environmental Inc.; *U.S. Public*, pg. 1222
PADDOCK POOL CONSTRUCTION CO., INC.; *U.S. Private*, pg. 833
PARAGON—Essef Corporation; *U.S. Public*, pg. 593
PATENT CONSTRUCTION SYSTEMS—Harsco Corporation; *U.S. Public*, pg. 793
HARRY S. PETERSON CO., INC.—Viag AG; *Int'l*, pg. 1465
POWER PROCESS PIPING, INC.; *U.S. Private*, pg. 878
PREMIER METAL PRODUCTS CO.; *U.S. Private*, pg. 881
PROCESS SYSTEMS INC.; *U.S. Private*, pg. 888
RK MECHANICAL, INC.; *U.S. Private*, pg. 904
ROCHE CONSTRUCTORS, INC.; *U.S. Private*, pg. 937
ROYER INDUSTRIES, INC.—Powerscreen International Plc; *Int'l*, pg. 1066
RUBEROID AG—Ruetgers A.G.; *Int'l*, pg. 1148
SCS FIELD SERVICES, INC.—SCS Engineers; *U.S. Private*, pg. 956
ST PIPING, INC.—Serv-Tech, Inc.; *U.S. Public*, pg. 1460
SIMPLEX CONSTRUCTION CO. INC.—Simplex Industries, Inc.; *U.S. Private*, pg. 1001
SMITH TECHNOLOGIES CORP.—Smith Environmental Technologies Corp.; *U.S. Public*, pg. 1478
SOUTHERN PETROLEUM EQUIPMENT CO., INC.—Kennedy Tank & Manufacturing Co., Inc.; *U.S. Private*, pg. 614
SOUTHWEST RECREATIONAL INDUSTRIES INC.; *U.S. Private*, pg. 1018
SPECIAL ERECTION SERVICES, INC.—Construction Specialties, Inc.; *U.S. Private*, pg. 266
STABILATOR AB—Skanska AB; *Int'l*, pg. 1261
STEBBINS ENGINEERING & MFG. CO.; *U.S. Private*, pg. 1037
STEEL TANK & FABRICATING CORP.—Kennedy Tank & Manufacturing Co., Inc.; *U.S. Private*, pg. 615
SUPERIOR INDUSTRIES OF NEBRASKA, INC.; *U.S. Private*, pg. 1055
TECSYN INTERNATIONAL, INC.; *Int'l*, pg. 1361
TELEFONICA DE ESPANA, S.A.; *Int'l*, pg. 1371
TESTRONICS—Gulf States, Inc.; *U.S. Private*, pg. 487
TIDEL ENGINEERING, INC.—Tidel Technologies, Inc.; *U.S. Public*, pg. 1608
TRANSCOAT INC.—Transco Inc.; *U.S. Private*, pg. 1097
UNITED ECO SYSTEMS—American Eco Corporation; *Int'l*, pg. 74
UNIVERSAL BUILDERS SUPPLY, INC.; *U.S. Private*, pg. 1126
UNIVERSAL INSULATION, INC.—Davenport Insulation, Inc; *U.S. Private*, pg. 314
UTILX CORPORATION; *U.S. Public*, pg. 1701
WEBB, MURRAY & ASSOCIATES; *U.S. Private*, pg. 1157
WELSBACH ELECTRIC CORP.—EMCOR Group, Inc.; *U.S. Public*, pg. 572
WENGER CORPORATION; *U.S. Private*, pg. 1162
WESTERN WATERPROOFING CO. OF AMERICA, INC.—The Western Group; *U.S. Private*, pg. 1165
WINTERS WELDING WORKS, INC.; *U.S. Private*, pg. 1183
YEOMANS & PARTNERS LTD.—The Peninsular and Oriental Steam Navigation Company; *Int'l*, pg. 1035
YOUNG ELECTRIC SIGN COMPANY; *U.S. Private*, pg. 1201

2011 — MEAT PACKING PLANTS

ABBYLAND FOODS, INC.; *U.S. Private*, pg. 10
ABBYLAND ILLINOIS, INC.—Abbyland Foods, Inc.; *U.S. Private*, pg. 10
AGROPECUARIA DE GUISSONA, S. COOP. LTDA.; *Int'l*, pg. 31
ALPINE PACKING COMPANY; *U.S. Private*, pg. 45
AMERICAN FOODS GROUP, INC.; *U.S. Private*, pg. 54
THE AMERICAN MEAT PACKING CORP.—The Iowa Packing Co.; *U.S. Private*, pg. 575
AURORA PACKING CO., INC.; *U.S. Private*, pg. 99
BAKER COMMODITIES, INC.; *U.S. Private*, pg. 111
BAR-S FOODS CO.; *U.S. Private*, pg. 114
BEEFAMERICA OPERATING CO., INC.; *U.S. Private*, pg. 130
BELL-GRUPPE—Coop Switzerland; *Int'l*, pg. 329
BERNARD MATTHEWS PLC; *Int'l*, pg. 189
BESSIN CORPORATION—Sara Lee Corporation; *U.S. Public*, pg. 1433
BIG FOOT CATTLE CO.—Vienna Sausage Mfg. Co.; *U.S. Private*, pg. 1140
BROOKS COUNTY SAUSAGE—Smithfield Foods, Inc.; *U.S. Public*, pg. 1479
BRYAN FOODS—Sara Lee Corporation; *U.S. Public*, pg. 1433
BUNKER HILL FOODS INC.—Castleberry/Snow's Brands Inc.; *U.S. Private*, pg. 219
BUTLER FOODS, INC.; *U.S. Private*, pg. 190
CARGILL; *U.S. Private*, pg. 210
CATTLEMAN'S, INC.; *U.S. Public*, pg. 318
CHAMPION BOXED BEEF; *U.S. Private*, pg. 228
CHARCUTERIE LA TOUR EIFFEL INC.—McCain Foods Limited; *Int'l*, pg. 850
CONAGRA, INC.; *U.S. Public*, pg. 425
CONAGRA RED MEAT COMPANIES—ConAgra, Inc.; *U.S. Public*, pg. 427
CONTADINA/LIBBY/TRENTON DIV.—Nestle S.A.; *Int'l*, pg. 916
CULINARY FOODS GROUP—Nestle S.A.; *Int'l*, pg. 917
DAKOTA PORK INDUSTRIES—American Foods Group, Inc.; *U.S. Private*, pg. 54
DEVAULT FOODS; *U.S. Private*, pg. 329
DIXIE PACKERS—Winn-Dixie Stores, Inc.; *U.S. Public*, pg. 1772
ESS-FOOD; *Int'l*, pg. 429
ESSKAY—Smithfield Foods, Inc.; *U.S. Public*, pg. 1479
EXCEL CORP.—Cargill; *U.S. Private*, pg. 210
FARMERS UNION MARKETING & PROCESSING ASSOCIATION; *U.S. Private*, pg. 395
FARMLAND NATIONAL BEEF PACKING COMPANY, LP—Farmland Industries, Inc.; *U.S. Private*, pg. 396
FARMSTEAD—Farmland Industries, Inc.; *U.S. Private*, pg. 396
FIELD PACKING COMPANY; *U.S. Private*, pg. 403
FISCHER PACKING CO.—Bongrain S.A.; *Int'l*, pg. 201
FRESH MARK, INC.; *U.S. Private*, pg. 427
GFI AMERICA; *U.S. Private*, pg. 435
GALLO/GALILEO SALAME—Sara Lee Corporation; *U.S. Public*, pg. 1433
GELDERLANDER FLEISCHWAREN GMBH—Koninklijke BolsWessanen nv; *Int'l*, pg. 752
GOOCH PACKING CO., INC.—Randalls Food Markets, Inc.; *U.S. Private*, pg. 909
GREEN BAY DRESSED BEEF COMPANY—American Foods Group, Inc.; *U.S. Private*, pg. 54
GWALTNEY OF SMITHFIELD, LTD.—Smithfield Foods, Inc.; *U.S. Public*, pg. 1479
HARRIS FARMS, INC.; *U.S. Private*, pg. 505
HARRIS RANCH BEEF CO.—Harris Farms, Inc.; *U.S. Private*, pg. 505
HATFIELD QUALITY MEATS; *U.S. Private*, pg. 510
HILLSHIRE FARM & KAHN'S—Sara Lee Corporation; *U.S. Public*, pg. 1433
HILLSHIRE FARM COMPANY—Sara Lee Corporation; *U.S. Public*, pg. 1433
HYGRADE FOOD PRODUCTS CORPORATION—Sara Lee Corporation; *U.S. Public*, pg. 1433
IBP, INC.; *U.S. Public*, pg. 852
THE IOWA PACKING CO.; *U.S. Private*, pg. 575
JONES DAIRY FARM; *U.S. Private*, pg. 596
LARS JONSSON AB—Nestle S.A.; *Int'l*, pg. 922
JORDAN'S FOODS-CARIBOU DIVISION—Jordan's Meats; *U.S. Private*, pg. 599
KF/KONSUM COOP GROUP; *Int'l*, pg. 718
KANE-MILLER CORP.; *U.S. Private*, pg. 607
KERRY GROUP PLC; *Int'l*, pg. 731
KOWALSKI SAUSAGE CO., INC.; *U.S. Private*, pg. 634
KRAFT FOODS, INC.—Philip Morris Companies Inc.; *U.S. Public*, pg. 1287

LEONARD & HARRAL PACKING CO.; U.S. Private, pg. 660
LONG PRAIRIE PACKING CO.—Rosens Diversified, Inc.; U.S. Private, pg. 945
LOWELL PACKING COMPANY; U.S. Private, pg. 679
LUNDY PACKING CO.; U.S. Private, pg. 681
MAPLE LEAF FOODS INC.; Int'l, pg. 841
MAPLE LEAF MEATS—Maple Leaf Foods Inc.; Int'l, pg. 841
MATTESSONS WALLS LTD.—Unilever Plc; Int'l, pg. 1434
MONFORT, INC.—ConAgra, Inc.; U.S. Public, pg. 427
JOHN MORRELL & CO.—Smithfield Foods, Inc.; U.S. Public, pg. 1479
MOYER PACKING COMPANY; U.S. Private, pg. 765
NEW HORIZONS LLC; U.S. Private, pg. 794
NEW MARKET FOODS—J. Sainsbury plc; Int'l, pg. 1170
NIPPON MEAT PACKERS, INC.; Int'l, pg. 936
NUBURN CAPITAL; Int'l, pg. 990
PACKERLAND PACKING CO.; U.S. Private, pg. 833
PARKS LLC; U.S. Private, pg. 840
PARTRIDGE MEATS, INC.—American Financial Group; U.S. Public, pg. 75
PEYTON MEATS—American Financial Group; U.S. Public, pg. 75
PHARMACIA & UPJOHN, INC.; Int'l, pg. 1047
PORK FARMS/BOWYERS—Northern Foods plc; Int'l, pg. 968
PROCORDIA FOOD AB—Orkla A.S.A.; Int'l, pg. 1011
PRODUCTOS BORDEN, INC.—Borden, Inc.; U.S. Private, pg. 158
PROVIMI VEAL CORPORATION; U.S. Private, pg. 892
ROCCO INC.; U.S. Private, pg. 937
ROSENS DIVERSIFIED, INC.; U.S. Private, pg. 945
J.H. ROUTH PACKING CO.; U.S. Private, pg. 948
RUSSER FOODS—Zemco Industries, Inc.; U.S. Private, pg. 1204
SADIA GROUP; Int'l, pg. 1168
J. SAINSBURY PLC; Int'l, pg. 1169
SARA LEE CORPORATION; U.S. Public, pg. 1432
SEITZ FOODS INC.—Sara Lee Corporation; U.S. Public, pg. 1434
THE SMITHFIELD COMPANIES, INC.; U.S. Public, pg. 1479
SMITHFIELD FOODS, INC.; U.S. Public, pg. 1479
THE SMITHFIELD PACKING CO., INC.—Smithfield Foods, Inc.; U.S. Public, pg. 1479
SNOW BRAND FOOD CO., LTD.—Snow Brand Milk Products Co. Ltd.; Int'l, pg. 1272
STOCK YARDS PACKING CO., INC.; U.S. Private, pg. 1043
SUNHILL FOOD OF VERMONT, INC.—Vestjyske Slagterier; Int'l, pg. 1464
SUNNYLAND INC.—Smithfield Foods, Inc.; U.S. Public, pg. 1479
SWIFT & COMPANY—ConAgra, Inc.; U.S. Public, pg. 426
TENNESSEE DRESSED BEEF COMPANY; U.S. Private, pg. 1076
THORN APPLE VALLEY-CAROLINA DIVISION—Thorn Apple Valley, Inc.; U.S. Public, pg. 1603
THORN APPLE VALLEY-FREDERICK DIVISION—Thorn Apple Valley, Inc.; U.S. Public, pg. 1603
THORN APPLE VALLEY-GRAND RAPIDS DIVISION—Thorn Apple Valley, Inc.; U.S. Public, pg. 1603
THORN APPLE VALLEY, INC.; U.S. Public, pg. 1602
TOM THUMB FOOD & PHARMACY—Randalls Food Markets, Inc.; U.S. Private, pg. 909
TOMAHAWK FARMS, INC.—Lundy Packing Co.; U.S. Private, pg. 681
UNIGATE PLC; Int'l, pg. 1433
VALLEYDALE FOODS, INC.—Smithfield Foods, Inc.; U.S. Public, pg. 1479
VESTJYSKE SLAGTERIER; Int'l, pg. 1464
WEINSTEIN INTERNATIONAL SEAFOOD—American Foods Group, Inc.; U.S. Private, pg. 54
WINN-DIXIE STORES, INC.; U.S. Public, pg. 1771
WORLDWIDE FOOD PRODUCTS INC.; U.S. Private, pg. 1191
ZEMCO INDUSTRIES, INC.; U.S. Private, pg. 1204

2013 — SAUSAGES & OTHER PREPARED MEAT PRODUCTS

RALPH & PAUL ADAMS, INC.—Jones Dairy Farm; U.S. Private, pg. 596
AGROPECUARIA DE GUISSONA, S. COOP. LTDA.; Int'l, pg. 31
AMERICAN FOODS GROUP, INC.; U.S. Private, pg. 54
AMERICAN FOODSERVICE CORP.; U.S. Private, pg. 54
ARMOUR FOOD COMPANY—ConAgra, Inc.; U.S. Public, pg. 427
ARMOUR SWIFT ECKRICH—ConAgra, Inc.; U.S. Public, pg. 426
ATALANTA CORPORATION; U.S. Private, pg. 93
BAR-S FOODS CO.; U.S. Private, pg. 114
BARONE FOODS—Clayton, Dubilier & Rice, Inc; U.S. Private, pg. 244
BEEFAMERICA OPERATING CO., INC.; U.S. Private, pg. 130
BELL-GRUPPE—Coop Switzerland; Int'l, pg. 329
BERNARD MATTHEWS PLC; Int'l, pg. 189
BESSIN CORPORATION—Sara Lee Corporation; U.S. Public, pg. 1433
BEST PROVISION CO., INC.; U.S. Private, pg. 140
BIL MAR FOODS, INC.—Sara Lee Corporation; U.S. Public, pg. 1433
BLUE GRASS QUALITY MEATS; U.S. Private, pg. 152
BRIDGFORD FOODS CORPORATION; U.S. Public, pg. 252
CARL BUDDIG & COMPANY; U.S. Private, pg. 178
BUNKER HILL FOODS INC.—Castleberry/Snow's Brands Inc.; U.S. Private, pg. 219
BYRON'S, INC.—Rich Products Corp.; U.S. Private, pg. 928
C.C.K., INC.—Kunzler & Company, Inc.; U.S. Private, pg. 637
CASTLEBERRY/SNOW'S BRANDS INC.; U.S. Private, pg. 219
CHARCUTERIE LA TOUR EIFFEL INC.—McCain Foods Limited; Int'l, pg. 850
CHESEBROUGH-POND'S—Unilever Plc; Int'l, pg. 1436
CHIPICO PICKLES—Vienna Sausage Mfg. Co.; U.S. Private, pg. 1140
CITY MEATS & PROVISIONS - SAN DIEGO—Clayton, Dubilier & Rice, Inc; U.S. Private, pg. 244
CONAGRA, INC.; U.S. Public, pg. 425
CONAGRA INTERNATIONAL PTE. LTD.—ConAgra, Inc.; U.S. Public, pg. 429
CONTADINA/LIBBY/TRENTON DIV.—Nestle S.A.; Int'l, pg. 916
CUCINA CLASSICA ITALIANA, INC.—Saratoga Brands, Inc.; U.S. Public, pg. 1435
PATRICK CUDAHY INC.—Smithfield Foods, Inc.; U.S. Public, pg. 1479
CULINARY FOODS GROUP—Nestle S.A.; Int'l, pg. 917
DEVRO-TEEPAK, INC.—Devro International Plc; Int'l, pg. 408
DOLD FOODS—Hormel Foods Corp.; U.S. Public, pg. 840
TONY DOWNS FOODS COMPANY; U.S. Private, pg. 342
DYNA S.A.—Nestle S.A.; Int'l, pg. 916
ESS-FOOD; Int'l, pg. 429
BOB EVANS FARMS, INC.; U.S. Public, pg. 596
EXCEL CORP.—Cargill; U.S. Private, pg. 210
FIELD PACKING COMPANY; U.S. Private, pg. 403
FOODBRANDS AMERICA, INC.—IBP, Inc.; U.S. Public, pg. 852
GFI AMERICA; U.S. Private, pg. 435
GAGLIARDI BROTHERS INC.—H.J. Heinz Company; U.S. Public, pg. 805
GALLO/GALILEO SALAME—Sara Lee Corporation; U.S. Public, pg. 1433
GELDERLANDER FLEISCHWAREN GMBH—Koninklijke BolsWessanen nv; Int'l, pg. 752
GOODMARK FOODS, INC.; U.S. Public, pg. 751
GORGES/QUIK-TO-FIX FOODS; U.S. Private, pg. 465
M.H. GREENEBAUM, INC.; U.S. Private, pg. 477
HEBREW NATIONAL KOSHER FOODS DIV.—ConAgra, Inc.; U.S. Public, pg. 429
HENNINGSEN NEDERLAND B.V.—Q.P. Corporation; Int'l, pg. 1074
HILLSDOWN LTD.—Hillsdown Holdings Plc; Int'l, pg. 619
HILLSHIRE FARM & KAHN'S—Sara Lee Corporation; U.S. Public, pg. 1433
HILLSHIRE FARM COMPANY—Sara Lee Corporation; U.S. Public, pg. 1433
HYGRADE FOOD PRODUCTS CORPORATION—Sara Lee Corporation; U.S. Public, pg. 1433
I.B.I.S.-S.P.A.; Int'l, pg. 642
JAC PAC FOODS, LTD.; U.S. Private, pg. 579
JIMMY DEAN FOODS—Sara Lee Corporation; U.S. Public, pg. 1433
JOHNSONVILLE FOODS, INC.; U.S. Private, pg. 595
JOHNSONVILLE SAUSAGE, INC.—Johnsonville Foods, Inc.; U.S. Private, pg. 595
D.R. JOHNSTON GROUP PTY. LTD.—ConAgra, Inc.; U.S. Public, pg. 429
JONES DAIRY FARM; U.S. Private, pg. 596
LARS JONSSON AB—Nestle S.A.; Int'l, pg. 922
JORDAN'S FOODS-CARIBOU DIVISION—Jordan's Meats; U.S. Private, pg. 599
JORDAN'S MEATS; U.S. Private, pg. 599
KF/KONSUM COOP GROUP; Int'l, pg. 718
SAM KANE BEEF PROCESSORS, INC.; U.S. Private, pg. 607
KAYEM FOODS, INC.; U.S. Private, pg. 610
KEYSTONE FOODS CORPORATION; U.S. Private, pg. 619
JOSEPH KIRSCHNER CO.—Jordan's Meats; U.S. Private, pg. 599
A.C. KISSLING, INC.; U.S. Private, pg. 624
E.W. KNAUSS & SON, INC.; U.S. Private, pg. 626
KOWALSKI SAUSAGE CO., INC.; U.S. Private, pg. 634
KRAFT FOODS, INC.—Philip Morris Companies Inc.; U.S. Public, pg. 1287
KUNZLER & COMPANY, INC.; U.S. Private, pg. 636
LAKESIDE FOODS, INC.; U.S. Private, pg. 643
LAY'S FINE FOODS; U.S. Private, pg. 655
LEVONIAN BROTHERS INC.; U.S. Private, pg. 663
LYKES MEAT GROUP—Smithfield Foods, Inc.; U.S. Public, pg. 1479
MAPLE LEAF MEATS—Maple Leaf Foods Inc.; Int'l, pg. 841
MARUBENI CORPORATION; Int'l, pg. 844
MATTESSONS WALLS LTD.—Unilever Plc; Int'l, pg. 1434
MCDOUGALLS CATERING FOODS LIMITED—Tomkins PLC; Int'l, pg. 1396
MCKENZIES OF VERMONT, INC.; U.S. Private, pg. 723
E.A. MILLER COMPANY—ConAgra, Inc.; U.S. Public, pg. 428
THE MILNOT COMPANY; U.S. Private, pg. 749
NATIONAL FOODS INC.—ConAgra, Inc.; U.S. Public, pg. 429
NATIONWIDE BEEF, INC.; U.S. Private, pg. 788
NESTLE S.A.; Int'l, pg. 915
NIPPON MEAT PACKERS, INC.; Int'l, pg. 936
NORTHERN FOODS PLC; Int'l, pg. 967
OHSE FOODS INC.—Farmland Industries, Inc.; U.S. Private, pg. 396
OLD WISCONSIN SAUSAGE—Carl Buddig & Company; U.S. Private, pg. 178
OWENS COUNTRY SAUSAGE, INC.—Bob Evans Farms, Inc.; U.S. Public, pg. 596
PACKERLAND PACKING CO.; U.S. Private, pg. 833
PARKS LLC; U.S. Private, pg. 840
PERRI SAUSAGE, INC.—Johnsonville Foods, Inc.; U.S. Private, pg. 595
PETER'S SAVOURY PRODUCTS—Diageo Plc; Int'l, pg. 410
PEYTON MEATS—American Financial Group; U.S. Public, pg. 75
PHARMACIA & UPJOHN, INC.; Int'l, pg. 1047
PHILIP MORRIS COMPANIES INC.; U.S. Public, pg. 1287
PRINCIPAL MARQUES MEAT CO.—Maple Leaf Foods Inc.; Int'l, pg. 841
PROCESSED MEATS/POULTRY—ConAgra, Inc.; U.S. Public, pg. 426
PROCORDIA FOOD AB—Orkla A.S.A.; Int'l, pg. 1011
RAGU FOODS, INC.—Unilever Plc; Int'l, pg. 1436
AB RESTAURANGFRYS—Nestle S.A.; Int'l, pg. 920
ROCCO INC.; U.S. Private, pg. 937
ROSE PACKING COMPANY; U.S. Private, pg. 945
RUSSER FOODS—Zemco Industries, Inc.; U.S. Private, pg. 1204
RYMER FOODS INC.; U.S. Public, pg. 1414
RYMER MEAT INC.—Rymer Foods Inc.; U.S. Public, pg. 1414
SADIA GROUP; Int'l, pg. 1168
J. SAINSBURY PLC; Int'l, pg. 1169
SARA LEE CORPORATION; U.S. Public, pg. 1432
SCHNEIDER CORP.; Int'l, pg. 1207
SHOFAR KOSHER FOODS—Sara Lee Corporation; U.S. Public, pg. 1433
SIEGRA—ConAgra, Inc.; U.S. Public, pg. 429
SORENSENS LIVS AB—Nestle S.A.; Int'l, pg. 922
STAR FOOD PRODUCTS, INC.; U.S. Private, pg. 1034
SUGAR CREEK PACKING CO.; U.S. Private, pg. 1049
SUNHILL FOOD OF VERMONT, INC.—Vestjyske Slagterier; Int'l, pg. 1464
SUPERIOR'S BRAND MEATS—Fresh Mark, Inc.; U.S. Private, pg. 427
SURLEAN MEAT CO.—Leonard & Harral Packing Co.; U.S. Private, pg. 660
SWIFT & COMPANY—ConAgra, Inc.; U.S. Public, pg. 426
THORN APPLE VALLEY-DELI & SMOKED MEATS DIVISION—Thorn Apple Valley, Inc.; U.S. Public, pg. 1603
THORN APPLE VALLEY, INC.; U.S. Public, pg. 1602
TYSON FOODS, INC.; U.S. Public, pg. 1652
FRED USINGER, INC.; U.S. Private, pg. 1129
VESTJYSKE SLAGTERIER; Int'l, pg. 1464
VIENNA SAUSAGE MFG. CO.; U.S. Private, pg. 1139
VISTA INTERNATIONAL PACKAGING INC.—Hormel Foods Corp.; U.S. Public, pg. 840
WEINSTEIN INTERNATIONAL SEAFOOD—American Foods Group, Inc.; U.S. Private, pg. 54
WORLDWIDE FOOD PRODUCTS INC.; U.S. Private, pg. 1191
WRIGHT BRAND FOODS, INC.; U.S. Private, pg. 1192
ZEMCO INDUSTRIES, INC.; U.S. Private, pg. 1204
ZWANENBERG DE MEXICO S.A.—Unilever Plc; Int'l, pg. 1439

2015 — POULTRY SLAUGHTERING & PROCESSING

ACME POULTRY COMPANY, INC.; U.S. Private, pg. 13
ALIMENTS FLAMINGO; Int'l, pg. 57
ARMOUR SWIFT ECKRICH—ConAgra, Inc.; U.S. Public, pg. 426
AUSTRALIAN POULTRY LTD.—Goodman Fielder Limited; Int'l, pg. 555
BAR-S FOODS CO.; U.S. Private, pg. 114
BERNARD MATTHEWS PLC; Int'l, pg. 189
BUTTERBALL TURKEY COMPANY—ConAgra, Inc.; U.S. Public, pg. 426
BYRON'S, INC.—Rich Products Corp.; U.S. Private, pg. 928
CAGLE'S INC.; U.S. Public, pg. 291
CAL-MAINE FOODS, INC.; U.S. Public, pg. 292
CAMPBELL SOUP COMPANY; U.S. Public, pg. 298
CAMPBELL USA—Campbell Soup Company; U.S. Public, pg. 299
CARGILL; U.S. Private, pg. 210
CHARLES RIVER FOODS, INC.; U.S. Private, pg. 230
COLUMBIA FARMS INC.; U.S. Private, pg. 255
CONAGRA BROILER CO.—ConAgra, Inc.; U.S. Public, pg. 427
CONAGRA, INC.; U.S. Public, pg. 425
CONAGRA POULTRY CO.—ConAgra, Inc.; U.S. Public, pg. 427
CONAGRA POULTRY COMPANY—ConAgra, Inc.; U.S. Public, pg. 427
CONAGRA SPAIN—ConAgra, Inc.; U.S. Public, pg. 429
CONAGRA TURKEY COMPANY—ConAgra, Inc.; U.S. Public, pg. 427
CUISINE SOLUTIONS, INC.; U.S. Public, pg. 466
EMPIRE KOSHER POULTRY, INC.; U.S. Private, pg. 374
FARMER'S PRIDE, INC.; U.S. Private, pg. 395
FIELDALE CORPORATION; U.S. Private, pg. 403
GELDERLANDER FLEISCHWAREN GMBH—Koninklijke BolsWessanen nv; Int'l, pg. 752
GOLD KIST, INC.; U.S. Private, pg. 459
GRESS FOODS INC.; U.S. Private, pg. 480
HENNINGSEN FOODS, INC.—Q.P. Corporation; Int'l, pg. 1074
HENNINGSEN-VAN DEN BURG—Q.P. Corporation; Int'l, pg. 1074
HOUSE OF RAEFORD FARMS, INC.; U.S. Private, pg. 542
JENNIE-O FOODS, INC.—Hormel Foods Corp.; U.S. Public, pg. 840
JEROME FOODS INC.; U.S. Private, pg. 586
KOUDIJS-WOUDA VOEDERS B.V.—Goodman Fielder Limited; Int'l, pg. 555
KRAFT FOODS, INC.—Philip Morris Companies Inc.; U.S. Public, pg. 1287
LONGMONT FOODS—ConAgra, Inc.; U.S. Public, pg. 426
MAPLE LEAF FOODS INC.; Int'l, pg. 841
MAR-JAC POULTRY INC.; U.S. Private, pg. 701
MOLINAS DE PUERTO RICO—ConAgra, Inc.; U.S. Public, pg. 426
MONARK EGG CORPORATION—Michael Foods, Inc.; U.S. Public, pg. 1104

NATIONAL FOODS INC.—ConAgra, Inc.; *U.S. Public*, pg. 429
OSCAR MAYER FOODS CORP.—Philip Morris Companies Inc.; *U.S. Public*, pg. 1288
OVERHILL FARMS, INC.—Polyphase Corporation; *U.S. Public*, pg. 1315
PERDUE FARMS, INC.—Perdue Farms Incorporated; *U.S. Private*, pg. 852
PERDUE FARMS INCORPORATED; *U.S. Private*, pg. 852
PHILIP MORRIS COMPANIES INC.; *U.S. Public*, pg. 1287
PILGRIM'S PRIDE WEST DIVISION—Pilgrim's Pride Corporation; *U.S. Public*, pg. 1296
PROCESSED MEATS/POULTRY—ConAgra, Inc.; *U.S. Public*, pg. 426
ROCCO INC.; *U.S. Private*, pg. 937
SANDERSON FARMS FOODS DIV.—Sanderson Farms, Inc.; *U.S. Public*, pg. 1431
SANDERSON FARMS, INC.; *U.S. Public*, pg. 1430
SANDERSON FARMS PROCESSING DIV.—Sanderson Farms, Inc.; *U.S. Public*, pg. 1431
SANDERSON FARMS PRODUCTION DIV.—Sanderson Farms, Inc.; *U.S. Public*, pg. 1431
SEABOARD CORPORATION; *U.S. Public*, pg. 1448
SEABOARD FLOUR CORPORATION—Seaboard Corporation; *U.S. Public*, pg. 1449
SHADY BROOK FARMS—Rocco Inc.; *U.S. Private*, pg. 937
SUNNY FRESH FOODS—Cargill; *U.S. Private*, pg. 210
TALMADGE FARMS—Cagle's Inc.; *U.S. Public*, pg. 292
TOWNSENDS, INC.; *U.S. Private*, pg. 1094
TYSON FOODS, INC.—Tyson Foods, Inc.; *U.S. Public*, pg. 1652
TYSON FOODS, INC.; *U.S. Public*, pg. 1652
TYSON FOODS OF TEXAS, INC.—Tyson Foods, Inc.; *U.S. Public*, pg. 1652
VALLEY FRESH, INC.; *U.S. Private*, pg. 1132
VALLEY FRESH, INC.—Valley Fresh, Inc.; *U.S. Private*, pg. 1132
WLR FOODS, INC.; *U.S. Public*, pg. 1727
WATSON'S QUALITY TURKEY PRODUCTS, INC.; *U.S. Private*, pg. 1154
WRIGHT BRAND FOODS, INC.; *U.S. Private*, pg. 1192
ZACKY FARMS, INC.; *U.S. Private*, pg. 1203

2021 — CREAMERY BUTTER

AGROPUR; *Int'l*, pg. 31
AVONMORE WATERFORD GROUP PLC; *Int'l*, pg. 102
BONGARDS CREAMERIES INC.; *U.S. Private*, pg. 156
BONGRAIN S.A.; *Int'l*, pg. 201
BROUGHTON FOODS COMPANY; *U.S. Public*, pg. 259
CABOT CREAMERY CO-OPERATIVE INC.—Agri-Mark, Inc.; *U.S. Private*, pg. 26
CASS-CLAY CREAMERY; *U.S. Private*, pg. 218
CONAGRA DAIRY & FOOD OILS—ConAgra, Inc.; *U.S. Public*, pg. 427
COUNTRY CLASSIC DAIRIES, INC.; *U.S. Private*, pg. 278
CRYSTAL CREAM & BUTTER COMPANY; *U.S. Private*, pg. 294
DANONE—Danone Group; *Int'l*, pg. 379
DIETRICH'S MILK PRODUCTS, INC.; *U.S. Private*, pg. 332
EDEN VALE FOOD INGREDIENTS—Northern Foods plc; *Int'l*, pg. 968
ENTREMONT S.A.; *Int'l*, pg. 458
FOREMOST FARMS USA COOPERATIVE; *U.S. Private*, pg. 418
HYGEIA DAIRY CO., INC.; *U.S. Private*, pg. 552
INDUSTRIAS ALIMENTICIAS CLUB S.A.—Nestle S.A.; *Int'l, pg. 920*
KERRY GROUP PLC; *Int'l*, pg. 731
LACTOS PTY. LTD.—Bongrain S.A.; *Int'l*, pg. 201
LAITERIE DE VILLECOMTAL—Danone Group; *Int'l*, pg. 379
LAND O'LAKES, INC.; *U.S. Private*, pg. 645
MADISON DAIRY PRODUCE COMPANY; *U.S. Private*, pg. 694
MANTEQUERIAS ARIAS S. A.—Bongrain S.A.; *Int'l*, pg. 201
MARGARINBOLAGET AB—Nestle S.A.; *Int'l*, pg. 922
MARYLAND & VIRGINIA MILK PRODUCERS COOPERATIVE ASSOCIATION, INC.; *U.S. Private*, pg. 711
MICHAEL FOODS, INC.; *U.S. Public*, pg. 1103
MID-AMERICA DAIRYMEN, INC.; *U.S. Private*, pg. 743
MILKCO, INC.—Ingles Markets, Incorporated; *U.S. Public*, pg. 878
NATREL INC.—Agropur; *Int'l*, pg. 32
NEW ENGLAND DAIRIES, INC.; *U.S. Private*, pg. 793
OLD HOME FOODS, INC.; *U.S. Private*, pg. 814
PETERS & BROWNES FOODS LTD.; *Int'l*, pg. 1040
PRAIRIE FARMS DAIRY, INC.; *U.S. Private*, pg. 878
SANCOR COOPERATIVAS UNIDAS LIMITADAS; *Int'l*, pg. 1183
SHAMROCK FOODS COMPANY; *U.S. Private*, pg. 989
SNOW BRAND MILK PRODUCTS CO. LTD.; *Int'l*, pg. 1271
SUPERIOR DAIRY, INC.; *U.S. Private*, pg. 1054
TINE-VESTLANDSMEIERIET; *Int'l*, pg. 1390
VERIFINE DAIRY PRODUCTS CORP.—Dean Foods Company; *U.S. Public*, pg. 491
ZANDER'S CREAMERY INC.; *U.S. Private*, pg. 1203

2022 — NATURAL, PROCESSED & IMITATION CHEESE

AGRILINK FOODS, INC.—Pro-Fac Cooperative, Inc.; *U.S. Private*, pg. 887
AGROPUR; *Int'l*, pg. 31
ALISA, S.A.—Borden, Inc.; *U.S. Private*, pg. 159
ALLIANT FOODSERVICE, INC.—Clayton, Dubilier & Rice, Inc; *U.S. Private*, pg. 244
ALTO DAIRY COOPERATIVE; *U.S. Private*, pg. 47
ANCO INTERNATIONAL—Philip Morris Companies Inc.; *U.S. Public*, pg. 1287
ARMOUR FOOD COMPANY—ConAgra, Inc.; *U.S. Public*, pg. 427
ARMOUR SWIFT ECKRICH—ConAgra, Inc.; *U.S. Public*, pg. 426
AVONMORE WATERFORD GROUP PLC; *Int'l*, pg. 102
BC-USA—Bongrain S.A.; *Int'l*, pg. 201
BG SAS—Bongrain S.A.; *Int'l*, pg. 201
BAYERNLAND GMBH & CO. KG; *Int'l*, pg. 181
BEATRICE CHEESE CO.—ConAgra, Inc.; *U.S. Public*, pg. 426
BEL/KAUKAUNA USA; *U.S. Private*, pg. 130
BIG STONE CHEESE FACTORY—Stella Foods, Inc.; *U.S. Private*, pg. 1040
BONGARDS CREAMERIES INC.; *U.S. Private*, pg. 156
BONGRAIN CHEESE USA—Bongrain S.A.; *Int'l*, pg. 201
BONGRAIN - GERARD & CIE.—Bongrain S.A.; *Int'l*, pg. 201
BONGRAIN S.A.; *Int'l*, pg. 201
THE BORDEN COMPANY LIMITED (CANADA)—Borden, Inc.; *U.S. Private*, pg. 159
BORDEN, INC.; *U.S. Private*, pg. 157
CABOT CREAMERY CO-OPERATIVE INC.—Agri-Mark, Inc.; *U.S. Private*, pg. 26
CACIQUE, INC.; *U.S. Private*, pg. 198
CHURNY COMPANY INC.—Philip Morris Companies Inc.; *U.S. Public*, pg. 1288
COASTAL WHOLESALE, INC.; *U.S. Private*, pg. 248
COLEMAN DAIRY LLC; *U.S. Private*, pg. 251
CONAGRA DAIRY & FOOD OILS—ConAgra, Inc.; *U.S. Public*, pg. 427
CONTADINA/LIBBY/TRENTON DIV.—Nestle S.A.; *Int'l*, pg. 916
COUNTRY CLASSIC DAIRIES, INC.; *U.S. Private*, pg. 278
CUCINA CLASSICA ITALIANA, INC.—Saratoga Brands, Inc.; *U.S. Public*, pg. 1435
CULINARY FOODS GROUP—Nestle S.A.; *Int'l*, pg. 917
DANONE—Danone Group; *Int'l*, pg. 379
DANONE B.V.—Danone Group; *Int'l*, pg. 379
DANONE S.A.—Danone Group; *Int'l*, pg. 379
DANONE S.P.A.—Danone Group; *Int'l*, pg. 379
DEAN FOODS—Dean Foods Company; *U.S. Public*, pg. 490
DEEP SOUTH PRODUCTS—Winn-Dixie Stores, Inc.; *U.S. Public*, pg. 1772
DIETRICH'S MILK PRODUCTS, INC.; *U.S. Private*, pg. 332
EMPIRE CHEESE, INC.—The Great Lakes Cheese Co.; *U.S. Private*, pg. 474
ENTREMONT S.A.; *Int'l*, pg. 458
FIRST DISTRICT ASSOCIATION; *U.S. Private*, pg. 406
FOREMOST FARMS USA COOPERATIVE; *U.S. Private*, pg. 418
FRIENDSHIP DAIRIES, INC.; *U.S. Private*, pg. 429
FROMAGERIE DES CHAUMES S.A.—Bongrain S.A.; *Int'l*, pg. 201
FROMAGERIE PERRAULT S.A.—Bongrain S.A.; *Int'l*, pg. 201
FROMAGERIE RAMBOL S.A.—Bongrain S.A.; *Int'l*, pg. 201
FROMARSAC SARL—Bongrain S.A.; *Int'l*, pg. 201
GALAXY FOOD COMPANY; *U.S. Public*, pg. 697
GALBANI—Danone Group; *Int'l*, pg. 380
GERVAIS DANONE AG—Danone Group; *Int'l*, pg. 380
THE GREAT LAKES CHEESE CO.; *U.S. Private*, pg. 473
GREAT LAKES CHEESE OF LA CROSSE WISCONSIN, INC.—The Great Lakes Cheese Co.; *U.S. Private*, pg. 474
HELUVA GOOD CHEESE INC.—Koninklijke BolsWessanen nv; *Int'l*, pg. 752
INDUSTRIAS ALIMENTICIAS CLUB S.A.—Nestle S.A.; *Int'l, pg. 920*
KERRY GROUP PLC; *Int'l*, pg. 731
KONINKLIJKE BOLSWESSANEN NV; *Int'l*, pg. 750
KRAFT CANADA INC.—Philip Morris Companies Inc.; *U.S. Public*, pg. 1288
KRAFT FOOD INGREDIENTS CORP.—Philip Morris Companies Inc.; *U.S. Public*, pg. 1288
KRAFT FOODS A/S—Philip Morris Companies Inc.; *U.S. Public*, pg. 1290
KRAFT FOODS INC.—Philip Morris Companies Inc.; *U.S. Public*, pg. 1288
KRAFT JACOBS SUCHARD—Philip Morris Companies Inc.; *U.S. Public*, pg. 1290
THE KROGER CO.; *U.S. Public*, pg. 967
LPC INDUSTRIAS ALIMENTICIAS S.A.—Danone Group; *Int'l*, pg. 380
LACTOS PTY. LTD.—Bongrain S.A.; *Int'l*, pg. 201
LAITERIE DE VILLECOMTAL—Danone Group; *Int'l*, pg. 379
LAND O'LAKES, INC.; *U.S. Private*, pg. 645
LEPRINO FOODS; *U.S. Private*, pg. 660
LOSURDO FOODS, INC.; *U.S. Private*, pg. 677
B.V. LYEMPF—Koninklijke BolsWessanen nv; *Int'l*, pg. 752
MAJOR SMITH INC.—Bongrain S.A.; *Int'l*, pg. 201
MANTEQUERIAS ARIAS S. A.—Bongrain S.A.; *Int'l*, pg. 201
MAPLEHURST FARMS, INC.—Dean Foods Company; *U.S. Public*, pg. 490
MARATHON CHEESE CORP.; *U.S. Private*, pg. 701
MCCAIN FOODS (GB) LIMITED—McCain Foods Limited; *Int'l*, pg. 850
MCCAIN REFRIGERATED FOODS INC.—McCain Foods Limited; *Int'l*, pg. 850
MEIJERIOSUUSKUNTA/MEJERIANDELSLAGET MILKA; *Int'l*, pg. 854
MICHAEL FOODS, INC.; *U.S. Public*, pg. 1103
MID-AMERICA DAIRYMEN, INC.; *U.S. Private*, pg. 743
MILKCO, INC.—Ingles Markets, Incorporated; *U.S. Public*, pg. 878
MORINAGA MILK INDUSTRY CO., LTD.; *Int'l*, pg. 895
NATREL INC.—Agropur; *Int'l*, pg. 32
NESTLE ITALIANA S.P.A.—Nestle S.A.; *Int'l*, pg. 921
NEW ENGLAND DAIRIES, INC.; *U.S. Private*, pg. 793
OLD WISCONSIN CHEESE CO., INC.—Carl Buddig & Company; *U.S. Private*, pg. 178
PACE DAIRY FOODS—The Kroger Co.; *U.S. Public*, pg. 967
PASTA & CHEESE, INC.—Nestle S.A.; *Int'l*, pg. 918
THE PERRIER GROUP OF AMERICA—Nestle S.A.; *Int'l*, pg. 919
PETERS & BROWNES FOODS LTD.; *Int'l*, pg. 1040
PHILIPPINES DAIRY PRODUCTS CORP.—New Zealand Dairy Board; *Int'l*, pg. 923
PRO-FAC COOPERATIVE, INC.; *U.S. Private*, pg. 887
PROCESSED MEATS/POULTRY—ConAgra, Inc.; *U.S. Public*, pg. 426
Q.U.F. INDUSTRIES LTD.; *Int'l*, pg. 1074
RJR NABISCO HOLDINGS CORP.; *U.S. Public*, pg. 1354
SANCOR COOPERATIVAS UNIDAS LIMITADAS; *Int'l*, pg. 1183
SARGENTO FOODS INC.; *U.S. Private*, pg. 966
SCHREIBER FOODS, INC.; *U.S. Private*, pg. 972
SMITH ENTERPRISES; *U.S. Private*, pg. 1007
SNOW BRAND FOOD CO., LTD.—Snow Brand Milk Products Co. Ltd.; *Int'l*, pg. 1272
SNOW BRAND MILK PRODUCTS CO. LTD.; *Int'l*, pg. 1271
SORRENTO CHEESE COMPANY, INC.—Compagnie Laitiere BESNIER; *Int'l*, pg. 323
STELLA FOODS, INC.; *U.S. Private*, pg. 1040
SUN DEW CORP.—Investcorp International; *Int'l*, pg. 686
SUPERIOR DAIRY, INC.; *U.S. Private*, pg. 1054
SUPREMA SPECIALTIES, INC.; *U.S. Public*, pg. 1541
SUPREMA SPECIALTIES WEST, INC.—Suprema Specialties, Inc.; *U.S. Public*, pg. 1541
THIEL CHEESE CO.; *U.S. Private*, pg. 1081
TILLAMOOK COUNTY CREAMERY ASSN.; *U.S. Private*, pg. 1086
TINE-VESTLANDSMEIERIET; *Int'l*, pg. 1390
UNIL-IT S.P.A.—Unilever Plc; *Int'l*, pg. 1438
VAN HEEL B.V.—Koninklijke BolsWessanen nv; *Int'l*, pg. 751
WATERFORD CONTINENTAL CHEESE LIMITED—Avonmore Waterford Group plc; *Int'l*, pg. 102
WINN-DIXIE STORES, INC.; *U.S. Public*, pg. 1771
ZUIVELFABRIEK 'SALLAND' BV—Koninklijke BolsWessanen nv; *Int'l*, pg. 752
ZUIVELONDERNEMING DE VIJFHEERENLANDEN B.V.—Koninklijke BolsWessanen nv; *Int'l*, pg. 751

2023 — DRY, CONDENSED & EVAPORATED DAIRY PRODUCTS

ABBOTT LABORATORIES; *U.S. Public*, pg. 12
AGROPUR; *Int'l*, pg. 31
ALBERTO-CULVER COMPANY; *U.S. Public*, pg. 37
ALLGAUER ALPENMILCH A.G.—Nestle S.A.; *Int'l*, pg. 918
ALTO DAIRY COOPERATIVE; *U.S. Private*, pg. 47
AMERICAN HOME PRODUCTS CORPORATION; *U.S. Public*, pg. 79
AMWAY CORPORATION; *U.S. Private*, pg. 69
AVONMORE WATERFORD GROUP PLC; *Int'l*, pg. 102
BG FINANS A/S—Solvay S.A.; *Int'l*, pg. 1279
BARBADOS DAIRY INDUSTRIES LTD.—New Zealand Dairy Board; *Int'l*, pg. 923
BASKIN-ROBBINS CANADA—Allied Domecq PLC; *Int'l*, pg. 63
BASKIN ROBBINS PRODUCTION FACILITY—Allied Domecq PLC; *Int'l*, pg. 63
BAYER CORPORATION/CONSUMER CARE DIVISION—Bayer AG; *Int'l*, pg. 173
BONGARDS CREAMERIES INC.; *U.S. Private*, pg. 156
BONGRAIN S.A.; *Int'l*, pg. 201
BORDEN, INC.; *U.S. Private*, pg. 157
BRISTOL-MYERS SQUIBB COMPANY; *U.S. Public*, pg. 253
CADBURY CHOCOLATE CANADA, INC.—Cadbury Schweppes p.l.c.; *Int'l*, pg. 248
CALPIS FOOD INDUSTRY CO. LTD.; *Int'l*, pg. 252
CARNATION DE MEXICO S.A. DE C.V.—Nestle S.A.; *Int'l*, pg. 919
CARNATION FOODS LTD.—Nestle S.A.; *Int'l*, pg. 919
CARNATION HELLAS S.A.I.—Nestle S.A.; *Int'l*, pg. 919
CARNATION ITALIA S.P.A.—Nestle S.A.; *Int'l*, pg. 919
CARNATION MANUFACTURING CO. (THAILAND) LTD.—Nestle S.A.; *Int'l*, pg. 919
CARNATION NEDERLAND B.V.—Nestle S.A.; *Int'l*, pg. 919
CARNATION PRODUCTS DIV.—Nestle S.A.; *Int'l*, pg. 916
COCIO CHOKOLADEMAELK—Borden, Inc.; *U.S. Private*, pg. 159
CIA. COLOMBIANA DE ALIMENTOS LACETOS, S.A.—Borden, Inc.; *U.S. Private*, pg. 159
CONAGRA, INC.; *U.S. Public*, pg. 425
CROWLEY FOODS, INC.—Koninklijke BolsWessanen nv; *Int'l*, pg. 752
DANMARK PROTEIN A/S—Solvay S.A.; *Int'l*, pg. 1279
DANONE—Danone Group; *Int'l*, pg. 379
DEAN FOOD PRODUCTS DIVISION—Dean Foods Company; *U.S. Public*, pg. 490
DIEHL INC.; *U.S. Private*, pg. 332
DIETRICH'S MILK PRODUCTS, INC.; *U.S. Private*, pg. 332
DONG-SUH FOODS CORPORATION; *Int'l*, pg. 416
EDEN VALE FOOD INGREDIENTS—Northern Foods plc; *Int'l*, pg. 968
ESKIMO FLAVORS—Eskimo Pie Corporation; *U.S. Public*, pg. 592
FAVORITE FOODS, INC.—Suiza Foods Corporation; *U.S. Public*, pg. 1527
FOREMOST FARMS USA COOPERATIVE; *U.S. Private*, pg. 418
FRIENDSHIP DAIRIES, INC.; *U.S. Private*, pg. 429
GAGE FOOD PRODUCTS COMPANY—DG Foods, LLC; *U.S. Private*, pg. 301
GERBER PRODUCTS DIVISION-BABY CARE—Novartis AG; *Int'l*, pg. 973
GERBER PRODUCTS, S.A. DE C.V.—Novartis AG; *Int'l*, pg. 973
GERVAIS DANONE AG—Danone Group; *Int'l*, pg. 380
GUIGOZ FRANCE S.A.—Nestle S.A.; *Int'l*, pg. 920
GUIGOZ S.A.—Nestle S.A.; *Int'l*, pg. 916

H.J. HEINZ COMPANY, LIMITED—H.J. Heinz Company; U.S. Public, pg. 806
HILLAND DAIRY COMPANY—Prairie Farms Dairy, Inc.; U.S. Private, pg. 879
IDAL-BENAVENTE—H.J. Heinz Company; U.S. Public, pg. 807
IDAL(INDUSTRIAS DE ALIMENTACAO, LDA.)—H.J. Heinz Company; U.S. Public, pg. 807
IBARAGI SNOW BRAND MILK CO., LTD.—Snow Brand Milk Products Co. Ltd.; Int'l, pg. 1272
INDUSTRIAS ALIMENTICIAS CLUB S.A.—Nestle S.A.; Int'l, pg. 920
INTEGRATED BRANDS INC.; U.S. Public, pg. 883
KONINKLIJKE BOLSWESSANEN NV; Int'l, pg. 750
KRAFT FOOD INGREDIENTS CORP.—Philip Morris Companies Inc.; U.S. Public, pg. 1288
LAIT MONT BLANC S.A.—Nestle S.A.; Int'l, pg. 920
LAITERIE DE VILLECOMTAL—Danone Group; Int'l, pg. 379
LYEMPF/VAN HEEL B.V.—Koninklijke BolsWessanen nv; Int'l, pg. 752
MAGGI AG—Nestle S.A.; Int'l, pg. 916
MARYLAND & VIRGINIA MILK PRODUCERS COOPERATIVE ASSOCIATION, INC.; U.S. Private, pg. 711
MEIJI MILK PRODUCTS CO., LTD.; Int'l, pg. 855
MICHAEL FOODS, INC.; U.S. Public, pg. 1103
MILEI GMBH—Morinaga Milk Industry Co., Ltd.; Int'l, pg. 895
MILKCO, INC.—Ingles Markets, Incorporated; U.S. Public, pg. 878
THE MILNOT COMPANY; U.S. Private, pg. 749
MILUPA S.A.—Nutricia BV; Int'l, pg. 991
MORINAGA MILK INDUSTRY CO., LTD.; Int'l, pg. 895
THE MORNING STAR GROUP—Suiza Foods Corporation; U.S. Public, pg. 1527
NESTLE NEDERLAND B.V.—Nestle S.A.; Int'l, pg. 921
NESTLE S.A.; Int'l, pg. 915
NESTLE (THAILAND) LTD.—Nestle S.A.; Int'l, pg. 921
NESTLE USA—Nestle S.A.; Int'l, pg. 916
NUTRICIA IRELAND LTD.—Nutricia BV; Int'l, pg. 992
OLD HOME FOODS, INC.; U.S. Private, pg. 814
OUTLOOK FOODS, INC.—Outlook Group Corporation; U.S. Public, pg. 1235
PRODUCTOS GERBER DE CENTROAMERICA, S.A.—Novartis AG; Int'l, pg. 973
PURAC BIOQUIMICA S.A.—CSM N.V.; Int'l, pg. 244
PURAC SINTESES—CSM N.V.; Int'l, pg. 245
RICHARDSON-VICKS, INC.—The Procter & Gamble Company; U.S. Public, pg. 1331
RONEY OTMAN; U.S. Private, pg. 943
ROSS PRODUCTS—Abbott Laboratories; U.S. Public, pg. 13
SAHAPATHANAPIBUL PUBLIC COMPANY LIMITED; Int'l, pg. 1169
SANCOR COOPERATIVAS UNIDAS LIMITADAS; Int'l, pg. 1183
SHOWA BUSSAN CO., LTD.—Snow Brand Milk Products Co. Ltd.; Int'l, pg. 1272
SNOW BRAND FOOD CO., LTD.—Snow Brand Milk Products Co. Ltd.; Int'l, pg. 1272
SNOW BRAND MILK PRODUCTS CO. LTD.; Int'l, pg. 1271
SNOW BRAND ROLLY CO., LTD.—Snow Brand Milk Products Co. Ltd.; Int'l, pg. 1272
SNOW BRAND SHOJI CO., LTD.—Snow Brand Milk Products Co. Ltd.; Int'l, pg. 1272
SUPERIOR DAIRY, INC.; U.S. Private, pg. 1054
UPSTATE MILK COOPERATIVES INC.; U.S. Private, pg. 1129
WANDER AG—Novartis AG; Int'l, pg. 972
WANDER (AUSTRALIA) PTY. LTD.—Novartis AG; Int'l, pg. 986
WANDER DE VENEZUELA S.A.—Novartis AG; Int'l, pg. 986
WANDER LTD.—Novartis AG; Int'l, pg. 973
WANDER PHARMA G.M.B.H.—Novartis AG; Int'l, pg. 986
WANDER (THAILAND) LTD.—Novartis AG; Int'l, pg. 986
WYETH-AYERST INTERNATIONAL, INC.—American Home Products Corporation; U.S. Public, pg. 80
YATSUGATAKE SNOW BRAND MILK CO., LTD.—Snow Brand Milk Products Co. Ltd.; Int'l, pg. 1272

2024 — ICE CREAM & FROZEN DESSERTS

AGROPUR; Int'l, pg. 31
ALIMENTOS FINDAS S.A. DE C.V.—Nestle S.A.; Int'l, pg. 918
AMBOY SPECIALTY FOODS—Dean Foods Company; U.S. Public, pg. 490
AMERICAN GLACE—Integrated Brands Inc.; U.S. Public, pg. 883
ARTIC N.V. S.A.—TLC Beatrice International Holdings Inc.; U.S. Private, pg. 1064
BARBER ICE CREAM COMPANY—Barber Dairies, Inc.; U.S. Private, pg. 115
BASKIN-ROBBINS CANADA—Allied Domecq PLC; Int'l, pg. 63
BASKIN-ROBBINS INCORPORATED—Allied Domecq PLC; Int'l, pg. 63
BASKIN ROBBINS PRODUCTION FACILITY—Allied Domecq PLC; Int'l, pg. 63
BASKIN-ROBBINS USA CO.—Allied Domecq PLC; Int'l, pg. 63
BELL DAIRY PRODUCTS, INC.—Dean Foods Company; U.S. Public, pg. 490
BEN & JERRY'S HOMEMADE INC.; U.S. Public, pg. 210
BIRDS EYE WALLS LTD.—Unilever Plc; Int'l, pg. 1434
BLUE BELL CREAMERIES, L.P.; U.S. Private, pg. 150
BORDEN, INC.; U.S. Private, pg. 157
BRAUM ICE CREAM STORES INC.; U.S. Private, pg. 166
BRIGHAM'S, INC.—Grotech Capital Group, Inc.; U.S. Private, pg. 483
BROUGHTON FOODS COMPANY; U.S. Public, pg. 259
CLR CORPORATION—Empire of Carolina, Inc.; U.S. Public, pg. 579
CPC RUFHAN LIMITED—Bestfoods; U.S. Public, pg. 225
CHARLIE'S SPECIALTIES INC.—Byrnes & Kiefer Company; U.S. Private, pg. 191
COASTAL WHOLESALE, INC.; U.S. Private, pg. 248
COGESAL S.A.—Unilever Plc; Int'l, pg. 1436
COLEMAN DAIRY LLC; U.S. Private, pg. 251
COUNTRY CLASSIC DAIRIES, INC.; U.S. Private, pg. 278
COUNTRY FRESH, INC.—Suiza Foods Corporation; U.S. Public, pg. 1526
CROWLEY FOODS, INC.—Koninklijke BolsWessanen nv; Int'l, pg. 752
CRYSTAL CREAM & BUTTER COMPANY; U.S. Private, pg. 294
DAIRY FRESH CORP.; U.S. Private, pg. 307
DAIRY FRESH ICE CREAM—Dairy Fresh Corp.; U.S. Private, pg. 307
DAIRY VALE CO-OP. LTD.; Int'l, pg. 372
THE DANNON CO.—Danone Group; Int'l, pg. 379
DANONE—Danone Group; Int'l, pg. 379
DANONE B.V.—Danone Group; Int'l, pg. 379
DANONE DE MEXICO—Danone Group; Int'l, pg. 379
DANONE S.A.—Danone Group; Int'l, pg. 379
DEAN FOODS COMPANY; U.S. Public, pg. 489
DEERING ICE CREAM, INC.—FieldBrook Farms, Inc.; U.S. Private, pg. 403
DEN HERTOG B.V.—Koninklijke BolsWessanen nv; Int'l, pg. 752
DERIVADOS LACTEOS Y ALIMENTICIOS S.A.—Nestle S.A.; Int'l, pg. 920
DOVE EUROPE—Mars, Incorporated; U.S. Private, pg. 707
DREYER'S GRAND ICE CREAM, INC.; U.S. Public, pg. 529
DREYER'S GRAND ICE CREAM, INC.—Dreyer's Grand Ice Cream, Inc.; U.S. Public, pg. 529
EAGLE ICE CREAM DIV.—Giant Eagle, Inc.; U.S. Private, pg. 451
ELGIN DAIRY FOODS, INC.; U.S. Private, pg. 370
FARMER JACK SUPERMARKETS—Tengelmann Warenhandelsgesellschaft; Int'l, pg. 1375
FAVORITE FOODS, INC.—Suiza Foods Corporation; U.S. Public, pg. 1527
FIELDBROOK FARMS, INC.; U.S. Private, pg. 403
FOSTERS FREEZE INTERNATIONAL, INC.; U.S. Public, pg. 677
FRANCE GLACES-FINDUS S.A.—Nestle S.A.; Int'l, pg. 920
FREESIA—Dairy Vale Co-op. Ltd.; Int'l, pg. 372
FRIENDLY ICE CREAM CORP.; U.S. Public, pg. 682
FRIENDSHIP DAIRIES, INC.; U.S. Private, pg. 429
FRISCO-FINDUS AG—Nestle S.A.; Int'l, pg. 916
FROZFRUIT CORPORATION; U.S. Private, pg. 430
GALBANI—Danone Group; Int'l, pg. 380
GOLD COAST MILK PTY. LTD.—Q.U.F. Industries Ltd.; Int'l, pg. 1074
GOOD HUMOR/BREYERS ICE CREAM—Unilever Plc; Int'l, pg. 1435
GRANDMET FOODS UK—Diageo Plc; Int'l, pg. 408
GUIGOZ S.A.—Nestle S.A.; Int'l, pg. 916
HB ICE CREAM LTD.—Unilever Plc; Int'l, pg. 1437
THE HAAGEN-DAZS COMPANY INC.—Diageo Plc; Int'l, pg. 411
HERSHEY CREAMERY COMPANY; U.S. Private, pg. 524
HYGEIA DAIRY CO., INC.; U.S. Private, pg. 552
IBARAGI SNOW BRAND MILK CO., LTD.—Snow Brand Milk Products Co. Ltd.; Int'l, pg. 1272
IGLO INDUSTRIAS DE GELADOS, LDA.—Unilever Plc; Int'l, pg. 1437
IGLO-OLA B.V.—Unilever Plc; Int'l, pg. 1437
IGLO-OLA N.V.—Unilever Plc; Int'l, pg. 1437
INTEGRATED BRANDS INC.; U.S. Public, pg. 883
KEMPS FOODS, INC.—Koninklijke BolsWessanen nv; Int'l, pg. 752
KONINKLIJKE BOLSWESSANEN NV; Int'l, pg. 750
LAND O'LAKES, INC.; U.S. Private, pg. 645
LAND-O-SUN DAIRIES, INC.; U.S. Private, pg. 646
LARRY'S INDUSTRIES, INC.—Yogen Fruz Worldwide Inc.; Int'l, pg. 1520
LOTTE ICE CREAM CORP. LTD.—Lotte Company Ltd.; Int'l, pg. 819
M&M/MARS—Mars, Incorporated; U.S. Private, pg. 707
MAPLEHURST FARMS, INC.—Dean Foods Company; U.S. Public, pg. 490
MARGARINBOLAGET AB—Nestle S.A.; Int'l, pg. 922
MARYLAND & VIRGINIA MILK PRODUCERS COOPERATIVE ASSOCIATION, INC.; U.S. Private, pg. 711
MAYFIELD DAIRY FARMS INC.—Dean Foods Company; U.S. Public, pg. 490
MEDICAL MEADOW GOLD DAIRIES, INC.—Southern Foods Group; U.S. Private, pg. 1016
MEIJI FROZEN DESSERT CORP.—Meiji Seika Kaisha, Ltd.; Int'l, pg. 855
MEIJI MILK PRODUCTS CO., LTD.; Int'l, pg. 855
MELLOBUTTERCUP ICE CREAM INC.; U.S. Private, pg. 730
MELODY FOODS, INC.; U.S. Private, pg. 730
MICHAEL FOODS, INC.; U.S. Public, pg. 1103
MID-AMERICA DAIRYMEN, INC.; U.S. Private, pg. 743
MILKCO, INC.—Ingles Markets, Incorporated; U.S. Public, pg. 878
MISTER COOKIE FACE, INC.; U.S. Private, pg. 753
MRS. SMITH'S BAKERY OF PENNSYLVANIA—Flowers Industries, Inc.; U.S. Public, pg. 658
NDS—Nestle S.A.; Int'l, pg. 918
NESTLE CHOCOLATE & CONFECTION—Nestle S.A.; Int'l, pg. 917
NESTLE ICE CREAM CO.—Nestle S.A.; Int'l, pg. 918
NESTLE INDUSTRIAL E COMMERCIAL LTDA.—Nestle S.A.; Int'l, pg. 921
NESTLE LYONS MAID—Nestle S.A.; Int'l, pg. 918
NESTLE S.A.; Int'l, pg. 915
NESTLE USA—Nestle S.A.; Int'l, pg. 916
NORTHERN FOODS PLC; Int'l, pg. 967
ORANGE JULIUS CANADA, LTD.—Berkshire Hathaway Inc.; U.S. Public, pg. 221
PENGUIN'S INDUSTRIES—Bongrain S.A.; Int'l, pg. 201
PERRY'S ICE CREAM CO., INC.; U.S. Private, pg. 855
PETERS & BROWNES FOODS LTD.; Int'l, pg. 1040
PETER'S SAVOURY PRODUCTS—Diageo Plc; Int'l, pg. 410
THE PILLSBURY COMPANY—Diageo Plc; Int'l, pg. 411
PRICE'S CREAMERIES—Dean Foods Company; U.S. Public, pg. 491
RAWMARSH FOODS—Northern Foods plc; Int'l, pg. 968
REITER DAIRY, INC.—Dean Foods Company; U.S. Public, pg. 491
RINI-REGO SUPERMARKETS, INC.—Giant Eagle, Inc.; U.S. Private, pg. 451
RISER FOODS, INC.—Giant Eagle, Inc.; U.S. Private, pg. 450
RONEY OTMAN; U.S. Private, pg. 943
SAGIT S.P.A.—Unilever Plc; Int'l, pg. 1438
SANCOR COOPERATIVAS UNIDAS LIMITADAS; Int'l, pg. 1183
SCANGAS BROTHERS HOLDINGS, INC.; U.S. Private, pg. 969
SCHNEIDER FARMS DAIRY—Schneider's Dairy, Inc.; U.S. Private, pg. 971
SCHOEP'S ICE CREAM, INC.; U.S. Private, pg. 972
SCHWAN'S SALES ENTERPRISES; U.S. Private, pg. 974
SHAMROCK FOODS COMPANY; U.S. Private, pg. 989
SNOW BRAND MILK PRODUCTS CO. LTD.; Int'l, pg. 1271
SOKOL & COMPANY; U.S. Private, pg. 1012
STEWART'S ICE CREAM CO., INC.; U.S. Private, pg. 1043
STREETS ICE CREAM PTY. LTD.—Unilever Plc; Int'l, pg. 1438
SUGAR CREEK FOODS—Eskimo Pie Corporation; U.S. Public, pg. 592
SUPERIOR DAIRY, INC.; U.S. Private, pg. 1054
TCBY ENTERPRISES INC.; U.S. Public, pg. 1553
TILLAMOOK COUNTY CREAMERY ASSN.; U.S. Private, pg. 1086
TURKEY HILL DAIRY, INC.; U.S. Private, pg. 1109
TURNER HOLDING LLC; U.S. Private, pg. 1109
TUSCAN/LEHIGH DAIRIES LP; U.S. Private, pg. 1110
UNIFROST NAHRUNGSMITTEL GES. M.B.H.—Unilever Plc; Int'l, pg. 1439
UNILEVER N.V.—Unilever Plc; Int'l, pg. 1434
UNILEVER PLC; Int'l, pg. 1433
VALLEY BELL DAIRY CO.—Borden, Inc.; U.S. Private, pg. 158
VERIFINE DAIRY PRODUCTS CORP.—Dean Foods Company; U.S. Public, pg. 491
VITAFREZE FROZEN CONFECTIONS—Crystal Cream & Butter Company; U.S. Private, pg. 294
WEEKS DAIRY FOODS, INC.—Koninklijke BolsWessanen nv; Int'l, pg. 752
WELSH FARMS, INC.; U.S. Private, pg. 1162
WESLEY'S QUAKER MAID ICE CREAM—Tengelmann Warenhandelsgesellschaft; Int'l, pg. 1375
WEST LYNN CREAMERY, INC.—Scangas Brothers Holdings, Inc.; U.S. Private, pg. 969
WINN-DIXIE STORES, INC.; U.S. Public, pg. 1771
WINN DIXIE SUPERBRAND DAIRIES—Winn-Dixie Stores, Inc.; U.S. Public, pg. 1771
YATSUGATAKE SNOW BRAND MILK CO., LTD.—Snow Brand Milk Products Co. Ltd.; Int'l, pg. 1272

2026 — FLUID MILK

AGROPUR; Int'l, pg. 31
ALTA-DENA CERTIFIED DAIRY—Bongrain S.A.; Int'l, pg. 201
ALTO DAIRY COOPERATIVE; U.S. Private, pg. 47
BC-USA—Bongrain S.A.; Int'l, pg. 201
BARBER DAIRIES, INC.; U.S. Private, pg. 115
BECKER MILK CO. LTD.; Int'l, pg. 182
BELL DAIRY PRODUCTS, INC.—Dean Foods Company; U.S. Public, pg. 490
BIOLAC—Solvay S.A.; Int'l, pg. 1278
BONGRAIN S.A.; Int'l, pg. 201
BORDEN, INC.; U.S. Private, pg. 157
BROUGHTON FOODS COMPANY; U.S. Public, pg. 259
C.F. BURGER CREAMERY COMPANY; U.S. Private, pg. 182
CABOT CREAMERY CO-OPERATIVE INC.—Agri-Mark, Inc.; U.S. Private, pg. 26
CASS-CLAY CREAMERY; U.S. Private, pg. 218
CHAMBOURCY FOOD CO. LTD.—Nestle S.A.; Int'l, pg. 920
CHAMBOURCY HOCHE AUX FEES & CIE—Nestle S.A.; Int'l, pg. 920
COASTAL WHOLESALE, INC.; U.S. Private, pg. 248
COCIO CHOKOLADEMAELK—Borden, Inc.; U.S. Private, pg. 159
COLEMAN DAIRY LLC; U.S. Private, pg. 251
COUNTRY CLASSIC DAIRIES, INC.; U.S. Private, pg. 278
COUNTRY FRESH, INC.—Suiza Foods Corporation; U.S. Public, pg. 1526
CREAMLAND DAIRIES, INC.—Dean Foods Company; U.S. Public, pg. 490
CROWLEY FOODS, INC.—Koninklijke BolsWessanen nv; Int'l, pg. 752
CRYSTAL CREAM & BUTTER COMPANY; U.S. Private, pg. 294
DAIRY FRESH CORP.; U.S. Private, pg. 307
DAIRY MART FARMS, INC.—Dairy Mart Convenience Stores, Inc.; U.S. Public, pg. 476
DAIRY QUEEN OF GEORGIA, INC.—Berkshire Hathaway Inc.; U.S. Public, pg. 220
DAIRY VALE CO-OP. LTD.; Int'l, pg. 372
DALE FARM DAIRIES LTD.—Northern Foods plc; Int'l, pg. 968
THE DANNON CO.—Danone Group; Int'l, pg. 379
DANONE—Danone Group; Int'l, pg. 379

DANONE DE MEXICO—Danone Group; *Int'l*, pg. 379
DANONE GROUP; *Int'l*, pg. 379
DANONE S.A.—Danone Group; *Int'l*, pg. 379
DANONE S.P.A.—Danone Group; *Int'l*, pg. 379
DARIGOLD, INC.; *U.S. Private*, pg. 311
DEAN DAIRY PRODUCTS CO.—Dean Foods Company; *U.S. Public*, pg. 490
DEAN FOODS—Dean Foods Company; *U.S. Public*, pg. 490
DEAN FOODS COMPANY; *U.S. Public*, pg. 489
DEAN FOODS COMPANY—Dean Foods Company; *U.S. Public*, pg. 490
DEAN FOODS SPECIALTY PRODUCTS—Dean Foods Company; *U.S. Public*, pg. 490
DERIVADOS LACTEOS Y ALIMENTICIOS S.A.—Nestle S.A.; *Int'l*, pg. 920
DIEHL INC.; *U.S. Private*, pg. 332
DIXIE DAIRY COMPANY; *U.S. Private*, pg. 337
EAST SMITHFIELD FARMS INC.—Bongrain S.A.; *Int'l*, pg. 201
EDEN VALE—Northern Foods plc; *Int'l*, pg. 968
ELGIN DAIRY FOODS, INC.; *U.S. Private*, pg. 370
EQUITY SUPPLY COMPANY; *U.S. Private*, pg. 380
FAIRMONT PRODUCTS—Dean Foods Company; *U.S. Public*, pg. 490
FARMER JACK SUPERMARKETS—Tengelmann Warenhandelsgesellschaft; *Int'l*, pg. 1375
FOREMOST FARMS USA COOPERATIVE; *U.S. Private*, pg. 418
FRIENDSHIP DAIRIES, INC.; *U.S. Private*, pg. 429
GALBANI—Danone Group; *Int'l*, pg. 380
GARELICK FARMS, INC.—Suiza Foods Corporation; *U.S. Public*, pg. 1527
GENERAL MILLS, INC.; *U.S. Public*, pg. 717
GERVAIS DANONE AG—Danone Group; *Int'l*, pg. 380
GOLD COAST MILK PTY. LTD.—Q.U.F. Industries Ltd.; *Int'l*, pg. 1074
GRANDMET FOODS EUROPE—Diageo Plc; *Int'l*, pg. 408
HASTINGS CO-OP CREAMERY COMPANY; *U.S. Private*, pg. 510
H.J. HEINZ COMPANY, LIMITED—H.J. Heinz Company; *U.S. Public*, pg. 806
HYGEIA DAIRY CO., INC.; *U.S. Private*, pg. 552
KEMPS FOODS, INC.—Koninklijke BolsWessanen nv; *Int'l*, pg. 752
KERRY GROUP PLC; *Int'l*, pg. 731
KONINKLIJKE BOLSWESSANEN NV; *Int'l*, pg. 750
LAITERIE DE VILLECOMTAL—Danone Group; *Int'l*, pg. 379
LANCASHIRE DAIRIES LTD.; *Int'l*, pg. 798
LAND O'LAKES, INC.; *U.S. Private*, pg. 645
LAND-O-SUN DAIRIES, INC.; *U.S. Private*, pg. 646
LIBERTY DAIRY—Dean Foods Company; *U.S. Public*, pg. 490
B.V. LYEMPF—Koninklijke BolsWessanen nv; *Int'l*, pg. 752
MANTEQUERIAS ARIAS S. A.—Bongrain S.A.; *Int'l*, pg. 201
MAPLEHURST FARMS, INC.—Dean Foods Company; *U.S. Public*, pg. 490
MARYLAND & VIRGINIA MILK PRODUCERS COOPERATIVE ASSOCIATION, INC.; *U.S. Private*, pg. 711
MAYFIELD DAIRY FARMS INC.—Dean Foods Company; *U.S. Public*, pg. 490
MCCOLLS DAIRY—Crystal Cream & Butter Company; *U.S. Private*, pg. 294
MEDICAL MEADOW GOLD DAIRIES, INC.—Southern Foods Group; *U.S. Private*, pg. 1016
MEIJERIOSUUSKUNTA/MEJERIANDELSLAGET MILKA; *Int'l*, pg. 854
MEIJI MILK PRODUCTS CO., LTD.; *Int'l*, pg. 855
MELODY FOODS, INC.; *U.S. Private*, pg. 730
MICHAEL FOODS, INC.; *U.S. Public*, pg. 1103
MICHIGAN MILK PRODUCERS ASSOCIATION; *U.S. Private*, pg. 741
MID-AMERICA DAIRYMEN, INC.; *U.S. Private*, pg. 743
MILKCO, INC.—Ingles Markets, Incorporated; *U.S. Public*, pg. 878
NATREL INC.—Agropur; *Int'l*, pg. 32
NESTLE (MALAYSIA), SDN. BHD., NESMAL—Nestle S.A.; *Int'l*, pg. 921
NESTLE NEDERLAND B.V.—Nestle S.A.; *Int'l*, pg. 921
NESTLE S.A.; *Int'l*, pg. 915
NEW ENGLAND DAIRIES, INC.; *U.S. Private*, pg. 793
NORTHERN DAIRIES—Northern Foods plc; *Int'l*, pg. 968
NORTHERN DAIRIES LTD.—Northern Foods plc; *Int'l*, pg. 968
NUTRICIA BV; *Int'l*, pg. 991
OAKHURST DAIRY; *U.S. Private*, pg. 809
OLD HOME FOODS, INC.; *U.S. Private*, pg. 814
PARMALAT CANADA LTD.—Parmalat S.p.A.; *Int'l*, pg. 1023
PARMALAT S.P.A.; *Int'l*, pg. 1023
PARMALAT USA CORPORATION—Parmalat S.p.A.; *Int'l*, pg. 1023
PETERS & BROWNES FOODS LTD.; *Int'l*, pg. 1040
PEVELY DAIRY COMPANY—Prairie Farms Dairy, Inc.; *U.S. Private*, pg. 879
PRAIRIE FARMS DAIRY, INC.; *U.S. Private*, pg. 878
PRICE'S CREAMERIES—Dean Foods Company; *U.S. Public*, pg. 491
PRODUCTOS QUAKER, C.A.—The Quaker Oats Company; *U.S. Public*, pg. 1348
PURITY DAIRIES INC.; *U.S. Private*, pg. 895
Q.U.F. INDUSTRIES LTD.; *Int'l*, pg. 1074
REITER DAIRY, INC.—Dean Foods Company; *U.S. Public*, pg. 491
ROSENBERGERS DAIRIES, INC.; *U.S. Private*, pg. 945
RYAN FOODS—Dean Foods Company; *U.S. Public*, pg. 491
SANTEE DAIRIES—Quality Food Centers, Inc.; *U.S. Public*, pg. 1349
SCANGAS BROTHERS HOLDINGS, INC.; *U.S. Private*, pg. 969
SCHNEIDER FARMS DAIRY—Schneider's Dairy, Inc.; *U.S. Private*, pg. 971
SCHNEIDER'S DAIRY, INC.; *U.S. Private*, pg. 971
SHAMROCK FOODS COMPANY; *U.S. Private*, pg. 989
SMITH BROTHERS FARMS, INC.; *U.S. Private*, pg. 1007
SNOW BRAND MILK PRODUCTS CO. LTD.; *Int'l*, pg. 1271
SOUTHERN BELLE DAIRY COMPANY; *U.S. Private*, pg. 1015
THE STOP & SHOP COMPANIES, INC.—Koninklijke Ahold NV; *Int'l*, pg. 750
SUPERIOR DAIRIES, INC.—Borden, Inc.; *U.S. Private*, pg. 158
SUPERIOR DAIRY, INC.; *U.S. Private*, pg. 1054
TILLAMOOK COUNTY CREAMERY ASSN.; *U.S. Private*, pg. 1086
TINE-VESTLANDSMEIERIET; *Int'l*, pg. 1390
TURNER HOLDING LLC; *U.S. Private*, pg. 1109
TUSCAN/LEHIGH DAIRIES LP; *U.S. Private*, pg. 1110
UNIGATE PLC; *Int'l*, pg. 1433
UNITED DAIRY FARMERS, INC.; *U.S. Private*, pg. 1121
VALLEY BELL DAIRY CO.—Borden, Inc.; *U.S. Private*, pg. 158
VAN HEEL B.V.—Koninklijke BolsWessanen nv; *Int'l*, pg. 751
VERIFINE DAIRY PRODUCTS CORP.—Dean Foods Company; *U.S. Public*, pg. 491
VITAMILK DAIRY, INC.; *U.S. Private*, pg. 1142
WEEKS DAIRY FOODS, INC.—Koninklijke BolsWessanen nv; *Int'l*, pg. 752
WELSH FARMS, INC.; *U.S. Private*, pg. 1162
WEST LYNN CREAMERY, INC.—Scangas Brothers Holdings, Inc.; *U.S. Private*, pg. 969
WHOLESOME DAIRY—Borden, Inc.; *U.S. Private*, pg. 158
WINN-DIXIE STORES, INC.; *U.S. Public*, pg. 1771
YOPLAIT USA—General Mills, Inc.; *U.S. Public*, pg. 718

2032 — CANNED SPECIALTIES

ALIMA-GERBER SA—Novartis AG; *Int'l*, pg. 973
ALIMENTOS HEINZ C.A.—H.J. Heinz Company; *U.S. Public*, pg. 806
ALLGAUER ALPENMILCH A.G.—Nestle S.A.; *Int'l*, pg. 918
ALLIED OLD ENGLISH, INC.; *U.S. Private*, pg. 39
H.J. BAKER & BRO., INC.; *U.S. Private*, pg. 112
BATCHELORS (IRELAND) LTD.—Northern Foods plc; *Int'l*, pg. 968
BEECH-NUT NUTRITION CORPORATION—Ralcorp Holdings Inc.; *U.S. Public*, pg. 1359
BISON CANNING CO., INC.—Goya Foods, Inc.; *U.S. Private*, pg. 468
BISTRO SOUPS, LTD.—Vienna Sausage Mfg. Co.; *U.S. Private*, pg. 1140
BOOKER PLC; *Int'l*, pg. 202
BUITONI SPA—Nestle S.A.; *Int'l*, pg. 919
BUNKER HILL FOODS INC.—Castleberry/Snow's Brands Inc.; *U.S. Private*, pg. 219
BURNS, PHILP & COMPANY LIMITED; *Int'l*, pg. 236
CPC/AJI (HONG KONG) LTD.—Bestfoods; *U.S. Public*, pg. 225
CALAVO FOODS, INC.—Calavo Growers of California; *U.S. Private*, pg. 199
CAMPBELL GROCERY PRODUCTS LTD.—Campbell Soup Company; *U.S. Public*, pg. 299
CAMPBELL SOUP COMPANY; *U.S. Public*, pg. 298
CAMPBELL SOUP COMPANY LTD.—Campbell Soup Company; *U.S. Public*, pg. 299
CAMPBELL SOUP (TEXAS) INC.—Campbell Soup Company; *U.S. Public*, pg. 299
CAMPBELL USA—Campbell Soup Company; *U.S. Public*, pg. 299
CAMPBELL'S SOUPS (AUST.) PTY. LTD.—Campbell Soup Company; *U.S. Public*, pg. 299
CAMPBELL'S (U.K.) LIMITED—Campbell Soup Company; *U.S. Public*, pg. 299
CASTLEBERRY/SNOW'S BRANDS INC.; *U.S. Private*, pg. 219
CENTRAL COMMISSARY, INC.—Cornucopia, Inc.; *U.S. Private*, pg. 276
CHEIL FOODS & CHEMICALS INC.—Samsung Group; *Int'l*, pg. 1181
CONDAL DISTRIBUTORS INC.; *U.S. Private*, pg. 262
CONNELLY CONTAINERS, INC.; *U.S. Private*, pg. 264
CONSERVENFABRIK EUGEN LACROIX GMBH—Campbell Soup Company; *U.S. Public*, pg. 299
CONTADINA DALLA CASA BUITONI—Nestle S.A.; *Int'l*, pg. 916
COPAIS FOOD & BEVERAGE COMPANY S.A.—H.J. Heinz Company; *U.S. Public*, pg. 806
CORNUCOPIA, INC.; *U.S. Private*, pg. 276
CRESTAR FOOD PRODUCTS, INC.—H.J. Heinz Company; *U.S. Public*, pg. 805
DANONE GROUP; *Int'l*, pg. 379
DEL MONTE FOODS; *U.S. Private*, pg. 321
DEL MONTE ROYAL CORPORATION; *Int'l*, pg. 388
FERROSAN INTERNATIONAL A/S—Novo Nordisk A/S; *Int'l*, pg. 987
GERBER FRANCE—Novartis AG; *Int'l*, pg. 973
GERBER POLSKA—Novartis AG; *Int'l*, pg. 973
GERBER PRODUCTS COMPANY—Novartis AG; *Int'l*, pg. 973
GERBER PRODUCTS DIVISION-BABY CARE—Novartis AG; *Int'l*, pg. 973
GERBER PRODUCTS, S.A. DE C.V.—Novartis AG; *Int'l*, pg. 973
GOLDEN TIGER—Windsor Quality Food Co., Ltd.; *U.S. Private*, pg. 1182
GOYA FOODS OF FLORIDA—Goya Foods, Inc.; *U.S. Private*, pg. 468
THE HAIN FOOD GROUP INC.; *U.S. Public*, pg. 774
H.J. HEINZ CENTRAL EUROPE S.A.—H.J. Heinz Company; *U.S. Public*, pg. 806
H.J. HEINZ COMPANY; *U.S. Public*, pg. 805
H.J. HEINZ COMPANY AUSTRALIA LTD.—H.J. Heinz Company; *U.S. Public*, pg. 807
H.J. HEINZ COMPANY, LIMITED—H.J. Heinz Company; *U.S. Public*, pg. 806
H.J. HEINZ GMBH—H.J. Heinz Company; *U.S. Public*, pg. 806
HEINZ JAPAN LTD.—H.J. Heinz Company; *U.S. Public*, pg. 806
HUNT-WESSON FOODSERVICE DIVISION—ConAgra, Inc.; *U.S. Public*, pg. 428
HUNT-WESSON, INC.—ConAgra, Inc.; *U.S. Public*, pg. 428
INTERNATIONAL HOME FOODS INC.—Hicks, Muse, Tate & Furst Inc.; *U.S. Private*, pg. 526
LA PREFERIDA, INC.; *U.S. Private*, pg. 640
LAKESIDE PACKING CO.—Lakeside Foods, Inc.; *U.S. Private*, pg. 644
LIPTON—Unilever Plc; *Int'l*, pg. 1438
LONDON BREWERY—Interbrew S.A.; *Int'l*, pg. 679
MAJOR SMITH INC.—Bongrain S.A.; *Int'l*, pg. 201
THE B. MANISCHEWITZ COMPANY; *U.S. Private*, pg. 699
MCILHENNY COMPANY; *U.S. Private*, pg. 722
MILUPA S.A.—Nutricia BV; *Int'l*, pg. 991
MOORE'S FOOD SERVICE PRODUCTS—H.J. Heinz Company; *U.S. Public*, pg. 805
MORGAN FOODS, INC.; *U.S. Private*, pg. 761
MORINAGA MILK INDUSTRY CO., LTD.; *Int'l*, pg. 895
MORINAGA NUTRITIONAL FOODS, INC.—Morinaga Milk Industry Co., Ltd.; *Int'l*, pg. 895
NESTLE CANADA INC.—Nestle S.A.; *Int'l*, pg. 921
NESTLE USA—Nestle S.A.; *Int'l*, pg. 916
NOVARTIS AG; *Int'l*, pg. 971
NOVARTIS NUTRITION CORPORATION—Novartis AG; *Int'l*, pg. 974
NOZAKI AMERICA, INC.—Nozaki & Company Ltd.; *Int'l*, pg. 990
NOZAKI & COMPANY LTD.; *Int'l*, pg. 990
PARMALAT S.P.A.; *Int'l*, pg. 1023
PLADA S.P.A.—H.J. Heinz Company; *U.S. Public*, pg. 807
PRODUCTOS DEL TROPICO C. POR A.—Borden, Inc.; *U.S. Private*, pg. 160
PRODUCTOS GERBER DE CENTROAMERICA, S.A.—Novartis AG; *Int'l*, pg. 973
Q.P. CORPORATION; *Int'l*, pg. 1074
QUAKER BRASIL, LTDA.—The Quaker Oats Company; *U.S. Public*, pg. 1348
RJR NABISCO HOLDINGS CORP.; *U.S. Public*, pg. 1354
RALSTON PURINA COMPANY; *U.S. Public*, pg. 1359
RANKS HOVIS MCDOUGALL LIMITED—Tomkins PLC; *Int'l*, pg. 1395
RECKITT & COLMAN INC.—Reckitt & Colman plc; *Int'l*, pg. 1090
RECKITT & COLMAN PLC; *Int'l*, pg. 1089
SAHAPATHANAPIBUL PUBLIC COMPANY LIMITED; *Int'l*, pg. 1169
SANDOZ FOOD SERVICE & INDUSTRIAL DIVISION—Novartis AG; *Int'l*, pg. 974
SCHWAN'S SALES ENTERPRISES; *U.S. Private*, pg. 974
J.A. SHARWOOD & COMPANY LIMITED—Tomkins PLC; *Int'l*, pg. 1396
SINO-AMERICAN GREAT WALL FOOD INDUSTRIES CO., LTD.—Diageo Plc; *Int'l*, pg. 411
STEGNER FOOD PRODUCTS CO.; *U.S. Private*, pg. 1039
WANDER AG—Novartis AG; *Int'l*, pg. 972
WANDER G.M.B.H.—Novartis AG; *Int'l*, pg. 986
WILSON PRODUCTS CO.; *U.S. Private*, pg. 1181
WOLF BRAND PRODUCTS—ConAgra, Inc.; *U.S. Public*, pg. 428
WORLDWIDE FOODS, INC.—La Preferida, Inc.; *U.S. Private*, pg. 640
THE WORNICK COMPANY; *U.S. Private*, pg. 1191

2033 — CANNED FRUITS, VEGETABLES, PRESERVES, JAMS & JELLIES

AGRILINK FOODS, INC.—Pro-Fac Cooperative, Inc.; *U.S. Private*, pg. 887
AGRIPAC INC.; *U.S. Private*, pg. 26
ALGOOD FOOD COMPANY; *U.S. Private*, pg. 34
ALIMENTOS HEINZ C.A.—H.J. Heinz Company; *U.S. Public*, pg. 806
ALLEN CANNING COMPANY; *U.S. Private*, pg. 36
ALLGAUER ALPENMILCH A.G.—Nestle S.A.; *Int'l*, pg. 918
ALLIANT FOODSERVICE—Clayton, Dubilier & Rice, Inc; *U.S. Private*, pg. 244
ALLIANT FOODSERVICE, INC.—Clayton, Dubilier & Rice, Inc; *U.S. Private*, pg. 244
AMERICAN BEVERAGE CORPORATION—Koninklijke BolsWessanen nv; *Int'l*, pg. 752
AMERICAN FINE FOODS, INC.—Chiquita Brands International, Inc.; *U.S. Public*, pg. 349
ARTICHOKE INDUSTRIES, INC.; *U.S. Private*, pg. 86
B&G FOODS, INC.; *U.S. Private*, pg. 105
H.J. BAKER & BRO., INC.; *U.S. Private*, pg. 112
BATCHELORS (IRELAND) LTD.—Northern Foods plc; *Int'l*, pg. 968
BELL-CARTER FOODS, INC.; *U.S. Private*, pg. 131
BERRIEL VITTEL FRANCE—Nestle S.A.; *Int'l*, pg. 918
BEST FOODS—Bestfoods; *U.S. Public*, pg. 224
BEST FOODS CANADA, INC.—Bestfoods; *U.S. Public*, pg. 224
BEST FOODS CARIBBEAN, INC.—Bestfoods; *U.S. Public*, pg. 224
BESTFOODS; *U.S. Public*, pg. 223
BORDEN FOODS CANADA—Borden, Inc.; *U.S. Private*, pg. 159
BRIGHT'S & MARTIN'S FOODS—Diageo Plc; *Int'l*, pg. 411
BROOKS FOODS—Pro-Fac Cooperative, Inc.; *U.S. Private*, pg. 887
BUSH BROTHERS & COMPANY; *U.S. Private*, pg. 189
BUSH BROTHERS & COMPANY PLANT—Bush Brothers & Company; *U.S. Private*, pg. 189
BUTTER KERNEL PRODUCTS—Faribault Foods Inc.; *U.S. Private*, pg. 393
CPC ASIA CONSUMER FOODS DIVISION—Bestfoods; *U.S. Public*, pg. 224

CPC RUFHAN LIMITED—Bestfoods; *U.S. Public*, pg. 225
CSR PAMPRYL—Groupe Pernod Ricard; *Int'l*, pg. 566
CADBURY BEVERAGES CANADA INC.—Cadbury Schweppes p.l.c.; *Int'l*, pg. 248
CALIFORNIA CUSTOM FOODS—Pacific Coast Producers; *U.S. Private*, pg. 831
CAMPBELL GROCERY PRODUCTS LTD.—Campbell Soup Company; *U.S. Public*, pg. 299
CAMPBELL SOUP COMPANY; *U.S. Public*, pg. 298
CAMPBELL SOUP COMPANY LTD.—Campbell Soup Company; *U.S. Public*, pg. 299
CAMPBELL USA—Campbell Soup Company; *U.S. Public*, pg. 299
CAMPBELL'S DE MEXICO, S.A. DE C.V.—Campbell Soup Company; *U.S. Public*, pg. 299
CAPRI SUN INC.—Philip Morris Companies Inc.; *U.S. Public*, pg. 1288
CARAVAN PRODUCTS COMPANY, INC.; *U.S. Private*, pg. 208
CARGILL CITRO-AMERICA, INC.—Cargill; *U.S. Private*, pg. 210
CASE-SWAYNE CO. INC.; *U.S. Private*, pg. 218
CEREBOS AUSTRALIA LIMITED—Suntory Ltd.; *Int'l*, pg. 1322
CHEIL FOODS & CHEMICALS INC.—Samsung Group; *Int'l*, pg. 1181
CHERRY CENTRAL COOPERATIVE; *U.S. Private*, pg. 233
CLEMENTS FOODS CO.; *U.S. Private*, pg. 245
COMPANIA PERUANA DE ALIMENTOS S.A.—Nestle S.A.; *Int'l*, pg. 920
COMSTOCK FOODS—Pro-Fac Cooperative, Inc.; *U.S. Private*, pg. 887
CONCENTRATE DIVISION—Orange-Co., Inc.; *U.S. Public*, pg. 1229
COOP SWITZERLAND; *Int'l*, pg. 329
COPAIS FOOD & BEVERAGE COMPANY S.A.—H.J. Heinz Company; *U.S. Public*, pg. 806
CORN PRODUCTS CO. (INDIA) LTD.—Bestfoods; *U.S. Public*, pg. 224
CURTICE BURNS FOODS—Pro-Fac Cooperative, Inc.; *U.S. Private*, pg. 887
DAIRY MART FARMS, INC.—Dairy Mart Convenience Stores, Inc.; *U.S. Public*, pg. 476
DANONE GROUP; *Int'l*, pg. 379
DEAN FOODS VEGETABLE COMPANY—Dean Foods Company; *U.S. Public*, pg. 490
DEAN PICKLES & SPECIALTY PRODUCTS—Dean Foods Company; *U.S. Public*, pg. 490
DEL MONTE FOODS; *U.S. Private*, pg. 321
DEL MONTE FOODS INTERNATIONAL LIMITED—Del Monte Royal Corporation; *Int'l*, pg. 388
DIAGEO PLC; *Int'l*, pg. 408
THE DICKINSON FAMILY, INC.—J.M. Smucker Company; *U.S. Public*, pg. 1480
ECKES AG; *Int'l*, pg. 432
EHIME KANZUME CO., LTD.—Meiji Seika Kaisha, Ltd.; *Int'l*, pg. 855
EVERFRESH BEVERAGES INC.—National Beverage Corp.; *U.S. Public*, pg. 1153
FARIBAULT FOODS INC.; *U.S. Private*, pg. 393
THE FIGARO COMPANY, INC.; *U.S. Private*, pg. 404
AB FINDUS—Nestle S.A.; *Int'l*, pg. 920
THE FREMONT CO.; *U.S. Private*, pg. 426
FRESH JUICE COMPANY; *U.S. Private*, pg. 427
FRUTERA COLOMBIANA S.A.—Corn Products International, Inc.; *U.S. Public*, pg. 447
FURMAN FOODS, INC.; *U.S. Private*, pg. 431
GAGE FOOD PRODUCTS COMPANY—DG Foods, LLC; *U.S. Private*, pg. 301
GERVAIS DANONE AG—Danone Group; *Int'l*, pg. 380
GRAND METROPOLITAN PLC—Diageo Plc; *Int'l*, pg. 408
GREEN GIANT INTERNATIONAL, INC.—Diageo Plc; *Int'l*, pg. 411
GROUPE PERNOD RICARD; *Int'l*, pg. 566
GRUPO INDUSTRIAL BIMBO S.A. DE C.V.; *Int'l*, pg. 575
H.J. HEINZ B.V.—H.J. Heinz Company; *U.S. Public*, pg. 806
H.J. HEINZ COMPANY; *U.S. Public*, pg. 805
H.J. HEINZ COMPANY, LIMITED—H.J. Heinz Company; *U.S. Public*, pg. 806
H.J. HEINZ CO. OF CANADA LTD.—H.J. Heinz Company; *U.S. Public*, pg. 806
H.J. HEINZ GMBH—H.J. Heinz Company; *U.S. Public*, pg. 806
HEINZ JAPAN LTD.—H.J. Heinz Company; *U.S. Public*, pg. 806
HEINZ-UFE LTD.—H.J. Heinz Company; *U.S. Public*, pg. 807
HILLSDOWN LTD.—Hillsdown Holdings Plc; *Int'l*, pg. 619
HUNT-WESSON, INC.—ConAgra, Inc.; *U.S. Public*, pg. 428
INDUSTRIAS DE MAIZ Y ALIMENTOS S.A.—Corn Products International, Inc.; *U.S. Public*, pg. 447
INDUSTRIAS LA FAMOSA, INC.—Borden, Inc.; *U.S. Private*, pg. 158
INTERNATIONAL HOME FOODS INC.—Hicks, Muse, Tate & Furst Inc.; *U.S. Private*, pg. 526
JMS SPECIALTY FOODS, INC.—J.M. Smucker Company; *U.S. Public*, pg. 1480
HENRY JONES FOODS PTY. LTD.—J.M. Smucker Company; *U.S. Public*, pg. 1480
A.C. KISSLING, INC.; *U.S. Private*, pg. 624
KNOTT'S BERRY FARM; *U.S. Private*, pg. 627
KNOUSE FOODS INC.; *U.S. Private*, pg. 627
KONINKLIJKE DE RUYTER BV—CSM N.V.; *Int'l*, pg. 244
KRAFT CANADA INC.—Philip Morris Companies Inc.; *U.S. Public*, pg. 1288
KRAFT FOODS INC.—Philip Morris Companies Inc.; *U.S. Public*, pg. 1288
KUNER-EMPSON COMPANY—Faribault Foods Inc.; *U.S. Private*, pg. 393
LA VICTORIA FOODS, INC.; *U.S. Private*, pg. 641
LAKESIDE FOODS, INC.; *U.S. Private*, pg. 643
MARGETTS FOODS LIMITED—Kerry Group PLC; *Int'l*, pg. 732
MARY ELLEN, INC.—J.M. Smucker Company; *U.S. Public*, pg. 1480
MAUI PINEAPPLE CO., LTD.—Maui Land & Pineapple Co., Inc.; *U.S. Public*, pg. 1060
MCCORMICK & COMPANY, INCORPORATED; *U.S. Public*, pg. 1066
MCILHENNY COMPANY; *U.S. Private*, pg. 722
METAL BOX PLC., FOOD PACKAGING—Caradon Plc; *Int'l*, pg. 267
MORGAN FOODS, INC.; *U.S. Private*, pg. 761
MORINAGA MILK INDUSTRY CO., LTD.; *Int'l*, pg. 895
MOTT'S CANADA DIVISION—Cadbury Schweppes p.l.c.; *Int'l*, pg. 248
MOTT'S INC.—Cadbury Schweppes p.l.c.; *Int'l*, pg. 248
NALLEYS FINE FOODS—Pro-Fac Cooperative, Inc.; *U.S. Private*, pg. 887
NANCE'S FOOD PRODUCTS, INC.—The Quaker Oats Company; *U.S. Public*, pg. 1347
NATIONAL GRAPE CO-OP ASSOCIATION, INC.; *U.S. Private*, pg. 784
NESTLE (MALAYSIA), SDN. BHD., NESMAL—Nestle S.A.; *Int'l*, pg. 921
NESTLE PANAMA S.A.—Nestle S.A.; *Int'l*, pg. 921
NESTLE S.A.; *Int'l*, pg. 915
NEWMAN'S OWN, INC.; *U.S. Private*, pg. 797
NORPAC FOODS, INC.; *U.S. Private*, pg. 802
OCEAN SPRAY CRANBERRIES, INC.; *U.S. Private*, pg. 811
OCONOMOWOC CANNING COMPANY—Stokely USA, Inc.; *U.S. Public*, pg. 1519
OKAYAMAKEN SHOKUHIN CO., LTD.—Meiji Seika Kaisha, Ltd.; *Int'l*, pg. 855
ORANGINA FRANCE—Groupe Pernod Ricard; *Int'l*, pg. 566
OWATONNA CANNING COMPANY—Chiquita Brands International, Inc.; *U.S. Public*, pg. 349
PACIFIC COAST PRODUCERS; *U.S. Private*, pg. 830
PARAMOUNT CITRUS ASSOCIATION—Roll International Corporation; *U.S. Private*, pg. 941
PHARMACIA & UPJOHN, INC.; *Int'l*, pg. 1047
THE PILLSBURY COMPANY—Diageo Plc; *Int'l*, pg. 411
PLADA S.P.A.—H.J. Heinz Company; *U.S. Public*, pg. 807
PORTLAND FOOD PRODUCTS COMPANY; *U.S. Private*, pg. 876
PRESTO FOOD PRODUCTS, INC.—Suiza Foods Corporation; *U.S. Public*, pg. 1527
PRINCEVILLE CANNING CO.—Chiquita Brands International, Inc.; *U.S. Public*, pg. 349
PRIVATE BRANDS—Harvest States Cooperatives; *U.S. Private*, pg. 508
PRO-FAC COOPERATIVE, INC.; *U.S. Private*, pg. 887
PRODUCTOS DELTROPICO C. PAR A.—Borden, Inc.; *U.S. Private*, pg. 158
QUINCY CORP.—Sylvan Inc.; *U.S. Public*, pg. 1545
RAISIO GROUP PLC—Raisio Group; *Int'l*, pg. 1085
RED WING COMPANY—Tomkins PLC; *Int'l*, pg. 1398
RED WING CO. INC.—Tomkins PLC; *Int'l*, pg. 1398
RED WINGS INC.—Tomkins PLC; *Int'l*, pg. 1398
ROSE & LAFLAMME CO. LTD.—Saskatchewan Wheat Pool; *Int'l*, pg. 1195
SIAS - MPA—Groupe Pernod Ricard; *Int'l*, pg. 566
SAN MIGUEL CORP.; *Int'l*, pg. 1183
SCHWAN'S SALES ENTERPRISES; *U.S. Private*, pg. 974
THE SEAGRAM BEVERAGE GROUP—The Seagram Company Ltd.; *Int'l*, pg. 1217
SENECA FOODS CORPORATION; *U.S. Public*, pg. 1456
SENECA FOODS-KENNETT DIVISION—Seneca Foods Corporation; *U.S. Public*, pg. 1457
SILVER SPRINGS CITRUS CO-OP; *U.S. Private*, pg. 1000
E.D. SMITH; *Int'l*, pg. 1263
SMUCKER GRANDVIEW PLANT—J.M. Smucker Company; *U.S. Public*, pg. 1480
J.M. SMUCKER COMPANY; *U.S. Public*, pg. 1480
SNOKIST GROWERS; *U.S. Private*, pg. 1011
SNOW BRAND MILK PRODUCTS CO. LTD.; *Int'l*, pg. 1271
SPECIALTY BRANDS—Burns, Philp & Company Limited; *Int'l*, pg. 237
SPICE PLANT—McCormick & Company, Incorporated; *U.S. Public*, pg. 1066
STAR FINE FOODS, INC.; *U.S. Private*, pg. 1034
STEINER CORPORATION; *U.S. Private*, pg. 1039
STILWELL FOODS, INC.—Flowers Industries, Inc.; *U.S. Public*, pg. 658
STOKELY USA, INC.; *U.S. Public*, pg. 1518
SUNDOR BRANDS INC.—The Procter & Gamble Company; *U.S. Public*, pg. 1331
SUNPURE LTD.; *U.S. Private*, pg. 1053
THE SWISS COLONY, INC.; *U.S. Private*, pg. 1059
TAIYO SHOKUHIN CO., LTD.—Meiji Seika Kaisha, Ltd.; *Int'l*, pg. 855
TREE TOP, INC.; *U.S. Private*, pg. 1098
TRI VALLEY GROWERS; *U.S. Private*, pg. 1101
TROPICANA DOLE BEVERAGES NORTH AMERICA—The Seagram Company Ltd.; *Int'l*, pg. 1217
UWAJIMA CANNING CO., LTD.—Meiji Seika Kaisha, Ltd.; *Int'l*, pg. 855
VACU-DRY COMPANY; *U.S. Public*, pg. 1704
VACU-DRY COMPANY PLANT—Vacu-Dry Company; *U.S. Public*, pg. 1704
VENTURA COASTAL CORPORATION; *U.S. Private*, pg. 1136
VENTURA FOODS—Harvest States Cooperatives; *U.S. Private*, pg. 508
VERYFINE PRODUCTS, INC.; *U.S. Private*, pg. 1137
WANDER S.A.—Novartis AG; *Int'l*, pg. 986
WARNER VINEYARDS; *U.S. Private*, pg. 1151
WELCH FOODS INC., A COOPERATIVE—National Grape Co-Op Association, Inc.; *U.S. Private*, pg. 784
WESTIN, INC.; *U.S. Private*, pg. 1169
WILLIAMS FOODS INC.; *U.S. Private*, pg. 1178
WORTHINGTON FOODS INC.; *U.S. Public*, pg. 1780

2034 — DRIED & DEHYDRATED FRUITS & VEGETABLES & SOUP MIXES

ARMOUR SWIFT ECKRICH—ConAgra, Inc.; *U.S. Public*, pg. 426
ARROW INDUSTRIES, INC.—ConAgra, Inc.; *U.S. Public*, pg. 426
BASIC AMERICAN FOODS; *U.S. Private*, pg. 121
BATCHELORS FOODS, LTD.—Unilever Plc; *Int'l*, pg. 1434
BEAU MARAIS S.A. (FRANCE)—McCain Foods Limited; *Int'l*, pg. 850
BESAN-BESIN SANAYI VE TICARET A.S.—Bestfoods; *U.S. Public*, pg. 224
BEST FOODS CANADA, INC.—Bestfoods; *U.S. Public*, pg. 224
BESTFOODS; *U.S. Public*, pg. 223
BETTY CROCKER PRODUCTS—General Mills, Inc.; *U.S. Public*, pg. 718
GEORGE F. BROCKE & SONS, INC.; *U.S. Private*, pg. 170
CFP FOODS—Saskatchewan Wheat Pool; *Int'l*, pg. 1195
CPC ASIA CONSUMER FOODS DIVISION—Bestfoods; *U.S. Public*, pg. 224
CPC FOODS A/S—Bestfoods; *U.S. Public*, pg. 225
CPC SPECIALTY MARKETS GROUP—Bestfoods; *U.S. Public*, pg. 224
CSM FOOD DIVISION—CSM N.V.; *Int'l*, pg. 243
CSM N.V.; *Int'l*, pg. 243
CALIFORNIA B.V.—CSM N.V.; *Int'l*, pg. 243
CAMPBELL SOUP COMPANY; *U.S. Public*, pg. 298
CAMPBELL USA—Campbell Soup Company; *U.S. Public*, pg. 299
JOHN COPES FOOD PRODUCTS, INC.; *U.S. Private*, pg. 274
CROMPTON & KNOWLES CORPORATION; *U.S. Public*, pg. 459
DG FOODS, LLC; *U.S. Private*, pg. 301
DALE FOODS—DG Foods, LLC; *U.S. Private*, pg. 301
DEL MONTE FOODS; *U.S. Private*, pg. 321
FARLEY CANDY COMPANY—Favorite Brands International, Inc.; *U.S. Private*, pg. 397
FOODCORP LIMITED; *Int'l*, pg. 496
FOODIE OY—Raisio Group; *Int'l*, pg. 1085
4C FOODS CORPORATION; *U.S. Private*, pg. 421
FRUTERA COLOMBIANA S.A.—Corn Products International, Inc.; *U.S. Public*, pg. 447
GAGE FOOD PRODUCTS COMPANY—DG Foods, LLC; *U.S. Private*, pg. 301
GENESEE CORPORATION; *U.S. Public*, pg. 728
GILROY ENERGY COMPANY—Calpine Corporation; *U.S. Public*, pg. 296
GILROY FOODS, INC.—ConAgra, Inc.; *U.S. Public*, pg. 428
HENNINGSEN FOODS, INC.—Q.P. Corporation; *Int'l*, pg. 1074
HONIG MERKARTIKELEN B.V.—CSM N.V.; *Int'l*, pg. 244
HUNT-WESSON, INC.—ConAgra, Inc.; *U.S. Public*, pg. 428
IDAHO SUPREME COMPANY; *U.S. Private*, pg. 557
IDAHOAN FOODS; *U.S. Private*, pg. 557
INDUSTRIAS DE MAIZ Y ALIMENTOS S.A.—Corn Products International, Inc.; *U.S. Public*, pg. 447
INTERNUT—Snack America; *U.S. Private*, pg. 1010
ISRAEL EDIBLE PRODUCTS LTD.—Bestfoods; *U.S. Public*, pg. 225
C.H. KNORR NAHRUNGSMITTELFABRIK, GES. MB H.—Bestfoods; *U.S. Public*, pg. 225
KNORR-NAHRMITTEL AKTIENGESELLSCHAFT—Bestfoods; *U.S. Public*, pg. 225
KNORR PORTUGUESA-PRODUTOS ALIMENTARES S.A.—Bestfoods; *U.S. Public*, pg. 225
LIEBIG BENELUX NV—Danone Group; *Int'l*, pg. 380
LIPTON—Unilever Plc; *Int'l*, pg. 1438
MAGGI AG—Nestle S.A.; *Int'l*, pg. 916
MAGIC VALLEY FOODS, INC.; *U.S. Private*, pg. 695
THE B. MANISCHEWITZ COMPANY; *U.S. Private*, pg. 699
MARUCHAN INC.; *U.S. Private*, pg. 710
MCCAIN ALIMENTAIRE SA—McCain Foods Limited; *Int'l*, pg. 850
MCCAIN ESPANA S.A. (SPAIN)—McCain Foods Limited; *Int'l*, pg. 850
MCCAIN FOODS (AUSTRALIA) PTY. LTD.—McCain Foods Limited; *Int'l*, pg. 850
MCCAIN FOODS HOLLAND B.V. (THE NETHERLANDS)—McCain Foods Limited; *Int'l*, pg. 850
MCCORMICK & COMPANY, INCORPORATED; *U.S. Public*, pg. 1066
MCDOUGALLS CATERING FOODS LIMITED—Tomkins PLC; *Int'l*, pg. 1396
NESTLE NEDERLAND B.V.—Nestle S.A.; *Int'l*, pg. 921
ONTARIO FOODS, INC.—Genesee Corporation; *U.S. Public*, pg. 728
PROCESSED MEATS/POULTRY—ConAgra, Inc.; *U.S. Public*, pg. 426
PRODUCTOS DE MAIZ S.A.—Corn Products International, Inc.; *U.S. Public*, pg. 447
RANKS HOVIS MCDOUGALL LIMITED—Tomkins PLC; *Int'l*, pg. 1395
REFINACOES DE MILHO, BRASIL LTDA.—Corn Products International, Inc.; *U.S. Public*, pg. 448
REFINERIAS DE MAIZ S.A.I.C.F.—Corn Products International, Inc.; *U.S. Public*, pg. 448
WILLIAM B. REILY & CO., INC.; *U.S. Private*, pg. 919
ROGERS FOODS—Universal Foods Corporation; *U.S. Public*, pg. 1696
SPECIALTY BRANDS—Burns, Philp & Company Limited; *Int'l*, pg. 237
SUN DIAMOND GROWERS OF CALIFORNIA; *U.S. Private*, pg. 1051
SUPERIOR COFFEE AND FOODS—Sara Lee Corporation; *U.S. Public*, pg. 1434
TONE BROTHERS INC.—Burns, Philp & Company Limited; *Int'l*, pg. 237
TREE TOP, INC.; *U.S. Private*, pg. 1098
UNIVERSAL FOODS CORPORATION; *U.S. Public*, pg. 1695

UNIVERSAL FOODS CORP.-DEHYDRATED PRODUCTS DIV.—Universal Foods Corporation; *U.S. Public*, pg. 1696
VACU-DRY COMPANY; *U.S. Public*, pg. 1704
VACU-DRY COMPANY PLANT—Vacu-Dry Company; *U.S. Public*, pg. 1704
VALLEY FIG GROWERS—Sun Diamond Growers of California; *U.S. Private*, pg. 1051
WILLIAMSBURG FOODS, INC.—The Smithfield Companies, Inc.; *U.S. Public*, pg. 1479
WORTHINGTON FOODS INC.; *U.S. Public*, pg. 1780

2035 — PICKLED FRUITS & VEGETABLES, VEGETABLE SAUCES & SEASONINGS & SALAD DRESSINGS

AJINOMOTO COMPANY INC.; *Int'l*, pg. 40
ALIMENTOS HEINZ C.A.—H.J. Heinz Company; *U.S. Public*, pg. 806
ALIMENTOS Y PRODUCTOS DE MAIZ S.A.—Corn Products International, Inc.; *U.S. Public*, pg. 447
ALIVEN S.A.—Corn Products International, Inc.; *U.S. Public*, pg. 447
ALLEN FOODS, INC.; *U.S. Private*, pg. 37
ALLIANT FOODSERVICE—Clayton, Dubilier & Rice, Inc; *U.S. Private*, pg. 244
ALLIANT FOODSERVICE, INC.—Clayton, Dubilier & Rice, Inc; *U.S. Private*, pg. 244
BEST FOODS—Bestfoods; *U.S. Public*, pg. 224
BEST FOODS CANADA, INC.—Bestfoods; *U.S. Public*, pg. 224
BEST FOODS CARIBBEAN, INC.—Bestfoods; *U.S. Public*, pg. 224
BESTFOODS; *U.S. Public*, pg. 223
BICK'S PICKLES & RELISHES—International Multifoods Corporation; *U.S. Public*, pg. 901
BRUCE FOODS CORP.; *U.S. Private*, pg. 175
CPC/AJI (HONG KONG) LTD.—Bestfoods; *U.S. Public*, pg. 225
CPC ASIA CONSUMER FOODS DIVISION—Bestfoods; *U.S. Public*, pg. 224
CPC FOODS A.S.—Bestfoods; *U.S. Public*, pg. 225
CALIFORNIA MFG. CO., INC.—Bestfoods; *U.S. Public*, pg. 225
CAMPBELL SALES—Campbell Soup Company; *U.S. Public*, pg. 299
CAMPBELL SOUP COMPANY; *U.S. Public*, pg. 298
CAMPBELL SOUP COMPANY LTD.—Campbell Soup Company; *U.S. Public*, pg. 299
CAMPBELL USA—Campbell Soup Company; *U.S. Public*, pg. 299
CAMPBELL'S DE MEXICO, S.A. DE C.V.—Campbell Soup Company; *U.S. Public*, pg. 299
CENTRAL COMMISSARY, INC.—Cornucopia, Inc.; *U.S. Private*, pg. 276
CEREBOS AUSTRALIA LIMITED—Suntory Ltd.; *Int'l*, pg. 1322
CLEMENTS FOODS CO.; *U.S. Private*, pg. 245
THE CLOROX COMPANY; *U.S. Public*, pg. 386
CONDIMENT PLANT—McCormick & Company, Incorporated; *U.S. Public*, pg. 1066
CONNELLY CONTAINERS, INC.; *U.S. Private*, pg. 264
CONTADINA DALLA CASA BUITONI—Nestle S.A.; *Int'l*, pg. 916
CONWAY IMPORT CO. INC.; *U.S. Private*, pg. 272
CORN PRODUCTS CO. (INDIA) LTD.—Bestfoods; *U.S. Public*, pg. 224
CORNUCOPIA, INC.; *U.S. Private*, pg. 276
DG FOODS, LLC; *U.S. Private*, pg. 301
DALE FOODS—DG Foods, LLC; *U.S. Private*, pg. 301
DANONE GROUP; *Int'l*, pg. 379
DEAN FOODS COMPANY; *U.S. Public*, pg. 489
DEAN PICKLE & SPECIALTY PRODUCTS—Dean Foods Company; *U.S. Public*, pg. 490
DEAN PICKLE & SPECIALTY PRODUCTS CO.—Dean Foods Company; *U.S. Public*, pg. 490
DEAN PICKLES & SPECIALTY PRODUCTS—Dean Foods Company; *U.S. Public*, pg. 490
J.L. DEGRAFFENREID & SONS, INC.—DG Foods, LLC; *U.S. Private*, pg. 301
DEL MONTE FOODS; *U.S. Private*, pg. 321
FARIBAULT FOODS INC.; *U.S. Private*, pg. 393
FARMAN BROTHERS PICKLE COMPANY—Pro-Fac Cooperative, Inc.; *U.S. Private*, pg. 887
FRUTERA COLOMBIANA S.A.—Corn Products International, Inc.; *U.S. Public*, pg. 447
GRAVYMASTER INC.; *U.S. Private*, pg. 471
GREAT LAKES KRAUT CO.—Pro-Fac Cooperative, Inc.; *U.S. Private*, pg. 887
GREAT LAKES KRAUT CO., L.L.C.—Pro-Fac Cooperative, Inc.; *U.S. Private*, pg. 887
GRIFFIN MANUFACTURING CO.; *U.S. Private*, pg. 481
HP FOODS—Danone Group; *Int'l*, pg. 380
THE HVR COMPANY—The Clorox Company; *U.S. Public*, pg. 387
H.J. HEINZ GMBH—H.J. Heinz Company; *U.S. Public*, pg. 806
HONIG MERKARTIKELEN B.V.—CSM N.V.; *Int'l*, pg. 244
IMSA S.A.—Corn Products International, Inc.; *U.S. Public*, pg. 447
INDUSTRIAS DE MAIZ Y ALIMENTOS S.A.—Corn Products International, Inc.; *U.S. Public*, pg. 447
INTERNATIONAL MULTIFOODS CORPORATION; *U.S. Public*, pg. 900
ISRAEL EDIBLE PRODUCTS LTD.—Bestfoods; *U.S. Public*, pg. 225
JMS SPECIALTY FOODS, INC.—J.M. Smucker Company; *U.S. Public*, pg. 1480
KIKKOMAN CORPORATION; *Int'l*, pg. 733
KIKKOMAN FOODS, INC.—Kikkoman Corporation; *Int'l*, pg. 733
KIKKOMAN (S) PTE. LTD.—Kikkoman Corporation; *Int'l*, pg. 733
A.C. KISSLING, INC.; *U.S. Private*, pg. 624
C.H. KNORR NAHRUNGSMITTELFABRIK, GES. MB H.—Bestfoods; *U.S. Public*, pg. 225
KNORR-NAHRMITTEL AKTIENGESELLSCHAFT—Bestfoods; *U.S. Public*, pg. 225
KNORR PORTUGUESA-PRODUTOS ALIMENTARES S.A.—Bestfoods; *U.S. Public*, pg. 225
KOIPE S.A.—Compart SpA; *Int'l*, pg. 324
KRAFT CANADA INC.—Philip Morris Companies Inc.; *U.S. Public*, pg. 1288
KRAFT FOODS, INC.—Philip Morris Companies Inc.; *U.S. Public*, pg. 1287
KRAFT FOODS INC.—Philip Morris Companies Inc.; *U.S. Public*, pg. 1288
LANCASTER COLONY CORPORATION; *U.S. Public*, pg. 976
LEA & PERRINS, INC.—Danone Group; *Int'l*, pg. 380
LIEBIG MAILLE AMORA—Danone Group; *Int'l*, pg. 380
LIPTON—Unilever Plc; *Int'l*, pg. 1438
LOSURDO FOODS, INC.; *U.S. Private*, pg. 677
MAGGI GMBH—Nestle S.A.; *Int'l*, pg. 920
T. MARZETTI COMPANY—Lancaster Colony Corporation; *U.S. Public*, pg. 977
T. MARZETTI COMPANY - WEST—Lancaster Colony Corporation; *U.S. Public*, pg. 977
MATTESSONS WALLS LTD.—Unilever Plc; *Int'l*, pg. 1434
MCCORMICK & COMPANY, INCORPORATED; *U.S. Public*, pg. 1066
NANCE'S FOOD PRODUCTS, INC.—The Quaker Oats Company; *U.S. Public*, pg. 1347
NATIONAL FOODS INC.—ConAgra, Inc.; *U.S. Public*, pg. 429
NESTLE (MALAYSIA), SDN. BHD., NESMAL—Nestle S.A.; *Int'l*, pg. 921
NESTLE S.A.; *Int'l*, pg. 915
NEWMAN'S OWN, INC.; *U.S. Private*, pg. 797
OTT FOOD PRODUCTS; *U.S. Private*, pg. 821
PFEIFFER FOODS, INC.—Lancaster Colony Corporation; *U.S. Public*, pg. 977
PIKNIK PRODUCTS COMPANY, INC.; *U.S. Private*, pg. 865
PRESIDENT FOODS CO., LTD.—President Enterprises Corp.; *Int'l*, pg. 1069
PRIVATE BRANDS—Harvest States Cooperatives; *U.S. Private*, pg. 508
PRODUCTOS DE MAIZ S.A.—Corn Products International, Inc.; *U.S. Public*, pg. 447
PRODUCTOS DE MAIZ Y ALIMENTOS, S.A.—Corn Products International, Inc.; *U.S. Public*, pg. 447
PURITY PRODUCTS INC.; *U.S. Private*, pg. 896
Q & B FOODS, INC.—Q.P. Corporation; *Int'l*, pg. 1074
Q.P. CORPORATION; *Int'l*, pg. 1074
RHM INGREDIENTS, LTD.—Newly Weds Foods Inc.; *U.S. Private*, pg. 797
RJR NABISCO HOLDINGS CORP.; *U.S. Public*, pg. 1354
RANKS HOVIS MCDOUGALL LIMITED—Tomkins PLC; *Int'l*, pg. 1395
RE-MI FOODS INC.—Borden, Inc.; *U.S. Private*, pg. 158
RECKITT & COLMAN INC.—Reckitt & Colman plc; *Int'l*, pg. 1090
RECKITT & COLMAN PLC; *Int'l*, pg. 1089
RED WING CO. INC.—Tomkins PLC; *Int'l*, pg. 1398
RED WINGS INC.—Tomkins PLC; *Int'l*, pg. 1398
REFINACOES DE MILHO, BRASIL LTDA.—Corn Products International, Inc.; *U.S. Public*, pg. 448
REFINERIAS DE MAIZ S.A.I.C.F.—Corn Products International, Inc.; *U.S. Public*, pg. 448
WILLIAM B. REILY & CO., INC.; *U.S. Private*, pg. 919
ROBIN HOOD MULTIFOODS INC.—International Multifoods Corporation; *U.S. Public*, pg. 901
SAN-JIRUSHI; *Int'l*, pg. 1183
J.A. SHARWOOD & COMPANY LIMITED—Tomkins PLC; *Int'l*, pg. 1396
THE SWISS COLONY, INC; *U.S. Private*, pg. 1059
TRAPPEY'S FINE FOODS, INC.—B&G Foods, Inc.; *U.S. Private*, pg. 105
TRI VALLEY GROWERS; *U.S. Private*, pg. 1101
UNIL-IT S.P.A.—Unilever Plc; *Int'l*, pg. 1438
VENTRE PACKING COMPANY, INC.; *U.S. Private*, pg. 1135
VENTURA FOODS—Harvest States Cooperatives; *U.S. Private*, pg. 508
VERYFINE PRODUCTS, INC.; *U.S. Private*, pg. 1137
VICTORIA PACKING CORPORATION; *U.S. Private*, pg. 1139
VIENNA SAUSAGE MFG. CO.; *U.S. Private*, pg. 1139
WILLIAMS FOODS INC.; *U.S. Private*, pg. 1178

2037 — FROZEN FRUITS, FRUIT JUICES & VEGETABLES

ADAMS WINE CO.; *U.S. Private*, pg. 17
AGRILINK FOODS, INC.—Pro-Fac Cooperative, Inc.; *U.S. Private*, pg. 887
AGRIPAC INC.; *U.S. Private*, pg. 26
AMERICAN BEVERAGE CORPORATION—Koninklijke BolsWessanen nv; *Int'l*, pg. 752
APPLETISER SOUTH AFRICA (PTY) LTD.—South African Breweries, Ltd.; *Int'l*, pg. 1286
ARDMORE FARMS—The Quaker Oats Company; *U.S. Public*, pg. 1348
ARTICHOKE INDUSTRIES, INC.; *U.S. Private*, pg. 86
BENTLEY & BENTLEY—J.R. Wood Inc.; *U.S. Private*, pg. 1186
BIG VALLEY MARKETING CORP.—J.R. Wood Inc.; *U.S. Private*, pg. 1186
BIRDS EYE WALLS LTD.—Unilever Plc; *Int'l*, pg. 1434
CADBURY BEVERAGES CANADA INC.—Cadbury Schweppes p.l.c.; *Int'l*, pg. 248
CADBURY BEVERAGES NORTH AMERICA—Cadbury Schweppes p.l.c.; *Int'l*, pg. 248
CAMPBELL'S DE MEXICO, S.A. DE C.V.—Campbell Soup Company; *U.S. Public*, pg. 299
CAMPBELL'S SOUPS (AUST.) PTY. LTD.—Campbell Soup Company; *U.S. Public*, pg. 299
CITRUS WORLD INC.; *U.S. Private*, pg. 241
THE COCA-COLA COMPANY; *U.S. Public*, pg. 392
CONAGRA, INC.; *U.S. Public*, pg. 425
JOHN COPES FOOD PRODUCTS, INC.; *U.S. Private*, pg. 274
DEAN FOODS VEGETABLE COMPANY—Dean Foods Company; *U.S. Public*, pg. 490
DELAGRA CORPORATION; *U.S. Private*, pg. 321
DIAGEO PLC; *Int'l*, pg. 408
ECKES AG; *Int'l*, pg. 432
ERLY INDUSTRIES, INC.; *U.S. Public*, pg. 591
EVERFRESH BEVERAGES INC.—National Beverage Corp.; *U.S. Public*, pg. 1153
FRESH JUICE COMPANY; *U.S. Private*, pg. 427
FRISCO-FINDUS AG—Nestle S.A.; *Int'l*, pg. 916
GERBER PRODUCTS DIVISION-BABY CARE—Novartis AG; *Int'l*, pg. 973
GERBER PRODUCTS, S.A. DE C.V.—Novartis AG; *Int'l*, pg. 973
GIGANTE VERTE S.A.—Diageo Plc; *Int'l*, pg. 409
GOLDEN GEM GROWERS INC.; *U.S. Private*, pg. 460
GRAND METROPOLITAN PLC—Diageo Plc; *Int'l*, pg. 408
GREEN GIANT INTERNATIONAL, INC.—Diageo Plc; *Int'l*, pg. 411
J. HUNGERFORD SMITH COMPANY—ConAgra, Inc.; *U.S. Public*, pg. 428
J & J SNACK FOODS CORPORATION; *U.S. Public*, pg. 916
JMS SPECIALTY FOODS, INC.—J.M. Smucker Company; *U.S. Public*, pg. 1480
JOHANNA FOODS INC.; *U.S. Private*, pg. 589
JUGOS DEL VALLE, S.A. DE C.V.; *Int'l*, pg. 716
KEIZER B.V. (WASPIK)—McCain Foods Limited; *Int'l*, pg. 850
KNUDSEN & SONS, INC.—J.M. Smucker Company; *U.S. Public*, pg. 1480
KRAFT FOODS, INC.—Philip Morris Companies Inc.; *U.S. Public*, pg. 1287
LAMB-WESTON—ConAgra, Inc.; *U.S. Public*, pg. 427
LAMB-WESTON, INC.—ConAgra, Inc.; *U.S. Public*, pg. 427
LAND-O-SUN DAIRIES, INC.; *U.S. Private*, pg. 646
LORENZ & LIHN OBST-EDEL-ERZEUGNISSE GMBH—Eckes AG; *Int'l*, pg. 433
MAGIC VALLEY FOODS, INC.; *U.S. Private*, pg. 695
MCCAIN CITRUS INC.—McCain Foods Limited; *Int'l*, pg. 850
MCCAIN FOODS (AUSTRALIA) PTY. LTD.—McCain Foods Limited; *Int'l*, pg. 850
MCCAIN FOODS BELGIUM N.V. (BELGIUM)—McCain Foods Limited; *Int'l*, pg. 850
MCCAIN FOODS INC.—McCain Foods Limited; *Int'l*, pg. 850
MCCAIN FOODS LIMITED; *Int'l*, pg. 850
MCCAIN SUNNYLAND BELGIUM—McCain Foods Limited; *Int'l*, pg. 850
MCCORMICK & COMPANY, INCORPORATED; *U.S. Public*, pg. 1066
MILNE FOOD PRODUCTS, INC.—Ocean Spray Cranberries, Inc.; *U.S. Private*, pg. 811
THE MINUTE MAID COMPANY—The Coca-Cola Company; *U.S. Public*, pg. 392
MOTT'S INC.—Cadbury Schweppes p.l.c.; *Int'l*, pg. 248
NATIONAL FROZEN FOODS CORP.; *U.S. Private*, pg. 783
NATIONAL GRAPE CO-OP ASSOCIATION, INC.; *U.S. Private*, pg. 784
NICHIREI CORPORATION; *Int'l*, pg. 928
NORPAC FOODS, INC.; *U.S. Private*, pg. 802
OCEAN SPRAY CRANBERRIES, INC.; *U.S. Private*, pg. 811
OH BOY CORPORATION; *U.S. Private*, pg. 812
ORE-IDA FOODS, INC.—H.J. Heinz Company; *U.S. Public*, pg. 805
PATTERSON FROZEN FOODS, INC.; *U.S. Private*, pg. 843
PENOBSCOT FROZEN FOODS, INC.; *U.S. Private*, pg. 850
PETERS & BROWNES FOODS LTD.; *Int'l*, pg. 1040
PHILIP MORRIS COMPANIES INC.; *U.S. Public*, pg. 1287
THE PILLSBURY COMPANY—Diageo Plc; *Int'l*, pg. 411
PRO-FAC COOPERATIVE, INC.; *U.S. Private*, pg. 887
PROCTER & GAMBLE BEVERAGE DIV.—The Procter & Gamble Company; *U.S. Public*, pg. 1330
PRODUCTOS GERBER DE CENTROAMERICA, S.A.—Novartis AG; *Int'l*, pg. 973
Q.P. CORPORATION; *Int'l*, pg. 1074
Q.U.F. INDUSTRIES LTD.; *Int'l*, pg. 1074
SCANGAS BROTHERS HOLDINGS, INC.; *U.S. Private*, pg. 969
SEABROOK BROTHERS & SONS, INC.; *U.S. Private*, pg. 978
SENECA FOODS CORPORATION; *U.S. Public*, pg. 1456
J.R. SIMPLOT COMPANY; *U.S. Private*, pg. 1002
SMITH FROZEN FOODS, INC.; *U.S. Private*, pg. 1008
J.M. SMUCKER COMPANY; *U.S. Public*, pg. 1480
STOKELY USA, INC.; *U.S. Public*, pg. 1518
STOKELY USA, INC.—Stokely USA, Inc.; *U.S. Public*, pg. 1519
SUNDOR BRANDS INC.—The Procter & Gamble Company; *U.S. Public*, pg. 1331
SUNKIST GROWERS, INC.; *U.S. Private*, pg. 1052
SWANSON—Campbell Soup Company; *U.S. Public*, pg. 299
SYSTEMS BIO INDUSTRIES—Elf Aquitane; *Int'l*, pg. 445
TINE-VESTLANDSMEIERIET; *Int'l*, pg. 1390
TROPICANA DOLE BEVERAGES NORTH AMERICA—The Seagram Company Ltd.; *Int'l*, pg. 1217
TWIN CITY FOODS, INC.; *U.S. Private*, pg. 1111
UNIFROST NAHRUNGSMITTEL GES. M.B.H.—Unilever Plc; *Int'l*, pg. 1439
UNILEVER N.V.—Unilever Plc; *Int'l*, pg. 1434
UNILEVER PLC; *Int'l*, pg. 1433
UNITED FOODS, INC.; *U.S. Public*, pg. 1677
UNIVERSAL FOODS CORPORATION; *U.S. Public*, pg. 1695
VACU-DRY COMPANY; *U.S. Public*, pg. 1704

VACU-DRY COMPANY PLANT—Vacu-Dry Company; U.S. Public, pg. 1704
WELCH FOODS INC., A COOPERATIVE—National Grape Co-Op Association, Inc.; U.S. Private, pg. 784
WESTIN, INC.; U.S. Private, pg. 1169
WHITE ROCK PRODUCTS CORP.; U.S. Private, pg. 1173
J.R. WOOD INC.; U.S. Private, pg. 1186

2038 — FROZEN SPECIALTIES, NEC

ALIMENTOS FINDAS S.A. DE C.V.—Nestle S.A.; Int'l, pg. 918
ARDEN INTERNATIONAL KITCHENS, INC.—Schreiber Foods, Inc.; U.S. Private, pg. 972
BAKERY & CONFECTIONARY DIVISION—Campbell Soup Company; U.S. Public, pg. 299
BEAU MARAIS S.A. (FRANCE)—McCain Foods Limited; Int'l, pg. 850
BERNARDI ITALIAN FOODS—Windsor Quality Food Co., Ltd.; U.S. Private, pg. 1182
BIRDS EYE WALLS LTD.—Unilever Plc; Int'l, pg. 1434
BOOKER PLC; Int'l, pg. 202
BUITONI SPA—Nestle S.A.; Int'l, pg. 919
CFP FOODS—Saskatchewan Wheat Pool; Int'l, pg. 1195
CAMPBELL SOUP COMPANY; U.S. Public, pg. 298
CAMPBELL SOUP COMPANY LTD.—Campbell Soup Company; U.S. Public, pg. 299
CAMPBELL USA—Campbell Soup Company; U.S. Public, pg. 299
CASA DI BERTACCHI—Rich Products Corp.; U.S. Private, pg. 928
CELENTANO BROS. INC.; U.S. Private, pg. 221
CONAGRA FROZEN FOOD COMPANY—ConAgra, Inc.; U.S. Public, pg. 427
CONAGRA PREPARED FOOD COMPANIES—ConAgra, Inc.; U.S. Public, pg. 427
DEAN FOODS VEGETABLE COMPANY—Dean Foods Company; U.S. Public, pg. 490
DORSET CHILLED FOOD PRODUCTS LTD.—Northern Foods plc; Int'l, pg. 968
TONY DOWNS FOODS COMPANY; U.S. Private, pg. 342
EDISON OPERATION—Nozaki & Company Ltd.; Int'l, pg. 990
AB FINDUS—Nestle S.A.; Int'l, pg. 920
FREEZER QUEEN FOODS INC.—James Crean PLC; Int'l, pg. 340
FROZEN SPECIALTIES, INC.—Citicorp; U.S. Public, pg. 378
GOLDEN TIGER—Windsor Quality Food Co., Ltd.; U.S. Private, pg. 1182
THE HAIN FOOD GROUP INC.; U.S. Public, pg. 774
H.J. HEINZ COMPANY; U.S. Public, pg. 805
ICEE-USA CORP.—J & J Snack Foods Corporation; U.S. Public, pg. 916
INTERNATIONAL HOME FOODS INC.—Hicks, Muse, Tate & Furst Inc.; U.S. Private, pg. 526
J & J SNACK FOODS CORPORATION; U.S. Public, pg. 916
THE JEL SERT CO.; U.S. Private, pg. 585
JUS-ROL LTD.—Diageo Plc; Int'l, pg. 411
KERRY INGREDIENTS UK LTD.—Kerry Group PLC; Int'l, pg. 732
KEYSTONE FOODS CORPORATION; U.S. Private, pg. 619
LANCASTER COLONY CORPORATION; U.S. Public, pg. 976
LEVER S.A.—Unilever Plc; Int'l, pg. 1438
LITTLE LADY FOODS, INC.; U.S. Private, pg. 671
LONDON BREWERY—Interbrew S.A.; Int'l, pg. 679
MCCAIN ALIMENTAIRE SA—McCain Foods Limited; Int'l, pg. 850
MCCAIN ARGENTINA SA—McCain Foods Limited; Int'l, pg. 850
MCCAIN-ELLIOS FOOD INC.—McCain Foods Limited; Int'l, pg. 850
MCCAIN ESPANA S.A. (SPAIN)—McCain Foods Limited; Int'l, pg. 850
MCCAIN FOODS (AUSTRALIA) PTY, LTD.—McCain Foods Limited; Int'l, pg. 850
MCCAIN FOODS BELGIUM N.V. (BELGIUM)—McCain Foods Limited; Int'l, pg. 850
MCCAIN FOODS (GB) LIMITED—McCain Foods Limited; Int'l, pg. 850
MCCAIN FOODS HOLLAND B.V. (THE NETHERLANDS)—McCain Foods Limited; Int'l, pg. 850
MCCAIN FOODS INC.—McCain Foods Limited; Int'l, pg. 850
MCCAIN FOODS LIMITED; Int'l, pg. 850
NESTLE FROZEN, REFRIGERATED, AND ICE CREAM COMPANIES—Nestle S.A.; Int'l, pg. 918
NESTLE S.A.; Int'l, pg. 915
NEW YORK FROZEN FOODS, INC.—Lancaster Colony Corporation; U.S. Public, pg. 977
NOZAKI AMERICA, INC.—Nozaki & Company Ltd.; Int'l, pg. 990
NOZAKI & COMPANY LTD.; Int'l, pg. 990
OH BOY CORPORATION; U.S. Private, pg. 812
ON-COR FROZEN FOODS INC.; U.S. Private, pg. 817
OVERHILL FARMS, INC.—Polyphase Corporation; U.S. Public, pg. 1315
PENOBSCOT FROZEN FOODS, INC.; U.S. Private, pg. 850
PEPPERIDGE FARM, INCORPORATED—Campbell Soup Company; U.S. Public, pg. 299
PHARMACIA & UPJOHN, INC.; Int'l, pg. 1047
PILLSBURY CO.—Diageo Plc; Int'l, pg. 411
THE PILLSBURY COMPANY—Diageo Plc; Int'l, pg. 411
THE QUAKER OATS COMPANY; U.S. Public, pg. 1347
THE QUAKER OATS CO. OF CANADA LTD.—The Quaker Oats Company; U.S. Public, pg. 1348
RECKITT & COLMAN INC.—Reckitt & Colman plc; Int'l, pg. 1090
REDI-SERVE FOODS—On-Cor Frozen Foods Inc.; U.S. Private, pg. 817
AB RESTAURANGFRYS—Nestle S.A.; Int'l, pg. 920
RICH PRODUCTS CORP.; U.S. Private, pg. 928
ROMAN MEAL COMPANY; U.S. Private, pg. 942
SARA LEE BAKERY—Sara Lee Corporation; U.S. Public, pg. 1433
SNOW BRAND PILLSBURY INC.—Diageo Plc; Int'l, pg. 411
TOMBSTONE PIZZA CORPORATION—Philip Morris Companies Inc.; U.S. Public, pg. 1288
TOTINO'S/WELLSTON—Diageo Plc; Int'l, pg. 411
UB FROZEN & CHILLED LIMITED—United Biscuits (Holdings) Plc; Int'l, pg. 1442
UNIFROST NAHRUNGSMITTEL GES. M.B.H.—Unilever Plc; Int'l, pg. 1439
WEIGHT WATCHERS GOURMET FOOD COMPANY—H.J. Heinz Company; U.S. Public, pg. 806
WINDSOR QUALITY FOOD CO., LTD.; U.S. Private, pg. 1182

2041 — FLOUR & OTHER GRAIN MILL PRODUCTS

ADM MILLING CO.—Archer Daniels Midland Company (ADM); U.S. Public, pg. 128
ALICORP S.A.; Int'l, pg. 57
THE ANDERSONS INCORPORATED; U.S. Public, pg. 111
ARCHER DANIELS MIDLAND COMPANY (ADM); U.S. Public, pg. 127
ARROWHEAD MILLS, INC.; U.S. Private, pg. 86
AVANA BAKERIES LTD.—Tomkins PLC; Int'l, pg. 1396
BOCM PAULS LIMITED—Harrisons & Crosfield plc; Int'l, pg. 598
BARTLETT AND COMPANY; U.S. Private, pg. 118
BAY STATE MILLING CO.; U.S. Private, pg. 124
BESTFOODS; U.S. Public, pg. 223
BIOTER-BIONA S.A.—ConAgra, Inc.; U.S. Public, pg. 429
F.M. BROWN SONS, INC.; U.S. Private, pg. 174
BURNS, PHILP & COMPANY LIMITED; Int'l, pg. 236
CPC/AJI (HONG KONG) LTD.—Bestfoods; U.S. Public, pg. 225
CPC/AJI (SINGAPORE) PTE. LTD.—Bestfoods; U.S. Public, pg. 225
CARGILL; U.S. Private, pg. 210
CARGILL FLOUR DIV.—Cargill; U.S. Private, pg. 210
CHEIL FOODS & CHEMICALS INC.—Samsung Group; Int'l, pg. 1181
CONAGRA-EUROPE, INC.—ConAgra, Inc.; U.S. Public, pg. 429
CONAGRA GROCERY PRODUCTS PACKAGING COMPANY—ConAgra, Inc.; U.S. Public, pg. 428
CONAGRA, INC.; U.S. Public, pg. 425
CONAGRA TRADING & PROCESSING COMPANIES—ConAgra, Inc.; U.S. Public, pg. 428
CORN PRODUCTS INTERNATIONAL, INC.; U.S. Public, pg. 447
COUNTRY PRODUCTS GROUP—Agway, Inc.; U.S. Private, pg. 27
CRESTAR FOODS INC.—H.J. Heinz Company; U.S. Public, pg. 805
DARWIN BAKERY PTY. LTD.—Q.U.F. Industries Ltd.; Int'l, pg. 1074
DOVER FLOUR MILLS—Dover Industries Limited; Int'l, pg. 417
DOVER INDUSTRIES LIMITED; Int'l, pg. 417
DOVER MILLS LIMITED—Dover Industries Limited; Int'l, pg. 417
E & D GRAIN MARKETING CO—EDI International, Inc.; U.S. Private, pg. 353
EDI INTERNATIONAL, INC.; U.S. Private, pg. 353
ECKES AG; Int'l, pg. 432
FIROILLO A. CO. INC.—Seaboard Corporation; U.S. Public, pg. 1449
FISHER COMPANIES INC.; U.S. Public, pg. 647
FISHER MILLS, INC.—Fisher Companies Inc.; U.S. Public, pg. 648
FRUEN OAT MILLING CO.—ConAgra, Inc.; U.S. Public, pg. 428
GENERAL MILLS CANADA INC.—General Mills, Inc.; U.S. Public, pg. 718
GENERAL MILLS, INC.; U.S. Public, pg. 717
GOLD MEDAL DIV.—General Mills, Inc.; U.S. Public, pg. 718
GOOCH FOODS, INC.—Archer Daniels Midland Company (ADM); U.S. Public, pg. 128
GOODMAN FIELDER MILLS (NZ) LTD.—Goodman Fielder Limited; Int'l, pg. 556
GRAIN FLOUR MILLING CO.—ConAgra, Inc.; U.S. Public, pg. 428
GRAND METROPOLITAN PLC—Diageo Plc; Int'l, pg. 408
GRANDE SEMOULERIE DE L'OUEST A GOND-PONTOUVRE—Grands Moulins de Paris S.A.; Int'l, pg. 556
GRANDS MOULINS DE PARIS S.A.; Int'l, pg. 556
GREEN FLOUR MILLS LIMITED—Harrisons & Crosfield plc; Int'l, pg. 598
HODGSON MILL, INC.—Siemer Milling Company; U.S. Private, pg. 998
HOPKINSVILLE MILLING CO.; U.S. Private, pg. 538
ROBERT HUTCHISON LIMITED—Harrisons & Crosfield plc; Int'l, pg. 598
INDUSTRIAL DIVISION—Grist Mill Company; U.S. Public, pg. 766
INTERNATIONAL MULTIFOODS CORPORATION; U.S. Public, pg. 900
JAMAICA FLOUR MILLS, LTD.—Diageo Plc; Int'l, pg. 411
KHONG GUAN FLOUR MILLING LIMITED; Int'l, pg. 732
KING MILLING COMPANY; U.S. Private, pg. 621
LOSURDO FOODS, INC.; U.S. Private, pg. 677
THE B. MANISCHEWITZ COMPANY; U.S. Private, pg. 699
MAPLE LEAF FOODS INC.; Int'l, pg. 841
MCDOUGALLS CATERING FOODS LIMITED—Tomkins PLC; Int'l, pg. 1396
MENEBA MEEL B.V.—Goodman Fielder Limited; Int'l, pg. 555
MENEBA N.V.—Goodman Fielder Limited; Int'l, pg. 555
MIDWEST GRAIN PRODUCTS, INC.; U.S. Public, pg. 1111
MINN-DAK GROWERS, LTD.; U.S. Private, pg. 750
MINOTERIE COOP RIVAZ—Coop Switzerland; Int'l, pg. 330
MOLINAS DE PUERTO RICO—ConAgra, Inc.; U.S. Public, pg. 426
MOLINOS CARACAS MARACAIBO S.A.—Diageo Plc; Int'l, pg. 411
MOLINOS EL SALVADOR, S.A.—Diageo Plc; Int'l, pg. 411
MOLINOS MODERNOS, S.A.—Diageo Plc; Int'l, pg. 411
MOLINOS NACIONALES, C.A. (VENEZUELA)—International Multifoods Corporation; U.S. Public, pg. 901
NABISCO INC.—RJR Nabisco Holdings Corp.; U.S. Public, pg. 1355
NEWLY WEDS FOODS INC.; U.S. Private, pg. 796
NORTH DAKOTA MILL & ELEVATOR ASSOCIATION; U.S. Private, pg. 804
NORTHERN FOODS PLC; Int'l, pg. 967
PASTA FOODS LIMITED—Tomkins PLC; Int'l, pg. 1396
PAULS PLC—Harrisons & Crosfield plc; Int'l, pg. 598
THE PILLSBURY COMPANY—Diageo Plc; Int'l, pg. 411
PILMICO—Diageo Plc; Int'l, pg. 411
PIONEER FLOUR MILLS; U.S. Private, pg. 866
PRESIDENT ENTERPRISES CORP.; Int'l, pg. 1068
QUAKER OATS B.V.—The Quaker Oats Company; U.S. Public, pg. 1348
THE QUAKER OATS COMPANY; U.S. Public, pg. 1347
QUAKER OATS LIMITED—The Quaker Oats Company; U.S. Public, pg. 1348
RANK HOVIS LIMITED—Tomkins PLC; Int'l, pg. 1396
RANKS HOVIS MCDOUGALL LIMITED—Tomkins PLC; Int'l, pg. 1395
AB RESTAURANGFRYS—Nestle S.A.; Int'l, pg. 920
ROBIN HOOD MULTIFOODS INC.—International Multifoods Corporation; U.S. Public, pg. 901
ROMAN MEAL COMPANY; U.S. Private, pg. 942
ROUSH PRODUCTS CO., INC.—Diageo Plc; Int'l, pg. 411
SEABOARD CORPORATION; U.S. Public, pg. 1448
SEABOARD FLOUR CORPORATION—Seaboard Corporation; U.S. Public, pg. 1449
SHENANDOAH MILLS, INC.; U.S. Private, pg. 992
SIEMER MILLING COMPANY; U.S. Private, pg. 998
SMITHS FLOUR MILLS LTD.—Northern Foods plc; Int'l, pg. 968
SOCIETE TOULOUSAINE DE MINOTERIE A REVEL—Grands Moulins de Paris S.A.; Int'l, pg. 557
SODEVA—Grands Moulins de Paris S.A.; Int'l, pg. 557
SOO LINE MILLS LIMITED—George Weston Limited; Int'l, pg. 1495
SOVEX NATURAL FOODS—McKee Foods Corporation; U.S. Private, pg. 723
SPANGLES' FLOUR MILLS OF MT. JOY—Wilkins-Rogers Incorporated; U.S. Private, pg. 1176
SPILLERS MILLING—Dalgety Plc; Int'l, pg. 376
TATA OIL & MILLS COMPANY—Unilever Plc; Int'l, pg. 1437
THAI FOOD COATINGS—Newly Weds Foods Inc.; U.S. Private, pg. 797
THE UHLMANN CO.; U.S. Private, pg. 1115
WESSANEN MEEL B.V.—Koninklijke BolsWessanen nv; Int'l, pg. 751
GEORGE WESTON LIMITED; Int'l, pg. 1494
WILKINS-ROGERS INCORPORATED; U.S. Private, pg. 1176

2043 — CEREAL BREAKFAST FOODS

ALIMENTOS KELLOGG S.A.—Kellogg Company; U.S. Public, pg. 947
ALTANA AG; Int'l, pg. 65
BEECH-NUT NUTRITION CORPORATION—Ralcorp Holdings Inc.; U.S. Public, pg. 1359
BIG 'G' DIV.—General Mills, Inc.; U.S. Public, pg. 718
BLUEBIRD FOODS LTD—Goodman Fielder Limited; Int'l, pg. 556
CFP FOODS—Saskatchewan Wheat Pool; Int'l, pg. 1195
CSM N.V.; Int'l, pg. 243
CEREAL PARTNERS WORLDWIDE—General Mills, Inc.; U.S. Public, pg. 718
CEREAL PARTNERS WORLDWIDE—Nestle S.A.; Int'l, pg. 916
CHESHIRE WHOLEFOODS PLC—Koninklijke BolsWessanen nv; Int'l, pg. 752
CONAGRA FRUEN MILLING CO.—ConAgra, Inc.; U.S. Public, pg. 428
CONAGRA GROCERY PRODUCTS PACKAGING COMPANY—ConAgra, Inc.; U.S. Public, pg. 428
DELICIA B.V.—Koninklijke BolsWessanen nv; Int'l, pg. 752
DONG-SUH FOODS CORPORATION; Int'l, pg. 416
ELABORADORA ARGENTINA DE CEREALES, S.A.—The Quaker Oats Company; U.S. Public, pg. 1348
FOOD SPECIALTIES LTD.—Nestle S.A.; Int'l, pg. 920
FRUEN OAT MILLING CO.—ConAgra, Inc.; U.S. Public, pg. 428
GAGE FOOD PRODUCTS COMPANY—DG Foods, LLC; U.S. Private, pg. 301
GENERAL MILLS, INC.; U.S. Public, pg. 717
GERBER PRODUCTS COMPANY—Novartis AG; Int'l, pg. 973
GERBER PRODUCTS DIVISION-BABY CARE—Novartis AG; Int'l, pg. 973
GERBER PRODUCTS, S.A. DE C.V.—Novartis AG; Int'l, pg. 973
GRIST MILL COMPANY; U.S. Public, pg. 766
GROCERY DIVISION—Grist Mill Company; U.S. Public, pg. 766
H&C CEREALES S.A.—Koninklijke BolsWessanen nv; Int'l, pg. 752
INDUSTRIAL DIVISION—Grist Mill Company; U.S. Public, pg. 766
ISRAEL EDIBLE PRODUCTS LTD.—Bestfoods; U.S. Public, pg. 225
KELLOGG (AUST.) PROPRIETARY LTD.—Kellogg Company; U.S. Public, pg. 947

KELLOGG BRASIL & CIA—Kellogg Company; U.S. Public, pg. 947
KELLOGG CANADA INC.—Kellogg Company; U.S. Public, pg. 947
KELLOGG COMPANY; U.S. Public, pg. 947
KELLOGG COMPANY ARGENTINA S.A.C.I.F.—Kellogg Company; U.S. Public, pg. 947
KELLOGG COMPANY OF GREAT BRITAIN LTD.—Kellogg Company; U.S. Public, pg. 947
KELLOGG COMPANY OF SOUTH AFRICA (PROPRIETARY) LIMITED—Kellogg Company; U.S. Public, pg. 947
KELLOGG DE COLOMBIA S.A.—Kellogg Company; U.S. Public, pg. 947
KELLOGG DE MEXICO S.A. DE C.V.—Kellogg Company; U.S. Public, pg. 948
KELLOGG (DEUTSCHLAND) GESELLSCHAFT MIT BESCHRANKTER HARTUNG (GMBH)—Kellogg Company; U.S. Public, pg. 948
KELLOGG ESPANA, S.A.—Kellogg Company; U.S. Public, pg. 948
KELLOGG (JAPAN) K.K.—Kellogg Company; U.S. Public, pg. 948
KELLOGG NORTH AMERICA DIVISION—Kellogg Company; U.S. Public, pg. 947
KELLOGG SALES COMPANY—Kellogg Company; U.S. Public, pg. 947
KELLOGG USA INC.—Kellogg Company; U.S. Public, pg. 947
KELLOGG'S PRODUITS ALIMENTAIRES, S.A.—Kellogg Company; U.S. Public, pg. 948
KERRY INGREDIENTS, BROXBURN—Kerry Group PLC; Int'l, pg. 732
KERRY INGREDIENTS UK LTD.—Kerry Group PLC; Int'l, pg. 732
C.H. KNORR NAHRUNGSMITTELFABRIK, GES. MB H.—Bestfoods; U.S. Public, pg. 225
KRAFT CANADA INC.—Philip Morris Companies Inc.; U.S. Public, pg. 1288
KRAFT FOODS, INC.—Philip Morris Companies Inc.; U.S. Public, pg. 1287
KRAFT FOODS INC.—Philip Morris Companies Inc.; U.S. Public, pg. 1288
LANCASTER PLANT-KELLOGG U.S.A.—Kellogg Company; U.S. Public, pg. 947
MALT-O-MEAL COMPANY; U.S. Private, pg. 699
MCCAIN FOODS LIMITED; Int'l, pg. 850
MEMPHIS PLANT-KELLOGG U.S.A.—Kellogg Company; U.S. Public, pg. 947
MILUPA A.G.—Nutricia BV; Int'l, pg. 991
MILUPA LTD.—Nutricia BV; Int'l, pg. 991
MILUPA S.A.—Nutricia BV; Int'l, pg. 991
NABISCO INC.—RJR Nabisco Holdings Corp.; U.S. Public, pg. 1355
NESTLE S.A.; Int'l, pg. 915
NHONG SHIM KELLOGG CO. LTD.—Kellogg Company; U.S. Public, pg. 948
NORDISK KELLOGGS A/S—Kellogg Company; U.S. Public, pg. 948
OMAHA PLANT-KELLOGG USA—Kellogg Company; U.S. Public, pg. 947
PRESCO INTERNATIONAL B.V.—Koninklijke BolsWessanen nv; Int'l, pg. 752
PRODUCTOS GERBER DE CENTROAMERICA, S.A.—Novartis AG; Int'l, pg. 973
PRODUCTOS QUAKER, C.A.—The Quaker Oats Company; U.S. Public, pg. 1348
PRODUCTOS QUAKER, S.A.—The Quaker Oats Company; U.S. Public, pg. 1348
PURINA GROCERY PRODUCTS GROUP—Ralston Purina Company; U.S. Public, pg. 1360
THE QUAKER OATS COMPANY; U.S. Public, pg. 1347
THE QUAKER OATS CO. OF CANADA LTD.—The Quaker Oats Company; U.S. Public, pg. 1348
RJR NABISCO HOLDINGS CORP.; U.S. Public, pg. 1354
RALSTON PURINA COMPANY; U.S. Public, pg. 1359
STADTMUHLE CMZ ZURICH—Coop Switzerland; Int'l, pg. 330
TELFORD FOODS LTD.—Koninklijke BolsWessanen nv; Int'l, pg. 753
THOMI & FRANCK AG—Nestle S.A.; Int'l, pg. 916
WANDER AG—Novartis AG; Int'l, pg. 972
THE WEETABIX COMPANY, INC.—Weetabix Limited; Int'l, pg. 1488
WEETABIX LIMITED; Int'l, pg. 1488
WEETABIX OF CANADA (MFG.) LIMITED—Weetabix Limited; Int'l, pg. 1488
WESSANEN MEEL B.V.—Koninklijke BolsWessanen nv; Int'l, pg. 751

2044 — RICE MILLING

AMERICAN RICE INC.—Erly Industries, Inc.; U.S. Public, pg. 591
CARGILL; U.S. Private, pg. 210
COMET RICE, INC.-STUTTGART—Erly Industries, Inc.; U.S. Public, pg. 591
COMET VENTURES, INC.—Erly Industries, Inc.; U.S. Public, pg. 591
CORMIER RICE MILLING COMPANY, INC.; U.S. Private, pg. 276
ERLY INDUSTRIES, INC.; U.S. Public, pg. 591
EURYZA BV—CSM N.V.; Int'l, pg. 243
EURYZA INTERNATIONAL AG—CSM N.V.; Int'l, pg. 244
EURYZA REIS GMBH—CSM N.V.; Int'l, pg. 244
INDUSTRIAL DIVISION—Grist Mill Company; U.S. Public, pg. 766
KOREA BORDEN CHUSIK HOESA—Borden, Inc.; U.S. Private, pg. 159
MARS, INCORPORATED; U.S. Private, pg. 707
MOLINOS NACIONALES, C.A. (VENEZUELA)—International Multifoods Corporation; U.S. Public, pg. 901
PRESIDENT ENTERPRISES CORP.; Int'l, pg. 1068
PRODUCERS RICE MILL INC.; U.S. Private, pg. 888
PRODUCTOS QUAKER, C.A.—The Quaker Oats Company; U.S. Public, pg. 1348
RICE GROWERS ASSOCIATION OF CALIFORNIA; U.S. Private, pg. 927
RICELAND FOODS, INC.; U.S. Private, pg. 928
RIVIANA FOODS INC.; U.S. Public, pg. 1392
UNCLE BEN'S, INC.—Mars, Incorporated; U.S. Private, pg. 707

2045 — PREPARED FLOUR MIXES & DOUGHS

ALL-AMERICAN SYSTEMS—NCI Building Systems, Inc.; U.S. Public, pg. 1146
J.W. ALLEN & COMPANY; U.S. Private, pg. 37
BAUKJE BEHEER BV—CSM N.V.; Int'l, pg. 243
BLUEBIRD FOODS LTD—Goodman Fielder Limited; Int'l, pg. 556
BRIDGFORD FOODS CORPORATION; U.S. Public, pg. 252
BURNS, PHILP & COMPANY LIMITED; Int'l, pg. 236
CSM N.V.; Int'l, pg. 243
CARAVAN PRODUCTS COMPANY, INC.; U.S. Private, pg. 208
CHELSEA MILLING CO.; U.S. Private, pg. 231
CONTINENTAL MILLS, INC.; U.S. Private, pg. 269
D H FOOD CO.—The Procter & Gamble Company; U.S. Public, pg. 1331
DARWIN BAKERY PTY. LTD.—Q.U.F. Industries Ltd.; Int'l, pg. 1074
DAWN FOOD PRODUCTS, INC.; U.S. Private, pg. 316
DIAGEO PLC; Int'l, pg. 408
FLEISCHMANN'S YEAST—Burns, Philp & Company Limited; Int'l, pg. 237
4C FOODS CORPORATION; U.S. Private, pg. 421
GENERAL MILLS, INC.; U.S. Public, pg. 717
GILSTER MARY LEE CORP.; U.S. Private, pg. 455
GOLD MEDAL DIV.—General Mills, Inc.; U.S. Public, pg. 718
GOODMAN FIELDER LIMITED; Int'l, pg. 555
GOODMAN FIELDER MILLS LTD.—Goodman Fielder Limited; Int'l, pg. 555
GRAND METROPOLITAN PLC—Diageo Plc; Int'l, pg. 408
HENRY & HENRY, INC.—CSM N.V.; Int'l, pg. 244
HINES-PARK FOODS, INC.—The Procter & Gamble Company; U.S. Public, pg. 1331
HONIG MERKARTIKELEN B.V.—CSM N.V.; Int'l, pg. 244
HUBBARD FEEDS INC.—Ridley Canada Limited; Int'l, pg. 1116
INTERNATIONAL MULTIFOODS CORPORATION; U.S. Public, pg. 900
KENLAKE FOODS—The Kroger Co.; U.S. Public, pg. 967
KIRKLAND & ROSE LTD.—CSM N.V.; Int'l, pg. 244
THE KROGER CO.; U.S. Public, pg. 967
THE B. MANISCHEWITZ COMPANY; U.S. Private, pg. 699
MOLINOS CARACAS MARACAIBO S.A.—Diageo Plc; Int'l, pg. 411
MOLINOS NACIONALES, C.A. (VENEZUELA)—International Multifoods Corporation; U.S. Public, pg. 901
NEWLY WEDS FOODS INC.; U.S. Private, pg. 796
NIPPON FLOUR MILLS CO., LTD.—Newly Weds Foods Inc.; U.S. Private, pg. 797
NORTH AMERICA FOODS—International Multifoods Corporation; U.S. Public, pg. 901
PAPUA-NEW GUINEA DIVISION—Goodman Fielder Limited; Int'l, pg. 556
PARK FOODS L.P.; U.S. Private, pg. 839
PARTY PAC DIV.—Gilster Mary Lee Corp.; U.S. Private, pg. 455
THE PILLSBURY COMPANY—Diageo Plc; Int'l, pg. 411
PRESCO INTERNATIONAL B.V.—Koninklijke BolsWessanen nv; Int'l, pg. 752
PROCTER & GAMBLE FOOD PRODUCTS DIV.—The Procter & Gamble Company; U.S. Public, pg. 1331
PY-O-MY DIV.—Gilster Mary Lee Corp.; U.S. Private, pg. 455
THE QUAKER OATS COMPANY; U.S. Public, pg. 1347
RHM INGREDIENTS, LTD.—Newly Weds Foods Inc.; U.S. Private, pg. 797
READY BAKE FOODS INC.—George Weston Limited; Int'l, pg. 1495
ROBIN HOOD MULTIFOODS INC.—International Multifoods Corporation; U.S. Public, pg. 901
SMITHS FLOUR MILLS LTD.—Northern Foods plc; Int'l, pg. 968
SPECIALTY BRANDS—Burns, Philp & Company Limited; Int'l, pg. 237
THAI FOOD COATINGS—Newly Weds Foods Inc.; U.S. Private, pg. 797
THE UNCLE TOBY'S COMPANY LTD.—Goodman Fielder Limited; Int'l, pg. 555
WESTCO PRODUCTS, INC.—CSM N.V.; Int'l, pg. 244

2046 — WET CORN MILLING

ADM CORN PROCESSING DIVISION—Archer Daniels Midland Company (ADM); U.S. Public, pg. 127
AKZO CHEMICALS INC.—Akzo Nobel N.V.; Int'l, pg. 47
AMYLUM N.V.—Tate & Lyle PLC; Int'l, pg. 1357
ARCHER DANIELS MIDLAND COMPANY (ADM); U.S. Public, pg. 127
BEST FOODS CANADA, INC.—Bestfoods; U.S. Public, pg. 224
BEST FOODS SAUDI ARABIA CO. LTD.—Bestfoods; U.S. Public, pg. 225
BESTFOODS; U.S. Public, pg. 223
CPC/AJI (SINGAPORE) PTE. LTD.—Bestfoods; U.S. Public, pg. 225
CPC ASIA CONSUMER FOODS DIVISION—Bestfoods; U.S. Public, pg. 224
CPC JAPAN, LTD.—Corn Products International, Inc.; U.S. Public, pg. 447
CARGILL; U.S. Private, pg. 210
CASCO INC.—Corn Products International, Inc.; U.S. Public, pg. 448
CERESTAR HOLDING B.V.—Compart SpA; Int'l, pg. 324
CLEARWATER MILL, INC.—Fleming Companies, Inc.; U.S. Public, pg. 653
CORN PRODUCTS INTERNATIONAL, INC.; U.S. Public, pg. 447
CORN PRODUCTS NORTH AMERICA DIV.—Corn Products International, Inc.; U.S. Public, pg. 448
CUSTOM FARM SEED—Unilever Plc; Int'l, pg. 1435
ERIDANIA BEGHIN-SAY GROUP—Compart SpA; Int'l, pg. 324
FOOD OILS CORPORATION—Trinidad/Benham Corp.; U.S. Private, pg. 1103
GRAIN PROCESSING CORP.—Varied Investments, Inc.; U.S. Private, pg. 1134
IPOK—Corn Products International, Inc.; U.S. Public, pg. 447
OY KATIONI AB—Raisio Group; Int'l, pg. 1085
LATENSTEIN ZETMEEL B.V.—Koninklijke BolsWessanen nv; Int'l, pg. 752
LEVER S.A.—Unilever Plc; Int'l, pg. 1438
LOU ANA FOODS, INC.—Mitsui & Co., Ltd.; Int'l, pg. 879
MONTEDISON S.P.A.—Compart SpA; Int'l, pg. 324
NACAN PRODUCTS LTD.—Unilever Plc; Int'l, pg. 1436
NEW ZEALAND STARCH—Goodman Fielder Limited; Int'l, pg. 555
NIHON SHOKUHIN KAKO CO., LTD.—Corn Products International, Inc.; U.S. Public, pg. 447
PAULS PLC—Harrisons & Crosfield plc; Int'l, pg. 598
PENFORD CORP.; U.S. Public, pg. 1269
PENFORD PRODUCTS—Penford Corp.; U.S. Public, pg. 1269
PENFORD PRODUCTS CO.—Penford Corp.; U.S. Public, pg. 1269
PRESCO INTERNATIONAL B.V.—Koninklijke BolsWessanen nv; Int'l, pg. 752
PRODUCTOS DE MAIZ S.A.—Corn Products International, Inc.; U.S. Public, pg. 448
QUAKER OATS B.V.—The Quaker Oats Company; U.S. Public, pg. 1348
RAISIO GROUP; Int'l, pg. 1085
RAISIO GROUP PLC—Raisio Group; Int'l, pg. 1085
RAISIO, INC.—Raisio Group; Int'l, pg. 1086
RAISIO SVENSKA AB—Raisio Group; Int'l, pg. 1086
ALFONZO RIVAS CO., C.A.—Corn Products International, Inc.; U.S. Public, pg. 447
ROQUETTE AMERICA INC.; U.S. Private, pg. 944
A.E. STALEY MANUFACTURING CO.—Tate & Lyle PLC; Int'l, pg. 1356
STAMFORD FOOD INDUSTRIES SDN. BERHAD—Corn Products International, Inc.; U.S. Public, pg. 447
STARCH AUSTRALASIA—Bestfoods; U.S. Public, pg. 224
STARCH AUSTRALIA—Goodman Fielder Limited; Int'l, pg. 555

2047 — DOG & CAT FOOD

ALLIED FOODS, INC.; U.S. Private, pg. 39
ALPO PET FOODS—Nestle S.A.; Int'l, pg. 917
ALTAIR CORPORATION; U.S. Private, pg. 46
ARCHER DANIELS MIDLAND COMPANY (ADM); U.S. Public, pg. 127
BENCO PET FOODS, INC.—Ralston Purina Company; U.S. Public, pg. 1360
BIOPRODUCTS, INC.; U.S. Private, pg. 145
BLUE SEAL FEEDS, INC.—Varied Investments, Inc.; U.S. Private, pg. 1134
CARGILL; U.S. Private, pg. 210
CARGILL ANIMAL NUTRITION DIV.—Cargill; U.S. Private, pg. 210
CARTER-WALLACE, INC.; U.S. Public, pg. 309
CHAMPION VALLEY FARMS—H.J. Heinz Company; U.S. Public, pg. 806
COLGATE-PALMOLIVE COMPANY; U.S. Public, pg. 397
CONAGRA CONSUMER DIRECT, INC.—ConAgra, Inc.; U.S. Public, pg. 426
CONTINENTAL GRAIN COMPANY; U.S. Private, pg. 268
DCV INC.; U.S. Private, pg. 301
DAD'S PRODUCTS CO., INC.; U.S. Private, pg. 306
DALGETY PLC; Int'l, pg. 376
DALGETY SPILLERS FOODS LTD.—Dalgety Plc; Int'l, pg. 376
DANISCO INGREDIENTS USA, INC.—Danisco A/S; Int'l, pg. 378
DOANE PRODUCTS CO.; U.S. Private, pg. 337
DUCOA L.P.—DCV Inc.; U.S. Private, pg. 301
DUQUESNE-PURINA S.A.—Ralston Purina Company; U.S. Public, pg. 1360
FRISKIES PETCARE DIV.—Nestle S.A.; Int'l, pg. 917
GALLINA BLANCA PURINA—Borden, Inc.; U.S. Private, pg. 159
GALLINA BLANCA PURINA—Ralston Purina Company; U.S. Public, pg. 1360
HARTZ GROUP—The Hartz Mountain Corp.; U.S. Private, pg. 508
HARVEST INDUSTRIES, INC.—Altair Corporation; U.S. Private, pg. 46
H.J. HEINZ COMPANY; U.S. Public, pg. 805
HILL'S PET NUTRITION—Colgate-Palmolive Company; U.S. Public, pg. 397
HILLSDOWN LTD.—Hillsdown Holdings Plc; Int'l, pg. 619
HUBBARD FEEDS INC.—Ridley Canada Limited; Int'l, pg. 1116
A.C. HUMKO—Associated British Foods plc; Int'l, pg. 92
IAMS COMPANY; U.S. Private, pg. 556
INDUSTRIAS PURINA, S.A. DE C.V.—Ralston Purina Company; U.S. Public, pg. 1360
THE JIM DANDY CO., INC.—Nestle S.A.; Int'l, pg. 918
KAL KAN FOODS, INC.—Mars, Incorporated; U.S. Private, pg. 707
KENT FEEDS INC.—Varied Investments, Inc.; U.S. Private, pg. 1134

KERN LIVESTOCK SUPPLEMENT CO., INC.—Altair Corporation; U.S. Private, pg. 46
LAMBERT-KAY DIV.—Carter-Wallace, Inc.; U.S. Public, pg. 310
LIV-A-SNAPS, INC.—Nestle S.A.; Int'l, pg. 917
MFA INCORPORATED; U.S. Private, pg. 686
MANNA PRO CORPORATION; U.S. Private, pg. 700
MARS, INCORPORATED; U.S. Private, pg. 707
MARS PETFOODS (UNISABI)—Mars, Incorporated; U.S. Private, pg. 707
MENU FOODS, INC.; U.S. Private, pg. 731
META FARM—Triple F, Inc.; U.S. Private, pg. 1104
NABISCO INC.—RJR Nabisco Holdings Corp.; U.S. Public, pg. 1355
NATURE'S RECIPE PET FOODS; U.S. Private, pg. 789
NESTLE CANADA INC.—Nestle S.A.; Int'l, pg. 921
NESTLE S.A.; Int'l, pg. 915
NESTLE USA—Nestle S.A.; Int'l, pg. 916
NULAID FOODS; U.S. Private, pg. 809
PANZALIM—Danone Group; Int'l, pg. 381
PET LIFE FOODS, INC.; U.S. Private, pg. 856
PURINA ALIMENTOS LTDA.—Ralston Purina Company; U.S. Public, pg. 1360
RJR NABISCO HOLDINGS CORP.; U.S. Public, pg. 1354
RALSTON PURINA CANADA AGRI-DIVISION—Ralston Purina Company; U.S. Public, pg. 1360
RALSTON PURINA CANADA INC.—Ralston Purina Company; U.S. Public, pg. 1360
RALSTON PURINA COMPANY; U.S. Public, pg. 1359
SPILLERS FOODS—Dalgety Plc; Int'l, pg. 376
STAR-KIST FOODS, INC.—H.J. Heinz Company; U.S. Public, pg. 806
SUPERIOR BRANDS, INC.—Nestle S.A.; Int'l, pg. 917
SVENSKA FODER AB—Cultor Ltd.; Int'l, pg. 350
TENNESSEE FARMERS CO-OP; U.S. Private, pg. 1076
TETRA HEIMTIERBEDARF G.M.B.H.—Warner-Lambert Company; U.S. Public, pg. 1739
TRIUMPH PET INDUSTRIES, INC.; U.S. Private, pg. 1104
W-P MILLING CO., INC.—Altair Corporation; U.S. Private, pg. 46
WARNER-LAMBERT—Warner-Lambert Company; U.S. Public, pg. 1739

2048 — PREPARED FEEDS & FEED INGREDIENTS FOR ANIMALS & FOWLS, EXCEPT DOGS & CATS

ADM CORN PROCESSING DIVISION—Archer Daniels Midland Company (ADM); U.S. Public, pg. 127
ADM PROCESSING DIV.—Archer Daniels Midland Company (ADM); U.S. Public, pg. 127
AG PROCESSING INC., A COOPERATIVE; U.S. Private, pg. 26
AGRILAND COMPANY; U.S. Private, pg. 26
AGROPECUARIA DE GUISSONA, S. COOP. LTDA.; Int'l, pg. 31
AGWAY AGRICULTURAL PRODUCTS (AAP)—Agway, Inc.; U.S. Private, pg. 27
ALIMENTOS BALANCEADOS PILGRIM'S PRIDE—Pilgrim's Pride Corporation; U.S. Public, pg. 1296
ALTAIR CORPORATION; U.S. Private, pg. 46
AMERICAN NUTRITION, INC.; U.S. Private, pg. 60
ANIMAL NUTRITION DIV.—Continental Grain Company; U.S. Private, pg. 268
ARCHER DANIELS MIDLAND COMPANY (ADM); U.S. Public, pg. 127
AVICOLA PILGRIM'S PRIDE DE MEXICO, S.A. DE C.V.—Pilgrim's Pride Corporation; U.S. Public, pg. 1296
AYRSHIRE LAND COMPANY—Cyprus Amax Minerals Company; U.S. Public, pg. 471
BOCM SILCOCK LTD.—Unilever Plc; Int'l, pg. 1434
BP AMERICA INC.—The British Petroleum Company P.L.C.; Int'l, pg. 220
BAKER COMMODITIES, INC.; U.S. Private, pg. 111
H.J. BAKER & BRO., INC.; U.S. Private, pg. 112
BEST FOODS CARIBBEAN, INC.—Bestfoods; U.S. Public, pg. 224
BIOKYOWA INC.—Kyowa Hakko Kogyo Company, Ltd.; Int'l, pg. 778
BIOPRODUCTS, INC.; U.S. Private, pg. 145
BIOTER-BIONA S.A.—ConAgra, Inc.; U.S. Public, pg. 429
BLUE SEAL FEEDS, INC.—Varied Investments, Inc.; U.S. Private, pg. 1134
F.M. BROWN SONS, INC.; U.S. Private, pg. 174
BUMBLE BEE SEAFOODS INC.—Hicks, Muse, Tate & Furst Inc.; U.S. Private, pg. 526
CAGLE'S INC.; U.S. Public, pg. 291
CARGILL; U.S. Private, pg. 210
CARGILL ANIMAL NUTRITION DIV.—Cargill; U.S. Private, pg. 210
CARGILL LTD.—Cargill; U.S. Private, pg. 210
CHAMPAIGN LANDMARK, INC.; U.S. Private, pg. 227
CHINA NATIONAL CEREALS, OILS & FOODSTUFFS CORPORATION (COFCO); Int'l, pg. 285
CLEARWATER MILL, INC.—Fleming Companies, Inc.; U.S. Public, pg. 653
COLBORN-DAWES AUSTRALIA (PTY.) LIMITED—Roche Holding Ltd.; Int'l, pg. 1121
COLBORN-DAWES IRELAND LTD.—Roche Holding Ltd.; Int'l, pg. 1121
COLBORN-DAWES JAPAN LTD.—Roche Holding Ltd.; Int'l, pg. 1121
CONAGRA AGRI-PRODUCTS CO.—ConAgra, Inc.; U.S. Public, pg. 426
CONAGRA-EUROPE, INC.—ConAgra, Inc.; U.S. Public, pg. 429
CONAGRA FEED CO.—ConAgra, Inc.; U.S. Public, pg. 428
CONAGRA FEED INGREDIENT—ConAgra, Inc.; U.S. Public, pg. 426
CONAGRA, INC.; U.S. Public, pg. 425
CONAGRA SPAIN—ConAgra, Inc.; U.S. Public, pg. 429
CONASAN, S.A.—ConAgra, Inc.; U.S. Public, pg. 429
COOP SWITZERLAND; Int'l, pg. 329
COUNTRYMARK FEED PLANT—Countrymark Cooperative, Inc.; U.S. Private, pg. 279
CULTOR LTD.; Int'l, pg. 349
DCV INC.; U.S. Private, pg. 301
DAD'S PRODUCTS CO., INC.; U.S. Private, pg. 306
DALGETY PLC; Int'l, pg. 376
DARLING INTERNATIONAL, INC; U.S. Public, pg. 484
DONG YANG ELANCO CO., LTD.—Eli Lilly and Company; U.S. Public, pg. 993
DUCOA L.P.—DCV Inc.; U.S. Private, pg. 301
DUNN NUTRATECH—Archer Daniels Midland Company (ADM); U.S. Public, pg. 128
DUQUESNE-PURINA S.A.—Ralston Purina Company; U.S. Public, pg. 1360
ELANCO ANIMAL HEALTH—Eli Lilly and Company; U.S. Public, pg. 993
ELANCO IHARA K. K.—Eli Lilly and Company; U.S. Public, pg. 993
ELANCO PREMEZCLAS, S.A.—Eli Lilly and Company; U.S. Public, pg. 993
ELANCO QUIMICA LIMITADA—Eli Lilly and Company; U.S. Public, pg. 993
ELANCO S.A.—Eli Lilly and Company; U.S. Public, pg. 993
EVERGREEN MILLS INC.—Varied Investments, Inc.; U.S. Private, pg. 1134
EWOS AB—Cultor Ltd.; Int'l, pg. 349
FARMERS UNION MARKETING & PROCESSING ASSOCIATION; U.S. Private, pg. 395
FARMLAND INDUSTRIES, INC.; U.S. Private, pg. 395
FEDERAL-MOGUL SERVICES—Kyowa Hakko Kogyo Company, Ltd.; Int'l, pg. 778
FEED SERVICE CORP.; U.S. Private, pg. 399
FERMENTACIONES MEXICANAS, S.A. DE C.V. (FERMEX)—Kyowa Hakko Kogyo Company, Ltd.; Int'l, pg. 778
FINNEWOS AQUA OY—Cultor Ltd.; Int'l, pg. 349
FLINT RIVER MILLS; U.S. Private, pg. 413
FOUR-F NUTRITION—Tate & Lyle PLC; Int'l, pg. 1356
FURST-MCNESS COMPANY; U.S. Private, pg. 432
GOLD KIST, INC.; U.S. Private, pg. 459
GOLDEN GEM GROWERS INC.; U.S. Private, pg. 460
GOLDEN SUN FEEDS, INC.—Purina Mills, Inc.; U.S. Private, pg. 895
GOODMAN FIELDER LIMITED; Int'l, pg. 555
GROWMARK, INC.; U.S. Private, pg. 484
HARRISONS & CROSFIELD PLC; Int'l, pg. 598
HARVEST INDUSTRIES, INC.—Altair Corporation; U.S. Private, pg. 46
HARVEST STATE FEED, INC.—Harvest States Cooperatives; U.S. Private, pg. 508
HINDUSTAN LEVER LTD.—Unilever Plc; Int'l, pg. 1437
HOECHST MARION ROUSSEL, INC.—Hoechst Aktiengesellschaft; Int'l, pg. 624
HOLMQUIST GRAIN & LUMBER CO.; U.S. Private, pg. 535
HUBBARD FEEDS INC.—Ridley Canada Limited; Int'l, pg. 1116
HUNT-WESSON, INC.—ConAgra, Inc.; U.S. Public, pg. 428
INDUSTRIAS DE MAIZ Y ALIMENTOS S.A.—Corn Products International, Inc.; U.S. Public, pg. 447
INDUSTRIAS PURINA, S.A. DE C.V.—Ralston Purina Company; U.S. Public, pg. 1360
JAPAN ELANCO COMPANY LIMITED (JELCO)—Eli Lilly and Company; U.S. Public, pg. 994
KENT FEEDS INC.—Varied Investments, Inc.; U.S. Private, pg. 1134
KERN LIVESTOCK SUPPLEMENT CO., INC.—Altair Corporation; U.S. Private, pg. 46
KOUDIJS-WOUDA VOEDERS B.V.—Goodman Fielder Limited; Int'l, pg. 555
KYOWA HAKKO EUROPE GMBH—Kyowa Hakko Kogyo Company, Ltd.; Int'l, pg. 778
KYOWA HAKKO (H.K.) CO., LTD.—Kyowa Hakko Kogyo Company, Ltd.; Int'l, pg. 778
LA HACIENDA S.A. DE C.V.—International Multifoods Corporation; U.S. Public, pg. 901
ELI LILLY AND COMPANY; U.S. Public, pg. 992
MFA INCORPORATED; U.S. Private, pg. 686
MANNA PRO CORPORATION; U.S. Private, pg. 700
MAPLE LEAF FOODS INC.; Int'l, pg. 841
MEIJI SEIKA KAISHA, LTD.; Int'l, pg. 855
MENEBA N.V.—Goodman Fielder Limited; Int'l, pg. 555
META FARM—Triple F, Inc.; U.S. Private, pg. 1104
MID-KANSAS CO-OP ASSOCIATION; U.S. Private, pg. 743
MID-SOUTH MILLING COMPANY, INC.; U.S. Private, pg. 744
MILK SPECIALTIES COMPANY; U.S. Private, pg. 746
MILLTECH—Tate & Lyle PLC; Int'l, pg. 1356
MINN-DAK GROWERS, LTD.; U.S. Private, pg. 750
MIRACLE FEEDS INC.—Furst-McNess Company; U.S. Private, pg. 432
MOLINAS DE PUERTO RICO—ConAgra, Inc.; U.S. Public, pg. 426
MOLINOS NACIONALES, C.A. (VENEZUELA)—International Multifoods Corporation; U.S. Public, pg. 901
MONAS FEED OY AB—Raisio Group; Int'l, pg. 1085
MONTEDISON S.P.A.—Compart SpA; Int'l, pg. 324
MOORMAN'S INC.; U.S. Private, pg. 760
NRV, INC.—Alto Dairy Cooperative; U.S. Private, pg. 47
NESTLE NEDERLAND B.V.—Nestle S.A.; Int'l, pg. 921
NULAID FOODS; U.S. Private, pg. 809
NUTRIUS DAIRY FEED SUPPLEMENTS DIV.—Bioproducts, Inc.; U.S. Private, pg. 145
PCS PHOSPHATE - RALEIGH—Potash Corporation of Saskatchewan Inc.; Int'l, pg. 1064
PAPUA-NEW GUINEA DIVISION—Goodman Fielder Limited; Int'l, pg. 556
PAUL & VINCENT LTD.—Unilever Plc; Int'l, pg. 1438
PET AG INC.—Milk Specialties Company; U.S. Private, pg. 746
PETERS & BROWNES FOODS LTD.; Int'l, pg. 1040
PILGRIM'S PRIDE CORPORATION; U.S. Public, pg. 1296
PRODUCERS CO-OP ASSOCIATION, INC.; U.S. Private, pg. 888
PROTEIN BLENDERS—Ridley Canada Limited; Int'l, pg. 1116
PURINA ALIMENTOS LTDA.—Ralston Purina Company; U.S. Public, pg. 1360
PURINA-HAGE LTD.—Ralston Purina Company; U.S. Public, pg. 1360
PURINA KOREA INC.—Ralston Purina Company; U.S. Public, pg. 1360
PURINA MILLS, INC.; U.S. Private, pg. 895
RAISIO GROUP; Int'l, pg. 1085
RALSTON PURINA CANADA INC.—Ralston Purina Company; U.S. Public, pg. 1360
RALSTON PURINA COMPANY; U.S. Public, pg. 1359
RANCH-WAY FEED INC.; U.S. Private, pg. 908
RANGEN, INC.; U.S. Private, pg. 909
RICHARDS BROTHERS OF MOUNTAIN GROVE; U.S. Private, pg. 928
RIDLEY CANADA LIMITED; Int'l, pg. 1116
ROCCO INC.; U.S. Private, pg. 937
RUMENCO—Tate & Lyle PLC; Int'l, pg. 1356
SF SERVICES; U.S. Private, pg. 956
SAPROPUR, S.A.R.L.—ConAgra, Inc.; U.S. Public, pg. 429
SCHREIER MALTING CO.; U.S. Private, pg. 972
SEABOARD CORPORATION; U.S. Public, pg. 1448
SEABOARD FLOUR CORPORATION—Seaboard Corporation; U.S. Public, pg. 1449
SNOW BRAND SEED CO., LTD.—Snow Brand Milk Products Co. Ltd.; Int'l, pg. 1272
SODEVA—Grands Moulins de Paris S.A.; Int'l, pg. 557
JACOB STERN & SONS, INC.; U.S. Private, pg. 1041
SVENSKA FODER AB—Cultor Ltd.; Int'l, pg. 350
SYNTEX AGRIBUSINESS, INC.—Roche Holding Ltd.; Int'l, pg. 1120
TECHNOSTAAL SCHOUTEN BV—Tate & Lyle PLC; Int'l, pg. 1357
TENNESSEE FARMERS CO-OP; U.S. Private, pg. 1076
TYSON FOODS, INC.; U.S. Public, pg. 1652
UNICORD PUBLIC CO. LTD.; Int'l, pg. 1432
P.T. UNILEVER INDONESIA—Unilever Plc; Int'l, pg. 1439
UNILEVER N.V.—Unilever Plc; Int'l, pg. 1434
UNILEVER PLC; Int'l, pg. 1433
UNITED AGRICULTURAL MERCHANTS LTD.—Unilever Plc; Int'l, pg. 1434
UNITED FEEDS, INC.; U.S. Private, pg. 1122
VAASAMILLS LTD.—Cultor Ltd.; Int'l, pg. 349
VIGORTONE AG PRODUCTS, INC.—Tate & Lyle PLC; Int'l, pg. 1357
W-P MILLING CO., INC.—Altair Corporation; U.S. Private, pg. 46
WESSANEN MEEL B.V.—Koninklijke BolsWessanen nv; Int'l, pg. 751
WEST CENTRAL COOPERATIVE; U.S. Private, pg. 1163
WINDY HILL PET FOOD CO.; U.S. Private, pg. 1182
WINDY HILL PET FOOD CO.—Windy Hill Pet Food Co.; U.S. Private, pg. 1182

2051 — BREAD & OTHER BAKERY PRODUCTS, EXCEPT COOKIES & CRACKERS

ALBRO BAKKERIJEN ZWANENBURG B.V.—Goodman Fielder Limited; Int'l, pg. 555
ALIMENTOS Y PRODUCTOS DE MAIZ S.A.—Corn Products International, Inc.; U.S. Public, pg. 447
ALIVEN S.A.—Corn Products International, Inc.; U.S. Public, pg. 447
ALLGAUER ALPENMILCH A.G.—Nestle S.A.; Int'l, pg. 918
AMANA SOCIETY, INC.; U.S. Private, pg. 48
ANHEUSER-BUSCH COMPANIES, INC.; U.S. Public, pg. 113
APRIL HILL, INC.—Grocers Baking Co.; U.S. Private, pg. 483
ARCHER DANIELS MIDLAND COMPANY (ADM); U.S. Public, pg. 127
AU BON PAIN CO., INC.; U.S. Public, pg. 146
AZTECA FOODS, INCORPORATED; U.S. Private, pg. 104
BAGLEY S.A.—Danone Group; Int'l, pg. 379
BAKERS AS—Orkla A.S.A.; Int'l, pg. 1010
BAKERY & CONFECTIONARY DIVISION—Campbell Soup Company; U.S. Public, pg. 299
BENSON'S, INC.; U.S. Private, pg. 134
BEST BRANDS—Hero; Int'l, pg. 617
BEST FOODS—Bestfoods; U.S. Public, pg. 224
BESTFOODS; U.S. Public, pg. 223
BETTER BAKED FOODS, INC.; U.S. Private, pg. 141
BIMBO S.A.—The Earthgrains Company; U.S. Public, pg. 548
BISCUITERIE MUGUET N.V.—Borden, Inc.; U.S. Private, pg. 159
BISCUITERIE VINCHON-JEANETTE S.A.—Sara Lee Corporation; U.S. Public, pg. 1435
N.V. BISCUITS DELACRE S.A.—Campbell Soup Company; U.S. Public, pg. 300
BORDEX (BELGIUM) N.V.—Borden, Inc.; U.S. Private, pg. 159
BRIDGFORD FOODS CORPORATION; U.S. Public, pg. 252
BRIDGFORD FROZEN-RITE FOODS—Bridgford Foods Corporation; U.S. Public, pg. 252
BRITISH BAKERIES LIMITED—Tomkins PLC; Int'l, pg. 1396
BRITISH BAKERIES (MIDLANDS) LIMITED—Tomkins PLC; Int'l, pg. 1396
BRITISH BAKERIES (SCOTLAND) LIMITED—Tomkins PLC; Int'l, pg. 1396
BUITONI SPA—Nestle S.A.; Int'l, pg. 919
BUNNY BREAD CO., INC.—Flowers Industries, Inc.; U.S. Public, pg. 657
BYRNES & KIEFER COMPANY; U.S. Private, pg. 191
CPC BAKING BUSINESS—Bestfoods; U.S. Public, pg. 224
CPC RUFHAN LIMITED—Bestfoods; U.S. Public, pg. 225
CAMPBELL SOUP COMPANY; U.S. Public, pg. 298
CERTIFIED BAKERS—Fleming Companies, Inc.; U.S. Public, pg. 653

CERTIFIED GROCERS OF CALIFORNIA; *U.S. Private*, pg. 226
CLOVERHILL BAKERY; *U.S. Private*, pg. 247
COMESTIBLES LA ROSA S.A.—Nestle S.A.; *Int'l*, pg. 920
CONSOLIDATED BISCUIT CO.; *U.S. Private*, pg. 265
CORPORATE FOODS LTD.—Maple Leaf Foods Inc.; *Int'l*, pg. 841
COTTONS BREAD BAKERIES—Interstate Bakeries Corporation; *U.S. Public*, pg. 909
CRESTAR FOOD PRODUCTS, INC.—H.J. Heinz Company; *U.S. Public*, pg. 805
CRESTAR FOODS INC.—H.J. Heinz Company; *U.S. Public*, pg. 805
CRESTWOOD BAKERY—Fleming Companies, Inc.; *U.S. Public*, pg. 653
CROWN CONFECTIONERY CO., LTD.; *Int'l*, pg. 348
CULINAR INC.; *Int'l*, pg. 348
DANONE GROUP; *Int'l*, pg. 379
DE GRAAF'S BAKKERIJEN BV—Koninklijke BolsWessanen nv; *Int'l*, pg. 752
DERST BAKING COMPANY, INC.; *U.S. Private*, pg. 326
DIAGEO PLC; *Int'l*, pg. 408
DOLLY MADISON BAKERIES—Interstate Bakeries Corporation; *U.S. Public*, pg. 909
JON DONAIRE DESSERTS, INC.—Suiza Foods Corporation; *U.S. Public*, pg. 1527
DRIEHOEK—Sara Lee Corporation; *U.S. Public*, pg. 1435
THE EARTHGRAINS COMPANY; *U.S. Public*, pg. 547
EDWARDS BAKING CO.; *U.S. Private*, pg. 365
ELI'S CHEESE CAKE COMPANY; *U.S. Private*, pg. 371
ELKES BISCUITS—Northern Foods plc; *Int'l*, pg. 968
EMERALD INDUSTRIES INC.—Flowers Industries, Inc.; *U.S. Public*, pg. 657
EUROPEAN BAKERS, LTD—Flowers Industries, Inc.; *U.S. Public*, pg. 657
EVESHAM FOODS—Northern Foods plc; *Int'l*, pg. 968
FLEMING COMPANY—Fleming Companies, Inc.; *U.S. Public*, pg. 653
FLOWERS BAKING CO. OF GADSDEN, INC.—Flowers Industries, Inc.; *U.S. Public*, pg. 657
FLOWERS INDUSTRIES, INC.; *U.S. Public*, pg. 656
FOUR-S BAKING COMPANY; *U.S. Private*, pg. 422
FRANKLIN BAKING CO., INC.; *U.S. Private*, pg. 424
FRANZ SEATTLE—United States Bakery; *U.S. Private*, pg. 1124
FRUTERA COLOMBIANA S.A.—Corn Products International, Inc.; *U.S. Public*, pg. 447
GAI'S NORTHWEST BAKERIES—United States Bakery; *U.S. Private*, pg. 1124
GEORGE & THOMAS CONE CO.; *U.S. Private*, pg. 448
GERBER PRODUCTS DIVISION-BABY CARE—Novartis AG; *Int'l*, pg. 973
GERBER PRODUCTS, S.A. DE C.V.—Novartis AG; *Int'l*, pg. 973
GONNELLA BAKING CO.; *U.S. Private*, pg. 463
GOODMAN FIELDER LIMITED; *Int'l*, pg. 555
GRAND METROPOLITAN PLC—Diageo Plc; *Int'l*, pg. 408
GRANDMET FOODS UK—Diageo Plc; *Int'l*, pg. 408
GRANNY GOOSE FOODS, INC.; *U.S. Private*, pg. 469
THE GREAT AUSTRALIAN PIE COMPANY PTY. LTD.—Q.U.F. Industries Ltd.; *Int'l*, pg. 1074
GRIST MILL COMPANY; *U.S. Public*, pg. 766
GUNSTONES BAKERY—Northern Foods plc; *Int'l*, pg. 968
HARDIN'S BAKERY, INC.—Flowers Industries, Inc.; *U.S. Public*, pg. 657
HEUDEBERT—Danone Group; *Int'l*, pg. 380
HOLSUM BAKERY, INC.; *U.S. Private*, pg. 536
HOLSUM BREAD BAKERIES—Interstate Bakeries Corporation; *U.S. Public*, pg. 909
HOLSUM OF FORT WAYNE, INC.—Lewis Brothers Bakeries, Inc.; *U.S. Private*, pg. 665
HOSTESS FRITO-LAY CO.—PepsiCo, Inc.; *U.S. Public*, pg. 1277
HUVAL BAKERY, INC.—Flowers Industries, Inc.; *U.S. Public*, pg. 657
INTERSTATE BAKERIES CORPORATION; *U.S. Public*, pg. 909
INTERSTATE BRANDS CORPORATION—Interstate Bakeries Corporation; *U.S. Public*, pg. 909
INTERSTATE CORP.—Interstate Bakeries Corporation; *U.S. Public*, pg. 909
J.M.P. BAKERY CO., INC.; *U.S. Private*, pg. 578
JAEGER BAKING CO.—Specialty Foods Corporation; *U.S. Private*, pg. 1022
KARL JAUS GMBH—Borden, Inc.; *U.S. Private*, pg. 159
KITCHENS OF SARA LEE-UNITED KINGDOM—Sara Lee Corporation; *U.S. Public*, pg. 1434
KLEMME GMBH & GO., K.G.—Borden, Inc.; *U.S. Private*, pg. 160
KLOSTERMAN BAKING COMPANY, INC.; *U.S. Private*, pg. 626
KRAFT FOODS A/S—Philip Morris Companies Inc.; *U.S. Public*, pg. 1290
KRAFT FOODS INC.—Philip Morris Companies Inc.; *U.S. Public*, pg. 1288
KRAFT JACOBS SUCHARD—Philip Morris Companies Inc.; *U.S. Public*, pg. 1290
D. LAZZARONI & C. S.P.A.; *Int'l*, pg. 804
LEISI AG NAHRUNGSMITTELFABRIK—Nestle S.A.; *Int'l*, pg. 916
LENDER'S BAGEL BAKERY—Philip Morris Companies Inc.; *U.S. Public*, pg. 1288
LEPAGE BAKERY, INC.; *U.S. Private*, pg. 660
LEWIS BROTHERS BAKERIES, INC.; *U.S. Private*, pg. 665
THE LONG COMPANY; *U.S. Private*, pg. 674
MANOR BAKERIES LIMITED—Tomkins PLC; *Int'l*, pg. 1396
MAPLE LEAF FOODS INC.; *Int'l*, pg. 841
MARTINO'S BAKERY, INC.; *U.S. Private*, pg. 710
MARTIN'S FAMOUS PASTRY SHOPPES; *U.S. Private*, pg. 710
MARUBENI CORPORATION; *Int'l*, pg. 844
MCCAIN FOODS BELGIUM N.V. (BELGIUM)—McCain Foods Limited; *Int'l*, pg. 850
MCCAIN FOODS LIMITED; *Int'l*, pg. 850
MCGAVIN FOODS LTD.—Maple Leaf Foods Inc.; *Int'l*, pg. 841
MCKEE FOODS CORPORATION; *U.S. Private*, pg. 723
MEIJI BAKING CO., LTD.—Meiji Seika Kaisha, Ltd.; *Int'l*, pg. 855
MEIJI-MCVITIE, LTD.—Meiji Seika Kaisha, Ltd.; *Int'l*, pg. 855
JULIUS MEINL AG; *Int'l*, pg. 856
MEMORY LANE CAKES LTD.—Diageo Plc; *Int'l*, pg. 410
MENEBA N.V.—Goodman Fielder Limited; *Int'l*, pg. 555
MERITA BREAD BAKERIES—Interstate Bakeries Corporation; *U.S. Public*, pg. 909
METZ BAKING COMPANY—Specialty Foods Corporation; *U.S. Private*, pg. 1022
MILLBROOK BREAD BAKERIES—Interstate Bakeries Corporation; *U.S. Public*, pg. 909
MRS. BAIRD'S BAKERIES, INC.; *U.S. Private*, pg. 765
MRS. CUBBISON'S FOODS, INC.—Interstate Bakeries Corporation; *U.S. Public*, pg. 909
MRS. SMITH'S BAKERIES OF PENNSYLVANIA, INC.—Flowers Industries, Inc.; *U.S. Public*, pg. 658
NATIONAL BAKING—Specialty Foods Corporation; *U.S. Private*, pg. 1022
THE NEW BAKERY COMPANY OF OHIO, INC.—Wendy's International Inc.; *U.S. Public*, pg. 1754
ALFRED NICKLES BAKERY, INC.; *U.S. Private*, pg. 799
NISSHO IWAI CORPORATION; *Int'l*, pg. 946
NORTH AMERICA FOODS—International Multifoods Corporation; *U.S. Public*, pg. 901
NORTHERN FOODS PLC; *Int'l*, pg. 967
ORVAL KENT FOOD CO.; *U.S. Private*, pg. 820
P & C FOOD MARKETS, INC.—The Penn Traffic Company; *U.S. Public*, pg. 1270
PAIN JACQUET S.A.; *Int'l*, pg. 1021
PALETHORPES—Northern Foods plc; *Int'l*, pg. 968
PANOFINA AG—Coop Switzerland; *Int'l*, pg. 330
PANZALIM—Danone Group; *Int'l*, pg. 381
PAPUA-NEW GUINEA DIVISION—Goodman Fielder Limited; *Int'l*, pg. 556
PARISIAN BAKERIES—Interstate Bakeries Corporation; *U.S. Public*, pg. 909
PARK CAKES LTD.—Northern Foods plc; *Int'l*, pg. 968
PEPPERIDGE FARM, INCORPORATED—Campbell Soup Company; *U.S. Public*, pg. 299
PIE PIPER PRODUCTS, LTD.—Vienna Sausage Mfg. Co.; *U.S. Private*, pg. 1140
PRESIDENT BAKING-BISHOP DIV.—President Enterprises Corp.; *Int'l*, pg. 1069
PRO-PASTRIES INC.—H.J. Heinz Company; *U.S. Public*, pg. 806
PRODUCTOS ALIMENTICIOS IMPERIAL, S.A.—Diageo Plc; *Int'l*, pg. 411
PRODUCTOS GERBER DE CENTROAMERICA, S.A.—Novartis AG; *Int'l*, pg. 973
PURITAN BAKERY, INC.; *U.S. Private*, pg. 895
QUALITY BAKERS AUSTRALIA LTD.—Goodman Fielder Limited; *Int'l*, pg. 555
QUALITY BAKERS NEDERLAND B.V.—Goodman Fielder Limited; *Int'l*, pg. 555
QUALITY BAKERS OF AMERICA COOPERATIVE, INC.; *U.S. Private*, pg. 898
THE QUALITY BAKERY CO., INC.—Lancaster Colony Corporation; *U.S. Public*, pg. 977
QUALITY NATURALLY FOODS; *U.S. Private*, pg. 899
RALSTON PURINA COMPANY; *U.S. Public*, pg. 1359
RANKS HOVIS MCDOUGALL LIMITED—Tomkins PLC; *Int'l*, pg. 1395
RHODES INTERNATIONAL, INC.; *U.S. Private*, pg. 927
RIPON FOODS, INC.; *U.S. Private*, pg. 931
SAETRE AS—Orkla A.S.A.; *Int'l*, pg. 1011
SAN FRANCISCO FRENCH BREAD COMPANY—Interstate Bakeries Corporation; *U.S. Public*, pg. 909
SCHMIDT BAKING CO., INC.; *U.S. Private*, pg. 970
SCHOTT'S BAKERY, INC.—Flowers Industries, Inc.; *U.S. Public*, pg. 658
SHAKLEE CORPORATION—Yamanouchi Pharmaceutical Co. Ltd.; *Int'l*, pg. 1518
SHIKISHIMA BAKING CO., LTD.; *Int'l*, pg. 1231
STEFANSBACK BACKWAREN GMBH—Borden, Inc.; *U.S. Private*, pg. 160
THE STOP & SHOP COMPANIES, INC.—Koninklijke Ahold NV; *Int'l*, pg. 750
STROEHMANN BAKERIES—George Weston Limited; *Int'l*, pg. 1495
STROEHMANN BAKERIES, L.C.—George Weston Limited; *Int'l*, pg. 1495
THE SWISS COLONY, INC; *U.S. Private*, pg. 1059
T A HOLDINGS LIMITED; *Int'l*, pg. 1334
TASTY BAKING COMPANY; *U.S. Public*, pg. 1561
TAYSTEE BAKERIES—Specialty Foods Corporation; *U.S. Private*, pg. 1022
TRAFFORD PARK BAKERY—Northern Foods plc; *Int'l*, pg. 968
UNCLE B'S BAKERY, INC.; *U.S. Public*, pg. 1664
UNIFERM GMBH & CO.—Royal Gist-Brocades N.V.; *Int'l*, pg. 1143
UNITED BISCUITS ASIA PACIFIC—United Biscuits (Holdings) Plc; *Int'l*, pg. 1442
UNITED BISCUITS (HOLDINGS) PLC; *Int'l*, pg. 1442
VICOM PRODUCTION AND DISTRIBUTION CO.—Vicorp Restaurants, Inc.; *U.S. Public*, pg. 1719
WILHELM WEBER GMBH—Borden, Inc.; *U.S. Private*, pg. 160
WEBER'S BREAD BAKERIES—Interstate Bakeries Corporation; *U.S. Public*, pg. 909
WESTON BAKERIES LIMITED—George Weston Limited; *Int'l*, pg. 1495
WHITE CASTLE BAKERY DIVISION—White Castle System, Inc.; *U.S. Private*, pg. 1172
WILTON INDUSTRIES, INC.; *U.S. Private*, pg. 1181
WINCHELL'S DONUT HOUSES, L.P.—Shato Holdings Ltd.; *Int'l*, pg. 1230
WURZNER DAUERBACKWAREN GMBH; *Int'l*, pg. 1514
ZENIMMO N.V.—Borden, Inc.; *U.S. Private*, pg. 160

2052 — COOKIES & CRACKERS

ANDERSON BAKERY CO., INC.—Amerifoods Inc.; *U.S. Private*, pg. 65
ARCHWAY COOKIES, INC.; *U.S. Private*, pg. 80
ARNI AG—Coop Switzerland; *Int'l*, pg. 329
ARNOTTS LIMITED—Campbell Soup Company; *U.S. Public*, pg. 299
AUSTIN QUALITY FOODS; *U.S. Private*, pg. 100
BAGLEY S.A.—Danone Group; *Int'l*, pg. 379
BAKE-LINE PRODUCTS, INC.—Flowers Industries, Inc.; *U.S. Public*, pg. 657
BAKERY & CONFECTIONARY DIVISION—Campbell Soup Company; *U.S. Public*, pg. 299
BEATRICE CORPORATION—Mrs. Alison's Cookie Company; *U.S. Private*, pg. 765
BELIN/LU—Danone Group; *Int'l*, pg. 380
BESTFOODS; *U.S. Public*, pg. 223
BISCUITERIE BOONE S.A.—Diageo Plc; *Int'l*, pg. 411
N.V. BISCUITS DELACRE S.A.—Campbell Soup Company; *U.S. Public*, pg. 300
BREAD & ROLLS DISTRIBUTION—Campbell Soup Company; *U.S. Public*, pg. 299
BROSSARD—Sara Lee Corporation; *U.S. Public*, pg. 1435
CADBURY SCHWEPPES P.L.C.; *Int'l*, pg. 247
CALIFORNIA PRETZEL COMPANY—GF Industries, Inc.; *U.S. Private*, pg. 434
CAMPBELL SOUP COMPANY; *U.S. Public*, pg. 298
CHIPS-OLW AB—Novartis AG; *Int'l*, pg. 975
COKOLADOVNY—Nestle S.A.; *Int'l*, pg. 922
CONSOLIDATED BISCUIT CO.; *U.S. Private*, pg. 265
CONTINENTAL EUROPE—United Biscuits (Holdings) Plc; *Int'l*, pg. 1442
CRACKIN' GOOD BAKERS—Winn-Dixie Stores, Inc.; *U.S. Public*, pg. 1772
CROWN CONFECTIONERY CO., LTD.; *Int'l*, pg. 348
CULTOR LTD.; *Int'l*, pg. 349
DARE FOODS LIMITED; *Int'l*, pg. 383
DE GRAAF'S BAKKERIJEN BV—Koninklijke BolsWessanen nv; *Int'l*, pg. 752
DESOBRY S.A.—Sara Lee Corporation; *U.S. Public*, pg. 1435
DOVER INDUSTRIES LIMITED; *Int'l*, pg. 417
EMERALD INDUSTRIES INC.—Flowers Industries, Inc.; *U.S. Public*, pg. 657
FAVORITE BRANDS INTERNATIONAL, INC.; *U.S. Private*, pg. 397
FLORIDOR S.A.—Novartis AG; *Int'l*, pg. 972
FOX'S BISCUITS LTD.—Northern Foods plc; *Int'l*, pg. 968
FRANZ SEATTLE—United States Bakery; *U.S. Private*, pg. 1124
FRITO-LAY COMPANY—PepsiCo, Inc.; *U.S. Public*, pg. 1277
GF INDUSTRIES, INC.; *U.S. Private*, pg. 434
GAI'S NORTHWEST BAKERIES—United States Bakery; *U.S. Private*, pg. 1124
GENERAL BISCUITS BELGIE N.V.—Danone Group; *Int'l*, pg. 380
GENERAL BISCUITS ESPANA (GBE)—Danone Group; *Int'l*, pg. 381
GENERAL BISCUITS GMBH (GBG)—Danone Group; *Int'l*, pg. 381
GENERAL BISCUITS NEDERLAND (GBNL)—Danone Group; *Int'l*, pg. 381
GENERAL BISCUITS OSTERREICH (GBO)—Danone Group; *Int'l*, pg. 381
GEORGE & THOMAS CONE CO.; *U.S. Private*, pg. 448
GOLDEN ENTERPRISES INC.; *U.S. Public*, pg. 749
GOODMAN FIELDER LIMITED; *Int'l*, pg. 555
IDEAL WASA A/S—Novartis AG; *Int'l*, pg. 982
INDUSTRIAS PURINA, S.A. DE C.V.—Ralston Purina Company; *U.S. Public*, pg. 1360
INTERBAKE FOODS INC.—George Weston Limited; *Int'l*, pg. 1495
IRISH BISCUITS; *Int'l*, pg. 688
IRISH BISCUITS (N.I.)—Irish Biscuits; *Int'l*, pg. 688
J & J SNACK FOODS CORPORATION; *U.S. Public*, pg. 916
THE JACOB'S BAKERY LTD.—Danone Group; *Int'l*, pg. 381
KEEBLER COMPANY—Flowers Industries, Inc.; *U.S. Public*, pg. 657
KRAFT FOODS A/S—Philip Morris Companies Inc.; *U.S. Public*, pg. 1290
KRAFT FOODS, INC.—Philip Morris Companies Inc.; *U.S. Public*, pg. 1287
KRAFT JACOBS SUCHARD—Philip Morris Companies Inc.; *U.S. Public*, pg. 1290
LANCE, INC.; *U.S. Public*, pg. 977
D. LAZZARONI & C. S.P.A.; *Int'l*, pg. 804
MRS. FIELDS' ORIGINAL COOKIES, INC.; *U.S. Private*, pg. 688
THE B. MANISCHEWITZ COMPANY; *U.S. Private*, pg. 699
MARTIN'S FAMOUS PASTRY SHOPPES; *U.S. Private*, pg. 710
MCKEE FOODS CORPORATION; *U.S. Private*, pg. 723
MECOR, INC.—Meiji Seika Kaisha, Ltd.; *Int'l*, pg. 855
MRS. ALISON'S COOKIE COMPANY; *U.S. Private*, pg. 765
NABISCO INC.—RJR Nabisco Holdings Corp.; *U.S. Public*, pg. 1355
NESTLE DEL URUGUAY S.A.—Nestle S.A.; *Int'l*, pg. 921
NORTHERN FOODS PLC; *Int'l*, pg. 967
NOVARTIS AG; *Int'l*, pg. 971
OLW-SNACKS AB—Novartis AG; *Int'l*, pg. 983
PAPUA-NEW GUINEA DIVISION—Goodman Fielder Limited; *Int'l*, pg. 556
PEPPERIDGE FARM, INCORPORATED—Campbell Soup Company; *U.S. Public*, pg. 299
PRESIDENT BAKING COMPANY—President Enterprises Corp.; *Int'l*, pg. 1069
PRESIDENT BAKING INC.—President Enterprises Corp.; *Int'l*, pg. 1069
PRESIDENT BAKING-LOUISVILLE—President Enterprises Corp.; *Int'l*, pg. 1069

PROCTER & GAMBLE FOOD PRODUCTS DIV.—The Procter & Gamble Company; U.S. Public, pg. 1331
QUALITY BAKERS NEDERLAND B.V.—Goodman Fielder Limited; Int'l, pg. 555
QUINLAN PRETZEL CO., INC.—Borden, Inc.; U.S. Private, pg. 158
RHM INGREDIENT SUPPLIES LIMITED—Tomkins PLC; Int'l, pg. 1396
RJR NABISCO HOLDINGS CORP.; U.S. Public, pg. 1354
ROBINSON CONE—Dover Industries Limited; Int'l, pg. 417
C. ROHER INC.; U.S. Private, pg. 940
ROLAND MURTEN AG—Novartis AG; Int'l, pg. 972
RONEY OTMAN; U.S. Private, pg. 943
SME INTERNATIONAL—IRI Istituto Ricostruzione Industriale; Int'l, pg. 655
SAIWA—Danone Group; Int'l, pg. 381
SANDOZ NUTRITION LTD.—Novartis AG; Int'l, pg. 972
SCHULZE & BURCH BISCUIT COMPANY; U.S. Private, pg. 973
SOCIEDADE PORTUGUESA DE PRODUTOS WANDER LDA.—Novartis AG; Int'l, pg. 985
D.F. STAUFFER BISCUIT CO.—Meiji Seika Kaisha, Ltd.; Int'l, pg. 855
SUNSHINE BISCUITS, INC.—GF Industries, Inc.; U.S. Private, pg. 434
SUNSHINE BISCUITS, INC.—Flowers Industries, Inc.; U.S. Public, pg. 657
SVENSKA KNACKE AB—Novartis AG; Int'l, pg. 986
TEMATI S.A. DE C.V.—PepsiCo, Inc.; U.S. Public, pg. 1278
TROTTER SOFT PRETZELS, INC.—J & J Snack Foods Corporation; U.S. Public, pg. 916
TROYER POTATO PRODUCTS, INC.; U.S. Private, pg. 1106
UNITED BISCUITS (HOLDINGS) PLC; Int'l, pg. 1442
UNITED BISCUITS (UK) LIMITED—United Biscuits (Holdings) Plc; Int'l, pg. 1442
UTZ QUALITY FOODS, INC.; U.S. Private, pg. 1130
VAASAMILLS LTD.—Cultor Ltd.; Int'l, pg. 349
VAN DEN BERGH FOODS COMPANY—Unilever Plc; Int'l, pg. 1436
VISTA BAKERY, INC.—Lance, Inc.; U.S. Public, pg. 977
WASA G.M.B.H.—Novartis AG; Int'l, pg. 986
WASABROD AB—Novartis AG; Int'l, pg. 986
WEETABIX LIMITED; Int'l, pg. 1488
WESTON BAKERIES LIMITED—George Weston Limited; Int'l, pg. 1495
GEORGE WESTON LIMITED; Int'l, pg. 1494

2053 — FROZEN BAKING PRODUCTS, EXCEPT BREAD

APRIL HILL, INC.—Grocers Baking Co.; U.S. Private, pg. 483
AVANA BAKERIES LTD.—Tomkins PLC; Int'l, pg. 1396
BAKERY & CONFECTIONARY DIVISION—Campbell Soup Company; U.S. Public, pg. 299
BISCUITERIE VINCHON-JEANETTE S.A.—Sara Lee Corporation; U.S. Public, pg. 1435
BROSSARD—Sara Lee Corporation; U.S. Public, pg. 1435
CAMPBELL SOUP COMPANY; U.S. Public, pg. 298
CLOVERHILL BAKERY; U.S. Private, pg. 247
CORPORATE FOODS LTD.—Maple Leaf Foods Inc.; Int'l, pg. 841
COUNTRY HOME BAKERY, INC.; U.S. Private, pg. 278
DE GRAAF'S BAKKERIJEN BV—Koninklijke BolsWessanen nv; Int'l, pg. 752
DRIEHOEK—Sara Lee Corporation; U.S. Public, pg. 1435
EDWARDS BAKING CO.; U.S. Private, pg. 365
ELI'S CHEESE CAKE COMPANY; U.S. Private, pg. 371
INTERNATIONAL MULTIFOODS CORPORATION; U.S. Public, pg. 900
J & J SNACK FOODS CORPORATION; U.S. Public, pg. 916
JUS-ROL LTD.—Diageo Plc; Int'l, pg. 411
KELLOGG COMPANY; U.S. Public, pg. 947
KITCHENS OF SARA LEE-UNITED KINGDOM—Sara Lee Corporation; U.S. Public, pg. 1434
NORTH AMERICA FOODS—International Multifoods Corporation; U.S. Public, pg. 901
PERFECTION BAKERIES INC.; U.S. Private, pg. 852
SARA LEE CORPORATION; U.S. Public, pg. 1432
WANDER AG—Novartis AG; Int'l, pg. 972

2061 — CANE SUGAR, EXCEPT REFINING

A & B-HAWAII, INC.—Alexander & Baldwin, Inc.; U.S. Public, pg. 39
ALEXANDER & BALDWIN, INC.; U.S. Public, pg. 39
AMFAC, INC.—JMB Realty Corporation; U.S. Private, pg. 577
ATLANTIC SUGAR ASSOCIATION, INC.; U.S. Private, pg. 95
BOOKER PLC; Int'l, pg. 202
C. BREWER & COMPANY, LIMITED—Buyco, Inc.; U.S. Private, pg. 190
BRYANT SUGAR HOUSE—United States Sugar Corporation; U.S. Private, pg. 1126
CALIFORNIA & HAWAIIAN SUGAR COMPANY INC.—Alexander & Baldwin, Inc.; U.S. Public, pg. 39
CANADA WEST INDIES MOLASSES CO. LTD.—Tate & Lyle PLC; Int'l, pg. 1357
CARIBBEAN ANTILLES MOLASSES CO. LTD.—Tate & Lyle PLC; Int'l, pg. 1357
CARIBBEAN MOLASSES CO. LTD.—Tate & Lyle PLC; Int'l, pg. 1357
CLEWISTON SUGAR HOUSE—United States Sugar Corporation; U.S. Private, pg. 1126
CORA TEXAS MANUFACTURING CO., INC.; U.S. Private, pg. 275
CROMPTON & KNOWLES CORPORATION; U.S. Public, pg. 459
CULTOR LTD.; Int'l, pg. 349
GRANDMA FOOD PRODUCTS LIMITED—Crompton & Knowles Corporation; U.S. Public, pg. 460
KAUAI SUGAR STORAGE CO.—JMB Realty Corporation; U.S. Private, pg. 578
KEKAHA SUGAR COMPANY, LIMITED—JMB Realty Corporation; U.S. Private, pg. 578
THE LIHUE PLANTATION COMPANY, LIMITED—JMB Realty Corporation; U.S. Private, pg. 578
MITSUI SUGAR CO., LTD.—Mitsui & Co., Ltd.; Int'l, pg. 879
PHARMACIA & UPJOHN, INC.; Int'l, pg. 1047
PIONEER MILL COMPANY, LTD.—JMB Realty Corporation; U.S. Private, pg. 578
PROCORDIA FOOD AB—Orkla A.S.A.; Int'l, pg. 1011
SOUTHERN MINNESOTA BEET SUGAR COOPERATIVE; U.S. Private, pg. 1016
SUCRERIE ET DISTILLERIE DE SOUPPES OUVRE ET FILS S.A.—Generale Sucriere SNC; Int'l, pg. 549
SUDZUCKER AG MANNHEIM/OCHSENFURT; Int'l, pg. 1305
SUGAR CANE GROWERS COOPERATIVE OF FLORIDA; U.S. Private, pg. 1049
TALISMAN SUGAR CORP.—St. Joe Corp.; U.S. Public, pg. 1427
TATE & LYLE PLC; Int'l, pg. 1356
UNITED STATES SUGAR CORPORATION; U.S. Private, pg. 1126
WHITFIELD FOODS, INC.; U.S. Private, pg. 1173

2062 — CANE SUGAR REFINING

ALEXANDER & BALDWIN, INC.; U.S. Public, pg. 39
AMYLUM N.V.—Tate & Lyle PLC; Int'l, pg. 1357
ARCHER DANIELS MIDLAND COMPANY (ADM); U.S. Public, pg. 127
B C SUGAR REFINERY, LTD.; Int'l, pg. 103
CSM SUGAR DIVISION—CSM N.V.; Int'l, pg. 243
CSR LIMITED; Int'l, pg. 245
CALIFORNIA & HAWAIIAN SUGAR COMPANY INC.—Alexander & Baldwin, Inc.; U.S. Public, pg. 39
CHEIL FOODS & CHEMICALS INC.—Samsung Group; Int'l, pg. 1181
CORA TEXAS MANUFACTURING CO., INC.; U.S. Private, pg. 275
DIXIE CRYSTALS BRANDS, INC.—Imperial Holly Corporation; U.S. Public, pg. 872
DOMINO SUGAR CORPORATION—Tate & Lyle PLC; Int'l, pg. 1356
ERIDANIA BEGHIN-SAY GROUP—Compart SpA; Int'l, pg. 324
EVERGLADES SUGAR REFINERY, INC.—Imperial Holly Corporation; U.S. Public, pg. 873
CHARLES E. FORD, LIMITED—Tate & Lyle PLC; Int'l, pg. 1356
FUJI SEITO CO., LTD.—Nissho Iwai Corporation; Int'l, pg. 947
GENERALE SUCRIERE SNC; Int'l, pg. 548
GRIFFIN MANUFACTURING CO.; U.S. Private, pg. 481
GROUPE SAINT LOUIS; Int'l, pg. 567
IMPERIAL HOLLY CORPORATION; U.S. Public, pg. 872
KENANA SUGAR CO., LTD.—Nissho Iwai Corporation; Int'l, pg. 948
MITSUI SUGAR CO., LTD.—Mitsui & Co., Ltd.; Int'l, pg. 878
M.A. PATOUT & SON; U.S. Private, pg. 843
PROCORDIA FOOD AB—Orkla A.S.A.; Int'l, pg. 1011
RACELAND RAW SUGAR CORP.—M.A. Patout & Son; U.S. Private, pg. 843
REDPATH INDUSTRIES LTD.—Tate & Lyle PLC; Int'l, pg. 1357
REFINED SUGARS, INC.—Jannock Limited; Int'l, pg. 699
SAVANNAH FOODS & INDUSTRIES, INC.—Imperial Holly Corporation; U.S. Public, pg. 872
SAVANNAH INVESTMENT COMPANY—Imperial Holly Corporation; U.S. Public, pg. 873
SHADY MAPLE FARMS LTD.—H.J. Heinz Company; U.S. Public, pg. 806
SHIN-MEITO CO., LTD.—Nissho Iwai Corporation; Int'l, pg. 947
SUDZUCKER AG MANNHEIM/OCHSENFURT; Int'l, pg. 1305
TAITO CO., LTD.—Mitsui & Co., Ltd.; Int'l, pg. 878
TATE & LYLE PLC; Int'l, pg. 1356
TATE & LYLE SUGARS—Tate & Lyle PLC; Int'l, pg. 1356
TUNNEL REFINERIES LIMITED—Tate & Lyle PLC; Int'l, pg. 1356

2063 — BEET SUGAR MANUFACTURING

THE AMALGAMATED SUGAR COMPANY LLC; U.S. Private, pg. 48
AMERICAN CRYSTAL SUGAR COMPANY; U.S. Private, pg. 52
ARCHER DANIELS MIDLAND COMPANY (ADM); U.S. Public, pg. 127
ATELIERS SUCRE LIQUIDE ET CONDITIONNEMENT-LABORATOIRE DE RECHERCHE DE NASSANDRES—Generale Sucriere SNC; Int'l, pg. 549
BREDA SUGAR FACTORY—CSM N.V.; Int'l, pg. 244
CSM N.V.; Int'l, pg. 243
CSM SUIKER BV—CSM N.V.; Int'l, pg. 243
CANADA WEST INDIES MOLASSES CO. LTD.—Tate & Lyle PLC; Int'l, pg. 1357
DIXIE CRYSTALS BRANDS, INC.—Imperial Holly Corporation; U.S. Public, pg. 872
ERIDANIA BEGHIN-SAY GROUP—Compart SpA; Int'l, pg. 324
HOLLY SUGAR CORPORATION—Imperial Holly Corporation; U.S. Public, pg. 872
IMPERIAL HOLLY CORPORATION; U.S. Public, pg. 872
MICHIGAN SUGAR COMPANY—Imperial Holly Corporation; U.S. Public, pg. 873
PROCORDIA FOOD AB—Orkla A.S.A.; Int'l, pg. 1011
RAFFINERIE DE MARSEILLE—Generale Sucriere SNC; Int'l, pg. 549
REDPATH INDUSTRIES LTD.—Tate & Lyle PLC; Int'l, pg. 1357
SAVANNAH FOODS & INDUSTRIES, INC.—Imperial Holly Corporation; U.S. Public, pg. 872
SAVANNAH INVESTMENT COMPANY—Imperial Holly Corporation; U.S. Public, pg. 873
SOUTHERN MINNESOTA BEET SUGAR COOPERATIVE; U.S. Private, pg. 1016
SUCRERIE D'AULNOIS-SOUS-LAON—Generale Sucriere SNC; Int'l, pg. 549
SUCRERIE DE CAGNY—Generale Sucriere SNC; Int'l, pg. 549
SUCRERIE DE ROYE—Generale Sucriere SNC; Int'l, pg. 549
SUCRERIE D'EPPEVILLE/HAM—Generale Sucriere SNC; Int'l, pg. 549
SUCRERIE D'ETREPAGNY—Generale Sucriere SNC; Int'l, pg. 549
SUDZUCKER AG MANNHEIM/OCHSENFURT; Int'l, pg. 1305
VIERVERLATEN SUGAR FACTORY—CSM N.V.; Int'l, pg. 244
THE WESTERN SUGAR COMPANY—Tate & Lyle PLC; Int'l, pg. 1357

2064 — CANDY & OTHER CONFECTIONERY PRODUCTS

ADAMS, S.A.—Warner-Lambert Company; U.S. Public, pg. 1739
ADAMS U.S.A.—Warner-Lambert Company; U.S. Public, pg. 1739
AMUROL CONFECTIONS CO.—Wm. Wrigley Jr. Company; U.S. Public, pg. 1781
ANDERSON, CLAYTON & CO. S.A.—Unilever Plc; Int'l, pg. 1436
ANDES CANDIES INC.—Brach & Brock Confections, Inc.; U.S. Private, pg. 163
ANNABELLE CANDY COMPANY, INC.; U.S. Private, pg. 75
ARCHIBALD CANDY COMPANY—The Jordan Company; U.S. Private, pg. 597
ASHER CANDY COMPANY—Marvel Entertainment Group; U.S. Public, pg. 1052
BAKERY & CONFECTIONARY DIVISION—Campbell Soup Company; U.S. Public, pg. 299
KATHRYN BEICH, INC.—Nestle S.A.; Int'l, pg. 917
BERKSHIRE HATHAWAY INC.; U.S. Public, pg. 217
BERLI JUCKER PUBLIC CO. LTD.—First Pacific Company Limited; Int'l, pg. 487
BEWLEY'S MANUFACTURING LTD.—Campbells/Bewley Group; Int'l, pg. 254
BOYER CANDY COMPANY INC.; U.S. Private, pg. 162
BRACH & BROCK CONFECTIONS, INC.; U.S. Private, pg. 163
BRACH & BROCK CONFECTIONS INC.—Brach & Brock Confections, Inc.; U.S. Private, pg. 163
E.J. BRACH, INC.—Brach & Brock Confections, Inc.; U.S. Private, pg. 163
BRIGHAM'S, INC.—Grotech Capital Group, Inc.; U.S. Private, pg. 483
BROWN & HALEY; U.S. Private, pg. 173
BUITONI SPA—Nestle S.A.; Int'l, pg. 919
CPC ASIA CONSUMER FOODS DIVISION—Bestfoods; U.S. Public, pg. 224
CADBURY IRELAND P.L.C.—Cadbury Schweppes p.l.c.; Int'l, pg. 248
CADBURY LIMITED—Cadbury Schweppes p.l.c.; Int'l, pg. 248
CADBURY SCHWEPPES P.L.C.; Int'l, pg. 247
CAMPBELL SOUP COMPANY; U.S. Public, pg. 298
CAMPBELL USA—Campbell Soup Company; U.S. Public, pg. 299
CE DE CANDY, INC.; U.S. Private, pg. 220
CELLA'S CONFECTIONS, INC.—Tootsie Roll Industries, Inc.; U.S. Public, pg. 1621
CHARMS COMPANY—Tootsie Roll Industries, Inc.; U.S. Public, pg. 1621
CHICLE ADAMS S.A.—Warner-Lambert Company; U.S. Public, pg. 1739
CHICLE ADAMS, S.A. DE C.V.—Warner-Lambert Company; U.S. Public, pg. 1739
COKOLADOVNY—Nestle S.A.; Int'l, pg. 922
COTE D'OR S.A.—Philip Morris Companies Inc.; U.S. Public, pg. 1288
CROWN CONFECTIONERY CO., LTD.; Int'l, pg. 348
CRUSPI S.A.; Int'l, pg. 348
CULINAR INC.; Int'l, pg. 348
DOHNAN SHOKUHIN CO., LTD.—Meiji Seika Kaisha, Ltd.; Int'l, pg. 855
DROSTE B.V.—CSM N.V.; Int'l, pg. 243
DRYDEN & PALMER COMPANY—Gravymaster Inc.; U.S. Private, pg. 471
FANNIE MAY CANDY SHOPS, INC.—The Jordan Company; U.S. Private, pg. 598
FERRERO; Int'l, pg. 480
FERRERO INC.—Ferrero; Int'l, pg. 480
FLEER-SKYBOX INTERNATIONAL INC.—Marvel Entertainment Group; U.S. Public, pg. 1052
GENERAL MILLS EUROPE LIMITED—General Mills, Inc.; U.S. Public, pg. 718
GERTRUDE HAWK CHOCOLATES, INC.; U.S. Private, pg. 449
GILLIAM CANDY BRANDS; U.S. Private, pg. 454
GODIVA CHOCOLATIER, INC.—Campbell Soup Company; U.S. Public, pg. 299
GOLDENBERG CANDY COMPANY; U.S. Private, pg. 461
GRAVYMASTER INC.; U.S. Private, pg. 471
GREAT LAKES CONFECTIONERY—Midial S.A.; Int'l, pg. 865
GRIST MILL COMPANY; U.S. Public, pg. 766
GRIST MILL COMPANY—Grist Mill Company; U.S. Public, pg. 766

GROCERY DIVISION—Grist Mill Company; *U.S. Public*, pg. 766
HALBA AG—Coop Switzerland; *Int'l*, pg. 330
HALL BROTHERS (WHITEFIELD) LIMITED—Warner-Lambert Company; *U.S. Public*, pg. 1739
HARMONY FOODS CORPORATION; *U.S. Private*, pg. 503
HAVILAND CANDY INC.—UIS, Inc.; *U.S. Private*, pg. 1113
HERSHEY CANADA INC.—Hershey Foods Corporation; *U.S. Public*, pg. 812
HUHTAMAKI OY; *Int'l*, pg. 638
JACOBS SUCHARD (AUSTRALIA) PTY. LTD.—Philip Morris Companies Inc.; *U.S. Public*, pg. 1288
JACOBS SUCHARD JAPAN CO., LTD.—Philip Morris Companies Inc.; *U.S. Public*, pg. 1289
JACOBS SUCHARD PAVLIDES S.A.—Philip Morris Companies Inc.; *U.S. Public*, pg. 1289
JACOBS SUCHARD TOBLER AG—Philip Morris Companies Inc.; *U.S. Public*, pg. 1288
JUDSON-ATKINSON CANDIES, INC.; *U.S. Private*, pg. 602
JUST BORN, INC.; *U.S. Private*, pg. 602
KRAFT FOODS INC.—Philip Morris Companies Inc.; *U.S. Public*, pg. 1288
KRAFT JACOBS SUCHARD AG—Philip Morris Companies Inc.; *U.S. Public*, pg. 1288
LABATT BREWING COMPANY LIMITED—Interbrew S.A.; *Int'l*, pg. 679
LANCE, INC.; *U.S. Public*, pg. 977
LEAF BALTICS—Huhtamaki Oy; *Int'l*, pg. 638
LEAF CHINA—Huhtamaki Oy; *Int'l*, pg. 638
LEAF FINLAND—Huhtamaki Oy; *Int'l*, pg. 638
LEAF GERMANY—Huhtamaki Oy; *Int'l*, pg. 638
LEAF GROUP B.V.—Huhtamaki Oy; *Int'l*, pg. 638
LEAF HOLLAND B.V.—Huhtamaki Oy; *Int'l*, pg. 638
LEAF IBERIA S.A.—Huhtamaki Oy; *Int'l*, pg. 638
LEAF IRELAND LTD.—Huhtamaki Oy; *Int'l*, pg. 638
LEAF NORWAY A/S—Huhtamaki Oy; *Int'l*, pg. 638
LEAF POLAND SP.Z.O.O—Huhtamaki Oy; *Int'l*, pg. 638
LEAF RUSSIA—Huhtamaki Oy; *Int'l*, pg. 638
LEAF SWEDEN—Huhtamaki Oy; *Int'l*, pg. 638
LEAF SWITZERLAND—Huhtamaki Oy; *Int'l*, pg. 638
LEAF UNITED KINGDOM LTD.—Huhtamaki Oy; *Int'l*, pg. 638
LOTTE SHOPPING CO. LTD.—Lotte Company Ltd.; *Int'l*, pg. 819
LUDEN'S INC.—Hershey Foods Corporation; *U.S. Public*, pg. 812
M&M/MARS—Mars, Incorporated; *U.S. Private*, pg. 707
MARS, INCORPORATED; *U.S. Private*, pg. 707
MASTER FOODS—Mars, Incorporated; *U.S. Private*, pg. 707
MAUNA LOA MACADAMIA NUT CORPORATION—Buyco, Inc.; *U.S. Private*, pg. 190
MEIJI SANGYO CO., LTD.—Meiji Seika Kaisha, Ltd.; *Int'l*, pg. 855
MEIJI SEIKA KAISHA, LTD.; *Int'l*, pg. 855
MEIJI SEIKA (SINGAPORE) PTE. LTD.—Meiji Seika Kaisha, Ltd.; *Int'l*, pg. 856
MIDIAL S.A.; *Int'l*, pg. 865
MIRABELL SALZBURGER CONFISERIE-UND BISQUIT-GES.M.B.H—Philip Morris Companies Inc.; *U.S. Public*, pg. 1289
BEN MYERSON CANDY COMPANY, INC.; *U.S. Private*, pg. 771
NABISCO INC.—RJR Nabisco Holdings Corp.; *U.S. Public*, pg. 1355
NATIONAL FOOD STORES, INC.; *U.S. Private*, pg. 783
NESTLE CHOCOLATE & CONFECTION—Nestle S.A.; *Int'l*, pg. 917
NESTLE CONFECTIONERY—Nestle S.A.; *Int'l*, pg. 922
NESTLE (MALAYSIA), SDN. BHD., NESMAL—Nestle S.A.; *Int'l*, pg. 921
NESTLE-ROWNTREE LTD.—Nestle S.A.; *Int'l*, pg. 921
NEW ENGLAND CONFECTIONERY CO.—UIS, Inc.; *U.S. Private*, pg. 1113
NIDAR AS—Orkla A.S.A.; *Int'l*, pg. 1011
NORFOODS, INC.; *U.S. Private*, pg. 802
OLD DUTCH FOODS, INC.; *U.S. Private*, pg. 814
R.M. PALMER COMPANY; *U.S. Private*, pg. 835
PANGBURN CANDY COMPANY; *U.S. Private*, pg. 836
PECO SUIKERWERKEN B.V.—Van Melle N.V.; *Int'l*, pg. 1451
PEERLESS CONFECTION COMPANY; *U.S. Private*, pg. 847
PERUGINA BRANDS OF AMERICA—Nestle S.A.; *Int'l*, pg. 917
PETER PAUL—Hershey Foods Corporation; *U.S. Public*, pg. 812
PHARMACIA & UPJOHN, INC.; *Int'l*, pg. 1047
PLANTERS COMPANY—RJR Nabisco Holdings Corp.; *U.S. Public*, pg. 1355
PORTLAND FOOD PRODUCTS COMPANY; *U.S. Private*, pg. 876
RJR NABISCO HOLDINGS CORP.; *U.S. Public*, pg. 1354
RAGOLDS SUSSWAREN GMBH & CO.; *Int'l*, pg. 1084
RED BAND—CSM N.V.; *Int'l*, pg. 244
RED BAND SUSSWAREN VERTRIEBS GMBH—CSM N.V.; *Int'l*, pg. 244
RED BAND VENCO—CSM N.V.; *Int'l*, pg. 244
RUSSELL STOVER CANDIES, INC.; *U.S. Private*, pg. 953
SANBORN HERMANOS—Grupo Carso S.A. de C.V.; *Int'l*, pg. 573
SATHERS INC.—Favorite Brands International, Inc.; *U.S. Private*, pg. 397
SEE'S CANDIES, INC.—Berkshire Hathaway Inc.; *U.S. Public*, pg. 221
SEE'S CANDY SHOPS, INC.—Berkshire Hathaway Inc.; *U.S. Public*, pg. 221
SHADE FOODS, INC.—Norfoods, Inc.; *U.S. Private*, pg. 802
SHELLY BROS., INC.—Brach & Brock Confections, Inc.; *U.S. Private*, pg. 163
SORBEE INTERNATIONAL LTD.; *U.S. Private*, pg. 1014
SPANGLER CANDY COMPANY; *U.S. Private*, pg. 1020
SPERLARI, S.R.L.—Hershey Foods Corporation; *U.S. Public*, pg. 812
STANDARD CANDY CO., INC.; *U.S. Private*, pg. 1030
STARK CANDY COMPANY—UIS, Inc.; *U.S. Private*, pg. 1113
STORCK INTERNATIONAL GMBH; *Int'l*, pg. 1304
STORCK U.S.A., L.P.—Storck International GmbH; *Int'l*, pg. 1304
THE SWEETS MIX COMPANY, INC.—Tootsie Roll Industries, Inc.; *U.S. Public*, pg. 1621
THE SWISS COLONY, INC; *U.S. Private*, pg. 1059
TRI INTERNATIONAL CO.—Tootsie Roll Industries, Inc.; *U.S. Public*, pg. 1621
TENNANT & RUTTLE LIMITED—James Crean PLC; *Int'l*, pg. 340
TERRY'S GROUP—Philip Morris Companies Inc.; *U.S. Public*, pg. 1290
THORNTONS PLC; *Int'l*, pg. 1386
TOBLER CHOCOLAT AG—Philip Morris Companies Inc.; *U.S. Public*, pg. 1288
TONNEMA B.V.—CSM N.V.; *Int'l*, pg. 244
THE TOOTSIE ROLL COMPANY—Tootsie Roll Industries, Inc.; *U.S. Public*, pg. 1621
TOOTSIE ROLL INDUSTRIES, INC.; *U.S. Public*, pg. 1621
TOOTSIE ROLL MANAGEMENT, INC.—Tootsie Roll Industries, Inc.; *U.S. Public*, pg. 1621
TOOTSIE ROLL MANUFACTURING INC.—Tootsie Roll Industries, Inc.; *U.S. Public*, pg. 1621
TOPPS ARGENTINA S.A.—The Topps Company, Inc.; *U.S. Public*, pg. 1622
TOPPS BRASIL LTDA.—The Topps Company, Inc.; *U.S. Public*, pg. 1622
THE TOPPS COMPANY, INC.; *U.S. Public*, pg. 1621
TOPPS IRELAND LTD.—The Topps Company, Inc.; *U.S. Public*, pg. 1622
TOPPS MEXICO, S.A. DE C.V.—The Topps Company, Inc.; *U.S. Public*, pg. 1622
TREBOR BASSETT LTD.—Cadbury Schweppes p.l.c.; *Int'l*, pg. 248
TUSTI S.A. DE C.V.—Tootsie Roll Industries, Inc.; *U.S. Public*, pg. 1621
VAN MELLE BRASIL LTDA.—Van Melle N.V.; *Int'l*, pg. 1451
VAN MELLE N.V.; *Int'l*, pg. 1450
VAN MELLE-(PHILS.) INC.—Van Melle N.V.; *Int'l*, pg. 1451
VANDAMME - PIE QUI CHANTE—Danone Group; *Int'l*, pg. 380
WARNER-LAMBERT COMPANY; *U.S. Public*, pg. 1738
GEORGE WESTON LIMITED; *Int'l*, pg. 1494
WHITMAN'S CANDIES, INC.—Russell Stover Candies, Inc.; *U.S. Private*, pg. 953
WILLIAMSBURG FOODS, INC.—The Smithfield Companies, Inc.; *U.S. Public*, pg. 1479
WORLD TRADE & MARKETING, LTD.—Tootsie Roll Industries, Inc.; *U.S. Public*, pg. 1621
Y & S CANDIES—Hershey Foods Corporation; *U.S. Public*, pg. 812
ZAO RUSSIA—Huhtamaki Oy; *Int'l*, pg. 638
ZAO SHOKUHIN CO., LTD.—Meiji Seika Kaisha, Ltd.; *Int'l*, pg. 855

2066 — CHOCOLATE & COCOA PRODUCTS

ADM COCOA, INC.—Archer Daniels Midland Company (ADM); *U.S. Public*, pg. 127
ANDERSON, CLAYTON & CO. S.A.—Unilever Plc; *Int'l*, pg. 1436
ANDES CANDIES INC.—Brach & Brock Confections, Inc.; *U.S. Private*, pg. 163
ANNABELLE CANDY COMPANY, INC.; *U.S. Private*, pg. 75
BAKERY & CONFECTIONARY DIVISION—Campbell Soup Company; *U.S. Public*, pg. 299
BARRY CALLEBAUT—Barry Callebaut N.V.; *Int'l*, pg. 252
BEWLEY'S MANUFACTURING LTD.—Campbells/Bewley Group; *Int'l*, pg. 254
BLOMMER CHOCOLATE CO.; *U.S. Private*, pg. 150
BRACH & BROCK CONFECTIONS, INC.; *U.S. Private*, pg. 163
BRACH & BROCK CONFECTIONS INC.—Brach & Brock Confections, Inc.; *U.S. Private*, pg. 163
E.J. BRACH, INC.—Brach & Brock Confections, Inc.; *U.S. Private*, pg. 163
BROWN & HALEY; *U.S. Private*, pg. 173
BUITONI SPA—Nestle S.A.; *Int'l*, pg. 919
CLR CORPORATION—Empire of Carolina, Inc.; *U.S. Public*, pg. 579
CACAO DE ZAAN B.V.—Archer Daniels Midland Company (ADM); *U.S. Public*, pg. 128
CADBURY CHOCOLATE CANADA, INC.—Cadbury Schweppes p.l.c.; *Int'l*, pg. 248
CADBURY SCHWEPPES P.L.C.; *Int'l*, pg. 247
CADBURY SCHWEPPES SOUTH AFRICA LTD.—Cadbury Schweppes p.l.c.; *Int'l*, pg. 248
BARRY CALLEBAUT N.V.; *Int'l*, pg. 252
CELLA'S CONFECTIONS, INC.—Tootsie Roll Industries, Inc.; *U.S. Public*, pg. 1621
CHOCOLATE PRODUCTS CO. LTD.—George Weston Limited; *Int'l*, pg. 1495
COMPANIA PERUANA DE ALIMENTOS S.A.—Nestle S.A.; *Int'l*, pg. 920
COOK CHOCOLATE CANADA LTD.—World's Finest Chocolate, Inc.; *U.S. Private*, pg. 1191
CROWN CONFECTIONERY CO., LTD.; *Int'l*, pg. 348
DE ZAAN FAR EAST PTE. LTD.—Archer Daniels Midland Company (ADM); *U.S. Public*, pg. 128
DELICIA B.V.—Koninklijke BolsWessanen nv; *Int'l*, pg. 752
DOHNAN SHOKUHIN CO., LTD.—Meiji Seika Kaisha, Ltd.; *Int'l*, pg. 855
DROSTE B.V.—CSM N.V.; *Int'l*, pg. 243
FARLEY CANDY COMPANY—Favorite Brands International, Inc.; *U.S. Private*, pg. 397
FOOD SERVICES DIVISION—Nestle S.A.; *Int'l*, pg. 917
GILSTER MARY LEE CORP.—Gilster Mary Lee Corp.; *U.S. Private*, pg. 455
GRACE COCOA/AMBROSIA CHOCOLATE—Archer Daniels Midland Company (ADM); *U.S. Public*, pg. 128
GRACE COCOA/MERCKENS—Archer Daniels Midland Company (ADM); *U.S. Public*, pg. 128
GRUPO INDUSTRIAL BIMBO S.A. DE C.V.; *Int'l*, pg. 575
HALBA AG—Coop Switzerland; *Int'l*, pg. 330
HERSHEY CANADA INC.—Hershey Foods Corporation; *U.S. Public*, pg. 812
HERSHEY CHOCOLATE U.S.A.—Hershey Foods Corporation; *U.S. Public*, pg. 812
HERSHEY FOODS CORPORATION; *U.S. Public*, pg. 811
HERSHEY JAPAN CO., LTD.—Hershey Foods Corporation; *U.S. Public*, pg. 812
HUNT-WESSON, INC.—ConAgra, Inc.; *U.S. Public*, pg. 428
ISRAEL EDIBLE PRODUCTS LTD.—Bestfoods; *U.S. Public*, pg. 225
JACOBS SUCHARD (AUSTRALIA) PTY. LTD.—Philip Morris Companies Inc.; *U.S. Public*, pg. 1288
JACOBS SUCHARD ESPANA S.A.—Philip Morris Companies Inc.; *U.S. Public*, pg. 1289
JACOBS SUCHARD JAPAN CO., LTD.—Philip Morris Companies Inc.; *U.S. Public*, pg. 1289
JACOBS SUCHARD LTD.—Philip Morris Companies Inc.; *U.S. Public*, pg. 1289
JACOBS SUCHARD PAVLIDES S.A.—Philip Morris Companies Inc.; *U.S. Public*, pg. 1289
JACOBS SUCHARD TOBLER AG—Philip Morris Companies Inc.; *U.S. Public*, pg. 1288
M&M/MARS—Mars, Incorporated; *U.S. Private*, pg. 707
MALAYSIA COCOA MANUFACTURING, SDN. BHD.—Nestle S.A.; *Int'l*, pg. 920
MARS, INCORPORATED; *U.S. Private*, pg. 707
MASTER FOODS—Mars, Incorporated; *U.S. Private*, pg. 707
JULIUS MEINL AG; *Int'l*, pg. 856
MIDIAL S.A.; *Int'l*, pg. 865
MULTIFOOD INTERNATIONAL—Meiji Seika Kaisha, Ltd.; *Int'l*, pg. 855
NESTLE CANADA INC.—Nestle S.A.; *Int'l*, pg. 921
NESTLE CHINA LTD.—Nestle S.A.; *Int'l*, pg. 921
NESTLE CHOCOLATE & CONFECTION—Nestle S.A.; *Int'l*, pg. 917
NESTLE DANMARK A/S—Nestle S.A.; *Int'l*, pg. 921
NESTLE DEL URUGUAY S.A.—Nestle S.A.; *Int'l*, pg. 921
NESTLE FOODSERVICE CANADA—Nestle S.A.; *Int'l*, pg. 922
NESTLE INDUSTRIAL E COMMERCIAL LTDA.—Nestle S.A.; *Int'l*, pg. 921
NESTLE S.A.; *Int'l*, pg. 915
NORFOODS, INC.; *U.S. Private*, pg. 802
ORVAL KENT FOOD CO.; *U.S. Private*, pg. 820
PERUGINA BRANDS OF AMERICA—Nestle S.A.; *Int'l*, pg. 917
PORTLAND FOOD PRODUCTS COMPANY; *U.S. Private*, pg. 876
PY-O-MY DIV.—Gilster Mary Lee Corp.; *U.S. Private*, pg. 455
H.B. REESE CANDY CO.—Hershey Foods Corporation; *U.S. Public*, pg. 812
RONDE CORP.—Meiji Seika Kaisha, Ltd.; *Int'l*, pg. 855
RUSSELL STOVER CANDIES, INC.; *U.S. Private*, pg. 953
S & A LESME CALLEBAUT—Barry Callebaut N.V.; *Int'l*, pg. 252
SME INTERNATIONAL—IRI Istituto Ricostruzione Industriale; *Int'l*, pg. 655
SHADE FOODS, INC.—Norfoods, Inc.; *U.S. Private*, pg. 802
SOPHIE MAE DIVISION—Gilliam Candy Brands; *U.S. Private*, pg. 454
STORCK INTERNATIONAL GMBH; *Int'l*, pg. 1304
STORCK U.S.A., L.P.—Storck International GmbH; *Int'l*, pg. 1304
SUCHARD SCHOKOLADE GES.M.B.H—Philip Morris Companies Inc.; *U.S. Public*, pg. 1289
THE SWISS COLONY, INC; *U.S. Private*, pg. 1059
THORNTONS PLC; *Int'l*, pg. 1386
TREBOR BASSETT LTD.—Cadbury Schweppes p.l.c.; *Int'l*, pg. 248
VAN MELLE BRASIL LTDA.—Van Melle N.V.; *Int'l*, pg. 1451
VAN MELLE N.V.; *Int'l*, pg. 1450
VAN MELLE-(PHILS.) INC.—Van Melle N.V.; *Int'l*, pg. 1451
WANDER LTD.—Novartis AG; *Int'l*, pg. 986
GEORGE WESTON LIMITED; *Int'l*, pg. 1494
WILBUR CHOCOLATE CO., INC.—Cargill; *U.S. Private*, pg. 210
WORLD'S FINEST CHOCOLATE AUSTRALIA PTY. LTD.—World's Finest Chocolate, Inc.; *U.S. Private*, pg. 1191
WORLD'S FINEST CHOCOLATE, INC.; *U.S. Private*, pg. 1191
ZAO SHOKUHIN CO., LTD.—Meiji Seika Kaisha, Ltd.; *Int'l*, pg. 855

2067 — CHEWING GUM

ADAMS, S.A.—Warner-Lambert Company; *U.S. Public*, pg. 1739
ADAMS U.S.A.—Warner-Lambert Company; *U.S. Public*, pg. 1739
AMUROL CONFECTIONS CO.—Wm. Wrigley Jr. Company; *U.S. Public*, pg. 1781
CHICLE ADAMS S.A.—Warner-Lambert Company; *U.S. Public*, pg. 1739
CHICLE ADAMS, S.A. DE C.V.—Warner-Lambert Company; *U.S. Public*, pg. 1739
CLARK GUM COMPANY; *U.S. Private*, pg. 243
CRUSPI S.A.; *Int'l*, pg. 348
DEUTSCHE WRIGLEY G.M.B.H—Wm. Wrigley Jr. Company; *U.S. Public*, pg. 1781
L.A. DREYFUS CO.—Wm. Wrigley Jr. Company; *U.S. Public*, pg. 1781
FLEER-SKYBOX INTERNATIONAL INC.—Marvel Entertainment Group; *U.S. Public*, pg. 1052
HUHTAMAKI OY; *Int'l*, pg. 638

LEAF CHINA—Huhtamaki Oy; *Int'l*, pg. 638
LEAF GROUP B.V.—Huhtamaki Oy; *Int'l*, pg. 638
LEAF HOLLAND B.V.—Huhtamaki Oy; *Int'l*, pg. 638
LEAF IBERIA S.A.—Huhtamaki Oy; *Int'l*, pg. 638
LEAF IRELAND LTD.—Huhtamaki Oy; *Int'l*, pg. 638
LEAF NORWAY A/S—Huhtamaki Oy; *Int'l*, pg. 638
LEAF RUSSIA—Huhtamaki Oy; *Int'l*, pg. 638
LEAF SWITZERLAND—Huhtamaki Oy; *Int'l*, pg. 638
LEAF UNITED KINGDOM LTD.—Huhtamaki Oy; *Int'l*, pg. 638
LOTTE COMPANY LTD.; *Int'l*, pg. 819
LOTTE U.S.A., INC.—Lotte Company Ltd.; *Int'l*, pg. 819
MEIJI CHEWING GUM CO, LTD.—Meiji Seika Kaisha, Ltd.; *Int'l*, pg. 855
RJR NABISCO HOLDINGS CORP.; *U.S. Public*, pg. 1354
SMITH'S CHEWING SWEETS MIJ. B.V.—Van Melle N.V.; *Int'l*, pg. 1451
THE TOPPS COMPANY, INC.; *U.S. Public*, pg. 1621
TOPPS IRELAND LTD.—The Topps Company, Inc.; *U.S. Public*, pg. 1622
WARNER-LAMBERT COMPANY; *U.S. Public*, pg. 1738
WARNER-LAMBERT (PORTUGAL) COMERCIO E INDUSTRIA LIMITADA—Warner-Lambert Company; *U.S.* Public, pg. 1740
WARNER-LAMBERT—Warner-Lambert Company; *U.S. Public*, pg. 1739
WRIGLEY AUSTRIA GES.M.B.H—Wm. Wrigley Jr. Company; *U.S. Public*, pg. 1781
WRIGLEY CANADA INC.—Wm. Wrigley Jr. Company; *U.S. Public*, pg. 1781
THE WRIGLEY CO., (EAST AFRICA) LTD.—Wm. Wrigley Jr. Company; *U.S. Public*, pg. 1781
THE WRIGLEY COMPANY (H.K.) LTD.—Wm. Wrigley Jr. Company; *U.S. Public*, pg. 1781
WRIGLEY COMPANY, LTD., JAPAN—Wm. Wrigley Jr. Company; *U.S. Public*, pg. 1781
THE WRIGLEY COMPANY LTD.—Wm. Wrigley Jr. Company; *U.S. Public*, pg. 1781
THE WRIGLEY COMPANY (MALAYSIA) SDN. BHD.—Wm. Wrigley Jr. Company; *U.S. Public*, pg. 1781
THE WRIGLEY COMPANY (N.Z.) LTD.—Wm. Wrigley Jr. Company; *U.S. Public*, pg. 1781
THE WRIGLEY COMPANY (P.N.G.) PTY. LTD.—Wm. Wrigley Jr. Company; *U.S. Public*, pg. 1781
THE WRIGLEY CO. PTY. LTD.—Wm. Wrigley Jr. Company; *U.S. Public*, pg. 1781
WRIGLEY CO. S.A.—Wm. Wrigley Jr. Company; *U.S. Public*, pg. 1781
WRIGLEY N.V.—Wm. Wrigley Jr. Company; *U.S. Public*, pg. 1781
WRIGLEY PHILIPPINES, INC.—Wm. Wrigley Jr. Company; *U.S. Public*, pg. 1781
WRIGLEY S.A.—Wm. Wrigley Jr. Company; *U.S. Public*, pg. 1781
WRIGLEY SCANDINAVIA AB—Wm. Wrigley Jr. Company; *U.S. Public*, pg. 1781
OY WRIGLEY SCANDINAVIA AB—Wm. Wrigley Jr. Company; *U.S. Public*, pg. 1781
WRIGLEY SCANDINAVIA A/S—Wm. Wrigley Jr. Company; *U.S. Public*, pg. 1781
WRIGLEY TAIWAN LTD.—Wm. Wrigley Jr. Company; *U.S. Public*, pg. 1781
WM. WRIGLEY JR. COMPANY; *U.S. Public*, pg. 1781
ZAO RUSSIA—Huhtamaki Oy; *Int'l*, pg. 638

2068 — SALTED & ROASTED NUTS & SEEDS

BLUEBIRD FOODS LTD—Goodman Fielder Limited; *Int'l*, pg. 556
C. BREWER & COMPANY, LIMITED—Buyco, Inc.; *U.S. Private*, pg. 190
CADBURY IRELAND P.L.C.—Cadbury Schweppes p.l.c.; *Int'l*, pg. 248
CADBURY SCHWEPPES P.L.C.; *Int'l*, pg. 247
COUNTRY PRODUCTS GROUP—Agway, Inc.; *U.S. Private*, pg. 27
DAVID & SONS—Nestle S.A.; *Int'l*, pg. 917
FAIRMONT SNACK GROUP, INC.; *U.S. Private*, pg. 392
FLAVOR HOUSE PRODUCTS, INC.; *U.S. Private*, pg. 410
FRUISEC S.A.—Bongrain S.A.; *Int'l*, pg. 201
GENERAL MILLS EUROPE LIMITED—General Mills, Inc.; *U.S. Public*, pg. 718
GRANNY GOOSE FOODS, INC.; *U.S. Private*, pg. 469
INTERNATIONAL HOME FOODS INC.—Hicks, Muse, Tate & Furst Inc.; *U.S. Private*, pg. 526
LABATT BREWING COMPANY LIMITED—Interbrew S.A.; *Int'l*, pg. 679
MAUNA KEA AGRIBUSINESS CO., INC.—Buyco, Inc.; *U.S.* Private, pg. 190
MAUNA LOA MACADAMIA NUT CORPORATION—Buyco, Inc.; *U.S. Private*, pg. 190
RJR NABISCO HOLDINGS CORP.; *U.S. Public*, pg. 1354
JOHN B. SANFILIPPO & SON, INC.; *U.S. Public*, pg. 1431
THE SWISS COLONY, INC; *U.S. Private*, pg. 1059
TOM'S FOODS, INC.; *U.S. Private*, pg. 1090
WAILUKU AGRIBUSINESS CO., INC.—Buyco, Inc.; *U.S. Private*, pg. 191
WILLIAMSBURG FOODS, INC.—The Smithfield Companies, Inc.; *U.S. Public*, pg. 1479

2074 — COTTONSEED OIL MILLS

ANDERSON, CLAYTON S.A.—Unilever Plc; *Int'l*, pg. 1436
ARCHER DANIELS MIDLAND COMPANY (ADM); *U.S. Public*, pg. 127
BUCKEYE CELLULOSE CORP.—The Procter & Gamble Company; *U.S. Public*, pg. 1331
THE BUCKEYE OILSEED PRODUCTS CO.—The Procter & Gamble Company; *U.S. Public*, pg. 1331
CHICKASHA COTTON OIL CO.—Tomen Corporation; *Int'l*, pg. 1395
COMPANIA COLOMBIANA DE GRASAS "COGRA-LEVER" S.A.—Unilever Plc; *Int'l*, pg. 1436
MALLET & CO.; *U.S. Private*, pg. 698
PLAINS CO-OP OIL MILL; *U.S. Private*, pg. 868
RANCHERS COTTON OIL; *U.S. Private*, pg. 908
SOUTHERN COTTON OIL CO., INC.—Archer Daniels Midland Company (ADM); *U.S. Public*, pg. 128

2075 — SOYBEAN OIL MILLS

AG PROCESSING INC., A COOPERATIVE; *U.S. Private*, pg. 26
ARCHER DANIELS MIDLAND COMPANY (ADM); *U.S. Public*, pg. 127
CARGILL; *U.S. Private*, pg. 210
CENTRAL SOYA COMPANY, INC.—Compart SpA; *Int'l*, pg. 324
DU PONT PROTEIN TECHNOLOGIES INTERNATIONAL—Du Pont (E.I. Du Pont De Nemours & Co.); *U.S. Public*, pg. 531
DURABLE SPECIALTIES DIVISION—FiberMark Inc.; *U.S. Public*, pg. 620
ERIDANIA BEGHIN-SAY GROUP—Compart SpA; *Int'l*, pg. 324
MALLET & CO.; *U.S. Private*, pg. 698
MOORMAN'S INC.; *U.S. Private*, pg. 760
OWENSBORO GRAIN CO., INC.; *U.S. Private*, pg. 824
PURINA PROTEIN EUROPE S.A.—Ralston Purina Company; *U.S. Public*, pg. 1360
RICELAND FOODS, INC.; *U.S. Private*, pg. 928
SOUTHERN COTTON OIL CO., INC.—Archer Daniels Midland Company (ADM); *U.S. Public*, pg. 128
A.E. STALEY MANUFACTURING CO.—Tate & Lyle PLC; *Int'l*, pg. 1356
TATA OIL & MILLS COMPANY—Unilever Plc; *Int'l*, pg. 1437
WEST CENTRAL COOPERATIVE; *U.S. Private*, pg. 1163

2076 — VEGETABLE OIL MILLS, EXCEPT CORN, COTTONSEED, & SOYBEAN

ARCHER DANIELS MIDLAND COMPANY (ADM); *U.S. Public*, pg. 127
H.J. BAKER & BRO., INC.; *U.S. Private*, pg. 112
CARGILL; *U.S. Private*, pg. 210
CASCHEM INC.—Cambrex Corporation; *U.S. Public*, pg. 297
COAST PACKING COMPANY; *U.S. Private*, pg. 248
COLFAX, INC.; *U.S. Private*, pg. 252
COMPANIA COLOMBIANA DE GRASAS "COGRA-LEVER" S.A.—Unilever Plc; *Int'l*, pg. 1436
FARMERS UNION MARKETING & PROCESSING ASSOCIATION; *U.S. Private*, pg. 395
GOODMAN FIELDER LIMITED; *Int'l*, pg. 555
LOU ANA FOODS, INC.—Mitsui & Co., Ltd.; *Int'l*, pg. 879
MALLET & CO.; *U.S. Private*, pg. 698
PRESIDENT ENTERPRISES CORP.; *Int'l*, pg. 1068
RJR NABISCO HOLDINGS CORP.; *U.S. Public*, pg. 1354
REFINED OIL PRODUCTS (PTY.) LTD.—H.J. Heinz Company; *U.S. Public*, pg. 806
SIME DARBY COMMODITY TRADING & PLANTATIONS DIVISION—Sime Darby Berhad; *Int'l*, pg. 1250
SOUTHERN COTTON OIL CO., INC.—Archer Daniels Midland Company (ADM); *U.S. Public*, pg. 128
TATA OIL & MILLS COMPANY—Unilever Plc; *Int'l*, pg. 1437

2077 — ANIMAL & MARINE FATS & OILS

BAKER COMMODITIES, INC.; *U.S. Private*, pg. 111
H.J. BAKER & BRO., INC.; *U.S. Private*, pg. 112
CBP RESOURCES, INC.; *U.S. Private*, pg. 192
CBP RESOURCES-NORFOLK DIVISION—CBP Resources, Inc.; *U.S. Private*, pg. 192
COAST PACKING COMPANY; *U.S. Private*, pg. 248
COLFAX, INC.; *U.S. Private*, pg. 252
DARLING INTERNATIONAL, INC; *U.S. Public*, pg. 484
FARMERS UNION MARKETING & PROCESSING ASSOCIATION; *U.S. Private*, pg. 395
GRIFFIN INDUSTRIES, INC.; *U.S. Private*, pg. 480
HRR ENTERPRISES, INC.—Kane-Miller Corp.; *U.S. Private*, pg. 607
HYGRADE FOOD PRODUCTS CORPORATION—Sara Lee Corporation; *U.S. Public*, pg. 1433
IBP, INC.; *U.S. Public*, pg. 852
JONES DAIRY FARM; *U.S. Private*, pg. 596
KANE-MILLER CORP.; *U.S. Private*, pg. 607
KVAERNER EUREKA, BRYNE DIVISION—Kvaerner a.s.a.; *Int'l*, pg. 767
MOYER PACKING COMPANY; *U.S. Private*, pg. 765
NIPPON SUISAN KAISHA, LTD.; *Int'l*, pg. 940
REFINED OIL PRODUCTS (PTY.) LTD.—H.J. Heinz Company; *U.S. Public*, pg. 806
JACOB STERN & SONS, INC.; *U.S. Private*, pg. 1041
THE TATA IRON AND STEEL CO. LTD.; *Int'l*, pg. 1356
TYSON FOODS, INC.; *U.S. Public*, pg. 1652
ZAPATA CORPORATION; *U.S. Public*, pg. 1789

2079 — SHORTENING, TABLE OILS, MARGARINE & OTHER EDIBLE FATS & OILS, NEC

AGRA S.A.—Unilever Plc; *Int'l*, pg. 1436
AJINOMOTO COMPANY INC.; *Int'l*, pg. 40
ALBERTO-CULVER COMPANY; *U.S. Public*, pg. 37
ALFA SOLO MARGARINEFABRIKKEN AS—Unilever Plc; *Int'l*, pg. 1436
ALICORP S.A.; *Int'l*, pg. 57
ALLIANT FOODSERVICE—Clayton, Dubilier & Rice, Inc; *U.S. Private*, pg. 244
ALLIANT FOODSERVICE, INC.—Clayton, Dubilier & Rice, Inc; *U.S. Private*, pg. 244
ARMOUR FOOD COMPANY—ConAgra, Inc.; *U.S. Public*, pg. 427
ASTRA-CALVE S.A.—Unilever Plc; *Int'l*, pg. 1436
ASTRA FETT-UND OELWERKE AG—Unilever Plc; *Int'l*, pg. 1436
BEST FOODS—Bestfoods; *U.S. Public*, pg. 224
BEST FOODS CARIBBEAN, INC.—Bestfoods; *U.S. Public*, pg. 224
BESTFOODS; *U.S. Public*, pg. 223
BLOHORN S.A.—Unilever Plc; *Int'l*, pg. 1436
BRISTOL-MYERS SQUIBB COMPANY; *U.S. Public*, pg. 253
CAILA Y PARES SA—Akzo Nobel N.V.; *Int'l*, pg. 47
CENTRAL SOYA COMPANY, INC.—Compart SpA; *Int'l*, pg. 324
CHESEBROUGH-POND'S—Unilever Plc; *Int'l*, pg. 1436
COAST PACKING COMPANY; *U.S. Private*, pg. 248
COLFAX, INC.; *U.S. Private*, pg. 252
COMPAGNIE DES MARGARINES, SAVONS ET COSMETIQUES AU ZAIRE S.A.R.L.—Unilever Plc; *Int'l*, pg. 1436
COMPANIA COLOMBIANA DE GRASAS "COGRA-LEVER" S.A.—Unilever Plc; *Int'l*, pg. 1436
CROKLAAN B.V.—Unilever Plc; *Int'l*, pg. 1436
DEEP SOUTH PRODUCTS—Winn-Dixie Stores, Inc.; *U.S. Public*, pg. 1772
EAST AFRICA INDUSTRIES LTD.—Unilever Plc; *Int'l*, pg. 1436
ERIDANIA BEGHIN-SAY GROUP—Compart SpA; *Int'l*, pg. 324
FIMA-PRODUCTOS ALIMENTARES, LDA; *Int'l*, pg. 471
FOOD OILS CORPORATION—Trinidad/Benham Corp.; *U.S. Private*, pg. 1103
GOODMAN FIELDER LIMITED; *Int'l*, pg. 555
GREGG FOODS OF GARDEN GROVE, INC.—Borden, Inc.; *U.S. Private*, pg. 158
HINDUSTAN LEVER LTD.—Unilever Plc; *Int'l*, pg. 1437
HUNT-WESSON, INC.—ConAgra, Inc.; *U.S. Public*, pg. 428
INDUSTRIAS GESSY LEVER LTDA.—Unilever Plc; *Int'l*, pg. 1437
KANE-MILLER CORP.; *U.S. Private*, pg. 607
KARLSHAMNS AB—KF/Konsum Coop Group; *Int'l*, pg. 718
KONINKLIJKE BUNGE B.V.; *Int'l*, pg. 753
KRAFT FOOD INGREDIENTS CORP.—Philip Morris Companies Inc.; *U.S. Public*, pg. 1288
KRAFT FOODS INC.—Philip Morris Companies Inc.; *U.S. Public*, pg. 1288
LEVER CHILE S.A.—Unilever Plc; *Int'l*, pg. 1437
LEVER Y ASOCIADOS SACIF—Unilever Plc; *Int'l*, pg. 1438
LODERS & NUCOLINE LTD.—Unilever Plc; *Int'l*, pg. 1434
LOU ANA FOODS, INC.—Mitsui & Co., Ltd.; *Int'l*, pg. 879
MADISON DAIRY PRODUCE COMPANY; *U.S. Private*, pg. 694
MALLET & CO.; *U.S. Private*, pg. 698
MAPLE LEAF FOODS INC.; *Int'l*, pg. 841
MARGARINBOLAGET AB—Nestle S.A.; *Int'l*, pg. 922
MARSA KRAFT JACOBS SUCHARD SABANCI GIDA SANAYI VE TICARET A.S—Sabanci Holding A.S.; *Int'l*, pg. 1168
MARSA KRAFT JACOBS SUCHARD SABANCI GIDA SANAYI VE TICARET A.S—Philip Morris Companies Inc.; *U.S. Public*, pg. 1290
MARUBENI CORPORATION; *Int'l*, pg. 844
W. & C. MCDONNELL LTD.—Unilever Plc; *Int'l*, pg. 1438
MEADOW LEA FOODS LTD.—Goodman Fielder Limited; *Int'l*, pg. 555
MEISTERMARKEN-WERKE G.M.B.H., SPEZIALFABRIK BACK-UND GROSSKUCHENBEDARF—Unilever Plc; *Int'l*, pg. 1438
NABISCO INC.—RJR Nabisco Holdings Corp.; *U.S. Public*, pg. 1355
NIPPON LEVER BV—Unilever Plc; *Int'l*, pg. 1438
OSTERREICHISCHE UNILEVER GES. M.B.H.—Unilever Plc; *Int'l*, pg. 1438
OTT FOOD PRODUCTS; *U.S. Private*, pg. 821
PAASIVAARA OY—Unilever Plc; *Int'l*, pg. 1438
PHILIPPINE REFINING COMPANY INC.—Unilever Plc; *Int'l*, pg. 1438
PHILIPPINES DAIRY PRODUCTS CORP.—New Zealand Dairy Board; *Int'l*, pg. 923
POMPEIIAN, INC.; *U.S. Private*, pg. 875
PREMIER EDIBLE OILS CORP.—Mitsubishi Corporation; *Int'l*, pg. 872
PROCTER & GAMBLE FOOD PRODUCTS DIV.—The Procter & Gamble Company; *U.S. Public*, pg. 1331
RJR NABISCO HOLDINGS CORP.; *U.S. Public*, pg. 1354
RAISIO GROUP; *Int'l*, pg. 1085
RAISIO GROUP PLC—Raisio Group; *Int'l*, pg. 1085
RAISIO GROUP PLC-MARGARINF—Raisio Group; *Int'l*, pg. 1085
RICELAND FOODS, INC.; *U.S. Private*, pg. 928
SAIS—Unilever Plc; *Int'l*, pg. 1438
SME INTERNATIONAL—IRI Istituto Ricostruzione Industriale; *Int'l*, pg. 655
SABANCI HOLDING A.S.; *Int'l*, pg. 1167
A.E. STALEY MANUFACTURING CO.—Tate & Lyle PLC; *Int'l*, pg. 1356
STAR FINE FOODS, INC.; *U.S. Private*, pg. 1034
SUNNYLAND REFINING CO., INC.—Kane-Miller Corp.; *U.S. Private*, pg. 607
TURUN SAIPPUA OY—Unilever Plc; *Int'l*, pg. 1438
UMEX COMPANY—Unilever Plc; *Int'l*, pg. 1435
UNI-DAN A/S—Unilever Plc; *Int'l*, pg. 1438
UNIL-IT S.P.A.—Unilever Plc; *Int'l*, pg. 1438
UNILEVER AUSTRALIA LTD.—Unilever Plc; *Int'l*, pg. 1439
P.T. UNILEVER INDONESIA—Unilever Plc; *Int'l*, pg. 1439
UNILEVER IS TICARET VE SANAYI TURK LIMITED SIRKETI—Unilever Plc; *Int'l*, pg. 1439
UNILEVER N.V.—Unilever Plc; *Int'l*, pg. 1434
UNILEVER PLC; *Int'l*, pg. 1433
UNIMILLS B.V.—Unilever Plc; *Int'l*, pg. 1439
UNION DEUTSCHE LEBENSMITTELWERKE G.M.B.H.—Unilever Plc; *Int'l*, pg. 1439
UNION N.V.—Unilever Plc; *Int'l*, pg. 1439

VAN DEN BERGH & JURGENS (PTY.) LTD.—Unilever Plc; *Int'l*, pg. 1439
VAN DEN BERGH EN JURGENS B.V.—Unilever Plc; *Int'l*, pg. 1439
VAN DEN BERGH FOODS COMPANY—Unilever Plc; *Int'l*, pg. 1436
VANDEMOORTELE N.V.; *Int'l*, pg. 1451
VENTURA FOODS LLC—Mitsui & Co., Ltd.; *Int'l*, pg. 879
WILSEY FOODS, INC.—Mitsui & Co., Ltd.; *Int'l*, pg. 879

2082 — MALT BEVERAGES

ALKEN-MAES—Danone Group; *Int'l*, pg. 381
AMPLEFLOW LTD.—Whitbread PLC; *Int'l*, pg. 1499
ANHEUSER-BUSCH COMPANIES, INC.; *U.S. Public*, pg. 113
ASAHI BREWERIES LTD.; *Int'l*, pg. 83
ASCOT HOLDINGS PLC; *Int'l*, pg. 87
ASIA PACIFIC BREWERIES LTD.—Heineken N.V.; *Int'l*, pg. 608
ATHENIAN BREWERY S.A.—Heineken N.V.; *Int'l*, pg. 608
BAKERY INGREDIENTS DIVISION—Royal Gist-Brocades N.V.; *Int'l*, pg. 1142
BASS BREWERS LTD.—Bass PLC; *Int'l*, pg. 170
BASS PLC; *Int'l*, pg. 169
BEAMISH & CRAWFORD PLC—Scottish & Newcastle plc; *Int'l*, pg. 1212
BIERBRAUEREI FOHRENBURG; *Int'l*, pg. 194
BIRRA MORETTI S.P.A.—Interbrew S.A.; *Int'l*, pg. 680
BIRRA PERONI INDUSTRIALE—Danone Group; *Int'l*, pg. 381
BITBURGER BRAUEREI TH. SIMON GMBH; *Int'l*, pg. 197
BOSTON BEER COMPANY; *U.S. Public*, pg. 246
BRASSERIES ET LIMONADERIES DU BURUNDI "BRARUDI" S.A.R.L.—Heineken N.V.; *Int'l*, pg. 608
BRAUEREI AG—Feldschlosschen Hurlimann Holding; *Int'l*, pg. 479
BRAUEREI EICHHOF; *Int'l*, pg. 213
MATHEW BROWN PLC—Scottish & Newcastle plc; *Int'l*, pg. 1211
CANADA MALTING CO. LIMITED—ConAgra, Inc.; *U.S. Public*, pg. 428
CARLTON & UNITED BREWERIES LTD.—Foster's Brewing Group Limited; *Int'l*, pg. 500
CARLTON BREWERY (FIJI) LIMITED—Foster's Brewing Group Limited; *Int'l*, pg. 501
CARLTON SPECIAL BEVERAGES—Foster's Brewing Group Limited; *Int'l*, pg. 501
CENTRAL DE CERVEJAS, S.A.; *Int'l*, pg. 279
CERVEJARIAS KAISER BRASIL LTDA.; *Int'l*, pg. 279
ADOLPH COORS COMPANY; *U.S. Public*, pg. 445
COORS BREWING COMPANY—Adolph Coors Company; *U.S. Public*, pg. 445
CROMPTON & KNOWLES CORPORATION; *U.S. Public*, pg. 459
DANONE GROUP; *Int'l*, pg. 379
DIAGEO PLC; *Int'l*, pg. 408
DIEBELS PRIVATE BREWERY; *Int'l*, pg. 413
DIXIE BREWING CO., INC.; *U.S. Private*, pg. 336
ELDERS LIMITED—Foster's Brewing Group Limited; *Int'l*, pg. 500
EUROCERMEX N.V.—Anheuser-Busch Companies, Inc.; *U.S. Public*, pg. 115
FOSTER'S BREWING GROUP LIMITED; *Int'l*, pg. 500
FULLER, SMITH & TURNER PLC; *Int'l*, pg. 529
THE GENESEE BREWING COMPANY, INC.—Genesee Corporation; *U.S. Public*, pg. 728
GENESEE CORPORATION; *U.S. Public*, pg. 728
GRANDMA FOOD PRODUCTS LIMITED—Crompton & Knowles Corporation; *U.S. Public*, pg. 460
GREAT WESTERN MALTING CO.—ConAgra, Inc.; *U.S. Public*, pg. 428
GROLSCH N.V.; *Int'l*, pg. 559
GRUPO MODELO S.A.—Anheuser-Busch Companies, Inc.; *U.S. Public*, pg. 115
GUINNESS BREWING WORLDWIDE LTD.—Diageo Plc; *Int'l*, pg. 412
GUINNESS IRELAND (HOLDINGS) LTD.—Diageo Plc; *Int'l*, *pg. 412*
GUINNESS NORTHERN IRELAND LIMITED—Diageo Plc; *Int'l*, pg. 412
GUINNESS PLC—Diageo Plc; *Int'l*, pg. 412
THE HARP LAGER CO. LTD.—Diageo Plc; *Int'l*, pg. 412
HARRISONS & CROSFIELD PLC; *Int'l*, pg. 598
HEINEKEN ITALIA S.P.A.—Heineken N.V.; *Int'l*, pg. 608
HEINEKEN NEDERLAND BV—Heineken N.V.; *Int'l*, pg. 608
HEINEKEN N.V.; *Int'l*, pg. 608
HOBART BREWERY—Foster's Brewing Group Limited; *Int'l*, pg. 501
HOME BREWERY PLC—Scottish & Newcastle plc; *Int'l*, pg. 1211
JOSEPH HUBER BREWING CO., INC.; *U.S. Private*, pg. 545
HUDEPOHL-SCHOENLING BREWING COMPANY; *U.S. Private*, pg. 545
INTERBREW ITALIA S.P.A.—Interbrew S.A.; *Int'l*, pg. 679
INTERBREW NETHERLANDS—Interbrew S.A.; *Int'l*, pg. 679
INTERBREW S.A.; *Int'l*, pg. 679
KANTERBRAU S.A.—Danone Group; *Int'l*, pg. 381
KIRIN BREWERY CO., LTD.; *Int'l*, pg. 735
KRONENBOURG—Danone Group; *Int'l*, pg. 381
LABATT BREWERIES OF CANADA—Interbrew S.A.; *Int'l*, pg. 679
LABATT BREWING COMPANY LIMITED—Interbrew S.A.; *Int'l*, pg. 679
LATROBE BREWING CO.—Interbrew S.A.; *Int'l*, pg. 680
JACOB LEINENKUGEL BREWING CO.—Philip Morris Companies Inc.; *U.S. Public*, pg. 1289
THE LION BREWERY, INC.; *U.S. Public*, pg. 1000
LONRHO PLC; *Int'l*, pg. 817
MAHOU S.A.—Danone Group; *Int'l*, pg. 381
THE F.X. MATT BREWING CO.; *U.S. Private*, pg. 714
MILLER BREWING COMPANY—Philip Morris Companies Inc.; *U.S. Public*, pg. 1289
MINNESOTA BREWING COMPANY; *U.S. Public*, pg. 1115
MOLSON ALBERTA BREWERY LTD.—The Molson Companies Limited; *Int'l*, pg. 887
MOLSON BREWERIES—The Molson Companies Limited; *Int'l*, pg. 887
MOLSON BREWERY B.C. LTD.—The Molson Companies Limited; *Int'l*, pg. 887
MOLSON BREWERY QUEBEC LIMITED—The Molson Companies Limited; *Int'l*, pg. 887
THE MOLSON COMPANIES LIMITED; *Int'l*, pg. 887
MOLSON SASKATCHEWAN BREWERY LTD.—The Molson Companies Limited; *Int'l*, pg. 887
P.T. MULTI BINTANG INDONESIA—Heineken N.V.; *Int'l*, pg. 608
MURPHY BREWERY IRELAND LTD.—Heineken N.V.; *Int'l*, pg. 608
NATIONAL SORGHUM BEER BREWERIES PTY. LTD. HIGHVELD DIVISION; *Int'l*, pg. 909
THE NEWCASTLE BREWERIES, LTD.—Scottish & Newcastle plc; *Int'l*, pg. 1211
NOR-CAL BEVERAGE CO., INC.; *U.S. Private*, pg. 801
OZEKI CORPORATION; *Int'l*, pg. 1019
OZEKI SAKE (U.S.A.) INC.—Ozeki Corporation; *Int'l*, pg. 1019
PABST BREWING CO./MILWAUKEE—S & P Company; *U.S. Private*, pg. 954
PHARMACIA & UPJOHN, INC.; *Int'l*, pg. 1047
PITTSBURGH BREWING COMPANY—Keystone Brewers, Inc.; *U.S. Private*, pg. 619
PRINZ BRAU ITALIA S.P.A.—Interbrew S.A.; *Int'l*, pg. 680
PYRAMID BREWERIES, INC.; *U.S. Public*, pg. 1345
S & P COMPANY; *U.S. Private*, pg. 954
SAN MIGUEL CORP.; *Int'l*, pg. 1183
SANDOZ NUTRITION LTD.—Novartis AG; *Int'l*, pg. 972
SAPPORO BREWERIES LTD.; *Int'l*, pg. 1193
SCOTTISH & COURAGE BEER DIV.—Scottish & Newcastle plc; *Int'l*, pg. 1212
SCOTTISH & COURAGE BEER PRODUCTION LIMITED—Scottish & Newcastle plc; *Int'l*, pg. 1212
SCOTTISH & NEWCASTLE PLC; *Int'l*, pg. 1211
SCOTTISH COURAGE LIMITED—Scottish & Newcastle plc; *Int'l*, pg. 1212
SOGEBRA S.A.—Heineken N.V.; *Int'l*, pg. 608
SOUTH AFRICAN BREWERIES, LTD.; *Int'l*, pg. 1286
SOUTHCORP HOLDINGS LTD.; *Int'l*, pg. 1287
STEVENS POINT BREWERY—Canandaigua Wine Company, Inc.; *U.S. Public*, pg. 300
THE STROH BREWERY COMPANY; *U.S. Private*, pg. 1047
STROTHMANN BRENNEREIEN G.M.B.H.—Koninklijke BolsWessanen nv; *Int'l*, pg. 751
UNICER-UNIAO CERVEJEIRA, S.A.; *Int'l*, pg. 1432
VAUX BREWERIES LTD.—Vaux Group Plc; *Int'l*, pg. 1454
VAUX GROUP PLC; *Int'l*, pg. 1453
S.H. WARD INC.—Vaux Group Plc; *Int'l*, pg. 1454
WARSTEINER BRAUEREI HAUS CRAMER GMBH & CO.; *Int'l*, pg. 1486
WATKINS INCORPORATED; *U.S. Private*, pg. 1153
WHITBREAD BEER COMPANY—Whitbread PLC; *Int'l*, pg. 1498
WHITBREAD PLC; *Int'l*, pg. 1498
WHITE ROCK PRODUCTS CORP.; *U.S. Private*, pg. 1173

2083 — MALT

ABM CHEMICALS LTD.—Rhone-Poulenc S.A.; *Int'l*, pg. 1113
ARCHER DANIELS MIDLAND COMPANY (ADM); *U.S. Public*, pg. 127
BOCM PAULS LIMITED—Harrisons & Crosfield plc; *Int'l*, pg. 598
HUGH BAIRD & SONS LIMITED—ConAgra, Inc.; *U.S. Public*, pg. 428
BARLEY EXPORTS LIMITED—Avonmore Waterford Group plc; *Int'l*, pg. 102
CANADA MALTING CO. LIMITED—ConAgra, Inc.; *U.S. Public*, pg. 428
CARGILL; *U.S. Private*, pg. 210
FLEISCHMANN MALTING COMPANY, INC.—Archer Daniels Midland Company (ADM); *U.S. Public*, pg. 128
GREAT WESTERN MALTING CO.—ConAgra, Inc.; *U.S. Public*, pg. 428
KIRIN BREWERY CO., LTD.; *Int'l*, pg. 735
LABATT BREWERIES OF CANADA—Interbrew S.A.; *Int'l*, pg. 679
MORAY FIRTH MALTINGS—Scottish & Newcastle plc; *Int'l*, pg. 1211
PABST BREWING CO./MILWAUKEE—S & P Company; *U.S. Private*, pg. 954
PAULS MALT LIMITED—Harrisons & Crosfield plc; *Int'l*, pg. 598
PAULS PLC—Harrisons & Crosfield plc; *Int'l*, pg. 598
PHILIP MORRIS COMPANIES INC.; *U.S. Public*, pg. 1287
SCHREIER MALTING CO.; *U.S. Private*, pg. 972
SCOTTISH & NEWCASTLE PLC; *Int'l*, pg. 1211
WATERLOO MALTING CO., INC.—Philip Morris Companies Inc.; *U.S. Public*, pg. 1289
WHITBREAD PLC; *Int'l*, pg. 1498

2084 — WINES, BRANDY & BRANDY SPIRITS

ADAMS WINE CO.; *U.S. Private*, pg. 17
ALLIED DOMECQ SPIRITS & WINE—Allied Domecq PLC; *Int'l*, pg. 63
ANDRES WINES LTD.; *Int'l*, pg. 75
ANGLO ESPANOLA DE DISTRIBUCION, AED SA—Diageo Plc; *Int'l*, pg. 409
BALLATORE CHAMPAGNE CELLARS—E. & J. Gallo Winery; *U.S. Private*, pg. 438
BANFI PRODUCT CORP—Banfi Vintners; *U.S. Private*, pg. 113
BARBERO 1891 SPA; *Int'l*, pg. 164
BATAVIA WINE CELLARS—Canandaigua Wine Company, Inc.; *U.S. Public*, pg. 300
BEAULIEU VINEYARD—Diageo Plc; *Int'l*, pg. 410
BERINGER WINE ESTATES HOLDINGS, INC.—Texas Pacific Group; *U.S. Private*, pg. 1078
BETTER BRANDS OF ATLANTA, INC.; *U.S. Private*, pg. 141
THE BEVERAGE SOURCE, INC.—Erly Industries, Inc.; *U.S. Public*, pg. 591
BISCEGLIA BROTHERS WINE CO.—Canandaigua Wine Company, Inc.; *U.S. Public*, pg. 300
BOLS-CYNAR, AG—Koninklijke BolsWessanen nv; *Int'l*, pg. 751
BOLS INTERNATIONAL B.V.—Koninklijke BolsWessanen nv; *Int'l*, pg. 751
BOLS MILANI LTD.—Koninklijke BolsWessanen nv; *Int'l*, pg. 751
BOLS ROYAL DISTILLERIES—Koninklijke BolsWessanen nv; *Int'l*, pg. 751
BOLS STROTHMANN BRENNEREIEN GMBH & CO. KG—Koninklijke BolsWessanen nv; *Int'l*, pg. 751
BUENA VISTA WINERY—A. Racke GmbH; *Int'l*, pg. 1083
CALLAWAY VINEYARD & WINERY—Allied Domecq PLC; *Int'l*, pg. 63
CANANDAIGUA WINE COMPANY, INC.; *U.S. Public*, pg. 300
CASTELLO BANFI SRL.—Banfi Vintners; *U.S. Private*, pg. 113
CHATEAU ST. JEAN WINERY—Suntory Ltd.; *Int'l*, pg. 1321
FRANCESCO CINZANO & C.IA SPA—Diageo Plc; *Int'l*, pg. 409
COGRAMI S.A.E.—Koninklijke BolsWessanen nv; *Int'l*, pg. 751
CORBETT CANYON VINEYARDS—The Wine Group; *U.S. Private*, pg. 1183
DAVIDE CAMPARI; *Int'l*, pg. 385
DELAFORCE SONS & CA VINHOS LDA.—Diageo Plc; *Int'l*, *pg. 409*
DELICATO VINEYARDS; *U.S. Private*, pg. 322
B.V. DISTILLERDERIJ 'DE FRANSCHE KROON' V/H HARTEVELT EN ZOON—Koninklijke BolsWessanen nv; *Int'l*, pg. 751
DOMAINE CARNEROS—Taittinger; *Int'l*, pg. 1348
E & J DISTILLERS BRANDY—E. & J. Gallo Winery; *U.S. Private*, pg. 438
ERLY INDUSTRIES, INC.; *U.S. Public*, pg. 591
ERVEN LUCAS BOLS ITALIA S.P.A.—Koninklijke BolsWessanen nv; *Int'l*, pg. 751
ERVEN LUCAS BOLS S.A.—Koninklijke BolsWessanen nv; *Int'l*, pg. 751
FRANZIA BROTHERS WINERY—The Wine Group; *U.S. Private*, pg. 1183
E. & J. GALLO WINERY; *U.S. Private*, pg. 438
GIBSON WINE COMPANY; *U.S. Private*, pg. 452
GIUMARRA VINEYARDS; *U.S. Private*, pg. 455
GLEN ELLEN WINERY; *U.S. Private*, pg. 455
GRANDES MARCAS SA—Diageo Plc; *Int'l*, pg. 409
GROUPE PERNOD RICARD; *Int'l*, pg. 566
HARVEYS OF BRISTOL LIMITED—Allied Domecq PLC; *Int'l*, pg. 63
HECK CELLARS WINERY—F. Korbel Bros. Inc.; *U.S. Private*, pg. 632
JA. HENNESSY & CO.—LVMH Moet Hennessy Louis Vuitton; *Int'l*, pg. 780
HEUBLEIN DO BRASIL—Diageo Plc; *Int'l*, pg. 410
HEUBLEIN INC.—Diageo Plc; *Int'l*, pg. 410
HEUBLEIN, INC.—Diageo Plc; *Int'l*, pg. 410
IDV AFRICA & LATIN AMERICA—Diageo Plc; *Int'l*, pg. 409
IDV ASIA PACIFIC—Diageo Plc; *Int'l*, pg. 409
IDV NORTH AMERICA—Diageo Plc; *Int'l*, pg. 409
IDV FRANCE—Diageo Plc; *Int'l*, pg. 410
INTERBREW NETHERLANDS—Interbrew S.A.; *Int'l*, pg. 679
INTERNATIONAL DISTILLERS & VINTNERS-EUROPE—Diageo Plc; *Int'l*, pg. 409
INTERNATIONAL DISTILLERS SOUTH ASIA—Diageo Plc; *Int'l*, pg. 410
INTERNATIONAL WINE & SPIRITS LTD.—UST Inc.; *U.S. Public*, pg. 1661
JBB WORLDWIDE, INC.—Fortune Brands, Inc.; *U.S. Public*, *pg. 675*
CHARLES JACQUIN ET CIE, INC.; *U.S. Private*, pg. 580
KYOWA HAKKO KOGYO COMPANY, LTD.; *Int'l*, pg. 778
LVMH MOET HENNESSY LOUIS VUITTON; *Int'l*, pg. 779
LA TONDENA DISTILLERS, INC.; *Int'l*, pg. 785
LABATT BREWING COMPANY LIMITED—Interbrew S.A.; *Int'l*, pg. 679
LAIRD & COMPANY; *U.S. Private*, pg. 642
LANCERS—Diageo Plc; *Int'l*, pg. 411
LONDON BREWERY—Interbrew S.A.; *Int'l*, pg. 679
LONRHO PLC; *Int'l*, pg. 817
MAISON DEUTZ WINERY—Nestle S.A.; *Int'l*, pg. 917
MANASCHEWITZ WINE COMPANY—Canandaigua Wine Company, Inc.; *U.S. Public*, pg. 300
MARCO DEL PONT S.A.; *Int'l*, pg. 842
MARIE BRIZARD WINES & SPIRITS USA; *U.S. Private*, pg. 702
MARKHAM VINEYARDS—Mercian Corporation; *Int'l*, pg. 858
MARQINT MARCAS INTERNACIONALES SA—Diageo Plc; *Int'l*, pg. 410
MARTELL ET CIE. S.A.—The Seagram Company Ltd.; *Int'l*, *pg. 1217*
MATTHEW CLARK BRANDS—Matthew Clark Taunton, Ltd.; *Int'l*, pg. 848
MATTHEW CLARK TAUNTON, LTD.; *Int'l*, pg. 848
MEIJI SHOKUHIN CO., LTD.—Meiji Seika Kaisha, Ltd.; *Int'l*, *pg. 855*
MERCIAN CORPORATION; *Int'l*, pg. 858
MOGEN DAVID WINE CORP.—The Wine Group; *U.S. Private*, pg. 1183
NESTLE S.A.; *Int'l*, pg. 915
ORLANDO WYNDHAM—Groupe Pernod Ricard; *Int'l*, pg. 567

OTTAVIO RICCADONNA S.P.A.—Koninklijke BolsWessanen nv; *Int'l*, pg. 751
PENAFLOR S.A.; *Int'l*, pg. 1032
PEPSICO WINES & SPIRITS INTERNATIONAL—PepsiCo, Inc.; *U.S. Public*, pg. 1277
PIAT PERE & FILS—Diageo Plc; *Int'l*, pg. 410
PINE STATE BEVERAGE—Pine State Trading Company; *U.S. Private*, pg. 865
A. RACKE GMBH; *Int'l*, pg. 1083
RACKE USA—A. Racke GmbH; *Int'l*, pg. 1083
REMY AMERIQUE INC.—Remy Cointreau; *Int'l*, pg. 1102
REMY COINTREAU; *Int'l*, pg. 1102
RENAULT BISQUIT—Groupe Pernod Ricard; *Int'l*, pg. 566
ROBERT MONDAVI WINERY, INC.; *U.S. Public*, pg. 1393
ST. CLEMENT VINEYARDS—Sapporo Breweries Ltd.; *Int'l*, pg. 1193
SAPPORO BREWERIES LTD.; *Int'l*, pg. 1193
SARA LEE/DE—Sara Lee Corporation; *U.S. Public*, pg. 1434
SAXONY DISTILLERS ET CIE, INC.—Charles Jacquin et Cie, Inc.; *U.S. Private*, pg. 580
SCOTTISH & COURAGE BEER DIV.—Scottish & Newcastle plc; *Int'l*, pg. 1212
SEAGRAM BEVERAGE CO.—The Seagram Company Ltd.; *Int'l*, pg. 1215
THE SEAGRAM BEVERAGE GROUP—The Seagram Company Ltd.; *Int'l*, pg. 1217
SEAGRAM CANADA—The Seagram Company Ltd.; *Int'l*, pg. 1217
THE SEAGRAM CLASSICS WINE COMPANY—The Seagram Company Ltd.; *Int'l*, pg. 1215
THE SEAGRAM COMPANY LTD.; *Int'l*, pg. 1214
JOSEPH E. SEAGRAM & SONS, INC.—The Seagram Company Ltd.; *Int'l*, pg. 1215
THE SEAGRAM SPIRITS AND WINE GROUP—The Seagram Company Ltd.; *Int'l*, pg. 1217
SILENO, SOC DISTRIBUIDORA DE BEBIDAS—Diageo Plc; *Int'l*, pg. 410
SIMI WINERY—LVMH Moet Hennessy Louis Vuitton; *Int'l*, pg. 781
SOCIETA INDUSTRIE LIQUORISTICHE S.A.S.—Koninklijke BolsWessanen nv; *Int'l*, pg. 751
SOCIETA ITALIANA PER IL CYNAR S.P.A.—Koninklijke BolsWessanen nv; *Int'l*, pg. 751
SOVEDI BENELUX-BELGIUM—Diageo Plc; *Int'l*, pg. 410
SOVEDI BENELUX-NEDERLAND—Diageo Plc; *Int'l*, pg. 410
SOVEDI FRANCE—Diageo Plc; *Int'l*, pg. 410
STABBURET A/S—Orkla A.S.A.; *Int'l*, pg. 1011
ROBERT STEMMLER WINERY—A. Racke GmbH; *Int'l*, pg. 1083
STIMSON LANE LTD.—UST Inc.; *U.S. Public*, pg. 1661
SUNBELT BEVERAGES; *U.S. Private*, pg. 1051
SUNTORY LTD.; *Int'l*, pg. 1321
SUTTER HOME WINERY, INC.; *U.S. Private*, pg. 1057
TAITTINGER; *Int'l*, pg. 1348
TOTT'S CHAMPAGNE CELLARS—E. & J. Gallo Winery; *U.S. Private*, pg. 438
UST INC.; *U.S. Public*, pg. 1660
VEUVE CLICQUOT PONSARDIN—LVMH Moet Hennessy Louis Vuitton; *Int'l*, pg. 781
VINCOR INTERNATIONAL; *Int'l*, pg. 1468
W & A GILBEY SA—Diageo Plc; *Int'l*, pg. 409
WARNER VINEYARDS; *U.S. Private*, pg. 1151
WEIBEL WINERY; *U.S. Private*, pg. 1159
WELTMARKEN IMPORT SPIRITUOSEN UND WEINE GMBH—Diageo Plc; *Int'l*, pg. 410
WHITE ROCK DISTILLERIES INC.; *U.S. Private*, pg. 1173
WIDMER'S WINE CELLARS, INC.—Canandaigua Wine Company, Inc.; *U.S. Public*, pg. 300
THE WINE ALLIANCE—Allied Domecq PLC; *Int'l*, pg. 63
THE WINE GROUP; *U.S. Private*, pg. 1182
WINE WORLD ESTATES COMPANY—Nestle S.A.; *Int'l*, pg. 917
WINEQUEST—Delicato Vineyards; *U.S. Private*, pg. 322
WINONA S.A.R.L.—Andres Wines Ltd.; *Int'l*, pg. 76
YAMANASHI JOZO CO., LTD.—Meiji Seika Kaisha, Ltd.; *Int'l*, pg. 855

2085 — DISTILLED & BLENDED LIQUORS

ALLIED DOMECQ SPIRITS & WINE—Allied Domecq PLC; *Int'l*, pg. 63
ANGLO ESPANOLA DE DISTRIBUCION, AED SA—Diageo Plc; *Int'l*, pg. 409
GW ARCHER & CO.—Diageo Plc; *Int'l*, pg. 409
ASBACH GMBH & CO.—Diageo Plc; *Int'l*, pg. 412
BACARDI CORPORATION—Bacardi Limited; *Int'l*, pg. 131
R & A BAILEY & CO.—Diageo Plc; *Int'l*, pg. 409
BARBERO 1891 SPA; *Int'l*, pg. 164
BARTON INCORPORATED—Canandaigua Wine Company, Inc.; *U.S. Public*, pg. 300
BOLS-CYNAR, AG—Koninklijke BolsWessanen nv; *Int'l*, pg. 751
BOLS INTERNATIONAL B.V.—Koninklijke BolsWessanen nv; *Int'l*, pg. 751
BOLS MILANI LTD.—Koninklijke BolsWessanen nv; *Int'l*, pg. 751
BOLS ROYAL DISTILLERIES—Koninklijke BolsWessanen nv; *Int'l*, pg. 751
BOLS STROTHMANN BRENNEREIEN GMBH & CO. KG—Koninklijke BolsWessanen nv; *Int'l*, pg. 751
THE BOMBAY SPIRITS COMPANY—Diageo Plc; *Int'l*, pg. 409
BONOMELLI S.R.L.; *Int'l*, pg. 201
BROWN-FORMAN BEVERAGES WORLDWIDE—Brown-Forman Corporation; *U.S. Public*, pg. 261
BROWN-FORMAN CORPORATION; *U.S. Public*, pg. 261
H.P. BULMER HOLDINGS PLC; *Int'l*, pg. 232
CSR PAMPRYL—Groupe Pernod Ricard; *Int'l*, pg. 566
CANADIAN MIST DISTILLERS LTD.—Brown-Forman Corporation; *U.S. Public*, pg. 262
CARILLON IMPORTERS, LTD.—Diageo Plc; *Int'l*, pg. 409
CHANTRE & CIE GMBH—Eckes AG; *Int'l*, pg. 433
CLINTOCK LIMITED—Brown-Forman Corporation; *U.S. Public*, pg. 262
COGRAMI S.A.E.—Koninklijke BolsWessanen nv; *Int'l*, pg. 751
CORMAGIC N.V.—Koninklijke BolsWessanen nv; *Int'l*, pg. 751
CROFT & COMPANHIA LIMITADA—Diageo Plc; *Int'l*, pg. 409
DAVIDE CAMPARI; *Int'l*, pg. 385
DISTILERIA BAGO, INC. (DBI)—La Tondena Distillers, Inc.; *Int'l*, pg. 785
B.V. DISTILLERDERIJ 'DE FRANSCHE KROON' V/H HARTEVELT EN ZOON—Koninklijke BolsWessanen nv; *Int'l*, pg. 751
DISTILLERS CORPORATION S.A.—Rothmans UK Holdings Limited; *Int'l*, pg. 1129
DUNHILL SCOTCH WHISKY SALES LIMITED—Diageo Plc; *Int'l*, pg. 409
EARLY TIMES DISTILLERS CO.—Brown-Forman Corporation; *U.S. Public*, pg. 261
ECKES AG; *Int'l*, pg. 432
ERVEN LUCAS BOLS ITALIA S.P.A.—Koninklijke BolsWessanen nv; *Int'l*, pg. 751
ERVEN LUCAS BOLS S.A.—Koninklijke BolsWessanen nv; *Int'l*, pg. 751
FAIRVIEW WINE CO.—White Rock Distilleries Inc.; *U.S. Private*, pg. 1173
FELDSCHLOSSCHEN HURLIMANN HOLDING; *Int'l*, pg. 479
FORTUNE BRANDS, INC.; *U.S. Public*, pg. 674
GILBEY CANADA INC.—Diageo Plc; *Int'l*, pg. 409
GLENROTHES DISTILLERY—The Highland Distilleries Company plc; *Int'l*, pg. 619
GLENTURRET DISTILLERY LIMITED—The Highland Distilleries Company plc; *Int'l*, pg. 619
MATTHEW GLOAG & SON LIMITED—The Highland Distilleries Company plc; *Int'l*, pg. 619
GRAIN PROCESSING CORP.—Varied Investments, Inc.; *U.S. Private*, pg. 1134
GRANDES MARCAS SA—Diageo Plc; *Int'l*, pg. 409
WILLIAM GRANT & SONS DISTILLERS LTD.; *Int'l*, pg. 557
JOHN GROSS & CO.; *U.S. Private*, pg. 483
GROUPE PERNOD RICARD; *Int'l*, pg. 566
HEUBLEIN DO BRASIL—Diageo Plc; *Int'l*, pg. 410
HEUBLEIN, INC.—Diageo Plc; *Int'l*, pg. 410
THE HIGHLAND DISTILLERIES COMPANY PLC; *Int'l*, pg. 619
HIRAM WALKER—Allied Domecq PLC; *Int'l*, pg. 63
HIRAM WALKER & SONS LIMITED—Allied Domecq PLC; *Int'l*, pg. 63
IDV AFRICA & LATIN AMERICA—Diageo Plc; *Int'l*, pg. 409
IDV ASIA PACIFIC—Diageo Plc; *Int'l*, pg. 409
IDV CENTRAL EUROPE—Diageo Plc; *Int'l*, pg. 410
IDV NORTH AMERICA—Diageo Plc; *Int'l*, pg. 409
INTERBREW NETHERLANDS—Interbrew S.A.; *Int'l*, pg. 679
INTERNATIONAL DISTILLERS AFRICA—Diageo Plc; *Int'l*, pg. 410
INTERNATIONAL DISTILLERS & VINTNERS-EUROPE—Diageo Plc; *Int'l*, pg. 409
INTERNATIONAL DISTILLERS SOUTH ASIA—Diageo Plc; *Int'l*, pg. 410
IRISH DISTILLERS LTD.—Groupe Pernod Ricard; *Int'l*, pg. 567
J&B SCOTLAND—Diageo Plc; *Int'l*, pg. 410
JBB WORLDWIDE, INC.—Fortune Brands, Inc.; *U.S. Public*, pg. 675
JACK DANIELS DISTILLERY—Brown-Forman Corporation; *U.S. Public*, pg. 261
CHARLES JACQUIN ET CIE, INC.; *U.S. Private*, pg. 580
JENKINS SPIRITS CORP. LTD.; *U.S. Private*, pg. 585
JUSTERINI & BROOKS LTD.—Diageo Plc; *Int'l*, pg. 409
KASSER/LAIRD DISTILLING CO.—Laird & Company; *U.S. Private*, pg. 643
KYOWA HAKKO KOGYO COMPANY, LTD.; *Int'l*, pg. 778
LA TONDENA DISTILLERS, INC.; *Int'l*, pg. 785
LABATT BREWING COMPANY LIMITED—Interbrew S.A.; *Int'l*, pg. 679
LAIRD & COMPANY; *U.S. Private*, pg. 642
LAWRENCE & COMPANY—White Rock Distilleries Inc.; *U.S. Private*, pg. 1173
D. LAZZARONI & C. S.P.A.; *Int'l*, pg. 804
LONRHO PLC; *Int'l*, pg. 817
MAINE BOTTLERS—White Rock Distilleries Inc.; *U.S. Private*, pg. 1173
MAKER'S MARK DISTILLERY, INC.—Allied Domecq PLC; *Int'l*, pg. 63
MARQINT MARCAS INTERNACIONALES SA—Diageo Plc; *Int'l*, pg. 410
MATTHEW CLARK TAUNTON, LTD.; *Int'l*, pg. 848
MCCORMICK DISTILLING CO.; *U.S. Private*, pg. 720
METAXA DISTILLERIES—Diageo Plc; *Int'l*, pg. 410
MIDWEST GRAIN PRODUCTS, INC.; *U.S. Public*, pg. 1111
MONTEBELLO BRANDS INC.; *U.S. Private*, pg. 758
MT. EAGLE CORPORATION—Brown-Forman Corporation; *U.S. Public*, pg. 261
AUSTIN NICHOLS & CO. INC.—Groupe Pernod Ricard; *Int'l*, pg. 567
OTTAVIO RICCADONNA S.P.A.—Koninklijke BolsWessanen nv; *Int'l*, pg. 751
OZEKI CORPORATION; *Int'l*, pg. 1019
PERNOD—Groupe Pernod Ricard; *Int'l*, pg. 566
PEZZIOL B.V.—Koninklijke BolsWessanen nv; *Int'l*, pg. 751
REMY AMERIQUE INC.—Remy Cointreau; *Int'l*, pg. 1102
RENAULT BISQUIT—Groupe Pernod Ricard; *Int'l*, pg. 566
RICARD—Groupe Pernod Ricard; *Int'l*, pg. 566
SARA LEE/DE—Sara Lee Corporation; *U.S. Public*, pg. 1434
SAXONY DISTILLERS ET CIE, INC.—Charles Jacquin et Cie, Inc.; *U.S. Private*, pg. 580
SEAGRAM CANADA—The Seagram Company Ltd.; *Int'l*, pg. 1217
THE SEAGRAM COMPANY LTD.; *Int'l*, pg. 1214
SEAGRAM EUROPE AND AFRICA—The Seagram Company Ltd.; *Int'l*, pg. 1217
JOSEPH E. SEAGRAM & SONS, INC.—The Seagram Company Ltd.; *Int'l*, pg. 1215
THE SEAGRAM SPIRITS AND WINE GROUP—The Seagram Company Ltd.; *Int'l*, pg. 1217
SILENO, SOC DISTRIBUIDORA DE BEBIDAS—Diageo Plc; *Int'l*, pg. 410
THE SINGLETON OF AUCHROISK—Diageo Plc; *Int'l*, pg. 409
THE PIERRE SMIRNOFF COMPANY—Diageo Plc; *Int'l*, pg. 411
SOCIETA INDUSTRIE LIQUORISTICHE S.A.S.—Koninklijke BolsWessanen nv; *Int'l*, pg. 751
SOCIETA ITALIANA PER IL CYNAR S.P.A.—Koninklijke BolsWessanen nv; *Int'l*, pg. 751
SOVEDI BENELUX-BELGIUM—Diageo Plc; *Int'l*, pg. 410
SOVEDI BENELUX-NEDERLAND—Diageo Plc; *Int'l*, pg. 410
SOVEDI FRANCE—Diageo Plc; *Int'l*, pg. 410
STEWART & SON OF DUNDEE LIMITED—Allied Domecq PLC; *Int'l*, pg. 63
SUNTORY LTD.; *Int'l*, pg. 1321
WM. TEACHER & SONS LIMITED—Allied Domecq PLC; *Int'l*, pg. 63
TENNESSEE DICKEL DISTILLING CO.—Diageo Plc; *Int'l*, pg. 412
TWELVE ISLANDS SHIPPING COMPANY—Diageo Plc; *Int'l*, pg. 409
UNITED DISTILLERS BLENDING & BOTTLING LTD.—Diageo Plc; *Int'l*, pg. 412
UNITED DISTILLERS PLC—Diageo Plc; *Int'l*, pg. 412
UNITED DISTILLERS USA, INC.—Diageo Plc; *Int'l*, pg. 412
W & A GILBEY—Diageo Plc; *Int'l*, pg. 409
W & A GILBEY SA—Diageo Plc; *Int'l*, pg. 409
M.S. WALKER, INC.; *U.S. Private*, pg. 1147
WHITE ROCK DISTILLERIES INC.; *U.S. Private*, pg. 1173
THE WHYTE & MACKAY GROUP PLC.—Fortune Brands, Inc.; *U.S. Public*, pg. 675

2086 — BOTTLED & CANNED SOFT DRINKS & CARBONATED WATERS

ALL AMERICAN BOTTLING CORP.; *U.S. Private*, pg. 34
ALLEGHENY PEPSI-COLA BOTTLING COMPANY—PepsiCo, Inc.; *U.S. Public*, pg. 1277
ALLIED DOMECQ PLC; *Int'l*, pg. 62
AMERICAN BEVERAGE CORPORATION—Koninklijke BolsWessanen nv; *Int'l*, pg. 752
AMERICA'S BEVERAGE CO.—The Kroger Co.; *U.S. Public*, pg. 967
ANJOU INTERNATIONAL COMPANY—Compagnie Generale Des Eaux; *Int'l*, pg. 321
APOLLINARIS & SCHWEPPES GMBH & CO.; *Int'l*, pg. 78
ARROWHEAD MOUNTAIN SPRING WATER COMPANY—Nestle S.A.; *Int'l*, pg. 919
ASAHI BREWERIES LTD.; *Int'l*, pg. 83
B & C BOTTLERS CORP.—Bacardi Limited; *Int'l*, pg. 131
BARBERO S.P.A.—Allied Domecq PLC; *Int'l*, pg. 64
BERRIEL VITTEL FRANCE—Nestle S.A.; *Int'l*, pg. 918
BEVERAGE AMERICA, INC.; *U.S. Private*, pg. 141
BEVERAGE CANNERS INTERNATIONAL CORP.—BCI Holding Corporation; *U.S. Private*, pg. 106
BIERBRAUEREI FOHRENBURG; *Int'l*, pg. 194
BLAUE QUELLEN MINERAL- UND HEILBRUNNEN AG—Nestle S.A.; *Int'l*, pg. 919
BOLS ROYAL DISTILLERIES—Koninklijke BolsWessanen nv; *Int'l*, pg. 751
BRASSERIES, LIMONADERIES ET MALTERIES DU ZAIRE "BRALIMA" S.A.R.L.—Heineken N.V.; *Int'l*, pg. 608
BRITVIC SOFT DRINKS LTD.—Whitbread PLC; *Int'l*, pg. 1499
BROOKS BEVERAGE MANAGEMENT, INC.—Beverage America, Inc.; *U.S. Private*, pg. 142
BUFFALO ROCK COMPANY; *U.S. Private*, pg. 179
H.P. BULMER HOLDINGS PLC; *Int'l*, pg. 232
C & C (WHOLESALE) LTD..—Allied Domecq PLC; *Int'l*, pg. 64
C C BEVERAGE PACKING INC.—Coca-Cola Bottling Co. Consolidated; *U.S. Public*, pg. 391
CADBURY BEVERAGES—Cadbury Schweppes p.l.c.; *Int'l*, pg. 248
CADBURY BEVERAGES CANADA INC.—Cadbury Schweppes p.l.c.; *Int'l*, pg. 248
CADBURY BEVERAGES NORTH AMERICA—Cadbury Schweppes p.l.c.; *Int'l*, pg. 248
CADBURY BEVERAGES SEVEN UP—Cadbury Schweppes p.l.c.; *Int'l*, pg. 248
CADBURY KENYA LIMITED—Cadbury Schweppes p.l.c.; *Int'l*, pg. 248
CADBURY SCHWEPPES P.L.C.; *Int'l*, pg. 247
CALLITHEKE INTERNATIONAL LTD.—Diageo Plc; *Int'l*, pg. 409
CALPIS FOOD INDUSTRY CO. LTD.; *Int'l*, pg. 252
CANADA DRY DIVISION—Cadbury Schweppes p.l.c.; *Int'l*, pg. 248
CANTRELL & COCHRANE GROUP—Allied Domecq PLC; *Int'l*, pg. 63
CENTRAL COCA-COLA BOTTLING COMPANY, INC.; *U.S.* Private, pg. 222
CENTRAL DE CERVEJAS, S.A.; *Int'l*, pg. 279
CHATEAUNEUF-LES-BAINS S.A.—Nestle S.A.; *Int'l*, pg. 918
CLEARLY CANADIAN BEVERAGE CORP.; *Int'l*, pg. 297
COCA-COLA BOTTLING CO. CONSOLIDATED; *U.S. Public*, pg. 391
COCA-COLA BOTTLING CO. OF CHICAGO; *U.S. Private*, pg. 248
COCA-COLA BOTTLING CO. OF ELIZABETHTOWN; *U.S.* Private, pg. 248
COCA-COLA BOTTLING CO. OF NEW ENGLAND—Coca-Cola Enterprises Inc.; *U.S. Public*, pg. 393

THE COCA-COLA BOTTLING CO. OF NEW YORK, INC.—Coca-Cola Enterprises Inc.; U.S. Public, pg. 393
COCA-COLA BOTTLING CO. OF SHREVEPORT—Coca-Cola Enterprises Inc.; U.S. Public, pg. 393
COCA-COLA BOTTLING CO. OF THE SOUTHWEST; U.S. Private, pg. 248
THE COCA-COLA COMPANY; U.S. Public, pg. 392
COCA-COLA/DR. PEPPER BOTTLING CO. OF SOUTH ARKANSAS—Coca-Cola Enterprises Inc.; U.S. Public, pg. 393
COCA-COLA ENTERPRISES - EASTERN GROUP/ SOUTHEAST REGION—Coca-Cola Enterprises Inc.; U.S. Public, pg. 393
COCA-COLA ENTERPRISES INC.; U.S. Public, pg. 393
THE COCA-COLA EXPORT CORPORATION—The Coca-Cola Company; U.S. Public, pg. 392
COLUMBUS COCA-COLA BOTTLING CO.—Coca-Cola Bottling Co. Consolidated; U.S. Public, pg. 392
COMPAGNIE FERMIERE DE L'ETABLISSEMENT THERMAL DE VICHY—Nestle S.A.; Int'l, pg. 919
COMPAGNIE FRANCAISE DE BOISSONS GAZEUSES—Nestle S.A.; Int'l, pg. 918
THE CONCENTRATE COMPANY OF IRELAND—PepsiCo, Inc.; U.S. Public, pg. 1277
R.J. CORR NATURALS, INC.; U.S. Private, pg. 276
COTT CORPORATION; Int'l, pg. 337
JAMES CREAN PLC; Int'l, pg. 340
CRODO SUD S.P.A.—Koninklijke BolsWessanen nv; Int'l, pg. 751
CRUSH INTERNATIONAL—Cadbury Schweppes p.l.c.; Int'l, pg. 248
CRUSH INTERNATIONAL (OVERSEAS)—Cadbury Schweppes p.l.c.; Int'l, pg. 248
CRUSH U.S.A.—Cadbury Schweppes p.l.c.; Int'l, pg. 248
CRYSTAL GEYSER; U.S. Private, pg. 294
DANONE GROUP; Int'l, pg. 379
DEL MONTE FOODS; U.S. Private, pg. 321
DIAGEO PLC; Int'l, pg. 408
DOUBLE-COLA CO.-USA; U.S. Private, pg. 341
DR. PEPPER CO.—Cadbury Schweppes p.l.c.; Int'l, pg. 248
A. DUDA & SONS INC.; U.S. Private, pg. 344
EAU MINERALE DE PLANCOET—Nestle S.A.; Int'l, pg. 919
EMBOLTELLADORA DEL URUGUAY, S.A.—PepsiCo, Inc.; U.S. Public, pg. 1277
EMBOTELLADORES DEL VALLE DE ANAHUAC S.A. DE C.V.; Int'l, pg. 452
EVIAN—Danone Group; Int'l, pg. 381
FAYGO BEVERAGES, INC.—National Beverage Corp.; U.S. Public, pg. 1153
AB FINDUS—Nestle S.A.; Int'l, pg. 920
FONT VELLA—Danone Group; Int'l, pg. 381
FRANCE ST.-YORRE—Nestle S.A.; Int'l, pg. 919
FULL SERVICE BEVERAGE COMPANY—All American Bottling Corp.; U.S. Private, pg. 34
GATORADE WORLDWIDE DIVISION—The Quaker Oats Company; U.S. Public, pg. 1347
GLOBAL BEVERAGE CO.; U.S. Private, pg. 457
GRAND METROPOLITAN PLC—Diageo Plc; Int'l, pg. 408
GRANT-LYDICK BEVERAGE CO.; U.S. Private, pg. 470
GREEN SPOT PACKAGING INC.; U.S. Private, pg. 477
GROUPE PERNOD RICARD; Int'l, pg. 566
GRUPO CONTINENTAL S.A.; Int'l, pg. 573
GRUPO EMBOTELLADORAS UNIDAS SA DE CV; Int'l, pg. 574
HEIL-UND MINERALQUELLEN GMBH—Nestle S.A.; Int'l, pg. 920
HEINEKEN N.V.; Int'l, pg. 608
HINCKLEY & SCHMITT, INC.—Suntory Ltd.; Int'l, pg. 1322
HOKKAIDO COCA-COLA BOTTLING CO., LTD.—Dai Nippon Printing Co., Ltd.; Int'l, pg. 363
HOME JUICE CO.; U.S. Private, pg. 537
HONICKMAN AFFILIATES; U.S. Private, pg. 537
INTERBREW NETHERLANDS—Interbrew S.A.; Int'l, pg. 679
INTERBREW S.A.; Int'l, pg. 679
INTERNATIONAL QUAKER FOOD PRODUCTS—The Quaker Oats Company; U.S. Public, pg. 1347
IONICS, INCORPORATED; U.S. Public, pg. 912
KRIER FOODS, INC.; U.S. Private, pg. 636
THE KROGER CO.; U.S. Public, pg. 967
THE LOUISIANA COCA-COLA BOTTLING COMPANY LIMITED—Coca-Cola Enterprises Inc.; U.S. Public, pg. 393
MCKESSON CORPORATION; U.S. Public, pg. 1072
METAL BOX PLC BEVERAGE CAN DIV.—Caradon Plc; Int'l, pg. 267
MID CONTINENT BOTTLERS, INC—Beverage America, Inc.; U.S. Private, pg. 142
MINERAL UND HEILQUELLEN AG, ADELBODEN—Koninklijke BolsWessanen nv; Int'l, pg. 751
MITSUI NORIN CO., LTD.—Mitsui & Co., Ltd.; Int'l, pg. 878
THE MONARCH COMPANY, INC.; U.S. Private, pg. 756
MORINAGA MILK INDUSTRY CO., LTD.; Int'l, pg. 895
NATIONAL BEVERAGE CORP.; U.S. Public, pg. 1153
NESTLE S.A.; Int'l, pg. 915
NEWMAN'S OWN, INC.; U.S. Private, pg. 797
NOEL CANNING CORPORATION; U.S. Private, pg. 800
NOR-CAL BEVERAGE CO., INC.; U.S. Private, pg. 801
OKAYAMAKEN SHOKUHIN CO., LTD.—Meiji Seika Kaisha, Ltd.; Int'l, pg. 855
ORANGINA FRANCE—Groupe Pernod Ricard; Int'l, pg. 566
OTTAVIO RICCADONNA S.P.A.—Koninklijke BolsWessanen nv; Int'l, pg. 751
OUACHITA COCA-COLA BOTTLING COMPANY—Coca-Cola Enterprises Inc.; U.S. Public, pg. 393
PANAMA CITY COCA-COLA BOTTLING CO.—Coca-Cola Bottling Co. Consolidated; U.S. Public, pg. 392
PEPCOM INDUSTRIES, INC.—Suntory Ltd.; Int'l, pg. 1321
PEPSI-COLA ALBANY BOTTLING CO., INC.; U.S. Private, pg. 852
PEPSI-COLA BOTTLING CO.; U.S. Public, pg. 1276
PEPSI-COLA BOTTLING COMPANY OF CHARLOTTE INC.; U.S. Private, pg. 852
PEPSI-COLA GENERAL BOTTLERS, INC.—PepsiCo, Inc.; U.S. Public, pg. 1277
PEPSI-COLA GENERAL BOTTLERS, INC.—Whitman Corporation; U.S. Public, pg. 1766
PEPSI-GEMEX SA DE CV; Int'l, pg. 1036
PEPSICO, INC.; U.S. Public, pg. 1276
PHARMACIA & UPJOHN, INC.; Int'l, pg. 1047
PHILADELPHIA COCA-COLA BOTTLING CO.; U.S. Private, pg. 861
POLAR BEVERAGES; U.S. Private, pg. 873
PROCORDIA FOOD AB—Orkla A.S.A.; Int'l, pg. 1011
PURE SOLUTIONS—Ionics, Incorporated; U.S. Public, pg. 912
THE QUAKER OATS COMPANY; U.S. Public, pg. 1347
SMDA—Danone Group; Int'l, pg. 381
SABANCI HOLDING A.S.; Int'l, pg. 1167
SANGEMINI S.P.A.; Int'l, pg. 1188
SAPPORO BREWERIES LTD.; Int'l, pg. 1193
SCHWEPPES FRANCE S.A.—Cadbury Schweppes p.l.c.; Int'l, pg. 248
SCHWEPPES S.A.—Cadbury Schweppes p.l.c.; Int'l, pg. 248
SEAGRAM BEVERAGE CO.—The Seagram Company Ltd.; Int'l, pg. 1215
SELECT BEVERAGES, INC.; U.S. Private, pg. 982
SELECT CANFIELD—Select Beverages, Inc.; U.S. Private, pg. 982
SEVEN-UP BOTTLING CO. OF ST. LOUIS—Beverage America, Inc.; U.S. Private, pg. 142
SEVEN-UP CONCESSIONES S.A.—PepsiCo, Inc.; U.S. Public, pg. 1278
SEVEN-UP EUROPE—PepsiCo, Inc.; U.S. Public, pg. 1278
SEVEN-UP IRELAND LTD.—PepsiCo, Inc.; U.S. Public, pg. 1278
SEVEN-UP NEDERLANDS N.V.—PepsiCo, Inc.; U.S. Public, pg. 1278
7-UP OF CORPUS CHRISTI—Grant-Lydick Beverage Co.; U.S. Private, pg. 470
SEVEN-UP PHILIPPINES, INC.—PepsiCo, Inc.; U.S. Public, pg. 1278
SHASTA BEVERAGES, INC.—National Beverage Corp.; U.S. Public, pg. 1153
SIERRA SPRING WATER COMPANY—Compagnie Generale Des Eaux; Int'l, pg. 322
SISTEMA ARGOS S.A.; Int'l, pg. 1256
SMITHKLINE BEECHAM CONSUMER BRANDS—SmithKline Beecham plc; Int'l, pg. 1264
SMITHKLINE BEECHAM OF IRELAND LTD.—SmithKline Beecham plc; Int'l, pg. 1266
SNAPPLE BEVERAGE COMPANY—Triarc Companies, Inc.; U.S. Public, pg. 1635
SOCIETE COMMERCIALE DES EAUX MINERALES DU BASSIN DE VICHY SAINT-YORRE—Nestle S.A.; Int'l, pg. 919
SOCIETE DES EAUX MINERALES DE THONON-LES-BAINS—Nestle S.A.; Int'l, pg. 919
SOUTHERN BEVERAGE PACKERS, INC.; U.S. Private, pg. 1015
STABBURET A/S—Orkla A.S.A.; Int'l, pg. 1011
STEWART'S ICE CREAM CO., INC.; U.S. Private, pg. 1043
THE STOP & SHOP COMPANIES, INC.—Koninklijke Ahold NV; Int'l, pg. 750
SUNDOR BRANDS INC.—The Procter & Gamble Company; U.S. Public, pg. 1331
SUNDOR BRANDS INC./LINCOLN—The Procter & Gamble Company; U.S. Public, pg. 1331
SUNDROP—Cadbury Schweppes p.l.c.; Int'l, pg. 248
SUNTORY LTD.; Int'l, pg. 1321
SUNTORY WATER GROUP, INC.—Suntory Ltd.; Int'l, pg. 1321
TLC BEATRICE INTERNATIONAL HOLDINGS INC.; U.S. Private, pg. 1064
TERME DI CRODO S.P.A.—Koninklijke BolsWessanen nv; Int'l, pg. 751
TONE BROTHERS INC.—Burns, Philp & Company Limited; Int'l, pg. 237
TRIARC BEVERAGE GROUP—Triarc Companies, Inc.; U.S. Public, pg. 1635
TRIARC COMPANIES, INC.; U.S. Public, pg. 1634
UNICER-UNIAO CERVEJEIRA, S.A.; Int'l, pg. 1432
UNITED BEVERAGES LIMITED—James Crean PLC; Int'l, pg. 340
VAUX GROUP PLC; Int'l, pg. 1453
VITASOY (U.S.A.) INC.—Vitasoy International Holdings Ltd.; Int'l, pg. 1469
VOLVIC—Danone Group; Int'l, pg. 381
WHITE ROCK PRODUCTS CORP.; U.S. Private, pg. 1173
WHITMAN CORPORATION; U.S. Public, pg. 1766
WORLDWIDE QUAKER BEVERAGES—The Quaker Oats Company; U.S. Public, pg. 1347
YOO HOO CHOCOLATE BEVERAGE CORP.—Groupe Pernod Ricard; Int'l, pg. 567

2087 — FLAVORING EXTRACTS & FLAVORING SYRUPS, NEC

ADAMS EXTRACT CO., INC.; U.S. Private, pg. 16
ALLEN FOODS, INC.; U.S. Private, pg. 37
AMERICAN BEVERAGE CORPORATION—Koninklijke BolsWessanen nv; Int'l, pg. 752
BARBADOS DAIRY INDUSTRIES LTD.—New Zealand Dairy Board; Int'l, pg. 923
BAYER CORPORATION—Bayer AG; Int'l, pg. 172
BAYER CORPORATION/CONSUMER CARE DIVISION—Bayer AG; Int'l, pg. 173
BESTFOODS; U.S. Public, pg. 223
BOAM PRODUCE (OVERSEAS) LTD.—MacAndrews & Forbes Holdings Inc.; U.S. Private, pg. 689
BRADY ENTERPRISES, INC.; U.S. Private, pg. 165
BYRNES & KIEFER COMPANY; U.S. Private, pg. 191
CADBURY BEVERAGES—Cadbury Schweppes p.l.c.; Int'l, pg. 248
CADBURY BEVERAGES NORTH AMERICA—Cadbury Schweppes p.l.c.; Int'l, pg. 248
CADBURY BEVERAGES SEVEN UP—Cadbury Schweppes p.l.c.; Int'l, pg. 248
CADBURY SCHWEPPES P.L.C.; Int'l, pg. 247
CAMPBELL'S SOUPS (AUST.) PTY. LTD.—Campbell Soup Company; U.S. Public, pg. 299
CANADA DRY DIVISION—Cadbury Schweppes p.l.c.; Int'l, pg. 248
CARAVAN PRODUCTS COMPANY, INC.; U.S. Private, pg. 208
CERATONIA S.A.—Hercules Incorporated; U.S. Public, pg. 810
THE COCA-COLA COMPANY; U.S. Public, pg. 392
THE COCA-COLA EXPORT CORPORATION—The Coca-Cola Company; U.S. Public, pg. 392
COCA-COLA INTERAMERICAN CORP.—The Coca-Cola Company; U.S. Public, pg. 392
COCA-COLA USA—The Coca-Cola Company; U.S. Public, pg. 392
CORN PRODUCTS CO. (INDIA) LTD.—Bestfoods; U.S. Public, pg. 224
CROMPTON & KNOWLES CORPORATION; U.S. Public, pg. 459
DG FOODS, LLC; U.S. Private, pg. 301
DALE FOODS—DG Foods, LLC; U.S. Private, pg. 301
DAWN FOOD PRODUCTS, INC.; U.S. Private, pg. 316
DOUBLE-COLA CO.-USA; U.S. Private, pg. 341
DR. PEPPER CO.—Cadbury Schweppes p.l.c.; Int'l, pg. 248
ELECTROCHEMICAL INDUSTRIES (FRUTAROM) LTD.—ICC Industries, Inc.; U.S. Private, pg. 553
EMBOTELLADORES DEL VALLE DE ANAHUAC S.A. DE C.V.; Int'l, pg. 452
FELTON WORLDWIDE LTD.—Universal Foods Corporation; U.S. Public, pg. 1696
FIDCO—Nestle S.A.; Int'l, pg. 916
FIRMENICH—Firmenich S.A.; Int'l, pg. 486
FIRMENICH S.A.; Int'l, pg. 486
FLORASYNTH AUSTRALASIA PTY. LTD.—Bayer AG; Int'l, pg. 173
FLORASYNTH GMBH—Bayer AG; Int'l, pg. 173
FLORASYNTH INC.—Bayer AG; Int'l, pg. 173
FLORASYNTH ITALIA S.R.L.—Bayer AG; Int'l, pg. 173
FLORASYNTH S.A. DE C.V.—Bayer AG; Int'l, pg. 174
FLORASYNTH SINGAPORE PTE LTD.—Bayer AG; Int'l, pg. 174
FRUTAROM MEER CORPORATION—ICC Industries, Inc.; U.S. Private, pg. 554
GILETTE FOOD FLAVORINGS, INC.; U.S. Private, pg. 453
GLORIA S.A.—Nestle S.A.; Int'l, pg. 920
HEG HOPFENEXTRAKTION GMBH—Viag AG; Int'l, pg. 1464
HAARMANN & REIMER CORP.—Bayer AG; Int'l, pg. 173
CHR. HANSEN (UK) LTD.—Chr. Hansen Holding A/S; Int'l, pg. 289
HARRISONS & CROSFIELD PLC; Int'l, pg. 598
HOKKAIDO COCA-COLA BOTTLING CO., LTD.—Dai Nippon Printing Co., Ltd.; Int'l, pg. 363
IFF CONCENTRATES, INC.—International Flavors & Fragrances, Inc.; U.S. Public, pg. 899
IFF FSC, INC.—International Flavors & Fragrances, Inc.; U.S. Public, pg. 899
ITC FLAVOR & SEASONING DIV.—Crompton & Knowles Corporation; U.S. Public, pg. 459
INDUSTRIAS DE MAIZ Y ALIMENTOS S.A.—Corn Products International, Inc.; U.S. Public, pg. 447
INTERNATIONAL FLAVORS & FRAGRANCES, INC.; U.S. Public, pg. 898
J. HUNGERFORD SMITH COMPANY—ConAgra, Inc.; U.S. Public, pg. 428
THE JEL SERT CO.; U.S. Private, pg. 585
JUGOS DEL VALLE, S.A. DE C.V.; Int'l, pg. 716
KALSEC, INC.—Kalamazoo Holdings, Inc.; U.S. Private, pg. 606
L. KARP & SONS, INC.; U.S. Private, pg. 607
KELLOGG CONVENIENCE FOOD PLANT—Kellogg Company; U.S. Public, pg. 947
KRAFT FOOD INGREDIENTS CORP.—Philip Morris Companies Inc.; U.S. Public, pg. 1288
KRAFT FOODS, INC.—Philip Morris Companies Inc.; U.S. Public, pg. 1287
LOTTE SHOPPING CO. LTD.—Lotte Company Ltd.; Int'l, pg. 819
LUCAS INGREDIENTS—Dalgety Plc; Int'l, pg. 376
MACANDREWS & FORBES HOLDINGS INC.; U.S. Private, pg. 689
MAFCO WORLDWIDE CORP.—MacAndrews & Forbes Holdings Inc.; U.S. Private, pg. 690
MCCORMICK & COMPANY, INCORPORATED; U.S. Public, pg. 1066
DAVID MICHAEL & CO. INC.; U.S. Private, pg. 740
L.J. MINOR CORPORATION—Nestle S.A.; Int'l, pg. 917
THE MINUTE MAID COMPANY—The Coca-Cola Company; U.S. Public, pg. 392
M.F. NEAL & CO.,INC.—MacAndrews & Forbes Holdings Inc.; U.S. Private, pg. 689
NOKIA GENERAL COMMUNICATIONS LTD.—Oy Nokia Ab/Nokia Group; Int'l, pg. 954
NORTHWESTERN FLAVORS INC.—Wm. Wrigley Jr. Company; U.S. Public, pg. 1781
NUTRICIA BV; Int'l, pg. 991
PAULS PLC—Harrisons & Crosfield plc; Int'l, pg. 598
PEPSI-COLA GENERAL BOTTLERS, INC.—PepsiCo, Inc.; U.S. Public, pg. 1277
PEPSI-COLA GENERAL BOTTLERS, INC.—Whitman Corporation; U.S. Public, pg. 1766
PEPSICO, INC.; U.S. Public, pg. 1276
PHILIP MORRIS COMPANIES INC.; U.S. Public, pg. 1287
PURITY PRODUCTS INC.; U.S. Private, pg. 896
QUEST INC.—Unilever Plc; Int'l, pg. 1435
QUEST INTERNATIONAL FLAVORS & FOODS INC.—Unilever Plc; Int'l, pg. 1436
RECKITT & COLMAN PLC; Int'l, pg. 1089
RED WINGS INC.—Tomkins PLC; Int'l, pg. 1398

ROBERTET FLAVORS—Robertet S.A.; *Int'l*, pg. 1119
ROSE & LAFLAMME CO. LTD.—Saskatchewan Wheat Pool; *Int'l*, pg. 1195
SAGIT S.P.A.—Unilever Plc; *Int'l*, pg. 1438
SARA LEE/DE—Sara Lee Corporation; *U.S. Public*, pg. 1434
SCHILLING PLANT—McCormick & Company, Incorporated; *U.S. Public*, pg. 1066
SEAGRAM'S CORP. RESEARCH AND DEVELOPMENT—The Seagram Company Ltd.; *Int'l*, pg. 1217
SOUTHERN TEA CO.—The Tetley Group Limited; *Int'l*, pg. 1377
STEPAN COMPANY; *U.S. Public*, pg. 1514
SUNDROP—Cadbury Schweppes p.l.c.; *Int'l*, pg. 248
THE SWISS COLONY, INC; *U.S. Private*, pg. 1059
TONE BROTHERS INC.—Burns, Philp & Company Limited; *Int'l*, pg. 237
TRIARC COMPANIES, INC.; *U.S. Public*, pg. 1634
UNIVERSAL FLAVORS—Universal Foods Corporation; *U.S. Public*, pg. 1695
UNIVERSAL FLAVORS CORP.—Universal Foods Corporation; *U.S. Public*, pg. 1695
UNIVERSAL FLAVORS-U.S.A.—Universal Foods Corporation; *U.S. Public*, pg. 1696
UNIVERSAL FOODS CORPORATION; *U.S. Public*, pg. 1695
UNIVERSAL FOODS PRODUCTS INTERNATIONAL LTD.—Universal Foods Corporation; *U.S. Public*, pg. 1696
WARNER-JENKINSON—Universal Foods Corporation; *U.S. Public*, pg. 1696
WHITMAN CORPORATION; *U.S. Public*, pg. 1766

2091 — CANNED & CURED FISH & SEAFOODS

ALPESCA, S.A.—National Sea Products Limited; *Int'l*, pg. 909
H.J. BAKER & BRO., INC.; *U.S. Private*, pg. 112
BORDEN, INC.; *U.S. Private*, pg. 157
BRITISH COLUMBIA PACKERS LIMITED—George Weston Limited; *Int'l*, pg. 1495
BRUCE FOODS CORP.; *U.S. Private*, pg. 175
BUMBLE BEE INTERNATIONAL INC.—Hicks, Muse, Tate & Furst Inc.; *U.S. Private*, pg. 526
BUMBLE BEE SEAFOODS INC.—Hicks, Muse, Tate & Furst Inc.; *U.S. Private*, pg. 526
CAMPBELL SOUP COMPANY; *U.S. Public*, pg. 298
CAMPBELL USA—Campbell Soup Company; *U.S. Public*, pg. 299
CONAGRA, INC.; *U.S. Public*, pg. 425
CONAGRA SHRIMP COMPANY—ConAgra, Inc.; *U.S. Public*, pg. 427
CONNORS BROS. LIMITED—George Weston Limited; *Int'l*, pg. 1495
CONNORS BRUNSWICK, INC.; *U.S. Private*, pg. 264
COPAIS FOOD & BEVERAGE COMPANY S.A.—H.J. Heinz Company; *U.S. Public*, pg. 806
DEEP SEA CLAM COMPANY LIMITED—National Sea Products Limited; *Int'l*, pg. 909
DIAGEO PLC; *Int'l*, pg. 408
THE GORTON GROUP—Unilever Plc; *Int'l*, pg. 1434
GRAND METROPOLITAN PLC—Diageo Plc; *Int'l*, pg. 408
H.J. HEINZ COMPANY; *U.S. Public*, pg. 805
ICICLE SEAFOODS, INC.; *U.S. Private*, pg. 556
KYOKUYO CO. LTD.; *Int'l*, pg. 777
KYOWA HAKKO KOGYO COMPANY, LTD.; *Int'l*, pg. 778
LOS ANGELES SMOKING & CURING COMPANY—Ocean Beauty Seafoods, Inc.; *U.S. Private*, pg. 810
MARIE ELISABETH PRODUTOS ALIMENTARES S.A.—H.J. Heinz Company; *U.S. Public*, pg. 807
MARIFARMS, INC.—Hanson PLC; *Int'l*, pg. 593
MCCAIN FOODS (GB) LIMITED—McCain Foods Limited; *Int'l*, pg. 850
NATIONAL SEA PRODUCTS LIMITED; *Int'l*, pg. 909
NICHIRO CORPORATION; *Int'l*, pg. 928
NIKO CO., LTD.—Mitsukoshi, Ltd.; *Int'l*, pg. 883
NIPPON SUISAN KAISHA, LTD.; *Int'l*, pg. 940
NORDSEE DEUTSCHE HOCHSEEFISCHEREI G.M.B.H.—Unilever Plc; *Int'l*, pg. 1438
OCEAN BEAUTY SEAFOODS, INC.; *U.S. Private*, pg. 810
O'DONNELL-USEN FISHERIES CORP.—ConAgra, Inc.; *U.S. Public*, pg. 427
ORLEANS FOOD CO.—Borden, Inc.; *U.S. Private*, pg. 158
PETER PAN SEAFOODS, INC.—Nichiro Corporation; *Int'l*, pg. 928
RYMER INTERNATIONAL SEAFOOD INC.—Rymer Foods Inc.; *U.S. Public*, pg. 1414
SAU-SEA FOODS, INC.; *U.S. Private*, pg. 967
SEA WATCH INTERNATIONAL, LTD.—Nichirei Corporation; *Int'l*, pg. 928
SEAFOOD IMPORTERS, INC.—Hicks, Muse, Tate & Furst Inc.; *U.S. Private*, pg. 526
STAR-KIST CARIBE, INC.—H.J. Heinz Company; *U.S. Public*, pg. 806
STAR-KIST EUROPE, INC.—H.J. Heinz Company; *U.S. Public*, pg. 807
STAR-KIST FOODS INC.—H.J. Heinz Company; *U.S. Public*, pg. 805
STINSON SEAFOOD COMPANY; *U.S. Private*, pg. 1043
TAIYO SHOKUHIN CO., LTD.—Meiji Seika Kaisha, Ltd.; *Int'l*, pg. 855
TOGIAK FISHERIES INC.—Marubeni Corporation; *Int'l*, pg. 845
TRANS OCEAN PRODUCTS, INC.—Maruha Corporation; *Int'l*, pg. 845
UNICORD PUBLIC CO. LTD.; *Int'l*, pg. 1432
UNISEA FOODS, INC.—Nippon Suisan Kaisha, Ltd.; *Int'l*, pg. 940
VITA FOOD PRODUCTS, INC.; *U.S. Private*, pg. 1142
WESTERN ALASKA FISHERIES INC.—Maruha Corporation; *Int'l*, pg. 845
GEORGE WESTON LIMITED; *Int'l*, pg. 1494
ZAPATA HAYNIE CORP.—Zapata Corporation; *U.S. Public*, pg. 1789

2092 — PREPARED FRESH OR FROZEN FISH & SEAFOODS

ALLIANT FOODSERVICE—Clayton, Dubilier & Rice, Inc; *U.S. Private*, pg. 244
ALPESCA, S.A.—National Sea Products Limited; *Int'l*, pg. 909
ALYESKA SEAFOODS, INC.—Maruha Corporation; *Int'l*, pg. 845
ARCTIC ALASKA FISHERIES CORPORATION—Tyson Foods, Inc.; *U.S. Public*, pg. 1652
ARCTIC ALASKA SEAFOODS, INC.—Tyson Foods, Inc.; *U.S. Public*, pg. 1652
BIRDS EYE WALLS LTD.—Unilever Plc; *Int'l*, pg. 1434
BRITISH COLUMBIA PACKERS LIMITED—George Weston Limited; *Int'l*, pg. 1495
CAMPBELL SOUP COMPANY; *U.S. Public*, pg. 298
CAMPBELL USA—Campbell Soup Company; *U.S. Public*, pg. 299
CARTER HOLT HARVEY LIMITED—International Paper Company; *U.S. Public*, pg. 904
COLDWATER SEAFOOD CORPORATION; *U.S. Private*, pg. 251
CONAGRA, INC.; *U.S. Public*, pg. 425
CONAGRA SEAFOOD COMPANIES—ConAgra, Inc.; *U.S. Public*, pg. 427
CONAGRA SHRIMP COMPANY—ConAgra, Inc.; *U.S. Public*, pg. 427
CONNORS BRUNSWICK, INC.; *U.S. Private*, pg. 264
COUNTRY SKILLET CATFISH CO.—ConAgra, Inc.; *U.S. Public*, pg. 428
CRYOGENIC STRUCTURES CORPORATION—Baltek Corporation; *U.S. Public*, pg. 172
DEEP SEA CLAM COMPANY LIMITED—National Sea Products Limited; *Int'l*, pg. 909
DELTA PRIDE CATFISH, INC.; *U.S. Private*, pg. 322
ENTREE CORPORATION—Coyote Network Systems, Inc.; *U.S. Public*, pg. 455
AB FINDUS—Nestle S.A.; *Int'l*, pg. 920
A/S FINDUS—Nestle S.A.; *Int'l*, pg. 920
FISHKING PROCESSORS, INC.—Nippon Suisan Kaisha, Ltd.; *Int'l*, pg. 940
FRIONOR A/S; *Int'l*, pg. 516
FRIONOR FABRIKKER A/S—Frionor A/S; *Int'l*, pg. 516
THE GORTON GROUP—Unilever Plc; *Int'l*, pg. 1434
HOSHO AMERICA INC.—Kibun Co. Ltd.; *Int'l*, pg. 733
ICELAND SEAFOOD CORPORATION; *U.S. Private*, pg. 556
KIBUN CO. LTD.; *Int'l*, pg. 733
KITCHENS OF THE OCEANS, INC.; *U.S. Private*, pg. 625
KYOKUYO AMERICA CORP.—Kyokuyo Co. Ltd.; *Int'l*, pg. 777
KYOKUYO CO. LTD.; *Int'l*, pg. 777
KYOWA HAKKO KOGYO COMPANY, LTD.; *Int'l*, pg. 778
LYONS SEAFOODS LIMITED; *Int'l*, pg. 824
MARIFARMS, INC.—Hanson PLC; *Int'l*, pg. 593
MARUBENI CORPORATION; *Int'l*, pg. 844
NATIONAL SEA PRODUCTS INCORPORATED—National Sea Products Limited; *Int'l*, pg. 909
NATIONAL SEA PRODUCTS LIMITED; *Int'l*, pg. 909
NESTLE-FINDUS OY—Nestle S.A.; *Int'l*, pg. 921
NICHIREI CORPORATION; *Int'l*, pg. 928
NICHIRO CORPORATION; *Int'l*, pg. 928
NIPPON SUISAN KAISHA, LTD.; *Int'l*, pg. 940
O'DONNELL-USEN FISHERIES CORP.—ConAgra, Inc.; *U.S. Public*, pg. 427
PETER PAN SEAFOODS, INC.—Nichiro Corporation; *Int'l*, pg. 928
PHARMACIA & UPJOHN, INC.; *Int'l*, pg. 1047
QF, INC.—Nippon Suisan Kaisha, Ltd.; *Int'l*, pg. 940
QUAKER BRASIL, LTDA.—The Quaker Oats Company; *U.S. Public*, pg. 1348
RICH PRODUCTS CORP.; *U.S. Private*, pg. 928
SAU-SEA FOODS, INC.; *U.S. Private*, pg. 967
SINGLETON SEAFOOD CO.—ConAgra, Inc.; *U.S. Public*, pg. 427
STINSON SEAFOOD COMPANY; *U.S. Private*, pg. 1043
THE STOP & SHOP COMPANIES, INC.—Koninklijke Ahold NV; *Int'l*, pg. 750
SUPERIOR BLENDS, INC.—Tyson Foods, Inc.; *U.S. Public*, pg. 1652
SWANSON—Campbell Soup Company; *U.S. Public*, pg. 299
TOGIAK FISHERIES INC.—Marubeni Corporation; *Int'l*, pg. 845
TRANS OCEAN PRODUCTS, INC.—Maruha Corporation; *Int'l*, pg. 845
TRIDENT SEAFOOD CORPORATION—ConAgra, Inc.; *U.S. Public*, pg. 429
TYSON FOODS, INC.; *U.S. Public*, pg. 1652
UB FROZEN & CHILLED LIMITED—United Biscuits (Holdings) Plc; *Int'l*, pg. 1442
UNICORD PUBLIC CO. LTD.; *Int'l*, pg. 1432
WESTERN ALASKA FISHERIES INC.—Maruha Corporation; *Int'l*, pg. 845
GEORGE WESTON LIMITED; *Int'l*, pg. 1494
WESTWARD SEAFOODS, INC.—Maruha Corporation; *Int'l*, pg. 845

2095 — ROASTED COFFEE

ALEXANDER & BALDWIN, INC.; *U.S. Public*, pg. 39
ALOIS DALLMAYR KAFFEE OHG—Nestle S.A.; *Int'l*, pg. 918
ASTOR PRODUCTS—Winn-Dixie Stores, Inc.; *U.S. Public*, pg. 1772
BEWLEY'S TEA & COFFEE LTD.—Campbells/Bewley Group; *Int'l*, pg. 254
BROTHERS GOURMET COFFEES, INC.; *U.S. Public*, pg. 259
CAFE GRAND MERE S.A.—Philip Morris Companies Inc.; *U.S. Public*, pg. 1289
CAFES LA ESTRELLA S.A.—Nestle S.A.; *Int'l*, pg. 919
CAIN'S COFFEE CO.—Chock Full O' Nuts Corporation; *U.S. Public*, pg. 351
CALPIS FOOD INDUSTRY CO. LTD.; *Int'l*, pg. 252
CHASE & SANBORN COFFEE, INC.—Nestle S.A.; *Int'l*, pg. 917
CHOCK FULL O' NUTS COFFEE COMPANY—Chock Full O' Nuts Corporation; *U.S. Public*, pg. 351
CHOCK FULL O' NUTS CORPORATION; *U.S. Public*, pg. 351
CHOCK FULL O' NUTS - FOOD SERVICE DIV.—Chock Full O' Nuts Corporation; *U.S. Public*, pg. 351
COMPACK DOUWE EGBERTS RT—Sara Lee Corporation; *U.S. Public*, pg. 1434
COMPANIA PERUANA DE ALIMENTOS S.A.—Nestle S.A.; *Int'l*, pg. 920
COMPASS FOODS, INC.—Tengelmann Warenhandelsgesellschaft; *Int'l*, pg. 1375
DONG-SUH FOODS CORPORATION; *Int'l*, pg. 416
EPPENS SMITH CO.—Chock Full O' Nuts Corporation; *U.S. Public*, pg. 351
FARMER BROTHERS COMPANY; *U.S. Public*, pg. 613
THE FOLGER COFFEE COMPANY—The Procter & Gamble Company; *U.S. Public*, pg. 1331
FOOD SERVICES DIVISION—Nestle S.A.; *Int'l*, pg. 917
GREEN MOUNTAIN COFFEE ROASTERS, INC.; *U.S. Public*, pg. 761
IRELAND COFFEE TEA, INC.—Chock Full O' Nuts Corporation; *U.S. Public*, pg. 351
IRISH BISCUITS; *Int'l*, pg. 688
JACOBS KAFFEE GES.M.B.H.—Philip Morris Companies Inc.; *U.S. Public*, pg. 1288
JACOBS SUCHARD BERLIN GMBH & CO. KG—Philip Morris Companies Inc.; *U.S. Public*, pg. 1288
JACOBS SUCHARD ERZEUGNISSE GMBH & CO. KG—Philip Morris Companies Inc.; *U.S. Public*, pg. 1289
JACOBS SUCHARD FRANCE S.A.—Philip Morris Companies Inc.; *U.S. Public*, pg. 1289
JACOBS SUCHARD INTERNATIONAL MFG. GMBH & CO. KG—Philip Morris Companies Inc.; *U.S. Public*, pg. 1289
JACOBS SUCHARD KAFFE A/S—Philip Morris Companies Inc.; *U.S. Public*, pg. 1289
AB KAFFEBONANS ROSTERI—Nestle S.A.; *Int'l*, pg. 920
KRAFT CANADA INC.—Philip Morris Companies Inc.; *U.S. Public*, pg. 1288
KRAFT FOODS, INC.—Philip Morris Companies Inc.; *U.S. Public*, pg. 1287
KRAFT FOODS INC.—Philip Morris Companies Inc.; *U.S. Public*, pg. 1288
KRAFT JACOBS SUCHARD—Philip Morris Companies Inc.; *U.S. Public*, pg. 1290
KRAFT JACOBS SUCHARD AG—Philip Morris Companies Inc.; *U.S. Public*, pg. 1288
MELITTA KAFFEE GMBH & CO., KOMMANDIT GESELLSCHAFT—Melitta Unternehmensgruppe Bentz KG; *Int'l*, pg. 857
MELITTA NORTH AMERICA, INC.—Melitta Unternehmensgruppe Bentz KG; *Int'l*, pg. 857
MELITTA UNTERNEHMENSGRUPPE BENTZ KG; *Int'l*, pg. 856
MELITTA U.S.A., INC.—Melitta Unternehmensgruppe Bentz KG; *Int'l*, pg. 857
MILLSTONE COFFEE, INC.—The Procter & Gamble Company; *U.S. Public*, pg. 1331
NABOB FOODS LIMITED—Philip Morris Companies Inc.; *U.S. Public*, pg. 1289
NESTLE BEVERAGE COMPANY—Nestle S.A.; *Int'l*, pg. 917
NESTLE CANADA INC.—Nestle S.A.; *Int'l*, pg. 921
NESTLE FOODSERVICE CANADA—Nestle S.A.; *Int'l*, pg. 922
NESTLE INDUSTRIAL E COMMERCIAL LTDA.—Nestle S.A.; *Int'l*, pg. 921
NESTLE NEDERLAND B.V.—Nestle S.A.; *Int'l*, pg. 921
NESTLE S.A.; *Int'l*, pg. 915
NEW ENGLAND COFFEE COMPANY; *U.S. Private*, pg. 792
NOVARTIS AG; *Int'l*, pg. 971
PARK FOODS L.P.; *U.S. Private*, pg. 839
PROCTER & GAMBLE BEVERAGE DIV.—The Procter & Gamble Company; *U.S. Public*, pg. 1330
REILY FOODS & CO.—William B. Reily & Co., Inc.; *U.S. Private*, pg. 919
WILLIAM B. REILY & CO., INC.; *U.S. Private*, pg. 919
S&D COFFEE INC.; *U.S. Private*, pg. 954
S.D.D. S.R.L.—Viag AG; *Int'l*, pg. 1466
SANDOZ NUTRITION LTD.—Novartis AG; *Int'l*, pg. 972
SARA LEE CORPORATION; *U.S. Public*, pg. 1432
SARA LEE/DE—Sara Lee Corporation; *U.S. Public*, pg. 1434
SIERRA SPRING WATER COMPANY—Compagnie Generale Des Eaux; *Int'l*, pg. 322
STARBUCKS COFFEE COMPANY; *U.S. Public*, pg. 1510
SUPERIOR COFFEE AND FOODS—Sara Lee Corporation; *U.S. Public*, pg. 1434
SUPERIOR COFFEE & FOODS/HAWAII—Buyco, Inc.; *U.S. Private*, pg. 191
TALOCA & CIA LTDA—Philip Morris Companies Inc.; *U.S. Public*, pg. 1289
THE TETLEY GROUP LIMITED; *Int'l*, pg. 1377
TETLEY USA INC.—The Tetley Group Limited; *Int'l*, pg. 1377
THAI SOLUBLE COFFEE COMPANY LTD.—Nestle S.A.; *Int'l*, pg. 922
TOFA- TORREFACCAO DE CAFES DE PORTUGAL, S.A.R.L.—Nestle S.A.; *Int'l*, pg. 922
TORKE COFFEE ROASTING COMPANY; *U.S. Private*, pg. 1092
WECHSLER COFFEE CORP.; *U.S. Private*, pg. 1158
AB ZOEGAS KAFFE—Nestle S.A.; *Int'l*, pg. 922

2096 — POTATO CHIPS, CORN CHIPS & SIMILAR SNACKS

AGWAY, INC.; *U.S. Private,* pg. 27
AMERIFOODS SNACKS—Amerifoods Inc.; *U.S. Private,* pg. 65
AZTECA FOODS, INCORPORATED; *U.S. Private,* pg. 104
BACHMAN COMPANY; *U.S. Private,* pg. 109
BARREL O'FUN SNACK FOODS CO.; *U.S. Private,* pg. 118
BLUEBIRD FOODS LTD—Goodman Fielder Limited; *Int'l,* pg. 556
BON TON FOODS, INC.—Amerifoods Inc.; *U.S. Private,* pg. 65
BORDEN, INC.; *U.S. Private,* pg. 157
CAPE COD POTATO CHIP COMPANY; *U.S. Private,* pg. 205
CHIPS-OLW AB—Novartis AG; *Int'l,* pg. 975
CRACKER JACK DIVISION—Borden, Inc.; *U.S. Private,* pg. 157
DIAGEO PLC; *Int'l,* pg. 408
EL MOLINO FOODS, INC.—Borden, Inc.; *U.S. Private,* pg. 158
FAMILY SMACKS, INC.; *U.S. Private,* pg. 393
FARIBAULT FOODS INC.; *U.S. Private,* pg. 393
GOLDEN ENTERPRISES INC.; *U.S. Public,* pg. 749
GRAND METROPOLITAN PLC—Diageo Plc; *Int'l,* pg. 408
GRANNY GOOSE FOODS—Granny Goose Foods, Inc.; *U.S. Private,* pg. 469
GRANNY GOOSE FOODS, INC.; *U.S. Private,* pg. 469
HOSTESS FRITO-LAY CO.—PepsiCo, Inc.; *U.S. Public,* pg. 1277
HUSMAN SNACK FOODS, CO.—Pro-Fac Cooperative, Inc.; *U.S. Private,* pg. 887
JAYS FOODS LLC; *U.S. Private,* pg. 584
LITTLE BEAR ORGANIC FOODS, INC.—The Hain Food Group Inc.; *U.S. Public,* pg. 774
MARTIN'S SNACK DIVISION—Martin's Famous Pastry Shoppes; *U.S. Private,* pg. 710
MOORE'S QUALITY SNACK FOODS, INC.—Borden, Inc.; *U.S. Private,* pg. 158
OLW-SNACKS AB—Novartis AG; *Int'l,* pg. 983
OLD DUTCH FOODS, INC.; *U.S. Private,* pg. 814
PEPSI FOODS PRIVATE LTD.—PepsiCo, Inc.; *U.S. Public,* pg. 1277
THE POPCORN FACTORY—Foster & Gallagher, Inc.; *U.S. Private,* pg. 421
PRESIDENT FRITO-LAY CORP.—President Enterprises Corp.; *Int'l,* pg. 1069
RJR NABISCO HOLDINGS CORP.; *U.S. Public,* pg. 1354
RED SEAL QUALITY FOODS, INC.—Borden, Inc.; *U.S. Private,* pg. 158
RUDOLPH FOODS COMPANY; *U.S. Private,* pg. 950
SEYFERT FOODS, INC.; *U.S. Private,* pg. 988
THE SIMBA GROUP—Foodcorp Limited; *Int'l,* pg. 496
SMITH'S CRISPS, LTD.—PepsiCo, Inc.; *U.S. Public,* pg. 1278
SNACK AMERICA; *U.S. Private,* pg. 1010
SNYDER BERLIN—Pro-Fac Cooperative, Inc.; *U.S. Private,* pg. 887
SVENSKA KNACKE AB—Novartis AG; *Int'l,* pg. 986
TROYER POTATO PRODUCTS, INC.; *U.S. Private,* pg. 1106
UTZ QUALITY FOODS, INC.; *U.S. Private,* pg. 1130
C.J. VITNER CO.; *U.S. Private,* pg. 1142
WALKER'S CRISPS, LTD.—PepsiCo, Inc.; *U.S. Public,* pg. 1278
WEAVER POPCORN COMPANY, INC.; *U.S. Private,* pg. 1156
WESTBRAE NATURAL FOODS, INC.—The Hain Food Group Inc.; *U.S. Public,* pg. 774
WESTBRAE NATURAL, INC.—The Hain Food Group Inc.; *U.S. Public,* pg. 774

2097 — MANUFACTURED ICE

CASSCO ICE & COLD STORAGE, INC.—WLR Foods, Inc.; *U.S. Public,* pg. 1727
KOLD DRAFT—Uniflow Manufacturing Co.; *U.S. Private,* pg. 1117
MIDSOUTH ICE CO.—Spencer Companies Inc.; *U.S. Private,* pg. 1025
ROTELLE, INC.—Richfood Holdings, Inc.; *U.S. Public,* pg. 1389
SISTEMA ARGOS S.A.; *Int'l,* pg. 1256
SPENCER COMPANIES INC.; *U.S. Private,* pg. 1024
WARNER-JENKINSON S.A. DE C.V.—Universal Foods Corporation; *U.S. Public,* pg. 1696

2098 — MACARONI, SPAGHETTI, VERMICELLI & NOODLES

AGNESI SPA—Danone Group; *Int'l,* pg. 380
AMERICAN BEAUTY MACARONI—Hershey Foods Corporation; *U.S. Public,* pg. 812
AMERICAN ITALIAN PASTA COMPANY; *U.S. Public,* pg. 85
ANCO N.V.—CSM N.V.; *Int'l,* pg. 244
ANTHONY MACARONI CO., INC.—Borden, Inc.; *U.S. Private,* pg. 158
BESTFOODS; *U.S. Public,* pg. 223
BLUEBIRD FOODS LTD—Goodman Fielder Limited; *Int'l,* pg. 556
BORDEN FOODS, INC.—Borden, Inc.; *U.S. Private,* pg. 158
BORDEN, INC.; *U.S. Private,* pg. 157
BORDEN ITALIAN FOODS—Borden, Inc.; *U.S. Private,* pg. 158
BUITONI SPA—Nestle S.A.; *Int'l,* pg. 919
CPC ASIA CONSUMER FOODS DIVISION—Bestfoods; *U.S. Public,* pg. 224
CPC FOODS A/S—Bestfoods; *U.S. Public,* pg. 225
CSM N.V.; *Int'l,* pg. 243
CALIFORNIA MFG. CO., INC.—Bestfoods; *U.S. Public,* pg. 225
CONTADINA DALLA CASA BUITONI—Nestle S.A.; *Int'l,* pg. 916
COOP SWITZERLAND; *Int'l,* pg. 329
THE CREAMETTE CO. OF CANADA LTD.—Borden, Inc.; *U.S. Private,* pg. 159
DANONE GROUP; *Int'l,* pg. 379
DELMONICO FOODS—Hershey Foods Corporation; *U.S. Public,* pg. 812
FOULDS INC.; *U.S. Private,* pg. 421
GILSTER MARY LEE CORP.; *U.S. Private,* pg. 455
GOLDEN GRAIN COMPANY—The Quaker Oats Company; *U.S. Public,* pg. 1348
GOOCH FOODS, INC.—Archer Daniels Midland Company (ADM); *U.S. Public,* pg. 128
A. GOODMAN & SONS, INC.—Borden, Inc.; *U.S. Private,* pg. 158
HERSHEY FOODS CORPORATION; *U.S. Public,* pg. 811
HERSHEY PASTA AND GROCERY GROUP—Hershey Foods Corporation; *U.S. Public,* pg. 812
HONIG MERKARTIKELEN B.V.—CSM N.V.; *Int'l,* pg. 244
KRAFT FOODS INC.—Philip Morris Companies Inc.; *U.S. Public,* pg. 1288
LANCIA-BRAVO FOODS—Borden, Inc.; *U.S. Private,* pg. 159
THOMAS J. LIPTON COMPANY—Unilever Plc; *Int'l,* pg. 1435
MERLINO'S MACARONI, INC.—Borden, Inc.; *U.S. Private,* pg. 158
NISSIN FOOD PRODUCTS CO., LTD.; *Int'l,* pg. 949
NISSIN FOODS (U.S.A.) CO. LTD.—Nissin Food Products Co., Ltd.; *Int'l,* pg. 949
PAJIAS MILANI, S.A.—Diageo Plc; *Int'l,* pg. 411
PANZALIM—Danone Group; *Int'l,* pg. 381
THE PRINCE CO. OF MICHIGAN—Borden, Inc.; *U.S. Private,* pg. 158
QUAKER OATS LIMITED—The Quaker Oats Company; *U.S. Public,* pg. 1348
RANKS HOVIS MCDOUGALL LIMITED—Tomkins PLC; *Int'l,* pg. 1395
REAMES FOODS INC.—Lancaster Colony Corporation; *U.S. Public,* pg. 977
N.V. RED BAND S.A.—CSM N.V.; *Int'l,* pg. 245
SAN GIORGIO MACARONI—Hershey Foods Corporation; *U.S. Public,* pg. 812
SANWA FOODS, INC.—Campbell Soup Company; *U.S. Public,* pg. 299
SKINNER MACARONI—Hershey Foods Corporation; *U.S. Public,* pg. 812
VANDAMME - PIE QUI CHANTE—Danone Group; *Int'l,* pg. 380
VENEPASTAS C.A.—Nestle S.A.; *Int'l,* pg. 922
VIVIANO MACARONI CO.—Borden, Inc.; *U.S. Private,* pg. 158
WESTERN GLOBE PRODUCTS, INC.—Borden, Inc.; *U.S. Private,* pg. 158
A. ZEREGAS SONS, INC.; *U.S. Private,* pg. 1204

2099 — FOOD PREPARATIONS, NEC

ADM ARKADY—Archer Daniels Midland Company (ADM); *U.S. Public,* pg. 127
APV FRANKLIN INC.—Siebe plc; *Int'l,* pg. 1240
ADAMS EXTRACT CO., INC.; *U.S. Private,* pg. 16
ADOLPH'S LTD.—Unilever Plc; *Int'l,* pg. 1435
ADRIA PRODUCTOS ALIMENTICOS LTDA—Borden, Inc.; *U.S. Private,* pg. 158
ALBERTO-CULVER COMPANY; *U.S. Public,* pg. 37
ALBERTO-CULVER USA, INC.—Alberto-Culver Company; *U.S. Public,* pg. 38
ALGAS MARINAS S.A.—Hercules Incorporated; *U.S. Public,* pg. 810
ALGEL S.P.A.—Unilever Plc; *Int'l,* pg. 1436
ALGOOD FOOD COMPANY; *U.S. Private,* pg. 34
J.W. ALLEN & COMPANY; *U.S. Private,* pg. 37
ALLEN MILK CO.—Lancaster Colony Corporation; *U.S. Public,* pg. 977
ALLIANT FOODSERVICE—Clayton, Dubilier & Rice, Inc; *U.S. Private,* pg. 244
ALLIED OLD ENGLISH, INC.; *U.S. Private,* pg. 39
ALSO S.P.A.—Unilever Plc; *Int'l,* pg. 1436
AMBOY SPECIALTY FOODS—Dean Foods Company; *U.S.* Public, pg. 490
AMERICAN NUT CO.—Clements Foods Co.; *U.S. Private,* pg. 245
AMERICANA FOODS, INC.—TCBY Enterprises Inc.; *U.S. Public,* pg. 1554
APONTI GMBH—Nestle S.A.; *Int'l,* pg. 918
ARCHER DANIELS MIDLAND COMPANY (ADM); *U.S. Public,* pg. 127
ARROW INDUSTRIES, INC.—ConAgra, Inc.; *U.S. Public,* pg. 426
AZTECA FOODS, INCORPORATED; *U.S. Private,* pg. 104
BSB NAHRUNGSMITTEL GMBH—Danone Group; *Int'l,* pg. 380
BACHMAN COMPANY; *U.S. Private,* pg. 109
BAKERY INGREDIENTS DIVISION—Royal Gist-Brocades N.V.; *Int'l,* pg. 1142
BANNER PHARMACAPS INC.—Sobel NV; *Int'l,* pg. 1272
BATCHELORS FOODS, LTD.—Unilever Plc; *Int'l,* pg. 1434
BEAUDREY MAPLE PRODUCTS, INC.—Borden, Inc.; *U.S. Private,* pg. 159
BELIZE FOOD PRODUCTS LTD.—Nestle S.A.; *Int'l,* pg. 918
BENSDROP GES. M.B.H.—Unilever Plc; *Int'l,* pg. 1436
BERNARDI ITALIAN FOODS—Windsor Quality Food Co., Ltd.; *U.S. Private,* pg. 1182
BEST FOODS—Bestfoods; *U.S. Public,* pg. 224
BEST FOODS CANADA, INC.—Bestfoods; *U.S. Public,* pg. 224
BEST FOODS CARIBBEAN, INC.—Bestfoods; *U.S. Public,* pg. 224
BESTFOODS; *U.S. Public,* pg. 223
BEWLEY'S TEA & COFFEE LTD.—Campbells/Bewley Group; *Int'l,* pg. 254
BIMAR BAKERIES—Grupo Industrial Bimbo S.A. de C.V.; *Int'l,* pg. 575
BLUEBIRD FOODS LTD—Goodman Fielder Limited; *Int'l,* pg. 556
BOB'S INDUSTRIA E COMERCIA LTDA.—Nestle S.A.; *Int'l, pg. 919*
BOEHRINGER INGELHEIM PHARMACEUTICALS, INC.—Boehringer Ingelheim GmbH; *Int'l,* pg. 199
BONIFACE THIEM S.A.—Borden, Inc.; *U.S. Private,* pg. 159
BONOMELLI S.R.L.; *Int'l,* pg. 201
BORDEN FOODS CANADA—Borden, Inc.; *U.S. Private,* pg. 159
BORDEN, INC.; *U.S. Private,* pg. 157
BRIGHAM'S, INC.—Grotech Capital Group, Inc.; *U.S. Private,* pg. 483
BRITISH FERMENTATION PRODUCTS LTD.—Royal Gist-Brocades N.V.; *Int'l,* pg. 1143
BRITISH PEPPER & SPICE CO. LTD.—Burns, Philp & Company Limited; *Int'l,* pg. 236
BROEX, S.A.—Borden, Inc.; *U.S. Private,* pg. 159
H.P. BULMER HOLDINGS PLC; *Int'l,* pg. 232
BURNS, PHILP & CO.—Burns, Philp & Company Limited; *Int'l,* pg. 236
BURNS, PHILP & COMPANY LIMITED; *Int'l,* pg. 236
BURNS, PHILP INC.—Burns, Philp & Company Limited; *Int'l,* pg. 236
BUTLER'S (GRINDERS & OPERATORS) LTD.—The Peninsular and Oriental Steam Navigation Company; *Int'l,* pg. 1033
CPC/AJI (HONG KONG) LTD.—Bestfoods; *U.S. Public,* pg. 225
CPC/AJI (SINGAPORE) PTE. LTD.—Bestfoods; *U.S. Public, pg. 225*
CPC ASIA CONSUMER FOODS DIVISION—Bestfoods; *U.S. Public,* pg. 224
CPC FOODS A/S—Bestfoods; *U.S. Public,* pg. 225
CPC FOODS A.S.—Bestfoods; *U.S. Public,* pg. 225
CPC RUFHAN LIMITED—Bestfoods; *U.S. Public,* pg. 225
CSM FOOD DIVISION—CSM N.V.; *Int'l,* pg. 243
CALIFORNIA MFG. CO., INC.—Bestfoods; *U.S. Public,* pg. 225
CALVE-DE BETUWE B.V.—Unilever Plc; *Int'l,* pg. 1436
JOSEPH CAMPBELL COMPANY—Campbell Soup Company; *U.S. Public,* pg. 299
CAMPBELL SOUP COMPANY; *U.S. Public,* pg. 298
CAMPBELL USA—Campbell Soup Company; *U.S. Public,* pg. 299
CAMPBELL'S DE MEXICO, S.A. DE C.V.—Campbell Soup Company; *U.S. Public,* pg. 299
CASE-SWAYNE CO. INC.; *U.S. Private,* pg. 218
CECA S.A.—Elf Aquitane; *Int'l,* pg. 445
CELESTIAL BEVERAGES, INC.—Celestial Seasonings; *U.S.* Public, pg. 320
CELESTIAL SEASONINGS; *U.S. Public,* pg. 319
CEREAL WANDER—Novartis AG; *Int'l,* pg. 975
CEREOL S.A.—Compart SpA; *Int'l,* pg. 324
CEYLON NUTRITIONAL FOODS LTD.—Nestle S.A.; *Int'l,* pg. 919
CHEIL FOODS & CHEMICALS INC.—Samsung Group; *Int'l, pg. 1181*
CHESEBROUGH-POND'S—Unilever Plc; *Int'l,* pg. 1436
CHESEBROUGH-POND'S USA CO.—Unilever Plc; *Int'l,* pg. 1435
CHESHIRE WHOLEFOODS PLC—Koninklijke BolsWessanen nv; *Int'l,* pg. 752
CHIPS-OLW AB—Novartis AG; *Int'l,* pg. 975
CHIQUITA BRANDS INTERNATIONAL, INC.; *U.S. Public,* pg. 349
CIA. CHIRICANA DE LECHE, S.A.—Borden, Inc.; *U.S. Private,* pg. 159
CHOCK FULL O' NUTS - FOOD SERVICE DIV.—Chock Full O' Nuts Corporation; *U.S. Public,* pg. 351
CLEMENTS FOODS CO.; *U.S. Private,* pg. 245
CLEMENTS NUT CO.—Clements Foods Co.; *U.S. Private,* pg. 245
CLEMENTS VINEGAR COMPANY—Clements Foods Co.; *U.S. Private,* pg. 245
COGESAL S.A.—Unilever Plc; *Int'l,* pg. 1436
COMPAGNIE AFRICAINE DE PREPARATIONS ALIMENTAIRES CAPRAL NESTLE—Nestle S.A.; *Int'l,* pg. 920
COMPANHIA PRODUTORA DE ALIMENTOS S.A.—Nestle S.A.; *Int'l,* pg. 920
CONAGRA FRUEN MILLING CO.—ConAgra, Inc.; *U.S. Public,* pg. 428
CONAGRA, INC.; *U.S. Public,* pg. 425
CONSUMER PRODUCTS COMPANY—Alltrista Corporation; *U.S. Public,* pg. 56
COOP SWITZERLAND; *Int'l,* pg. 329
JOHN COPES FOOD PRODUCTS, INC.; *U.S. Private,* pg. 274
CORN PRODUCTS CO. (INDIA) LTD.—Bestfoods; *U.S. Public,* pg. 224
CORN PRODUCTS INTERNATIONAL, INC.; *U.S. Public,* pg. 447
CORPORATE FOODS LTD.—Maple Leaf Foods Inc.; *Int'l,* pg. 841
CROMPTON & KNOWLES CORPORATION; *U.S. Public,* pg. 459
CULINAR INC.; *Int'l,* pg. 348
CUMBERLAND PACKING CORP.; *U.S. Private,* pg. 295
CURTICE BURNS FOODS—Pro-Fac Cooperative, Inc.; *U.S.* Private, pg. 887
CUSTOM FOOD PRODUCTS INC.—Griffith Laboratories Worldwide, Inc.; *U.S. Private,* pg. 481
DANISCO A/S; *Int'l,* pg. 378
DANISCO INGREDIENTS USA, INC.—Danisco A/S; *Int'l,* pg. 378
DEAN FOODS SPECIALTY PRODUCTS—Dean Foods Company; *U.S. Public,* pg. 490

DEAN PICKLES & SPECIALTY PRODUCTS—Dean Foods Company; *U.S. Public*, pg. 490
DEL MONTE FOODS; *U.S. Private*, pg. 321
DERIVADOS LACTEOS Y ALIMENTICIOS S.A.—Nestle S.A.; *Int'l*, pg. 920
DEUTSCHE LIBBY GMBH—Nestle S.A.; *Int'l*, pg. 920
H.B. DEVINEY CO.—J.M. Smucker Company; *U.S. Public*, pg. 1480
DEVRO-TEEPAK, INC.—Devro International Plc; *Int'l*, pg. 408
DIAGEO PLC; *Int'l*, pg. 408
DIAMOND CRYSTAL SPECIALTY FOODS, INC.; *U.S. Private*, pg. 330
DIEPAL-N.S.A.—Danone Group; *Int'l*, pg. 380
DON MIGUEL MEXICAN FOODS, INC.; *U.S. Private*, pg. 339
DONG-SUH FOODS CORPORATION; *Int'l*, pg. 416
DR. RITTER GMBH & CO.—Nestle S.A.; *Int'l*, pg. 920
ELF SANOFI S.A.—Elf Aquitane; *Int'l*, pg. 445
EMPIRE KOSHER POULTRY, INC.; *U.S. Private*, pg. 374
ENZOPAC, INC.; *U.S. Private*, pg. 379
ESPECIALIDADES ALIMENTICIAS S.A.—Nestle S.A.; *Int'l*, pg. 920
EXPORTSLACHTERIJ UDEMA B.V.—Unilever Plc; *Int'l*, pg. 1437
FIDCO (FOOD INGREDIENT DEVELOPMENT COMPANY)—Nestle S.A.; *Int'l*, pg. 917
FIMA-PRODUCTOS ALIMENTARES, LDA; *Int'l*, pg. 471
FARMER BROTHERS COMPANY; *U.S. Public*, pg. 613
FERROSAN DANMARK A/S—Novo Nordisk A/S; *Int'l*, pg. 987
FERROSAN INTERNATIONAL A/S—Novo Nordisk A/S; *Int'l*, pg. 987
FIRMENICH—Firmenich S.A.; *Int'l*, pg. 486
FLAVORITE LABORATORIES—A.M. Todd Company; *U.S. Private*, pg. 1090
FLEISCHMANN'S YEAST—Burns, Philp & Company Limited; *Int'l*, pg. 237
FLEISCHMANN'S YEAST CONSUMER PRODUCTS DIV.—Burns, Philp & Company Limited; *Int'l*, pg. 237
FLOWERS INDUSTRIES, INC.; *U.S. Public*, pg. 656
FONT VELLA—Danone Group; *Int'l*, pg. 381
FOOD & NUTRITIONAL PRODUCTS (PTY.) LTD.—Nestle S.A.; *Int'l*, pg. 920
FOOD INGREDIENTS SPECIALTIES S.A.—Nestle S.A.; *Int'l*, pg. 916
FOOD SERVICES DIVISION—Nestle S.A.; *Int'l*, pg. 917
FOOD SPECIALTIES GHANA LTD.—Nestle S.A.; *Int'l*, pg. 920
P.T. FOOD SPECIALTIES INDONESIA—Nestle S.A.; *Int'l*, pg. 920
FOOD SPECIALTIES JAMAICA LTD.—Nestle S.A.; *Int'l*, pg. 920
FOOD SPECIALTIES (NIGERIA) LTD.—Nestle S.A.; *Int'l*, pg. 920
FOOD SPECIALTIES (PVT.) LTD.—Nestle S.A.; *Int'l*, pg. 920
FOODCORP LIMITED; *Int'l*, pg. 496
FRANCAISE D'ALIMENTATION ET DE BOISSONS S.A.—Unilever Plc; *Int'l*, pg. 1437
FRIGO S.A.—Unilever Plc; *Int'l*, pg. 1437
FRITO-LAY COMPANY—PepsiCo, Inc.; *U.S. Public*, pg. 1277
FRUTAROM MEER CORPORATION—ICC Industries, Inc.; *U.S. Private*, pg. 554
FRUTERA COLOMBIANA S.A.—Corn Products International, Inc.; *U.S. Public*, pg. 447
GV NESTLE GMBH FUR GROSSVERBRAUCHERZENGNISSE—Nestle S.A.; *Int'l*, pg. 920
GAGE FOOD PRODUCTS COMPANY—DG Foods, LLC; *U.S. Private*, pg. 301
GALLINA BLANCA S.A.—Borden, Inc.; *U.S. Private*, pg. 159
GENERALE TRAITEUR—Danone Group; *Int'l*, pg. 380
GERMANTOWN INTERNATIONAL—Goodman Fielder Limited; *Int'l*, pg. 555
GERMANTOWN (USA) CO.—Goodman Fielder Limited; *Int'l*, pg. 555
GILROY FOODS, INC.—ConAgra, Inc.; *U.S. Public*, pg. 428
GIST-BROCADES FRANCE S.A.—Royal Gist-Brocades N.V.; *Int'l*, pg. 1143
GIST-BROCADES, INC.—Royal Gist-Brocades N.V.; *Int'l*, pg. 1143
GIVAUDAN-ROURE DO BRAZIL LTDA—Roche Holding Ltd.; *Int'l*, pg. 1120
GIVAUDAN-ROURE GMBH—Roche Holding Ltd.; *Int'l*, pg. 1120
GOLDEN ENTERPRISES INC.; *U.S. Public*, pg. 749
GOLDEN GRAIN COMPANY—The Quaker Oats Company; *U.S. Public*, pg. 1348
GOLDEN VALLEY MICROWAVE FOODS, INC.—ConAgra, Inc.; *U.S. Public*, pg. 427
GORGES/QUIK-TO-FIX FOODS; *U.S. Private*, pg. 465
GRAND METROPOLITAN PLC—Diageo Plc; *Int'l*, pg. 408
GRANDMET FOODS UK—Diageo Plc; *Int'l*, pg. 408
GRANNY GOOSE FOODS, INC.; *U.S. Private*, pg. 469
GRAVYMASTER INC.; *U.S. Private*, pg. 471
GREEN SPOT PACKAGING INC.; *U.S. Private*, pg. 477
GRIFFITH COLOMBIA S.A.—Griffith Laboratories Worldwide, Inc.; *U.S. Private*, pg. 481
GRIFFITH LABORATORIES WORLDWIDE, INC.; *U.S. Private*, pg. 481
GROUPE PERNOD RICARD; *Int'l*, pg. 566
GROUPE SERVAIR (COMPAGNIE D'EXPLOITATION DES SERVICES AUXILIAIRES AERIENS)—Groupe Air France; *Int'l*, pg. 560
GUIGOZ FRANCE S.A.—Nestle S.A.; *Int'l*, pg. 920
HP FOODS—Danone Group; *Int'l*, pg. 380
THE HAIN FOOD GROUP INC.; *U.S. Public*, pg. 774
HANOVER FOODS CORPORATION; *U.S. Private*, pg. 499
HANSEO FOOD CO. LTD.—Nestle S.A.; *Int'l*, pg. 920
HARMONY FOODS CORPORATION; *U.S. Private*, pg. 503
S.A. HARTOG N.V.—Unilever Plc; *Int'l*, pg. 1437
HEIMBS & SOHN GMBH & CO KG—Nestle S.A.; *Int'l*, pg. 920
H.J. HEINZ B.V.—H.J. Heinz Company; *U.S. Public*, pg. 806
H.J. HEINZ COMPANY; *U.S. Public*, pg. 805
H.J. HEINZ COMPANY AUSTRALIA LTD.—H.J. Heinz Company; *U.S. Public*, pg. 807
H.J. HEINZ CO. OF CANADA LTD.—H.J. Heinz Company; *U.S. Public*, pg. 806
H.J. HEINZ GMBH—H.J. Heinz Company; *U.S. Public*, pg. 806
HEINZ JAPAN LTD.—H.J. Heinz Company; *U.S. Public*, pg. 806
HELADOS BORDEN, S.A.—Borden, Inc.; *U.S. Private*, pg. 159
HELLER SEASONINGS & INGREDIENTS, INC.; *U.S. Private*, pg. 520
HELMSLEY ENTERPRISES, INC.; *U.S. Private*, pg. 521
HELMSLEY-SPEAR INC.—Helmsley Enterprises, Inc.; *U.S. Private*, pg. 521
HERTA (U.K.) LTD.—Nestle S.A.; *Int'l*, pg. 920
HORMEL FOODS CORP.; *U.S. Public*, pg. 840
THE HUDSON CORPORATION—Nature's Bounty Inc.; *U.S. Public*, pg. 1166
A.C. HUMKO—Associated British Foods plc; *Int'l*, pg. 92
IMSA S.A.—Corn Products International, Inc.; *U.S. Public*, pg. 447
IDAHO POTATO OPERS.—Diageo Plc; *Int'l*, pg. 411
IGLO INDUSTRIAS DE GELADOS, LDA.—Unilever Plc; *Int'l*, pg. 1437
INDRA AB—Nestle S.A.; *Int'l*, pg. 920
INDUSTRIAS DE MAIZ Y ALIMENTOS S.A.—Corn Products International, Inc.; *U.S. Public*, pg. 447
INTERNATIONAL DIVERSE FOODS—Levmark Capital Corporation; *U.S. Private*, pg. 663
INTERNATIONAL HOME FOODS INC.—Hicks, Muse, Tate & Furst Inc.; *U.S. Private*, pg. 526
INTERNATIONAL MULTIFOODS CORPORATION; *U.S. Public*, pg. 900
IRISH BISCUITS; *Int'l*, pg. 688
ISRAEL EDIBLE PRODUCTS LTD.—Bestfoods; *U.S. Public*, pg. 225
J. HUNGERFORD SMITH COMPANY—ConAgra, Inc.; *U.S. Public*, pg. 428
N.V. JACKY, S.A.—Unilever Plc; *Int'l*, pg. 1437
GEBR. JUNG GMBH & CO. OHG—Nestle S.A.; *Int'l*, pg. 920
M. KAMENSTEIN, INC.; *U.S. Private*, pg. 606
KANE-MILLER CORP.; *U.S. Private*, pg. 607
L. KARP & SONS, INC.; *U.S. Private*, pg. 607
KEIZER B.V. (WASPIK)—McCain Foods Limited; *Int'l*, pg. 850
KELLOGG (AUST.) PROPRIETARY LTD.—Kellogg Company; *U.S. Public*, pg. 947
KELLOGG BRASIL & CIA—Kellogg Company; *U.S. Public*, pg. 947
KELLOGG CANADA INC.—Kellogg Company; *U.S. Public*, pg. 947
KELLOGG COMPANY; *U.S. Public*, pg. 947
KELLOGG COMPANY ARGENTINA S.A.C.I.F.—Kellogg Company; *U.S. Public*, pg. 947
KELLOGG COMPANY OF GREAT BRITAIN LTD.—Kellogg Company; *U.S. Public*, pg. 947
KELLOGG DE MEXICO S.A. DE C.V.—Kellogg Company; *U.S. Public*, pg. 948
KELLOGG (DEUTSCHLAND) GESELLSCHAFT MIT BESCHRANKTER HARTUNG (GMBH)—Kellogg Company; *U.S. Public*, pg. 948
KELLOGG SALES COMPANY—Kellogg Company; *U.S. Public*, pg. 947
C.H. KNORR NAHRUNGSMITTELFABRIK, GES. MB H.—Bestfoods; *U.S. Public*, pg. 225
KNORR-NAHRMITTEL AKTIENGESELLSCHAFT—Bestfoods; *U.S. Public*, pg. 225
KNORR PORTUGUESA-PRODUTOS ALIMENTARES S.A.—Bestfoods; *U.S. Public*, pg. 225
KNOUSE FOODS INC.; *U.S. Private*, pg. 627
KOIPE S.A.—Compart SpA; *Int'l*, pg. 324
KONINKLIJKE BUNGE B.V.; *Int'l*, pg. 753
KONINKLIJKE MAATSCHAPPIJ DE BETUWE B.V.—Unilever Plc; *Int'l*, pg. 1437
KRAFT CANADA INC.—Philip Morris Companies Inc.; *U.S. Public*, pg. 1288
KRAFT FOODS, INC.—Philip Morris Companies Inc.; *U.S. Public*, pg. 1287
KRAFT FOODS LTD., YEAST EXTRACT PLANT—Philip Morris Companies Inc.; *U.S. Public*, pg. 1290
KRAFT JACOBS SUCHARD—Philip Morris Companies Inc.; *U.S. Public*, pg. 1290
THE KROGER CO.; *U.S. Public*, pg. 967
KVAERNER EUREKA, BRYNE DIVISION—Kvaerner a.s.a.; *Int'l*, pg. 767
KYOWA HAKKO EUROPE GMBH—Kyowa Hakko Kogyo Company, Ltd.; *Int'l*, pg. 778
KYOWA HAKKO (H.K.) CO., LTD.—Kyowa Hakko Kogyo Company, Ltd.; *Int'l*, pg. 778
KYOWA HAKKO KOGYO COMPANY, LTD.; *Int'l*, pg. 778
KYOWA HAKKO U.S.A., INC.—Kyowa Hakko Kogyo Company, Ltd.; *Int'l*, pg. 778
KYOWA HAKKO-WEST COAST OFFICE—Kyowa Hakko Kogyo Company, Ltd.; *Int'l*, pg. 778
LA REINA, INC.; *U.S. Private*, pg. 640
LANCE, INC.; *U.S. Public*, pg. 977
LANGNESE-IGLO G.M.B.H.—Unilever Plc; *Int'l*, pg. 1437
LAWRY'S FOODS, INC.—Unilever Plc; *Int'l*, pg. 1435
A.C. LEGG PACKING COMPANY, INC.; *U.S. Private*, pg. 658
LEINER-DAVIS INTERNATIONAL LIMITED—Goodman Fielder Limited; *Int'l*, pg. 555
LEINER HEALTH PRODUCTS, INC.; *U.S. Private*, pg. 659
LEVER S.A.—Unilever Plc; *Int'l*, pg. 1438
LIEBIG BENELUX NV—Danone Group; *Int'l*, pg. 380
LIPTON—Unilever Plc; *Int'l*, pg. 1438
LIPTON PAKISTAN LTD.—Unilever Plc; *Int'l*, pg. 1438
LIPTON (SA) (PTY.) LTD.—Unilever Plc; *Int'l*, pg. 1438
THOMAS J. LIPTON COMPANY—Unilever Plc; *Int'l*, pg. 1435
LUCAS AARDENBURG B.V.—Unilever Plc; *Int'l*, pg. 1438
LUCAS INGREDIENTS—Dalgety Plc; *Int'l*, pg. 376
MJB RICE COMPANY—Nestle S.A.; *Int'l*, pg. 917
MAGGI AG—Nestle S.A.; *Int'l*, pg. 916
THE B. MANISCHEWITZ COMPANY; *U.S. Private*, pg. 699
MARVELO B.V.—Koninklijke Ahold NV; *Int'l*, pg. 749
MCCAIN FOODS LIMITED; *Int'l*, pg. 850
MCCAIN FOODS (NZ) LTD.—McCain Foods Limited; *Int'l*, pg. 850
MCCORMICK & COMPANY, INCORPORATED; *U.S. Public*, pg. 1066
MEDICORNEA S.A.—Nestle S.A.; *Int'l*, pg. 920
MEESTER WIJHE BV—Koninklijke Ahold NV; *Int'l*, pg. 749
JULIUS MEINL AG; *Int'l*, pg. 856
MELISSA—Danone Group; *Int'l*, pg. 380
DAVID MICHAEL & CO. INC.; *U.S. Private*, pg. 740
MICHAEL FOODS, INC.; *U.S. Public*, pg. 1103
MILWAUKEE SEASONINGS, INC.—Bestfoods; *U.S. Public*, pg. 224
MITSUI NORIN CO., LTD.—Mitsui & Co., Ltd.; *Int'l*, pg. 878
MITSUKAN & NAKANO VINEGAR COMPANY LTD.; *Int'l*, pg. 883
MOLINOS NACIONALES, C.A. (VENEZUELA)—International Multifoods Corporation; *U.S. Public*, pg. 901
MONTEDISON S.P.A.—Compart SpA; *Int'l*, pg. 324
MORINAGA MILK INDUSTRY CO., LTD.; *Int'l*, pg. 895
MORINAGA NUTRITIONAL FOODS, INC.—Morinaga Milk Industry Co., Ltd.; *Int'l*, pg. 895
MRS. GILES COUNTRY KITCHENS, INC.—Bob Evans Farms, Inc.; *U.S. Public*, pg. 596
MUELLER'S MUEHLE GMBH; *Int'l*, pg. 896
MY OWN MEALS, INC.; *U.S. Private*, pg. 770
NABISCO INC.—RJR Nabisco Holdings Corp.; *U.S. Public*, pg. 1355
NAKANO FOODS—Mitsukan & Nakano Vinegar Company Ltd.; *Int'l*, pg. 883
NAKANO FOODS INC.—Mitsukan & Nakano Vinegar Company Ltd.; *Int'l*, pg. 883
NATIONAL FRUIT PRODUCT COMPANY; *U.S. Private*, pg. 783
NATIONAL STARCH AND CHEMICAL COMPANY—Unilever Plc; *Int'l*, pg. 1435
NESTLE AUSTRALIA LTD.—Nestle S.A.; *Int'l*, pg. 920
NESTLE BELGILUX S.A.—Nestle S.A.; *Int'l*, pg. 921
NESTLE CANADA INC.—Nestle S.A.; *Int'l*, pg. 921
NESTLE CARIBBEAN, INC.—Nestle S.A.; *Int'l*, pg. 921
NESTLE CHILE S.A.—Nestle S.A.; *Int'l*, pg. 921
NESTLE CHINA LTD.—Nestle S.A.; *Int'l*, pg. 921
NESTLE CHOCOLATE & CONFECTION—Nestle S.A.; *Int'l*, pg. 917
S.A. NESTLE DE PRODUCTOS ALIMENTICIOS—Nestle S.A.; *Int'l*, pg. 921
NESTLE DEL URUGUAY S.A.—Nestle S.A.; *Int'l*, pg. 921
NESTLE ERZEUGNISSE GMBH—Nestle S.A.; *Int'l*, pg. 921
NESTLE FOODS KENYA LTD.—Nestle S.A.; *Int'l*, pg. 921
NESTLE FOODSERVICE CANADA—Nestle S.A.; *Int'l*, pg. 922
NESTLE HELLAS S.A.I.—Nestle S.A.; *Int'l*, pg. 921
NESTLE HONDURENA S.A.—Nestle S.A.; *Int'l*, pg. 921
NESTLE INDUSTRIAL E COMMERCIAL LTDA.—Nestle S.A.; *Int'l*, pg. 921
NESTLE (IRELAND) LTD.—Nestle S.A.; *Int'l*, pg. 921
NESTLE ITALIANA S.P.A.—Nestle S.A.; *Int'l*, pg. 921
NESTLE KK—Nestle S.A.; *Int'l*, pg. 921
NESTLE LANKA LTD.—Nestle S.A.; *Int'l*, pg. 921
A/S NESTLE NORGE—Nestle S.A.; *Int'l*, pg. 921
NESTLE PANAMA S.A.—Nestle S.A.; *Int'l*, pg. 921
NESTLE PORTUGAL, S.A.—Nestle S.A.; *Int'l*, pg. 921
NESTLE PRODUCTS (MAURITIUS) LTD.—Nestle S.A.; *Int'l*, pg. 921
NESTLE-ROWNTREE LTD.—Nestle S.A.; *Int'l*, pg. 921
NESTLE S.A.; *Int'l*, pg. 915
NESTLE SINGAPORE PTE. LTD.—Nestle S.A.; *Int'l*, pg. 921
NESTLE U.K. LTD.—Nestle S.A.; *Int'l*, pg. 922
NESTLE USA—Nestle S.A.; *Int'l*, pg. 916
NEWLY WEDS FOODS INC.; *U.S. Private*, pg. 796
NEWMAN'S OWN, INC.; *U.S. Private*, pg. 797
NIKO CO., LTD.—Mitsukoshi, Ltd.; *Int'l*, pg. 883
NIPPON LEVER BV—Unilever Plc; *Int'l*, pg. 1438
NORDSEE DEUTSCHE HOCHSEEFISCHEREI G.M.B.H.—Unilever Plc; *Int'l*, pg. 1438
NORDSEE GES. M.B.H.—Unilever Plc; *Int'l*, pg. 1438
NORFOODS, INC.; *U.S. Private*, pg. 802
NOVALIM-NESTLE—Nestle S.A.; *Int'l*, pg. 922
NOVARTIS AG; *Int'l*, pg. 971
NOVIA LIVSMEDELSINDUSTRIER AB—Unilever Plc; *Int'l*, pg. 1438
NOZAKI & COMPANY LTD.; *Int'l*, pg. 990
NUTREX AG—Coop Switzerland; *Int'l*, pg. 330
NUTRILITE PRODUCTS, INC.—Amway Corporation; *U.S. Private*, pg. 69
NUTRINSA, S.A.—Borden, Inc.; *U.S. Private*, pg. 160
OLW-SNACKS AB—Novartis AG; *Int'l*, pg. 983
THE O'BOISE CORPORATION; *U.S. Private*, pg. 810
OH BOY CORPORATION; *U.S. Private*, pg. 812
OLD DUTCH FOODS, INC.; *U.S. Private*, pg. 814
OLIVIERI FOODS—Maple Leaf Foods Inc.; *Int'l*, pg. 841
OREGON FREEZE DRY, INC.; *U.S. Private*, pg. 819
THE ORIGINAL CHILI BOWL, INC.—Windsor Quality Food Co., Ltd.; *U.S. Private*, pg. 1182
ORVAL KENT FOOD CO.; *U.S. Private*, pg. 820
OSTERREICHISCHE UNILEVER GES. M.B.H.—Unilever Plc; *Int'l*, pg. 1438
PPF INTL. LTD., FOOD INDUSTRIES DIV.—Unilever Plc; *Int'l*, pg. 1434
PARADISE, INC.; *U.S. Public*, pg. 1256
PASTA & CHEESE, INC.—Nestle S.A.; *Int'l*, pg. 918
PASTA FOODS LIMITED—Tomkins PLC; *Int'l*, pg. 1396
PASTA GALA SA—Coop Switzerland; *Int'l*, pg. 330
THE PASTENE COMPANIES LTD.; *U.S. Private*, pg. 842
PAULS PLC—Harrisons & Crosfield plc; *Int'l*, pg. 598

PEPSICO, INC.; *U.S. Public*, pg. 1276
PETER'S SAVOURY PRODUCTS—Diageo Plc; *Int'l*, pg. 410
PHILIP MORRIS COMPANIES INC.; *U.S. Public*, pg. 1287
PRESIDENT ENTERPRISES CORP.; *Int'l*, pg. 1068
PRESTO FOOD PRODUCTS, INC.—Suiza Foods Corporation; *U.S. Public*, pg. 1527
PRINCE FOODS CANNING DIV.—Borden, Inc.; *U.S. Private*, pg. 158
PRINCIPAL MARQUES MEAT CO.—Maple Leaf Foods Inc.; *Int'l*, pg. 841
PROCTER & GAMBLE OF PERU—The Procter & Gamble Company; *U.S. Public*, pg. 1332
PROCTER & GAMBLE FOOD PRODUCTS DIV.—The Procter & Gamble Company; *U.S. Public*, pg. 1331
PRODUCTOS ALIMENTICIOS IMPERIAL, S.A.—Diageo Plc; *Int'l*, pg. 411
PRODUCTOS ALIMENTICIOS SAVORY S.A.I.C.—Nestle S.A.; *Int'l*, pg. 922
PRODUCTOS DE MAIZ S.A.—Corn Products International, Inc.; *U.S. Public*, pg. 447
PRODUCTOS NESTLE (COSTA RICA) S.A.—Nestle S.A.; *Int'l*, pg. 922
PRODUCTOS NESTLE (EL SALVADOR) S.A.—Nestle S.A.; *Int'l*, pg. 922
PRODUCTOS NESTLE (GUATEMALA) S.A.—Nestle S.A.; *Int'l*, pg. 922
PRODUCTOS NESTLE (NICARAGUA) S.A.—Nestle S.A.; *Int'l*, pg. 922
QA PRODUCTS, INC.—CSM N.V.; *Int'l*, pg. 244
THE QUAKER OATS COMPANY; *U.S. Public*, pg. 1347
RHM INGREDIENTS, LTD.—Newly Weds Foods Inc.; *U.S. Private*, pg. 797
RJR NABISCO HOLDINGS CORP.; *U.S. Public*, pg. 1354
RAGU FOODS, INC.—Unilever Plc; *Int'l*, pg. 1436
RALEIGH NUTRITIONAL PRODUCTS LTD.—Nestle S.A.; *Int'l*, pg. 922
RALSTON PURINA COMPANY; *U.S. Public*, pg. 1359
RED CARNATION GUMS LTD.—The Peninsular and Oriental Steam Navigation Company; *Int'l*, pg. 1034
RED STAR DE PUERTO RICO, S.A.—Universal Foods Corporation; *U.S. Public*, pg. 1696
RED STAR YEAST & PRODUCTS DIV.—Universal Foods Corporation; *U.S. Public*, pg. 1695
RED WING COMPANY—Tomkins PLC; *Int'l*, pg. 1398
RED WING CO. INC.—Tomkins PLC; *Int'l*, pg. 1398
REFINERIAS DE MAIZ S.A.I.C.F.—Corn Products International, Inc.; *U.S. Public*, pg. 448
REILY FOODS & CO.—William B. Reily & Co., Inc.; *U.S. Private*, pg. 919
WILLIAM B. REILY & CO., INC.; *U.S. Private*, pg. 919
REXALL SUNDOWN INC.; *U.S. Public*, pg. 1384
RICH PRODUCTS CORP.; *U.S. Private*, pg. 928
RICHARDSON-VICKS, INC.—The Procter & Gamble Company; *U.S. Public*, pg. 1331
ROBERTET FLAVORS—Robertet S.A.; *Int'l*, pg. 1119
ROBIN HOOD MULTIFOODS INC.—International Multifoods Corporation; *U.S. Public*, pg. 901
ROKEACH FOOD DISTRIBUTING INC.; *U.S. Private*, pg. 940
ROSELLA LIPTON PTY. LTD.—Unilever Plc; *Int'l*, pg. 1438
ROYAL GIST-BROCADES N.V.; *Int'l*, pg. 1142
RUIZ FOOD PRODUCTS, INC.; *U.S. Private*, pg. 951
S&D COFFEE INC.; *U.S. Private*, pg. 954
S.A.E. WANDER—Novartis AG; *Int'l*, pg. 984
SME INTERNATIONAL—IRI Istituto Ricostruzione Industriale; *Int'l*, pg. 655
SABRITAS S.A. DE C.V.—PepsiCo, Inc.; *U.S. Public*, pg. 1278
SAGIT S.P.A.—Unilever Plc; *Int'l*, pg. 1438
SANDOZ NUTRITION LTD.—Novartis AG; *Int'l*, pg. 972
SANWA FOODS, INC.—Campbell Soup Company; *U.S. Public*, pg. 299
SARA LEE/DE—Sara Lee Corporation; *U.S. Public*, pg. 1434
SAROTTI GMBH—Nestle S.A.; *Int'l*, pg. 922
SAUDI FOOD INDUSTRIES LTD. LIABILITY CO.—Nestle S.A.; *Int'l*, pg. 922
SAVANNAH FOODS & INDUSTRIES, INC.—Imperial Holly Corporation; *U.S. Public*, pg. 872
SCHAFFT FLEISCHWERKE G.M.B.H.—Unilever Plc; *Int'l*, pg. 1438
SCHILLING PLANT—McCormick & Company, Incorporated; *U.S. Public*, pg. 1066
SCHWAN'S SALES ENTERPRISES; *U.S. Private*, pg. 974
SHADE PASTA, INC.—Norfoods, Inc.; *U.S. Private*, pg. 802
SHADY MAPLE FARMS LTD.—H.J. Heinz Company; *U.S. Public*, pg. 806
SMARTFOODS, INC.—PepsiCo, Inc.; *U.S. Public*, pg. 1277
E.D. SMITH; *Int'l*, pg. 1263
J.M. SMUCKER COMPANY; *U.S. Public*, pg. 1480
SNACK AMERICA; *U.S. Private*, pg. 1010
SNOW BRAND FOOD CO., LTD.—Snow Brand Milk Products Co. Ltd.; *Int'l*, pg. 1272
SNYDER'S OF HANOVER, INC.; *U.S. Private*, pg. 1011
SOCIEDAD DOMINICANA DE CONSERVAS Y ALIMENTOS S.A.—Nestle S.A.; *Int'l*, pg. 916
SOCIEDADE PORTUGUESA DE PRODUTOS WANDER LDA.—Novartis AG; *Int'l*, pg. 985
SOCIETE DE PRODUITS ALIMETAIRES ET DIETETIQUES, SOPAD-NESTLE S.A.—Nestle S.A.; *Int'l*, pg. 922
SOKOL & COMPANY; *U.S. Private*, pg. 1012
SOUTHERN TEA CO.—The Tetley Group Limited; *Int'l*, pg. 1377
SPECIALTY BRANDS—Burns, Philp & Company Limited; *Int'l*, pg. 237
SPICE PLANT—McCormick & Company, Incorporated; *U.S. Public*, pg. 1066
STANGE (JAPAN) K.K.—McCormick & Company, Incorporated; *U.S. Public*, pg. 1067
STAR FINE FOODS, INC.; *U.S. Private*, pg. 1034
STAR FOOD PROCESSING, INC.; *U.S. Private*, pg. 1034
STAR S.P.A.—Danone Group; *Int'l*, pg. 380
STARLUX—Bestfoods; *U.S. Public*, pg. 225
STEGNER FOOD PRODUCTS CO.; *U.S. Private*, pg. 1039
STOEFFLER—Danone Group; *Int'l*, pg. 380
THE STOP & SHOP COMPANIES, INC.—Koninklijke Ahold NV; *Int'l*, pg. 750
SUNNYLAND REFINING CO., INC.—Kane-Miller Corp.; *U.S. Private*, pg. 607
SVENSKA KNACKE AB—Novartis AG; *Int'l*, pg. 986
TLC BEATRICE INTERNATIONAL HOLDINGS INC.; *U.S. Private*, pg. 1064
TARA FOODS—The Kroger Co.; *U.S. Public*, pg. 967
TAUNTON CIDER COMPANY P.L.C.—Matthew Clark Taunton, Ltd.; *Int'l*, pg. 849
TAUNTON CIDER SCOTLAND—Matthew Clark Taunton, Ltd.; *Int'l*, pg. 849
TELFORD FOODS LTD.—Koninklijke BolsWessanen nv; *Int'l*, pg. 753
TEMATI S.A. DE C.V.—PepsiCo, Inc.; *U.S. Public*, pg. 1278
THE TETLEY GROUP LIMITED; *Int'l*, pg. 1377
TETLEY USA INC.—The Tetley Group Limited; *Int'l*, pg. 1377
TINO LEBENSMITTEL GMBH—Nestle S.A.; *Int'l*, pg. 922
TOM'S FOODS, INC.; *U.S. Private*, pg. 1090
TONE BROTHERS INC.—Burns, Philp & Company Limited; *Int'l*, pg. 237
TRINIDAD FOOD PRODUCTS LTD.—Nestle S.A.; *Int'l*, pg. 922
TRINKS GMBH—Nestle S.A.; *Int'l*, pg. 922
TROPONWERKE GMBH & CO., KG—Bayer AG; *Int'l*, pg. 175
TYSON FOODS, INC.; *U.S. Public*, pg. 1652
UVG NEDERLAND B.V.—Unilever Plc; *Int'l*, pg. 1438
UNICER-UNIAO CERVEJEIRA, S.A.; *Int'l*, pg. 1432
UNIFERM GMBH & CO.—Royal Gist-Brocades N.V.; *Int'l*, pg. 1143
UNIFRANCK LEBENSMITTELWERKE GMBH—Nestle S.A.; *Int'l*, pg. 922
UNIFROST NAHRUNGSMITTEL GES. M.B.H.—Unilever Plc; *Int'l*, pg. 1439
UNILEVER NEW ZEALAND LTD.—Unilever Plc; *Int'l*, pg. 1439
UNILEVER N.V.—Unilever Plc; *Int'l*, pg. 1434
UNILEVER PLC; *Int'l*, pg. 1433
UNITED BISCUITS (HOLDINGS) PLC; *Int'l*, pg. 1442
UNITED BISCUITS (UK) LIMITED—United Biscuits (Holdings) Plc; *Int'l*, pg. 1442
U.S. & CANADIAN FOOD PRODUCTS—The Quaker Oats Company; *U.S. Public*, pg. 1347
UNIVERSAL FOODS CORPORATION-BAKERY PRODUCTS DIV.—Universal Foods Corporation; *U.S. Public*, pg. 1696
UNIVERSAL FOODS PRODUCTS INTERNATIONAL LTD.—Universal Foods Corporation; *U.S. Public*, pg. 1696
VAN DEN BERGH EN JURGENS B.V.—Unilever Plc; *Int'l*, pg. 1439
VAN DEN BERGH FOODS COMPANY—Unilever Plc; *Int'l*, pg. 1436
VAN DEN BERGH FOODS LTD.—Unilever Plc; *Int'l*, pg. 1434
VANDEMOORTELE N.V.; *Int'l*, pg. 1451
VENTRE PACKING COMPANY, INC.; *U.S. Private*, pg. 1135
VICTORIA PACKING CORPORATION; *U.S. Private*, pg. 1139
VOGEL POPCORN COMPANY—ConAgra, Inc.; *U.S. Public*, pg. 427
WANDER AG—Novartis AG; *Int'l*, pg. 972
WANDER LTD.—Novartis AG; *Int'l*, pg. 973
WANDER PHARMA G.M.B.H.—Novartis AG; *Int'l*, pg. 986
WANDER (PHILIPPINES) INC.—Novartis AG; *Int'l*, pg. 986
WANDER (PORTUGAL) ALIMENTOCAO LDA.—Novartis AG; *Int'l*, pg. 986
WANDER S.A.—Novartis AG; *Int'l*, pg. 986
WANDER (SINGAPORE) PTY. LTD.—Novartis AG; *Int'l*, pg. 986
WANDER (THAILAND) LTD.—Novartis AG; *Int'l*, pg. 986
WARNER-JENKINSON CANADA—Universal Foods Corporation; *U.S. Public*, pg. 1696
WATKINS INCORPORATED; *U.S. Private*, pg. 1153
WEI-CHUAN FOODS CORPORATION; *Int'l*, pg. 1488
WEIGHT WATCHERS FOODS CENTRAL EUROPE B.V.—H.J. Heinz Company; *U.S. Public*, pg. 807
JOHN WEST FOODS LTD.—Unilever Plc; *Int'l*, pg. 1434
WEST LYNN CREAMERY, INC.—Scangas Brothers Holdings, Inc.; *U.S. Private*, pg. 969
WHITFIELD FOODS, INC.; *U.S. Private*, pg. 1173
WILBUR CHOCOLATE CO., INC.—Cargill; *U.S. Private*, pg. 210
WILLIAMS FOODS INC.; *U.S. Private*, pg. 1178
THE WORNICK COMPANY; *U.S. Private*, pg. 1191
WORTHINGTON FOODS INC.; *U.S. Public*, pg. 1780
WYANDOT INC.; *U.S. Private*, pg. 1193
ZWANENBERG DE MEXICO S.A.—Unilever Plc; *Int'l*, pg. 1439

2111 — CIGARETTES

AMER GROUP LTD.; *Int'l*, pg. 72
AMER TOBACCO LTD.—Amer Group Ltd.; *Int'l*, pg. 72
ARDATH TOBACCO CO. LTD.—B.A.T Industries P.L.C.; *Int'l*, pg. 111
B.A.T CIGARETTENFABRIKEN B.A.T.—B.A.T Industries P.L.C.; *Int'l*, pg. 111
B.A.T FINLAND—B.A.T Industries P.L.C.; *Int'l*, pg. 111
B.A.T INDUSTRIES P.L.C.; *Int'l*, pg. 110
B.A.T (UK & EXPORT) LTD.—B.A.T Industries P.L.C.; *Int'l*, pg. 111
BENSON & HEDGES LIMITED—Gallaher Limited; *Int'l*, pg. 539
BRITISH-AMERICAN TOBACCO CO. LTD.—B.A.T Industries P.L.C.; *Int'l*, pg. 111
BRITISH-AMERICAN TOBACCO (GERMANY) GMBH—B.A.T Industries P.L.C.; *Int'l*, pg. 111
BROOKE GROUP LTD.; *U.S. Public*, pg. 259
BROWN & WILLIAMSON TOBACCO CORP.—B.A.T Industries P.L.C.; *Int'l*, pg. 111
CITA TABACOS DE CANARIAS, S.A.—Tabacalera, S.A.; *Int'l*, pg. 1346
CARITAS CENTRALE D'ARTICLES DE MARQUES S.A.—Reemtsma Cigarettenfabriken GmbH, Hamburg; *Int'l*, pg. 1101
P.J. CARROLL HOLDINGS P.L.C.—Rothmans UK Holdings Limited; *Int'l*, pg. 1130
C.A. CIGARRERA BIGOTT, SUCS.—B.A.T Industries P.L.C.; *Int'l*, pg. 111
CIGARRERIA MORAZAN SA DE CV—B.A.T Industries P.L.C.; *Int'l*, pg. 111
CINTA COMPAGNIE INDEPENDANTE DES TABACS S.A.—Reemtsma Cigarettenfabriken GmbH, Hamburg; *Int'l*, pg. 1101
DUBEK LTD.; *Int'l*, pg. 421
FABRIQUES DE TABAC REUNIS SA—Philip Morris Companies Inc.; *U.S. Public*, pg. 1290
GALLAHER (DUBLIN) LTD.—Gallaher Limited; *Int'l*, pg. 539
GALLAHER INVESTMENTS LIMITED—Gallaher Limited; *Int'l*, pg. 539
GALLAHER LIMITED; *Int'l*, pg. 539
GALLAHER TOBACCO LTD.—Gallaher Limited; *Int'l*, pg. 539
IMASCO B.V.—B.A.T Industries P.L.C.; *Int'l*, pg. 112
IMASCO B.V.-FRIBOURG BRANCH—B.A.T Industries P.L.C.; *Int'l*, pg. 112
IMASCO LIMITED—B.A.T Industries P.L.C.; *Int'l*, pg. 112
IMPERIAL TOBACCO GROUP, LTD.; *Int'l*, pg. 666
IMPERIAL TOBACCO LTD., SOUTHERN TRADING DIV.—Imperial Tobacco Group, Ltd.; *Int'l*, pg. 666
JOHN PLAYER & SONS IRELAND—Hanson PLC; *Int'l*, pg. 595
KARELIA TOBACCO COMPANY INC.; *Int'l*, pg. 724
KRAFT FOODS ASIA/PACIFIC, INC.—Philip Morris Companies Inc.; *U.S. Public*, pg. 1288
LIGGETT GROUP INC.—Brooke Group Ltd.; *U.S. Public*, pg. 259
LOEWS CORPORATION; *U.S. Public*, pg. 1010
LORILLARD TOBACCO COMPANY—Loews Corporation; *U.S. Public*, pg. 1011
MASSALIN PARTICULARES S.A.—Reemtsma Cigarettenfabriken GmbH, Hamburg; *Int'l*, pg. 1101
NATIONAL FOOD STORES, INC.; *U.S. Private*, pg. 783
NOBLEZA-PICCARDO SAICF—B.A.T Industries P.L.C.; *Int'l*, pg. 111
PHILIP MORRIS COMPANIES INC.; *U.S. Public*, pg. 1287
PHILIP MORRIS ESPANA, S.A.—Tabacalera, S.A.; *Int'l*, pg. 1346
RJR NABISCO HOLDINGS CORP.; *U.S. Public*, pg. 1354
REEMTSMA CHERKASSY TYUTYUNOVA FABRIKA—Reemtsma Cigarettenfabriken GmbH, Hamburg; *Int'l*, pg. 1101
REEMTSMA CIGARETTEN AG—Reemtsma Cigarettenfabriken GmbH, Hamburg; *Int'l*, pg. 1101
REEMTSMA CIGARETTENFABRIKEN GMBH, HAMBURG; *Int'l*, pg. 1100
REEMTSMA DEBRECENI DOHANYGYAR KFT—Reemtsma Cigarettenfabriken GmbH, Hamburg; *Int'l*, pg. 1101
REEMTSMA DISTRIBUTION COMPANY ITALY S.R.L.—Reemtsma Cigarettenfabriken GmbH, Hamburg; *Int'l*, pg. 1101
REEMTSMA ESPANA S.A.—Reemtsma Cigarettenfabriken GmbH, Hamburg; *Int'l*, pg. 1101
H.F. & PH. F. REEMTSMA GMBH—Reemtsma Cigarettenfabriken GmbH, Hamburg; *Int'l*, pg. 1101
REEMTSMA HUNGARY KERESKEDELMI KFT.—Reemtsma Cigarettenfabriken GmbH, Hamburg; *Int'l*, pg. 1101
REEMTSMA INTERNATIONAL CHINA LTD.—Reemtsma Cigarettenfabriken GmbH, Hamburg; *Int'l*, pg. 1101
REEMTSMA INTERNATIONAL PRAHA SPOL. S.R.O.—Reemtsma Cigarettenfabriken GmbH, Hamburg; *Int'l*, pg. 1101
REEMTSMA KIEW TYUTYUNOVA FABRIKA—Reemtsma Cigarettenfabriken GmbH, Hamburg; *Int'l*, pg. 1101
REEMTSMA NEDERLAND B.V.—Reemtsma Cigarettenfabriken GmbH, Hamburg; *Int'l*, pg. 1101
REPUBLIC TOBACCO CO. S.A.—B.A.T Industries P.L.C.; *Int'l*, pg. 111
R.J. REYNOLDS TOBACCO COMPANY—RJR Nabisco Holdings Corp.; *U.S. Public*, pg. 1355
R.J. REYNOLDS ESPANA, S.L.—Tabacalera, S.A.; *Int'l*, pg. 1346
ROTHMANS BENSON & HEDGES INC.—Rothmans UK Holdings Limited; *Int'l*, pg. 1130
SEITA, SOCIETE NATIONALE D'EXPLOITATION INDUSTRIELLE DES TABACS ET DES ALLUMETTES; *Int'l*, pg. 1219
SENIOR SERVICE TOBACCO LTD.—Gallaher Limited; *Int'l*, pg. 539
SLOVAK INTERNATIONAL TABAK, A.S. (S.I.T.)—Reemtsma Cigarettenfabriken GmbH, Hamburg; *Int'l*, pg. 1101
SOUZA CRUZ, S.A.—B.A.T Industries P.L.C.; *Int'l*, pg. 112
TABACALERA ISTMENA SA—B.A.T Industries P.L.C.; *Int'l*, pg. 111
WWT (WYTWORNIA WYROBOW TYTONIOWYCH) S.A.—Reemtsma Cigarettenfabriken GmbH, Hamburg; *Int'l*, pg. 1101
W.D. & H.O. WILLS (AUSTRALIA) LTD.—B.A.T Industries P.L.C.; *Int'l*, pg. 112
HENRI WINTERMANS' SIGARENFABRIEKEN B.V.—B.A.T Industries P.L.C.; *Int'l*, pg. 111

2121 — CIGARS

BENSON & HEDGES LIMITED—Gallaher Limited; *Int'l*, pg. 539
BRITISH-AMERICAN TOBACCO CO. LTD.—B.A.T Industries P.L.C.; *Int'l*, pg. 111

CITA TABACOS DE CANARIAS, S.A.—Tabacalera, S.A.; *Int'l*, pg. 1346
CONSOLIDATED CIGAR CORPORATION—MacAndrews & Forbes Holdings Inc.; *U.S. Private*, pg. 690
DEMERARA TOBACCO CO. LTD.—B.A.T Industries P.L.C.; *Int'l*, pg. 111
FABRICA DE MOLDURAS Y CAJAS, S.A.—UST Inc.; *U.S. Public*, pg. 1661
J.R. FREEMAN & SON LIMITED—Gallaher Limited; *Int'l*, pg. 539
GALLAHER INTERNATIONAL LIMITED—Gallaher Limited; *Int'l*, pg. 539
GENERAL CIGAR COMPANY, INC.—General Cigar Holdings Inc; *U.S. Public*, pg. 708
GENERAL CIGAR HOLDINGS INC; *U.S. Public*, pg. 707
HAVATAMPA, INC.; *U.S. Private*, pg. 510
IMASCO B.V.—B.A.T Industries P.L.C.; *Int'l*, pg. 112
IMASCO B.V.-FRIBOURG BRANCH—B.A.T Industries P.L.C.; *Int'l*, pg. 112
IMASCO LIMITED—B.A.T Industries P.L.C.; *Int'l*, pg. 112
IMPERIAL TOBACCO GROUP, LTD.; *Int'l*, pg. 666
IMPERIAL TOBACCO LTD., SOUTHERN TRADING DIV.—Imperial Tobacco Group, Ltd.; *Int'l*, pg. 666
JOHN PLAYER & SONS IRELAND—Hanson PLC; *Int'l*, pg. 595
LANE LIMITED—Rothmans UK Holdings Limited; *Int'l*, pg. 1129
R.J. REYNOLDS ESPANA, S.L.—Tabacalera, S.A.; *Int'l*, pg. 1346
SEITA, SOCIETE NATIONALE D'EXPLOITATION INDUSTRIELLE DES TABACS ET DES ALLUMETTES; *Int'l*, pg. 1219
SWISHER INTERNATIONAL GROUP, INC.; *U.S. Public*, pg. 1543
UST INC.; *U.S. Public*, pg. 1660
UNITED STATES TOBACCO COMPANY—UST Inc.; *U.S. Public*, pg. 1661
VELASQUES SIGARENFABRIEKEN N.V.—B.A.T Industries P.L.C.; *Int'l*, pg. 111
VILLAZON COMPANY INC.; *U.S. Private*, pg. 1140

2131 — TOBACCO (CHEWING & SMOKING) & SNUFF

B.A.T CIGARETTENFABRIKEN B.A.T—B.A.T Industries P.L.C.; *Int'l*, pg. 111
B.A.T INDUSTRIES P.L.C.; *Int'l*, pg. 110
BADISCHE TABAKMANUFAKTUR ROTH-HANDLE GMBH—Reemtsma Cigarettenfabriken GmbH, Hamburg; *Int'l*, pg. 1101
BANGLADESH TOBACCO CO. LTD.—B.A.T Industries P.L.C.; *Int'l*, pg. 111
BRITISH-AMERICAN TOBACCO CO. (BARBADOS) LTD.—B.A.T Industries P.L.C.; *Int'l*, pg. 111
BRITISH-AMERICAN TOBACCO CO. LTD.—B.A.T Industries P.L.C.; *Int'l*, pg. 111
BRITISH-AMERICAN TOBACCO (GERMANY) GMBH—B.A.T Industries P.L.C.; *Int'l*, pg. 111
BROWN & WILLIAMSON TOBACCO CORP.—B.A.T Industries P.L.C.; *Int'l*, pg. 111
P.J. CARROLL HOLDINGS P.L.C.—Rothmans UK Holdings Limited; *Int'l*, pg. 1130
CEYLON TOBACCO CO. LTD.—B.A.T Industries P.L.C.; *Int'l*, pg. 111
CONSOLIDATED CIGAR CORPORATION—MacAndrews & Forbes Holdings Inc.; *U.S. Private*, pg. 690
CONWOOD COMPANY L.P.; *U.S. Private*, pg. 272
DUBEK LTD.; *Int'l*, pg. 421
IMASCO B.V.—B.A.T Industries P.L.C.; *Int'l*, pg. 112
IMASCO B.V.-FRIBOURG BRANCH—B.A.T Industries P.L.C.; *Int'l*, pg. 112
IMASCO LIMITED—B.A.T Industries P.L.C.; *Int'l*, pg. 112
IMPERIAL TOBACCO GROUP, LTD.; *Int'l*, pg. 666
IMPERIAL TOBACCO LIMITED—B.A.T Industries P.L.C.; *Int'l*, pg. 112
IMPERIAL TOBACCO LTD., CIGAR DIV.—Imperial Tobacco Group, Ltd.; *Int'l*, pg. 666
IMPERIAL TOBACCO LTD., SOUTHERN TRADING DIV.—Imperial Tobacco Group, Ltd.; *Int'l*, pg. 666
JOHN PLAYER & SONS IRELAND—Hanson PLC; *Int'l*, pg. 595
LANE LIMITED—Rothmans UK Holdings Limited; *Int'l*, pg. 1129
MALAYSIAN TOBACCO CO./B.A.T. INDUST.—B.A.T Industries P.L.C.; *Int'l*, pg. 111
PAKISTAN TOBACCO CO. LTD.—B.A.T Industries P.L.C.; *Int'l*, pg. 111
PHARMACIA & UPJOHN, INC.; *Int'l*, pg. 1047
R.J. REYNOLDS SCANDINAVIA AB—RJR Nabisco Holdings Corp.; *U.S. Public*, pg. 1355
R.J. REYNOLDS TOBACCO COMPANY—RJR Nabisco Holdings Corp.; *U.S. Public*, pg. 1355
ROTHMANS BENSON & HEDGES INC.—Rothmans UK Holdings Limited; *Int'l*, pg. 1130
SCOTT TOBACCO—Conwood Company L.P.; *U.S. Private*, pg. 272
SOUZA CRUZ, S.A.—B.A.T Industries P.L.C.; *Int'l*, pg. 112
TABACALERA HONDURENVA SA—B.A.T Industries P.L.C.; *Int'l*, pg. 111
TABACALERA NICARAGUENSE S.A.—B.A.T Industries P.L.C.; *Int'l*, pg. 111
TABACALERA, S.A.; *Int'l*, pg. 1345
TAYLOR BROS.—Conwood Company L.P.; *U.S. Private*, pg. 272
J.L. TIEDEMANNS TOBAKSFABRIK—Tiedemanns - Joh.H.Andresen ANS; *Int'l*, pg. 1390
TIEDEMANNS - JOH.H.ANDRESEN ANS; *Int'l*, pg. 1389
UST INC.; *U.S. Public*, pg. 1660
UNITED STATES TOBACCO COMPANY—UST Inc.; *U.S. Public*, pg. 1661
W.D. & H.O. WILLS (AUSTRALIA) LTD.—B.A.T Industries P.L.C.; *Int'l*, pg. 112

2141 — TOBACCO STEMMING & REDRYING

DIMON, INCORPORATED; *U.S. Public*, pg. 509
DIMON, INTERNATIONAL, INC.—DIMON, Incorporated; *U.S. Public*, pg. 510
K.R. EDWARDS LEAF TOBACCO CO., INC.—Universal Corporation; *U.S. Public*, pg. 1694
FENNER DRIVES; *U.S. Private*, pg. 400
GENERAL PROCESSORS, INC.—Standard Commercial Corporation; *U.S. Public*, pg. 1502
LANCASTER LEAF TOBACCO CO. OF PENNSYLVANIA—Universal Corporation; *U.S. Public*, pg. 1695
MACLIN-ZIMMER MCGILL TOBACCO COMPANY, INC.—Universal Corporation; *U.S. Public*, pg. 1695
RJR NABISCO HOLDINGS CORP.; *U.S. Public*, pg. 1354
R.J. REYNOLDS TOBACCO COMPANY—RJR Nabisco Holdings Corp.; *U.S. Public*, pg. 1355
SEITA, SOCIETE NATIONALE D'EXPLOITATION INDUSTRIELLE DES TABACS ET DES ALLUMETTES; *Int'l*, pg. 1219
SIMCOE LEAF TOBACCO COMPANY, LTD.—Universal Corporation; *U.S. Public*, pg. 1695
SOUTHERN PROCESSORS, INC.—Universal Corporation; *U.S. Public*, pg. 1695
SOUTHWESTERN TOBACCO CO., INC.—Universal Corporation; *U.S. Public*, pg. 1695
J.P. TAYLOR CO., INC.—Universal Corporation; *U.S. Public*, pg. 1695
UNIVERSAL LEAF TOBACCO COMPANY, INC.—Universal Corporation; *U.S. Public*, pg. 1694

2211 — BROAD WOVEN FABRIC MILLS, COTTON

AG STANLEY LIMITED—The Boots Company PLC; *Int'l*, pg. 202
ABERDEEN MFG. CORPORATION—Trace International Holdings, Inc.; *U.S. Private*, pg. 1094
ALBANY INTERNATIONAL/PRESS FABRICS DIVISION—Albany International Corp.; *U.S. Public*, pg. 36
ALLISON CORPORATION—Allison Corporation; *U.S. Private*, pg. 41
APPLETON WIRE DIV., ALBANY INTERNATIONAL—Albany International Corp.; *U.S. Public*, pg. 36
AVONDALE FOREIGN SALES CORPORATION—Avondale Incorporated; *U.S. Private*, pg. 103
AVONDALE MILLS, INC.—Avondale Incorporated; *U.S. Private*, pg. 102
BALSON-HERCULES LTD.—Consoltex Group Inc.; *Int'l*, pg. 326
BEACON MFG. CO.—Pillowtex Corporation; *U.S. Public*, pg. 1296
F.H. BONN COMPANY; *U.S. Private*, pg. 156
BRUNSCHWIG & FILS, INC.; *U.S. Private*, pg. 176
BURLINGTON DENIM—Burlington Industries, Inc.; *U.S. Public*, pg. 268
BURLINGTON INDUSTRIES, INC.; *U.S. Public*, pg. 268
CC INDUSTRIES, INC.; *U.S. Private*, pg. 192
CMI INDUSTRIES, INC.; *U.S. Private*, pg. 195
CS BROOKS CANADA INC.; *U.S. Private*, pg. 197
CANON BUSINESS MACHINES INC.—Canon Inc.; *Int'l*, pg. 261
CAROLINA MILLS, INC.; *U.S. Private*, pg. 214
CYRUS CLARK CO., INC.; *U.S. Private*, pg. 242
COLLINS & AIKMAN CORPORATION; *U.S. Public*, pg. 399
CONCORD FABRICS INC.; *U.S. Public*, pg. 429
CONE APPAREL PRODUCTS—Cone Mills Corporation; *U.S. Public*, pg. 430
CONE MILLS CORPORATION; *U.S. Public*, pg. 430
CONSOLTEX GROUP INC.; *Int'l*, pg. 326
CRAFTEX MILLS INC. OF PENNSYLVANIA; *U.S. Private*, pg. 284
CROWN CRAFTS, INC.; *U.S. Public*, pg. 465
CULP, INC.; *U.S. Public*, pg. 467
DAN RIVER INC.; *U.S. Public*, pg. 478
DAN RIVER SPINDALE INC.—Dan River Inc.; *U.S. Public*, pg. 479
J.L. DE BALL CANADA INC.—Girmes GmbH; *Int'l*, pg. 552
J.L. DE BALL-GIRMES OF AMERICA, INC.—Girmes GmbH; *Int'l*, pg. 552
DELTA WOODSIDE INDUSTRIES, INC.; *U.S. Public*, pg. 497
DOMINION INDUSTRIAL FABRICS COMPANY—Dominion Textile Inc.; *Int'l*, pg. 415
EASTERN CANVAS PRODUCTS, INC.; *U.S. Private*, pg. 357
ESPE OY—Royal Dutch/Shell Group of Companies; *Int'l*, pg. 1138
FARLEY, INC.; *U.S. Private*, pg. 394
FIELDCREST/CANNON BED FASHIONS DIVISION—Pillowtex Corporation; *U.S. Public*, pg. 1296
FIELDCREST CANNON, INC.—Pillowtex Corporation; *U.S. Public*, pg. 1296
FORBO CONTRACT FABRICS LTD.—Forbo Holding SA; *Int'l*, pg. 497
GIRMES GMBH; *Int'l*, pg. 552
GLEN RAVEN MILLS, INC.; *U.S. Private*, pg. 456
GLEN RAVEN MILLS, INC.-CUSTOM FABRICS DIVISION-EQUINOX PLANT—Glen Raven Mills, Inc.; *U.S. Private*, pg. 456
GLENOIT MILLS, INC.; *U.S. Private*, pg. 456
GRANITEVILLE COMPANY—Avondale Incorporated; *U.S. Private*, pg. 103
GREENWOOD MILLS, INC.; *U.S. Private*, pg. 479
HART HOLDING COMPANY, INC.; *U.S. Private*, pg. 507
INMAN MILLS; *U.S. Private*, pg. 564
INTERFACE INC.; *U.S. Public*, pg. 889
JPS TEXTILE GROUP, INC.; *U.S. Private*, pg. 578
JOHNSON & JOHNSON; *U.S. Public*, pg. 927
JOHNSTON INDUSTRIES COMPOSITE REINFORCEMENTS—Johnston Industries, Inc.; *U.S. Public*, pg. 933
JOHNSTON INDUSTRIES, INC.; *U.S. Public*, pg. 933
LESHNER MILLS. INC.; *U.S. Private*, pg. 660
LONRHO PLC; *Int'l*, pg. 817
MART CORPORATION—Damsmith Corp.; *U.S. Private*, pg. 309
MAYFAIR MILLS, INC.; *U.S. Private*, pg. 718
METRO AG; *Int'l*, pg. 863
MITCHELL CO.—Stonecutter Mills Corp.; *U.S. Private*, pg. 1044
MOUNT VERNON MILLS, INC.—R.B. Pamplin Corp.; *U.S. Private*, pg. 835
NOEL JOANNA, INC.—Crown Crafts, Inc.; *U.S. Public*, pg. 465
OPP MICOLAS MILLS INC.—Johnston Industries, Inc.; *U.S. Public*, pg. 933
PHILIP METALS/STEINER-LIFF—Philip Services Corp.; *Int'l*, pg. 1050
PLAINS COTTON CO-OP ASSOCIATION; *U.S. Private*, pg. 868
POLYTECH NETTING INDUSTRIES—TecSyn International, Inc.; *Int'l*, pg. 1362
PUBLICKER INDUSTRIES INC.; *U.S. Public*, pg. 1341
QST FAR EAST LIMITED—QST Industries, Inc.; *U.S. Private*, pg. 897
QST INDUSTRIES, INC.; *U.S. Private*, pg. 897
RAYTEX FINISHING CO.—Cone Mills Corporation; *U.S. Public*, pg. 430
REEVES BROTHERS, INC.—Hart Holding Company, Inc.; *U.S. Private*, pg. 507
RUSSELL CORPORATION; *U.S. Public*, pg. 1413
SAVOY DRAPERY DIV.—Trace International Holdings, Inc.; *U.S. Private*, pg. 1094
SHELBY YARN COMPANY; *U.S. Private*, pg. 991
SHERIDAN AUSTRALIA LTD.—CS Brooks Canada Inc.; *U.S. Private*, pg. 197
SMITH & NEPHEW MEDICAL FABRICS—Smith & Nephew PLC; *Int'l*, pg. 1263
SOUTHERN PHENIX TEXTILES, INC.—Johnston Industries, Inc.; *U.S. Public*, pg. 933
SPARTAN MILLS; *U.S. Private*, pg. 1020
SPECIALTY TEXTILE PRODUCTS; *U.S. Private*, pg. 1023
SPINNERIN INC.; *U.S. Private*, pg. 1025
SPRINGS CANADA, LTD.—Springs Industries, Inc.; *U.S. Public*, pg. 1500
SPRINGS INDUSTRIES, INC.; *U.S. Public*, pg. 1499
STANDARD TEXTILE CO., INC.; *U.S. Private*, pg. 1032
STERN & STERN INDUSTRIES INC.; *U.S. Private*, pg. 1041
STONECUTTER MILLS CORP.; *U.S. Private*, pg. 1044
SWIFT DENIM INC.—Dominion Textile Inc.; *Int'l*, pg. 415
SWIFT TEXTILES, INC.—Dominion Textile Inc.; *Int'l*, pg. 415
TBA INDUSTRIAL PRODUCTS LTD.—T & N Plc; *Int'l*, pg. 1334
TECSYN INTERNATIONAL, INC.; *Int'l*, pg. 1361
RICHARD E. THIBAUT, INC.—RPM, Inc.; *U.S. Public*, pg. 1358
THOMASTON MILLS, INC.; *U.S. Public*, pg. 1599
TOYOBO CO., LTD.; *Int'l*, pg. 1411
TRADICION TEXTIL, S.A.; *Int'l*, pg. 1416
VERATEC DIVISION—International Paper Company; *U.S. Public*, pg. 904
VORWERK TEXTIL FRANCE S.A.R.L.—Vorwerk & Co.; *Int'l*, pg. 1481
WALLBERGS FABRIKS AKTIEBOLAG—Albany International Corp.; *U.S. Public*, pg. 37
WALTON FABRIC DIVISION OF AVONDALE MILLS—Avondale Incorporated; *U.S. Private*, pg. 103
WATEREE TEXTILE CORP.—Marubeni Corporation; *Int'l*, pg. 845
WEST RIDING WORSTED & WOOLEN MILLS LIMITED—Coats Viyella plc; *Int'l*, pg. 299
DAVID WHITEHEAD & SONS LTD.—Lonrho plc; *Int'l*, pg. 818
FRANK W. WINNE & SON, INC.; *U.S. Private*, pg. 1183
WOODHEAD SPECIALTY FABRICS—Avondale Incorporated; *U.S. Private*, pg. 103
WOODMARK ORIGINALS INC.—Howard Miller; *U.S. Private*, pg. 747

2221 — BROAD WOVEN FABRIC MILLS, MAN-MADE FIBER & SILK

ACME MILLS CO. INC.; *U.S. Private*, pg. 13
ALBANY INTERNATIONAL/PRESS FABRICS DIVISION—Albany International Corp.; *U.S. Public*, pg. 36
AMETEX FABRICS, INC.—Furnishings International, Inc.; *U.S. Private*, pg. 432
AMOCO CORPORATION; *U.S. Public*, pg. 101
AMOCO DEUTSCHLAND GMBH—Amoco Corporation; *U.S. Public*, pg. 103
AMOCO FABRICS & FIBERS COMPANY—Amoco Corporation; *U.S. Public*, pg. 102
AMOCO FABRICS & FIBERS, LTD.—Amoco Corporation; *U.S. Public*, pg. 102
AMOCO FABRICS (U.K.) LTD.—Amoco Corporation; *U.S. Public*, pg. 103
AMOCO (U.K.) LTD.—Amoco Corporation; *U.S. Public*, pg. 103
APEX MILLS CORPORATION; *U.S. Private*, pg. 77
APPLETON WIRE DIV., ALBANY INTERNATIONAL—Albany International Corp.; *U.S. Public*, pg. 36
ASHWORTH BROS., INC.; *U.S. Private*, pg. 89
BTR NYLEX LIMITED—BTR plc; *Int'l*, pg. 129
BEACON MFG. CO.—Pillowtex Corporation; *U.S. Public*, pg. 1296
BLOOMSBURG MILLS INC.; *U.S. Private*, pg. 150
BLUMENTHAL PRINT WORKS, INC.; *U.S. Private*, pg. 153
BRUNSCHWIG & FILS, INC.; *U.S. Private*, pg. 176
BURLINGTON INDUSTRIES, INC.; *U.S. Public*, pg. 268
BURLINGTON MENSWEAR—Burlington Industries, Inc.; *U.S. Public*, pg. 268
CS BROOKS CANADA INC.; *U.S. Private*, pg. 197

CV WOVEN FABRICS LIMITED—Coats Viyella plc; Int'l, pg. 299
CHEMICAL FABRICS LIMITED—Chemfab Corporation; U.S. Public, pg. 344
COLLINS & AIKMAN CORPORATION; U.S. Public, pg. 399
CONE APPAREL PRODUCTS—Cone Mills Corporation; U.S. Public, pg. 430
CONE DECORATIVE FABRICS—Cone Mills Corporation; U.S. Public, pg. 430
CONE FINISHING COMPANY—Cone Mills Corporation; U.S. Public, pg. 430
CONE MILLS CORPORATION; U.S. Public, pg. 430
COPLAND FABRICS, INC.; U.S. Private, pg. 274
CRAFTEX MILLS INC. OF PENNSYLVANIA; U.S. Private, pg. 284
DAN RIVER INC.; U.S. Public, pg. 478
J.L. DE BALL CANADA INC.—Girmes GmbH; Int'l, pg. 552
J.L. DE BALL-GIRMES OF AMERICA, INC.—Girmes GmbH; Int'l, pg. 552
DOMINION TEXTILE INC.; Int'l, pg. 415
DU PONT-TORAY COMPANY, LTD.—Du Pont (E.I. Du Pont De Nemours & Co.); U.S. Public, pg. 533
FARLEY, INC.; U.S. Private, pg. 394
FIELDCREST CANNON, INC.—Pillowtex Corporation; U.S. Public, pg. 1296
FORBO CONTRACT FABRICS LTD.—Forbo Holding SA; Int'l, pg. 497
FORMOSA PLASTICS CORPORATION; Int'l, pg. 498
FRANK IX & SONS, INC.; U.S. Private, pg. 423
GIRMES GMBH; Int'l, pg. 552
GLEN RAVEN MILLS, INC.; U.S. Private, pg. 456
GRANITEVILLE COMPANY—Avondale Incorporated; U.S. Private, pg. 103
GREENWOOD MILLS, INC.; U.S. Private, pg. 479
GUILFORD OF MAINE, INC.—Interface Inc.; U.S. Public, pg. 889
HART HOLDING COMPANY, INC.; U.S. Private, pg. 507
HEXCEL CORPORATION; U.S. Public, pg. 824
HEXCEL, FAR EAST—Hexcel Corporation; U.S. Public, pg. 824
HEXCEL KNYTEX—Hexcel Corporation; U.S. Public, pg. 824
HEXCEL (LYON) S.A.—Hexcel Corporation; U.S. Public, pg. 824
HEXCEL, S.A.—Hexcel Corporation; U.S. Public, pg. 824
HEXCEL, U.K.—Hexcel Corporation; U.S. Public, pg. 824
HI-TEMP MATERIALS, INC.—Chemfab Corporation; U.S. Public, pg. 344
HOME FURNISHINGS SEGMENT—Springs Industries, Inc.; U.S. Public, pg. 1500
INDO RAMA SYNTHETICS P.T.; Int'l, pg. 673
S.A. INDUSTRIAS VOTORANTIM; Int'l, pg. 677
INTERFACE INC.; U.S. Public, pg. 889
J & R INTERFACING—William Prym GmbH & Co. KG; Int'l, pg. 1499
JPS AUTOMOTIVE L.P.—Trace International Holdings, Inc.; U.S. Private, pg. 1095
JPS CONVERTER & INDUSTRIAL CORP.—JPS Textile Group, Inc.; U.S. Private, pg. 578
JPS TEXTILE GROUP, INC.; U.S. Private, pg. 578
JOAN FABRICS CORP.; U.S. Private, pg. 588
JOHNSTON INDUSTRIES, INC.; U.S. Public, pg. 933
THE KIPLINGER WASHINGTON EDITORS, INC.; U.S. Private, pg. 623
KLOPMAN FABRICS DIV.—Burlington Industries, Inc.; U.S. Public, pg. 268
LONRHO TEXTILES LTD.—Lonrho plc; Int'l, pg. 817
LOUISVILLE BEDDING COMPANY; U.S. Private, pg. 677
MALDEN MILLS INDUSTRIES, INC.; U.S. Private, pg. 698
J.B. MARTIN COMPANY; U.S. Private, pg. 709
MAYFAIR MILLS, INC.; U.S. Private, pg. 718
MILLIKEN & COMPANY; U.S. Private, pg. 748
MITCHELL CO.—Stonecutter Mills Corp.; U.S. Private, pg. 1044
MOUNT VERNON TEXTILE GROUP—R.B. Pamplin Corp.; U.S. Private, pg. 836
NEW YORK WIRE CO.; U.S. Private, pg. 795
NORDLYS SA—Dominion Textile Inc.; Int'l, pg. 415
OPP MICOLAS MILLS INC.—Johnston Industries, Inc.; U.S. Public, pg. 933
QUAKER FABRIC CORPORATION; U.S. Public, pg. 1347
RHODIA S.A.—Rhone-Poulenc S.A.; Int'l, pg. 1112
SCALAMANDRE, INC.; U.S. Private, pg. 969
SCHNEIDER MILLS, INC.; U.S. Private, pg. 971
SCHULLER INTERNATIONAL, INC.—Johns Manville Corporation; U.S. Public, pg. 927
SHELBY WILLIAMS TEXTILES—Shelby Williams Industries, Inc.; U.S. Public, pg. 1465
SHELBY YARN COMPANY; U.S. Private, pg. 991
SHERIDAN AUSTRALIA LTD.—CS Brooks Canada Inc.; U.S. Private, pg. 197
SLEEPEEZEE LIMITED; Int'l, pg. 1263
SOUTHERN PHENIX TEXTILES, INC.—Johnston Industries, Inc.; U.S. Public, pg. 933
SPRINGS INDUSTRIES, INC.; U.S. Public, pg. 1499
STONECUTTER MILLS CORP.; U.S. Private, pg. 1044
TETKO, INC.; U.S. Private, pg. 1078
TEXFI BLENDS DIVISION—Texfi Industries, Inc.; U.S. Public, pg. 1588
TEXFI INDUSTRIES, INC.; U.S. Public, pg. 1588
THOMASTON MILLS, INC.; U.S. Public, pg. 1599
TONG SHING INC.—Toray Industries, Inc.; Int'l, pg. 1400
TRADICION TEXTIL, S.A.; Int'l, pg. 1416
TYGAFLOR LTD.—Chemfab Corporation; U.S. Public, pg. 344
VANTONA LTD.—Coats Viyella plc; Int'l, pg. 299
VORWERK TEXTIL FRANCE S.A.R.L.—Vorwerk & Co.; Int'l, pg. 1481
WESTERN POWER PRODUCTS, INC.—Cooper Industries, Inc.; U.S. Public, pg. 444
DAVID WHITEHEAD & SONS LTD.—Lonrho plc; Int'l, pg. 818

2231 — BROAD WOVEN FABRIC MILLS, WOOL (INCLUDING DYEING & FINISHING)

AMANA SOCIETY, INC.; U.S. Private, pg. 48
AMERBELLE CORPORATION; U.S. Private, pg. 48
BEACON MFG. CO.—Pillowtex Corporation; U.S. Public, pg. 1296
BELMONT DYERS COMPANY—Meridian Industries, Inc.; U.S. Private, pg. 732
BOZZALLA & LESNA S.P.A.; Int'l, pg. 209
ETS, BRICQ & CIE S.A.—Scapa Group Plc; Int'l, pg. 1202
BRITISH MOHAIR SPINNERS LIMITED—British Mohair Holdings Plc; Int'l, pg. 219
BRUZA GUSUM VIROR AB—Scapa Group Plc; Int'l, pg. 1202
BURLINGTON INDUSTRIES, INC.; U.S. Public, pg. 268
BURLINGTON MENSWEAR—Burlington Industries, Inc.; U.S. Public, pg. 268
CAROLINA MILLS, INC.; U.S. Private, pg. 214
CENTRAL/SHIPPEE, INC.; U.S. Private, pg. 224
CHEIL INDUSTRIES INC.—Samsung Group; Int'l, pg. 1181
COLLINS & AIKMAN PRODUCTS CO.—Collins & Aikman Corporation; U.S. Public, pg. 399
CRAFTEX MILLS INC. OF PENNSYLVANIA; U.S. Private, pg. 284
CULP, INC.; U.S. Public, pg. 467
FARIBAULT WOOLEN MILL CO.; U.S. Private, pg. 394
FELTRAX INTERNATIONAL, INC.—BTR plc; Int'l, pg. 130
FORSTMANN & COMPANY, INC.; U.S. Public, pg. 670
GAMMA HOLDING N.V.; Int'l, pg. 539
GIRMES GMBH; Int'l, pg. 552
GLEN RAVEN MILLS, INC.-CUSTOM FABRICS DIVISION-EQUINOX PLANT—Glen Raven Mills, Inc.; U.S. Private, pg. 456
GLENOIT MILLS, INC.; U.S. Private, pg. 456
GUILFORD OF MAINE, INC.—Interface Inc.; U.S. Public, pg. 889
HART HOLDING COMPANY, INC.; U.S. Private, pg. 507
MERIDIAN INDUSTRIES, INC.; U.S. Private, pg. 732
MILLIKEN & COMPANY; U.S. Private, pg. 748
F. OBERDORFER SIEBTECHNIK GMBH—Scapa Group Plc; Int'l, pg. 1202
PENDLETON WOOLEN MILLS, INC.; U.S. Private, pg. 848
PUBLICKER INDUSTRIES INC.; U.S. Public, pg. 1341
SCALAMANDRE, INC.; U.S. Private, pg. 969
SCAPA GROUP PLC; Int'l, pg. 1202
SCAPA SCANDIA LTD.—Scapa Group Plc; Int'l, pg. 1202
STANDARD COMMERCIAL CORPORATION; U.S. Public, pg. 1501
TEXTILES MORELOS S.A. DE C.V.—Burlington Industries, Inc.; U.S. Public, pg. 268
UNAFORM LTD.—Scapa Group Plc; Int'l, pg. 1202
UNAFORM SOUTH AFRICA (PTY) LTD.—Scapa Group Plc; Int'l, pg. 1203
UNITED PIECE DYE WORKS, LP; U.S. Private, pg. 1123
VORWERK TEXTIL FRANCE S.A.R.L.—Vorwerk & Co.; Int'l, pg. 1481
WOOL FILTERS INTL.—Fruit of the Loom, Inc.; U.S. Public, pg. 686
WOOLCAN—Woolrich, Inc.; U.S. Private, pg. 1188
WOOLRICH, INC.; U.S. Private, pg. 1188

2241 — NARROW FABRICS & OTHER SMALLWARES MILLS: COTTON, WOOL, SILK, & MAN-MADE FIBER

AMERICAN FABRICS COMPANY; U.S. Private, pg. 53
BBA GROUP PLC; Int'l, pg. 112
BRITISH TRIMMINGS LTD.—Conso Products Company; U.S. Public, pg. 434
CYDSA S.A.; Int'l, pg. 246
COATS & CLARK INC.—Coats Viyella plc; Int'l, pg. 300
COATS CADENA SA—Coats Viyella plc; Int'l, pg. 300
COATS CUCIRINI S.P.A.—Coats Viyella plc; Int'l, pg. 300
COATS HARLANDER G.M.B.H—Coats Viyella plc; Int'l, pg. 300
COATS MEZ INDUSTRIEAHFADEN G.M.B.H.—Coats Viyella plc; Int'l, pg. 300
COATS PAKISTAN LIMITED—Coats Viyella plc; Int'l, pg. 300
COATS PATONS—Coats Viyella plc; Int'l, pg. 300
COATS (TURKEY) IPLIK SANAYII AS—Coats Viyella plc; Int'l, pg. 300
COLLITEX SRL—PAXAR Corporation; U.S. Public, pg. 1266
COMPAC CORPORATION—Masco Corporation; U.S. Public, pg. 1054
COMPOFLEX—Senior Engineering Group, plc.; Int'l, pg. 1221
CONSO PRODUCTS COMPANY; U.S. Public, pg. 434
DA GAMA TEXTILE COMPANY—South African Breweries, Ltd.; Int'l, pg. 1287
CIA. DE LINHA COATS & CLARK LDA.—Coats Viyella plc; Int'l, pg. 300
DELAWARE RIBBON MANUFACTURERS, INC.; U.S. Private, pg. 322
DURHAM TUBE—Senior Engineering Group, plc.; Int'l, pg. 1221
EAGLE BUTTON CO., INC.; U.S. Private, pg. 354
THE EAST ASIATIC COMPANY LTD. A/S; Int'l, pg. 430
EASTERN CANVAS PRODUCTS, INC.; U.S. Private, pg. 357
FARLEY, INC.; U.S. Private, pg. 394
GLENOIT MILLS, INC.; U.S. Private, pg. 456
HABISAT GLOBE INC.—Habisat Svergie AB; Int'l, pg. 585
HABISAT SVERGIE AB; Int'l, pg. 585
INDUSTRIAS TRATERH, S.A.—Senior Engineering Group, plc.; Int'l, pg. 1222
P.T. KANEBO-NISSHO IWAI-SAHABAT TEXTILE INDUSTRIES—Nissho Iwai Corporation; Int'l, pg. 948
LESHNER MILLS. INC.; U.S. Private, pg. 660
LINHAS CORRENTE LTDA.—Coats Viyella plc; Int'l, pg. 301
F.G. MONTABERT; U.S. Private, pg. 758
MOORE COMPANY; U.S. Private, pg. 759
MOUNT VERNON MILLS, INC.—R.B. Pamplin Corp.; U.S. Private, pg. 835
NARROW FABRIC INDUSTRIES, INC.; U.S. Private, pg. 774
NATIVE TEXTILES—U.S. Industries, Inc.; U.S. Public, pg. 1684
ORVAC SPA—PAXAR Corporation; U.S. Public, pg. 1266
PAXAR GRAPHICS—PAXAR Corporation; U.S. Public, pg. 1266
PAXAR PRINTED LABELS—PAXAR Corporation; U.S. Public, pg. 1266
PAXAR WOVEN LABELS—PAXAR Corporation; U.S. Public, pg. 1266
DAVID L. PEISTER CO., INC.; U.S. Private, pg. 848
PHOENIX STEEL TUBE—Senior Engineering Group, plc.; Int'l, pg. 1221
POWERFLEX—Senior Engineering Group, plc.; Int'l, pg. 1221
PRECISION DRAWN TUBE—Senior Engineering Group, plc.; Int'l, pg. 1222
RHODIA S.A.—Rhone-Poulenc S.A.; Int'l, pg. 1112
RIBBON NARROW FABRIC COMPANY; U.S. Private, pg. 927
SAAR-GUMMIWERK GMBH—Saarbergwerke Aktiengesellschaft; Int'l, pg. 1167
SAMSUNG GROUP; Int'l, pg. 1181
SECURALL, INC.—Damsmith Corp.; U.S. Private, pg. 309
SENIOR BIGWOOD LIMITED—Senior Engineering Group, plc.; Int'l, pg. 1220
SENIOR ENGINEERING PRODUCTS BUSINESS AREA—Senior Engineering Group, plc.; Int'l, pg. 1220
SENIOR ENGINEERING TIFT GMBH—Senior Engineering Group, plc.; Int'l, pg. 1223
SENIOR FOSTER WHEELER CONSTRUCTION DIVISION—Senior Engineering Group, plc.; Int'l, pg. 1221
SENIOR FOSTER WHEELER INDUSTRIAL BOILER DIVISION—Senior Engineering Group, plc.; Int'l, pg. 1221
SENIOR FOSTER WHEELER POWER DIVISION—Senior Engineering Group, plc.; Int'l, pg. 1221
SENIOR GREEN ECONOMISER DIVISION—Senior Engineering Group, plc.; Int'l, pg. 1221
SENIOR HEAT TREATMENT LIMITED—Senior Engineering Group, plc.; Int'l, pg. 1221
SENIOR LUKE MATERIALS HANDLING DIVISION—Senior Engineering Group, plc.; Int'l, pg. 1221
SENIOR TIFT B.V.—Senior Engineering Group, plc.; Int'l, pg. 1223
SENIOR TIFT, INC.—Senior Engineering Group, plc.; Int'l, pg. 1222
SENIOR TIFT LIMITED—Senior Engineering Group, plc.; Int'l, pg. 1221
SENIOR TIFT PTE. LTD.—Senior Engineering Group, plc.; Int'l, pg. 1223
SENIOR TUBE LIMITED—Senior Engineering Group, plc.; Int'l, pg. 1221
SHELBY WILLIAMS TEXTILES—Shelby Williams Industries, Inc.; U.S. Public, pg. 1465
SPRINGS INDUSTRIES, INC.; U.S. Public, pg. 1499
STANDARD COMMERCIAL CORPORATION; U.S. Public, pg. 1501
TP MANIPULATIONS—Senior Engineering Group, plc.; Int'l, pg. 1222
TRIMTEX CO. INC.; U.S. Private, pg. 1103
TUBE PRODUCTS—Senior Engineering Group, plc.; Int'l, pg. 1222
UNITED FLEXIBLE—Senior Engineering Group, plc.; Int'l, pg. 1221

2251 — WOMEN'S FULL-LENGTH & KNEE-LENGTH HOSIERY, EXCEPT SOCKS

AWI RETAIL—Alba-Waldensian, Inc.; U.S. Public, pg. 36
ADMIRATION HOSIERY MILLS, INC.—Highland Mills Inc.; U.S. Private, pg. 528
ALBA-WALDENSIAN EXPORT CORP.—Alba-Waldensian, Inc.; U.S. Public, pg. 36
ALBA-WALDENSIAN, INC.; U.S. Public, pg. 35
ARGO AG—Coop Switzerland; Int'l, pg. 329
CHARNOS PLC; Int'l, pg. 280
COOP SWITZERLAND; Int'l, pg. 329
DANCE FRANCE LTD.—Danskin Inc.; U.S. Public, pg. 483
DIM S.A.—Sara Lee Corporation; U.S. Public, pg. 1434
GREAT AMERICAN KNITTING MILLS—Bidermann International S.A.; Int'l, pg. 194
GRUPO SYNKRO, S.A. DE C.V.; Int'l, pg. 576
HAMPSHIRE DESIGNERS INC.—Hampshire Group, Ltd.; U.S. Public, pg. 778
HAMPSHIRE GROUP, LTD.; U.S. Public, pg. 778
HAMPSHIRE HOSIERY, INC.—Hampshire Group, Ltd.; U.S. Public, pg. 778
HANES HOSIERY, INC.—Sara Lee Corporation; U.S. Public, pg. 1434
THE HARTSTONE GROUP PLC; Int'l, pg. 599
HIGHLAND MILLS INC.; U.S. Private, pg. 528
HOLT HOSIERY MILLS, INC.; U.S. Private, pg. 536
ITHACA INDUSTRIES, INC.; U.S. Private, pg. 576
KAYSER-ROTH CORPORATION, INC.—Grupo Synkro, S.A. de C.V.; Int'l, pg. 576
L'EGGS PRODUCTS, INC.—Sara Lee Corporation; U.S. Public, pg. 1434
MAYER/BERKSHIRE CORPORATION; U.S. Private, pg. 717
PENNACO HOSIERY—Danskin Inc.; U.S. Public, pg. 483
PRETTY POLLY LIMITED—Sara Lee Corporation; U.S. Public, pg. 1434
SANS, S.A.—Sara Lee Corporation; U.S. Public, pg. 1434
SARA LEE CORPORATION; U.S. Public, pg. 1432
SARA LEE HOSIERY—Sara Lee Corporation; U.S. Public, pg. 1434
SLANE HOSIERY MILLS, INC.; U.S. Private, pg. 1005

STERLING HOSIERY CO.—Heyman Corporation; U.S. Private, pg. 525
TRIMFIT, INC.; U.S. Private, pg. 1103
UNION UNDERWEAR CO., INC.—Fruit of the Loom, Inc.; U.S. Public, pg. 686

2252 — HOSIERY, NEC

ADMIRATION HOSIERY MILLS, INC.—Highland Mills Inc.; U.S. Private, pg. 528
ARCOPLUS ARGENTINA—Grupo Synkro, S.A. de C.V.; Int'l, pg. 576
ARGO AG—Coop Switzerland; Int'l, pg. 329
AUBURN HOSIERY MILLS, INC.; U.S. Private, pg. 98
CHIPMAN-UNION, INC.; U.S. Private, pg. 237
CLAYSON KNITTING CO. INC.; U.S. Private, pg. 244
COOP SWITZERLAND; Int'l, pg. 329
FARLEY, INC.; U.S. Private, pg. 394
FRUIT OF THE LOOM, INC.; U.S. Public, pg. 685
GREAT AMERICAN KNITTING MILLS—Bidermann International S.A.; Int'l, pg. 194
GRUPO SYNKRO, S.A. DE C.V.; Int'l, pg. 576
HAMPSHIRE DESIGNERS INC.—Hampshire Group, Ltd.; U.S. Public, pg. 778
HARRISS & COVINGTON HOSIERY MILLS; U.S. Private, pg. 506
THE HARTSTONE GROUP PLC; Int'l, pg. 599
HIGHLAND MILLS INC.; U.S. Private, pg. 528
ITHACA INDUSTRIES, INC.; U.S. Private, pg. 576
K-SWISS INC.; U.S. Public, pg. 937
KAYSER-ROTH CORPORATION, INC.—Grupo Synkro, S.A. de C.V.; Int'l, pg. 576
MAUNEY HOSIERY MILLS, INC.; U.S. Private, pg. 715
MAYER/BERKSHIRE CORPORATION; U.S. Private, pg. 717
RELIABLE KNITTING WORKS; U.S. Private, pg. 920
RENFRO CORP.; U.S. Private, pg. 922
RIDGEVIEW, INC.; U.S. Private, pg. 930
SARA LEE SOCK COMPANY—Sara Lee Corporation; U.S. Public, pg. 1434
SLANE HOSIERY MILLS, INC.; U.S. Private, pg. 1005
TRIMFIT, INC.; U.S. Private, pg. 1103
UNION UNDERWEAR CO., INC.—Fruit of the Loom, Inc.; U.S. Public, pg. 686
WIGWAM MILLS, INC.; U.S. Private, pg. 1175

2253 — KNIT OUTERWEAR MILLS

AMERICAN MARKETING WORK, INC.—Signal Apparel Company, Inc.; U.S. Public, pg. 1472
AUTHENTIC FITNESS CORP.; U.S. Public, pg. 147
AUTHENTIC FITNESS CORP. EAST COAST REGION—Authentic Fitness Corp.; U.S. Public, pg. 148
BELFE S.P.A.; Int'l, pg. 185
BONHOMME—Randa Corp.; U.S. Private, pg. 909
THE WILLIAM CARTER COMPANY; U.S. Private, pg. 217
COURTAULDS TEXTILES PLC; Int'l, pg. 339
COVINGTON INDUSTRIES; U.S. Private, pg. 280
CROSS CREEK APPAREL, INC.—Russell Corporation; U.S. Public, pg. 1413
DALKEITH KNITWEAR LIMITED—Coats Viyella plc; Int'l, pg. 299
DANCE FRANCE LTD.—Danskin Inc.; U.S. Public, pg. 483
THE ECHO DESIGN GROUP, INC.; U.S. Private, pg. 359
ERIMA GMBH & CO.—Adidas AG; Int'l, pg. 24
FRUIT OF THE LOOM, INC.; U.S. Public, pg. 685
GERRY SPORTSWEAR COMPANY; U.S. Private, pg. 449
GLAMOURETTE FASHION MILLS—Hampshire Group, Ltd.; U.S. Public, pg. 779
GRANITEVILLE COMPANY—Avondale Incorporated; U.S. Private, pg. 103
GRIFFON CORP.; U.S. Public, pg. 766
GUILFORD OF MAINE, INC.—Interface Inc.; U.S. Public, pg. 889
HALPER BROS.—Reliable Knitting Works; U.S. Private, pg. 920
HAMPSHIRE DESIGNERS INC.—Hampshire Group, Ltd.; U.S. Public, pg. 778
HAMPSHIRE GROUP, LTD.; U.S. Public, pg. 778
HARPER INDUSTRIES, INC.—Harcrest International, Ltd.; U.S. Private, pg. 501
HERITAGE SPORTSWEAR—Signal Apparel Company, Inc.; U.S. Public, pg. 1472
IZOD—Phillips-Van Heusen Corporation; U.S. Public, pg. 1292
JAEGER HOLDINGS LIMITED—Coats Viyella plc; Int'l, pg. 300
JOHNSTOWN KNITTING MILL CO.; U.S. Private, pg. 595
CHARLES KOMAR & SONS, INC.; U.S. Private, pg. 631
TONY LAMBERT COMPANY; U.S. Private, pg. 644
LIBERTY FABRICS, INC.—Courtaulds Textiles Plc; Int'l, pg. 340
LOGA ATHLETIC/HEADWEAR INC.—Tultex Corporation; U.S. Public, pg. 1644
LONDON FOG INDUSTRIES, INC.; U.S. Private, pg. 673
MALDEN MILLS INDUSTRIES, INC.; U.S. Private, pg. 698
NATALIE KNITTING MILLS—Hampshire Group, Ltd.; U.S. Public, pg. 779
PHILLIPS-VAN HEUSEN CORPORATION; U.S. Public, pg. 1291
POCONO KNITS, INC.—Jack Young Associates; U.S. Private, pg. 1201
RELIABLE KNITTING WORKS; U.S. Private, pg. 920
RUSSELL CORPORATION; U.S. Public, pg. 1413
SARA LEE CORPORATION; U.S. Public, pg. 1432
SCHOOL APPAREL, INC.; U.S. Private, pg. 972
SCHRADER BELLOWS DIVISION—Parker Hannifin Corporation; U.S. Public, pg. 1261
SIGNAL APPAREL COMPANY, INC.; U.S. Public, pg. 1472
SIGNAL ARTWEAR—Signal Apparel Company, Inc.; U.S. Public, pg. 1472
SIGNAL KNITWEAR—Signal Apparel Company, Inc.; U.S. Public, pg. 1472
SOMERSET KNITTING MILLS—Phillips-Van Heusen Corporation; U.S. Public, pg. 1291
TRIUMPH INTERNATIONAL—Triumph International Gruppe Deutschland; Int'l, pg. 1424
TULTEX CORPORATION; U.S. Public, pg. 1644
VF CORPORATION; U.S. Public, pg. 1702
WHALING INDUSTRIES, INC.; U.S. Private, pg. 1170
WIGWAM MILLS, INC.; U.S. Private, pg. 1175
WINONA KNITTING MILLS, INC.—Hampshire Group, Ltd.; U.S. Public, pg. 779
JACK YOUNG ASSOCIATES; U.S. Private, pg. 1201
YOUNG STUFF APPAREL GROUP, INC.; U.S. Private, pg. 1202

2254 — KNIT UNDERWEAR & NIGHTWEAR MILLS

AWI RETAIL—Alba-Waldensian, Inc.; U.S. Public, pg. 36
ALBA-WALDENSIAN, INC.; U.S. Public, pg. 35
DALKEITH KNITWEAR LIMITED—Coats Viyella plc; Int'l, pg. 299
DAMART S.A.; Int'l, pg. 376
DELTA WOODSIDE INDUSTRIES, INC.; U.S. Public, pg. 497
FRUIT OF THE LOOM, INC.; U.S. Public, pg. 685
GRIFFON CORP.; U.S. Public, pg. 766
HELLY-HANSEN (US), INC.—Orkla A.S.A.; Int'l, pg. 1010
JAEGER HOLDINGS LIMITED—Coats Viyella plc; Int'l, pg. 300
JOCKEY INTERNATIONAL, INC.; U.S. Private, pg. 588
JOHNSTOWN KNITTING MILL CO.; U.S. Private, pg. 595
CHARLES KOMAR & SONS, INC.; U.S. Private, pg. 631
MAYER/BERKSHIRE CORPORATION; U.S. Private, pg. 717
J.E. MORGAN KNITTING MILLS INC.—Dawson International PLC; Int'l, pg. 386
SALANT CHILDRENS APPAREL GROUP—Salant Corporation; U.S. Public, pg. 1429
SARA LEE HOSIERY—Sara Lee Corporation; U.S. Public, pg. 1434
SPARTAN MILLS; U.S. Private, pg. 1020
VF CORPORATION; U.S. Public, pg. 1702

2257 — CIRCULAR KNIT FABRIC MILLS

AMERICAN FABRICS COMPANY; U.S. Private, pg. 53
BRITTANY DYEING & PRINTING CORPORATION; U.S. Private, pg. 170
BURLINGTON INDUSTRIES, INC.; U.S. Public, pg. 268
CARO KNIT (JEFFERSON PLANT)—The Dixie Group, Inc.; U.S. Public, pg. 514
COATS VIYELLA PLC; Int'l, pg. 299
COLLINS & AIKMAN CORPORATION; U.S. Public, pg. 399
GLENOIT MILLS, INC.; U.S. Private, pg. 456
GUILFORD MILLS, INC.; U.S. Public, pg. 768
LORBER INDUSTRIES OF CALIFORNIA; U.S. Private, pg. 675
MALHARIA INDUSTRIAL DO NORDESTE S.A.—Solvay S.A.; Int'l, pg. 1279
SCOTT MILLS—Kleinert's, Inc.; U.S. Private, pg. 625
VANTONA LTD.—Coats Viyella plc; Int'l, pg. 299

2258 — LACE & WARP KNIT FABRIC MILLS

AMERICAN FABRICS COMPANY; U.S. Private, pg. 53
APEX MILLS CORPORATION; U.S. Private, pg. 77
CMI INDUSTRIES, INC.; U.S. Private, pg. 195
COATS VIYELLA PLC; Int'l, pg. 299
COLLINS & AIKMAN CORPORATION; U.S. Public, pg. 399
COURTAULDS TEXTILES PLC; Int'l, pg. 339
FORBO CONTRACT FABRICS LTD.—Forbo Holding SA; Int'l, pg. 497
GUILFORD EUROPE, LTD.—Guilford Mills, Inc.; U.S. Public, pg. 769
GUILFORD MILLS (APPAREL, HOME & INDUSTRIAL FABRICS)—Guilford Mills, Inc.; U.S. Public, pg. 769
GUILFORD MILLS, INC.; U.S. Public, pg. 768
HUNTER DOUGLAS VERTICALS—Hunter Douglas N.V.; Int'l, pg. 639
LIBERTY FABRICS, INC.—Courtaulds Textiles Plc; Int'l, pg. 340
MOORE COMPANY; U.S. Private, pg. 759
RAVAL LACE DIVISION—Fab Industries, Inc.; U.S. Public, pg. 603
SPARTAN MILLS; U.S. Private, pg. 1020
VANTONA LTD.—Coats Viyella plc; Int'l, pg. 299
WESTCHESTER LACE, INC.; U.S. Private, pg. 1163

2259 — KNITTING MILLS, NEC

CAROLINA GLOVE CO.; U.S. Private, pg. 214
CHRONOS RICHARDSON GMBH—Staveley Industries PLC; Int'l, pg. 1299
DYERSBURG CORPORATION; U.S. Public, pg. 538
HUNTER DOUGLAS VERTICALS—Hunter Douglas N.V.; Int'l, pg. 639
HUYCK LTD.—BTR plc; Int'l, pg. 124
JOMAC, INC.; U.S. Private, pg. 595
SARA LEE HOSIERY—Sara Lee Corporation; U.S. Public, pg. 1434
TOTES/ISOTONER, INC.—Sara Lee Corporation; U.S. Public, pg. 1433
TRENTON MILLS—Dyersburg Corporation; U.S. Public, pg. 538

2261 — FINISHERS OF BROAD WOVEN FABRICS OF COTTON

AMERBELLE CORPORATION; U.S. Private, pg. 48
AMERICAN FAST PRINT, LIMITED; U.S. Private, pg. 53
AMERICAN PAD AND PAPER COMPANY; U.S. Public, pg. 88
BRITTANY DYEING & PRINTING CORPORATION; U.S. Private, pg. 170
CLAREMONT FLOCK CORPORATION; U.S. Private, pg. 241
CONCORD FABRICS INC.; U.S. Public, pg. 429
CRANSTON PRINT WORKS COMPANY; U.S. Private, pg. 286
DEITSCH PLASTICS COMPANY; U.S. Private, pg. 320
DOMINION INDUSTRIAL FABRICS COMPANY—Dominion Textile Inc.; Int'l, pg. 415
DOMINION TEXTILE INC.; Int'l, pg. 415
FACEMATE CORP.—Facemate Corporation; U.S. Private, pg. 391
FACEMATE CORPORATION; U.S. Private, pg. 391
G.Y. INDUSTRIES, INC.—American Pad and Paper Company; U.S. Public, pg. 89
GRANITEVILLE COMPANY—Avondale Incorporated; U.S. Private, pg. 103
HANES COMPANIES, INC.—Leggett & Platt, Incorporated; U.S. Public, pg. 986
THE HARODITE FINISHING COMPANY INC.; U.S. Private, pg. 503
HART HOLDING COMPANY, INC.; U.S. Private, pg. 507
HOLOUBEK INC.; U.S. Private, pg. 536
HOME FURNISHINGS SEGMENT—Springs Industries, Inc.; U.S. Public, pg. 1500
LIBERTY PLC; Int'l, pg. 807
LORBER INDUSTRIES OF CALIFORNIA; U.S. Private, pg. 675
MERIDIAN INDUSTRIES, INC.; U.S. Private, pg. 732
MITCHELL CO.—Stonecutter Mills Corp.; U.S. Private, pg. 1044
PEELERS RUG COMPANY, INC.; U.S. Private, pg. 846
PRIORITY FINISHING CORP.; U.S. Private, pg. 887
PUBLICKER INDUSTRIES INC.; U.S. Public, pg. 1341
R.A. BRIGGS & CO.—Home Innovations, Inc.; U.S. Private, pg. 536
RUSSELL CORPORATION; U.S. Public, pg. 1413
SANTEE PRINT WORKS, INC.; U.S. Private, pg. 965
SCALAMANDRE, INC.; U.S. Private, pg. 969
SPRINGS INDUSTRIES, INC.; U.S. Public, pg. 1499
STONECUTTER MILLS CORP.; U.S. Private, pg. 1044
THOMASTON MILLS, INC.; U.S. Public, pg. 1599
TOOTAL GROUP PLC—Coats Viyella plc; Int'l, pg. 300
UNITED PIECE DYE WORKS, LP; U.S. Private, pg. 1123
WESTGATE FABRICS, INC.; U.S. Private, pg. 1169
WILLIAMHOUSE-REGENCY, INC.—American Pad and Paper Company; U.S. Public, pg. 89

2262 — FINISHERS OF BROAD WOVEN FABRICS OF MAN-MADE FIBER & SILK

AMERBELLE CORPORATION; U.S. Private, pg. 48
BALLIEVEY LTD.—Lamont Holdings Plc; Int'l, pg. 797
BLUMENTHAL PRINT WORKS, INC.; U.S. Private, pg. 153
CLAREMONT FLOCK CORPORATION; U.S. Private, pg. 241
COLLINS & AIKMAN CORPORATION; U.S. Public, pg. 399
CRANSTON PRINT WORKS COMPANY; U.S. Private, pg. 286
ERNST MICHALKE GMBH—Hoechst Aktiengesellschaft; Int'l, pg. 624
FACEMATE CORP.—Facemate Corporation; U.S. Private, pg. 391
FACEMATE CORPORATION; U.S. Private, pg. 391
GLEN RAVEN MILLS, INC.; U.S. Private, pg. 456
GRANITEVILLE COMPANY—Avondale Incorporated; U.S. Private, pg. 103
HAMPTON PRINT WORKS, INC.; U.S. Private, pg. 498
HANES COMPANIES, INC.—Leggett & Platt, Incorporated; U.S. Public, pg. 986
THE HARODITE FINISHING COMPANY INC.; U.S. Private, pg. 503
HART HOLDING COMPANY, INC.; U.S. Private, pg. 507
IMPRESSIONS ET TEINTURES DE TOURNON S.A.—Liberty PLC; Int'l, pg. 807
LIBERTY PLC; Int'l, pg. 807
LORBER INDUSTRIES OF CALIFORNIA; U.S. Private, pg. 675
MITCHELL CO.—Stonecutter Mills Corp.; U.S. Private, pg. 1044
PERFORMANCE PRODUCTS DIVISION—Springs Industries, Inc.; U.S. Public, pg. 1500
PRIORITY FINISHING CORP.; U.S. Private, pg. 887
PUBLICKER INDUSTRIES INC.; U.S. Public, pg. 1341
SPRINGS INDUSTRIES, INC.; U.S. Public, pg. 1499
STONECUTTER MILLS CORP.; U.S. Private, pg. 1044
THOMASTON MILLS, INC.; U.S. Public, pg. 1599
TOOTAL GROUP PLC—Coats Viyella plc; Int'l, pg. 300
UNITED PIECE DYE WORKS, LP; U.S. Private, pg. 1123

2269 — FINISHERS OF TEXTILES, NEC

BEACON MFG. CO.—Pillowtex Corporation; U.S. Public, pg. 1296
COLLINS & AIKMAN CORPORATION; U.S. Public, pg. 399
GLEN RAVEN MILLS, INC.; U.S. Private, pg. 456
THE HARODITE FINISHING COMPANY INC.; U.S. Private, pg. 503
LIBERTY PLC; Int'l, pg. 807
MOUNT VERNON MILLS, INC.—R.B. Pamplin Corp.; U.S. Private, pg. 835
PAXAR CORPORATION; U.S. Public, pg. 1266

PUBLICKER INDUSTRIES INC.; U.S. Public, pg. 1341
SCALAMANDRE, INC.; U.S. Private, pg. 969
SPARTAN MILLS; U.S. Private, pg. 1020
STOWE-PHARR MILLS, INC.; U.S. Private, pg. 1045

2273 — CARPETS & RUGS

THE AKRO CORPORATION—Collins & Aikman Corporation; U.S. Public, pg. 399
ALADDIN MILLS—Mohawk Industries, Inc.; U.S. Public, pg. 1121
AMERICAN RUG CRAFTSMEN—Mohawk Industries, Inc.; U.S. Public, pg. 1121
ASHLEY CARPET—Shaw Industries, Inc.; U.S. Public, pg. 1464
BEAULIEU UNITED—Beaulieu Group; U.S. Private, pg. 128
BENTLEY MILLS, INC.—Interface Inc.; U.S. Public, pg. 889
BRETLIN, INC.—The Dixie Group, Inc.; U.S. Public, pg. 514
BUCHANAN INDUSTRIES, INC.—Martin Color-Fi; U.S. Public, pg. 1052
BURLINGTON HOUSE AREA RUGS—Burlington Industries, Inc.; U.S. Public, pg. 268
BURLINGTON INDUSTRIES, INC.; U.S. Public, pg. 268
C&C ASSOCIATES—Couristan Inc.; U.S. Private, pg. 279
CABIN CRAFTS CARPETS—Shaw Industries, Inc.; U.S. Public, pg. 1464
CARRIAGE DESIGNS, INC.—The Dixie Group, Inc.; U.S. Public, pg. 514
CARRIAGE INDUSTRIES, INC.—The Dixie Group, Inc.; U.S. Public, pg. 514
COLLINS & AIKMAN CORPORATION; U.S. Public, pg. 399
COLLINS & AIKMAN FLOORCOVERINGS, INC.—CAF Holding Company; U.S. Private, pg. 192
COLLINS & AIKMAN PRODUCTS CO.—Collins & Aikman Corporation; U.S. Public, pg. 399
COURI CARPET CO.—Couristan Inc.; U.S. Private, pg. 279
COURI-MURAD & CO.—Couristan Inc.; U.S. Private, pg. 279
COURISTAN INC.; U.S. Private, pg. 279
THE DIXIE GROUP, INC.; U.S. Public, pg. 514
EVANS-BLACK CARPET MILLS—Shaw Industries, Inc.; U.S. Public, pg. 1464
FATATI-BTR S.A.—BTR plc; Int'l, pg. 130
FELTRAX INTERNATIONAL, INC.—BTR plc; Int'l, pg. 130
FORBO HOLDING SA; Int'l, pg. 496
GALAXY CARPET MILLS, INC.—Mohawk Industries, Inc.; U.S. Public, pg. 1121
GAMMA HOLDING N.V.; Int'l, pg. 539
GENERAL FELT INDUSTRIES, INC.—Trace International Holdings, Inc.; U.S. Private, pg. 1094
GOLDEN STAR INC.; U.S. Private, pg. 460
HOLLYBANK BLEACH & DYE WORKS LTD.—Lamont Holdings Plc; Int'l, pg. 798
HOLLYTEX CARPET MILLS, INC.; U.S. Private, pg. 535
HOME FURNISHINGS SEGMENT—Springs Industries, Inc.; U.S. Public, pg. 1500
HOWARD CARPET MILLS, INC.—Shaw Industries, Inc.; U.S. Public, pg. 1464
INTERFACE EUROPE B.V.—Interface Inc.; U.S. Public, pg. 889
INTERFACE FLOORING SYSTEMS INC.—Interface Inc.; U.S. Public, pg. 889
INTERFACE INC.; U.S. Public, pg. 889
KARASTAN—Mohawk Industries, Inc.; U.S. Public, pg. 1121
KELLER LADDERS INC.—U.S. Industries, Inc.; U.S. Public, pg. 1684
LEES CARPETS—Burlington Industries, Inc.; U.S. Public, pg. 268
THE MAGEE CARPET COMPANY; U.S. Private, pg. 694
MAJESTIC CARPET MILLS—Shaw Industries, Inc.; U.S. Public, pg. 1464
MARGLEN INDUSTRIES; U.S. Private, pg. 702
MARGLEN YARN PLANT—Marglen Industries; U.S. Private, pg. 702
MASLAND—Lear Corporation; U.S. Public, pg. 981
MASLAND CARPETS, INC.—The Dixie Group, Inc.; U.S. Public, pg. 514
MILLIKEN & COMPANY; U.S. Private, pg. 748
MITCHELL CORPORATION OF OWOSSO; U.S. Private, pg. 753
MITSUBISHI-BURLINGTON CO.—Burlington Industries, Inc.; U.S. Public, pg. 268
MOHAWK COMMERCIAL CARPET—Mohawk Industries, Inc.; U.S. Public, pg. 1121
NOBILES-LEES S.A. DE C.V.—Burlington Industries, Inc.; U.S. Public, pg. 268
OKA TEPPICHWERKE GMBH.—Vorwerk & Co.; Int'l, pg. 1480
PATCRAFT COMMERCIAL CARPET—Queen Carpet Corporation; U.S. Private, pg. 900
PEELERS RUG COMPANY, INC.; U.S. Private, pg. 846
PEERLESS CARPET CORPORATION; Int'l, pg. 1032
PHILADELPHIA CARPET DIV.—Shaw Industries, Inc.; U.S. Public, pg. 1464
PLAYFIELD INDUSTRIES INC.—TecSyn International, Inc.; Int'l, pg. 1362
QUEEN CARPET CORPORATION; U.S. Private, pg. 900
SALEM CARPET MILLS, INC.—Shaw Industries, Inc.; U.S. Public, pg. 1464
SCALAMANDRE, INC.; U.S. Private, pg. 969
SHAW INDUSTRIES, INC.; U.S. Public, pg. 1464
SPRINGS CANADA, LTD.—Springs Industries, Inc.; U.S. Public, pg. 1500
SPRINGS INDUSTRIES, INC.; U.S. Public, pg. 1499
VORWERK & CO.; Int'l, pg. 1480
VORWERK & CO. TEPPICH-BETEILIGUNGSGESELLSCHAFT MBH.—Vorwerk & Co.; Int'l, pg. 1480
VORWERK & CO. TEPPICHWERKE GMBH. & CO. KG.—Vorwerk & Co.; Int'l, pg. 1480
WINSTON CARPET CO.—Shaw Industries, Inc.; U.S. Public, pg. 1464
WORLD CARPETS, INC.; U.S. Private, pg. 1190

2281 — YARN SPINNING MILLS: COTTON, MAN-MADE FIBERS, SILK, WOOL, MOHAIR & ANIMAL FIBERS

ACS INDUSTRIES, INC.; U.S. Private, pg. 3
AMES EUROPE LTD.—Gamma Holding N.V.; Int'l, pg. 540
AMICALE INDUSTRIES, INC.; U.S. Private, pg. 66
AMOCO FABRICS & FIBERS COMPANY—Amoco Corporation; U.S. Public, pg. 102
AMOCO FABRICS & FIBERS, LTD.—Amoco Corporation; U.S. Public, pg. 102
ARTEE-WRAP SPUN—Culp, Inc.; U.S. Public, pg. 467
AVONDALE FOREIGN SALES CORPORATION—Avondale Incorporated; U.S. Private, pg. 103
AVONDALE MILLS, INC.—Avondale Incorporated; U.S. Private, pg. 102
BASF CORPORATION FIBER PRODUCTS DIVISION—BASF AG; Int'l, pg. 105
BEACON MFG. CO.—Pillowtex Corporation; U.S. Public, pg. 1296
THE BRAIDWATER SPINNING COMPANY LTD.—Lamont Holdings Plc; Int'l, pg. 797
BRITISH MOHAIR SPINNERS LIMITED—British Mohair Holdings Plc; Int'l, pg. 219
CMI INDUSTRIES, INC.; U.S. Private, pg. 195
CYDSA S.A.; Int'l, pg. 246
CANDLEWICK GROUP—The Dixie Group, Inc.; U.S. Public, pg. 514
CAROLINA MILLS, INC.; U.S. Private, pg. 214
CARON INTERNATIONAL—National Spinning Co., Inc.; U.S. Private, pg. 786
CHERAW YARN MILLS, INC.; U.S. Private, pg. 233
CHINA THREAD DEVELOPMENT CO. LTD.—Coats Viyella plc; Int'l, pg. 299
COATS CADENA SA—Coats Viyella plc; Int'l, pg. 300
COATS CUCIRINI S.P.A.—Coats Viyella plc; Int'l, pg. 300
COATS HARLANDER G.M.B.H—Coats Viyella plc; Int'l, pg. 300
COATS MEZ INDUSTRIEAHFADEN G.M.B.H.—Coats Viyella plc; Int'l, pg. 300
COATS PAKISTAN LIMITED—Coats Viyella plc; Int'l, pg. 300
COATS PATONS—Coats Viyella plc; Int'l, pg. 300
COATS (TURKEY) IPLIK SANAYII AS—Coats Viyella plc; Int'l, pg. 300
COLLINS & AIKMAN CORPORATION; U.S. Public, pg. 399
COURTAULDS PLC; Int'l, pg. 338
CUSTOM COLORANTS, INC.—Martin Color-Fi; U.S. Public, pg. 1052
DAIWA DO BRASIL TEXTIL LTDA.—Nissho Iwai Corporation; Int'l, pg. 947
DAN RIVER DANVILLE MFG. DIV.—Dan River Inc.; U.S. Public, pg. 479
CIA. DE LINHA COATS & CLARK LDA.—Coats Viyella plc; Int'l, pg. 300
THE DIXIE GROUP, INC.; U.S. Public, pg. 514
DIXIE SYNTHETIC YARN GROUP—The Dixie Group, Inc.; U.S. Public, pg. 514
DUSA ENDUSTRIYEL IPLIK SANAYI VE TICARET A.S.—Du Pont (E.I. Du Pont De Nemours & Co.); U.S. Public, pg. 533
DUSA ENDUSTRIYEL IPLIK SANAYI VE TICARET A.S.—Sabanci Holding A.S.; Int'l, pg. 1167
FIELDCREST CANNON, INC.—Pillowtex Corporation; U.S. Public, pg. 1296
THE FIRST REPUBLIC CORPORATION OF AMERICA; U.S. Public, pg. 637
FORMOSA PLASTICS CORPORATION; Int'l, pg. 498
GLEN RAVEN MILLS, INC.; U.S. Private, pg. 456
GLEN RAVEN MILLS, INC.-NORLINA PLANT—Glen Raven Mills, Inc.; U.S. Private, pg. 456
GLEN RAVEN MILLS, INC.-ULTRASPUN PLANT—Glen Raven Mills, Inc.; U.S. Private, pg. 456
GOLDEN STAR INC.; U.S. Private, pg. 460
HANORA SPINNING, INC.—The First Republic Corporation of America; U.S. Public, pg. 637
HARBINGER CARPET—Mohawk Industries, Inc.; U.S. Public, pg. 1121
HARRIET & HENDERSON YARNS, INC.; U.S. Private, pg. 504
INDO RAMA SYNTHETICS P.T.; Int'l, pg. 673
JPS CONVERTER & INDUSTRIAL CORP.—JPS Textile Group, Inc.; U.S. Private, pg. 578
KANEBO, LTD.; Int'l, pg. 722
KARASTAN BIGELOW COMMERCIAL—Mohawk Industries, Inc.; U.S. Public, pg. 1121
THE KENT MANUFACTURING CO.; U.S. Private, pg. 615
KEUM KANG DEVELOPMENT INDUSTRIAL CO., LTD.—Hyundai Motor Company; Int'l, pg. 642
KUNZ & DIETFURT—Oerlikon-Buhrle Holding AG; Int'l, pg. 998
KUNZ SPINNING MILLS LTD.—Oerlikon-Buhrle Holding AG; Int'l, pg. 998
LINHAS CORRENTE LTDA.—Coats Viyella plc; Int'l, pg. 301
LION BRAND YARN CO.; U.S. Private, pg. 669
LORBER INDUSTRIES OF CALIFORNIA; U.S. Private, pg. 675
MARTIN COLOR-FI; U.S. Public, pg. 1052
B.H. MCCLEERY & CO. LTD.—Lamont Holdings Plc; Int'l, pg. 797
MITCHELL CO.—Stonecutter Mills Corp.; U.S. Private, pg. 1044
MOHAWK INDUSTRIES, INC.; U.S. Public, pg. 1121
NATIONAL SPINNING CO., INC.; U.S. Private, pg. 786
NATIONAL SPINNING CO.—National Spinning Co., Inc.; U.S. Private, pg. 787
NATIONAL YARN CRAFTS—National Spinning Co., Inc.; U.S. Private, pg. 787
NATIVE TEXTILES—U.S. Industries, Inc.; U.S. Public, pg. 1684
ORCHARD YARN & THREAD CO., INC.—Lion Brand Yarn Co.; U.S. Private, pg. 669
ORIX INTERIOR CORPORATION—Orix Corporation; Int'l, pg. 1008
THE OSTERNECK CO. INC.; U.S. Private, pg. 821
PALMETTO SPINNING CORP.—Martin Color-Fi; U.S. Public, pg. 1052
PARKDALE MILLS; U.S. Private, pg. 840
POLYLOOM CORP. OF AMERICA; U.S. Private, pg. 875
RUDDICK CORPORATION; U.S. Public, pg. 1412
SCT YARNS, INC.; U.S. Private, pg. 956
SABANCI HOLDING A.S.; Int'l, pg. 1167
SHUFORD MILLS, INC.; U.S. Private, pg. 996
SPINNSTOFFFABRIK ZEHLENDORF AG—Hoechst Aktiengesellschaft; Int'l, pg. 626
SPRINGS INDUSTRIES, INC.; U.S. Public, pg. 1499
STONECUTTER MILLS CORP.; U.S. Private, pg. 1044
STOWE-PHARR MILLS, INC.; U.S. Private, pg. 1045
TAINAN SPINNING CO., LTD.; Int'l, pg. 1347
TEXFI INDUSTRIES, INC.; U.S. Public, pg. 1588
THOMASTON MILLS, INC.; U.S. Public, pg. 1599
TRENTON MILLS—Dyersburg Corporation; U.S. Public, pg. 538
TUSCARORA YARNS INC.; U.S. Private, pg. 1110
WALTON FABRIC DIVISION OF AVONDALE MILLS—Avondale Incorporated; U.S. Private, pg. 103

2282 — YARN TEXTURIZING, THROWING, TWISTING & WINDING MILLS

BARBOUR THREAD—Hicking Pentecost Plc; Int'l, pg. 618
COLLINS & AIKMAN CORPORATION; U.S. Public, pg. 399
COOP SWITZERLAND; Int'l, pg. 329
CUSTOM COLORANTS, INC.—Martin Color-Fi; U.S. Public, pg. 1052
DERIVADOS ACRILICOS, S.A. DE C.V.—CYDSA S.A.; Int'l, pg. 246
GUDEBROD, INC.; U.S. Private, pg. 486
JEFFERSON MILLS, INC.; U.S. Private, pg. 584
KANEBO, LTD.; Int'l, pg. 722
THE KENT MANUFACTURING CO.; U.S. Private, pg. 615
KUNZ & DIETFURT—Oerlikon-Buhrle Holding AG; Int'l, pg. 998
LEON-FERENBACH INC.; U.S. Private, pg. 660
LINDUSTRIES LTD.—Hanson PLC; Int'l, pg. 593
LION BRAND YARN CO.; U.S. Private, pg. 669
MARTIN COLOR-FI; U.S. Public, pg. 1052
PALMETTO SPINNING CORP.—Martin Color-Fi; U.S. Public, pg. 1052
SOLUTIA INC.—Solutia Inc.; U.S. Public, pg. 1484
UNIFI INC.; U.S. Public, pg. 1665

2284 — THREAD MILLS

ALLIED THREAD CO. INC.—Coats Viyella plc; Int'l, pg. 299
AMERICAN & EFIRD, INC.—Ruddick Corporation; U.S. Public, pg. 1412
ARAMIDE MAATSCHAPPIJ VOF—Akzo Nobel N.V.; Int'l, pg. 45
AUSTRALIAN THREAD PTY. LTD.—Coats Viyella plc; Int'l, pg. 299
BARBOUR THREAD INC.—Hicking Pentecost Plc; Int'l, pg. 618
WM. BRIGGS & CO. LIMITED—Coats Viyella plc; Int'l, pg. 299
BURLINGTON MADISON YARN—Burlington Industries, Inc.; U.S. Public, pg. 268
CAROLINA MAIDEN CORP.—Carolina Mills, Inc.; U.S. Private, pg. 214
CHINA THREAD DEVELOPMENT CO. LTD.—Coats Viyella plc; Int'l, pg. 299
THE CHUO WOOLLEN MILLS, LTD.—Nissho Iwai Corporation; Int'l, pg. 946
COATS & CLARK INC.—Coats Viyella plc; Int'l, pg. 300
COATS BELL—Coats Viyella plc; Int'l, pg. 299
COATS LIMITED—Coats Viyella plc; Int'l, pg. 299
COATS NORTH AMERICA—Coats Viyella plc; Int'l, pg. 300
COATS VIYELLA PLC; Int'l, pg. 299
COURTAULDS PLC; Int'l, pg. 338
DOMINION INDUSTRIAL FABRICS COMPANY—Dominion Textile Inc.; Int'l, pg. 415
EZ INTERNATIONAL—Wm. E. Wright Limited Partnership; U.S. Private, pg. 1192
ENKA BV—Akzo Nobel N.V.; Int'l, pg. 45
GUDEBROD, INC.; U.S. Private, pg. 486
HICKING PENTECOST PLC; Int'l, pg. 618
HILANA C.A.—Nissho Iwai Corporation; Int'l, pg. 947
HILOS MAGIC H.M. DE VENEZUELA CA—Mantex, S.A.C.A.; Int'l, pg. 840
ICI (SINGAPORE) PRIVATE LIMITED—Imperial Chemical Industries PLC; Int'l, pg. 665
IRISH SEWING LTD.—Coats Viyella plc; Int'l, pg. 299
J. & P. COATS LIMITED—Coats Viyella plc; Int'l, pg. 299
KUAGGARN TEXTIL AG—Akzo Nobel N.V.; Int'l, pg. 46
LINDUSTRIES LTD.—Hanson PLC; Int'l, pg. 593
LUDLOW TEXTILES CO., INC.; U.S. Private, pg. 680
NATAL THREAD CO. (PTY) LTD.—Coats Viyella plc; Int'l, pg. 299
RHENANIA A.G.—Coats Viyella plc; Int'l, pg. 299
RUDDICK CORPORATION; U.S. Public, pg. 1412
SCT YARNS, INC.; U.S. Private, pg. 956
THO-RO PRODUCTS, INC.—Eagle Button Co., Inc.; U.S. Private, pg. 354
TOOTAL THREAD HONG KONG LTD.—Coats Viyella plc; Int'l, pg. 299
TOOTAL THREAD MALACCA SDN BDN—Coats Viyella plc; Int'l, pg. 299
TOOTAL THREAD (PTE.) LTD.—Coats Viyella plc; Int'l, pg. 299

P.T. TOOTAL THREAD WDONGSLA—Coats Viyella plc; *Int'l*, pg. 299
TOYOBO CO., LTD.; *Int'l*, pg. 1411
TOYODA BOSHOFU CORPORATION—Toyota Motor Corporation; *Int'l*, pg. 1412
ZENECA AB—Zeneca Group Plc; *Int'l*, pg. 1526
ZENECA HELLAS S.A.—Zeneca Group Plc; *Int'l*, pg. 1526
ZENECA OY—Zeneca Group Plc; *Int'l*, pg. 1527
ZENECA POLAND SP. Z.O.O.—Zeneca Group Plc; *Int'l*, pg. 1527
ZENECA ZIMBABWE (PRIVATE) LIMITED—Zeneca Group Plc; *Int'l*, pg. 1527

2295 — COATED FABRICS, NOT RUBBERIZED

ACME CHEMICALS & INSULATION CO.—Insulating Materials, Inc.; *U.S. Private*, pg. 565
ALDAN INDUSTRIES; *U.S. Private*, pg. 33
ALPHA ASSOCIATES, INC.; *U.S. Private*, pg. 44
AMERBELLE CORPORATION; *U.S. Private*, pg. 48
AMERCOAT ESPANA, S.A.—Ameron International Corporation; *U.S. Public*, pg. 99
AMERICAN BILTRITE INC.; *U.S. Public*, pg. 68
ATHOL CORPORATION; *U.S. Private*, pg. 94
BROOKWOOD COMPANIES INC.—The Hallwood Group Incorporated; *U.S. Public*, pg. 777
CC INDUSTRIES, INC.; *U.S. Private*, pg. 192
CHR INDUSTRIES, INC.—Furon Company; *U.S. Public*, pg. 689
CHASE & SONS DIVISION—Chase Corporation; *U.S. Public*, pg. 337
CHASE & SONS-WEBSTER BRANCH—Chase Corporation; *U.S. Public*, pg. 337
CHASE CORPORATION; *U.S. Public*, pg. 337
CHEMFAB CORPORATION; *U.S. Public*, pg. 344
CHOMERICS INC.—Parker Hannifin Corporation; *U.S. Public*, pg. 1262
COLLINS & AIKMAN CORPORATION; *U.S. Public*, pg. 399
COOLEY, INC.; *U.S. Private*, pg. 273
DOMINION INDUSTRIAL FABRICS COMPANY—Dominion Textile Inc.; *Int'l*, pg. 415
FORBO LANCASTER LTD.—Forbo Holding SA; *Int'l*, pg. 497
FORBO-STAMOID AG—Forbo Holding SA; *Int'l*, pg. 497
FREUDENBERG NONWOVENS LIMITED PARTNERSHIP—Freudenberg & Company; *Int'l*, pg. 505
HART HOLDING COMPANY, INC.; *U.S. Private*, pg. 507
HEALTH-CHEM CORPORATION; *U.S. Public*, pg. 802
HERCULITE PRODUCTS, INC.—Health-Chem Corporation; *U.S. Public*, pg. 802
HEXCEL, FAR EAST—Hexcel Corporation; *U.S. Public*, pg. 824
HEXCEL, S.A.—Hexcel Corporation; *U.S. Public*, pg. 824
HEXCEL, U.K.—Hexcel Corporation; *U.S. Public*, pg. 824
HOECHST CELANESE FINE CHEMICAL DIVISION—Hoechst Aktiengesellschaft; *Int'l*, pg. 625
INDUSTRIAL COATINGS GROUP, INC.—GCI Holdings Corporation; *U.S. Private*, pg. 434
INTERPLAST UNIVERSAL INDUSTRIES, INC.; *U.S. Private*, pg. 572
J. JOSEPHSON, INC.; *U.S. Private*, pg. 601
MARTIN MATHYS, NV—RPM, Inc.; *U.S. Public*, pg. 1358
MERIDIAN INDUSTRIES, INC.; *U.S. Private*, pg. 732
NORWOOD INDUSTRIES, INC.—Seton Company; *U.S. Private*, pg. 987
OCE-VAN DER GRINTEN N.V.; *Int'l*, pg. 993
THE OSTERNECK CO. INC.; *U.S. Private*, pg. 821
PACIFIC COMBINING CORP.—Health-Chem Corporation; *U.S. Public*, pg. 802
PAXAR APPAREL IDENTIFICATION SYSTEMS—PAXAR Corporation; *U.S. Public*, pg. 1266
PAXAR CORPORATION; *U.S. Public*, pg. 1266
PAXAR EUROPE LTD.—PAXAR Corporation; *U.S. Public*, pg. 1267
PERMACEL—Nitto Denko Corporation; *Int'l*, pg. 950
PERMACEL TAPE—Avery Dennison Corporation; *U.S. Public*, pg. 153
RAINFAIR, INC.; *U.S. Private*, pg. 907
REEVES-INDUSTRIAL COATED FABRICS PLANT—Hart Holding Company, Inc.; *U.S. Private*, pg. 507
SCHNELLER, INC.; *U.S. Private*, pg. 971
SETON COMPANY; *U.S. Private*, pg. 987
THE STIFFEL COMPANY; *U.S. Private*, pg. 1043
TEXON MATERIALS INC.; *U.S. Private*, pg. 1079
3M; *U.S. Public*, pg. 1604

2296 — TIRE CORD & FABRIC

BTR PLC; *Int'l*, pg. 124
BRIDGESTONE/FIRESTONE, INC.—Bridgestone Corporation; *Int'l*, pg. 213
CONTINENTAL GENERAL TIRE, INC.—Continental AG; *Int'l*, pg. 327
FIRESTONE FIBERS & TEXTILES CO.—Bridgestone Corporation; *Int'l*, pg. 214
FIRESTONE TEXTILES COMPANY—Bridgestone Corporation; *Int'l*, pg. 214
RICHMOND CONVERTERS, INC.—Pirelli S.p.A.; *Int'l*, pg. 1059
STERN & STERN INDUSTRIES INC.; *U.S. Private*, pg. 1041

2297 — NONWOVEN FABRICS

ALDINE TECHNOLOGIES INDUSTRIES INC.; *U.S. Private*, pg. 33
AMOCO FABRICS & FIBERS COMPANY—Amoco Corporation; *U.S. Public*, pg. 102
AMOCO NISSEKI CLAF INC. (ANCI)—Amoco Corporation; *U.S. Public*, pg. 102
AVENT, S.A. DE C.V.—Kimberly-Clark Corporation; *U.S. Public*, pg. 959
BEACON MFG. CO.—Pillowtex Corporation; *U.S. Public*, pg. 1296
BLYDENSTEIN-WILLINK N.V.; *Int'l*, pg. 198
BONDED FIBRE FABRIC LTD.—Lamont Holdings Plc; *Int'l*, pg. 798
CSS INDUSTRIES, INC.; *U.S. Public*, pg. 283
CARPENTER CO.; *U.S. Private*, pg. 214
CHASE & SONS DIVISION—Chase Corporation; *U.S. Public*, pg. 337
CHASE & SONS-WEBSTER BRANCH—Chase Corporation; *U.S. Public*, pg. 337
CHASE CORPORATION; *U.S. Public*, pg. 337
COLBOND BV—Akzo Nobel N.V.; *Int'l*, pg. 45
COMPOSITE MATERIALS DIV.—Rogers Corporation; *U.S. Public*, pg. 1402
CONSTRUCTION & HOME IMPROVEMENT MARKETS DIVISION—3M; *U.S. Public*, pg. 1605
DEXTER NONWOVENS DIVISION—The Dexter Corporation; *U.S. Public*, pg. 504
ENKA BV—Akzo Nobel N.V.; *Int'l*, pg. 45
FARLEY, INC.; *U.S. Private*, pg. 394
FIRET, B.V.—Fruit of the Loom, Inc.; *U.S. Public*, pg. 686
FORT JAMES CORPORATION; *U.S. Public*, pg. 670
FOSS MANUFACTURING COMPANY INCORPORATED; *U.S. Private*, pg. 420
CARL FREUDENBERG—Freudenberg & Company; *Int'l*, pg. 505
FREUDENBERG NONWOVENS—Freudenberg & Company; *Int'l*, pg. 505
FREUDENBERG NONWOVENS LIMITED PARTNERSHIP—Freudenberg & Company; *Int'l*, pg. 505
FREUDENBERG PELLON CORPORATION—Freudenberg & Company; *Int'l*, pg. 507
FREUDENBERG SPUNWEB CO.—Freudenberg & Company; *Int'l*, pg. 505
GAMMA HOLDING N.V.; *Int'l*, pg. 539
GLENOIT MILLS, INC.; *U.S. Private*, pg. 456
ALBERT HARTLEY LIMITED—Coats Viyella plc; *Int'l*, pg. 299
HOECHST MARION ROUSSEL, INC.—Hoechst Aktiengesellschaft; *Int'l*, pg. 624
HOF TEXTILES INC.—Neuebaum Woll-Spinnerei Und Weberei Hof A.G.; *Int'l*, pg. 923
KIMBERLY-CLARK CORPORATION; *U.S. Public*, pg. 958
KIMBERLY-CLARK HOSPITAL SERVICE PRODUCTS—Kimberly-Clark Corporation; *U.S. Public*, pg. 959
KIMBERLY-CLARK LIMITED—Kimberly-Clark Corporation; *U.S. Public*, pg. 959
LYDALL AXOHM—Lydall, Inc.; *U.S. Public*, pg. 1021
LYDALL, INC.; *U.S. Public*, pg. 1020
NAN WOVEN—BBA Group plc; *Int'l*, pg. 113
NEUEBAUM WOLL-SPINNEREI UND WEBEREI HOF A.G.; *Int'l*, pg. 922
R.B. PAMPLIN CORP.; *U.S. Private*, pg. 835
POLY-BOND INC.—Dominion Textile Inc.; *Int'l*, pg. 415
RIBBON NARROW FABRIC COMPANY; *U.S. Private*, pg. 927
RUDDICK CORPORATION; *U.S. Public*, pg. 1412
SACKNER-CENTRAL—Jason Incorporated; *U.S. Public*, pg. 924
SACKNER PRODUCTS—Jason Incorporated; *U.S. Public*, pg. 924
SACKNER-SOUTHEAST DIV.—Jason Incorporated; *U.S. Public*, pg. 924
SCHLEGEL OKLAHOMA, INC.—BTR plc; *Int'l*, pg. 128
SUDAMTEX DE URUGUAY, S.A.; *Int'l*, pg. 1304
TAMROCK CORP.; *Int'l*, pg. 1352
THE TRANZONIC COMPANIES; *U.S. Public*, pg. 1632
TRANZONIC INDUSTRIAL TEXTILES DIVISION—The Tranzonic Companies; *U.S. Public*, pg. 1632
TRI-CHEM, INC.; *U.S. Private*, pg. 1100
TROY MILLS, INC.; *U.S. Private*, pg. 1106
VERATEC DIVISION—International Paper Company; *U.S. Public*, pg. 904

2298 — CORDAGE & TWINE

ANCRA INTERNATIONAL LLC; *U.S. Private*, pg. 71
BARBOUR THREAD, INC.—Hicking Pentecost Plc; *Int'l*, pg. 618
BRIDON CORDAGE INC.—Bridon PLC; *Int'l*, pg. 215
BRIDON PLC; *Int'l*, pg. 215
BRIDPORT AVIATION PRODUCTS—Bridport-Gundry p.l.c.; *Int'l*, pg. 215
BRIDPORT-GRUNDY MARINE—Bridport-Gundry p.l.c.; *Int'l*, pg. 215
BRIDPORT-GRUNDY NETTING LIMITED—Bridport-Gundry p.l.c.; *Int'l*, pg. 215
BRIDPORT-GUNDRY P.L.C.; *Int'l*, pg. 215
COLUMBIAN ROPE COMPANY; *U.S. Private*, pg. 256
COLUMBUS MILLS, INC.; *U.S. Private*, pg. 256
CORTLAND LINE CO., INC.; *U.S. Private*, pg. 277
CROSBY-NATIONAL SWAGE CO.—FKI Plc; *Int'l*, pg. 473
CROWE ROPE INDUSTRIES L.L.C.; *U.S. Private*, pg. 291
GLADDING BRAIDED PRODUCTS LLC—Crowe Rope Industries L.L.C.; *U.S. Private*, pg. 291
GUDEBROD, INC.; *U.S. Private*, pg. 486
LOTUS CARPET DIVISION—Columbus Mills, Inc.; *U.S. Private*, pg. 257
LUDLOW TEXTILES CO., INC.; *U.S. Private*, pg. 680
POLI-TWINE CANADA (BELLEVILLE)—TecSyn International, Inc.; *Int'l*, pg. 1361
POLI-TWINE SOUTHERN INC.—TecSyn International, Inc.; *Int'l*, pg. 1362
POLI-TWINE WESTERN INC.—TecSyn International, Inc.; *Int'l*, pg. 1362
POLYTECH NETTING INDUSTRIES—TecSyn International, Inc.; *Int'l*, pg. 1362
SHAKESPEARE MONOFILAMENT—K2 Inc.; *U.S. Public*, pg. 940
SHAKESPEARE MONOFILAMENT U.K. LTD.—K2 Inc.; *U.S. Public*, pg. 940
SUPERIOR TELECOMMUNICATIONS—The Alpine Group, Inc.; *U.S. Public*, pg. 58
THOMASTON MILLS, INC.; *U.S. Public*, pg. 1599
UNIVERSAL COOPERATIVES, INC.; *U.S. Private*, pg. 1127

2299 — TEXTILE GOODS, NEC

ACME MILLS CO. INC.; *U.S. Private*, pg. 13
ROBERT ALLEN AMETEK—Furnishings International, Inc.; *U.S. Private*, pg. 432
ANGLO FABRICS COMPANY, INC.; *U.S. Private*, pg. 74
ARMSTRONG WORLD INDUSTRIES-A.C.I. B.V.—Armstrong World Industries, Inc.; *U.S. Public*, pg. 132
BGF INDUSTRIES INC.; *U.S. Private*, pg. 106
BARNHARDT MANUFACTURING CO.; *U.S. Private*, pg. 116
BEKAERT TEXTILES N.V.—Gamma Holding N.V.; *Int'l*, pg. 540
F.H. BONN COMPANY; *U.S. Private*, pg. 156
BUCILLA CORPORATION—The Dyson-Kissner-Moran Corporation; *U.S. Private*, pg. 352
WM. T. BURNETT & CO., INC.; *U.S. Private*, pg. 186
CALWER DECKEN-UND TUCHFABRIKEN AG; *Int'l*, pg. 253
CAROLE FABRICS CORP.—Hunter Douglas N.V.; *Int'l*, pg. 639
CAROLINA MILLS, INC.; *U.S. Private*, pg. 214
CERTAINTEED CORPORATION—Saint-Gobain; *Int'l*, pg. 1170
CHEMISCHE FABRIK GRUNAU GMBH—Henkel KGaA; *Int'l*, pg. 609
CHRIS-CRAFT INDUSTRIES, INC.; *U.S. Public*, pg. 351
COLOMBIANA UNIVERSAL DE PAPELES S.A.—Kimberly-Clark Corporation; *U.S. Public*, pg. 959
DAN RIVER DANVILLE MFG. DIV.—Dan River Inc.; *U.S. Public*, pg. 479
C.R. DANIELS, INC.; *U.S. Private*, pg. 310
DELAWARE VALLEY WOOL SCOURING CO.—Mohawk Industries, Inc.; *U.S. Public*, pg. 1121
EUREKA MANUFACTURING CO., INC.—Reed & Barton Corporation; *U.S. Private*, pg. 916
FACEMATE CORPORATION; *U.S. Private*, pg. 391
THE FELTERS COMPANY; *U.S. Private*, pg. 400
GENERAL FELT INDUSTRIES, INC.—Trace International Holdings, Inc.; *U.S. Private*, pg. 1094
GLENOIT MILLS, INC.; *U.S. Private*, pg. 456
GOLDEN STAR INC.; *U.S. Private*, pg. 460
GRUPO SYNKRO, S.A. DE C.V.; *Int'l*, pg. 576
GUILFORD OF MAINE, INC.—Interface Inc.; *U.S. Public*, pg. 889
HERMANN WANGNER, GMBH—Transworld Interweaving AG (TIAG); *Int'l*, pg. 1418
INSITUFORM TECHNOLOGIES, INC.; *U.S. Public*, pg. 881
JASON INCORPORATED; *U.S. Public*, pg. 923
K-C DO BRASIL LTDA.—Kimberly-Clark Corporation; *U.S. Public*, pg. 959
KTI, INC.; *U.S. Public*, pg. 939
KALDNES MILJOTEKNOLOGI A/S—Norsk Vekst ASA; *Int'l*, pg. 965
KAYSER-ROTH CORPORATION, INC.—Grupo Synkro, S.A. de C.V.; *Int'l*, pg. 576
KIMBERLY-CLARK AUSTRALIA PTY. LTD.—Kimberly-Clark Corporation; *U.S. Public*, pg. 959
KIMBERLY-CLARK DE CENTRO AMERICA S.A.—Kimberly-Clark Corporation; *U.S. Public*, pg. 959
KIMBERLY-CLARK GMBH—Kimberly-Clark Corporation; *U.S. Public*, pg. 959
KIMBERLY-CLARK PHILIPPINES INC.—Kimberly-Clark Corporation; *U.S. Public*, pg. 959
KIMBERLY-CLARK SOPALIN S.A.—Kimberly-Clark Corporation; *U.S. Public*, pg. 959
KUNZ & DIETFURT—Oerlikon-Buhrle Holding AG; *Int'l*, pg. 998
LESHNER MILLS, INC.; *U.S. Private*, pg. 660
LIBERTY OF LONDON PRINTS LIMITED—Liberty PLC; *Int'l*, pg. 807
LUDLOW CORPORATION—Tyco International Ltd.; *U.S. Public*, pg. 1651
THE LUX CO., INC.—Coachmen Industries, Inc.; *U.S. Public*, pg. 388
MELLON CORPORATION; *U.S. Private*, pg. 730
MOHICAN MILLS DIVISION—Fab Industries, Inc.; *U.S. Public*, pg. 603
MOMENTUM—PrimeSource Corporation; *U.S. Public*, pg. 1329
MOUNT VERNON DRYER FABRICS—R.B. Pamplin Corp.; *U.S. Private*, pg. 835
NASHVILLE TEXTILE CORP.—House of Ronnie, Inc.; *U.S. Private*, pg. 542
NATIVE TEXTILES—U.S. Industries, Inc.; *U.S. Public*, pg. 1684
ORCHARD YARN & THREAD CO., INC.—Lion Brand Yarn Co.; *U.S. Private*, pg. 669
THE ORR FELT COMPANY; *U.S. Private*, pg. 820
OSMAN TEXTILES—Coats Viyella plc; *Int'l*, pg. 300
OUIMET CORP.; *U.S. Private*, pg. 821
P&O (NEW ZEALAND) LTD.—The Peninsular and Oriental Steam Navigation Company; *Int'l*, pg. 1035
SINGER RETAIL DIVISION—Fab Industries, Inc.; *U.S. Public*, pg. 603
SOUTHERN MILLS, INC.; *U.S. Private*, pg. 1016
SPRINGS INDUSTRIES, INC.; *U.S. Public*, pg. 1499
TOOTAL GROUP PLC—Coats Viyella plc; *Int'l*, pg. 300
TOOTAL TEXTILES LTD.—Coats Viyella plc; *Int'l*, pg. 300
TRACE INTERNATIONAL HOLDINGS, INC.; *U.S. Private*, pg. 1094
TRADICION TEXTIL, S.A.; *Int'l*, pg. 1416
TRANSWORLD INTERWEAVING AG (TIAG); *Int'l*, pg. 1418
TROY MILLS, INC.; *U.S. Private*, pg. 1106

VORWERK & CO. MOBELSTOFF-BETEILIGUNGSGESELLSCHAFT MBH.—Vorwerk & Co.; *Int'l*, pg. 1480
VORWERK & CO. MOBELSTOFFWERKE GMBH. & CO. KG—Vorwerk & Co.; *Int'l*, pg. 1480
WANGNER SYSTEMS CORPORATION—Transworld Interweaving AG (TIAG); *Int'l*, pg. 1418
WELLMAN WOOL DIV.—Wellman, Inc.; *U.S. Public*, pg. 1753
YUHAN-KIMBERLY, LTD.—Kimberly-Clark Corporation; *U.S. Public*, pg. 960

2311 — MEN'S & BOYS' SUITS, COATS & OVERCOATS

AMERICAN TROUSER, INC.; *U.S. Private*, pg. 64
AMERICAN UNIFORM CO.—Steiner Corporation; *U.S. Private*, pg. 1039
ARIS INDUSTRIES, INC.; *U.S. Public*, pg. 129
ARNAV INDUSTRIES, INC.; *U.S. Private*, pg. 83
ARROW SHIRT COMPANY—Bidermann International S.A.; *Int'l*, pg. 194
AUSTIN REED LIMITED—Hartmarx Corporation; *U.S. Public*, pg. 796
BARCO OF CALIFORNIA; *U.S. Private*, pg. 115
BAYER CLOTHING GROUP; *U.S. Private*, pg. 124
BENETTON U.S.A. CORPORATION—Benetton Group S.p.A.; *Int'l*, pg. 186
STANLEY BLACKER, INC.; *U.S. Private*, pg. 147
BROOKHURST, INC.; *U.S. Private*, pg. 171
BURBERRYS SHIRTS—Bidermann International S.A.; *Int'l*, pg. 194
ELDER MANUFACTURING COMPANY; *U.S. Private*, pg. 367
HARDWICK CLOTHES INC.; *U.S. Private*, pg. 502
HART SCHAFFNER & MARX CLOTHES—Hartmarx Corporation; *U.S. Public*, pg. 795
HARTMARX CORPORATION; *U.S. Public*, pg. 795
HARVE BENARD LTD.; *U.S. Private*, pg. 508
HICKEY-FREEMAN/BOBBY JONES—Hartmarx Corporation; *U.S. Public*, pg. 795
HORACE SMALL APPAREL COMPANY—Horace Small Apparel PLC; *Int'l*, pg. 635
HUGO BOSS AG; *Int'l*, pg. 637
HUGO BOSS FASHIONS INC.—Hugo Boss AG; *Int'l*, pg. 637
HYOSUNG GROUP; *Int'l*, pg. 640
INTERCONTINENTAL BRANDED APPAREL—Hartmarx Corporation; *U.S. Public*, pg. 796
JOHNNY CARSON APPAREL, INC.—Hartmarx Corporation; *U.S. Public*, pg. 796
H. R. KAMINSKY & SONS, INC.; *U.S. Private*, pg. 606
KEUM KANG DEVELOPMENT INDUSTRIAL CO., LTD.—Hyundai Motor Company; *Int'l*, pg. 642
KOSUGI SANGYO CO., LTD.; *Int'l*, pg. 759
LANIER CLOTHES—Oxford Industries, Inc.; *U.S. Public*, pg. 1239
LONDON FOG INDUSTRIES, INC.; *U.S. Private*, pg. 673
THE MENSWEAR COMPANY—Coats Viyella plc; *Int'l*, pg. 300
NANBU SEN-I KOGYO CO., LTD.—Kosugi Sangyo Co., Ltd.; *Int'l*, pg. 759
ORGANIZACION ROBERTS S.A. DE C.V.—Hartmarx Corporation; *U.S. Public*, pg. 796
PHILLIPS-VAN HEUSEN CORPORATION; *U.S. Public*, pg. 1291
PIERRE CARDIN FORMAL WEAR—West Mill Clothes, Inc.; *U.S. Private*, pg. 1163
JOS. J. PIETRAFESA CO.; *U.S. Private*, pg. 865
PINCUS BROS., INC.; *U.S. Private*, pg. 865
POLO/RALPH LAUREN—Polo/Ralph Lauren Corporation; *U.S. Private*, pg. 875
POLO/RALPH LAUREN CORPORATION; *U.S. Private*, pg. 874
RAVEN INDUSTRIES, INC.; *U.S. Public*, pg. 1361
REFRIGIWEAR, INC.; *U.S. Private*, pg. 917
RIVERSIDE MANUFACTURING CO.; *U.S. Private*, pg. 934
SCHOTT BROTHERS, INC.; *U.S. Private*, pg. 972
SHEPARD CLOTHING COMPANY; *U.S. Private*, pg. 992
STANDARD TEXTILE CO., INC.; *U.S. Private*, pg. 1032
SUPERIOR SURGICAL MFG. CO., INC.; *U.S. Public*, pg. 1539
TRAIN KOGYO CO., LTD.—Kosugi Sangyo Co., Ltd.; *Int'l*, pg. 759
UNITOG COMPANY; *U.S. Public*, pg. 1693
WEST MILL CLOTHES, INC.; *U.S. Private*, pg. 1163
WHITEVILLE APPAREL CORP.—Hartmarx Corporation; *U.S. Public*, pg. 796
Z. CAVARICCI INC.; *U.S. Private*, pg. 1203

2321 — MEN'S & BOYS' SHIRTS, EXCEPT WORK SHIRTS

AMERICAN MARKETING INDUSTRIES, INC.; *U.S. Private*, *pg. 58*
THE APPAREL GROUP, LTD.; *U.S. Private*, pg. 78
ARIS INDUSTRIES, INC.; *U.S. Public*, pg. 129
ARROW DE CENTRO-AMERICA LTDA.—Bidermann International S.A.; *Int'l*, pg. 194
ARROW DE MEXICO S.A. DE C.V.—Bidermann International S.A.; *Int'l*, pg. 194
AUSTRIA PUMA DASSLER GES.M.B.H.—Proventus AB; *Int'l*, pg. 1072
BASSETT-WALKER—VF Corporation; *U.S. Public*, pg. 1702
BENETTON U.S.A. CORPORATION—Benetton Group S.p.A.; *Int'l*, pg. 186
BIDERMANN INTERNATIONAL S.A.; *Int'l*, pg. 194
BIG DOG HOLDINGS INC.; *U.S. Public*, pg. 227
BLOCK INDUSTRIES, INC.; *U.S. Private*, pg. 150
BON JOUR INTERNATIONAL LTD.; *U.S. Private*, pg. 156
BONHOMME—Randa Corp.; *U.S. Private*, pg. 909
THE BRITISH VAN HEUSEN COMPANY LIMITED—Coats Viyella plc; *Int'l*, pg. 299
DICK BRUHN INCORPORATED; *U.S. Private*, pg. 175
CALVIN KLEIN, INC.; *U.S. Private*, pg. 202
CAPITAL MERCURY SHIRT; *U.S. Private*, pg. 206
CARRINGTON VIYELLA GARMENTS LTD.—Coats Viyella plc; *Int'l*, pg. 299
CHAMPION PRODUCTS INC.—Sara Lee Corporation; *U.S. Public*, pg. 1433
CHEROKEE INC.; *U.S. Public*, pg. 345
CLAIBORNE MENSWEAR DIV.—Liz Claiborne, Inc.; *U.S. Public*, pg. 1006
CLUETT, PEABODY CANADA INC.—Bidermann International S.A.; *Int'l*, pg. 194
CODI INTERNATIONAL B.V.—Fruit of the Loom, Inc.; *U.S. Public*, pg. 686
COM CORP FACTORS, INC.—Kennington Ltd., Inc.; *U.S. Private*, pg. 615
COVINGTON INDUSTRIES; *U.S. Private*, pg. 280
CUSTOM SHOP SHIRTMAKERS INC.—HC Holdings; *U.S. Private*, pg. 490
DOTHAN APPAREL, INC.—Host Apparel, Inc.; *U.S. Private*, *pg. 540*
ELBECO INCORPORATED; *U.S. Private*, pg. 367
ELDER MANUFACTURING COMPANY; *U.S. Private*, pg. 367
FARAH AUSTRALIA PTY. LIMITED—Farah Incorporated; *U.S. Public*, pg. 613
M. FINE & SONS MANUFACTURING CO., INC.; *U.S. Private*, pg. 405
FRUIT OF THE LOOM, INC.; *U.S. Public*, pg. 685
GANT—Phillips-Van Heusen Corporation; *U.S. Public*, pg. 1291
GANT RETAIL—Phillips-Van Heusen Corporation; *U.S. Public*, pg. 1292
GARAN, INCORPORATED; *U.S. Public*, pg. 703
GARANIMALS—Garan, Incorporated; *U.S. Public*, pg. 703
HAMPTON INDUSTRIES, INC.; *U.S. Public*, pg. 779
HARCREST INTERNATIONAL, LTD.; *U.S. Private*, pg. 500
HARDWICK CLOTHES INC.; *U.S. Private*, pg. 502
THE HARWOOD COMPANIES, INC.—Sara Lee Corporation; *U.S. Public*, pg. 1433
C.F. HATHAWAY; *U.S. Private*, pg. 510
HOLOUBEK INC.; *U.S. Private*, pg. 536
HUGO BOSS AG; *Int'l*, pg. 637
HUGO BOSS FASHIONS INC.—Hugo Boss AG; *Int'l*, pg. 637
JOSTENS SPORTSWEAR—Fruit of the Loom, Inc.; *U.S. Public*, pg. 686
K-SWISS INC.; *U.S. Public*, pg. 937
KARSTEN MANUFACTURING CORPORATION; *U.S. Private*, pg. 608
KENNINGTON LTD., INC.; *U.S. Private*, pg. 615
KEUM KANG DEVELOPMENT INDUSTRIAL CO., LTD.—Hyundai Motor Company; *Int'l*, pg. 642
KING LOUIE INTERNATIONAL; *U.S. Private*, pg. 621
KNAPP SHOES INC.—Fenway Partners Inc.; *U.S. Private*, pg. 401
KOBRA INTERNATIONAL LTD; *U.S. Private*, pg. 628
KOSUGI SANGYO CO., LTD.; *Int'l*, pg. 759
LSJ SPORTSWEAR INC.—Merchant Capital Group Ltd.; *U.S. Private*, pg. 732
LEVI STRAUSS & CO.; *U.S. Private*, pg. 662
LIZ CLAIBORNE, INC.; *U.S. Public*, pg. 1005
MANHATTAN ACCESSORIES DIV.—Salant Corporation; *U.S. Public*, pg. 1429
MANHATTAN FACTORY—Salant Corporation; *U.S. Public*, pg. 1429
MANHATTAN INDUSTRIES INTL. DIV.—Salant Corporation; *U.S. Public*, pg. 1429
THE MANHATTAN SHIRT CO.—Salant Corporation; *U.S. Public*, pg. 1429
MASS MARKET DIVISION—VF Corporation; *U.S. Public*, pg. 1702
MCCRORY CORPORATION; *U.S. Private*, pg. 720
MERCHANT CAPITAL GROUP LTD.; *U.S. Private*, pg. 732
MORLEY SHIRT COMPANY—HC Holdings; *U.S. Private*, pg. 490
NANBU SEN-I KOGYO CO., LTD.—Kosugi Sangyo Co., Ltd.; *Int'l*, pg. 759
NISSHO IWAI APPAREL CO., LTD.—Nissho Iwai Corporation; *Int'l*, pg. 946
OSHKOSH B'GOSH, INC.; *U.S. Public*, pg. 1232
OXFORD APPAREL, INC.—Oxford Industries, Inc.; *U.S. Public*, pg. 1239
OXFORD INDUSTRIES, INC.; *U.S. Public*, pg. 1239
OXFORD INTERNATIONAL, INC.—Oxford Industries, Inc.; *U.S. Public*, pg. 1239
OXFORD MEN'S WEAR DIVISION—Oxford Industries, Inc.; *U.S. Public*, pg. 1239
PHILLIPS-VAN HEUSEN CORPORATION; *U.S. Public*, pg. 1291
PREMIUMWEAR, INC.; *U.S. Public*, pg. 1323
RAM GOLF CORPORATION; *U.S. Private*, pg. 908
RIVERSIDE MANUFACTURING CO.; *U.S. Private*, pg. 934
RUSSELL CORPORATION; *U.S. Public*, pg. 1413
SALANT CORPORATION; *U.S. Public*, pg. 1429
SAO PAULO ALPARGATAS S.A.; *Int'l*, pg. 1193
SEATTLE PACIFIC INDUSTRIES, INC.; *U.S. Private*, pg. 980
SMART SHIRTS (LANKA) LIMITED—Kellwood Company; *U.S. Public*, pg. 948
SMART SHIRTS LTD.—Kellwood Company; *U.S. Public*, pg. 948
STANLEIGH INTERNATIONAL, INC.—Kennington Ltd., Inc.; *U.S. Private*, pg. 615
SVENSKA CELLULOSA AKTIEBOLAGET (SCA); *Int'l*, pg. 1326
THOMSON COMPANY, INC.—Salant Corporation; *U.S. Public*, pg. 1429
TOOTAL CLOTHING LTD.—Coats Viyella plc; *Int'l*, pg. 300
TOOTAL GROUP PLC—Coats Viyella plc; *Int'l*, pg. 300
TOUCHE INDUSTRIAL, S.A. DE C.V.—Farah Incorporated; *U.S. Public*, pg. 613
TRAIN KOGYO CO., LTD.—Kosugi Sangyo Co., Ltd.; *Int'l*, pg. 759
VF CORPORATION; *U.S. Public*, pg. 1702
THE VAN HEUSEN GROUP OF COMPANIES—Phillips-Van Heusen Corporation; *U.S. Public*, pg. 1291
WARNACO INC.-MENSWEAR DIV.—Warnaco Inc.; *U.S. Public*, pg. 1738
WARNACO OF CANADA LIMITED—Warnaco Inc.; *U.S. Public*, pg. 1738
WEMCO, INC.—Randa Corp.; *U.S. Private*, pg. 909
WEST MILL CLOTHES, TUXEDO ACCESSORIES DIV.—West Mill Clothes, Inc.; *U.S. Private*, pg. 1163

2322 — MEN'S & BOYS' UNDERWEAR & NIGHTWEAR

AMERICAN MARKETING INDUSTRIES, INC.; *U.S. Private*, *pg. 58*
THE WILLIAM CARTER COMPANY; *U.S. Private*, pg. 217
CHAMPION PRODUCTS—Sara Lee Corporation; *U.S. Public*, pg. 1433
CHEROKEE INC.; *U.S. Public*, pg. 345
DELTA APPAREL—Delta Woodside Industries, Inc.; *U.S. Public*, pg. 498
DELTA WOODSIDE INDUSTRIES, INC.; *U.S. Public*, pg. 497
DIM S.A.—Sara Lee Corporation; *U.S. Public*, pg. 1434
DOTHAN APPAREL, INC.—Host Apparel, Inc.; *U.S. Private*, *pg. 540*
ELDER MANUFACTURING COMPANY; *U.S. Private*, pg. 367
FARLEY, INC.; *U.S. Private*, pg. 394
FRUIT OF THE LOOM, INC.; *U.S. Public*, pg. 685
THE HARWOOD COMPANIES, INC.—Sara Lee Corporation; *U.S. Public*, pg. 1433
HELLY-HANSEN A/S—Orkla A.S.A.; *Int'l*, pg. 1010
HOST APPAREL, INC.; *U.S. Private*, pg. 540
JOCKEY INTERNATIONAL, INC.; *U.S. Private*, pg. 588
KEUM KANG DEVELOPMENT INDUSTRIAL CO., LTD.—Hyundai Motor Company; *Int'l*, pg. 642
KOMBI, LTD.; *U.S. Private*, pg. 631
NANTUCKET INDUSTRIES, INC.; *U.S. Public*, pg. 1151
SANS, S.A.—Sara Lee Corporation; *U.S. Public*, pg. 1434
SARA LEE HOSIERY—Sara Lee Corporation; *U.S. Public*, pg. 1434
SARA LEE KNIT PRODUCTS—Sara Lee Corporation; *U.S. Public*, pg. 1434
SCHIESSER EMINENCE HOLDING AG—Hesta Tex AG; *Int'l*, pg. 618
SCHOENECKERS, INC.; *U.S. Private*, pg. 971
UMBRO INTERNATIONAL, INC.; *U.S. Private*, pg. 1116
UNION UNDERWEAR CO., INC.—Fruit of the Loom, Inc.; *U.S. Public*, pg. 686

2323 — MEN'S & BOYS' NECKWEAR

THE APPAREL GROUP, LTD.; *U.S. Private*, pg. 78
ARROW SHIRT COMPANY—Bidermann International S.A.; *Int'l*, pg. 194
BIDERMANN SHIRT GROUP—Bidermann International S.A.; *Int'l*, pg. 194
HUGO BOSS AG; *Int'l*, pg. 637
HUGO BOSS FASHIONS INC.—Hugo Boss AG; *Int'l*, pg. 637
SUPERBA, INC.; *U.S. Private*, pg. 1054
TIE RACK CORPORATE NECKWEAR—Tie Rack plc; *Int'l*, pg. 1389
WEMCO, INC.—Randa Corp.; *U.S. Private*, pg. 909

2325 — MEN'S & BOYS' TROUSERS & SLACKS

AMERICAN TROUSER, INC.; *U.S. Private*, pg. 64
ARIS INDUSTRIES, INC.; *U.S. Public*, pg. 129
ARROW DE CENTRO-AMERICA LTDA.—Bidermann International S.A.; *Int'l*, pg. 194
AUSTIN REED LIMITED—Hartmarx Corporation; *U.S. Public*, pg. 796
BENETTON U.S.A. CORPORATION—Benetton Group S.p.A.; *Int'l*, pg. 186
BIDERMANN INTERNATIONAL S.A.; *Int'l*, pg. 194
STANLEY BLACKER, INC.; *U.S. Private*, pg. 147
BON JOUR INTERNATIONAL LTD.; *U.S. Private*, pg. 156
CALVIN KLEIN, INC.; *U.S. Private*, pg. 202
CARHARTT, INC.; *U.S. Private*, pg. 210
CHAPS BY RALPH LAUREN—Warnaco Inc.; *U.S. Public*, pg. 1738
CLUETT, PEABODY CANADA INC.—Bidermann International S.A.; *Int'l*, pg. 194
CODI INTERNATIONAL B.V.—Fruit of the Loom, Inc.; *U.S. Public*, pg. 686
COVINGTON INDUSTRIES; *U.S. Private*, pg. 280
D'ARMIGENE DESIGN CENTER—Superior Surgical Mfg. Co., Inc.; *U.S. Public*, pg. 1539
DUCK HEAD APPAREL—Delta Woodside Industries, Inc.; *U.S. Public*, pg. 498
ELBECO INCORPORATED; *U.S. Private*, pg. 367
ELDER MANUFACTURING COMPANY; *U.S. Private*, pg. 367
FTX, INC.—Farah Incorporated; *U.S. Public*, pg. 613
FARAH AUSTRALIA PTY. LIMITED—Farah Incorporated; *U.S. Public*, pg. 613
FARAH CLOTHING, INC.—Farah Incorporated; *U.S. Public*, *pg. 613*
FARAH INCORPORATED; *U.S. Public*, pg. 612
FILA SPORT S.P.A.; *Int'l*, pg. 484
M. FINE & SONS MANUFACTURING CO., INC.; *U.S. Private*, pg. 405
FISHMAN & TOBIN, INC.; *U.S. Private*, pg. 408
H. FREEMAN & SON, INC.; *U.S. Private*, pg. 426
GANT—Phillips-Van Heusen Corporation; *U.S. Public*, pg. 1291
GARAN, INCORPORATED; *U.S. Public*, pg. 703

GLEN OAKS INDUSTRIES, INC.; *U.S. Private*, pg. 456
HAGGAR CORPORATION; *U.S. Public*, pg. 774
HARDWICK CLOTHES INC.; *U.S. Private*, pg. 502
HARTMARX CORPORATION; *U.S. Public*, pg. 795
HUGO BOSS AG; *Int'l*, pg. 637
HUGO BOSS FASHIONS INC.—Hugo Boss AG; *Int'l*, pg. 637
H. R. KAMINSKY & SONS, INC.; *U.S. Private*, pg. 606
KNAPP SHOES INC.—Fenway Partners Inc.; *U.S. Private*, pg. 401
KOBRA INTERNATIONAL LTD; *U.S. Private*, pg. 628
KOSUGI SANGYO CO., LTD.; *Int'l*, pg. 759
LSJ SPORTSWEAR INC.—Merchant Capital Group Ltd.; *U.S. Private*, pg. 732
LEVI STRAUSS & CO.; *U.S. Private*, pg. 662
LEVI'S BRAND—Levi Strauss & Co.; *U.S. Private*, pg. 663
LIZ CLAIBORNE, INC.; *U.S. Public*, pg. 1005
MASS MARKET DIVISION—VF Corporation; *U.S. Public*, pg. 1702
MASTER INDUSTRIES CORP.; *U.S. Private*, pg. 713
MASTER TROUSER/ MASTER APPAREL/ BOTANY 500 SLACKS LTD.—Master Industries Corp.; *U.S. Private*, pg. 713
THE MENSWEAR COMPANY—Coats Viyella plc; *Int'l*, pg. 300
MERCHANT CAPITAL GROUP LTD.; *U.S. Private*, pg. 732
MUDD JEANS, INC.; *U.S. Private*, pg. 766
NANBU SEN-I KOGYO CO., LTD.—Kosugi Sangyo Co., Ltd.; *Int'l*, pg. 759
NOEL OF JAMAICA LTD.—Fruit of the Loom, Inc.; *U.S. Public*, pg. 686
ORGANIZACION ROBERTS S.A. DE C.V.—Hartmarx Corporation; *U.S. Public*, pg. 796
OSHKOSH B'GOSH, INC.; *U.S. Public*, pg. 1232
OXFORD INDUSTRIES, INC.; *U.S. Public*, pg. 1239
OXFORD SLACKS DIVISION—Oxford Industries, Inc.; *U.S. Public*, pg. 1239
PHILLIPS-VAN HEUSEN CORPORATION; *U.S. Public*, pg. 1291
PINCUS BROS., INC.; *U.S. Private*, pg. 865
RAM GOLF CORPORATION; *U.S. Private*, pg. 908
SALANT CORPORATION; *U.S. Public*, pg. 1429
SAO PAULO ALPARGATAS S.A.; *Int'l*, pg. 1193
SASSON LICENSING CORP.; *U.S. Private*, pg. 967
SCHOOL APPAREL, INC.; *U.S. Private*, pg. 972
SEATTLE PACIFIC INDUSTRIES, INC.; *U.S. Private*, pg. 980
THE SPENCER GROUP INC.; *U.S. Private*, pg. 1025
SVENSKA CELLULOSA AKTIEBOLAGET (SCA); *Int'l*, pg. 1326
THOMSON COMPANY, INC.—Salant Corporation; *U.S. Public*, pg. 1429
TOUCHE INDUSTRIAL, S.A. DE C.V.—Farah Incorporated; *U.S. Public*, pg. 613
TRAIN KOGYO CO., LTD.—Kosugi Sangyo Co., Ltd.; *Int'l*, pg. 759
TRANS-APPAREL GROUP—Hartmarx Corporation; *U.S. Public*, pg. 796
TROPICAL SPORTSWEAR INTERNATIONAL; *U.S. Private*, pg. 1105
VF CORPORATION; *U.S. Public*, pg. 1702
WARNACO OF CANADA LIMITED—Warnaco Inc.; *U.S. Public*, pg. 1738
WEMCO, INC.—Randa Corp.; *U.S. Private*, pg. 909
Z. CAVARICCI INC.; *U.S. Private*, pg. 1203

2326 — MEN'S & BOYS' WORK CLOTHING

ANGELICA CORPORATION; *U.S. Public*, pg. 113
APPEL UNIFORMS DIV.—Superior Surgical Mfg. Co., Inc.; *U.S. Public*, pg. 1539
ARAMARK UNIFORM SERVICES OF PUERTO RICO—Aramark Corp.; *U.S. Private*, pg. 79
BERKSHIRE HATHAWAY INC.; *U.S. Public*, pg. 217
BLAUER MANUFACTURING CO., INC.; *U.S. Private*, pg. 149
CCM LIMITED—Sketchley Plc; *Int'l*, pg. 1261
CARHARTT, INC.; *U.S. Private*, pg. 210
DESIGN USA—Jacmar Companies, Inc.; *U.S. Private*, pg. 580
DOWLING TEXTILE MANUFACTURING CO.; *U.S. Private*, pg. 341
ELDER MANUFACTURING COMPANY; *U.S. Private*, pg. 367
FECHHEIMER BROS. CO.—Berkshire Hathaway Inc.; *U.S. Public*, pg. 217
M. FINE & SONS MANUFACTURING CO., INC.; *U.S. Private*, pg. 405
FISHMAN & TOBIN, INC.; *U.S. Private*, pg. 408
MARITHE AND FRANCOIS GIRBAUD N.A.—VF Corporation; *U.S. Public*, pg. 1702
HORACE SMALL APPAREL COMPANY—Horace Small Apparel PLC; *Int'l*, pg. 635
INTERSTATE UNIFORM MANUFACTURING OF PUERTO RICO, INC.—UniFirst Corporation; *U.S. Public*, pg. 1665
JACMAR COMPANIES, INC.; *U.S. Private*, pg. 580
KEY INDUSTRIES, INC.; *U.S. Private*, pg. 618
LAMAR CARIBBEAN SALES DIV.—Superior Surgical Mfg. Co., Inc.; *U.S. Public*, pg. 1539
MARTIN'S UNIFORMS DIV.—Superior Surgical Mfg. Co., Inc.; *U.S. Public*, pg. 1539
MARTIN'S UNIFORMS DIV.- NEW ORLEANS—Superior Surgical Mfg. Co., Inc.; *U.S. Public*, pg. 1539
QUIKSILVER, INC.; *U.S. Public*, pg. 1353
R & R UNIFORMS—Horace Small Apparel PLC; *Int'l*, pg. 635
M. RUBIN & SONS INC.; *U.S. Private*, pg. 949
SERVICE UNIFORMS DIV.—Superior Surgical Mfg. Co., Inc.; *U.S. Public*, pg. 1539
SHANE UNIFORMS—Superior Surgical Mfg. Co., Inc.; *U.S. Public*, pg. 1539
SKETCHLEY PLC; *Int'l*, pg. 1261
SOUTHERN UNIFORMS DIV.—Superior Surgical Mfg. Co., Inc.; *U.S. Public*, pg. 1539
I. SPIEWAK & SONS, INC.; *U.S. Private*, pg. 1025
SUPERIOR SURGICAL MFG. CO., INC.; *U.S. Public*, pg. 1539
UNITOG COMPANY; *U.S. Public*, pg. 1693
UNIVERSAL OVERALL COMPANY; *U.S. Private*, pg. 1127
VF CORPORATION; *U.S. Public*, pg. 1702
THE VERNON COMPANY; *U.S. Private*, pg. 1137
WHITESWAN/META—Dowling Textile Manufacturing Co.; *U.S. Private*, pg. 342
WILLIAMSON-DICKIE MFG. CO.; *U.S. Private*, pg. 1179
WORKLON DIV.—Superior Surgical Mfg. Co., Inc.; *U.S. Public*, pg. 1539

2329 — MEN'S & BOYS' CLOTHING, NEC

ADIDAS ESPANA, S.A.—Adidas AG; *Int'l*, pg. 25
ADIDAS SPORTSCHUHFABRIKEN GMBH—Adidas AG; *Int'l*, pg. 25
ADIDAS (UK) LTD.—Adidas AG; *Int'l*, pg. 25
ADLER MODEMARKTE GMBH—Metro AG; *Int'l*, pg. 863
ALPHA MILLS CORP.; *U.S. Private*, pg. 45
AMERICAN MARKETING INDUSTRIES, INC.; *U.S. Private*, pg. 58
ANDOVER TOGS, INC.; *U.S. Public*, pg. 112
THE APPAREL GROUP, LTD.; *U.S. Private*, pg. 78
ARROW DE CENTRO-AMERICA LTDA.—Bidermann International S.A.; *Int'l*, pg. 194
ARROW DE MEXICO S.A. DE C.V.—Bidermann International S.A.; *Int'l*, pg. 194
ARROW SHIRT COMPANY—Bidermann International S.A.; *Int'l*, pg. 194
THE ARROW SHIRT COMPANY—Bidermann International S.A.; *Int'l*, pg. 194
ASICS TIGER CORPORATION; *U.S. Private*, pg. 89
AUSTRIA PUMA DASSLER GES.M.B.H.—Proventus AB; *Int'l*, pg. 1072
AUTHENTIC FITNESS CORP.; *U.S. Public*, pg. 147
AUTHENTIC FITNESS CORP. EAST COAST REGION—Authentic Fitness Corp.; *U.S. Public*, pg. 148
BASSETT-WALKER—VF Corporation; *U.S. Public*, pg. 1702
BELFE S.P.A.; *Int'l*, pg. 185
BENETTON GROUP S.P.A.; *Int'l*, pg. 186
BENETTON U.S.A. CORPORATION—Benetton Group S.p.A.; *Int'l*, pg. 186
BIDERMANN INTERNATIONAL S.A.; *Int'l*, pg. 194
BIG DOG HOLDINGS INC.; *U.S. Public*, pg. 227
BILTWELL COMPANY, INC.—Hartmarx Corporation; *U.S. Public*, pg. 795
STANLEY BLACKER, INC.; *U.S. Private*, pg. 147
BLOCK INDUSTRIES, INC.; *U.S. Private*, pg. 150
BON JOUR INTERNATIONAL LTD.; *U.S. Private*, pg. 156
BOSS MANUFACTURING COMPANY—Vista 2000, Inc.; *U.S. Private*, pg. 1142
CB NORTH AMERICA, INC.; *U.S. Private*, pg. 192
CGS INDUSTRIES, INC.; *U.S. Private*, pg. 194
CAPUCCI CREATIONS INTERNATIONAL, INC.; *U.S. Private*, pg. 207
CARHARTT, INC.; *U.S. Private*, pg. 210
CHAMPION PRODUCTS—Sara Lee Corporation; *U.S. Public*, pg. 1433
CHAMPION PRODUCTS INC.—Sara Lee Corporation; *U.S. Public*, pg. 1433
CLUETT, PEABODY CANADA INC.—Bidermann International S.A.; *Int'l*, pg. 194
COVINGTON INDUSTRIES; *U.S. Private*, pg. 280
CROSS CREEK APPAREL, INC.—Russell Corporation; *U.S. Public*, pg. 1413
DANSKIN—Danskin Inc.; *U.S. Public*, pg. 483
DANSKIN INC.; *U.S. Public*, pg. 483
DELTA APPAREL—Delta Woodside Industries, Inc.; *U.S. Public*, pg. 498
DESCENTE AMERICA INC.—Descente Ltd.; *Int'l*, pg. 395
DESIGNERS KNITTING MILLS—Hampshire Group, Ltd.; *U.S. Public*, pg. 778
DON ALLESON, INC.; *U.S. Private*, pg. 339
DOTHAN APPAREL, INC.—Host Apparel, Inc.; *U.S. Private*, pg. 540
DYLEX LIMITED; *Int'l*, pg. 425
EDDIE BAUER, INC.—Spiegel, Inc.; *U.S. Public*, pg. 1499
ELDER MANUFACTURING COMPANY; *U.S. Private*, pg. 367
ERIMA GMBH & CO.—Adidas AG; *Int'l*, pg. 24
FAMA DE DURANGO, S.A. DE C.V.—Farah Incorporated; *U.S. Public*, pg. 613
FARAH (FAR EAST) LIMITED—Farah Incorporated; *U.S. Public*, pg. 613
FARAH INCORPORATED; *U.S. Public*, pg. 612
FARAH JAPAN LIMITED—Farah Incorporated; *U.S. Public*, pg. 613
FARAH MFG. CO. OF NEW MEXICO—Farah Incorporated; *U.S. Public*, pg. 613
FARAH MANUFACTURING SERVICES, INC.—Farah Incorporated; *U.S. Public*, pg. 613
FARAH MANUFACTURING (U.K.) LIMITED—Farah Incorporated; *U.S. Public*, pg. 613
FARAH U.S.A., INC.—Farah Incorporated; *U.S. Public*, pg. 613
FISHMAN & TOBIN, INC.; *U.S. Private*, pg. 408
FRED PERRY SPORTSWEAR LTD.—Hit Union Company Ltd.; *Int'l*, pg. 620
GANT—Phillips-Van Heusen Corporation; *U.S. Public*, pg. 1291
THE GENERRA COMPANY; *U.S. Private*, pg. 446
GENESCO INC.; *U.S. Public*, pg. 728
GERRY SPORTSWEAR COMPANY; *U.S. Private*, pg. 449
GOLDEN FLEECE OUTERWEAR CO.—I. Spiewak & Sons, Inc.; *U.S. Private*, pg. 1025
GOODY'S FAMILY CLOTHING, INC.; *U.S. Public*, pg. 753
GRAFTON FRASER INC.; *Int'l*, pg. 556
GRANITEVILLE COMPANY—Avondale Incorporated; *U.S. Private*, pg. 103
GUESS ?, INC.; *U.S. Public*, pg. 768
HARCREST INTERNATIONAL, LTD.; *U.S. Private*, pg. 500
HARDWICK CLOTHES INC.; *U.S. Private*, pg. 502
THE HARWOOD COMPANIES, INC.—Sara Lee Corporation; *U.S. Public*, pg. 1433
HILTON ACTIVE APPAREL—K2 Inc.; *U.S. Public*, pg. 940
HOLOUBEK INC.; *U.S. Private*, pg. 536
HUTCH SPORTS USA, INC.—RDM Sports Group; *U.S. Public*, pg. 1354
TOM JAMES COMPANY; *U.S. Private*, pg. 580
JANTZEN—VF Corporation; *U.S. Public*, pg. 1702
JOSTENS SPORTSWEAR—Fruit of the Loom, Inc.; *U.S. Public*, pg. 686
K2 INC.; *U.S. Public*, pg. 940
H. R. KAMINSKY & SONS, INC.; *U.S. Private*, pg. 606
KARSTEN MANUFACTURING CORPORATION; *U.S. Private*, pg. 608
KATIN—K2 Inc.; *U.S. Public*, pg. 940
KELLWOOD COMPANY; *U.S. Public*, pg. 948
KELLWOOD LINGERIE/ACTIVE GROUP—Kellwood Company; *U.S. Public*, pg. 948
KIMBERLY-CLARK DURAFAB, INC.—Kimberly-Clark Corporation; *U.S. Public*, pg. 959
KING LOUIE INTERNATIONAL; *U.S. Private*, pg. 621
KNAPP SHOES INC.—Fenway Partners Inc.; *U.S. Private*, pg. 401
TONY LAMBERT COMPANY; *U.S. Private*, pg. 644
LEE EUROPE N.V.—VF Corporation; *U.S. Public*, pg. 1702
THE LESLIE FAY COMPANIES, INC.; *U.S. Public*, pg. 989
LEVI'S BRAND—Levi Strauss & Co.; *U.S. Private*, pg. 663
LITTLEFIELD, ADAMS & COMPANY; *U.S. Public*, pg. 1001
LIZ CLAIBORNE, INC.; *U.S. Public*, pg. 1005
LOST ARROW CORPORATION; *U.S. Private*, pg. 676
LUCKY GOLDSTAR INTERNATIONAL CORP.—LG Group; *Int'l*, pg. 779
MANHATTAN ACCESSORIES DIV.—Salant Corporation; *U.S. Public*, pg. 1429
MANHATTAN FACTORY—Salant Corporation; *U.S. Public*, pg. 1429
THE MANHATTAN SHIRT CO.—Salant Corporation; *U.S. Public*, pg. 1429
MARTIN'S UNIFORMS DIV.—Superior Surgical Mfg. Co., Inc.; *U.S. Public*, pg. 1539
MCCRORY CORPORATION; *U.S. Private*, pg. 720
MEMBERS ONLY BY EUROPE CRAFT—Aris Industries, Inc.; *U.S. Public*, pg. 129
MITRE SPORTS (U.S.)—Pentland Group PLC; *Int'l*, pg. 1036
MIZUNO USA, INC.—Mizuno Corporation; *Int'l*, pg. 885
MUDD JEANS, INC.; *U.S. Private*, pg. 766
NEW BALANCE ATHLETIC SHOE, INC.; *U.S. Private*, pg. 792
OXFORD INDUSTRIES, INC.; *U.S. Public*, pg. 1239
OXFORD SHIRTS—Oxford Industries, Inc.; *U.S. Public*, pg. 1239
PASOLDS LIMITED—Coats Viyella plc; *Int'l*, pg. 300
PATAGONIA—Lost Arrow Corporation; *U.S. Private*, pg. 677
PENDLETON WOOLEN MILLS, INC.; *U.S. Private*, pg. 848
PENTLAND GROUP PLC; *Int'l*, pg. 1035
PERRY ELLIS—Salant Corporation; *U.S. Public*, pg. 1429
DAVID PEYSER SPORTSWEAR INC.; *U.S. Private*, pg. 860
POCONO KNITS, INC.—Jack Young Associates; *U.S. Private*, pg. 1201
POLO/RALPH LAUREN CORPORATION; *U.S. Private*, pg. 874
PREMIUMWEAR, INC.; *U.S. Public*, pg. 1323
PUMA AG RUDOLF DASSLER SPORT—Proventus AB; *Int'l*, pg. 1072
QUIKSILVER, INC.; *U.S. Public*, pg. 1353
RADCO SPORTSWEAR, INC.—Farah Incorporated; *U.S. Public*, pg. 613
RAVEN INDUSTRIES, INC.; *U.S. Public*, pg. 1361
RAWLINGS SPORTING GOODS COMPANY; *U.S. Public*, pg. 1361
REEBOK INTERNATIONAL LTD.; *U.S. Public*, pg. 1369
RENNOC CORPORATION; *U.S. Private*, pg. 922
S. ROTHCHILD & CO., INC.; *U.S. Private*, pg. 947
M. RUBIN & SONS INC.; *U.S. Private*, pg. 949
RUSSELL CORPORATION; *U.S. Public*, pg. 1413
SALANT CORPORATION; *U.S. Public*, pg. 1429
SASSON LICENSING CORP.; *U.S. Private*, pg. 967
SCHOTT BROTHERS, INC.; *U.S. Private*, pg. 972
SEATTLE PACIFIC INDUSTRIES, INC.; *U.S. Private*, pg. 980
SLATES BRAND—Levi Strauss & Co.; *U.S. Private*, pg. 663
SMART SHIRTS (LANKA) LIMITED—Kellwood Company; *U.S. Public*, pg. 948
SPEEDO (EUROPE) LTD.—Pentland Group PLC; *Int'l*, pg. 1036
THE SPENCER GROUP INC.; *U.S. Private*, pg. 1025
I. SPIEWAK & SONS, INC.; *U.S. Private*, pg. 1025
STANDARD MANUFACTURING CO., INC.; *U.S. Private*, pg. 1031
STARTER CORP.; *U.S. Public*, pg. 1511
SUPERIOR SURGICAL MFG. CO., INC.; *U.S. Public*, pg. 1539
TEXAS APPAREL—Salant Corporation; *U.S. Public*, pg. 1429
THAW & WALRUS, INC.—Recreational Equipment, Inc.; *U.S. Private*, pg. 914
THE TIMBERLAND COMPANY; *U.S. Public*, pg. 1609
TOMMY HILFIGER CORPORATION; *Int'l*, pg. 1398
TRAPPINGS CO.—I. Spiewak & Sons, Inc.; *U.S. Private*, pg. 1025
TULTEX CORPORATION; *U.S. Public*, pg. 1644
UMBRO INTERNATIONAL, INC.; *U.S. Private*, pg. 1116
VF CORPORATION; *U.S. Public*, pg. 1702
VALUE CLOTHING COMPANY, INC.—Farah Incorporated; *U.S. Public*, pg. 613
VARSITY SPIRIT CORPORATION—Riddell Sports, Inc.; *U.S. Public*, pg. 1389
VENDEX INTERNATIONAL N.V.; *Int'l*, pg. 1462

WARNACO INC.; *U.S. Public*, pg. 1738
WARNACO INC.-MENSWEAR DIV.—Warnaco Inc.; *U.S. Public*, pg. 1738
WOLF MANUFACTURING COMPANY; *U.S. Private*, pg. 1186
WOOLCAN—Woolrich, Inc.; *U.S. Private*, pg. 1188
WOOLRICH, INC.; *U.S. Private*, pg. 1188
JACK YOUNG ASSOCIATES; *U.S. Private*, pg. 1201

2331 — WOMEN'S, MISSES' & JUNIORS' BLOUSES & SHIRTS

THE APPAREL GROUP, LTD.; *U.S. Private*, pg. 78
ARIS INDUSTRIES, INC.; *U.S. Public*, pg. 129
AUSTRIA PUMA DASSLER GES.M.B.H.—Proventus AB; *Int'l*, pg. 1072
BASSETT-WALKER—VF Corporation; *U.S. Public*, pg. 1702
BENETTON U.S.A. CORPORATION—Benetton Group S.p.A.; *Int'l*, pg. 186
BIDERMANN INTERNATIONAL S.A.; *Int'l*, pg. 194
STANLEY BLACKER, INC.; *U.S. Private*, pg. 147
BODY DRAMA (FAR EAST) LTD.—Niches, Inc.; *U.S. Public*, pg. 1182
THE BRITISH VAN HEUSEN COMPANY LIMITED—Coats Viyella plc; *Int'l*, pg. 299
BYER CALIFORNIA; *U.S. Private*, pg. 191
CARRINGTON VIYELLA GARMENTS LTD.—Coats Viyella plc; *Int'l*, pg. 299
CASTLEBERRY KNITS, LTD.—The Leslie Fay Companies, Inc.; *U.S. Public*, pg. 989
CHEROKEE INC.; *U.S. Public*, pg. 345
DONNKENNY, INC.; *U.S. Public*, pg. 519
ELDER MANUFACTURING COMPANY; *U.S. Private*, pg. 367
ELISABETH DIVISION—Liz Claiborne, Inc.; *U.S. Public*, pg. 1006
ESPRIT DE CORP.; *U.S. Private*, pg. 383
FARLEY, INC.; *U.S. Private*, pg. 394
HAMPTON INDUSTRIES, INC.; *U.S. Public*, pg. 779
HARDWICK CLOTHES INC.; *U.S. Private*, pg. 502
HARVE BENARD LTD.; *U.S. Private*, pg. 508
HOUSE OF PERFECTION, INC.; *U.S. Private*, pg. 542
IVY—Kellwood Company; *U.S. Public*, pg. 948
JACQUES MORET, INC.; *U.S. Private*, pg. 580
JERELL, INC.; *U.S. Private*, pg. 586
JONES APPAREL GROUP, INC.; *U.S. Public*, pg. 933
K-SWISS INC.; *U.S. Public*, pg. 937
KAMYN INDUSTRIES (TANZANIA) LTD.—Nissho Iwai Corporation; *Int'l*, pg. 948
KELLWOOD ASIA LIMITED—Kellwood Company; *U.S. Public*, pg. 948
KEUM KANG DEVELOPMENT INDUSTRIAL CO., LTD.—Hyundai Motor Company; *Int'l*, pg. 642
KING LOUIE INTERNATIONAL; *U.S. Private*, pg. 621
KOBRA INTERNATIONAL LTD; *U.S. Private*, pg. 628
KOSUGI SANGYO CO., LTD.; *Int'l*, pg. 759
LSJ SPORTSWEAR INC.—Merchant Capital Group Ltd.; *U.S. Private*, pg. 732
LAND N SEA, INC.; *U.S. Private*, pg. 645
THE LESLIE FAY COMPANIES, INC.; *U.S. Public*, pg. 989
LEVI STRAUSS & CO.; *U.S. Private*, pg. 662
LIZ & CO.—Liz Claiborne, Inc.; *U.S. Public*, pg. 1006
LIZ CLAIBORNE, INC.; *U.S. Public*, pg. 1005
LIZWEAR DIVISION—Liz Claiborne, Inc.; *U.S. Public*, pg. 1006
LUCKY WINNER, INC.; *U.S. Private*, pg. 679
THE MANHATTAN SHIRT CO.—Salant Corporation; *U.S. Public*, pg. 1429
MASS MARKET DIVISION—VF Corporation; *U.S. Public*, pg. 1702
MERCHANT CAPITAL GROUP LTD.; *U.S. Private*, pg. 732
MICKEY & COMPANY—Donnkenny, Inc.; *U.S. Public*, pg. 519
NANBU SEN-I KOGYO CO., LTD.—Kosugi Sangyo Co., Ltd.; *Int'l*, pg. 759
NICHES, INC.; *U.S. Public*, pg. 1181
NISSHO IWAI APPAREL CO., LTD.—Nissho Iwai Corporation; *Int'l*, pg. 946
NITCHES (FAR EAST) LTD.—Niches, Inc.; *U.S. Public*, pg. 1182
OUTLANDER—The Leslie Fay Companies, Inc.; *U.S. Public*, pg. 989
OXFORD INDUSTRIES, INC.; *U.S. Public*, pg. 1239
PUMA AG RUDOLF DASSLER SPORT—Proventus AB; *Int'l*, pg. 1072
RAYSIL GOWNS LTD.—Coats Viyella plc; *Int'l*, pg. 300
RETROSPETTIVA, INC.; *U.S. Public*, pg. 1383
SAMSON APPAREL CORP.—Hampton Industries, Inc.; *U.S. Public*, pg. 779
SEATTLE PACIFIC INDUSTRIES, INC.; *U.S. Private*, pg. 980
SMART SHIRTS (LANKA) LIMITED—Kellwood Company; *U.S. Public*, pg. 948
SMART SHIRTS LTD.—Kellwood Company; *U.S. Public*, pg. 948
TANNER CO.; *U.S. Private*, pg. 1068
TRAIN KOGYO CO., LTD.—Kosugi Sangyo Co., Ltd.; *Int'l*, pg. 759
TRANS-APPAREL GROUP—Hartmarx Corporation; *U.S. Public*, pg. 796
VF CORPORATION; *U.S. Public*, pg. 1702
THE VAN HEUSEN GROUP OF COMPANIES—Phillips-Van Heusen Corporation; *U.S. Public*, pg. 1291
VAN RAALTE DE VENEZUELA C.A.—Fruit of the Loom, Inc.; *U.S. Public*, pg. 686
VENDEX INTERNATIONAL N.V.; *Int'l*, pg. 1462
HOWARD B. WOLF, INC.; *U.S. Public*, pg. 1774
Z. CAVARICCI INC.; *U.S. Private*, pg. 1203

2335 — WOMEN'S, MISSES' & JUNIORS' DRESSES

ARIS INDUSTRIES, INC.; *U.S. Public*, pg. 129
ARROW SHIRT COMPANY—Bidermann International S.A.; *Int'l*, pg. 194
BENETTON U.S.A. CORPORATION—Benetton Group S.p.A.; *Int'l*, pg. 186
BYER CALIFORNIA; *U.S. Private*, pg. 191
CHORUS LINE CORPORATION; *U.S. Private*, pg. 238
COMING EVENT FASHIONS LTD.—Shirmax Leasing Ltd.; *Int'l*, pg. 1235
CRICKET LANE—Kellwood Company; *U.S. Public*, pg. 948
DANI MICHAELS, INC.; *U.S. Private*, pg. 309
DAWN JOY FASHIONS, INC.; *U.S. Private*, pg. 316
DECORP—Kellwood Company; *U.S. Public*, pg. 948
DONNKENNY, INC.; *U.S. Public*, pg. 519
ELDER MANUFACTURING COMPANY; *U.S. Private*, pg. 367
ELISABETH DIVISION—Liz Claiborne, Inc.; *U.S. Public*, pg. 1006
ESPRIT DE CORP.; *U.S. Private*, pg. 383
HARDWICK CLOTHES INC.; *U.S. Private*, pg. 502
HARVE BENARD LTD.; *U.S. Private*, pg. 508
HOUSE OF BIANCHI, INC.; *U.S. Private*, pg. 541
JERELL, INC.; *U.S. Private*, pg. 586
JONES APPAREL GROUP, INC.; *U.S. Public*, pg. 933
KAMYN INDUSTRIES (TANZANIA) LTD.—Nissho Iwai Corporation; *Int'l*, pg. 948
KELLWOOD COMPANY; *U.S. Public*, pg. 948
KELLWOOD LINGERIE/ACTIVE GROUP—Kellwood Company; *U.S. Public*, pg. 948
KEUM KANG DEVELOPMENT INDUSTRIAL CO., LTD.—Hyundai Motor Company; *Int'l*, pg. 642
KOBRA INTERNATIONAL LTD; *U.S. Private*, pg. 628
LANZ, INC.; *U.S. Private*, pg. 650
GUY LAROCHE SA—Societe BIC S.A.; *Int'l*, pg. 1273
LAURA ASHLEY LTD.—Laura Ashley Holdings Plc; *Int'l*, pg. 804
THE LESLIE FAY COMPANIES, INC.; *U.S. Public*, pg. 989
LESLIE FAY DRESS—The Leslie Fay Companies, Inc.; *U.S. Public*, pg. 989
LIZ & CO.—Liz Claiborne, Inc.; *U.S. Public*, pg. 1006
LIZ CLAIBORNE DRESS DIVISION—Liz Claiborne, Inc.; *U.S. Public*, pg. 1006
LIZ CLAIBORNE, INC.; *U.S. Public*, pg. 1005
LIZWEAR DIVISION—Liz Claiborne, Inc.; *U.S. Public*, pg. 1006
SHERRI MARTIN—Dawn Joy Fashions, Inc.; *U.S. Private*, pg. 316
JESSICA MCCLINTOCK INC.; *U.S. Private*, pg. 719
OXFORD INDUSTRIES, INC.; *U.S. Public*, pg. 1239
RAYSIL GOWNS LTD.—Coats Viyella plc; *Int'l*, pg. 300
RETROSPETTIVA, INC.; *U.S. Public*, pg. 1383
S.A.S.I. CORPORATION; *U.S. Private*, pg. 955
SALLY LOU FASHIONS CORPORATION; *U.S. Private*, pg. 962
TANNER CO.; *U.S. Private*, pg. 1068
TOOTAL CLOTHING LTD.—Coats Viyella plc; *Int'l*, pg. 300
TOOTAL GROUP PLC—Coats Viyella plc; *Int'l*, pg. 300
TRANS-APPAREL GROUP—Hartmarx Corporation; *U.S. Public*, pg. 796
VAN RAALTE DE VENEZUELA C.A.—Fruit of the Loom, Inc.; *U.S. Public*, pg. 686
VIVIAN & ELLIETTE, INC.; *U.S. Private*, pg. 1142
HOWARD B. WOLF, INC.; *U.S. Public*, pg. 1774

2337 — WOMEN'S, MISSES' & JUNIORS' SUITS, SKIRTS & COATS

AMERICAN UNIFORM CO.—Steiner Corporation; *U.S. Private*, pg. 1039
ARAMARK UNIFORM SERVICES OF PUERTO RICO—Aramark Corp.; *U.S. Private*, pg. 79
ARIS INDUSTRIES, INC.; *U.S. Public*, pg. 129
ARNAV INDUSTRIES, INC.; *U.S. Private*, pg. 83
AUSTIN REED LIMITED—Hartmarx Corporation; *U.S. Public*, pg. 796
BARCO OF CALIFORNIA; *U.S. Private*, pg. 115
BENETTON U.S.A. CORPORATION—Benetton Group S.p.A.; *Int'l*, pg. 186
BIDERMANN INTERNATIONAL S.A.; *Int'l*, pg. 194
BISCAYNE APPAREL INC.; *U.S. Public*, pg. 232
STANLEY BLACKER, INC.; *U.S. Private*, pg. 147
BROOKHURST, INC.; *U.S. Private*, pg. 171
DICK BRUHN INCORPORATED; *U.S. Private*, pg. 175
CALVIN KLEIN, INC.; *U.S. Private*, pg. 202
CRICKET LANE—Kellwood Company; *U.S. Public*, pg. 948
DANA BUCHMAN DIV.—Liz Claiborne, Inc.; *U.S. Public*, pg. 1006
DESIGN USA—Jacmar Companies, Inc.; *U.S. Private*, pg. 580
DESIGNERS KNITTING MILLS—Hampshire Group, Ltd.; *U.S. Public*, pg. 778
DONNA KARAN; *U.S. Public*, pg. 517
E.N.C.—Kellwood Company; *U.S. Public*, pg. 948
ELDER MANUFACTURING COMPANY; *U.S. Private*, pg. 367
KENNETH GORDON IAG, INC.—Tom James Company; *U.S. Private*, pg. 581
HARDWICK CLOTHES INC.; *U.S. Private*, pg. 502
HARTMARX CORPORATION; *U.S. Public*, pg. 795
HARVE BENARD LTD.; *U.S. Private*, pg. 508
HELENA SPORTSWEAR CO.—Hartmarx Corporation; *U.S. Public*, pg. 795
HYOSUNG GROUP; *Int'l*, pg. 640
INTERNATIONAL WOMEN'S APPAREL GROUP—Hartmarx Corporation; *U.S. Public*, pg. 796
JACMAR COMPANIES, INC.; *U.S. Private*, pg. 580
JANTZEN—VF Corporation; *U.S. Public*, pg. 1702
JARAN INC.; *U.S. Private*, pg. 582
ANDY JOHNS FASHIONS, INC.—Biscayne Apparel Inc.; *U.S. Public*, pg. 233
JONES APPAREL GROUP, INC.; *U.S. Public*, pg. 933
KELLWOOD COMPANY; *U.S. Public*, pg. 948
KELLWOOD LINGERIE/ACTIVE GROUP—Kellwood Company; *U.S. Public*, pg. 948
KEUM KANG DEVELOPMENT INDUSTRIAL CO., LTD.—Hyundai Motor Company; *Int'l*, pg. 642
KING LOUIE INTERNATIONAL; *U.S. Private*, pg. 621
KOBRA INTERNATIONAL LTD; *U.S. Private*, pg. 628
LANZ, INC.; *U.S. Private*, pg. 650
THE LESLIE FAY COMPANIES, INC.; *U.S. Public*, pg. 989
LILLI ANN CORPORATION—Jaran Inc.; *U.S. Private*, pg. 582
LIZ CLAIBORNE COLLECTION DIVISION—Liz Claiborne, Inc.; *U.S. Public*, pg. 1006
LIZ CLAIBORNE, INC.; *U.S. Public*, pg. 1005
LIZ CLAIBORNE SUIT DIVISION—Liz Claiborne, Inc.; *U.S. Public*, pg. 1006
LIZSPORT DIVISION—Liz Claiborne, Inc.; *U.S. Public*, pg. 1006
LIZWEAR DIVISION—Liz Claiborne, Inc.; *U.S. Public*, pg. 1006
MELROSE—Kellwood Company; *U.S. Public*, pg. 948
MUDD JEANS, INC.; *U.S. Private*, pg. 766
OXFORD INDUSTRIES, INC.; *U.S. Public*, pg. 1239
PHILLIPS-VAN HEUSEN CORPORATION; *U.S. Public*, pg. 1291
PINCUS BROS., INC.; *U.S. Private*, pg. 865
RAVEN INDUSTRIES, INC.; *U.S. Public*, pg. 1361
RAYSIL GOWNS LTD.—Coats Viyella plc; *Int'l*, pg. 300
RETROSPETTIVA, INC.; *U.S. Public*, pg. 1383
SAG HARBOR—Kellwood Company; *U.S. Public*, pg. 948
HENRY I. SIEGEL COMPANY, INC.; *U.S. Private*, pg. 998
SUPERIOR SURGICAL MFG. CO., INC.; *U.S. Public*, pg. 1539
SVENSKA CELLULOSA AKTIEBOLAGET (SCA); *Int'l*, pg. 1326
TANNER CO.; *U.S. Private*, pg. 1068
TOOTAL GROUP PLC—Coats Viyella plc; *Int'l*, pg. 300
TRANS-APPAREL GROUP—Hartmarx Corporation; *U.S. Public*, pg. 796
VF CORPORATION; *U.S. Public*, pg. 1702
WOOLCAN—Woolrich, Inc.; *U.S. Private*, pg. 1188
WOOLRICH, INC.; *U.S. Private*, pg. 1188
Z. CAVARICCI INC.; *U.S. Private*, pg. 1203

2339 — WOMEN'S, MISSES' & JUNIORS' OUTERWEAR, NEC

ADIDAS ESPANA, S.A.—Adidas AG; *Int'l*, pg. 25
ADIDAS SPORTSCHUHFABRIKEN GMBH—Adidas AG; *Int'l*, pg. 25
ADIDAS (UK) LTD.—Adidas AG; *Int'l*, pg. 25
ALPHA MILLS CORP.; *U.S. Private*, pg. 45
ANGELICA CORPORATION; *U.S. Public*, pg. 113
APPARAL AMERICA, INC.—Apparel America, Inc.; *U.S. Public*, pg. 120
APPAREL AMERICA, INC.; *U.S. Public*, pg. 120
APPAREL VENTURES, INC.; *U.S. Private*, pg. 78
APPEL UNIFORMS DIV.—Superior Surgical Mfg. Co., Inc.; *U.S. Public*, pg. 1539
ARROW SHIRT COMPANY—Bidermann International S.A.; *Int'l*, pg. 194
ASICS TIGER CORPORATION; *U.S. Private*, pg. 89
AUSTRIA PUMA DASSLER GES.M.B.H.—Proventus AB; *Int'l*, pg. 1072
AUTHENTIC FITNESS CORP.; *U.S. Public*, pg. 147
AUTHENTIC FITNESS CORP. EAST COAST REGION—Authentic Fitness Corp.; *U.S. Public*, pg. 148
BAAR & BEARDS—Paris Accessories; *U.S. Private*, pg. 839
BARCO OF CALIFORNIA; *U.S. Private*, pg. 115
BASSETT-WALKER—VF Corporation; *U.S. Public*, pg. 1702
BEACH PATROL INC.; *U.S. Private*, pg. 125
BELFE S.P.A.; *Int'l*, pg. 185
BENETTON GROUP S.P.A.; *Int'l*, pg. 186
BENETTON U.S.A. CORPORATION—Benetton Group S.p.A.; *Int'l*, pg. 186
BIDERMANN INTERNATIONAL S.A.; *Int'l*, pg. 194
BIG DOG HOLDINGS INC.; *U.S. Public*, pg. 227
BLAUER MANUFACTURING CO., INC.; *U.S. Private*, pg. 149
BOSS MANUFACTURING COMPANY—Vista 2000, Inc.; *U.S. Private*, pg. 1142
BURBERRYS SHIRTS—Bidermann International S.A.; *Int'l*, pg. 194
BYER CALIFORNIA; *U.S. Private*, pg. 191
CAPEZIO BALLET MAKERS INC.; *U.S. Private*, pg. 205
CHAMPION PRODUCTS INC.—Sara Lee Corporation; *U.S. Public*, pg. 1433
CHRISTIANSBURG GARMENT CO. INC.—Donnkenny, Inc.; *U.S. Public*, pg. 520
COATS VIYELLA PLC; *Int'l*, pg. 299
COVINGTON INDUSTRIES; *U.S. Private*, pg. 280
DANCE FRANCE LTD.—Danskin Inc.; *U.S. Public*, pg. 483
D'ARMIGENE DESIGN CENTER—Superior Surgical Mfg. Co., Inc.; *U.S. Public*, pg. 1539
DELTA APPAREL—Delta Woodside Industries, Inc.; *U.S. Public*, pg. 498
DESCENTE AMERICA INC.—Descente Ltd.; *Int'l*, pg. 395
DESIGNERS KNITTING MILLS—Hampshire Group, Ltd.; *U.S. Public*, pg. 778
DONKENNY APPAREL, INC.—Donnkenny, Inc.; *U.S. Public*, pg. 520
DOWLING TEXTILE MANUFACTURING CO.; *U.S. Private*, pg. 341
DURLACHER & CO., INC.; *U.S. Private*, pg. 348
E.N.C.—Kellwood Company; *U.S. Public*, pg. 948
THE ECHO DESIGN GROUP, INC.; *U.S. Private*, pg. 359
EDDIE BAUER, INC.—Spiegel, Inc.; *U.S. Public*, pg. 1499
ELDER MANUFACTURING COMPANY; *U.S. Private*, pg. 367
ELLEN TRACY INC.; *U.S. Private*, pg. 372
FARAH MFG. CO. OF NEW MEXICO—Farah Incorporated; *U.S. Public*, pg. 613

FARAH MANUFACTURING SERVICES, INC.—Farah Incorporated; *U.S. Public*, pg. 613
FARAH U.S.A., INC.—Farah Incorporated; *U.S. Public*, pg. 613
FARLEY, INC.; *U.S. Private*, pg. 394
FILA SPORT S.P.A.; *Int'l*, pg. 484
FRED PERRY SPORTSWEAR LTD.—Hit Union Company Ltd.; *Int'l*, pg. 620
FRUIT OF THE LOOM, INC.; *U.S. Public*, pg. 685
GARAN, INCORPORATED; *U.S. Public*, pg. 703
THE GENERRA COMPANY; *U.S. Private*, pg. 446
GERRY SPORTSWEAR COMPANY; *U.S. Private*, pg. 449
MARITHE AND FRANCOIS GIRBAUD N.A.—VF Corporation; *U.S. Public*, pg. 1702
GRANITEVILLE COMPANY—Avondale Incorporated; *U.S. Private*, pg. 103
GRAPHIC JACKETS—PPG Inc.; *U.S. Private*, pg. 827
GUESS ?, INC.; *U.S. Public*, pg. 768
HABITS, INC.—Saul Bros. & Company, Inc.; *U.S. Private*, pg. 968
HAMPTON INDUSTRIES, INC.; *U.S. Public*, pg. 779
HARDWICK CLOTHES INC.; *U.S. Private*, pg. 502
HELENA SPORTSWEAR CO.—Hartmarx Corporation; *U.S. Public*, pg. 795
HILTON ACTIVE APPAREL—K2 Inc.; *U.S. Public*, pg. 940
HONEY FASHIONS LTD.; *U.S. Private*, pg. 537
HORACE SMALL APPAREL COMPANY—Horace Small Apparel PLC; *Int'l*, pg. 635
JBQ SPORT LLC; *U.S. Private*, pg. 577
JACQUES MORET, INC.; *U.S. Private*, pg. 580
JANTZEN—VF Corporation; *U.S. Public*, pg. 1702
ANDY JOHNS FASHIONS, INC.—Biscayne Apparel Inc.; *U.S. Public*, pg. 233
JONES APPAREL GROUP, INC.; *U.S. Public*, pg. 933
JOSTENS SPORTSWEAR—Fruit of the Loom, Inc.; *U.S. Public*, pg. 686
JUNIOR GALLERY LTD.; *U.S. Private*, pg. 602
K2 INC.; *U.S. Public*, pg. 940
KARSTEN MANUFACTURING CORPORATION; *U.S. Private*, pg. 608
KELLWOOD COMPANY; *U.S. Public*, pg. 948
KELLWOOD SPORTSWEAR—Kellwood Company; *U.S. Public*, pg. 948
KEUM KANG DEVELOPMENT INDUSTRIAL CO., LTD.—Hyundai Motor Company; *Int'l*, pg. 642
KIMBERLY-CLARK DURAFAB, INC.—Kimberly-Clark Corporation; *U.S. Public*, pg. 959
KING LOUIE INTERNATIONAL; *U.S. Private*, pg. 621
KOBRA INTERNATIONAL LTD; *U.S. Private*, pg. 628
LSJ SPORTSWEAR INC.—Merchant Capital Group Ltd.; *U.S. Private*, pg. 732
LAMAR CARIBBEAN SALES DIV.—Superior Surgical Mfg. Co., Inc.; *U.S. Public*, pg. 1539
LANZ, INC.; *U.S. Private*, pg. 650
LAURA ASHLEY LTD.—Laura Ashley Holdings Plc; *Int'l*, pg. 804
THE LESLIE FAY COMPANIES, INC.; *U.S. Public*, pg. 989
LEVI STRAUSS & CO.; *U.S. Private*, pg. 662
LARRY LEVINE—S. Rothchild & Co., Inc.; *U.S. Private*, pg. 947
LEVI'S BRAND—Levi Strauss & Co.; *U.S. Private*, pg. 663
LITTLEFIELD, ADAMS & COMPANY; *U.S. Public*, pg. 1001
LUCKY WINNER, INC.; *U.S. Private*, pg. 679
THE MANHATTAN SHIRT CO.—Salant Corporation; *U.S. Public*, pg. 1429
MARISA CHRISTINA INC.; *U.S. Public*, pg. 1044
MARTIN'S UNIFORMS DIV.—Superior Surgical Mfg. Co., Inc.; *U.S. Public*, pg. 1539
MARTIN'S UNIFORMS DIV.- NEW ORLEANS—Superior Surgical Mfg. Co., Inc.; *U.S. Public*, pg. 1539
GILDA MARX INC.; *U.S. Private*, pg. 710
MASS MARKET DIVISION—VF Corporation; *U.S. Public*, pg. 1702
MASTER INDUSTRIES CORP.; *U.S. Private*, pg. 713
MAXINE OF HOLLYWOOD, INC.; *U.S. Private*, pg. 716
MELROSE—Kellwood Company; *U.S. Public*, pg. 948
MERCHANT CAPITAL GROUP LTD.; *U.S. Private*, pg. 732
MIZUNO USA, INC.—Mizuno Corporation; *Int'l*, pg. 885
MUDD JEANS, INC.; *U.S. Private*, pg. 766
PPG INC.; *U.S. Private*, pg. 827
PARIS ACCESSORIES; *U.S. Private*, pg. 839
PASOLDS LIMITED—Coats Viyella plc; *Int'l*, pg. 300
PENDLETON WOOLEN MILLS, INC.; *U.S. Private*, pg. 848
PENTLAND GROUP PLC; *Int'l*, pg. 1035
PERRY ELLIS—Salant Corporation; *U.S. Public*, pg. 1429
JOS. J. PIETRAFESA CO.; *U.S. Private*, pg. 865
PRENATAL, S.A.; *Int'l*, pg. 1068
PUMA AG RUDOLF DASSLER SPORT—Proventus AB; *Int'l*, pg. 1072
QUANTUM SPORT; *U.S. Private*, pg. 900
RADCO SPORTSWEAR, INC.—Farah Incorporated; *U.S. Public*, pg. 613
RALPH LAUREN WOMENSWEAR CO., L.P.—Polo/Ralph Lauren Corporation; *U.S. Private*, pg. 875
RAVEN INDUSTRIES, INC.; *U.S. Public*, pg. 1361
RED KAP INDUSTRIES—VF Corporation; *U.S. Public*, pg. 1702
REEBOK INTERNATIONAL LTD.; *U.S. Public*, pg. 1369
RENNOC CORPORATION; *U.S. Private*, pg. 922
RIVERSIDE MANUFACTURING CO.; *U.S. Private*, pg. 934
ROBBY LEN FASHIONS—Apparel America, Inc.; *U.S. Public*, pg. 121
S. ROTHCHILD & CO., INC.; *U.S. Private*, pg. 947
RUSSELL CORPORATION; *U.S. Public*, pg. 1413
SAMSON MANUFACTURING CORP.—Hampton Industries, Inc.; *U.S. Public*, pg. 779
SARA LEE HOSIERY—Sara Lee Corporation; *U.S. Public*, pg. 1434
SASSON LICENSING CORP.; *U.S. Private*, pg. 967
SAUL BROS. & COMPANY, INC.; *U.S. Private*, pg. 968
SEATTLE PACIFIC INDUSTRIES, INC.; *U.S. Private*, pg. 980
SERVICE UNIFORMS DIV.—Superior Surgical Mfg. Co., Inc.; *U.S. Public*, pg. 1539
SHANE UNIFORMS—Superior Surgical Mfg. Co., Inc.; *U.S. Public*, pg. 1539
SOUTHERN UNIFORMS DIV.—Superior Surgical Mfg. Co., Inc.; *U.S. Public*, pg. 1539
SPEEDO (EUROPE) LTD.—Pentland Group PLC; *Int'l*, pg. 1036
I. SPIEWAK & SONS, INC.; *U.S. Private*, pg. 1025
SUPERIOR SURGICAL MFG. CO., INC.; *U.S. Public*, pg. 1539
SVENSKA CELLULOSA AKTIEBOLAGET (SCA); *Int'l*, pg. 1326
SWIRL, II LTD; *U.S. Private*, pg. 1059
TIE RACK CORPORATE NECKWEAR—Tie Rack plc; *Int'l*, pg. 1389
TIGHE INDUSTRIES, INC.; *U.S. Private*, pg. 1086
THE TOG SHOP; *U.S. Private*, pg. 1090
TRU-FIT GLOVE & HEADWEAR DIV.—Heyman Corporation; *U.S. Private*, pg. 525
TULTEX CORPORATION; *U.S. Public*, pg. 1644
UNION UNDERWEAR CO., INC.—Fruit of the Loom, Inc.; *U.S. Public*, pg. 686
VF CORPORATION; *U.S. Public*, pg. 1702
VALUE CLOTHING COMPANY, INC.—Farah Incorporated; *U.S. Public*, pg. 613
VAN RAALTE DE VENEZUELA C.A.—Fruit of the Loom, Inc.; *U.S. Public*, pg. 686
VARSITY SPIRIT CORPORATION—Riddell Sports, Inc.; *U.S. Public*, pg. 1389
THE VERNON COMPANY; *U.S. Private*, pg. 1137
WACOAL AMERICA INC.—Wacoal Corporation; *Int'l*, pg. 1484
WACOAL CORPORATION; *Int'l*, pg. 1484
WARNACO OF CANADA LIMITED—Warnaco Inc.; *U.S. Public*, pg. 1738
WHITESWAN/META—Dowling Textile Manufacturing Co.; *U.S. Private*, pg. 342
WOOLCAN—Woolrich, Inc.; *U.S. Private*, pg. 1188
WOOLRICH, INC.; *U.S. Private*, pg. 1188
WORKLON DIV.—Superior Surgical Mfg. Co., Inc.; *U.S. Public*, pg. 1539
CAROLE WREN, INC.; *U.S. Private*, pg. 1192

2341 — WOMEN'S, MISSES', CHILDREN'S & INFANTS' UNDERWEAR & NIGHTWEAR

ALPHA MILLS CORP.; *U.S. Private*, pg. 45
I. APPEL CORPORATION; *U.S. Private*, pg. 78
BERKLIFF CORPORATION; *U.S. Private*, pg. 135
BISCAYNE APPAREL INC.; *U.S. Public*, pg. 232
BODY DRAMA, INC.—Niches, Inc.; *U.S. Public*, pg. 1182
BRISTOL LINGERIE—House of Ronnie, Inc.; *U.S. Private*, pg. 542
THE WILLIAM CARTER COMPANY; *U.S. Private*, pg. 217
CHARNOS PLC; *Int'l*, pg. 280
CHEROKEE INC.; *U.S. Public*, pg. 345
DIM S.A.—Sara Lee Corporation; *U.S. Public*, pg. 1434
DONNKENNY, INC.; *U.S. Public*, pg. 519
EDELSON & SONS CORPORATION; *U.S. Private*, pg. 363
FARLEY, INC.; *U.S. Private*, pg. 394
LEWIS FRIMEL—Donnkenny, Inc.; *U.S. Public*, pg. 519
FRUIT OF THE LOOM, INC.; *U.S. Public*, pg. 685
GLENCRAFT LINGERIE, INC.; *U.S. Private*, pg. 456
HELLY-HANSEN A/S—Orkla A.S.A.; *Int'l*, pg. 1010
HOST APPAREL, INC.; *U.S. Private*, pg. 540
HOST FOR HER—Host Apparel, Inc.; *U.S. Private*, pg. 540
HOUSE OF RONNIE, INC.; *U.S. Private*, pg. 542
JASPER TEXTILE—House of Ronnie, Inc.; *U.S. Private*, pg. 542
JOCKEY INTERNATIONAL, INC.; *U.S. Private*, pg. 588
ANDY JOHNS FASHIONS, INC.—Biscayne Apparel Inc.; *U.S. Public*, pg. 233
KELLWOOD COMPANY; *U.S. Public*, pg. 948
KELLWOOD LINGERIE/ACTIVE GROUP—Kellwood Company; *U.S. Public*, pg. 948
KEUM KANG DEVELOPMENT INDUSTRIAL CO., LTD.—Hyundai Motor Company; *Int'l*, pg. 642
KLEINERT'S, INC.; *U.S. Private*, pg. 625
KLEINERT'S, INC., OF ALABAMA—Kleinert's, Inc.; *U.S. Private*, pg. 625
CHARLES KOMAR & SONS, INC.; *U.S. Private*, pg. 631
MAIDENFORM WORLDWIDE; *U.S. Private*, pg. 697
MCCRORY CORPORATION; *U.S. Private*, pg. 720
MISS ELAINE INC.; *U.S. Private*, pg. 752
MOUNT VERNON MILLS, INC.—R.B. Pamplin Corp.; *U.S. Private*, pg. 835
MOVIE STAR, INC.; *U.S. Public*, pg. 1140
NANTUCKET INDUSTRIES, INC.; *U.S. Public*, pg. 1151
NATIONAL CORSET SUPPLY HOUSE; *U.S. Private*, pg. 781
NEW AGE INTIMATES INC.; *U.S. Private*, pg. 792
OBION COMPANY, INC.—Salant Corporation; *U.S. Public*, pg. 1429
O'BRYAN BROTHERS INC.; *U.S. Private*, pg. 810
SCHIESSER EMINENCE HOLDING AG—Hesta Tex AG; *Int'l*, pg. 618
S. SCHWAB COMPANY; *U.S. Private*, pg. 974
SPENCER'S INC.; *U.S. Private*, pg. 1025
TEENFORM INC.—Wacoal Corporation; *Int'l*, pg. 1484
TRIUMPH INTERNATIONAL—Triumph International Gruppe Deutschland; *Int'l*, pg. 1424
UNION UNDERWEAR CO., INC.—Fruit of the Loom, Inc.; *U.S. Public*, pg. 686
VF CORPORATION; *U.S. Public*, pg. 1702
VAN RAALTE DE VENEZUELA C.A.—Fruit of the Loom, Inc.; *U.S. Public*, pg. 686
VANITY FAIR—VF Corporation; *U.S. Public*, pg. 1702
VARON—Biscayne Apparel Inc.; *U.S. Public*, pg. 233
WACOAL AMERICA INC.—Wacoal Corporation; *Int'l*, pg. 1484
WACOAL CORPORATION; *Int'l*, pg. 1484
WARNACO INC.; *U.S. Public*, pg. 1738
WARNACO OF CANADA LIMITED—Warnaco Inc.; *U.S. Public*, pg. 1738
WARNER'S—Warnaco Inc.; *U.S. Public*, pg. 1738
WARNER'S DE MEXICO, S.A. DE C.V.—Warnaco Inc.; *U.S. Public*, pg. 1738
WARNER'S (UNITED KINGDOM) LIMITED—Warnaco Inc.; *U.S. Public*, pg. 1738

2342 — BRASSIERES, GIRDLES & ALLIED GARMENTS

AGP INDUSTRIAL CORPORATION; *Int'l*, pg. 14
BESTFORM FOUNDATIONS, INC.; *U.S. Private*, pg. 140
CANADELLE, INC.—Sara Lee Corporation; *U.S. Public*, pg. 1434
CARNIVAL CREATIONS; *U.S. Private*, pg. 213
EXQUISITE FORM BRASSIERE (GB) LTD.—AGP Industrial Corporation; *Int'l*, pg. 14
GLAMORISE FOUNDATIONS, INC.; *U.S. Private*, pg. 455
GODDESS BRA COMPANY; *U.S. Private*, pg. 458
INNER SECRETS, INC.; *U.S. Private*, pg. 564
LADY MARLENE SALES CORP.; *U.S. Private*, pg. 642
LILYETTE BRASSIERE CO.—Maidenform Worldwide; *U.S. Private*, pg. 697
MAIDENFORM WORLDWIDE; *U.S. Private*, pg. 697
NCC INDUSTRIES, INC.—Maidenform Worldwide; *U.S. Private*, pg. 697
NEW AGE INTIMATES INC.; *U.S. Private*, pg. 792
OLGA DIV.—Warnaco Inc.; *U.S. Public*, pg. 1738
PLAYTEX APPAREL CANADA, LTD.—Sara Lee Corporation; *U.S. Public*, pg. 1433
PLAYTEX APPAREL CANADA, LTD., TORONTO—Sara Lee Corporation; *U.S. Public*, pg. 1433
QUANTUM SPORT—JbQ Sport LLC; *U.S. Private*, pg. 577
SARA LEE HOSIERY—Sara Lee Corporation; *U.S. Public*, pg. 1434
SPIRITE INDUSTRIES, INC.; *U.S. Private*, pg. 1026
SPLENDOR FORM BRASSIERE, INC.—New Age Intimates Inc.; *U.S. Private*, pg. 792
THE STROUSE, ADLER COMPANY; *U.S. Private*, pg. 1047
TEENFORM INC.—Wacoal Corporation; *Int'l*, pg. 1484
TRIUMPH INTERNATIONAL—Triumph International Gruppe Deutschland; *Int'l*, pg. 1424
TRIUMPH INTERNATIONAL GRUPPE DEUTSCHLAND; *Int'l*, pg. 1424
VF CORPORATION; *U.S. Public*, pg. 1702
VANITY FAIR—VF Corporation; *U.S. Public*, pg. 1702
WACOAL AMERICA INC.—Wacoal Corporation; *Int'l*, pg. 1484
WACOAL CORPORATION; *Int'l*, pg. 1484

2353 — HATS, CAPS & MILLINERY

AJD—HATCO, Inc.; *U.S. Private*, pg. 510
ADCOM OF IOWA, INC.—The Vernon Company; *U.S. Private*, pg. 1137
BOLLMAN HAT CO.; *U.S. Private*, pg. 155
DURLACHER & CO., INC.; *U.S. Private*, pg. 348
M. GROSSMAN & SON, INC.; *U.S. Private*, pg. 483
HATCO, INC.; *U.S. Private*, pg. 510
K-SWISS INC.; *U.S. Public*, pg. 937
KING LOUIE INTERNATIONAL; *U.S. Private*, pg. 621
THE VERNON COMPANY; *U.S. Private*, pg. 1137
VOYAGER EMBLEMS, INC.; *U.S. Private*, pg. 1143

2361 — GIRLS', CHILDREN'S, & INFANTS' DRESSES, BLOUSES & SHIRTS

BABY TOGS, INC.; *U.S. Private*, pg. 108
BENTEX KIDDIE CORPORATION; *U.S. Private*, pg. 134
CAPITAL CITY MANUFACTURING COMPANY—House of Perfection, Inc.; *U.S. Private*, pg. 542
CHEROKEE INC.; *U.S. Public*, pg. 345
COVINGTON INDUSTRIES; *U.S. Private*, pg. 280
EVY OF CALIFORNIA, INC.; *U.S. Private*, pg. 387
GARAN, INCORPORATED; *U.S. Public*, pg. 703
GARANIMALS—Garan, Incorporated; *U.S. Public*, pg. 703
GERSON & GERSON, INC.; *U.S. Private*, pg. 449
HEALTHTEX—VF Corporation; *U.S. Public*, pg. 1702
HOUSE OF PERFECTION, INC.; *U.S. Private*, pg. 542
ISFEL COMPANY, INC.; *U.S. Private*, pg. 576
JUMPING JACKS—Munro & Company, Inc.; *U.S. Private*, pg. 767
LAND N SEA, INC.; *U.S. Private*, pg. 645
THE MAY APPAREL GROUP, INC.; *U.S. Private*, pg. 717
OSHKOSH B'GOSH, INC.; *U.S. Public*, pg. 1232
OXFORD COLLECTION—Oxford Industries, Inc.; *U.S. Public*, pg. 1239
OXFORD SEPARATES—Oxford Industries, Inc.; *U.S. Public*, pg. 1239
STAR CHILDREN'S DRESS COMPANY, INC.; *U.S. Private*, pg. 1034

2369 — GIRLS', CHILDREN'S & INFANTS' OUTERWEAR, NEC

ANDOVER TOGS, INC.; *U.S. Public*, pg. 112
BABY TOGS, INC.; *U.S. Private*, pg. 108
BASSETT-WALKER—VF Corporation; *U.S. Public*, pg. 1702
BENTEX KIDDIE CORPORATION; *U.S. Private*, pg. 134
BUSTER BROWN APPAREL, INC.; *U.S. Private*, pg. 189
CAPEZIO BALLET MAKERS INC.; *U.S. Private*, pg. 205
COVINGTON INDUSTRIES; *U.S. Private*, pg. 280
E.N.C.—Kellwood Company; *U.S. Public*, pg. 948
EVY OF CALIFORNIA, INC.; *U.S. Private*, pg. 387
FRUIT OF THE LOOM, INC.; *U.S. Public*, pg. 685
GERRY SPORTSWEAR COMPANY; *U.S. Private*, pg. 449
GYMBOREE CORPORATION; *U.S. Public*, pg. 770
HEALTHTEX—VF Corporation; *U.S. Public*, pg. 1702
HOUSE OF PERFECTION, INC.; *U.S. Private*, pg. 542
JACQUES MORET, INC.; *U.S. Private*, pg. 580
ANDY JOHNS MACKINTOSH—Biscayne Apparel Inc.; *U.S. Public*, pg. 233

JUMPING JACKS—Munro & Company, Inc.; *U.S. Private*, pg. 767
KLEINERT'S, INC.; *U.S. Private*, pg. 625
KLEINERT'S, INC., OF ALABAMA—Kleinert's, Inc.; *U.S. Private*, pg. 625
OSHKOSH B'GOSH, INC.; *U.S. Public*, pg. 1232
PRENATAL, S.A.; *Int'l*, pg. 1068
S. ROTHCHILD & CO., INC.; *U.S. Private*, pg. 947
ROTHCHILD'S LARRY L.—S. Rothchild & Co., Inc.; *U.S. Private*, pg. 947
S. SCHWAB COMPANY; *U.S. Private*, pg. 974
TAWIL ASSOCIATES INC.; *U.S. Private*, pg. 1070
TRU-FIT GLOVE & HEADWEAR DIV.—Heyman Corporation; *U.S. Private*, pg. 525
VF CORPORATION; *U.S. Public*, pg. 1702
WELLMADE INDUSTRIES, INCORPORATED; *U.S. Private*, pg. 1161
CAROLE WREN, INC.; *U.S. Private*, pg. 1192

2371 — FUR GOODS

J.L. DE BALL OF AMERICA LTD. APPAREL DIV.—Girmes GmbH; *Int'l*, pg. 552
EVANS, INC.; *U.S. Public*, pg. 596
EVANS, INC. (MA)—Evans, Inc.; *U.S. Public*, pg. 596
MCCLELLAND & STEWART; *Int'l*, pg. 851
ROSENDORF/EVANS—Evans, Inc.; *U.S. Public*, pg. 597

2381 — DRESS & WORK GLOVES, EXCEPT KNIT & ALL LEATHER

AMERICAN CONSUMER PRODUCTS—Vista 2000, Inc.; *U.S. Private*, pg. 1142
BASEL TRADING COMPANY LTD.; *Int'l*, pg. 169
BERLIN GLOVE COMPANY LTD.; *U.S. Private*, pg. 136
BOSS MANUFACTURING COMPANY—Vista 2000, Inc.; *U.S. Private*, pg. 1142
CAROLINA GLOVE CO.; *U.S. Private*, pg. 214
FOWNES BROTHERS & CO., INC.; *U.S. Private*, pg. 422
THE GRANDOE CORP.; *U.S. Private*, pg. 469
HONEY FASHIONS LTD.; *U.S. Private*, pg. 537
JOMAC, INC.; *U.S. Private*, pg. 595
KIMBERLY-CLARK CORPORATION; *U.S. Public*, pg. 958
THE MARMON GROUP, INC.; *U.S. Private*, pg. 706
MID-WESTERN—Berlin Glove Company Ltd.; *U.S. Private*, pg. 136
NORTH SAFETY PRODUCTS, HAND PROTECTION DIVISION—Siebe plc; *Int'l*, pg. 1243
SPENCO MEDICAL CORPORATION—SBS Enterprises Inc.; *U.S. Private*, pg. 955

2384 — ROBES & DRESSING GOWNS

I. APPEL CORPORATION; *U.S. Private*, pg. 78
CINEMA ETOILE DIVISION—Movie Star, Inc.; *U.S. Public*, pg. 1141
CROWNTUFT MANUFACTURING CO.—Kellwood Company; *U.S. Public*, pg. 948
EDELSON & SONS CORPORATION; *U.S. Private*, pg. 363
THE HARWOOD COMPANIES, INC.—Sara Lee Corporation; *U.S. Public*, pg. 1433
NABI; *U.S. Public*, pg. 1148
SANMARK GROUP—Movie Star, Inc.; *U.S. Public*, pg. 1141
SWIRL, II LTD; *U.S. Private*, pg. 1059
VF CORPORATION; *U.S. Public*, pg. 1702
VANITY FAIR—VF Corporation; *U.S. Public*, pg. 1702

2385 — RAINCOATS & WATERPROOF OUTERWEAR

AMERICAN CONSUMER PRODUCTS—Vista 2000, Inc.; *U.S. Private*, pg. 1142
HELLY-HANSEN A/S—Orkla A.S.A.; *Int'l*, pg. 1010
KAPPLER EUROPE, LTD.—Kappler Safety Group, Inc.; *U.S. Private*, pg. 607
LONDON FOG INDUSTRIES, INC.; *U.S. Private*, pg. 673
PYRAMID HANDBAGS INC.; *U.S. Private*, pg. 896
RAINFAIR, INC.; *U.S. Private*, pg. 907
TOTES INCORPORATED—Bain Capital; *U.S. Private*, pg. 111
WHALING INDUSTRIES, INC.; *U.S. Private*, pg. 1170

2386 — LEATHER & SHEEP-LINED CLOTHING

BELFE S.P.A.; *Int'l*, pg. 185
CAPUCCI CREATIONS INTERNATIONAL, INC.; *U.S. Private*, pg. 207
EMPIRE CLOTHING—Excelled Sheepskin & Leather Coat Corporation; *U.S. Private*, pg. 387
EXCELLED SHEEPSKIN & LEATHER COAT CORPORATION; *U.S. Private*, pg. 387
LEATHER WAREHOUSE, INC.; *U.S. Private*, pg. 656
LONDON FOG INDUSTRIES, INC.; *U.S. Private*, pg. 673
LUCKY GOLDSTAR INTERNATIONAL CORP.—LG Group; *Int'l*, pg. 779
SCHOTT BROTHERS, INC.; *U.S. Private*, pg. 972

2387 — APPAREL BELTS

CHEROKEE INC.; *U.S. Public*, pg. 345
CRESTLINE DIV.—Swank, Inc.; *U.S. Public*, pg. 1543
THE ECHO DESIGN GROUP, INC.; *U.S. Private*, pg. 359
ETIENNE AIGNER; *U.S. Private*, pg. 384
JUSTIN INDUSTRIES, INC.; *U.S. Public*, pg. 936
H.A. SHELDON, INC.—Tandy Brands Accessories, Inc.; *U.S. Public*, pg. 1560
SWANK, INC.; *U.S. Public*, pg. 1543
TBAC - CANTERBURY, INC.—Tandy Brands Accessories, Inc.; *U.S. Public*, pg. 1560
TBAC - PRINCE GARDNER, INC.—Tandy Brands Accessories, Inc.; *U.S. Public*, pg. 1560
VP-SCHICKEDANZ AG—The Procter & Gamble Company; *U.S. Public*, pg. 1333

2389 — APPAREL & ACCESSORIES, NEC

AMER GROUP LTD.; *Int'l*, pg. 72
AUGSBURG FORTRESS, PUBLISHERS; *U.S. Private*, pg. 98
AVENT, INC.—Kimberly-Clark Corporation; *U.S. Public*, pg. 959
BAAR & BEARDS—Paris Accessories; *U.S. Private*, pg. 839
BON JOUR INTERNATIONAL LTD.; *U.S. Private*, pg. 156
CAMELIA WERK AG—Kimberly-Clark Corporation; *U.S. Public*, pg. 959
CAMP HEALTHCARE—True Life; *Int'l*, pg. 1425
CAPEZIO BALLET MAKERS INC.; *U.S. Private*, pg. 205
CHEMLAND INDUSTRIES, INC.—Lakeland Industries, Inc.; *U.S. Public*, pg. 975
CHICOPEE—BBA Group plc; *Int'l*, pg. 113
CONVERTORS/CUSTOM STERILE—Allegiance Healthcare Corp.; *U.S. Public*, pg. 44
COUNTDOWN CLEAN SYSTEMS LIMITED—Laporte plc; *Int'l*, pg. 802
COUNTY SEAT STORES, INC.; *U.S. Private*, pg. 279
CRAMERTON AUTOMOTIVE PRODUCTS, L.P.—Trace International Holdings, Inc.; *U.S. Private*, pg. 1095
G-III APPAREL GROUP, LTD.; *U.S. Public*, pg. 690
GEM-DANDY, INC.; *U.S. Private*, pg. 442
PAUL HARRIS STORES OF VIRGINIA, INC.—Paul Harris Stores, Inc.; *U.S. Public*, pg. 792
HELLY-HANSEN AB—Orkla A.S.A.; *Int'l*, pg. 1010
HELLY-HANSEN A/S—Orkla A.S.A.; *Int'l*, pg. 1010
HELLY-HANSEN CONFECCOES LDA.—Orkla A.S.A.; *Int'l*, pg. 1010
HELLY-HANSEN DISTRIBUTIE B.V.—Orkla A.S.A.; *Int'l*, pg. 1010
HELLY-HANSEN GMBH—Orkla A.S.A.; *Int'l*, pg. 1011
HELLY-HANSEN (SUISSE) SA—Orkla A.S.A.; *Int'l*, pg. 1011
HELLY-HANSEN (UK) LTD.—Orkla A.S.A.; *Int'l*, pg. 1011
HEYMAN CORPORATION; *U.S. Private*, pg. 524
HONEY FASHIONS LTD.; *U.S. Private*, pg. 537
LAKELAND INDUSTRIES, INC.; *U.S. Public*, pg. 975
MANSFIELD KNITWEAR LIMITED—Coats Viyella plc; *Int'l*, pg. 300
MAR-MAC MANUFACTURING COMPANY, INC.; *U.S. Private*, pg. 701
E.R. MOORE CO.; *U.S. Private*, pg. 759
NUTMEG MILLS INC.—VF Corporation; *U.S. Public*, pg. 1702
PARIS ACCESSORIES; *U.S. Private*, pg. 839
SUMIKIN BUSSAN CORPORATION; *Int'l*, pg. 1308
SUPERIOR SURGICAL MFG. CO., INC.; *U.S. Public*, pg. 1539
TEMPO ESPANA S.A. Y CIA S.E.C.—The Procter & Gamble Company; *U.S. Public*, pg. 1333
TIGHE INDUSTRIES, INC.; *U.S. Private*, pg. 1086

2391 — CURTAINS & DRAPERIES

ABERDEEN MFG. CORPORATION—Trace International Holdings, Inc.; *U.S. Private*, pg. 1094
CC INDUSTRIES, INC.; *U.S. Private*, pg. 192
CAMEO WINDOW FURNISHINGS—Trace International Holdings, Inc.; *U.S. Private*, pg. 1094
CHARLES CURTAIN COMPANY, INC.; *U.S. Private*, pg. 229
COACHMEN INDUSTRIES, INC.; *U.S. Public*, pg. 387
CROSCILL, INC.; *U.S. Private*, pg. 290
DECORATOR INDUSTRIES, INC.; *U.S. Public*, pg. 491
EASTERN CANVAS PRODUCTS, INC.; *U.S. Private*, pg. 357
HALEYVILLE DRAPERY—Decorator Industries, Inc.; *U.S. Public*, pg. 491
HALEYVILLE DRAPERY MANUFACTURING DIVISION—Decorator Industries, Inc.; *U.S. Public*, pg. 491
HALEYVILLE MANUFACTURING—Decorator Industries, Inc.; *U.S. Public*, pg. 491
HALEYVILLE MANUFACTURING OF ELKHART—Decorator Industries, Inc.; *U.S. Public*, pg. 491
HOME CURTAIN CORPORATION—Home Innovations, Inc.; *U.S. Private*, pg. 536
HOME FURNISHINGS SEGMENT—Springs Industries, Inc.; *U.S. Public*, pg. 1500
HOME INNOVATIONS, INC.; *U.S. Private*, pg. 536
LIBERIA MFG. CO.—Decorator Industries, Inc.; *U.S. Public*, pg. 491
MILLER CURTAIN CO., INC.; *U.S. Private*, pg. 746
PERFECT FIT INDUSTRIES, INC.; *U.S. Private*, pg. 852
ROBERTSON FACTORIES, INC.; *U.S. Private*, pg. 936
SOUTHERN INTERIORS—Decorator Industries, Inc.; *U.S. Public*, pg. 491
SPECIALTY WINDOW COVERINGS—Decorator Industries, Inc.; *U.S. Public*, pg. 491
SPRINGS INDUSTRIES, INC.; *U.S. Public*, pg. 1499
TEXTILE PRODUCTS DIV.—Berkshire Hathaway Inc.; *U.S. Public*, pg. 217
THOMASTON MILLS, INC.; *U.S. Public*, pg. 1599
TRACE INTERNATIONAL HOLDINGS, INC.; *U.S. Private*, pg. 1094
VKO, INC.; *U.S. Private*, pg. 1130
WHITING MANUFACTURING CO., INC.; *U.S. Private*, pg. 1174

2392 — HOUSEFURNISHINGS, EXCEPT CURTAINS & DRAPERIES

ABERDEEN MFG. CORPORATION—Trace International Holdings, Inc.; *U.S. Private*, pg. 1094
ARLEY CORPORATION—VKO, Inc.; *U.S. Private*, pg. 1130
BALSON-HERCULES LTD.—Consoltex Group Inc.; *Int'l*, pg. 326
BOMAINE CORPORATION; *U.S. Private*, pg. 155
BRISTOL-MYERS SQUIBB COMPANY; *U.S. Public*, pg. 253
BURLINGTON BASKET CO.; *U.S. Private*, pg. 183
CC INDUSTRIES, INC.; *U.S. Private*, pg. 192
CALEFFI S.P.A.; *Int'l*, pg. 252
CAMEO WINDOW FURNISHINGS—Trace International Holdings, Inc.; *U.S. Private*, pg. 1094
CHARLES CURTAIN COMPANY, INC.; *U.S. Private*, pg. 229
CROSCILL, INC.; *U.S. Private*, pg. 290
DAKOTAH, INC.; *U.S. Public*, pg. 477
EARLE INDUSTRIES, INC.; *U.S. Private*, pg. 356
EASY DAY MANUFACTURING COMPANY; *U.S. Private*, pg. 358
FARLEY, INC.; *U.S. Private*, pg. 394
FIELDCREST/CANNON BED FASHIONS DIVISION—Pillowtex Corporation; *U.S. Public*, pg. 1296
FIELDCREST CANNON, INC.—Pillowtex Corporation; *U.S. Public*, pg. 1296
GAMMA HOLDING N.V.; *Int'l*, pg. 539
GEDY S.P.A.; *Int'l*, pg. 542
LOUIS HAND DIV.—Trace International Holdings, Inc.; *U.S. Private*, pg. 1094
HOME CURTAIN CORPORATION—Home Innovations, Inc.; *U.S. Private*, pg. 536
HOME FURNISHINGS SEGMENT—Springs Industries, Inc.; *U.S. Public*, pg. 1500
HOME INNOVATIONS, INC.; *U.S. Private*, pg. 536
JAKSON-A CHF COMPANY—Trace International Holdings, Inc.; *U.S. Private*, pg. 1094
KEUM KANG DEVELOPMENT INDUSTRIAL CO., LTD.—Hyundai Motor Company; *Int'l*, pg. 642
LASTING PRODUCTS, INC.; *U.S. Private*, pg. 652
LAURA ASHLEY LTD.—Laura Ashley Holdings Plc; *Int'l*, pg. 804
LESHNER MILLS, INC.; *U.S. Private*, pg. 660
LOUISVILLE BEDDING COMPANY; *U.S. Private*, pg. 677
MAGLA PRODUCTS; *U.S. Private*, pg. 695
METRO AG; *Int'l*, pg. 863
MILLER CURTAIN CO., INC.; *U.S. Private*, pg. 746
MOUNT VERNON MILLS, INC.—R.B. Pamplin Corp.; *U.S. Private*, pg. 835
NEWELL CO.; *U.S. Public*, pg. 1176
NOEL JOANNA, INC.—Crown Crafts, Inc.; *U.S. Public*, pg. 465
NORTHSIDE DIV.—Thomaston Mills, Inc.; *U.S. Public*, pg. 1599
PERFECT FIT INDUSTRIES, INC.; *U.S. Private*, pg. 852
PILLOWTEX CORPORATION; *U.S. Public*, pg. 1296
RUBBERMAID INCORPORATED; *U.S. Public*, pg. 1411
ARTHUR SANDERSON AND SONS LTD.—Gamma Holding N.V.; *Int'l*, pg. 540
CECIL SAYDAH COMPANY; *U.S. Private*, pg. 969
SPRINGS INDUSTRIES, INC.; *U.S. Public*, pg. 1499
TEXTRON MARINE & LAND SYSTEMS—Textron Inc.; *U.S. Public*, pg. 1589
TRADICION TEXTIL, S.A.; *Int'l*, pg. 1416
VKO, INC.; *U.S. Private*, pg. 1130
WELLINGTON INDUSTRIES INC.; *U.S. Private*, pg. 1161
WHITE MOP WRINGER COMPANY; *U.S. Private*, pg. 1172
WHITING MANUFACTURING CO., INC.; *U.S. Private*, pg. 1174
WILEN MANUFACTURING COMPANY, INC.; *U.S. Private*, pg. 1176
WORLD CARPETS, INC.; *U.S. Private*, pg. 1190

2393 — TEXTILE BAGS

DRUMHELLER BAG & SUPPLY—Norfoods, Inc.; *U.S. Private*, pg. 802
JANSPORT—VF Corporation; *U.S. Public*, pg. 1702
KELLWOOD COMPANY; *U.S. Public*, pg. 948
LANGSTON COMPANIES; *U.S. Private*, pg. 650
MAINE POTATO GROWERS, INC.; *U.S. Private*, pg. 697
NORFOODS, INC.; *U.S. Private*, pg. 802
PUMA AG RUDOLF DASSLER SPORT—Proventus AB; *Int'l*, pg. 1072
REEBOK INTERNATIONAL LTD.; *U.S. Public*, pg. 1369
WILLIAM B. REILY & CO., INC.; *U.S. Private*, pg. 919
SUPERIOR SURGICAL MFG. CO., INC.; *U.S. Public*, pg. 1539
UNIVERSAL LAUNDRY BAGS DIV.—Superior Surgical Mfg. Co., Inc.; *U.S. Public*, pg. 1539
VF CORPORATION; *U.S. Public*, pg. 1702

2394 — CANVAS & RELATED PRODUCTS

ACME CANVAS CO., INC.; *U.S. Private*, pg. 13
AMERICAN RECREATION PRODUCTS, INC.—Kellwood Company; *U.S. Public*, pg. 948
ANCHOR INDUSTRIES INC.; *U.S. Private*, pg. 71
F.H. BONN COMPANY; *U.S. Private*, pg. 156
BOSS MANUFACTURING COMPANY—Vista 2000, Inc.; *U.S. Private*, pg. 1142
CENTURY PRODUCTS INC.—Acme Canvas Co., Inc.; *U.S. Private*, pg. 13
THE COLEMAN COMPANY—MacAndrews & Forbes Holdings Inc.; *U.S. Private*, pg. 691
COLEMAN (DEUTSCHLAND) GMBH—MacAndrews & Forbes Holdings Inc.; *U.S. Private*, pg. 691
COOLEY, INC.; *U.S. Private*, pg. 273
C.R. DANIELS, INC.; *U.S. Private*, pg. 310
GENERAL TRADE ASSOCIATES—Georgia Tent & Awning Inc.; *U.S. Private*, pg. 448
GEORGIA TENT & AWNING INC.; *U.S. Private*, pg. 448
GRANITEVILLE COMPANY—Avondale Incorporated; *U.S. Private*, pg. 103
INDUSTRIAS KOLMEX, S.A.—MacAndrews & Forbes Holdings Inc.; *U.S. Private*, pg. 690
JINWOONG INC.; *Int'l*, pg. 706

JINWOONG LANKA (PVT) LTD.—Jinwoong Inc.; *Int'l*, pg. 707
THE JOHN JOHNSON CO.; *U.S. Private*, pg. 591
KELLWOOD COMPANY; *U.S. Public*, pg. 948
KLEIN TOOLS INC.; *U.S. Private*, pg. 625
NORTH AMERICAN RECREATION PRODUCTS COMPANY—MacAndrews & Forbes Holdings Inc.; *U.S. Private*, pg. 691
OUTDOOR VENTURE CORP.; *U.S. Private*, pg. 822
RAVEN INDUSTRIES, INC.; *U.S. Public*, pg. 1361
SAO PAULO ALPARGATAS S.A.; *Int'l*, pg. 1193
WOODHEAD SPECIALTY FABRICS—Avondale Incorporated; *U.S. Private*, pg. 103
XIAMEN JINWOONG ENTERPRISE CO., LTD.—Jinwoong Inc.; *Int'l*, pg. 707

2395 — PLEATING, DECORATIVE & NOVELTY STITCHING & TUCKING FOR THE TRADE

A-B EMBLEM DIV. OF CONRAD INDUSTRIES, INC.; *U.S. Private*, pg. 2
ACTIVE QUILTING DIV.—Rockville Fabrics Corporation; *U.S. Private*, pg. 938
BUCILLA CORPORATION—The Dyson-Kissner-Moran Corporation; *U.S. Private*, pg. 352
DIMENSIONS INC.—Coats Viyella plc; *Int'l*, pg. 300
HIRSCH INTERNATIONAL CORP.; *U.S. Public*, pg. 829
HOUSE OF BIANCHI, INC.; *U.S. Private*, pg. 541
LION BROTHERS COMPANY, INC.; *U.S. Private*, pg. 669
NEWELL CO.; *U.S. Public*, pg. 1176
DAVID L. PEISTER CO., INC.; *U.S. Private*, pg. 848
THE PENN COMPANIES; *U.S. Private*, pg. 849
PENN EMBLEM CO.—The Penn Companies; *U.S. Private*, pg. 849
JOHN SOLOMON, INC.; *U.S. Private*, pg. 1013
TEAM EDITION APPAREL, INC.—Woolworth Corporation; *U.S. Public*, pg. 1777
UNITOG COMPANY; *U.S. Public*, pg. 1693
VOYAGER EMBLEMS, INC.; *U.S. Private*, pg. 1143

2396 — AUTOMOTIVE TRIMMINGS, APPAREL FINDINGS & RELATED PRODUCTS

AMERICAN FAST PRINT, LIMITED; *U.S. Private*, pg. 53
BERWICK INDUSTRIES, INC.—CSS Industries, Inc.; *U.S. Public*, pg. 284
BRAZOS SPORTSWEAR INC.; *U.S. Public*, pg. 251
CADILLAC PRODUCTS, INC.; *U.S. Private*, pg. 198
FACEMATE CORPORATION; *U.S. Private*, pg. 391
THE HARODITE FINISHING COMPANY INC.; *U.S. Private*, pg. 503
HOME CURTAIN CORPORATION—Home Innovations, Inc.; *U.S. Private*, pg. 536
JOHNSON CONTROLS, INC.—Johnson Controls, Inc.; *U.S. Public*, pg. 932
LSJ SPORTSWEAR INC.—Merchant Capital Group Ltd.; *U.S. Private*, pg. 732
LEAR CORPORATION—Lear Corporation; *U.S. Public*, pg. 982
LIBERTY FABRICS, INC.—Courtaulds Textiles Plc; *Int'l*, pg. 340
MAGNA INTERNATIONAL INC.; *Int'l*, pg. 829
MASLAND—Lear Corporation; *U.S. Public*, pg. 981
MERCHANT CAPITAL GROUP LTD.; *U.S. Private*, pg. 732
MEXICAN INDUSTRIES IN MICHIGAN; *U.S. Private*, pg. 739
QST INDUSTRIES, INC.; *U.S. Private*, pg. 897
ROUSH INDUSTRIES INC.; *U.S. Private*, pg. 948
SACKNER-AUTOMOTIVE SALES OFFICE—Jason Incorporated; *U.S. Public*, pg. 924
SACKNER PRODUCTS—Jason Incorporated; *U.S. Public*, pg. 924
SCALAMANDRE, INC.; *U.S. Private*, pg. 969
JOHN SOLOMON, INC.; *U.S. Private*, pg. 1013
SPECIALTY TEXTILE PRODUCTS; *U.S. Private*, pg. 1023
STAFLEX/HAROTEX—The Harodite Finishing Company Inc.; *U.S. Private*, pg. 504
TEAM EDITION APPAREL, INC.—Woolworth Corporation; *U.S. Public*, pg. 1777
TEXTRON AUTOMOTIVE TRIM OPERATIONS—Textron Inc.; *U.S. Public*, pg. 1590
3M; *U.S. Public*, pg. 1604
TROY MILLS, INC.—Troy Mills, Inc.; *U.S. Private*, pg. 1106
WM. E. WRIGHT LIMITED PARTNERSHIP; *U.S. Private*, pg. 1192

2397 — SCHIFFLI MACHINE EMBROIDERIES

C S CRABLE SPORTSWEAR, INC.—The Midland Company; *U.S. Public*, pg. 1111
SWISS-M-TEX, L.P.; *U.S. Private*, pg. 1059

2399 — FABRICATED TEXTILE PRODUCTS, NEC

A & S TRIBAL INDUSTRIES; *U.S. Private*, pg. 1
ALLISON CORPORATION—Allison Corporation; *U.S. Private*, pg. 41
AMFAC, INC.—JMB Realty Corporation; *U.S. Private*, pg. 577
ANNIN & COMPANY; *U.S. Private*, pg. 75
AUTOLIV DEVELOPMENT AB—Electrolux, AB; *Int'l*, pg. 438
AUTOLIV STIL AB—Electrolux, AB; *Int'l*, pg. 438
BTR, INC.—BTR plc; *Int'l*, pg. 127
BTR PAPER GROUP—BTR plc; *Int'l*, pg. 127
BLOCH/NEW ENGLAND, INC.; *U.S. Private*, pg. 149
BLYDENSTEIN-WILLINK N.V.; *Int'l*, pg. 198
BREED TECHNOLOGIES—Breed Technologies, Inc.; *U.S. Public*, pg. 251
BRITAX-EXCELSIOR LIMITED—Britax International plc; *Int'l*, pg. 216
BRITAX INTERNATIONAL PLC; *Int'l*, pg. 216
C S CRABLE SPORTSWEAR, INC.—The Midland Company; *U.S. Public*, pg. 1111
CALEFFI S.P.A.; *Int'l*, pg. 252
CALWER DECKEN-UND TUCHFABRIKEN AG; *Int'l*, pg. 253
CAMELIA WERK AG—Kimberly-Clark Corporation; *U.S. Public*, pg. 959
CHARGEURS; *Int'l*, pg. 280
CHICOPEE INC.—BBA Group plc; *Int'l*, pg. 113
THE COLEMAN COMPANY—MacAndrews & Forbes Holdings Inc.; *U.S. Private*, pg. 691
COLLEGEVILLE FLAG & MFG. COMPANY; *U.S. Private*, pg. 252
COLLEGEVILLE/IMAGINEERING L.P.—Collegeville Flag & Mfg. Company; *U.S. Private*, pg. 252
C.R. DANIELS, INC.; *U.S. Private*, pg. 310
DESIGN USA—Jacmar Companies, Inc.; *U.S. Private*, pg. 580
DETTRA FLAG COMPANY; *U.S. Private*, pg. 328
DRYPER'S CORP.; *U.S. Private*, pg. 344
DURAY, INC.—Newell Co.; *U.S. Public*, pg. 1177
ERO INDUSTRIES, INC.—Hicks, Muse, Tate & Furst Inc.; *U.S. Private*, pg. 526
EASTCO INDUSTRIAL SAFETY CORP.; *U.S. Public*, pg. 548
ELECTROLUX AUTOLIV—Electrolux, AB; *Int'l*, pg. 439
FAB INDUSTRIES, INC.; *U.S. Public*, pg. 603
FLEXSTEEL DIVISION—Flexsteel Industries, Inc.; *U.S. Public*, pg. 654
HIGHLAND INDUSTRIES INC.; *U.S. Private*, pg. 528
ITC INLAND TEKNIK OTO YAN SANAYI LIMITED SIRKETI—General Motors Corporation; *U.S. Public*, pg. 723
JACMAR COMPANIES, INC.; *U.S. Private*, pg. 580
JINWOONG INC.; *Int'l*, pg. 706
JINWOONG LANKA (PVT) LTD.—Jinwoong Inc.; *Int'l*, pg. 707
LITTLEFIELD, ADAMS & COMPANY; *U.S. Public*, pg. 1001
LYDALL, INC.; *U.S. Public*, pg. 1020
LYDALL WESTEX—Lydall, Inc.; *U.S. Public*, pg. 1021
LYM-TECH SCIENTIFIC—John R. Lyman Company; *U.S. Private*, pg. 683
JOHN R. LYMAN COMPANY; *U.S. Private*, pg. 683
NSK-AUTOLIV, INC.—Electrolux, AB; *Int'l*, pg. 439
NSK-AUTOLIV, INC.—NSK Ltd.; *Int'l*, pg. 903
NATIONAL BANNER COMPANY, INC.; *U.S. Private*, pg. 780
NOEL JOANNA, INC.—Crown Crafts, Inc.; *U.S. Public*, pg. 465
OUTDOOR VENTURE CORP.; *U.S. Private*, pg. 822
THE PENN COMPANIES; *U.S. Private*, pg. 849
POLYTECH NETTING INDUSTRIES—TecSyn International, Inc.; *Int'l*, pg. 1362
RAINSFORDS METAL PRODUCTS PTY. LIMITED—Britax International plc; *Int'l*, pg. 217
RAVEN INDUSTRIES, INC.; *U.S. Public*, pg. 1361
RECREATIONAL EQUIPMENT, INC.; *U.S. Private*, pg. 914
ROMER-BRITAX AUTOGURTE GMBH—Britax International plc; *Int'l*, pg. 217
SACKNER PRODUCTS—Jason Incorporated; *U.S. Public*, pg. 924
SAO PAULO ALPARGATAS S.A.; *Int'l*, pg. 1193
SCANDURA CANADA INC.—BBA Group plc; *Int'l*, pg. 114
SCANDURA INC.—BBA Group plc; *Int'l*, pg. 113
SCANDURA OHIO INC.—BBA Group plc; *Int'l*, pg. 113
SCAPA SCANDIA AB—Scapa Group Plc; *Int'l*, pg. 1203
SCHLEGEL CORPORATION—BTR plc; *Int'l*, pg. 128
SCHLEGEL INDUSTRIAL PRODUCTS DIV.—BTR plc; *Int'l*, pg. 128
SCHLEGEL ROCHESTER DIV.—BTR plc; *Int'l*, pg. 128
SUPERIOR SURGICAL MFG. CO., INC.; *U.S. Public*, pg. 1539
TRW OCCUPANT RESTRAINTS SYSTEMS—TRW Inc.; *U.S. Public*, pg. 1558
TAKATTA INC.—Highland Industries Inc.; *U.S. Private*, pg. 528
TAYLOR MADE GROUP, INC.; *U.S. Private*, pg. 1070
TEMPO ESPANA S.A. Y CIA S.E.C.—The Procter & Gamble Company; *U.S. Public*, pg. 1333
THOMASTON MILLS, INC.; *U.S. Public*, pg. 1599
3M; *U.S. Public*, pg. 1604
VOYAGER EMBLEMS, INC.; *U.S. Private*, pg. 1143
XIAMEN JINWOONG ENTERPRISE CO., LTD.—Jinwoong Inc.; *Int'l*, pg. 707

2411 — LOGGING CAMPS & LOGGING CONTRACTORS

AEC FOREST PRODUCTS—Alberta Energy Company, Ltd.; *Int'l*, pg. 48
AVENOR, INC.; *Int'l*, pg. 101
BOISE CASCADE CORPORATION; *U.S. Public*, pg. 242
BOISE CASCADE TIMBER & WOOD PRODUCTS DIVISION—Boise Cascade Corporation; *U.S. Public*, pg. 243
BRIDGEWATER RESOURCES CORPORATION; *U.S. Private*, pg. 168
CALIFORNIA CEDAR PRODUCTS, INC.; *U.S. Private*, pg. 200
CANADIAN FOREST PRODUCTS LTD., ENGLEWOOD LOGGING DIVISION—Canfor Corporation; *Int'l*, pg. 260
CANFOR CORPORATION; *Int'l*, pg. 260
CONNOR FOREST INDUSTRIES, INC.—Bridgewater Resources Corporation; *U.S. Private*, pg. 168
DOMAN INDUSTRIES LIMITED; *Int'l*, pg. 414
ENSO OYJ; *Int'l*, pg. 455
FLETCHER CHALLENGE LIMITED; *Int'l*, pg. 494
KELSEY BAY DIV.—MacMillan Bloedel Limited; *Int'l*, pg. 828
KORSNAS AB; *Int'l*, pg. 759
LONGVIEW FIBRE COMPANY; *U.S. Public*, pg. 1013
LOUISIANA PACIFIC WESTERN DIV.—Louisiana Pacific Corporation; *U.S. Public*, pg. 1015
MACMILLAN BLOEDEL SPECIALTIES—MacMillan Bloedel Limited; *Int'l*, pg. 828
MANKE LUMBER COMPANY, INC.; *U.S. Private*, pg. 699
THE MEAD CORPORATION; *U.S. Public*, pg. 1074
MENASHA CORPORATION; *U.S. Private*, pg. 731
MO OCH DOMSJO AB; *Int'l*, pg. 885
NORANDA FOREST INC.—EdperBrascan Corporation; *Int'l*, pg. 434
NORSK VIRKE NORSKE SKOGINDUSTRIER BA FIBRE—Norske Skogindustrier A.S; *Int'l*, pg. 966
NORSKE SKOGINDUSTRIER A.S; *Int'l*, pg. 965
PLUM CREEK MANUFACTURING—Plum Creek Timber Co., L.P.; *U.S. Public*, pg. 1311
PONTMEYER NV—Meyer International PLC; *Int'l*, pg. 864
POTLATCH CORPORATION; *U.S. Public*, pg. 1318
RLC INDUSTRIES CO.; *U.S. Private*, pg. 905
RAYONIER INC.; *U.S. Public*, pg. 1363
RAYONIER NEW ZEALAND LIMITED—Rayonier Inc.; *U.S. Public*, pg. 1363
SAUGBRUGSFORENINGEN AS—Norske Skogindustrier A.S; *Int'l*, pg. 966
SIMPSON INVESTMENT CO.; *U.S. Private*, pg. 1003
STORA KOPPARBERGS BERGSLAGS AB; *Int'l*, pg. 1302
ALLEN TAYLOR & CO. LIMITED—Boral Limited; *Int'l*, pg. 203
J.E. THERRIEN, INC.—Quebecor Inc.; *Int'l*, pg. 1075
TRANS-SERVE, INC.—Kansas City Southern Industries, Inc.; *U.S. Public*, pg. 944
WEYERHAEUSER CANADA LTD.—Weyerhaeuser Company; *U.S. Public*, pg. 1764
WEYERHAEUSER FOREST PRODUCTS COMPANY—Weyerhaeuser Company; *U.S. Public*, pg. 1764

2421 — SAWMILLS & PLANING MILLS, GENERAL

ALABAMA RIVER CHIP MILLS, INC.—Parsons & Whittemore, Inc.; *U.S. Private*, pg. 841
ALLEN-ROGERS CO.—Davis Mining & Manufacturing; *U.S. Private*, pg. 315
ANTHONY FOREST DIV.—Anthony Forest Products Co., Inc.; *U.S. Private*, pg. 76
ANTHONY FOREST PRODUCTS CO., INC.; *U.S. Private*, pg. 76
ARMATRON INTERNATIONAL, INC.; *U.S. Public*, pg. 131
ARTEK OY AB—Proventus AB; *Int'l*, pg. 1072
ATLANTIC LUMBER COMPANY—Sabbeth Industries Ltd; *U.S. Private*, pg. 959
BALFOUR GUTHRIE FOREST PRODUCTS INC.—Canfor Corporation; *Int'l*, pg. 260
BALMANTA S.A.—Baltek Corporation; *U.S. Public*, pg. 172
BALTEK CORPORATION; *U.S. Public*, pg. 171
BEADLES LUMBER COMPANY, INC.; *U.S. Private*, pg. 126
BEARDEN LUMBER COMPANY, INC.; *U.S. Private*, pg. 127
BERGHUIZER-ENSO FORMAATFABRIEK B.V.—Enso Oyj; *Int'l*, pg. 458
BIBLER BROTHERS, INC.; *U.S. Private*, pg. 142
BOISE CASCADE CORPORATION; *U.S. Public*, pg. 242
BOISE CASCADE TIMBER & WOOD PRODUCTS DIVISION—Boise Cascade Corporation; *U.S. Public*, pg. 243
BOXHOLMS SKOGAR AB/SKANSKA FORESTRY GROUP—Skanska AB; *Int'l*, pg. 1260
BRIDGEWATER RESOURCES CORPORATION; *U.S. Private*, pg. 168
WILLIAM BROJACK LUMBER COMPANY; *U.S. Private*, pg. 171
BRUNSWICK PULP & PAPER COMPANY—Georgia-Pacific Corporation; *U.S. Public*, pg. 736
CALIFORNIA WOODFIBER CORP.—Marubeni Corporation; *Int'l*, pg. 845
CANADIAN FOREST PRODUCTS LTD.—Canfor Corporation; *Int'l*, pg. 260
CANADIAN FOREST PRODUCTS LTD., NETHERLANDS DIVISION—Canfor Corporation; *Int'l*, pg. 260
CANFOR CORPORATION; *Int'l*, pg. 260
CANFOR U.S.A., BELLINGHAM DIVISION—Canfor Corporation; *Int'l*, pg. 260
CANFOR U.S.A. CORPORATION—Canfor Corporation; *Int'l*, pg. 260
CARTER HOLT HARVEY TIMBER LIMITED—International Paper Company; *U.S. Public*, pg. 904
CAVENHAM FOREST INDUSTRIES INC.—Hanson PLC; *Int'l*, pg. 593
CHAPLEAU FOREST PRODUCTS—MacMillan Bloedel Limited; *Int'l*, pg. 828
COASTAL LUMBER COMPANY; *U.S. Private*, pg. 248
THE COE MANUFACTURING COMPANY; *U.S. Private*, pg. 249
COMPANIA ECUATORIANA DE BALSA S.A.—Baltek Corporation; *U.S. Public*, pg. 172
CONNOR FOREST INDUSTRIES, INC.—Bridgewater Resources Corporation; *U.S. Private*, pg. 168
DMI FURNITURE INC.; *U.S. Public*, pg. 473
DMI FURNITURE, INC.—DMI Furniture Inc.; *U.S. Public*, pg. 473
DELTIC TIMBER CORPORATION; *U.S. Public*, pg. 498
DOMAN INDUSTRIES LIMITED; *Int'l*, pg. 414
DOMTAR INC.; *Int'l*, pg. 416
DONOHUE INC.—Quebecor Inc.; *Int'l*, pg. 1075
DONOHUE MATANE, INC.—Quebecor Inc.; *Int'l*, pg. 1075
EASTERN SOFTWOOD SAWMILL—Georgia-Pacific Corporation; *U.S. Public*, pg. 738
ENSO OYJ; *Int'l*, pg. 455
FLETCHER CHALLENGE CANADA LIMITED—Fletcher Challenge Limited; *Int'l*, pg. 495
FLETCHER CHALLENGE LIMITED; *Int'l*, pg. 494

FRASER PAPER LIMITED—EdperBrascan Corporation; Int'l, pg. 434
GILMAN BUILDING PRODUCTS CO.—Gilman Investment Company, Inc.; U.S. Private, pg. 454
GREEN FOREST LUMBER CORPORATION—MacMillan Bloedel Limited; Int'l, pg. 828
GREENSBURG MANUFACTURING—Kimball International, Inc.; U.S. Public, pg. 957
GULF LUMBER COMPANY, INC.; U.S. Private, pg. 487
GULF STATES PAPER CORPORATION; U.S. Private, pg. 487
HAMPTON RESOURCES INC.; U.S. Private, pg. 498
HANEL LUMBER CO., INC.—Hood Lumber Co.; U.S. Private, pg. 538
HARDWOODS OF MICHIGAN, INC.; U.S. Private, pg. 502
HAUSER LAKE LUMBER OPERATION, INC.—Fleetwood Enterprises, Inc.; U.S. Public, pg. 652
HIGHLAND LAND MINERALS, INC.—National Fuel Gas Company; U.S. Public, pg. 1156
EDWARD HINES LUMBER CO.; U.S. Private, pg. 530
HOOD LUMBER CO.; U.S. Private, pg. 538
HUTTIG SASH & DOOR CO.—Crane Co.; U.S. Public, pg. 457
HYUNDAI WOOD INDUSTRIES CO., LTD.—Hyundai Motor Company; Int'l, pg. 642
IDAHO FOREST INDUSTRY, INC.; U.S. Private, pg. 556
INDIANA HARDWOODS—Kimball International, Inc.; U.S. Public, pg. 957
INDIANA HARDWOODS, CLOVERPORT MILL—Kimball International, Inc.; U.S. Public, pg. 957
INKEROINEN SAWMILL—Enso Oyj; Int'l, pg. 456
INTERNATIO HOUT B.V.—Internatio-Muller N.V.; Int'l, pg. 682
INTERNATIONAL PAPER COMPANY; U.S. Public, pg. 901
KAIBAB INDUSTRIES; U.S. Private, pg. 605
KALMAR KOCKUM A/S—Trelleborg AB; Int'l, pg. 1421
KAUKAS SAWN GOODS INDUSTRY—UPM-Kymmene Corporation; Int'l, pg. 1428
KIMBALL INTERNATIONAL, INC.; U.S. Public, pg. 956
KIMBERLY-CLARK INC.—Kimberly-Clark Corporation; U.S. Public, pg. 959
KOHLBECHER & CO. GMBH—Saarbergwerke Aktiengesellschaft; Int'l, pg. 1166
KORSNAS AB; Int'l, pg. 759
KOTOBUKI SEATING CO.; Int'l, pg. 759
J. PAUL LEVESQUE & SONS INC—EdperBrascan Corporation; Int'l, pg. 434
LONGVIEW FIBRE COMPANY; U.S. Public, pg. 1013
LOUISIANA PACIFIC CORPORATION; U.S. Public, pg. 1015
LOUISIANA PACIFIC NORTHERN DIV.—Louisiana Pacific Corporation; U.S. Public, pg. 1015
LOUISIANA PACIFIC WESTERN DIV.—Louisiana Pacific Corporation; U.S. Public, pg. 1015
MACMILLAN BLOEDEL LIMITED; Int'l, pg. 828
MADERAS SECAS C.A. (MASECA)—Baltek Corporation; U.S. Public, pg. 172
MALLERY LUMBER CORP.; U.S. Private, pg. 698
MAXXAM INC.; U.S. Public, pg. 1062
THE MEAD CORPORATION; U.S. Public, pg. 1074
METTOWEE LUMBER & PLASTIC CO., INC.—Telescope Casual Furniture, Inc.; U.S. Private, pg. 1074
MO OCH DOMSJO AB; Int'l, pg. 885
MORGAN LUMBER SALES CO.; U.S. Private, pg. 761
NEW ZEALAND FOREST PRODUCTS LIMITED—International Paper Company; U.S. Public, pg. 905
NICKERSON LUMBER COMPANY; U.S. Private, pg. 798
NORANDA FOREST INC.—EdperBrascan Corporation; Int'l, pg. 434
NORANDA INC.—EdperBrascan Corporation; Int'l, pg. 433
NORTHWOOD FOREST INDUSTRIES, LTD.—The Mead Corporation; U.S. Public, pg. 1076
NORTHWOOD PULP & TIMBER LTD.—The Mead Corporation; U.S. Public, pg. 1076
OCHOCO LUMBER COMPANY; U.S. Private, pg. 811
PACIFIC LUMBER & SHIPPING CO.; U.S. Private, pg. 832
THE PACIFIC LUMBER COMPANY—Maxxam Inc.; U.S. Public, pg. 1062
FRANK PAXTON LUMBER COMPANY—Jeld-Wen, Inc.; U.S. Private, pg. 585
PINKHAM LUMBER—Bowater Incorporated; U.S. Public, pg. 248
PLUM CREEK TIMBER CO., L.P.; U.S. Public, pg. 1311
PLUNKETT-WEBSTER, INC.; U.S. Private, pg. 872
POLAR DIVISION—Canfor Corporation; Int'l, pg. 260
POPE & TALBOT, INC.; U.S. Public, pg. 1316
POPE & TALBOT LTD.—Pope & Talbot, Inc.; U.S. Public, pg. 1317
POTLATCH CORPORATION; U.S. Public, pg. 1318
PREMDOR WOOD PRODUCTS—Premdor Inc.; Int'l, pg. 1067
E.R. PROBYN LTD.; Int'l, pg. 1071
PRODUCTOS DEL PACIFICO S.A.—Baltek Corporation; U.S. Public, pg. 172
PYRAMID MOUNTAIN LUMBER; U.S. Private, pg. 896
RLC INDUSTRIES CO.; U.S. Private, pg. 905
THE RTZ CORPORATION PLC—Rio Tinto PLC; Int'l, pg. 1118
REPAP NEW BRUNSWICK INC.—Repap Enterprises Inc.; Int'l, pg. 1104
RILEY CREEK LUMBER COMPANY; U.S. Private, pg. 931
ROBBINS MANUFACTURING COMPANY; U.S. Private, pg. 935
ROSEBURG FOREST PRODUCTS CO.—RLC Industries Co.; U.S. Private, pg. 905
SCHAUMAN WOOD OY—UPM-Kymmene Corporation; Int'l, pg. 1428
SIERRA PACIFIC INDUSTRIES; U.S. Private, pg. 998
SIMMONS JUVENILE PRODUCTS; U.S. Private, pg. 1001
SIMPSON INVESTMENT CO.; U.S. Private, pg. 1003
SIMPSON TIMBER CO.—Simpson Investment Co.; U.S. Private, pg. 1003
SKANSKA AB; Int'l, pg. 1260
SKEENA CELLULOSE INC.; Int'l, pg. 1261
JEFFERSON SMURFIT CORPORATION—Jefferson Smurfit Group p.l.c.; Int'l, pg. 1269
JEFFERSON SMURFIT GROUP P.L.C.; Int'l, pg. 1269
SOKNABRUKET—Norske Skogindustrier A.S; Int'l, pg. 965
SONOCO FOREST PRODUCTS DIVISION—Sonoco Products Company; U.S. Public, pg. 1486
SOUTHERN HARDWOOD SAWMILL—Georgia-Pacific Corporation; U.S. Public, pg. 738
SPARTYWOOD PRODUCTS, INC.—Semac Industries Inc.; U.S. Private, pg. 983
STANDARD PLYWOODS, INC.; U.S. Private, pg. 1032
STETTIN BAY LUMBER CO., PTY., LTD.—Nissho Iwai Corporation; Int'l, pg. 949
F.H. STOLTZE LAND & LUMBER COMPANY; U.S. Private, pg. 1044
STONE CONTAINER CORPORATION; U.S. Public, pg. 1520
STORA KOPPARBERGS BERGSLAGS AB; Int'l, pg. 1302
TASMAN LUMBER COMPANY LIMITED—Fletcher Challenge Limited; Int'l, pg. 495
TEMBEC FOREST PRODUCTS INC.—Tembec Inc.; Int'l, pg. 1375
TEMLAM INC.—Tembec Inc.; Int'l, pg. 1375
TEMPLE-INLAND FOREST PRODUCTS CORPORATION—Temple-Inland Inc.; U.S. Public, pg. 1575
TEMPLE-INLAND FOREST PRODUCTS CORP.-BUILDING PRODUCTS GROUP—Temple-Inland Inc.; U.S. Public, pg. 1575
TEMPLE-INLAND INC.; U.S. Public, pg. 1574
TENNESSEE RIVER PULP & PAPER CO.—Tenneco Inc.; U.S. Public, pg. 1579
J.E. THERRIEN, INC.—Quebecor Inc.; Int'l, pg. 1075
TOLKKINEN SAWMILL—Enso Oyj; Int'l, pg. 456
TOLKO INDUSTRIES LTD.; Int'l, pg. 1395
TOLLESON LUMBER COMPANY, INC.; U.S. Private, pg. 1090
USG INTERIORS, INC.—USG Corporation; U.S. Public, pg. 1660
UNION CAMP CORPORATION; U.S. Public, pg. 1665
VAAGEN BROTHERS LUMBER, INC.; U.S. Private, pg. 1131
VALLEY FOREST RESOURCES CO.—Villaume Industries, Inc.; U.S. Private, pg. 1140
VANPORT MANUFACTURING, INC.; U.S. Private, pg. 1134
WDK, INC.—Lindal Cedar Homes, Inc.; U.S. Public, pg. 999
WEABER, INC; U.S. Private, pg. 1155
WELCO LUMBER COMPANY; U.S. Private, pg. 1161
WEST BUILDING MATERIALS; U.S. Private, pg. 1163
WESTAR GROUP LTD.; Int'l, pg. 1491
WESTCOAST CELLUFIBRE—Canfor Corporation; Int'l, pg. 261
WESTVACO DEVELOPMENT CORP.—Westvaco Corporation; U.S. Public, pg. 1762
WETSEL-OVIATT LUMBER COMPANY; U.S. Private, pg. 1170
WEYERHAEUSER COMPANY; U.S. Public, pg. 1764
WEYERHAEUSER FOREST PRODUCTS COMPANY—Weyerhaeuser Company; U.S. Public, pg. 1764
WILLAMETTE INDUSTRIES, INC.—Willamette Industries, Inc.; U.S. Public, pg. 1769
WILLAMINA LUMBER CO. INC.—Hampton Resources Inc.; U.S. Private, pg. 498
WISAFOREST OY AB—UPM-Kymmene Corporation; Int'l, pg. 1429
WISAPAK OY AB—UPM-Kymmene Corporation; Int'l, pg. 1429

2426 — HARDWOOD DIMENSION & FLOORING MILLS

AIRLINE MANUFACTURING COMPANY, INC.; U.S. Private, pg. 29
ANDERSON-TULLY CO.; U.S. Private, pg. 73
ARTWOOD PRODUCTS—Semac Industries Inc.; U.S. Private, pg. 983
BABCOCK LUMBER COMPANY; U.S. Private, pg. 108
BRIDGEWATER RESOURCES CORPORATION; U.S. Private, pg. 168
WILLIAM BROJACK LUMBER COMPANY; U.S. Private, pg. 171
BRUCE HARDWOOD FLOORS—Triangle Pacific Corporation; U.S. Public, pg. 1634
CANTERBURY TIMBER PRODUCTS LIMITED—International Paper Company; U.S. Public, pg. 905
CARTER HOLT HARVEY TIMBER LIMITED—International Paper Company; U.S. Public, pg. 904
DALE WOOD MANUFACTURING—Kimball International, Inc.; U.S. Public, pg. 957
DAVIS MINING & MANUFACTURING; U.S. Private, pg. 315
FITZPATRICK & WELLER, INC.; U.S. Private, pg. 409
GEORGIA-PACIFIC CORPORATION; U.S. Public, pg. 735
HANCOCK LUMBER, INC.; U.S. Private, pg. 498
HARDWOODS OF MICHIGAN, INC.; U.S. Private, pg. 502
HARTCO FLOORING COMPANY—Premark International, Inc.; U.S. Public, pg. 1322
ICD GROUP INTERNATIONAL INC.; U.S. Private, pg. 554
INTERNATIO HOUT B.V.—Internatio-Muller N.V.; Int'l, pg. 682
KIMBALL INTERNATIONAL, INC.; U.S. Public, pg. 956
KING ARTHUR INC.—Shelby Williams Industries, Inc.; U.S. Public, pg. 1465
LAFAYETTE MANUFACTURING—Kimball International, Inc.; U.S. Public, pg. 957
LANGMOEN PARKETT—Norske Skogindustrier A.S; Int'l, pg. 965
LOUISIANA PACIFIC CORPORATION; U.S. Public, pg. 1015
THE MEAD CORPORATION; U.S. Public, pg. 1074
MILLER & CO.; U.S. Private, pg. 746
NORSKE SKOGINDUSTRIER A.S; Int'l, pg. 965
NORWALK FURNITURE CORPORATION; U.S. Private, pg. 807
PFLEIDERER INDUSTRIE GMBH WIRUS-WERKE GUETERSLOH—Pfleiderer AG; Int'l, pg. 1047
PREMARK INTERNATIONAL, INC.; U.S. Public, pg. 1321
ROBBINS, INC.; U.S. Private, pg. 934
TATE ACCESS FLOORS, INC.; U.S. Private, pg. 1069
TEMPLE-INLAND FOREST PRODUCTS CORPORATION—Temple-Inland Inc.; U.S. Public, pg. 1575
TOLKO INDUSTRIES LTD.; Int'l, pg. 1395
TRIANGLE PACIFIC CORPORATION; U.S. Public, pg. 1634
WTD INDUSTRIES, INC.; U.S. Public, pg. 1729
WESTERN TIMBER CO.—WTD Industries, Inc.; U.S. Public, pg. 1729
WOODCRAFT INDUSTRIES, INC.; U.S. Private, pg. 1187

2429 — SPECIAL PRODUCT SAWMILLS, NEC

ANTHONY FOREST PRODUCTS CO., INC.; U.S. Private, pg. 76
THE COE MANUFACTURING COMPANY; U.S. Private, pg. 249
GEORGIA-PACIFIC CORPORATION; U.S. Public, pg. 735
KIMBERLY-CLARK, NOVA SCOTIA—Kimberly-Clark Corporation; U.S. Public, pg. 959
LEUCADIA INC. MANUFACTURING DIVISION—Leucadia National Corporation; U.S. Public, pg. 990
SHAKERTOWN 1992, INC.—The Clark Group; Int'l, pg. 296
STORA TIMBER AB—Stora Kopparbergs Bergslags AB; Int'l, pg. 1303
TANDYCRAFTS, INC.; U.S. Public, pg. 1561

2431 — MILLWORK

AHI ROLL-A-DOOR—International Paper Company; U.S. Public, pg. 904
APL CORPORATION; U.S. Private, pg. 7
ACCURATE DOOR & HARDWARE DIVISION—Acklands Limited; Int'l, pg. 23
ALCOA BUILDING PRODUCTS, INC.—Aluminum Company of America; U.S. Public, pg. 61
ALUMINIO REYNOLDS, SANTO DOMINGO, S.A.—Reynolds Metals Company; U.S. Public, pg. 1386
AMERICAN ARCHITECTURAL PRODUCTS, INC.; U.S. Public, pg. 67
AMERICAN DOOR COMPANY OF MICHIGAN, INC.—Premdor Inc.; Int'l, pg. 1067
ANDERSEN CORPORATION; U.S. Private, pg. 71
ANTHONY FOREST PRODUCTS CO., INC.; U.S. Private, pg. 76
ARTEAGA, SOCIEDAD ANOMIMA, "ARTEAGA, S.A."—Reynolds Metals Company; U.S. Public, pg. 1386
ATRIUM COMPANIES, INC.; U.S. Private, pg. 98
ATRIUM COMPANIES, INC.—Atrium Companies, Inc.; U.S. Private, pg. 98
BARNETT MILLWORKS, INC.; U.S. Private, pg. 116
BAY INDUSTRIES INC.; U.S. Private, pg. 124
BILTBEST WINDOWS—U.S. Industries, Inc.; U.S. Public, pg. 1683
BLACK MILLWORK CO., INC.; U.S. Private, pg. 147
THE BRAAS GROUP—Redland PLC; Int'l, pg. 1091
BUFFELEN WOODWORKING COMPANY; U.S. Private, pg. 179
CURT BULLOCK BUILDERS, INC.; U.S. Private, pg. 180
CARADCO—Aluminum Company of America; U.S. Public, pg. 61
CARDO DOOR AB—Cardo AB; Int'l, pg. 269
CARDO DOOR PRODUCTION AB—Cardo AB; Int'l, pg. 269
CARDO DOOR PRODUCTION A/S—Cardo AB; Int'l, pg. 269
CAROLINA BUILDERS CORPORATION—Wolseley Plc.; Int'l, pg. 1512
CARTER HOLT HARVEY GARAGE DOORS—International Paper Company; U.S. Public, pg. 904
CENTURY DOOR U.S.A. INC.—Premdor Inc.; Int'l, pg. 1067
CLEVER S.A.—Cardo AB; Int'l, pg. 269
CLOPAY CORPORATION—Griffon Corp.; U.S. Public, pg. 766
COMPLAST, INC.; U.S. Private, pg. 259
CONESTOGA WOOD SPECIALTIES CORP.; U.S. Private, pg. 262
CRANE CO.; U.S. Public, pg. 456
CRAWFORD DEUR B.V.—Cardo AB; Int'l, pg. 269
CRAWFORD DOOR A/S—Cardo AB; Int'l, pg. 269
CRAWFORD DOOR (FAR EAST) PTE LTD.—Cardo AB; Int'l, pg. 269
CRAWFORD DOOR FORSALJNINGS AB—Cardo AB; Int'l, pg. 269
S.A. CRAWFORD DOOR N.V.—Cardo AB; Int'l, pg. 269
CRAWFORD DOOR S.A.—Cardo AB; Int'l, pg. 269
CRAWFORD DOOR S.R.L.—Cardo AB; Int'l, pg. 269
CRAWFORD GARAGE DOOR SYSTEMS AB—Cardo AB; Int'l, pg. 269
CRAWFORD TOR GES.M.B.H.—Cardo AB; Int'l, pg. 269
CRAWMATOR AB—Cardo AB; Int'l, pg. 269
CROWN DOOR CORP.—Premdor Inc.; Int'l, pg. 1067
DOORCRAFT & CHALLENGE—Jeld-Wen, Inc.; U.S. Private, pg. 585
THE DORRIS LUMBER & MOULDING CO.; U.S. Private, pg. 341
EAGLE WINDOW & DOOR, INC.—American Architectural Products, Inc.; U.S. Public, pg. 67
ESPE WINDOW SYSTEMS LTD.—Stora Kopparbergs Bergslags AB; Int'l, pg. 1302
FALTEC BENELUX B.V.—Cardo AB; Int'l, pg. 269
FALTEC PORTE A/S—Cardo AB; Int'l, pg. 269
FALTEC TORE GMBH—Cardo AB; Int'l, pg. 269
FIBO-TRESPO—Norske Skogindustrier A.S; Int'l, pg. 965
FIMBEL DOOR CORPORATION; U.S. Private, pg. 404
FRASER VALLEY FOREST INC.—Premdor Inc.; Int'l, pg. 1067

FRASER VALLEY FOREST PRODUCTS LIMITED—Premdor Inc.; *Int'l*, pg. 1067
GANAHL LUMBER COMPANY; *U.S. Private*, pg. 439
GEORGIA-PACIFIC CORPORATION; *U.S. Public*, pg. 735
GRAHAM MANUFACTURING CO.—Assa Abloy AB; *Int'l*, pg. 18
GRIFFON CORP.; *U.S. Public*, pg. 766
HARVEY INDUSTRIES, INC.; *U.S. Private*, pg. 508
HURD MILLWORK COMPANY, INC.—UIS, Inc.; *U.S. Private*, pg. 1113
HUTTIG SASH & DOOR CO.—Crane Co.; *U.S. Public*, pg. 457
IGELFORS PORTSYSTEM AB—Cardo AB; *Int'l*, pg. 269
INTERDOCK—Cardo AB; *Int'l*, pg. 269
INTERNATIONAL DOOR AUTOMATION AB—Cardo AB; *Int'l*, pg. 269
J.W. WINDOW COMPONENTS, INC.—Walter Industries, Inc.; *U.S. Public*, pg. 1736
JELD-WEN, INC.; *U.S. Private*, pg. 585
H. KRUEGER MASCHINENFABRIK GMBH—Cardo AB; *Int'l*, pg. 269
LENNAR CORPORATION; *U.S. Public*, pg. 987
LIFETIME DOORS INC.; *U.S. Private*, pg. 666
LOVENE DORR AB—Stora Kopparbergs Bergslags AB; *Int'l*, pg. 1302
MW MANUFACTURERS INC.—Hanson PLC; *Int'l*, pg. 593
MACMILLAN BLOEDEL INC—MacMillan Bloedel Limited; *Int'l*, pg. 828
MALTA DIV.-TOMKINS INDUSTRIES, INC.—Tomkins PLC; *Int'l*, pg. 1398
MARLITE; *U.S. Private*, pg. 705
MARVIN LUMBER & CEDAR COMPANY; *U.S. Private*, pg. 710
MATSUSHITA ELECTRIC WORKS, LTD.; *Int'l*, pg. 847
MEGADOOR AB—Cardo AB; *Int'l*, pg. 269
MEGADOOR INC.—Cardo AB; *Int'l*, pg. 269
MEYER INTERNATIONAL PLC; *Int'l*, pg. 864
MOHAWK FLUSH DOORS, INC.—Premdor Inc.; *Int'l*, pg. 1067
MORGAN MANUFACTURING—Morgan Products Ltd.; *U.S. Public*, pg. 1132
MORGAN PRODUCTS LTD.; *U.S. Public*, pg. 1132
NACOMA PRODUCTS, INC.; *U.S. Private*, pg. 773
NATIONAL WOOD PRODUCTS, CO.—Saunders Brothers; *U.S. Private*, pg. 968
NORSKE SKOGINDUSTRIER A.S; *Int'l*, pg. 965
ODL INCORPORATED; *U.S. Private*, pg. 809
VICENTE PUIG OLIVER S.A.; *Int'l*, pg. 1001
OVERHEAD DOOR CORPORATION; *U.S. Private*, pg. 822
PABCO METALS CORPORATION—A.J. Gerrard and Company; *U.S. Private*, pg. 449
PATRICK INDUSTRIES INC.; *U.S. Public*, pg. 1264
PEASE INDUSTRIES, INC.; *U.S. Private*, pg. 845
PELLA CORPORATION; *U.S. Private*, pg. 848
PFLEIDERER INDUSTRIE GMBH WIRUS-WERKE GUETERSLOH—Pfleiderer AG; *Int'l*, pg. 1047
PIONEER PLASTICS CORPORATION; *U.S. Private*, pg. 867
PREMDOR ENTRY SYSTEMS—Premdor Inc.; *Int'l*, pg. 1067
PREMDOR INC.; *Int'l*, pg. 1066
PREMDOR INC.-ATLANTIC DIVISION—Premdor Inc.; *Int'l*, pg. 1067
PREMDOR MOULDINGS INC.—Premdor Inc.; *Int'l*, pg. 1067
THE RESIDENTIAL PRODUCTS GROUP—Tomkins PLC; *Int'l*, pg. 1398
REYNOLDS ALUMINUM OF CANADA—Reynolds Metals Company; *U.S. Public*, pg. 1387
REYNOLDS INTERNATIONAL, INC.—Reynolds Metals Company; *U.S. Public*, pg. 1387
REYNOLDS METALS COMPANY-ILLINOIS—Reynolds Metals Company; *U.S. Public*, pg. 1385
RIVERSIDE MILLWORK COMPANY, INC.; *U.S. Private*, pg. 934
ROONEY BROTHERS COMPANY; *U.S. Private*, pg. 943
RUTT CUSTOM CABINETRY—Harrow Industries; *U.S. Private*, pg. 507
SNE ENTERPRISES, INC.—Nortek, Inc.; *U.S. Public*, pg. 1193
SO ÖVITEOLLISUUS OY—Stora Kopparbergs Bergslags AB; *Int'l*, pg. 1302
SP-SNICKERIER AB—Stora Kopparbergs Bergslags AB; *Int'l*, pg. 1302
SAUDI CRAWFORD DOORS FACTORY LTD.—Cardo AB; *Int'l*, pg. 270
SAUNDERS BROTHERS; *U.S. Private*, pg. 968
SCHUCK & SONS CONSTRUCTION CO.; *U.S. Private*, pg. 973
SETZER FOREST PRODUCTS; *U.S. Private*, pg. 987
SHAKERTOWN 1992, INC.—The Clark Group; *Int'l*, pg. 296
SIERRA PACIFIC INDUSTRIES; *U.S. Private*, pg. 998
SIMPSON DOOR COMPANY—Simpson Investment Co.; *U.S. Private*, pg. 1003
SIMPSON INVESTMENT CO.; *U.S. Private*, pg. 1003
SIMPSON TIMBER CO.—Simpson Investment Co.; *U.S. Private*, pg. 1003
L.J. SMITH, INC.—Marmac Corporation; *U.S. Private*, pg. 706
SOUTHERN RECLAMATION COMPANY—Reynolds Metals Company; *U.S. Public*, pg. 1386
STEGBAR BIFOLD DOORS—BTR plc; *Int'l*, pg. 128
STEGBAR WINDOWALLS PTY. LTD.—BTR plc; *Int'l*, pg. 128
STEVES & SONS, INC.; *U.S. Private*, pg. 1042
STORA BUILDING PRODUCTS AB—Stora Kopparbergs Bergslags AB; *Int'l*, pg. 1302
SUPREME LUMBER & MILLWORK CO.—Lennar Corporation; *U.S. Public*, pg. 989
SWEDOOR AB-ASTORP—Stora Kopparbergs Bergslags AB; *Int'l*, pg. 1303
SWEDOOR AB-FORSERUM—Stora Kopparbergs Bergslags AB; *Int'l*, pg. 1303
SWEDOOR AB-VETLANDA—Stora Kopparbergs Bergslags AB; *Int'l*, pg. 1303
SWEDOOR A/S-GRAN—Stora Kopparbergs Bergslags AB; *Int'l*, pg. 1303
TJ INTERNATIONAL, INC.; *U.S. Public*, pg. 1556
THE TANEY CORPORATION; *U.S. Private*, pg. 1067
TEMPLE-INLAND FOREST PRODUCTS CORP.-BUILDING PRODUCTS GROUP—Temple-Inland Inc.; *U.S. Public*, pg. 1575
THERMA-TRU CORP.; *U.S. Private*, pg. 1079
THERMWELL PRODUCTS CO., INC.; *U.S. Private*, pg. 1081
TOMKINS INDUSTRIES INC.—Tomkins PLC; *Int'l*, pg. 1397
TREND-LINES INC.; *U.S. Private*, pg. 1099
WM. S. TRIMBLE COMPANY, INC.; *U.S. Private*, pg. 1103
TRUS JOIST MACMILLAN—TJ International, Inc.; *U.S. Public*, pg. 1556
UNIVERSAL BUILDERS SUPPLY, INC.; *U.S. Private*, pg. 1126
VICTORIA JOINERY LTD.—John Laing PLC; *Int'l*, pg. 796
VIVIAN MILLWORKS; *U.S. Private*, pg. 1143
WAYNE DALTON CORPORATION; *U.S. Private*, pg. 1155
WESTAG & GETALIT AG; *Int'l*, pg. 1491
WIGAND CORPORATION—Steelcase Inc.; *U.S. Private*, pg. 1038
WINDOW FURNISHINGS SINGAPORE PTE. LTD.—Hunter Douglas N.V.; *Int'l*, pg. 640
WINDOWVISIONS INC.—Lindal Cedar Homes, Inc.; *U.S. Public*, pg. 999
WINDSOR DOOR—American Buildings Co.; *U.S. Public*, pg. 69
WING INDUSTRIES, INC.; *U.S. Private*, pg. 1183
WING INDUSTRIES SOUTH CENTRAL—Wing Industries, Inc.; *U.S. Private*, pg. 1183
WOODGRAIN MILLWORK; *U.S. Private*, pg. 1187

2434 — WOOD KITCHEN CABINETS

APL CORPORATION; *U.S. Private*, pg. 7
ALNO AG; *Int'l*, pg. 65
AMERICAN WOODMARK CORPORATION; *U.S. Public*, pg. 96
ARISTOKRAFT, INC.—Fortune Brands, Inc.; *U.S. Public*, pg. 675
BALLINGSLOVS AB—Electrolux, AB; *Int'l*, pg. 438
CRYSTAL CABINET WORKS, INC.; *U.S. Private*, pg. 293
FIBO-TRESPO—Norske Skogindustrier A.S; *Int'l*, pg. 965
FIELDSTONE CABINETRY INC.—Masco Corporation; *U.S. Public*, pg. 1053
FORTUNE BRANDS, INC.; *U.S. Public*, pg. 674
GENERAL MARBLE CORPORATION—Leucadia National Corporation; *U.S. Public*, pg. 990
IXL CABINETS—Triangle Pacific Corporation; *U.S. Public*, pg. 1634
KELLER KITCHEN CABINETS; *U.S. Private*, pg. 612
KELLER LADDERS INC.—U.S. Industries, Inc.; *U.S. Public*, pg. 1684
LEUCADIA NATIONAL CORPORATION; *U.S. Public*, pg. 989
MAGNET LTD.—Berisford plc; *Int'l*, pg. 188
MARSH FURNITURE COMPANY; *U.S. Private*, pg. 708
MASCO CORPORATION; *U.S. Public*, pg. 1052
MASCO CORPORATION LIMITED—Masco Corporation; *U.S. Public*, pg. 1054
MCCONNELL CABINETS, INC.; *U.S. Private*, pg. 720
MERILLAT CORPORATION—Masco Corporation; *U.S. Public*, pg. 1054
MERILLAT INDUSTRIES INC.—Masco Corporation; *U.S. Public*, pg. 1053
NORCRAFT COMPANIES, INC.; *U.S. Private*, pg. 801
NORTEK, INC.; *U.S. Public*, pg. 1192
PACIFIC TRI-VIEW CORPORATION—Leucadia National Corporation; *U.S. Public*, pg. 990
RIVERSIDE MILLWORK COMPANY, INC.; *U.S. Private*, pg. 934
RUTT CUSTOM CABINETRY—Harrow Industries; *U.S. Private*, pg. 507
STAR MOBELWERK GMBH—Stora Kopparbergs Bergslags AB; *Int'l*, pg. 1303
TRIANGLE PACIFIC CORPORATION; *U.S. Public*, pg. 1634
UNIVERSAL-RUNDLE CORP.—Nortek, Inc.; *U.S. Public*, pg. 1193
YORKTOWNE, INC.; *U.S. Private*, pg. 1196

2435 — HARDWOOD VENEER & PLYWOOD

AMOS-HILL ASSOCIATES, INC.; *U.S. Private*, pg. 67
BERGHUIZER-ENSO FORMAATFABRIEK B.V.—Enso Oyj; *Int'l*, pg. 458
BEST-WOOD LIMITED—International Paper Company; *U.S. Public*, pg. 905
BRIDGEWATER RESOURCES CORPORATION; *U.S. Private*, pg. 168
WILLIAM BROJACK LUMBER COMPANY; *U.S. Private*, pg. 171
CAMDEN MILL, WOOD PRODUCTS DIV.—Champion International Corp.; *U.S. Public*, pg. 334
CANFOR U.S.A., BELLINGHAM DIVISION—Canfor Corporation; *Int'l*, pg. 260
CANFOR U.S.A. CORPORATION—Canfor Corporation; *Int'l*, pg. 260
CAVENHAM FOREST INDUSTRIES INC.—Hanson PLC; *Int'l*, pg. 593
CHAMPION INTERNATIONAL CORP.; *U.S. Public*, pg. 333
CHAMPION INTERNATIONAL CORP., WOOD PRODUCTS DIV.—Champion International Corp.; *U.S. Public*, pg. 334
DARLINGTON VENEER COMPANY; *U.S. Private*, pg. 311
EVANSVILLE VENEER & LUMBER CO.—Kimball International, Inc.; *U.S. Public*, pg. 957
FLETCHER WOOD PANELS LIMITED—Fletcher Challenge Limited; *Int'l*, pg. 495
GEORGIA-PACIFIC CORPORATION; *U.S. Public*, pg. 735
GEORGIA-PACIFIC MID-CONTINENT WOOD PRODS. MFG. DIV.—Georgia-Pacific Corporation; *U.S. Public*, pg. 735
HEINOLA MILL—UPM-Kymmene Corporation; *Int'l*, pg. 1428
JASPER LAMINATES—Kimball International, Inc.; *U.S. Public*, pg. 957
KIMBALL INTERNATIONAL, INC.; *U.S. Public*, pg. 956
LADD FURNITURE, INC.; *U.S. Public*, pg. 974
LAHTI MILLS—UPM-Kymmene Corporation; *Int'l*, pg. 1429
LEA LUMBER & PLYWOOD LLC; *U.S. Private*, pg. 655
MW MANUFACTURERS INC.—Hanson PLC; *Int'l*, pg. 593
MALLERY LUMBER CORP.; *U.S. Private*, pg. 698
MALVAUX S.A.—UPM-Kymmene Corporation; *Int'l*, pg. 1429
MASONITE CORPORATION—International Paper Company; *U.S. Public*, pg. 904
MILLER & CO.; *U.S. Private*, pg. 746
MITSUI HOME CO., LTD.—Mitsui & Co., Ltd.; *Int'l*, pg. 877
MITSUI LUMBER CO., LTD.—Mitsui & Co., Ltd.; *Int'l*, pg. 877
NORTHERN MICHIGAN VENEERS, INC.; *U.S. Private*, pg. 805
NORTHWOOD FOREST INDUSTRIES, LTD.—The Mead Corporation; *U.S. Public*, pg. 1076
NORTHWOOD PULP & TIMBER LTD.—The Mead Corporation; *U.S. Public*, pg. 1076
PELLOS MILLS—UPM-Kymmene Corporation; *Int'l*, pg. 1429
PLY-GEM MANUFACTURING—Nortek, Inc.; *U.S. Public*, pg. 1193
PULASKI FURNITURE-DUBLIN—Pulaski Furniture Corporation; *U.S. Public*, pg. 1343
SARMIENTO RAPPAN INDUSTRIES; *Int'l*, pg. 1194
SAVONLINNA MILL—UPM-Kymmene Corporation; *Int'l*, pg. 1429
SCHAUMAN WOOD OY—UPM-Kymmene Corporation; *Int'l*, pg. 1428
SIMPSON TIMBER CO.—Simpson Investment Co.; *U.S. Private*, pg. 1003
SLOCAN FOREST PRODUCTS LTD.; *Int'l*, pg. 1263
STONE FOREST INDUSTRIES—Stone Container Corporation; *U.S. Public*, pg. 1521
TEMBEC INC.; *Int'l*, pg. 1374
TENNESSEE RIVER PULP & PAPER CO.—Tenneco Inc.; *U.S. Public*, pg. 1579
TIMBER PRODUCTS COMPANY, LP; *U.S. Private*, pg. 1086
UNIVERSAL WOODS, INCORPORATED—Universal Corporation; *U.S. Public*, pg. 1695
WELDWOOD OF CANADA LIMITED—Champion International Corp.; *U.S. Public*, pg. 334
WESTAG & GETALIT AG; *Int'l*, pg. 1491
WEYERHAEUSER COMPANY; *U.S. Public*, pg. 1764

2436 — SOFTWOOD VENEER & PLYWOOD

BOISE CASCADE CORPORATION; *U.S. Public*, pg. 242
BOISE CASCADE TIMBER & WOOD PRODUCTS DIVISION—Boise Cascade Corporation; *U.S. Public*, pg. 243
DAVIS WOOD PRODUCTS, INC.; *U.S. Private*, pg. 315
FLETCHER WOOD PANELS LIMITED—Fletcher Challenge Limited; *Int'l*, pg. 495
GEORGIA-PACIFIC CORPORATION; *U.S. Public*, pg. 735
GLIDE LUMBER PRODUCTS CO.—WTD Industries, Inc.; *U.S. Public*, pg. 1729
EDWARD HINES LUMBER CO.; *U.S. Private*, pg. 530
HYUNDAI WOOD INDUSTRIES CO., LTD.—Hyundai Motor Company; *Int'l*, pg. 642
LEA LUMBER & PLYWOOD LLC; *U.S. Private*, pg. 655
LOUISIANA PACIFIC CORPORATION; *U.S. Public*, pg. 1015
LOUISIANA PACIFIC NORTHERN DIV.—Louisiana Pacific Corporation; *U.S. Public*, pg. 1015
MASONITE CORPORATION—International Paper Company; *U.S. Public*, pg. 904
MITSUI HOME CO., LTD.—Mitsui & Co., Ltd.; *Int'l*, pg. 877
MITSUI LUMBER CO., LTD.—Mitsui & Co., Ltd.; *Int'l*, pg. 877
MO OCH DOMSJO AB; *Int'l*, pg. 885
MORTON FOREST PRODUCTS CO.—WTD Industries, Inc.; *U.S. Public*, pg. 1730
NORTH POWDER LUMBER CO.—WTD Industries, Inc.; *U.S. Public*, pg. 1730
PACIFIC HARDWOODS-SOUTH BEND CO.—WTD Industries, Inc.; *U.S. Public*, pg. 1730
PACIFIC LUMBER & SHIPPING CO.; *U.S. Private*, pg. 832
PHILOMATH FOREST PRODUCTS CO.—WTD Industries, Inc.; *U.S. Public*, pg. 1730
POTLATCH CORPORATION; *U.S. Public*, pg. 1318
PULASKI FURNITURE-DUBLIN—Pulaski Furniture Corporation; *U.S. Public*, pg. 1343
RLC INDUSTRIES CO.; *U.S. Private*, pg. 905
ROSEBURG FOREST PRODUCTS CO.—RLC Industries Co.; *U.S. Private*, pg. 905
SARMIENTO RAPPAN INDUSTRIES; *Int'l*, pg. 1194
SEDRO-WOOLLEY LUMBER CO.—WTD Industries, Inc.; *U.S. Public*, pg. 1730
SIMPSON INVESTMENT CO.; *U.S. Private*, pg. 1003
SIMPSON TIMBER CO.—Simpson Investment Co.; *U.S. Private*, pg. 1003
SPANAWAY LUMBER CO.—WTD Industries, Inc.; *U.S. Public*, pg. 1730
TEMBEC INC.; *Int'l*, pg. 1374
TENNESSEE RIVER PULP & PAPER CO.—Tenneco Inc.; *U.S. Public*, pg. 1579
TIMBER PRODUCTS COMPANY, LP; *U.S. Private*, pg. 1086
TUMWATER LUMBER CO.—WTD Industries, Inc.; *U.S. Public*, pg. 1730
VIVIAN MILLWORKS; *U.S. Private*, pg. 1143
WTD INDUSTRIES, INC.; *U.S. Public*, pg. 1729

WELDWOOD OF CANADA LIMITED—Champion International Corp.; *U.S. Public*, pg. 334
WESTERN TIMBER CO.—WTD Industries, Inc.; *U.S. Public*, *pg. 1729*
WEYERHAEUSER COMPANY; *U.S. Public*, pg. 1764
WILLAMETTE INDUSTRIES, INC.; *U.S. Public*, pg. 1768
WILLAMETTE INDUSTRIES, INC.—Willamette Industries, Inc.; *U.S. Public*, pg. 1769

2439 — STRUCTURAL WOOD MEMBERS, NEC

ACI AMERICA HOLDINGS INC.—BTR plc; *Int'l*, pg. 129
ACI INTERNATIONAL LTD.—BTR plc; *Int'l*, pg. 128
ACI KIMTRUSS CORP.—BTR plc; *Int'l*, pg. 129
BOISE CASCADE CORPORATION; *U.S. Public*, pg. 242
BOISE CASCADE TIMBER & WOOD PRODUCTS DIVISION—Boise Cascade Corporation; *U.S. Public*, pg. 243
CALCASIEU LUMBER COMPANY; *U.S. Private*, pg. 200
CARDO DOOR AB—Cardo AB; *Int'l*, pg. 269
CARDO DOOR PRODUCTION AB—Cardo AB; *Int'l*, pg. 269
CARDO DOOR PRODUCTION A/S—Cardo AB; *Int'l*, pg. 269
CAROLINA BUILDERS CORPORATION—Wolseley Plc.; *Int'l*, pg. 1512
CLEVER S.A.—Cardo AB; *Int'l*, pg. 269
CRAWFORD DEUR B.V.—Cardo AB; *Int'l*, pg. 269
CRAWFORD DOOR A/S—Cardo AB; *Int'l*, pg. 269
CRAWFORD DOOR (FAR EAST) PTE LTD.—Cardo AB; *Int'l*, pg. 269
CRAWFORD DOOR FORSALJNINGS AB—Cardo AB; *Int'l*, pg. 269
S.A. CRAWFORD DOOR N.V.—Cardo AB; *Int'l*, pg. 269
CRAWFORD DOOR S.A.—Cardo AB; *Int'l*, pg. 269
CRAWFORD DOOR S.R.L.—Cardo AB; *Int'l*, pg. 269
CRAWFORD GARAGE DOOR SYSTEMS AB—Cardo AB; *Int'l*, pg. 269
CRAWFORD TOR GES.M.B.H.—Cardo AB; *Int'l*, pg. 269
CRAWMATOR AB—Cardo AB; *Int'l*, pg. 269
ENGINEERED WOOD DIV.—Anthony Forest Products Co., Inc.; *U.S. Private*, pg. 76
FALTEC BENELUX B.V.—Cardo AB; *Int'l*, pg. 269
FALTEC PORTE A/S—Cardo AB; *Int'l*, pg. 269
FALTEC TORE GMBH—Cardo AB; *Int'l*, pg. 269
GEORGIA-PACIFIC CORPORATION; *U.S. Public*, pg. 735
GREAT PLAINS COMPANIES, INC.; *U.S. Private*, pg. 475
JAMES HARDIE BUILDING PRODUCTS INC.—James Hardie Industries Ltd.; *Int'l*, pg. 597
IGELFORS PORTSYSTEM AB—Cardo AB; *Int'l*, pg. 269
INTERDOCK—Cardo AB; *Int'l*, pg. 269
INTERNATIONAL DOOR AUTOMATION AB—Cardo AB; *Int'l*, pg. 269
H. KRUEGER MASCHINENFABRIK GMBH—Cardo AB; *Int'l*, pg. 269
LITTFIN LUMBER COMPANY; *U.S. Private*, pg. 670
LOUISIANA PACIFIC NORTHERN DIV.—Louisiana Pacific Corporation; *U.S. Public*, pg. 1015
MATSUSHITA ELECTRIC WORKS, LTD.; *Int'l*, pg. 847
MEGADOOR AB—Cardo AB; *Int'l*, pg. 269
MEGADOOR INC.—Cardo AB; *Int'l*, pg. 269
NATIONAL LUMBER CO.; *U.S. Private*, pg. 785
NICKERSON LUMBER COMPANY; *U.S. Private*, pg. 798
PLUM BUILDING SYSTEMS, INC.—Great Plains Companies, Inc.; *U.S. Private*, pg. 475
PRECONAL—Falkema AB; *Int'l*, pg. 477
RICHARDSON INDUSTRIES, INC.; *U.S. Private*, pg. 929
RICHCO STRUCTURES—Richardson Industries, Inc.; *U.S. Private*, pg. 929
SAUDI CRAWFORD DOORS FACTORY LTD.—Cardo AB; *Int'l*, pg. 270
SCHUCK & SONS CONSTRUCTION CO.; *U.S. Private*, pg. 973
SEAMAN TIMBER COMPANY, INC.; *U.S. Private*, pg. 979
TJ INTERNATIONAL, INC.; *U.S. Public*, pg. 1556
TRUS JOIST MACMILLAN LIMITED—TJ International, Inc.; *U.S. Public*, pg. 1556
TRUS JOIST (WESTERN) LTD.—TJ International, Inc.; *U.S. Public*, pg. 1556
VILLAUME INDUSTRIES, INC.; *U.S. Private*, pg. 1140

2441 — NAILED & LOCK CORNER WOODEN BOXES & SHOOK

L.P. FOREMAN & SONS LTD.—The General Electric Company, p.l.c.; *Int'l*, pg. 543
SEATTLE PACKAGING CORPORATION; *U.S. Private*, pg. 980
VILLAUME INDUSTRIES, INC.; *U.S. Private*, pg. 1140

2448 — WOOD PALLETS & SKIDS

AAR CADILLAC MANUFACTURING DIV.—AAR Corp.; *U.S. Public*, pg. 1
CHEP USA—Brambles Industries Limited; *Int'l*, pg. 211
CHEP USA—GKN plc; *Int'l*, pg. 535
ELBERTA CRATE & BOX COMPANY; *U.S. Private*, pg. 367
GKN CHEP SA (PTY) LTD.—GKN plc; *Int'l*, pg. 536
STEPHEN GOULD PAPER CO., INC.; *U.S. Private*, pg. 467
A. JALANDER OY—Kemira Oy; *Int'l*, pg. 727
JELD-WEN, INC.; *U.S. Private*, pg. 585
LOVE PACKAGING GROUP; *U.S. Private*, pg. 677
SEAMAN TIMBER COMPANY, INC.; *U.S. Private*, pg. 979
SEMAC INDUSTRIES INC.; *U.S. Private*, pg. 983
SPARTYWOOD PRODUCTS, INC.—Semac Industries Inc.; *U.S. Private*, pg. 983
VILLAUME INDUSTRIES, INC.; *U.S. Private*, pg. 1140

2449 — WOOD CONTAINERS, NEC

BPB INDUSTRIES PLC; *Int'l*, pg. 122
BPB PAPER & PACKAGING LTD.—BPB Industries PLC; *Int'l*, pg. 122
BLUE GRASS COOPERAGE CO.—Brown-Forman Corporation; *U.S. Public*, pg. 261
ELBERTA CRATE & BOX COMPANY; *U.S. Private*, pg. 367
GREIF BROTHERS CORPORATION; *U.S. Public*, pg. 763
HORN PACKAGING CORPORATION; *U.S. Private*, pg. 539
KVAERNER ENERGY A.S.—Kvaerner a.s.a.; *Int'l*, pg. 767
L & L NURSERY SUPPLY, INC.; *U.S. Private*, pg. 638
SEMAC INDUSTRIES INC.; *U.S. Private*, pg. 983
SKYDYNE DIV.—AAR Corp.; *U.S. Public*, pg. 1
VILLAUME INDUSTRIES, INC.; *U.S. Private*, pg. 1140
WATKINS MANUFACTURING CORP./HOT SPRING PORTABLE SPAS—Masco Corporation; *U.S. Public*, pg. 1054
WETSEL-OVIATT LUMBER COMPANY; *U.S. Private*, pg. 1170

2451 — MOBILE HOMES

ALL AMERICAN HOMES OF IOWA INC.—Coachmen Industries, Inc.; *U.S. Public*, pg. 388
ATLANTIC HOMES DIV.—Champion Enterprises, Inc.; *U.S. Public*, pg. 332
B & B HOMES CORPORATION; *U.S. Private*, pg. 105
CMH MANUFACTURING, INC.—Clayton Homes, Inc.; *U.S. Public*, pg. 383
CAVCO INDUSTRIES, INC.—Centex Corporation; *U.S. Public*, pg. 323
CHAMPION ENTERPRISES, INC.; *U.S. Public*, pg. 332
CHAMPION HOME BUILDERS CO.—Champion Enterprises, Inc.; *U.S. Public*, pg. 332
CHAMPION MOTOR COACH, INC.—Champion Enterprises, Inc.; *U.S. Public*, pg. 332
CHANDELEUR HOMES, INC.—Champion Enterprises, Inc.; *U.S. Public*, pg. 333
CHATEAU COMMUNITIES, INC.; *U.S. Public*, pg. 341
CHIEF INDUSTRIES - HOUSING DIV.—Chief Industries, Inc.; *U.S. Private*, pg. 236
CHIEF INDUSTRIES, INC.; *U.S. Private*, pg. 236
CLAYTON HOMES, INC.; *U.S. Public*, pg. 382
COACHMEN INDUSTRIES, INC.; *U.S. Public*, pg. 387
CREST RIDGE HOMES, INC.—Champion Enterprises, Inc.; *U.S. Public*, pg. 333
DESTINY INDUSTRIES INC.—Oakwood Homes Corporation; *U.S. Public*, pg. 1209
DUTCH HOUSING, INC.—Champion Enterprises, Inc.; *U.S. Public*, pg. 333
FAIRMONT HOMES, INC.; *U.S. Private*, pg. 391
FLEETWOOD ENTERPRISES, INC.; *U.S. Public*, pg. 650
FLEETWOOD HOMES OF GEORGIA, INC. 651
FLEETWOOD HOMES OF INDIANA, INC.—Fleetwood Enterprises, Inc.; *U.S. Public*, pg. 651
FLEETWOOD HOMES OF TEXAS—Fleetwood Enterprises, Inc.; *U.S. Public*, pg. 651
GOLDEN WEST HOMES—Oakwood Homes Corporation; *U.S. Public*, pg. 1209
GRIFFON CORP.; *U.S. Public*, pg. 766
HOMES OF MERIT INC.; *U.S. Private*, pg. 537
HOMETTE CORPORATION—Skyline Corporation; *U.S. Public*, pg. 1476
HORTON HOMES, INC.; *U.S. Private*, pg. 540
JACOBSEN MANUFACTURING, INC.; *U.S. Private*, pg. 580
KIT MANUFACTURING COMPANY; *U.S. Public*, pg. 962
LB INDUSTRIES INC.; *U.S. Private*, pg. 639
LAYTON HOMES CORP.—Skyline Corporation; *U.S. Public*, *pg. 1476*
LIBERTY HOMES, INC.; *U.S. Public*, pg. 992
M1 KIT MFG. CO.—Kit Manufacturing Company; *U.S. Public*, pg. 962
MANUFACTURED HOUSING DIV.—Kit Manufacturing Company; *U.S. Public*, pg. 962
MARLETTE HOMES, INC.—Schult Homes Corporation; *U.S. Public*, pg. 1442
NASHUA HOMES OF IDAHO INC.; *U.S. Private*, pg. 774
NOBILITY HOMES, INC.; *U.S. Public*, pg. 1186
OAKWOOD HOMES CORPORATION; *U.S. Public*, pg. 1209
PALM HARBOR HOMES—Palm Harbor Homes, Inc.; *U.S. Public*, pg. 1255
PALM HARBOR HOMES, INC.; *U.S. Public*, pg. 1254
PARK MANUFACTURING, INC.; *U.S. Private*, pg. 840
SCHULT HOMES CORPORATION; *U.S. Public*, pg. 1442
SKYLINE HOMES, INC.—Skyline Corporation; *U.S. Public*, pg. 1476
TAMARACK HOMES DIV.—Champion Enterprises, Inc.; *U.S. Public*, pg. 332
TITAN HOMES DIV.—Champion Enterprises, Inc.; *U.S. Public*, pg. 332
WICK BUILDING SYSTEMS; *U.S. Private*, pg. 1174
WICK BLDG. SYSTEMS INC. MANUFACTURED HOMES DIV.—Wick Building Systems; *U.S. Private*, pg. 1174
WILLIAMS SCOTSMAN GROUP, INC.—Scotsman Holding Inc.; *U.S. Private*, pg. 977

2452 — PREFABRICATED WOOD BUILDINGS & COMPONENTS

ACI HOMES—BTR plc; *Int'l*, pg. 128
ACTIVE HOMES CORP.—Active Tool & Manufacturing Co., Inc.; *U.S. Private*, pg. 16
ACTIVE TOOL & MANUFACTURING CO., INC.; *U.S. Private*, pg. 16
BARDEN & ROBESON CORPORATION; *U.S. Private*, pg. 116
BERKS PRODUCTS CORPORATION; *U.S. Private*, pg. 136
CALCASIEU LUMBER COMPANY; *U.S. Private*, pg. 200
CARLSBERG FINANCIAL CORP.; *U.S. Private*, pg. 211
CAROLINA BUILDERS CORPORATION—Wolseley Plc.; *Int'l*, pg. 1512
COLEMAN SPAS, INC.—MacAndrews & Forbes Holdings Inc.; *U.S. Private*, pg. 691
COLUMBIA LUMBER & MANUFACTURING CO.; *U.S. Private*, pg. 255
CONTEMPRI HOMES, INC.; *U.S. Public*, pg. 439
DECK HOUSE INC.; *U.S. Private*, pg. 320
DELAIR GROUP, L.L.C.—Aluminum Shapes, LLC; *U.S. Private*, pg. 47
DELUXE HOMES OF PA., INC.; *U.S. Private*, pg. 323
DIXIE ROYAL HOMES, INC.—Family Inns of America, Inc.; *U.S. Private*, pg. 392
GAME TIME, INC.—Swing-N-Slide Corp.; *U.S. Public*, pg. 1543
LESTER BUILDINGS DIVISION—Butler Manufacturing Company; *U.S. Public*, pg. 271
LINDAL CEDAR HOMES, INC.; *U.S. Public*, pg. 998
METALLIC BUILDING COMPANY—NCI Building Systems, Inc.; *U.S. Public*, pg. 1146
MIDWEST STEEL BUILDING COMPANY—NCI Building Systems, Inc.; *U.S. Public*, pg. 1146
MODTECH, INC.; *U.S. Public*, pg. 1121
MODULINE INDUSTRIES, INC.—Champion Enterprises, Inc.; *U.S. Public*, pg. 333
MODULINE INTERNATIONAL, INC.—Champion Enterprises, Inc.; *U.S. Public*, pg. 333
NVR, INC.; *U.S. Public*, pg. 1148
NATIONWIDE HOMES, INC.; *U.S. Private*, pg. 788
NICKERSON LUMBER COMPANY; *U.S. Private*, pg. 798
PHILADELPHIA SIGN COMPANY; *U.S. Private*, pg. 861
RIDG-U-RAK, INC.; *U.S. Private*, pg. 930
RIEMEIER LUMBER COMPANY, INC.; *U.S. Private*, pg. 930
SEKISUI CHEMICAL CO., LTD.; *Int'l*, pg. 1219
SIMPLEX INDUSTRIES, INC.; *U.S. Private*, pg. 1001
SKYLINE CORPORATION; *U.S. Public*, pg. 1476
STEEL SYSTEMS INC.—NCI Building Systems, Inc.; *U.S. Public*, pg. 1146
TJ INTERNATIONAL, INC.; *U.S. Public*, pg. 1556
VILLAUME INDUSTRIES, INC.; *U.S. Private*, pg. 1140
VORWERK FRANCE SA—Vorwerk & Co.; *Int'l*, pg. 1481
WALPOLE WOODWORKERS, INC.; *U.S. Private*, pg. 1148
WAUSAU HOMES, INC.; *U.S. Private*, pg. 1154
WICK BUILDING SYSTEMS; *U.S. Private*, pg. 1174
WILLIAMS SCOTSMAN GROUP, INC.—Scotsman Holding Inc.; *U.S. Private*, pg. 977
ZENKER HAUSBAU GMBH & CO.—Philipp Holzmann AG; *Int'l*, pg. 633

2491 — WOOD PRESERVING

J.H. BAXTER & COMPANY; *U.S. Private*, pg. 124
BROWN WOOD PRESERVING COMPANY; *U.S. Private*, pg. 174
CAVENHAM FOREST INDUSTRIES INC.—Hanson PLC; *Int'l*, pg. 593
COASTAL LUMBER COMPANY; *U.S. Private*, pg. 248
CONSTRUCTION & HOME IMPROVEMENT MARKETS DIVISION—3M; *U.S. Public*, pg. 1605
CONTINENTAL WOOD PRESERVERS, INC.—Nortek, Inc.; *U.S. Public*, pg. 1193
COX WOOD PRESERVING CO.; *U.S. Private*, pg. 283
GEORGIA-PACIFIC INDUSTRIAL WOOD PRODUCTS DIV.—Georgia-Pacific Corporation; *U.S. Public*, pg. 735
HALVIC KUNSTSTOFFWERKE GMBH—Solvay S.A.; *Int'l*, pg. 1278
HICKSON TIMBER PRODUCTS LTD.—Hickson International Plc; *Int'l*, pg. 619
HOOVER TREATED WOOD PRODUCTS, INC.—Nortek, Inc.; *U.S. Public*, pg. 1193
HYUNDAI WOOD INDUSTRIES CO., LTD.—Hyundai Motor Company; *Int'l*, pg. 642
KERR-MCGEE CHEMICAL CORP.—Kerr-McGee Corporation; *U.S. Public*, pg. 952
MANKE LUMBER COMPANY, INC.; *U.S. Private*, pg. 699
MASONITE DIVISION—International Paper Company; *U.S. Public*, pg. 903
OSMOSE WOOD PRESERVING, INC.; *U.S. Private*, pg. 821
PSR; *U.S. Private*, pg. 828
RAILROAD CONCRETE CROSSTIE CORP.—St. Joe Corp.; *U.S. Public*, pg. 1427
RICHARDSON INDUSTRIES, INC.; *U.S. Private*, pg. 929
ROBBINS MANUFACTURING COMPANY; *U.S. Private*, pg. 935
SARMIENTO RAPPAN INDUSTRIES; *Int'l*, pg. 1194
SEAMAN TIMBER COMPANY, INC.; *U.S. Private*, pg. 979
SWANER HARDWOOD COMPANY, INC.; *U.S. Private*, pg. 1057
TATE ACCESS FLOORS—International Paper Company; *U.S. Public*, pg. 905
TEXAS ELECTRIC COOPERATIVES, INC.; *U.S. Private*, pg. 1078
TOLLESON LUMBER COMPANY, INC.; *U.S. Private*, pg. 1090
WEYERHAEUSER COMPANY; *U.S. Public*, pg. 1764
WOOD MOULDING PLANT—Georgia-Pacific Corporation; *U.S. Public*, pg. 738

2493 — RECONSTITUTED WOOD PRODUCTS

ABT BUILDING PRODUCTS CORPORATION—Abitibi-Consolidated Inc.; *Int'l*, pg. 20
AEC FOREST PRODUCTS—Alberta Energy Company, Ltd.; *Int'l*, pg. 48
ANTHONY FOREST PRODUCTS CO., INC.; *U.S. Private*, pg. 76
BMCA INSULATION PRODUCTS, INC.—GAF Corporation; *U.S. Private*, pg. 433
BPCO—Emco Limited; *Int'l*, pg. 453
BOISE CASCADE CORPORATION; *U.S. Public*, pg. 242

BOISE CASCADE TIMBER & WOOD PRODUCTS DIVISION—Boise Cascade Corporation; *U.S. Public*, pg. 243
CANADIAN WHITE PINE DIVISION—MacMillan Bloedel Limited; *Int'l*, pg. 828
CANFOR U.S.A., BELLINGHAM DIVISION—Canfor Corporation; *Int'l*, pg. 260
CANFOR U.S.A. CORPORATION—Canfor Corporation; *Int'l*, *pg. 260*
CHIPMILL—Anthony Forest Products Co., Inc.; *U.S. Private*, *pg. 76*
CLADWOOD DIV. (CENTRAL OFFICE)—Jefferson Smurfit Group p.l.c.; *Int'l*, pg. 1270
COMPAGNIE DE SAINT-GOBAIN-PONT-A MOUSSON—Compagnie de Suez; *Int'l*, pg. 313
DAISHOWA PAPER MFG. CO., LTD.; *Int'l*, pg. 373
DAVIS WOOD PRODUCTS, INC.; *U.S. Private*, pg. 315
DUFAYLITE DEVELOPMENTS LIMITED—SLD Holdings Ltd.; *Int'l*, pg. 1160
EMCO BUILDING PRODUCTS—Emco Limited; *Int'l*, pg. 453
EMCO LIMITED; *Int'l*, pg. 452
GYPROC INSULATION LTD.—BPB Industries PLC; *Int'l*, pg. 123
J.M. HUBER, WOOD PRODUCTS DIV.—J.M. Huber Corporation; *U.S. Private*, pg. 545
INDUSTRIAS DE TABLEROS Y DERIVADOS DE LA MADERA, S.A.—International Paper Company; *U.S. Public*, pg. 905
THE KAY COMPANY, INC.; *U.S. Private*, pg. 610
LOUISIANA PACIFIC CORPORATION; *U.S. Public*, pg. 1015
LOUISIANA PACIFIC NORTHERN DIV.—Louisiana Pacific Corporation; *U.S. Public*, pg. 1015
LOUISIANA PACIFIC WESTERN DIV.—Louisiana Pacific Corporation; *U.S. Public*, pg. 1015
MALETTE QUEBEC, INC.; *Int'l*, pg. 833
MANVILLE GREAT BRITAIN LTD. (BRISTOL)—Johns Manville Corporation; *U.S. Public*, pg. 927
MANVILLE GREAT BRITAIN LTD. (LEEDS)—Johns Manville Corporation; *U.S. Public*, pg. 927
MASONITE CORPORATION—International Paper Company; *U.S. Public*, pg. 904
MO OCH DOMSJO AB; *Int'l*, pg. 885
OVERHEAD DOOR CORPORATION; *U.S. Private*, pg. 822
PACIFIC LUMBER & SHIPPING CO.; *U.S. Private*, pg. 832
PANEL PROCESSING, INC.; *U.S. Private*, pg. 836
PANNEAUX MALETTE-OSB INC.—Malette Quebec, Inc.; *Int'l*, pg. 833
PFLEIDERER INDUSTRIE GMBH WIRUS-WERKE GUETERSLOH—Pfleiderer AG; *Int'l*, pg. 1047
POTLATCH CORPORATION; *U.S. Public*, pg. 1318
RLC INDUSTRIES CO.; *U.S. Private*, pg. 905
ROSEBURG FOREST PRODUCTS CO.—RLC Industries Co.; *U.S. Private*, pg. 905
JEFFERSON SMURFIT CORPORATION—Jefferson Smurfit Group p.l.c.; *Int'l*, pg. 1269
JEFFERSON SMURFIT GROUP P.L.C.; *Int'l*, pg. 1269
TEMPLE-INLAND FOREST PRODUCTS CORP.-BUILDING PRODUCTS GROUP—Temple-Inland Inc.; *U.S. Public*, pg. 1575
TEMPLE-INLAND INC.; *U.S. Public*, pg. 1574
TIMBER PRODUCTS COMPANY, LP; *U.S. Private*, pg. 1086
TRIWOOD, INC.—Bassett Furniture Industries, Incorporated; *U.S. Public*, pg. 193
UNIBOARD CANADA INC.; *Int'l*, pg. 1431
UNION CAMP CORPORATION; *U.S. Public*, pg. 1665
WEYERHAEUSER COMPANY; *U.S. Public*, pg. 1764
WILLAMETTE INDUSTRIES, INC.—Willamette Industries, Inc.; *U.S. Public*, pg. 1769

2499 — WOOD PRODUCTS, NEC

AARON BROTHERS, INC.—Michaels Stores, Inc.; *U.S. Public*, pg. 1104
ACME FRAME PRODUCTS, INC.—American Greetings Corporation; *U.S. Public*, pg. 78
ACME RULER CO. LTD.—Acme United Corporation; *U.S. Public*, pg. 17
ALLEN-ROGERS CO.—Davis Mining & Manufacturing; *U.S. Private*, pg. 315
ANNIN & COMPANY; *U.S. Private*, pg. 75
APPLAUSE INC.; *U.S. Private*, pg. 78
BALSA DEVELOPMENT CORPORATION—Baltek Corporation; *U.S. Public*, pg. 171
BALSA ECUADOR LUMBER CORPORATION—Baltek Corporation; *U.S. Public*, pg. 171
BALTEK CORPORATION; *U.S. Public*, pg. 171
JOHN BOOS & COMPANY; *U.S. Private*, pg. 156
BOWATER WINDOWS—Rexam PLC; *Int'l*, pg. 1106
BRIDGEWATER RESOURCES CORPORATION; *U.S. Private*, pg. 168
BRUNER-IVORY HANDLE COMPANY—O.P. Link Handle Company; *U.S. Private*, pg. 669
BURLINGTON BASKET CO.; *U.S. Private*, pg. 183
C.K. TRADING CORP.—Baltek Corporation; *U.S. Public*, pg. 172
CALIFORNIA CEDAR PRODUCTS, INC., *U.S. Private*, pg. 200
CARRIS OF CALIFORNIA, INC.—Carris Financial Group; *U.S. Private*, pg. 215
CARRIS OF CONNECTICUT, INC.—Carris Financial Group; *U.S. Private*, pg. 215
CARRIS REELS, INC.—Carris Financial Group; *U.S. Private*, *pg. 215*
CHESAPEAKE FOREST PRODUCTS CO.—Chesapeake Corporation; *U.S. Public*, pg. 346
CLOPAY CORPORATION—Griffon Corp.; *U.S. Public*, pg. 766
COASTAL LUMBER COMPANY; *U.S. Private*, pg. 248
CRANE CREEK CEDAR—E.R. Probyn Ltd.; *Int'l*, pg. 1071
CROWN CORK & SEAL (PORTUGAL) S.A.—Crown Cork & Seal Company, Inc.; *U.S. Public*, pg. 464
DAVIS WOOD PRODUCTS, INC.; *U.S. Private*, pg. 315
DIAMOND BRANDS, INC.; *U.S. Private*, pg. 330
DODGE REGUPOL, INC.; *U.S. Private*, pg. 337
DURAFLAME, INC.; *U.S. Private*, pg. 348
ECODYNE COOLING TOWER SERVICES—Air & Water Technologies Corporation; *U.S. Public*, pg. 29
EUREKA MANUFACTURING CO., INC.—Reed & Barton Corporation; *U.S. Private*, pg. 916
FAYETTE ENTERPRISES INC.—Furniture Brands International Inc.; *U.S. Public*, pg. 688
FISKARS-GERBER—Fiskars Oy AB; *Int'l*, pg. 492
FOREST INDUSTRIES, INC.—Saunders Brothers; *U.S. Private*, pg. 968
GEC ZAMBIA LTD.—The General Electric Company, p.l.c.; *Int'l*, pg. 546
GEORGIA-PACIFIC CORPORATION; *U.S. Public*, pg. 735
GEORGIA PACIFIC HARDBOARD—Georgia-Pacific Corporation; *U.S. Public*, pg. 736
GRIFFON CORP.; *U.S. Public*, pg. 766
HIG HOLZLEIMBAU-INDUSTRIE GMBH—Philipp Holzmann AG; *Int'l*, pg. 632
HARVEST PRODUCTS PTY. LTD.—Internatio-Muller N.V.; *Int'l*, pg. 682
HOWARD MANUFACTURING—Greenbull Inc.; *U.S. Private*, *pg. 477*
INCENTIVE AB; *Int'l*, pg. 666
INDUSTRIAS DE TABLEROS Y DERIVADOS DE LA MADERA, S.A.—International Paper Company; *U.S. Public*, pg. 905
INTERCRAFT COMPANY—Newell Co.; *U.S. Public*, pg. 1177
INTERCRAFT INDUSTRIES OF CANADA, LTD.—Newell Co.; *U.S. Public*, pg. 1178
M. KAMENSTEIN, INC.; *U.S. Private*, pg. 606
KILLINGTON WOOD PRODUCTS, INC.—Carris Financial Group; *U.S. Private*, pg. 215
LEUCADIA INC. MANUFACTURING DIVISION—Leucadia National Corporation; *U.S. Public*, pg. 990
O.P. LINK HANDLE COMPANY; *U.S. Private*, pg. 668
THE LONGABERGER COMPANY; *U.S. Private*, pg. 675
LOUISIANA PACIFIC CORPORATION; *U.S. Public*, pg. 1015
LOUISVILLE LADDER DIV.—Emerson Electric Co.; *U.S. Public*, pg. 574
MAESTRO PRODUCTS INC.—International Aluminum Corporation; *U.S. Public*, pg. 895
MAGEE CO.—Tandycrafts, Inc.; *U.S. Public*, pg. 1561
MALLERY LUMBER CORP.; *U.S. Private*, pg. 698
MASONITE CORPORATION—International Paper Company; *U.S. Public*, pg. 904
MOORE COMPANY; *U.S. Private*, pg. 759
AB CARL MUNTERS—Incentive AB; *Int'l*, pg. 669
MURPHY COMPANY; *U.S. Private*, pg. 768
NICOR GAS EXCHANGE COMPANY—NICOR Inc.; *U.S. Public*, pg. 1182
NORTH AMERICAN ENCLOSURES, INC.; *U.S. Private*, pg. 803
PATRICK INDUSTRIES INC.; *U.S. Public*, pg. 1264
PLUM CREEK MANUFACTURING—Plum Creek Timber Co., L.P.; *U.S. Public*, pg. 1311
POPE & TALBOT, INC.; *U.S. Public*, pg. 1316
POSTERLOID CORPORATION—PolyVision Corp.; *U.S. Public*, pg. 1315
E.R. PROBYN LTD.; *Int'l*, pg. 1071
PROCESSED TIMBER PRODUCTS—UPM-Kymmene Corporation; *Int'l*, pg. 1428
RAGLAND MANUFACTURING COMPANY INC.—International Aluminum Corporation; *U.S. Public*, pg. 895
REED & BARTON CORPORATION; *U.S. Private*, pg. 916
ROYAL OAK ENTERPRISES, INC.; *U.S. Private*, pg. 948
SANLAM CORPORATION—Baltek Corporation; *U.S. Public*, *pg. 172*
SAUNDERS BROTHERS; *U.S. Private*, pg. 968
SEQUATCHIE HANDLE WORKS, INC.—O.P. Link Handle Company; *U.S. Private*, pg. 669
SHARON CONCEPTS; *U.S. Private*, pg. 990
SIERRA PACIFIC INDUSTRIES; *U.S. Private*, pg. 998
SIMPSON TIMBER CO.—Simpson Investment Co.; *U.S. Private*, pg. 1003
JEFFERSON SMURFIT CORPORATION—Jefferson Smurfit Group p.l.c.; *Int'l*, pg. 1269
SOLON MANUFACTURING COMPANY; *U.S. Private*, pg. 1013
STRUCTURAL INDUSTRIES, INC.; *U.S. Private*, pg. 1048
SUPREME INDUSTRIES, INC.; *U.S. Public*, pg. 1541
THREE BRANCHES, INC.—Carris Financial Group; *U.S. Private*, pg. 215
TRUE TEMPER SPORTS DIVISION—The Black & Decker Corporation; *U.S. Public*, pg. 233
TUBAFOR MILL INC.—E.R. Probyn Ltd.; *Int'l*, pg. 1071
TURNER, DAY & WOOLWORTH HANDLE CORP.—O.P. Link Handle Company; *U.S. Private*, pg. 669
VERMONT TUBBS, INC.—Carris Financial Group; *U.S. Private*, pg. 215
VILLAUME INDUSTRIES, INC.; *U.S. Private*, pg. 1140
WALPOLE WOODWORKERS, INC.; *U.S. Private*, pg. 1148
WESTON GALLERY—Wilton Industries, Inc.; *U.S. Private*, pg. 1182
WILLAMETTE INDUSTRIES, INC.—Willamette Industries, Inc.; *U.S. Public*, pg. 1769
ZENITH PRODUCTS CORP.—Masco Corporation; *U.S. Public*, pg. 1054
ZIMDAR ENTERPRISES/FRAMES UNLIMITED; *U.S. Private*, pg. 1206

2511 — WOOD HOUSEHOLD FURNITURE, EXCEPT UPHOLSTERED

ACCENTRICS DIVISION—Pulaski Furniture Corporation; *U.S. Public*, pg. 1342
ACMETRACK—BTR plc; *Int'l*, pg. 129
AMANA SOCIETY, INC.; *U.S. Private*, pg. 48
AMERICAN DREW—Ladd Furniture, Inc.; *U.S. Public*, pg. 974
AMERICAN FURNITURE COMPANY, INCORPORATED—Ladd Furniture, Inc.; *U.S. Public*, pg. 974
AMERIWOOD INDUSTRIES INTERNATIONAL INC.; *U.S. Public*, pg. 98
ARMSTRONG WORLD INDUSTRIES, INC.; *U.S. Public*, pg. 131
ASAHI KOGYO CO., LTD.—Hitachi, Ltd.; *Int'l*, pg. 621
ASSOCIATED FURNITURE COMPANIES LTD.—South African Breweries, Ltd.; *Int'l*, pg. 1286
BASIC AMERICAN MEDICAL PRODUCTS, INC.—Graham-Field Health Products, Inc.; *U.S. Public*, pg. 758
BASSETT CHAIR CO.—Bassett Furniture Industries, Incorporated; *U.S. Public*, pg. 193
BASSETT FURNITURE CO.—Bassett Furniture Industries, Incorporated; *U.S. Public*, pg. 193
BASSETT FURNITURE INDUSTRIES, INCORPORATED; *U.S. Public*, pg. 193
BASSETT FURNITURE INDUSTRIES OF NORTH CAROLINA INC.—Bassett Furniture Industries, Incorporated; *U.S. Public*, pg. 193
BASSETT SUPERIOR LINES—Bassett Furniture Industries, Incorporated; *U.S. Public*, pg. 193
BASSETT TABLE CO.—Bassett Furniture Industries, Incorporated; *U.S. Public*, pg. 193
W.M. BASSETT FURNITURE CO.—Bassett Furniture Industries, Incorporated; *U.S. Public*, pg. 193
S. BENT & BROTHERS, INC.; *U.S. Private*, pg. 134
BERNHARDT FURNITURE CO.; *U.S. Private*, pg. 137
BRITTANY CORPORATION; *U.S. Private*, pg. 169
BROWN JORDAN COMPANY; *U.S. Private*, pg. 174
BROYHILL FURNITURE INDUSTRIES, INC.—Furniture Brands International Inc.; *U.S. Public*, pg. 688
BRUNSCHWIG & FILS, INC.; *U.S. Private*, pg. 176
BUSH INDUSTRIES INC.; *U.S. Public*, pg. 270
CARFTIQUE, INC.—Pulaski Furniture Corporation; *U.S. Public*, pg. 1342
CENTURY FURNITURE INDUSTRIES; *U.S. Private*, pg. 226
CENTURY PRODUCTS CO.; *U.S. Private*, pg. 226
CHROMCRAFT REVINGTON, INC.; *U.S. Public*, pg. 352
CLEVELAND CHAIR COMPANY—Jackson Furniture Industries; *U.S. Private*, pg. 579
COCHRANE FURNITURE CO., INC.—Chromcraft Revington, Inc.; *U.S. Public*, pg. 352
COMMERCIAL SEATING DIVISION—Flexsteel Industries, Inc.; *U.S. Public*, pg. 654
CRAFTIQUE—Pulaski Furniture Corporation; *U.S. Public*, pg. 1343
DMI FURNITURE INC.; *U.S. Public*, pg. 473
DMI FURNITURE, INC.—DMI Furniture Inc.; *U.S. Public*, pg. 473
DINAIRE CORP.; *U.S. Private*, pg. 334
DIRECTIONAL FURNITURE—CF Group; *U.S. Private*, pg. 193
DREXEL HERITAGE FURNISHINGS INC.—Furnishings International, Inc.; *U.S. Private*, pg. 432
ETHAN ALLEN, INC.—Ethan Allen Interiors Inc.; *U.S. Public*, pg. 595
ETHAN ALLEN INTERIORS INC.; *U.S. Public*, pg. 595
EVENFLO COMPANY, INC.—Kohlberg Kravis Roberts & Co.; *U.S. Private*, pg. 629
FOLEY MARTENS COMPANY—Foley-Belsaw Company; *U.S. Private*, pg. 416
FOURNIER FURNITURE; *U.S. Private*, pg. 422
FURNITURE BRANDS INTERNATIONAL INC.; *U.S. Public*, *pg. 688*
GOOD COMPANIES; *U.S. Private*, pg. 463
GORDON'S INC.—Furniture Brands International Inc.; *U.S. Public*, pg. 688
HAMMARY FURNITURE CO.—La-Z-Boy Incorporated; *U.S. Public*, pg. 973
HELIKON FURNITURE CO., INC.; *U.S. Private*, pg. 520
HENREDON FURNITURE INDUSTRIES, INC.—Furnishings International, Inc.; *U.S. Private*, pg. 432
HENREDON UPHOLSTERY—Furnishings International, Inc.; *U.S. Private*, pg. 432
HILL-ROM COMPANY, INC.—Hillenbrand Industries, Inc.; *U.S. Public*, pg. 828
HOMEWORTHY FURNITURE LTD.—Silentnight Holdings Plc; *Int'l*, pg. 1249
HOOKER FURNITURE CORPORATION; *U.S. Private*, pg. 538
IDEAL FORM TEAM S.R.L.; *Int'l*, pg. 659
IMPACT FURNITURE CO. INC.—Bassett Furniture Industries, Incorporated; *U.S. Public*, pg. 193
THE KARGES FURNITURE COMPANY INC.; *U.S. Private*, pg. 607
THE KELLER MANUFACTURING CO., INC.; *U.S. Private*, pg. 612
KIMBALL INTERNATIONAL, INC.; *U.S. Public*, pg. 956
KINCAID FURNITURE CO., INC.—La-Z-Boy Incorporated; *U.S. Public*, pg. 972
KINDEL FURNITURE COMPANY; *U.S. Private*, pg. 620
KITCHEN KOMPACT, INC.; *U.S. Private*, pg. 624
LA-Z-BOY INCORPORATED; *U.S. Public*, pg. 972
LADD FURNITURE, INC.; *U.S. Public*, pg. 974
THE LANE COMPANY, INC.—Furniture Brands International Inc.; *U.S. Public*, pg. 688
LEA INDUSTRIES—Ladd Furniture, Inc.; *U.S. Public*, pg. 974
LEGGETT & PLATT, INCORPORATED; *U.S. Public*, pg. 985
LEISURE LIFE, INC.—Ajay Sports Inc.; *U.S. Public*, pg. 34
LEXINGTON FURNITURE INDUSTRIES—Furnishings International, Inc.; *U.S. Private*, pg. 432
LIFESTYLE FURNISHINGS INTERNATIONAL, LTD.—Furnishings International, Inc.; *U.S. Private*, pg. 431
MAITLAND-SMITH U.S., INC.—Furnishings International, Inc.; *U.S. Private*, pg. 432
MASCO CORPORATION; *U.S. Public*, pg. 1052

MASCO CORPORATION LIMITED—Masco Corporation; *U.S. Public*, pg. 1054
METRO AG; *Int'l*, pg. 863
MOBEL UNGER GMBH—Metro AG; *Int'l*, pg. 863
MUEBLES FINO BUENO—Good Companies; *U.S. Private*, pg. 463
NATIONAL BEDDING CO.—National Bedding Co.; *U.S. Private*, pg. 780
NORWALK FURNITURE CORPORATION; *U.S. Private*, pg. 807
NORWALK FURNITURE CORPORATION OF TENNESSEE—Norwalk Furniture Corporation; *U.S. Private*, pg. 808
OKLA HOMER SMITH FURNITURE CO.—Century Products Co.; *U.S. Private*, pg. 226
THE PACE COLLECTION; *U.S. Private*, pg. 829
PAOLI, INC.; *U.S. Private*, pg. 837
PARK-OHIO INDUSTRIES, INC.; *U.S. Public*, pg. 1258
PETERS-REVINGTON CORP.—Chromcraft Revington, Inc.; *U.S. Public*, pg. 352
PULASKI FURNITURE CORPORATION; *U.S. Public*, pg. 1342
PULASKI FURNITURE-DUBLIN—Pulaski Furniture Corporation; *U.S. Public*, pg. 1343
PULASKI FURNITURE-MARTINSVILLE—Pulaski Furniture Corporation; *U.S. Public*, pg. 1343
RED CALLIOPE & ASSOCIATES, INC.—Crown Crafts, Inc.; *U.S. Public*, pg. 465
RESTONIC MATTRESS CORPORATION; *U.S. Private*, pg. 925
RICHARDSON INDUSTRIES, INC.; *U.S. Private*, pg. 929
ROSPATCH JESSCO, INC.—Ameriwood Industries International Inc.; *U.S. Public*, pg. 98
ROWE FURNITURE CORP.; *U.S. Public*, pg. 1410
SAUDER WOODWORKING CO.; *U.S. Private*, pg. 967
SAUNDERS BROTHERS; *U.S. Private*, pg. 968
SCHNADIG CORPORATION; *U.S. Private*, pg. 971
SEALY CORPORATION; *U.S. Private*, pg. 978
SILENTNIGHT HOLDINGS PLC; *Int'l*, pg. 1249
SILVER FURNITURE CO., INC.—Chromcraft Revington, Inc.; *U.S. Public*, pg. 352
SIMMONS JUVENILE PRODUCTS; *U.S. Private*, pg. 1001
SPALDING & EVENFLO COMPANIES, INC.—Kohlberg Kravis Roberts & Co.; *U.S. Private*, pg. 629
SPECTRUM INDUSTRIES, INC.; *U.S. Private*, pg. 1024
STANLEY FURNITURE CO. INC.; *U.S. Public*, pg. 1508
STONEVILLE FURNITURE CO. INC.; *U.S. Private*, pg. 1045
SUNLITE FURNITURE—U.S. Industries, Inc.; *U.S. Public*, pg. 1684
SWANER HARDWOOD COMPANY, INC.; *U.S. Private*, pg. 1057
TELESCOPE CASUAL FURNITURE, INC.; *U.S. Private*, pg. 1074
THOMASVILLE FURNITURE INDUSTRIES, INC.—Furniture Brands International Inc.; *U.S. Public*, pg. 688
TOWNE SQUARE FURNITURE, INC.; *U.S. Private*, pg. 1093
TRU-SPACE—Therma-Tru Corp.; *U.S. Private*, pg. 1080
UNION CITY CHAIR CO.—Brittany Corporation; *U.S. Private*, pg. 170
U.S. FURNITURE INDUSTRIES, INC.; *U.S. Private*, pg. 1125
UNIVERSAL FURNITURE INDUSTRIES, INC.—Furnishings International, Inc.; *U.S. Private*, pg. 432
WOODLORE—Allen-Edmonds Shoe Corp.; *U.S. Private*, pg. 37
WOODSTUFF MANUFACTURING, INC.; *U.S. Private*, pg. 1187

2512 — WOOD HOUSEHOLD FURNITURE, UPHOLSTERED

ACCENTRICS DIVISION—Pulaski Furniture Corporation; *U.S. Public*, pg. 1342
ACTION INDUSTRIES, INC.—Furniture Brands International Inc.; *U.S. Public*, pg. 688
AMERICAN DREW—Ladd Furniture, Inc.; *U.S. Public*, pg. 974
AMERICAN FURNITURE COMPANY, INCORPORATED—Ladd Furniture, Inc.; *U.S. Public*, pg. 974
AVON WORKSHOP FICKS REED; *U.S. Private*, pg. 102
BARCALOUNGER COMPANY—Consolidated Furniture Corporation; *U.S. Private*, pg. 265
BARCLAY FURNITURE COMPANY—Ladd Furniture, Inc.; *U.S. Public*, pg. 974
BASSETT FURNITURE INDUSTRIES, INCORPORATED; *U.S. Public*, pg. 193
BASSETT MOTION DIVISION—Bassett Furniture Industries, Incorporated; *U.S. Public*, pg. 193
BASSETT UPHOLSTERY DIVISION—Bassett Furniture Industries, Incorporated; *U.S. Public*, pg. 193
BENCH CRAFT, INC.—Furnishings International, Inc.; *U.S. Private*, pg. 432
THE BERKLINE CORPORATION—Furnishings International, Inc.; *U.S. Private*, pg. 432
BERKLINE, INC.—Furnishings International, Inc.; *U.S. Private*, pg. 432
BERKSHIRE FURNITURE CO.—Leggett & Platt, Incorporated; *U.S. Public*, pg. 985
BERNHARDT FURNITURE CO.; *U.S. Private*, pg. 137
BROYHILL FURNITURE INDUSTRIES, INC.—Furniture Brands International Inc.; *U.S. Public*, pg. 688
CARLTON MANUFACTURING, INC.; *U.S. Private*, pg. 212
CENTURY FURNITURE INDUSTRIES; *U.S. Private*, pg. 226
CHROMCRAFT REVINGTON, INC.; *U.S. Public*, pg. 352
CLAYTON-MARCUS COMPANY, INC.—Ladd Furniture, Inc.; *U.S. Public*, pg. 975
COCHRANE FURNITURE CO., INC.—Chromcraft Revington, Inc.; *U.S. Public*, pg. 352
COMMERCIAL SEATING DIVISION—Flexsteel Industries, Inc.; *U.S. Public*, pg. 654
CONSOLIDATED FURNITURE CORPORATION; *U.S. Private*, pg. 265
COX FURNITURE; *U.S. Private*, pg. 283
DIRECTIONAL FURNITURE—CF Group; *U.S. Private*, pg. 193
DREXEL HERITAGE FURNISHINGS INC.—Furnishings International, Inc.; *U.S. Private*, pg. 432
ENGLAND/CORSAIR—La-Z-Boy Incorporated; *U.S. Public*, pg. 972
ETHAN ALLEN, INC.—Ethan Allen Interiors Inc.; *U.S. Public*, pg. 595
ETHAN ALLEN INTERIORS INC.; *U.S. Public*, pg. 595
FLEXSTEEL DIVISION—Flexsteel Industries, Inc.; *U.S. Public*, pg. 654
FLEXSTEEL INDUSTRIES, INC.; *U.S. Public*, pg. 653
FRAENKEL COMPANY; *U.S. Private*, pg. 423
FURNISHINGS INTERNATIONAL, INC.; *U.S. Private*, pg. 431
FURNITURE BRANDS INTERNATIONAL INC.; *U.S. Public*, pg. 688
GROUPE STRAFOR FACOM; *Int'l*, pg. 569
HAMMARY FURNITURE CO.—La-Z-Boy Incorporated; *U.S. Public*, pg. 973
HARDEN FURNITURE COMPANY; *U.S. Private*, pg. 501
HENREDON FURNITURE INDUSTRIES, INC.—Furnishings International, Inc.; *U.S. Private*, pg. 432
HICKORY CHAIR DIV.—Furniture Brands International Inc.; *U.S. Public*, pg. 688
HICKORY HILL FURNITURE CORPORATION—Norwalk Furniture Corporation; *U.S. Private*, pg. 808
HITCHCOCK CHAIR COMPANY LTD; *U.S. Private*, pg. 531
HOMEWORTHY FURNITURE LTD.—Silentnight Holdings Plc; *Int'l*, pg. 1249
JACKSON FURNITURE INDUSTRIES; *U.S. Private*, pg. 579
KIMBALL FURNITURE REPRODUCTIONS—Kimball International, Inc.; *U.S. Public*, pg. 957
KIMBALL INTERNATIONAL, INC.; *U.S. Public*, pg. 956
KINDEL FURNITURE COMPANY; *U.S. Private*, pg. 620
KLAUSSNER CORPORATION; *U.S. Private*, pg. 625
KLAUSSNER FURNITURE INDUSTRY—Klaussner Corporation; *U.S. Private*, pg. 625
KROEHLER FURNITURE MANUFACTURING COMPANY, INC.—Schottenstein Stores Corporation; *U.S. Private*, pg. 972
LA-Z-BOY ARKANSAS—La-Z-Boy Incorporated; *U.S. Public*, pg. 973
LA-Z-BOY CANADA LTD.—La-Z-Boy Incorporated; *U.S. Public*, pg. 973
LA-Z-BOY EAST—La-Z-Boy Incorporated; *U.S. Public*, pg. 973
LA-Z-BOY LELAND—La-Z-Boy Incorporated; *U.S. Public*, pg. 973
LA-Z-BOY MIDWEST—La-Z-Boy Incorporated; *U.S. Public*, pg. 973
LA-Z-BOY SOUTH—La-Z-Boy Incorporated; *U.S. Public*, pg. 973
LA-Z-BOY TENNESSEE—La-Z-Boy Incorporated; *U.S. Public*, pg. 973
LA-Z-BOY UTAH—La-Z-Boy Incorporated; *U.S. Public*, pg. 973
LA-Z-BOY WEST—La-Z-Boy Incorporated; *U.S. Public*, pg. 973
LADD FURNITURE, INC.; *U.S. Public*, pg. 974
THE LANE COMPANY, INC.—Furniture Brands International Inc.; *U.S. Public*, pg. 688
LANE UPHOLSTERY—Furniture Brands International Inc.; *U.S. Public*, pg. 688
LAYEZEE BEDS—Silentnight Holdings Plc; *Int'l*, pg. 1249
LEATHER CENTER, INC.; *U.S. Private*, pg. 656
LEXINGTON FURNITURE INDUSTRIES—Furnishings International, Inc.; *U.S. Private*, pg. 432
LIFESTYLE FURNISHINGS INTERNATIONAL, LTD.—Furnishings International, Inc.; *U.S. Private*, pg. 431
MACTAVISH FURNITURE INDUSTRIES—Aaron Rents, Inc.; *U.S. Public*, pg. 12
MACTAVISH FURNITURE INDUSTRIES, COOLIDGE FACTORY—Aaron Rents, Inc.; *U.S. Public*, pg. 12
MASCO CORPORATION; *U.S. Public*, pg. 1052
MASCO CORPORATION LIMITED—Masco Corporation; *U.S. Public*, pg. 1054
METRO AG; *Int'l*, pg. 863
MOBEL UNGER GMBH—Metro AG; *Int'l*, pg. 863
NORWALK FURNITURE CORPORATION; *U.S. Private*, pg. 807
CLYDE PEARSON DIV.—Furniture Brands International Inc.; *U.S. Public*, pg. 688
PENNSYLVANIA HOUSE CASEGOODS—Ladd Furniture, Inc.; *U.S. Public*, pg. 975
PULASKI FURNITURE-CHRISTIANSBURG—Pulaski Furniture Corporation; *U.S. Public*, pg. 1343
PULASKI FURNITURE CORPORATION; *U.S. Public*, pg. 1342
ROWE FURNITURE CORP.; *U.S. Public*, pg. 1410
SCHNADIG CORPORATION; *U.S. Private*, pg. 971
SHELBY WILLIAMS INDUSTRIES, INC.; *U.S. Public*, pg. 1464
SILENTNIGHT HOLDINGS PLC; *Int'l*, pg. 1249
STAKMORE INC.; *U.S. Private*, pg. 1029
STANLEY FURNITURE CO. INC.; *U.S. Public*, pg. 1508
STRATOLOUNGER—Consolidated Furniture Corporation; *U.S. Private*, pg. 265
TELESCOPE CASUAL FURNITURE, INC.; *U.S. Private*, pg. 1074
THOMASVILLE UPHOLSTERY, INC.—Furniture Brands International Inc.; *U.S. Public*, pg. 688
UNION CITY CHAIR CO.—Brittany Corporation; *U.S. Private*, pg. 170
U.S. FURNITURE INDUSTRIES, INC.; *U.S. Private*, pg. 1125
VENTURE FURNITURE DIV.—Furniture Brands International Inc.; *U.S. Public*, pg. 688
WEIMAN—Bassett Furniture Industries, Incorporated; *U.S. Public*, pg. 193
WOODMARK ORIGINALS INC.—Howard Miller; *U.S. Private*, pg. 747

2514 — METAL HOUSEHOLD FURNITURE

ACCENTRICS DIVISION—Pulaski Furniture Corporation; *U.S. Public*, pg. 1342
ALL-LUMINUM PRODUCTS, INC.; *U.S. Private*, pg. 34
ASAHI KOGYO CO., LTD.—Hitachi, Ltd.; *Int'l*, pg. 621
BENCH CRAFT, INC.—Furnishings International, Inc.; *U.S. Private*, pg. 432
BENSON CORP.—Gem Industries Finance Corporation; *U.S. Private*, pg. 443
BERKSHIRE FURNITURE CO.—Leggett & Platt, Incorporated; *U.S. Public*, pg. 985
CC INDUSTRIES, INC.; *U.S. Private*, pg. 192
CASTELLI S.P.A.—Haworth, Inc.; *U.S. Private*, pg. 512
CHROMCRAFT CORPORATION—Chromcraft Revington, Inc.; *U.S. Public*, pg. 352
CHROMCRAFT REVINGTON, INC.; *U.S. Public*, pg. 352
CLAIRSON INTERNATIONAL CORP.—Emerson Electric Co.; *U.S. Public*, pg. 575
CLEVELAND CHAIR COMPANY—Jackson Furniture Industries; *U.S. Private*, pg. 579
COSCO, INC.; *U.S. Private*, pg. 277
DIRECTIONAL FURNITURE—CF Group; *U.S. Private*, pg. 193
DRESHER, INC.—Leggett & Platt, Incorporated; *U.S. Public*, pg. 986
ENERGY BROKERS GUILD; *U.S. Private*, pg. 376
FANTA FURNITURE—All-Luminum Products, Inc.; *U.S. Private*, pg. 35
FINKEL OUTDOOR PRODUCTS, INC.—Trace International Holdings, Inc.; *U.S. Private*, pg. 1094
FLANDERS INDUSTRIES, INC.; *U.S. Private*, pg. 410
FLEXIBLE FLYER TOYS; *U.S. Private*, pg. 412
GEM INDUSTRIES NE INC.—Gem Industries Finance Corporation; *U.S. Private*, pg. 442
GEM SOUTHEAST, INC.—Gem Industries Finance Corporation; *U.S. Private*, pg. 443
GORDON'S INC.—Furniture Brands International Inc.; *U.S. Public*, pg. 688
HEDSTROM CORPORATION—Hicks, Muse, Tate & Furst Inc.; *U.S. Private*, pg. 526
HUNTER DOUGLAS FABRICATION COMPANY—Hunter Douglas N.V.; *Int'l*, pg. 639
IXL CABINETS—Triangle Pacific Corporation; *U.S. Public*, pg. 1634
JENSEN INDUSTRIES—Nortek, Inc.; *U.S. Public*, pg. 1193
KELLER LADDERS INC.—U.S. Industries, Inc.; *U.S. Public*, pg. 1684
LABARGE MIRRORS, INC.—Furnishings International, Inc.; *U.S. Private*, pg. 432
LADD FURNITURE, INC.; *U.S. Public*, pg. 974
LEGGETT & PLATT, INCORPORATED; *U.S. Public*, pg. 985
LIFESTYLE FURNISHINGS INTERNATIONAL, LTD.—Furnishings International, Inc.; *U.S. Private*, pg. 431
MASTERCRAFT FURNITURE CORP.; *U.S. Private*, pg. 714
MEADOWCRAFT, INC.; *U.S. Private*, pg. 725
MECO CORPORATION; *U.S. Private*, pg. 726
MOBEL UNGER GMBH—Metro AG; *Int'l*, pg. 863
MOHAWK FURNITURE, INC.—Gem Industries Finance Corporation; *U.S. Private*, pg. 443
NORTEK, INC.; *U.S. Public*, pg. 1192
PARK-OHIO INDUSTRIES, INC.; *U.S. Public*, pg. 1258
RENCO GROUP; *U.S. Private*, pg. 922
RESTONIC MATTRESS CORPORATION; *U.S. Private*, pg. 925
ROWE FURNITURE CORP.; *U.S. Public*, pg. 1410
SILVER FURNITURE CO., INC.—Chromcraft Revington, Inc.; *U.S. Public*, pg. 352
SLEEPEEZEE LIMITED; *Int'l*, pg. 1263
STANLEY FURNITURE CO. INC.; *U.S. Public*, pg. 1508
STONEVILLE FURNITURE CO. INC.; *U.S. Private*, pg. 1045
TAKARA STANDARD CO., LTD.—Takara Belmont Co., Ltd.; *Int'l*, pg. 1349
TELESCOPE CASUAL FURNITURE, INC.; *U.S. Private*, pg. 1074
THE TURNER & SEYMOUR MFG. COMPANY; *U.S. Private*, pg. 1109
UNITED RECEPTICAL, INC.; *U.S. Private*, pg. 1123
U.S. FURNITURE INDUSTRIES, INC.; *U.S. Private*, pg. 1125
VIRCO MFG. CORPORATION; *U.S. Public*, pg. 1721
VIRSAN S.A. DE C.V.—Virco Mfg. Corporation; *U.S. Public*, pg. 1721
WELLINGTON INDUSTRIES INC.; *U.S. Private*, pg. 1161
WOODARD INC.—CC Industries, Inc.; *U.S. Private*, pg. 192
ZENITH PRODUCTS CORP.—Masco Corporation; *U.S. Public*, pg. 1054

2515 — MATTRESSES, FOUNDATIONS & CONVERTIBLE BEDS

W.S. BADCOCK CORPORATION; *U.S. Private*, pg. 109
BASSETT FURNITURE INDUSTRIES, INCORPORATED; *U.S. Public*, pg. 193
BLUE BELL/KING KOIL, INC.; *U.S. Private*, pg. 150
CENTRAL DE INDUSTRIAS, S.A.—Lear Corporation; *U.S. Public*, pg. 982
CHITTENDEN & EASTMAN CO.; *U.S. Private*, pg. 237
COSCO, INC.; *U.S. Private*, pg. 277
CRAFTMATIC INDUSTRIES, INC.; *U.S. Private*, pg. 284
DRESHER, INC.—Leggett & Platt, Incorporated; *U.S. Public*, pg. 986
EASTMAN HOUSE OF ALABAMA, INC.—Chittenden & Eastman Co.; *U.S. Private*, pg. 238
EASTMAN HOUSE OF CALIFORNIA, INC.—Chittenden & Eastman Co.; *U.S. Private*, pg. 238

ETHAN ALLEN INTERIORS INC.; *U.S. Public*, pg. 595
FRAENKEL COMPANY; *U.S. Private*, pg. 423
GERBER PRODUCTS DIVISION-BABY CARE—Novartis AG; *Int'l*, pg. 973
HAMMARY FURNITURE CO.—La-Z-Boy Incorporated; *U.S. Public*, pg. 973
JAMISON BEDDING, INC.; *U.S. Private*, pg. 581
KING KOIL LICENSING COMPANY INC.; *U.S. Private*, pg. 621
LAYEZEE BEDS—Silentnight Holdings Plc; *Int'l*, pg. 1249
LEGGETT & PLATT, INCORPORATED; *U.S. Public*, pg. 985
E.B. MALONE CORP.—Bassett Furniture Industries, Incorporated; *U.S. Public*, pg. 193
MERINOS; *Int'l*, pg. 858
NATIONAL BEDDING CO.; *U.S. Private*, pg. 780
NATIONAL BEDDING CO.—National Bedding Co.; *U.S. Private*, pg. 780
NOEL JOANNA, INC.—Crown Crafts, Inc.; *U.S. Public*, pg. 465
THE OHIO MATTRESS COMPANY LICENSING & COMPONENTS GROUP—Sealy Corporation; *U.S. Private*, pg. 979
OHIO-SEALY MATTRESS MANUFACTURING CO.-FORT WORTH—Sealy Corporation; *U.S. Private*, pg. 979
OHIO-SEALY MATTRESS MANUFACTURING CO.-HOUSTON—Sealy Corporation; *U.S. Private*, pg. 979
RED CALLIOPE & ASSOCIATES, INC.—Crown Crafts, Inc.; *U.S. Public*, pg. 465
RESTONIC MATTRESS CORPORATION; *U.S. Private*, pg. 925
SCHUBERT INDUSTRIES INC.; *U.S. Private*, pg. 973
SEALY CORPORATION; *U.S. Private*, pg. 978
SEALY OF MARYLAND & VIRGINIA, INC.—Sealy Corporation; *U.S. Private*, pg. 979
SEALY OF MINNESOTA, INC.—Sealy Corporation; *U.S. Private*, pg. 979
SERTA, INC.—Serta Mattress Company; *U.S. Private*, pg. 985
SERTA MATTRESS COMPANY; *U.S. Private*, pg. 985
SILENTNIGHT HOLDINGS PLC; *Int'l*, pg. 1249
SIMMONS COMPANY—Investcorp International; *Int'l*, pg. 686
SLEEPEEZE LIMITED; *Int'l*, pg. 1263
SPAN-AMERICA MEDICAL SYSTEMS INC.; *U.S. Public*, pg. 1495
THE SPRINGWALL MATTRESS CO.—Schubert Industries Inc.; *U.S. Private*, pg. 973
THE STEARNS & FOSTER BEDDING COMPANY—Sealy Corporation; *U.S. Private*, pg. 979
STRATOLOUNGER—Consolidated Furniture Corporation; *U.S. Private*, pg. 265
THERAPEDIC ASSOCIATES, INC.; *U.S. Private*, pg. 1079
VI-SPRING LIMITED—Newmond PLC; *Int'l*, pg. 925
YOUNG SPRING & WIRE COMPANY—Leggett & Platt, Incorporated; *U.S. Public*, pg. 987

2517 — WOOD TELEVISION, RADIO, PHONOGRAPH & SEWING MACHINE CABINETS

AMERIWOOD INDUSTRIES INTERNATIONAL INC.; *U.S. Public*, pg. 98
BOSE CANADA, INC.—Bose Corporation; *U.S. Private*, pg. 161
HERITAGE HILLS—Kimball International, Inc.; *U.S. Public*, pg. 957
JASPER CORPORATION—Kimball International, Inc.; *U.S. Public*, pg. 957
KIMBALL INTERNATIONAL, INC.; *U.S. Public*, pg. 956
THE PACE COLLECTION; *U.S. Private*, pg. 829
RUTT CUSTOM CABINETRY—Harrow Industries; *U.S. Private*, pg. 507
SPRINGS VALLEY MFG.—Kimball International, Inc.; *U.S. Public*, pg. 957
TIFFIN ENTERPRISES, INC.—Ameriwood Industries International Inc.; *U.S. Public*, pg. 98
TOSHIBA ELECTROMEX, S.A. DE C.V.—Toshiba Corporation; *Int'l*, pg. 1406
WILLCOX & GIBBS, INC.; *U.S. Private*, pg. 1177

2519 — HOUSEHOLD FURNITURE, NEC

ACCENTRICS DIVISION—Pulaski Furniture Corporation; *U.S. Public*, pg. 1342
ALL-LUMINUM PRODUCTS, INC.; *U.S. Private*, pg. 34
ARTEK OY AB—Proventus AB; *Int'l*, pg. 1072
AVON WORKSHOP FICKS REED; *U.S. Private*, pg. 102
BERKSHIRE FURNITURE CO.—Leggett & Platt, Incorporated; *U.S. Public*, pg. 985
BURLINGTON BASKET CO.; *U.S. Private*, pg. 183
DIRECTIONAL FURNITURE—CF Group; *U.S. Private*, pg. 193
FANTA FURNITURE—All-Luminum Products, Inc.; *U.S. Private*, pg. 35
FOURNIER FURNITURE; *U.S. Private*, pg. 422
HOOKER FURNITURE CORPORATION; *U.S. Private*, pg. 538
M. KAMENSTEIN, INC.; *U.S. Private*, pg. 606
KETER PLASTIC LTD.; *Int'l*, pg. 732
LADD FURNITURE, INC.; *U.S. Public*, pg. 974
LAWNWARE PRODUCTS, INC.; *U.S. Private*, pg. 653
LEATHER CENTER, INC.; *U.S. Private*, pg. 656
MOBEL UNGER GMBH—Metro AG; *Int'l*, pg. 863
PIONEER PLASTICS CORPORATION; *U.S. Private*, pg. 867
PULASKI FURNITURE CORPORATION; *U.S. Public*, pg. 1342
PULASKI FURNITURE-MARTINSVILLE—Pulaski Furniture Corporation; *U.S. Public*, pg. 1343
ROWE FURNITURE CORP.; *U.S. Public*, pg. 1410
STANLEY FURNITURE CO. INC.; *U.S. Public*, pg. 1508
THE STEARNS & FOSTER BEDDING COMPANY—Sealy Corporation; *U.S. Private*, pg. 979
THIS END UP FURNITURE; *U.S. Private*, pg. 1081
TOSHIBA ELECTROMEX, S.A. DE C.V.—Toshiba Corporation; *Int'l*, pg. 1406
TROPITONE FURNITURE CO. INC.; *U.S. Private*, pg. 1105
UNIVERSAL (HONG KONG TEAKWOOD)—Furnishings International, Inc.; *U.S. Private*, pg. 432
ZENITH PRODUCTS CORP.—Masco Corporation; *U.S. Public*, pg. 1054

2521 — WOOD OFFICE FURNITURE

AF SISTEMAS SA—Groupe Strafor Facom; *Int'l*, pg. 569
ABCO—Jami, Inc.; *U.S. Private*, pg. 581
ACCO EUROPE PLC—Fortune Brands, Inc.; *U.S. Public*, pg. 674
ACCO FRANCE S.A.—Fortune Brands, Inc.; *U.S. Public*, pg. 675
ACCO UK LIMITED—Fortune Brands, Inc.; *U.S. Public*, pg. 675
ANDERSON HICKEY, INC.—Haworth, Inc.; *U.S. Private*, pg. 512
ARTEC MANUFACTURING—Kimball International, Inc.; *U.S. Public*, pg. 957
ASHBY & HORNER JOINERY LTD.—The Peninsular and Oriental Steam Navigation Company; *Int'l*, pg. 1032
ASSOCIATED FURNITURE COMPANIES LTD.—South African Breweries, Ltd.; *Int'l*, pg. 1286
BASSETT FURNITURE INDUSTRIES, INCORPORATED; *U.S. Public*, pg. 193
BELVEDERE COMPANY—Smith Investment Company; *U.S. Private*, pg. 1008
BRAYTON INTERNATIONAL INC.—Steelcase Inc.; *U.S. Private*, pg. 1038
BRODART COMPANY; *U.S. Private*, pg. 170
BUSH INDUSTRIES INC.; *U.S. Public*, pg. 270
CARTER HOLT HARVEY LIMITED—International Paper Company; *U.S. Public*, pg. 904
CASSINA—Groupe Strafor Facom; *Int'l*, pg. 570
CEMAC COMMERCIAL INTERIORS LTD.—International Paper Company; *U.S. Public*, pg. 905
CHROMCRAFT CORPORATION—Chromcraft Revington, Inc.; *U.S. Public*, pg. 352
CHROMCRAFT REVINGTON, INC.; *U.S. Public*, pg. 352
CLESTRA HAUSERMAN KOREA—Groupe Strafor Facom; *Int'l*, pg. 569
COLLIER-KEYWORTH, INC.—Leggett & Platt, Incorporated; *U.S. Public*, pg. 985
COMMUNITY—Jasper Seating Co., Inc.; *U.S. Private*, pg. 583
CORRYHIEBERT CORPORATION—HON Industries Inc.; *U.S. Public*, pg. 772
CRAMER INC.; *U.S. Private*, pg. 285
DMI FURNITURE INC.; *U.S. Public*, pg. 473
DMI FURNITURE, INC.—DMI Furniture Inc.; *U.S. Public*, pg. 473
DOMORE CORPORATION; *U.S. Private*, pg. 339
EAC CORPORATION; *U.S. Private*, pg. 353
ETHAN ALLEN INTERIORS INC.; *U.S. Public*, pg. 595
EUROSEEL EQUIPAMENTOS METALICOS, SA—Groupe Strafor Facom; *Int'l*, pg. 569
EWING TOWNSHIP-NEW JERSEY DIV.—EAC Corporation; *U.S. Private*, pg. 353
FALCON-BELDING—Falcon Products, Inc.; *U.S. Public*, pg. 611
FALCON DE JUAREZ, S.A. DE C.V.—Falcon Products, Inc.; *U.S. Public*, pg. 611
FALCON-LEWISVILLE—Falcon Products, Inc.; *U.S. Public*, pg. 611
FALCON-NEWPORT—Falcon Products, Inc.; *U.S. Public*, pg. 611
FALCON PRODUCTS, INC.; *U.S. Public*, pg. 611
FELTRAX INTERNATIONAL, INC.—BTR plc; *Int'l*, pg. 130
FIXTURES FURNITURE—Jami, Inc.; *U.S. Private*, pg. 581
FLEWELLING DIV.—EAC Corporation; *U.S. Private*, pg. 353
FRENCH LICK FURNITURE—Kimball International, Inc.; *U.S. Public*, pg. 957
FURNITURE GROUP INDUSTRIES; *U.S. Private*, pg. 432
GF OFFICE FURNITURE LTD.; *U.S. Private*, pg. 434
GLOBE BUSINESS FURNITURE, INC.—Haworth, Inc.; *U.S. Private*, pg. 512
THE GUNLOCKE COMPANY—HON Industries Inc.; *U.S. Public*, pg. 772
THE HON CO.—HON Industries Inc.; *U.S. Public*, pg. 772
HON INDUSTRIES INC.; *U.S. Public*, pg. 772
HALI-BUROMOBEL VERTRIEBS GESMBH; *Int'l*, pg. 589
HAWORTH, INC.; *U.S. Private*, pg. 511
HERMAN MILLER MEXICO—Herman Miller, Inc.; *U.S. Public*, pg. 1112
THE HON CO., LOUISBURG PLANT—HON Industries Inc.; *U.S. Public*, pg. 772
THE HON CO., OWENSBORO PLANT—HON Industries Inc.; *U.S. Public*, pg. 772
THE HON CO., WILLIAMSPORT PLANT—HON Industries Inc.; *U.S. Public*, pg. 772
HOWE FURNITURE CORPORATION; *U.S. Private*, pg. 543
HYUNDAI WOOD INDUSTRIES CO., LTD.—Hyundai Motor Company; *Int'l*, pg. 642
JSI—Jasper Seating Co., Inc.; *U.S. Private*, pg. 583
JAMI, INC.; *U.S. Private*, pg. 581
JASPER SEATING CO., INC.; *U.S. Private*, pg. 583
JOFCO INC.; *U.S. Private*, pg. 588
KIMBALL INTERNATIONAL, INC.; *U.S. Public*, pg. 956
KIMBALL OFFICE FURNITURE MANUFACTURING—Kimball International, Inc.; *U.S. Public*, pg. 957
KIMBALL UPHOLSTERED PRODUCTS—Kimball International, Inc.; *U.S. Public*, pg. 957
KINETICS, INC., A HAWORTH CO.—Haworth, Inc.; *U.S. Private*, pg. 512
KLAUSSNER FURNITURE INDUSTRY—Klaussner Corporation; *U.S. Private*, pg. 625
KNOLL, INC.; *U.S. Private*, pg. 627
KNOLL INTL., INC.—Knoll, Inc.; *U.S. Private*, pg. 627
LUNSTEAD, A HAWORTH CO.—Haworth, Inc.; *U.S. Private*, pg. 512
MACTAVISH FURNITURE INDUSTRIES—Aaron Rents, Inc.; *U.S. Public*, pg. 12
MACTAVISH FURNITURE INDUSTRIES, QUINCY OFFICE PLANT—Aaron Rents, Inc.; *U.S. Public*, pg. 12
MADISON FURNITURE INDUSTRIES—Shelby Williams Industries, Inc.; *U.S. Public*, pg. 1465
METROPOLITAN FURNITURE CORPORATION—Steelcase Inc.; *U.S. Private*, pg. 1038
HERMAN MILLER, INC.; *U.S. Public*, pg. 1111
MYRTLE/MUELLER, A HAWORTH CO.—Haworth, Inc.; *U.S. Private*, pg. 512
NATIONAL METAL INDUSTRIES—Standex International Corporation; *U.S. Public*, pg. 1506
NATIONAL MOUNT AIRY—Bassett Furniture Industries, Incorporated; *U.S. Public*, pg. 193
NATIONAL OFFICE FURNITURE MANUFACTURING—Kimball International, Inc.; *U.S. Public*, pg. 957
OSI—Tang Industries Inc.; *U.S. Private*, pg. 1068
O'SULLIVAN INDUSTRIES HOLDINGS; *U.S. Public*, pg. 1234
PCI TANDEM DIV.—Standard Pacific Corp.; *U.S. Public*, pg. 1504
THE PACE COLLECTION; *U.S. Private*, pg. 829
PAOLI, INC.; *U.S. Private*, pg. 837
POHLSCHRODER GMBH & CO. KG—Steelcase Inc.; *U.S. Private*, pg. 1038
PRECISION—Jami, Inc.; *U.S. Private*, pg. 581
ROWE FURNITURE CORP.; *U.S. Public*, pg. 1410
SAUDER MANUFACTURING CORPORATION; *U.S. Private*, pg. 967
SICAN CORP.; *U.S. Private*, pg. 997
SPECTRUM INDUSTRIES, INC.; *U.S. Private*, pg. 1024
STANDARD MANIFOLD COMPANY, INC.; *U.S. Private*, pg. 1031
STATHAM INDUSTRIES—International Paper Company; *U.S. Public*, pg. 905
STEELCASE INC.; *U.S. Private*, pg. 1038
STEELCASE STRAFOR—Groupe Strafor Facom; *Int'l*, pg. 569
STOW DAVIS FURNITURE CO.—Steelcase Inc.; *U.S. Private*, pg. 1038
THONET—Shelby Williams Industries, Inc.; *U.S. Public*, pg. 1465
UNITED CHAIR, INC.—Haworth, Inc.; *U.S. Private*, pg. 512
U.S. FURNITURE INDUSTRIES, INC.; *U.S. Private*, pg. 1125
WESTINGHOUSE INDUSTRIES & TECHNOLOGIES GROUP—CBS Corporation; *U.S. Public*, pg. 273

2522 — METAL OFFICE FURNITURE

ADI DATA FURNITURE—Esselte AB; *Int'l*, pg. 460
ADMC INC—Artco-Bell Corporation; *U.S. Private*, pg. 86
AF SISTEMAS SA—Groupe Strafor Facom; *Int'l*, pg. 569
AFD CONTRACT FURNITURE; *U.S. Private*, pg. 5
ABCO—Jami, Inc.; *U.S. Private*, pg. 581
ACCO EUROPE PLC—Fortune Brands, Inc.; *U.S. Public*, pg. 674
ACCO FRANCE S.A.—Fortune Brands, Inc.; *U.S. Public*, pg. 675
ACCO UK LIMITED—Fortune Brands, Inc.; *U.S. Public*, pg. 675
ACME DESIGN TECHNOLOGY, CO.; *U.S. Private*, pg. 13
ALLSTEEL, INC.—HON Industries Inc.; *U.S. Public*, pg. 772
AMES COLOR FILE DIVISION—Ames Safety Envelope Company, Inc.; *U.S. Private*, pg. 66
AMES SAFETY ENVELOPE COMPANY, INC.; *U.S. Private*, pg. 66
ANDERSON HICKEY, INC.—Haworth, Inc.; *U.S. Private*, pg. 512
APPLIED POWER INC.; *U.S. Public*, pg. 124
ARTCO-BELL CORPORATION; *U.S. Private*, pg. 86
BALTIMORE STATIONERY CO./TOTAL OFFICE; *U.S. Private*, pg. 113
BELVEDERE COMPANY—Smith Investment Company; *U.S. Private*, pg. 1008
BRODART COMPANY; *U.S. Private*, pg. 170
CARTER HOLT HARVEY LIMITED—International Paper Company; *U.S. Public*, pg. 904
CASSINA—Groupe Strafor Facom; *Int'l*, pg. 570
CEMAC COMMERCIAL INTERIORS LTD.—International Paper Company; *U.S. Public*, pg. 905
CHROMCRAFT CORPORATION—Chromcraft Revington, Inc.; *U.S. Public*, pg. 352
CHROMCRAFT REVINGTON, INC.; *U.S. Public*, pg. 352
CLESTRA HAUSERMAN KOREA—Groupe Strafor Facom; *Int'l*, pg. 569
COLLIER-KEYWORTH, INC.—Leggett & Platt, Incorporated; *U.S. Public*, pg. 985
COMFORTO GROUP—Haworth, Inc.; *U.S. Private*, pg. 512
CORRYHIEBERT CORPORATION—HON Industries Inc.; *U.S. Public*, pg. 772
CRAMER INC.; *U.S. Private*, pg. 285
DIRECTIONAL FURNITURE—CF Group; *U.S. Private*, pg. 193
DOMORE CORPORATION; *U.S. Private*, pg. 339
EAC CORPORATION; *U.S. Private*, pg. 353
EMPIRE OFFICE EQUIPMENT, INC.; *U.S. Private*, pg. 374
ESSELTE AB; *Int'l*, pg. 459
ESSELTE PENDAFLEX CANADA, INC.—Esselte AB; *Int'l*, pg. 460
EUROSEEL EQUIPAMENTOS METALICOS, SA—Groupe Strafor Facom; *Int'l*, pg. 569
EWING TOWNSHIP-NEW JERSEY DIV.—EAC Corporation; *U.S. Private*, pg. 353
FELTRAX INTERNATIONAL, INC.—BTR plc; *Int'l*, pg. 130
FIRE KING INTERNATIONAL, INC.; *U.S. Private*, pg. 406
FIXTURES FURNITURE—Jami, Inc.; *U.S. Private*, pg. 581
FLEWELLING DIV.—EAC Corporation; *U.S. Private*, pg. 353
GF OFFICE FURNITURE LTD.; *U.S. Private*, pg. 434

GLOBE BUSINESS FURNITURE, INC.—Haworth, Inc.; *U.S. Private*, pg. 512
THE GUNLOCKE COMPANY—HON Industries Inc.; *U.S. Public*, pg. 772
THE HON CO.—HON Industries Inc.; *U.S. Public*, pg. 772
THE HON CO. SYSTEMS FURNITURE PLANT—HON Industries Inc.; *U.S. Public*, pg. 772
HON INDUSTRIES INC.; *U.S. Public*, pg. 772
HALI-BUROMOBEL VERTRIEBS GESMBH; *Int'l*, pg. 589
HARPERS MANUFACTURING—Kimball International, Inc.; *U.S. Public*, pg. 957
HARTER—Jami, Inc.; *U.S. Private*, pg. 581
HARVARD INDUSTRIES, INC.; *U.S. Public*, pg. 796
HARVARD INTERIORS MANUFACTURING CO.—Harvard Industries, Inc.; *U.S. Public*, pg. 796
HAWORTH, INC.; *U.S. Private*, pg. 511
HOLGA INC.—HON Industries Inc.; *U.S. Public*, pg. 772
THE HON CO., SULPHUR SPRINGS PLANT—HON Industries Inc.; *U.S. Public*, pg. 772
THE HON CO., WINNSBORO PLANT—HON Industries Inc.; *U.S. Public*, pg. 772
HOOKER FURNITURE CORPORATION; *U.S. Private*, pg. 538
HOWE FURNITURE CORPORATION; *U.S. Private*, pg. 543
INTEGRATED METAL TECHNOLOGIES, INC.—Herman Miller, Inc.; *U.S. Public*, pg. 1112
INVINCIBLE OFFICE FURNITURE; *U.S. Private*, pg. 575
JAMESTOWN METAL PRODUCTS, INC.—Brittany Corporation; *U.S. Private*, pg. 169
JAMI, INC.; *U.S. Private*, pg. 581
JOYCE INTERNATIONAL, INC.; *U.S. Private*, pg. 602
KIMBALL INTERNATIONAL, INC.; *U.S. Public*, pg. 956
KINETICS, INC., A HAWORTH CO.—Haworth, Inc.; *U.S. Private*, pg. 512
KNOLL, INC.; *U.S. Private*, pg. 627
KNOLL INTL., INC.—Knoll, Inc.; *U.S. Private*, pg. 627
KNURR AG; *Int'l*, pg. 739
KNURR AG—Knurr AG; *Int'l*, pg. 739
KNURR-LOMMATEC GMBH & CO. KG—Knurr AG; *Int'l*, pg. 739
KNURR NEDERLAND B.V.—Knurr AG; *Int'l*, pg. 739
KNURR-NORGE AS—Knurr AG; *Int'l*, pg. 739
KNURR NV BELGIE—Knurr AG; *Int'l*, pg. 739
KNURR-SPECTRA (S.E.A.) PTE. LTD.—Knurr AG; *Int'l*, pg. 739
KNURR SVERIGE AB—Knurr AG; *Int'l*, pg. 739
KNURR (UK) LTD.—Knurr AG; *Int'l*, pg. 739
KNURR USA, INC.—Knurr AG; *Int'l*, pg. 739
LUXOR—EBSCO Industries, Inc.; *U.S. Private*, pg. 359
MADISON FURNITURE INDUSTRIES—Shelby Williams Industries, Inc.; *U.S. Public*, pg. 1465
THE MARVEL GROUP, INC.—Masco Corporation; *U.S. Public*, pg. 1053
MASTER PRODUCTS MFG. CO.—James Crean PLC; *Int'l*, pg. 340
MERIDIAN INC.—Herman Miller, Inc.; *U.S. Public*, pg. 1112
HERMAN MILLER, INC.; *U.S. Public*, pg. 1111
HERMAN MILLER, LTD.—Herman Miller, Inc.; *U.S. Public*, pg. 1112
OLIVETTI SYNTHESIS—Olivetti SpA; *Int'l*, pg. 1002
O'SULLIVAN INDUSTRIES HOLDINGS; *U.S. Public*, pg. 1234
PANEL CONCEPTS, L.P.—Standard Pacific Corp.; *U.S. Public*, pg. 1504
PARK-OHIO INDUSTRIES, INC.; *U.S. Public*, pg. 1258
POHLSCHRODER GMBH & CO. KG—Steelcase Inc.; *U.S. Private*, pg. 1038
PRECISION—Jami, Inc.; *U.S. Private*, pg. 581
PRECISION OFFICE INDUSTRIES—International Paper Company; *U.S. Public*, pg. 904
PRODUCTOS MAESTROS—James Crean PLC; *Int'l*, pg. 341
ROWE FURNITURE CORP.; *U.S. Public*, pg. 1410
SCHWAB CORP.; *U.S. Private*, pg. 974
SMITH SYSTEM MANUFACTURING COMPANY; *U.S. Private*, pg. 1009
STATHAM INDUSTRIES—International Paper Company; *U.S. Public*, pg. 905
STEELCASE INC.; *U.S. Private*, pg. 1038
STEELCASE, INC./ATHENS PLANT—Steelcase Inc.; *U.S. Private*, pg. 1038
STEELCASE STRAFOR—Groupe Strafor Facom; *Int'l*, pg. 569
STEELWORKS, INCORPORATED; *U.S. Private*, pg. 1039
STEELWORKS, INC. DOVER DIVISION—Steelworks, Incorporated; *U.S. Private*, pg. 1039
TAB PRODUCTS CO.; *U.S. Public*, pg. 1559
TAB PRODUCTS EUROPA B.V.—Tab Products Co.; *U.S. Public*, pg. 1559
TAB PRODUCTS OF CANADA, LTD.—Tab Products Co.; *U.S. Public*, pg. 1559
TENNSCO CORPORATION; *U.S. Private*, pg. 1077
THONET—Shelby Williams Industries, Inc.; *U.S. Public*, pg. 1465
TRENDWAY CORPORATION; *U.S. Private*, pg. 1099
UNITED CHAIR, INC.—Haworth, Inc.; *U.S. Private*, pg. 512
U.S. FURNITURE INDUSTRIES, INC.; *U.S. Private*, pg. 1125
WESTINGHOUSE INDUSTRIES & TECHNOLOGIES GROUP—CBS Corporation; *U.S. Public*, pg. 273
ZERO PLASTICS—Zero Corporation; *U.S. Public*, pg. 1791

2531 — PUBLIC BUILDING & RELATED FURNITURE

AMI INDUSTRIES, INC.—Coltec Holdings Inc; *U.S. Public*, pg. 401
AMERICAN SEATING COMPANY; *U.S. Private*, pg. 61
THE APOGEE COMPANIES, INC.; *U.S. Private*, pg. 77
ARTCO-BELL CORPORATION; *U.S. Private*, pg. 86
B/E AEROSPACE SEATING PRODUCTS—B/E Aerospace, Inc.; *U.S. Public*, pg. 159
B/E SERVICES—B/E Aerospace, Inc.; *U.S. Public*, pg. 159
BALTIMORE STATIONERY CO./TOTAL OFFICE; *U.S. Private*, pg. 113
BASIC AMERICAN MEDICAL PRODUCTS, INC.—Graham-Field Health Products, Inc.; *U.S. Public*, pg. 758
BLOCKHOUSE CO., INC.; *U.S. Private*, pg. 150
BOSTROM SEATING, INC.—Johnstown America Industries; *U.S. Public*, pg. 933
BRITAX INTERNATIONAL PLC; *Int'l*, pg. 216
BRODART COMPANY; *U.S. Private*, pg. 170
BUTLER CAPITAL CORP.; *U.S. Private*, pg. 190
CENTRAL DE INDUSTRIAS, S.A.—Lear Corporation; *U.S. Public*, pg. 982
CLARIN; *U.S. Private*, pg. 242
COLUMBIA MANUFACTURING INC.; *U.S. Private*, pg. 255
CUTLER MANUFACTURING CORPORATION; *U.S. Private*, pg. 298
DMI FURNITURE INC.; *U.S. Public*, pg. 473
EAC CORPORATION; *U.S. Private*, pg. 353
FLEXSTEEL DIVISION—Flexsteel Industries, Inc.; *U.S. Public*, pg. 654
GAME TIME, INC.—Swing-N-Slide Corp.; *U.S. Public*, pg. 1543
J.L. HAMMETT COMPANY; *U.S. Private*, pg. 498
HUSSEY CORPORATION; *U.S. Private*, pg. 550
HUSSEY PRODUCTS CO.—Hussey Corporation; *U.S. Private*, pg. 550
HUSSEY SEATING COMPANY—Hussey Corporation; *U.S. Private*, pg. 550
ITC INLAND TEKNIK OTO YAN SANAYI LIMITED SIRKETI—General Motors Corporation; *U.S. Public*, pg. 723
INTERKAL, INC.—Kotobuki Seating Co.; *Int'l*, pg. 759
LEAR CORPORATION; *U.S. Public*, pg. 981
MIRACLE RECREATION EQUIPMENT COMPANY; *U.S. Private*, pg. 752
NAMBA PRESS WORKS CO., LTD.; *Int'l*, pg. 904
NATIONAL SEATING CO.; *U.S. Private*, pg. 786
NEMSCHOFF CHAIRS, INC.; *U.S. Private*, pg. 791
NORTHLAND FURNITURE CO., LLC—The Apogee Companies, Inc.; *U.S. Private*, pg. 77
OVERHOLTZER CHURCH FURNITURE, INC.; *U.S. Private*, pg. 823
RECARO NORTH AMERICA, INC.; *U.S. Private*, pg. 914
ROWE FURNITURE CORP.; *U.S. Public*, pg. 1410
L.A. RUMBOLD LIMITED—Britax International plc; *Int'l*, pg. 216
SAFWAY STEEL PRODUCTS INC.—Thyssen AG; *Int'l*, pg. 1389
SAUDER MANUFACTURING CORPORATION; *U.S. Private*, pg. 967
SEATS INCORPORATED—Flambeau Corporation; *U.S. Private*, pg. 410
SHAIN/SHOPBILT—John Boos & Company; *U.S. Private*, pg. 156
SICAN CORP.; *U.S. Private*, pg. 997
SICO INCORPORATED; *U.S. Private*, pg. 997
SICO NORTH AMERICA INC.—Sico Incorporated; *U.S. Private*, pg. 997
SMITH SYSTEM MANUFACTURING COMPANY; *U.S. Private*, pg. 1009
VIRCO MFG. CORPORATION; *U.S. Public*, pg. 1721
WOOD COLONY MILLWORKS—Overholtzer Church Furniture, Inc.; *U.S. Private*, pg. 823

2541 — WOOD PARTITIONS, SHELVING, LOCKERS & OFFICE & STORE FIXTURES

A.G. INDUSTRIES INC.—American Greetings Corporation; *U.S. Public*, pg. 78
ABCO—Jami, Inc.; *U.S. Private*, pg. 581
ABRAMS FIXTURE CORPORATION—Abrams Industries, Inc.; *U.S. Public*, pg. 14
ABRAMS INDUSTRIES, INC.; *U.S. Public*, pg. 14
AMERICAN GREETINGS CORPORATION; *U.S. Public*, pg. 77
AMSTORE CORPORATION; *U.S. Private*, pg. 68
ASHBY & HORNER JOINERY LTD.—The Peninsular and Oriental Steam Navigation Company; *Int'l*, pg. 1032
BERG CO.—DEC International, Inc.; *U.S. Private*, pg. 301
BRODART COMPANY; *U.S. Private*, pg. 170
CAPITOL CONSTRUCTION GROUP, INC.; *U.S. Private*, pg. 206
COLUMBUS SHOW CASE COMPANY; *U.S. Private*, pg. 257
COLUMBUS SHOWCASE, ASHLAND DIVISION—Columbus Show Case Company; *U.S. Private*, pg. 257
DANN DEE DISPLAY FIXTURES; *U.S. Private*, pg. 310
DECORA'—Fortune Brands, Inc.; *U.S. Public*, pg. 675
DORFILE COMPANY—Newell Co.; *U.S. Public*, pg. 1177
DURAND INC.—L & D Group; *U.S. Private*, pg. 638
EUROSEEL EQUIPAMENTOS METALICOS, SA—Groupe Strafor Facom; *Int'l*, pg. 569
GLOBE BUSINESS FURNITURE, INC.—Haworth, Inc.; *U.S. Private*, pg. 512
GOER MANUFACTURING CO.—RHC/Spacemaster Corporation; *U.S. Private*, pg. 904
THE H.T. HACKNEY CO.; *U.S. Private*, pg. 493
HANDY STORE FIXTURES, INC.; *U.S. Private*, pg. 499
HODGES DIVISION—Leggett & Platt, Incorporated; *U.S. Public*, pg. 985
HOLCOMB & HOKE MFG. COMPANY, INC.; *U.S. Private*, pg. 533
HOOKER FURNITURE CORPORATION; *U.S. Private*, pg. 538
JAMI, INC.; *U.S. Private*, pg. 581
M. KAMENSTEIN, INC.; *U.S. Private*, pg. 606
KING ARTHUR INC.—Shelby Williams Industries, Inc.; *U.S. Public*, pg. 1465
KNAPE & VOGT MFG. CO.; *U.S. Public*, pg. 963
KNAPE & VOGT MFG. CO.—Knape & Vogt Mfg. Co.; *U.S. Public*, pg. 963
LOZIER CORPORATION; *U.S. Private*, pg. 679
LUNDIA DIV. OF MII, INC.; *U.S. Private*, pg. 680
MEG; *U.S. Private*, pg. 686
MARLITE; *U.S. Private*, pg. 705
PARISI INC./ROYAL STORE FIXTURE; *U.S. Private*, pg. 839
PHILADELPHIA SIGN COMPANY; *U.S. Private*, pg. 861
PIONEER PLASTICS CORPORATION; *U.S. Private*, pg. 867
PLASTAG CORPORATION; *U.S. Private*, pg. 870
PRECISION OFFICE INDUSTRIES—International Paper Company; *U.S. Public*, pg. 904
RHC/SPACEMASTER CORPORATION; *U.S. Private*, pg. 904
ROLL-IT—Knape & Vogt Mfg. Co.; *U.S. Public*, pg. 963
ROWE FURNITURE CORP.; *U.S. Public*, pg. 1410
RYNONE MANUFACTURING CORPORATION; *U.S. Private*, pg. 953
SAUNDERS BROTHERS; *U.S. Private*, pg. 968
SICAN CORP.; *U.S. Private*, pg. 997
SPARTAN SHOWCASE, INC.—RHC/Spacemaster Corporation; *U.S. Private*, pg. 904
SPEEDFAM CO LTD.—SpeedFan International, Inc.; *U.S. Public*, pg. 1498
SPEEDRACK PRODUCTS GROUP, LTD.; *U.S. Private*, pg. 1024
TANDY CABINETS—Tandy Corporation; *U.S. Public*, pg. 1560
WM. S. TRIMBLE COMPANY, INC.; *U.S. Private*, pg. 1103
VOLUNTEER FABRICATORS, INC.—The H.T. Hackney Co.; *U.S. Private*, pg. 493
WADDELL DISPLAY CASES DIV. OF GHENT MFG. CO.—Ghent Manufacturing, Inc.; *U.S. Private*, pg. 450

2542 — OFFICE & STORE FIXTURES, PARTITIONS, SHELVING & LOCKERS, EXCEPT WOOD

A.G. INDUSTRIES INC.—American Greetings Corporation; *U.S. Public*, pg. 78
ABCO—Jami, Inc.; *U.S. Private*, pg. 581
ABRAMS FIXTURE CORPORATION—Abrams Industries, Inc.; *U.S. Public*, pg. 14
ABRAMS INDUSTRIES, INC.; *U.S. Public*, pg. 14
AMERICAN LOCKER CO., INC.—American Locker Group, Inc.; *U.S. Public*, pg. 86
AMERICAN LOCKER CO. OF CANADA LTD.—American Locker Group, Inc.; *U.S. Public*, pg. 86
AMERICAN LOCKER GROUP, INC.; *U.S. Public*, pg. 85
AMERICAN LOCKER SECURITY SYSTEMS, INC.—American Locker Group, Inc.; *U.S. Public*, pg. 86
AMERICAN SPECIALTIES INC.; *U.S. Private*, pg. 62
BRODART COMPANY; *U.S. Private*, pg. 170
BURTMAN IRON WORKS, INC.; *U.S. Private*, pg. 188
CANADIAN LOCKER CO., LTD.—American Locker Group, Inc.; *U.S. Public*, pg. 86
CAPITOL HARDWARE, INC.—RHC/Spacemaster Corporation; *U.S. Private*, pg. 904
CLAIRSON INTERNATIONAL CORP.—Emerson Electric Co.; *U.S. Public*, pg. 575
CLARK SPECIALTY CO., INC.; *U.S. Private*, pg. 243
CLESTRA HAUSERMAN—Groupe Strafor Facom; *Int'l*, pg. 569
CLESTRA HAUSERMAN, INC.—Groupe Strafor Facom; *Int'l*, pg. 569
COLUMBUS SHOW CASE COMPANY; *U.S. Private*, pg. 257
COLUMBUS SHOWCASE, ASHLAND DIVISION—Columbus Show Case Company; *U.S. Private*, pg. 257
CRAMER INC.; *U.S. Private*, pg. 285
DANN DEE DISPLAY FIXTURES; *U.S. Private*, pg. 310
DELUXE STORAGE SYSTEMS, INC.; *U.S. Private*, pg. 323
DEXION (AUSTRALIA) PTY. LTD.—The Interlake Corporation; *U.S. Public*, pg. 893
DEXION GMBH—The Interlake Corporation; *U.S. Public*, pg. 893
DEXION GROUP PLC—The Interlake Corporation; *U.S. Public*, pg. 893
DEXION LTD.-STORAGE DIV.—The Interlake Corporation; *U.S. Public*, pg. 893
S.A. DEXION REDIRACK—The Interlake Corporation; *U.S. Public*, pg. 893
DOMORE CORPORATION; *U.S. Private*, pg. 339
DURAND INC.—L & D Group; *U.S. Private*, pg. 638
DYNABILT PRODUCTS—Burtman Iron Works, Inc.; *U.S. Private*, pg. 188
EBSCO INDUSTRIES, INC.; *U.S. Private*, pg. 358
ESSELTE AB; *Int'l*, pg. 459
EUROSEEL EQUIPAMENTOS METALICOS, SA—Groupe Strafor Facom; *Int'l*, pg. 569
FOGA SYSTEM INTERNATIONAL AB; *Int'l*, pg. 496
FOGA SYSTEMS—Foga System International AB; *Int'l*, pg. 496
GLOBAL STEEL PRODUCTS CORPORATION; *U.S. Private*, pg. 457
GLOBE BUSINESS FURNITURE, INC.—Haworth, Inc.; *U.S. Private*, pg. 512
HANDY STORE FIXTURES, INC.; *U.S. Private*, pg. 499
HARVARD INTERIORS MANUFACTURING CO.—Harvard Industries, Inc.; *U.S. Public*, pg. 796
HIRSH COMPANY—Knape & Vogt Mfg. Co.; *U.S. Public*, pg. 963
HOLCOMB & HOKE MFG. COMPANY, INC.; *U.S. Private*, pg. 533
THE INTERLAKE CORPORATION; *U.S. Public*, pg. 892
INTERLAKE MATERIAL HANDLING DIV.—The Interlake Corporation; *U.S. Public*, pg. 893
JAMI, INC.; *U.S. Private*, pg. 581
JANNOCK LIMITED; *Int'l*, pg. 698
JANNOCK STEEL FABRICATING COMPANY—Jannock Limited; *Int'l*, pg. 698
KNOLL, INC.; *U.S. Private*, pg. 627
LIST INDUSTRIES, INC.; *U.S. Private*, pg. 669
LONRHO PLC; *Int'l*, pg. 817
LOZIER CORPORATION; *U.S. Private*, pg. 679

LUNDIA DIV. OF MII, INC.; U.S. Private, pg. 680
LUXOR—EBSCO Industries, Inc.; U.S. Private, pg. 359
LYON METAL PRODUCTS, INC.—L & D Group; U.S. Private, pg. 638
MEG; U.S. Private, pg. 686
MANHATTAN STORE INTERIORS, INC.; U.S. Private, pg. 699
MARDAKLEVS INDUSTRI AB—ACTIVE BioTech AB; Int'l, pg. 23
MARKETING DISPLAYS INTERNATIONAL; U.S. Private, pg. 705
HERMAN MILLER, LTD.—Herman Miller, Inc.; U.S. Public, pg. 1112
MORGAN MARSHALL INDUSTRIES, INC.—RHC/Spacemaster Corporation; U.S. Private, pg. 904
MOSLER INC.; U.S. Private, pg. 763
NEWELL CO.; U.S. Public, pg. 1176
OLIVETTI SPA; Int'l, pg. 1002
PACIFIC WESTEEL—Jannock Limited; Int'l, pg. 698
PALTIER INC.—L & D Group; U.S. Private, pg. 638
PARISI INC./ROYAL STORE FIXTURE; U.S. Private, pg. 839
PENCO PRODUCTS; U.S. Private, pg. 848
POLYMER PLASTICS CORPORATION; U.S. Private, pg. 875
RHC/SPACEMASTER CORPORATION; U.S. Private, pg. 904
READY METAL MANUFACTURING COMPANY; U.S. Private, pg. 913
REGION GOTEBORG—ACTIVE BioTech AB; Int'l, pg. 23
REGION JONKOPING—ACTIVE BioTech AB; Int'l, pg. 23
REGION STOCKHOLM—ACTIVE BioTech AB; Int'l, pg. 23
REGION SUNDSVALL—ACTIVE BioTech AB; Int'l, pg. 23
REPUBLIC STORAGE SYSTEMS COMPANY INC.; U.S. Private, pg. 924
ROWE FURNITURE CORP.; U.S. Public, pg. 1410
SONESSON INDRETNING APS—ACTIVE BioTech AB; Int'l, pg. 23
SONESSON INREDNINGAR AB—ACTIVE BioTech AB; Int'l, pg. 23
SPEEDRACK PRODUCTS GROUP, LTD.; U.S. Private, pg. 1024
SYCAMORE SYSTEMS, INC.—L & D Group; U.S. Private, pg. 638
SYNDICATE SYSTEMS, INC.; U.S. Private, pg. 1060
TANDY CABINETS—Tandy Corporation; U.S. Public, pg. 1560
TRENDWAY CORPORATION; U.S. Private, pg. 1099
VIRGINIA METAL INDUSTRIES, INC.; U.S. Private, pg. 1141
WADDELL DISPLAY CASES DIV. OF GHENT MFG. CO.—Ghent Manufacturing, Inc.; U.S. Private, pg. 450

2591 — DRAPERY HARDWARE & WINDOW BLINDS & SHADES

CC INDUSTRIES, INC.; U.S. Private, pg. 192
DURAL LEEDS PTY. LTD.—Hunter Douglas N.V.; Int'l, pg. 639
ESSROC CANADA—Ciments Francais; Int'l, pg. 292
FABRICATION PLANT/CUSTOM PRODUCTS—Newell Co.; U.S. Public, pg. 1177
GRIFFON CORP.; U.S. Public, pg. 766
HARDWARE & COMPONENTS OPERATION—Newell Co.; U.S. Public, pg. 1177
HARRISON DRAPE—McKechnie PLC; Int'l, pg. 851
HOME FURNISHINGS SEGMENT—Springs Industries, Inc.; U.S. Public, pg. 1500
HUNTER DOUGLAS CANADA INC.—Hunter Douglas N.V.; Int'l, pg. 639
HUNTER DOUGLAS DO BRAZIL LTDA.—Hunter Douglas N.V.; Int'l, pg. 640
HUNTER DOUGLAS FABRICATION COMPANY—Hunter Douglas N.V.; Int'l, pg. 639
HUNTER DOUGLAS HOLDINGS LTD.—Hunter Douglas N.V.; Int'l, pg. 640
HUNTER DOUGLAS LTD.-SYDNEY—Hunter Douglas N.V.; Int'l, pg. 640
HUNTER DOUGLAS N.V.; Int'l, pg. 639
HUNTER DOUGLAS PLEATED SHADE CORP.—Hunter Douglas N.V.; Int'l, pg. 639
HUNTER DOUGLAS SINGAPORE PTE. LTD.—Hunter Douglas N.V.; Int'l, pg. 640
KENNEY MANUFACTURING COMPANY; U.S. Private, pg. 615
KIRSCH—Newell Co.; U.S. Public, pg. 1176
LEVOLOR HOME FASHIONS—Newell Co.; U.S. Public, pg. 1177
E.L. MANSURE DIV.—Trace International Holdings, Inc.; U.S. Private, pg. 1094
NEWELL CO.; U.S. Public, pg. 1176
NEWELL WINDOW FURNISHINGS CO.—Newell Co., U.S. Public, pg. 1177
AB SANI-MASKINER—Cooper Industries, Inc.; U.S. Public, pg. 444
SPRINGS INDUSTRIES, INC.; U.S. Public, pg. 1499
SWISH PRODUCTS LTD.—Newmond PLC; Int'l, pg. 925
WAUSAU METALS CORP.—Apogee Enterprises, Inc.; U.S. Public, pg. 120
WAUSAU METALS, NANIK DIVISION—Springs Industries, Inc.; U.S. Public, pg. 1500

2599 — FURNITURE & FIXTURES, NEC

BPI INC.—HON Industries Inc.; U.S. Public, pg. 772
BPI INC., SALISBURY PLANT—HON Industries Inc.; U.S. Public, pg. 772
BASIC AMERICAN MEDICAL PRODUCTS, INC.—Graham-Field Health Products, Inc.; U.S. Public, pg. 758
BASIC AMERICAN METAL PRODUCTS—Columbia/HCA Healthcare Corporation; U.S. Public, pg. 404
BASIC AMERICAN WOOD PRODUCTS—Columbia/HCA Healthcare Corporation; U.S. Public, pg. 404
BATESVILLE AMERICAN MFG.—Kimball International, Inc.; U.S. Public, pg. 957
BELVEDERE COMPANY—Smith Investment Company; U.S. Private, pg. 1008
CR LLC; U.S. Private, pg. 196
CHARTER HOUSE INCORPORATED—Stainless Incorporated; U.S. Private, pg. 1029
THE CORNELIUS COMPANY—IMI Plc; Int'l, pg. 646
COSCO, INC.; U.S. Private, pg. 277
CRAMER INC.; U.S. Private, pg. 285
DIRECTIONAL FURNITURE—CF Group; U.S. Private, pg. 193
FAIRFIELD PURCHASING & DESIGN, INC.—Fairfield Communities, Inc.; U.S. Public, pg. 611
FISHER SCIENTIFIC INTERNATIONAL—Thomas H. Lee Co.; U.S. Private, pg. 658
GEM SOUTHEAST, INC.—Gem Industries Finance Corporation; U.S. Private, pg. 443
THE HON CO.—HON Industries Inc.; U.S. Public, pg. 772
HARVARD INTERIORS MANUFACTURING CO.—Harvard Industries, Inc.; U.S. Public, pg. 796
HILL-ROM COMPANY, INC.—Hillenbrand Industries, Inc.; U.S. Public, pg. 828
HILL-ROM/LE COUVIOUR S.A.—Hillenbrand Industries, Inc.; U.S. Public, pg. 828
HILLENBRAND INDUSTRIES, INC.; U.S. Public, pg. 828
HIRSH COMPANY—Knape & Vogt Mfg. Co.; U.S. Public, pg. 963
HOUSTON FOODS COMPANY; U.S. Private, pg. 542
JASPER FURNITURE COMPANY—Kimball International, Inc.; U.S. Public, pg. 957
KENNEDY MANUFACTURING COMPANY; U.S. Private, pg. 614
KIDRON INC.; U.S. Private, pg. 619
KING ARTHUR INC.—Shelby Williams Industries, Inc.; U.S. Public, pg. 1465
LISTA HOLDING AG; Int'l, pg. 812
LISTA INTERNATIONAL CORPORATION—Lista Holding AG; Int'l, pg. 812
MANHATTAN STORE INTERIORS, INC.; U.S. Private, pg. 699
METRO AG; Int'l, pg. 863
MILCARE, INC.—Herman Miller, Inc.; U.S. Public, pg. 1112
HERMAN MILLER, INC.; U.S. Public, pg. 1111
HERMAN MILLER, LTD.—Herman Miller, Inc.; U.S. Public, pg. 1112
MOHAWK FURNITURE, INC.—Gem Industries Finance Corporation; U.S. Private, pg. 443
NATIONAL METAL INDUSTRIES—Standex International Corporation; U.S. Public, pg. 1506
O'SULLIVAN INDUSTRIES HOLDINGS; U.S. Public, pg. 1234
PIOLE—Groupe Strafor Facom; Int'l, pg. 570
L.A. RUMBOLD LIMITED—Britax International plc; Int'l, pg. 216
SALON & FITNESS SYSTEMS; U.S. Private, pg. 962
SBARRO OF ROOSEVELT FIELD INC.—Sbarro, Inc.; U.S. Public, pg. 1436
SHAFER COMMERCIAL SEATING INC.; U.S. Private, pg. 988
SIMMONS JUVENILE PRODUCTS; U.S. Private, pg. 1001
STAINLESS INCORPORATED; U.S. Private, pg. 1029
SUNRISE MEDICAL, INC.; U.S. Public, pg. 1535
THERADYNE CORPORATION—Kurt Manufacturing Co. Inc.; U.S. Private, pg. 637
TURNBULL ENTERPRISES, INC.; U.S. Private, pg. 1109
UNIVERSAL LAUNDRY BAGS DIV.—Superior Surgical Mfg. Co., Inc.; U.S. Public, pg. 1539
VIRCO MFG. CORPORATION; U.S. Public, pg. 1721
WASSALL PLC; Int'l, pg. 1486

2611 — PULP MILLS

AEC FOREST PRODUCTS—Alberta Energy Company, Ltd.; Int'l, pg. 48
ALABAMA PINE PULP COMPANY, INC.—Parsons & Whittemore, Inc.; U.S. Private, pg. 841
ARACRUZ CELULOSE S.A.; Int'l, pg. 78
ASPA BRUK—Trelleborg AB; Int'l, pg. 1423
BOISE CASCADE CORPORATION; U.S. Public, pg. 242
BOISE CASCADE PAPER DIV.—Boise Cascade Corporation; U.S. Public, pg. 243
BOWATER COATED PAPER & PULP DIV.—Bowater Incorporated; U.S. Public, pg. 248
BOWATER INCORPORATED; U.S. Public, pg. 247
BOWATER NEWSPRINT DIVISION—Bowater Incorporated; U.S. Public, pg. 248
BRANT ALLEN INDUSTRIES, INC.; U.S. Private, pg. 165
BRUNSWICK PULP & PAPER COMPANY—Georgia-Pacific Corporation; U.S. Public, pg. 736
CANADIAN FOREST PRODUCTS LTD., PRINCE GEORGE PULP & PAPER MILLS DIV.—Canfor Corporation; Int'l, pg. 260
CANFOR CORPORATION; Int'l, pg. 260
CANFOR U.S.A., BELLINGHAM DIVISION—Canfor Corporation; Int'l, pg. 260
CANFOR U.S.A. CORPORATION—Canfor Corporation; Int'l, pg. 260
CARTIERA DI SUBIACO S.P.A.—Groupe Saint Louis; Int'l, pg. 567
CARTONAJES INTERNATIONAL, S.A.—International Paper Company; U.S. Public, pg. 905
CELBI SA—Stora Kopparbergs Bergslags AB; Int'l, pg. 1303
CELULOSAS DE ASTURIAS—Groupe Saint Louis; Int'l, pg. 567
CLEANERS HANGER CO.; U.S. Private, pg. 245
COLOMBIANA KIMBERLY S.A.—Kimberly-Clark Corporation; U.S. Public, pg. 959
CRESTBROOK FOREST INDUSTRIES LTD.; Int'l, pg. 348
DOMTAR INC.; Int'l, pg. 416
DONOHUE INC.—Quebecor Inc.; Int'l, pg. 1075
DONOHUE MATANE, INC.—Quebecor Inc.; Int'l, pg. 1075
E.B. EDDY FOREST PRODUCTS LTD.—George Weston Limited; Int'l, pg. 1495
E.B. EDDY PAPER, INC.—George Weston Limited; Int'l, pg. 1495
ENVASES INTERNACIONAL S.A.—International Paper Company; U.S. Public, pg. 906
ESCANABA PAPER CO.—The Mead Corporation; U.S. Public, pg. 1076
FEDERAL PAPER BOARD COMPANY, INC.—International Paper Company; U.S. Public, pg. 903
FLETCHER CHALLENGE CANADA LIMITED—Fletcher Challenge Limited; Int'l, pg. 495
FLETCHER CHALLENGE LIMITED; Int'l, pg. 494
FOLLA CTMP A/S—Norske Skogindustrier A.S; Int'l, pg. 966
FORT JAMES CORPORATION; U.S. Public, pg. 670
FORT JAMES-MARATHON, LTD.—Fort James Corporation; U.S. Public, pg. 672
GSF VERPAKKINGEN—N.V. Koninklijke KNP BT; Int'l, pg. 756
GEORGIA-PACIFIC CORPORATION; U.S. Public, pg. 735
GEORGIA-PACIFIC PULP & PAPER DIVISION—Georgia-Pacific Corporation; U.S. Public, pg. 735
GROUPE SAINT LOUIS; Int'l, pg. 567
ELOF HANSSON PULP, INC.—Elof Hansson AB; Int'l, pg. 595
HERZBERGER PAPIERFABRIK LUDWIG OSTHUSHANRICH GMBH & CO. KG—N.V. Koninklijke KNP BT; Int'l, pg. 757
HOWE SOUND PULP & PAPER LIMITED—Canfor Corporation; Int'l, pg. 260
INTERNATIONAL PAPER COMPANY; U.S. Public, pg. 901
JAMONT N.V.—Fort James Corporation; U.S. Public, pg. 672
K & P LEYKAM AUSTRIA—N.V. Koninklijke KNP BT; Int'l, pg. 757
KNP BT NEDERLAND B.V.—N.V. Koninklijke KNP BT; Int'l, pg. 756
KNP INTERNATIONAL B.V.—N.V. Koninklijke KNP BT; Int'l, pg. 756
KNP LEYKAM B.V.—N.V. Koninklijke KNP BT; Int'l, pg. 756
KNP MAASTRICHT B.V.—N.V. Koninklijke KNP BT; Int'l, pg. 756
KNP OUD PAPIER B.V.—N.V. Koninklijke KNP BT; Int'l, pg. 756
KAPPA B.V.—N.V. Koninklijke KNP BT; Int'l, pg. 756
KAPPA SCHOLTEN B.V.—N.V. Koninklijke KNP BT; Int'l, pg. 756
KETCHIKAN PULP CO.—Louisiana Pacific Corporation; U.S. Public, pg. 1015
KIMBERLY-CLARK AUSTRALIA PTY. LTD.—Kimberly-Clark Corporation; U.S. Public, pg. 959
KIMBERLY-CLARK DE MEXICO, S.A. DE C.V.—Kimberly-Clark Corporation; U.S. Public, pg. 960
KIMBERLY-CLARK INC.—Kimberly-Clark Corporation; U.S. Public, pg. 959
KIMBERLY-CLARK, NOVA SCOTIA—Kimberly-Clark Corporation; U.S. Public, pg. 959
KIMBERLY-CLARK SOPALIN S.A.—Kimberly-Clark Corporation; U.S. Public, pg. 959
KINLEITH MILL—International Paper Company; U.S. Public, pg. 905
N.V. KONINKLIJKE KNP BT; Int'l, pg. 756
KVAERNER A.S.A.; Int'l, pg. 766
KYMI PAPER MILLS LTD.—UPM-Kymmene Corporation; Int'l, pg. 1428
LEAF RIVER FOREST PRODUCTS, INC.—Georgia-Pacific Corporation; U.S. Public, pg. 736
LONGVIEW FIBRE COMPANY; U.S. Public, pg. 1013
LOUISIANA PACIFIC CORPORATION; U.S. Public, pg. 1015
LOUISIANA PACIFIC WESTERN DIV.—Louisiana Pacific Corporation; U.S. Public, pg. 1015
THE MEAD CORPORATION; U.S. Public, pg. 1074
METSA-SERLA CORPORATION; Int'l, pg. 863
MIRAMICHI PULP & PAPER INC.—Repap Enterprises Inc.; Int'l, pg. 1104
MO OCH DOMSJO AB; Int'l, pg. 885
MODO PAPER AB—Mo och Domsjo AB; Int'l, pg. 886
NEW YORK TIMES COMPANY FOREST PRODUCTS GROUP—The New York Times Company; U.S. Public, pg. 1174
NORSKE SKOGINDUSTRIER A.S; Int'l, pg. 965
NORTHWOOD FOREST INDUSTRIES, LTD.—The Mead Corporation; U.S. Public, pg. 1076
NORTHWOOD PULP & TIMBER LTD.—The Mead Corporation; U.S. Public, pg. 1076
OMNITRAX INC.—Broe Companies; U.S. Private, pg. 171
PKF/JONGEKRIJG HOLDING B.V.—N.V. Koninklijke KNP BT; Int'l, pg. 756
PAPELES VENEZOLANOS, S.A.—Kruger Inc.; Int'l, pg. 762
PARSONS & WHITTEMORE, INC.; U.S. Private, pg. 840
PORT TOWNSEND PAPER CORPORATION—Haindl Papier GmbH; Int'l, pg. 586
POTLATCH CORPORATION; U.S. Public, pg. 1318
PRIMARY PULP & PAPER PLANT—Georgia-Pacific Corporation; U.S. Public, pg. 736
PROCTER & GAMBLE INC.—The Procter & Gamble Company; U.S. Public, pg. 1332
PRODUCTORA DE PAPELES S.A. (PROPAL)—International Paper Company; U.S. Public, pg. 906
RAYONIER INC.; U.S. Public, pg. 1363
REPAP NEW BRUNSWICK INC.—Repap Enterprises Inc.; Int'l, pg. 1104
ST. ANNE - NACKAWIC PULP CO., LTD.—Parsons & Whittemore, Inc.; U.S. Private, pg. 841
ST. JOE CORP.; U.S. Public, pg. 1426
SAPPI LIMITED; Int'l, pg. 1193
SIAM CELLULOSE CO., LTD.—The Siam Cement Public Company Limited; Int'l, pg. 1238
THE SIAM PULP AND PAPER CO., LTD.—The Siam Cement Public Company Limited; Int'l, pg. 1238
SIMPSON INVESTMENT CO.; U.S. Private, pg. 1003

SIMPSON PAPER CO.—Simpson Investment Co.; *U.S. Private*, pg. 1003
SKEENA CELLULOSE INC.; *Int'l*, pg. 1261
SOCIETE GUADELOUPEENE DE CARTON ONDULE—International Paper Company; *U.S. Public*, pg. 906
SOCIETE MARTINIQUAISE DE CARTON ONDULE—International Paper Company; *U.S. Public*, pg. 906
SODRA CELL AB; *Int'l*, pg. 1275
SOPORCEL-SOCIEDADE PORTUGUESA DE CELULOSE S.A.—Groupe Saint Louis; *Int'l*, pg. 567
STONE CONTAINER CORPORATION; *U.S. Public*, pg. 1520
STORA BILLERUD AB—Stora Kopparbergs Bergslags AB; *Int'l*, pg. 1302
STORA BILLERUD PAPER GMBH—Stora Kopparbergs Bergslags AB; *Int'l*, pg. 1302
STORA BILLERUD PAPER S.A.—Stora Kopparbergs Bergslags AB; *Int'l*, pg. 1302
STORA CELL AB—Stora Kopparbergs Bergslags AB; *Int'l*, pg. 1303
STORA FOREST INDUSTRIES—Stora Kopparbergs Bergslags AB; *Int'l*, pg. 1304
STORA KOPPARBERGS BERGSLAGS AB; *Int'l*, pg. 1302
STORA PAPYRUS AB—Stora Kopparbergs Bergslags AB; *Int'l*, pg. 1303
STORA SKUTSKAR AB—Stora Kopparbergs Bergslags AB; *Int'l*, pg. 1303
SULPHITE PULP—Tembec Inc.; *Int'l*, pg. 1375
SUMMA MILLS—Enso Oyj; *Int'l*, pg. 457
TAMROCK CORP.; *Int'l*, pg. 1352
TASMAN PULP & PAPER COMPANY LIMITED—Fletcher Challenge Limited; *Int'l*, pg. 495
TEMBEC INC.; *Int'l*, pg. 1374
TEMPLE-INLAND FOREST PRODUCTS CORP.-BLEACHED PAPERBOARD GROUP—Temple-Inland Inc.; *U.S. Public*, pg. 1575
TEMPLE-INLAND INC.; *U.S. Public*, pg. 1574
UPM-KYMMENE CORPORATION; *Int'l*, pg. 1427
UNION CAMP CORPORATION; *U.S. Public*, pg. 1665
UNITED PAPER MILLS LTD.—UPM-Kymmene Corporation; *Int'l*, pg. 1429
VEDENA B.V.—N.V. Koninklijke KNP BT; *Int'l*, pg. 757
VERATEC JAPAN, LTD.—International Paper Company; *U.S. Public*, pg. 906
VERATEC S.A.—International Paper Company; *U.S. Public*, pg. 906
WEYERHAEUSER COMPANY; *U.S. Public*, pg. 1764
WEYERHAEUSER FOREST PRODUCTS COMPANY—Weyerhaeuser Company; *U.S. Public*, pg. 1764
WIGGINS ARJO IRELAND (HOLDINGS) LTD.—Groupe Saint Louis; *Int'l*, pg. 567
WILLAMETTE INDUSTRIES, INC.; *U.S. Public*, pg. 1768
WILLAMETTE INDUSTRIES, INC.—Willamette Industries, Inc.; *U.S. Public*, pg. 1768
WISAFOREST OY AB—UPM-Kymmene Corporation; *Int'l*, pg. 1429
WISAPAK OY AB—UPM-Kymmene Corporation; *Int'l*, pg. 1429

2621 — PAPER MILLS

APL CORPORATION; *U.S. Private*, pg. 7
ABITIBI-CONSOLIDATED INC.; *Int'l*, pg. 19
ACHOIA PAPERMILL S.A.—Fort James Corporation; *U.S. Public*, pg. 672
AMCOR LIMITED; *Int'l*, pg. 71
AMERICAN ISRAELI PAPER MILLS LTD.; *Int'l*, pg. 74
AMERICAN TISSUE CORPORATION; *U.S. Private*, pg. 63
AMERICAN TISSUE, INC.—American Tissue Corporation; *U.S. Private*, pg. 63
APPLETON PAPERS INC.—Groupe Saint Louis; *Int'l*, pg. 567
ARJO WIGGINS APPLETON PLC—Groupe Saint Louis; *Int'l*, pg. 567
ARJO WIGGINS EUROPE HOLDINGS, LTD.—Groupe Saint Louis; *Int'l*, pg. 567
ARVEY PAPER & OFFICE PRODUCTS—International Paper Company; *U.S. Public*, pg. 903
ATHENS MILL—Fort James Corporation; *U.S. Public*, pg. 672
AUSTRALIAN NEWSPRINT MILLS—Fletcher Challenge Limited; *Int'l*, pg. 495
AVENOR, INC.; *Int'l*, pg. 101
AVIGLIANO MILL—Fort James Corporation; *U.S. Public*, pg. 673
BADGER PAPER MILLS, INC.; *U.S. Public*, pg. 165
BEAR ISLAND PAPER CO.—Brant Allen Industries, Inc.; *U.S. Private*, pg. 166
BEAR ISLAND PAPER CO.—Dow Jones & Company, Inc.; *U.S. Public*, pg. 525
BEAR ISLAND PAPER CO.—The Washington Post Company; *U.S. Public*, pg. 1743
BECKETT PAPERS—International Paper Company; *U.S. Public*, pg. 903
BELL PACKAGING CORPORATION-MARION DIV.—Pratt Industries; *Int'l*, pg. 1066
BERGHUIZER-ENSO FORMAATFABRIEK B.V.—Enso Oyj; *Int'l*, pg. 458
BERGSTROM PAPER DIV.—P.H. Glatfelter Company; *U.S. Public*, pg. 746
BLANDIN PAPER COMPANY—Fletcher Challenge Limited; *Int'l*, pg. 495
BOISE CASCADE CORPORATION; *U.S. Public*, pg. 242
BOISE CASCADE PAPER DIV.—Boise Cascade Corporation; *U.S. Public*, pg. 243
BOWATER COATED PAPER & PULP DIV.—Bowater Incorporated; *U.S. Public*, pg. 248
BOWATER INCORPORATED; *U.S. Public*, pg. 247
BOWATER MERSEY PAPER COMPANY, LTD.—Bowater Incorporated; *U.S. Public*, pg. 248
BOWATER MERSEY PAPER COMPANY, LTD.—The Washington Post Company; *U.S. Public*, pg. 1743
BOWATER NEWSPRINT DIVISION—Bowater Incorporated; *U.S. Public*, pg. 248
BRANT ALLEN INDUSTRIES, INC.; *U.S. Private*, pg. 165
BRIDGEND PAPER MILL—Fort James Corporation; *U.S. Public*, pg. 672
BRIDGEWATER PAPER LIMITED—Abitibi-Consolidated Inc.; *Int'l*, pg. 20
BRUNSCHWIG & FILS, INC.; *U.S. Private*, pg. 176
BUNZL PLC; *Int'l*, pg. 232
BURROWS PAPER CORPORATION; *U.S. Private*, pg. 188
CALEDONIAN PAPER PLC—UPM-Kymmene Corporation; *Int'l*, pg. 1430
CALENZANO PLANT—Fort James Corporation; *U.S. Public*, pg. 673
CANADIAN FOREST PRODUCTS LTD., PRINCE GEORGE PULP & PAPER MILLS DIV.—Canfor Corporation; *Int'l*, pg. 260
CANTON MILL, CHAMPION INTERNATIONAL CORPORATION—Champion International Corp.; *U.S. Public*, pg. 334
CARTER HOLT HARVEY LIMITED—International Paper Company; *U.S. Public*, pg. 904
CARTIERA DEL TIRRENO MILL—Fort James Corporation; *U.S. Public*, pg. 673
CARTONAJES INTERNATIONAL, S.A.—International Paper Company; *U.S. Public*, pg. 905
CASCADES, INC.—The Cascades Group; *Int'l*, pg. 273
CASCADES INDUSTRIES INC.—The Cascades Group; *Int'l*, pg. 274
THE CAXTON GROUP OF COMPANIES—International Paper Company; *U.S. Public*, pg. 905
CHAMPION INTERNATIONAL CORP.; *U.S. Public*, pg. 333
CHAMPION INTERNATIONAL CORP., PAPER DIV.—Champion International Corp.; *U.S. Public*, pg. 334
CHAMPION PAPEL E CELULOSE, S.A.—Champion International Corp.; *U.S. Public*, pg. 334
CHAPELLE DARBLAY GRAND COURONNE—UPM-Kymmene Corporation; *Int'l*, pg. 1428
CHAPELLE DARBLAY GRAND COURONNE S.A.—UPM-Kymmene Corporation; *Int'l*, pg. 1430
CHAPELLE DARBLAY SAINT ETIENNE S.A.—UPM-Kymmene Corporation; *Int'l*, pg. 1430
CHONJU PAPER MFG. CO., LTD.—Samsung Group; *Int'l*, pg. 1181
CINDU CHEMICALS B.V.—Koninklijke Hoogovens N.V.; *Int'l*, pg. 754
CONNELLY CONTAINERS, INC.; *U.S. Private*, pg. 264
CONNELLY PAPER MILL—Connelly Containers, Inc.; *U.S. Private*, pg. 264
CONSOLIDATED PAPERS, INC.; *U.S. Public*, pg. 436
CONTINENTAL PLASTIC CONTAINERS, INC.—Continental Can Co.; *U.S. Public*, pg. 440
CONVERTING DIV.—Consolidated Papers, Inc.; *U.S. Public*, pg. 436
COPAMEX INDUSTRIAS S.A. DE C.V.; *Int'l*, pg. 330
COURTLAND MILL, CHAMPION INTERNATIONAL CORPORATION—Champion International Corp.; *U.S. Public*, pg. 334
CRANE & CO., INC.; *U.S. Private*, pg. 286
CROWN VANTAGE INC.; *U.S. Public*, pg. 465
THE CRYSTAL TISSUE CO.; *U.S. Private*, pg. 294
CURRAN PLANT—Fort James Corporation; *U.S. Public*, pg. 672
DAI NIPPON PRINTING CO., LTD.; *Int'l*, pg. 363
THE DEXTER CORPORATION; *U.S. Public*, pg. 504
DOMTAR INC.; *Int'l*, pg. 416
DONOHUE INC.—Quebecor Inc.; *Int'l*, pg. 1075
DONOHUE MALBAIE, INC.—The New York Times Company; *U.S. Public*, pg. 1174
EASTERN FINE PAPER; *U.S. Private*, pg. 357
ECUSTA AUSTRALIA PTY. LIMITED—P.H. Glatfelter Company; *U.S. Public*, pg. 746
ECUSTA DIVISION—P.H. Glatfelter Company; *U.S. Public*, pg. 746
ECUSTA FIBRES LTD.—P.H. Glatfelter Company; *U.S. Public*, pg. 746
E.B. EDDY FOREST PRODUCTS LTD.—George Weston Limited; *Int'l*, pg. 1495
E.B. EDDY PAPER, INC.—George Weston Limited; *Int'l*, pg. 1495
EDWARDS DUNLOP & CO. PTY. LTD.—Amcor Limited; *Int'l*, pg. 72
EEKLO MILL—Fort James Corporation; *U.S. Public*, pg. 673
ENOCELL OY—Enso Oyj; *Int'l*, pg. 455
ENSO OYJ; *Int'l*, pg. 455
ENSO PUBLICATION PAPERS OY LTD.—Enso Oyj; *Int'l*, pg. 457
ENVASES INTERNACIONAL S.A.—International Paper Company; *U.S. Public*, pg. 906
ERVING INDUSTRIES, INC.; *U.S. Private*, pg. 382
ESCANABA PAPER CO.—The Mead Corporation; *U.S. Public*, pg. 1076
FEDERAL PAPER BOARD COMPANY, INC.—International Paper Company; *U.S. Public*, pg. 903
FIBERMARK INC.; *U.S. Public*, pg. 620
FINE ART DEVELOPMENTS PLC; *Int'l*, pg. 485
FINE PAPER DIV.—The Mead Corporation; *U.S. Public*, pg. 1074
FLAMBEAU MILL—EdperBrascan Corporation; *Int'l*, pg. 434
FLETCHER CHALLENGE CANADA LIMITED—Fletcher Challenge Limited; *Int'l*, pg. 495
FLETCHER CHALLENGE LIMITED; *Int'l*, pg. 494
FOLLUM FABRIKKER—Norske Skogindustrier A.S; *Int'l*, pg. 965
FORT JAMES CORPORATION; *U.S. Public*, pg. 670
FOX RIVER PAPER COMPANY—Fox Valley Corporation; *U.S. Private*, pg. 422
FOX VALLEY CORPORATION; *U.S. Private*, pg. 422
FRASER PAPERS, INC.—EdperBrascan Corporation; *Int'l*, pg. 434
GB PAPERS LIMITED—Fort James Corporation; *U.S. Public*, pg. 672
GARDEN STATE PAPER CO., INC.—Media General, Inc.; *U.S. Public*, pg. 1078
GAYLORD CONTAINER CORPORATION; *U.S. Public*, pg. 704
GEORGIA-PACIFIC CORPORATION; *U.S. Public*, pg. 735
GEORGIA-PACIFIC PORT EDWARDS OPERATIONS—Georgia-Pacific Corporation; *U.S. Public*, pg. 736
GEORGIA-PACIFIC PULP & PAPER DIVISION—Georgia-Pacific Corporation; *U.S. Public*, pg. 735
GIEN MILL—Fort James Corporation; *U.S. Public*, pg. 673
GILBERT PAPER—The Mead Corporation; *U.S. Public*, pg. 1074
P.H. GLATFELTER COMPANY; *U.S. Public*, pg. 746
GOULD PAPER CORPORATION; *U.S. Private*, pg. 466
GREAT NORTHERN PAPER, INC.—Bowater Incorporated; *U.S. Public*, pg. 248
GRENOBLE MILL—Fort James Corporation; *U.S. Public*, pg. 673
HAINDL PAPIER GMBH; *Int'l*, pg. 586
HAMMERMILL PAPERS—International Paper Company; *U.S. Public*, pg. 902
HERLITZ PBS AKTIENGESELLSCHAFT; *Int'l*, pg. 616
HOBART/MCINTOSH PAPER COMPANY—Amer Group Ltd.; *Int'l*, pg. 72
HOLLINGSWORTH & VOSE CO.; *U.S. Private*, pg. 534
HOLMEN PAPER AB—Mo och Domsjo AB; *Int'l*, pg. 885
HOUNDOUVILLE MILL—Fort James Corporation; *U.S. Public*, pg. 673
HOVOMEX S.A. DE C.V.—Hollingsworth & Vose Co.; *U.S. Private*, pg. 535
IMPERIAL BONDWARE CORP.—International Paper Company; *U.S. Public*, pg. 903
INTERNATIONAL PAPER COMPANY; *U.S. Public*, pg. 901
INVERCON PAPERMILLS LTD.—Fort James Corporation; *U.S. Public*, pg. 672
JA/MONT IRELAND LTD.—Fort James Corporation; *U.S. Public*, pg. 673
JAMONT N.V.—Fort James Corporation; *U.S. Public*, pg. 672
JOHNS MANVILLE CORPORATION; *U.S. Public*, pg. 927
K & P LEYKAM AUSTRIA—N.V. Koninklijke KNP BT; *Int'l*, pg. 757
KANZAKI SPECIALTY PAPERS INC.—Oji Paper Co., Ltd.; *Int'l*, pg. 998
KARAMURSEL MILL—Fort James Corporation; *U.S. Public*, pg. 673
KENG HUA PAPER PRODUCTS CO., INC.; *Int'l*, pg. 729
KIMBERLY-CLARK—Kimberly-Clark Corporation; *U.S. Public*, pg. 959
KIMBERLY-CLARK CORPORATION; *U.S. Public*, pg. 958
KIMBERLY-CLARK HOME HEALTHCARE—Kimberly-Clark Corporation; *U.S. Public*, pg. 959
KIMBERLY-CLARK INTERNATIONAL SERVICES CORP.—Kimberly-Clark Corporation; *U.S. Public*, pg. 959
P.T. KIMSARI PAPER-INDONESIA—Kimberly-Clark Corporation; *U.S. Public*, pg. 959
KINLEITH MILL—International Paper Company; *U.S. Public*, pg. 905
KOTKA MILLS—Enso Oyj; *Int'l*, pg. 457
KRUGER INC.; *Int'l*, pg. 761
KRUPP HOESCH BERUFSBILDUNG GMBH—Fried. Krupp AG; *Int'l*, pg. 512
KUNHEIM CONSUMER PRODUCTS DIV.—Fort James Corporation; *U.S. Public*, pg. 673
KURTZ BROS., INC.; *U.S. Private*, pg. 637
KYMI PAPER MILLS LTD.—UPM-Kymmene Corporation; *Int'l*, pg. 1428
LAKE SUPERIOR PAPER INDUSTRIES—Consolidated Papers, Inc.; *U.S. Public*, pg. 436
LANGASJONAS PAPER MILL—Duni AB; *Int'l*, pg. 421
LANGSTON COMPANIES; *U.S. Private*, pg. 650
LAPPEENRANTA PAPER MILL—UPM-Kymmene Corporation; *Int'l*, pg. 1428
LES PAPIERS GRAPHIQUES ROLLAND—The Cascades Group; *Int'l*, pg. 274
LIVERIGHT PUBLISHING CORP.—W.W. Norton & Company, Inc.; *U.S. Private*, pg. 807
LONGVIEW FIBRE COMPANY; *U.S. Public*, pg. 1013
LUFKIN MILL, CHAMPION INTERNATIONAL CORPORATION—Champion International Corp.; *U.S. Public*, pg. 334
LYDALL AXOHM—Lydall, Inc.; *U.S. Public*, pg. 1021
LYDALL, INC.; *U.S. Public*, pg. 1020
MACMILLAN BLOEDEL LIMITED; *Int'l*, pg. 828
MACMILLAN BLOEDEL SPECIALTIES—MacMillan Bloedel Limited; *Int'l*, pg. 828
MADISON PAPER INDUSTRIES—The New York Times Company; *U.S. Public*, pg. 1174
MARCAL PAPER MILLS, INC.; *U.S. Private*, pg. 701
MASONITE CORPORATION—International Paper Company; *U.S. Public*, pg. 904
MEAD COATED BOARD EUROPE KARTONVERTRIEBS-A.G.—The Mead Corporation; *U.S. Public*, pg. 1076
THE MEAD CORPORATION; *U.S. Public*, pg. 1074
MEAD PUBLISHING PAPER—The Mead Corporation; *U.S. Public*, pg. 1074
MEAD SPECIALTY PAPER—The Mead Corporation; *U.S. Public*, pg. 1074
MEAUX—Fort James Corporation; *U.S. Public*, pg. 673
MEDIA GENERAL, INC.; *U.S. Public*, pg. 1077
MEDITE CORPORATION—SierraPine Limited; *U.S. Private*, pg. 999
MELITTA NORTH AMERICA, INC.—Melitta Unternehmensgruppe Bentz KG; *Int'l*, pg. 857
MELITTA UNTERNEHMENSGRUPPE BENTZ KG; *Int'l*, pg. 856
MELITTA U.S.A., INC.—Melitta Unternehmensgruppe Bentz KG; *Int'l*, pg. 857
MIAMI MILL—EdperBrascan Corporation; *Int'l*, pg. 434
MINNESOTA PAPER, INCORPORATED—Minnesota Power; *U.S. Public*, pg. 1116
MINNESOTA POWER; *U.S. Public*, pg. 1116
MO OCH DOMSJO AB; *Int'l*, pg. 885
MODO PAPER AB—Mo och Domsjo AB; *Int'l*, pg. 886
MOHAWK PAPER MILLS, INC.; *U.S. Private*, pg. 755

NEENAH PAPER—Kimberly-Clark Corporation; *U.S. Public*, pg. 958
THE NEW YORK TIMES COMPANY; *U.S. Public*, pg. 1173
NEW YORK TIMES COMPANY FOREST PRODUCTS GROUP—The New York Times Company; *U.S. Public*, pg. 1174
NEW ZEALAND FOREST PRODUCTS LIMITED—International Paper Company; *U.S. Public*, pg. 905
NEWCASTLE PLANT—Fort James Corporation; *U.S. Public*, *pg. 672*
NEWSPRINT SOUTH, INC.; *U.S. Private*, pg. 797
NIAGARA OF WISCONSIN—Consolidated Papers, Inc.; *U.S. Public*, pg. 436
NIAGARA OF WISCONSIN PAPER CORP.—Consolidated Papers, Inc.; *U.S. Public*, pg. 436
NICOLET PAPER COMPANY—International Paper Company; *U.S. Public*, pg. 903
NIPPON PAPER INDUSTRIES COMPANY LIMITED; *Int'l*, pg. 937
NOKIAN PAPERI OY—Fort James Corporation; *U.S. Public*, *pg. 673*
NORANDA FOREST INC.—EdperBrascan Corporation; *Int'l*, *pg. 434*
NORSKE SKOGINDUSTRIER A.S; *Int'l*, pg. 965
NORSKE SKOGINDUSTRIER A.S-PAPER—Norske Skogindustrier A.S; *Int'l*, pg. 965
NORTH AMERICAN PULP & PAPER SECTOR—Kimberly-Clark Corporation; *U.S. Public*, pg. 958
NORTHERN SC PAPER CORPORATION—The New York Times Company; *U.S. Public*, pg. 1174
OFFICE PRODUCTS DIVISION—FiberMark Inc.; *U.S. Public*, pg. 620
OJI PAPER CO., LTD.; *Int'l*, pg. 998
ORCHIDS PAPER PRODUCTS CO.; *U.S. Private*, pg. 819
OUGHTIBRIDGE MILL—Fort James Corporation; *U.S. Public*, pg. 672
PWA ROLLAND DECOR INC.—The Cascades Group; *Int'l*, pg. 274
PANKAKOSKI BOARDS OY LTD.—Enso Oyj; *Int'l*, pg. 456
PAPEL DE IMPRENSA, S.A.—Fletcher Challenge Limited; *Int'l*, pg. 495
PAPELES VENEZOLANOS, S.A.—Kruger Inc.; *Int'l*, pg. 762
PAPER RECYCLING INTERNATIONAL—Stone Container Corporation; *U.S. Public*, pg. 1522
PAPETERIES DE DOCELLES—UPM-Kymmene Corporation; *Int'l*, pg. 1430
PAPETERIES DE MALAUCENE S.A.—Kimberly-Clark Corporation; *U.S. Public*, pg. 959
PAPETERIES DE MAUDIT S.A.—Kimberly-Clark Corporation; *U.S. Public*, pg. 959
PAPIERFABRIK MELITTA-WERK BENTZ KG—Melitta Unternehmensgruppe Bentz KG; *Int'l*, pg. 857
PARENCO B.V.—Haindl Papier GmbH; *Int'l*, pg. 586
PARSONS PAPER DIV. OF NVF CO.—NVF Company; *U.S. Private*, pg. 772
PEGLER-HATTERSLEY PLC—Tomkins PLC; *Int'l*, pg. 1395
PENSACOLA MILL, CHAMPION INTERNATIONAL CORPORATION—Champion International Corp.; *U.S. Public*, pg. 334
PLAS-TECHS, INC.—Badger Paper Mills, Inc.; *U.S. Public*, pg. 165
POPE & TALBOT, INC.; *U.S. Public*, pg. 1316
PORT TOWNSEND PAPER CORPORATION—Haindl Papier GmbH; *Int'l*, pg. 586
POTLATCH CORPORATION; *U.S. Public*, pg. 1318
PRAT DE ALLO MILL—Fort James Corporation; *U.S. Public*, pg. 673
PRIMARY PULP & PAPER PLANT—Georgia-Pacific Corporation; *U.S. Public*, pg. 736
PRODUCTORA DE PAPELES S.A. (PROPAL)—International Paper Company; *U.S. Public*, pg. 906
RITTENHOUSE PAPER CO.—Rittenhouse Inc.; *U.S. Private*, pg. 933
RIVERWOOD INTERNATIONAL CORPORATION; *U.S. Public*, pg. 1391
ROANOKE RAPIDS MILL, CHAMPION INTERNATIONAL CORPORATION—Champion International Corp.; *U.S. Public*, pg. 334
ROCHEFORT PLANT—Fort James Corporation; *U.S. Public*, pg. 673
ROLLAND INC., FINE PAPERS DIVISION—The Cascades Group; *Int'l*, pg. 274
ROSELLE PAPER CO., INC.; *U.S. Private*, pg. 945
SABANCI HOLDING A.S.; *Int'l*, pg. 1167
SABIN ROBBINS PAPER CO.; *U.S. Private*, pg. 959
ST. JUST MILL—Fort James Corporation; *U.S. Public*, pg. 673
SAMSUNG GROUP; *Int'l*, pg. 1181
SANDE PAPER MILL A/S—Norske Skogindustrier A.S; *Int'l*, *pg. 965*
SAPPI LIMITED; *Int'l*, pg. 1193
SARRIO TISU S.A.—Fort James Corporation; *U.S. Public*, pg. 673
SAUGBRUGSFORENINGEN AS—Norske Skogindustrier A.S; *Int'l*, pg. 966
SCOTT CONTINENTAL N.V.—Kimberly-Clark Corporation; *U.S. Public*, pg. 960
SCOTT IBERICA, S.A.—Kimberly-Clark Corporation; *U.S. Public*, pg. 960
SCOTT LIMITED—Kimberly-Clark Corporation; *U.S. Public*, pg. 960
SCOTT PAPER CO. DE COSTA RICA, S.A.—Kimberly-Clark Corporation; *U.S. Public*, pg. 960
SCOTT S.N.C.—Kimberly-Clark Corporation; *U.S. Public*, pg. 960
SCOTT S.P.A.—Kimberly-Clark Corporation; *U.S. Public*, pg. 960
SEIKO TIME CORP.—Seiko Corporation; *Int'l*, pg. 1218
SHELDON MILL, CHAMPION INTERNATIONAL CORPORATION—Champion International Corp.; *U.S. Public*, pg. 334
SIMPSON INVESTMENT CO.; *U.S. Private*, pg. 1003
SIMPSON PAPER CO.—Simpson Investment Co.; *U.S. Private*, pg. 1003
JEFFERSON SMURFIT CORPORATION—Jefferson Smurfit Group p.l.c.; *Int'l*, pg. 1269
JEFFERSON SMURFIT GROUP P.L.C.; *Int'l*, pg. 1269
SMURFIT PACKAGING CORPORATION—Jefferson Smurfit Group p.l.c.; *Int'l*, pg. 1271
SMURFIT PAPER & BOX MILLS (BURNLEY) LTD.—Jefferson Smurfit Group p.l.c.; *Int'l*, pg. 1271
SMURFIT PAPER MILLS (TAMWORTH) LTD.—Jefferson Smurfit Group p.l.c.; *Int'l*, pg. 1271
SOCIETE GUADELOUPEENE DE CARTON ONDULE—International Paper Company; *U.S. Public*, pg. 906
SOCIETE MARTINIQUAISE DE CARTON ONDULE—International Paper Company; *U.S. Public*, pg. 906
SODIPAN BIESSARD—Fort James Corporation; *U.S. Public*, pg. 673
SODIPAN S.A.—Fort James Corporation; *U.S. Public*, pg. 673
THE SORG PAPER CO.—Wausau-Mosinee Paper Corporation; *U.S. Public*, pg. 1747
SPECIALTY PRODUCTS—Kimberly-Clark Corporation; *U.S. Public*, pg. 958
SPICERS PAPER—Amcor Limited; *Int'l*, pg. 72
SPICERS PAPER LIMITED—Amcor Limited; *Int'l*, pg. 72
SSANGYONG BUSINESS GROUP; *Int'l*, pg. 1291
SSANGYONG PAPER CO., LTD.—Ssangyong Business Group; *Int'l*, pg. 1292
STONE CONTAINER CORPORATION; *U.S. Public*, pg. 1520
STORA CELL AB—Stora Kopparbergs Bergslags AB; *Int'l*, pg. 1303
STORA CELL NORRSUNDET AB—Stora Kopparbergs Bergslags AB; *Int'l*, pg. 1303
STORA FELDMUHLE AG—Stora Kopparbergs Bergslags AB; *Int'l*, pg. 1303
STORA KOPPARBERGS BERGSLAGS AB; *Int'l*, pg. 1302
STRATHMORE PAPER—International Paper Company; *U.S. Public*, pg. 903
SUMMA MILLS—Enso Oyj; *Int'l*, pg. 457
A/S SUNLAND-EKER PAPIRFABRIKKER—Trelleborg AB; *Int'l*, pg. 1420
SVENSKA CELLULOSA AKTIEBOLAGET (SCA); *Int'l*, pg. 1326
TAIWAN SCOTT PAPER CORP.—Kimberly-Clark Corporation; *U.S. Public*, pg. 960
TAMROCK CORP.; *Int'l*, pg. 1352
TASMAN PULP & PAPER COMPANY LIMITED—Fletcher Challenge Limited; *Int'l*, pg. 495
TECHNICAL PAPER—Kimberly-Clark Corporation; *U.S. Public*, pg. 958
TECHNICAL SPECIALTIES DIVISION—FiberMark Inc.; *U.S. Public*, pg. 620
TERVAKOSKI OY—Enso Oyj; *Int'l*, pg. 456
THILMANY DIVISION—International Paper Company; *U.S. Public*, pg. 903
TIME INDEX, INC.—Time Systems, Inc.; *U.S. Private*, pg. 1087
TOLKO MANITOBA, INC.—Tolko Industries Ltd.; *Int'l*, pg. 1395
TOWNSEND HOOK LTD.—Jefferson Smurfit Group p.l.c.; *Int'l*, pg. 1271
UPM-KYMMENE CORPORATION; *Int'l*, pg. 1427
UNIKAY S.R.L.—Fort James Corporation; *U.S. Public*, pg. 673
UNION CAMP CORPORATION; *U.S. Public*, pg. 1665
UNITED PAPER MILLS LTD.—UPM-Kymmene Corporation; *Int'l*, pg. 1429
UNITED STATES GYPSUM CO.—USG Corporation; *U.S. Public*, pg. 1660
U.S. PULP AND NEWSPRINT—Kimberly-Clark Corporation; *U.S. Public*, pg. 959
VAN LEER VERPACKUNGEN GMBH—Royal Packaging Industries Van Leer B.V.; *Int'l*, pg. 1147
VERATEC JAPAN, LTD.—International Paper Company; *U.S. Public*, pg. 906
VERATEC S.A.—International Paper Company; *U.S. Public*, pg. 906
WAUSAU-MOSINEE PAPER CORPORATION; *U.S. Public*, pg. 1747
WAUSAU-MOSINEE PAPERS SPECIALTY PAPERS GROUP—Wausau-Mosinee Paper Corporation; *U.S. Public*, pg. 1747
WAUSAU PAPERS - PRINTING & WRITING DIV.—Wausau-Mosinee Paper Corporation; *U.S. Public*, pg. 1747
WESTERN PULP & PAPER DIV.—Georgia-Pacific Corporation; *U.S. Public*, pg. 736
WESTVACO CORPORATION; *U.S. Public*, pg. 1762
WEYERHAEUSER COMPANY; *U.S. Public*, pg. 1764
WHATMAN INC.—Whatman plc; *Int'l*, pg. 1498
WHATMAN PLC; *Int'l*, pg. 1498
WIGGINS TEAPE (STATIONERY) LTD.—Groupe Saint Louis; *Int'l*, pg. 567
WILLAMETTE INDUSTRIES, INC.; *U.S. Public*, pg. 1768
WILLAMETTE INDUSTRIES, INC.—Willamette Industries, Inc.; *U.S. Public*, pg. 1768
WISAFOREST OY AB—UPM-Kymmene Corporation; *Int'l*, pg. 1429
WISCONSIN TISSUE—Chesapeake Corporation; *U.S. Public*, pg. 347
WISCONSIN TISSUE MILLS, INC.—Chesapeake Corporation; *U.S. Public*, pg. 347
WOOD PRODUCTS/FOREST RESOURCES/ENERGY RESOURCE DIV.—Plum Creek Timber Co., L.P.; *U.S. Public*, pg. 1311
YORK WALLCOVERINGS INC.; *U.S. Private*, pg. 1196
ZELHEM PLANT—Fort James Corporation; *U.S. Public*, pg. 672

2631 — PAPERBOARD MILLS

BELL PACKAGING CORPORATION-MARION DIV.—Pratt Industries; *Int'l*, pg. 1066
BERGHUIZER-ENSO FORMAATFABRIEK B.V.—Enso Oyj; *Int'l*, pg. 458
BEVERIDGE PAPER CO.—Simkins Industries, Inc.; *U.S. Private*, pg. 1000
CARAUSTAR INDUSTRIES, INC.; *U.S. Public*, pg. 303
CASCADES EAST ANGUS INC.—The Cascades Group; *Int'l*, pg. 273
CASCADES, INC.—The Cascades Group; *Int'l*, pg. 273
CHAMPION INTERNATIONAL CORP.; *U.S. Public*, pg. 333
CORENSO UNITED OY LTD.—Enso Oyj; *Int'l*, pg. 456
DAIO PAPER CORPORATION; *Int'l*, pg. 372
DOMTAR INC.; *Int'l*, pg. 416
DURALAM, INC.—Sargento Foods Inc.; *U.S. Private*, pg. 966
ENSO OYJ; *Int'l*, pg. 455
FEDERAL PAPER BOARD COMPANY, INC.—International Paper Company; *U.S. Public*, pg. 903
FIBERMARK INC.; *U.S. Public*, pg. 620
GSF VERPAKKINGEN—N.V. Koninklijke KNP BT; *Int'l*, pg. 756
GAYLORD CONTAINER CORPORATION; *U.S. Public*, pg. 704
GEORGIA-PACIFIC CORPORATION; *U.S. Public*, pg. 735
GOLFKARTONFABRIEK VAN DAM B.V.—N.V. Koninklijke KNP BT; *Int'l*, pg. 756
GOULD PAPER CORPORATION; *U.S. Private*, pg. 466
GREEN BAY PACKAGING INC.; *U.S. Private*, pg. 476
GRUPO INDUSTRIAL DURANGO S.A. DE C.V.; *Int'l*, pg. 575
GULF STATES PAPER CORPORATION; *U.S. Private*, pg. 487
HOMASOTE COMPANY; *U.S. Public*, pg. 831
IGGESUND CONVERTERS LTD.—Mo och Domsjo AB; *Int'l*, pg. 886
IGGESUND PAPERBOARD AB—Mo och Domsjo AB; *Int'l*, pg. 886
IGGESUND PAPERBOARD (WORKINGTON) LTD.—Mo och Domsjo AB; *Int'l*, pg. 886
IMPERIAL BONDWARE CORP.—International Paper Company; *U.S. Public*, pg. 903
INTERNATIONAL PAPER COMPANY; *U.S. Public*, pg. 901
INTERSTATE CORE PACK—Interstate Resources, Inc.; *U.S. Private*, pg. 573
INTERSTATE PAPER CORPORATION—Interstate Resources, Inc.; *U.S. Private*, pg. 573
INTERSTATE RESOURCES, INC.; *U.S. Private*, pg. 573
K & M PRODUCTS DIVISION—Avery Dennison Corporation; *U.S. Public*, pg. 152
KNP BT NEDERLAND B.V.—N.V. Koninklijke KNP BT; *Int'l*, *pg. 756*
KNP INTERNATIONAL B.V.—N.V. Koninklijke KNP BT; *Int'l*, *pg. 756*
KNP LEYKAM B.V.—N.V. Koninklijke KNP BT; *Int'l*, pg. 756
KNP MAASTRICHT B.V.—N.V. Koninklijke KNP BT; *Int'l*, pg. 756
KAPPA B.V.—N.V. Koninklijke KNP BT; *Int'l*, pg. 756
KAPPA ESKABOARD B.V.—N.V. Koninklijke KNP BT; *Int'l*, pg. 756
KAPPA GOLFKARTON B.V.—N.V. Koninklijke KNP BT; *Int'l*, pg. 756
KAPPA SCHOLTEN B.V.—N.V. Koninklijke KNP BT; *Int'l*, pg. 756
KENG HUA PAPER PRODUCTS CO., INC.; *Int'l*, pg. 729
N.V. KONINKLIJKE KNP BT; *Int'l*, pg. 756
KORSNAS AB; *Int'l*, pg. 759
KRUGER INC.; *Int'l*, pg. 761
LHOMME S.A.—Sonoco Products Company; *U.S. Public*, pg. 1487
LONGVIEW FIBRE COMPANY; *U.S. Public*, pg. 1013
LOWE PAPER CO.—Simkins Industries, Inc.; *U.S. Private*, pg. 1000
LYDALL & FOULDS DIV.—Lydall, Inc.; *U.S. Public*, pg. 1021
LYDALL COMPOSITE MATERIALS—Lydall, Inc.; *U.S. Public*, pg. 1021
LYDALL, INC.; *U.S. Public*, pg. 1020
MACMILLAN BLOEDEL LIMITED; *Int'l*, pg. 828
MEAD COATED BOARD—The Mead Corporation; *U.S. Public*, pg. 1074
THE MEAD CORPORATION; *U.S. Public*, pg. 1074
MENASHA CORPORATION; *U.S. Private*, pg. 731
MUNKSJO AB—Trelleborg AB; *Int'l*, pg. 1423
MUNKSJOE FORPACKNINGAR AB—Trelleborg AB; *Int'l*, pg. 1423
NEWPORT TIMBER—Interstate Resources, Inc.; *U.S. Private*, pg. 573
NORSKE SKOGINDUSTRIER A.S; *Int'l*, pg. 965
OFFICE PRODUCTS DIVISION—FiberMark Inc.; *U.S. Public*, pg. 620
PKF/JONGEKRIJG HOLDING B.V.—N.V. Koninklijke KNP BT; *Int'l*, pg. 756
PAKENSO OY—Enso Oyj; *Int'l*, pg. 456
PAPELES VENEZOLANOS, S.A.—Kruger Inc.; *Int'l*, pg. 762
POTLATCH CORPORATION; *U.S. Public*, pg. 1318
PRIMARY PULP & PAPER PLANT—Georgia-Pacific Corporation; *U.S. Public*, pg. 736
QUEENS GROUP, INC.; *U.S. Private*, pg. 900
RP EUROPE B.V.—N.V. Koninklijke KNP BT; *Int'l*, pg. 757
REPUBLIC GROUP INCORPORATED; *U.S. Public*, pg. 1378
REPUBLIC PAPERBOARD CO.-COMMERCE CITY MILL—Republic Group Incorporated; *U.S. Public*, pg. 1378
REPUBLIC PAPERBOARD CO.-HUTCHINSON MILL—Republic Group Incorporated; *U.S. Public*, pg. 1378
RIVERWOOD INTERNATIONAL CORPORATION; *U.S. Public*, pg. 1391
ROCK-TENN COMPANY; *U.S. Public*, pg. 1396
ROCK-TENN COMPANY, MILL DIVISION, INC.—Rock-Tenn Company; *U.S. Public*, pg. 1397
ST. JOE CORP.; *U.S. Public*, pg. 1426
SCHAUMAN WOOD OY—UPM-Kymmene Corporation; *Int'l*, *pg. 1428*
SETTSU CORPORATION; *Int'l*, pg. 1225
SIMKINS INDUSTRIES, INC.; *U.S. Private*, pg. 1000

SIMPLEX PRODUCTS—K2 Inc.; *U.S. Public*, pg. 940
SIMPSON INVESTMENT CO.; *U.S. Private*, pg. 1003
SIMPSON PAPER CO.—Simpson Investment Co.; *U.S. Private*, pg. 1003
SMURFIT CARTON Y PAPEL DE MEXICO—Jefferson Smurfit Group p.l.c.; *Int'l*, pg. 1271
JEFFERSON SMURFIT CORPORATION—Jefferson Smurfit Group p.l.c.; *Int'l*, pg. 1269
JEFFERSON SMURFIT FOLDING CARTON & BOXBOARD MILLS DIV.—Jefferson Smurfit Group p.l.c.; *Int'l*, pg. 1270
JEFFERSON SMURFIT GROUP P.L.C.; *Int'l*, pg. 1269
SMURFIT LIMITED—Jefferson Smurfit Group p.l.c.; *Int'l*, pg. 1271
SMURFIT PACKAGING CORPORATION—Jefferson Smurfit Group p.l.c.; *Int'l*, pg. 1271
SONOCO PRODUCTS COMPANY; *U.S. Public*, pg. 1485
STAHL GMBH & CO.; *Int'l*, pg. 1293
STONE CONTAINER CORPORATION; *U.S. Public*, pg. 1520
STONE SAVANNAH RIVER PULP AND PAPER—Stone Container Corporation; *U.S. Public*, pg. 1520
STORA BILLERUD AB—Stora Kopparbergs Bergslags AB; *Int'l*, pg. 1302
STORA FELDMUHLE AG—Stora Kopparbergs Bergslags AB; *Int'l*, pg. 1303
TECHNICAL SPECIALTIES DIVISION—FiberMark Inc.; *U.S. Public*, pg. 620
TEMBEC INC.; *Int'l*, pg. 1374
TEMPLE-INLAND FOREST PRODUCTS CORP.-BLEACHED PAPERBOARD GROUP—Temple-Inland Inc.; *U.S. Public*, pg. 1575
TEMPLE-INLAND INC.; *U.S. Public*, pg. 1574
TENNECO PACKAGING—Tenneco Inc.; *U.S. Public*, pg. 1579
TENNESSEE RIVER PULP & PAPER CO.—Tenneco Inc.; *U.S. Public*, pg. 1579
UNION CAMP CORPORATION; *U.S. Public*, pg. 1665
VEDENA B.V.—N.V. Koninklijke KNP BT; *Int'l*, pg. 757
WESTON PAPER & MANUFACTURING CO.; *U.S. Private*, pg. 1169
WESTVACO CORPORATION; *U.S. Public*, pg. 1762
WEYERHAEUSER COMPANY; *U.S. Public*, pg. 1764
WHAKATANE BOARD MILL—International Paper Company; *U.S. Public*, pg. 905
WHITE PIGEON PAPER COMPANY—Artistic Carton Company; *U.S. Private*, pg. 87
YORKTOWNE PAPERBOARD CORP.—The Newark Group, Inc.; *U.S. Private*, pg. 796

2652 — SET-UP PAPERBOARD BOXES

ARTISTIC CARTON COMPANY; *U.S. Private*, pg. 87
BANKERS BOX/RECORDS STORAGE SYSTEMS—Fellowes Manufacturing Co.; *U.S. Private*, pg. 400
COPYHOLDER DIVISION—Fellowes Manufacturing Co.; *U.S. Private*, pg. 400
DOMINO SUGAR CORPORATION—Tate & Lyle PLC; *Int'l*, pg. 1356
DOVER INDUSTRIES LIMITED; *Int'l*, pg. 417
FELLOWES MANUFACTURING CO.; *U.S. Private*, pg. 400
OLD DOMINION BOX CO., INC.; *U.S. Private*, pg. 814
PRINTPAC-UEB CARTON GROUP—International Paper Company; *U.S. Public*, pg. 905
REXAM CARTONS—Rexam PLC; *Int'l*, pg. 1106
ST. JOE CORP.; *U.S. Public*, pg. 1426
SCHWARZ PAPER COMPANY; *U.S. Private*, pg. 974
SPENCER'S INC.; *U.S. Private*, pg. 1025
TEMPLE-INLAND INC.; *U.S. Public*, pg. 1574
C.W. ZUMBIEL COMPANY; *U.S. Private*, pg. 1207

2653 — CORRUGATED & SOLID FIBER BOXES

ACCO WORLD CORPORATION—Fortune Brands, Inc.; *U.S. Public*, pg. 674
ACCURATE BOX CO., INC.; *U.S. Private*, pg. 11
ADVANCE PACKAGING CORPORATION; *U.S. Private*, pg. 18
ADVANCE PACKAGING CORPORATION-JACKSON FACILITY—Advance Packaging Corporation; *U.S. Private*, pg. 18
AKERS PACKAGING SERVICE INC.; *U.S. Private*, pg. 29
ALL SIZE CORRUGATED—Buckeye Corrugated Inc.; *U.S. Private*, pg. 177
ARMIN PLASTICS DIVISION—Tyco International Ltd.; *U.S. Public*, pg. 1647
BATES CONTAINER, INC.; *U.S. Private*, pg. 122
BEACON CONTAINER CORPORATION; *U.S. Private*, pg. 125
BEACON CONTAINER OF PA—Beacon Container Corporation; *U.S. Private*, pg. 125
BELL PACKAGING CORPORATION-MARION DIV.—Pratt Industries; *Int'l*, pg. 1066
BELL PACKAGING CORPORATION-MENOMINEE DIV.—Pratt Industries; *Int'l*, pg. 1066
BOISE CASCADE CORPORATION; *U.S. Public*, pg. 242
BOISE CASCADE PAPER DIV.—Boise Cascade Corporation; *U.S. Public*, pg. 243
BOX USA INC.—Four M Corporation, Inc.; *U.S. Private*, pg. 421
BRADFORD COMPANY; *U.S. Private*, pg. 163
BRITISH PRINTING COMPANY LTD.; *Int'l*, pg. 220
BROCKHOUSE MODERNFOLD LIMITED—EIP Group plc; *Int'l*, pg. 426
BUCKEYE CONTAINER—Buckeye Corrugated Inc.; *U.S. Private*, pg. 177
C.D. PACKAGING SYSTEMS LTD.—American Israeli Paper Mills Ltd.; *Int'l*, pg. 75
CALUMET CARTON COMPANY; *U.S. Private*, pg. 201
CASTLE ROCK CONTAINER CO.—Consolidated Papers, Inc.; *U.S. Public*, pg. 436
CHESAPEAKE CORPORATION; *U.S. Public*, pg. 346
CLARKE CONTAINER COMPANY, INC.—Mark IV Industries Inc.; *U.S. Public*, pg. 1045
COLOR-BOX, INC.—Chesapeake Corporation; *U.S. Public*, pg. 347
CONCORD SPECIALTY CORP.—Buckeye Corrugated Inc.; *U.S. Private*, pg. 177
CONNECTICUT CONTAINER CORPORATION; *U.S. Private*, pg. 263
CONNELLY CONTAINERS, INC.; *U.S. Private*, pg. 264
DAI NIPPON PRINTING CO., LTD.; *Int'l*, pg. 363
DOMTAR INC.; *Int'l*, pg. 416
EARLE INDUSTRIES, INC.; *U.S. Private*, pg. 356
ENSO OYJ; *Int'l*, pg. 455
ENVASES INDUSTRIALES DE COSTA RICA, S.A.—Georgia-Pacific Corporation; *U.S. Public*, pg. 739
EUROPA CARTON AG—Abitibi-Consolidated Inc.; *Int'l*, pg. 20
FLETCHER CHALLENGE CANADA LIMITED—Fletcher Challenge Limited; *Int'l*, pg. 495
GAYLORD CONTAINER CORPORATION; *U.S. Public*, pg. 704
GEORGIA-PACIFIC CORPORATION; *U.S. Public*, pg. 735
STEPHEN GOULD PAPER CO., INC.; *U.S. Private*, pg. 467
GREATER NEW YORK BOX CO.; *U.S. Private*, pg. 476
GREEN BAY PACKAGING INC.; *U.S. Private*, pg. 476
GREIF BROTHERS CORPORATION; *U.S. Public*, pg. 763
GRUPO INDUSTRIAL DURANGO S.A. DE C.V.; *Int'l*, pg. 575
HORN PACKAGING CORPORATION; *U.S. Private*, pg. 539
INDUSTRIA PANAMENA DE PAPEL, S.A.—Georgia-Pacific Corporation; *U.S. Public*, pg. 739
INLAND CONTAINER-CONTAINERBOARD DIVISION—Temple-Inland Inc.; *U.S. Public*, pg. 1575
INLAND CONTAINER CORPORATION—Temple-Inland Inc.; *U.S. Public*, pg. 1575
INTERSTATE CONTAINER CORPORATION—Interstate Resources, Inc.; *U.S. Private*, pg. 573
INTERSTATE RESOURCES, INC.; *U.S. Private*, pg. 573
J & J CORRUGATED BOX—Georgia-Pacific Corporation; *U.S. Public*, pg. 736
KEY CONTAINER CORPORATION; *U.S. Private*, pg. 617
KOCH CONTAINER—Buckeye Corrugated Inc.; *U.S. Private*, pg. 177
KRUGER INC.; *Int'l*, pg. 761
L & M CORRUGATED CONTAINER CORP.—Stone Container Corporation; *U.S. Public*, pg. 1521
LAWRENCE PAPER COMPANY; *U.S. Private*, pg. 654
LONE STAR CORRUGATED CONTAINER CORPORATION; *U.S. Private*, pg. 674
LONGVIEW FIBRE COMPANY; *U.S. Public*, pg. 1013
LONGVIEW FIBRE CO. WESTERN CONTAINER DIVISION—Longview Fibre Company; *U.S. Public*, pg. 1014
LOVE PACKAGING GROUP; *U.S. Private*, pg. 677
MACMILLAN BATHURST INC.—Abitibi-Consolidated Inc.; *Int'l*, pg. 20
MACMILLAN BATHURST INC.—MacMillan Bloedel Limited; *Int'l*, pg. 828
MALAYAN FIBRE CONTAINERS SDN. BHD.—BTR plc; *Int'l*, pg. 129
MASSACHUSETTS CONTAINER CORPORATION—Connecticut Container Corporation; *U.S. Private*, pg. 263
MEAD CONTAINERBOARD—The Mead Corporation; *U.S. Public*, pg. 1074
THE MEAD CORPORATION; *U.S. Public*, pg. 1074
MEBANE PACKAGING GROUP; *U.S. Private*, pg. 726
MEBANE PACKAGING GROUP—Mebane Packaging Group; *U.S. Private*, pg. 726
MENASHA CORPORATION; *U.S. Private*, pg. 731
MERTON CONTAINERS—BPB Industries PLC; *Int'l*, pg. 123
MITCHEL-LINCOLN PACKAGING; *Int'l*, pg. 870
MO OCH DOMSJO AB; *Int'l*, pg. 885
NEKOOSA PACKAGING COMPANY—Georgia-Pacific Corporation; *U.S. Public*, pg. 736
OLD DOMINION BOX CO., INC.; *U.S. Private*, pg. 814
PAKENSO OY—Enso Oyj; *Int'l*, pg. 456
PAPELES VENEZOLANOS, S.A.—Kruger Inc.; *Int'l*, pg. 762
PRATT INDUSTRIES; *Int'l*, pg. 1066
PRINTPAC-UEB CARTON GROUP—International Paper Company; *U.S. Public*, pg. 905
PUERTO RICO CONTAINER CO.—Union Camp Corporation; *U.S. Public*, pg. 1666
QUALITY PACKAGING PRODUCTS, INC.; *U.S. Private*, pg. 899
REPUBLIC CONTAINER CORP.; *U.S. Private*, pg. 923
RIGESA, LTDA.—Westvaco Corporation; *U.S. Public*, pg. 1762
ROCK-TENN COMPANY; *U.S. Public*, pg. 1396
ROCK-TENN CONVERTING CO.—Rock-Tenn Company; *U.S. Public*, pg. 1397
ST. JOE CONTAINER CO.—St. Joe Corp.; *U.S. Public*, pg. 1427
SEATTLE PACKAGING CORPORATION; *U.S. Private*, pg. 980
SHOREWOOD PACKAGING CORPORATION; *U.S. Public*, pg. 1468
SHOREWOOD PACKAGING CORPORATION OF CANADA, LTD.—Shorewood Packaging Corporation; *U.S. Public*, pg. 1468
SHOWA PRODUCTS CO., LTD.—Sonoco Products Company; *U.S. Public*, pg. 1487
SMURFIT CARTONS (CONGLETON) LTD.—Jefferson Smurfit Group p.l.c.; *Int'l*, pg. 1271
SMURFIT CARTONS (LEEDS) LTD.—Jefferson Smurfit Group p.l.c.; *Int'l*, pg. 1271
SMURFIT CARTONS (WITHAM) LTD.—Jefferson Smurfit Group p.l.c.; *Int'l*, pg. 1271
SMURFIT CORRUGATED CASES (WARRINGTON) LTD.—Jefferson Smurfit Group p.l.c.; *Int'l*, pg. 1271
SMURFIT CORRUGATED (UK) LIMITED—Jefferson Smurfit Group p.l.c.; *Int'l*, pg. 1271
SMURFIT FIBREBOARD CONVERTERS LTD.—Jefferson Smurfit Group p.l.c.; *Int'l*, pg. 1271
JEFFERSON SMURFIT CORPORATION—Jefferson Smurfit Group p.l.c.; *Int'l*, pg. 1269
JEFFERSON SMURFIT GROUP P.L.C.; *Int'l*, pg. 1269
SOUTHERN MISSOURI CONTAINERS INC.; *U.S. Private*, pg. 1017
SPECIALTY INDUSTRIES, INC.; *U.S. Private*, pg. 1022
STONE CONTAINER CORPORATION; *U.S. Public*, pg. 1520
STONE SOUTHWEST CORP.—Stone Container Corporation; *U.S. Public*, pg. 1521
SUNCLIPSE, INC.—Amcor Limited; *Int'l*, pg. 72
TE PAPAPA PAPER MILL—International Paper Company; *U.S. Public*, pg. 905
TENNECO PACKAGING—Tenneco Inc.; *U.S. Public*, pg. 1579
TENNESSEE PACKAGING—Buckeye Corrugated Inc.; *U.S. Private*, pg. 177
THAI CONTAINERS INDUSTRY CO., LTD.—The Siam Cement Public Company Limited; *Int'l*, pg. 1238
THAI CONTAINERS LTD.—The Siam Cement Public Company Limited; *Int'l*, pg. 1238
THAI CONTAINERS RATCHABURI (1989) CO., LTD.—The Siam Cement Public Company Limited; *Int'l*, pg. 1238
THOROBRED CONTAINERS INCORPORATED—Interlock Industries, Inc.; *U.S. Private*, pg. 567
TUSCARORA INCORPORATED; *U.S. Public*, pg. 1646
UNION CAMP CORPORATION; *U.S. Public*, pg. 1665
U.S. CONTAINER DIV.—International Paper Company; *U.S. Public*, pg. 903
VP-SCHICKEDANZ AG—The Procter & Gamble Company; *U.S. Public*, pg. 1333
WABASH FIBRE BOX CO.—Weston Paper & Manufacturing Co.; *U.S. Private*, pg. 1170
WABASH FIBRE BOX CO.-COLUMBIA—Weston Paper & Manufacturing Co.; *U.S. Private*, pg. 1170
WABASH FIBRE BOX COMPANY—Weston Paper & Manufacturing Co.; *U.S. Private*, pg. 1170
WABASH PIONEER CONTAINER DIVISION—Weston Paper & Manufacturing Co.; *U.S. Private*, pg. 1170
WESTON PAPER & MANUFACTURING CO.; *U.S. Private*, pg. 1169
WEYERHAEUSER COMPANY; *U.S. Public*, pg. 1764
WILLAMETTE INDUSTRIES, INC.; *U.S. Public*, pg. 1768
WILLAMETTE INDUSTRIES INC.—Willamette Industries, Inc.; *U.S. Public*, pg. 1768
WURZBURG, INC.; *U.S. Private*, pg. 1192

2655 — FIBER CANS, TUBES, DRUMS & SIMILAR PRODUCTS

ACI INTERNATIONAL LTD.—BTR plc; *Int'l*, pg. 128
BARBOUR THREAD INC.—Hicking Pentecost Plc; *Int'l*, pg. 618
CEBAL S.A.—Pechiney S.A.; *Int'l*, pg. 1028
CEBAL VERPACKUNGEN GMBH & CO. KG—Pechiney S.A.; *Int'l*, pg. 1030
CENTRAL STATES CAN CO.—Crown Cork & Seal Company, Inc.; *U.S. Public*, pg. 463
CLARCOR, INC.; *U.S. Public*, pg. 381
CONTINENTAL PLASTIC CONTAINERS, INC.—Continental Can Co.; *U.S. Public*, pg. 440
CORENSO UNITED OY LTD.—Enso Oyj; *Int'l*, pg. 456
CROWN CORK & SEAL COMPANY, INC.; *U.S. Public*, pg. 462
EAGLE INDUSTRIES, INC.—Great American Management & Investment, Inc.; *U.S. Private*, pg. 473
FIBRO TAMBOR—Sonoco Products Company; *U.S. Public*, pg. 1487
GREIF BROTHERS CORPORATION; *U.S. Public*, pg. 763
HARRIS ALLIED SYSTEMS—Harris Corporation; *U.S. Public*, pg. 791
MB GENERAL PACKAGING DIV.—Caradon Plc; *Int'l*, pg. 266
MILTON CAN CO., INC.; *U.S. Private*, pg. 749
NEWARK PAPERBOARD PRODUCTS MERCER DIV.—The Newark Group, Inc.; *U.S. Private*, pg. 796
PAK PACIFIC CORP. PTY. LTD.—BTR plc; *Int'l*, pg. 129
PIONEER PAPER CORPORATION; *U.S. Private*, pg. 867
PRECISION PRODUCTS CORPORATION; *U.S. Private*, pg. 879
RADCLIFFE PAPER TUBES—BPB Industries PLC; *Int'l*, pg. 123
REPUBLIC CONTAINER CORP.; *U.S. Private*, pg. 923
SHOWA PRODUCTS CO., LTD.—Sonoco Products Company; *U.S. Public*, pg. 1487
JEFFERSON SMURFIT CORPORATION—Jefferson Smurfit Group p.l.c.; *Int'l*, pg. 1269
JEFFERSON SMURFIT GROUP P.L.C.; *Int'l*, pg. 1269
SONOCO COLOMBIANA S.A.—Sonoco Products Company; *U.S. Public*, pg. 1487
SONOCO CONSUMER PACKAGING GROUP—Sonoco Products Company; *U.S. Public*, pg. 1486
SONOCO CONTAINERS, INC.—Sonoco Products Company; *U.S. Public*, pg. 1487
SONOCO PRODUCTS COMPANY; *U.S. Public*, pg. 1485
STONE INDUSTRIAL—Precision Products Corporation; *U.S. Private*, pg. 880
TBG MANAGEMENT S.A.M.; *Int'l*, pg. 1335
T.P.T. LTD.—Sonoco Products Company; *U.S. Public*, pg. 1487
TRANSLOGIC CORP.—Thyssen AG; *Int'l*, pg. 1387

2656 — SANITARY FOOD CONTAINERS, EXCEPT FOLDING

A J M PACKAGING CORPORATION; *U.S. Private*, pg. 2
ACCURATE BOX CO., INC.; *U.S. Private*, pg. 11
ARABIAN PAPER PRODUCTS COMPANY (APPCO)—Huhtamaki Oy; *Int'l*, pg. 639
BPB INDUSTRIES PLC; *Int'l*, pg. 122
BPB PAPER & PACKAGING LTD.—BPB Industries PLC; *Int'l*, pg. 122

CAMBRO MANUFACTURING COMPANY; *U.S. Private*, pg. 203
CHAMPION DAIRYPAK DIV.—Champion International Corp.; *U.S. Public*, pg. 334
CHAMPION INTERNATIONAL CORP.; *U.S. Public*, pg. 333
CLARCOR, INC.; *U.S. Public*, pg. 381
DANONE GROUP; *Int'l*, pg. 379
DEEKO PLC—Fort James Corporation; *U.S. Public*, pg. 672
DEUTSCHE DUNI GMBH—Duni AB; *Int'l*, pg. 421
DIXIE BENDERS LIMITED—Fort James Corporation; *U.S. Public*, pg. 672
DIXIE FOODSERVICE—Fort James Corporation; *U.S. Public*, pg. 671
DOVER INDUSTRIES LIMITED; *Int'l*, pg. 417
DUBREUIL FOREST PRODUCTS, LTD.—Fort James Corporation; *U.S. Public*, pg. 672
DUNI AG—Duni AB; *Int'l*, pg. 421
DUNI A/S—Duni AB; *Int'l*, pg. 421
DUNI BELGIUM NV—Duni AB; *Int'l*, pg. 421
DUNI GMBH—Duni AB; *Int'l*, pg. 421
DUNI IBERICA S.L.—Duni AB; *Int'l*, pg. 421
DUNI INC.—Duni AB; *Int'l*, pg. 421
DUNI LTD.—Duni AB; *Int'l*, pg. 421
DUNI NEDERLAND B.V.—Duni AB; *Int'l*, pg. 421
DUNI SARL—Duni AB; *Int'l*, pg. 421
ELOPAK A/S—Tiedemanns - Joh.H.Andresen ANS; *Int'l*, pg. 1389
ELOPAK, INC.—Tiedemanns - Joh.H.Andresen ANS; *Int'l*, pg. 1390
FEDERAL PAPER BOARD COMPANY, INC.—International Paper Company; *U.S. Public*, pg. 903
FORT JAMES CORPORATION; *U.S. Public*, pg. 670
FRANCIA-LOTUS S.A.—Fort James Corporation; *U.S. Public*, pg. 672
GASTRA SPOL. S.R.O.—Huhtamaki Oy; *Int'l*, pg. 638
HUHTAMAKI OY; *Int'l*, pg. 638
HYGIE FRANCE—Fort James Corporation; *U.S. Public*, pg. 672
INGRID DIVISION OF LAWNWARE—Lawnware Products, Inc.; *U.S. Private*, pg. 654
INLAND CONTAINER-CONTAINER DIVISION—Temple-Inland Inc.; *U.S. Public*, pg. 1575
POLARCUP (AUSTRALIA) LTD.—Huhtamaki Oy; *Int'l*, pg. 638
POLARCUP BENELUX B.V.—Huhtamaki Oy; *Int'l*, pg. 638
POLARCUP FINLAND—Huhtamaki Oy; *Int'l*, pg. 638
POLARCUP GERMANY—Huhtamaki Oy; *Int'l*, pg. 638
POLARCUP GROUP HEADQUARTERS—Huhtamaki Oy; *Int'l*, pg. 638
POLARCUP NORWAY—Huhtamaki Oy; *Int'l*, pg. 638
POLARCUP (N.Z.) LIMITED—Huhtamaki Oy; *Int'l*, pg. 638
POLARCUP POLAND SP. Z.O.O.—Huhtamaki Oy; *Int'l*, pg. 638
POLARCUP PORTUGAL—Huhtamaki Oy; *Int'l*, pg. 639
POLARCUP S.A.—Huhtamaki Oy; *Int'l*, pg. 638
POLARCUP SINGAPORE PTE. LTD.—Huhtamaki Oy; *Int'l*, pg. 639
POLARCUP S.R.L.—Huhtamaki Oy; *Int'l*, pg. 639
POLARCUP SWEDEN—Huhtamaki Oy; *Int'l*, pg. 639
POLARCUP UNITED KINGDOM LTD.—Huhtamaki Oy; *Int'l*, pg. 638
PRINTPAC-UEB CARTON GROUP—International Paper Company; *U.S. Public*, pg. 905
SEALRIGHT COMPANY, INC.; *U.S. Public*, pg. 1451
JEFFERSON SMURFIT CORPORATION—Jefferson Smurfit Group p.l.c.; *Int'l*, pg. 1269
JEFFERSON SMURFIT FOLDING CARTON & BOXBOARD MILLS DIV.—Jefferson Smurfit Group p.l.c.; *Int'l*, pg. 1270
SOLO CUP COMPANY; *U.S. Private*, pg. 1013
SOLO CUP COMPANY—Solo Cup Company; *U.S. Private*, pg. 1013
TIEDEMANNS - JOH.H.ANDRESEN ANS; *Int'l*, pg. 1389
TRIMAS CORPORATION—Masco Corporation; *U.S. Public*, pg. 1054
WESTVACO CORPORATION; *U.S. Public*, pg. 1762

2657 — FOLDING PAPERBOARD BOXES, INCLUDING SANITARY

ACI INTERNATIONAL LTD.—BTR plc; *Int'l*, pg. 128
ACCURATE BOX CO., INC.; *U.S. Private*, pg. 11
AKROSIL EUROPE B.V.—International Paper Company; *U.S. Public*, pg. 904
AMCO FOLDING CARTONS, INC.; *U.S. Private*, pg. 48
AMERICAN PACKAGING CORPORATION; *U.S. Private*, pg. 60
ARKAY PACKAGING CORPORATION; *U.S. Private*, pg. 82
BELL PACKAGING CORPORATION-MENOMINEE DIV.—Pratt Industries; *Int'l*, pg. 1066
BLOHORN S.A.—Unilever Plc; *Int'l*, pg. 1436
BUFKOR, INC.; *U.S. Private*, pg. 179
BURD & FLETCHER COMPANY, *U.S. Private*, pg. 181
F.N. BURT COMPANY, INC.; *U.S. Private*, pg. 188
CARTON-CRAFT CORPORATION; *U.S. Private*, pg. 217
CARTONAJES INTERNATIONAL, S.A.—International Paper Company; *U.S. Public*, pg. 905
CONTEMPO COLORS; *U.S. Private*, pg. 267
DRG CARTONS LTD.—Johns Manville Corporation; *U.S. Public*, pg. 927
DEE PAPER COMPANY; *U.S. Private*, pg. 320
DUBREUIL FOREST PRODUCTS, LTD.—Fort James Corporation; *U.S. Public*, pg. 672
DURALAM, INC.—Sargento Foods Inc.; *U.S. Private*, pg. 966
ECONOMY FOLDING BOX CORP.; *U.S. Private*, pg. 362
FIELD CONTAINER COMPANY, L.P.; *U.S. Private*, pg. 403
FLETCHER CHALLENGE CANADA LIMITED—Fletcher Challenge Limited; *Int'l*, pg. 495
FORT JAMES CANADA, INC.—Fort James Corporation; *U.S. Public*, pg. 672
FORT JAMES CORPORATION; *U.S. Public*, pg. 670
GREATER NEW YORK BOX CO.; *U.S. Private*, pg. 476
GREEN BAY PACKAGING INC.; *U.S. Private*, pg. 476
GULF STATES PAPER CORPORATION; *U.S. Private*, pg. 487
GUNTHER MELE LIMITED; *Int'l*, pg. 578
HAMMERMILL PAPER GMBH—International Paper Company; *U.S. Public*, pg. 905
ICE CREAM SPECIALTIES, INC.—Prairie Farms Dairy, Inc.; *U.S. Private*, pg. 879
IMPERIAL BONDWARE CORP.—International Paper Company; *U.S. Public*, pg. 903
INLAND CONTAINER-CONTAINER DIVISION—Temple-Inland Inc.; *U.S. Public*, pg. 1575
INTERNATIONAL PAPER COMPANY; *U.S. Public*, pg. 901
LANDOR CARTONS; *Int'l*, pg. 801
LAWSON MARDON PACKAGING INC.—Alusuisse-Lonza Holding Ltd.; *Int'l*, pg. 68
LAWSON MARDON SUPERIOR PACKAGING—Alusuisse-Lonza Holding Ltd.; *Int'l*, pg. 69
LAWSON MARDON THYNE LTD—Alusuisse-Lonza Holding Ltd.; *Int'l*, pg. 69
LAWSON MARDON TRENTESAUX SA—Alusuisse-Lonza Holding Ltd.; *Int'l*, pg. 69
MANUFACTURERS FOLDING CARTON, INC.—Stone Container Corporation; *U.S. Public*, pg. 1521
THE MEAD CORPORATION; *U.S. Public*, pg. 1074
MEAD-EMBALLAGE S.A.—The Mead Corporation; *U.S. Public*, pg. 1076
MEAD KK—The Mead Corporation; *U.S. Public*, pg. 1076
MEAD PACKAGING—The Mead Corporation; *U.S. Public*, pg. 1074
MEAD PACKAGING (CANADA) LTD.—The Mead Corporation; *U.S. Public*, pg. 1076
MEAD PACKAGING KOREA, INC.—The Mead Corporation; *U.S. Public*, pg. 1076
MEAD VERPACKUNG G.M.B.H.—The Mead Corporation; *U.S. Public*, pg. 1077
MEAD VERPAKKING B.V.—The Mead Corporation; *U.S. Public*, pg. 1076
MEBANE PACKAGING GROUP; *U.S. Private*, pg. 726
MEBANE PACKAGING GROUP.—Mebane Packaging Group; *U.S. Private*, pg. 726
MOD-PAC CORP—Astronics Corporation; *U.S. Public*, pg. 142
NDS—Nestle S.A.; *Int'l*, pg. 918
NESTLE DAIRY SYSTEMS-PACKAGING/MACHINERY DIVISION—Nestle S.A.; *Int'l*, pg. 918
OLD DOMINION BOX CO., INC.; *U.S. Private*, pg. 814
ORLANDI INC.—Jefferson Smurfit Group p.l.c.; *Int'l*, pg. 1269
PAK PACIFIC (SOUTH EAST ASIA) PTE. LTD.—BTR plc; *Int'l*, pg. 129
PACKAGE PRODUCTS SPECIALTY-PAPERBOARD DIV.—Sonoco Products Company; *U.S. Public*, pg. 1486
PACKAGING BUSINESS—Fort James Corporation; *U.S. Public*, pg. 671
PRATT INDUSTRIES; *Int'l*, pg. 1066
REXAM INC.—Rexam PLC; *Int'l*, pg. 1106
ROCK-TENN CO.—Rock-Tenn Company; *U.S. Public*, pg. 1397
ROCK-TENN COMPANY; *U.S. Public*, pg. 1396
ROTOPACK SAHRE GMBH—Alusuisse-Lonza Holding Ltd.; *Int'l*, pg. 69
ROYAL PAPER BOX OF CALIFORNIA; *U.S. Private*, pg. 949
SCHWARZ PAPER COMPANY; *U.S. Private*, pg. 974
SIMKINS CAROLINA FOLDING BOX DIV.—Simkins Industries, Inc.; *U.S. Private*, pg. 1000
SIMKINS INDUSTRIES, INC.; *U.S. Private*, pg. 1000
JEFFERSON SMURFIT GROUP P.L.C.; *Int'l*, pg. 1269
SOCIETE GUADELOUPEENE DE CARTON ONDULE—International Paper Company; *U.S. Public*, pg. 906
SOCIETE MARTINIQUAISE DE CARTON ONDULE—International Paper Company; *U.S. Public*, pg. 906
SONOCO ENGRAPH, INC.—Sonoco Products Company; *U.S. Public*, pg. 1486
STERLING PAPER CO.; *U.S. Private*, pg. 1041
TEMPLE-INLAND FOREST PRODUCTS CORPORATION—Temple-Inland Inc.; *U.S. Public*, pg. 1575
TEMPLE-INLAND INC.; *U.S. Public*, pg. 1574
TENNECO PACKAGING—Tenneco Inc.; *U.S. Public*, pg. 1579
TETRA LAVAL GROUP; *Int'l*, pg. 1377
TETRA-PAK ROMONT SA—Tetra Laval Group; *Int'l*, pg. 1380
UNIVERSAL FOLDING BOX COMPANY, INC.; *U.S. Private*, pg. 1127
WESTVACO CORPORATION; *U.S. Public*, pg. 1762
WESTVACO CORPORATION-CONSUMER PACKAGING DIV.—Westvaco Corporation; *U.S. Public*, pg. 1762
WINCHESTER CARTON CORP.—Rock-Tenn Company; *U.S. Public*, pg. 1397

2671 — COATED & LAMINATED PAPER & PLASTICS FILM

AHLSTROM PAPER AG—A. Ahlstrom Corporation; *Int'l*, pg. 35
AMCOR LIMITED; *Int'l*, pg. 71
AMERICAN NATIONAL CAN COMPANY—Pechiney S.A.; *Int'l*, pg. 1029
APPLETON PAPERS INC.—Groupe Saint Louis; *Int'l*, pg. 567
ARJO WIGGINS APPLETON PLC—Groupe Saint Louis; *Int'l*, pg. 567
ARJO WIGGINS BELGIUM S.A.—Groupe Saint Louis; *Int'l*, pg. 568
ARJO WIGGINS OVERSEAS LTD.—Groupe Saint Louis; *Int'l*, pg. 567
AVERY ETICHETTE ITALIA S.P.A.—Avery Dennison Corporation; *U.S. Public*, pg. 153
AVERY INTERNATIONAL CONVERTING GROUP—Avery Dennison Corporation; *U.S. Public*, pg. 152
AVERY LABEL LTD.—Avery Dennison Corporation; *U.S. Public*, pg. 153
BTR PAPER GROUP—BTR plc; *Int'l*, pg. 127
BAGCRAFT CORPORATION OF AMERICA—Artra Group Incorporated; *U.S. Public*, pg. 136
BAGPAK DIV.—International Paper Company; *U.S. Public*, pg. 901
BAKERS CHOICE PRODUCTS, INC.—Reynolds Metals Company; *U.S. Public*, pg. 1386
BEMIS COMPANY, INC.; *U.S. Public*, pg. 210
BLOHORN S.A.—Unilever Plc; *Int'l*, pg. 1436
BORDEN DECORATIVE PRODUCTS—Borden, Inc.; *U.S. Private*, pg. 158
BROWN-BRIDGE—Lynch Corporation; *U.S. Public*, pg. 1022
BRYCE LLC CORPORATION; *U.S. Private*, pg. 177
BUCKSPORT MILL, CHAMPION INTERNATIONAL CORP.—Champion International Corp.; *U.S. Public*, pg. 334
BUNZL EXTRUSION—Bunzl PLC; *Int'l*, pg. 232
C P CONVERTERS, INC.; *U.S. Private*, pg. 192
CHR INDUSTRIES, INC.—Furon Company; *U.S. Public*, pg. 689
CPS CORPORATION—Fox Valley Corporation; *U.S. Private*, pg. 422
CADILLAC PRODUCTS, INC.; *U.S. Private*, pg. 198
CARTER HOLT HARVEY LIMITED—International Paper Company; *U.S. Public*, pg. 904
THE CAXTON GROUP OF COMPANIES—International Paper Company; *U.S. Public*, pg. 905
CAXTON PAPER LIMITED—International Paper Company; *U.S. Public*, pg. 905
CELLOGLAS LIMITED—Alusuisse-Lonza Holding Ltd.; *Int'l*, pg. 69
CENTRAL NATIONAL-GOTTESMAN INC.; *U.S. Private*, pg. 224
CONTINENTAL PLASTIC CARD CO.; *U.S. Private*, pg. 269
CURWOOD PACKAGING (CANADA) LTD.—Bemis Company, Inc.; *U.S. Public*, pg. 210
CYDSA S.A. PACKAGING DIV.—CYDSA S.A.; *Int'l*, pg. 246
DEFERIET MILL, CHAMPION INTERNATIONAL CORP.—Champion International Corp.; *U.S. Public*, pg. 334
DENNISON MANUFACTURING CANADA, INC.—Avery Dennison Corporation; *U.S. Public*, pg. 153
DENNISON PLC—Avery Dennison Corporation; *U.S. Public*, pg. 153
DINAGRAPHICS, INC.—Jefferson Smurfit Group p.l.c.; *Int'l*, pg. 1270
DOW CHEM CO.- FRESNO PLANT—The Dow Chemical Company; *U.S. Public*, pg. 523
DUNI/FINESS HYGIENE—Duni AB; *Int'l*, pg. 421
DUNMORE CORPORATION/BREWSTER—Dunmore Corporation; *U.S. Private*, pg. 347
EGAN MACHINERY DIVISION—Kvaerner a.s.a.; *Int'l*, pg. 774
ERVING INDUSTRIES, INC.; *U.S. Private*, pg. 382
ESSELTE CORPORATION—Esselte AB; *Int'l*, pg. 459
EUL & GUNTHER GMBH & CO KG—Melitta Unternehmensgruppe Bentz KG; *Int'l*, pg. 857
FARDEM BV—DSM N.V.; *Int'l*, pg. 352
FASSON ADHESIVE PRODUCTS, LTD.—Avery Dennison Corporation; *U.S. Public*, pg. 154
FASSON DE MEXICO, S.A.—Avery Dennison Corporation; *U.S. Public*, pg. 154
FASSON GESELLSCHAFT GMBH—Avery Dennison Corporation; *U.S. Public*, pg. 154
FASSON HANDELSGESELLSHAFT GMBH—Avery Dennison Corporation; *U.S. Public*, pg. 154
FASSON PRODUCTEN VERKOOPMAATSHAPPIJ B.V.—Avery Dennison Corporation; *U.S. Public*, pg. 154
FASSON PRODUTOS ADESIVOS LTDA.—Avery Dennison Corporation; *U.S. Public*, pg. 154
FASSON PTY. LTD.—Avery Dennison Corporation; *U.S. Public*, pg. 154
FASSON ROLL DIV.—Avery Dennison Corporation; *U.S. Public*, pg. 153
FASSON ROLL MATERIALS DIV.—Avery Dennison Corporation; *U.S. Public*, pg. 153
FILPAC, INC.—Bunzl PLC; *Int'l*, pg. 233
FORT JAMES CORPORATION; *U.S. Public*, pg. 670
FORTIFIBER CORPORATION; *U.S. Private*, pg. 419
FOX VALLEY CORPORATION; *U.S. Private*, pg. 422
GEORGIA-BONDED FIBERS, INC.; *U.S. Public*, pg. 734
GRIFFON CORP.; *U.S. Public*, pg. 766
GROUPE SAINT LOUIS; *Int'l*, pg. 567
HEXCEL, S.A.—Hexcel Corporation; *U.S. Public*, pg. 824
HEXCEL, U.K.—Hexcel Corporation; *U.S. Public*, pg. 824
INNOVATIVE SOUTH—Innovative Plastics Corporation; *U.S. Private*, pg. 565
KCL CORPORATION; *U.S. Private*, pg. 603
THE KENDALL-BETHAM DIVISION—Tyco International Ltd.; *U.S. Public*, pg. 1647
KENG HUA PAPER PRODUCTS CO., INC.; *Int'l*, pg. 729
LAWSON MARDON PACKAGING INC.—Alusuisse-Lonza Holding Ltd.; *Int'l*, pg. 68
LAWSON MARDON SUPERIOR PACKAGING—Alusuisse-Lonza Holding Ltd.; *Int'l*, pg. 69
LAWSON MARDON TRENTESAUX SA—Alusuisse-Lonza Holding Ltd.; *Int'l*, pg. 69
LUDLOW CORPORATION—Tyco International Ltd.; *U.S. Public*, pg. 1651
LUDLOW LAMINATING & COATING DIV.—Tyco International Ltd.; *U.S. Public*, pg. 1647
LUDLOW TECHNICAL PRODUCTS DIV.—Tyco International Ltd.; *U.S. Public*, pg. 1647
MD PAPIER GMBH—Metsa-Serla Corporation; *Int'l*, pg. 864
MACTAC MORGAN ADHESIVE COMPANY—Bemis Company, Inc.; *U.S. Public*, pg. 210
MATERIALS GROUP NORTH AMERICA—Avery Dennison Corporation; *U.S. Public*, pg. 153
MATTHEY BEYRAND & CIE S.A.—Johnson Matthey Public Limited Company; *Int'l*, pg. 714
MODO PAPER AB—Mo och Domsjo AB; *Int'l*, pg. 886

MOSINEE CONVERTED PRODUCTS DIV.—Wausau-Mosinee Paper Corporation; *U.S. Public*, pg. 1747
NOREL PAPER CORPORATION—Unisource Worldwide, Inc.; *U.S. Public*, pg. 1671
OCE-VAN DER GRINTEN N.V.; *Int'l*, pg. 993
OJI PAPER CO., LTD.; *Int'l*, pg. 998
ORLANDI INC.—Jefferson Smurfit Group p.l.c.; *Int'l*, pg. 1269
OUTLOOK PACKAGING, INC.—Outlook Group Corporation; *U.S. Public*, pg. 1236
PAK PACIFIC (SOUTH EAST ASIA) PTE. LTD.—BTR plc; *Int'l*, pg. 129
PACKAGING BUSINESS—Fort James Corporation; *U.S. Public*, pg. 671
PITNEY BOWES INC.; *U.S. Public*, pg. 1303
PLASTAG CORPORATION; *U.S. Private*, pg. 870
REXAM CUSTOM—Rexam PLC; *Int'l*, pg. 1106
REXAM EXTRUSIONS—Rexam PLC; *Int'l*, pg. 1106
REXAM INC.—Rexam PLC; *Int'l*, pg. 1106
REXAM MEDICAL PACKAGING—Rexam PLC; *Int'l*, pg. 1106
REXAM MEDICAL PACKAGING, INC.—Rexam PLC; *Int'l*, pg. 1107
ROHRER CORPORATION; *U.S. Private*, pg. 940
ROHRER CORPORATION—Rohrer Corporation; *U.S. Private*, pg. 940
SARTELL MILL, CHAMPION INTERNATIONAL CORP.—Champion International Corp.; *U.S. Public*, pg. 334
SEALED AIR B.V.—Sealed Air Corporation; *U.S. Public*, pg. 1451
SEALED AIR ESPANA, S.A.—Sealed Air Corporation; *U.S. Public*, pg. 1451
SEALED AIR G.M.B.H.—Sealed Air Corporation; *U.S. Public*, pg. 1451
SEALED AIR JAPAN LTD.—Sealed Air Corporation; *U.S. Public*, pg. 1451
SEALED AIR LIMITED—Sealed Air Corporation; *U.S. Public*, pg. 1451
SEALED AIR (MALAYSIA) SDN BHD—Sealed Air Corporation; *U.S. Public*, pg. 1451
SEALED AIR OF CANADA INC.—Sealed Air Corporation; *U.S. Public*, pg. 1451
SEALED AIR S.P.A.—Sealed Air Corporation; *U.S. Public*, pg. 1451
SEALED AIR SYSTEMS—Sealed Air Corporation; *U.S. Public*, pg. 1451
SEALRIGHT COMPANY, INC.; *U.S. Public*, pg. 1451
SEALRIGHT MFG. EAST, INC.—Sealright Company, Inc.; *U.S. Public*, pg. 1452
SIERRA COATING TECHNOLOGIES; *U.S. Private*, pg. 998
SIME DARBY BERHAD MALAYSIA REGION—Sime Darby Berhad; *Int'l*, pg. 1250
SMURFIT GIFTWRAP—Jefferson Smurfit Group p.l.c.; *Int'l*, pg. 1271
JEFFERSON SMURFIT GROUP P.L.C.; *Int'l*, pg. 1269
SMURFIT LIMITED—Jefferson Smurfit Group p.l.c.; *Int'l*, pg. 1271
SMURFIT PACKAGING PRODUCTS—Jefferson Smurfit Group p.l.c.; *Int'l*, pg. 1271
SOUZA CRUZ, S.A.—B.A.T Industries P.L.C.; *Int'l*, pg. 112
SPICERS PAPER LIMITED—Amcor Limited; *Int'l*, pg. 72
TESA-WERKE OFFENBURG GMBH—Beiersdorf Group; *Int'l*, pg. 182
THAI PAPER CO., LTD.—The Siam Cement Public Company Limited; *Int'l*, pg. 1239
3M; *U.S. Public*, pg. 1604
U.K. PAPER PLC—Fletcher Challenge Limited; *Int'l*, pg. 495
UNICOVER CORPORATION; *U.S. Private*, pg. 1117
UNIFOIL CORPORATION; *U.S. Private*, pg. 1117
UNILEVER AUSTRALIA LTD.—Unilever Plc; *Int'l*, pg. 1439
UNION INDUSTRIES, INC.; *U.S. Private*, pg. 1119
UNIPLAST INDUSTRIES, INC.—Trimin Enterprises, Inc.; *Int'l*, pg. 1424
VPI MIRREX CORP.—Vinyl Plastics Incorporated; *U.S. Private*, pg. 1141
VINYL PLASTICS INCORPORATED; *U.S. Private*, pg. 1141
WAUSAU-MOSINEE PAPER CORPORATION; *U.S. Public*, pg. 1747
WESTVACO CORPORATION; *U.S. Public*, pg. 1762
WISAFOREST OY AB—UPM-Kymmene Corporation; *Int'l*, pg. 1429
WISAPAK OY AB—UPM-Kymmene Corporation; *Int'l*, pg. 1429
WRAPPING SPECIALISTS PTY. LTD.—Borden, Inc.; *U.S. Private*, pg. 160
X-RITE, INCORPORATED; *U.S. Public*, pg. 1783
ZIMMER CUSTOM-MADE PACKAGING CO.—Norse Dairy Systems; *U.S. Private*, pg. 802

2672 — COATED & LAMINATED PAPER, NEC

A.F. & D. MACKAY LTD.—Norske Skogindustrier A.S; *Int'l*, pg. 966
AGENCE BELGE BULOW BENNET & CIE—Norske Skogindustrier A.S; *Int'l*, pg. 966
AHLSTROM PAPER AG—A. Ahlstrom Corporation; *Int'l*, pg. 35
AKROSIL—International Paper Company; *U.S. Public*, pg. 903
AMCOR LIMITED; *Int'l*, pg. 71
AMERICAN BILTRITE FAR EAST, INC.—American Biltrite Inc.; *U.S. Public*, pg. 69
AMERICAN TAPE CO.—Intertape Polymer Group Inc.; *Int'l*, pg. 685
ANCHOR CONTINENTAL INCORPORATED; *U.S. Private*, pg. 70
APPLETON PAPERS INC.—Groupe Saint Louis; *Int'l*, pg. 567
ARJO WIGGINS APPLETON PLC—Groupe Saint Louis; *Int'l*, pg. 567
ASSI FRANCE S.A.R.L.—Norske Skogindustrier A.S; *Int'l*, pg. 966
ASSI ITALIANA S.R.L.—Norske Skogindustrier A.S; *Int'l*, pg. 966
ASSI PULP & PAPER SALES (UK) LTD.—Norske Skogindustrier A.S; *Int'l*, pg. 967
AUTRON INCORPORATED—Marubeni Corporation; *Int'l*, pg. 845
AVERY DENNISON CORPORATION; *U.S. Public*, pg. 152
AVERY DENNISON CORPORATION LABEL GROUP—Avery Dennison Corporation; *U.S. Public*, pg. 153
AVERY ETICHETTE ITALIA S.P.A.—Avery Dennison Corporation; *U.S. Public*, pg. 153
AVERY INTERNATIONAL CONVERTING GROUP—Avery Dennison Corporation; *U.S. Public*, pg. 152
BAKERS CHOICE PRODUCTS, INC.—Reynolds Metals Company; *U.S. Public*, pg. 1386
BEIERSDORF GROUP; *Int'l*, pg. 182
S.A. BEIERSDORF NV—Beiersdorf Group; *Int'l*, pg. 183
BELL PACKAGING CORPORATION-MENOMINEE DIV.—Pratt Industries; *Int'l*, pg. 1066
BEMIS COMPANY, INC.; *U.S. Public*, pg. 210
BEMIS CRAFTIL, S.A.—Bemis Company, Inc.; *U.S. Public*, pg. 210
BEMIS MARAL, S.A. DE C.V.—Bemis Company, Inc.; *U.S. Public*, pg. 210
BLANDIN PAPER COMPANY—Fletcher Challenge Limited; *Int'l*, pg. 495
BOMARKO, INC.; *U.S. Private*, pg. 156
BORDEN DECORATIVE PRODUCTS—Borden, Inc.; *U.S. Private*, pg. 158
CADILLAC PRODUCTS, INC.; *U.S. Private*, pg. 198
CAL EMBLEM LABELS, INC.; *U.S. Private*, pg. 199
CARTER HOLT HARVEY LIMITED—International Paper Company; *U.S. Public*, pg. 904
THE CAXTON GROUP OF COMPANIES—International Paper Company; *U.S. Public*, pg. 905
CENTRAL NATIONAL-GOTTESMAN INC.; *U.S. Private*, pg. 224
CHAMPION INTERNATIONAL CORP.; *U.S. Public*, pg. 333
COMPAC CORPORATION—Masco Corporation; *U.S. Public*, pg. 1054
CONSTRUCTION & HOME IMPROVEMENT MARKETS DIVISION—3M; *U.S. Public*, pg. 1605
CUSTOM-MADE PACKAGING, INC.—Norse Dairy Systems; *U.S. Private*, pg. 803
DAUBERT COATED PRODUCTS, INC.—Daubert Industries, Inc.; *U.S. Private*, pg. 313
DENNISON MANUFACTURING CANADA, INC.—Avery Dennison Corporation; *U.S. Public*, pg. 153
DENNISON PLC—Avery Dennison Corporation; *U.S. Public*, pg. 153
DENNISON SPECIALTY PRODUCTS DIV.—Avery Dennison Corporation; *U.S. Public*, pg. 152
DENNISON TRADING HONG KONG LTD.—Avery Dennison Corporation; *U.S. Public*, pg. 153
THE DEXTER CORPORATION; *U.S. Public*, pg. 504
DIELECTRIC POLYMERS, INC.—Park Electrochemical Corporation; *U.S. Public*, pg. 1258
DURABLE SPECIALTIES DIVISION—FiberMark Inc.; *U.S. Public*, pg. 620
EASTERN FINE PAPER; *U.S. Private*, pg. 357
ELECTRICAL PRODUCTS DIVISION—3M; *U.S. Public*, pg. 1605
ENSO OYJ; *Int'l*, pg. 455
FABRICON PRODUCTS—Eagle-Picher Industries, Inc.; *U.S. Private*, pg. 355
FASSON ADHESIVE PRODUCTS, LTD.—Avery Dennison Corporation; *U.S. Public*, pg. 154
FASSON DE MEXICO, S.A.—Avery Dennison Corporation; *U.S. Public*, pg. 154
FASSON FILMS—Avery Dennison Corporation; *U.S. Public*, pg. 153
FASSON FRANCE S.A.R.L.—Avery Dennison Corporation; *U.S. Public*, pg. 154
FASSON GESELLSCHAFT GMBH—Avery Dennison Corporation; *U.S. Public*, pg. 154
FASSON HANDELSGESELLSHAFT GMBH—Avery Dennison Corporation; *U.S. Public*, pg. 154
N.V. FASSON INDUS. DIV.—Avery Dennison Corporation; *U.S. Public*, pg. 154
FASSON IRELAND LTD.—Avery Dennison Corporation; *U.S. Public*, pg. 154
FASSON ITALIA S.P.A.—Avery Dennison Corporation; *U.S. Public*, pg. 154
FASSON PRODUCTEN VERKOOPMAATSHAPPIJ B.V.—Avery Dennison Corporation; *U.S. Public*, pg. 154
FASSON PRODUCTS (PTY) LTD.—Avery Dennison Corporation; *U.S. Public*, pg. 154
FASSON PTY. LTD.—Avery Dennison Corporation; *U.S. Public*, pg. 154
FASSON VERTRIEBS, AG—Avery Dennison Corporation; *U.S. Public*, pg. 154
FIBERMARK INC.; *U.S. Public*, pg. 620
FIBO-TRESPO-LANGMOEN—Norske Skogindustrier A.S; *Int'l*, pg. 966
FORT JAMES CORPORATION; *U.S. Public*, pg. 670
FORTIFIBER CORPORATION; *U.S. Private*, pg. 419
FRYETECH, INC.; *U.S. Private*, pg. 430
GOULD PACKAGING, INC.; *U.S. Private*, pg. 466
GRAPHIC TECHNOLOGY, INC.—Nitto Denko Corporation; *Int'l*, pg. 950
GRAPHICS SYSTEMS DIVISION—Avery Dennison Corporation; *U.S. Public*, pg. 153
GUNNAR OLSSON TRANSPORTKONSULT AB—Norske Skogindustrier A.S; *Int'l*, pg. 966
HOECHST MARION ROUSSEL, INC.—Hoechst Aktiengesellschaft; *Int'l*, pg. 624
HUNT CORPORATION; *U.S. Public*, pg. 848
HURUM PAPIRFABRIKK—Norske Skogindustrier A.S; *Int'l*, pg. 965
IDEAL TAPE-BELGIUM—American Biltrite Inc.; *U.S. Public*, pg. 69
IDEAL TAPE COMPANY—American Biltrite Inc.; *U.S. Public*, pg. 69
INTERLAKE PAPERS, INC.—Consolidated Papers, Inc.; *U.S. Public*, pg. 436
INTERNATIONAL PAPER CANADA, INC.—International Paper Company; *U.S. Public*, pg. 905
INTERTAPE POLYMER GROUP—Intertape Polymer Group Inc.; *Int'l*, pg. 685
R. ANCKER JORGENSEN A/S—Avery Dennison Corporation; *U.S. Public*, pg. 153
K & P LEYKAM AUSTRIA—N.V. Koninklijke KNP BT; *Int'l*, pg. 757
K2 INC.; *U.S. Public*, pg. 940
THE KENDALL-BETHAM DIVISION—Tyco International Ltd.; *U.S. Public*, pg. 1647
KORSNAS AB; *Int'l*, pg. 759
LABEL ART LIMITED—James Crean PLC; *Int'l*, pg. 340
LABELON CORPORATION; *U.S. Private*, pg. 641
LAMINATING PAPERS LTD.—Enso Oyj; *Int'l*, pg. 457
LEPAGE'S, INC.—The Jordan Company; *U.S. Private*, pg. 598
LORBER INDUSTRIES OF CALIFORNIA; *U.S. Private*, pg. 675
LUFT, MAACK & CO. GMBH—Norske Skogindustrier A.S; *Int'l*, pg. 966
LYNCH CORPORATION; *U.S. Public*, pg. 1021
MD PAPIER GMBH—Metsa-Serla Corporation; *Int'l*, pg. 864
MACTAC EUROPE S.A.—Bemis Company, Inc.; *U.S. Public*, pg. 210
MACTAC MEXICO, S.A.—Bemis Company, Inc.; *U.S. Public*, pg. 210
MACTAC MORGAN ADHESIVE COMPANY—Bemis Company, Inc.; *U.S. Public*, pg. 210
MACTAC NORTH AMERICA—Bemis Company, Inc.; *U.S. Public*, pg. 210
MARSON/CREATIVE FASTENER, INC.; *U.S. Private*, pg. 708
MCCOURT LABEL CO.; *U.S. Private*, pg. 720
THE MEAD CORPORATION; *U.S. Public*, pg. 1074
METSA-SERLA CORPORATION; *Int'l*, pg. 863
THE MEYERCORD COMPANY—Illinois Tool Works Inc.; *U.S. Public*, pg. 867
NOPI GMBH—Beiersdorf Group; *Int'l*, pg. 182
NASHUA CORPORATION; *U.S. Public*, pg. 1152
NITTO DENKO CORPORATION; *Int'l*, pg. 950
NORSKE SKOGINDUSTRIER A.S; *Int'l*, pg. 965
OFFICE PRODUCTS DIVISION—FiberMark Inc.; *U.S. Public*, pg. 620
ORGANISATION DE VENTE DES PRODUITS FASSON S.A.R.L.—Avery Dennison Corporation; *U.S. Public*, pg. 154
PACKAGE SERVICE COMPANY, LLC.; *U.S. Private*, pg. 833
PAPERDIRECT, INC.—Deluxe Corporation; *U.S. Public*, pg. 498
PERFECSEAL COMPANY—Bemis Company, Inc.; *U.S. Public*, pg. 210
POLYKEN TECHNOLOGIES—Tyco International Ltd.; *U.S. Public*, pg. 1647
PRATT INDUSTRIES; *Int'l*, pg. 1066
PRINT-O-TAPE, INC.; *U.S. Private*, pg. 886
REPAP NEW BRUNSWICK INC.—Repap Enterprises Inc.; *Int'l*, pg. 1104
RESPATEX VERTRIEB—Norske Skogindustrier A.S; *Int'l*, pg. 966
REXAM CUSTOM—Rexam PLC; *Int'l*, pg. 1106
REXAM DSI—Rexam PLC; *Int'l*, pg. 1106
REXAM GRAPHICS—Rexam PLC; *Int'l*, pg. 1107
REXAM INC.—Rexam PLC; *Int'l*, pg. 1106
REXAM MEDICAL PACKAGING—Rexam PLC; *Int'l*, pg. 1106
REXAM RELEASE, INC.—Rexam PLC; *Int'l*, pg. 1107
SELIX F. SCHOELLER LTD.; *Int'l*, pg. 1209
SIERRA COATING TECHNOLOGIES; *U.S. Private*, pg. 998
SIME DARBY BERHAD MALAYSIA REGION—Sime Darby Berhad; *Int'l*, pg. 1250
SOABAR MARKING SYSTEMS LTD.—Avery Dennison Corporation; *U.S. Public*, pg. 154
SOABAR SYSTEMS (HONG KONG) LTD.—Avery Dennison Corporation; *U.S. Public*, pg. 154
SODER S.A.—Norske Skogindustrier A.S; *Int'l*, pg. 966
SPECIALTY TAPES AND ADHESIVES GROUP—Avery Dennison Corporation; *U.S. Public*, pg. 153
SPICERS PAPER LIMITED—Amcor Limited; *Int'l*, pg. 72
STORA DALUM A/S—Stora Kopparbergs Bergslags AB; *Int'l*, pg. 1303
W. SWANSTROM & CO. S.P.R.L.—Norske Skogindustrier A.S; *Int'l*, pg. 966
TAPECOAT COMPANY—T C Manufacturing Company, Inc.; *U.S. Private*, pg. 1062
TAPEMARK; *U.S. Private*, pg. 1068
THAI UNION PAPER CO., LTD.—The Siam Cement Public Company Limited; *Int'l*, pg. 1239
3M; *U.S. Public*, pg. 1604
3M CANADA INC.—3M; *U.S. Public*, pg. 1606
TIMEMED LABELING SYSTEMS, INC.; *U.S. Private*, pg. 1087
UNIVERSAL BLUEPRINT PAPER CO.—Wilco Reprographic, Inc.; *U.S. Private*, pg. 1176
VAN LEER METALLIZED PRODUCTS LTD.—Royal Packaging Industries Van Leer B.V.; *Int'l*, pg. 1147
A/S P. WALLMANN & CO.—Norske Skogindustrier A.S; *Int'l*, pg. 966
WISCONSIN PHARMACAL CO., INC.; *U.S. Private*, pg. 1185
WURZBURG, INC.; *U.S. Private*, pg. 1192
ZIMMER CUSTOM-MADE PACKAGING CO.—Norse Dairy Systems; *U.S. Private*, pg. 802

2673 — PLASTICS, FOIL & COATED PAPER BAGS

AMCEL CORP.; *U.S. Private*, pg. 48
APPLIED EXTRUSION TECHNOLOGIES, INC.; *U.S. Public*, pg. 122

ARMIN PLASTICS DIVISION—Tyco International Ltd.; *U.S. Public*, pg. 1647
ARROW INDUSTRIES, INC.—ConAgra, Inc.; *U.S. Public*, pg. 426
BPB INDUSTRIES PLC; *Int'l*, pg. 122
BPB PAPER & PACKAGING LTD.—BPB Industries PLC; *Int'l*, pg. 122
BEMIS COMPANY, INC.; *U.S. Public*, pg. 210
BRAWNEY PLASTICS, INC.; *U.S. Private*, pg. 166
BRAWNY PLASTICS WEST—Brawney Plastics, Inc.; *U.S. Private*, pg. 166
CADILLAC PRODUCTS, INC.; *U.S. Private*, pg. 198
DOMINO SUGAR CORPORATION—Tate & Lyle PLC; *Int'l*, pg. 1356
ENSO OYJ; *Int'l*, pg. 455
EQUITABLE BAG COMPANY, INC.; *U.S. Private*, pg. 380
FARDEM NV—DSM N.V.; *Int'l*, pg. 353
FIRST BRANDS ASIA—First Brands Corporation; *U.S. Public*, pg. 627
FIRST BRANDS (CANADA) CORP.—First Brands Corporation; *U.S. Public*, pg. 627
FIRST BRANDS CORPORATION; *U.S. Public*, pg. 626
FIRST BRANDS PUERTO RICO—First Brands Corporation; *U.S. Public*, pg. 627
FORT JAMES CORPORATION; *U.S. Public*, pg. 670
FORTIFIBER CORPORATION; *U.S. Private*, pg. 419
FRANCIA-LOTUS S.A.—Fort James Corporation; *U.S. Public*, pg. 672
HIMOLENE CORP.—First Brands Corporation; *U.S. Public*, pg. 627
INTERNATIONAL PAPER CO.—International Paper Company; *U.S. Public*, pg. 902
IVEX PACKAGING CORPORATION; *U.S. Public*, pg. 915
LAWSON MARDON SUPERIOR PACKAGING—Alusuisse-Lonza Holding Ltd.; *Int'l*, pg. 69
LAWSON MARDON TRENTESAUX SA—Alusuisse-Lonza Holding Ltd.; *Int'l*, pg. 69
MILPRINT INC.—Bemis Company, Inc.; *U.S. Public*, pg. 210
MINIGRIP ZIP-PAK—Illinois Tool Works Inc.; *U.S. Public*, pg. 867
NOTEWORTHY INDUSTRIES INC.; *U.S. Private*, pg. 808
PAK PACIFIC (SOUTH EAST ASIA) PTE. LTD.—BTR plc; *Int'l*, pg. 129
PAK-SAK INDUSTRIES, INC.—Maxco, Inc.; *U.S. Public*, pg. 1061
POLY PAK AMERICA, INC.; *U.S. Private*, pg. 875
PRIMEPAK COMPANY; *U.S. Private*, pg. 884
PRINTPACK INC.; *U.S. Private*, pg. 886
PUERTO RICAN CEMENT CO., INC.; *U.S. Public*, pg. 1341
REXAM FLEXIBLE PACKAGING—Rexam PLC; *Int'l*, pg. 1106
REXAM INC.—Rexam PLC; *Int'l*, pg. 1106
REXAM MEDICAL PACKAGING, INC.—Rexam PLC; *Int'l*, pg. 1106
SONOCO ENGRAPH, INC.—Sonoco Products Company; *U.S. Public*, pg. 1486
SOUTHERN CONTAINER CORPORATION; *U.S. Private*, pg. 1016
SPAN-AMERICA MEDICAL SYSTEMS INC.; *U.S. Public*, pg. 1495
STONE CONTAINER CORPORATION; *U.S. Public*, pg. 1520
STORA BILLERUD AB—Stora Kopparbergs Bergslags AB; *Int'l*, pg. 1302
TIFFANY EXTRUDERS, INC.; *U.S. Private*, pg. 1085
UNION INDUSTRIES, INC.; *U.S. Private*, pg. 1119
UNITED RECEPTICAL, INC.; *U.S. Private*, pg. 1123

2674 — UNCOATED PAPER & MULTIWALL BAGS

A J M PACKAGING CORPORATION; *U.S. Private*, pg. 2
ABERTAY PAPER SACKS LTD.—BPB Industries PLC; *Int'l*, pg. 122
AHLSTROM PAPER AG—A. Ahlstrom Corporation; *Int'l*, pg. 35
BEMIS COMPANY, INC.; *U.S. Public*, pg. 210
BES-PAK & CO., INC.—Chelsea Industries, Inc.; *U.S. Private*, pg. 231
CADILLAC PRODUCTS, INC.; *U.S. Private*, pg. 198
CENTRAL STATES DIVERSIFIED, INC.; *U.S. Private*, pg. 224
CIMENTS FRANCAIS; *Int'l*, pg. 292
COPAMEX INDUSTRIAS S.A. DE C.V.; *Int'l*, pg. 330
CROWN SACKS & SYSTEMS (AINTREE) LTD.—Korsnas AB; *Int'l*, pg. 759
EASTERN FINE PAPER; *U.S. Private*, pg. 357
EASY DAY MANUFACTURING COMPANY; *U.S. Private*, pg. 358
EQUITABLE BAG COMPANY, INC.; *U.S. Private*, pg. 380
GEORGIA-PACIFIC CORPORATION; *U.S. Public*, pg. 735
GRUPO INDUSTRIAL DURANGO S.A. DE C.V.; *Int'l*, pg. 575
INDUSTRISKOG AB—Mo och Domsjo AB; *Int'l*, pg. 886
IVEX PACKAGING CORPORATION; *U.S. Public*, pg. 915
KORSNAS AB; *Int'l*, pg. 759
LONGVIEW FIBRE COMPANY; *U.S. Public*, pg. 1013
LONGVIEW FIBRE CO. WESTERN CONTAINER DIVISION—Longview Fibre Company; *U.S. Public*, pg. 1014
MAINE POTATO GROWERS, INC.; *U.S. Private*, pg. 697
MULTIWALL PACKAGING LIMITED—International Paper Company; *U.S. Public*, pg. 905
NOTEWORTHY INDUSTRIES INC.; *U.S. Private*, pg. 808
PAPER SACKS LIMITED—Korsnas AB; *Int'l*, pg. 759
PAPIERSACKFABRIK JUNEMANN GMBH—Korsnas AB; *Int'l*, pg. 759
RED-E-CRETE, INC.—Lonrho plc; *Int'l*, pg. 818
REXAM MULOX—Rexam PLC; *Int'l*, pg. 1106
REXAM MULOX USA—Rexam PLC; *Int'l*, pg. 1106
SOUTHERN BAG CORPORATION; *U.S. Private*, pg. 1015
SOUTHERN CONTAINER CORPORATION; *U.S. Private*, pg. 1016
UNION CAMP CORPORATION; *U.S. Public*, pg. 1665
WEBSTER INDUSTRIES DIV.—Chelsea Industries, Inc.; *U.S. Private*, pg. 231
WERTHAN PACKAGING, INC.; *U.S. Private*, pg. 1162
WESTVACO CORPORATION; *U.S. Public*, pg. 1762
WILHELMSTAL-WERKE GMBH PAPIERSACKFABRIKEN—Korsnas AB; *Int'l*, pg. 759
WISAFOREST OY AB—UPM-Kymmene Corporation; *Int'l*, pg. 1429
WISAPAK OY AB, KARHULA FACTORY—UPM-Kymmene Corporation; *Int'l*, pg. 1429

2675 — DIE-CUT PAPER, PAPERBOARD & CARDBOARD

AMERICAN ISRAELI PAPER MILLS LTD.; *Int'l*, pg. 74
AMERICAN TRADING AND PRODUCTION CORPORATION; *U.S. Private*, pg. 63
ASTRONICS CORPORATION; *U.S. Public*, pg. 142
AB CERBO—Trelleborg AB; *Int'l*, pg. 1423
CHAMPION PAPEL E CELULOSE, S.A.—Champion International Corp.; *U.S. Public*, pg. 334
COLAD GROUP INC.; *U.S. Private*, pg. 250
DAISHOWA PAPER MFG. CO., LTD.; *Int'l*, pg. 373
ELECTRONIC DATA MAGNETICS, INC.; *U.S. Private*, pg. 370
ENSO OYJ; *Int'l*, pg. 455
ESSELTE AB; *Int'l*, pg. 459
ESSELTE CORPORATION—Esselte AB; *Int'l*, pg. 459
FIBERMARK INC.; *U.S. Public*, pg. 620
GUSSCO MANUFACTURING, INC.; *U.S. Private*, pg. 488
HILROY—Abitibi-Consolidated Inc.; *Int'l*, pg. 20
JEN-COAT INC.—American Business Products, Inc.; *U.S. Public*, pg. 70
LETRASET NIELSEN & BAINBRIDGE—Esselte AB; *Int'l*, pg. 460
LHOMME S.A.—Sonoco Products Company; *U.S. Public*, pg. 1487
MARION 100, INC.—Marsh Company; *U.S. Private*, pg. 708
MONARCH INDUSTRIES, INC.—Avery Dennison Corporation; *U.S. Public*, pg. 153
MUNKSJO AB—Trelleborg AB; *Int'l*, pg. 1423
NIELSEN—Esselte AB; *Int'l*, pg. 460
NIELSEN & BAINBRIDGE—Esselte AB; *Int'l*, pg. 460
OMNITRAX INC.—Broe Companies; *U.S. Private*, pg. 171
PAK PACIFIC (SOUTH EAST ASIA) PTE. LTD.—BTR plc; *Int'l*, pg. 129
QUALITY PARK PRODUCTS—Mail-Well Inc.; *U.S. Public*, pg. 1038
RAPID MOUNTING & FINISHING CO.; *U.S. Private*, pg. 910
REXAM INC.—Rexam PLC; *Int'l*, pg. 1106
ROHRER CORPORATION; *U.S. Private*, pg. 940
ROHRER CORPORATION—Rohrer Corporation; *U.S. Private*, pg. 940
RUBBERMAID INCORPORATED; *U.S. Public*, pg. 1411
SIME DARBY BERHAD MALAYSIA REGION—Sime Darby Berhad; *Int'l*, pg. 1250
SIMPSON PAPER CO.—Simpson Investment Co.; *U.S. Private*, pg. 1003
SMEAD MANUFACTURING COMPANY; *U.S. Private*, pg. 1006
SMURFIT CARTON Y PAPEL DE MEXICO—Jefferson Smurfit Group p.l.c.; *Int'l*, pg. 1271
SMURFIT PACKAGING CORPORATION—Jefferson Smurfit Group p.l.c.; *Int'l*, pg. 1271
SONOCO DEUTSCHLAND—Sonoco Products Company; *U.S. Public*, pg. 1487
STORA BILLERUD AB—Stora Kopparbergs Bergslags AB; *Int'l*, pg. 1302
STORA DALUM A/S—Stora Kopparbergs Bergslags AB; *Int'l*, pg. 1303
SULA SUPPLY—Vienna Sausage Mfg. Co.; *U.S. Private*, pg. 1140
TAB PRODUCTS CO.; *U.S. Public*, pg. 1559
TAB PRODUCTS EUROPA B.V.—Tab Products Co.; *U.S. Public*, pg. 1559
TAB PRODUCTS OF CANADA, LTD.—Tab Products Co.; *U.S. Public*, pg. 1559
TAPEMARK; *U.S. Private*, pg. 1068
TEMPLE-INLAND FOREST PRODUCTS CORPORATION—Temple-Inland Inc.; *U.S. Public*, pg. 1575
TEMPLE-INLAND INC.; *U.S. Public*, pg. 1574
THAI UNION PAPER CO., LTD.—The Siam Cement Public Company Limited; *Int'l*, pg. 1239
20TH CENTURY PRODUCTS DIV.—Avery Dennison Corporation; *U.S. Public*, pg. 153
UNISOURCE (S.E. REGIONAL OFFICE)—Unisource Worldwide, Inc.; *U.S. Public*, pg. 1671
UNIVERSAL PAPER GOODS—Esselte AB; *Int'l*, pg. 460
WEBER MARKING SYSTEMS, INC.; *U.S. Private*, pg. 1157
WHAKATANE BOARD MILL—International Paper Company; *U.S. Public*, pg. 905
WURZBURG, INC.; *U.S. Private*, pg. 1192

2676 — SANITARY PAPER PRODUCTS

APL CORPORATION; *U.S. Private*, pg. 7
AMERICAN ISRAELI PAPER MILLS LTD.; *Int'l*, pg. 74
AMERICAN TISSUE, INC.—American Tissue Corporation; *U.S. Private*, pg. 63
AMERICAN TISSUE MILLS OF GREENWICH—American Tissue Corporation; *U.S. Private*, pg. 63
BESS HYGIENE AG—The Procter & Gamble Company; *U.S. Public*, pg. 1333
BRITISH TISSUES LIMITED—Fort James Corporation; *U.S. Public*, pg. 672
CAMELIA WERK AG—Kimberly-Clark Corporation; *U.S. Public*, pg. 959
CARLTON PAPER CORP. LTD.—Kimberly-Clark Corporation; *U.S. Public*, pg. 959
CHICOPEE—BBA Group plc; *Int'l*, pg. 113
THE CLINIPAD CORPORATION; *U.S. Private*, pg. 246
COMPANIA INDUSTRIAL DE SAN CRISTOBAL, S.A.—Kimberly-Clark Corporation; *U.S. Public*, pg. 960
CONSUMER PRODUCTS BUSINESS—Fort James Corporation; *U.S. Public*, pg. 671
CONTEMPO COLORS; *U.S. Private*, pg. 267
DRYPER'S CORP.; *U.S. Private*, pg. 344
DUBREUIL FOREST PRODUCTS, LTD.—Fort James Corporation; *U.S. Public*, pg. 672
DUNI AB; *Int'l*, pg. 421
DUNI AB-FINESS FORSALJNING—Duni AB; *Int'l*, pg. 421
DUNI/FINESS HYGIENE—Duni AB; *Int'l*, pg. 421
DUNI LTD.—Duni AB; *Int'l*, pg. 421
ELITE PERSONALIZED CREATIONS—American Pad and Paper Company; *U.S. Public*, pg. 89
ERVING INDUSTRIES, INC.; *U.S. Private*, pg. 382
FOOD SERVICE & LODGING PRODUCTS DIV.—The Procter & Gamble Company; *U.S. Public*, pg. 1330
FORT JAMES CORPORATION; *U.S. Public*, pg. 670
FRANCIA-LOTUS S.A.—Fort James Corporation; *U.S. Public*, pg. 672
GEORGIA-PACIFIC CORPORATION; *U.S. Public*, pg. 735
GOLDEN BOOKS FAMILY ENTERTAINMENT INC.; *U.S. Public*, pg. 749
GUEST SUPPLY, INC.; *U.S. Public*, pg. 768
HERMANN WANGNER, GMBH—Transworld Interweaving AG (TIAG); *Int'l*, pg. 1418
HOGLA-KIMBERLY LTD.—American Israeli Paper Mills Ltd.; *Int'l*, pg. 75
HOGLA-KIMBERLY LTD.—Kimberly-Clark Corporation; *U.S. Public*, pg. 959
HYGIE FRANCE—Fort James Corporation; *U.S. Public*, pg. 672
INTERNATIONAL CONSUMER & SERVICE SECTOR—Kimberly-Clark Corporation; *U.S. Public*, pg. 958
IVEX PACKAGING CORPORATION; *U.S. Public*, pg. 915
JANSSEN-CILAG PTY. LTD.—Johnson & Johnson; *U.S. Public*, pg. 929
JOHNSON & JOHNSON; *U.S. Public*, pg. 927
JOHNSON & JOHNSON (IRELAND) LTD.—Johnson & Johnson; *U.S. Public*, pg. 930
KAO CORPORATION; *Int'l*, pg. 717
KIMBERLY-CLARK BENELUX OPERATIONS B.V.—Kimberly-Clark Corporation; *U.S. Public*, pg. 959
KIMBERLY-CLARK BENELUX OPERATIONS B.V.-WEST OFFICE—Kimberly-Clark Corporation; *U.S. Public*, pg. 959
KIMBERLY-CLARK CONSUMER PRODUCTS—Kimberly-Clark Corporation; *U.S. Public*, pg. 959
KIMBERLY-CLARK CORPORATION; *U.S. Public*, pg. 958
KIMBERLY-CLARK DE MEXICO, S.A. DE C.V.—Kimberly-Clark Corporation; *U.S. Public*, pg. 960
KIMBERLY-CLARK FAR EAST PTE. LTD.—Kimberly-Clark Corporation; *U.S. Public*, pg. 959
KIMBERLY-CLARK INTERNATIONAL, S.A.—Kimberly-Clark Corporation; *U.S. Public*, pg. 959
KIMBERLY-CLARK MALAYSIA SENDIRIAN BERHAD—Kimberly-Clark Corporation; *U.S. Public*, pg. 960
KIMBERLY-CLARK THAILAND LTD.—Kimberly-Clark Corporation; *U.S. Public*, pg. 959
LENSCLEAN, INC.—H.L. Bouton Company Inc.; *U.S. Private*, pg. 162
MEGAS BEAUTY CARE, INC.; *U.S. Private*, pg. 729
MOLETT MARKETING—American Israeli Paper Mills Ltd.; *Int'l*, pg. 75
MUNKSJOE HYGIEN AB—Trelleborg AB; *Int'l*, pg. 1423
PEAUDOUCE S.A. BABY PRODUCTS—Svenska Cellulosa Aktiebolaget (SCA); *Int'l*, pg. 1326
PERSONAL CARE SECTOR—Kimberly-Clark Corporation; *U.S. Public*, pg. 958
PERSONAL PRODUCTS CO.—Johnson & Johnson; *U.S. Public*, pg. 929
PLAYTEX PRODUCTS CORP.—Playtex Products Inc.; *U.S. Public*, pg. 1311
POTLATCH CORPORATION; *U.S. Public*, pg. 1318
PROCTER & GAMBLE CLEANING & PAPER PRODUCTS DIV.—The Procter & Gamble Company; *U.S. Public*, pg. 1330
ROCHESTER MIDLAND CORPORATION; *U.S. Private*, pg. 937
SCOTT CONTINENTAL N.V.—Kimberly-Clark Corporation; *U.S. Public*, pg. 960
SCOTT IBERICA, S.A.—Kimberly-Clark Corporation; *U.S. Public*, pg. 960
SCOTT LIMITED—Kimberly-Clark Corporation; *U.S. Public*, pg. 960
SCOTT PAPER CO. DE COSTA RICA, S.A.—Kimberly-Clark Corporation; *U.S. Public*, pg. 960
SCOTT PAPER LIMITED—Kruger Inc.; *Int'l*, pg. 762
SCOTT PAPER (MALAYSIA) SDN. BHD.—Kimberly-Clark Corporation; *U.S. Public*, pg. 960
SCOTT PAPER (SINGAPORE) PTE. LTD.—Kimberly-Clark Corporation; *U.S. Public*, pg. 960
SCOTT S.N.C.—Kimberly-Clark Corporation; *U.S. Public*, pg. 960
SCOTT S.P.A.—Kimberly-Clark Corporation; *U.S. Public*, pg. 960
SEALED AIR CORPORATION; *U.S. Public*, pg. 1450
SHANGHAI JOHNSON & JOHNSON LTD.—Johnson & Johnson; *U.S. Public*, pg. 932
SHIKMA—American Israeli Paper Mills Ltd.; *Int'l*, pg. 75
SKAPAFORS PAPER MILL—Duni AB; *Int'l*, pg. 421
SMITH & NEPHEW CONSUMER PRODUCTS LTD.—Smith & Nephew PLC; *Int'l*, pg. 1263
SSANGYONG BUSINESS GROUP; *Int'l*, pg. 1291
SSANGYONG PAPER CO., LTD.—Ssangyong Business Group; *Int'l*, pg. 1292
SSANGYONG UNI-CHARM CO., LTD.—Ssangyong Business Group; *Int'l*, pg. 1291
STORA DALUM A/S—Stora Kopparbergs Bergslags AB; *Int'l*, pg. 1303
SVENSKA CELLULOSA AKTIEBOLAGET (SCA); *Int'l*, pg. 1326
TAIWAN SCOTT PAPER CORP.—Kimberly-Clark Corporation; *U.S. Public*, pg. 960

TAMBRANDS INC.—The Procter & Gamble Company; *U.S. Public*, pg. 1331
TEMCA CHEMISCHE UNION GMBH—The Procter & Gamble Company; *U.S. Public*, pg. 1333
TEMPO ESPANA S.A. Y CIA S.E.C.—The Procter & Gamble Company; *U.S. Public*, pg. 1333
TEMPO SANYS S.A.—The Procter & Gamble Company; *U.S. Public*, pg. 1333
THAI-SCOTT PAPER COMPANY, LTD.—Kimberly-Clark Corporation; *U.S. Public*, pg. 960
THE TRANZONIC COMPANIES; *U.S. Public*, pg. 1632
TRANZONIC PERSONAL CARE DIVISION—The Tranzonic Companies; *U.S. Public*, pg. 1632
UNILEVER AUSTRALIA LTD.—Unilever Plc; *Int'l*, pg. 1439
VP-SCHICKEDANZ AG—The Procter & Gamble Company; *U.S. Public*, pg. 1333
WAUSAU-MOSINEE PAPER CORPORATION; *U.S. Public*, pg. 1747
WINCUP; *U.S. Private*, pg. 1182
WISCONSIN TISSUE—Chesapeake Corporation; *U.S. Public*, pg. 347
WUHRLIN-SOPLAMED S.A.—Fort James Corporation; *U.S. Public*, pg. 673
YUHAN-KIMBERLY, LTD.—Kimberly-Clark Corporation; *U.S. Public*, pg. 960

2677 — ENVELOPES

AMERICAN MAIL-WELL ENVELOPE—Mail-Well Inc.; *U.S. Public*, pg. 1038
AMERICAN PAD AND PAPER COMPANY; *U.S. Public*, pg. 88
AMERICAN PAPER GROUP, INC.; *U.S. Private*, pg. 60
ARVEY PAPER & OFFICE PRODUCTS—International Paper Company; *U.S. Public*, pg. 903
ATLANTIC ENVELOPE CO.—National Service Industries, Inc.; *U.S. Public*, pg. 1160
CC INDUSTRIES, INC.; *U.S. Private*, pg. 192
CHAMPION INTERNATIONAL CORP.; *U.S. Public*, pg. 333
CHAPMAN INDUSTRIES PLC—Trelleborg AB; *Int'l*, pg. 1420
CURTIS 1000 EUROPE GMBH—American Business Products, Inc.; *U.S. Public*, pg. 70
DARLING ENVELOPE CORPORATION; *U.S. Private*, pg. 311
DUPLEX ENVELOPE CO.—International Paper Company; *U.S. Public*, pg. 903
GILMORE ENVELOPE CORP.; *U.S. Private*, pg. 454
GRIFFIN ENVELOPE, INC.—Mail-Well Inc.; *U.S. Public*, pg. 1038
GROUPE SAINT LOUIS; *Int'l*, pg. 567
THE INSTANT WEB COMPANIES; *U.S. Private*, pg. 565
INTERNATIONAL ENVELOPE COMPANY—American Business Products, Inc.; *U.S. Public*, pg. 70
IVEX PACKAGING CORPORATION; *U.S. Public*, pg. 915
KENT PAPER CO., INC.—American Pad and Paper Company; *U.S. Public*, pg. 89
MASSACHUSETTS ENVELOPE CO.; *U.S. Private*, pg. 712
MEAD SCHOOL & OFFICE PRODUCTS—The Mead Corporation; *U.S. Public*, pg. 1074
NATIONAL SERVICE INDUSTRIES, INC.; *U.S. Public*, pg. 1160
NOTEWORTHY INDUSTRIES INC.; *U.S. Private*, pg. 808
PANEL CONCEPTS, L.P.—Standard Pacific Corp.; *U.S. Public*, pg. 1504
PAVEY ENVELOPE & TAG CORP.—Mail-Well Inc.; *U.S. Public*, pg. 1038
QUALITY PARK PRODUCTS—Mail-Well Inc.; *U.S. Public*, pg. 1038
SEALED AIR CORPORATION; *U.S. Public*, pg. 1450
SEALED AIR PACKAGING PRODUCTS DIVISION—Sealed Air Corporation; *U.S. Public*, pg. 1451
AB STURE LJUNGDAHL—Trelleborg AB; *Int'l*, pg. 1423
TENSION ENVELOPE CORP.; *U.S. Private*, pg. 1077
TRANSCOAST ENVELOPE CO.—Tension Envelope Corp.; *U.S. Private*, pg. 1077
TRANSO ENVELOPE CO./GLENDALE—Tension Envelope Corp.; *U.S. Private*, pg. 1077
UNISOURCE (S.E. REGIONAL OFFICE)—Unisource Worldwide, Inc.; *U.S. Public*, pg. 1671
WEST SHORE ENVELOPE COMPANY, INC.; *U.S. Private*, pg. 1163
WESTERN STATES ENVELOPE CO.; *U.S. Private*, pg. 1168
WESTVACO CORPORATION; *U.S. Public*, pg. 1762
WESTVACO CORPORATION-ENVELOPE DIV.—Westvaco Corporation; *U.S. Public*, pg. 1762
WIGGINS ARJO IRELAND (HOLDINGS) LTD.—Groupe Saint Louis; *Int'l*, pg. 567
WILLIAMHOUSE OF CALIFORNIA, INC.—American Pad and Paper Company; *U.S. Public*, pg. 89
WILLIAMHOUSE-REGENCY, INC.—American Pad and Paper Company; *U.S. Public*, pg. 89

2678 — STATIONERY, TABLETS & RELATED PRODUCTS

ACCO EUROPE PLC—Fortune Brands, Inc.; *U.S. Public*, pg. 674
ACCO-REXEL GROUP SERVICES PLC—Fortune Brands, Inc.; *U.S. Public*, pg. 674
ACCO WORLD CORPORATION—Fortune Brands, Inc.; *U.S. Public*, pg. 674
AMERICAN TRADING AND PRODUCTION CORPORATION; *U.S. Private*, pg. 63
ARTISTIC GREETINGS, INC.; *U.S. Public*, pg. 136
AVENOR, INC.; *Int'l*, pg. 101
CAPITAL IMAGING; *U.S. Private*, pg. 206
CHAMPION INTERNATIONAL CORP.; *U.S. Public*, pg. 333
COMPANIA INDUSTRIAL DE SAN CRISTOBAL, S.A.—Kimberly-Clark Corporation; *U.S. Public*, pg. 960
CONTEMPO COLORS; *U.S. Private*, pg. 267
CRAWFORD INDUSTRIES—American Trading and Production Corporation; *U.S. Private*, pg. 64
CROSS POINTE PAPER CORPORATION—EdperBrascan Corporation; *Int'l*, pg. 434
THE CRYSTAL TISSUE CO.; *U.S. Private*, pg. 294
CULLMAN VENTURES, INC.; *U.S. Private*, pg. 294
DAIO PAPER CORPORATION; *Int'l*, pg. 372
DISCOUNT LABELS, INC.—American Business Products, Inc.; *U.S. Public*, pg. 70
ELTIS PRECISION PRINTING LIMITED—HSBC Holdings plc; *Int'l*, pg. 581
FOX VALLEY CORPORATION; *U.S. Private*, pg. 422
GEORGIA-PACIFIC CORPORATION; *U.S. Public*, pg. 735
C.R. GIBSON CO.—Thomas Nelson Inc.; *U.S. Public*, pg. 1168
GOLDEN BOOKS FAMILY ENTERTAINMENT INC.; *U.S. Public*, pg. 749
DON GRESSWELL LTD.—U.S. Office Products Company; *U.S. Public*, pg. 1687
HALLMARK CARDS, INC.; *U.S. Private*, pg. 495
HERLITZ PBS AKTIENGESELLSCHAFT; *Int'l*, pg. 616
HETZEL GMBH—Fortune Brands, Inc.; *U.S. Public*, pg. 675
INTERNATIONAL PAPER COMPANY; *U.S. Public*, pg. 901
IVEX PACKAGING CORPORATION; *U.S. Public*, pg. 915
K & M PRODUCTS DIVISION—Avery Dennison Corporation; *U.S. Public*, pg. 152
KIMBERLY-CLARK DE MEXICO, S.A. DE C.V.—Kimberly-Clark Corporation; *U.S. Public*, pg. 960
KURTZ BROS., INC.; *U.S. Private*, pg. 637
L.C.G. MALMBERG BV—VNU Verenigde Nederlandse Uitgeversbedrijven B.V.; *Int'l*, pg. 1445
MASSACHUSETTS ENVELOPE CO.; *U.S. Private*, pg. 712
MATAURA PAPER MILL—International Paper Company; *U.S. Public*, pg. 905
MEAD SCHOOL & OFFICE PRODUCTS—The Mead Corporation; *U.S. Public*, pg. 1074
JAY NORRIS CANADA INC.—Russel Metals Inc.; *Int'l*, pg. 1150
PWA ROLLAND DECOR INC.—The Cascades Group; *Int'l*, pg. 274
PARSONS PAPER DIV. OF NVF CO.—NVF Company; *U.S. Private*, pg. 772
PEN-TAB INDUSTRIES, INC.; *U.S. Private*, pg. 848
PERFECSEAL COMPANY—Bemis Company, Inc.; *U.S. Public*, pg. 210
PRIMES DE LUXE INC.—Russel Metals Inc.; *Int'l*, pg. 1150
RANK XEROX AG—Xerox Corporation; *U.S. Public*, pg. 1785
REGAL GREETINGS & GIFTS—Russel Metals Inc.; *Int'l*, pg. 1150
RING KING VISIBLES, INC.—Esselte AB; *Int'l*, pg. 460
RITTENHOUSE INC.; *U.S. Private*, pg. 933
ROLLAND INC.—The Cascades Group; *Int'l*, pg. 273
RUNDEL PRODUCTS, INC.; *U.S. Private*, pg. 951
SCHWARZ PAPER COMPANY; *U.S. Private*, pg. 974
SHEAFFER INC.—Gefinor S.A. Luxembourg; *Int'l*, pg. 542
STUART HALL CO., INC.—Newell Co.; *U.S. Public*, pg. 1178
AB STURE LJUNGDAHL—Trelleborg AB; *Int'l*, pg. 1423
SULA SUPPLY—Vienna Sausage Mfg. Co.; *U.S. Private*, pg. 1140
SVENSKA CELLULOSA AKTIEBOLAGET (SCA); *Int'l*, pg. 1326
TAB PRODUCTS CO.; *U.S. Public*, pg. 1559
3M; *U.S. Public*, pg. 1604

2679 — CONVERTED PAPER & PAPERBOARD PRODUCTS, NEC

ACI INTERNATIONAL LTD.—BTR plc; *Int'l*, pg. 128
AG STANLEY LIMITED—The Boots Company PLC; *Int'l*, pg. 202
ACCO EASTLIGHT LIMITED—Fortune Brands, Inc.; *U.S. Public*, pg. 674
A. AHLSTROM CORPORATION; *Int'l*, pg. 32
AHLSTROM ALCORE LTD—A. Ahlstrom Corporation; *Int'l*, pg. 32
AHLSTROM CONSUMER PRODUCTS LTD.—A. Ahlstrom Corporation; *Int'l*, pg. 32
AHLSTROM KAUTTUA LTD.—A. Ahlstrom Corporation; *Int'l*, pg. 35
AHLSTROM KOREA CO., LTD.—A. Ahlstrom Corporation; *Int'l*, pg. 35
AHLSTROM PAPEIS LTDA.—A. Ahlstrom Corporation; *Int'l*, pg. 35
AHLSTROM PAPER AG—A. Ahlstrom Corporation; *Int'l*, pg. 35
AHLSTROM PAPIER B.V.—A. Ahlstrom Corporation; *Int'l*, pg. 35
AHLSTROMFORETAGEN SVENSKA AB-MARKARYD CORE PLANT—A. Ahlstrom Corporation; *Int'l*, pg. 33
AHLSTROMFORETAGEN SVENSKA AB-MATFORS CORE PLANT—A. Ahlstrom Corporation; *Int'l*, pg. 33
AHLSTROMFORETAGEN SVENSKA AB-NORRKOPING CORE PLANT—A. Ahlstrom Corporation; *Int'l*, pg. 33
AKERLUND & RAUSING—A. Ahlstrom Corporation; *Int'l*, pg. 33
AB AKERLUND & RAUSING—A. Ahlstrom Corporation; *Int'l*, pg. 33
AKERLUND & RAUSING A/S—A. Ahlstrom Corporation; *Int'l*, pg. 33
A/S AKERLUND & RAUSING—A. Ahlstrom Corporation; *Int'l*, pg. 33
AB AKERLUND & RAUSING GROUP—A. Ahlstrom Corporation; *Int'l*, pg. 33
AKERLUND & RAUSING LTD.—A. Ahlstrom Corporation; *Int'l*, pg. 33
AKERLUND & RAUSING S.A.R.L.—A. Ahlstrom Corporation; *Int'l*, pg. 33
AKERLUND & RAUSING VERPACKUNG GMBH—A. Ahlstrom Corporation; *Int'l*, pg. 33
ALDEN ELECTRONICS, INC.—Platinum Equity Holdings, LLC; *U.S. Private*, pg. 872
AMCOR LIMITED; *Int'l*, pg. 71
AMERICAN ENVIRONMENTAL PRODUCTS, INC.—Washington Gas Light Co.; *U.S. Public*, pg. 1741
AMERICAN EXCELSIOR COMPANY; *U.S. Private*, pg. 53
AMERICAN GREETINGS CORPORATION; *U.S. Public*, pg. 77
ATLAS TAG & LABEL INC.—Bissell Inc.; *U.S. Private*, pg. 145
BAKERS CHOICE PRODUCTS, INC.—Reynolds Metals Company; *U.S. Public*, pg. 1386
BAY WEST PAPER CORPORATION—Wausau-Mosinee Paper Corporation; *U.S. Public*, pg. 1747
J. BIBBY & SONS PLC—Barlow Ltd.; *Int'l*, pg. 167
BIENFANG PAPER DIV.—Hunt Corporation; *U.S. Public*, pg. 849
BORDEN DECORATIVE PRODUCTS—Borden, Inc.; *U.S. Private*, pg. 158
BOSSO CARTE SPECIALI S.P.A.—A. Ahlstrom Corporation; *Int'l*, pg. 35
BRADFORD COMPANY; *U.S. Private*, pg. 163
CPS CORPORATION—Fox Valley Corporation; *U.S. Private*, pg. 422
CSS INDUSTRIES, INC.; *U.S. Public*, pg. 283
CASCADE DIAMOND—The Cascades Group; *Int'l*, pg. 274
CASCADE DJUPAGOW AB—The Cascades Group; *Int'l*, pg. 274
CASCADE DUFFEL NV—The Cascades Group; *Int'l*, pg. 274
CASCADES DOMINION INC.—The Cascades Group; *Int'l*, pg. 273
CASCADES, INC.—The Cascades Group; *Int'l*, pg. 273
CASCADES MOULDED PULP, INC.—The Cascades Group; *Int'l*, pg. 274
CASCADES NIAGARA FALLS—The Cascades Group; *Int'l*, pg. 274
CAXTON PAPER LIMITED—International Paper Company; *U.S. Public*, pg. 905
CENTRAL STATES DIVERSIFIED, INC.; *U.S. Private*, pg. 224
CHAMPION INTERNATIONAL CORP.; *U.S. Public*, pg. 333
CHAPMAN INDUSTRIES PLC—Trelleborg AB; *Int'l*, pg. 1420
THE CHINET CO.—Royal Packaging Industries Van Leer B.V.; *Int'l*, pg. 1146
CLEO INC.—CSS Industries, Inc.; *U.S. Public*, pg. 284
COLAD GROUP INC.; *U.S. Private*, pg. 250
COLUMBIAN ROPE COMPANY; *U.S. Private*, pg. 256
CONSOLIDATED CONVERTING CO.—Cubic Corporation; *U.S. Public*, pg. 466
CONTEMPO COLORS; *U.S. Private*, pg. 267
CORRUGATED EUROPE BV—N.V. Koninklijke KNP BT; *Int'l*, pg. 756
CROWN WALLCOVERINGS FRANCE, S.A.—Borden, Inc.; *U.S. Private*, pg. 159
DAIO PAPER CORPORATION; *Int'l*, pg. 372
DOMTAR PACKAGING DIVISION—Domtar Inc.; *Int'l*, pg. 416
DORET S.A.—Avery Dennison Corporation; *U.S. Public*, pg. 154
DUBREUIL FOREST PRODUCTS, LTD.—Fort James Corporation; *U.S. Public*, pg. 672
DURABLE SPECIALTIES DIVISION—FiberMark Inc.; *U.S. Public*, pg. 620
DURACELL INC. ENVIRONMENTAL—The Gillette Company; *U.S. Public*, pg. 743
EDDY PAPER COMPANY LIMITED—George Weston Limited; *Int'l*, pg. 1495
ENSO OYJ; *Int'l*, pg. 455
EUL & GUNTHER GMBH & CO KG—Melitta Unternehmensgruppe Bentz KG; *Int'l*, pg. 857
FASSON ADHESIVE PRODUCTS, LTD.—Avery Dennison Corporation; *U.S. Public*, pg. 154
FIBERMARK INC.; *U.S. Public*, pg. 620
FIBRE PRODUCTS NEW ZEALAND LIMITED—International Paper Company; *U.S. Public*, pg. 905
FINE ART DEVELOPMENTS PLC; *Int'l*, pg. 485
FORBO-GIUBIASCO SA—Forbo Holding SA; *Int'l*, pg. 497
FORBO HOLDING SA; *Int'l*, pg. 496
FORT JAMES CORPORATION; *U.S. Public*, pg. 670
FORT ORANGE PAPER CO., INC.—Relm Wireless Corp.; *U.S. Public*, pg. 1376
FORTIFIBER CORPORATION; *U.S. Private*, pg. 419
FOX VALLEY CORPORATION; *U.S. Private*, pg. 422
GEORGIA-PACIFIC CORPORATION; *U.S. Public*, pg. 735
C.R. GIBSON CO.—Thomas Nelson Inc.; *U.S. Public*, pg. 1168
GILMAN PAPER CO.—Gilman Investment Company, Inc.; *U.S. Private*, pg. 454
GOLDEN BOOKS FAMILY ENTERTAINMENT INC.; *U.S. Public*, pg. 749
GOLDENBERG GROUP, INC.—Nortek, Inc.; *U.S. Public*, pg. 1193
GREEN MOUNTAIN COFFEE ROASTERS, INC.; *U.S. Public*, pg. 761
GULF STATES PAPER CORPORATION; *U.S. Private*, pg. 487
HALLMARK CARDS, INC.; *U.S. Private*, pg. 495
HEE SUNG CO. LTD.—LG Group; *Int'l*, pg. 779
HEXCEL, FAR EAST—Hexcel Corporation; *U.S. Public*, pg. 824
HEXCEL, S.A.—Hexcel Corporation; *U.S. Public*, pg. 824
HEXCEL, U.K.—Hexcel Corporation; *U.S. Public*, pg. 824
HOLLYMATIC CORPORATION; *U.S. Private*, pg. 535
HUNT CORPORATION; *U.S. Public*, pg. 848
INTERNATIONAL PAINTS (CANADA) LTD.—Courtaulds plc; *Int'l*, pg. 339
IVEX PACKAGING CORPORATION; *U.S. Public*, pg. 915
JEN-COAT INC.—American Business Products, Inc.; *U.S. Public*, pg. 70
K2 INC.; *U.S. Public*, pg. 940
KAMMERER GMBH—A. Ahlstrom Corporation; *Int'l*, pg. 35
KIMBERLY-CLARK LIMITED—Kimberly-Clark Corporation; *U.S. Public*, pg. 959
N.V. KONINKLIJKE KNP BT; *Int'l*, pg. 756

PERRY H. KOPLIK & SONS; *U.S. Private*, pg. 632
KVAERNER ENERGY A.S.—Kvaerner a.s.a.; *Int'l*, pg. 767
LYDALL, INC.; *U.S. Public*, pg. 1020
LYDALL SOUTHERN PRODUCTS—Lydall, Inc.; *U.S. Public*, pg. 1021
MD PAPIER GMBH—Metsa-Serla Corporation; *Int'l*, pg. 864
MARCAL PAPER MILLS, INC.; *U.S. Private*, pg. 701
MASONITE CORPORATION—International Paper Company; *U.S. Public*, pg. 904
MASSACHUSETTS ENVELOPE CO.; *U.S. Private*, pg. 712
MATSUSHITA ELECTRIC WORKS, LTD.; *Int'l*, pg. 847
MEAD COATED BOARD EUROPE B.V.—The Mead Corporation; *U.S. Public*, pg. 1076
MELITTA CANADA INC.—Melitta Unternehmensgruppe Bentz KG; *Int'l*, pg. 857
MELLON CORPORATION; *U.S. Private*, pg. 730
MENASHA CORPORATION; *U.S. Private*, pg. 731
MIAMI MILL—EdperBrascan Corporation; *Int'l*, pg. 434
MO OCH DOMSJO AB; *Int'l*, pg. 885
MUNKSJO AB—Trelleborg AB; *Int'l*, pg. 1423
MUNSKJOE PAPER AB—Trelleborg AB; *Int'l*, pg. 1423
M. MYERS & SON PLC—Avery Dennison Corporation; *U.S. Public*, pg. 154
NCR CORPORATION; *U.S. Public*, pg. 1146
NIAGARA OF WISCONSIN PAPER CORP.—Consolidated Papers, Inc.; *U.S. Public*, pg. 436
OFFICE PRODUCTS DIVISION—FiberMark Inc.; *U.S. Public*, pg. 620
PAK PACIFIC (SOUTH EAST ASIA) PTE. LTD.—BTR plc; *Int'l*, pg. 129
PACKAGE SERVICE COMPANY, LLC.; *U.S. Private*, pg. 833
PAPER-FIN S.P.A.—A. Ahlstrom Corporation; *Int'l*, pg. 35
THE PAPER MAGIC GROUP, INC.—CSS Industries, Inc.; *U.S. Public*, pg. 284
PARAMOUNT TUBE—Precision Products Corporation; *U.S. Private*, pg. 880
PEN-TAB INDUSTRIES, INC.; *U.S. Private*, pg. 848
PERSTORP A/S DECORATIVE LAMINATE—Perstorp AB; *Int'l*, pg. 1038
PERSTORP FLOORING AB—Perstorp AB; *Int'l*, pg. 1039
PERSTORP FLOORING BV—Perstorp AB; *Int'l*, pg. 1039
PERSTORP FLOORING GMBH—Perstorp AB; *Int'l*, pg. 1039
PERSTORP FLOORING NV—Perstorp AB; *Int'l*, pg. 1039
PERSTORP GMBH DECORATIVE LAMINATE—Perstorp AB; *Int'l*, pg. 1038
PERSTORP GMBH-SBU FURNITURE (UNIDUR)—Perstorp AB; *Int'l*, pg. 1038
PERSTORP GULV A/S—Perstorp AB; *Int'l*, pg. 1039
PERSTORP IKI OY DECORATIVE LAMINATE—Perstorp AB; *Int'l*, pg. 1038
PERSTORP S.A. DECORATIVE LAMINATE—Perstorp AB; *Int'l*, pg. 1038
PERSTORP SURFACE MATERIALS—Perstorp AB; *Int'l*, pg. 1038
PERSTORP UNIDUR BEIJING OFFICE—Perstorp AB; *Int'l*, pg. 1038
PERSTORP UNIDUR, INC.—Perstorp AB; *Int'l*, pg. 1038
PERSTORP UNIDUR LTD.—Perstorp AB; *Int'l*, pg. 1039
PERSTORP WARERITE LTD.—Perstorp AB; *Int'l*, pg. 1039
PIONEER PLASTICS CORPORATION; *U.S. Private*, pg. 867
PITNEY BOWES INC.; *U.S. Public*, pg. 1303
PLUS MARK, INC.—American Greetings Corporation; *U.S. Public*, pg. 78
PLYMKRAFT INC.—Columbian Rope Company; *U.S. Private*, pg. 256
POLARCUP FINLAND—Huhtamaki Oy; *Int'l*, pg. 638
POLARCUP GERMANY—Huhtamaki Oy; *Int'l*, pg. 638
POLARCUP GROUP HEADQUARTERS—Huhtamaki Oy; *Int'l*, pg. 638
PROOST EN BRANDT NV—N.V. Koninklijke KNP BT; *Int'l*, pg. 756
RP EUROPE B.V.—N.V. Koninklijke KNP BT; *Int'l*, pg. 757
REXAM DSI—Rexam PLC; *Int'l*, pg. 1106
RISING PAPER PRODUCTS PRIVATE LIMITED—Sime Darby Berhad; *Int'l*, pg. 1251
RIXIE PAPER PRODUCTS—Sonoco Products Company; *U.S. Public*, pg. 1486
ROOSEVELT PAPER CO.; *U.S. Private*, pg. 943
ROOSEVELT PAPER COMPANY—Roosevelt Paper Co.; *U.S. Private*, pg. 943
ROSELLE PAPER CO., INC.; *U.S. Private*, pg. 945
ROYAL PACKAGING INDUSTRIES VAN LEER B.V.; *Int'l*, pg. 1145
RUBBERMAID INCORPORATED; *U.S. Public*, pg. 1411
SELIX F. SCHOELLER LTD.; *Int'l*, pg. 1209
SCHWARZ PAPER COMPANY; *U.S. Private*, pg. 974
SEALED AIR CORPORATION; *U.S. Public*, pg. 1450
SEALED AIR FOOD PACKAGING DIVISION—Sealed Air Corporation; *U.S. Public*, pg. 1451
SEALED AIR PACKAGING PRODUCTS DIVISION—Sealed Air Corporation; *U.S. Public*, pg. 1451
SERVICE & INDUSTRIAL SECTOR—Kimberly-Clark Corporation; *U.S. Public*, pg. 958
SHOWA PRODUCTS CO., LTD.—Sonoco Products Company; *U.S. Public*, pg. 1487
HCH. SIEGER GMBH UND CO. KG.—N.V. Koninklijke KNP BT; *Int'l*, pg. 757
SIGNATURE BRANDS USA, INC.; *U.S. Public*, pg. 1472
SIME RENGO PACKAGING SINGAPORE LIMITED—Sime Darby Berhad; *Int'l*, pg. 1251
SMITH-LEE CO., INC.; *U.S. Private*, pg. 1009
SMURFIT CARTON Y PAPEL DE MEXICO—Jefferson Smurfit Group p.l.c.; *Int'l*, pg. 1271
SMURFIT PACKAGING CORPORATION—Jefferson Smurfit Group p.l.c.; *Int'l*, pg. 1271
SOLO CUP COMPANY—Solo Cup Company; *U.S. Private*, pg. 1013
SONOCO COLOMBIANA S.A.—Sonoco Products Company; *U.S. Public*, pg. 1487
SONOCO ENGRAPH, INC.—Sonoco Products Company; *U.S. Public*, pg. 1486
SONOCO PRODUCTS COMPANY; *U.S. Public*, pg. 1485
SPICERS PAPER LIMITED—Amcor Limited; *Int'l*, pg. 72
STANDARD CAP & SEAL—Sonoco Products Company; *U.S. Public*, pg. 1486
STONE SAVANNAH RIVER PULP AND PAPER—Stone Container Corporation; *U.S. Public*, pg. 1520
STORA DALUM A/S—Stora Kopparbergs Bergslags AB; *Int'l*, pg. 1303
STOREYS DECORATIVE PRODUCTS LTD.—Borden, Inc.; *U.S. Private*, pg. 160
STUDLEY PRODUCTS CO.—Nortek, Inc.; *U.S. Public*, pg. 1193
SULLIVAN PAPER COMPANY; *U.S. Private*, pg. 1050
SUNCLIPSE, INC.—Amcor Limited; *Int'l*, pg. 72
SWEETHEART CUP COMPANY INC.; *U.S. Private*, pg. 1058
SWEETHEART CUP COMPANY INC.—Sweetheart Cup Company Inc.; *U.S. Private*, pg. 1058
T.P.T. LTD.—Sonoco Products Company; *U.S. Public*, pg. 1487
TENNECO PACKAGING—Tenneco Inc.; *U.S. Public*, pg. 1579
TEXALES LTD.—Borden, Inc.; *U.S. Private*, pg. 160
RICHARD E. THIBAUT, INC.—RPM, Inc.; *U.S. Public*, pg. 1358
THOMAS TAIT & SONS, LTD.—International Paper Company; *U.S. Public*, pg. 904
3M; *U.S. Public*, pg. 1604
UPM-KYMMENE CORPORATION; *Int'l*, pg. 1427
UNIWOOD DIV.—International Paper Company; *U.S. Public*, pg. 903
VAN LEER PACKAGING SYSTEMS LTD.—Royal Packaging Industries Van Leer B.V.; *Int'l*, pg. 1147
WALL TRENDS, INC.—Solvay S.A.; *Int'l*, pg. 1278
WASHINGTON GAS LIGHT CO.; *U.S. Public*, pg. 1740
WISCONSIN LABEL CORPORATION; *U.S. Private*, pg. 1184
YORK WALLCOVERINGS INC.; *U.S. Private*, pg. 1196
ZIMMER CUSTOM-MADE PACKAGING CO.—Norse Dairy Systems; *U.S. Private*, pg. 802

2711 — NEWSPAPERS: PUBLISHING, OR PUBLISHING & PRINTING

ACBJ BUSINESS JOURNALS, INC.—Advance Publications Inc.; *U.S. Private*, pg. 19
ACBJ BUSINESS PUBLICATIONS, INC.—Advance Publications Inc.; *U.S. Private*, pg. 19
AP-DOW JONES NEWS SERVICE—Dow Jones & Company, Inc.; *U.S. Public*, pg. 524
ABERDEEN CITIZEN NEWS-RECORD—Media General, Inc.; *U.S. Public*, pg. 1079
ABERDEEN NEWS COMPANY—Knight-Ridder, Inc.; *U.S. Public*, pg. 963
ABILENE REPORTER NEWS—Harte-Hanks Communications, Inc.; *U.S. Public*, pg. 793
ABINGTON-ROCKLAND MARINER—Gannett Company, Inc.; *U.S. Public*, pg. 700
ACTION MUNICIPALE—C.E.P. Communication Group; *Int'l*, pg. 239
ADVANCE PUBLICATIONS INC.; *U.S. Private*, pg. 18
ADVERTISER—The Gazette Company; *U.S. Private*, pg. 442
THE ADVERTISER—Journal Register Company; *U.S. Public*, pg. 934
THE ADVERTISER CO.—Gannett Company, Inc.; *U.S. Public*, pg. 699
THE ADVOCATE; *U.S. Private*, pg. 23
THE ADVOCATE—The Times Mirror Company; *U.S. Public*, pg. 1616
AFTONBLADET AB; *Int'l*, pg. 29
ALBANY DEMOCRAT-HERALD—Lee Enterprises, Incorporated; *U.S. Public*, pg. 983
THE ALBANY HERALD PUBLISHING CO., INC.—Gray Communications Systems, Inc.; *U.S. Public*, pg. 759
ALBANY TIMES UNION—The Hearst Corporation; *U.S. Private*, pg. 517
THE ALBUQUERQUE TRIBUNE—The E.W. Scripps Company; *U.S. Public*, pg. 1447
ALTON TELEGRAPH—Journal Register Company; *U.S. Public*, pg. 934
AMADOR LEDGER-DISPATCH—Central Valley Publishing; *U.S. Private*, pg. 225
AMERICAN CITIES BUSINESS JOURNALS, INC.—Advance Publications Inc.; *U.S. Private*, pg. 19
AMERICAN CITY BUSINESS JOURNALS, INC.—Advance Publications Inc.; *U.S. Private*, pg. 19
AMERICAN PUBLISHING MANAGEMENT SERVICES INC.—Hollinger Inc.; *Int'l*, pg. 632
THE ANDERSON NEWS—Landmark Communications, Inc.; *U.S. Private*, pg. 648
THE ARDMORE DAILY ARDMOREITE—Shivers Trading & Operating Co.; *U.S. Private*, pg. 995
THE ARIZONA DAILY STAR—Pulitzer Publishing Company; *U.S. Public*, pg. 1343
THE ARKANSAS CITY DAILY TRAVELER—Shivers Trading & Operating Co.; *U.S. Private*, pg. 995
THE ARLINGTON CITIZEN-JOURNAL—The Walt Disney Company; *U.S. Public*, pg. 512
ARMADA TIMES—The Walt Disney Company; *U.S. Public*, pg. 513
ARMY TIMES PUBLISHING CO.—Gannett Company, Inc.; *U.S. Public*, pg. 699
ASBURY PARK PRESS, INC.—Gannett Company, Inc.; *U.S. Public*, pg. 699
ASHEVILLE CITIZEN TIMES—Gannett Company, Inc.; *U.S. Public*, pg. 699
ASIAN WALL STREET JOURNAL—Dow Jones & Company, Inc.; *U.S. Public*, pg. 525
THE ASIAN WALL STREET JOURNAL WEEKLY—Dow Jones & Company, Inc.; *U.S. Public*, pg. 524
ASSOCIATED NEWSPAPER HOLDINGS LTD.—Daily Mail & General Trust PLC; *Int'l*, pg. 366
ATHENS NEWSPAPERS, INC.—Shivers Trading & Operating Co.; *U.S. Private*, pg. 996
AUBURNDALE STAR—Shivers Trading & Operating Co.; *U.S. Private*, pg. 995
AUSTRALIAN FINANCIAL REVIEW—John Fairfax Holdings Limited; *Int'l*, pg. 477
AUTOMOTIVE NEWS—Crain Communications, Inc.; *U.S. Private*, pg. 284
THE AVENAL PROGRESS—Pulitzer Publishing Company; *U.S. Public*, pg. 1343
AXEL SPRINGER VERLAG AG; *Int'l*, pg. 102
BPI COMMUNICATIONS INC.—VNU Verenigde Nederlandse Uitgeversbedrijven B.V.; *Int'l*, pg. 1446
THE BAKERSFIELD CALIFORNIAN; *U.S. Private*, pg. 112
BALTIMORE BUSINESS PUBLICATIONS, INC.—Advance Publications Inc.; *U.S. Private*, pg. 19
THE BALTIMORE SUN NEWSPAPERS—The Times Mirror Company; *U.S. Public*, pg. 1616
BARRON'S THE DOW JONES BUSINESS & FINANCIAL WEEKLY—Dow Jones & Company, Inc.; *U.S. Public*, pg. 524
BATTLE CREEK ENQUIRER—Gannett Company, Inc.; *U.S. Public*, pg. 700
THE BAXTER BULLETIN—Gannett Company, Inc.; *U.S. Public*, pg. 699
BAXTER COUNTY NEWSPAPERS, INC.—Gannett Company, Inc.; *U.S. Public*, pg. 699
THE BEACON JOURNAL PUBLISHING COMPANY—Knight-Ridder, Inc.; *U.S. Public*, pg. 963
THE BEACON-NEWS—The Copley Press, Inc.; *U.S. Private*, pg. 275
BEAUMONT ENTERPRISE—The Hearst Corporation; *U.S. Private*, pg. 517
BEDFORD BULLETIN—Landmark Communications, Inc.; *U.S. Private*, pg. 648
BELLEVILLE NEWS-DEMOCRAT—Knight-Ridder, Inc.; *U.S. Public*, pg. 964
THE BELLINGHAM HERALD—Gannett Company, Inc.; *U.S. Public*, pg. 700
A.H. BELO CORPORATION; *U.S. Public*, pg. 209
JOHN BENJAMINS BV; *Int'l*, pg. 187
JOHN BENJAMINS NORTH AMERICA INC—John Benjamins BV; *Int'l*, pg. 187
BERGEN RECORD CORP.—Macromedia Incorporated; *U.S. Private*, pg. 693
BERKSHIRE HATHAWAY INC.; *U.S. Public*, pg. 217
THE BILLINGS GAZETTE—Lee Enterprises, Incorporated; *U.S. Public*, pg. 983
BIRMINGHAM NEWS—Advance Publications Inc.; *U.S. Private*, pg. 20
BIRMINGHAM POST-HERALD COMPANY—The E.W. Scripps Company; *U.S. Public*, pg. 1447
THE BISMARCK TRIBUNE—Lee Enterprises, Incorporated; *U.S. Public*, pg. 983
BLADE COMMUNICATIONS, INC.; *U.S. Private*, pg. 147
BLUE SPRINGS EXAMINER—Shivers Trading & Operating Co.; *U.S. Private*, pg. 995
BOCA RATON NEWS, INC.—Community Newspaper Holdings Inc.; *U.S. Private*, pg. 259
BOOTH NEWSPAPERS, INC.; *U.S. Private*, pg. 157
THE BOSTON GLOBE—The New York Times Company; *U.S. Public*, pg. 1175
THE BOSTON HERALD—The News Corporation Limited; *Int'l*, pg. 926
BOULDER PUBLISHING, INC.—The E.W. Scripps Company; *U.S. Public*, pg. 1447
BOWES PUBLISHERS LIMITED—Sun Media Corporation; *Int'l*, pg. 1320
THE BRADENTON HERALD, INC.—Knight-Ridder, Inc.; *U.S. Public*, pg. 964
BRAINERD DAILY DISPATCH—Shivers Trading & Operating Co.; *U.S. Private*, pg. 995
BRAINTREE FORUM—Gannett Company, Inc.; *U.S. Public*, pg. 700
BRANFORD REVIEW—Journal Register Company; *U.S. Public*, pg. 934
BREHM COMMUNICATIONS INC.; *U.S. Private*, pg. 166
BREMERTON SUN—The E.W. Scripps Company; *U.S. Public*, pg. 1447
BROWN CITY BANNER—The Walt Disney Company; *U.S. Public*, pg. 513
BUFFALO EVENING NEWS, INC.—Berkshire Hathaway Inc.; *U.S. Public*, pg. 217
BUFORD GAZETTE—McClatchy Newspapers Inc.; *U.S. Public*, pg. 1065
THE BULLETIN COMPANY—Gannett Company, Inc.; *U.S. Public*, pg. 700
BURLINGTON FREE PRESS—Gannett Company, Inc.; *U.S. Public*, pg. 700
BUSINESS FIRST OF NEW YORK, INC.—Advance Publications Inc.; *U.S. Private*, pg. 10
THE BUSINESS JOURNAL OF PORTLAND, INC.—Advance Publications Inc.; *U.S. Private*, pg. 19
BUSINESS JOURNAL PUBLICATIONS, INC.—Advance Publications Inc.; *U.S. Private*, pg. 19
BUSINESS JOURNALS OF NORTH CAROLINA, LLC—Advance Publications Inc.; *U.S. Private*, pg. 19
CALGARY HERALD—Hollinger Inc.; *Int'l*, pg. 631
THE CALGARY SUN—Sun Media Corporation; *Int'l*, pg. 1320
CALIFORNIA NEWSPAPERS, INC.—Gannett Company, Inc.; *U.S. Public*, pg. 700
CANTON NEWS—Gannett Company, Inc.; *U.S. Public*, pg. 700
CAPE PUBLICATIONS, INC.—Gannett Company, Inc.; *U.S. Public*, pg. 700
CAPITAL-GAZETTE COMMUNICATIONS, INC.—Landmark Communications, Inc.; *U.S. Private*, pg. 649
CAPITOL CITY PUBLISHING CO., INC.-THE TRENTONIAN—Journal Register Company; *U.S. Public*, pg. 934
CARROLL COUNTY TIMES—Landmark Communications, Inc.; *U.S. Private*, pg. 648

THE CASEY COUNTY NEWS—Landmark Communications, Inc.; U.S. Private, pg. 648
CENTRAL KENTUCKY NEWS-JOURNAL—Landmark Communications, Inc.; U.S. Private, pg. 648
CENTRAL MAINE NEWSPAPERS—Guy Gannett Communications; U.S. Private, pg. 439
CENTRAL NEWSPAPERS, INC.; U.S. Public, pg. 326
CENTRAL VALLEY PUBLISHING; U.S. Private, pg. 225
CENTRE DAILY TIMES, INC.—Knight-Ridder, Inc.; U.S. Public, pg. 964
THE CHARLOTTE OBSERVER—Knight-Ridder, Inc.; U.S. Public, pg. 964
CHICAGO READER, INC.; U.S. Private, pg. 235
CHICAGO SUN TIMES—Hollinger Inc.; Int'l, pg. 632
CHICAGO TRIBUNE CO.—Tribune Company; U.S. Public, pg. 1635
CHILDREN'S BUSINESS—The Walt Disney Company; U.S. Public, pg. 513
CHILLICOTHE NEWSPAPERS—Gannett Company, Inc.; U.S. Public, pg. 700
CHRONICLE PUBLISHING CO. INC.; U.S. Private, pg. 239
CHRONICLE-TRIBUNE—Gannett Company, Inc.; U.S. Public, pg. 700
THE CINCINNATI ENQUIRER, INC.—Gannett Company, Inc.; U.S. Public, pg. 700
THE CINCINNATI POST—The E.W. Scripps Company; U.S. Public, pg. 1447
CITIZEN PUBLISHING CO.—Gannett Company, Inc.; U.S. Public, pg. 700
CITRUS COUNTY CHRONICLE—Landmark Communications, Inc.; U.S. Private, pg. 648
THE CLARION-LEDGER—Gannett Company, Inc.; U.S. Public, pg. 700
CLAUSEN & BOSSE GMBH—Georg von Holtzbrinck GmbH; Int'l, pg. 1478
CLINTON RECORDER—Journal Register Company; U.S. Public, pg. 934
CLOVIS INDEPENDENT—McClatchy Newspapers Inc.; U.S. Public, pg. 1065
THE COALINGA RECORD—Pulitzer Publishing Company; U.S. Public, pg. 1343
COHASSET MARINER—Gannett Company, Inc.; U.S. Public, pg. 700
COLDWATER REPORTER, INC.—Media General, Inc.; U.S. Public, pg. 1077
THE COLUMBUS LEDGER & ENQUIRER—Knight-Ridder, Inc.; U.S. Public, pg. 964
COMET-PRESS NEWSPAPERS, INC.—The New York Times Company; U.S. Public, pg. 1175
THE COMMERCIAL APPEAL—The E.W. Scripps Company; U.S. Public, pg. 1447
COMMERCIAL-NEWS—Gannett Company, Inc.; U.S. Public, pg. 700
COMMUNITY NEWSPAPER HOLDINGS INC.; U.S. Private, pg. 259
COMMUNITY NEWSPAPERS—Gannett Company, Inc.; U.S. Public, pg. 701
THE CONCORD TRIBUNE, INC.—Media General, Inc.; U.S. Public, pg. 1078
CONSOLIDATED PUBLISHING COMPANY; U.S. Private, pg. 266
JACK KENT COOKE, INC.; U.S. Private, pg. 273
COOKE MEDIA GROUP, INC.—Jack Kent Cooke, Inc.; U.S. Private, pg. 273
THE COPLEY PRESS, INC.; U.S. Private, pg. 275
CORPUS CHRISTI CALLER-TIMES—Harte-Hanks Communications, Inc.; U.S. Public, pg. 793
CORVALLIS GAZETTE-TIMES—Lee Enterprises, Incorporated; U.S. Public, pg. 983
COTTAGE GROVE SENTINEL—Lee Enterprises, Incorporated; U.S. Public, pg. 983
COUNTRY WEEKLY, INC.—American Media, Inc.; U.S. Public, pg. 87
THE COURIER JOURNAL—The E.W. Scripps Company; U.S. Public, pg. 1447
THE COURIER-JOURNAL LOUISVILLE TIMES CO.—Gannett Company, Inc.; U.S. Public, pg. 700
COURIER-NEWS CO.—Gannett Company, Inc.; U.S. Public, pg. 700
COURIER-POST—Gannett Company, Inc.; U.S. Public, pg. 700
COWLES MEDIA COMPANY; U.S. Private, pg. 280
COX ENTERPRISES, INC.; U.S. Private, pg. 281
COX NEWSPAPERS, INC.—Cox Enterprises, Inc.; U.S. Private, pg. 281
COX TEXAS PUBLICATIONS, INC.—Cox Enterprises, Inc.; U.S. Private, pg. 281
CRAIN COMMUNICATIONS, INC.; U.S. Private, pg. 284
CROSSROADS PRESS, INC.—Advance Publications Inc.; U.S. Private, pg. 19
CROWN PUBLISHERS, INC.—Advance Publications Inc.; U.S. Private, pg. 21
CYNTHIANA DEMOCRAT—Landmark Communications, Inc.; U.S. Private, pg. 648
DAGBLADET BOERSEN A/S; Int'l, pg. 359
THE DAILY & SUNDAY OKLAHOMAN—Oklahoma Publishing Company; U.S. Private, pg. 813
THE DAILY BREEZE—The Copley Press, Inc.; U.S. Private, pg. 275
THE DAILY CHRONICLE—Pulitzer Publishing Company; U.S. Public, pg. 1343
THE DAILY COMET—The New York Times Company; U.S. Public, pg. 1175
DAILY COURIER-NEWS—The Copley Press, Inc.; U.S. Private, pg. 275
THE DAILY HERALD—Pulitzer Publishing Company; U.S. Public, pg. 1343
DAILY HERALD CO.—The Washington Post Company; U.S. Public, pg. 1743
THE DAILY JOURNAL—Pulitzer Publishing Company; U.S. Public, pg. 1343
THE DAILY JOURNAL (NJ)—Gannett Company, Inc.; U.S. Public, pg. 700
DAILY MAIL & GENERAL TRUST PLC; Int'l, pg. 366
DAILY NEWS—Hollinger Inc.; Int'l, pg. 632
THE DAILY NEWS—Pulitzer Publishing Company; U.S. Public, pg. 1343
THE DAILY NEWS LEADER—Gannett Company, Inc.; U.S. Public, pg. 699
DAILY NEWS RECORD—The Walt Disney Company; U.S. Public, pg. 513
THE DAILY PRESS, INCORPORATED—Tribune Company; U.S. Public, pg. 1635
THE DAILY SENTINEL—Gannett Company, Inc.; U.S. Public, pg. 699
THE DAILY TIDINGS—Lee Enterprises, Incorporated; U.S. Public, pg. 983
THE DAILY WORLD—The New York Times Company; U.S. Public, pg. 1175
DALLAS-FT. WORTH SUBURBAN NEWSPAPERS, INC.—A.H. Belo Corporation; U.S. Public, pg. 209
THE DALLAS MORNING NEWS, INC.—A.H. Belo Corporation; U.S. Public, pg. 209
DAYTON NEWSPAPERS, INC.—Cox Enterprises, Inc.; U.S. Private, pg. 281
DECATUR HERALD & REVIEW—Lee Enterprises, Incorporated; U.S. Public, pg. 983
DEMOCRAT & CHRONICLE—Gannett Company, Inc.; U.S. Public, pg. 699
THE DENVER BUSINESS JOURNAL, LLC—Advance Publications Inc.; U.S. Private, pg. 19
DES MOINES REGISTER & TRIBUNE CO.—Gannett Company, Inc.; U.S. Public, pg. 700
DESERET NEWS—Deseret Management Corporation; U.S. Private, pg. 327
THE DESERT SUN—Gannett Company, Inc.; U.S. Public, pg. 700
THE DETROIT NEWS—Gannett Company, Inc.; U.S. Public, pg. 700
DETROIT NEWSPAPERS—Knight-Ridder, Inc.; U.S. Public, pg. 965
DEVILS LAKE JOURNAL—Media General, Inc.; U.S. Public, pg. 1078
THE DISPATCH PRINTING COMPANY; U.S. Private, pg. 334
THE DISPATCH PUBLISHING COMPANY, INC.—The New York Times Company; U.S. Public, pg. 1175
DODGE CITY DAILY GLOBE—Shivers Trading & Operating Co.; U.S. Private, pg. 995
DODGE CITY SHOPPER'S WEEKLY—Shivers Trading & Operating Co.; U.S. Private, pg. 995
F.W. DODGE GROUP—The McGraw-Hill Companies; U.S. Public, pg. 1070
THE DOLPHIN—Journal Register Company; U.S. Public, pg. 934
DOW JONES & COMPANY, INC.; U.S. Public, pg. 524
DOW JONES FINANCIAL NEWS SERVICES—Dow Jones & Company, Inc.; U.S. Public, pg. 524
DOW JONES INTERACTIVE PUBLISHING—Dow Jones & Company, Inc.; U.S. Public, pg. 524
DOW JONES PUBLISHING CO. (ASIA), INC.—Dow Jones & Company, Inc.; U.S. Public, pg. 525
DULUTH NEWS-TRIBUNE—Knight-Ridder, Inc.; U.S. Public, pg. 964
THE ECONOMIST GROUP LIMITED.—Pearson plc; Int'l, pg. 1026
EDEN NEWS—Media General, Inc.; U.S. Public, pg. 1078
EDITRICE LA STAMPA S.P.A.—Fiat Auto SpA; Int'l, pg. 482
THE EDMONTON JOURNAL—Hollinger Inc.; Int'l, pg. 631
THE EDMONTON SUN—Sun Media Corporation; Int'l, pg. 1320
EDWARDSVILLE INTELLIGENCER—The Hearst Corporation; U.S. Private, pg. 517
EL PASO HERALD-POST—The E.W. Scripps Company; U.S. Public, pg. 1447
EL PASO TIMES, INC.—Gannett Company, Inc.; U.S. Public, pg. 700
ELMIRA STAR-GAZETTE—Gannett Company, Inc.; U.S. Public, pg. 700
THE EVANSVILLE COURIER—The E.W. Scripps Company; U.S. Public, pg. 1447
THE EVENING CALL PUBLISHING CO.-THE CALL—Journal Register Company; U.S. Public, pg. 934
EVENING POST PUBLISHING CO.; U.S. Private, pg. 385
THE EXPOSITOR—Hollinger Inc.; Int'l, pg. 631
EXPRESS NEWSPAPERS PLC—United News & Media plc; Int'l, pg. 1443
EXTEL—Pearson plc; Int'l, pg. 1025
F.T. PUBLICATIONS INC.—Pearson plc; Int'l, pg. 1026
FAIRCHILD PUBLICATIONS—The Walt Disney Company; U.S. Public, pg. 513
JOHN FAIRFAX HOLDINGS LIMITED; Int'l, pg. 477
FARM PRESS—Primedia Inc.; U.S. Public, pg. 1328
FERNANDINA BEACH NEWS LEADER, INC.—The New York Times Company; U.S. Public, pg. 1175
THE FINANCIAL POST—Sun Media Corporation; Int'l, pg. 1320
THE FINANCIAL TIMES LTD.—Pearson plc; Int'l, pg. 1025
FINGER LAKES PRINTING COMPANY—Independent Publications, Inc.; U.S. Private, pg. 559
FLORIDA SUN PUBLICATIONS, INC.—Pearson plc; Int'l, pg. 1026
FOOTWEAR NEWS—The Walt Disney Company; U.S. Public, pg. 513
FORT COLLINS NEWSPAPERS, INC.—Gannett Company, Inc.; U.S. Public, pg. 700
FORT WAYNE NEWSPAPERS, INC.—Knight-Ridder, Inc.; U.S. Public, pg. 964
FORUM COMMUNICATIONS COMPANY; U.S. Private, pg. 420
FREEDOM COMMUNICATION INC.; U.S. Private, pg. 425
FREMONT NEWS-MESSENGER—Gannett Company, Inc.; U.S. Public, pg. 700
THE FRESNO BEE—McClatchy Newspapers Inc.; U.S. Public, pg. 1065
G.T.C. TRANSCONTINENTAL GROUP LTD.; Int'l, pg. 538
THE GADSDEN TIMES—The New York Times Company; U.S. Public, pg. 1175
GAINESVILLE SUN PUBLISHING COMPANY—The New York Times Company; U.S. Public, pg. 1175
GALLIPOLIS DAILY TRIBUNE—Gannett Company, Inc.; U.S. Public, pg. 699
GANNETT COMPANY, INC.; U.S. Public, pg. 698
GUY GANNETT COMMUNICATIONS; U.S. Private, pg. 439
GANNETT OFFSET-SPRINGFIELD PLANT—Gannett Company, Inc.; U.S. Public, pg. 700
GANNETT SATELLITE INFORMATION NETWORK, INC.—Gannett Company, Inc.; U.S. Public, pg. 700
GANNETT SUBURBAN NEWSPAPERS—Gannett Company, Inc.; U.S. Public, pg. 700
GANNETT SUPPLY CORP.—Gannett Company, Inc.; U.S. Public, pg. 699
THE GARDEN ISLAND—Pulitzer Publishing Company; U.S. Public, pg. 1343
GARDEN STATE NEWSPAPERS, INC.—MediaNews Group Inc.; U.S. Private, pg. 727
THE GAZETTE—Landmark Communications, Inc.; U.S. Private, pg. 648
THE GAZETTE COMPANY; U.S. Private, pg. 442
GAZETTE TELEGRAPH—Freedom Communication Inc.; U.S. Private, pg. 425
GILROY DISPATCH—Central Valley Publishing; U.S. Private, pg. 225
GLENWOOD POST—Shivers Trading & Operating Co.; U.S. Private, pg. 995
GLOBE-GAZETTE—Lee Enterprises, Incorporated; U.S. Public, pg. 983
GLOBE NEWSPAPER COMPANY—The New York Times Company; U.S. Public, pg. 1175
GRAND FORKS HERALD, INCORPORATED—Knight-Ridder, Inc.; U.S. Public, pg. 964
THE GRAND ISLAND DAILY INDEPENDENT—Shivers Trading & Operating Co.; U.S. Private, pg. 995
GRAND JUNCTION NEWSPAPERS, INC.—Cox Enterprises, Inc.; U.S. Private, pg. 281
GRANT COUNTY NEWS—Landmark Communications, Inc.; U.S. Private, pg. 648
GRAY COMMUNICATIONS SYSTEMS, INC.; U.S. Public, pg. 759
GREAT FALLS TRIBUNE—Gannett Company, Inc.; U.S. Public, pg. 700
GREAT LAKES MEDIA, INC.—The Walt Disney Company; U.S. Public, pg. 513
GREEN BAY PRESS-GAZETTE—Gannett Company, Inc.; U.S. Public, pg. 700
THE GREENVILLE NEWS—Gannett Company, Inc.; U.S. Public, pg. 699
GRESHAM OUTLOOK—Lee Enterprises, Incorporated; U.S. Public, pg. 983
GUAM PUBLICATIONS, INC.—Gannett Company, Inc.; U.S. Public, pg. 702
GUARD PUBLISHING COMPANY; U.S. Private, pg. 485
GUARDIAN & OBSERVER—Guardian Media Group plc; Int'l, pg. 577
GUARDIAN MEDIA GROUP PLC; Int'l, pg. 577
GULF PUBLISHING COMPANY, INC.—Knight-Ridder, Inc.; U.S. Public, pg. 964
HAINES CITY HERALD & RIDGE SHOPPER—Shivers Trading & Operating Co.; U.S. Private, pg. 995
HAMDEN CHRONICLE—Journal Register Company; U.S. Public, pg. 935
THE HANFORD SENTINEL—Pulitzer Publishing Company; U.S. Public, pg. 1343
THE HANNIBAL COURIER-POST—Shivers Trading & Operating Co.; U.S. Private, pg. 995
HANOVER MARINER—Gannett Company, Inc.; U.S. Public, pg. 701
THE HARLAN DAILY ENTERPRISE—Hollinger Inc.; Int'l, pg. 632
HARRIMAN RECORD—Landmark Communications, Inc.; U.S. Private, pg. 648
HARRIS ENTERPRISES INC.; U.S. Private, pg. 505
HARTE-HANKS COMMUNICATIONS, INC.; U.S. Public, pg. 793
HARTE-HANKS COMMUNITY NEWSPAPERS, INC.—Harte-Hanks Communications, Inc.; U.S. Public, pg. 793
HARTE-HANKS SHOPPER MIAMI—Harte-Hanks Communications, Inc.; U.S. Public, pg. 794
THE HARTFORD COURANT COMPANY—The Times Mirror Company; U.S. Public, pg. 1616
HATTIESBURG AMERICAN—Gannett Company, Inc.; U.S. Public, pg. 701
THE HAVERHILL GAZETTE—Pulitzer Publishing Company; U.S. Public, pg. 1343
HAWAII NEWSPAPER AGENCY, INC.—Gannett Company, Inc.; U.S. Public, pg. 701
THE HEARST CORPORATION; U.S. Private, pg. 515
HEARST ENTERPRISES DIVISION—The Hearst Corporation; U.S. Private, pg. 516
HEARST NEWSPAPERS—The Hearst Corporation; U.S. Private, pg. 517
HENDERSONVILLE NEWSPAPER CORPORATION—The New York Times Company; U.S. Public, pg. 1175
HENRY COUNTY LOCAL—Landmark Communications, Inc.; U.S. Private, pg. 648
THE HERALD-DISPATCH—Gannett Company, Inc.; U.S. Public, pg. 701
HERALD-NEWS—The Copley Press, Inc.; U.S. Private, pg. 275
HERALD VOICE—Pulitzer Publishing Company; U.S. Public, pg. 1343
THE HERALD & WEEKLY TIMES LTD.—The News Corporation Limited; Int'l, pg. 925
HIGHLAND NEWS-LEADER—Knight-Ridder, Inc.; U.S. Public, pg. 964
HILLSDALE DAILY NEWS—Shivers Trading & Operating Co.; U.S. Private, pg. 995
HILTON HEAD ISLAND PACKET—McClatchy Newspapers Inc.; U.S. Public, pg. 1065

HINGHAM MARINER—Gannett Company, Inc.; *U.S. Public, pg. 701*
THE HOLBROOK SUN—Gannett Company, Inc.; *U.S. Public*, pg. 701
THE HOLLAND SENTINEL—Shivers Trading & Operating Co.; *U.S. Private*, pg. 995
HOLLINGER INC.; *Int'l*, pg. 630
HOLLISTER FREE LANCE—Central Valley Publishing; *U.S. Private*, pg. 225
HOME FURNISHINGS DAILY—The Walt Disney Company; *U.S. Public*, pg. 513
HOMESTEAD PUBLISHING—The Times Mirror Company; *U.S. Public*, pg. 1616
HOMETOWN COMMUNICATIONS NETWORK, INC.; *U.S. Private*, pg. 537
HOMETOWN PUBLICATIONS—Journal Communications Inc.; *U.S. Private*, pg. 601
THE HOUMA COURIER NEWSPAPER CORPORATION—The New York Times Company; *U.S. Public*, pg. 1175
HURON DAILY TRIBUNE—The Hearst Corporation; *U.S. Private*, pg. 517
ITEDI S.P.A.—Fiat Auto SpA; *Int'l*, pg. 482
THE IDAHO STATESMAN—Gannett Company, Inc.; *U.S. Public*, pg. 701
ILLINOIS STAR-COURIER—Lee Enterprises, Incorporated; *U.S. Public*, pg. 983
THE INDEPENDENCE EXAMINER—Shivers Trading & Operating Co.; *U.S. Private*, pg. 995
INDEPENDENT PUBLICATIONS, INC.; *U.S. Private*, pg. 559
INDEPENDENT PUBLISHING COMPANY—Harte-Hanks Communications, Inc.; *U.S. Public*, pg. 794
THE INDEPENDENT RECORD—Lee Enterprises, Incorporated; *U.S. Public*, pg. 983
INSTITUTIONAL INVESTOR, INC.—The Walt Disney Company; *U.S. Public*, pg. 513
INTERACTIVE MEDIA, INC.—The Gazette Company; *U.S. Private*, pg. 442
INTERNATIONAL HERALD TRIBUNE S.A.—The New York Times Company; *U.S. Public*, pg. 1176
INTERNATIONAL THOMSON BUSINESS PUBLISHING—The Thomson Corporation; *U.S. Public*, pg. 1601
INTERNATIONAL THOMSON PUBLISHING LIMITED—The Thomson Corporation; *U.S. Public*, pg. 1600
ITHACA JOURNAL—Gannett Company, Inc.; *U.S. Public*, pg. 700
JACKSON SUN, INC.—Gannett Company, Inc.; *U.S. Public, pg. 701*
THE JAPAN TIMES, LTD.—Nifco Inc.; *Int'l*, pg. 928
JASPER NEWS-BOY—The Hearst Corporation; *U.S. Private*, pg. 517
JERUSALEM POST PUBLICATIONS LTD.—Hollinger Inc.; *Int'l*, pg. 632
JOHNSON NEWSPAPER CORPORATION; *U.S. Private*, pg. 591
THE JOURNAL; *U.S. Private*, pg. 601
JOURNAL & COURIER—Gannett Company, Inc.; *U.S. Public*, pg. 701
JOURNAL COMMUNICATIONS INC.; *U.S. Private*, pg. 601
JOURNAL OF COMMERCE, INC.—Pearson plc; *Int'l*, pg. 1026
JOURNAL REGISTER COMPANY; *U.S. Public*, pg. 934
JOURNAL STAR LINCOLN—Lee Enterprises, Incorporated; *U.S. Public*, pg. 983
THE JOURNAL TIMES—Lee Enterprises, Incorporated; *U.S. Public*, pg. 983
THE KAMLOOPS DAILY NEWS—Hollinger Inc.; *Int'l*, pg. 631
THE KANSAS CITY STAR COMPANY—Knight-Ridder, Inc.; *U.S. Public*, pg. 964
KELTATIM PUBLISHING COMPANY; *U.S. Private*, pg. 613
THE KENTUCKY POST—The E.W. Scripps Company; *U.S. Public*, pg. 1447
KENTUCKY STANDARD—Landmark Communications, Inc.; *U.S. Private*, pg. 648
KEYNOTER PUBLISHING COMPANY, INC.—Knight-Ridder, Inc.; *U.S. Public*, pg. 964
KINGSTON INDEPENDENT VOICE—Gannett Company, Inc.; *U.S. Public*, pg. 701
KINGSTON WHIG-STANDARD—Hollinger Inc.; *Int'l*, pg. 631
THE KNIGHT PUBLISHING CO.—Knight-Ridder, Inc.; *U.S. Public*, pg. 964
KNIGHT-RIDDER, INC.; *U.S. Public*, pg. 963
KNOXVILLE NEWS-SENTINEL COMPANY—The E.W. Scripps Company; *U.S. Public*, pg. 1448
KODANSHA INTERNATIONAL LTD—Kodansha Ltd.; *Int'l*, pg. 742
KODANSHA LTD.; *Int'l*, pg. 742
KODANSHA SCIENTIFIC LTD.—Kodansha Ltd.; *Int'l*, pg. 742
LA CROSSE TRIBUNE—Lee Enterprises, Incorporated; *U.S. Public*, pg. 983
LA NACION S.A.; *Int'l*, pg. 785
LA PRENSA ASOCIADA, INC.—The Associated Press; *U.S.* Private, pg. 92
LAKE CITY REPORTER, INC.—The New York Times Company; *U.S. Public*, pg. 1175
LAKE WALES DAILY HIGHLANDER—Shivers Trading & Operating Co.; *U.S. Private*, pg. 995
LAKELAND LEDGER PUBLISHING CORPORATION—The New York Times Company; *U.S. Public*, pg. 1175
THE LANCASTER NEWS—Landmark Communications, Inc.; *U.S. Private*, pg. 648
LANDMARK COMMUNICATIONS, INC.; *U.S. Private*, pg. 647
LANSING STATE JOURNAL—Gannett Company, Inc.; *U.S.* Public, pg. 701
LAREDO MORNING TIMES—The Hearst Corporation; *U.S. Private*, pg. 517
LAS VEGAS SUN; *U.S. Private*, pg. 652
LAUSITZER RUNDSCHAU VERLAG UND DRUCKEREI GMBH—Georg von Holtzbrinck GmbH; *Int'l*, pg. 1478
LEAF-CHRONICLE CO.—Gannett Company, Inc.; *U.S. Public*, pg. 699
THE LEBANON ENTERPRISE—Landmark Communications, Inc.; *U.S. Private*, pg. 648
LEBANON EXPRESS—Lee Enterprises, Incorporated; *U.S. Public*, pg. 983
LEBHAR-FRIEDMAN, INC.; *U.S. Private*, pg. 656
LEE ENTERPRISES, INCORPORATED; *U.S. Public*, pg. 983
THE LEMOORE ADVANCE—Pulitzer Publishing Company; *U.S. Public*, pg. 1343
LES ECHOS SA—Pearson plc; *Int'l*, pg. 1027
LINCOLN COURIER—The Copley Press, Inc.; *U.S. Private*, pg. 275
LINCOLN NEWS MESSENGER—Brehm Communications Inc.; *U.S. Private*, pg. 167
LOCKPORT UNION SUN & JOURNAL—Media General, Inc.; *U.S. Public*, pg. 1078
LONG BEACH PRESS-TELEGRAM—MediaNews Group Inc.; *U.S. Private*, pg. 727
LONRHO PLC; *Int'l*, pg. 817
THE LORAIN JOURNAL COMPANY-THE MORNING JOURNAL—Journal Register Company; *U.S. Public*, pg. 935
LOS ALAMOS MONITOR—Landmark Communications, Inc.; *U.S. Private*, pg. 648
LOS ANGELES TIMES—The Times Mirror Company; *U.S. Public*, pg. 1616
LYKE CORPORATION; *U.S. Private*, pg. 682
MACON TELEGRAPH PUBLISHING COMPANY—Knight-Ridder, Inc.; *U.S. Public*, pg. 964
MACROMEDIA INCORPORATED; *U.S. Private*, pg. 693
MADISON NEWSPAPERS, INC.—Lee Enterprises, Incorporated; *U.S. Public*, pg. 984
MANCHESTER GUARDIAN—Guardian Media Group plc; *Int'l*, pg. 577
MARCO ISLAND EAGLE—The New York Times Company; *U.S. Public*, pg. 1175
MARSHFIELD MARINER—Gannett Company, Inc.; *U.S. Public*, pg. 701
MCALESTER NEWS-CAPITAL & DEMOCRAT—Media General, Inc.; *U.S. Public*, pg. 1078
MCALESTER PUBLISHING CO.—Media General, Inc.; *U.S. Public*, pg. 1078
MCCLATCHY NEWSPAPERS INC.; *U.S. Public*, pg. 1065
MCDOWELL NEWS—Media General, Inc.; *U.S. Public*, pg. 1078
THE MCGRAW-HILL COMPANIES; *U.S. Public*, pg. 1069
MEDIA GENERAL, INC.; *U.S. Public*, pg. 1077
MEDIANEWS GROUP INC.; *U.S. Private*, pg. 727
MEDICINE HAT NEWS—Hollinger Inc.; *Int'l*, pg. 631
MEDINA JOURNAL-REGISTER—Media General, Inc.; *U.S. Public*, pg. 1079
MEMPHIS PUBLISHING CO.—The E.W. Scripps Company; *U.S. Public*, pg. 1448
METROPOLITAN SUNDAY NEWSPAPERS, INC.; *U.S. Private*, pg. 739
THE MIAMI HERALD—Knight-Ridder, Inc.; *U.S. Public*, pg. 964
THE MIDDLESEX NEWS—Harte-Hanks Communications, Inc.; *U.S. Public*, pg. 794
MIDLAND DAILY NEWS—The Hearst Corporation; *U.S. Private*, pg. 517
MILWAUKEE JOURNAL SENTINEL—Journal Communications Inc.; *U.S. Private*, pg. 601
MIRROR GROUP PLC; *Int'l*, pg. 869
THE MISSOULIAN—Lee Enterprises, Incorporated; *U.S. Public*, pg. 984
THE MONITOR—Freedom Communication Inc.; *U.S. Private*, pg. 425
THE MONTANA STANDARD—Lee Enterprises, Incorporated; *U.S. Public*, pg. 984
MOORESVILLE TRIBUNE INC.—Media General, Inc.; *U.S. Public*, pg. 1079
MORGAN COUNTY NEWS—Landmark Communications, Inc.; *U.S. Private*, pg. 648
MORGAN HILL TIMES—McClatchy Newspapers Inc.; *U.S. Public*, pg. 1065
MORGANTON NEWS-HERALD—Media General, Inc.; *U.S. Public*, pg. 1079
MORGENPOST DRUCK & VERLAGSANSTALT GMBH & CO.—Bertelsmann AG; *Int'l*, pg. 190
THE MORNING CALL—The Times Mirror Company; *U.S. Public*, pg. 1616
MORRIS COMMUNICATIONS CORPORATION—Shivers Trading & Operating Co.; *U.S. Private*, pg. 995
MORRIS NEWSPAPER CORPORATION; *U.S. Private*, pg. 762
MOUNT VERNON DEMOCRAT—Landmark Communications, Inc.; *U.S. Private*, pg. 648
MULTIMEDIA PUBLISHING OF NORTH CAROLINA, INC.—Gannett Company, Inc.; *U.S. Public*, pg. 699
MULTIMEDIA PUBLISHING OF SOUTH CAROLINA, INC.—Gannett Company, Inc.; *U.S. Public*, pg. 699
MUSCATINE JOURNAL—Lee Enterprises, Incorporated; *U.S. Public*, pg. 984
NANBEI LTD.—Dow Jones & Company, Inc.; *U.S. Public*, pg. 525
THE NAPA VALLEY REGISTER—Pulitzer Publishing Company; *U.S. Public*, pg. 1343
NAPLES DAILY NEWS—The E.W. Scripps Company; *U.S. Public*, pg. 1448
NATIONAL BUSINESS EMPLOYMENT WEEKLY—Dow Jones & Company, Inc.; *U.S. Public*, pg. 524
THE NATIONAL ENQUIRER—American Media, Inc.; *U.S. Public*, pg. 87
NATIONAL TELEGRAPH—Independent Publications, Inc.; *U.S. Private*, pg. 559
THE NETWORK OF CITY BUSINESS JOURNALS, INC.—Advance Publications Inc.; *U.S. Private*, pg. 19
NEW ALBANY GAZETTE—Landmark Communications, Inc.; *U.S. Private*, pg. 648
NEW ENGLAND NEWSPAPERS, INC.-THE TIMES—Journal Register Company; *U.S. Public*, pg. 935
NEW HAVEN REGISTER, INC.—Journal Register Company; *U.S. Public*, pg. 935
THE NEW YORK OBSERVER—Shepaug Corporation; *U.S. Private*, pg. 993
THE NEW YORK POST—The News Corporation Limited; *Int'l*, pg. 927
THE NEW YORK TIMES—The New York Times Company; *U.S. Public*, pg. 1174
THE NEW YORK TIMES COMPANY; *U.S. Public*, pg. 1173
THE NEW YORK TIMES COMPANY REGIONAL NEWSPAPER GROUP—The New York Times Company; *U.S. Public*, pg. 1174
NEW YORK TIMES NEWSPAPER GROUP—The New York Times Company; *U.S. Public*, pg. 1174
THE NEWPORT DAILY EXPRESS—Pulitzer Publishing Company; *U.S. Public*, pg. 1343
NEWPORT-NEWS TIMES—Lee Enterprises, Incorporated; *U.S. Public*, pg. 984
NEWS AMERICA PUBLISHING INC.—The News Corporation Limited; *Int'l*, pg. 925
NEWS & RECORD—Landmark Communications, Inc.; *U.S. Private*, pg. 649
THE NEWS AND REPORTER—Landmark Communications, Inc.; *U.S. Private*, pg. 648
THE NEWS CORPORATION LIMITED; *Int'l*, pg. 925
THE NEWS-DEMOCRAT—Landmark Communications, Inc.; *U.S. Private*, pg. 648
NEWS-ENTERPRISE—Landmark Communications, Inc.; *U.S. Private*, pg. 648
NEWS HERALD—Freedom Communication Inc.; *U.S. Private*, pg. 425
THE NEWS-HERALD (LAKE COUNTY)—Journal Register Company; *U.S. Public*, pg. 935
NEWS INTERNATIONAL PLC—The News Corporation Limited; *Int'l*, pg. 927
THE NEWS-JOURNAL COMPANY—Gannett Company, Inc.; *U.S. Public*, pg. 699
NEWS LIMITED OF AUSTRALIA—The News Corporation Limited; *Int'l*, pg. 925
THE NEWS-PILOT—The Copley Press, Inc.; *U.S. Private*, pg. 275
NEWS-PRESS & GAZETTE COMPANY; *U.S. Private*, pg. 797
NEWS-PRESS PUBLISHING CO.—Gannett Company, Inc.; *U.S. Public*, pg. 701
NEWS PUBLISHING COMPANY—Knight-Ridder, Inc.; *U.S. Public*, pg. 964
NEWS-STAR PUBLISHING COMPANY—Gannett Company, Inc.; *U.S. Public*, pg. 700
THE NEWS-SUN—The Copley Press, Inc.; *U.S. Private*, pg. 275
THE NEWS TRIBUNE—McClatchy Newspapers Inc.; *U.S. Public*, pg. 1066
NEWSPAPER ENTERPRISE ASSOC.—The E.W. Scripps Company; *U.S. Public*, pg. 1448
NEWSPAPER ENTERPRISE ASSOCIATION—The E.W. Scripps Company; *U.S. Public*, pg. 1448
NEWSPAPERS FIRST—Knight-Ridder, Inc.; *U.S. Public*, pg. 964
NEWSQUEST MEDIA GROUP; *Int'l*, pg. 927
THE NEWTON KANSAN—Shivers Trading & Operating Co.; *U.S. Private*, pg. 995
NIANTIC NEWS—Journal Register Company; *U.S. Public*, pg. 935
NIHON KEIZAI SHIMBUN AMERICA, INC.—Nihon Keizai Shimbun, Inc.; *Int'l*, pg. 929
NIHON KEIZAI SHIMBUN EUROPE LTD.—Nihon Keizai Shimbun, Inc.; *Int'l*, pg. 929
NIHON KEIZAI SHIMBUN, INC.; *Int'l*, pg. 929
NIHON KEIZAI SHIMBUN SINGAPORE PTE. LTD.—Nihon Keizai Shimbun, Inc.; *Int'l*, pg. 930
THE NIKKAN KOGYO SHIMBUN-CHUGOKU—The Nikkan Kogyo Shimbun, Ltd.; *Int'l*, pg. 930
THE NIKKAN KOGYO SHIMBUN, LTD.; *Int'l*, pg. 930
NITTANY PRINTING & PUBLISHING CO.—Knight-Ridder, Inc.; *U.S. Public*, pg. 964
NORTH AMERICAN PUBLISHING COMPANY; *U.S. Private*, pg. 803
NORTHEAST PUBLISHING, INC.-THE HERALD NEWS—Journal Register Company; *U.S. Public*, pg. 935
NORTHWEST FLORIDA DAILY NEWS—Freedom Communication Inc.; *U.S. Private*, pg. 425
NORWELL MARINER—Gannett Company, Inc.; *U.S. Public, pg. 701*
THE NUGGET—Hollinger Inc.; *Int'l*, pg. 631
OAK GROVE PUBLICATIONS, INC.—Shivers Trading & Operating Co.; *U.S. Private*, pg. 995
THE OAK RIDGER—Shivers Trading & Operating Co.; *U.S. Private*, pg. 995
OCALA STAR-BANNER CORPORATION—The New York Times Company; *U.S. Public*, pg. 1175
O'FALLON PROGRESS—Knight-Ridder, Inc.; *U.S. Public*, pg. 964
OGDEN NEWSPAPERS, INC.; *U.S. Private*, pg. 812
OHIO VALLEY PUBLISHING CO.—Gannett Company, Inc.; *U.S. Public*, pg. 701
OKLAHOMA PRESS PUBLISHING CO.—Gannett Company, Inc.; *U.S. Public*, pg. 701
OKLAHOMA PUBLISHING COMPANY; *U.S. Private*, pg. 813
OLATHE DAILY NEWS—Keltatim Publishing Company; *U.S.* Private, pg. 613
THE OLDHAM ERA—Landmark Communications, Inc.; *U.S.* Private, pg. 648
THE OLYMPIAN—Gannett Company, Inc.; *U.S. Public*, pg. 701
ON TRACK—Advance Publications Inc.; *U.S. Private*, pg. 19
OPINION-TRIBUNE—Landmark Communications, Inc.; *U.S. Private*, pg. 648
THE ORANGE COUNTY REGISTER—Freedom Communication Inc.; *U.S. Private*, pg. 425
ORLANDO SENTINEL COMMUNICATIONS—Tribune Company; *U.S. Public*, pg. 1636

THE OTTAWA CITIZEN—Hollinger Inc.; *Int'l*, pg. 631
THE OTTAWA SUN—Sun Media Corporation; *Int'l*, pg. 1320
OTTAWAY NEWSPAPERS, INC.—Dow Jones & Company, Inc.; *U.S. Public*, pg. 525
OTTUMWA COURIER—Lee Enterprises, Incorporated; *U.S. Public*, pg. 984
THE OUTLOOK—The Copley Press, Inc.; *U.S. Private*, pg. 275
GEORGE OUTRAM & COMPANY LTD.—Lonrho plc; *Int'l*, pg. 817
OVERSEA COURIER SERVICE CO., LTD.—Nihon Keizai Shimbun, Inc.; *Int'l*, pg. 929
PC WEEK—Softbank Corporation; *Int'l*, pg. 1276
PG PUBLISHING CO.—Blade Communications, Inc.; *U.S. Private*, pg. 147
PACIFIC MEDIA, INC.—Gannett Company, Inc.; *U.S. Public*, *pg. 702*
PACIFIC PRESS LTD.—Hollinger Inc.; *Int'l*, pg. 631
PADDOCK PUBLICATIONS, INC.; *U.S. Private*, pg. 833
THE R.W. PAGE CORP.—Knight-Ridder, Inc.; *U.S. Public*, pg. 964
THE PALATKA DAILY NEWS, INC.—The New York Times Company; *U.S. Public*, pg. 1175
PALLADIUM PUBLISHING CORP.—Gannett Company, Inc.; *U.S. Public*, pg. 701
PEARSON, INC.—Pearson plc; *Int'l*, pg. 1026
PEARSON PLC; *Int'l*, pg. 1025
PEMBROKE MARINER—Gannett Company, Inc.; *U.S. Public*, pg. 701
PENDULUM—Journal Register Company; *U.S. Public*, pg. 935
PENNY SAVER—The Gazette Company; *U.S. Private*, pg. 442
PENNYSAVER—Harte-Hanks Communications, Inc.; *U.S. Public*, pg. 794
PENSACOLA NEWS-JOURNAL, INC.—Gannett Company, Inc.; *U.S. Public*, pg. 701
PEORIA JOURNAL STAR, INC.—The Copley Press, Inc.; *U.S. Private*, pg. 275
PERRY COUNTY NEWS—Landmark Communications, Inc.; *U.S. Private*, pg. 648
PHILADELPHIA DAILY NEWS—Knight-Ridder, Inc.; *U.S. Public*, pg. 964
THE PHILADELPHIA INQUIRER—Knight-Ridder, Inc.; *U.S. Public*, pg. 964
PHILADELPHIA NEWSPAPERS, INC.—Knight-Ridder, Inc.; *U.S. Public*, pg. 964
PHOENIX NEWSPAPERS, INC.—Central Newspapers, Inc.; *U.S. Public*, pg. 326
PHOENIXVILLE NEWSPAPERS, INC.—Journal Register Company; *U.S. Public*, pg. 935
THE PICTORIAL GAZETTE—Journal Register Company; *U.S. Public*, pg. 935
PIEDMONT PUBLISHING CO., INC.—Media General, Inc.; *U.S. Public*, pg. 1079
PIERCE COUNTY HERALD—McClatchy Newspapers Inc.; *U.S. Public*, pg. 1066
PIONEER NEWS—Landmark Communications, Inc.; *U.S. Private*, pg. 648
PIONEER PRESS NEWSPAPERS INC.—Hollinger Inc.; *Int'l*, *pg. 632*
PITTSBURG MORNING SUN—Shivers Trading & Operating Co.; *U.S. Private*, pg. 995
PLAINVIEW DAILY HERALD—The Hearst Corporation; *U.S. Private*, pg. 517
POINT PLEASANT REGISTER CO.—Gannett Company, Inc.; *U.S. Public*, pg. 701
THE PORTLAND NEWSPAPERS—Guy Gannett Communications; *U.S. Private*, pg. 439
POTPOURRI (HARTE-HANKS NORTHERN CALIFORNIA CDM, INC.)—Harte-Hanks Communications, Inc.; *U.S. Public*, pg. 794
POUGHKEEPSIE NEWSPAPERS—Gannett Company, Inc.; *U.S. Public*, pg. 700
PRATTVILLE PROGRESS—Gannett Company, Inc.; *U.S. Public*, pg. 699
GEORGE W. PRESCOTT PUBLISHING CO.; *U.S. Private*, pg. 882
PRESS & SUN-BULLETIN—Gannett Company, Inc.; *U.S. Public*, pg. 700
PRESS-CITIZEN COMPANY, INC.—Gannett Company, Inc.; *U.S. Public*, pg. 701
THE PRESS DEMOCRAT—The New York Times Company; *U.S. Public*, pg. 1175
PRESS ENTERPRISE COMPANY—A.H. Belo Corporation; *U.S. Public*, pg. 209
PRIMEDIA INC.; *U.S. Public*, pg. 1327
PRIMEDIA INFORMATIN GROUP—Primedia Inc.; *U.S. Public*, pg. 1328
THE PRINCE GEORGE CITIZEN—Hollinger Inc.; *Int'l*, pg. 631
PROVIDENCE JOURNAL-BULLETIN—A.H. Belo Corporation; *U.S. Public*, pg. 209
PULITZER PUBLISHING COMPANY; *U.S. Public*, pg. 1343
QUAD-CITY TIMES—Lee Enterprises, Incorporated; *U.S. Public*, pg. 984
QUEBECOR INC.; *Int'l*, pg. 1075
QUEBECOR PRINTING AURORA—Quebecor Inc.; *Int'l*, pg. 1076
RAMA GROUP OF COMPANIES; *U.S. Private*, pg. 908
RANDOLPH MARINER—Gannett Company, Inc.; *U.S. Public*, pg. 701
RAPID CITY JOURNAL—Lee Enterprises, Incorporated; *U.S. Public*, pg. 984
RAVALLI REPUBLIC—Pulitzer Publishing Company; *U.S. Public*, pg. 1343
READING EAGLE COMPANY; *U.S. Private*, pg. 913
THE RECORD-JOURNAL PUBLISHING COMPANY; *U.S. Private*, pg. 914
RED OAK EXPRESS—Landmark Communications, Inc.; *U.S. Private*, pg. 648
RED WING PUBLISHING COMPANY; *U.S. Private*, pg. 915
REDDING RECORD SEARCHLIGHT—The E.W. Scripps Company; *U.S. Public*, pg. 1448
REED ELSEVIER BUSINESS INFORMATION—Reed Elsevier plc; *Int'l*, pg. 1095
REED ELSEVIER BUSINESS INFORMATION-NEW YORK—Reed Elsevier plc; *Int'l*, pg. 1095
REED ELSEVIER PLC; *Int'l*, pg. 1093
THE REGIONAL STANDARD—Journal Register Company; *U.S. Public*, pg. 935
RELOCATION CONSULTANTS—Tribune Company; *U.S. Public*, pg. 1635
RENO GAZETTE JOURNAL—Gannett Company, Inc.; *U.S. Public*, pg. 701
AB REPORTAGEBILD—Aftonbladet AB; *Int'l*, pg. 29
THE REPORTER EQUITABLE PUBLISHING CO.—Gannett Company, Inc.; *U.S. Public*, pg. 701
RICHMOND NEWSPAPERS, INC.—Media General, Inc.; *U.S. Public*, pg. 1079
RINGIER AG; *Int'l*, pg. 1118
ROANE COUNTY NEWS—Landmark Communications, Inc.; *U.S. Private*, pg. 648
ROBESONIAN—Media General, Inc.; *U.S. Public*, pg. 1078
ROCK HILL HERALD—McClatchy Newspapers Inc.; *U.S. Public*, pg. 1066
THE ROCKDALE CITIZEN PUBLISHING COMPANY—Gray Communications Systems, Inc.; *U.S. Public*, pg. 759
ROCKFORD NEWSPAPERS, INC.—Gannett Company, Inc.; *U.S. Public*, pg. 701
ROCKWOOD TIMES—Landmark Communications, Inc.; *U.S. Private*, pg. 648
ROCKY MOUNTAIN NEWS—The E.W. Scripps Company; *U.S. Public*, pg. 1448
SAARBRUCKER ZEITUNG VERLAG UND DRUCKEREI GMBH—Georg von Holtzbrinck GmbH; *Int'l*, pg. 1478
THE SACRAMENTO BEE—McClatchy Newspapers Inc.; *U.S. Public*, pg. 1066
ST. CLOUD DAILY TIMES, INC.—Gannett Company, Inc.; *U.S. Public*, pg. 701
ST. LOUIS BUSINESS JOURNAL CORP.—Advance Publications Inc.; *U.S. Private*, pg. 20
ST. LOUIS COUNTIAN—The Walt Disney Company; *U.S. Public*, pg. 513
ST. LOUIS DAILY RECORD—The Walt Disney Company; *U.S. Public*, pg. 513
ST. LOUIS POST-DISPATCH—Pulitzer Publishing Company; *U.S. Public*, pg. 1343
SAINT PAUL PIONEER PRESS DIVISION—Knight-Ridder, Inc.; *U.S. Public*, pg. 964
ST. PETERSBURG TIMES—The Times Publishing Co.; *U.S.* Private, pg. 1088
SALINAS CALIFORNIAN—Gannett Company, Inc.; *U.S. Public*, pg. 701
SAMSON INDEPENDENT, INC.—Media General, Inc.; *U.S. Public*, pg. 1078
SAMSUNG GROUP; *Int'l*, pg. 1181
SAN ANGELO STANDARD, INC.—Harte-Hanks Communications, Inc.; *U.S. Public*, pg. 794
SAN ANTONIO EXPRESS NEWS—The Hearst Corporation; *U.S. Private*, pg. 517
SAN DIEGO UNION TRIBUNE—The Copley Press, Inc.; *U.S. Private*, pg. 275
SAN FRANCISCO EXAMINER—The Hearst Corporation; *U.S. Private*, pg. 518
SAN JOSE MERCURY NEWS—Knight-Ridder, Inc.; *U.S. Public*, pg. 964
SAN LUIS OBISPO TELEGRAM-TRIBUNE—Knight-Ridder, Inc.; *U.S. Public*, pg. 964
SANDY POST—Lee Enterprises, Incorporated; *U.S. Public*, pg. 984
SANTA BARBARA NEWS-PRESS—The New York Times Company; *U.S. Public*, pg. 1175
SANTA MARIA TIMES—Pulitzer Publishing Company; *U.S. Public*, pg. 1343
SARASOTA HERALD-TRIBUNE COMPANY—The New York Times Company; *U.S. Public*, pg. 1175
THE SARATOGIAN—Gannett Company, Inc.; *U.S. Public*, pg. 700
THE SAULT STAR LTD.—Hollinger Inc.; *Int'l*, pg. 631
SCHURZ COMMUNICATIONS, INC.; *U.S. Private*, pg. 973
SCITUATE MARINER—Gannett Company, Inc.; *U.S. Public*, *pg. 701*
SCOTTISH & UNIVERSAL NEWSPAPERS LIMITED—Lonrho plc; *Int'l*, pg. 817
THE E.W. SCRIPPS COMPANY; *U.S. Public*, pg. 1447
THE SEATTLE BUSINESS JOURNAL, INC.—Advance Publications Inc.; *U.S. Private*, pg. 20
SEATTLE POST-INTELLIGENCER—The Hearst Corporation; *U.S. Private*, pg. 517
SEATTLE TIMES COMPANY; *U.S. Private*, pg. 980
SEBRING NEWS-SUN—The New York Times Company; *U.S. Public*, pg. 1175
SENIOR SPECTRUM—McClatchy Newspapers Inc.; *U.S. Public*, pg. 1066
SENTINEL-NEWS—Landmark Communications, Inc.; *U.S. Private*, pg. 648
SHAWNEE NEWS-STAR—Shivers Trading & Operating Co.; *U.S. Private*, pg. 995
SHEARMAN CORPORATION; *U.S. Private*, pg. 991
SHEPARD'S—Reed Elsevier plc; *Int'l*, pg. 1095
SHEPARD'S—The Times Mirror Company; *U.S. Public*, pg. 1616
SHIVERS TRADING & OPERATING CO.; *U.S. Private*, pg. 994
SHOPPER PUBLISHING GROUP—Shivers Trading & Operating Co.; *U.S. Private*, pg. 995
SINGAPORE PRESS HOLDINGS LTD.; *Int'l*, pg. 1253
SIOUX FALLS ARGUS LEADER—Gannett Company, Inc.; *U.S. Public*, pg. 701
AB SKANE-REPORTAGE—Aftonbladet AB; *Int'l*, pg. 29
SOAP OPERA MAGAZINE—American Media, Inc.; *U.S. Public*, pg. 87
THE SOUTH CHINA MORNING POST, LIMITED—The News Corporation Limited; *Int'l*, pg. 925
SOUTHAM INC.—Hollinger Inc.; *Int'l*, pg. 631
SOUTHAM MAGAZINE AND INFORMATION GROUP—Hollinger Inc.; *Int'l*, pg. 631
SOUTHEASTERN NEWSPAPERS CORPORATION—Shivers Trading & Operating Co.; *U.S. Private*, pg. 996
SOUTHEASTERN PRINTING COMPANY INC.—MasTec, Inc.; *U.S. Public*, pg. 1056
SOUTHERN ILLINOISAN—Lee Enterprises, Incorporated; *U.S. Public*, pg. 984
SOUTHLAND PUBLISHING CO.—Gannett Company, Inc.; *U.S. Public*, pg. 701
SPARTANBURG HERALD-JOURNAL—The New York Times Company; *U.S. Public*, pg. 1175
THE SPECTATOR, HAMILTON—Hollinger Inc.; *Int'l*, pg. 631
SPENCER COUNTY JOURNAL-DEMOCRAT—Landmark Communications, Inc.; *U.S. Private*, pg. 648
SPENCER MAGNET—Landmark Communications, Inc.; *U.S. Private*, pg. 648
FRANZ SPIEGEL BUCH GMBH—Georg von Holtzbrinck GmbH; *Int'l*, pg. 1478
SPRINGFIELD NEWS—Lee Enterprises, Incorporated; *U.S. Public*, pg. 984
THE SPRINGFIELD NEWS LEADER—Gannett Company, Inc.; *U.S. Public*, pg. 701
SPRINGFIELD NEWSPAPERS, INC.—Cox Enterprises, Inc.; *U.S. Private*, pg. 281
THE SPRINGFIELD SUN—Landmark Communications, Inc.; *U.S. Private*, pg. 648
STANDARD EXAMINER; *U.S. Private*, pg. 1031
STAR EDITORIAL, INC.—American Media, Inc.; *U.S. Public*, *pg. 87*
STAR PUBLICATIONS—Hollinger Inc.; *Int'l*, pg. 632
STAR-TELEGRAM NEWSPAPER, INC.—Knight-Ridder, Inc.; *U.S. Public*, pg. 964
STAR TRIBUNE, MINNEAPOLIS-ST. PAUL—Cowles Media Company; *U.S. Private*, pg. 281
THE STATE JOURNAL-REGISTER—The Copley Press, Inc.; *U.S. Private*, pg. 275
THE STATE-RECORD COMPANY—Knight-Ridder, Inc.; *U.S. Public*, pg. 964
STATESMAN-JOURNAL CO., INC.—Gannett Company, Inc.; *U.S. Public*, pg. 701
STATESVILLE RECORD AND LANDMARK—Media General, Inc.; *U.S. Public*, pg. 1078
STAUFFER COMMUNICATIONS, INC.—Shivers Trading & Operating Co.; *U.S. Private*, pg. 995
STAUNTON LEADER PUBLISHING CO.—Gannett Company, Inc.; *U.S. Public*, pg. 701
STERLING NEWSPAPERS LTD.—Hollinger Inc.; *Int'l*, pg. 632
STUART NEWS COMPANY—The E.W. Scripps Company; *U.S. Public*, pg. 1448
SUBURBAN NEWSPAPER GROUP—Gannett Company, Inc.; *U.S. Public*, pg. 700
SUBURBAN PUBLICATIONS, INC.—Journal Register Company; *U.S. Public*, pg. 935
SUDKURIER GMBH—Georg von Holtzbrinck GmbH; *Int'l*, pg. 1478
SUMTER COUNTY TIMES—Landmark Communications, Inc.; *U.S. Private*, pg. 648
THE SUN—The News Corporation Limited; *Int'l*, pg. 927
THE SUN CO.—Gannett Company, Inc.; *U.S. Public*, pg. 701
SUN HERALD—Knight-Ridder, Inc.; *U.S. Public*, pg. 964
THE SUN-HERALD—John Fairfax Holdings Limited; *Int'l*, pg. 477
SUN-LITHO—Morris Newspaper Corporation; *U.S. Private*, pg. 762
THE SUN NEWS—Knight-Ridder, Inc.; *U.S. Public*, pg. 964
SUN PUBLISHING COMPANY, INC.—Knight-Ridder, Inc.; *U.S. Public*, pg. 964
SUN-SENTINEL COMPANY—Tribune Company; *U.S. Public*, pg. 1636
THE SUN TIMES—Hollinger Inc.; *Int'l*, pg. 631
SUNBELT NEWSPAPERS, INC.—Media General, Inc.; *U.S. Public*, pg. 1079
SUPERMARKET NEWS—The Walt Disney Company; *U.S. Public*, pg. 513
THE SYDNEY MORNING HERALD—John Fairfax Holdings Limited; *Int'l*, pg. 477
T-R PRINTING & PUBLISHING—Tribune Review Publishing Co.; *U.S. Private*, pg. 1102
TS PUBLICATIONS (FLORIDA), INC.—Sun Media Corporation; *Int'l*, pg. 1320
TSP NEWSPAPERS, INC.—The New York Times Company; *U.S. Public*, pg. 1175
TALLAHASSEE DEMOCRAT, INC.—Knight-Ridder, Inc.; *U.S. Public*, pg. 964
THE TAMPA TRIBUNE—Media General, Inc.; *U.S. Public*, pg. 1079
THE TELEGRAPH PLC—Hollinger Inc.; *Int'l*, pg. 632
TEMPLE-INLAND INC.; *U.S. Public*, pg. 1574
TENNESSEAN NEWSPAPERS, INC.—Gannett Company, Inc.; *U.S. Public*, pg. 701
THOMSON AUSTRALIAN HOLDINGS PTY. LTD.—The Thomson Corporation; *U.S. Public*, pg. 1601
THE THOMSON CORPORATION PLC—The Thomson Corporation; *U.S. Public*, pg. 1601
THE THOMSON CORPORATION; *U.S. Public*, pg. 1599
THOMSON REGIONAL NEWSPAPERS LTD.—The Thomson Corporation; *U.S. Public*, pg. 1601
THOMSON U.S. INC.—The Thomson Corporation; *U.S. Public*, pg. 1601
THOUSAND OAKS NEWS-CHRONICLE—The E.W. Scripps Company; *U.S. Public*, pg. 1448
THE TIMES—Gannett Company, Inc.; *U.S. Public*, pg. 700
THE TIMES CO.—Gannett Company, Inc.; *U.S. Public*, pg. 700
TIMES DAILY, INC.—The New York Times Company; *U.S. Public*, pg. 1175
THE TIMES HERALD CO.—Gannett Company, Inc.; *U.S. Public*, pg. 701
THE TIMES LEADER—Knight-Ridder, Inc.; *U.S. Public*, pg. 963

THE TIMES MIRROR COMPANY; *U.S. Public*, pg. 1615
TIMES-NEWS—The New York Times Company; *U.S. Public*, pg. 1175
TIMES NEWSPAPERS LTD.—The News Corporation Limited; *Int'l*, pg. 927
THE TIMES-PICAYUNE PUBLISHING CORP.; *U.S. Private, pg. 1087*
THE TIMES PUBLISHING CO.; *U.S. Private*, pg. 1087
THE TIMES REPORTER—Journal Register Company; *U.S. Public*, pg. 935
THE TOPEKA CAPITAL-JOURNAL—Shivers Trading & Operating Co.; *U.S. Private*, pg. 995
TORONTO STAR NEWSPAPERS LTD.—Torstar Corporation; *Int'l*, pg. 1402
THE TORONTO SUN PUBLISHING CORPORATION—Sun Media Corporation; *Int'l*, pg. 1320
TORSTAR CORPORATION; *Int'l*, pg. 1402
TRI-CITY HERALD—McClatchy Newspapers Inc.; *U.S. Public*, pg. 1066
THE TRIBUNE—The Thomson Corporation; *U.S. Public*, pg. 1601
TRIBUNE COMPANY; *U.S. Public*, pg. 1635
TRIBUNE PUBLISHING COMPANY—Tribune Company; *U.S. Public*, pg. 1636
TRIBUNE REVIEW PUBLISHING CO.; *U.S. Private*, pg. 1102
TRIMBLE BANNER DEMOCRAT—Landmark Communications, Inc.; *U.S. Private*, pg. 648
TROY PUBLISHING COMPANY, INC.—Journal Register Company; *U.S. Public*, pg. 935
TUCSON NEWSPAPERS, INC.—Gannett Company, Inc.; *U.S. Public*, pg. 701
THE TUSCALOOSA NEWS—The New York Times Company; *U.S. Public*, pg. 1175
THE TWIN CITIES TIMES/RIVERDALE FREE PRESS—Pulitzer Publishing Company; *U.S. Public*, pg. 1343
ULLSTEIN GMBH—Axel Springer Verlag AG; *Int'l*, pg. 102
UNIMEDIA INC.—Hollinger Inc.; *Int'l*, pg. 632
THE UNION-RECORDER—Community Newspaper Holdings Inc.; *U.S. Private*, pg. 259
UNITED ADVERTISING PUBLICATIONS, INC.—United News & Media plc; *Int'l*, pg. 1443
UNITED NEWS & MEDIA PLC; *Int'l*, pg. 1443
USA TODAY—Gannett Company, Inc.; *U.S. Public*, pg. 700
UNIVERSAL STUDIOS MUSIC LTD.—The Seagram Company Ltd.; *Int'l*, pg. 1217
USMEDIA GROUP—Central Valley Publishing; *U.S. Private*, pg. 225
UTICA OBSERVER-DISPATCH—Gannett Company, Inc.; *U.S. Public*, pg. 700
VNU DAGBLADENGROEP B.V.—VNU Verenigde Nederlandse Uitgeversbedrijven B.V.; *Int'l*, pg. 1445
VNU VERENIGDE NEDERLANDSE UITGEVERSBEDRIJVEN B.V.; *Int'l*, pg. 1445
VV PUBLISHING CORP.; *U.S. Private*, pg. 1131
THE VANCOUVER SUN—Hollinger Inc.; *Int'l*, pg. 631
VANDALIA LEADER-UNION—Landmark Communications, Inc.; *U.S. Private*, pg. 648
VENTURA COUNTY STAR-FREE PRESS—The E.W. Scripps Company; *U.S. Public*, pg. 1448
THE VIRGIN ISLANDS DAILY NEWS—Gannett Company, Inc.; *U.S. Public*, pg. 702
THE VIRGINIAN-PILOT—Landmark Communications, Inc.; *U.S. Private*, pg. 649
VISALIA TIMES-DELTA—Gannett Company, Inc.; *U.S. Public*, pg. 702
THE WALL STREET JOURNAL—Dow Jones & Company, Inc.; *U.S. Public*, pg. 524
THE WALL STREET JOURNAL EUROPE—Dow Jones & Company, Inc.; *U.S. Public*, pg. 525
WALLA WALLA UNION BULLETIN—Seattle Times Company; *U.S. Private*, pg. 980
WASHINGTON BUSINESS JOURNAL, INC.—Advance Publications Inc.; *U.S. Private*, pg. 20
THE WASHINGTON POST COMPANY; *U.S. Public*, pg. 1742
THE WASHINGTON POST NATIONAL WEEKLY EDITION—The Washington Post Company; *U.S. Public*, pg. 1743
WASHINGTON POST NEWSPAPER DIVISION—The Washington Post Company; *U.S. Public*, pg. 1743
THE WASHINGTON POST WRITERS GROUP—The Washington Post Company; *U.S. Public*, pg. 1743
WAUSAU DAILY HERALD—Gannett Company, Inc.; *U.S. Public*, pg. 700
WAYNE INDEPENDENT—Media General, Inc.; *U.S. Public*, pg. 1078
WEEKLY WORLD NEWS, INC.—American Media, Inc.; *U.S.* Public, pg. 87
WEHCO MEDIA, INC.; *U.S. Private*, pg. 1159
WEYMOUTH NEWS—Gannett Company, Inc.; *U.S. Public*, pg. 702
WIARTON ECHO GROUP—Hollinger Inc.; *Int'l*, pg. 632
WICHITA BUSINESS JOURNAL, INC.—Advance Publications Inc.; *U.S. Private*, pg. 20
THE WICHITA EAGLE AND BEACON PUBLISHING CO., INC.—Knight-Ridder, Inc.; *U.S. Public*, pg. 964
WICHITA FALLS TIMES & RECORD NEWS—Harte-Hanks Communications, Inc.; *U.S. Public*, pg. 794
WILMINGTON MORNING STAR—The New York Times Company; *U.S. Public*, pg. 1175
WILMINGTON STAR-NEWS, INC.—The New York Times Company; *U.S. Public*, pg. 1175
THE WINDSOR STAR—Hollinger Inc.; *Int'l*, pg. 632
WINONA DAILY NEWS—Lee Enterprises, Incorporated; *U.S. Public*, pg. 984
WINTER HAVEN NEWS CHIEF—Shivers Trading & Operating Co.; *U.S. Private*, pg. 995
WISCONSIN STATE JOURNAL—Lee Enterprises, Incorporated; *U.S. Public*, pg. 984
WOMEN'S WEAR DAILY—The Walt Disney Company; *U.S.* Public, pg. 513
THE WORLD—Pulitzer Publishing Company; *U.S. Public*, pg. 1343
WORLD PUBLISHING COMPANY; *U.S. Private*, pg. 1190
WORRELL ENTERPRISES, INC.; *U.S. Private*, pg. 1191
THE YANKTON PRINTING COMPANY—Shivers Trading & Operating Co.; *U.S. Private*, pg. 995
THE YORK NEWS-TIMES—Shivers Trading & Operating Co.; *U.S. Private*, pg. 995
THE YUMA DAILY SUN—The Thomson Corporation; *U.S. Public*, pg. 1601

2721 — PERIODICALS: PUBLISHING, OR PUBLISHING & PRINTING

A/S/M COMMUNICATIONS, INC.—VNU Verenigde Nederlandse Uitgeversbedrijven B.V.; *Int'l*, pg. 1446
ABC, INC—The Walt Disney Company; *U.S. Public*, pg. 511
ADD, INC.—Journal Communications Inc.; *U.S. Private*, pg. 601
AP JOURNALS, INC.—Harcourt General, Inc.; *U.S. Public*, pg. 783
ACADEMIC PRESS INTERNATIONAL CORP.—Harcourt General, Inc.; *U.S. Public*, pg. 783
ADAMS BUSINESS MEDIA; *U.S. Private*, pg. 16
ADAMS BUSINESS MEDIA—Adams Business Media; *U.S. Private*, pg. 16
ADAPT ELECTRONIC PUBLISHING—Bertelsmann AG; *Int'l*, pg. 191
ADVANCE PUBLICATIONS INC.; *U.S. Private*, pg. 18
ADVANSTAR COMMUNICATIONS; *U.S. Private*, pg. 22
ADVERTISING AGE—Crain Communications, Inc.; *U.S. Private*, pg. 284
AGRICULTURAL PUBLISHING GROUP—The Walt Disney Company; *U.S. Public*, pg. 512
ALLURE—Advance Publications Inc.; *U.S. Private*, pg. 20
AMERICAN ARBITRATION ASSOCIATION; *U.S. Private*, pg. 50
AMERICAN ARTIST—VNU Verenigde Nederlandse Uitgeversbedrijven B.V.; *Int'l*, pg. 1446
AMERICAN BANKER BOND BUYER—The Thomson Corporation; *U.S. Public*, pg. 1600
AMERICAN CITY BUSINESS JOURNALS, INC.—Advance Publications Inc.; *U.S. Private*, pg. 19
AMERICAN EXPORT REGISTER—Thomas Publishing Company; *U.S. Private*, pg. 1082
AMERICAN EXPRESS COMPANY; *U.S. Public*, pg. 73
AMERICAN EXPRESS PUBLISHING CORPORATION—American Express Company; *U.S. Public*, pg. 74
AMERICAN FAMILY PUBLISHERS—Time Warner Inc.; *U.S.* Public, pg. 1612
AMERICAN HEALTH CONSULTANTS—The Thomson Corporation; *U.S. Public*, pg. 1601
AMERICAN HERITAGE MAGAZINE—Forbes, Inc.; *U.S. Private*, pg. 417
AMERICAN HOME STYLE—Bertelsmann AG; *Int'l*, pg. 190
AMERICAN JOURNAL OF NURSING COMPANY—Wolters Kluwer N.V.; *Int'l*, pg. 1513
AMERICAN LITERATURE REVIEW—Thomas Publishing Company; *U.S. Private*, pg. 1082
AMERICAN PHOTO—Lagardere Groupe; *Int'l*, pg. 795
AMUSEMENT BUSINESS—VNU Verenigde Nederlandse Uitgeversbedrijven B.V.; *Int'l*, pg. 1446
APPLIED GRAPHICS TECHNOLOGY—U.S. News & World Report; *U.S. Private*, pg. 1125
ARCHITECTURAL RECORD—The McGraw-Hill Companies; *U.S. Public*, pg. 1070
ARCHITECTURE—VNU Verenigde Nederlandse Uitgeversbedrijven B.V.; *Int'l*, pg. 1446
ARGUS PUBLISHERS—Primedia Inc.; *U.S. Public*, pg. 1328
ASIAWEEK LTD.—Time Warner Inc.; *U.S. Public*, pg. 1613
ASPEN PUBLISHERS, INC.—Wolters Kluwer N.V.; *Int'l*, pg. 1513
THE ATLANTIC MONTHLY MAGAZINE; *U.S. Private*, pg. 95
AUTOMOBILE MAGAZINE—Primedia Inc.; *U.S. Public*, pg. 1328
AUTOMOTIVE NEWS—Crain Communications, Inc.; *U.S. Private*, pg. 284
AUTOWEEK—Crain Communications, Inc.; *U.S. Private*, pg. 284
AXEL SPRINGER VERLAG AG; *Int'l*, pg. 102
B.A.S.S., INC.; *U.S. Private*, pg. 105
BBC MAGAZINES; *Int'l*, pg. 114
BCA—Bertelsmann AG; *Int'l*, pg. 192
BCA—Reed Elsevier plc; *Int'l*, pg. 1094
BEI GRAPHICS—The New Yorker Magazine; *U.S. Private*, pg. 796
BNA ENVIRONMENT & SAFETY SERVICES DIV.—The Bureau of National Affairs, Inc.; *U.S. Private*, pg. 182
BNA INTERNATIONAL INC.—The Bureau of National Affairs, Inc.; *U.S. Private*, pg. 182
BNA LEGAL SERVICES DIV.—The Bureau of National Affairs, Inc.; *U.S. Private*, pg. 182
BPA INTERNATIONAL; *U.S. Private*, pg 107
BPI COMMUNICATIONS INC.—VNU Verenigde Nederlandse Uitgeversbedrijven B.V.; *Int'l*, pg. 1446
BZV ZEITSCHRIFTEN VERLAG GMBH & CO. KG—Burda Holding GmbH & Co., KG; *Int'l*, pg. 233
BACKSTAGE—VNU Verenigde Nederlandse Uitgeversbedrijven B.V.; *Int'l*, pg. 1446
BACON'S INFORMATION, INC.—Primedia Inc.; *U.S. Public, pg. 1327*
BALL PUBLISHING—W. Atlee Burpee Co.; *U.S. Private*, pg. 188
BAM MEDIA; *U.S. Private*, pg. 113
BANCROFT-WHITNEY CO.—The Thomson Corporation; *U.S. Public*, pg. 1602
BANTA PUBLICATIONS GROUP—Banta Corporation; *U.S. Public*, pg. 188
BANTAM BOOKS LTD.—Bertelsmann AG; *Int'l*, pg. 191
BANTAM DOUBLEDAY DELL PUBLISHING GROUP, INC.—Bertelsmann AG; *Int'l*, pg. 191
BANTAM PAPERBACKS UK—Bertelsmann AG; *Int'l*, pg. 191
BANTAM PRESS UK—Bertelsmann AG; *Int'l*, pg. 191
BASS ANGLER SPORTSMAN SOCIETY—B.A.S.S., Inc.; *U.S. Private*, pg. 105
BASSMASTER MAGAZINE—B.A.S.S., Inc.; *U.S. Private*, pg. 105
BAUVERLAG G.M.B.H.—Rogers Communications, Inc.; *Int'l*, pg. 1124
BENJAMIN FRANKLIN LITERARY & MEDICAL SOCIETY, INC.; *U.S. Private*, pg. 133
BEREAN CHRISTIAN STORES—Standex International Corporation; *U.S. Public*, pg. 1506
BERTELSMANN AG; *Int'l*, pg. 189
BERTELSMANN INC.—Bertelsmann AG; *Int'l*, pg. 191
CHANNING L. BETE CO., INC.; *U.S. Private*, pg. 140
BETRIEBSWINTSCHAFT LICHER VERLAG DR. TH. GABLER GMBH—Bertelsmann AG; *Int'l*, pg. 189
BETTER HOMES AND GARDENS BOOKS—Meredith Corporation; *U.S. Public*, pg. 1094
BETTER HOMES AND GARDENS MAGAZINE—Meredith Corporation; *U.S. Public*, pg. 1094
BETTER HOMES AND GARDENS SPECIAL INTEREST PUBLICATIONS—Meredith Corporation; *U.S. Public*, pg. 1094
BETTER HOMES AND GARDENS WOOD MAGAZINE—Meredith Corporation; *U.S. Public*, pg. 1094
BILL COMMUNICATIONS, INC.—VNU Verenigde Nederlandse Uitgeversbedrijven B.V.; *Int'l*, pg. 1446
BILLBOARD MAGAZINE—VNU Verenigde Nederlandse Uitgeversbedrijven B.V.; *Int'l*, pg. 1446
BILLCOM AKRON—VNU Verenigde Nederlandse Uitgeversbedrijven B.V.; *Int'l*, pg. 1446
BOBIT PUBLISHING COMPANY; *U.S. Private*, pg. 154
BONAVENTURA—Reed Elsevier plc; *Int'l*, pg. 1099
BRIDE'S—Advance Publications Inc.; *U.S. Private*, pg. 20
BUFFALO LAW JOURNAL—Advance Publications Inc.; *U.S. Private*, pg. 19
BURDA GMBH—Burda Holding GmbH & Co., KG; *Int'l*, pg. 233
BURDA HOLDING GMBH & CO., KG; *Int'l*, pg. 233
BURDA PUBLICATIONS, INC.—Burda Holding GmbH & Co., KG; *Int'l*, pg. 233
THE BUREAU OF NATIONAL AFFAIRS, INC.; *U.S. Private*, pg. 181
BUSINESS GUIDES INC.—Lebhar-Friedman, Inc.; *U.S. Private*, pg. 656
BUSINESS INSURANCE—Crain Communications, Inc.; *U.S.* Private, pg. 285
BUSINESS MAGAZINE—Pearson plc; *Int'l*, pg. 1025
BUSINESS MARKETING—Crain Communications, Inc.; *U.S.* Private, pg. 285
BUSINESS WEEK—The McGraw-Hill Companies; *U.S. Public*, pg. 1069
BUTTERICK COMPANY, INC.; *U.S. Private*, pg. 190
BUTTERWORTHS ASIA—Reed Elsevier plc; *Int'l*, pg. 1095
BUTTERWORTHS BRITISH AND IRISH LEGAL—Reed Elsevier plc; *Int'l*, pg. 1095
BYTE PUBLICATIONS—The McGraw-Hill Companies; *U.S. Public*, pg. 1070
CCB/NILS, INC.—The Walt Disney Company; *U.S. Public*, pg. 512
CCH ASIA LIMITED—Wolters Kluwer N.V.; *Int'l*, pg. 1513
CCH AUSTRALIA LIMITED—Wolters Kluwer N.V.; *Int'l*, pg. 1513
CCH CANADIAN LTD.—Wolters Kluwer N.V.; *Int'l*, pg. 1513
CCH EDITIONS LIMITED—Wolters Kluwer N.V.; *Int'l*, pg. 1514
CCH JAPAN LIMITED—Wolters Kluwer N.V.; *Int'l*, pg. 1513
CCH LEGAL INFORMATION SERVICES, INC.—Wolters Kluwer N.V.; *Int'l*, pg. 1513
CCH NEW ZEALAND LIMITED—Wolters Kluwer N.V.; *Int'l*, pg. 1513
C.E.P. COMMUNICATION GROUP; *Int'l*, pg. 239
CIO PUBLISHING CORP.—International Data Group; *U.S. Private*, pg. 569
CMP MEDIA, INC.; *U.S. Public*, pg. 279
CT CORPORATION SYSTEM—Wolters Kluwer N.V.; *Int'l*, pg. 1513
CADMUS COMMUNICATIONS CORPORATION; *U.S. Public*, pg. 290
CALIFORNIA OFFSET PRINTERS, INC.—COP Communications; *U.S. Private*, pg. 196
CANADIAN PUBLISHING—Rogers Communications, Inc.; *Int'l*, pg. 1123
CANON COMMUNICATIONS—Canon Inc.; *Int'l*, pg. 261
CAPITAL CITIES/ABC PUBLISHING GROUP—The Walt Disney Company; *U.S. Public*, pg. 512
CAR AND DRIVER—Lagardere Groupe; *Int'l*, pg. 795
CATHOLIC DIGEST; *U.S. Private*, pg. 220
CENTURY PUBLISHING COMPANY; *U.S. Private*, pg. 226
CHEMICAL ENGINEERING—The McGraw-Hill Companies; *U.S. Public*, pg. 1071
CHICAGO MAGAZINE—Primedia Inc.; *U.S. Public*, pg. 1328
CHILD MAGAZINE—Bertelsmann AG; *Int'l*, pg. 190
CHRISTIANITY TODAY, INC.; *U.S. Private*, pg. 238
CLIGGOTT PUBLISHING; *U.S. Private*, pg. 246
THE COBB GROUP—Softbank Corporation; *Int'l*, pg. 1276
COLONIAL HOMES—The Hearst Corporation; *U.S. Private*, pg. 517
COLOR MEDIA AG—Fotolabo S.A.; *Int'l*, pg. 501
COMMTEK COMMUNICATIONS, CORP.; *U.S. Private*, pg. 258
COMPENDIUM SYSTEMS CORPORATION; *U.S. Private*, pg. 259
COMPUTER SHOPPER—Softbank Corporation; *Int'l*, pg. 1276
COMPUTERWORLD, INC.—International Data Group; *U.S. Private*, pg. 569
THE CONDE NAST PUBLICATIONS INC.—Advance Publications Inc.; *U.S. Private*, pg. 20
CONDE NAST TRAVELER—Advance Publications Inc.; *U.S. Private*, pg. 20
CONGRESSIONAL QUARTERLY—The Times Publishing Co.; *U.S. Private*, pg. 1088
CORGI BOOKS LTD.—Bertelsmann AG; *Int'l*, pg. 191

CORPORATE FINANCE MAGAZINE—Financial World Partners; *U.S. Private*, pg. 405
COSMOPOLITAN—The Hearst Corporation; *U.S. Private*, pg. 517
COUNTRY AMERICA MAGAZINE—Meredith Corporation; *U.S. Public*, pg. 1094
COUNTRY HOME MAGAZINE—Meredith Corporation; *U.S. Public*, pg. 1094
COUNTRY LIVING—The Hearst Corporation; *U.S. Private*, pg. 517
COWLES BUSINESS MEDIA, INC.—Cowles Media Company; *U.S. Private*, pg. 281
COWLES ENTHUSIAST MEDIA, INC.—Cowles Media Company; *U.S. Private*, pg. 281
COWLES HISTORY GROUP, INC.—Cowles Media Company; *U.S. Private*, pg. 281
CRAFTWAYS CORP.—Meredith Corporation; *U.S. Public*, pg. 1094
CRAIN COMMUNICATIONS, INC.; *U.S. Private*, pg. 284
CRAIN'S NEW YORK BUSINESS—Crain Communications, Inc.; *U.S. Private*, pg. 285
CROWN PUBLISHERS, INC.—Advance Publications Inc.; *U.S. Private*, pg. 21
DC COMICS, INC.—Time Warner Inc.; *U.S. Public*, pg. 1614
DMG BUSINESS MEDIA LTD.—Daily Mail & General Trust PLC; *Int'l*, pg. 366
DAI NIPPON PRINTING CO., LTD.; *Int'l*, pg. 363
DAILY RACING FORM, INC.—Primedia Inc.; *U.S. Public*, pg. 1327
DATA COMMUNICATIONS—The McGraw-Hill Companies; *U.S. Public*, pg. 1070
MARCEL DEKKER, INC.; *U.S. Private*, pg. 321
DEPARTURES—American Express Company; *U.S. Public*, pg. 74
DETAILS MAGAZINE—Advance Publications Inc.; *U.S. Private*, pg. 20
DETROIT MONTHLY—Crain Communications, Inc.; *U.S. Private*, pg. 285
DEUTSCHER PRESS VERTRIEB BUCH-HANSA GMBH—Bertelsmann AG; *Int'l*, pg. 190
DIAMOND COMIC DISTRIBUTORS, INC.; *U.S. Private*, pg. 330
DISCOVER—The Walt Disney Company; *U.S. Public*, pg. 513
DISNEY PUBLISHING GROUP—The Walt Disney Company; *U.S. Public*, pg. 511
DIVERSION—The Hearst Corporation; *U.S. Private*, pg. 516
DOW JONES & COMPANY, INC.; *U.S. Public*, pg. 524
E.P. GRAPHICS, INC.; *U.S. Private*, pg. 354
EDITIONS LAMY—Wolters Kluwer N.V.; *Int'l*, pg. 1513
EDITRICE LA STAMPA S.P.A.—Fiat Auto SpA; *Int'l*, pg. 482
EDWARDS BROTHERS, INC.; *U.S. Private*, pg. 365
ELECTRICAL WORLD—The McGraw-Hill Companies; *U.S. Public*, pg. 1071
ELECTRONIC MEDIA—Crain Communications, Inc.; *U.S. Private*, pg. 285
ELECTRONIC PRODUCTS MAGAZINE—The Hearst Corporation; *U.S. Private*, pg. 516
ELLE PUBLISHING, L.P.—Lagardere Groupe; *Int'l*, pg. 795
ELSEVIER BEDRIJFINFORMATIE B.V.—Reed Elsevier plc; *Int'l*, pg. 1099
ELSEVIER BUSINESS INFORMATION—Reed Elsevier plc; *Int'l*, pg. 1099
ELSEVIER NV—Reed Elsevier plc; *Int'l*, pg. 1093
ELSEVIER SCIENCE (INTERNATIONAL)—Reed Elsevier plc; *Int'l*, pg. 1099
ELSEVIER THOMAS FACHVERLAG GMBH—Reed Elsevier plc; *Int'l*, pg. 1100
ELSEVIER TRENDS JOURNALS—Reed Elsevier plc; *Int'l*, pg. 1100
EMAP PLC; *Int'l*, pg. 451
ENDLESS VACATION—Cendant Corporation; *U.S. Public*, pg. 322
ENGINEERING NEWS-RECORD MAGAZINE—The McGraw-Hill Companies; *U.S. Public*, pg. 1070
ESQUIRE—The Hearst Corporation; *U.S. Private*, pg. 517
ESSENCE COMMUNICATIONS INC.; *U.S. Private*, pg. 383
EUROMARKETING—Crain Communications, Inc.; *U.S. Private*, pg. 285
EUROPEAN MAGAZINES LIMITED—IPC Magazines Limited; *Int'l*, pg. 651
EUROPEAN RUBBER JOURNAL—Crain Communications, Inc.; *U.S. Private*, pg. 285
EXPECTING—Bertelsmann AG; *Int'l*, pg. 190
F & W PUBLICATIONS, INC.; *U.S. Private*, pg. 388
FCW PUBLISHING CORP.—International Data Group; *U.S. Private*, pg. 569
FAIRCHILD PUBLICATIONS—The Walt Disney Company; *U.S. Public*, pg. 513
THE FAMILY CIRCLE, INC.—Bertelsmann AG; *Int'l*, pg. 190
FARM JOURNAL INC.; *U.S. Private*, pg. 394
FARM PROGRESS PUBLICATIONS—The Walt Disney Company; *U.S. Public*, pg. 513
FIELD & STREAM—The Times Mirror Company; *U.S. Public*, pg. 1617
FIRST DATABANK—The Hearst Corporation; *U.S. Private*, pg. 515
FISHING TACKLE RETAILER—B.A.S.S., Inc.; *U.S. Private*, pg. 105
FLOOR COVERING WEEKLY—The Hearst Corporation; *U.S. Private*, pg. 516
FLORIDA TREND MAGAZINE—The Times Publishing Co.; *U.S. Private*, pg. 1088
FOCUS MAGAZIN VERLAG—Burda Holding GmbH & Co., KG; *Int'l*, pg. 233
FOOD & WINE—American Express Company; *U.S. Public*, pg. 74
FOODSERVICE DIRECTOR—VNU Verenigde Nederlandse Uitgeversbedrijven B.V.; *Int'l*, pg. 1446
FOR BETTER LIVING, INC.; *U.S. Private*, pg. 417
FORBES, INC.; *U.S. Private*, pg. 417
FORBES MAGAZINE DIVISION—Forbes, Inc.; *U.S. Private*, pg. 417
FORTUNE—Time Warner Inc.; *U.S. Public*, pg. 1613
G.T.C. TRANSCONTINENTAL GROUP LTD.; *Int'l*, pg. 538
GALE RESEARCH INC.—The Thomson Corporation; *U.S. Public*, pg. 1600
GAMEPRO—International Data Group; *U.S. Private*, pg. 569
GANNETT COMPANY, INC.; *U.S. Public*, pg. 698
GARDNER PUBLICATIONS, INC.; *U.S. Private*, pg. 440
GENERAL MEDIA INTERNATIONAL INC.; *U.S. Private*, pg. 444
GENTLEMEN'S QUARTERLY—Advance Publications Inc.; *U.S. Private*, pg. 20
GEYER-MCALLISTER PUBLICATIONS, INC.; *U.S. Private*, pg. 450
GLAMOUR—Advance Publications Inc.; *U.S. Private*, pg. 20
THE GOLDHIRSH GROUP; *U.S. Private*, pg. 461
GOLF FOR WOMEN—Meredith Corporation; *U.S. Public*, pg. 1094
GOLF MAGAZINE—The Times Mirror Company; *U.S. Public*, pg. 1617
GOLF SHOP OPERATIONS—The New York Times Company; *U.S. Public*, pg. 1174
GOLF WORLD—The New York Times Company; *U.S. Public*, pg. 1174
GOOD FOOD MAGAZINE—The News Corporation Limited; *Int'l*, pg. 925
GOOD HOUSEKEEPING—The Hearst Corporation; *U.S. Private*, pg. 517
GORDON PUBLICATIONS, INC.—Reed Elsevier plc; *Int'l*, pg. 1096
GOURMET—Advance Publications Inc.; *U.S. Private*, pg. 20
GOVERNING MAGAZINE—The Times Publishing Co.; *U.S. Private*, pg. 1088
GRAHAM & TROTMAN—Wolters Kluwer N.V.; *Int'l*, pg. 1513
EARL G. GRAVES, LTD.; *U.S. Private*, pg. 471
EARL G. GRAVES PUBLISHING CO., INC.—Earl G. Graves, Ltd.; *U.S. Private*, pg. 471
GROUPE DE LA CITE—Alcatel Alsthom Compagnie Generale D'Electricite; *Int'l*, pg. 53
GROUPE L.S.A.—C.E.P. Communication Group; *Int'l*, pg. 239
GRUNER + JAHR AG & CO.—Bertelsmann AG; *Int'l*, pg. 190
GRUNER + JAHR AG & CO. DRUCK UND VERLAGSHAUS—Bertelsmann AG; *Int'l*, pg. 190
GRUNER + JAHR AG (SCHWEIZ)—Bertelsmann AG; *Int'l*, pg. 190
GRUNER + JAHR USA PUBLISHING, INC.—Bertelsmann AG; *Int'l*, pg. 190
GRUNER + JAHR VERLAGS-GMBH—Bertelsmann AG; *Int'l*, pg. 191
GUESTINFORMANT, INC.—AT&T Corporation; *U.S. Public*, pg. 11
GUIDEPOSTS ASSOCIATES, INC.; *U.S. Private*, pg. 487
HACHETTE FILIPACCHI MAGAZINES INC.—Lagardere Groupe; *Int'l*, pg. 794
HACHETTE FILIPACCHI PRESSE—Lagardere Groupe; *Int'l*, pg. 794
HACHETTE FILIPACCHI USA—Lagardere Groupe; *Int'l*, pg. 794
HANDELSBLATT-DOW JONES GMBH—Georg von Holtzbrinck GmbH; *Int'l*, pg. 1479
HANKOOK ILBO TIME-LIFE LTD.—Time Warner Inc.; *U.S. Public*, pg. 1615
HARCOURT BRACE & COMPANY - ELEMENTARY DIV.—Harcourt General, Inc.; *U.S. Public*, pg. 783
HARCOURT BRACE & COMPANY FARM PUBLICATIONS INC.—Harcourt General, Inc.; *U.S. Public*, pg. 783
HARMON PUBLISHING—United News & Media plc; *Int'l*, pg. 1443
HARPER'S BAZAAR—The Hearst Corporation; *U.S. Private*, pg. 517
HARTE-HANKS SHOPPERS—Harte-Hanks Communications, Inc.; *U.S. Public*, pg. 794
HEALTHCARE GROUP—The Hearst Corporation; *U.S. Private*, pg. 515
HEARST BOOKS/BUSINESS PUBLISHING GROUP—The Hearst Corporation; *U.S. Private*, pg. 515
THE HEARST CORPORATION; *U.S. Private*, pg. 515
HEARST MAGAZINES DIVISION—The Hearst Corporation; *U.S. Private*, pg. 516
HEARST MAGAZINES INTERNATIONAL—The Hearst Corporation; *U.S. Private*, pg. 517
HIGHLIGHTS FOR CHILDREN, INC.; *U.S. Private*, pg. 528
HOLLINGER INC.; *Int'l*, pg. 630
THE HOLLYWOOD REPORTER—VNU Verenigde Nederlandse Uitgeversbedrijven B.V.; *Int'l*, pg. 1446
HOME FASHIONS—The Walt Disney Company; *U.S. Public*, pg. 513
HOME MAGAZINE PUBLISHING CORP.—Lagardere Groupe; *Int'l*, pg. 795
HOSPITALITY DESIGN—VNU Verenigde Nederlandse Uitgeversbedrijven B.V.; *Int'l*, pg. 1446
HOUSE BEAUTIFUL—The Hearst Corporation; *U.S. Private*, pg. 517
HOUSE OF WHITE BIRCHES, INC.; *U.S. Private*, pg. 542
HYPERMEDIA COMMUNICATIONS, INC.; *U.S. Public*, pg. 851
ICA FORLAGET AB—ICA Handlarnas AB; *Int'l*, pg. 643
ID MAGAZINE—VNU Verenigde Nederlandse Uitgeversbedrijven B.V.; *Int'l*, pg. 1446
IPC MAGAZINES LIMITED; *Int'l*, pg. 651
IPSOA S.A.R.L.—Wolters Kluwer N.V.; *Int'l*, pg. 1514
ITEDI S.P.A.—Fiat Auto SpA; *Int'l*, pg. 482
IGAKU-SHOIN MYW LTD.—Waverly, Inc.; *U.S. Public*, pg. 1748
ILLUSTRATED LONDON NEWS—Sea Containers Ltd.; *Int'l*, pg. 1214
INCENTIVE—VNU Verenigde Nederlandse Uitgeversbedrijven B.V.; *Int'l*, pg. 1446
INDUSTRIAL EQUIPMENT NEWS—Thomas Publishing Company; *U.S. Private*, pg. 1082
INFORMATION ET TECHNOLOGIES—C.E.P. Communication Group; *Int'l*, pg. 239
INFOWORLD PUBLISHING, INC.—International Data Group; *U.S. Private*, pg. 569
INSIDE SPORTS, INC.—Century Publishing Company; *U.S. Private*, pg. 226
INSTITUTE FOR SCIENTIFIC INFORMATION—The Thomson Corporation; *U.S. Public*, pg. 1600
INTERAVIA PUBLISHING GROUP—The Thomson Corporation; *U.S. Public*, pg. 1601
INTERIORS—VNU Verenigde Nederlandse Uitgeversbedrijven B.V.; *Int'l*, pg. 1446
INTERNATIONAL DATA GROUP; *U.S. Private*, pg. 569
INTERNATIONAL EQUIPMENT NEWS EUROPE NV—Reed Elsevier plc; *Int'l*, pg. 1099
INTERNATIONAL HORTICULTURE PUBLICATIONS COMPANY—Watt Publishing Co.; *U.S. Private*, pg. 1154
INTERNATIONAL THOMSON BUSINESS PUBLISHING—The Thomson Corporation; *U.S. Public*, pg. 1601
INTERNATIONAL THOMSON PUBLISHING LIMITED—The Thomson Corporation; *U.S. Public*, pg. 1600
INTERTEC PRESENTATIONS—Primedia Inc.; *U.S. Public*, pg. 1328
INTERTEC PUBLISHING—Primedia Inc.; *U.S. Public*, pg. 1327
JANE'S INFORMATION GROUP—The Thomson Corporation; *U.S. Public*, pg. 1601
JOBBER RETAILER—VNU Verenigde Nederlandse Uitgeversbedrijven B.V.; *Int'l*, pg. 1446
JOHNSON PUBLISHING COMPANY, INC.; *U.S. Private*, pg. 591
K-III MEDIA GROUP—Primedia Inc.; *U.S. Public*, pg. 1328
KALMBACH PUBLISHING CO.; *U.S. Private*, pg. 606
KLUWER ACADEMIC PUBLISHERS—Wolters Kluwer N.V.; *Int'l*, pg. 1513
KRAUSE PUBLICATIONS, INC.; *U.S. Private*, pg. 635
L.C.G. MALMBERG BV—VNU Verenigde Nederlandse Uitgeversbedrijven B.V.; *Int'l*, pg. 1445
LADIES' HOME JOURNAL—Meredith Corporation; *U.S. Public*, pg. 1094
LAGARDERE GROUPE NORTH AMERICA—Lagardere Groupe; *Int'l*, pg. 794
THE LANCET LIMITED—Reed Elsevier plc; *Int'l*, pg. 1100
LANDESVERLAGS UND DRUCKGESELLSCHAFT MBH - MECKLENBURG & CO. KG—Burda Holding GmbH & Co., KG; *Int'l*, pg. 233
LANDMARK COMMUNICATIONS, INC.; *U.S. Private*, pg. 647
LAWYERS COOPERATIVE PUBLISHING CO.—The Thomson Corporation; *U.S. Public*, pg. 1602
LEBHAR-FRIEDMAN, INC.; *U.S. Private*, pg. 656
LECTORUM PUBLICATIONS—Scholastic Corporation; *U.S. Public*, pg. 1440
LIFE MAGAZINE—Time Warner Inc.; *U.S. Public*, pg. 1613
LINK HOUSE ADVERTISING PERIODICALS LTD.—United News & Media plc; *Int'l*, pg. 1443
LIPPINCOTT-RAVEN PUBLISHING—Wolters Kluwer N.V.; *Int'l*, pg. 1513
LITTLE BROWN & CO. (CANADA) LTD.—Time Warner Inc.; *U.S. Public*, pg. 1615
LITTLE NICKEL WANT ADS—Lee Enterprises, Incorporated; *U.S. Public*, pg. 983
LOGICAL OPERATIONS—Softbank Corporation; *Int'l*, pg. 1276
LONGEVITY INTERNATIONAL, LTD.—General Media International Inc.; *U.S. Private*, pg. 444
L'OREAL S.A.; *Int'l*, pg. 818
LOS ANGELES MAGAZINE, INC.—The Walt Disney Company; *U.S. Public*, pg. 513
MVT MAGAZIN VERLAG GMBH & CO. KG—Burda Holding GmbH & Co., KG; *Int'l*, pg. 233
MACDONALD COMMUNICATIONS; *U.S. Private*, pg. 691
MACLEAN HUNTER GMBH—Rogers Communications, Inc.; *Int'l*, pg. 1124
MACLEAN HUNTER LIMITED—Rogers Communications, Inc.; *Int'l*, pg. 1124
MACLEAN HUNTER PUBLISHING LTD.—Rogers Communications, Inc.; *Int'l*, pg. 1123
MACLEAN HUNTER S.R.L.—Rogers Communications, Inc.; *Int'l*, pg. 1124
MACUSER—Softbank Corporation; *Int'l*, pg. 1276
MACWORLD—International Data Group; *U.S. Private*, pg. 569
MADEMOISELLE—Advance Publications Inc.; *U.S. Private*, pg. 20
MAGAZINES MACLEAN HUNTER QUEBEC—Rogers Communications, Inc.; *Int'l*, pg. 1123
MANAGER MAGAZIN VERLAGSGESELLSCHAFT MBH—Bertelsmann AG; *Int'l*, pg. 190
MANAGING AUTOMATION—Thomas Publishing Company; *U.S. Private*, pg. 1082
MARKET STATISTICS—VNU Verenigde Nederlandse Uitgeversbedrijven B.V.; *Int'l*, pg. 1446
MARVEL ENTERTAINMENT GROUP; *U.S. Public*, pg. 1052
MCCALL'S MAGAZINE—Bertelsmann AG; *Int'l*, pg. 190
MCGRAW-HILL AVIATION WEEK GROUP—The McGraw-Hill Companies; *U.S. Public*, pg. 1070
THE MCGRAW-HILL COMPANIES; *U.S. Public*, pg. 1069
MCGRAW-HILL HEALTHCARE PUBLICATIONS GROUP—The McGraw-Hill Companies; *U.S. Public*, pg. 1071
MCGRAW-HILL INTERNATIONAL PUBLICATIONS CO. LTD.—The McGraw-Hill Companies; *U.S. Public*, pg. 1072
MCGRAW-HILL PUBLICATIONS SERVICES GROUP—The McGraw-Hill Companies; *U.S. Public*, pg. 1071
MCKNIGHT MEDICAL COMMUNICATIONS COMPANY—The Thomson Corporation; *U.S. Public*, pg. 1601
MCMULLEN/ARGUS PUBLISHERS—Primedia Inc.; *U.S. Public*, pg. 1328
MEDIA-DATEN VERLAGSGESELLSCHAFT—Rogers Communications, Inc.; *Int'l*, pg. 1124
MEDIA GENERAL FINANCIAL SERVICES, INC.—Media General, Inc.; *U.S. Public*, pg. 1078
MEDIA GENERAL, INC.; *U.S. Public*, pg. 1077

MEDIA INTERNATIONAL DATA S.A.—Rogers Communications, Inc.; *Int'l*, pg. 1124
MEDIA SERVICES, INC.—Time Warner Inc.; *U.S. Public*, pg. 1613
MEDIATEX COMMUNICATIONS CORPORATION; *U.S. Private*, pg. 727
MEDICAL DEVICE REGISTER—The Thomson Corporation; *U.S. Public*, pg. 1600
MEDICAL ECONOMICS COMPANY INC.—The Thomson Corporation; *U.S. Public*, pg. 1601
MEN'S JOURNAL—Wenner Media; *U.S. Private*, pg. 1162
MEREDITH CORPORATION; *U.S. Public*, pg. 1094
MEREDITH PUBLISHING GROUP—Meredith Corporation; *U.S. Public*, pg. 1094
MEREDITH PUBLISHING SERVICES—Meredith Corporation; *U.S. Public*, pg. 1094
MERRILL CORPORATION; *U.S. Public*, pg. 1097
METROPOLITAN SUNDAY NEWSPAPERS, INC.; *U.S. Private*, pg. 739
MIDWEST LIVING MAGAZINE—Meredith Corporation; *U.S. Public*, pg. 1094
MILLER ACCOUNTING PUBLICATIONS, INC.—Harcourt General, Inc.; *U.S. Public*, pg. 784
MILLER FREEMAN INC.—United News & Media plc; *Int'l*, pg. 1443
MILLER FREEMAN PLC—United News & Media plc; *Int'l*, pg. 1443
MILLER FREEMAN PTE LTD.—United News & Media plc; *Int'l*, pg. 1443
MISSET—Reed Elsevier plc; *Int'l*, pg. 1099
MODERN HEALTHCARE—Crain Communications, Inc.; *U.S. Private*, pg. 285
MODERN PLASTICS—The McGraw-Hill Companies; *U.S. Public*, pg. 1071
MODERN TIRE DEALER—VNU Verenigde Nederlandse Uitgeversbedrijven B.V.; *Int'l*, pg. 1446
ARNOLDO MONDADORI EDITORE S.P.A.; *Int'l*, pg. 887
MONEY—Time Warner Inc.; *U.S. Public*, pg. 1613
MOODY'S INVESTORS SERVICE LTD.—The Dun & Bradstreet Corporation; *U.S. Public*, pg. 537
MOODY'S JAPAN KK—The Dun & Bradstreet Corporation; *U.S. Public*, pg. 537
MORROW JUNIOR BOOKS—The Hearst Corporation; *U.S. Private*, pg. 515
MOSBY-YEAR BOOK, INC.—The Times Mirror Company; *U.S. Public*, pg. 1616
MOTHER EARTH NEWS—Sussex Publishers, Inc.; *U.S. Private*, pg. 1056
MOTOR BOATING & SAILING—The Hearst Corporation; *U.S. Private*, pg. 517
MOTOR MAGAZINE—The Hearst Corporation; *U.S. Private*, *pg. 516*
MOTOR PUBLICATIONS—The Hearst Corporation; *U.S. Private*, pg. 516
MURDOCH MAGAZINES—The News Corporation Limited; *Int'l*, pg. 925
MUSIC & MEDIA—VNU Verenigde Nederlandse Uitgeversbedrijven B.V.; *Int'l*, pg. 1446
MUSIC CITY NEWS—Gannett Company, Inc.; *U.S. Public*, pg. 701
MUSICIAN MAGAZINE—VNU Verenigde Nederlandse Uitgeversbedrijven B.V.; *Int'l*, pg. 1446
THE NATIONAL ASSOCIATION FOR FEMALE EXECUTIVES, INC.—MacDonald Communications; *U.S. Private*, pg. 691
NATIONAL AUTO RESEARCH—The Hearst Corporation; *U.S. Private*, pg. 516
NATIONAL GEOGRAPHIC SOCIETY; *U.S. Private*, pg. 783
NATIONAL JOURNAL GROUP; *U.S. Private*, pg. 785
NATIONAL LAW PUBLISHING CO.—The Nomura Securities Co., Ltd.; *Int'l*, pg. 956
THE NATIONAL MAGAZINE COMPANY LTD.—The Hearst Corporation; *U.S. Private*, pg. 518
NEPA—C.E.P. Communication Group; *Int'l*, pg. 239
NETWORK WORLD, INC.—International Data Group; *U.S. Private*, pg. 569
NEW WOMAN MAGAZINE—Rodale Press, Inc.; *U.S. Private*, pg. 939
NEW YORK LAW JOURNAL—The Nomura Securities Co., Ltd.; *Int'l*, pg. 956
NEW YORK MAGAZINE—Primedia Inc.; *U.S. Public*, pg. 1328
THE NEW YORK TIMES COMPANY; *U.S. Public*, pg. 1173
THE NEW YORKER MAGAZINE; *U.S. Private*, pg. 795
NEWS AMERICA PUBLISHING INC.—The News Corporation Limited; *Int'l*, pg. 925
THE NEWS CORPORATION LIMITED; *Int'l*, pg. 925
NEWS LIMITED OF AUSTRALIA—The News Corporation Limited; *Int'l*, pg. 925
NEWSWEEK, INC.—The Washington Post Company; *U.S. Public*, pg. 1743
NICKEL ADS—Lee Enterprises, Incorporated; *U.S. Public*, pg. 984
NICKEL NIK—Lee Enterprises, Incorporated; *U.S. Public*, pg. 984
THE NIKKAN KOGYO SHIMBUN, LTD.; *Int'l*, pg. 930
NILS PUBLISHING COMPANY—Wolters Kluwer N.V.; *Int'l*, pg. 1513
NORTH AMERICAN PUBLISHING COMPANY; *U.S. Private*, pg. 803
OAG—Reed Elsevier plc; *Int'l*, pg. 1097
OGDEN PUBLISHING—Ogden Newspapers, Inc.; *U.S. Private*, pg. 812
OMNI PUBLICATIONS INTERNATIONAL LTD.—General Media International Inc.; *U.S. Private*, pg. 444
OUTDOOR LIFE—The Times Mirror Company; *U.S. Public*, pg. 1617
OXMOOR HOUSE, INC.—Time Warner Inc.; *U.S. Public*, pg. 1613
PC COMPUTING—Softbank Corporation; *Int'l*, pg. 1276
PC MAGAZINE—Softbank Corporation; *Int'l*, pg. 1276
PC WORLD—International Data Group; *U.S. Private*, pg. 569
PCI; *U.S. Private*, pg. 826
PAISANO PUBLICATIONS, INC.; *U.S. Private*, pg. 834
PAN EUROPEAN PUBLISHING CO.—Reed Elsevier plc; *Int'l*, pg. 1099
PARADE PUBLICATIONS INC.—Advance Publications Inc.; *U.S. Private*, pg. 20
PARENTING MAGAZINE PARTNERS—Time Warner Inc.; *U.S. Public*, pg. 1614
PARENTS MAGAZINE—Bertelsmann AG; *Int'l*, pg. 191
PATCH COMMUNICATIONS; *U.S. Private*, pg. 842
PATIENT CARE COMMUNICATIONS, INC.—The Thomson Corporation; *U.S. Public*, pg. 1601
PEARSON PLC; *Int'l*, pg. 1025
PENNYPOWER SHOPPING NEWS, INC.—Harte-Hanks Communications, Inc.; *U.S. Public*, pg. 794
PENSIONS & INVESTMENTS—Crain Communications, Inc.; *U.S. Private*, pg. 285
PENTON PUBLISHING, INC.—Pittway Corporation; *U.S. Public*, pg. 1306
PEOPLE—Time Warner Inc.; *U.S. Public*, pg. 1613
PETERSEN PUBLISHING COMPANY, L.L.C.; *U.S. Private*, pg. 856
PHILLIPS PUBLISHING INTERNATIONAL, INC.; *U.S. Private*, pg. 862
PHOTO DESIGN—VNU Verenigde Nederlandse Uitgeversbedrijven B.V.; *Int'l*, pg. 1446
THE PHYSICIAN AND SPORTSMEDICINE—The McGraw-Hill Companies; *U.S. Public*, pg. 1071
PIKE & FISCHER—The Bureau of National Affairs, Inc.; *U.S. Private*, pg. 182
PITTWAY CORPORATION; *U.S. Public*, pg. 1305
PLANTS, SITES & PARKS—VNU Verenigde Nederlandse Uitgeversbedrijven B.V.; *Int'l*, pg. 1446
PLASTICS NEWS—Crain Communications, Inc.; *U.S. Private*, pg. 285
PLASTICS TECHNOLOGY—VNU Verenigde Nederlandse Uitgeversbedrijven B.V.; *Int'l*, pg. 1446
PLAYBOY ENTERPRISES, INC.; *U.S. Public*, pg. 1309
PLAZA Y JANES S.A.—Bertelsmann AG; *Int'l*, pg. 192
PLEASANT COMPANY; *U.S. Private*, pg. 872
POPULAR MECHANICS—The Hearst Corporation; *U.S. Private*, pg. 517
POPULAR SCIENCE—The Times Mirror Company; *U.S. Public*, pg. 1617
POSTGRADUATE MEDICINE—The McGraw-Hill Companies; *U.S. Public*, pg. 1071
POWER—The McGraw-Hill Companies; *U.S. Public*, pg. 1071
PRESIDENT INC.—Time Warner Inc.; *U.S. Public*, pg. 1615
PRIMEDIA INC.; *U.S. Public*, pg. 1327
PRIMEDIA INC.—Primedia Inc.; *U.S. Public*, pg. 1328
PRIMEDIA INFORMATIN GROUP—Primedia Inc.; *U.S. Public*, pg. 1328
PRIMEDIA INFORMATION INC.—Primedia Inc.; *U.S. Public*, *pg. 1328*
PRISMA PRESSE & CIE—Bertelsmann AG; *Int'l*, pg. 191
PRISMA-VERLAG GMBH & CO. KG—Bertelsmann AG; *Int'l*, pg. 190
PROGNOS AG—Georg von Holtzbrinck GmbH; *Int'l*, pg. 1480
PROGRESSIVE FARMER, INC.—Time Warner Inc.; *U.S. Public*, pg. 1613
PSYCHOLOGY TODAY—Sussex Publishers, Inc.; *U.S. Private*, pg. 1056
PULSE MAGAZINE—MTS, Inc.; *U.S. Private*, pg. 688
PUTMAN PUBLISHING CO.; *U.S. Private*, pg. 896
QUEBECOR PRINTING DICKSON INC.—Quebecor Inc.; *Int'l*, pg. 1078
QUEBECOR PRINTING ST. PAUL INC.—Quebecor Inc.; *Int'l*, pg. 1078
QUILLET S.A.—Lagardere Groupe; *Int'l*, pg. 793
RCR PUBLICATIONS—Crain Communications, Inc.; *U.S. Private*, pg. 285
R.C.S. EDITORI S.P.A.; *Int'l*, pg. 1078
RD MANUFACTURING CORPORATION—The Reader's Digest Association, Inc.; *U.S. Public*, pg. 1367
RD PUBLICATIONS, INC.—The Reader's Digest Association, Inc.; *U.S. Public*, pg. 1367
RAE-PRINT PRINTING & PACKAGING—McRae Industries, Inc.; *U.S. Public*, pg. 1074
REACT MAGAZINE—Advance Publications Inc.; *U.S. Private*, pg. 20
THE READER'S DIGEST ASSOCIATION, INC.; *U.S. Public*, pg. 1367
REDBOOK—The Hearst Corporation; *U.S. Private*, pg. 517
REED BUSINESS INFORMATION—Reed Elsevier plc; *Int'l*, *pg. 1094*
REED ELSEVIER BUSINESS INFORMATION—Reed Elsevier plc; *Int'l*, pg. 1095
REED ELSEVIER BUSINESS INFORMATION-DES PLAINES—Reed Elsevier plc; *Int'l*, pg. 1095
REED ELSEVIER BUSINESS INFORMATION-NEW YORK—Reed Elsevier plc; *Int'l*, pg. 1095
REED ELSEVIER NEDERLAND BV—Reed Elsevier plc; *Int'l*, pg. 1100
REED ELSEVIER PLC; *Int'l*, pg. 1093
REED INTERNATIONAL P.L.C.—Reed Elsevier plc; *Int'l*, pg. 1093
REED TRAVEL GROUP—Reed Elsevier plc; *Int'l*, pg. 1097
REISREVUE AND MEDICAL JOURNALS—Reed Elsevier plc; *Int'l*, pg. 1099
REQUEST—Musicland Group Inc.; *U.S. Public*, pg. 1142
RESEARCH INSTITUTE OF AMERICA—The Thomson Corporation; *U.S. Public*, pg. 1602
RESTAURANT BUSINESS—VNU Verenigde Nederlandse Uitgeversbedrijven B.V.; *Int'l*, pg. 1446
RETIREMENT ADVISORS, INC.—The Hearst Corporation; *U.S. Private*, pg. 516
REVIEW PUBLISHING COMPANY LTD.—Dow Jones & Company, Inc.; *U.S. Public*, pg. 525
RINGIER AG; *Int'l*, pg. 1118
ROAD AND TRACK—Lagardere Groupe; *Int'l*, pg. 795
RODALE PRESS, INC.; *U.S. Private*, pg. 939
A.I. ROOT COMPANY; *U.S. Private*, pg. 944
RUBBER & PLASTICS NEWS—Crain Communications, Inc.; *U.S. Private*, pg. 285
SKI—The Times Mirror Company; *U.S. Public*, pg. 1617
SAILING WORLD—The New York Times Company; *U.S. Public*, pg. 1174
ST. CROIX PRESS, INC.; *U.S. Private*, pg. 960
SALES AND MARKETING MANAGEMENT—VNU Verenigde Nederlandse Uitgeversbedrijven B.V.; *Int'l*, pg. 1446
SALT WATER SPORTSMAN—The Times Mirror Company; *U.S. Public*, pg. 1617
THE SATURDAY EVENING POST SOCIETY—Benjamin Franklin Literary & Medical Society, Inc.; *U.S. Private*, pg. 133
SATURDAY NIGHT MAGAZINE LIMITED—Hollinger Inc.; *Int'l*, pg. 631
W.B. SAUNDERS COMPANY—Harcourt General, Inc.; *U.S. Public*, pg. 784
K.G. SAUR—Reed Elsevier plc; *Int'l*, pg. 1099
SCHOLASTIC CORPORATION; *U.S. Public*, pg. 1440
SCHOLASTIC INC. NATIONAL DISTRIBUTION CENTER—Scholastic Corporation; *U.S. Public*, pg. 1440
SCHOLASTIC PUBLICATIONS LTD.—Scholastic Corporation; *U.S. Public*, pg. 1441
SCIENTIFIC AMERICAN, INC.—Georg von Holtzbrinck GmbH; *Int'l*, pg. 1479
SCIENTIFIC AMERICAN MAGAZINE—Georg von Holtzbrinck GmbH; *Int'l*, pg. 1479
THE E.W. SCRIPPS COMPANY; *U.S. Public*, pg. 1447
SELECTION DU READER'S DIGEST S.A.—The Reader's Digest Association, Inc.; *U.S. Public*, pg. 1368
SELF—Advance Publications Inc.; *U.S. Private*, pg. 20
SEVENTEEN MAGAZINE—Primedia Inc.; *U.S. Public*, pg. 1328
SHEPARD'S—Reed Elsevier plc; *Int'l*, pg. 1095
SHEPARD'S—The Times Mirror Company; *U.S. Public*, pg. 1616
THE SHERIDAN GROUP; *U.S. Private*, pg. 993
THE SHERIDAN PRESS, INC.—The Sheridan Group; *U.S. Private*, pg. 993
SIMMONS-BOARDMAN PUBLISHING CORP.; *U.S. Private*, *pg. 1000*
SKIING—The Times Mirror Company; *U.S. Public*, pg. 1617
SNOW COUNTRY—The New York Times Company; *U.S. Public*, pg. 1174
SOAP OPERA DIGEST—Primedia Inc.; *U.S. Public*, pg. 1328
SOAP OPERA WEEKLY—Primedia Inc.; *U.S. Public*, pg. 1328
STE. SOCIDOC—C.E.P. Communication Group; *Int'l*, pg. 239
SOUTHAM INC.—Hollinger Inc.; *Int'l*, pg. 631
SOUTHERN ACCENTS, INC.—Time Warner Inc.; *U.S. Public*, pg. 1613
SOUTHERN LIVING, INC.—Time Warner Inc.; *U.S. Public*, pg. 1613
SOUTHERN OUTDOORS MAGAZINE—B.A.S.S., Inc.; *U.S. Private*, pg. 106
SOUTHERN PROGRESS CORPORATION—Time Warner Inc.; *U.S. Public*, pg. 1612
SOUTHWESTERN/GREAT AMERICAN INC.; *U.S. Private*, pg. 1018
SPANGLER INC.; *U.S. Private*, pg. 1020
SPECIAL EDITIONS, LTD.—Playboy Enterprises, Inc.; *U.S. Public*, pg. 1310
SPEKTRUM DER WISSENSCHAFT VERLAGSGESELLSCHAFT MBH—Georg von Holtzbrinck GmbH; *Int'l*, pg. 1478
SPIEGEL-VERLAG RUDOLF AUGSTEIN GMBH & CO.—Bertelsmann AG; *Int'l*, pg. 190
THE SPORTING NEWS PUBLISHING COMPANY—The Times Mirror Company; *U.S. Public*, pg. 1616
SPORTS AFIELD—The Hearst Corporation; *U.S. Private*, pg. 517
SPORTS ILLUSTRATED—Time Warner Inc.; *U.S. Public*, pg. 1613
SPORTS/LEISURE MAGAZINES GROUP—The New York Times Company; *U.S. Public*, pg. 1174
SPORTSTYLE—The Walt Disney Company; *U.S. Public*, pg. 513
SPRINGER-VERLAG GMBH & CO. KG; *Int'l*, pg. 1291
SPRINGER-VERLAG NEW YORK INC.—Springer-Verlag GmbH & Co. KG; *Int'l*, pg. 1291
SPRINGHOUSE CORPORATION—Reed Elsevier plc; *Int'l*, pg. 1100
STANDARD PUBLISHING—Standex International Corporation; *U.S. Public*, pg. 1506
SUCCESSFUL FARMING MAGAZINE—Meredith Corporation; *U.S. Public*, pg. 1094
SUCCESSFUL MEETINGS—VNU Verenigde Nederlandse Uitgeversbedrijven B.V.; *Int'l*, pg. 1446
SURFER PUBLICATIONS, INC.—For Better Living, Inc.; *U.S. Private*, pg. 417
SUSSEX PUBLISHERS, INC.; *U.S. Private*, pg. 1056
TSR, INC.—Wizards of the Coast; *U.S. Private*, pg. 1185
TV GUIDE MAGAZINE—The News Corporation Limited; *Int'l*, pg. 925
TV HOST INC.; *U.S. Private*, pg. 1066
TABAPRESS, S.A.—Tabacalera, S.A.; *Int'l*, pg. 1346
TAX MANAGEMENT, INC.—The Bureau of National Affairs, Inc.; *U.S. Private*, pg. 182
TELEMEDIA INC.; *Int'l*, pg. 1373
TENNIS—The New York Times Company; *U.S. Public*, pg. 1174
TENNIS BUYER'S GUIDE—The New York Times Company; *U.S. Public*, pg. 1174
TEXAS MONTHLY, INC.—Mediatex Communications Corporation; *U.S. Private*, pg. 727
THOMAS PUBLISHING COMPANY; *U.S. Private*, pg. 1082
THOMAS REGISTER—Thomas Publishing Company; *U.S. Private*, pg. 1082
THOMSON AUSTRALIAN HOLDINGS PTY. LTD.—The Thomson Corporation; *U.S. Public*, pg. 1601

THE THOMSON CORPORATION PLC—The Thomson Corporation; U.S. Public, pg. 1601
THE THOMSON CORPORATION; U.S. Public, pg. 1599
THOMSON HEALTHCARE COMMUNICATIONS—The Thomson Corporation; U.S. Public, pg. 1602
THOMSON INTERNATIONAL HOLDINGS LIMITED—The Thomson Corporation; U.S. Public, pg. 1600
THOMSON PROFESSIONAL PUBLISHING—The Thomson Corporation; U.S. Public, pg. 1601
THOMSON U.S. INC.—The Thomson Corporation; U.S. Public, pg. 1601
D.W. THORPE-AUSTRALIA—Reed Elsevier plc; Int'l, pg. 1095
AB TIDNINGEN VI—KF/Konsum Coop Group; Int'l, pg. 718
TIME—Time Warner Inc.; U.S. Public, pg. 1613
TIME CANADA LTD.—Time Warner Inc.; U.S. Public, pg. 1615
TIME INC.—Time Warner Inc.; U.S. Public, pg. 1612
TIME INC. HEALTH—Time Warner Inc.; U.S. Public, pg. 1613
TIME-LIFE BOOKS B.V.—Time Warner Inc.; U.S. Public, pg. 1615
TIME-LIFE INTERNATIONAL B.V.—Time Warner Inc.; U.S. Public, pg. 1615
TIME PUBLISHING VENTURES, INC.—Time Warner Inc.; U.S. Public, pg. 1613
TIME WARNER INC.; U.S. Public, pg. 1610
TIME WARNER PUBLISHING INC.—Time Warner Inc.; U.S. Public, pg. 1614
TIME WOMEN'S PUBLICATIONS INC.—Time Warner Inc.; U.S. Public, pg. 1614
THE TIMES MIRROR COMPANY; U.S. Public, pg. 1615
TIMES MIRROR MAGAZINES, INC.—The Times Mirror Company; U.S. Public, pg. 1616
TIMESFAX—The New York Times Company; U.S. Public, pg. 1174
TIRE BUSINESS—Crain Communications, Inc.; U.S. Private, pg. 285
TODAY'S HOMEOWNER—The Times Mirror Company; U.S. Public, pg. 1617
THE TOPPS COMPANY, INC.; U.S. Public, pg. 1621
TOWN & COUNTRY—The Hearst Corporation; U.S. Private, pg. 517
TRADITIONAL HOME—Meredith Corporation; U.S. Public, pg. 1094
TRAFFIC WORLD—Pearson plc; Int'l, pg. 1026
TRANSWORLD (AUSTRALIA) PTY. LTD.—Bertelsmann AG; Int'l, pg. 191
TRANSWORLD PUBLISHERS LTD.—Bertelsmann AG; Int'l, pg. 191
TRANSWORLD PUBLISHERS (NZ) LTD.—Bertelsmann AG; Int'l, pg. 191
TRAVEL & LEISURE—American Express Company; U.S. Public, pg. 74
TRIBUNE COMPANY; U.S. Public, pg. 1635
TUFF STUFF PUBLICATIONS, INC.—Cadmus Communications Corporation; U.S. Public, pg. 291
TYNDALE HOUSE PUBLISHERS, INC.; U.S. Private, pg. 1112
UNITED ADVERTISING PUBLICATIONS PLC—United News & Media plc; Int'l, pg. 1443
UNITED NEWS & MEDIA PLC; Int'l, pg. 1443
U.S. NEWS & WORLD REPORT; U.S. Private, pg. 1125
USA WEEKEND—Gannett Company, Inc.; U.S. Public, pg. 701
URBAN & VOGEL GMBH—Waverly, Inc.; U.S. Public, pg. 1748
URETHANES TECHNOLOGY—Crain Communications, Inc.; U.S. Private, pg. 285
US MAGAZINE—Wenner Media; U.S. Private, pg. 1162
GROUPE USINE NOUVELLE—C.E.P. Communication Group; Int'l, pg. 239
VDI-VERLAG GMBH—Georg von Holtzbrinck GmbH; Int'l, pg. 1479
VNU TIJDSCHRIFTENGROEP NEDERLAND BV—VNU Verenigde Nederlandse Uitgeversbedrijven B.V.; Int'l, pg. 1445
VNU VERENIGDE NEDERLANDSE UITGEVERSBEDRIJVEN B.V.; Int'l, pg. 1445
VANCE PUBLISHING CORPORATION; U.S. Private, pg. 1133
VANITY FAIR—Advance Publications Inc.; U.S. Private, pg. 20
VEGETARIAN TIMES—Cowles Media Company; U.S. Private, pg. 281
VERLAG KREMAYR UND SCHERIAU—Bertelsmann AG; Int'l, pg. 192
VERLAGSGRUPPE HANDELSBLATT GMBH—Georg von Holtzbrinck GmbH; Int'l, pg. 1479
VERLEGERDIENST MUNCHEN—Waverly, Inc.; U.S. Public, pg. 1748
VETERINARY MEDICINE PUBLISHING CO., INC.—The Thomson Corporation; U.S. Public, pg. 1600
VICTORIA—The Hearst Corporation; U.S. Private, pg. 517
VOGUE MAGAZINE—Advance Publications Inc.; U.S. Private, pg. 20
WM WIRTSCHAFTS-MEDIEN AG—Georg von Holtzbrinck GmbH; Int'l, pg. 1480
WWT PARTNERSHIP—Time Warner Inc.; U.S. Public, pg. 1614
WARNER COMMUNICATIONS INC.—Time Warner Inc.; U.S. Public, pg. 1611
WATT PUBLISHING CO.; U.S. Private, pg. 1154
WEEKLY READER CORP.—Primedia Inc.; U.S. Public, pg. 1328
WEIDER PUBLICATIONS, INC.; U.S. Private, pg. 1159
WEIGHT WATCHERS INTERNATIONAL, INC.—H.J. Heinz Company; U.S. Public, pg. 806
WEIGHT WATCHERS MAGAZINE—Time Warner Inc.; U.S. Public, pg. 1612
WENNER MEDIA; U.S. Private, pg. 1162
WHITTLE COMMUNICATIONS L.P.—Time Warner Inc.; U.S. Public, pg. 1614
WILEY EUROPE LIMITED—John Wiley & Sons, Inc.; U.S. Public, pg. 1768
JOHN WILEY & SONS, INC.; U.S. Public, pg. 1768
WILLIAMS & WILKINS ASIA PACIFIC LTD.—Waverly, Inc.; U.S. Public, pg. 1748
WIRTSCHAFTSWOCHE ZEITSCHRIFTEN-VERLAGSGESELLSCHAFT M.B.H. & CO. KG—Georg von Holtzbrinck GmbH; Int'l, pg. 1479
WIZARDS OF THE COAST; U.S. Private, pg. 1185
WOLTERS KLUWER ACADEMIC PUBLISHERS—Wolters Kluwer N.V.; Int'l, pg. 1512
WOLTERS KLUWER BELGIUM—Wolters Kluwer N.V.; Int'l, pg. 1513
WOLTERS KLUWER BUSINESS PUBLISHING—Wolters Kluwer N.V.; Int'l, pg. 1513
WOLTERS KLUWER EDUCATIONAL ACTIVITIES—Wolters Kluwer N.V.; Int'l, pg. 1513
WOLTERS KLUWER FRANCE—Wolters Kluwer N.V.; Int'l, pg. 1513
WOLTERS KLUWER GERMANY—Wolters Kluwer N.V.; Int'l, pg. 1513
WOLTERS KLUWER LAW AND TAXATION—Wolters Kluwer N.V.; Int'l, pg. 1513
WOLTERS KLUWER SPAIN—Wolters Kluwer N.V.; Int'l, pg. 1514
WOLTERS KLUWER SWEDEN—Wolters Kluwer N.V.; Int'l, pg. 1514
WOLTERS KLUWER TRADE PUBLISHING—Wolters Kluwer N.V.; Int'l, pg. 1513
WOLTERS KLUWER U.K.—Wolters Kluwer N.V.; Int'l, pg. 1514
WOMAN'S DAY—Lagardere Groupe; Int'l, pg. 795
WORLD PUBLISHING COMPANY—Century Publishing Company; U.S. Private, pg. 226
YACHTING—The Times Mirror Company; U.S. Public, pg. 1617
YANKEE PUBLISHING INCORPORATED; U.S. Private, pg. 1195
ZIFF-DAVIS BUSINESS MEDIA GROUP—Softbank Corporation; Int'l, pg. 1276
ZIFF-DAVIS GERMANY—Softbank Corporation; Int'l, pg. 1276
ZIFF-DAVIS PUBLISHING COMPANY—Softbank Corporation; Int'l, pg. 1276

2731 — BOOKS: PUBLISHING, OR PUBLISHING & PRINTING

ABINGDON PRESS—The United Methodist Publishing House; U.S. Private, pg. 1123
ABRAMS & CO. PUBLISHING INC.; U.S. Private, pg. 10
ACADEMIC PRESS, INC.—Harcourt General, Inc.; U.S. Public, pg. 783
ACADEMIC PRESS INTERNATIONAL CORP.—Harcourt General, Inc.; U.S. Public, pg. 783
ADDISON-WESLEY HIGHER EDUCATION—Pearson plc; Int'l, pg. 1026
ADDISON-WESLEY LONGMAN—Pearson plc; Int'l, pg. 1026
ADDISON-WESLEY LONGMAN, INC.—Pearson plc; Int'l, pg. 1026
ADDISON-WESLEY PUBLISHERS JAPAN LTD.—Pearson plc; Int'l, pg. 1027
ADDISON-WESLEY PUBLISHERS LTD.—Pearson plc; Int'l, pg. 1027
ADDISON-WESLEY PUBLISHERS PTY. LTD.—Pearson plc; Int'l, pg. 1027
ADVANCE PUBLICATIONS INC.; U.S. Private, pg. 18
ALBRECHT KNAUS VERLAG—Bertelsmann AG; Int'l, pg. 190
ALHAMBRA LONGMAN S.A.—Pearson plc; Int'l, pg. 1025
ALLYN & BACON—National Amusements, Inc.; U.S. Private, pg. 778
AMERICAN ARBITRATION ASSOCIATION; U.S. Private, pg. 50
AMERICAN BIBLE SOCIETY; U.S. Private, pg. 51
AMERICAN DEMOGRAPHICS, INC.—Cowles Media Company; U.S. Private, pg. 281
AMERICAN KENNEL CLUB, INC.; U.S. Private, pg. 58
AMERICAN LIBRARY ASSOCIATION; U.S. Private, pg. 58
AMERICAN MATHEMATICAL SOCIETY, INC.; U.S. Private, pg. 59
AMERICAN TECHNICAL PUBLISHERS, INC.; U.S. Private, pg. 63
AMSCO SCHOOL PUBLICATIONS, INC.; U.S. Private, pg. 67
AMWAY CORPORATION; U.S. Private, pg. 69
APPLETON & LANGE—National Amusements, Inc.; U.S. Private, pg. 778
ASHTON/SCHOLASTIC PTY. LTD.—Scholastic Corporation; U.S. Public, pg. 1440
ASPEN PUBLISHERS, INC.—Wolters Kluwer N.V.; Int'l, pg. 1513
ASSOCIATED DIRECTORY SERVICES—SBC Communications Inc.; U.S. Public, pg. 1415
AUTOMOTIVE NEWS—Crain Communications, Inc.; U.S. Private, pg. 284
AVON BOOKS—The Hearst Corporation; U.S. Private, pg. 515
AXEL SPRINGER VERLAG AG; Int'l, pg. 102
BNA INTERNATIONAL INC.—The Bureau of National Affairs, Inc.; U.S. Private, pg. 182
BNA PLUS—The Bureau of National Affairs, Inc.; U.S. Private, pg. 182
BALLANTINE BOOKS—Advance Publications Inc.; U.S. Private, pg. 21
BALLINGER PUBLISHING CO.—The News Corporation Limited; Int'l, pg. 927
BARANSKI PUBLISHING COMPANY—Barancorp; U.S. Private, pg. 115
BASIC BOOKS, INC.—The News Corporation Limited; Int'l, pg. 927
BEECH TREE BOOKS—The Hearst Corporation; U.S. Private, pg. 515
BEGINNING READERS' PROGRAM—Lagardere Groupe; Int'l, pg. 794
BELL ATLANTIC YELLOW PAGES—Bell Atlantic Corporation; U.S. Public, pg. 203
MATTHEW BENDER & COMPANY, INCORPORATED—The Times Mirror Company; U.S. Public, pg. 1616
THE BENJAMIN/CUMMINGS PUBLISHING COMPANY—Pearson plc; Int'l, pg. 1026
JOHN BENJAMINS BV; Int'l, pg. 187
JOHN BENJAMINS NORTH AMERICA INC—John Benjamins BV; Int'l, pg. 187
BERKLEY PUBLISHING CORP.—Pearson plc; Int'l, pg. 1027
BERKSHIRE HATHAWAY INC.; U.S. Public, pg. 217
BERLITZ PUBLISHING COMPANY INC.—Berlitz International, Inc.; U.S. Public, pg. 221
BERTELSMANN AG; Int'l, pg. 189
BERTELSMANN INC.—Bertelsmann AG; Int'l, pg. 191
BERTELSMANN LEXIKOTHEK VERLAG GMBH—Bertelsmann AG; Int'l, pg. 189
BERTELSMANN PRINTING & MANUFACTURING CORP.—Bertelsmann AG; Int'l, pg. 191
CHANNING L. BETE CO., INC.; U.S. Private, pg. 140
BETRIEBSWINTSCHAFT LICHER VERLAG DR. TH. GABLER GMBH—Bertelsmann AG; Int'l, pg. 189
BLACKWELL PUBLISHERS, INC.—B.H. Blackwell Ltd.; Int'l, pg. 197
BLACKWELL PUBLISHERS LTD.—B.H. Blackwell Ltd.; Int'l, pg. 197
BLACKWELL SCIENTIFIC PUBLICATIONS (AUSTRALIA) PTY. LTD.—B.H. Blackwell Ltd.; Int'l, pg. 197
BLANVALET VERLAG GMBH—Bertelsmann AG; Int'l, pg. 190
BOOKS FOR PROFESSIONALS, INC.—Harcourt General, Inc.; U.S. Public, pg. 783
BOUNTY BOOKS—Reed Elsevier plc; Int'l, pg. 1093
BRAUN-BRUMFIELD, INC.—The Sheridan Group; U.S. Private, pg. 993
BROOKS/COLE PUBLISHING CO.—The Thomson Corporation; U.S. Public, pg. 1600
THE BUREAU OF NATIONAL AFFAIRS, INC.; U.S. Private, pg. 181
BUTTERWORTH & CO. PUBLISHERS LTD.—Reed Elsevier plc; Int'l, pg. 1095
BUTTERWORTH-HEINEMANN LIMITED—Reed Elsevier plc; Int'l, pg. 1094
BUTTERWORTHS AUSTRALIA—Reed Elsevier plc; Int'l, pg. 1095
BUTTERWORTHS BRITISH AND IRISH LEGAL—Reed Elsevier plc; Int'l, pg. 1095
BUTTERWORTHS CANADA—Reed Elsevier plc; Int'l, pg. 1095
BUTTERWORTHS NEW ZEALAND—Reed Elsevier plc; Int'l, pg. 1095
CCH AUSTRALIA LIMITED—Wolters Kluwer N.V.; Int'l, pg. 1513
CCH CANADIAN LTD.—Wolters Kluwer N.V.; Int'l, pg. 1513
CCH EDITIONS LIMITED—Wolters Kluwer N.V.; Int'l, pg. 1514
CCH INCORPORATED—Wolters Kluwer N.V.; Int'l, pg. 1513
C.E.P. COMMUNICATION GROUP; Int'l, pg. 239
THE CAXTON PRINTERS LTD.; U.S. Private, pg. 220
CHILDRENS PRESS INC.—Lagardere Groupe; Int'l, pg. 794
CHURCHILL PPS-KK—Pearson plc; Int'l, pg. 1025
CINEBOOKS, INC.—The News Corporation Limited; Int'l, pg. 925
CLARION BOOKS—Houghton Mifflin Company; U.S. Public, pg. 841
COMMUNICATIONS INTERNATIONAL (NY); U.S. Private, pg. 259
COMPUTER SCIENCE PRESS, INC.—Georg von Holtzbrinck GmbH; Int'l, pg. 1479
CONGRESSIONAL QUARTERLY—The Times Publishing Co.; U.S. Private, pg. 1088
CONRAN OCTOPUS LIMITED—Reed Elsevier plc; Int'l, pg. 1093
COOK COMMUNICATION MINISTRIES; U.S. Private, pg. 272
CORON VERLAG MONIKA SCHOELLER & CO.—Georg von Holtzbrinck GmbH; Int'l, pg. 1479
COURIER CORPORATION; U.S. Public, pg. 453
COURIER INTERNATIONAL, LTD.—Courier Corporation; U.S. Public, pg. 453
COURIER WESTFORD, INC.—Courier Corporation; U.S. Public, pg. 453
COWARD-MCCANN, INC.—Pearson plc; Int'l, pg. 1027
THE CREATIVE SERVICES INC.—Proudfoot plc; Int'l, pg. 1072
CROWN PUBLISHERS, INC.—Advance Publications Inc.; U.S. Private, pg. 21
DK PUBLISHING—Dorling Kindersley Holdings plc; Int'l, pg. 417
DA CAPO PRESS, INC.—Plenum Publishing Corporation; U.S. Public, pg. 1311
DAI NIPPON PRINTING CO. (HONG KONG) LTD.—Dai Nippon Printing Co., Ltd.; Int'l, pg. 363
P.T. DAI NIPPON PRINTING INDONESIA—Dai Nippon Printing Co., Ltd.; Int'l, pg. 363
THE DARTNELL CORPORATION; U.S. Private, pg. 312
MARCEL DEKKER, INC.; U.S. Private, pg. 321
DELL PUBLISHING—Bertelsmann AG; Int'l, pg. 191
DELMAR PUBLISHERS INC.—The Thomson Corporation; U.S. Public, pg. 1600
DELTA EDUCATION, INC.—Torstar Corporation; Int'l, pg. 1402
DESERET BOOK CO.—Deseret Management Corporation; U.S. Private, pg. 327
DORLING KINDERSLEY HOLDINGS PLC; Int'l, pg. 416
DORLING KINDERSLEY LTD.—Dorling Kindersley Holdings plc; Int'l, pg. 417

DOUBLEDAY AUSTRALIA PTY. LTD.—Bertelsmann AG; *Int'l*, pg. 192
DOUBLEDAY NEW ZEALAND LTD.—Bertelsmann AG; *Int'l*, *pg. 192*
DOUBLEDAY PUBLISHING COMPANY—Bertelsmann AG; *Int'l*, pg. 191
DOW JONES PUBLISHING COMPANY (EUROPE) INC.—Dow Jones & Company, Inc.; *U.S. Public*, pg. 525
DROEMERSCHE VERLAGSANSTALT TH. KNAUR NACHF. GMBH & CO.—Georg von Holtzbrinck GmbH; *Int'l*, pg. 1478
THE DRYDEN PRESS, A DIVISION OF HOLT, RINEHART AND WINSTON COLLEGE DIVISION—Harcourt General, Inc.; *U.S. Public*, pg. 783
E.D.I.C.E.F.—Lagardere Groupe; *Int'l*, pg. 792
EMC CORPORATION; *U.S. Public*, pg. 545
E.P. GRAPHICS, INC.; *U.S. Private*, pg. 354
EDITIONS BORDAS—C.E.P. Communication Group; *Int'l*, pg. 239
EDITIONS DU JURIS-CLASSEUR—Reed Elsevier plc; *Int'l*, pg. 1095
EDITIONS DU MONITEUR—C.E.P. Communication Group; *Int'l*, pg. 239
EDITIONS EDOUARD PRIVAT SA—C.E.P. Communication Group; *Int'l*, pg. 239
EDITIONS FRANCAISES INC.—C.E.P. Communication Group; *Int'l*, pg. 240
EDITIONS GARNIER—C.E.P. Communication Group; *Int'l*, pg. 239
EDITIONS GRASSET-FASQUELLE—Lagardere Groupe; *Int'l*, pg. 792
EDITIONS JEAN-CLAUDE LATTES—Lagardere Groupe; *Int'l*, pg. 794
EDITIONS SCIENTIFIQUES ET MEDICALES ELSEVIER—Reed Elsevier plc; *Int'l*, pg. 1099
EDITIONS WILSON & LAFLEUR, MARTEL LTEE—Quebecor Inc.; *Int'l*, pg. 1076
EDITORA CAMPUS LTDA.—Reed Elsevier plc; *Int'l*, pg. 1100
EDITORIAL ALHAMBRA MEXICANA S.A. DE C.V.—Pearson plc; *Int'l*, pg. 1025
EDITORIAL CARIBE INC.—Thomas Nelson Inc.; *U.S. Public*, pg. 1168
EDITORIAL DIANA, S.A. DE C.V.—Corporacion MAPFRE, Compania Internacional de Reaseguros, S.A.; *Int'l*, pg. 334
EDITORIAL PLANETA - DEAGOSTINI, S.A.; *Int'l*, pg. 433
EDITRICE LA STAMPA S.P.A.—Fiat Auto SpA; *Int'l*, pg. 482
THE EDUCATION PUBLISHING GROUP—Pearson plc; *Int'l*, pg. 1026
EDWARDS BROTHERS, INC.; *U.S. Private*, pg. 365
ELSEVIER ELECTRONIC PUBLISHING SERVICES—Reed Elsevier plc; *Int'l*, pg. 1100
ELSEVIER NV—Reed Elsevier plc; *Int'l*, pg. 1093
ELSEVIER SCIENCE (INTERNATIONAL)—Reed Elsevier plc; *Int'l*, pg. 1099
ELSEVIER SCIENCE (THE NETHERLANDS)—Reed Elsevier plc; *Int'l*, pg. 1099
ENCYCLOPAEDIA BRITANNICA DIRECT, INC.—Encyclopaedia Britannica, Inc.; *U.S. Private*, pg. 375
ENCYCLOPAEDIA BRITANNICA EDUCATIONAL CORPORATION—Encyclopaedia Britannica, Inc.; *U.S. Private*, pg. 375
ENCYCLOPAEDIA BRITANNICA, INC.; *U.S. Private*, pg. 375
EVERYDAY LEARNING/CREATIVE PUBLICATIONS GROUP—Tribune Company; *U.S. Public*, pg. 1635
EXCERPTA MEDICA INC.—Reed Elsevier plc; *Int'l*, pg. 1100
EXCERPTA MEDICA MEDICAL COMMUNICATIONS BV—Reed Elsevier plc; *Int'l*, pg. 1099
F & W PUBLICATIONS, INC.; *U.S. Private*, pg. 388
FALMER PRESS LTD.—Taylor & Francis Group Ltd.; *Int'l*, pg. 1358
FARRAR, STRAUS & GIROUX, INC.—Georg von Holtzbrinck GmbH; *Int'l*, pg. 1479
FAWCETT BOOKS—Advance Publications Inc.; *U.S. Private*, pg. 21
FERGUSON PUBLISHING COMPANY; *U.S. Private*, pg. 401
FIRESIDE BOOKS—National Amusements, Inc.; *U.S. Private*, pg. 777
S. FISCHER VERLAG GMBH—Georg von Holtzbrinck GmbH; *Int'l*, pg. 1478
FISCHER TASCHENBUCH VERLAG GMBH—Georg von Holtzbrinck GmbH; *Int'l*, pg. 1478
FODOR'S TRAVEL PUBLICATIONS, INC.—Advance Publications Inc.; *U.S. Private*, pg. 21
FONDO EDUCATIVO INTERAMERICANO—Pearson plc; *Int'l*, pg. 1027
W.H. FREEMAN & CO.—Georg von Holtzbrinck GmbH; *Int'l*, pg. 1479
GANNETT NEW MEDIA—Gannett Company, Inc.; *U.S. Public*, pg. 699
GARDNER PUBLICATIONS, INC.; *U.S. Private*, pg. 440
GENERAL MEDIA INTERNATIONAL INC.; *U.S. Private*, pg. 444
THE GENERAL PUBLISHING GROUP—Pearson plc; *Int'l*, pg. 1026
GEOCENTER VERLAGSVERTRIEB GMBH—Bertelsmann AG; *Int'l*, pg. 190
GEOGRAPHIA LTD.—The News Corporation Limited; *Int'l*, pg. 927
C.R. GIBSON CO.—Thomas Nelson Inc.; *U.S. Public*, pg. 1168
GINN & CO. LIMITED—Reed Elsevier plc; *Int'l*, pg. 1094
GIUFFRE EDITORE SPA—Reed Elsevier plc; *Int'l*, pg. 1095
GLENCOE/MC-GRAW HILL—The McGraw-Hill Companies; *U.S. Public*, pg. 1070
GLENCOE/MCGRAW HILL—The McGraw-Hill Companies; *U.S. Public*, pg. 1070
GOLDEN BOOKS FAMILY ENTERTAINMENT INC.; *U.S. Public*, pg. 749
GOLDEN BOOKS PUBLISHING—Golden Books Family Entertainment Inc.; *U.S. Public*, pg. 749
WILHELM GOLDMANN VERLAG GMBH—Bertelsmann AG; *Int'l*, pg. 190
GOODHEART-WILLCOX PUBLISHER; *U.S. Private*, pg. 464
GRAHAM & TROTMAN—Wolters Kluwer N.V.; *Int'l*, pg. 1513
GRAPHIC LEARNING—Abrams & Co. Publishing Inc.; *U.S. Private*, pg. 10
GRAY PRINTING CO.; *U.S. Private*, pg. 472
GREENWILLOW BOOKS—The Hearst Corporation; *U.S. Private*, pg. 515
GREENWOOD PUBLISHING GROUP INC.—Reed Elsevier plc; *Int'l*, pg. 1094
GROLIER ENTERPRISES INC.—Lagardere Groupe; *Int'l*, pg. 794
GROLIER INC.—Lagardere Groupe; *Int'l*, pg. 794
GROLIER LIMITED—Lagardere Groupe; *Int'l*, pg. 794
GROSSET & DUNLAP, INC.—Pearson plc; *Int'l*, pg. 1027
GROUPE DE LA CITE—Alcatel Alsthom Compagnie Generale D'Electricite; *Int'l*, pg. 53
GROVE'S DICTIONARIES OF MUSIC INC.—Georg von Holtzbrinck GmbH; *Int'l*, pg. 1479
GRUNER + JAHR AG & CO.—Bertelsmann AG; *Int'l*, pg. 190
GRUNER + JAHR AG & CO. DRUCK UND VERLAGSHAUS—Bertelsmann AG; *Int'l*, pg. 190
GRUNER + JAHR (ESPANA) DISTRIBUIDORA S.A.—Bertelsmann AG; *Int'l*, pg. 190
GRUNER + JAHR OF THE UK—Bertelsmann AG; *Int'l*, pg. 190
GRUNER + JAHR USA PUBLISHING, INC.—Bertelsmann AG; *Int'l*, pg. 190
GUIDEPOSTS ASSOCIATES, INC.; *U.S. Private*, pg. 487
GUINNESS ENTERPRISES LTD.—Diageo Plc; *Int'l*, pg. 412
GUINNESS PUBLISHING LTD.—Diageo Plc; *Int'l*, pg. 412
HBC INFORMATIONAL AND INSTRUCTIONAL SERVICES, INC.—Harcourt General, Inc.; *U.S. Public*, pg. 783
HACHETTE LATINO AMERICA S.A. DE C.V.—Lagardere Groupe; *Int'l*, pg. 796
HADDON CRAFTSMEN, INC.—R.R. Donnelley & Sons Company; *U.S. Public*, pg. 518
HAMLYN/OCTOPUS—Reed Elsevier plc; *Int'l*, pg. 1093
HANLEY & BELFUS, INC.—Georg von Holtzbrinck GmbH; *Int'l*, pg. 1479
HARCOURT-BRACE—Harcourt General, Inc.; *U.S. Public*, pg. 783
HARCOURT BRACE & COMPANY - ELEMENTARY DIV.—Harcourt General, Inc.; *U.S. Public*, pg. 783
HARCOURT BRACE & COMPANY LEGAL AND PROFESSIONAL PUBLICATIONS, INC.—Harcourt General, Inc.; *U.S. Public*, pg. 783
HARLEQUIN ENTERPRISES LTD.—Torstar Corporation; *Int'l*, pg. 1402
HARPER AUDIO—The News Corporation Limited; *Int'l*, pg. 926
HARPER REFERENCE—The News Corporation Limited; *Int'l*, pg. 927
HARPERCOLLINS ADULT TRADE DIVISION—The News Corporation Limited; *Int'l*, pg. 926
HARPERCOLLINS JUNIOR BOOKS DIVISION—The News Corporation Limited; *Int'l*, pg. 927
HARPERCOLLINS PUBLISHERS—The News Corporation Limited; *Int'l*, pg. 926
HARPERCOLLINS SAN FRANCISCO—The News Corporation Limited; *Int'l*, pg. 927
HEARST BOOK GROUP—The Hearst Corporation; *U.S. Private*, pg. 515
HEARST BOOKS/BUSINESS PUBLISHING GROUP—The Hearst Corporation; *U.S. Private*, pg. 515
THE HEARST CORPORATION; *U.S. Private*, pg. 515
HEARST MAGAZINES DIVISION—The Hearst Corporation; *U.S. Private*, pg. 516
HEARST MARINE BOOKS—The Hearst Corporation; *U.S. Private*, pg. 515
HEINEMANN USA—Reed Elsevier plc; *Int'l*, pg. 1094
HIGHER EDUCATION DIVISION—National Amusements, Inc.; *U.S. Private*, pg. 778
HENRY HOLT & CO. PUBLISHING—Georg von Holtzbrinck GmbH; *Int'l*, pg. 1479
HOLT, RINEHART AND WINSTON COLLEGE DIVISION—Harcourt General, Inc.; *U.S. Public*, pg. 783
HOLT, RINEHART AND WINSTON, INC.—Harcourt General, Inc.; *U.S. Public*, pg. 783
HOLT, RINEHART AND WINSTON SCHOOL DIVISION—Harcourt General, Inc.; *U.S. Public*, pg. 783
HORST & SONS FORLAG A/S—B.H. Blackwell Ltd.; *Int'l*, pg. 197
HOUGHTON MIFFLIN COLLEGE DIV.—Houghton Mifflin Company; *U.S. Public*, pg. 841
HOUGHTON MIFFLIN COMPANY; *U.S. Public*, pg. 841
HOUGHTON MIFFLIN TRADE & REFERENCE DIV.—Houghton Mifflin Company; *U.S. Public*, pg. 841
HUMAN SCIENCES PRESS, INC.—Plenum Publishing Corporation; *U.S. Public*, pg. 1311
ICA FORLAGET AB—ICA Handlarnas AB; *Int'l*, pg. 643
ICIS LOR-EUROPE—Reed Elsevier plc; *Int'l*, pg. 1094
IDG BOOKS WORLDWIDE—International Data Group; *U.S. Private*, pg. 569
IPSOA S.A.R.L.—Wolters Kluwer N.V.; *Int'l*, pg. 1514
ITEDI S.P.A.—Fiat Auto SpA; *Int'l*, pg. 482
ITT CORPORATION—Starwood Hotels & Resorts; *U.S. Public*, pg. 1512
ITT PROMEDIA N.V.—VNU Verenigde Nederlandse Uitgeversbedrijven B.V.; *Int'l*, pg. 1447
IGAKU-SHOIN MYW LTD.—Waverly, Inc.; *U.S. Public*, pg. 1748
IMPRIMERIE GAUTHIER-VILLARS—C.E.P. Communication Group; *Int'l*, pg. 239
INDUSTRIAL INFORMATION HEADQUARTERS CO.—Bearing Headquarters Co.; *U.S. Private*, pg. 127
INFORMATION RESOURCES DIVISION—The Bureau of National Affairs, Inc.; *U.S. Private*, pg. 182
INTEGRITY INCORPORATED; *U.S. Public*, pg. 886
THE INTERNATIONAL PUBLISHING GROUP—Pearson plc; *Int'l*, pg. 1027
INTERNATIONAL RESEARCH & EVALUATION; *U.S. Private*, pg. 571
INTERNATIONAL THOMSON BUSINESS PUBLISHING—The Thomson Corporation; *U.S. Public*, pg. 1601
INTERNATIONAL THOMSON PUBLISHING LIMITED—The Thomson Corporation; *U.S. Public*, pg. 1600
JACARANDA WILEY LTD.—John Wiley & Sons, Inc.; *U.S. Public*, pg. 1768
JAENEUNG EDUCATION CO., LTD.; *Int'l*, pg. 697
JOSSEY-BASS, INC.—National Amusements, Inc.; *U.S. Private*, pg. 778
JOVE PUBLICATIONS, INC.—Pearson plc; *Int'l*, pg. 1027
JUSTIN INDUSTRIES, INC.; *U.S. Public*, pg. 936
KCI COMMUNICATIONS, INC—National Information Corporation; *U.S. Private*, pg. 784
J.J. KELLER & ASSOCIATES, INC.; *U.S. Private*, pg. 612
KINDLER VERLAG GMBH—Georg von Holtzbrinck GmbH; *Int'l*, pg. 1478
KLUWER ACADEMIC PUBLISHERS—Wolters Kluwer N.V.; *Int'l*, pg. 1513
KLUWER LAW INTERNATIONAL—Wolters Kluwer N.V.; *Int'l*, pg. 1512
ALFRED A. KNOPF, INC.—Advance Publications Inc.; *U.S. Private*, pg. 21
KODANSHA AMERICA, INC.—Kodansha Ltd.; *Int'l*, pg. 742
KODANSHA INTERNATIONAL LTD—Kodansha Ltd.; *Int'l*, pg. 742
KODANSHA LTD.; *Int'l*, pg. 742
KODANSHA SCIENTIFIC LTD.—Kodansha Ltd.; *Int'l*, pg. 742
KRAMES COMMUNICATIONS—The Times Mirror Company; *U.S. Public*, pg. 1616
KRAUSE PUBLICATIONS, INC.; *U.S. Private*, pg. 635
WOLFGANG KRUGER VERLAG GMBH—Georg von Holtzbrinck GmbH; *Int'l*, pg. 1478
L.C.G. MALMBERG BV—VNU Verenigde Nederlandse Uitgeversbedrijven B.V.; *Int'l*, pg. 1445
LADYBIRD BOOKS LTD.—Pearson plc; *Int'l*, pg. 1025
LAGARDERE GROUPE NORTH AMERICA—Lagardere Groupe; *Int'l*, pg. 794
LAIDLAW BROTHERS—Bertelsmann AG; *Int'l*, pg. 191
EDICIONES LAROUSSE ARGENTINA SA—C.E.P. Communication Group; *Int'l*, pg. 240
EDICIONES LAROUSSE COLOMBIANA LTDA.—C.E.P. Communication Group; *Int'l*, pg. 240
LIBRAIRIE LAROUSSE—C.E.P. Communication Group; *Int'l*, *pg. 239*
LAROUSSE (SUISSE) SA—C.E.P. Communication Group; *Int'l*, pg. 240
LAWYERS COOPERATIVE PUBLISHING CO.—The Thomson Corporation; *U.S. Public*, pg. 1602
LE LIVRE DE PARIS—Lagardere Groupe; *Int'l*, pg. 792
LECTORUM PUBLICATIONS—Scholastic Corporation; *U.S. Public*, pg. 1440
LES EDITIONS CEC INC.—Lagardere Groupe; *Int'l*, pg. 794
LES EDITIONS CEC INC.—Quebecor Inc.; *Int'l*, pg. 1078
LES PRESSES DE LA CITE—Alcatel Alsthom Compagnie Generale D'Electricite; *Int'l*, pg. 53
LES PRESSES DE LA CITE—C.E.P. Communication Group; *Int'l*, pg. 240
LIBRAIRIE ARTHEME FAYARD—Lagardere Groupe; *Int'l*, pg. 792
LIBRAIRIE DES CHAMPS-ELYSEES—Lagardere Groupe; *Int'l*, pg. 792
LIBRAIRIE GENERALE FRANCAISE—Lagardere Groupe; *Int'l*, pg. 792
J.B. LIPPINCOTT COMPANY—Wolters Kluwer N.V.; *Int'l*, pg. 1513
LIPPINCOTT-RAVEN PUBLISHING—Wolters Kluwer N.V.; *Int'l*, pg. 1513
LITTLE, BROWN & CO.—Time Warner Inc.; *U.S. Public*, pg. 1612
LITTLE BROWN & CO. (CANADA) LTD.—Time Warner Inc.; *U.S. Public*, pg. 1615
LONDON HOUSE—The McGraw-Hill Companies; *U.S. Public*, pg. 1070
LONGMAN BOTSWANA (PTY) LTD.—Pearson plc; *Int'l*, pg. 1025
LONGMAN CHESHIRE PTY. LTD.—Pearson plc; *Int'l*, pg. 1025
LONGMAN FRANCE SA—Pearson plc; *Int'l*, pg. 1025
LONGMAN GROUP (OVERSEAS HOLDING) LIMITED—Pearson plc; *Int'l*, pg. 1025
LONGMAN GROUP UK LTD.—Pearson plc; *Int'l*, pg. 1025
LONGMAN ITALIA SRL—Pearson plc; *Int'l*, pg. 1025
LONGMAN KENYA LTD.—Pearson plc; *Int'l*, pg. 1027
LONGMAN MALAYSIA SDN. BHD.—Pearson plc; *Int'l*, pg. 1025
LONGMAN NIGERIA LTD.—Pearson plc; *Int'l*, pg. 1027
LONGMAN PAUL LTD.—Pearson plc; *Int'l*, pg. 1025
LONGMAN PENGUIN JAPAN CO. LTD.—Pearson plc; *Int'l*, *pg. 1025*
LONGMAN PENGUIN LIMITED—Pearson plc; *Int'l*, pg. 1025
LONGMAN SINGAPORE PUBLISHERS (PTE.) LTD.—Pearson plc; *Int'l*, pg. 1025
LONGMAN SWAZILAND (PTY) LTD.—Pearson plc; *Int'l*, pg. 1026
LONGMAN ZIMBABWE (PTE) LTD.—Pearson plc; *Int'l*, pg. 1026
LOTHROP, LEE & SHEPARD BOOKS—The Hearst Corporation; *U.S. Private*, pg. 515
MAC AMERICA COMMUNICATIONS, INC.; *U.S. Private*, pg. 685
MACDONALD & CO. (PUBLISHERS) LTD.—Time Warner Inc.; *U.S. Public*, pg. 1615
MACK PRINTING GROUP (EPHRATA DIV.)—Mack Printing Company; *U.S. Private*, pg. 692
MACMILLAN BOLESWA PUBLISHING (PTY) LTD.—Georg von Holtzbrinck GmbH; *Int'l*, pg. 1479

MACMILLAN BOTSWANA PUBLISHING CO.—Georg von Holtzbrinck GmbH; *Int'l*, pg. 1479
MACMILLAN CHILDREN'S BOOKS LIMITED—Georg von Holtzbrinck GmbH; *Int'l*, pg. 1479
THE MACMILLAN CO. OF AUSTRALIA PTY. LTD.—Georg von Holtzbrinck GmbH; *Int'l*, pg. 1480
THE MACMILLAN CO. OF NEW ZEALAND LTD.—Georg von Holtzbrinck GmbH; *Int'l*, pg. 1480
MACMILLAN EDUCATION LTD.—Georg von Holtzbrinck GmbH; *Int'l*, pg. 1479
MACMILLAN LONDON LTD.—Georg von Holtzbrinck GmbH; *Int'l*, pg. 1479
MACMILLAN LTD.—Georg von Holtzbrinck GmbH; *Int'l*, pg. 1479
MACMILLAN/MCGRAW-HILL SCHOOL PUBLISHING COMPANY—The McGraw-Hill Companies; *U.S. Public*, pg. 1070
MACMILLAN NIGERIA PUBLISHERS LTD.—Georg von Holtzbrinck GmbH; *Int'l*, pg. 1480
MACMILLAN PUBLISHERS (CHINA) LTD.—Georg von Holtzbrinck GmbH; *Int'l*, pg. 1480
MACMILLAN PUBLISHING USA—National Amusements, Inc.; *U.S. Private*, pg. 777
MACMILLAN SWAZILAND NATIONAL PUBLISHING CO.—Georg von Holtzbrinck GmbH; *Int'l*, pg. 1480
MAD MAGAZINE, E. C. CREATIONS, INC.—Time Warner Inc.; *U.S. Public*, pg. 1614
MARINELLO SCHOOLS OF BEAUTY—Scope Industries; *U.S. Public*, pg. 1444
MARSHALL PICKERING HOLDINGS, LTD.—The News Corporation Limited; *Int'l*, pg. 927
MARUZEN ASIA PRIVATE LTD.—Maruzen Company Limited; *Int'l*, pg. 846
MARUZEN BOOKMATES CO., LTD.—Maruzen Company Limited; *Int'l*, pg. 846
MARUZEN COMPANY LIMITED; *Int'l*, pg. 845
MARUZEN INTERNATIONAL CO., LTD.—Maruzen Company Limited; *Int'l*, pg. 846
MATHEMATICAL REVIEWS—American Mathematical Society, Inc.; *U.S. Private*, pg. 59
MCDOUGAL/LITTELL—Houghton Mifflin Company; *U.S. Public*, pg. 841
THE MCGRAW-HILL COMPANIES; *U.S. Public*, pg. 1069
MCKNIGHT MEDICAL COMMUNICATIONS—The Thomson Corporation; *U.S. Public*, pg. 1600
MEREDITH CORPORATION; *U.S. Public*, pg. 1094
MEREDITH PUBLISHING SERVICES—Meredith Corporation; *U.S. Public*, pg. 1094
MERRIAM-WEBSTER, INC.—Encyclopaedia Britannica, Inc.; *U.S. Private*, pg. 375
MERRILL CORPORATION; *U.S. Public*, pg. 1097
METROLAND PRINTING & DISTRIBUTING—Torstar Corporation; *Int'l*, pg. 1402
J.B. METZLER VERLAG—Georg von Holtzbrinck GmbH; *Int'l*, pg. 1478
MICROSOFT PRESS—Microsoft Corporation; *U.S. Public*, pg. 1107
MILLER FREEMAN INC.—United News & Media plc; *Int'l*, pg. 1443
MILLER FREEMAN PLC—United News & Media plc; *Int'l*, pg. 1443
MILLER'S PUBLICATIONS—Reed Elsevier plc; *Int'l*, pg. 1093
MILLS & BOON LTD.—Torstar Corporation; *Int'l*, pg. 1402
MITCHELL BEAZLEY—Reed Elsevier plc; *Int'l*, pg. 1093
ARNOLDO MONDADORI EDITORE S.P.A.; *Int'l*, pg. 887
MONEY MARKET DIRECTORIES—The McGraw-Hill Companies; *U.S. Public*, pg. 1071
JOSHUA MORRIS PUBLISHING, INC.—The Reader's Digest Association, Inc.; *U.S. Public*, pg. 1367
WILLIAM MORROW & CO., INC.—The Hearst Corporation; *U.S. Private*, pg. 515
MOSAIK VERLAG—Bertelsmann AG; *Int'l*, pg. 190
MOSBY - WILLIAMS & WILKINS PTY. LTD.—Waverly, Inc.; *U.S. Public*, pg. 1748
MOSBY-YEAR BOOK, INC.—The Times Mirror Company; *U.S. Public*, pg. 1616
MOSTRUPS FORLAG A/S—The Thomson Corporation; *U.S. Public*, pg. 1602
MOTOR PUBLICATIONS—The Hearst Corporation; *U.S. Private*, pg. 516
MUNKSGAARD INTERNATIONAL BOOKSELLERS & PUBLISHERS LTD.—B.H. Blackwell Ltd.; *Int'l*, pg. 197
NAL/PENGUIN INC.—Pearson plc; *Int'l*, pg. 1027
NTC/CONTEMPORARY PUBLISHING GROUP—Tribune Company; *U.S. Public*, pg. 1635
FERNAND NATHAN—C.E.P. Communication Group; *Int'l*, pg. 240
NATIONAL GEOGRAPHIC SOCIETY; *U.S. Private*, pg. 783
NATIONAL INSTITUTE OF BUSINESS MANAGEMENT, INC.—National Information Corporation; *U.S. Private*, pg. 785
NATIONAL PUBLISHING CO.—Courier Corporation; *U.S. Public*, pg. 453
NELSON CANADA—The Thomson Corporation; *U.S. Public*, pg. 1601
THOMAS NELSON & SONS LTD.—The Thomson Corporation; *U.S. Public*, pg. 1601
THOMAS NELSON AUSTRALIA—The Thomson Corporation; *U.S. Public*, pg. 1601
NEW DIMENSIONS IN EDUCATION—Abrams & Co. Publishing Inc.; *U.S. Private*, pg. 10
NEW YORK INSTITUTE OF FINANCE—National Amusements, Inc.; *U.S. Private*, pg. 778
THE NEWS CORPORATION LIMITED; *Int'l*, pg. 925
NEWS LIMITED OF AUSTRALIA—The News Corporation Limited; *Int'l*, pg. 925
NIHON KEIZAI SHIMBUN, INC.; *Int'l*, pg. 929
NIKKEI BUSINESS PUBLICATIONS INC.—Nihon Keizai Shimbun, Inc.; *Int'l*, pg. 929
NIKKEI CUSTOM PUBLISHING SERVICES, INC.—Nihon Keizai Shimbun, Inc.; *Int'l*, pg. 929
NIKKEI HOME PUBLISHING, INC.—Nihon Keizai Shimbun, Inc.; *Int'l*, pg. 929
NORTH AMERICAN PUBLISHING COMPANY; *U.S. Private*, pg. 803
NORTHLAND PUBLISHING CO.—Justin Industries, Inc.; *U.S. Public*, pg. 937
W.W. NORTON & COMPANY, INC.; *U.S. Private*, pg. 807
NOUVELLES EDITIONS MARABOUT—Lagardere Groupe; *Int'l*, pg. 796
ORIENT LONGMAN LTD.—Pearson plc; *Int'l*, pg. 1026
OSBORNE/MCGRAW-HILL—The McGraw-Hill Companies; *U.S. Public*, pg. 1071
OSPREY—Reed Elsevier plc; *Int'l*, pg. 1093
OUR SUNDAY VISITOR, INC.; *U.S. Private*, pg. 821
OXFORD UNIVERSITY PRESS; *Int'l*, pg. 1018
PRC, INC.—Litton Industries, Inc.; *U.S. Public*, pg. 1003
PWS-KENT PUBLISHING CO.—The Thomson Corporation; *U.S. Public*, pg. 1600
PANEL PUBLISHERS, INC.—Wolters Kluwer N.V.; *Int'l*, pg. 1513
PANTHEON BOOKS, INC.—Advance Publications Inc.; *U.S. Private*, pg. 21
PASSPORT BOOKS—Tribune Company; *U.S. Public*, pg. 1636
PEARSON, INC.—Pearson plc; *Int'l*, pg. 1026
PEARSON LONGMAN INC.—Pearson plc; *Int'l*, pg. 1026
PEARSON PLC; *Int'l*, pg. 1025
THE PENGUIN PUBLISHING CO. LTD.—Pearson plc; *Int'l*, pg. 1026
PENGUIN PUTNAM INC.—Pearson plc; *Int'l*, pg. 1027
GEORGE PHILIP LIMITED—Reed Elsevier plc; *Int'l*, pg. 1093
THE PHOENIX LEARNING GROUP, INC.; *U.S. Private*, pg. 863
PHOENIX LEARNING RESOURCES—The Phoenix Learning Group, Inc.; *U.S. Private*, pg. 863
PHOENIX MAGAZINE—MAC America Communications, Inc.; *U.S. Private*, pg. 685
PIKE & FISCHER—The Bureau of National Affairs, Inc.; *U.S. Private*, pg. 182
PITKIN GUIDES—Reed Elsevier plc; *Int'l*, pg. 1094
PITMAN PUBLISHING LTD.—Pearson plc; *Int'l*, pg. 1025
PLENUM PUBLISHING COMPANY, LTD.—Plenum Publishing Corporation; *U.S. Public*, pg. 1311
PLENUM PUBLISHING CORPORATION; *U.S. Public*, pg. 1311
POCKET BOOKS—National Amusements, Inc.; *U.S. Private*, pg. 777
PRENTICE HALL BUSINESS PUBLISHING—National Amusements, Inc.; *U.S. Private*, pg. 778
PRIMEDIA INC.; *U.S. Public*, pg. 1327
PRIMEDIA INC.—Primedia Inc.; *U.S. Public*, pg. 1328
PRINCETON UNIVERSITY PRESS; *U.S. Private*, pg. 885
PRISMA PRESSE & CIE—Bertelsmann AG; *Int'l*, pg. 191
PRISMA VERLAG GMBH—Bertelsmann AG; *Int'l*, pg. 190
PRODUCERS MASTERGUIDE—VNU Verenigde Nederlandse Uitgeversbedrijven B.V.; *Int'l*, pg. 1446
PROFESSIONAL PUBLISHING LTD.—The Thomson Corporation; *U.S. Public*, pg. 1601
THE PUTNAM & GROSSET GROUP—Pearson plc; *Int'l*, pg. 1027
THE PUTNAM BERKLEY GROUP, INC.—Pearson plc; *Int'l*, pg. 1027
QUEBECOR PRINTING BOOK PRESS INC.—Quebecor Inc.; *Int'l*, pg. 1078
QUILL TRADE PAPERBACKS—The Hearst Corporation; *U.S. Private*, pg. 515
R.C.S. EDITORI S.P.A.; *Int'l*, pg. 1078
RAND MCNALLY & COMPANY; *U.S. Private*, pg. 908
RANDOM HOUSE ADULT TRADE BOOKS—Advance Publications Inc.; *U.S. Private*, pg. 21
RANDOM HOUSE, INC.—Advance Publications Inc.; *U.S. Private*, pg. 20
THE READER'S DIGEST ASSOCIATION, INC.; *U.S. Public*, pg. 1367
READING EAGLE COMPANY; *U.S. Private*, pg. 913
REED BOOKS—Reed Elsevier plc; *Int'l*, pg. 1093
REED BOOKS AUSTRALIA—Reed Elsevier plc; *Int'l*, pg. 1094
REED BUSINESS INFORMATION-EAST GRINSTEAD—Reed Elsevier plc; *Int'l*, pg. 1094
REED EDUCATIONAL AND PROFESSIONAL PUBLISHING—Reed Elsevier plc; *Int'l*, pg. 1094
REED ELSEVIER PLC; *Int'l*, pg. 1093
REED ELSEVIER (SINGAPORE) PTE LIMITED—Reed Elsevier plc; *Int'l*, pg. 1095
REED INTERNATIONAL P.L.C.—Reed Elsevier plc; *Int'l*, pg. 1093
REED PUBLISHING (NZ) LTD.—Reed Elsevier plc; *Int'l*, pg. 1094
REED TRAVEL GROUP—Reed Elsevier plc; *Int'l*, pg. 1097
REISE-UND VERKEHRS VERLAG GMBH—Bertelsmann AG; *Int'l*, pg. 190
HANS REITZELS FORLAG A/S—B.H. Blackwell Ltd.; *Int'l*, pg. 197
RESEARCH INSTITUTE OF AMERICA—The Thomson Corporation; *U.S. Public*, pg. 1602
RICHARD DE BOO PUBLISHERS—The Thomson Corporation; *U.S. Public*, pg. 1601
RIGBY EDUCATION—Reed Elsevier plc; *Int'l*, pg. 1094
RIGBY HEINEMANN—Reed Elsevier plc; *Int'l*, pg. 1095
RINGIER AG; *Int'l*, pg. 1118
THE RIVERSIDE PUBLISHING CO.—Houghton Mifflin Company; *U.S. Public*, pg. 841
ROLLING STONE MAGAZINE—Wenner Media; *U.S. Private*, pg. 1162
ROWMAN & LITTLEFIELD PUBLISHERS, INC.—University Press of America, Inc.; *U.S. Private*, pg. 1128
ROWOHLT BERLIN VERLAG GMBH—Georg von Holtzbrinck GmbH; *Int'l*, pg. 1478
ROWOHLT TASCHENBUCH VERLAG GMBH—Georg von Holtzbrinck GmbH; *Int'l*, pg. 1478
ROWOHLT VERLAG GMBH—Georg von Holtzbrinck GmbH; *Int'l*, pg. 1478
WILLIAM H. SADLIER, INC.; *U.S. Public*, pg. 1422
SAMMLER KABINETT, INC.—Time Warner Inc.; *U.S. Public*, pg. 1613
SANGAM BOOKS LTD.—Pearson plc; *Int'l*, pg. 1026
W.B. SAUNDERS COMPANY—Harcourt General, Inc.; *U.S. Public*, pg. 784
SCARECROW PRESS, INC.—Lagardere Groupe; *Int'l*, pg. 794
SCHAFFER-POESCHEL VERLAG—Georg von Holtzbrinck GmbH; *Int'l*, pg. 1478
SCHOCKEN BOOKS—Advance Publications Inc.; *U.S. Private*, pg. 21
SCHOLASTIC-CANADA, LTD.—Scholastic Corporation; *U.S. Public*, pg. 1440
SCHOLASTIC PUBLICATIONS LTD.—Scholastic Corporation; *U.S. Public*, pg. 1441
SCHROEDEL SCHULBUCHVERLAG GMBH—Georg von Holtzbrinck GmbH; *Int'l*, pg. 1478
SCHULVERLAG VIEWEG GMBH—Bertelsmann AG; *Int'l*, pg. 190
SCIENTIFIC AMERICAN, INC.—Georg von Holtzbrinck GmbH; *Int'l*, pg. 1479
SCOTT FORSEMAN/ADDISON WESLEY—The News Corporation Limited; *Int'l*, pg. 927
SELECTION DU READER'S DIGEST S.A.—The Reader's Digest Association, Inc.; *U.S. Public*, pg. 1368
SHEPARD'S—Reed Elsevier plc; *Int'l*, pg. 1095
SHEPARD'S—The Times Mirror Company; *U.S. Public*, pg. 1616
THE SHERIDAN GROUP; *U.S. Private*, pg. 993
THE SHERIDAN PRESS, INC.—The Sheridan Group; *U.S. Private*, pg. 993
SHESHUNOFF INFORMATION SERVICES, INC.—The Thomson Corporation; *U.S. Public*, pg. 1601
SIGHT AND SOUND—Golden Books Family Entertainment Inc.; *U.S. Public*, pg. 749
SILHOUETTE BOOKS—Torstar Corporation; *Int'l*, pg. 1402
SILVER BURDETT DIVISION—National Amusements, Inc.; *U.S. Private*, pg. 778
SILVER BURDETT GINN—National Amusements, Inc.; *U.S. Private*, pg. 778
SIMON & SCHUSTER—National Amusements, Inc.; *U.S. Private*, pg. 777
SIMON & SCHUSTER INTERNATIONAL & BUSINESS & PROFESSIONAL GROUP—National Amusements, Inc.; *U.S. Private*, pg. 778
SMITH-EDWARDS-DUNLAP COMPANY; *U.S. Private*, pg. 1007
W.H. SMITH GROUP PLC; *Int'l*, pg. 1264
SOUTHWESTERN BELL PRINTING COMPANY—SBC Communications Inc.; *U.S. Public*, pg. 1415
SOUTHWESTERN/GREAT AMERICAN INC.; *U.S. Private*, pg. 1018
SPEKTRUM AKADEMISCHER VERLAG GMBH—Georg von Holtzbrinck GmbH; *Int'l*, pg. 1478
SPEKTRUM FACHVERLAGE GMBH—Georg von Holtzbrinck GmbH; *Int'l*, pg. 1478
SPRINGER-VERLAG GMBH & CO. KG; *Int'l*, pg. 1291
SPRINGER-VERLAG NEW YORK INC.—Springer-Verlag GmbH & Co. KG; *Int'l*, pg. 1291
STANDARD PUBLISHING—Standex International Corporation; *U.S. Public*, pg. 1506
STECK-VAUGHN COMPANY—Harcourt General, Inc.; *U.S. Public*, pg. 784
STECK-VAUGHN PUBLISHING CORPORATION—Harcourt General, Inc.; *U.S. Public*, pg. 784
SUNSET PUBLISHING CORPORATION—Time Warner Inc.; *U.S. Public*, pg. 1613
SUTTLE PRESS, INC—Telephone and Data Systems, Inc.; *U.S. Public*, pg. 1570
SYBEX, INC.; *U.S. Private*, pg. 1059
TABAPRESS, S.A.—Tabacalera, S.A.; *Int'l*, pg. 1346
TAFT GROUP—The Thomson Corporation; *U.S. Public*, pg. 1601
TAMBOURINE BOOKS—The Hearst Corporation; *U.S. Private*, pg. 515
TATA MCGRAW-HILL PUBLISHING CO., PRIVATE LIMITED—The McGraw-Hill Companies; *U.S. Public*, pg. 1072
TAX MANAGEMENT, INC.—The Bureau of National Affairs, Inc.; *U.S. Private*, pg. 182
TAYLOR & FRANCIS—Taylor & Francis Group Ltd.; *Int'l*, pg. 1358
TAYLOR & FRANCIS GROUP LTD.; *Int'l*, pg. 1357
TAYLOR & FRANCIS PHILADELPHIA—Taylor & Francis Group Ltd.; *Int'l*, pg. 1358
THOMSON AUSTRALIAN HOLDINGS PTY. LTD.—The Thomson Corporation; *U.S. Public*, pg. 1601
THOMSON BOOK/REFERENCE GROUP—The Thomson Corporation; *U.S. Public*, pg. 1600
THE THOMSON CORPORATION PLC—The Thomson Corporation; *U.S. Public*, pg. 1601
THE THOMSON CORPORATION; *U.S. Public*, pg. 1599
THOMSON DIRECTORIES—U S West Inc.; *U.S. Public*, pg. 1689
THOMSON HOLDINGS INC.—The Thomson Corporation; *U.S. Public*, pg. 1601
THOMSON INTERNATIONAL HOLDINGS LIMITED—The Thomson Corporation; *U.S. Public*, pg. 1600
THOMSON PROFESSIONAL PUBLISHING—The Thomson Corporation; *U.S. Public*, pg. 1601
THOMSON U.S. INC.—The Thomson Corporation; *U.S. Public*, pg. 1601
THORNDIKE PRESS—National Amusements, Inc.; *U.S. Private*, pg. 777
TIEN WAH PRESS (PTE.) LTD.—Dai Nippon Printing Co., Ltd.; *Int'l*, pg. 363
THE TIME INC. BOOK COMPANY—Time Warner Inc.; *U.S. Public*, pg. 1613
TIME-LIFE BOOKS (EUROPE), INC.—Time Warner Inc.; *U.S. Public*, pg. 1613
TIME-LIFE, INC.—Time Warner Inc.; *U.S. Public*, pg. 1613
TIME-LIFE LIBRARIES, INC.—Time Warner Inc.; *U.S. Public*, pg. 1613

TIME PUBLISHING VENTURES, INC.—Time Warner Inc.; *U.S. Public*, pg. 1613
TIME WARNER INC.; *U.S. Public*, pg. 1610
TIME WARNER PUBLISHING INC.—Time Warner Inc.; *U.S.* Public, pg. 1614
TIME WARNER TRADE PUBLISHING—Time Warner Inc.; *U.S. Public*, pg. 1614
TIMES BOOKS—Advance Publications Inc.; *U.S. Private*, pg. 21
TIMES JOURNAL PUBLISHING—SBC Communications Inc.; *U.S. Public*, pg. 1415
THE TIMES MIRROR COMPANY; *U.S. Public*, pg. 1615
TIMES MIRROR MAGAZINES, INC.—The Times Mirror Company; *U.S. Public*, pg. 1616
TIMES PUBLISHING LIMITED; *Int'l*, pg. 1390
TOLLEY PUBLISHING LTD.—Reed Elsevier plc; *Int'l*, pg. 1095
TORSTAR CORPORATION; *Int'l*, pg. 1402
TRIBUNE COMPANY; *U.S. Public*, pg. 1635
TRIBUNE EDUCATION—Tribune Company; *U.S. Public*, pg. 1636
TRUMPET BOOK CLUBS—Scholastic Corporation; *U.S. Public*, pg. 1440
TUNDRA BOOKS INC.—McClelland & Stewart; *Int'l*, pg. 851
TYNDALE HOUSE PUBLISHERS, INC.; *U.S. Private*, pg. 1112
UTP (UNITED TECHNICAL PUBLICATIONS) DIVISION—The Hearst Corporation; *U.S. Private*, pg. 516
THE UNITED METHODIST PUBLISHING HOUSE; *U.S. Private*, pg. 1122
UNIVERSITY PRESS OF AMERICA, INC.; *U.S. Private*, pg. 1127
THE UPPER ROOM; *U.S. Private*, pg. 1129
URBAN & SCHWARZENBERG GMBH—Waverly, Inc.; *U.S. Public*, pg. 1748
VGM CAREER HORIZONS—Tribune Company; *U.S. Public*, *pg. 1636*
VALUE LINE PUBLISHING—Arnold Bernhard & Co.; *U.S. Private*, pg. 137
VAN NOSTRAND REINHOLD CO.—The Thomson Corporation; *U.S. Public*, pg. 1600
VERLAG DR. MAX GEHLEN GMBH & CO. KG—Georg von Holtzbrinck GmbH; *Int'l*, pg. 1479
VERLEGERDIENST MUNCHEN—Waverly, Inc.; *U.S. Public*, *pg. 1748*
FRIEDRICH VIEWEG & SOHN VERLAGSGESELLSCHAFT MBH—Bertelsmann AG; *Int'l*, pg. 190
VILLARD BOOKS—Advance Publications Inc.; *U.S. Private*, pg. 21
VOLT-AUTOLOGIC DIRECTORIES S.A.—Volt Information Sciences, Inc.; *U.S. Public*, pg. 1724
GEORG VON HOLTZBRINCK GMBH; *Int'l*, pg. 1478
WADSWORTH PUBLISHING CO.—The Thomson Corporation; *U.S. Public*, pg. 1600
WALSWORTH PUBLISHING COMPANY, INC.; *U.S. Private*, pg. 1148
WARNER BOOKS, INC.—Time Warner Inc.; *U.S. Public*, pg. 1614
WARNER COMMUNICATIONS INC.—Time Warner Inc.; *U.S. Public*, pg. 1611
WARNER PRESS, INC.; *U.S. Private*, pg. 1150
WARNER PUBLISHER SERVICES, INC.—Time Warner Inc.; *U.S. Public*, pg. 1614
WARREN GORHAM LAMONT—The Thomson Corporation; *U.S. Public*, pg. 1602
WAVERLY EUROPE LTD.—Waverly, Inc.; *U.S. Public*, pg. 1748
WAVERLY HISPANICA S.A.—Waverly, Inc.; *U.S. Public*, pg. 1748
WAVERLY, INC.; *U.S. Public*, pg. 1748
WERK-VERLAG—Reed Elsevier plc; *Int'l*, pg. 1099
WEST INFORMATION PUBLISHING GROUP—The Thomson Corporation; *U.S. Public*, pg. 1602
WESTDEUTSCHER VERLAG GMBH—Bertelsmann AG; *Int'l*, pg. 190
WILEY EUROPE LIMITED—John Wiley & Sons, Inc.; *U.S. Public*, pg. 1768
JOHN WILEY & SONS, CANADA, LTD.—John Wiley & Sons, Inc.; *U.S. Public*, pg. 1768
JOHN WILEY & SONS, INC.; *U.S. Public*, pg. 1768
WILEY-VCH—John Wiley & Sons, Inc.; *U.S. Public*, pg. 1768
WILLIAMS & WILKINS BOOK PUBLISHING—Waverly, Inc.; *U.S. Public*, pg. 1748
WILLIAMS & WILKINS PERIODICAL PUBLISHING—Waverly, Inc.; *U.S. Public*, pg. 1748
WILSON & LAFLEUR, LIMITEE—Quebecor Inc.; *Int'l*, pg. 1076
THE H.W. WILSON CO.; *U.S. Private*, pg. 1180
WOLTERS KLUWER ACADEMIC PUBLISHERS—Wolters Kluwer N.V.; *Int'l*, pg. 1512
WOLTERS KLUWER BELGIUM—Wolters Kluwer N.V.; *Int'l*, *pg. 1513*
WOLTERS KLUWER EDUCATIONAL ACTIVITIES—Wolters Kluwer N.V.; *Int'l*, pg. 1513
WOLTERS KLUWER FRANCE—Wolters Kluwer N.V.; *Int'l*, pg. 1513
WOLTERS KLUWER GERMANY—Wolters Kluwer N.V.; *Int'l*, pg. 1513
WOLTERS KLUWER LAW AND TAXATION—Wolters Kluwer N.V.; *Int'l*, pg. 1513
WOLTERS KLUWER SPAIN—Wolters Kluwer N.V.; *Int'l*, pg. 1514
WOLTERS KLUWER SWEDEN—Wolters Kluwer N.V.; *Int'l*, pg. 1514
WOLTERS KLUWER TRADE PUBLISHING—Wolters Kluwer N.V.; *Int'l*, pg. 1513
WOLTERS KLUWER U.K.—Wolters Kluwer N.V.; *Int'l*, pg. 1514
WOLTERS KLUWER U.S.—Wolters Kluwer N.V.; *Int'l*, pg. 1513
WORD, INCORPORATED—Gaylord Entertainment Co.; *U.S.* Public, pg. 704
THE WORLD ALMANAC—Primedia Inc.; *U.S. Public*, pg. 1328
WORLD BOOK CHILDCRAFT DIVISION—Berkshire Hathaway Inc.; *U.S. Public*, pg. 218
WORLD BOOK, INC.—Berkshire Hathaway Inc.; *U.S. Public*, pg. 218
WORLD BOOK PUBLISHING—Berkshire Hathaway Inc.; *U.S. Public*, pg. 218
WORTH PUBLISHER INC.—Georg von Holtzbrinck GmbH; *Int'l*, pg. 1479
WRIGHT GROUP PUBLISHING, INC.—Tribune Company; *U.S. Public*, pg. 1636
WUNDERLICH VERLAG—Georg von Holtzbrinck GmbH; *Int'l*, pg. 1479
XYVISION, INC.; *U.S. Public*, pg. 1787
XYVISION LIMITED—Xyvision, Inc.; *U.S. Public*, pg. 1787
YALE UNIVERSITY PRESS; *U.S. Private*, pg. 1195
ZD PRESS—Softbank Corporation; *Int'l*, pg. 1276
THE ZONDERVAN CORPORATION—The News Corporation Limited; *Int'l*, pg. 927

2732 — BOOK PRINTING

AURUM PRESS LIMITED—Really Useful Holdings Limited; *Int'l*, pg. 1089
BANTA BOOK GROUP-HARRISONBURG—Banta Corporation; *U.S. Public*, pg. 188
BANTA CORPORATION; *U.S. Public*, pg. 187
BOOKCRAFTERS U.S.A. INC.—American Business Products, Inc.; *U.S. Public*, pg. 70
BRITISH PRINTING COMPANY LTD.; *Int'l*, pg. 220
CADMUS—Cadmus Communications Corporation; *U.S. Public*, pg. 290
CADMUS COMMUNICATIONS CORPORATION; *U.S. Public*, pg. 290
COURIER CONNECTION, INC.—Courier Corporation; *U.S. Public*, pg. 453
COURIER CORPORATION; *U.S. Public*, pg. 453
COURIER INTERNATIONAL, LTD.—Courier Corporation; *U.S. Public*, pg. 453
COURIER KENDALLVILLE, INC.—Courier Corporation; *U.S.* Public, pg. 453
COURIER STOUGHTON, INC.—Courier Corporation; *U.S. Public*, pg. 453
COURIER WESTFORD, INC.—Courier Corporation; *U.S. Public*, pg. 453
DELMAR PHOTOGRAPHIC AND PRINTING COMPANY—Continental Graphics Holdings, Inc.; *U.S. Private*, pg. 268
G.T.C. TRANSCONTINENTAL GROUP LTD.; *Int'l*, pg. 538
HARCOURT BRACE & COMPANY - ELEMENTARY DIV.—Harcourt General, Inc.; *U.S. Public*, pg. 783
JOSTENS; *U.S. Public*, pg. 934
JUDD'S INCORPORATED—Perry Graphic Communications, Inc.; *U.S. Private*, pg. 855
JUSTIN INDUSTRIES, INC.; *U.S. Public*, pg. 936
LAWYERS COOPERATIVE PUBLISHING CO.—The Thomson Corporation; *U.S. Public*, pg. 1602
MALLOY LITHOGRAPHING INC.; *U.S. Private*, pg. 698
MCNAUGHTON & GUNN, INC.; *U.S. Private*, pg. 724
MCPHERSON'S LIMITED; *Int'l*, pg. 852
MERRILL CORPORATION; *U.S. Public*, pg. 1097
ARNOLDO MONDADORI EDITORE S.P.A.; *Int'l*, pg. 887
NISSAN GRAPHIC ARTS CO., LTD.—Nissan Motor Co., Ltd.; *Int'l*, pg. 944
NORTHPRINT B.V.—Reed Elsevier plc; *Int'l*, pg. 1100
OPTIC GRAPHICS, INC.; *U.S. Private*, pg. 818
PANTHEON BOOKS, INC.—Advance Publications Inc.; *U.S.* Private, pg. 21
PERRY GRAPHIC COMMUNICATIONS, INC.; *U.S. Private*, *pg. 855*
RAND MCNALLY & COMPANY; *U.S. Private*, pg. 908
ROSE PRINTING COMPANY, INC.; *U.S. Private*, pg. 945
SCHOCKEN BOOKS—Advance Publications Inc.; *U.S. Private*, pg. 21
SCHOOL PRODUCTS GROUP—Jostens; *U.S. Public*, pg. 934
SCIENCE & TECHNOLOGY GROUP—The McGraw-Hill Companies; *U.S. Public*, pg. 1071
THE SEGERDAHL CORP.; *U.S. Private*, pg. 981
STECK-VAUGHN PUBLISHING CORPORATION—Harcourt General, Inc.; *U.S. Public*, pg. 784
WEST INFORMATION PUBLISHING GROUP—The Thomson Corporation; *U.S. Public*, pg. 1602
WORZALLA PUBLISHING CO., INC.; *U.S. Private*, pg. 1191

2741 — MISCELLANEOUS PUBLISHING

A/S/M COMMUNICATIONS, INC.—VNU Verenigde Nederlandse Uitgeversbedrijven B.V.; *Int'l*, pg. 1446
ALLTEL CORPORATION; *U.S. Public*, pg. 55
ALLTEL PUBLISHING CORPORATION—ALLTEL Corporation; *U.S. Public*, pg. 56
AMER GROUP LTD.; *Int'l*, pg. 72
AMERICAN AUTOMOBILE ASSOCIATION; *U.S. Private*, pg. 50
AMERICAN BUSINESS INFORMATION, INC.; *U.S. Public*, pg. 69
AMERICAN RADIO RELAY LEAGUE; *U.S. Private*, pg. 60
AMERITECH CORPORATION; *U.S. Public*, pg. 97
AMERITECH PUBLISHING, INC.—Ameritech Corporation; *U.S. Public*, pg. 98
AMWAY CORPORATION; *U.S. Private*, pg. 69
ARANDELL CORPORATION; *U.S. Private*, pg. 79
ARKANSAS ELECTRIC COOPERATIVES INC.; *U.S. Private*, pg. 82
ASPEN PUBLISHERS, INC.—Wolters Kluwer N.V.; *Int'l*, pg. 1513
ASSOCIATED MUSIC PUBLISHERS—Music Sales Corporation; *U.S. Private*, pg. 768
AUGSBURG FORTRESS, PUBLISHERS; *U.S. Private*, pg. 98
BMG ARIOLA MUSICA S.P.A.—Bertelsmann AG; *Int'l*, pg. 192
BMG ARIOLA S.A. (FRANCE)—Bertelsmann AG; *Int'l*, pg. 192
BARANCORP; *U.S. Private*, pg. 115
BELLSOUTH CORPORATION; *U.S. Public*, pg. 207
JOHN BENJAMINS BV; *Int'l*, pg. 187
JOHN BENJAMINS NORTH AMERICA INC—John Benjamins BV; *Int'l*, pg. 187
BERTELSMANN MUSIC GROUP—Bertelsmann AG; *Int'l*, pg. 191
A.M. BEST COMPANY; *U.S. Private*, pg. 139
CHANNING L. BETE CO., INC.; *U.S. Private*, pg. 140
BONANZA BOOKS—Advance Publications Inc.; *U.S. Private*, pg. 21
BOOKAZINE COMPANY, INC.; *U.S. Private*, pg. 156
BOOKER ENTERTAINMENT—Booker PLC; *Int'l*, pg. 202
R.R. BOWKER—Reed Elsevier plc; *Int'l*, pg. 1096
BOWKER-SAUR LTD.—Reed Elsevier plc; *Int'l*, pg. 1094
BUTLER CAPITAL CORP.; *U.S. Private*, pg. 190
BUTTERICK COMPANY, INC.; *U.S. Private*, pg. 190
CCH AUSTRALIA LIMITED—Wolters Kluwer N.V.; *Int'l*, pg. 1513
CCH CANADIAN LTD.—Wolters Kluwer N.V.; *Int'l*, pg. 1513
CCH EDITIONS LIMITED—Wolters Kluwer N.V.; *Int'l*, pg. 1514
CCH INCORPORATED—Wolters Kluwer N.V.; *Int'l*, pg. 1513
C.E.P. COMMUNICATION GROUP; *Int'l*, pg. 239
CMP MEDIA, INC.; *U.S. Public*, pg. 279
CANADIAN ART PRINTS—Devon Group, Inc.; *U.S. Public*, pg. 503
CAPITOL INDUSTRIES-EMI INC.—EMI Group plc; *Int'l*, pg. 427
CAREERTRACK INC.—TCI Communications, Inc.; *U.S. Public*, pg. 1555
CINCINNATI BELL DIRECTORY INC.—Cincinnati Bell Telephone; *U.S. Public*, pg. 367
COMMUNICATIONS INTERNATIONAL (NY); *U.S. Private*, pg. 259
COMPAGNIE GENERALE DES ETABLISSEMENTS MICHELIN; *Int'l*, pg. 322
COMPUTER INTELLIGENCE—Softbank Corporation; *Int'l*, pg. 1276
CONCORDIA PUBLISHING HOUSE; *U.S. Private*, pg. 261
CONTINENTAL WEB PRESS OF KENTUCKY—Continental Web Press, Inc.; *U.S. Private*, pg. 269
COURIER COMPANIES, INC.—Courier Corporation; *U.S. Public*, pg. 453
COURIER CORPORATION; *U.S. Public*, pg. 453
COURIER INTERNATIONAL, LTD.—Courier Corporation; *U.S. Public*, pg. 453
COWLES SYNDICATE, INC.—The Hearst Corporation; *U.S.* Private, pg. 518
COX ENTERPRISES, INC.; *U.S. Private*, pg. 281
THE CREATIVE SERVICES INC.—Proudfoot plc; *Int'l*, pg. 1072
CRONER PUBLICATIONS, LTD.—Wolters Kluwer N.V.; *Int'l*, *pg. 1514*
CROWN PUBLISHERS, INC.—Advance Publications Inc.; *U.S. Private*, pg. 21
DRI EUROPE, INC.—The McGraw-Hill Companies; *U.S. Public*, pg. 1072
DRI EUROPE (U.K.) LTD.—The McGraw-Hill Companies; *U.S. Public*, pg. 1072
DA CAPO PRESS, INC.—Plenum Publishing Corporation; *U.S. Public*, pg. 1311
THE DARTNELL CORPORATION; *U.S. Private*, pg. 312
DATA NATIONAL—Volt Information Sciences, Inc.; *U.S. Public*, pg. 1724
DATA SOURCES—The Thomson Corporation; *U.S. Public*, pg. 1600
DATAPRO INFORMATION SERVICES GRP.—The McGraw-Hill Companies; *U.S. Public*, pg. 1070
DELMAR—Herff Jones Inc.; *U.S. Private*, pg. 523
DERWENT PUBLICATIONS LTD.—The Thomson Corporation; *U.S. Public*, pg. 1601
DEVON GROUP, INC.; *U.S. Public*, pg. 503
DEVON PUBLISHING GROUP—Devon Group, Inc.; *U.S. Public*, pg. 503
DISPATCH CONSUMER SERVICES—The Dispatch Printing Company; *U.S. Private*, pg. 335
DIVERSIFIED COMMUNICATIONS; *U.S. Private*, pg. 336
DONNELLEY INFORMATION PUBLISHING, INC.—The Dun & Bradstreet Corporation; *U.S. Public*, pg. 535
R.R. DONNELLEY NORWEST DIV.-GREELEY—R.R. Donnelley & Sons Company; *U.S. Public*, pg. 518
THE REUBEN H. DONNELLEY CORPORATION—The Dun & Bradstreet Corporation; *U.S. Public*, pg. 535
DONTECH—Ameritech Corporation; *U.S. Public*, pg. 98
DONTECH—The Dun & Bradstreet Corporation; *U.S. Public*, pg. 535
DOODLE ART DIV.—The Seagram Company Ltd.; *Int'l*, pg. 1215
THE DUN & BRADSTREET CORPORATION; *U.S. Public*, pg. 535
EMC CORPORATION; *U.S. Public*, pg. 545
EMI MUSIC PUBLISHING—EMI Group plc; *Int'l*, pg. 427
E.Z. EDITIONS ZURICH AG.—Philip Morris Companies Inc.; *U.S. Public*, pg. 1288
EATEL PUBLISHING INC.—Eatelcorp Inc.; *U.S. Private*, pg. 358
THE ECONOMICS PRESS, INC.; *U.S. Private*, pg. 362
ELECTRONIC ENGINEERS MASTER—The Hearst Corporation; *U.S. Private*, pg. 516
ELSEVIER EDITORIAL SERVICES—Reed Elsevier plc; *Int'l*, *pg. 1100*
ELSEVIER ELECTRONIC PUBLISHING SERVICES—Reed Elsevier plc; *Int'l*, pg. 1100
ELSEVIER NV—Reed Elsevier plc; *Int'l*, pg. 1093
ELSEVIER REED FINANCE BV—Reed Elsevier plc; *Int'l*, pg. 1093
ENCYCLOPAEDIA BRITANNICA, INC.; *U.S. Private*, pg. 375

ENTERTAINMENT PUBLICATIONS, INC.—Cendant Corporation; *U.S. Public*, pg. 320
FAMOUS MUSIC CORPORATION—National Amusements, Inc.; *U.S. Private*, pg. 777
FINANCIAL TRAINING COMPANY—Wolters Kluwer N.V.; *Int'l*, pg. 1514
FINANCIAL WORLD PARTNERS; *U.S. Private*, pg. 404
FOTOLAB LIMITED—Tie Rack plc; *Int'l*, pg. 1389
GTE INFORMATION SERVICES INCORPORATED—GTE Corporation; *U.S. Public*, pg. 696
GANNETT COMPANY, INC.; *U.S. Public*, pg. 698
GENERAL MEDIA INTERNATIONAL INC.; *U.S. Private*, pg. 444
GEYER-MCALLISTER PUBLICATIONS, INC.; *U.S. Private*, *pg. 450*
MARY GLASGOW PUBLICATIONS LTD.—Wolters Kluwer N.V.; *Int'l*, pg. 1514
GOLDEN BOOKS FAMILY ENTERTAINMENT INC.; *U.S. Public*, pg. 749
GOLDEN BOOKS PUBLISHING—Golden Books Family Entertainment Inc.; *U.S. Public*, pg. 749
GORDON PUBLICATIONS, INC.—Reed Elsevier plc; *Int'l*, pg. 1096
GRAHAM & TROTMAN—Wolters Kluwer N.V.; *Int'l*, pg. 1513
HAAS PUBLISHING COMPANIES, INC.—Primedia Inc.; *U.S. Public*, pg. 1327
HAKUHODO CORPORATE SOUND DESIGN CO., LTD.—Hakuhodo Incorporated; *Int'l*, pg. 587
HANDELSBLATT-DOW JONES GMBH—Georg von Holtzbrinck GmbH; *Int'l*, pg. 1479
HARCOURT BRACE & COMPANY MEDIA SYSTEMS CORPORATION—Harcourt General, Inc.; *U.S. Public*, pg. 783
HARMONY BOOKS—Advance Publications Inc.; *U.S. Private*, pg. 21
HEALTHCARE MANAGEMENT GROUP—The McGraw-Hill Companies; *U.S. Public*, pg. 1071
IPSOA S.A.R.L.—Wolters Kluwer N.V.; *Int'l*, pg. 1514
IMPRIMERIE WALLON—Nestle S.A.; *Int'l*, pg. 919
IMPRINT NEWPAPERS—Journal Register Company; *U.S. Public*, pg. 935
INFOCORP—Softbank Corporation; *Int'l*, pg. 1276
INFORMATION ACCESS CO.—The Thomson Corporation; *U.S. Public*, pg. 1600
INSTITUTE FOR SCIENTIFIC INFORMATION—The Thomson Corporation; *U.S. Public*, pg. 1600
INTEGRATED CIRCUITS MASTER CATALOG—The Hearst Corporation; *U.S. Private*, pg. 516
INTERAVIA PUBLISHING GROUP—The Thomson Corporation; *U.S. Public*, pg. 1601
ISLAND MUSIC, INC.—Philips Electronics N.V.; *Int'l*, pg. 1052
JII/SALES PROMOTION ASSOCIATES, INC.—Jordan Industries, Inc.; *U.S. Private*, pg. 598
JANE'S INFORMATION GROUP—The Thomson Corporation; *U.S. Public*, pg. 1601
JANOME SEWING MACHINE CO., LTD.; *Int'l*, pg. 699
JEPPESEN AND CO. GMBH—The Times Mirror Company; *U.S. Public*, pg. 1617
JULIAN PRESS—Advance Publications Inc.; *U.S. Private*, pg. 21
KCI COMMUNICATIONS, INC—National Information Corporation; *U.S. Private*, pg. 784
J.J. KELLER & ASSOCIATES, INC.; *U.S. Private*, pg. 612
KLUWER ACADEMIC PUBLISHERS—Wolters Kluwer N.V.; *Int'l*, pg. 1513
KODANSHA INTERNATIONAL LTD—Kodansha Ltd.; *Int'l*, pg. 742
KODANSHA LTD.; *Int'l*, pg. 742
KODANSHA SCIENTIFIC LTD.—Kodansha Ltd.; *Int'l*, pg. 742
LEISURE ARTS, INC.—Time Warner Inc.; *U.S. Public*, pg. 1613
LES PUBLICATIONS CCH/FM LTEE—Wolters Kluwer N.V.; *Int'l*, pg. 1513
LIPPINCOTT-RAVEN PUBLISHING—Wolters Kluwer N.V.; *Int'l*, pg. 1513
LONGMAN GROUP UK LTD.—Pearson plc; *Int'l*, pg. 1025
LONGMAN GROUP USA INC.—Pearson plc; *Int'l*, pg. 1026
MACK PRINTING COMPANY; *U.S. Private*, pg. 691
MACMILLAN PUBLISHING USA—National Amusements, Inc.; *U.S. Private*, pg. 777
MANUFACTURERS' NEWS, INC.; *U.S. Private*, pg. 700
MARQUIS WHO'S WHO—Reed Elsevier plc; *Int'l*, pg. 1096
MARTIN LAWRENCE LIMITED EDITIONS, INC.; *U.S. Private*, pg. 709
MARTINDALE-HUBBELL—Reed Elsevier plc; *Int'l*, pg. 1096
MARUZEN ASIA PRIVATE LTD.—Maruzen Company Limited; *Int'l*, pg. 846
MARUZEN BOOKMATES CO., LTD.—Maruzen Company Limited; *Int'l*, pg. 846
MARUZEN COMPANY LIMITED; *Int'l*, pg. 845
MARUZEN INTERNATIONAL CO., LTD.—Maruzen Company Limited; *Int'l*, pg. 846
MAXWELL MACMILLAN PROFESSIONAL & BUSINESS REFERENCE PUBLISHING—The Thomson Corporation; *U.S. Public*, pg. 1602
MCARDLE PRINTING CO., INC.—The Bureau of National Affairs, Inc.; *U.S. Private*, pg. 182
MCCLATCHY NEWSPAPERS INC.; *U.S. Public*, pg. 1065
THE MCGRAW-HILL COMPANIES; *U.S. Public*, pg. 1069
MCGRAW-HILL INFORMATION SYSTEMS CO. OF CANADA LTD.—The McGraw-Hill Companies; *U.S. Public*, pg. 1072
THE MEAD CORPORATION; *U.S. Public*, pg. 1074
MEDIA GENERAL, INC.; *U.S. Public*, pg. 1077
MEDICAL ECONOMICS COMPANY INC.—The Thomson Corporation; *U.S. Public*, pg. 1601
MEREDITH VIDEO PUBLISHING—Meredith Corporation; *U.S. Public*, pg. 1094
MERRILL CORPORATION; *U.S. Public*, pg. 1097
METROPOLITAN SUNDAY NEWSPAPERS, INC.; *U.S. Private*, pg. 739
MITCHELL INTERNATIONAL—The Thomson Corporation; *U.S. Public*, pg. 1601
MOTHER EARTH NEWS—Sussex Publishers, Inc.; *U.S. Private*, pg. 1056
MOTOR CRASH ESTIMATING GUIDE—The Hearst Corporation; *U.S. Private*, pg. 516
MULTI-LOCAL MEDIA CORPORATION; *U.S. Private*, pg. 767
MUSEUM BOUTIQUE INTERCONTINENTAL, LTD.; *U.S. Private*, pg. 768
MUSIC SALES CORPORATION; *U.S. Private*, pg. 768
NTS—First Data Corporation; *U.S. Public*, pg. 631
NATIONAL INSTITUTE OF BUSINESS MANAGEMENT, INC.—National Information Corporation; *U.S. Private*, pg. 785
NATIONAL REGISTER PUBLISHING—Reed Elsevier plc; *Int'l*, pg. 1096
NELSON PUBLICATIONS—Primedia Inc.; *U.S. Public*, pg. 1328
NORWEST DIVISION—R.R. Donnelley & Sons Company; *U.S. Public*, pg. 518
OAG—Reed Elsevier plc; *Int'l*, pg. 1097
O'NEIL DATA SYSTEMS, INC.—William O'Neil & Co., Inc.; *U.S. Private*, pg. 817
O'RYAN BOOKS—Advance Publications Inc.; *U.S. Private*, pg. 21
PACIFIC TELECOM, INC.—Century Telephone Enterprises, Inc.; *U.S. Public*, pg. 330
PEARSON PLC; *Int'l*, pg. 1025
GEORGE PHILIP LIMITED—Reed Elsevier plc; *Int'l*, pg. 1094
PHILLIPS PUBLISHING INTERNATIONAL, INC.; *U.S. Private*, pg. 862
PITKIN GUIDES—Reed Elsevier plc; *Int'l*, pg. 1094
R.L. POLK & CO.; *U.S. Private*, pg. 874
POLYGRAM INTERNATIONAL LTD.—Philips Electronics N.V.; *Int'l*, pg. 1053
POLYGRAM MUSIC PUBLISHING, INC.—Philips Electronics N.V.; *Int'l*, pg. 1052
POLYGRAM N.V.—Philips Electronics N.V.; *Int'l*, pg. 1051
PORTAL AIRD PUBLICATIONS PTY. LTD.—Devon Group, Inc.; *U.S. Public*, pg. 503
PORTAL PUBLICATIONS, LTD.—Devon Group, Inc.; *U.S. Public*, pg. 503
PORTAL PUBLICATIONS LTD.—Devon Group, Inc.; *U.S. Public*, pg. 503
PORTLAND HOUSE—Advance Publications Inc.; *U.S. Private*, pg. 21
CLARKSON N. POTTER, INC.—Advance Publications Inc.; *U.S. Private*, pg. 21
PRACTITIONERS PUBLISHING CO.—The Thomson Corporation; *U.S. Public*, pg. 1601
PREDICASTS—The Thomson Corporation; *U.S. Public*, pg. 1600
PRENTICE-HALL HISPANOAMERICANA, S.A.—National Amusements, Inc.; *U.S. Private*, pg. 778
PRICE STERN SLOAN INC.—The Seagram Company Ltd.; *Int'l*, pg. 1215
PRIMEDIA INFORMATIN GROUP—Primedia Inc.; *U.S. Public*, pg. 1328
PRINTING HOUSE, INC.; *U.S. Private*, pg. 886
PROFESSIONAL PUBLISHING LTD.—The Thomson Corporation; *U.S. Public*, pg. 1601
PROGNOS AG—Georg von Holtzbrinck GmbH; *Int'l*, pg. 1480
THE PSYCHOLOGICAL CORP.—Harcourt General, Inc.; *U.S. Public*, pg. 784
QUEBECOR PRINTING ST. PAUL INC.—Quebecor Inc.; *Int'l*, pg. 1078
QUESTRON DIV.—The Seagram Company Ltd.; *Int'l*, pg. 1215
RAND MCNALLY & COMPANY; *U.S. Private*, pg. 908
REED BUSINESS INFORMATION—Reed Elsevier plc; *Int'l*, *pg. 1094*
REED BUSINESS INFORMATION (USA)—Reed Elsevier plc; *Int'l*, pg. 1094
REED ELSEVIER NEDERLAND BV—Reed Elsevier plc; *Int'l*, pg. 1100
REED ELSEVIER PLC; *Int'l*, pg. 1093
REED INTERNATIONAL P.L.C.—Reed Elsevier plc; *Int'l*, pg. 1093
RENAISSANCE PUBLISHING CO., INC.—Bemrose Corporation; *Int'l*, pg. 185
RESEARCH PUBLICATIONS, INC.—The Thomson Corporation; *U.S. Public*, pg. 1600
RICHARD DE BOO PUBLISHERS—The Thomson Corporation; *U.S. Public*, pg. 1601
SRA MCGRAW HILL—The McGraw-Hill Companies; *U.S. Public*, pg. 1070
SRDS; *U.S. Private*, pg. 958
WILLIAM H. SADLIER, INC.; *U.S. Public*, pg. 1422
ST. LOUIS BUSINESS JOURNAL CORP.—Advance Publications Inc.; *U.S. Private*, pg. 20
ST. MARTINS PRESS, INC.—Georg von Holtzbrinck GmbH; *Int'l*, pg. 1479
SAMPLER PUBLICATIONS INC.; *U.S. Private*, pg. 963
K.G. SAUR—Reed Elsevier plc; *Int'l*, pg. 1099
G. SCHIRMER, INC.—Music Sales Corporation; *U.S. Private*, pg. 768
SCHOOL ANNUAL PUBLISHING CO.—Jordan Industries, Inc.; *U.S. Private*, pg. 598
SCICOM DATA SERVICES, LTD.; *U.S. Private*, pg. 975
THE E.W. SCRIPPS COMPANY; *U.S. Public*, pg. 1447
SHAWNEE PRESS, INC.—Music Sales Corporation; *U.S. Private*, pg. 768
SIMPLICITY HOLDINGS INC.; *U.S. Private*, pg. 1002
SONY MUSIC, NASHVILLE—Sony Corporation; *Int'l*, pg. 1284
SOUTH-WESTERN PUBLISHING COMPANY—The Thomson Corporation; *U.S. Public*, pg. 1600
SOUTHAM INC.—Hollinger Inc.; *Int'l*, pg. 631
SPEKTRUM DER WISSENSCHAFT VERLAGSGESELLSCHAFT MBH—Georg von Holtzbrinck GmbH; *Int'l*, pg. 1478
SPRINT PUBLISHING & ADVERTISING—Sprint Corporation; *U.S. Public*, pg. 1501
STANDARD & POOR'S INTERNATIONAL S.A.—The McGraw-Hill Companies; *U.S. Public*, pg. 1072
STREAM—Telecom Italia S.p.A.; *Int'l*, pg. 1363
SUNDAY MAGAZINE NETWORK—Metropolitan Sunday Newspapers, Inc.; *U.S. Private*, pg. 739
SWEET'S DIV.—The McGraw-Hill Companies; *U.S. Public*, pg. 1070
TATA MCGRAW-HILL PUBLISHING CO., PRIVATE LIMITED—The McGraw-Hill Companies; *U.S. Public*, pg. 1072
TAYLOR PUBLISHING CO.—Insilco Corporation; *U.S. Public*, pg. 881
TECHNICAL INFORMATION (SINTEP)—Petrobras - Petroleo Brasileiro S.A.; *Int'l*, pg. 1042
TELEFONICA PUBLICIDAD E INFORMAC.—Telefonica de Espana, S.A.; *Int'l*, pg. 1372
TELUS ADVERTISING SERVICES—Telus Corporation; *Int'l*, *pg. 1374*
TEXAS ELECTRIC COOPERATIVES, INC.; *U.S. Private*, pg. 1078
THOMAS PUBLISHING COMPANY; *U.S. Private*, pg. 1082
THOMSON BOOK/REFERENCE GROUP—The Thomson Corporation; *U.S. Public*, pg. 1600
THE THOMSON CORPORATION; *U.S. Public*, pg. 1599
THOMSON INTERNATIONAL HOLDINGS LIMITED—The Thomson Corporation; *U.S. Public*, pg. 1600
THOMSON PROFESSIONAL PUBLISHING—The Thomson Corporation; *U.S. Public*, pg. 1601
THOMSON U.S. INC.—The Thomson Corporation; *U.S. Public*, pg. 1601
D.W. THORPE-AUSTRALIA—Reed Elsevier plc; *Int'l*, pg. 1095
TIE RACK PLC; *Int'l*, pg. 1389
TIME/SYSTEM INTERNATIONAL A/S—Amer Group Ltd.; *Int'l*, pg. 73
TOKYO LIFESTYLES INSTITUTE, INC.—Matsuya Company Ltd.; *Int'l*, pg. 848
TOP VALUE MEDIA—Metropolitan Sunday Newspapers, Inc.; *U.S. Private*, pg. 739
THE TOPPS COMPANY, INC.; *U.S. Public*, pg. 1621
TURNER MUSIC PUBLISHING, INC.—Time Warner Inc.; *U.S. Public*, pg. 1615
UNITED ADVERTISING PUBLICATIONS, INC.—United News & Media plc; *Int'l*, pg. 1443
U S WEST DEX—U S West Inc.; *U.S. Public*, pg. 1689
U S WEST INC.; *U.S. Public*, pg. 1688
UNIVERSAL STUDIOS, INC.—The Seagram Company Ltd.; *Int'l*, pg. 1215
UNIVERSAL STUDIOS MUSIC KK—The Seagram Company Ltd.; *Int'l*, pg. 1217
VDI-VERLAG GMBH—Georg von Holtzbrinck GmbH; *Int'l*, pg. 1479
VALUE LINE, INC.—Arnold Bernhard & Co.; *U.S. Private*, pg. 137
VERLAGSGRUPPE HANDELSBLATT GMBH—Georg von Holtzbrinck GmbH; *Int'l*, pg. 1479
VISPAC INC.—VSI Holdings, Inc.; *U.S. Public*, pg. 1703
VOLT-AUTOLOGIC DIRECTORIES S.A.—Volt Information Sciences, Inc.; *U.S. Public*, pg. 1724
VOLT DIRECTORY SERVICES—Volt Information Sciences, Inc.; *U.S. Public*, pg. 1724
VOLT INFORMATION SCIENCES, INC.; *U.S. Public*, pg. 1724
W/A MUSIC CORPORATION—Baton Broadcasting Incorporated; *Int'l*, pg. 171
WM WIRTSCHAFTS-MEDIEN AG—Georg von Holtzbrinck GmbH; *Int'l*, pg. 1480
WAL-MART STORES, INC.; *U.S. Public*, pg. 1732
WARNER MUSIC GROUP, INC.—Time Warner Inc.; *U.S. Public*, pg. 1612
WARREN GORHAM LAMONT—The Thomson Corporation; *U.S. Public*, pg. 1602
WENNER MEDIA; *U.S. Private*, pg. 1162
WEST INFORMATION PUBLISHING GROUP—The Thomson Corporation; *U.S. Public*, pg. 1602
WESTERN STATES ASSOC.—Metropolitan Sunday Newspapers, Inc.; *U.S. Private*, pg. 739
WESTINGHOUSE INDUSTRIES & TECHNOLOGIES GROUP—CBS Corporation; *U.S. Public*, pg. 273
JOHN WILEY & SONS, INC.; *U.S. Public*, pg. 1768
THE H.W. WILSON CO.; *U.S. Private*, pg. 1180
THE WINN ART GROUP, LTD.—Devon Group, Inc.; *U.S. Public*, pg. 503
WINSTON CUP SCENE—Advance Publications Inc.; *U.S. Private*, pg. 20
WIRTSCHAFTSWOCHE ZEITSCHRIFTEN-VERLAGSGESELLSCHAFT M.B.H. & CO. KG—Georg von Holtzbrinck GmbH; *Int'l*, pg. 1479
WOLFER PRINTING COMPANY; *U.S. Private*, pg. 1186
WOLTERS KLUWER ACADEMIC PUBLISHERS—Wolters Kluwer N.V.; *Int'l*, pg. 1512
WOLTERS KLUWER BELGIUM—Wolters Kluwer N.V.; *Int'l*, *pg. 1513*
WOLTERS KLUWER EDUCATIONAL ACTIVITIES—Wolters Kluwer N.V.; *Int'l*, pg. 1513
WOLTERS KLUWER FRANCE—Wolters Kluwer N.V.; *Int'l*, pg. 1513
WOLTERS KLUWER GERMANY—Wolters Kluwer N.V.; *Int'l*, pg. 1513
WOLTERS KLUWER LAW AND TAXATION—Wolters Kluwer N.V.; *Int'l*, pg. 1513
WOLTERS KLUWER N.V.; *Int'l*, pg. 1512
WOLTERS KLUWER SPAIN—Wolters Kluwer N.V.; *Int'l*, pg. 1514
WOLTERS KLUWER SWEDEN—Wolters Kluwer N.V.; *Int'l*, pg. 1514
WOLTERS KLUWER TRADE PUBLISHING—Wolters Kluwer N.V.; *Int'l*, pg. 1513
WOLTERS KLUWER U.K.—Wolters Kluwer N.V.; *Int'l*, pg. 1514
WONDERLAND MUSIC CO., INC.—The Walt Disney Company; *U.S. Public*, pg. 514

WORLD COLOR-CHICAGO DIV.—World Color Press, Inc.; *U.S. Public*, pg. 1778
WORLD COLOR PRESS, INC.; *U.S. Public*, pg. 1778
XYVISION, INC.; *U.S. Public*, pg. 1787
XYVISION LIMITED—Xyvision, Inc.; *U.S. Public*, pg. 1787
YANKEE PUBLISHING INCORPORATED; *U.S. Private*, pg. 1195
ZIFF-DAVIS PUBLISHING COMPANY—Softbank Corporation; *Int'l*, pg. 1276
ZIFF INFORMATION SERVICES—Softbank Corporation; *Int'l*, pg. 1276
THE ZONDERVAN CORPORATION—The News Corporation Limited; *Int'l*, pg. 927

2752 — COMMERCIAL PRINTING, LITHOGRAPHIC

ADAMS BUSINESS FORMS; *U.S. Private*, pg. 16
ADVANCE BUSINESS GRAPHICS; *U.S. Private*, pg. 18
ALAN LITHOGRAPH, INC.; *U.S. Private*, pg. 31
ALCOM PRINTING GROUP, INC.; *U.S. Private*, pg. 33
ALDEN PRESS—World Color Press, Inc.; *U.S. Public*, pg. 1778
AMERICAN BANKERS INSURANCE GROUP, INC.; *U.S. Public*, pg. 67
AMERICAN DECAL & MFG. CO.; *U.S. Private*, pg. 53
AMERICAN GREETINGS U.S. GREETING CARD DIVISION—American Greetings Corporation; *U.S. Public*, *pg. 78*
ANDERSON LITHOGRAPH COMPANY; *U.S. Private*, pg. 72
W.E. ANDREWS CO., INC.—Wallace Computer Services, Inc.; *U.S. Public*, pg. 1735
W.E. ANDREWS CO., INC., OF CONNECTICUT—Wallace Computer Services, Inc.; *U.S. Public*, pg. 1735
APPLIED GRAPHICS—U.S. News & World Report; *U.S. Private*, pg. 1125
APPLIED GRAPHICS TECHNOLOGIES—U.S. News & World Report; *U.S. Private*, pg. 1125
ARANDELL CORPORATION; *U.S. Private*, pg. 79
ARCADE INC.; *U.S. Private*, pg. 79
ARROW INTERNATIONAL; *U.S. Private*, pg. 85
ARTHUR-JONES LITHOGRAPHING LIMITED—Jannock Limited; *Int'l*, pg. 698
ARTS & CRAFTS PRESS—Continental Graphics Holdings, Inc.; *U.S. Private*, pg. 268
THE AT-A-GLANCE GROUP—Cullman Ventures, Inc.; *U.S. Private*, pg. 295
AUTOMATIC LIQUID PACKAGING, INC.; *U.S. Private*, pg. 101
AVANTI PRESS INC.; *U.S. Private*, pg. 101
AVERY DENNISON CORPORATION; *U.S. Public*, pg. 152
BAC COLOR FRANSEWEG; *Int'l*, pg. 131
BANKERS SYSTEMS INCORPORATED; *U.S. Private*, pg. 114
BANTA CATALOG GROUP—Banta Corporation; *U.S. Public*, pg. 188
BANTA CORPORATION; *U.S. Public*, pg. 187
BANTA DIGITAL GROUP—Banta Corporation; *U.S. Public*, pg. 188
BANTA DIRECT MARKETING GROUP—Banta Corporation; *U.S. Public*, pg. 188
BANTA INFORMATION SERVICES GROUP—Banta Corporation; *U.S. Public*, pg. 188
BANTA PUBLICATIONS GROUP—Banta Corporation; *U.S. Public*, pg. 188
BARTON PRESS, INC.; *U.S. Private*, pg. 120
BAT OFFICE PRODUCTS—U.S. Office Products Company; *U.S. Public*, pg. 1686
BAUM PRINTING HOUSE, INC.—Wallace Computer Services, Inc.; *U.S. Public*, pg. 1735
BAWDEN CORPORATION; *U.S. Private*, pg. 124
BAZAAR & NOVELTY—Stuart Entertainment Inc.; *U.S. Public*, pg. 1526
BEMIS COMPANY, INC.; *U.S. Public*, pg. 210
BERLIN INDUSTRIES, INC.; *U.S. Private*, pg. 136
BERLIN INDUSTRIES, INC.—Berlin Industries, Inc.; *U.S. Private*, pg. 136
CHANNING L. BETE CO., INC.; *U.S. Private*, pg. 140
BOWNE & CO., INC.; *U.S. Public*, pg. 248
BRAUN-BRUMFIELD, INC.—The Sheridan Group; *U.S. Private*, pg. 993
BRIAN UNLIMITED DISTRIBUTION COMPANY, INC.; *U.S. Private*, pg. 167
BRITISH PRINTING COMPANY LTD.; *Int'l*, pg. 220
BROWN PRINTING CO., INC.—Bertelsmann AG; *Int'l*, pg. 190
BROWN PRINTING EAST—Bertelsmann AG; *Int'l*, pg. 190
BUREAU OF ENGRAVING; *U.S. Private*, pg. 181
CGF INDUSTRIES; *U.S. Private*, pg. 194
CSS INDUSTRIES, INC.; *U.S. Public*, pg. 283
CADMUS COMMUNICATIONS CORPORATION; *U.S. Public*, pg. 290
CADMUS JOURNAL SERVICES—Cadmus Communications Corporation; *U.S. Public*, pg. 291
CADMUS MARKETING SERVICES—Cadmus Communications Corporation; *U.S. Public*, pg. 291
CADMUS PROMOTIONAL PRINTING—Cadmus Communications Corporation; *U.S. Public*, pg. 291
CAPITAL CITY PRESS, INC.; *U.S. Private*, pg. 205
CASA GRANDE MFG. DIVISION—R.R. Donnelley & Sons Company; *U.S. Public*, pg. 518
THE CAXTON PRINTERS LTD.; *U.S. Private*, pg. 220
THE CENTRAL PRESS OF MIAMI, INC.—Wallace Computer Services, Inc.; *U.S. Public*, pg. 1735
CENTRAL STATES CAN CO.—Crown Cork & Seal Company, Inc.; *U.S. Public*, pg. 463
CENTURY PRINTING & PUBLISHING CO.—Century Telephone Enterprises, Inc.; *U.S. Public*, pg. 330
CHAMPION BUSINESS FORMS; *U.S. Private*, pg. 228
CHAMPION INDUSTRIES; *U.S. Public*, pg. 333
CHEMGRAPHICS SYSTEMS, INC.—The Chase Manhattan Corporation; *U.S. Public*, pg. 338
COLFAX ENVELOPE CORPORATION; *U.S. Private*, pg. 252
COLLMAN GRAPHICS, INC.; *U.S. Private*, pg. 253
COLONY PRINTING & LABELING—Lancaster Colony Corporation; *U.S. Public*, pg. 976
COLOR DATA EAST—Schawk, Inc.; *U.S. Public*, pg. 1437
COLWELL INDUSTRIES, INC.; *U.S. Private*, pg. 257
COMMAND WEB OFFSET CO.—MacNaughton Einson Graphics; *U.S. Private*, pg. 693
COMMUNICORP, INC.—AFLAC Incorporated; *U.S. Public*, pg. 28
CONCORD LITHO CO., INC.; *U.S. Private*, pg. 261
CONSOLIDATED GRAPHIC COMMUNICATIONS—Champion Industries; *U.S. Public*, pg. 333
CONSOLIDATED GRAPHICS, INC.; *U.S. Private*, pg. 265
CONTINENTAL GRAPHICS CORPORATION—Continental Graphics Holdings, Inc.; *U.S. Private*, pg. 268
CONTINENTAL WEB PRESS, INC.; *U.S. Private*, pg. 269
COOKSON MATTHEY PRINT—Johnson Matthey Public Limited Company; *Int'l*, pg. 713
COSCO INDUSTRIES; *U.S. Private*, pg. 277
COSMOS COMMUNICATIONS, INC.; *U.S. Private*, pg. 278
COVINGTON SPECIALTY PRINT—John H. Harland Company; *U.S. Public*, pg. 786
CRAFTSMAN PRINTING COMPANY—Wallace Computer Services, Inc.; *U.S. Public*, pg. 1735
CUMMINS-ALLISON CORP.; *U.S. Private*, pg. 295
CURTIS 1000, INC.—American Business Products, Inc.; *U.S. Public*, pg. 70
DANIELS PRINTING COMPANY; *U.S. Private*, pg. 310
DAVIDSON PRINTING COMPANY; *U.S. Private*, pg. 314
DAY INTERNATIONAL PRINTING PRODUCTS CO.—American Industrial Partners; *U.S. Private*, pg. 56
DEMOCRAT PRINTING & LITHOGRAPH COMPANY; *U.S. Private*, pg. 323
DES MOINES MFG. DIVISION—R.R. Donnelley & Sons Company; *U.S. Public*, pg. 518
DICKINSON PRESS, INC.; *U.S. Private*, pg. 331
DIRECT PRESS MODERN LITHO CORPORATION; *U.S. Private*, pg. 334
DIXONWEB PRINTING COMPANY—Sleepeck Printing Company; *U.S. Private*, pg. 1005
R.R. DONNELLEY & SONS COMPANY; *U.S. Public*, pg. 517
R.R. DONNELLEY, LIMITED-YORK—R.R. Donnelley & Sons Company; *U.S. Public*, pg. 519
DOT PRINTER, INC.; *U.S. Private*, pg. 341
DROYHURST LIMITED—James Crean PLC; *Int'l*, pg. 341
EPX; *U.S. Private*, pg. 354
EASTERN COLOR PRINTING COMPANY; *U.S. Private*, pg. 357
EDITORS PRESS, INC.—The Kiplinger Washington Editors, Inc.; *U.S. Private*, pg. 623
EDWARDS & BROUGHTON COMPANY—Wallace Computer Services, Inc.; *U.S. Public*, pg. 1735
ELLISON GRAPHICS—Herlin Press Inc.; *U.S. Private*, pg. 524
ENTERPRISE; *U.S. Private*, pg. 377
F C L GRAPHICS; *U.S. Private*, pg. 389
FEATHER FINE SERVICES—Pittway Corporation; *U.S. Public*, pg. 1306
FENTON PRESS, INC.; *U.S. Private*, pg. 400
FLEMING PACKAGING CORP.; *U.S. Private*, pg. 411
FORT DEARBORN COMPANY; *U.S. Private*, pg. 419
FORUM COMMUNICATIONS COMPANY; *U.S. Private*, pg. 420
THE FRANKLIN MINT—Roll International Corporation; *U.S. Private*, pg. 941
FREDERIC PRINTING COMPANY—Consolidated Graphics, Inc.; *U.S. Private*, pg. 265
GAC COLOR GRAPHICS—Mail-Well Inc.; *U.S. Public*, pg. 1038
GANNETT COMPANY, INC.; *U.S. Public*, pg. 698
GANNETT OFFSET—Gannett Company, Inc.; *U.S. Public*, pg. 699
THE GARBER COMPANY—Caraustar Industries, Inc.; *U.S. Public*, pg. 303
GATEWAY PRESS, INC.; *U.S. Private*, pg. 441
GAYLORD PRINTING, INC.; *U.S. Private*, pg. 441
GENERAL BUSINESS FORMS LTD.—Data Business Forms Limited; *Int'l*, pg. 384
GEORGE LITHOGRAPH; *U.S. Private*, pg. 448
GRANDVILLE PRINTING COMPANY; *U.S. Private*, pg. 469
GRAPHIC DIRECT, INC.—Wallace Computer Services, Inc.; *U.S. Public*, pg. 1735
GRAPHIC INDUSTRIES, INC.—Wallace Computer Services, Inc.; *U.S. Public*, pg. 1735
GRAPHIC TECHNOLOGY, INC.—Nitto Denko Corporation; *Int'l*, pg. 950
GRAPHICS ARTS CENTER—Mail-Well Inc.; *U.S. Public*, pg. 1038
GREAT LAKES LITHOGRAPH CO.; *U.S. Private*, pg. 474
JOHN H. HARLAND COMPANY; *U.S. Public*, pg. 785
JOHN H. HARLAND CO. OF PUERTO RICO—John H. Harland Company; *U.S. Public*, pg. 786
HART GRAPHICS INC.; *U.S. Private*, pg. 507
THE HENNEGAN COMPANY; *U.S. Private*, pg. 522
HERFF JONES YEARBOOKS—Herff Jones Inc.; *U.S. Private*, pg. 524
HERITAGE PRESS, INC.—Wallace Computer Services, Inc.; *U.S. Public*, pg. 1735
HERLIN PRESS INC.; *U.S. Private*, pg. 524
HICKORY PRINTING GROUP, INC.; *U.S. Private*, pg. 525
HOLOUBEK INC.; *U.S. Private*, pg. 536
IPD PRINTING & DISTRIBUTING, INC.—Wallace Computer Services, Inc.; *U.S. Public*, pg. 1735
IMPERIAL LITHO & DRYOGRAPHY, INC.; *U.S. Private*, pg. 558
IMPRESORA DONNECO INTERNACIONAL, S.A. DE C.V.—R.R. Donnelley & Sons Company; *U.S. Public*, pg. 519
INLAND PRINTING CO., INC.; *U.S. Private*, pg. 564
THE INSTANT WEB COMPANIES; *U.S. Private*, pg. 565
INTERFORM CORPORATION—Champion Industries; *U.S. Public*, pg. 333
INTERNATIONAL CENTER FOR ENTREPRENEURIAL DEVELOPMENT, INC.; *U.S. Private*, pg. 568
JANNOCK LIMITED; *Int'l*, pg. 698
JAPS-OLSON COMPANY; *U.S. Private*, pg. 582
JOHNSON & QUIN, INC.; *U.S. Private*, pg. 590
JOHNSON MATTHEY PUBLIC LIMITED COMPANY; *Int'l*, pg. 713
JOHNSON PRESS—Johnson Publishing Company, Inc.; *U.S. Private*, pg. 592
JOHNSON PRINTING CO.—Johnson Publishing Company, Inc.; *U.S. Private*, pg. 592
JOSTENS; *U.S. Public*, pg. 934
JOURNAL COMMUNICATIONS INC.; *U.S. Private*, pg. 601
JUDD'S, INC.—Perry Graphic Communications, Inc.; *U.S. Private*, pg. 855
JUDD'S INCORPORATED—Perry Graphic Communications, Inc.; *U.S. Private*, pg. 855
JUSTIN INDUSTRIES, INC.; *U.S. Public*, pg. 936
KOA HOLDINGS; *U.S. Private*, pg. 603
KERVICK ENTERPRISES, INC.; *U.S. Private*, pg. 616
KINKO'S SERVICE CORP.—Kinko's Corporation; *U.S. Private*, pg. 622
KRIPS REPRO B.V.—Reed Elsevier plc; *Int'l*, pg. 1100
KRUPP DRUCKEREIBETRIEBE GMBH—Fried. Krupp AG; *Int'l*, pg. 513
KRUPP HOESCH DIENSTLEISTIGUNGEN GMBH—Fried. Krupp AG; *Int'l*, pg. 512
KURTZ BROS., INC.; *U.S. Private*, pg. 637
LSI/KALA—Schawk, Inc.; *U.S. Public*, pg. 1437
LABEL ART, INC.—National Fiberstock Corporation; *U.S. Private*, pg. 782
LABEL PRODUCTS & DESIGN DIVISION—Journal Communications Inc.; *U.S. Private*, pg. 602
LAKE COUNTY PRESS; *U.S. Private*, pg. 643
LANE PRESS, INC.; *U.S. Private*, pg. 650
LASON, INC.—Lason, Inc.; *U.S. Public*, pg. 979
LAWSON MARDON PACKAGING INC.—Alusuisse-Lonza Holding Ltd.; *Int'l*, pg. 68
LITHO COLORPLATE—Schawk, Inc.; *U.S. Public*, pg. 1437
LITHO-KROME COMPANY—Hallmark Cards, Inc.; *U.S. Private*, pg. 496
LITHOGRAPH PRINTING COMPANY, INC.—Master Graphic, Inc.; *U.S. Private*, pg. 713
LITHOGRAPHIX, INC.; *U.S. Private*, pg. 670
LITHOTYPE COMPANY, INC.; *U.S. Private*, pg. 670
JOHN D. LUCAS PRINTING COMPANY—Collman Graphics, Inc.; *U.S. Private*, pg. 253
LYKE CORPORATION; *U.S. Private*, pg. 682
LYNCHBURG GRAPHICS SERVICE CENTER—R.R. Donnelley & Sons Company; *U.S. Public*, pg. 518
MACK PRINTING COMPANY; *U.S. Private*, pg. 691
MACK PRINTING GROUP (EAST STROUDSBURG DIV.)—Mack Printing Company; *U.S. Private*, pg. 692
MACNAUGHTON EINSON GRAPHICS; *U.S. Private*, pg. 692
MADISON GRAHAM COLORGRAPHICS, INC.; *U.S. Private*, pg. 694
MASTER GRAPHIC, INC.; *U.S. Private*, pg. 713
MAUL-BELSER GMBH; *Int'l*, pg. 849
MCCLATCHY NEWSPAPERS INC.; *U.S. Public*, pg. 1065
MCCLATCHY PRINTING SERVICE—McClatchy Newspapers Inc.; *U.S. Public*, pg. 1066
MCRAE INDUSTRIES, INC.; *U.S. Public*, pg. 1073
MEDIA PRINTING CORPORATION; *U.S. Private*, pg. 726
MENASHA CORPORATION; *U.S. Private*, pg. 731
MERCHANTS PUBLISHING CO.; *U.S. Private*, pg. 732
MERCURY PRINTING COMPANY, INC.—Wallace Computer Services, Inc.; *U.S. Public*, pg. 1736
MERRILL CORPORATION; *U.S. Public*, pg. 1097
THE MERTEN COMPANY—Champion Industries; *U.S. Public*, pg. 333
THE MEYERCORD COMPANY—Illinois Tool Works Inc.; *U.S. Public*, pg. 867
MICKELBERRY COMMUNICATIONS, INC.; *U.S. Private*, pg. 741
MIDWEST LITHO ARTS—World Color Press, Inc.; *U.S. Public*, pg. 1779
MIKEN COMPANIES, INC.; *U.S. Private*, pg. 745
H.C. MILLER COMPANY; *U.S. Private*, pg. 747
MONROE LITHO INC.—Wallace Computer Services, Inc.; *U.S. Public*, pg. 1736
MOORE CORPORATION LIMITED; *Int'l*, pg. 888
NATIONAL BANNER COMPANY, INC.; *U.S. Private*, pg. 780
NATIONAL COMPUTER SUPPLIES—Riccobon & Company, Inc.; *U.S. Private*, pg. 927
NATIONAL POSTERS, INC.—National Print Group, Inc.; *U.S. Private*, pg. 786
NATIONAL PRINT GROUP, INC.; *U.S. Private*, pg. 785
NEW ENGLAND BUSINESS SERVICE—New England Business Service, Inc.; *U.S. Public*, pg. 1171
NEW ENGLAND BUSINESS SERVICE INC.—New England Business Service, Inc.; *U.S. Public*, pg. 1171
NEWS & RECORD—Landmark Communications, Inc.; *U.S. Private*, pg. 649
NEWTON-SOUTHEASTERN MFG. DIV.—R.R. Donnelley & Sons Company; *U.S. Public*, pg. 518
THE NIELSEN COMPANY; *U.S. Private*, pg. 799
NORTH STAR/NORWAY—Journal Communications Inc.; *U.S. Private*, pg. 602
NORTH STAR PRINT GROUP INC.—Journal Communications Inc.; *U.S. Private*, pg. 601
OFFICE ELECTRONICS, INC.; *U.S. Private*, pg. 812
OPTIC GRAPHICS, INC.; *U.S. Private*, pg. 818
OUTLOOK GROUP CORPORATION; *U.S. Public*, pg. 1235
PACE PRESS, INC.; *U.S. Private*, pg. 829
PACE RESOURCES, INC.; *U.S. Private*, pg. 829
PANEL PRINTS, INC.; *U.S. Private*, pg. 836
PATSON'S PRESS; *U.S. Private*, pg. 843
PAXAR CORPORATION; *U.S. Public*, pg. 1266
PEAKE PRINTERS, INC.; *U.S. Private*, pg. 845
PEARL-PRESSMAN-LIBERTY COMMUNICATIONS GROUP; *U.S. Private*, pg. 845
DAVID L. PEISTER CO., INC.; *U.S. Private*, pg. 848

PERLMUTER PRINTING COMPANY—St. Ives plc; *Int'l*, pg. 1177
PERRY GRAPHIC COMMUNICATIONS, INC.; *U.S. Private*, pg. 855
PETERSEN GRAPHICS GROUP; *U.S. Private*, pg. 856
PETTY COMPANY, INC.; *U.S. Private*, pg. 860
PHIPPS PRESS, INC.—Jannock Limited; *Int'l*, pg. 699
PHOTO MECHANICAL SERVICES INC.—Proto Systems of Atlanta; *U.S. Private*, pg. 891
PHOTOTYPE COLOR GRAPHICS, INC.; *U.S. Private*, pg. 864
PIONEER PAPER CORPORATION; *U.S. Private*, pg. 867
PORT CITY PRESS, INC.—Perry Graphic Communications, Inc.; *U.S. Private*, pg. 855
POTOMAC GRAPHIC INDUSTRIES, INC.—Jannock Limited; *Int'l*, pg. 699
PRINT NORTHWEST COMPANY, L.P.—Quebecor Inc.; *Int'l*, pg. 1076
PRINT-O-STAT, INC.—Pace Resources, Inc.; *U.S. Private*, pg. 830
PRINTCO GROUP—Big Flower Press Holdings, Inc.; *U.S. Public*, pg. 228
PRINTING HOUSE, INC.; *U.S. Private*, pg. 886
PRINTING SERVICE INCORPORATED—Wallace Computer Services, Inc.; *U.S. Public*, pg. 1736
PROCESS COLOR PLATE—Schawk, Inc.; *U.S. Public*, pg. 1437
PROGRESS PRINTING COMPANY; *U.S. Private*, pg. 890
QUAD/GRAPHICS, INC.; *U.S. Private*, pg. 897
QUAD/WEST PRE-PRESS—Quad/Graphics, Inc.; *U.S. Private*, pg. 898
QUEBECOR LITHO PLUS—Quebecor Inc.; *Int'l*, pg. 1076
QUEBECOR PRINTING FEDERATED INC.—Quebecor Inc.; *Int'l*, pg. 1078
QUEBECOR PRINTING ST. PAUL INC.—Quebecor Inc.; *Int'l*, pg. 1078
QUIK PRINT INC.—Foster Management Co.; *U.S. Private*, pg. 421
RAMA GROUP OF COMPANIES; *U.S. Private*, pg. 908
RAND MCNALLY & COMPANY; *U.S. Private*, pg. 908
READING EAGLE COMPANY; *U.S. Private*, pg. 913
REGENCY GROUP INC.; *U.S. Private*, pg. 918
RICCOBON & COMPANY, INC.; *U.S. Private*, pg. 927
GEORGE RICE & SONS—World Color Press, Inc.; *U.S. Public*, pg. 1779
RINGIER AG; *Int'l*, pg. 1118
RINGIER AMERICA, JONESBORO DIVISION—World Color Press, Inc.; *U.S. Public*, pg. 1778
RINGIER AMERICA, NEW BERLIN DIVISION—World Color Press, Inc.; *U.S. Public*, pg. 1778
RIPLEY GRAPHICS—American Greetings Corporation; *U.S. Public*, pg. 78
JOHN ROBERTS COMPANY; *U.S. Private*, pg. 935
RUSH PRESS—Continental Graphics Holdings, Inc.; *U.S. Private*, pg. 268
S & S GRAPHICS, INC.; *U.S. Private*, pg. 955
S L C GRAPHICS, LP; *U.S. Private*, pg. 955
SNC-LAVALIN GROUP INC.; *Int'l*, pg. 1161
SVG LITHOGRAPHY SYSTEMS—Silicon Valley Group, Inc.; *U.S. Public*, pg. 1474
SAN FRANCISCO NEWSPAPER AGENCY—Chronicle Publishing Co. Inc.; *U.S. Private*, pg. 239
SCANFORMS, INC.—Big Flower Press Holdings, Inc.; *U.S. Public*, pg. 228
SCHAWK, INC.; *U.S. Public*, pg. 1437
SCHAWKGRAPHICS—Schawk, Inc.; *U.S. Public*, pg. 1437
SCHLUMBERGER MALCO INC.—N. Schlumberger & Cie; *Int'l*, pg. 1206
SCHOOL PRODUCTS GROUP—Jostens; *U.S. Public*, pg. 934
SCOTT PRINTING CORPORATION; *U.S. Private*, pg. 977
SCOVILLE PRESS, INC.; *U.S. Private*, pg. 977
THE SEGERDAHL CORP.; *U.S. Private*, pg. 981
SELECTO-FLASH, INC.; *U.S. Private*, pg. 982
SEQUOIA-PACIFIC SYSTEMS CORP.—Jefferson Smurfit Group p.l.c.; *Int'l*, pg. 1270
SERIGRAPH, INC.; *U.S. Private*, pg. 985
SHANDWICK INTERNATIONAL PLC; *Int'l*, pg. 1226
SHEA COMMUNICATIONS CO.; *U.S. Private*, pg. 990
THE SHERIDAN GROUP; *U.S. Private*, pg. 993
THE SHERIDAN PRESS, INC.—The Sheridan Group; *U.S. Private*, pg. 993
SHOREWOOD PACKAGING COMPANY OF ILLINOIS, INC.—Shorewood Packaging Corporation; *U.S. Public*, pg. 1468
SHOREWOOD PACKAGING CORPORATION; *U.S. Public*, pg. 1468
SINCLAIR PRINTING & LITHO, INC.; *U.S. Private*, pg. 1003
SLEEPECK PRINTING COMPANY; *U.S. Private*, pg. 1005
SMITH-EDWARDS-DUNLAP COMPANY; *U.S. Private*, pg. 1007
JEFFERSON SMURFIT CORPORATION—Jefferson Smurfit Group p.l.c.; *Int'l*, pg. 1269
SMYTH, CO.; *U.S. Private*, pg. 1010
SOABAR GRAPHICS DIVISION—Avery Dennison Corporation; *U.S. Public*, pg. 153
SOABAR PRODUCTS GROUP—Avery Dennison Corporation; *U.S. Public*, pg. 153
SOABAR SYSTEMS DIVISION—Avery Dennison Corporation; *U.S. Public*, pg. 153
SOLAR COMMUNICATIONS—Solar Communications, Inc.; *U.S. Private*, pg. 1012
SOLAR COMMUNICATIONS, INC.; *U.S. Private*, pg. 1012
SONOCO ENGRAPH, INC.—Sonoco Products Company; *U.S. Public*, pg. 1486
SPANGLER INC.; *U.S. Private*, pg. 1020
SPENCER PRESS, INC.; *U.S. Private*, pg. 1025
THE STATE PRINTING COMPANY, INC.—Wallace Computer Services, Inc.; *U.S. Public*, pg. 1736
THE STEIN PRINTING COMPANY, INC.—Wallace Computer Services, Inc.; *U.S. Public*, pg. 1736
STEPHENSON, INC.; *U.S. Private*, pg. 1040
STERLING COLOR PROCESS—The Excellence Group; *U.S. Private*, pg. 387
STUART ENTERTAINMENT INC.; *U.S. Public*, pg. 1526
STUART ENTERTAINMENT, S.A. DE C.V.—Stuart Entertainment Inc.; *U.S. Public*, pg. 1526
SUPERIOR PRINTING CO.; *U.S. Private*, pg. 1055
TAYLOR CORPORATION; *U.S. Private*, pg. 1070
TELEGRAPHICS PRINTING—Telescope Casual Furniture, Inc.; *U.S. Private*, pg. 1074
3 SCORE, INC.—Cadmus Communications Corporation; *U.S. Public*, pg. 291
TIMES PRINTING COMPANY, INC.; *U.S. Private*, pg. 1087
TRADE PRODUCTS—Stuart Entertainment Inc.; *U.S. Public*, pg. 1526
TREASURE CHEST ADVERTISING—Big Flower Press Holdings, Inc.; *U.S. Public*, pg. 228
TREASURE CHEST ADVERTISING CO., INC.—Big Flower Press Holdings, Inc.; *U.S. Public*, pg. 228
TREND OFFSET PRINTING SERVICES; *U.S. Private*, pg. 1099
TWEDDLE LITHO COMPANY; *U.S. Private*, pg. 1111
ULTRATECH STEPPER, INC.; *U.S. Public*, pg. 1663
UNITED GRAPHICS, INC.—Banta Corporation; *U.S. Public*, pg. 188
THE VERNON COMPANY; *U.S. Private*, pg. 1137
VIDEOJET LTD.—The General Electric Company, p.l.c.; *Int'l*, pg. 546
VILE-GOLLER, FINE ART PRINTING & LITHOGRAPHY; *U.S. Private*, pg. 1140
VISION ONE; *U.S. Private*, pg. 1141
WALLE CORPORATION; *U.S. Private*, pg. 1148
WARRENS WALLER PRESS, INC.; *U.S. Private*, pg. 1151
WASHBURN GRAPHICS, INC.—Cadmus Communications Corporation; *U.S. Public*, pg. 291
WEB PRESS GRAPHICS LTD.—Quebecor Inc.; *Int'l*, pg. 1077
WEBCRAFT TECHNOLOGIES, INC.—Big Flower Press Holdings, Inc.; *U.S. Public*, pg. 228
WEST SHORE ENVELOPE COMPANY, INC.; *U.S. Private*, pg. 1163
WESTON ENGRAVING—Schawk, Inc.; *U.S. Public*, pg. 1437
WETMORE & COMPANY—Wallace Computer Services, Inc.; *U.S. Public*, pg. 1736
WILLIAMS PRINTING COMPANY—Wallace Computer Services, Inc.; *U.S. Public*, pg. 1736
WINTHROP PRINTING COMPANY, INC.; *U.S. Private*, pg. 1184
WOLFER PRINTING COMPANY; *U.S. Private*, pg. 1186
YORK LITHOGRAPHING—Rogers Communications, Inc.; *Int'l*, pg. 1123
THE YORKVILLE PRINTING GROUP LIMITED—G.T.C. Transcontinental Group Ltd.; *Int'l*, pg. 538
ZYAN, INC.—Foster Management Co.; *U.S. Private*, pg. 421

2754 — COMMERCIAL PRINTING, GRAVURE

AMERICAN BANKNOTE CORP.; *U.S. Public*, pg. 68
ARMIN PLASTICS, NORTHEAST DIVISION—Tyco International Ltd.; *U.S. Public*, pg. 1647
AUSTILL PACKAGING—Jefferson Smurfit Group p.l.c.; *Int'l*, pg. 1269
B.A. BANK NOTE—Quebecor Inc.; *Int'l*, pg. 1077
BATTEN GRAPHICS—Schawk, Inc.; *U.S. Public*, pg. 1437
BELL ATLANTIC DIRECTORY GRAPHICS, INC.—Bell Atlantic Corporation; *U.S. Public*, pg. 203
BEMIS COMPANY, INC.; *U.S. Public*, pg. 210
BROWN PRINTING CENTRAL—Bertelsmann AG; *Int'l*, pg. 190
BROWN PRINTING CO., INC.—Bertelsmann AG; *Int'l*, pg. 190
BUREAU OF ENGRAVING; *U.S. Private*, pg. 181
CADMUS COMMUNICATIONS CORPORATION; *U.S. Public*, pg. 290
THE CASE-HOYT CORPORATION—Avanti Press Inc.; *U.S. Private*, pg. 101
CHRISTIES INTERNATIONAL PLC; *Int'l*, pg. 289
CONSOLIDATED GROUP, INC.—The Dyson-Kissner-Moran Corporation; *U.S. Private*, pg. 351
COURIER COMPANIES, INC.—Courier Corporation; *U.S. Public*, pg. 453
CURTIS 1000 EUROPE GMBH—American Business Products, Inc.; *U.S. Public*, pg. 70
CURWOOD, INC.—Bemis Company, Inc.; *U.S. Public*, pg. 210
DAI NIPPON PRINTING CO., LTD.; *Int'l*, pg. 363
DENNISON THERIMAGE DIV.—Avery Dennison Corporation; *U.S. Public*, pg. 152
DENNISON TRANSOCEANIC CORPORATION—Avery Dennison Corporation; *U.S. Public*, pg. 153
R.R. DONNELLEY & SONS COMPANY; *U.S. Public*, pg. 517
DROYHURST LIMITED—James Crean PLC; *Int'l*, pg. 341
IMPRESORA DONNECO INTERNACIONAL, S.A. DE C.V.—R.R. Donnelley & Sons Company; *U.S. Public*, pg. 519
INLAND PRINTING CO., INC.; *U.S. Private*, pg. 564
INTERNATIONAL CENTER FOR ENTREPRENEURIAL DEVELOPMENT, INC.; *U.S. Private*, pg. 568
JANNOCK LIMITED; *Int'l*, pg. 698
MACKAY, INC.—Bemis Company, Inc.; *U.S. Public*, pg. 210
MCCLATCHY PRINTING SERVICE—McClatchy Newspapers Inc.; *U.S. Public*, pg. 1066
MENASHA CORPORATION; *U.S. Private*, pg. 731
MEREDITH CORPORATION; *U.S. Public*, pg. 1094
THE MORRILL PRESS—Sonoco Products Company; *U.S. Public*, pg. 1486
OFFICE ELECTRONICS, INC.; *U.S. Private*, pg. 812
O'NEIL DATA SYSTEMS, INC.—William O'Neil & Co., Inc.; *U.S. Private*, pg. 817
PAMCO PRINTED TAPE & LABEL COMPANY, INC.—Jordan Industries, Inc.; *U.S. Private*, pg. 598
PHIPPS PRESS, INC.—Jannock Limited; *Int'l*, pg. 699
PITNEY BOWES INC.; *U.S. Public*, pg. 1303
QUAD/GRAPHICS, INC.; *U.S. Private*, pg. 897
QUEBECOR PRINTING DICKSON INC.—Quebecor Inc.; *Int'l*, pg. 1078
RJR NABISCO HOLDINGS CORP.; *U.S. Public*, pg. 1354
RELIEF PRINTING; *U.S. Private*, pg. 921
RINGIER AG; *Int'l*, pg. 1118
SNC-LAVALIN GROUP INC.; *Int'l*, pg. 1161
THE SEGERDAHL CORP.; *U.S. Private*, pg. 981
JEFFERSON SMURFIT CORPORATION—Jefferson Smurfit Group p.l.c.; *Int'l*, pg. 1269
SONOCO ENGRAPH, INC.—Sonoco Products Company; *U.S. Public*, pg. 1486
SOUTHERN GRAPHICS SYSTEMS—Reynolds Metals Company; *U.S. Public*, pg. 1386
UNITED NEWS & MEDIA PLC; *Int'l*, pg. 1443
THE VERNON COMPANY; *U.S. Private*, pg. 1137
WOODS OF PERTH—Christies International plc; *Int'l*, pg. 290

2759 — COMMERCIAL PRINTING, NEC

A.C. SCANNING, INC.—Wallace Computer Services, Inc.; *U.S. Public*, pg. 1735
AGI INC.; *U.S. Private*, pg. 5
ALCO GRAVURE INDUSTRIES, INC.—Quebecor Inc.; *Int'l*, pg. 1076
ALLIED PRINTING SERVICES, INC.; *U.S. Private*, pg. 40
AMERICAN BANKNOTE COMPANY GRAFICA E SERVICOS LTDA.—American Banknote Corp.; *U.S. Public*, pg. 68
AMERICAN BANKNOTE CORP.; *U.S. Public*, pg. 68
AMERICAN BANKNOTE HOLOGRAPHICS—American Banknote Corp.; *U.S. Public*, pg. 68
AMERICAN COLOR GRAPHICS—Morgan Stanley Dean Witter & Co.; *U.S. Public*, pg. 1132
AMERICAN DECAL & MFG. CO.; *U.S. Private*, pg. 53
AMERICAN PAD AND PAPER COMPANY; *U.S. Public*, pg. 88
AMERICAN SPEEDY PRINTING CENTERS, INC.; *U.S. Private*, pg. 62
AMERICAN STATIONERY CO., INC.; *U.S. Private*, pg. 62
W.E. ANDREWS CO., INC.—Wallace Computer Services, Inc.; *U.S. Public*, pg. 1735
APPLIED GRAPHICS—U.S. News & World Report; *U.S. Private*, pg. 1125
ARCO BLUEPRINTERS—Wallace Computer Services, Inc.; *U.S. Public*, pg. 1735
ARISTON—Sonoco Products Company; *U.S. Public*, pg. 1486
ASHDOWN PRESS LTD.—Shandwick International Plc; *Int'l*, pg. 1226
ASHER CANDY COMPANY—Marvel Entertainment Group; *U.S. Public*, pg. 1052
ATLANTA BLUEPRINT COMPANY—Wallace Computer Services, Inc.; *U.S. Public*, pg. 1735
AUTOCOMP, INC.—Wallace Computer Services, Inc.; *U.S. Public*, pg. 1735
AVERY CONVERTED PRODUCTS GROUP—Avery Dennison Corporation; *U.S. Public*, pg. 152
AVERY DENNISON CORPORATION; *U.S. Public*, pg. 152
BAC COLOR FRANSEWEG; *Int'l*, pg. 131
L.G. BALFOUR CO., INC.—Commemorative Brands, Inc.; *U.S. Private*, pg. 258
BANTA BOOK GROUP-HARRISONBURG—Banta Corporation; *U.S. Public*, pg. 188
BANTA DIGITAL GROUP—Banta Corporation; *U.S. Public*, pg. 188
BANTA INFORMATION SERVICES GROUP—Banta Corporation; *U.S. Public*, pg. 188
BANTA MERCHANDISING PRODUCTS—Banta Corporation; *U.S. Public*, pg. 188
BAT OFFICE PRODUCTS—U.S. Office Products Company; *U.S. Public*, pg. 1686
BEACON PRESS, INC.—Media General, Inc.; *U.S. Public*, pg. 1077
BERRYVILLE GRAPHICS INC.—Bertelsmann AG; *Int'l*, pg. 191
BIC SPECIAL MKTS. DIV.—Societe BIC S.A.; *Int'l*, pg. 1273
BIG FLOWER PRESS HOLDINGS, INC.; *U.S. Public*, pg. 228
BOWATER INCORPORATED; *U.S. Public*, pg. 247
BOWATER MERSEY PAPER COMPANY, LTD.—Bowater Incorporated; *U.S. Public*, pg. 248
BOWATER MERSEY PAPER COMPANY, LTD.—The Washington Post Company; *U.S. Public*, pg. 1743
BOWNE & CO., INC.; *U.S. Public*, pg. 248
BOWNE BUSINESS COMMUNICATIONS, INC.—Bowne & Co., Inc.; *U.S. Public*, pg. 248
BOWNE INSURANCE DIVISION—Bowne & Co., Inc.; *U.S. Public*, pg. 248
BRADLEY PRINTING COMPANY—World Color Press, Inc.; *U.S. Public*, pg. 1778
BRIGHT OF AMERICA, INC.—Russ Berrie and Company, Inc.; *U.S. Public*, pg. 223
BRODART COMPANY; *U.S. Private*, pg. 170
BROWN & BIGELOW, INC.; *U.S. Private*, pg. 172
BUREAU OF ENGRAVING; *U.S. Private*, pg. 181
CCL INDUSTRIES, INC.; *Int'l*, pg. 238
CADMUS COMMUNICATIONS CORPORATION; *U.S. Public*, pg. 290
CADMUS MARKETING SERVICES—Cadmus Communications Corporation; *U.S. Public*, pg. 291
CALIFORNIA OFFSET PRINTERS, INC.—COP Communications; *U.S. Private*, pg. 196
CARSTENS INC.; *U.S. Private*, pg. 216
CARVEL PRINT GRUPO SERIGRAPH—Serigraph, Inc.; *U.S. Private*, pg. 985
CASA GRANDE MFG. DIVISION—R.R. Donnelley & Sons Company; *U.S. Public*, pg. 518
CENTRAL STATES DIVERSIFIED, INC.; *U.S. Private*, pg. 224
CHRISTIES INTERNATIONAL PLC; *Int'l*, pg. 289
CINE MAGNETICS, INC.; *U.S. Private*, pg. 240

COLOR ARTS, INC.; *U.S. Private*, pg. 254
COLOR DATA EAST—Schawk, Inc.; *U.S. Public*, pg. 1437
COMMUNICORP, INC.—AFLAC Incorporated; *U.S. Public*, pg. 28
CON-WEB PRESS INC.—Quebecor Inc.; *Int'l*, pg. 1076
CONSOLIDATED COMMUNICATIONS DIRECTORIES, INC.—McLeodUSA Incorporated; *U.S. Public*, pg. 1073
CONSOLIDATED GROUP, INC.—The Dyson-Kissner-Moran Corporation; *U.S. Private*, pg. 351
COURIER COMPANIES, INC.—Courier Corporation; *U.S. Public*, pg. 453
COVINGTON SPECIALTY PRINT—John H. Harland Company; *U.S. Public*, pg. 786
H.S. CROCKER CO., INC.; *U.S. Private*, pg. 290
CULLMAN VENTURES, INC.; *U.S. Private*, pg. 294
CURTIS 1000 EUROPE GMBH—American Business Products, Inc.; *U.S. Public*, pg. 70
DAI NIPPON PRINTING CO. (HONG KONG) LTD.—Dai Nippon Printing Co., Ltd.; *Int'l*, pg. 363
DAI NIPPON PRINTING CO., LTD.; *Int'l*, pg. 363
P.T. DAI NIPPON PRINTING INDONESIA—Dai Nippon Printing Co., Ltd.; *Int'l*, pg. 363
DE LA RUE FARADAY—De La Rue plc; *Int'l*, pg. 387
DE LA RUE PLC; *Int'l*, pg. 386
DE LA RUE SMURFIT LIMITED—De La Rue plc; *Int'l*, pg. 386
THOMAS DE LA RUE AND COMPANY LIMITED—De La Rue plc; *Int'l*, pg. 386
THOMAS DE LA RUE INC.—De La Rue plc; *Int'l*, pg. 387
DES MOINES MFG. DIVISION—R.R. Donnelley & Sons Company; *U.S. Public*, pg. 518
R.R. DONNELLEY FAR EAST LIMITED—R.R. Donnelley & Sons Company; *U.S. Public*, pg. 519
DOUBLEDAY BROS. & CO.—Standex International Corporation; *U.S. Public*, pg. 1506
DOWNEY PRINTING; *U.S. Private*, pg. 342
DROYHURST LIMITED—James Crean PLC; *Int'l*, pg. 341
EASTERN COLOR PRINTING COMPANY; *U.S. Private*, pg. 357
EDWARDS & BROUGHTON COMPANY—Wallace Computer Services, Inc.; *U.S. Public*, pg. 1735
ELTIS PRECISION PRINTING LIMITED—HSBC Holdings plc; *Int'l*, pg. 581
ENGRAPH MACHINE GROUP—Sonoco Products Company; *U.S. Public*, pg. 1486
ENGRAPH PUERTO RICO—Sonoco Products Company; *U.S. Public*, pg. 1486
ETIQUETAS INTERNACIONALES, INC.—Bacardi Limited; *Int'l*, pg. 132
THE EXCELLENCE GROUP; *U.S. Private*, pg. 387
FINE ART DEVELOPMENTS PLC; *Int'l*, pg. 485
FLASHMEDIA ADVERTISING INC.—Quebecor Inc.; *Int'l*, pg. 1076
FLEER-SKYBOX INTERNATIONAL INC.—Marvel Entertainment Group; *U.S. Public*, pg. 1052
FLEMING PACKAGING CORP.; *U.S. Private*, pg. 411
FORBO SCANACHROME LTD.—Forbo Holding SA; *Int'l*, pg. 498
G.T.C. TRANSCONTINENTAL GROUP LTD.; *Int'l*, pg. 538
GEIGER BROTHERS; *U.S. Private*, pg. 442
GOLDEN BOOKS FAMILY ENTERTAINMENT INC.; *U.S. Public*, pg. 749
GOLDEN BOOKS PUBLISHING—Golden Books Family Entertainment Inc.; *U.S. Public*, pg. 749
GOVERNMENT FORMS & SYSTEMS, INC.—National Fiberstock Corporation; *U.S. Private*, pg. 782
GRAPHIC CONTROLS CORPORATION; *U.S. Private*, pg. 470
GRAPHIC DIRECT, INC.—Wallace Computer Services, Inc.; *U.S. Public*, pg. 1735
GRAPHIC INDUSTRIES, INC.—Wallace Computer Services, Inc.; *U.S. Public*, pg. 1735
GRAPHIC RESOURCES, INC.—Sonoco Products Company; *U.S. Public*, pg. 1486
GRAY PRINTING CO.; *U.S. Private*, pg. 472
GREAT NORTHERN PAPER, INC.—Bowater Incorporated; *U.S. Public*, pg. 248
GREENAWAY-HARRISON LTD. D/B/A GREENAWAYS—Lonrho plc; *Int'l*, pg. 817
HARCOURT BRACE & COMPANY - ELEMENTARY DIV.—Harcourt General, Inc.; *U.S. Public*, pg. 783
JOHN H. HARLAND COMPANY; *U.S. Public*, pg. 785
JOHN H. HARLAND CO. OF PUERTO RICO—John H. Harland Company; *U.S. Public*, pg. 786
HARRISON & SONS LTD.—Lonrho plc; *Int'l*, pg. 817
HARTE HANKS SHOPPERS—Harte-Hanks Communications, Inc.; *U.S. Public*, pg. 794
HEBDO MAG. INC.—Cendant Corporation; *U.S. Public*, pg. 321
HERFF JONES INC.; *U.S. Private*, pg. 523
HERITAGE PRESS, INC.—Wallace Computer Services, Inc.; *U.S. Public*, pg. 1735
HOLYOKE LITHOGRAPH CO., INC.—Quebecor Inc.; *Int'l*, pg. 1078
HOYLE PRODUCTS—Brown & Bigelow, Inc.; *U.S. Private*, pg. 172
IPD PRINTING & DISTRIBUTING, INC.—Wallace Computer Services, Inc.; *U.S. Public*, pg. 1735
IMAGE REPROGRAPHICS—Day & Zimmermann, Inc.; *U.S. Private*, pg. 317
IMPRIMERIE QUEBECOR INC.—Quebecor Inc.; *Int'l*, pg. 1077
IMPRIMERIE QUEBECOR JOLIETTE—Quebecor Inc.; *Int'l*, pg. 1077
INSIGHT GRAPHIC SYSTEMS—LSI Industries, Inc.; *U.S. Public*, pg. 971
THE INSTANT WEB COMPANIES; *U.S. Private*, pg. 565
INTERMEC MEDIA PRODUCTS—UNOVA, Inc.; *U.S. Public*, pg. 1699
INTERNATIONAL CENTER FOR ENTREPRENEURIAL DEVELOPMENT, INC.; *U.S. Private*, pg. 568
INTERNATIONAL PAPER LABEL DIV.—International Paper Company; *U.S. Public*, pg. 903
JAPS-OLSON COMPANY; *U.S. Private*, pg. 582
KAL GRAFX—The Excellence Group; *U.S. Private*, pg. 387
KREPE-KRAFT, INC.—Astronics Corporation; *U.S. Public*, pg. 142
LSI/KALA—Schawk, Inc.; *U.S. Public*, pg. 1437
LAWSON MARDON PACKAGING INC.—Alusuisse-Lonza Holding Ltd.; *Int'l*, pg. 68
THE LEHIGH PRESS, INC.; *U.S. Private*, pg. 658
LEHIGH PRESS LITHOGRAPHERS—The Lehigh Press, Inc.; *U.S. Private*, pg. 659
LES PUBLICATIONS MDN INC.—Quebecor Inc.; *Int'l*, pg. 1076
LITHO COLORPLATE—Schawk, Inc.; *U.S. Public*, pg. 1437
LYNCHBURG GRAPHICS SERVICE CENTER—R.R. Donnelley & Sons Company; *U.S. Public*, pg. 518
MACK PRINTING COMPANY; *U.S. Private*, pg. 691
MACK PRINTING GROUP (EPHRATA DIV.)—Mack Printing Company; *U.S. Private*, pg. 692
MASTER CRAFT CORP.—Caradon Plc; *Int'l*, pg. 267
MAUL-BELSER GMBH; *Int'l*, pg. 849
MENASHA CORPORATION; *U.S. Private*, pg. 731
MERRILL CORPORATION; *U.S. Public*, pg. 1097
METRO LABEL CORP.; *U.S. Private*, pg. 736
H.C. MILLER COMPANY; *U.S. Private*, pg. 747
MILPRINT INC.—Bemis Company, Inc.; *U.S. Public*, pg. 210
MINUTEMAN PRESS INTERNATIONAL; *U.S. Private*, pg. 752
MIRCOR INC.—Quebecor Inc.; *Int'l*, pg. 1075
MORRIS NEWSPAPER CORPORATION; *U.S. Private*, pg. 762
MULTI-AD SERVICES, INCORPORATED; *U.S. Private*, pg. 766
NATIONAL FIBERSTOCK CORPORATION; *U.S. Private*, pg. 782
NATIONAL PRINT GROUP, INC.; *U.S. Private*, pg. 785
NEWTON-SOUTHEASTERN MFG. DIV.—R.R. Donnelley & Sons Company; *U.S. Public*, pg. 518
NOLL PRINTING CORPORATION—Our Sunday Visitor, Inc.; *U.S. Private*, pg. 821
OBERLANDER RECYCLING TECHNIK GMBH—Fried. Krupp AG; *Int'l*, pg. 513
OFFICE ELECTRONICS, INC.; *U.S. Private*, pg. 812
ONENA BOLSAS DE PAPEL, S.A.—Continental Can Co.; *U.S. Public*, pg. 440
OUTLOOK LABEL SYSTEMS, INC.—Outlook Group Corporation; *U.S. Public*, pg. 1235
PACKAGE PRODUCTS SPECIALTY-LABELS DIV.—Sonoco Products Company; *U.S. Public*, pg. 1486
PACKAGE PRODUCTS SPECIALTY-PAPERBOARD DIV.—Sonoco Products Company; *U.S. Public*, pg. 1486
PATSON'S PRESS; *U.S. Private*, pg. 843
PATTON—Sonoco Products Company; *U.S. Public*, pg. 1486
PHIPPS PRESS, INC.—Jannock Limited; *Int'l*, pg. 699
PINNACLE BRANDS, INC.; *U.S. Private*, pg. 866
PIP PRINTING—Franchise Services, Inc.; *U.S. Private*, pg. 423
PITNEY BOWES INC.; *U.S. Public*, pg. 1303
POWER PLASTICS INC.—Tiffany Extruders, Inc.; *U.S. Private*, pg. 1086
PRECISION PRINTING & PACKAGING—Anheuser-Busch Companies, Inc.; *U.S. Public*, pg. 115
PROCESS COLOR PLATE—Schawk, Inc.; *U.S. Public*, pg. 1437
PUB/DATA, INC.—Quebecor Inc.; *Int'l*, pg. 1076
QUEBECOR COMMUNICATIONS, INC.—Quebecor Inc.; *Int'l*, pg. 1076
QUEBECOR PRINTING CORPORATION—Quebecor Inc.; *Int'l*, pg. 1078
QUEBECOR PRINTING (USA) CORP.—Quebecor Inc.; *Int'l*, pg. 1078
QUEENS GROUP, INC.; *U.S. Private*, pg. 900
REGENCY ENGRAVERS, INC.—American Pad and Paper Company; *U.S. Public*, pg. 89
REGENCY THERMOGRAPHICS OF WASHINGTON, INC.—American Pad and Paper Company; *U.S. Public*, pg. 89
RELIEF PRINTING; *U.S. Private*, pg. 921
RISDON CORPORATION—Crown Cork & Seal Company, Inc.; *U.S. Public*, pg. 463
SCHAWK, INC.; *U.S. Public*, pg. 1437
SCHAWKGRAPHICS—Schawk, Inc.; *U.S. Public*, pg. 1437
SCHLUMBERGER MALCO INC.—N. Schlumberger & Cie; *Int'l*, pg. 1206
SCREEN ART—Sonoco Products Company; *U.S. Public*, pg. 1486
SCREEN GRAPHICS, INC.—Sonoco Products Company; *U.S. Public*, pg. 1486
THE SEGERDAHL CORP.; *U.S. Private*, pg. 981
SERIGRAPH, INC.; *U.S. Private*, pg. 985
SERVICE WEB OFFSET CORPORATION; *U.S. Private*, pg. 987
SHEA COMMUNICATIONS CO.; *U.S. Private*, pg. 990
SKYBOX INTERNATIONAL INC.—Marvel Entertainment Group; *U.S. Public*, pg. 1052
SMITH & MCLAURIN LIMITED—Rexam PLC; *Int'l*, pg. 1107
SMITH-EDWARDS-DUNLAP COMPANY; *U.S. Private*, pg. 1007
JEFFERSON SMURFIT CORPORATION—Jefferson Smurfit Group p.l.c.; *Int'l*, pg. 1269
SMYTH, CO.; *U.S. Private*, pg. 1010
SOABAR GRAPHICS DIVISION—Avery Dennison Corporation; *U.S. Public*, pg. 153
SOABAR PRODUCTS GROUP—Avery Dennison Corporation; *U.S. Public*, pg. 153
SONOCO ENGRAPH, INC.—Sonoco Products Company; *U.S. Public*, pg. 1486
SONY MUSIC ENTERTAINMENT, INC.—Sony Corporation; *Int'l*, pg. 1281
SONY MUSIC ENTERTAINMENT (UK) LIMITED—Sony Corporation; *Int'l*, pg. 1284
SPECIALTIES BINDERY, INC.—Quebecor Inc.; *Int'l*, pg. 1078
STANDARD PUBLISHING—Standex International Corporation; *U.S. Public*, pg. 1506
STATIONERY HOUSE, INC.—American Pad and Paper Company; *U.S. Public*, pg. 89
SUN-LITHO—Morris Newspaper Corporation; *U.S. Private*, pg. 762
SUNGARD MAILING SERVICES—SunGard Data Systems Inc.; *U.S. Public*, pg. 1534
SUPERIOR LABEL SYSTEMS, INC.; *U.S. Private*, pg. 1055
TAPE & LABEL ENGINEERING—Weber Marking Systems, Inc.; *U.S. Private*, pg. 1157
TAYLOR CORPORATION; *U.S. Private*, pg. 1070
TECHNICAL IMAGE PRODUCTS, INC./DGI; *U.S. Private*, pg. 1072
TIEN WAH PRESS (PTE.) LTD.—Dai Nippon Printing Co., Ltd.; *Int'l*, pg. 363
TOPFLIGHT CORP.; *U.S. Private*, pg. 1091
TOPPAN PRINTING CO. (AMERICA) INC.-NEW JERSEY—Toppan Printing Company, Ltd.; *Int'l*, pg. 1399
TOPPAN PRINTING COMPANY, LTD.; *Int'l*, pg. 1399
TRADEMARK PRESS, INC.—Harte-Hanks Communications, Inc.; *U.S. Public*, pg. 794
TRANSPORT GRAPHICOR INC.—Quebecor Inc.; *Int'l*, pg. 1075
THE UPPER DECK COMPANY, LLC; *U.S. Private*, pg. 1129
VALASSIS COMMUNICATIONS, INC.; *U.S. Public*, pg. 1704
WEB GRAPHICS, INC.—American Pad and Paper Company; *U.S. Public*, pg. 89
WEBER MARKING SYSTEMS, INC.; *U.S. Private*, pg. 1157
WELDON, WILLIAMS & LICK, INC.; *U.S. Private*, pg. 1161
WERTHAN PACKAGING, INC.; *U.S. Private*, pg. 1162
WESTON ENGRAVING—Schawk, Inc.; *U.S. Public*, pg. 1437
WETMORE & COMPANY—Wallace Computer Services, Inc.; *U.S. Public*, pg. 1736
WILLIAMHOUSE-REGENCY, INC.—American Pad and Paper Company; *U.S. Public*, pg. 89
WILLIAMS PRINTING COMPANY—Wallace Computer Services, Inc.; *U.S. Public*, pg. 1736
WINTHROP-ATKINS CO., INC.; *U.S. Private*, pg. 1183
WINTHROP PRINTING COMPANY, INC.; *U.S. Private*, pg. 1184
WOODS OF PERTH—Christies International plc; *Int'l*, pg. 290
WORLD PUBLISHING COMPANY; *U.S. Private*, pg. 1190
ZEBRA TECHNOLOGIES CORPORATION; *U.S. Public*, pg. 1790
ZENGER-MILLER—The Times Mirror Company; *U.S. Public*, pg. 1617

2761 — MANIFOLD BUSINESS FORMS

ADAMS BUSINESS FORMS; *U.S. Private*, pg. 16
ADAMS INVESTMENT COMPANY; *U.S. Private*, pg. 16
AMERICAN TRADING AND PRODUCTION CORPORATION; *U.S. Private*, pg. 63
APPERSON BUSINESS FORMS, INC.; *U.S. Private*, pg. 78
CAPITAL GRAPHICS INC.; *U.S. Private*, pg. 206
CENTRAL STATES MULTIPLEX—Adams Investment Company; *U.S. Private*, pg. 16
COMPUTER STOCK FORMS, INC.—Rotary Forms Press, Inc.; *U.S. Private*, pg. 947
CONSOLIDATED GRAPHIC COMMUNICATIONS—Champion Industries; *U.S. Public*, pg. 333
CRABAR BUSINESS SYSTEMS; *U.S. Private*, pg. 283
CRANE & CO., INC.; *U.S. Private*, pg. 286
CULLMAN VENTURES, INC.; *U.S. Private*, pg. 294
CURTIS 1000, INC.—American Business Products, Inc.; *U.S. Public*, pg. 70
DAI NIPPON PRINTING CO., LTD.; *Int'l*, pg. 363
DATA DOCUMENTS, INC.—Corporate Express, Inc.; *U.S. Public*, pg. 449
DATAFORMS, INC.—The Reynolds and Reynolds Company; *U.S. Public*, pg. 1385
DELUXE BUSINESS SYSTEMS DIVISION—Deluxe Corporation; *U.S. Public*, pg. 498
DELUXE CORPORATION; *U.S. Public*, pg. 498
ENNIS BUSINESS FORMS, INC.; *U.S. Public*, pg. 583
ENNIS-TEXAS TAG—Ennis Business Forms, Inc.; *U.S. Public*, pg. 583
FEDERAL BUSINESS PRODUCTS, INC.; *U.S. Private*, pg. 398
FORMULARIOS MOORE DE COSTA RICA S.A. DE CV—Moore Corporation Limited; *Int'l*, pg. 889
FORMULARIOS MOORE DE GUATEMALA, S.A.—Moore Corporation Limited; *Int'l*, pg. 889
FRYETECH, INC.; *U.S. Private*, pg. 430
GOVERNMENT FORMS & SYSTEMS, INC.—National Fiberstock Corporation; *U.S. Private*, pg. 782
HANO DOCUMENT PRINTERS, INC.—U.S. Office Products Company; *U.S. Public*, pg. 1686
INTERFORM CORPORATION—Champion Industries; *U.S. Public*, pg. 333
INTERNATIONAL PAPER COMPANY; *U.S. Public*, pg. 901
JOHNSON & QUIN, INC.; *U.S. Private*, pg. 590
WARD KRAFT, INC.; *U.S. Private*, pg. 634
LABEL ART, INC.—National Fiberstock Corporation; *U.S. Private*, pg. 782
GEORGES LANG CONTINU S.A.—Moore Corporation Limited; *Int'l*, pg. 889
MB AMERICA, INC.—Caradon Plc; *Int'l*, pg. 267
MASTER CRAFT CORP.—Caradon Plc; *Int'l*, pg. 267
MCBEE SYSTEMS, INC.; *U.S. Private*, pg. 718
THE MEAD CORPORATION; *U.S. Public*, pg. 1074
MIAMI SYSTEMS CORPORATION; *U.S. Private*, pg. 740
MOORE BUSINESS FORMS & SYSTEMS DIV.—Moore Corporation Limited; *Int'l*, pg. 890
MOORE BUSINESS FORMS & SYSTEMS LTD.—Moore Corporation Limited; *Int'l*, pg. 889
MOORE BUSINESS FORMS DE CENTRO AMERICA, S.A. DE C.V.—Moore Corporation Limited; *Int'l*, pg. 889
MOORE BUSINESS FORMS DE PUERTO RICO, S.A.—Moore Corporation Limited; *Int'l*, pg. 889

MOORE BUSINESS FORMS U.K. LTD.—Moore Corporation Limited; *Int'l*, pg. 889
MOORE BUSINESS SYSTEMS AUSTRALIA LTD.—Moore Corporation Limited; *Int'l*, pg. 889
MOORE BUSINESS SYSTEMS PTY. LTD.—Moore Corporation Limited; *Int'l*, pg. 889
MOORE CORPORATION LIMITED; *Int'l*, pg. 888
MOORE DOCUMENT SOLUTIONS—Moore Corporation Limited; *Int'l*, pg. 890
MOORE FORMULARIOS LIMITADA—Moore Corporation Limited; *Int'l*, pg. 889
MOORE INTERNATIONAL B.V.—Moore Corporation Limited; *Int'l*, pg. 889
MOORE NEDERLAND B.V.—Moore Corporation Limited; *Int'l*, pg. 890
MOORE PARAGON AUSTRALIA LIMITED—Moore Corporation Limited; *Int'l*, pg. 889
MOORE PARAGON (CARIBBEAN) LIMITED—Moore Corporation Limited; *Int'l*, pg. 889
MOORE PARAGON CENTRAL AFRICA LIMITED—Moore Corporation Limited; *Int'l*, pg. 890
MOORE PARAGON NORGE A/S—Moore Corporation Limited; *Int'l*, pg. 889
MOORE PARAGON (SUISSE) S.A.—Moore Corporation Limited; *Int'l*, pg. 890
MOORE PARAGON SVENSKA AB—Moore Corporation Limited; *Int'l*, pg. 890
MOORE PARAGON U.K. LIMITED—Moore Corporation Limited; *Int'l*, pg. 889
MOORE PORTUGUESA LIMITADA—Moore Corporation Limited; *Int'l*, pg. 890
MOORE SIGMA, S.P.A.—Moore Corporation Limited; *Int'l*, pg. 890
NCR CORPORATION; *U.S. Public*, pg. 1146
NEW ENGLAND BUSINESS SERVICE—New England Business Service, Inc.; *U.S. Public*, pg. 1171
NEW ENGLAND BUSINESS SERVICE, INC.; *U.S. Public*, pg. 1170
NEW ENGLAND BUSINESS SERVICE INC.—New England Business Service, Inc.; *U.S. Public*, pg. 1171
OFFICE CONNECTION, INC.—U.S. Office Products Company; *U.S. Public*, pg. 1687
OFFICE ELECTRONICS, INC.; *U.S. Private*, pg. 812
QUALITY COMPUTER FORMS, INC.—Rotary Forms Press, Inc.; *U.S. Private*, pg. 947
REYNOLDS AND REYNOLDS—The Reynolds and Reynolds Company; *U.S. Public*, pg. 1385
REYNOLDS AND REYNOLDS-BUSINESS FORMS DIVISION—The Reynolds and Reynolds Company; *U.S. Public*, pg. 1385
REYNOLDS AND REYNOLDS (CANADA) LTD.—The Reynolds and Reynolds Company; *U.S. Public*, pg. 1385
THE REYNOLDS AND REYNOLDS COMPANY; *U.S. Public*, pg. 1384
RING KING VISIBLES, INC.—Esselte AB; *Int'l*, pg. 460
ROTARY FORMS PRESS, INC.; *U.S. Private*, pg. 947
ROTARY MULTIFORMS, INC.; *U.S. Private*, pg. 947
SHADE/ALLIED, INC.—American Pad and Paper Company; *U.S. Public*, pg. 89
STANDARD REGISTER-BARRINGTON—The Standard Register Company; *U.S. Public*, pg. 1505
THE STANDARD REGISTER COMPANY; *U.S. Public*, pg. 1505
STANFAST, INC.—The Standard Register Company; *U.S. Public*, pg. 1505
STUART HALL CO., INC.—Newell Co.; *U.S. Public*, pg. 1178
TFP DATA SYSTEMS—Taylor Corporation; *U.S. Private*, pg. 1070
TST/IMPRESO, INC.; *U.S. Private*, pg. 1066
TRANSKRIT CORPORATION—National Fiberstock Corporation; *U.S. Private*, pg. 782
UFORMA SHELBY BUSINESS FORMS—Miami Systems Corporation; *U.S. Private*, pg. 740
UNITS SETS, INC.—Rotary Forms Press, Inc.; *U.S. Private*, pg. 947
WALLACE COMPUTER SERVICES, INC.; *U.S. Public*, pg. 1735
WEBER MARKING SYSTEMS, INC.; *U.S. Private*, pg. 1157
WILLAMETTE INDUSTRIES, INC.; *U.S. Public*, pg. 1768
WOODBURY BUSINESS FORMS, INC.; *U.S. Private*, pg. 1186
WURZBURG, INC.; *U.S. Private*, pg. 1192

2771 — GREETING CARD PUBLISHING & PRINTING

AMERICAN GREETINGS CORPORATION; *U.S. Public*, pg. 77
AMERICAN GREETINGS U.S. GREETING CARD DIVISION—American Greetings Corporation; *U.S. Public*, pg. 78
AMERICAN PAD AND PAPER COMPANY; *U.S. Public*, pg. 88
ARTISTIC GREETINGS, INC.; *U.S. Public*, pg. 136
BRIGHT OF AMERICA, INC.—Russ Berrie and Company, Inc.; *U.S. Public*, pg. 223
BURGOYNE, INC.; *U.S. Private*, pg. 182
CSS INDUSTRIES, INC.; *U.S. Public*, pg. 283
CARLTON CARDS DIVISION—American Greetings Corporation; *U.S. Public*, pg. 78
CARLTON CARDS FRANCE—American Greetings Corporation; *U.S. Public*, pg. 78
CARLTON CARDS, LTD.—American Greetings Corporation; *U.S. Public*, pg. 78
CELEBRATION ARTS GROUP LIMITED—American Greetings Corporation; *U.S. Public*, pg. 78
CLEO INC.—CSS Industries, Inc.; *U.S. Public*, pg. 284
COOK COMMUNICATION MINISTRIES; *U.S. Private*, pg. 272
CREATIVE CARD CO.—American Pad and Paper Company; *U.S. Public*, pg. 89
DELUXE CORPORATION; *U.S. Public*, pg. 498
DENISON COLOUR LIMITED—American Greetings Corporation; *U.S. Public*, pg. 78
FELICITACIONES NACIONALES S.A. DE C.V—American Greetings Corporation; *U.S. Public*, pg. 78
FINE ART DEVELOPMENTS PLC; *Int'l*, pg. 485
FINE ART GRAPHICS LTD.—Fine Art Developments plc; *Int'l*, pg. 485
GIBSON GREETINGS, INC.; *U.S. Public*, pg. 742
GIBSON GREETINGS INTERNATIONAL LIMITED—Gibson Greetings, Inc.; *U.S. Public*, pg. 742
GRAKO OY—American Greetings Corporation; *U.S. Public*, pg. 78
HALLMARK CARDS, INC.; *U.S. Private*, pg. 495
HAMBLEDON STUDIOS LTD.—Fine Art Developments plc; *Int'l*, pg. 485
HANSON WHITE LTD.—Pentland Group PLC; *Int'l*, pg. 1035
A/S MULVA GRAFISKE PRODUKTER—American Greetings Corporation; *U.S. Public*, pg. 78
MUVA GREETINGS B.V.—American Greetings Corporation; *U.S. Public*, pg. 78
MUVA GREETINGS S.A.—American Greetings Corporation; *U.S. Public*, pg. 78
NEW ENGLAND BUSINESS SERVICE, INC.; *U.S. Public*, pg. 1170
THE PAPER FACTORY OF WISCONSIN, INC.—Gibson Greetings, Inc.; *U.S. Public*, pg. 742
THE PAPER MAGIC GROUP, INC.—CSS Industries, Inc.; *U.S. Public*, pg. 284
RUST CRAFT CANADA, INC.—American Greetings Corporation; *U.S. Public*, pg. 78
RUST CRAFT GREETING CARDS (U.K.) LIMITED—American Greetings Corporation; *U.S. Public*, pg. 78
RUST CRAFT INTERNATIONAL, S.A.—American Greetings Corporation; *U.S. Public*, pg. 78
SANGAMON INDUSTRIES; *U.S. Private*, pg. 965
STUDIO CARDS LTD.—Fine Art Developments plc; *Int'l*, pg. 485
SUMMIT-CANADA—American Greetings Corporation; *U.S. Public*, pg. 78
ANDREW VALENTINE HOLDINGS LIMITED—American Greetings Corporation; *U.S. Public*, pg. 78
THE VERNON COMPANY; *U.S. Private*, pg. 1137
WILLIAMHOUSE OF TEXAS—American Pad and Paper Company; *U.S. Public*, pg. 89
WILLIAMHOUSE-REGENCY, INC.—American Pad and Paper Company; *U.S. Public*, pg. 89

2782 — BLANKBOOKS, LOOSE LEAF BINDERS & DEVICES

ACCO CANADA INC.—Fortune Brands, Inc.; *U.S. Public*, pg. 674
ACCO FRANCE S.A.—Fortune Brands, Inc.; *U.S. Public*, pg. 675
ACCO UK LIMITED—Fortune Brands, Inc.; *U.S. Public*, pg. 675
ACCO WORLD CORPORATION—Fortune Brands, Inc.; *U.S. Public*, pg. 674
AMERICAN PAD AND PAPER COMPANY; *U.S. Public*, pg. 88
AMERICAN TRADING AND PRODUCTION CORPORATION; *U.S. Private*, pg. 63
BENSONS INTERNATIONAL SYSTEMS INC.—Esselte AB; *Int'l*, pg. 460
BRODART COMPANY; *U.S. Private*, pg. 170
BROWN INDUSTRIES, INC.; *U.S. Private*, pg. 174
JAMES BURN INTERNATIONAL LIMITED—Standex International Corporation; *U.S. Public*, pg. 1507
CLARKE AMERICAN CORP.—Caradon Plc; *Int'l*, pg. 267
COLAD GROUP INC.; *U.S. Private*, pg. 250
DAVIS & HENDERSON LIMITED—Data Business Forms Limited; *Int'l*, pg. 384
DAY-TIMERS, INC.—Fortune Brands, Inc.; *U.S. Public*, pg. 674
DAY-TIMERS OF CANADA, LIMITED—Fortune Brands, Inc.; *U.S. Public*, pg. 674
DELUXE CORPORATION; *U.S. Public*, pg. 498
DORET S.A.—Avery Dennison Corporation; *U.S. Public*, pg. 154
EBSCO INDUSTRIES, INC.; *U.S. Private*, pg. 358
ESSELTE PENDAFLEX CANADA, INC.—Esselte AB; *Int'l*, pg. 460
FORTUNE BRANDS, INC.; *U.S. Public*, pg. 674
GEIGER BROTHERS; *U.S. Private*, pg. 442
GENERAL BINDING CORPORATION; *U.S. Public*, pg. 707
C.R. GIBSON CO.—Thomas Nelson Inc.; *U.S. Public*, pg. 1168
GRAPHIC CONTROLS CORPORATION; *U.S. Private*, pg. 470
IVY HILL CORPORATION—Time Warner Inc.; *U.S. Public*, pg. 1611
JM COMPANY; *U.S. Private*, pg. 577
KLEER-VU PLASTICS, INC.; *U.S. Public*, pg. 962
KLEER-VU PLASTICS CORP.—Kleer-Vu Plastics, Inc.; *U.S. Public*, pg. 962
CHARLES LEONARD, INC.; *U.S. Private*, pg. 660
CHARLES LEONARD WESTERN, INC.—Charles Leonard, Inc.; *U.S. Private*, pg. 660
MASTER PRODUCTS MFG. CO.—James Crean PLC; *Int'l*, pg. 340
THE MEAD CORPORATION; *U.S. Public*, pg. 1074
MEAD SCHOOL & OFFICE PRODUCTS—The Mead Corporation; *U.S. Public*, pg. 1074
H.C. MILLER COMPANY; *U.S. Private*, pg. 747
M. MYERS & SON PLC—Avery Dennison Corporation; *U.S. Public*, pg. 154
MYRON MANUFACTURING CORPORATION; *U.S. Private*, pg. 771
OPTIC GRAPHICS, INC.; *U.S. Private*, pg. 818
PITNEY BOWES INC.; *U.S. Public*, pg. 1303
PRODUCTOS MAESTROS—James Crean PLC; *Int'l*, pg. 341
QUALITY SERVICES INTERNATIONAL, INC.—Encore Marketing International, Inc.; *U.S. Public*, pg. 580
THE REYNOLDS AND REYNOLDS COMPANY; *U.S. Public*, pg. 1384
RING KING VISIBLES, INC.—Esselte AB; *Int'l*, pg. 460
STUART HALL CO., INC.—Newell Co.; *U.S. Public*, pg. 1178
U.S. RING BINDER CORP.—General Binding Corporation; *U.S. Public*, pg. 707
U.S. RING-ST. LOUIS—General Binding Corporation; *U.S. Public*, pg. 707
VIA TECH PUBLISHING SOLUTIONS; *U.S. Private*, pg. 1138
WILLIAMHOUSE-REGENCY, INC.—American Pad and Paper Company; *U.S. Public*, pg. 89

2789 — BOOKBINDING & RELATED WORK

AMERICAN BINDRY-MIDWEST—The American Companies, Inc.; *U.S. Private*, pg. 52
AMERICAN BINDRY-SOUTH—The American Companies, Inc.; *U.S. Private*, pg. 52
THE AMERICAN COMPANIES, INC.; *U.S. Private*, pg. 52
BERRYVILLE GRAPHICS INC.—Bertelsmann AG; *Int'l*, pg. 191
BRADLEY PRINTING COMPANY—World Color Press, Inc.; *U.S. Public*, pg. 1778
BRODART COMPANY; *U.S. Private*, pg. 170
BROWN INDUSTRIES, INC.; *U.S. Private*, pg. 174
COLWELL INDUSTRIES, INC.; *U.S. Private*, pg. 257
COURIER CONNECTION, INC.—Courier Corporation; *U.S. Public*, pg. 453
COURIER INTERNATIONAL, LTD.—Courier Corporation; *U.S. Public*, pg. 453
COURIER KENDALLVILLE, INC.—Courier Corporation; *U.S. Public*, pg. 453
COURIER WESTFORD, INC.—Courier Corporation; *U.S. Public*, pg. 453
DAI NIPPON BOOK BINDING CO., LTD.—Dai Nippon Printing Co., Ltd.; *Int'l*, pg. 363
DELTA LITHOGRAPH CO.—Bertelsmann AG; *Int'l*, pg. 191
E.P. GRAPHICS, INC.; *U.S. Private*, pg. 354
ECONO-CLAD BOOKS—The American Companies, Inc.; *U.S. Private*, pg. 52
EDITORS PRESS, INC.—The Kiplinger Washington Editors, Inc.; *U.S. Private*, pg. 623
GEIGER BROTHERS; *U.S. Private*, pg. 442
C.R. GIBSON CO.—Thomas Nelson Inc.; *U.S. Public*, pg. 1168
GROUPE DE LA CITE—Alcatel Alsthom Compagnie Generale D'Electricite; *Int'l*, pg. 53
LANE GRAPHICS PRODUCTS DIV.—General Binding Corporation; *U.S. Public*, pg. 707
LAWYERS COOPERATIVE PUBLISHING CO.—The Thomson Corporation; *U.S. Public*, pg. 1602
MCCORQUODALE COLORCARD, INC.—Rexam PLC; *Int'l*, pg. 1106
MIKEN COMPANIES, INC.; *U.S. Private*, pg. 745
NATIONAL PUBLISHING CO.—Courier Corporation; *U.S. Public*, pg. 453
PREBOUND PERIODICALS, INC.—The American Companies, Inc.; *U.S. Private*, pg. 52
RAND MCNALLY & COMPANY; *U.S. Private*, pg. 908
ROSE PRINTING COMPANY, INC.; *U.S. Private*, pg. 945
THE SEGERDAHL CORP.; *U.S. Private*, pg. 981
SMITH-EDWARDS-DUNLAP COMPANY; *U.S. Private*, pg. 1007
TREND OFFSET PRINTING SERVICES; *U.S. Private*, pg. 1099
VAN NOSTRAND REINHOLD—The Thomson Corporation; *U.S. Public*, pg. 1600
VIA TECH PUBLISHING SOLUTIONS; *U.S. Private*, pg. 1138
WORZALLA PUBLISHING CO., INC.; *U.S. Private*, pg. 1191

2791 — TYPESETTING

ALCOM PRINTING GROUP, INC.; *U.S. Private*, pg. 33
AUTOLOGIC INFORMATION INTERNATIONAL, INC.—Volt Information Sciences, Inc.; *U.S. Public*, pg. 1724
BLACK DOT GRAPHICS, INC.—Devon Group, Inc.; *U.S. Public*, pg. 503
CAPITAL GRAPHICS INC.; *U.S. Private*, pg. 206
CASTCRAFT INDUSTRIES, INC.; *U.S. Private*, pg. 219
CASTCRAFT SOFTWARE OPTIFONT—Castcraft Industries, Inc.; *U.S. Private*, pg. 219
THE CLARINDA COMPANY—Capital Graphics Inc.; *U.S. Private*, pg. 206
COOPER & BEATTY—Jannock Limited; *Int'l*, pg. 698
COSMOS COMMUNICATIONS, INC.; *U.S. Private*, pg. 278
DEVON GROUP, INC.; *U.S. Public*, pg. 503
GEORGE LITHOGRAPH; *U.S. Private*, pg. 448
GOLDEN BOOKS FAMILY ENTERTAINMENT INC.; *U.S. Public*, pg. 749
GOLDEN BOOKS PUBLISHING—Golden Books Family Entertainment Inc.; *U.S. Public*, pg. 749
IMPERIAL LITHO & DRYOGRAPHY, INC.; *U.S. Private*, pg. 558
JANNOCK IMAGING COMPANIES LIMITED—Jannock Limited; *Int'l*, pg. 698
MCLEAN BROTHERS—Jannock Limited; *Int'l*, pg. 698
O'NEIL DATA SYSTEMS, INC.—William O'Neil & Co., Inc.; *U.S. Private*, pg. 817
PEARL-PRESSMAN-LIBERTY COMMUNICATIONS GROUP; *U.S. Private*, pg. 845
POTOMAC GRAPHIC INDUSTRIES, INC.—Jannock Limited; *Int'l*, pg. 699
ST. CROIX PRESS, INC.; *U.S. Private*, pg. 960
SHANDWICK INTERNATIONAL PLC; *Int'l*, pg. 1226
SMITH-EDWARDS-DUNLAP COMPANY; *U.S. Private*, pg. 1007
TWEDDLE LITHO COMPANY; *U.S. Private*, pg. 1111

TYPO-GRAPHICS, INC.—Devon Group, Inc.; *U.S. Public*, pg. 503
UNIDIGITAL/CARDINAL CORP.—Unidigital Inc.; *U.S. Public*, pg. 1664
VOLT-AUTOLOGIC DIRECTORIES S.A.—Volt Information Sciences, Inc.; *U.S. Public*, pg. 1724
VOLT INFORMATION SCIENCES, INC.; *U.S. Public*, pg. 1724

2796 — PLATEMAKING AND RELATED SERVICES

AMERICAN BANKNOTE CORP.; *U.S. Public*, pg. 68
AMERICAN COLOR—Morgan Stanley Dean Witter & Co.; *U.S. Public*, pg. 1133
ANCHOR INC.—International Paper Company; *U.S. Public*, pg. 903
BANTA DIGITAL GROUP—Banta Corporation; *U.S. Public*, pg. 188
BATTEN CONVERTER SERVICES—Jannock Limited; *Int'l*, pg. 698
BUREAU OF ENGRAVING; *U.S. Private*, pg. 181
CADMUS FINANCIAL—Cadmus Communications Corporation; *U.S. Public*, pg. 291
CLARINDA COLOR L.L.C.—Capital Graphics Inc.; *U.S. Private*, pg. 206
THE CLARINDA COMPANY—Capital Graphics Inc.; *U.S. Private*, pg. 206
COLOR DATA EAST—Schawk, Inc.; *U.S. Public*, pg. 1437
COOKSON GROUP PLC; *Int'l*, pg. 328
FUJI PHOTO FILM B.V.—Fuji Photo Film Co., Ltd.; *Int'l*, pg. 524
FUJI PHOTO FILM CO., LTD.; *Int'l*, pg. 523
FUJI PHOTO FILM, INC.—Fuji Photo Film Co., Ltd.; *Int'l*, pg. 524
GAMMA ONE, INC.—Big Flower Press Holdings, Inc.; *U.S. Public*, pg. 228
HOECHST SPECIALTY PRODUCTS GROUP—Hoechst Aktiengesellschaft; *Int'l*, pg. 625
JANNOCK LIMITED; *Int'l*, pg. 698
KAL GRAFX—The Excellence Group; *U.S. Private*, pg. 387
KELLER-DORIAN GRAVEURS, DIV. OF ROEHLEN INDUSTRIES/EUROPE—Standex International Corporation; *U.S. Public*, pg. 1507
LSI/KALA—Schawk, Inc.; *U.S. Public*, pg. 1437
LITHO COLORPLATE—Schawk, Inc.; *U.S. Public*, pg. 1437
MOLD-TECH PORTUGAL—Standex International Corporation; *U.S. Public*, pg. 1507
NAPP SYSTEMS INC—Lee Enterprises, Incorporated; *U.S. Public*, pg. 984
POLYCHROME CORP. DIV.—Dainippon Ink & Chemicals, Inc.; *Int'l*, pg. 370
POTOMAC GRAPHIC INDUSTRIES, INC.—Jannock Limited; *Int'l*, pg. 699
PREPLINK—Great Lakes Lithograph Co.; *U.S. Private*, pg. 475
PRINTING DEVELOPMENTS, INC.—The General Chemical Group, Inc.; *U.S. Public*, pg. 707
PROCESS COLOR PLATE—Schawk, Inc.; *U.S. Public*, pg. 1437
ROEHLEN ENGLAND—Standex International Corporation; *U.S. Public*, pg. 1507
ROEHLEN INDUSTRIES PTY. LTD. (SIDNEY DIVISION)—Standex International Corporation; *U.S. Public*, pg. 1507
SAFEGUARD BUSINESS SYSTEMS LIMITED—Safeguard Business Systems, Inc.; *U.S. Private*, pg. 960
SCHAWK, INC.; *U.S. Public*, pg. 1437
SCHAWKGRAPHICS—Schawk, Inc.; *U.S. Public*, pg. 1437
STANDEX INTERNATIONAL GMBH—Standex International Corporation; *U.S. Public*, pg. 1507
STANDEX INTERNATIONAL S.R.L. (MOLD-TECH DIVISION)—Standex International Corporation; *U.S. Public*, pg. 1508
TAKAGI CHOKOKU CO., LTD.; *Int'l*, pg. 1349
VIKING ENGRAVING CORP. INC.—Borden, Inc.; *U.S. Private*, pg. 158
WESTON ENGRAVING—Schawk, Inc.; *U.S. Public*, pg. 1437

2812 — ALKALIES & CHLORINE

AKZO COATINGS B.V.—Akzo Nobel N.V.; *Int'l*, pg. 42
AKZO NOBEL INC.—Akzo Nobel N.V.; *Int'l*, pg. 47
ARM & HAMMER CONSUMER PRODUCTS—Church & Dwight Co., Inc.; *U.S. Public*, pg. 356
ATOCHEM UK LTD.—Elf Aquitane; *Int'l*, pg. 446
BASF AG; *Int'l*, pg. 103
CASTROL INDUSTRIAL—Burmah Castrol plc; *Int'l*, pg. 235
CHURCH & DWIGHT CO., INC.; *U.S. Public*, pg. 355
CHURCH & DWIGHT CO., INC. LTD.—Church & Dwight Co., Inc.; *U.S. Public*, pg. 356
CHURCH & DWIGHT SPECIALTY PRODUCTS DIVISION—Church & Dwight Co., Inc.; *U.S. Public*, pg. 356
DEUTSCHE ICI GMBH—Imperial Chemical Industries PLC; *Int'l*, pg. 664
THE DOW CHEMICAL COMPANY; *U.S. Public*, pg. 522
ELECTROCHEMICAL INDUSTRIES (FRUTAROM) LTD.—ICC Industries, Inc.; *U.S. Private*, pg. 553
ELF AQUITAINE, INC.—Elf Aquitane; *Int'l*, pg. 445
ELF ATOCHEM S.A.—Elf Aquitane; *Int'l*, pg. 445
FMC ALKALI CHEMICALS DIV.—FMC Corporation; *U.S. Public*, pg. 605
FORMOSA PLASTICS CORPORATION; *Int'l*, pg. 498
GENERAL CHEMICAL CORPORATION—The General Chemical Group, Inc.; *U.S. Public*, pg. 707
GEORGIA GULF CORPORATION; *U.S. Public*, pg. 734
HAVILAND ENTERPRISES; *U.S. Private*, pg. 511
HERCULES CHEMICAL CO., INC.; *U.S. Private*, pg. 523
HUBBARD HALL INC.; *U.S. Private*, pg. 544
HYDRITE CHEMICAL COMPANY; *U.S. Private*, pg. 551
ICI ATLANTIK GMBH—Imperial Chemical Industries PLC; *Int'l*, pg. 664
ICI FRANCE SA—Imperial Chemical Industries PLC; *Int'l*, pg. 665
ICI OESTERREICH GMBH—Imperial Chemical Industries PLC; *Int'l*, pg. 665
ICI (PERU) S.A.—Imperial Chemical Industries PLC; *Int'l*, pg. 665
ICI (PHILIPPINES) INC.—Imperial Chemical Industries PLC; *Int'l*, pg. 665
ICI (SINGAPORE) PRIVATE LIMITED—Imperial Chemical Industries PLC; *Int'l*, pg. 665
ICI ZAMBIA LIMITED—Imperial Chemical Industries PLC; *Int'l*, pg. 665
IMPERIAL CHEMICAL INDUSTRIES PLC; *Int'l*, pg. 662
ISHIHARA SANGYO KAISHA, LTD.; *Int'l*, pg. 689
JONES CHEMICALS, INC.; *U.S. Private*, pg. 596
KALI UND SALZ BETEILIGUNGS AG—BASF AG; *Int'l*, pg. 104
KINLEITH MILL—International Paper Company; *U.S. Public*, pg. 905
LAPORTE INC.—Laporte plc; *Int'l*, pg. 802
LONZA INC.—Alusuisse-Lonza Holding Ltd.; *Int'l*, pg. 67
MATTHES & WEBER GMBH—Henkel KGaA; *Int'l*, pg. 610
NIACHLOR—Olin Corporation; *U.S. Public*, pg. 1219
NORSK HYDRO A.S; *Int'l*, pg. 959
OCCIDENTAL CHEMICAL CORPORATION—Occidental Petroleum Corporation; *U.S. Public*, pg. 1210
OLIN CORPORATION; *U.S. Public*, pg. 1218
PCS PHOSPHATE - RALEIGH—Potash Corporation of Saskatchewan Inc.; *Int'l*, pg. 1064
PPG INDUSTRIES, INC.; *U.S. Public*, pg. 1245
SOLVAY CHEMIE B.V.—Solvay S.A.; *Int'l*, pg. 1279
SOLVAY OSTERREICH AG—Solvay S.A.; *Int'l*, pg. 1280
SOLVAY PORTUGAL PRODUCTOS QUIMICOS S.A.—Solvay S.A.; *Int'l*, pg. 1280
SOLVAY S.A.; *Int'l*, pg. 1277
SOLVAY SCHWEIZ S.A.—Solvay S.A.; *Int'l*, pg. 1280
TOKUYAMA CORPORATION; *Int'l*, pg. 1393
VULCAN CHEMICALS—Vulcan Materials Company; *U.S. Public*, pg. 1725
VULCAN MATERIALS COMPANY; *U.S. Public*, pg. 1725
WEYERHAEUSER COMPANY; *U.S. Public*, pg. 1764
ZENECA AB—Zeneca Group Plc; *Int'l*, pg. 1526
ZENECA HELLAS S.A.—Zeneca Group Plc; *Int'l*, pg. 1526
ZENECA OY—Zeneca Group Plc; *Int'l*, pg. 1527
ZENECA POLAND SP. Z.O.O.—Zeneca Group Plc; *Int'l*, pg. 1527
ZENECA ZIMBABWE (PRIVATE) LIMITED—Zeneca Group Plc; *Int'l*, pg. 1527

2813 — INDUSTRIAL GASES

AGA AB; *Int'l*, pg. 12
OY AGA AB—AGA AB; *Int'l*, pg. 13
AGA AG—AGA AB; *Int'l*, pg. 13
AGA ARGENTINA SACIFIMR—AGA AB; *Int'l*, pg. 13
AGA A/S—AGA AB; *Int'l*, pg. 13
AGA CHILE S.A.—AGA AB; *Int'l*, pg. 13
AGA DE MEXICO S.A. DE C.V.—AGA AB; *Int'l*, pg. 13
AGA DEL ECUADOR C.A.—AGA AB; *Int'l*, pg. 13
CIA. AGA DEL PERU S.A.—AGA AB; *Int'l*, pg. 13
AGA-FANO S.A.—AGA AB; *Int'l*, pg. 13
AGA GAS AB—AGA AB; *Int'l*, pg. 12
AGA GAS B.V.—AGA AB; *Int'l*, pg. 13
AGA GAS GMBH—AGA AB; *Int'l*, pg. 13
AGA GAS, INC.—AGA AB; *Int'l*, pg. 13
AGA GES.M.B.H.—AGA AB; *Int'l*, pg. 13
AGA PROGAS A/S—AGA AB; *Int'l*, pg. 13
AGA S.A.—AGA AB; *Int'l*, pg. 13
AGA SPECIALGAS AB—AGA AB; *Int'l*, pg. 13
AGA VENEZOLANA C.A.—AGA AB; *Int'l*, pg. 14
AGANOR S.A.—AGA AB; *Int'l*, pg. 13
AIR LIQUIDE AMERICA CORPORATION—Air Liquide S.A.; *Int'l*, pg. 37
AIR LIQUIDE ITALY/SIO—Air Liquide S.A.; *Int'l*, pg. 37
AIR LIQUIDE S.A.; *Int'l*, pg. 37
AIR PRODUCTS AND CHEMICALS, INC.; *U.S. Public*, pg. 30
AIRGAS, INC.; *U.S. Public*, pg. 33
ALBRIGHT & WILSON (AUSTRALIA) LIMITED—Albright & Wilson plc; *Int'l*, pg. 49
ALBRIGHT & WILSON, INC.—Albright & Wilson plc; *Int'l*, pg. 49
ALPHAGAZ DIVISION—Air Liquide S.A.; *Int'l*, pg. 37
BOC—The BOC Group plc; *Int'l*, pg. 121
BOC BANGLADESH LTD.—The BOC Group plc; *Int'l*, pg. 121
BOC CANADA LTD.—The BOC Group plc; *Int'l*, pg. 121
BOC GASES ANBA NV—The BOC Group plc; *Int'l*, pg. 121
BOC GASES AUSTRALIA LTD.—The BOC Group plc; *Int'l*, pg. 121
BOC GASES FIJI LTD.—The BOC Group plc; *Int'l*, pg. 121
P.T. BOC GASES INDONESIA—The BOC Group plc; *Int'l*, pg. 121
BOC GASES IRELAND LTD.—The BOC Group plc; *Int'l*, pg. 121
BOC GASES NEW ZEALAND LTD—The BOC Group plc; *Int'l*, pg. 121
BOC GASES PAPUA NEW GUINEA PTY LTD.—The BOC Group plc; *Int'l*, pg. 121
THE BOC GROUP INC. (DELAWARE)—The BOC Group plc; *Int'l*, pg. 121
THE BOC GROUP PLC; *Int'l*, pg. 121
BOC INDIA LTD.—The BOC Group plc; *Int'l*, pg. 122
BOC KENYA LTD.—The BOC Group plc; *Int'l*, pg. 122
BOC LIEN HWA INDUSTRIAL GASES CO. LTD.—The BOC Group plc; *Int'l*, pg. 122
BOC PAKISTAN LTD.—The BOC Group plc; *Int'l*, pg. 122
BOC ZIMBABWE—The BOC Group plc; *Int'l*, pg. 122
BANGKOK INDUSTRIAL GAS CO., LTD.—Air Products and Chemicals, Inc.; *U.S. Public*, pg. 32
BAYOU COGENERATION—Air Liquide S.A.; *Int'l*, pg. 37
BEIJING AP BEIFEN GASES INDUSTRY COMPANY, LTD.—Air Products and Chemicals, Inc.; *U.S. Public*, pg. 32
CANADIAN LIQUID AIR LTD.-AIR LIQUIDE CANADA LTEE—Air Liquide S.A.; *Int'l*, pg. 37
CANADIAN LIQUIDAIRE PROPERTIES LTD.—Air Liquide S.A.; *Int'l*, pg. 37
CARBIDE PRODUCTS—The Carbide/Graphite Group, Inc.; *U.S. Public*, pg. 304
S.E. CARBUROS METALICOS S.A.—Air Products and Chemicals, Inc.; *U.S. Public*, pg. 32
CARDOX DIVISION—Air Liquide S.A.; *Int'l*, pg. 37
CHUN WANG INDUSTRIAL GASES, LIMITED—Air Products and Chemicals, Inc.; *U.S. Public*, pg. 32
THE COASTAL CORPORATION; *U.S. Public*, pg. 389
CONSOLIDACION COMERCIAL INFRA, S.A. DE C.V.—Air Products and Chemicals, Inc.; *U.S. Public*, pg. 32
CONSOLIDATED INDUSTRIAL GASES INC.—The BOC Group plc; *Int'l*, pg. 122
CRYOINFRA S.A. DE C.V.—Air Products and Chemicals, Inc.; *U.S. Public*, pg. 32
DAIDO HOXAN INC.; *Int'l*, pg. 363
ENRON CORP.; *U.S. Public*, pg. 584
HOECHST MARION ROUSSEL AG—Hoechst Aktiengesellschaft; *Int'l*, pg. 624
HOECHST MARION ROUSSEL, INC.—Hoechst Aktiengesellschaft; *Int'l*, pg. 624
HOECHST SPECIALTY PRODUCTS GROUP—Hoechst Aktiengesellschaft; *Int'l*, pg. 625
HONG KONG OXYGEN & ACETYLENE CO. LTD.—The BOC Group plc; *Int'l*, pg. 122
IBERICA AGA S.A.—AGA AB; *Int'l*, pg. 14
INDUSTRIAL GASES LTD.—The BOC Group plc; *Int'l*, pg. 122
ISHIHARA SANGYO KAISHA, LTD.; *Int'l*, pg. 689
K.K. JAPAN HELIUM CENTER—The BOC Group plc; *Int'l*, pg. 122
KEEN COMPRESSED GAS CO.; *U.S. Private*, pg. 611
KEEN WELDING DIVISION—Keen Compressed Gas Co.; *U.S. Private*, pg. 611
KOREA INDUSTRIAL GASES LTD.—Air Products and Chemicals, Inc.; *U.S. Public*, pg. 32
LAROCHE INDUSTRIES INC.; *U.S. Private*, pg. 651
LINDE AG; *Int'l*, pg. 810
LINDE AG WERKSGRUPPE TECHNISCHE GASE—Linde AG; *Int'l*, pg. 810
MALAYSIAN OXYGEN BERHAD—The BOC Group plc; *Int'l*, pg. 122
MIDDLETOWN OXYGEN CO., INC.—Air Products and Chemicals, Inc.; *U.S. Public*, pg. 31
NATIONAL WELDERS SUPPLY CO. INC.; *U.S. Private*, pg. 788
NIPPON BOC KK—The BOC Group plc; *Int'l*, pg. 122
NIPPON SANSO CORPORATION; *Int'l*, pg. 938
NITROUS OXIDE CORP. (DONORA)—Airgas, Inc.; *U.S. Public*, pg. 33
NORSK HYDRO A.S; *Int'l*, pg. 959
OXIGENIO DO BRASIL S.A., CONSOLIDEE—Air Liquide S.A.; *Int'l*, pg. 37
PRODAIR, S.A.—Air Products and Chemicals, Inc.; *U.S. Public*, pg. 32
SAN FU CHEMICAL CO., LTD.—Air Products and Chemicals, Inc.; *U.S. Public*, pg. 32
SCOTT SPECIALTY GASES; *U.S. Private*, pg. 977
SINGAPORE OXYGEN AIR LIQUIDE PTE LTD.—The BOC Group plc; *Int'l*, pg. 122
SITT TATT INDUSTRIAL GASES SDN. BHD.—Air Products and Chemicals, Inc.; *U.S. Public*, pg. 32
SOLVAY CHEMIE B.V.—Solvay S.A.; *Int'l*, pg. 1279
SOLVAY SCHWEIZ S.A.—Solvay S.A.; *Int'l*, pg. 1280
TECHNISCHE GASE GMBH—AGA AB; *Int'l*, pg. 14
THERMICE CORPORATION—Publicker Industries Inc.; *U.S. Public*, pg. 1341
TRAFALGAR HOUSE OFFSHORE FABRICATORS LIMITED (PORT CLARENCE)—Kvaerner a.s.a.; *Int'l*, pg. 773
TRAFALGAR HOUSE OFFSHORE FABRICATORS LIMITED (METHIL WORKS)—Kvaerner a.s.a.; *Int'l*, pg. 773
UNION CARBIDE BENELUX NV—Union Carbide Corporation; *U.S. Public*, pg. 1667
VITALAIRE CORPORATION—Air Liquide S.A.; *Int'l*, pg. 37
VULCAN CHEMICALS—Vulcan Materials Company; *U.S. Public*, pg. 1725
VULCAN MATERIALS COMPANY; *U.S. Public*, pg. 1725
WELSCO INC.; *U.S. Private*, pg. 1161

2816 — INORGANIC PIGMENTS

AMERICAN EMULSIONS CO., INC.—RPM, Inc.; *U.S. Public*, pg. 1357
AMERICAN THERMOPLASTICS CORPORATION—Phillips Petroleum Company; *U.S. Public*, pg. 1291
BASF MAROC S.A.—BASF AG; *Int'l*, pg. 106
BAYER AG—Bayer AG; *Int'l*, pg. 172
BAYER CORPORATION—Bayer AG; *Int'l*, pg. 172
BROWNING CHEMICAL CORPORATION; *U.S. Private*, pg. 175
C & C - COLORING & COMPOUNDING SRL—Mazzucchelli Polimeri Srl; *Int'l*, pg. 850
CERDEC CORPORATION—Ciba Specialty Chemicals Holding Inc.; *Int'l*, pg. 292
CIBA-GEIGY AUSTRALIA LTD.—Novartis AG; *Int'l*, pg. 976
CIBA-GEIGY CANADA LTD.—Novartis AG; *Int'l*, pg. 976
CIBA-GEIGY (CHINA) LIMITED—Novartis AG; *Int'l*, pg. 976
CIBA-GEIGY (CHINA) LIMITED-GUANGZHOU BRANCH OFFICE—Novartis AG; *Int'l*, pg. 976
CIBA-GEIGY (CHINA) LIMITED-SHANGHAI BRANCH—Novartis AG; *Int'l*, pg. 976
CIBA-GEIGY ILAC VE KIMYA URUNLERI SANAYI VE TICARET AS—Novartis AG; *Int'l*, pg. 977
CIBA-GEIGY JAPAN LIMITED-TOKYO BRANCH—Novartis AG; *Int'l*, pg. 977

CIBA-GEIGY KOREA LTD.—Novartis AG; *Int'l*, pg. 977
CIBA-GEIGY LTD.-TECHNICAL ASSISTANCE OFFICE—Novartis AG; *Int'l*, pg. 978
CIBA-GEIGY MAROC SA—Novartis AG; *Int'l*, pg. 978
CIBA-GEIGY MEXICANA SA DE CV—Novartis AG; *Int'l*, pg. 978
CIBA-GEIGY QUIMICA S.A.—Novartis AG; *Int'l*, pg. 979
CIBA-GEIGY S.A.—Novartis AG; *Int'l*, pg. 979
CIBA-GEIGY SERVICES AG—Novartis AG; *Int'l*, pg. 979
CIBA-GEIGY SERVICES AG-TECHNICAL ADVISORY OFFICE—Novartis AG; *Int'l*, pg. 979
CIBA-GEIGY (THAILAND) LTD.—Novartis AG; *Int'l*, pg. 980
CIBA-GEIGY TRADING AND MARKETING SERVICES CO. LTD.—Novartis AG; *Int'l*, pg. 980
CIBA PIGMENTS—Ciba Specialty Chemicals Holding Inc.; *Int'l*, pg. 292
COOKSON MATTHEY (AUSTRALIA)—Johnson Matthey Public Limited Company; *Int'l*, pg. 714
COOKSON MATTHEY B.V.—Johnson Matthey Public Limited Company; *Int'l*, pg. 714
COOKSON MATTHEY CERAMICS PLC—Johnson Matthey Public Limited Company; *Int'l*, pg. 713
COOKSON MATTHEY SPA—Johnson Matthey Public Limited Company; *Int'l*, pg. 714
CREATIVE CARD CO.—American Pad and Paper Company; *U.S. Public*, pg. 89
DAIHAN SWISS CHEMICAL CORPORATION—Ciba Specialty Chemicals Holding Inc.; *Int'l*, pg. 292
DEUTSCHE BARYT-INDUSTRIE DR. RUDOLF ALBERTI & CO.—Solvay S.A.; *Int'l*, pg. 1278
DEXTER CHEMICAL CORP.; *U.S. Private*, pg. 329
EGE FERRO KIMYA SANAYI VE TICARRET—Ferro Corporation; *U.S. Public*, pg. 619
ENGELHARD CORPORATION; *U.S. Public*, pg. 582
FERRO CORPORATION; *U.S. Public*, pg. 618
FERRO (ITALIA) S.R.L.—Ferro Corporation; *U.S. Public*, pg. 619
FINE INORGANIC CHEMICALS—Rhone-Poulenc S.A.; *Int'l*, pg. 1109
HAMMOND GROUP INC.; *U.S. Private*, pg. 498
HARRISONS & CROSFIELD PLC; *Int'l*, pg. 598
HINDUSTAN CIBA-GEIGY LIMITED—Novartis AG; *Int'l*, pg. 982
HITOX CORPORATION OF AMERICA; *U.S. Public*, pg. 829
HOECHST AUSTRALIA LTD.—Hoechst Aktiengesellschaft; *Int'l*, pg. 626
HOOGOVENS GROEP B.V.—Koninklijke Hoogovens N.V.; *Int'l*, pg. 753
J.M. HUBER, CHEMICALS DIVISION—J.M. Huber Corporation; *U.S. Private*, pg. 545
J.M. HUBER CORPORATION; *U.S. Private*, pg. 544
ICI CHEMICALS & POLYMERS—Imperial Chemical Industries PLC; *Int'l*, pg. 663
ICI COLORS—Imperial Chemical Industries PLC; *Int'l*, pg. 663
JOHNSON MATTHEY INC.—Johnson Matthey Public Limited Company; *Int'l*, pg. 713
KEMIRA INCORPORATED—Kemira Oy; *Int'l*, pg. 729
KERR-MCGEE CHEMICAL CORP.—Kerr-McGee Corporation; *U.S. Public*, pg. 952
KERR-MCGEE CORPORATION; *U.S. Public*, pg. 952
KRONOS, INC.—Contran Corporation; *U.S. Private*, pg. 270
KRONOS TITAN GMBH—Contran Corporation; *U.S. Private*, pg. 271
LEARONAL AG—LeaRonal, Inc.; *U.S. Public*, pg. 982
LEARONAL FRANCE—LeaRonal, Inc.; *U.S. Public*, pg. 982
LEARONAL GMBH—LeaRonal, Inc.; *U.S. Public*, pg. 982
LEARONAL, INC.; *U.S. Public*, pg. 982
LEARONAL JAPAN INC.—LeaRonal, Inc.; *U.S. Public*, pg. 982
LEARONAL UK LTD.—LeaRonal, Inc.; *U.S. Public*, pg. 982
LIMOX CHEMIE B.V.—Harrisons & Crosfield plc; *Int'l*, pg. 599
MAGNETICS INTERNATIONAL, INC.—Inland Steel Industries, Inc.; *U.S. Public*, pg. 879
MERCK KOREA, LTD.—Merck & Co., Inc.; *U.S. Public*, pg. 1092
MOONEY CHEMICALS—OM Group; *U.S. Public*, pg. 1208
NL INDUSTRIES, INC.—Contran Corporation; *U.S. Private*, pg. 270
NOVARTIS—Novartis AG; *Int'l*, pg. 972
PPG INDUSTRIES, INC.; *U.S. Public*, pg. 1245
PENTEX AUSTRALIA PTY. LTD.—Novartis AG; *Int'l*, pg. 983
PHELPS DODGE CORPORATION; *U.S. Public*, pg. 1286
PIGMENTS & ADDITIVES—Engelhard Corporation; *U.S. Public*, pg. 582
PREP - STAT/SPECTRUM; *U.S. Private*, pg. 882
PRODUCTOS CIBA SA—Novartis AG; *Int'l*, pg. 983
REEDSPECTRUM—Hoechst Aktiengesellschaft; *Int'l*, pg. 624
SCM CHEM COLORS & SILICA DIV.—Hanson PLC; *Int'l*, pg. 594
SACHTLEBEN CHEMIE GMBH—Metallgesellschaft AG; *Int'l*, pg. 861
THE SHERWIN-WILLIAMS COMPANY; *U.S. Public*, pg. 1465
SHINTO PAINT CO., LTD.—Sumitomo Chemical Company, Ltd.; *Int'l*, pg. 1311
SOCIETE NOUVELLE DE CHIMIE INDUSTRIELLE (SNCI)—Novartis AG; *Int'l*, pg. 986
SOCIETE ZAIRO-SUISSE DE PRODUITS CHIMIQUES S.A.R.L.—Novartis AG; *Int'l*, pg. 986
SOVEREIGN CHEMICAL INDUSTRIES LIMITED—Laporte plc; *Int'l*, pg. 802
SWISS NIGERIAN CHEMICAL CO. LTD.—Novartis AG; *Int'l*, pg. 986
TAITO CO., LTD.—Mitsui & Co., Ltd.; *Int'l*, pg. 878
TAMMS INDUSTRIES—Laporte plc; *Int'l*, pg. 803
TEKNOR COLOR COMPANY—Teknor Apex Company; *U.S. Private*, pg. 1073
TIOXIDE AUSTRALIA PROPRIETARY LIMITED—Imperial Chemical Industries PLC; *Int'l*, pg. 665
TIOXIDE CANADA INC.—Imperial Chemical Industries PLC; *Int'l*, pg. 665
TIOXIDE EUROPE GMBH—Imperial Chemical Industries PLC; *Int'l*, pg. 666
TIOXIDE EUROPE LIMITED—Imperial Chemical Industries PLC; *Int'l*, pg. 663
TIOXIDE EUROPE NV/SA—Imperial Chemical Industries PLC; *Int'l*, pg. 666
TIOXIDE EUROPE S.A.—Imperial Chemical Industries PLC; *Int'l*, pg. 666
TIOXIDE EUROPE SRL—Imperial Chemical Industries PLC; *Int'l*, pg. 666
TIOXIDE GROUP LIMITED—Imperial Chemical Industries PLC; *Int'l*, pg. 663
TIOXIDE JAPAN KK—Imperial Chemical Industries PLC; *Int'l*, pg. 666
TIOXIDE (MALAYSIA) SDN BHD—Imperial Chemical Industries PLC; *Int'l*, pg. 666
TIOXIDE SOUTHERN AFRICA (PTY) LTD.—Imperial Chemical Industries PLC; *Int'l*, pg. 666
VALHI, INC.—Contran Corporation; *U.S. Private*, pg. 270
VAN HEMELRIJCK—GIB Group; *Int'l*, pg. 533
WARNER-JENKINSON CO.—Universal Foods Corporation; *U.S. Public*, pg. 1696
WARNER-JENKINSON COSMETIC COLORS—Universal Foods Corporation; *U.S. Public*, pg. 1696
WAYNE CHEMICAL CORPORATION—Harrisons & Crosfield plc; *Int'l*, pg. 599
WELLBORN - DE CORP.—Dunn-Edwards Corporation; *U.S. Private*, pg. 347
WHITTAKER, CLARK & DANIELS, INC.; *U.S. Private*, pg. 1174
ZEOFINN OY—J.M. Huber Corporation; *U.S. Private*, pg. 545
ZINC CORPORATION OF AMERICA—Horsehead Industries, Inc.; *U.S. Private*, pg. 540

2819 — INDUSTRIAL INORGANIC CHEMICALS, NEC

ABB COMBUSTION ENGINEERING NUCLEAR POWER—ABB Asea Brown Boveri (Holding) Ltd.; *Int'l*, pg. 3
ACAP CHEMICALS PTE. LTD.—Aluminum Company of America; *U.S. Public*, pg. 61
OY ALGOL AB; *Int'l*, pg. 15
ABBEY CHEMICALS, LTD.—Contran Corporation; *U.S. Private*, pg. 271
AFRICAN OXYGEN LTD.—The BOC Group plc; *Int'l*, pg. 121
AIR PRODUCTS AND CHEMICALS, INC.; *U.S. Public*, pg. 30
AKZO CHEMICALS B.V.—Akzo Nobel N.V.; *Int'l*, pg. 42
AKZO CHEMICALS S.P.A.—Akzo Nobel N.V.; *Int'l*, pg. 46
AKZO CHEMIE—Akzo Nobel N.V.; *Int'l*, pg. 46
AKZO CHEMIE BRASIL—Akzo Nobel N.V.; *Int'l*, pg. 46
AKZO CHEMIE FRANCE S.A.R.L.—Akzo Nobel N.V.; *Int'l*, pg. 47
AKZO CHEMIE GMBH—Akzo Nobel N.V.; *Int'l*, pg. 47
AKZO CHEMIE LTD.—Akzo Nobel N.V.; *Int'l*, pg. 47
AKZO CHEMIE NEDERLAND BV—Akzo Nobel N.V.; *Int'l*, pg. 46
AKZO CHEMIE U.K. LTD.—Akzo Nobel N.V.; *Int'l*, pg. 47
AKZO CHEMIE UK LTD.—Akzo Nobel N.V.; *Int'l*, pg. 47
AKZO COATINGS SA—Akzo Nobel N.V.; *Int'l*, pg. 43
AKZO DREELAND—Akzo Nobel N.V.; *Int'l*, pg. 48
AKZO NOBEL INC.—Akzo Nobel N.V.; *Int'l*, pg. 47
AKZO SALT SPA.—Akzo Nobel N.V.; *Int'l*, pg. 47
ALBA AMAZONIA S.A. INDUSTRIAS QUIMICAS—Borden, Inc.; *U.S. Private*, pg. 158
ALBA NORDESTE SA INDUSTRIES QUIMICAS—Borden, Inc.; *U.S. Private*, pg. 158
ALBRIGHT & WILSON (AUSTRALIA) LIMITED—Albright & Wilson plc; *Int'l*, pg. 49
ALCAN CHEMICALS EUROPE—Alcan Aluminium Limited; *Int'l*, pg. 51
ALCOA CHEMIE NEDERLAND B.V.—Aluminum Company of America; *U.S. Public*, pg. 61
ALCOA FUJIKURA GMBH—Aluminum Company of America; *U.S. Public*, pg. 62
ALCOA PROPPANTS, INC.—Aluminum Company of America; *U.S. Public*, pg. 61
ALCOA S.A.—Aluminum Company of America; *U.S. Public*, pg. 62
ALCOLAC LTD.—Rhone-Poulenc S.A.; *Int'l*, pg. 1113
ALGINATE INDUSTRIES—Merck & Co., Inc.; *U.S. Public*, pg. 1091
ALLIED DIAGNOSTIC IMAGING RESOURCES, INC.—CPAC, Inc.; *U.S. Public*, pg. 282
ALLIEDSIGNAL CHEMICALS—AlliedSignal Inc.; *U.S. Public*, pg. 52
ALLIEDSIGNAL CHEMICALS CANADA INC.—AlliedSignal Inc.; *U.S. Public*, pg. 52
ALLIEDSIGNAL CHEMICALS DO BRASIL—AlliedSignal Inc.; *U.S. Public*, pg. 52
ALLIEDSIGNAL CHEMICALS N.Z. LTD.—AlliedSignal Inc.; *U.S. Public*, pg. 52
ALLIEDSIGNAL INC.; *U.S. Public*, pg. 49
ALLIEDSIGNAL PERFORMANCE ADDITIVES—AlliedSignal Inc.; *U.S. Public*, pg. 53
ALRO GROUP; *U.S. Private*, pg. 45
ALTOS HORNOS DE MEXICO, S.A.; *Int'l*, pg. 66
ALUMAR CONSORTIUM—Aluminum Company of America; *U.S. Public*, pg. 62
ALUMINA COMPANY LIMITED—Alcan Aluminium Limited; *Int'l*, pg. 51
ALUMINUM DE GRECE—Pechiney S.A.; *Int'l*, pg. 1030
ALUMINUM OXID STADE GESELLSCHAFT MIT BESCHRANKTER HAFTUNG—Reynolds Metals Company; *U.S. Public*, pg. 1386
ALUSUISSE-LONZA HOLDING LTD.; *Int'l*, pg. 66
AMERICAN CHROME & CHEMICALS, INC.—Harrisons & Crosfield plc; *Int'l*, pg. 598
AMERICAN NORIT CO. INC.—NORIT N.V.; *Int'l*, pg. 958
AMERICAN PACIFIC CORPORATION; *U.S. Public*, pg. 88
AMERSHAM BUCHLER GMBH & CO. KG—Nycomed Amersham plc; *Int'l*, pg. 992
AMINKEMI AB—Kemira Oy; *Int'l*, pg. 728
AMOCO CORPORATION; *U.S. Public*, pg. 101
ANCHOR CHEMICAL GROUP PLC—Air Products and Chemicals, Inc.; *U.S. Public*, pg. 32
ANEDCO, INC.—The Lubrizol Corporation; *U.S. Public*, pg. 1016
ANGLO BLACKWELLS LTD.—Viag AG; *Int'l*, pg. 1465
APPLIED BIOSYSTEMS—The Perkin-Elmer Corporation; *U.S. Public*, pg. 1279
AQUACHLOR (PROPRIETARY) LIMITED—Olin Corporation; *U.S. Public*, pg. 1219
ARKANSAS CHEMICALS, INC.—Great Lakes Chemical Corporation; *U.S. Public*, pg. 760
ASAHI CHEMICAL INDUSTRY AMERICA, INC.—Asahi Chemical Industry Co., Ltd.; *Int'l*, pg. 84
ASAHI GLASS CO., LTD.; *Int'l*, pg. 84
ASARCO INCORPORATED; *U.S. Public*, pg. 137
ASHLAND CHEMICAL—Ashland, Inc.; *U.S. Public*, pg. 139
ASIAN BLEACHING EARTH CO., LTD.—Laporte plc; *Int'l*, pg. 803
ASPA BRUK—Trelleborg AB; *Int'l*, pg. 1423
ATLANTIC METALS CORPORATION; *U.S. Private*, pg. 95
ATLANTIC RICHFIELD COMPANY; *U.S. Public*, pg. 144
ATOCHEM CANADA INC.—Elf Aquitane; *Int'l*, pg. 446
AUSIMONT S.P.A.—Compart SpA; *Int'l*, pg. 324
AUSTRALIAN CHEMICAL HOLDINGS LTD.—Hercules Incorporated; *U.S. Public*, pg. 810
BASF MAROC S.A.—BASF AG; *Int'l*, pg. 106
BK LADENBURG GMBH—Hoechst Aktiengesellschaft; *Int'l*, pg. 626
BNFL; *Int'l*, pg. 120
THE BOC GROUP PLC; *Int'l*, pg. 121
BP AUSTRALIA LTD.—The British Petroleum Company P.L.C.; *Int'l*, pg. 220
BP CHEMICALS, INC.—The British Petroleum Company P.L.C.; *Int'l*, pg. 220
BP CHEMICALS LTD.—The British Petroleum Company P.L.C.; *Int'l*, pg. 220
BP JAPAN KK—The British Petroleum Company P.L.C.; *Int'l*, pg. 220
H.J. BAKER & BRO., INC.; *U.S. Private*, pg. 112
BARCROFT CO.—Rhone-Poulenc S.A.; *Int'l*, pg. 1110
BASIC CHEMICALS DIV.—Rhone-Poulenc S.A.; *Int'l*, pg. 1109
THE BAXENDEN CHEMICAL CO., LTD.—Witco Corporation; *U.S. Public*, pg. 1774
BAXENDEN SCANDINAVIA APS—Witco Corporation; *U.S. Public*, pg. 1774
BAYER AG—Bayer AG; *Int'l*, pg. 172
BAYER B.V.—Bayer AG; *Int'l*, pg. 175
BAYER CORPORATION—Bayer AG; *Int'l*, pg. 172
BAYER HISPANIA INDUSTRIAL, S.A.—Bayer AG; *Int'l*, pg. 175
BENTONE-SUD S.A.—Contran Corporation; *U.S. Private*, pg. 271
BERTELLI SPA—Akzo Nobel N.V.; *Int'l*, pg. 47
BERWIND CORPORATION; *U.S. Private*, pg. 138
BEVALOID CHEMICALS LTD.—Rhone-Poulenc S.A.; *Int'l*, pg. 1113
BEVALOID SA—Rhone-Poulenc S.A.; *Int'l*, pg. 1113
BIO-RAD LABORATORIES, INC.; *U.S. Public*, pg. 230
BOEHRINGER INGELHEIM—Boehringer Ingelheim GmbH; *Int'l*, pg. 199
BORDEN AUSTRALIA (PTY) LTD.—Borden, Inc.; *U.S. Private*, pg. 159
BORDEX B.V.—Borden, Inc.; *U.S. Private*, pg. 159
BRISTOL-MYERS SQUIBB COMPANY; *U.S. Public*, pg. 253
BRITISH CHROME & CHEMICALS LTD.—Harrisons & Crosfield plc; *Int'l*, pg. 598
BROTHERTON CHEMICALS LTD.—Church & Dwight Co., Inc.; *U.S. Public*, pg. 356
BROWNING CHEMICAL CORPORATION; *U.S. Private*, pg. 175
BULAB HOLDINGS, INC.; *U.S. Private*, pg. 180
BUREAU RHONE-POULENC—Rhone-Poulenc S.A.; *Int'l*, pg. 1112
CM CHEMICAL—Metallgesellschaft AG; *Int'l*, pg. 861
CSR LIMITED; *Int'l*, pg. 245
CYDSA S.A.; *Int'l*, pg. 246
CAB-O-SIL DIV. CABOT CORP.—Cabot Corporation; *U.S. Public*, pg. 289
CABOT CORPORATION; *U.S. Public*, pg. 288
CABOT HULS GMBH—Veba AG; *Int'l*, pg. 1454
CAFFARO S.P.A.; *Int'l*, pg. 248
CALGON CARBON CORPORATION; *U.S. Public*, pg. 292
CALGON CARBON CORP., NEVILLE ISLAND—Calgon Carbon Corporation; *U.S. Public*, pg. 293
CALGON CORPORATION—English China Clays Plc; *Int'l*, pg. 455
CALGON INTERAMERICAN CORP.—English China Clays Plc; *Int'l*, pg. 455
CALLERY CHEMICAL CO.—Mine Safety Appliances Co.; *U.S. Public*, pg. 1114
CANADIAN REYNOLDS METALS COMPANY, LTD.—Reynolds Metals Company; *U.S. Public*, pg. 1386
CANATOM HEAVY WATER LIMITED—Texas Utilities Company; *U.S. Public*, pg. 1587
THE CARBIDE/GRAPHITE GROUP, INC.; *U.S. Public*, pg. 304
CARBIDE PRODUCTS—The Carbide/Graphite Group, Inc.; *U.S. Public*, pg. 304
CARBOSULF CHEMISCHE WERKE GMBH—Akzo Nobel N.V.; *Int'l*, pg. 47
CAROLINA METALS, INC.—Starmet Corporation; *U.S. Public*, pg. 1511
CARUS CHEMICAL COMPANY, CHEMICAL DIV.—Carus Corporation; *U.S. Private*, pg. 217
CARUS CORPORATION; *U.S. Private*, pg. 217
CATALYSTS & CHEMICALS—Johnson Matthey Public Limited Company; *Int'l*, pg. 713

CECA S.A.—Elf Aquitane; *Int'l*, pg. 445
CHEMDESIGN CORPORATION—Bayer AG; *Int'l*, pg. 173
CHEMETALL GMBH GESELLSCHAFT FUER CHEMISCH TECHNISCHE VERFAHREN—Metallgesellschaft AG; *Int'l*, pg. 861
CHEMICAL EXCHANGE INDUSTRIES; *U.S. Private*, pg. 232
CHEMICAL SPECIALTIES, INC.—Laporte plc; *Int'l*, pg. 802
CHEMOXY INTERNATIONAL PLC—Ascot Holdings Plc; *Int'l*, pg. 88
CHEMTECH PRODUCTS INC.—Allied Industrial Group, Inc.; *U.S. Private*, pg. 39
CHEMVIRON CARBON—Calgon Carbon Corporation; *U.S. Public*, pg. 293
CHEMVIRON CARBON GMBH—Calgon Carbon Corporation; *U.S. Public*, pg. 293
CHEMVIRON SPECIALTY CHEMICALS—Merck & Co., Inc.; *U.S. Public*, pg. 1091
CHESSCO INDUSTRIES, INC.; *U.S. Private*, pg. 234
CHIMIQUE DE LA MEDITERRANEE—Royal Dutch/Shell Group of Companies; *Int'l*, pg. 1138
CHURCH & DWIGHT CO., INC.; *U.S. Public*, pg. 355
CILAG AG—Johnson & Johnson; *U.S. Public*, pg. 929
THE CLOROX COMPANY; *U.S. Public*, pg. 386
THE CLOROX COMPANY OF CANADA LTD.—The Clorox Company; *U.S. Public*, pg. 387
COLLOIDS CANADA INC.—Rhone-Poulenc S.A.; *Int'l*, pg. 1113
COMINCO, LTD.; *Int'l*, pg. 307
COMPANIA QUIMICA BORDEN, S.A.—Borden, Inc.; *U.S. Private*, pg. 159
COMURHEX—COGEMA - Compagnie Generale des Matieres Nucleaires; *Int'l*, pg. 305
CONDEA VISTA COMPANY—Condea Chemie GmbH; *Int'l*, pg. 325
CORMETECH INC.—Corning Incorporated; *U.S. Public*, pg. 449
CRITERION CATALYST COMPANY L.P.—Royal Dutch/Shell Group of Companies; *Int'l*, pg. 1136
JOSEPH CROSFIELD & SONS LTD.—Unilever Plc; *Int'l*, pg. 1434
CROSSFIELD CHEMICAL—Unilever Plc; *Int'l*, pg. 1435
CYANAMID-KETJEN KATALYSATOR BV—Akzo Nobel N.V.; *Int'l*, pg. 47
CYANAMID MEXICO—American Home Products Corporation; *U.S. Public*, pg. 81
CYANAMID OF GREAT BRITAIN LTD.—American Home Products Corporation; *U.S. Public*, pg. 81
DSM CHEMICALS ROTTERDAM—DSM N.V.; *Int'l*, pg. 353
DSM CHEMIE LINZ GMBH—DSM N.V.; *Int'l*, pg. 356
DSM N.V.; *Int'l*, pg. 352
DAEHAN SPECIALTY CHEMICALS COMPANY, LTD.—Solvay S.A.; *Int'l*, pg. 1279
DAINIPPON INK & CHEMICALS, INC.; *Int'l*, pg. 369
DANSK STYROPACK—Royal Dutch/Shell Group of Companies; *Int'l*, pg. 1138
DEASUNG-HENKEL CHEMICAL CO., LTD.—Henkel KGaA; *Int'l*, pg. 614
DEGUSSA AG; *Int'l*, pg. 388
DEGUSSA CORPORATION—Degussa AG; *Int'l*, pg. 388
DELTA FOREMOST CHEMICAL CORP.; *U.S. Private*, pg. 322
DESC, S.A. DE C.V.; *Int'l*, pg. 395
DETREX CORPORATION; *U.S. Public*, pg. 501
DEUTSCHE HEY'DI CHEMISCHE GMBH—Laporte plc; *Int'l*, *pg. 803*
DEUTSCHE SHELL AG—Royal Dutch/Shell Group of Companies; *Int'l*, pg. 1138
DEXTER AEROSPACE MATERIALS DIVISION—The Dexter Corporation; *U.S. Public*, pg. 504
DEXTER CHEMICAL CORP.; *U.S. Private*, pg. 329
THE DEXTER CORPORATION; *U.S. Public*, pg. 504
DEXTER ELECTRONIC MATERIALS—The Dexter Corporation; *U.S. Public*, pg. 505
DEXTER ELECTRONIC MATERIALS DIVISION—The Dexter Corporation; *U.S. Public*, pg. 504
DEXTER S.A.—The Dexter Corporation; *U.S. Public*, pg. 505
DEXTER SPECIALTY MATERIALS, LTD.—The Dexter Corporation; *U.S. Public*, pg. 505
DIRECT TOOL INC.—Cold Heading Co.; *U.S. Private*, pg. 250
DONAU CHEMIE AG—Rhone-Poulenc S.A.; *Int'l*, pg. 1112
DOVER CHEMICAL CORP.—ICC Industries, Inc.; *U.S. Private*, pg. 553
THE DOW CHEMICAL COMPANY; *U.S. Public*, pg. 522
DU PONT (E.I. DU PONT DE NEMOURS & CO.); *U.S. Public*, pg. 530
DUROFORM-J. FRITZ GMBH & CO KG—Alusuisse-Lonza Holding Ltd.; *Int'l*, pg. 68
EKA NOBEL AB—Akzo Nobel N.V.; *Int'l*, pg. 48
EAGLE-PICHER INDUSTRIES, INC.; *U.S. Private*, pg. 355
EASTMAN KODAK COMPANY; *U.S. Public*, pg. 550
ELECTRO QUIMICA MEXICANA S.A. DE C.V.—FMC Corporation; *U.S. Public*, pg. 606
ELECTROCHEMICAL INDUSTRIES (FRUTAROM) LTD.—ICC Industries, Inc.; *U.S. Private*, pg. 553
ELF AQUITAINE, INC.—Elf Aquitane; *Int'l*, pg. 445
ELF ATOCHEM NORTH AMERICA, BASIC CHEMICALS DIV.—Elf Aquitane; *Int'l*, pg. 446
ELF ATOCHEM NORTH AMERICA, INC.—Elf Aquitane; *Int'l*, pg. 445
ELKEM-AMERICAN CARBIDE COMPANY (ASHTABULA)—Airgas, Inc.; *U.S. Public*, pg. 33
ELKEM-AMERICAN CARBIDE COMPANY (PITTSBURGH)—Airgas, Inc.; *U.S. Public*, pg. 33
ELKEM-AMERICAN CARBIDE COMPANY (PRYOR)—Airgas, Inc.; *U.S. Public*, pg. 33
ELKEM MARIETTA—Elkem ASA; *Int'l*, pg. 447
ELMER'S PRODUCTS, INC.—Borden, Inc.; *U.S. Private*, pg. 158
EMBECON (NEW ZEALAND) LIMITED—Novartis AG; *Int'l*, pg. 982
ENGELHARD CANADA LIMITED—Engelhard Corporation; *U.S. Public*, pg. 582
ESPECIALIDADES QUIMICAS SA DE CV—Rhone-Poulenc S.A.; *Int'l*, pg. 1113
ESSEX CHEMICAL CORPORATION—The Dow Chemical Company; *U.S. Public*, pg. 523
ESSEX INDUSTRIAL CHEMICALS, INC.—The Dow Chemical Company; *U.S. Public*, pg. 523
ESSO MALAYSIA BERHAD—Exxon Corporation; *U.S. Public*, pg. 602
EXXON CHEMICAL COMPANY—Exxon Corporation; *U.S. Public*, pg. 601
EXXON CHEMICAL POLYMERES, SNC—Exxon Corporation; *U.S. Public*, pg. 602
EXXON CORPORATION; *U.S. Public*, pg. 601
FMC CORPORATION; *U.S. Public*, pg. 604
FMC CORP., LITHIUM DIVISION—FMC Corporation; *U.S. Public*, pg. 605
FMC PEROXYGEN CHEMICALS DIV.—FMC Corporation; *U.S. Public*, pg. 605
FMC PHOSPHORUS CHEMICALS DIV.—FMC Corporation; *U.S. Public*, pg. 605
FARMLAND INDUSTRIES, INC.; *U.S. Private*, pg. 395
FARNAM COMPANIES, INC.; *U.S. Private*, pg. 396
FEDERAL LABORATORIES—Mace Security International, Inc.; *U.S. Public*, pg. 1030
FERRIKLOR AB—Kemira Oy; *Int'l*, pg. 728
FERRO CORPORATION; *U.S. Public*, pg. 618
FERRO ECUATORIANA S.A.—Ferro Corporation; *U.S. Public*, pg. 619
FERRO FRANCE-EUROSTAR—Ferro Corporation; *U.S. Public*, pg. 619
FERRO (HOLLAND) B.V.—Ferro Corporation; *U.S. Public*, pg. 619
FESLENTE BONIFACE S.A.—Borden, Inc.; *U.S. Private*, pg. 159
FINA CHEMICALS ANTWERPEN N.V.—Petrofina S.A.; *Int'l*, *pg. 1043*
FINA CHEMICALS FELUY S.A.—Petrofina S.A.; *Int'l*, pg. 1043
FINE INORGANIC CHEMICALS—Rhone-Poulenc S.A.; *Int'l*, *pg. 1109*
OY FINNISH PEROXIDES AB—UPM-Kymmene Corporation; *Int'l*, pg. 1430
FISHER SCIENTIFIC COMPANY—Thomas H. Lee Co.; *U.S. Private*, pg. 658
FOKAB AB—Axel Johnson AB; *Int'l*, pg. 708
FORMOSA PLASTICS CORPORATION; *Int'l*, pg. 498
FOSROC INC.—Burmah Castrol plc; *Int'l*, pg. 234
FRITZ INDUSTRIES INC.; *U.S. Private*, pg. 429
GEMISA S.A. DE C.V.—Henkel KGaA; *Int'l*, pg. 614
GENERAL ALUM & CHEMICAL; *U.S. Private*, pg. 443
THE GEON COMPANY; *U.S. Public*, pg. 733
GEORGIA GULF CORPORATION; *U.S. Public*, pg. 734
GLUCONA VOF—Akzo Nobel N.V.; *Int'l*, pg. 47
THE GOODYEAR TIRE & RUBBER COMPANY; *U.S. Public*, pg. 752
GRACE SILICA N.V.—W.R. Grace & Co.; *U.S. Public*, pg. 756
GRAIN PROCESSING CORP.—Varied Investments, Inc.; *U.S. Private*, pg. 1134
GRANT CHEMICAL DIV.—Ferro Corporation; *U.S. Public*, pg. 618
GRAPHITWERK KROPFMUEHL AG—Viag AG; *Int'l*, pg. 1464
GREAT LAKES BIOCHEMICAL CO., INC.—Laporte plc; *Int'l*, pg. 802
GREAT LAKES CHEMICAL CORPORATION; *U.S. Public*, pg. 760
GREAT SALT LAKE MINERALS CORP.—Harris Chemical Group, Inc.; *U.S. Private*, pg. 505
HCI CHEMTECH; *U.S. Private*, pg. 490
HAARMAN & REIMER AROMA CHEMICALS—Bayer AG; *Int'l*, pg. 173
HACH COMPANY; *U.S. Public*, pg. 773
HAMMOND GROUP INC.; *U.S. Private*, pg. 498
HANDY & HARMAN; *U.S. Public*, pg. 780
HARCROS CHEMICALS INC.—Harrisons & Crosfield plc; *Int'l*, pg. 598
HARRISONS & CROSFIELD PLC; *Int'l*, pg. 598
HAWKINS CHEMICAL, INC.; *U.S. Public*, pg. 800
HEAT BATH PARK METALLURGICAL CORP.; *U.S. Private*, pg. 518
HELMERICH & PAYNE, INC.; *U.S. Public*, pg. 808
HENKEL & CIE AG—Henkel KGaA; *Int'l*, pg. 611
HENKEL & CIE GMBH—Henkel KGaA; *Int'l*, pg. 609
HENKEL BELGIUM S.A.—Henkel KGaA; *Int'l*, pg. 612
HENKEL CHEMICALS (BARBADOS) LTD.—Henkel KGaA; *Int'l*, pg. 614
HENKEL CHEMICALS LTD.—Henkel KGaA; *Int'l*, pg. 612
HENKEL CORP.- PROCESS CHEMICALS—Henkel KGaA; *Int'l*, pg. 611
HENKEL CORPORATION MINERALS INDUSTRY DIV.—Henkel KGaA; *Int'l*, pg. 610
HENKEL COSMETIC GMBH—Henkel KGaA; *Int'l*, pg. 609
HENKEL-DAESUNG CO.—Henkel KGaA; *Int'l*, pg. 612
HENKEL FRANCE S.A.—Henkel KGaA; *Int'l*, pg. 612
HENKEL HAKUSUI CORPORATION—Henkel KGaA; *Int'l*, pg. 612
HENKEL IBERICA S.A.—Henkel KGaA; *Int'l*, pg. 612
HENKEL INDUSTRIE AG—Henkel KGaA; *Int'l*, pg. 612
HENKEL ITALIANA S.P.A.—Henkel KGaA; *Int'l*, pg. 613
HENKEL KGAA; *Int'l*, pg. 609
HENKEL OLEOCHEMICALS (MALAYSIA) SND. BHD.—Henkel KGaA; *Int'l*, pg. 613
HENKEL PHILIPPINES INC.—Henkel KGaA; *Int'l*, pg. 614
HENKEL SINGAPORE PTE., LTD.—Henkel KGaA; *Int'l*, pg. 613
HENKEL SOUTH AFRICA (PTY.) LTD.—Henkel KGaA; *Int'l*, *pg. 614*
HENKEL TAIWAN LTD.—Henkel KGaA; *Int'l*, pg. 613
HENKEL THAI LTD.—Henkel KGaA; *Int'l*, pg. 613
OY HERCOFINN AB—Hercules Incorporated; *U.S. Public*, pg. 810
HERCULES CHEMICAL CO., INC.; *U.S. Private*, pg. 523
HERCULES KOREA CHEMICAL CO. LTD.—Hercules Incorporated; *U.S. Public*, pg. 811
HICKSON & WELCH LTD.—Hickson International Plc; *Int'l*, pg. 619
HICKSON CORPORATION—Hickson International Plc; *Int'l*, *pg. 619*
HINDUSTAN GUM & CHEMICALS LTD.—Rhone-Poulenc S.A.; *Int'l*, pg. 1113
HITACHI-BORDEN CHEMICAL PRODUCTS, INC.—AEP Industries, Inc.; *U.S. Public*, pg. 5
HITACHI-BORDEN CHEMICAL PRODUCTS, INC.—Hitachi, Ltd.; *Int'l*, pg. 622
HOECHST CELANESE FINE CHEMICAL DIVISION—Hoechst Aktiengesellschaft; *Int'l*, pg. 625
HOECHST MARION ROUSSEL, INC.—Hoechst Aktiengesellschaft; *Int'l*, pg. 624
HOECHST SPECIALTY CHEMICALS GROUP—Hoechst Aktiengesellschaft; *Int'l*, pg. 624
HOLLOW SPHERES BUSINESS—PQ Corporation; *U.S. Private*, pg. 827
HUBBARD HALL INC.; *U.S. Private*, pg. 544
J.M. HUBER, SOLEM DIV.—J.M. Huber Corporation; *U.S. Private*, pg. 545
HUMBROL LIMITED—Borden, Inc.; *U.S. Private*, pg. 159
HYDRITE CHEMICAL COMPANY; *U.S. Private*, pg. 551
HYSOL JAPAN LIMITED—The Dexter Corporation; *U.S. Public*, pg. 505
ICI CHEMICALS & POLYMERS LTD.—Imperial Chemical Industries PLC; *Int'l*, pg. 663
ICI POLYURETHANES GROUP—Imperial Chemical Industries PLC; *Int'l*, pg. 664
ICN PHARMACEUTICALS, INC.; *U.S. Public*, pg. 853
IMAGE TECHNOLOGY CORPORATION—Olin Corporation; *U.S. Public*, pg. 1219
IMPERIAL CHEMICAL INDUSTRIES PLC; *Int'l*, pg. 662
IMPERIAL OIL LIMITED—Exxon Corporation; *U.S. Public*, pg. 602
INCO LIMITED; *Int'l*, pg. 672
INDUSTRIAL RESEARCH (SUPESQ)—Petrobras - Petroleo Brasileiro S.A.; *Int'l*, pg. 1042
INDUSTRIAS QUIMICAS CARABOBO, C.A.—Novartis AG; *Int'l*, pg. 982
S.A. INDUSTRIAS VOTORANTIM; *Int'l*, pg. 677
INORGANIC COLLOIDS BUSINESS—PQ Corporation; *U.S. Private*, pg. 827
INTERMARINE S.P.A.—Compart SpA; *Int'l*, pg. 324
INTERMARINE U.S.A. INC.—Compart SpA; *Int'l*, pg. 324
INTEROX SOLVAY—Solvay S.A.; *Int'l*, pg. 1278
ISHIHARA SANGYO KAISHA, LTD.; *Int'l*, pg. 689
ITALCOLOR, S.A.—Borden, Inc.; *U.S. Private*, pg. 159
AXEL JOHNSON AB; *Int'l*, pg. 707
AXEL JOHNSON CHEMICALS AB—Axel Johnson AB; *Int'l*, *pg. 708*
JOHNSON MATTHEY CATALOG CO.—Johnson Matthey Public Limited Company; *Int'l*, pg. 713
JOHNSON MATTHEY INC.—Johnson Matthey Public Limited Company; *Int'l*, pg. 713
JOHNSON MATTHEY PUBLIC LIMITED COMPANY; *Int'l*, pg. 713
JONES CHEMICALS, INC.; *U.S. Private*, pg. 596
KAO CORPORATION; *Int'l*, pg. 717
KALI-CHEMIE AKTIENGESELLSCHAFT—Solvay S.A.; *Int'l*, pg. 1278
KATALYSATORENWERKE HULS GMBH—Veba AG; *Int'l*, pg. 1454
KAYAKU-NOURY K.K.—Akzo Nobel N.V.; *Int'l*, pg. 47
KEMIRA AGRO OY—Kemira Oy; *Int'l*, pg. 727
KEMIRA IBERICA S.A.—Kemira Oy; *Int'l*, pg. 728
KEMIRA KEMI AB—Kemira Oy; *Int'l*, pg. 728
KEMIRA THAI CO. LTD.—Kemira Oy; *Int'l*, pg. 728
KEMIRA-UBE LTD.—Kemira Oy; *Int'l*, pg. 728
KEMWATER A/S—Kemira Oy; *Int'l*, pg. 728
KENYA SHELL LTD.—Royal Dutch/Shell Group of Companies; *Int'l*, pg. 1136
KEPEC CHEMISCHE FABRIK GMBH—Henkel KGaA; *Int'l*, pg. 610
KERR-MCGEE CHEMICAL CORP.—Kerr-McGee Corporation; *U.S. Public*, pg. 952
KERR-MCGEE CORPORATION; *U.S. Public*, pg. 952
THE KINGSFORD PRODUCTS COMPANY—The Clorox Company; *U.S. Public*, pg. 387
KINLEITH MILL—International Paper Company; *U.S. Public*, *pg. 905*
KNOLL PHARMACEUTICAL COMPANY—BASF AG; *Int'l*, pg. 105
KOHAP FINE CHEMICAL LTD.—KOHAP Group; *Int'l*, pg. 742
KONEZO, DIV. OF AKZO BELGIE N.V.—Akzo Nobel N.V.; *Int'l*, pg. 44
KRONOS SA/NV—Contran Corporation; *U.S. Private*, pg. 271
KRONOS TITAN A/S—Contran Corporation; *U.S. Private*, pg. 271
LA CORNUBIA—McKechnie PLC; *Int'l*, pg. 852
LA DOMINCIA, S.A. DE C.V.—Du Pont (E.I. Du Pont De Nemours & Co.); *U.S. Public*, pg. 533
LANKEM CEYLON—Royal Dutch/Shell Group of Companies; *Int'l*, pg. 1140
LAPORTE ABSORBENTS-HOLLAND—Laporte plc; *Int'l*, pg. 803
LAPORTE CHEMICALS (MALAYSIA) SDN BHD—Laporte plc; *Int'l*, pg. 803
LAPORTE ESD-GERMANY—Laporte plc; *Int'l*, pg. 803
LAPORTE FLUORIDES—Laporte plc; *Int'l*, pg. 802
LAPORTE INC.—Laporte plc; *Int'l*, pg. 802
LAPORTE INDUSTRIES (SINGAPORE) PTE LIMITED—Laporte plc; *Int'l*, pg. 803
LAPORTE KEMWOOD AB—Laporte plc; *Int'l*, pg. 803
LAPORTE (MALAYSIA) SDN BHD—Laporte plc; *Int'l*, pg. 803
LAPORTE PLC; *Int'l*, pg. 801
LAPORTE (TAIWAN) LIMITED—Laporte plc; *Int'l*, pg. 803
LAPORTE (THAILAND) LTD.—Laporte plc; *Int'l*, pg. 803

P.T. LAUTAN OTSUKA CHEMICAL—Otsuka Pharmaceutical Co., Ltd.; *Int'l*, pg. 1014
LEARONAL, INC.; *U.S. Public*, pg. 982
LEPAGE'S LIMITED—Henkel KGaA; *Int'l*, pg. 613
LION AKZO CO. K.K.—Akzo Nobel N.V.; *Int'l*, pg. 47
LIPHA CHEMICALS S.A.; *Int'l*, pg. 812
LITHION, INC.—Ener-Tek International Corporation; *U.S. Private*, pg. 376
LIXTON SPEZIALREINIGER GMBH—Henkel KGaA; *Int'l*, pg. 610
LONZA AG—Alusuisse-Lonza Holding Ltd.; *Int'l*, pg. 67
LONZA BIOTEC SRO—Alusuisse-Lonza Holding Ltd.; *Int'l*, pg. 69
LONZA HONGKONG LTD.—Alusuisse-Lonza Holding Ltd.; *Int'l*, pg. 69
LONZA IBERICA S.A.—Alusuisse-Lonza Holding Ltd.; *Int'l*, pg. 69
LONZA INC.—Alusuisse-Lonza Holding Ltd.; *Int'l*, pg. 67
LUCIDOL YOSHITOMI LTD.—Elf Aquitane; *Int'l*, pg. 446
MAGMA-PINTO VALLEY MINING DIVISION—The Broken Hill Proprietary Company Limited; *Int'l*, pg. 224
MAGMA-SAN MANUEL MINING DIVISION—The Broken Hill Proprietary Company Limited; *Int'l*, pg. 224
MAGMA-SUPERIOR MINING DIVISION—The Broken Hill Proprietary Company Limited; *Int'l*, pg. 224
MAGNOLIA CHEMICALS & SOLVENTS—Preussag AG; *Int'l*, pg. 1071
MALAKOFF INDUSTRIES—Reynolds Metals Company; *U.S. Public*, pg. 1386
MALLINCKRODT BAKER INC.—Mallinckrodt Inc.; *U.S. Public*, pg. 1039
MANCHEM LTD.—Rhone-Poulenc S.A.; *Int'l*, pg. 1113
MARTINSWERK GMBH FUR CHEMISCHE UND METALLURGISCHE PRODUKTION—Alusuisse-Lonza Holding Ltd.; *Int'l*, pg. 69
MARUBENI CORPORATION; *Int'l*, pg. 844
MATERIALES MOLDEABLES S.A. DE C.V.—Borden, Inc.; *U.S. Private*, pg. 159
MATTHES & WEBER GMBH—Henkel KGaA; *Int'l*, pg. 610
MAY & BAKER NIGERIA LTD.—Rhone-Poulenc S.A.; *Int'l*, pg. 1112
MCGEAN-ROHCO, INC.; *U.S. Private*, pg. 721
MEAD JOHNSON DE MEXICO, S.A. DE C.V.—Bristol-Myers Squibb Company; *U.S. Public*, pg. 256
MIDDLETOWN OXYGEN CO., INC.—Air Products and Chemicals, Inc.; *U.S. Public*, pg. 31
MIDWEST CARBIDE CORPORATION—Airgas, Inc.; *U.S. Public*, pg. 33
MILLENNIUM CHEMICALS INC.; *U.S. Public*, pg. 1111
MILLENNIUM PETROCHEMICALS, INC.—Hanson PLC; *Int'l*, pg. 594
MINAS DE GADOR S.A.—Laporte plc; *Int'l*, pg. 803
MINE SAFETY APPLIANCES CO.; *U.S. Public*, pg. 1114
MINE SAFETY APPLIANCES CO.—Mine Safety Appliances Co.; *U.S. Public*, pg. 1114
MINERAL RESEARCH & DEVELOPMENT CORP.—Laporte plc; *Int'l*, pg. 802
MITCHELL-BRADFORD INTERNATIONAL—Hubbard Hall Inc.; *U.S. Private*, pg. 544
MITSUBISHI YUKA—Royal Dutch/Shell Group of Companies; *Int'l*, pg. 1139
MOLDING COMPOUNDS SPA—Alusuisse-Lonza Holding Ltd.; *Int'l*, pg. 69
MONTEDISON S.P.A.—Compart SpA; *Int'l*, pg. 324
MOONEY CHEMICALS—OM Group; *U.S. Public*, pg. 1208
MORALCO LTD.—Aluminum Company of America; *U.S. Public*, pg. 62
MORTON INTERNATIONAL INC.; *U.S. Public*, pg. 1134
MUNKSJO AB—Trelleborg AB; *Int'l*, pg. 1423
N.E. CHEMCAT—Engelhard Corporation; *U.S. Public*, pg. 583
NL INDUSTRIES, INC.—Contran Corporation; *U.S. Private*, pg. 270
NL SPECIALTY CHEMICALS LTD.—Contran Corporation; *U.S. Private*, pg. 271
NSO CO.—Rhone-Poulenc S.A.; *Int'l*, pg. 1110
NTC GROUP; *U.S. Private*, pg. 772
NABALCO PTY. LTD.—Alusuisse-Lonza Holding Ltd.; *Int'l*, pg. 69
NACAN PRODUCTS LTD.—Unilever Plc; *Int'l*, pg. 1436
NALCO CHEMICAL COMPANY; *U.S. Public*, pg. 1150
NATIONAL ORGANIC CHEMICAL INDUSTRIES—Royal Dutch/Shell Group of Companies; *Int'l*, pg. 1139
NATIONAL SILICATES LTD.—PQ Corporation; *U.S. Private*, pg. 827
NATURAL GAS ODORIZING—Occidental Petroleum Corporation; *U.S. Public*, pg. 1210
NEYNABER CHEMIE GMBH—Henkel KGaA; *Int'l*, pg. 610
NIPPON KETJEN K.K.—Akzo Nobel N.V.; *Int'l*, pg. 47
NOPCO INDUSTRIAL S.A. DE C.V.—Henkel KGaA; *Int'l*, pg. 614
NORDESCLOR S.A.—Olin Corporation; *U.S. Public*, pg. 1219
NORDION INTERNATIONAL INC.—MDS Inc.; *Int'l*, pg. 827
NORIT N.V.; *Int'l*, pg. 958
NORIT (UK) LTD.—NORIT N.V.; *Int'l*, pg. 958
NORSK HYDRO A.S; *Int'l*, pg. 959
NUCOR IRON CARBIDE—Nucor Corporation; *U.S. Public*, pg. 1206
NYACOL PRODUCTS, INC.—PQ Corporation; *U.S. Private*, pg. 827
OCG MICROELECTRONIC MATERIALS AG—Novartis AG; *Int'l*, pg. 973
OCG MICROELECTRONIC MATERIALS AG—Olin Corporation; *U.S. Public*, pg. 1220
OCG MICROELECTRONIC MATERIALS GMBH—Olin Corporation; *U.S. Public*, pg. 1219
OCG MICROELECTRONIC MATERIALS LIMITED—Olin Corporation; *U.S. Public*, pg. 1220
OCG MICROELECTRONIC MATERIALS S.A.—Olin Corporation; *U.S. Public*, pg. 1220
OCCIDENTAL CHEMICAL CORPORATION—Occidental Petroleum Corporation; *U.S. Public*, pg. 1210
OCTAGON PROCESS INC.; *U.S. Private*, pg. 811
ODDA SMELTEVERK A/S—The BOC Group plc; *Int'l*, pg. 122
OKUMURA METALS CO., LTD.—The Furukawa Electric Co., Ltd.; *Int'l*, pg. 530
OLD WORLD INDUSTRIES, INC.; *U.S. Private*, pg. 814
OLIN CANADA INC.—Olin Corporation; *U.S. Public*, pg. 1220
OLIN CORPORATION; *U.S. Public*, pg. 1218
N.V. OLIN HUNT TRADING—Olin Corporation; *U.S. Public*, pg. 1220
OMEGA SOUFRE, S.A.—Solvay S.A.; *Int'l*, pg. 1279
ONCOMEMBRANE, INC.—Otsuka Pharmaceutical Co., Ltd.; *Int'l*, pg. 1013
PMC, INC.; *U.S. Private*, pg. 827
PQ AUSTRALIA PTY., LTD.—PQ Corporation; *U.S. Private*, pg. 827
PQ CORPORATION; *U.S. Private*, pg. 827
PVS CHEMICALS, INC.; *U.S. Private*, pg. 828
PVS TECHNOLOGIES, INC.—PVS Chemicals, Inc.; *U.S. Private*, pg. 828
PACIFIC ANCHOR CHEMICAL CORPORATION—Air Products and Chemicals, Inc.; *U.S. Public*, pg. 31
PAKISTAN GUM & CHEMICALS LTD.—Rhone-Poulenc S.A.; *Int'l*, pg. 1113
PARKER & AMCHEM—Henkel KGaA; *Int'l*, pg. 612
PATEX CHEMIE GMBH—Hercules Incorporated; *U.S. Public*, pg. 811
PECHINEY S.A.; *Int'l*, pg. 1027
PERSTORP FERGUSON LTD.-CHEMITEC & COMPOUNDS—Perstorp AB; *Int'l*, pg. 1037
PERSTORP FORMOX—Perstorp AB; *Int'l*, pg. 1038
PERSTORP SPA-POLYOLS DIV.—Perstorp AB; *Int'l*, pg. 1038
PERSTORP SPECIALTY CHEMICALS—Perstorp AB; *Int'l*, pg. 1038
PERWAKILAN BUREAU TECHNIQUE RHONE-POULENC—Rhone-Poulenc S.A.; *Int'l*, pg. 1112
PETROFERM INC.; *U.S. Private*, pg. 858
PHARMACIA & UPJOHN BIOSYSTEMS AB—Pharmacia & Upjohn, Inc.; *Int'l*, pg. 1047
PHILLIPS PETROLEUM CHEMICALS S.A.—Phillips Petroleum Company; *U.S. Public*, pg. 1291
PHILLIPS PETROLEUM COMPANY; *U.S. Public*, pg. 1290
PHOSPHATES DIVISION, ALBRIGHT & WILSON LIMITED—Albright & Wilson plc; *Int'l*, pg. 49
POLYMER CHEMICALS ADDITIVES GROUP—Witco Corporation; *U.S. Public*, pg. 1774
POLYMER CHEMICALS GROUP—Witco Corporation; *U.S. Public*, pg. 1774
POLYPURE RHONE-POULENC—Rhone-Poulenc S.A.; *Int'l*, pg. 1110
POMOSIN GMBH—Hercules Incorporated; *U.S. Public*, pg. 811
POWER CONVERSION, INC.—BTR plc; *Int'l*, pg. 127
PREMIER INDUSTRIES, INC.; *U.S. Private*, pg. 881
PROCTER & GAMBLE OF PERU—The Procter & Gamble Company; *U.S. Public*, pg. 1332
PRODUTOS QUIMICAS ALBA S.A.—Borden, Inc.; *U.S. Private*, pg. 160
QUAKER CHEMICAL CORPORATION; *U.S. Public*, pg. 1346
QUIMICA BORDEN ECUATORIANA, S.A.—Borden, Inc.; *U.S. Private*, pg. 160
QUIMICA DOMINICANA—Royal Dutch/Shell Group of Companies; *Int'l*, pg. 1141
QUIMICA FLUOR, S.A. DE C.V.—Du Pont (E.I. Du Pont De Nemours & Co.); *U.S. Public*, pg. 533
QUIMICA HERCULES, S.A. DE C.V.—Hercules Incorporated; *U.S. Public*, pg. 811
QUIMICA NICARAGUENSE—Royal Dutch/Shell Group of Companies; *Int'l*, pg. 1141
QUIMICA S.A. DE C.V.—Henkel KGaA; *Int'l*, pg. 614
RAISIO CHEMICALS CANADA INC.—Raisio Group; *Int'l*, pg. 1086
RAISIO FRANCE S.A.—Raisio Group; *Int'l*, pg. 1086
RAISIO GROUP; *Int'l*, pg. 1085
RASCHIG GMBH—PMC, Inc.; *U.S. Private*, pg. 827
REGLAR SRL—Alusuisse-Lonza Holding Ltd.; *Int'l*, pg. 69
REICHHOLD CHEMICALS, INC.—Dainippon Ink & Chemicals, Inc.; *Int'l*, pg. 370
REICHHOLD CHEMIE AG—Dainippon Ink & Chemicals, Inc.; *Int'l*, pg. 370
REICHHOLD LIMITED—Dainippon Ink & Chemicals, Inc.; *Int'l*, pg. 370
REILLY INDUSTRIES, INC.; *U.S. Private*, pg. 919
BV RENTOKIL CHEMIE—Sophus Berendsen A/S; *Int'l*, pg. 1286
RESART GMBH—BASF AG; *Int'l*, pg. 104
RESINMEC SPA—Alusuisse-Lonza Holding Ltd.; *Int'l*, pg. 69
RHEOX—Contran Corporation; *U.S. Private*, pg. 270
RHODANID CHEMIE GMBH—Akzo Nobel N.V.; *Int'l*, pg. 47
RHONE-POULENC—Rhone-Poulenc S.A.; *Int'l*, pg. 1109
RHONE-POULENC AFRIQUE CENTRALE—Rhone-Poulenc S.A.; *Int'l*, pg. 1112
RHONE-POULENC ARGENTINA S.A.—Rhone-Poulenc S.A.; *Int'l*, pg. 1112
RHONE-POULENC AUSTRALIA HOLDINGS PTY. LTD.—Rhone-Poulenc S.A.; *Int'l*, pg. 1112
RHONE-POULENC BANGLADESH LTD.—Rhone-Poulenc S.A.; *Int'l*, pg. 1112
RHONE-POULENC BASIC CHEMICALS CO.—Rhone-Poulenc S.A.; *Int'l*, pg. 1110
RHONE-POULENC BELGIQUE S.A.—Rhone-Poulenc S.A.; *Int'l*, pg. 1112
RHONE-POULENC, CHEMICAL DIVISION—Rhone-Poulenc S.A.; *Int'l*, pg. 1109
RHONE-POULENC CHEMICALS (INDIA)—Rhone-Poulenc S.A.; *Int'l*, pg. 1112
RHONE-POULENC CHEMICALS LTD.—Rhone-Poulenc S.A.; *Int'l*, pg. 1109
RHONE-POULENC DE MEXICO S.A. DE C.V.—Rhone-Poulenc S.A.; *Int'l*, pg. 1112
RHONE-POULENC DE VENEZUELA—Rhone-Poulenc S.A.; *Int'l*, pg. 1113
RHONE-POULENC DELEGATION GENERALE—Rhone-Poulenc S.A.; *Int'l*, pg. 1113
RHONE-POULENC HELLAS—Rhone-Poulenc S.A.; *Int'l*, pg. 1113
RHONE-POULENC ITALIA SPA—Rhone-Poulenc S.A.; *Int'l*, pg. 1113
RHONE-POULENC KENYA LTD.—Rhone-Poulenc S.A.; *Int'l*, pg. 1113
RHONE-POULENC KIMYEVI MADDELER LTD.—Rhone-Poulenc S.A.; *Int'l*, pg. 1113
RHONE-POULENC MALAYSIA SDN, BHD—Rhone-Poulenc S.A.; *Int'l*, pg. 1113
RHONE-POULENC MAROC—Rhone-Poulenc S.A.; *Int'l*, pg. 1113
RHONE-POULENC NEDERLAND B.V.—Rhone-Poulenc S.A.; *Int'l*, pg. 1113
RHONE-POULENC NEW ZEALAND LTD.—Rhone-Poulenc S.A.; *Int'l*, pg. 1113
RHONE-POULENC OY—Rhone-Poulenc S.A.; *Int'l*, pg. 1113
RHONE-POULENC PAKISTAN (PVT.) LTD.—Rhone-Poulenc S.A.; *Int'l*, pg. 1113
RHONE-POULENC PERFORMANCE RESINS & COATINGS—Rhone-Poulenc S.A.; *Int'l*, pg. 1110
RHONE-POULENC RORER LTD.—Rhone-Poulenc S.A.; *Int'l*, pg. 1110
RHONE-POULENC S.A.; *Int'l*, pg. 1108
RHONE-POULENC S.A.—Rhone-Poulenc S.A.; *Int'l*, pg. 1113
RHONE-POULENC SANTE C,I.—Rhone-Poulenc S.A.; *Int'l*, pg. 1114
RHONE-POULENC SENEGAL-SSPT—Rhone-Poulenc S.A.; *Int'l*, pg. 1114
RHONE-POULENC SINGAPORE PTE. LTD.—Rhone-Poulenc S.A.; *Int'l*, pg. 1114
RHONE-POULENC SVERIGE AB—Rhone-Poulenc S.A.; *Int'l*, pg. 1114
RHONE-POULENC TAIWAN LTD.—Rhone-Poulenc S.A.; *Int'l*, pg. 1114
RHONE-POULENC VISCOSUISSE—Rhone-Poulenc S.A.; *Int'l*, pg. 1114
RICHARDSON-VICKS, INC.—The Procter & Gamble Company; *U.S. Public*, pg. 1331
RIEDEL-DE HAEN AG—Hoechst Aktiengesellschaft; *Int'l*, pg. 625
ROCKLAND REACT-RITE, INC.—Interface Inc.; *U.S. Public*, pg. 889
ROHM & HAAS (AUSTRALIA) PTY. LTD.—Rohm and Haas Company; *U.S. Public*, pg. 1404
ROYAL OAK ENTERPRISES, INC.; *U.S. Private*, pg. 948
ST. ANNE CHEMICAL CO., LTD.—Parsons & Whittemore, Inc.; *U.S. Private*, pg. 841
SANDOZ CHEMICAL CORP., PURCHASING—Novartis AG; *Int'l*, pg. 974
SANDOZ CHEMICALS (THAILAND) LTD.—Novartis AG; *Int'l*, pg. 984
SANDOZ CHIMICA S.P.A.—Novartis AG; *Int'l*, pg. 984
SANDOZ KOREA LTD.—Novartis AG; *Int'l*, pg. 985
SANDOZ PRODUCTS (SWITZERLAND) LTD.—Novartis AG; *Int'l*, pg. 972
SANDOZ URUNLERI LTD.—Novartis AG; *Int'l*, pg. 985
AB SANDVIK HARD MATERIALS—Sandvik AB; *Int'l*, pg. 1185
SANDVIK HARD MATERIALS NORDEN AB—Sandvik AB; *Int'l*, pg. 1185
SANDVIK LTD.—Sandvik AB; *Int'l*, pg. 1186
SCOTCH PREMIUM MEAT—FMC Corporation; *U.S. Public*, pg. 607
SEMILAB AG—Laporte plc; *Int'l*, pg. 803
SEQUA CHEMICALS, INC.—Sequa Corporation; *U.S. Public*, pg. 1459
SEQUA CORPORATION; *U.S. Public*, pg. 1458
SETTEF SPA—Laporte plc; *Int'l*, pg. 803
SHELL BRASIL SA (PETROLEO)—Royal Dutch/Shell Group of Companies; *Int'l*, pg. 1141
SHELL CHEMICAL (AUSTRALIA)—Royal Dutch/Shell Group of Companies; *Int'l*, pg. 1137
SHELL CHEMICAL CO. (PHILIPPINES) INC.—Royal Dutch/Shell Group of Companies; *Int'l*, pg. 1140
SHELL CHEMICALS & SERVICES (EAST CARIBBEAN) LTD—Royal Dutch/Shell Group of Companies; *Int'l*, pg. 1141
SHELL CHEMICALS (HELLAS) LTD.—Royal Dutch/Shell Group of Companies; *Int'l*, pg. 1138
SHELL CHEMICALS U.K.—Royal Dutch/Shell Group of Companies; *Int'l*, pg. 1139
SHELL CHEMICALS (ZAMBIA) LTD.—Royal Dutch/Shell Group of Companies; *Int'l*, pg. 1136
SHELL CHILE SA COMERCIAL E INDUSTRIAL—Royal Dutch/Shell Group of Companies; *Int'l*, pg. 1142
SHELL CHIMIE—Royal Dutch/Shell Group of Companies; *Int'l*, pg. 1138
SHELL CURACAO N.V.—Royal Dutch/Shell Group of Companies; *Int'l*, pg. 1141
SHELL DEVELOPMENT CO.—Royal Dutch/Shell Group of Companies; *Int'l*, pg. 1136
SHELL MALAWI LTD.—Royal Dutch/Shell Group of Companies; *Int'l*, pg. 1136
SHELL MEXICO, SA DE CV—Royal Dutch/Shell Group of Companies; *Int'l*, pg. 1141
SHELL QUIMICA DE EL SALVADOR—Royal Dutch/Shell Group of Companies; *Int'l*, pg. 1141
SHELL QUIMICA DE VENEZUELA, C.A.—Royal Dutch/Shell Group of Companies; *Int'l*, pg. 1142
SHELL ZIMBABWE (PRIVATE) LTD.—Royal Dutch/Shell Group of Companies; *Int'l*, pg. 1136
THE SHERWIN-WILLIAMS COMPANY; *U.S. Public*, pg. 1465
SHIMURA KAKO COMPANY, LTD.—Inco Limited; *Int'l*, pg. 673
SHIMURA KAKO COMPANY, LTD.—Mitsui & Co., Ltd.; *Int'l*, pg. 879

SHIN-ETSU CHEMICAL CO. LTD.; *Int'l*, pg. 1234
SHIPLEY CO., LLC—Rohm and Haas Company; *U.S. Public*, pg. 1403
SIGNUM ARZNELMITTEL GMBH—Solvay S.A.; *Int'l*, pg. 1278
SKANDINAVISK HENKEL A/S—Henkel KGaA; *Int'l*, pg. 614
SOCIETA BARIO E DERIVATI, S.P.A.—Solvay S.A.; *Int'l*, pg. 1279
SOCIETE D'APPLICATION DU FLOCKAGE—Borden, Inc.; *U.S. Private*, pg. 160
SOCIETE NOUVELLE CELLONITE—Borden, Inc.; *U.S. Private*, pg. 160
SOLUTIA INC.; *U.S. Public*, pg. 1483
SOLVAY INTEROX—Solvay S.A.; *Int'l*, pg. 1280
SOLVAY INTEROX AMERICA—Solvay S.A.; *Int'l*, pg. 1277
SOLVAY INTEROX CHEMICALS PTY. LTD.—Solvay S.A.; *Int'l*, pg. 1280
SOLVAY INTEROX S.A.—Solvay S.A.; *Int'l*, pg. 1277
SOLVAY INTEROX S.P.A.—Solvay S.A.; *Int'l*, pg. 1280
SOLVAY PORTUGAL PRODUCTOS QUIMICOS S.A.—Solvay S.A.; *Int'l*, pg. 1280
SOLVAY S.A.; *Int'l*, pg. 1277
SOPRELEC SA—Laporte plc; *Int'l*, pg. 803
SOVEREIGN CHEMICAL INDUSTRIES LIMITED—Laporte plc; *Int'l*, pg. 802
SPECIA COLOMBIA—Rhone-Poulenc S.A.; *Int'l*, pg. 1114
SPECIALTY CHEMICALS DIV.—Rhone-Poulenc S.A.; *Int'l*, pg. 1109
SPECIALTYCHEM PRODUCTS CORPORATION—Bayer AG; *Int'l*, pg. 173
STERLING CHEMICALS HOLDINGS, INC.; *U.S. Public*, pg. 1515
STERLING PULP CHEMICALS, LTD.—Tenneco Inc.; *U.S. Public*, pg. 1580
STURGE, LIFFORD—Rhone-Poulenc S.A.; *Int'l*, pg. 1113
STURGE S.A.—Rhone-Poulenc S.A.; *Int'l*, pg. 1113
SUMITOMO CHEMICAL COMPANY, LTD.; *Int'l*, pg. 1310
OY SUOMEN HENKEL AB—Henkel KGaA; *Int'l*, pg. 614
SUOMEN UNIPOL OY—Oy Algol AB; *Int'l*, pg. 15
SWISS ALUMINIUM AUSTRALIA LTD.—Alusuisse-Lonza Holding Ltd.; *Int'l*, pg. 69
SYBRON CHEMICALS INC.; *U.S. Public*, pg. 1544
SYNTEX—Roche Holding Ltd.; *Int'l*, pg. 1120
SYREMONT S.P.A.—Compart SpA; *Int'l*, pg. 324
TKM LIMITED—Aluminum Company of America; *U.S. Public*, pg. 62
TR-METRO CHEM, INC.—Preussag AG; *Int'l*, pg. 1071
TRL S.A.—Borden, Inc.; *U.S. Private*, pg. 160
TAIWAN HERCULES CHEMICALS, INC.—Hercules Incorporated; *U.S. Public*, pg. 811
TAKEDA CHEMICAL INDUSTRIES, LTD.; *Int'l*, pg. 1350
TALOQUIMIA, S.A.—Hercules Incorporated; *U.S. Public*, pg. 811
TAMMS INDUSTRIES—Laporte plc; *Int'l*, pg. 803
TECHNIC INCORPORATED; *U.S. Private*, pg. 1071
TEIJIN LIMITED; *Int'l*, pg. 1362
TENNECO ORGANICS LTD.—Tenneco Inc.; *U.S. Public*, pg. 1580
TETRA TECHNOLOGIES; *U.S. Public*, pg. 1582
TETRAETILO DE MEXICO, S.A.—Du Pont (E.I. Du Pont De Nemours & Co.); *U.S. Public*, pg. 533
TEXACO INC.; *U.S. Public*, pg. 1582
THANN ET MULHOUSE—Millennium Chemicals Inc.; *U.S. Public*, pg. 1111
3M; *U.S. Public*, pg. 1604
TIRAM KIMIA—Royal Dutch/Shell Group of Companies; *Int'l*, pg. 1140
TOSHIBA CHEMICAL CORPORATION—Toshiba Corporation; *Int'l*, pg. 1403
TRANSELCO DIV.—Ferro Corporation; *U.S. Public*, pg. 619
TREBLA CHEMICAL COMPANY—CPAC, Inc.; *U.S. Public*, pg. 282
UF6 FLOURINE SPECIALTIES—AlliedSignal Inc.; *U.S. Public*, pg. 51
UNILEVER N.V.—Unilever Plc; *Int'l*, pg. 1434
UNILEVER PLC; *Int'l*, pg. 1433
UNION CARBIDE CORPORATION; *U.S. Public*, pg. 1666
UNIROYAL CHEMICAL LTD.—Crompton & Knowles Corporation; *U.S. Public*, pg. 460
U.S. BORAX INC.—Rio Tinto PLC; *Int'l*, pg. 1119
UNIVERSAL PROPULSION CO., INC.—Carpenter Technology Corporation; *U.S. Public*, pg. 308
R.T. VANDERBILT COMPANY, INC.; *U.S. Private*, pg. 1133
VELSICOL CHEMICAL CORPORATION; *U.S. Private*, pg. 1135
VULCAN CHEMICALS—Vulcan Materials Company; *U.S. Public*, pg. 1725
VULCAN MATERIALS COMPANY; *U.S. Public*, pg. 1725
VULNAX INTERNATIONAL LTD.—Akzo Nobel N.V.; *Int'l*, pg. 47
WARWICK INTERNATIONAL LTD.—Sequa Corporation; *U.S. Public*, pg. 1459
WAYNE CHEMICAL CORPORATION—Harrisons & Crosfield plc; *Int'l*, pg. 599
WEST CHEMICAL PRODUCTS, INC.—Wechco, Inc.; *U.S. Private*, pg. 1158
WEST PENETONE CORPORATION—Wechco, Inc.; *U.S. Private*, pg. 1158
WESTERN ELECTROCHEMICAL COMPANY—American Pacific Corporation; *U.S. Public*, pg. 88
WESTVACO CORPORATION-CHEMICAL DIV.—Westvaco Corporation; *U.S. Public*, pg. 1762
WHATMAN INC.—Whatman plc; *Int'l*, pg. 1498
WHITTAKER, CLARK & DANIELS, INC.; *U.S. Private*, pg. 1174
WITCO CORPORATION; *U.S. Public*, pg. 1773
WITCO ITALIANA—Witco Corporation; *U.S. Public*, pg. 1774
WITCO LTD.—Witco Corporation; *U.S. Public*, pg. 1774
YUKA SHELL EPOXY—Royal Dutch/Shell Group of Companies; *Int'l*, pg. 1140
ZEOLYST INTERNATIONAL—PQ Corporation; *U.S. Private*, pg. 827

2821 — PLASTICS MATERIALS, SYNTHETIC RESINS & NONVULCANIZABLE ELASTOMERS

ASI INVESTMENTS HOLDING CO.—A. Schulman, Inc.; *U.S. Public*, pg. 1441
AAKRONITE NEW ZEALAND—International Paper Company; *U.S. Public*, pg. 904
ACME CHEMICALS & INSULATION CO.—Insulating Materials, Inc.; *U.S. Private*, pg. 565
ACME RESIN CORP.—Borden, Inc.; *U.S. Private*, pg. 157
AIR PRODUCTS AND CHEMICALS, INC.; *U.S. Public*, pg. 30
AKEMI PLASTICS INC.—Maxco, Inc.; *U.S. Public*, pg. 1061
AKZO COATINGS INC. (MI)—Akzo Nobel N.V.; *Int'l*, pg. 46
AKZO ENGINEERING PLASTICS, INC.—Akzo Nobel N.V.; *Int'l*, pg. 47
AKZO LANCHEM CORP.—Akzo Nobel N.V.; *Int'l*, pg. 47
AKZO NOBEL COATINGS INC.—Akzo Nobel N.V.; *Int'l*, pg. 48
AKZO NOBEL FORTAFIL FIBERS INC.—Akzo Nobel N.V.; *Int'l*, pg. 48
AKZO NOBEL INC.—Akzo Nobel N.V.; *Int'l*, pg. 47
AL-JUBAIL PETROCHEMICAL COMPANY—Exxon Corporation; *U.S. Public*, pg. 601
ALCOA MINERALS OF JAMAICA, INC.—Aluminum Company of America; *U.S. Public*, pg. 62
ALLIEDSIGNAL INC.; *U.S. Public*, pg. 49
THE ALPHA CORPORATION OF TENNESSEE; *U.S. Private*, pg. 44
ALPHA/OWENS CORNING LLC—The Alpha Corporation Of Tennessee; *U.S. Private*, pg. 45
ALUSUISSE-LONZA HOLDING LTD.; *Int'l*, pg. 66
AMICON POLYMERS (H.K.) LTD.—Millipore Corporation; *U.S. Public*, pg. 1113
AMOCO CHEMICALS—Amoco Corporation; *U.S. Public*, pg. 102
AMOCO CORPORATION; *U.S. Public*, pg. 101
AMOCO PERFORMANCE PRODUCTS, INC.—Amoco Corporation; *U.S. Public*, pg. 102
AMPACET CORPORATION; *U.S. Private*, pg. 67
AQUALON—Hercules Incorporated; *U.S. Public*, pg. 810
AQUALON BELGIUM N.V.—Hercules Incorporated; *U.S. Public*, pg. 810
AQUALON B.V.—Hercules Incorporated; *U.S. Public*, pg. 810
AQUALON CANADA INC.—Hercules Incorporated; *U.S. Public*, pg. 810
AQUALON FRANCE B.V.—Hercules Incorporated; *U.S. Public*, pg. 810
AQUALON GMBH—Hercules Incorporated; *U.S. Public*, pg. 810
AQUALON-HOPEWELL—Hercules Incorporated; *U.S. Public*, pg. 810
AQUALON ITALIA S.P.A.—Hercules Incorporated; *U.S. Public*, pg. 810
AQUALON-LOUISIANA—Hercules Incorporated; *U.S. Public*, pg. 810
AQUALON (UK) LIMITED—Hercules Incorporated; *U.S. Public*, pg. 810
ARISTECH CHEMICAL CORPORATION—Mitsubishi Corporation; *Int'l*, pg. 872
ASAHI CHEMICAL INDUSTRY CO., LTD.; *Int'l*, pg. 83
ASAHI GLASS CO., LTD.; *Int'l*, pg. 84
ASHLAND CHEMICAL—Ashland, Inc.; *U.S. Public*, pg. 139
ASHLAND CHEMICAL ITALIANA S.P.A.—Ashland, Inc.; *U.S. Public*, pg. 139
AVERY DENNISON CORPORATION; *U.S. Public*, pg. 152
AXSON ESPANA—Axson S.A.; *Int'l*, pg. 103
AXSON FRANCE—Axson S.A.; *Int'l*, pg. 103
BASF ESPANOLA S.A.—BASF AG; *Int'l*, pg. 106
BASF INDIA LTD.—BASF AG; *Int'l*, pg. 106
BASF MAROC S.A.—BASF AG; *Int'l*, pg. 106
BHP PETROLEUM PTY LTD.—The Broken Hill Proprietary Company Limited; *Int'l*, pg. 225
BP CHEMICALS, INC.—The British Petroleum Company P.L.C.; *Int'l*, pg. 220
BASIC CHEMICALS DIV.—Rhone-Poulenc S.A.; *Int'l*, pg. 1109
BAYER AG—Bayer AG; *Int'l*, pg. 172
BAYER B.V.—Bayer AG; *Int'l*, pg. 175
BAYER CORPORATION—Bayer AG; *Int'l*, pg. 172
BEAUMONT POLYETHYLENE PLANT—Mobil Oil Corporation; *U.S. Public*, pg. 1118
BIO-RAD LABORATORIES, INC.; *U.S. Public*, pg. 230
BORDEN, INC.; *U.S. Private*, pg. 157
WM. T. BURNETT & CO., INC.; *U.S. Private*, pg. 186
C & C - COLORING & COMPOUNDING SRL—Mazzucchelli Polimeri Srl; *Int'l*, pg. 850
CPC-COMPANHIA PETROQUIMICA CAMACCARI LTDA.—Nissho Iwai Corporation; *Int'l*, pg. 947
CERTAINTEED CORPORATION—Saint-Gobain; *Int'l*, pg. 1170
CESTIDUR INDUSTRIES SA—DSM N.V.; *Int'l*, pg. 354
CHASE & SONS DIVISION—Chase Corporation; *U.S. Public*, pg. 337
CHASE CORPORATION; *U.S. Public*, pg. 337
CHEM-PLAST S.P.A.—Henkel KGaA; *Int'l*, pg. 611
CHEMDESIGN CORPORATION—Bayer AG; *Int'l*, pg. 173
CHEMETALL GMBH GESELLSCHAFT FUER CHEMISCH TECHNISCHE VERFAHREN—Metallgesellschaft AG; *Int'l*, pg. 861
CHIMIQUE DE LA MEDITERRANEE—Royal Dutch/Shell Group of Companies; *Int'l*, pg. 1138
CHROMA CORPORATION; *U.S. Private*, pg. 238
CHUGAI BOYEKI CO., LTD.; *Int'l*, pg. 290
CIBA-GEIGY (CHINA) LIMITED-SHANGHAI BRANCH—Novartis AG; *Int'l*, pg. 976
CIBA SPECIALTY CHEMICALS—Ciba Specialty Chemicals Holding Inc.; *Int'l*, pg. 291
CIBA SPECIALTY CHEMICALS HOLDING INC.; *Int'l*, pg. 291
CIQUINE-COMPANHIA PETROQUIMICA—Nissho Iwai Corporation; *Int'l*, pg. 947
CLARIANT CORPORATION—Hoechst Aktiengesellschaft; *Int'l*, pg. 624
CLEANING SOLUTIONS GROUP/CELLO—The Sherwin-Williams Company; *U.S. Public*, pg. 1466
CONAP INC.; *U.S. Private*, pg. 261
CONDEA VISTA COMPANY—Condea Chemie GmbH; *Int'l*, pg. 325
CORDES & CO. GMBH—Henkel KGaA; *Int'l*, pg. 609
CORNING INCORPORATED; *U.S. Public*, pg. 448
CRAY VALLEY PRODUCTS—Total S.A.; *Int'l*, pg. 1410
JOSEPH CROSFIELD & SONS LTD.—Unilever Plc; *Int'l*, pg. 1434
CYANAMID DE VENEZUELA CA—American Home Products Corporation; *U.S. Public*, pg. 80
CYANAMID-KETJEN KATALYSATOR BV—Akzo Nobel N.V.; *Int'l*, pg. 47
CYTEC FIBERITE INC.—Cytec Industries Inc.; *U.S. Public*, pg. 471
CYTEC INDUSTRIES INC.; *U.S. Public*, pg. 471
DSM BELGIUM N.V.—DSM N.V.; *Int'l*, pg. 355
DSM DEUTSCHLAND GMBH & CO.—DSM N.V.; *Int'l*, pg. 356
DSM ENGINEERING PLASTIC PRODUCTS—DSM N.V.; *Int'l*, pg. 354
DSM FRANCE SA—DSM N.V.; *Int'l*, pg. 355
DSM IDEMITSU CORP. LTD.—DSM N.V.; *Int'l*, pg. 356
DSM ITALIA—DSM N.V.; *Int'l*, pg. 355
DSM ITALIA SRL—DSM N.V.; *Int'l*, pg. 355
DSM KUNSTHARZE GMBH—DSM N.V.; *Int'l*, pg. 355
DSM KUNSTSTOFFEN B.V.—DSM N.V.; *Int'l*, pg. 353
DSM POLYMERS INTERNATIONAL—DSM N.V.; *Int'l*, pg. 353
DSM RESEARCH B.V.—DSM N.V.; *Int'l*, pg. 353
DSM RESINS BELGIUM N.V.—DSM N.V.; *Int'l*, pg. 355
DSM RESINS B.V.—DSM N.V.; *Int'l*, pg. 353
DSM RESINS ESPANA SA—DSM N.V.; *Int'l*, pg. 355
DSM RESINS FRANCE S.A.—DSM N.V.; *Int'l*, pg. 355
DSM RESINS UK LTD.—DSM N.V.; *Int'l*, pg. 355
DSM RIM NYLON VOF—DSM N.V.; *Int'l*, pg. 353
DSM SCANDINAVIA AB—DSM N.V.; *Int'l*, pg. 355
DSM VERKOOPKANTOOR POLYMEREN NEDERLAND—DSM N.V.; *Int'l*, pg. 353
DAICEL CHEMICAL INDUSTRIES LTD.—Mitsui & Co., Ltd.; *Int'l*, pg. 877
DAINICHISEIKA COLOUR & CHEMICALS MFG. CO., LTD.; *Int'l*, pg. 369
DAINIPPON INK & CHEMICALS, INC.; *Int'l*, pg. 369
DAUBERT INDUSTRIES, INC.; *U.S. Private*, pg. 313
DAY-GLO COLOR CORP.—RPM, Inc.; *U.S. Public*, pg. 1357
DELTA RESINS & REFRACTORIES, INC.; *U.S. Private*, pg. 323
DENKI KAGAKU KOGYO KABUSHIKI KAISHA—Mitsui & Co., Ltd.; *Int'l*, pg. 877
DENNIS CHEMICAL CO., INC.; *U.S. Private*, pg. 324
DERIVADOS DEL PROPILENO, S.A. (DERPROSA)—Compania Espanola de Petroleos, S.A. (CEPSA); *Int'l*, pg. 323
DEUTSCHE SHELL AG—Royal Dutch/Shell Group of Companies; *Int'l*, pg. 1138
DIVERSIFIED COMPOUNDERS—Dennis Chemical Co., Inc.; *U.S. Private*, pg. 324
THE DOW CHEMICAL COMPANY; *U.S. Public*, pg. 522
DOW CORNING TORAY SILICON CO., LTD.—Toray Industries, Inc.; *Int'l*, pg. 1400
DOW HELLAS—The Dow Chemical Company; *U.S. Public*, pg. 524
DOWBRANDS, L.P.—The Dow Chemical Company; *U.S. Public*, pg. 523
DOWTY WOODVILLE POLYMER—TI Group plc; *Int'l*, pg. 1338
DU PONT CANADA-MONTREAL—Du Pont (E.I. Du Pont De Nemours & Co.); *U.S. Public*, pg. 532
DU PONT DE NEMOURS (DEUTSCHLAND) GMBH, PLANT UENTROP—Du Pont (E.I. Du Pont De Nemours & Co.); *U.S. Public*, pg. 532
DU PONT DE NEMOURS (NEDERLAND) B.V.—Du Pont (E.I. Du Pont De Nemours & Co.); *U.S. Public*, pg. 532
DU PONT (E.I. DU PONT DE NEMOURS & CO.); *U.S. Public*, pg. 530
DU PONT MITSUI POLYCHEMICALS CO., LTD.—Du Pont (E.I. Du Pont De Nemours & Co.); *U.S. Public*, pg. 533
DU PONT PHOTOLUX S.A.—Du Pont (E.I. Du Pont De Nemours & Co.); *U.S. Public*, pg. 533
DU PONT PROTEIN TECHNOLOGIES INTERNATIONAL—Du Pont (E.I. Du Pont De Nemours & Co.); *U.S. Public*, pg. 531
DUCILO S.A.—Du Pont (E.I. Du Pont De Nemours & Co.); *U.S. Public*, pg. 533
DUROFORM-J. FRITZ GMBH & CO KG—Alusuisse-Lonza Holding Ltd.; *Int'l*, pg. 68
EAGLE-PICHER ESPANA, S.A.—Eagle-Picher Industries, Inc.; *U.S. Private*, pg. 355
EAGLE-PICHER FLUID SYSTEMS LIMITED—Eagle-Picher Industries, Inc.; *U.S. Private*, pg. 355
EASTMAN CHEMICAL COMPANY; *U.S. Public*, pg. 550
EDISON FOAM PROCESSING CORP.—Leggett & Platt, Incorporated; *U.S. Public*, pg. 986
ELASTOGRAN FRANCE S.A.—BASF AG; *Int'l*, pg. 108
ELASTOGRAN GMBH—BASF AG; *Int'l*, pg. 104
ELASTOGRAN HEADWAY URETHANES CO., LTD.—BASF AG; *Int'l*, pg. 108
ELASTOGRAN ITALIA S.P.A.—BASF AG; *Int'l*, pg. 108
ELASTOGRAN S.A.—BASF AG; *Int'l*, pg. 108
ELASTOGRAN SCHWARZHEIDE GMBH—BASF AG; *Int'l*, pg. 104
ELASTOGRAN UK LIMITED—BASF AG; *Int'l*, pg. 108
ELECTRICAL PRODUCTS DIVISION—3M; *U.S. Public*, pg. 1605
ELF AQUITAINE, INC.—Elf Aquitane; *Int'l*, pg. 445

ELF ATOCHEM NORTH AMERICA, FLUOROCHEMICAL DIV.—Elf Aquitane; *Int'l*, pg. 446
ELF ATOCHEM NORTH AMERICA, INC.—Elf Aquitane; *Int'l*, pg. 445
ELF ATOCHEM ORGANIC PEROXIDES PLANT—Elf Aquitane; *Int'l*, pg. 446
ENGINEERED POLYMERS CORPORATION—Cookson Group plc; *Int'l*, pg. 328
ENVIRODYNE LIMITED—Envirodyne Industries, Inc.; *U.S. Public*, pg. 586
EPOXYLITE CORPORATION-RESIN DIV.; *U.S. Private*, pg. 379
ERTA (ARNOLD) UK LTD.—DSM N.V.; *Int'l*, pg. 354
EVODE GROUP LTD.—Laporte plc; *Int'l*, pg. 802
EXPOXIQUIM, C.A.—Corporacion Grupo Quimico, S.A.C.A.; *Int'l*, pg. 332
FERRO CORPORATION; *U.S. Public*, pg. 618
FIBERCOTE INDUSTRIES, INC.—Park Electrochemical Corporation; *U.S. Public*, pg. 1258
FIRESTONE TEXTILES COMPANY—Bridgestone Corporation; *Int'l*, pg. 214
THE FLECTO CO., INC.; *U.S. Private*, pg. 410
FLETCHER CHALLENGE METHANOL LIMITED—Fletcher Challenge Limited; *Int'l*, pg. 495
FLEXIBLE PRODUCTS COMPANY; *U.S. Private*, pg. 412
FLUORPLAST NEDERLAND B.V.—Saint-Gobain; *Int'l*, pg. 1174
FOAMEX INTERNATIONAL INC.—Trace International Holdings, Inc.; *U.S. Private*, pg. 1094
FORMOSA PLASTICS CORPORATION; *Int'l*, pg. 498
FORMOSA PLASTICS CORP., U.S.A.—Formosa Plastics Corporation; *Int'l*, pg. 498
FREEMAN DISTRIBUTION LTD.—DSM N.V.; *Int'l*, pg. 355
G.E. PLASTICS—General Electric Company; *U.S. Public*, pg. 710
G.E. PLASTICS-AMERICA—General Electric Company; *U.S. Public*, pg. 711
G.E. SILICONES—General Electric Company; *U.S. Public*, pg. 711
G.E. SPECIALTY CHEMICALS—General Electric Company; *U.S. Public*, pg. 711
GATOR INDUSTRIES INC.; *U.S. Private*, pg. 441
GEMISA S.A. DE C.V.—Henkel KGaA; *Int'l*, pg. 614
GENERAL ELECTRIC COMPANY; *U.S. Public*, pg. 709
GENEVAD CELLPLAST—Scancem AB; *Int'l*, pg. 1199
THE GEON COMPANY; *U.S. Public*, pg. 733
GEORGIA DUCK & CORDAGE MILLS; *U.S. Private*, pg. 448
GEORGIA GULF CORPORATION; *U.S. Public*, pg. 734
GEORGIA-PACIFIC CORPORATION; *U.S. Public*, pg. 735
M.C. GILL CORPORATION; *U.S. Private*, pg. 453
GIST-BROCADES FRANCE S.A.—Royal Gist-Brocades N.V.; *Int'l*, pg. 1143
GLUCONA VOF—Akzo Nobel N.V.; *Int'l*, pg. 47
THE B.F. GOODRICH COMPANY; *U.S. Public*, pg. 751
THE GOODYEAR TIRE & RUBBER COMPANY; *U.S. Public*, pg. 752
GRACE PACKAGING—W.R. Grace & Co.; *U.S. Public*, pg. 755
GRACE (SWEDEN) AB—W.R. Grace & Co.; *U.S. Public*, pg. 756
GRANITEVILLE COMPANY—Avondale Incorporated; *U.S. Private*, pg. 103
GUNDLE/SLT ENVIRONMENTAL, INC.; *U.S. Public*, pg. 769
HAMWORTHY INDUSTRAMAR LIMITED—Powell Duffryn PLC; *Int'l*, pg. 1065
M.A. HANNA COLOR—M.A. Hanna Company; *U.S. Public*, pg. 781
M.A. HANNA COMPANY; *U.S. Public*, pg. 780
M.A. HANNA ENGINEERED MATERIALS—M.A. Hanna Company; *U.S. Public*, pg. 781
HARDMAN DIVISION OF HARCROS CHEMICALS, INC.—Harrisons & Crosfield plc; *Int'l*, pg. 598
HARIMA M.I.D., INC.—The Mead Corporation; *U.S. Public*, pg. 1077
A.C. HATRICK CHEMICALS PTY. LIMITED—Hercules Incorporated; *U.S. Public*, pg. 811
A.C. HATRICK (N.Z.) LTD.—Hercules Incorporated; *U.S. Public*, pg. 811
HENKEL-EYTESA S.A.—Henkel KGaA; *Int'l*, pg. 612
HENKEL FUNCTIONAL PRODUCTS DIV.—Henkel KGaA; *Int'l*, pg. 610
HENKEL KGAA; *Int'l*, pg. 609
HEPWORTH PLC; *Int'l*, pg. 614
HERCULES BELGIUM N.V.—Hercules Incorporated; *U.S. Public*, pg. 810
HERCULES CHEMICALS INVESTMENTS PTY. LTD.—Hercules Incorporated; *U.S. Public*, pg. 811
HERCULES INCORPORATED; *U.S. Public*, pg. 809
HERCULES INC.-JEFFERSON—Hercules Incorporated; *U.S. Public*, pg. 810
HERCULES TRADING CORP.—Hercules Incorporated; *U.S. Public*, pg. 810
HEXCEL CORPORATION; *U.S. Public*, pg. 824
HISPAVIC INDUSTRIAL S.A.—Solvay S.A.; *Int'l*, pg. 1278
HOECHST CELANESE ADVANCED MATERIALS—Hoechst Aktiengesellschaft; *Int'l*, pg. 624
HOECHST CELANESE CORP. SPUNBOND PRODUCTS—Hoechst Aktiengesellschaft; *Int'l*, pg. 626
HOECHST CELANESE FINE CHEMICAL DIVISION—Hoechst Aktiengesellschaft; *Int'l*, pg. 625
HOECHST MARION ROUSSEL AG—Hoechst Aktiengesellschaft; *Int'l*, pg. 624
HOECHST SPECIALTY CHEMICALS GROUP—Hoechst Aktiengesellschaft; *Int'l*, pg. 624
HOECHST SPECIALTY PRODUCTS GROUP—Hoechst Aktiengesellschaft; *Int'l*, pg. 625
HULS AG—Veba AG; *Int'l*, pg. 1454
HULS AMERICA PLASTICS DIVISION—Veba AG; *Int'l*, pg. 1455
HUNTSMAN CORPORATION; *U.S. Private*, pg. 549
ICC INDUSTRIES, INC.; *U.S. Private*, pg. 553
ICI ADVANCED MATERIALS—Imperial Chemical Industries PLC; *Int'l*, pg. 663
ICI AMERICAS, INC.—Imperial Chemical Industries PLC; *Int'l*, pg. 663
ICI CHEMICALS & POLYMERS—Imperial Chemical Industries PLC; *Int'l*, pg. 663
ICI CHEMICALS & POLYMERS LTD.—Imperial Chemical Industries PLC; *Int'l*, pg. 663
ICI FIBERITE—Imperial Chemical Industries PLC; *Int'l*, pg. 664
ICI FILMS—Imperial Chemical Industries PLC; *Int'l*, pg. 664
ICI FRANCE SA—Imperial Chemical Industries PLC; *Int'l*, pg. 665
ICI NEW ZEALAND LIMITED—Imperial Chemical Industries PLC; *Int'l*, pg. 665
ICI OESTERREICH GMBH—Imperial Chemical Industries PLC; *Int'l*, pg. 665
ICI PAINTS—Imperial Chemical Industries PLC; *Int'l*, pg. 664
ICI (PERU) S.A.—Imperial Chemical Industries PLC; *Int'l*, pg. 665
ICI (PHILIPPINES) INC.—Imperial Chemical Industries PLC; *Int'l*, pg. 665
ICI POLYESTER POLYMER—Imperial Chemical Industries PLC; *Int'l*, pg. 664
ICI PRETECHNIK GGS FUER POLYURETHANE-ROHSTOFFE MBH—Imperial Chemical Industries PLC; *Int'l*, pg. 665
ICI RESINS B.V.—Imperial Chemical Industries PLC; *Int'l*, pg. 665
ICI RESINS CANADA INC.—Imperial Chemical Industries PLC; *Int'l*, pg. 665
ICI (SINGAPORE) PRIVATE LIMITED—Imperial Chemical Industries PLC; *Int'l*, pg. 665
ICI ZAMBIA LIMITED—Imperial Chemical Industries PLC; *Int'l*, pg. 665
IGLOO PRODUCTS CORPORATION—Brunswick Corporation; *U.S. Public*, pg. 265
IMPERIAL OIL LIMITED—Exxon Corporation; *U.S. Public*, pg. 602
INDO RAMA SYNTHETICS P.T.; *Int'l*, pg. 673
INDUSQUIMA S.A.—Henkel KGaA; *Int'l*, pg. 613
INDUSTRIAL LATEX ADHESIVES LTD.—The Dow Chemical Company; *U.S. Public*, pg. 523
INDUSTRIAS CYDSA BAYER, S.A. DE C.V.—CYDSA S.A.; *Int'l*, pg. 246
INTERFACE INC.; *U.S. Public*, pg. 889
INTERMARINE U.S.A. INC.—Compart SpA; *Int'l*, pg. 324
INTEROX AMERICA—Solvay S.A.; *Int'l*, pg. 1278
INTERPLASTIC CORP.; *U.S. Private*, pg. 572
JAPAN ACRYLIC CHEMICAL CO., LTD.—Rohm and Haas Company; *U.S. Public*, pg. 1404
JONES BLAIR COMPANY; *U.S. Private*, pg. 596
JOTUN A/S; *Int'l*, pg. 714
JOTUN POLYMER A/S—Jotun A/S; *Int'l*, pg. 714
OY JOTUN SCANPOL AB—Jotun A/S; *Int'l*, pg. 715
KENYA SHELL LTD.—Royal Dutch/Shell Group of Companies; *Int'l*, pg. 1136
KEYSOR CENTURY CORPORATION; *U.S. Private*, pg. 618
KOHAP ENGINEERING PLASTICS LTD.—KOHAP Group; *Int'l*, pg. 742
KOHAP GROUP; *Int'l*, pg. 742
KOHAP INC.—KOHAP Group; *Int'l*, pg. 742
KONINKLIJKE TALENS BV—Akzo Nobel N.V.; *Int'l*, pg. 42
KYODO TDI LIMITED COMPANY—Olin Corporation; *U.S. Public*, pg. 1219
LANKEM CEYLON—Royal Dutch/Shell Group of Companies; *Int'l*, pg. 1140
LAPORTE ALPHAGARY LTD.—Laporte plc; *Int'l*, pg. 802
LAUBECK CORPORATION/CROSS; *U.S. Private*, pg. 652
LAWTER INTERNATIONAL, INC.; *U.S. Public*, pg. 980
LAWTER INTL. APS—Lawter International, Inc.; *U.S. Public*, *pg. 981*
LEE PHARMACEUTICALS; *U.S. Public*, pg. 984
LIGNIN PRODUCTS—Georgia-Pacific Corporation; *U.S. Public*, pg. 737
LIMBURGSE VINYL MAATSCHAPPIJ NV—DSM N.V.; *Int'l*, pg. 355
LINATEX CORPORATION OF AMERICA—Harrisons & Crosfield plc; *Int'l*, pg. 599
LOCTITE CORPORATION—Henkel KGaA; *Int'l*, pg. 611
LONZA AG—Alusuisse-Lonza Holding Ltd.; *Int'l*, pg. 67
LONZA BIOTEC SRO—Alusuisse-Lonza Holding Ltd.; *Int'l*, pg. 69
LONZA HONGKONG LTD.—Alusuisse-Lonza Holding Ltd.; *Int'l*, pg. 69
LONZA IBERICA S.A.—Alusuisse-Lonza Holding Ltd.; *Int'l*, pg. 69
LONZA INC.—Alusuisse-Lonza Holding Ltd.; *Int'l*, pg. 67
LUCKY LTD.—LG Group; *Int'l*, pg. 779
LYONDELL PETROCHEMICAL COMPANY; *U.S. Public*, pg. 1022
M.A. HANNA COLOR—M.A. Hanna Company; *U.S. Public*, pg. 781
MEMC ELECTRONIC MATERIALS, INC.—Veba AG; *Int'l*, pg. 1455
MACDERMID INCORPORATED; *U.S. Public*, pg. 1029
MARSON/CREATIVE FASTENER, INC.; *U.S. Private*, pg. 708
MARVAL INDUSTRIES, INC.; *U.S. Private*, pg. 710
MAZZUCCHELLI 1849 S.P.A.; *Int'l*, pg. 849
MAZZUCCHELLI POLIMERI SRL; *Int'l*, pg. 850
THE MCCLOSKEY CORPORATION—McWhorter Technologies, Inc.; *U.S. Public*, pg. 1074
MCWHORTER TECHNOLOGIES, INC.; *U.S. Public*, pg. 1074
MENASHA CORP., POLY HI SOLIDUR—Menasha Corporation; *U.S. Private*, pg. 731
MICAFIL AG—ABB Asea Brown Boveri (Holding) Ltd.; *Int'l*, pg. 2
MILLENNIUM PETROCHEMICALS, INC.—Hanson PLC; *Int'l*, pg. 594
MILPRINT INC.—Bemis Company, Inc.; *U.S. Public*, pg. 210
MITSUBISHI CHEMICAL BASF CO., LTD.—BASF AG; *Int'l*, pg. 106
MITSUBISHI CHEMICAL CORPORATION; *Int'l*, pg. 870
MITSUBISHI CHEMICAL MKV CO.—Mitsubishi Chemical Corporation; *Int'l*, pg. 871
MITSUBISHI MONSANTO CHEMICAL CO.—Monsanto Company; *U.S. Public*, pg. 1125
MITSUBISHI RAYON CO., LTD.; *Int'l*, pg. 876
MITSUBISHI YUKA—Royal Dutch/Shell Group of Companies; *Int'l*, pg. 1139
MITSUI TOATSU CHEMICALS, INC.—Mitsui & Co., Ltd.; *Int'l*, pg. 877
MOBIL FILMS AND PACKAGING—Mobil Oil Corporation; *U.S. Public*, pg. 1118
MOBIL OIL CORPORATION; *U.S. Public*, pg. 1118
MOLDING COMPOUNDS SPA—Alusuisse-Lonza Holding Ltd.; *Int'l*, pg. 69
MOLDING MATERIALS DIV.—Rogers Corporation; *U.S. Public*, pg. 1403
MONSANTO DO BRASIL LTDA. (MOBRA S.A.)—Monsanto Company; *U.S. Public*, pg. 1125
MONSANTO EUROPE S.A.—Monsanto Company; *U.S. Public*, pg. 1125
MONTEDISON S.P.A.—Compart SpA; *Int'l*, pg. 324
MORTON THIOKOL S.A. DE C.V.—Morton International Inc.; *U.S. Public*, pg. 1136
NL INDUSTRIES, INC.—Contran Corporation; *U.S. Private*, pg. 270
NVF COMPANY; *U.S. Private*, pg. 772
NACAN PRODUCTS LTD.—Unilever Plc; *Int'l*, pg. 1436
NATIONAL ORGANIC CHEMICAL INDUSTRIES—Royal Dutch/Shell Group of Companies; *Int'l*, pg. 1139
NATIONAL STARCH AND CHEMICAL COMPANY—Unilever Plc; *Int'l*, pg. 1435
NESTE CANADA INC.—Neste Oy; *Int'l*, pg. 914
NESTE OXO AB—Neste Oy; *Int'l*, pg. 915
NESTE RESINS CORPORATION—Neste Oy; *Int'l*, pg. 915
NIPPON DYNEEMA CO., LTD.—DSM N.V.; *Int'l*, pg. 354
NIPPON MAGPHANE COMPANY—Rhone-Poulenc S.A.; *Int'l*, pg. 1109
AB NOBEL PLAST—Akzo Nobel N.V.; *Int'l*, pg. 48
NORTON MATERIAUX AVANCES S.A.R.L.—Saint-Gobain; *Int'l*, pg. 1175
NORTON PAMPUS GMBH—Saint-Gobain; *Int'l*, pg. 1175
NORTON PAMPUS LIMITED—Saint-Gobain; *Int'l*, pg. 1175
NOVARTIS AG; *Int'l*, pg. 971
NYLTECH NORTH AMERICA INC.—Fiat Auto SpA; *Int'l*, pg. 482
OCCIDENTAL CHEMICAL CORPORATION—Occidental Petroleum Corporation; *U.S. Public*, pg. 1210
OLIN CORPORATION; *U.S. Public*, pg. 1218
OLIN MICROELECTRONIC MATERIALS, INC.—Olin Corporation; *U.S. Public*, pg. 1219
OWENS CORNING; *U.S. Public*, pg. 1236
OWENS-CORNING CANADA—Owens Corning; *U.S. Public*, *pg. 1237*
PMC, INC.; *U.S. Private*, pg. 827
PPG INDUSTRIES, INC.; *U.S. Public*, pg. 1245
PVC COMPOUNDERS—Group Dekko; *U.S. Private*, pg. 484
PACIFIC PLASTICS (THAILAND) LTD.—The Siam Cement Public Company Limited; *Int'l*, pg. 1238
PALMER INTERNATIONAL, INC.; *U.S. Private*, pg. 834
P.T. PARDIC JAYA CHEMICALS—Nissho Iwai Corporation; *Int'l*, pg. 949
C.H. PATRICK & CO., INC.—The B.F. Goodrich Company; *U.S. Public*, pg. 751
PENFORD CORP.; *U.S. Public*, pg. 1269
PERSTORP COMPOUNDS INC.—Perstorp AB; *Int'l*, pg. 1037
PHILLIPS PETROLEUM COMPANY; *U.S. Public*, pg. 1290
PIGGING PRODUCTS—T.D. Williamson, Inc.; *U.S. Private*, pg. 1180
PLASCAL CORPORATION; *U.S. Private*, pg. 870
PLASCOAT SYSTEMS LIMITED—BTR plc; *Int'l*, pg. 129
PLAVINA & CIE S.N.C.—Solvay S.A.; *Int'l*, pg. 1277
POLIALDEN-PETROQUIMICA S.A.—Nissho Iwai Corporation; *Int'l*, pg. 949
POLICYD, S.A. DE C.V.—CYDSA S.A.; *Int'l*, pg. 246
POLYFLUORO PRIVATE LIMITED—Saint-Gobain; *Int'l*, pg. 1175
POLYMER CHEMICALS GROUP—Witco Corporation; *U.S. Public*, pg. 1774
POLYSAR—Bayer AG; *Int'l*, pg. 174
PRIMEX PLASTICS CORP.—ICC Industries, Inc.; *U.S. Private*, pg. 553
QUAKER CHEMICAL CORPORATION; *U.S. Public*, pg. 1346
QUANTUM, USI DIVISION—Quantum Corporation; *U.S. Public*, pg. 1350
QUIMICA DOMINICANA—Royal Dutch/Shell Group of Companies; *Int'l*, pg. 1141
QUIMICA NICARAGUENSE—Royal Dutch/Shell Group of Companies; *Int'l*, pg. 1141
R-CUBED COMPOSITES INC.—Perstorp AB; *Int'l*, pg. 1037
RASCHIG GMBH—PMC, Inc.; *U.S. Private*, pg. 827
REED PLASTICS (MI)—Novartis AG; *Int'l*, pg. 974
REED PLASTICS (TX)—Novartis AG; *Int'l*, pg. 974
REGLAR SRL—Alusuisse-Lonza Holding Ltd.; *Int'l*, pg. 69
REICHHOLD CHEMICALS DIV.—Dainippon Ink & Chemicals, Inc.; *Int'l*, pg. 370
REICHHOLD CHEMICALS, INC.—Dainippon Ink & Chemicals, Inc.; *Int'l*, pg. 370
REICHHOLD CHEMIE AG—Dainippon Ink & Chemicals, Inc.; *Int'l*, pg. 370
REICHHOLD LIMITED—Dainippon Ink & Chemicals, Inc.; *Int'l*, pg. 370
REPSOL QUIMICA—Repsol S.A.; *Int'l*, pg. 1104
RESIN FORMULATORS—E.V. Roberts & Associates, Inc.; *U.S. Private*, pg. 935
RESINMEC SPA—Alusuisse-Lonza Holding Ltd.; *Int'l*, pg. 69
RESINS & ORGANICS DIVISION, ALBRIGHT & WILSON LIMITED—Albright & Wilson plc; *Int'l*, pg. 49
REXAM RELEASE—Rexam PLC; *Int'l*, pg. 1107

REXENE CORPORATION—Huntsman Corporation; *U.S. Private*, pg. 549
RHEIN CHEMIE CORPORATION—Bayer AG; *Int'l*, pg. 173
RHEINISCHE OLEFINWERKE GMBH—BASF AG; *Int'l*, pg. 105
RHEINISCHE OLEFINWERKE GMBH—Royal Dutch/Shell Group of Companies; *Int'l*, pg. 1137
RHODIA NORDESTE—Rhone-Poulenc S.A.; *Int'l*, pg. 1109
RHONE-POULENC, CHEMICAL DIVISION—Rhone-Poulenc S.A.; *Int'l*, pg. 1109
RHONE-POULENC FILMS—Rhone-Poulenc S.A.; *Int'l*, pg. 1109
RHONE-POULENC INC.—Rhone-Poulenc S.A.; *Int'l*, pg. 1112
RHONE-POULENC S.A.; *Int'l*, pg. 1108
RHONE-POULENC WALSH—Rhone-Poulenc S.A.; *Int'l*, pg. 1110
E.V. ROBERTS & ASSOCIATES, INC.; *U.S. Private*, pg. 935
RODGARD CORPORATION—Astronics Corporation; *U.S. Public*, pg. 142
ROGERS INOAC CORPORATION—Rogers Corporation; *U.S. Public*, pg. 1403
ROHM AND HAAS COMPANY; *U.S. Public*, pg. 1403
ROHM GMBH—Veba AG; *Int'l*, pg. 1454
ROTTERDAMSE POLYOLEFINEN—Royal Dutch/Shell Group of Companies; *Int'l*, pg. 1135
ROYSTON LABORATORIES—Chase Corporation; *U.S. Public*, pg. 337
RUETGERS A.G.; *Int'l*, pg. 1147
SALSBURY CHEMICALS, INC.—Cambrex Corporation; *U.S. Public*, pg. 297
SASOL LIMITED; *Int'l*, pg. 1196
SAUDI INDUSTRIAL RESINS LTD.—Ashland, Inc.; *U.S. Public*, pg. 140
SCHENECTADY INTERNATIONAL, INC.; *U.S. Private*, pg. 969
A. SCHULMAN AG—A. Schulman, Inc.; *U.S. Public*, pg. 1441
A. SCHULMAN CANADA LTD.—A. Schulman, Inc.; *U.S. Public*, pg. 1441
A. SCHULMAN, INC.; *U.S. Public*, pg. 1441
A. SCHULMAN PLASTICS S.A.—A. Schulman, Inc.; *U.S. Public*, pg. 1442
A. SCHULMAN S.A.—A. Schulman, Inc.; *U.S. Public*, pg. 1441
SELLERS & JOSEPHSON—Shelby Williams Industries, Inc.; *U.S. Public*, pg. 1465
SHELL BRASIL SA (PETROLEO)—Royal Dutch/Shell Group of Companies; *Int'l*, pg. 1141
SHELL CANADA LTD.—Royal Dutch/Shell Group of Companies; *Int'l*, pg. 1138
SHELL CHEMICAL (AUSTRALIA)—Royal Dutch/Shell Group of Companies; *Int'l*, pg. 1137
SHELL CHEMICAL CO. (PHILIPPINES) INC.—Royal Dutch/Shell Group of Companies; *Int'l*, pg. 1140
SHELL CHEMICALS & SERVICES (EAST CARIBBEAN) LTD—Royal Dutch/Shell Group of Companies; *Int'l*, pg. 1141
SHELL CHEMICALS (HELLAS) LTD.—Royal Dutch/Shell Group of Companies; *Int'l*, pg. 1138
SHELL CHEMICALS U.K.—Royal Dutch/Shell Group of Companies; *Int'l*, pg. 1139
SHELL CHEMICALS (ZAMBIA) LTD.—Royal Dutch/Shell Group of Companies; *Int'l*, pg. 1136
SHELL CHILE SA COMERCIAL E INDUSTRIAL—Royal Dutch/Shell Group of Companies; *Int'l*, pg. 1142
SHELL CHIMIE—Royal Dutch/Shell Group of Companies; *Int'l*, pg. 1138
SHELL CURACAO N.V.—Royal Dutch/Shell Group of Companies; *Int'l*, pg. 1141
SHELL MALAWI LTD.—Royal Dutch/Shell Group of Companies; *Int'l*, pg. 1136
SHELL MEXICO, SA DE CV—Royal Dutch/Shell Group of Companies; *Int'l*, pg. 1141
SHELL NEDERLAND CHEMIE—Royal Dutch/Shell Group of Companies; *Int'l*, pg. 1135
SHELL QUIMICA DE EL SALVADOR—Royal Dutch/Shell Group of Companies; *Int'l*, pg. 1141
SHELL QUIMICA DE VENEZUELA, C.A.—Royal Dutch/Shell Group of Companies; *Int'l*, pg. 1142
SHELL REFINING (AUSTRALIA) PTY. LTD.—Royal Dutch/Shell Group of Companies; *Int'l*, pg. 1137
SHELL ZIMBABWE (PRIVATE) LTD.—Royal Dutch/Shell Group of Companies; *Int'l*, pg. 1136
SHIN-ETSU CHEMICAL CO. LTD.; *Int'l*, pg. 1234
SHIN-ETSU POLYMER AMERICA, INC.—Shin-Etsu Chemical Co. ltd.; *Int'l*, pg. 1234
SHIN-ETSU POLYMER CO. LTD.—Shin-Etsu Chemical Co. ltd.; *Int'l*, pg. 1234
SHINTECH INC.—Shin-Etsu Chemical Co. ltd.; *Int'l*, pg. 1234
SHOWA DENKO KAWASAKI WORKS—Showa Denko K.K.; *Int'l*, pg. 1236
SHOWA DENKO K.K.; *Int'l*, pg. 1236
SHOWPLA ASIA LIMITED; *Int'l*, pg. 1237
SIC PLASTICS FRANCE S.A.—Mazzucchelli 1849 S.p.a.; *Int'l*, pg. 850
SIC PLASTICS GMBH—Mazzucchelli 1849 S.p.a.; *Int'l*, pg. 850
SIKA CORPORATION—Sika Finanz AG; *Int'l*, pg. 1249
SIKKENS AEROSPACE FINISHERS—Akzo Nobel N.V.; *Int'l*, pg. 48
SIKKENS B.V.—Akzo Nobel N.V.; *Int'l*, pg. 42
SILICONE PRODUCTS DIV.—General Electric Company; *U.S. Public*, pg. 711
SINCLAIR/AMERITONE PAINT CORP.—Imperial Chemical Industries PLC; *Int'l*, pg. 663
SINOCHEM INTERNATIONAL PETROLEUM CO. LTD.; *Int'l*, pg. 1254
SOCIETE ANONYME INDUSTRIELLE DE RESINES—Tenneco Inc.; *U.S. Public*, pg. 1580
SOLAR PLASTICS-MINNEAPOLIS—Upper Midwest Industries, Incorporated; *U.S. Private*, pg. 1129
SOLUTIA INC.; *U.S. Public*, pg. 1483
SOLVAY DE BRASIL S/A—Solvay S.A.; *Int'l*, pg. 1280
SOLVAY INTEROX CHEMICALS PTY. LTD.—Solvay S.A.; *Int'l*, pg. 1280
SOLVAY POLYMERS INC.—Solvay S.A.; *Int'l*, pg. 1278
SOLVAY S.A.; *Int'l*, pg. 1277
SPENCER KELLOGG—Dainippon Ink & Chemicals, Inc.; *Int'l*, pg. 370
STEPAN COMPANY; *U.S. Public*, pg. 1514
STEPAN EUROPE—Stepan Company; *U.S. Public*, pg. 1514
SUMITOMO BAYER URETHANE CO., LTD.—Bayer AG; *Int'l*, pg. 174
SUMITOMO CHEMICAL COMPANY, LTD.; *Int'l*, pg. 1310
SVENSKA POLYSTYREN FABRIKEN AB—Veba AG; *Int'l*, pg. 1456
SYNTHESE BV—Akzo Nobel N.V.; *Int'l*, pg. 43
SYNTHOMER GMBH—Dainippon Ink & Chemicals, Inc.; *Int'l*, pg. 370
SYNTHOMER, LTD.—Dainippon Ink & Chemicals, Inc.; *Int'l*, pg. 370
TEIJIN LIMITED; *Int'l*, pg. 1362
TEKNOR APEX COMPANY; *U.S. Private*, pg. 1073
TEMBEC INC.; *Int'l*, pg. 1374
TEXAS RESIN—Jones Blair Company; *U.S. Private*, pg. 596
TEXTRON SYSTEMS CORPORATION—Textron Inc.; *U.S. Public*, pg. 1589
THAI POLYETHYLENE CO., LTD.—The Siam Cement Public Company Limited; *Int'l*, pg. 1239
THANN ET MULHOUSE—Millennium Chemicals Inc.; *U.S. Public*, pg. 1111
THERMO ELECTRON CORPORATION; *U.S. Public*, pg. 1591
TIRAM KIMIA—Royal Dutch/Shell Group of Companies; *Int'l*, pg. 1140
TOKUYAMA CORPORATION; *Int'l*, pg. 1393
TOKYO PRINTING INK MANUFACTURING CO., LTD.; *Int'l*, pg. 1394
TOSHIBA CHEMICAL CORPORATION—Toshiba Corporation; *Int'l*, pg. 1403
TRANSILWRAP COMPANY, INC.; *U.S. Private*, pg. 1097
TRIARC COMPANIES, INC.; *U.S. Public*, pg. 1634
UBE INDUSTRIES LTD.; *Int'l*, pg. 1426
UNILEVER N.V.—Unilever Plc; *Int'l*, pg. 1434
UNILEVER PLC; *Int'l*, pg. 1433
UNION CARBIDE CORPORATION; *U.S. Public*, pg. 1666
UNION POLYMER CO., LTD.—Nissho Iwai Corporation; *Int'l*, pg. 949
UNIROYAL TECHNOLOGY CORPORATION; *U.S. Public*, pg. 1670
UNITEX LIMITED—Smiths Industries plc; *Int'l*, pg. 1267
UPPER MIDWEST INDUSTRIES, INCORPORATED; *U.S. Private*, pg. 1129
VALCHEM AUSTRALIA PTY—Imperial Chemical Industries PLC; *Int'l*, pg. 666
VINAMUL LTD.—Unilever Plc; *Int'l*, pg. 1434
VINICLOR S.A.—Solvay S.A.; *Int'l*, pg. 1280
VYNCOLIT N.V.—Perstorp AB; *Int'l*, pg. 1037
WACKER-CHEMIE GMBH—Hoechst Aktiengesellschaft; *Int'l*, pg. 625
WACKER MEXICANA, S.A. DE C.V.—Hoechst Aktiengesellschaft; *Int'l*, pg. 625
WACKER SILICONES CORPORATION—Hoechst Aktiengesellschaft; *Int'l*, pg. 625
WELLMAN ENGINEERING RESINS DIV.—Wellman, Inc.; *U.S. Public*, pg. 1752
WELLMAN, INC.; *U.S. Public*, pg. 1752
WESTVACO CORPORATION; *U.S. Public*, pg. 1762
WESTVACO CORPORATION-CHEMICAL DIV.—Westvaco Corporation; *U.S. Public*, pg. 1762
WILSON COLOR—M.A. Hanna Company; *U.S. Public*, pg. 781
YUKA SHELL EPOXY—Royal Dutch/Shell Group of Companies; *Int'l*, pg. 1140
ZEELAND CHEMICALS, INC.—Cambrex Corporation; *U.S. Public*, pg. 297
ZENECA AB—Zeneca Group Plc; *Int'l*, pg. 1526
ZENECA HELLAS S.A.—Zeneca Group Plc; *Int'l*, pg. 1526
ZENECA OY—Zeneca Group Plc; *Int'l*, pg. 1527
ZENECA POLAND SP. Z.O.O.—Zeneca Group Plc; *Int'l*, pg. 1527
ZENECA ZIMBABWE (PRIVATE) LIMITED—Zeneca Group Plc; *Int'l*, pg. 1527

2822 — SYNTHETIC RUBBER (VULCANIZABLE ELASTOMERS)

AL-JUBAIL PETROCHEMICAL COMPANY—Exxon Corporation; *U.S. Public*, pg. 601
ALDAN INDUSTRIES; *U.S. Private*, pg. 33
AMERIPOL SYNPOL CORP.; *U.S. Private*, pg. 65
ASAHI GLASS CO., LTD.; *Int'l*, pg. 84
BWH KOUTSCHUR GMBH—Veba AG; *Int'l*, pg. 1454
BAYER AG; *Int'l*, pg. 171
BAYER AG—Bayer AG; *Int'l*, pg. 172
BAYER CORPORATION—Bayer AG; *Int'l*, pg. 172
BAYER (INDIA) LTD.—Bayer AG; *Int'l*, pg. 174
SAMUEL BINGHAM CO; *U.S. Private*, pg. 144
BRIDGESTONE/FIRESTONE, INC.—Bridgestone Corporation; *Int'l*, pg. 213
CHR DIVISION—Furon Company; *U.S. Public*, pg. 689
CAFFARO S.P.A.; *Int'l*, pg. 248
CASCHEM INC.—Cambrex Corporation; *U.S. Public*, pg. 297
CHASE & SONS DIVISION—Chase Corporation; *U.S. Public*, pg. 337
CHASE & SONS-WEBSTER BRANCH—Chase Corporation; *U.S. Public*, pg. 337
CHASE CORPORATION; *U.S. Public*, pg. 337
CHOMERICS INC.—Parker Hannifin Corporation; *U.S. Public*, pg. 1262
CHUGAI BOYEKI CO., LTD.; *Int'l*, pg. 290
DSM KUNSTSTOFFEN B.V.—DSM N.V.; *Int'l*, pg. 353
DAICEL HULS LTD.—Veba AG; *Int'l*, pg. 1455
DOW CORNING CORPORATION—The Dow Chemical Company; *U.S. Public*, pg. 523
DU PONT-SHOWA DENKO CO., LTD.—Du Pont (E.I. Du Pont De Nemours & Co.); *U.S. Public*, pg. 533
DYNAGEN INC.—Continental AG; *Int'l*, pg. 327
EAGLE-PICHER ESPANA, S.A.—Eagle-Picher Industries, Inc.; *U.S. Private*, pg. 355
EAGLE-PICHER FLUID SYSTEMS LIMITED—Eagle-Picher Industries, Inc.; *U.S. Private*, pg. 355
EASTMAN CHEMICAL COMPANY; *U.S. Public*, pg. 550
EASTMAN KODAK COMPANY; *U.S. Public*, pg. 550
ESSEX CHEMICAL CORPORATION—The Dow Chemical Company; *U.S. Public*, pg. 523
ESSEX SPECIALTY PRODUCTS, INC.—The Dow Chemical Company; *U.S. Public*, pg. 523
FERRO CORPORATION; *U.S. Public*, pg. 618
FIRESTONE SYNTHETIC RUBBER & LATEX CO.—Bridgestone Corporation; *Int'l*, pg. 214
THE FLECTO CO., INC.; *U.S. Private*, pg. 410
FORMOSA PLASTICS CORPORATION; *Int'l*, pg. 498
FREUDENBERG NOK—Freudenberg & Company; *Int'l*, pg. 505
GATOR INDUSTRIES INC.; *U.S. Private*, pg. 441
GENCORP INC.; *U.S. Public*, pg. 705
GENCORP VEHICLE SEALING DIV.—GenCorp Inc.; *U.S. Public*, pg. 706
GENERAL LATEX & CHEMICAL CORPORATION; *U.S. Private*, pg. 444
B.F. GOODRICH CHEMICAL (BELGIE) N.V.—The B.F. Goodrich Company; *U.S. Public*, pg. 752
THE GOODYEAR TIRE & RUBBER COMPANY; *U.S. Public*, pg. 752
HEAT BATH PARK METALLURGICAL CORP.; *U.S. Private*, pg. 518
HERTFORDSHIRE BTR LTD.—BTR plc; *Int'l*, pg. 126
HOECHST CELANESE ADVANCED MATERIALS—Hoechst Aktiengesellschaft; *Int'l*, pg. 624
INSTA-FOAM PRODUCTS, INC.—Flexible Products Company; *U.S. Private*, pg. 412
MACROTECH PLYSEAL, INC.; *U.S. Private*, pg. 693
MINOR RUBBER CO., INC.; *U.S. Private*, pg. 751
MITSUBISHI MONSANTO CHEMICAL CO.—Monsanto Company; *U.S. Public*, pg. 1125
MOELLER PRODUCTS CO., INC.; *U.S. Private*, pg. 755
MONROE CLEVITE—Tenneco Inc.; *U.S. Public*, pg. 1577
MONSANTO DO BRASIL LTDA. (MOBRA S.A.)—Monsanto Company; *U.S. Public*, pg. 1125
MONSANTO EUROPE S.A.—Monsanto Company; *U.S. Public*, pg. 1125
NIPPON KAYAKU CO. LTD.; *Int'l*, pg. 934
NIPPON SHOKUBAI CO., LTD.; *Int'l*, pg. 939
PALMER INTERNATIONAL, INC.; *U.S. Private*, pg. 834
PAMOL (NIGERIA) LTD.—Unilever Plc; *Int'l*, pg. 1438
PHILLIPS PETROLEUM COMPANY; *U.S. Public*, pg. 1290
PIRELLI ARGENTINA DE MANDATOS S.A.—Pirelli S.p.A.; *Int'l*, pg. 1059
PIRELLI ARMSTRONG TIRE CORPORATION—Pirelli S.p.A.; *Int'l*, pg. 1058
QUIMICA ORGANICA DE MEXICO, S.A. DE C.V.—CYDSA S.A.; *Int'l*, pg. 246
REEVES-INDUSTRIAL COATED FABRICS PLANT—Hart Holding Company, Inc.; *U.S. Private*, pg. 507
REEVES INTERNATIONAL—Hart Holding Company, Inc.; *U.S. Private*, pg. 507
RHEIN CHEMIE CORPORATION—Bayer AG; *Int'l*, pg. 173
RHEIN-CHEMIE RHEINAU GMBH—Bayer AG; *Int'l*, pg. 174
RHONE-POULENC, SPECIALTY PLASTICS DIVISION—Rhone-Poulenc S.A.; *Int'l*, pg. 1110
SAFIC ALCAN & CIE S.A.—Metallgesellschaft AG; *Int'l*, pg. 862
SHELL DEVELOPMENT CO.—Royal Dutch/Shell Group of Companies; *Int'l*, pg. 1136
SHIN-ETSU POLYMER AMERICA, INC.—Shin-Etsu Chemical Co. ltd.; *Int'l*, pg. 1234
SHIN-ETSU POLYMER CO. LTD.—Shin-Etsu Chemical Co. ltd.; *Int'l*, pg. 1234
SILICONE PRODUCTS DIV.—General Electric Company; *U.S. Public*, pg. 711
SOLUTIA INC.; *U.S. Public*, pg. 1483
SOPHISTICATED PRODUCTS DIV.—Nippon Kayaku Co. Ltd.; *Int'l*, pg. 934
SPECIALTY POLYMERS & CHEMICALS DIVISION—The B.F. Goodrich Company; *U.S. Public*, pg. 751
ALBERT TROSTEL & SONS CO.; *U.S. Private*, pg. 1105
ALBERT TROSTEL PACKINGS LTD.—Albert Trostel & Sons Co.; *U.S. Private*, pg. 1105

2823 — CELLULOSIC MAN-MADE FIBERS

ALBA QUIMICA S.A. INDUSTRIA E COMMERCIO—Borden, Inc.; *U.S. Private*, pg. 158
ALLIEDSIGNAL INC.; *U.S. Public*, pg. 49
BAYER AG—Bayer AG; *Int'l*, pg. 172
BONTEX S.A.—Georgia-Bonded Fibers, Inc.; *U.S. Public*, pg. 734
BUCKEYE CELLULOSE CORP.—The Procter & Gamble Company; *U.S. Public*, pg. 1331
CYDSA S.A.; *Int'l*, pg. 246
CELLATEX—Rhone-Poulenc S.A.; *Int'l*, pg. 1109
CELULOSA Y DERIVADOS, S.A. DE C.V.—CYDSA S.A.; *Int'l*, pg. 246
CENTURY ENKA LTD.—Akzo Nobel N.V.; *Int'l*, pg. 46
CHEIL INDUSTRIES INC.—Samsung Group; *Int'l*, pg. 1181
COBAFI, COMPANHIA BAHIANA DE FIBRAS SA—Akzo Nobel N.V.; *Int'l*, pg. 46
COURTAULDS (CANADA) INC.—Courtaulds plc; *Int'l*, pg. 339
COURTAULDS EUROPEAN FIBRES—Courtaulds plc; *Int'l*, pg. 339
COURTAULDS EUROPEAN FIBRES—Hoechst Aktiengesellschaft; *Int'l*, pg. 626
COURTAULDS FIBERS INC.—Courtaulds plc; *Int'l*, pg. 339

COURTAULDS PLC; *Int'l*, pg. 338
COURTAULDS STRUCTURAL COMPOSITES INC.—Courtaulds plc; *Int'l*, pg. 338
CYDSA S.A. FIBERS DIV.—CYDSA S.A.; *Int'l*, pg. 246
DERIVADOS ACRILICOS, S.A. DE C.V.—CYDSA S.A.; *Int'l*, pg. 246
DU PONT CANADA-MONTREAL—Du Pont (E.I. Du Pont De Nemours & Co.); *U.S. Public*, pg. 532
EASTMAN CHEMICAL COMPANY; *U.S. Public*, pg. 550
ENKA AG—Akzo Nobel N.V.; *Int'l*, pg. 46
ENKA BV—Akzo Nobel N.V.; *Int'l*, pg. 45
ENKA DE COLOMBIA S.A.—Akzo Nobel N.V.; *Int'l*, pg. 46
ENKA ITALIANA SRL.—Akzo Nobel N.V.; *Int'l*, pg. 46
ENKA UK LTD.—Akzo Nobel N.V.; *Int'l*, pg. 46
ENKADOR S.A.—Akzo Nobel N.V.; *Int'l*, pg. 46
FIBRAS QUIMICAS SA—Akzo Nobel N.V.; *Int'l*, pg. 46
HERCULES INC., ABSORBENT & TEXTILE PRODUCTS GROUP—Hercules Incorporated; *U.S. Public*, pg. 810
HOECHST MARION ROUSSEL AG—Hoechst Aktiengesellschaft; *Int'l*, pg. 624
HOECHST MARION ROUSSEL, INC.—Hoechst Aktiengesellschaft; *Int'l*, pg. 624
S.A. INDUSTRIAS VOTORANTIM; *Int'l*, pg. 677
KEMIRA FIBRES OY—Kemira Oy; *Int'l*, pg. 728
LA SEDA DE BARCELONA—Akzo Nobel N.V.; *Int'l*, pg. 46
LA SEDA DE BARCELONA S.A.—Akzo Nobel N.V.; *Int'l*, pg. 46
LESHNER MILLS, INC.; *U.S. Private*, pg. 660
MILLIKEN & COMPANY; *U.S. Private*, pg. 748
NIPPON MAGPHANE COMPANY—Rhone-Poulenc S.A.; *Int'l*, pg. 1109
POLYENKA SA—Akzo Nobel N.V.; *Int'l*, pg. 46
RHODIA A.G.—Rhone-Poulenc S.A.; *Int'l*, pg. 1112
RHODIA NORDESTE—Rhone-Poulenc S.A.; *Int'l*, pg. 1109
RHONE-POULENC FIBRES—Rhone-Poulenc S.A.; *Int'l*, pg. 1109
RHONE-POULENC FILMS—Rhone-Poulenc S.A.; *Int'l*, pg. 1109
RHONE-POULENC MULTI-TECHNIQUES—Rhone-Poulenc S.A.; *Int'l*, pg. 1109
RHONE-POULENC-TEXTILE—Rhone-Poulenc S.A.; *Int'l*, pg. 1109
RHOVYL—Rhone-Poulenc S.A.; *Int'l*, pg. 1109
SAFA—Rhone-Poulenc S.A.; *Int'l*, pg. 1114
SHOWA DENKO KAWASAKI WORKS—Showa Denko K.K.; *Int'l*, pg. 1236
VISCOSUISSE S.A.—Rhone-Poulenc S.A.; *Int'l*, pg. 1114
ZAZULA PROCESS EQUIP. LTD.—ABB Asea Brown Boveri (Holding) Ltd.; *Int'l*, pg. 6

2824 — SYNTHETIC ORGANIC FIBERS EXCEPT CELLULOSIC

ALLIEDSIGNAL INC.; *U.S. Public*, pg. 49
ALLIEDSIGNAL INC., FLUOROCARBONS—AlliedSignal Inc.; *U.S. Public*, pg. 51
AMOCO FABRICS & FIBERS COMPANY—Amoco Corporation; *U.S. Public*, pg. 102
ASAHI CHEMICAL INDUSTRY CO., LTD.; *Int'l*, pg. 83
BASF CORPORATION FIBER PRODUCTS DIVISION—BASF AG; *Int'l*, pg. 105
BTR NYLEX LIMITED—BTR plc; *Int'l*, pg. 129
BASIC CHEMICALS DIV.—Rhone-Poulenc S.A.; *Int'l*, pg. 1109
BAYER AG—Bayer AG; *Int'l*, pg. 172
BAYER ARGENTINA S.A.—Bayer AG; *Int'l*, pg. 175
BAYER INDUSTRIAL S.A.—Bayer AG; *Int'l*, pg. 175
BRIDGESTONE/FIRESTONE, INC.—Bridgestone Corporation; *Int'l*, pg. 213
CYDSA S.A.; *Int'l*, pg. 246
CELANESE CANADA, INC.—Hoechst Aktiengesellschaft; *Int'l*, pg. 625
CELANESE CANADA TEXTILE GROUP—Hoechst Aktiengesellschaft; *Int'l*, pg. 625
CELULOSA Y DERIVADOS, S.A. DE C.V.—CYDSA S.A.; *Int'l*, pg. 246
COURTAULDS EUROPEAN FIBRES—Courtaulds plc; *Int'l*, pg. 339
COURTAULDS EUROPEAN FIBRES—Hoechst Aktiengesellschaft; *Int'l*, pg. 626
CYDSA S.A. FIBERS DIV.—CYDSA S.A.; *Int'l*, pg. 246
DSM ENGINEERING PLASTIC PRODUCTS—DSM N.V.; *Int'l*, pg. 354
DU PONT (AUSTRALIA) LTD.—Du Pont (E.I. Du Pont De Nemours & Co.); *U.S. Public*, pg. 532
DU PONT DE NEMOURS (NEDERLAND) B.V.—Du Pont (E.I. Du Pont De Nemours & Co.); *U.S. Public*, pg. 532
DU PONT DO BRASIL S.A.—Du Pont (E.I. Du Pont De Nemours & Co.); *U.S. Public*, pg. 532
DU PONT (E.I. DU PONT DE NEMOURS & CO.); *U.S. Public*, pg. 530
DU PONT, S.A. DE C.V.—Du Pont (E.I. Du Pont De Nemours & Co.); *U.S. Public*, pg. 533
DUCILO S.A.—Du Pont (E.I. Du Pont De Nemours & Co.); *U.S. Public*, pg. 533
P.T. EASTERNTEX—Toray Industries, Inc.; *Int'l*, pg. 1400
EASTMAN CHEMICAL COMPANY; *U.S. Public*, pg. 550
EASTMAN KODAK COMPANY; *U.S. Public*, pg. 550
EXXON CHEMICAL OLEFINS INC.—Exxon Corporation; *U.S. Public*, pg. 602
GEORGIA-BONDED FIBERS, INC.; *U.S. Public*, pg. 734
HERCULES INCORPORATED; *U.S. Public*, pg. 809
HERCULES INC.-OXFORD—Hercules Incorporated; *U.S. Public*, pg. 810
HILANA C.A.—Nissho Iwai Corporation; *Int'l*, pg. 947
HISPAN CORP.—Hercules Incorporated; *U.S. Public*, pg. 810
HOECHST MARION ROUSSEL AG—Hoechst Aktiengesellschaft; *Int'l*, pg. 624
HOECHST MARION ROUSSEL, INC.—Hoechst Aktiengesellschaft; *Int'l*, pg. 624
ICI OESTERREICH GMBH—Imperial Chemical Industries PLC; *Int'l*, pg. 665
ICI (SINGAPORE) PRIVATE LIMITED—Imperial Chemical Industries PLC; *Int'l*, pg. 665
ICI ZAMBIA LIMITED—Imperial Chemical Industries PLC; *Int'l*, pg. 665
INDO RAMA SYNTHETICS P.T.; *Int'l*, pg. 673
INTERFACE INC.; *U.S. Public*, pg. 889
KOHAP ENGINEERING PLASTICS LTD.—KOHAP Group; *Int'l*, pg. 742
KOHAP INC.—KOHAP Group; *Int'l*, pg. 742
KURARAY CO., LTD.; *Int'l*, pg. 764
MITSUBISHI RAYON CO., LTD.; *Int'l*, pg. 876
MONROE CLEVITE—Tenneco Inc.; *U.S. Public*, pg. 1577
NUREL S.A.—Imperial Chemical Industries PLC; *Int'l*, pg. 665
NYLON DE MEXICO, S.A.—Du Pont (E.I. Du Pont De Nemours & Co.); *U.S. Public*, pg. 533
PENFABRIC SDN. BERHAD—Toray Industries, Inc.; *Int'l*, pg. 1400
POLYPENCO CANADA LTD.—DSM N.V.; *Int'l*, pg. 354
RHODIA S.A.—Rhone-Poulenc S.A.; *Int'l*, pg. 1112
RHONE-POULENC S.A.; *Int'l*, pg. 1108
SAFA—Rhone-Poulenc S.A.; *Int'l*, pg. 1114
SASOL FIBRES—Sasol Limited; *Int'l*, pg. 1196
SASOL LIMITED; *Int'l*, pg. 1196
SNIA FIBRE S.P.A.—Fiat Auto SpA; *Int'l*, pg. 482
SOLUTIA INC.; *U.S. Public*, pg. 1483
SPECIAL FILAMENTS ODENTON—APEX Specialty Materials, Inc.; *U.S. Private*, pg. 77
SPECIALTY FILAMENTS INC.—APEX Specialty Materials, Inc.; *U.S. Private*, pg. 77
SPINNSTOFFFABRIK ZEHLENDORF AG—Hoechst Aktiengesellschaft; *Int'l*, pg. 626
STERLING CHEMICALS HOLDINGS, INC.; *U.S. Public*, pg. 1515
TEIJIN LIMITED; *Int'l*, pg. 1362
THAI TORAY TEXTILE MILLS PUBLIC COMPANY LIMITED—Toray Industries, Inc.; *Int'l*, pg. 1400
TORAY COMPOSITES (AMERICA), INC.—Toray Industries, Inc.; *Int'l*, pg. 1400
TORAY FIBERS (THAILAND), LTD.—Toray Industries, Inc.; *Int'l*, pg. 1400
TORAY INDUSTRIES, INC.; *Int'l*, pg. 1399
TORAY PLASTICS (AMERICA), INC.—Toray Industries, Inc.; *Int'l*, pg. 1400
TORAY RESEARCH CENTER, INC.—Toray Industries, Inc.; *Int'l*, pg. 1399
TORAY TEXTILES EUROPE LTD.—Toray Industries, Inc.; *Int'l*, pg. 1400
WACKER-CHEMIE GMBH—Hoechst Aktiengesellschaft; *Int'l*, pg. 625
WELLMAN BONDED FIBERS DIV.—Wellman, Inc.; *U.S. Public*, pg. 1753
WELLMAN, INC.; *U.S. Public*, pg. 1752
WELLMAN INTERNATIONAL LTD.—Wellman, Inc.; *U.S. Public*, pg. 1753
WELLMAN MAN-MADE FIBERS DIV.—Wellman, Inc.; *U.S. Public*, pg. 1752
WELLMAN NONWOVENS DIV.—Wellman, Inc.; *U.S. Public*, pg. 1753
ZENECA AB—Zeneca Group Plc; *Int'l*, pg. 1526
ZENECA OY—Zeneca Group Plc; *Int'l*, pg. 1527
ZENECA POLAND SP. Z.O.O.—Zeneca Group Plc; *Int'l*, pg. 1527
ZENECA ZIMBABWE (PRIVATE) LIMITED—Zeneca Group Plc; *Int'l*, pg. 1527

2833 — MEDICINAL CHEMICAL & BOTANICAL PRODUCTS

AKZO NOBEL INC.—Akzo Nobel N.V.; *Int'l*, pg. 47
AKZO PHARMA B.V.—Akzo Nobel N.V.; *Int'l*, pg. 44
ALGAS MARINAS S.A.—Hercules Incorporated; *U.S. Public*, pg. 810
ALPHARMA INC.; *U.S. Public*, pg. 57
ALRA LABORATORIES, INC.; *U.S. Private*, pg. 45
AMGEN BOULDER, INC.—Amgen Inc.; *U.S. Public*, pg. 101
BASIC CHEMICALS DIV.—Rhone-Poulenc S.A.; *Int'l*, pg. 1109
BAYER AG—Bayer AG; *Int'l*, pg. 172
BAYER CORP. PHARMACEUTICALS—Bayer AG; *Int'l*, pg. 173
BAYER CORPORATION—Bayer AG; *Int'l*, pg. 172
BAYER HISPANIA INDUSTRIAL, S.A.—Bayer AG; *Int'l*, pg. 175
BOEHRINGER INGELHEIM—Boehringer Ingelheim GmbH; *Int'l*, pg. 199
BOEHRINGER MANNHEIM GMBH—Corange Limited; *Int'l*, pg. 331
BONOMELLI S.R.L.; *Int'l*, pg. 201
B. BRAUN-DEXON SA—American Home Products Corporation; *U.S. Public*, pg. 80
BRISTOL-MYERS SQUIBB COMPANY; *U.S. Public*, pg. 253
THE BRULIN CORPORATION; *U.S. Private*, pg. 176
CAMBREX CORPORATION; *U.S. Public*, pg. 297
CARRINGTON LABORATORIES, INC.; *U.S. Public*, pg. 309
CHEMDESIGN CORPORATION—Bayer AG; *Int'l*, pg. 173
CHEMVIRON SPECIALTY CHEMICALS—Merck & Co., Inc.; *U.S. Public*, pg. 1091
CHIRON CORPORATION—Chiron Corporation; *U.S. Public*, pg. 350
CONTINENTAL CARBON COMPANY—China Synthetic Rubber Corporation; *Int'l*, pg. 286
CROSSFIELD CHEMICAL—Unilever Plc; *Int'l*, pg. 1435
CYANAMID CANADA INC.—American Home Products Corporation; *U.S. Public*, pg. 80
CYANAMID IBERICA, S.A.—American Home Products Corporation; *U.S. Public*, pg. 81
CYANAMID LATIN AMERICA GROUP—American Home Products Corporation; *U.S. Public*, pg. 79
DIOSYNTH FRANCE SA—Akzo Nobel N.V.; *Int'l*, pg. 44
DIOSYNTH, INC.—Akzo Nobel N.V.; *Int'l*, pg. 48
EASTMAN KODAK LIFE SCIENCES DIV.—Eastman Kodak Company; *U.S. Public*, pg. 551
ELF SANOFI INC.—Elf Aquitane; *Int'l*, pg. 445
EVERGOOD PRODUCTS CORPORATION; *U.S. Private*, pg. 386
EXXON CHEMICAL POLYMERES, SNC—Exxon Corporation; *U.S. Public*, pg. 602
FERMENTA AB; *Int'l*, pg. 480
FERROSAN DANMARK A/S—Novo Nordisk A/S; *Int'l*, pg. 987
GAMMA BIOLOGICALS INC.; *U.S. Public*, pg. 698
GENERAL NUTRITION PRODUCTS, INC.—General Nutrition, Inc.; *U.S. Public*, pg. 725
GENZYME DIAGNOSTICS, MEDIX BIOTECH—Genzyme Corporation; *U.S. Public*, pg. 733
GREAT LAKES CHEMICAL (EUROPE) LTD.—Great Lakes Chemical Corporation; *U.S. Public*, pg. 760
HALSEY DRUG COMPANY; *U.S. Private*, pg. 496
HENKEL CORPORATION FINE CHEMICALS DIV.—Henkel KGaA; *Int'l*, pg. 610
HENKEL KGAA; *Int'l*, pg. 609
WALTER HIRSCH ADM—BASF AG; *Int'l*, pg. 108
HOECHST CELANESE FINE CHEMICAL DIVISION—Hoechst Aktiengesellschaft; *Int'l*, pg. 625
HOECHST MARION ROUSSEL, INC.—Hoechst Aktiengesellschaft; *Int'l*, pg. 624
HOECHST MARION ROUSSEL NORTH AMERICA—Hoechst Aktiengesellschaft; *Int'l*, pg. 625
HOFFMANN-LA ROCHE AG—Roche Holding Ltd.; *Int'l*, pg. 1121
F. HOFFMANN-LA ROCHE LTD.—Roche Holding Ltd.; *Int'l*, pg. 1119
HOFFMANN-LA ROCHE INC.—Roche Holding Ltd.; *Int'l*, pg. 1120
HYGEIA SCIENCES, INC.—Carter-Wallace, Inc.; *U.S. Public*, pg. 310
ICN PHARMACEUTICALS, INC.; *U.S. Public*, pg. 853
ISK BIOTECH—Ishihara Sangyo Kaisha, Ltd.; *Int'l*, pg. 689
INDUSTRIAL PHARMACEUTICAL PRODUCTS DIVISION—Royal Gist-Brocades N.V.; *Int'l*, pg. 1142
INTERFACE RESEARCH CORPORATION—Interface Inc.; *U.S. Public*, pg. 889
ISHIHARA SANGYO KAISHA, LTD.; *Int'l*, pg. 689
ISTITUTO DELLE VITAMINE S.P.A.—Roche Holding Ltd.; *Int'l*, pg. 1121
J B LABS, INC.; *U.S. Private*, pg. 576
KV PHARMACEUTICAL COMPANY; *U.S. Public*, pg. 941
KNOLL AG—BASF AG; *Int'l*, pg. 104
KNOLL ALMAN ILAC VE ECZA TIC. LTD. STI.—BASF AG; *Int'l*, pg. 108
KNOLL BEIJING—BASF AG; *Int'l*, pg. 108
KNOLL BELGIUM S.A./N.V.—BASF AG; *Int'l*, pg. 108
KNOLL-BIORESEARCH S.A.—BASF AG; *Int'l*, pg. 108
KNOLL CENTROAMERICANA S.A.—BASF AG; *Int'l*, pg. 108
KNOLL COLOMBIANA S.A.—BASF AG; *Int'l*, pg. 108
KNOLL DEUTSCHLAND GMBH—BASF AG; *Int'l*, pg. 104
KNOLL FARMACEUTICI S.P.A—BASF AG; *Int'l*, pg. 108
KNOLL JAPAN K.K.—BASF AG; *Int'l*, pg. 108
KNOLL LUSITANA, LDA.—BASF AG; *Int'l*, pg. 109
KNOLL PHARMA—BASF AG; *Int'l*, pg. 109
KNOLL PHARMACEUTICALS SOUTH AFRICA (PTY.) LTD.—BASF AG; *Int'l*, pg. 109
KNOLL PHARMACEUTICALS TAIWAN—BASF AG; *Int'l*, pg. 109
KNOLL S.A. PRODUTOS QUIMICOS E FARMACEUTICOS—BASF AG; *Int'l*, pg. 109
KNOLL SCIENTIFIC OFFICE—BASF AG; *Int'l*, pg. 109
KNOLL SPOL. S.R.O.—BASF AG; *Int'l*, pg. 109
KOHLENSAUREWERK DEUTSCHLAND GMBH—Solvay S.A.; *Int'l*, pg. 1278
ELI LILLY AND COMPANY; *U.S. Public*, pg. 992
MALLINCKRODT BAKER INC.—Mallinckrodt Inc.; *U.S. Public*, pg. 1039
MALLINCKRODT INC.; *U.S. Public*, pg. 1039
THE R.J. MARSHALL CO.; *U.S. Private*, pg. 708
MEAD JOHNSON DE MEXICO, S.A. DE C.V.—Bristol-Myers Squibb Company; *U.S. Public*, pg. 256
EDWARD MENDELL CO.—Penford Corp.; *U.S. Public*, pg. 1269
MERCK & CO., INC.; *U.S. Public*, pg. 1090
MERCK HUMAN HEALTH DIVISION—Merck & Co., Inc.; *U.S. Public*, pg. 1090
MERCK MANUFACTURING DIV.—Merck & Co., Inc.; *U.S. Public*, pg. 1091
MILLENNIUM CHEMICALS INC.; *U.S. Public*, pg. 1111
MONSANTO COMPANY; *U.S. Public*, pg. 1124
NATIONAL HEALTH PRODUCTS; *U.S. Private*, pg. 784
NATURE'S BOUNTY INC.; *U.S. Public*, pg. 1166
NATURE'S SUNSHINE PRODUCTS, INC.; *U.S. Public*, pg. 1166
NEPERA INC.—Cambrex Corporation; *U.S. Public*, pg. 297
NIPPON ROCHE K.K.—Roche Holding Ltd.; *Int'l*, pg. 1121
NOBEL BIOCARE; *Int'l*, pg. 951
NORTON HEALTHCARE LIMITED—IVAX Corporation; *U.S. Public*, pg. 915
NOVARTIS AG; *Int'l*, pg. 971
NOVO NORDISK A/S; *Int'l*, pg. 987
NOVO NORDISK BIOINDUSTRIAL DO BRASIL LTDA.—Novo Nordisk A/S; *Int'l*, pg. 988
NOVO NORDISK CANADA, INC.—Novo Nordisk A/S; *Int'l*, pg. 988
NOVO NORDISK COMERCIO DE PRODUTOS FARMACEUTICOS, LDA—Novo Nordisk A/S; *Int'l*, pg. 988
NOVO NORDISK FARMA B.V.—Novo Nordisk A/S; *Int'l*, pg. 988
NOVO NORDISK FARMA OY—Novo Nordisk A/S; *Int'l*, pg. 988
NOVO NORDISK FARMACEUTICI SRL—Novo Nordisk A/S; *Int'l*, pg. 988
NOVO NORDISK FARMAKA DANMARK A/S—Novo Nordisk A/S; *Int'l*, pg. 987

NOVO NORDISK HELLAS LTD.—Novo Nordisk A/S; *Int'l*, pg. 988
NOVO NORDISK PHARMA AB—Novo Nordisk A/S; *Int'l*, pg. 988
NOVO NORDISK PHARMA AG—Novo Nordisk A/S; *Int'l*, pg. 988
NOVO NORDISK PHARMA A/S—Novo Nordisk A/S; *Int'l*, pg. 988
NOVO NORDISK PHARMA GESELLSCHAFT MBH—Novo Nordisk A/S; *Int'l*, pg. 988
NOVO NORDISK PHARMA GMBH—Novo Nordisk A/S; *Int'l*, pg. 988
S.A. NOVO NORDISK PHARMA NV—Novo Nordisk A/S; *Int'l*, pg. 988
NOVO NORDISK PHARMA S.A.—Novo Nordisk A/S; *Int'l*, pg. 988
NOVO NORDISK PHARMA (THAILAND) LTD.—Novo Nordisk A/S; *Int'l*, pg. 988
NOVO NORDISK PHARMACEUTICALS LTD.—Novo Nordisk A/S; *Int'l*, pg. 988
NOVO NORDISK PHARMACEUTICALS PTY. LTD.—Novo Nordisk A/S; *Int'l*, pg. 988
NOVO NORDISK PHARMACEUTIQUE S.A.—Novo Nordisk A/S; *Int'l*, pg. 988
NOVO NORDISK (PTY) LTD.—Novo Nordisk A/S; *Int'l*, pg. 988
ODG—Witco Corporation; *U.S. Public*, pg. 1774
OLEOCHEMICALS & DERIVATIVES GROUP—Witco Corporation; *U.S. Public*, pg. 1774
ORGANON ARGENTINA S.A.—Akzo Nobel N.V.; *Int'l*, pg. 45
ORGANON INC.—Akzo Nobel N.V.; *Int'l*, pg. 48
ORGANON IRELAND LTD.—Akzo Nobel N.V.; *Int'l*, pg. 45
PARTICLE DYNAMICS, INC.—KV Pharmaceutical Company; *U.S. Public*, pg. 941
PENFORD CORP.; *U.S. Public*, pg. 1269
PENWEST PHARM. CO.—Penford Corp.; *U.S. Public*, pg. 1269
PERRIGO OF TENNESSEE—L. Perrigo Company; *U.S. Public*, pg. 1280
PHARMACEUTICALS DIVISION—3M; *U.S. Public*, pg. 1605
PHARMACIA & UPJOHN—Pharmacia & Upjohn, Inc.; *Int'l*, pg. 1048
PHARMACIA & UPJOHN BIOSYSTEMS AB—Pharmacia & Upjohn, Inc.; *Int'l*, pg. 1047
PIERCE CHEMICAL COMPANY—Perstorp AB; *Int'l*, pg. 1037
PRODUCTOS FARMOQUIMICOS ROCHE LTDA.—Roche Holding Ltd.; *Int'l*, pg. 1121
PRODUCTOS ROCHE QUIMICA FARMACEUTICA S.A.—Roche Holding Ltd.; *Int'l*, pg. 1121
PRODUCTOS ROCHE S.A.—Roche Holding Ltd.; *Int'l*, pg. 1121
PRODUITS ROCHE S.A.—Roche Holding Ltd.; *Int'l*, pg. 1121
PRODUTOS ROCHE QUIMICOS E FARMACEUTICOS S.A.—Roche Holding Ltd.; *Int'l*, pg. 1121
QUIMICA KNOLL DE MEXICO, S.A. DE C.V. BASF PHARMA—BASF AG; *Int'l*, pg. 109
RHONE-POULENC RORER LTD.—Rhone-Poulenc S.A.; *Int'l*, pg. 1110
RICHARDSON-VICKS, INC.—The Procter & Gamble Company; *U.S. Public*, pg. 1331
ROCHE AB—Roche Holding Ltd.; *Int'l*, pg. 1121
ROCHE (HELLAS) S.A.—Roche Holding Ltd.; *Int'l*, pg. 1121
ROCHE INTERNATIONAL LTD.—Roche Holding Ltd.; *Int'l*, pg. 1121
ROCHE KOREA COMPANY LTD.—Roche Holding Ltd.; *Int'l*, pg. 1121
ROCHE MALAYSIA SDN. BHD.—Roche Holding Ltd.; *Int'l*, pg. 1121
ROCHE MEXICANA DE FARMACOS, S.A. DE C.V. EL SALTO (JALISCO)—Roche Holding Ltd.; *Int'l*, pg. 1121
ROCHE MUSTAHZARLARI SANAYI LIMITED SIRKETI—Roche Holding Ltd.; *Int'l*, pg. 1121
ROCHE (NIGERIA) LTD.—Roche Holding Ltd.; *Int'l*, pg. 1121
ROCHE PHARMACEUTICALS & CHEMICALS LTD.—Roche Holding Ltd.; *Int'l*, pg. 1121
ROCHE (PHILIPPINES) INC.—Roche Holding Ltd.; *Int'l*, pg. 1121
ROCHE PRODUCTS LTD.—Roche Holding Ltd.; *Int'l*, pg. 1121
ROCHE PRODUCTS (NEW ZEALAND) LTD.—Roche Holding Ltd.; *Int'l*, pg. 1122
ROCHE PRODUCTS (PTY.) LTD.—Roche Holding Ltd.; *Int'l*, pg. 1122
ROCHE THAILAND LTD.—Roche Holding Ltd.; *Int'l*, pg. 1122
ROUSSEL UCLAF S.A.—Hoechst Aktiengesellschaft; *Int'l*, pg. 626
SABANCI HOLDING A.S.; *Int'l*, pg. 1167
SANDOZ PHARMA LTD.—Novartis AG; *Int'l*, pg. 972
SASOL LIMITED; *Int'l*, pg. 1196
SCHERING MEXICANA SA—Schering AG; *Int'l*, pg. 1204
SEARLE & CO.—Monsanto Company; *U.S. Public*, pg. 1125
SELECCIONES MERCANTILES, S.A. DE C.V.—Bristol-Myers Squibb Company; *U.S. Public*, pg. 256
SETON COMPANY; *U.S. Private*, pg. 987
SEVEN SEAS LIMITED—Hanson PLC; *Int'l*, pg. 593
SHAKLEE CORPORATION—Yamanouchi Pharmaceutical Co. Ltd.; *Int'l*, pg. 1518
SIGMA CHEMICAL CO.—Sigma-Aldrich Corporation; *U.S. Public*, pg. 1472
SIGMA CHEMICAL CO., LTD.—Sigma-Aldrich Corporation; *U.S. Public*, pg. 1472
SIGMA CHIMIE S.A.R.L.—Sigma-Aldrich Corporation; *U.S. Public*, pg. 1472
SIGMA ISRAEL CHEMICAL CO., LTD.—Sigma-Aldrich Corporation; *U.S. Public*, pg. 1472
SIGMA REDEVELOPMENT CORP.—Sigma-Aldrich Corporation; *U.S. Public*, pg. 1472
SIGMA SECOND STREET REDEVELOPMENT CORP.—Sigma-Aldrich Corporation; *U.S. Public*, pg. 1472
SIGMA-TAU FINANZIARIA S.P.A.; *Int'l*, pg. 1248
SMITHKLINE BEECHAM LABS—SmithKline Beecham plc; *Int'l*, pg. 1265
SOCIETE CHIMIQUE ROCHE S.A.—Roche Holding Ltd.; *Int'l*, pg. 1121
SPECIALTY CHEMICALS DIV.—Rhone-Poulenc S.A.; *Int'l*, pg. 1109
STURGE BIOCHEMICALS—Rhone-Poulenc S.A.; *Int'l*, pg. 1113
TEIJIN LIMITED; *Int'l*, pg. 1362
THOMPSON NUTRITIONAL PRODUCTS—Rexall Sundown Inc.; *U.S. Public*, pg. 1384
TSUMURA & CO.; *Int'l*, pg. 1425
UBE INDUSTRIES LTD.; *Int'l*, pg. 1426
VESTRETUNG DES KNOLL AG—BASF AG; *Int'l*, pg. 110
VITAMIN WORLD—Nature's Bounty Inc.; *U.S. Public*, pg. 1166

2834 — PHARMACEUTICAL PREPARATIONS

OY ALGOL AB; *Int'l*, pg. 15
AMBI INC.; *U.S. Public*, pg. 7
ABBOTT LABORATORIES; *U.S. Public*, pg. 12
ACCRA PAC GROUP; *U.S. Private*, pg. 11
ACETO CORPORATION; *U.S. Public*, pg. 15
ADVANCED CARE PRODUCTS—Johnson & Johnson; *U.S. Public*, pg. 928
ADVANCED POLYMER SYSTEMS; *U.S. Public*, pg. 22
AGIS INDUSTRIES LTD.; *Int'l*, pg. 30
AGOURON PHARMACEUTICALS, INC.; *U.S. Public*, pg. 28
AGREVO GMBH—Hoechst Aktiengesellschaft; *Int'l*, pg. 624
AGREVO GMBH—Schering AG; *Int'l*, pg. 1203
AKORN, INC.; *U.S. Public*, pg. 34
AKORN MANUFACTURING, INC.—Akorn, Inc.; *U.S. Public*, pg. 34
AKZO NOBEL INC.—Akzo Nobel N.V.; *Int'l*, pg. 47
AKZO NOBEL N.V.; *Int'l*, pg. 42
AKZO PHARMA B.V.—Akzo Nobel N.V.; *Int'l*, pg. 44
AKZO PHARMA NEDERLAND B.V.—Akzo Nobel N.V.; *Int'l*, pg. 44
ALCON CANADA, INC.—Nestle S.A.; *Int'l*, pg. 918
ALCON-COUVREUR N.V.—Nestle S.A.; *Int'l*, pg. 918
ALCON ITALIA S.P.A.—Nestle S.A.; *Int'l*, pg. 918
ALCON LABORATORIES ARGENTINA S.A.—Nestle S.A.; *Int'l*, pg. 918
ALCON LABORATORIES (AUSTRALIA) PTY. LTD.—Nestle S.A.; *Int'l*, pg. 918
ALCON LABORATORIES, INC.—Nestle S.A.; *Int'l*, pg. 916
ALCON LABORATORIOS DO BRASIL S.A.—Nestle S.A.; *Int'l*, pg. 918
ALCON LABORATORIOS S.A. DE C.V.—Nestle S.A.; *Int'l*, pg. 918
ALCON PHARMACEUTICALS LTD.—Nestle S.A.; *Int'l*, pg. 916
ALCON (PUERTO RICO) INC.—Nestle S.A.; *Int'l*, pg. 916
ALLEGIANCE HEALTHCARE CORP.—Allegiance Healthcare Corp.; *U.S. Public*, pg. 44
ALLEGIANCE HEALTHCARE INTERNATIONAL—Allegiance Healthcare Corp.; *U.S. Public*, pg. 45
ALLEN & HANBURYS LIMITED—Glaxo Wellcome plc; *Int'l*, pg. 552
ALLERGAN DIV.—SmithKline Beecham plc; *Int'l*, pg. 1265
ALLERGAN, INC.; *U.S. Public*, pg. 46
ALPHA THERAPEUTIC CORP.—The Green Cross Corporation; *Int'l*, pg. 558
ALPHARMA INC.; *U.S. Public*, pg. 57
ALRA LABORATORIES, INC.; *U.S. Private*, pg. 45
ALTANA AG; *Int'l*, pg. 65
ALTANA, INC.—Altana AG; *Int'l*, pg. 66
ALVA/AMCO PHARMACAL COMPANIES, INC.; *U.S. Private*, pg. 47
ALZA CORPORATION; *U.S. Public*, pg. 62
ALZA DEVELOPMENT CORPORATION—Alza Corporation; *U.S. Public*, pg. 62
AMAFRUTAS S.A.—Novartis AG; *Int'l*, pg. 974
AMERICAN DRUG CORPORATION—American Home Products Corporation; *U.S. Public*, pg. 80
AMERICAN HOME PRODUCTS CORPORATION; *U.S. Public*, pg. 79
AMGEN BOULDER, INC.—Amgen Inc.; *U.S. Public*, pg. 101
AMGEN DEVELOPMENT CORPORATION—Amgen Inc.; *U.S. Public*, pg. 101
AMGEN INC.; *U.S. Public*, pg. 100
ANIMAL HEALTH—Alpharma Inc.; *U.S. Public*, pg. 58
ANTIBIOTICOS S.A.—Compart SpA; *Int'l*, pg. 324
AQUATIC ANIMAL HEALTH—Alpharma Inc.; *U.S. Public*, pg. 58
ASCHE AG—Schering AG; *Int'l*, pg. 1203
ASIA PACIFIC RESIN CORPORATION—Novartis AG; *Int'l*, pg. 975
ASTRA AB; *Int'l*, pg. 93
ASTRA CHEMICALS S.A.—Astra AB; *Int'l*, pg. 93
ASTRA DRACO AB—Astra AB; *Int'l*, pg. 93
ASTRA GMBH—Astra AB; *Int'l*, pg. 93
ASTRA-IDL LTD.—Astra AB; *Int'l*, pg. 93
ASTRA JAPAN—Astra AB; *Int'l*, pg. 94
ASTRA JAPAN—Fujisawa Pharmaceutical Co. Ltd.; *Int'l*, pg. 525
ASTRA/MERCK GROUP—Merck & Co., Inc.; *U.S. Public*, pg. 1091
ASTRA MERCK INC.—Astra AB; *Int'l*, pg. 93
ASTRA PHARMA INC.—Astra AB; *Int'l*, pg. 94
ASTRA PHARMACEUTICAL PRODUCTION AB—Astra AB; *Int'l*, pg. 93
ASTRA PHARMACEUTICALS PTY. LTD.—Astra AB; *Int'l*, pg. 94
N.V. ASTRA PHARMACEUTICALS S.A.—Astra AB; *Int'l*, pg. 94
ASTRA S.A. PRODUCTOS FARMACEUTICOS Y QUIMICOS—Astra AB; *Int'l*, pg. 94
ASTRA USA, INC.—Astra AB; *Int'l*, pg. 93
ASTRE CORPORATE GROUP; *U.S. Private*, pg. 93
AYERST, MCKENNA & HARRISON INC.—American Home Products Corporation; *U.S. Public*, pg. 80
AYERST-WYETH PHARMACEUTICALS, INC.—American Home Products Corporation; *U.S. Public*, pg. 79
AYRTON SAUNDERS—Franz Haniel & Cie, GmbH; *Int'l*, pg. 591
THE B-M GROUP (PTY.) LTD.—Bristol-Myers Squibb Company; *U.S. Public*, pg. 255
BASF AG; *Int'l*, pg. 103
B.L. PHARMACEUTICALS (PTY.) LTD.—Bristol-Myers Squibb Company; *U.S. Public*, pg. 255
BYK GULDEN-LOMBERG GMBH—Altana AG; *Int'l*, pg. 66
BYK GULDEN, S.A. DE C.V.—Altana AG; *Int'l*, pg. 66
BYK LIPRANDI S.A.C.E.L.—Altana AG; *Int'l*, pg. 66
BYK QUIMICA E FARMACEUTICA LTDA.—Altana AG; *Int'l*, pg. 66
BAKER NORTON PHARMACEUTICALS, INC.—IVAX Corporation; *U.S. Public*, pg. 914
BANNER PHARMACAPS INC.—Sobel NV; *Int'l*, pg. 1272
BARETT S.A.—Rohto Pharmaceutical Co.; *Int'l*, pg. 1126
BARR LABORATORIES INC.; *U.S. Public*, pg. 191
BAUSCH & LOMB INCORPORATED; *U.S. Public*, pg. 194
BAUSCH & LOMB PHARMACEUTICAL DIVISION—Bausch & Lomb Incorporated; *U.S. Public*, pg. 194
BAXTER HEALTHCARE CORPORATION—Baxter International Inc.; *U.S. Public*, pg. 196
BAXTER INTERNATIONAL INC.; *U.S. Public*, pg. 196
BAXTER RESEARCH MEDICAL, INC.—Baxter International Inc.; *U.S. Public*, pg. 196
BAYER AG; *Int'l*, pg. 171
BAYER AG—Bayer AG; *Int'l*, pg. 172
BAYER ARGENTINA S.A.—Bayer AG; *Int'l*, pg. 175
BAYER B.V.—Bayer AG; *Int'l*, pg. 175
BAYER CORP. PHARMACEUTICALS—Bayer AG; *Int'l*, pg. 173
BAYER CORPORATION—Bayer AG; *Int'l*, pg. 172
BAYER CORPORATION/AGRICULTURE DIVISION—Bayer AG; *Int'l*, pg. 173
BAYER CORPORATION/CONSUMER CARE DIVISION—Bayer AG; *Int'l*, pg. 173
BAYER CORPORATION/PHARMACEUTICAL DIVISION—Bayer AG; *Int'l*, pg. 173
BAYER DE MEXICO, S.A. DE C.V.—Bayer AG; *Int'l*, pg. 175
BAYER DO BRAZIL S.A.—Bayer AG; *Int'l*, pg. 175
BAYER (INDIA) LTD.—Bayer AG; *Int'l*, pg. 174
BAYER YAKUHIN, LTD.—Bayer AG; *Int'l*, pg. 174
BECTON DICKINSON CONSUMER PRODS.—Becton Dickinson & Company; *U.S. Public*, pg. 199
BECTON DICKINSON VACUTAINER SYSTEMS EUROPE—Becton Dickinson & Company; *U.S. Public*, pg. 200
BEECHAM (AUSTRALIA) PTY. LTD.—SmithKline Beecham plc; *Int'l*, pg. 1265
BEECHAM-WULFING G.M.B.H. & CO. K.G.—SmithKline Beecham plc; *Int'l*, pg. 1266
BEHRINGWERKE AG—Hoechst Aktiengesellschaft; *Int'l*, pg. 624
BEIERSDORF GROUP; *Int'l*, pg. 182
S.A. BEIERSDORF NV—Beiersdorf Group; *Int'l*, pg. 183
BEIJING CIBA-GEIGY PHARMA LTD.—Novartis AG; *Int'l*, pg. 975
BEIJING JIAI PHARMACEUTICALS LIMITED LIABILITY COMPANY—IVAX Corporation; *U.S. Public*, pg. 915
BENTLEY PHARMACEUTICALS, INC.; *U.S. Public*, pg. 212
BERK PHARMACEUTICALS LTD.—Rhone-Poulenc S.A.; *Int'l*, pg. 1111
BERLEX CANADA, INC.—Schering AG; *Int'l*, pg. 1204
BERLI JUCKER PUBLIC CO. LTD.—First Pacific Company Limited; *Int'l*, pg. 487
BERLEX LABORATORIES INC.—Schering AG; *Int'l*, pg. 1204
BERTEK, INC.—Mylan Laboratories, Inc.; *U.S. Public*, pg. 1143
BERWIND PHARMACEUTICAL SERVICES, INC.—Berwind Corporation; *U.S. Private*, pg. 139
BEUTLICH, L.P.; *U.S. Private*, pg. 141
BIO DERMIS CORPORATION—Inamed Corporation; *U.S. Public*, pg. 873
BIO-LAB, INC.—Great Lakes Chemical Corporation; *U.S. Public*, pg. 760
BIOCHEMIE GESELLSCHAFT M.B.H.—Novartis AG; *Int'l*, pg. 975
BIOCINE COMPANY—Novartis AG; *Int'l*, pg. 973
BIOCRAFT CEPHALOSPORIN DOSAGE PLANT—Teva Pharmaceutical Industries Ltd.; *Int'l*, pg. 1381
BIOCRAFT NON-PENICILLIN PLANT—Teva Pharmaceutical Industries Ltd.; *Int'l*, pg. 1381
BIOCRAFT PENICILLIN DOSAGE PLANT—Teva Pharmaceutical Industries Ltd.; *Int'l*, pg. 1381
BIOGALENICA QUIMICA E FARMACEUTICA LTDA.—Novartis AG; *Int'l*, pg. 975
BIOGEN, INC.; *U.S. Public*, pg. 230
BLISTEX, INC.; *U.S. Private*, pg. 149
BLOCK DRUG CO. (CANADA) LTD.—Block Drug Company, Inc.; *U.S. Public*, pg. 237
BLOCK DRUG COMPANY, INC.; *U.S. Public*, pg. 236
BLOCK DRUG CO. (PHILIPPINES) INC.—Block Drug Company, Inc.; *U.S. Public*, pg. 237
BLOCK DRUG CORPORATION—Block Drug Company, Inc.; *U.S. Public*, pg. 237
BOEHRINGER INGELHEIM—Boehringer Ingelheim GmbH; *Int'l*, pg. 199
BOEHRINGER INGELHEIM ANIMAL HEALTH INC.—Boehringer Ingelheim GmbH; *Int'l*, pg. 199
BOEHRINGER INGELHEIM GMBH; *Int'l*, pg. 199
BOEHRINGER INGELHEIM ITALIA S.P.A.—Boehringer Ingelheim GmbH; *Int'l*, pg. 199
BOEHRINGER INGELHEIM PHARMACEUTICALS, INC.—Boehringer Ingelheim GmbH; *Int'l*, pg. 199
BOEHRINGER MANNHEIM GMBH—Corange Limited; *Int'l*, pg. 331

BOEHRINGER MANNHEIM JAPAN K.K.—Corange Limited; *Int'l*, pg. 331
BOEHRINGER MANNHEIM YAMANOUCHI K.K.—Corange Limited; *Int'l*, pg. 331
BONOMELLI S.R.L.; *Int'l*, pg. 201
THE BOOTS COMPANY PLC; *Int'l*, pg. 202
BRACCO S.P.A.; *Int'l*, pg. 209
BRADLEY PHARMACEUTICALS; *U.S. Public*, pg. 249
GEORG A. BRENNER ARZNEIMITTEL-FABRIK GMBH—American Home Products Corporation; *U.S. Public*, pg. 80
BRIMMS INC.; *U.S. Private*, pg. 169
BRISTOL-MYERS SQUIBB COMPANY; *U.S. Public*, pg. 253
BRITCAIR, LTD.—Merck & Co., Inc.; *U.S. Public*, pg. 1091
DR. CHRISTIAN BRUNNENGRABER CHEMISCHE FABRIK GMBH—Novartis AG; *Int'l*, pg. 975
BURROUGHS WELLCOME & CO. (HONG KONG) LTD.—Glaxo Wellcome plc; *Int'l*, pg. 553
BURROUGHS WELLCOME INTL. LTD.—Glaxo Wellcome plc; *Int'l*, pg. 552
BUTLER PHARMA PAK, INC.—Sunstar Inc.; *Int'l*, pg. 1320
CBP RESOURCES, INC.; *U.S. Private*, pg. 192
CRA LIMITED—Rio Tinto PLC; *Int'l*, pg. 1119
P.T. CANDRA SARI—Novartis AG; *Int'l*, pg. 975
S.A. CAPSUGEL N.V.—Warner-Lambert Company; *U.S. Public*, pg. 1739
CARDINAL HEALTH INC.; *U.S. Public*, pg. 304
CARNRICK LABORATORIES, INC.—GWC Health, Inc.; *U.S. Private*, pg. 436
CAROLINA ABSORBENT COTTON CO.—Barnhardt Manufacturing Co.; *U.S. Private*, pg. 117
CARRINGTON LABORATORIES, INC.; *U.S. Public*, pg. 309
CARTER-WALLACE, INC.; *U.S. Public*, pg. 309
CEBRIS S.P.A.—Bristol-Myers Squibb Company; *U.S. Public*, pg. 256
CENTRE DE RECHERCHE DE L'INSTITUT MERIEUX—Rhone-Poulenc S.A.; *Int'l*, pg. 1109
CHATTEM, INC.; *U.S. Public*, pg. 341
CHATTEM, INC., CONSUMER PRODUCTS DIVISION—Chattem, Inc.; *U.S. Public*, pg. 341
CHATTEM (U.K.) LTD.—Chattem, Inc.; *U.S. Public*, pg. 342
CHEFARO INTERNATIONAL B.V.—Akzo Nobel N.V.; *Int'l*, pg. 44
CHEFARO NEDERLAND B.V.—Akzo Nobel N.V.; *Int'l*, pg. 44
CHEIL CIBA-GEIGY CO, LTD—Novartis AG; *Int'l*, pg. 975
CHEMAG AKTIENGESELLSCHAFT—BASF AG; *Int'l*, pg. 104
CHEMDEX, INC.—Polydex Pharmaceuticals Limited; *Int'l*, pg. 1063
CHEMISCHE FABRIK PROMONTA GMBH—Altana AG; *Int'l*, pg. 66
CHINA OTSUKA PHARMACEUTICAL CO., LTD.—Otsuka Pharmaceutical Co., Ltd.; *Int'l*, pg. 1014
CHIRON CORPORATION—Chiron Corporation; *U.S. Public*, *pg. 350*
CHIRON CORPORATION; *U.S. Public*, pg. 349
CHIRON DIAGNOSTICS—Chiron Corporation; *U.S. Public*, pg. 350
CHIRON VISION—Chiron Corporation; *U.S. Public*, pg. 350
CHUGAI PHARMACEUTICAL CO., LTD.; *Int'l*, pg. 290
CIBA CORNING DIAGNOSTICS GMBH—Novartis AG; *Int'l*, pg. 975
CIBA CORNING DIAGNOSTICS KK—Novartis AG; *Int'l*, pg. 975
CIBA CORNING DIAGNOSTICS LIMITED—Novartis AG; *Int'l*, pg. 978
S.A. CIBA CORNING DIAGNOSTICS NV—Novartis AG; *Int'l*, pg. 975
CIBA CORNING DIAGNOSTICS S.A.—Novartis AG; *Int'l*, pg. 975
CIBA CORNING DIAGNOSTICS SPA—Novartis AG; *Int'l*, pg. 975
CIBA-GEIGY ARGENTINA S.A.I.C. Y F.—Novartis AG; *Int'l*, pg. 976
CIBA-GEIGY (BANGLADESH) LIMITED-PHARMACEUTICALS PLANT—Novartis AG; *Int'l*, pg. 976
CIBA-GEIGY CANADA LTD.—Novartis AG; *Int'l*, pg. 976
CIBA-GEIGY (CHINA) LIMITED—Novartis AG; *Int'l*, pg. 976
CIBA-GEIGY (CHINA) LIMITED-GUANGZHOU BRANCH OFFICE—Novartis AG; *Int'l*, pg. 976
CIBA-GEIGY GMBH—Novartis AG; *Int'l*, pg. 977
CIBA-GEIGY HELLAS S.A.—Novartis AG; *Int'l*, pg. 977
CIBA-GEIGY ILAC VE KIMYA URUNLERI SANAYI VE TICARET AS—Novartis AG; *Int'l*, pg. 977
P.T. CIBA-GEIGY INDONESIA—Novartis AG; *Int'l*, pg. 977
CIBA-GEIGY JAPAN LIMITED-SASAYAMA FACTORY—Novartis AG; *Int'l*, pg. 977
CIBA-GEIGY MAROC SA—Novartis AG; *Int'l*, pg. 978
CIBA-GEIGY MEXICANA SA DE CV—Novartis AG; *Int'l*, pg. 978
CIBA-GEIGY (MPL) LIMITED—Novartis AG; *Int'l*, pg. 978
CIBA-GEIGY PERUANA S.A.—Novartis AG; *Int'l*, pg. 978
CIBA-GEIGY PHARMA MAROC SA—Novartis AG; *Int'l*, pg. 978
CIBA-GEIGY PHARMACEUTICALS—Novartis AG; *Int'l*, pg. 978
CIBA-GEIGY QUIMICA S.A.—Novartis AG; *Int'l*, pg. 979
CIBA-GEIGY-SCIENTIFIC OFFICE PHARMACEUTICALS—Novartis AG; *Int'l*, pg. 979
CIBA-GEIGY SERVICES AG—Novartis AG; *Int'l*, pg. 979
CIBA-GEIGY SERVICES AG-TAO RIGA—Novartis AG; *Int'l*, *pg. 979*
CIBA-GEIGY SERVICES LIMITED-SCIENTIFIC OFFICE—Novartis AG; *Int'l*, pg. 980
CIBA-GEIGY SERVICES S.A.—Novartis AG; *Int'l*, pg. 980
CIBA-GEIGY SERVICES SA—Novartis AG; *Int'l*, pg. 980
CIBA-GEIGY SERVICES SA-TECHNICAL ADVISORY OFFICE—Novartis AG; *Int'l*, pg. 979
CIBA-GEIGY SPA—Novartis AG; *Int'l*, pg. 980
CIBA-GEIGY (THAILAND) LTD.—Novartis AG; *Int'l*, pg. 980
CIBA-GEIGY TRADING AND MARKETING SERVICES CO. LTD.—Novartis AG; *Int'l*, pg. 980
CIBA-GEIGY ZIMBABWE (PRIVATE) LIMITED—Novartis AG; *Int'l*, pg. 980
CIBA HUNGARIA KFT.—Novartis AG; *Int'l*, pg. 980
CIBA PHARMACEUTICALS—Novartis AG; *Int'l*, pg. 981
CIBA SELF-MEDICATION, INC.—Novartis AG; *Int'l*, pg. 973
CIBA SPECIALTY CHEMICALS—Ciba Specialty Chemicals Holding Inc.; *Int'l*, pg. 291
CIBA SPECIALTY CHEMICALS HOLDING INC.; *Int'l*, pg. 291
CIBATUL LTD.—Novartis AG; *Int'l*, pg. 981
CILAG AG—Johnson & Johnson; *U.S. Public*, pg. 929
CIRCA PHARMACEUTICALS, INC.—Watson Pharmaceuticals, Inc.; *U.S. Public*, pg. 1746
CLAY-PARK LABS, INC.—Agis Industries Ltd.; *Int'l*, pg. 30
THE CLAYTON ANILINE COMPANY—Novartis AG; *Int'l*, pg. 981
THE CLINIPAD CORPORATION; *U.S. Private*, pg. 246
CO-OPERATIVE ANIMAL HEALTH LIMITED—Avonmore Waterford Group plc; *Int'l*, pg. 102
COLUMBIA LABORATORIES, INC.; *U.S. Public*, pg. 405
COMBE INCORPORATED; *U.S. Private*, pg. 257
COMMERCE DRUG CANADA LTD.—Del Laboratories, Inc.; *U.S. Public*, pg. 494
COMPANIA FARMACEUTICA UPJOHN S.A.—Pharmacia & Upjohn, Inc.; *Int'l*, pg. 1049
COMPANIA MEDICINAL LA CAMPANA, S.A. DE C.V.—Warner-Lambert Company; *U.S. Public*, pg. 1739
CONKLIN CO. INC.; *U.S. Private*, pg. 263
COOP SWITZERLAND; *Int'l*, pg. 329
THE COOPER COMPANIES, INC.; *U.S. Public*, pg. 442
COOPER, MCDOUGALL & ROBERTSON LTD.—Glaxo Wellcome plc; *Int'l*, pg. 552
COPLEY PHARMACEUTICALS, INC.; *U.S. Public*, pg. 446
COVIGAL SA—Novartis AG; *Int'l*, pg. 981
CURATIO VERSIGHERUNGS-VERMITTLUNGS GMBH—Solvay S.A.; *Int'l*, pg. 1278
CUSSONS (U.K.) LTD.—Paterson Zochonis Plc; *Int'l*, pg. 1024
CUTTER LABORATORIES INC.—Bayer AG; *Int'l*, pg. 174
CYANAMID AGRICULTURAL PRODUCTS DIVISION—American Home Products Corporation; *U.S. Public*, pg. 79
CYANAMID AUSTRALIA, PTY., LTD.—American Home Products Corporation; *U.S. Public*, pg. 80
CYANAMID CANADA INC.—American Home Products Corporation; *U.S. Public*, pg. 80
CYANAMID DE VENEZUELA CA—American Home Products Corporation; *U.S. Public*, pg. 80
CYANAMID IBERICA, S.A.—American Home Products Corporation; *U.S. Public*, pg. 81
CYANAMID INDIA LTD.—American Home Products Corporation; *U.S. Public*, pg. 81
CYANAMID MEXICO—American Home Products Corporation; *U.S. Public*, pg. 81
CYANAMID OF GREAT BRITAIN LTD.—American Home Products Corporation; *U.S. Public*, pg. 81
CYTOGEN CORPORATION; *U.S. Public*, pg. 471
D & K HEALTHCARE RESOURCES, INC.; *U.S. Public*, pg. 471
DADE BEHRING-MICROSCAN DIV.—Bain Capital; *U.S. Private*, pg. 110
DANBURY PHARMACAL INC.—Schein Pharmaceutical, Inc.; *U.S. Private*, pg. 969
DANSK KENRAL A.P.S.—Pharmacia & Upjohn, Inc.; *Int'l*, pg. 1049
DEGUSSA AG; *Int'l*, pg. 388
DEL LABORATORIES (CANADA) LTD.—Del Laboratories, Inc.; *U.S. Public*, pg. 494
DEL LABORATORIES, INC.; *U.S. Public*, pg. 494
DEL PHARMACEUTICALS, INC.—Del Laboratories, Inc.; *U.S. Public*, pg. 494
DELTA WEST PTY. LTD.—Pharmacia & Upjohn, Inc.; *Int'l*, pg. 1049
DENVER CHEMICAL (PR) INC.—Carter-Wallace, Inc.; *U.S. Public*, pg. 310
DEP CORPORATION; *U.S. Public*, pg. 500
DERMIK LABORATORIES, INC.—Rhone-Poulenc S.A.; *Int'l*, *pg. 1110*
DEXTRAN PRODUCTS LIMITED—Polydex Pharmaceuticals Limited; *Int'l*, pg. 1063
DEY LABORATORIES INC.—Lipha Chemicals S.A.; *Int'l*, pg. 812
DIFFUCAP-EURAND S.A.—American Home Products Corporation; *U.S. Public*, pg. 81
DIOSYNTH BV—Akzo Nobel N.V.; *Int'l*, pg. 44
DISPERSA AG—Novartis AG; *Int'l*, pg. 972
DISTA PRODUCTS LTD.—Eli Lilly and Company; *U.S. Public*, pg. 993
DISTA, S.A.—Eli Lilly and Company; *U.S. Public*, pg. 993
DR. MANN PHARMA—Bausch & Lomb Incorporated; *U.S. Public*, pg. 196
DONG-MYUNG INDUSTRIAL CO., LTD.—Meiji Seika Kaisha, Ltd.; *Int'l*, pg. 856
DOW HICKAM PHARMACEUTICALS INC.—Mylan Laboratories, Inc.; *U.S. Public*, pg. 1143
DRESSIN KOSMETIK-U. PHARMA GMBH—The Procter & Gamble Company; *U.S. Public*, pg. 1333
DU PONT (E.I. DU PONT DE NEMOURS & CO.); *U.S. Public*, pg. 530
THE DU PONT MERCK PHARMACEUTICAL COMPANY—Du Pont (E.I. Du Pont De Nemours & Co.); *U.S. Public*, pg. 531
THE DU PONT MERCK PHARMACEUTICAL COMPANY—Merck & Co., Inc.; *U.S. Public*, pg. 1091
DUNCAN FLOCKHART & CO. LIMITED—Glaxo Wellcome plc; *Int'l*, pg. 552
DUPHAR & CIE S.N.C.—Solvay S.A.; *Int'l*, pg. 1277
DUPONT MERCK PHARM—Merck & Co., Inc.; *U.S. Public*, pg. 1091
DUREX CONSUMER PRODUCTS—London International Group plc; *Int'l*, pg. 815
E-Z-EM CANADA INC.—E-Z-Em, Inc.; *U.S. Public*, pg. 540
E-Z-EM, INC.; *U.S. Public*, pg. 540
EFEKA FRIEDRICH & KAUFMANN GMBH & CO.—American Home Products Corporation; *U.S. Public*, pg. 81
EVSCO PHARMACEUTICALS—IGI, Inc.; *U.S. Public*, pg. 855
EGYPT OTSUKA PHARMACEUTICAL CO., S.A.E.—Otsuka Pharmaceutical Co., Ltd.; *Int'l*, pg. 1014
EISAI CO., LTD.; *Int'l*, pg. 435
ELAN CORPORATION PLC; *Int'l*, pg. 435
ELAN PHARMA INC.—Elan Corporation Plc; *Int'l*, pg. 436
ELAN PHARMA LTD.—Elan Corporation Plc; *Int'l*, pg. 436
ELAN/PRI LTD.—Elan Corporation Plc; *Int'l*, pg. 436
ELAN TRANSDERMAL LTD.—Elan Corporation Plc; *Int'l*, pg. 436
ELANCO, VETERINARIA, S.A.—Eli Lilly and Company; *U.S. Public*, pg. 993
ELDON LABORATORIES LIMITED—Alliance UniChem PLC; *Int'l*, pg. 58
ELF SANOFI INC.—Elf Aquitane; *Int'l*, pg. 445
ELF SANOFI S.A.—Elf Aquitane; *Int'l*, pg. 445
ELKINS-SINN, INC.-LEDERLE—American Home Products Corporation; *U.S. Public*, pg. 79
EMPRESAS BRISTOL DE COSTA RICA, S.A.—Bristol-Myers Squibb Company; *U.S. Public*, pg. 256
EON LABS—Eon Labs Manufacturing, Inc.; *U.S. Private*, pg. 379
EON LABS MANUFACTURING, INC.; *U.S. Private*, pg. 379
ESKAYEF LTD.—SmithKline Beecham plc; *Int'l*, pg. 1265
EURAND FRANCE S.A.—American Home Products Corporation; *U.S. Public*, pg. 81
EURAND INTERNATIONAL S.P.A.—American Home Products Corporation; *U.S. Public*, pg. 81
EVERGOOD PRODUCTS CORPORATION; *U.S. Private*, pg. 386
FMC CORP. PHARMACEUTICAL & BIOSCIENCE PRODUCTS DIV.—FMC Corporation; *U.S. Public*, pg. 605
FARNAM COMPANIES, INC.; *U.S. Private*, pg. 396
FERRO CORPORATION; *U.S. Public*, pg. 618
FINE CHEMICALS—Alpharma Inc.; *U.S. Public*, pg. 58
FISONS CONSUMER HEALTH PLC—Rhone-Poulenc S.A.; *Int'l*, pg. 1110
C. B. FLEET CO., INC.; *U.S. Private*, pg. 410
FOREST LABORATORIES CARIBE, INC.—Forest Laboratories, Inc.; *U.S. Public*, pg. 670
FOREST LABORATORIES, INC.; *U.S. Public*, pg. 670
FOREST PHARMACEUTICALS, INC.—Forest Laboratories, Inc.; *U.S. Public*, pg. 670
FORT DODGE ANIMAL HEALTH—American Home Products Corporation; *U.S. Public*, pg. 79
FRESENIUS AG; *Int'l*, pg. 505
FRUTAROM MEER CORPORATION—ICC Industries, Inc.; *U.S. Private*, pg. 554
FUJISAWA FISONS KK—Rhone-Poulenc S.A.; *Int'l*, pg. 1111
FUJISAWA PHARMACEUTICAL CO. LTD.; *Int'l*, pg. 525
FUJISAWA U.S.A. INC.—Fujisawa Pharmaceutical Co. Ltd.; *Int'l*, pg. 525
GP STRATEGIES CORPORATION; *U.S. Public*, pg. 694
GALDERMA LABORATORIES, INC.—Nestle S.A.; *Int'l*, pg. 918
GEMA S.A.—Novartis AG; *Int'l*, pg. 982
GEN TRAC—Jones Medical Industries Inc.; *U.S. Public*, pg. 934
GENERAL NUTRITION PRODUCTS, INC.—General Nutrition, Inc.; *U.S. Public*, pg. 725
GENETICS INSTITUTE, INC.—American Home Products Corporation; *U.S. Public*, pg. 79
GENEVA PHARMACEUTICALS, INC.—Novartis AG; *Int'l*, pg. 973
GENZYME CORPORATION; *U.S. Public*, pg. 733
GIULINI PHARMA GMBH—Solvay S.A.; *Int'l*, pg. 1278
GLAXO DEVELOPMENT PTE. LTD.—Glaxo Wellcome plc; *Int'l*, pg. 553
GLAXO LABORATORIES LIMITED—Glaxo Wellcome plc; *Int'l*, pg. 552
GLAXO PHARMACEUTICALS—Glaxo Wellcome plc; *Int'l*, pg. 552
GLAXO TECHNICAL OPERATIONS—Glaxo Wellcome plc; *Int'l*, pg. 552
GLAXO WELLCOME AUSTRALIA LTD.—Glaxo Wellcome plc; *Int'l*, pg. 553
GLAXO WELLCOME GMBH—Glaxo Wellcome plc; *Int'l*, pg. 553
GLAXO WELLCOME INC.—Glaxo Wellcome plc; *Int'l*, pg. 552
GLAXO WELLCOME PLC; *Int'l*, pg. 552
GLAXOCHEM PTE. LTD.—Glaxo Wellcome plc; *Int'l*, pg. 553
GOEDECKE A.G.—Warner-Lambert Company; *U.S. Public*, pg. 1739
GRAHAM-FIELD HEALTH PRODUCTS, INC.; *U.S. Public*, pg. 757
GREAT LAKES WHOLESALE DRUGS; *U.S. Private*, pg. 475
GRIMA QUIMICA, S.A.—Eli Lilly and Company; *U.S. Public*, *pg. 994*
GRUPPO LEPETIT S.P.A.—The Dow Chemical Company; *U.S. Public*, pg. 524
GUANGDONG OTSUKA PHARMACEUTICAL CO., LTD.—Otsuka Pharmaceutical Co., Ltd.; *Int'l*, pg. 1014
GUIGOZ FRANCE S.A.—Nestle S.A.; *Int'l*, pg. 920
HALSEY DRUG COMPANY; *U.S. Private*, pg. 496
HAN WHA PHARMA CO. LTD.—Akzo Nobel N.V.; *Int'l*, pg. 44
HAVILAND ENTERPRISES; *U.S. Private*, pg. 511
HAW PAR BROTHERS INTERNATIONAL LIMITED; *Int'l*, pg. 603
HEALTH-CHEM CORPORATION; *U.S. Public*, pg. 802
HEICO CHEMICALS, INC.—Cambrex Corporation; *U.S. Public*, pg. 297
HENKEL CORPORATION FINE CHEMICALS DIV.—Henkel KGaA; *Int'l*, pg. 610

HENKEL CORPORATION FUNCTIONAL PRODUCTS DIV.—Henkel KGaA; *Int'l*, pg. 610
HENKEL COSMETIC GMBH—Henkel KGaA; *Int'l*, pg. 609
HENKEL GENTHIN GMBH—Henkel KGaA; *Int'l*, pg. 610
HENKEL KGAA; *Int'l*, pg. 609
HERCON LABORATORIES CORP.—Health-Chem Corporation; *U.S. Public*, pg. 802
HERMAL KURT HERRMANN & CO.; *Int'l*, pg. 616
HESS & CLARK COMPANY—ConAgra, Inc.; *U.S. Public*, pg. 426
HI-TECH PHARMACAL CO., INC.; *U.S. Public*, pg. 825
HINDUSTAN CIBA-GEIGY LIMITED—Novartis AG; *Int'l*, pg. 982
WALTER HIRSCH ADM—BASF AG; *Int'l*, pg. 108
HOECHST AUSTRALIA LTD.—Hoechst Aktiengesellschaft; *Int'l*, pg. 626
HOECHST MARION ROUSSEL AG—Hoechst Aktiengesellschaft; *Int'l*, pg. 624
HOECHST MARION ROUSSEL, INC.—Hoechst Aktiengesellschaft; *Int'l*, pg. 624
HOECHST MARION ROUSSEL ITALY—Hoechst Aktiengesellschaft; *Int'l*, pg. 625
HOECHST MARION ROUSSEL NORTH AMERICA—Hoechst Aktiengesellschaft; *Int'l*, pg. 625
HOECHST MARION ROUSSEL RESEARCH—Hoechst Aktiengesellschaft; *Int'l*, pg. 625
HOFFMANN-LA ROCHE AG—Roche Holding Ltd.; *Int'l*, pg. 1121
F. HOFFMANN-LA ROCHE LTD.—Roche Holding Ltd.; *Int'l*, pg. 1119
HOFFMANN-LA ROCHE INC.—Roche Holding Ltd.; *Int'l*, pg. 1120
HOFFMANN-LA ROCHE LTD.—Roche Holding Ltd.; *Int'l*, pg. 1121
HOFFMANN-LA ROCHE WIEN GMBH—Roche Holding Ltd.; *Int'l*, pg. 1121
HOHN & HOHN GMBH—American Home Products Corporation; *U.S. Public*, pg. 81
HORMOQUIMICA DE CHILE LTDA.—Akzo Nobel N.V.; *Int'l*, pg. 44
FRANK W. HORNER INC. (CANADA)—Carter-Wallace, Inc.; *U.S. Public*, pg. 310
THE HUDSON CORPORATION—Nature's Bounty Inc.; *U.S. Public*, pg. 1166
HUMANPHARMAKOLOGISCHES INSTITUT CIBA-GEIGY GMBH—Novartis AG; *Int'l*, pg. 982
HYCOR BIOMEDICAL, INC.; *U.S. Public*, pg. 851
ICC COMERCIO E INDUSTRIA LTDS.—ICC Industries, Inc.; *U.S. Private*, pg. 554
ICC HANDELS AG—ICC Industries, Inc.; *U.S. Private*, pg. 554
ICC INDUSTRIES, INC.; *U.S. Private*, pg. 553
ICI AUSTRALIA HOSPITAL PRODUCTS PTY LTD—Imperial Chemical Industries PLC; *Int'l*, pg. 664
P.T. ICI FARMASI INDONESIA—Imperial Chemical Industries PLC; *Int'l*, pg. 666
P.T. ICI FARMASI INDONESIA—Zeneca Group Plc; *Int'l*, pg. 1527
ICI FRANCE SA—Imperial Chemical Industries PLC; *Int'l*, pg. 665
ICI INDIA LIMITED—Imperial Chemical Industries PLC; *Int'l*, pg. 665
ICI ZAMBIA LIMITED—Imperial Chemical Industries PLC; *Int'l*, pg. 665
ICN PHARMACEUTICALS, INC.; *U.S. Public*, pg. 853
IGI, INC.; *U.S. Public*, pg. 855
INAC INDUSTRIA NACIONAL DE PRODUTOS QUIMICOS LDA.—Novartis AG; *Int'l*, pg. 982
IPR PHARMACEUTICALS, INC.—Zeneca Group Plc; *Int'l*, pg. 1524
IMASCO LIMITED—B.A.T Industries P.L.C.; *Int'l*, pg. 112
IMMUNEX CORPORATION; *U.S. Public*, pg. 871
IMMUNEX MANUFACTURING CORPORATION—Immunex Corporation; *U.S. Public*, pg. 871
INDUSTRIAS FARMACEUTICAS FONTOURA WYETH S.A.—American Home Products Corporation; *U.S. Public*, pg. 81
INDUSTRIAS QUIMICAS DE NAVARRA S.A.—Novartis AG; *Int'l*, pg. 982
INDUSTRIAS WYETH S.A.—American Home Products Corporation; *U.S. Public*, pg. 81
INFAR (INDIA) LTD.—Akzo Nobel N.V.; *Int'l*, pg. 45
INNOVIR GMBH—VIMRx Pharmaceuticals, Inc.; *U.S. Public*, pg. 1703
INNOVIR LABORATORIES, INC.—VIMRx Pharmaceuticals, Inc.; *U.S. Public*, pg. 1702
INNOVIR (UK) LTD—VIMRx Pharmaceuticals, Inc.; *U.S. Public*, pg. 1703
INTERFERON SCIENCES DEVELOPMENT CORP.—GP Strategies Corporation; *U.S. Public*, pg. 694
INTERFERON SCIENCES, INC.—GP Strategies Corporation; *U.S. Public*, pg. 694
INTERNATIONAL PHARMACEUTICALS—Alpharma Inc.; *U.S. Public*, pg. 58
INTERVET AMERICA, INC.—Akzo Nobel N.V.; *Int'l*, pg. 48
INTERVET INTERNATIONAL BV—Akzo Nobel N.V.; *Int'l*, pg. 44
INTERVET MEXICO SA DE CV—Akzo Nobel N.V.; *Int'l*, pg. 45
INTERVET (U.K.) LTD.—Akzo Nobel N.V.; *Int'l*, pg. 45
INWOOD LABORATORIES, INC.—Forest Laboratories, Inc.; *U.S. Public*, pg. 670
S.P.A. ITALIANA LABORATORI BOUTY (ITALY)—Carter-Wallace, Inc.; *U.S. Public*, pg. 310
IVAX CORPORATION; *U.S. Public*, pg. 914
J B LABS, INC.; *U.S. Private*, pg. 576
JMI-CANTON PHARMACEUTICALS, INC.—Jones Medical Industries Inc.; *U.S. Public*, pg. 934
JMI-DANIELS PHARMACEUTICALS, INC.—Jones Medical Industries Inc.; *U.S. Public*, pg. 934
JAPAN PHARMACIA & UPJOHN LIMITED—Pharmacia & Upjohn, Inc.; *Int'l*, pg. 1049
JOHNSON & JOHNSON; *U.S. Public*, pg. 927
JOHNSON MATTHEY PHARMACEUTICALS MATERIALS—Johnson Matthey Public Limited Company; *Int'l*, pg. 713
JOHNSON MATTHEY PUBLIC LIMITED COMPANY; *Int'l*, pg. 713
JONES MEDICAL INDUSTRIES INC.; *U.S. Public*, pg. 933
KHR; *U.S. Private*, pg. 603
KV PHARMACEUTICAL COMPANY; *U.S. Public*, pg. 941
KALI-CHEMIE AKTIENGESELLSCHAFT—Solvay S.A.; *Int'l*, pg. 1278
KALI-CHEMIE PHARMA GESELLSCHAFT MBH—Solvay S.A.; *Int'l*, pg. 1279
KALI-CHEMIE PHARMA GMBH—Solvay S.A.; *Int'l*, pg. 1278
KALI-DUPHAR K.K.—Solvay S.A.; *Int'l*, pg. 1279
KALIFARMA S.A.—Solvay S.A.; *Int'l*, pg. 1279
KAZ, INC.; *U.S. Private*, pg. 610
KENRAL INC.—Pharmacia & Upjohn, Inc.; *Int'l*, pg. 1049
KENYA-SWISS CHEMICAL CO. LTD.—Novartis AG; *Int'l*, pg. 983
KEY PHARMACEUTICALS—Schering-Plough Corporation; *U.S. Public*, pg. 1438
KIRIN AMGEN, INC.—Amgen Inc.; *U.S. Public*, pg. 101
KIRIN U.S.A. C/O NOMUSA & CO.—Kirin Brewery Co., Ltd.; *Int'l*, pg. 736
KIWI BRANDS PTY. LTD.—Sara Lee Corporation; *U.S. Public*, pg. 1434
KNOLL AG—BASF AG; *Int'l*, pg. 104
KNOLL AG WERK UETERSEN—BASF AG; *Int'l*, pg. 104
KNOLL ALMAN ILAC VE ECZA TIC. LTD. STI.—BASF AG; *Int'l*, pg. 108
KNOLL BEIJING—BASF AG; *Int'l*, pg. 108
KNOLL BELGIUM S.A./N.V.—BASF AG; *Int'l*, pg. 108
KNOLL-BIORESEARCH S.A.—BASF AG; *Int'l*, pg. 108
KNOLL CENTROAMERICANA S.A.—BASF AG; *Int'l*, pg. 108
KNOLL COLOMBIANA S.A.—BASF AG; *Int'l*, pg. 108
KNOLL DEUTSCHLAND GMBH—BASF AG; *Int'l*, pg. 104
KNOLL FARMACEUTICI S.P.A—BASF AG; *Int'l*, pg. 108
KNOLL JAPAN K.K.—BASF AG; *Int'l*, pg. 108
KNOLL LUSITANA, LDA.—BASF AG; *Int'l*, pg. 109
KNOLL PHARMA—BASF AG; *Int'l*, pg. 109
KNOLL PHARMACEUTICAL COMPANY—BASF AG; *Int'l*, pg. 105
KNOLL PHARMACEUTICALS SOUTH AFRICA (PTY.) LTD.—BASF AG; *Int'l*, pg. 109
KNOLL PHARMACEUTICALS TAIWAN—BASF AG; *Int'l*, pg. 109
KNOLL S.A. PRODUTOS QUIMICOS E FARMACEUTICOS—BASF AG; *Int'l*, pg. 109
KNOLL SCIENTIFIC OFFICE—BASF AG; *Int'l*, pg. 109
KNOLL SPOL. S.R.O.—BASF AG; *Int'l*, pg. 109
KNOLLPHARMA INC.—BASF AG; *Int'l*, pg. 109
KOBAYASHI-BLOCK CO. LTD.—Block Drug Company, Inc.; *U.S. Public*, pg. 237
KOBAYASHI PHARMACEUTICAL CO., LTD.; *Int'l*, pg. 740
KOLANA S.A.—American Home Products Corporation; *U.S. Public*, pg. 81
KOREA & PHARMACIA UPJOHN LIMITED—Pharmacia & Upjohn, Inc.; *Int'l*, pg. 1049
KOREA OTSUKA PHARMACEUTICAL CO., LTD.—Otsuka Pharmaceutical Co., Ltd.; *Int'l*, pg. 1014
KYOWA HAKKO EUROPE GMBH—Kyowa Hakko Kogyo Company, Ltd.; *Int'l*, pg. 778
KYOWA HAKKO (H.K.) CO., LTD.—Kyowa Hakko Kogyo Company, Ltd.; *Int'l*, pg. 778
KYOWA HAKKO KOGYO COMPANY, LTD.; *Int'l*, pg. 778
KYOWA HAKKO (MALAYSIA) SDN BHD.—Kyowa Hakko Kogyo Company, Ltd.; *Int'l*, pg. 778
KYOWA HAKKO (THAILAND) LTD.—Kyowa Hakko Kogyo Company, Ltd.; *Int'l*, pg. 778
KYOWA HAKKO U.K. LTD.—Kyowa Hakko Kogyo Company, Ltd.; *Int'l*, pg. 778
KYOWA HAKKO U.S.A., INC.—Kyowa Hakko Kogyo Company, Ltd.; *Int'l*, pg. 778
KYOWA HAKKO-WEST COAST OFFICE—Kyowa Hakko Kogyo Company, Ltd.; *Int'l*, pg. 778
KYOWA ITALIANA FARMACEUTICI S.R.L.—Kyowa Hakko Kogyo Company, Ltd.; *Int'l*, pg. 778
KYTTA-WERK SAUTER GMBH—American Home Products Corporation; *U.S. Public*, pg. 81
L.P.B. INSTITUTO FARMACEUTICO S.P.A.—Novartis AG; *Int'l*, pg. 983
LABORATOIRE ALLARD S.A.—Bristol-Myers Squibb Company; *U.S. Public*, pg. 256
LABORATOIRE LACHARTRE S.A.—The Procter & Gamble Company; *U.S. Public*, pg. 1331
LABORATOIRE ROGER BELLON—Rhone-Poulenc S.A.; *Int'l*, pg. 1109
LABORATOIRE WELLCOME GLAXO S.A.—Glaxo Wellcome plc; *Int'l*, pg. 553
LABORATOIRES ALCON S.A.R.L.—Nestle S.A.; *Int'l*, pg. 920
LABORATOIRES BRISTOL S.A.—Bristol-Myers Squibb Company; *U.S. Public*, pg. 256
LABORATOIRES CIBA-GEIGY S.A.—Novartis AG; *Int'l*, pg. 983
LABORATOIRES DE THERAPEUTHIQUE MODERNE LTM S.A.—Solvay S.A.; *Int'l*, pg. 1279
LABORATOIRES DUPHAR S.A.—Solvay S.A.; *Int'l*, pg. 1279
LABORATOIRES FUMOUZE S.A.—Carter-Wallace, Inc.; *U.S. Public*, pg. 310
LABORATOIRES NEOLAIT S.A.—SmithKline Beecham plc; *Int'l*, pg. 1265
LABORATOIRES PHARMACIA & UPJOHN SARL—Pharmacia & Upjohn, Inc.; *Int'l*, pg. 1049
LABORATOIRES SANDOZ S.A.R.L.—Novartis AG; *Int'l*, pg. 983
LABORATOIRES SAUTER S.A.—Roche Holding Ltd.; *Int'l*, pg. 1120
LABORATOIRES SOBIO S.A.—SmithKline Beecham plc; *Int'l*, pg. 1265
LABORATOIRES SYNTHELABO FRANCE—L'Oreal S.A.; *Int'l*, pg. 818
LABORATOIRES WYETH FRANCE—American Home Products Corporation; *U.S. Public*, pg. 81
LABORATORIES ASTRA FRANCE—Astra AB; *Int'l*, pg. 94
LABORATORIES WELLCOME S.A.—Glaxo Wellcome plc; *Int'l*, pg. 553
LABORATORIO NORMAL PRODUCTOS FARMACEUTICOS, LDA.—Novartis AG; *Int'l*, pg. 983
LABORATORIO PADRO SA—Novartis AG; *Int'l*, pg. 983
LABORATORIOS BRISTOL DE VENEZUELA, S.A.—Bristol-Myers Squibb Company; *U.S. Public*, pg. 256
LABORATORIOS BRISTOL DEL ECUADOR S.A.—Bristol-Myers Squibb Company; *U.S. Public*, pg. 256
LABORATORIOS INTERVET S.A.—Akzo Nobel N.V.; *Int'l*, pg. 45
LABORATORIOS MIQUEL, S.A.—Otsuka Pharmaceutical Co., Ltd.; *Int'l*, pg. 1014
LABORATORIOS PHARMACIA & UPJOHN, C.A.—Pharmacia & Upjohn, Inc.; *Int'l*, pg. 1049
LABORATORIOS SUBSTANTIA, C.A.—Warner-Lambert Company; *U.S. Public*, pg. 1739
LABORATORIOS WYETH-WHITEHALL LTD.—American Home Products Corporation; *U.S. Public*, pg. 81
LANDER CO., INC.; *U.S. Private*, pg. 647
LANGFORD INC.—American Home Products Corporation; *U.S. Public*, pg. 81
LEE PHARMACEUTICALS; *U.S. Public*, pg. 984
LEINER HEALTH PRODUCTS, INC.; *U.S. Private*, pg. 659
LEIRAS OY—Huhtamaki Oy; *Int'l*, pg. 639
LENSCLEAN, INC.—H.L. Bouton Company Inc.; *U.S. Private*, pg. 162
LES LABORATOIRES BEECHAM S.A.—SmithKline Beecham plc; *Int'l*, pg. 1265
LEVER S.A.—Unilever Plc; *Int'l*, pg. 1438
LIBAMEDI S.A.—American Home Products Corporation; *U.S. Public*, pg. 81
ELI LILLY AND COMPANY; *U.S. Public*, pg. 992
ELI LILLY Y COMPANIA DE VENEZUELA, S.A.—Eli Lilly and Company; *U.S. Public*, pg. 994
LILLY-FARMA PRODUTOS FARMACEUTICOS, LDA.—Eli Lilly and Company; *U.S. Public*, pg. 994
LILLY FRANCE S.A.—Eli Lilly and Company; *U.S. Public*, pg. 994
LILLY INDUSTRIES LIMITED—Eli Lilly and Company; *U.S. Public*, pg. 994
LIPHA PHARMACEUTICALS, INC.—Lipha Chemicals S.A.; *Int'l*, pg. 812
THE LIPOSOME COMPANY, INC.; *U.S. Public*, pg. 1000
LONDON INTERNATIONAL GROUP PLC; *Int'l*, pg. 815
LONDON INTERNATIONAL, U.S. HOLDINGS INC.—London International Group plc; *Int'l*, pg. 815
L'OREAL S.A.; *Int'l*, pg. 818
LOREX PHARMACEUTICALS LTD.—L'Oreal S.A.; *Int'l*, pg. 818
LYSSIA GMBH—Solvay S.A.; *Int'l*, pg. 1278
MGI PHARMA INC.; *U.S. Public*, pg. 1026
MSD AGVET (EC OFFICE)—Merck & Co., Inc.; *U.S. Public*, pg. 1092
MSD SHARP & DOHME GMBH—Merck & Co., Inc.; *U.S. Public*, pg. 1092
MACANDREWS & FORBES HOLDINGS INC.; *U.S. Private*, pg. 689
MADDEN & LAYMAN LIMITED—Bausch & Lomb Incorporated; *U.S. Public*, pg. 196
MAJOR PHARMACEUTICALS—Great Lakes Wholesale Drugs; *U.S. Private*, pg. 475
MALLINCKRODT INC.; *U.S. Public*, pg. 1039
MALLINCKRODT MEDICAL—Mallinckrodt Inc.; *U.S. Public*, pg. 1040
MCKESSON CORPORATION; *U.S. Public*, pg. 1072
MCNEIL CONSUMER PRODUCTS COMPANY—Johnson & Johnson; *U.S. Public*, pg. 928
MCNEIL SPECIALTY PRODUCTS COMPANY—Johnson & Johnson; *U.S. Public*, pg. 928
MEDEVA PHARMACEUTICALS—Medeva PLC; *Int'l*, pg. 852
MEDEVA PLC; *Int'l*, pg. 852
MEDICIS PHARMACEUTICAL CORP.; *U.S. Public*, pg. 1080
MEDTECH INC.; *U.S. Private*, pg. 728
P.T. MEIJI INDONESIAN PHARMACEUTICAL INDUSTRIES—Meiji Seika Kaisha, Ltd.; *Int'l*, pg. 856
MEIJI MILK PRODUCTS CO., LTD.; *Int'l*, pg. 855
MEIJI SEIKA KAISHA, LTD.; *Int'l*, pg. 855
MEIJI SEIKA PHARMA INTERNATIONAL, LTD.—Meiji Seika Kaisha, Ltd.; *Int'l*, pg. 855
MENLEY & JAMES LABORATORIES, INC.; *U.S. Public*, pg. 1086
MENTHOLATUM CANADA LTD.—Rohto Pharmaceutical Co.; *Int'l*, pg. 1126
MENTHOLATUM COMPANY—Rohto Pharmaceutical Co.; *Int'l*, pg. 1126
MEPHICO SAL—Novartis AG; *Int'l*, pg. 983
P.T. MERAPI UTAMA PHARMA—Otsuka Pharmaceutical Co., Ltd.; *Int'l*, pg. 1014
MERCK & CO., INC.; *U.S. Public*, pg. 1090
MERCK HUMAN HEALTH DIVISION—Merck & Co., Inc.; *U.S. Public*, pg. 1090
MERCK HUMAN HEALTH DIVISION (U.S. HUMAN HEALTH)—Merck & Co., Inc.; *U.S. Public*, pg. 1091
MERCK SHARP & DOHME-HOLLAND—Merck & Co., Inc.; *U.S. Public*, pg. 1092
MERIAL LTD.—Merck & Co., Inc.; *U.S. Public*, pg. 1092
MERIAL SAS—Rhone-Poulenc S.A.; *Int'l*, pg. 1114
MERIDIAN INDUSTRIES, INC.; *U.S. Private*, pg. 732
MENTHOLATUM PTY. LTD.—Rohto Pharmaceutical Co.; *Int'l*, pg. 1126
MILES LABORATORIES AUSTRALIA PTY. LTD.—Bayer AG; *Int'l*, pg. 175
MITSUBISHI CHEMICAL CORPORATION; *Int'l*, pg. 870
MITSUI PHARMACEUTICALS, INC.—Mitsui & Co., Ltd.; *Int'l*, pg. 877
MODIPACK BV—Novartis AG; *Int'l*, pg. 983
MONSANTO COMPANY; *U.S. Public*, pg. 1124
MONTEDISON S.P.A.—Compart SpA; *Int'l*, pg. 324

MONTICELLO DRUG CO.—The Monticello Companies, Inc.; U.S. Private, pg. 759
MOORMAN'S INC.; U.S. Private, pg. 760
MORINAGA MILK INDUSTRY CO., LTD.; Int'l, pg. 895
MUCH PHARMA—American Home Products Corporation; U.S. Public, pg. 81
MULTIPHARMA BV—Novartis AG; Int'l, pg. 983
MURO PHARMACEUTICAL, INC.; U.S. Private, pg. 767
MUSASHINO-GEIGY CO. LTD.—Novartis AG; Int'l, pg. 983
MYLAN LABORATORIES, INC.; U.S. Public, pg. 1143
MYLAN PHARMACEUTICALS INC.—Mylan Laboratories, Inc.; U.S. Public, pg. 1143
NAGASE-CIBA LTD.—Novartis AG; Int'l, pg. 983
NASCO MODESTO—Geneve Corporation; U.S. Private, pg. 446
NATURE'S BOUNTY INC.; U.S. Public, pg. 1166
NATURE'S SUNSHINE PRODUCTS, INC.; U.S. Public, pg. 1166
OY NEOREMEDIA AB—Oy Algol AB; Int'l, pg. 15
NEORX CORPORATION; U.S. Private, pg. 791
NESTLE S.A.; Int'l, pg. 915
NEW BRUNSWICK SCIENTIFIC CO., INC.; U.S. Public, pg. 1169
NEXSTAR PHARMACEUTICALS, INC.; U.S. Public, pg. 1180
NEXSTAR PHARMACEUTICALS, INC.—Nexstar Pharmaceuticals, Inc.; U.S. Public, pg. 1180
NEZEL S.A.—Solvay S.A.; Int'l, pg. 1279
NIPPON BECTON DICKINSON COMPANY LTD.—Becton Dickinson & Company; U.S. Public, pg. 200
NIPPON BYK GULDEN CO., LTD.—Altana AG; Int'l, pg. 66
NIPPON KAYAKU CO. LTD.; Int'l, pg. 934
NIPPON KAYAKU PHARMACEUTICAL DIV.—Nippon Kayaku Co. Ltd.; Int'l, pg. 934
NIPPON ROCHE K.K.—Roche Holding Ltd.; Int'l, pg. 1121
NIPPON VICKS K.K.—The Procter & Gamble Company; U.S. Public, pg. 1331
NORAMCO, INC.—Johnson & Johnson; U.S. Public, pg. 929
NORDION INTERNATIONAL INC.—MDS Inc.; Int'l, pg. 827
NORTON HEALTHCARE LIMITED—IVAX Corporation; U.S. Public, pg. 915
A. NOTTERMANN & CIE GMBH—Rhone-Poulenc S.A.; Int'l, pg. 1112
NOVARTIS—Novartis AG; Int'l, pg. 972
NOVARTIS AG; Int'l, pg. 971
NOVARTIS NUTRITION CORPORATION—Novartis AG; Int'l, pg. 974
NOVARTIS-PHARMA GMBH—Novartis AG; Int'l, pg. 984
NOVARTIS PHARMACEUTICALS—Novartis AG; Int'l, pg. 973
NOVO NORDISK COMERCIO DE PRODUTOS FARMACEUTICOS, LDA—Novo Nordisk A/S; Int'l, pg. 988
NOVO NORDISK FARMAKA DANMARK A/S—Novo Nordisk A/S; Int'l, pg. 987
NYCOMED AMERSHAM—Nycomed Amersham plc; Int'l, pg. 993
OCLASSEN PHARMACEUTICALS—Watson Pharmaceuticals, Inc.; U.S. Public, pg. 1746
OHKURA PHARMACEUTICAL—Meiji Milk Products Co., Ltd.; Int'l, pg. 855
OHMEDA—The BOC Group plc; Int'l, pg. 121
OHMEDA CARIBE, INC.—The BOC Group plc; Int'l, pg. 121
OHMEDA, INC.—The BOC Group plc; Int'l, pg. 121
OMAHA VACCINE COMPANY—KHR; U.S. Private, pg. 603
OMNICARE PHARMACY SERVICES—Omnicare, Inc.; U.S. Public, pg. 1223
ORGANON (BANGLADESH) LTD.—Akzo Nobel N.V.; Int'l, pg. 45
ORGANON BELGIE NV—Akzo Nobel N.V.; Int'l, pg. 45
ORGANON CANADA LTD.—Akzo Nobel N.V.; Int'l, pg. 45
LAB. ORGANON DO BRAZIL LTDA.—Akzo Nobel N.V.; Int'l, pg. 45
ORGANON ESPANOLA SA—Akzo Nobel N.V.; Int'l, pg. 45
ORGANON GMBH—Akzo Nobel N.V.; Int'l, pg. 45
ORGANON INC.—Akzo Nobel N.V.; Int'l, pg. 48
P.T. ORGANON INDONESIA—Akzo Nobel N.V.; Int'l, pg. 45
ORGANON INTERNATIONAL B.V.—Akzo Nobel N.V.; Int'l, pg. 44
ORGANON LABORATORIES LTD.—Akzo Nobel N.V.; Int'l, pg. 45
ORGANON MEXICANA SA—Akzo Nobel N.V.; Int'l, pg. 45
ORGANON PAKISTAN (PRIVATE) LIMITED—Akzo Nobel N.V.; Int'l, pg. 45
ORGANON SA—Akzo Nobel N.V.; Int'l, pg. 45
ORGANON VENEZOLANA SA—Akzo Nobel N.V.; Int'l, pg. 45
ORTHO-MCNEIL PHARMACEUTICAL CORPORATION—Johnson & Johnson; U.S. Public, pg. 929
OTSUKA AMERICA PHARMACEUTICAL, INC.—Otsuka Pharmaceutical Co., Ltd.; Int'l, pg. 1013
P.T. OTSUKA INDONESIA—Otsuka Pharmaceutical Co., Ltd.; Int'l, pg. 1014
P.T. OTSUKA JAYA INDAH—Otsuka Pharmaceutical Co., Ltd.; Int'l, pg. 1014
OTSUKA PAKISTAN LTD.—Otsuka Pharmaceutical Co., Ltd.; Int'l, pg. 1014
OTSUKA PHARMACEUTICAL CO., LTD.; Int'l, pg. 1013
PALM BEACH BEAUTY PRODUCTS CO.; U.S. Private, pg. 834
PARKE-DAVIS GROUP—Warner-Lambert Company; U.S. Public, pg. 1739
PARTICLE DYNAMICS, INC.—KV Pharmaceutical Company; U.S. Public, pg. 941
PATERSON ZOCHONIS PLC; Int'l, pg. 1024
PENFORD FOOD INGREDIENTS COMPANY—Penford Corp.; U.S. Public, pg. 1269
PERMARK INTERNATIONAL (PTY.) LTD.; Int'l, pg. 1036
L. PERRIGO COMPANY; U.S. Public, pg. 1280
PERRIGO OF TENNESSEE—L. Perrigo Company; U.S. Public, pg. 1280
PERSTORP PHARMA AB—Perstorp AB; Int'l, pg. 1036
PERSTORP PHARMA LTD. WOUND CARE DIVISION—Perstorp AB; Int'l, pg. 1037
PFIZER AB—Pfizer Inc.; U.S. Public, pg. 1282
PFIZER INC.; U.S. Public, pg. 1281
PHARM-ALLERGAN GMBH—Allergan, Inc.; U.S. Public, pg. 46
PHARMACEUTICAL BASICS, INC.—Akzo Nobel N.V.; Int'l, pg. 48
PHARMACEUTICAL FORMULATIONS, INC.; U.S. Public, pg. 1284
PHARMACEUTICAL RESOURCES; U.S. Public, pg. 1285
PHARMACEUTICALS DIVISION—3M; U.S. Public, pg. 1605
PHARMACIA & UPJOHN—Pharmacia & Upjohn, Inc.; Int'l, pg. 1048
PHARMACIA & UPJOHN AB—Pharmacia & Upjohn, Inc.; Int'l, pg. 1049
PHARMACIA & UPJOHN BIOTECH AB—Pharmacia & Upjohn, Inc.; Int'l, pg. 1047
PHARMACIA & UPJOHN COMPANIA LIMITADA—Pharmacia & Upjohn, Inc.; Int'l, pg. 1049
PHARMACIA & UPJOHN COMPANY HONG KONG BRANCH—Pharmacia & Upjohn, Inc.; Int'l, pg. 1049
PHARMACIA & UPJOHN COMPANY LIMITED—Pharmacia & Upjohn, Inc.; Int'l, pg. 1049
PHARMACIA & UPJOHN COMPANY S.A.—Pharmacia & Upjohn, Inc.; Int'l, pg. 1049
PHARMACIA & UPJOHN FARMOQUIMICA, S.A.—Pharmacia & Upjohn, Inc.; Int'l, pg. 1049
PHARMACIA & UPJOHN GMBH—Pharmacia & Upjohn, Inc.; Int'l, pg. 1049
PHARMACIA & UPJOHN, INC.; Int'l, pg. 1047
PHARMACIA & UPJOHN, INC.—Pharmacia & Upjohn, Inc.; Int'l, pg. 1049
P.T. PHARMACIA & UPJOHN INDONESIA—Pharmacia & Upjohn, Inc.; Int'l, pg. 1049
PHARMACIA & UPJOHN LABORATORIES LIMITED—Pharmacia & Upjohn, Inc.; Int'l, pg. 1049
PHARMACIA & UPJOHN LIMITED—Pharmacia & Upjohn, Inc.; Int'l, pg. 1049
PHARMACIA & UPJOHN MANUFACTURING CO.—Pharmacia & Upjohn, Inc.; Int'l, pg. 1048
PHARMACIA & UPJOHN OPHTHALMICS—Pharmacia & Upjohn, Inc.; Int'l, pg. 1048
PHARMACIA & UPJOHN PEPTIDE HORMONES—Pharmacia & Upjohn, Inc.; Int'l, pg. 1048
PHARMACIA & UPJOHN PHARMACEUTICAL DIV.—Pharmacia & Upjohn, Inc.; Int'l, pg. 1048
PHARMACIA & UPJOHN PLASMA PRODUCTS—Pharmacia & Upjohn, Inc.; Int'l, pg. 1048
PHARMACIA & UPJOHN PTY. LIMITED—Pharmacia & Upjohn, Inc.; Int'l, pg. 1049
PHARMACIA & UPJOHN S.A. DE C.V.—Pharmacia & Upjohn, Inc.; Int'l, pg. 1049
N.V. PHARMACIA & UPJOHN S.A.—Pharmacia & Upjohn, Inc.; Int'l, pg. 1049
PHARMACIA & UPJOHN S.P.A.—Pharmacia & Upjohn, Inc.; Int'l, pg. 1049
PHARMACIA & UPJOHN THERAPEUTICS—Pharmacia & Upjohn, Inc.; Int'l, pg. 1048
PHARMAVITE CORP.; U.S. Private, pg. 860
PHARMAX LTD.—Forest Laboratories, Inc.; U.S. Public, pg. 670
PHARMERICA-REGIONAL OFFICE—PharMerica, Inc.; U.S. Public, pg. 1286
PHARMETRIX CORPORATION—Recordati Industria Chimica e Farmaceutica S.p.A.; Int'l, pg. 1090
PHARMOSOL CORPORATION—Elf Aquitane; Int'l, pg. 446
PIERRE FABRE S.A.; Int'l, pg. 1056
PILKINGTON PLC; Int'l, pg. 1056
PLOUGH U.S.A.—Schering-Plough Corporation; U.S. Public, pg. 1438
POLIVE/TRICOSTERIL—Fort James Corporation; U.S. Public, pg. 673
POLYDEX PHARMACEUTICALS LIMITED; Int'l, pg. 1062
PROCTER & GAMBLE HEALTH & BEAUTY CARE SO. EUROPE—The Procter & Gamble Company; U.S. Public, pg. 1332
PROCTER & GAMBLE HEALTH & PERSONAL CARE DIV.—The Procter & Gamble Company; U.S. Public, pg. 1331
PROCTER & GAMBLE OF PERU—The Procter & Gamble Company; U.S. Public, pg. 1332
PROCTER & GAMBLE PHARMACEUTICALS, INC.—The Procter & Gamble Company; U.S. Public, pg. 1331
PRODUCTOS CIBA SA—Novartis AG; Int'l, pg. 983
PRODUCTOS FARMOQUIMICOS ROCHE LTDA.—Roche Holding Ltd.; Int'l, pg. 1121
PRODUCTOS ROCHE QUIMICA FARMACEUTICA S.A.—Roche Holding Ltd.; Int'l, pg. 1121
PRODUCTOS ROCHE S.A.—Roche Holding Ltd.; Int'l, pg. 1121
PRODUITS ALIMENTAIRES ET DIETETIQUES (SIDPAD)—Nestle S.A.; Int'l, pg. 922
PRODUITS ROCHE S.A.—Roche Holding Ltd.; Int'l, pg. 1121
PRODUTOS ROCHE QUIMICOS E FARMACEUTICOS S.A.—Roche Holding Ltd.; Int'l, pg. 1121
PRODUTOS SANDOZ LDA.—Novartis AG; Int'l, pg. 983
PROLIMPER S.A.—Henkel KGaA; Int'l, pg. 612
PROQUIMO PRODS. QUIMS OPOT. LTDA.—Akzo Nobel N.V.; Int'l, pg. 45
QUIMICA ESTEROIDAL SA DE CV—Akzo Nobel N.V.; Int'l, pg. 45
QUIMICA FARMACEUTICA BAYER, S.A.—Bayer AG; Int'l, pg. 175
QUIMICA KNOLL DE MEXICO, S.A. DE C.V. BASF PHARMA—BASF AG; Int'l, pg. 109
QUIMICA SCHERING COLOMBIANA S. A.—Schering AG; Int'l, pg. 1204
QUIMIFAR, LDA.—Solvay S.A.; Int'l, pg. 1279
RECKITT & COLMAN PHARMACEUTICALS—Reckitt & Colman plc; Int'l, pg. 1090
RECKITT & COLMAN PLC; Int'l, pg. 1089
RECKITT & COLMAN PRODUCTS—Reckitt & Colman plc; Int'l, pg. 1090
RECORDATI FARMA S.R.L.—Recordati Industria Chimica e Farmaceutica S.p.A.; Int'l, pg. 1090
RECORDATI INDUSTRIA CHIMICA E FARMACEUTICA S.P.A.; Int'l, pg. 1090
RECORDATI PHARMACEUTICAL CHEMICALS DIVISION:—Recordati Industria Chimica e Farmaceutica S.p.A.; Int'l, pg. 1090
REEDCO, INC.—Block Drug Company, Inc.; U.S. Public, pg. 237
REPRESENTATION OF CIBA-GEIGY SERVICES LTD.—Novartis AG; Int'l, pg. 984
RETI SA—Akzo Nobel N.V.; Int'l, pg. 45
REXALL INC. CONSUMER PRODUCTS DIV.—Rexall Sundown Inc.; U.S. Public, pg. 1384
REXALL SUNDOWN INC.; U.S. Public, pg. 1384
RHEIN-PHARMA ARZNEIMITTELWERK GMBH—Zeneca Group Plc; Int'l, pg. 1525
RHODIA A.G.—Rhone-Poulenc S.A.; Int'l, pg. 1112
RHODIA S.A.—Rhone-Poulenc S.A.; Int'l, pg. 1112
RHONE-POULENC INC.—Rhone-Poulenc S.A.; Int'l, pg. 1112
RHONE-POULENC RORER LTD.—Rhone-Poulenc S.A.; Int'l, pg. 1110
RHONE-POULENC RORER PHILIPPINES INC.—Rhone-Poulenc S.A.; Int'l, pg. 1111
RHONE-POULENC RORER - U.S.—Rhone-Poulenc S.A.; Int'l, pg. 1110
RHONE-POULENC SANTE—Rhone-Poulenc S.A.; Int'l, pg. 1109
RICHARDSON-VICKS, INC.—The Procter & Gamble Company; U.S. Public, pg. 1331
RICHARDSON-VICKS, INC., HEALTH CARE PRODUCTS—The Procter & Gamble Company; U.S. Public, pg. 1331
RICHARDSON-VICKS, INC. PERSONAL CARE PRODUCTS DIV.—The Procter & Gamble Company; U.S. Public, pg. 1331
A.H. ROBINS FARMACEUTICA, S.A.—American Home Products Corporation; U.S. Public, pg. 82
A.H. ROBINS INTERNATIONAL, S.A.—American Home Products Corporation; U.S. Public, pg. 82
A.H. ROBINS (IRAN) COMPANY—American Home Products Corporation; U.S. Public, pg. 82
ROCHE AB—Roche Holding Ltd.; Int'l, pg. 1121
ROCHE AG—Roche Holding Ltd.; Int'l, pg. 1120
ROCHE FARMACEUTICA QUIMICA LIMITADA—Roche Holding Ltd.; Int'l, pg. 1121
ROCHE (HELLAS) S.A.—Roche Holding Ltd.; Int'l, pg. 1121
ROCHE HOLDING LTD.; Int'l, pg. 1119
ROCHE INTERNATIONAL LTD.—Roche Holding Ltd.; Int'l, pg. 1121
ROCHE KIMYASAL URUNLER VE TEKNIK CIHAZLAR LTD.—Roche Holding Ltd.; Int'l, pg. 1121
ROCHE KOREA COMPANY LTD.—Roche Holding Ltd.; Int'l, pg. 1121
ROCHE MALAYSIA SDN. BHD.—Roche Holding Ltd.; Int'l, pg. 1121
ROCHE MEXICANA DE FARMACOS, S.A. DE C.V. EL SALTO (JALISCO)—Roche Holding Ltd.; Int'l, pg. 1121
ROCHE MUSTAHZARLARI SANAYI LIMITED SIRKETI—Roche Holding Ltd.; Int'l, pg. 1121
ROCHE (NIGERIA) LTD.—Roche Holding Ltd.; Int'l, pg. 1121
ROCHE PAKISTAN LTD.—Roche Holding Ltd.; Int'l, pg. 1121
ROCHE PHARMACEUTICAL (IRELAND) LIMITED—Roche Holding Ltd.; Int'l, pg. 1121
ROCHE PHARMACEUTICALS & CHEMICALS LTD.—Roche Holding Ltd.; Int'l, pg. 1121
ROCHE (PHILIPPINES) INC.—Roche Holding Ltd.; Int'l, pg. 1121
ROCHE PRODUCTS LTD.—Roche Holding Ltd.; Int'l, pg. 1121
ROCHE PRODUCTS (NEW ZEALAND) LTD.—Roche Holding Ltd.; Int'l, pg. 1122
ROCHE PRODUCTS (PTY.) LTD.—Roche Holding Ltd.; Int'l, pg. 1122
ROCHE THAILAND LTD.—Roche Holding Ltd.; Int'l, pg. 1122
ROHTO PHARMACEUTICAL CO.; Int'l, pg. 1126
RORER ARGENTINA S.A.—Rhone-Poulenc S.A.; Int'l, pg. 1111
RORER AUSTRALIA PTY. LTD.—Rhone-Poulenc S.A.; Int'l, pg. 1111
RORER B.V.—Rhone-Poulenc S.A.; Int'l, pg. 1111
RORER (CARIBBEAN) CORP.—Rhone-Poulenc S.A.; Int'l, pg. 1111
RORER DE CENTRO AMERICA (GUATEMALA) S.A.—Rhone-Poulenc S.A.; Int'l, pg. 1111
RORER DE CENTRO AMERICA S.A. DE C.V.—Rhone-Poulenc S.A.; Int'l, pg. 1111
RORER DE ECUADOR, S.A.—Rhone-Poulenc S.A.; Int'l, pg. 1111
RORER DE MEXICO, S.A. DE C.V.—Rhone-Poulenc S.A.; Int'l, pg. 1111
RORER DO BRASIL QUIMICA E. FARMACEUTICA LTDA.—Rhone-Poulenc S.A.; Int'l, pg. 1111
RORER GMBH—Rhone-Poulenc S.A.; Int'l, pg. 1111
RORER HEALTH CARE LTD.—Rhone-Poulenc S.A.; Int'l, pg. 1112
RORER-INTER-AMERICAN CORP.—Rhone-Poulenc S.A.; Int'l, pg. 1111
RORER IRELAND, LTD.—Rhone-Poulenc S.A.; Int'l, pg. 1112
RORER JAPAN, INC.—Rhone-Poulenc S.A.; Int'l, pg. 1112
S.A. RORER N.V.—Rhone-Poulenc S.A.; Int'l, pg. 1112
RORER PANAMA S.A.—Rhone-Poulenc S.A.; Int'l, pg. 1112
RORER PHARMACEUTICAL (SINGAPORE) PTE. LTD.—Rhone-Poulenc S.A.; Int'l, pg. 1112
RORER PUERTO RICO INC.—Rhone-Poulenc S.A.; Int'l, pg. 1111
RORER, S.A.—Rhone-Poulenc S.A.; Int'l, pg. 1112

RORER S.P.A.—Rhone-Poulenc S.A.; *Int'l*, pg. 1112
ROSS PRODUCTS—Abbott Laboratories; *U.S. Public*, pg. 13
ROTTA FARMACEUTICI, S.P.A.—Rhone-Poulenc S.A.; *Int'l*, *pg. 1112*
ROUSSEL UCLAF S.A.—Hoechst Aktiengesellschaft; *Int'l*, pg. 626
ROVITHAI LIMITED—Roche Holding Ltd.; *Int'l*, pg. 1122
ROXANE LABORATORIES, INC.—Boehringer Ingelheim GmbH; *Int'l*, pg. 199
ROYAL GIST-BROCADES N.V.; *Int'l*, pg. 1142
ROYCE LABORATORIES—Watson Pharmaceuticals, Inc.; *U.S. Public*, pg. 1746
RUETGERS A.G.; *Int'l*, pg. 1147
RYSTAN COMPANY, INC.—GWC Health, Inc.; *U.S. Private*, *pg. 436*
SABANCI HOLDING A.S.; *Int'l*, pg. 1167
SANDOZ AUSTRALIA PTY. LTD.—Novartis AG; *Int'l*, pg. 984
P.T. SANDOZ-BIOCHEMIE FARMA INDONESIA—Novartis AG; *Int'l*, pg. 984
SANDOZ CLINICAL & NUTRITION DIV.—Novartis AG; *Int'l*, *pg. 974*
SANDOZ COLOMBIANA S.A.—Novartis AG; *Int'l*, pg. 984
SANDOZ CORPORATION—Novartis AG; *Int'l*, pg. 974
SANDOZ DE MEXICO S.A. DE C.V.—Novartis AG; *Int'l*, pg. 984
SANDOZ DONGKOOK LTD.—Novartis AG; *Int'l*, pg. 984
SANDOZ FARMACEUTICA LTDA.—Novartis AG; *Int'l*, pg. 984
SANDOZ FORSCHUNGSINSTITUT GESELLSCHAFT M.B.H.—Novartis AG; *Int'l*, pg. 984
SANDOZ (HELLAS) S.A.C.I.—Novartis AG; *Int'l*, pg. 984
SANDOZ (INDIA) LTD.—Novartis AG; *Int'l*, pg. 984
SANDOZ KIMYA SANAYII LTD. SIRKETI—Novartis AG; *Int'l*, pg. 984
SANDOZ PERU S.A.—Novartis AG; *Int'l*, pg. 985
SANDOZ PHARMA LTD.—Novartis AG; *Int'l*, pg. 972
SANDOZ PHARMA S.A.E.—Novartis AG; *Int'l*, pg. 985
SANDOZ PHARMACEUTICALS CORP.—Novartis AG; *Int'l*, pg. 974
SANDOZ (PHILIPPINES) INC.—Novartis AG; *Int'l*, pg. 985
SANDOZ PRODOTTI FARMACEUTICI S.P.A.—Novartis AG; *Int'l*, pg. 985
SANDOZ PRODUCTS (IRELAND) LTD.—Novartis AG; *Int'l*, pg. 985
SANDOZ PRODUCTS LTD.—Novartis AG; *Int'l*, pg. 985
SANDOZ PRODUCTS (MALAYSIA) SDN. BHD.—Novartis AG; *Int'l*, pg. 985
SANDOZ QUIMICA Y FARMACEUTICA S.A.—Novartis AG; *Int'l*, pg. 985
SANDOZ RESEARCH INSTITUTE—Novartis AG; *Int'l*, pg. 974
SANDOZ RESEARCH INSTITUTE BERNE LTD.—Novartis AG; *Int'l*, pg. 972
SANDOZ RINGASKIDDY LTD.—Novartis AG; *Int'l*, pg. 985
SANDOZ YAKUHIN K.K.—Novartis AG; *Int'l*, pg. 985
SANI-MIST, INC.; *U.S. Private*, pg. 965
SANI-TECH INC.—Sybron International Corporation; *U.S. Public*, pg. 1545
SANKYO COMPANY LIMITED; *Int'l*, pg. 1189
SANOFI—Elf Aquitane; *Int'l*, pg. 446
SANOFI CANADA—Elf Aquitane; *Int'l*, pg. 445
SANOFI-MEIJI PHARMACEUTICALS CO., LTD.—Meiji Seika Kaisha, Ltd.; *Int'l*, pg. 855
SANOFI PHARMACEUTICALS INC.—Elf Aquitane; *Int'l*, pg. 445
SANOFI PHARMACEUTICALS, INC.—Elf Aquitane; *Int'l*, pg. 445
SANORANIA GMBH—Pharmacia & Upjohn, Inc.; *Int'l*, pg. 1049
SCHEIN PHARMACEUTICAL, INC.; *U.S. Private*, pg. 969
SCHERAX ARZNEIMITTEL GMBH—Schering AG; *Int'l*, pg. 1203
R.P. SCHERER CORPORATION; *U.S. Public*, pg. 1437
R.P. SCHERER NORTH AMERICA—R.P. Scherer Corporation; *U.S. Public*, pg. 1438
SCHERING AG; *Int'l*, pg. 1203
SCHERING A/S—Schering AG; *Int'l*, pg. 1204
SCHERING MEXICANA SA—Schering AG; *Int'l*, pg. 1204
SCHERING-PLOUGH CORPORATION; *U.S. Public*, pg. 1438
SCHERING PTY. LTD.—Schering AG; *Int'l*, pg. 1204
N.V. SCHERING S.A./BELGIEN—Schering AG; *Int'l*, pg. 1204
E. SCHEURICH PHARMWERK GMBH—American Home Products Corporation; *U.S. Public*, pg. 82
SCHWARZ PHARMA AG; *Int'l*, pg. 1211
SCHWARZ PHARMA INC.—Schwarz Pharma AG; *Int'l*, pg. 1211
SCHWARZ PHARMA MANUFACTURING, INC.—Schwarz Pharma AG; *Int'l*, pg. 1211
SCIENTIFIC PROTEIN LABORATORIES, INC.—American Home Products Corporation; *U.S. Public*, pg. 80
SEARLE & CO.—Monsanto Company; *U.S. Public*, pg. 1125
SEARLE CANADA INC.—Monsanto Company; *U.S. Public*, pg. 1126
SEARLE CHEMICALS, INC.—Monsanto Company; *U.S. Public*, pg. 1125
SEARLE CIBA-GEIGY KOREA LTD.—Novartis AG; *Int'l*, pg. 985
G.D. SEARLE & COMPANY LIMITED—Monsanto Company; *U.S. Public*, pg. 1126
SEARLE LABORATORIES—Monsanto Company; *U.S. Public*, pg. 1125
SEIN MENDEZ LABORATORIES, INC.—Forest Laboratories, Inc.; *U.S. Public*, pg. 670
SENTINEL CONSUMER PRODUCTS, INC.; *U.S. Private*, pg. 984
SENTINEL CONSUMER PRODUCTS, INC.—Sentinel Consumer Products, Inc.; *U.S. Private*, pg. 984
SEQUUS PHARMACEUTICALS, INC.; *U.S. Public*, pg. 1460
SERVIPHARM LTD.—Novartis AG; *Int'l*, pg. 972
SETON COMPANY; *U.S. Private*, pg. 987
SEVEN SEAS LIMITED—Hanson PLC; *Int'l*, pg. 593
SHIONOGI & CO., LTD.; *Int'l*, pg. 1234
SHIONOGI LILLY KABUSHIKI KAISHA—Eli Lilly and Company; *U.S. Public*, pg. 994
SIEBE NORTH INC.—Siebe plc; *Int'l*, pg. 1242
SIGMA-TAU FINANZIARIA S.P.A.; *Int'l*, pg. 1248
SMITH & NEPHEW UNITED INC.—Smith & Nephew PLC; *Int'l*, pg. 1263
SMITHKLINE & FRENCH (BANGLADESH) LTD.—SmithKline Beecham plc; *Int'l*, pg. 1265
SMITHKLINE & FRENCH B.V.—SmithKline Beecham plc; *Int'l*, pg. 1265
SMITHKLINE & FRENCH, C.A.—SmithKline Beecham plc; *Int'l*, pg. 1265
SMITHKLINE & FRENCH INTER-AMERICAN CORP.—SmithKline Beecham plc; *Int'l*, pg. 1265
SMITHKLINE & FRENCH INTL., GMBH—SmithKline Beecham plc; *Int'l*, pg. 1265
SMITHKLINE & FRENCH NIGERIA, LTD.—SmithKline Beecham plc; *Int'l*, pg. 1265
SMITHKLINE & FRENCH OF IRAN LIMITED—SmithKline Beecham plc; *Int'l*, pg. 1265
SMITHKLINE & FRENCH PAKISTAN, LTD.—SmithKline Beecham plc; *Int'l*, pg. 1265
SMITHKLINE & FRENCH PORTUGUESA—SmithKline Beecham plc; *Int'l*, pg. 1265
SMITHKLINE & FRENCH (PROPRIETARY) LTD.—SmithKline Beecham plc; *Int'l*, pg. 1265
SMITHKLINE & FRENCH, S.A.—SmithKline Beecham plc; *Int'l*, pg. 1265
SMITHKLINE & FRENCH SWITZERLAND LTD.—SmithKline Beecham plc; *Int'l*, pg. 1265
SMITHKLINE BEECHAM A.G.—SmithKline Beecham plc; *Int'l*, pg. 1265
SMITHKLINE BEECHAM BIOLOGICALS S.A.—SmithKline Beecham plc; *Int'l*, pg. 1265
SMITHKLINE BEECHAM CANADA, INC.—SmithKline Beecham plc; *Int'l*, pg. 1265
SMITHKLINE BEECHAM C.I.S.A.—SmithKline Beecham plc; *Int'l*, pg. 1265
SMITHKLINE BEECHAM CONSUMER BRANDS—SmithKline Beecham plc; *Int'l*, pg. 1264
SMITHKLINE BEECHAM CONSUMER HEALTHCARE, U.S.—SmithKline Beecham plc; *Int'l*, pg. 1264
SMITHKLINE BEECHAM CONSUMER PRODUCTS—SmithKline Beecham plc; *Int'l*, pg. 1264
SMITHKLINE BEECHAM CORPORATION—SmithKline Beecham plc; *Int'l*, pg. 1264
SMITHKLINE BEECHAM-DAUELSBERG G.M.B.H & CO.—SmithKline Beecham plc; *Int'l*, pg. 1266
SMITHKLINE BEECHAM DE MEXICO S.A. DE C.V.—SmithKline Beecham plc; *Int'l*, pg. 1266
SMITHKLINE BEECHAM DIERGENEESKUNDIGE PRODUCTEN B.V.—SmithKline Beecham plc; *Int'l*, pg. 1266
SMITHKLINE BEECHAM DIVISION VETERINARIA—SmithKline Beecham plc; *Int'l*, pg. 1266
SMITHKLINE BEECHAM ITALIA S.P.A.—SmithKline Beecham plc; *Int'l*, pg. 1266
SMITHKLINE BEECHAM LABORATORIES—SmithKline Beecham plc; *Int'l*, pg. 1264
SMITHKLINE BEECHAM LABORATORIES LTD.—SmithKline Beecham plc; *Int'l*, pg. 1266
SMITHKLINE BEECHAM (NEW ZEALAND) LTD.—SmithKline Beecham plc; *Int'l*, pg. 1266
SMITHKLINE BEECHAM PAKISTAN (PRIVATE) LIMITED—SmithKline Beecham plc; *Int'l*, pg. 1266
SMITHKLINE BEECHAM PHARMA S.A.—SmithKline Beecham plc; *Int'l*, pg. 1266
SMITHKLINE BEECHAM PHARMACEUTICALS—SmithKline Beecham plc; *Int'l*, pg. 1264
SMITHKLINE BEECHAM PHARMACEUTICALS INC.—SmithKline Beecham plc; *Int'l*, pg. 1266
SMITHKLINE BEECHAM PHARMACEUTICALS (PTY.) LTD.—SmithKline Beecham plc; *Int'l*, pg. 1266
SMITHKLINE BEECHAM PLC; *Int'l*, pg. 1264
SMITHKLINE BEECHAM PORTUGUESA PRODUCTOS FARMACEUTICOS E QUIMICOS LDA.—SmithKline Beecham plc; *Int'l*, pg. 1266
SMITHKLINE BEECHAM RESEARCH LIMITED—SmithKline Beecham plc; *Int'l*, pg. 1266
SMITHKLINE BEECHAM S.A.—SmithKline Beecham plc; *Int'l*, pg. 1266
SMITHKLINE BEECHAM SAUDE ANIMAL—SmithKline Beecham plc; *Int'l*, pg. 1266
SMITHKLINE BEECHAM (VENEZUELA) S.A.—SmithKline Beecham plc; *Int'l*, pg. 1266
SMITHKLINE BEECHAM YAKUHIN K.K.—SmithKline Beecham plc; *Int'l*, pg. 1266
SOCHIM COTE-D'IVOIRE SA—Novartis AG; *Int'l*, pg. 985
SOCIETE CAMEROUNAISE DE PRODUITS ALIMETAIRES, DIETETIQUES ET AUTRES (CAMAD)—Nestle S.A.; *Int'l*, *pg. 922*
SOCIETE CHIMIQUE ROCHE S.A.—Roche Holding Ltd.; *Int'l*, pg. 1121
SOCIETE DE PRODUITS ALIMETAIRES ET DIETETIQUES, SOPAD-NESTLE S.A.—Nestle S.A.; *Int'l*, pg. 922
SOCIETE FRANCAISE LABORATOIRE ABBOTT—Abbott Laboratories; *U.S. Public*, pg. 14
SOCIETE GABONAISE DE PRODUITS ALIMETAIRES (SOGAPRAL)—Nestle S.A.; *Int'l*, pg. 922
SOLVAY ANIMAL HEALTH, INC.—Solvay S.A.; *Int'l*, pg. 1277
SOLVAY DUPHAR B.V.—Solvay S.A.; *Int'l*, pg. 1279
SOLVAY OSTERREICH AG—Solvay S.A.; *Int'l*, pg. 1280
SOLVAY PERFORMANCE CHEMICALS—Solvay S.A.; *Int'l*, pg. 1278
SOLVAY PHARMACEUTICALS, INC.—Solvay S.A.; *Int'l*, pg. 1278
SOLVAY S.A.; *Int'l*, pg. 1277
SOLVAY VETERINARY LTD.—Solvay S.A.; *Int'l*, pg. 1280
SOMERSET PHARMACEUTICALS INC.—Mylan Laboratories, Inc.; *U.S. Public*, pg. 1143
SPECIA—Rhone-Poulenc S.A.; *Int'l*, pg. 1109
SQUIBB-CONTAVEC SA—Bristol-Myers Squibb Company; *U.S. Public*, pg. 256
E.R. SQUIBB & SONS LTD.—Bristol-Myers Squibb Company; *U.S. Public*, pg. 256
SQUIBB EUROPE INC.—Bristol-Myers Squibb Company; *U.S. Public*, pg. 256
SQUIBB MANUFACTURING INC.—Bristol-Myers Squibb Company; *U.S. Public*, pg. 254
SQUIBB SPA—Bristol-Myers Squibb Company; *U.S. Public*, pg. 256
STABILMENTI CHIMICO FARMACEUTICI DOTT. R. RAVASINI & CIA. SPA—Akzo Nobel N.V.; *Int'l*, pg. 45
STAMFORD HOLDINGS B.V. (NETHERLANDS)—Bristol-Myers Squibb Company; *U.S. Public*, pg. 256
STANBACK COMPANY; *U.S. Private*, pg. 1030
STERIS LABORATORIES, INC.—Schein Pharmaceutical, Inc.; *U.S. Private*, pg. 969
STIEFEL LABORATORIES, INC.; *U.S. Private*, pg. 1043
STURGE BIOCHEMICALS—Rhone-Poulenc S.A.; *Int'l*, pg. 1113
SUBSTANTIA GESELLSCHAFT M.B.H.—Warner-Lambert Company; *U.S. Public*, pg. 1739
SUMITOMO CHEMICAL COMPANY, LTD.; *Int'l*, pg. 1310
SUMITOMO PHARMACEUTICALS CO., LTD.—Sumitomo Chemical Company, Ltd.; *Int'l*, pg. 1311
SWISS NIGERIAN CHEMICAL CO. LTD.—Novartis AG; *Int'l*, pg. 986
SWISSPHARMA S.A.E.—Novartis AG; *Int'l*, pg. 986
SWISSPHARMA TAIWAN LTD.—Novartis AG; *Int'l*, pg. 986
SYLAMERICA—L'Oreal S.A.; *Int'l*, pg. 818
SYNTEX—Roche Holding Ltd.; *Int'l*, pg. 1120
SYNTEX AGRIBUSINESS, INC.—Roche Holding Ltd.; *Int'l*, pg. 1120
SYNTHELABO S.A.—L'Oreal S.A.; *Int'l*, pg. 818
T C MANUFACTURING COMPANY, INC.; *U.S. Private*, pg. 1062
TUCO ANIMAL HEALTH—Pharmacia & Upjohn, Inc.; *Int'l*, pg. 1048
TAISHO PHARMACEUTICAL CO., LTD.; *Int'l*, pg. 1348
TAITO CO., LTD.—Mitsui & Co., Ltd.; *Int'l*, pg. 878
TAIWAN OTSUKA PHARMACEUTICAL CO., LTD.—Otsuka Pharmaceutical Co., Ltd.; *Int'l*, pg. 1014
TAKEDA CHEMICAL INDUSTRIES, LTD.; *Int'l*, pg. 1350
TANABE SEIYAKU CO., LTD.; *Int'l*, pg. 1354
TARGETED GENETICS CORP.—Immunex Corporation; *U.S. Public*, pg. 871
TASMANIAN ALKALOIDS PTY. LTD.—Johnson & Johnson; *U.S. Public*, pg. 932
TAXANDRIA PHARMACEUTICA B.V.—Johnson & Johnson; *U.S. Public*, pg. 932
TERUMO CORPORATION; *Int'l*, pg. 1375
TEVA USA - BIOCRAFT—Teva Pharmaceutical Industries Ltd.; *Int'l*, pg. 1381
THAI MEIJI PHARMACEUTICAL CO., LTD.—Meiji Seika Kaisha, Ltd.; *Int'l*, pg. 856
THAI OTSUKA PHARMACEUTICAL CO., LTD.—Otsuka Pharmaceutical Co., Ltd.; *Int'l*, pg. 1014
THEON CO. LTD.—Del Laboratories, Inc.; *U.S. Public*, pg. 494
THIEMANN ARZNEIMITTEL GMBH—Akzo Nobel N.V.; *Int'l*, *pg. 45*
THOMPSON MEDICAL COMPANY, INC.; *U.S. Private*, pg. 1083
3M; *U.S. Public*, pg. 1604
TIGER MEDICALS LTD.—Haw Par Brothers International Limited; *Int'l*, pg. 603
TOHO KAGAKU KENKYUSHO CO., LTD.—E-Z-Em, Inc.; *U.S. Public*, pg. 540
TOLBIACHIM—American Home Products Corporation; *U.S. Public*, pg. 82
TONWERKE ERPEL WERNER E. GABLER GMBH—Solvay S.A.; *Int'l*, pg. 1278
TOSARA GROUP—Forest Laboratories, Inc.; *U.S. Public*, pg. 670
TRIOSOL, S.A.—Solvay S.A.; *Int'l*, pg. 1279
TRIPLE F, INC.; *U.S. Private*, pg. 1104
TROPONWERKE GMBH & CO., KG—Bayer AG; *Int'l*, pg. 175
UAD LABORATORIES—Forest Laboratories, Inc.; *U.S. Public*, pg. 670
UCB, S.A.; *Int'l*, pg. 1427
USV (P.R) DEVELOPMENT CORPORATION—Rhone-Poulenc S.A.; *Int'l*, pg. 1111
UNION TECHNIQUE INDUSTRIELLE S.A.—Bristol-Myers Squibb Company; *U.S. Public*, pg. 256
UNIONE CHIMICA MEDICAMENTI-DIFME-S.P.A.—Solvay S.A.; *Int'l*, pg. 1279
UNIPHARMA S.A.—Pharmacia & Upjohn, Inc.; *Int'l*, pg. 1048
U.S. BIOSCIENCE, INC.; *U.S. Public*, pg. 1681
U.S. PHARMACEUTICALS—Alpharma Inc.; *U.S. Public*, pg. 58
VIMRX PHARMACEUTICALS, INC.; *U.S. Public*, pg. 1702
VP-SCHICKEDANZ AG—The Procter & Gamble Company; *U.S. Public*, pg. 1333
VPF B.V.—Akzo Nobel N.V.; *Int'l*, pg. 44
VEMIE-VETRINAR-CHEMIE GMBH—Akzo Nobel N.V.; *Int'l*, *pg. 45*
BEN VENUE LABORATORIES, INC.; *U.S. Private*, pg. 1136
VESTRETUNG DES KNOLL AG—BASF AG; *Int'l*, pg. 110
VETERINARY LABORATORIES, INC.—Polydex Pharmaceuticals Limited; *Int'l*, pg. 1063
VIGORTONE AG PRODUCTS, INC.—Tate & Lyle PLC; *Int'l*, *pg. 1357*
VINELAND LABORATORIES INC.—IGI, Inc.; *U.S. Public*, pg. 855
VITALINK PHARMACY SERVICES, INC.—Manor Care, Inc.; *U.S. Public*, pg. 1041
VITAMIN WORLD—Nature's Bounty Inc.; *U.S. Public*, pg. 1166
VITATECH INTERNATIONAL, INC.; *U.S. Private*, pg. 1142

WALLACE LABORATORIES—Carter-Wallace, Inc.; U.S. Public, pg. 310
WARNER-CHILCOTT LABORATORIES, INC.—Elan Corporation Plc; Int'l, pg. 436
WARNER-LAMBERT—Warner-Lambert Company; U.S. Public, pg. 1739
WARNER-LAMBERT COMPANY; U.S. Public, pg. 1738
WARNER-LAMBERT (PORTUGAL) COMERCIO E INDUSTRIA LIMITADA—Warner-Lambert Company; U.S. Public, pg. 1740
WARNER-LAMBERT SCANDINAVIA AKTIEBOLAG—Warner-Lambert Company; U.S. Public, pg. 1740
WARNER-LAMBERT (SCHWEIZ) AG—Warner-Lambert Company; U.S. Public, pg. 1740
WATERFORD PHARMACEUTICALS LTD.—IVAX Corporation; U.S. Public, pg. 915
WATSON LABORATORIES, INC.—Watson Pharmaceuticals, Inc.; U.S. Public, pg. 1746
WATSON PHARMACEUTICALS, INC.; U.S. Public, pg. 1746
WELLCOME AUSTRALIA LTD.—Glaxo Wellcome plc; Int'l, pg. 553
WELLCOME GMBH—Glaxo Wellcome plc; Int'l, pg. 553
WELLCOME IRELAND LTD.—Glaxo Wellcome plc; Int'l, pg. 553
N.V. WELLCOME S.A.—Glaxo Wellcome plc; Int'l, pg. 553
WELLCOME SINGAPORE PRIVATE LTD.—Glaxo Wellcome plc; Int'l, pg. 553
WELLCOME THAILAND LTD.—Glaxo Wellcome plc; Int'l, pg. 553
WESTWOOD PRODUCTS, S.A.—Bristol-Myers Squibb Company; U.S. Public, pg. 256
WESTWOOD-SQUIBB PHARMACEUTICALS INC.—Bristol-Myers Squibb Company; U.S. Public, pg. 255
WHITBY, INC.—UCB, S.A.; Int'l, pg. 1427
WHITEHALL LABORATORIES PTY. LIMITED—American Home Products Corporation; U.S. Public, pg. 82
WHITEHALL-ROBINS DE MEXICO, S.A. DE C.V.—American Home Products Corporation; U.S. Public, pg. 82
WHITEHALL-ROBINS HEALTHCARE—American Home Products Corporation; U.S. Public, pg. 80
WHITEHALL-ROBINS INC.—American Home Products Corporation; U.S. Public, pg. 82
WHITEHALL-ROBINS INTERNATIONAL, INC.—American Home Products Corporation; U.S. Public, pg. 80
WHITEHALL-ROBINS LABORATORIES LTD.—American Home Products Corporation; U.S. Public, pg. 82
WINDSOR HEALTHCARE LTD.—Boehringer Ingelheim GmbH; Int'l, pg. 199
WOELM PHARMA GMBH & CO.—Rhone-Poulenc S.A.; Int'l, pg. 1112
WYETH AUSTRALIA PTY. LTD.—American Home Products Corporation; U.S. Public, pg. 82
WYETH-AYERST INTERNATIONAL, INC.—American Home Products Corporation; U.S. Public, pg. 80
WYETH-AYERST LABORATORIES-DOMESTIC—American Home Products Corporation; U.S. Public, pg. 80
WYETH-AYERST LABORATORIES, INC.—American Home Products Corporation; U.S. Public, pg. 80
WYETH-AYERST LABORATORIES-RESEARCH & DEVELOPMENT—American Home Products Corporation; U.S. Public, pg. 80
WYETH (JAPAN) CORPORATION—American Home Products Corporation; U.S. Public, pg. 82
JOHN WYETH & BROTHER LTD.—American Home Products Corporation; U.S. Public, pg. 82
JOHN WYETH & BROTHER (N.Z.) LTD.—American Home Products Corporation; U.S. Public, pg. 82
WYETH LTD.—American Home Products Corporation; U.S. Public, pg. 82
WYETH-ORFI S.A.—American Home Products Corporation; U.S. Public, pg. 82
WYETH-PHARMA GMBH—American Home Products Corporation; U.S. Public, pg. 82
WYETH S.A.—American Home Products Corporation; U.S. Public, pg. 82
WYETH S.P.A.—American Home Products Corporation; U.S. Public, pg. 82
WYETH-SUACO LABORATORIES, INC.—American Home Products Corporation; U.S. Public, pg. 82
XIAN-JANSSEN PHARMACEUTICAL LTD.—Johnson & Johnson; U.S. Public, pg. 932
XOMA CORPORATION; U.S. Public, pg. 1786
YAMANOUCHI PHARMACEUTICAL CO. LTD.; Int'l, pg. 1518
DR. LO. ZAMBELETTI S.P.A.—SmithKline Beecham plc; Int'l, pg. 1266
ZENECA AB—Zeneca Group Plc; Int'l, pg. 1526
ZENECA A/S—Zeneca Group Plc; Int'l, pg. 1526
ZENECA AS—Zeneca Group Plc; Int'l, pg. 1526
ZENECA INC.—Zeneca Group Plc; Int'l, pg. 1525
ZENECA KK—Zeneca Group Plc; Int'l, pg. 1527
ZENECA OY—Zeneca Group Plc; Int'l, pg. 1527
ZENECA-PHARMA S.A.—Zeneca Group Plc; Int'l, pg. 1527
ZENECA POLAND SP. Z.O.O.—Zeneca Group Plc; Int'l, pg. 1527
ZENECA SA—Zeneca Group Plc; Int'l, pg. 1527
ZENECA ZIMBABWE (PRIVATE) LIMITED—Zeneca Group Plc; Int'l, pg. 1527
ZENITH GOLDLINE PHARMACEUTICALS—IVAX Corporation; U.S. Public, pg. 915
ZIMBRA INDUSTRIA E COMERCIO LTDA.—Bristol-Myers Squibb Company; U.S. Public, pg. 257
ZYMA-GEBRO ARZNEIMITTEL GMBH—Novartis AG; Int'l, pg. 986
ZYMA GMBH—Novartis AG; Int'l, pg. 986
ZYMA-NEDERLAND—Novartis AG; Int'l, pg. 986
ZYMA SA—Novartis AG; Int'l, pg. 972
ZYMA S.P.A—Novartis AG; Int'l, pg. 986
ZYMA (UNITED KINGDOM) LIMITED—Novartis AG; Int'l, pg. 986

2835 — IN VITRO & IN VIVO DIAGNOSTIC SUBSTANCES

ABBOTT LABORATORIES; U.S. Public, pg. 12
ADVANCED MAGNETICS, INC.; U.S. Public, pg. 20
AKZO PHARMA B.V.—Akzo Nobel N.V.; Int'l, pg. 44
AMERSHAM CORPORATION—Nycomed Amersham plc; Int'l, pg. 992
AMERSHAM HEALTHCARE—Nycomed Amersham plc; Int'l, pg. 992
AQUILA BIOPHARMACEUTICALS, INC.; U.S. Public, pg. 126
BASIC CHEMICALS DIV.—Rhone-Poulenc S.A.; Int'l, pg. 1109
BAUSCH & LOMB INCORPORATED; U.S. Public, pg. 194
BAYER CORPORATION—Bayer AG; Int'l, pg. 172
BAYER CORPORATION/CONSUMER CARE DIVISION—Bayer AG; Int'l, pg. 173
BECTON DICKINSON IMMUNOCYTOMETRY SYSTEMS—Becton Dickinson & Company; U.S. Public, pg. 199
BEHRINGWERKE AG—Hoechst Aktiengesellschaft; Int'l, pg. 624
BIO-RAD CLINICAL DIV.—Bio-Rad Laboratories, Inc.; U.S. Public, pg. 230
BIO-RAD LABORATORIES AG—Bio-Rad Laboratories, Inc.; U.S. Public, pg. 230
BIO-RAD LABORATORIES (CANADA) LTD.—Bio-Rad Laboratories, Inc.; U.S. Public, pg. 230
BIO-RAD LABORATORIES, GES.M.B.H.—Bio-Rad Laboratories, Inc.; U.S. Public, pg. 230
BIO-RAD LABORATORIES, GMBH—Bio-Rad Laboratories, Inc.; U.S. Public, pg. 230
BIO-RAD LABORATORIES, INC.; U.S. Public, pg. 230
BIO-RAD LABORATORIES S.R.L.—Bio-Rad Laboratories, Inc.; U.S. Public, pg. 230
BIO-RAD S.A.—Bio-Rad Laboratories, Inc.; U.S. Public, pg. 230
BIO-RAD S.P.D.—Bio-Rad Laboratories, Inc.; U.S. Public, pg. 230
BIOCHEM IMMUNOSYSTEMS, INC.—BioChem Pharma Inc.; Int'l, pg. 196
BIOMAKOR LTD.—Sigma-Aldrich Corporation; U.S. Public, pg. 1472
BIOWHITTAKER, INC.—Cambrex Corporation; U.S. Public, pg. 297
BOEHRINGER MANNHEIM GMBH—Corange Limited; Int'l, pg. 331
BRISTOL-MYERS SQUIBB COMPANY; U.S. Public, pg. 253
CRA LIMITED—Rio Tinto PLC; Int'l, pg. 1119
CENTOCOR DIAGNOSTICS DIV.—Centocor, Inc.; U.S. Public, pg. 323
CENTOCOR, INC.; U.S. Public, pg. 323
CENTOCOR PHARMACEUTICAL DIVISION—Centocor, Inc.; U.S. Public, pg. 323
CHIRON CORPORATION; U.S. Public, pg. 349
CIBA-GEIGY SERVICES LIMITED-SCIENTIFIC & ADVISORY OFFICE—Novartis AG; Int'l, pg. 980
CIBA-GEIGY TRADING AND MARKETING SERVICES CO. LTD.-REGIONAL OFFICE—Novartis AG; Int'l, pg. 980
CIBA GRIMSBY—Novartis AG; Int'l, pg. 980
CILAG AG—Johnson & Johnson; U.S. Public, pg. 929
CORANGE U.S. HOLDINGS, INC—Corange Limited; Int'l, pg. 331
CYANAMID PERUANA SA—American Home Products Corporation; U.S. Public, pg. 81
CYTOGEN CORPORATION; U.S. Public, pg. 471
DADE BEHRING INC.—Bain Capital; U.S. Private, pg. 110
DADE BEHRING INC.—Hoechst Aktiengesellschaft; Int'l, pg. 626
DIAGNOSTIC PRODUCTS CORPORATION; U.S. Public, pg. 505
DIAMEDIX CORPORATION—IVAX Corporation; U.S. Public, pg. 914
E-Z-EM IMAGING PRODUCTS DIVISION—E-Z-Em, Inc.; U.S. Public, pg. 540
EG & G WALLAC OY—EG & G, Inc.; U.S. Public, pg. 544
EASTMAN KODAK LIFE SCIENCES DIV.—Eastman Kodak Company; U.S. Public, pg. 551
ELAN CORPORATION PLC; Int'l, pg. 435
ENTERIC PRODUCTS, INC.—E-Z-Em, Inc.; U.S. Public, pg. 540
FORT DODGE ANIMAL HEALTH—American Home Products Corporation; U.S. Public, pg. 79
GAMMA BIOLOGICALS, B.V.—Gamma Biologicals Inc.; U.S. Public, pg. 698
GAMMA BIOLOGICALS INC.; U.S. Public, pg. 698
GENOME THERAPEUTICS CORPORATION; U.S. Public, pg. 730
GENZYME BIOCHEMICALS LTD.—Genzyme Corporation; U.S. Public, pg. 733
GENZYME CORPORATION; U.S. Public, pg. 733
GENZYME FINE CHEMICALS—Genzyme Corporation; U.S. Public, pg. 733
GENZYME JAPAN—Genzyme Corporation; U.S. Public, pg. 733
HICHEM DIAGNOSTICS B.V.—Elan Corporation Plc; Int'l, pg. 436
HICHEM DIAGNOSTICS, INC.—Elan Corporation Plc; Int'l, pg. 436
HOECHST MARION ROUSSEL AG—Hoechst Aktiengesellschaft; Int'l, pg. 624
HOECHST MARION ROUSSEL NORTH AMERICA—Hoechst Aktiengesellschaft; Int'l, pg. 625
F. HOFFMANN-LA ROCHE LTD.—Roche Holding Ltd.; Int'l, pg. 1119
HOFFMANN-LA ROCHE INC.—Roche Holding Ltd.; Int'l, pg. 1120
IMMUNEX CORPORATION; U.S. Public, pg. 871
INCSTAR CORPORATION—Fiat Auto SpA; Int'l, pg. 483
INCSTAR LTD.—Fiat Auto SpA; Int'l, pg. 483
INTERGEN CENTER FOR DIAGNOSTIC PRODUCTS—Intergen Company; U.S. Private, pg. 567
INTERGEN COMPANY; U.S. Private, pg. 567
INTERNATIONAL MUREX TECHNOLOGIES CORPORATION; Int'l, pg. 684
JANSSEN-CILAG LTD.—Johnson & Johnson; U.S. Public, pg. 929
KALI-CHEMIE AKTIENGESELLSCHAFT—Solvay S.A.; Int'l, pg. 1278
LIFESCAN, INC.—Johnson & Johnson; U.S. Public, pg. 928
ELI LILLY AND COMPANY; U.S. Public, pg. 992
MALLINCKRODT AUSTRALIA PTY. LTD.—Mallinckrodt Inc.; U.S. Public, pg. 1040
MALLINCKRODT CANADA, INC.—Mallinckrodt Inc.; U.S. Public, pg. 1040
MALLINCKRODT INC.; U.S. Public, pg. 1039
MALLINCKRODT MEDICAL B.V.—Mallinckrodt Inc.; U.S. Public, pg. 1040
MALLINCKRODT MEDICAL GMBH—Mallinckrodt Inc.; U.S. Public, pg. 1040
MEDICAL ANALYSIS SYSTEMS INC.; U.S. Private, pg. 727
MEDICORE INC.; U.S. Public, pg. 1080
MERIDIAN DIAGNOSTICS, INC.; U.S. Public, pg. 1094
NABI; U.S. Public, pg. 1148
NIPPON BIO-RAD LABORATORIES K.K.—Bio-Rad Laboratories, Inc.; U.S. Public, pg. 230
NYCOMED AMERSHAM PLC; Int'l, pg. 992
ORGANON TEKNIKA CORP.—Akzo Nobel N.V.; Int'l, pg. 46
ORTHO CLINICAL DIAGNOSTIC SYSTEMS INC.—Johnson & Johnson; U.S. Public, pg. 929
PHARMACIA & UPJOHN BIOSYSTEMS AB—Pharmacia & Upjohn, Inc.; Int'l, pg. 1047
PHARMACIA & UPJOHN, INC.; Int'l, pg. 1047
QUIDEL CORPORATION; U.S. Public, pg. 1352
RHONE-POULENC RORER LTD.—Rhone-Poulenc S.A.; Int'l, pg. 1110
RICHARDSON-VICKS, INC.—The Procter & Gamble Company; U.S. Public, pg. 1331
SANDOZ PHARMA LTD.—Novartis AG; Int'l, pg. 972
SANOFI, DIAGNOSTIAS PASTEUR—Elf Aquitane; Int'l, pg. 446
SERADYN, INC.—Mitsubishi Chemical Corporation; Int'l, pg. 871
SEROLOGICALS CORPORATION; U.S. Public, pg. 1460
SIGMA CHEMIE GMBH—Sigma-Aldrich Corporation; U.S. Public, pg. 1472
SIGMA DIAGNOSTICS DIV.—Sigma-Aldrich Corporation; U.S. Public, pg. 1472
SORIN BIOMEDICA S.P.A.—Fiat Auto SpA; Int'l, pg. 483
TSI CORPORATION—Genzyme Corporation; U.S. Public, pg. 733
TAMBRANDS INC.—The Procter & Gamble Company; U.S. Public, pg. 1331
TARGETED GENETICS CORP.—Immunex Corporation; U.S. Public, pg. 871
TECHNE CORPORATION; U.S. Public, pg. 1563
3M; U.S. Public, pg. 1604
WHITTAKER CORPORATION; U.S. Public, pg. 1766

2836 — BIOLOGICAL PRODUCTS, EXCEPT DIAGNOSTIC SUBSTANCES

ADM FOOD ADDITIVES DIVISION—Archer Daniels Midland Company (ADM); U.S. Public, pg. 127
AMERICAN HOME PRODUCTS CORPORATION; U.S. Public, pg. 79
AMGEN BOULDER, INC.—Amgen Inc.; U.S. Public, pg. 101
AMGEN INC.; U.S. Public, pg. 100
ANIMAL HEALTH—Alpharma Inc.; U.S. Public, pg. 58
ATLANTIC ANTIBODIES, INC.—Fiat Auto SpA; Int'l, pg. 483
BAYER AG—Bayer AG; Int'l, pg. 172
BAYER CORPORATION—Bayer AG; Int'l, pg. 172
BECTON DICKINSON PRIMARY CARE DIAGNOSTICS—Becton Dickinson & Company; U.S. Public, pg. 199
BIO-RAD LABORATORIES, INC.; U.S. Public, pg. 230
BOEHRINGER INGELHEIM ANIMAL HEALTH INC.—Boehringer Ingelheim GmbH; Int'l, pg. 199
BUCKMAN LABORATORIES INC.—Bulab Holdings, Inc.; U.S. Private, pg. 180
CAMBRIDGE RESEARCH BIOCHEMICALS LIMITED—Zeneca Group Plc; Int'l, pg. 1524
CAROLINA BIOLOGICAL SUPPLY CO.; U.S. Private, pg. 213
CENTEON, L.L.C.—Hoechst Aktiengesellschaft; Int'l, pg. 626
CENTEON, L.L.C.—Rhone-Poulenc S.A.; Int'l, pg. 1110
CENTER LABORATORIES, INC.—Heska Corporation; U.S. Public, pg. 813
CENTOCOR B.V.—Centocor, Inc.; U.S. Public, pg. 323
CENTOCOR, INC.; U.S. Public, pg. 323
CHEMETALL GMBH GESELLSCHAFT FUER CHEMISCH TECHNISCHE VERFAHREN—Metallgesellschaft AG; Int'l, pg. 861
CHIRON CORPORATION—Chiron Corporation; U.S. Public, pg. 350
CHR. HANSEN HOLDING A/S; Int'l, pg. 288
CONNAUGHT LABORATORIES, INC.—Rhone-Poulenc S.A.; Int'l, pg. 1109
CONNAUGHT LABORATORIES LIMITED—Rhone-Poulenc S.A.; Int'l, pg. 1109
CORDIS, A JOHNSON & JOHNSON COMPANY—Johnson & Johnson; U.S. Public, pg. 928
THE DOW CHEMICAL COMPANY; U.S. Public, pg. 522
ENZON, INC.; U.S. Public, pg. 587
ENZON, INC.—Enzon, Inc.; U.S. Public, pg. 588
FERRO CORPORATION; U.S. Public, pg. 618
GP STRATEGIES CORPORATION; U.S. Public, pg. 694
GENENTECH, INC.—Roche Holding Ltd.; Int'l, pg. 1120
GENZYME CORPORATION; U.S. Public, pg. 733
GREAT YEAR TRADING CO. LTD.—The Green Cross Corporation; Int'l, pg. 558

THE GREEN CROSS CORP.-NEW YORK REPRESENTATIVE OFFICE—The Green Cross Corporation; Int'l, pg. 558
THE GREEN CROSS CORPORATION; Int'l, pg. 558
CHR. HANSEN, INC.—Chr. Hansen Holding A/S; Int'l, pg. 288
HEARTLAND LYSINE INC.—Ajinomoto Company Inc.; Int'l, pg. 40
HESKA CORPORATION; U.S. Public, pg. 812
HOECHST MARION ROUSSEL, INC.—Hoechst Aktiengesellschaft; Int'l, pg. 624
HOECHST MARION ROUSSEL NORTH AMERICA—Hoechst Aktiengesellschaft; Int'l, pg. 625
HOFFMANN-LA ROCHE INC.—Roche Holding Ltd.; Int'l, pg. 1120
HYCLONE LABORATORIES INC.—Perstorp AB; Int'l, pg. 1037
INTERBIO INC.; U.S. Private, pg. 566
KODAK BIO-PRODUCTS DIVISION—Eastman Kodak Company; U.S. Public, pg. 551
KODAK BIOSCIENCE / EMERGING BUSINESS DIVISION—Eastman Kodak Company; U.S. Public, pg. 551
LAFARGE S.A.; Int'l, pg. 788
LANGFORD INC.—American Home Products Corporation; U.S. Public, pg. 81
LIFE TECHNOLOGIES, INC.—The Dexter Corporation; U.S. Public, pg. 504
MEAD JOHNSON DE MEXICO, S.A. DE C.V.—Bristol-Myers Squibb Company; U.S. Public, pg. 256
MERCIA DIAGNOSTICS LIMITED—Centocor, Inc.; U.S. Public, pg. 323
MERCK VACCINE DIVISION—Merck & Co., Inc.; U.S. Public, pg. 1091
MERIAL SAS—Rhone-Poulenc S.A.; Int'l, pg. 1114
MERIDIAN DIAGNOSTICS, INC.; U.S. Public, pg. 1094
MICROBE MASTERS—InterBio Inc.; U.S. Private, pg. 567
NABI; U.S. Public, pg. 1148
NOBEL BIOCARE; Int'l, pg. 951
NOVARTIS AG; Int'l, pg. 971
NOVO NORDISK A/S; Int'l, pg. 987
NOVO NORDISK BIOCHEM, INC.—Novo Nordisk A/S; Int'l, pg. 987
ORGANON INC.—Akzo Nobel N.V.; Int'l, pg. 48
PASTEUR MERIEUX SERUMS ET VACCINS—Rhone-Poulenc S.A.; Int'l, pg. 1109
PHARMACIA & UPJOHN, INC.; Int'l, pg. 1047
PIONEER HI-BRED INTERNATIONAL, INC.; U.S. Public, pg. 1298
RHONE-POULENC INC.—Rhone-Poulenc S.A.; Int'l, pg. 1112
RICERA INC.—Ishihara Sangyo Kaisha, Ltd.; Int'l, pg. 689
SANDOZ PHARMA LTD.—Novartis AG; Int'l, pg. 972
SANDOZ RESEARCH INSTITUTE—Novartis AG; Int'l, pg. 974
SCIENTIFIC IMAGING SYSTEMS—Eastman Kodak Company; U.S. Public, pg. 550
SEROLOGICALS CORPORATION; U.S. Public, pg. 1460
SIGMA CHEMICAL CO.—Sigma-Aldrich Corporation; U.S. Public, pg. 1472
SIGMA CHEMIE GMBH—Sigma-Aldrich Corporation; U.S. Public, pg. 1472
SMITHKLINE BEECHAM DIERGENEESKUNDIGE PRODUCTEN B.V.—SmithKline Beecham plc; Int'l, pg. 1266
SMITHKLINE BEECHAM DIVISION VETERINARIA—SmithKline Beecham plc; Int'l, pg. 1266
SMITHKLINE BEECHAM SAUDE ANIMAL—SmithKline Beecham plc; Int'l, pg. 1266
SOLVAY ANIMAL HEALTH, INC.—Solvay S.A.; Int'l, pg. 1277
STURGE BIOCHEMICALS—Rhone-Poulenc S.A.; Int'l, pg. 1113
TECHNE CORPORATION; U.S. Public, pg. 1563
TORAY INDUSTRIES, INC.; Int'l, pg. 1399
ZENECA GROUP PLC; Int'l, pg. 1524

2841 — SOAP & OTHER DETERGENTS, EXCEPT SPECIALTY CLEANERS

AKZO NOBEL INC.—Akzo Nobel N.V.; Int'l, pg. 47
ALCO CHEMICAL—Unilever Plc; Int'l, pg. 1435
ALICORP S.A.; Int'l, pg. 57
AMWAY CORPORATION; U.S. Private, pg. 69
ARLINGTON, LTD.—Avon Products, Inc.; U.S. Public, pg. 156
ARM & HAMMER CONSUMER PRODUCTS—Church & Dwight Co., Inc.; U.S. Public, pg. 356
JAMES AUSTIN CO.; U.S. Private, pg. 99
BALLARD MEDICAL PRODUCTS; U.S. Public, pg. 171
BAR SOAP & HOUSEHOLD CLEANING PRODUCTS DIV.—The Procter & Gamble Company; U.S. Public, pg. 1330
BAYER CORPORATION—Bayer AG; Int'l, pg. 172
BAYER CORPORATION/CONSUMER CARE DIVISION—Bayer AG; Int'l, pg. 173
BENCKISER CONSUMER PRODUCTS INC.—Joh. A. Benckiser GmbH; Int'l, pg. 185
JOH. A. BENCKISER GMBH; Int'l, pg. 185
BLOHORN S.A.—Unilever Plc; Int'l, pg. 1436
BLUE CROSS LABORATORIES; U.S. Private, pg. 152
BOEHME FETTCHEMIE GMBH—Henkel KGaA; Int'l, pg. 609
BREWER ENVIRONMENTAL INDUSTRIES, LLC—Buyco, Inc.; U.S. Private, pg. 190
THE BRULIN CORPORATION; U.S. Private, pg. 176
THE BUTCHER COMPANY; U.S. Private, pg. 189
CARCLIN S.A.—Henkel KGaA; Int'l, pg. 612
S.A. CASMITJANA MENSA—Henkel KGaA; Int'l, pg. 612
CERAS JOHNSON DE PORTUGAL, LDA.—S.C. Johnson & Son, Inc.; U.S. Private, pg. 592
CERAS JOHNSON LTDA.—S.C. Johnson & Son, Inc.; U.S. Private, pg. 593
CHURCH & DWIGHT CO., INC.; U.S. Public, pg. 355
CLEANING SOLUTIONS GROUP/CELLO—The Sherwin-Williams Company; U.S. Public, pg. 1466
CLOROX ARGENTINA S.A.—The Clorox Company; U.S. Public, pg. 387
THE CLOROX COMPANY; U.S. Public, pg. 386
THE CLOROX CO. OF PUERTO RICO—The Clorox Company; U.S. Public, pg. 387
COLGATE-CLOROX (FAR EAST) LTD.—The Clorox Company; U.S. Public, pg. 387
COLGATE-PALMOLIVE COMPANY; U.S. Public, pg. 397
COLGATE-PALMOLIVE, INC.—Colgate-Palmolive Company; U.S. Public, pg. 398
COLUMBIA COSMETICS GMBH—Henkel KGaA; Int'l, pg. 609
COMMERCIAL HENKEL S.A. (COHESA)—Henkel KGaA; Int'l, pg. 611
COMPAGNIE DES MARGARINES, SAVONS ET COSMETIQUES AU ZAIRE S.A.R.L.—Unilever Plc; Int'l, pg. 1436
COMPANIA COLOMBIANA DE GRASAS "COGRA-LEVER" S.A.—Unilever Plc; Int'l, pg. 1436
COOP SWITZERLAND; Int'l, pg. 329
CUSSONS GROUP LTD.—Paterson Zochonis Plc; Int'l, pg. 1024
CUSSONS INTERNATIONAL LTD.—Paterson Zochonis Plc; Int'l, pg. 1024
CUSSONS (U.K.) LTD.—Paterson Zochonis Plc; Int'l, pg. 1024
DARLING INTERNATIONAL, INC; U.S. Public, pg. 484
DESOTO INC.—Keystone Consolidated Industries, Inc.; U.S. Public, pg. 956
DETERGENTS DIVISION, ALBRIGHT & WILSON LIMITED—Albright & Wilson plc; Int'l, pg. 49
THE DIAL CORPORATION; U.S. Public, pg. 505
DIAMOND CHEMICAL CO., INC.; U.S. Private, pg. 330
DOUGLAS/QUIKUT—Berkshire Hathaway Inc.; U.S. Public, pg. 217
DOWBRANDS, L.P.—The Dow Chemical Company; U.S. Public, pg. 523
DUBOIS CHEMICALS—Unilever Plc; Int'l, pg. 1437
EAST AFRICA INDUSTRIES LTD.—Unilever Plc; Int'l, pg. 1436
ECOLAB INC.; U.S. Public, pg. 562
ELIDA FABERGE—Unilever Plc; Int'l, pg. 1434
EMERY GROUP HENKEL CORP.—Henkel KGaA; Int'l, pg. 611
H.B. FULLER COMPANY; U.S. Public, pg. 686
GO JO INDUSTRIES; U.S. Private, pg. 458
GRANITEVILLE COMPANY—Avondale Incorporated; U.S. Private, pg. 103
GROW GROUP, INC.—Imperial Chemical Industries PLC; Int'l, pg. 663
HAVILAND ENTERPRISES; U.S. Private, pg. 511
HENKEL & CIE AG—Henkel KGaA; Int'l, pg. 611
HENKEL & CIE GMBH—Henkel KGaA; Int'l, pg. 609
HENKEL AUSTRIA GROUP—Henkel KGaA; Int'l, pg. 611
HENKEL BAUTECHNIK GMBH—Henkel KGaA; Int'l, pg. 609
HENKEL BELGIUM S.A.—Henkel KGaA; Int'l, pg. 612
HENKEL CHIMICA S.P.A.—Henkel KGaA; Int'l, pg. 612
HENKEL ENTRETIEN S.A.—Henkel KGaA; Int'l, pg. 612
HENKEL FRANCE S.A.—Henkel KGaA; Int'l, pg. 612
HENKEL GENTHIN GMBH—Henkel KGaA; Int'l, pg. 610
HENKEL HELLAS, S.A.—Henkel KGaA; Int'l, pg. 612
HENKEL IBERICA S.A.—Henkel KGaA; Int'l, pg. 612
HENKEL ITALIANA S.P.A.—Henkel KGaA; Int'l, pg. 613
HENKEL KGAA; Int'l, pg. 609
HENKEL NEDERLAND B.V.—Henkel KGaA; Int'l, pg. 613
HENKEL SUD S.P.A.—Henkel KGaA; Int'l, pg. 613
HILLS COLGATE JAPAN LTD.—Colgate-Palmolive Company; U.S. Public, pg. 399
HINDUSTAN LEVER LTD.—Unilever Plc; Int'l, pg. 1437
HITACHI CHEMICAL CO., LTD.—Hitachi, Ltd.; Int'l, pg. 621
HOUSEHOLD PRODUCTS—The Clorox Company; U.S. Public, pg. 387
HOUSEHOLD PRODUCTS CO.—The Clorox Company; U.S. Public, pg. 387
INX INTERNATIONAL—Sumitomo Chemical Company, Ltd.; Int'l, pg. 1311
INDUSTRIAL DETERGENTS, LTD.—Henkel KGaA; Int'l, pg. 612
INDUSTRIAS LEVER PORTUGUESA, LDA.—Unilever Plc; Int'l, pg. 1437
INDUSTRIAS PACOCHA S.A. (UNILEVER)—Unilever Plc; Int'l, pg. 1437
INDUSTRIE HELLENIQUE DE DETERGENTS S.A. (E.V.A.)—Unilever Plc; Int'l, pg. 1437
INTERGEN BEAUTY PRODUCTS—Franz Haniel & Cie, GmbH; Int'l, pg. 591
JOHNSON COMPANY, LTD.—S.C. Johnson & Son, Inc.; U.S. Private, pg. 593
JOHNSON NEDERLAND B.V.—S.C. Johnson & Son, Inc.; U.S. Private, pg. 593
S.C. JOHNSON & SON, INC.; U.S. Private, pg. 592
N.V. JOHNSON WAX BELGIUM S.A.—S.C. Johnson & Son, Inc.; U.S. Private, pg. 593
KAO CORPORATION; Int'l, pg. 717
KGALAGADI SOAP INDUSTRIES(PTY) LTD.—H.J. Heinz Company; U.S. Public, pg. 806
KOREA JOHNSON CO., LTD.—S.C. Johnson & Son, Inc.; U.S. Private, pg. 593
LA JOHNSON FRANCAISE S.A.—S.C. Johnson & Son, Inc.; U.S. Private, pg. 593
LANG APPARATEBAU GMBH—Henkel KGaA; Int'l, pg. 610
LE SOLEIL S.A.—Henkel KGaA; Int'l, pg. 613
LEVER—Unilever Plc; Int'l, pg. 1435
LEVER & KITCHEN PTY. LTD.—Unilever Plc; Int'l, pg. 1437
LEVER BROTHERS LTD.—Unilever Plc; Int'l, pg. 1434
LEVER IBERICA S.A.—Unilever Plc; Int'l, pg. 1437
LEVER INDUSTRIAL B.V.—Unilever Plc; Int'l, pg. 1437
LEVER N.V.—Unilever Plc; Int'l, pg. 1438
LEVER POND'S LIMITED—Unilever Plc; Int'l, pg. 1438
LEVER S.A.—Unilever Plc; Int'l, pg. 1438
LEVER SUNLIGHT B.V.—Unilever Plc; Int'l, pg. 1438
LEVER SUNLIGHT G.M.B.H.—Unilever Plc; Int'l, pg. 1438
LEVER Y ASOCIADOS SACIF—Unilever Plc; Int'l, pg. 1438
LEVERINDUS AB—Unilever Plc; Int'l, pg. 1438
OY LEVERINDUS AB—Unilever Plc; Int'l, pg. 1438
LION HENKEL CORPORATION—Henkel KGaA; Int'l, pg. 614
LIXTON SPEZIALREINIGER GMBH—Henkel KGaA; Int'l, pg. 610
MALCO PRODUCTS, INC.; U.S. Private, pg. 698
MARIETTA, INC.—Marietta Corporation; U.S. Private, pg. 703
MOLETT MARKETING—American Israeli Paper Mills Ltd.; Int'l, pg. 75
MONA INDUSTRIES, INC.; U.S. Private, pg. 756
MURPHY-PHOENIX CO.—Colgate-Palmolive Company; U.S. Public, pg. 397
NAMICO, INC.; U.S. Private, pg. 773
NELSEN S.P.A.—The Procter & Gamble Company; U.S. Public, pg. 1333
SOPHIE NERVAL S.A.—Henkel KGaA; Int'l, pg. 612
NEUTROGENA CORPORATION—Johnson & Johnson; U.S. Public, pg. 928
NEUTROGENA PROVENCE SARL—Johnson & Johnson; U.S. Public, pg. 928
NIPPON LEVER BV—Unilever Plc; Int'l, pg. 1438
OAKITE CANADA, LTD.—Metallgesellschaft AG; Int'l, pg. 861
OLIVINE INDUSTRIES (PRIVATE) LIMITED—H.J. Heinz Company; U.S. Public, pg. 807
OSTERREICHISCHE UNILEVER GES. M.B.H.—Unilever Plc; Int'l, pg. 1438
PARAGERM FRANCE S.A.—Henkel KGaA; Int'l, pg. 612
PARKER CHEMICAL COMPANY PTE. LTD.—Henkel KGaA; Int'l, pg. 613
PATERSON ZOCHONIS PLC; Int'l, pg. 1024
C.H. PATRICK & CO., INC.—The B.F. Goodrich Company; U.S. Public, pg. 751
PHILIPPINE REFINING COMPANY INC.—Unilever Plc; Int'l, pg. 1438
PRISM INTEGRATED SANITATION MANAGEMENT, INC.—S.C. Johnson & Son, Inc.; U.S. Private, pg. 592
THE PROCTER & GAMBLE COMPANY; U.S. Public, pg. 1330
PURITAN/CHURCHILL CHEMICAL COMPANY; U.S. Private, pg. 895
QUAKER CHEMICAL CORPORATION; U.S. Public, pg. 1346
QUIMICA PARKER S.A. DE C.V.—Henkel KGaA; Int'l, pg. 614
QUIMICA S.C. JOHNSON & SON CHILENA S.A.C.I.—S.C. Johnson & Son, Inc.; U.S. Private, pg. 593
RAKONA—The Procter & Gamble Company; U.S. Public, pg. 1333
THE RAMSEY COMPANY—The Butcher Company; U.S. Private, pg. 189
RECKITT & COLMAN PLC; Int'l, pg. 1089
RECKITT & COLMAN S.A.—Reckitt & Colman plc; Int'l, pg. 1090
ROCHESTER MIDLAND CORPORATION; U.S. Private, pg. 937
ROCHESTER-MIDLAND ICL—Rochester Midland Corporation; U.S. Private, pg. 937
SBS HOLDINGS, INC.; U.S. Private, pg. 955
SBS PRODUCTS, INC.—SBS Holdings, Inc.; U.S. Private, pg. 955
SCIOM S.A.—Henkel KGaA; Int'l, pg. 614
SHAKLEE CORPORATION—Yamanouchi Pharmaceutical Co. Ltd.; Int'l, pg. 1518
SKANDINAVISK HENKEL A/S—Henkel KGaA; Int'l, pg. 614
SMITHKLINE BEECHAM CONSUMER BRANDS—SmithKline Beecham plc; Int'l, pg. 1264
SMITHKLINE BEECHAM CONSUMER HEALTHCARE—Hoechst Aktiengesellschaft; Int'l, pg. 625
SMITHKLINE BEECHAM PLC; Int'l, pg. 1264
SMITHKLINE BEECHAM PRODUCTS WESTERN HEMISPHERE DIV., INTL.—SmithKline Beecham plc; Int'l, pg. 1264
SOFTSOAP ENTERPRISES, INC.—Colgate-Palmolive Company; U.S. Public, pg. 397
SOILAX DE MEXICO S.A.—Ecolab Inc.; U.S. Public, pg. 562
SOLUTIA INC.; U.S. Public, pg. 1483
STANHOME INC.; U.S. Public, pg. 1508
STEPAN COLOMBIANA—Stepan Company; U.S. Public, pg. 1514
STEPAN COMPANY; U.S. Public, pg. 1514
STEPAN EUROPE—Stepan Company; U.S. Public, pg. 1514
THE STOP & SHOP COMPANIES, INC.—Koninklijke Ahold NV, Int'l, pg. 750
AB SUNLIGHT—Unilever Plc; Int'l, pg. 1438
SUNLIGHT, AG—Unilever Plc; Int'l, pg. 1438
A. SUTTER AG—Unilever Plc; Int'l, pg. 1438
SVENSKA JOHNSON'S VAX AB—S.C. Johnson & Son, Inc.; U.S. Private, pg. 594
THEOCHEM LABS., INC.; U.S. Private, pg. 1079
THERA COSMETIC GMBH—Henkel KGaA; Int'l, pg. 610
TIME PRODUCTS, INC.—Theochem Labs., Inc.; U.S. Private, pg. 1079
TRIARC COMPANIES, INC.; U.S. Public, pg. 1634
TURYAG TURKLYE YAG VE MAMULATI A.S.—Henkel KGaA; Int'l, pg. 614
TWINCRAFT, INC.; U.S. Private, pg. 1111
UMEX COMPANY—Unilever Plc; Int'l, pg. 1435
UNI-DAN A/S—Unilever Plc; Int'l, pg. 1438
UNIL-IT S.P.A.—Unilever Plc; Int'l, pg. 1438
P.T. UNILEVER INDONESIA—Unilever Plc; Int'l, pg. 1439
UNILEVER NEW ZEALAND LTD.—Unilever Plc; Int'l, pg. 1439
UNILEVER N.V.—Unilever Plc; Int'l, pg. 1434
UNILEVER PLC; Int'l, pg. 1433

UNION GENERALE DE SAVONNERIE (UGS)—Henkel KGaA; Int'l, pg. 612
USA DETERGENTS, INC.; U.S. Public, pg. 1685
WEST PENETONE INC.—Wechco, Inc.; U.S. Private, pg. 1158
ZEEPFABRIEK DE FENIX B.V.—Unilever Plc; Int'l, pg. 1439

2842 — SPECIALTY CLEANING, POLISHING & SANITATION PREPARATIONS

ABM INDUSTRIES; U.S. Public, pg. 2
ADVANCE MACHINE COMPANY—Nilfisk A/S; Int'l, pg. 932
AIR-SCENT INTERNATIONAL—Surco Products, Inc.; U.S. Private, pg. 1056
ALBERTO-CULVER COMPANY; U.S. Public, pg. 37
ALFA LAVAL INC.—Tetra Laval Group; Int'l, pg. 1378
ALLIEDSIGNAL INC., FLUOROCARBONS—AlliedSignal Inc.; U.S. Public, pg. 51
AMERICO MANUFACTURING CO., INC.; U.S. Private, pg. 64
AMWAY CORPORATION; U.S. Private, pg. 69
APPLIED BIOCHEMIST INC.—Laporte plc; Int'l, pg. 802
ARMOR ALL PRODUCTS GROUP—The Clorox Company; U.S. Public, pg. 387
JAMES AUSTIN CO.; U.S. Private, pg. 99
W.M. BARR & CO., INC.; U.S. Private, pg. 117
BAYER CORPORATION/CONSUMER CARE DIVISION—Bayer AG; Int'l, pg. 173
BISSELL INC.; U.S. Private, pg. 145
BLOCK DRUG COMPANY, INC.; U.S. Public, pg. 236
BLUE CORAL/SLICK 50—Quaker State Corporation; U.S. Public, pg. 1348
BLUE CROSS LABORATORIES; U.S. Private, pg. 152
BLUE DEVIL INDUSTRIES, INC.—Laporte plc; Int'l, pg. 802
BRESLUBE DIVISION OF SAFETY-KLEEN CANADA INC.—Safety-Kleen Corp.; U.S. Public, pg. 1426
BRISTOL-MYERS SQUIBB COMPANY; U.S. Public, pg. 253
THE BRULIN CORPORATION; U.S. Private, pg. 176
THE BUTCHER COMPANY; U.S. Private, pg. 189
CPAC, INC.; U.S. Public, pg. 282
CAR BRITE, INC.—E & A Industries, Inc.; U.S. Private, pg. 352
CASTROL INDUSTRIAL—Burmah Castrol plc; Int'l, pg. 235
CERAS ALEX S.A.—Henkel KGaA; Int'l, pg. 611
CERAS JOHNSON DE PORTUGAL, LDA.—S.C. Johnson & Son, Inc.; U.S. Private, pg. 592
CERAS JOHNSON LTDA.—S.C. Johnson & Son, Inc.; U.S. Private, pg. 593
CHEMETALL GMBH GESELLSCHAFT FUER CHEMISCH TECHNISCHE VERFAHREN—Metallgesellschaft AG; Int'l, pg. 861
CHEMICAL SPECIALTIES MANUFACTURING CORP.—RPM, Inc.; U.S. Public, pg. 1357
A.W. CHESTERTON COMPANY; U.S. Private, pg. 234
CHURCH & DWIGHT CO., INC.; U.S. Public, pg. 355
CLAIRE MANUFACTURING CO.—Goldner Hawn Johnsons & Morrison Incorporated; U.S. Private, pg. 462
CLARIANT CORPORATION—Hoechst Aktiengesellschaft; Int'l, pg. 624
CLAYTON INDUSTRIES CO.; U.S. Private, pg. 245
CLEANING SOLUTIONS GROUP/CELLO—The Sherwin-Williams Company; U.S. Public, pg. 1466
THE CLOROX COMPANY; U.S. Public, pg. 386
CLOROX DE MEXICO S.A. DE C.V.—The Clorox Company; U.S. Public, pg. 387
THE CLOROX INTERNATIONAL CO.—The Clorox Company; U.S. Public, pg. 387
CLOROX PROFESSIONAL PRODUCTS COMPANY—The Clorox Company; U.S. Public, pg. 387
COLGATE-CLOROX (FAR EAST) LTD.—The Clorox Company; U.S. Public, pg. 387
COLUMBIA COSMETICS GMBH—Henkel KGaA; Int'l, pg. 609
CONKLIN CO. INC.; U.S. Private, pg. 263
CONSTRUCTION & HOME IMPROVEMENT MARKETS DIVISION—3M; U.S. Public, pg. 1605
CREED CO.—NCH Corporation; U.S. Public, pg. 1145
CUSSONS GROUP LTD.—Paterson Zochonis Plc; Int'l, pg. 1024
CUSSONS INTERNATIONAL LTD.—Paterson Zochonis Plc; Int'l, pg. 1024
CUSSONS (U.K.) LTD.—Paterson Zochonis Plc; Int'l, pg. 1024
DANCO PRODUCTS—NCH Corporation; U.S. Public, pg. 1145
DANSK INTERNATIONAL DESIGNS LTD.—Brown-Forman Corporation; U.S. Public, pg. 261
DESOTO INC.—Keystone Consolidated Industries, Inc.; U.S. Public, pg. 956
DETREX CORPORATION; U.S. Public, pg. 501
DIAMOND CHEMICAL CO., INC.; U.S. Private, pg. 330
DIVERSEY WATER TECHNOLOGIES, INC.—Nalco Chemical Company; U.S. Public, pg. 1150
DOWBRANDS, L.P.—The Dow Chemical Company; U.S. Public, pg. 523
E & A INDUSTRIES, INC.; U.S. Private, pg. 352
EKC TECHNOLOGY, INC.—ChemFirst Inc.; U.S. Public, pg. 344
EASTERDAY JANITORIAL SUPPLY CO.—ABM Industries; U.S. Public, pg. 2
ECOLAB INC.; U.S. Public, pg. 562
ELDORADO CHEMICAL COMPANY; U.S. Private, pg. 367
FERRO CORPORATION; U.S. Public, pg. 618
FIRST BRANDS (CANADA) CORP.—First Brands Corporation; U.S. Public, pg. 627
FIRST BRANDS CORPORATION; U.S. Public, pg. 626
FOOD & BEVERAGE—Ecolab Inc.; U.S. Public, pg. 562
FREEMAN MANUFACTURING & SUPPLY COMPANY; U.S. Private, pg. 426
FUCHS PETROLUB AG OEL + CHEMIE; Int'l, pg. 517
THE FULLER BRUSH COMPANY—CPAC, Inc.; U.S. Public, pg. 282
THE GENERAL CHEMICAL GROUP, INC.; U.S. Public, pg. 707
GOLDEN STAR INC.; U.S. Private, pg. 460
GREAT LAKES BIOCHEMICAL CO., INC.—Laporte plc; Int'l, pg. 802
GROW GROUP, INC.—Imperial Chemical Industries PLC; Int'l, pg. 663
GUARDSMAN CONSUMER PRODUCTS DIV.—Lilly Industries, Inc.; U.S. Public, pg. 995
GUEST INTERNATIONAL (CANADA) LTD.—Guest Supply, Inc.; U.S. Public, pg. 768
GUEST INTERNATIONAL (ENGLAND) LTD.—Guest Supply, Inc.; U.S. Public, pg. 768
GUEST INTERNATIONAL (NEW ZEALAND) LTD.—Guest Supply, Inc.; U.S. Public, pg. 768
GUEST SUPPLY, INC.; U.S. Public, pg. 768
THE HARTZ MOUNTAIN CORP.; U.S. Private, pg. 508
HAVILAND ENTERPRISES; U.S. Private, pg. 511
HAWKINS CHEMICAL, INC.; U.S. Public, pg. 800
HENKEL CHEMICALS (INDIA) LTD.—Henkel KGaA; Int'l, pg. 614
HENKEL-EYTESA S.A.—Henkel KGaA; Int'l, pg. 612
HENKEL LEATHER CHEMICALS DIV.—Henkel KGaA; Int'l, pg. 610
HENKEL PORTUGUESA PRODUCTOS QUIMICOS LDA.—Henkel KGaA; Int'l, pg. 613
HENKEL SURFACE TECHNOLOGIES—Henkel KGaA; Int'l, pg. 610
HOECHST CELANESE FINE CHEMICAL DIVISION—Hoechst Aktiengesellschaft; Int'l, pg. 625
J.I. HOLCOMB MFG.—Premier Farnell plc; Int'l, pg. 1068
HOUSEHOLD PRODUCTS CO.—The Clorox Company; U.S. Public, pg. 387
INDUSTRIA QUIMICA DEL ISTMO, S.A. DE C.V.—CYDSA S.A.; Int'l, pg. 246
IONICS, INCORPORATED; U.S. Public, pg. 912
JELMAR COMPANY; U.S. Private, pg. 585
JOHNSON COMPANY, LTD.—S.C. Johnson & Son, Inc.; U.S. Private, pg. 593
JOHNSON NEDERLAND B.V.—S.C. Johnson & Son, Inc.; U.S. Private, pg. 593
S.C. JOHNSON & SON, INC.; U.S. Private, pg. 592
S.C. JOHNSON & SON INC.—S.C. Johnson & Son, Inc.; U.S. Private, pg. 592
N.V. JOHNSON WAX BELGIUM S.A.—S.C. Johnson & Son, Inc.; U.S. Private, pg. 593
KAALUNDS PRODUKTION A/S—Henkel KGaA; Int'l, pg. 613
KINLEITH MILL—International Paper Company; U.S. Public, pg. 905
KIWI BRANDS—Sara Lee Corporation; U.S. Public, pg. 1433
KIWI BRANDS PTY. LTD.—Sara Lee Corporation; U.S. Public, pg. 1434
KNOMARK, INC.; U.S. Private, pg. 627
KOREA JOHNSON CO., LTD.—S.C. Johnson & Son, Inc.; U.S. Private, pg. 593
L&R MANUFACTURING CO.; U.S. Private, pg. 638
LA JOHNSON FRANCAISE S.A.—S.C. Johnson & Son, Inc.; U.S. Private, pg. 593
LAMINAIRE CORPORATION—Thermo-Mizer Environmental Corp.; U.S. Public, pg. 1596
LANG APPARATEBAU GMBH—Henkel KGaA; Int'l, pg. 610
LAPORTE PLC; Int'l, pg. 801
LEISURE TIME INDUSTRIES—Laporte plc; Int'l, pg. 802
LEVER Y ASOCIADOS SACIF—Unilever Plc; Int'l, pg. 1438
LIPPERT ABRASIVES INC.—Fuchs Petrolub AG Oel + Chemie; Int'l, pg. 518
MAGIC AMERICAN CORPORATION; U.S. Private, pg. 695
MALCO PRODUCTS, INC.; U.S. Private, pg. 698
MAN-GILL CHEMICAL COMPANY; U.S. Private, pg. 699
MINUTEMAN INTERNATIONAL, INC.—Hako-Werke GmbH & Co.; Int'l, pg. 587
MORTON AUTOMOTIVE COATINGS—Morton International Inc.; U.S. Public, pg. 1135
MORTON THIOKOL S.A. DE C.V.—Morton International Inc.; U.S. Public, pg. 1136
MURPHY-PHOENIX CO.—Colgate-Palmolive Company; U.S. Public, pg. 397
NCH CORPORATION; U.S. Public, pg. 1145
NATIONAL CLEANING PRODUCTS LTD.—The Clorox Company; U.S. Public, pg. 387
NATIONAL SERVICE INDUSTRIES, INC.; U.S. Public, pg. 1160
SOPHIE NERVAL S.A.—Henkel KGaA; Int'l, pg. 612
NORTHERN LABS, INC.; U.S. Private, pg. 805
NOVARTIS AG; Int'l, pg. 971
OAKITE PRODUCTS, INC.—Metallgesellschaft AG; Int'l, pg. 861
OCEAN BIO-CHEM INC.; U.S. Public, pg. 1211
OCTAGON PROCESS INC.; U.S. Private, pg. 811
PACE INTERNATIONAL L.P.; U.S. Private, pg. 829
PATERSON ZOCHONIS PLC; Int'l, pg. 1024
PATTERSON LABORATORIES, INC.; U.S. Private, pg. 843
PIONEER/ECLIPSE CORP.—Amano Corporation; Int'l, pg. 71
PLASTROM S.A.—Henkel KGaA; Int'l, pg. 612
PLUMBMASTER INC.—NCH Corporation; U.S. Public, pg. 1145
PREMIER FARNELL—Premier Farnell plc; Int'l, pg. 1068
PRESTONE PRODUCTS CORPORATION—AlliedSignal Inc.; U.S. Public, pg. 51
PRISM INTEGRATED SANITATION MANAGEMENT, INC.—S.C. Johnson & Son, Inc.; U.S. Private, pg. 592
THE PROCTER & GAMBLE COMPANY; U.S. Public, pg. 1330
PURITAN/CHURCHILL CHEMICAL COMPANY; U.S. Private, pg. 895
QUAKER CHEMICAL CORPORATION; U.S. Public, pg. 1346
QUIMICA S.C. JOHNSON & SON CHILENA S.A.C.I.—S.C. Johnson & Son, Inc.; U.S. Private, pg. 593
RECKITT & COLMAN CANADA INC.—Reckitt & Colman plc; Int'l, pg. 1090
RECKITT & COLMAN INC.—Reckitt & Colman plc; Int'l, pg. 1090
RECKITT & COLMAN INDUSTRIAL LTDA.—Reckitt & Colman plc; Int'l, pg. 1090
RECKITT & COLMAN PLC; Int'l, pg. 1089
RECKITT & COLMAN PRODUCTS—Reckitt & Colman plc; Int'l, pg. 1090
RECKITT & COLMAN PRODUCTS LTD.—Reckitt & Colman plc; Int'l, pg. 1090
RECKITT & COLMAN S.A.—Reckitt & Colman plc; Int'l, pg. 1090
RHONE-POULENC AGROCHIMIE—Rhone-Poulenc S.A.; Int'l, pg. 1109
RHONE-POULENC S.A.; Int'l, pg. 1108
RICHARDSON-VICKS, INC.—The Procter & Gamble Company; U.S. Public, pg. 1331
ROCHESTER MIDLAND CORPORATION; U.S. Private, pg. 937
ROCHESTER-MIDLAND ICL—Rochester Midland Corporation; U.S. Private, pg. 937
RONSON CONSUMER PRODUCTS CORP.—Ronson Corporation; U.S. Public, pg. 1405
FRANK B. ROSS CO. INC.; U.S. Private, pg. 946
SLG CHEMICALS, INC.—Scott's Liquid Gold-Inc.; U.S. Public, pg. 1447
STP PRODUCTS, INC.—First Brands Corporation; U.S. Public, pg. 627
SAFETY-KLEEN CANADA, LTD.—Safety-Kleen Corp.; U.S. Public, pg. 1426
SAFETY-KLEEN CORP.; U.S. Public, pg. 1425
SAHAPATHANAPIBUL PUBLIC COMPANY LIMITED; Int'l, pg. 1169
SANITARIA MEXICANA S.A. DE C.V.—Henkel KGaA; Int'l, pg. 614
SARA LEE CORPORATION; U.S. Public, pg. 1432
SCOT LABORATORIES—Berkshire Hathaway Inc.; U.S. Public, pg. 218
SCOTT'S LIQUID GOLD-INC.; U.S. Public, pg. 1447
SELIG CHEMICAL INDUSTRIES—National Service Industries, Inc.; U.S. Public, pg. 1160
SERVAAS, INC.; U.S. Private, pg. 986
THE SERVICEMASTER COMPANY; U.S. Public, pg. 1461
SERVICEMASTER MANUFACTURING SERVICES—The ServiceMaster Company; U.S. Public, pg. 1462
SIME DARBY BERHAD MALAYSIA REGION—Sime Darby Berhad; Int'l, pg. 1250
SMITH & NEPHEW PLC; Int'l, pg. 1263
STANHOME DE MEXICO, S.A. DE C.V.—Stanhome Inc.; U.S. Public, pg. 1508
STANHOME INC.; U.S. Public, pg. 1508
STANHOME PANAMERICANA, C.A.—Stanhome Inc.; U.S. Public, pg. 1508
STARBRITE CORP.; U.S. Public, pg. 1510
SURCO PRODUCTS, INC.; U.S. Private, pg. 1056
SVENSKA JOHNSON'S VAX AB—S.C. Johnson & Son, Inc.; U.S. Private, pg. 594
TENNANT COMPANY; U.S. Public, pg. 1577
TEXAS REFINERY CORP.; U.S. Private, pg. 1078
THE TEXWIPE CO., INC.; U.S. Private, pg. 1079
THEOCHEM LABS., INC.; U.S. Private, pg. 1079
THETFORD CORPORATION—The Dyson-Kissner-Moran Corporation; U.S. Private, pg. 352
THE THOMPSON'S COMPANY—The Sherwin-Williams Company; U.S. Public, pg. 1466
TIME PRODUCTS, INC.—Theochem Labs., Inc.; U.S. Private, pg. 1079
TOPAKA SCIENTIFIC SAFETY CO.—Amano Corporation; Int'l, pg. 71
TURCO PRODUCTS DIVISION—Elf Aquitane; Int'l, pg. 446
TURTLE WAX, INC.; U.S. Private, pg. 1110
TURTLE WAX MANUFACTURING LTD.—Turtle Wax, Inc.; U.S. Private, pg. 1110
UNITED LABORATORIES, INC.; U.S. Private, pg. 1122
UNIVERSAL PHOTONICS, INC.; U.S. Private, pg. 1127
UNSMOKE INTERNATIONAL—Surco Products, Inc.; U.S. Private, pg. 1056
THE VALVOLINE COMPANY—Ashland, Inc.; U.S. Public, pg. 139
WCM CO.—NCH Corporation; U.S. Public, pg. 1145
WEST CHEMICAL PRODUCTS, INC.—Wechco, Inc.; U.S. Private, pg. 1158
WEST PENETONE CORPORATION—Wechco, Inc.; U.S. Private, pg. 1158
WEST PENETONE INC.—Wechco, Inc.; U.S. Private, pg. 1158
WILLERT HOME PRODUCTS, INC.; U.S. Private, pg. 1177
WISCONSIN PHARMACAL CO., INC.; U.S. Private, pg. 1185
WITCO CORPORATION; U.S. Public, pg. 1773
ZEP EUROPE B.V.—National Service Industries, Inc.; U.S. Public, pg. 1160
ZEP MANUFACTURING—National Service Industries, Inc.; U.S. Public, pg. 1160
ZEP MANUFACTURING COMPANY—National Service Industries, Inc.; U.S. Public, pg. 1160

2843 — SURFACE ACTIVE AGENTS, FINISHING AGENTS, SULFONATED OILS & ASSISTANTS

AKZO NOBEL INC.—Akzo Nobel N.V.; Int'l, pg. 47
ATLAS REFINERY; U.S. Private, pg. 96
BLUE CROSS LABORATORIES; U.S. Private, pg. 152
BOEHME FILATEX INC.—Dr. Th. Boehme KG Chem. Fabrik GmbH & Co.; Int'l, pg. 199
DR. TH. BOEHME KG CHEM. FABRIK GMBH & CO.; Int'l, pg. 199
CBP RESOURCES, INC.; U.S. Private, pg. 192
CASTROL INDUSTRIAL—Burmah Castrol plc; Int'l, pg. 235
CHEMETALL GMBH GESELLSCHAFT FUER CHEMISCH TECHNISCHE VERFAHREN—Metallgesellschaft AG; Int'l, pg. 861

CLOUGH CHEMICAL CO., LTD.—Dr. Th. Boehme KG Chem. Fabrik GmbH & Co.; Int'l, pg. 199
CONKLIN CO. INC.; U.S. Private, pg. 263
DOW CORNING CORPORATION—The Dow Chemical Company; U.S. Public, pg. 523
EASTMAN CHEMICAL COMPANY; U.S. Public, pg. 550
GRANITEVILLE COMPANY—Avondale Incorporated; U.S. Private, pg. 103
HCI CHEMTECH; U.S. Private, pg. 490
HARCROS CHEMICALS INC.—Harrisons & Crosfield plc; Int'l, pg. 598
HENKEL CHEMICAL SPECIALTIES DIV.—Henkel KGaA; Int'l, pg. 610
HENKEL CORPORATION TEXTILE CHEMICALS—Henkel KGaA; Int'l, pg. 610
HENKEL KGAA; Int'l, pg. 609
HIGH POINT CHEMICAL CORPORATION—Kao Corporation; Int'l, pg. 717
HOECHST SPECIALTY CHEMICALS GROUP—Hoechst Aktiengesellschaft; Int'l, pg. 624
ICI FRANCE SA—Imperial Chemical Industries PLC; Int'l, pg. 665
ICI OESTERREICH GMBH—Imperial Chemical Industries PLC; Int'l, pg. 665
ICI (PERU) S.A.—Imperial Chemical Industries PLC; Int'l, pg. 665
ICI (PHILIPPINES) INC.—Imperial Chemical Industries PLC; Int'l, pg. 665
ICI (SINGAPORE) PRIVATE LIMITED—Imperial Chemical Industries PLC; Int'l, pg. 665
ICI SPECIALTIES—Imperial Chemical Industries PLC; Int'l, pg. 664
ICI ZAMBIA LIMITED—Imperial Chemical Industries PLC; Int'l, pg. 665
INDUSTRIAS QUIMICAS CARABOBO, C.A.—Novartis AG; Int'l, pg. 982
KELCO DIV.—Monsanto Company; U.S. Public, pg. 1125
KELCO INTERNATIONAL LTD.—Merck & Co., Inc.; U.S. Public, pg. 1091
THE KENDALL COMPANY—Tyco International Ltd.; U.S. Public, pg. 1647
MBT HOLDING, LTD.—Viag AG; Int'l, pg. 1465
MONA INDUSTRIES, INC.; U.S. Private, pg. 756
MONTEREY KELP CORP.—Monsanto Company; U.S. Public, pg. 1125
NATIONAL STARCH AND CHEMICAL COMPANY—Unilever Plc; Int'l, pg. 1435
NOVARTIS AG; Int'l, pg. 971
THE NUTRASWEET KELCO COMPANY—Monsanto Company; U.S. Public, pg. 1125
PACE INTERNATIONAL L.P.; U.S. Private, pg. 829
C.H. PATRICK & CO., INC.—The B.F. Goodrich Company; U.S. Public, pg. 751
PATTERSON LABORATORIES, INC.; U.S. Private, pg. 843
QUAKER CHEMICAL CORPORATION; U.S. Public, pg. 1346
SANDOZ CHEMICALS (THAILAND) LTD.—Novartis AG; Int'l, pg. 984
SANDOZ PRODUCTS (SWITZERLAND) LTD.—Novartis AG; Int'l, pg. 972
SANDOZ-QUINN PRODUCKTIE GMBH—Novartis AG; Int'l, pg. 985
SANDOZ URUNLERI LTD.—Novartis AG; Int'l, pg. 985
SEVEN SEAS LIMITED—Hanson PLC; Int'l, pg. 593
STAHL ASIA PTE LTD—Zeneca Group Plc; Int'l, pg. 1526
STAHL AUSTRALIA PTY LTD—Zeneca Group Plc; Int'l, pg. 1526
STAHL CANADA LIMITED—Zeneca Group Plc; Int'l, pg. 1526
STAHL DE MEXICO, S.A. DE C.V.—Zeneca Group Plc; Int'l, pg. 1526
STAHL FRANCE S.A.R.L.—Zeneca Group Plc; Int'l, pg. 1526
STAHL GB LIMITED—Zeneca Group Plc; Int'l, pg. 1524
STAHL HOLLAND B.V.—Zeneca Group Plc; Int'l, pg. 1526
STAHL IBERICA, S.A.—Zeneca Group Plc; Int'l, pg. 1526
STEPAN COLOMBIANA—Stepan Company; U.S. Public, pg. 1514
STEPAN COMPANY; U.S. Public, pg. 1514
STEPAN EUROPE—Stepan Company; U.S. Public, pg. 1514
THE STEPHAN COMPANY; U.S. Public, pg. 1514
JACOB STERN & SONS, INC.; U.S. Private, pg. 1041
3M; U.S. Public, pg. 1604
TRIARC COMPANIES, INC.; U.S. Public, pg. 1634
TURK HENKEL A.S.—Henkel KGaA; Int'l, pg. 614
WESTVACO CORPORATION; U.S. Public, pg. 1762
WESTVACO CORPORATION-CHEMICAL DIV.—Westvaco Corporation; U.S. Public, pg. 1762
ZENECA AB—Zeneca Group Plc; Int'l, pg. 1526
ZENECA GROUP PLC; Int'l, pg. 1524
ZENECA OY—Zeneca Group Plc; Int'l, pg. 1527
ZENECA POLAND SP. Z O.O.—Zeneca Group Plc; Int'l, pg. 1527
ZENECA ZIMBABWE (PRIVATE) LIMITED—Zeneca Group Plc; Int'l, pg. 1527

2844 — PERFUMES, COSMETICS & OTHER TOILET PREPARATIONS

All CLUBMAN—American International Industries; U.S. Private, pg. 57
AOK-NERVAL COSMETICS & PERFUMES GMBH—Henkel KGaA; Int'l, pg. 609
ADVANCED CARE PRODUCTS—Johnson & Johnson; U.S. Public, pg. 928
ADVANTAGE LIFE PRODUCTS, INC.; U.S. Public, pg. 22
AIR-SCENT INTERNATIONAL—Surco Products, Inc.; U.S. Private, pg. 1056
ALBERTO-CULVER COMPANY; U.S. Public, pg. 37
ALBERTO-CULVER INTERNATIONAL, INC.—Alberto-Culver Company; U.S. Public, pg. 38
ALBERTO-CULVER USA, INC.—Alberto-Culver Company; U.S. Public, pg. 38
ALFIN, INC.; U.S. Public, pg. 40
ALOETTE COSMETICS, INC.; U.S. Public, pg. 57
AMERCHOL CORPORATION—Union Carbide Corporation; U.S. Public, pg. 1667
AMERICAN DRUG CORPORATION—American Home Products Corporation; U.S. Public, pg. 80
AMERICAN INTERNATIONAL INDUSTRIES; U.S. Private, pg. 57
AMERICAN SAFETY RAZOR COMPANY—The Jordan Company; U.S. Private, pg. 597
AMWAY CORPORATION; U.S. Private, pg. 69
ANDREA INTERNATIONAL—American International Industries; U.S. Private, pg. 57
BENJAMIN ANSEHL COMPANY; U.S. Private, pg. 75
ARDELL INTERNATIONAL, INC.—American International Industries; U.S. Private, pg. 57
ADRIEN ARPEL—Alfin, Inc.; U.S. Public, pg. 40
AVON PRODUCTS, INC.; U.S. Public, pg. 155
THE B-M GROUP (PTY.) LTD.—Bristol-Myers Squibb Company; U.S. Public, pg. 255
BDF DE CENTROAMERICA S.A.—Beiersdorf Group; Int'l, pg. 182
BDF DE CHILE S.A.—Beiersdorf Group; Int'l, pg. 182
BDF EAST AFRICA LTD.—Beiersdorf Group; Int'l, pg. 183
BDF MEXICO S.A. DE C.V.—Beiersdorf Group; Int'l, pg. 183
BDF NIVEA LTDA.—Beiersdorf Group; Int'l, pg. 183
BABYLISS. SA—Conair Corporation; U.S. Private, pg. 261
BASEL TRADING COMPANY LTD.; Int'l, pg. 169
BAUSCH & LOMB INCORPORATED; U.S. Public, pg. 194
BAUSCH & LOMB ORAL CARE DIVISION—Bausch & Lomb Incorporated; U.S. Public, pg. 194
BAYER ARGENTINA S.A.—Bayer AG; Int'l, pg. 175
BAYER DE MEXICO, S.A. DE C.V.—Bayer AG; Int'l, pg. 175
BAYER DO BRAZIL S.A.—Bayer AG; Int'l, pg. 175
BEAUTICONTROL COSMETICS, INC.; U.S. Public, pg. 198
GEOFFREY BEENE FRAGRANCES—French Fragrances Inc.; U.S. Public, pg. 681
BEIERSDORF GROUP; Int'l, pg. 182
BEIERSDORF S.A.—Beiersdorf Group; Int'l, pg. 183
JOH. A. BENCKISER GMBH; Int'l, pg. 185
BILL BLASS, INC.—MacAndrews & Forbes Holdings Inc.; U.S. Private, pg. 689
BIOTON AG INDUSTRIEAKTIENGESELLSCHAFT FUR KOSMETIK UND FRISEURBEDARF—Wella Group; Int'l, pg. 1489
BLENDAX-RICHARDSON AG—The Procter & Gamble Company; U.S. Public, pg. 1331
THE BODY SHOP INTERNATIONAL; Int'l, pg. 199
BOOTS CONTRACT MANUFACTURING—The Boots Company PLC; Int'l, pg. 202
BRIMMS INC.; U.S. Private, pg. 169
BRISTOL-MYERS DE VENEZUELA, S.A.—Bristol-Myers Squibb Company; U.S. Public, pg. 255
BRISTOL-MYERS (HONG KONG) LIMITED—Bristol-Myers Squibb Company; U.S. Public, pg. 255
BRISTOL-MYERS (N.Z.) LIMITED—Bristol-Myers Squibb Company; U.S. Public, pg. 255
BRISTOL-MYERS (PACIFIC) LIMITED—Bristol-Myers Squibb Company; U.S. Public, pg. 255
BRISTOL-MYERS PRODUCTS S.A.—Bristol-Myers Squibb Company; U.S. Public, pg. 255
BRISTOL-MYERS SQUIBB—Bristol-Myers Squibb Company; U.S. Public, pg. 256
BRISTOL-MYERS SQUIBB COMPANY; U.S. Public, pg. 253
E.T. BROWNE DRUG CO., INC.; U.S. Private, pg. 175
JOHN O. BUTLER CO.—Sunstar Inc.; Int'l, pg. 1320
CCA INDUSTRIES, INC.; U.S. Public, pg. 276
CCL INDUSTRIES, INC.; Int'l, pg. 238
CWK AG—Coop Switzerland; Int'l, pg. 329
CALVIN KLEIN COSMETICS COMPANY—Unilever Plc; Int'l, pg. 1435
CARME' COSMECEUTICAL SCIENCES, INC.; U.S. Private, pg. 213
CARRINGTON LABORATORIES, INC.; U.S. Public, pg. 309
CARRINGTON PARFUMS LTD.—MacAndrews & Forbes Holdings Inc.; U.S. Private, pg. 689
CARSON PRODUCTS COMPANY; U.S. Public, pg. 309
CARTER PRODUCTS DIV.—Carter-Wallace, Inc.; U.S. Public, pg. 310
CARTER-WALLACE, INC.; U.S. Public, pg. 309
CHARLES OF THE RITZ GROUP LTD.—MacAndrews & Forbes Holdings Inc.; U.S. Private, pg. 689
CHATTEM, INC.; U.S. Public, pg. 341
CHATTEM, INC., CONSUMER PRODUCTS DIVISION—Chattem, Inc.; U.S. Public, pg. 341
CHEMAG AKTIENGESELLSCHAFT—BASF AG; Int'l, pg. 104
CHEMISCHE FABRIK GRUNAU GMBH—Henkel KGaA; Int'l, pg. 609
CHESEBROUGH-POND'S INTERNATIONAL LTD.—Unilever Plc; Int'l, pg. 1436
CHESEBROUGH-POND'S MFG. CO.—Unilever Plc; Int'l, pg. 1435
CHESEBROUGH-POND'S USA CO.—Unilever Plc; Int'l, pg. 1435
CHRISTIAN DIOR PERFUMES INC.—LVMH Moet Hennessy Louis Vuitton; Int'l, pg. 781
CLAIROL CARIBE—Bristol-Myers Squibb Company; U.S. Public, pg. 254
CLAIROL DIVISION—Bristol-Myers Squibb Company; U.S. Public, pg. 255
CLAIROL, INC.—Bristol-Myers Squibb Company; U.S. Public, pg. 254
CLAIROL (TAIWAN) LTD.—Bristol-Myers Squibb Company; U.S. Public, pg. 256
CLARINS; Int'l, pg. 295
CLARINS DE MEXICO SADE CV—Clarins; Int'l, pg. 295
CLARINS LTD.—Clarins; Int'l, pg. 295
CLARINS PTE LTD.—Clarins; Int'l, pg. 295
CLARINS SDN BHD—Clarins; Int'l, pg. 295
CLARINS USA INC.—Clarins; Int'l, pg. 295
CLARION COSMETICS—The Procter & Gamble Company; U.S. Public, pg. 1330
COLGATE ORAL PHARMACEUTICAL—Colgate-Palmolive Company; U.S. Public, pg. 397
COLGATE-PALMOLIVE COMPANY; U.S. Public, pg. 397
COLUMBIA COSMETICS GMBH—Henkel KGaA; Int'l, pg. 609
COMBE INCORPORATED; U.S. Private, pg. 257
COMMERCE DRUG CANADA LTD.—Del Laboratories, Inc.; U.S. Public, pg. 494
COMPAGNIE DES MARGARINES, SAVONS ET COSMETIQUES AU ZAIRE S.A.R.L.—Unilever Plc; Int'l, pg. 1436
COMPANIA COLOMBIANA DE GRASAS "COGRA-LEVER" S.A.—Unilever Plc; Int'l, pg. 1436
CONAIR CORPORATION; U.S. Private, pg. 261
COSMAIR CANADA INC.—L'Oreal S.A.; Int'l, pg. 819
COSMAIR, INC.—L'Oreal S.A.; Int'l, pg. 818
COSMED-PRODUKTIONS GMBH—Beiersdorf Group; Int'l, pg. 182
THE COSMETIC CENTER INC.—MacAndrews & Forbes Holdings Inc.; U.S. Private, pg. 689
COSMETIC GROUP, U.S.A.; U.S. Private, pg. 277
COSMEUROP S.A.—Clarins; Int'l, pg. 295
COSMOLAB DIV.—Koh-I-Noor, Inc.; U.S. Private, pg. 629
COTY INC.—Joh. A. Benckiser GmbH; Int'l, pg. 185
COVER GIRL COSMETICS—The Procter & Gamble Company; U.S. Public, pg. 1330
JAMES CREAN PLC; Int'l, pg. 340
CREATIONS AROMATIQUES, INC.—Bayer AG; Int'l, pg. 173
CUSSONS GROUP LTD.—Paterson Zochonis Plc; Int'l, pg. 1024
CUSSONS INTERNATIONAL LTD.—Paterson Zochonis Plc; Int'l, pg. 1024
CUSSONS (U.K.) LTD.—Paterson Zochonis Plc; Int'l, pg. 1024
DANA PERFUMES CORP.—Renaissance Cosmetics, Inc.; U.S. Private, pg. 922
DEL LABORATORIES, INC.; U.S. Public, pg. 494
DELORE—American International Industries; U.S. Private, pg. 57
DEMERT & DOUGHERTY, INC.; U.S. Private, pg. 323
DENA CORPORATION; U.S. Private, pg. 324
DENTCO, INC.—Block Drug Company, Inc.; U.S. Public, pg. 237
DEP CORPORATION; U.S. Public, pg. 500
DEP INTERNATIONAL, LTD.—Dep Corporation; U.S. Public, pg. 500
DIAMOND BRANDS, INC.; U.S. Private, pg. 330
DIAMOND PRODUCTS COMPANY—Havatampa, Inc.; U.S. Private, pg. 510
DIVERSIFIED GROUP—The Gillette Company; U.S. Public, pg. 743
DOAK DERMATOLOGICS—Bradley Pharmaceuticals; U.S. Public, pg. 250
DRESSIN KOSMETIK-U. PHARMA GMBH—The Procter & Gamble Company; U.S. Public, pg. 1333
EAST AFRICA INDUSTRIES LTD.—Unilever Plc; Int'l, pg. 1436
ELF SANOFI S.A.—Elf Aquitane; Int'l, pg. 445
ELIDA COSMETIC AG—Unilever Plc; Int'l, pg. 1437
ELIDA FABERGE—Unilever Plc; Int'l, pg. 1437
ELIDA FABERGE—Unilever Plc; Int'l, pg. 1434
ELIDA FABERGE (IRELAND) LTD.—Unilever Plc; Int'l, pg. 1437
ELIDA-GIBBS G.M.B.H.—Unilever Plc; Int'l, pg. 1437
ELIDA-GIBBS (PTY.) LTD.—Unilever Plc; Int'l, pg. 1437
ELITE PARFUMS, LTD.—Jean Philippe Fragrances, Inc.; U.S. Public, pg. 924
ELIZABETH ARDEN COMPANY—Unilever Plc; Int'l, pg. 1435
ELIZABETH ARDEN DE MEXICO, S.A.—Unilever Plc; Int'l, pg. 1437
ESTEE LAUDER—Estee Lauder Companies Inc.; U.S. Public, pg. 594
ESTEE LAUDER COMPANIES INC.; U.S. Public, pg. 594
EYELET IBERICA, S.A.—Crown Cork & Seal Company, Inc.; U.S. Public, pg. 464
EYELET MEXICANA S.A. DE C.V.—Crown Cork & Seal Company, Inc.; U.S. Public, pg. 464
FSP LABORATOIRES PHARMEUROP S.A.—Unilever Plc; Int'l, pg. 1437
FELTON WORLDWIDE LTD.—Universal Foods Corporation; U.S. Public, pg. 1696
FIRMENICH S.A.; Int'l, pg. 486
C. B. FLEET CO., INC.; U.S. Private, pg. 410
FLORASYNTH AUSTRALASIA PTY. LTD.—Bayer AG; Int'l, pg. 173
FLORASYNTH GMBH—Bayer AG; Int'l, pg. 173
FLORASYNTH INC.—Bayer AG; Int'l, pg. 173
FLORASYNTH S.A. DE C.V.—Bayer AG; Int'l, pg. 174
FLORASYNTH SINGAPORE PTE LTD.—Bayer AG; Int'l, pg. 174
FOOD SERVICE & LODGING PRODUCTS DIV.—The Procter & Gamble Company; U.S. Public, pg. 1330
FORT PITT ACQUISITIONS, INC.; U.S. Private, pg. 419
FRAMESI USA, INC./ROFFLER INDUSTRIES, INC./CASA DI COLORE, INC.—Fort Pitt Acquisitions, Inc.; U.S. Private, pg. 419
FREEMAN COSMETIC CORP.; U.S. Private, pg. 426
FRENCH FRAGRANCES INC.; U.S. Public, pg. 681
FRUEHLING COSMETICS CO. LTD.—Wella Group; Int'l, pg. 1490
RENE GARRAUD S.A.—Wella Group; Int'l, pg. 1490
GIBBS AB—Unilever Plc; Int'l, pg. 1437
GIGI—American International Industries; U.S. Private, pg. 57
GILLETTE ARGENTINA S.A.—The Gillette Company; U.S. Public, pg. 744

GILLETTE CANADA INC.—The Gillette Company; *U.S. Public*, pg. 744
THE GILLETTE COMPANY; *U.S. Public*, pg. 743
THE GILLETTE COMPANY, PERSONAL CARE GROUP—The Gillette Company; *U.S. Public*, pg. 744
GILLETTE DO BRASIL & CIA—The Gillette Company; *U.S. Public*, pg. 744
GILLETTE GROUP ITALY S.R.L.—The Gillette Company; *U.S. Public*, pg. 745
GILLETTE (PHILIPPINES), INC.—The Gillette Company; *U.S. Public*, pg. 745
GILLETTE SOUTH AFRICA LIMITED—The Gillette Company; *U.S. Public*, pg. 745
GIORGIO BEVERLY HILLS—The Procter & Gamble Company; *U.S. Public*, pg. 1331
GIVAUDAN-ROURE DO BRAZIL LTDA—Roche Holding Ltd.; *Int'l*, pg. 1120
GIVAUDAN-ROURE INC.—Roche Holding Ltd.; *Int'l*, pg. 1120
GIVAUDAN-ROURE S.A.—Roche Holding Ltd.; *Int'l*, pg. 1119
GIVAUDAN-ROURE, S.A. DE C.V.—Roche Holding Ltd.; *Int'l*, pg. 1120
GIVAUDAN-ROURE S.P.A.—Roche Holding Ltd.; *Int'l*, pg. 1120
GOLDWELL A.G.—Kao Corporation; *Int'l*, pg. 717
GOODY CANADA LIMITED—Newell Co.; *U.S. Public*, pg. 1177
GUERLAIN, INC.—LVMH Moet Hennessy Louis Vuitton; *Int'l*, pg. 780
GUERLAIN S.A.—LVMH Moet Hennessy Louis Vuitton; *Int'l*, *pg. 780*
GUEST INTERNATIONAL (CANADA) LTD.—Guest Supply, Inc.; *U.S. Public*, pg. 768
GUEST INTERNATIONAL (ENGLAND) LTD.—Guest Supply, Inc.; *U.S. Public*, pg. 768
GUEST INTERNATIONAL (NEW ZEALAND) LTD.—Guest Supply, Inc.; *U.S. Public*, pg. 768
GUEST SUPPLY, INC.; *U.S. Public*, pg. 768
HAARMANN & REIMER CORP.—Bayer AG; *Int'l*, pg. 173
HAGEMEYER N.V.—First Pacific Company Limited; *Int'l*, pg. 487
HALSTON ENTERPRISES, INC.—MacAndrews & Forbes Holdings Inc.; *U.S. Private*, pg. 690
HASK TOILETRIES; *U.S. Private*, pg. 509
HAWLEY & HAZEL CHEMICAL CO., (HONG KONG) LTD.—Colgate-Palmolive Company; *U.S. Public*, pg. 399
HAZEL BISHOP INTERNATIONAL; *U.S. Private*, pg. 514
HELENE CURTIS INDUSTRIES, INC.—Unilever Plc; *Int'l*, pg. 1434
HENKEL & CIE AG—Henkel KGaA; *Int'l*, pg. 611
HENKEL ARGENTINA S.A.—Henkel KGaA; *Int'l*, pg. 611
HENKEL BAUTECHNIK GMBH—Henkel KGaA; *Int'l*, pg. 609
HENKEL BELGIUM S.A.—Henkel KGaA; *Int'l*, pg. 612
HENKEL CHEMICAL SPECIALTIES DIV.—Henkel KGaA; *Int'l*, pg. 610
HENKEL COSMETIC GMBH—Henkel KGaA; *Int'l*, pg. 609
HENKEL COSMETICS GES.MBH—Henkel KGaA; *Int'l*, pg. 612
HENKEL FRANCE S.A.—Henkel KGaA; *Int'l*, pg. 612
HENKEL HELLAS, S.A.—Henkel KGaA; *Int'l*, pg. 612
P.T. HENKEL INDONESIA—Henkel KGaA; *Int'l*, pg. 614
HENKEL ITALIANA S.P.A.—Henkel KGaA; *Int'l*, pg. 613
HENKEL KENYA LTD.—Henkel KGaA; *Int'l*, pg. 613
HENKEL KGAA; *Int'l*, pg. 609
HENKEL NEDERLAND B.V.—Henkel KGaA; *Int'l*, pg. 613
JA. HENNESSY & CO.—LVMH Moet Hennessy Louis Vuitton; *Int'l*, pg. 780
HERMES INTERNATIONAL; *Int'l*, pg. 617
HEWITT SOAP CO.—The Jordan Company; *U.S. Private*, pg. 597
HILLS COLGATE JAPAN LTD.—Colgate-Palmolive Company; *U.S. Public*, pg. 399
HINDUSTAN LEVER LTD.—Unilever Plc; *Int'l*, pg. 1437
HOECHST MARION ROUSSEL AG—Hoechst Aktiengesellschaft; *Int'l*, pg. 624
F. HOFFMANN-LA ROCHE LTD.—Roche Holding Ltd.; *Int'l*, *pg. 1119*
HOME SHOWCASE PRODUCTS—Tri Tech Laboratories, Inc.; *U.S. Private*, pg. 1101
ICC INDUSTRIES, INC.; *U.S. Private*, pg. 553
IFF FSC, INC.—International Flavors & Fragrances, Inc.; *U.S. Public*, pg. 899
ICART S.A.—Carter-Wallace, Inc.; *U.S. Public*, pg. 310
IMASCO LIMITED—B.A.T Industries P.L.C.; *Int'l*, pg. 112
INDUSTRIAS LEVER PORTUGUESA, LDA.—Unilever Plc; *Int'l*, pg. 1437
INDUSTRIAS PACOCHA S.A. (UNILEVER)—Unilever Plc; *Int'l*, pg. 1437
INTER PARFUMS-SELECTIVE INDUSTRIE—Jean Philippe Fragrances, Inc.; *U.S. Public*, pg. 924
INTERCOSMETICS, INC.—Wella Group; *Int'l*, pg. 1489
INTERNATIONAL FLAVORS & FRAGRANCES, INC.; *U.S. Public*, pg. 898
INVERNESS CORP.; *U.S. Private*, pg. 574
INVERNESS UK LTD.—Inverness Corp.; *U.S. Private*, pg. 574
JEAN PHILIPPE FRAGRANCES, INC.; *U.S. Public*, pg. 924
THE ANDREW JERGENS COMPANY—Kao Corporation; *Int'l*, pg. 717
JIL SANDERS COSMETICS G.M.B.H.—SmithKline Beecham plc; *Int'l*, pg. 1265
JOHNSON & JOHNSON CONSUMER PRODUCTS—Johnson & Johnson; *U.S. Public*, pg. 928
JOHNSON PRODUCTS CO., INC.—IVAX Corporation; *U.S. Public*, pg. 915
JOHNSON PUBLISHING COMPANY, INC.; *U.S. Private*, pg. 591
S.C. JOHNSON & SON, INC.; *U.S. Private*, pg. 592
JORDACHE FRAGRANCES & COSMETICS—Jean Philippe Fragrances, Inc.; *U.S. Public*, pg. 924
JORDAN A/S; *Int'l*, pg. 714
JOY CORPORATION—Bristol-Myers Squibb Company; *U.S. Public*, pg. 256
KAO CORPORATION; *Int'l*, pg. 717
KADABELL GMBH & CO. KG—Wella Group; *Int'l*, pg. 1489
KAISER WHOLESALE, INC.; *U.S. Private*, pg. 605
KALIFARMA S.A.—Solvay S.A.; *Int'l*, pg. 1279
KANEBO, LTD.; *Int'l*, pg. 722
EMIL KIESSLING & CIE. G.M.B.H.—Wella Group; *Int'l*, pg. 1489
KIWI BRANDS PTY. LTD.—Sara Lee Corporation; *U.S. Public*, pg. 1434
GEORGETTE KLINGER, INC.; *U.S. Private*, pg. 626
KNOMARK, INC.; *U.S. Private*, pg. 627
KOLMAR (AUST.) PTY LTD.—CCL Industries, Inc.; *Int'l*, pg. 239
KOLMAR DE MEXICO, S.A.—CCL Industries, Inc.; *Int'l*, pg. 239
KOLMAR LABORATORIES—CCL Industries, Inc.; *Int'l*, pg. 239
KOLMAR LABORATORIES, INC.—CCL Industries, Inc.; *Int'l*, pg. 239
KYOWA HAKKO KOGYO COMPANY, LTD.; *Int'l*, pg. 778
L.A.D.V. (LABORATOIRES D'APPLICATIONS DERMATOLOGIQUES DE VICHY)—L'Oreal S.A.; *Int'l*, pg. 818
LVMH MOET HENNESSY LOUIS VUITTON; *Int'l*, pg. 779
LA SALLE LABS DIV.—Del Laboratories, Inc.; *U.S. Public*, pg. 494
LABORATOIRES GARNIER PARIS—L'Oreal S.A.; *Int'l*, pg. 818
LANCASTER GROUP WORLDWIDE—Joh. A. Benckiser GmbH; *Int'l*, pg. 185
LANCASTER S.A.M.—Joh. A. Benckiser GmbH; *Int'l*, pg. 186
LANCOME INSTITUT & CIE—L'Oreal S.A.; *Int'l*, pg. 818
LANCOME PARFUMS ET BEAUTE—L'Oreal S.A.; *Int'l*, pg. 818
LANVIN PARFUMS—L'Oreal S.A.; *Int'l*, pg. 818
LAPORTE PLC; *Int'l*, pg. 801
LE SOLEIL S.A.—Henkel KGaA; *Int'l*, pg. 613
LEE PHARMACEUTICALS; *U.S. Public*, pg. 984
LENSCLEAN, INC.—H.L. Bouton Company Inc.; *U.S. Private*, pg. 162
LEVER S.A.—Unilever Plc; *Int'l*, pg. 1438
LEVER Y ASOCIADOS SACIF—Unilever Plc; *Int'l*, pg. 1438
LEVLAD, INC.; *U.S. Private*, pg. 663
LION HENKEL CORPORATION—Henkel KGaA; *Int'l*, pg. 614
LIZ CLAIBORNE COSMETICS, INC.—Liz Claiborne, Inc.; *U.S. Public*, pg. 1006
LONDON INTERNATIONAL GROUP PLC; *Int'l*, pg. 815
L'OREAL PRODESCA S.A.—L'Oreal S.A.; *Int'l*, pg. 819
L'OREAL S.A.; *Int'l*, pg. 818
L'OREAL (UK) LIMITED—L'Oreal S.A.; *Int'l*, pg. 819
M & E MANUFACTURING CO.—Plastek Group; *U.S. Private*, pg. 870
MACANDREWS & FORBES HOLDINGS INC.; *U.S. Private*, *pg. 689*
MARY KAY CORPORATION; *U.S. Private*, pg. 710
MARY KAY COSMETICS, INC.—Mary Kay Corporation; *U.S. Private*, pg. 711
MARY KAY, INC.—Mary Kay Corporation; *U.S. Private*, pg. 711
MATRIX ESSENTIALS, INC.—Bristol-Myers Squibb Company; *U.S. Public*, pg. 254
MAYBELLINE, INC.—L'Oreal S.A.; *Int'l*, pg. 819
MCNEIL CONSUMER PRODUCTS COMPANY—Johnson & Johnson; *U.S. Public*, pg. 931
MEGAS BEAUTY CARE, INC.; *U.S. Private*, pg. 729
MENLEY & JAMES LABORATORIES, INC.; *U.S. Public*, pg. 1086
MERLE NORMAN COSMETICS, INC.; *U.S. Private*, pg. 733
THIERRY MUGLER PARFUMS—Clarins; *Int'l*, pg. 295
NATIONAL STARCH AND CHEMICAL COMPANY—Unilever Plc; *Int'l*, pg. 1435
NATURISTICS—Del Laboratories, Inc.; *U.S. Public*, pg. 494
NEOTERIC COSMETICS, INC.—Scott's Liquid Gold-Inc.; *U.S. Public*, pg. 1447
SOPHIE NERVAL S.A.—Henkel KGaA; *Int'l*, pg. 612
NICE-PAK PRODUCTS, INC.; *U.S. Private*, pg. 798
NIPPON LEVER BV—Unilever Plc; *Int'l*, pg. 1438
NIVEA-KAO CO. LTD.—Beiersdorf Group; *Int'l*, pg. 183
NOBEL CONSUMER GOODS AB—Akzo Nobel N.V.; *Int'l*, pg. 48
NORELL PERFUMES, INC.—MacAndrews & Forbes Holdings Inc.; *U.S. Private*, pg. 690
NORTHERN LABS, INC.; *U.S. Private*, pg. 805
NOVILLE; *U.S. Private*, pg. 808
NOXELL CORPORATION—The Procter & Gamble Company; *U.S. Public*, pg. 1330
NUEVO FEDERAL S.A.; *Int'l*, pg. 990
NUTRI-TONIC DIV.—Del Laboratories, Inc.; *U.S. Public*, pg. 494
ORLANE; *Int'l*, pg. 1011
PALM BEACH BEAUTY PRODUCTS CO.; *U.S. Private*, pg. 834
THE PANTENE CO.—The Procter & Gamble Company; *U.S. Public*, pg. 1330
PANTENE GMBH—The Procter & Gamble Company; *U.S. Public*, pg. 1331
PARFUMS ET BEAUTE FRANCE & CIE.—L'Oreal S.A.; *Int'l*, pg. 818
PARFUMS DE COEUR LTD.; *U.S. Private*, pg. 839
PARFUMS INTERNATIONAL LTD.—Unilever Plc; *Int'l*, pg. 1435
PARFUMS RALPH LAUREN—L'Oreal S.A.; *Int'l*, pg. 818
PARFUMS ROCHAS S.A.—Wella Group; *Int'l*, pg. 1490
PARFUMS VAN CLEEF & ARPELS—Elf Aquitane; *Int'l*, pg. 445
PARKS PRODUCTS, INC.; *U.S. Private*, pg. 840
PARLUX FRAGRANCES INC.; *U.S. Public*, pg. 1264
PARLUX, LTD.—Parlux Fragrances Inc.; *U.S. Public*, pg. 1264
PATERSON ZOCHONIS PLC; *Int'l*, pg. 1024
PERMARK INTERNATIONAL (PTY.) LTD.; *Int'l*, pg. 1036
L. PERRIGO COMPANY; *U.S. Public*, pg. 1280
PHILIPPINE REFINING COMPANY INC.—Unilever Plc; *Int'l*, *pg. 1438*
PALOMA PICASSO & CIE.—L'Oreal S.A.; *Int'l*, pg. 818
PIERRE FABRE—Pierre Fabre S.A.; *Int'l*, pg. 1056
PIERRE FABRE S.A.; *Int'l*, pg. 1056
PIERRE ROBERT AB—Unilever Plc; *Int'l*, pg. 1438
PLAYTEX BEAUTY CARE, INC.—Playtex Products Inc.; *U.S. Public*, pg. 1311
PLOUGH U.S.A.—Schering-Plough Corporation; *U.S. Public*, *pg. 1438*
POLAROME INTERNATIONAL; *U.S. Private*, pg. 874
POLIVE/TRICOSTERIL—Fort James Corporation; *U.S. Public*, pg. 673
POLO/RALPH LAUREN CORPORATION; *U.S. Private*, pg. 874
PRESTIGE ET COLLECTIONS INTER. & CIE.—L'Oreal S.A.; *Int'l*, pg. 818
THE PRINCESS MARCELLA BORGHESE, INC.—MacAndrews & Forbes Holdings Inc.; *U.S. Private*, pg. 690
PROCTER & GAMBLE BEAUTY CARE DIV.—The Procter & Gamble Company; *U.S. Public*, pg. 1330
THE PROCTER & GAMBLE COMPANY; *U.S. Public*, pg. 1330
PROCTER & GAMBLE COSMETICS CO.—The Procter & Gamble Company; *U.S. Public*, pg. 1330
PROCTER & GAMBLE HEALTH & BEAUTY CARE BELGIUM—The Procter & Gamble Company; *U.S. Public*, pg. 1332
PROCTER & GAMBLE HEALTH & BEAUTY CARE GERMANY—The Procter & Gamble Company; *U.S. Public*, pg. 1332
PROCTER & GAMBLE (HEALTH & BEAUTY CARE) LIMITED—The Procter & Gamble Company; *U.S. Public*, *pg. 1332*
PROCTER & GAMBLE HEALTH & BEAUTY CARE SCANDINAVIA—The Procter & Gamble Company; *U.S. Public*, pg. 1332
PROCTER & GAMBLE HEALTH & BEAUTY CARE SO. EUROPE—The Procter & Gamble Company; *U.S. Public*, *pg. 1332*
PROCTER & GAMBLE HEALTH & PERSONAL CARE DIV.—The Procter & Gamble Company; *U.S. Public*, pg. 1331
PROCTER & GAMBLE INC.—The Procter & Gamble Company; *U.S. Public*, pg. 1332
PROCTER & GAMBLE INDIA—The Procter & Gamble Company; *U.S. Public*, pg. 1332
PROCTER & GAMBLE OF PERU—The Procter & Gamble Company; *U.S. Public*, pg. 1332
PRODUCTORA DE COSMETICOS S.A.—Wella Group; *Int'l*, *pg. 1490*
PRODUCTOS AVON DE GUATEMALA S.A.—Avon Products, Inc.; *U.S. Public*, pg. 156
QUENCHER DIV.—Del Laboratories, Inc.; *U.S. Public*, pg. 494
QUEST INTERNATIONAL FRAGRANCES INC.—Unilever Plc; *Int'l*, pg. 1436
RAKONA—The Procter & Gamble Company; *U.S. Public*, pg. 1333
RANIR CORPORATION/DCP; *U.S. Private*, pg. 909
RECKITT & COLMAN PLC; *Int'l*, pg. 1089
RECKITT & COLMAN S.A.—Reckitt & Colman plc; *Int'l*, pg. 1090
RED SEAL LABORATORIES LTD.—Wella Group; *Int'l*, pg. 1490
REEDCO, INC.—Block Drug Company, Inc.; *U.S. Public*, pg. 237
REJUVIA PROD. GROUP—Del Laboratories, Inc.; *U.S. Public*, pg. 494
REVLON INTERNATIONAL CORPORATION—MacAndrews & Forbes Holdings Inc.; *U.S. Private*, pg. 690
REVLON MANUFACTURING FACILITIES—MacAndrews & Forbes Holdings Inc.; *U.S. Private*, pg. 690
REVLON-REALISTIC PROFESSIONAL PRODUCTS, INC.—MacAndrews & Forbes Holdings Inc.; *U.S. Private*, pg. 690
REVLON SERVICE, INC.—MacAndrews & Forbes Holdings Inc.; *U.S. Private*, pg. 690
CHARLES REVSON, INC.—MacAndrews & Forbes Holdings Inc.; *U.S. Private*, pg. 690
RHONE-POULENC AGROCHIMIE—Rhone-Poulenc S.A.; *Int'l*, pg. 1109
RHONE-POULENC S.A.; *Int'l*, pg. 1108
RICHARDSON-VICKS, INC.—The Procter & Gamble Company; *U.S. Public*, pg. 1331
RICHARDSON-VICKS, INC. PERSONAL CARE PRODUCTS DIV.—The Procter & Gamble Company; *U.S. Public*, pg. 1331
ROCHE HOLDING LTD.; *Int'l*, pg. 1119
SBS PRODUCTS, INC.—SBS Holdings, Inc.; *U.S. Private*, pg. 955
SALLY HANSEN—Del Laboratories, Inc.; *U.S. Public*, pg. 494
SALON DIVISION—Wella Group; *Int'l*, pg. 1489
SANKYO COMPANY LIMITED; *Int'l*, pg. 1189
SANOFI BEAUTE, INC.—Elf Aquitane; *Int'l*, pg. 445
SARA LEE CORPORATION; *U.S. Public*, pg. 1432
SCHERING PLOUGH BRASIL—Schering-Plough Corporation; *U.S. Public*, pg. 1439
SCHERING-PLOUGH CORPORATION; *U.S. Public*, pg. 1438
SCHOLLS INC.; *U.S. Private*, pg. 972
HANS SCHWARZKOPF GMBH—Henkel KGaA; *Int'l*, pg. 610
SCOTT'S LIQUID GOLD-INC.; *U.S. Public*, pg. 1447
SENTINEL CONSUMER PRODUCTS, INC.; *U.S. Private*, pg. 984
SENTINEL CONSUMER PRODUCTS, INC.—Sentinel Consumer Products, Inc.; *U.S. Private*, pg. 984
SHAKLEE CORPORATION—Yamanouchi Pharmaceutical Co. Ltd.; *Int'l*, pg. 1518

SHISEIDO COMPANY LTD.; *Int'l*, pg. 1235
SHISEIDO COSMETICS (AMERICA) LTD.—Shiseido Company Ltd.; *Int'l*, pg. 1235
IRMA SHORELL, INC.—Tri Tech Laboratories, Inc.; *U.S. Private*, pg. 1101
SMITHKLINE BEECHAM CONSUMER BRANDS—SmithKline Beecham plc; *Int'l*, pg. 1264
SMITHKLINE BEECHAM CONSUMER BRANDS BV—SmithKline Beecham plc; *Int'l*, pg. 1266
SMITHKLINE BEECHAM CONSUMER BRANDS (PTY) LTD.—SmithKline Beecham plc; *Int'l*, pg. 1265
SMITHKLINE BEECHAM CONSUMER BRANDS SDN. BHD.—SmithKline Beecham plc; *Int'l*, pg. 1265
SMITHKLINE BEECHAM CONSUMER HEALTHCARE—Hoechst Aktiengesellschaft; *Int'l*, pg. 625
SMITHKLINE BEECHAM PLC; *Int'l*, pg. 1264
SMITHKLINE BEECHAM PRODUCTS FRANCE S.A.—SmithKline Beecham plc; *Int'l*, pg. 1266
SMITHKLINE BEECHAM PRODUCTS WESTERN HEMISPHERE DIV., INTL.—SmithKline Beecham plc; *Int'l*, pg. 1264
SOFT SHEEN PRODUCTS, INC.; *U.S. Private*, pg. 1012
SOFTSOAP ENTERPRISES, INC.—Colgate-Palmolive Company; *U.S. Public*, pg. 397
SONATA LABORATORIES LTD.—Wella Group; *Int'l*, pg. 1490
STANHOME DE MEXICO, S.A. DE C.V.—Stanhome Inc.; *U.S. Public*, pg. 1508
STANHOME INC.; *U.S. Public*, pg. 1508
STENDHAL—Elf Aquitane; *Int'l*, pg. 445
THE STEPHAN COMPANY; *U.S. Public*, pg. 1514
AB SUNLIGHT—Unilever Plc; *Int'l*, pg. 1438
SUNLIGHT, AG—Unilever Plc; *Int'l*, pg. 1438
SUNSTAR INC.; *Int'l*, pg. 1320
SUPERNAIL—American International Industries; *U.S. Private*, pg. 57
SURCO PRODUCTS, INC.; *U.S. Private*, pg. 1056
SVENSKA CELLULOSA AKTIEBOLAGET (SCA); *Int'l*, pg. 1326
SYSTEMS BIO INDUSTRIES—Elf Aquitane; *Int'l*, pg. 445
TAKEDA CHEMICAL INDUSTRIES, LTD.; *Int'l*, pg. 1350
TANNING RESEARCH LABS., INC.; *U.S. Private*, pg. 1068
DR. RER. NAT. PETER THEISS NATURWAREN—Wella Group; *Int'l*, pg. 1489
THOMPSON NUTRITIONAL PRODUCTS—Rexall Sundown Inc.; *U.S. Public*, pg. 1384
TIME-MIST DIV.—Carpenter Technology Corporation; *U.S. Public*, pg. 308
TREND LABORATORIES INC.; *U.S. Public*, pg. 1634
TREND MEDIA—Trend Laboratories Inc.; *U.S. Public*, pg. 1634
TRESSA, INC.; *U.S. Private*, pg. 1100
TRI-K INDUSTRIES, INC.; *U.S. Private*, pg. 1100
TRI TECH LABORATORIES, INC.; *U.S. Private*, pg. 1101
TRISTAR CORP.; *U.S. Public*, pg. 1640
TROPONWERKE GMBH & CO., KG—Bayer AG; *Int'l*, pg. 175
TSUMURA & CO.; *Int'l*, pg. 1425
TURK HENKEL A.S.—Henkel KGaA; *Int'l*, pg. 614
TURUN SAIPPUA OY—Unilever Plc; *Int'l*, pg. 1438
UNI-DAN A/S—Unilever Plc; *Int'l*, pg. 1438
UNIL-IT S.P.A.—Unilever Plc; *Int'l*, pg. 1438
UNILEVER AUSTRALIA LTD.—Unilever Plc; *Int'l*, pg. 1439
P.T. UNILEVER INDONESIA—Unilever Plc; *Int'l*, pg. 1439
UNILEVER NEW ZEALAND LTD.—Unilever Plc; *Int'l*, pg. 1439
U.S. DIRECT SELLING DIVISION—Avon Products, Inc.; *U.S. Public*, pg. 156
UNSMOKE INTERNATIONAL—Surco Products, Inc.; *U.S. Private*, pg. 1056
VP-SCHICKEDANZ AG—The Procter & Gamble Company; *U.S. Public*, pg. 1333
VIDAL SASSOON—The Procter & Gamble Company; *U.S. Public*, pg. 1330
WARNER-JENKINSON CO.—Universal Foods Corporation; *U.S. Public*, pg. 1696
WARNER-LAMBERT SCANDINAVIA AKTIEBOLAG—Warner-Lambert Company; *U.S. Public*, pg. 1740
WARNER-LAMBERT (SCHWEIZ) AG—Warner-Lambert Company; *U.S. Public*, pg. 1740
WARNER-LAMBERT SHAVING PRODUCTS GROUP—Warner-Lambert Company; *U.S. Public*, pg. 1739
WATERBURY COMPANIES, INC.-INDEPENDENCE DIV.—Carpenter Technology Corporation; *U.S. Public*, pg. 308
WEEKS AND LEO CO., INC.; *U.S. Private*, pg. 1158
WELLA CANADA INC.—Wella Group; *Int'l*, pg. 1489
THE WELLA CORPORATION—Wella Group; *Int'l*, pg. 1489
WELLA FRISEURBEDARF GMBH—Wella Group; *Int'l*, pg. 1489
WELLA GROUP; *Int'l*, pg. 1489
WESTWOOD-SQUIBB PHARMACEUTICALS INC.—Bristol-Myers Squibb Company; *U.S. Public*, pg. 255
WHITEHALL-ROBINS HEALTHCARE—American Home Products Corporation; *U.S. Public*, pg. 00
YVES SAINT LAURENT PARFUMS S.A.—Elf Aquitane; *Int'l*, pg. 445
ZOTOS INTERNATIONAL—Shiseido Company Ltd.; *Int'l*, pg. 1236

2851 — PAINTS, VARNISHES, LACQUERS, ENAMELS & ALLIED PRODUCTS

APL CORPORATION; *U.S. Private*, pg. 7
M. ABELMAN COMPANY, INC.—GP Strategies Corporation; *U.S. Public*, pg. 694
ACHESON INDUSTRIES, INC.; *U.S. Private*, pg. 12
ACHILLES CORPORATION; *Int'l*, pg. 22
AKZO COATINGS BELGIUM, DIV. OF AKZO BELGIE NV—Akzo Nobel N.V.; *Int'l*, pg. 43
AKZO COATINGS GES. M.B.H.—Akzo Nobel N.V.; *Int'l*, pg. 43
AKZO COATINGS GMBH—Akzo Nobel N.V.; *Int'l*, pg. 43
AKZO COATINGS INC.—Akzo Nobel N.V.; *Int'l*, pg. 46
AKZO COATINGS NEDERLAND B.V.—Akzo Nobel N.V.; *Int'l*, pg. 42
AKZO COATINGS SA—Akzo Nobel N.V.; *Int'l*, pg. 43
AKZO COATINGS (THAILAND LTD.)—Akzo Nobel N.V.; *Int'l*, pg. 43
AKZO COATINGS-TINTAS WANDA—Akzo Nobel N.V.; *Int'l*, pg. 43
AKZO NOBEL AB—Akzo Nobel N.V.; *Int'l*, pg. 48
AKZO NOBEL COATINGS INC.—Akzo Nobel N.V.; *Int'l*, pg. 48
AKZO NOBEL INC.—Akzo Nobel N.V.; *Int'l*, pg. 43
ALCAN POWDERS & PIGMENTS DIVISION—Alcan Aluminium Limited; *Int'l*, pg. 50
ALOX CORPORATION—RPM, Inc.; *U.S. Public*, pg. 1357
ALPHA MUURVERFFABRIEKEN BV—Akzo Nobel N.V.; *Int'l*, pg. 43
AMERCOAT ESPANA, S.A.—Ameron International Corporation; *U.S. Public*, pg. 99
AMERCOAT MEXICANA S.A. DE C.V.—Ameron International Corporation; *U.S. Public*, pg. 99
AMERON B.V., PROTECTIVE COATINGS DIVISION-EUROPE—Ameron International Corporation; *U.S. Public*, pg. 99
AMERON INTERNATIONAL CORPORATION; *U.S. Public*, pg. 98
AMERON PROTECTIVE COATINGS DIV.—Ameron International Corporation; *U.S. Public*, pg. 99
AMERON PROTECTIVE COATINGS GROUP—Ameron International Corporation; *U.S. Public*, pg. 99
ANCHOR INC.—International Paper Company; *U.S. Public*, pg. 903
ANZON INC.—Cookson Group plc; *Int'l*, pg. 328
ARTEX LTD.—BPB Industries PLC; *Int'l*, pg. 122
BASF AG; *Int'l*, pg. 103
BASF ARGENTINA S.A.—BASF AG; *Int'l*, pg. 105
BASF AUSTRALIA LTD.—BASF AG; *Int'l*, pg. 105
BASF INDIA LTD.—BASF AG; *Int'l*, pg. 106
BASF JAPAN LTD.—BASF AG; *Int'l*, pg. 106
BASF NORGE A/S—BASF AG; *Int'l*, pg. 106
BASF PEINTURES & ENCRES S.A.—BASF AG; *Int'l*, pg. 107
BASF QUIMICA COLOMBIANA S.A.—BASF AG; *Int'l*, pg. 107
BASF S.A.—BASF AG; *Int'l*, pg. 107
BJN (FIJI) LIMITED—Imperial Chemical Industries PLC; *Int'l*, pg. 664
BUFA BAEUERLE GMBH & CO.—Viag AG; *Int'l*, pg. 1464
BALZERS DUNNSCHICHT-KOMPONENTEN GMBH—Oerlikon-Buhrle Holding AG; *Int'l*, pg. 997
BALZERS SANDVIK COATING AB—Oerlikon-Buhrle Holding AG; *Int'l*, pg. 997
BAYER B.V.—Bayer AG; *Int'l*, pg. 175
BENJAMIN MOORE & CO.; *U.S. Private*, pg. 133
BIO-KIL LABORATORIES LIMITED—Laporte plc; *Int'l*, pg. 802
BONDEX INTL., INC.—RPM, Inc.; *U.S. Public*, pg. 1357
BONDO/MAR-HYDE CORPORATION—RPM, Inc.; *U.S. Public*, pg. 1357
BRADSHAW-PRAEGER CO.—RPM, Inc.; *U.S. Public*, pg. 1358
M.A. BRUDER & SONS, INCORPORATED; *U.S. Private*, pg. 175
THE BRULIN CORPORATION; *U.S. Private*, pg. 176
BRUNING PAINT COMPANY; *U.S. Private*, pg. 176
SAMUEL CABOT, INC.; *U.S. Private*, pg. 198
CALIFORNIA PRODUCTS CORP.; *U.S. Private*, pg. 201
CASCO NOBEL AB—Akzo Nobel N.V.; *Int'l*, pg. 48
CASTROL INDUSTRIAL—Burmah Castrol plc; *Int'l*, pg. 235
CEILCOTE COMPANY—Viag AG; *Int'l*, pg. 1465
CEILCOTE KORROSIONSTECHNIK G.M.B.H.—Novartis AG; *Int'l*, pg. 975
CERDEC CORPORATION—Ciba Specialty Chemicals Holding Inc.; *Int'l*, pg. 292
CETA-BEVER BV—Akzo Nobel N.V.; *Int'l*, pg. 43
CHASE CORPORATION; *U.S. Public*, pg. 337
CHEMICAL COATINGS, INC.—RPM, Inc.; *U.S. Public*, pg. 1357
CHEMICAL COMPANY OF MALAYSIA BERHAD—Imperial Chemical Industries PLC; *Int'l*, pg. 664
CHEMICAL SPECIALTIES, INC.—Laporte plc; *Int'l*, pg. 802
CHEMICAL SPECIALTIES MANUFACTURING CORP.—RPM, Inc.; *U.S. Public*, pg. 1357
CHEMWEST CORP.—Corporacion Grupo Quimico, S.A.C.A.; *Int'l*, pg. 332
COLONY PAINTS—The Valspar Corporation; *U.S. Public*, pg. 1707
COLOR CORP. OF AMERICA—The Valspar Corporation; *U.S. Public*, pg. 1707
COMPAGNIE DES VERNIS VALENTINE SA—Imperial Chemical Industries PLC; *Int'l*, pg. 664
COMPAGNIE EUROPEENNE DES PEINTURES JULIEN SA—Imperial Chemical Industries PLC; *Int'l*, pg. 664
COMPANIA SHERWIN-WILLIAMS, S.A. DE C.V.—The Sherwin-Williams Company; *U.S. Public*, pg. 1466
CONSOLIDATED COATINGS CORP.—RPM, Inc.; *U.S. Public*, pg. 1357
CONSTRUCTION & HOME IMPROVEMENT MARKETS DIVISION—3M; *U.S. Public*, pg. 1605
COOK COMPOSITES & POLYMERS INC.—Total S.A.; *Int'l*, pg. 1409
COOKSON AMERICA INC.—Cookson Group plc; *Int'l*, pg. 328
COOKSON GROUP PLC; *Int'l*, pg. 328
COOKSON MATTHEY CERAMICS PLC—Johnson Matthey Public Limited Company; *Int'l*, pg. 713
CORONADO PAINT COMPANY—Wattyl; *Int'l*, pg. 1488
CORRO CLARK COATINGS LTD.—Jotun A/S; *Int'l*, pg. 715
CORRO-COAT A/S—Jotun A/S; *Int'l*, pg. 714
CORRO-COAT (MALAYSIA) SDN. BHD.—Jotun A/S; *Int'l*, pg. 715
CORRO-COAT (THAILAND) LTD.—Jotun A/S; *Int'l*, pg. 715
CORRO-COAT TOZ BOYA SAN.VE TIC. A.S.—Jotun A/S; *Int'l*, pg. 715
COURTAULDS COATINGS INC.—Courtaulds plc; *Int'l*, pg. 338
COURTAULDS COATINGS LTD.—Courtaulds plc; *Int'l*, pg. 338
CROFT METALS, INC.; *U.S. Private*, pg. 290
CUPRINOL LIMITED—Williams Holdings Plc; *Int'l*, pg. 1501
DACRAL EUROPE—Akzo Nobel N.V.; *Int'l*, pg. 43
DAIHAN SWISS CHEMICAL CORPORATION—Ciba Specialty Chemicals Holding Inc.; *Int'l*, pg. 292
DAVIS PAINT COMPANY; *U.S. Private*, pg. 315
DAY-GLO COLOR CORP.—RPM, Inc.; *U.S. Public*, pg. 1357
DENNIS CHEMICAL CO., INC.; *U.S. Private*, pg. 324
DEUTSCHE ICI GMBH—Imperial Chemical Industries PLC; *Int'l*, pg. 664
DEVOE & RAYNOLDS—Imperial Chemical Industries PLC; *Int'l*, pg. 663
THE DEXTER CORPORATION; *U.S. Public*, pg. 504
DEXTER ELECTRONIC MATERIALS DIVISION—The Dexter Corporation; *U.S. Public*, pg. 504
DEXTER MIDLAND CO. LTD.—The Dexter Corporation; *U.S. Public*, pg. 505
DEXTER PACKAGING PRODUCTS DIV.—The Dexter Corporation; *U.S. Public*, pg. 505
DULUX PAPUA NEW GUINEA PTY LTD—Imperial Chemical Industries PLC; *Int'l*, pg. 664
DUNN-EDWARDS CORPORATION; *U.S. Private*, pg. 347
DURON, INC.; *U.S. Private*, pg. 349
EL-MOHANDES JOTUN EGYPT—Jotun A/S; *Int'l*, pg. 715
ELIXIR INDUSTRIES; *U.S. Private*, pg. 371
ESSEX SPECIALTY PRODUCTS, INC.—The Dow Chemical Company; *U.S. Public*, pg. 523
FARMLAND INDUSTRIES, INC.; *U.S. Private*, pg. 395
FERRO CORPORATION; *U.S. Public*, pg. 618
FERRO (GREAT BRITAIN) LIMITED—Ferro Corporation; *U.S. Public*, pg. 619
FIBERLOCK TECHNOLOGIES, INC.—California Products Corp.; *U.S. Private*, pg. 201
FIGUEROA—Imetal; *Int'l*, pg. 662
FINGERLE LUMBER CO.; *U.S. Private*, pg. 405
THE FLECTO CO., INC.; *U.S. Private*, pg. 410
FLEXA FABRIEKEN B.V.—Akzo Nobel N.V.; *Int'l*, pg. 43
THE FLOOD COMPANY; *U.S. Private*, pg. 414
FLOQUIL-POLLY S COLOR CORP.—RPM, Inc.; *U.S. Public*, pg. 1357
FOAMEX INTERNATIONAL INC.—Trace International Holdings, Inc.; *U.S. Private*, pg. 1094
FRAZEE INDUSTRIES INC.—Williams Holdings Plc; *Int'l*, pg. 1501
FREUDENBERG NOK—Freudenberg & Company; *Int'l*, pg. 505
H.B. FULLER COMPANY; *U.S. Public*, pg. 686
GENERAL PAINT LTD.—Williams Holdings Plc; *Int'l*, pg. 1501
GLASURIT DE ARGENTINA S.A.—BASF AG; *Int'l*, pg. 105
THE GLIDDEN COMPANY (CANADA) LIMITED—Imperial Chemical Industries PLC; *Int'l*, pg. 664
THE B.F. GOODRICH COMPANY; *U.S. Public*, pg. 751
GRAHAM PAINT AND VARNISH COMPANY; *U.S. Private*, pg. 468
GROW GROUP CANADA LTD.—Imperial Chemical Industries PLC; *Int'l*, pg. 663
GROW GROUP, INC.—Imperial Chemical Industries PLC; *Int'l*, pg. 663
GRUPO ICI DE MEXICO, S.A. DE C.V.—Imperial Chemical Industries PLC; *Int'l*, pg. 664
GULF STATES ASPHALT COMPANY, INC.; *U.S. Private*, pg. 487
HAGEMEYER N.V.—First Pacific Company Limited; *Int'l*, pg. 487
HARRISON PAINT CORP.; *U.S. Private*, pg. 506
HENKEL-EYTESA S.A.—Henkel KGaA; *Int'l*, pg. 612
HENKEL NOPCO AB—Henkel KGaA; *Int'l*, pg. 613
HENKEL NOPCO OY—Henkel KGaA; *Int'l*, pg. 614
HENKEL SURFACE TECHNOLOGIES—Henkel KGaA; *Int'l*, pg. 610
HENKEL TAIWAN LTD.—Henkel KGaA; *Int'l*, pg. 613
HERBERTS GMBH—Hoechst Aktiengesellschaft; *Int'l*, pg. 625
HERBERTS-O'BRIEN INC.—Hoechst Aktiengesellschaft; *Int'l*, pg. 626
HERCULES CHEMICAL CO., INC.; *U.S. Private*, pg. 523
HERESITE PROTECTIVE COATINGS INC.; *U.S. Private*, pg. 523
HERPU S.A.—Akzo Nobel N.V.; *Int'l*, pg. 43
HULS AMERICA INC.—Veba AG; *Int'l*, pg. 1455
ICI CANADA INC.—Imperial Chemical Industries PLC; *Int'l*, pg. 664
ICI FRANCE SA—Imperial Chemical Industries PLC; *Int'l*, pg. 665
ICI INDIA LIMITED—Imperial Chemical Industries PLC; *Int'l*, pg. 665
ICI LACKE FARBEN GMBH—Imperial Chemical Industries PLC; *Int'l*, pg. 665
ICI NEW ZEALAND LIMITED—Imperial Chemical Industries PLC; *Int'l*, pg. 665
ICI OESTERREICH GMBH—Imperial Chemical Industries PLC; *Int'l*, pg. 665
ICI PAINTS—Imperial Chemical Industries PLC; *Int'l*, pg. 664
ICI PAINTS (CANADA) INC.—Imperial Chemical Industries PLC; *Int'l*, pg. 665
ICI PAINTS ESPANA SA—Imperial Chemical Industries PLC; *Int'l*, pg. 665
ICI PAINTS (MALAYSIA) SDN BHD—Imperial Chemical Industries PLC; *Int'l*, pg. 665
ICI PAINTS (SINGAPORE) PRIVATE LIMITED—Imperial Chemical Industries PLC; *Int'l*, pg. 665
ICI (PERU) S.A.—Imperial Chemical Industries PLC; *Int'l*, pg. 665
ICI (PHILIPPINES) INC.—Imperial Chemical Industries PLC; *Int'l*, pg. 665
ICI (SINGAPORE) PRIVATE LIMITED—Imperial Chemical Industries PLC; *Int'l*, pg. 665

ICI SPECIALTIES—Imperial Chemical Industries PLC; *Int'l*, pg. 664
ICI SWIRE PAINTS LIMITED—Imperial Chemical Industries PLC; *Int'l*, pg. 665
ICI (SWITZERLAND) AG—Imperial Chemical Industries PLC; *Int'l*, pg. 665
ICI TAIWAN LIMITED—Imperial Chemical Industries PLC; *Int'l*, pg. 665
ICI ZAMBIA LIMITED—Imperial Chemical Industries PLC; *Int'l*, pg. 665
ISK BIOSCIENCES—Ishihara Sangyo Kaisha, Ltd.; *Int'l*, pg. 689
IMPERIAL CHEMICAL INDUSTRIES PLC; *Int'l*, pg. 662
INDUSTRIAL BRUGER SA—Akzo Nobel N.V.; *Int'l*, pg. 43
INTERNATIONAL PAINT CO., INC.—Courtaulds plc; *Int'l*, pg. 338
INTERNATIONAL PAINT GULF DIV.—Courtaulds plc; *Int'l*, pg. 339
INTERNATIONAL PAINT POWDER COATINGS DIV.—Courtaulds plc; *Int'l*, pg. 339
INTERNATIONAL PAINT SOUTHWEST DIV.—Courtaulds plc; *Int'l*, pg. 339
INTERNATIONAL PAINTS (CANADA) LTD.—Courtaulds plc; *Int'l*, pg. 339
IOWA PAINT MFG. COMPANY, INC.; *U.S. Private*, pg. 575
JOHNSON MATTHEY PUBLIC LIMITED COMPANY; *Int'l*, pg. 713
JONES BLAIR COMPANY; *U.S. Private*, pg. 596
JOTUN A/S; *Int'l*, pg. 714
JOTUN-HENRY CLARK LTD.—Jotun A/S; *Int'l*, pg. 715
JOTUN L.L.C.—Jotun A/S; *Int'l*, pg. 716
JOTUN (MALAYSIA) SDN. BHD.—Jotun A/S; *Int'l*, pg. 715
JOTUN NOF SINGAPORE PTE. LTD.—Jotun A/S; *Int'l*, pg. 715
JOTUN POLYMER (UK) LTD.—Jotun A/S; *Int'l*, pg. 714
JOTUN S.A.E.—Jotun A/S; *Int'l*, pg. 715
JOTUN SAUDIA CO. LTD.—Jotun A/S; *Int'l*, pg. 716
JOTUN THAILAND LTD.—Jotun A/S; *Int'l*, pg. 715
JOTUN U.A.E. LTD.—Jotun A/S; *Int'l*, pg. 716
K.C.I. COATINGS, INC.—Progress Paint Mfg. Co.; *U.S. Private*, pg. 890
KANSAI PAINT CO., LTD.; *Int'l*, pg. 723
KELLY-MOORE PAINT COMPANY, INC.; *U.S. Private*, pg. 613
KEMIRA COATINGS LTD.—Kemira Oy; *Int'l*, pg. 729
KEMIRA COLOR B.V.—Kemira Oy; *Int'l*, pg. 729
KEMIRA COLOR N.V.—Kemira Oy; *Int'l*, pg. 729
KEMIRA PIGMENTS OY—Kemira Oy; *Int'l*, pg. 729
KING INDUSTRIES, INC.; *U.S. Private*, pg. 620
KONINKLIJKE TALENS BV—Akzo Nobel N.V.; *Int'l*, pg. 42
KOOL SEAL, INC.; *U.S. Private*, pg. 632
KWAL-HOWELLS, INC.(DENVER)—Williams Holdings Plc; *Int'l*, pg. 1501
LPS LABORATORIES INC.—Morgan Crucible Co. Plc; *Int'l*, pg. 892
LAWTER INTERNATIONAL, INC.; *U.S. Public*, pg. 980
LEPAGE'S LIMITED—Henkel KGaA; *Int'l*, pg. 613
S.A. LEVIS—Akzo Nobel N.V.; *Int'l*, pg. 43
LEVIS SAPT. SA—Akzo Nobel N.V.; *Int'l*, pg. 43
LILLY INDUSTRIES (FAR EAST), LTD.—Lilly Industries, Inc.; *U.S. Public*, pg. 995
LILLY INDUSTRIES, INC.; *U.S. Public*, pg. 994
LILLY INDUSTRIES, INC.—Lilly Industries, Inc.; *U.S. Public*, pg. 995
LILLY INDUSTRIES (MALAYSIA) SND. BHD.—Lilly Industries, Inc.; *U.S. Public*, pg. 995
LORD CORPORATION; *U.S. Private*, pg. 675
M.A.B. PAINTS—M.A. Bruder & Sons, Incorporated; *U.S. Private*, pg. 175
ML CAMPBELL & FABULON—The Sherwin-Williams Company; *U.S. Public*, pg. 1466
J.P. MACDOUGALL & CO. LIMITED—Imperial Chemical Industries PLC; *Int'l*, pg. 663
MANTROSE BRADSHAW ZINSSER GROUP—RPM, Inc.; *U.S. Public*, pg. 1358
MAR-HYDE CORPORATION—RPM, Inc.; *U.S. Public*, pg. 1357
SA MAROCAINE DES PEINTURES ASTRAL CELLUCO (SAMPAC)—Akzo Nobel N.V.; *Int'l*, pg. 43
MARSON/CREATIVE FASTENER, INC.; *U.S. Private*, pg. 708
MASTERCHEM INDUSTRIES—Williams Holdings Plc; *Int'l*, pg. 1501
MASURY PAINT—The Valspar Corporation; *U.S. Public*, pg. 1707
MAUTZ PAINT CO.; *U.S. Private*, pg. 715
MAXCO, INC.; *U.S. Public*, pg. 1061
THE MCCLOSKEY CORPORATION—McWhorter Technologies, Inc.; *U.S. Public*, pg. 1074
MCCORMICK PAINT WORKS COMPANY; *U.S. Private*, pg. 720
MEYNADIER AG—Viag AG; *Int'l*, pg. 1465
MILUZ SAICIF—Akzo Nobel N.V.; *Int'l*, pg. 43
MINERAL RESEARCH & DEVELOPMENT CORP.—Laporte plc; *Int'l*, pg. 802
MINWAX COMPANY DIV.—The Sherwin-Williams Company; *U.S. Public*, pg. 1466
MOHAWK FINISHING PRODUCTS, INC.—RPM, Inc.; *U.S. Public*, pg. 1357
MORTON AUTOMOTIVE COATINGS—Morton International Inc.; *U.S. Public*, pg. 1135
MORTON INTERNATIONAL, LTD.—Morton International Inc.; *U.S. Public*, pg. 1136
MURALO CO., INC.; *U.S. Private*, pg. 767
NOF JOTUN (H.K.) LTD.—Jotun A/S; *Int'l*, pg. 716
NASCO INDUSTRIES INC.; *U.S. Private*, pg. 774
NATIONAL LABEL COMPANY; *U.S. Private*, pg. 785
THE NEOGARD CORPORATION—Jones Blair Company; *U.S. Private*, pg. 596
NIPPON PAINT COMPANY LTD.; *Int'l*, pg. 937
NISSHOKU SCHENECTADY CHEMICALS, INC.—Schenectady International, Inc.; *U.S. Private*, pg. 970
NODEST A/S—Jotun A/S; *Int'l*, pg. 715
NOPCO INDUSTRIAL S.A. DE C.V.—Henkel KGaA; *Int'l*, pg. 614
NOPCO ITALIANA SPA—Henkel KGaA; *Int'l*, pg. 612
OASIS-AMERON, LTD.—Ameron International Corporation; *U.S. Public*, pg. 99
PPG INDUSTRIES, INC.; *U.S. Public*, pg. 1245
PACIFIC PAINTS PTY LTD.—Imperial Chemical Industries PLC; *Int'l*, pg. 665
PARAGON PAINT & VARNISH CORP.; *U.S. Private*, pg. 838
PAREX, INC.—Lafarge S.A.; *Int'l*, pg. 789
PARKER PAINT MANUFACTURING CO. INC.—Williams Holdings Plc; *Int'l*, pg. 1501
PARKS CORPORATION; *U.S. Private*, pg. 840
PERRY & DERRICK CO.; *U.S. Private*, pg. 854
PERSTORP FERGUSON LTD.-CHEMITEC & COMPOUNDS—Perstorp AB; *Int'l*, pg. 1037
PERSTORP FORMOX—Perstorp AB; *Int'l*, pg. 1038
PERSTORP POLYOLS INC.—Perstorp AB; *Int'l*, pg. 1038
PERSTORP SPA-POLYOLS DIV.—Perstorp AB; *Int'l*, pg. 1038
PERSTORP SPECIALTY CHEMICALS—Perstorp AB; *Int'l*, pg. 1038
THE PERVO PAINT COMPANY; *U.S. Private*, pg. 856
PETROFINA S.A.; *Int'l*, pg. 1043
PIERCE & STEVENS CORP.—Sovereign Specialty Chemical, Inc.; *U.S. Private*, pg. 1019
PLASTI-KOTE COMPANY INC.; *U.S. Private*, pg. 870
POLYMER PLASTICS CORPORATION; *U.S. Private*, pg. 875
PRATT & LAMBERT UNITED, INC.—The Sherwin-Williams Company; *U.S. Public*, pg. 1466
PREMIER COATINGS, INC.—Wattyl; *Int'l*, pg. 1488
PREMIUM POLYMERS INC.—Flexible Products Company; *U.S. Private*, pg. 412
PRESERVATIVE PAINT COMPANY—Kelly-Moore Paint Company, Inc.; *U.S. Private*, pg. 613
PROGRESS PAINT MFG. CO.; *U.S. Private*, pg. 890
PROTIM SOLIGNUM LTD.—Burmah Castrol plc; *Int'l*, pg. 234
RPM BELGIUM N.V.—RPM, Inc.; *U.S. Public*, pg. 1357
RPM, INC.; *U.S. Public*, pg. 1356
RAFFI & SWANSON, INC.; *U.S. Private*, pg. 907
RECREATIONAL PRODUCTS DIV.—California Products Corp.; *U.S. Private*, pg. 201
RED SPOT PAINT & VARNISH CO.; *U.S. Private*, pg. 915
RED SPOT WESTLAND INC.—Red Spot Paint & Varnish Co.; *U.S. Private*, pg. 915
REICHHOLD CHEMIE AG—Dainippon Ink & Chemicals, Inc.; *Int'l*, pg. 370
DR. RENGER GMBH—Morton International Inc.; *U.S. Public*, pg. 1135
RENTOKIL LABORATORIES LTD.—Sophus Berendsen A/S; *Int'l*, pg. 1286
RHONE-POULENC PERFORMANCE RESINS & COATINGS—Rhone-Poulenc S.A.; *Int'l*, pg. 1110
RICHARDSON-VICKS, INC.—The Procter & Gamble Company; *U.S. Public*, pg. 1331
ROYSTON LABORATORIES—Chase Corporation; *U.S. Public*, pg. 337
RUHR PULVERLACK G.M.B.H.—Ferro Corporation; *U.S. Public*, pg. 620
RULE INDUSTRIES, INC.—Kennametal Inc.; *U.S. Public*, pg. 950
RUST-OLEUM CORPORATION—RPM, Inc.; *U.S. Public*, pg. 1358
RUST-OLEUM NEDERLAND B.V.—RPM, Inc.; *U.S. Public*, pg. 1358
SANKO-STEVENS CHEMICAL, INC.—The Sherwin-Williams Company; *U.S. Public*, pg. 1466
THE SAVOGRAN COMPANY; *U.S. Private*, pg. 968
A/S SCANDIA KJEMISKE—Jotun A/S; *Int'l*, pg. 715
EARL SCHEIB AUTOMOTIVE PAINT FINISHES, INC.—Earl Scheib, Inc.; *U.S. Public*, pg. 1437
EARL SCHEIB, INC.; *U.S. Public*, pg. 1437
SCHENECTADY INTERNATIONAL, INC.; *U.S. Private*, pg. 969
SEIBERT-OXIDERMO, INC.—Detrex Corporation; *U.S. Public*, pg. 502
SEYMOUR OF SYCAMORE, INC.; *U.S. Private*, pg. 988
THE SHERWIN-WILLIAMS COMPANY; *U.S. Public*, pg. 1465
SICO INC.; *Int'l*, pg. 1239
SIGMA COATINGS, INC.—Petrofina S.A.; *Int'l*, pg. 1044
SIGMA COATINGS S.A.—Petrofina S.A.; *Int'l*, pg. 1044
SIKA CORPORATION—Sika Finanz AG; *Int'l*, pg. 1249
SIKKENS B.V.—Akzo Nobel N.V.; *Int'l*, pg. 42
SIKKENS LINVEA SPA—Akzo Nobel N.V.; *Int'l*, pg. 43
SIMONIZ USA, INC.; *U.S. Private*, pg. 1001
SINCLAIR/AMERITONE PAINT CORP.—Imperial Chemical Industries PLC; *Int'l*, pg. 663
SINCLAIR PAINT CO.—Imperial Chemical Industries PLC; *Int'l*, pg. 663
SINOCHEM INTERNATIONAL PETROLEUM CO. LTD.; *Int'l*, pg. 1254
SOC. ABIDJANISE D'EXPANSION CHIMIQUE (SAEC) SA—Akzo Nobel N.V.; *Int'l*, pg. 43
SOC. AFRICAINE D'EXPANSION CHIMIQUE (SAEC) SA—Akzo Nobel N.V.; *Int'l*, pg. 43
SOC. AFRICAINE DES PRODUITS CHEMIQUES, AGRICOLES ET MENAGERS SA (SAPCAM)—Akzo Nobel N.V.; *Int'l*, pg. 43
SOUTHWESTERN PETROLEUM CORPORATION; *U.S. Private*, pg. 1019
SPECTRUM INDUSTRIES; *U.S. Private*, pg. 1024
STAR BRONZE COMPANY; *U.S. Private*, pg. 1034
STAR FINISHING PRODUCTS, INC.—RPM, Inc.; *U.S. Public*, pg. 1358
STONHARD, INC.—RPM, Inc.; *U.S. Public*, pg. 1358
TAMBOUR LIMITED—IDB Holding Corporation; *Int'l*, pg. 644
TAMMS INDUSTRIES—Laporte plc; *Int'l*, pg. 803
TAMMS INDUSTRIES CO.—Laporte plc; *Int'l*, pg. 803
THE TESTOR CORPORATION—RPM, Inc.; *U.S. Public*, pg. 1358
TEXAS RESIN—Jones Blair Company; *U.S. Private*, pg. 596
THE THOMPSON-MINWAX COMPANY—The Sherwin-Williams Company; *U.S. Public*, pg. 1466
THE THOMPSON'S COMPANY—The Sherwin-Williams Company; *U.S. Public*, pg. 1466
THORO—Harris Chemical Group, Inc.; *U.S. Private*, pg. 505
3M; *U.S. Public*, pg. 1604
TIKKURILA OY—Kemira Oy; *Int'l*, pg. 729
TORNE-JOTUN S.A.—Jotun A/S; *Int'l*, pg. 716
TROY CORPORATION; *U.S. Private*, pg. 1105
UNITED COATINGS, INC.—The Sherwin-Williams Company; *U.S. Public*, pg. 1466
UNITED PAINT CO.—The Sherwin-Williams Company; *U.S. Public*, pg. 1466
UNITEX LIMITED—Smiths Industries plc; *Int'l*, pg. 1267
THE VALSPAR CORPORATION; *U.S. Public*, pg. 1707
THE VALSPAR CORP. PROTECTIVE COATINGS DIV.—The Valspar Corporation; *U.S. Public*, pg. 1707
VALSPAR, INC.—The Valspar Corporation; *U.S. Public*, pg. 1707
VAN HEMELRIJCK—GIB Group; *Int'l*, pg. 533
VERCOLAC SPA—Akzo Nobel N.V.; *Int'l*, pg. 43
VEROC TECHNOLOGY A/S—Jotun A/S; *Int'l*, pg. 714
WATTYL; *Int'l*, pg. 1488
WELLBORN - DE CORP.—Dunn-Edwards Corporation; *U.S. Private*, pg. 347
WINTER-BOUTS B.V.—Kemira Oy; *Int'l*, pg. 729
WISCONSIN PROTECTIVE COATINGS CORP.—RPM, Inc.; *U.S. Public*, pg. 1358
WITCO CORPORATION; *U.S. Public*, pg. 1773
YENKIN-MAJESTIC PAINT CORPORATION; *U.S. Private*, pg. 1195
ZENECA AB—Zeneca Group Plc; *Int'l*, pg. 1526
ZENECA HELLAS S.A.—Zeneca Group Plc; *Int'l*, pg. 1526
ZENECA OY—Zeneca Group Plc; *Int'l*, pg. 1527
ZENECA POLAND SP. Z.O.O.—Zeneca Group Plc; *Int'l*, pg. 1527
ZENECA ZIMBABWE (PRIVATE) LIMITED—Zeneca Group Plc; *Int'l*, pg. 1527
WM. ZINSSER & CO., INC.—RPM, Inc.; *U.S. Public*, pg. 1358

2861 — GUM & WOOD CHEMICALS

ARIZONA CHEMICAL DIV.—International Paper Company; *U.S. Public*, pg. 901
ARROW INDUSTRIES, INC.—ConAgra, Inc.; *U.S. Public*, pg. 426
CALGON CARBON CORPORATION; *U.S. Public*, pg. 292
CASCO NOBEL AB—Akzo Nobel N.V.; *Int'l*, pg. 48
CIBA SPECIALTY CHEMICALS—Ciba Specialty Chemicals Holding Inc.; *Int'l*, pg. 291
CIBA SPECIALTY CHEMICALS HOLDING INC.; *Int'l*, pg. 291
DSM N.V.; *Int'l*, pg. 352
DR. WOLMANN GMBH—BASF AG; *Int'l*, pg. 104
FLETCHER CHALLENGE METHANOL LIMITED—Fletcher Challenge Limited; *Int'l*, pg. 495
FORT JAMES CORPORATION; *U.S. Public*, pg. 670
GEORGIA-PACIFIC CORPORATION; *U.S. Public*, pg. 735
GREAT LAKES BIOCHEMICAL CO., INC.—Laporte plc; *Int'l*, pg. 802
HERCULES INC.-BRUNSWICK—Hercules Incorporated; *U.S. Public*, pg. 810
HICKORY SPECIALTIES, INC.—Bob Evans Farms, Inc.; *U.S. Public*, pg. 596
KINLEITH MILL—International Paper Company; *U.S. Public*, pg. 905
LAPORTE PLC; *Int'l*, pg. 801
THE MEAD CORPORATION; *U.S. Public*, pg. 1074
METHANEX CORPORATION; *Int'l*, pg. 862
METHANOR VOF—Akzo Nobel N.V.; *Int'l*, pg. 43
METHANOR VOF—DSM N.V.; *Int'l*, pg. 354
MINERAL RESEARCH & DEVELOPMENT CORP.—Laporte plc; *Int'l*, pg. 802
NIPPON KAYAKU CO. LTD.; *Int'l*, pg. 934
PERKINS INDUSTRIES, INC.—Borden, Inc.; *U.S. Private*, pg. 158
REICHHOLD CHEMICALS, INC.—Dainippon Ink & Chemicals, Inc.; *Int'l*, pg. 370
SANDOZ HUNINGUE S.A.—Novartis AG; *Int'l*, pg. 984
JEFFERSON SMURFIT CORPORATION—Jefferson Smurfit Group p.l.c.; *Int'l*, pg. 1269
TENNESSEE RIVER PULP & PAPER CO.—Tenneco Inc.; *U.S. Public*, pg. 1579
UNION CAMP CORPORATION; *U.S. Public*, pg. 1665
WESTVACO CORPORATION; *U.S. Public*, pg. 1762
WESTVACO CORPORATION-CHEMICAL DIV.—Westvaco Corporation; *U.S. Public*, pg. 1762

2865 — CYCLIC ORGANIC CRUDES & INTERMEDIATES, ORGANIC DYES AND PIGMENTS

ABM CHEMICALS LTD.—Rhone-Poulenc S.A.; *Int'l*, pg. 1113
AIR PRODUCTS AND CHEMICALS, INC.; *U.S. Public*, pg. 30
AKZO NOBEL AB—Akzo Nobel N.V.; *Int'l*, pg. 48
ALBRIGHT & WILSON, INC.—Albright & Wilson plc; *Int'l*, pg. 49
AMOCO CHEMICALS—Amoco Corporation; *U.S. Public*, pg. 102
AMOCO CORPORATION; *U.S. Public*, pg. 101
APOLLO COLORS INC.; *U.S. Private*, pg. 77
ASHLAND CHEMICAL—Ashland, Inc.; *U.S. Public*, pg. 139
BASF-FINLAY (PVT.) LTD.—BASF AG; *Int'l*, pg. 106
BASF LACKE & FARBEN VERTRIEBSGESELLSCHAFT MBH—BASF AG; *Int'l*, pg. 106
BASF S.A.—BASF AG; *Int'l*, pg. 107

BAYER ARGENTINA S.A.—Bayer AG; *Int'l*, pg. 175
BAYER CORPORATION—Bayer AG; *Int'l*, pg. 172
BERWIND CORPORATION; *U.S. Private*, pg. 138
BLACKMAN UHLER CHEMICAL CO.—Synalloy Corporation; *U.S. Public*, pg. 1548
BRISTOL-MYERS SQUIBB COMPANY; *U.S. Public*, pg. 253
BUFFALO COLOR CORPORATION; *U.S. Private*, pg. 178
BURKE MILLS, INC.; *U.S. Public*, pg. 267
C & K COLOURS (UK) LTD.—Crompton & Knowles Corporation; *U.S. Public*, pg. 460
CDR PIGMENTS & DISPERSIONS—Flint Ink Corp.; *U.S. Private*, pg. 413
CAFFARO S.P.A.; *Int'l*, pg. 248
P.T. CANDRA SARI—Novartis AG; *Int'l*, pg. 975
CERESIT GMBH—Henkel KGaA; *Int'l*, pg. 609
CHEMDESIGN CORPORATION—Bayer AG; *Int'l*, pg. 173
CHEMFIRST INC.; *U.S. Public*, pg. 344
CHEMRICH, INC.—Albright & Wilson plc; *Int'l*, pg. 49
CIBA-GEIGY ARGENTINA S.A.I.C. Y F.—Novartis AG; *Int'l*, pg. 976
CIBA-GEIGY AUSTRALIA LTD.—Novartis AG; *Int'l*, pg. 976
CIBA-GEIGY (CHINA) LIMITED-GUANGZHOU BRANCH OFFICE—Novartis AG; *Int'l*, pg. 976
CIBA-GEIGY (CHINA) LIMITED-SHANGHAI BRANCH—Novartis AG; *Int'l*, pg. 976
CIBA-GEIGY GESELLSCHAFT MBH—Novartis AG; *Int'l*, pg. 977
CIBA-GEIGY GMBH—Novartis AG; *Int'l*, pg. 977
CIBA-GEIGY HELLAS S.A.—Novartis AG; *Int'l*, pg. 977
CIBA-GEIGY (HONG KONG) LIMITED—Novartis AG; *Int'l*, pg. 977
CIBA-GEIGY IRELAND LIMITED—Novartis AG; *Int'l*, pg. 977
CIBA-GEIGY KOREA LTD.—Novartis AG; *Int'l*, pg. 977
CIBA-GEIGY LTD.-TECHNICAL ASSISTANCE OFFICE—Novartis AG; *Int'l*, pg. 978
CIBA-GEIGY MAROC SA—Novartis AG; *Int'l*, pg. 978
CIBA-GEIGY MEXICANA SA DE CV—Novartis AG; *Int'l*, pg. 978
CIBA-GEIGY QUIMICA S.A.—Novartis AG; *Int'l*, pg. 979
CIBA-GEIGY S.A.—Novartis AG; *Int'l*, pg. 979
CIBA-GEIGY SERVICES AG—Novartis AG; *Int'l*, pg. 979
CIBA-GEIGY SERVICES AG-TECHNICAL ADVISORY OFFICE—Novartis AG; *Int'l*, pg. 979
CIBA-GEIGY SERVICES S.A.—Novartis AG; *Int'l*, pg. 980
CIBA-GEIGY SERVICES SA—Novartis AG; *Int'l*, pg. 980
CIBA-GEIGY TAO—Novartis AG; *Int'l*, pg. 980
CIBA-GEIGY (THAILAND) LTD.—Novartis AG; *Int'l*, pg. 980
CIBA-GEIGY TRADING AND MARKETING SERVICES CO. LTD.-REGIONAL OFFICE—Novartis AG; *Int'l*, pg. 980
CIBA GRIMSBY—Novartis AG; *Int'l*, pg. 980
CIBA SPECIALTY CHEMICALS—Ciba Specialty Chemicals Holding Inc.; *Int'l*, pg. 291
CIBA SPECIALTY CHEMICALS HOLDING INC.; *Int'l*, pg. 291
CLARIANT CORPORATION—Hoechst Aktiengesellschaft; *Int'l*, pg. 624
THE CLAYTON ANILINE COMPANY—Novartis AG; *Int'l*, pg. 981
COLORANTS & AUXILIARIES—Hoechst Aktiengesellschaft; *Int'l*, pg. 626
COLORCON—Berwind Corporation; *U.S. Private*, pg. 139
COMPANHIA BRASILEIRA DE ESTIRENO—Monsanto Company; *U.S. Public*, pg. 1125
COOKSON MATTHEY (AUSTRALIA)—Johnson Matthey Public Limited Company; *Int'l*, pg. 714
COOKSON MATTHEY B.V.—Johnson Matthey Public Limited Company; *Int'l*, pg. 714
COOKSON MATTHEY SPA—Johnson Matthey Public Limited Company; *Int'l*, pg. 714
COS-MAR, INC.—Petrofina S.A.; *Int'l*, pg. 1044
COZ PLASTICS INC.—PMC, Inc.; *U.S. Private*, pg. 827
CROMPTON & KNOWLES CORPORATION; *U.S. Public*, pg. 459
DSM CHEMICALS SALES GMBH—DSM N.V.; *Int'l*, pg. 353
DSM FRANCE SA—DSM N.V.; *Int'l*, pg. 355
DSM UNITED KINGDOM LIMITED—DSM N.V.; *Int'l*, pg. 353
DAIHAN SWISS CHEMICAL CORPORATION—Ciba Specialty Chemicals Holding Inc.; *Int'l*, pg. 292
DAINICHISEIKA COLOUR & CHEMICALS MFG. CO., LTD.; *Int'l*, pg. 369
DEXTER CHEMICAL CORP.; *U.S. Private*, pg. 329
DUSSEK CAMPBELL PTY LTD.—Burmah Castrol plc; *Int'l*, pg. 236
EGE FERRO KIMYA SANAYI VE TICARRET—Ferro Corporation; *U.S. Public*, pg. 619
EASTMAN CHEMICAL COMPANY; *U.S. Public*, pg. 550
FERRO CORPORATION; *U.S. Public*, pg. 618
FINE ORGANICS LIMITED—Laporte plc; *Int'l*, pg. 802
FIRST CHEMICAL CORP.—ChemFirst Inc.; *U.S. Public*, pg. 344
FLINT INK CORP.; *U.S. Private*, pg. 413
FOSROC EXPANDITE (AUSTRALIA) PTY. LTD.—Burmah Castrol plc; *Int'l*, pg. 236
FUCHS PETROLUB AG OEL + CHEMIE; *Int'l*, pg. 517
FUJI-HUNT ELECTRONICS TECHNOLOGY CO., LTD.—Olin Corporation; *U.S. Public*, pg. 1219
GRANITEVILLE COMPANY—Avondale Incorporated; *U.S. Private*, pg. 103
GREAT LAKES BIOCHEMICAL CO., INC.—Laporte plc; *Int'l*, pg. 802
HALTERMANN LTD.—Haltermann AG; *Int'l*, pg. 590
HALVIC KUNSTSTOFFWERKE GMBH—Solvay S.A.; *Int'l*, pg. 1278
HARWICK STANDARD DISTRIBUTION CORPORATION; *U.S. Private*, pg. 509
HENKEL-EYTESA S.A.—Henkel KGaA; *Int'l*, pg. 612
HENKEL PORTUGUESA PRODUCTOS QUIMICOS LDA.—Henkel KGaA; *Int'l*, pg. 613
HINDUSTAN CIBA-GEIGY LIMITED—Novartis AG; *Int'l*, pg. 982
HINKLE EASTER PRODUCTS—Life-Like Products, Inc.; *U.S. Private*, pg. 666
HOECHST AUSTRALIA LTD.—Hoechst Aktiengesellschaft; *Int'l*, pg. 626
HOECHST CELANESE FILM & FIBER INTERMEDIATES GROUP—Hoechst Aktiengesellschaft; *Int'l*, pg. 626
HOECHST CELANESE FINE CHEMICAL DIVISION—Hoechst Aktiengesellschaft; *Int'l*, pg. 625
HOECHST SPECIALTY CHEMICALS GROUP—Hoechst Aktiengesellschaft; *Int'l*, pg. 624
HOECHST SPECIALTY PRODUCTS GROUP—Hoechst Aktiengesellschaft; *Int'l*, pg. 625
HULS AMERICA INC.—Veba AG; *Int'l*, pg. 1455
HULS CANADA INC.—Veba AG; *Int'l*, pg. 1455
INAC INDUSTRIA NACIONAL DE PRODUTOS QUIMICOS LDA.—Novartis AG; *Int'l*, pg. 982
INDUSTRIAS QUIMICAS CARABOBO, C.A.—Novartis AG; *Int'l*, pg. 982
INDUSTRIAS QUIMICAS RESENDE S.A.—Novartis AG; *Int'l*, pg. 983
ISHIHARA SANGYO KAISHA, LTD.; *Int'l*, pg. 689
ISOTECH G.M.B.H.—Novartis AG; *Int'l*, pg. 983
JOHNSON MATTHEY PUBLIC LIMITED COMPANY; *Int'l*, pg. 713
KENYA-SWISS CHEMICAL CO. LTD.—Novartis AG; *Int'l*, pg. 983
KONICA SUPPLIES MANUFACTURING U.S.A., INC.—Konica Corporation; *Int'l*, pg. 749
KRONOS TITAN GMBH—Contran Corporation; *U.S. Private*, pg. 271
MAGRUDER COLOR COMPANY, INC.; *U.S. Private*, pg. 696
MAKHTESHIM CHEMICAL WORKS LTD.; *Int'l*, pg. 830
MANOX LTD.—Rhone-Poulenc S.A.; *Int'l*, pg. 1113
MARVAL INDUSTRIES, INC.; *U.S. Private*, pg. 710
METAL PORTUGUESA S.A.—Ferro Corporation; *U.S. Public*, pg. 619
NIPPON KAYAKU CO. LTD.; *Int'l*, pg. 934
NOVARTIS—Novartis AG; *Int'l*, pg. 972
NOVARTIS AG; *Int'l*, pg. 971
OLIN CORPORATION; *U.S. Public*, pg. 1218
PMC, INC.; *U.S. Private*, pg. 827
C.H. PATRICK & CO., INC.—The B.F. Goodrich Company; *U.S. Public*, pg. 751
PENTAGON CHEMICALS LIMITED—Ascot Holdings Plc; *Int'l*, pg. 88
PERSTORP POLYOLS INC.—Perstorp AB; *Int'l*, pg. 1038
PFERSEE CHEMIE GMBH—Novartis AG; *Int'l*, pg. 983
PHENOLCHEMIE GMBH—Veba AG; *Int'l*, pg. 1454
PHILLIPS PETROLEUM COMPANY; *U.S. Public*, pg. 1290
PIERCE CHEMICAL COMPANY—Perstorp AB; *Int'l*, pg. 1037
PRODUCTOS CIBA SA—Novartis AG; *Int'l*, pg. 983
REILLY INDUSTRIES, INC.; *U.S. Private*, pg. 919
RIEDEL-DE HAEN AG—Hoechst Aktiengesellschaft; *Int'l*, pg. 625
SANDOZ AUSTRALIA PTY. LTD.—Novartis AG; *Int'l*, pg. 984
SANDOZ CHEMICALS LTD.—Novartis AG; *Int'l*, pg. 972
SANDOZ CHEMICALS (THAILAND) LTD.—Novartis AG; *Int'l*, pg. 984
SANDOZ DE MEXICO S.A. DE C.V.—Novartis AG; *Int'l*, pg. 984
SANDOZ INDUSTRIAL CHEMICALS LTD.—Novartis AG; *Int'l*, pg. 984
SANDOZ PRODUCTS LTD.—Novartis AG; *Int'l*, pg. 985
SANDOZ PRODUCTS (SWITZERLAND) LTD.—Novartis AG; *Int'l*, pg. 972
SANDOZ S.P.A.—Novartis AG; *Int'l*, pg. 985
SANDOZ URUNLERI LTD.—Novartis AG; *Int'l*, pg. 985
SASOL LIMITED; *Int'l*, pg. 1196
SCHELDE CHEMIE BRUNSBUTTEL GMBH—Bayer AG; *Int'l*, pg. 172
SCHENECTADY INTERNATIONAL, INC.; *U.S. Private*, pg. 969
SHELL NEDERLAND RAFFINADERIJ—Royal Dutch/Shell Group of Companies; *Int'l*, pg. 1135
SHELL SPECIALTY CHEMICALS—Royal Dutch/Shell Group of Companies; *Int'l*, pg. 1139
SOCHIM COTE-D'IVOIRE SA—Novartis AG; *Int'l*, pg. 985
SOCIETE ZAIRO-SUISSE DE PRODUITS CHIMIQUES S.A.R.L.—Novartis AG; *Int'l*, pg. 986
SOLUTIA INC.; *U.S. Public*, pg. 1483
STANDARD CHLORINE CLOROBEN CHEMICAL CORPORATION; *U.S. Private*, pg. 1031
STEPAN COMPANY; *U.S. Public*, pg. 1514
STEPAN EUROPE—Stepan Company; *U.S. Public*, pg. 1514
STERLING CHEMICALS HOLDINGS, INC.; *U.S. Public*, pg. 1515
SUMITOMO CHEMICAL COMPANY, LTD.; *Int'l*, pg. 1310
SWISSCOLOR D.O.O.—Novartis AG; *Int'l*, pg. 986
SWISSCOLOR SRL—Novartis AG; *Int'l*, pg. 986
SYNALLOY CORPORATION; *U.S. Public*, pg. 1547
TEROCHEM LABORATORIES LIMITED A/K/A RAYLO CHEMICALS—Laporte plc; *Int'l*, pg. 803
TEXFI INDUSTRIES, INC.; *U.S. Public*, pg. 1588
TRIARC COMPANIES, INC.; *U.S. Public*, pg. 1634
UNIVERSAL FLAVORS—Universal Foods Corporation; *U.S. Public*, pg. 1695
UNIVERSAL FOODS CORPORATION; *U.S. Public*, pg. 1695
VELSICOL CHEMICAL CORPORATION; *U.S. Private*, pg. 1135
VULCAN CHEMICALS—Vulcan Materials Company; *U.S. Public*, pg. 1725
VULCAN MATERIALS COMPANY; *U.S. Public*, pg. 1725
WARNER-JENKINSON CO.—Universal Foods Corporation; *U.S. Public*, pg. 1696
WARNER-JENKINSON COSMETIC COLORS—Universal Foods Corporation; *U.S. Public*, pg. 1696
WHITTAKER, CLARK & DANIELS, INC.; *U.S. Private*, pg. 1174

2869 — INDUSTRIAL ORGANIC CHEMICALS, NEC

ABB COMBUSTION ENGINEERING NUCLEAR POWER—ABB Asea Brown Boveri (Holding) Ltd.; *Int'l*, pg. 3
ABM CHEMICALS LTD.—Rhone-Poulenc S.A.; *Int'l*, pg. 1113
APP CHEMICALS LIMITED—Burmah Castrol plc; *Int'l*, pg. 234
AVC CHEMICAL CORPORATION—Ishihara Sangyo Kaisha, Ltd.; *Int'l*, pg. 689
ABBOTT AUSTRALIA/ASIA PTY. LTD.—Abbott Laboratories; *U.S. Public*, pg. 13
ABEL LEMON & BLEAKLEY—Laporte plc; *Int'l*, pg. 803
ADHESIVE SOLUTIONS LIMITED—Burmah Castrol plc; *Int'l*, pg. 234
AETHYLEN ROHRLEITUNGS GESELLSCHAFT MBH & CO. KG—DSM N.V.; *Int'l*, pg. 356
AIR PRODUCTS AND CHEMICALS, INC.; *U.S. Public*, pg. 30
AJINOMOTO COMPANY INC.; *Int'l*, pg. 40
AKROSIL DIVISION—International Paper Company; *U.S. Public*, pg. 901
AKZO COATINGS INC. (MI)—Akzo Nobel N.V.; *Int'l*, pg. 46
AKZO NOBEL CHEMICALS INC.—Akzo Nobel N.V.; *Int'l*, pg. 47
AKZO NOBEL COATINGS INC.—Akzo Nobel N.V.; *Int'l*, pg. 48
AKZO NOBEL INC.—Akzo Nobel N.V.; *Int'l*, pg. 47
AKZO ZOUT CHEMIE B.V.—Akzo Nobel N.V.; *Int'l*, pg. 43
ALCOA CHEMIE GMBH—Aluminum Company of America; *U.S. Public*, pg. 61
ALDRICH CHEMICAL CO., INC.—Sigma-Aldrich Corporation; *U.S. Public*, pg. 1471
ALDRICH CHEMICAL CO., LTD.—Sigma-Aldrich Corporation; *U.S. Public*, pg. 1472
ALDRICH CHEMIE GMBH & CO. K.G.—Sigma-Aldrich Corporation; *U.S. Public*, pg. 1472
ALLIEDSIGNAL INC.; *U.S. Public*, pg. 49
AMERICAN SWEETNERS, INC.; *U.S. Private*, pg. 63
AMERSHAM BUCHLER GMBH & CO. KG—Nycomed Amersham plc; *Int'l*, pg. 992
AMOCO CHEMICAL BELGIUM N.V.—Amoco Corporation; *U.S. Public*, pg. 103
AMOCO CHEMICAL (EUROPE) S.A.—Amoco Corporation; *U.S. Public*, pg. 103
AMOCO CHEMICAL (UK) LTD.—Amoco Corporation; *U.S. Public*, pg. 103
AMOCO CHEMICALS—Amoco Corporation; *U.S. Public*, pg. 102
AMOCO CORPORATION; *U.S. Public*, pg. 101
AMOCO FINA N.V.—Amoco Corporation; *U.S. Public*, pg. 102
AMSPEC CHEMICAL CORPORATION; *U.S. Private*, pg. 67
ANGUS CHEMICAL COMPANY; *U.S. Private*, pg. 75
ANGUS CHEMICAL (SINGAPORE) PTE. LTD.—ANGUS Chemical Company; *U.S. Private*, pg. 75
ANGUS CHEMIE GMBH—ANGUS Chemical Company; *U.S. Private*, pg. 75
APPLETON PAPERS-PORTAGE PLANT—Groupe Saint Louis; *Int'l*, pg. 567
AQUALON-LOUISIANA—Hercules Incorporated; *U.S. Public*, pg. 810
ARCHER DANIELS MIDLAND COMPANY (ADM); *U.S. Public*, pg. 127
ARISTECH CHEMICAL CORPORATION—Mitsubishi Corporation; *Int'l*, pg. 872
ARJO WIGGINS CHEMIE GMBH—Groupe Saint Louis; *Int'l*, pg. 568
ASAHI-PENN CHEMICAL COMPANY LIMITED—PPG Industries, Inc.; *U.S. Public*, pg. 1245
ASHLAND CHEMICAL—Ashland, Inc.; *U.S. Public*, pg. 139
ASIAN BLEACHING EARTH CO., LTD.—Laporte plc; *Int'l*, pg. 803
ATLANTIC METALS CORPORATION; *U.S. Private*, pg. 95
ATLANTIC RICHFIELD COMPANY; *U.S. Public*, pg. 144
ATOCHEM CANADA INC.—Elf Aquitane; *Int'l*, pg. 446
ATOCHEM SAIC—Elf Aquitane, *Int'l*, pg. 446
AUSTRALIAN PERLITE—Laporte plc; *Int'l*, pg. 803
BASF-FINLAY (PVT.) LTD.—BASF AG; *Int'l*, pg. 106
BASF INDIA LTD.—BASF AG; *Int'l*, pg. 106
BASF MAROC S.A.—BASF AG; *Int'l*, pg. 106
BP AMERICA INC.—The British Petroleum Company P.L.C.; *Int'l*, pg. 220
BAKERY INGREDIENTS DIVISION—Royal Gist-Brocades N.V.; *Int'l*, pg. 1142
BASIC CHEMICALS DIV.—Rhone-Poulenc S.A.; *Int'l*, pg. 1109
BAYER AG—Bayer AG; *Int'l*, pg. 172
BAYER A/S—Bayer AG; *Int'l*, pg. 174
BAYER CORPORATION—Bayer AG; *Int'l*, pg. 172
BAYER CORPORATION/CONSUMER CARE DIVISION—Bayer AG; *Int'l*, pg. 173
BEAUMONT PETROCHEMICAL PLANT—Mobil Oil Corporation; *U.S. Public*, pg. 1118
BEIERSDORF (THAILAND) CO. LTD.—Beiersdorf Group; *Int'l*, pg. 183
BERK SPENCER ACIDS LTD.—Rhone-Poulenc S.A.; *Int'l*, pg. 1113
BEVALOID LTD.—Rhone-Poulenc S.A.; *Int'l*, pg. 1113
BIOZYM GESELLSCHAFT M.B.H.—Novartis AG; *Int'l*, pg. 986
BLEAKLEY FINE CHEMICALS—Laporte plc; *Int'l*, pg. 803
BREYER CHEMIE B.V.—Harrisons & Crosfield plc; *Int'l*, pg. 599
BRISTOL ORGANICS, LTD.—Sigma-Aldrich Corporation; *U.S. Public*, pg. 1472
BULAB HOLDINGS, INC.; *U.S. Private*, pg. 180
BURMAH CASTROL CHEMICALS LTD.—Burmah Castrol plc; *Int'l*, pg. 234
BURMAH CASTROL PLC; *Int'l*, pg. 234
BUSH BOAKE ALLEN, INC—Union Camp Corporation; *U.S. Public*, pg. 1666

BUSH BOAKE ALLEN LTD.—Union Camp Corporation; *U.S. Public*, pg. 1666
BUTACHIMIE—Du Pont (E.I. Du Pont De Nemours & Co.); *U.S. Public*, pg. 533
CSM INGREDIENTS DIVISION—CSM N.V.; *Int'l*, pg. 243
CSM N.V.; *Int'l*, pg. 243
CARPENTER CO.; *U.S. Private*, pg. 214
CASTROL (U.K.) LIMITED—Burmah Castrol plc; *Int'l*, pg. 234
CECA S.A.—Elf Aquitane; *Int'l*, pg. 445
CELANESE CANADA, INC.—Hoechst Aktiengesellschaft; *Int'l*, pg. 625
CHEM-TREND INCORPORATED—Burmah Castrol plc; *Int'l*, pg. 235
CHEMDESIGN CORPORATION—Bayer AG; *Int'l*, pg. 173
CHEMICAL EXCHANGE INDUSTRIES; *U.S. Private*, pg. 232
CHEMRICH, INC.—Albright & Wilson plc; *Int'l*, pg. 49
CHEMVIRON SPECIALTY CHEMICALS—Merck & Co., Inc.; *U.S. Public*, pg. 1091
CHEVRON CHEMICAL CO.—Chevron Corporation; *U.S. Public*, pg. 348
CHEVRON CORPORATION; *U.S. Public*, pg. 347
CHIEF ETHANOL FUELS, INC.—Chief Industries, Inc.; *U.S. Private*, pg. 236
CHINA AMERICAN PETROCHEMICAL CO., LTD.—Amoco Corporation; *U.S. Public*, pg. 102
CHR. HANSEN HOLDING A/S; *Int'l*, pg. 288
CHRISTIAN DIOR PERFUMES INC.—LVMH Moet Hennessy Louis Vuitton; *Int'l*, pg. 781
S.A. CITRIQUE BELGE N.V.—Roche Holding Ltd.; *Int'l*, pg. 1121
CLAEYS SEMENCES—Lafarge S.A.; *Int'l*, pg. 790
CLARIANT CORPORATION—Hoechst Aktiengesellschaft; *Int'l*, pg. 624
CLEANING SOLUTIONS GROUP/CELLO—The Sherwin-Williams Company; *U.S. Public*, pg. 1466
COGEMA - COMPAGNIE GENERALE DES MATIERES NUCLEAIRES; *Int'l*, pg. 304
COLORANTS & AUXILIARIES—Hoechst Aktiengesellschaft; *Int'l*, pg. 626
COLOUR SERVICES—Laporte plc; *Int'l*, pg. 803
COMMERCIAL HENKEL S.A. (COHESA)—Henkel KGaA; *Int'l*, pg. 611
COSAN CHEMICAL CORP.—Cambrex Corporation; *U.S. Public*, pg. 297
COURTAULDS PLC; *Int'l*, pg. 338
CRANSTON PRINT WORKS COMPANY; *U.S. Private*, pg. 286
CREEKSIDE INDUSTRIAL; *U.S. Private*, pg. 288
CULTOR LTD.; *Int'l*, pg. 349
CYANAMID DE COLUMBIA SA—American Home Products Corporation; *U.S. Public*, pg. 80
CYANAMID GMBH—American Home Products Corporation; *U.S. Public*, pg. 81
CYANAMID INTER-AMERICAN CORPORATION—American Home Products Corporation; *U.S. Public*, pg. 81
CYANAMID ITALIA S.P.A—American Home Products Corporation; *U.S. Public*, pg. 81
CYANAMID (JAPAN) LTD.—American Home Products Corporation; *U.S. Public*, pg. 81
CYANAMID KOREA, INC.—American Home Products Corporation; *U.S. Public*, pg. 81
CYANAMID MEXICO—American Home Products Corporation; *U.S. Public*, pg. 81
CYANAMID OF GREAT BRITAIN LTD.—American Home Products Corporation; *U.S. Public*, pg. 81
CYANAMID PHILIPPINES, INC.—American Home Products Corporation; *U.S. Public*, pg. 81
CYANAMID TAIWAN CORP.—American Home Products Corporation; *U.S. Public*, pg. 81
DSM CHEMIE LINZ GMBH—DSM N.V.; *Int'l*, pg. 356
DSM FRANCE SA—DSM N.V.; *Int'l*, pg. 355
DSM N.V.; *Int'l*, pg. 352
DAICEL CHEMICAL INDUSTRIES LTD.—Mitsui & Co., Ltd.; *Int'l*, pg. 877
DAVCO SERVICES—Laporte plc; *Int'l*, pg. 803
DECCO DIV.—Elf Aquitane; *Int'l*, pg. 446
DEGUSSA AG; *Int'l*, pg. 388
DEGUSSA CORPORATION—Degussa AG; *Int'l*, pg. 388
DETREX CORPORATION; *U.S. Public*, pg. 501
DEUTSCHE HEY'DI CHEMISCHE GMBH—Laporte plc; *Int'l*, pg. 803
DOBER CHEMICAL CORP.; *U.S. Private*, pg. 337
DOVER CHEMICAL CORP.—ICC Industries, Inc.; *U.S. Private*, pg. 553
THE DOW CHEMICAL COMPANY; *U.S. Public*, pg. 522
DOW CORNING CORPORATION—The Dow Chemical Company; *U.S. Public*, pg. 523
DU PONT CHAMBERS WORKS—Du Pont (E.I. Du Pont De Nemours & Co.); *U.S. Public*, pg. 531
DU PONT (E.I. DU PONT DE NEMOURS & CO.); *U.S. Public*, pg. 530
DUSSEK BROS. (SA) (PTY.) LTD.—Burmah Castrol plc; *Int'l*, pg. 236
EC ERDOLCHEMIE GMBH—Bayer AG; *Int'l*, pg. 172
EASTEX HYDROCARBONS, INC.—El Paso Natural Gas Co.; *U.S. Public*, pg. 567
EASTMAN CHEMICAL COMPANY; *U.S. Public*, pg. 550
EASTMAN FINE CHEMICALS—Eastman Kodak Company; *U.S. Public*, pg. 550
ELF AQUITAINE, INC.—Elf Aquitane; *Int'l*, pg. 445
ELF ATOCHEM NORTH AMERICA, INC.—Elf Aquitane; *Int'l*, pg. 445
ELF ATOCHEM ROTTERDAH B.V.—Elf Aquitane; *Int'l*, pg. 446
ELQUIBER, S.A.—Eli Lilly and Company; *U.S. Public*, pg. 994
EMBECON (NEW ZEALAND) LIMITED—Novartis AG; *Int'l*, pg. 982
ENZYME BIO-SYSTEMS, LTD.—Corn Products International, Inc.; *U.S. Public*, pg. 448
ESSEX INDUSTRIAL CHEMICALS, INC.—The Dow Chemical Company; *U.S. Public*, pg. 523
ETOXYL, C.A.—Olin Corporation; *U.S. Public*, pg. 1219
EUROCHEM DIVISION—Baker Hughes Incorporated; *U.S. Public*, pg. 166
EUROLYSINE SA—Ajinomoto Company Inc.; *Int'l*, pg. 41
EWOS AB—Cultor Ltd.; *Int'l*, pg. 349
EXPANDITE S.A.—Burmah Castrol plc; *Int'l*, pg. 236
EXXON CORPORATION; *U.S. Public*, pg. 601
FMC CORP., LITHIUM DIVISION—FMC Corporation; *U.S. Public*, pg. 605
FMC MARINE COLLOIDS DIV.—FMC Corporation; *U.S. Public*, pg. 605
FERRO CORPORATION; *U.S. Public*, pg. 618
FILTROL CORPORATION—Akzo Nobel N.V.; *Int'l*, pg. 47
FINNFEEDS INTERNATIONAL LTD.—Cultor Ltd.; *Int'l*, pg. 349
FINNSUGAR BIOPRODUCTS—Cultor Ltd.; *Int'l*, pg. 349
FISHER SCIENTIFIC COMPANY—Thomas H. Lee Co.; *U.S. Private*, pg. 658
FISHER SCIENTIFIC INTERNATIONAL—Thomas H. Lee Co.; *U.S. Private*, pg. 658
FLETCHER CHALLENGE METHANOL LIMITED—Fletcher Challenge Limited; *Int'l*, pg. 495
FLOORDRESS REINIGUNGSMASCHINEN AG—Henkel KGaA; *Int'l*, pg. 611
FLORIDA LIME CORP.—Puerto Rican Cement Co., Inc.; *U.S. Public*, pg. 1342
FOSROC EXPANDITE LTD.—Burmah Castrol plc; *Int'l*, pg. 236
FOSROC EXPANDITE SB—Burmah Castrol plc; *Int'l*, pg. 236
FURON FLUORGLAS PRODUCTS—Furon Company; *U.S. Public*, pg. 689
GAF-HULS CHEMIE GMBH—Veba AG; *Int'l*, pg. 1454
GEMISA S.A. DE C.V.—Henkel KGaA; *Int'l*, pg. 614
GENERAL CHEMICAL CORPORATION—The General Chemical Group, Inc.; *U.S. Public*, pg. 707
GEORGIA GULF CORPORATION; *U.S. Public*, pg. 734
GERMANTOWN INTERNATIONAL—Goodman Fielder Limited; *Int'l*, pg. 555
GIANT INDUSTRIES INC.; *U.S. Public*, pg. 741
GIST-BROCADES FRANCE S.A.—Royal Gist-Brocades N.V.; *Int'l*, pg. 1143
GIVAUDAN-ROURE, S.A. DE C.V.—Roche Holding Ltd.; *Int'l*, pg. 1120
GRACE, S.A.—W.R. Grace & Co.; *U.S. Public*, pg. 756
W.R. GRACE OY—W.R. Grace & Co.; *U.S. Public*, pg. 756
GRANT CHEMICAL DIV.—Ferro Corporation; *U.S. Public*, pg. 618
GREAT LAKES BIOCHEMICAL CO., INC.—Laporte plc; *Int'l*, pg. 802
GREAT LAKES CHEMICAL CORPORATION; *U.S. Public*, pg. 760
GROW GROUP, INC.—Imperial Chemical Industries PLC; *Int'l*, pg. 663
HAARMANN & REIMER CORP.—Bayer AG; *Int'l*, pg. 173
HAARMANN & REIMER FOOD INGREDIENTS DIV.—Bayer AG; *Int'l*, pg. 173
THE C.P. HALL COMPANY; *U.S. Private*, pg. 495
HALTERMANN AG; *Int'l*, pg. 590
HALTERMANN LTD.—Haltermann AG; *Int'l*, pg. 590
HALVIC KUNSTSTOFFWERKE GMBH—Solvay S.A.; *Int'l*, pg. 1278
HAMPSHIRE CHEMICAL CORP.; *U.S. Private*, pg. 498
M.A. HANNA RUBBER COMPOUNDING—M.A. Hanna Company; *U.S. Public*, pg. 781
HARCROS CHEMICALS—Harrisons & Crosfield plc; *Int'l*, pg. 599
HELMERICH & PAYNE, INC.; *U.S. Public*, pg. 808
HENKEL & CIE AG—Henkel KGaA; *Int'l*, pg. 611
HENKEL BELGIUM S.A.—Henkel KGaA; *Int'l*, pg. 612
HENKEL CHEMICALS LTD.—Henkel KGaA; *Int'l*, pg. 612
HENKEL FRANCE S.A.—Henkel KGaA; *Int'l*, pg. 612
HENKEL IBERICA S.A.—Henkel KGaA; *Int'l*, pg. 612
HENKEL KGAA; *Int'l*, pg. 609
HENKEL MEXICANA S.A. DE C.V.—Henkel KGaA; *Int'l*, pg. 614
HENKEL RIKA (M) SDN. BHD.—Henkel KGaA; *Int'l*, pg. 613
HERCULES FOOD & FUNCTIONAL PRODUCTS CO.—Hercules Incorporated; *U.S. Public*, pg. 810
HERCULES INCORPORATED; *U.S. Public*, pg. 809
HEXAQUIMIA SA—Akzo Nobel N.V.; *Int'l*, pg. 47
HIGH PLAINS CORPORATION; *U.S. Public*, pg. 825
HOECHST CELANESE FINE CHEMICAL DIVISION—Hoechst Aktiengesellschaft; *Int'l*, pg. 625
HOECHST MARION ROUSSEL, INC.—Hoechst Aktiengesellschaft; *Int'l*, pg. 624
HOECHST SPECIALTY CHEMICALS GROUP—Hoechst Aktiengesellschaft; *Int'l*, pg. 624
HOECHST SPECIALTY PRODUCTS GROUP—Hoechst Aktiengesellschaft; *Int'l*, pg. 625
F. HOFFMANN-LA ROCHE LTD.—Roche Holding Ltd.; *Int'l*, pg. 1119
HSIN-FENG CHEMICAL CORP.—Jason Incorporated; *U.S. Public*, pg. 924
THE HUMPHREY CHEMICAL COMPANY, INC.—Cambrex Corporation; *U.S. Public*, pg. 297
HYDROCHIM, S.A.—Olin Corporation; *U.S. Public*, pg. 1219
ICC INDUSTRIES, INC.; *U.S. Private*, pg. 553
ICI AMERICAS, INC.—Imperial Chemical Industries PLC; *Int'l*, pg. 663
ICI KATALCO—Imperial Chemical Industries PLC; *Int'l*, pg. 664
ISC CHEMICALS LTD.—Rhone-Poulenc S.A.; *Int'l*, pg. 1113
ISK SINGAPORE PTE. LTD.—Ishihara Sangyo Kaisha, Ltd.; *Int'l*, pg. 689
ISK TAIWAN CO., LTD.—Ishihara Sangyo Kaisha, Ltd.; *Int'l*, pg. 689
ITW FLUID PRODUCTS GROUP—Illinois Tool Works Inc.; *U.S. Public*, pg. 866
INDUSTRIAS RESISTOL, S.A.—Monsanto Company; *U.S. Public*, pg. 1125
INTERNATIONAL SPECIALTY PRODUCTS, INC.—ISP Holdings, Inc.; *U.S. Public*, pg. 858
ISHIHARA ARGENTINA S.A.—Ishihara Sangyo Kaisha, Ltd.; *Int'l*, pg. 689
ISHIHARA SANGYO KAISHA, LTD.; *Int'l*, pg. 689
ISHIHARA TRADING CO., LTD.—Ishihara Sangyo Kaisha, Ltd.; *Int'l*, pg. 689
J.U.L. SEILAZ AG—Henkel KGaA; *Int'l*, pg. 613
JAPAN NUCLEAR FUEL CO., LTD.—Toshiba Corporation; *Int'l*, pg. 1403
AXEL JOHNSON CHEMICALS AB—Axel Johnson AB; *Int'l*, pg. 708
KAO CORPORATION; *Int'l*, pg. 717
KEIL CHEMICAL DIV.—Ferro Corporation; *U.S. Public*, pg. 619
KELCO DIV.—Monsanto Company; *U.S. Public*, pg. 1125
KELCO INTERNATIONAL LTD.—Merck & Co., Inc.; *U.S. Public*, pg. 1091
KEMIRA AGRO OY—Kemira Oy; *Int'l*, pg. 727
KEMIRA CHIMIE S.A.—Kemira Oy; *Int'l*, pg. 728
KING INDUSTRIES, INC.; *U.S. Private*, pg. 620
KNOLL PHARMACEUTICAL COMPANY—BASF AG; *Int'l*, pg. 105
KRONOS SA/NV—Contran Corporation; *U.S. Private*, pg. 271
KUWAIT PETROLEUM CORPORATION; *Int'l*, pg. 764
KYOWA HAKKO EUROPE GMBH—Kyowa Hakko Kogyo Company, Ltd.; *Int'l*, pg. 778
KYOWA HAKKO (H.K.) CO., LTD.—Kyowa Hakko Kogyo Company, Ltd.; *Int'l*, pg. 778
KYOWA HAKKO U.S.A., INC.—Kyowa Hakko Kogyo Company, Ltd.; *Int'l*, pg. 778
KYOWA HAKKO-WEST COAST OFFICE—Kyowa Hakko Kogyo Company, Ltd.; *Int'l*, pg. 778
LPS LABORATORIES INC.—Morgan Crucible Co. Plc; *Int'l*, pg. 892
LAMBENT TECHNOLOGIES INC.—Petroferm Inc.; *U.S. Private*, pg. 858
LAPORTE ABSORBENTS-HOLLAND—Laporte plc; *Int'l*, pg. 803
LAPORTE CHEMICALS (MALAYSIA) SDN BHD—Laporte plc; *Int'l*, pg. 803
LAPORTE ESD-GERMANY—Laporte plc; *Int'l*, pg. 803
LAPORTE INDUSTRIES (SINGAPORE) PTE LIMITED—Laporte plc; *Int'l*, pg. 803
LAPORTE KEMWOOD AB—Laporte plc; *Int'l*, pg. 803
LAPORTE (MALAYSIA) SDN BHD—Laporte plc; *Int'l*, pg. 803
LAPORTE PLC; *Int'l*, pg. 801
LAPORTE (TAIWAN) LIMITED—Laporte plc; *Int'l*, pg. 803
LAPORTE (THAILAND) LTD.—Laporte plc; *Int'l*, pg. 803
LEDERLE (JAPAN) LTD.—American Home Products Corporation; *U.S. Public*, pg. 81
ELI LILLY AND COMPANY; *U.S. Public*, pg. 992
LONZA-WERKE GMBH—Alusuisse-Lonza Holding Ltd.; *Int'l*, pg. 67
LORD CORPORATION; *U.S. Private*, pg. 675
THE LUBRIZOL CORPORATION; *U.S. Public*, pg. 1016
MALLINCKRODT BAKER INC.—Mallinckrodt Inc.; *U.S. Public*, pg. 1039
MANOX LTD.—Rhone-Poulenc S.A.; *Int'l*, pg. 1113
MARSON/CREATIVE FASTENER, INC.; *U.S. Private*, pg. 708
MAZZUCCHELLI 1849 S.P.A.; *Int'l*, pg. 849
MCCORMICK INGREDIENTS SOUTHEAST ASIA PVT., LTD.—McCormick & Company, Incorporated; *U.S. Public*, pg. 1067
MCGHAN LIMITED—Inamed Corporation; *U.S. Public*, pg. 874
MERCK & CO., INC.; *U.S. Public*, pg. 1090
METHANEX CORPORATION; *Int'l*, pg. 862
METHANOL CHEMIE NEDERLAND VOF—Akzo Nobel N.V.; *Int'l*, pg. 43
METHANOR VOF—Akzo Nobel N.V.; *Int'l*, pg. 43
METHANOR VOF—DSM N.V.; *Int'l*, pg. 354
MILLENNIUM INORGANIC CHEMICALS—Hanson PLC; *Int'l*, pg. 593
MINAS DE GADOR S.A.—Laporte plc; *Int'l*, pg. 803
MINERAL RESEARCH & DEVELOPMENT CORP.—Laporte plc; *Int'l*, pg. 802
MITCHELL COTTS CHEMICALS LIMITED—Ascot Holdings Plc; *Int'l*, pg. 88
MITSUI PETROCHEMICAL INDUSTRIES, LTD.—Mitsui & Co., Ltd.; *Int'l*, pg. 877
MITSUI TOATSU CHEMICALS, INC.—Mitsui & Co., Ltd.; *Int'l*, pg. 877
MOBIL LAND DEVELOPMENT CORPORATION—Mobil Oil Corporation; *U.S. Public*, pg. 1118
MOBIL OIL CORPORATION; *U.S. Public*, pg. 1118
MOBIL PETROCHEMICALS DIV.—Mobil Oil Corporation; *U.S. Public*, pg. 1118
MONSANTO EUROPE S.A.—Monsanto Company; *U.S. Public*, pg. 1125
MONTEREY KELP CORP.—Monsanto Company; *U.S. Public*, pg. 1125
MOONEY CHEMICALS—OM Group; *U.S. Public*, pg. 1208
MORFLEX, INC.—Reilly Industries, Inc.; *U.S. Private*, pg. 919
NL INDUSTRIES, INC.—Contran Corporation; *U.S. Private*, pg. 270
NALCO CHEMICAL COMPANY; *U.S. Public*, pg. 1150
NATIONAL STARCH AND CHEMICAL COMPANY—Unilever Plc; *Int'l*, pg. 1435
NATURAL GAS ODORIZING—Occidental Petroleum Corporation; *U.S. Public*, pg. 1210
NICOLET DIVISION—International Paper Company; *U.S. Public*, pg. 903
NOVILLE; *U.S. Private*, pg. 808
NOVO NORDISK A/S; *Int'l*, pg. 987
NOVO NORDISK A/S—Novo Nordisk A/S; *Int'l*, pg. 989
NOVO NORDISK BIOCHEMICALS KK—Novo Nordisk A/S; *Int'l*, pg. 989
NOVO NORDISK BIOINDUSTRIALE SRL—Novo Nordisk A/S; *Int'l*, pg. 989
NOVO NORDISK BIOINDUSTRIE S.A.—Novo Nordisk A/S; *Int'l*, pg. 989

NOVO NORDISK BIOINDUSTRIES UK LTD.—Novo Nordisk A/S; *Int'l*, pg. 989
NOVO NORDISK BIOINDUSTRY LTD—Novo Nordisk A/S; *Int'l*, pg. 989
NOVO NORDISK BIOTECHNOLOGIE GMBH—Novo Nordisk A/S; *Int'l*, pg. 989
NOVO NORDISK FERMENT LTD.—Novo Nordisk A/S; *Int'l*, pg. 989
NUCLEAR AND ADVANCED TECHNOLOGY DIVISION—CBS Corporation; *U.S. Public*, pg. 273
NUEVO FEDERAL S.A.; *Int'l*, pg. 990
NUTRASWEET INTERNATIONAL, LTD.—Monsanto Company; *U.S. Public*, pg. 1125
THE NUTRASWEET KELCO COMPANY—Monsanto Company; *U.S. Public*, pg. 1125
OCCIDENTAL CHEMICAL CORPORATION—Occidental Petroleum Corporation; *U.S. Public*, pg. 1210
OLIN BRAZIL LTDA.—Olin Corporation; *U.S. Public*, pg. 1220
OLIN CHEMICALS, B.V.—Olin Corporation; *U.S. Public*, pg. 1220
OLIN CORPORATION; *U.S. Public*, pg. 1218
ONCOMEMBRANE, INC.—Otsuka Pharmaceutical Co., Ltd.; *Int'l*, pg. 1013
ORSAN—Lafarge S.A.; *Int'l*, pg. 791
PPG INDUSTRIES, INC.; *U.S. Public*, pg. 1245
THE PAKS CORP.—International Flavors & Fragrances, Inc.; *U.S. Public*, pg. 899
PALINTEST LIMITED—Halma p.l.c.; *Int'l*, pg. 589
PARKS CORPORATION; *U.S. Private*, pg. 840
PENRECO—Pennzoil Company; *U.S. Public*, pg. 1273
PENTAGON CHEMICALS LIMITED—Ascot Holdings Plc; *Int'l*, pg. 88
PERFORMANCE POLYMERS B.V.—Burmah Castrol plc; *Int'l*, pg. 236
PEROXIDES ARGENTINOS SA—Akzo Nobel N.V.; *Int'l*, pg. 47
PEROXIDOS DO BRAZIL—Solvay S.A.; *Int'l*, pg. 1279
PERSTORP AB; *Int'l*, pg. 1036
PERSTORP FERGUSON LTD.-CHEMITEC & COMPOUNDS—Perstorp AB; *Int'l*, pg. 1037
PERSTORP FORMOX—Perstorp AB; *Int'l*, pg. 1038
PERSTORP SPA-POLYOLS DIV.—Perstorp AB; *Int'l*, pg. 1038
PERSTORP SPECIALTY CHEMICALS—Perstorp AB; *Int'l*, pg. 1038
PETROFERM INC.; *U.S. Private*, pg. 858
PETROLEUM SPECIALTIES GROUP—Witco Corporation; *U.S. Public*, pg. 1774
PHILIPP BROTHERS CHEMICALS, INC.; *U.S. Private*, pg. 861
PHILLIPS PETROLEUM COMPANY; *U.S. Public*, pg. 1290
POLYMER CHEMICALS GROUP—Witco Corporation; *U.S. Public*, pg. 1774
PREMIER CHEMICAL PLANT—Crompton & Knowles Corporation; *U.S. Public*, pg. 460
PREUSSENELEKTRA-KERNBRENNSTOFF GMBH—Veba AG; *Int'l*, pg. 1457
PROCTER & GAMBLE OF PERU—The Procter & Gamble Company; *U.S. Public*, pg. 1332
PRODUCTORA DE ALCOHOLES HIDRATADOS, C.A. (PRALCA)—Olin Corporation; *U.S. Public*, pg. 1220
PRONOVA A/S—Norsk Hydro a.s; *Int'l*, pg. 961
PRONOVA BIOPOLYMERS A/S—Norsk Hydro a.s; *Int'l*, pg. 961
PULCRA S.A.—Henkel KGaA; *Int'l*, pg. 612
QUAKER CHEMICAL CORPORATION; *U.S. Public*, pg. 1346
QUALITY CHEMICALS, INC.—ChemFirst Inc.; *U.S. Public*, pg. 344
QUEST INTERNATIONAL—Unilever Plc; *Int'l*, pg. 1438
QUIMICA S.A. DE C.V.—Henkel KGaA; *Int'l*, pg. 614
QUIMOBASICOS, S.A. DE C.V.—CYDSA S.A.; *Int'l*, pg. 247
RASCHIG GMBH—PMC, Inc.; *U.S. Private*, pg. 827
RECORDATI INDUSTRIA CHIMICA E FARMACEUTICA S.P.A.; *Int'l*, pg. 1090
REPSOL EXPLORACION—Repsol S.A.; *Int'l*, pg. 1104
REPSOL S.A.; *Int'l*, pg. 1104
RHODIACO INDUSTRIES QUIMICAS LTDA.—Amoco Corporation; *U.S. Public*, pg. 103
RHONE-POULENC ALCOLAC—Rhone-Poulenc S.A.; *Int'l*, pg. 1110
RHONE-POULENC, CHEMICAL DIVISION—Rhone-Poulenc S.A.; *Int'l*, pg. 1109
RHONE-POULENC INC.—Rhone-Poulenc S.A.; *Int'l*, pg. 1112
RHONE-POULENC SPECIALTY CHEMICALS—Rhone-Poulenc S.A.; *Int'l*, pg. 1110
RHONE-POULENC, SPECIALTY PLASTICS DIVISION—Rhone-Poulenc S.A.; *Int'l*, pg. 1110
RICHARDSON-VICKS, INC.—The Procter & Gamble Company; *U.S. Public*, pg. 1331
RIEDEL-DE HAEN AG—Hoechst Aktiengesellschaft; *Int'l*, pg. 625
RIOQUIMA S.A.—Novartis AG; *Int'l*, pg. 984
ROHM AND HAAS COMPANY; *U.S. Public*, pg. 1403
ROHM & HAAS CO. RESEARCH LABS—Rohm and Haas Company; *U.S. Public*, pg. 1403
ROHM GMBH—Veba AG; *Int'l*, pg. 1454
RUBICON INC.—Crompton & Knowles Corporation; *U.S. Public*, pg. 460
RUETGERS A.G.; *Int'l*, pg. 1147
RUETGERS-NEASE CORPORATION—Ruetgers A.G.; *Int'l*, pg. 1148
SCM GLIDCO ORGANIC—Hanson PLC; *Int'l*, pg. 594
SCM SPECIALTY CHEMICALS INC.—Hanson PLC; *Int'l*, pg. 594
SAMSUNG PETROCHEMICAL CO. LTD.—Amoco Corporation; *U.S. Public*, pg. 102
SANABO GESELLSCHAFT M.B.H.—Novartis AG; *Int'l*, pg. 984
SASOL SYNTHETIC FUELS (PTY.) LTD.—Sasol Limited; *Int'l*, pg. 1197
SCIOM S.A.—Henkel KGaA; *Int'l*, pg. 614
SEMILAB AG—Laporte plc; *Int'l*, pg. 803
SEQUA CORPORATION; *U.S. Public*, pg. 1458
SERVO DELDEN B.V.—Veba AG; *Int'l*, pg. 1456
SETTEF SPA—Laporte plc; *Int'l*, pg. 803
SHELL CHEMICAL CO.—Royal Dutch/Shell Group of Companies; *Int'l*, pg. 1136
THE SHERWIN-WILLIAMS COMPANY; *U.S. Public*, pg. 1465
SHIPLEY CO., LLC—Rohm and Haas Company; *U.S. Public*, pg. 1403
SIGMA-ALDRICH CORPORATION; *U.S. Public*, pg. 1471
SIGMA-ALDRICH FS CORP.—Sigma-Aldrich Corporation; *U.S. Public*, pg. 1472
SIGMA ALDRICH JAPAN—Sigma-Aldrich Corporation; *U.S. Public*, pg. 1472
SIGMA-ALDRICH N.V.—Sigma-Aldrich Corporation; *U.S. Public*, pg. 1472
SIKKENS AEROSPACE FINISHERS—Akzo Nobel N.V.; *Int'l*, pg. 48
SOCIETE DES PRODUITS CHIMIQUES DU SIDOBRE-SINNOVA S.A.—Henkel KGaA; *Int'l*, pg. 614
SOLKATRONIC CHEMICALS, INC.—Air Products and Chemicals, Inc.; *U.S. Public*, pg. 31
SOLUTIA INC.; *U.S. Public*, pg. 1483
SOLVAY ENZYMES GMBH & CO.—Solvay S.A.; *Int'l*, pg. 1279
SOLVENTS & ENVIRONMENTAL SERVICES DIV.—Detrex Corporation; *U.S. Public*, pg. 502
SOPRELEC SA—Laporte plc; *Int'l*, pg. 803
SPECIALTY CHEMICALS DIV.—Rhone-Poulenc S.A.; *Int'l*, pg. 1109
SPECIALTY POLYMERS & CHEMICALS DIVISION—The B.F. Goodrich Company; *U.S. Public*, pg. 751
SPECIALTYCHEM PRODUCTS CORPORATION—Bayer AG; *Int'l*, pg. 173
SPHINX CHEMICALS—Henkel KGaA; *Int'l*, pg. 614
STEPAN COLOMBIANA—Stepan Company; *U.S. Public*, pg. 1514
STEPAN COMPANY; *U.S. Public*, pg. 1514
STEPAN EUROPE—Stepan Company; *U.S. Public*, pg. 1514
STERLING CHEMICALS HOLDINGS, INC.; *U.S. Public*, pg. 1515
SYBRON CHEMICALS INC.—Sybron Chemicals Inc.; *U.S. Public*, pg. 1544
SYBRON CHEMICALS, INC.—Sybron Chemicals Inc.; *U.S. Public*, pg. 1544
SYNTEX CHEMICALS, INC.—Roche Holding Ltd.; *Int'l*, pg. 1120
TAMPERE SALES OFFICE & STORAGE DEPOT—Oy Algol AB; *Int'l*, pg. 15
THE TATA IRON AND STEEL CO. LTD.; *Int'l*, pg. 1356
TATE & LYLE PLC; *Int'l*, pg. 1356
TECH SPRAY, INC.; *U.S. Private*, pg. 1071
TEKNOR APEX COMPANY; *U.S. Private*, pg. 1073
TEMBEC INC.; *Int'l*, pg. 1374
THANN ET MULHOUSE—Millennium Chemicals Inc.; *U.S. Public*, pg. 1111
3M; *U.S. Public*, pg. 1604
TOSHIBA SILICONE CO., LTD.—Toshiba Corporation; *Int'l*, pg. 1405
TURKU SALES OFFICE & STORAGE DEPOT—Oy Algol AB; *Int'l*, pg. 15
UNICHEMA-CHEMIE B.V.—Unilever Plc; *Int'l*, pg. 1438
UNION CAMP CORPORATION; *U.S. Public*, pg. 1665
UNION CARBIDE CORPORATION; *U.S. Public*, pg. 1666
UNIROYAL CHEMICAL CORPORATION—Crompton & Knowles Corporation; *U.S. Public*, pg. 459
UNIVERSAL FOODS CORPORATION; *U.S. Public*, pg. 1695
VALQUIMICA, S.A.—Eli Lilly and Company; *U.S. Public*, pg. 994
R.T. VANDERBILT COMPANY, INC.; *U.S. Private*, pg. 1133
VELSICOL CHEMICAL CORPORATION; *U.S. Private*, pg. 1135
VULCAN CHEMICALS—Vulcan Materials Company; *U.S. Public*, pg. 1725
VULCAN MATERIALS COMPANY; *U.S. Public*, pg. 1725
WACKER-CHEMIE GMBH—Hoechst Aktiengesellschaft; *Int'l*, pg. 625
WEST CHEMICAL PRODUCTS, INC.—Wechco, Inc.; *U.S. Private*, pg. 1158
WESTRALIAN SANDS LIMITED—Ishihara Sangyo Kaisha, Ltd.; *Int'l*, pg. 689
WESTVACO CORPORATION; *U.S. Public*, pg. 1762
WESTVACO CORPORATION-CHEMICAL DIV.—Westvaco Corporation; *U.S. Public*, pg. 1762
WITCO CORPORATION; *U.S. Public*, pg. 1773

2873 — NITROGENOUS FERTILIZERS

AGLUKON SPEZIALDUNGER GMBH—Schering AG; *Int'l*, pg. 1203
AGRIUM INC.; *Int'l*, pg. 31
AGROFERM HUNGARIAN JAPANESE FERMENTATION INDUSTRY LTD.—Kyowa Hakko Kogyo Company, Ltd.; *Int'l*, pg. 778
AIR PRODUCTS AND CHEMICALS, INC.; *U.S. Public*, pg. 30
AQUALON-LOUISIANA—Hercules Incorporated; *U.S. Public*, pg. 810
H.J. BAKER & BRO., INC.; *U.S. Private*, pg. 112
BANDINI FERTILIZER COMPANY; *U.S. Private*, pg. 113
BAYER AG—Bayer AG; *Int'l*, pg. 172
BAYER CORPORATION—Bayer AG; *Int'l*, pg. 172
CF INDUSTRIES, INC.; *U.S. Private*, pg. 193
CENEX/LAND O'LAKES, INC.—CENEX, Inc.; *U.S. Private*, pg. 222
CHEMICAL COMPANY OF MALAYSIA BERHAD—Imperial Chemical Industries PLC; *Int'l*, pg. 664
THE COASTAL CORPORATION; *U.S. Public*, pg. 389
COMINCO AMERICAN INCORPORATED—Cominco, Ltd.; *Int'l*, pg. 308
CONKLIN CO. INC.; *U.S. Private*, pg. 263
COUNTRYMARK COOPERATIVE, INC.; *U.S. Private*, pg. 279
DSM AGARHANDELEN GMBH—DSM N.V.; *Int'l*, pg. 355
DSM ENGRAIS FRANCE SA—DSM N.V.; *Int'l*, pg. 355
DSM FRANCE SA—DSM N.V.; *Int'l*, pg. 355
DSM MESTSTOFFEN B.V.—DSM N.V.; *Int'l*, pg. 353
ELF ATOCHEM NORTH AMERICA, AGRICHEMICALS DIV.—Elf Aquitane; *Int'l*, pg. 446
ESSO MALAYSIA BERHAD—Exxon Corporation; *U.S. Public*, pg. 602
FARMLAND INDUSTRIES, INC.; *U.S. Private*, pg. 395
FREEPORT-MCMORAN RESOURCE PARTNERS, LTD.—Freeport-McMoRan Inc.; *U.S. Public*, pg. 681
GENERAL CHEMICAL CORPORATION—The General Chemical Group, Inc.; *U.S. Public*, pg. 707
GRASSLAND FERTILISERS (KILKENNY) LIMITED—Avonmore Waterford Group plc; *Int'l*, pg. 102
GROW FORCE AUSTRALIA LIMITED—Imperial Chemical Industries PLC; *Int'l*, pg. 664
GRUPO ACERERO DEL NORTE S.A. DE C.V. (GAN); *Int'l*, *pg. 572*
ICI CANADA INC.—Imperial Chemical Industries PLC; *Int'l*, pg. 664
ICI FERTILIZERS (MALAYSIA) SDN BERHAD—Imperial Chemical Industries PLC; *Int'l*, pg. 665
ICI FRANCE SA—Imperial Chemical Industries PLC; *Int'l*, pg. 665
ICI INDIA LIMITED—Imperial Chemical Industries PLC; *Int'l*, *pg. 665*
IMC AGRIBUSINESS—IMC Global; *U.S. Public*, pg. 856
IMC GLOBAL; *U.S. Public*, pg. 856
INCITEC LTD—Imperial Chemical Industries PLC; *Int'l*, pg. 665
KALI UND SALZ BETEILIGUNGS AG—BASF AG; *Int'l*, pg. 104
KEMIRA AGRO OY—Kemira Oy; *Int'l*, pg. 727
KEMIRA N.I. LIMITED—Kemira Oy; *Int'l*, pg. 728
LAROCHE INDUSTRIES INC.; *U.S. Private*, pg. 651
LEBANON SEABOARD CORPORATION; *U.S. Private*, pg. 656
MFA INCORPORATED; *U.S. Private*, pg. 686
MARUBENI CORPORATION; *Int'l*, pg. 844
METHANEX CORPORATION; *Int'l*, pg. 862
MILLER CHEMICAL & FERTILIZER CORP.—Alco Industries, Inc.; *U.S. Private*, pg. 33
MISSISSIPPI CHEMICAL CORPORATION; *U.S. Public*, pg. 1117
MONSANTO CANADA, INC.—Monsanto Company; *U.S. Public*, pg. 1125
MONSANTO CHEMICALS OF INDIA LIMITED—Monsanto Company; *U.S. Public*, pg. 1125
MONSANTO EUROPE S.A.—Monsanto Company; *U.S. Public*, pg. 1125
MONSANTO (MALAYSIA) SENDIRIAN BERHAD—Monsanto Company; *U.S. Public*, pg. 1126
NORSK HYDRO A.S; *Int'l*, pg. 959
PCS NITROGEN—Potash Corporation of Saskatchewan Inc.; *Int'l*, pg. 1064
PACE INTERNATIONAL L.P.; *U.S. Private*, pg. 829
PAX COMPANY—Zipp Industries; *U.S. Private*, pg. 1207
PERSTORP CHEMITEC—Perstorp AB; *Int'l*, pg. 1037
PERSTORP SPA-DIV. COMPOUNDS—Perstorp AB; *Int'l*, pg. 1037
PHOENIX CHEMICAL COMPANY—IMC Global; *U.S. Public*, *pg. 856*
RICHARDSON-VICKS, INC.—The Procter & Gamble Company; *U.S. Public*, pg. 1331
RINGER CORPORATION; *U.S. Public*, pg. 1390
ROYSTER-CLARK, INC.; *U.S. Private*, pg. 949
SASOL FERTILIZERS—Sasol Limited; *Int'l*, pg. 1196
THE SCOTTS COMPANY; *U.S. Public*, pg. 1446
SCOTT'S MIRACLE-GRO PRODUCTS, INC.—The Scotts Company; *U.S. Public*, pg. 1447
J.R. SIMPLOT COMPANY; *U.S. Private*, pg. 1002
SINOCHEM INTERNATIONAL PETROLEUM CO. LTD.; *Int'l*, pg. 1254
T A HOLDINGS LIMITED; *Int'l*, pg. 1334
TENNESSEE FARMERS CO-OP; *U.S. Private*, pg. 1076
TERRA NITROGEN COMPANY, L.P.; *U.S. Public*, pg. 1581
TRIAD CHEMICAL—Mississippi Chemical Corporation; *U.S. Public*, pg. 1117
TRIAD NITROGEN, INC.—Mississippi Chemical Corporation; *U.S. Public*, pg. 1117
TRUGREEN-CHEMLAWN—The ServiceMaster Company; *U.S. Public*, pg. 1461
UNITED AGRI PRODUCTS CO.—ConAgra, Inc.; *U.S. Public*, pg. 426
UNOCAL AGRICULTURAL PRODUCTS GROUP—Unocal Corporation; *U.S. Public*, pg. 1698
UNOCAL CORPORATION; *U.S. Public*, pg. 1698
THE VIGORO CORPORATION—IMC Global; *U.S. Public*, pg. 856
WEATHERLY CONSUMER PRODUCTS—U.S. Home & Garden Inc.; *U.S. Public*, pg. 1682
WILDHAWK, INC.—Northland Cranberries, Inc.; *U.S. Public*, *pg. 1197*
ZENECA AB—Zeneca Group Plc; *Int'l*, pg. 1526
ZENECA HELLAS S.A.—Zeneca Group Plc; *Int'l*, pg. 1526
ZENECA OY—Zeneca Group Plc; *Int'l*, pg. 1527
ZENECA POLAND SP. Z.O.O.—Zeneca Group Plc; *Int'l*, pg. 1527
ZENECA ZIMBABWE (PRIVATE) LIMITED—Zeneca Group Plc; *Int'l*, pg. 1527
ZIPP INDUSTRIES; *U.S. Private*, pg. 1207

2874 — PHOSPHATIC FERTILIZERS

AGLUKON SPEZIALDUNGER GMBH—Schering AG; *Int'l*, pg. 1203
AGRIUM INC.; *Int'l*, pg. 31

S.I.C. Index

AGROFERM HUNGARIAN JAPANESE FERMENTATION INDUSTRY LTD.—Kyowa Hakko Kogyo Company, Ltd.; *Int'l*, pg. 778
AKZO NOBEL INC.—Akzo Nobel N.V.; *Int'l*, pg. 47
H.J. BAKER & BRO., INC.; *U.S. Private*, pg. 112
BANDINI FERTILIZER COMPANY; *U.S. Private*, pg. 113
BAYER AG—Bayer AG; *Int'l*, pg. 172
CF INDUSTRIES, INC.; *U.S. Private*, pg. 193
CARGILL; *U.S. Private*, pg. 210
CENEX/LAND O'LAKES, INC.—CENEX, Inc.; *U.S. Private*, pg. 222
COMINCO AMERICAN INCORPORATED—Cominco, Ltd.; *Int'l*, pg. 308
DSM AGARHANDELEN GMBH—DSM N.V.; *Int'l*, pg. 355
DSM CHEMIE LINZ GMBH—DSM N.V.; *Int'l*, pg. 356
DSM ENGRAIS FRANCE SA—DSM N.V.; *Int'l*, pg. 355
DSM MESTSTOFFEN B.V.—DSM N.V.; *Int'l*, pg. 353
EL DORADO CHEMICAL—LSB Industries, Inc.; *U.S. Public*, *pg. 970*
ELF AQUITAINE, INC.—Elf Aquitane; *Int'l*, pg. 445
ELF AQUITANE; *Int'l*, pg. 444
ELF ATOCHEM NORTH AMERICA, AGRICHEMICALS DIV.—Elf Aquitane; *Int'l*, pg. 446
FARMERS CHEMICAL CO.—Farmland Industries, Inc.; *U.S.* Private, pg. 396
FLORIDA FAVORITE FERTILIZER—Potash Corporation of Saskatchewan Inc.; *Int'l*, pg. 1064
FREEPORT-MCMORAN INC.; *U.S. Public*, pg. 680
FREEPORT-MCMORAN RESOURCE PARTNERS, LTD.—Freeport-McMoRan Inc.; *U.S. Public*, pg. 681
GOODPASTURE, INC.; *U.S. Private*, pg. 464
GROWMARK, INC.; *U.S. Private*, pg. 484
HYDRITE CHEMICAL COMPANY; *U.S. Private*, pg. 551
IMC AGRIBUSINESS—IMC Global; *U.S. Public*, pg. 856
KALI UND SALZ BETEILIGUNGS AG—BASF AG; *Int'l*, pg. 104
KEMIRA AGRO OY—Kemira Oy; *Int'l*, pg. 727
LEBANON SEABOARD CORPORATION; *U.S. Private*, pg. 656
THE CHAS. H. LILLY CO.; *U.S. Private*, pg. 667
MFA INCORPORATED; *U.S. Private*, pg. 686
MILLER CHEMICAL & FERTILIZER CORP.—Alco Industries, Inc.; *U.S. Private*, pg. 33
MISSISSIPPI CHEMICAL CORPORATION; *U.S. Public*, pg. 1117
MISSISSIPPI PHOSPHATES CORP.—Mississippi Chemical Corporation; *U.S. Public*, pg. 1117
MOBIL MINING & MINERALS COMPANY—Mobil Oil Corporation; *U.S. Public*, pg. 1118
MONSANTO CANADA, INC.—Monsanto Company; *U.S. Public*, pg. 1125
MONSANTO CHEMICALS OF INDIA LIMITED—Monsanto Company; *U.S. Public*, pg. 1125
MONSANTO COMPANY; *U.S. Public*, pg. 1124
MONSANTO EUROPE S.A.—Monsanto Company; *U.S. Public*, pg. 1125
MONSANTO (MALAYSIA) SENDIRIAN BERHAD—Monsanto Company; *U.S. Public*, pg. 1126
NORSK HYDRO A.S; *Int'l*, pg. 959
PCS PHOSPHATE - RALEIGH—Potash Corporation of Saskatchewan Inc.; *Int'l*, pg. 1064
RINGER CORPORATION; *U.S. Public*, pg. 1390
SASOL LIMITED; *Int'l*, pg. 1196
THE SCOTTS COMPANY; *U.S. Public*, pg. 1446
SCOTT'S MIRACLE-GRO PRODUCTS, INC.—The Scotts Company; *U.S. Public*, pg. 1447
J.R. SIMPLOT COMPANY; *U.S. Private*, pg. 1002
J.R. SIMPLOT COMPANY LATHROP PLANT—J.R. Simplot Company; *U.S. Private*, pg. 1002
SUMITOMO CHEMICAL COMPANY, LTD.; *Int'l*, pg. 1310
TENNESSEE FARMERS CO-OP; *U.S. Private*, pg. 1076
TRUGREEN-CHEMLAWN—The ServiceMaster Company; *U.S. Public*, pg. 1461
WEATHERLY CONSUMER PRODUCTS—U.S. Home & Garden Inc.; *U.S. Public*, pg. 1682

2875 — FERTILIZERS, MIXING ONLY

AGWAY AGRICULTURAL PRODUCTS (AAP)—Agway, Inc.; *U.S. Private*, pg. 27
THE ANDERSONS INCORPORATED; *U.S. Public*, pg. 111
ARMATRON INTERNATIONAL, INC.; *U.S. Public*, pg. 131
BRUNSWICK MINING & SMELTING CORP. LTD.—EdperBrascan Corporation; *Int'l*, pg. 434
CHAMPAIGN LANDMARK, INC.; *U.S. Private*, pg. 227
DSM AGARHANDELEN GMBH—DSM N.V.; *Int'l*, pg. 355
DSM ENGRAIS FRANCE SA—DSM N.V.; *Int'l*, pg. 355
DSM MESTSTOFFEN B.V.—DSM N.V.; *Int'l*, pg. 353
FISONS HORTICULTURE—Rhone-Poulenc S.A.; *Int'l*, pg. 1110
GOLD KIST, INC.; *U.S. Private*, pg. 459
GREENWAY CO-OP SERVICE; *U.S. Private*, pg. 478
HYPONEX CORPORATION—The Scotts Company; *U.S. Public*, pg. 1447
JIFFY PRODUCTS INTERNATIONAL LTD.; *Int'l*, pg. 706
KALI UND SALZ BETEILIGUNGS AG—BASF AG; *Int'l*, pg. 104
KLOECKNER DURILIT GMBH—Klockner-Werke AG; *Int'l*, pg. 737
LEBANON SEABOARD CORPORATION; *U.S. Private*, pg. 656
LOFTS SEED, INC.—AgriBioTech, Inc.; *U.S. Public*, pg. 29
MAPCO INC.; *U.S. Public*, pg. 1042
MITSUI TOATSU CHEMICALS, INC.—Mitsui & Co., Ltd.; *Int'l*, pg. 877
NA-CHURS PLANT FOOD COMPANY—Trans Resources, Inc.; *U.S. Private*, pg. 1096
NOBEL CONSUMER GOODS AB—Akzo Nobel N.V.; *Int'l*, pg. 48
PURSELL INDUSTRIES; *U.S. Private*, pg. 896
ROSENS DIVERSIFIED, INC.; *U.S. Private*, pg. 945
J.R. SIMPLOT COMPANY; *U.S. Private*, pg. 1002
THAI CHEMICAL & ENGINEERING CO. LTD.—Nissho Iwai Corporation; *Int'l*, pg. 949
WESTERN MINING CORPORATION HOLDINGS LIMITED; *Int'l*, pg. 1494

2879 — PESTICIDES & AGRICULTURAL CHEMICALS, NEC

AAKO INC.—Makhteshim Chemical Works Ltd.; *Int'l*, pg. 830
ARS CHEMICAL (THAILAND) CO., LTD.—Otsuka Pharmaceutical Co., Ltd.; *Int'l*, pg. 1014
ABBOTT LABORATORIES; *U.S. Public*, pg. 12
ACETO AGRICULTURAL CHEMICALS CORP.—Aceto Corporation; *U.S. Public*, pg. 15
AGREVO USA COMPANY—Schering AG; *Int'l*, pg. 1203
THE AGRICULTURAL GROUP, MONSANTO COMPANY—Monsanto Company; *U.S. Public*, pg. 1125
AGRICUR-DEFENSIVOS AGRICOLAS LTD.—Makhteshim Chemical Works Ltd.; *Int'l*, pg. 830
AGROCHEMICALS DIV.—Nippon Kayaku Co. Ltd.; *Int'l*, pg. 934
AGROLINZ AGRARCHEMIKALIEN GESELLSCHAFTMBH BERLIN—DSM N.V.; *Int'l*, pg. 356
AGROLINZ AGRARCHEMIKALIEN MUNCHEN GESMBH—DSM N.V.; *Int'l*, pg. 356
AGROLINZ INC.—DSM N.V.; *Int'l*, pg. 356
AGROLINZ MELAMIN GMBH—DSM N.V.; *Int'l*, pg. 356
AGSCO, INC.; *U.S. Private*, pg. 27
AKZO NOBEL INC.—Akzo Nobel N.V.; *Int'l*, pg. 47
ALFA AGRICULTURAL SUPPLIES LTD.—Makhteshim Chemical Works Ltd.; *Int'l*, pg. 830
BASF ESPANOLA S.A.—BASF AG; *Int'l*, pg. 106
BASF QUIMICA COLOMBIANA S.A.—BASF AG; *Int'l*, pg. 107
BASF S.A.—BASF AG; *Int'l*, pg. 107
BANDINI FERTILIZER COMPANY; *U.S. Private*, pg. 113
BATTAILLE S.A.—Kemira Oy; *Int'l*, pg. 728
BAYER AG—Bayer AG; *Int'l*, pg. 172
BAYER ARGENTINA S.A.—Bayer AG; *Int'l*, pg. 175
BAYER B.V.—Bayer AG; *Int'l*, pg. 175
BAYER CORPORATION—Bayer AG; *Int'l*, pg. 172
BAYER CORPORATION/AGRICULTURE DIVISION—Bayer AG; *Int'l*, pg. 173
BAYER DE MEXICO, S.A. DE C.V.—Bayer AG; *Int'l*, pg. 175
BAYER DO BRAZIL S.A.—Bayer AG; *Int'l*, pg. 175
BAYER (INDIA) LTD.—Bayer AG; *Int'l*, pg. 174
BIOPRODUCTS, INC.; *U.S. Private*, pg. 145
BOEHRINGER INGELHEIM ANIMAL HEALTH INC.—Boehringer Ingelheim GmbH; *Int'l*, pg. 199
BRISTOL-MYERS SQUIBB COMPANY; *U.S. Public*, pg. 253
BUSHWHACKER ASSOCIATES, INC.—Bethurum Research & Development, Inc.; *U.S. Private*, pg. 141
CARIBE BIOCHEMICALS, INC.—Du Pont (E.I. Du Pont De Nemours & Co.); *U.S. Public*, pg. 531
CERAS JOHNSON LTDA.—S.C. Johnson & Son, Inc.; *U.S. Private*, pg. 593
CHEMAG AKTIENGESELLSCHAFT—BASF AG; *Int'l*, pg. 104
CIBA-GEIGY LTD.-TECHNICAL ASSISTANCE OFFICE—Novartis AG; *Int'l*, pg. 978
CIBA SPECIALTY CHEMICALS—Ciba Specialty Chemicals Holding Inc.; *Int'l*, pg. 291
CIBA SPECIALTY CHEMICALS HOLDING INC.; *Int'l*, pg. 291
CLAIRE MANUFACTURING CO.—Goldner Hawn Johnsons & Morrison Incorporated; *U.S. Private*, pg. 462
COMPO GMBH PRODUKTIONS UND VERTRIEBSGESELLSCHAFT—BASF AG; *Int'l*, pg. 104
CONAGRA, INC.; *U.S. Public*, pg. 425
COOPERATIVE FEDEREE DE QUEBEC; *Int'l*, pg. 330
CYANAMID AGRICULTURAL PRODUCTS DIVISION—American Home Products Corporation; *U.S. Public*, pg. 79
CYANAMID CHILE LTDA.—American Home Products Corporation; *U.S. Public*, pg. 80
CYANAMID DE ARGENTINA S.A.I.C.—American Home Products Corporation; *U.S. Public*, pg. 80
CYANAMID DE VENEZUELA CA—American Home Products Corporation; *U.S. Public*, pg. 80
CYANAMID FRANCE—American Home Products Corporation; *U.S. Public*, pg. 81
CYANAMID INDIA LTD.—American Home Products Corporation; *U.S. Public*, pg. 81
CYANAMID MEXICO—American Home Products Corporation; *U.S. Public*, pg. 81
CYANAMID OF GREAT BRITAIN LTD.—American Home Products Corporation; *U.S. Public*, pg. 81
CYANAMID QUIMICA DO BRASIL LTDA.—American Home Products Corporation; *U.S. Public*, pg. 81
DSM CHEMIE LINZ GMBH—DSM N.V.; *Int'l*, pg. 356
DSM N.V.; *Int'l*, pg. 352
DEXOL—Ringer Corporation; *U.S. Public*, pg. 1390
DOLISOS—Groupe Limagrain; *Int'l*, pg. 566
DONG YANG ELANCO CO., LTD.—Eli Lilly and Company; *U.S. Public*, pg. 993
THE DOW CHEMICAL COMPANY; *U.S. Public*, pg. 522
DU PONT AGRICULTURAL PRODUCTS—Du Pont (E.I. Du Pont De Nemours & Co.); *U.S. Public*, pg. 531
DU PONT (AUSTRALIA) LTD.—Du Pont (E.I. Du Pont De Nemours & Co.); *U.S. Public*, pg. 532
DU PONT DE COLOMBIA S.A.—Du Pont (E.I. Du Pont De Nemours & Co.); *U.S. Public*, pg. 532
DU PONT DE NEMOURS (FRANCE) S.A.—Du Pont (E.I. Du Pont De Nemours & Co.); *U.S. Public*, pg. 532
DU PONT DE VENEZUELA C.A.—Du Pont (E.I. Du Pont De Nemours & Co.); *U.S. Public*, pg. 532
DU PONT DO BRASIL S.A.—Du Pont (E.I. Du Pont De Nemours & Co.); *U.S. Public*, pg. 532
DU PONT (E.I. DU PONT DE NEMOURS & CO.); *U.S. Public*, pg. 530
DU PONT, S.A. DE C.V.—Du Pont (E.I. Du Pont De Nemours & Co.); *U.S. Public*, pg. 533
DU PONT/SHELL—Du Pont (E.I. Du Pont De Nemours & Co.); *U.S. Public*, pg. 531
DUNN NUTRATECH—Archer Daniels Midland Company (ADM); *U.S. Public*, pg. 128
ECOSCIENCE CORPORATION; *U.S. Public*, pg. 563
ELANCO IHARA K. K.—Eli Lilly and Company; *U.S. Public*, pg. 993
ELANCO QUIMICA LIMITADA—Eli Lilly and Company; *U.S.* Public, pg. 993
ELANCO S.A.—Eli Lilly and Company; *U.S. Public*, pg. 993
ELCO DOMINICANA, S.A.—Eli Lilly and Company; *U.S. Public*, pg. 993
ELF ATOCHEM NORTH AMERICA, AGRICHEMICALS DIV.—Elf Aquitane; *Int'l*, pg. 446
ELF ATOCHEM ROTTERDAH B.V.—Elf Aquitane; *Int'l*, pg. 446
EUROCHEM DIVISION—Baker Hughes Incorporated; *U.S. Public*, pg. 166
EWOS AB—Cultor Ltd.; *Int'l*, pg. 349
FMC AGROQUIMICA DE MEXICO SI DE R.L. DE C.V.—FMC Corporation; *U.S. Public*, pg. 606
FMC CORPORATION; *U.S. Public*, pg. 604
FMC CORP., AGRICULTURAL PRODUCTS GROUP—FMC Corporation; *U.S. Public*, pg. 605
FMC FOOD MACHINERY FRANCE, S.A.—FMC Corporation; *U.S. Public*, pg. 606
FARNAM COMPANIES, INC.; *U.S. Private*, pg. 396
FIGUEROA—Imetal; *Int'l*, pg. 662
W.A. FLICK & CO. PTY. LIMITED; *Int'l*, pg. 495
GREAT LAKES BIOCHEMICAL CO., INC.—Laporte plc; *Int'l*, pg. 802
GREAT LAKES CHEMICAL CORPORATION; *U.S. Public*, pg. 760
GRIFFIN CORPORATION; *U.S. Private*, pg. 480
GUSTAFSON, INC.—Crompton & Knowles Corporation; *U.S. Public*, pg. 460
HELENA CHEMICAL COMPANY—Marubeni Corporation; *Int'l*, pg. 845
HENKEL KGAA; *Int'l*, pg. 609
HERCULES INC.-BRUNSWICK—Hercules Incorporated; *U.S. Public*, pg. 810
HUNGAROFERT CHEMIKALIEN HANDELSGESMBH—DSM N.V.; *Int'l*, pg. 356
HYPONEX CORPORATION—The Scotts Company; *U.S. Public*, pg. 1447
ICI AGRICULTURAL PRODUCTS—Imperial Chemical Industries PLC; *Int'l*, pg. 663
IMC AGRIBUSINESS—IMC Global; *U.S. Public*, pg. 856
INSECT CONTROL & RESEARCH CORP.—McLaughlin Gormley King Company; *U.S. Private*, pg. 724
INTERNATIO (PTY.) LTD.—Internatio-Muller N.V.; *Int'l*, pg. 682
JAPAN ELANCO COMPANY LIMITED (JELCO)—Eli Lilly and Company; *U.S. Public*, pg. 994
S.C. JOHNSON & SON, INC.; *U.S. Private*, pg. 592
KEMIRA DANMARK A/S—Kemira Oy; *Int'l*, pg. 728
KEMIRA DEUTSCHLAND GMBH—Kemira Oy; *Int'l*, pg. 728
KEMIRA INCE LTD.—Kemira Oy; *Int'l*, pg. 728
KEMIRA IRELAND LTD.—Kemira Oy; *Int'l*, pg. 728
KEMIRA LTD.—Kemira Oy; *Int'l*, pg. 728
KEMIRA N.I. LIMITED—Kemira Oy; *Int'l*, pg. 728
KEMIRA THAI CO. LTD.—Kemira Oy; *Int'l*, pg. 728
THE KINGSFORD PRODUCTS COMPANY—The Clorox Company; *U.S. Public*, pg. 387
KODAK BIOSCIENCE / EMERGING BUSINESS DIVISION—Eastman Kodak Company; *U.S. Public*, pg. 551
KORAG COMPANY, LTD.—Monsanto Company; *U.S. Public*, pg. 1126
KYOWA HAKKO KOGYO COMPANY, LTD.; *Int'l*, pg. 778
LABORATORIES LEDERLE SA—American Home Products Corporation; *U.S. Public*, pg. 81
LAPORTE PLC; *Int'l*, pg. 801
LEBANON SEABOARD CORPORATION; *U.S. Private*, pg. 656
LEDERLE (JAPAN) LTD.—American Home Products Corporation; *U.S. Public*, pg. 81
LEU & GYGAX AG—DSM N.V.; *Int'l*, pg. 356
LIPHATECH, INC.—Lipha Chemicals S.A.; *Int'l*, pg. 812
LIVING EARTH TECHNOLOGY CO.—Republic Industries, Inc.; *U.S. Public*, pg. 1379
LOFTS SEED, INC.—AgriBioTech, Inc.; *U.S. Public*, pg. 29
MAKHTESHIM-AGAN ESPANA S.L.—Makhteshim Chemical Works Ltd.; *Int'l*, pg. 830
MAKHTESHIM-AGAN FRANCE S.A.R.L.—Makhteshim Chemical Works Ltd.; *Int'l*, pg. 830
MAKHTESHIM AGAN OF NORTH AMERICA INC.—Makhteshim Chemical Works Ltd.; *Int'l*, pg. 830
MAKHTESHIM-AGAN ROMANIA S.R.L.—Makhteshim Chemical Works Ltd.; *Int'l*, pg. 831
MAKHTESHIM-AGAN (U.K.) LTD.—Makhteshim Chemical Works Ltd.; *Int'l*, pg. 831
MAKHTESHIM CHEMICAL WORKS LTD.; *Int'l*, pg. 830
MCLAUGHLIN GORMLEY KING COMPANY; *U.S. Private*, pg. 723
MERCK SHARP & DOHME-HOLLAND—Merck & Co., Inc.; *U.S. Public*, pg. 1092
MILLER CHEMICAL & FERTILIZER CORP.—Alco Industries, Inc.; *U.S. Private*, pg. 33
MONSANTO CANADA, INC.—Monsanto Company; *U.S. Public*, pg. 1125
MONSANTO CHEMICALS OF INDIA LIMITED—Monsanto Company; *U.S. Public*, pg. 1125
MONSANTO COMPANY; *U.S. Public*, pg. 1124
MONSANTO EUROPE S.A.—Monsanto Company; *U.S. Public*, pg. 1125
MONSANTO (MALAYSIA) SENDIRIAN BERHAD—Monsanto Company; *U.S. Public*, pg. 1126
MORFLEX, INC.—Reilly Industries, Inc.; *U.S. Private*, pg. 919
MYCOGEN CORPORATION; *U.S. Public*, pg. 1142

MYCOGEN CROP PROTECTION—Mycogen Corporation; *U.S. Public*, pg. 1142
NIHON TOKUSHU NOYAKU SEIZO K.K.—Bayer AG; *Int'l*, pg. 174
NIPPON KAYAKU CO. LTD.; *Int'l*, pg. 934
NOVARTIS—Novartis AG; *Int'l*, pg. 972
NOVARTIS AG; *Int'l*, pg. 971
NUEVO FEDERAL S.A.; *Int'l*, pg. 990
NUTRIUS DAIRY FEED SUPPLEMENTS DIV.—Bioproducts, Inc.; *U.S. Private*, pg. 145
OCTAGON PROCESS INC.; *U.S. Private*, pg. 811
PACE INTERNATIONAL L.P.; *U.S. Private*, pg. 829
PHARMACIA & UPJOHN—Pharmacia & Upjohn, Inc.; *Int'l*, pg. 1048
PHILIPP BROTHERS CHEMICALS, INC.; *U.S. Private*, pg. 861
PREMIER CHEMICAL PLANT—Crompton & Knowles Corporation; *U.S. Public*, pg. 460
PRENTISS INCORPORATED; *U.S. Private*, pg. 882
QUIMICA SCHERING COLOMBIANA S. A.—Schering AG; *Int'l*, pg. 1204
RHONE-POULENC, AGROCHEMICAL DIVISION—Rhone-Poulenc S.A.; *Int'l*, pg. 1109
RHONE-POULENC AGROCHIMIE—Rhone-Poulenc S.A.; *Int'l*, pg. 1109
RHONE-POULENC INC.—Rhone-Poulenc S.A.; *Int'l*, pg. 1112
RHONE-POULENC RORER LTD.—Rhone-Poulenc S.A.; *Int'l*, pg. 1110
RHONE-POULENC S.A.; *Int'l*, pg. 1108
RIGO/BLACK LEAF—Ringer Corporation; *U.S. Public*, pg. 1390
RIVERDALE CHEMICAL CO.; *U.S. Private*, pg. 934
ROCHESTER MIDLAND CORPORATION; *U.S. Private*, pg. 937
ROLLINS, INC.; *U.S. Public*, pg. 1404
ROUSSEL CORPORATION—Hoechst Aktiengesellschaft; *Int'l*, pg. 625
ROUSSEL UCLAF S.A.—Hoechst Aktiengesellschaft; *Int'l*, pg. 626
RUBICON INC.—Crompton & Knowles Corporation; *U.S. Public*, pg. 460
SDS BIOTECH K.K.—Novartis AG; *Int'l*, pg. 984
SANDOZ AGRO CORPORATION—Novartis AG; *Int'l*, pg. 974
SANDOZ AGRO, INC.—Novartis AG; *Int'l*, pg. 974
SANDOZ AGRO LTD.—Novartis AG; *Int'l*, pg. 972
SANDOZ AGRO S.A.—Novartis AG; *Int'l*, pg. 984
SANDOZ AGRO S.A.E.—Novartis AG; *Int'l*, pg. 984
SANDOZ AGRO S.P.A.—Novartis AG; *Int'l*, pg. 984
SANDOZ (PAKISTAN) LTD.—Novartis AG; *Int'l*, pg. 985
SCHERING AGRO B.V.—Schering AG; *Int'l*, pg. 1203
SCHERING A/S—Schering AG; *Int'l*, pg. 1204
SCHERING PTY. LTD.—Schering AG; *Int'l*, pg. 1204
N.V. SCHERING S.A./BELGIEN—Schering AG; *Int'l*, pg. 1204
SHELL CANADA LTD.—Royal Dutch/Shell Group of Companies; *Int'l*, pg. 1138
SHELL DEVELOPMENT CO.—Royal Dutch/Shell Group of Companies; *Int'l*, pg. 1136
SHELL NEDERLAND CHEMIE—Royal Dutch/Shell Group of Companies; *Int'l*, pg. 1135
SHOWA DENKO KAWASAKI WORKS—Showa Denko K.K.; *Int'l*, pg. 1236
SHOWA DENKO K.K.; *Int'l*, pg. 1236
J.R. SIMPLOT COMPANY; *U.S. Private*, pg. 1002
SOLPLANT—Zeneca Group Plc; *Int'l*, pg. 1524
SOUTHERN AGRICULTURAL INSECTICIDES, INC.; *U.S. Private*, pg. 1015
SPRAYWAY, INC.—Goldner Hawn Johnsons & Morrison Incorporated; *U.S. Private*, pg. 462
STEPAN COMPANY; *U.S. Public*, pg. 1514
STEPAN EUROPE—Stepan Company; *U.S. Public*, pg. 1514
SUMITOMO CHEMICAL ASIA PTE LTD.—Sumitomo Chemical Company, Ltd.; *Int'l*, pg. 1311
SUMITOMO CHEMICAL COMPANY, LTD.; *Int'l*, pg. 1310
SURECO INC.—Ringer Corporation; *U.S. Public*, pg. 1390
TUCO ANIMAL HEALTH—Pharmacia & Upjohn, Inc.; *Int'l*, pg. 1048
TAKEDA CHEMICAL INDUSTRIES, LTD.; *Int'l*, pg. 1350
TENNESSEE FARMERS CO-OP; *U.S. Private*, pg. 1076
THOMPSON-SIEGEL GMBH—Henkel KGaA; *Int'l*, pg. 610
TIME-MIST DIV.—Carpenter Technology Corporation; *U.S. Public*, pg. 308
TRANS RESOURCES, INC.; *U.S. Private*, pg. 1096
TROY CORPORATION; *U.S. Private*, pg. 1105
UNIVERSAL COOPERATIVES, INC.; *U.S. Private*, pg. 1127
WACKER-CHEMIE GMBH—Hoechst Aktiengesellschaft; *Int'l*, pg. 625
WATERBURY COMPANIES, INC.-INDEPENDENCE DIV.—Carpenter Technology Corporation; *U.S. Public*, pg. 308
WATKINS INCORPORATED; *U.S. Private*, pg. 1153
WEATHERLY CONSUMER PRODUCTS—U.S. Home & Garden Inc.; *U.S. Public*, pg. 1682
WHITMIRE MICRO-GEN RESEARCH LABORATORIES INC.—S.C. Johnson & Son, Inc.; *U.S. Private*, pg. 592
WILLERT HOME PRODUCTS, INC.; *U.S. Private*, pg. 1177
WISCONSIN PHARMACAL CO., INC.; *U.S. Private*, pg. 1185

2891 — ADHESIVES & SEALANTS

AC PRODUCTS, INC.—Quaker Chemical Corporation; *U.S. Public*, pg. 1346
ACI INDUSTRIES PTY. LTD.—BTR plc; *Int'l*, pg. 128
ACI INTERNATIONAL LTD.—BTR plc; *Int'l*, pg. 128
AFE (HONG KONG) LTD.—BTR plc; *Int'l*, pg. 129
ABLESTIK LABORATORIES—Unilever Plc; *Int'l*, pg. 1435
ADENAX SPA—Scapa Group Plc; *Int'l*, pg. 1202
ADHESIVE FILMS—Bairnco Corporation; *U.S. Public*, pg. 165
ADHESIVE RESEARCH, INC.—Topflight Corp.; *U.S. Private*, pg. 1091
ADHESIVES & CHEMICALS—Borden, Inc.; *U.S. Private*, pg. 157
ADHESIVES (FAR EAST) PTE. LTD.—BTR plc; *Int'l*, pg. 129
ADHESIVES (MALAYSIA) SDN. BHD.—BTR plc; *Int'l*, pg. 129
ADHESIVES (THAILAND) LTD.—BTR plc; *Int'l*, pg. 129
AKZO COATINGS BELGIUM, DIV. OF AKZO BELGIE NV—Akzo Nobel N.V.; *Int'l*, pg. 43
AKZO COATINGS GES. M.B.H.—Akzo Nobel N.V.; *Int'l*, pg. 43
AKZO COATINGS GMBH—Akzo Nobel N.V.; *Int'l*, pg. 43
AKZO COATINGS SA—Akzo Nobel N.V.; *Int'l*, pg. 43
AKZO COATINGS (THAILAND LTD.)—Akzo Nobel N.V.; *Int'l*, pg. 43
AKZO COATINGS-TINTAS WANDA—Akzo Nobel N.V.; *Int'l*, pg. 43
AKZO NOBEL INC.—Akzo Nobel N.V.; *Int'l*, pg. 43
ALBA QUIMICA S.A. INDUSTRIA E COMMERCIO—Borden, Inc.; *U.S. Private*, pg. 158
ATO-FINDLEY, INC.—Elf Aquitane; *Int'l*, pg. 445
AUTOMOTIVE DIVISION, GROW GROUP, INC.—Imperial Chemical Industries PLC; *Int'l*, pg. 663
AXSON FRANCE—Axson S.A.; *Int'l*, pg. 103
BWK KRIEGLACH BAUWERKSTOFFE GES. M. B. H.—Viag AG; *Int'l*, pg. 1465
BAYER CORPORATION—Bayer AG; *Int'l*, pg. 172
BESTOLIFE CORP.—Quexco Incorporated; *U.S. Private*, pg. 900
BETON DE PARIS—Lafarge S.A.; *Int'l*, pg. 788
BETTOR S.A.—Viag AG; *Int'l*, pg. 1465
BINNEY & SMITH INC.—Hallmark Cards, Inc.; *U.S. Private*, pg. 496
BIXBY INTERNATIONAL CORP.; *U.S. Private*, pg. 146
BLUE CORAL/SLICK 50—Quaker State Corporation; *U.S. Public*, pg. 1348
BONDO/MAR-HYDE CORPORATION—RPM, Inc.; *U.S. Public*, pg. 1357
BORDEN, INC.; *U.S. Private*, pg. 157
BORDEN (NEDERLAND) B.V.—Borden, Inc.; *U.S. Private*, pg. 159
BORDEN THERMOFORMING, B.V.—Borden, Inc.; *U.S. Private*, pg. 159
BORDEX (NEDERLAND), B.V.—Borden, Inc.; *U.S. Private*, pg. 159
BOSTIK, INC.—Total S.A.; *Int'l*, pg. 1409
BOSTIK LTD.—Total S.A.; *Int'l*, pg. 1409
BURMAH ADHESIVES & SEALANTS (PTY) LTD.—Burmah Castrol plc; *Int'l*, pg. 235
CANADIAN ADHESIVES LTD.—Viag AG; *Int'l*, pg. 1466
CARLISLE COMPANIES INCORPORATED; *U.S. Public*, pg. 305
CASCO NOBEL AB—Akzo Nobel N.V.; *Int'l*, pg. 48
CEDEST CIMENTS—Lafarge S.A.; *Int'l*, pg. 788
CEILCOTE COMPANY—Viag AG; *Int'l*, pg. 1465
CEILCOTE KORROSIONSTECHNIK G.M.B.H.—Novartis AG; *Int'l*, pg. 975
CHASE CORPORATION; *U.S. Public*, pg. 337
CHEMETALL GMBH GESELLSCHAFT FUER CHEMISCH TECHNISCHE VERFAHREN—Metallgesellschaft AG; *Int'l*, pg. 861
CHEMIONICS CORPORATION—Chessco Industries, Inc.; *U.S. Private*, pg. 234
CHEMPLAST, INC.—Saint-Gobain; *Int'l*, pg. 1174
CHEMREX INC.—Viag AG; *Int'l*, pg. 1465
CHESSCO INDUSTRIES, INC.; *U.S. Private*, pg. 234
CHOMERICS INC.—Parker Hannifin Corporation; *U.S. Public*, pg. 1262
S.A. CIMENTERIES CBR—Heidelberger Zement A.G.; *Int'l*, pg. 605
CIMENTS FRANCAIS; *Int'l*, pg. 292
CLAYTON CORPORATION; *U.S. Private*, pg. 244
COATED SPECIALITIES LTD.—Hunt Corporation; *U.S. Public*, pg. 849
COATES CHEMIE COMPOUNDS (PTY.) LTD.—Total S.A.; *Int'l*, pg. 1410
COLAS PRODUCTS LTD.—Royal Dutch/Shell Group of Companies; *Int'l*, pg. 1139
COLUMBIA CEMENT CO. INC.—Burmah Castrol plc; *Int'l*, pg. 235
COMPAGNIE DES SABLIERES DE LA SEINE—Lafarge S.A.; *Int'l*, pg. 788
CONAP INC.; *U.S. Private*, pg. 261
CONSTRUCTION & HOME IMPROVEMENT MARKETS DIVISION—3M; *U.S. Public*, pg. 1605
COURTAULDS AEROSPACE—Courtaulds plc; *Int'l*, pg. 339
DACRAL EUROPE—Akzo Nobel N.V.; *Int'l*, pg. 43
DAP INC.—Wassall Plc; *Int'l*, pg. 1486
DAUBERT INDUSTRIES, INC.; *U.S. Private*, pg. 313
DEKKO HEATING TECHNOLOGIES, INC.—Group Dekko; *U.S. Private*, pg. 484
DELTA RESINS & REFRACTORIES, INC.; *U.S. Private*, pg. 323
DENNIS CHEMICAL CO., INC.; *U.S. Private*, pg. 324
DEXTER AEROSPACE MATERIALS DIVISION—The Dexter Corporation; *U.S. Public*, pg. 504
THE DEXTER CORPORATION; *U.S. Public*, pg. 504
DEXTER ELECTRONIC MATERIALS DIVISION—The Dexter Corporation; *U.S. Public*, pg. 504
DEXTER PACKAGING PRODUCTS—The Dexter Corporation; *U.S. Public*, pg. 504
DIELECTRIC POLYMERS, INC.—Park Electrochemical Corporation; *U.S. Public*, pg. 1258
P.T. DIMET INDONESIA—BTR plc; *Int'l*, pg. 129
DIMET (THAILAND) LTD.—BTR plc; *Int'l*, pg. 129
DOW CORNING CORPORATION—The Dow Chemical Company; *U.S. Public*, pg. 523
DUBIN-CLARK & COMPANY; *U.S. Private*, pg. 344
DUNLOP ADHESIVES—BTR plc; *Int'l*, pg. 125
E.J. FOOTWEAR CORP.—U.S. Industries, Inc.; *U.S. Public*, pg. 1684
ELCO CONSTRUCTION PRODUCTS DIVISION—Textron Inc.; *U.S. Public*, pg. 1590
ELIXIR INDUSTRIES; *U.S. Private*, pg. 371
ELIXIR INDUSTRIES—Elixir Industries; *U.S. Private*, pg. 371
EMERSON & CUMING SPECIALTY POLYMERS—Unilever Plc; *Int'l*, pg. 1435
EMPRESAS FRISCO SA DE CV—Grupo Carso S.A. de C.V.; *Int'l*, pg. 572
EPOXYLITE CORPORATION-RESIN DIV.; *U.S. Private*, pg. 379
ESPECIALIDADES QUIMICIAS GRACE DE MEXICO S.A. DE C.V.—W.R. Grace & Co.; *U.S. Public*, pg. 755
ESSEX CHEMICAL CORPORATION—The Dow Chemical Company; *U.S. Public*, pg. 523
ESSEX SPECIALTY PRODUCTS, INC.—The Dow Chemical Company; *U.S. Public*, pg. 523
ESSEX SPECIALTY PRODUCTS, INC., CANADA—The Dow Chemical Company; *U.S. Public*, pg. 523
EVANS ADHESIVE CORP.; *U.S. Private*, pg. 384
EVODE LTD.—Laporte plc; *Int'l*, pg. 802
EVODE SPECIALTY ADHESIVES LTD.—Laporte plc; *Int'l*, pg. 802
FERRO CORPORATION; *U.S. Public*, pg. 618
FLUIDTEC ENGINEER PRODUCTS—Coltec Holdings Inc; *U.S. Public*, pg. 401
FORBO HELMITIN GMBH—Forbo Holding SA; *Int'l*, pg. 497
FORMICA CORPORATION—BTR plc; *Int'l*, pg. 129
FORTON B.V.—DSM N.V.; *Int'l*, pg. 354
FOSROC EXPANDITE LTD.—Burmah Castrol plc; *Int'l*, pg. 234
FOSROC EXPANDITE (PTE) LTD.—Burmah Castrol plc; *Int'l*, pg. 236
FOSROC INC.—Burmah Castrol plc; *Int'l*, pg. 234
FOSTER PRODUCTS CORPORATION—H.B. Fuller Company; *U.S. Public*, pg. 686
H.B. FULLER COMPANY; *U.S. Public*, pg. 686
H.B. FULLER ECUADOR, S.A.—H.B. Fuller Company; *U.S. Public*, pg. 687
H.B. FULLER NETHERLANDS B.V.—H.B. Fuller Company; *U.S. Public*, pg. 687
GEMISA S.A. DE C.V.—Henkel KGaA; *Int'l*, pg. 614
GENCORP SPECIALTY PRODUCT DIV.—GenCorp Inc.; *U.S. Public*, pg. 706
GEORGIA-PACIFIC CORPORATION; *U.S. Public*, pg. 735
THE GIBSON-HOMANS COMPANY; *U.S. Private*, pg. 451
GIFFORD-HILL COMPANY—Hanson PLC; *Int'l*, pg. 593
THE B.F. GOODRICH COMPANY; *U.S. Public*, pg. 751
THE GOODYEAR TIRE & RUBBER COMPANY; *U.S. Public*, pg. 752
GRACE CENTRAL AMERICA—W.R. Grace & Co.; *U.S. Public*, pg. 755
GRACE ESPECIALIDADES QUIMICOS E PLASTICAS—W.R. Grace & Co.; *U.S. Public*, pg. 755
GRACE G.M.B.H.—W.R. Grace & Co.; *U.S. Public*, pg. 755
GRACE HELLAS INDUSTRIAL & COMMERCIAL L.L.C.—W.R. Grace & Co.; *U.S. Public*, pg. 756
GRACE ITALIANA S.P.A.—W.R. Grace & Co.; *U.S. Public*, pg. 756
GRACE JAPAN K.K.—W.R. Grace & Co.; *U.S. Public*, pg. 756
GRACE PORTUGUESA LDA.—W.R. Grace & Co.; *U.S. Public*, pg. 756
GRACE, S.A.—W.R. Grace & Co.; *U.S. Public*, pg. 756
GRACE VENEZUELA S.A.—W.R. Grace & Co.; *U.S. Public*, pg. 756
W.R. GRACE & CO. OF CANADA LTD., GRACE CONSTRUCTION PRODUCTS—W.R. Grace & Co.; *U.S. Public*, pg. 755
W.R. GRACE AUSTRALIA LTD.—W.R. Grace & Co.; *U.S. Public*, pg. 755
W.R. GRACE LTD.—W.R. Grace & Co.; *U.S. Public*, pg. 756
GROW GROUP, INC.—Imperial Chemical Industries PLC; *Int'l*, pg. 663
GULF STATE SPECIALTIES, INC.—Gulf States Asphalt Company, Inc.; *U.S. Private*, pg. 487
HALOGEN INSULATOR & SEAL CORP.—Saint-Gobain; *Int'l*, pg. 1174
HARDMAN DIVISION OF HARCROS CHEMICALS, INC.—Harrisons & Crosfield plc; *Int'l*, pg. 598
HEICO CHEMICALS, INC.—Cambrex Corporation; *U.S. Public*, pg. 297
HENKEL ADHESIVES CORPORATION—Henkel KGaA; *Int'l*, pg. 610
HENKEL & CIE AG—Henkel KGaA; *Int'l*, pg. 611
HENKEL ARGENTINA S.A.—Henkel KGaA; *Int'l*, pg. 611
HENKEL BELGIUM S.A.—Henkel KGaA; *Int'l*, pg. 612
HENKEL CANADA LTD.—Henkel KGaA; *Int'l*, pg. 612
HENKEL CHEMICALS (CARIBBEAN) LTD.—Henkel KGaA; *Int'l*, pg. 614
HENKEL CHEMICALS LTD.—Henkel KGaA; *Int'l*, pg. 612
HENKEL CORPORATION POLYMERS DIVISION—Henkel KGaA; *Int'l*, pg. 610
HENKEL FRANCE S.A.—Henkel KGaA; *Int'l*, pg. 612
HENKEL HELLAS—Henkel KGaA; *Int'l*, pg. 612
HENKEL IBERICA S.A.—Henkel KGaA; *Int'l*, pg. 612
P.T. HENKEL INDONESIA—Henkel KGaA; *Int'l*, pg. 614
HENKEL KEMI AB—Henkel KGaA; *Int'l*, pg. 613
HENKEL KENYA LTD.—Henkel KGaA; *Int'l*, pg. 613
HENKEL KGAA; *Int'l*, pg. 609
HENKEL NEDERLAND B.V.—Henkel KGaA; *Int'l*, pg. 613
HENKEL NOPCO AG—Henkel KGaA; *Int'l*, pg. 613
HENKEL NOPCO A/S—Henkel KGaA; *Int'l*, pg. 613
HENKEL NOPCO LTD.—Henkel KGaA; *Int'l*, pg. 613
HENKEL NOPCO S.A.—Henkel KGaA; *Int'l*, pg. 613
HENKEL NOPCO TAIWAN—Henkel KGaA; *Int'l*, pg. 613
HENKEL PORTUGUESA PRODUCTOS QUIMICOS LDA.—Henkel KGaA; *Int'l*, pg. 613
HENKEL S/A. INDUSTRIAS QUIMICAS—Henkel KGaA; *Int'l*, pg. 613
HENKEL SOUTH AFRICA (PTY.) LTD.—Henkel KGaA; *Int'l*, pg. 614
HENKEL VENEZOLANA S.A.—Henkel KGaA; *Int'l*, pg. 614

HENKEL ZIMBABWE (PVT) LTD.—Henkel KGaA; Int'l, pg. 613
HERCULES CHEMICAL CO., INC.; U.S. Private, pg. 523
HERPU S.A.—Akzo Nobel N.V.; Int'l, pg. 43
HEXCEL CORPORATION; U.S. Public, pg. 824
HILTI AG; Int'l, pg. 619
HUMISEAL DIV.—Chase Corporation; U.S. Public, pg. 337
ICI PAINTS—Imperial Chemical Industries PLC; Int'l, pg. 664
INX INTERNATIONAL—Sumitomo Chemical Company, Ltd.; Int'l, pg. 1311
ITW ADHESIVES—Illinois Tool Works Inc.; U.S. Public, pg. 866
ITW DEVCON INDUSTRIAL—Illinois Tool Works Inc.; U.S. Public, pg. 866
ITW IRATHANE—Illinois Tool Works Inc.; U.S. Public, pg. 866
ITW PHILADELPHIA RESINS—Illinois Tool Works Inc.; U.S. Public, pg. 867
IGLOO PRODUCTS CORPORATION—Brunswick Corporation; U.S. Public, pg. 265
ILLINOIS TOOL WORKS INC.; U.S. Public, pg. 865
IMPERIAL ADHESIVES & CHEMICALS, INC.—NS Group, Inc.; U.S. Public, pg. 1147
INDUSTRIAL ADHESIVES LTD.—Burmah Castrol plc; Int'l, pg. 234
INDUSTRIAL BRUGER SA—Akzo Nobel N.V.; Int'l, pg. 43
INSTALLATION PRODUCTS DIV.—Armstrong World Industries, Inc.; U.S. Public, pg. 132
INTERNACIONAL DE CERAMICA S.A. DE C.V.; Int'l, pg. 680
IRISH CEMENT LTD.—CRH, plc; Int'l, pg. 242
ISOTECH G.M.B.H.—Novartis AG; Int'l, pg. 983
KATIVO CHEMICAL INDUSTRIES, S.A.—H.B. Fuller Company; U.S. Public, pg. 687
KATIVO DE GUATEMALA, S.A.—H.B. Fuller Company; U.S. Public, pg. 687
KATIVO DE HONDURAS, S.A.—H.B. Fuller Company; U.S. Public, pg. 687
KATIVO DE PANAMA S.A.—H.B. Fuller Company; U.S. Public, pg. 687
KATIVO EL SALVADOR, S.A.—H.B. Fuller Company; U.S. Public, pg. 687
KATIVO NICARAGUA, S.A.—H.B. Fuller Company; U.S. Public, pg. 687
LAFARGE CONCRETE LTD.—Lafarge S.A.; Int'l, pg. 789
LAFARGE S.A.; Int'l, pg. 788
LAKIN GENERAL CORPORATION; U.S. Private, pg. 644
LAPORTE PLC; Int'l, pg. 801
LEPAGE'S, INC.—The Jordan Company; U.S. Private, pg. 598
S.A. LEVIS—Akzo Nobel N.V.; Int'l, pg. 43
LEVIS SAPT. SA—Akzo Nobel N.V.; Int'l, pg. 43
LOCTITE CORP. NORTH AMERICAN GROUP—Henkel KGaA; Int'l, pg. 611
LOCTITE CORPORATION—Henkel KGaA; Int'l, pg. 611
LOCTITE PUERTO RICO, INC.—Henkel KGaA; Int'l, pg. 611
LORD CORPORATION; U.S. Private, pg. 675
MW MANUFACTURERS INC.—Hanson PLC; Int'l, pg. 593
SA MAROCAINE DES PEINTURES ASTRAL CELLUCO (SAMPAC)—Akzo Nobel N.V.; Int'l, pg. 43
MASTER BUILDERS INC.—Viag AG; Int'l, pg. 1465
MAXCO, INC.; U.S. Public, pg. 1061
METHODE DEVELOPMENT COMPANY—Methode Electronics Inc.; U.S. Public, pg. 1101
MEYNADIER AG—Viag AG; Int'l, pg. 1465
MILUZ SAICIF—Akzo Nobel N.V.; Int'l, pg. 43
MIRACLE ADHESIVES—The Sherwin-Williams Company; U.S. Public, pg. 1466
MITSUI TOATSU CHEMICALS, INC.—Mitsui & Co., Ltd.; Int'l, pg. 877
MOHAWK FINISHING PRODUCTS, INC.—RPM, Inc.; U.S. Public, pg. 1357
MORTON CHEMICAL DIV.—Morton International Inc.; U.S. Public, pg. 1135
MORTON INTERNATIONAL G.M.B.H.—Morton International Inc.; U.S. Public, pg. 1135
MORTON THIOKOL S.A. DE C.V.—Morton International Inc.; U.S. Public, pg. 1136
NATIONAL STARCH AND CHEMICAL COMPANY—Unilever Plc; Int'l, pg. 1435
NESTE RESINS OY—Neste Oy; Int'l, pg. 913
NEVAMAR DIVISION—International Paper Company; U.S. Public, pg. 903
NORDISK BYGGE KEMI A/S—Viag AG; Int'l, pg. 1466
NORTON GMBH—Saint-Gobain; Int'l, pg. 1175
NORTON PERFORMANCE PLASTICS—Saint-Gobain; Int'l, pg. 1174
NORTON PTY. LTD.—Saint-Gobain; Int'l, pg. 1175
NORTON S.A.—Saint-Gobain; Int'l, pg. 1175
NORTON S.A. INDUSTRIA E COMERCIO—Saint-Gobain; Int'l, pg. 1175
NOVARTIS AG; Int'l, pg. 971
OHIO SEALANTS INC.—Laporte plc; Int'l, pg. 802
OMNITECHNIC GMBH—Henkel KGaA; Int'l, pg. 610
PCI AUGSBURG GMBH—Viag AG; Int'l, pg. 1464
PRC (UK) LTD.—Courtaulds plc; Int'l, pg. 339
PALMER INTERNATIONAL, INC.; U.S. Private, pg. 834
PARK ELECTROCHEMICAL CORPORATION; U.S. Public, pg. 1258
PERMABOND INTERNATIONAL—Unilever Plc; Int'l, pg. 1435
HARRY S. PETERSON CO., INC.—Viag AG; Int'l, pg. 1465
PITNEY BOWES INC.; U.S. Public, pg. 1303
PLASTIC PADDING A/S—Henkel KGaA; Int'l, pg. 611
PLASTOMER PRODUCTS DIV.—Coltec Holdings Inc; U.S. Public, pg. 402
POLYKEN TECHNOLOGIES—Tyco International Ltd.; U.S. Public, pg. 1647
POLYMER PLASTICS CORPORATION; U.S. Private, pg. 875
PRAKOLL, S.A.—H.B. Fuller Company; U.S. Public, pg. 687
PRATT & LAMBERT UNITED, INC.—The Sherwin-Williams Company; U.S. Public, pg. 1466
PREMARK INTERNATIONAL, INC.; U.S. Public, pg. 1321
QUAKER CHEMICAL CORPORATION; U.S. Public, pg. 1346
QUIMICA HARTING S.A.—Henkel KGaA; Int'l, pg. 614
QUIMICA HENKEL CENTROAMERICANA S.A.—Henkel KGaA; Int'l, pg. 613
QUIMICA HENKEL S.A. DE C.V.—Henkel KGaA; Int'l, pg. 613
RPM BELGIUM N.V.—RPM, Inc.; U.S. Public, pg. 1357
RSR CORPORATION—Quexco Incorporated; U.S. Private, pg. 900
RAFFI & SWANSON, INC.; U.S. Private, pg. 907
RECORDATI PHARMACEUTICAL CHEMICALS PRODUCTIONS—Recordati Industria Chimica e Farmaceutica S.p.A.; Int'l, pg. 1090
RED DEVIL INC.; U.S. Private, pg. 915
REINZ-DICHTUNGS-GMBH—Dana Corporation; U.S. Public, pg. 480
REXAM INC.—Rexam PLC; Int'l, pg. 1106
E.V. ROBERTS & ASSOCIATES, INC.; U.S. Private, pg. 935
ROCKWELL INTERNATIONAL CORPORATION; U.S. Public, pg. 1397
ROYSTON LABORATORIES—Chase Corporation; U.S. Public, pg. 337
RUBSON S.A.F.—Henkel KGaA; Int'l, pg. 614
SAIM SOCIETE LES ADHESIFS ET INSONORISANTS MODERNES, SA—Henkel KGaA; Int'l, pg. 614
SKW BAUWERKSTOFFE PIESTERITZ GMBH—Viag AG; Int'l, pg. 1465
SKW CHEMICALS CANADA INC.—Viag AG; Int'l, pg. 1466
SAAR-GUMMIWERK GMBH—Saarbergwerke Aktiengesellschaft; Int'l, pg. 1167
SANFORD CORPORATION—Newell Co.; U.S. Public, pg. 1178
SICHEL-WERKE GMBH—Henkel KGaA; Int'l, pg. 610
SIERRACIN CORPORATION; U.S. Private, pg. 999
SIKA CORPORATION—Sika Finanz AG; Int'l, pg. 1249
SIKKENS LINVEA SPA—Akzo Nobel N.V.; Int'l, pg. 43
SKANDINAVISK HENKEL A/S—Henkel KGaA; Int'l, pg. 614
SMITH & MCLAURIN LIMITED—Rexam PLC; Int'l, pg. 1107
SOC. ABIDJANISE D'EXPANSION CHIMIQUE (SAEC) SA—Akzo Nobel N.V.; Int'l, pg. 43
SOC. AFRICAINE D'EXPANSION CHIMIQUE (SAEC) SA—Akzo Nobel N.V.; Int'l, pg. 43
SOC. AFRICAINE DES PRODUITS CHEMIQUES, AGRICOLES ET MENAGERS SA (SAPCAM)—Akzo Nobel N.V.; Int'l, pg. 43
SONOCO ADHESIVES DIVISION—Sonoco Products Company; U.S. Public, pg. 1486
SONOCO PRODUCTS COMPANY; U.S. Public, pg. 1485
SOVEREIGN SPECIALTY CHEMICAL, INC.; U.S. Private, pg. 1019
SPECIALTY POLYMERS & CHEMICALS DIVISION—The B.F. Goodrich Company; U.S. Public, pg. 751
STALO CHEMICALS GMBH—Henkel KGaA; Int'l, pg. 610
STAR FINISHING PRODUCTS, INC.—RPM, Inc.; U.S. Public, pg. 1358
OY SUOMEN HENKEL AB—Henkel KGaA; Int'l, pg. 614
THE SYRACUSE ADHESIVES COMPANY—Laporte plc; Int'l, pg. 803
TEC INCORPORATED—H.B. Fuller Company; U.S. Public, pg. 687
TAMMS INDUSTRIES—Laporte plc; Int'l, pg. 803
TAMMS INDUSTRIES CO.—Laporte plc; Int'l, pg. 803
THE TESTOR CORPORATION—RPM, Inc.; U.S. Public, pg. 1358
TEXAS REFINERY CORP.; U.S. Private, pg. 1078
THOMPSON-SIEGEL GMBH—Henkel KGaA; Int'l, pg. 610
3M CANADA INC.—3M; U.S. Public, pg. 1606
TOPFLIGHT CORP.; U.S. Private, pg. 1091
TRICOSAL GMBH—Henkel KGaA; Int'l, pg. 610
TURK HENKEL A.S.—Henkel KGaA; Int'l, pg. 614
TURTLE WAX, INC.; U.S. Private, pg. 1110
USG CORPORATION; U.S. Public, pg. 1660
UNICHEMA U.S.A.—Unilever Plc; Int'l, pg. 1436
UNIROYAL TECHNOLOGY CORPORATION; U.S. Public, pg. 1670
UNISEAL, INC.—George Koch Sons, Inc.; U.S. Private, pg. 628
UNITED MARKETING (LEICESTER) LTD.—The Black & Decker Corporation; U.S. Public, pg. 234
UNITED STATES GYPSUM CO.—USG Corporation; U.S. Public, pg. 1660
VAN NEERBOS-PCI B.V.—Viag AG; Int'l, pg. 1466
VERCOLAC SPA—Akzo Nobel N.V.; Int'l, pg. 43
VREDESTEIN ICOPRO B.V.—Vredestein N.V.; Int'l, pg. 1481
WESTVACO CORPORATION-CHEMICAL DIV.—Westvaco Corporation; U.S. Public, pg. 1762
RALPH WILSON PLASTICS CO.—Premark International, Inc.; U.S. Public, pg. 1322
WILTIC CHEMICAL MANUFACTURING—Genova Products, Inc.; U.S. Private, pg. 447

2892 — EXPLOSIVES

ALLIANT TECHSYSTEMS (AEROSPACE DIVISION)—Alliant Techsystems; U.S. Public, pg. 47
ATLANTIC EXPLOSIVES—Imperial Chemical Industries PLC; Int'l, pg. 664
ATLAS DE MEXICO, S.A. DE C.V.—Imperial Chemical Industries PLC; Int'l, pg. 664
AUSTIN POWDER CO.; U.S. Private, pg. 100
CXA LTD.—Imperial Chemical Industries PLC; Int'l, pg. 664
CELSIUS INVEST AB—Celsius AB; Int'l, pg. 276
DAISY MANUFACTURING COMPANY, INC.; U.S. Private, pg. 308
DAVIS MINING & MANUFACTURING; U.S. Private, pg. 315
DU PONT DO BRASIL S.A.—Du Pont (E.I. Du Pont De Nemours & Co.); U.S. Public, pg. 532
DU PONT, S.A. DE C.V.—Du Pont (E.I. Du Pont De Nemours & Co.); U.S. Public, pg. 533
DYNAMIT NOBEL AG—Metallgesellschaft AG; Int'l, pg. 861
EXPLO-MIDWEST, INC.—Imperial Chemical Industries PLC; Int'l, pg. 663
EXPLONOR, INC.—Imperial Chemical Industries PLC; Int'l, pg. 664
EXPLOSIVES DIV.—Nippon Kayaku Co. Ltd.; Int'l, pg. 934
EXPLOSIVOS MEXICANOS S.A. DE C.V.—Imperial Chemical Industries PLC; Int'l, pg. 664
HALLIBURTON COMPANY; U.S. Public, pg. 775
HALLIBURTON ENERGY SERVICES, INC.—Halliburton Company; U.S. Public, pg. 776
HENKEL ITALIANA S.P.A.—Henkel KGaA; Int'l, pg. 613
ICI AMERICAS, INC.—Imperial Chemical Industries PLC; Int'l, pg. 663
ICI CANADA INC.—Imperial Chemical Industries PLC; Int'l, pg. 664
ICI EXPLOSIVES—Imperial Chemical Industries PLC; Int'l, pg. 664
ICI EXPLOSIVES USA INC.—Imperial Chemical Industries PLC; Int'l, pg. 663
ICI EXPLOSIVES—Imperial Chemical Industries PLC; Int'l, pg. 664
ICI FRANCE SA—Imperial Chemical Industries PLC; Int'l, pg. 665
ICI INDIA LIMITED—Imperial Chemical Industries PLC; Int'l, pg. 665
ICI NEW ZEALAND LIMITED—Imperial Chemical Industries PLC; Int'l, pg. 665
ICI OESTERREICH GMBH—Imperial Chemical Industries PLC; Int'l, pg. 665
ICI ZAMBIA LIMITED—Imperial Chemical Industries PLC; Int'l, pg. 665
IMPERIAL CHEMICAL INDUSTRIES PLC; Int'l, pg. 662
KINEPAK, INCORPORATED—Imperial Chemical Industries PLC; Int'l, pg. 664
MARTIN ELECTRONICS, INC.; U.S. Private, pg. 709
MINING SERVICES INTERNATIONAL, INC.; U.S. Public, pg. 1115
NATIONAL DYNAMICS—Sperry Owens, Inc.; U.S. Private, pg. 1025
NIPPON KAYAKU CO. LTD.; Int'l, pg. 934
NOBEL'S EXPLOSIVES COMPANY LIMITED—Imperial Chemical Industries PLC; Int'l, pg. 663
PHILIPPINES EXPLOSIVES CORPORATION—Imperial Chemical Industries PLC; Int'l, pg. 665
PRIMEX TECHNOLOGIES, INC.; U.S. Public, pg. 1329
SASOL LIMITED; Int'l, pg. 1196
SOUTHWESTERN EXPLOSIVES—Austin Powder Co.; U.S. Private, pg. 100
SPECIAL DEVICES, INCORPORATED; U.S. Public, pg. 1496
STAR EXPORT SERVICES INC.—Imperial Chemical Industries PLC; Int'l, pg. 664
WESTERN STATES ENERGY—Imperial Chemical Industries PLC; Int'l, pg. 664
ZENECA AB—Zeneca Group Plc; Int'l, pg. 1526
ZENECA HELLAS S.A.—Zeneca Group Plc; Int'l, pg. 1526
ZENECA OY—Zeneca Group Plc; Int'l, pg. 1527
ZENECA POLAND SP. Z.O.O.—Zeneca Group Plc; Int'l, pg. 1527
ZENECA ZIMBABWE (PRIVATE) LIMITED—Zeneca Group Plc; Int'l, pg. 1527

2893 — PRINTING INK

ACME PRINTING INK CO., INC.—Sumitomo Chemical Company, Ltd.; Int'l, pg. 1311
AKZO RESINS & VEHICLES—Akzo Nobel N.V.; Int'l, pg. 48
AMERICAN INKS & COATINGS CORP.; U.S. Private, pg. 56
BASF COATINGS & INKS HONG KONG LTD.—BASF AG; Int'l, pg. 105
BASF COATINGS & INKS PHILIPPINES, INC.—BASF AG; Int'l, pg. 105
BASF LACKE & FARBEN VERTRIEBSGESELLSCHAFT MBH—BASF AG; Int'l, pg. 106
BAYER ANTWERPEN N.V.—Bayer AG; Int'l, pg. 174
CORDES & CO. GMBH—Henkel KGaA; Int'l, pg. 609
DIC TRADING (USA) INC.—Dainippon Ink & Chemicals, Inc.; Int'l, pg. 369
DAINIPPON INK & CHEMICALS, INC.; Int'l, pg. 369
FIELD CONTAINER COMPANY, L.P.; U.S. Private, pg. 403
FLINT INK CORP.; U.S. Private, pg. 413
FORT JAMES CORPORATION; U.S. Public, pg. 670
GANS INK & SUPPLY COMPANY, INC.; U.S. Private, pg. 440
THE GENERAL CHEMICAL GROUP, INC.; U.S. Public, pg. 707
GENERAL PRINTING INK—Dainippon Ink & Chemicals, Inc.; Int'l, pg. 370
HANDSCHY INDUSTRIES—Field Container Company, L.P.; U.S. Private, pg. 403
HERITAGE INKS INTERNATIONAL; U.S. Private, pg. 524
J.M. HUBER CORPORATION; U.S. Private, pg. 544
ICI PACKAGING INKS—Imperial Chemical Industries PLC; Int'l, pg. 664
ICI SPECIALTIES—Imperial Chemical Industries PLC; Int'l, pg. 664
INX INTERNATIONAL—Sumitomo Chemical Company, Ltd.; Int'l, pg. 1311
THE INCTEC INC.—Dai Nippon Printing Co., Ltd.; Int'l, pg. 363
KOHL & MADDEN PRINTING INK CORP. DIV.—Dainippon Ink & Chemicals, Inc.; Int'l, pg. 370
MARKEM CORPORATION; U.S. Private, pg. 704
MATTHEWS INTERNATIONAL CORP.; U.S. Public, pg. 1059
THE MEAD CORPORATION; U.S. Public, pg. 1074
MELLON CORPORATION; U.S. Private, pg. 730

MIDLAND SEABOARD PRINTING INK, INC.—Sumitomo Chemical Company, Ltd.; *Int'l*, pg. 1311
NAZ-DAR COMPANY—Thrall Enterprises, Inc.; *U.S. Private*, *pg. 1084*
NU-KOTE INTERNATIONAL; *U.S. Public*, pg. 1205
RAFFI & SWANSON, INC.; *U.S. Private*, pg. 907
SAKATA INX CORPORATION—Sumitomo Chemical Company, Ltd.; *Int'l*, pg. 1311
SERICOL INTERNATIONAL LTD.—Burmah Castrol plc; *Int'l*, pg. 235
THRALL ENTERPRISES, INC.; *U.S. Private*, pg. 1084
TOKYO PRINTING INK MANUFACTURING CO., LTD.; *Int'l*, pg. 1394
VAN SON HOLLAND INK CORP. OF AMERICA; *U.S. Private*, pg. 1133
VERATEC DIVISION—International Paper Company; *U.S. Public*, pg. 904

2895 — CARBON BLACK

CABOT CORPORATION; *U.S. Public*, pg. 288
CHINA SYNTHETIC RUBBER CORPORATION; *Int'l*, pg. 286
CONTINENTAL CARBON COMPANY—China Synthetic Rubber Corporation; *Int'l*, pg. 286
ENGINEERED CARBONS INC.—Ameripol Synpol Corp.; *U.S. Private*, pg. 65
J.M. HUBER CORPORATION; *U.S. Private*, pg. 544
LUCKY ADVANCED MATERIALS INC.—LG Group; *Int'l*, pg. 779
PHELPS DODGE CORPORATION; *U.S. Public*, pg. 1286

2899 — CHEMICALS & CHEMICAL PREPARATIONS, NEC

ABIETA CHEMIE GMBH—Hercules Incorporated; *U.S. Public*, pg. 810
ACETO CORPORATION; *U.S. Public*, pg. 15
ACHESON INDUSTRIES, INC.; *U.S. Private*, pg. 12
AGREVO USA COMPANY—Schering AG; *Int'l*, pg. 1203
AIR PRODUCTS—Air Products and Chemicals, Inc.; *U.S. Public*, pg. 30
AKZO CHEMIE—Akzo Nobel N.V.; *Int'l*, pg. 46
AKZO CHEMIE FRANCE S.A.R.L.—Akzo Nobel N.V.; *Int'l*, pg. 47
AKZO CHEMIE U.K. LTD.—Akzo Nobel N.V.; *Int'l*, pg. 47
AKZO SALT INC.—Akzo Nobel N.V.; *Int'l*, pg. 48
AKZO SALT OF UTAH—Akzo Nobel N.V.; *Int'l*, pg. 48
AKZO SALT SPA.—Akzo Nobel N.V.; *Int'l*, pg. 47
ALBRIGHT & WILSON INTERTRADE LTD.—Albright & Wilson plc; *Int'l*, pg. 49
ALBRIGHT & WILSON PLC; *Int'l*, pg. 49
ALCO INDUSTRIES, INC.; *U.S. Private*, pg. 32
ALLIED COLLOIDS GROUP PLC.; *Int'l*, pg. 62
ALLIEDSIGNAL INC.; *U.S. Public*, pg. 49
ALPHA METALS, INC.—Cookson Group plc; *Int'l*, pg. 328
ALTANA AG; *Int'l*, pg. 65
ALUPOWER, INC.—Ener-Tek International Corporation; *U.S. Private*, pg. 376
AMERICAN CHROME & CHEMICALS, INC.—Harrisons & Crosfield plc; *Int'l*, pg. 598
AMERICAN VANGUARD CORPORATION; *U.S. Public*, pg. 94
AMICON POLYMERS (H.K.) LTD.—Millipore Corporation; *U.S. Public*, pg. 1113
AMSPEC CHEMICAL CORPORATION; *U.S. Private*, pg. 67
AMVAC CHEMICAL CORPORATION—American Vanguard Corporation; *U.S. Public*, pg. 94
ANGUS CHEMICAL COMPANY; *U.S. Private*, pg. 75
ANGUS CHEMICAL (SINGAPORE) PTE. LTD.—ANGUS Chemical Company; *U.S. Private*, pg. 75
ANGUS CHEMIE GMBH—ANGUS Chemical Company; *U.S. Private*, pg. 75
ARCO CHEMICAL CO.—Atlantic Richfield Company; *U.S. Public*, pg. 144
ARROW FASTENER CO., INC.; *U.S. Private*, pg. 85
ARROW INDUSTRIES, INC.—ConAgra, Inc.; *U.S. Public*, pg. 426
ASHLAND-AVEBENE—Ashland, Inc.; *U.S. Public*, pg. 139
ASHLAND CHEMICAL—Ashland, Inc.; *U.S. Public*, pg. 139
ASHLAND CHEMICAL CANADA, LTD.—Ashland, Inc.; *U.S. Public*, pg. 139
ASHLAND CHEMICAL LTD.—Ashland, Inc.; *U.S. Public*, pg. 139
ASHLAND DE MEXICO S.A. DE C.V.—Ashland, Inc.; *U.S. Public*, pg. 139
ASHLAND OIL INTL. LTD.—Ashland, Inc.; *U.S. Public*, pg. 139
ASHLAND-SUEDCHEMIE-KERNFEST GMBH—Ashland, Inc.; *U.S. Public*, pg. 140
B.V. ASHLAND-SUEDCHEMIE V.H. NECOF—Ashland, Inc.; *U.S. Public*, pg. 140
ASIAN PVS CHEMICAL CO., LTD.—PVS Chemicals, Inc.; *U.S. Private*, pg. 828
ATLANTA MFG. FACILITY—L.M. Scofield Company; *U.S. Private*, pg. 976
ATLANTIC RICHFIELD COMPANY; *U.S. Public*, pg. 144
ATOTECH U.S.A. INC.; *U.S. Private*, pg. 97
AUSTRALIAN CHEMICAL HOLDINGS LTD.—Hercules Incorporated; *U.S. Public*, pg. 810
AVERY DENNISON CORPORATION; *U.S. Public*, pg. 152
BASF AUSTRALIA LTD.—BASF AG; *Int'l*, pg. 105
BK LADENBURG GMBH—Hoechst Aktiengesellschaft; *Int'l*, *pg. 626*
BWK KRIEGLACH BAUWERKSTOFFE GES. M. B. H.—Viag AG; *Int'l*, pg. 1465
BADGER FIRE PROTECTION INC.—Williams Holdings Plc; *Int'l*, pg. 1500
BAKER HUGHES INCORPORATED; *U.S. Public*, pg. 165
BAKER PETROLITE CORPORATION—Baker Hughes Incorporated; *U.S. Public*, pg. 166
BAROID DRILLING FLUIDS DIVISION—Dresser Industries, Inc.; *U.S. Public*, pg. 528
BAYER AG—Bayer AG; *Int'l*, pg. 172
BAYER CORPORATION—Bayer AG; *Int'l*, pg. 172
BAYER CORPORATION/CONSUMER CARE DIVISION—Bayer AG; *Int'l*, pg. 173
BAYLOR COMPANY—Royal Begemann Group; *Int'l*, pg. 1134
BENSONS—Esselte AB; *Int'l*, pg. 460
BERCEN INC.—Cranston Print Works Company; *U.S. Private*, pg. 287
BERGVIK CHEMIE B.V.—International Paper Company; *U.S. Public*, pg. 904
BERGVIK CHEMIE GMBH—International Paper Company; *U.S. Public*, pg. 904
BERGVIK KEMI AB—International Paper Company; *U.S. Public*, pg. 906
BERGVIK SALES LIMITED—International Paper Company; *U.S. Public*, pg. 904
BERNER LTD.; *Int'l*, pg. 189
BETTOR S.A.—Viag AG; *Int'l*, pg. 1465
BETZDEARBORN INC.; *U.S. Public*, pg. 226
BETZDEARBORN K.K.—BetzDearborn Inc.; *U.S. Public*, pg. 227
BETZDEARBORN OY—BetzDearborn Inc.; *U.S. Public*, pg. 227
BEVALOID LTD.—Rhone-Poulenc S.A.; *Int'l*, pg. 1113
SAMUEL BINGHAM CO; *U.S. Private*, pg. 144
BIO-KIL LABORATORIES LIMITED—Laporte plc; *Int'l*, pg. 802
BITUMEX S.A. DE C.V.—Kao Corporation; *Int'l*, pg. 717
BLUE DEVIL INDUSTRIES, INC.—Laporte plc; *Int'l*, pg. 802
BONDO/MAR-HYDE CORPORATION—RPM, Inc.; *U.S. Public*, pg. 1357
BORREGAARD INDUSTRIES LIMITED—Orkla A.S.A.; *Int'l*, pg. 1011
BRINER PAINT MANUFACTURING CO., INC.—RPM, Inc.; *U.S. Public*, pg. 1358
BRITISH CHROME & CHEMICALS LTD.—Harrisons & Crosfield plc; *Int'l*, pg. 598
BUCKMAN LABORATORIES INC.—Bulab Holdings, Inc.; *U.S. Private*, pg. 180
CEPSA ITALIA, S.P.A.—Compania Espanola de Petroleos, S.A. (CEPSA); *Int'l*, pg. 323
CEPSA U.K., LTD.—Compania Espanola de Petroleos, S.A. (CEPSA); *Int'l*, pg. 323
CPAC ITALIA, S.R.L./CHIMIFOTO ORNANO—CPAC, Inc.; *U.S. Public*, pg. 282
CPC SPECIALTY MARKETS GROUP—Bestfoods; *U.S. Public*, pg. 224
CPS CHEMICAL COMPANY INC.; *U.S. Private*, pg. 196
CAILA Y PARES SA—Akzo Nobel N.V.; *Int'l*, pg. 47
CALGON CORPORATION—English China Clays Plc; *Int'l*, pg. 455
CALGON INTERAMERICAN CORP.—English China Clays Plc; *Int'l*, pg. 455
CANCARB LIMITED—Transcanada Pipelines Limited; *Int'l*, pg. 1417
CARL FR. CAPPEL—BASF AG; *Int'l*, pg. 104
CARBIDE PRODUCTS—The Carbide/Graphite Group, Inc.; *U.S. Public*, pg. 304
CARBOLINE CO.—RPM, Inc.; *U.S. Public*, pg. 1357
CARBOSULF CHEMISCHE WERKE GMBH—Akzo Nobel N.V.; *Int'l*, pg. 47
CARGILL SALT—Cargill; *U.S. Private*, pg. 210
CARGILL SALT INC.—Akzo Nobel N.V.; *Int'l*, pg. 48
CASTING MATERIALS DIVISION—Hickman, Williams & Co. Inc.; *U.S. Private*, pg. 525
CERAS JOHNSON DE PORTUGAL, LDA.—S.C. Johnson & Son, Inc.; *U.S. Private*, pg. 592
CERESIT GMBH—Henkel KGaA; *Int'l*, pg. 609
CERTIFIED LABS—NCH Corporation; *U.S. Public*, pg. 1145
CHEMAG AKTIENGESELLSCHAFT—BASF AG; *Int'l*, pg. 104
CHEMDESIGN CORPORATION—Bayer AG; *Int'l*, pg. 173
CHEMETALL GMBH GESELLSCHAFT FUER CHEMISCH TECHNISCHE VERFAHREN—Metallgesellschaft AG; *Int'l*, pg. 861
CHEMETICS INTERNATIONAL COMPANY LTD VANCOUVER OPERATIONS—Kvaerner a.s.a.; *Int'l*, pg. 774
CHEMISCHE FABRIK GRUNAU GMBH—Henkel KGaA; *Int'l*, pg. 609
CHEMISCHE FABRIK KALK GMBH—BASF AG; *Int'l*, pg. 104
CHEMONICS FIRE-TROL, INC.—Erly Industries, Inc.; *U.S. Public*, pg. 591
CHEMONICS INDUSTRIES (CANADA) LTD.—Erly Industries, Inc.; *U.S. Public*, pg. 591
CHEMOXY INTERNATIONAL PLC—Ascot Holdings Plc; *Int'l*, pg. 88
CHEMREX INC.—Viag AG; *Int'l*, pg. 1465
CHEMVIRON SPECIALTY CHEMICALS—Merck & Co., Inc.; *U.S. Public*, pg. 1091
CHESEBROUGH-POND'S HOUSEHOLD PRODUCTS DIV.—Unilever Plc; *Int'l*, pg. 1435
CHESSCO INDUSTRIES, INC.; *U.S. Private*, pg. 234
CILAG AG—Johnson & Johnson; *U.S. Public*, pg. 929
CLARIANT CORPORATION—Hoechst Aktiengesellschaft; *Int'l*, pg. 624
CLEANING SOLUTIONS GROUP/CELLO—The Sherwin-Williams Company; *U.S. Public*, pg. 1466
COATES BROTHERS PLC—Total S.A.; *Int'l*, pg. 1409
COATES BROTHERS (SOUTH AFRICA) LTD.—Total S.A.; *Int'l*, pg. 1409
COLLOID ENVIRONMENTAL TECHNOLOGIES COMPANY (CETCO)—AMCOL International Corp.; *U.S. Public*, pg. 64
COLORANTS & AUXILIARIES—Hoechst Aktiengesellschaft; *Int'l*, pg. 626
COMMERCIAL HENKEL S.A. (COHESA)—Henkel KGaA; *Int'l*, pg. 611
COMPUGRAPHICS INTERNATIONAL LIMITED—Laporte plc; *Int'l*, pg. 802
CONAP INC.; *U.S. Private*, pg. 261
CONOCO INC.—Du Pont (E.I. Du Pont De Nemours & Co.); *U.S. Public*, pg. 531
CONSOLIDATED COATINGS CORP.—RPM, Inc.; *U.S. Public*, pg. 1357
CONSTRUCTION & HOME IMPROVEMENT MARKETS DIVISION—3M; *U.S. Public*, pg. 1605
CONTINENTAL INDUSTRIES INC.—Handy & Harman; *U.S. Public*, pg. 780
COOKSON MATTHEY PRINT—Johnson Matthey Public Limited Company; *Int'l*, pg. 713
CORPORACION GRUPO QUIMICO, S.A.C.A.; *Int'l*, pg. 331
CRANSTON PRINT WORKS COMPANY; *U.S. Private*, pg. 286
CYANTEK CORPORATION—Laporte plc; *Int'l*, pg. 802
CYDSA S.A. CHEMICAL DIV.—CYDSA S.A.; *Int'l*, pg. 246
DIC TRADING (USA) INC.—Dainippon Ink & Chemicals, Inc.; *Int'l*, pg. 369
DSM FRANCE SA—DSM N.V.; *Int'l*, pg. 355
DSM N.V.; *Int'l*, pg. 352
DAINIPPON INK & CHEMICALS, INC.; *Int'l*, pg. 369
DAMPIER SALT LTD.—Nissho Iwai Corporation; *Int'l*, pg. 947
P.T. DARYA-VARIA LABORATORIA—First Pacific Company Limited; *Int'l*, pg. 487
DAUBERT CHEMICAL COMPANY, INC.—Daubert Industries, Inc.; *U.S. Private*, pg. 313
DAY-GLO COLOR CORP.—RPM, Inc.; *U.S. Public*, pg. 1357
DEAN FOODS/MCDONALD'S SALES DIVISION—Dean Foods Company; *U.S. Public*, pg. 490
DEASUNG-HENKEL CHEMICAL CO., LTD.—Henkel KGaA; *Int'l*, pg. 614
DEEPWATER CHEMICALS, INC.—Tomen Corporation; *Int'l*, *pg. 1395*
DEER PARK SPRING WATER, INC.—Nestle S.A.; *Int'l*, pg. 919
DELAMINE B.V.—Tosoh Corporation; *Int'l*, pg. 1408
DELTA RESINS & REFRACTORIES, INC.; *U.S. Private*, pg. 323
DETREX GENERAL CHEMICALS & SOLVENTS DIV.—Detrex Corporation; *U.S. Public*, pg. 501
DEUTSCHE HERAKLITH A.G.—RGP Holding, Inc.; *U.S. Private*, pg. 903
THE DEXTER CORPORATION; *U.S. Public*, pg. 504
DEXTER ELECTRONIC MATERIALS DIVISION—The Dexter Corporation; *U.S. Public*, pg. 504
DINOL AB—Novartis AG; *Int'l*, pg. 981
DINOL AUSTRALIA PTY. LTD.—Novartis AG; *Int'l*, pg. 981
DINOL FRANCE S.A.R.L.—Novartis AG; *Int'l*, pg. 981
DINOL INDUSTRIAL CANADA INC.—Novartis AG; *Int'l*, pg. 982
DINOL JAPAN—Novartis AG; *Int'l*, pg. 982
DINOL KOREA LTD.—Novartis AG; *Int'l*, pg. 982
DINOL NORGE A/S—Novartis AG; *Int'l*, pg. 982
DINOL OY—Novartis AG; *Int'l*, pg. 982
DINOL PROTECTOL LTD.—Novartis AG; *Int'l*, pg. 982
DINOL-SHROFF (INDIA) PVT. LTD.—Novartis AG; *Int'l*, pg. 982
DIVERSEY WATER TECHNOLOGIES, INC.—Nalco Chemical Company; *U.S. Public*, pg. 1150
THE DOW CHEMICAL COMPANY; *U.S. Public*, pg. 522
DOW CHEMICAL NORTH AMERICA—The Dow Chemical Company; *U.S. Public*, pg. 522
DYNACHEM SINGAPORE PTE. LTD.—Morton International Inc.; *U.S. Public*, pg. 1135
ECC INTERNATIONAL LTD.—English China Clays Plc; *Int'l*, *pg. 455*
EGE FERRO KIMYA SANAYI VE TICARRET—Ferro Corporation; *U.S. Public*, pg. 619
EMS-TOGO—Novartis AG; *Int'l*, pg. 981
EASTMAN CHEMICAL COMPANY; *U.S. Public*, pg. 550
EASTMAN GELATINE CORP.—Eastman Kodak Company; *U.S. Public*, pg. 551
EASTMAN KODAK COMPANY; *U.S. Public*, pg. 550
ECOLOGICAL CHEMICAL PRODUCTS CO.—Du Pont (E.I. Du Pont De Nemours & Co.); *U.S. Public*, pg. 531
ECUATORIANA DE SAL Y PRODUCTOS QUIMICOS C.A. (ECUASAL)—Morton International Inc.; *U.S. Public*, pg. 1135
ELECTRICAL PRODUCTS DIVISION—3M; *U.S. Public*, pg. 1605
ELECTRO-COATINGS, INC.; *U.S. Private*, pg. 368
ELECTRO-SCIENCE LABORATORIES, INC.; *U.S. Private*, pg. 369
EMERSON & CUMING SPECIALTY POLYMERS—Unilever Plc; *Int'l*, pg. 1435
ENER-TEK INTERNATIONAL CORPORATION; *U.S. Private*, pg. 376
ENGLISH CHINA CLAYS PLC; *Int'l*, pg. 455
ENICHEM S.P.A.—ENI S.p.A.; *Int'l*, pg. 428
ENTHONE OMI-BRIDGEVIEW—Asarco Incorporated; *U.S. Public*, pg. 138
ENTHONE-OMI, INC.—Asarco Incorporated; *U.S. Public*, pg. 138
ENTHONE OMI-LONG BEACH—Asarco Incorporated; *U.S. Public*, pg. 138
ERLY INDUSTRIES, INC.; *U.S. Public*, pg. 591
ESCO—Esco Corporation; *U.S. Private*, pg. 383
ESQUIRE CANADA, INC.—Strombecker Corporation; *U.S. Private*, pg. 1047
ETHONE OMI-WARREN—Asarco Incorporated; *U.S. Public*, *pg. 138*
ETHONE OMI-WEST HAVEN—Asarco Incorporated; *U.S. Public*, pg. 138
ETHYL PETROLEUM ADDITIVES LTD.—Ethyl Corporation; *U.S. Public*, pg. 595
THE EUCLID CHEMICAL COMPANY—RPM, Inc.; *U.S. Public*, pg. 1358
EUROGENETICS N.V.—Tosoh Corporation; *Int'l*, pg. 1408
EXXON CHEMICAL POLYMERS, ENG.—Exxon Corporation; *U.S. Public*, pg. 601
EZON PRODUCTS, INC.; *U.S. Private*, pg. 388
FMC FOOD INGREDIENTS DIV.—FMC Corporation; *U.S. Public*, pg. 605

FMC OF CANADA LIMITED—FMC Corporation; *U.S. Public, pg. 606*
FATTY CHEMICAL (MALAYSIA) SDN., BHD.—Kao Corporation; *Int'l*, pg. 717
FAVORITE PRODUCTS CO.—Oil-Dri Corporation of America; *U.S. Public*, pg. 1215
FERRO CORPORATION; *U.S. Public*, pg. 618
FERRO (DEUTSCHLAND) GMBH—Ferro Corporation; *U.S. Public*, pg. 619
FERRO ECUATORIANA S.A.—Ferro Corporation; *U.S. Public*, pg. 619
FERRO (GREAT BRITAIN) LIMITED—Ferro Corporation; *U.S. Public*, pg. 619
FERRO (HOLLAND) B.V.—Ferro Corporation; *U.S. Public*, pg. 619
FERRO (ITALIA) S.R.L.—Ferro Corporation; *U.S. Public*, pg. 619
P.T. FERRO MAS DINAMIKA—Ferro Corporation; *U.S. Public*, pg. 619
FERRO TOYO CO. LIMITED—Ferro Corporation; *U.S. Public*, pg. 619
FIRST BRANDS AFRICA (PTY) LTD.—First Brands Corporation; *U.S. Public*, pg. 627
FIRST BRANDS (CANADA) CORP.—First Brands Corporation; *U.S. Public*, pg. 627
FIRST BRANDS CORPORATION; *U.S. Public*, pg. 626
FIRST BRANDS (EUROPE) LTD.—First Brands Corporation; *U.S. Public*, pg. 627
FIRST BRANDS PHILIPPINES—First Brands Corporation; *U.S. Public*, pg. 627
FIRST CHEMICAL CORP.—ChemFirst Inc.; *U.S. Public*, pg. 344
FLEXIBLE PRODUCTS COMPANY; *U.S. Private*, pg. 412
FLORASYNTH INC.—Bayer AG; *Int'l*, pg. 173
FLORASYNTH S.A. DE C.V.—Bayer AG; *Int'l*, pg. 174
FLORASYNTH SINGAPORE PTE LTD.—Bayer AG; *Int'l*, pg. 174
FLOURO-PRECISION COATINGS—TI Group plc; *Int'l*, pg. 1338
FOOD INGREDIENTS LIMITED—FMC Corporation; *U.S. Public*, pg. 606
FOOD INGREDIENTS (PHILLIPINES) INC.—FMC Corporation; *U.S. Public*, pg. 606
FOSECO INC.—Burmah Castrol plc; *Int'l*, pg. 234
FOSECO PLC—Burmah Castrol plc; *Int'l*, pg. 234
FRAGRANCE RESOURCES, INC.; *U.S. Private*, pg. 423
FRANKLIN OIL CORP.—Morgan Crucible Co. Plc; *Int'l*, pg. 892
FRIT DIVISION—Ferro Corporation; *U.S. Public*, pg. 619
THE FULLER BRUSH COMPANY—CPAC, Inc.; *U.S. Public, pg. 282*
GEMISA S.A. DE C.V.—Henkel KGaA; *Int'l*, pg. 614
GERHARD COLLARDIN GMBH—Henkel KGaA; *Int'l*, pg. 609
GESTETNER MANUFACTURING LIMITED—Ricoh Company, Ltd.; *Int'l*, pg. 1114
GIFFORD-HILL COMPANY—Hanson PLC; *Int'l*, pg. 593
GIVAUDAN-ROURE INC.—Roche Holding Ltd.; *Int'l*, pg. 1120
GOLD EAGLE COMPANY; *U.S. Private*, pg. 459
GOLDMAN FINANCIAL GROUP; *U.S. Private*, pg. 461
THE B.F. GOODRICH COMPANY; *U.S. Public*, pg. 751
THE GOODYEAR TIRE & RUBBER COMPANY; *U.S. Public*, pg. 752
GOTEK GMBH—Metallgesellschaft AG; *Int'l*, pg. 861
GRACE CONSTRUCTION PRODUCTS—W.R. Grace & Co.; *U.S. Public*, pg. 755
W.R. GRACE AB—W.R. Grace & Co.; *U.S. Public*, pg. 755
W.R. GRACE LTD.—W.R. Grace & Co.; *U.S. Public*, pg. 756
GREAT LAKES BIOCHEMICAL CO., INC.—Laporte plc; *Int'l*, pg. 802
GREAT LAKES CHEMICAL CORPORATION; *U.S. Public*, pg. 760
GREAT LAKES CHEMICAL (EUROPE) LTD.—Great Lakes Chemical Corporation; *U.S. Public*, pg. 760
GRUPO CEMENTOS DE CHIHUAHUA S.A. DE C.V.; *Int'l*, pg. 573
GUANO-WERKE H GMBH—BASF AG; *Int'l*, pg. 104
GULF STATES ASPHALT COMPANY, INC.; *U.S. Private*, pg. 487
HCI CHEMTECH; *U.S. Private*, pg. 490
HAARMAN & REIMER AROMA CHEMICALS—Bayer AG; *Int'l*, pg. 173
HALLIBURTON COMPANY; *U.S. Public*, pg. 775
HALLIBURTON ENERGY SERVICES, INC.—Halliburton Company; *U.S. Public*, pg. 776
HALTERMANN AG; *Int'l*, pg. 590
HALTERMANN LTD.—Haltermann AG; *Int'l*, pg. 590
HARCROS CHEMICALS INC.—Harrisons & Crosfield plc; *Int'l*, pg. 598
HARDMAN DIVISION OF HARCROS CHEMICALS, INC.—Harrisons & Crosfield plc; *Int'l*, pg. 598
HARRIS SPECIALTY CHEMICAL—Harris Chemical Group, Inc.; *U.S. Private*, pg. 505
HAVILAND ENTERPRISES; *U.S. Private*, pg. 511
HAWKINS CHEMICAL, INC.; *U.S. Public*, pg. 800
HEAT BATH PARK METALLURGICAL CORP.; *U.S. Private*, pg. 518
HEMOCUE AB—Mallinckrodt Inc.; *U.S. Public*, pg. 1040
HENKEL CORPORATION - CHEMICALS GROUP—Henkel KGaA; *Int'l*, pg. 610
HENKEL-DAESUNG CO.—Henkel KGaA; *Int'l*, pg. 612
HENKEL-EYTESA S.A.—Henkel KGaA; *Int'l*, pg. 612
HENKEL (IRELAND) LTD.—Henkel KGaA; *Int'l*, pg. 612
HENKEL KGAA; *Int'l*, pg. 609
HENKEL KIMIANIKA (M) SDN. BHD.—Henkel KGaA; *Int'l*, pg. 614
HENKEL NEW ZEALAND LTD.—Henkel KGaA; *Int'l*, pg. 613
HENKEL NOPCO AB—Henkel KGaA; *Int'l*, pg. 613
HENKEL NOPCO OY—Henkel KGaA; *Int'l*, pg. 614
HENKEL PHILIPPINES INC.—Henkel KGaA; *Int'l*, pg. 614
HENKEL SINGAPORE PTE., LTD.—Henkel KGaA; *Int'l*, pg. 613
HENKEL SURFACE TECHNOLOGIES—Henkel KGaA; *Int'l*, *pg. 610*
HENKEL TAIWAN LTD.—Henkel KGaA; *Int'l*, pg. 613
HEPWORTH MINERALIEN UND CHEMICALIEN GMBH—Hepworth Plc; *Int'l*, pg. 615
HEPWORTH PLC; *Int'l*, pg. 614
OY HERCOFINN AB—Hercules Incorporated; *U.S. Public*, pg. 810
HERCULES AB—Hercules Incorporated; *U.S. Public*, pg. 810
HERCULES B.V.—Hercules Incorporated; *U.S. Public*, pg. 810
HERCULES CHEMICAL CO., INC.; *U.S. Private*, pg. 523
HERCULES DO BRASIL PRODUTOS QUIMICOS LTDA.—Hercules Incorporated; *U.S. Public*, pg. 811
S.A. HERCULES EUROPE N.V.—Hercules Incorporated; *U.S. Public*, pg. 811
HERCULES FRANCE, S.A.—Hercules Incorporated; *U.S. Public*, pg. 811
HERCULES INCORPORATED; *U.S. Public*, pg. 809
HERCULES ITALIA S.P.A.—Hercules Incorporated; *U.S. Public*, pg. 811
HERCULES JAPAN LTD.—Hercules Incorporated; *U.S. Public*, pg. 811
HERCULES KOREA CHEMICAL CO. LTD.—Hercules Incorporated; *U.S. Public*, pg. 811
P.T. HERCULES MAS INDONESIA—Hercules Incorporated; *U.S. Public*, pg. 811
HERCULES OVERSEAS CORPORATION—Hercules Incorporated; *U.S. Public*, pg. 810
HEXCEL CORPORATION; *U.S. Public*, pg. 824
HITACHI CHEMICAL CO., LTD.—Hitachi, Ltd.; *Int'l*, pg. 621
HITACHI KIDEN KOGYO, LTD.—Hitachi, Ltd.; *Int'l*, pg. 621
HOECHST SPECIALTY CHEMICALS GROUP—Hoechst Aktiengesellschaft; *Int'l*, pg. 624
HOLLAND SWEETENER COMPANY V.O.F.—Tosoh Corporation; *Int'l*, pg. 1408
HOLLAND SWEETENER NORTH AMERICA, INC.—Tosoh Corporation; *Int'l*, pg. 1407
HOOKER INDUSTRIES; *U.S. Private*, pg. 538
HOUGHTON INTERNATIONAL INC.; *U.S. Private*, pg. 541
J.M. HUBER CORPORATION; *U.S. Private*, pg. 544
HULS AMERICA INC.—Veba AG; *Int'l*, pg. 1455
HYDRITE CHEMICAL COMPANY; *U.S. Private*, pg. 551
HYPONEX CORPORATION—The Scotts Company; *U.S. Public*, pg. 1447
ICN PHARMACEUTICALS, INC.; *U.S. Public*, pg. 853
ITW FLUID PRODUCTS GROUP—Illinois Tool Works Inc.; *U.S. Public*, pg. 866
INDUSTRIAL ENVIRONMENTAL PRODUCTS, INC.—Oil-Dri Corporation of America; *U.S. Public*, pg. 1215
INDUSTRIAL MAINTENANCE CORP.—Ecolab Inc.; *U.S. Public*, pg. 562
INDUSTRIAS LUBRIZOL S.A. DE C.V.—The Lubrizol Corporation; *U.S. Public*, pg. 1017
INDUSTRIAS QUIMICAS CARABOBO, C.A.—Novartis AG; *Int'l*, pg. 982
INTERCONTINENTAL QUIMICA, S.A. (INTERQUISA)—Compania Espanola de Petroleos, S.A. (CEPSA); *Int'l*, pg. 323
INVIRECHEM—Pace International L.P.; *U.S. Private*, pg. 829
IONICS, INCORPORATED; *U.S. Public*, pg. 912
ISOTECH G.M.B.H.—Novartis AG; *Int'l*, pg. 983
JARCHEM INDUSTRIES, INC.; *U.S. Private*, pg. 582
JOHNSON COMPANY, LTD.—S.C. Johnson & Son, Inc.; *U.S. Private*, pg. 593
JOHNSON NEDERLAND B.V.—S.C. Johnson & Son, Inc.; *U.S. Private*, pg. 593
S.C. JOHNSON & SON, INC.; *U.S. Private*, pg. 592
N.V. JOHNSON WAX BELGIUM S.A.—S.C. Johnson & Son, Inc.; *U.S. Private*, pg. 593
KAO CORPORATION; *Int'l*, pg. 717
KALI-CHEMIE AKTIENGESELLSCHAFT—Solvay S.A.; *Int'l*, pg. 1278
KALI-CHEMIE IBERIA, S.A.—Solvay S.A.; *Int'l*, pg. 1279
KALI UND SALZ BETEILIGUNGS AG—BASF AG; *Int'l*, pg. 104
KAYAKU-NOURY K.K.—Akzo Nobel N.V.; *Int'l*, pg. 47
KEMIRA CHEMICALS OY—Kemira Oy; *Int'l*, pg. 728
KEMIRA CHIMIE S.A.—Kemira Oy; *Int'l*, pg. 728
KEMIRA IRELAND LTD.—Kemira Oy; *Int'l*, pg. 728
KEMIRA WATER TREATMENT, INC.—Kemira Oy; *Int'l*, pg. 728
KENT INDUSTRIES—Premier Farnell plc; *Int'l*, pg. 1068
KERNITE—NCH Corporation; *U.S. Public*, pg. 1145
KIDDE-GRAVINER LTD.—Williams Holdings Plc; *Int'l*, pg. 1500
KILGORE OPERATIONS—Alliant Techsystems; *U.S. Public, pg. 47*
KING INDUSTRIES, INC.; *U.S. Private*, pg. 620
KIWI BRANDS—Sara Lee Corporation; *U.S. Public*, pg. 1433
KOCH NITROGEN DIVISION—Koch Industries, Incorporated; *U.S. Private*, pg. 628
KOEI CHEMICAL COMPANY, LTD.—Sumitomo Chemical Company, Ltd.; *Int'l*, pg. 1311
KOREA JOHNSON CO., LTD.—S.C. Johnson & Son, Inc.; *U.S. Private*, pg. 593
KRONOS EUROPE, INC.—Contran Corporation; *U.S. Private*, pg. 271
KRONOS, INC.—Contran Corporation; *U.S. Private*, pg. 270
KRONOS SA/NV—Contran Corporation; *U.S. Private*, pg. 271
KVAERNER ROSENBERG A/S KVAERNER EGERSUND—Kvaerner a.s.a.; *Int'l*, pg. 769
LSB CHEMICAL CORP.—LSB Industries, Inc.; *U.S. Public*, pg. 971
LSB INDUSTRIES, INC.; *U.S. Public*, pg. 970
LA-CO INDUSTRIES MARKAL COMPANY; *U.S. Private*, pg. 640
LA JOHNSON FRANCAISE S.A.—S.C. Johnson & Son, Inc.; *U.S. Private*, pg. 593
LABORA MANNHEIM GMBH FUR LABORTECHNIK—Corange Limited; *Int'l*, pg. 331
LANE LIMITED—Rothmans UK Holdings Limited; *Int'l*, pg. 1129
LAPORTE ABSORBENTS EUROPE—Laporte plc; *Int'l*, pg. 802
LAPORTE ELECTRONICS—Laporte plc; *Int'l*, pg. 802
LAPORTE INC.—Laporte plc; *Int'l*, pg. 802
LAPORTE PLC; *Int'l*, pg. 801
LAPORTE WOOD PRESERVATION—Laporte plc; *Int'l*, pg. 802
LEISURE TIME INDUSTRIES—Laporte plc; *Int'l*, pg. 802
LITHION, INC.—Ener-Tek International Corporation; *U.S. Private*, pg. 376
LONZA INC.—Alusuisse-Lonza Holding Ltd.; *Int'l*, pg. 67
LUBRASYSTEMS—NCH Corporation; *U.S. Public*, pg. 1145
MBT AUSTRIA GESELLSCHAFT M.B.H.—Viag AG; *Int'l*, pg. 1465
MBT DE VENEZUELA, C.A.—Viag AG; *Int'l*, pg. 1465
MBT (NEW ZEALAND) LTD.—Viag AG; *Int'l*, pg. 1465
MACDERMID INCORPORATED; *U.S. Public*, pg. 1029
MACDERMID SYSTEMS, INC.—MacDermid Incorporated; *U.S. Public*, pg. 1030
MAGNOMIN-GENERAL MINING S.A.—RGP Holding, Inc.; *U.S. Private*, pg. 904
MALLINCKRODT BAKER INC.—Mallinckrodt Inc.; *U.S. Public*, pg. 1039
MANCHEM LTD.—Rhone-Poulenc S.A.; *Int'l*, pg. 1113
MANTEK—NCH Corporation; *U.S. Public*, pg. 1145
MARCHON ESPANOLA S.A.—Tenneco Inc.; *U.S. Public*, pg. 1580
MARCHON FRANCE S.A.—Tenneco Inc.; *U.S. Public*, pg. 1580
MARCHON HELLAS LIMITED—Tenneco Inc.; *U.S. Public*, pg. 1580
MARCHON ITALIANA S.P.A.—Tenneco Inc.; *U.S. Public*, pg. 1580
MARTIN ELECTRONICS, INC.; *U.S. Private*, pg. 709
MASTER BUILDERS INC.—Viag AG; *Int'l*, pg. 1465
MASTER BUILDERS TECHNOLOGIES LTD.—Viag AG; *Int'l*, pg. 1465
MCGEAN-ROHCO, INC.; *U.S. Private*, pg. 721
MERCK & CO., INC.; *U.S. Public*, pg. 1090
MESSER GRIESHEIM GMBH—Hoechst Aktiengesellschaft; *Int'l*, pg. 626
MET-PRO CORPORATION; *U.S. Public*, pg. 1100
METAL PORTUGUESA S.A.—Ferro Corporation; *U.S. Public*, pg. 619
METALLGESELLSCHAFT AG; *Int'l*, pg. 860
MITSUBISHI CHEMICAL CORPORATION; *Int'l*, pg. 870
MITSUBISHI MONSANTO CHEMICAL CO.—Monsanto Company; *U.S. Public*, pg. 1125
MOHAWK LABORATORIES DIV.—NCH Corporation; *U.S. Public*, pg. 1145
MOLECULAR PACKAGING SYSTEMS, INC.—IGI, Inc.; *U.S. Public*, pg. 855
MONSANTO DO BRASIL LTDA. (MOBRA S.A.)—Monsanto Company; *U.S. Public*, pg. 1125
MORFECOR, C.A.—Morton International Inc.; *U.S. Public*, pg. 1135
MORGAN CRUCIBLE CO. PLC; *Int'l*, pg. 890
MORTON INTERNATIONAL INC.; *U.S. Public*, pg. 1134
N.V. MORTON THIOKOL S.A.—Morton International Inc.; *U.S. Public*, pg. 1136
NFE CO., LTD.—Ferro Corporation; *U.S. Public*, pg. 620
NATIONAL CHEMSEARCH—NCH Corporation; *U.S. Public, pg. 1145*
NATIONAL CHEMSEARCH OF CANADA LTD.—NCH Corporation; *U.S. Public*, pg. 1145
NATIONAL STARCH AND CHEMICAL COMPANY—Unilever Plc; *Int'l*, pg. 1435
NEWELL CO.; *U.S. Public*, pg. 1176
NIGU CHEMIE-BETEILIGUNGS GMBH—Viag AG; *Int'l*, pg. 1465
NIPPON MACDERMID K.K.—MacDermid Incorporated; *U.S. Public*, pg. 1030
NIPPON QUAKER CHEMICAL, LTD.—Quaker Chemical Corporation; *U.S. Public*, pg. 1346
NISSAN FERRO ORGANIC CHEMICAL CO. LTD.—Ferro Corporation; *U.S. Public*, pg. 620
NOPCO INDUSTRIAL S.A. DE C.V.—Henkel KGaA; *Int'l*, pg. 614
NOPCO ITALIANA SPA—Henkel KGaA; *Int'l*, pg. 612
NORDIC SYNTHESIS AB—Cambrex Corporation; *U.S. Public*, pg. 297
NORDISK BYGGE KEMI A/S—Viag AG; *Int'l*, pg. 1466
NORTH AMERICAN SALT COMPANY—Harris Chemical Group, Inc.; *U.S. Private*, pg. 505
NORTON-ALCOA PROPPANTS—Saint-Gobain; *Int'l*, pg. 1174
NORTON CHEMICAL PROCESS PRODUCTS (EUROPE) LIMITED—Saint-Gobain; *Int'l*, pg. 1175
NOVARTIS AG; *Int'l*, pg. 971
NOVILLE; *U.S. Private*, pg. 808
OAKITE PRODUCTS, INC.—Metallgesellschaft AG; *Int'l*, pg. 861
OCTAGON PROCESS INC.; *U.S. Private*, pg. 811
OESTERREICHISCH HERAKLITH, A.G.—RGP Holding, Inc.; *U.S. Private*, pg. 904
OIL-DRI CORPORATION OF AMERICA; *U.S. Public*, pg. 1214
OIL-DRI CORPORATION OF GEORGIA—Oil-Dri Corporation of America; *U.S. Public*, pg. 1215
OIL-DRI PRODUCTION CO.—Oil-Dri Corporation of America; *U.S. Public*, pg. 1215
OIL-DRI (U.K.) LTD.—Oil-Dri Corporation of America; *U.S. Public*, pg. 1215
OLD WORLD AUTOMOTIVE PRODUCTS—Old World Industries, Inc.; *U.S. Private*, pg. 814
OLD WORLD INDUSTRIES, INC.; *U.S. Private*, pg. 814
OLDHAM FRANCE SA—BTR plc; *Int'l*, pg. 125
OMNITECHNIC GMBH—Henkel KGaA; *Int'l*, pg. 610

PCS NITROGEN—Potash Corporation of Saskatchewan Inc.; Int'l, pg. 1064
PPF INTERNATIONAL LIMITED—Unilever Plc; Int'l, pg. 1434
PACE INTERNATIONAL L.P.; U.S. Private, pg. 829
S.A. PAPER CHEMICALS (PROPRIETARY), LIMITED—Tenneco Inc.; U.S. Public, pg. 1580
PARKER CHEMICAL COMPANY PTE. LTD.—Henkel KGaA; Int'l, pg. 613
PARKER CHEMICAL CORP. LTD.—Henkel KGaA; Int'l, pg. 613
PETRESA INTERNATIONAL N.V.—Compania Espanola de Petroleos, S.A. (CEPSA); Int'l, pg. 323
PETROLEOS MEXICANOS; Int'l, pg. 1046
PETROLEUM SPECIALTIES GROUP—Witco Corporation; U.S. Public, pg. 1774
PETROQUIMICA ESPANOLA, S.A. (PETRESA)—Compania Espanola de Petroleos, S.A. (CEPSA); Int'l, pg. 323
PHILIPPINE REFINING COMPANY INC.—Unilever Plc; Int'l, pg. 1438
PHILLIPS PETROLEUM COMPANY; U.S. Public, pg. 1290
PILIPINAS KAO INC.—Kao Corporation; Int'l, pg. 718
POLAROME INTERNATIONAL; U.S. Private, pg. 874
P.T. POLEKAO INDONESIA CHEMICALS—Kao Corporation; Int'l, pg. 718
POLO INDUSTRIA E COMERCIO LTDA.—Hercules Incorporated; U.S. Public, pg. 811
POLYFIBRON TECHNOLOGIES CORP.; U.S. Private, pg. 875
POLYKEN TECHNOLOGIES—Tyco International Ltd.; U.S. Public, pg. 1647
POLYMER CHEMICALS GROUP—Witco Corporation; U.S. Public, pg. 1774
POLYMER PLASTICS CORPORATION; U.S. Private, pg. 875
PONCE SALT INDUSTRIES CORP.—Morton International Inc.; U.S. Public, pg. 1135
PREMIER FARNELL—Premier Farnell plc; Int'l, pg. 1068
PREMIER FARNELL PLC; Int'l, pg. 1068
PRODORITE LTD.—Ameron International Corporation; U.S. Public, pg. 99
PRODUTEC HOUGHTON S.A.—Houghton International Inc.; U.S. Private, pg. 541
PRONOVA OLEOCHEMICALS A.S.—Norsk Hydro a.s; Int'l, pg. 961
PURITAN/CHURCHILL CHEMICAL COMPANY; U.S. Private, pg. 895
QUAKER CHEMICAL (AUSTRALASIA) PTY. LTD.—Quaker Chemical Corporation; U.S. Public, pg. 1346
QUAKER CHEMICAL B.V.—Quaker Chemical Corporation; U.S. Public, pg. 1346
QUAKER CHEMICAL CORPORATION; U.S. Public, pg. 1346
QUAKER CHEMICAL LIMITED—Quaker Chemical Corporation; U.S. Public, pg. 1347
QUAKER CHEMICAL, S.A.—Quaker Chemical Corporation; U.S. Public, pg. 1347
QUAKER CHEMICAL S.A.—Quaker Chemical Corporation; U.S. Public, pg. 1347
QUAKER CHEMICAL SOUTH AFRICA (PTY.) LTD.—Quaker Chemical Corporation; U.S. Public, pg. 1347
QUANTIC INDUSTRIES INC.—Quantic Industries, Inc.; U.S. Private, pg. 899
QUIMI-KAO S.A. DE C.V.—Kao Corporation; Int'l, pg. 718
QUIMICA NALCO DE COLOMBIA, S.A.—Nalco Chemical Company; U.S. Public, pg. 1151
QUIMICA PARKER S.A. DE C.V.—Henkel KGaA; Int'l, pg. 614
QUIMICA S.A. DE C.V.—Henkel KGaA; Int'l, pg. 614
QUIMICA S.C. JOHNSON & SON CHILENA S.A.C.I.—S.C. Johnson & Son, Inc.; U.S. Private, pg. 593
RPM BELGIUM N.V.—RPM, Inc.; U.S. Public, pg. 1357
RADIATOR SPECIALTY COMPANY; U.S. Private, pg. 906
RASCHIG AG (FRANCE)—PMC, Inc.; U.S. Private, pg. 827
RASCHIG GMBH—PMC, Inc.; U.S. Private, pg. 827
WILLIAM B. REILY & CO., INC.; U.S. Private, pg. 919
REPUBLIC ENVIRONMENTAL SYSTEMS LTD.—Republic Industries, Inc.; U.S. Public, pg. 1380
REPUBLIC POWDERED METALS, INC.—RPM, Inc.; U.S. Public, pg. 1357
RESINAS SINTETICAS, S.A. (RESISA)—Compania Espanola de Petroleos, S.A. (CEPSA); Int'l, pg. 323
RHODIA S.A.—Rhone-Poulenc S.A.; Int'l, pg. 1112
RHONE-POULENC RORER LTD.—Rhone-Poulenc S.A.; Int'l, pg. 1110
RHONE-POULENC SPECIALTY CHEMICALS—Rhone-Poulenc S.A.; Int'l, pg. 1110
RHONE POULENC - WATER TREATMENT CHEMICALS—Rhone-Poulenc S.A.; Int'l, pg. 1112
RICHARDSON-VICKS, INC.—The Procter & Gamble Company; U.S. Public, pg. 1331
ROBERTET, INC.—Robertet S.A.; Int'l, pg. 1119
ROCHE AG—Roche Holding Ltd.; Int'l, pg. 1120
ROHM GMBH—Veba AG; Int'l, pg. 1454
RUHR PULVERLACK G.M.B.H.—Ferro Corporation; U.S. Public, pg. 620
RUST-OLEUM CORPORATION—RPM, Inc.; U.S. Public, pg. 1358
RUST-OLEUM NEDERLAND B.V.—RPM, Inc.; U.S. Public, pg. 1358
SCM CHEMICALS - EUROPE—Hanson PLC; Int'l, pg. 593
SKS TECHNIK SAURE UND KORROSIONSSCHUTZ GMBH—Viag AG; Int'l, pg. 1465
SKW BAUWERKSTOFFE PIESTERITZ GMBH—Viag AG; Int'l, pg. 1465
STP PRODUCTS, INC.—First Brands Corporation; U.S. Public, pg. 627
SAKATA INX CORPORATION—Sumitomo Chemical Company, Ltd.; Int'l, pg. 1311
SALES DEL ISTMO, S.A. DE C.V.—CYDSA S.A.; Int'l, pg. 247
SALZGEWINNUNGSGESELLSCHAFT WESTFALEN MBH—Solvay S.A.; Int'l, pg. 1279
SAN NOPCO LTD.—Henkel KGaA; Int'l, pg. 614
SANDOZ AUSTRALIA PTY. LTD.—Novartis AG; Int'l, pg. 984
SANDOZ CHEMICALS (THAILAND) LTD.—Novartis AG; Int'l, pg. 984
SANDOZ PRODUCTS LTD.—Novartis AG; Int'l, pg. 985
SANDOZ PRODUCTS (SWITZERLAND) LTD.—Novartis AG; Int'l, pg. 972
SARA LEE/DE—Sara Lee Corporation; U.S. Public, pg. 1434
R.P. SCHERER NORTH AMERICA—R.P. Scherer Corporation; U.S. Public, pg. 1438
N.V. SCHERING S.A./BELGIEN—Schering AG; Int'l, pg. 1204
SCHMIDT & HAGEN GMBH & CO. KG—Henkel KGaA; Int'l, pg. 610
SCIOM S.A.—Henkel KGaA; Int'l, pg. 614
L.M. SCOFIELD COMPANY; U.S. Private, pg. 976
SEALED AIR CORPORATION; U.S. Public, pg. 1450
SEALED AIR SVENSKA A.B.—Sealed Air Corporation; U.S. Public, pg. 1451
SEKISUI CHEMICAL CO., LTD.; Int'l, pg. 1219
SENTRY POLYMERS, INC.—RPM, Inc.; U.S. Public, pg. 1357
SEQUA CORPORATION; U.S. Public, pg. 1458
SHELL NEDERLAND CHEMIE—Royal Dutch/Shell Group of Companies; Int'l, pg. 1135
SHIPLEY CO., LLC—Rohm and Haas Company; U.S. Public, pg. 1403
SICHEL-WERKE GMBH—Henkel KGaA; Int'l, pg. 610
SIEGERT & CIE GMBH—Henkel KGaA; Int'l, pg. 610
SIERRACIN CORPORATION; U.S. Private, pg. 999
SIFTO CANADA, INC.—Harris Chemical Group, Inc.; U.S. Private, pg. 505
SIKA CORPORATION—Sika Finanz AG; Int'l, pg. 1249
SINOCHEM INTERNATIONAL PETROLEUM CO. LTD.; Int'l, pg. 1254
A.O. SMITH CORPORATION; U.S. Public, pg. 1476
SNOWMAX TECHNOLOGIES—Eastman Kodak Company; U.S. Public, pg. 551
SOCIETE FINANCIERE ET COMMERCIALE DE CADILLAC—Warner-Lambert Company; U.S. Public, pg. 1739
SOCIETE INDUSTRIELLE ET SALINES DE BAYONNE S.A.—Solvay S.A.; Int'l, pg. 1279
SONOCO ADHESIVES DIVISION—Sonoco Products Company; U.S. Public, pg. 1486
SPHINX CHEMICALS—Henkel KGaA; Int'l, pg. 614
STATIONERY PRODUCTS DIVISION—The Gillette Company; U.S. Public, pg. 744
STAVELEY INDUSTRIES PLC; Int'l, pg. 1298
STEPAN COMPANY; U.S. Public, pg. 1514
STEPAN EUROPE—Stepan Company; U.S. Public, pg. 1514
JACOB STERN & SONS, INC.; U.S. Private, pg. 1041
SUMIKA-HERCULES CO. LTD.—Hercules Incorporated; U.S. Public, pg. 811
SUMITOMO DOW LTD.—Sumitomo Chemical Company, Ltd.; Int'l, pg. 1311
SUN CHEMICAL CORP.—Dainippon Ink & Chemicals, Inc.; Int'l, pg. 370
OY SUOMEN HENKEL AB—Henkel KGaA; Int'l, pg. 614
SUPACRYL (PTY.) LTD.—Veba AG; Int'l, pg. 1456
SUPREME SALT COMPANY LIMITED—Tomkins PLC; Int'l, pg. 1396
SURCO PRODUCTS, INC.; U.S. Private, pg. 1056
SVENSKA JOHNSON'S VAX AB—S.C. Johnson & Son, Inc.; U.S. Private, pg. 594
T C MANUFACTURING COMPANY, INC.; U.S. Private, pg. 1062
TAOKA CHEMICAL CO., LTD.—Sumitomo Chemical Company, Ltd.; Int'l, pg. 1311
TECHNIC INCORPORATED; U.S. Private, pg. 1071
TECNIQUIMIA MEXICANA S.A. DE C.V.—Quaker Chemical Corporation; U.S. Public, pg. 1347
TEIJIN-HERCULES LTD.—Hercules Incorporated; U.S. Public, pg. 811
TENNECO MALROS LTD.—Tenneco Inc.; U.S. Public, pg. 1580
TENNECO TRANSICOL B.V.—Tenneco Inc.; U.S. Public, pg. 1580
TENNECO UNITED KINGDOM HOLDINGS LIMITED—Tenneco Inc.; U.S. Public, pg. 1580
TENSID CHEMIE VERTRIEBSGESELLSCHAFT MBH—BASF AG; Int'l, pg. 104
TERANOL AG—Roche Holding Ltd.; Int'l, pg. 1120
THAI MASTER BUILDERS CO. LTD.—Novartis AG; Int'l, pg. 986
THE THOMPSON'S COMPANY—The Sherwin-Williams Company; U.S. Public, pg. 1466
3M; U.S. Public, pg. 1604
A.M. TODD COMPANY; U.S. Private, pg. 1089
TORAY INDUSTRIES, INC.; Int'l, pg. 1399
TOSOH CORPORATION; Int'l, pg. 1407
TOYO-MORTON, LTD.—Morton International Inc.; U.S. Public, pg. 1136
TRICON INDUSTRIES, INC.; U.S. Private, pg. 1102
TRICOSAL GMBH—Henkel KGaA; Int'l, pg. 610
TROPONWERKE GMBH & CO., KG—Bayer AG; Int'l, pg. 175
TUNGSTONE BATTERIES LTD.—BTR plc; Int'l, pg. 124
TURTLE WAX, INC.; U.S. Private, pg. 1110
UNICHEMA CHEMICALS LTD.—Unilever Plc; Int'l, pg. 1434
UNICHEMA-CHEMIE B.V.—Unilever Plc; Int'l, pg. 1438
UNICHEMA CHEMIE G.M.B.H.—Unilever Plc; Int'l, pg. 1438
VDL GROEP BV; Int'l, pg. 1444
VAN NEERBOS-PCI B.V.—Viag AG; Int'l, pg. 1466
VERATEC DIVISION—International Paper Company; U.S. Public, pg. 904
VININGS INDUSTRIES INC.; U.S. Private, pg. 1141
VULNAX INTERNATIONAL LTD.—Akzo Nobel N.V.; Int'l, pg. 47
WARNER-LAMBERT COMPANY; U.S. Public, pg. 1738
WARREN DISTRIBUTION, INC.; U.S. Private, pg. 1151
WAVERLEY MINERAL CORPORATION—Laporte plc; Int'l, pg. 803
WEBER MARKING SYSTEMS, INC.; U.S. Private, pg. 1157
WEST CHEMICAL PRODUCTS, INC.—Wechco, Inc.; U.S. Private, pg. 1158
WEST PENETONE CORPORATION—Wechco, Inc.; U.S. Private, pg. 1158
WESTVACO CORPORATION; U.S. Public, pg. 1762
WESTVACO CORPORATION-CHEMICAL DIV.—Westvaco Corporation; U.S. Public, pg. 1762
WHATMAN INC.—Whatman plc; Int'l, pg. 1498
WHITTAKER, CLARK & DANIELS, INC.; U.S. Private, pg. 1174
WISCONSIN PHARMACAL CO., INC.; U.S. Private, pg. 1185
WYNN OIL COMPANY—Wynn's International, Inc.; U.S. Public, pg. 1782
WYNN'S INTERNATIONAL, INC.; U.S. Public, pg. 1782
YARDNEY TECHNICAL PRODUCTS, INC.—Ener-Tek International Corporation; U.S. Private, pg. 376
YORKSHIRE CHEMICALS PLC; Int'l, pg. 1522

2911 — PETROLEUM REFINING

AGIP DEUTSCHLAND AG—ENI S.p.A.; Int'l, pg. 428
AGIP PETROLI—ENI S.p.A.; Int'l, pg. 428
AGIP SPA—ENI S.p.A.; Int'l, pg. 428
ABU DHABI COMPANY FOR ONSHORE OIL OPERATIONS—Royal Dutch/Shell Group of Companies; Int'l, pg. 1140
AFRICAINE DE RAFFINAGE—Royal Dutch/Shell Group of Companies; Int'l, pg. 1136
ALASKA REFINERY—Mapco Inc.; U.S. Public, pg. 1042
ALFA, S.A. DE C.V.; Int'l, pg. 56
LANDULPHO ALVES REFINERY—Petrobras - Petroleo Brasileiro S.A.; Int'l, pg. 1042
AMERADA HESS CORPORATION; U.S. Public, pg. 65
AMOCO CORPORATION; U.S. Public, pg. 101
AMOCO OIL COMPANY—Amoco Corporation; U.S. Public, pg. 102
AMOCO OIL REFINERY—Amoco Corporation; U.S. Public, pg. 103
ANADOLU TASFIYEHANESI—Royal Dutch/Shell Group of Companies; Int'l, pg. 1141
ARCO PRODUCTS CO.—Atlantic Richfield Company; U.S. Public, pg. 144
ARCTIC SLOPE REGIONAL CORPORATION; U.S. Private, pg. 80
ASBURY GRAPHITE INC. OF CALIFORNIA—Asbury Carbons, Inc.; U.S. Private, pg. 87
ASBURY LOUISIANA, INC.—Asbury Carbons, Inc.; U.S. Private, pg. 87
ASFALTOS ESPANOLES, S.A. (ASESA)—Compania Espanola de Petroleos, S.A. (CEPSA); Int'l, pg. 323
ASPHALT PLANT—Petrobras - Petroleo Brasileiro S.A.; Int'l, pg. 1042
ATLANTIC RICHFIELD COMPANY; U.S. Public, pg. 144
BHP HAWAII, INC.—The Broken Hill Proprietary Company Limited; Int'l, pg. 225
BP AUSTRALIA LTD.—The British Petroleum Company P.L.C.; Int'l, pg. 220
BP FRANCE—The British Petroleum Company P.L.C.; Int'l, pg. 220
BP INTERNATIONAL LTD.—The British Petroleum Company P.L.C.; Int'l, pg. 220
BP OIL CO.—The British Petroleum Company P.L.C.; Int'l, pg. 220
BP OIL INTERNATIONAL LIMITED—The British Petroleum Company P.L.C.; Int'l, pg. 220
BAKER PETROLITE CORPORATION—Baker Hughes Incorporated; U.S. Public, pg. 166
BASIS PETROLEUM, INC.—Valero Energy Corporation; U.S. Public, pg. 1704
BELGIAN SHELL, S.A.—Royal Dutch/Shell Group of Companies; Int'l, pg. 1138
THE BRITISH PETROLEUM COMPANY P.L.C.; Int'l, pg. 219
BRUNEI SHELL PETROLEUM CO SDN BHD—Royal Dutch/Shell Group of Companies; Int'l, pg. 1139
BURMAH CASTROL CHEMICALS LTD.—Burmah Castrol plc; Int'l, pg. 234
CEDIPSA—Compania Espanola de Petroleos, S.A. (CEPSA); Int'l, pg. 323
CEPSA CIA. PORTUGUESA DE PETROLEOS, LDA.—Compania Espanola de Petroleos, S.A. (CEPSA); Int'l, pg. 323
CEPSA ESTACIONES DE SERVICIO, S.A.—Compania Espanola de Petroleos, S.A. (CEPSA); Int'l, pg. 323
CEPSA GIBRALTAR, LTD.—Compania Espanola de Petroleos, S.A. (CEPSA); Int'l, pg. 323
CEPSA ITALIA, S.P.A.—Compania Espanola de Petroleos, S.A. (CEPSA); Int'l, pg. 323
CEPSA U.K., LTD.—Compania Espanola de Petroleos, S.A. (CEPSA); Int'l, pg. 323
CMI OIL CORPORATION—CMI Corporation; U.S. Public, pg. 279
CANADIAN ROXY PETROLEUM LTD.—Westcoast Energy Inc.; Int'l, pg. 1492
CASTROL LTD.—Burmah Castrol plc; Int'l, pg. 234
CASTROL OVERSEAS LTD.—Burmah Castrol plc; Int'l, pg. 234
CASTROL (U.K.) LIMITED—Burmah Castrol plc; Int'l, pg. 234
CENEX, INC.; U.S. Private, pg. 221
CHEVRON CORPORATION; U.S. Public, pg. 347
CHEVRON USA PRODUCTS CO.—Chevron Corporation; U.S. Public, pg. 348
CHINESE PETROLEUM CORPORATION; Int'l, pg. 286
CIT-CON OIL CORPORATION—Petroleos de Venezuela S.A.; Int'l, pg. 1045
CITGO CARIBBEAN CORPORATION—Petroleos de Venezuela S.A.; Int'l, pg. 1045

CITGO PETROLEUM CORPORATION—Petroleos de Venezuela S.A.; *Int'l*, pg. 1045
CLARK OIL & REFINING CORPORATION-BLUE ISLAND REFINERY—Clark Refining & Marketing Inc.; *U.S. Private*, pg. 243
CLARK OIL & REFINING CORPORATION-WOOD RIVER REFINERY—Clark Refining & Marketing Inc.; *U.S. Private*, pg. 243
CLARK REFINING & MARKETING INC.; *U.S. Private*, pg. 243
COASTAL (BERMUDA) PETROLEUM LIMITED—The Coastal Corporation; *U.S. Public*, pg. 390
THE COASTAL CORPORATION; *U.S. Public*, pg. 389
COASTAL REFINING & MARKETING—The Coastal Corporation; *U.S. Public*, pg. 390
COASTAL STATES PETROLEUM (U.K.) LIMITED—The Coastal Corporation; *U.S. Public*, pg. 391
COLAS EAST AFRICA—Royal Dutch/Shell Group of Companies; *Int'l*, pg. 1136
COMMANDER OIL CORPORATION; *U.S. Private*, pg. 257
COMPANIA ESPANOLA DE PETROLEOS, S.A. (CEPSA); *Int'l*, pg. 323
CONOCO OIL REFINERY—Du Pont (E.I. Du Pont De Nemours & Co.); *U.S. Public*, pg. 531
CROWN CENTRAL PETROLEUM CORPORATION; *U.S. Public*, pg. 462
CROWNCEN INTL. N.V.—Crown Central Petroleum Corporation; *U.S. Public*, pg. 462
DSM N.V.; *Int'l*, pg. 352
A/S DANSK SHELL—Royal Dutch/Shell Group of Companies; *Int'l*, pg. 1138
DEUTSCHE SHELL AG—Royal Dutch/Shell Group of Companies; *Int'l*, pg. 1138
CIA. DISTRIBUIDORA DE PETROLEOS, S.A. (CEDIPSA)—Compania Espanola de Petroleos, S.A. (CEPSA); *Int'l*, pg. 323
DISTRIBUIDORA DE PRODUCTOS PETROLIFEROS, S.A. (DISPESA)—Compania Espanola de Petroleos, S.A. (CEPSA); *Int'l*, pg. 323
DITEP—Petrobras - Petroleo Brasileiro S.A.; *Int'l*, pg. 1042
DITEQ—Petrobras - Petroleo Brasileiro S.A.; *Int'l*, pg. 1042
DRAKE PETROLEUM COMPANY, INC.—Warren Equities Inc.; *U.S. Private*, pg. 1151
DU PONT (E.I. DU PONT DE NEMOURS & CO.); *U.S. Public*, pg. 530
DUSSEK CAMPBELL, INC.—Burmah Castrol plc; *Int'l*, pg. 234
ENI S.P.A.; *Int'l*, pg. 428
ELF ERDOEL UNDERDGAS DEUTSCHLAND GMBH—Elf Aquitane; *Int'l*, pg. 446
ELF FRANCE—Elf Aquitane; *Int'l*, pg. 445
ELF SANOFI S.A.—Elf Aquitane; *Int'l*, pg. 445
ERGON, INC.; *U.S. Private*, pg. 380
CIA. ESPANOLA DE PETROLEOS ATLANTICO, S.A.—Compania Espanola de Petroleos, S.A. (CEPSA); *Int'l*, pg. 323
ESSO INC.—Exxon Corporation; *U.S. Public*, pg. 602
EXXON BIOMEDICAL SCIENCES INC.—Exxon Corporation; *U.S. Public*, pg. 601
EXXON COMPANY, U.S.A.—Exxon Corporation; *U.S. Public*, pg. 601
EXXON CORPORATION; *U.S. Public*, pg. 601
FINA, INC.—Petrofina S.A.; *Int'l*, pg. 1044
FINA OIL & CHEMICAL CO. (BIG SPRING)—Petrofina S.A.; *Int'l*, pg. 1044
FINA OLEOCHEMICALS N.V.—Petrofina S.A.; *Int'l*, pg. 1043
FINA PETROLEOS DE ANGOLA, S.A.R.L.—Petrofina S.A.; *Int'l*, pg. 1044
FRONTIER HOLDINGS INC.—Wainoco Oil Corporation; *U.S. Public*, pg. 1732
FRONTIER OIL CORPORATION—Wainoco Oil Corporation; *U.S. Public*, pg. 1732
FRONTIER REFINING, INC.—Wainoco Oil Corporation; *U.S. Public*, pg. 1732
GK GESELLSCHAFT FUER KOHLEVERFLUESSIGUNG MBH—Saarbergwerke Aktiengesellschaft; *Int'l*, pg. 1166
GSF ENERGY INC.—Air Products and Chemicals, Inc.; *U.S. Public*, pg. 31
GARY-WILLIAMS ENERGY CORPORATION; *U.S. Private*, pg. 440
GETTY GAS GATHERING, INC.—Texaco Inc.; *U.S. Public*, pg. 1583
GETTY OIL EXPLORATION CO.—Texaco Inc.; *U.S. Public*, pg. 1583
GIANT INDUSTRIES ARIZONA, INC.—Giant Industries Inc.; *U.S. Public*, pg. 742
GIANT INDUSTRIES INC.; *U.S. Public*, pg. 741
GIANT REFINING COMPANY—Giant Industries Inc.; *U.S. Public*, pg. 742
GIRARD POINT REFINERY—Sun Company, Inc.; *U.S. Public*, pg. 1530
GOLDEN WEST REFINING COMPANY—Thrifty Oil Co.; *U.S. Private*, pg. 1084
GREAT LAKES CARBON CORP.—Horsehead Industries, Inc.; *U.S. Private*, pg. 540
GROWMARK, INC.; *U.S. Private*, pg. 484
HALTERMANN AG; *Int'l*, pg. 590
HARBERT CORPORATION; *U.S. Private*, pg. 500
HAWAIIAN INDEPENDENT REFINERY, INC.—The Broken Hill Proprietary Company Limited; *Int'l*, pg. 225
HI-PURE CHEMICALS, INC.—Olin Corporation; *U.S. Public*, pg. 1219
HOLLY CORPORATION; *U.S. Public*, pg. 830
HONAM OIL REFINERY CO. LTD.—LG Group; *Int'l*, pg. 779
HONDO OIL & GAS COMPANY—Lonrho plc; *Int'l*, pg. 818
HUNT OIL COMPANY; *U.S. Private*, pg. 548
HUNTSMAN CORPORATION—Huntsman Corporation; *U.S. Private*, pg. 549
HUSKY OIL INTL. LTD.—Husky Oil Ltd.; *Int'l*, pg. 640
HUSKY OIL LTD.; *Int'l*, pg. 640
HUSKY OIL OPERATIONS LTD.—Husky Oil Ltd.; *Int'l*, pg. 640
ITT BARTON INSTRUMENTS—ITT Industries, Inc.; *U.S. Public*, pg. 860
IMPERIAL OIL LIMITED—Exxon Corporation; *U.S. Public*, pg. 602
INTERCONTINENTAL QUIMICA, S.A. (INTERQUISA)—Compania Espanola de Petroleos, S.A. (CEPSA); *Int'l*, pg. 323
INTERNATIONAL MARKETING & REFINING DIVISION—Mobil Oil Corporation; *U.S. Public*, pg. 1118
JAPAN ENERGY CORPORATION; *Int'l*, pg. 702
KAOHSIUNG REFINERY—Chinese Petroleum Corporation; *Int'l*, pg. 286
KENYA PETROLEUM REFINERIES—Royal Dutch/Shell Group of Companies; *Int'l*, pg. 1136
KENYON OIL COMPANY, INC.—Warren Equities Inc.; *U.S. Private*, pg. 1151
KOCH INDUSTRIES, INCORPORATED; *U.S. Private*, pg. 628
KOHAP PETROCHEMICAL CORPORATION—KOHAP Group; *Int'l*, pg. 742
KRAFFT, S.A.—Compania Espanola de Petroleos, S.A. (CEPSA); *Int'l*, pg. 323
KUKDONG SHELL OIL CO., LTD.—Royal Dutch/Shell Group of Companies; *Int'l*, pg. 1140
KUWAIT PETROLEUM CORPORATION; *Int'l*, pg. 764
KYOKUTO PETROLEUM INDUSTRIES LTD.—Mitsui & Co., Ltd.; *Int'l*, pg. 877
HENRIQUE LAGE REFINERY—Petrobras - Petroleo Brasileiro S.A.; *Int'l*, pg. 1042
LINDSEY OIL REFINERY—Petrofina S.A.; *Int'l*, pg. 1043
LITTLE AMERICA REFINING, INC.—Sinclair Oil Corp.; *U.S. Private*, pg. 1003
THE LOUISIANA LAND AND EXPLORATION COMPANY—Burlington Resources Inc.; *U.S. Public*, pg. 269
LUBRICANTES DEL SUR, S.A. (LUBRISUR)—Compania Espanola de Petroleos, S.A. (CEPSA); *Int'l*, pg. 323
LUBRICATION CONSULTANTS, L.L.C.—Mid-Kansas Co-op Association; *U.S. Private*, pg. 743
LUBRINER (LUBRICATES DEL NERVION, S.A.)—Compania Espanola de Petroleos, S.A. (CEPSA); *Int'l*, pg. 323
LYONDELL PETROCHEMICAL COMPANY; *U.S. Public*, pg. 1022
MFA OIL COMPANY; *U.S. Private*, pg. 687
MAPCO INC.; *U.S. Public*, pg. 1042
MAPCO PETROLEUM INC.—Mapco Inc.; *U.S. Public*, pg. 1042
MARATHON ASHLAND PETROLEUM LLC—Ashland, Inc.; *U.S. Public*, pg. 139
MARATHON ASHLAND PETROLEUM LLC—USX Corporation; *U.S. Public*, pg. 1662
MARATHON ASHLAND PETROLEUM LLC RETAIN MARKETING—USX Corporation; *U.S. Public*, pg. 1662
MCKEE COMPLEX—Ultramar Diamond Shamrock Corporation; *U.S. Public*, pg. 1663
MID-VALLEY OIL COMPANY, INC.—Warren Equities Inc.; *U.S. Private*, pg. 1151
MITSUI OIL CO., LTD.—Mitsui & Co., Ltd.; *Int'l*, pg. 877
MOBIL OIL COMPANY, LTD.—Mobil Oil Corporation; *U.S. Public*, pg. 1119
MOBIL OIL CORPORATION; *U.S. Public*, pg. 1118
MOBIL SOUTH, MARKETING & REFINING DIVISION—Mobil Oil Corporation; *U.S. Public*, pg. 1118
MONT BELVIEU OPERATIONS—Ultramar Diamond Shamrock Corporation; *U.S. Public*, pg. 1663
MONTANA REFINING CO.—Holly Corporation; *U.S. Public*, pg. 830
MURCO PETROLEUM LTD.—Murphy Oil Corporation; *U.S. Public*, pg. 1142
MURPHY OIL CORPORATION; *U.S. Public*, pg. 1141
MURPHY OIL USA, INC.—Murphy Oil Corporation; *U.S. Public*, pg. 1142
NATIONAL COOPERATIVE REFINERY ASSOCIATION; *U.S. Private*, pg. 781
NAVAJO CORP.—Holly Corporation; *U.S. Public*, pg. 830
NAVAJO REFINING CO.—Holly Corporation; *U.S. Public*, pg. 830
NESTE OY; *Int'l*, pg. 912
NEWHALL REFINING CO.—Lonrho plc; *Int'l*, pg. 818
NIPPON OIL COMPANY, LIMITED (NISSEKI); *Int'l*, pg. 936
NORSK HYDRO A.S; *Int'l*, pg. 959
A/S NORSKE SHELL—Royal Dutch/Shell Group of Companies; *Int'l*, pg. 1139
NUCLEST—Petrobras - Petroleo Brasileiro S.A.; *Int'l*, pg. 1042
OBERRHEINISCHE MINERALOELWERKE GMBH—Du Pont (E.I. Du Pont De Nemours & Co.); *U.S. Public*, pg. 533
OIL SHALE PLANT—Petrobras - Petroleo Brasileiro S.A.; *Int'l*, pg. 1042
PAKISTAN REFINERY—Royal Dutch/Shell Group of Companies; *Int'l*, pg. 1140
R.B. PAMPLIN CORP.; *U.S. Private*, pg. 835
PARAMOUNT PETROLEUM CORP.; *U.S. Private*, pg. 838
PAULINIA REFINERY—Petrobras - Petroleo Brasileiro S.A.; *Int'l*, pg. 1042
PECKHAM INDUSTRIES, INC.; *U.S. Private*, pg. 846
PEERLESS DISTRIBUTING CO.; *U.S. Private*, pg. 847
PENNZOIL COMPANY; *U.S. Public*, pg. 1272
PENNZOIL PRODUCTS CO.—Pennzoil Company; *U.S. Public*, pg. 1272
PENRECO—Pennzoil Company; *U.S. Public*, pg. 1273
PETRESA INTERNATIONAL N.V.—Compania Espanola de Petroleos, S.A. (CEPSA); *Int'l*, pg. 323
PETRO STAR INC.—Arctic Slope Regional Corporation; *U.S. Private*, pg. 80
PETROBRAS - PETROLEO BRASILEIRO S.A.; *Int'l*, pg. 1041
PETROFINA S.A.; *Int'l*, pg. 1043
PETROLEOS DE CANARIAS, S.A. (PETROCAN)—Compania Espanola de Petroleos, S.A. (CEPSA); *Int'l*, pg. 323
PETROLEOS DE VENEZUELA S.A.; *Int'l*, pg. 1045
PETROLEOS DEL SUR, S.A. (PETROSUR)—Compania Espanola de Petroleos, S.A. (CEPSA); *Int'l*, pg. 323
PETROLEOS MEXICANOS; *Int'l*, pg. 1046
PETROLEUM DEVELOPMENT OMAN LLC—Royal Dutch/Shell Group of Companies; *Int'l*, pg. 1141
PETROLEUM REFINERIES (AUSTRALIA) PTY., LTD.—Mobil Oil Corporation; *U.S. Public*, pg. 1120
PETROLEUM SPECIALTIES GROUP—Witco Corporation; *U.S. Public*, pg. 1774
PETROQUIMICA ESPANOLA, S.A. (PETRESA)—Compania Espanola de Petroleos, S.A. (CEPSA); *Int'l*, pg. 323
PHILLIPS PETROLEUM COMPANY; *U.S. Public*, pg. 1290
PILIPINAS SHELL PETROLEUM CORPORATION—Royal Dutch/Shell Group of Companies; *Int'l*, pg. 1140
POCO PETROLEUMS LTD.; *Int'l*, pg. 1061
POINT BREEZE REFINERY—Sun Company, Inc.; *U.S. Public*, pg. 1530
POUNDER EMULSIONS, LTD.—Husky Oil Ltd.; *Int'l*, pg. 640
POWERINE OIL COMPANY—Castle Energy Corporation; *U.S. Public*, pg. 314
PREEM PETROLEUM AB; *Int'l*, pg. 1066
PRESIDENTE BERNARDES REFINERY—Petrobras - Petroleo Brasileiro S.A.; *Int'l*, pg. 1042
PRESIDENTE GETULIO VARGAS REFINERY—Petrobras - Petroleo Brasileiro S.A.; *Int'l*, pg. 1042
PRODUCTOS ASFALTICOS, S.A. (PROAS)—Compania Espanola de Petroleos, S.A. (CEPSA); *Int'l*, pg. 323
PURITAN OIL COMPANY, INC.—Warren Equities Inc.; *U.S. Private*, pg. 1151
RAFFINERIA DI ROMA SPA—Petrofina S.A.; *Int'l*, pg. 1043
RAFFINERIE DE CRESSIER, S.A.—Royal Dutch/Shell Group of Companies; *Int'l*, pg. 1139
RAFFINERIE DES ANTILLES—Royal Dutch/Shell Group of Companies; *Int'l*, pg. 1141
JOHN G. RATHBORNE—Royal Dutch/Shell Group of Companies; *Int'l*, pg. 1138
REFINERIA DOMINICANA DE PETROLEO, S.A.—Royal Dutch/Shell Group of Companies; *Int'l*, pg. 1141
REFINERIA PANAMA S.A.—Texaco Inc.; *U.S. Public*, pg. 1584
REFINERIA PETROLERA ACAJUTLA, S.A.—Royal Dutch/Shell Group of Companies; *Int'l*, pg. 1141
REFINERIA TEXACO DE HONDURAS, S.A.—Texaco Inc.; *U.S. Public*, pg. 1584
REPSOL EXPLORACION—Repsol S.A.; *Int'l*, pg. 1104
REPSOL S.A.; *Int'l*, pg. 1104
RESINAS SINTETICAS, S.A. (RESISA)—Compania Espanola de Petroleos, S.A. (CEPSA); *Int'l*, pg. 323
RHENANE DE RAFFINAGE—Royal Dutch/Shell Group of Companies; *Int'l*, pg. 1136
ROBERTET S.A.; *Int'l*, pg. 1119
ROHOL-AUFSUCHUNGS—Royal Dutch/Shell Group of Companies; *Int'l*, pg. 1138
ROLLS-ROYCE PLC; *Int'l*, pg. 1126
ROSE FUEL CORPORATION—Bayside Fuel Oil Depot Corp.; *U.S. Private*, pg. 125
ROYAL DUTCH/SHELL GROUP OF COMPANIES; *Int'l*, pg. 1135
SARAWAK SHELL—Royal Dutch/Shell Group of Companies; *Int'l*, pg. 1140
SASOL OIL (PTY) LTD.—Sasol Limited; *Int'l*, pg. 1197
SEIBU SEKIYO—Royal Dutch/Shell Group of Companies; *Int'l*, pg. 1139
SHELL ARGENTINA DE PETROLEO—Royal Dutch/Shell Group of Companies; *Int'l*, pg. 1141
SHELL CANADA LTD.—Royal Dutch/Shell Group of Companies; *Int'l*, pg. 1138
SHELL COMPANY OF PAKISTAN LTD—Royal Dutch/Shell Group of Companies; *Int'l*, pg. 1140
SHELL COTE D'IVOIRE—Royal Dutch/Shell Group of Companies; *Int'l*, pg. 1137
SHELL CURACAO N.V.—Royal Dutch/Shell Group of Companies; *Int'l*, pg. 1141
SHELL DEVELOPMENT CO.—Royal Dutch/Shell Group of Companies; *Int'l*, pg. 1136
SHELL EASTERN PETROLEUM—Royal Dutch/Shell Group of Companies; *Int'l*, pg. 1140
SHELL FRANCAISE—Royal Dutch/Shell Group of Companies; *Int'l*, pg. 1138
SHELL GABON—Royal Dutch/Shell Group of Companies; *Int'l*, pg. 1137
SHELL GAS PHILIPPINES, INC.—Royal Dutch/Shell Group of Companies; *Int'l*, pg. 1140
SHELL INTERNATIONAL PETROLEUM CO. LTD.—Royal Dutch/Shell Group of Companies; *Int'l*, pg. 1139
SHELL MALAYSIA LTD—Royal Dutch/Shell Group of Companies; *Int'l*, pg. 1140
SHELL NEDERLAND RAFFINADERIJ—Royal Dutch/Shell Group of Companies; *Int'l*, pg. 1135
SHELL OIL COMPANY—Royal Dutch/Shell Group of Companies; *Int'l*, pg. 1136
SHELL OLIE-OG GASUDVINDING DANMARK—Royal Dutch/Shell Group of Companies; *Int'l*, pg. 1138
THE SHELL PETROLEUM DEVELOPMENT COMPANY OF NIGERIA LTD.—Royal Dutch/Shell Group of Companies; *Int'l*, pg. 1137
SHELL REFINING (AUSTRALIA) PTY. LTD.—Royal Dutch/Shell Group of Companies; *Int'l*, pg. 1137
SHELL REFINING (F.O.M.) BHD.—Royal Dutch/Shell Group of Companies; *Int'l*, pg. 1140
SHELL SOUTH AFRICA (PTY) LTD.—Royal Dutch/Shell Group of Companies; *Int'l*, pg. 1136
SHELL (SWITZERLAND)—Royal Dutch/Shell Group of Companies; *Int'l*, pg. 1139
SHELL THAILAND MANUFACTURING, LTD.—Royal Dutch/Shell Group of Companies; *Int'l*, pg. 1140
SHOWA SHELL SEKIYU KK—Royal Dutch/Shell Group of Companies; *Int'l*, pg. 1140
SHOWA YOKKAICHI SEKIYU CO. LTD.—Royal Dutch/Shell Group of Companies; *Int'l*, pg. 1140
SIERRA LEONE PETROLEUM REFINING—Royal Dutch/Shell Group of Companies; *Int'l*, pg. 1137
SINCLAIR OIL CORP.; *U.S. Private*, pg. 1003

SINGAPORE PETROLEUM CO. (HK) LTD.—Amoco Corporation; U.S. Public, pg. 102
SNAMPROGETTI S.P.A.—ENI S.p.A.; Int'l, pg. 429
SOMERSET REFINERY INC.; U.S. Private, pg. 1013
SOUTHLAND OIL COMPANY; U.S. Private, pg. 1018
SOUTHWESTERN PETROLEUM CORPORATION; U.S. Private, pg. 1019
SSANGYONG BUSINESS GROUP; Int'l, pg. 1291
SSANGYONG OIL REFINING CO. LTD.—Ssangyong Business Group; Int'l, pg. 1292
SUN COMPANY, INC.; U.S. Public, pg. 1530
SUN REFINING & MARKETING CO. OPERATIONS DIV.—Sun Company, Inc.; U.S. Public, pg. 1530
SUNCOR INC.; Int'l, pg. 1320
SUNDA SHELL—Royal Dutch/Shell Group of Companies; Int'l, pg. 1139
SUNOCO GROUP—Suncor Inc.; Int'l, pg. 1320
SUNOCO SARNIA REFINERY—Suncor Inc.; Int'l, pg. 1320
AB SVENSKA SHELL—Royal Dutch/Shell Group of Companies; Int'l, pg. 1139
T A HOLDINGS LIMITED; Int'l, pg. 1334
TRMI HOLDINGS INC.—Texaco Inc.; U.S. Public, pg. 1583
TAOYUAN REFINERY—Chinese Petroleum Corporation; Int'l, pg. 286
TENNECO OIL & MINERALS OF AUSTRALIA, INC.—Tenneco Inc.; U.S. Public, pg. 1580
TENNESSEE REFINERY—Mapco Inc.; U.S. Public, pg. 1042
TESORO ALASKA PETROLEUM CO.—Tesoro Petroleum Corporation; U.S. Public, pg. 1582
TESORO PETROLEUM CORPORATION; U.S. Public, pg. 1581
TEXACO INC.; U.S. Public, pg. 1582
S.A. TEXACO PETROLEUM N.V.—Texaco Inc.; U.S. Public, pg. 1584
TEXACO REFINING & MARKETING, INC.—Texaco Inc.; U.S. Public, pg. 1583
TEXACO RESEARCH CENTER—Texaco Inc.; U.S. Public, pg. 1583
THAI OIL REFINERY—Royal Dutch/Shell Group of Companies; Int'l, pg. 1140
THREE RIVERS REFINERY—Ultramar Diamond Shamrock Corporation; U.S. Public, pg. 1663
THRIFTY OIL CO.; U.S. Private, pg. 1084
TIMEC COMPANY; U.S. Private, pg. 1087
TONEN CORPORATION; Int'l, pg. 1398
TOSCO CORPORATION; U.S. Public, pg. 1624
TOSCO REFINING COMPANY—Tosco Corporation; U.S. Public, pg. 1625
TOTAL PETROLEUM, INC.—Ultramar Diamond Shamrock Corporation; U.S. Public, pg. 1663
TOTAL RAFFINAGE DISTRIBUTION S.A.—Total S.A.; Int'l, pg. 1409
TOTAL S.A.; Int'l, pg. 1408
TRANS MOUNTAIN ENTERPRISES OF BRITISH COLUMBIA LIMITED—BC Gas Inc.; Int'l, pg. 114
TURKSE SHELL—Royal Dutch/Shell Group of Companies; Int'l, pg. 1141
USX CORPORATION; U.S. Public, pg. 1661
ULTRAMAR DIAMOND SHAMROCK CORPORATION; U.S. Public, pg. 1663
UNITED ACQUISITION CORPORATION—Red Apple Companies; U.S. Private, pg. 915
UNITED REFINING COMPANY—Red Apple Companies; U.S. Private, pg. 915
UNITED REFINING INC.—Red Apple Companies; U.S. Private, pg. 915
U.S. OIL & REFINING CO.—Time Oil Company; U.S. Private, pg. 1086
VALERO MARKETING & SUPPLY COMPANY—Valero Energy Corporation; U.S. Public, pg. 1704
VALERO REFINING COMPANY—Valero Energy Corporation; U.S. Public, pg. 1704
VALVOLINE, INC.—Ashland, Inc.; U.S. Public, pg. 139
VEBA OEL AG—Veba AG; Int'l, pg. 1460
VENTURE PROCESSING COMPANY—Stone & Webster, Incorporated; U.S. Public, pg. 1519
VULCAN ASPHALT REFINING COMPANY—Red Apple Companies; U.S. Private, pg. 915
WILSHIRE OIL CO. OF TEXAS; U.S. Public, pg. 1770
WITCO CORPORATION; U.S. Public, pg. 1773
WORLD OIL CORP.; U.S. Private, pg. 1190
Y.P.F., S.A.; Int'l, pg. 1515
YATES INVESTMENT CASTING WAX INC.—Burmah Castrol plc; Int'l, pg. 234
YOUNG REFINING CORP.; U.S. Private, pg. 1202
ZIEGLER CHEMICAL & MINERAL CORP.; U.S. Private, pg. 1205

2951 — ASPHALT PAVING MIXTURES & BLOCKS

AJAX PAVING INDUSTRIES INC.; U.S. Private, pg. 29
ASHLAND, INC.; U.S. Public, pg. 138
ASSOCIATED SAND & GRAVEL CO., INC.—CSR Limited; Int'l, pg. 245
BANKHEAD ENTERPRISES INC.; U.S. Private, pg. 114
BARLETTA MATERIALS & CONSTRUCTION; U.S. Private, pg. 116
HANS BERNEBURG GMBH & CO. KG—Philipp Holzmann AG; Int'l, pg. 632
BITUMINOUS ROADWAYS, INC.; U.S. Private, pg. 146
BORAL LIMITED; Int'l, pg. 203
BORAL RESOURCES LTD.—Boral Limited; Int'l, pg. 203
CENTRAL ALLIED ENTERPRISES; U.S. Private, pg. 222
COAST ASPHALT, INC.—CalMat Co.; U.S. Public, pg. 295
CRAFCO, INC.—Ergon, Inc.; U.S. Private, pg. 381
CURRAN GROUP, INC.; U.S. Private, pg. 297
DEUTSCHE ASPHALT GMBH—Philipp Holzmann AG; Int'l, pg. 632
ELASTIC MATERIALS, INC.; U.S. Private, pg. 367
ELF AQUITAINE ASPHALT, INC.—Elf Aquitane; Int'l, pg. 445
ELF AQUITAINE, INC.—Elf Aquitane; Int'l, pg. 445
THE GIBSON-HOMANS COMPANY; U.S. Private, pg. 451
GOHMANN ASPHALT & CONSTRUCTION INC.; U.S. Private, pg. 459
GOHMANN ASPHALT & CONSTRUCTION OF KY., INC.—Gohmann Asphalt & Construction Inc.; U.S. Private, pg. 459
GULF STATES ASPHALT COMPANY, INC.; U.S. Private, pg. 487
GLENN O. HAWBAKER, INC.; U.S. Private, pg. 511
HUNTMIX, INC.—CalMat Co.; U.S. Public, pg. 296
IA CONSTRUCTION CORP.; U.S. Private, pg. 552
ICOPAL A/S; Int'l, pg. 658
K.F. JACOBSON CO.—R.B. Pamplin Corp.; U.S. Private, pg. 836
KEATING MATERIALS—P.J. Keating Company; U.S. Private, pg. 611
P.J. KEATING COMPANY; U.S. Private, pg. 610
KOCH MATERIALS DIVISION—Koch Industries, Incorporated; U.S. Private, pg. 628
LAFARGE CIMENTS—Lafarge S.A.; Int'l, pg. 788
LAFARGE CONSTRUCTION MATERIALS—Lafarge S.A.; Int'l, pg. 788
EDWARD C. LEVY CO.; U.S. Private, pg. 664
N.C. PRODUCTS CORP.—CRH, plc; Int'l, pg. 242
OHIO TAR ASPHALT—Central Allied Enterprises; U.S. Private, pg. 222
R.B. PAMPLIN CORP.; U.S. Private, pg. 835
PECKHAM INDUSTRIES, INC.; U.S. Private, pg. 846
PIKE INDUSTRIES INC.—CRH, plc; Int'l, pg. 242
PIONEER INTERNATIONAL LTD.; Int'l, pg. 1058
PROMSA—Ciments Francais; Int'l, pg. 292
RASCHIG GMBH—PMC, Inc.; U.S. Private, pg. 827
RITCHIE CORPORATION; U.S. Private, pg. 933
RIVER BEND CORP.—CalMat Co.; U.S. Public, pg. 296
ROGERS GROUP INC.; U.S. Private, pg. 939
ROSS ISLAND SAND & GRAVEL CO., INC.—R.B. Pamplin Corp.; U.S. Private, pg. 836
RUETGERS A.G.; Int'l, pg. 1147
JOSEF SKIPIOL STRASSENBAUSTOFFE GMBH & CO. KG—Philipp Holzmann AG; Int'l, pg. 633
STABLER COMPANIES, INC.; U.S. Private, pg. 1028
TARMAC PLC; Int'l, pg. 1355
TARMAC QUARRY PRODUCTS LTD.—Tarmac plc; Int'l, pg. 1355
TARMAC ROADSTONE LTD.—Tarmac plc; Int'l, pg. 1355
THOMPSON-MCCULLY CO.; U.S. Private, pg. 1083
TILCON, INC.; U.S. Private, pg. 1086
TRUMBULL CORPORATION/P.J. DICK, INC.; U.S. Private, pg. 1107
UNIMIX—Ciments Francais; Int'l, pg. 292
UNITED REFINING COMPANY—Red Apple Companies; U.S. Private, pg. 915
VALLEY ASPHALT CORPORATION; U.S. Private, pg. 1131
VULCAN MATERIALS COMPANY; U.S. Public, pg. 1725
WESTERN MOBILE INC.—Redland PLC; Int'l, pg. 1091
WINDSOR SERVICE, INC.—Haines Kibblehouse; U.S. Private, pg. 494

2952 — ASPHALT FELTS & COATINGS

ABT BUILDING PRODUCTS CORPORATION—Abitibi-Consolidated Inc.; Int'l, pg. 20
AC PRODUCTS, INC.—Quaker Chemical Corporation; U.S. Public, pg. 1346
D. ANDERSON & SON LTD.—Icopal a/s; Int'l, pg. 659
AQUASEAL LTD.—Tarmac plc; Int'l, pg. 1355
BPB INDUSTRIES PLC; Int'l, pg. 122
BPCO—Emco Limited; Int'l, pg. 453
BALZARETTI MODIGLIANI—Saint-Gobain; Int'l, pg. 1177
BENCHMARK INDUSTRIES; U.S. Private, pg. 132
BIRD INCORPORATED—Saint-Gobain; Int'l, pg. 1170
BIRD ROOFING PRODUCTS, INC.—Saint-Gobain; Int'l, pg. 1171
BUILDING MATERIALS CORPORATION OF AMERICA—GAF Corporation; U.S. Private, pg. 433
CSR CENTRAL—CSR Limited; Int'l, pg. 245
CSR LIMITED; Int'l, pg. 245
CSR WEST—CSR Limited; Int'l, pg. 245
CELOTEX CORPORATION; U.S. Private, pg. 221
CERTAINTEED CORPORATION—Saint-Gobain; Int'l, pg. 1170
CHASE CORPORATION; U.S. Public, pg. 337
CONKLIN CO. INC.; U.S. Private, pg. 263
CONSOLIDATED COATINGS CORP.—RPM, Inc.; U.S. Public, pg. 1357
DELTA RESINS & REFRACTORIES, INC.; U.S. Private, pg. 323
DEUTSCHE ASPHALT GMBH—Philipp Holzmann AG; Int'l, pg. 632
DURO-LAST ROOFING, INC.; U.S. Private, pg. 349
ELCOR CORPORATION; U.S. Public, pg. 567
ELK CORP. OF ALABAMA—Elcor Corporation; U.S. Public, pg. 568
ELK CORPORATION OF DALLAS—Elcor Corporation; U.S. Public, pg. 568
ELK CORPORATION OF TEXAS—Elcor Corporation; U.S. Public, pg. 568
EMCO BUILDING PRODUCTS—Emco Limited; Int'l, pg. 453
EMCO LIMITED; Int'l, pg. 452
EVERITE S.A.—Saint-Gobain; Int'l, pg. 1170
FOSTER PRODUCTS CORPORATION—H.B. Fuller Company; U.S. Public, pg. 686
GATE PETROLEUM COMPANY; U.S. Private, pg. 441
GEORGIA-PACIFIC CORPORATION; U.S. Public, pg. 735
THE GIBSON-HOMANS COMPANY; U.S. Private, pg. 451
THE B.F. GOODRICH COMPANY; U.S. Public, pg. 751
GULF STATES ASPHALT COMPANY, INC.; U.S. Private, pg. 487
JAMES HARDIE USA—James Hardie Industries Ltd.; Int'l, pg. 597
HEMPT BROTHERS, INC.; U.S. Private, pg. 521
ICOPAL AB—Icopal a/s; Int'l, pg. 659
ICOPAL A/S; Int'l, pg. 658
ICOPAL OY—Icopal a/s; Int'l, pg. 659
ICOPAL-SIPLAST GMBH—Icopal a/s; Int'l, pg. 659
INSTALLATION PRODUCTS DIV.—Armstrong World Industries, Inc.; U.S. Public, pg. 132
K.F. JACOBSON CO.—R.B. Pamplin Corp.; U.S. Private, pg. 836
JANESVILLE PRODUCTS—Jason Incorporated; U.S. Public, pg. 924
JOHNS MANVILLE CORPORATION; U.S. Public, pg. 927
KARNAK CORPORATION; U.S. Private, pg. 607
KOOL SEAL, INC.; U.S. Private, pg. 632
HERBERT MALARKEY ROOFING COMPANY; U.S. Private, pg. 698
MATSUSHITA ELECTRIC WORKS, LTD.; Int'l, pg. 847
MONSEY-BAKOR; U.S. Private, pg. 757
NOVARTIS AG; Int'l, pg. 971
POLYCOAT SYSTEMS, INC.; U.S. Private, pg. 875
QUAKER CHEMICAL CORPORATION; U.S. Public, pg. 1346
REA CONSTRUCTION CO.—Philipp Holzmann AG; Int'l, pg. 633
ROSS ISLAND SAND & GRAVEL CO., INC.—R.B. Pamplin Corp.; U.S. Private, pg. 836
ROYSTON LABORATORIES—Chase Corporation; U.S. Public, pg. 337
SIPLAST INC.—Icopal a/s; Int'l, pg. 659
SPECIALTY POLYMERS & CHEMICALS DIVISION—The B.F. Goodrich Company; U.S. Public, pg. 751
TARCO; U.S. Private, pg. 1068
TECHNI-THERM INC.—Domtar Inc.; Int'l, pg. 416
TEXAS REFINERY CORP.; U.S. Private, pg. 1078
TREMCO, INC.—RPM, Inc.; U.S. Public, pg. 1358
TRUMBULL CORPORATION/P.J. DICK, INC.; U.S. Private, pg. 1107
U.S. INTEC, INC.—GAF Corporation; U.S. Private, pg. 433
WINDSOR SERVICE, INC.—Haines Kibblehouse; U.S. Private, pg. 494
ZIEGLER CHEMICAL & MINERAL CORP.; U.S. Private, pg. 1205

2992 — LUBRICATING OILS & GREASES

ACEITES LUBRICANTES Y GRASAS CASTROL S.A.—Burmah Castrol plc; Int'l, pg. 235
ACHESON COLLOIDS COMPANY—Acheson Industries, Inc.; U.S. Private, pg. 12
ACHESON INDUSTRIES, INC.; U.S. Private, pg. 12
ATOCHEM CANADA INC.—Elf Aquitane; Int'l, pg. 446
BP INTERNATIONAL LTD.—The British Petroleum Company P.L.C.; Int'l, pg. 220
BP OIL CO.—The British Petroleum Company P.L.C.; Int'l, pg. 220
BEL-RAY COMPANY, INC.; U.S. Private, pg. 130
BERNER LTD.; Int'l, pg. 189
BOSTIK, INC.—Total S.A.; Int'l, pg. 1409
BROOKS TECHNOLOGY—Premier Farnell plc; Int'l, pg. 1068
BURMAH CASTROL PLC; Int'l, pg. 234
BURMAH CASTROL USA INC.—Burmah Castrol plc; Int'l, pg. 235
CASTROL AB—Burmah Castrol plc; Int'l, pg. 235
CASTROL A/S—Burmah Castrol plc; Int'l, pg. 235
CASTROL HELLAS S.A.—Burmah Castrol plc; Int'l, pg. 235
CASTROL INDUSTRIAL—Burmah Castrol plc; Int'l, pg. 235
CASTROL ITALIANA SPA—Burmah Castrol plc; Int'l, pg. 236
CASTROL K.K.—Burmah Castrol plc; Int'l, pg. 236
CASTROL LTD.—Burmah Castrol plc; Int'l, pg. 234
CASTROL NORTH AMERICA—Burmah Castrol plc; Int'l, pg. 235
CASTROL OVERSEAS LTD.—Burmah Castrol plc; Int'l, pg. 234
CASTROL SINGAPORE PTE. LTD.—Burmah Castrol plc; Int'l, pg. 236
CATO OIL & GREASE CO.—Petroleos de Venezuela S.A.; Int'l, pg. 1045
CENEX, INC.; U.S. Private, pg. 221
CENTURY OILS (CANADA), INC.—Fuchs Petrolub AG Oel + Chemie; Int'l, pg. 518
CENTURY OILS LTD.—Fuchs Petrolub AG Oel + Chemie; Int'l, pg. 518
CHEM-TREND INCORPORATED—Burmah Castrol plc; Int'l, pg. 235
CHEVRON CHEMICAL S.A.—Chevron Corporation; U.S. Public, pg. 348
AB AXEL CHRISTIERNSSON—Axel Johnson AB; Int'l, pg. 708
CONKLIN CO. INC.; U.S. Private, pg. 263
CORPORACION GRUPO QUIMICO, S.A.C.A.; Int'l, pg. 331
D-A LUBRICANT CO., INC.—Premier Farnell plc; Int'l, pg. 1068
DAUBERT INDUSTRIES, INC.; U.S. Private, pg. 313
DELTA RESINS & REFRACTORIES, INC.; U.S. Private, pg. 323
DETREX INDUSTRIAL CHEMICAL SPECIALTIES DIV.—Detrex Corporation; U.S. Public, pg. 502
DINOL GMBH—Novartis AG; Int'l, pg. 982
DRYDEN OIL COMPANY, INC.—Burmah Castrol plc; Int'l, pg. 235
DRYDEN OIL OF NEW ENGLAND—Burmah Castrol plc; Int'l, pg. 235
THE ELCO CORP.—Detrex Corporation; U.S. Public, pg. 502
ESSO MALAYSIA BERHAD—Exxon Corporation; U.S. Public, pg. 602
FARMLAND INDUSTRIES, INC.; U.S. Private, pg. 395
FIRST BRANDS (CANADA) CORP.—First Brands Corporation; U.S. Public, pg. 627
FIRST BRANDS CORPORATION; U.S. Public, pg. 626

FIRST BRANDS (EUROPE) LTD.—First Brands Corporation; U.S. Public, pg. 627
FIRST BRANDS PHILIPPINES—First Brands Corporation; U.S. Public, pg. 627
FISKE BROTHERS REFINING COMPANY; U.S. Private, pg. 408
FISKE BROTHERS REFINING, TOLEDO DIV.—Fiske Brothers Refining Company; U.S. Private, pg. 409
FRANKLIN OIL CORP.—Morgan Crucible Co. Plc; Int'l, pg. 892
H. FUCHS DO BRAZIL S.A.—Fuchs Petrolub AG Oel + Chemie; Int'l, pg. 517
FUCHS LUBRICANTES S.A.—Fuchs Petrolub AG Oel + Chemie; Int'l, pg. 518
FUCHS LUBRICANTS, MIDLANTIC DIV.—Fuchs Petrolub AG Oel + Chemie; Int'l, pg. 518
FUCHS LUBRIFICANTES LDA—Fuchs Petrolub AG Oel + Chemie; Int'l, pg. 518
FUCHS-MONTGOMERY COMPANY, INC.—Fuchs Petrolub AG Oel + Chemie; Int'l, pg. 518
FUCHS PETROLUB AG—Fuchs Petrolub AG Oel + Chemie; Int'l, pg. 517
FUCHS PETROLUB AG OEL + CHEMIE; Int'l, pg. 517
FUCHS (UK) P.L.C.—Fuchs Petrolub AG Oel + Chemie; Int'l, pg. 518
GRAFO COLLOIDS DIVISION—Fuchs Petrolub AG Oel + Chemie; Int'l, pg. 518
GREAT LAKES CHEMICAL CORPORATION; U.S. Public, pg. 760
GUMOUT DIVISION—Pennzoil Company; U.S. Public, pg. 1273
HALOCARBON PRODUCTS CORP.; U.S. Private, pg. 496
HOUGHTON INTERNATIONAL INC.; U.S. Private, pg. 541
HYDROTEX INC.—Morgan Crucible Co. Plc; Int'l, pg. 892
AXEL JOHNSON AB; Int'l, pg. 707
KING INDUSTRIES, INC.; U.S. Private, pg. 620
KRONOS EUROPE, INC.—Contran Corporation; U.S. Private, pg. 271
LPS LABORATORIES INC.—Morgan Crucible Co. Plc; Int'l, pg. 892
LUBECON SYSTEMS, INC.; U.S. Private, pg. 679
LUBRICATION CONSULTANTS, L.L.C.—Mid-Kansas Co-op Association; U.S. Private, pg. 743
LUBRICATION ENGINEERS, INC.; U.S. Private, pg. 679
MFA OIL COMPANY; U.S. Private, pg. 687
MAINTENANCE, INC.—Premier Farnell plc; Int'l, pg. 1068
METAL LUBRICANTS CO.—Fuchs Petrolub AG Oel + Chemie; Int'l, pg. 518
NASCO INDUSTRIES INC.; U.S. Private, pg. 774
OCTAGON PROCESS INC.; U.S. Private, pg. 811
OPTIMOL OELWERKE GMBH—Burmah Castrol plc; Int'l, pg. 236
PACE INTERNATIONAL L.P.; U.S. Private, pg. 829
PENNZOIL COMPANY; U.S. Public, pg. 1272
PENNZOIL PRODUCTS CO.—Pennzoil Company; U.S. Public, pg. 1272
PETROBRAS - PETROLEO BRASILEIRO S.A.; Int'l, pg. 1041
PETROLEOS DE VENEZUELA S.A.; Int'l, pg. 1045
PETROLEUM SPECIALTIES GROUP—Witco Corporation; U.S. Public, pg. 1774
PETRON CORPORATION—Wechco, Inc.; U.S. Private, pg. 1158
PHOENIX OIL COMPANY (UK) LIMITED—Fuchs Petrolub AG Oel + Chemie; Int'l, pg. 519
PREMIER FARNELL—Premier Farnell plc; Int'l, pg. 1068
QUAKER CHEMICAL CORPORATION; U.S. Public, pg. 1346
RESEARCH ENVIRONMENTAL INDUSTRIES, INC.; U.S. Private, pg. 924
STP CORPORATION—First Brands Corporation; U.S. Public, pg. 627
STP PRODUCTS, INC.—First Brands Corporation; U.S. Public, pg. 627
SAFETY-KLEEN CORP.; U.S. Public, pg. 1425
SERICOL AG—Burmah Castrol plc; Int'l, pg. 236
SILKOLENE LUBRICANTS PLC—Fuchs Petrolub AG Oel + Chemie; Int'l, pg. 519
SILKOLENE PLC—Fuchs Petrolub AG Oel + Chemie; Int'l, pg. 518
SIMONIZ INTERNATIONAL PLC—Burmah Castrol plc; Int'l, pg. 235
SOUTHWESTERN PETROLEUM CORPORATION; U.S. Private, pg. 1019
THE L.S. STARRETT COMPANY; U.S. Public, pg. 1511
D.A. STUART COMPANY; U.S. Private, pg. 1048
SUPERIOR GRAPHITE CO.; U.S. Private, pg. 1054
SUPERIOR GRAPHITE EUROPE, LTD.—Superior Graphite Co.; U.S. Private, pg. 1055
TEXACO INC.; U.S. Public, pg. 1582
TEXAS REFINERY CORP.; U.S. Private, pg. 1078
3M; U.S. Public, pg. 1604
UNIVERSAL COOPERATIVES, INC.; U.S. Private, pg. 1127
VALVOLINE CANADA LTD.—Ashland, Inc.; U.S. Public, pg. 140
VALVOLINE OIL CO. LTD.—Ashland, Inc.; U.S. Public, pg. 140
VALVOLINE OIL NEDERLAND B.V.—Ashland, Inc.; U.S. Public, pg. 140
VEEDOL INTERNATIONAL LTD.—Burmah Castrol plc; Int'l, pg. 235
VELSICOL CHEMICAL CORPORATION; U.S. Private, pg. 1135
WD-40 COMPANY; U.S. Public, pg. 1726
WEST PENETONE INC.—Wechco, Inc.; U.S. Private, pg. 1158
WITCO CANADA, INC.—Witco Corporation; U.S. Public, pg. 1774
WITCO CORPORATION; U.S. Public, pg. 1773
WOLF'S HEAD OIL COMPANY—Pennzoil Company; U.S. Public, pg. 1273
WYNN OIL COMPANY—Wynn's International, Inc.; U.S. Public, pg. 1782
WYNN'S INTERNATIONAL, INC.; U.S. Public, pg. 1782

2999 — PRODUCTS OF PETROLEUM & COAL, NEC

AKZO NOBEL INC.—Akzo Nobel N.V.; Int'l, pg. 47
ASBURY CARBONS, INC.; U.S. Private, pg. 87
CENEX, INC.; U.S. Private, pg. 221
COASTAL STOCK CO., LTD.—The Coastal Corporation; U.S. Public, pg. 390
COLGATE-PALMOLIVE IPD—Colgate-Palmolive Company; U.S. Public, pg. 397
COPETRO, S.A.—Horsehead Industries, Inc.; U.S. Private, pg. 540
COUNTRYMARK COOPERATIVE, INC.; U.S. Private, pg. 279
DELTA RESINS & REFRACTORIES, INC.; U.S. Private, pg. 323
EMBERS CHARCOAL COMPANY, INC.; U.S. Private, pg. 373
ESSO AUSTRALIA RESOURCES LTD.—Exxon Corporation; U.S. Public, pg. 602
ETHYL CORPORATION; U.S. Public, pg. 595
FABRICA DE VALVULAS—Fruit of the Loom, Inc.; U.S. Public, pg. 686
GREAT LAKES CARBON CORP.—Horsehead Industries, Inc.; U.S. Private, pg. 540
GULF STATES ASPHALT COMPANY, INC.; U.S. Private, pg. 487
HOLBORN OIL TRADING LTD.—The Coastal Corporation; U.S. Public, pg. 390
HORSEHEAD INDUSTRIES, INC.; U.S. Private, pg. 540
IDEMITSU KOSAN CO., LTD.; Int'l, pg. 659
MITSUBISHI CHEMICAL CORPORATION; Int'l, pg. 870
MITSUI MINING CO., LTD.—Mitsui & Co., Ltd.; Int'l, pg. 878
MOOSE JAW PLANT—The Clorox Company; U.S. Public, pg. 387
PETROCOQUE S.A.—Alcan Aluminium Limited; Int'l, pg. 52
REYNOLDS METALS COMPANY-BATON ROUGE—Reynolds Metals Company; U.S. Public, pg. 1385
SUPERIOR GRAPHITE CO.; U.S. Private, pg. 1054
SUPERIOR GRAPHITE EUROPE, LTD.—Superior Graphite Co.; U.S. Private, pg. 1055
TEXACO INC.; U.S. Public, pg. 1582
TOTAL PETROLEUM, INC.—Ultramar Diamond Shamrock Corporation; U.S. Public, pg. 1663
UNOCAL CARBON & MINERALS—Unocal Corporation; U.S. Public, pg. 1698
WALTER INDUSTRIES, INC.; U.S. Public, pg. 1736
WESTERN MINING CORPORATION HOLDINGS LIMITED; Int'l, pg. 1494
WINTERSHALL AG—BASF AG; Int'l, pg. 104

3011 — TIRES & INNER TUBES

BTR PLC; Int'l, pg. 124
BANDAG CANADA, LTD.—Bandag, Incorporated; U.S. Public, pg. 178
BANDAG DO BRASIL LTDA.—Bandag, Incorporated; U.S. Public, pg. 178
BANDAG EUROPE NV—Bandag, Incorporated; U.S. Public, pg. 178
BANDAG, INCORPORATED; U.S. Public, pg. 177
BANDAG INC. OF S.A. (PTY.) LTD.—Bandag, Incorporated; U.S. Public, pg. 178
BANDAG LICENSING CORPORATION—Bandag, Incorporated; U.S. Public, pg. 177
BANDAG NEW ZEALAND LTD.—Bandag, Incorporated; U.S. Public, pg. 178
BARUM CONTINENTAL SPOL. S.R.O.—Continental AG; Int'l, pg. 327
BEKSA CELIK KORD SANAYI VE TICARET A.S.—N.V. Bekaert S.A.; Int'l, pg. 185
BEKSA CELIK KORD SANAYI VE TICARET A.S.—Sabanci Holding A.S.; Int'l, pg. 1167
BRIDGESTONE CORPORATION; Int'l, pg. 213
BRIDGESTONE/FIRESTONE, INC.—Bridgestone Corporation; Int'l, pg. 213
BRIDGESTONE TAIWAN CO., LTD.—Bridgestone Corporation; Int'l, pg. 214
BRISA BRIDGESTONE SABANCI LASTIK SANAYI VE TICARET A.S.—Bridgestone Corporation; Int'l, pg. 213
CARLISLE TIRE & WHEEL COMPANY—Carlisle Companies Incorporated; U.S. Public, pg. 305
COLTEC HOLDINGS INC; U.S. Public, pg. 401
COMMERCIAL PLASTICS & SUPPLIES CORP.; U.S. Private, pg. 258
COMPAGNIE GENERALE DES ETABLISSEMENTS MICHELIN; Int'l, pg. 322
COMPANHIA GOODYEAR DO BRASIL PRODUTOS DE BORRACHA—The Goodyear Tire & Rubber Company; U.S. Public, pg. 753
COMPANIA ANONIMA GOODYEAR DE VENEZUELA—The Goodyear Tire & Rubber Company; U.S. Public, pg. 753
COMPANIA GOODYEAR DEL PERU, S.A.—The Goodyear Tire & Rubber Company; U.S. Public, pg. 753
COMPANIA HULERA GOODYEAR-OXO SOCIEDAD ANONIMA—The Goodyear Tire & Rubber Company; U.S. Public, pg. 753
CONDERE CORPORATION; U.S. Private, pg. 262
CONTINENTAL AG; Int'l, pg. 327
CONTINENTAL GENERAL TIRE, INC.—Continental AG; Int'l, pg. 327
CONTINENTAL MABOR INDUSTRIA DE ANEUS S.A.—Continental AG; Int'l, pg. 328
COOPER TIRE & RUBBER COMPANY; U.S. Public, pg. 445
THE COOPER TIRE COMPANY—Cooper Tire & Rubber Company; U.S. Public, pg. 445
CUSTOM BRANDS DIV.—The Goodyear Tire & Rubber Company; U.S. Public, pg. 753
DMIB BERHAD—Sime Darby Berhad; Int'l, pg. 1250
DEUTSCHE GOODYEAR GMBH—The Goodyear Tire & Rubber Company; U.S. Public, pg. 753
DMIB EARTHMOVER TYRES SDN. BHD.—Sime Darby Berhad; Int'l, pg. 1250
DUNLOP AIRCRAFT TYRES DIV.—BTR plc; Int'l, pg. 125
DUNLOP INTERNATIONAL PROJECTS—BTR plc; Int'l, pg. 126
DUNLOP TIRE CORPORATION—Sumitomo Rubber Industries Ltd.; Int'l, pg. 1317
DUNLOP TIRE CORPORATION (HUNTSVILLE)—Sumitomo Rubber Industries Ltd.; Int'l, pg. 1317
FATE S.A.; Int'l, pg. 478
FIDELITY TIRE MFG. CO.—Condere Corporation; U.S. Private, pg. 262
FIRESTONE FRANCE S.A.—Bridgestone Corporation; Int'l, pg. 214
FIRESTONE TIRE & RUBBER CO. OF NEW ZEALAND, LTD.—Bridgestone Corporation; Int'l, pg. 214
C.A. FIRESTONE VENEZOLANA—Bridgestone Corporation; Int'l, pg. 215
FREDESTEIN BANDEN; Int'l, pg. 504
GTY TIRE CO.—Continental AG; Int'l, pg. 327
GEN CORP INC.—Toyo Tire & Rubber Co., Ltd.; Int'l, pg. 1411
GENERAL TIRE & RUBBER CO. OF MOROCCO—Continental AG; Int'l, pg. 327
GENERAL TYRE EAST AFRICA LTD.—Continental AG; Int'l, pg. 327
GOODALL RUBBER COMPANY—Trelleborg AB; Int'l, pg. 1423
THE GOODYEAR TIRE & RUBBER COMPANY; U.S. Public, pg. 752
GRAN INDUSTRIA DE NEUMATICOS CENTROAMERICANA, S.A.—The Goodyear Tire & Rubber Company; U.S. Public, pg. 753
GUMMIWERKE FULDA—The Goodyear Tire & Rubber Company; U.S. Public, pg. 753
THE HERCULES TIRE & RUBBER COMPANY; U.S. Private, pg. 523
HUBER & SUHNER AG; Int'l, pg. 637
INDUSTRIA DE PNEUMATICOS FIRESTONE LTDA.—Bridgestone Corporation; Int'l, pg. 215
GAY JOHNSON'S INC.; U.S. Private, pg. 595
KELLY BRANDS DIVISION—The Goodyear Tire & Rubber Company; U.S. Public, pg. 753
THE KELLY-SPRINGFIELD TIRE COMPANY—The Goodyear Tire & Rubber Company; U.S. Public, pg. 753
KEX PRODUCTS, INC.—Berwind Corporation; U.S. Private, pg. 138
KLEBER INDUSTRIE GMBH—Compagnie Generale des Etablissements Michelin; Int'l, pg. 322
KLEBER ITALIANA S.P.A.—Compagnie Generale des Etablissements Michelin; Int'l, pg. 322
KLEBER PNEUMATIQUES SA—Compagnie Generale des Etablissements Michelin; Int'l, pg. 322
KLEBER REIFEN UND TECHNISCHE GUMMIWAREN AG—Compagnie Generale des Etablissements Michelin; Int'l, pg. 322
KRUPP MASCHINENTECHNIK GMBH—Fried. Krupp AG; Int'l, pg. 510
LONG MILE RUBBER COMPANY—The Standard Products Company; U.S. Public, pg. 1504
MALOYA FREDESTEIN—Fredestein Banden; Int'l, pg. 505
MANUFACTURE FRANCAISE DES PNEUMATIQUES MICHELIN—Compagnie Generale des Etablissements Michelin; Int'l, pg. 322
MICHELIN AIRCRAFT TIRE CORPORATION—Compagnie Generale des Etablissements Michelin; Int'l, pg. 322
MICHELIN AMERICAS SMALL TIRES (MAST)—Compagnie Generale des Etablissements Michelin; Int'l, pg. 322
MICHELIN CORPORATION—Compagnie Generale des Etablissements Michelin; Int'l, pg. 322
MICHELIN NORTH AMERICA—Compagnie Generale des Etablissements Michelin; Int'l, pg. 322
MICHELIN REIFENWERKE KGAA—Compagnie Generale des Etablissements Michelin; Int'l, pg. 322
MICHELIN SIAM CO., LTD.—The Siam Cement Public Company Limited; Int'l, pg. 1238
MICHELIN TYRE P.L.C.—Compagnie Generale des Etablissements Michelin; Int'l, pg. 322
MYERS INDUSTRIES, INC.; U.S. Public, pg. 1143
MYERS INTERNATIONAL, INC.—Myers Industries, Inc.; U.S. Public, pg. 1143
NEUMATICOS GOODYEAR SA—The Goodyear Tire & Rubber Company; U.S. Public, pg. 753
OLIVER RUBBER CO.—The Standard Products Company; U.S. Public, pg. 1504
OLIVER RUBBER EUROPA LTD.—The Standard Products Company; U.S. Public, pg. 1505
PATCH RUBBER COMPANY—Myers Industries, Inc.; U.S. Public, pg. 1143
PERFECT EQUIPMENT CORP.—Berwind Corporation; U.S. Private, pg. 138
PIRELLI ARGENTINA DE MANDATOS S.A.—Pirelli S.p.A.; Int'l, pg. 1059
PIRELLI ARMSTRONG MIDWEST DIVISION—Pirelli S.p.A.; Int'l, pg. 1058
PIRELLI ARMSTRONG PACIFIC COAST DIVISION—Pirelli S.p.A.; Int'l, pg. 1058
PIRELLI ARMSTRONG SOUTHEAST DIVISION—Pirelli S.p.A.; Int'l, pg. 1058
PIRELLI ARMSTRONG TIRE CORPORATION—Pirelli S.p.A.; Int'l, pg. 1058
PIRELLI S.P.A.; Int'l, pg. 1058
PIRELLI TIRE INC.—Pirelli S.p.A.; Int'l, pg. 1059
PIRELLI TYRES BENELUX S.A.—Pirelli S.p.A.; Int'l, pg. 1059
PIRELLI U.K. TYRES LIMITED—Pirelli S.p.A.; Int'l, pg. 1059
PNEU UNIROYAL ENGLEBERT S.A.—Continental AG; Int'l, pg. 327
SABANCI HOLDING A.S.; Int'l, pg. 1167
SAVSJO FALGAR AB—Trelleborg AB; Int'l, pg. 1422
SEMPERIT REIFEN AG—Continental AG; Int'l, pg. 328
SIAM TYRE CO., LTD.—The Siam Cement Public Company Limited; Int'l, pg. 1238

SIAM TYRE INDUSTRY CO., LTD.—The Siam Cement Public Company Limited; *Int'l*, pg. 1238
SIME AIRCRAFT TYRE COMPANY SDN. BHD.—Sime Darby Berhad; *Int'l*, pg. 1250
SIME DARBY BERHAD; *Int'l*, pg. 1249
SIME DARBY BERHAD MALAYSIA REGION—Sime Darby Berhad; *Int'l*, pg. 1250
SKEGA AB—Svedala Industri AB; *Int'l*, pg. 1323
SOCIETA PNEUMATICI PIRELLI S.P.A.—Pirelli S.p.A.; *Int'l*, pg. 1058
SOUTH PACIFIC TYRES—Pacific Dunlop Limited; *Int'l*, pg. 1021
THE STANDARD PRODUCTS COMPANY; *U.S. Public*, pg. 1504
SUMITOMO RUBBER INDUSTRIES LTD.; *Int'l*, pg. 1316
SWEDISH TYRE TUBE AB—Trelleborg AB; *Int'l*, pg. 1422
THAI BRIDGESTONE CO., LTD.—Bridgestone Corporation; *Int'l*, pg. 214
TITAN TIRE CORPORATION OF TN—Titan International, Inc.; *U.S. Public*, pg. 1618
TOYO TIRE & RUBBER CO., LTD.; *Int'l*, pg. 1411
TOYO TIRE (U.S.A.) CORPORATION—Toyo Tire & Rubber Co., Ltd.; *Int'l*, pg. 1411
TREAD RUBBER PLANT—Bandag, Incorporated; *U.S. Public*, pg. 177
TRELLEBORG AB; *Int'l*, pg. 1419
TRELLEBORG ATLAS A/S—Trelleborg AB; *Int'l*, pg. 1423
TRELLEBORG FABRIEKEN B.V.—Trelleborg AB; *Int'l*, pg. 1423
TRELLEBORG RUBBER & PLASTICS DIV.—Trelleborg AB; *Int'l*, pg. 1422
TRELLEBORGDACK AB—Trelleborg AB; *Int'l*, pg. 1422
UNIROYAL ENGLEBERT REIFEN GMBH—Continental AG; *Int'l*, pg. 327
UNIROYAL ENGLEBERT TYRES LTD.—Continental AG; *Int'l*, pg. 327
UNIROYAL GOODRICH CANADA INC.—Compagnie Generale des Etablissements Michelin; *Int'l*, pg. 322
UNIVERSAL COOPERATIVES, INC.; *U.S. Private*, pg. 1127
VISKAFORS AB—Trelleborg AB; *Int'l*, pg. 1423
VREDESTEIN BANDEN B.V.—Vredestein N.V.; *Int'l*, pg. 1481
VREDESTEIN FIETSBANDEN B.V.—Vredestein N.V.; *Int'l*, pg. 1481
YOKOHAMA CORPORATION OF NORTH AMERICA—The Yokohama Rubber Co., Ltd.; *Int'l*, pg. 1521
THE YOKOHAMA RUBBER CO., LTD.; *Int'l*, pg. 1521
YOKOHAMA TIRE CANADA INC.—The Yokohama Rubber Co., Ltd.; *Int'l*, pg. 1521
YOKOHAMA TIRE CORPORATION—The Yokohama Rubber Co., Ltd.; *Int'l*, pg. 1521
YOKOHAMA TYRE AUSTRALIAN PTY., LTD.—The Yokohama Rubber Co., Ltd.; *Int'l*, pg. 1522

3021 — RUBBER & PLASTICS FOOTWEAR

AMERICAN BILTRITE (CANADA) LTD.—American Biltrite Inc.; *U.S. Public*, pg. 69
AMERICAN CONSUMER PRODUCTS—Vista 2000, Inc.; *U.S. Private*, pg. 1142
BANGKOK RUBBER PUBLIC CO., LTD.; *Int'l*, pg. 146
COLE-HAAN—Nike, Inc.; *U.S. Public*, pg. 1184
COMMERCIAL PLASTICS & SUPPLIES CORP.; *U.S. Private*, pg. 258
COMPANIA HULERA SULA, S.A. DE C.V.—American Biltrite Inc.; *U.S. Public*, pg. 69
DACOR CORPORATION; *U.S. Private*, pg. 306
DR. SCHOLL'S SPA—Scholl Plc; *Int'l*, pg. 1209
E.J. FOOTWEAR CORP.—U.S. Industries, Inc.; *U.S. Public*, pg. 1684
ETONIC TRETORN—Kohlberg Kravis Roberts & Co.; *U.S. Private*, pg. 629
GATOR INDUSTRIES INC.; *U.S. Private*, pg. 441
GENFOOT INC.; *Int'l*, pg. 549
GOODALL RUBBER COMPANY—Trelleborg AB; *Int'l*, pg. 1423
THE GOODYEAR TIRE & RUBBER COMPANY; *U.S. Public*, pg. 752
HEVEA B.V.—Vredestein N.V.; *Int'l*, pg. 1481
HYDE ATHLETIC INDUSTRIES, INC.; *U.S. Public*, pg. 851
LUDLOW COMPOSITES CORPORATION; *U.S. Private*, pg. 680
MASON SHOE MFG. CO.; *U.S. Private*, pg. 712
PACIFIC BRANDS—Pacific Dunlop Limited; *Int'l*, pg. 1021
PONY U.S.A.—Pentland Group PLC; *Int'l*, pg. 1036
SIME DARBY BERHAD; *Int'l*, pg. 1249
SIME DARBY BERHAD TYRE MANUFACTURING DIVISION—Sime Darby Berhad; *Int'l*, pg. 1250
THE STRIDE RITE CORPORATION; *U.S. Public*, pg. 1524
TOTES INCORPORATED—Bain Capital; *U.S. Private*, pg. 111
TRANSMARCO LIMITED; *Int'l*, pg. 1417
TRETORN—Proventus AB, *Int'l*, pg. 1072
TRETORN AB—Proventus AB; *Int'l*, pg. 1072

3052 — RUBBER & PLASTICS HOSE & BELTING

ACTION CLINTON—Action Technology Company; *U.S. Private*, pg. 15
ACTION ROCKAWAY—Action Technology Company; *U.S. Private*, pg. 15
ACTION TECHNOLOGY COMPANY; *U.S. Private*, pg. 15
AEROQUIP CORPORATION—Aeroquip-Vickers, Inc.; *U.S. Public*, pg. 24
AEROQUIP IBERICA S.A. (AUTOMOTIVE GROUP)—Aeroquip-Vickers, Inc.; *U.S. Public*, pg. 25
AEROQUIP MEXICANA S.A. DE C.V.—Aeroquip-Vickers, Inc.; *U.S. Public*, pg. 25
AEROQUIP-VICKERS, INC.; *U.S. Public*, pg. 24
ALLIED DIGITAL TECHNOLOGIES; *U.S. Public*, pg. 48
AMERICAN GASKET & RUBBER—Action Technology Company; *U.S. Private*, pg. 15
ANGUS FIRE ARMOUR CORP.—Williams Holdings Plc; *Int'l*, pg. 1500
AQUAPORE MOISTURE SYSTEMS, INC.—Powell Duffryn PLC; *Int'l*, pg. 1066
AUTOMOTIVE DISTRIBUTION SALES DIV.—Dana Corporation; *U.S. Public*, pg. 479
AUTOMOTIVE GROUP—Aeroquip-Vickers, Inc.; *U.S. Public*, pg. 24
BTR NYLEX LIMITED—BTR plc; *Int'l*, pg. 129
BOSTON WEATHERHEAD DIV.—Dana Corporation; *U.S. Public*, pg. 479
BRAKES INDIA LTD.—LucasVarity plc; *Int'l*, pg. 820
BRIDGESTONE CORPORATION; *Int'l*, pg. 213
CALLAHAN MINING CORPORATION—Coeur D'Alene Mines Corporation; *U.S. Public*, pg. 394
CATERPILLAR INC.; *U.S. Public*, pg. 315
COMMERCIAL PLASTICS & SUPPLIES CORP.; *U.S. Private*, pg. 258
COMPANHIA GOODYEAR DO BRASIL PRODUTOS DE BORRACHA—The Goodyear Tire & Rubber Company; *U.S. Public*, pg. 753
COMPANIA HULERA GOODYEAR-OXO SOCIEDAD ANONIMA—The Goodyear Tire & Rubber Company; *U.S. Public*, pg. 753
COSMOFLEX, INC.—The Goodyear Tire & Rubber Company; *U.S. Public*, pg. 753
CRANE CO.; *U.S. Public*, pg. 456
CRANE RESISTOFLEX/DEFENSE—Crane Co.; *U.S. Public*, pg. 457
CRANE RESISTOFLEX/INDUSTRIAL—Crane Co.; *U.S. Public*, pg. 457
DSM ENGINEERING PLASTIC PRODUCTS—DSM N.V.; *Int'l*, pg. 354
C.R. DANIELS, INC.; *U.S. Private*, pg. 310
DAYCO PRODUCTS INC.—Mark IV Industries Inc.; *U.S. Public*, pg. 1045
DAYCO PTI, INC.—Mark IV Industries Inc.; *U.S. Public*, pg. 1045
DAYCO SWAN CORPORATION—Mark IV Industries Inc.; *U.S. Public*, pg. 1045
DERLAN INDUSTRIES LIMITED; *Int'l*, pg. 395
DEUTSCHE GOODYEAR GMBH—The Goodyear Tire & Rubber Company; *U.S. Public*, pg. 753
DOWTY SILCOFAB—TI Group plc; *Int'l*, pg. 1338
DUNLOP HIFLEX LTD.—BTR plc; *Int'l*, pg. 125
DUNLOP INDUSTRIAL HOSE LTD.—BTR plc; *Int'l*, pg. 125
DYNACRAFT—Paccar Inc.; *U.S. Public*, pg. 1246
ENGINEERED SYSTEMS GROUP—Aeroquip-Vickers, Inc.; *U.S. Public*, pg. 24
FEDERAL HOSE MANUFACTURING CORP.—Flexfab Horizons International, Inc.; *U.S. Private*, pg. 412
FIRESTONE INDUSTRIAL PRODUCTS CO.—Bridgestone Corporation; *Int'l*, pg. 214
THE FLEXAUST CO.—Coeur D'Alene Mines Corporation; *U.S. Public*, pg. 394
FLEXFAB HORIZONS INTERNATIONAL, INC.; *U.S. Private*, pg. 412
FLUID CONNECTORS GROUP, PARKER HANNIFIN (U.K.) LTD.—Parker Hannifin Corporation; *U.S. Public*, pg. 1261
FLUID PRODUCT SALES DIV.—Dana Corporation; *U.S. Public*, pg. 479
FREIOS VARGA S/A—LucasVarity plc; *Int'l*, pg. 820
FURON COMPANY; *U.S. Public*, pg. 688
GATES CANADA INC.—Tomkins PLC; *Int'l*, pg. 1396
THE GATES CORPORATION—Tomkins PLC; *Int'l*, pg. 1396
GATES DO BRASIL IND. E COM. LTDA.—Tomkins PLC; *Int'l*, pg. 1396
GATES EUROPE—Tomkins PLC; *Int'l*, pg. 1396
GATES HYDRAULICS LTD.—Tomkins PLC; *Int'l*, pg. 1397
GATES RUBBER CO. INC.—Tomkins PLC; *Int'l*, pg. 1396
THE GATES RUBBER COMPANY LIMITED—Tomkins PLC; *Int'l*, pg. 1397
GATES RUBBER DE MEXICO—Tomkins PLC; *Int'l*, pg. 1397
GATES SPAIN AUTOMOTIVE PRODUCTS DIVISION—Tomkins PLC; *Int'l*, pg. 1397
GILMOUR HOSE COMPANY—Emerson Electric Co.; *U.S. Public*, pg. 575
GOODALL RUBBER COMPANY—Trelleborg AB; *Int'l*, pg. 1423
THE GOODYEAR TIRE & RUBBER COMPANY; *U.S. Public*, pg. 752
GRANFORD MANUFACTURING, INC.—The Goodyear Tire & Rubber Company; *U.S. Public*, pg. 753
HBD INDUSTRIES, INC.; *U.S. Private*, pg. 489
HABISAT GLOBE INC.—Habisat Svergie AB; *Int'l*, pg. 585
HABISAT SVERGIE AB; *Int'l*, pg. 585
HYDRAULICS INC.—Echlin Inc.; *U.S. Public*, pg. 560
IPC-INTERNATIONAL PARTS CORP.—Whitman Corporation; *U.S. Public*, pg. 1766
INDUSTRIAL AMERICAS GROUP—Aeroquip-Vickers, Inc.; *U.S. Public*, pg. 24
INTRALOX A/S—The Laitram Corporation; *U.S. Private*, pg. 643
JAFFREY FIRE PROTECTION CO.—D.D. Bean & Sons Co.; *U.S. Private*, pg. 127
JASON INDUSTRIAL, INC.; *U.S. Private*, pg. 583
LUCAS LIGHT VEHICLE BRAKING SYSTEMS—LucasVarity plc; *Int'l*, pg. 819
MARK IV AUTOMOTIVE CANADA INC.—Mark IV Industries Inc.; *U.S. Public*, pg. 1045
MELNOR INC.—O'Sullivan Corporation; *U.S. Public*, pg. 1234
MULHERN BELTING, INC.; *U.S. Private*, pg. 766
NEUMATICOS GOODYEAR SA—The Goodyear Tire & Rubber Company; *U.S. Public*, pg. 753
NIEDNER LIMITED—Wajax Limited; *Int'l*, pg. 1485
PIRELLI ARMSTRONG TIRE CORPORATION—Pirelli S.p.A.; *Int'l*, pg. 1058
PLASTRON—Action Technology Company; *U.S. Private*, pg. 15
PLASTRON DALTON—Action Technology Company; *U.S. Private*, pg. 15
PLUMLEY COMPANIES—Dana Corporation; *U.S. Public*, pg. 480
POLYFLEX BUSINESS UNIT—Parker Hannifin Corporation; *U.S. Public*, pg. 1260
RAIN BIRD SPRINKLERS MANUFACTURING CORP.; *U.S. Private*, pg. 907
REEVES INTERNATIONAL—Hart Holding Company, Inc.; *U.S. Private*, pg. 507
SNAP-TITE HOSE, INC.—Snap-Tite, Inc.; *U.S. Private*, pg. 1010
SNAP-TITE, INC.; *U.S. Private*, pg. 1010
STARCAN CORPORATION; *Int'l*, pg. 1297
SYNFLEX DIVISION—Furon Company; *U.S. Public*, pg. 689
TEKNOR APEX COMPANY; *U.S. Private*, pg. 1073
TIGERFLEX CORPORATION—Tigers Polymer Corporation; *Int'l*, pg. 1390
TIGERPOLY MANUFACTURING, INC.—Tigers Polymer Corporation; *Int'l*, pg. 1390
TIGERS POLYMER CORPORATION; *Int'l*, pg. 1390
TRELLEBORG AB; *Int'l*, pg. 1419
TRELLEBORG-BOLIDEN—Trelleborg AB; *Int'l*, pg. 1423
TRELLEBORG RUBBER & PLASTICS DIV.—Trelleborg AB; *Int'l*, pg. 1422
TRELLEX AB—Svedala Industri AB; *Int'l*, pg. 1324
TRELLEX AB—Trelleborg AB; *Int'l*, pg. 1423
TRINOVA DO BRAZIL S.A.-DIVISAO AEROQUIP—Aeroquip-Vickers, Inc.; *U.S. Public*, pg. 25
TRINOVA LIMITED AEROQUIP AUTOMOTIVE OPERATIONS—Aeroquip-Vickers, Inc.; *U.S. Public*, pg. 25
TRINOVA S.A.-AEROQUIP DIV.—Aeroquip-Vickers, Inc.; *U.S. Public*, pg. 25
VERMONT AMERICAN TOOL CORP.—Emerson Electric Co.; *U.S. Public*, pg. 575
WAJAX LIMITED; *Int'l*, pg. 1484
WEATHERHEAD BRAKE DIV.—Dana Corporation; *U.S. Public*, pg. 480

3053 — GASKETS, PACKING & SEALING DEVICES

ACTION CLINTON—Action Technology Company; *U.S. Private*, pg. 15
ACTION ROCKAWAY—Action Technology Company; *U.S. Private*, pg. 15
ACTION TECHNOLOGY COMPANY; *U.S. Private*, pg. 15
AMERICAN GASKET & RUBBER—Action Technology Company; *U.S. Private*, pg. 15
AUTOMOTIVE DISTRIBUTION SALES DIV.—Dana Corporation; *U.S. Public*, pg. 479
BUNDY BELGIUM SA—TI Group plc; *Int'l*, pg. 1341
FEODOR BURGMANN DICHTUNGSWERKE GMBH; *Int'l*, pg. 233
BURGMANN MALAYSIA SDN BHD—Feodor Burgmann Dichtungswerke GmbH; *Int'l*, pg. 233
BURGMANN SEALS AMERICA, INC.—Feodor Burgmann Dichtungswerke GmbH; *Int'l*, pg. 233
CHEMOFLON GMBH—Martin Merkel GmbH & Co. KG; *Int'l*, pg. 859
A.W. CHESTERTON COMPANY; *U.S. Private*, pg. 234
CHOMERICS EUROPE/U.K.—Parker Hannifin Corporation; *U.S. Public*, pg. 1262
COLTEC HOLDINGS INC; *U.S. Public*, pg. 401
COOPERS PAYEN LTD.—T & N Plc; *Int'l*, pg. 1334
JOHN CRANE AUSTRALIA PTY, LTD.—TI Group plc; *Int'l*, pg. 1339
S.A. JOHN CRANE BELGIUM N.V.—TI Group plc; *Int'l*, pg. 1339
JOHN CRANE BRASIL INDUSTRIAL LTDA.—TI Group plc; *Int'l*, pg. 1339
JOHN CRANE CANADA, INC.—TI Group plc; *Int'l*, pg. 1339
JOHN CRANE GMBH—TI Group plc; *Int'l*, pg. 1339
JOHN CRANE GROUP—TI Group plc; *Int'l*, pg. 1338
JOHN CRANE IBERICA S.A.—TI Group plc; *Int'l*, pg. 1339
JOHN CRANE ITALIA SPA—TI Group plc; *Int'l*, pg. 1339
JOHN CRANE (JAPAN), INC.—TI Group plc; *Int'l*, pg. 1339
JOHN CRANE (KOREA) CO., LTD.—TI Group plc; *Int'l*, pg. 1339
JOHN CRANE KUWAIT—TI Group plc; *Int'l*, pg. 1339
JOHN CRANE LTD.—TI Group plc; *Int'l*, pg. 1339
JOHN CRANE MECHANICAL SEALS—TI Group plc; *Int'l*, pg. 1339
JOHN CRANE SAUDI ARABIA LTD.—TI Group plc; *Int'l*, pg. 1339
JOHN CRANE SINGAPORE PTE. LTD.—TI Group plc; *Int'l*, pg. 1339
JOHN CRANE (TAIWAN) CO. LTD.—TI Group plc; *Int'l*, pg. 1339
JOHN CRANE UK LTD.—TI Group plc; *Int'l*, pg. 1338
DEEP SEA SEALS LTD.—TI Group plc; *Int'l*, pg. 1339
DELTA RUBBER COMPANY; *U.S. Private*, pg. 323
DETROIT GASKET—Indian Head Industries Inc.; *U.S. Private*, pg. 560
DIEHL & EAGLE-PICHER GMBH—Eagle-Picher Industries, Inc.; *U.S. Private*, pg. 355
DODGE REGUPOL, INC.; *U.S. Private*, pg. 337
DOWTY O RINGS & ACTUATION POLYMERS—TI Group plc; *Int'l*, pg. 1338
DOWTY PALMER-CHENARD—TI Group plc; *Int'l*, pg. 1338
DOWTY TECMOLD—TI Group plc; *Int'l*, pg. 1338
DRIVETRAIN SERVICE DIV.—Dana Corporation; *U.S. Public*, pg. 479
DURAMETALLIC CORP.—Flowserve Corporation; *U.S. Public*, pg. 658
EG & G AEROSPACE & ENGINEERED PRODUCTS—EG & G, Inc.; *U.S. Public*, pg. 542
EG & G SEALOL EAGLE—EG & G, Inc.; *U.S. Public*, pg. 544
EG & G SEALOL ENGINEERED PRODUCTS DIVISION—EG & G, Inc.; *U.S. Public*, pg. 542
EG & G SEALOL-INDUSTRIAL DIVISION—EG & G, Inc.; *U.S. Public*, pg. 543

EAGLE-PICHER WOLVERINE GMBH—Eagle-Picher Industries, Inc.; U.S. Private, pg. 355
ENGINEERED SEALS—TI Group plc; Int'l, pg. 1338
FARNAM SEALING SYSTEMS DIVISION—Coltec Holdings Inc; U.S. Public, pg. 401
FEL-PRO INCORPORATED; U.S. Private, pg. 399
FLUID PRODUCT SALES DIV.—Dana Corporation; U.S. Public, pg. 479
FLUIDTEC ENGINEER PRODUCTS—Coltec Holdings Inc; U.S. Public, pg. 401
FREUDENBERG-NOK; U.S. Private, pg. 427
FURON COMPANY; U.S. Public, pg. 688
GNC CORP—Goshen Rubber Co., Inc.; U.S. Private, pg. 466
GRN CORP.—Goshen Rubber Co., Inc.; U.S. Private, pg. 466
GSH CORP.—Goshen Rubber Co., Inc.; U.S. Private, pg. 466
GEMSTONE GASKET CO.—Dana Corporation; U.S. Public, pg. 480
GLACIER VANDERVELL, INC.—T & N Plc; Int'l, pg. 1334
GOETZE CORP. OF AMERICA—T & N Plc; Int'l, pg. 1335
AE GOETZE GMBH—T & N Plc; Int'l, pg. 1334
GOODALL RUBBER COMPANY—Trelleborg AB; Int'l, pg. 1423
GOSHEN RUBBER OF CANADA LTD.—Goshen Rubber Co., Inc.; U.S. Private, pg. 466
HUTCHENSON SEAL CORPORATION; U.S. Private, pg. 550
HUTCHINSON S.A.—Total S.A.; Int'l, pg. 1409
JADE S.A.—Martin Merkel GmbH & Co. KG; Int'l, pg. 859
JOHN CRANE INC.—TI Group plc; Int'l, pg. 1338
KSA DICHTSYSTEME G.M.B.H & CO. KG—Svedala Industri AB; Int'l, pg. 1323
KAMAN INDUSTRIAL TECHNOLOGIES CORP.—Kaman Corporation; U.S. Public, pg. 942
KAYDON RING & SEAL, INC.—Kaydon Corporation; U.S. Public, pg. 946
KLOCKNER-DOWTY—TI Group plc; Int'l, pg. 1338
LAMONS METAL GASKET CO.—Masco Corporation; U.S. Public, pg. 1054
MARQUETTE COPPERSMITHING CO., INC.; U.S. Private, pg. 706
MCCORD PAYEN INC.—T & N Plc; Int'l, pg. 1334
MARTIN MERKEL GMBH & CO. KG; Int'l, pg. 859
METALLIC GASKET DIVISION—Furon Company; U.S. Public, pg. 689
MR. GASKET INC.—Echlin Inc.; U.S. Public, pg. 560
NHK GASKET SINGAPORE CO. (PTE.) LTD.—Nissho Iwai Corporation; Int'l, pg. 948
O-RING DIV.—Parker Hannifin Corporation; U.S. Public, pg. 1262
O-SEAL DIV.—Parker Hannifin Corporation; U.S. Public, pg. 1262
PARKER HANNIFIN GMBH, O-RING DIV. EUROPE—Parker Hannifin Corporation; U.S. Public, pg. 1263
PAWLING CORPORATION; U.S. Private, pg. 844
THE PAYNE INVESTMENT COMPANY—Brittany Corporation; U.S. Private, pg. 169
PLASTOMER CORP.; U.S. Private, pg. 872
PLASTRON—Action Technology Company; U.S. Private, pg. 15
PLASTRON DALTON—Action Technology Company; U.S. Private, pg. 15
PLUMLEY COMPANIES—Dana Corporation; U.S. Public, pg. 480
POLAR SEALS APS; PTFE-PACKING MFG. OPERATION—Parker Hannifin Corporation; U.S. Public, pg. 1262
REINZ-DICHTUNGS-GMBH—Dana Corporation; U.S. Public, pg. 480
RUBBER MOLDING DIVISION—Eagle-Picher Industries, Inc.; U.S. Private, pg. 355
RUBBERHIDE COMPANY—Trelleborg AB; Int'l, pg. 1423
SI SEALING PARTS SPA—TI Group plc; Int'l, pg. 1338
SIG SCHWEIZERSICHE INDUSTRIE-GESELLSCHAFT HOLDING AG; Int'l, pg. 1156
SCHLEGEL MARYLAND—BTR plc; Int'l, pg. 128
SCHLEGEL TENNESSEE, INC.—BTR plc; Int'l, pg. 128
SEALING DEVICES INC.; U.S. Private, pg. 978
SEALING EQUIPMENT PRODUCTS CO., INC.; U.S. Private, pg. 978
SEALS N.V./S.A.—Furon Company; U.S. Public, pg. 689
SPECIFICATION RUBBER PRODUCTS INC.—American Cast Iron Pipe Co.; U.S. Private, pg. 52
STAND-COTE INDUSTRIAL COATINGS DIV.—Standco Industries, Inc.; U.S. Private, pg. 1032
STANDCO INDUSTRIES, INC.; U.S. Private, pg. 1032
STANHOPE PRODUCTS COMPANY—Brittany Corporation; U.S. Private, pg. 169
STERLING RUBBER & GASKET—Standco Industries, Inc.; U.S. Private, pg. 1032
T & N INDUSTRIES, INC.—T & N Plc; Int'l, pg. 1334
THIOKOL CORPORATION; U.S. Public, pg. 1596
3M; U.S. Public, pg. 1604
TOTAL S.A.; Int'l, pg. 1408
TRELLEBORG RUBBER & PLASTICS DIV.—Trelleborg AB; Int'l, pg. 1422
ALBERT TROSTEL & SONS CO.; U.S. Private, pg. 1105
ALBERT TROSTEL PACKINGS LTD.—Albert Trostel & Sons Co.; U.S. Private, pg. 1105
VICTOR PRODUCTS—Dana Corporation; U.S. Public, pg. 480
JAMES WALKER & CO. LIMITED; Int'l, pg. 1485
JAMES WALKER MFG. CO.—James Walker & Co. Limited; Int'l, pg. 1485
WYNN'S INTERNATIONAL, INC.; U.S. Public, pg. 1782
WYNN'S-PRECISION FLUID SEALING DIV.—Wynn's International, Inc.; U.S. Public, pg. 1783
WYNN'S-PRECISION, INC.—Wynn's International, Inc.; U.S. Public, pg. 1783
WYNN'S-PRECISION, INC., ARIZONA DIV.—Wynn's International, Inc.; U.S. Public, pg. 1783

3061 — MOLDED, EXTRUDED & LATHE-CUT RUBBER GOODS

AKROCHEM CORPORATION; U.S. Private, pg. 30
BEEBE RUBBER COMPANY—The Chardon Rubber Co.; U.S. Private, pg. 229
CHAD THERAPEUTICS; U.S. Public, pg. 332
CHARDON ELECTRICAL COMPONENTS, INC.—The Chardon Rubber Co.; U.S. Private, pg. 229
THE CHARDON RUBBER CO.; U.S. Private, pg. 229
DAYCO PRODUCTS INC.—Mark IV Industries Inc.; U.S. Public, pg. 1045
DELTA RUBBER COMPANY; U.S. Private, pg. 323
DOWTY SILCOFAB—TI Group plc; Int'l, pg. 1338
ENIDINE INCORPORATED; U.S. Private, pg. 377
EVANS INDUSTRIES, INC.; U.S. Private, pg. 385
CARL FREUDENBERG—Freudenberg & Company; Int'l, pg. 505
GOODALL RUBBER COMPANY—Trelleborg AB; Int'l, pg. 1423
HORDA PACKINGSINDUSTRI AB—Trelleborg AB; Int'l, pg. 1422
HUBER & SUHNER AG; Int'l, pg. 637
HUTCHENSON SEAL CORPORATION; U.S. Private, pg. 550
HYDRIL COMPANY; U.S. Private, pg. 551
HYDRIL RUBBER OPERS.—Hydril Company; U.S. Private, pg. 551
IMAS S.A.—Clouth Gummiwerke AG; Int'l, pg. 298
JBL DIV.—Parker Hannifin Corporation; U.S. Public, pg. 1262
KWG KUNSTSTOFFWERK GESSMANN GMBH & CO.—DSM N.V.; Int'l, pg. 355
KINUGAWA RUBBER INDUSTRIAL CO., LTD.—Nissan Motor Co., Ltd.; Int'l, pg. 944
LEXINGTON PRECISION CORPORATION; U.S. Public, pg. 991
THE LEYLAND & BIRMINGHAM RUBBER GROUP—BTR plc; Int'l, pg. 125
LINATEX CORPORATION OF AMERICA—Harrisons & Crosfield plc; Int'l, pg. 599
LONSTROFF-BTR AG—BTR plc; Int'l, pg. 130
MEDICAL RUBBER AB—Perstorp AB; Int'l, pg. 1036
MOORE COMPANY; U.S. Private, pg. 759
MOX-MED, INC.—Applied Power Inc.; U.S. Public, pg. 124
NEUMATICOS GOODYEAR SA—The Goodyear Tire & Rubber Company; U.S. Public, pg. 753
OMNI PRODUCTS, INC.; U.S. Private, pg. 816
OMNI PRODUCTS, INC.—OMNI Products, Inc.; U.S. Private, pg. 816
PAWLING CORPORATION; U.S. Private, pg. 844
PIRELLI ARMSTRONG EXTRUDED PRODUCTS DIVISION—Pirelli S.p.A.; Int'l, pg. 1058
POREX TECHNOLOGIES CORP. OF GEORGIA—Synetic, Inc.; U.S. Public, pg. 1548
ROUSH INDUSTRIES INC.; U.S. Private, pg. 948
RUBBER MOLDING DIVISION—Eagle-Picher Industries, Inc.; U.S. Private, pg. 355
SIGMA AB—Trelleborg AB; Int'l, pg. 1422
SIME DARBY BERHAD; Int'l, pg. 1249
SIME DARBY BERHAD TYRE MANUFACTURING DIVISION—Sime Darby Berhad; Int'l, pg. 1250
TFX MEDICAL INC.—Teleflex Incorporated; U.S. Public, pg. 1570
3M; U.S. Public, pg. 1604
TRELLEBORG AB; Int'l, pg. 1419
TRELLEBORG RUBBER & PLASTICS DIV.—Trelleborg AB; Int'l, pg. 1422
TRELLEBORG YSH, INC.—Trelleborg AB; Int'l, pg. 1422
ALBERT TROSTEL PACKINGS LTD.—Albert Trostel & Sons Co.; U.S. Private, pg. 1105
AB VARANMO GUMMIFABRIK—Trelleborg AB; Int'l, pg. 1422
VERNAY LABORATORIES, INC.; U.S. Private, pg. 1137
VISKAFORS AB—Trelleborg AB; Int'l, pg. 1423
VREDESTEIN N.V.; Int'l, pg. 1481

3069 — FABRICATED RUBBER PRODUCTS, NEC

A&A MANUFACTURING CO.; U.S. Private, pg. 1
ABBOTT LABORATORIES/ASHLAND—Abbott Laboratories; U.S. Public, pg. 13
ACE COMB COMPANY INC.—Newell Co.; U.S. Public, pg. 1177
ADVANCED POLYMERS DIVISION - KENT FACILITY—Furon Company; U.S. Public, pg. 689
AIR CRUISERS CO.—Groupe Zodiac; Int'l, pg. 572
AKVAMATIK AB—Trelleborg AB; Int'l, pg. 1422
ALCO INDUSTRIES, INC.; U.S. Private, pg. 32
ALDAN INDUSTRIES; U.S. Private, pg. 33
AMERICAN BILTRITE (CANADA) LTD.—American Biltrite Inc.; U.S. Public, pg. 69
AMERICAN BILTRITE INC.; U.S. Public, pg. 68
AMERICAN CAST IRON PIPE CO.; U.S. Private, pg. 51
AMERICAN EXCELSIOR COMPANY; U.S. Private, pg. 53
AMERICAN FUEL CELL & COATED FABRICS CO. (AMFUEL); U.S. Private, pg. 55
ANSELL INTERNATIONAL—Pacific Dunlop Limited; Int'l, pg. 1021
AUTOMOTIVE ORIGINAL EQUIPMENT DIV.—Mark IV Industries Inc.; U.S. Public, pg. 1045
BTR, INC.—BTR plc; Int'l, pg. 127
BARRY CONTROLS INDUSTRIAL/DEFENSE—Applied Power Inc.; U.S. Public, pg. 124
BATA SHOE CO., INC.—CHB Corp.; U.S. Private, pg. 195
THE BILTRITE CORPORATION; U.S. Private, pg. 144
SAMUEL BINGHAM CO; U.S. Private, pg. 144
BINKS DE MEXICO, S.A. DE S.V.—Binks Sames Corporation; U.S. Public, pg. 229
BOSCH BRAKING SYSTEMS-NORTH AMERICA—Robert Bosch GmbH; Int'l, pg. 204
BOSS CANADA, INC.—Vista 2000, Inc.; U.S. Private, pg. 1142
BOSS DE MEXICO, S.A.—Vista 2000, Inc.; U.S. Private, pg. 1142
BRIDGESTONE/FIRESTONE, INC.—Bridgestone Corporation; Int'l, pg. 213
BUCKHORN RUBBER PRODUCTS INC.—Myers Industries, Inc.; U.S. Public, pg. 1143
BUNNELL PLASTICS DIVISION—Furon Company; U.S. Public, pg. 689
BURKE INDUSTRIES, INC.; U.S. Private, pg. 183
CHB CORP.; U.S. Private, pg. 194
CHR DIVISION—Furon Company; U.S. Public, pg. 689
CHR INDUSTRIES, INC.—Furon Company; U.S. Public, pg. 689
CANADIAN FABRICATED PRODUCTS—Chrysler Corporation; U.S. Public, pg. 354
CARLISLE COMPANIES INCORPORATED; U.S. Public, pg. 305
CARLISLE SYNTEC INC.—Carlisle Companies Incorporated; U.S. Public, pg. 305
CASTLE RUBBER CO.—Park-Ohio Industries, Inc.; U.S. Public, pg. 1258
CENTRAL RUBBER COMPANY—Woodhead Industries, Inc.; U.S. Public, pg. 1776
CHARDON ELECTRICAL COMPONENTS, INC.—The Chardon Rubber Co.; U.S. Private, pg. 229
THE CHARDON RUBBER CO.; U.S. Private, pg. 229
CHASE & SONS DIVISION—Chase Corporation; U.S. Public, pg. 337
CHASE & SONS-WEBSTER BRANCH—Chase Corporation; U.S. Public, pg. 337
CLOUTH GUMMIWERKE AG; Int'l, pg. 297
COMMERCIAL PLASTICS & SUPPLIES CORP.; U.S. Private, pg. 258
COMPANIA HULERA SULA, S.A. DE C.V.—American Biltrite Inc.; U.S. Public, pg. 69
CONNOR CORPORATION—Connor Corporation; U.S. Private, pg. 264
CONTINENTAL AMERICAN CORP.; U.S. Private, pg. 267
H A COOMBS LIMITED—SLD Holdings Ltd.; Int'l, pg. 1160
COOPER TIRE & RUBBER COMPANY; U.S. Public, pg. 445
COW PROOFINGS LIMITED—BTR plc; Int'l, pg. 124
DACOR CORPORATION; U.S. Private, pg. 306
DAIKYO SEIKO CO., LTD.—The West Company, Incorporated; U.S. Public, pg. 1756
DAYCO MOLDED PRODUCTS—Mark IV Industries Inc.; U.S. Public, pg. 1045
DAYCO RUBBER INDUSTRIAL SALES DIVISION—Mark IV Industries Inc.; U.S. Public, pg. 1045
DAYCO RUBBER PRODUCTS CO.—Mark IV Industries Inc.; U.S. Public, pg. 1045
DAYFLEX WORLDWIDE—Mark IV Industries Inc.; U.S. Public, pg. 1045
DELTA RUBBER COMPANY; U.S. Private, pg. 323
DEPUY, INC.—Corange Limited; Int'l, pg. 331
DIEHL & EAGLE-PICHER GMBH—Eagle-Picher Industries, Inc.; U.S. Private, pg. 355
DIXON TICONDEROGA COMPANY; U.S. Public, pg. 514
DODGE REGUPOL, INC.; U.S. Private, pg. 337
DURAKON INDUSTRIES, INC.; U.S. Public, pg. 537
DURHAM CHEMICALS LTD.—Harrisons & Crosfield plc; Int'l, pg. 598
EAGLE-PICHER INDUSTRIES, INC.; U.S. Private, pg. 355
EASY DAY MANUFACTURING COMPANY; U.S. Private, pg. 358
ELASTOMER COMPONENTS UNIT—Rogers Corporation; U.S. Public, pg. 1402
ENIDINE INCORPORATED; U.S. Private, pg. 377
EVENFLO COMPANY, INC.—Kohlberg Kravis Roberts & Co.; U.S. Private, pg. 629
FO-MAC DIVISION—Furon Company; U.S. Public, pg. 689
FABREEKA INTERNATIONAL, INC.; U.S. Private, pg. 390
FEL-PRO INCORPORATED; U.S. Private, pg. 399
FELTRAX INTERNATIONAL, INC.—BTR plc; Int'l, pg. 130
FIRESTONE INDUSTRIAL PRODUCTS CO.—Bridgestone Corporation; Int'l, pg. 214
THE FIRST YEARS INC.; U.S. Public, pg. 642
5 RUBBER CORPORATION—The Standard Products Company; U.S. Public, pg. 1504
FLEXFAB HORIZONS INTERNATIONAL, INC.; U.S. Private, pg. 412
FLUID PRODUCT SALES DIV.—Dana Corporation; U.S. Public, pg. 479
FLUIDTEC ENGINEER PRODUCTS—Coltec Holdings Inc; U.S. Public, pg. 401
FOAMEX, L.P.—Trace International Holdings, Inc.; U.S. Private, pg. 1094
FREUDENBERG & COMPANY; Int'l, pg. 505
CARL FREUDENBERG—Freudenberg & Company; Int'l, pg. 505
FREUDENBERG NOK—Freudenberg & Company; Int'l, pg. 507
FURON COMPANY; U.S. Public, pg. 688
FURON FLUORGLAS PRODUCTS—Furon Company; U.S. Public, pg. 689
GKK AUTOMOTIVE—GenCorp Inc.; U.S. Public, pg. 706
GAMMA HOLDING N.V.; Int'l, pg. 539
GARLOCK SEALING TECHNOLOGIES—Coltec Holdings Inc; U.S. Public, pg. 402
THE GATES CORPORATION—Tomkins PLC; Int'l, pg. 1396
GENCORP INC.; U.S. Public, pg. 705
GENCORP VEHICLE SEALING DIV.—GenCorp Inc.; U.S. Public, pg. 706
GENERAL FELT, FAIRLESS HILLS—Trace International Holdings, Inc.; U.S. Private, pg. 1094
GENERAL FELT INDUSTRIES, INC.—Trace International Holdings, Inc.; U.S. Private, pg. 1094
GERBER PRODUCTS DIVISION-BABY CARE—Novartis AG; Int'l, pg. 973
GOODALL RUBBER COMPANY—Trelleborg AB; Int'l, pg. 1423

THE GOODYEAR TIRE & RUBBER COMPANY; *U.S. Public*, pg. 752
GOSHEN RUBBER CO., INC.; *U.S. Private*, pg. 465
GOULD PACKAGING, INC.; *U.S. Private*, pg. 466
GROUPE ZODIAC; *Int'l*, pg. 572
HAARTZ-MASON, INC.—RPM, Inc.; *U.S. Public*, pg. 1358
HABISAT GLOBE INC.—Habisat Svergie AB; *Int'l*, pg. 585
HABISAT SVERGIE AB; *Int'l*, pg. 585
HALLIBURTON ENERGY SERVICES—Halliburton Company; *U.S. Public*, pg. 776
HALSTEAD INDUSTRIAL PRODS. DIV.—Halstead Industries, Inc.; *U.S. Private*, pg. 497
HALSTEAD INDUSTRIES, INC.; *U.S. Private*, pg. 496
M.A. HANNA COMPANY; *U.S. Public*, pg. 780
M.A. HANNA RUBBER COMPOUNDING—M.A. Hanna Company; *U.S. Public*, pg. 781
HART HOLDING COMPANY, INC.; *U.S. Private*, pg. 507
HEDSTROM CORPORATION—Hicks, Muse, Tate & Furst Inc.; *U.S. Private*, pg. 526
THE HERCULES TIRE & RUBBER COMPANY; *U.S. Private*, pg. 523
HUBER & SUHNER AG; *Int'l*, pg. 637
HUTCHINSON S.A.—Total S.A.; *Int'l*, pg. 1409
IER DIVISION—Furon Company; *U.S. Public*, pg. 689
INAMED CORPORATION; *U.S. Public*, pg. 873
INDUSTRIAL LATEX COMPOUNDS LTD.—The Dow Chemical Company; *U.S. Public*, pg. 523
JASON INDUSTRIAL, INC.; *U.S. Private*, pg. 583
JOMAC, INC.; *U.S. Private*, pg. 595
KLEBER PNEUMATIQUES SA—Compagnie Generale des Etablissements Michelin; *Int'l*, pg. 322
KONETA RUBBER CO. DIV.—Lancaster Colony Corporation; *U.S. Public*, pg. 976
KRACO ENTERPRISES, INC.; *U.S. Private*, pg. 634
LAGRANGE MOLDED PRODUCTS, INC.—Lancaster Colony Corporation; *U.S. Public*, pg. 977
LAKIN GENERAL CORPORATION; *U.S. Private*, pg. 644
LANCASTER COLONY AUTOMOTIVE GROUP—Lancaster Colony Corporation; *U.S. Public*, pg. 977
LAVELLE INDUSTRIES INC.; *U.S. Private*, pg. 653
LINATEX AUSTRALIA PTY. LTD.—Harrisons & Crosfield plc; *Int'l*, pg. 599
LINATEX CANADA INC.—Harrisons & Crosfield plc; *Int'l*, pg. 599
LINATEX LIMITED—Harrisons & Crosfield plc; *Int'l*, pg. 598
LONDON INTERNATIONAL GROUP PLC; *Int'l*, pg. 815
LORD CORPORATION; *U.S. Private*, pg. 675
LORD CORPORATION—Lord Corporation; *U.S. Private*, pg. 676
LUDLOW COMPOSITES CORPORATION; *U.S. Private*, pg. 680
M & C SPECIALTIES COMPANY; *U.S. Private*, pg. 684
M & C SPECIALTIES (IRELAND) LIMITED—M & C Specialties Company; *U.S. Private*, pg. 684
M & C REMCO TAPE PRODUCTS CO.—M & C Specialties Company; *U.S. Private*, pg. 684
MAGLA PRODUCTS; *U.S. Private*, pg. 695
MALOYA FREDESTEIN—Fredestein Banden; *Int'l*, pg. 505
MANCHEM LTD.—Rhone-Poulenc S.A.; *Int'l*, pg. 1113
MAPA—Total S.A.; *Int'l*, pg. 1409
MAPA PIONEER CORPORATION—Total S.A.; *Int'l*, pg. 1409
MARIGOLD GLOVE DIVISION—London International Group plc; *Int'l*, pg. 815
MATTHEWS INTERNATIONAL CORP.; *U.S. Public*, pg. 1059
MATTHEWS INTL. CORP.-GRAPHIC SYSTEMS DIV.—Matthews International Corp.; *U.S. Public*, pg. 1060
MEDAES INCORPORATED—Cravey, Green & Wahlen, Incorporated; *U.S. Private*, pg. 287
MEDICAL RUBBER AB—Perstorp AB; *Int'l*, pg. 1036
MERIDIAN INDUSTRIES, INC.; *U.S. Private*, pg. 732
MILLER PRODUCTS COMPANY, INC.; *U.S. Private*, pg. 747
MILTON INDUSTRIES, INC.; *U.S. Private*, pg. 749
MINOR RUBBER CO., INC.; *U.S. Private*, pg. 751
MITCHELL CORPORATION OF OWOSSO; *U.S. Private*, pg. 753
MOELLER PRODUCTS CO., INC.; *U.S. Private*, pg. 755
MOORE COMPANY; *U.S. Private*, pg. 759
MOXNESS PRODUCTS EAST TROY DIVISION—Applied Power Inc.; *U.S. Public*, pg. 124
MOXNESS PRODUCTS, INC.—Applied Power Inc.; *U.S. Public*, pg. 124
NI INDUSTRIES, INC.—Masco Corporation; *U.S. Public*, pg. 1054
THE NATIONAL LATEX PRODUCTS CO.; *U.S. Private*, pg. 785
NEUMATICOS GOODYEAR SA—The Goodyear Tire & Rubber Company; *U.S. Public*, pg. 753
NORTH SAFETY PRODUCTS, HAND PROTECTION DIVISION—Siebe plc; *Int'l*, pg. 1243
OLIN-ASAHI INTERCONNECT TECHNOLOGIES—Olin Corporation; *U.S. Public*, pg. 1219
OMNI PRODUCTS, INC.; *U.S. Private*, pg. 816
OMNI PRODUCTS, INC.—OMNI Products, Inc.; *U.S. Private*, pg. 816
O'SULLIVAN CORPORATION; *U.S. Public*, pg. 1234
OUIMET CORP.; *U.S. Private*, pg. 821
PHB PLASTIC & RUBBER MOLDING DIVISION—PHB Die Casting; *U.S. Private*, pg. 826
PACIFIC DUNLOP LIMITED; *Int'l*, pg. 1021
PAMOL (NIGERIA) LTD.—Unilever Plc; *Int'l*, pg. 1438
PANDEL, INC.—Interface Inc.; *U.S. Public*, pg. 889
PARK-OHIO INDUSTRIES, INC.; *U.S. Public*, pg. 1258
PARKER SEAL DE MEXICO SA—Parker Hannifin Corporation; *U.S. Public*, pg. 1262
PAULSTRA CRC CORPORATION—Total S.A.; *Int'l*, pg. 1410
PAWLING CORPORATION; *U.S. Private*, pg. 844
PEGLER-HATTERSLEY PLC—Tomkins PLC; *Int'l*, pg. 1395
PERFORMANCE ELASTOMERS DIVISION—Furon Company; *U.S. Public*, pg. 689
PERMACEL—Nitto Denko Corporation; *Int'l*, pg. 950
PHOENIX MEDICAL TECHNOLOGY, INC.; *U.S. Public*, pg. 1292
PIRELLI ARGENTINA DE MANDATOS S.A.—Pirelli S.p.A.; *Int'l*, pg. 1059
PIRELLI U.K. TYRES LIMITED—Pirelli S.p.A.; *Int'l*, pg. 1059
PITNEY BOWES INC.; *U.S. Public*, pg. 1303
PLAYTEX PRODUCTS CORP.—Playtex Products Inc.; *U.S. Public*, pg. 1311
PLAYTEX PRODUCTS INC.; *U.S. Public*, pg. 1310
PLYMOUTH RUBBER COMPANY, INC.; *U.S. Public*, pg. 1311
POLYSAR RUBBER CORPORATION—Bayer AG; *Int'l*, pg. 175
PRIDE PRODUCTS, INC.; *U.S. Private*, pg. 883
QUADION CORPORATION; *U.S. Private*, pg. 898
QUIXOTE CORPORATION; *U.S. Public*, pg. 1353
RBX CORPORATION—American Industrial Partners; *U.S. Private*, pg. 56
R.C.A. RUBBER COMPANY; *U.S. Private*, pg. 902
RPM, INC.; *U.S. Public*, pg. 1356
RTE FAR EAST CORPORATION—Cooper Industries, Inc.; *U.S. Public*, pg. 445
RADIATOR SPECIALTY COMPANY; *U.S. Private*, pg. 906
REESE ENTERPRISES, INC.; *U.S. Private*, pg. 916
REEVES BROTHERS, INC.—Hart Holding Company, Inc.; *U.S. Private*, pg. 507
REEVES-INDUSTRIAL COATED FABRICS PLANT—Hart Holding Company, Inc.; *U.S. Private*, pg. 507
REEVES INTERNATIONAL—Hart Holding Company, Inc.; *U.S. Private*, pg. 507
REHRIG INTERNATIONAL—Cravey, Green & Wahlen, Incorporated; *U.S. Private*, pg. 287
REICHHOLD CHEMICALS, INC.—Dainippon Ink & Chemicals, Inc.; *Int'l*, pg. 370
ROPPE CORP.; *U.S. Private*, pg. 944
ROYSTON LABORATORIES—Chase Corporation; *U.S. Public*, pg. 337
RUBATEX CORPORATION—American Industrial Partners; *U.S. Private*, pg. 56
RUBBER PRODUCTS DIV.—Vulcan International Corporation; *U.S. Public*, pg. 1725
RUBBERMAID CANADA INC. CONSUMER PRODUCTS—Rubbermaid Incorporated; *U.S. Public*, pg. 1411
RUBBERMAID HOME PRODUCTS DIV.—Rubbermaid Incorporated; *U.S. Public*, pg. 1411
RUBBERMAID INCORPORATED; *U.S. Public*, pg. 1411
RUTLAND PLASTIC TECHNOLOGIES, INC.—Florida Capital Partners; *U.S. Private*, pg. 414
SAAR-GUMMIWERK GMBH—Saarbergwerke Aktiengesellschaft; *Int'l*, pg. 1167
SAFESKIN CORPORATION; *U.S. Public*, pg. 1425
ST. CLAIRE PLASTICS CO.; *U.S. Private*, pg. 960
W.H. SALISBURY & COMPANY—Siebe plc; *Int'l*, pg. 1244
SCHLEGEL NAAO—BTR plc; *Int'l*, pg. 128
SCHLEGEL OKLAHOMA, INC.—BTR plc; *Int'l*, pg. 128
SCHUBERT SEALS A/S—The West Company, Incorporated; *U.S. Public*, pg. 1755
SENETICS—The West Company, Incorporated; *U.S. Public*, *pg. 1755*
SERADYN, INC.—Mitsubishi Chemical Corporation; *Int'l*, pg. 871
SIAM SYNTHETIC LATEX CO., LTD.—The Siam Cement Public Company Limited; *Int'l*, pg. 1238
SIME CHEMICAL PRODUCTS SDN. BHD.—Sime Darby Berhad; *Int'l*, pg. 1250
SINOCHEM INTERNATIONAL PETROLEUM CO. LTD.; *Int'l*, pg. 1254
SKEGA AB—Svedala Industri AB; *Int'l*, pg. 1323
OY SKEGA AB—Svedala Industri AB; *Int'l*, pg. 1323
SKEGA CANADA LTD.—Svedala Industri AB; *Int'l*, pg. 1323
SKEGA CHILENA S.A.—Svedala Industri AB; *Int'l*, pg. 1323
SKEGA FAR EAST PTE. LTD.—Svedala Industri AB; *Int'l*, pg. 1323
SKEGA GMBH—Svedala Industri AB; *Int'l*, pg. 1323
SKEGA MEXICANA SA DE CV—Svedala Industri AB; *Int'l*, pg. 1324
SKEGA (PTY) LTD.—Svedala Industri AB; *Int'l*, pg. 1324
SMITH TECHNOLOGIES CORP.—Smith Environmental Technologies Corp.; *U.S. Public*, pg. 1478
SPECIALTY CHEMICALS DIV.—Rhone-Poulenc S.A.; *Int'l*, pg. 1109
STAND-COTE INDUSTRIAL COATINGS DIV.—Standco Industries, Inc.; *U.S. Private*, pg. 1032
STANDARD PRODUCTS (CANADA) LTD.—The Standard Products Company; *U.S. Public*, pg. 1505
THE STANDARD PRODUCTS COMPANY; *U.S. Public*, pg. 1504
STANDARD PRODUCTS INDUSTRIAL—The Standard Products Company; *U.S. Public*, pg. 1505
STANDARD PRODUCTS LIMITED—The Standard Products Company; *U.S. Public*, pg. 1505
STANDCO INDUSTRIES, INC.; *U.S. Private*, pg. 1032
STAPLES DISPOSABLES LIMITED—James Crean Plc; *Int'l*, pg. 341
SUMITOMO CHEMICAL COMPANY, LTD.; *Int'l*, pg. 1310
TWC OF FLORIDA, INCORPORATED—The West Company, Incorporated; *U.S. Public*, pg. 1755
TABAPACK, S.A.—Tabacalera, S.A.; *Int'l*, pg. 1346
TEKNOR APEX COMPANY; *U.S. Private*, pg. 1073
TEXON MATERIALS INC.; *U.S. Private*, pg. 1079
TEXTILE RUBBER & CHEMICAL COMPANY; *U.S. Private*, *pg. 1079*
THERAPEDIC ASSOCIATES, INC.; *U.S. Private*, pg. 1079
THERMWELL PRODUCTS CO., INC.; *U.S. Private*, pg. 1081
TIGERS POLYMER CORPORATION; *Int'l*, pg. 1390
TINGLEY RUBBER CORPORATION; *U.S. Private*, pg. 1088
THE TOY FACTORY—Pride Products, Inc.; *U.S. Private*, pg. 883
TOYO TIRE & RUBBER CO., LTD.; *Int'l*, pg. 1411
TOYODA GOSEI CO. LTD.—Toyota Motor Corporation; *Int'l*, pg. 1412
TRELLEBORG AB; *Int'l*, pg. 1419
TRELLEBORG-BOLIDEN—Trelleborg AB; *Int'l*, pg. 1423
ALBERT TROSTEL & SONS CO.; *U.S. Private*, pg. 1105
VARNAMO ISOLERDUK—Trelleborg AB; *Int'l*, pg. 1422
VERNAY LABORATORIES, INC.; *U.S. Private*, pg. 1137
VIKING FOTTOY A.S.—Orkla A.S.A.; *Int'l*, pg. 1011
VREDESTEIN RUBBER RECYCLING B.V.—Vredestein N.V.; *Int'l*, pg. 1481
VULCAN CORPORATION—Vulcan International Corporation; *U.S. Public*, pg. 1725
VULCAN INTERNATIONAL CORPORATION; *U.S. Public*, pg. 1725
THE WALWORTH COMPANY USA; *U.S. Private*, pg. 1149
WATERVILLE TG INC.; *Int'l*, pg. 1487
WAYCROSS MOLDED PRODUCTS, INC.—Lancaster Colony Corporation; *U.S. Public*, pg. 977
THE WEST COMPANY, INCORPORATED; *U.S. Public*, pg. 1755
WESTERN SKY INDUSTRIES, INC.; *U.S. Private*, pg. 1168
WILHOLD INC.—American Greetings Corporation; *U.S. Public*, pg. 78
WILLIAM WARNE LIMITED—SLD Holdings Ltd.; *Int'l*, pg. 1160
WINSTAR GLOBAL PRODUCTS, INC.—Winstar Communications; *U.S. Public*, pg. 1772
WYNN'S-PRECISION, INC.—Wynn's International, Inc.; *U.S. Public*, pg. 1783
THE YOKOHAMA RUBBER CO., LTD.; *Int'l*, pg. 1521

3081 — UNSUPPORTED PLASTICS FILM & SHEET

A & B PLASTICS, INC.—Bunzl PLC; *Int'l*, pg. 232
A & B PLASTICS-SOUTHWEST, INC.—Bunzl PLC; *Int'l*, pg. 232
AET PACKAGING FILMS—Applied Extrusion Technologies, Inc.; *U.S. Public*, pg. 122
AEROQUIP STERLING GMBH—Aeroquip-Vickers, Inc.; *U.S. Public*, pg. 25
ALLIEDSIGNAL INC.; *U.S. Public*, pg. 49
ALLTRISTA CORPORATION; *U.S. Public*, pg. 56
ARISTECH CHEMICAL CORPORATION—Mitsubishi Corporation; *Int'l*, pg. 872
ATLANTIS PLASTIC FILMS, INC.—Atlantis Plastic, Inc.; *U.S. Public*, pg. 145
ATLAS ALCHEM PLASTICS, INC.—Spartech Corporation; *U.S. Public*, pg. 1496
BTR NYLEX LIMITED—BTR plc; *Int'l*, pg. 129
BARRIER FILMS CORP.—World Class Film Corporation; *U.S. Private*, pg. 1190
BEMIS COMPANY, INC.; *U.S. Public*, pg. 210
BIRD VINYL—Jannock Limited; *Int'l*, pg. 699
BLESSINGS CORPORATION—Williamson-Dickie Mfg. Co.; *U.S. Private*, pg. 1179
BOEKELO FOLIEN B.V.—Solvay S.A.; *Int'l*, pg. 1278
BRASILIT DA AMAZONIA—Saint-Gobain; *Int'l*, pg. 1171
BUNZL EXTRUSION—Bunzl PLC; *Int'l*, pg. 232
CMS GILBRETH PACKAGING SYSTEMS—IMPAXX, Inc.; *U.S. Private*, pg. 558
CABOT CORPORATION; *U.S. Public*, pg. 288
CABOT PLASTICS INTERNATIONAL—Cabot Corporation; *U.S. Public*, pg. 289
CELLO BAG COMPANY, INC.—Amcor Limited; *Int'l*, pg. 72
CLOPAY CORPORATION—Griffon Corp.; *U.S. Public*, pg. 766
CONSTRUCTION & HOME IMPROVEMENT MARKETS DIVISION—3M; *U.S. Public*, pg. 1605
CONTINENTAL CAN CO.; *U.S. Public*, pg. 439
COOK COMPOSITES & POLYMERS INC.—Total S.A.; *Int'l*, *pg. 1409*
COURTAULDS FILMS HOLDINGS LTD.—Courtaulds plc; *Int'l*, pg. 339
COURTAULDS PERFORMANCE FILMS INC.—Courtaulds plc; *Int'l*, pg. 339
DSM SHEFFIELD PLASTICS—DSM N.V.; *Int'l*, pg. 354
DIXIE UNION VERPACKUNGEN GMBH—Continental Can Co.; *U.S. Public*, pg. 440
DRAKA POLVA B.V.—Solvay S.A.; *Int'l*, pg. 1278
DU PONT DE NEMOURS (LUXEMBOURG) S.A.—Du Pont (E.I. Du Pont De Nemours & Co.); *U.S. Public*, pg. 532
DU PONT ELECTRONICS INFORMATION STORAGE DIVISION—Du Pont (E.I. Du Pont De Nemours & Co.); *U.S. Public*, pg. 531
DUALL PLASTICS, INC.—Bunzl PLC; *Int'l*, pg. 233
DUPERIAL 9 DE JULIO S.A.I.C.—Imperial Chemical Industries PLC; *Int'l*, pg. 664
DYNACAST—Coats Viyella plc; *Int'l*, pg. 300
EASTMAN CHEMICAL COMPANY; *U.S. Public*, pg. 550
ENKA BV—Akzo Nobel N.V.; *Int'l*, pg. 45
EVERITE S.A.—Saint-Gobain; *Int'l*, pg. 1170
FLEXA SPA—Chargeurs; *Int'l*, pg. 280
FLEXCON CO., INC.; *U.S. Private*, pg. 412
FORMOSA PLASTICS CORPORATION; *Int'l*, pg. 498
FRANKLIN-BURLINGTON PLASTICS—Spartech Corporation; *U.S. Public*, pg. 1496
GENERAL CIGAR HOLDINGS INC; *U.S. Public*, pg. 707
GOMAR MANUFACTURING CO., INC.—AlliedSignal Inc.; *U.S. Public*, pg. 51
HEDWIN CORPORATION—Solvay S.A.; *Int'l*, pg. 1278
HOPPLE PLASTICS, INC.; *U.S. Private*, pg. 538
ICC INDUSTRIES, INC.; *U.S. Private*, pg. 553
ICI AMERICAS, INC.—Imperial Chemical Industries PLC; *Int'l*, pg. 663
ICI FILMS—Imperial Chemical Industries PLC; *Int'l*, pg. 664
ICI FRANCE SA—Imperial Chemical Industries PLC; *Int'l*, pg. 665
ICI JAPAN LIMITED—Imperial Chemical Industries PLC; *Int'l*, pg. 665
ICI OESTERREICH GMBH—Imperial Chemical Industries PLC; *Int'l*, pg. 665
ICI (PERU) S.A.—Imperial Chemical Industries PLC; *Int'l*, pg. 665
ICI (PHILIPPINES) INC.—Imperial Chemical Industries PLC; *Int'l*, pg. 665

ICI (SINGAPORE) PRIVATE LIMITED—Imperial Chemical Industries PLC; *Int'l*, pg. 665
ICI (SWITZERLAND) AG—Imperial Chemical Industries PLC; *Int'l*, pg. 665
ICI ZAMBIA LIMITED—Imperial Chemical Industries PLC; *Int'l*, pg. 665
IMPAXX, INC.; *U.S. Private*, pg. 558
IMPERIAL CHEMICAL INDUSTRIES PLC; *Int'l*, pg. 662
INDUSTRIAL PLASTICS COMPANY—Alltrista Corporation; *U.S. Public*, pg. 56
INTEX CORP.; *U.S. Private*, pg. 574
INTEX PLASTICS CORPORATION—Intex Corp.; *U.S. Private*, pg. 574
K & M PRODUCTS DIVISION—Avery Dennison Corporation; *U.S. Public*, pg. 152
KEY PLASTICS, INC.; *U.S. Private*, pg. 618
KLEER-VU PLASTICS CORP.—Kleer-Vu Plastics, Inc.; *U.S. Public*, pg. 962
KLOECKNER PENTAPLAST LTD.—Klockner-Werke AG; *Int'l*, pg. 737
KUSS CORPORATION—Cummins Engine Company, Inc.; *U.S. Public*, pg. 468
MASTERPAK, S.A. DE C.V.—CYDSA S.A.; *Int'l*, pg. 246
MAXCO, INC.; *U.S. Public*, pg. 1061
MOHAWK PLASTICS, INC.; *U.S. Private*, pg. 755
MOHAWK PLASTICS, INC.—Mohawk Plastics, Inc.; *U.S. Private*, pg. 755
MOUNT VERNON PLASTICS COMPANY—Reynolds Metals Company; *U.S. Public*, pg. 1386
NESTE CELLPLAST AB—Neste Oy; *Int'l*, pg. 914
NEXUS PLASTICS, INC.; *U.S. Private*, pg. 797
AB NOBEL PLAST—Akzo Nobel N.V.; *Int'l*, pg. 48
NORTON PERFORMANCE PLASTICS—Saint-Gobain; *Int'l*, pg. 1174
OLEFINAS, S.A.—McNeel International Corp.; *U.S. Private*, pg. 725
PHILLIPS-JOANNA, INC.—GCI Holdings Corporation; *U.S. Private*, pg. 434
PLASBOARD PLASTICS LIMITED—James Crean PLC; *Int'l*, *pg. 341*
PLASTAG CORPORATION; *U.S. Private*, pg. 870
PLASTIC PACKAGING COMPANY—Alltrista Corporation; *U.S. Public*, pg. 57
PLASTIC SUPPLIERS, INC.; *U.S. Private*, pg. 871
PLASTIC SUPPLIERS, INC.—Plastic Suppliers, Inc.; *U.S. Private*, pg. 871
PLASTICOS PLAVINIL S.A.—Solvay S.A.; *Int'l*, pg. 1279
PLASTOMER CORP.; *U.S. Private*, pg. 872
PLYMOUTH RUBBER COMPANY, INC.; *U.S. Public*, pg. 1311
POLY PAK AMERICA, INC.; *U.S. Private*, pg. 875
POLYVINYL FILMS, INC.; *U.S. Private*, pg. 875
PORTH PLASTIC CO.—Bunzl PLC; *Int'l*, pg. 233
RAVEN INDUSTRIES, INC.; *U.S. Public*, pg. 1361
RHONE-POULENC INC., FILMS DIVISION—Rhone-Poulenc S.A.; *Int'l*, pg. 1110
W. ROSENLEW LTD.—UPM-Kymmene Corporation; *Int'l*, pg. 1428
SNYDER INDUSTRIES, INC.; *U.S. Private*, pg. 1011
SOCIEDAD GENERAL DE HULES S.A.—Solvay S.A.; *Int'l*, pg. 1279
SOLUTIA INC.; *U.S. Public*, pg. 1483
SOUTHERN PLASTICS CO.—Bunzl PLC; *Int'l*, pg. 233
SPARTECH CORPORATION; *U.S. Public*, pg. 1495
STRAUSS 9 DE JULIO S.A.I.C.—Imperial Chemical Industries PLC; *Int'l*, pg. 665
3M/ECC EUROPA BV—Bowthorpe plc; *Int'l*, pg. 209
TRANSILWRAP COMPANY, INC.; *U.S. Private*, pg. 1097
TREDEGAR INDUSTRIES INC.; *U.S. Public*, pg. 1633
TRI-LITE PLASTICS, INC.—Bunzl PLC; *Int'l*, pg. 233
TRI-LITE PLASTICS SOUTH, INC.—Bunzl PLC; *Int'l*, pg. 233
TRIMIN ENTERPRISES, INC.; *Int'l*, pg. 1424
VAN LEER FLEXIBLES, INC.—Royal Packaging Industries Van Leer B.V.; *Int'l*, pg. 1146
VAN LEER NEW ZEALAND LTD.—Royal Packaging Industries Van Leer B.V.; *Int'l*, pg. 1147
WORLD CLASS FILM CORPORATION; *U.S. Private*, pg. 1190
ZENECA AB—Zeneca Group Plc; *Int'l*, pg. 1526
ZENECA HELLAS S.A.—Zeneca Group Plc; *Int'l*, pg. 1526
ZENECA OY—Zeneca Group Plc; *Int'l*, pg. 1527
ZENECA POLAND SP. Z.O.O.—Zeneca Group Plc; *Int'l*, pg. 1527
ZENECA ZIMBABWE (PRIVATE) LIMITED—Zeneca Group Plc; *Int'l*, pg. 1527

3082 — UNSUPPORTED PLASTICS PROFILE SHAPES

A & B PLASTICS, INC.—Bunzl PLC; *Int'l*, pg. 232
A & B PLASTICS-SOUTHWEST, INC.—Bunzl PLC; *Int'l*, pg. 232
BUNZL EXTRUSION—Bunzl PLC; *Int'l*, pg. 232
DSM ENGINEERING PLASTIC PRODUCTS—DSM N.V.; *Int'l*, pg. 354
DSM SHEFFIELD PLASTICS—DSM N.V.; *Int'l*, pg. 354
DUALL PLASTICS, INC.—Bunzl PLC; *Int'l*, pg. 233
EAGLE ELECTRIC MFG. CO., INC.; *U.S. Private*, pg. 354
G.I. PLASTEK; *U.S. Private*, pg. 435
KENTILE OPERTING CO.; *U.S. Private*, pg. 615
NITTO DENKO CORPORATION; *Int'l*, pg. 950
AB NOBEL PLAST—Akzo Nobel N.V.; *Int'l*, pg. 48
NORTON PERFORMANCE PLASTICS—Saint-Gobain; *Int'l*, pg. 1174
POLYPENCO LTD.—DSM N.V.; *Int'l*, pg. 354
PORTH PLASTIC CO.—Bunzl PLC; *Int'l*, pg. 233
RAYCHEM CORPORATION; *U.S. Public*, pg. 1362
SOUTHERN PLASTICS CO.—Bunzl PLC; *Int'l*, pg. 233
TRI-LITE PLASTICS, INC.—Bunzl PLC; *Int'l*, pg. 233
TRI-LITE PLASTICS SOUTH, INC.—Bunzl PLC; *Int'l*, pg. 233

3083 — LAMINATED PLASTICS, PLATE, SHEET & PROFILE SHAPES

ALKOR PLASTICS LTD.—Solvay S.A.; *Int'l*, pg. 1278
ALLIEDSIGNAL ENVIRONMENTAL CATALYSTS—AlliedSignal Inc.; *U.S. Public*, pg. 51
ALLIEDSIGNAL INC.; *U.S. Public*, pg. 49
ALLIEDSIGNAL LAMINATE SYSTEMS—AlliedSignal Inc.; *U.S. Public*, pg. 53
ALLIEDSIGNAL LAMINATE SYSTEMS S.A.—AlliedSignal Inc.; *U.S. Public*, pg. 53
APPLIED EXTRUSION TECHNOLOGIES, INC.; *U.S. Public*, pg. 122
AXXIS NV—DSM N.V.; *Int'l*, pg. 354
BIXBY INTERNATIONAL CORP.; *U.S. Private*, pg. 146
BUNNELL PLASTICS DIVISION—Furon Company; *U.S. Public*, pg. 689
CAMBRO MANUFACTURING COMPANY; *U.S. Private*, pg. 203
COASTAL WOOD PRODUCTS, INC.—McConnell Cabinets, Inc.; *U.S. Private*, pg. 720
COLTEC HOLDINGS INC; *U.S. Public*, pg. 401
COMPOSITE MATERIALS DIV.—Rogers Corporation; *U.S. Public*, pg. 1402
DSM ENGINEERING PLASTICS—Akzo Nobel N.V.; *Int'l*, pg. 46
DEITSCH PLASTICS COMPANY; *U.S. Private*, pg. 320
DEKORON DIVISION—Furon Company; *U.S. Public*, pg. 689
DISCOVERY PLASTICS, INC.—RHC/Spacemaster Corporation; *U.S. Private*, pg. 904
DUNMORE CORPORATION; *U.S. Private*, pg. 346
DUNMORE CORPORATION/BREWSTER—Dunmore Corporation; *U.S. Private*, pg. 347
DYNACAST—Coats Viyella plc; *Int'l*, pg. 300
EASTMAN CHEMICAL COMPANY; *U.S. Public*, pg. 550
FERRO FRANCE-EUROSTAR—Ferro Corporation; *U.S. Public*, pg. 619
FORMICA ASIA LIMITED—BTR plc; *Int'l*, pg. 129
FORMICA CORP.—BTR plc; *Int'l*, pg. 129
FORMICA CORPORATION—BTR plc; *Int'l*, pg. 129
FORMICA ESPANOLA S.A.—BTR plc; *Int'l*, pg. 129
FORMICA ITALIA S.R.1.—BTR plc; *Int'l*, pg. 129
FORMICA LIMITED—BTR plc; *Int'l*, pg. 129
FORMICA NEDERLAND B.V.—BTR plc; *Int'l*, pg. 129
FORMICA SWITZERLAND AG—BTR plc; *Int'l*, pg. 129
FORMICA TAIWAN CORPORATION—BTR plc; *Int'l*, pg. 130
M.C. GILL CORPORATION; *U.S. Private*, pg. 453
HALLIBURTON ENERGY SERVICES—Halliburton Company; *U.S. Public*, pg. 776
HOECHST MARION ROUSSEL, INC.—Hoechst Aktiengesellschaft; *Int'l*, pg. 624
KUSS CORPORATION—Cummins Engine Company, Inc.; *U.S. Public*, pg. 468
LABELON CORPORATION; *U.S. Private*, pg. 641
LASCO FLUID DISTRIBUTION PRODUCTS—Tomkins PLC; *Int'l*, pg. 1398
LASCO PANEL PRODUCTS—Tomkins PLC; *Int'l*, pg. 1398
LATI INDUSTRIA TERMOPLASTICI S.P.A.; *Int'l*, pg. 804
MASONITE DIVISION—International Paper Company; *U.S. Public*, pg. 903
MICROWAVE MATERIALS GROUP-MICROWAVE MATERIALS DIV.—Rogers Corporation; *U.S. Public*, pg. 1402
NVF COMPANY; *U.S. Private*, pg. 772
NEW ZEALAND FIBRE GLASS—International Paper Company; *U.S. Public*, pg. 904
NITTOBO NORPLEX OAK CO., LTD. (NNO)—AlliedSignal Inc.; *U.S. Public*, pg. 53
AB NOBEL PLAST—Akzo Nobel N.V.; *Int'l*, pg. 48
NORTON PERFORMANCE PLASTICS—Saint-Gobain; *Int'l*, pg. 1174
O'KEEFFE'S, INC.; *U.S. Private*, pg. 813
OTIS SPECIALTY PAPERS—Rexam PLC; *Int'l*, pg. 1107
PLASTAG CORPORATION; *U.S. Private*, pg. 870
PLASTIC SUPPLIERS, INC.; *U.S. Private*, pg. 871
PLASTOMER CORP.; *U.S. Private*, pg. 872
PLIX PACKAGING LIMITED—International Paper Company; *U.S. Public*, pg. 904
PROPAK—International Paper Company; *U.S. Public*, pg. 904
REXAM CUSTOM—Rexam PLC; *Int'l*, pg. 1106
ROGERS CORPORATION; *U.S. Public*, pg. 1402
SAUDER WOODWORKING CO.; *U.S. Private*, pg. 967
SCHLUMBERGER MALCO INC.—N. Schlumberger & Cie; *Int'l*, pg. 1206
SCHNELLER, INC.; *U.S. Private*, pg. 971
SIGNTECH USA, LTD.; *U.S. Private*, pg. 999
SOCIETE ANONYME FORMICA (FRANCE)—BTR plc; *Int'l*, *pg. 130*
SPARTAN INTERNATIONAL INC.; *U.S. Private*, pg. 1020
SPARTECH PLASTICS—Spartech Corporation; *U.S. Public*, *pg. 1496*
TEKNOR APEX COMPANY; *U.S. Private*, pg. 1073
TETRA PLASTICS—Nike, Inc.; *U.S. Public*, pg. 1184
TRIO PRODUCTS INC.—Ivex Packaging Corporation; *U.S. Public*, pg. 915
UFP TECHNOLOGY; *U.S. Private*, pg. 1112
UNIROYAL TECHNOLOGY CORPORATION; *U.S. Public*, pg. 1670
VPI MIRREX CORP.—Vinyl Plastics Incorporated; *U.S. Private*, pg. 1141
WILDON INDUSTRIES, INC.—BTR plc; *Int'l*, pg. 129
WILSON-FIBERFIL FRANCE SA—Akzo Nobel N.V.; *Int'l*, pg. 46
WILSON-FIBERFIL INTERNATIONAL SA—Akzo Nobel N.V.; *Int'l*, pg. 46
WILSON-FIBERFIL SWEDEN AB—Akzo Nobel N.V.; *Int'l*, pg. 46
THE ZIPPERTUBING CO.; *U.S. Private*, pg. 1207

3084 — PLASTICS PIPE

APACHE PLASTICS, L.P.; *U.S. Private*, pg. 77
BTR SILVERTOWN LTD.—BTR plc; *Int'l*, pg. 125
CELLO BAG COMPANY, INC.—Amcor Limited; *Int'l*, pg. 72
CRESLINE PLASTIC PIPE CO. INC.; *U.S. Private*, pg. 289
GRUPO CONDUMEX—Grupo Carso S.A. de C.V.; *Int'l*, pg. 572
J-M MANUFACTURING CO., INC.—Formosa Plastics Corporation; *Int'l*, pg. 498
KETER PLASTIC LTD.; *Int'l*, pg. 732
THE LAMSON & SESSIONS CO.; *U.S. Public*, pg. 976
LONSTROFF-BTR AG—BTR plc; *Int'l*, pg. 130
NORTON PERFORMANCE PLASTICS—Saint-Gobain; *Int'l*, pg. 1174
PAWLING CORPORATION; *U.S. Private*, pg. 844
PHILLIPS PETROLEUM COMPANY; *U.S. Public*, pg. 1290
PLASTILON FRANCE S.A.—Neste Oy; *Int'l*, pg. 915
SOLUTIA INC.; *U.S. Public*, pg. 1483
SOLVIC & CIE S.N.C.—Solvay S.A.; *Int'l*, pg. 1277
VANGUARD PLASTICS, INC.; *U.S. Private*, pg. 1134
WHEATLAND TUBE COMPANY; *U.S. Private*, pg. 1170
WINROCK ENTERPRISES, INC.; *U.S. Private*, pg. 1183

3085 — PLASTICS BOTTLES

AMERICAN NATIONAL CAN COMPANY—Pechiney S.A.; *Int'l*, pg. 1029
ATLANTIS PLASTIC, INC.; *U.S. Public*, pg. 145
CARTER HOLT HARVEY PLASTIC PRODUCTS-BEVERAGE DIVISION—International Paper Company; *U.S. Public*, pg. 904
CROWN CORK & SEAL COMPANY, INC.; *U.S. Public*, pg. 462
DOUGLAS STEPHEN PLASTICS, INC.; *U.S. Private*, pg. 341
HEDWIN CORPORATION—Solvay S.A.; *Int'l*, pg. 1278
IGLOO PRODUCTS CORPORATION—Brunswick Corporation; *U.S. Public*, pg. 265
KEYSOR CENTURY CORPORATION; *U.S. Private*, pg. 618
MONTAGUE MOULDERS PTY. LTD.—Q.U.F. Industries Ltd.; *Int'l*, pg. 1074
NUNC A/S—BTR plc; *Int'l*, pg. 130
PORT CURTIS MOULDERS PTY. LTD.—Q.U.F. Industries Ltd.; *Int'l*, pg. 1074
SANTA MARINA—Saint-Gobain; *Int'l*, pg. 1177
SILGAN CORPORATION; *U.S. Public*, pg. 1473
WADDINGTON & DUVAL (HOLDINGS) LTD.—BTR plc; *Int'l*, pg. 129

3086 — PLASTICS FOAM PRODUCTS

ACI LIQUITAINERS—BTR plc; *Int'l*, pg. 128
AIR CARGO EQUIPMENT CORPORATION—Zero Corporation; *U.S. Public*, pg. 1791
ALADDIN INDUSTRIES, INCORPORATED; *U.S. Private*, pg. 30
AMERICAN EXCELSIOR COMPANY; *U.S. Private*, pg. 53
AMOCO CORPORATION; *U.S. Public*, pg. 101
AMOCO FOAM PRODUCTS CO.—Amoco Corporation; *U.S. Public*, pg. 102
ASTRO POLYFOAM LTD.—N.V. Koninklijke KNP BT; *Int'l*, pg. 756
ASTRO-VALCOUR INC.—N.V. Koninklijke KNP BT; *Int'l*, pg. 756
BT-U.S.A., INC.—N.V. Koninklijke KNP BT; *Int'l*, pg. 756
BAY INSULATION—Bay Industries Inc.; *U.S. Private*, pg. 124
BISCHOF & KLEIN (U.K.) LTD.—BPB Industries PLC; *Int'l*, pg. 122
BRADFORD COMPANY; *U.S. Private*, pg. 163
BRIDGESTONE CORPORATION; *Int'l*, pg. 213
CMT ENGINEERING INSULATION—Caparo Group Ltd.; *Int'l*, pg. 265
CARPENTER CO.; *U.S. Private*, pg. 214
CELFORTEC INC.—Jannock Limited; *Int'l*, pg. 698
CELOTEX CORPORATION; *U.S. Private*, pg. 221
THE COLEMAN COMPANY—MacAndrews & Forbes Holdings Inc.; *U.S. Private*, pg. 691
COLLECTIBLES PLANT—Fort James Corporation; *U.S. Public*, pg. 672
CONSOLIDATED METCO, INC.—Varlen Corporation; *U.S. Public*, pg. 1710
COOK COMPOSITES & POLYMERS INC.—Total S.A.; *Int'l*, *pg. 1409*
CORRECTA GMBH—Bayer AG; *Int'l*, pg. 172
H.S. CROCKER CO., INC.; *U.S. Private*, pg. 290
DSM ENGINEERING PLASTICS—Akzo Nobel N.V.; *Int'l*, pg. 46
E&S INSULATION—Egan Cos.; *U.S. Private*, pg. 366
EGAN COS.; *U.S. Private*, pg. 365
ENERGY CONTROL PRODUCTS—TI Group plc; *Int'l*, pg. 1338
FLEXIBLE PRODUCTS COMPANY; *U.S. Private*, pg. 412
FOAM PLUS LIMITED—James Crean PLC; *Int'l*, pg. 341
FOAMEX—Trace International Holdings, Inc.; *U.S. Private*, pg. 1094
FORT JAMES CORPORATION; *U.S. Public*, pg. 670
FUTURE FOAM, INC.; *U.S. Private*, pg. 433
HP PACKAGING HOLDINGS—Hargro Enterprises, Inc.; *U.S. Private*, pg. 502
IGLOO PRODUCTS CORPORATION—Brunswick Corporation; *U.S. Public*, pg. 265
INNOVATIVE PLASTICS CORPORATION; *U.S. Private*, pg. 565
ISORA OY—Neste Oy; *Int'l*, pg. 913
JANNOCK LIMITED; *Int'l*, pg. 698
LINPAC MOULDINGS LIMITED; *Int'l*, pg. 811
LUDLOW COMPOSITES CORPORATION; *U.S. Private*, pg. 680
NESTE CELLPLAST AB—Neste Oy; *Int'l*, pg. 914
NOMACO, INC.; *U.S. Private*, pg. 801

NORTON PERFORMANCE PLASTICS—Saint-Gobain; Int'l, pg. 1174
OLIVER PRODUCTS COMPANY; U.S. Private, pg. 815
OWENS-CORNING BUILDING PRODUCTS UK LTD.—Owens Corning; U.S. Public, pg. 1237
OWENS CORNING/FOAMULAR—Owens Corning; U.S. Public, pg. 1237
PACKAGING RESOURCES, INCORPORATED; U.S. Private, pg. 833
PACO PHARMACEUTICAL SERVICES, INC.—The West Company, Incorporated; U.S. Public, pg. 1755
PLASBOARD PLASTICS LIMITED—James Crean PLC; Int'l, pg. 341
PLASTOMER CORP.; U.S. Private, pg. 872
PORON MATERIALS UNIT—Rogers Corporation; U.S. Public, pg. 1403
RAYCHEM LTD.—Raychem Corporation; U.S. Public, pg. 1362
RAYCHEM N.V.—Raychem Corporation; U.S. Public, pg. 1362
RAYCHEM TECHNOLOGIAS—Raychem Corporation; U.S. Public, pg. 1363
RENOSOL CORP.; U.S. Private, pg. 922
REXAM MEDICAL PACKAGING—Rexam PLC; Int'l, pg. 1106
RUBBERMAID INCORPORATED; U.S. Public, pg. 1411
SAINT-GOBAIN; Int'l, pg. 1170
SEALED AIR B.V.—Sealed Air Corporation; U.S. Public, pg. 1451
SEALED AIR CORPORATION; U.S. Public, pg. 1450
SEALED AIR ESPANA, S.A.—Sealed Air Corporation; U.S. Public, pg. 1451
SEALED AIR G.M.B.H.—Sealed Air Corporation; U.S. Public, pg. 1451
SEALED AIR JAPAN LTD.—Sealed Air Corporation; U.S. Public, pg. 1451
SEALED AIR LIMITED—Sealed Air Corporation; U.S. Public, pg. 1451
SEALED AIR (MALAYSIA) SDN BHD—Sealed Air Corporation; U.S. Public, pg. 1451
SEALED AIR OF CANADA INC.—Sealed Air Corporation; U.S. Public, pg. 1451
SEALED AIR S.P.A.—Sealed Air Corporation; U.S. Public, pg. 1451
SEALED AIR SVENSKA A.B.—Sealed Air Corporation; U.S. Public, pg. 1451
SEALED AIR SYSTEMS—Sealed Air Corporation; U.S. Public, pg. 1451
SMYTH, CO.; U.S. Private, pg. 1010
SOLO CUP COMPANY; U.S. Private, pg. 1013
SOLUTIA INC.; U.S. Public, pg. 1483
SPAN-AMERICA MEDICAL SYSTEMS INC.; U.S. Public, pg. 1495
TECH-AEROFOAM PRODUCTS, INC.—Great American Industries, Inc.; U.S. Private, pg. 473
P.T. TOPPAN SAMPOERNA INDONESIA—Toppan Printing Company, Ltd.; Int'l, pg. 1399
TRACE INTERNATIONAL HOLDINGS, INC.; U.S. Private, pg. 1094
TUSCARORA INCORPORATED; U.S. Public, pg. 1646
UFP TECHNOLOGY; U.S. Private, pg. 1112
VARLEN CORPORATION; U.S. Public, pg. 1710
VITRO, SOCIEDAD ANONIMA - CHEMICAL, FIBERS & MINING—Vitro, Sociedad Anonima; Int'l, pg. 1469
WILSON-FIBERFIL FRANCE SA—Akzo Nobel N.V.; Int'l, pg. 46
WILSON-FIBERFIL INTERNATIONAL SA—Akzo Nobel N.V.; Int'l, pg. 46
WILSON-FIBERFIL SWEDEN AB—Akzo Nobel N.V.; Int'l, pg. 46
WINCUP; U.S. Private, pg. 1182

3087 — CUSTOM COMPOUNDING OF PURCHASED PLASTICS RESINS

ASI INVESTMENTS HOLDING CO.—A. Schulman, Inc.; U.S. Public, pg. 1441
AKEMI PLASTICS INC.—Maxco, Inc.; U.S. Public, pg. 1061
AKZO NOBEL INC.—Akzo Nobel N.V.; Int'l, pg. 47
ATLAS ALCHEM PLASTICS, INC.—Spartech Corporation; U.S. Public, pg. 1496
ATREX INCORPORATED; U.S. Private, pg. 97
COM ALLOY INTERNATIONAL COMPANY—A. Schulman, Inc.; U.S. Public, pg. 1441
COMALLOY INTERNATIONAL COMPANY—A. Schulman, Inc.; U.S. Public, pg. 1441
D.I.W.S.—Olivetti SpA; Int'l, pg. 1002
DSM N.V.; Int'l, pg. 352
EVANS INDUSTRIES, INC.; U.S. Private, pg. 385
EXEL OSTERREICH—Neste Oy; Int'l, pg. 914
FLEXIBLE PRODUCTS COMPANY; U.S. Private, pg. 412
FRANKLIN-BURLINGTON PLASTICS—Spartech Corporation; U.S. Public, pg. 1496
ICI AMERICAS, INC.—Imperial Chemical Industries PLC; Int'l, pg. 663
INTERNATIONAL PLASTICS COMPANY; U.S. Private, pg. 571
KEYSOR CENTURY CORPORATION; U.S. Private, pg. 618
MICRONYL-WEDCO S.A.—ICO, Inc.; U.S. Public, pg. 854
N.V.A. SCHULMAN PLASTICS, S.A.—A. Schulman, Inc.; U.S. Public, pg. 1441
PHILLIPS PETROLEUM COMPANY; U.S. Public, pg. 1290
PLASTEK INDUSTRIES, INC.—Plastek Group; U.S. Private, pg. 870
PLASTIGAGE CORPORATION; U.S. Private, pg. 871
POLYMER COMPOSITES INC.—Hoechst Aktiengesellschaft; Int'l, pg. 624
REEDSPECTRUM—Hoechst Aktiengesellschaft; Int'l, pg. 624
RENOSOL CORP.; U.S. Private, pg. 922
THE RESIN EXCHANGE—Spartech Corporation; U.S. Public, pg. 1496
A. SCHULMAN CANADA LTD.—A. Schulman, Inc.; U.S. Public, pg. 1441
A. SCHULMAN GMBH—A. Schulman, Inc.; U.S. Public, pg. 1441
A. SCHULMAN, INC.; U.S. Public, pg. 1441
A. SCHULMAN, INC.—A. Schulman, Inc.; U.S. Public, pg. 1441
A. SCHULMAN INC. LIMITED—A. Schulman, Inc.; U.S. Public, pg. 1441
SIOUX MANUFACTURING CORP.; U.S. Private, pg. 1003
SPARTECH CORPORATION; U.S. Public, pg. 1495
TEXAS POLYMER SERVICES, INC.—A. Schulman, Inc.; U.S. Public, pg. 1441
THERMON MANUFACTURING COMPANY; U.S. Private, pg. 1080
UNITIKA LTD.; Int'l, pg. 1444
WEDCO HOLLAND B.V.—ICO, Inc.; U.S. Public, pg. 854
WEDCO, INC.—ICO, Inc.; U.S. Public, pg. 854
WEDCO TECHNOLOGY—ICO, Inc.; U.S. Public, pg. 854
WEDCO TECHNOLOGY U.K. LTD.—ICO, Inc.; U.S. Public, pg. 854
WEDTECH INC.—ICO, Inc.; U.S. Public, pg. 854

3088 — PLASTICS PLUMBING FIXTURES

ALSONS CORPORATION—Masco Corporation; U.S. Public, pg. 1053
AMERICAN FLANGE & MANUFACTURING CO. INC.—Royal Packaging Industries Van Leer B.V.; Int'l, pg. 1146
BENEKE—Sanderson Plumbing Products Inc.; U.S. Private, pg. 964
BRIGGS INDUSTRIES, INC.; U.S. Private, pg. 168
COLEMAN SPAS, INC.—MacAndrews & Forbes Holdings Inc.; U.S. Private, pg. 691
COMPAGNIE INTERNATIONALE DES PRODUITS SANITAIRES (CIPS) JACOB DELAFON—Kohler Company; U.S. Private, pg. 631
EMCO LIMITED; Int'l, pg. 452
FLAMBEAU SOUTHEAST CO.—Flambeau Corporation; U.S. Private, pg. 409
GENOVA PRODUCTS, INC.; U.S. Private, pg. 447
HARRINGTON INDUSTRIAL PLASTICS INC.—Glynwed International PLC; Int'l, pg. 554
KOHLER LTD.—Kohler Company; U.S. Private, pg. 631
LASCO BATHWARE—Tomkins PLC; Int'l, pg. 1398
MELARD MANUFACTURING CORPORATION; U.S. Private, pg. 729
METPAR CORP.; U.S. Private, pg. 735
MOEN INCORPORATED—Fortune Brands, Inc.; U.S. Public, pg. 675
NORTEK, INC.; U.S. Public, pg. 1192
PLASKOLITE INC.; U.S. Private, pg. 870
ROLLEPAAL B.V.—Royal Dutch/Shell Group of Companies; Int'l, pg. 1136
A.O. SMITH CORPORATION; U.S. Public, pg. 1476
SMITH FIBERGLASS PRODUCTS INC.—A.O. Smith Corporation; U.S. Public, pg. 1477
THETFORD (AQUA) PRODUCTS, LTD.—The Dyson-Kissner-Moran Corporation; U.S. Private, pg. 352
THETFORD CORPORATION—The Dyson-Kissner-Moran Corporation; U.S. Private, pg. 352
THETFORD CORP. MFG. FACILITY—The Dyson-Kissner-Moran Corporation; U.S. Private, pg. 352
UNIVERSAL-RUNDLE CORP.—Nortek, Inc.; U.S. Public, pg. 1193
WESTERN AMERICAN MANUFACTURING, INC.—Waxman Industries, Inc.; U.S. Public, pg. 1749

3089 — PLASTICS PRODUCTS, NEC

ACI INTERNATIONAL LTD.—BTR plc; Int'l, pg. 128
ACI OPERATIONS PTY. LTD.—BTR plc; Int'l, pg. 128
ACI PLASTICS CLOSURES—BTR plc; Int'l, pg. 128
AEP INDUSTRIES, INC.; U.S. Public, pg. 4
AGRA PLASTICS INC.—Agra Inc.; Int'l, pg. 30
APL CORPORATION; U.S. Private, pg. 7
AWC MANUFACTURING FACILITY—Nortek, Inc.; U.S. Public, pg. 1193
ABBOTT LABORATORIES/ASHLAND—Abbott Laboratories; U.S. Public, pg. 13
ACHILLES CORPORATION; Int'l, pg. 22
ACMIL INDUSTRIES PTY. LTD.—BTR plc; Int'l, pg. 129
ADHESIVE FILMS—Bairnco Corporation; U.S. Public, pg. 165
ADMIRAL PACKAGING, INC.—Union Industries, Inc.; U.S. Private, pg. 1119
ADRIAPLAST S.P.A.—Solvay S.A.; Int'l, pg. 1278
AEROQUIP-VICKERS, INC.; U.S. Public, pg. 24
AGRICULTURAL PRODUCTS, INC.—Summa Industries; U.S. Public, pg. 1527
AIR CRUISERS CO.—Groupe Zodiac; Int'l, pg. 572
AIREX AG (AIREX)—Alusuisse-Lonza Holding Ltd.; Int'l, pg. 67
AKZO ENGINEERING PLASTICS, INC.—Akzo Nobel N.V.; Int'l, pg. 47
AKZO NOBEL AB—Akzo Nobel N.V.; Int'l, pg. 48
ALBA QUIMICA S.A. INDUSTRIA E COMMERCIO—Borden, Inc.; U.S. Private, pg. 158
ALBANY INTERNATIONAL CORP.; U.S. Public, pg. 36
ALCO INDUSTRIES, INC.; U.S. Private, pg. 32
ALCOA BUILDING PRODUCTS, INC.—Aluminum Company of America; U.S. Public, pg. 61
ALCOA CLOSURE SYSTEMS, INTERNATIONAL—Aluminum Company of America; U.S. Public, pg. 60
ALKOR GMBH KUNSTSTOFFE—Solvay S.A.; Int'l, pg. 1278
ALLIED PRODUCTS CORPORATION; U.S. Public, pg. 48
ALLIEDSIGNAL INC.; U.S. Public, pg. 49
ALLIEDSIGNAL LAMINATE SYSTEMS—AlliedSignal Inc.; U.S. Public, pg. 51
ALLTRISTA CORPORATION; U.S. Public, pg. 56
ALPHAGARY CORPORATION—Laporte plc; Int'l, pg. 802
ALRO GROUP; U.S. Private, pg. 45
ALUMINUM DECIN SPOL. S.R.O.—Alusuisse-Lonza Holding Ltd.; Int'l, pg. 68
ALUPLAST S.A. DE C.V.—The West Company, Incorporated; U.S. Public, pg. 1756
ALUSUISSE AUSTRIA GMBH—Alusuisse-Lonza Holding Ltd.; Int'l, pg. 68
ALUSUISSE FRANCE PRODUITS INDUSTRIELS S.A.—Alusuisse-Lonza Holding Ltd.; Int'l, pg. 68
ALUSUISSE-LONZA HUNGARIA KFT.—Alusuisse-Lonza Holding Ltd.; Int'l, pg. 68
ALUSUISSE-LONZA TRADING LTD.—Alusuisse-Lonza Holding Ltd.; Int'l, pg. 67
ALUSUISSE PRODUITS SPECIAUX SARL—Alusuisse-Lonza Holding Ltd.; Int'l, pg. 68
ALUSUISSE SWISS ALUMINIUM LTD.—Alusuisse-Lonza Holding Ltd.; Int'l, pg. 67
AMERICAN BILTRITE (CANADA) LTD.—American Biltrite Inc.; U.S. Public, pg. 69
AMERICAN BILTRITE INC.; U.S. Public, pg. 68
AMERICAN EXCELSIOR COMPANY; U.S. Private, pg. 53
AMERICAN INTERNATIONAL CONTAINER, INC.; U.S. Private, pg. 57
AMERICAN METAL & PLASTICS INC.; U.S. Private, pg. 59
AMERICAN NATIONAL CAN CANADA INC.—Pechiney S.A.; Int'l, pg. 1029
AMERICAN NATIONAL CAN COMPANY—Pechiney S.A.; Int'l, pg. 1029
AMERICAN TECHNOLOGY CORPORATION; U.S. Private, pg. 63
AMERON B.V., FIBERGLASS PIPE DIVISION-EUROPE—Ameron International Corporation; U.S. Public, pg. 99
AMERON FIBERGLASS PIPE GROUP—Ameron International Corporation; U.S. Public, pg. 99
AMERON (PTE) LTD.—Ameron International Corporation; U.S. Public, pg. 99
AMES COMPANY—U.S. Industries, Inc.; U.S. Public, pg. 1683
AMETEK, INC.; U.S. Public, pg. 99
ANCHOR HOCKING PLASTICS—Newell Co.; U.S. Public, pg. 1177
ANGLERS ROSLYN GROUP LTD.; U.S. Private, pg. 74
APACHE PLASTICS, L.P.; U.S. Private, pg. 77
APPLIED EXTRUSION TECHNOLOGIES, INC.; U.S. Public, pg. 122
APTARGROUP, INC.; U.S. Public, pg. 125
ARISTO MANUFACTURING CO.—The Metal Ware Corp.; U.S. Private, pg. 735
ARLON, INC.—Bairnco Corporation; U.S. Public, pg. 165
ARMIN PLASTICS DIVISION—Tyco International Ltd.; U.S. Public, pg. 1647
ARMIN PLASTICS, TYCO LABS—Tyco International Ltd.; U.S. Public, pg. 1647
ARTRA GROUP INCORPORATED; U.S. Public, pg. 136
ASSOCIATED SPRING SPEC, LTD.—Barnes Group Inc.; U.S. Public, pg. 190
ASTROTURF MANUFACTURING—Southwest Recreational Industries Inc.; U.S. Private, pg. 1018
ATKINSON; U.S. Public, pg. 143
ATLANTIS MOLDED PLASTICS, INC.—Atlantis Plastic, Inc.; U.S. Public, pg. 145
ATLANTIS PLASTIC, INC.; U.S. Public, pg. 145
ATREX INCORPORATED; U.S. Private, pg. 97
AUTOMOTIVE GROUP—Aeroquip-Vickers, Inc.; U.S. Public, pg. 24
AUTOMOTIVE WORLDWIDE SECTOR—TRW Inc.; U.S. Public, pg. 1558
AYDIN MOLDED DEVICES DIV.—Aydin Corporation; U.S. Public, pg. 158
AZON CORPORATION; U.S. Private, pg. 104
B&B MOLDERS; U.S. Private, pg. 105
B & L PLASTICS INC.—Illinois Tool Works Inc.; U.S. Public, pg. 867
B-BAR-B FLEXIBLE PACKAGING SYSTEMS—Liqui-Box Corporation; U.S. Public, pg. 1000
BASF ESPANOLA S.A.—BASF AG; Int'l, pg. 106
BDW - BAYERISCHES DRUCKGUSS-WERK THURNER GMBH & CO KG—Alusuisse-Lonza Holding Ltd.; Int'l, pg. 68
BFX HOSPITALITY GROUP, INC.; U.S. Public, pg. 160
BPB INDUSTRIES PLC; Int'l, pg. 122
BPB PAPER & PACKAGING LTD.—BPB Industries PLC; Int'l, pg. 122
BPC DIVISION—Heywood Williams Group PLC; Int'l, pg. 618
BTR, INC.—BTR plc; Int'l, pg. 127
BTR PLC; Int'l, pg. 124
BAIRNCO CORPORATION; U.S. Public, pg. 165
BAYER CORPORATION—Bayer AG; Int'l, pg. 172
BAYER CORPORATION/CONSUMER CARE DIVISION—Bayer AG; Int'l, pg. 173
BECTON DICKINSON & COMPANY; U.S. Public, pg. 199
BEDFORD INDUSTRIES, INC.; U.S. Private, pg. 129
BEEMAK PLASTICS—Jordan Industries, Inc.; U.S. Private, pg. 598
BELMONT PLASTICS CO.—Foam Pro Manufacturing; U.S. Private, pg. 415
BELVEDERE—Excel Industries, Inc.; U.S. Public, pg. 598
BEMIS POLYETHYLENE PACKAGING DIV.—Bemis Company, Inc.; U.S. Public, pg. 210
BENTON PLASTICS, INC.—Durakon Industries, Inc.; U.S. Public, pg. 537
BERRY PLASTICS CORPORATION; U.S. Private, pg. 137
BIC CORPORATION—Societe BIC S.A.; Int'l, pg. 1273
BIC INC.—Societe BIC S.A.; Int'l, pg. 1273
THE BILTRITE CORPORATION; U.S. Private, pg. 144
SAMUEL BINGHAM CO; U.S. Private, pg. 144
BINNING'S BUILDING PRODUCTS, INC.—American Architectural Products, Inc.; U.S. Public, pg. 67
BIRD INCORPORATED—Saint-Gobain; Int'l, pg. 1170
BIRO BIC LTD.—Societe BIC S.A.; Int'l, pg. 1273
BIXBY INTERNATIONAL CORP.; U.S. Private, pg. 146
BLESSINGS CORPORATION—Williamson-Dickie Mfg. Co.; U.S. Private, pg. 1179

BONDSTRAND, LTD.—Ameron International Corporation; U.S. Public, pg. 99
BORDEN, INC.; U.S. Private, pg. 157
BORDEN (U.K.) LTD.—Borden, Inc.; U.S. Private, pg. 159
ROBERT BOSCH GMBH; Int'l, pg. 203
BOSS CANADA, INC.—Vista 2000, Inc.; U.S. Private, pg. 1142
BOSS DE MEXICO, S.A.—Vista 2000, Inc.; U.S. Private, pg. 1142
BOWTHORPE-HELLERMANN (PTY.) LTD.—Bowthorpe plc; Int'l, pg. 208
THE BRAAS GROUP—Redland PLC; Int'l, pg. 1091
BRADFORD COMPANY; U.S. Private, pg. 163
BRASILIT DA AMAZONIA—Saint-Gobain; Int'l, pg. 1171
BRASILIT S.A.—Saint-Gobain; Int'l, pg. 1171
BRAWNEY PLASTICS, INC.; U.S. Private, pg. 166
BRAWNEY PLASTICS WEST—Brawney Plastics, Inc.; U.S. Private, pg. 166
BRISTILE CLAY TILES, LTD.; Int'l, pg. 216
BRISTOL-MYERS SQUIBB COMPANY; U.S. Public, pg. 253
BRISTOLIPE DIVISION—Heywood Williams Group PLC; Int'l, pg. 618
BRITAX CHILDCARE PRODUCTS PTY.—Britax International plc; Int'l, pg. 216
BRITAX-EXCELSIOR LIMITED—Britax International plc; Int'l, pg. 216
BRITTANY CORPORATION; U.S. Private, pg. 169
BROCK MANUFACTURING—CTB International Corp.; U.S. Public, pg. 285
BROCKWAY STANDARD OHIO, INC.—BWAY Corp.; U.S. Public, pg. 164
BRONSON SPECIALTIES, INC.—Solvay S.A.; Int'l, pg. 1277
E.J. BROOKS COMPANY; U.S. Private, pg. 172
BUCKHORN CANADA LTD.—Myers Industries, Inc.; U.S. Public, pg. 1143
BUCKHORN MATERIAL HANDLING GROUP INC.—Myers Industries, Inc.; U.S. Public, pg. 1143
THE BUDD COMPANY—Thyssen AG; Int'l, pg. 1388
BUDD PLASTICS DESIGN CENTER—Thyssen AG; Int'l, pg. 1388
BULL CP8, S.A.—Compagnie des Machines Bull; Int'l, pg. 316
BUNNELL PLASTICS DIVISION—Furon Company; U.S. Public, pg. 689
C-LINE PRODUCTS, INC.; U.S. Private, pg. 192
CCL INDUSTRIES, INC.; Int'l, pg. 238
CMIC SA—Alusuisse-Lonza Holding Ltd.; Int'l, pg. 68
CTI SINGAPORE, PTE—M.A. Hanna Company; U.S. Public, pg. 781
CYDSA S.A.; Int'l, pg. 246
CABOT PLASTICS INTERNATIONAL—Cabot Corporation; U.S. Public, pg. 289
CADILLAC PRODUCTS, INC.; U.S. Private, pg. 198
CAMBRIDGE INDUSTRIES INC.; U.S. Private, pg. 202
CAMBRIDGE INDUSTRIES, INC.—Cambridge Industries Inc.; U.S. Private, pg. 202
CAMBRIDGE INDUSTRIES - WOODSTOCK—Cambridge Industries Inc.; U.S. Private, pg. 202
CAMBRO MANUFACTURING COMPANY; U.S. Private, pg. 203
CAMPBELL PLASTICS DIV.—The Standard Products Company; U.S. Public, pg. 1504
THE CANADIAN COLEMAN CO., LTD.—MacAndrews & Forbes Holdings Inc.; U.S. Private, pg. 691
CANADIAN OCCIDENTAL PETROLEUM LTD.—Occidental Petroleum Corporation; U.S. Public, pg. 1210
CANANDAIGUA PLASTICS DIV.—Cambridge Industries Inc.; U.S. Private, pg. 202
CANIDA RUBBER COMPANY—Lancaster Colony Corporation; U.S. Public, pg. 976
CANNON RUBBER LTD.; Int'l, pg. 261
CANTEX INC.—Sumitomo Corporation; Int'l, pg. 1312
CAPSEALS, LIMITED—Sonoco Products Company; U.S. Public, pg. 1486
CAPSONIC GROUP, INC.; U.S. Private, pg. 207
CAPTIVE PLASTICS; U.S. Private, pg. 207
CARADON PLC; Int'l, pg. 266
CARADON (USA) INC.—Caradon Plc; Int'l, pg. 267
CARBOLON DIVISION—High Voltage Engineering Corporation; U.S. Private, pg. 528
CAREFREE OF COLORADO—Berkshire Hathaway Inc.; U.S. Public, pg. 217
CARLISLE COMPANIES INCORPORATED; U.S. Public, pg. 305
CARLISLE FOOD SERVICE PRODUCTS—Carlisle Companies Incorporated; U.S. Public, pg. 305
CARNAUDMETALBOX—Crown Cork & Seal Company, Inc.; U.S. Public, pg. 463
CARSON INDUSTRIES—Millhouse Group; U.S. Private, pg. 748
CARTER HOLT HARVEY PLASTIC PRODUCTS—International Paper Company; U.S. Public, pg. 904
CARTER HOLT HARVEY PLASTIC PRODUCTS-BEVERAGE DIVISION—International Paper Company; U.S. Public, pg. 904
CARTER HOLT HARVEY ROOFING INTERNATIONAL—International Paper Company; U.S. Public, pg. 904
CENTRAL STATES DIVERSIFIED, INC.; U.S. Private, pg. 224
CENTREX CORPORATION; U.S. Private, pg. 225
CERTAINTEED CORPORATION—Saint-Gobain; Int'l, pg. 1170
THE CHARDON RUBBER CO.; U.S. Private, pg. 229
CHELSEA INDUSTRIES, INC.; U.S. Private, pg. 231
CHEM-TAINER INDUSTRIES; U.S. Private, pg. 231
CHEMDAL CORPORATION—AMCOL International Corp.; U.S. Public, pg. 64
CHEMOFLON GMBH—Martin Merkel GmbH & Co. KG; Int'l, pg. 859
THE CHINET CO.—Royal Packaging Industries Van Leer B.V.; Int'l, pg. 1146
CHOMERICS INC.—Parker Hannifin Corporation; U.S. Public, pg. 1262
CHRIS-CRAFT INDUSTRIAL PRODUCTS, INC.—Chris-Craft Industries, Inc.; U.S. Public, pg. 351
CHRIS-CRAFT INDUSTRIAL PRODUCTS, INC., MONO-SOL DIV.—Chris-Craft Industries, Inc.; U.S. Public, pg. 351
CHRIS-CRAFT INDUSTRIES, INC.; U.S. Public, pg. 351
CIBA-GEIGY (CHINA) LIMITED—Novartis AG; Int'l, pg. 976
CIBA-GEIGY FORMULATED SYSTEMS GROUP (AUTOMOTIVE CENTER)—Novartis AG; Int'l, pg. 973
CIBA-GEIGY ILAC VE KIMYA URUNLERI SANAYI VE TICARET AS—Novartis AG; Int'l, pg. 977
P.T. CIBA-GEIGY INDONESIA—Novartis AG; Int'l, pg. 977
CIBA-GEIGY JAPAN LIMITED-TOKYO BRANCH—Novartis AG; Int'l, pg. 977
CIBA-GEIGY KOREA LTD.—Novartis AG; Int'l, pg. 977
CIBA-GEIGY PLASTICS (EGYPT) S.A.E.—Novartis AG; Int'l, pg. 978
CIBA-GEIGY SERVICES S.A.—Novartis AG; Int'l, pg. 980
CIBA-GEIGY TRADING AND MARKETING SERVICES CO. LTD.—Novartis AG; Int'l, pg. 980
CIBA GRIMSBY—Novartis AG; Int'l, pg. 980
CIBA POLYMERS—Ciba Specialty Chemicals Holding Inc.; Int'l, pg. 292
CIBATUL LTD.—Novartis AG; Int'l, pg. 981
CIMCO—Intesys Technologies; U.S. Private, pg. 574
CIRCLE PLASTICS PRODUCTS, INC.; U.S. Private, pg. 240
CIRCUIT MATERIALS DIVISION—Rogers Corporation; U.S. Public, pg. 1402
CLARCOR, INC.; U.S. Public, pg. 381
CLARKE CONTAINER COMPANY, INC.—Mark IV Industries Inc.; U.S. Public, pg. 1045
CLAYTON CORPORATION; U.S. Private, pg. 244
CLAYTON PLASTICS CORP.—Clayton Corporation; U.S. Private, pg. 244
CLEAR SHIELD NATIONAL, INC.—Envirodyne Industries, Inc.; U.S. Public, pg. 586
CLOPAY CORPORATION—Griffon Corp.; U.S. Public, pg. 766
COACHMEN INDUSTRIES, INC.; U.S. Public, pg. 387
COATS & CLARK INC.—Coats Viyella plc; Int'l, pg. 300
COLEX INTERNATIONAL, LTD.—NewAge Industries Inc.; U.S. Private, pg. 796
COLLECTIBLES PLANT—Fort James Corporation; U.S. Public, pg. 672
COLLINS & AIKMAN CORPORATION; U.S. Public, pg. 399
COLTEC HOLDINGS INC; U.S. Public, pg. 401
COMBI BLOCK, INC.—PKL Verpackungssysteme GmbH; Int'l, pg. 1020
COMMAND PLASTIC CORPORATION; U.S. Private, pg. 257
COMMERCIAL PLASTICS & SUPPLIES CORP.; U.S. Private, pg. 258
COMPANIA HULERA GOODYEAR-OXO SOCIEDAD ANONIMA—The Goodyear Tire & Rubber Company; U.S. Public, pg. 753
COMPOSITE MATERIALS DIV.—Rogers Corporation; U.S. Public, pg. 1402
CONAIR CORPORATION; U.S. Private, pg. 261
CONCRETE & STEEL PIPE GROUP (SOUTHERN DIV.)—Ameron International Corporation; U.S. Public, pg. 99
CONNOR CORPORATION—Connor Corporation; U.S. Private, pg. 264
CONSTAR INTERNATIONAL, INC.—Crown Cork & Seal Company, Inc.; U.S. Public, pg. 463
CONSTRUCTION & HOME IMPROVEMENT MARKETS DIVISION—3M; U.S. Public, pg. 1605
CONTAINER STRAPPING—Illinois Tool Works Inc.; U.S. Public, pg. 867
CONTICO CONTAINER COMPANY—Contico International, Inc.; U.S. Private, pg. 267
CONTICO INTERNATIONAL, INC.; U.S. Private, pg. 267
CONTINENTAL AG; Int'l, pg. 327
CONTINENTAL INDUSTRIES INC.—Handy & Harman; U.S. Public, pg. 780
CONTINENTAL PLASTIC CONTAINERS, INC.—Continental Can Co.; U.S. Public, pg. 440
CONWED PLASTICS/N.V. S.A.—Leucadia National Corporation; U.S. Public, pg. 990
CORNING COSTAR CORPORATION—Corning Incorporated; U.S. Public, pg. 448
CORTEC COMPANY—Crane Co.; U.S. Public, pg. 456
COSCO INDUSTRIES; U.S. Private, pg. 277
COSTAR EUROPE, LTD.—Corning Incorporated; U.S. Public, pg. 448
COSTAR GMBH—Corning Incorporated; U.S. Public, pg. 448
COSTAR ITALIA, S.R.L.—Corning Incorporated; U.S. Public, pg. 448
COSTAR UK LTD.—Corning Incorporated; U.S. Public, pg. 448
COURTAULDS AEROSPACE—Courtaulds plc; Int'l, pg. 339
COZ PLASTICS INC.—PMC, Inc.; U.S. Private, pg. 827
CRANE CO.; U.S. Public, pg. 456
CRANE PLASTICS COMPANY; U.S. Private, pg. 286
CRANE RESISTOFLEX/DEFENSE—Crane Co.; U.S. Public, pg. 457
CRANE RESISTOFLEX/INDUSTRIAL—Crane Co.; U.S. Public, pg. 457
CRAWAL—Buckeye Corrugated Inc.; U.S. Private, pg. 177
CREDIT CARD SENTINEL—Montgomery Ward & Co., Inc.; U.S. Private, pg. 759
CREST-FOAM CORPORATION—Leggett & Platt, Incorporated; U.S. Public, pg. 986
CREST-HOOD FOAM COMPANY, INC.—Leggett & Platt, Incorporated; U.S. Public, pg. 986
CROWN CORK & SEAL COMPANY, INC.; U.S. Public, pg. 462
CROWN OBRIST AG—Crown Cork & Seal Company, Inc.; U.S. Public, pg. 465
CURVER B.V.—DSM N.V.; Int'l, pg. 352
CURVER KFT—DSM N.V.; Int'l, pg. 353
CUSTOM PAK, INC.; U.S. Private, pg. 298
CUTLER MANUFACTURING CORPORATION; U.S. Private, pg. 298
CYDSA S.A. PACKAGING DIV.—CYDSA S.A.; Int'l, pg. 246
DH COMPOUNDING CO.—M.A. Hanna Company; U.S. Public, pg. 781
DSM ENGINEERING PLASTIC PRODUCTS—DSM N.V.; Int'l, pg. 354
DSM PLASTIC PRODUCTS—DSM N.V.; Int'l, pg. 353
DACOR CORPORATION; U.S. Private, pg. 306
DAICEL CHEMICAL INDUSTRIES LTD.—Mitsui & Co., Ltd.; Int'l, pg. 877
DANAFILMS, INC.; U.S. Private, pg. 309
DANAHER CORPORATION; U.S. Public, pg. 480
DANBRAND PRODUCTS AUSTRALASIA—International Paper Company; U.S. Public, pg. 904
C.R. DANIELS, INC.; U.S. Private, pg. 310
DANONE GROUP; Int'l, pg. 379
DANSK INTERNATIONAL DESIGNS LTD.—Brown-Forman Corporation; U.S. Public, pg. 261
DART ARGENTINA S.A.—Premark International, Inc.; U.S. Public, pg. 1322
DART CONTAINER CORP.; U.S. Private, pg. 311
DART DO BRASIL INDUSTRIA E COMERCIO LTDA.—Premark International, Inc.; U.S. Public, pg. 1322
DART EUROPE S.A.—Premark International, Inc.; U.S. Public, pg. 1322
DART INDUSTRIES BELGIUM NV—Premark International, Inc.; U.S. Public, pg. 1322
DART INDUSTRIES LTD.—Premark International, Inc.; U.S. Public, pg. 1322
DART S.A. DE C.V.—Premark International, Inc.; U.S. Public, pg. 1322
DATACARD CORPORATION; U.S. Private, pg. 312
DATACARD EUROPE LTD.—DataCard Corporation; U.S. Private, pg. 312
DAVIES SHEPHARD PTY. LTD.—ABB Asea Brown Boveri (Holding) Ltd.; Int'l, pg. 2
DE LA RUE CARD TECHNOLOGY LIMITED—De La Rue plc; Int'l, pg. 387
DEERFIELD URETHANE, INC.—Bayer AG; Int'l, pg. 173
DELTA CONSOLIDATED INDUSTRIES, INC. (CO. HEADQUARTERS)—Danaher Corporation; U.S. Public, pg. 481
DENKI KAGAKU KOGYO KABUSHIKI KAISHA—Mitsui & Co., Ltd.; Int'l, pg. 877
DENNISON DO BRAZIL COMMERCIAL LTDA.—Avery Dennison Corporation; U.S. Public, pg. 153
DENNISON FASTENER DIV.—Avery Dennison Corporation; U.S. Public, pg. 152
DENNISON TRANSOCEANIC CORPORATION—Avery Dennison Corporation; U.S. Public, pg. 154
DESOTO INC.—Keystone Consolidated Industries, Inc.; U.S. Public, pg. 956
DETREX INDUSTRIAL CHEMICAL SPECIALTIES DIV.—Detrex Corporation; U.S. Public, pg. 502
DEUTSCHE DUNI GMBH—Duni AB; Int'l, pg. 421
THE DEXTER CORPORATION; U.S. Public, pg. 504
DEXTER GMBH—The Dexter Corporation; U.S. Public, pg. 505
DICKTEN & MASCH MANUFACTURING CO.; U.S. Private, pg. 331
DIEMOLDING CORP.; U.S. Private, pg. 332
DIMCO-GRAY COMPANY; U.S. Private, pg. 333
DOMINIQUE DUTSCHER, S.A.—Corning Incorporated; U.S. Public, pg. 448
DONNELLY CORPORATION; U.S. Public, pg. 519
DOUGLAS STEPHEN PLASTICS, INC.; U.S. Private, pg. 341
DOVER INDUSTRIES LIMITED; Int'l, pg. 417
THE DOW CHEMICAL COMPANY; U.S. Public, pg. 522
DOW KAKOH KABASHIKI KAISHA—The Dow Chemical Company; U.S. Public, pg. 524
DU PONT (E.I. DU PONT DE NEMOURS & CO.); U.S. Public, pg. 530
DUNMORE CORPORATION; U.S. Private, pg. 346
DURACO PRODUCTS, INC.; U.S. Private, pg. 348
DURACO PRODUCTS INC. OF SOUTH CAROLINA—Duraco Products, Inc.; U.S. Private, pg. 348
DURAKON INDUSTRIES, INC.; U.S. Public, pg. 537
DURAKON MEXICANA, S.A. DE C.V.—Durakon Industries, Inc.; U.S. Public, pg. 537
DURANT ELECTRONICS, INC.—Strombecker Corporation; U.S. Private, pg. 1047
DURAY, INC.—Newell Co.; U.S. Public, pg. 1177
DURO BAG MANUFACTURING CO.; U.S. Private, pg. 348
DURO PAPER BAG MFG. CO.—Duro Bag Manufacturing Co.; U.S. Private, pg. 349
ECW, INC.—The Dow Chemical Company; U.S. Public, pg. 523
ENPAC—Essef Corporation; U.S. Public, pg. 592
EAGLE AFFILIATES, INC.—APL Corporation; U.S. Private, pg. 7
EAGLE INDUSTRIES, INC.—Great American Management & Investment, Inc.; U.S. Private, pg. 473
EDISON PLASTICS CO.—Williamson-Dickie Mfg. Co.; U.S. Private, pg. 1179
EDISON PLASTICS DIV.—Williamson-Dickie Mfg. Co.; U.S. Private, pg. 1179
EKCO GROUP, INC.; U.S. Public, pg. 566
EKCO HOUSEWARES, INC.—Ekco Group, Inc.; U.S. Public, pg. 566
ELASTOGRAN FRANCE S.A.—BASF AG; Int'l, pg. 108
ELASTOGRAN GMBH—BASF AG; Int'l, pg. 104
ELASTOGRAN HEADWAY URETHANES CO., LTD.—BASF AG; Int'l, pg. 108
ELASTOGRAN ITALIA S.P.A.—BASF AG; Int'l, pg. 108
ELASTOGRAN S.A.—BASF AG; Int'l, pg. 108
ELASTOGRAN SCHWARZHEIDE GMBH—BASF AG; Int'l, pg. 104
ELASTOGRAN UK LIMITED—BASF AG; Int'l, pg. 108
ELCO TEXTRON—Textron Inc.; U.S. Public, pg. 1590

ELECTRICAL PRODUCTS DIVISION—3M; *U.S. Public*, pg. 1605
ELECTRONIC SOLUTIONS—Zero Corporation; *U.S. Public*, *pg. 1791*
ELKAY PLASTICS COMPANY, INC.; *U.S. Private*, pg. 372
ELKAY PRODUCTS, INC.; *U.S. Private*, pg. 372
ELTA PLASTICS LIMITED—Nifco Inc.; *Int'l*, pg. 929
ENERGY ABSORPTION SYSTEMS, INC.—Quixote Corporation; *U.S. Public*, pg. 1353
ENERGY CONTROL PRODUCTS—TI Group plc; *Int'l*, pg. 1338
ENVASES VALENCIANOS, S.A.—Reynolds Metals Company; *U.S. Public*, pg. 1386
ENVASES Y ALIMENTACION MADRID, S.A.—Reynolds Metals Company; *U.S. Public*, pg. 1386
ENVASES Y ALIMENTACION, S.A.—Reynolds Metals Company; *U.S. Public*, pg. 1387
ENVIRODYNE INDUSTRIES, INC.; *U.S. Public*, pg. 586
ERTA NV—DSM N.V.; *Int'l*, pg. 354
ERTA PLASTICS GMBH—DSM N.V.; *Int'l*, pg. 354
ESPECIALIDADES QUIMICIAS GRACE DE MEXICO S.A. DE C.V.—W.R. Grace & Co.; *U.S. Public*, pg. 755
ESSEF CORPORATION; *U.S. Public*, pg. 592
ESSEX POLYTECH, INC.—The Dow Chemical Company; *U.S. Public*, pg. 523
EUROCARBON TILBURG B.V.—DSM N.V.; *Int'l*, pg. 354
EVANS INDUSTRIES, INC.; *U.S. Private*, pg. 385
EVART PRODUCTS CO.—Chrysler Corporation; *U.S. Public*, pg. 353
EVENFLO COMPANY, INC.—Kohlberg Kravis Roberts & Co.; *U.S. Private*, pg. 629
EVENFLO MEXICO S.A.—Kohlberg Kravis Roberts & Co.; *U.S. Private*, pg. 630
EVODE CLEAREX LTD.—Laporte plc; *Int'l*, pg. 802
EVODE GROUP LTD.—Laporte plc; *Int'l*, pg. 802
EXCEL INDUSTRIES, INC.; *U.S. Public*, pg. 598
FMC FOODTECH/FRAN RICA—FMC Corporation; *U.S. Public*, pg. 605
FO-MAC DIVISION—Furon Company; *U.S. Public*, pg. 689
THE FABRI-FORM COMPANY; *U.S. Private*, pg. 390
FARDEM BV—DSM N.V.; *Int'l*, pg. 352
FASSON DE MEXICO, S.A.—Avery Dennison Corporation; *U.S. Public*, pg. 154
FASSON GESELLSCHAFT GMBH—Avery Dennison Corporation; *U.S. Public*, pg. 154
FASSON HANDELSGESELLSHAFT GMBH—Avery Dennison Corporation; *U.S. Public*, pg. 154
FAWN INDUSTRIES, INC.; *U.S. Private*, pg. 397
FEDERAL PAPER BOARD COMPANY, INC.—International Paper Company; *U.S. Public*, pg. 903
FEDERAL PROCESS CORP.; *U.S. Private*, pg. 399
FELTRAX INTERNATIONAL, INC.—BTR plc; *Int'l*, pg. 130
OY FENNOFELT AB-FORMING & FABRICS DRYER PLANT—Albany International Corp.; *U.S. Public*, pg. 37
OY FENNOFELT AB-PRESS FABRIC PLANT—Albany International Corp.; *U.S. Public*, pg. 37
FIBERESIN INDUSTRIES INC.; *U.S. Private*, pg. 402
FIBERLUX, INC.—Tredegar Industries Inc.; *U.S. Public*, pg. 1634
FILM PRODUCTS DIVISION—General Binding Corporation; *U.S. Public*, pg. 707
GEORG FISCHER LTD.; *Int'l*, pg. 488
FLAMBEAU CORPORATION; *U.S. Private*, pg. 409
FLAMBEAU CORPORATION—Flambeau Corporation; *U.S. Private*, pg. 409
FLAMBEAU PRODUCTS CORP.—Flambeau Corporation; *U.S. Private*, pg. 409
FLAMBEAU SOUTHEAST CO.—Flambeau Corporation; *U.S. Private*, pg. 409
FLEX-O-GLASS, INC.; *U.S. Private*, pg. 412
FLEXCON CO., INC.; *U.S. Private*, pg. 412
FLO CONTROL, INC.; *U.S. Private*, pg. 414
FLOWSERVE CORPORATION, ENGINEERED PLASTIC PRODUCTS DIV.—Flowserve Corporation; *U.S. Public*, pg. 658
FOAM MOLDING CORP.—FMC Corporation; *U.S. Public*, pg. 605
FOR BETTER LIVING, INC.; *U.S. Private*, pg. 417
FORBO-GIUBIASCO SA—Forbo Holding SA; *Int'l*, pg. 497
FORBO HELMITIN GMBH—Forbo Holding SA; *Int'l*, pg. 497
FORBO HOLDING SA; *Int'l*, pg. 496
FORBO NOVILON GMBH—Forbo Holding SA; *Int'l*, pg. 497
FORD PLASTIC & TRIM PRODUCTS INTERNATIONAL, INC.—Ford Motor Company; *U.S. Public*, pg. 662
FORT JAMES CORPORATION; *U.S. Public*, pg. 670
FOSTER PRODUCTS CORPORATION—H.B. Fuller Company; *U.S. Public*, pg. 686
FUJI BONDSTRAND CO., LTD.—Ameron International Corporation; *U.S. Public*, pg. 99
FURON COMPANY; *U.S. Public*, pg. 688
FUTTY & COMPANY—NCH Corporation; *U.S. Public*, pg. 1145
GEC REINFORCED PLASTICS LTD.—The General Electric Company, p.l.c.; *Int'l*, pg. 544
G.I. PLASTEK; *U.S. Private*, pg. 435
GST INDUSTRIES, INC.—Summa Industries; *U.S. Public*, pg. 1527
GAMCO PRODUCTS CO.—Masco Corporation; *U.S. Public*, *pg. 1053*
GARELICK FARMS, INC.—Suiza Foods Corporation; *U.S. Public*, pg. 1527
GATES FORMED-FIBRE PRODUCTS—Tomkins PLC; *Int'l*, pg. 1396
GEDY S.P.A.; *Int'l*, pg. 542
GENCORP DECORATIVE PRODUCT MANUFACTURING DIV.—GenCorp Inc.; *U.S. Public*, pg. 706
GENCORP INC.; *U.S. Public*, pg. 705
GENERAL CABLE CO.—Wassall Plc; *Int'l*, pg. 1487
GERBER PRODUCTS DIVISION-BABY CARE—Novartis AG; *Int'l*, pg. 973
A.J. GERRARD AND COMPANY; *U.S. Private*, pg. 449
M.C. GILL CORPORATION; *U.S. Private*, pg. 453
GLASSMASTER COMPANY; *U.S. Public*, pg. 745
GLASSTITE, INC.—Raven Industries, Inc.; *U.S. Public*, pg. 1361
GLASTIC CORPORATION—Kobe Steel, Ltd.; *Int'l*, pg. 740
GLYNWED INTERNATIONAL PLC; *Int'l*, pg. 554
GOLD SHIELD FIBERGLASS, INC.—Fleetwood Enterprises, Inc.; *U.S. Public*, pg. 652
GOLDEN BOOKS FAMILY ENTERTAINMENT INC.; *U.S. Public*, pg. 749
GOLDSHIELD FIBERGLASS OF INDIANA, INC.—Fleetwood Enterprises, Inc.; *U.S. Public*, pg. 652
GORVI S.A.—Solvay S.A.; *Int'l*, pg. 1278
GOULD PACKAGING, INC.; *U.S. Private*, pg. 466
STEPHEN GOULD PAPER CO., INC.; *U.S. Private*, pg. 467
GRABER-ROGG, INC.; *U.S. Private*, pg. 468
GRACE ARGENTINA S.A.—W.R. Grace & Co.; *U.S. Public*, *pg. 755*
GRACE CENTRAL AMERICA—W.R. Grace & Co.; *U.S. Public*, pg. 755
GRACE ESPECIALIDADES QUIMICOS E PLASTICAS—W.R. Grace & Co.; *U.S. Public*, pg. 755
GRACE G.M.B.H.—W.R. Grace & Co.; *U.S. Public*, pg. 755
GRACE HELLAS INDUSTRIAL & COMMERCIAL L.L.C.—W.R. Grace & Co.; *U.S. Public*, pg. 756
GRACE ITALIANA S.P.A.—W.R. Grace & Co.; *U.S. Public*, pg. 756
GRACE JAPAN K.K.—W.R. Grace & Co.; *U.S. Public*, pg. 756
GRACE PORTUGUESA LDA.—W.R. Grace & Co.; *U.S. Public*, pg. 756
GRACE, S.A.—W.R. Grace & Co.; *U.S. Public*, pg. 756
GRACE VENEZUELA S.A.—W.R. Grace & Co.; *U.S. Public*, *pg. 756*
W.R. GRACE AUSTRALIA LTD.—W.R. Grace & Co.; *U.S. Public*, pg. 755
W.R. GRACE LTD.—W.R. Grace & Co.; *U.S. Public*, pg. 756
W.R. GRACE OY—W.R. Grace & Co.; *U.S. Public*, pg. 756
GRIFFIN TECHNOLOGY INCORPORATED—Diebold, Incorporated; *U.S. Public*, pg. 506
GUARDIAN AUTOMOTIVE—Guardian Industries Corp.; *U.S. Private*, pg. 486
GUILD MOLDERS DIVISION—Crown Cork & Seal Company, Inc.; *U.S. Public*, pg. 463
HON INDUSTRIES INC.; *U.S. Public*, pg. 772
HANDGARDS INC.; *U.S. Private*, pg. 499
M.A. HANNA ENGINEERED MATERIALS—M.A. Hanna Company; *U.S. Public*, pg. 781
M.A. HANNA RUBBER COMPOUNDING—M.A. Hanna Company; *U.S. Public*, pg. 781
HANSEN PLASTICS DIVISION—Tuthill Corporation; *U.S. Private*, pg. 1110
HARTWELL COMMERCIAL DIVISION—Western Sky Industries, Inc.; *U.S. Private*, pg. 1168
HARTWELL CORPORATION—Western Sky Industries, Inc.; *U.S. Private*, pg. 1168
HARVEL PLASTICS, INC.—Detrex Corporation; *U.S. Public*, *pg. 502*
HEARTLAND BUILDING PRODUCTS, INC.—Jannock Limited; *Int'l*, pg. 699
H.E.I.L.—Dover Corporation; *U.S. Public*, pg. 521
HELLERMANN ELECTRIC—Bowthorpe plc; *Int'l*, pg. 207
HELLERMANN FRANCE SA—Bowthorpe plc; *Int'l*, pg. 209
HELLERMANN INSULOID—Bowthorpe plc; *Int'l*, pg. 207
HELLERMANN NORGE A/S—Bowthorpe plc; *Int'l*, pg. 209
PAUL HELLERMANN GMBH—Bowthorpe plc; *Int'l*, pg. 209
HELLERMANN SCANDINAVIA AB—Bowthorpe plc; *Int'l*, pg. 209
HENNELLS, INC.; *U.S. Private*, pg. 522
HEPWORTH PLC; *Int'l*, pg. 614
HERCULES INCORPORATED; *U.S. Public*, pg. 809
HIGH DENSITY FILM PRODS. DIV.—Sonoco Products Company; *U.S. Public*, pg. 1486
HILLS PRECISION COMPONENTS LTD.—PSA Peugeot Citroen; *Int'l*, pg. 1021
HINDUSTAN CIBA-GEIGY LIMITED—Novartis AG; *Int'l*, pg. 982
HOECHST CELANESE FILM & FIBER INTERMEDIATES GROUP—Hoechst Aktiengesellschaft; *Int'l*, pg. 626
HOECHST SPECIALTY PRODUCTS GROUP—Hoechst Aktiengesellschaft; *Int'l*, pg. 625
HOFFER PLASTICS CORPORATION; *U.S. Private*, pg. 532
HOLCOMB & HOKE MFG. COMPANY, INC.; *U.S. Private*, pg. 533
HOLM INDUSTRIES, INC.—The Standard Products Company; *U.S. Public*, pg. 1504
HOPPLE PLASTICS, INC.; *U.S. Private*, pg. 538
HUBBELL INCORPORATED; *U.S. Public*, pg. 844
HUBBELL PLASTICS, INC.—Hubbell Incorporated; *U.S. Public*, pg. 844
HUBER & SUHNER AG; *Int'l*, pg. 637
HUHTAMAKI OY; *Int'l*, pg. 638
HULS AMERICA INC.—Veba AG; *Int'l*, pg. 1455
HYOSUNG-BASF CO., LTD.—BASF AG; *Int'l*, pg. 108
ICI ACRYLICS INC.—Imperial Chemical Industries PLC; *Int'l*, pg. 663
IER DIVISION—Furon Company; *U.S. Public*, pg. 689
ITW FIXLOCK AB—Illinois Tool Works Inc.; *U.S. Public*, pg. 868
ITW NIFCO, INC.—Illinois Tool Works Inc.; *U.S. Public*, pg. 867
ITW PLASTIGLIDE LTD. OF CANADA/ ITW FASTEX—Illinois Tool Works Inc.; *U.S. Public*, pg. 869
ITW SIGNODE—Illinois Tool Works Inc.; *U.S. Public*, pg. 867
ICOPAL AB—Icopal a/s; *Int'l*, pg. 659
ICOPAL A/S; *Int'l*, pg. 658
ICORE INTERNATIONAL INC.—Smiths Industries plc; *Int'l*, pg. 1268
IDEAL-STANDARD S.A.I.—American Standard Inc.; *U.S. Public*, pg. 92
IGLOO PRODUCTS CORPORATION—Brunswick Corporation; *U.S. Public*, pg. 265
ILLINOIS TOOL WORKS INC.; *U.S. Public*, pg. 865
IMPERIAL CHEMICAL INDUSTRIES PLC; *Int'l*, pg. 662
IMPROVED BLOW MOLDING EQUIPMENT COMPANY, INC.—Goodman Equipment Corp.; *U.S. Private*, pg. 464
P.T. INDONESIA TORAY SYNTHETICS—Mitsui & Co., Ltd.; *Int'l*, pg. 882
INDUSTRIAL CUSTOM PRODUCTS L.L.C.—E & A Industries, Inc.; *U.S. Private*, pg. 352
INDUSTRIAL PLASTICS COMPANY—Alltrista Corporation; *U.S. Public*, pg. 56
INGRID DIVISION OF LAWNWARE—Lawnware Products, Inc.; *U.S. Private*, pg. 654
INJECTRON CORPORATION; *U.S. Private*, pg. 563
INNOVATIVE SOUTH—Innovative Plastics Corporation; *U.S. Private*, pg. 565
INTERNATIO (PTY.) LTD.—Internatio-Muller N.V.; *Int'l*, pg. 682
INTERNATIONAL CHEMPACK INC.—The Dow Chemical Company; *U.S. Public*, pg. 523
INTERNATIONAL CONTAINER SYSTEMS—Intertape Polymer Group Inc.; *Int'l*, pg. 685
INTERPLASTIC CORP.; *U.S. Private*, pg. 572
INTERTAPE POLYMER GROUP INC.; *Int'l*, pg. 684
INTERTRADE INDUSTRIES; *U.S. Private*, pg. 573
INTESYS OF CALIFORNIA—Intesys Technologies; *U.S. Private*, pg. 574
INTESYS TECHNOLOGIES; *U.S. Private*, pg. 574
INTEX CORP.; *U.S. Private*, pg. 574
INTEX PLASTICS CORPORATION—Intex Corp.; *U.S. Private*, pg. 574
IVEX PACKAGING CORPORATION; *U.S. Public*, pg. 915
J & B PRODUCTS, INC.—Federal Process Corp.; *U.S. Private*, pg. 399
JM COMPANY; *U.S. Private*, pg. 577
JACKSON CORP.—Lancaster Colony Corporation; *U.S. Public*, pg. 977
JADE S.A.—Martin Merkel GmbH & Co. KG; *Int'l*, pg. 859
JAMISON PLASTIC CORPORATION; *U.S. Private*, pg. 581
JANNOCK LIMITED; *Int'l*, pg. 698
JASPER PLASTICS—Kimball International, Inc.; *U.S. Public*, *pg. 957*
JELD-WEN, INC.; *U.S. Private*, pg. 585
AXEL JOHNSON AB; *Int'l*, pg. 707
JOHNSON CONTROLS, INC. (ENGINEERED PLASTICS DIV.)—Johnson Controls, Inc.; *U.S. Public*, pg. 932
JOHNSON CONTROLS, INC., PLASTICS TECHNOLOGY GROUP—Johnson Controls, Inc.; *U.S. Public*, pg. 932
JUNO, INC.—The Cretex Companies; *U.S. Private*, pg. 290
KVP SYSTEMS, INC.—Summa Industries; *U.S. Public*, pg. 1527
KANAFLEX DO BRASIL INDUSTRIA DE PLASTICOS LTDA.—Nissho Iwai Corporation; *Int'l*, pg. 948
KAPA GMBH LEICHTSOFFTECHNIK—Alusuisse-Lonza Holding Ltd.; *Int'l*, pg. 68
KAUFEL AMERICA INC.—Kaufel Group Ltd.; *Int'l*, pg. 725
KEENEY MANUFACTURING CO.; *U.S. Private*, pg. 611
KELLER BUILDING PRODUCTS OF CHARLOTTE, INC.; *U.S. Private*, pg. 612
KEMLITE COMPANY—Crane Co.; *U.S. Public*, pg. 457
KERR GROUP, INC.; *U.S. Public*, pg. 952
KETER PLASTIC LTD.; *Int'l*, pg. 732
KEY PLASTICS FRANCE SA—Key Plastics, Inc.; *U.S. Private*, pg. 618
KEY PLASTICS UK—Key Plastics, Inc.; *U.S. Private*, pg. 618
KEYSOR CENTURY CORPORATION; *U.S. Private*, pg. 618
KIMBALL INTERNATIONAL, INC.; *U.S. Public*, pg. 956
KIMBLE GLASS INC.—Viag AG; *Int'l*, pg. 1464
KINARK CORPORATION; *U.S. Public*, pg. 960
KINPAK, INC.—Ocean Bio-Chem Inc.; *U.S. Public*, pg. 1211
KLEER-VU—Kleer-Vu Plastics, Inc.; *U.S. Public*, pg. 962
KLEER-VU PLASTICS CORP.—Kleer-Vu Plastics, Inc.; *U.S. Public*, pg. 962
KLOCKNER-PENTAPLAST GMBH—Klockner-Werke AG; *Int'l*, pg. 737
KLOCKNER PENTAPLAST OF AMERICA, INC.—Klockner-Werke AG; *Int'l*, pg. 737
KLOCKNER-WERKE AG; *Int'l*, pg. 736
KOCH INDUSTRIES, INCORPORATED; *U.S. Private*, pg. 628
KOHLER COMPANY; *U.S. Private*, pg. 630
KOLLER ENTERPRISES, INC.; *U.S. Private*, pg. 631
KRACO ENTERPRISES, INC.; *U.S. Private*, pg. 634
KURZ-KASCH, INC.—Kurz-Kasch, Inc.; *U.S. Private*, pg. 637
KUSS CORPORATION—Cummins Engine Company, Inc.; *U.S. Public*, pg. 468
KYOWA ELECTRIC WIRE CO., LTD.—The Furukawa Electric Co., Ltd.; *Int'l*, pg. 530
LEC, INC.—Nifco Inc.; *Int'l*, pg. 929
LSP SPECIALTY PRODUCTS CO.—NCH Corporation; *U.S. Public*, pg. 1145
LA SALLE LABS DIV.—Del Laboratories, Inc.; *U.S. Public*, pg. 494
LAKE RIVER CORPORATION—Kinark Corporation; *U.S. Public*, pg. 961
LASALLE BRISTOL CORP.—Heywood Williams Group PLC; *Int'l*, pg. 618
LASCO BATHWARE—Tomkins PLC; *Int'l*, pg. 1397
LASCO FLUID DISTRIBUTION PRODUCTS—Tomkins PLC; *Int'l*, pg. 1398
LASCO PANEL PRODUCTS—Tomkins PLC; *Int'l*, pg. 1398
LATSHAW ENTERPRISES, INC.; *U.S. Public*, pg. 979
LAUGHTON & SONS, LTD.; *Int'l*, pg. 804
LAWNWARE PRODUCTS, INC.; *U.S. Private*, pg. 653
LAWSON MARDON PACKAGING INC.—Alusuisse-Lonza Holding Ltd.; *Int'l*, pg. 68
LEAR CORPORATION—Lear Corporation; *U.S. Public*, pg. 982
LEAR PLASTICS CORP.—Lear Corporation; *U.S. Public*, pg. 982
LEON PLASTICS, INC.—U.S. Industries, Inc.; *U.S. Public*, pg. 1684
LETICA CORPORATION; *U.S. Private*, pg. 661
LEUCADIA NATIONAL CORPORATION; *U.S. Public*, pg. 989

S.I.C. Index

LEXALITE INTERNATIONAL CORPORATION—Summa Industries; *U.S. Public*, pg. 1527
LIFE SCIENCES INTERNATIONAL (EUROPE) LIMITED—Thermo Electron Corporation; *U.S. Public*, pg. 1594
LIFE SCIENCES INTERNATIONAL PLC—Thermo Electron Corporation; *U.S. Public*, pg. 1594
LINCOLN INDUSTRIES, INC.—Zoeller Co.; *U.S. Private*, pg. 1207
LIQUI-BOX ACQUISITION CORPORATION—Liqui-Box Corporation; *U.S. Public*, pg. 1000
LIQUI-BOX CORP.—Liqui-Box Corporation; *U.S. Public*, pg. 1000
LIQUI-BOX CORPORATION; *U.S. Public*, pg. 1000
LIQUID COATINGS & DISPERSIONS DIVISION—Ferro Corporation; *U.S. Public*, pg. 619
LONDON INDUSTRIES, INC.—Worthington Industries, Inc.; *U.S. Public*, pg. 1780
LONZA-FOLIEN GMBH—Alusuisse-Lonza Holding Ltd.; *Int'l*, *pg. 69*
LONZA JAPAN LTD.—Alusuisse-Lonza Holding Ltd.; *Int'l*, pg. 69
LORD CORPORATION; *U.S. Private*, pg. 675
LOVDAHL MANUFACTURING—Kurz-Kasch, Inc.; *U.S. Private*, pg. 637
LOXCREEN COMPANY; *U.S. Private*, pg. 679
LUCAS-TVS LTD.—LucasVarity plc; *Int'l*, pg. 820
LUCKY LTD.—LG Group; *Int'l*, pg. 779
LUDLOW COMPOSITES CORPORATION; *U.S. Private*, pg. 680
MB AMERICA, INC.—Caradon Plc; *Int'l*, pg. 267
MB GENERAL PACKAGING DIV.—Caradon Plc; *Int'l*, pg. 266
MFG TRAY CO.—Molded Fiber Glass Companies; *U.S. Private*, pg. 756
MFG UNION CITY OPERATIONS—Molded Fiber Glass Companies; *U.S. Private*, pg. 756
MPC EASLEY—McKechnie PLC; *Int'l*, pg. 851
MPC MINNEAPOLIS—McKechnie PLC; *Int'l*, pg. 851
MPC STAMFORD BRIDGE—McKechnie PLC; *Int'l*, pg. 851
MACHINE-RITE PRODUCTS—Excel Industries, Inc.; *U.S. Public*, pg. 599
MACK MOLDING COMPANY INC.; *U.S. Private*, pg. 691
MACLEAN-FOGG CO.; *U.S. Private*, pg. 692
MAGLA PRODUCTS; *U.S. Private*, pg. 695
MANCHESTER PLASTICS—Collins & Aikman Corporation; *U.S. Public*, pg. 399
MANCHESTER PLASTICS CO., INC.—Summa Industries; *U.S. Public*, pg. 1527
MANUFACTURAS RODEX S.A.—DSM N.V.; *Int'l*, pg. 355
MARIETTA CORPORATION; *U.S. Private*, pg. 702
MARK IV INDUSTRIES INC.; *U.S. Public*, pg. 1044
MARK I MOLDED PLASTICS, INC.—Excel Industries, Inc.; *U.S. Public*, pg. 599
MARLEY MOULDINGS INC.—Marley PLC; *Int'l*, pg. 843
MARLEY PLC; *Int'l*, pg. 843
MARSHALLAN INDUSTRIES—Park-Ohio Industries, Inc.; *U.S. Public*, pg. 1259
MARTEL CATALA ET CIE—Albany International Corp.; *U.S.* Public, pg. 37
MARUBENI CORPORATION; *Int'l*, pg. 844
MARYLAND PLASTICS, INC.—Lab Products, Inc.; *U.S. Private*, pg. 641
MASCO CORPORATION; *U.S. Public*, pg. 1052
MASCO CORPORATION LIMITED—Masco Corporation; *U.S. Public*, pg. 1054
MASTER MOLDED PRODUCTS CORPORATION; *U.S. Private*, pg. 714
MASTER SHIELD BUILDING PRODUCTS—Jannock Limited; *Int'l*, pg. 698
MATSUSHITA ELECTRIC WORKS, LTD.; *Int'l*, pg. 847
MATTEL T COMPANY LTD.—Mattel, Inc.; *U.S. Public*, pg. 1059
MAUI CUP—Letica Corporation; *U.S. Private*, pg. 661
MAXCO, INC.; *U.S. Public*, pg. 1061
MAYFAIR MOLDED PRODUCTS CORPORATION—Wozniak Industries, Inc.; *U.S. Private*, pg. 1192
MAZZUCCHELLI 1849 S.P.A.; *Int'l*, pg. 849
MCCORMICK & COMPANY, INCORPORATED; *U.S. Public*, pg. 1066
MCKECHNIE PLC; *Int'l*, pg. 851
MEDLINE INDUSTRIES, INC.; *U.S. Private*, pg. 728
MELNOR INC.—O'Sullivan Corporation; *U.S. Public*, pg. 1234
MEMBRANA GMBH—Akzo Nobel N.V.; *Int'l*, pg. 46
MENASHA CORP., TRAEX DIVISION—Menasha Corporation; *U.S. Private*, pg. 731
MENASHA CORPORATION; *U.S. Private*, pg. 731
MERCER PRODUCTS CO.—Laporte plc; *Int'l*, pg. 802
MARTIN MERKEL GMBH & CO. KG; *Int'l*, pg. 859
METALLGESELLSCHAFT AG; *Int'l*, pg. 860
METTOWEE LUMBER & PLASTIC CO., INC.—Telescope Casual Furniture, Inc.; *U.S. Private*, pg. 1074
MEXALIT S.A.—Saint-Gobain; *Int'l*, pg. 1171
MICRO CARD TECHNOLOGIES INC.—Compagnie des Machines Bull; *Int'l*, pg. 316
MIKRON AG BIEL—Mikron Holding AG; *Int'l*, pg. 866
MIKRON CORP. ANDERSON—Mikron Holding AG; *Int'l*, pg. 866
MIKRON CORP. STRATFORD—Mikron Holding AG; *Int'l*, pg. 867
MIKRON SPA ZINGONIA—Mikron Holding AG; *Int'l*, pg. 867
MIKRON SRL TREZZO SULL'ADDA—Mikron Holding AG; *Int'l*, pg. 867
MIKRON U.K. LTD.—Mikron Holding AG; *Int'l*, pg. 867
MIKUNI INDUSTRY CO., LTD.—Oki Electric Industry Company, Ltd.; *Int'l*, pg. 999
MILLER PRODUCTS COMPANY, INC.; *U.S. Private*, pg. 747
MILLHOUSE GROUP; *U.S. Private*, pg. 748
MILPRINT INC.—Bemis Company, Inc.; *U.S. Public*, pg. 210
MILTON CAN CO., INC.; *U.S. Private*, pg. 749
MINIATURE PRECISION COMPONENTS; *U.S. Private*, pg. 750
MINIGRIP ZIP-PAK—Illinois Tool Works Inc.; *U.S. Public*, pg. 867
MITCHEL-LINCOLN PACKAGING; *Int'l*, pg. 870
MITSUI TOATSU CHEMICALS, INC.—Mitsui & Co., Ltd.; *Int'l*, pg. 877
MOBIL FILMS AND PACKAGING—Mobil Oil Corporation; *U.S. Public*, pg. 1118
MOBIL OIL CORPORATION; *U.S. Public*, pg. 1118
MOLDED FIBER GLASS COMPANIES; *U.S. Private*, pg. 755
MONOFORT—Saint-Gobain; *Int'l*, pg. 1177
MORTON AUTOMOTIVE COATINGS—Morton International Inc.; *U.S. Public*, pg. 1135
MOSSBERG INDUSTRIES, HUBBARD DIVISION—Mossberg Industries, Inc.; *U.S. Private*, pg. 764
MOSSBERG INDUSTRIES, INC.; *U.S. Private*, pg. 763
MULAY PLASTICS INC.—Dubin-Clark & Company; *U.S. Private*, pg. 344
MUSKIN LEISURE PRODUCTS, INC.; *U.S. Private*, pg. 768
MYERS INDUSTRIES, INC.; *U.S. Public*, pg. 1143
MYTTON'S LIMITED—Bristile Clay Tiles, Ltd.; *Int'l*, pg. 216
NALLE PLASTICS INC.; *U.S. Private*, pg. 773
NAPCO PLASTICS CO.—Electrolux, AB; *Int'l*, pg. 440
THE NATIONAL LATEX PRODUCTS CO.; *U.S. Private*, pg. 785
NATIONAL TOOL & MANUFACTURING COMPANY; *U.S. Private*, pg. 787
NATIONAL UNION ELECTRIC CORP.—Electrolux, AB; *Int'l*, *pg. 440*
NEWELL CO.; *U.S. Public*, pg. 1176
NIBCO, INC.; *U.S. Private*, pg. 798
NIFCO INC.; *Int'l*, pg. 928
NOMACO, INC.; *U.S. Private*, pg. 801
NORDISKAFILT AB—Albany International Corp.; *U.S. Public*, pg. 37
NORDISKAFILT A/S—Albany International Corp.; *U.S. Public*, pg. 37
NORDISKAFILT GMBH—Albany International Corp.; *U.S. Public*, pg. 37
NOREL PAPER CORPORATION—Unisource Worldwide, Inc.; *U.S. Public*, pg. 1671
NORSK HYDRO A.S; *Int'l*, pg. 959
NORTH AMERICAN RECREATION PRODUCTS COMPANY—MacAndrews & Forbes Holdings Inc.; *U.S. Private*, pg. 691
NORTH CAROLINA FOAM INDUSTRIES, INC.—Barnhardt Manufacturing Co.; *U.S. Private*, pg. 117
NORTHLAND ALUMINUM PRODUCTS, INC.; *U.S. Private*, pg. 805
NORTON PERFORMANCE PLASTICS—Saint-Gobain; *Int'l*, pg. 1174
NORWESCO, INC.; *U.S. Private*, pg. 808
NOVARTIS—Novartis AG; *Int'l*, pg. 972
NUNC A/S—BTR plc; *Int'l*, pg. 130
NY-GLASS PLASTICS, INC.—Summa Industries; *U.S. Public*, pg. 1527
NYLONCRAFT—Excel Industries, Inc.; *U.S. Public*, pg. 599
THE OHIO ART COMPANY, INC.; *U.S. Public*, pg. 1214
OLSONITE CORPORATION; *U.S. Private*, pg. 815
OMICRON PROPRIETARY LTD.—W.R. Grace & Co.; *U.S. Public*, pg. 756
OMNIPLASTIC—Lafarge S.A.; *Int'l*, pg. 789
ONEIDA ROSTONE CORPORATION—Reunion Industries, Inc.; *U.S. Public*, pg. 1383
OUIMET CORP.; *U.S. Private*, pg. 821
OVERPELT-PLASCOBEL, INC.—Union Miniere; *Int'l*, pg. 1442
AB OVERUMS FONSTERFABRIK—Electrolux, AB; *Int'l*, pg. 439
OWENS-BROCKWAY PLASTIC CONTAINERS—Owens-Illinois, Inc.; *U.S. Public*, pg. 1238
OWENS-BROCKWAY PRESCRIPTION PRODUCTS—Owens-Illinois, Inc.; *U.S. Public*, pg. 1238
OWENS CORNING; *U.S. Public*, pg. 1236
OWENS CORNING/FOAMULAR—Owens Corning; *U.S. Public*, pg. 1237
OWENS-ILLINOIS, INC.; *U.S. Public*, pg. 1238
P & M MANUFACTURING—NCH Corporation; *U.S. Public*, pg. 1145
PCM BELGIUM—DSM N.V.; *Int'l*, pg. 356
PCM-EWP—DSM N.V.; *Int'l*, pg. 356
PCM FRANCE SA—DSM N.V.; *Int'l*, pg. 356
PEC EL PASO—Plastic Engineered Components Inc.; *U.S. Private*, pg. 871
PEC MICHIGAN—Plastic Engineered Components Inc.; *U.S.* Private, pg. 871
PEC MOARK—Plastic Engineered Components Inc.; *U.S. Private*, pg. 871
PEC WISCONSIN—Plastic Engineered Components Inc.; *U.S. Private*, pg. 871
PKL VERPACKUNGSSYSTEME GMBH; *Int'l*, pg. 1020
PTA CORPORATION; *U.S. Private*, pg. 828
PACESETTER CORPORATION; *U.S. Private*, pg. 830
PACKAGE SERVICE COMPANY, LLC.; *U.S. Private*, pg. 833
PACKAGING & CONTAINER MANUFACTURERS LTD.—DSM N.V.; *Int'l*, pg. 356
PAK-SHER CO.—T C Manufacturing Company, Inc.; *U.S. Private*, pg. 1062
PAR INDUSTRIES, INC.; *U.S. Private*, pg. 838
PARISI INC./ROYAL STORE FIXTURE; *U.S. Private*, pg. 839
PARK-OHIO INDUSTRIES, INC.; *U.S. Public*, pg. 1258
PATHWAY BELLOWS, INC.—Dover Corporation; *U.S. Public*, pg. 521
PEERLESS TUBE COMPANY; *U.S. Public*, pg. 1269
PENN ERIE DIV.—Plastek Group; *U.S. Private*, pg. 870
PENT PLASTICS, INC.—Group Dekko; *U.S. Private*, pg. 484
PEREGRINE INCORPORATED; *U.S. Private*, pg. 852
PERFECSEAL, INC.—Bemis Company, Inc.; *U.S. Public*, pg. 210
PERSTORP COMPONENTS—Perstorp AB; *Int'l*, pg. 1040
PERSTORP FORM—Perstorp AB; *Int'l*, pg. 1037
PERSTORP FORM LTD.—Perstorp AB; *Int'l*, pg. 1038
PERSTORP FORM OY—Perstorp AB; *Int'l*, pg. 1038
PERSTORP PLASTIC SYSTEMS—Perstorp AB; *Int'l*, pg. 1037
PERSTORP S.A.-DIV. BAKELITE—Perstorp AB; *Int'l*, pg. 1037
PERSTORP S.A.-DIV. COMPONENTS FRANCE—Perstorp AB; *Int'l*, pg. 1040
PERSTORP S.A.-DIV. PERSTORP STAMP—Perstorp AB; *Int'l*, pg. 1038
PERSTORP SPA-DIV. COMPOUNDS—Perstorp AB; *Int'l*, pg. 1037
PERSTORP XYTEC, INC.—Perstorp AB; *Int'l*, pg. 1037
PHILADELPHIA SIGN COMPANY; *U.S. Private*, pg. 861
PHILLIPS DRISCOPIPE, INC.—Phillips Petroleum Company; *U.S. Public*, pg. 1291
PHILLIPS PETROLEUM COMPANY; *U.S. Public*, pg. 1290
PHILLIPS PLASTICS CORPORATION; *U.S. Private*, pg. 862
PIETRO COSTA & C SRL—Alusuisse-Lonza Holding Ltd.; *Int'l*, pg. 69
PIONEER PAPER CORPORATION; *U.S. Private*, pg. 867
PIONEER TOOL & MOLD, INC.—Plastek Group; *U.S. Private*, pg. 870
PLANO MOLDING CO.; *U.S. Private*, pg. 869
PLASKOLITE INC.; *U.S. Private*, pg. 870
PLASTECH CORPORATION; *U.S. Private*, pg. 870
PLASTEK GROUP; *U.S. Private*, pg. 870
PLASTI-LINE, INC.; *U.S. Public*, pg. 1308
PLASTIC ENGINEERED COMPONENTS INC.; *U.S. Private*, *pg. 870*
PLASTIC MOLDINGS CORP.; *U.S. Private*, pg. 871
PLASTIC PACKAGING COMPANY—Alltrista Corporation; *U.S. Public*, pg. 57
PLASTIC PACKAGING, INC.; *U.S. Private*, pg. 871
PLASTIC PARTS, INC.—Myers Industries, Inc.; *U.S. Public*, pg. 1143
PLASTIC SUPPLIERS, INC.; *U.S. Private*, pg. 871
PLASTIC TRIM, INC.—JPE, Inc.; *U.S. Public*, pg. 919
PLASTICOS BEST SA—Saint-Gobain; *Int'l*, pg. 1171
PLASTICOS EXTRUIDOS, S.A.—FMC Corporation; *U.S. Public*, pg. 607
PLASTICOS MARATON, S.A.—Mattel, Inc.; *U.S. Public*, pg. 1059
PLASTICOS REX. S.A. DE C.V.—CYDSA S.A.; *Int'l*, pg. 246
PLASTICS, INC.—Newell Co.; *U.S. Public*, pg. 1177
PLASTICS MANUFACTURING COMPANY—Sun Coast Industries, Inc; *U.S. Public*, pg. 1530
PLASTIPAK PACKAGING INC.; *U.S. Private*, pg. 872
PLAXICON COMPANY—Vorwerk & Co.; *Int'l*, pg. 1481
PLEXCO/SPIROLITE—Chevron Corporation; *U.S. Public*, pg. 348
PLIX PACKAGING LIMITED—International Paper Company; *U.S. Public*, pg. 904
PLYMOUTH RUBBER COMPANY, INC.; *U.S. Public*, pg. 1311
POLARCUP FINLAND—Huhtamaki Oy; *Int'l*, pg. 638
POLARCUP GERMANY—Huhtamaki Oy; *Int'l*, pg. 638
POLARCUP GROUP HEADQUARTERS—Huhtamaki Oy; *Int'l*, pg. 638
POLARCUP UNITED KINGDOM LTD.—Huhtamaki Oy; *Int'l*, *pg. 639*
POLY-SEAL CORPORATION; *U.S. Private*, pg. 875
POLYFIBRON TECHNOLOGIES CORP.; *U.S. Private*, pg. 875
POLYFLON COMPANY—Crane Co.; *U.S. Public*, pg. 457
POLYMER PLASTICS CORPORATION; *U.S. Private*, pg. 875
POLYPENCO B.V.—DSM N.V.; *Int'l*, pg. 354
POLYPENCO G.M.B.H.—DSM N.V.; *Int'l*, pg. 354
POLYPENCO LTD.—DSM N.V.; *Int'l*, pg. 354
POLYPENCO NV—DSM N.V.; *Int'l*, pg. 354
POLYPENCO S.R.L.—DSM N.V.; *Int'l*, pg. 354
POSSO S.A.; *Int'l*, pg. 1064
PRECISION DYNAMICS CORPORATION; *U.S. Private*, pg. 879
PRECISION PLASTICS INC.; *U.S. Private*, pg. 879
PRETTY NEAT PRODUCTS—Newell Co.; *U.S. Public*, pg. 1177
PRODUCTS RESEARCH & CHEMICAL CORP. MANUFACTURING FACILITIES DIV.—Courtaulds plc; *Int'l*, pg. 339
PROGRAMMED COMPOSITES, INC.—Pressure Systems, Inc.; *U.S. Private*, pg. 882
PROPAK—International Paper Company; *U.S. Public*, pg. 904
PROTECTIVE CLOSURES CO., INC.—Mark IV Industries Inc.; *U.S. Public*, pg. 1045
PUGET PLASTICS CORPORATION—Arctic Slope Regional Corporation; *U.S. Private*, pg. 80
Q3 INDUSTRIES—Q3 Stamped Metal; *U.S. Private*, pg. 897
QUADION CORPORATION; *U.S. Private*, pg. 898
QUAKER INDUSTRIES—Park-Ohio Industries, Inc.; *U.S. Public*, pg. 1259
THE QUIKSET ORGANIZATION—For Better Living, Inc.; *U.S. Private*, pg. 417
QUIXOTE CORPORATION; *U.S. Public*, pg. 1353
R & B MACHINE TOOL CO.; *U.S. Private*, pg. 901
R & R PLASTICS—Fulton Industries Inc.; *U.S. Private*, pg. 431
RANDALL TEXTRON—Textron Inc.; *U.S. Public*, pg. 1590
RANIR CORPORATION/DCP; *U.S. Private*, pg. 909
RANTOUL PRODUCTS TEXTRON INC.—Textron Inc.; *U.S.* Public, pg. 1589
RAPID INDUSTRIAL PLASTICS COMPANY; *U.S. Private*, pg. 910
RAUCH INDUSTRIES, INC.—Syratech Corporation; *U.S. Private*, pg. 1061
RAVEN INDUSTRIES, INC.; *U.S. Public*, pg. 1361
RED WING PRODUCTS, INC.—Ferguson International Holdings; *Int'l*, pg. 480
REDPATH INDUSTRIES LTD.—Tate & Lyle PLC; *Int'l*, pg. 1357
REESE ENTERPRISES, INC.; *U.S. Private*, pg. 916

REEVES BROTHERS, INC.—Hart Holding Company, Inc.; U.S. Private, pg. 507
REEVES INTERNATIONAL—Hart Holding Company, Inc.; U.S. Private, pg. 507
REEVES RUBBER—BTR plc; Int'l, pg. 127
REHRIG PACIFIC COMPANY; U.S. Private, pg. 919
REICHHOLD CHEMICALS, INC.—Dainippon Ink & Chemicals, Inc.; Int'l, pg. 370
REINHOLD INDUSTRIES INC.; U.S. Private, pg. 920
REXAM CLOSURES—Rexam PLC; Int'l, pg. 1106
REXAM CONTAINERS—Rexam PLC; Int'l, pg. 1107
REXAM CONTAINERS - US—Rexam PLC; Int'l, pg. 1106
REXAM MEDICAL PACKAGING LTD.—Rexam PLC; Int'l, pg. 1106
REXAM PERFORMANCE PRODUCTS—Rexam PLC; Int'l, pg. 1106
RHONE-POULENC INC.—Rhone-Poulenc S.A.; Int'l, pg. 1112
RICHCO INC.; U.S. Private, pg. 929
RICHMOND TECHNOLOGY INC.; U.S. Private, pg. 929
RIKEN ELECTRIC WIRE CO., LTD.—The Furukawa Electric Co., Ltd.; Int'l, pg. 530
RIMIR, S.A. DE C.V.—General Motors Corporation; U.S. Public, pg. 723
RISDON CORPORATION—Crown Cork & Seal Company, Inc.; U.S. Public, pg. 463
ROBINSON CONE—Dover Industries Limited; Int'l, pg. 417
ROCKWELL PLASTIC PRODUCTS—BBA Group plc; Int'l, pg. 113
ROMER-BRITAX AUTOGURTE GMBH—Britax International plc; Int'l, pg. 217
ROPAK ATLANTIC INC.—Linpac Mouldings Limited; Int'l, pg. 811
ROPAK CENTRAL INC.—Linpac Mouldings Limited; Int'l, pg. 811
ROPAK CORPORATION—Linpac Mouldings Limited; Int'l, pg. 811
ROPAK MATERIALS HANDLING DIV.—Linpac Mouldings Limited; Int'l, pg. 812
ROPAK NORTHWEST INC.—Linpac Mouldings Limited; Int'l, pg. 812
ROPAK SOUTHWEST INC.—Linpac Mouldings Limited; Int'l, pg. 812
ROPAK WEST—Linpac Mouldings Limited; Int'l, pg. 812
ROTATIONAL MOLDING, INC.—Rotonics Manufacturing Inc.; U.S. Public, pg. 1406
ROTONICS MANUFACTURING INC.; U.S. Public, pg. 1406
ROYAL PLASTIC—M.C. Gill Corporation; U.S. Private, pg. 453
RUBBERMAID CANADA INC. COMMERCIAL PRODUCTS—Rubbermaid Incorporated; U.S. Public, pg. 1411
RUBBERMAID CANADA INC. CONSUMER PRODUCTS—Rubbermaid Incorporated; U.S. Public, pg. 1411
RUBBERMAID HOME PRODUCTS DIV.—Rubbermaid Incorporated; U.S. Public, pg. 1411
RUBBERMAID INCORPORATED; U.S. Public, pg. 1411
RUBBERMAID-STATESVILLE INC.—Rubbermaid Incorporated; U.S. Public, pg. 1411
RUETGERS A.G.; Int'l, pg. 1147
RUTLAND PLASTIC TECHNOLOGIES, INC.—Florida Capital Partners; U.S. Private, pg. 414
SFP CORPORATION—Kerr Group, Inc.; U.S. Public, pg. 952
SLG PLASTICS, INC.—Scott's Liquid Gold-Inc.; U.S. Public, pg. 1447
SAAR-GUMMIWERK GMBH—Saarbergwerke Aktiengesellschaft; Int'l, pg. 1167
ST. CLAIRE PLASTICS CO.; U.S. Private, pg. 960
SAMBOW PLASTICS CO., LTD.—Nissho Iwai Corporation; Int'l, pg. 947
SAMSILL CORPORATION; U.S. Private, pg. 963
SANDUSKY PLASTICS, INC.—Envirodyne Industries, Inc.; U.S. Public, pg. 586
SCHLEGEL CORPORATION—BTR plc; Int'l, pg. 128
SCHLEGEL ROCHESTER DIV.—BTR plc; Int'l, pg. 128
A. SCHULMAN, INC.; U.S. Public, pg. 1441
SCRIPTO-TOKAI CORP.; U.S. Private, pg. 977
SEALED AIR B.V.—Sealed Air Corporation; U.S. Public, pg. 1451
SEALED AIR CORPORATION; U.S. Public, pg. 1450
SEALED AIR ESPANA, S.A.—Sealed Air Corporation; U.S. Public, pg. 1451
SEALED AIR G.M.B.H.—Sealed Air Corporation; U.S. Public, pg. 1451
SEALED AIR JAPAN LTD.—Sealed Air Corporation; U.S. Public, pg. 1451
SEALED AIR LIMITED—Sealed Air Corporation; U.S. Public, pg. 1451
SEALED AIR (MALAYSIA) SDN BHD—Sealed Air Corporation; U.S. Public, pg. 1451
SEALED AIR OF CANADA INC.—Sealed Air Corporation; U.S. Public, pg. 1451
SEALED AIR PACKAGING PRODUCTS DIVISION—Sealed Air Corporation; U.S. Public, pg. 1451
SEALED AIR S.P.A.—Sealed Air Corporation; U.S. Public, pg. 1451
SEALED AIR SVENSKA A.B.—Sealed Air Corporation; U.S. Public, pg. 1451
SEALED AIR SYSTEMS—Sealed Air Corporation; U.S. Public, pg. 1451
SEALRIGHT COMPANY, INC.; U.S. Public, pg. 1451
SEALRIGHT MFG. EAST, INC.—Sealright Company, Inc.; U.S. Public, pg. 1452
SEALRIGHT MFG. WEST, INC.—Sealright Company, Inc.; U.S. Public, pg. 1452
SEASON-ALL INDUSTRIES, INC.—Caradon Plc; Int'l, pg. 267
SEATTLE PACKAGING CORPORATION; U.S. Private, pg. 980
SECURITY PLASTICS CARIBE, INC.—Security Plastics, Inc.; U.S. Private, pg. 981
SECURITY PLASTICS DE MEXICO—Security Plastics, Inc.; U.S. Private, pg. 981
SECURITY PLASTICS, INC.; U.S. Private, pg. 981
SECURITY PLASTICS WEST, INC.—Security Plastics, Inc.; U.S. Private, pg. 981
SEKISUI CHEMICAL CO., LTD.; Int'l, pg. 1219
SELFIX, INC.—Home Products International, Inc.; U.S. Public, pg. 832
SENETICS—The West Company, Incorporated; U.S. Public, pg. 1755
SEQUENTIA INC.; U.S. Private, pg. 985
SETCO, INC.—McCormick & Company, Incorporated; U.S. Public, pg. 1066
SHIN-ETSU POLYMER CO. LTD.—Shin-Etsu Chemical Co. ltd.; Int'l, pg. 1234
SHOWPLA ASIA LIMITED; Int'l, pg. 1237
SHUTTERS, INC.—Home Products International, Inc.; U.S. Public, pg. 832
SIC PLASTICS FRANCE S.A.—Mazzucchelli 1849 S.p.a.; Int'l, pg. 850
SIC PLASTICS GMBH—Mazzucchelli 1849 S.p.a.; Int'l, pg. 850
SIERRACIN CORPORATION; U.S. Private, pg. 999
SIGNET SCIENTIFIC CO.—Georg Fischer Ltd.; Int'l, pg. 489
SILLCOCKS PLASTICS, INC.—American Technology Corporation; U.S. Private, pg. 63
SIMPSON INVESTMENT CO.; U.S. Private, pg. 1003
SISTEMA ARGOS S.A.; Int'l, pg. 1256
GEORGE FISCHER SLOANE, INC.—ETEX; Int'l, pg. 430
SMALL PARTS, INC.-NAPCO DIVISION—Small Parts, Inc.; U.S. Private, pg. 1006
A.O. SMITH CORPORATION; U.S. Public, pg. 1476
SMITH & SMITH GLASS LTD.—International Paper Company; U.S. Public, pg. 904
SMITH MCDONALD CORP.; U.S. Private, pg. 1009
SMITHS INDUSTRIES PLC; Int'l, pg. 1266
SMURFIT PLASTIC PACKAGING DIV.—Jefferson Smurfit Group p.l.c.; Int'l, pg. 1271
SNYDER-CROWN, INC.—Snyder Industries, Inc.; U.S. Private, pg. 1011
SNYDER SOUTHEAST DIV.—Snyder Industries, Inc.; U.S. Private, pg. 1011
SOCIETE DE TRANSFORMATION DES MATIERES PLASTIQUES-S.T.M.P. S.A.—Solvay S.A.; Int'l, pg. 1279
SOCIETE ZAIRO-SUISSE DE PRODUITS CHIMIQUES S.A.R.L.—Novartis AG; Int'l, pg. 986
SOLO CUP COMPANY—Solo Cup Company; U.S. Private, pg. 1013
SOLUTIA INC.; U.S. Public, pg. 1483
SOLVAY AUTOMOTIVE INC.—Solvay S.A.; Int'l, pg. 1277
SOLVAY S.A.; Int'l, pg. 1277
SONOCO PRODUCTS COMPANY; U.S. Public, pg. 1485
SOPLACHIM S.A.—Solvay S.A.; Int'l, pg. 1280
SOUTH BEND PLASTICS, INC.; U.S. Private, pg. 1014
SOUTHWEST CHEMICAL/SERVICES—M.A. Hanna Company; U.S. Public, pg. 781
SPALDING & EVENFLO COMPANIES, INC.—Kohlberg Kravis Roberts & Co.; U.S. Private, pg. 629
SPALDING & EVENFLO JUVENILE FURNITURE COMPANY—Kohlberg Kravis Roberts & Co.; U.S. Private, pg. 630
SPARTAN PLASTICS CANADA—Spartan International Inc.; U.S. Private, pg. 1020
SPARTECH CORPORATION; U.S. Public, pg. 1495
SPECTRUM MOLDING—Plastek Group; U.S. Private, pg. 870
SPEEDLING INCORPORATED; U.S. Private, pg. 1024
SPIN-CAST PLASTICS, INC.—Quixote Corporation; U.S. Public, pg. 1353
SPONTEX, INC.—Total S.A.; Int'l, pg. 1409
SPONTEX S.A.—Total S.A.; Int'l, pg. 1409
STADIUM LIMITED; Int'l, pg. 1293
STANDARD PRODUCTS (CANADA) LTD.—The Standard Products Company; U.S. Public, pg. 1505
THE STANDARD PRODUCTS COMPANY; U.S. Public, pg. 1504
STANDARD PRODUCTS LIMITED—The Standard Products Company; U.S. Public, pg. 1505
STANT MANUFACTURING INC.—Tomkins PLC; Int'l, pg. 1397
STERILITE CORPORATION; U.S. Private, pg. 1040
STERLING PLASTICS CO.—Newell Co.; U.S. Public, pg. 1178
THE STOLLE CORPORATION—Aluminum Company of America; U.S. Public, pg. 61
STONE CONTAINER CORPORATION; U.S. Public, pg. 1520
STROMBECKER CORPORATION; U.S. Private, pg. 1047
STRUCTURAL EUROPE—Essef Corporation; U.S. Public, pg. 593
STRUCTURAL FOAM PLASTICS—Structural Foam Plastics, Inc.; U.S. Private, pg. 1048
STRUCTURAL FOAM PLASTICS, INC.; U.S. Private, pg. 1047
STRUCTURAL FOAM PLASTICS, INC.—Structural Foam Plastics, Inc.; U.S. Private, pg. 1048
SUMMA INDUSTRIES; U.S. Public, pg. 1527
SUMMIT PLASTIC CO.—Novartis AG; Int'l, pg. 974
SUMMIT PLASTIC SOLUTIONS, INC.; U.S. Private, pg. 1050
SUN COAST CLOSURES OF FLORIDA, INC.—Sun Coast Industries, Inc; U.S. Public, pg. 1530
SUN COAST INDUSTRIES, INC; U.S. Public, pg. 1529
SUNPRENE CO.—A. Schulman, Inc.; U.S. Public, pg. 1441
SUPERFORM METALS—Alcan Aluminium Limited; Int'l, pg. 52
SWEETHEART CUP COMPANY INC.; U.S. Private, pg. 1058
SWEETHEART CUP COMPANY INC.—Sweetheart Cup Company Inc.; U.S. Private, pg. 1058
SWISS NIGERIAN CHEMICAL CO. LTD.—Novartis AG; Int'l, pg. 986
SYNETIC, INC.; U.S. Public, pg. 1548
SYNRES-ALMOCO B.V.—DSM N.V.; Int'l, pg. 354
SYNRES-ALMOCO FRANCE S.A.R.L.—DSM N.V.; Int'l, pg. 356
SYNRES-ALMOCO UK LTD.—DSM N.V.; Int'l, pg. 356
TII-DITEL—TII Industries, Inc.; U.S. Public, pg. 1556
TII DOMINICANA INC.—TII Industries, Inc.; U.S. Public, pg. 1556
TII INDUSTRIES, INC.; U.S. Public, pg. 1556
T O PLASTICS, INC.; U.S. Private, pg. 1065
TAIYO CHEMICAL INDUSTRY CO., LTD.—Nissho Iwai Corporation; Int'l, pg. 947
TAIYO KOGYO CORPORATION; Int'l, pg. 1348
TALLEY INDUSTRIES, INC.—Carpenter Technology Corporation; U.S. Public, pg. 307
TAMROCK CORP.; Int'l, pg. 1352
TAPCO INTERNATIONAL CORPORATION; U.S. Private, pg. 1068
TAYLOR MADE GROUP, INC.; U.S. Private, pg. 1070
THE TECH GROUP; U.S. Private, pg. 1071
TECH GROUP PHOENIX, INC.—The Tech Group; U.S. Private, pg. 1071
TECH GROUP SCOTTSDALE, INC.—The Tech Group; U.S. Private, pg. 1071
TECH GROUP TEMPE INC.—The Tech Group; U.S. Private, pg. 1071
TECH INDUSTRIES, INC.; U.S. Private, pg. 1071
TECHNIFORM CORP.—LSB Industries, Inc.; U.S. Public, pg. 971
TECHNOMER (PRIVATE) LTD.—BTR plc; Int'l, pg. 129
TECSYN INTERNATIONAL, INC.; Int'l, pg. 1361
TEKNI-PLEX, INC.; U.S. Private, pg. 1073
TEKNI-PLEX, INC.—Tekni-Plex, Inc.; U.S. Private, pg. 1073
TELEFLEX INCORPORATED; U.S. Public, pg. 1569
TENAX CORPORATION—Bespak plc; Int'l, pg. 193
TENELUX—Kaufel Group Ltd.; Int'l, pg. 725
TENNECO PACKAGING, CONSUMER PRODUCTS GROUP—Tenneco Inc.; U.S. Public, pg. 1579
TEXTRON AUTOMOTIVE INTERIORS COMPANY—Textron Inc.; U.S. Public, pg. 1590
THERMAL TECHNOLOGY INDUSTRIES; U.S. Private, pg. 1080
THERMOPLAST UND APPARATEBAU GMBH; Int'l, pg. 1381
THERMOPLASTICS, INC.—Textron Inc.; U.S. Public, pg. 1590
THOMAS & BETTS CORPORATION; U.S. Public, pg. 1597
THOROUGHBRED PLASTICS CORP.—Brown-Forman Corporation; U.S. Public, pg. 261
TOMKINS INDUSTRIES INC.—Tomkins PLC; Int'l, pg. 1397
TOPPAN MOORE DATA PRODUCTS LTD.—DataCard Corporation; U.S. Private, pg. 313
TOTER INCORPORATED; U.S. Private, pg. 1092
TOYODA GOSEI CO. LTD.—Toyota Motor Corporation; Int'l, pg. 1412
TRANSILWRAP COMPANY, INC.; U.S. Private, pg. 1097
TRAYCO, INC.—Masco Corporation; U.S. Public, pg. 1054
TRI-CHEM, INC.; U.S. Private, pg. 1100
TRIANGLE TOOL CO.—Plastek Group; U.S. Private, pg. 870
TRICON INDUSTRIES, INC.; U.S. Private, pg. 1102
TRIENDA CORPORATION; U.S. Private, pg. 1103
TRIO PRODUCTS INC.—Ivex Packaging Corporation; U.S. Public, pg. 915
TRIPLE S PLASTICS, INC.; U.S. Public, pg. 1639
TROY MILLS, INC.; U.S. Private, pg. 1106
TUBED PRODUCTS, INC.—McCormick & Company, Incorporated; U.S. Public, pg. 1066
TUCKER HOUSEWARES—Mobil Oil Corporation; U.S. Public, pg. 1118
TULIP CORPORATION; U.S. Private, pg. 1109
TUPPERWARE CORPORATION; U.S. Public, pg. 1644
TUSCARORA INCORPORATED; U.S. Public, pg. 1646
20TH CENTURY PRODUCTS DIV.—Avery Dennison Corporation; U.S. Public, pg. 153
TWINPAK INC.—Amcor Limited; Int'l, pg. 72
TYTON HELLERMANN ASIA PACIFIC LTD.—Bowthorpe plc; Int'l, pg. 209
TYTON HELLERMANN CANADA INCORPORATED—Bowthorpe plc; Int'l, pg. 209
UBE INDUSTRIES LTD.; Int'l, pg. 1426
UFE INCORPORATED; U.S. Private, pg. 1112
UFE PTE LTD—UFE Incorporated; U.S. Private, pg. 1112
UTA HOLLAND PLANT—United Technologies Corporation; U.S. Public, pg. 1691
UTA THOMPSON PLANT—United Technologies Corporation; U.S. Public, pg. 1691
ULTRA PAC, INC.; U.S. Public, pg. 1662
ULTRA TOOL & PLASTICS, INC.; U.S. Private, pg. 1116
ULTRAFORM COMPANY—BASF AG; Int'l, pg. 105
UNIFLEX, INC.; U.S. Public, pg. 1665
UNIMARK PLASTICS COMPANY—Alltrista Corporation; U.S. Public, pg. 57
UNIROYAL TECHNOLOGY CORPORATION; U.S. Public, pg. 1670
UNITED INDUSTRIAL CORPORATION; U.S. Public, pg. 1679
UNITED STATES CORRULITE CORPORATION—United States Sugar Corporation; U.S. Private, pg. 1126
U.S. CAN COMPANY—U.S. Can Company; U.S. Public, pg. 1681
VALLEN CORPORATION; U.S. Public, pg. 1705
VALPAK PTY. LTD.—Nissho Iwai Corporation; Int'l, pg. 949
VAN LEER AUSTRALIA PTY. LTD.—Royal Packaging Industries Van Leer B.V.; Int'l, pg. 1146
VAN LEER CONTAINERS, INC.—Royal Packaging Industries Van Leer B.V.; Int'l, pg. 1146
VAN LEER (MALAYSIA) SDN. BHD.—Royal Packaging Industries Van Leer B.V.; Int'l, pg. 1147
VAN LEER SINGAPORE PTE. LTD.—Royal Packaging Industries Van Leer B.V.; Int'l, pg. 1147
VAN LEER (U.K.) LTD.—Royal Packaging Industries Van Leer B.V.; Int'l, pg. 1147
VARIFORM, INC.—Nortek, Inc.; U.S. Public, pg. 1193
VENTURI INC.; U.S. Private, pg. 1136
VERA KLIPPAN AB—Jotun A/S; Int'l, pg. 715

S.I.C. Index

VIKING FORMED PRODUCTS—Coachmen Industries, Inc.; *U.S. Public*, pg. 388
VIKING MJOENDALEN A/S—Trelleborg AB; *Int'l*, pg. 1423
VINYLIUM CORP.—HIG Capital Management; *U.S. Private*, pg. 491
VISKASE CANADA INC.—Envirodyne Industries, Inc.; *U.S. Public*, pg. 586
VISKASE CORPORATION—Envirodyne Industries, Inc.; *U.S. Public*, pg. 586
VISKASE UNITED KINGDOM LIMITED—Envirodyne Industries, Inc.; *U.S. Public*, pg. 586
WADDINGTON & DUVAL (HOLDINGS) LTD.—BTR plc; *Int'l*, pg. 129
WATERBURY COMPANIES, INC.—Carpenter Technology Corporation; *U.S. Public*, pg. 308
WATERLOO INDUSTRIES, INC.—Fortune Brands, Inc.; *U.S. Public*, pg. 675
WATKINS MANUFACTURING CORP./HOT SPRING PORTABLE SPAS—Masco Corporation; *U.S. Public*, pg. 1054
WATTOHM—Imetal; *Int'l*, pg. 662
WAVIN BV—Royal Dutch/Shell Group of Companies; *Int'l*, pg. 1135
WE VAC PLASTICS—E & A Industries, Inc.; *U.S. Private*, pg. 352
WEBER PLASTICS CO. LTD.—Leggett & Platt, Incorporated; *U.S. Public*, pg. 987
THE WEST COMPANY ARGENTINA S.A.—The West Company, Incorporated; *U.S. Public*, pg. 1755
THE WEST COMPANY BRASIL LTDA.—The West Company, Incorporated; *U.S. Public*, pg. 1755
THE WEST COMPANY HOLDING, G.M.B.H—The West Company, Incorporated; *U.S. Public*, pg. 1756
THE WEST COMPANY, INCORPORATED; *U.S. Public*, pg. 1755
THE WEST COMPANY OF PUERTO RICO, INC.—The West Company, Incorporated; *U.S. Public*, pg. 1755
THE WEST COMPANY SINGAPORE PTY. LTD.—The West Company, Incorporated; *U.S. Public*, pg. 1756
WESTCHESTER PLASTICS—AMETEK, Inc.; *U.S. Public*, pg. 100
WESTINGHOUSE POWER SYSTEMS GROUP—CBS Corporation; *U.S. Public*, pg. 273
WHALE SCIENTIFIC INC.—Thermo Electron Corporation; *U.S. Public*, pg. 1595
WHEATLAND TUBE COMPANY; *U.S. Private*, pg. 1170
WHEATON INC.—Alusuisse-Lonza Holding Ltd.; *Int'l*, pg. 67
WHEATON PLASTIC PRODUCTS—Alusuisse-Lonza Holding Ltd.; *Int'l*, pg. 68
WHITE CAP, INC.—Schmalbach-Lubeca AG; *Int'l*, pg. 1207
WHITE MOP WRINGER COMPANY; *U.S. Private*, pg. 1172
WILHOLD INC.—American Greetings Corporation; *U.S. Public*, pg. 78
RALPH WILSON PLASTICS CO.—Premark International, Inc.; *U.S. Public*, pg. 1322
WOLVERINE VINYL SIDING—Saint-Gobain; *Int'l*, pg. 1171
WOODHEAD INDUSTRIES, INC.; *U.S. Public*, pg. 1776
WOODSTREAM CORPORATION—Ekco Group, Inc.; *U.S. Public*, pg. 566
WORTHINGTON CUSTOM PLASTICS—Worthington Industries, Inc.; *U.S. Public*, pg. 1780
WORTHINGTON INDUSTRIES, INC.; *U.S. Public*, pg. 1780
WOZNIAK INDUSTRIES, INC.; *U.S. Private*, pg. 1192
WRIGHT PLASTIC PRODUCTS, INC.—Maxco, Inc.; *U.S. Public*, pg. 1061
XERXES CORPORATION; *U.S. Private*, pg. 1194
YORK WALLCOVERINGS INC.; *U.S. Private*, pg. 1196
ZANUSSI COMPONENTI PLASTICA S.P.A.—Electrolux, AB; *Int'l*, pg. 442
ZAPPA PLASTICS—E.J. Brooks Company; *U.S. Private*, pg. 172
ZENKER-FENSTER GMBH & CO KG—Philipp Holzmann AG; *Int'l*, pg. 633
ZERO PLASTICS—Zero Corporation; *U.S. Public*, pg. 1791
THE ZIPPERTUBING CO.; *U.S. Private*, pg. 1207

3111 — LEATHER TANNING & FINISHING

AAF INDUSTRIES PLC; *Int'l*, pg. 1
BERLIN GLOVE COMPANY LTD.; *U.S. Private*, pg. 136
COACH—Sara Lee Corporation; *U.S. Public*, pg. 1433
DARLING INTERNATIONAL, INC; *U.S. Public*, pg. 484
E.J. FOOTWEAR CORP.—U.S. Industries, Inc.; *U.S. Public*, pg. 1684
EAGLE-OTTAWA LEATHER CO.—Albert Trostel & Sons Co.; *U.S. Private*, pg. 1105
S.B. FOOT TANNING CO.—Red Wing Shoe Co., Inc.; *U.S. Private*, pg. 915
GENESCO INC.; *U.S. Public*, pg. 728
WM. HAUGHTON & CO. LTD.—Foster's Brewing Group Limited; *Int'l*, pg. 501
HOWES LEATHER CORPORATION; *U.S. Private*, pg. 543
IRVING TANNING CO.; *U.S. Private*, pg. 575
LEATHERS BEST; *U.S. Private*, pg. 656
LUCKY GOLDSTAR INTERNATIONAL CORP.—LG Group; *Int'l*, pg. 779
MID-WESTERN—Berlin Glove Company Ltd.; *U.S. Private*, pg. 136
NOZAKI & COMPANY LTD.; *Int'l*, pg. 990
OUIMET CORP.; *U.S. Private*, pg. 821
PRIME TANNING CO., INC.; *U.S. Private*, pg. 884
SALZ LEATHERS, INC.; *U.S. Private*, pg. 963
SETON CO.—Seton Company; *U.S. Private*, pg. 987
SETON COMPANY; *U.S. Private*, pg. 987
ALBERT TROSTEL & SONS CO.; *U.S. Private*, pg. 1105
VOLUNTEER LEATHER CO.—Genesco Inc.; *U.S. Public*, pg. 728
WOLVERINE LEATHER DIV.—Wolverine World Wide, Inc.; *U.S. Public*, pg. 1775
WOLVERINE WORLD WIDE, INC.; *U.S. Public*, pg. 1775

3131 — BOOT & SHOE CUT STOCK & FINDINGS

ALLEN-EDMONDS SHOE CORP.; *U.S. Private*, pg. 36
BATA SHOE CO., INC.—CHB Corp.; *U.S. Private*, pg. 195
BIXBY INTERNATIONAL CORP.; *U.S. Private*, pg. 146
BROWN SHOE COMPANY—Brown Group, Inc.; *U.S. Public*, pg. 262
CHB CORP.; *U.S. Private*, pg. 194
CLARKS INTERNATIONAL; *Int'l*, pg. 296
HOWES LEATHER CORPORATION; *U.S. Private*, pg. 543
INJECTION FOOTWEAR CORP.; *U.S. Private*, pg. 563
JUSTIN BOOT COMPANY—Justin Industries, Inc.; *U.S. Public*, pg. 937
JUSTIN INDUSTRIES, INC.; *U.S. Public*, pg. 936
NOCONA BOOT CO.—Justin Industries, Inc.; *U.S. Public*, pg. 937
OUIMET CORP.; *U.S. Private*, pg. 821
STANBEE COMPANY, INC.; *U.S. Private*, pg. 1030
EDWIN B. STIMPSON COMPANY, INC.; *U.S. Private*, pg. 1043

3142 — HOUSE SLIPPERS

BARRY OF CIUDAD ACUNA—R.G. Barry Corporation; *U.S. Public*, pg. 192
BARRY OF LAREDO—R.G. Barry Corporation; *U.S. Public*, pg. 192
BARRY OF NUEVO LAREDO—R.G. Barry Corporation; *U.S. Public*, pg. 192
BARRY OF SAN ANGELO—R.G. Barry Corporation; *U.S. Public*, pg. 192
R.G. BARRY CORPORATION; *U.S. Public*, pg. 192
DEXTER SHOE COMPANY—Berkshire Hathaway Inc.; *U.S. Public*, pg. 217
ETONIC TRETORN—Kohlberg Kravis Roberts & Co.; *U.S. Private*, pg. 629
DANIEL GREEN CO.; *U.S. Private*, pg. 477
MUNRO & COMPANY, INC.; *U.S. Private*, pg. 767
SCHOENECKERS, INC.; *U.S. Private*, pg. 971
TRETORN AB—Proventus AB; *Int'l*, pg. 1072
TRU-STITCH FOOTWEAR DIV.—Wolverine World Wide, Inc.; *U.S. Public*, pg. 1775
WOLVERINE WORLD WIDE, INC.; *U.S. Public*, pg. 1775

3143 — MEN'S FOOTWEAR, EXCEPT ATHLETIC

ACME BOOT CO., INC.—Farley, Inc.; *U.S. Private*, pg. 394
STACY ADAMS SHOE CO.—Weyco Group, Inc.; *U.S. Public*, pg. 1763
AGNEW GROUP—The Bentley Agnew Group Inc.; *Int'l*, pg. 187
AGUADILLA SHOE DIV.—Wolverine World Wide, Inc.; *U.S. Public*, pg. 1775
ALDEN SHOE CO., INC.; *U.S. Private*, pg. 33
ALLEN-EDMONDS SHOE CORP.; *U.S. Private*, pg. 36
ALTAMA DELTA CORPORATION; *U.S. Private*, pg. 47
BALLY-BIVER S.A.R.L.—Oerlikon-Buhrle Holding AG; *Int'l*, pg. 997
BALLY DEUTSCHLAND GMBH—Oerlikon-Buhrle Holding AG; *Int'l*, pg. 997
BALLY GROUP (UK) LIMITED—Oerlikon-Buhrle Holding AG; *Int'l*, pg. 997
BALLY MANAGEMENT AG—Oerlikon-Buhrle Holding AG; *Int'l*, pg. 996
BALLY SCHOENHANDEL B.V.—Oerlikon-Buhrle Holding AG; *Int'l*, pg. 997
BALLY SHOE CO. LTD.—Oerlikon-Buhrle Holding AG; *Int'l*, pg. 997
BALLY'S SHOE FACTORIES (NORWICH) LTD.—Oerlikon-Buhrle Holding AG; *Int'l*, pg. 997
R.G. BARRY CORPORATION; *U.S. Public*, pg. 192
G.H. BASS & CO.—Phillips-Van Heusen Corporation; *U.S. Public*, pg. 1291
BATES DIV.—Wolverine World Wide, Inc.; *U.S. Public*, pg. 1775
THE BENTLEY AGNEW GROUP INC.; *Int'l*, pg. 187
BROWN GROUP, INC.; *U.S. Public*, pg. 262
H.H. BROWN SHOE COMPANY, INC.—Berkshire Hathaway Inc.; *U.S. Public*, pg. 217
BROWN SHOE COMPANY—Brown Group, Inc.; *U.S. Public*, pg. 262
BROWN SHOE CO. OF CANADA LTD.—Brown Group, Inc.; *U.S. Public*, pg. 262
CAROLINA SHOE COMPANY—Berkshire Hathaway Inc.; *U.S. Public*, pg. 217
CHAUSSURES BALLY-FRANCE S.A.—Oerlikon-Buhrle Holding AG; *Int'l*, pg. 997
S.A. CHAUSSURES BALLY SCHOENEN N.V.—Oerlikon-Buhrle Holding AG; *Int'l*, pg. 997
CHEROKEE INC.; *U.S. Public*, pg. 345
CLARKS INTERNATIONAL; *Int'l*, pg. 296
COVE SHOE COMPANY—Berkshire Hathaway Inc.; *U.S. Public*, pg. 217
COWTOWN BOOT COMPANY; *U.S. Private*, pg. 281
CRADDOCK-TERRY INC.; *U.S. Private*, pg. 284
DECKERS OUTDOOR CORPORATION; *U.S. Public*, pg. 491
DEXTER SHOE COMPANY—Berkshire Hathaway Inc.; *U.S. Public*, pg. 217
DOCKERS FOOTWEAR—Genesco Inc.; *U.S. Public*, pg. 728
DOUBLE H BOOT CO.—Berkshire Hathaway Inc.; *U.S. Public*, pg. 217
DR. SCHOLL'S SPA—Scholl Plc; *Int'l*, pg. 1209
E.J. FOOTWEAR CORP.—U.S. Industries, Inc.; *U.S. Public*, pg. 1684
ELEFANTEN-SCHUH GMBH—Freudenberg & Company; *Int'l*, pg. 505
ENCORE SHOE CORPORATION; *U.S. Private*, pg. 375
FARLEY, INC.; *U.S. Private*, pg. 394
FILA USA—Fila Sport S.p.A.; *Int'l*, pg. 484
FROLIC FOOTWEAR DIV.—Wolverine World Wide, Inc.; *U.S. Public*, pg. 1775
GENESCO INC.; *U.S. Public*, pg. 728
GENFOOT INC.; *Int'l*, pg. 549
GEORGIA/DURANGO BOOT COMPANY—U.S. Industries, Inc.; *U.S. Public*, pg. 1684
GUCCIO GUCCI S.P.A.—Investcorp International; *Int'l*, pg. 686
HANOVER SHOE CO.—Clarks International; *Int'l*, pg. 297
JOS. M. HERMAN SHOE CO.; *U.S. Private*, pg. 524
HUSH PUPPIES COMPANY—Wolverine World Wide, Inc.; *U.S. Public*, pg. 1775
INJECTION FOOTWEAR CORP.; *U.S. Private*, pg. 563
IRON AGE CORPORATION—Fenway Partners Inc.; *U.S. Private*, pg. 401
JARMAN SHOE CO.—Genesco Inc.; *U.S. Public*, pg. 728
JOHNSTON & MURPHY CO.—Genesco Inc.; *U.S. Public*, pg. 728
JUSTIN BOOT COMPANY—Justin Industries, Inc.; *U.S. Public*, pg. 937
JUSTIN INDUSTRIES, INC.; *U.S. Public*, pg. 936
K-SWISS INC.; *U.S. Public*, pg. 937
KAMIK—Genfoot Inc.; *Int'l*, pg. 549
KAUFMAN FOOTWEAR; *Int'l*, pg. 725
KEUM KANG DEVELOPMENT INDUSTRIAL CO., LTD.—Hyundai Motor Company; *Int'l*, pg. 642
KNAPP SHOES INC.—Fenway Partners Inc.; *U.S. Private*, pg. 401
L.L. BEAN, INC.; *U.S. Private*, pg. 639
LAREDO BOOT CO.—Genesco Inc.; *U.S. Public*, pg. 728
LUCKY GOLDSTAR INTERNATIONAL CORP.—LG Group; *Int'l*, pg. 779
MASON SHOE MFG. CO.; *U.S. Private*, pg. 712
MCRAE FOOTWEAR DIV.—McRae Industries, Inc.; *U.S. Public*, pg. 1073
MCRAE INDUSTRIES, INC.; *U.S. Public*, pg. 1073
MID-WESTERN—Berlin Glove Company Ltd.; *U.S. Private*, pg. 136
P.W. MINOR & SON, INC.; *U.S. Private*, pg. 751
MORSE SHOE, INC.—J. Baker, Inc.; *U.S. Public*, pg. 168
NAUTICA FOOTWEAR—Genesco Inc.; *U.S. Public*, pg. 728
NOCONA BOOT CO.—Justin Industries, Inc.; *U.S. Public*, pg. 937
NUNN-BUSH SHOE CO.—Weyco Group, Inc.; *U.S. Public*, pg. 1763
PHILLIPS-VAN HEUSEN CORPORATION; *U.S. Public*, pg. 1291
PRIESTLEY FOOTWEAR LTD.—Pentland Group PLC; *Int'l*, pg. 1036
THE RIGHT SHOE ONLY, INC.—Brown Group, Inc.; *U.S. Public*, pg. 262
ROCKY SHOES & BOOTS, INC.; *U.S. Public*, pg. 1402
SPORTO CORP.; *U.S. Private*, pg. 1026
THE STRIDE RITE CORPORATION; *U.S. Public*, pg. 1524
SUNBELT FOOTWEAR, LTD.—Brown Group, Inc.; *U.S. Public*, pg. 262
THE TIMBERLAND COMPANY; *U.S. Public*, pg. 1609
TRANSMARCO LIMITED; *Int'l*, pg. 1417
UNIVERSAL SHOE MFG. CO.—Craddock-Terry Inc.; *U.S. Private*, pg. 284
VIKING FOTTOY A.S.—Orkla A.S.A.; *Int'l*, pg. 1011
B.B. WALKER COMPANY; *U.S. Public*, pg. 1734
WEINBRENNER SHOE COMPANY, INC.; *U.S. Private*, pg. 1160
WEYCO GROUP, INC.; *U.S. Public*, pg. 1763
WOLVERINE BOOT CO.—Wolverine World Wide, Inc.; *U.S. Public*, pg. 1775
WOLVERINE BRAND DIV.—Wolverine World Wide, Inc.; *U.S. Public*, pg. 1775
WOLVERINE WORLD WIDE, INC.; *U.S. Public*, pg. 1775

3144 — WOMEN'S FOOTWEAR, EXCEPT ATHLETIC

ASHWORTH YOUNG & CO., LTD.—Pentland Group PLC; *Int'l*, pg. 1035
BALLY-BIVER S.A.R.L.—Oerlikon-Buhrle Holding AG; *Int'l*, pg. 997
BALLY DEUTSCHLAND GMBH—Oerlikon-Buhrle Holding AG; *Int'l*, pg. 997
BALLY GROUP (UK) LIMITED—Oerlikon-Buhrle Holding AG; *Int'l*, pg. 997
BALLY MANAGEMENT AG—Oerlikon-Buhrle Holding AG; *Int'l*, pg. 996
BALLY SCHOENHANDEL B.V.—Oerlikon-Buhrle Holding AG; *Int'l*, pg. 997
BALLY SHOE CO. LTD.—Oerlikon-Buhrle Holding AG; *Int'l*, pg. 997
BALLY'S SHOE FACTORIES (NORWICH) LTD.—Oerlikon-Buhrle Holding AG; *Int'l*, pg. 997
R.G. BARRY CORPORATION; *U.S. Public*, pg. 192
G.H. BASS & CO.—Phillips-Van Heusen Corporation; *U.S. Public*, pg. 1291
BROWN GROUP, INC.; *U.S. Public*, pg. 262
BROWN SHOE COMPANY—Brown Group, Inc.; *U.S. Public*, pg. 262
BROWN SHOE CO. OF CANADA LTD.—Brown Group, Inc.; *U.S. Public*, pg. 262
C & J CLARK AMERICA, INC.—Clarks International; *Int'l*, pg. 297
CHAUSSURES BALLY-FRANCE S.A.—Oerlikon-Buhrle Holding AG; *Int'l*, pg. 997
S.A. CHAUSSURES BALLY SCHOENEN N.V.—Oerlikon-Buhrle Holding AG; *Int'l*, pg. 997
CHEROKEE INC.; *U.S. Public*, pg. 345
CLARKS INTERNATIONAL; *Int'l*, pg. 296
COOP SWITZERLAND; *Int'l*, pg. 329
CRADDOCK-TERRY INC.; *U.S. Private*, pg. 284
DECKERS OUTDOOR CORPORATION; *U.S. Public*, pg. 491
DEXTER SHOE COMPANY—Berkshire Hathaway Inc.; *U.S. Public*, pg. 217
DR. SCHOLL'S SPA—Scholl Plc; *Int'l*, pg. 1209

E.J. FOOTWEAR CORP.—U.S. Industries, Inc.; *U.S. Public*, pg. 1684
EASTLAND SHOE MANUFACTURING CORPORATION; *U.S. Private*, pg. 357
ENCORE SHOE CORPORATION; *U.S. Private*, pg. 375
ETIENNE AIGNER; *U.S. Private*, pg. 384
FARLEY, INC.; *U.S. Private*, pg. 394
FILA USA—Fila Sport S.p.A.; *Int'l*, pg. 484
FRANKLIN SHOE CO.—Shaer Shoe Corporation; *U.S. Private*, pg. 988
GENESCO INC.; *U.S. Public*, pg. 728
GENFOOT INC.; *Int'l*, pg. 549
GEORGIA/DURANGO BOOT COMPANY—U.S. Industries, Inc.; *U.S. Public*, pg. 1684
GUCCIO GUCCI S.P.A.—Investcorp International; *Int'l*, pg. 686
HANNA—Genfoot Inc.; *Int'l*, pg. 549
INJECTION FOOTWEAR CORP.; *U.S. Private*, pg. 563
IRON AGE CORPORATION—Fenway Partners Inc.; *U.S. Private*, pg. 401
ISABELA SHOE CORP.—Berkshire Hathaway Inc.; *U.S. Public*, pg. 217
K-SWISS INC.; *U.S. Public*, pg. 937
KAGAN LOWN—Penobscot Shoe Company; *U.S. Public*, pg. 1273
KAMIK—Genfoot Inc.; *Int'l*, pg. 549
KAUFMAN FOOTWEAR; *Int'l*, pg. 725
KENNETH COLE PRODUCTIONS; *U.S. Public*, pg. 951
KNAPP SHOES INC.—Fenway Partners Inc.; *U.S. Private*, pg. 401
LIZ CLAIBORNE SHOE DIVISION—Liz Claiborne, Inc.; *U.S. Public*, pg. 1006
LOWELL SHOE, INC.—Berkshire Hathaway Inc.; *U.S. Public*, pg. 217
LUCKY GOLDSTAR INTERNATIONAL CORP.—LG Group; *Int'l*, pg. 779
MASON SHOE MFG. CO.; *U.S. Private*, pg. 712
MID-WESTERN—Berlin Glove Company Ltd.; *U.S. Private*, pg. 136
P.W. MINOR & SON, INC.; *U.S. Private*, pg. 751
MORSE SHOE, INC.—J. Baker, Inc.; *U.S. Public*, pg. 168
MUNRO & COMPANY, INC.; *U.S. Private*, pg. 767
OOMPHIES, INC.; *U.S. Private*, pg. 817
PENOBSCOT SHOE COMPANY; *U.S. Public*, pg. 1273
PHILLIPS-VAN HEUSEN CORPORATION; *U.S. Public*, pg. 1291
PRIESTLEY FOOTWEAR LTD.—Pentland Group PLC; *Int'l*, pg. 1036
RED WING SHOE CO., INC.; *U.S. Private*, pg. 915
THE RIGHT SHOE ONLY, INC.—Brown Group, Inc.; *U.S. Public*, pg. 262
ROCKY SHOES & BOOTS, INC.; *U.S. Public*, pg. 1402
SHAER SHOE CORPORATION; *U.S. Private*, pg. 988
SPORTO CORP.; *U.S. Private*, pg. 1026
SUNBELT FOOTWEAR, LTD.—Brown Group, Inc.; *U.S. Public*, pg. 262
THE TIMBERLAND COMPANY; *U.S. Public*, pg. 1609
TRANSMARCO LIMITED; *Int'l*, pg. 1417
UNIVERSAL SHOE MFG. CO.—Craddock-Terry Inc.; *U.S. Private*, pg. 284
VIKING FOTTOY A.S.—Orkla A.S.A.; *Int'l*, pg. 1011
WEINBRENNER SHOE COMPANY, INC.; *U.S. Private*, pg. 1160
WOLVERINE WORLD WIDE, INC.; *U.S. Public*, pg. 1775

3149 — FOOTWEAR, EXCEPT RUBBER, NEC

ACUSHNET COMPANY—Fortune Brands, Inc.; *U.S. Public*, pg. 675
ADIDAS AG; *Int'l*, pg. 24
ADIDAS ESPANA, S.A.—Adidas AG; *Int'l*, pg. 25
ADIDAS SPORTSCHUHFABRIKEN GMBH—Adidas AG; *Int'l*, pg. 25
ADIDAS (UK) LTD.—Adidas AG; *Int'l*, pg. 25
AIRBORNE LEISURE LTD.—Pentland Group PLC; *Int'l*, pg. 1035
AMERICAN CONSUMER PRODUCTS—Vista 2000, Inc.; *U.S. Private*, pg. 1142
AMERICAN SPORTING GOODS CORPORATION; *U.S. Private*, pg. 62
ASICS TIGER CORPORATION; *U.S. Private*, pg. 89
AUSTRIA PUMA DASSLER GES.M.B.H.—Proventus AB; *Int'l*, pg. 1072
AVIA—American Sporting Goods Corporation; *U.S. Private*, pg. 62
BALLY-BIVER S.A.R.L.—Oerlikon-Buhrle Holding AG; *Int'l*, pg. 997
BALLY SCHOENHANDEL B.V.—Oerlikon-Buhrle Holding AG; *Int'l*, pg. 997
G.H. BASS & CO.—Phillips-Van Heusen Corporation; *U.S. Public*, pg. 1291
BOSS CANADA, INC.—Vista 2000, Inc.; *U.S. Private*, pg. 1142
BOSS DE MEXICO, S.A.—Vista 2000, Inc.; *U.S. Private*, pg. 1142
BROWN GROUP, INC.; *U.S. Public*, pg. 262
BROWN SHOE COMPANY—Brown Group, Inc.; *U.S. Public*, pg. 262
BROWN SHOE CO. OF CANADA LTD.—Brown Group, Inc.; *U.S. Public*, pg. 262
CAPEZIO BALLET MAKERS INC.; *U.S. Private*, pg. 205
CAPEZIO BALLET MAKERS, INC.—Capezio Ballet Makers Inc.; *U.S. Private*, pg. 205
S.A. CHAUSSURES BALLY SCHOENEN N.V.—Oerlikon-Buhrle Holding AG; *Int'l*, pg. 997
CHEROKEE INC.; *U.S. Public*, pg. 345
CLARKS INTERNATIONAL; *Int'l*, pg. 296
CONVERSE INC.; *U.S. Public*, pg. 441
DEXTER SHOE COMPANY—Berkshire Hathaway Inc.; *U.S. Public*, pg. 217
E.J. FOOTWEAR CORP.—U.S. Industries, Inc.; *U.S. Public*, pg. 1684
ELEFANTEN-SCHUH GMBH—Freudenberg & Company; *Int'l*, pg. 505
EMPIRE DIVISION—U.S. Industries, Inc.; *U.S. Public*, pg. 1684
ETONIC TRETORN—Kohlberg Kravis Roberts & Co.; *U.S. Private*, pg. 629
FILA USA—Fila Sport S.p.A.; *Int'l*, pg. 484
FLORSHEIM GROUP INC.; *U.S. Public*, pg. 656
FORTUNE BRANDS, INC.; *U.S. Public*, pg. 674
THE FRYE COMPANY; *U.S. Private*, pg. 430
GENFOOT INC.; *Int'l*, pg. 549
GEORGIA/DURANGO BOOT COMPANY—U.S. Industries, Inc.; *U.S. Public*, pg. 1684
DANIEL GREEN CO.; *U.S. Private*, pg. 477
HANG TEN—Genfoot Inc.; *Int'l*, pg. 549
HEAD USA, INC.; *U.S. Private*, pg. 514
HYDE ATHLETIC INDUSTRIES, INC.; *U.S. Public*, pg. 851
JUMPING JACKS—Munro & Company, Inc.; *U.S. Private*, pg. 767
K-SWISS INC.; *U.S. Public*, pg. 937
KAMIK—Genfoot Inc.; *Int'l*, pg. 549
L.A. GEAR CALIFORNIA, INC.—L.A. Gear, Inc.; *U.S. Public*, pg. 969
L.A. GEAR, INC.; *U.S. Public*, pg. 969
LOTTO S.P.A.; *Int'l*, pg. 819
LOTTO SPORT U.S.A.—Lotto S.p.A.; *Int'l*, pg. 819
LOWELL SHOE, INC.—Berkshire Hathaway Inc.; *U.S. Public*, pg. 217
MITRE SPORTS (U.S.)—Pentland Group PLC; *Int'l*, pg. 1036
MIZUNO USA, INC.—Mizuno Corporation; *Int'l*, pg. 885
MO-KA SHOE CORP.—Wellco Enterprises, Inc.; *U.S. Public*, pg. 1752
MUNRO & COMPANY, INC.; *U.S. Private*, pg. 767
NEW BALANCE ATHLETIC SHOE, INC.; *U.S. Private*, pg. 792
NIKE, INC.; *U.S. Public*, pg. 1184
PENTLAND GROUP PLC; *Int'l*, pg. 1035
PRIESTLEY FOOTWEAR LTD.—Pentland Group PLC; *Int'l*, pg. 1036
PUMA AG RUDOLF DASSLER SPORT—Proventus AB; *Int'l*, pg. 1072
PUMA NORTH AMERICA—Proventus AB; *Int'l*, pg. 1072
REEBOK INTERNATIONAL LTD.; *U.S. Public*, pg. 1369
THE ROCKPORT COMPANY—Reebok International Ltd.; *U.S. Public*, pg. 1370
ROCKY SHOES & BOOTS, INC.; *U.S. Public*, pg. 1402
SAO PAULO ALPARGATAS S.A.; *Int'l*, pg. 1193
SPORTO CORP.; *U.S. Private*, pg. 1026
STRIDE RITE CHILDREN'S GROUP-WHOLESALE DIV.—The Stride Rite Corporation; *U.S. Public*, pg. 1525
THE STRIDE RITE CORPORATION; *U.S. Public*, pg. 1524
TRANSMARCO LIMITED; *Int'l*, pg. 1417
TRETORN—Proventus AB; *Int'l*, pg. 1072
TRETORN AB—Proventus AB; *Int'l*, pg. 1072
TRIMFOOT COMPANY—U.S. Industries, Inc.; *U.S. Public*, pg. 1684
WELLCO ENTERPRISES, INC.; *U.S. Public*, pg. 1752
WEYCO GROUP, INC.; *U.S. Public*, pg. 1763

3151 — LEATHER GLOVES & MITTENS

BERLIN GLOVE CO.—Berlin Glove Company Ltd.; *U.S. Private*, pg. 136
BERLIN GLOVE COMPANY LTD.; *U.S. Private*, pg. 136
BOSS DE MEXICO, S.A.—Vista 2000, Inc.; *U.S. Private*, pg. 1142
BOSS MANUFACTURING COMPANY—Vista 2000, Inc.; *U.S. Private*, pg. 1142
CAROLINA GLOVE CO.; *U.S. Private*, pg. 214
KLEIN TOOLS INC.; *U.S. Private*, pg. 625
MID-WESTERN—Berlin Glove Company Ltd.; *U.S. Private*, pg. 136
NORTH SAFETY PRODUCTS, HAND PROTECTION DIVISION—Siebe plc; *Int'l*, pg. 1243
SARA LEE HOSIERY—Sara Lee Corporation; *U.S. Public*, pg. 1434
SHELBY GROUP INTERNATIONAL, INC.; *U.S. Private*, pg. 991
TOTES/ISOTONER, INC.—Sara Lee Corporation; *U.S. Public*, pg. 1433

3161 — LUGGAGE

AMERICAN TOURISTER, INC.—Samsonite Corporation; *U.S. Public*, pg. 1430
ANDIAMO, INC.; *U.S. Private*, pg. 73
ANVIL CASES, INC.—Zero Corporation; *U.S. Public*, pg. 1791
ATLAS CO. OF BOSTON, INC.—Tom James Company; *U.S. Private*, pg. 581
BROWN-FORMAN CORPORATION; *U.S. Public*, pg. 261
COAST MANUFACTURING COMPANY; *U.S. Private*, pg. 248
DUNSTON LEATHERS, INC.—United States Luggage Company; *U.S. Private*, pg. 1125
DURAY, INC.—Newell Co.; *U.S. Public*, pg. 1177
EASTERN CANVAS PRODUCTS, INC.; *U.S. Private*, pg. 357
SAMUEL GROVES & CO., LTD.—Zero Corporation; *U.S. Public*, pg. 1791
HARTMANN LUGGAGE & LEATHER GOODS GROUP—Brown-Forman Corporation; *U.S. Public*, pg. 261
KEUM KANG DEVELOPMENT INDUSTRIAL CO., LTD.—Hyundai Motor Company; *Int'l*, pg. 642
LVMH MOET HENNESSY LOUIS VUITTON; *Int'l*, pg. 779
LARK LUGGAGE COMPANY, INC.—Samsonite Corporation; *U.S. Public*, pg. 1430
G. LEBLANC CORPORATION; *U.S. Private*, pg. 656
LENOX, INCORPORATED—Brown-Forman Corporation; *U.S. Public*, pg. 261
LOUIS VUITTON MALLETIER—LVMH Moet Hennessy Louis Vuitton; *Int'l*, pg. 781
MONARCH LUGGAGE CO. INC.; *U.S. Private*, pg. 757
POLO/RALPH LAUREN CORPORATION; *U.S. Private*, pg. 874
PONY U.S.A.—Pentland Group PLC; *Int'l*, pg. 1036
SAMSONITE CORPORATION; *U.S. Public*, pg. 1430
SAMSONITE OF CANADA—Samsonite Corporation; *U.S. Public*, pg. 1430
SEWARD INC.; *U.S. Private*, pg. 988
TEXON MATERIALS INC.; *U.S. Private*, pg. 1079
TRAFALGAR GHURKA LTD.; *U.S. Private*, pg. 1095
UNITED STATES LUGGAGE COMPANY; *U.S. Private*, pg. 1125
ZERO CORPORATION; *U.S. Public*, pg. 1791

3171 — WOMEN'S HANDBAGS & PURSES

AETNA HANDBAGS—Jaclyn, Inc.; *U.S. Public*, pg. 920
F.J. BENJAMIN FASHIONS (M) SDN. BHD.—F. J. Benjamin Holdings Ltd.; *Int'l*, pg. 187
BERLIN GLOVE COMPANY LTD.; *U.S. Private*, pg. 136
BONNIE INTERNATIONAL—Jaclyn, Inc.; *U.S. Public*, pg. 920
CHEROKEE INC.; *U.S. Public*, pg. 345
DOVER HANDBAG CO., INC.—Michael Stevens Ltd.; *U.S. Private*, pg. 1042
EMPRESS HANDBAGS—Jaclyn, Inc.; *U.S. Public*, pg. 920
ETIENNE AIGNER; *U.S. Private*, pg. 384
GUCCIO GUCCI S.P.A.—Investcorp International; *Int'l*, pg. 686
THE HARTSTONE GROUP PLC; *Int'l*, pg. 599
JACLYN, INC.; *U.S. Public*, pg. 920
KORET PIERRE CARDIN; *U.S. Private*, pg. 632
LVMH MOET HENNESSY LOUIS VUITTON; *Int'l*, pg. 779
LIZ CLAIBORNE OUTLET DIVISION—Liz Claiborne, Inc.; *U.S. Public*, pg. 1006
LOUIS VUITTON NORTH AMERICA, INC.—LVMH Moet Hennessy Louis Vuitton; *Int'l*, pg. 781
MID-WESTERN—Berlin Glove Company Ltd.; *U.S. Private*, pg. 136
RENCO GROUP; *U.S. Private*, pg. 922
TRAFALGAR GHURKA LTD.; *U.S. Private*, pg. 1095

3172 — PERSONAL LEATHER GOODS, EXCEPT WOMEN'S HANDBAGS & PURSES

AR ACCESSORIES GROUP, INC.; *U.S. Private*, pg. 7
AMERICAN CONSUMER PRODUCTS—Vista 2000, Inc.; *U.S. Private*, pg. 1142
AMITY—AR Accessories Group, Inc.; *U.S. Private*, pg. 7
F.J. BENJAMIN FASHIONS (AUST) PTY. LTD.—F. J. Benjamin Holdings Ltd.; *Int'l*, pg. 187
F.J. BENJAMIN FASHIONS (SINGAPORE) PTE. LTD.—F. J. Benjamin Holdings Ltd.; *Int'l*, pg. 187
HUGO BOSCA CO., INC.; *U.S. Private*, pg. 160
CRESTLINE DIV.—Swank, Inc.; *U.S. Public*, pg. 1543
DHP LIMITED PARTNERSHIP; *U.S. Private*, pg. 302
DAY-TIMERS, INC.—Fortune Brands, Inc.; *U.S. Public*, pg. 674
ENGER-KRESS COMPANY; *U.S. Private*, pg. 376
KORET PIERRE CARDIN; *U.S. Private*, pg. 632
LVMH MOET HENNESSY LOUIS VUITTON; *Int'l*, pg. 779
TONY LAMA CO., INC.—Justin Industries, Inc.; *U.S. Public*, pg. 937
LOUIS VUITTON MALLETIER—LVMH Moet Hennessy Louis Vuitton; *Int'l*, pg. 781
PRETTY NEAT PRODUCTS—Newell Co.; *U.S. Public*, pg. 1177
PYRAMID HANDBAGS INC.; *U.S. Private*, pg. 896
ROLFS—AR Accessories Group, Inc.; *U.S. Private*, pg. 7
SWANK, INC.; *U.S. Public*, pg. 1543
TANDY LEATHER CO.—Tandycrafts, Inc.; *U.S. Public*, pg. 1561
TANDYCRAFTS, INC.; *U.S. Public*, pg. 1561
TRAFALGAR GHURKA LTD.; *U.S. Private*, pg. 1095
WILLMOTTS LIMITED—Ascot Holdings Plc; *Int'l*, pg. 88

3199 — LEATHER GOODS, NEC

A&A MANUFACTURING CO.; *U.S. Private*, pg. 1
BENDIX ATLANTIC INFLATER CO.—AlliedSignal Inc.; *U.S. Public*, pg. 51
HUGO BOSCA CO., INC.; *U.S. Private*, pg. 160
DHP LIMITED PARTNERSHIP; *U.S. Private*, pg. 302
GEIGER BROTHERS; *U.S. Private*, pg. 442
KLEIN TOOLS INC.; *U.S. Private*, pg. 625
KORET PIERRE CARDIN; *U.S. Private*, pg. 632
TONY LAMA CO., INC.—Justin Industries, Inc.; *U.S. Public*, pg. 937
THE MARMON GROUP, INC.; *U.S. Private*, pg. 706
NSK-AUTOLIV, INC.—Electrolux, AB; *Int'l*, pg. 439
NSK-AUTOLIV, INC.—NSK Ltd.; *Int'l*, pg. 903
H.A. SHELDON, INC.—Tandy Brands Accessories, Inc.; *U.S. Public*, pg. 1560
TBAC - CANTERBURY, INC.—Tandy Brands Accessories, Inc.; *U.S. Public*, pg. 1560
TBAC - PRINCE GARDNER, INC.—Tandy Brands Accessories, Inc.; *U.S. Public*, pg. 1560
TANDY BRANDS ACCESSORIES, INC.; *U.S. Public*, pg. 1560
TANDYCRAFTS, INC.; *U.S. Public*, pg. 1561
TEXON MATERIALS INC.; *U.S. Private*, pg. 1079
TRAFALGAR GHURKA LTD.; *U.S. Private*, pg. 1095
WINGS LUGGAGE—Brown-Forman Corporation; *U.S. Public*, pg. 262

3211 — FLAT GLASS

AFG INDUSTRIES, INC.—Asahi Glass Co., Ltd.; *Int'l*, pg. 84
AFGD—Asahi Glass Co., Ltd.; *Int'l*, pg. 84
APOGEE ENTERPRISES, INC.; *U.S. Public*, pg. 120

ASAHI GLASS CO., LTD.; *Int'l*, pg. 84
J.E. BERKOWITZ, LP; *U.S. Private*, pg. 135
CEBRACE—Saint-Gobain; *Int'l*, pg. 1177
CEBRACE CRISTAL PLANO LTDA.—Pilkington Plc; *Int'l*, pg. 1057
CENTRE EST VITRAGE—Saint-Gobain; *Int'l*, pg. 1172
COMPAGNIE DE SAINT-GOBAIN-PONT-A MOUSSON—Compagnie de Suez; *Int'l*, pg. 313
COMPANHIA VIDRARIA SANTA MARINA—Saint-Gobain; *Int'l*, pg. 1172
CORNING ASAHI VIDEO PRODUCTS COMPANY—Corning Incorporated; *U.S. Public*, pg. 449
CORNING INCORPORATED; *U.S. Public*, pg. 448
CORNING INTERNATIONAL CORPORATION—Corning Incorporated; *U.S. Public*, pg. 448
DEUTSCHE SPEZIALGLAS AG—Carl-Zeiss-Stiftung; *Int'l*, pg. 1523
EOMAG AG - ERSTE OSTERREICHISCHE MACHINGLASINDUSTRIE BRUNN AM GEBIRGE—Pilkington Plc; *Int'l*, pg. 1056
EXCEL INDUSTRIES, INC.; *U.S. Public*, pg. 598
FLACHGLAS AG—Pilkington Plc; *Int'l*, pg. 1056
FLORAL GLASS & MIRROR, INC.; *U.S. Private*, pg. 414
FORD GLASS & METAL, INC.—Ford Motor Company; *U.S. Public*, pg. 664
FORD MOTOR COMPANY; *U.S. Public*, pg. 661
FOURCO GLASS CO.—Asahi Glass Co., Ltd.; *Int'l*, pg. 84
GLACERIES DE SAINT-ROCH—Saint-Gobain; *Int'l*, pg. 1172
GLASFABRICK SAS VAN GENT B.V.—Saint-Gobain; *Int'l*, pg. 1173
GLAVERBEL S.A.—Asahi Glass Co., Ltd.; *Int'l*, pg. 85
GLOBE-AMERADA GLASS COMPANY; *U.S. Private*, pg. 458
GUARDIAN INDUSTRIES CORP.; *U.S. Private*, pg. 485
GYPROC INSULATION LTD.—BPB Industries PLC; *Int'l*, pg. 123
HANKUK SAFETY GLASS LIMITED—Pilkington Plc; *Int'l*, pg. 1057
INSOLAIR INDUSTRIES—Apogee Enterprises, Inc.; *U.S. Public*, pg. 120
INTERNATIONAL ALUMINUM CORPORATION; *U.S. Public*, pg. 894
L-ZOS OPTICS, LTD.; *U.S. Private*, pg. 639
LA VENECIANA S.A.—Saint-Gobain; *Int'l*, pg. 1173
LIBBEY OWENS FORD CO.—Pilkington Plc; *Int'l*, pg. 1056
MACHINE-RITE PRODUCTS—Excel Industries, Inc.; *U.S. Public*, pg. 599
MASSGLAS B.V.—Asahi Glass Co., Ltd.; *Int'l*, pg. 85
MONSANTO EUROPE S.A.—Monsanto Company; *U.S. Public*, pg. 1125
MOY INSULATION LTD.—BPB Industries PLC; *Int'l*, pg. 123
NKK AMERICA INC.—NKK Corporation; *Int'l*, pg. 902
NKK EUROPE LTD.-LONDON OFFICE—NKK Corporation; *Int'l*, pg. 903
NYLONCRAFT—Excel Industries, Inc.; *U.S. Public*, pg. 599
O'KEEFFE'S, INC.; *U.S. Private*, pg. 813
OWENS-CORNING BUILDING PRODUCTS UK LTD.—Owens Corning; *U.S. Public*, pg. 1237
PPG INDUSTRIES, INC.; *U.S. Public*, pg. 1245
PILKINGTON (AUSTRALIA) OPERATIONS LIMITED—Pilkington Plc; *Int'l*, pg. 1057
PILKINGTON LAHDEN LASITEHDAS OY—Pilkington Plc; *Int'l*, pg. 1056
PILKINGTON LAMINO OY—Pilkington Plc; *Int'l*, pg. 1057
PILKINGTON (NEW ZEALAND) LIMITED—Pilkington Plc; *Int'l*, pg. 1057
PILKINGTON PLC; *Int'l*, pg. 1056
PILKINGTON UNITED KINGDOM LIMITED—Pilkington Plc; *Int'l*, pg. 1056
PILKINGTON VIDROS LTDA—Pilkington Plc; *Int'l*, pg. 1057
PITTSBURGH CORNING CORPORATION—Corning Incorporated; *U.S. Public*, pg. 449
PITTSBURGH CORNING EUROPE, N.V.—Corning Incorporated; *U.S. Public*, pg. 449
SAINT-GOBAIN; *Int'l*, pg. 1170
SAINT-GOBAIN VITRAGE—Saint-Gobain; *Int'l*, pg. 1172
SAINT-GOBAIN VITRO ITALIA—Saint-Gobain; *Int'l*, pg. 1173
SAMSUNG-CORNING COMPANY LTD.—Corning Incorporated; *U.S. Public*, pg. 449
SANTA MARINA—Saint-Gobain; *Int'l*, pg. 1177
SCANGLAS A/S—Saint-Gobain; *Int'l*, pg. 1173
SOLARIUM SYSTEMS, INC.—Apogee Enterprises, Inc.; *U.S. Public*, pg. 120
SUPER SKY PRODUCTS, INC.; *U.S. Private*, pg. 1054
T.G.U.S. CORP.—Taiwan Glass Industry Corp.; *Int'l*, pg. 1348
TAIWAN GLASS INDUSTRY CORP.; *Int'l*, pg. 1348
TOSCANA GLAS S.P.A.—Saint-Gobain; *Int'l*, pg. 1173
TREMPEX AB—Saint-Gobain; *Int'l*, pg. 1173
TRIPLEX SAFETY GLASS LIMITED—Pilkington Plc; *Int'l*, pg. 1056
VEGLA VEREINIGTE GLASWERKE GMBH—Saint-Gobain; *Int'l*, pg. 1173
VIDRIERIA ARGENTINA SA—Pilkington Plc; *Int'l*, pg. 1057
VIDRIERIAS ESPANOLAS VICASA—Saint-Gobain; *Int'l*, pg. 1176
VIRACON/CURVLITE, INC.—Apogee Enterprises, Inc.; *U.S. Public*, pg. 120
VIRACON, INC.—Apogee Enterprises, Inc.; *U.S. Public*, pg. 120
VIRACON OF ILLINOIS, INC.—Apogee Enterprises, Inc.; *U.S. Public*, pg. 120
VITRO, SOCIEDAD ANONIMA - FLAT GLASS DIV.—Vitro, Sociedad Anonima; *Int'l*, pg. 1469

3221 — GLASS CONTAINERS

ACI INTERNATIONAL LTD.—BTR plc; *Int'l*, pg. 128
AHLSTROM GLASSFIBRE LTD.-KARHULA PLANT—A. Ahlstrom Corporation; *Int'l*, pg. 32
ANCHOR GLASS CONTAINER CORPORATION—Consumers Packaging Inc.; *Int'l*, pg. 327
AUSTRALIAN GLASS MANUFACTURERS CO.—BTR plc; *Int'l*, pg. 128
BSN VIDRIO ESPANA—Danone Group; *Int'l*, pg. 381
BERNARDIN OF CANADA, LTD.—Alltrista Corporation; *U.S. Public*, pg. 56
CHATAS GLASS CO., INC.—Publicker Industries Inc.; *U.S. Public*, pg. 1341
COCA-COLA BOTTLING CO. UNITED, INC.; *U.S. Private*, pg. 248
COMPAGNIE DE SAINT-GOBAIN-PONT-A MOUSSON—Compagnie de Suez; *Int'l*, pg. 313
CONSUMER PRODUCTS COMPANY—Alltrista Corporation; *U.S. Public*, pg. 56
CONSUMERS PACKAGING INC.; *Int'l*, pg. 326
EMMABODA GLAS AB—Saint-Gobain; *Int'l*, pg. 1173
GLENSHAW GLASS CO. INC.; *U.S. Private*, pg. 457
KUALA LUMPUR GLASS MANUFACTURERS CO. SDN. BHD.—BTR plc; *Int'l*, pg. 129
MB GENERAL PACKAGING DIV.—Caradon Plc; *Int'l*, pg. 266
NEW ZEALAND GLASS MANUFACTURERS CO.—BTR plc; *Int'l*, pg. 129
NEWELL CO.; *U.S. Public*, pg. 1176
OWENS-BROCKWAY GLASS CONTAINERS—Owens-Illinois, Inc.; *U.S. Public*, pg. 1238
OWENS-BROCKWAY PRESCRIPTION PRODUCTS—Owens-Illinois, Inc.; *U.S. Public*, pg. 1238
OWENS-ILLINOIS, INC.; *U.S. Public*, pg. 1238
PHILIP MORRIS COMPANIES INC.; *U.S. Public*, pg. 1287
QUEENSLAND GLASS MANUFACTURERS CO.—BTR plc; *Int'l*, pg. 128
S.E.A. GLASS IND. PTE. LTD.—Taiwan Glass Industry Corp.; *Int'l*, pg. 1348
SGD GLASHUTTENWERKE GMBH—Saint-Gobain; *Int'l*, pg. 1171
SAINT-GOBAIN DESJONQUERES—Saint-Gobain; *Int'l*, pg. 1171
SAINT-GOBAIN EMBALLAGE—Saint-Gobain; *Int'l*, pg. 1171
SANTA MARINA—Saint-Gobain; *Int'l*, pg. 1177
SOVIS, SOCIETE DE VERRERIE SCIENTIFIQUE ET INDUSTRIELLE—Saint-Gobain; *Int'l*, pg. 1172
TBG SERVICES, INC.—TBG Management S.A.M.; *Int'l*, pg. 1335
TAIWAN GLASS INDUSTRY CORP.; *Int'l*, pg. 1348
THAI GLASS INDUSTRIES LTD.—BTR plc; *Int'l*, pg. 129
N.V. VEREENIGDE GLASFABRIEKEN—Danone Group; *Int'l*, pg. 381
VERRERIES SOUCHEN NEUVESEL—Danone Group; *Int'l*, pg. 381
VIDRIERIAS ESPANOLAS VICASA—Saint-Gobain; *Int'l*, pg. 1176
VITRO, SOCIEDAD ANONIMA; *Int'l*, pg. 1469

3229 — PRESSED & BLOWN GLASS & GLASSWARE, NEC

ACI INTERNATIONAL LTD.—BTR plc; *Int'l*, pg. 128
ANCHOR HOCKING—Newell Co.; *U.S. Public*, pg. 1177
ASAHI GLASS CO., LTD.; *Int'l*, pg. 84
BTR PERMALI RP LTD.—BTR plc; *Int'l*, pg. 124
BALZARETTI MODIGLIANI—Saint-Gobain; *Int'l*, pg. 1177
BERLI JUCKER PUBLIC CO. LTD.—First Pacific Company Limited; *Int'l*, pg. 487
BROWN-FORMAN CORPORATION; *U.S. Public*, pg. 261
BUILDING MATERIALS CORPORATION OF AMERICA—GAF Corporation; *U.S. Private*, pg. 433
CAMBRO MANUFACTURING COMPANY; *U.S. Private*, pg. 203
CASSIDY'S LTD.; *Int'l*, pg. 275
CERTAINTEED CORPORATION—Saint-Gobain; *Int'l*, pg. 1170
CHATAS GLASS CO., INC.—Publicker Industries Inc.; *U.S. Public*, pg. 1341
CHUGAI BOYEKI CO., LTD.; *Int'l*, pg. 290
COLGATE-PALMOLIVE COMPANY; *U.S. Public*, pg. 397
CORNING AUSTRALIA PTY. LIMITED—Corning Incorporated; *U.S. Public*, pg. 448
CORNING CANADA INC.—Corning Incorporated; *U.S. Public*, pg. 448
CORNING GMBH—Corning Incorporated; *U.S. Public*, pg. 449
CORNING INCORPORATED; *U.S. Public*, pg. 448
CRAFTLITE—The Genlyte Group Incorporated; *U.S. Public*, pg. 730
CRISTALERIA ESPANOLA S.A.—Saint-Gobain; *Int'l*, pg. 1176
CROWN CORNING LTD.—BTR plc; *Int'l*, pg. 128
CROWN CRYSTAL GLASS—BTR plc; *Int'l*, pg. 129
CRYSTAL CLEAR INDUSTRIES; *U.S. Private*, pg. 293
DANSK INTERNATIONAL DESIGNS LTD.—Brown-Forman Corporation; *U.S. Public*, pg. 261
DEUTSCHE SPEZIALGLAS AG—Carl-Zeiss-Stiftung; *Int'l*, pg. 1523
DR. GENTHE GMBH & CO. KG—Carl-Zeiss-Stiftung; *Int'l*, pg. 1523
EVENFLO COMPANY, INC.—Kohlberg Kravis Roberts & Co.; *U.S. Private*, pg. 629
EVENFLO MEXICO S.A.—Kohlberg Kravis Roberts & Co.; *U.S. Private*, pg. 630
FORD GLASS & METAL, INC.—Ford Motor Company; *U.S. Public*, pg. 664
GALILEO CORP.; *U.S. Public*, pg. 698
GLAVERBEL S.A.—Asahi Glass Co., Ltd.; *Int'l*, pg. 85
INDIANA GLASS COMPANY—Lancaster Colony Corporation; *U.S. Public*, pg. 976
INGRID DIVISION OF LAWNWARE—Lawnware Products, Inc.; *U.S. Private*, pg. 654
IWAKI-CORNING (MALAYSIA) SDN. BHD.—Corning Incorporated; *U.S. Public*, pg. 449
P.T. KANGAR CONSOLIDATED INDUSTRIES—BTR plc; *Int'l*, pg. 129
KRUG INTERNATIONAL TECHNOLOGY/SCIENTIFIC SERVICES, INC.—Krug International Corp.; *U.S. Public*, pg. 968
LALIQUE NORTH AMERICA—Lalique S.A.; *Int'l*, pg. 797
LALIQUE S.A.; *Int'l*, pg. 797
LANCASTER COLONY CORPORATION; *U.S. Public*, pg. 976
LANCASTER GLASS CORPORATION—Lancaster Colony Corporation; *U.S. Public*, pg. 977
LE VITRAGE DU MIDI—Saint-Gobain; *Int'l*, pg. 1172
LENOX PRODUCTS GROUP—Brown-Forman Corporation; *U.S. Public*, pg. 261
MASON CANDLELIGHT—Standex International Corporation; *U.S. Public*, pg. 1506
MCGRAW GLASS DIV.—Chrysler Corporation; *U.S. Public*, pg. 353
MYTTON'S LIMITED—Bristile Clay Tiles, Ltd.; *Int'l*, pg. 216
NEWELL CO.; *U.S. Public*, pg. 1176
NEWELL PUERTO RICO, LTD.—Newell Co.; *U.S. Public*, pg. 1177
OPTICAL FIBRES—Corning Incorporated; *U.S. Public*, pg. 449
OPTICAL WAVEGUIDES AUSTRALIA PTY,. LIMITED—Corning Incorporated; *U.S. Public*, pg. 449
OWENS CORNING; *U.S. Public*, pg. 1236
PPG INDUSTRIES, INC.; *U.S. Public*, pg. 1245
PALLFLEX, INC.—Pall Corporation; *U.S. Public*, pg. 1254
THE PFALTZGRAFF CO.—The Pfaltzgraff Co.; *U.S. Private*, pg. 860
PILKINGTON (AUSTRALIA) OPERATIONS LIMITED—Pilkington Plc; *Int'l*, pg. 1057
PILKINGTON PLC; *Int'l*, pg. 1056
Q.V.F. GLASTECHNIK GMBH—Corning Incorporated; *U.S. Public*, pg. 449
ROYAL COPENHAGEN A/S; *Int'l*, pg. 1134
ROYAL DOULTON PLC.; *Int'l*, pg. 1135
S.E.A. GLASS IND. PTE. LTD.—Taiwan Glass Industry Corp.; *Int'l*, pg. 1348
SAINT-GOBAIN ADVANCED MATERIALS CORPORATION—Saint-Gobain; *Int'l*, pg. 1173
SAINT-GOBAIN DESJONQUERES—Saint-Gobain; *Int'l*, pg. 1171
SAINT-GOBAIN EMBALLAGE—Saint-Gobain; *Int'l*, pg. 1171
SAINT-GOBAIN VITRO ITALIA—Saint-Gobain; *Int'l*, pg. 1173
SALADMASTER; *U.S. Private*, pg. 961
SAMCOR GLASS LIMITED—Corning Incorporated; *U.S. Public*, pg. 449
SANTA MARINA—Saint-Gobain; *Int'l*, pg. 1177
SCHOTT GLASS TECHNOLOGIES, INC.—Carl-Zeiss-Stiftung; *Int'l*, pg. 1523
SCHULLER GMBH—Johns Manville Corporation; *U.S. Public*, pg. 927
SHANGHAI CORNING ENGINEERING CORPORATION—Corning Incorporated; *U.S. Public*, pg. 449
SIECOR GMBH & CO. KG—Corning Incorporated; *U.S. Public*, pg. 449
SOCIETE VERRIERE D'ATLANTIQUE (SVA)—Saint-Gobain; *Int'l*, pg. 1172
SOPROVER—Saint-Gobain; *Int'l*, pg. 1172
SPALDING & EVENFLO JUVENILE FURNITURE COMPANY—Kohlberg Kravis Roberts & Co.; *U.S. Private*, pg. 630
SPECTRAN CORPORATION; *U.S. Public*, pg. 1497
TAIWAN GLASS INDUSTRY CORP.; *Int'l*, pg. 1348
TOSHIBA CERAMICS CO., LTD.—Toshiba Corporation; *Int'l*, pg. 1403
TOSHIBA GLASS CO., LTD.—Toshiba Corporation; *Int'l*, pg. 1404
VERRERIES SOUCHEN NEUVESEL—Danone Group; *Int'l*, pg. 381
VIDRIERIA ARGENTINA SA—Pilkington Plc; *Int'l*, pg. 1057
VIDRIERIAS ESPANOLAS VICASA—Saint-Gobain; *Int'l*, pg. 1176
VILLEROY & BOCH AG; *Int'l*, pg. 1468
WANNER Y VINYAS—Saint-Gobain; *Int'l*, pg. 1176
WATERFORD CRYSTAL LTD.—Waterford Wedgwood Plc; *Int'l*, pg. 1487
WATERFORD WEDGWOOD PLC; *Int'l*, pg. 1487
WATERFORD WEDGWOOD UK PLC—Waterford Wedgwood Plc; *Int'l*, pg. 1487
WHEATON GLASS PRODUCTS—Alusuisse-Lonza Holding Ltd.; *Int'l*, pg. 67
WHEATON INC.—Alusuisse-Lonza Holding Ltd.; *Int'l*, pg. 67
WHEATON SCIENTIFIC PRODUCTS—Alusuisse-Lonza Holding Ltd.; *Int'l*, pg. 68
WORLD TABLEWARE, INC.—Pilkington Plc; *Int'l*, pg. 1056

3231 — GLASS PRODUCTS, MADE OF PURCHASED GLASS

ACI AMERICA HOLDINGS INC.—BTR plc; *Int'l*, pg. 129
ACI INTERNATIONAL LTD.—BTR plc; *Int'l*, pg. 128
AP TECHNO GLASS COMPANY—Asahi Glass Co., Ltd.; *Int'l*, pg. 84
ACE GLASS INCORPORATED; *U.S. Private*, pg. 12
ACMIL INDUSTRIES PTY. LTD.—BTR plc; *Int'l*, pg. 129
ACORN WINDOW SYSTEMS INC.; *U.S. Private*, pg. 14
ALADDIN INDUSTRIES, INCORPORATED; *U.S. Private*, pg. 30
ALBANY GLASS—BTR plc; *Int'l*, pg. 129
AMERICAN GLASSMITH, INC.—American Architectural Products, Inc.; *U.S. Public*, pg. 67
APOGEE ENTERPRISES, INC.; *U.S. Public*, pg. 120
ARDCO, INC.; *U.S. Private*, pg. 80
ASAHI GLASS CO., LTD.; *Int'l*, pg. 84
ASSURANCE GLASS CO. OF ALABAMA—Globe-Amerada Glass Company; *U.S. Private*, pg. 458
BACCARAT (CIE DES CRISTALLERIES); *Int'l*, pg. 132
BENTLEY INTERNATIONAL, INC.; *U.S. Public*, pg. 212
J.E. BERKOWITZ, LP; *U.S. Private*, pg. 135
BRITAX (GECO) S.A.—Britax International plc; *Int'l*, pg. 216
BRITAX INTERNATIONAL PLC; *Int'l*, pg. 216

BRITAX WINGARD LIMITED—Britax International plc; *Int'l*, pg. 216
BRITE VUE GLASS SYSTEMS—Alumax Inc.; *U.S. Public*, pg. 60
CAROLINA MIRROR COMPANY; *U.S. Private*, pg. 214
CENTURY DOOR U.S.A. INC.—Premdor Inc.; *Int'l*, pg. 1067
CORNING GMBH—Corning Incorporated; *U.S. Public*, pg. 449
CORNING INCORPORATED; *U.S. Public*, pg. 448
CRYCO QUARTZ, INC.—Tosoh Corporation; *Int'l*, pg. 1408
D&A TECHNOLOGY—Asahi Glass Co., Ltd.; *Int'l*, pg. 85
DERLAN INDUSTRIES LIMITED; *Int'l*, pg. 395
DONNELLY CORPORATION; *U.S. Public*, pg. 519
DONNELLY EURO GLAS SYSTEMS—Donnelly Corporation; *U.S. Public*, pg. 519
DONNELLY MIRRORS, LIMITED—Donnelly Corporation; *U.S. Public*, pg. 519
EASTCO INDUSTRIAL SAFETY CORP.; *U.S. Public*, pg. 548
ERIE SCIENTIFIC CO.—Sybron International Corporation; *U.S. Public*, pg. 1545
FIMBEL DOOR CORPORATION; *U.S. Private*, pg. 404
FISHER SCIENTIFIC INTERNATIONAL—Thomas H. Lee Co.; *U.S. Private*, pg. 658
FLORAL GLASS & MIRROR, INC.; *U.S. Private*, pg. 414
LEONARD FLORENCE ASSOCIATES—Syratech Corporation; *U.S. Private*, pg. 1061
ABDULLA FOUAD-TESTRADE MIDDLE EAST—Abdulla Fouad Co. Ltd.; *Int'l*, pg. 502
GEMTRON CORPORATION—Carl-Zeiss-Stiftung; *Int'l*, pg. 1523
GENTEX CORPORATION; *U.S. Public*, pg. 731
GLASS PRODUCTS, INC.—Asahi Glass Co., Ltd.; *Int'l*, pg. 84
GLOBE-AMERADA GLASS COMPANY; *U.S. Private*, pg. 458
GREAT LAKES WINDOW, INC.—Nortek, Inc.; *U.S. Public*, pg. 1193
GROTE INDUSTRIES; *U.S. Private*, pg. 483
GROUPE STRAFOR FACOM; *Int'l*, pg. 569
GUARDIAN INDUSTRIES CORP.; *U.S. Private*, pg. 485
HUEPPE GMBH—Masco Corporation; *U.S. Public*, pg. 1055
HUEPPE SARL—Masco Corporation; *U.S. Public*, pg. 1054
INTERNATIONAL ALUMINUM CORPORATION; *U.S. Public*, pg. 894
INTERNATIONAL CALIFORNIA GLASS CORP.—International Aluminum Corporation; *U.S. Public*, pg. 895
INTERNATIONAL CAROLINA GLASS CORP.—International Aluminum Corporation; *U.S. Public*, pg. 895
ISOVER SAINT-GOBAIN—Saint-Gobain; *Int'l*, pg. 1176
K-D LAMP COMPANY; *U.S. Private*, pg. 603
KONTES GLASS COMPANY—Viag AG; *Int'l*, pg. 1464
LIBBEY OWENS FORD CO.—Pilkington Plc; *Int'l*, pg. 1056
LONDON LABORATORIES GMBH—Lilly Industries, Inc.; *U.S. Public*, pg. 995
MASON CANDLELIGHT—Standex International Corporation; *U.S. Public*, pg. 1506
MASSGLAS B.V.—Asahi Glass Co., Ltd.; *Int'l*, pg. 85
NAUGATUCK GLASS COMPANY; *U.S. Private*, pg. 789
NEWELL CO.; *U.S. Public*, pg. 1176
NORITAKE CO., LIMITED; *Int'l*, pg. 958
NORTEK, INC.; *U.S. Public*, pg. 1192
PQ CORPORATION; *U.S. Private*, pg. 827
PELLA CORPORATION; *U.S. Private*, pg. 848
PEREGRINE INCORPORATED; *U.S. Private*, pg. 852
PITTSBURGH CORNING CORPORATION—Corning Incorporated; *U.S. Public*, pg. 449
Q.V.F. GLASTECHNIK GMBH—Corning Incorporated; *U.S. Public*, pg. 449
RAINSFORDS METAL PRODUCTS PTY. LIMITED—Britax International plc; *Int'l*, pg. 217
RAUCH INDUSTRIES, INC.—Syratech Corporation; *U.S. Private*, pg. 1061
C.J. RUSH INC.—Derlan Industries Limited; *Int'l*, pg. 395
S & B ALTIM—BTR plc; *Int'l*, pg. 129
SEIKO EPSON CORPORATION; *Int'l*, pg. 1219
SINGAPORE GLASS (1974) LTD.—BTR plc; *Int'l*, pg. 129
SIVAQ—Saint-Gobain; *Int'l*, pg. 1172
SMITH & SMITH GLASS LTD.—International Paper Company; *U.S. Public*, pg. 904
SYRATECH CORPORATION; *U.S. Private*, pg. 1060
T & K GLASS CO.—BTR plc; *Int'l*, pg. 129
TAIWAN GLASS INDUSTRY CORP.; *Int'l*, pg. 1348
TAYLOR MADE GROUP, INC.; *U.S. Private*, pg. 1070
TAYLOR MADE-NEW YORK—Taylor Made Group, Inc.; *U.S. Private*, pg. 1070
THAI GLASS INDUSTRIES LTD.—BTR plc; *Int'l*, pg. 129
TOSHIBA BALLOTINE CO., LTD.—Toshiba Corporation; *Int'l*, pg. 1403
UNIVERSAL-RUNDLE CORP.—Nortek, Inc.; *U.S. Public*, pg. 1193
VANCE INDUSTRIES, INC.; *U.S. Private*, pg. 1133
VERRERIES DE L'ORNE—Saint-Gobain; *Int'l*, pg. 1171
VERRERIES SOUCHEN NEUVESEL—Danone Group; *Int'l*, pg. 381
VIRACON/CURVLITE, INC.—Apogee Enterprises, Inc.; *U.S. Public*, pg. 120
VIRACON, INC.—Apogee Enterprises, Inc.; *U.S. Public*, pg. 120
VIRACON OF ILLINOIS, INC.—Apogee Enterprises, Inc.; *U.S. Public*, pg. 120
VITRO, SOCIEDAD ANONIMA - CHEMICAL, FIBERS & MINING—Vitro, Sociedad Anonima; *Int'l*, pg. 1469
WK MFG. COMPANY—K-D Lamp Company; *U.S. Private*, pg. 603
WEISS GLASS TECHNOLOGIES, INC.—Tosoh Corporation; *Int'l*, pg. 1408
WEISS SCIENTIFIC GLASS BLOWING CO., INC.—Tosoh Corporation; *Int'l*, pg. 1408
WINDOWVISIONS INC.—Lindal Cedar Homes, Inc.; *U.S. Public*, pg. 999
WORLD TABLEWARE, INC.—Pilkington Plc; *Int'l*, pg. 1056
ZENITH PRODUCTS CORP.—Masco Corporation; *U.S. Public*, pg. 1054

3241 — CEMENT, HYDRAULIC

AKER RAJ ASA; *Int'l*, pg. 41
ALLENTOWN CEMENT CO. INC.—Scancem AB; *Int'l*, pg. 1201
ASH GROVE CEMENT COMPANY; *U.S. Private*, pg. 87
ASH GROVE CEMENT PLANT—Ash Grove Cement Company; *U.S. Private*, pg. 88
ASLAN CIMENTO AS—Lafarge S.A.; *Int'l*, pg. 788
ASSOCIATED PAN MALAYSIA CEMENT SDN. BERHAD—Blue Circle Industries PLC; *Int'l*, pg. 198
BLG BETONLIEFERUNGSGESELLSCHAFT GMBH—Heidelberger Zement A.G.; *Int'l*, pg. 606
BAMBURI PORTLAND CEMENT CO LTD—Lafarge S.A.; *Int'l*, pg. 789
BEAZER GROUP PLC; *Int'l*, pg. 181
BETECNA—Lafarge S.A.; *Int'l*, pg. 789
BETON DE PARIS—Lafarge S.A.; *Int'l*, pg. 788
BLUE CIRCLE SOUTHERN CEMENT LIMITED—Boral Limited; *Int'l*, pg. 203
CALCIA—Ciments Francais; *Int'l*, pg. 292
CASTLE CEMENT LIMITED—Scancem AB; *Int'l*, pg. 1201
CASTLE CEMENT LTD. (CLITHEROE)—Scancem AB; *Int'l*, pg. 1201
CASTLE CEMENT LTD. (GRAYS)—Scancem AB; *Int'l*, pg. 1201
CASTLE CEMENT LTD. (MOLD)—Scancem AB; *Int'l*, pg. 1201
CASTLE CEMENT LTD. (STAMFORD)—Scancem AB; *Int'l*, pg. 1201
CASTLE CEMENT LTD. (STRATHCLYDE)—Scancem AB; *Int'l*, pg. 1201
CEDEST CIMENTS—Lafarge S.A.; *Int'l*, pg. 788
CEMENTA AB—Scancem AB; *Int'l*, pg. 1198
CEMENTA AB (DEGERHAMN)—Scancem AB; *Int'l*, pg. 1199
CEMENTA AB (MALMO)—Scancem AB; *Int'l*, pg. 1198
CEMENTA AB (SKOVDE)—Scancem AB; *Int'l*, pg. 1199
CEMENTA AB (SLITE)—Scancem AB; *Int'l*, pg. 1199
CEMENTA AB (STOCKHOLM)—Scancem AB; *Int'l*, pg. 1198
CEMENTOS CARIBE C.A.—Holderbank Financiere Glaris Ltd.; *Int'l*, pg. 629
CEMENTOS NOLINS FINANCERA MINERA—Ciments Francais; *Int'l*, pg. 292
CENTEX CORPORATION; *U.S. Public*, pg. 322
CIMENTO MAUA S.A.—Lafarge S.A.; *Int'l*, pg. 789
CIMENTS DE L'ADOUR—Ciments Francais; *Int'l*, pg. 292
CIMENTS DU TOGO, S.A.—Scancem AB; *Int'l*, pg. 1201
CIMENTS DUNAROC—Ciments Francais; *Int'l*, pg. 292
CIMENTS LUXEMBOURGEOIS S.A.—Arbed S.A.; *Int'l*, pg. 80
COMPAGNIE DES SABLIERES DE LA SEINE—Lafarge S.A.; *Int'l*, pg. 788
COMPANHIA NACIONAL DE CIMENTO PORTLAND (C.N.C.P.)—Lafarge S.A.; *Int'l*, pg. 789
CONTINENTAL CEMENT CO. INC.—Scancem AB; *Int'l*, pg. 1201
CONTINENTAL CEMENT CO. OF FLORIDA INC.—Scancem AB; *Int'l*, pg. 1201
DUNDEE CEMENT CO.—Holderbank Financiere Glaris Ltd.; *Int'l*, pg. 628
DYCKERHOFF AG; *Int'l*, pg. 422
ELKEM MATERIALS—Elkem ASA; *Int'l*, pg. 447
ESSROC CANADA—Ciments Francais; *Int'l*, pg. 292
ESSROC CEMENT, CORP.; *U.S. Private*, pg. 384
ESSROC MATERIALS INC.—Ciments Francais; *Int'l*, pg. 292
FINNSEMENTTI OY AB—Scancem AB; *Int'l*, pg. 1198
FLORIDA CRUSHED STONE COMPANY; *U.S. Private*, pg. 414
FONDARGE (PTY.) LTD.—Lafarge S.A.; *Int'l*, pg. 790
GHACEM, LTD.—Scancem AB; *Int'l*, pg. 1201
GIANT CEMENT COMPANY—Giant Cement Holding Inc.; *U.S. Public*, pg. 741
GIANT CEMENT HOLDING INC.; *U.S. Public*, pg. 741
GIFFORD-HILL CEMENT COMPANY OF SOUTH CAROLINA—Hanson PLC; *Int'l*, pg. 593
GLENS FALLS CEMENT CO.—Dyckerhoff AG; *Int'l*, pg. 423
GOLDEN BAY CEMENT LTD.—Fletcher Challenge Limited; *Int'l*, pg. 495
GRUPO CEMENTOS DE CHIHUAHUA S.A. DE C.V.; *Int'l*, pg. 573
HISALBA - HORNOS IBERICOS ALBA S.A.—Holderbank Financiere Glaris Ltd.; *Int'l*, pg. 629
HAGERSTOWN CEMENT PLANT INDEPENDENT CEMENT CORP.—Holderbank Financiere Glaris Ltd.; *Int'l*, pg. 629
HEIDELBERGER BAUSTOFFTECHNIK GMBH—Heidelberger Zement A.G.; *Int'l*, pg. 605
HEIDELBERGER ZEMENT A.G.; *Int'l*, pg. 605
HILLS MATERIALS CO.—Northwestern Engineering Co.; *U.S. Private*, pg. 806
HOKURYU CEMENT CORP.—Ssangyong Business Group; *Int'l*, pg. 1291
HOLNAM INC.—Holderbank Financiere Glaris Ltd.; *Int'l*, pg. 628
HOLNAM INC. (WEST DIVISION)—Holderbank Financiere Glaris Ltd.; *Int'l*, pg. 628
IDEAL CEMENT COMPANY (B.C.) LTD.—Holderbank Financiere Glaris Ltd.; *Int'l*, pg. 628
IDEAL CONCRETE—Holderbank Financiere Glaris Ltd.; *Int'l*, pg. 628
ILIGAN CEMENT CORPORATION—Holderbank Financiere Glaris Ltd.; *Int'l*, pg. 629
ILLINOIS CEMENT CO.—Centex Corporation; *U.S. Public*, pg. 322
INDEPENDENT CEMENT CORPORATION—Holderbank Financiere Glaris Ltd.; *Int'l*, pg. 629
INDUSTRIA NACIONAL DE CEMENTO S.A.—Holderbank Financiere Glaris Ltd.; *Int'l*, pg. 630
S.A. INDUSTRIAS VOTORANTIM; *Int'l*, pg. 677
INTERMOSELLE—Ciments Francais; *Int'l*, pg. 292
INTERMOSELLE S.A.R.L.—Arbed S.A.; *Int'l*, pg. 80
KAISER CEMENT CORPORATION—Hanson PLC; *Int'l*, pg. 593
KAISER INTERNATIONAL SERVICES CORP.—Hanson PLC; *Int'l*, pg. 593
KARSDORFER ZEMENT BETEILIGUNGS GMBH—Lafarge S.A.; *Int'l*, pg. 789
KEYSTONE CEMENT CO.—Giant Cement Holding Inc.; *U.S. Public*, pg. 741
KOSMOS CEMENT COMPANY—Lone Star Industries, Inc.; *U.S. Public*, pg. 1012
LAFARGE ALUMINATES—Lafarge S.A.; *Int'l*, pg. 789
LAFARGE ALUMINATES CO. LTD.—Lafarge S.A.; *Int'l*, pg. 790
LAFARGE ALUMINOSO DO BRAZIL—Lafarge S.A.; *Int'l*, pg. 790
LAFARGE ALUMINOUS CEMENT CO. LTD.—Lafarge S.A.; *Int'l*, pg. 790
LAFARGE CALCIUM ALUMINATE—Lafarge S.A.; *Int'l*, pg. 791
LAFARGE CANADA INC.—Lafarge S.A.; *Int'l*, pg. 789
LAFARGE CIMENTS—Lafarge S.A.; *Int'l*, pg. 788
LAFARGE CONCRETE LTD.—Lafarge S.A.; *Int'l*, pg. 789
LAFARGE CORPORATION—Lafarge S.A.; *Int'l*, pg. 788
LAFARGE S.A.; *Int'l*, pg. 788
LEHIGH PORTLAND CEMENT COMPANY—Heidelberger Zement A.G.; *Int'l*, pg. 605
LIBERIA CEMENT CORP.—Scancem AB; *Int'l*, pg. 1201
LONE STAR INDUSTRIES, INC.; *U.S. Public*, pg. 1012
MBT AUSTRIA GESELLSCHAFT M.B.H.—Viag AG; *Int'l*, pg. 1465
MBT FRANCE S.A.—Viag AG; *Int'l*, pg. 1465
MBT (NEW ZEALAND) LTD.—Viag AG; *Int'l*, pg. 1465
MBT PORTUGAL LDA.—Viag AG; *Int'l*, pg. 1465
MALAYAN CEMENT BERHAD—Blue Circle Industries PLC; *Int'l*, pg. 198
MASTER BUILDERS INC.—Viag AG; *Int'l*, pg. 1465
MASTER BUILDERS TECHNOLOGIES (HONG KONG) LTD.—Viag AG; *Int'l*, pg. 1465
MASTER BUILDERS TECHNOLOGIES LTD.—Viag AG; *Int'l*, pg. 1465
MEDUSA CORPORATION; *U.S. Public*, pg. 1084
MEYNADIER AG—Viag AG; *Int'l*, pg. 1465
MISSOURI PORTLAND CEMENT HOLDING—Lafarge S.A.; *Int'l*, pg. 788
MONARCH CEMENT CO.; *U.S. Public*, pg. 1123
MOUNTAIN CEMENT COMPANY—Centex Corporation; *U.S. Public*, pg. 323
NEVADA CEMENT CO.—Centex Corporation; *U.S. Public*, pg. 323
NORCEM CEMENT A/S—Aker Raj Asa; *Int'l*, pg. 42
NORCEM INDUSTRIER—Aker Raj Asa; *Int'l*, pg. 42
NORDCEMENT AG—Holderbank Financiere Glaris Ltd.; *Int'l*, pg. 628
NORTHWESTERN ENGINEERING CO.; *U.S. Private*, pg. 806
NORTHWESTERN STATES PORTLAND CEMENT—Holderbank Financiere Glaris Ltd.; *Int'l*, pg. 628
NORVAL, INC.—Scancem AB; *Int'l*, pg. 1201
NOVARTIS AG; *Int'l*, pg. 971
PAN MALAYSIA CEMENT WORKS (SINGAPORE) PTE. LTD.—Blue Circle Industries PLC; *Int'l*, pg. 198
PERAK HANJUNG SINIEN SDN. BHD.—Korea Heavy Industries & Construction Co., Ltd.; *Int'l*, pg. 758
PROMSA—Ciments Francais; *Int'l*, pg. 292
PUERTO RICAN CEMENT CO., INC.; *U.S. Public*, pg. 1341
QUEBEC & MARITIMES DIV. ST. LAWRENCE CEMENT—Holderbank Financiere Glaris Ltd.; *Int'l*, pg. 629
QUEENSLAND CEMENT LTD.—Holderbank Financiere Glaris Ltd.; *Int'l*, pg. 629
CIE. RHODANIENNE DE DEVELOPPEMENT—Lafarge S.A.; *Int'l*, pg. 788
RIVERSIDE CEMENT CO.—Ssangyong Business Group; *Int'l*, pg. 1293
SAINT-GOBAIN; *Int'l*, pg. 1170
ST. LAWRENCE CEMENT INC.—Holderbank Financiere Glaris Ltd.; *Int'l*, pg. 628
SCANCEM AB; *Int'l*, pg. 1198
SCANCEM INDUSTRIES, INC.—Scancem AB; *Int'l*, pg. 1201
SHAMROCK AGGREGATES, INC.—Ash Grove Cement Company; *U.S. Private*, pg. 88
SHINRYU CEMENT CORP.—Ssangyong Business Group; *Int'l*, pg. 1291
SOCIETE DES CIMENTS DU CONGO S.A.—Scancem AB; *Int'l*, pg. 1200
SOUTHDOWN CEMENT GROUP—Southdown, Inc.; *U.S. Public*, pg. 1489
SOUTHDOWN, INC.; *U.S. Public*, pg. 1488
SSANGYONG AUSTRALIA PTY., LTD.—Ssangyong Business Group; *Int'l*, pg. 1291
SSANGYONG CEMENT INDUSTRIAL CO., LTD.—Ssangyong Business Group; *Int'l*, pg. 1291
SSANGYONG CEMENT (SINGAPORE) LTD.—Ssangyong Business Group; *Int'l*, pg. 1293
SSANGYONG PACIFIC—Ssangyong Business Group; *Int'l*, pg. 1292
STANDARD CONCRETE—Heidelberger Zement A.G.; *Int'l*, pg. 605
SUEDBAYERISCHES PORTLAND SIMNING ZEMENTWERK GEBR. WIESBOECK & CO. GMBH—Heidelberger Zement A.G.; *Int'l*, pg. 605
TARMAC AMERICA, INC.—Tarmac plc; *Int'l*, pg. 1355
TECNOCRETO S.A. DE C.V.—Novartis AG; *Int'l*, pg. 986
TERRAZUL—Ciments Francais; *Int'l*, pg. 292
TEXAS INDUSTRIES, INC.; *U.S. Public*, pg. 1585
TEXAS-LEHIGH CEMENT CO.—Centex Corporation; *U.S. Public*, pg. 323
TEXAS SUNBELT CEMENT—Centex Corporation; *U.S. Public*, pg. 323
THAI MASTER BUILDERS CO. LTD.—Novartis AG; *Int'l*, pg. 986
TILCON, INC.; *U.S. Private*, pg. 1086
TOKUYAMA CORPORATION; *Int'l*, pg. 1393

S.I.C. Index

TORYU CEMENT CORP.—Ssangyong Business Group; Int'l, pg. 1291
USX FAIRFIELD WORKS—USX Corporation; U.S. Public, pg. 1662
UNIBETON—Ciments Francais; Int'l, pg. 292
UNITED CEMENT CO.—Holderbank Financiere Glaris Ltd.; Int'l, pg. 628
VICAT S.A.—Heidelberger Zement A.G.; Int'l, pg. 606
VYNEX S.R.L.—Dyckerhoff AG; Int'l, pg. 423
WOSSINGER ZEMENT—Lafarge S.A.; Int'l, pg. 789
H.B. ZACHRY COMPANY—H.B. Zachry; U.S. Private, pg. 1203
ZEAG ZEMENTWERK LAUFFEN-ELEKTRIZITAETSWERK HEILBRONN AG—Heidelberger Zement A.G.; Int'l, pg. 605

3251 — BRICK & STRUCTURAL CLAY TILE

ACI INTERNATIONAL LTD.—BTR plc; Int'l, pg. 128
ACME BRICK CO.—Justin Industries, Inc.; U.S. Public, pg. 936
ARMOR BOND BUILDING PRODUCTS, INC.—Jannock Limited; Int'l, pg. 699
ATHENS BRICK CO.—Texas Industries, Inc.; U.S. Public, pg. 1585
BORAL BRICKS INC.—Boral Limited; Int'l, pg. 203
BORAL BRICKS PTY. LTD.—Boral Limited; Int'l, pg. 203
BOREN CLAY PRODUCTS COMPANY—Jannock Limited; Int'l, pg. 699
BRISTILE CLAY TILES, LTD.; Int'l, pg. 216
BUTTERLEY BRICK LTD.—Hanson PLC; Int'l, pg. 592
CANADA BRICK DIV.—Jannock Limited; Int'l, pg. 698
CERAMICA SYRE S.A.—Lafarge S.A.; Int'l, pg. 790
COOKSON GROUP PLC; Int'l, pg. 328
GAF PREMIUM PRODUCTS, INC.—GAF Corporation; U.S. Private, pg. 433
GENERAL SHALE PRODUCTS CORP.—Marley PLC; Int'l, pg. 843
GLEN-GERY CORPORATION—Ibstock Plc; Int'l, pg. 658
HOLLY SPRINGS BRICK AND TILE, INC.—Jannock Limited; Int'l, pg. 699
HUGUENOT-FENAL—Imetal; Int'l, pg. 661
IBSTOCK PLC; Int'l, pg. 658
INTERSTATE BRICK COMPANY—Pacific Coast Building Products Inc.; U.S. Private, pg. 830
JANNOCK BRICK GROUP-HEAD OFFICE—Jannock Limited; Int'l, pg. 698
JANNOCK LIMITED; Int'l, pg. 698
JUSTIN INDUSTRIES, INC.; U.S. Public, pg. 936
LINEAR DYNAMICS INC.; U.S. Private, pg. 668
NORCEM A.S.—Aker Raj Asa; Int'l, pg. 42
PAVIMENTOS CERAMICOS S.A.—Lafarge S.A.; Int'l, pg. 790
REAL BRICK PRODUCTS, INC.—Jannock Limited; Int'l, pg. 699
REDLAND KORAMIC BRICKS N.V.—Redland PLC; Int'l, pg. 1093
REDLAND PLC; Int'l, pg. 1090
RICHTEX CORPORATION—Jannock Limited; Int'l, pg. 699
ST. LAWRENCE BRICK DIVISION—Jannock Limited; Int'l, pg. 698
SCANCEM AB; Int'l, pg. 1198
TEMCO FIREPLACE PRODUCTS, INC.—Temtex Industries Inc.; U.S. Public, pg. 1576
TEMTEX INDUSTRIES INC.; U.S. Public, pg. 1575
U.S. BRICK, INC.—Jannock Limited; Int'l, pg. 699
VITROMEX, S.A.; Int'l, pg. 1469
WESTBRICK LIMITED—Tarmac plc; Int'l, pg. 1355
YORKSHIRE BRICK COMPANY—Franz Haniel & Cie, GmbH; Int'l, pg. 591

3253 — CERAMIC WALL & FLOOR TILE

ACI AMERICA HOLDINGS INC.—BTR plc; Int'l, pg. 129
ACI INTERNATIONAL LTD.—BTR plc; Int'l, pg. 128
ACME BRICK CO.—Justin Industries, Inc.; U.S. Public, pg. 936
ARMSTRONG WORLD INDUSTRIES, INC.; U.S. Public, pg. 131
CERAMICA SYRE S.A.—Lafarge S.A.; Int'l, pg. 790
COOKSON GROUP PLC; Int'l, pg. 328
CURRAN GROUP, INC.; U.S. Private, pg. 297
DAL KEYSTONE—Dal-Tile International; U.S. Private, pg. 308
DAL-TILE CORP.—Dal-Tile International; U.S. Private, pg. 308
DAL-TILE INTERNATIONAL; U.S. Private, pg. 308
FLORIDA TILE INDUSTRIES, INC.—Premark International, Inc.; U.S. Public, pg. 1322
HUNTINGTON TILE, INC.—Pacific Holding Corporation; U.S. Private, pg. 831
INNER CERAMIC USA; U.S. Private, pg. 564
INTERNACIONAL DE CERAMICA S.A. DE C.V.; Int'l, pg. 680
JUSTIN INDUSTRIES, INC.; U.S. Public, pg. 936
MONARCH TILE, INC.—Cravey, Green & Wahlen, Incorporated; U.S. Private, pg. 287
NARUMI CHINA CORPORATION; Int'l, pg. 906
PGH EUREKA CERAMICS—BTR plc; Int'l, pg. 128
PACIFIC HOLDING CORPORATION; U.S. Private, pg. 831
PILKINGTON'S TILES LTD.—BTR plc; Int'l, pg. 124
PORCELANITE, INC.—Grupo Carso S.A. de C.V.; Int'l, pg. 573
PORCELANITE SA DE CV—Grupo Carso S.A. de C.V.; Int'l, pg. 572
PRECISION DIE & ENGINEERING, INC.—Premark International, Inc.; U.S. Public, pg. 1322
ANN SACKS TILE & STONE, INC.—Kohler Company; U.S. Private, pg. 630
TILECERA, INC.—The Siam Cement Public Company Limited; Int'l, pg. 1239
TOINDUSTRIE HEISTERHOLZ ERNST RAUCH GMBH & CO. KG—Redland PLC; Int'l, pg. 1091

UNITED STATES CERAMIC TILE CO.; U.S. Private, pg. 1124
VILLEROY & BOCH AG; Int'l, pg. 1468
VILLEROY & BOCH (USA) INC.—Villeroy & Boch AG; Int'l, pg. 1468
VITROMEX, S.A.; Int'l, pg. 1469

3255 — CLAY REFRACTORIES

ACI INDUSTRIES PTY. LTD.—BTR plc; Int'l, pg. 128
AKER RAJ ASA; Int'l, pg. 41
ASLAND S.A.—Lafarge S.A.; Int'l, pg. 790
BETAO LIZ S.A.—Lafarge S.A.; Int'l, pg. 790
BLUE CIRCLE SOUTHERN CEMENT LIMITED—Boral Limited; Int'l, pg. 203
BORAL LIMITED; Int'l, pg. 203
C&W REFRACTORIES, LTD.—CFB Industries, Inc.; U.S. Private, pg. 194
CFB INDUSTRIES, INC.; U.S. Private, pg. 194
CANADA BRICK DIV.—Jannock Limited; Int'l, pg. 698
THE CARBORUNDUM CORPORATION—Saint-Gobain; Int'l, pg. 1173
CEMENLAND S.A.—Lafarge S.A.; Int'l, pg. 790
CEMENTOS ASLAND S.A.—Lafarge S.A.; Int'l, pg. 790
CEMENTOS PEYLAND S.A.—Lafarge S.A.; Int'l, pg. 790
CERTECH, INC.—Carpenter Technology Corporation; U.S. Public, pg. 307
CHICAGO FIRE BRICK CO.—CFB Industries, Inc.; U.S. Private, pg. 194
CHICAGO FIRE BRICK OF DELAWARE, INC.—CFB Industries, Inc.; U.S. Private, pg. 194
DFC CERAMICS INC.—Morgan Crucible Co. Plc; Int'l, pg. 893
DIXON TICONDEROGA COMPANY; U.S. Public, pg. 514
ENSR; U.S. Private, pg. 354
ELKEM MATERIALS—Elkem ASA; Int'l, pg. 447
EMCO LIMITED; Int'l, pg. 452
EMPRESA DE REFRACTARIOS COLOMBIANOS S.A.—RGP Holding, Inc.; U.S. Private, pg. 903
FERRO CORPORATION; U.S. Public, pg. 618
A.P. GREEN INDUSTRIES, INC.; U.S. Public, pg. 761
HARBISON-WALKER REFRACTORIES—Global Industrial Technologies; U.S. Public, pg. 748
HEIDELBERGER DAEMMSYSTEME GMBH—Heidelberger Zement A.G.; Int'l, pg. 606
HEPWORTH PLC; Int'l, pg. 614
HEPWORTH REFRACTORIES (CANADA) LIMITED—Hepworth Plc; Int'l, pg. 615
HISPACEMENT S.A.—Lafarge S.A.; Int'l, pg. 790
JANNOCK BRICK GROUP-HEAD OFFICE—Jannock Limited; Int'l, pg. 698
LAFARGE REFRACTAIRES MONOLITHIQUES—Lafarge S.A.; Int'l, pg. 789
LAPORTE PLC; Int'l, pg. 801
LONDON BRICK COMPANY LTD.—Hanson PLC; Int'l, pg. 593
MORGANITE CANADA CORPORATION—Morgan Crucible Co. Plc; Int'l, pg. 895
NEW CASTLE REFRACTORY CO.—Dixon Ticonderoga Company; U.S. Public, pg. 515
NORTH AMERICAN REFRACTORIES COMPANY; U.S. Private, pg. 803
OPTIROC AS—Scancem AB; Int'l, pg. 1200
OPTIROC GROUP AB—Scancem AB; Int'l, pg. 1200
PACIFIC CLAY PRODUCTS—Pacific Holding Corporation; U.S. Private, pg. 831
PACIFIC HOLDING CORPORATION; U.S. Private, pg. 831
PERAK HANJUNG SINIEN SDN. BHD.—Korea Heavy Industries & Construction Co., Ltd.; Int'l, pg. 758
PORTCEMEN S.A.—Lafarge S.A.; Int'l, pg. 790
RADEX AUSTRIA, A.G.—RGP Holding, Inc.; U.S. Private, pg. 904
RESCO PRODUCTS, INC.; U.S. Private, pg. 924
SABANCI HOLDING A.S.; Int'l, pg. 1167
ST. LAWRENCE BRICK DIVISION—Jannock Limited; Int'l, pg. 698
THE SIAM CEMENT PUBLIC COMPANY LIMITED; Int'l, pg. 1237
TYK REFRACTORIES CO.—TYK Corporation; Int'l, pg. 1345
THERMAL CERAMICS INC.—Morgan Crucible Co. Plc; Int'l, pg. 894
TOSHIBA CERAMICS CO., LTD.—Toshiba Corporation; Int'l, pg. 1403
WATTS BLAKE BEARNE & CO. PLC; Int'l, pg. 1487
WELLSVILLE FIRE BRICK COMPANY—CFB Industries, Inc.; U.S. Private, pg. 194

3259 — STRUCTURAL CLAY PRODUCTS, NEC

CARTER HOLT HARVEY ROOFING INTERNATIONAL—International Paper Company; U.S. Public, pg. 904
CRAMIQUES TECHNIQUES DESMARQUEST—Pechiney S.A.; Int'l, pg. 1028
HEPWORTH PLC; Int'l, pg. 614
INDUSTRIAS TRANSFORMADORAS DEL CEMENTO ETERNIT SA—Redland PLC; Int'l, pg. 1092
LUDOWICI ROOF TILE, INC.—Saint-Gobain; Int'l, pg. 1171
LUSOCERAM-EMPREENDIMENTOS CERAMICOS, S.A.—Redland PLC; Int'l, pg. 1092
MALAYSIAN ROOFING INDUSTRIES SDN. BHD.—BTR plc; Int'l, pg. 129
MARLEY PLC; Int'l, pg. 843
MARLEY ROOF TILES HOLDINGS (U.S.A.) INC.—Marley PLC; Int'l, pg. 844
MEYNADIER AG—Viag AG; Int'l, pg. 1465
MONIER INC.—Redland PLC; Int'l, pg. 1091
PACIFIC COAST BUILDING PRODUCTS INC.; U.S. Private, pg. 830
ROOF TILE MANUFACTURING CO.—International Paper Company; U.S. Public, pg. 905
RUPPKERAMIK GMBH—Redland PLC; Int'l, pg. 1093

SELKIRK METALBESTOS—Zurn Industries, Inc.; U.S. Public, pg. 1794
SIPLAST INC.—Icopal a/s; Int'l, pg. 659
SIPLAST S.A.—Icopal a/s; Int'l, pg. 659
TARCO; U.S. Private, pg. 1068

3261 — VITREOUS CHINA PLUMBING FIXTURES & CHINA & EARTHENWARE FITTINGS & BATHROOM ACCESSORIES

AAA PLUMBING POTTERY CORP.—Gerber Plumbing Fixtures Corporation; U.S. Private, pg. 449
AMERICAN STANDARD INC.; U.S. Public, pg. 91
AMERICAN STANDARD SANITARYWARE (THAILAND) LTD.—American Standard Inc.; U.S. Public, pg. 92
ARMITAGE SHANKS LIMITED—Blue Circle Industries PLC; Int'l, pg. 197
BLUE CIRCLE INDUSTRIES PLC; Int'l, pg. 197
BRIGGS INDUSTRIES, INC.; U.S. Private, pg. 168
CC INDUSTRIES, INC.; U.S. Private, pg. 192
CERAMICA DOLOMITE S.P.A.—Blue Circle Industries PLC; Int'l, pg. 198
COMPAGNIE INTERNATIONALE DES PRODUITS SANITAIRES (CIPS) JACOB DELAFON—Kohler Company; U.S. Private, pg. 631
DAIDO HOXAN INC.; Int'l, pg. 363
DAMIXA ARMATUREN, GMBH—Masco Corporation; U.S. Public, pg. 1054
DAMIXA LTD.—Masco Corporation; U.S. Public, pg. 1055
DAMIXA S.A.—Masco Corporation; U.S. Public, pg. 1054
DURST CORPORATION; U.S. Private, pg. 349
EAGLE INDUSTRIES, INC.—Great American Management & Investment, Inc.; U.S. Private, pg. 473
ELJER INDUSTRIES—Zurn Industries, Inc.; U.S. Public, pg. 1795
FINNAIR—FinnAir Oy; Int'l, pg. 486
GENERAL MARBLE CORPORATION—Leucadia National Corporation; U.S. Public, pg. 990
GERBER PLUMBING FIXTURES CORPORATION; U.S. Private, pg. 449
HUEPPE GMBH—Masco Corporation; U.S. Public, pg. 1055
HUEPPE SARL—Masco Corporation; U.S. Public, pg. 1054
IDEAL-STANDARD BRAZIL—American Standard Inc.; U.S. Public, pg. 92
IDEAL-STANDARD GMBH—American Standard Inc.; U.S. Public, pg. 92
IDEAL-STANDARD LTD.—American Standard Inc.; U.S. Public, pg. 92
IDEAL-STANDARD, S.A. DE C.V.—American Standard Inc.; U.S. Public, pg. 92
IDEAL-STANDARD S.A.I.—American Standard Inc.; U.S. Public, pg. 92
IDEAL-STANDARD S.P.A.—American Standard Inc.; U.S. Public, pg. 92
INDUSTRIA CENTROAMERICANA DE SANITARIOS, S.A.—American Standard Inc.; U.S. Public, pg. 92
INDUSTRIA CERAMICA CENTROAMERICANA, S.A.—American Standard Inc.; U.S. Public, pg. 92
INDUSTRIA CERAMICA COSTARRICENSE, S.A.—American Standard Inc.; U.S. Public, pg. 92
JACLO INC.—Durst Corporation; U.S. Private, pg. 349
KALLISTA, INC.—Kohler Company; U.S. Private, pg. 630
KOHLER COMPANY; U.S. Private, pg. 630
KOKOMO SANITARY POTTERY CORP.—Gerber Plumbing Fixtures Corporation; U.S. Private, pg. 449
LEUCADIA NATIONAL CORPORATION; U.S. Public, pg. 989
MIX-A-MIX A/S—Masco Corporation; U.S. Public, pg. 1054
NORTEK, INC.; U.S. Public, pg. 1192
PEERLESS POTTERY, INC.; U.S. Private, pg. 847
QUALITAS BATHROOMS LTD.—Blue Circle Industries PLC; Int'l, pg. 197
QUEROY S.A.—American Standard Inc.; U.S. Public, pg. 92
SANITARIOS DOMINICANOS, S.A.—American Standard Inc.; U.S. Public, pg. 92
SANITARY WARES MFG. CORP.—American Standard Inc.; U.S. Public, pg. 92
UNIVERSAL-RUNDLE CORP.—Nortek, Inc.; U.S. Public, pg. 1193
VILLEROY & BOCH AG; Int'l, pg. 1468
VILLEROY & BOCH (USA) INC.—Villeroy & Boch AG; Int'l, pg. 1468
WESTERN AMERICAN MANUFACTURING, INC.—Waxman Industries, Inc.; U.S. Public, pg. 1749
WOODBRIDGE SANITARY POTTERY CORP.—Gerber Plumbing Fixtures Corporation; U.S. Private, pg. 449

3262 — VITREOUS CHINA TABLE & KITCHEN ARTICLES

BACCARAT (CIE DES CRISTALLERIES); Int'l, pg. 132
ROBERT BOSCH GMBH; Int'l, pg. 203
BROWN-FORMAN CORPORATION; U.S. Public, pg. 261
BUFFALO CHINA, INC.—Oneida Ltd.; U.S. Public, pg. 1226
H.F. COORS CHINA CO.—Standex International Corporation; U.S. Public, pg. 1506
DANSK INTERNATIONAL DESIGNS LTD.—Brown-Forman Corporation; U.S. Public, pg. 261
FINETECH CO., LTD.—Skylark Co., Ltd.; Int'l, pg. 1262
THE HALL CHINA COMPANY; U.S. Private, pg. 494
HERMES INTERNATIONAL; Int'l, pg. 617
THE HOMER LAUGHLIN CHINA COMPANY; U.S. Private, pg. 653
LENOX BRANDS—Brown-Forman Corporation; U.S. Public, pg. 261
LENOX, INCORPORATED—Brown-Forman Corporation; U.S. Public, pg. 261
LENOX PRODUCTS GROUP—Brown-Forman Corporation; U.S. Public, pg. 261
NARUMI CHINA CORPORATION; Int'l, pg. 906
NORDIC WARE—Northland Aluminum Products, Inc.; U.S. Private, pg. 806

NORITAKE CO., LIMITED; *Int'l*, pg. 958
ONEIDA LTD.; *U.S. Public*, pg. 1225
THE PFALTZGRAFF CO.—The Pfaltzgraff Co.; *U.S. Private*, *pg. 860*
REVERE WARE CORPORATION—Corning Incorporated; *U.S. Public*, pg. 448
ROSENTHAL AG; *Int'l*, pg. 1127
ROYAL DOULTON PLC.; *Int'l*, pg. 1135
VILLEROY & BOCH TABLEWARE, LTD.—Villeroy & Boch AG; *Int'l*, pg. 1468
WATERFORD WEDGWOOD PLC; *Int'l*, pg. 1487
WATERFORD WEDGWOOD UK PLC—Waterford Wedgwood Plc; *Int'l*, pg. 1487
WEST BEND OF CANADA LTD.—Premark International, Inc.; *U.S. Public*, pg. 1323

3263 — FINE EARTHENWARE (WHITEWARE) TABLE & KITCHEN ARTICLES

M. BLOCK & SONS, INC.; *U.S. Private*, pg. 150
FINETECH CO., LTD.—Skylark Co., Ltd.; *Int'l*, pg. 1262
GROUPE SEB CR—Groupe SEB; *Int'l*, pg. 568
GROUPE SEB HUNGARY—Groupe SEB; *Int'l*, pg. 568
GROUPE SEB POLSKA—Groupe SEB; *Int'l*, pg. 568
GROUPE SEB SLOVENSKO—Groupe SEB; *Int'l*, pg. 568
NARUMI CHINA CORPORATION; *Int'l*, pg. 906
NORDIC WARE—Northland Aluminum Products, Inc.; *U.S. Private*, pg. 806
NORITAKE CO., LIMITED; *Int'l*, pg. 958
ONEIDA LTD.; *U.S. Public*, pg. 1225
PERSTORP CHEMITEC—Perstorp AB; *Int'l*, pg. 1037
THE PFALTZGRAFF CO.; *U.S. Private*, pg. 860
THE PFALTZGRAFF CO.—The Pfaltzgraff Co.; *U.S. Private*, *pg. 860*
REVERE WARE CORPORATION—Corning Incorporated; *U.S. Public*, pg. 448
ROSENTHAL AG; *Int'l*, pg. 1127
ROWOCO—Wilton Industries, Inc.; *U.S. Private*, pg. 1182
WATERFORD WEDGWOOD PLC; *Int'l*, pg. 1487
WATERFORD WEDGWOOD UK PLC—Waterford Wedgwood Plc; *Int'l*, pg. 1487

3264 — PORCELAIN ELECTRICAL SUPPLIES

AIMANTS UGIMAG—Pechiney S.A.; *Int'l*, pg. 1028
ALCOA ELECTRONIC PACKAGING, INC.—Aluminum Company of America; *U.S. Public*, pg. 60
THE ARNOLD ENGINEERING COMPANY—SPS Technologies, Inc.; *U.S. Public*, pg. 1420
THE BENTLEY-HARRIS MANUFACTURING CO.—T & N Plc; *Int'l*, pg. 1334
BRUSH WELLMAN INC.; *U.S. Public*, pg. 266
COLTEC HOLDINGS INC; *U.S. Public*, pg. 401
EDO CERAMICS—EDO Corporation; *U.S. Public*, pg. 542
EAGLE INDUSTRIES, INC.—Great American Management & Investment, Inc.; *U.S. Private*, pg. 473
ELECTRICAL PRODUCTS DIVISION—3M; *U.S. Public*, pg. 1605
FERRO (THAILAND) CO. LTD.—Ferro Corporation; *U.S. Public*, pg. 619
GEC ALSTHOM-INTERMAGNETICS S.A.—Alcatel Alsthom Compagnie Generale D'Electricite; *Int'l*, pg. 56
GEC ALSTHOM-INTERMAGNETICS S.A.—Intermagnetics General Corporation; *U.S. Public*, pg. 894
GRUPO INDUSTRIAL MORGAN, S.A. DE C.V.—Morgan Crucible Co. Plc; *Int'l*, pg. 895
INDUSTRIAL CERAMICS, INC.; *U.S. Private*, pg. 560
KNOX PORCELAIN CORP.—Carpenter Technology Corporation; *U.S. Public*, pg. 308
KYOCERA CORPORATION; *Int'l*, pg. 775
LAPP INSULATOR COMPANY—Great American Management & Investment, Inc.; *U.S. Private*, pg. 473
MORGAN MATROC INC.-EAST COAST SALES DIVISION—Morgan Crucible Co. Plc; *Int'l*, pg. 893
NATIONAL BERYLLIA DIV.—Tokuyama Corporation; *Int'l*, pg. 1394
PERMALI LTD.—BTR plc; *Int'l*, pg. 126
PORCELAIN METALS CORP.; *U.S. Private*, pg. 876
PORCELAIN PRODUCTS—Carpenter Technology Corporation; *U.S. Public*, pg. 308
SPS TECHNOLOGIES, INC.; *U.S. Public*, pg. 1419
TALLEY INDUSTRIES, INC.—Carpenter Technology Corporation; *U.S. Public*, pg. 307

3269 — POTTERY PRODUCTS, NEC

AMERICAN GREETINGS CORPORATION; *U.S. Public*, pg. 77
APPLAUSE INC.; *U.S. Private*, pg. 78
BRITTANY CORPORATION; *U.S. Private*, pg. 169
CABOT CORPORATION; *U.S. Public*, pg. 288
COPCO—Wilton Industries, Inc.; *U.S. Private*, pg. 1182
HAEGER INDUSTRIES, INC.; *U.S. Private*, pg. 493
HAEGER POTTERIES, INC.—Haeger Industries, Inc.; *U.S. Private*, pg. 493
HAEGER POTTERIES OF MACOMB, INC.—Haeger Industries, Inc.; *U.S. Private*, pg. 493
JIFFY PRODUCTS INTERNATIONAL LTD.; *Int'l*, pg. 706
KYOCERA CORPORATION; *Int'l*, pg. 775
THE LONGABERGER COMPANY; *U.S. Private*, pg. 675
MARYLAND RIBBON COMPANY—C.M. Offray & Son Inc.; *U.S. Private*, pg. 812
MATTHEY BEYRAND & CIE S.A.—Johnson Matthey Public Limited Company; *Int'l*, pg. 714
MCCORMICK DISTILLING CO.; *U.S. Private*, pg. 720
MIRRO COMPANY—Newell Co.; *U.S. Public*, pg. 1177
MORGAN MATROC INC.-EAST COAST SALES DIVISION—Morgan Crucible Co. Plc; *Int'l*, pg. 893
NEW ZEALAND FIBRE GLASS—International Paper Company; *U.S. Public*, pg. 904
NORDIC WARE—Northland Aluminum Products, Inc.; *U.S. Private*, pg. 806
NORTHLAND ALUMINUM PRODUCTS, INC.; *U.S. Private*, pg. 805
C.M. OFFRAY & SON—C.M. Offray & Son Inc.; *U.S. Private*, pg. 812
C.M. OFFRAY & SON INC.; *U.S. Private*, pg. 812
PPC, INC.—Thomas Nelson Inc.; *U.S. Public*, pg. 1168
THE PAYNE INVESTMENT COMPANY—Brittany Corporation; *U.S. Private*, pg. 169
THE PFALTZGRAFF CO.; *U.S. Private*, pg. 860
THE PFALTZGRAFF CO.—The Pfaltzgraff Co.; *U.S. Private*, *pg. 860*
PORCELAIN METALS CORP.; *U.S. Private*, pg. 876
REMA BAKEWARE—Newell Co.; *U.S. Public*, pg. 1177
ROBINSON-RANSBOTTOM POTTERY COMPANY—Brittany Corporation; *U.S. Private*, pg. 169
ROSS & CATHERALL CERAMICS LIMITED—Vickers PLC; *Int'l*, pg. 1467
ROWOCO—Wilton Industries, Inc.; *U.S. Private*, pg. 1182
ROYAL COPENHAGEN A/S; *Int'l*, pg. 1134
UNITED DESIGN CORPORATION; *U.S. Private*, pg. 1121

3271 — CONCRETE BLOCK & BRICK

ADAMS PRODUCTS COMPANY—CRH, plc; *Int'l*, pg. 242
AMCOR, INC.—CRH, plc; *Int'l*, pg. 242
AMERON INTERNATIONAL CORPORATION; *U.S. Public*, pg. 98
ATLAS STONE PRODUCTS LIMITED—Hanson PLC; *Int'l*, pg. 592
BIG RIVER INDUSTRIES—CRH, plc; *Int'l*, pg. 242
BRISTOL CONCRETE PRODS. CORP.—Marley PLC; *Int'l*, pg. 843
BROOKLYNS LIMITED—Tarmac plc; *Int'l*, pg. 1355
CRH, PLC; *Int'l*, pg. 242
CSR AMERICA INC.—CSR Limited; *Int'l*, pg. 245
CSR CENTRAL—CSR Limited; *Int'l*, pg. 245
CSR FLORIDA—CSR Limited; *Int'l*, pg. 245
CSR LIMITED; *Int'l*, pg. 245
CALLANAN INDUSTRIES, INC.—CRH, plc; *Int'l*, pg. 242
CARSON INDUSTRIES—Millhouse Group; *U.S. Private*, pg. 748
CONTRACTORS SUPPLIES, INC.; *U.S. Private*, pg. 270
DEMCO INC.; *U.S. Private*, pg. 323
ESSROC MATERIALS INC.—Ciments Francais; *Int'l*, pg. 292
EVANS INDUSTRIES, INC.; *U.S. Private*, pg. 385
FEATHERLITE BUILDING PRODUCTS OPERATION—Justin Industries, Inc.; *U.S. Public*, pg. 936
FISCHER COMPANIES; *U.S. Private*, pg. 408
FLORIDA ROCK INDUSTRIES, INC.; *U.S. Public*, pg. 655
GLEN-GERY CORPORATION—Ibstock Plc; *Int'l*, pg. 658
HC&D DIV.—Ameron International Corporation; *U.S. Public*, *pg. 99*
HAWAIIAN DREDGING & CONSTRUCTION COMPANY—Dillingham Construction Corporation; *U.S. Private*, pg. 333
E.P. HENRY CORPORATION; *U.S. Private*, pg. 522
IMPERIA BROS., INC.; *U.S. Private*, pg. 558
K.F. JACOBSON CO.—R.B. Pamplin Corp.; *U.S. Private*, pg. 836
JUSTIN INDUSTRIES, INC.; *U.S. Public*, pg. 936
KALKZANDSTEENFABRIEK HOOGDONK B.V.—Scancem AB; *Int'l*, pg. 1199
KALKZANDSTEENFABRIEK RIJSBERGEN B.V.—Scancem AB; *Int'l*, pg. 1199
LAFARGE CANADA INC.—Lafarge S.A.; *Int'l*, pg. 789
LOUISIANA INDUSTRIES DIV.—Texas Industries, Inc.; *U.S. Public*, pg. 1585
MILLHOUSE GROUP; *U.S. Private*, pg. 748
MITSUI HARBOUR & URBAN CONSTRUCTION CO., LTD.—Mitsui & Co., Ltd.; *Int'l*, pg. 877
NORCEM INDUSTRIER—Aker Raj Asa; *Int'l*, pg. 42
THE OCKLEY BRICK CO. LTD.—Blue Circle Industries PLC; *Int'l*, pg. 197
ORCO BLOCK COMPANY; *U.S. Private*, pg. 819
PGH BRICKS PTY. LTD.—BTR plc; *Int'l*, pg. 128
PGH EUREKA CERAMICS—BTR plc; *Int'l*, pg. 128
PLASTICRETE BLOCK & SUPPLY CORP.; *U.S. Private*, pg. 871
QANBAR DYWIDAG PRECAST CONCRETE LTD.—Dyckerhoff & Widmann AG; *Int'l*, pg. 425
READYMIX QATAR WLL & THE QUATAR QUARRY CO. WLL—Redland PLC; *Int'l*, pg. 1092
RINKER MATERIALS CORP.—CSR Limited; *Int'l*, pg. 246
ROSS ISLAND SAND & GRAVEL CO., INC.—R.B. Pamplin Corp.; *U.S. Private*, pg. 836
SCANCEM AB; *Int'l*, pg. 1198
N.V. SILICAATSTEEN—Scancem AB; *Int'l*, pg. 1199
SSANGYONG BUSINESS GROUP; *Int'l*, pg. 1291
STEENFABRIEK BOUDEWIJN B.V.—Scancem AB; *Int'l*, pg. 1199
TARMAC AMERICA, INC.—Tarmac plc; *Int'l*, pg. 1355
TARMAC TOPBLOCK LIMITED—Tarmac plc; *Int'l*, pg. 1355
TERRE HILL CONCRETE PRODUCTS, INC.; *U.S. Private*, pg. 1077
TEXAS INDUSTRIES, INC.; *U.S. Public*, pg. 1585
TRI-STATE CONCRETE PRODUCTS CO., INC.—Marley PLC; *Int'l*, pg. 843
UTILITY VAULT CO., INC.—CRH, plc; *Int'l*, pg. 242
YORK BUILDING PRODUCTS CO., INC.; *U.S. Private*, pg. 1196

3272 — CONCRETE PRODUCTS, EXCEPT BLOCK & BRICK

ARC CENTRAL—Hanson PLC; *Int'l*, pg. 592
ARC LIMITED—Hanson PLC; *Int'l*, pg. 592
ARC NORTHERN—Hanson PLC; *Int'l*, pg. 592
ARC PIPES LIMITED—Hanson PLC; *Int'l*, pg. 592
ABETONG AMERICA INC.—Scancem AB; *Int'l*, pg. 1199
ABETONG MILJO AB—Scancem AB; *Int'l*, pg. 1199
ABETONG PREFAB AB—Scancem AB; *Int'l*, pg. 1199
AKER RAJ ASA; *Int'l*, pg. 41
AMERICAN AGGREGATES CORP.—CSR Limited; *Int'l*, pg. 245
AMERICAN LIMESTONE CO.—Asarco Incorporated; *U.S. Public*, pg. 138
AMERICAN PIPE AND CONSTRUCTION INTERNATIONAL—Ameron International Corporation; *U.S. Public*, pg. 99
AMERICAN PRECAST CONCRETE, INC.; *U.S. Private*, pg. 60
AMERON INTERNATIONAL CORPORATION; *U.S. Public*, pg. 98
AMERON POLE PRODUCTS & SYSTEMS—Ameron International Corporation; *U.S. Public*, pg. 99
AMERON SAUDI ARABIA, LTD.—Ameron International Corporation; *U.S. Public*, pg. 99
ASLAND S.A.—Lafarge S.A.; *Int'l*, pg. 790
ASSOCIATED CONCRETE PRODUCTS, INC.—For Better Living, Inc.; *U.S. Private*, pg. 417
ASSOCIATED PLASTICS, INC.—For Better Living, Inc.; *U.S. Private*, pg. 417
ASSOCIATED SAND & GRAVEL CO., INC.—CSR Limited; *Int'l*, pg. 245
ASSOCIATION SAND & GRAVEL—CSR Limited; *Int'l*, pg. 246
ATLANTA MFG. FACILITY—L.M. Scofield Company; *U.S. Private*, pg. 976
ATLANTIC CONCRETE PRODUCTS, INC.; *U.S. Private*, pg. 95
ATLAS BUILDING SYSTEMS, INC.—Scancem AB; *Int'l*, pg. 1201
B&C DANMARK BETONTAGSTENSVAERKENE A/S—Redland PLC; *Int'l*, pg. 1092
BARDON (ENGLAND) LTD.—Bardon Group PLC; *Int'l*, pg. 166
BASALT PRECAST DIVISION—Dillingham Construction Corporation; *U.S. Private*, pg. 333
BEAZER GROUP PLC; *Int'l*, pg. 181
BETAO LIZ S.A.—Lafarge S.A.; *Int'l*, pg. 790
BETONGINDUSTRI AB—Scancem AB; *Int'l*, pg. 1199
BLUE CIRCLE INDUSTRIES PLC; *Int'l*, pg. 197
BORAL CONCRETE PRODUCTS INC.—Boral Limited; *Int'l*, pg. 203
BORAL LIMITED; *Int'l*, pg. 203
THE BRAAS GROUP—Redland PLC; *Int'l*, pg. 1091
BRAMAC DACHSYSTEME INTERNATIONAL GMBH—Redland PLC; *Int'l*, pg. 1092
BRAMAC KFT—Redland PLC; *Int'l*, pg. 1092
BRASWELL CONCRETE PRODUCTS, INC.—Holderbank Financiere Glaris Ltd.; *Int'l*, pg. 628
BRASWELL INDUSTRIES—Holderbank Financiere Glaris Ltd.; *Int'l*, pg. 628
BROOKLYNS LIMITED—Tarmac plc; *Int'l*, pg. 1355
C.I. HOLDINGS BERHAD—Redland PLC; *Int'l*, pg. 1092
THE CPAC CONCRETE PRODUCTS CO., LTD.—The Siam Cement Public Company Limited; *Int'l*, pg. 1237
THE CPAC ROOF TILE CO., LTD.—The Siam Cement Public Company Limited; *Int'l*, pg. 1237
CRH, PLC; *Int'l*, pg. 242
CSR AMERICA INC.—CSR Limited; *Int'l*, pg. 245
CSR LIMITED; *Int'l*, pg. 245
CADILLAC PIPE—Premarc Corporation; *U.S. Private*, pg. 881
CARDER CONCRETE PRODUCTS CO.; *U.S. Private*, pg. 208
CAROLINA STEEL CORPORATION; *U.S. Private*, pg. 214
CARSON INDUSTRIES—Millhouse Group; *U.S. Private*, pg. 748
CARTER HOLT HARVEY ROOFING INTERNATIONAL—International Paper Company; *U.S. Public*, pg. 904
CEMEX, S.A. DE C.V.; *Int'l*, pg. 278
CHOCTAW, INC.; *U.S. Private*, pg. 238
CLARK PACIFIC; *U.S. Private*, pg. 243
CONCRETE INDUSTRIES SECTOR—Fletcher Challenge Limited; *Int'l*, pg. 495
THE CONCRETE PRODUCTS AND AGGREGATE INDUSTRY CO., LTD.—The Siam Cement Public Company Limited; *Int'l*, pg. 1237
CONCRETE PRODUCTS GROUP—Southdown, Inc.; *U.S. Public*, pg. 1489
CONCRETE TECHNOLOGY CORP.; *U.S. Private*, pg. 262
COTTO COPERTURE S.P.A.—Redland PLC; *Int'l*, pg. 1092
COVERLAND S.A.—Redland PLC; *Int'l*, pg. 1092
THE CRETEX COMPANIES; *U.S. Private*, pg. 289
CUSTODIS-COTTRELL, INC.—Air & Water Technologies Corporation; *U.S. Public*, pg. 29
DALWORTH CONCRETE PRODUCTS, INC.—For Better Living, Inc.; *U.S. Private*, pg. 417
DAYTON SUPERIOR CANADA LTD.—Ripplewood Holdings L.L.C.; *U.S. Private*, pg. 932
DAYTON SUPERIOR CORPORATION—Ripplewood Holdings L.L.C.; *U.S. Private*, pg. 931
DEKALB CONCRETE PRODUCTS, INC.—For Better Living, Inc.; *U.S. Private*, pg. 417
DEMCO INC.; *U.S. Private*, pg. 323
DIRECTIONAL FURNITURE—CF Group; *U.S. Private*, pg. 193
DONLEY'S, INC.; *U.S. Private*, pg. 340
EMCO LIMITED; *Int'l*, pg. 452
EUROC BETON AB—Scancem AB; *Int'l*, pg. 1199
FELS-WERKE GMBH—Preussag AG; *Int'l*, pg. 1069
FIBREBOND CORPORATION; *U.S. Private*, pg. 402
FLORIDA MINING & MATERIALS CONCRETE CORP.—Southdown, Inc.; *U.S. Public*, pg. 1489
FOR BETTER LIVING, INC.; *U.S. Private*, pg. 417
FRITZ INDUSTRIES INC.; *U.S. Private*, pg. 429
GAF PREMIUM PRODUCTS, INC.—GAF Corporation; *U.S. Private*, pg. 433
GSW INC.; *Int'l*, pg. 538
GARY CONCRETE PRODUCTS INC.—Zurn Industries, Inc.; *U.S. Public*, pg. 1795
GIFFORD-HILL-AMERICAN, INC.—Ameron International Corporation; *U.S. Public*, pg. 99
GIFFORD-HILL CONCRETE PRODUCTS INC.—Hanson PLC; *Int'l*, pg. 593

GRAND RIVER INFRASTRUCTURE, INC.—Premarc Corporation; *U.S. Private*, pg. 881
HC&D DIV.—Ameron International Corporation; *U.S. Public*, pg. 99
HANIEL BAUSTOFF-INDUSTRIE GMBH—Franz Haniel & Cie, GmbH; *Int'l*, pg. 592
HANIEL BAUSTOFF-INDUSTRIE GMBH—Philipp Holzmann AG; *Int'l*, pg. 633
HAWAIIAN DREDGING & CONSTRUCTION COMPANY—Dillingham Construction Corporation; *U.S. Private*, pg. 333
HEMPT BROTHERS, INC.; *U.S. Private*, pg. 521
HEPWORTH PLC; *Int'l*, pg. 614
HIGH INDUSTRIES, INC.; *U.S. Private*, pg. 528
HYDRO CONDUIT CORP.—CSR Limited; *Int'l*, pg. 245
ICOPAL A/S; *Int'l*, pg. 658
IMBAU INDUSTRIELLES BAUEN GMBH—Philipp Holzmann AG; *Int'l*, pg. 633
INDUSTRIAS TRANSFORMADORAS DEL CEMENTO ETERNIT SA—Redland PLC; *Int'l*, pg. 1092
K.F. JACOBSON CO.—R.B. Pamplin Corp.; *U.S. Private*, pg. 836
A/S JOTUL INDUSTRIER—Aker Raj Asa; *Int'l*, pg. 42
JUSTIN INDUSTRIES, INC.; *U.S. Public*, pg. 936
KLOECKNER DURILIT GMBH—Klockner-Werke AG; *Int'l*, pg. 737
LAFARGE CIMENTS—Lafarge S.A.; *Int'l*, pg. 788
LAFARGE CORPORATION—Lafarge S.A.; *Int'l*, pg. 788
LAFARGE S.A.; *Int'l*, pg. 788
LINEAR DYNAMICS INC.; *U.S. Private*, pg. 668
LOUISIANA INDUSTRIES DIV.—Texas Industries, Inc.; *U.S. Public*, pg. 1585
MAC S.P.A., MODERN ADVANCED CONCRETE—Novartis AG; *Int'l*, pg. 983
MARSH PRODUCTS CO.—Premarc Corporation; *U.S. Private*, pg. 881
MARTIN INDUSTRIES, INC. (AL); *U.S. Private*, pg. 709
MASTRAK SDN BHD—Scancem AB; *Int'l*, pg. 1199
MILES SAND & GRAVEL COMPANY; *U.S. Private*, pg. 745
MILLHOUSE GROUP; *U.S. Private*, pg. 748
MODERN CONCRETE SEPTIC TANK COMPANY; *U.S. Private*, pg. 754
MONIER INC.—Redland PLC; *Int'l*, pg. 1091
P.T. MONIER INDONESIA—Redland PLC; *Int'l*, pg. 1091
NATIONAL CONCRETE PRODUCTS COMPANY; *U.S. Private*, pg. 781
NATIONAL CONSOLIDATED; *Int'l*, pg. 908
NIPPON MONIER CO. LTD.—Redland PLC; *Int'l*, pg. 1092
NORCEM INDUSTRIER—Aker Raj Asa; *Int'l*, pg. 42
THE NORTHUMBERLAND CONCRETE COMPANY LIMITED—Tarmac plc; *Int'l*, pg. 1355
P.G. BELL DIV.—Jannock Limited; *Int'l*, pg. 698
PERMACRETE PRODUCTS CORPORATION—CSR Limited; *Int'l*, pg. 245
PHELPS TOINTON INC.; *U.S. Private*, pg. 860
THE PILOT CORPORATION; *Int'l*, pg. 1057
PLASTICRETE BLOCK & SUPPLY CORP.; *U.S. Private*, pg. 871
PRECON AB—Scancem AB; *Int'l*, pg. 1199
PREMARC CORPORATION; *U.S. Private*, pg. 881
PRICE BROTHERS CO.; *U.S. Private*, pg. 883
THE QUIKSET ORGANIZATION—For Better Living, Inc.; *U.S. Private*, pg. 417
RBB NV—Redland PLC; *Int'l*, pg. 1092
RAVO INTERNATIONAL—Federal Signal Corporation; *U.S. Public*, pg. 617
REDLAND DAKPRODUKTEN B.V.—Redland PLC; *Int'l*, pg. 1093
REDLAND IBERICA S.A.—Redland PLC; *Int'l*, pg. 1093
REDLAND PLC; *Int'l*, pg. 1090
REDLAND READYMIX LTD.—Redland PLC; *Int'l*, pg. 1091
REDLAND ROOF TILES LTD.—Redland PLC; *Int'l*, pg. 1091
REDLAND TILE & BRICK—Redland PLC; *Int'l*, pg. 1091
CIE. RHODANIENNE DE DEVELOPPEMENT—Lafarge S.A.; *Int'l*, pg. 788
RINKER MATERIALS CORP.—CSR Limited; *Int'l*, pg. 246
RITCHIE CORPORATION; *U.S. Private*, pg. 933
ROCKVILLE CRUSHED STONE, INC.—Bardon Group PLC; *Int'l*, pg. 166
ROSS ISLAND SAND & GRAVEL CO., INC.—R.B. Pamplin Corp.; *U.S. Private*, pg. 836
S&G PRESTRESS CO.—Florida Rock Industries, Inc.; *U.S. Public*, pg. 656
SAUDI ARABIA CONCRETE PRODUCTS LTD.—Ameron International Corporation; *U.S. Public*, pg. 99
SCANCEM AB; *Int'l*, pg. 1198
L.M. SCOFIELD COMPANY; *U.S. Private*, pg. 976
SCORI—Lafarge S.A.; *Int'l*, pg. 788
THE SIAM CEMENT PUBLIC COMPANY LIMITED; *Int'l*, pg. 1237
SIKA CORPORATION—Sika Finanz AG; *Int'l*, pg. 1249
SIMIA AB—Scancem AB; *Int'l*, pg. 1199
SIPLAST INC.—Icopal a/s; *Int'l*, pg. 659
SIPLAST S.A.—Icopal a/s; *Int'l*, pg. 659
SKANSKA AB; *Int'l*, pg. 1260
SKANSKA PREFAB AB—Skanska AB; *Int'l*, pg. 1261
JOSEF SKIPIOL STRASSENBAUSTOFFE GMBH & CO. KG—Philipp Holzmann AG; *Int'l*, pg. 633
THE SOMERSET GROUP, INC.; *U.S. Public*, pg. 1484
SUMITOMO METAL MINING CO., LTD.; *Int'l*, pg. 1316
TXI STRUCTURAL PRODUCTS, INC.—Texas Industries, Inc.; *U.S. Public*, pg. 1585
TAMMS INDUSTRIES—Laporte plc; *Int'l*, pg. 803
TAMMS INDUSTRIES CO.—Laporte plc; *Int'l*, pg. 803
TARCO; *U.S. Private*, pg. 1068
TARMAC AMERICA, INC.—Tarmac plc; *Int'l*, pg. 1355
A. TEICHERT & SON, INC.; *U.S. Private*, pg. 1072
TEMCO FIREPLACE PRODUCTS, INC. (PERRIS)—Temtex Industries Inc.; *U.S. Public*, pg. 1576
TERRE HILL CONCRETE PRODUCTS, INC.; *U.S. Private*, pg. 1077
TEXAS INDUSTRIES, INC.; *U.S. Public*, pg. 1585
TOLMEX S.A. DE C.V.—Cemex, S.A. de C.V.; *Int'l*, pg. 278
TRANSIT MIX CONCRETE CO.—Continental Materials Corporation; *U.S. Public*, pg. 441
TRANSMIX CORPORATION—Southdown, Inc.; *U.S. Public*, pg. 1489
USG INTERIORS, INC.—USG Corporation; *U.S. Public*, pg. 1660
VERMICULITE INDUSTRIES LTD.—Ssangyong Business Group; *Int'l*, pg. 1293
WEHRUNG FAMILY HOME CENTER—Modern Concrete Septic Tank Company; *U.S. Private*, pg. 754
WYOMING CONCRETE PRODUCTS CO.—Carder Concrete Products Co.; *U.S. Private*, pg. 208

3273 — READY-MIXED CONCRETE

ALRASHID-ABETONG CO. LTD.—Scancem AB; *Int'l*, pg. 1199
ASARCO INCORPORATED; *U.S. Public*, pg. 137
BACCO CONSTRUCTION CO.; *U.S. Private*, pg. 109
BARDON GROUP PLC; *Int'l*, pg. 166
BARLETTA MATERIALS & CONSTRUCTION; *U.S. Private*, pg. 116
BEAZER GROUP PLC; *Int'l*, pg. 181
BERKS PRODUCTS CORPORATION; *U.S. Private*, pg. 136
BLUE CIRCLE INDUSTRIES PLC; *Int'l*, pg. 197
BLUE CIRCLE MATERIALS, INC.—Blue Circle Industries PLC; *Int'l*, pg. 198
BORAL LIMITED; *Int'l*, pg. 203
BORAL RESOURCES LTD.—Boral Limited; *Int'l*, pg. 203
BRECKENRIDGE MATERIAL COMPANY; *U.S. Private*, pg. 166
CALMAT CO. OF ARIZONA—CalMat Co.; *U.S. Public*, pg. 295
CALMAT CO. OF NEW MEXICO—CalMat Co.; *U.S. Public*, pg. 295
CALMAT OF CENTRAL CALIFORNIA—CalMat Co.; *U.S. Public*, pg. 295
CANTON AGGREGATE DIVISION—Central Allied Enterprises; *U.S. Private*, pg. 222
CARDINAL CONCRETE CO.—Florida Rock Industries, Inc.; *U.S. Public*, pg. 656
CEMEX, S.A. DE C.V.; *Int'l*, pg. 278
CENTEX CORPORATION; *U.S. Public*, pg. 322
CENTEX MATERIALS, INC.—Centex Corporation; *U.S. Public*, pg. 322
CENTRAL ALLIED ENTERPRISES; *U.S. Private*, pg. 222
CENTURY CONCRETE, INC.—Ash Grove Cement Company; *U.S. Private*, pg. 88
CHAMPION, INC.; *U.S. Private*, pg. 228
CHICHIBU ONODA CEMENT CORPORATION; *Int'l*, pg. 284
CLEMS READY-MIX—Holderbank Financiere Glaris Ltd.; *Int'l*, pg. 629
COMMERCIAL PRODUCTS, INC.—The Dickerson Group, Inc.; *U.S. Private*, pg. 331
THE CONCRETE PRODUCTS AND AGGREGATE CO., LTD.—The Siam Cement Public Company Limited; *Int'l*, pg. 1238
CONTINENTAL MATERIALS CORPORATION; *U.S. Public*, pg. 441
CONTRACTORS SUPPLIES, INC.; *U.S. Private*, pg. 270
CUSTOM CONCRETE—Holderbank Financiere Glaris Ltd.; *Int'l*, pg. 629
DELMON READY MIXED CONCRETE & PRODUCTS CO. W.L.L. (BAHRAIN)—Redland PLC; *Int'l*, pg. 1092
DUFFERIN-CUSTOM CONCRETE GROUP—Holderbank Financiere Glaris Ltd.; *Int'l*, pg. 628
EUROC BETONG & BALLAST AB—Scancem AB; *Int'l*, pg. 1200
FLORIDA ROCK INDUSTRIES, INC.; *U.S. Public*, pg. 655
FORDYCE CONCRETE CO., INC.—Ash Grove Cement Company; *U.S. Private*, pg. 88
JOHN FYFE LTD.—Bardon Group PLC; *Int'l*, pg. 166
GENERAL SHALE PRODUCTS CORP.—Marley PLC; *Int'l*, pg. 843
HARDAWAY CONCRETE CO., INC.; *U.S. Private*, pg. 501
HECK INDUSTRIES; *U.S. Private*, pg. 519
K.F. JACOBSON CO.—R.B. Pamplin Corp.; *U.S. Private*, pg. 836
LEGRAND JOHNSON CONSTRUCTION CO.; *U.S. Private*, pg. 591
P.J. KEATING COMPANY; *U.S. Private*, pg. 610
LAFARGE CIMENTS—Lafarge S.A.; *Int'l*, pg. 788
EDWARD C. LEVY CO.; *U.S. Private*, pg. 664
LONE STAR INDUSTRIES, INC.; *U.S. Public*, pg. 1012
LOUISIANA INDUSTRIES DIV.—Texas Industries, Inc.; *U.S. Public*, pg. 1585
MATERIAL SERVICE CORP.—General Dynamics Corporation; *U.S. Public*, pg. 709
MATHEWS READYMIX, INC.—Centex Corporation; *U.S. Public*, pg. 323
MCCOWAN MOBILE MIX—Holderbank Financiere Glaris Ltd.; *Int'l*, pg. 629
MCNEILUS COMPANIES; *U.S. Private*, pg. 725
H.B. MELLOTT ESTATE, INC.; *U.S. Private*, pg. 730
NORCEM BETONG A/S—Aker Raj Asa; *Int'l*, pg. 42
ONODA NORTHWEST, INC.—Chichibu Onoda Cement Corporation; *Int'l*, pg. 284
PALOMAR TRANSIT MIX CO.—CalMat Co.; *U.S. Public*, pg. 296
PETERBOROUGH PORT HOPE READY MIX—Holderbank Financiere Glaris Ltd.; *Int'l*, pg. 629
PIONEER CONCRETE OF AMERICA—Pioneer International Ltd.; *Int'l*, pg. 1058
PIONEER CONCRETE OF TEXAS, INC.—Pioneer International Ltd.; *Int'l*, pg. 1058
PIONEER INTERNATIONAL LTD.; *Int'l*, pg. 1058
PRE-MIX CONCRETE CO.—H.G. Fenton Material Company; *U.S. Private*, pg. 400
QANBAR STEETLEY (SAUDI) LIMITED—Redland PLC; *Int'l*, pg. 1092
READYMIX GULF LTD.—Redland PLC; *Int'l*, pg. 1092
READYMIX MUSCAT LLC & PREMIX LLC—Redland PLC; *Int'l*, pg. 1092
READYMIX MUSCAT LLC & PREMIX LLC—Royal Dutch/Shell Group of Companies; *Int'l*, pg. 1136
REDLAND GRANULATS SA—Redland PLC; *Int'l*, pg. 1093
REDLAND STONE PRODUCTS CO.—Redland PLC; *Int'l*, pg. 1091
ROBATOR AB—Scancem AB; *Int'l*, pg. 1199
ROCK HILL MATERIALS COMPANY; *U.S. Private*, pg. 938
ROGERS GROUP INC.; *U.S. Private*, pg. 939
ROSS ISLAND SAND & GRAVEL CO., INC.—R.B. Pamplin Corp.; *U.S. Private*, pg. 836
S&G CONCRETE CO.—Florida Rock Industries, Inc.; *U.S. Public*, pg. 656
SADLER MATERIALS CORP.—Florida Rock Industries, Inc.; *U.S. Public*, pg. 656
SAKRETE, INC.; *U.S. Private*, pg. 961
SCANCEM AB; *Int'l*, pg. 1198
THE SIAM CEMENT PUBLIC COMPANY LIMITED; *Int'l*, pg. 1237
SUPER CONCRETE CORP.—Bardon Group PLC; *Int'l*, pg. 166
TARMAC AMERICA, INC.—Tarmac plc; *Int'l*, pg. 1355
TEXAS INDUSTRIES, INC.; *U.S. Public*, pg. 1585
THOMPSON-MCCULLY CO.; *U.S. Private*, pg. 1083
TOLMEX S.A. DE C.V.—Cemex, S.A. de C.V.; *Int'l*, pg. 278
TRANSIT MIX CONCRETE CO.—Continental Materials Corporation; *U.S. Public*, pg. 441
VIRGINIA CONCRETE CO., INC.—Florida Rock Industries, Inc.; *U.S. Public*, pg. 656
VULCAN MATERIALS COMPANY; *U.S. Public*, pg. 1725
WESTERN MOBILE INC.—Redland PLC; *Int'l*, pg. 1091
WESTERN MOBILE KANSAS INC.—Redland PLC; *Int'l*, pg. 1091
WILLIAMS BROS.—Blue Circle Industries PLC; *Int'l*, pg. 198

3274 — LIME

APG LIME CORP.—A.P. Green Industries, Inc.; *U.S. Public*, pg. 761
A.P.G. LIME CORP.—A.P. Green Industries, Inc.; *U.S. Public*, pg. 761
ARKANSAS LIME CO.—United States Lime & Minerals; *U.S. Public*, pg. 1685
ASH GROVE CEMENT COMPANY; *U.S. Private*, pg. 87
BAUSTOFFWERKE DURMERSHEIM GMBH & CO. KG—Heidelberger Zement A.G.; *Int'l*, pg. 606
CALCIA—Ciments Francais; *Int'l*, pg. 292
CARBIDE PRODUCTS—The Carbide/Graphite Group, Inc.; *U.S. Public*, pg. 304
CORSON LIME COMPANY—United States Lime & Minerals; *U.S. Public*, pg. 1685
DRAVO CORPORATION; *U.S. Public*, pg. 527
DRAVO LIME COMPANY—Dravo Corporation; *U.S. Public*, pg. 527
KALKWERK D. FUNK GMBH & CO. KG—Heidelberger Zement A.G.; *Int'l*, pg. 606
GOLDCORP INC.—CSA Management Inc.; *Int'l*, pg. 243
A.P. GREEN INDUSTRIES, INC.; *U.S. Public*, pg. 761
HAVELOCK LIME DIV.—CSA Management Inc.; *Int'l*, pg. 243
S.A. INDUSTRIAS VOTORANTIM; *Int'l*, pg. 677
KLOECKNER DURILIT GMBH—Klockner-Werke AG; *Int'l*, pg. 737
MARBLEHEAD LIME CO.—General Dynamics Corporation; *U.S. Public*, pg. 709
MARTIN MARIETTA MAGNESIA SPECIALTIES, INC.—Lockheed Martin Corporation; *U.S. Public*, pg. 1007
MARTIN MARIETTA MATERIALS, INC.—Lockheed Martin Corporation; *U.S. Public*, pg. 1007
MISSISSIPPI LIME CO.; *U.S. Private*, pg. 753
PUERTO RICAN CEMENT CO., INC.; *U.S. Public*, pg. 1341
REDLAND OHIO INC.—Redland PLC; *Int'l*, pg. 1091
SCANCEM AB; *Int'l*, pg. 1198
SOLVAY OSTERREICH AG—Solvay S.A.; *Int'l*, pg. 1280
TEXAS LIME CO.—United States Lime & Minerals; *U.S. Public*, pg. 1685
UNITED STATES LIME & MINERALS; *U.S. Public*, pg. 1684
VULCAN MATERIALS COMPANY; *U.S. Public*, pg. 1725

3275 — GYPSUM PRODUCTS

BPB INDUSTRIES PLC; *Int'l*, pg. 122
THE BEAVER WOOD FIBER COMPANY LTD.—Georgia-Pacific Corporation; *U.S. Public*, pg. 739
BETECNA—Lafarge S.A.; *Int'l*, pg. 789
BORAL AUSTRALIAN GYPSUM LTD.—Boral Limited; *Int'l*, pg. 203
BORAL GYPSUM INC.—Boral Limited; *Int'l*, pg. 203
BRITISH GYPSUM LTD.—BPB Industries PLC; *Int'l*, pg. 122
CGC INC.—USG Corporation; *U.S. Public*, pg. 1660
CSR LIMITED; *Int'l*, pg. 245
CELOTEX CORPORATION; *U.S. Private*, pg. 221
CENTEX AMERICAN GYPSUM CO.—Centex Corporation; *U.S. Public*, pg. 322
CENTEX CORPORATION; *U.S. Public*, pg. 322
CERESIT GMBH—Henkel KGaA; *Int'l*, pg. 609
CHAMBERS PACKAGING—BPB Industries PLC; *Int'l*, pg. 123
THE COE MANUFACTURING COMPANY; *U.S. Private*, pg. 249
THE COE MFG. LTD.—The Coe Manufacturing Company; *U.S. Private*, pg. 249
CONGLETON BOARD—BPB Industries PLC; *Int'l*, pg. 123
DEITERMANN CHEMIEWERK GMBH & CO. K.G.—Heidelberger Zement A.G.; *Int'l*, pg. 606
ERSTE SALZBURGER GIPSWERKS-GESELLSCHAFT CHRISTIAN MOLDAN KG—Heidelberger Zement A.G.; *Int'l*, pg. 606
GEORGIA-PACIFIC CORPORATION; *U.S. Public*, pg. 735
GYPROC AB—BPB Industries PLC; *Int'l*, pg. 122

GYPROC AB—Scancem AB; *Int'l*, pg. 1200
GYPROC BALSTA PLANT—Scancem AB; *Int'l*, pg. 1200
GYPROC GIPSPLATEFABRIKK A/S—Scancem AB; *Int'l*, pg. 1200
GYPROC INSULATION LTD.—BPB Industries PLC; *Int'l*, pg. 123
GYPROC OY—Scancem AB; *Int'l*, pg. 1200
GYPSUM INDUSTRIES PLC.—BPB Industries PLC; *Int'l*, pg. 123
JAMES HARDIE GYPSUM WASHINGTON—James Hardie Industries Ltd.; *Int'l*, pg. 597
JAMES HARDIE USA—James Hardie Industries Ltd.; *Int'l*, pg. 597
HEIDELBERGER ZEMENT A.G.; *Int'l*, pg. 605
INDUSTRIAL ACOUSTICS COMPANY, INC.; *U.S. Public*, pg. 875
KARTONFABRIEK "DE EENDRACHT" N.V.—BPB Industries PLC; *Int'l*, pg. 123
LAFARGE PLATRESINTERNATIONAL—Lafarge S.A.; *Int'l*, pg. 789
LAFARGE PLATREUROPE S.A.—Lafarge S.A.; *Int'l*, pg. 788
LAFARGE S.A.; *Int'l*, pg. 788
LAFARGESSI SPA—Lafarge S.A.; *Int'l*, pg. 789
LAPORTE PLC; *Int'l*, pg. 801
LOUISIANA PACIFIC NORTHERN DIV.—Louisiana Pacific Corporation; *U.S. Public*, pg. 1015
MOY INSULATION LTD.—BPB Industries PLC; *Int'l*, pg. 123
NATIONAL GYPSUM COMPANY—Lafarge S.A.; *Int'l*, pg. 790
PLACOPLATRE S.A.—BPB Industries PLC; *Int'l*, pg. 123
REDLAND PLASTERBOARD HOLDINGS—Lafarge S.A.; *Int'l*, pg. 789
REPUBLIC GROUP INCORPORATED; *U.S. Public*, pg. 1378
RIGIPS AUSTRIA GMBH—BPB Industries PLC; *Int'l*, pg. 123
RIGIPS GMBH—BPB Industries PLC; *Int'l*, pg. 123
SCANCEM AB; *Int'l*, pg. 1198
THE SIAM GYPSUM INDUSTRY CO., LTD.—The Siam Cement Public Company Limited; *Int'l*, pg. 1238
TEMPLE-INLAND FOREST PRODUCTS CORP.-BUILDING PRODUCTS GROUP—Temple-Inland Inc.; *U.S. Public*, pg. 1575
TEMPLE-INLAND INC.; *U.S. Public*, pg. 1574
THAI UNION PAPER INDUSTRY CO., LTD.—The Siam Cement Public Company Limited; *Int'l*, pg. 1239
USG CORPORATION; *U.S. Public*, pg. 1660
UNITED STATES GYPSUM CO.—USG Corporation; *U.S. Public*, pg. 1660
WESTROC INDUSTRIES LIMITED—BPB Industries PLC; *Int'l*, pg. 123
WINSTONE WALLBOARDS LIMITED—Fletcher Challenge Limited; *Int'l*, pg. 495
YESO PANAMERICANO, S.A. DE C.V.—USG Corporation; *U.S. Public*, pg. 1660

3281 — CUT STONE & STONE PRODUCTS

BARDON (ENGLAND) LTD.—Bardon Group PLC; *Int'l*, pg. 166
BARDON GROUP PLC; *Int'l*, pg. 166
BAUSTOFFWERKE DURMERSHEIM GMBH & CO. KG—Heidelberger Zement A.G.; *Int'l*, pg. 606
CRH, PLC; *Int'l*, pg. 242
CAROLINA QUARRIES, INC.—Rock of Ages Corporation; *U.S. Public*, pg. 1396
GEORGIA STONE INDUSTRIES, INC.—New England Stone Industries, Inc.; *U.S. Private*, pg. 793
ICOPAL AB—Icopal a/s; *Int'l*, pg. 659
KELIM TOTO CO., LTD.—Toto Ltd.; *Int'l*, pg. 1410
KEYSTONE & CHILDS, INC.—Rock of Ages Corporation; *U.S. Public*, pg. 1396
KLOECKNER DURILIT GMBH—Klockner-Werke AG; *Int'l*, pg. 737
MARMORAN AG—Heidelberger Zement A.G.; *Int'l*, pg. 606
MATTHEWS INTERNATIONAL CORP.; *U.S. Public*, pg. 1059
MONROC, INC.; *U.S. Public*, pg. 1124
NATURAL STONE PRODUCTS LIMITED—Tarmac plc; *Int'l*, *pg. 1355*
NEW ENGLAND STONE INDUSTRIES, INC.; *U.S. Private*, pg. 793
PECKHAM INDUSTRIES, INC.; *U.S. Private*, pg. 846
PENNSYLVANIA GRANITE CORP.—Rock of Ages Corporation; *U.S. Public*, pg. 1396
ROCK OF AGES CANADA, INC.—Rock of Ages Corporation; *U.S. Public*, pg. 1396
ROCK OF AGES CORPORATION; *U.S. Public*, pg. 1396
ROCKVILLE CRUSHED STONE, INC.—Bardon Group PLC; *Int'l*, pg. 166
RYNONE MANUFACTURING CORPORATION; *U.S. Private*, pg. 953
SELLERSBURG STONE COMPANY, INC.—Gohmann Asphalt & Construction Inc.; *U.S. Private*, pg. 459
STARRETT GRANITE SURFACE PLATE DIVISION—The L.S. Starrett Company; *U.S. Public*, pg. 1511
THE L.S. STARRETT COMPANY; *U.S. Public*, pg. 1511
TARCO; *U.S. Private*, pg. 1068
YORK BUILDING PRODUCTS CO., INC.; *U.S. Private*, pg. 1196

3291 — ABRASIVE PRODUCTS

AHLSELL AB—Trelleborg AB; *Int'l*, pg. 1422
AMPLEX/SGNIC—Saint-Gobain; *Int'l*, pg. 1173
ARENDAL SMELTEVERCK A.S.—Saint-Gobain; *Int'l*, pg. 1174
AUSTRALIAN ABRASIVES PTY. LTD.—Saint-Gobain; *Int'l*, pg. 1174
BAYER CORPORATION/CONSUMER CARE DIVISION—Bayer AG; *Int'l*, pg. 173
CARBORUNDUM ABRASIVES INC./CARBORUNDUM ABRASIFS INC.—Saint-Gobain; *Int'l*, pg. 1174
CARBORUNDUM ABRASIVES NORTH AMERICA—Saint-Gobain; *Int'l*, pg. 1174
CLIPPER ABRASIVES INC.—Saint-Gobain; *Int'l*, pg. 1174
CONSTRUCTION & HOME IMPROVEMENT MARKETS DIVISION—3M; *U.S. Public*, pg. 1605
CURTIS-TOLEDO, INC.; *U.S. Private*, pg. 298
DIAMOND PRODUCTIONS, INC.; *U.S. Private*, pg. 330
ELKEM MATERIALS—Elkem ASA; *Int'l*, pg. 447
B. ELLIOTT PLC.; *Int'l*, pg. 448
ERVIN AMASTEEL DIV.—Ervin Industries, Inc.; *U.S. Private*, pg. 382
ERVIN INDUSTRIES, INC.; *U.S. Private*, pg. 382
EXOLON-ESK COMPANY; *U.S. Public*, pg. 600
THE EXOLON-ESK COMPANY OF CANADA LTD.—Exolon-Esk Company; *U.S. Public*, pg. 600
FAG AUSTRIA WAELZLAGER AG—FAG Group; *Int'l*, pg. 469
FAG GROUP; *Int'l*, pg. 468
FIELD NORTON (PVT.) LIMITED—Saint-Gobain; *Int'l*, pg. 1174
FOSECO PLC—Burmah Castrol plc; *Int'l*, pg. 234
G.E. SUPERABRASIVES—General Electric Company; *U.S. Public*, pg. 711
GARRYSON-INSLEY LTD.—B. Elliott plc.; *Int'l*, pg. 448
GLIT—Katy Industries, Inc.; *U.S. Public*, pg. 944
GRINDWELL NORTON LTD.—Saint-Gobain; *Int'l*, pg. 1174
HERKULESSTEINE GMBH—Dyckerhoff & Widmann AG; *Int'l*, pg. 423
HERMANN H.C. STARCK BERLIN GBMH & CO. KG—Bayer AG; *Int'l*, pg. 174
INTERNATIONAL STEEL WOOL CORPORATION—F.H. Bonn Company; *U.S. Private*, pg. 156
JACKSONLEA—Jason Incorporated; *U.S. Public*, pg. 924
JASON INCORPORATED; *U.S. Public*, pg. 923
KURE-NORTON CO., LTD.—Saint-Gobain; *Int'l*, pg. 1174
LONZA-WERKE GMBH—Alusuisse-Lonza Holding Ltd.; *Int'l*, pg. 67
METABO CORPORATION; *U.S. Private*, pg. 734
MINERALS TECHNOLOGIES, INC.; *U.S. Public*, pg. 1115
NICSAND, INC.; *U.S. Private*, pg. 799
NORTON ABRASIVES LIMITED—Saint-Gobain; *Int'l*, pg. 1174
NORTON A/S—Saint-Gobain; *Int'l*, pg. 1174
NORTON B.V.—Saint-Gobain; *Int'l*, pg. 1175
NORTON CANADA INC.—Saint-Gobain; *Int'l*, pg. 1175
NORTON CAPITAL INC. (CANADA)—Saint-Gobain; *Int'l*, pg. 1175
NORTON COMPANY—Saint-Gobain; *Int'l*, pg. 1173
NORTON DO NORDESTE S.A. INDUSTRIA E COMERCIO—Saint-Gobain; *Int'l*, pg. 1175
NORTON GMBH—Saint-Gobain; *Int'l*, pg. 1175
NORTON (NEW ZEALAND) LIMITED—Saint-Gobain; *Int'l*, pg. 1175
NORTON PIKE DIVISION—Saint-Gobain; *Int'l*, pg. 1176
NORTON PTE. LTD.—Saint-Gobain; *Int'l*, pg. 1175
NORTON PTY. LTD.—Saint-Gobain; *Int'l*, pg. 1175
NORTON S.A.—Saint-Gobain; *Int'l*, pg. 1175
NORTON S.A. INDUSTRIA E COMERCIO—Saint-Gobain; *Int'l*, pg. 1175
NORTON S.A./N.V.—Saint-Gobain; *Int'l*, pg. 1175
NORTON SCANDINAVIA AB—Saint-Gobain; *Int'l*, pg. 1175
NORTON S.P.A.—Saint-Gobain; *Int'l*, pg. 1175
NORTONMAS SDN. BHD.—Saint-Gobain; *Int'l*, pg. 1175
K/S ORKLA EXOLON A/S & CO.—Exolon-Esk Company; *U.S. Public*, pg. 600
OSBORN MANUFACTURING—Jason Incorporated; *U.S. Public*, pg. 924
PACKAGING RESOURCES, INCORPORATED; *U.S. Private*, pg. 833
PECHINEY ELECTROMETALLURGIE—Pechiney S.A.; *Int'l*, pg. 1028
PFERD/AUGUST RUEGGEBERG; *Int'l*, pg. 1046
SANDVIK HARD MATERIALS A/S—Sandvik AB; *Int'l*, pg. 1186
SIAM MAGOTTEAUX CO., LTD.—The Siam Cement Public Company Limited; *Int'l*, pg. 1238
TECHNICAL SPECIALTIES DIVISION—FiberMark Inc.; *U.S. Public*, pg. 620
UNIVERSAL PHOTONICS, INC.; *U.S. Private*, pg. 1127
WILTON CORPORATION; *U.S. Private*, pg. 1181

3292 — ASBESTOS PRODUCTS

BALZARETTI MODIGLIANI—Saint-Gobain; *Int'l*, pg. 1176
BRASILIT DA AMAZONIA—Saint-Gobain; *Int'l*, pg. 1171
BRASILIT S.A.—Saint-Gobain; *Int'l*, pg. 1171
EMCO LIMITED; *Int'l*, pg. 452
GRUNZWEIG & HARTMANN UND GLASFASER AG—Saint-Gobain; *Int'l*, pg. 1176
MEXALIT S.A.—Saint-Gobain; *Int'l*, pg. 1171
MONOFORT—Saint-Gobain; *Int'l*, pg. 1177
MOY INSULATION LTD.—BPB Industries PLC; *Int'l*, pg. 123
THE PILOT CORPORATION; *Int'l*, pg. 1057
QUARTZ & SILICE—Saint-Gobain; *Int'l*, pg. 1176
RAYBESTOS INDUSTRIE-PRODUKTE GMBH—Raytech Corporation; *U.S. Public*, pg. 1364

3295 — MINERALS & EARTHS, GROUND OR OTHERWISE TREATED

AMERICAN GRAPHITE CO.—Dixon Ticonderoga Company; *U.S. Public*, pg. 515
AMOL DICALITE LTD.—RGP Holding, Inc.; *U.S. Private*, pg. 903
ASBURY GRAPHITE MILLS, INC.—Asbury Carbons, Inc.; *U.S. Private*, pg. 87
BELMONT INDUSTRIES, INC.—RGP Holding, Inc.; *U.S. Private*, pg. 903
BURGESS PIGMENT CO.; *U.S. Private*, pg. 182
CARBONE-LORRAINE NORTH AMERICA—Pechiney S.A.; *Int'l*, pg. 1028
CARBONE OF AMERICA—Pechiney S.A.; *Int'l*, pg. 1028
CHEMROCK CORPORATION—RGP Holding, Inc.; *U.S. Private*, pg. 903
CONSTRUCTION & HOME IMPROVEMENT MARKETS DIVISION—3M; *U.S. Public*, pg. 1605
DICALITE CORPORATION—RGP Holding, Inc.; *U.S. Private*, pg. 903
DICALITE EUROPE NORD, S.A.—RGP Holding, Inc.; *U.S. Private*, pg. 903
DICALITE ORIENT CO. LTD.—RGP Holding, Inc.; *U.S. Private*, pg. 903
DICASER S.A. DE C.V.—RGP Holding, Inc.; *U.S. Private*, pg. 903
DIXON TICONDEROGA COMPANY; *U.S. Public*, pg. 514
ENGELHARD CORP.-QUINCY OPERATIONS—Engelhard Corporation; *U.S. Public*, pg. 582
FMC CORP., LITHIUM DIVISION—FMC Corporation; *U.S. Public*, pg. 605
GLASS ROCK PLANT—Oglebay Norton Company; *U.S. Public*, pg. 1213
GOLDEN CAT CORPORATION—Ralston Purina Company; *U.S. Public*, pg. 1360
GREAT LAKES CARBON CORP.—Horsehead Industries, Inc.; *U.S. Private*, pg. 540
GREFCO, INC.—RGP Holding, Inc.; *U.S. Private*, pg. 903
GLENN O. HAWBAKER, INC.; *U.S. Private*, pg. 511
HEMPT BROTHERS, INC.; *U.S. Private*, pg. 521
HEPWORTH MINERALS AND CHEMICALS LIMITED—Hepworth Plc; *Int'l*, pg. 615
HEPWORTH PLC; *Int'l*, pg. 614
HILL & GRIFFITH COMPANY; *U.S. Private*, pg. 529
J.M. HUBER CORPORATION; *U.S. Private*, pg. 544
INDUPLEX, INC.—RGP Holding, Inc.; *U.S. Private*, pg. 904
INTERNATIONAL SPECIALTY PRODUCTS, INC.—ISP Holdings, Inc.; *U.S. Public*, pg. 858
LAFARGE CONSTRUCTION MATERIALS—Lafarge S.A.; *Int'l*, pg. 788
LAPORTE ABSORBENTS (BAULKING) LIMITED—Laporte plc; *Int'l*, pg. 802
LAPORTE PLC; *Int'l*, pg. 801
MILLWOOD PLANT—Oglebay Norton Company; *U.S. Public*, pg. 1213
MINERALS DIV.—Eagle-Picher Industries, Inc.; *U.S. Private*, *pg. 355*
OLYMPIC MILL SERVICES—Tube City Inc.; *U.S. Private*, pg. 1108
PENN VIRGINIA CORPORATION; *U.S. Public*, pg. 1271
PERCHEM LTD.—Akzo Nobel N.V.; *Int'l*, pg. 47
PERCHEM SA—Akzo Nobel N.V.; *Int'l*, pg. 47
RGP HOLDING, INC.; *U.S. Private*, pg. 903
REED MINERALS—Harsco Corporation; *U.S. Public*, pg. 793
RHONE POULENC INC.—Rhone-Poulenc S.A.; *Int'l*, pg. 1112
SAINT-GOBAIN ADVANCED MATERIALS CORPORATION—Saint-Gobain; *Int'l*, pg. 1173
SARCAL—Imetal; *Int'l*, pg. 662
SILBRICO CORPORATION; *U.S. Private*, pg. 1000
SIPLAST S.A.—Icopal a/s; *Int'l*, pg. 659
SOUTHWESTERN GRAPHITE CO.—Dixon Ticonderoga Company; *U.S. Public*, pg. 515
STANHOPE PRODUCTS COMPANY—Brittany Corporation; *U.S. Private*, pg. 169
SUPERIOR GRAPHITE CO.; *U.S. Private*, pg. 1054
SUPERIOR GRAPHITE EUROPE, LTD.—Superior Graphite Co.; *U.S. Private*, pg. 1055
THERMIC REFRACTORIES INC.—Morgan Crucible Co. Plc; *Int'l*, pg. 894
3M; *U.S. Public*, pg. 1604
TREIBACHER SCHLEIFMITTEL CORP.; *U.S. Private*, pg. 1099
VOLCLAY LIMITED—AMCOL International Corp.; *U.S. Public*, pg. 64
VOLCLAY STANDARD PTY. LTD.—AMCOL International Corp.; *U.S. Public*, pg. 64
VULCAN MATERIALS COMPANY; *U.S. Public*, pg. 1725
WATTS BLAKE BEARNE & CO. PLC; *Int'l*, pg. 1487
WAVERLEY MINERAL CORPORATION—Laporte plc; *Int'l*, pg. 803
WHIBCO, INC.; *U.S. Private*, pg. 1171
ZEMEX CORPORATION; *Int'l*, pg. 1523

3296 — MINERAL WOOL

ACI FIBREGLASS—BTR plc; *Int'l*, pg. 128
ADVANCE THERMAL CORP.—Transco Inc.; *U.S. Private*, pg. 1096
AMIANTIT FIBREGLASS INDUS., LTD.—Owens Corning; *U.S. Public*, pg. 1237
ARABIAN FIBERGLASS INSULATION CO.—Owens Corning; *U.S. Public*, pg. 1237
ARMSTRONG WORLD INDUSTRIES, INC.; *U.S. Public*, pg. 131
BPB INDUSTRIES PLC; *Int'l*, pg. 122
BPCO—Emco Limited; *Int'l*, pg. 453
BALDT, INC.; *U.S. Private*, pg. 112
E.J. BARTELLS CO.; *U.S. Private*, pg. 118
BAYER OWENS/CORNING GLASSWOOL S.A.—Bayer AG; *Int'l*, pg. 175
THE BENTLEY-HARRIS MANUFACTURING CO.—T & N Plc; *Int'l*, pg. 1334
BRITISH GYPSUM LTD.—BPB Industries PLC; *Int'l*, pg. 122
CCX FIBERGLASS PRODUCTS—CCX, Inc.; *U.S. Private*, pg. 193
CELOTEX CORPORATION; *U.S. Private*, pg. 221
CERTAINTEED CORPORATION—Saint-Gobain; *Int'l*, pg. 1170
COMPANHIA VIDRARIA SANTA MARINA—Saint-Gobain; *Int'l*, pg. 1172
CRISTALERIA ESPANOLA S.A.—Saint-Gobain; *Int'l*, pg. 1176

EMCO BUILDING PRODUCTS—Emco Limited; *Int'l*, pg. 453
GEVETEX TEXTILGLAS GMBH—Saint-Gobain; *Int'l*, pg. 1177
A.P. GREEN INDUSTRIES, INC.; *U.S. Public*, pg. 761
GRUNZWEIG & HARTMANN UND GLASFASER AG—Saint-Gobain; *Int'l*, pg. 1176
GULLFIBER AB—Saint-Gobain; *Int'l*, pg. 1176
HERCULES INC.-MAGNA—Hercules Incorporated; *U.S. Public*, pg. 810
HYUNDAI WOOD INDUSTRIES CO., LTD.—Hyundai Motor Company; *Int'l*, pg. 642
INDUSTRIAL ACOUSTICS COMPANY, INC.; *U.S. Public*, pg. 875
INDUSTRIAL ACOUSTICS COMPANY, LTD.—Industrial Acoustics Company, Inc.; *U.S. Public*, pg. 875
ISOVER S.A.—Saint-Gobain; *Int'l*, pg. 1176
JOHNS MANVILLE CORPORATION; *U.S. Public*, pg. 927
MOY INSULATION LTD.—BPB Industries PLC; *Int'l*, pg. 123
OWENS CORNING; *U.S. Public*, pg. 1236
OWENS-CORNING BUILDING PRODUCTS UK LTD.—Owens Corning; *U.S. Public*, pg. 1237
OWENS-CORNING VEIL NETHERLANDS B.V.—Owens Corning; *U.S. Public*, pg. 1237
OWENS-CORNING VEIL U.K. LIMITED—Owens Corning; *U.S. Public*, pg. 1237
PACOR, INC.; *U.S. Private*, pg. 833
SFIC—Saint-Gobain; *Int'l*, pg. 1176
SAINT-GOBAIN; *Int'l*, pg. 1170
SCHULLER INTERNATIONAL, INC.—Johns Manville Corporation; *U.S. Public*, pg. 927
SPECIALTY PRODUCTS AND INSULATION COMPANY—Irex Corporation; *U.S. Public*, pg. 913
TRANSCO INC.; *U.S. Private*, pg. 1096
USG CORPORATION; *U.S. Public*, pg. 1660
USG INTERIORS, INC.—USG Corporation; *U.S. Public*, pg. 1660
VETROTEX FRANCE—Saint-Gobain; *Int'l*, pg. 1177
VETROTEX ITALIA—Saint-Gobain; *Int'l*, pg. 1177
VIDRIERIA ARGENTINA SA—Pilkington Plc; *Int'l*, pg. 1057
VITRO-FIBRAS, S.A.—Owens Corning; *U.S. Public*, pg. 1238
VITROFIL S.P.A.—Saint-Gobain; *Int'l*, pg. 1177
WANNER Y VINYAS—Saint-Gobain; *Int'l*, pg. 1176

3297 — NONCLAY REFRACTORIES

ALLIED MINERAL PRODUCTS, INC.; *U.S. Private*, pg. 39
AMERICAN GRAPHITE CO.—Dixon Ticonderoga Company; *U.S. Public*, pg. 515
E.J. BARTELLS CO.; *U.S. Private*, pg. 118
CARBONE-LORRAINE NORTH AMERICA—Pechiney S.A.; *Int'l*, pg. 1028
CARBONE OF AMERICA—Pechiney S.A.; *Int'l*, pg. 1028
THE CARBORUNDUM CORPORATION—Saint-Gobain; *Int'l*, pg. 1173
CHISHOLM, BOYD & WHITE CO.—Venturedyne, Ltd.; *U.S. Private*, pg. 1136
COMPAGNIE DE SAINT-GOBAIN-PONT-A MOUSSON—Compagnie de Suez; *Int'l*, pg. 313
DANREC—Imetal; *Int'l*, pg. 662
DETRICK REFRACTORY FIBERS, INC.—A.P. Green Industries, Inc.; *U.S. Public*, pg. 761
DIXON TICONDEROGA COMPANY; *U.S. Public*, pg. 514
FLO-CON ITALIANA S.R.L.—Zimmermann & Jansen GmbH; *Int'l*, pg. 1529
GENERAL SIGNAL CORPORATION; *U.S. Public*, pg. 726
A.P. GREEN INDUSTRIES, INC.; *U.S. Public*, pg. 761
HEPWORTH PLC; *Int'l*, pg. 614
HUGUENOT-FENAL—Imetal; *Int'l*, pg. 661
INDIANA PLANT—Oglebay Norton Company; *U.S. Public*, pg. 1214
S.A. INDUSTRIAS VOTORANTIM; *Int'l*, pg. 677
KYOCERA CORPORATION; *Int'l*, pg. 775
KYOCERA INDUSTRIAL CERAMICS CORP.—Kyocera Corporation; *Int'l*, pg. 776
LAFARGE MATERIAUX DE SPECIALITES—Lafarge S.A.; *Int'l*, pg. 789
LAFARGE S.A.; *Int'l*, pg. 788
MAGNECO/METREL, INC.; *U.S. Private*, pg. 695
MARTIN MARIETTA MAGNESIA SPECIALTIES, INC.—Lockheed Martin Corporation; *U.S. Public*, pg. 1007
MARTIN MARIETTA MATERIALS, INC.—Lockheed Martin Corporation; *U.S. Public*, pg. 1007
NORTH AMERICAN REFRACTORIES COMPANY; *U.S. Private*, pg. 803
NORTON ADVANCED CERAMICS LIMITED—Saint-Gobain; *Int'l*, pg. 1174
NORTON ADVANCED CERAMICS OF CANADA INC.—Saint-Gobain; *Int'l*, pg. 1174
NORTON CONSTRUCTION PRODUCTS—Saint-Gobain; *Int'l*, pg. 1177
NORTON PTY. LTD.—Saint-Gobain; *Int'l*, pg. 1175
NORTON SCANDINAVIA AB—Saint-Gobain; *Int'l*, pg. 1175
OGLEBAY NORTON COMPANY; *U.S. Public*, pg. 1213
OGLEBAY NORTON REFRACTORIES & MINERALS, INC.—Oglebay Norton Company; *U.S. Public*, pg. 1214
OPTIROC AS—Scancem AB; *Int'l*, pg. 1200
OPTIROC GROUP AB—Scancem AB; *Int'l*, pg. 1200
PACIFIC HOLDING CORPORATION; *U.S. Private*, pg. 831
PAKCO INDUSTRIAL CERAMICS, INC.—Saint-Gobain; *Int'l*, pg. 1174
PECHINEY ELECTROMETALLURGIE—Pechiney S.A.; *Int'l*, pg. 1028
PERMATECH, INC.—Aluminum Company of America; *U.S. Public*, pg. 61
PLIBRICO CO.; *U.S. Private*, pg. 872
PREMIER REFRACTORIES (CANADA) LTD.—The Alpine Group, Inc.; *U.S. Public*, pg. 58
PREMIER REFRACTORIES INTERNATIONAL INC.—The Alpine Group, Inc.; *U.S. Public*, pg. 58
RADEX DEUTSCHLAND, A.G.—RGP Holding, Inc.; *U.S. Private*, pg. 904
REFRACTARIOS NORTON, S.A.—Saint-Gobain; *Int'l*, pg. 1175
REFRADIGE—Saint-Gobain; *Int'l*, pg. 1176
RESCO PRODUCTS, INC.; *U.S. Private*, pg. 924
RHEINISCHE CHAMOTTE UND DINAS GMBH—Viag AG; *Int'l*, pg. 1464
SAVOIE REFRACTAIRES—Saint-Gobain; *Int'l*, pg. 1176
SOCIETE EUROPEENNE DES PRODUCTS REFRACTARIES (SEPR)—Saint-Gobain; *Int'l*, pg. 1175
TYK CORPORATION; *Int'l*, pg. 1345
TYK REFRACTORIES CO.—TYK Corporation; *Int'l*, pg. 1345
THERMAL CERAMICS INC.—Morgan Crucible Co. Plc; *Int'l*, *pg. 894*

3299 — NONMETALLIC MINERAL PRODUCTS, NEC

AEARO COMPANY; *U.S. Private*, pg. 23
AMERICAN FOUNDRY GROUP, INC.; *U.S. Private*, pg. 54
AUSTIN PRODUCTIONS, INC.; *U.S. Private*, pg. 100
BARDON (ENGLAND) LTD.—Bardon Group PLC; *Int'l*, pg. 166
BARDON GROUP PLC; *Int'l*, pg. 166
CAPE PLC.—Charter plc; *Int'l*, pg. 280
THE CARBORUNDUM CORPORATION—Saint-Gobain; *Int'l*, pg. 1173
CERADYNE, INC; *U.S. Public*, pg. 330
CERAMATEC—Elkem ASA; *Int'l*, pg. 448
CERASIV GMBH—Metallgesellschaft AG; *Int'l*, pg. 861
COOKSON GROUP PLC; *Int'l*, pg. 328
DIAMONITE PLANT—Ferro Corporation; *U.S. Public*, pg. 618
DOW CORNING CORPORATION—The Dow Chemical Company; *U.S. Public*, pg. 523
EXXON COAL AND MINERALS COMPANY—Exxon Corporation; *U.S. Public*, pg. 601
FREEPORT-MCMORAN RESOURCE PARTNERS, LTD.—Freeport-McMoRan Inc.; *U.S. Public*, pg. 681
GENERAL CERAMICS, INC.—Tokuyama Corporation; *Int'l*, pg. 1394
HYBRID PRODUCTS—Sony Corporation; *Int'l*, pg. 1283
KERLANE—Saint-Gobain; *Int'l*, pg. 1176
KIRKWOOD INDUSTRIES, INC.; *U.S. Private*, pg. 623
KLOECKNER-WILHELMSBURGER GMBH—Klockner-Werke AG; *Int'l*, pg. 737
KYOCERA AMERICA, INC.—Kyocera Corporation; *Int'l*, pg. 775
KYOCERA CORPORATION; *Int'l*, pg. 775
KYOCERA INDUSTRIAL CERAMICS CORP.—Kyocera Corporation; *Int'l*, pg. 776
KYOCERA MEXICANA S.A. DE C.V.—Kyocera Corporation; *Int'l*, pg. 776
MAGNECO/METREL, INC.; *U.S. Private*, pg. 695
MATERIALS RESEARCH CORPORATION—Sony Corporation; *Int'l*, pg. 1283
NORITAKE CO., LIMITED; *Int'l*, pg. 958
PAVIMENTOS CERAMICOS S.A.—Lafarge S.A.; *Int'l*, pg. 790
PENTEL CO., LTD.; *Int'l*, pg. 1035
POWDERTECH CORPORATION—Mitsui & Co., Ltd.; *Int'l*, pg. 878
REFRADIGE—Saint-Gobain; *Int'l*, pg. 1176
RESCO PRODUCTS, INC.; *U.S. Private*, pg. 924
SOCIETE EUROPEENNE DES PRODUCTS REFRACTARIES (SEPR)—Saint-Gobain; *Int'l*, pg. 1175
SUPERIOR BRANDS, INC.—Nestle S.A.; *Int'l*, pg. 917
SUZORITE MICA PRODUCTS INC.—Zemex Corporation; *Int'l*, pg. 1523
WARREN PLANT—Oglebay Norton Company; *U.S. Public*, pg. 1214

3312 — STEEL WORKS, BLAST FURNACES, INCLUDING COKE OVENS & ROLLING MILLS

ABB ISOPROFIL GMBH STAHLPROFIL-UND WARMWALZWERK—ABB Asea Brown Boveri (Holding) Ltd.; *Int'l*, pg. 2
AK STEEL CORPORATION; *U.S. Public*, pg. 7
AM GENERAL CORPORATION—Renco Group; *U.S. Private*, pg. 922
ABBOTT BALL COMPANY; *U.S. Private*, pg. 9
ACME METALS INCORPORATED; *U.S. Public*, pg. 16
ACME STEEL CO.—Acme Metals Incorporated; *U.S. Public*, *pg. 16*
ACOS VILLARES S.A.; *Int'l*, pg. 23
ACOS VILLARES STEEL UNIT—Acos Villares S.A.; *Int'l*, pg. 23
AIRFORGE S.A.—Groupe Usinor; *Int'l*, pg. 571
ALFA-LAVAL HAMILTON PTY LTD.—Tetra Laval Group; *Int'l*, pg. 1379
ALGOMA STEEL INC.; *Int'l*, pg. 56
ALLEGHENY LUDLUM-WATERBURY—Allegheny Teledyne Incorporated; *U.S. Public*, pg. 43
ALLOY TOOL STEEL INC.—Nissho Iwai Corporation; *Int'l*, pg. 947
AMERICAN STEEL CORP.—NKK Corporation; *Int'l*, pg. 903
AMERISTEEL; *U.S. Private*, pg. 65
AMERON INTERNATIONAL CORPORATION; *U.S. Public*, pg. 98
APOLO PRODUTOS DE ACO S.A.; *Int'l*, pg. 78
ARBED S.A.; *Int'l*, pg. 78
ARMCO INC.; *U.S. Public*, pg. 131
ARMCO INC.-BUTLER OPERS.—Armco Inc.; *U.S. Public*, pg. 131
ARMCO INC.-MANSFIELD OPERATIONS—Armco Inc.; *U.S. Public*, pg. 131
ARNOLD WRAGG (BOLTS & NUTS) LTD.—Haden Maclellan Holdings plc; *Int'l*, pg. 586
ASCOMETAL—Groupe Usinor; *Int'l*, pg. 570
ATLANTIC STEEL INDUSTRIES, INC.—The Ivaco Group; *Int'l*, pg. 696
AUSTRALIAN NATIONAL INDUSTRIES LIMITED; *Int'l*, pg. 100
AVESTA ABE AB—British Steel Plc; *Int'l*, pg. 221
AVESTA CALAMO AB—British Steel Plc; *Int'l*, pg. 221
AVESTA NORDS AB—British Steel Plc; *Int'l*, pg. 221
AVESTA PREFAB AB—British Steel Plc; *Int'l*, pg. 221
AVESTA SHEFFIELD AB—British Steel Plc; *Int'l*, pg. 221
AVESTA SHEFFIELD EAST, INC.—British Steel Plc; *Int'l*, pg. 221
AVESTA SHEFFIELD PLATE INC.—British Steel Plc; *Int'l*, pg. 221
AVESTA VALBRUNA AB—British Steel Plc; *Int'l*, pg. 221
AVESTA WELDING AB—British Steel Plc; *Int'l*, pg. 221
BHP STEEL—The Broken Hill Proprietary Company Limited; *Int'l*, pg. 225
BABCOCK & WILCOX CO.—McDermott International, Inc.; *U.S. Public*, pg. 1068
BACHMANN GMBH—Fried. Krupp AG; *Int'l*, pg. 514
BANGKOK STEEL INDUSTRY CO. LTD.—Nissho Iwai Corporation; *Int'l*, pg. 947
BAYOU STEEL CORPORATION; *U.S. Public*, pg. 197
BERENFIELD CONTAINERS, INC.; *U.S. Private*, pg. 135
BERENFIELD CONTAINERS LTD.—Berenfield Containers, Inc.; *U.S. Private*, pg. 135
BERGMAN MANUFACTURING—Datron Incorporated; *U.S. Private*, pg. 313
BETHLEHEM STEEL CORPORATION; *U.S. Public*, pg. 226
BETHLEHEM STEEL-STRUCTURAL PRODUCTS DIVISION—Bethlehem Steel Corporation; *U.S. Public*, pg. 226
BILLING METAL TRADING AB—British Steel Plc; *Int'l*, pg. 221
BIRMINGHAM AL STEEL DIVISION—Birmingham Steel Corporation; *U.S. Public*, pg. 232
BIRMINGHAM SOUTHEAST—Birmingham Steel Corporation; *U.S. Public*, pg. 232
BIRMINGHAM STEEL CORP., CLEVELAND DIV.—Birmingham Steel Corporation; *U.S. Public*, pg. 232
BIRMINGHAM STEEL CORPORATION; *U.S. Public*, pg. 232
BJORNEBORGS JERNVERKS AB—Axel Johnson AB; *Int'l*, *pg. 708*
BOCK INDUSTRIES INC.—Caparo Group Ltd.; *Int'l*, pg. 265
BOHLER UDDEHOLM AG—Voest-Alpine Stahl AG; *Int'l*, pg. 1471
BOHLERIT GES.M.B.H.—Voest-Alpine Stahl AG; *Int'l*, pg. 1470
BORAL LIMITED; *Int'l*, pg. 203
BOWEN COKE PTY. LTD.—M.I.M. Holdings Ltd.; *Int'l*, pg. 827
BRAEBURN ALLOY STEEL—CCX, Inc.; *U.S. Private*, pg. 193
BROCKHOUSE CANADA LIMITED—EIP Group plc; *Int'l*, pg. 426
BRUDI, INC.—Long Reach Holdings Inc.; *U.S. Private*, pg. 675
CCX, INC.; *U.S. Private*, pg. 193
CF & I STEEL, L.P.—Oregon Steel Mills Inc.; *U.S. Public*, pg. 1230
CSC, LTD.—The Reserve Group; *U.S. Private*, pg. 924
CSP PACIFIC—Fletcher Challenge Limited; *Int'l*, pg. 495
CAMDEL METALS DIVISION—Handy & Harman; *U.S. Public*, pg. 780
CANRON FABRICATION CORPORATION - EASTERN DIVISION—The Ivaco Group; *Int'l*, pg. 695
CANRON FABRICATION CORPORATION - WESTERN DIVISION—The Ivaco Group; *Int'l*, pg. 695
CANRON INC.—The Ivaco Group; *Int'l*, pg. 695
CAPARO MERCHANT BAR PLC—Caparo Group Ltd.; *Int'l*, pg. 265
CAPITOL METALS COMPANY; *U.S. Private*, pg. 206
CARGILL; *U.S. Private*, pg. 210
CARPENTER TECHNOLOGY CORPORATION; *U.S. Public*, *pg. 307*
CASCADE STEEL ROLLING MILLS, INC.—Schnitzer Steel Industries, Inc.; *U.S. Public*, pg. 1440
CENTURY FENCE COMPANY; *U.S. Private*, pg. 226
CERTIFIED ALLOY PRODUCTS, INC.—Vickers PLC; *Int'l*, pg. 1467
CHAPARRAL STEEL CO.—Texas Industries, Inc.; *U.S. Public*, pg. 1585
CHICAGO HEIGHTS STEEL; *U.S. Private*, pg. 234
CHINA STEEL CHEMICAL CORP.—China Steel Corporation; *Int'l*, pg. 286
CITATION CORPORATION; *U.S. Public*, pg. 376
CLYDESDALE ENGINEERING—Caparo Group Ltd.; *Int'l*, pg. 265
COIL PLUS-ILLINOIS INC.—Mitsubishi Corporation; *Int'l*, pg. 872
COLTEC HOLDINGS INC; *U.S. Public*, pg. 401
COMMERCIAL METALS COMPANY; *U.S. Public*, pg. 411
COMMONWEALTH STEEL CO. LTD.—Australian National Industries Limited; *Int'l*, pg. 101
COMPAGNIE FRANCAISE DE FORGES ET FONDRIES (C3F)—Groupe Usinor; *Int'l*, pg. 571
COMPANHIA NIPO-BRASILEIRA DE PELOTIZACAO-NIBRASCO—NKK Corporation; *Int'l*, pg. 903
COMPANHIA NIPO-BRASILEIRA DE PELOTIZACAO-NIBRASCO—Nissho Iwai Corporation; *Int'l*, pg. 949
COMPANHIA SIDERURGICA BELGO-MINEIRA—Arbed S.A.; *Int'l*, pg. 79
COMPANHIA SIDERURGICA BELGO-MINEIRA—Nissho Iwai Corporation; *Int'l*, pg. 949
COMPANIA ESPANOLA PARA LA FABRICACION DE ACERO INOXIDABLE S.A.—Nissho Iwai Corporation; *Int'l*, pg. 947
CONTRAN CORPORATION; *U.S. Private*, pg. 270
CO-STEEL SAYREVILLE INC.—Co-Steel Inc.; *Int'l*, pg. 298
CREUSOT-LOIRE INDUSTRIE—Groupe Usinor; *Int'l*, pg. 571
CRITCHLEY, SHARP & TETLOW—Carclo Engineering Group plc; *Int'l*, pg. 268

CRUCIBLE MATERIALS CORP.; *U.S. Private*, pg. 293
THE CYPRESS COMPANIES; *U.S. Private*, pg. 299
DSC LTD.; *U.S. Private*, pg. 305
DAIDO STEEL CO., LTD.; *Int'l*, pg. 364
DANA CANADA INC.—Dana Corporation; *U.S. Public*, pg. 480
DAVUM-ARMATURES—Groupe Usinor; *Int'l*, pg. 571
DER DILLINGER HUETTENWERKE AG—Groupe Usinor; *Int'l*, pg. 572
DIMOND INDUSTRIES—Fletcher Challenge Limited; *Int'l*, pg. 495
DOFASCO, INC.; *Int'l*, pg. 414
DOMTECH HOLDINGS, INC.—Leucadia National Corporation; *U.S. Public*, pg. 990
DOUBLECOAT, L.L.C.—Consolidated Systems, Inc.; *U.S. Private*, pg. 266
DRUMMOND COMPANY, INC.; *U.S. Private*, pg. 343
DUBIN-CLARK & COMPANY; *U.S. Private*, pg. 344
EDGEWATER STEEL COMPANY; *U.S. Private*, pg. 364
EISENMETALL GESELLSCHAFT MBH—Fried. Krupp AG; *Int'l*, pg. 514
EISENMETALL LAGER GMBH—Fried. Krupp AG; *Int'l*, pg. 514
B. ELLIOTT PLC.; *Int'l*, pg. 448
ELLWOOD CRANKSHAFT & MACHINE COMPANY—Ellwood Group, Inc.; *U.S. Private*, pg. 373
ELLWOOD GROUP, INC.; *U.S. Private*, pg. 373
EWALD GLEBEL LUXEMBOURG G.M.B.H.—Arbed S.A.; *Int'l*, pg. 79
FAGERSTA STAINLESS AB; *Int'l*, pg. 476
FARMERS MARINE COPPER WORKS—Four Winds Investment Corp.; *U.S. Private*, pg. 422
FERROUS PROCESSING & TRADING CO.; *U.S. Private*, pg. 402
A. FINKL & SONS CO.; *U.S. Private*, pg. 405
FIRSTMISS STEEL, INC.—ChemFirst Inc.; *U.S. Public*, pg. 344
FIRTH-RIXSON FORGINGS—Firth-Rixson Plc; *Int'l*, pg. 487
FORMEX, INC. - PERMANENT STEEL FORMS—Omega Environmental Inc.; *U.S. Public*, pg. 1222
FREEDOM FORGE CORPORATION; *U.S. Private*, pg. 425
FROG SWITCH & MANUFACTURING COMPANY; *U.S. Private*, pg. 429
FUDICKAR METALL GMBH—Fried. Krupp AG; *Int'l*, pg. 514
GKN WALTERSCHEID PRESSWERK GMBH—GKN plc; *Int'l*, pg. 536
GKN WHEELS NAGBOL A/S—GKN plc; *Int'l*, pg. 535
GS INDUSTRIES, INC.; *U.S. Private*, pg. 435
GALVANO DIVISION—The Ivaco Group; *Int'l*, pg. 696
GARY STEEL CO., INC.—Primac Corp.; *U.S. Private*, pg. 884
GENEVA STEEL; *U.S. Public*, pg. 729
GOLDMAN FINANCIAL GROUP; *U.S. Private*, pg. 461
GRUPO IMSA S.A. DE C.V.; *Int'l*, pg. 575
GRUPO INDUSTRIAL CAMESA S.A. DE C.V.; *Int'l*, pg. 575
HAMILTON SPECIALTY BAR—Slater Industries Inc.; *Int'l*, pg. 1262
FRANZ HANIEL & CIE, GMBH; *Int'l*, pg. 591
HEIN, LEHMANN AG—Arbed S.A.; *Int'l*, pg. 80
HIDRO NITRO ESPANOLA—Pechiney S.A.; *Int'l*, pg. 1030
HIGHVELD STEEL & VANADIUM CORPORATION—Anglo American Corporation of South Africa Limited; *Int'l*, pg. 76
HOESCH HOHENLIMBURG GMBH—Fried. Krupp AG; *Int'l*, *pg. 508*
HOOGOVENS BUIZEN B.V.—Koninklijke Hoogovens N.V.; *Int'l*, pg. 754
HOOGOVENS IJMUIDEN—Koninklijke Hoogovens N.V.; *Int'l*, pg. 753
HOVELMANN & CO. EISENGROSSHANDLUNG GMBH—Fried. Krupp AG; *Int'l*, pg. 514
HUNTCO INC.; *U.S. Public*, pg. 849
HUNTCO STEEL CO.—Huntco Inc.; *U.S. Public*, pg. 849
HURON VALLEY STEEL CORP.; *U.S. Private*, pg. 549
HYUNDAI HEAVY INDUSTRIES CO., LTD.—Hyundai Motor Company; *Int'l*, pg. 641
HYUNDAI MOTOR COMPANY; *Int'l*, pg. 641
HYUNDAI PIPE CO., LTD.—Hyundai Motor Company; *Int'l*, pg. 642
ILRO SRL; *Int'l*, pg. 646
IMPHY S.A.—Groupe Usinor; *Int'l*, pg. 571
INCHON IRON & STEEL CO., LTD.—Hyundai Motor Company; *Int'l*, pg. 642
P.T. INDONESIA STEEL TUBE WORKS LTD.—Nissho Iwai Corporation; *Int'l*, pg. 948
INLAND STEEL PRODUCTS COMPANY—Inland Steel Industries, Inc.; *U.S. Public*, pg. 879
INTERNATIONAL TUBULAR PRODUCTS, INC.—Acme Tube Inc.; *U.S. Private*, pg. 14
INTERSTATE STEEL CO. INC.—Groupe Usinor; *Int'l*, pg. 572
P.T. IRON WIRE WORKS INDONESIA—Nissho Iwai Corporation; *Int'l*, pg. 948
ISCOR; *Int'l*, pg. 688
THE IVACO GROUP; *Int'l*, pg. 695
IVACO ROLLING MILLS LIMITED PARTNERSHIP—The Ivaco Group; *Int'l*, pg. 696
J & L SPECIALTY PRODUCTS CORP.—Groupe Usinor; *Int'l*, pg. 572
OY JA-RO AB—Outokumpu Oyj; *Int'l*, pg. 1018
JACKSON MS STEEL DIVISION—Birmingham Steel Corporation; *U.S. Public*, pg. 232
AXEL JOHNSON AB; *Int'l*, pg. 707
AXEL JOHNSON LAB SYSTEMS A/S—Axel Johnson AB; *Int'l*, pg. 711
KANKAKEE, IL STEEL DIVISION—Birmingham Steel Corporation; *U.S. Public*, pg. 232
KEENEY MANUFACTURING CO.; *U.S. Private*, pg. 611
KEYSTONE CONSOLIDATED INDUSTRIES, INC.; *U.S. Public*, pg. 955
KEYSTONE STEEL & WIRE CO.—Keystone Consolidated Industries, Inc.; *U.S. Public*, pg. 955
KLOCKNER-WERKE AG; *Int'l*, pg. 736
KOMATSUGAWA KOKI CO., LTD.—Nissho Iwai Corporation; *Int'l*, pg. 946
KOPPEL STEEL CORP.—NS Group, Inc.; *U.S. Public*, pg. 1147
KRUPP EDELSTAHLPROFILE GMBH—Fried. Krupp AG; *Int'l*, pg. 512
KRUPP HOESCH METALLHANDEL GMBH—Fried. Krupp AG; *Int'l*, pg. 514
KRUPP HOESCH STAHLEXPORT GMBH—Fried. Krupp AG; *Int'l*, pg. 515
KRUPP HOESCH STAHLHANDEL GMBH—Fried. Krupp AG; *Int'l*, pg. 514
KRUPP HOESCH STAHLHANDEL RHEINLAND GMBH—Fried. Krupp AG; *Int'l*, pg. 514
KRUPP STAHLBAU BERLIN GMBH & CO. KG—Fried. Krupp AG; *Int'l*, pg. 508
KRUPP WILPUTTE CORP.—Fried. Krupp AG; *Int'l*, pg. 512
KWANGYANG WORKS—Pohang Iron & Steel Co., Ltd.; *Int'l*, pg. 1061
THE LTV CORPORATION; *U.S. Public*, pg. 971
LACLEDE - ALTON PLANT—Laclede Steel Company; *U.S. Public*, pg. 974
LACLEDE MID AMERICA INC.—Laclede Steel Company; *U.S. Public*, pg. 974
LACLEDE STEEL COMPANY; *U.S. Public*, pg. 974
LATROBE STEEL COMPANY—The Timken Company; *U.S. Public*, pg. 1617
LEBUS MANUFACTURING CO.—FKI Plc; *Int'l*, pg. 473
LONE STAR STEEL COMPANY—Lone Star Technologies, Inc.; *U.S. Public*, pg. 1012
LORLEA ARCHITECTURAL SYSTEMS DIVISION—Jannock Limited; *Int'l*, pg. 698
LUKENS INC.; *U.S. Public*, pg. 1019
LUKENS STEEL COMPANY—Lukens Inc.; *U.S. Public*, pg. 1020
LURGI AG—Metallgesellschaft AG; *Int'l*, pg. 861
LURGI ESPANOLA S.A.—Metallgesellschaft AG; *Int'l*, pg. 861
MSP STEEL WORKS LTD.—Nissho Iwai Corporation; *Int'l*, pg. 948
MACSTEEL DIV.—Quanex Corporation; *U.S. Public*, pg. 1349
MANNESMANN HOESCH PRAZISROHR GMBH—Fried. Krupp AG; *Int'l*, pg. 513
MARCLIN WESTEEL DIVISION—Jannock Limited; *Int'l*, pg. 698
MARSHALL STEEL, INC.—Steel of West Virginia, Inc.; *U.S. Public*, pg. 1513
MARYLAND SPECIALTY WIRE, INC.—Handy & Harman; *U.S. Public*, pg. 780
THE MASAN STEEL TUBE WORKS CO. LTD.—Nissho Iwai Corporation; *Int'l*, pg. 948
MAXCO, INC.; *U.S. Public*, pg. 1061
MCWANE, INC.; *U.S. Private*, pg. 725
MERIDIAN NATIONAL CORPORATION; *U.S. Public*, pg. 1095
METAL MASTERS FOODSERVICE EQUIPMENT; *U.S. Private*, pg. 734
METALART CORPORATION—Nissho Iwai Corporation; *Int'l*, pg. 946
MITSUI COKE CO., LTD.—Mitsui & Co., Ltd.; *Int'l*, pg. 877
MOLY-COP CANADA—Stelco Inc.; *Int'l*, pg. 1300
MONROE FORGINGS INC.—Firth-Rixson Plc; *Int'l*, pg. 488
MYTTON'S LIMITED—Bristile Clay Tiles, Ltd.; *Int'l*, pg. 216
NKK CORPORATION; *Int'l*, pg. 902
NAPA PIPE CORPORATION—Oregon Steel Mills Inc.; *U.S. Public*, pg. 1230
NATIONAL FORGE COMPANY; *U.S. Private*, pg. 783
NATIONAL STEEL CORPORATION—NKK Corporation; *Int'l*, pg. 902
NATIONAL STEEL CORP., GRANITE CITY DIVISION—NKK Corporation; *Int'l*, pg. 902
NATIONAL STEEL CORP., GREAT LAKES DIVISION—NKK Corporation; *Int'l*, pg. 903
NAYLOR PIPE COMPANY; *U.S. Private*, pg. 789
NEWPORT STEEL CORPORATION—NS Group, Inc.; *U.S. Public*, pg. 1147
NIAGARA COLD DRAWN CORP.—Niagara Corporation; *U.S. Public*, pg. 1181
NISSHIN STEEL CO., LTD.; *Int'l*, pg. 946
NISSHO IWAI (CHILE) LTDA—Nissho Iwai Corporation; *Int'l*, pg. 948
NISSHO IWAI CORPORATION; *Int'l*, pg. 946
NORTH STAR STEEL CO.—Cargill; *U.S. Private*, pg. 210
NORTHWESTERN STEEL & WIRE CO.; *U.S. Public*, pg. 1201
NUCOR CORPORATION; *U.S. Public*, pg. 1205
NUCOR STEEL-ARKANSAS—Nucor Corporation; *U.S. Public*, pg. 1205
NUCOR STEEL-INDIANA—Nucor Corporation; *U.S. Public*, pg. 1205
NUCOR STEEL-SOUTH CAROLINA—Nucor Corporation; *U.S. Public*, pg. 1205
NUCOR-YAMATO STEEL COMPANY—Nucor Corporation; *U.S. Public*, pg. 1206
OMNITRAX INC.—Broe Companies; *U.S. Private*, pg. 171
OREGON STEEL MILLS INC.; *U.S. Public*, pg. 1230
ORNSKOLDSVIKS MEKANISKA VERKSTAD (OMV)—British Steel Plc; *Int'l*, pg. 221
OUTOKUMPU OYJ; *Int'l*, pg. 1015
OUTOKUMPU STEEL OY—Outokumpu Oyj; *Int'l*, pg. 1018
OVAKO STEEL AB—AB SKF; *Int'l*, pg. 1157
PACIFIC COILCOATERS LIMITED—Fletcher Challenge Limited; *Int'l*, pg. 495
PACIFIC STEEL LTD.—Fletcher Challenge Limited; *Int'l*, pg. 495
PACIFIC SYNTHETIC FUEL COMPANY—Pacific Enterprises; *U.S. Public*, pg. 1249
PACIFIC WESTEEL—Jannock Limited; *Int'l*, pg. 698
PECHINEY ELECTROMETALLURGIE—Pechiney S.A.; *Int'l*, pg. 1028
PECHINEY S.A.; *Int'l*, pg. 1027
PERSTORP SPA-DIV. COMPOUNDS—Perstorp AB; *Int'l*, pg. 1037
PHELPS TOINTON INC.; *U.S. Private*, pg. 860
PILLAR BUILDING PRODUCTS LTD.—Caradon Plc; *Int'l*, pg. 267
PIPER IMPACT, INC.—Quanex Corporation; *U.S. Public*, pg. 1349
PITTSBURGH-CANFIELD CORP.—WHX Corporation; *U.S. Public*, pg. 1726
PLAND STAINLESS LTD.—Lonrho plc; *Int'l*, pg. 817
POHANG IRON & STEEL CO., LTD.; *Int'l*, pg. 1061
POHANG STEEL AUSTRALIA PTY, LTD.(POSA)—Pohang Iron & Steel Co., Ltd.; *Int'l*, pg. 1062
POHANG STEEL CANADA LTD.(POSCAN)—Pohang Iron & Steel Co., Ltd.; *Int'l*, pg. 1062
POHANG WORKS—Pohang Iron & Steel Co., Ltd.; *Int'l*, pg. 1062
PORTEC, INC.; *U.S. Public*, pg. 1317
POSCO ASIA CO., LTD. (POA)—Pohang Iron & Steel Co., Ltd.; *Int'l*, pg. 1062
POSCO INTERNATIONAL OSAKA (PIO)—Pohang Iron & Steel Co., Ltd.; *Int'l*, pg. 1062
POSTRADE RIO OFFICE—Pohang Iron & Steel Co., Ltd.; *Int'l*, pg. 1062
PRECISION SPECIALTY METALS, INC.—Dubin-Clark & Company; *U.S. Private*, pg. 344
PRECISION STEEL WAREHOUSE, INC.—Berkshire Hathaway Inc.; *U.S. Public*, pg. 217
PRIMARY STEEL, INC.—Primac Corp.; *U.S. Private*, pg. 884
QUANEX CORPORATION; *U.S. Public*, pg. 1349
RAUTARUUKKI OY; *Int'l*, pg. 1088
RENCO GROUP; *U.S. Private*, pg. 922
RENOWN STEEL—Slater Industries Inc.; *Int'l*, pg. 1262
REPUBLIC ENGINEERED STEELS, INC.; *U.S. Public*, pg. 1378
REYNOLDS WHEELS S.P.A.—Reynolds Metals Company; *U.S. Public*, pg. 1387
RIGBY-MARYLAND (STAINLESS) LTD.—Handy & Harman; *U.S. Public*, pg. 780
RIO ALGOM LIMITED; *Int'l*, pg. 1118
ROANOKE ELECTRIC STEEL CORPORATION; *U.S. Public*, pg. 1392
ROTTERDAM VENTURES INC.—Galesi Group; *U.S. Private*, pg. 437
SMI STEEL, INC.—Commercial Metals Company; *U.S. Public*, pg. 412
SMR (SOCIÉTÉ METALLURGIQUE DE REVIGNY)—Groupe Usinor; *Int'l*, pg. 571
SMS AKTIENGESELLSCHAFT—MAN Aktiengesellschaft; *Int'l*, pg. 825
SMS SCHLOEMANN-SIEMAG AG—MAN Aktiengesellschaft; *Int'l*, pg. 826
SAARBERGWERKE AKTIENGESELLSCHAFT; *Int'l*, pg. 1166
SASOL LIMITED; *Int'l*, pg. 1196
SAWHILL TUBULAR DIV.—Armco Inc.; *U.S. Public*, pg. 131
SCHNITZER STEEL INDUSTRIES, INC.; *U.S. Public*, pg. 1439
SCHULTZ STEEL COMPANY; *U.S. Private*, pg. 973
SEATTLE WA STEEL DIVISION—Birmingham Steel Corporation; *U.S. Public*, pg. 232
SHEFFIELD STEEL CORPORATION-JOLIET; *U.S. Private*, *pg. 991*
SHELBY STEEL PROCESSING CO.—McClain Industries, Inc.; *U.S. Public*, pg. 1065
THE SIAM IRON AND STEEL CO., LTD.—The Siam Cement Public Company Limited; *Int'l*, pg. 1238
SLAB & PLATE PRODUCTS DIVISION—The Broken Hill Proprietary Company Limited; *Int'l*, pg. 227
SLATER INDUSTRIES INC.; *Int'l*, pg. 1262
SLATER STEELS CORPORATION—Slater Industries Inc.; *Int'l*, pg. 1263
SNIJBRANDCENTRUM ROERMOND—Koninklijke Hoogovens N.V.; *Int'l*, pg. 754
SONCO STEEL TUBE DIV., FERRUM INC.—Jannock Limited; *Int'l*, pg. 699
SOUTHEASTERN COATED PRODUCTS—Consolidated Systems, Inc.; *U.S. Private*, pg. 266
SOUTHERN STEEL COMPANY—Phelps Tointon Inc.; *U.S. Private*, pg. 861
STAHLWERKE BREMEN GMBH—Arbed S.A.; *Int'l*, pg. 79
STANDARD STEEL—Freedom Forge Corporation; *U.S. Private*, pg. 425
STANDARD TUBE CANADA INC.—Jannock Limited; *Int'l*, pg. 699
STEEL OF WEST VIRGINIA, INC.; *U.S. Public*, pg. 1513
STELCO INC.; *Int'l*, pg. 1299
STRUCTURAL METALS, INC.—Commercial Metals Company; *U.S. Public*, pg. 412
SUPERIOR GROUP, INC.; *U.S. Private*, pg. 1055
TRP-PROFILE UND BAUELEMENTE GMBH—Fried. Krupp AG; *Int'l*, pg. 508
TALLEY INDUSTRIES, INC.—Carpenter Technology Corporation; *U.S. Public*, pg. 307
TALLEY METALS TECHNOLOGY, INC.—Carpenter Technology Corporation; *U.S. Public*, pg. 308
TAMCO—Ameron International Corporation; *U.S. Public*, pg. 99
THE TATA IRON AND STEEL CO. LTD.; *Int'l*, pg. 1356
TATA-YODOGAWA LTD.—Nissho Iwai Corporation; *Int'l*, pg. 949
TECHNOARBED LUXEMBOURG S.A.R.L.—Arbed S.A.; *Int'l*, pg. 80
TEXAS INDUSTRIES, INC.; *U.S. Public*, pg. 1585
THOMAS STEEL STRIP CORP.—Koninklijke Hoogovens N.V.; *Int'l*, pg. 756
THYSSEN STAHL AG—Thyssen AG; *Int'l*, pg. 1388
THE TIMKEN COMPANY; *U.S. Public*, pg. 1617
TITAN UMREIFUNGSTECHNIK GMBH—Fried. Krupp AG; *Int'l*, pg. 509
TITAN WHEEL-PEORIA—Titan International, Inc.; *U.S. Public*, pg. 1619
TOLES IVOIRE S.A. SOCIETE DE GALVANIZATION DE TOLES EN COTE IVOIRE—Nissho Iwai Corporation; *Int'l*, pg. 949

TOSHIBA STEEL TUBE CO., LTD.—Toshiba Corporation; Int'l, pg. 1405
TRU-WELD GRATING, INC.; U.S. Private, pg. 1107
TRU-WELD LTD—Tru-Weld Grating, Inc.; U.S. Private, pg. 1107
TUBE-FAB LTD.—HMI Industries; U.S. Public, pg. 771
TUSCALOOSA STEEL CORP.—British Steel Plc; Int'l, pg. 221
USS KOBE STEEL—Kobe Steel, Ltd.; Int'l, pg. 741
USS-POSCO INDUSTRIES—USX Corporation; U.S. Public, pg. 1662
USX CORPORATION; U.S. Public, pg. 1661
USX GARY WORKS, STEEL PRODUCTION—USX Corporation; U.S. Public, pg. 1662
UDDEHOLM KRAFT AB—Voest-Alpine Stahl AG; Int'l, pg. 1471
UDDEHOLM TOOLING AB—Voest-Alpine Stahl AG; Int'l, pg. 1471
UGINE ACIERS DE CHATILLON ET GUEUGNON S.A.—Groupe Usinor; Int'l, pg. 571
U.S. STEEL INTERNATIONAL, INC.—USX Corporation; U.S. Public, pg. 1661
VALEX CORP.—Reliance Steel & Aluminum Co.; U.S. Public, pg. 1375
VICWEST STEEL DIVISION NORTH AMERICAN BUILDING PRODUCTS—Jannock Limited; Int'l, pg. 698
VOEST-ALPINE INDUSTRIES, INC.—Voest-Alpine Stahl AG; Int'l, pg. 1470
VOEST-ALPINE INTERNATIONAL CORPORATION—Voest-Alpine Stahl AG; Int'l, pg. 1470
VOEST-ALPINE STAHL AG; Int'l, pg. 1470
VOEST-ALPINE STAHL TRAISEN GES.M.B.H.—Voest-Alpine Stahl AG; Int'l, pg. 1470
VOEST-ALPINE STEEL CORP.—Voest-Alpine Stahl AG; Int'l, pg. 1471
THE VOLLRATH COMPANY, L.L.C.; U.S. Private, pg. 1143
VON ROLL AG DEPARTEMENT STAHLPRODUKTE—Von Roll AG; Int'l, pg. 1480
WHX CORPORATION; U.S. Public, pg. 1726
WMF/USA; U.S. Private, pg. 1144
WEBB FORGING—Jervis B. Webb Company; U.S. Private, pg. 1156
WEIRTON STEEL CORPORATION; U.S. Public, pg. 1751
WESCO FINANCIAL CORPORATION—Berkshire Hathaway Inc.; U.S. Public, pg. 217
WIDISA METAL S.A.—FKI Plc; Int'l, pg. 474
WISCONSIN WIRE & STEEL—Maxco, Inc.; U.S. Public, pg. 1061
PAUL WURTH S.A.—Arbed S.A.; Int'l, pg. 80
WYMAN-GORDON LIMITED—Wyman-Gordon; U.S. Public, pg. 1782
XTEK CANADA, LTD.—Xtek, Inc.; U.S. Private, pg. 1194

3313 — ELECTROMETALLURGICAL PRODUCTS, EXCEPT STEEL

THE ALUMINUM POWDER COMPANY—Metallurg, Inc.; U.S. Private, pg. 735
APPLIED INDUSTRIAL MATERIALS CORPORATION—Walter Industries, Inc.; U.S. Public, pg. 1736
BRAEBURN ALLOY STEEL—CCX, Inc.; U.S. Private, pg. 193
CCX, INC.; U.S. Private, pg. 193
CANNON-MUSKEGON CORP.—SPS Technologies, Inc.; U.S. Public, pg. 1420
CHAPARRAL STEEL CO.—Texas Industries, Inc.; U.S. Public, pg. 1585
COMPAGNIE FRANCAISE DE FORGES ET FONDRIES (C3F)—Groupe Usinor; Int'l, pg. 571
COMPANHIA BRASILIERA CARBURETO DE CALCIO—Solvay S.A.; Int'l, pg. 1278
COMPANIA MINERA AUTLAN S.A. DE C.V.; Int'l, pg. 324
COPPERWELD INTERNATIONAL CO.—Imetal; Int'l, pg. 662
COPPERWELD SHELBY DIVISION—Imetal; Int'l, pg. 662
CYPRUS FOOTE MINERAL CO.—Cyprus Amax Minerals Company; U.S. Public, pg. 471
DELTA PLC; Int'l, pg. 389
DRIVER-HARRIS COMPANY; U.S. Public, pg. 530
DRIVER-HARRIS, S.A.—Kanthal AB; Int'l, pg. 723
ELEKTROWERK WEISWEILER GMBH—Metallurg, Inc.; U.S. Private, pg. 735
ELKEM ASA; Int'l, pg. 446
ELKEM CHICOUTIMI—Elkem ASA; Int'l, pg. 448
ELKEM MANGAN—Elkem ASA; Int'l, pg. 447
ELKEM MANGAN PEA—Elkem ASA; Int'l, pg. 447
ELKEM MARIETTA—Elkem ASA; Int'l, pg. 447
ELKEM RANA—Elkem ASA; Int'l, pg. 447
ELKEM SALTEN—Elkem ASA; Int'l, pg. 448
ELKEM SAUDEFALDLNE—Elkem ASA; Int'l, pg. 447
ELKEM THAMSHAVN—Elkem ASA; Int'l, pg. 448
AB FERROLEGERINGAR—Metallurg, Inc.; U.S. Private, pg. 735
FERROUS PROCESSING & TRADING CO.; U.S. Private, pg. 402
HAYNES INTERNATIONAL, INC.; U.S. Public, pg. 801
HERMANN H.C. STARCK BERLIN GBMH & CO. KG—Bayer AG; Int'l, pg. 174
ICELANDIC ALLOYS—Elkem ASA; Int'l, pg. 448
IMPHY S.A.—Groupe Usinor; Int'l, pg. 571
KRUPP MATERIALS HANDLING LTD.—Fried. Krupp AG; Int'l, pg. 511
LONDON & SCANDINAVIAN METALLURGICAL CO. LIMITED—Metallurg, Inc.; U.S. Private, pg. 735
MARKIN TUBING, INC.; U.S. Private, pg. 705
MATEC CORPORATION; U.S. Public, pg. 1056
METALCHIMICA SRL—Metallurg, Inc.; U.S. Private, pg. 735
METALLURG, INC.; U.S. Private, pg. 735
NIPPON TUNGSTEN CO., LTD.—Toshiba Corporation; Int'l, pg. 1403
OUTOKUMPU CHROME OY—Outokumpu Oyj; Int'l, pg. 1018
REACTIVE METALS & ALLOYS CORPORATION (REMACOR); U.S. Private, pg. 913
ROYAL ORDNANCE SPECIALTY METALS LTD.—British Aerospace p.l.c.; Int'l, pg. 217
SPS TECHNOLOGIES, INC.; U.S. Public, pg. 1419
SHOWA DENKO KAWASAKI WORKS—Showa Denko K.K.; Int'l, pg. 1236
SHOWA DENKO K.K.; Int'l, pg. 1236
WARATOKU STEEL CO., LTD.—Oki Electric Industry Company, Ltd.; Int'l, pg. 999

3315 — STEEL WIREDRAWING & STEEL NAILS & SPIKES

ACOR (ACIERS DE CONSTRUCTIONS RATIONALISES)—Groupe Usinor; Int'l, pg. 570
ABERDARE CABLES LTD.—Pirelli S.p.A.; Int'l, pg. 1059
ACCO WORLD CORPORATION—Fortune Brands, Inc.; U.S. Public, pg. 674
ACOS VILLARES S.A.; Int'l, pg. 23
ADCOM WIRE COMPANY—Leggett & Platt, Incorporated; U.S. Public, pg. 986
ALCOA FUJIKURA—Aluminum Company of America; U.S. Public, pg. 60
AMERICAN INSULATED WIRE CORP.—Leviton Mfg. Co., Inc.; U.S. Private, pg. 663
AMERON INTERNATIONAL CORPORATION; U.S. Public, pg. 98
AMSTED INDUSTRIES INCORPORATED; U.S. Private, pg. 68
ARBED S.A.; Int'l, pg. 78
ARROW FASTENER CO., INC.; U.S. Private, pg. 85
ASSOCIATED MATERIALS INCORPORATED; U.S. Private, pg. 91
ATLAS STEEL & WIRE—AmeriSteel; U.S. Private, pg. 65
AUSTRALIAN NATIONAL INDUSTRIES LIMITED; Int'l, pg. 100
BEKAERT CORPORATION—N.V. Bekaert S.A.; Int'l, pg. 184
N.V. BEKAERT S.A.; Int'l, pg. 183
BRIDON PLC; Int'l, pg. 215
THE BROKEN HILL PROPRIETARY COMPANY LIMITED; Int'l, pg. 223
CF & I STEEL, L.P.—Oregon Steel Mills Inc.; U.S. Public, pg. 1230
CABOT CORPORATION; U.S. Public, pg. 288
CAPARO WIRE COMPANY LTD.—Caparo Group Ltd.; Int'l, pg. 265
CARCLO ENGINEERING GROUP PLC; Int'l, pg. 268
CARPENTER STEEL DIV.—Carpenter Technology Corporation; U.S. Public, pg. 307
CARPENTER TECHNOLOGY CORPORATION; U.S. Public, pg. 307
CENTURY FENCE COMPANY; U.S. Private, pg. 226
CHICAGO STEEL & WIRE—MCM Enterprises, Inc.; U.S. Private, pg. 686
CLEANERS HANGER CO.; U.S. Private, pg. 245
COMPAGNIE GENERALE DES ETABLISSEMENTS MICHELIN; Int'l, pg. 322
CONTINENTAL/MIDLAND, INC.; U.S. Private, pg. 268
CONTRAN CORPORATION; U.S. Private, pg. 270
COPPERWELD FAYETTEVILLE DIVISION—Imetal; Int'l, pg. 662
DELTA ENFIELD CABLES (HOLDINGS) LTD.—Delta plc; Int'l, pg. 390
DELTA ENFIELD LTD.—Delta plc; Int'l, pg. 390
DOMTECH HOLDINGS, INC.—Leucadia National Corporation; U.S. Public, pg. 990
DUO-FAST CORPORATION; U.S. Private, pg. 347
E.C.D., INC.; U.S. Private, pg. 353
ELECTRONIC MATERIALS & REFRACTORY METALS DIV.—Cabot Corporation; U.S. Public, pg. 289
FANSTEEL, INC.; U.S. Public, pg. 612
FILERGIE S.N.C.—Pirelli S.p.A.; Int'l, pg. 1059
FOX VALLEY STEEL & WIRE CO.—Keystone Consolidated Industries, Inc.; U.S. Public, pg. 956
G.E. INFORMATION SERVICES—General Electric Company; U.S. Public, pg. 710
GS INDUSTRIES, INC.; U.S. Private, pg. 435
GENERAL CABLE CO.—Wassall Plc; Int'l, pg. 1487
A.J. GERRARD AND COMPANY; U.S. Private, pg. 449
GILL'S CABLES LIMITED—Carclo Engineering Group plc; Int'l, pg. 268
GOLDSTAR CABLE CO. LTD.—LG Group; Int'l, pg. 778
GUNNEBO INDUSTRIER AB; Int'l, pg. 578
HANDY & HARMAN; U.S. Public, pg. 780
HILTI INC.—Hilti AG; Int'l, pg. 620
ILRO SRL; Int'l, pg. 646
IMPHY S.A.—Groupe Usinor; Int'l, pg. 571
INDEPENDENT NAIL COMPANY—Maze Nails; U.S. Private, pg. 718
INDUSTRIAL WIRE PRODUCTS CORPORATION; U.S. Private, pg. 561
THE IVACO GROUP; Int'l, pg. 695
IVACO ROLLING MILLS LIMITED PARTNERSHIP—The Ivaco Group; Int'l, pg. 696
KEYSTONE CONSOLIDATED INDUSTRIES, INC.; U.S. Public, pg. 955
KEYSTONE FASTENERS—Keystone Consolidated Industries, Inc.; U.S. Public, pg. 956
KEYSTONE STEEL & WIRE CO.—Keystone Consolidated Industries, Inc.; U.S. Public, pg. 955
LACLEDE MID AMERICA INC.—Laclede Steel Company; U.S. Public, pg. 974
LEGGETT WIRE COMPANY—Leggett & Platt, Incorporated; U.S. Public, pg. 986
LOOS & CO., INC.; U.S. Private, pg. 675
MCM ENTERPRISES, INC.; U.S. Private, pg. 686
MMI PRODUCTS, INC.; U.S. Private, pg. 687
MACWHYTE CO.—Amsted Industries Incorporated; U.S. Private, pg. 68
MARYLAND SPECIALTY WIRE, INC.—Handy & Harman; U.S. Public, pg. 780
MAXCO, INC.; U.S. Public, pg. 1061
MAZE NAILS; U.S. Private, pg. 718
MECASLIN STREET CORPORATION—The Ivaco Group; Int'l, pg. 696
MERIT STEEL COMPANY, INC.—Leggett & Platt, Incorporated; U.S. Public, pg. 986
MID-STATE WIRE COMPANY—MCM Enterprises, Inc.; U.S. Private, pg. 686
NAGANO OKI ELECTRIC CO., LTD.—Oki Electric Industry Company, Ltd.; Int'l, pg. 999
NASHVILLE WIRE PRODUCT CO.; U.S. Private, pg. 775
NATIONAL-STANDARD CO.; U.S. Public, pg. 1160
NATIONAL-STANDARD CO. LTD.—National-Standard Co.; U.S. Public, pg. 1161
NATIONAL-STANDARD CO. CANADA—National-Standard Co.; U.S. Public, pg. 1161
NELSEN STEEL & WIRE CO.; U.S. Private, pg. 790
NOKIA SOURCING, INC.—Oy Nokia Ab/Nokia Group; Int'l, pg. 953
NORTHWESTERN STEEL & WIRE CO.; U.S. Public, pg. 1201
NORTHWESTERN STEEL & WIRE COMPANY-KENTUCKY, A DELAWARE CORP.—Northwestern Steel & Wire Co.; U.S. Public, pg. 1201
PEACE INDUSTRIES INC.; U.S. Private, pg. 845
PIRELLI CABLE CORPORATION—Pirelli S.p.A.; Int'l, pg. 1059
PIRELLI CABLE, POWER CABLE DIV.—Pirelli S.p.A.; Int'l, pg. 1059
PIRELLI S.P.A.; Int'l, pg. 1058
POLYMET CORP.; U.S. Private, pg. 875
PRICE BROTHERS CO.; U.S. Private, pg. 883
REEVES SOUTHEASTERN CORPORATION; U.S. Private, pg. 916
RIGBY-MARYLAND (STAINLESS) LTD.—Handy & Harman; U.S. Public, pg. 780
ROLLED ALLOYS/ATEK METALS DIVISION—Rolled Alloys, Inc.; U.S. Private, pg. 941
ROYAL PAPER BOX OF CALIFORNIA; U.S. Private, pg. 949
RUBBER GROUP—National-Standard Co.; U.S. Public, pg. 1160
SAM (SOCIETE DES ACIERIES DE MONTEREAU)—Groupe Usinor; Int'l, pg. 571
SMN (SOCIETE METALLURGIQUE DE NORMANDIE)—Groupe Usinor; Int'l, pg. 571
SANDVIK AB; Int'l, pg. 1185
SANDVIK BAHCO NORDEN AB—Sandvik AB; Int'l, pg. 1185
SANDVIK STAL FORSALJNINGS AB—Sandvik AB; Int'l, pg. 1185
SANDVIK STEEL CO.—Sandvik AB; Int'l, pg. 1185
SENCO PRODUCTS, INC.—SENCORP; U.S. Private, pg. 984
SENCORP; U.S. Private, pg. 983
SIVACO GEORGIA—The Ivaco Group; Int'l, pg. 696
SIVACO NEW YORK, INC.—The Ivaco Group; Int'l, pg. 696
SIVACO ONTARIO—The Ivaco Group; Int'l, pg. 696
SIVACO QUEBEC—The Ivaco Group; Int'l, pg. 696
SPECIALTY PRODUCTS GROUP—National-Standard Co.; U.S. Public, pg. 1160
STELWIRE LTD.—Stelco Inc.; Int'l, pg. 1299
STRANDFLEX DIVISION—Handy & Harman; U.S. Public, pg. 780
SUNRACK OYODO CO., LTD.—Nissho Iwai Corporation; Int'l, pg. 947
JOSEPH SYKES BROTHERS LTD.—Carclo Engineering Group plc; Int'l, pg. 268
THE TATA IRON AND STEEL CO. LTD.; Int'l, pg. 1356
TECHALLOY CO., INC.—Groupe Usinor; Int'l, pg. 572
THOMAS STEEL STRIP CORP.—Koninklijke Hoogovens N.V.; Int'l, pg. 756
TREFILARBED ARKANSAS INC.—Arbed S.A.; Int'l, pg. 80
TREFILARBED BETTEMBOURG S.A.R.L—Arbed S.A.; Int'l, pg. 80
TREFILARBED BISSEN S.A.R.L—Arbed S.A.; Int'l, pg. 80
TREFILARBED GREMBERGEN S.A.—Arbed S.A.; Int'l, pg. 80
TREFILUNION—Groupe Usinor; Int'l, pg. 571
THE TURNER & SEYMOUR MFG. COMPANY; U.S. Private, pg. 1109
UGINE-SAVOIE—Groupe Usinor; Int'l, pg. 571
ULBRICH STAINLESS STEELS & SPECIAL METALS, INC.; U.S. Private, pg. 1115
ULBRICH WIRE, INC.—Ulbrich Stainless Steels & Special Metals, Inc.; U.S. Private, pg. 1115
UNIMETAL—Groupe Usinor; Int'l, pg. 571
WHX CORPORATION; U.S. Public, pg. 1726
WALKER WIRE & STEEL COMPANY; U.S. Private, pg. 1147
WASHINGTON MANUFACTURING COMPANY, INC.—Fansteel, Inc.; U.S. Public, pg. 612
WATERLOO FURNITURE COMPONENTS LIMITED—Contran Corporation; U.S. Private, pg. 270
WEBSTER WIRE, INC.—Leggett & Platt, Incorporated; U.S. Public, pg. 986
WILLING B WIRE CORPORATION—Handy & Harman; U.S. Public, pg. 780
WILSON STEEL & WIRE CO.—MCM Enterprises, Inc.; U.S. Private, pg. 686
WIRE ROPE CORPORATION OF AMERICA, INC.; U.S. Private, pg. 1184
WIRE TECH, INC.—Hicks, Muse, Tate & Furst Inc.; U.S. Private, pg. 526
WIREMAKERS LIMITED—Fletcher Challenge Limited; Int'l, pg. 495
WISCONSIN WIRE & STEEL—Maxco, Inc.; U.S. Public, pg. 1061
JONAS WOODHEAD LIMITED—Carclo Engineering Group plc; Int'l, pg. 268

3316 — COLD ROLLED STEEL SHEET, STRIP & BARS

ALZ N.V.—Arbed S.A.; *Int'l*, pg. 79
THE AARQUE COMPANIES; *U.S. Private*, pg. 9
ACOS VILLARES S.A.; *Int'l*, pg. 23
ACOS VILLARES STEEL UNIT—Acos Villares S.A.; *Int'l*, pg. 23
ALFA, S.A. DE C.V.; *Int'l*, pg. 56
ALGOMA STEEL INC.; *Int'l*, pg. 56
ALLEGHENY LUDLUM-WASHINGTON PLANT—Allegheny Teledyne Incorporated; *U.S. Public*, pg. 43
ALLEGHENY TELEDYNE INCORPORATED; *U.S. Public*, pg. 43
ANCHOR LAMINA INC.; *Int'l*, pg. 75
ANCIENS ESTABLISSEMENTS GOYOT ET CIE—Standex International Corporation; *U.S. Public*, pg. 1507
ARBED S.A.; *Int'l*, pg. 78
ARMCO INC.-COSHOCTON OPERATIONS—Armco Inc.; *U.S. Public*, pg. 131
ARMCO INC.-MANSFIELD OPERATIONS—Armco Inc.; *U.S. Public*, pg. 131
ARMTEC—Jannock Limited; *Int'l*, pg. 698
ASSOCIATION COOPERATIVE ZELANDAISE DE CARBONISATION—Groupe Usinor; *Int'l*, pg. 572
BALDWIN INTERNATIONAL, INC.—Russel Metals Inc.; *Int'l*, pg. 1150
BALDWINS STEEL (PTY) LIMITED—Dorbyl Limited; *Int'l*, pg. 416
BIRFIELD PLANT OF GKN HARDY SPICER—GKN plc; *Int'l*, pg. 534
BOHLER GES.M.B.H.—Voest-Alpine Stahl AG; *Int'l*, pg. 1470
BOHLER UDDEHOLM AG—Voest-Alpine Stahl AG; *Int'l*, pg. 1471
BRUNTONS AREO PRODUCT—Carclo Engineering Group plc; *Int'l*, pg. 268
CTL STEEL CO.—Clark Grave Vault Co.; *U.S. Private*, pg. 243
CARCLO ENGINEERING GROUP PLC; *Int'l*, pg. 268
CARPENTER TECHNOLOGY CORPORATION; *U.S. Public*, pg. 307
CAVEXSA—Magellan International Trading; *U.S. Private*, pg. 694
CHAVANNE KETTIN—Groupe Usinor; *Int'l*, pg. 571
CISATOL—Groupe Usinor; *Int'l*, pg. 571
SIGMUND COHN CORP.; *U.S. Private*, pg. 250
COLTEC HOLDINGS INC; *U.S. Public*, pg. 401
CONSOLIDATED METAL PRODUCTS, INC.; *U.S. Private*, pg. 265
COSTAIN GROUP PLC; *Int'l*, pg. 336
CREUSOT-LOIRE INDUSTRIE—Groupe Usinor; *Int'l*, pg. 571
CROMDANE STEEL & ENGINEERING LIMITED—Australian National Industries Limited; *Int'l*, pg. 101
DSC LTD.; *U.S. Private*, pg. 305
E.S.P. EUROPESE STAALPREFABRICATLE N.V.—Arbed S.A.; *Int'l*, pg. 79
ESCO CORPORATION; *U.S. Private*, pg. 382
ETILAM-GRAVIGNY—Groupe Usinor; *Int'l*, pg. 571
FORECAST INTERNATIONAL—Groupe Usinor; *Int'l*, pg. 571
GPRI—Groupe Usinor; *Int'l*, pg. 571
A.J. GERRARD AND COMPANY; *U.S. Private*, pg. 449
GIBRALTAR STEEL CORP.; *U.S. Public*, pg. 742
GREER LIMESTONE CO.—Greer Steel Co.; *U.S. Private*, pg. 479
GREER STEEL CO.; *U.S. Private*, pg. 479
GREER STEEL COMPANY FERNDALE MICHIGAN SERVICE CENTER—Greer Steel Co.; *U.S. Private*, pg. 479
GRUPO IMSA S.A. DE C.V.; *Int'l*, pg. 575
HEIN, LEHMANN AG—Arbed S.A.; *Int'l*, pg. 80
HIGHVELD STEEL & VANADIUM CORPORATION—Anglo American Corporation of South Africa Limited; *Int'l*, pg. 76
HYNES INDUSTRIES INC.; *U.S. Private*, pg. 552
HYUNDAI STEEL INDUSTRIES INC.—Hyundai Motor Company; *Int'l*, pg. 642
I/N KOTE—Inland Steel Industries, Inc.; *U.S. Public*, pg. 879
I/N TEK—Inland Steel Industries, Inc.; *U.S. Public*, pg. 879
IMPHY S.A.—Groupe Usinor; *Int'l*, pg. 571
INLAND STEEL PRODUCTS COMPANY—Inland Steel Industries, Inc.; *U.S. Public*, pg. 879
J & L SPECIALTY PRODUCTS CORP.—Groupe Usinor; *Int'l*, pg. 572
JAPAN ALUMOWELD CO., LTD.—Imetal; *Int'l*, pg. 662
KAWASAKI STEEL CORPORATION; *Int'l*, pg. 726
KRUPP EDELSTAHLPROFILE GMBH—Fried. Krupp AG; *Int'l*, pg. 512
KRUPP HOESCH STAHLEXPORT GMBH—Fried. Krupp AG; *Int'l*, pg. 515
KRUPP STAHL KALTFORM GMBH—Fried. Krupp AG; *Int'l*, pg. 508
LAMINOIRS DE BRETAGNE—Groupe Usinor; *Int'l*, pg. 571
LASALLE STEEL COMPANY—Niagara Corporation; *U.S. Public*, pg. 1181
LEE STEEL STRIP LIMITED—Carclo Engineering Group plc; *Int'l*, pg. 268
LEE STEEL WIRE LIMITED—Carclo Engineering Group plc; *Int'l*, pg. 268
MMRA METALLURGIQUE ET MINIERE DE RODANGE-ATHUS S.A.—Arbed S.A.; *Int'l*, pg. 80
MARUBENI CORPORATION; *Int'l*, pg. 844
METALESCAUT (SOCIETE METALLURGIQUE DE L'ESCAUT)—Groupe Usinor; *Int'l*, pg. 571
METCRAFT, INC.—Emco Limited; *Int'l*, pg. 453
MOLTRUP STEEL PRODUCTS COMPANY; *U.S. Private*, pg. 756
NKK CORPORATION; *Int'l*, pg. 902
NS SALES INC.—Nippon Steel Corporation; *Int'l*, pg. 940
NATIONAL STEEL CORPORATION—NKK Corporation; *Int'l*, pg. 902
NATIONAL STEEL CORP., GRANITE CITY DIVISION—NKK Corporation; *Int'l*, pg. 902
NELSEN STEEL & WIRE CO.; *U.S. Private*, pg. 790
NEUMEYER FLIESSPRESSEN GMBH—Koninklijke Hoogovens N.V.; *Int'l*, pg. 755
NIPPON KOSHUHA STEEL CO., LTD.—Kobe Steel, Ltd.; *Int'l*, pg. 740
NISSHIN STEEL CO., LTD.; *Int'l*, pg. 946
NUCOR CORPORATION; *U.S. Public*, pg. 1205
NUCOR STEEL-SOUTH CAROLINA—Nucor Corporation; *U.S. Public*, pg. 1205
NUCOR WIRE—Nucor Corporation; *U.S. Public*, pg. 1205
OMNITRAX INC.—Broe Companies; *U.S. Private*, pg. 171
ORBEL CORPORATION; *U.S. Private*, pg. 819
PAV (SOCIETE INDUSTRIELE DE PRE A VAROIS)—Groupe Usinor; *Int'l*, pg. 570
PRECISION STEEL WAREHOUSE, INC.—Berkshire Hathaway Inc.; *U.S. Public*, pg. 217
QATAR STEEL CO. LTD.—Kobe Steel, Ltd.; *Int'l*, pg. 741
QUANEX CORPORATION; *U.S. Public*, pg. 1349
RAHNS SPECIALTY METALS, INC.—Groupe Usinor; *Int'l*, pg. 572
RATHBONE PRECISION METALS—Carpenter Technology Corporation; *U.S. Public*, pg. 307
RELIANCE STEEL FABRICATORS LIMITED—Anchor Lamina Inc.; *Int'l*, pg. 75
RENCO GROUP; *U.S. Private*, pg. 922
ROLLED STEEL PRODUCTS CORPORATION; *U.S. Private*, pg. 941
ROME STRIP STEEL CO., INC.; *U.S. Private*, pg. 942
SAM (SOCIETE DES ACIERIES DE MONTEREAU)—Groupe Usinor; *Int'l*, pg. 571
SNLFT (SOCIETE NOUVELLE DES LAMINOIRS A FROID DE THIONVILLE)—Groupe Usinor; *Int'l*, pg. 571
SAMSUNG SHIPBUILDING & HEAVY INDUSTRIES CO. LTD.—Samsung Group; *Int'l*, pg. 1183
SANDVIK AB; *Int'l*, pg. 1185
SANDVIK STEEL CO.—Sandvik AB; *Int'l*, pg. 1185
SCAW METAL LTD.—Anglo American Corporation of South Africa Limited; *Int'l*, pg. 76
SENIOR ENGINEERING GROUP, PLC.; *Int'l*, pg. 1220
P.T. SERNIWA STEEL WORKS—Nissho Iwai Corporation; *Int'l*, pg. 949
SIDMAR N.V.—Arbed S.A.; *Int'l*, pg. 79
SMITH WIRES LIMITED—Carclo Engineering Group plc; *Int'l*, pg. 268
SOCIETE METALLURGIQUE DE SAINT-CHELY D'APACHER—Groupe Usinor; *Int'l*, pg. 571
STEEL TECHNOLOGIES INC.; *U.S. Public*, pg. 1513
STEWARTS & LLOYDS TRADING (PTY) LIMITED—Dorbyl Limited; *Int'l*, pg. 416
THE TATA IRON AND STEEL CO. LTD.; *Int'l*, pg. 1356
THOMAS STEEL STRIP CORP.—Koninklijke Hoogovens N.V.; *Int'l*, pg. 756
THOMPSON STEEL CO., INC.; *U.S. Private*, pg. 1083
TREFILARBED KOREA CO. LTD.—Arbed S.A.; *Int'l*, pg. 80
USS-POSCO INDUSTRIES—USX Corporation; *U.S. Public*, pg. 1662
UDDEHOLM KRAFT AB—Voest-Alpine Stahl AG; *Int'l*, pg. 1471
UGINE ACG (ACIERS DE CHATILLON ET GUEUGNON)—Groupe Usinor; *Int'l*, pg. 571
UGINE-SAVOIE—Groupe Usinor; *Int'l*, pg. 571
ULBRICH STAINLESS STEELS & SPECIAL METALS, INC.; *U.S. Private*, pg. 1115
UNIMETAL—Groupe Usinor; *Int'l*, pg. 571
USINES LAPRADE—Groupe Usinor; *Int'l*, pg. 571
VOEST-ALPINE INTERNATIONAL CORPORATION—Voest-Alpine Stahl AG; *Int'l*, pg. 1470
VOEST-ALPINE STAHL JUDENBURG GES.M.B.H.—Voest-Alpine Stahl AG; *Int'l*, pg. 1470
VOEST-ALPINE STAHL LINZ GES.M.B.H.—Voest-Alpine Stahl AG; *Int'l*, pg. 1470
WHX CORPORATION; *U.S. Public*, pg. 1726
WESCO FINANCIAL CORPORATION—Berkshire Hathaway Inc.; *U.S. Public*, pg. 217
WORTHINGTON INDUSTRIES, INC.; *U.S. Public*, pg. 1780
WORTHINGTON STEEL CO.—Worthington Industries, Inc.; *U.S. Public*, pg. 1780
THE WORTHINGTON STEEL COMPANY-PENNSYLAVNIA—Worthington Industries, Inc.; *U.S. Public*, pg. 1780
PAUL WURTH S.A.—Arbed S.A.; *Int'l*, pg. 80

3317 — STEEL PIPE & TUBES

ABBEY ETNA MACHINE COMPANY; *U.S. Private*, pg. 9
ACME TUBE INC.; *U.S. Private*, pg. 14
ACOS VILLARES S.A.; *Int'l*, pg. 23
ALGOMA STEEL INC.; *Int'l*, pg. 56
ALLIED TUBE & CONDUIT CORPORATION—Tyco International Ltd.; *U.S. Public*, pg. 1650
ALPHA TUBE—Acme Metals Incorporated; *U.S. Public*, pg. 17
AMERICAN CAST IRON PIPE CO.; *U.S. Private*, pg. 51
AMERICAN PIPE AND CONSTRUCTION INTERNATIONAL—Ameron International Corporation; *U.S. Public*, pg. 99
AVESTA SANDVIK TUBE AB—British Steel Plc; *Int'l*, pg. 221
AVIS INDUSTRIAL CORPORATION; *U.S. Private*, pg. 102
BABCOCK CALORIZING LTD.—Babcock International Group PLC; *Int'l*, pg. 130
BARTON CONDUITS—Caparo Group Ltd.; *Int'l*, pg. 264
BARTON ENGINEERING LTD.—Caparo Group Ltd.; *Int'l*, pg. 264
BETA TUBE—Acme Metals Incorporated; *U.S. Public*, pg. 17
BOHLER UDDEHOLM AG—Voest-Alpine Stahl AG; *Int'l*, pg. 1471
BORAL LIMITED; *Int'l*, pg. 203
BRITISH STEEL SEAMLESS TUBES—British Steel Plc; *Int'l*, pg. 221
BRITISH STEEL SEAMLESS TUBES-WEDNESFIELD WORKS—British Steel Plc; *Int'l*, pg. 220
BRITISH STEEL TUBES & PIPES—British Steel Plc; *Int'l*, pg. 221
THE BROKEN HILL PROPRIETARY COMPANY LIMITED; *Int'l*, pg. 223
BULL MOOSE TUBES LTD.—Caparo Group Ltd.; *Int'l*, pg. 265
BUNDY AB—TI Group plc; *Int'l*, pg. 1341
BUNDY A/S—TI Group plc; *Int'l*, pg. 1341
BUNDY COLOMBIA S.A.—TI Group plc; *Int'l*, pg. 1342
BUNDY G.M.B.H.—TI Group plc; *Int'l*, pg. 1341
BUNDY GROUP—TI Group plc; *Int'l*, pg. 1341
BUNDY INTERNATIONAL—TI Group plc; *Int'l*, pg. 1340
BUNDY NORTH AMERICA—TI Group plc; *Int'l*, pg. 1340
BUNDY OF CANADA LTD.—TI Group plc; *Int'l*, pg. 1341
BUNDY SA—TI Group plc; *Int'l*, pg. 1341
BUNDY SNC—TI Group plc; *Int'l*, pg. 1342
BUNDY SPA—TI Group plc; *Int'l*, pg. 1341
BUNDY TUBING CO. (AUSTRALIA) PTY. LTD.—TI Group plc; *Int'l*, pg. 1341
BUNDY VENEZOLANA C.A.—TI Group plc; *Int'l*, pg. 1342
BURTCO, INC.; *U.S. Private*, pg. 188
CF & I STEEL, L.P.—Oregon Steel Mills Inc.; *U.S. Public*, pg. 1230
CAMROSE PIPE COMPANY—Oregon Steel Mills Inc.; *U.S. Public*, pg. 1230
CARGILL; *U.S. Private*, pg. 210
CENTRAL ILLINOIS STEEL COMPANY; *U.S. Private*, pg. 223
CERTIFIED ALLOY PRODUCTS, INC.—Vickers PLC; *Int'l*, pg. 1467
CONSOLIDATED PIPE & SUPPLY COMPANY; *U.S. Private*, pg. 266
COPPERWELD CHICAGO DIVISION—Imetal; *Int'l*, pg. 662
COPPERWELD FAYETTEVILLE DIVISION—Imetal; *Int'l*, pg. 662
COPPERWELD MIAMI DIVISION—Imetal; *Int'l*, pg. 662
COPPERWELD MIAMI INDUSTRIES—Imetal; *Int'l*, pg. 662
COPPERWELD TUBING—Imetal; *Int'l*, pg. 662
DUBIN-CLARK & COMPANY; *U.S. Private*, pg. 344
EATON INTERNATIONAL CORP.—Eaton Corporation; *U.S. Public*, pg. 558
EMAIL LIMITED-METALS GROUP—Email Limited; *Int'l*, pg. 450
ERLANGER TUBULAR CORPORATION—NS Group, Inc.; *U.S. Public*, pg. 1147
FERRO UNION, INC.; *U.S. Private*, pg. 402
CARL FROH GMBH & CO.—Rautaruukki Oy; *Int'l*, pg. 1088
GTS INDUSTRIES—Groupe Usinor; *Int'l*, pg. 571
GRANGES HEDLUND AB—Electrolux, AB; *Int'l*, pg. 439
HANDY & HARMAN; *U.S. Public*, pg. 780
HANDY & HARMAN TUBE CO., INC.—Handy & Harman; *U.S. Public*, pg. 780
HOFMANN INDUSTRIES, INC.; *U.S. Private*, pg. 533
INDIANA TUBE CORP.—Handy & Harman; *U.S. Public*, pg. 780
INTERNATIONAL COMFORT PRODUCTS; *U.S. Public*, pg. 898
JAMES STEEL & TUBE COMPANY—Avis Industrial Corporation; *U.S. Private*, pg. 102
JOHNSON METALL AB—Electrolux, AB; *Int'l*, pg. 439
KRUPP STAHL WOHNUNGSBAU GMBH—Fried. Krupp AG; *Int'l*, pg. 512
LA MEUSIENNE—Groupe Usinor; *Int'l*, pg. 571
LONE STAR STEEL COMPANY—Lone Star Technologies, Inc.; *U.S. Public*, pg. 1012
MANNESMANN A.G.; *Int'l*, pg. 834
MANNESMANN HANDEL AG—Mannesmann A.G.; *Int'l*, pg. 838
MANNESMANNROHREN-WERKE AG—Mannesmann A.G.; *Int'l*, pg. 835
MARKIN TUBING, INC.; *U.S. Private*, pg. 705
MARUICHI AMERICAN CORP.—Nissho Iwai Corporation; *Int'l*, pg. 947
MAVERICK TUBE CORPORATION; *U.S. Public*, pg. 1060
MCWANE CAST IRON PIPE CO.—McWane, Inc.; *U.S. Private*, pg. 725
MICHIGAN TUBE CO.—Hofmann Industries, Inc.; *U.S. Private*, pg. 533
MORRIS COUPLING CO.; *U.S. Private*, pg. 762
ROBERT MORTON AEROSPACE LIMITED—SLD Holdings Ltd.; *Int'l*, pg. 1160
NAYLOR PIPE COMPANY; *U.S. Private*, pg. 789
NEWPORT STEEL CORPORATION—NS Group, Inc.; *U.S. Public*, pg. 1147
NISSHO IWAI CORPORATION; *Int'l*, pg. 946
PALMER TUBE—Australian National Industries Limited; *Int'l*, pg. 101
PEERLESS TUBE CO. OF PUERTO RICO, INC.—Peerless Tube Company; *U.S. Public*, pg. 1269
PITT-DES MOINES, INC.; *U.S. Public*, pg. 1304
PITTSBURGH TUBE CO.; *U.S. Private*, pg. 867
PLYMOUTH TUBE COMPANY; *U.S. Private*, pg. 873
QUANEX CORPORATION; *U.S. Public*, pg. 1349
RAUTARUUKKI OY; *Int'l*, pg. 1088
SAMSTEEL, INC.—Ferro Union, Inc.; *U.S. Private*, pg. 402
SANDVIK AB; *Int'l*, pg. 1185
SANDVIK STEEL CANADA—Sandvik AB; *Int'l*, pg. 1188
SANDVIK STEEL CO.—Sandvik AB; *Int'l*, pg. 1185
SAWHILL TUBULAR DIV.—Armco Inc.; *U.S. Public*, pg. 131
SENIOR ENGINEERING GROUP, PLC.; *Int'l*, pg. 1220
SHAPCO, INC.; *U.S. Private*, pg. 989
SHARON TUBE COMPANY; *U.S. Private*, pg. 990
SOUTHERN CROSS INVESTMENT CO.—Imetal; *Int'l*, pg. 662
STEWARTS & LLOYDS TRADING (PTY) LIMITED—Dorbyl Limited; *Int'l*, pg. 416
STUPP BROS, INC.; *U.S. Private*, pg. 1048
SUPERIOR GROUP, INC.; *U.S. Private*, pg. 1055
SUPERIOR TUBE COMPANY; *U.S. Private*, pg. 1056
THE TATA IRON AND STEEL CO. LTD.; *Int'l*, pg. 1356
TUBE BEND—Macristy Industries, Inc.; *U.S. Private*, pg. 693

TUBE FORM, INC.—HMI Industries; U.S. Public, pg. 771
TUBETEC—Plymouth Tube Company; U.S. Private, pg. 873
TUBOS DE ACERO DE MEXICO, S.A.; Int'l, pg. 1426
UNR-LEAVITT DIV.—ROHN Industries, Inc.; U.S. Public, pg. 1404
UDDEHOLM KRAFT AB—Voest-Alpine Stahl AG; Int'l, pg. 1471
UNIVERSAL STEEL TUBE CO. LIMITED—Plymouth Tube Company; U.S. Private, pg. 873
USUI BUNDY TUBING CO. LTD.—TI Group plc; Int'l, pg. 1341
VALEXY—Groupe Usinor; Int'l, pg. 571
VALMONT INDUSTRIES, INC.; U.S. Public, pg. 1706
VAN LEEUWEL TUBES LTD.—Van Leeuwen Pipe and Tube Group B.V.; Int'l, pg. 1450
VAN LEEUWEN BUIZEN BELGIUM N.V.—Van Leeuwen Pipe and Tube Group B.V.; Int'l, pg. 1450
P. VAN LEEUWEN JR'S BUIZENHANDEL B.V.—Van Leeuwen Pipe and Tube Group B.V.; Int'l, pg. 1449
VAN LEEUWEN PIPE AND TUBE EASTERN AUSTRALIA PTY. LTD.—Van Leeuwen Pipe and Tube Group B.V.; Int'l, pg. 1450
VAN LEEUWEN PIPE AND TUBE GROUP B.V.; Int'l, pg. 1449
VAN LEEUWEN PRECISION BV—Van Leeuwen Pipe and Tube Group B.V.; Int'l, pg. 1449
VAN LEEUWEN ROHREN GMBH—Van Leeuwen Pipe and Tube Group B.V.; Int'l, pg. 1450
VAN LEEUWEN STAINLESS—Van Leeuwen Pipe and Tube Group B.V.; Int'l, pg. 1449
VAN LEEUWEN TUBES LTD.—Van Leeuwen Pipe and Tube Group B.V.; Int'l, pg. 1450
VAN LEEUWEN TUBES SA—Van Leeuwen Pipe and Tube Group B.V.; Int'l, pg. 1450
VAN LEEUWEN TUBOS ESPANA S.A.E.—Van Leeuwen Pipe and Tube Group B.V.; Int'l, pg. 1450
VOEST-ALPINE KREMS GES.M.B.H.—Voest-Alpine Stahl AG; Int'l, pg. 1470
VOEST-ALPINE STAHLROHR KINDBERG GES.M.B.H.—Voest-Alpine Stahl AG; Int'l, pg. 1470
VOEST-ALPINE STEEL CORP.—Voest-Alpine Stahl AG; Int'l, pg. 1471
VON ROLL AG; Int'l, pg. 1480
WAUKESHA CHERRY-BURRELL—United Dominion Industries, Ltd.; U.S. Public, pg. 1677
WELDED TUBE—Australian National Industries Limited; Int'l, pg. 101
WELDED TUBE COMPANY—Australian National Industries Limited; Int'l, pg. 101
WELLAND PIPE LTD.—Stelco Inc.; Int'l, pg. 1299
WHEATLAND TUBE COMPANY; U.S. Private, pg. 1170

3321 — GRAY & DUCTILE IRON FOUNDRIES

ACME FOUNDRY, INC.; U.S. Private, pg. 13
ALVESTA GJUTERI AB—Svedala Industri AB; Int'l, pg. 1323
ALVESTA GJUTERI AB—Trelleborg AB; Int'l, pg. 1419
AMERICAN CAST IRON PIPE CO.; U.S. Private, pg. 51
AMSTED INDUSTRIES INCORPORATED; U.S. Private, pg. 68
ARMTEC—Jannock Limited; Int'l, pg. 698
ATCHISON CASTING CORPORATION; U.S. Public, pg. 142
JOHN BOUCHARD & SONS COMPANY; U.S. Private, pg. 161
BRITT INDUSTRIES, INC.—Kurdziel Industries, Inc.; U.S. Private, pg. 637
BRITTANY CORPORATION; U.S. Private, pg. 169
THE BUDD COMPANY—Thyssen AG; Int'l, pg. 1388
BURNHAM; U.S. Public, pg. 270
CMI INTERNATIONAL INC.; U.S. Private, pg. 195
CWC CASTINGS TEXTRON—Textron Inc.; U.S. Public, pg. 1590
CWC TEXTRON COMPANY—Textron Inc.; U.S. Public, pg. 1590
CAST METALS OPERATIONS—Zurn Industries, Inc.; U.S. Public, pg. 1794
CATERPILLAR INC.; U.S. Public, pg. 315
CENTEC ROLL CORPORATION—Park Corp.; U.S. Private, pg. 839
CENTRE FOUNDRY & MACHINE CO.—The Dyson-Kissner-Moran Corporation; U.S. Private, pg. 351
CERTIFIED ALLOY PRODUCTS, INC.—Vickers PLC; Int'l, pg. 1467
CINCINNATI MILACRON U.K. LIMITED—Cincinnati Milacron Inc.; U.S. Public, pg. 368
CITATION CORPORATION; U.S. Public, pg. 376
CLOW WATER SYSTEMS CORP.—McWane, Inc.; U.S. Private, pg. 725
DENVER THOMAS, INC.—Svedala Industri AB; Int'l, pg. 1325
DERLAN INDUSTRIES LIMITED; Int'l, pg. 395
DEXTER COMPANY; U.S. Private, pg. 329
DOCK FOUNDRY COMPANY; U.S. Private, pg. 337
EMG EISEN-UND METALLGUSSWERK GMBH—Deutsche Babcock AG; Int'l, pg. 400
EAGLE INDUSTRIES, INC.—Great American Management & Investment, Inc.; U.S. Private, pg. 473
EAST JORDAN IRON WORKS; U.S. Private, pg. 356
ELECTRON CORP.; U.S. Private, pg. 370
B. ELLIOTT PLC.; Int'l, pg. 448
ELYRIA FOUNDRY COMPANY; U.S. Private, pg. 373
EMPIRE FOUNDRY—Crane Co.; U.S. Public, pg. 457
GEORG FISCHER LTD.; Int'l, pg. 488
FLENDER GUSS GMBH—Deutsche Babcock AG; Int'l, pg. 400
FUNDITUBO—Saint-Gobain; Int'l, pg. 1176
G & H CASTINGS CORPORATION—ITT Industries, Inc.; U.S. Public, pg. 861
GIW INDUSTRIES, INC.—KSB Aktiengesellschaft; Int'l, pg. 721
GENERAL HOUSEWARES CORP.; U.S. Public, pg. 715
GENERAL MOTORS CANADA FOUNDRY DIV.—General Motors Corporation; U.S. Public, pg. 722
GIDDINGS & LEWIS CASTING TECHNOLOGY—Thyssen AG; Int'l, pg. 1389
GIDDINGS & LEWIS, INC.—Thyssen AG; Int'l, pg. 1389
GOETZE CORP. OF AMERICA—T & N Plc; Int'l, pg. 1335
GOUGLER INDUSTRIES, INC.; U.S. Private, pg. 466
GOULDS PUMPS, INCORPORATED—ITT Industries, Inc.; U.S. Public, pg. 860
GREAT LAKES CASTINGS CORPORATION—Brittany Corporation; U.S. Private, pg. 169
GREDE FOUNDRIES, INC.; U.S. Private, pg. 476
GREDE-PRYOR, INC.—Grede Foundries, Inc.; U.S. Private, pg. 476
GREGG INDUSTRIES, INC.; U.S. Private, pg. 480
GRIFFIN PIPE PRODUCTS CO.—Amsted Industries Incorporated; U.S. Private, pg. 68
HALBERGERHUTTE GMBH—Saint-Gobain; Int'l, pg. 1176
HELMICK CORPORATION; U.S. Private, pg. 520
RODNEY HUNT COMPANY; U.S. Private, pg. 549
HYUNDAI PRECISION & INDUSTRY CO., LTD.—Hyundai Motor Company; Int'l, pg. 642
INDUSTRIJA DELOVA AUTOMOBILA, KIKINDA—General Motors Corporation; U.S. Public, pg. 724
JTC LLC; U.S. Private, pg. 579
JANNOCK LIMITED; Int'l, pg. 698
JOHNSTOWN CORPORATION; U.S. Private, pg. 595
KATY INDUSTRIES, INC.; U.S. Public, pg. 944
KNORR-BREMSE AG; Int'l, pg. 738
KOBE STEEL, LTD.; Int'l, pg. 740
KOHLER COMPANY; U.S. Private, pg. 630
KUBOTA CORP.; Int'l, pg. 762
KURDZIEL INDUSTRIES, INC.; U.S. Private, pg. 637
KURDZIEL IRON OF ROTHBURY, INC.—Kurdziel Industries, Inc.; U.S. Private, pg. 637
KURDZIEL IRON OF WAUSEON, INC.—Kurdziel Industries, Inc.; U.S. Private, pg. 637
AB LJUNGBY STALGJUTERI—Trelleborg AB; Int'l, pg. 1419
LORFONTE—Groupe Usinor; Int'l, pg. 571
MAGIC CIRCLE MANUFACTURING DIV.—Acme Foundry, Inc.; U.S. Private, pg. 13
MCWANE CAST IRON PIPE CO.—McWane, Inc.; U.S. Private, pg. 725
MCWANE, INC.; U.S. Private, pg. 725
MILWAUKEE GREY IRON—JTC LLC; U.S. Private, pg. 579
NEENAH FOUNDRY COMPANY; U.S. Private, pg. 790
NORTH AMERICAN ROYALTIES, INC.; U.S. Private, pg. 803
OSCO INDUSTRIES INC.; U.S. Private, pg. 820
PENTAIR, INC.; U.S. Public, pg. 1273
PREUSSAG INTERNATIONAL STEEL CORP.—Preussag AG; Int'l, pg. 1070
PROSPECT FOUNDRY, INC.—Atchison Casting Corporation; U.S. Public, pg. 142
SWAYNE ROBINSON & COMPANY; U.S. Private, pg. 936
ROSS ALUMINUM FOUNDRIES—Eagle-Picher Industries, Inc.; U.S. Private, pg. 355
RUSSELL CASTINGS LTD.—B. Elliott plc.; Int'l, pg. 449
SCAW METAL LTD.—Anglo American Corporation of South Africa Limited; Int'l, pg. 76
I.H. SCHLEZINGER, INC.—Worthington Industries, Inc.; U.S. Public, pg. 1780
SPECIALTY CASTINGS—The Johnson Corporation; U.S. Private, pg. 591
STANTON PLC—Saint-Gobain; Int'l, pg. 1177
STEEL PRODUCTS DIV.—Carlyle Holding Corporation; U.S. Private, pg. 213
STURGIS FOUNDRY CORP.—Armstrong International, Inc.; U.S. Private, pg. 83
TB WOOD'S CORPORATION; U.S. Public, pg. 1562
THE TURNER & SEYMOUR MFG. COMPANY; U.S. Private, pg. 1109
UBE INDUSTRIES LTD.; Int'l, pg. 1426
UGINE ACG (ACIERS DE CHATILLON ET GUEUGNON)—Groupe Usinor; Int'l, pg. 571
UNITED STATES LOCK & HARDWARE CO.—York Barbell Co., Inc.; U.S. Private, pg. 1196
UNITED STATES PIPE & FOUNDRY COMPANY, INC.—Walter Industries, Inc.; U.S. Public, pg. 1736
VON ROLL AG; Int'l, pg. 1480
WAGNER CASTINGS COMPANY—Intermet Corporation; U.S. Public, pg. 894
WAGNERWARE CORPORATION; U.S. Private, pg. 1146
WALTER INDUSTRIES, INC.; U.S. Public, pg. 1736
WARD MANUFACTURING, INC.; U.S. Private, pg. 1149
WATEROUS COMPANY—American Cast Iron Pipe Co.; U.S. Private, pg. 52
WAUPACA FOUNDRY INC.—Thyssen AG; Int'l, pg. 1389
WESTCODE SEMICONDUCTORS INC. (U.S.A.)—BTR plc; Int'l, pg. 127
YORK BARBELL CO., INC.; U.S. Private, pg. 1196

3322 — MALLEABLE IRON FOUNDRIES

CMI INTERNATIONAL INC.; U.S. Private, pg. 195
DENVER THOMAS, INC.—Svedala Industri AB; Int'l, pg. 1325
EAGLE INDUSTRIES, INC.—Great American Management & Investment, Inc.; U.S. Private, pg. 473
GEORG FISCHER LTD.; Int'l, pg. 488
FRAZER & JONES DIV.—The Eastern Company; U.S. Public, pg. 548
GAS EQUIPMENT COMPANY, INC.; U.S. Private, pg. 440
GENERAL SIGNAL CORPORATION; U.S. Public, pg. 726
KOBE STEEL, LTD.; Int'l, pg. 740
KOBE STEEL U.S.A. INC. (NEW YORK)—Kobe Steel, Ltd.; Int'l, pg. 740
LANCASTER MALLEABLE CASTINGS COMPANY; U.S. Private, pg. 645
MCWANE, INC.; U.S. Private, pg. 725
TBV, INC.—Victaulic Company of America; U.S. Private, pg. 1138
VICTAULIC COMPANY OF AMERICA; U.S. Private, pg. 1138
VICTAULIC COMPANY OF CANADA LIMITED—Victaulic Company of America; U.S. Private, pg. 1138
VICTAULIC TOOL COMPANY—Victaulic Company of America; U.S. Private, pg. 1138
VON ROLL AG; Int'l, pg. 1480
VON ROLL EISEN & STAHLGIESSEREI AG—Von Roll AG; Int'l, pg. 1480
WARD MANUFACTURING, INC.; U.S. Private, pg. 1149
WEBSTER INDUSTRIES INC.; U.S. Private, pg. 1157

3324 — STEEL INVESTMENT FOUNDRIES

AMERICAN FOUNDRY GROUP, INC.; U.S. Private, pg. 54
BUCKEYE STEEL CASTINGS COMPANY—Worthington Industries, Inc.; U.S. Public, pg. 1780
CMI INTERNATIONAL INC.; U.S. Private, pg. 195
ESCAST, INC.—Fansteel, Inc.; U.S. Public, pg. 612
FANSTEEL, INC.; U.S. Public, pg. 612
HOWMET CORPORATION—Carlyle Holding Corporation; U.S. Private, pg. 213
HOWMET CORPORATION—Thiokol Corporation; U.S. Public, pg. 1597
HOWMET TURBINE COMPONENT CORPORATION—Carlyle Holding Corporation; U.S. Private, pg. 213
KUBOTA CORP.; Int'l, pg. 762
MICROFUSION—Pechiney S.A.; Int'l, pg. 1028
PCC EXPORTS, INC.—Precision Castparts Corp.; U.S. Public, pg. 1320
PRECISION CASTPARTS CORP.; U.S. Public, pg. 1320
SMS AKTIENGESELLSCHAFT—MAN Aktiengesellschaft; Int'l, pg. 825
SMS SCHLOEMANN-SIEMAG AG—MAN Aktiengesellschaft; Int'l, pg. 826
SIERRA CAST INC.—Wyman-Gordon; U.S. Public, pg. 1782
UDDEHOLM TOOLING AB—Voest-Alpine Stahl AG; Int'l, pg. 1471
WORTHINGTON INDUSTRIES, INC.; U.S. Public, pg. 1780
WYMAN-GORDON; U.S. Public, pg. 1782
WYMAN-GORDON INVESTMENT CASTINGS—Wyman-Gordon; U.S. Public, pg. 1782
WYMAN-GORDON INVESTMENT CASTINGS, INC.—Wyman-Gordon; U.S. Public, pg. 1782

3325 — STEEL FOUNDRIES, NEC

APV REFINERY PRODUCTS CORP.—Siebe plc; Int'l, pg. 1241
AHLSTROM MACHINERY KARHULA STEEL FOUNDRY—A. Ahlstrom Corporation; Int'l, pg. 33
AICHI STEEL WORKS, LTD.; Int'l, pg. 35
AG AJIKAWA CORPORATION; Int'l, pg. 39
AMCAST INDUSTRIAL CORPORATION; U.S. Public, pg. 63
AMERICAN CAST IRON PIPE CO.; U.S. Private, pg. 51
AMERICAN FOUNDRY GROUP, INC.; U.S. Private, pg. 54
AMERICAN STEEL FOUNDRIES—Amsted Industries Incorporated; U.S. Private, pg. 68
AMSTED INDUSTRIES INCORPORATED; U.S. Private, pg. 68
ATCHISON CASTING CORPORATION; U.S. Public, pg. 142
ATLAS FOUNDRY & MACHINE CO.—TIC United Corporation; U.S. Private, pg. 1063
BACHMANN GMBH—Fried. Krupp AG; Int'l, pg. 514
BOHLER UDDEHOLM AG—Voest-Alpine Stahl AG; Int'l, pg. 1471
C.I.S. CO. OF ALABAMA—Central Illinois Steel Company; U.S. Private, pg. 223
CMI INTERNATIONAL INC.; U.S. Private, pg. 195
CERTIFIED ALLOY PRODUCTS, INC.—Vickers PLC; Int'l, pg. 1467
CHINA STEEL CORPORATION; Int'l, pg. 285
CIREX BV—Koninklijke Hoogovens N.V.; Int'l, pg. 753
COMPOFLEX—Senior Engineering Group, plc.; Int'l, pg. 1221
COSTAIN GROUP PLC; Int'l, pg. 336
DE GLOBE BV—Koninklijke Hoogovens N.V.; Int'l, pg. 753
DENVER THOMAS, INC.—Svedala Industri AB; Int'l, pg. 1325
DURALOY TECHNOLOGIES—Park Corp.; U.S. Private, pg. 839
DURHAM TUBE—Senior Engineering Group, plc.; Int'l, pg. 1221
EISENMETALL GESELLSCHAFT MBH—Fried. Krupp AG; Int'l, pg. 514
EISENMETALL LAGER GMBH—Fried. Krupp AG; Int'l, pg. 514
ESCO CORPORATION; U.S. Private, pg. 382
ESCO LTD.—Esco Corporation; U.S. Private, pg. 383
FERRUM INC.—DoFasco, Inc.; Int'l, pg. 414
FERRUM INC.—Jannock Limited; Int'l, pg. 699
FORD CASTING DIVISION—Ford Motor Company; U.S. Public, pg. 662
FROG SWITCH & MANUFACTURING COMPANY; U.S. Private, pg. 429
GLYNWED CONSUMER & CONSTRUCTION PRODUCTS LTD.—Glynwed International PLC; Int'l, pg. 554
GLYNWED INTERNATIONAL PLC; Int'l, pg. 554
GOULDS PUMPS, INCORPORATED—ITT Industries, Inc.; U.S. Public, pg. 860
GREDE FOUNDRIES, INC.; U.S. Private, pg. 476
GRIFFIN CANADA INC.—Amsted Industries Incorporated; U.S. Private, pg. 68
GRIFFIN WHEEL CO.—Amsted Industries Incorporated; U.S. Private, pg. 68
GROUPE USINOR; Int'l, pg. 570
GUSAB STAINLESS AB—Sandvik AB; Int'l, pg. 1185
HILL-LOMA, INC.—Goldman Financial Group; U.S. Private, pg. 461
HOESCH ROTHE ERDE AG—Fried. Krupp AG; Int'l, pg. 509

HOOGOVENS GROEP B.V.—Koninklijke Hoogovens N.V.; *Int'l*, pg. 753
HOVELMANN & CO. EISENGROSSHANDLUNG GMBH—Fried. Krupp AG; *Int'l*, pg. 514
HUTCHENS INDUSTRIES INC.; *U.S. Private*, pg. 550
INDUSTRIAS TRATERH, S.A.—Senior Engineering Group, plc.; *Int'l*, pg. 1222
J & L FIBER SERVICES, INC.—Harnischfeger Industries, Inc.; *U.S. Public*, pg. 789
JANNOCK LIMITED; *Int'l*, pg. 698
THE JAPAN STEEL WORKS, LTD.—Mitsui & Co., Ltd.; *Int'l*, pg. 878
JOHNSON METALL AB—Electrolux, AB; *Int'l*, pg. 439
JOHNSTOWN CORPORATION; *U.S. Private*, pg. 595
KERVICK ENTERPRISES, INC.; *U.S. Private*, pg. 616
KLOCKNER-WERKE AG; *Int'l*, pg. 736
KOHLSWA JERNVERK AB—Electrolux, AB; *Int'l*, pg. 439
KRUPP EDELSTAHLPROFILE GMBH—Fried. Krupp AG; *Int'l*, pg. 512
KRUPP HOESCH STAHLEXPORT GMBH—Fried. Krupp AG; *Int'l*, pg. 515
KRUPP HOESCH STAHLHANDEL GMBH—Fried. Krupp AG; *Int'l*, pg. 514
KRUPP HOESCH STAHLHANDEL RHEINLAND GMBH—Fried. Krupp AG; *Int'l*, pg. 514
KRUPP NIROSTA GMBH—Fried. Krupp AG; *Int'l*, pg. 513
MANNESMANN HOESCH PRAZISROHR GMBH—Fried. Krupp AG; *Int'l*, pg. 513
MARUBENI CORPORATION; *Int'l*, pg. 844
MAYNARD STEEL CASTING COMPANY; *U.S. Private*, pg. 718
MCGRAW/KOKOSING, INC.—Kokosing Construction Company, Inc.; *U.S. Private*, pg. 631
MILLER & CO.—Veba AG; *Int'l*, pg. 1458
NIPPON STEEL CORPORATION; *Int'l*, pg. 939
OLSONITE CORPORATION; *U.S. Private*, pg. 815
OTTO JUNKER GMBH LAMMERSDORF; *Int'l*, pg. 1014
PACIFIC STEEL CASTING CO.; *U.S. Private*, pg. 832
PHOENIX STEEL TUBE—Senior Engineering Group, plc.; *Int'l*, pg. 1221
PIEDMONT METAL PRODUCTS, INC.—Williams Industries, Inc.; *U.S. Public*, pg. 1770
POWERFLEX—Senior Engineering Group, plc.; *Int'l*, pg. 1221
PRECISION DRAWN TUBE—Senior Engineering Group, plc.; *Int'l*, pg. 1222
RIVERSIDE PRODUCTS DIV.—Everett Smith Group, Ltd.; *U.S. Private*, pg. 1008
ROLOCK, INC.; *U.S. Private*, pg. 942
ROSS & CATHERALL LIMITED—Vickers PLC; *Int'l*, pg. 1467
S.C.I. STEEL MILL PTY. LTD.—Smorgon A.R.C.; *Int'l*, pg. 1269
SMS AKTIENGESELLSCHAFT—MAN Aktiengesellschaft; *Int'l*, pg. 825
SMS SCHLOEMANN-SIEMAG AG—MAN Aktiengesellschaft; *Int'l*, pg. 826
SANDUSKY INTERNATIONAL INC.; *U.S. Private*, pg. 964
SANDUSKY LIMITED—Sandusky International Inc.; *U.S. Private*, pg. 965
SANDVIK GMBH—Sandvik AB; *Int'l*, pg. 1186
SANDVIK LTD.—Sandvik AB; *Int'l*, pg. 1186
AB SANDVIK STEEL—Sandvik AB; *Int'l*, pg. 1185
SENIOR BIGWOOD LIMITED—Senior Engineering Group, plc.; *Int'l*, pg. 1220
SENIOR ENGINEERING PRODUCTS BUSINESS AREA—Senior Engineering Group, plc.; *Int'l*, pg. 1220
SENIOR ENGINEERING TIFT GMBH—Senior Engineering Group, plc.; *Int'l*, pg. 1223
SENIOR FOSTER WHEELER CONSTRUCTION DIVISION—Senior Engineering Group, plc.; *Int'l*, pg. 1221
SENIOR FOSTER WHEELER INDUSTRIAL BOILER DIVISION—Senior Engineering Group, plc.; *Int'l*, pg. 1221
SENIOR FOSTER WHEELER POWER DIVISION—Senior Engineering Group, plc.; *Int'l*, pg. 1221
SENIOR GREEN ECONOMISER DIVISION—Senior Engineering Group, plc.; *Int'l*, pg. 1221
SENIOR HEAT TREATMENT LIMITED—Senior Engineering Group, plc.; *Int'l*, pg. 1221
SENIOR LUKE MATERIALS HANDLING DIVISION—Senior Engineering Group, plc.; *Int'l*, pg. 1221
SENIOR TIFT B.V.—Senior Engineering Group, plc.; *Int'l*, pg. 1223
SENIOR TIFT, INC.—Senior Engineering Group, plc.; *Int'l*, pg. 1222
SENIOR TIFT LIMITED—Senior Engineering Group, plc.; *Int'l*, pg. 1221
SENIOR TIFT PTE. LTD.—Senior Engineering Group, plc.; *Int'l*, pg. 1223
SENIOR TUBE LIMITED—Senior Engineering Group, plc.; *Int'l*, pg. 1221
SHAW-PERKINS INC.—Reactive Metals & Alloys Corporation (REMACOR); *U.S. Private*, pg. 913
SIVYER STEEL CORPORATION—Everett Smith Group, Ltd.; *U.S. Private*, pg. 1008
SMORGON A.R.C.; *Int'l*, pg. 1269
SMORGON CONSOLIDATED INDUSTRIES—Smorgon A.R.C.; *Int'l*, pg. 1269
SOCIETE IVOIRIENNE DE PREFABRIQUES ET D'ACCESSOIRES INDUSTRIELS S.A.—Nissho Iwai Corporation; *Int'l*, pg. 949
STARMET CORPORATION; *U.S. Public*, pg. 1511
SUMITOMO METAL INDUSTRIES, LTD.; *Int'l*, pg. 1315
TP MANIPULATIONS—Senior Engineering Group, plc.; *Int'l*, pg. 1222
TRP-PROFILE UND BAUELEMENTE GMBH—Fried. Krupp AG; *Int'l*, pg. 508
THOMAS STEEL STRIP CORP.—Koninklijke Hoogovens N.V.; *Int'l*, pg. 756
THYSSEN AG; *Int'l*, pg. 1387
TUBE PRODUCTS—Senior Engineering Group, plc.; *Int'l*, pg. 1222
UDDEHOLM KRAFT AB—Voest-Alpine Stahl AG; *Int'l*, pg. 1471
UNITED FLEXIBLE—Senior Engineering Group, plc.; *Int'l*, pg. 1221
VON ROLL AG; *Int'l*, pg. 1480
YAMAHA CORPORATION; *Int'l*, pg. 1515
ZWJSEN B.V.—Koninklijke Hoogovens N.V.; *Int'l*, pg. 754

3331 — PRIMARY SMELTING & REFINING OF COPPER

ASARCO INCORPORATED; *U.S. Public*, pg. 137
CHINO MINES COMPANY—Phelps Dodge Corporation; *U.S. Public*, pg. 1287
COMPANIA MINERA DISPUTADA DE LAS CONDES S.S.—Exxon Corporation; *U.S. Public*, pg. 601
COPPER RANGE COMPANY—Metallgesellschaft AG; *Int'l*, pg. 862
GALAMBA METALS, INC.—Galamet, Inc.; *U.S. Private*, pg. 437
GALAMET, INC.; *U.S. Private*, pg. 437
KENNECOTT HOLDINGS CORPORATION—Rio Tinto PLC; *Int'l*, pg. 1119
KOBE STEEL, LTD.; *Int'l*, pg. 740
MAGMA METALS COMPANY—The Broken Hill Proprietary Company Limited; *Int'l*, pg. 224
MCKECHNIE METAL PRODUCTS—McKechnie PLC; *Int'l*, pg. 852
MINORCO—Anglo American Corporation of South Africa Limited; *Int'l*, pg. 77
OUTOKUMPU METALS (USA) INC.—Outokumpu Oyj; *Int'l*, pg. 1015
OUTOKUMPU WENMEC AB—Outokumpu Oyj; *Int'l*, pg. 1017
OUTOKUMPU WENMEC, INC.—Outokumpu Oyj; *Int'l*, pg. 1017
OUTOKUMPU WENMEC OY—Outokumpu Oyj; *Int'l*, pg. 1017
PALABORA MINING CO. LTD.—Rio Tinto PLC; *Int'l*, pg. 1119
PHELPS DODGE CORPORATION; *U.S. Public*, pg. 1286
REFRIGERATION & COPPER PRODUCT DIVISION—Parker Hannifin Corporation; *U.S. Public*, pg. 1259
SUMITOMO METAL MINING CO., LTD.; *Int'l*, pg. 1316
UNION MINIERE; *Int'l*, pg. 1441

3334 — PRIMARY PRODUCTION OF ALUMINUM

ADEC AUTOMATION—Adec International Automation Corp.; *U.S. Private*, pg. 17
ALCAN ALUMINIUM LIMITED; *Int'l*, pg. 50
ALCAN ENFIELD ALLOYS LTD.—Delta plc; *Int'l*, pg. 391
ALCAN FRANCE—Alcan Aluminium Limited; *Int'l*, pg. 51
ALCAN METAL CENTRES—Alcan Aluminium Limited; *Int'l*, pg. 51
ALCAN RECYCLING—Alcan Aluminium Limited; *Int'l*, pg. 51
ALCAN SIAM LIMITED—Alcan Aluminium Limited; *Int'l*, pg. 51
ALCAN SPECIALTY AEROSPACE—Alcan Aluminium Limited; *Int'l*, pg. 51
ALCOA ALUMINIO S.A.—Aluminum Company of America; *U.S. Public*, pg. 61
ALCOA NEDERLAND HOLDING B. V.—Aluminum Company of America; *U.S. Public*, pg. 62
ALCOA OF AUSTRALIA LIMITED—Aluminum Company of America; *U.S. Public*, pg. 62
ALUCAM-SOCTRAL—Pechiney S.A.; *Int'l*, pg. 1030
ALUMAR CONSORTIUM—Aluminum Company of America; *U.S. Public*, pg. 62
ALUMAX INC.; *U.S. Public*, pg. 59
ALUMAX OF SOUTH CAROLINA MT. HOLLY—Alumax Inc.; *U.S. Public*, pg. 60
ALUMAX PRIMARY ALUMINUM CORPORATION—Alumax Inc.; *U.S. Public*, pg. 60
ALUMINA PARTNERS OF JAMAICA (ALPART)—Maxxam Inc.; *U.S. Public*, pg. 1062
ALUMINUM DE GRECE—Pechiney S.A.; *Int'l*, pg. 1030
ALUMINUM PECHINEY—Pechiney S.A.; *Int'l*, pg. 1028
ALUMINUM SMELTING CO. OF NIGERIA—Reynolds Metals Company; *U.S. Public*, pg. 1386
ALUSUISSE-LONZA HOLDING LTD.; *Int'l*, pg. 66
BOYNE SMELTERS LIMITED—Comalco Limited; *Int'l*, pg. 307
BRITISH ALCAN ALUMINIUM PLC—Alcan Aluminium Limited; *Int'l*, pg. 51
CENTURY ALUMINUM COMPANY; *U.S. Public*, pg. 328
COLUMBIA FALLS ALUMINUM COMPANY; *U.S. Private*, pg. 255
COMALCO ALUMINIUM (BELL BAY) LIMITED—Comalco Limited; *Int'l*, pg. 307
COMALCO LIMITED; *Int'l*, pg. 307
COMALCO NEW ZEALAND—Comalco Limited; *Int'l*, pg. 307
COMALCO SMELTING—Comalco Limited; *Int'l*, pg. 307
CROFT METALS, INC.; *U.S. Private*, pg. 290
EASTALCO ALUMINUM COMPANY—Alumax Inc.; *U.S. Public*, pg. 60
ELKEM ASA; *Int'l*, pg. 446
GALAMBA METALS, INC.—Galamet, Inc.; *U.S. Private*, pg. 437
GALAMET, INC.; *U.S. Private*, pg. 437
GEDDES GRANT SPROSTONS INDUS., LTD.—Alcan Aluminium Limited; *Int'l*, pg. 52
HAMBURGER ALUMINIUM-WERK GESELLSCHAFT MIT BESCHRANKTER HAFTUNG—Reynolds Metals Company; *U.S. Public*, pg. 1387
HOOGOVENS ALUMINIUM BAUSYSTEME GMBH—Koninklijke Hoogovens N.V.; *Int'l*, pg. 755
HOOGOVENS ALUMINIUM GMBH—Koninklijke Hoogovens N.V.; *Int'l*, pg. 755
HOOGOVENS ALUMINIUM HUTTENWERK GMBH—Koninklijke Hoogovens N.V.; *Int'l*, pg. 755
HOOGOVENS ALUMINIUM WALZPRODUKTE GMBH—Koninklijke Hoogovens N.V.; *Int'l*, pg. 755
HUNTER ENGINEERING CO., INC.—FKI Plc; *Int'l*, pg. 474
INDIAN ALUMINIUM CO. LTD.—Alcan Aluminium Limited; *Int'l*, pg. 51
S.A. INDUSTRIAS VOTORANTIM; *Int'l*, pg. 677
INTALCO ALUMINUM CORP.—Alumax Inc.; *U.S. Public*, pg. 60
KAISER ALUMINUM & CHEMICAL CORPORATION—Maxxam Inc.; *U.S. Public*, pg. 1062
KAISER JAMAICA BAUXITE CO.—Maxxam Inc.; *U.S. Public*, pg. 1062
LINN PRODUCTS, INC.; *U.S. Private*, pg. 669
MAXXAM INC.; *U.S. Public*, pg. 1062
MINALEX—Alcan Aluminium Limited; *Int'l*, pg. 52
MINORCO—Anglo American Corporation of South Africa Limited; *Int'l*, pg. 77
NEW ZEALAND ALUMINIUM SMELTERS LTD.—Comalco Limited; *Int'l*, pg. 307
NORSK ALCOA A/S—Aluminum Company of America; *U.S. Public*, pg. 62
NORSK HYDRO A.S; *Int'l*, pg. 959
ORMET PRIMARY ALUMINUM CORP—Ormet Corporation; *U.S. Private*, pg. 820
PECHINEY CORPORATION-AUSTRALIAN BRANCH—Pechiney S.A.; *Int'l*, pg. 1031
PECHINEY NEDERLAND NV—Pechiney S.A.; *Int'l*, pg. 1031
PECHINEY S.A.; *Int'l*, pg. 1027
QAL GLADSTONE PLANT—Maxxam Inc.; *U.S. Public*, pg. 1062
QUADION CORPORATION; *U.S. Private*, pg. 898
QUEENSLAND ALUMINA LIMITED—Alcan Aluminium Limited; *Int'l*, pg. 52
QUEENSLAND ALUMINA LIMITED—Maxxam Inc.; *U.S. Public*, pg. 1063
RAVENSWOOD ALUMINUM CORP.—Century Aluminum Company; *U.S. Public*, pg. 328
REYNOLDS METALS COMPANY; *U.S. Public*, pg. 1385
REYNOLDS METALS COMPANY-TROUTDALE—Reynolds Metals Company; *U.S. Public*, pg. 1386
SORAL - SOR-NORGE ALUMINUM A/S—Alusuisse-Lonza Holding Ltd.; *Int'l*, pg. 69
VAW ALUMINUM AG—Viag AG; *Int'l*, pg. 1466
VASSEN ALUMINIUM BV—Koninklijke Hoogovens N.V.; *Int'l*, pg. 753
VOLTA ALUMINIUM CO. LTD. (VALCO)—Maxxam Inc.; *U.S. Public*, pg. 1063
WORTHINGTON CYLINDER CANADA—Worthington Industries, Inc.; *U.S. Public*, pg. 1781
WORTHINGTON CYLINDER CORPORATION—Worthington Industries, Inc.; *U.S. Public*, pg. 1780

3339 — PRIMARY SMELTING & REFINING OF NONFERROUS METALS, EXCEPT COPPER & ALUMINUM

ALCAN ALUMINIUM LIMITED; *Int'l*, pg. 50
ALCAN SMELTERS & CHEMICALS LTD.—Alcan Aluminium Limited; *Int'l*, pg. 50
ALTASTEEL LTD.—Stelco Inc.; *Int'l*, pg. 1299
BRITANNIA REFINED METALS LTD.—M.I.M. Holdings Ltd.; *Int'l*, pg. 827
BRUSH WELLMAN INC.; *U.S. Public*, pg. 266
CABOT CORPORATION; *U.S. Public*, pg. 288
CAROLMET DIVISION—Union Miniere; *Int'l*, pg. 1442
CEZUS—Framatome SA; *Int'l*, pg. 503
CEZUS—Pechiney S.A.; *Int'l*, pg. 1029
COOKSON GROUP PLC; *Int'l*, pg. 328
CORNING INCORPORATED; *U.S. Public*, pg. 448
CRUCIBLE MATERIALS CORP.; *U.S. Private*, pg. 293
DEGUSSA AG; *Int'l*, pg. 388
DEGUSSA CORPORATION—Degussa AG; *Int'l*, pg. 388
T.L. DIAMOND COMPANY; *U.S. Private*, pg. 330
THE DOW CHEMICAL COMPANY; *U.S. Public*, pg. 522
ELECTRONIC MATERIALS & REFRACTORY METALS DIV.—Cabot Corporation; *U.S. Public*, pg. 289
ELKEM ALLOY—Elkem ASA; *Int'l*, pg. 447
ELKEM FISKAA SILICON—Elkem ASA; *Int'l*, pg. 448
ENGELHARD CORPORATION; *U.S. Public*, pg. 582
FALCONBRIDGE NIKKELVERK A/S—EdperBrascan Corporation; *Int'l*, pg. 434
GALAMBA METALS, INC.—Galamet, Inc.; *U.S. Private*, pg. 437
GALAMET, INC.; *U.S. Private*, pg. 437
HANDY & HARMAN MANUFACTURING (SINGAPORE) PTE. LTD.—Handy & Harman; *U.S. Public*, pg. 780
HANDY & HARMAN OF CANADA LTD.—Handy & Harman; *U.S. Public*, pg. 780
HERMANN H.C. STARCK BERLIN GBMH & CO. KG—Bayer AG; *Int'l*, pg. 174
HIGHVELD STEEL & VANADIUM CORPORATION—Anglo American Corporation of South Africa Limited; *Int'l*, pg. 76
HUNTER ENGINEERING CO., INC.—FKI Plc; *Int'l*, pg. 474
IMETAL; *Int'l*, pg. 661
INDUSTRIAS PENOLES S.A. DE C.V.; *Int'l*, pg. 677
S.A. INDUSTRIAS VOTORANTIM; *Int'l*, pg. 677
INTERAMERICAN ZINC, INC.—IMCO Recycling Inc.; *U.S. Public*, pg. 871
KRONOS TITAN GMBH—Contran Corporation; *U.S. Private*, pg. 271
KRUPP VDM GMBH—Fried. Krupp AG; *Int'l*, pg. 509
LEACH & GARNER COMPANY; *U.S. Private*, pg. 655
LURGI AG—Metallgesellschaft AG; *Int'l*, pg. 861
MHD BERZELIUS DUISBURG GMBH—Metallgesellschaft AG; *Int'l*, pg. 861
MATERIALS RESEARCH CORPORATION—Sony Corporation; *Int'l*, pg. 1283
MCGEAN-ROHCO, INC.; *U.S. Private*, pg. 721
MINORCO—Anglo American Corporation of South Africa Limited; *Int'l*, pg. 77
MITSUBISHI MATERIALS CORP.; *Int'l*, pg. 874

MIZUNO HANDY HARMAN, LTD.—Handy & Harman; *U.S. Public*, pg. 780
MOLYCORP, INC.—Unocal Corporation; *U.S. Public*, pg. 1698
NRC INC.—Bayer AG; *Int'l*, pg. 173
NEY DENTAL INTERNATIONAL—Degussa AG; *Int'l*, pg. 388
NIHON SEIKO CO. LTD.—Nissho Iwai Corporation; *Int'l*, pg. 947
OUTOKUMPU WENMEC AB—Outokumpu Oyj; *Int'l*, pg. 1017
OUTOKUMPU WENMEC, INC.—Outokumpu Oyj; *Int'l*, pg. 1017
OUTOKUMPU WENMEC OY—Outokumpu Oyj; *Int'l*, pg. 1017
LOUIS PADNOS IRON & METAL CO.; *U.S. Private*, pg. 834
PYROMET, INC.; *U.S. Private*, pg. 897
QUALITY METALS—Sony Corporation; *Int'l*, pg. 1283
QUARTZ & SILICE—Saint-Gobain; *Int'l*, pg. 1176
REACTIVE METALS & ALLOYS CORPORATION (REMACOR); *U.S. Private*, pg. 913
REYNOLDS YILGARN GOLD OPERATIONS LIMITED—Reynolds Metals Company; *U.S. Public*, pg. 1387
SALEM MANUFACTURING FACILITY—Mitsubishi Materials Corp.; *Int'l*, pg. 875
STERN-LEACH COMPANY—Cookson Group plc; *Int'l*, pg. 329
STROUD RESOURCES LTD.; *Int'l*, pg. 1304
SUMITOMO METAL MINING CO., LTD.; *Int'l*, pg. 1316
TAISIL ELECTRONIC MATERIALS CORPORATION—China Steel Corporation; *Int'l*, pg. 286
TAM CERAMICS INC.—Cookson Group plc; *Int'l*, pg. 329
TITANIUM METALS CORPORATION—Contran Corporation; *U.S. Private*, pg. 270
TRELLEBORG MINING & METALS DIV.—Trelleborg AB; *Int'l*, pg. 1422
TREMONT CORPORATION—Contran Corporation; *U.S. Private*, pg. 270

3341 — SECONDARY SMELTING & REFINING OF NONFERROUS METALS

AFFIMET—Pechiney S.A.; *Int'l*, pg. 1028
ALCOA MANUFACTURING (G.B.) LTD.—Aluminum Company of America; *U.S. Public*, pg. 62
ALCOA RECYCLING CO.—Aluminum Company of America; *U.S. Public*, pg. 61
ALUMAX INC.; *U.S. Public*, pg. 59
ALUMINIUM DELFZIJL BV—Koninklijke Hoogovens N.V.; *Int'l*, pg. 753
ALUMINUM OF KOREA LTD.—Hyundai Motor Company; *Int'l*, pg. 641
ALUSUISSE-LONZA AMERICA INC.—Alusuisse-Lonza Holding Ltd.; *Int'l*, pg. 67
ANHEUSER-BUSCH RECYCLING CORPORATION—Anheuser-Busch Companies, Inc.; *U.S. Public*, pg. 114
ARORA-MATTHEY LIMITED—Johnson Matthey Public Limited Company; *Int'l*, pg. 714
B.U.S. BERZELIUS UMWELT-SERVICE GMBH—Metallgesellschaft AG; *Int'l*, pg. 860
JOSEPH BEHR & SONS INC.; *U.S. Private*, pg. 130
BELMONT METALS, INC.; *U.S. Private*, pg. 132
BRITANNIA REFINED METALS LTD.—M.I.M. Holdings Ltd.; *Int'l*, pg. 827
CANNON-MUSKEGON CORP.—SPS Technologies, Inc.; *U.S. Public*, pg. 1420
A. COHEN & CO. P.L.C.; *Int'l*, pg. 306
COLONIAL METALS CO.; *U.S. Private*, pg. 253
CONNELL LIMITED PARTNERSHIP; *U.S. Private*, pg. 264
COOKSON MATTHEY PRINT—Johnson Matthey Public Limited Company; *Int'l*, pg. 713
COPPER REFINERIES PTY. LTD.—M.I.M. Holdings Ltd.; *Int'l*, pg. 827
DEGUSSA AG; *Int'l*, pg. 388
EASCO INC.; *U.S. Public*, pg. 548
EL CAMPO ALUMINUM CO.—Reynolds Metals Company; *U.S. Public*, pg. 1386
ELIXIR INDUSTRIES; *U.S. Private*, pg. 371
A.W. FRASER—McKechnie PLC; *Int'l*, pg. 852
FURUKAWA ALUMINUM CO., LTD.—The Furukawa Electric Co., Ltd.; *Int'l*, pg. 530
THE FURUKAWA ELECTRIC CO., LTD.; *Int'l*, pg. 530
GEC ENGINEERING (ACCRINGTON) LTD.—The General Electric Company, p.l.c.; *Int'l*, pg. 544
GLINES & RHODES, INC.; *U.S. Private*, pg. 457
GRILLO-WERKE AG—Metallgesellschaft AG; *Int'l*, pg. 861
GULF COAST RECYCLING; *U.S. Private*, pg. 487
HANDY & HARMAN; *U.S. Public*, pg. 780
HERAEUS PRECIOUS METALS MANAGEMENT INC.—Heraeus Holding GmbH; *Int'l*, pg. 616
W.C. HERAEUS GMBH—Heraeus Holding GmbH; *Int'l*, pg. 616
HOOGOVENS METALS BV—Koninklijke Hoogovens N.V.; *Int'l*, pg. 754
HURON VALLEY STEEL CORP.; *U.S. Private*, pg. 549
IMCO RECYCLING INC.; *U.S. Public*, pg. 870
IMCO RECYCLING INC.—IMCO Recycling Inc.; *U.S. Public*, pg. 871
IMETAL; *Int'l*, pg. 661
IMPHY S.A.—Groupe Usinor; *Int'l*, pg. 571
IMSAMET, INC.—EnviroSource, Inc.; *U.S. Public*, pg. 587
INDUSTRIA NAVARRIA DEL ALUMINIO, S.A.—Reynolds Metals Company; *U.S. Public*, pg. 1387
ISCOR; *Int'l*, pg. 688
JOHNSON MATTHEY & BRANDENBERGER AG—Johnson Matthey Public Limited Company; *Int'l*, pg. 714
JOHNSON MATTHEY INC.—Johnson Matthey Public Limited Company; *Int'l*, pg. 713
JOHNSON MATTHEY LIMITED—Johnson Matthey Public Limited Company; *Int'l*, pg. 714
JOHNSON MATTHEY P.L.C.—Johnson Matthey Public Limited Company; *Int'l*, pg. 713
JOHNSON MATTHEY (PTY.) LIMITED—Johnson Matthey Public Limited Company; *Int'l*, pg. 714
JOHNSON MATTHEY PUBLIC LIMITED COMPANY; *Int'l*, pg. 713
JOHNSON MATTHEY REFINING, INC.—Johnson Matthey Public Limited Company; *Int'l*, pg. 713
S.A. JOHNSON MATTHEY NV.—Johnson Matthey Public Limited Company; *Int'l*, pg. 714
KAISER ALUMINUM & CHEMICAL CORPORATION—Maxxam Inc.; *U.S. Public*, pg. 1062
KAISER ALUMINUM & CHEMICAL OF CANADA LIMITED—Maxxam Inc.; *U.S. Public*, pg. 1062
KLIL INDUSTRIES LTD.—IDB Holding Corporation; *Int'l*, pg. 644
KRUPP VDM GMBH—Fried. Krupp AG; *Int'l*, pg. 509
LEACH & GARNER COMPANY; *U.S. Private*, pg. 655
MHD BERZELIUS DUISBURG GMBH—Metallgesellschaft AG; *Int'l*, pg. 861
MAGMA METALS COMPANY—The Broken Hill Proprietary Company Limited; *Int'l*, pg. 224
MCKECHNIE PACIFIC—McKechnie PLC; *Int'l*, pg. 852
METAL RESOURCES, INC.—IMCO Recycling Inc.; *U.S. Public*, pg. 871
METALLWERKE REFONDA AG—Alusuisse-Lonza Holding Ltd.; *Int'l*, pg. 67
MUELLER INDUSTRIES, INC.; *U.S. Public*, pg. 1141
NORDDEUTSCHE AFFINERIE AG—Metallgesellschaft AG; *Int'l*, pg. 861
NORTHLAND ALUMINUM PRODUCTS, INC.; *U.S. Private*, pg. 805
OKUMURA METALS CO., LTD.—The Furukawa Electric Co., Ltd.; *Int'l*, pg. 530
A.J. OSTER CARIBE, INC.—Olin Corporation; *U.S. Public*, pg. 1219
A.J. OSTER COMPANY—Olin Corporation; *U.S. Public*, pg. 1219
A.J. OSTER FOILS, INC.—Olin Corporation; *U.S. Public*, pg. 1219
A.J. OSTER WEST, INC.—Olin Corporation; *U.S. Public*, pg. 1219
OSTER ALLOYS—Cookson Group plc; *Int'l*, pg. 329
OUTOKUMPU METALS (USA) INC.—Outokumpu Oyj; *Int'l*, pg. 1015
P.C. WIAUX—Union Miniere; *Int'l*, pg. 1442
PALABORA MINING CO. LTD.—Rio Tinto PLC; *Int'l*, pg. 1119
PATRICK METALS—Patrick Industries Inc.; *U.S. Public*, pg. 1265
PECHINEY S.A.; *Int'l*, pg. 1027
QUANEX CORPORATION; *U.S. Public*, pg. 1349
QUEMETCO, INC.—Quexco Incorporated; *U.S. Private*, pg. 900
QUEXCO INCORPORATED; *U.S. Private*, pg. 900
RSR CORPORATION—Quexco Incorporated; *U.S. Private*, pg. 900
RECICLAJES ENVALIC, C.A.—Reynolds Metals Company; *U.S. Public*, pg. 1387
RECLAIMERS, INC.—Philip Services Corp.; *Int'l*, pg. 1050
REVERE SMELTING & REFINING CORP.—Quexco Incorporated; *U.S. Private*, pg. 901
REYNOLDS ALUMINIUM HOLLAND B.V.—Reynolds Metals Company; *U.S. Public*, pg. 1387
REYNOLDS METALS COMPANY; *U.S. Public*, pg. 1385
REYNOLDS PHILIPPINE CORPORATION—Reynolds Metals Company; *U.S. Public*, pg. 1387
ROESSING BRONZE CO.; *U.S. Private*, pg. 939
SPS TECHNOLOGIES, INC.; *U.S. Public*, pg. 1419
SASOL ALPHA OLEFINS—Sasol Limited; *Int'l*, pg. 1196
SAYANAL—Reynolds Metals Company; *U.S. Public*, pg. 1387
SHOWA ALUMINUM CORP.—Showa Denko K.K.; *Int'l*, pg. 1236
SHOWA ALUMINUM CORP. OF AMERICA—Showa Denko K.K.; *Int'l*, pg. 1236
SOUTH PACIFIC ALUMINUM—International Paper Company; *U.S. Public*, pg. 905
SOUTHWIRE COMPANY; *U.S. Private*, pg. 1019
TABER METALS, INC.—Tang Industries Inc.; *U.S. Private*, pg. 1068
TECHNIC INCORPORATED; *U.S. Private*, pg. 1071
TRARYDS METALL AB—Svedala Industri AB; *Int'l*, pg. 1323
TRARYDS METALL AB—Trelleborg AB; *Int'l*, pg. 1419
TRELLEBORG MINING & METALS DIV.—Trelleborg AB; *Int'l*, pg. 1422
UNION MINIERE; *Int'l*, pg. 1441
VAW ALUMINUM AG—Viag AG; *Int'l*, pg. 1466
VEM ERZ UND STAHL GMBH—Internatio-Muller N.V.; *Int'l*, pg. 682
VIKING METALLURGICAL CORPORATION—Firth-Rixson Plc; *Int'l*, pg. 488
WESTERN EXTRUSIONS; *U.S. Private*, pg. 1165

3351 — ROLLING, DRAWING & EXTRUDING OF COPPER

ALBION WIRE, INC.—Hicks, Muse, Tate & Furst Inc.; *U.S. Private*, pg. 526
ALBION WIRE INC., KENDALLVILLE WIRE DIVISION—Hicks, Muse, Tate & Furst Inc.; *U.S. Private*, pg. 526
ALGONA FOOD EQUIPMENT CO.—Hormel Foods Corp.; *U.S. Public*, pg. 840
AMPCO METAL INCORPORATED; *U.S. Private*, pg. 67
AMPCO METAL LTD.—Ampco Metal Incorporated; *U.S. Private*, pg. 67
AMPCO METAL S.A.—Ampco Metal Incorporated; *U.S. Private*, pg. 67
ANCIENS ESTABLISSEMENTS GOYOT ET CIE—Standex International Corporation; *U.S. Public*, pg. 1507
BULL MOOSE TUBE COMPANY—Caparo Group Ltd.; *Int'l*, pg. 265
CAMDEN WIRE CO., INC.—Hicks, Muse, Tate & Furst Inc.; *U.S. Private*, pg. 526
CHICAGO EXTRUDED METALS CO.; *U.S. Private*, pg. 234
CHICAGO MAGNET WIRE CORP.—Philips Electronics N.V.; *Int'l*, pg. 1054
COLEMAN CABLE SYSTEMS, INC.—Kuhlman Corporation; *U.S. Public*, pg. 968
DELTA ENFIELD METALS LTD.—Delta plc; *Int'l*, pg. 390
DELTA ENFIELD WIRES LTD.—Delta plc; *Int'l*, pg. 390
ELECTRONIC INTERNCONNECT SYSTEMS INC.—Noma Industries Limited; *Int'l*, pg. 955
ERICSSON, INC.—Telefonaktiebolaget LM Ericsson; *Int'l*, pg. 1364
ESSEX INTERNATIONAL, INC.; *U.S. Public*, pg. 593
FLECK MANUFACTURING INC.—Noma Industries Limited; *Int'l*, pg. 955
GUARDIAN PRODUCTS/CAPITAL WIRE—Wassall Plc; *Int'l*, pg. 1487
H & H TUBE & MANUFACTURING CO.; *U.S. Private*, pg. 489
HALSTEAD INDUSTRIES, INC.; *U.S. Private*, pg. 496
HANDY & HARMAN ELECTRONIC MATERIALS CORP.—Handy & Harman; *U.S. Public*, pg. 780
HOWELL METAL COMPANY—Commercial Metals Company; *U.S. Public*, pg. 413
IGC ADVANCED SUPERCONDUCTORS, INC.—Intermagnetics General Corporation; *U.S. Public*, pg. 893
IWG-ARDMORE—Hicks, Muse, Tate & Furst Inc.; *U.S. Private*, pg. 526
INTERMAGNETICS GENERAL CORPORATION; *U.S. Public*, pg. 893
KM-EUROPA METAL AKTIENGESELLSCHAFT; *Int'l*, pg. 719
KME IBERTUBOS S.A.—KM-Europa Metal Aktiengesellschaft; *Int'l*, pg. 719
THE KANTHAL CORPORATION—Kanthal AB; *Int'l*, pg. 723
E. & E. KAYE LIMITED; *Int'l*, pg. 727
KENNECOTT HOLDINGS CORPORATION—Rio Tinto PLC; *Int'l*, pg. 1119
THE MARMON GROUP, INC.; *U.S. Private*, pg. 706
THE NIPPERT COMPANY—Outokumpu Oyj; *Int'l*, pg. 1016
OLIN CORPORATION; *U.S. Public*, pg. 1218
ONEIDA LTD.; *U.S. Public*, pg. 1225
OUTOKUMPU AMERICAN BRASS CO.—Outokumpu Oyj; *Int'l*, pg. 1016
OUTOKUMPU COPPER BRASS ROD AB—Outokumpu Oyj; *Int'l*, pg. 1017
OUTOKUMPU COPPER KENOSHA, INC.—Outokumpu Oyj; *Int'l*, pg. 1017
OUTOKUMPU COPPER PARTNER AB—Outokumpu Oyj; *Int'l*, pg. 1017
OUTOKUMPU COPPER STRIP AB—Outokumpu Oyj; *Int'l*, pg. 1017
OUTOKUMPU COPPER STRIP B.V.—Outokumpu Oyj; *Int'l*, pg. 1017
OUTOKUMPU COPPER TUBES AB—Outokumpu Oyj; *Int'l*, pg. 1017
OUTOKUMPU PORICOPPER OY—Outokumpu Oyj; *Int'l*, pg. 1016
PHELPS DODGE COPPER PRODUCTS COMPANY—Phelps Dodge Corporation; *U.S. Public*, pg. 1287
PHELPS DODGE CORPORATION; *U.S. Public*, pg. 1286
READING TUBE CORP.—Cambridge-Lee Industries, Inc.; *U.S. Private*, pg. 202
ROESSING BRONZE CO.; *U.S. Private*, pg. 939
ROLL FORMING CORPORATION; *U.S. Private*, pg. 941
SERVAAS, INC.; *U.S. Private*, pg. 986
SHUNT TECHNOLOGY—Hicks, Muse, Tate & Furst Inc.; *U.S. Private*, pg. 526
SINGAPORE KOBE PRIVATE LIMITED—Kobe Steel, Ltd.; *Int'l*, pg. 741
SMALL TUBE PRODUCTS CO., INC.—Wolverine Tube Inc.; *U.S. Public*, pg. 1775
SOUTHWIRE COMPANY; *U.S. Private*, pg. 1019
SUPERIOR GROUP, INC.; *U.S. Private*, pg. 1055
TAMAQUA CABLE PRODUCTS CORP.—Draka Kabel B.V.; *Int'l*, pg. 417
TECHNICAL MATERIALS, INC.—Brush Wellman Inc.; *U.S. Public*, pg. 266
ULLRICH COPPER, INC.—Foster Wheeler Corporation; *U.S. Public*, pg. 677
WIDISA METAL S.A.—FKI Plc; *Int'l*, pg. 474
WOLVERINE TUBE INC.; *U.S. Public*, pg. 1774

3353 — ALUMINUM SHEET, PLATE & FOIL

ALCAN ALUMINIO DEL URUGUAY S.A.—Alcan Aluminium Limited; *Int'l*, pg. 50
ALCAN ALUMINIUM FOLIENWERK VERWALTUNGS GMBH—Alcan Aluminium Limited; *Int'l*, pg. 50
ALCAN ALUMINIUMFOLIENWERK GMBH & CO.—Alcan Aluminium Limited; *Int'l*, pg. 50
ALCAN CONSUMER PRODUCTS—Alcan Aluminium Limited; *Int'l*, pg. 51
ALCAN EKCO—Alcan Aluminium Limited; *Int'l*, pg. 51
ALCAN RORSCHACH AG—Alcan Aluminium Limited; *Int'l*, pg. 51
ALCONOR S.A.—Aluminum Company of America; *U.S. Public*, pg. 62
ALUMAX FOILS, INC.—Alumax Inc.; *U.S. Public*, pg. 60
ALUMAX INC.; *U.S. Public*, pg. 59
ALUMINIO REYNOLDS, SANTO DOMINGO, S.A.—Reynolds Metals Company; *U.S. Public*, pg. 1386
ARTEAGA, SOCIEDAD ANOMIMA, "ARTEAGA, S.A."—Reynolds Metals Company; *U.S. Public*, pg. 1386
BRADBURY COMPANY, INC.; *U.S. Private*, pg. 163
BRITISH ALCAN ALUMINIUM PLC—Alcan Aluminium Limited; *Int'l*, pg. 51
BRITISH ALCAN ROLLED PRODUCTS LIMITED—Alcan Aluminium Limited; *Int'l*, pg. 51
COMALCO LIMITED; *Int'l*, pg. 307
COMMONWEALTH ALUMINUM-LEWISPORT—Commonwealth Industries, Inc.; *U.S. Public*, pg. 415
COMMONWEALTH INDUSTRIES, INC.; *U.S. Public*, pg. 415

EG & G KT AEROFAB—EG & G, Inc.; *U.S. Public*, pg. 542
ELIXIR INDUSTRIES; *U.S. Private*, pg. 371
ENVASES VALENCIANOS, S.A.—Reynolds Metals Company; *U.S. Public*, pg. 1386
ENVASES Y ALIMENTACION MADRID, S.A.—Reynolds Metals Company; *U.S. Public*, pg. 1386
ENVASES Y ALIMENTACION, S.A.—Reynolds Metals Company; *U.S. Public*, pg. 1387
INDIAN ALUMINIUM CO. LTD.—Alcan Aluminium Limited; *Int'l*, pg. 51
INDUSTRIA NAVARRIA DEL ALUMINIO, S.A.—Reynolds Metals Company; *U.S. Public*, pg. 1387
J.W. ALUMINUM COMPANY—Walter Industries, Inc.; *U.S. Public*, pg. 1736
KAISER ALUMINUM & CHEMICAL CORPORATION—Maxxam Inc.; *U.S. Public*, pg. 1062
LAWSON MARDON FLEXIBLE PACKAGING, INC.—Alusuisse-Lonza Holding Ltd.; *Int'l*, pg. 67
LAWSON MARDON SINGEN GMBH—Alusuisse-Lonza Holding Ltd.; *Int'l*, pg. 69
MELITTA NORTH AMERICA, INC.—Melitta Unternehmensgruppe Bentz KG; *Int'l*, pg. 857
MELITTA U.S.A., INC.—Melitta Unternehmensgruppe Bentz KG; *Int'l*, pg. 857
NEW ZEALAND FIBRE GLASS—International Paper Company; *U.S. Public*, pg. 904
NICHOLS ALUMINUM—Quanex Corporation; *U.S. Public*, pg. 1350
NICHOLS-HOMESHIELD—Quanex Corporation; *U.S. Public*, *pg. 1350*
NICHOLS-HOMESHIELD CASTING—Quanex Corporation; *U.S. Public*, pg. 1350
NORANDAL U.S.A.—EdperBrascan Corporation; *Int'l*, pg. 434
PHENIX ALUMINIUM S.A.—Koninklijke Hoogovens N.V.; *Int'l*, pg. 755
RJR NABISCO HOLDINGS CORP.; *U.S. Public*, pg. 1354
REYNOLDS METALS COMPANY; *U.S. Public*, pg. 1385
ROLL FORMING CORPORATION; *U.S. Private*, pg. 941
RUEDAS DE ALUMINIO C.A. "RUALCA"—Reynolds Metals Company; *U.S. Public*, pg. 1387
SPECTRULITE CONSORTIUM, INC.; *U.S. Private*, pg. 1024
TENNECO PACKAGING—Tenneco Inc.; *U.S. Public*, pg. 1579
UNITED ALUMINUM CORPORATION; *U.S. Private*, pg. 1120

3354 — ALUMINUM EXTRUDED PRODUCTS

APL CORPORATION; *U.S. Private*, pg. 7
ADEC AUTOMATION—Adec International Automation Corp.; *U.S. Private*, pg. 17
ADVANCED METAL FORMING CV—Koninklijke Hoogovens N.V.; *Int'l*, pg. 753
ALCAN ALLUMINIO S.P.A.—Alcan Aluminium Limited; *Int'l*, pg. 50
ALCAN ALUMINIUM LIMITED; *Int'l*, pg. 50
ALCAN PRICE EXTRUSIONS LTD.—Alcan Aluminium Limited; *Int'l*, pg. 50
ALCAN SPECIALTY EXTRUSIONS—Alcan Aluminium Limited; *Int'l*, pg. 51
ALCAN TUBES—Alcan Aluminium Limited; *Int'l*, pg. 51
ALCOA DEUTSCHLAND GMBH-WORMS—Aluminum Company of America; *U.S. Public*, pg. 61
ALCOA EXTRUDED PRODUCTS (UK) LTD.—Aluminum Company of America; *U.S. Public*, pg. 62
ALCOA S.A.—Aluminum Company of America; *U.S. Public*, pg. 62
ALCONOR S.A.—Aluminum Company of America; *U.S. Public*, pg. 62
ALMETEX—Alcan Aluminium Limited; *Int'l*, pg. 51
ALUMA SYSTEMS CORP.—Tridel Enterprises Inc.; *Int'l*, pg. 1423
ALUMAX ENGINEERED METAL PROCESSES, INC.—Alumax Inc.; *U.S. Public*, pg. 60
ALUMAX EXTRUSIONS, INC.—Alumax Inc.; *U.S. Public*, pg. 59
ALUMAX INC.; *U.S. Public*, pg. 59
ALUMINIO REYNOLDS, SANTO DOMINGO, S.A.—Reynolds Metals Company; *U.S. Public*, pg. 1386
ALUMINIUM EUROPE S.A., EN ABREGE: "ALEUROPE S.A."—Reynolds Metals Company; *U.S. Public*, pg. 1386
ALUMINO REYNOLDS DE VENEZUELA, S.A.—Reynolds Metals Company; *U.S. Public*, pg. 1386
ALUMINUM CORPORATION—Alcan Aluminium Limited; *Int'l*, pg. 51
ALUMINUM SHAPES, LLC; *U.S. Private*, pg. 47
AMCAST INDUSTRIAL CORPORATION; *U.S. Public*, pg. 63
ANAHEIM EXTRUSION CO.—Universal Molding Company; *U.S. Private*, pg. 1127
ARTEAGA, SOCIEDAD ANOMIMA, "ARTEAGA, S.A."—Reynolds Metals Company; *U.S. Public*, pg. 1386
BRITISH ALCAN ALUMINIUM PLC—Alcan Aluminium Limited; *Int'l*, pg. 51
BRITISH ALCAN BUILDING PRODUCTS LTD.—Alcan Aluminium Limited; *Int'l*, pg. 51
BURTCO, INC.; *U.S. Private*, pg. 188
BUTLER MANUFACTURING COMPANY; *U.S. Public*, pg. 271
CALORSTAT INDUSTRIES SA—Senior Engineering Group, plc.; *Int'l*, pg. 1222
CAMEA S.A.—Alcan Aluminium Limited; *Int'l*, pg. 51
CARDINAL ALUMINUM CO.; *U.S. Private*, pg. 208
CONSTRUCTION SPECIALTIES OF CALIFORNIA—Construction Specialties, Inc.; *U.S. Private*, pg. 266
CROFT METALS, INC.; *U.S. Private*, pg. 290
EASCO INC.; *U.S. Public*, pg. 548
EGYPTIAN ALUMINIUM PRODUCTS COMPANY—Reynolds Metals Company; *U.S. Public*, pg. 1386
ELKHART PRODUCTS CORPORATION-INDUSTRIAL DIVISION—Amcast Industrial Corporation; *U.S. Public*, pg. 63
GKN SQUEEZEFORM—GKN plc; *Int'l*, pg. 534
GEMINI ALUMINUM CORPORATION; *U.S. Private*, pg. 443
GRANGES ALUMINIUM AB—Electrolux, AB; *Int'l*, pg. 439
GRUPO IMSA S.A. DE C.V.; *Int'l*, pg. 575
HANOVER MANUFACTURING CORPORATION—Reynolds Metals Company; *U.S. Public*, pg. 1386
HEPWORTH PLC; *Int'l*, pg. 614
HOOGOVENS ALUMINIUM NV—Koninklijke Hoogovens N.V.; *Int'l*, pg. 755
HOOGOVENS ALUMINIUM PROFILTECHNIK GMBH—Koninklijke Hoogovens N.V.; *Int'l*, pg. 755
HORIZON ALUMINIUM PRODS. LTD.—Alcan Aluminium Limited; *Int'l*, pg. 51
INDIAN ALUMINIUM CO. LTD.—Alcan Aluminium Limited; *Int'l*, pg. 51
INTERNATIONAL ALUMINUM CORPORATION; *U.S. Public*, pg. 894
INTERNATIONAL EXTRUSION CORP.—International Aluminum Corporation; *U.S. Public*, pg. 895
INTERNATIONAL EXTRUSION CORPORATION-TEXAS—International Aluminum Corporation; *U.S. Public*, pg. 895
KAISER ALUMINUM & CHEMICAL CORPORATION—Maxxam Inc.; *U.S. Public*, pg. 1062
KETEMA, INC.—KTM Holdings Corp.; *U.S. Private*, pg. 604
KEYMARK CORPORATION; *U.S. Private*, pg. 618
KOBE STEEL, LTD.; *Int'l*, pg. 740
LINN PRODUCTS, INC.; *U.S. Private*, pg. 669
LOXCREEN COMPANY; *U.S. Private*, pg. 679
LUXFER—Alcan Aluminium Limited; *Int'l*, pg. 51
MAKI CORPORATION; *U.S. Private*, pg. 697
MAKI HOME CENTER, INC.—Maki Corporation; *U.S. Private*, pg. 698
THE MARMON GROUP, INC.; *U.S. Private*, pg. 706
NIPPON LIGHT METAL CO. LTD.—Alcan Aluminium Limited; *Int'l*, pg. 52
OHIO VALLEY ALUMINUM COMPANY—Interlock Industries, Inc.; *U.S. Private*, pg. 567
PATRICK METALS—Patrick Industries Inc.; *U.S. Public*, pg. 1265
PILLAR BUILDING PRODUCTS LTD.—Caradon Plc; *Int'l*, pg. 267
PIMALCO INC.—Aluminum Company of America; *U.S. Public*, pg. 61
PRECISION EXTRUSIONS; *U.S. Private*, pg. 879
THE RTZ CORPORATION PLC—Rio Tinto PLC; *Int'l*, pg. 1118
RAMCO MANUFACTURING COMPANY—Reynolds Metals Company; *U.S. Public*, pg. 1386
REYNOLDS ALUMINUM DEUTSCHLAND, INC.—Reynolds Metals Company; *U.S. Public*, pg. 1387
REYNOLDS EXTRUSION COMPANY—Reynolds Metals Company; *U.S. Public*, pg. 1387
REYNOLDS METALS COMPANY; *U.S. Public*, pg. 1385
REYNOLDS METALS COMPANY-BELLWOOD—Reynolds Metals Company; *U.S. Public*, pg. 1385
RUEDAS DE ALUMINIO C.A. "RUALCA"—Reynolds Metals Company; *U.S. Public*, pg. 1387
SOUTHERN GRAPHICS SYSTEMS—Reynolds Metals Company; *U.S. Public*, pg. 1386
TIFTON ALUMINUM CO., INC.—Aluminum Company of America; *U.S. Public*, pg. 61
UNITED TECHNOLOGIES AUTOMOTIVE—United Technologies Corporation; *U.S. Public*, pg. 1691
VAN CAMPEN BENDING TECHNICS B.V.—Reynolds Metals Company; *U.S. Public*, pg. 1387
VAW OF AMERICA, INC.—Viag AG; *Int'l*, pg. 1466
WELLS ALUMINUM CORP.; *U.S. Private*, pg. 1161

3355 — ALUMINUM ROLLING & DRAWING, NEC

ANI AURORA PLC—Australian National Industries Limited; *Int'l*, pg. 101
ALCAN ALUMINUM CORPORATION—Alcan Aluminium Limited; *Int'l*, pg. 50
ALCAN ROLLED PRODUCTS DIVISION—Alcan Aluminium Limited; *Int'l*, pg. 50
ALCAN WIRE—Alcan Aluminium Limited; *Int'l*, pg. 51
ALUMAX ALUMINUM CORP., MILL PRODUCTS—Alumax Inc.; *U.S. Public*, pg. 59
ALUMAX MILL PRODUCTS, INC.—Alumax Inc.; *U.S. Public*, *pg. 59*
ALUMINUM COMPANY OF AMERICA; *U.S. Public*, pg. 60
ALUMINUM CO. OF MALAYSIA BERHAD—Alcan Aluminium Limited; *Int'l*, pg. 51
ALUMINUM NORF GMBH—Alcan Aluminium Limited; *Int'l*, pg. 51
AMPHENOL CORPORATION—Kohlberg Kravis Roberts & Co.; *U.S. Private*, pg. 629
ARCO ALUMINUM—Atlantic Richfield Company; *U.S. Public*, pg. 144
JOSEPH BEHR & SONS INC.; *U.S. Private*, pg. 130
BRITISH ALCAN ALUMINIUM PLC—Alcan Aluminium Limited; *Int'l*, pg. 51
CAPRAL ALUMINIUM LIMITED; *Int'l*, pg. 266
COLEMAN CABLE SYSTEMS, INC.—Kuhlman Corporation; *U.S. Public*, pg. 968
COMALCO-CHH ALUMINUM—International Paper Company; *U.S. Public*, pg. 905
ESCO CORPORATION; *U.S. Private*, pg. 382
ESSEX INTERNATIONAL, INC.; *U.S. Public*, pg. 593
FURUKAWA SANGYO KAISHA, LTD.—The Furukawa Electric Co., Ltd.; *Int'l*, pg. 530
HOOGOVENS ALUMINIUM BAUSYSTEME GMBH—Koninklijke Hoogovens N.V.; *Int'l*, pg. 755
HOOGOVENS ALUMINIUM WALZPRODUKTE GMBH—Koninklijke Hoogovens N.V.; *Int'l*, pg. 755
KB ALLOYS, INC.—Code, Hennessy & Simmons, Inc.; *U.S. Private*, pg. 249
KAISER ALUMINUM & CHEMICAL CORPORATION—Maxxam Inc.; *U.S. Public*, pg. 1062
E. & E. KAYE LIMITED; *Int'l*, pg. 727
THE RTZ CORPORATION PLC—Rio Tinto PLC; *Int'l*, pg. 1118
ROLL FORMING CORPORATION; *U.S. Private*, pg. 941
SOUTHWIRE COMPANY; *U.S. Private*, pg. 1019
THE STOLLE CORPORATION—Aluminum Company of America; *U.S. Public*, pg. 61
TOYO ALUMINIUM K.K.—Alcan Aluminium Limited; *Int'l*, pg. 52
UNIVERSAL MOLDING COMPANY; *U.S. Private*, pg. 1127

3356 — ROLLING, DRAWING & EXTRUDING OF NONFERROUS METALS, EXCEPT COPPER & ALUMINUM

AAR CORP.; *U.S. Public*, pg. 1
ADEC AUTOMATION—Adec International Automation Corp.; *U.S. Private*, pg. 17
ALLTRISTA CORPORATION; *U.S. Public*, pg. 56
ALPHA METALS, INC.—Cookson Group plc; *Int'l*, pg. 328
AMERICAN SHEAR KNIVE CO.—Asko, Inc; *U.S. Private*, pg. 89
AMETEK, INC.; *U.S. Public*, pg. 99
AMPHENOL CORPORATION—Kohlberg Kravis Roberts & Co.; *U.S. Private*, pg. 629
ARCONIUM SPECIALTY ALLOYS—Cookson Group plc; *Int'l*, pg. 328
ARMADA CORPORATION; *U.S. Private*, pg. 82
THE ARNOLD ENGINEERING COMPANY—SPS Technologies, Inc.; *U.S. Public*, pg. 1420
ARTESANIAS BAJA, S.A.—Hanson PLC; *Int'l*, pg. 594
ATLAS WIRE CORPORATION; *U.S. Private*, pg. 97
BRITISH ALCAN ALUMINIUM PLC—Alcan Aluminium Limited; *Int'l*, pg. 51
E.J. BROOKS COMPANY; *U.S. Private*, pg. 172
BRUSH WELLMAN INC.; *U.S. Public*, pg. 266
CARPENTER TECHNOLOGY CORPORATION; *U.S. Public*, *pg. 307*
CEZUS—Framatome SA; *Int'l*, pg. 503
CEZUS—Pechiney S.A.; *Int'l*, pg. 1029
COLTEC HOLDINGS INC; *U.S. Public*, pg. 401
COOKSON GROUP PLC; *Int'l*, pg. 328
DEKORON DIVISION—Furon Company; *U.S. Public*, pg. 689
DELTA EXTRUDED METALS CO. LTD.—Delta plc; *Int'l*, pg. 391
DRIVER-HARRIS, S.A.—Kanthal AB; *Int'l*, pg. 723
DU PONT, S.A. DE C.V. DIV. PIGMENTOS Y PRODUCTOS QUIMICOS—Du Pont (E.I. Du Pont De Nemours & Co.); *U.S. Public*, pg. 531
DYNAMET INC.—Carpenter Technology Corporation; *U.S. Public*, pg. 307
ENGELHARD CORPORATION; *U.S. Public*, pg. 582
ESSEX INTERNATIONAL, INC.; *U.S. Public*, pg. 593
FARMERS MARINE COPPER WORKS—Four Winds Investment Corp.; *U.S. Private*, pg. 422
GUARDIAN PRODUCTS/CAPITAL WIRE—Wassall Plc; *Int'l*, pg. 1487
HANDY & HARMAN; *U.S. Public*, pg. 780
HAYNES INTERNATIONAL, INC.; *U.S. Public*, pg. 801
HERMANN H.C. STARCK BERLIN GBMH & CO. KG—Bayer AG; *Int'l*, pg. 174
HILLE & MULLER—Koninklijke Hoogovens N.V.; *Int'l*, pg. 754
HOOGOVENS ALUMINIUM NV—Koninklijke Hoogovens N.V.; *Int'l*, pg. 755
HOSKINS MFG. CO.—Armada Corporation; *U.S. Private*, pg. 83
HYGRADE METAL MOULDING MFG. CORP.; *U.S. Private*, *pg. 552*
IMI PLC; *Int'l*, pg. 646
INCO ALLOYS INTERNATIONAL, INC.—Inco Limited; *Int'l*, pg. 672
INCO ALLOYS LIMITED—Inco Limited; *Int'l*, pg. 672
INCO LIMITED; *Int'l*, pg. 672
INSILCO CORPORATION; *U.S. Public*, pg. 881
INTERNATIONAL NICKEL, INC.—Inco Limited; *Int'l*, pg. 672
AXEL JOHNSON METALS, INC.—Axel Johnson AB; *Int'l*, pg. 709
JOHNSON MATTHEY INC.—Johnson Matthey Public Limited Company; *Int'l*, pg. 713
JOHNSON MATTHEY PUBLIC LIMITED COMPANY; *Int'l*, pg. 713
THE KANTHAL CORPORATION—Kanthal AB; *Int'l*, pg. 723
KRUPP VDM GMBH—Fried. Krupp AG; *Int'l*, pg. 509
LEACH & GARNER COMPANY; *U.S. Private*, pg. 655
MAGNESIUM ELEKTRON—Alcan Aluminium Limited; *Int'l*, pg. 51
THE MILLER COMPANY; *U.S. Private*, pg. 746
NRC INC.—Bayer AG; *Int'l*, pg. 173
NORSK HYDRO A.S; *Int'l*, pg. 959
OREGON METALLURGICAL CORPORATION—Allegheny Teledyne Incorporated; *U.S. Public*, pg. 43
PIPE FABRICATING & SUPPLY COMPANY; *U.S. Private*, pg. 867
QUANEX CORPORATION; *U.S. Public*, pg. 1349
QUEMETCO METALS LIMITED, INC.—Quexco Incorporated; *U.S. Private*, pg. 900
RMI TITANIUM COMPANY—USX Corporation; *U.S. Public*, pg. 1662
RSR CORPORATION—Quexco Incorporated; *U.S. Private*, pg. 900
RIGBY-MARYLAND (STAINLESS) LTD.—Handy & Harman; *U.S. Public*, pg. 780
ROLL FORMING CORPORATION; *U.S. Private*, pg. 941
SPS TECHNOLOGIES, INC.; *U.S. Public*, pg. 1419
SETTAS S.A.—Inco Limited; *Int'l*, pg. 673
SPECTRULITE CONSORTIUM, INC.; *U.S. Private*, pg. 1024
SUNBEAM CORPORATION; *U.S. Public*, pg. 1533
TARACORP, INC.; *U.S. Private*, pg. 1068
TECHALLOY CO., INC.—Groupe Usinor; *Int'l*, pg. 572
TITANIUM METALS CORPORATION—Contran Corporation; *U.S. Private*, pg. 270
TREDEGAR INDUSTRIES INC.; *U.S. Public*, pg. 1633

TREMONT CORPORATION—Contran Corporation; *U.S. Private*, pg. 270
TUBE FITTINGS—Caparo Group Ltd.; *Int'l*, pg. 265
ULBRICH WIRE, INC.—Ulbrich Stainless Steels & Special Metals, Inc.; *U.S. Private*, pg. 1115
VDM TECHNOLOGIES CORP.—Fried. Krupp AG; *Int'l*, pg. 509
VDM (U.K.) LTD.—Fried. Krupp AG; *Int'l*, pg. 509
VAN LEEUWEN PIPE AND TUBE (FAR EAST) PTE. LTD.—Van Leeuwen Pipe and Tube Group B.V.; *Int'l*, pg. 1450
ZINC PRODUCTS COMPANY—Alltrista Corporation; *U.S. Public*, pg. 57
ZIRCOTUBE—Framatome SA; *Int'l*, pg. 503

3357 — DRAWING & INSULATING OF NONFERROUS WIRE

ACS INTERNACIONAL S.A. DE C.V.—ACS Industries, Inc.; *U.S. Private*, pg. 4
AFC CABLE SYSTEMS, INC.; *U.S. Public*, pg. 6
ALCAN CABLE DIVISION—Alcan Aluminium Limited; *Int'l*, pg. 50
ALCATEL CABLE SYSTEMS GROUP—Alcatel Alsthom Compagnie Generale D'Electricite; *Int'l*, pg. 55
ALCATEL N.A. INC.—Alcatel Alsthom Compagnie Generale D'Electricite; *Int'l*, pg. 55
AMERCORD INC.—The Ivaco Group; *Int'l*, pg. 696
AMERICAN FINANCIAL GROUP—American Financial Group; *U.S. Public*, pg. 75
ANCHOR WIRE CORPORATION OF TENNESSEE—Textron Inc.; *U.S. Public*, pg. 1590
ANDREW CORPORATION; *U.S. Public*, pg. 112
ARTEL VIDEO SYSTEMS, INC.; *U.S. Private*, pg. 86
BICC BRAND-REX—BICC plc; *Int'l*, pg. 120
BICC CABLES CORPORATION—BICC plc; *Int'l*, pg. 120
BICC PYROTENAX—BICC plc; *Int'l*, pg. 120
BIW CABLE MANUFACTURING PLANT—Draka Kabel B.V.; *Int'l*, pg. 417
BIW CABLE SYSTEMS-CONNECTOR SYSTEMS DIV.—Draka Kabel B.V.; *Int'l*, pg. 417
BIW CABLE SYSTEMS, INC.—Draka Kabel B.V.; *Int'l*, pg. 417
BICC CABLES LIMITED—BICC plc; *Int'l*, pg. 120
BIRNBACH COMPANY, INC.—Bell Industries, Inc.; *U.S. Public*, pg. 207
WHITNEY BLAKE COMPANY OF VERMONT, INC.; *U.S. Private*, pg. 148
BRUNTONS AREO PRODUCT—Carclo Engineering Group plc; *Int'l*, pg. 268
C & M CORPORATION; *U.S. Private*, pg. 191
CABLE DESIGN TECHNOLOGIES CORPORATION; *U.S. Public*, pg. 287
CABLEWAVE SYSTEMS; *U.S. Private*, pg. 197
CARCLO ENGINEERING GROUP PLC; *Int'l*, pg. 268
CARLISLE COMPANIES INCORPORATED; *U.S. Public*, pg. 305
CHAMPLAIN CABLE CORP.—Huber & Suhner AG; *Int'l*, pg. 637
COLEMAN CABLE SYSTEMS, INC.—Kuhlman Corporation; *U.S. Public*, pg. 968
COMMSCOPE, INC.; *U.S. Public*, pg. 415
COMMUNICATION CABLE (CCI)-SILER CITY—Kuhlman Corporation; *U.S. Public*, pg. 968
COMMUNICATION CABLE, INC.—Kuhlman Corporation; *U.S. Public*, pg. 968
COPPERWELD BIMETALLICS PRODUCTS CO.—Imetal; *Int'l*, pg. 662
COPPERWELD FAYETTEVILLE DIVISION—Imetal; *Int'l*, pg. 662
CORNING INCORPORATED; *U.S. Public*, pg. 448
DEKKO HEATING TECHNOLOGIES, INC.—Group Dekko; *U.S. Private*, pg. 484
DEKORON DIVISION—Furon Company; *U.S. Public*, pg. 689
DEKORON WIRE & CABLE DIVISION—Furon Company; *U.S. Public*, pg. 689
DELTA (MANGANESE BRONZE) LTD.—Delta plc; *Int'l*, pg. 391
DERLAN INDUSTRIES LIMITED; *Int'l*, pg. 395
DRAKA KABEL B.V.; *Int'l*, pg. 417
DRIVER-HARRIS COMPANY; *U.S. Public*, pg. 530
ELECTRONIC INTERNCONNECT SYSTEMS INC.—Noma Industries Limited; *Int'l*, pg. 955
ERICSSON CABLES AB—Telefonaktiebolaget LM Ericsson; *Int'l*, pg. 1363
ESSEX INTERNATIONAL, INC.; *U.S. Public*, pg. 593
FIBER OPTIC PRODUCTS DIVISION—Methode Electronics Inc.; *U.S. Public*, pg. 1101
FITEL LUCENT—The Furukawa Electric Co., Ltd.; *Int'l*, pg. 530
FLECK MANUFACTURING INC.—Noma Industries Limited; *Int'l*, pg. 955
FORSLID AB—Telefonaktiebolaget LM Ericsson; *Int'l*, pg. 1363
FURON COMPANY; *U.S. Public*, pg. 688
G.E. INFORMATION SERVICES—General Electric Company; *U.S. Public*, pg. 710
GALILEO CORP.; *U.S. Public*, pg. 698
GENCAB OF CANADA LTD.—American Financial Group; *U.S. Public*, pg. 75
GENERAL CABLE CORPORATION—Wassall Plc; *Int'l*, pg. 1486
GENERAL SIGNAL CORPORATION; *U.S. Public*, pg. 726
W.L. GORE & ASSOCIATES, INC.; *U.S. Private*, pg. 465
GRUPO CONDUMEX—Grupo Carso S.A. de C.V.; *Int'l*, pg. 572
GUARDIAN PRODUCTS/CAPITAL WIRE—Wassall Plc; *Int'l*, pg. 1487
HELIX/HI-TEMP CABLES, INC.—Draka Kabel B.V.; *Int'l*, pg. 417
HENDRIX WIRE & CABLE—Thomas & Betts Corporation; *U.S. Public*, pg. 1598
HOOSIER WIRE, INC.—Hicks, Muse, Tate & Furst Inc.; *U.S. Private*, pg. 526
HUBBELL INCORPORATED; *U.S. Public*, pg. 844
HUBER & SUHNER AG; *Int'l*, pg. 637
IWG-ARDMORE—Hicks, Muse, Tate & Furst Inc.; *U.S. Private*, pg. 526
INDUSTRIAL ALLOYS, INC.—Industrial Wire Products Corporation; *U.S. Private*, pg. 561
INSILCO CORPORATION; *U.S. Public*, pg. 881
INTERCOMP (ICM)—Kuhlman Corporation; *U.S. Public*, pg. 968
IRISH DRIVER-HARRIS CO., LTD.—Driver-Harris Company; *U.S. Public*, pg. 530
JOHNSON MATTHEY PUBLIC LIMITED COMPANY; *Int'l*, pg. 713
KALAS MANUFACTURING, INC.; *U.S. Private*, pg. 606
KANTHAL AB; *Int'l*, pg. 723
THE KANTHAL CORPORATION—Kanthal AB; *Int'l*, pg. 723
THE KERITE COMPANY—Hubbell Incorporated; *U.S. Public*, pg. 844
KRUG INTERNATIONAL TECHNOLOGY/SCIENTIFIC SERVICES, INC.—Krug International Corp.; *U.S. Public*, pg. 968
LES CABLES DE LYON—Alcatel Alsthom Compagnie Generale D'Electricite; *Int'l*, pg. 56
LEVITON—Leviton Mfg. Co., Inc.; *U.S. Private*, pg. 663
JOHN MARTENSSON ELMATERIAL AB—Telefonaktiebolaget LM Ericsson; *Int'l*, pg. 1363
MARYLAND SPECIALTY WIRE, INC.—Handy & Harman; *U.S. Public*, pg. 780
MATH ASSOCIATES—General Microwave Corporation; *U.S. Public*, pg. 717
MELLANSVENSKA ELEKTRISKA AB—Telefonaktiebolaget LM Ericsson; *Int'l*, pg. 1363
MEYER WIRE & CABLE COMPANY—Cole Hersee Company; *U.S. Private*, pg. 251
MITSUBISHI CABLE INDUSTRIES, LTD.; *Int'l*, pg. 870
MOLEX CARIBE—Molex Incorporated; *U.S. Public*, pg. 1122
MOLEX INCORPORATED; *U.S. Public*, pg. 1121
NORDX/CDT—Cable Design Technologies Corporation; *U.S. Public*, pg. 287
NS FIBER OPTICS, INC.—Norfolk Southern Corporation; *U.S. Public*, pg. 1190
NEHRING ELECTRICAL WORKS COMPANY—Kuhlman Corporation; *U.S. Public*, pg. 968
NORTHERN TELECOM CANADA LIMITED, OUTSIDE PLANT DIV.—Northern Telecom Limited; *Int'l*, pg. 969
OKI ELECTRIC CABLE CO., LTD.—Oki Electric Industry Company, Ltd.; *Int'l*, pg. 999
THE OKONITE COMPANY; *U.S. Private*, pg. 813
ORBEL CORPORATION; *U.S. Private*, pg. 819
ORTRONICS, INC.—LeGrand S.A.; *Int'l*, pg. 806
PACIFIC DUNLOP CABLES GROUP—Pacific Dunlop Limited; *Int'l*, pg. 1021
PARLEX CORPORATION; *U.S. Public*, pg. 1264
PARLEX LAMINATED CABLE—Parlex Corporation; *U.S. Public*, pg. 1264
PHELPS DODGE COPPER PRODUCTS COMPANY—Phelps Dodge Corporation; *U.S. Public*, pg. 1287
PHELPS DODGE CORPORATION; *U.S. Public*, pg. 1286
PHELPS DODGE MAGNET WIRE CO.—Phelps Dodge Corporation; *U.S. Public*, pg. 1286
PHILIPSSONS GRAV & SCHAKT AB—Telefonaktiebolaget LM Ericsson; *Int'l*, pg. 1364
PIRELLI CABLE CORPORATION—Pirelli S.p.A.; *Int'l*, pg. 1059
PIRELLI CABLE, FIBER OPTIC DIV.—Pirelli S.p.A.; *Int'l*, pg. 1059
PIRELLI CABLE, POWER CABLE DIV.—Pirelli S.p.A.; *Int'l*, pg. 1059
PIRELLI CABLES AUSTRALIA LIMITED—Pirelli S.p.A.; *Int'l*, *pg. 1059*
PIRELLI ENFIELD SUPERTENSION CABLES LTD.—Pirelli S.p.A.; *Int'l*, pg. 1059
PIRELLI S.P.A.; *Int'l*, pg. 1058
PREFORMADOS DE MEXICO SA—Preformed Line Products; *U.S. Public*, pg. 1321
RADIX WIRE COMPANY; *U.S. Private*, pg. 907
RAYCHEM CORPORATION; *U.S. Public*, pg. 1362
RAYCHEM GMBH—Raychem Corporation; *U.S. Public*, pg. 1362
REA MAGNET WIRE COMPANY, INC.; *U.S. Private*, pg. 913
RIKEN ELECTRIC WIRE CO., LTD.—The Furukawa Electric Co., Ltd.; *Int'l*, pg. 530
ROME CABLE CORPORATION; *U.S. Private*, pg. 942
ROYLE SYSTEMS GROUP; *U.S. Private*, pg. 949
SAXTON—Kuhlman Corporation; *U.S. Public*, pg. 968
SCANCABLES AB—Telefonaktiebolaget LM Ericsson; *Int'l*, pg. 1363
SIECOR CORPORATION—Corning Incorporated; *U.S. Public*, pg. 449
SIECOR CORPORATION—Siemens AG; *Int'l*, pg. 1245
SILICONES, INC.—Hicks, Muse, Tate & Furst Inc.; *U.S. Private*, pg. 526
SOUTHWIRE COMPANY; *U.S. Private*, pg. 1019
SOUTHWIRE SPECIALTY PRODUCTS—Southwire Company; *U.S. Private*, pg. 1019
STORM PRODUCTS COMPANY, INC.; *U.S. Private*, pg. 1045
STRANDFLEX DIVISION—Handy & Harman; *U.S. Public*, pg. 780
SVENSKA ELGROSSIST AB SELGA—Telefonaktiebolaget LM Ericsson; *Int'l*, pg. 1363
TANDY CABLE PRODUCTS—Tandy Corporation; *U.S. Public*, pg. 1560
TANDY WIRE & CABLE—Tandy Corporation; *U.S. Public*, pg. 1560
TANDY WIRE FABRICATION—Tandy Corporation; *U.S. Public*, pg. 1560
TELEFONICA DE ESPANA, S.A.; *Int'l*, pg. 1371
TENSOLITE COMPANY—Carlisle Companies Incorporated; *U.S. Public*, pg. 305
TESSCO GROUP, INC.—Code-Alarm, Inc.; *U.S. Public*, pg. 394
THERMO ELECTRIC CO., INC.; *U.S. Private*, pg. 1080
THERMON MANUFACTURING COMPANY; *U.S. Private*, pg. 1080
TIMES FIBER COMMUNICATIONS, INC.—Kohlberg Kravis Roberts & Co.; *U.S. Private*, pg. 629
TOCKFORS VERKSTADS AB—Telefonaktiebolaget LM Ericsson; *Int'l*, pg. 1364
TREFICABLE PIRELLI S.N.C.—Pirelli S.p.A.; *Int'l*, pg. 1060
TRIBORO ELECTRIC CO.; *U.S. Private*, pg. 1102
TYTON HELLERMANN DO BRASIL INDUSTRIA E COMERCIO LTDA.—Bowthorpe plc; *Int'l*, pg. 209
WAGNER LIGHTING PRODUCTS—Cooper Industries, Inc.; *U.S. Public*, pg. 442
WIDISA METAL S.A.—FKI Plc; *Int'l*, pg. 474
WILLING B WIRE CORPORATION—Handy & Harman; *U.S.* Public, pg. 780
WIRELESS NETWORKS SKYLINE - NORTHERN TELECOM CANADA LIMITED—Northern Telecom Limited; *Int'l*, pg. 969
WIREMAKERS LIMITED—Fletcher Challenge Limited; *Int'l*, pg. 495
WOVEN PRODUCTS DIV.—National-Standard Co.; *U.S. Public*, pg. 1161

3363 — ALUMINUM DIE-CASTINGS

ADC L.P.; *U.S. Private*, pg. 4
AALLIED DIE CASTING MFG., INC.—RCM Industries; *U.S. Private*, pg. 903
ALUSUISSE-LONZA AMERICA INC.—Alusuisse-Lonza Holding Ltd.; *Int'l*, pg. 67
AMCAST INDUSTRIAL CORPORATION; *U.S. Public*, pg. 63
BTR PRECISION DIE CASTING, INC.—BTR plc; *Int'l*, pg. 127
BARTON ALUMINUM FOUNDRIES—Caparo Group Ltd.; *Int'l*, pg. 264
BARTON ENGINEERING LTD.—Caparo Group Ltd.; *Int'l*, pg. 264
BLUE RIDGE PRESSURE CASTINGS, INC.; *U.S. Private*, pg. 153
CMI INTERNATIONAL INC.; *U.S. Private*, pg. 195
C.V.G. ALUMINIO DEL CARONI, S.A.—Reynolds Metals Company; *U.S. Public*, pg. 1386
CAST-MATIC CORPORATION—Intermet Corporation; *U.S. Public*, pg. 894
CHICAGO WHITE METAL CASTING, INC.; *U.S. Private*, pg. 236
CONSOLIDATED FOUNDRIES; *U.S. Private*, pg. 265
CONSOLIDATED METCO, INC.—Varlen Corporation; *U.S. Public*, pg. 1710
CONTECH DIV. (KALAMAZOO)—SPX Corporation; *U.S. Public*, pg. 1421
CROFT METALS, INC.; *U.S. Private*, pg. 290
DAYCO PRODUCTS INC.—Mark IV Industries Inc.; *U.S. Public*, pg. 1045
DIEMAKERS, INC.; *U.S. Private*, pg. 332
DOEHLER-JARVIS, INC.—Harvard Industries, Inc.; *U.S. Public*, pg. 796
EMG EISEN-UND METALLGUSSWERK GMBH—Deutsche Babcock AG; *Int'l*, pg. 400
EVANS INDUSTRIES, INC.; *U.S. Private*, pg. 385
FABWEL INC.; *U.S. Private*, pg. 390
FEDERAL CHICAGO CORPORATION; *U.S. Private*, pg. 398
GEORG FISCHER AUTOMOBILGUSS GES.M.B.H.—Georg Fischer Ltd.; *Int'l*, pg. 488
GEORG FISCHER AUTOMOBILGUSS GMBH—Georg Fischer Ltd.; *Int'l*, pg. 488
GEORG FISCHER LTD.; *Int'l*, pg. 488
FUJITSU TEN CORP. OF AMERICA—Fujitsu Limited; *Int'l*, pg. 526
GIBBS DIE CASTING CORP.—George Koch Sons, Inc.; *U.S. Private*, pg. 628
HALEX DIV.—Berkshire Hathaway Inc.; *U.S. Public*, pg. 217
IMPERIAL DIE CASTING—RCM Industries; *U.S. Private*, pg. 903
INLAND DIE CASTING—RCM Industries; *U.S. Private*, pg. 903
KAISER ALUMINUM & CHEMICAL CORPORATION—Maxxam Inc.; *U.S. Public*, pg. 1062
KRONE CASTING CORP.; *U.S. Private*, pg. 636
LINDBERG CORPORATION; *U.S. Public*, pg. 999
METALLOY CORPORATION; *U.S. Private*, pg. 735
PHB DIE CASTING; *U.S. Private*, pg. 826
PACE DIE CAST PRODUCTS, INC.—Leggett & Platt, Incorporated; *U.S. Public*, pg. 986
PACE INDUSTRIES, INC.—Leggett & Platt, Incorporated; *U.S. Public*, pg. 986
PECO MFG. CO., INC.; *U.S. Private*, pg. 846
PEMCO DIE CASTING CORPORATION; *U.S. Private*, pg. 848
REULAND ELECTRIC COMPANY; *U.S. Private*, pg. 925
SPX CORPORATION; *U.S. Public*, pg. 1420
ST. PAUL METALCRAFT, INC.; *U.S. Private*, pg. 961
TCH INDUSTRIES INC.; *U.S. Private*, pg. 1063
TWIN CITY DIE CASTINGS CO.; *U.S. Private*, pg. 1111
VAW ALUMINUM AG—Viag AG; *Int'l*, pg. 1466
VARLEN CORPORATION; *U.S. Public*, pg. 1710
WALKER DIE CASTING, INC.; *U.S. Private*, pg. 1147
WYMAN-GORDON INVESTMENT CASTINGS, INC.—Wyman-Gordon; *U.S. Public*, pg. 1782

3364 — NONFERROUS DIE-CASTINGS, EXCEPT ALUMINUM

ADC L.P.; *U.S. Private*, pg. 4
AMERICAN FOUNDRY GROUP, INC.; *U.S. Private*, pg. 54
BAYCO INDUSTRIES—Derlan Industries Limited; *Int'l*, pg. 395

FRANCIS W. BIRKETT & SONS LIMITED—Carclo Engineering Group plc; *Int'l*, pg. 268
BLUE RIDGE PRESSURE CASTINGS, INC.; *U.S. Private*, pg. 153
CAST-MATIC CORPORATION—Intermet Corporation; *U.S. Public*, pg. 894
CHIAPHUA SHINKO COPPER ALLOY CO., LTD.—Kobe Steel, Ltd.; *Int'l*, pg. 741
CHIAPHUA SHINKO COPPER ALLOY CO., LTD.—Nissho Iwai Corporation; *Int'l*, pg. 946
CHICAGO WHITE METAL CASTING, INC.; *U.S. Private*, pg. 236
CHRYSLER CORPORATION; *U.S. Public*, pg. 352
CONSOLIDATED METCO, INC.—Varlen Corporation; *U.S. Public*, pg. 1710
CONTECH DIV. (KALAMAZOO)—SPX Corporation; *U.S. Public*, pg. 1421
DECO PRODUCTS CO.; *U.S. Private*, pg. 320
DERLAN INDUSTRIES LIMITED; *Int'l*, pg. 395
DIEMAKERS, INC.; *U.S. Private*, pg. 332
DOLPHIN, INC.—Karsten Manufacturing Corporation; *U.S. Private*, pg. 608
DYNACAST DE MEXICO, S.A. DE C.V.—Coats Viyella plc; *Int'l*, pg. 300
DYNACAST INTERNATIONAL LIMITED—Coats Viyella plc; *Int'l*, pg. 299
EVANS INDUSTRIES, INC.; *U.S. Private*, pg. 385
FAG GROUP; *Int'l*, pg. 468
FEDERAL CHICAGO CORPORATION; *U.S. Private*, pg. 398
FINNAIR—FinnAir Oy; *Int'l*, pg. 486
FUJITSU BUSINESS COMMUNICATION SYSTEMS—Fujitsu Limited; *Int'l*, pg. 526
THE FURUKAWA ELECTRIC CO., LTD.; *Int'l*, pg. 530
GREAT LAKES-EGLINTON—United Dominion Industries, Ltd.; *U.S. Public*, pg. 1676
HALEX DIV.—Berkshire Hathaway Inc.; *U.S. Public*, pg. 217
HILER INDUSTRIES; *U.S. Private*, pg. 529
HITCHINER MANUFACTURING COMPANY, INC.; *U.S. Private*, pg. 531
IMI PLC; *Int'l*, pg. 646
ILCO UNICAN INC. (CAPITOL DIVISION)—Unican Security Systems Ltd.; *Int'l*, pg. 1432
INVESTMENT ENGINEERING LTD.—Delta plc; *Int'l*, pg. 391
KARSTEN MANUFACTURING CORPORATION; *U.S. Private*, pg. 608
KRONE CASTING CORP.; *U.S. Private*, pg. 636
LA FRANCE CORPORATION; *U.S. Private*, pg. 640
LIPS UNITED B.V.; *Int'l*, pg. 812
OREGON METALLURGICAL CORPORATION—Allegheny Teledyne Incorporated; *U.S. Public*, pg. 43
PHB DIE CASTING; *U.S. Private*, pg. 826
PACE DIE CAST PRODUCTS, INC.—Leggett & Platt, Incorporated; *U.S. Public*, pg. 986
PECO MFG. CO., INC.; *U.S. Private*, pg. 846
PEERLESS TUBE COMPANY; *U.S. Public*, pg. 1269
PILLAR ENGINEERING LTD.—Caradon Plc; *Int'l*, pg. 267
THE RENOVATOR'S SUPPLY, INC.; *U.S. Private*, pg. 923
RYOBI LTD.; *Int'l*, pg. 1151
SPX CORPORATION; *U.S. Public*, pg. 1420
ST. PAUL METALCRAFT, INC.; *U.S. Private*, pg. 961
SERVAAS, INC.; *U.S. Private*, pg. 986
SHENANGO INDUSTRIES; *U.S. Private*, pg. 992
J.W. SINGER & SONS—Delta plc; *Int'l*, pg. 391
SOUTHWESTERN DIE CASTING, INC.—Baldor Electric Company; *U.S. Public*, pg. 169
STAHL SPECIALTY COMPANY; *U.S. Private*, pg. 1029
SWISSMETAL PLANT DORNACH—UMS Swiss Metalworks Holding Ltd; *Int'l*, pg. 1427
TCH INDUSTRIES INC.; *U.S. Private*, pg. 1063
TWIN CITY DIE CASTINGS CO.; *U.S. Private*, pg. 1111
UMS SWISS METALWORKS HOLDING LTD; *Int'l*, pg. 1427
UNITED STATES NAME PLATE—La France Corporation; *U.S. Private*, pg. 640
WAGNERWARE CORPORATION; *U.S. Private*, pg. 1146

3365 — ALUMINUM FOUNDRIES

A-MOLD CORP.—UBE Industries Ltd.; *Int'l*, pg. 1427
ADEC AUTOMATION—Adec International Automation Corp.; *U.S. Private*, pg. 17
AFFIMET—Pechiney S.A.; *Int'l*, pg. 1028
ALUFLUOR AKTIEBOLAG—Alusuisse-Lonza Holding Ltd.; *Int'l*, pg. 69
ALUFLUOR AKTIEBOLAG—Kemira Oy; *Int'l*, pg. 729
ALUMINIUM DELFZIJL BV—Koninklijke Hoogovens N.V.; *Int'l*, pg. 753
ALUMINUM DECIN SPOL. S.R.O.—Alusuisse-Lonza Holding Ltd.; *Int'l*, pg. 68
ALUMINUM SHAPES, LLC; *U.S. Private*, pg. 47
ALUSUISSE FRANCE PRODUITS INDUSTRIELS S.A.—Alusuisse-Lonza Holding Ltd.; *Int'l*, pg. 68
ALUSUISSE-LONZA HOLDING LTD.; *Int'l*, pg. 66
ALUSUISSE-LONZA SERVICES LTD.—Alusuisse-Lonza Holding Ltd.; *Int'l*, pg. 67
ALUSUISSE SWISS ALUMINIUM LTD.—Alusuisse-Lonza Holding Ltd.; *Int'l*, pg. 67
AMCAST AUTOMOTIVE-CEDARBURG PLANT—Amcast Industrial Corporation; *U.S. Public*, pg. 63
AMCAST AUTOMOTIVE-RICHMOND PLANT—Amcast Industrial Corporation; *U.S. Public*, pg. 63
AMCAST AUTOMOTIVE-WAPAKONETA PLANT—Amcast Industrial Corporation; *U.S. Public*, pg. 63
BDW - BAYERISCHES DRUCKGUSS-WERK THURNER GMBH & CO KG—Alusuisse-Lonza Holding Ltd.; *Int'l*, pg. 68
BARTON ALUMINUM FOUNDRIES—Caparo Group Ltd.; *Int'l*, pg. 264
CMI INTERNATIONAL INC.; *U.S. Private*, pg. 195
C.S. ALUMINIUM CORPORATION—China Steel Corporation; *Int'l*, pg. 285
CHUGAI BOYEKI CO., LTD.; *Int'l*, pg. 290
CITATION CORPORATION; *U.S. Public*, pg. 376
CONSOLIDATED INDUSTRIES, INC.; *U.S. Private*, pg. 265
CONSOLIDATED METCO, INC.—Varlen Corporation; *U.S. Public*, pg. 1710
COSWORTH CASTINGS LTD.—Vickers PLC; *Int'l*, pg. 1467
CUSTOM CASTING—Esco Corporation; *U.S. Private*, pg. 383
DELTA (MANGANESE BRONZE) LTD.—Delta plc; *Int'l*, pg. 391
EMG EISEN-UND METALLGUSSWERK GMBH—Deutsche Babcock AG; *Int'l*, pg. 400
EKCO HOUSEWARES, INC.—Ekco Group, Inc.; *U.S. Public*, pg. 566
ELKEM ALUMINIUM ANS—Elkem ASA; *Int'l*, pg. 446
ELKEM ALUMINIUM LISTA—Elkem ASA; *Int'l*, pg. 446
ELKEM ALUMINIUM MOSJOEN—Elkem ASA; *Int'l*, pg. 447
ELKEM ASA; *Int'l*, pg. 446
ELKEM FISKAA SILICON—Elkem ASA; *Int'l*, pg. 448
ELKEM MARIETTA—Elkem ASA; *Int'l*, pg. 447
FRONTIER FOUNDRY, INC.; *U.S. Private*, pg. 430
GENERAL HOUSEWARES CORP.; *U.S. Public*, pg. 715
HARRIS METALS—Lindberg Corporation; *U.S. Public*, pg. 999
HARRIS METALS-ARROW ACME CO.—Lindberg Corporation; *U.S. Public*, pg. 999
HITCHINER MANUFACTURING COMPANY, INC.; *U.S. Private*, pg. 531
HOOGOVENS ALUMINIUM NV—Koninklijke Hoogovens N.V.; *Int'l*, pg. 755
HOOGOVENS GROEP B.V.—Koninklijke Hoogovens N.V.; *Int'l*, pg. 753
ISAL ICELANDIC ALUMINIUM CO. LTD.—Alusuisse-Lonza Holding Ltd.; *Int'l*, pg. 68
ITALPLAN SRL—Alusuisse-Lonza Holding Ltd.; *Int'l*, pg. 68
KAPA GMBH LEICHTSOFFTECHNIK—Alusuisse-Lonza Holding Ltd.; *Int'l*, pg. 68
KONINKLIJKE HOOGOVENS N.V.; *Int'l*, pg. 753
LINCOLN FOODSERVICE PRODUCTS, INC.—Berisford plc; *Int'l*, pg. 188
LONZA-FOLIEN GMBH—Alusuisse-Lonza Holding Ltd.; *Int'l*, pg. 69
MAGNIFIN MAGNESIAPRODUKTE GMBH—Alusuisse-Lonza Holding Ltd.; *Int'l*, pg. 69
MANHATTAN BRASS & COPPER CO.; *U.S. Private*, pg. 699
NORTHLAND ALUMINUM PRODUCTS, INC.; *U.S. Private*, pg. 805
OBERDORFER INDUSTRIES, INC.; *U.S. Private*, pg. 810
PECHINEY S.A.; *Int'l*, pg. 1027
REGAL WARE, INC.; *U.S. Private*, pg. 917
RELIABLE CASTINGS CORPORATION; *U.S. Private*, pg. 920
RENOLD, INC.—Renold PLC; *Int'l*, pg. 1104
SHOWA ALUMINUM CORP.—Showa Denko K.K.; *Int'l*, pg. 1236
SHOWA ALUMINUM CORP. OF AMERICA—Showa Denko K.K.; *Int'l*, pg. 1236
SOUTHWESTERN DIE CASTING, INC.—Baldor Electric Company; *U.S. Public*, pg. 169
TWIN CITY DIE CASTINGS CO.; *U.S. Private*, pg. 1111
VARLEN CORPORATION; *U.S. Public*, pg. 1710
VASSEN ALUMINIUM BV—Koninklijke Hoogovens N.V.; *Int'l*, pg. 753
VAW OF AMERICA, INC.—Viag AG; *Int'l*, pg. 1466
WELLMAN DYNAMICS CORP.—Fansteel, Inc.; *U.S. Public*, pg. 612
CARL ZEISS CANADA LTD.—Carl-Zeiss-Stiftung; *Int'l*, pg. 1523
CARL-ZEISS-STIFTUNG; *Int'l*, pg. 1522

3366 — COPPER FOUNDRIES

AMCAST INDUSTRIAL CORPORATION; *U.S. Public*, pg. 63
AMERICAN FOUNDRY GROUP, INC.; *U.S. Private*, pg. 54
AMPCO METAL, INC.—Ampco Metal Incorporated; *U.S. Private*, pg. 67
AMPCO METAL INCORPORATED; *U.S. Private*, pg. 67
AMPCO METAL LTD.—Ampco Metal Incorporated; *U.S. Private*, pg. 67
AMPCO METAL S.A.—Ampco Metal Incorporated; *U.S. Private*, pg. 67
AMPCO SAFTEY TOOLS, DALLAS DIV.—Ampco Metal Incorporated; *U.S. Private*, pg. 67
ATLANTIC RICHFIELD COMPANY; *U.S. Public*, pg. 144
BRIDGEPORT BRASS CORPORATION—Olin Corporation; *U.S. Public*, pg. 1219
BRONZE DIV.—Matthews International Corp.; *U.S. Public*, pg. 1059
BRYAN METALS, INC.—Olin Corporation; *U.S. Public*, pg. 1219
CARBONE-LORRAINE NORTH AMERICA—Pechiney S.A.; *Int'l*, pg. 1028
CARBONE OF AMERICA—Pechiney S.A.; *Int'l*, pg. 1028
CARBONE OF AMERICA, ULTRA CARBON DIV.—Pechiney S.A.; *Int'l*, pg. 1028
DAEWOO METAL CO., LTD.—Daewoo Corporation; *Int'l*, pg. 357
ERICSSON, INC.—Telefonaktiebolaget LM Ericsson; *Int'l*, pg. 1364
ERIE BRONZE & ALUMINUM CO.—McInnes Steel Company; *U.S. Private*, pg. 722
KM-EUROPA METAL AKTIENGESELLSCHAFT; *Int'l*, pg. 719
LANGENBERG KUPFER UND MESSINGWERKE GMBH—Olin Corporation; *U.S. Public*, pg. 1219
MANHATTAN BRASS & COPPER CO.; *U.S. Private*, pg. 699
MATTHEWS INTERNATIONAL CORP.; *U.S. Public*, pg. 1059
MATTHEWS INTERNATIONAL MEMORIAL DIVISION—Matthews International Corp.; *U.S. Public*, pg. 1059
MCINNES STEEL COMPANY; *U.S. Private*, pg. 722
MICHIGAN WHEEL CORPORATION; *U.S. Private*, pg. 741
MITSUBISHI SHINDOH CO., LTD.—Mitsubishi Materials Corp.; *Int'l*, pg. 875
OUTOKUMPU COPPER PRODUCTS OY—Outokumpu Oyj; *Int'l*, pg. 1016
OUTOKUMPU OYJ; *Int'l*, pg. 1015
SANDUSKY INTERNATIONAL INC.; *U.S. Private*, pg. 964
SANDUSKY LIMITED—Sandusky International Inc.; *U.S. Private*, pg. 965
VDM TECHNOLOGIES CORP.—Fried. Krupp AG; *Int'l*, pg. 509
WILLIAM PRYM GMBH & CO. KG; *Int'l*, pg. 1499
YAMAHA-OLIN METAL CORPORATION—Olin Corporation; *U.S. Public*, pg. 1220

3369 — NONFERROUS FOUNDRIES, EXCEPT ALUMINUM & COPPER

ACTION MANUFACTURING CO.; *U.S. Private*, pg. 15
ALLIAGES FRITTES METAFRAM—Pechiney S.A.; *Int'l*, pg. 1028
AURORA METALS DIVISION L.P.C.—Hiler Industries; *U.S. Private*, pg. 529
BENGUET MANAGEMENT CORPORATION—Benguet Corporation; *Int'l*, pg. 186
BRUSH WELLMAN INC.; *U.S. Public*, pg. 266
CWC TEXTRON COMPANY—Textron Inc.; *U.S. Public*, pg. 1590
CUSTOM CASTING—Esco Corporation; *U.S. Private*, pg. 383
DEUMU DEUTSCHE ERZ- UND METALL-UNION GMBH—Preussag AG; *Int'l*, pg. 1069
DYNACAST—Coats Viyella plc; *Int'l*, pg. 300
FANSTEEL, INC.; *U.S. Public*, pg. 612
THE SCOTT FETZER COMPANY—Berkshire Hathaway Inc.; *U.S. Public*, pg. 217
FISHER GAUGE INC./FISHERCAST DIV.—Fisher Gauge Limited; *Int'l*, pg. 492
FISHER GAUGE LIMITED; *Int'l*, pg. 491
FISHERCAST—Fisher Gauge Limited; *Int'l*, pg. 491
FREEMAN PRODUCTS—Trophy Holdings Inc.; *U.S. Private*, pg. 1105
THE FURUKAWA ELECTRIC CO., LTD.; *Int'l*, pg. 530
GAMCO PRODUCTS CO.—Masco Corporation; *U.S. Public*, pg. 1053
GAS EQUIPMENT COMPANY, INC.; *U.S. Private*, pg. 440
GOULDS PUMPS, INCORPORATED—ITT Industries, Inc.; *U.S. Public*, pg. 860
GRAND RAPIDS DIE CASTING CORP.—Park Electrochemical Corporation; *U.S. Public*, pg. 1258
HALE PRODUCTS INC.—IDEX Corporation; *U.S. Public*, pg. 862
HAMWORTHY USA, INC.—Powell Duffryn PLC; *Int'l*, pg. 1066
HEXCEL CORPORATION; *U.S. Public*, pg. 824
HITCHCOCK INDUSTRIES, INC.; *U.S. Private*, pg. 531
HITCHINER MANUFACTURING COMPANY, INC.; *U.S. Private*, pg. 531
HOWMET CORPORATION—Carlyle Holding Corporation; *U.S. Private*, pg. 213
HOWMET CORPORATION—Thiokol Corporation; *U.S. Public*, pg. 1597
KARSTEN MANUFACTURING CORPORATION; *U.S. Private*, pg. 608
KERVICK ENTERPRISES, INC.; *U.S. Private*, pg. 616
LANDEGRENS MEKANISKA VERKSTAD AB—Trelleborg AB; *Int'l*, pg. 1419
LOS ANGELES DIE CASTING—Atchison Casting Corporation; *U.S. Public*, pg. 142
MAXIMET—Karsten Manufacturing Corporation; *U.S. Private*, pg. 608
NORTHWEST ALLOYS, INC.—Aluminum Company of America; *U.S. Public*, pg. 61
OREGON METALLURGICAL CORPORATION—Allegheny Teledyne Incorporated; *U.S. Public*, pg. 43
OSBY ARMATUR AB—Svedala Industri AB; *Int'l*, pg. 1323
OSBY ARMATUR AB—Trelleborg AB; *Int'l*, pg. 1419
PCC AIRFOILS, INC.—Precision Castparts Corp.; *U.S. Public*, pg. 1320
PCC EXPORTS, INC.—Precision Castparts Corp.; *U.S. Public*, pg. 1320
PHB MACHINING DIVISION—PHB Die Casting; *U.S. Private*, pg. 826
PARK ELECTROCHEMICAL CORPORATION; *U.S. Public*, pg. 1258
PEMCO DIE CASTING CORPORATION; *U.S. Private*, pg. 848
PRECISION CASTPARTS CORP.; *U.S. Public*, pg. 1320
PRECISION MOULDS, LTD.—Mattel, Inc.; *U.S. Public*, pg. 1059
SCALED COMPOSITES, INC.—Wyman-Gordon; *U.S. Public*, pg. 1782
SCHLOSSER CASTING COMPANY—Schlosser Forge Company; *U.S. Private*, pg. 970
SINERTECH—Groupe Usinor; *Int'l*, pg. 572
J.W. SINGER & SONS—Delta plc; *Int'l*, pg. 391
SONOCO PRODUCTS COMPANY; *U.S. Public*, pg. 1485
STARMET CORPORATION; *U.S. Public*, pg. 1511
TWIN CITY DIE CASTINGS CO.; *U.S. Private*, pg. 1111
VON ROLL AG; *Int'l*, pg. 1480
VON ROLL EISEN & STAHLGIESSEREI AG—Von Roll AG; *Int'l*, pg. 1480
W. & O. BERGMANN GMBH & CO. KG—Preussag AG; *Int'l*, pg. 1069
WALL COLMONOY CORP.; *U.S. Private*, pg. 1148
WALTEC AMERICAN FORGINGS, INC.—Emco Limited; *Int'l*, pg. 453
WELLMAN DYNAMICS CORP.—Fansteel, Inc.; *U.S. Public*, pg. 612
WYMAN-GORDON INVESTMENT CASTINGS, INC.—Wyman-Gordon; *U.S. Public*, pg. 1782

CARL ZEISS CANADA LTD.—Carl-Zeiss-Stiftung; *Int'l*, pg. 1523
CARL-ZEISS-STIFTUNG; *Int'l*, pg. 1522

3398 — METAL HEAT TREATING

ALLOY RING SERVICE—Handy & Harman; *U.S. Public*, pg. 780
ALLOY TECHNOLOGY INTERNATIONAL INC.; *U.S. Private*, pg. 42
ALUM-A-THERM—Lindberg Corporation; *U.S. Public*, pg. 999
COMPOFLEX—Senior Engineering Group, plc.; *Int'l*, pg. 1221
COOKSON AMERICA INC.—Cookson Group plc; *Int'l*, pg. 328
CURTISS-WRIGHT CORP.; *U.S. Public*, pg. 469
DAYTON PROCESS B.V.—Indivers B.V.; *Int'l*, pg. 673
DURHAM TUBE—Senior Engineering Group, plc.; *Int'l*, pg. 1221
ELDIM B.V.—Indivers B.V.; *Int'l*, pg. 673
ENVIROSOURCE-INTERNATIONAL MILL SERVICE, INC.—EnviroSource, Inc.; *U.S. Public*, pg. 587
FEDERAL SCREW WORKS; *U.S. Public*, pg. 616
FEDERATED FRY METALS, INC.—Cookson Group plc; *Int'l*, pg. 328
GKN BOUND BROOK LTD.—GKN plc; *Int'l*, pg. 534
GKN POWDER METALLURGY DIVISION—GKN plc; *Int'l*, pg. 534
HARRIS METALS—Lindberg Corporation; *U.S. Public*, pg. 999
HINDERLITER HEAT TREATING, INC.; *U.S. Private*, pg. 530
INDUSTRIAS TRATERH, S.A.—Senior Engineering Group, plc.; *Int'l*, pg. 1222
INTERTURBINE DALLAS AIRFOIL—United Technologies Corporation; *U.S. Public*, pg. 1690
INTERTURBINE DALLAS CASINGS—United Technologies Corporation; *U.S. Public*, pg. 1690
INTERTURBINE GERMANY GMBH—Indivers B.V.; *Int'l*, pg. 673
INTERTURBINE SINGAPORE PTE. LTD.—United Technologies Corporation; *U.S. Public*, pg. 1690
KARSTEN MANUFACTURING CORPORATION; *U.S. Private*, pg. 608
LINDBERG CORPORATION; *U.S. Public*, pg. 999
LINDBERG HEAT TREATING CO.—Lindberg Corporation; *U.S. Public*, pg. 999
LINDBERG HEAT TREATING COMPANY, BATSON DIV.—Lindberg Corporation; *U.S. Public*, pg. 999
LOI, INC.—Ruhrgas Aktiengesellschaft; *Int'l*, pg. 1149
MASCOTECH, INC.; *U.S. Public*, pg. 1055
METAL IMPROVEMENT CO.—Curtiss-Wright Corp.; *U.S. Public*, pg. 469
METAL TREATING, INC.—Thermo Electron Corporation; *U.S. Public*, pg. 1592
METALLURGICAL, INC.—Thermo Electron Corporation; *U.S. Public*, pg. 1594
OUTOKUMPU POLARIT OY—Outokumpu Oyj; *Int'l*, pg. 1018
PMC INDUSTRIES INC.; *U.S. Private*, pg. 827
PHOENIX STEEL TUBE—Senior Engineering Group, plc.; *Int'l*, pg. 1221
PIPE FABRICATING & SUPPLY COMPANY; *U.S. Private*, pg. 867
POWERFLEX—Senior Engineering Group, plc.; *Int'l*, pg. 1221
PRATT & WHITNEY—United Technologies Corporation; *U.S. Public*, pg. 1690
PRECISION DRAWN TUBE—Senior Engineering Group, plc.; *Int'l*, pg. 1222
QUANEX CORPORATION; *U.S. Public*, pg. 1349
SENIOR BIGWOOD LIMITED—Senior Engineering Group, plc.; *Int'l*, pg. 1220
SENIOR ENGINEERING GROUP, PLC.; *Int'l*, pg. 1220
SENIOR ENGINEERING PRODUCTS BUSINESS AREA—Senior Engineering Group, plc.; *Int'l*, pg. 1220
SENIOR ENGINEERING TIFT GMBH—Senior Engineering Group, plc.; *Int'l*, pg. 1223
SENIOR FOSTER WHEELER CONSTRUCTION DIVISION—Senior Engineering Group, plc.; *Int'l*, pg. 1221
SENIOR FOSTER WHEELER INDUSTRIAL BOILER DIVISION—Senior Engineering Group, plc.; *Int'l*, pg. 1221
SENIOR FOSTER WHEELER POWER DIVISION—Senior Engineering Group, plc.; *Int'l*, pg. 1221
SENIOR GREEN ECONOMISER DIVISION—Senior Engineering Group, plc.; *Int'l*, pg. 1221
SENIOR HEAT TREATMENT-ALDRIDGE—Senior Engineering Group, plc.; *Int'l*, pg. 1221
SENIOR HEAT TREATMENT LIMITED—Senior Engineering Group, plc.; *Int'l*, pg. 1221
SENIOR LUKE MATERIALS HANDLING DIVISION—Senior Engineering Group, plc.; *Int'l*, pg. 1221
SENIOR TIFT B.V.—Senior Engineering Group, plc.; *Int'l*, pg. 1223
SENIOR TIFT, INC.—Senior Engineering Group, plc.; *Int'l*, pg. 1222
SENIOR TIFT LIMITED—Senior Engineering Group, plc.; *Int'l*, pg. 1221
SENIOR TIFT PTE. LTD.—Senior Engineering Group, plc.; *Int'l*, pg. 1223
SENIOR TUBE LIMITED—Senior Engineering Group, plc.; *Int'l*, pg. 1221
SONEE HEAT TREATING—Karsten Manufacturing Corporation; *U.S. Private*, pg. 608
STEEL TECHNOLOGIES INC.; *U.S. Public*, pg. 1513
TP MANIPULATIONS—Senior Engineering Group, plc.; *Int'l*, pg. 1222
THERMO ELECTRON CORPORATION; *U.S. Public*, pg. 1591
THERMO PROCESS SYSTEMS INC./CAL-DORAN METALLURGICAL, INC.—Thermo Electron Corporation; *U.S. Public*, pg. 1594
THOMPSON STEEL CO., INC., *U.S. Private*, pg. 1083
TUBE PRODUCTS—Senior Engineering Group, plc.; *Int'l*, pg. 1222
UNITED FLEXIBLE—Senior Engineering Group, plc.; *Int'l*, pg. 1221
WALL COLMONOY CORP.; *U.S. Private*, pg. 1148

3399 — PRIMARY METAL PRODUCTS, NEC

ABBOTT BALL COMPANY; *U.S. Private*, pg. 9
ACME METALS INCORPORATED; *U.S. Public*, pg. 16
ACME PACKAGING CORPORATION—Acme Metals Incorporated; *U.S. Public*, pg. 16
ADVANCED FORMING TECHNOLOGY, INC.—Precision Castparts Corp.; *U.S. Public*, pg. 1320
ALCAN ALUMINUM CORPORATION—Alcan Aluminium Limited; *Int'l*, pg. 50
ALLOY TECHNOLOGY INTERNATIONAL INC.; *U.S. Private*, pg. 42
AMPHENOL CORPORATION—Kohlberg Kravis Roberts & Co.; *U.S. Private*, pg. 629
E.J. BROOKS COMPANY; *U.S. Private*, pg. 172
CARBOINDUSTRIAL—Elkem ASA; *Int'l*, pg. 447
CATALYSTS & CHEMICALS—Johnson Matthey Public Limited Company; *Int'l*, pg. 713
CHACE PRECISION METALS, INC.—Technitrol, Inc.; *U.S. Public*, pg. 1564
CONTINENTAL INDUSTRIES INC.—Handy & Harman; *U.S. Public*, pg. 780
DUO-FAST CORPORATION; *U.S. Private*, pg. 347
EMG EISEN-UND METALLGUSSWERK GMBH—Deutsche Babcock AG; *Int'l*, pg. 400
ELKEM ALLOY—Elkem ASA; *Int'l*, pg. 447
ELKEM CARBON—Elkem ASA; *Int'l*, pg. 447
ENGINEERED SINTERED COMPONENTS COMPANY—Eaton Corporation; *U.S. Public*, pg. 558
FATALUMINIUM—FKI Plc; *Int'l*, pg. 474
FLENDER GUSS GMBH—Deutsche Babcock AG; *Int'l*, pg. 400
HAMILTON PRECISION METALS—Katy Industries, Inc.; *U.S. Public*, pg. 944
HAMILTON SPECIALTY BAR—Slater Industries Inc.; *Int'l*, pg. 1262
HARSCO CORPORATION; *U.S. Public*, pg. 792
HECKETT MULTISERV—Harsco Corporation; *U.S. Public*, pg. 793
HILTI INC.—Hilti AG; *Int'l*, pg. 620
HOEGANAES CORP.—The Interlake Corporation; *U.S. Public*, pg. 893
HOOGOVENS GROEP B.V.—Koninklijke Hoogovens N.V.; *Int'l*, pg. 753
HORSEHEAD INDUSTRIES, INC.; *U.S. Private*, pg. 540
IMI PLC; *Int'l*, pg. 646
THE INTERLAKE CORPORATION; *U.S. Public*, pg. 892
ITOCHU BUILDING PRODUCTS CO., INC.—Itochu Corporation; *Int'l*, pg. 694
KEYSTONE POWDERED METAL COMPANY; *U.S. Private*, pg. 619
KVAERNER ROSENBERG A/S KVAERNER EGERSUND—Kvaerner a.s.a.; *Int'l*, pg. 769
LUCAS-MILHAUPT, INC.—Handy & Harman; *U.S. Public*, pg. 780
LUKENS INC.; *U.S. Public*, pg. 1019
LUKENS STEEL COMPANY—Lukens Inc.; *U.S. Public*, pg. 1020
MASCOTECH INDUSTRIAL COMPONENTS, INC.—MascoTech, Inc.; *U.S. Public*, pg. 1055
METHODE DEVELOPMENT COMPANY—Methode Electronics Inc.; *U.S. Public*, pg. 1101
NRC INC.—Bayer AG; *Int'l*, pg. 173
NATIONAL FORGE COMPANY; *U.S. Private*, pg. 783
NATIONAL LAMINATION CO.—Tang Industries Inc.; *U.S. Private*, pg. 1068
NEW HAMPSHIRE BALL BEARINGS, INC.—Minebea Co., Ltd.; *Int'l*, pg. 868
NORTHWEST INDUSTRIES, INC.—Triumph Group, Inc.; *U.S. Public*, pg. 1640
P/M STRUCTURAL PARTS DIV.—Keystone Powdered Metal Company; *U.S. Private*, pg. 619
PADNOS-SUMMIT—Louis Padnos Iron & Metal Co.; *U.S. Private*, pg. 834
PARMATECH CORPORATION—Carpenter Technology Corporation; *U.S. Public*, pg. 307
PYRON CORP.—Zemex Corporation; *Int'l*, pg. 1524
ETS RAFFEL SARREBOURG S.A.—Ascot Holdings Plc; *Int'l*, pg. 88
RENOWN STEEL—Slater Industries Inc.; *Int'l*, pg. 1262
RODNEY METALS—Allegheny Teledyne Incorporated; *U.S. Public*, pg. 43
SCM METAL PRODUCTS INC.—Hanson PLC; *Int'l*, pg. 594
SLATER INDUSTRIES INC.; *Int'l*, pg. 1262
SOUTHERN GRAPHICS SYSTEMS—Reynolds Metals Company; *U.S. Public*, pg. 1386
STACKPOLE LIMITED—Stackpole Ltd.; *U.S. Private*, pg. 1028
STARMET CORPORATION; *U.S. Public*, pg. 1511
SULZER, INC.—Sulzer Ltd.; *Int'l*, pg. 1306
SULZER PLASMA TECHNIK, INC.—Sulzer Ltd.; *Int'l*, pg. 1307
SUMIKIN BUSSAN CORPORATION; *Int'l*, pg. 1308
TECHLAM SA—SNECMA - Societe Nationale d'Etude et de Construction de Moteurs d'Aviation; *Int'l*, pg. 1166
TECHNITROL, INC.; *U.S. Public*, pg. 1564
TECOMET INC.—Thermo Electron Corporation; *U.S. Public*, pg. 1591
TECOMET-TEMPE—Thermo Electron Corporation; *U.S. Public*, pg. 1592
TECSYN P.M.P. INC.—TecSyn International, Inc.; *Int'l*, pg. 1362
TEXAS INSTRUMENTS INCORPORATED; *U.S. Public*, pg. 1585
TEXAS INSTRUMENTS MATERIALS & CONTROLS GROUP—Texas Instruments Incorporated; *U.S. Public*, pg. 1586
TEXTRON SYSTEMS CORPORATION—Textron Inc.; *U.S. Public*, pg. 1589
TREDEGAR INDUSTRIES INC.; *U.S. Public*, pg. 1633
UNITED STATES BRONZE POWDERS, INC.; *U.S. Private*, pg. 1124
WALL COLMONOY CORP.; *U.S. Private*, pg. 1148
WAYNE DALTON OF STERLING—Wayne Dalton Corporation; *U.S. Private*, pg. 1155
WESTERN MINING CORPORATION HOLDINGS LIMITED; *Int'l*, pg. 1494
ZEMEX CORPORATION; *Int'l*, pg. 1523
ZWJSEN B.V.—Koninklijke Hoogovens N.V.; *Int'l*, pg. 754

3411 — METAL CANS

A-L PACKAGING SERVICES LTD.—Alusuisse-Lonza Holding Ltd.; *Int'l*, pg. 67
ALISERE S.A.—Alusuisse-Lonza Holding Ltd.; *Int'l*, pg. 68
ALLIED FOODS, INC.; *U.S. Private*, pg. 39
ALLSTATE CAN CORPORATION; *U.S. Private*, pg. 44
ALUSINGEN GMBH—Alusuisse-Lonza Holding Ltd.; *Int'l*, pg. 68
AMERICAN NATIONAL CAN CANADA INC.—Pechiney S.A.; *Int'l*, pg. 1029
AMERICAN NATIONAL CAN COMPANY—Pechiney S.A.; *Int'l*, pg. 1029
ANHEUSER-BUSCH RECYCLING CORPORATION—Anheuser-Busch Companies, Inc.; *U.S. Public*, pg. 114
BWAY CORP.; *U.S. Public*, pg. 164
BALL CORPORATION; *U.S. Public*, pg. 170
BALL METAL BEVERAGE CONTAINER CORP.—Ball Corporation; *U.S. Public*, pg. 171
BALL METAL FOOD CONTAINER CORP.—Ball Corporation; *U.S. Public*, pg. 171
BALL PACKAGING HOLDINGS CORP.—Ball Corporation; *U.S. Public*, pg. 171
BALL PACKAGING PRODUCTS CANADA INC.—Ball Corporation; *U.S. Public*, pg. 171
BLITZ USA, INC.; *U.S. Private*, pg. 149
BORDEN INTL. PACKAGING, LTD.—Borden, Inc.; *U.S. Private*, pg. 159
BROCKWAY STANDARD OHIO, INC.—BWAY Corp.; *U.S. Public*, pg. 164
COPAL SNC—Alusuisse-Lonza Holding Ltd.; *Int'l*, pg. 68
CAN CORPORATION OF AMERICA; *U.S. Private*, pg. 204
CENTRAL STATES CAN CO.—Crown Cork & Seal Company, Inc.; *U.S. Public*, pg. 463
CENTRAL STATES CAN CO.-COMPOSITE OPERATIONS—Crown Cork & Seal Company, Inc.; *U.S. Public*, pg. 463
CLARCOR, INC.; *U.S. Public*, pg. 381
J.L. CLARK LANCASTER DIV.—CLARCOR, Inc.; *U.S. Public*, pg. 381
CONTINENTAL HOLDINGS INC.—Loews Corporation; *U.S. Public*, pg. 1011
CONTINENTAL PLASTIC CONTAINERS, INC.—Continental Can Co.; *U.S. Public*, pg. 440
ADOLPH COORS COMPANY; *U.S. Public*, pg. 445
N.V. CROWN-BAELE S. A.—Crown Cork & Seal Company, Inc.; *U.S. Public*, pg. 464
CROWN CORK & SEAL COMPANY, INC.; *U.S. Public*, pg. 462
CROWN LITOMETAL, S.A.—Crown Cork & Seal Company, Inc.; *U.S. Public*, pg. 465
DAVR - DEUTSCHE ALUMINIUM VERPACKUNG RECYCLING GMBH—Alusuisse-Lonza Holding Ltd.; *Int'l*, pg. 68
DEL MONTE FOODS; *U.S. Private*, pg. 321
EMIRATES CAN COMPANY LTD.—Crown Cork & Seal Company, Inc.; *U.S. Public*, pg. 465
FMC FOODTECH/FRAN RICA—FMC Corporation; *U.S. Public*, pg. 605
FAR FRANCE ALUMINIUM RECYCLAGE S.A.—Alusuisse-Lonza Holding Ltd.; *Int'l*, pg. 68
FEREMBAL S.A.—Continental Can Co.; *U.S. Public*, pg. 440
FOSHAN CROWN CAN COMPANY LTD.—Crown Cork & Seal Company, Inc.; *U.S. Public*, pg. 465
FOSHAN EASY-OPENING END COMPANY LTD.—Crown Cork & Seal Company, Inc.; *U.S. Public*, pg. 465
HANIL CAN CO., LTD.—Pechiney S.A.; *Int'l*, pg. 1029
HYUNDAI PRECISION & INDUSTRY CO., LTD.—Hyundai Motor Company; *Int'l*, pg. 642
INDEPENDENT CAN COMPANY; *U.S. Private*, pg. 559
INGRID DIVISION OF LAWNWARE—Lawnware Products, Inc.; *U.S. Private*, pg. 654
JEDDAH BEVERAGE CAN MAKING COMPANY LTD.—Crown Cork & Seal Company, Inc.; *U.S. Public*, pg. 465
JUSTRITE MANUFACTURING COMPANY—Federal Signal Corporation; *U.S. Public*, pg. 617
KERN INDUSTRIES; *U.S. Private*, pg. 616
LAGEEN BOX & CAN FACTORY, LTD.—Pechiney S.A.; *Int'l*, pg. 1029
LATAS DE ALUMINIO REYNOLDS, INC.—Reynolds Metals Company; *U.S. Public*, pg. 1386
LATAS DE ALUMINIO, S/A-LATASA—Reynolds Metals Company; *U.S. Public*, pg. 1387
LAWSON MARDON BOXAL FRANCE S.A.—Alusuisse-Lonza Holding Ltd.; *Int'l*, pg. 68
LAWSON MARDON BOXAL NEDERLAND B.V.—Alusuisse-Lonza Holding Ltd.; *Int'l*, pg. 68
LAWSON MARDON BOXAL SALES GMBH—Alusuisse-Lonza Holding Ltd.; *Int'l*, pg. 68
LAWSON MARDON CERLIVE S.A.—Alusuisse-Lonza Holding Ltd.; *Int'l*, pg. 68
LAWSON MARDON CHARMETTES S.A.—Alusuisse-Lonza Holding Ltd.; *Int'l*, pg. 68

LAWSON MARDON MORIN S.A.—Alusuisse-Lonza Holding Ltd.; Int'l, pg. 68
LAWSON MARDON PACKAGING INC.—Alusuisse-Lonza Holding Ltd.; Int'l, pg. 68
LAWSON MARDON PACKAGING S.A.—Alusuisse-Lonza Holding Ltd.; Int'l, pg. 69
LAWSON MARDON PICOPAC BV—Alusuisse-Lonza Holding Ltd.; Int'l, pg. 69
MB GENERAL PACKAGING DIV.—Caradon Plc; Int'l, pg. 266
METAL BOX PLC BEVERAGE CAN DIV.—Caradon Plc; Int'l, pg. 267
METAL CONTAINER CORPORATION—Anheuser-Busch Companies, Inc.; U.S. Public, pg. 114
MIDDLE EAST CAN MANUFACTURING COMPANY—Crown Cork & Seal Company, Inc.; U.S. Public, pg. 465
MILTON CAN CO., INC.; U.S. Private, pg. 749
NVF COMPANY; U.S. Private, pg. 772
NACANCO FRANCE S.A.—Pechiney S.A.; Int'l, pg. 1029
NACANCO GMBH & CO. KG—Pechiney S.A.; Int'l, pg. 1029
NACANCO IRELAND LTD.—Pechiney S.A.; Int'l, pg. 1029
NACANCO LTD.—Pechiney S.A.; Int'l, pg. 1029
NACANCO PAKETLEME SANAYI A.S.—Pechiney S.A.; Int'l, pg. 1029
NACANCO S.P.A.—Pechiney S.A.; Int'l, pg. 1029
NATIONAL CAN IBERICA SA—Pechiney S.A.; Int'l, pg. 1029
NIPPON NATIONAL SEIKAN CO., LTD.—Pechiney S.A.; Int'l, pg. 1029
PEARL CONTAINER CO.—S & P Company; U.S. Private, pg. 954
PHARMA-METALL GMBH—The West Company, Incorporated; U.S. Public, pg. 1755
REYNOLDS METALS COMPANY; U.S. Public, pg. 1385
S & P COMPANY; U.S. Private, pg. 954
SEQUA CORPORATION; U.S. Public, pg. 1458
SEXTON CAN CO., INC.; U.S. Private, pg. 988
SILGAN CORPORATION; U.S. Public, pg. 1473
SUPERENVASES ENVALIC C.A.—Reynolds Metals Company; U.S. Public, pg. 1387
SUPERIOR METAL PRINTING LIMITED; Int'l, pg. 1322
TOYO SEIKAN KAISHA, LTD.; Int'l, pg. 1411
TRI VALLEY GROWERS; U.S. Private, pg. 1101
TRIMAS CORPORATION—Masco Corporation; U.S. Public, pg. 1054
U.S. CAN COMPANY; U.S. Public, pg. 1681
VAN LEER FRANCE S.A.R.L.—Royal Packaging Industries Van Leer B.V.; Int'l, pg. 1147
VAN LEER ITALIA SPA—Royal Packaging Industries Van Leer B.V.; Int'l, pg. 1147
WHITE MOP WRINGER COMPANY; U.S. Private, pg. 1172

3412 — METAL SHIPPING BARRELS, DRUMS, KEGS, PAILS

CARMUN INTERNATIONAL—IMI Plc; Int'l, pg. 646
F.X. COUGHLIN CO.; U.S. Private, pg. 278
HOOVER GROUP, INC.; U.S. Private, pg. 538
HYOSUNG METAL PRODUCTS CO., LTD.—Hyosung Group; Int'l, pg. 641
HYUNDAI PRECISION & INDUSTRY CO., LTD.—Hyundai Motor Company; Int'l, pg. 642
PAULISTA CONTAINERS MARITIMOS LTDA.—Sea Containers Ltd.; Int'l, pg. 1214
RIEKE CORPORATION—Masco Corporation; U.S. Public, pg. 1054
ROYAL PACKAGING INDUSTRIES VAN LEER B.V.; Int'l, pg. 1145
RUBSTEEL AB—Royal Packaging Industries Van Leer B.V.; Int'l, pg. 1146
RUSSELL-STANLEY CORPORATION; U.S. Private, pg. 953
SEATTLE PACKAGING CORPORATION; U.S. Private, pg. 980
SOUTHERN FOODS GROUP; U.S. Private, pg. 1016
VAN LEER AUSTRALIA PTY. LTD.—Royal Packaging Industries Van Leer B.V.; Int'l, pg. 1146
VAN LEER BELGIUM BV—Royal Packaging Industries Van Leer B.V.; Int'l, pg. 1146
VAN LEER CONTAINERS, INC.—Royal Packaging Industries Van Leer B.V.; Int'l, pg. 1146
VAN LEER ELPACK A.E.B.E.—Royal Packaging Industries Van Leer B.V.; Int'l, pg. 1146
VAN LEER EMBALAGENS INDUSTRIAIS DO BRAZIL LTDA.—Royal Packaging Industries Van Leer B.V.; Int'l, pg. 1146
VAN LEER FRANCE S.A.R.L.—Royal Packaging Industries Van Leer B.V.; Int'l, pg. 1147
VAN LEER (MALAYSIA) SDN. BHD.—Royal Packaging Industries Van Leer B.V.; Int'l, pg. 1147
VAN LEER SINGAPORE PTE. LTD.—Royal Packaging Industries Van Leer B.V.; Int'l, pg. 1147
VAN LEER (U.K.) LTD.—Royal Packaging Industries Van Leer B.V.; Int'l, pg. 1147
VON ROLL AG DEPARTEMENT MASCHINEN & FORDERTECHN—Von Roll AG; Int'l, pg. 1480
WITT COMPANY; U.S. Private, pg. 1185

3421 — CUTLERY

ACME UNITED LTD.-SURMANCO DIVISION—Acme United Corporation; U.S. Public, pg. 17
ADAMS, S.A.—Warner-Lambert Company; U.S. Public, pg. 1739
AESCULAP AKTIENGESELLSCHAFT; Int'l, pg. 29
AMERICAN SAFETY RAZOR COMPANY—The Jordan Company; U.S. Private, pg. 597
AMES COMPANY—U.S. Industries, Inc.; U.S. Public, pg. 1683
ARDELL INDUSTRIES INC.—The Jordan Company; U.S. Private, pg. 597
ATLANTIC SERVICE CO., LTD.—Bairnco Corporation; U.S. Public, pg. 165
ATLANTIC SERVICE CO. (U.K.) LTD.—Bairnco Corporation; U.S. Public, pg. 165
BAIRNCO CORPORATION; U.S. Public, pg. 165
THE W.E. BASSETT COMPANY; U.S. Private, pg. 122
BERTRAM & GRAF GMBH—Bairnco Corporation; U.S. Public, pg. 165
BIC ASSEMBLAGE S.A.R.L.—Societe BIC S.A.; Int'l, pg. 1273
BIC CORPORATION—Societe BIC S.A.; Int'l, pg. 1273
BIC DE GUATEMALA—Societe BIC S.A.; Int'l, pg. 1273
BIC INC.—Societe BIC S.A.; Int'l, pg. 1273
BIRO BIC LTD.—Societe BIC S.A.; Int'l, pg. 1273
BUCK KNIVES, INC.; U.S. Private, pg. 177
CAMILLUS CUTLERY CO.; U.S. Private, pg. 203
CARVEL HALL—Syratech Corporation; U.S. Private, pg. 1061
W.R. CASE & SONS CUTLERY COMPANY—Zippo Manufacturing Company; U.S. Private, pg. 1207
CHICAGO CUTLERY, INC.—General Housewares Corp.; U.S. Public, pg. 716
COMPANIA MEDICINAL LA CAMPANA, S.A. DE C.V.—Warner-Lambert Company; U.S. Public, pg. 1739
THE COOK BATES DIVISION—London International Group plc; Int'l, pg. 815
CRESCENT MANUFACTURING COMPANY; U.S. Private, pg. 289
EKCO HOUSEWARES, INC.—Ekco Group, Inc.; U.S. Public, pg. 566
THE SCOTT FETZER COMPANY—Berkshire Hathaway Inc.; U.S. Public, pg. 217
FISKARS-GERBER—Fiskars Oy AB; Int'l, pg. 492
FISKARS INC.—Fiskars Oy AB; Int'l, pg. 492
GENERAL HOUSEWARES CORP.; U.S. Public, pg. 715
THE GILLETTE COMPANY; U.S. Public, pg. 743
THE GILLETTE COMPANY, GILLETTE GROOMING PRODUCTS, USA—The Gillette Company; U.S. Public, pg. 744
GILLETTE DA AMAZONIA S/A—The Gillette Company; U.S. Public, pg. 744
GILLETTE DO BRASIL & CIA—The Gillette Company; U.S. Public, pg. 744
GILLETTE GROUP ITALY S.R.L.—The Gillette Company; U.S. Public, pg. 745
GILLETTE (PHILIPPINES), INC.—The Gillette Company; U.S. Public, pg. 745
GILLETTE SOUTH AFRICA LIMITED—The Gillette Company; U.S. Public, pg. 745
HYDE MANUFACTURING CO.; U.S. Private, pg. 551
IMPERIAL SCHRADE CORP.; U.S. Private, pg. 559
IMPERIAL SCHRADE CORP.—Imperial Schrade Corp.; U.S. Private, pg. 559
IMPERIAL STAG LTD.—Imperial Schrade Corp.; U.S. Private, pg. 559
JMP NEWCOR HOLDINGS INC.—Patra Ceramics Co., Ltd.; Int'l, pg. 1025
KASCO CORPORATION—Bairnco Corporation; U.S. Public, pg. 165
KLEIN TOOLS INC.; U.S. Private, pg. 625
KVAERNER MESNA A/S—Kvaerner a.s.a.; Int'l, pg. 769
LABORATORIOS SUBSTANTIA, C.A.—Warner-Lambert Company; U.S. Public, pg. 1739
MCPHERSON'S LIMITED; Int'l, pg. 852
MIRRO COMPANY—Newell Co.; U.S. Public, pg. 1177
NORDIA S.A.—Duni AB; Int'l, pg. 421
ONTARIO KNIFE CO.—Servotronics, Inc.; U.S. Public, pg. 1462
PRYM-DRITZ CORPORATION—William Prym GmbH & Co. KG; Int'l, pg. 1499
QUEEN CUTLERY CO.—Servotronics, Inc.; U.S. Public, pg. 1462
REED & BARTON HOUSEWARES—Reed & Barton Corporation; U.S. Private, pg. 916
STANLEY ROBERTS, INC.; U.S. Private, pg. 936
ROBESON APPLIANCE, INC.; U.S. Public, pg. 1394
SAEL DECORS—Duni AB; Int'l, pg. 421
SCHICK NEDERLAND B.V.—Warner-Lambert Company; U.S. Public, pg. 1739
EMIL SCHLEMPER G.M.B.H.—Acme United Corporation; U.S. Public, pg. 17
SILUETT NORDIA AB—Duni AB; Int'l, pg. 421
SEYMOUR SMITH & SON—Emerson Electric Co.; U.S. Public, pg. 575
SPECTRUM RAZOR TOOLS—Pacific Handy Cutter, Inc.; U.S. Private, pg. 831
STANLEY TOOLS DIV.—The Stanley Works; U.S. Public, pg. 1509
STATESBORO PLANT—Cooper Industries, Inc.; U.S. Public, pg. 444
TONDEO-WERK GMBH—Wella Group; Int'l, pg. 1489
TRUE TEMPER HARDWARE COMPANY—Huffy Corporation; U.S. Public, pg. 846
THE VERNON COMPANY; U.S. Private, pg. 1137
VISTA 2000, INC.; U.S. Private, pg. 1142
WAHL CLIPPER CORP.; U.S. Private, pg. 1146
WARNER-LAMBERT (PORTUGAL) COMERCIO E INDUSTRIA LIMITADA—Warner-Lambert Company; U.S. Public, pg. 1740
WARNER-LAMBERT SCANDINAVIA AKTIEBOLAG—Warner-Lambert Company; U.S. Public, pg. 1740
WILSON MACHINE KNIFE CO., INC.—Hyde Manufacturing Co.; U.S. Private, pg. 551
ZIPPO MANUFACTURING COMPANY; U.S. Private, pg. 1207
ZIVI S.A. CUTELARIA; Int'l, pg. 1529

3423 — HAND & EDGE TOOLS, EXCEPT MACHINE TOOLS & HAND SAWS

A.T.I. TOOLS, INC.—Snap-On Tools Corporation; U.S. Public, pg. 1480
ACME METALS INCORPORATED; U.S. Public, pg. 16
ACME PACKAGING CORPORATION—Acme Metals Incorporated; U.S. Public, pg. 16
AMERICAN TOOL COMPANIES, INC.; U.S. Private, pg. 63
AMERICAN TOOL COMPANIES, INC.—American Tool Companies, Inc.; U.S. Private, pg. 63
AMERICAN WELDING & MANUFACTURING CO.—Freedom Forge Corporation; U.S. Private, pg. 425
AMES COMPANY—U.S. Industries, Inc.; U.S. Public, pg. 1683
AMES TAPING TOOL SYSTEMS CO.—AXIA Incorporated; U.S. Private, pg. 103
AMES TAPING TOOLS CO. OF CANADA LIMITED—AXIA Incorporated; U.S. Private, pg. 103
AMMCO TOOLS, INC.—Danaher Corporation; U.S. Public, pg. 480
AMPCO METAL INCORPORATED; U.S. Private, pg. 67
ARDELL INDUSTRIES INC.—The Jordan Company; U.S. Private, pg. 597
ARNO-SKIL FERRAMENTAS ELECTRICAS LTDA.—Emerson Electric Co.; U.S. Public, pg. 575
ARROW FASTENER CO., INC.; U.S. Private, pg. 85
ASKO, INC; U.S. Private, pg. 89
AUDITS & SURVEYS WORLDWIDE; U.S. Public, pg. 147
AXIA INCORPORATED; U.S. Private, pg. 103
B&D ELECTRODOMESTICOS LTDA.—The Black & Decker Corporation; U.S. Public, pg. 234
BELDRAY LIMITED—Krug International Corp.; U.S. Public, pg. 968
BLACK & DECKER CANADA INC.—The Black & Decker Corporation; U.S. Public, pg. 234
THE BLACK & DECKER CORPORATION; U.S. Public, pg. 233
BLACK & DECKER DE ESPANA S.A.—The Black & Decker Corporation; U.S. Public, pg. 234
BLACK & DECKER (SWITZERLAND) S.A.—The Black & Decker Corporation; U.S. Public, pg. 234
BRITOOL LTD.—Groupe Strafor Facom; Int'l, pg. 570
CKC—Asko, Inc; U.S. Private, pg. 89
CHANNELLOCK, INC.; U.S. Private, pg. 229
CHERAW PLANT—Cooper Industries, Inc.; U.S. Public, pg. 444
CLYDESDALE WHITEHOUSE & CO.—Caparo Group Ltd.; Int'l, pg. 265
COOPER INDUSTRIES, INC.; U.S. Public, pg. 442
THE CORNWALL & PATTERSON CO.—Pratt-Read Corporation; U.S. Private, pg. 879
CRESCENT/XCELITE—Cooper Industries, Inc.; U.S. Public, pg. 444
DANAHER TOOL GROUP—Danaher Corporation; U.S. Public, pg. 480
DANIELS MANUFACTURING CORPORATION; U.S. Private, pg. 310
DEXOL—Ringer Corporation; U.S. Public, pg. 1390
THE DISSTON CO.—Kennametal Inc.; U.S. Public, pg. 950
DRESSER OIL TOOLS—Dresser Industries, Inc.; U.S. Public, pg. 528
DUBIN-CLARK & COMPANY; U.S. Private, pg. 344
DUO-FAST CORPORATION; U.S. Private, pg. 347
DUO-FAST CORPORATION—Duo-Fast Corporation; U.S. Private, pg. 348
EDLUND COMPANY, INC.; U.S. Private, pg. 364
ESSEX INDUSTRIES—Assa Abloy AB; Int'l, pg. 18
EVANS RULE CO., INC.—The L.S. Starrett Company; U.S. Public, pg. 1511
FACOM—Groupe Strafor Facom; Int'l, pg. 570
FACOM TOOLS INC.—Groupe Strafor Facom; Int'l, pg. 570
FISKARS HAND TOOL DIVISION—Fiskars Oy AB; Int'l, pg. 492
GENERAL TOOLS MFG., CO. INC.; U.S. Private, pg. 445
A.J. GERRARD AND COMPANY; U.S. Private, pg. 449
GREENLEE TEXTRON—Textron Inc.; U.S. Public, pg. 1589
HERRAMIENTAS KLEIN S.A. DE C.V.—Klein Tools Inc.; U.S. Private, pg. 625
HERRAMIENTAS SNAP-ON DE MEXICO, S.A.—Snap-On Tools Corporation; U.S. Public, pg. 1481
HIRSH COMPANY—Knape & Vogt Mfg. Co.; U.S. Public, pg. 963
HYDE MANUFACTURING CO.; U.S. Private, pg. 551
INTERLOT GMBH—Rothenberger Group GmbH; Int'l, pg. 1128
KEN TOOL—Summit Tool Company; U.S. Private, pg. 1050
KESTER SOLDER—Litton Industries, Inc.; U.S. Public, pg. 1003
KLEIN TOOLS INC.; U.S. Private, pg. 625
KLOCKNER-BORSCH TOOLING TECHNOLOGIES—Klockner-Werke AG; Int'l, pg. 737
KVAERNER MESNA A/S—Kvaerner a.s.a.; Int'l, pg. 769
LINREAD NORTH BRIDGE—McKechnie PLC; Int'l, pg. 852
LOOS & CO., INC.; U.S. Private, pg. 675
MTD PRODUCTS, INC.; U.S. Private, pg. 688
MAGNA DIVISION—Emerson Electric Co.; U.S. Public, pg. 575
MANOIR INDUSTRIES—Groupe Strafor Facom; Int'l, pg. 570
MEADVILLE FORGING CO.; U.S. Private, pg. 726
MECHANICS TOOL DIV.—The Stanley Works; U.S. Public, pg. 1509
MIKRON AG NIDAU—Mikron Holding AG; Int'l, pg. 866
MILFORD FASTENING SYSTEMS; U.S. Private, pg. 745
MILTON INDUSTRIES, INC.; U.S. Private, pg. 749
MIRRO COMPANY—Newell Co.; U.S. Public, pg. 1177
NASCO MODESTO—Geneve Corporation; U.S. Private, pg. 446
NATIONAL HAND TOOLS—The Stanley Works; U.S. Public, pg. 1509
NICHOLSON FILE—Cooper Industries, Inc.; U.S. Public, pg. 444
PFERD/AUGUST RUEGGEBERG; Int'l, pg. 1046
POWER TEAM DIVISION—SPX Corporation; U.S. Public, pg. 1421
POWER-DYNE—Bidwell Industrial Group, Inc.; U.S. Private, pg. 142
POWERS FASTENING, INC.; U.S. Private, pg. 878
PRATT-READ CORPORATION; U.S. Private, pg. 879

PRECISION TWIST DRILL CO.—Sandvik AB; *Int'l*, pg. 1185
PREMIER DRYWALL TOOL COMPANY—Kelly-Moore Paint Company, Inc.; *U.S. Private*, pg. 613
RED DEVIL INC.; *U.S. Private*, pg. 915
REPUBLIC FASTENER PRODUCTS CORP.; *U.S. Private*, pg. 923
RIDGID FERRAMENTAS E MAGUINAS, LTDA.—Emerson Electric Co.; *U.S. Public*, pg. 577
RIDGID VAERKTOJ A/S—Emerson Electric Co.; *U.S. Public*, pg. 577
ROGERS TOOL WORKS, INC.—Kennametal Inc.; *U.S. Public*, pg. 950
RUGG MANUFACTURING COMPANY; *U.S. Private*, pg. 950
RULE CUTTING TOOLS, INC.—Kennametal Inc.; *U.S. Public*, pg. 951
RYOBI ELECTRIC TOOL MFG.—Ryobi Ltd.; *Int'l*, pg. 1151
RYOBI LTD.; *Int'l*, pg. 1151
RYOBI MOTOR PRODUCTS—Ryobi Ltd.; *Int'l*, pg. 1151
S-B POWER TOOL COMPANY—Robert Bosch GmbH; *Int'l*, pg. 205
SK HAND TOOL CORP.—Groupe Strafor Facom; *Int'l*, pg. 570
SPX CORPORATION; *U.S. Public*, pg. 1420
SANDVIK AB; *Int'l*, pg. 1185
AB SANDVIK HAND TOOLS—Sandvik AB; *Int'l*, pg. 1185
SANDVIK KOSTA GMBH—Sandvik AB; *Int'l*, pg. 1186
AB SANDVIK SAWS & TOOLS—Sandvik AB; *Int'l*, pg. 1185
SERVICE SOLUTION—SPX Corporation; *U.S. Public*, pg. 1421
SEYMOUR MANUFACTURING COMPANY; *U.S. Private*, pg. 988
SKILTOOLS DE MEXICO S.A. DE C.V.—Emerson Electric Co.; *U.S. Public*, pg. 578
SNAP-ON TOOLS CORPORATION; *U.S. Public*, pg. 1480
SNAP-ON TOOLS, GMBH—Snap-On Tools Corporation; *U.S. Public*, pg. 1481
STANLEY TOOLS DIV.—The Stanley Works; *U.S. Public*, pg. 1509
THE STANLEY WORKS; *U.S. Public*, pg. 1508
THE L.S. STARRETT COMPANY; *U.S. Public*, pg. 1511
L.S. STARRETT COMPANY OF CANADA—The L.S. Starrett Company; *U.S. Public*, pg. 1511
SUMMIT TOOL COMPANY; *U.S. Private*, pg. 1050
SYNEX CORP.—Berwind Corporation; *U.S. Private*, pg. 138
THE TATA IRON AND STEEL CO. LTD.; *Int'l*, pg. 1356
TATRY OFFICINA MECCANICA S.R.L.—The Black & Decker Corporation; *U.S. Public*, pg. 234
TECO MANUFACTURING, INC.—Team, Inc.; *U.S. Public*, pg. 1562
TRIUMPH TWIST DRILL CO.—Sandvik AB; *Int'l*, pg. 1185
TRUE TEMPER HARDWARE COMPANY—Huffy Corporation; *U.S. Public*, pg. 846
UNIONTOOLS, INC.—Acorn Products, Inc.; *U.S. Public*, pg. 17
U.S. HOME & GARDEN INC.; *U.S. Public*, pg. 1682
UNIVERSAL TOOL & STAMPING—Acme Metals Incorporated; *U.S. Public*, pg. 17
VERMONT AMERICAN CORPORATION-FOUNTAIN INN DIV.—Emerson Electric Co.; *U.S. Public*, pg. 575
VERMONT AMERICAN TOOL CORP.—Emerson Electric Co.; *U.S. Public*, pg. 575
VIRAX—Groupe Strafor Facom; *Int'l*, pg. 570
WEN PRODUCTS, INC.; *U.S. Private*, pg. 1144
WARREN TOOL GROUP—Wilton Corporation; *U.S. Private*, pg. 1181
J.H. WILLIAMS—Snap-On Tools Corporation; *U.S. Public*, pg. 1481
WILTON CORPORATION; *U.S. Private*, pg. 1181
WILTON TOOL CORP.—Wilton Corporation; *U.S. Private*, pg. 1181
ZIPPO MANUFACTURING COMPANY; *U.S. Private*, pg. 1207

3425 — HAND SAWS & SAW BLADES

AMERICAN SAW & MFG. COMPANY; *U.S. Private*, pg. 61
AMERICAN TOOL COMPANIES, INC.; *U.S. Private*, pg. 63
AVEN TOOLS LTD.—The Black & Decker Corporation; *U.S. Public*, pg. 234
BERTRAM & GRAF GMBH—Bairnco Corporation; *U.S. Public*, pg. 165
THE BLACK & DECKER CORPORATION; *U.S. Public*, pg. 233
BLOUNT, INC.—Blount International, Inc.; *U.S. Public*, pg. 238
BLOUNT INDUSTRIAL DE CORRENTES LTDA.—Blount International, Inc.; *U.S. Public*, pg. 239
BLOUNT INTERNATIONAL, INC.; *U.S. Public*, pg. 237
DML INDUSTRIAL DIV.—Emerson Electric Co.; *U.S. Public*, pg. 575
DML PRODUCTS—Emerson Electric Co.; *U.S. Public*, pg. 575
THE DISSTON CO.—Kennametal Inc.; *U.S. Public*, pg. 950
EVANS RULE CO., INC.—The L.S. Starrett Company; *U.S. Public*, pg. 1511
GREAT NECK SAW MANUFACTURERS, INC.; *U.S. Private*, pg. 475
KLEIN TOOLS INC.; *U.S. Private*, pg. 625
LARSAN MANUFACTURING CO.—Emerson Electric Co.; *U.S. Public*, pg. 575
LEITCHFIELD DIV.—Emerson Electric Co.; *U.S. Public*, pg. 575
MIDLAND FORGE DIVISION—Columbus McKinnon Corp.; *U.S. Public*, pg. 406
NICHOLSON—Cooper Industries, Inc.; *U.S. Public*, pg. 444
NICHOLSON FILE—Cooper Industries, Inc.; *U.S. Public*, pg. 444
PRECISION CARBIDE TOOL COMPANY, INC.; *U.S. Private*, pg. 879
PRIMARK TOOL GROUP—Emerson Electric Co.; *U.S. Public*, pg. 575
RULE CUTTING TOOLS, INC.—Kennametal Inc.; *U.S. Public*, pg. 951
RULE INDUSTRIES, INC.—Kennametal Inc.; *U.S. Public*, pg. 950
SANDVIK AB; *Int'l*, pg. 1185
SANDVIK/MILFORD CORPORATION—Sandvik AB; *Int'l*, pg. 1185
AB SANDVIK SAWS & TOOLS—Sandvik AB; *Int'l*, pg. 1185
SEMITEC, INC.—Kulicke & Soffa Industries, Inc.; *U.S. Public*, pg. 969
STANLEY TOOLS DIV.—The Stanley Works; *U.S. Public*, pg. 1509
THE L.S. STARRETT COMPANY; *U.S. Public*, pg. 1511
L.S. STARRETT CO. LTD.—The L.S. Starrett Company; *U.S. Public*, pg. 1511
L.S. STARRETT COMPANY OF CANADA—The L.S. Starrett Company; *U.S. Public*, pg. 1511
VERMONT AMERICAN CANADA, INC.—Emerson Electric Co.; *U.S. Public*, pg. 578
VERMONT AMERICAN TOOL CORP.—Emerson Electric Co.; *U.S. Public*, pg. 575

3429 — HARDWARE, NEC

ACI INTERNATIONAL LTD.—BTR plc; *Int'l*, pg. 128
ASSA ABLOY AB; *Int'l*, pg. 17
ACMETRACK—BTR plc; *Int'l*, pg. 129
ADAMS RITE MANUFACTURING CO.; *U.S. Private*, pg. 17
ADTEC DETENTION SYSTEMS; *U.S. Private*, pg. 18
ADVANCED ACCESSORIES SYSTEMS, LLC.; *U.S. Private*, pg. 21
AEROQUIP CORPORATION—Aeroquip-Vickers, Inc.; *U.S. Public*, pg. 24
AIRBORNE—Groupe Strafor Facom; *Int'l*, pg. 569
AKRON BRASS COMPANY—Premier Farnell plc; *Int'l*, pg. 1068
ALCATEL ALSTHOM COMPAGNIE GENERALE D'ELECTRICITE; *Int'l*, pg. 52
ALCOA COMPOSITES, INC.—Aluminum Company of America; *U.S. Public*, pg. 60
AMERICAN CONSUMER PRODUCTS—Vista 2000, Inc.; *U.S. Private*, pg. 1142
AMERICAN STRIP STEEL INC.; *U.S. Private*, pg. 62
AMEROCK CORPORATION—Newell Co.; *U.S. Public*, pg. 1177
ANCHOR STAMPINGS—Illinois Tool Works Inc.; *U.S. Public*, pg. 865
ANDERSON INDUSTRIES, INC.—Excel Industries, Inc.; *U.S. Public*, pg. 599
ANDROCK PRODUCTS/NEWELL BULLDOG—Newell Co.; *U.S. Public*, pg. 1178
ARMSTRONG INTERNATIONAL, INC.; *U.S. Private*, pg. 83
AUBREY MANUFACTURING COMPANY—Nortek, Inc.; *U.S. Public*, pg. 1193
AVIBANK MFG., INC.; *U.S. Private*, pg. 101
AVIS INDUSTRIAL CORPORATION; *U.S. Private*, pg. 102
BALDWIN HARDWARE CORPORATION—Masco Corporation; *U.S. Public*, pg. 1053
BALDWIN HARDWARE SERVICE CORPORATION—Masco Corporation; *U.S. Public*, pg. 1053
BAND-IT-IDEX, INC.—IDEX Corporation; *U.S. Public*, pg. 862
BASSICK BY KASPAR; *U.S. Private*, pg. 122
BEST ACCESS SYSTEMS; *U.S. Public*, pg. 223
BEST UNIVERSAL LOCK LTD.—Best Access Systems; *U.S. Public*, pg. 223
THE BLACK & DECKER CORPORATION; *U.S. Public*, pg. 233
BOMMER INDUSTRIES, INC.; *U.S. Private*, pg. 156
BORG WARNER AUTOMOTIVE-ALABAMA DIV.—Borg Warner Automotive, Inc.; *U.S. Public*, pg. 245
BREED TECHNOLOGIES—Breed Technologies, Inc.; *U.S. Public*, pg. 251
BREEZE INDUSTRIAL—TransTechnology Corporation; *U.S. Public*, pg. 1632
BRIGGS & STRATTON CORPORATION; *U.S. Public*, pg. 252
BULLDOG CO.—Newell Co.; *U.S. Public*, pg. 1176
BYERS PORTLAND WILLAMETTE—Byers Industries, Inc.; *U.S. Private*, pg. 191
CCL SECURITY PRODUCTS—The Eastern Company; *U.S. Public*, pg. 548
CEF SAFETY SYSTEMS B.V.—Halma p.l.c.; *Int'l*, pg. 590
CAM AM CASTERS—Standex International Corporation; *U.S. Public*, pg. 1507
THE CANADIAN COLEMAN CO., LTD.—MacAndrews & Forbes Holdings Inc.; *U.S. Private*, pg. 691
CANADIAN THERMOS PRODUCTS LTD.—Nippon Sanso Corporation; *Int'l*, pg. 938
CARCLO ENGINEERING GROUP PLC; *Int'l*, pg. 268
CASTELL INTERLOCKS INC.—Halma p.l.c.; *Int'l*, pg. 590
CASTELL SAFETY INTERNATIONAL LIMITED—Halma p.l.c.; *Int'l*, pg. 589
CERTANIUM B.V.—Premier Farnell plc; *Int'l*, pg. 1068
CHICAGO LOCK COMPANY; *U.S. Private*, pg. 235
COLE CONSUMER PRODUCTS—Vista 2000, Inc.; *U.S. Private*, pg. 1142
CONSTRUCCIONES RADIO ELECTRO MECANICAS S.A.—Caparo Group Ltd.; *Int'l*, pg. 265
CONTRAN CORPORATION; *U.S. Private*, pg. 270
CORBIN RUSSWIN, INC.—Williams Holdings Plc; *Int'l*, pg. 1499
CORTLAND PLANT—Cooper Industries, Inc.; *U.S. Public*, pg. 444
CROSBY CANADA LTD.—FKI Plc; *Int'l*, pg. 473
DOM AG SICHERHEITSTECHNIK—The Black & Decker Corporation; *U.S. Public*, pg. 233
DOM-SICHERHEITSTECHNIK GMBH & CO. KG—The Black & Decker Corporation; *U.S. Public*, pg. 233
DAYTON SUPERIOR CANADA LTD.—Ripplewood Holdings L.L.C.; *U.S. Private*, pg. 932
DAYTON SUPERIOR CORPORATION—Ripplewood Holdings L.L.C.; *U.S. Private*, pg. 931
DE-STA-CO, A DOVER RESOURCES CO.—Dover Corporation; *U.S. Public*, pg. 521
DECO PRODUCTS CO.; *U.S. Private*, pg. 320
DELPHI ENERGY & ENGINE MANAGEMENT SYSTEMS—General Motors Corporation; *U.S. Public*, pg. 719
DEUTSCHE BABCOCK AG; *Int'l*, pg. 398
DEUTSCHE BABCOCK TECHNOLOGIES, INC.—Deutsche Babcock AG; *Int'l*, pg. 401
DIEBEL MANUFACTURING CO.; *U.S. Private*, pg. 331
DIMCO-GRAY COMPANY; *U.S. Private*, pg. 333
J.B. DIONNE LTD.—Purdel, Cooperative Agro-Alimentaire; *Int'l*, pg. 1074
EG & G SEALOL INC.—EG & G, Inc.; *U.S. Public*, pg. 544
THE EASTERN COMPANY; *U.S. Public*, pg. 548
EBERHARD HARDWARE MANUFACTURING LTD.—The Eastern Company; *U.S. Public*, pg. 548
EBERHARD MANUFACTURING—The Eastern Company; *U.S. Public*, pg. 548
ELCO TEXTRON—Textron Inc.; *U.S. Public*, pg. 1590
ELECTROLUX AUTOLIV—Electrolux, AB; *Int'l*, pg. 439
EMTEC PRODUCTS CORPORATION—Kuhlman Corporation; *U.S. Public*, pg. 968
ERICO INTERNATIONAL; *U.S. Private*, pg. 381
ESSEX INDUSTRIES—Assa Abloy AB; *Int'l*, pg. 18
ESSEX INDUSTRIES, INC.—Assa Abloy AB; *Int'l*, pg. 18
EUROPEAN VACUUM INTERRUPTERS S.A.—Toshiba Corporation; *Int'l*, pg. 1405
EVANS INDUSTRIES, INC.; *U.S. Private*, pg. 385
FKI INDUSTRIES. INC.—FKI Plc; *Int'l*, pg. 472
FAULTLESS CASTER—FKI Plc; *Int'l*, pg. 473
FEENY MANUFACTURING COMPANY—Knape & Vogt Mfg. Co.; *U.S. Public*, pg. 963
FIBRE GLASS-EVERCOAT COMPANY—Illinois Tool Works Inc.; *U.S. Public*, pg. 866
FINGERLE LUMBER CO.; *U.S. Private*, pg. 405
FLANDERS INDUSTRIES, INC.; *U.S. Private*, pg. 410
FLUIDRIVE INC.; *U.S. Private*, pg. 415
FORT LOCK CORPORATION; *U.S. Private*, pg. 419
FORTUNE BRANDS, INC.; *U.S. Public*, pg. 674
GSW JACKES-EVANS MANUFACTURING CO.—GSW Inc.; *Int'l*, pg. 538
GATES HYDRAULICS LTD.—Tomkins PLC; *Int'l*, pg. 1397
GILMOUR MANUFACTURING CO.—Emerson Electric Co.; *U.S. Public*, pg. 575
GLOBE SPRING & CUSHION CO., LTD.—Leggett & Platt, Incorporated; *U.S. Public*, pg. 987
GRIFFON CORP.; *U.S. Public*, pg. 766
GROUPE STRAFOR FACOM; *Int'l*, pg. 569
A.L. HANSEN MANUFACTURING CO.; *U.S. Private*, pg. 500
HARTWELL CORPORATION—Western Sky Industries, Inc.; *U.S. Private*, pg. 1168
JOHN HASSALL, INC.; *U.S. Private*, pg. 509
HERRAMIENTAS SNAP-ON DE MEXICO, S.A.—Snap-On Tools Corporation; *U.S. Public*, pg. 1481
HIGHFIELD MANUFACTURING CO.—BTR plc; *Int'l*, pg. 127
HIGHLAND MANUFACTURING—Illinois Tool Works Inc.; *U.S. Public*, pg. 866
HILLENBRAND INDUSTRIES, INC.; *U.S. Public*, pg. 828
HILTI INC.—Hilti AG; *Int'l*, pg. 620
HIRSH COMPANY—Knape & Vogt Mfg. Co.; *U.S. Public*, pg. 963
HONDA LOCK MFG., CO., LTD.—Honda Motor Co., Ltd.; *Int'l*, pg. 634
HOUCK INDUSTRIES, INC.; *U.S. Private*, pg. 541
HURD LOCKS—Avis Industrial Corporation; *U.S. Private*, pg. 102
HYNES INDUSTRIES INC.; *U.S. Private*, pg. 552
IMI CORNELIUS, INC. (IA)—IMI Plc; *Int'l*, pg. 646
IPC-INTERNATIONAL PARTS CORP.—Whitman Corporation; *U.S. Public*, pg. 1766
ISI NORGEN, INC.—IMI Plc; *Int'l*, pg. 646
ITW SIGNODE—Illinois Tool Works Inc.; *U.S. Public*, pg. 867
IDEX CORPORATION; *U.S. Public*, pg. 862
ILCO UNICAN CORP., SAFELOCK DIVISION—Unican Security Systems Ltd.; *Int'l*, pg. 1432
ILCO UNICAN CORP., SIMPLEX ACCESS CONTROLS DIVISION—Unican Security Systems Ltd.; *Int'l*, pg. 1432
ILCO UNICAN CORP.—Unican Security Systems Ltd.; *Int'l*, pg. 1432
ILCO UNICAN INC. (CAPITOL DIVISION)—Unican Security Systems Ltd.; *Int'l*, pg. 1432
ILCO UNICAN MEXICO S.A. DE C.V.—Unican Security Systems Ltd.; *Int'l*, pg. 1432
THE ILLINOIS LOCK CO. DIV.—The Eastern Company; *U.S. Public*, pg. 548
INDUSTRIAL AMERICAS GROUP—Aeroquip-Vickers, Inc.; *U.S. Public*, pg. 24
INDUSTRIAL RETAINING RING COMPANY—TransTechnology Corporation; *U.S. Public*, pg. 1632
INGERSOLL-RAND COMPANY; *U.S. Public*, pg. 876
H.B. IVES—Harrow Industries; *U.S. Private*, pg. 506
JARVIS (EAST)—Standex International Corporation; *U.S. Public*, pg. 1506
JARVIS-PEMCO—Standex International Corporation; *U.S. Public*, pg. 1506
JARVIS (WEST)—Standex International Corporation; *U.S. Public*, pg. 1506
JASON INDUSTRIAL, INC.; *U.S. Private*, pg. 583
JEUMONT-SCHNEIDER TRENFORMETEURS; *Int'l*, pg. 706
JOHNSON CONTROLS, INC.; *U.S. Public*, pg. 932
KEELER BRASS COMPANY—FKI Plc; *Int'l*, pg. 473
KLEIN TOOLS INC.; *U.S. Private*, pg. 625
KNAPE & VOGT CANADA INC.—Knape & Vogt Mfg. Co.; *U.S. Public*, pg. 963
KNAPE & VOGT MFG. CO.; *U.S. Public*, pg. 963
KNAPE & VOGT MFG. CO.—Knape & Vogt Mfg. Co.; *U.S. Public*, pg. 963
KRAFT HARDWARE, INC.; *U.S. Private*, pg. 634
KWIKSET CORPORATION—The Black & Decker Corporation; *U.S. Public*, pg. 233

LARCH-LAP LIMITED—Newmond PLC; *Int'l*, pg. 925
LESLIE BUILDING PRODUCTS, INC.; *U.S. Public*, pg. 989
LESLIE - LOCKE, INC.—Leslie Building Products, Inc.; *U.S. Public*, pg. 989
LIEBHERR-AEROSPACE LINDENBERG GMBH—Liebherr-International AG; *Int'l*, pg. 808
LINN PRODUCTS, INC.; *U.S. Private*, pg. 669
MTD PRODUCTS, INC.; *U.S. Private*, pg. 688
MACHINING ENTERPRISES INC.; *U.S. Private*, pg. 691
MACKLANBURG-DUNCAN CO.; *U.S. Private*, pg. 692
MARLITE; *U.S. Private*, pg. 705
MASCO CORPORATION; *U.S. Public*, pg. 1052
MASCO CORPORATION LIMITED—Masco Corporation; *U.S. Public*, pg. 1054
MASTER LOCK COMPANY—Fortune Brands, Inc.; *U.S. Public*, pg. 675
MAUREY MANUFACTURING CORP.; *U.S. Private*, pg. 715
MEDECO SECURITY LOCKS, INC.—Hillenbrand Industries, Inc.; *U.S. Public*, pg. 828
MILWAUKEE LOCK COMPANY—Fortune Brands, Inc.; *U.S.* Public, pg. 675
MINER ENTERPRISES INC.; *U.S. Private*, pg. 749
MOELLER PRODUCTS CO., INC.; *U.S. Private*, pg. 755
MORRIS COUPLING CO.; *U.S. Private*, pg. 762
MOSLER INC.; *U.S. Private*, pg. 763
NT DOR-OMATIC; *U.S. Private*, pg. 771
NATIONAL CABINET LOCK, INC.—Contran Corporation; *U.S. Private*, pg. 270
NEMEF B.V.—The Black & Decker Corporation; *U.S. Public*, pg. 235
NEW COLEMAN HOLDINGS INC.—MacAndrews & Forbes Holdings Inc.; *U.S. Private*, pg. 690
NEWELL CO.; *U.S. Public*, pg. 1176
NIELSEN/SESSIONS—Zero Corporation; *U.S. Public*, pg. 1791
NORTH & JUDD; *U.S. Private*, pg. 804
NORTHFIELD METAL PRODUCTS LTD.—Leggett & Platt, Incorporated; *U.S. Public*, pg. 987
NORWALK POWDERED METALS, INC.; *U.S. Private*, pg. 808
ORION SPA.—Unican Security Systems Ltd.; *Int'l*, pg. 1432
P.E./DEL MAR, INC.—Watsco, Inc.; *U.S. Public*, pg. 1746
THE PALNUT COMPANY—TransTechnology Corporation; *U.S. Public*, pg. 1632
PANDROL INTERNATIONAL LIMITED—Charter plc; *Int'l*, pg. 280
PAYSON CASTERS, INC.; *U.S. Private*, pg. 844
PEGLER-HATTERSLEY PLC—Tomkins PLC; *Int'l*, pg. 1395
PETERSON AMERICAN CORP.; *U.S. Private*, pg. 857
PHELPS TOINTON INC.; *U.S. Private*, pg. 860
PLASTIMO S.A.—Johnson Worldwide Associates, Inc.; *U.S.* Public, pg. 933
POLYCELL PRODUCTS LIMITED—Williams Holdings Plc; *Int'l*, pg. 1501
PREMIER FARNELL—Premier Farnell plc; *Int'l*, pg. 1068
PRYM-DRITZ CORPORATION—William Prym GmbH & Co. KG; *Int'l*, pg. 1499
RAILROAD TRACK CONSTRUCTION CORP.—St. Joe Corp.; *U.S. Public*, pg. 1427
THE RAWLPLUG COMPANY LIMITED—Newmond PLC; *Int'l*, pg. 925
REV-A-SHELF; *U.S. Private*, pg. 925
ROLL-IT—Knape & Vogt Mfg. Co.; *U.S. Public*, pg. 963
ROLLEX CORPORATION; *U.S. Private*, pg. 941
RULE INDUSTRIES, INC.—Kennametal Inc.; *U.S. Public*, pg. 950
SERV TRAYVOU INTERVERROUILLAGE SA—Halma p.l.c.; *Int'l*, pg. 590
SMR (SOCIETE METALLURGIQUE DE REVIGNY)—Groupe Usinor; *Int'l*, pg. 571
SARGENT & GREENLEAF, INC.; *U.S. Private*, pg. 965
SARGENT MANUFACTURING COMPANY—Assa Abloy AB; *Int'l*, pg. 18
SCHLAGE LOCK COMPANY—Ingersoll-Rand Company; *U.S. Public*, pg. 876
SEA RANGER PRODUCTS—West Marine, Inc.; *U.S. Public*, *pg. 1756*
SECURITY GROUP INC.; *U.S. Private*, pg. 981
SELKIRK METALBESTOS—Zurn Industries, Inc.; *U.S. Public*, pg. 1794
SERVICE SUPPLY CO. INC. OF INDIANA; *U.S. Private*, pg. 987
THE SHELBURNE CORPORATION; *U.S. Private*, pg. 991
SHELBURNE HUSKY DIV.—The Shelburne Corporation; *U.S. Private*, pg. 991
SHUR-LOK CORPORATION; *U.S. Private*, pg. 997
SIGNFIX LTD.—IDEX Corporation; *U.S. Public*, pg. 862
SNAP-ON TOOLS, GMBH—Snap-On Tools Corporation; *U.S. Public*, pg. 1481
SNAP-TITE, INC.; *U.S. Private*, pg. 1010
SOSS OF SINGAPORE PTE. LTD.—United Dominion Industries, Ltd.; *U.S. Public*, pg. 1677
STANLEY HARDWARE DIV.—The Stanley Works; *U.S. Public*, pg. 1509
THE STANLEY WORKS; *U.S. Public*, pg. 1508
STANT CORPORATION—Tomkins PLC; *Int'l*, pg. 1396
JOHN STERLING CORPORATION; *U.S. Private*, pg. 1041
STEWART WARNER INSTRUMENTS CORPORATION; *U.S. Private*, pg. 1042
STEWART WARNER INSTRUMENTS CORPORATION—Stewart Warner Instruments Corporation; *U.S. Private*, pg. 1043
STRATTEC SECURITIES CORPORATION; *U.S. Public*, pg. 1523
SURCO PRODUCTS, INC.; *U.S. Private*, pg. 1056
TA MFG. CO.—Esterline Technologies Corporation; *U.S. Public*, pg. 594
TEMCO FIREPLACE PRODUCTS, INC.—Temtex Industries Inc.; *U.S. Public*, pg. 1576
THERMA-TRU INDIANA MFG. OPERS.—Therma-Tru Corp.; *U.S. Private*, pg. 1080
THERMA-TRU WESTERN MFG. OPERS.—Therma-Tru Corp.; *U.S. Private*, pg. 1080
THERMOS LIMITED—Nippon Sanso Corporation; *Int'l*, pg. 938
THE TOBIN CORPORATION—Avis Industrial Corporation; *U.S. Private*, pg. 102
TRANSTECHNOLOGY CORPORATION; *U.S. Public*, pg. 1632
TRIDON INC.—AT&T Corporation; *U.S. Public*, pg. 11
WM. S. TRIMBLE COMPANY, INC.; *U.S. Private*, pg. 1103
TRIPLE A SPECIALTY COMPANY; *U.S. Private*, pg. 1103
TRU-TURN CORPORATION—Hayes Wheels International, Inc.; *U.S. Private*, pg. 513
TUTHILL CORPORATION; *U.S. Private*, pg. 1110
UNICAN SECURITY SYSTEMS LTD.; *Int'l*, pg. 1432
U.S. LOCK—Waxman Industries, Inc.; *U.S. Public*, pg. 1748
UNITED TECHNOLOGIES, AUTOMOTIVE—United Technologies Corporation; *U.S. Public*, pg. 1691
UNIVERSAL INDUSTRIAL PRODUCTS CO.—United Dominion Industries, Ltd.; *U.S. Public*, pg. 1677
VERMONT AMERICAN TOOL CORP.—Emerson Electric Co.; *U.S. Public*, pg. 575
VOSS INDUSTRIES, INC.; *U.S. Private*, pg. 1143
W.J. & DENNIS CO.; *U.S. Private*, pg. 1144
WAGNER CASTERS AND WHEELS—E.R. Wagner Manufacturing; *U.S. Private*, pg. 1146
E.R. WAGNER MANUFACTURING; *U.S. Private*, pg. 1146
WATSCO, INC.; *U.S. Public*, pg. 1745
WAYNE DALTON OF STERLING—Wayne Dalton Corporation; *U.S. Private*, pg. 1155
WEBER-KNAPP COMPANY—FKI Plc; *Int'l*, pg. 473
N.V. WEISER EUROPE, S.A.—Masco Corporation; *U.S. Public*, pg. 1055
WEISER INC.—Masco Corporation; *U.S. Public*, pg. 1055
WEISER LOCK DIVISION—Masco Corporation; *U.S. Public*, *pg. 1053*
WEISER (U.K.) LTD.—Masco Corporation; *U.S. Public*, pg. 1055
WESLOCK NATIONAL, INC.; *U.S. Private*, pg. 1163
WESTERN FIRE EQUIP.—Premier Farnell plc; *Int'l*, pg. 1068
RALPH C. WILSON ENTERPRISES; *U.S. Private*, pg. 1181
WINFIELD LOCKS, INC.—Masco Corporation; *U.S. Public*, pg. 1053
WORLD LOCK CO. LTD.—The Eastern Company; *U.S. Public*, pg. 548
WYNN'S INTERNATIONAL, INC.; *U.S. Public*, pg. 1782
YALE SECURITY, INC.—Williams Holdings Plc; *Int'l*, pg. 1499
YALE SECURITY PRODUCTS, LTD.—Williams Holdings Plc; *Int'l*, pg. 1499
ZERO PLASTICS—Zero Corporation; *U.S. Public*, pg. 1791

3431 — ENAMELED IRON & METAL SANITARY WARE

ACORN ENGINEERING COMPANY; *U.S. Private*, pg. 14
ALSONS CORPORATION—Masco Corporation; *U.S. Public*, *pg. 1053*
AMERICAN SPECIALTIES INC.; *U.S. Private*, pg. 62
AMERICAN STANDARD INC.; *U.S. Public*, pg. 91
AQUA GLASS CORP.—Masco Corporation; *U.S. Public*, pg. 1053
BLUE CIRCLE INDUSTRIES PLC; *Int'l*, pg. 197
BOMMER INDUSTRIES, INC.; *U.S. Private*, pg. 156
BRADLEY CORPORATION; *U.S. Private*, pg. 164
BRADLEY WASHROOM ACCESSORIES DIV.—Bradley Corporation; *U.S. Private*, pg. 164
BRIGGS INDUSTRIES, INC.; *U.S. Private*, pg. 168
BULTHAUP GMBH & CO.—Toto Ltd.; *Int'l*, pg. 1410
CRANE CANADA INC.—Crane Co.; *U.S. Public*, pg. 457
DAIDO HOXAN INC.; *Int'l*, pg. 363
ELJER MANUFACTURING/HVAC GROUP—Zurn Industries, Inc.; *U.S. Public*, pg. 1794
ELJER PLUMBINGWARE—Zurn Industries, Inc.; *U.S. Public*, pg. 1794
ELKAY MANUFACTURING COMPANY; *U.S. Private*, pg. 372
EMAIL LIMITED-BUILDING PRODUCTS GROUP—Email Limited; *Int'l*, pg. 450
EXCELSIOR MANUFACTURING & SUPPLY CORP.; *U.S. Private*, pg. 387
GLOBAL STEEL PRODUCTS CORPORATION; *U.S. Private*, pg. 457
HMI INDUSTRIES; *U.S. Public*, pg. 771
HAWS DRINKING FAUCET CO.; *U.S. Private*, pg. 512
IDEAL-STANDARD—American Standard Inc.; *U.S. Public*, pg. 92
JOSAM COMPANY; *U.S. Private*, pg. 600
KALLISTA, INC.—Kohler Company; *U.S. Private*, pg. 630
KELIM TOTO CO., LTD.—Toto Ltd.; *Int'l*, pg. 1410
KERMI GMBH—Preussag AG; *Int'l*, pg. 1069
KINDRED INDUSTRIES—Emco Limited; *Int'l*, pg. 453
MAGLA PRODUCTS; *U.S. Private*, pg. 695
MELNOR INC.—O'Sullivan Corporation; *U.S. Public*, pg. 1234
METPAR CORP.; *U.S. Private*, pg. 735
MUELLER INDUSTRIES, INC.; *U.S. Public*, pg. 1141
NANJING TOTO CO., LTD.—Toto Ltd.; *Int'l*, pg. 1410
PARK ELECTROCHEMICAL CORPORATION; *U.S. Public*, pg. 1258
SEALAND TECHNOLOGY—Taylor Made Group, Inc.; *U.S. Private*, pg. 1071
SIAM SANITARY WARE CO., LTD.—Toto Ltd.; *Int'l*, pg. 1410
STANCO METAL PRODUCTS, INC.; *U.S. Private*, pg. 1030
SUN WAVE INDUSTRIAL CO.; *Int'l*, pg. 1320
P.T. SURYA TOTO INDONESIA—Toto Ltd.; *Int'l*, pg. 1410
TAKARA STANDARD CO., LTD.—Takara Belmont Co., Ltd.; *Int'l*, pg. 1349
TOTO LTD.; *Int'l*, pg. 1410
UNR HOME PRODUCTS DIV.—ROHN Industries, Inc.; *U.S.* Public, pg. 1404
WESTERN AMERICAN MANUFACTURING, INC.—Waxman Industries, Inc.; *U.S. Public*, pg. 1749

3432 — PLUMBING FIXTURE FITTINGS & TRIM

A.Y.M. INC.—A.Y. McDonald Industries, Inc.; *U.S. Private*, pg. 721
ACORN ENGINEERING COMPANY; *U.S. Private*, pg. 14
ALSONS CORPORATION—Masco Corporation; *U.S. Public*, *pg. 1053*
AMERICAN FLANGE & MANUFACTURING CO. INC.—Royal Packaging Industries Van Leer B.V.; *Int'l*, pg. 1146
AMERICAN STANDARD INC.; *U.S. Public*, pg. 91
ARTISTIC BRASS DIV.—Masco Corporation; *U.S. Public*, pg. 1054
THE BLACK & DECKER CORPORATION; *U.S. Public*, pg. 233
BRADLEY CORPORATION; *U.S. Private*, pg. 164
BRADLEY WASHROOM ACCESSORIES DIV.—Bradley Corporation; *U.S. Private*, pg. 164
BRASS-CRAFT CANADA, LTD.—Masco Corporation; *U.S. Public*, pg. 1054
BRASS-CRAFT HOLDING CO.—Masco Corporation; *U.S. Public*, pg. 1053
BRASS-CRAFT MANUFACTURING COMPANY—Masco Corporation; *U.S. Public*, pg. 1053
BRASS-CRAFT WESTERN COMPANY—Masco Corporation; *U.S. Public*, pg. 1053
BRIGGS INDUSTRIES, INC.; *U.S. Private*, pg. 168
THE CHICAGO FAUCET CO.; *U.S. Private*, pg. 234
COMPAGNIE INTERNATIONALE DES PRODUITS SANITAIRES (CIPS) JACOB DELAFON—Kohler Company; *U.S. Private*, pg. 631
CRANE LIMITED U.K.—Crane Co.; *U.S. Public*, pg. 458
DAIDO HOXAN INC.; *Int'l*, pg. 363
DAMIXA ARMATUREN, GMBH—Masco Corporation; *U.S. Public*, pg. 1054
DAMIXA LTD.—Masco Corporation; *U.S. Public*, pg. 1055
DAMIXA S.A.—Masco Corporation; *U.S. Public*, pg. 1054
DELTA CAPILLARY PRODUCTS—Delta plc; *Int'l*, pg. 390
DELTA FAUCET CORPORATION—Masco Corporation; *U.S. Public*, pg. 1053
DELTA FAUCET OF CANADA—Masco Corporation; *U.S. Public*, pg. 1053
DELTA PLC; *Int'l*, pg. 389
EAGLE INDUSTRIES, INC.—Great American Management & Investment, Inc.; *U.S. Private*, pg. 473
ELJER MANUFACTURING/HVAC GROUP—Zurn Industries, Inc.; *U.S. Public*, pg. 1794
ELJER PLUMBINGWARE—Zurn Industries, Inc.; *U.S. Public*, pg. 1794
FIRE PROTECTION INDUSTRIES, INC.—Compagnie Generale Des Eaux; *Int'l*, pg. 321
FORTUNE BRANDS, INC.; *U.S. Public*, pg. 674
GENOVA PRODUCTS, INC.; *U.S. Private*, pg. 447
GERBER PLUMBING FIXTURES CORPORATION; *U.S. Private*, pg. 449
GLOBE VALVE CORPORATION—Gerber Plumbing Fixtures Corporation; *U.S. Private*, pg. 449
FRIEDRICH GROHE ARMATURENFABRIK GMBH & CO.; *Int'l*, pg. 559
HARDEN INDUSTRIES, INC.; *U.S. Private*, pg. 501
JAMES HARDIE INDUSTRIES LTD.; *Int'l*, pg. 596
HARRINGTON INDUSTRIAL PLASTICS INC.—Glynwed International PLC; *Int'l*, pg. 554
HAWS DRINKING FAUCET CO.; *U.S. Private*, pg. 512
HYDROMECHANICS DIV.—Zurn Industries, Inc.; *U.S. Public*, pg. 1794
IMI PLC; *Int'l*, pg. 646
IDEAL-STANDARD GMBH—American Standard Inc.; *U.S. Public*, pg. 92
IDEAL-STANDARD, S.A. DE C.V.—American Standard Inc.; *U.S. Public*, pg. 92
IDEAL-STANDARD S.A.I.—American Standard Inc.; *U.S. Public*, pg. 92
INTERBATH, INC.; *U.S. Private*, pg. 566
INTERBATH OF CANADA LTD.—Interbath, Inc.; *U.S. Private*, pg. 566
IRRITOL SYSTEM—The Toro Company; *U.S. Public*, pg. 1624
JAMECO INDUSTRIES, INC.—Watts Industries, Inc.; *U.S. Public*, pg. 1746
JOSAM COMPANY; *U.S. Private*, pg. 600
KALLISTA, INC.—Kohler Company; *U.S. Private*, pg. 630
KEENEY MANUFACTURING CO.; *U.S. Private*, pg. 611
KOHLER COMPANY; *U.S. Private*, pg. 630
MACRISTY INDUSTRIES, INC.; *U.S. Private*, pg. 693
THE MARMON GROUP, INC.; *U.S. Private*, pg. 706
MASCO CORPORATION; *U.S. Public*, pg. 1052
MASCO CORPORATION LIMITED—Masco Corporation; *U.S. Public*, pg. 1054
A.Y. MCDONALD INDUSTRIES, INC.; *U.S. Private*, pg. 721
A.Y. MCDONALD MFG. CO.—A.Y. McDonald Industries, Inc.; *U.S. Private*, pg. 721
MCKECHNIE PACIFIC—McKechnie PLC; *Int'l*, pg. 852
MELARD MANUFACTURING CORPORATION; *U.S. Private*, pg. 729
METCRAFT, INC.—Emco Limited; *Int'l*, pg. 453
MOEN INCORPORATED—Fortune Brands, Inc.; *U.S. Public*, pg. 675
NI INDUSTRIES, INC.—Masco Corporation; *U.S. Public*, pg. 1054
L.R. NELSON CORPORATION; *U.S. Private*, pg. 790
NIBCO, INC.; *U.S. Private*, pg. 798
NORTEK, INC.; *U.S. Public*, pg. 1192
ONDINE DIV.—Interbath, Inc.; *U.S. Private*, pg. 566
PEERLESS FAUCET CORPORATION—Masco Corporation; *U.S. Public*, pg. 1053
PRICE PFISTER, INC.—The Black & Decker Corporation; *U.S. Public*, pg. 234
QUEROY S.A.—American Standard Inc.; *U.S. Public*, pg. 92
R.A. INDUSTRIES, INC.; *U.S. Private*, pg. 902
RAIN BIRD SPRINKLERS MANUFACTURING CORP.; *U.S. Private*, pg. 907
THE RENOVATOR'S SUPPLY, INC.; *U.S. Private*, pg. 923
ROYAL TOTO METAL CO., LTD.—Toto Ltd.; *Int'l*, pg. 1410

SANITARY-DASH MANUFACTURING CO., INC.—Zurn Industries, Inc.; *U.S. Public*, pg. 1795
THE SHANE GROUP INC.; *U.S. Private*, pg. 989
THE SIAM SANITARY FITTINGS CO., LTD.—The Siam Cement Public Company Limited; *Int'l*, pg. 1239
THE SIAM SANITARY FITTINGS CO., LTD.—Toto Ltd.; *Int'l*, pg. 1410
SLOAN VALVE COMPANY; *U.S. Private*, pg. 1006
SMITH INDUSTRIES, INC.; *U.S. Private*, pg. 1008
SPEAKMAN COMPANY; *U.S. Private*, pg. 1021
STOLBERGER METALLWERKE GMBH & CO. KG—KM-Europa Metal Aktiengesellschaft; *Int'l*, pg. 719
T & N INDUSTRIES, INC.—T & N Plc; *Int'l*, pg. 1334
T & S BRASS & BRONZE WORKS, INC.; *U.S. Private*, pg. 1061
TELSCO INDUSTRIES; *U.S. Private*, pg. 1074
TRIFLOW LTD.—Delta plc; *Int'l*, pg. 391
UNITED STATES BRASS CORPORATION—Zurn Industries, Inc.; *U.S. Public*, pg. 1795
UNIVERSAL-RUNDLE CORP.—Nortek, Inc.; *U.S. Public*, pg. 1193
VANCE INDUSTRIES, INC.; *U.S. Private*, pg. 1133
WALTEC COMPONENTS—Emco Limited; *Int'l*, pg. 453
WATTS INDUSTRIES EUROPE B.V.—Watts Industries, Inc.; *U.S. Public*, pg. 1747
WATTS INDUSTRIES, INC.; *U.S. Public*, pg. 1746
WATTS REGULATOR CO.—Watts Industries, Inc.; *U.S. Public*, pg. 1747
WILKINS-REGULATOR DIV.—Zurn Industries, Inc.; *U.S. Public*, pg. 1794
ZIN-PLAS CORPORATION—Park Electrochemical Corporation; *U.S. Public*, pg. 1258
ZURN INDUSTRIES, INC.; *U.S. Public*, pg. 1794

3433 — HEATING EQUIPMENT, EXCEPT ELECTRIC & WARM AIR FURNACES

AERCO INTERNATIONAL INC.; *U.S. Private*, pg. 23
AUTOMATIC ASSEMBLY—Research, Incorporated; *U.S. Public*, pg. 1382
BENTONE-ELECTRO OIL AB—Trelleborg AB; *Int'l*, pg. 1422
BURNER SYSTEMS INTERNATIONAL, INC.—The Dyson-Kissner-Moran Corporation; *U.S. Private*, pg. 351
BURNHAM; *U.S. Public*, pg. 270
CANEFCO LIMITED—Electric Furnace Co.; *U.S. Private*, pg. 368
CONTINENTAL MATERIALS CORPORATION; *U.S. Public*, pg. 441
CORBERO S.A.—Electrolux, AB; *Int'l*, pg. 443
DESA INTERNATIONAL; *U.S. Private*, pg. 326
DETROIT STOKER CO.—United Industrial Corporation; *U.S. Public*, pg. 1679
DONLEE TECHNOLOGIES INC.; *U.S. Private*, pg. 339
ECLIPSE COMBUSTION—Eclipse Inc.; *U.S. Private*, pg. 361
ECLIPSE INC.; *U.S. Private*, pg. 360
EDWARDS ENGINEERING CORPORATION; *U.S. Private*, pg. 365
ELJER MANUFACTURING/HVAC GROUP—Zurn Industries, Inc.; *U.S. Public*, pg. 1794
ENERTECH INDUSTRIES AB—Trelleborg AB; *Int'l*, pg. 1422
EXCELSIOR MANUFACTURING & SUPPLY CORP.; *U.S. Private*, pg. 387
GSW JACKES-EVANS MANUFACTURING CO.—GSW Inc.; *Int'l*, pg. 538
GAS-FIRED PRODUCTS, INC.; *U.S. Private*, pg. 440
GAS-FIRED PRODUCTS (U.K.) LTD.—Gas-Fired Products, Inc.; *U.S. Private*, pg. 440
GENERAL CABLE CO.—Wassall Plc; *Int'l*, pg. 1487
GOLDSTAR CO. LTD.—LG Group; *Int'l*, pg. 778
GOVERNALE CO., INC.—Burnham; *U.S. Public*, pg. 270
HON INDUSTRIES INC.; *U.S. Public*, pg. 772
HAMWORTHY COMBUSTION EQUIPMENT LIMITED—Powell Duffryn PLC; *Int'l*, pg. 1065
HARPER-WYMAN CO.—Oak Industries Inc.; *U.S. Public*, pg. 1209
HAUCK MFG. CO.; *U.S. Private*, pg. 510
HAUCK MANUFACTURING COMPANY INC.—Ruhrgas Aktiengesellschaft; *Int'l*, pg. 1149
HEATEC, INC.—Astec Industries, Inc.; *U.S. Public*, pg. 141
HEATILATOR INC.—HON Industries Inc.; *U.S. Public*, pg. 772
HEPWORTH HOME PRODUCTS LIMITED—Hepworth Plc; *Int'l*, pg. 615
HEPWORTH PLC; *Int'l*, pg. 614
HOLMAN BOILER WORKS, INC.—Copes-Vulcan Inc.; *U.S. Private*, pg. 274
INTERNATIO-MULLER N.V.; *Int'l*, pg. 680
KERMI GMBH—Preussag AG; *Int'l*, pg. 1069
KEWANEE BOILER MANUFACTURING COMPANY, INC.—Burnham; *U.S. Public*, pg. 270
KING COMPANY—United Dominion Industries, Ltd.; *U.S. Public*, pg. 1676
KOMLINE-SANDERSON ENGINEERING CORP.; *U.S. Private*, pg. 631
KYOCERA CORPORATION; *Int'l*, pg. 775
LENNOX INDUSTRIES (CANADA) LTD.—Lennox International Inc.; *U.S. Private*, pg. 660
LENTJES AG—Metallgesellschaft AG; *Int'l*, pg. 861
LESLIE CONTROLS, INC.—Watts Industries, Inc.; *U.S. Public*, pg. 1746
LONG MFG. NC, INC.; *U.S. Private*, pg. 674
MAN URANIT GRONAU GMBH—MAN Aktiengesellschaft; *Int'l*, pg. 825
M.E. MACK VALVES PTY. LIMITED—Senior Engineering Group, plc.; *Int'l*, pg. 1222
MACK VALVES-NSW—Senior Engineering Group, plc.; *Int'l*, pg. 1223
MACRISTY INDUSTRIES, INC.; *U.S. Private*, pg. 693
THE MARLEY COOLING TOWER CO.—United Dominion Industries, Ltd.; *U.S. Public*, pg. 1676
MARTIN INDUSTRIES, INC. (AL); *U.S. Private*, pg. 709
MAXON CORPORATION; *U.S. Private*, pg. 716
N.V. MAXON INTERNATIONAL S.A.—Maxon Corporation; *U.S. Private*, pg. 717
MESTEK, INC.; *U.S. Public*, pg. 1099
METALLGESELLSCHAFT AG; *Int'l*, pg. 860
MIDCO INTERNATIONAL INC.; *U.S. Private*, pg. 744
MODINE MANUFACTURING COMPANY; *U.S. Public*, pg. 1121
MUNROE, INC.; *U.S. Private*, pg. 767
NEW YORKER BOILER CO., INC.—Burnham; *U.S. Public*, pg. 270
THE NORTH AMERICAN MANUFACTURING CO.; *U.S. Private*, pg. 803
OSBY PARCA AB—Trelleborg AB; *Int'l*, pg. 1422
P & F INDUSTRIES, INC.; *U.S. Public*, pg. 1239
PALOMA INDUSTRIES LIMITED; *Int'l*, pg. 1022
PERFECTION-SCHWANK INC.; *U.S. Private*, pg. 853
POTTERTON MYSON—Blue Circle Industries PLC; *Int'l*, pg. 197
PRECISION PARTS CORP.; *U.S. Private*, pg. 879
PREFERRED UTILITIES MANUFACTURING CORP.; *U.S. Private*, pg. 881
RAYPAK CANADA, LTD.—Paloma Industries Limited; *Int'l*, pg. 1022
RAYPAK, INC.—Paloma Industries Limited; *Int'l*, pg. 1022
RHEEM AIR CONDITIONING DIV.—Paloma Industries Limited; *Int'l*, pg. 1022
RHEEM MANUFACTURING CO.—Paloma Industries Limited; *Int'l*, pg. 1022
RHEEM WATER HEATER-DIVISION HEADQUARTERS—Paloma Industries Limited; *Int'l*, pg. 1022
SNC-LAVALIN GROUP INC.; *Int'l*, pg. 1161
SECURITY CHIMNEYS INTERNATIONAL LTD.; *Int'l*, pg. 1217
SELKIRK CANADA LTD.—Zurn Industries, Inc.; *U.S. Public*, pg. 1795
SELKIRK EUROPE—Zurn Industries, Inc.; *U.S. Public*, pg. 1795
SELKIRK (HVAC) EUROPE—Zurn Industries, Inc.; *U.S. Public*, pg. 1795
SELKIRK METALBESTOS N.A.—Zurn Industries, Inc.; *U.S. Public*, pg. 1794
SENIOR AUSTRALIA LIMITED—Senior Engineering Group, plc.; *Int'l*, pg. 1222
SENIOR ENGINEERING—Senior Engineering Group, plc.; *Int'l*, pg. 1222
SENIOR ENGINEERING COMPANY-USA—Senior Engineering Group, plc.; *Int'l*, pg. 1222
SENIOR ENGINEERING (PTY) LIMITED-SOUTH AFRICA—Senior Engineering Group, plc.; *Int'l*, pg. 1223
SENIOR THERMAL ENGINEERING LIMITED—Senior Engineering Group, plc.; *Int'l*, pg. 1221
SENIOR TIFT AUSTRALIA PTY LIMITED—Senior Engineering Group, plc.; *Int'l*, pg. 1223
SENIOR TIFT-PROSPECT—Senior Engineering Group, plc.; *Int'l*, pg. 1223
SENIOR TIFT-WESTERN AUSTRALIA—Senior Engineering Group, plc.; *Int'l*, pg. 1223
SLANT/FIN CORPORATION; *U.S. Private*, pg. 1005
SLANT-FIN, LTD./LTEE—Slant/Fin Corporation; *U.S. Private*, pg. 1005
A.O. SMITH-ENTERPRISES LTD.—A.O. Smith Corporation; *U.S. Public*, pg. 1477
H.B. SMITH CO., INC.; *U.S. Private*, pg. 1008
SMITH METERS LTD.—Hanson PLC; *Int'l*, pg. 593
STELRAD DIV.—Caradon Plc; *Int'l*, pg. 267
STELRAD GROUP LIMITED—Caradon Plc; *Int'l*, pg. 267
TAMROCK OY—Tamrock Corp.; *Int'l*, pg. 1352
TEMCO FIREPLACE PRODUCTS, INC.—Temtex Industries Inc.; *U.S. Public*, pg. 1576
THERMO SOLUTIONS—Research, Incorporated; *U.S. Public*, pg. 1382
THERMON MANUFACTURING COMPANY; *U.S. Private*, pg. 1080
THE TRANE COMPANY—American Standard Inc.; *U.S. Public*, pg. 92
THE TRANE COMPANY NORTH AMERICAN COMMERCIAL GROUP—American Standard Inc.; *U.S. Public*, pg. 92
UNIVERSAL BOILERS CORP.; *U.S. Private*, pg. 1126
UTICA BOILERS INC.; *U.S. Private*, pg. 1129
VULCAN-ECLIPSE (PVT) LTD.—Eclipse Inc.; *U.S. Private*, pg. 361
W.N. BEST—Preferred Utilities Manufacturing Corp.; *U.S. Private*, pg. 881
WAYNE HOME EQUIPMENT DIV.—Berkshire Hathaway Inc.; *U.S. Public*, pg. 218
WEBSTER COMPANY, INC.—Danfoss A/S; *Int'l*, pg. 377
WEIL-MCLAIN—United Dominion Industries, Ltd.; *U.S. Public*, pg. 1676
THE WILL-BURT COMPANY; *U.S. Private*, pg. 1177
WILLIAMS FURNACE CO.—Continental Materials Corporation; *U.S. Public*, pg. 441
WOLF KLIMATECHNIK GMBH—Preussag AG; *Int'l*, pg. 1070
YOUNG RADIATOR COMPANY; *U.S. Private*, pg. 1201
JOHN ZINK CO.—Koch Industries, Incorporated; *U.S. Private*, pg. 628

3441 — FABRICATED STRUCTURAL METAL

ABROS, INC.—Art Iron, Inc.; *U.S. Private*, pg. 86
ADDISON STEEL INC.; *U.S. Private*, pg. 17
ALAMO INDUSTRIAL GROUP; *U.S. Private*, pg. 31
ALAMO IRON WORKS—Alamo Industrial Group; *U.S. Private*, pg. 31
ALLEN TELECOM, INC.; *U.S. Public*, pg. 45
ARNOLD STEEL COMPANY, INC.; *U.S. Private*, pg. 84
ART IRON, INC.; *U.S. Private*, pg. 86
AUSTRALASIAN HMT PTY. LTD.—ITEQ, Inc.; *U.S. Public*, pg. 914
B & K STEEL & SUPPLY, INC.; *U.S. Private*, pg. 105
BALDWINS STEEL (PTY) LIMITED—Dorbyl Limited; *Int'l*, pg. 416
BARBOT ENTERPRISE—Groupe Usinor; *Int'l*, pg. 571
BELMONT INDUSTRIES, INC.—RGP Holding, Inc.; *U.S. Private*, pg. 903
BENNINGTON IRON WORKS, INC.; *U.S. Private*, pg. 133
THE BERLIN STEEL CONSTRUCTION COMPANY; *U.S. Private*, pg. 136
BINKLEY COMPANY—The Holland Hitch Company; *U.S. Private*, pg. 534
BOWMAN & KEMP STEEL & SUPPLY COMPANY—B & K Steel & Supply, Inc.; *U.S. Private*, pg. 105
BRADEN MANUFACTURING CO.—Jason Incorporated; *U.S. Public*, pg. 924
BROWN & ROOT NEDERLAND B.V.—Halliburton Company; *U.S. Public*, pg. 776
BROWN-MINNEAPOLIS TANK & FABRICATING CO.—ITEQ, Inc.; *U.S. Public*, pg. 914
T. BRUCE SALES, INC.; *U.S. Private*, pg. 175
BURTCO, INC.; *U.S. Private*, pg. 188
BURTCO METAL SYSTEMS—Burtco, Inc.; *U.S. Private*, pg. 188
CAPITOL STEEL, INC.—Commercial Metals Company; *U.S. Public*, pg. 412
CAROLINA STEEL CORPORATION; *U.S. Private*, pg. 214
CAROLINA STEEL-HICKORY PLANT—Carolina Steel Corporation; *U.S. Private*, pg. 214
CAROLINA STEEL-SALEM PLANT—Carolina Steel Corporation; *U.S. Private*, pg. 214
W.C. CAYE & COMPANY, INC.; *U.S. Private*, pg. 220
CENTRAL ILLINOIS STEEL COMPANY; *U.S. Private*, pg. 223
CHINA STEEL STRUCTURE CO., LTD.—China Steel Corporation; *Int'l*, pg. 286
CIVES CORPORATION; *U.S. Private*, pg. 241
COAST STEEL FABRICATORS LTD.—Agra Inc.; *Int'l*, pg. 31
COCKERILL SAMBRE; *Int'l*, pg. 301
COMET STEEL, INC.—Commercial Metals Company; *U.S. Public*, pg. 412
COMMERCIAL METALS COMPANY; *U.S. Public*, pg. 411
CONSTRUCCIONES PITT-DES MOINES VENEZUELA, C.A.—Pitt-Des Moines, Inc.; *U.S. Public*, pg. 1304
CREST STEEL CORP.—Marubeni Corporation; *Int'l*, pg. 845
CUSTODIS-ECODYNE—Air & Water Technologies Corporation; *U.S. Public*, pg. 29
DENGYOSHA MACHINE WORKS CORPORATION—Toshiba Corporation; *Int'l*, pg. 1402
DERLAN INDUSTRIES LIMITED; *Int'l*, pg. 395
DISPLAY TECHNOLOGIES, INC.—Toshiba Corporation; *Int'l*, pg. 1402
DORBYL LIMITED; *Int'l*, pg. 416
DOUGLAS STEEL FABRICATING CORPORATION; *U.S. Private*, pg. 341
EAST COAST STEEL, INC.; *U.S. Private*, pg. 356
EAST MOLINE METAL PRODUCTS COMPANY; *U.S. Private*, pg. 357
EATON METAL PRODUCTS COMPANY; *U.S. Private*, pg. 358
ENVIRONMENTAL ELEMENTS CORPORATION; *U.S. Public*, pg. 586
ETILAM-GRAVIGNY—Groupe Usinor; *Int'l*, pg. 571
FORMEX, INC. - PERMANENT STEEL FORMS—Omega Environmental Inc.; *U.S. Public*, pg. 1222
L.B. FOSTER COMPANY-BEDFORD PLANT—L.B. Foster Company; *U.S. Public*, pg. 676
L.B. FOSTER COMPANY-DORAVILLE YARD/FABRICATION SHOP—L.B. Foster Company; *U.S. Public*, pg. 676
L.B. FOSTER COMPANY-EPHRATA PLANT—L.B. Foster Company; *U.S. Public*, pg. 676
JOHN S. FREY ENTERPRISES; *U.S. Private*, pg. 428
HMT RUBBER GLAS LTD.—ITEQ, Inc.; *U.S. Public*, pg. 914
H.S.C. CANADA INC.—Harris Chemical Group, Inc.; *U.S. Private*, pg. 505
HAMWORTHY INDUSTRAMAR LIMITED—Powell Duffryn PLC; *Int'l*, pg. 1065
JOHN W. HANCOCK JR., INC.—Roanoke Electric Steel Corporation; *U.S. Public*, pg. 1392
HAVENS STEEL CO.; *U.S. Private*, pg. 510
HIGH INDUSTRIES, INC.; *U.S. Private*, pg. 528
HIRSCHFELD, INC.; *U.S. Private*, pg. 530
HIRSCHFELD STEEL COMPANY, INC.—Hirschfeld, Inc.; *U.S. Private*, pg. 531
HOUSTON STEEL SERVICE COMPANY OF TEXAS—Commercial Metals Company; *U.S. Public*, pg. 412
RODNEY HUNT COMPANY; *U.S. Private*, pg. 549
HUNTING PLC; *Int'l*, pg. 640
HYSPAN PRECISION PRODUCTS, INC.; *U.S. Private*, pg. 552
IDEA ENGINEERING & FABRICATING; *U.S. Private*, pg. 557
IMPERIAL POOLS, INC.; *U.S. Private*, pg. 558
INDUSTRIAS CH, S.A. DE C.V.; *Int'l*, pg. 677
KEWAUNEE ENGINEERING CORP.—Marine Travelift, Inc.; *U.S. Private*, pg. 703
KILROY STRUCTURAL STEEL—Triumph Group, Inc.; *U.S. Public*, pg. 1640
KLINE IRON & STEEL CO., INC.; *U.S. Private*, pg. 626
KARL KOCH ERECTING CO. INC.—Skanska AB; *Int'l*, pg. 1261
KRUPP MONTAGE- UND SERVICETECHNIK GMBH—Fried. Krupp AG; *Int'l*, pg. 516
KRUPP STAHLBAU BERLIN GMBH & CO. KG—Fried. Krupp AG; *Int'l*, pg. 508
KVAERNER ENGINEERING, STAVANGER DIVISION—Kvaerner a.s.a.; *Int'l*, pg. 766
KVAERNER KLEVEN ROVDE A/S—Kvaerner a.s.a.; *Int'l*, pg. 769
KVAERNER SINGAPORE PTE LTD—Kvaerner a.s.a.; *Int'l*, pg. 768
LEBLANC COMMUNICATIONS, INC.; *U.S. Private*, pg. 656

LIPS B.V.—Lips United B.V.; *Int'l*, pg. 812
LIPS PROPELLERS, INC.—Lips United B.V.; *Int'l*, pg. 812
LIPS PROPELLERS WEST/COAST OPERATIONS—Lips United B.V.; *Int'l*, pg. 812
LIPS UNITED B.V.; *Int'l*, pg. 812
LIPS USA INC.—Lips United B.V.; *Int'l*, pg. 812
MACGREGOR GROUP—Incentive AB; *Int'l*, pg. 670
MACGREGOR (USA) INC.—Incentive AB; *Int'l*, pg. 670
MADISON INDUSTRIES—John S. Frey Enterprises; *U.S. Private*, pg. 428
MADISON INDUSTRIES INC. OF ARIZONA—John S. Frey Enterprises; *U.S. Private*, pg. 428
MARINE TRAVELIFT, INC.; *U.S. Private*, pg. 703
MERCON STEEL STRUCTURES B.V.; *Int'l*, pg. 858
MEXIA FABRICATORS, INC.—COMSAT Corporation; *U.S. Public*, pg. 424
MID AMERICA STEEL, INC.; *U.S. Private*, pg. 743
MISSOURI VALLEY STEEL CO.—Owen Industries, Inc.; *U.S. Private*, pg. 824
MODERN WELDING CO., INC.; *U.S. Private*, pg. 755
MUTUAL WELDING CO., LTD; *U.S. Private*, pg. 770
NASHVILLE MACHINE CO. INC.; *U.S. Private*, pg. 774
NUCOR BUILDING SYSTEMS—Nucor Corporation; *U.S. Public*, pg. 1205
NUCOR CORPORATION; *U.S. Public*, pg. 1205
OMEGA ENVIRONMENTAL INC.—Omega Environmental Inc.; *U.S. Public*, pg. 1222
ORLEANS MATERIALS & EQUIPMENT CO., INC.; *U.S. Private*, pg. 820
OWEN INDUSTRIES, INC.; *U.S. Private*, pg. 824
PDM BRIDGE—Pitt-Des Moines, Inc.; *U.S. Public*, pg. 1305
PDM BRIDGE CORP.—Pitt-Des Moines, Inc.; *U.S. Public*, pg. 1304
PDM LATIN AMERICA LTD.—Pitt-Des Moines, Inc.; *U.S. Public*, pg. 1304
PDM STROCAL, INC.—Pitt-Des Moines, Inc.; *U.S. Public*, pg. 1305
PAXTON & VIERLING—Owen Industries, Inc.; *U.S. Private*, pg. 824
PETERSEN ALUMINUM CORPORATION; *U.S. Private*, pg. 856
PITT-DES MOINES, INC.; *U.S. Public*, pg. 1304
PLANT CITY STEEL CO.—Harsco Corporation; *U.S. Public*, *pg. 793*
QUINCY DESIGN & MANUFACTURING—Brunner Engineering & Manufacturing, Inc.; *U.S. Private*, pg. 176
RGP HOLDING, INC.; *U.S. Private*, pg. 903
RESCO STEEL PRODUCTS CORP.—Roanoke Electric Steel Corporation; *U.S. Public*, pg. 1392
RIGGS INDUSTRIES, INC.; *U.S. Private*, pg. 930
H.H. ROBERTSON BURFORD PLANT—Robertson-Ceco Corporation; *U.S. Public*, pg. 1394
ROHN INDUSTRIES, INC.; *U.S. Public*, pg. 1404
SMI-OWEN STEEL COMPANY—Commercial Metals Company; *U.S. Public*, pg. 413
SAFETY RAILWAY SERVICE—Commercial Metals Company; *U.S. Public*, pg. 412
SAFETY STEEL SERVICE, INC.—Commercial Metals Company; *U.S. Public*, pg. 412
SAMSUNG SHIPBUILDING & HEAVY INDUSTRIES CO. LTD.—Samsung Group; *Int'l*, pg. 1183
SANDVIK SORTING SYSTEMS—Sandvik AB; *Int'l*, pg. 1186
SARGENT METAL FABRICATING—Todd & Sargent, Inc.; *U.S. Private*, pg. 1089
SECOM GENERAL CORPORATION; *U.S. Public*, pg. 1453
SOCAR, INC.—Roanoke Electric Steel Corporation; *U.S. Public*, pg. 1392
SOCAR OF OHIO, INC.—Roanoke Electric Steel Corporation; *U.S. Public*, pg. 1392
SOUTHEASTERN STEEL COMPANY; *U.S. Private*, pg. 1015
SOUTHERN OHIO FABRICATORS, INC.; *U.S. Private*, pg. 1017
SOUTHERN POST COMPANY—Commercial Metals Company; *U.S. Public*, pg. 412
SOUTHERN STATES STEEL COMPANY—Commercial Metals Company; *U.S. Public*, pg. 412
STANDEX INTERNATIONAL CORPORATION; *U.S. Public*, *pg. 1505*
STERLING STEEL COMPANY—Commercial Metals Company; *U.S. Public*, pg. 412
STEWARTS & LLOYDS TRADING (PTY) LIMITED—Dorbyl Limited; *Int'l*, pg. 416
STRUTHERS WELLS CORP.—Struthers Industries Inc.; *U.S. Private*, pg. 1048
STUPP BROS, INC.; *U.S. Private*, pg. 1048
SYSTEMS & ELECTRONICS INC.—ESCO Electronics Corporation; *U.S. Public*, pg. 547
THOMAS & BETTS LEHIGH LANCASTER—Thomas & Betts Corporation; *U.S. Public*, pg. 1597
TODD PACIFIC SHIPYARDS CORP.; *U.S. Public*, pg. 1619
TRINITY INDUSTRIES INC.; *U.S. Public*, pg. 1638
TRINITY-STRUCTURAL STEEL—Trinity Industries Inc.; *U.S. Public*, pg. 1639
UNR-LEAVITT DIV.—ROHN Industries, Inc.; *U.S. Public*, pg. 1404
UNR-ROHN DIV.—ROHN Industries, Inc.; *U.S. Public*, pg. 1404
UNIFAB INTERNATIONAL INC.; *U.S. Public*, pg. 1665
UNISTRUT CORPORATION—Tyco International Ltd.; *U.S. Public*, pg. 1651
UP-RIGHT, INC.; *U.S. Private*, pg. 1128
VALMONT—Valmont Industries, Inc.; *U.S. Public*, pg. 1707
VARI-FORM—TI Group plc; *Int'l*, pg. 1341
VESTAL MANUFACTURING—Walter Industries, Inc.; *U.S. Public*, pg. 1737
VINCENNES STEEL CORP.; *U.S. Private*, pg. 1141
VON ROLL AG; *Int'l*, pg. 1480
VULCRAFT DIV.—Nucor Corporation; *U.S. Public*, pg. 1206
WAGGONBAU BRUNINGHAUS GMBH—Fried. Krupp AG; *Int'l*, pg. 509
WESTERN INDUSTRIES, INC.; *U.S. Private*, pg. 1165
WHITING CORPORATION; *U.S. Private*, pg. 1173
WILLIAMS BRIDGE CO.—Williams Industries, Inc.; *U.S. Public*, pg. 1770

3442 — METAL DOORS, SASH, FRAMES, MOLDING & TRIM

APL CORPORATION; *U.S. Private*, pg. 7
ACCURATE DOOR & HARDWARE DIVISION—Acklands Limited; *Int'l*, pg. 23
ACORN WINDOW SYSTEMS INC.; *U.S. Private*, pg. 14
ALUMA SHIELD INDUSTRIES, INC.; *U.S. Private*, pg. 47
ALUMAX INC.; *U.S. Public*, pg. 59
AMERICAN ARCHITECTURAL PRODUCTS, INC.; *U.S. Public*, pg. 67
AMSCO—Quanex Corporation; *U.S. Public*, pg. 1350
APOGEE ENTERPRISES, INC.; *U.S. Public*, pg. 120
ARCH ALUMINIUM & GLASS L.C.; *U.S. Private*, pg. 79
ATLAS ROLL-LITE DOOR CORPORATION—Griffon Corp.; *U.S. Public*, pg. 766
BAIRNCO CORPORATION; *U.S. Public*, pg. 165
BAY INDUSTRIES INC.; *U.S. Private*, pg. 124
WILLIAM BAYLEY/FOLGER ADAM SECURITY, INC.; *U.S.* Private, pg. 125
BELVEDERE—Excel Industries, Inc.; *U.S. Public*, pg. 598
BERINGER DIVISION—Kvaerner a.s.a.; *Int'l*, pg. 774
BINNING'S BUILDING PRODUCTS, INC.—American Architectural Products, Inc.; *U.S. Public*, pg. 67
BLACK MILLWORK CO., INC.; *U.S. Private*, pg. 147
WILLIAM L. BONNELL CO., INC.—Tredegar Industries Inc.; *U.S. Public*, pg. 1634
BOON EDAM B.V.; *Int'l*, pg. 202
BOON EDAM INC.—Boon Edam B.V.; *Int'l*, pg. 202
BORAL LIMITED; *Int'l*, pg. 203
CURT BULLOCK BUILDERS, INC.; *U.S. Private*, pg. 180
CGF INDUSTRIES; *U.S. Private*, pg. 194
CALDWELL MANUFACTURING COMPANY; *U.S. Private*, pg. 200
CARTER HOLT HARVEY GARAGE DOORS—International Paper Company; *U.S. Public*, pg. 904
CASTLEGATE INC.—Premdor Inc.; *Int'l*, pg. 1067
CECO DOOR PRODUCTS—United Dominion Industries, Ltd.; *U.S. Public*, pg. 1676
CENTURY DOOR U.S.A. INC.—Premdor Inc.; *Int'l*, pg. 1067
CERTAINTEED CORPORATION—Saint-Gobain; *Int'l*, pg. 1170
CHAMPION ALUMINUM WINDOW CORPORATION; *U.S. Private*, pg. 227
CHOMERICS EUROPE/U.K.—Parker Hannifin Corporation; *U.S. Public*, pg. 1262
CLARK DOOR CO., INC.; *U.S. Private*, pg. 242
CLOPAY CORPORATION—Griffon Corp.; *U.S. Public*, pg. 766
CONSTRUCTION SPECIALTIES, INC.; *U.S. Private*, pg. 266
CORNELL IRON WORKS, INC.; *U.S. Private*, pg. 276
CORNELL STOREFRONT SYSTEMS, INC.—Cornell Iron Works, Inc.; *U.S. Private*, pg. 276
CREATION WINDOWS OF INDIANA, INC.; *U.S. Private*, pg. 287
CROFT METALS, INC.; *U.S. Private*, pg. 290
CULLMAN PRODUCTS CORPORATION; *U.S. Private*, pg. 294
CURRIES COMPANY—Assa Abloy AB; *Int'l*, pg. 18
D&A TECHNOLOGY—Asahi Glass Co., Ltd.; *Int'l*, pg. 85
DREW INDUSTRIES INCORPORATED; *U.S. Public*, pg. 529
DYNAMICS CORPORATION OF AMERICA—CTS Corporation; *U.S. Public*, pg. 286
EBE EDELSTAHL-BAUELEMENTE GMBH—Fried. Krupp AG; *Int'l*, pg. 508
EFCO CORPORATION; *U.S. Private*, pg. 353
ELAND-BRANDT, B.V.—International Aluminum Corporation; *U.S. Public*, pg. 895
ELIXIR INDUSTRIES; *U.S. Private*, pg. 371
ELIXIR INDUSTRIES—Elixir Industries; *U.S. Private*, pg. 371
EMAIL LIMITED-BUILDING PRODUCTS GROUP—Email Limited; *Int'l*, pg. 450
FSW LTD.—The Sherwin-Williams Company; *U.S. Public*, pg. 1466
FILMCO INDUSTRIES INC.—Thermwell Products Co., Inc.; *U.S. Private*, pg. 1081
FIMBEL DOOR CORPORATION; *U.S. Private*, pg. 404
FINISHLINE INDUSTRIES INC. OF GEORGIA—John S. Frey Enterprises; *U.S. Private*, pg. 428
FLEETWOOD ALUMINUM PRODUCTS; *U.S. Private*, pg. 410
FLORENCE CORPORATION; *U.S. Private*, pg. 414
FOGA SYSTEM INTERNATIONAL AB; *Int'l*, pg. 496
JOHN S. FREY ENTERPRISES; *U.S. Private*, pg. 428
GENERAL AMERICAN DOOR COMPANY—Merchant Capital Group Ltd.; *U.S. Private*, pg. 732
HARVEY INDUSTRIES, INC.; *U.S. Private*, pg. 500
HEHR INTERNATIONAL INC.; *U.S. Private*, pg. 519
HOMESHIELD FABRICATED PRODUCTS—Quanex Corporation; *U.S. Public*, pg. 1350
HOPE'S ARCHITECTURAL PRODUCTS INC.; *U.S. Private*, *pg. 538*
HORTON AUTOMATICS DIV.—Overhead Door Corporation; *U.S. Private*, pg. 823
HORTON AUTOMATICS, LTD.—Overhead Door Corporation; *U.S. Private*, pg. 823
INTERNATIONAL ALUMINUM CORPORATION; *U.S. Public*, pg. 894
INTERNATIONAL WINDOW-ARIZONA, INC.—International Aluminum Corporation; *U.S. Public*, pg. 895
INTERNATIONAL WINDOW CORP.—International Aluminum Corporation; *U.S. Public*, pg. 895
INTERNATIONAL WINDOW-NORTHERN CALIFORNIA—International Aluminum Corporation; *U.S. Public*, pg. 895
JAMISON DOOR COMPANY; *U.S. Private*, pg. 581
JELD-WEN, INC.; *U.S. Private*, pg. 585
KASSON & KELLER—Keymark Corporation; *U.S. Private*, pg. 618
KELLER BUILDING PRODUCTS OF CHARLOTTE, INC.; *U.S. Private*, pg. 612
KELLER LADDERS INC.—U.S. Industries, Inc.; *U.S. Public*, pg. 1684
KEYMARK CORPORATION; *U.S. Private*, pg. 618
KINGSTON-WARREN CORPORATION—Harvard Industries, Inc.; *U.S. Public*, pg. 796
KINRO, INC.—Drew Industries Incorporated; *U.S. Public*, pg. 529
LARSON MANUFACTURING COMPANY; *U.S. Private*, pg. 652
LOUISIANA PACIFIC CORPORATION; *U.S. Public*, pg. 1015
LOXCREEN COMPANY; *U.S. Private*, pg. 679
MW MANUFACTURERS INC.—Hanson PLC; *Int'l*, pg. 593
MACHINE-RITE PRODUCTS—Excel Industries, Inc.; *U.S. Public*, pg. 599
MAKI CORPORATION; *U.S. Private*, pg. 697
MAKI HOME CENTER, INC.—Maki Corporation; *U.S. Private*, pg. 698
MARTIN DOOR MFG., INC.; *U.S. Private*, pg. 708
MASTERVIEW WINDOW COMPANY, INC.—Publicker Industries Inc.; *U.S. Public*, pg. 1341
W.B. MCGUIRE CO.—Overhead Door Corporation; *U.S. Private*, pg. 823
MCKEE DOOR, INC.—American Buildings Co.; *U.S. Public*, pg. 69
MERCHANT CAPITAL GROUP LTD.; *U.S. Private*, pg. 732
MUL-T-LOCK LTD.—IDB Holding Corporation; *Int'l*, pg. 644
OHD THERMACORE DIV., OHD CORP.—Overhead Door Corporation; *U.S. Private*, pg. 822
O'KEEFFE'S, INC.; *U.S. Private*, pg. 813
OVERHEAD DOOR CORPORATION; *U.S. Private*, pg. 822
OVERLY MANUFACTURING CO.; *U.S. Private*, pg. 823
PACESETTER CORPORATION; *U.S. Private*, pg. 830
PEASE INDUSTRIES, INC.; *U.S. Private*, pg. 845
PEMKO MANUFACTURING—Pemko Manufacturing Company; *U.S. Private*, pg. 848
PEMKO MANUFACTURING COMPANY; *U.S. Private*, pg. 848
PEREGRINE INCORPORATED; *U.S. Private*, pg. 852
PERKASIE INDUSTRIES CORPORATION; *U.S. Private*, pg. 854
PHELPS TOINTON INC.; *U.S. Private*, pg. 860
PREMDOR ENTRY SYSTEMS—Premdor Inc.; *Int'l*, pg. 1067
PREMDOR INC.; *Int'l*, pg. 1066
PREMDOR, INC.—Premdor Inc.; *Int'l*, pg. 1067
QUANEX CORPORATION; *U.S. Public*, pg. 1349
RAGLAND MANUFACTURING COMPANY INC.—International Aluminum Corporation; *U.S. Public*, pg. 895
RAYNOR GARAGE DOORS; *U.S. Private*, pg. 912
ROLL FORMING CORPORATION; *U.S. Private*, pg. 941
SAB IBERICA S.A.—Cardo AB; *Int'l*, pg. 271
SAB SISTEMI S.P.A.—Cardo AB; *Int'l*, pg. 271
SAB WABCO AB—Cardo AB; *Int'l*, pg. 271
SAB WABCO BENELUX—Cardo AB; *Int'l*, pg. 271
SAB WABCO ENGINEERING S.R.L.—Cardo AB; *Int'l*, pg. 271
SAB WABCO HOLDINGS B.V.—Cardo AB; *Int'l*, pg. 271
SAB WABCO LTD.—Cardo AB; *Int'l*, pg. 271
SAB WABCO N.V.—Cardo AB; *Int'l*, pg. 271
SAB WABCO S.A.—Cardo AB; *Int'l*, pg. 271
SAB WABCO S.P.A.—Cardo AB; *Int'l*, pg. 271
SEASON-ALL INDUSTRIES, INC.—Caradon Plc; *Int'l*, pg. 267
SIEBAU SIEGENER STAHLBAUTEN GMBH—Fried. Krupp AG; *Int'l*, pg. 509
STANLEY DOOR SYSTEMS—The Stanley Works; *U.S. Public*, pg. 1509
STEELCRAFT MANUFACTURING COMPANY—Ingersoll-Rand Company; *U.S. Public*, pg. 877
STEVES & SONS, INC.; *U.S. Private*, pg. 1042
SUECOBRAS INDUSTRIA E COMERCIO LTDA.—Cardo AB; *Int'l*, pg. 271
TAYLOR BUILDING PRODUCTS COMPANY—American Architectural Products, Inc.; *U.S. Public*, pg. 67
THERMA-TRU CORP.; *U.S. Private*, pg. 1079
THERMAL INDUSTRIES, INC.—HIG Capital Management; *U.S. Private*, pg. 490
THERMWELL PRODUCTS CO., INC.; *U.S. Private*, pg. 1081
TODCO—Overhead Door Corporation; *U.S. Private*, pg. 823
TOMKINS INDUSTRIES INC.—Tomkins PLC; *Int'l*, pg. 1397
WM. S. TRIMBLE COMPANY, INC.; *U.S. Private*, pg. 1103
ULTRA INDUSTRIES, INC.—Macklanburg-Duncan Co.; *U.S.* Private, pg. 692
UNITED STATES ALUMINUM CORP.—International Aluminum Corporation; *U.S. Public*, pg. 895
UNITED STATES ALUMINUM CORP.-ILLINOIS—International Aluminum Corporation; *U.S. Public*, pg. 895
WASCO PRODUCTS, INC.; *U.S. Private*, pg. 1152
WAUSAU METALS CORP.—Apogee Enterprises, Inc.; *U.S. Public*, pg. 120
WAYNE DALTON CORPORATION; *U.S. Private*, pg. 1155
WAYNE DALTON OF STERLING—Wayne Dalton Corporation; *U.S. Private*, pg. 1155
WINDOW FURNISHINGS SINGAPORE PTE. LTD.—Hunter Douglas N.V.; *Int'l*, pg. 640
WINDSOR DOOR—American Buildings Co.; *U.S. Public*, pg. 69

3443 — FABRICATED PLATE WORK (BOILER SHOPS)

ABB AIR PREHEATER INC.—ABB Asea Brown Boveri (Holding) Ltd.; *Int'l*, pg. 3
ABB INC.—ABB Asea Brown Boveri (Holding) Ltd.; *Int'l*, pg. 3
ABB SELFA AB—ABB Asea Brown Boveri (Holding) Ltd.; *Int'l*, pg. 7
ABB STAL AB—ABB Asea Brown Boveri (Holding) Ltd.; *Int'l*, pg. 7

AGA-CRYO AB—AGA AB; Int'l, pg. 12
AGA-CRYO GMBH—AGA AB; Int'l, pg. 13
API KATEMA INC.—American Precision Industries Inc.; U.S. Public, pg. 90
AERCO INTERNATIONAL INC.; U.S. Private, pg. 23
AHLSTROM MACHINERY RECOVERY BOILERS—A. Ahlstrom Corporation; Int'l, pg. 34
AIR PRODUCTS A/S-GARDNER CRYOGENICS DIV.—Air Products and Chemicals, Inc.; U.S. Public, pg. 31
AIRGAS, INC.; U.S. Public, pg. 33
ALASKAN COPPER COMPANIES; U.S. Private, pg. 31
ALFA-LAVAL EQUIPAMENTOS LTDA.—Tetra Laval Group; Int'l, pg. 1379
ALFA LAVAL INC.—Tetra Laval Group; Int'l, pg. 1378
ALFA-LAVAL S.A.—Tetra Laval Group; Int'l, pg. 1379
ALFA-LAVAL THERMAL AB—Tetra Laval Group; Int'l, pg. 1378
ALFA LAVAL THERMAL INC.—Tetra Laval Group; Int'l, pg. 1378
AMERICAN PRECISION INDUSTRIES INC.; U.S. Public, pg. 90
AMERICAN TANK & FABRICATING CO.; U.S. Private, pg. 63
ANDERSEN 2000 INC.—Crown Andersen Inc.; U.S. Public, pg. 462
AQUA-CHEM INC.—Lyonnaise des Eaux S.A.; Int'l, pg. 824
ARDCO, INC.; U.S. Private, pg. 80
ARMSTRONG-HUNT, INC.—Armstrong International, Inc.; U.S. Private, pg. 83
ARMSTRONG INTERNATIONAL, INC.; U.S. Private, pg. 83
ARROW TANK & ENGINEERING CO.; U.S. Private, pg. 85
ARTEAGA, SOCIEDAD ANOMIMA, "ARTEAGA, S.A."—Reynolds Metals Company; U.S. Public, pg. 1386
B-LINE SYSTEMS, INC.—Sigma-Aldrich Corporation; U.S. Public, pg. 1471
BABCOCK & WILCOX CO.—McDermott International, Inc.; U.S. Public, pg. 1068
BABCOCK & WILCOX INTERNATIONAL—McDermott International, Inc.; U.S. Public, pg. 1068
BABCOCK SEMPELL AG—Deutsche Babcock AG; Int'l, pg. 399
BALL AEROSPACE & TECHNOLOGIES CORP.—Ball Corporation; U.S. Public, pg. 171
BASCO DIV.—American Precision Industries Inc.; U.S. Public, pg. 90
WILLIAM BAYLEY/FOLGER ADAM SECURITY, INC.; U.S. Private, pg. 125
BEAIRD INDUSTRIES, INC.—Trinity Industries Inc.; U.S. Public, pg. 1639
BEAIRD INDUSTRIES, INC. OF ORANGE—Trinity Industries Inc.; U.S. Public, pg. 1639
THE BETHLEHEM CORPORATION; U.S. Public, pg. 225
BROWN-MINNEAPOLIS TANK & FABRICATING CO.—ITEQ, Inc.; U.S. Public, pg. 914
BRUNNER ENGINEERING & MANUFACTURING, INC.; U.S. Private, pg. 176
BURNHAM; U.S. Public, pg. 270
BURTMAN IRON WORKS, INC.; U.S. Private, pg. 188
CALDWELL TANKS, INC.; U.S. Private, pg. 200
CAROLINA STEEL CORPORATION; U.S. Private, pg. 214
CENTRAL ILLINOIS STEEL COMPANY; U.S. Private, pg. 223
CHEMAP—Tetra Laval Group; Int'l, pg. 1380
CHEMAP, INC.—Tetra Laval Group; Int'l, pg. 1378
CHEMI-TROL CHEMICAL CO.; U.S. Public, pg. 345
THE CHINET CO.—Royal Packaging Industries Van Leer B.V.; Int'l, pg. 1146
CINCINNATI INDUSTRIAL MACHINERY DIV.—Eagle-Picher Industries, Inc.; U.S. Private, pg. 355
COMMERCIAL INTERTECH CORP.; U.S. Public, pg. 411
CONBRACO INDUSTRIES INC.; U.S. Private, pg. 261
CONNELL LIMITED PARTNERSHIP; U.S. Private, pg. 264
CONSOLIDATED SYSTEMS, INC.; U.S. Private, pg. 266
CONSTRUCCIONES PITT-DES MOINES VENEZUELA, C.A.—Pitt-Des Moines, Inc.; U.S. Public, pg. 1304
CRAIG SYSTEMS; U.S. Private, pg. 284
CROWN ANDERSEN INC.; U.S. Public, pg. 462
CUSTODIS-COTTRELL, INC.—Air & Water Technologies Corporation; U.S. Public, pg. 29
D.C.I., INC.; U.S. Private, pg. 301
DCI OF UTAH INC.—D.C.I., Inc.; U.S. Private, pg. 301
DE-STA-CO, A DOVER RESOURCES CO.—Dover Corporation; U.S. Public, pg. 521
DEDERT CORPORATION; U.S. Private, pg. 320
DELTA INDUSTRIES; U.S. Private, pg. 322
DELUXE SPECIALTIES MFG. CO.—Triumph Group, Inc.; U.S. Public, pg. 1640
DENVER AUTOMETRICS—Svedala Industri AB; Int'l, pg. 1325
DONLEE TECHNOLOGIES INC.; U.S. Private, pg. 339
DOVER DIVERSIFIED—Dover Corporation; U.S. Public, pg. 521
DYNABILT PRODUCTS—Burtman Iron Works, Inc.; U.S. Private, pg. 188
EAGLE-PICHER INDUSTRIES, INC.; U.S. Private, pg. 355
ENERFAB INC.; U.S. Private, pg. 376
ENGINEERS & FABRICATORS CO.; U.S. Private, pg. 377
FMP-RAUMA COMPANY—UPM-Kymmene Corporation; Int'l, pg. 1428
FARMERS MARINE COPPER WORKS—Four Winds Investment Corp.; U.S. Private, pg. 422
THE SCOTT FETZER COMPANY—Berkshire Hathaway Inc.; U.S. Public, pg. 217
FILTRATION SYSTEMS DIVISION—Aqua Care Systems Inc.; U.S. Public, pg. 126
THE FLOATING TECHNOLOGY CO—Taylor Woodrow plc; Int'l, pg. 1358
FOSTER WHEELER CORPORATION; U.S. Public, pg. 676
FOSTER WHEELER ENERGIA OY—Foster Wheeler Corporation; U.S. Public, pg. 677
FRIGID COIL WEST—York International Corporation; U.S. Public, pg. 1789
GKN WESTLAND AEROSPACE NORTH AMERICA INC.—GKN plc; Int'l, pg. 535
GASTON COUNTY DYEING MACHINE CO.; U.S. Private, pg. 441
GENERAL SIGNAL CORPORATION; U.S. Public, pg. 726
THE GERSTENSLAGER COMPANY—Worthington Industries, Inc.; U.S. Public, pg. 1780
GLITSCH INTERNATIONAL—Koch Industries, Incorporated; U.S. Private, pg. 628
GOTAVERKEN ENERGY AB—Kvaerner a.s.a.; Int'l, pg. 771
GRAHAM CORPORATION; U.S. Public, pg. 757
GREENEVILLE METAL MANUFACTURING, INC.—Newport News Shipbuilding, Inc.; U.S. Public, pg. 1180
HMT INC.—ITEQ, Inc.; U.S. Public, pg. 914
HMT TONKAWA TANK COMPANY, INC.—ITEQ, Inc.; U.S. Public, pg. 914
HARSCO CORPORATION; U.S. Public, pg. 792
HAVENS STEEL CO.; U.S. Private, pg. 510
HEIL ENVIRONMENTAL INDUSTRIES—Dover Corporation; U.S. Public, pg. 520
HEPWORTH HEATING LTD.—Hepworth Plc; Int'l, pg. 615
HOLMAN BOILER WORKS, INC.—Copes-Vulcan Inc.; U.S. Private, pg. 274
HOWDEN COMPRESSORS—Howden Group Plc; Int'l, pg. 636
HOWDEN GROUP PLC; Int'l, pg. 636
JAMES HOWDEN AMERICA INC.—Howden Group Plc; Int'l, pg. 636
HYUNDAI PRECISION & INDUSTRY CO., LTD.—Hyundai Motor Company; Int'l, pg. 642
ITT BELL & GOSSETT—ITT Industries, Inc.; U.S. Public, pg. 860
INTERNATIONAL COMFORT PRODUCTS; U.S. Public, pg. 898
IONICS, INCORPORATED—Ionics, Incorporated; U.S. Public, pg. 912
ISHIKAWAJIMA-HARIMA HEAVY INDUSTRIES CO., LTD.; Int'l, pg. 689
J&L TANK—Dover Corporation; U.S. Public, pg. 521
JUDD-OLIN (U.K.) LIMITED—Olin Corporation; U.S. Public, pg. 1219
JUSTISS OIL CO., INC.; U.S. Private, pg. 602
KENNEDY TANK & MANUFACTURING CO., INC.; U.S. Private, pg. 614
KLOECKNER-WILHELMSBURGER GMBH—Klockner-Werke AG; Int'l, pg. 737
KOCH ENGINEERING CO., INC.—Koch Industries, Incorporated; U.S. Private, pg. 628
GEORGE KOCH SONS, INC.; U.S. Private, pg. 628
KVAERNER ROSENBERG A.S.—Kvaerner a.s.a.; Int'l, pg. 769
KYOTO MACHINERY CO. LTD.—Tetra Laval Group; Int'l, pg. 1380
KYSOR/MICHIGAN FLEET—Kuhlman Corporation; U.S. Public, pg. 968
LAUBECK CORPORATION, LAUBENSTEIN DIVISION—Laubeck Corporation/Cross; U.S. Private, pg. 653
LENAPE FORGE, INC.; U.S. Private, pg. 659
LINDE AG; Int'l, pg. 810
LIVERNOIS ENGINEERING COMPANY; U.S. Private, pg. 672
LUKENS STEEL COMPANY—Lukens Inc.; U.S. Public, pg. 1020
LUXFER USA LTD.—Alcan Aluminium Limited; Int'l, pg. 50
LYTRON INCORPORATED; U.S. Private, pg. 684
M.E. MACK VALVES PTY. LIMITED—Senior Engineering Group, plc.; Int'l, pg. 1222
MACK VALVES-NSW—Senior Engineering Group, plc.; Int'l, pg. 1223
MANCHESTER TANK & EQUIPMENT COMPANY; U.S. Private, pg. 699
MANNING & LEWIS ENGINEERING CO.; U.S. Private, pg. 700
MANUFACTURERA THERMON DE MEXICO, S.A.—Thermon Manufacturing Company; U.S. Private, pg. 1081
THE MARLEY COOLING TOWER CO.—United Dominion Industries, Ltd.; U.S. Public, pg. 1676
MATRIX SERVICE COMPANY; U.S. Public, pg. 1057
MAXON INDUSTRIES, S.A. DE C.V.—Maxon Industries, Inc.; U.S. Private, pg. 717
MCDERMOTT SCOTLAND—McDermott International, Inc.; U.S. Public, pg. 1068
MELBEN PRODUCTS INC.—Berkshire Hathaway Inc.; U.S. Public, pg. 218
MERCON STEEL STRUCTURES B.V.; Int'l, pg. 858
MID AMERICA STEEL, INC.; U.S. Private, pg. 743
MILFORD FABRICATING CO.—Thyssen AG; Int'l, pg. 1388
MIURA CO., LTD.; Int'l, pg. 884
MODERN EQUIPMENT CO., INC.—Alco Industries, Inc.; U.S. Private, pg. 33
MODERN WELDING CO., INC.; U.S. Private, pg. 755
MODINE MANUFACTURING COMPANY; U.S. Public, pg. 1121
MONTAIR ANDERSEN B.V.—Crown Andersen Inc.; U.S. Public, pg. 462
MONTICELLO EXCHANGER & MANUFACTURING—Bryan Steam Corporation; U.S. Private, pg. 176
MORGANTOWN MACHINE & HYDRAULICS, INC.—Charter plc; Int'l, pg. 280
PAUL MUELLER COMPANY; U.S. Public, pg. 1141
MUNRO & COMPANY, INC.; U.S. Private, pg. 767
MUNROE, INC.; U.S. Private, pg. 767
MUTUAL WELDING CO., LTD; U.S. Private, pg. 770
NEO INDUSTRIES—Russel Metals Inc.; Int'l, pg. 1150
NATIONAL MINE SERVICE, INC.—Charter plc; Int'l, pg. 280
NATIONAL STEEL CORP., GRANITE CITY DIVISION—NKK Corporation; Int'l, pg. 902
NIAGARA BLOWER COMPANY; U.S. Private, pg. 798
NIPPON SANSO CORPORATION; Int'l, pg. 938
NITRAM ENERGY INC.; U.S. Private, pg. 799
NOOTER CORPORATION; U.S. Private, pg. 801
NOOTER FABRICATORS, INC.—Nooter Corporation; U.S. Private, pg. 801
NORRIS CYLINDER COMPANY—Masco Corporation; U.S. Public, pg. 1054
NORTHERN PIGMENT—Russel Metals Inc.; Int'l, pg. 1150
NUOVO PIGNONE S.P.A.; Int'l, pg. 990
OLIN FABRICATED METALS PRODUCTS, INC.—Olin Corporation; U.S. Public, pg. 1219
OLIN SPECIALTY METALS CORPORATION—Olin Corporation; U.S. Public, pg. 1219
PDM LATIN AMERICA LTD.—Pitt-Des Moines, Inc.; U.S. Public, pg. 1304
PAPER CALMENSON & CO.; U.S. Private, pg. 837
PATTERSON-KELLEY COMPANY—Harsco Corporation; U.S. Public, pg. 793
PEABODY ENGINEERING CANADA LTD.—Powell Duffryn PLC; Int'l, pg. 1066
PEABODY TECTANK, INC.—A.O. Smith Corporation; U.S. Public, pg. 1477
PEERLESS MFG. CO.; U.S. Public, pg. 1268
PERRY EQUIPMENT CORPORATION; U.S. Private, pg. 855
PERRY MACHINERY CORPORATION; U.S. Private, pg. 855
PIPE FABRICATING & SUPPLY COMPANY; U.S. Private, pg. 867
PITT-DES MOINES, INC.; U.S. Public, pg. 1304
PLANT CITY STEEL CO.—Harsco Corporation; U.S. Public, pg. 793
PLANT MAINTENANCE SERVICE CORPORATION; U.S. Private, pg. 869
POCONO FABRICATORS—Harsco Corporation; U.S. Public, pg. 793
PRECISION PARTS CORP.; U.S. Private, pg. 879
PRESSED STEEL TANK CO., INC.; U.S. Private, pg. 882
RP & C—Conbraco Industries Inc.; U.S. Private, pg. 261
RESEARCH COTTRELL, EUROPE—Air & Water Technologies Corporation; U.S. Public, pg. 29
RESORCOH INC.—Niagara Blower Company; U.S. Private, pg. 798
ROBBINS & MYERS, INC.; U.S. Public, pg. 1393
ROLOCK, INC.; U.S. Private, pg. 942
ROTTERDAM VENTURES INC.—Galesi Group; U.S. Private, pg. 437
SAUNIER DUVAL EAU CHAUDE CHAUFFAGE SA—Hepworth Plc; Int'l, pg. 615
SCHMALBACH-LUBECA AG; Int'l, pg. 1206
SCHUTTE & KOERTING DIVISION—KTM Holdings Corp.; U.S. Private, pg. 604
SEARLE (FRANCE)—Ascot Holdings Plc; Int'l, pg. 88
SEARLE MANUFACTURING CO.—Ascot Holdings Plc; Int'l, pg. 88
SECO WARWICK CORPORATION; U.S. Private, pg. 980
SENIOR AUSTRALIA LIMITED—Senior Engineering Group, plc.; Int'l, pg. 1222
SENIOR CHRISTCHURCH LIMITED—Senior Engineering Group, plc.; Int'l, pg. 1223
SENIOR ENGINEERING—Senior Engineering Group, plc.; Int'l, pg. 1222
SENIOR ENGINEERING COMPANY-USA—Senior Engineering Group, plc.; Int'l, pg. 1222
SENIOR ENGINEERING GROUP, PLC.; Int'l, pg. 1220
SENIOR ENGINEERING (PTY) LIMITED-SOUTH AFRICA—Senior Engineering Group, plc.; Int'l, pg. 1223
SENIOR THERMAL ENGINEERING LIMITED—Senior Engineering Group, plc.; Int'l, pg. 1221
SENIOR TIFT AUSTRALIA PTY LIMITED—Senior Engineering Group, plc.; Int'l, pg. 1223
SENIOR TIFT-PROSPECT—Senior Engineering Group, plc.; Int'l, pg. 1223
SENIOR TIFT-QUEENSLAND—Senior Engineering Group, plc.; Int'l, pg. 1223
SENIOR TIFT-VICTORIA—Senior Engineering Group, plc.; Int'l, pg. 1223
SENIOR TIFT-WESTERN AUSTRALIA—Senior Engineering Group, plc.; Int'l, pg. 1223
SENIOR WELLINGTON LIMITED—Senior Engineering Group, plc.; Int'l, pg. 1223
SERCK HEAT TRANSFER—BTR plc; Int'l, pg. 125
SIVALLS, INC.; U.S. Private, pg. 1004
A.O. SMITH CORPORATION; U.S. Public, pg. 1476
EVERETT SMITH GROUP, LTD.; U.S. Private, pg. 1007
H.B. SMITH CO., INC.; U.S. Private, pg. 1008
SNYDER-CROWN, INC.—Snyder Industries, Inc.; U.S. Private, pg. 1011
SNYDER INDUSTRIES, INC.; U.S. Private, pg. 1011
SOUTHERN OHIO FABRICATORS, INC.; U.S. Private, pg. 1017
SOUTHERN TANK & MANUFACTURING, INC.—Kennedy Tank & Manufacturing Co., Inc.; U.S. Private, pg. 614
STEEL TANK & FABRICATING CORP.—Kennedy Tank & Manufacturing Co., Inc.; U.S. Private, pg. 615
STEWART-WARNER SOUTH WIND CORP.—BTR plc; Int'l, pg. 127
STINNES CORPORATION—Veba AG; Int'l, pg. 1460
STRUTHERS INDUSTRIES INC.; U.S. Private, pg. 1048
STRUTHERS WELLS CORP.—Struthers Industries Inc.; U.S. Private, pg. 1048
SULZER IMMOBILIEN AG—Sulzer Ltd.; Int'l, pg. 1306
SVEDALA INDUSTRIES INC.—Svedala Industri AB; Int'l, pg. 1325
SYNALLOY CORPORATION; U.S. Public, pg. 1547
TIC UNITED CORPORATION; U.S. Private, pg. 1063
TII-DITEL—TII Industries, Inc.; U.S. Public, pg. 1556
TII DOMINICANA INC.—TII Industries, Inc.; U.S. Public, pg. 1556
TII INDUSTRIES, INC.; U.S. Public, pg. 1556
TACO INCORPORATED; U.S. Private, pg. 1066
TAYLOR-WHARTON GAS EQUIPMENT—Harsco Corporation; U.S. Public, pg. 793
TEXAS METAL FABRICATING—Trinity Industries Inc.; U.S. Public, pg. 1639
THERMAL TRANSFER CORP.—Air & Water Technologies Corporation; U.S. Public, pg. 29
THERMON AUSTRALIA—Thermon Manufacturing Company; U.S. Private, pg. 1081
TIMPTE INDUSTRIES, INC.; U.S. Private, pg. 1088
TODD PACIFIC SHIPYARDS CORP.; U.S. Public, pg. 1619

P.T. TOYO KANETSU INDONESIA—Nissho Iwai Corporation; *Int'l*, pg. 949
TRANTER, INC.—Dover Corporation; *U.S. Public*, pg. 521
TRANTER INC.-EDGEFIELD DIV.—Dover Corporation; *U.S. Public*, pg. 522
TRINITY INDUSTRIES INC.; *U.S. Public*, pg. 1638
UNITED AIR SPECIALISTS, INC.—CLARCOR, Inc.; *U.S. Public*, pg. 382
UNITED AIRCRAFT PRODUCTS—Parker Hannifin Corporation; *U.S. Public*, pg. 1262
UNITED MCGILL CORP.; *U.S. Private*, pg. 1122
UPPER MIDWEST INDUSTRIES, INCORPORATED; *U.S. Private*, pg. 1129
HENRY VOGT MACHINE CO.; *U.S. Private*, pg. 1143
VOSS INDUSTRIES, INC.; *U.S. Private*, pg. 1143
WAUKESHA CHERRY-BURRELL—United Dominion Industries, Ltd.; *U.S. Public*, pg. 1677
WHEELING CORRUGATING CO.—WHX Corporation; *U.S. Public*, pg. 1727
WHITING CORPORATION; *U.S. Private*, pg. 1173
WILKINSON COMPANY, INC.—Electric Furnace Co.; *U.S. Private*, pg. 368
WINTERS WELDING WORKS, INC.; *U.S. Private*, pg. 1183
XALOY, INC.; *U.S. Private*, pg. 1194
ZURN INDUSTRIES, INC.; *U.S. Public*, pg. 1794

3444 — SHEET METAL WORK

API GROUP INC.; *U.S. Private*, pg. 7
THE AARQUE COMPANIES; *U.S. Private*, pg. 9
AARQUE STEEL CORPORATION—The Aarque Companies; *U.S. Private*, pg. 9
ADVANCED MANUFACTURING & DEVELOPMENT; *U.S. Private*, pg. 22
AERO DATA METAL CRAFTERS; *U.S. Private*, pg. 23
AERO TECH MANUFACTURING INC.—Toromont Industries Ltd.; *Int'l*, pg. 1400
THE AIROLITE COMPANY; *U.S. Private*, pg. 29
AJAX MAGNETHERMIC CORP.—BBA Group plc; *Int'l*, pg. 113
ALUMAX INC.; *U.S. Public*, pg. 59
AMERICAN METAL PRODUCTS—Masco Corporation; *U.S. Public*, pg. 1053
AMERIMARK INC.—Owens Corning; *U.S. Public*, pg. 1237
ANEMOSTAT PRODUCTS—CTS Corporation; *U.S. Public*, pg. 286
ANEMOSTAT-WEST—CTS Corporation; *U.S. Public*, pg. 286
ARVIN INDUSTRIES, INC.; *U.S. Public*, pg. 136
AUBREY MANUFACTURING COMPANY—Nortek, Inc.; *U.S. Public*, pg. 1193
AUSTRALIAN WINDOW FURNISHINGS (NSW) PTY. LTD.—Hunter Douglas N.V.; *Int'l*, pg. 639
BS CONTINENTAL S.A. UTILIDADES DOMESTICAS; *Int'l*, pg. 123
BARBER & COLMAN LTD.—Siebe plc; *Int'l*, pg. 1243
BINKS SAMES CORPORATION; *U.S. Public*, pg. 229
BONLAND INDUSTRIES, INC.; *U.S. Private*, pg. 156
CALCOR SPACE FACILITY, INC.; *U.S. Private*, pg. 200
CARTER HOLT HARVEY ROOFING INTERNATIONAL—International Paper Company; *U.S. Public*, pg. 904
CHEMPOWER, INC.—American Eco Corporation; *Int'l*, pg. 74
CHIEF INDUSTRIES, INC.; *U.S. Private*, pg. 236
CHOMERICS EUROPE/U.K.—Parker Hannifin Corporation; *U.S. Public*, pg. 1262
CONSOLIDATED PIPE & SUPPLY COMPANY; *U.S. Private*, pg. 266
CORNERCROFT ENGINEERING LIMITED—Caparo Group Ltd.; *Int'l*, pg. 265
CORRUGATED METALS, INC.; *U.S. Private*, pg. 277
CUSTODIS-COTTRELL, INC.—Air & Water Technologies Corporation; *U.S. Public*, pg. 29
DALE INDUSTRIES INC.; *U.S. Private*, pg. 308
DELFIELD COMPANY—Scotsman Industries, Inc.; *U.S. Public*, pg. 1445
DELTA INDUSTRIES; *U.S. Private*, pg. 322
DOWNEY, INC.—K & G of Wisconsin, Inc.; *U.S. Private*, pg. 602
DURO DYNE CORPORATION; *U.S. Private*, pg. 349
DYNAMIC METAL PRODUCTS COMPANY; *U.S. Private*, pg. 350
DYNAMICS CORPORATION OF AMERICA—CTS Corporation; *U.S. Public*, pg. 286
EAGLE INDUSTRIES, INC.—Great American Management & Investment, Inc.; *U.S. Private*, pg. 473
ELIXIR INDUSTRIES; *U.S. Private*, pg. 371
ENGINEERED PRODUCTS, INC.; *U.S. Private*, pg. 376
ENVIRONMENTAL ELEMENTS CORPORATION; *U.S. Public*, pg. 586
EVENWOOD ENGINEERING—Brunel Holdings Plc; *Int'l*, pg. 231
FABWEL INC.; *U.S. Private*, pg. 390
FISHER SKYLIGHTS, INC.; *U.S. Private*, pg. 408
FLEXIBLE TECHNOLOGIES INC.—Smiths Industries plc; *Int'l*, pg. 1267
FRICKE GMBH & CO. KG—KM-Europa Metal Aktiengesellschaft; *Int'l*, pg. 719
GSW JACKES-EVANS MANUFACTURING CO.—GSW Inc.; *Int'l*, pg. 538
GENERAL AMERICAN DOOR COMPANY—Merchant Capital Group Ltd.; *U.S. Private*, pg. 732
GENERAL METAL PRODUCTS—Wozniak Industries, Inc.; *U.S. Private*, pg. 1192
GIDDINGS & LEWIS CASTING TECHNOLOGY—Thyssen AG; *Int'l*, pg. 1389
GRUPO IMSA S.A. DE C.V.; *Int'l*, pg. 575
H C PRODUCTS CO.—Aluminum Company of America; *U.S. Public*, pg. 61
HANCOCK MANUFACTURING—The Cypress Companies; *U.S. Private*, pg. 299
HARMONY ENGINEERING CORPORATION; *U.S. Private*, pg. 503
HARRIS AIR SYSTEMS COMPANY—Harris Contracting Co.; *U.S. Private*, pg. 505
HARTWELL COMMERCIAL DIVISION—Western Sky Industries, Inc.; *U.S. Private*, pg. 1168
HEIDTMAN STEEL PRODUCTS, INC.; *U.S. Private*, pg. 519
HOESCH SIEGERLANDWERKE GMBH—Fried. Krupp AG; *Int'l*, pg. 508
HOUSTON PRODUCTS—American Eco Corporation; *Int'l*, pg. 74
HUGHES-TREITLER MANUFACTURING CORPORATION; *U.S. Private*, pg. 547
HUNTER DOUGLAS ARCHITECTURAL PRODUCTS INC.—Hunter Douglas N.V.; *Int'l*, pg. 639
HUNTER DOUGLAS HOLDINGS LTD.—Hunter Douglas N.V.; *Int'l*, pg. 640
HUNTER DOUGLAS N.V.; *Int'l*, pg. 639
INCOR, INC.—Dale Industries Inc.; *U.S. Private*, pg. 308
INTEGRATED METAL TECHNOLOGIES, INC.—Herman Miller, Inc.; *U.S. Public*, pg. 1112
THE INTERTECH GROUP INC.—BBA Group plc; *Int'l*, pg. 113
K & G OF WISCONSIN, INC.; *U.S. Private*, pg. 602
GEORGE KOCH SONS, INC.; *U.S. Private*, pg. 628
KRUPP MONTAGE- UND SERVICETECHNIK GMBH—Fried. Krupp AG; *Int'l*, pg. 516
LAVELLE COMPANY; *U.S. Private*, pg. 653
LESLIE BUILDING PRODUCTS, INC.; *U.S. Public*, pg. 989
M M SYSTEMS CORPORATION; *U.S. Private*, pg. 685
MACHINE FABRICATORS—Brunel Holdings Plc; *Int'l*, pg. 231
THE MARLEY COOLING TOWER CO.—United Dominion Industries, Ltd.; *U.S. Public*, pg. 1676
AB MATAKI—Trelleborg AB; *Int'l*, pg. 1422
METAL SALES MANUFACTURING CORPORATION—Interlock Industries, Inc.; *U.S. Private*, pg. 567
METALTECH, INC.; *U.S. Private*, pg. 735
MONTEREY MECHANICAL COMPANY; *U.S. Private*, pg. 758
NUCOR CORPORATION; *U.S. Public*, pg. 1205
BENJAMIN OBDYKE, INC.; *U.S. Private*, pg. 810
OREGON CULVERT CO., INC.—Pitt-Des Moines, Inc.; *U.S. Public*, pg. 1305
OVERLY MANUFACTURING CO.; *U.S. Private*, pg. 823
PSB CO.—White Castle System, Inc.; *U.S. Private*, pg. 1172
RESEARCH COTTRELL, EUROPE—Air & Water Technologies Corporation; *U.S. Public*, pg. 29
H.H. ROBERTSON BURFORD PLANT—Robertson-Ceco Corporation; *U.S. Public*, pg. 1394
ROLL FORMING CORPORATION; *U.S. Private*, pg. 941
RUSKIN DIV.—Tomkins PLC; *Int'l*, pg. 1398
SENIOR ENGINEERING GROUP, PLC.; *Int'l*, pg. 1220
SENIOR FLEXONICS INC.—Senior Engineering Group, plc.; *Int'l*, pg. 1222
SHAW-PERKINS, INC.—Reactive Metals & Alloys Corporation (REMACOR); *U.S. Private*, pg. 913
SIMPSON DURA-VENT CO., INC.; *U.S. Public*, pg. 1474
SIPLAST S.A.—Icopal a/s; *Int'l*, pg. 659
EVERETT SMITH GROUP, LTD.; *U.S. Private*, pg. 1007
SMITH SYSTEM MANUFACTURING COMPANY; *U.S. Private*, pg. 1009
SOUTHWARK METAL MANUFACTURING COMPANY; *U.S. Private*, pg. 1018
STANCO METAL PRODUCTS, INC.; *U.S. Private*, pg. 1030
STANDEX INTERNATIONAL CORPORATION; *U.S. Public*, pg. 1505
STEELOX SYSTEMS INC.; *U.S. Private*, pg. 1038
STIFAB—Trelleborg AB; *Int'l*, pg. 1422
STOCKTON CULVERT—Pitt-Des Moines, Inc.; *U.S. Public*, pg. 1305
SUPER SKY PRODUCTS, INC.; *U.S. Private*, pg. 1054
SWIFT-COR TOOL ENGINEERING; *U.S. Private*, pg. 1058
SYMONS CORPORATION—Ripplewood Holdings L.L.C.; *U.S. Private*, pg. 932
TRP-PROFILE UND BAUELEMENTE GMBH—Fried. Krupp AG; *Int'l*, pg. 508
TARCO; *U.S. Private*, pg. 1068
E.H. TITCHENER & COMPANY; *U.S. Private*, pg. 1089
TOMKINS INDUSTRIES INC.—Tomkins PLC; *Int'l*, pg. 1397
UNISTRUT CORPORATION—Tyco International Ltd.; *U.S. Public*, pg. 1651
UNITED MCGILL CORP.; *U.S. Private*, pg. 1122
U.S. INTEC, INC.—GAF Corporation; *U.S. Private*, pg. 433
UPPER MIDWEST INDUSTRIES, INCORPORATED; *U.S. Private*, pg. 1129
VENTLINE DIV.—Tomkins PLC; *Int'l*, pg. 1398
VULCRAFT DIV.—Nucor Corporation; *U.S. Public*, pg. 1206
WHX CORPORATION; *U.S. Public*, pg. 1726
WASCO PRODUCTS, INC.; *U.S. Private*, pg. 1152
WASHINGTON CULVERT CO.—Pitt-Des Moines, Inc.; *U.S. Public*, pg. 1305
WHEELING CORRUGATING CO.—WHX Corporation; *U.S. Public*, pg. 1727
WOZNIAK INDUSTRIES, INC.; *U.S. Private*, pg. 1192
ZERO PLASTICS—Zero Corporation; *U.S. Public*, pg. 1791
ZIMMERMAN HOLDINGS, INC.; *U.S. Private*, pg. 1206

3446 — ARCHITECTURAL & ORNAMENTAL METAL WORK

AEP-SPAN—United Dominion Industries, Ltd.; *U.S. Public*, pg. 1676
ABROS, INC.—Art Iron, Inc.; *U.S. Private*, pg. 86
ABRU ALUMINIUM LIMITED—Hepworth Plc; *Int'l*, pg. 615
ALABAMA METAL INDUSTRIES CORPORATION; *U.S. Private*, pg. 30
ALTENBERG ZINK AG—Union Miniere; *Int'l*, pg. 1442
ALUMAX INC.; *U.S. Public*, pg. 59
AMERICAN METAL PRODUCTS—Masco Corporation; *U.S. Public*, pg. 1053
ANNIN & COMPANY; *U.S. Private*, pg. 75
ARCH ALUMINIUM & GLASS L.C.; *U.S. Private*, pg. 79
ART IRON, INC.; *U.S. Private*, pg. 86
AYDIN RAYTOR DIV.—Aydin Corporation; *U.S. Public*, pg. 158
BRITISH BUILDING & ENGINEERING APPLIANCES PLC; *Int'l*, pg. 219
BUTLER MANUFACTURING COMPANY; *U.S. Public*, pg. 271
EAGLE INDUSTRIES, INC.—Great American Management & Investment, Inc.; *U.S. Private*, pg. 473
FSW LTD.—The Sherwin-Williams Company; *U.S. Public*, pg. 1466
HAPCO/AMERICAN DIV.—The Dyson-Kissner-Moran Corporation; *U.S. Private*, pg. 351
HARSCO CORPORATION; *U.S. Public*, pg. 792
HUNTER DOUGLAS N.V.; *Int'l*, pg. 639
IKG INDUSTRIES—Harsco Corporation; *U.S. Public*, pg. 793
INDUSTRIAL ACOUSTICS COMPANY, INC.; *U.S. Public*, pg. 875
ITOCHU BUILDING PRODUCTS CO., INC.—Itochu Corporation; *Int'l*, pg. 694
J & J REGISTER DIV.—Tomkins PLC; *Int'l*, pg. 1397
KAWNEER COMPANY—Alumax Inc.; *U.S. Public*, pg. 60
LAPEYRE STAIR, INC.—The Laitram Corporation; *U.S. Private*, pg. 643
LAWRENCE METAL PRODUCTS, INC.; *U.S. Private*, pg. 654
LESLIE BUILDING PRODUCTS, INC.; *U.S. Public*, pg. 989
LLOYDAIRE/ELJER INC.—Zurn Industries, Inc.; *U.S. Public*, pg. 1795
LOUISVILLE LADDER DIV.—Emerson Electric Co.; *U.S. Public*, pg. 574
MACHINE FABRICATORS—Brunel Holdings Plc; *Int'l*, pg. 231
OKABE COMPANY LIMITED; *Int'l*, pg. 999
OVERHEAD DOOR CORPORATION; *U.S. Private*, pg. 822
PASCON LTD.—BTR plc; *Int'l*, pg. 124
PATENT CONSTRUCTION SYSTEMS—Harsco Corporation; *U.S. Public*, pg. 793
REESE ENTERPRISES, INC.; *U.S. Private*, pg. 916
ROLL FORMING CORPORATION; *U.S. Private*, pg. 941
SAFWAY STEEL PRODUCTS INC.—Thyssen AG; *Int'l*, pg. 1389
STAINLESS INCORPORATED; *U.S. Private*, pg. 1029
TATE ACCESS FLOORS—International Paper Company; *U.S. Public*, pg. 905
TITUS PRODUCTS DIV.—Tomkins PLC; *Int'l*, pg. 1398
TOMKINS INDUSTRIES INC.—Tomkins PLC; *Int'l*, pg. 1397
TRU-WELD GRATING, INC.; *U.S. Private*, pg. 1107
UNISTRUT CORPORATION—Tyco International Ltd.; *U.S. Public*, pg. 1651
UP-RIGHT, INC.; *U.S. Private*, pg. 1128
VIRGINIA METAL INDUSTRIES, INC.; *U.S. Private*, pg. 1141
VOEST-ALPINE STAHL DONAWITZ GES.M.B.H.—Voest-Alpine Stahl AG; *Int'l*, pg. 1470
WHX CORPORATION; *U.S. Public*, pg. 1726
WENGER CORPORATION; *U.S. Private*, pg. 1162

3448 — PREFABRICATED METAL BUILDINGS & COMPONENTS

A & S BUILDING SYSTEMS, INC.—NCI Building Systems, Inc.; *U.S. Public*, pg. 1146
AEP-SPAN—United Dominion Industries, Ltd.; *U.S. Public*, pg. 1676
ACORN ENGINEERING COMPANY; *U.S. Private*, pg. 14
ACORN STRUCTURES—Deck House Inc.; *U.S. Private*, pg. 320
ALL AMERICAN HOMES, INC.—Coachmen Industries, Inc.; *U.S. Public*, pg. 388
ALL-AMERICAN SYSTEMS—NCI Building Systems, Inc.; *U.S. Public*, pg. 1146
ALUMA SHIELD INDUSTRIES, INC.; *U.S. Private*, pg. 47
ALUMAX INC.; *U.S. Public*, pg. 59
AMERICAN BUILDINGS CO.; *U.S. Public*, pg. 69
AMERICAN MODULAR TECHNOLOGIES—American Buildings Co.; *U.S. Public*, pg. 69
AMERICAN MODULAR TECHNOLOGIES, LLC—American Buildings Co.; *U.S. Public*, pg. 69
ARMTEC—Jannock Limited; *Int'l*, pg. 698
ARROW GROUP INDUSTRIES, INC.—Leonard Green & Partners; *U.S. Private*, pg. 477
ASTRON S.A.R.L.—Commercial Intertech Corp.; *U.S. Public*, pg. 411
BACO LEISURE PRODUCTS—Alcan Aluminium Limited; *Int'l*, pg. 51
BEHLEN MFG. CO.; *U.S. Private*, pg. 130
BROCK MANUFACTURING—CTB International Corp.; *U.S. Public*, pg. 285
CURT BULLOCK BUILDERS, INC.; *U.S. Private*, pg. 180
BUTLER BUILDINGS DIVISION—Butler Manufacturing Company; *U.S. Public*, pg. 271
BUTLER MANUFACTURING COMPANY; *U.S. Public*, pg. 271
CANADIAN BUILDING SYSTEMS INC.—Jannock Limited; *Int'l*, pg. 698
CECO BUILDING SYSTEMS; *U.S. Private*, pg. 221
CECO BUILDING SYSTEMS-SOUTHERN REGION—Ceco Building Systems; *U.S. Private*, pg. 221
CECO DOOR PRODUCTS—United Dominion Industries, Ltd.; *U.S. Public*, pg. 1676
CENTRIA; *U.S. Private*, pg. 225
CHATWINS GROUP, INC.; *U.S. Private*, pg. 231
CHIEF INDUSTRIES - AGRI/INDUSTRIAL PRODUCTS DIV.—Chief Industries, Inc.; *U.S. Private*, pg. 236
CHIEF INDUSTRIES - BUILDINGS DIV.—Chief Industries, Inc.; *U.S. Private*, pg. 236
COMMERCIAL INTERTECH CORP.; *U.S. Public*, pg. 411
COMMERCIAL INTERTECH S.A.—Commercial Intertech Corp.; *U.S. Public*, pg. 411
CUPPLES PRODUCTS, INC.; *U.S. Private*, pg. 297
DANVILLE DIV.—Curt Bullock Builders, Inc.; *U.S. Private*, pg. 180

S.I.C. Index

DELUXE HOMES OF PA., INC.; *U.S. Private*, pg. 323
ELLIOTT GROUP LIMITED—The Davis Service Group Plc.; *Int'l*, pg. 385
FORMEX, INC. - PERMANENT STEEL FORMS—Omega Environmental Inc.; *U.S. Public*, pg. 1222
L.B. FOSTER COMPANY; *U.S. Public*, pg. 675
GRUPO IMSA S.A. DE C.V.; *Int'l*, pg. 575
GULF STATES MANUFACTURERS, INC.—Jannock Limited; *Int'l*, pg. 699
HOESCH RENOVA GMBH—Fried. Krupp AG; *Int'l*, pg. 508
HOESCH SIEGERLANDWERKE GMBH—Fried. Krupp AG; *Int'l*, pg. 508
HYOSUNG METAL PRODUCTS CO., LTD.—Hyosung Group; *Int'l*, pg. 641
IMBAU INDUSTRIELLES BAUEN GMBH—Philipp Holzmann AG; *Int'l*, pg. 633
JANNOCK LIMITED; *Int'l*, pg. 698
JANNOCK STEEL FABRICATING COMPANY—Jannock Limited; *Int'l*, pg. 698
JEWELL BUILDING SYSTEMS; *U.S. Private*, pg. 587
KIRBY BUILDING SYSTEMS, INC.—Jannock Limited; *Int'l*, pg. 699
KRUPP MONTAGE- UND SERVICETECHNIK GMBH—Fried. Krupp AG; *Int'l*, pg. 516
KRUPP STAHLBAU BERLIN GMBH & CO. KG—Fried. Krupp AG; *Int'l*, pg. 508
KYSOR PANEL SYSTEMS—Scotsman Industries, Inc.; *U.S. Public*, pg. 1445
LESTER BUILDINGS DIVISION—Butler Manufacturing Company; *U.S. Public*, pg. 271
MAGLINE, INC.; *U.S. Private*, pg. 695
METALLIC BUILDING COMPANY—NCI Building Systems, Inc.; *U.S. Public*, pg. 1146
MIDWEST STEEL BUILDING COMPANY—NCI Building Systems, Inc.; *U.S. Public*, pg. 1146
MITSUBISHI HEAVY INDUSTRIES LTD.; *Int'l*, pg. 873
MODULINE INDUSTRIES, INC.—Champion Enterprises, Inc.; *U.S. Public*, pg. 333
MUTUAL WELDING CO., LTD; *U.S. Private*, pg. 770
OMAHA DIV.—Curt Bullock Builders, Inc.; *U.S. Private*, pg. 180
OMEGA ENVIRONMENTAL INC.—Omega Environmental Inc.; *U.S. Public*, pg. 1222
PASCOE BUILDING SYSTEMS, INC.; *U.S. Private*, pg. 842
PRUM-TURENWERK GMBH—Hochtief AG; *Int'l*, pg. 623
RESDISPACE LTD.—Sophus Berendsen A/S; *Int'l*, pg. 1285
ROBERTSON-CECO CORPORATION; *U.S. Public*, pg. 1394
ROSS INDUSTRIE- UND FASSADENBAU GMBH—Fried. Krupp AG; *Int'l*, pg. 509
RUFFIN BUILDING SYSTEMS, INC.; *U.S. Private*, pg. 950
SAB PROFIEL B.V.—Koninklijke Hoogovens N.V.; *Int'l*, pg. 754
SAUDI BUILDING SYSTEMS, LTD.—Butler Manufacturing Company; *U.S. Public*, pg. 271
SEKISUI CHEMICAL CO., LTD.; *Int'l*, pg. 1219
A.O. SMITH CORPORATION; *U.S. Public*, pg. 1476
A.O. SMITH HARVESTORE PRODUCTS, INC.—A.O. Smith Corporation; *U.S. Public*, pg. 1477
SOUTH FRESH FARMS; *U.S. Private*, pg. 1014
STEEL SYSTEMS INC.—NCI Building Systems, Inc.; *U.S. Public*, pg. 1146
STEELOX SYSTEMS INC.; *U.S. Private*, pg. 1038
STREIF AG—Hochtief AG; *Int'l*, pg. 623
SUPER HOMES LTD.—John Laing PLC; *Int'l*, pg. 796
TOYOTA MOTOR CORPORATION; *Int'l*, pg. 1411
TRELLEBORG BUILDING & DISTRIBUTION DIV.—Trelleborg AB; *Int'l*, pg. 1421
TRI STATE STEEL CONSTRUCTION—National Engineering & Contracting Co.; *U.S. Private*, pg. 782
UNITED DOMINION INDUSTRIES, LTD.; *U.S. Public*, pg. 1675
VP BUILDINGS—The LTV Corporation; *U.S. Public*, pg. 972
VARCO-PRUDEN BUILDINGS—United Dominion Industries, Ltd.; *U.S. Public*, pg. 1677
VORWERK FRANCE SA—Vorwerk & Co.; *Int'l*, pg. 1481
WENINGER INDUSTRIES DIVISION—Jannock Limited; *Int'l*, pg. 698
WESTEEL AGRICULTURAL PRODUCTS DIVISION—Jannock Limited; *Int'l*, pg. 698
WHEELING CORRUGATING CO.—WHX Corporation; *U.S. Public*, pg. 1727
WICK BUILDING SYSTEMS; *U.S. Private*, pg. 1174
WILLIAMS SCOTSMAN GROUP, INC.—Scotsman Holding Inc.; *U.S. Private*, pg. 977
ZENKER HAUSBAU GMBH & CO.—Philipp Holzmann AG; *Int'l*, pg. 633

3449 — MISCELLANEOUS STRUCTURAL METAL WORK

AAR CORP.; *U.S. Public*, pg. 1
ALABAMA METAL INDUSTRIES CORPORATION; *U.S. Private*, pg. 30
AMERICAN TANK & FABRICATING CO.; *U.S. Private*, pg. 63
ARMCO INC.; *U.S. Public*, pg. 131
BOSTIK INC.—Total S.A.; *Int'l*, pg. 1409
BRODART COMPANY; *U.S. Private*, pg. 170
BUTLER MANUFACTURING COMPANY; *U.S. Public*, pg. 271
CAPITAL INDUSTRIES, INC.; *U.S. Private*, pg. 206
CROFT METALS, INC.; *U.S. Private*, pg. 290
DYWIDAG-SYSTEMS (U.K.) LTD.—Dyckerhoff & Widmann AG; *Int'l*, pg. 425
ELEKTRO METALL EXPORT GMBH—Datron Incorporated; *U.S. Private*, pg. 313
ENCO-JOHNSON CITY DIVISION—Enco Materials, Inc.; *U.S. Private*, pg. 375
ENCO MATERIALS, INC.; *U.S. Private*, pg. 375
GAME TIME, INC.—Swing-N-Slide Corp.; *U.S. Public*, pg. 1543
GARRETT PRODUCTS, INC.—Group Dekko; *U.S. Private*, pg. 484
GEM INDUSTRIES NE INC.—Gem Industries Finance Corporation; *U.S. Private*, pg. 442
HYDRO GROUP, INC.; *U.S. Private*, pg. 552
KALDNES HEAVY LIFT TRUCKS—Norsk Vekst ASA; *Int'l*, pg. 965
KALDNES INDUSTRI A/S—Norsk Vekst ASA; *Int'l*, pg. 965
GEORGE KOCH SONS, INC.; *U.S. Private*, pg. 628
MACHINE FABRICATORS—Brunel Holdings Plc; *Int'l*, pg. 231
MACHINING ENTERPRISES INC.; *U.S. Private*, pg. 691
MARKHON INDUSTRIES, INC—Kennedy Manufacturing Company; *U.S. Private*, pg. 614
NVF COMPANY; *U.S. Private*, pg. 772
NEWELL CO.; *U.S. Public*, pg. 1176
NOLTE MASTENFABRIEK—Valmont Industries, Inc.; *U.S. Public*, pg. 1707
NUCOR BUILDING SYSTEMS—Nucor Corporation; *U.S. Public*, pg. 1205
NUCOR CORPORATION; *U.S. Public*, pg. 1205
OGLEBAY NORTON REFRACTORIES & MINERALS, INC.—Oglebay Norton Company; *U.S. Public*, pg. 1214
O'KEEFFE'S, INC.; *U.S. Private*, pg. 813
PASCOE BUILDING SYSTEMS, INC.; *U.S. Private*, pg. 842
PAXTON & VIERLING—Owen Industries, Inc.; *U.S. Private*, pg. 824
PHELPS TOINTON INC.; *U.S. Private*, pg. 860
REINKE MANUFACTURING CO., INC.; *U.S. Private*, pg. 920
THOMAS ROBINSON GROUP PLC—Brunel Holdings Plc; *Int'l*, pg. 231
ROLL FORMING CORPORATION; *U.S. Private*, pg. 941
SMI-OWEN STEEL COMPANY—Commercial Metals Company; *U.S. Public*, pg. 413
SENIOR ENGINEERING GROUP, PLC.; *Int'l*, pg. 1220
SOUTHERN OHIO FABRICATORS, INC.; *U.S. Private*, pg. 1017
SOUTHWIRE COMPANY; *U.S. Private*, pg. 1019
M. SWIFT & SONS INC.; *U.S. Private*, pg. 1059
UNISTRUT CORPORATION—Tyco International Ltd.; *U.S. Public*, pg. 1651
UPPER MIDWEST INDUSTRIES, INCORPORATED; *U.S. Private*, pg. 1129
WHX CORPORATION; *U.S. Public*, pg. 1726
WASHINGTON SCIENTIFIC INDUSTRIES, INC.; *U.S. Public*, pg. 1744
WASHINGTON SCIENTIFIC INDUSTRIES—Washington Scientific Industries, Inc.; *U.S. Public*, pg. 1744

3451 — SCREW MACHINE PRODUCTS

AMERICAN LAUBSCHER CORP.; *U.S. Private*, pg. 58
N.V. ARO S.A.—Ingersoll-Rand Company; *U.S. Public*, pg. 877
CURTIS SCREW CO., INC.; *U.S. Private*, pg. 298
DELTA REPETITION COMPONENTS LTD.—Delta plc; *Int'l*, pg. 391
THE FAIRCHILD CORPORATION; *U.S. Public*, pg. 610
FEDERAL SCREW WORKS; *U.S. Public*, pg. 616
FRISBY P.M.C. INCORPORATED—Intermet Corporation; *U.S. Public*, pg. 894
HEADER PRODUCTS INC.; *U.S. Private*, pg. 514
HORIZON ENTERPRISES GROUP LLC; *U.S. Private*, pg. 539
HORIZON TECHNOLOGY GROUP LLC—Horizon Enterprises Group LLC; *U.S. Private*, pg. 539
D.M. HULL & CO. PTY. LTD.—Delta plc; *Int'l*, pg. 391
HURON MANUFACTURING DIV.—U.S. Industries, Inc.; *U.S. Public*, pg. 1684
ILSCO; *U.S. Private*, pg. 558
KURT MANUFACTURING CO. INC.; *U.S. Private*, pg. 637
LATSHAW ENTERPRISES, INC.; *U.S. Public*, pg. 979
MACHIN & EWIN PTY. LTD.—Delta plc; *Int'l*, pg. 392
MACHINING ENTERPRISES INC.; *U.S. Private*, pg. 691
MEDICO INDUSTRIES, INC.; *U.S. Private*, pg. 728
METAL SEAL & PRODUCTS, INC.; *U.S. Private*, pg. 734
MITCHEL & SCOTT MACHINE CO., INC.; *U.S. Private*, pg. 753
NATIONAL TOOL & MANUFACTURING COMPANY; *U.S. Private*, pg. 787
PENTAIR, INC.; *U.S. Public*, pg. 1273
PHILDAS LTD.—Haden Maclellan Holdings plc; *Int'l*, pg. 585
PIC DESIGN; *U.S. Private*, pg. 864
POWERS FASTENING, INC.; *U.S. Private*, pg. 878
QUALITY CONTROL CORPORATION; *U.S. Private*, pg. 898
RAMATECH LLC—Horizon Enterprises Group LLC; *U.S. Private*, pg. 539
ROCHESTER GEAR, INC.—Newcor, Inc.; *U.S. Public*, pg. 1176
ROUSE THOMPSON & LLOYD LTD.—Delta plc; *Int'l*, pg. 391
THE SHANE GROUP INC.; *U.S. Private*, pg. 989
SPIROL INTERNATIONAL CORP.; *U.S. Private*, pg. 1026
THE TORRINGTON CO.—Ingersoll-Rand Company; *U.S. Public*, pg. 877
TORRINGTON GMBH—Ingersoll-Rand Company; *U.S. Public*, pg. 878
J.J. TOUREK CO.—Tuthill Corporation; *U.S. Private*, pg. 1111
TRIANGLE MACHINE PRODUCT CO.—Freeway Corporation; *U.S. Private*, pg. 426
USECO—Litton Industries, Inc.; *U.S. Public*, pg. 1003
ASHLEY F. WARD, INC.; *U.S. Private*, pg. 1149
WEST FOOTSCRAY ENGINEERING WORKS PTY. LTD.—Delta plc; *Int'l*, pg. 392

3452 — BOLTS, NUTS, SCREWS, RIVETS & WASHERS

ATF, INC.; *U.S. Private*, pg. 8
ACCO-REXEL GROUP SERVICES PLC—Fortune Brands, Inc.; *U.S. Public*, pg. 674
AIR INDUSTRIES CORPORATION; *U.S. Private*, pg. 28
ALABAMA METAL INDUSTRIES CORPORATION; *U.S. Private*, pg. 30
ALLFAST FASTENING SYSTEMS, INC.; *U.S. Private*, pg. 37
ALLIED INTERNATIONAL-AMERICAN EAGLE TRADING CORP.—Itochu Corporation; *Int'l*, pg. 694
ALLOY RING SERVICE—Handy & Harman; *U.S. Public*, pg. 780
ALPHA BOLT COMPANY—Washers, Incorporated; *U.S. Private*, pg. 1152
AMATRON—NCH Corporation; *U.S. Public*, pg. 1145
AMERICAN CONSUMER PRODUCTS—Vista 2000, Inc.; *U.S. Private*, pg. 1142
ANCHOR FASTENERS—Illinois Tool Works Inc.; *U.S. Public*, pg. 865
ARMSTRONG FASTENINGS LTD.—Caparo Group Ltd.; *Int'l*, pg. 265
ARMSTRONG SCREWS & FIXINGS LTD.—Caparo Group Ltd.; *Int'l*, pg. 265
ARROW FASTENER CO., INC.; *U.S. Private*, pg. 85
AVIBANK MFG., INC.; *U.S. Private*, pg. 101
AVIS INDUSTRIAL CORPORATION; *U.S. Private*, pg. 102
AYLESBURY AUTOMATION LTD.—Clayhithe P.L.C.; *Int'l*, pg. 297
BAUMANN FEDERN AG; *Int'l*, pg. 171
BAUMANN GMBH—Baumann Federn AG; *Int'l*, pg. 171
BAUMANN SPRINGS & PRESSINGS (UK) LTD.—Baumann Federn AG; *Int'l*, pg. 171
THE BLACK & DECKER CORPORATION; *U.S. Public*, pg. 233
BRISTOL INDUSTRIES; *U.S. Private*, pg. 169
C-T ENGINEERING—Premier Farnell plc; *Int'l*, pg. 1068
CAMCAR TEXTRON—Textron Inc.; *U.S. Public*, pg. 1589
CAMLOC FASTENER GMBH—The Fairchild Corporation; *U.S. Public*, pg. 610
CAMLOC INTERNATIONAL—The Fairchild Corporation; *U.S. Public*, pg. 610
CAPARO INDUSTRIES PLC.—Caparo Group Ltd.; *Int'l*, pg. 265
CERTANIUM ALLOYS & RESEARCH—Premier Farnell plc; *Int'l*, pg. 1068
CHANDLER PRODUCTS, INC.—Elgin National Industries, Inc.; *U.S. Private*, pg. 370
CHERRY TEXTRON—Textron Inc.; *U.S. Public*, pg. 1589
CHICAGO RIVET & MACHINE COMPANY; *U.S. Public*, pg. 348
CLAYHITHE P.L.C.; *Int'l*, pg. 297
CLEVEDON RIVETS & TOOLS LTD.—Clayhithe P.L.C.; *Int'l*, pg. 297
COLD HEADING CO.; *U.S. Private*, pg. 250
CONTINENTAL/MIDLAND, INC.; *U.S. Private*, pg. 268
CORNELL MANUFACTURING COMPANY—Jupiter Industries, Inc.; *U.S. Private*, pg. 602
DANAHER TOOL GROUP-WEST HARTFORD OPERATIONS—Danaher Corporation; *U.S. Public*, pg. 481
DANUSER MACHINE CO.; *U.S. Private*, pg. 310
DE-STA-CO, A DOVER RESOURCES CO.—Dover Corporation; *U.S. Public*, pg. 521
DELTA REPETITION COMPONENTS LTD.—Delta plc; *Int'l*, pg. 391
THE DEUTSCH COMPANY; *U.S. Private*, pg. 328
DYNA SYSTEMS—NCH Corporation; *U.S. Public*, pg. 1145
EATON CORPORATION, ENGINEERED FASTENERS DIVISION—Eaton Corporation; *U.S. Public*, pg. 556
ELCO CONSTRUCTION PRODUCTS DIVISION—Textron Inc.; *U.S. Public*, pg. 1590
ELCO SDD—Textron Inc.; *U.S. Public*, pg. 1590
ELCO TEXTRON—Textron Inc.; *U.S. Public*, pg. 1590
B. ELLIOTT PLC.; *Int'l*, pg. 448
ESKAY SCREW CORPORATION—Masco Corporation; *U.S. Public*, pg. 1054
EUROPEAN INDUSTRIAL SERVICES—Brunel Holdings Plc; *Int'l*, pg. 231
THE FAIRCHILD CORPORATION; *U.S. Public*, pg. 610
FAIRCHILD FASTENERS FRANCE—The Fairchild Corporation; *U.S. Public*, pg. 610
FEDERAL SCREW WORKS; *U.S. Public*, pg. 616
THE FLEXITALLIC GROUP, INC.; *U.S. Private*, pg. 413
FOREST FASTENERS—Caparo Group Ltd.; *Int'l*, pg. 265
FREEWAY ROCKFORD—Freeway Corporation; *U.S. Private*, pg. 426
GENERAL CABLE CO.—Wassall Plc; *Int'l*, pg. 1487
THE B.F. GOODRICH COMPANY; *U.S. Public*, pg. 751
HALIFAX RACK & SCREW CUTTING CO., LTD.—B. Elliott plc.; *Int'l*, pg. 448
HARVARD INDUSTRIES, INC.; *U.S. Public*, pg. 796
HI-SHEAR CORP.—Hi-Shear Industries Inc.; *U.S. Public*, pg. 825
HI-SHEAR INDUSTRIES INC.; *U.S. Public*, pg. 824
IBL (BALLSCREWS) LTD.—FAG Group; *Int'l*, pg. 469
ITW SHAKEPROOF/AUTOMOTIVE PRODUCTS—Illinois Tool Works Inc.; *U.S. Public*, pg. 867
INDUSTRIAL & AUTOMOTIVE FASTENERS, INC.—JPE, Inc.; *U.S. Public*, pg. 919
INFASCO DIVISION—The Ivaco Group; *Int'l*, pg. 696
INFASCO NUT DIVISION—The Ivaco Group; *Int'l*, pg. 696
INGERSOLL FASTENERS DIVISION—The Ivaco Group; *Int'l*, pg. 696
ISELI COMPANY—Danaher Corporation; *U.S. Public*, pg. 481
ITOCHU BUILDING PRODUCTS CO., INC.—Itochu Corporation; *Int'l*, pg. 694
THE JEFFERSON DIVISION—Chicago Rivet & Machine Company; *U.S. Public*, pg. 349
KTI; *U.S. Public*, pg. 939
KAMAX-G.B. DUPONT L.P.; *U.S. Private*, pg. 606
KEYSTONE CONSOLIDATED INDUSTRIES, INC.; *U.S. Public*, pg. 955
LAKE ERIE SCREW CORPORATION—Masco Corporation; *U.S. Public*, pg. 1054

MNP CORP.; U.S. Private, pg. 687
MACLEAN-FOGG CO.; U.S. Private, pg. 692
THE MARMON GROUP, INC.; U.S. Private, pg. 706
MARSON/CREATIVE FASTENER, INC.; U.S. Private, pg. 708
METALAC S.A. INDUSTRIA E COMERCIO—SPS Technologies, Inc.; U.S. Public, pg. 1420
METFORM, INC.—Maclean-Fogg Co.; U.S. Private, pg. 692
MID-CONTINENT SCREW PRODUCTS CO.; U.S. Private, pg. 743
MIDWEST FASTENERS CORPORATION; U.S. Private, pg. 744
MONOGRAM AEROSPACE FASTENERS, INC.—Masco Corporation; U.S. Public, pg. 1054
NCH CORPORATION; U.S. Public, pg. 1145
NATIONAL RIVET & MANUFACTURING COMPANY; U.S. Private, pg. 786
NETTLEFOLDS LTD.—Brunel Holdings Plc; Int'l, pg. 231
O.A. NEWTON & SON CO.; U.S. Private, pg. 797
OHIO ROD PRODUCTS COMPANY, INC.—Elgin National Industries, Inc.; U.S. Private, pg. 370
OKABE COMPANY LIMITED; Int'l, pg. 999
PARKER KALON—The Black & Decker Corporation; U.S. Public, pg. 233
PAWTUCKET FASTENERS INC.; U.S. Private, pg. 844
PENN ENGINEERING & MANUFACTURING CORP.; U.S. Public, pg. 1269
PENN ENGINEERING & MANUFACTURING CORP. NORTH CAROLINA DIV.—Penn Engineering & Manufacturing Corp.; U.S. Public, pg. 1270
PHILDAS LTD.—Haden Maclellan Holdings plc; Int'l, pg. 585
PIC DESIGN; U.S. Private, pg. 864
POWERS FASTENING, INC.; U.S. Private, pg. 878
PRECISION FASTENERS LTD.—SPS Technologies, Inc.; U.S. Public, pg. 1420
PREMIER AUTOWARE—Premier Farnell plc; Int'l, pg. 1068
PREMIER FARNELL—Premier Farnell plc; Int'l, pg. 1068
PREMIER FASTENER—Premier Farnell plc; Int'l, pg. 1068
PREMIER FASTENER LTD.—Premier Farnell plc; Int'l, pg. 1068
PRESTIGE STAMPING, INC.; U.S. Private, pg. 882
PRODOTTI BAUMANN SPA—Baumann Federn AG; Int'l, pg. 171
RB&W CORPORATION—Park-Ohio Industries, Inc.; U.S. Public, pg. 1259
RAYMOND ENGINEERING—Kaman Corporation; U.S. Public, pg. 942
RING SCREW WORKS; U.S. Private, pg. 931
ROCKFORD PRODUCTS CORP.; U.S. Private, pg. 938
ROCKNEL FASTENER, INC.—Textron Inc.; U.S. Public, pg. 1590
ROTANIUM PRODUCTS—Premier Farnell plc; Int'l, pg. 1068
SKF SLEWING BEARINGS (RKS S.A)—AB SKF; Int'l, pg. 1159
SPS TECHNOLOGIES, INC.; U.S. Public, pg. 1419
SEMBLEX CORPORATION; U.S. Private, pg. 983
SERVICE SUPPLY CO. INC. OF INDIANA; U.S. Private, pg. 987
SHUR-LOK CORPORATION; U.S. Private, pg. 997
SPIROL INTERNATIONAL CORP.; U.S. Private, pg. 1026
SPIROLOX DIVISION—Kaydon Corporation; U.S. Public, pg. 946
STAMPTECH—Maclean-Fogg Co.; U.S. Private, pg. 692
STANDCO INDUSTRIES, INC.; U.S. Private, pg. 1032
STAR ANCHORS & FASTENERS; U.S. Private, pg. 1033
STAR EXPANSION SHIELDS LTD.—STAR Anchors & Fasteners; U.S. Private, pg. 1034
EDWIN B. STIMPSON COMPANY, INC.; U.S. Private, pg. 1043
TCR CORPORATION—TransTechnology Corporation; U.S. Public, pg. 1632
TII DOMINICANA INC.—TII Industries, Inc.; U.S. Public, pg. 1556
TII INDUSTRIES, INC.; U.S. Public, pg. 1556
THE TOBIN CORPORATION—Avis Industrial Corporation; U.S. Private, pg. 102
TRANSTECHNOLOGY CORPORATION; U.S. Public, pg. 1632
TRIMAS CORPORATION—Masco Corporation; U.S. Public, pg. 1054
TRU-FIT PRODUCTS CORP.; U.S. Private, pg. 1107
TUCKER FASTENERS LTD.—The Black & Decker Corporation; U.S. Public, pg. 234
UNBRAKO DIV.—SPS Technologies, Inc.; U.S. Public, pg. 1420
UNBRAKO PTY. LTD.—SPS Technologies, Inc.; U.S. Public, pg. 1420
VALLEY-TODECO, INC.—McKechnie PLC; Int'l, pg. 852
VOSS INDUSTRIES, INC.; U.S. Private, pg. 1143
WASHERS, INCORPORATED; U.S. Private, pg. 1152
WROUGHT WASHER MFG., INC.; U.S. Private, pg. 1192
X-ERGON—NCH Corporation; U.S. Public, pg. 1145
XALOY, INC.; U.S. Private, pg. 1194

3462 — IRON & STEEL FORGINGS

ANI AURORA PLC—Australian National Industries Limited; Int'l, pg. 101
ACCO PLATEN GMBH—FKI Plc; Int'l, pg. 473
ARMCO INC.; U.S. Public, pg. 131
AVIS INDUSTRIAL CORPORATION; U.S. Private, pg. 102
BALDT, INC.; U.S. Private, pg. 112
BAY CITY FORGE OPERATIONS—Zurn Industries, Inc.; U.S. Public, pg. 1794
BAYSIDE MOTION GROUP; U.S. Private, pg. 125
BERRY CONTRACTING; U.S. Private, pg. 137
BRIDON PLC; Int'l, pg. 215
BRITISH STEEL GENERAL STEELS DIVISION—British Steel Plc; Int'l, pg. 220
BRITISH STEEL PLC; Int'l, pg. 220
CALIFORNIA DROP FORGE—Fansteel, Inc.; U.S. Public, pg. 612
CANTON DROP FORGE; U.S. Private, pg. 205
CLEVELAND CITY FORGE—Park-Ohio Industries, Inc.; U.S. Public, pg. 1258
CLYDESDALE FORGE CO.—Caparo Group Ltd.; Int'l, pg. 265
COMMERCIAL FORGED PRODUCTS—Wozniak Industries, Inc.; U.S. Private, pg. 1192
CONE DRIVE TEXTRON—Textron Inc.; U.S. Public, pg. 1589
CONSOLIDATED INDUSTRIES, INC.; U.S. Private, pg. 265
CONTRAN CORPORATION; U.S. Private, pg. 270
CORNELL FORGE COMPANY; U.S. Private, pg. 276
THE CROSBY GROUP INC.—FKI Plc; Int'l, pg. 473
DANA CORPORATION; U.S. Public, pg. 479
DEFIANCE PRECISION PRODUCTS, INC.—Defiance, Inc.; U.S. Public, pg. 493
DELROYD WORM GEAR—IMO Industries Inc.; U.S. Public, pg. 857
DERLAN INDUSTRIES LIMITED; Int'l, pg. 395
EDGERTON FORGE, INC.—Avis Industrial Corporation; U.S. Private, pg. 102
EDGEWATER STEEL COMPANY; U.S. Private, pg. 364
ELLWOOD CRANKSHAFT & MACHINE COMPANY—Ellwood Group, Inc.; U.S. Private, pg. 373
ELLWOOD GROUP, INC.; U.S. Private, pg. 373
ENVIROTECH PUMPSYSTEMS—Weir Group PLC; Int'l, pg. 1489
FANSTEEL, INC.; U.S. Public, pg. 612
FOLEY-PLP COMPANY—Foley-Belsaw Company; U.S. Private, pg. 416
FREEDOM FORGE CORPORATION; U.S. Private, pg. 425
FROG SWITCH & MANUFACTURING COMPANY; U.S. Private, pg. 429
GEC ALSTHOM—Alcatel Alsthom Compagnie Generale D'Electricite; Int'l, pg. 52
GEAR RESEARCH INCORPORATED—Jordan Industries, Inc.; U.S. Private, pg. 598
GROUPE STRAFOR FACOM; Int'l, pg. 569
GUNNEBO FASTENING CORP.; U.S. Private, pg. 488
HFC ESTAMFOR—Groupe Usinor; Int'l, pg. 570
HYLAR METAL PRODUCTS—Degelman Industries Ltd.; Int'l, pg. 388
IMI MARSTON INC.—IMI Plc; Int'l, pg. 646
IDEAL FORGING CORPORATION; U.S. Private, pg. 557
ISHIKAWAJIMA-HARIMA HEAVY INDUSTRIES CO., LTD.; Int'l, pg. 689
JANNOCK STEEL FABRICATING, INC.—Jannock Limited; Int'l, pg. 699
JERNBERG INDUSTRIES, INC.; U.S. Private, pg. 586
JEUMONT-SCHNEIDER TRENFORMETEURS; Int'l, pg. 706
KERVICK ENTERPRISES, INC.; U.S. Private, pg. 616
KROPP FORGE CO.—TIC United Corporation; U.S. Private, pg. 1064
KRUPP GERLACH COMPANY—Fried. Krupp AG; Int'l, pg. 508
LENAPE FORGE, INC.; U.S. Private, pg. 659
LETTS INDUSTRIES, INC.; U.S. Private, pg. 661
MACLEAN-FOGG CO.; U.S. Private, pg. 692
MANNESMANN ANLAGENBAU AG—Mannesmann A.G.; Int'l, pg. 836
MANOIR ELECTROALLOYS CORPORATION—Groupe Strafor Facom; Int'l, pg. 570
MANOIR INDUSTRIES—Groupe Strafor Facom; Int'l, pg. 570
MASCOTECH FORMING TECHNOLOGIES—MascoTech, Inc.; U.S. Public, pg. 1055
MCINNES ROLLED RINGS—McInnes Steel Company; U.S. Private, pg. 722
MCINNES STEEL COMPANY; U.S. Private, pg. 722
MCKISSICK PRODUCTS CO.—FKI Plc; Int'l, pg. 473
MCWILLIAMS FORGE CO.; U.S. Private, pg. 725
MEADVILLE FORGING CO.; U.S. Private, pg. 726
MELLING FORGING COMPANY—Avis Industrial Corporation; U.S. Private, pg. 102
MERCER FORGE, INC.—Galesi Group; U.S. Private, pg. 438
MERITOR AUTOMOTIVE, INC.; U.S. Public, pg. 1096
METAL FORGE—General Signal Corporation; U.S. Public, pg. 727
MITCHELL SHACKLETON & CO. LTD.—National Forge Company; U.S. Private, pg. 783
MODERN DROP FORGE CO.; U.S. Private, pg. 754
NTC GROUP; U.S. Private, pg. 772
NASCO INTERNATIONAL, INC.—Geneve Corporation; U.S. Private, pg. 446
NATIONAL FORGE COMPANY; U.S. Private, pg. 783
NATIONAL MINE SERVICE, INC.—Charter plc; Int'l, pg. 280
NUCLEAR AND ADVANCED TECHNOLOGY DIVISION—CBS Corporation; U.S. Public, pg. 273
NUCOR CORPORATION; U.S. Public, pg. 1205
OSAKA CHAIN & MACHINERY, LTD.—Kobe Steel, Ltd.; Int'l, pg. 740
P.C. DROP FORGINGS DIVISION—The Ivaco Group; Int'l, pg. 695
PACIFIC FORGE, INC.—Avis Industrial Corporation; U.S. Private, pg. 102
PARK DROP FORGE DIV.—Park-Ohio Industries, Inc.; U.S. Public, pg. 1258
PARK-OHIO INDUSTRIES, INC.; U.S. Public, pg. 1258
PENN LOCOMOTIVE GEAR—Charter plc; Int'l, pg. 281
PENN MACHINE COMPANY—Charter plc; Int'l, pg. 281
PORTEC, INC.; U.S. Public, pg. 1317
RAIL PRODUCTS DIVISION—AmeriSteel; U.S. Private, pg. 65
RING SCREW WORKS; U.S. Private, pg. 931
ROCKWELL HEAVY VEHICLE SUSPENSION SYSTEMS COMPANY, INC.—Meritor Automotive, Inc.; U.S. Public, pg. 1096
ROLLS-ROYCE & ASSOCIATES LIMITED—FKI Plc; Int'l, pg. 472
SAFE S.A.—Groupe Usinor; Int'l, pg. 571
SCHLOSSER FORGE COMPANY; U.S. Private, pg. 970
SENIOR COLMAN LIMITED—Senior Engineering Group, plc.; Int'l, pg. 1220
SENIOR CONFLOW—Senior Engineering Group, plc.; Int'l, pg. 1220
SENIOR CONFLOW INC.—Senior Engineering Group, plc.; Int'l, pg. 1222
SENIOR CONSTRUCTION SERVICES LIMITED—Senior Engineering Group, plc.; Int'l, pg. 1220
SENIOR CONTROL ENGINEERING LIMITED—Senior Engineering Group, plc.; Int'l, pg. 1220
SENIOR DAVIS DERBY—Senior Engineering Group, plc.; Int'l, pg. 1220
SENIOR ENTEX—Senior Engineering Group, plc.; Int'l, pg. 1220
SENIOR HARGREAVES LIMITED—Senior Engineering Group, plc.; Int'l, pg. 1221
SENIOR MODUCEL LIMITED—Senior Engineering Group, plc.; Int'l, pg. 1221
SENIOR PHOENIX RFS LIMITED—Senior Engineering Group, plc.; Int'l, pg. 1221
SIFCO FORGE GROUP—Sifco Industries, Inc.; U.S. Public, pg. 1471
SIFCO INDUSTRIES, INC.; U.S. Public, pg. 1470
SIGLA EQUIPAMENTOS ELETRICOS LTDA.—Jeumont-Schneider Trenformeteurs; Int'l, pg. 706
STEEL PRODUCTS DIV.—Carlyle Holding Corporation; U.S. Private, pg. 213
STINNES CORPORATION—Veba AG; Int'l, pg. 1460
SUMITOMO METAL INDUSTRIES, LTD.; Int'l, pg. 1315
SWISS LOCOMOTIVE AND MACHINE WORKS—Sulzer Ltd.; Int'l, pg. 1307
TIFT SA—Senior Engineering Group, plc.; Int'l, pg. 1223
TSUBAKIMOTO CHAIN CO.; Int'l, pg. 1425
UIS, INC.; U.S. Private, pg. 1113
UNIT RAIL ANCHOR COMPANY—Varlen Corporation; U.S. Public, pg. 1711
USINE DE BOURGES—Groupe Strafor Facom; Int'l, pg. 570
USINE DE CUSTINES—Groupe Strafor Facom; Int'l, pg. 570
VARLEN CORPORATION; U.S. Public, pg. 1710
VICKERS PLC; Int'l, pg. 1466
VOEST-ALPINE STEEL CORP.—Voest-Alpine Stahl AG; Int'l, pg. 1471
VON ROLL AG DEPARTEMENT MASCHINEN & FORDERTECHN—Von Roll AG; Int'l, pg. 1480
WFI INTERNATIONAL, INC.; U.S. Private, pg. 1144
WEBB FORGING—Jervis B. Webb Company; U.S. Private, pg. 1156
JERVIS B. WEBB COMPANY; U.S. Private, pg. 1156
WEBSTER INDUSTRIES INC.; U.S. Private, pg. 1157
WELLAND FORGE DIV.—FKI Plc; Int'l, pg. 474
WOZNIAK INDUSTRIES, INC.; U.S. Private, pg. 1192
WYMAN-GORDON; U.S. Public, pg. 1782
WYMAN-GORDON FORGINGS, INC.—Wyman-Gordon; U.S. Public, pg. 1782

3463 — NONFERROUS FORGINGS

ANI AURORA PLC—Australian National Industries Limited; Int'l, pg. 101
ACCURATE FORGING CORP.—Delta plc; Int'l, pg. 391
ADEC AUTOMATION—Adec International Automation Corp.; U.S. Private, pg. 17
AVIS INDUSTRIAL CORPORATION; U.S. Private, pg. 102
CANTON DROP FORGE; U.S. Private, pg. 205
CAPSULAS METALICAS S.A.—Aluminum Company of America; U.S. Public, pg. 62
CEGEDUR PECHINEY—Pechiney S.A.; Int'l, pg. 1028
CONSOLIDATED INDUSTRIES, INC.; U.S. Private, pg. 265
CONTINENTAL FORGE COMPANY; U.S. Private, pg. 268
EMCO LIMITED; Int'l, pg. 452
FORGEAL—Pechiney S.A.; Int'l, pg. 1028
FORGES DE BOLOGNE—Aluminum Company of America; U.S. Public, pg. 62
HDA FORGINGS LTD.—BTR plc; Int'l, pg. 126
HOESCH ROTHE ERDE AG—Fried. Krupp AG; Int'l, pg. 509
ITW THIELEX PLASTICS CORP.—Illinois Tool Works Inc.; U.S. Public, pg. 867
JONATHAN MANUFACTURING CORP.; U.S. Private, pg. 595
KERVICK ENTERPRISES, INC.; U.S. Private, pg. 616
KROPP FORGE CO.—TIC United Corporation; U.S. Private, pg. 1064
KRUPP GERLACH COMPANY—Fried. Krupp AG; Int'l, pg. 508
LENAPE FORGE, INC.; U.S. Private, pg. 659
LETTS INDUSTRIES, INC.; U.S. Private, pg. 661
LETTS INDUSTRIES, PIONEER DIV.—Letts Industries, Inc.; U.S. Private, pg. 661
MANOIR INDUSTRIES—Groupe Strafor Facom; Int'l, pg. 570
MCWILLIAMS FORGE CO.; U.S. Private, pg. 725
NASCO INTERNATIONAL, INC.—Geneve Corporation; U.S. Private, pg. 446
PACIFIC FORGE, INC.—Avis Industrial Corporation; U.S. Private, pg. 102
PHILIPS ELMET CORPORATION—Philips Electronics N.V.; Int'l, pg. 1055
RING SCREW WORKS; U.S. Private, pg. 931
SCHLOSSER FORGE COMPANY; U.S. Private, pg. 970
SHIBAZAKI SEISAKUSHO LIMITED—Aluminum Company of America; U.S. Public, pg. 62
SIFCO FORGE GROUP—Sifco Industries, Inc.; U.S. Public, pg. 1471
SIFCO INDUSTRIES, INC.; U.S. Public, pg. 1470
UIS, INC.; U.S. Private, pg. 1113
USINE DE BOURGES—Groupe Strafor Facom; Int'l, pg. 570

VIKING METALLURGICAL CORPORATION—Firth-Rixson Plc; *Int'l*, pg. 488
WFI INTERNATIONAL, INC.; *U.S. Private*, pg. 1144
WALTEC AMERICAN FORGINGS, INC.—Emco Limited; *Int'l*, pg. 453
WYMAN-GORDON; *U.S. Public*, pg. 1782
WYMAN-GORDON FORGINGS—Wyman-Gordon; *U.S. Public*, pg. 1782

3465 — AUTOMOTIVE STAMPINGS

ACTIVE TOOL & MANUFACTURING CO., INC.; *U.S. Private*, pg. 16
AETNA INDUSTRIES, INC.; *U.S. Private*, pg. 25
AMERICAN METAL & PLASTICS INC.; *U.S. Private*, pg. 59
ANAMET INC.; *U.S. Private*, pg. 70
ANCHOR TOOL & DIE COMPANY; *U.S. Private*, pg. 71
ANDERSON INDUSTRIES, INC.—Excel Industries, Inc.; *U.S. Public*, pg. 599
ARROW METAL PRODUCTS CORPORATION; *U.S. Private*, pg. 85
ARVIN INDUSTRIES, INC.; *U.S. Public*, pg. 136
P.T. ASTRA DAIHATSU MOTOR—Daihatsu Motor Corporation, Ltd.; *Int'l*, pg. 365
BELVEDERE—Excel Industries, Inc.; *U.S. Public*, pg. 598
BENT TUBE, INC.; *U.S. Private*, pg. 134
BINDERLINE DEVELOPMENT, INC./DRAFTLINE ENGINEERING CO., INC.—Defiance, Inc.; *U.S. Public*, pg. 493
THE BUDD COMPANY—Thyssen AG; *Int'l*, pg. 1388
BUTLER METAL PRODUCTS—BBA Group plc; *Int'l*, pg. 113
CMC KALAMAZOO INC.—Stamford Capital; *U.S. Private*, pg. 1030
CHIVAS PRODUCTS LTD.; *U.S. Private*, pg. 238
CHRYSLER ADVANCE MANUFACTURING OPERATIONS—Chrysler Corporation; *U.S. Public*, pg. 353
CHRYSLER CORPORATION; *U.S. Public*, pg. 352
CONDOR TOOL & DIE, INC.—Anchor Tool & Die Company; *U.S. Private*, pg. 71
COSMA INTERNATIONAL INC.—Magna International Inc.; *Int'l*, pg. 829
CRAGAR INDUSTRIES, INC.; *U.S. Public*, pg. 456
CRESCIVE DIE & TOOL, INC.; *U.S. Private*, pg. 289
CRESIVE MILAN DIVISION—Crescive Die & Tool, Inc.; *U.S. Private*, pg. 289
DAVIS INDUSTRIES INC.; *U.S. Private*, pg. 315
DAVIS TOOL & ENGINEERING CO.—Davis Industries Inc.; *U.S. Private*, pg. 315
DEFIANCE PRECISION PRODUCTS, INC.—Defiance, Inc.; *U.S. Public*, pg. 493
DUFFY TOOL & STAMPING, INC.—Brittany Corporation; *U.S. Private*, pg. 169
EWI/SOUTH BEND STAMPING DIVISION—South Bend Stamping; *U.S. Private*, pg. 1014
EMTEC PRODUCTS CORPORATION—Kuhlman Corporation; *U.S. Public*, pg. 968
EXCEL INDUSTRIES, INC.; *U.S. Public*, pg. 598
THE GERSTENSLAGER COMPANY—Worthington Industries, Inc.; *U.S. Public*, pg. 1780
HAWK CORP.; *U.S. Private*, pg. 511
HOFLEY MANUFACTURING COMPANY; *U.S. Private*, pg. 532
HY-FORM PRODUCTS, INC.—Defiance, Inc.; *U.S. Public*, pg. 493
IROQUOIS DIE & MFG. CO.; *U.S. Private*, pg. 575
KAUFFMAN PRODUCTS, INC.; *U.S. Private*, pg. 609
THE OTTO KONIGSLOW MFG. CO.—Triumph Group, Inc.; *U.S. Public*, pg. 1640
LEAR CORPORATION; *U.S. Public*, pg. 981
LETTS INDUSTRIES, INC.; *U.S. Private*, pg. 661
LOGGHE STAMPING COMPANY; *U.S. Private*, pg. 672
LUCAS BODY SYSTEMS - NORTH AMERICA—LucasVarity plc; *Int'l*, pg. 820
MACHINE-RITE PRODUCTS—Excel Industries, Inc.; *U.S. Public*, pg. 599
MAGNA INTERNATIONAL INC.; *Int'l*, pg. 829
MAGNA LOMASON CORP.—Magna International Inc.; *Int'l*, pg. 830
MANUFACTURERS PRODUCTS COMPANY; *U.S. Private*, pg. 701
MASCOTECH, INC.; *U.S. Public*, pg. 1055
MASCOTECH SINTERED COMPONENTS, INC.—MascoTech, Inc.; *U.S. Public*, pg. 1055
MCCORD WINN TEXTRON COMPANY—Textron Inc.; *U.S. Public*, pg. 1590
MEANS INDUSTRIES, INC.—Varlen Corporation; *U.S. Public*, pg. 1711
MERITOR AUTOMOTIVE, INC.; *U.S. Public*, pg. 1096
MIDWAY PRODUCTS CORPORATION; *U.S. Private*, pg. 744
NI INDUSTRIES, INC.—Masco Corporation; *U.S. Public*, pg. 1054
NEW STANDARD CORPORATION; *U.S. Private*, pg. 794
NYLONCRAFT—Excel Industries, Inc.; *U.S. Public*, pg. 599
OAKLAND TOOL & MANUFACTURING COMPANY; *U.S. Private*, pg. 809
OXFORD AUTOMOTIVE, INC.; *U.S. Private*, pg. 825
PRESTIGE STAMPING, INC.; *U.S. Private*, pg. 882
PRIDGEON & CLAY, INC.; *U.S. Private*, pg. 883
PRINCE CORPORATION—Johnson Controls, Inc.; *U.S. Public*, pg. 932
PULLMAN INDUSTRIES, INC.; *U.S. Private*, pg. 894
RANDALL TEXTRON—Textron Inc.; *U.S. Public*, pg. 1590
REPUBLIC DIE & TOOL COMPANY; *U.S. Private*, pg. 923
ROCKWELL HEAVY VEHICLE SUSPENSION SYSTEMS COMPANY, INC.—Meritor Automotive, Inc.; *U.S. Public*, pg. 1096
A.G. SIMPSON CO. LIMITED; *Int'l*, pg. 1252
SINTERING TECHNOLOGIES, INC.—Cummins Engine Company, Inc.; *U.S. Public*, pg. 468
SOUTH CHARLESTON STAMPING & MANUFACTURING—Stamford Capital; *U.S. Private*, pg. 1030
SPARTANBURG STEEL PRODUCTS—The Cypress Companies; *U.S. Private*, pg. 300
STAMCO INDUSTRIES INC.; *U.S. Private*, pg. 1029
STARBOARD INDUSTRIES, INC.—JPE, Inc.; *U.S. Public*, pg. 919
STEEL PARTS CORP.—Insilco Corporation; *U.S. Public*, pg. 881
SYNERGIS TECHNOLOGIES GROUP; *U.S. Private*, pg. 1060
TEXTRON AUTOMOTIVE COMPANY—Textron Inc.; *U.S. Public*, pg. 1590
TEXTRON INC.; *U.S. Public*, pg. 1588
TITAN TIRE CORPORATION—Titan International, Inc.; *U.S. Public*, pg. 1618
TITAN WHEEL—Titan International, Inc.; *U.S. Public*, pg. 1618
TITAN WHEEL CORPORATION OF VIRGINIA—Titan International, Inc.; *U.S. Public*, pg. 1619
TITAN WHEEL CORPORATION OF WI—Titan International, Inc.; *U.S. Public*, pg. 1619
TOWER AUTOMOTIVE, INC.; *U.S. Public*, pg. 1625
VARLEN CORPORATION; *U.S. Public*, pg. 1710

3466 — METAL CROWNS & CLOSURES

ALLTRISTA CORPORATION; *U.S. Public*, pg. 56
AMERICAN FLANGE & MANUFACTURING CO. INC.—Royal Packaging Industries Van Leer B.V.; *Int'l*, pg. 1146
AMERICAN INTERNATIONAL CONTAINER, INC.; *U.S. Private*, pg. 57
BERNARDIN OF CANADA, LTD.—Alltrista Corporation; *U.S. Public*, pg. 56
CONSUMER PRODUCTS COMPANY—Alltrista Corporation; *U.S. Public*, pg. 56
N.V. CROWN-BAELE S. A.—Crown Cork & Seal Company, Inc.; *U.S. Public*, pg. 464
CROWN CORK & SEAL COMPANY, INC.; *U.S. Public*, pg. 462
H-C INDUSTRIES, INC.—Aluminum Company of America; *U.S. Public*, pg. 60
THE IRISH CROWN CORK CO., LTD.—Crown Cork & Seal Company, Inc.; *U.S. Public*, pg. 465
MOELLER PRODUCTS CO., INC.; *U.S. Private*, pg. 755
OWENS-ILLINOIS CLOSURE INC.—Owens-Illinois, Inc.; *U.S. Public*, pg. 1238
SILGAN CONTAINERS—Silgan Corporation; *U.S. Public*, pg. 1473
WHITE CAP, INC.—Schmalbach-Lubeca AG; *Int'l*, pg. 1207

3469 — METAL STAMPINGS, NEC

A & S TRIBAL INDUSTRIES; *U.S. Private*, pg. 1
APG DIVISION—Upper Midwest Industries, Incorporated; *U.S. Private*, pg. 1129
ATF, INC.; *U.S. Private*, pg. 8
AAKRONITE NEW ZEALAND—International Paper Company; *U.S. Public*, pg. 904
THE AARQUE COMPANIES; *U.S. Private*, pg. 9
ACCURATE PERFORATING CO.; *U.S. Private*, pg. 12
ACKLIN STAMPING DIV.—Tecumseh Products Company; *U.S. Public*, pg. 1565
ACTIVE TOOL & MANUFACTURING CO., INC.; *U.S. Private*, pg. 16
ALCO INDUSTRIES, INC.; *U.S. Private*, pg. 32
ALLIANCE AMERICA; *U.S. Private*, pg. 37
ALLIEDSIGNAL AMORPHOUS METALS—AlliedSignal Inc.; *U.S. Public*, pg. 51
ALPHA METALS, INC.—Cookson Group plc; *Int'l*, pg. 328
AMERICAN FLANGE & MANUFACTURING CO. INC.—Royal Packaging Industries Van Leer B.V.; *Int'l*, pg. 1146
AMERICAN MANUFACTURING COMPANY; *U.S. Private*, pg. 58
AMERICAN SPECIALTIES INC.; *U.S. Private*, pg. 62
AMHERST METAL PRODUCTS, INC.—Brittany Corporation; *U.S. Private*, pg. 169
AMTROL INC.—The Cypress Group LLC; *U.S. Private*, pg. 300
ANCHOR TOOL & DIE COMPANY; *U.S. Private*, pg. 71
ARMCO INC.-MANSFIELD OPERATIONS—Armco Inc.; *U.S. Public*, pg. 131
ARROW TRU-LINE, INC.; *U.S. Private*, pg. 85
ATKINSON; *U.S. Public*, pg. 143
AUGAT, INC., WIRING SYSTEMS & COMPONENTS GROUP—Thomas & Betts Corporation; *U.S. Public*, pg. 1598
BCL MAGNETICS—Tempel Steel Company; *U.S. Private*, pg. 1075
BATESVILLE AMERICAN MFG.—Kimball International, Inc.; *U.S. Public*, pg. 957
BAUMANN FEDERN AG; *Int'l*, pg. 171
BAUMANN GMBH—Baumann Federn AG; *Int'l*, pg. 171
BAUMANN SPRING CO. (S) PTE. LTD.—Baumann Federn AG; *Int'l*, pg. 171
BAUMANN SPRINGS & PRESSINGS (UK) LTD.—Baumann Federn AG; *Int'l*, pg. 171
BENSON CORP.—Gem Industries Finance Corporation; *U.S. Private*, pg. 443
BERMO, INC.; *U.S. Private*, pg. 136
BETTCHER MANUFACTURING CORP.—Brittany Corporation; *U.S. Private*, pg. 169
BETTCHER MANUFACTURING CORPORATION—Brittany Corporation; *U.S. Private*, pg. 169
BIRTCHER—Zero Corporation; *U.S. Public*, pg. 1791
BLISS MANUFACTURING COMPANY—HMI Industries; *U.S. Public*, pg. 771
BOMMER INDUSTRIES, INC.; *U.S. Private*, pg. 156
BRITTANY CORPORATION; *U.S. Private*, pg. 169
BRONZE HEADQUARTERS—Bearing Headquarters Co.; *U.S. Private*, pg. 127
CME—California Manufacturing Enterprises; *U.S. Private*, pg. 201
CALIFORNIA MANUFACTURING ENTERPRISES; *U.S. Private*, pg. 201
CARSTENS INC.; *U.S. Private*, pg. 216
CASH BASES INCORPORATED—Tridex Corporation; *U.S. Public*, pg. 1637
CHACE PRECISION METALS, INC.—Technitrol, Inc.; *U.S. Public*, pg. 1564
CLAYTON METALS CORP.—Clayton Corporation; *U.S. Private*, pg. 244
COMMERCIAL INTERTECH CORP.; *U.S. Public*, pg. 411
CONDOR TOOL & DIE, INC.—Anchor Tool & Die Company; *U.S. Private*, pg. 71
CONNECTICUT SPRING & STAMPING CORPORATION; *U.S. Private*, pg. 263
CONTICO INTERNATIONAL, INC.; *U.S. Private*, pg. 267
COPCO—Wilton Industries, Inc.; *U.S. Private*, pg. 1182
COSCO INDUSTRIES; *U.S. Private*, pg. 277
COWDEN METAL-SAN JOSE—Cowden Metal Specialties, Inc.; *U.S. Private*, pg. 280
COWDEN METAL SPECIALTIES, INC.; *U.S. Private*, pg. 280
CROWN CORK & SEAL COMPANY, INC.; *U.S. Public*, pg. 462
CULLMAN PRODUCTS CORPORATION; *U.S. Private*, pg. 294
DAVIS INDUSTRIES INC.; *U.S. Private*, pg. 315
DAYTON ROGERS MFG. CO.; *U.S. Private*, pg. 318
DAYTON ROGERS OF FLORIDA—Dayton Rogers Mfg. Co.; *U.S. Private*, pg. 318
DE-STA-CO, A DOVER RESOURCES CO.—Dover Corporation; *U.S. Public*, pg. 521
DELTA CONSOLIDATED INDUSTRIES, INC. (CO. HEADQUARTERS)—Danaher Corporation; *U.S. Public*, pg. 481
DETEX CORPORATION; *U.S. Private*, pg. 327
DIEBEL MANUFACTURING CO.; *U.S. Private*, pg. 331
THE DISSTON CO.—Kennametal Inc.; *U.S. Public*, pg. 950
DUAL MANUFACTURING & ENGINEERING, INC.—Furnishings International, Inc.; *U.S. Private*, pg. 432
DUDEK & BOCK SPRING MANUFACTURING COMPANY; *U.S. Private*, pg. 344
DUFFY TOOL & STAMPING, INC.—Brittany Corporation; *U.S. Private*, pg. 169
EAGLE INDUSTRIES, INC.—Great American Management & Investment, Inc.; *U.S. Private*, pg. 473
EAST MOLINE METAL PRODUCTS COMPANY; *U.S. Private*, pg. 357
EATON CORPORATION, ENGINEERED FASTENERS DIVISION—Eaton Corporation; *U.S. Public*, pg. 556
ECLIPSE MANUFACTURING COMPANY; *U.S. Private*, pg. 361
EKCO GROUP, INC.; *U.S. Public*, pg. 566
EKCO HOUSEWARES, INC.—Ekco Group, Inc.; *U.S. Public*, pg. 566
ELCO CONSUMER PRODUCTS CORP.—Textron Inc.; *U.S. Public*, pg. 1590
ELCO PRECISION FORMING DIV.—Textron Inc.; *U.S. Public*, pg. 1590
ELCO PRECISION STAMPING DIV.—Textron Inc.; *U.S. Public*, pg. 1590
ELCO TEXTRON—Textron Inc.; *U.S. Public*, pg. 1590
EMAIL LIMITED-BUILDING PRODUCTS GROUP—Email Limited; *Int'l*, pg. 450
EMTEC PRODUCTS CORPORATION—Kuhlman Corporation; *U.S. Public*, pg. 968
ERDLE PERFORATING CO.; *U.S. Private*, pg. 380
FERROUS PROCESSING & TRADING CO.; *U.S. Private*, pg. 402
FORTUNE BRANDS, INC.; *U.S. Public*, pg. 674
FREEWAY CORPORATION; *U.S. Private*, pg. 426
FULTON INDUSTRIES INC.; *U.S. Private*, pg. 431
FUTABA CORPORATION; *Int'l*, pg. 531
GEM SOUTHEAST, INC.—Gem Industries Finance Corporation; *U.S. Private*, pg. 443
GENERAL CABLE CO.—Wassall Plc; *Int'l*, pg. 1487
GENERAL HOUSEWARES CORP.; *U.S. Public*, pg. 715
GENERAL METAL PRODUCTS—Wozniak Industries, Inc.; *U.S. Private*, pg. 1192
GENESEE METAL STAMPINGS, INC.; *U.S. Private*, pg. 446
THE GERSTENSLAGER COMPANY—Worthington Industries, Inc.; *U.S. Public*, pg. 1780
HMI INDUSTRIES; *U.S. Public*, pg. 771
HACKNEY INC.—Trinity Industries Inc.; *U.S. Public*, pg. 1639
HAMLIN STEEL PRODUCTS—The Cypress Companies; *U.S. Private*, pg. 299
HANCOCK MANUFACTURING—The Cypress Companies; *U.S. Private*, pg. 299
HANDY & HARMAN ELECTRONIC MATERIALS CORP.—Handy & Harman; *U.S. Public*, pg. 780
HARRINGTON & KING; *U.S. Private*, pg. 504
HARRINGTON & KING, SOUTH, INC.—Harrington & King; *U.S. Private*, pg. 504
HEADCO MACHINE WORKS, INC.—Bearing Headquarters Co.; *U.S. Private*, pg. 127
HENDRICKSON INTERNATIONAL—Boler Company; *U.S. Private*, pg. 155
HENDRICKSON STAMPING—Boler Company; *U.S. Private*, pg. 155
HEXCEL, FAR EAST—Hexcel Corporation; *U.S. Public*, pg. 824
HOESCH ROTHE ERDE AG—Fried. Krupp AG; *Int'l*, pg. 509
HOFLEY MANUFACTURING COMPANY; *U.S. Private*, pg. 532
HUBBELL INCORPORATED; *U.S. Public*, pg. 844
IRI ISTITUTO RICOSTRUZIONE INDUSTRIALE; *Int'l*, pg. 652
INDIANA FINEBLANKING DIVISION—Klockner-Werke AG; *Int'l*, pg. 737

INSTRUMENT SPECIALTIES COMPANY; *U.S. Private*, pg. 565
INSTRUMENT SPECIALTIES - WESTERN DIVISION—Instrument Specialties Company; *U.S. Private*, pg. 565
INTEGRATED METAL TECHNOLOGIES, INC.—Herman Miller, Inc.; *U.S. Public*, pg. 1112
M. KAMENSTEIN, INC.; *U.S. Private*, pg. 606
KAUFEL AMERICA INC.—Kaufel Group Ltd.; *Int'l*, pg. 725
KAUFEL GROUP LTD.; *Int'l*, pg. 724
KAUFFMAN PRODUCTS, INC.; *U.S. Private*, pg. 609
KELLEMS DIV.—Hubbell Incorporated; *U.S. Public*, pg. 844
KENDALE INDUSTRIES, INC.; *U.S. Private*, pg. 614
KENNEDY MANUFACTURING COMPANY; *U.S. Private*, pg. 614
KEUM KANG DEVELOPMENT INDUSTRIAL CO., LTD.—Hyundai Motor Company; *Int'l*, pg. 642
KIMBALL INTERNATIONAL, INC.; *U.S. Public*, pg. 956
THE OTTO KONIGSLOW MFG. CO.—Triumph Group, Inc.; *U.S. Public*, pg. 1640
LAUGHTON & SONS, LTD.; *Int'l*, pg. 804
MTD PRODUCTS LIMITED—MTD Products, Inc.; *U.S. Private*, pg. 688
MAYVILLE ENGINEERING CO., INC.; *U.S. Private*, pg. 718
MCDOWELL MFG. CO. INC.—The Cypress Companies; *U.S. Private*, pg. 300
MECHANICS TOOL DIV.—The Stanley Works; *U.S. Public*, pg. 1509
MELITTA UNTERNEHMENSGRUPPE BENTZ KG; *Int'l*, pg. 856
MILFORD FABRICATING CO.—Thyssen AG; *Int'l*, pg. 1388
NI INDUSTRIES, INC.—Masco Corporation; *U.S. Public*, pg. 1054
NEW STANDARD CORPORATION; *U.S. Private*, pg. 794
NEWELL CO.; *U.S. Public*, pg. 1176
NORDIC WARE—Northland Aluminum Products, Inc.; *U.S. Private*, pg. 806
NORTHLAND ALUMINUM PRODUCTS, INC.; *U.S. Private*, pg. 805
NUPAR—Baldor Electric Company; *U.S. Public*, pg. 169
OBERG INDUSTRIES CORP.; *U.S. Private*, pg. 810
OBERG MFG. CO.—Oberg Industries Corp.; *U.S. Private*, pg. 810
THE OHIO ART COMPANY, INC.; *U.S. Public*, pg. 1214
ORANGE COUNTY METAL WORKS—Commercial Intertech Corp.; *U.S. Public*, pg. 411
PAR INDUSTRIES, INC.; *U.S. Private*, pg. 838
PETERSON AMERICAN CORP.; *U.S. Private*, pg. 857
PORCELAIN METALS CORP.; *U.S. Private*, pg. 876
PRECISION METALCRAFT—Bell Industries, Inc.; *U.S. Public*, pg. 205
PRECISION RESOURCE INC.; *U.S. Private*, pg. 880
PREMIER METAL PRODUCTS CO.; *U.S. Private*, pg. 881
PRIDGEON & CLAY, INC.; *U.S. Private*, pg. 883
PULLMAN INDUSTRIES, INC.; *U.S. Private*, pg. 894
Q3 INDUSTRIES—Q3 Stamped Metal; *U.S. Private*, pg. 897
Q3 STAMPED METAL; *U.S. Private*, pg. 897
RANDALL TEXTRON—Textron Inc.; *U.S. Public*, pg. 1590
RAYTHEON SYSTEMS COMPANY—Raytheon Company; *U.S. Public*, pg. 1365
REVERE WARE CORPORATION—Corning Incorporated; *U.S. Public*, pg. 448
ROLL INTERNATIONAL CORPORATION; *U.S. Private*, pg. 941
ROWOCO—Wilton Industries, Inc.; *U.S. Private*, pg. 1182
SEIKA ELECTRIC CO., LTD.; *Int'l*, pg. 1218
SMALL PARTS, INC.; *U.S. Private*, pg. 1006
SOUTH BEND STAMPING; *U.S. Private*, pg. 1014
SOUTHERN FINEBLANKING—Klockner-Werke AG; *Int'l*, pg. 737
SPINCRAFT MASSACHUSETTS—Standex International Corporation; *U.S. Public*, pg. 1506
SPIROL INTERNATIONAL CORP.; *U.S. Private*, pg. 1026
SPIROL INTERNATIONAL CORP.—Spirol International Corp.; *U.S. Private*, pg. 1026
SPRING ENGINEERS OF HOUSTON LTD.—SEI Holding Corp.; *U.S. Private*, pg. 956
STAHL DIV.—Berkshire Hathaway Inc.; *U.S. Public*, pg. 218
STAMCO INDUSTRIES INC.; *U.S. Private*, pg. 1029
EDWIN B. STIMPSON COMPANY, INC.; *U.S. Private*, pg. 1043
STOCKO CORP.—Stocko Metallwaren Fabriken Henkels & Sohn; *Int'l*, pg. 1301
STOCKO METALLWAREN FABRIKEN HENKELS & SOHN; *Int'l*, pg. 1301
RALPH J. STOLLE CO.; *U.S. Private*, pg. 1044
T & N INDUSTRIES, INC.—T & N Plc; *Int'l*, pg. 1334
TARGET STAMPED PRODUCTS CORP.; *U.S. Private*, pg. 1069
TECHNITROL, INC.; *U.S. Public*, pg. 1564
TECSYN P.M.P. INC.—TecSyn International, Inc.; *Int'l*, pg. 1362
TECUMSEH PRODUCTS COMPANY; *U.S. Public*, pg. 1565
TEMPEL STEEL COMPANY; *U.S. Private*, pg. 1075
THERMADOR—Masco Corporation; *U.S. Public*, pg. 1054
THOMAS & BETTS ELECTRONICS DIVISION—Thomas & Betts Corporation; *U.S. Public*, pg. 1597
TOLEDO STAMPING & MANUFACTURING CO.—The General Chemical Group, Inc.; *U.S. Public*, pg. 707
TOSHIBA SINGAPORE PTE., LTD.—Toshiba Corporation; *Int'l*, pg. 1407
TRINITY INDUSTRIES INC.; *U.S. Public*, pg. 1638
TRITON INDUSTRIES, INC.; *U.S. Private*, pg. 1104
TRUELOVE & MACLEAN INC.; *U.S. Private*, pg. 1107
UNICOVER CORPORATION; *U.S. Private*, pg. 1117
UNITED RECEPTICAL, INC.; *U.S. Private*, pg. 1123
UNIVERSAL INDUSTRIAL PRODUCTS CO.—United Dominion Industries, Ltd.; *U.S. Public*, pg. 1677
UNIVERSAL INSTRUMENTS CORPORATION—Dover Corporation; *U.S. Public*, pg. 522
VALHI, INC.—Contran Corporation; *U.S. Private*, pg. 270
VERMONT AMERICAN TOOL CORP.—Emerson Electric Co.; *U.S. Public*, pg. 575
THE VOLLRATH COMPANY, L.L.C.; *U.S. Private*, pg. 1143
VOLUNTEER ENGINEERING, INC.—Davis Industries Inc.; *U.S. Private*, pg. 315
WAGNERWARE CORPORATION; *U.S. Private*, pg. 1146
WATERLOO INDUSTRIES, INC.—Fortune Brands, Inc.; *U.S. Public*, pg. 675
WEBER-KNAPP COMPANY—FKI Plc; *Int'l*, pg. 473
WEISER LOCK—Masco Corporation; *U.S. Public*, pg. 1053
WEST BEND OF CANADA LTD.—Premark International, Inc.; *U.S. Public*, pg. 1323
WESTERN INDUSTRIES, INC.; *U.S. Private*, pg. 1165
WISCONSIN FINEBLANKING—Klockner-Werke AG; *Int'l*, pg. 737
WITT COMPANY; *U.S. Private*, pg. 1185
WOZNIAK INDUSTRIES, INC.; *U.S. Private*, pg. 1192
WROUGHT WASHER MFG., INC.; *U.S. Private*, pg. 1192
ZERO CORPORATION; *U.S. Public*, pg. 1791
ZERO PLASTICS—Zero Corporation; *U.S. Public*, pg. 1791

3471 — ELECTROPLATING, PLATING, POLISHING, ANODIZING & COLORING

AAR CORP.; *U.S. Public*, pg. 1
AFFIVAL S.A.—Viag AG; *Int'l*, pg. 1466
ANO-COIL CORPORATION; *U.S. Private*, pg. 75
AUTOMATION FINISHING INC.—Freeway Corporation; *U.S. Private*, pg. 426
BERLIMED-PRODUCTOS QUIMICOS FARMACEULICOS E BIOLOGICOS LTDA.—Schering AG; *Int'l*, pg. 1204
CALIFORNIA MANUFACTURING ENTERPRISES; *U.S. Private*, pg. 201
CHROMIUM CORP.—Elcor Corporation; *U.S. Public*, pg. 568
COMALCO-CHH ALUMINUM—International Paper Company; *U.S. Public*, pg. 905
CULLMAN PRODUCTS CORPORATION; *U.S. Private*, pg. 294
ELCOR CORPORATION; *U.S. Public*, pg. 567
F.R. GROSS COMPANY—Ampco-Pittsburgh Corporation; *U.S. Public*, pg. 103
FEDERATED METALS CORP.—Asarco Incorporated; *U.S. Public*, pg. 138
FELLOWES MANUFACTURING CO.; *U.S. Private*, pg. 400
FLUID POWER DIV.—Quanex Corporation; *U.S. Public*, pg. 1350
GENERAL MAGNAPLATE CORPORATION; *U.S. Public*, pg. 717
HANDY & HARMAN ELECTRONIC MATERIALS CORP.—Handy & Harman; *U.S. Public*, pg. 780
HARRIS-KAYOT, INC.; *U.S. Private*, pg. 506
HARRISON DRAPE—McKechnie PLC; *Int'l*, pg. 851
INDUSTRIAS UNIVERSALES UNIONS DE MEXICO SA—Superior Industries International, Inc.; *U.S. Public*, pg. 1539
KOLLER ENTERPRISES, INC.; *U.S. Private*, pg. 631
LEARONAL, INC.—LeaRonal, Inc.; *U.S. Public*, pg. 982
LINN PRODUCTS, INC.; *U.S. Private*, pg. 669
MARCO COLOR LABS, INC.; *U.S. Private*, pg. 702
MECO METAL FINISHING USA INC.—L. Possehl & Co. mbH; *Int'l*, pg. 1064
NEW CASTLE INDUSTRIES, INC.—Ampco-Pittsburgh Corporation; *U.S. Public*, pg. 104
NIHON SCHERING K.K.—Schering AG; *Int'l*, pg. 1204
PARAMOUNT METALIZING DIV.—Koller Enterprises, Inc.; *U.S. Private*, pg. 631
POSSEHL ELECTRONIC NEDERLAND BV—L. Possehl & Co. mbH; *Int'l*, pg. 1064
PRECISION ROLL GRINDERS, INC.; *U.S. Private*, pg. 880
REYNOLDS METALS COMPANY-LAKE CHARLES—Reynolds Metals Company; *U.S. Public*, pg. 1385
RISDON CORPORATION—Crown Cork & Seal Company, Inc.; *U.S. Public*, pg. 463
SKW FRANCE S.A.—Viag AG; *Int'l*, pg. 1466
SKW METALS U.K. LTD., MOLYPRESS DIVISION—Viag AG; *Int'l*, pg. 1465
SL INDUSTRIES, INC.; *U.S. Public*, pg. 1418
SL SURFACE TECHNOLOGY, INC.—SL Industries, Inc.; *U.S. Public*, pg. 1419
SCHERING ESPANA S. A.—Schering AG; *Int'l*, pg. 1204
SCHERING ESPANA S.A.—Schering AG; *Int'l*, pg. 1204
SCHERING (SCHWEIZ) AG—Schering AG; *Int'l*, pg. 1204
SCHERING S.P.A.—Schering AG; *Int'l*, pg. 1204
SCHERING WIEN GES.M.B.H.—Schering AG; *Int'l*, pg. 1204
SIFCO INDUSTRIES, INC.; *U.S. Public*, pg. 1470
SIFCO SELECTIVE PLATING—Sifco Industries, Inc.; *U.S. Public*, pg. 1471
SUMMIT CORPORATION OF AMERICA; *U.S. Private*, pg. 1050
TANNER PLATING DIV.—Ampco-Pittsburgh Corporation; *U.S. Public*, pg. 104
TORCAD LIMITED—Stelco Inc.; *Int'l*, pg. 1299
VACUUM METALIZING DIV.—Crown Cork & Seal Company, Inc.; *U.S. Public*, pg. 463
WALBRIDGE COATINGS, INC.—Inland Steel Industries, Inc.; *U.S. Public*, pg. 879

3479 — COATING, ENGRAVING & ALLIED SERVICES, NEC

AFFIVAL INC.—Viag AG; *Int'l*, pg. 1465
AFFIVAL S.A.—Viag AG; *Int'l*, pg. 1466
AG AJIKAWA CORPORATION; *Int'l*, pg. 39
ALLIANCE AMERICA; *U.S. Private*, pg. 37
ALUMINUM COMPANY OF AMERICA; *U.S. Public*, pg. 60
AMERCOAT MEXICANA S.A. DE C.V.—Ameron International Corporation; *U.S. Public*, pg. 99
AMERON B.V., PROTECTIVE COATINGS DIVISION-EUROPE—Ameron International Corporation; *U.S. Public*, pg. 99
AMSTED INDUSTRIES INCORPORATED; *U.S. Private*, pg. 68
ANDAL CORP.; *U.S. Public*, pg. 111
APPLIED COATINGS—Bel-Art Products; *U.S. Private*, pg. 130
ARIZONA GALVANIZING INC.—Aztec Manufacturing Co.; *U.S. Public*, pg. 159
ARVIN INDUSTRIES, INC.; *U.S. Public*, pg. 136
AZTEC INDUSTRIES, INC.—Aztec Manufacturing Co.; *U.S. Public*, pg. 159
AZTEC MANUFACTURING CO.; *U.S. Public*, pg. 159
BASF LACKE & FARBEN VERTRIEBSGESELLSCHAFT MBH—BASF AG; *Int'l*, pg. 106
BUFA BAEUERLE GMBH & CO.—Viag AG; *Int'l*, pg. 1464
BAYCOAT—DoFasco, Inc.; *Int'l*, pg. 414
BOYLES GALVANIZING CO.—Kinark Corporation; *U.S. Public*, pg. 960
BREDERO-SHAW—Dresser Industries, Inc.; *U.S. Public*, pg. 529
BRINER PAINT MANUFACTURING CO., INC.—RPM, Inc.; *U.S. Public*, pg. 1358
CALIFORNIA MANUFACTURING ENTERPRISES; *U.S. Private*, pg. 201
CARBOLINE CO.—RPM, Inc.; *U.S. Public*, pg. 1357
CINCINNATI THERMAL SPRAY, INC.; *U.S. Private*, pg. 240
CINCINNATI THERMAL SPRAY SOUTH—Cincinnati Thermal Spray, Inc.; *U.S. Private*, pg. 240
CONSOLIDATED SYSTEMS, INC.; *U.S. Private*, pg. 266
CORRO-COAT U.A.E. LTD.—Jotun A/S; *Int'l*, pg. 715
COURT GALVANIZING LIMITED—Jannock Limited; *Int'l*, pg. 698
CROWLEY GALVANIZING DIV.—Aztec Manufacturing Co.; *U.S. Public*, pg. 159
THE CROWN GROUP, INC.; *U.S. Private*, pg. 292
DNN GALVANIZING CORPORATION—DoFasco, Inc.; *Int'l*, pg. 414
DNN GALVANIZING CORPORATION—NKK Corporation; *Int'l*, pg. 903
DAUBERT INDUSTRIES, INC.; *U.S. Private*, pg. 313
DIMOND INDUSTRIES—Fletcher Challenge Limited; *Int'l*, pg. 495
DINOL GMBH—Novartis AG; *Int'l*, pg. 982
DU PONT PROTEIN TECHNOLOGIES INTERNATIONAL—Du Pont (E.I. Du Pont De Nemours & Co.); *U.S. Public*, pg. 531
DUNMORE CORPORATION; *U.S. Private*, pg. 346
DUNMORE CORPORATION/BREWSTER—Dunmore Corporation; *U.S. Private*, pg. 347
ESM II, INC.—Viag AG; *Int'l*, pg. 1465
EASTERN ENGRAVING—Standex International Corporation; *U.S. Public*, pg. 1506
ENCOAT-NORTH ARLINGTON, INC.—Lukens Inc.; *U.S. Public*, pg. 1020
EWALD GLEBEL LUXEMBOURG G.M.B.H.—Arbed S.A.; *Int'l*, pg. 79
L.B. FOSTER COMPANY-BIRMINGHAM PLANT—L.B. Foster Company; *U.S. Public*, pg. 676
L.B. FOSTER COMPANY-DORAVILLE YARD/COATED PIPE—L.B. Foster Company; *U.S. Public*, pg. 676
L.B. FOSTER COMPANY-NEWPORT PLANT—L.B. Foster Company; *U.S. Public*, pg. 676
H.B. FULLER COATINGS LTD.—H.B. Fuller Company; *U.S. Public*, pg. 686
GALVALANGE S.A.R.L.—Arbed S.A.; *Int'l*, pg. 79
GALVANO DIVISION—The Ivaco Group; *Int'l*, pg. 696
GENERAL MAGNAPLATE CALIFORNIA—General Magnaplate Corporation; *U.S. Public*, pg. 717
GENERAL MAGNAPLATE CANADA—General Magnaplate Corporation; *U.S. Public*, pg. 717
GENERAL MAGNAPLATE CORPORATION; *U.S. Public*, pg. 717
GENERAL MAGNAPLATE TEXAS—General Magnaplate Corporation; *U.S. Public*, pg. 717
GENERAL MAGNAPLATE WISCONSIN—General Magnaplate Corporation; *U.S. Public*, pg. 717
GROW GROUP, INC.—Imperial Chemical Industries PLC; *Int'l*, pg. 663
GULF COAST GALVANIZING INC.—Aztec Manufacturing Co.; *U.S. Public*, pg. 159
HOUSTON GALVANIZING DIV.—Aztec Manufacturing Co.; *U.S. Public*, pg. 159
HUMBERSIDE HOLDINGS LTD—Powell Duffryn PLC; *Int'l*, pg. 1065
HYUNDAI HEAVY INDUSTRIES CO., LTD.—Hyundai Motor Company; *Int'l*, pg. 641
HYUNDAI MOTOR COMPANY; *Int'l*, pg. 641
ICO, INC.; *U.S. Public*, pg. 853
INDUSTRIA NAVARRIA DEL ALUMINIO, S.A.—Reynolds Metals Company; *U.S. Public*, pg. 1387
INDUSTRIAL POWDER COATINGS, INC.—Intermet Corporation; *U.S. Public*, pg. 894
INDUSTRIAS DEL LACADO, S.A. (INDULACSA)—Reynolds Metals Company; *U.S. Public*, pg. 1387
ISOTECH G.M.B.H.—Novartis AG; *Int'l*, pg. 983
JANNOCK LIMITED; *Int'l*, pg. 698
JINBANG STEEL CO., LTD.—Ssangyong Business Group; *Int'l*, pg. 1291
KINARK CORPORATION; *U.S. Public*, pg. 960
KOP-COAT—RPM, Inc.; *U.S. Public*, pg. 1357
KRONOS EUROPE, INC.—Contran Corporation; *U.S. Private*, pg. 271
LEBLANC COMMUNICATIONS, INC.; *U.S. Private*, pg. 656
MMI PRODUCTS, INC.; *U.S. Private*, pg. 687
MATEC CORPORATION; *U.S. Public*, pg. 1056
MATERIAL SCIENCES CORPORATION; *U.S. Public*, pg. 1056
METFOILS AB—Perstorp AB; *Int'l*, pg. 1039
MOLD-TECH—Standex International Corporation; *U.S. Public*, pg. 1506
MOLD-TECH PORTUGAL—Standex International Corporation; *U.S. Public*, pg. 1507
MOLD-TECH S.A.—Standex International Corporation; *U.S. Public*, pg. 1507
MOLD-TECH S.A.R.L.—Standex International Corporation; *U.S. Public*, pg. 1507

MORTON AUTOMOTIVE COATINGS—Morton International Inc.; *U.S. Public*, pg. 1135
MORTON CHEMICAL POWDER COATINGS—Morton International Inc.; *U.S. Public*, pg. 1135
MULTI-ARC INC.—Saurer AG; *Int'l*, pg. 1198
MULTI-ARC (U.K.) LTD.—Saurer AG; *Int'l*, pg. 1198
NATIONAL FORGE COMPANY; *U.S. Private*, pg. 783
NESTAWAY—AXIA Incorporated; *U.S. Private*, pg. 103
NICHOLS ALUMINUM—Quanex Corporation; *U.S. Public*, pg. 1350
NORTHLAND ALUMINUM PRODUCTS, INC.; *U.S. Private*, pg. 805
PERSTORP DO BRASIL INDUSTRIA E COMERCIO LTDA.-DIV. CHEMITEC—Perstorp AB; *Int'l*, pg. 1037
PERSTORP VERTRIEBS AG—Perstorp AB; *Int'l*, pg. 1039
PILLAR ENGINEERING LTD.—Caradon Plc; *Int'l*, pg. 267
PLASMA TECHNOLOGY, INC.; *U.S. Private*, pg. 870
POLY COATING PLANT—Georgia-Pacific Corporation; *U.S. Public*, pg. 737
PRE FINISH METALS (EG) INC.—Bethlehem Steel Corporation; *U.S. Public*, pg. 226
PRE FINISH METALS (EG) INC.—Inland Steel Industries, Inc.; *U.S. Public*, pg. 879
PRE FINISH METALS INCORPORATED—Material Sciences Corporation; *U.S. Public*, pg. 1056
RAWAL ENGRAVERS—Standex International Corporation; *U.S. Public*, pg. 1506
REEVES SOUTHEASTERN CORPORATION; *U.S. Private*, pg. 916
REYNOLDS ALUMINIUM FRANCE—Reynolds Metals Company; *U.S. Public*, pg. 1387
ROEHLEN ENGRAVING—Standex International Corporation; *U.S. Public*, pg. 1506
ROEHLEN INDUSTRIES PTY. LTD. MOLD-TECH DIV.—Standex International Corporation; *U.S. Public*, pg. 1507
ROLL COATER, INC.—Arvin Industries, Inc.; *U.S. Public*, pg. 137
ROLLED ALLOYS/ATEK METALS DIVISION—Rolled Alloys, Inc.; *U.S. Private*, pg. 941
SKW ALLOYS, INC.—Viag AG; *Int'l*, pg. 1465
SKW CANADA INC.—Viag AG; *Int'l*, pg. 1466
SKW FRANCE S.A.—Viag AG; *Int'l*, pg. 1466
SKW METALS U.K. LTD., MOLYPRESS DIVISION—Viag AG; *Int'l*, pg. 1465
SKW STICKSTOFFWERKE PIESTERITZ GMBH—Viag AG; *Int'l*, pg. 1464
SENTRY POLYMERS, INC.—RPM, Inc.; *U.S. Public*, pg. 1357
SERMATECH INTERNATIONAL, INC.—Teleflex Incorporated; *U.S. Public*, pg. 1569
SERMATECH KLOCK—Teleflex Incorporated; *U.S. Public*, pg. 1570
SERMATECH MIDDLE ATLANTIC—Teleflex Incorporated; *U.S. Public*, pg. 1570
SERMATECH SOUTHWEST—Teleflex Incorporated; *U.S. Public*, pg. 1570
SERMATECH WEST, AIRFOIL MANAGEMENT CO.—Teleflex Incorporated; *U.S. Public*, pg. 1570
SICO INC.; *Int'l*, pg. 1239
SIKA CORPORATION—Sika Finanz AG; *Int'l*, pg. 1249
SIOUXLAND GALVANIZING CORP.—Leblanc Communications, Inc.; *U.S. Private*, pg. 656
A.O. SMITH CORPORATION; *U.S. Public*, pg. 1476
SOREVCO INC.—DoFasco, Inc.; *Int'l*, pg. 414
STANDEX INTERNATIONAL GMBH, MOLD-TECH I NORTH (GERMANY)—Standex International Corporation; *U.S. Public*, pg. 1507
STANDEX INTERNATIONAL GMBH, MOLD-TECH SOUTH—Standex International Corporation; *U.S. Public*, pg. 1507
STANDEX INTERNATIONAL LIMITED—Standex International Corporation; *U.S. Public*, pg. 1507
STANDEX INTERNATIONAL S.A.—Standex International Corporation; *U.S. Public*, pg. 1507
STOLLBERG GMBH—Viag AG; *Int'l*, pg. 1465
STOLLBERG INC.—Viag AG; *Int'l*, pg. 1465
SULZER PLASMA TECHNIK, INC.—Sulzer Ltd.; *Int'l*, pg. 1307
SURFACE TECHNOLOGY BUSINESS—Engelhard Corporation; *U.S. Public*, pg. 582
TELEFLEX INCORPORATED; *U.S. Public*, pg. 1569
TRANSCOAT INC.—Transco Inc.; *U.S. Private*, pg. 1097
VALVOLINE (AUSTRALIA) PTY. LTD.—Ashland, Inc.; *U.S. Public*, pg. 140
VERNICOLOR A.G.—The Dexter Corporation; *U.S. Public*, pg. 505
WHX CORPORATION; *U.S. Public*, pg. 1726
WITT COMPANY; *U.S. Private*, pg. 1185
WOLF RANGE CO.—Premark International, Inc.; *U.S. Public*, pg. 1322
YLA, INC.—Perstorp AB; *Int'l*, pg. 1037
THE ZIPPERTUBING CO.; *U.S. Private*, pg. 1207

3482 — SMALL ARMS AMMUNITION

ADEC INTERNATIONAL AUTOMATION CORP.; *U.S. Private*, pg. 17
BLOUNT, INC.—Blount International, Inc.; *U.S. Public*, pg. 238
BLOUNT, INC. SPORTING EQUIPMENT GROUP—Blount International, Inc.; *U.S. Public*, pg. 238
BLOUNT INTERNATIONAL, INC.; *U.S. Public*, pg. 237
BRITISH AEROSPACE P.L.C.; *Int'l*, pg. 217
FEDERAL CARTRIDGE CO.—Blount International, Inc.; *U.S. Public*, pg. 239
HORNADY MANUFACTURING COMPANY; *U.S. Private*, pg. 539
ICI FRANCE SA—Imperial Chemical Industries PLC; *Int'l*, pg. 665
LYMAN PRODUCTS CORPORATION; *U.S. Private*, pg. 683
MEDICO INDUSTRIES, INC.; *U.S. Private*, pg. 728
OERLIKON-CONTRAVES PYROTEC AG—Oerlikon-Buhrle Holding AG; *Int'l*, pg. 998
OLIN AUSTRALIA LIMITED—Olin Corporation; *U.S. Public*, pg. 1220
OLIN CORPORATION; *U.S. Public*, pg. 1218
ORBEA ARGENTINA SOCIEDAD ANONIMA—Imperial Chemical Industries PLC; *Int'l*, pg. 665
PRIMEX TECHNOLOGIES, INC.; *U.S. Public*, pg. 1329
UNITED INDUSTRIAL CORPORATION; *U.S. Public*, pg. 1679
ZENECA AB—Zeneca Group Plc; *Int'l*, pg. 1526
ZENECA HELLAS S.A.—Zeneca Group Plc; *Int'l*, pg. 1526
ZENECA OY—Zeneca Group Plc; *Int'l*, pg. 1527
ZENECA POLAND SP. Z.O.O.—Zeneca Group Plc; *Int'l*, pg. 1527
ZENECA ZIMBABWE (PRIVATE) LIMITED—Zeneca Group Plc; *Int'l*, pg. 1527

3483 — AMMUNITION, EXCEPT SMALL ARMS, NEC

ACCUDYNE CORPORATION—Alliant Techsystems; *U.S. Public*, pg. 47
R.P. ADAMS COMPANY, INC.; *U.S. Public*, pg. 19
ADEC INTERNATIONAL AUTOMATION CORP.; *U.S. Private*, pg. 17
ALLIANT TECHSYSTEMS; *U.S. Public*, pg. 47
ALLIANT TECHSYSTEMS-MAGNA—Alliant Techsystems; *U.S. Public*, pg. 47
ALLIED RESEARCH CORPORATION; *U.S. Public*, pg. 48
BEI DEFENSE SYSTEMS COMPANY—BEI Technologies, Inc.; *U.S. Public*, pg. 160
BRITISH AEROSPACE P.L.C.; *Int'l*, pg. 217
DAY & ZIMMERMANN KANSAS DIVISION—Day & Zimmermann, Inc.; *U.S. Private*, pg. 317
EG & G, INC.; *U.S. Public*, pg. 542
EG & G MOUND APPLIED TECHNOLOGIES—EG & G, Inc.; *U.S. Public*, pg. 543
GENCORP INC.; *U.S. Public*, pg. 705
IMI PLC; *Int'l*, pg. 646
KILGORE OPERATIONS—Alliant Techsystems; *U.S. Public*, pg. 47
MECAR S.A.—Allied Research Corporation; *U.S. Public*, pg. 49
MASON & HANGER CORPORATION, INC.; *U.S. Private*, pg. 711
MASON & HANGER CORPORATION, INC.—Mason & Hanger Corporation, Inc.; *U.S. Private*, pg. 711
NATIONAL DEFENSE CORP.—National Presto Industries, Inc.; *U.S. Public*, pg. 1159
NORTHROP GRUMMAN CORPORATION; *U.S. Public*, pg. 1197
OLIN CORPORATION; *U.S. Public*, pg. 1218
PRIMEX TECHNOLOGIES, INC.; *U.S. Public*, pg. 1329
RAYMOND ENGINEERING—Kaman Corporation; *U.S. Public*, pg. 942
SAAB MISSILES AB—Investor AB; *Int'l*, pg. 686
SPECIAL DEVICES, INCORPORATED; *U.S. Public*, pg. 1496
THIOKOL CORPORATION; *U.S. Public*, pg. 1596
THOMSON-TRT DEFENSE—Thomson S.A.; *Int'l*, pg. 1383

3484 — SMALL ARMS

ADEC INTERNATIONAL AUTOMATION CORP.; *U.S. Private*, pg. 17
ALLIED RESEARCH CORPORATION; *U.S. Public*, pg. 48
BRITISH AEROSPACE P.L.C.; *Int'l*, pg. 217
CELSIUS AB; *Int'l*, pg. 276
THE COLEMAN COMPANY, INC.—MacAndrews & Forbes Holdings Inc.; *U.S. Private*, pg. 690
CROSMAN AIRGUNS—Crosman Corp.; *U.S. Private*, pg. 291
FN HERSTAL S.A.—Herstal S.A.; *Int'l*, pg. 617
HECKLER & KOCH GMBH—British Aerospace p.l.c.; *Int'l*, pg. 217
HERSTAL S.A.; *Int'l*, pg. 617
O.F. MOSSBERG & SONS, INC.; *U.S. Private*, pg. 764
PINE TREE CASTINGS DIV.—Sturm, Ruger & Co., Inc.; *U.S. Public*, pg. 1526
REMINGTON ARMS COMPANY, INC.; *U.S. Private*, pg. 921
RUGER INVESTMENT CASTINGS—Sturm, Ruger & Co., Inc.; *U.S. Public*, pg. 1526
SIG SCHWEIZERSICHE INDUSTRIE-GESELLSCHAFT HOLDING AG; *Int'l*, pg. 1156
SISTO ARMATUREN S.A.—KSB Aktiengesellschaft; *Int'l*, pg. 721
SAVAGE ARMS INC.; *U.S. Private*, pg. 968
SMITH & WESSON CORP.—Tomkins PLC; *Int'l*, pg. 1397
STURM, RUGER & CO., INC.; *U.S. Public*, pg. 1526
U.S. REPEATING ARMS COMPANY; *U.S. Private*, pg. 1125
WEATHERBY, INC.; *U.S. Private*, pg. 1155

3489 — ORDNANCE & ACCESSORIES, NEC

ACTION MANUFACTURING CO.; *U.S. Private*, pg. 15
AEROSONIC CORPORATION; *U.S. Public*, pg. 25
ALLIED CHUCKER & ENGINEERING COMPANY; *U.S. Private*, pg. 38
ALLIED RESEARCH CORPORATION; *U.S. Public*, pg. 48
ARMTEC DEFENSE PRODUCTS CO.—Esterline Technologies Corporation; *U.S. Public*, pg. 594
BARNES & REINECKE, INC.—Allied Research Corporation; *U.S. Public*, pg. 49
P. BERETTA S.P.A.; *Int'l*, pg. 187
BERETTA U.S.A. CORP.—P. Beretta S.P.A.; *Int'l*, pg. 188
BOFORS AB—Celsius AB; *Int'l*, pg. 276
BRITISH AEROSPACE P.L.C.; *Int'l*, pg. 217
CHAMBERLAIN MANUFACTURING CORP.—Duchossois Industries, Inc.; *U.S. Private*, pg. 344
DEMPSTER EQUIPMENT—Toccoa Metal Technologies, Inc.; *U.S. Private*, pg. 1089
DUCHOSSOIS INDUSTRIES, INC.; *U.S. Private*, pg. 344
EG & G MOUND APPLIED TECHNOLOGIES—EG & G, Inc.; *U.S. Public*, pg. 543
FMC CORPORATION; *U.S. Public*, pg. 604
HARVARD INDUSTRIES, INC.; *U.S. Public*, pg. 796
HARVARD INTERIORS MANUFACTURING CO.—Harvard Industries, Inc.; *U.S. Public*, pg. 796
HECKLER & KOCH GMBH—British Aerospace p.l.c.; *Int'l*, pg. 217
HI-SHEAR INDUSTRIES INC.; *U.S. Public*, pg. 824
HISPANO-SUIZA S.A.—SNECMA - Societe Nationale d'Etude et de Construction de Moteurs d'Aviation; *Int'l*, pg. 1165
KDI PRECISION PRODUCTS, INC.; *U.S. Private*, pg. 603
MECAR S.A.—Allied Research Corporation; *U.S. Public*, pg. 49
NASCO INTERNATIONAL, INC.—Geneve Corporation; *U.S. Private*, pg. 446
OERLIKON-CONTRAVES AG—Oerlikon-Buhrle Holding AG; *Int'l*, pg. 998
OLIN CORPORATION; *U.S. Public*, pg. 1218
PRIMEX TECHNOLOGIES, INC.; *U.S. Public*, pg. 1329
QUANTIC INDUSTRIES, INC.; *U.S. Private*, pg. 899
SNECMA - SOCIETE NATIONALE D'ETUDE ET DE CONSTRUCTION DE MOTEURS D'AVIATION; *Int'l*, pg. 1165
SULZER METCO (WESTBURY) INC.—Sulzer Ltd.; *Int'l*, pg. 1307
THOMSON-TRT DEFENSE—Thomson S.A.; *Int'l*, pg. 1383
ULTRA ELECTRONICS COMMAND & CONTROL SYSTEMS—Ultra Electronics Holdings plc; *Int'l*, pg. 1431
WESTERN DESIGN CORPORATION—Howden Group Plc; *Int'l*, pg. 636

3491 — INDUSTRIAL VALVES

AKO ARMATUREN - VERTRIEKS GMBH—Axel Johnson AB; *Int'l*, pg. 710
AMOT CONTROLS CORPORATION—Roper Industries, Inc.; *U.S. Public*, pg. 1405
ANDERSON, GREENWOOD & CO.—Tyco International Ltd.; *U.S. Public*, pg. 1650
ANSALDO COMPONENTI SRL—IRI Istituto Ricostruzione Industriale; *Int'l*, pg. 653
BABCOCK SEMPELL AG—Deutsche Babcock AG; *Int'l*, pg. 399
BARKSDALE, INC.—Crane Co.; *U.S. Public*, pg. 457
BORSIG KUGELHAHN GMBH—Deutsche Babcock AG; *Int'l*, pg. 400
CASHCO, INC.; *U.S. Private*, pg. 218
CENTER LINE—Crane Co.; *U.S. Public*, pg. 457
CHARLES WINN (VALVES) LIMITED—Tyco International Ltd.; *U.S. Public*, pg. 1651
COLTEC HOLDINGS INC; *U.S. Public*, pg. 401
COPES-VULCAN INC.; *U.S. Private*, pg. 274
CRANE LIMITED U.K.—Crane Co.; *U.S. Public*, pg. 458
CRANE VALVES/NORTH AMERICAN—Crane Co.; *U.S. Public*, pg. 457
DENGYOSHA MACHINE WORKS CORPORATION—Toshiba Corporation; *Int'l*, pg. 1402
DEZURIK INTERNATIONAL LTD.—General Signal Corporation; *U.S. Public*, pg. 727
DRESSER INDUSTRIES, INC.; *U.S. Public*, pg. 528
DURCO B.V.—Flowserve Corporation; *U.S. Public*, pg. 659
S.A. DURCO EUROPE N.V.—Flowserve Corporation; *U.S. Public*, pg. 659
DURCO EUROPE S.R.L.—Flowserve Corporation; *U.S. Public*, pg. 659
DURCO-VALTEK (ASIA PACIFIC) PTE. LTD.—Flowserve Corporation; *U.S. Public*, pg. 659
EG & G WRIGHT COMPONENTS—EG & G, Inc.; *U.S. Public*, pg. 542
EAGLE VALVE CO., INC.—Watts Industries, Inc.; *U.S. Public*, pg. 1746
ECLIPSE COMBUSTION—Eclipse Inc.; *U.S. Private*, pg. 361
ECLIPSE INC.; *U.S. Private*, pg. 360
ERIE MANUFACTURING CO.—Siebe plc; *Int'l*, pg. 1241
FMC-CROSBY VALVE, INC.—FMC Corporation; *U.S. Public*, pg. 605
FIKE CORPORATION; *U.S. Private*, pg. 404
FLOWSEAL—Crane Co.; *U.S. Public*, pg. 457
FLOWSERVE CORPORATION, VALVE DIV.—Flowserve Corporation; *U.S. Public*, pg. 658
FRANCE COMPRESSOR PRODUCTS DIVISION—Coltec Holdings Inc; *U.S. Public*, pg. 402
GENERAL SIGNAL CORPORATION; *U.S. Public*, pg. 726
GROVE VALVE & REGULATOR COMPANY; *U.S. Private*, pg. 484
HALE OIL FIELD PRODUCTS CO.—Watts Industries, Inc.; *U.S. Public*, pg. 1746
HARLEY VALVE & INSTRUMENT CO.—Innovative Valve Technology, Inc.; *U.S. Public*, pg. 880
HAYS FLUID CONTROLS-DIVISION OF ROMAC INDUSTRIES—Romac Industries, Inc.; *U.S. Private*, pg. 942
HONEYWELL INC.; *U.S. Public*, pg. 833
J.M. HUBER CORPORATION; *U.S. Private*, pg. 544
HUNT VALVE; *U.S. Private*, pg. 549
ITT FLUID HANDLING—ITT Industries, Inc.; *U.S. Public*, pg. 860
JAMES JONES COMPANY—Tyco International Ltd.; *U.S. Public*, pg. 1650
KF INDUSTRIES—Watts Industries, Inc.; *U.S. Public*, pg. 1746
KENNEDY VALVE—McWane, Inc.; *U.S. Private*, pg. 725
KOLTEX, INC.—Tetra Laval Group; *Int'l*, pg. 1378
KVAERNER EUREKA, MOSS DIVISION—Kvaerner a.s.a.; *Int'l*, pg. 767

KVAERNER MASA-YARDS INC., PIIKKIO WORKS—Kvaerner a.s.a.; Int'l, pg. 771
KVAERNER ROSENBERG A.S.—Kvaerner a.s.a.; Int'l, pg. 769
LESLIE CONTROLS, INC.—Watts Industries, Inc.; U.S. Public, pg. 1746
LUKENHEIMER ENERGO VALVES INC.; U.S. Private, pg. 680
MAROTTA SCIENTIFIC CONTROLS, INC.; U.S. Private, pg. 706
MILTON INDUSTRIES, INC.; U.S. Private, pg. 749
MOGAS INDUSTRIES, INC.; U.S. Private, pg. 755
MUELLER CO.—Tyco International Ltd.; U.S. Public, pg. 1650
NAEGELEN S.A.—Emerson Electric Co.; U.S. Public, pg. 574
NICHOLSON STEAM TRAP—Watts Industries, Inc.; U.S. Public, pg. 1747
NUOVO PIGNONE S.P.A.; Int'l, pg. 990
PACIFIC VALVES—Crane Co.; U.S. Public, pg. 457
PARKER HANNIFIN RAK S.A.—Parker Hannifin Corporation; U.S. Public, pg. 1261
PUROFLOW INCORPORATED; U.S. Public, pg. 1345
RAUMA LTD.—UPM-Kymmene Corporation; Int'l, pg. 1428
RICHARDS INDUSTRIES, INC.; U.S. Private, pg. 929
ROCKWELL INTERNATIONAL CORPORATION; U.S. Public, pg. 1397
SENIOR NEW ZEALAND LIMITED—Senior Engineering Group, plc.; Int'l, pg. 1223
SERCK AUDCO VALVES—BTR plc; Int'l, pg. 125
SHERWOOD—Harsco Corporation; U.S. Public, pg. 793
SMITH FLOW CONTROL LIMITED—Halma p.l.c.; Int'l, pg. 590
SPENCE ENGINEERING CO.—Watts Industries, Inc.; U.S. Public, pg. 1747
SULZER (JAPAN) LTD.—Sulzer Ltd.; Int'l, pg. 1306
SUNTEC INDUSTRIES INC.; U.S. Private, pg. 1054
TARAS VALVE COMPANY, INC.—Watts Industries, Inc.; U.S. Public, pg. 1747
TELEDYNE FLUID SYSTEMS—Allegheny Teledyne Incorporated; U.S. Public, pg. 43
TRI-CLOVER INC.—Tetra Laval Group; Int'l, pg. 1379
TUFLIN AG—Emerson Electric Co.; U.S. Public, pg. 578
UNITED STATES PIPE & FOUNDRY COMPANY, INC.—Walter Industries, Inc.; U.S. Public, pg. 1736
VALTEK/AUSTRALIA—Flowserve Corporation; U.S. Public, pg. 659
VALTEK CONTROLS, LTD.—Flowserve Corporation; U.S. Public, pg. 659
VALTEK INTERNATIONAL—Flowserve Corporation; U.S. Public, pg. 658
VALTEK NEW ZEALAND, LTD.—Flowserve Corporation; U.S. Public, pg. 659
THE WALWORTH COMPANY USA; U.S. Private, pg. 1149
WATTS AUTOMATIC CONTROL VALVES, INC.—Watts Industries, Inc.; U.S. Public, pg. 1747
WATTS INDUSTRIES, INC.; U.S. Public, pg. 1746
WATTS REGULATOR/WATTS ACV—Watts Industries, Inc.; U.S. Public, pg. 1746
WORCESTER CONTROLS (UK) LTD.—BTR plc; Int'l, pg. 125
XOMOX CORP.—Emerson Electric Co.; U.S. Public, pg. 574
XOMOX K.K.—Emerson Electric Co.; U.S. Public, pg. 578
XOMOX S.A. DE C.V.—Emerson Electric Co.; U.S. Public, pg. 578
XOMOX U.K. LIMITED—Emerson Electric Co.; U.S. Public, pg. 578
YOKOGAWA-KITZ-VALTEK CORP. (Y-K-V)—Flowserve Corporation; U.S. Public, pg. 659

3492 — FLUID POWER VALVES & HOSE FITTINGS

AKO ARMATUREN - VERTRIEKS GMBH—Axel Johnson AB; Int'l, pg. 710
ACUTEX DIVISION—SPX Corporation; U.S. Public, pg. 1421
AEROQUIP DIVISION, VICKERS SYSTEMS PTY. LTD.—Aeroquip-Vickers, Inc.; U.S. Public, pg. 25
AEROQUIP MEXICANA S.A. DE C.V.—Aeroquip-Vickers, Inc.; U.S. Public, pg. 25
AEROQUIP-VICKERS, INC.; U.S. Public, pg. 24
ALEXANDER DOLL COMPANY, INC.; U.S. Private, pg. 33
ALLIEDSIGNAL INC.; U.S. Public, pg. 49
AMERICAN ELECTRONICS, INC.—AEI Holding Co., Inc.; U.S. Private, pg. 5
AMOT CONTROLS CORPORATION—Roper Industries, Inc.; U.S. Public, pg. 1405
ANDERSON, GREENWOOD & CO.—Tyco International Ltd.; U.S. Public, pg. 1650
APPLIED POWER INC.; U.S. Public, pg. 124
ARO CORPORATION S.A.R.L.—Ingersoll-Rand Company; U.S. Public, pg. 877
ARO FLUID PRODUCTS DIVISION—Ingersoll-Rand Company; U.S. Public, pg. 877
ARO GMBH—Ingersoll-Rand Company; U.S. Public, pg. 877
ASCOLECTRIC LIMITED—Emerson Electric Co.; U.S. Public, pg. 575
AUTOMOTIVE DISTRIBUTION SALES DIV.—Dana Corporation; U.S. Public, pg. 479
BABCOCK & WILCOX CO.—McDermott International, Inc.; U.S. Public, pg. 1068
ROBERT BOSCH CORPORATION—Robert Bosch GmbH; Int'l, pg. 204
BUNNELL PLASTICS DIVISION—Furon Company; U.S. Public, pg. 689
CGF INDUSTRIES; U.S. Private, pg. 194
COMMERCIAL HYDRAULICS KONTAK LTD.—Commercial Intertech Corp.; U.S. Public, pg. 411
COMMERCIAL INTERTECH CORP.; U.S. Public, pg. 411
COMPOFLEX—Senior Engineering Group, plc.; Int'l, pg. 1221
DANFOSS FLUID POWER—Danfoss A/S; Int'l, pg. 377
DEKORON/UNITHERM DIVISION—Furon Company; U.S. Public, pg. 689
DELTA POWER CO.; U.S. Private, pg. 322
DENGYOSHA MACHINE WORKS CORPORATION—Toshiba Corporation; Int'l, pg. 1402
DOWTY AEROSPACE YAKIMA—TI Group plc; Int'l, pg. 1337
DRIVETRAIN SERVICE DIV.—Dana Corporation; U.S. Public, pg. 479
DURHAM TUBE—Senior Engineering Group, plc.; Int'l, pg. 1221
DYNACRAFT—Paccar Inc.; U.S. Public, pg. 1246
EG & G AEROSPACE & ENGINEERED PRODUCTS—EG & G, Inc.; U.S. Public, pg. 542
EG & G SEALOL ENGINEERED PRODUCTS DIVISION—EG & G, Inc.; U.S. Public, pg. 542
EG & G SEALOL-INDUSTRIAL DIVISION—EG & G, Inc.; U.S. Public, pg. 543
EG & G WRIGHT COMPONENTS—EG & G, Inc.; U.S. Public, pg. 542
EATON INTERNATIONAL CORP.—Eaton Corporation; U.S. Public, pg. 558
FASCO CONTROLS CORPORATION—BTR plc; Int'l, pg. 125
FIKE CORPORATION; U.S. Private, pg. 404
FLUID CONNECTORS GROUP—Parker Hannifin Corporation; U.S. Public, pg. 1260
FLUID PRODUCT SALES DIV.—Dana Corporation; U.S. Public, pg. 479
FREMONT MFG.—The Oilgear Company; U.S. Public, pg. 1215
GENERAL VALVE—Parker Hannifin Corporation; U.S. Public, pg. 1262
GRINNELL CORPORATION—Tyco International Ltd.; U.S. Public, pg. 1651
GRISWOLD INDUSTRIES, INC.; U.S. Private, pg. 482
HANSEN COUPLING DIVISION—Tuthill Corporation; U.S. Private, pg. 1110
HONEYWELL INC.; U.S. Public, pg. 833
HOSE PRODUCTS DIV. PLANT—Parker Hannifin Corporation; U.S. Public, pg. 1260
HUMPHREY PRODUCTS COMPANY; U.S. Private, pg. 547
HYDRAULICS GROUP—Parker Hannifin Corporation; U.S. Public, pg. 1261
INDUSTRIAS TRATERH, S.A.—Senior Engineering Group, plc.; Int'l, pg. 1222
INGERSOLL-RAND COMPANY; U.S. Public, pg. 876
INSTRUMENTATION CONNECTORS DIV.—Parker Hannifin Corporation; U.S. Public, pg. 1261
INSTRUMENTATION GROUP—Parker Hannifin Corporation; U.S. Public, pg. 1261
INSTRUMENTATION VALVE DIVISION—Parker Hannifin Corporation; U.S. Public, pg. 1261
INTEGRAL HYDRAULIK & CO.; Int'l, pg. 679
INTEGRAL TECHNOLOGIE GMBH—Integral Hydraulik & Co.; Int'l, pg. 679
KEYSTONE INTERNATIONAL, INC.—Tyco International Ltd.; U.S. Public, pg. 1650
LESLIE CONTROLS, INC.—Watts Industries, Inc.; U.S. Public, pg. 1746
LUKENHEIMER ENERGO VALVES INC.; U.S. Private, pg. 680
MANNESMANN REXROTH GMBH—Mannesmann A.G.; Int'l, pg. 838
NEW HAVEN MFG. CORP.; U.S. Private, pg. 793
OILDYNE—Commercial Intertech Corp.; U.S. Public, pg. 411
THE OILGEAR COMPANY; U.S. Public, pg. 1215
OILGEAR GMBH—The Oilgear Company; U.S. Public, pg. 1215
OILGEAR MEXICANA S.A.—The Oilgear Company; U.S. Public, pg. 1215
OILGEAR/TOWLER AUSTRALIA PTY. LTD.—The Oilgear Company; U.S. Public, pg. 1215
OILGEAR TOWLER LTD.—The Oilgear Company; U.S. Public, pg. 1215
OILGEAR TOWLER LTD. (BEDFORD)—The Oilgear Company; U.S. Public, pg. 1215
OILGEAR TOWLER (LYON)—The Oilgear Company; U.S. Public, pg. 1215
OILGEAR TOWLER SA—The Oilgear Company; U.S. Public, pg. 1215
PARKER FLUID VERBINDUNGSTELLE GMBH—Parker Hannifin Corporation; U.S. Public, pg. 1260
PARKER HANNIFIN A/S—Parker Hannifin Corporation; U.S. Public, pg. 1263
PARTEK OPERATION—Parker Hannifin Corporation; U.S. Public, pg. 1262
PHOENIX STEEL TUBE—Senior Engineering Group, plc.; Int'l, pg. 1221
PNEUTRONICS DIV.—Parker Hannifin Corporation; U.S. Public, pg. 1262
POLYFLEX BUSINESS UNIT—Parker Hannifin Corporation; U.S. Public, pg. 1260
POWER-PACKER U.S.—Applied Power Inc.; U.S. Public, pg. 124
POWERFLEX—Senior Engineering Group, plc.; Int'l, pg. 1221
PRECISION DRAWN TUBE—Senior Engineering Group, plc.; Int'l, pg. 1222
PUROFLOW INCORPORATED; U.S. Public, pg. 1345
SPX CORPORATION; U.S. Public, pg. 1420
SALEM PRODUCTS—The Oilgear Company; U.S. Public, pg. 1215
SAUER SUNDSTRAND GMBH & CO.; Int'l, pg. 1198
SAUNDERS VALVE CO. LTD.—Tetra Laval Group; Int'l, pg. 1379
SENIOR BIGWOOD LIMITED—Senior Engineering Group, plc.; Int'l, pg. 1220
SENIOR CONFLOW—Senior Engineering Group, plc.; Int'l, pg. 1220
SENIOR CONFLOW INC.—Senior Engineering Group, plc.; Int'l, pg. 1222
SENIOR CONTROL ENGINEERING LIMITED—Senior Engineering Group, plc.; Int'l, pg. 1220
SENIOR DAVIS DERBY—Senior Engineering Group, plc.; Int'l, pg. 1220
SENIOR ENGINEERING PRODUCTS BUSINESS AREA—Senior Engineering Group, plc.; Int'l, pg. 1220
SENIOR ENGINEERING TIFT GMBH—Senior Engineering Group, plc.; Int'l, pg. 1223
SENIOR ENTEX—Senior Engineering Group, plc.; Int'l, pg. 1220
SENIOR FOSTER WHEELER CONSTRUCTION DIVISION—Senior Engineering Group, plc.; Int'l, pg. 1221
SENIOR FOSTER WHEELER INDUSTRIAL BOILER DIVISION—Senior Engineering Group, plc.; Int'l, pg. 1221
SENIOR FOSTER WHEELER POWER DIVISION—Senior Engineering Group, plc.; Int'l, pg. 1221
SENIOR GREEN ECONOMISER DIVISION—Senior Engineering Group, plc.; Int'l, pg. 1221
SENIOR HEAT TREATMENT LIMITED—Senior Engineering Group, plc.; Int'l, pg. 1221
SENIOR LUKE MATERIALS HANDLING DIVISION—Senior Engineering Group, plc.; Int'l, pg. 1221
SENIOR TIFT B.V.—Senior Engineering Group, plc.; Int'l, pg. 1223
SENIOR TIFT, INC.—Senior Engineering Group, plc.; Int'l, pg. 1222
SENIOR TIFT LIMITED—Senior Engineering Group, plc.; Int'l, pg. 1221
SENIOR TIFT PTE. LTD.—Senior Engineering Group, plc.; Int'l, pg. 1223
SENIOR TUBE LIMITED—Senior Engineering Group, plc.; Int'l, pg. 1221
SERCK AUDCO VALVES—BTR plc; Int'l, pg. 125
SKINNER VALVE DIVISION—Parker Hannifin Corporation; U.S. Public, pg. 1260
STRATOFLEX AEROSPACE/MILITARY CONNECTORS DIV.—Parker Hannifin Corporation; U.S. Public, pg. 1260
SWAGELOK COMPANY; U.S. Private, pg. 1057
SYNFLEX DIVISION—Furon Company; U.S. Public, pg. 689
TP MANIPULATIONS—Senior Engineering Group, plc.; Int'l, pg. 1222
TECNORD @ DELTA POWER CO.—Delta Power Co.; U.S. Private, pg. 322
TELEFLEX FLUID SYSTEMS INC.—Teleflex Incorporated; U.S. Public, pg. 1569
TOWLER PRODUCTS—The Oilgear Company; U.S. Public, pg. 1215
TRINOVA DO BRAZIL S.A.-DIVISAO AEROQUIP—Aeroquip-Vickers, Inc.; U.S. Public, pg. 25
TRINOVA GMBH—Aeroquip-Vickers, Inc.; U.S. Public, pg. 25
TRINOVA LIMITED AEROQUIP AUTOMOTIVE OPERATIONS—Aeroquip-Vickers, Inc.; U.S. Public, pg. 25
TUBE PRODUCTS—Senior Engineering Group, plc.; Int'l, pg. 1222
TUTHILL CORPORATION; U.S. Private, pg. 1110
UNITED FLEXIBLE—Senior Engineering Group, plc.; Int'l, pg. 1221
VALCOR ENGINEERING CORP.; U.S. Private, pg. 1131
VICKERS, INCORPORATED—Aeroquip-Vickers, Inc.; U.S. Public, pg. 24
VICKERS INDUSTRIAL—Aeroquip-Vickers, Inc.; U.S. Public, pg. 24
VICKERS MODULAR—Aeroquip-Vickers, Inc.; U.S. Public, pg. 25
VICKERS STERER ENGINEERING—Aeroquip-Vickers, Inc.; U.S. Public, pg. 25
THE WALWORTH COMPANY USA; U.S. Private, pg. 1149
WATEROUS COMPANY—American Cast Iron Pipe Co.; U.S. Private, pg. 52
WICOR, INC.; U.S. Public, pg. 1767
YOKOHAMA AEROQUIP KK—The Yokohama Rubber Co., Ltd.; Int'l, pg. 1521

3493 — STEEL SPRINGS, EXCEPT WIRE

ALLIANT TECHSYSTEMS-MAGNA—Alliant Techsystems; U.S. Public, pg. 47
AMERICAN STEEL FOUNDRIES—Amsted Industries Incorporated; U.S. Private, pg. 68
AMETEK, INC.; U.S. Public, pg. 99
AMSTED INDUSTRIES INCORPORATED; U.S. Private, pg. 68
BAUMANN FEDERN AG; Int'l, pg. 171
BAUMANN GMBH—Baumann Federn AG; Int'l, pg. 171
BAUMANN MUELLES, S.A.—Baumann Federn AG; Int'l, pg. 171
BAUMANN SPRING CO. (S) PTE. LTD.—Baumann Federn AG; Int'l, pg. 171
BAUMANN SPRINGS & PRESSINGS (UK) LTD.—Baumann Federn AG; Int'l, pg. 171
CMT DYNAMICS—Caparo Group Ltd.; Int'l, pg. 265
COMPANIA NHK CIMEBRA-COMERCIAL INDUSTRIAL E MECANICA BRASILEIRA—Nissho Iwai Corporation; Int'l, pg. 947
CORPORACION INDUSTRIAL SANLUIS; Int'l, pg. 332
DUDEK & BOCK SPRING MANUFACTURING COMPANY; U.S. Private, pg. 344
HARBOUR GROUP LTD.; U.S. Private, pg. 500
HOESCH HOHENLIMBURG GMBH—Fried. Krupp AG; Int'l, pg. 508
LEE SPRING CO., LTD.—The Unimax Corporation; U.S. Private, pg. 1118
THE MARMON GROUP, INC.; U.S. Private, pg. 706
MATTHEW WARREN INC.—Harbour Group Ltd.; U.S. Private, pg. 500
MERITOR AUTOMOTIVE, INC.; U.S. Public, pg. 1096
PETERSON AMERICAN CORP.; U.S. Private, pg. 857

ROCKWELL HEAVY VEHICLE SUSPENSION SYSTEMS COMPANY, INC.—Meritor Automotive, Inc.; *U.S. Public*, pg. 1096
SANDVIK STEEL CO.—Sandvik AB; *Int'l*, pg. 1185
SMALL PARTS, INC.; *U.S. Private*, pg. 1006
SPICER TRAILER PRODUCTS DIV.—Dana Corporation; *U.S. Public*, pg. 479
STEMCO TRUCK PRODUCTS DIVISION—Coltec Holdings Inc; *U.S. Public*, pg. 402
UNIMAX CORP.—Shepaug Corporation; *U.S. Private*, pg. 993
THE UNIMAX CORPORATION; *U.S. Private*, pg. 1118
JONAS WOODHEAD LIMITED—Carclo Engineering Group plc; *Int'l*, pg. 268

3494 — VALVES & PIPE FITTINGS, NEC

AMRI INC.—KSB Aktiengesellschaft; *Int'l*, pg. 721
AMRI NEDERLAND B.V.—KSB Aktiengesellschaft; *Int'l*, pg. 721
AMRI PTE. LTD.—KSB Aktiengesellschaft; *Int'l*, pg. 721
APL CORPORATION; *U.S. Private*, pg. 7
A.Y.M. INC.—A.Y. McDonald Industries, Inc.; *U.S. Private*, pg. 721
AERCO INTERNATIONAL INC.; *U.S. Private*, pg. 23
AEROQUIP-VICKERS, INC.; *U.S. Public*, pg. 24
AGUADOR S.A.—KSB Aktiengesellschaft; *Int'l*, pg. 721
AMCAST INDUSTRIAL CORPORATION; *U.S. Public*, pg. 63
AMERICAN CAST IRON PIPE CO.; *U.S. Private*, pg. 51
AMERICAN STANDARD INC.; *U.S. Public*, pg. 91
AMERICAN VALVE & HYDRANT CO.—American Cast Iron Pipe Co.; *U.S. Private*, pg. 52
AMOT CONTROLS CORPORATION—Roper Industries, Inc.; *U.S. Public*, pg. 1405
AMTROL INC.—The Cypress Group LLC; *U.S. Private*, pg. 300
ANDERSON, GREENWOOD & CO.—Tyco International Ltd.; *U.S. Public*, pg. 1650
ANGAR SCIENTIFIC CO., INC.—Emerson Electric Co.; *U.S. Public*, pg. 574
APEX GALVANIZING CORP.—Victaulic Company of America; *U.S. Private*, pg. 1138
AQUAMINE, LLC—Victaulic Company of America; *U.S. Private*, pg. 1138
ARMSTRONG INTERNATIONAL, INC.; *U.S. Private*, pg. 83
ARMSTRONG INTERNATIONAL, S.A.—Armstrong International, Inc.; *U.S. Private*, pg. 83
ARMSTRONG-YOSHITAKE, INC.—Armstrong International, Inc.; *U.S. Private*, pg. 83
ATWOOD & MORRILL CO., INC.—Weir Group PLC; *Int'l*, pg. 1489
AUTOMATIC MACHINE PRODUCTS COMPANY; *U.S. Private*, pg. 101
AUTOMOTIVE DISTRIBUTION SALES DIV.—Dana Corporation; *U.S. Public*, pg. 479
BABCOCK SEMPELL AG—Deutsche Babcock AG; *Int'l*, pg. 399
BADGER METER EUROPE GMBH—Badger Meter, Inc.; *U.S. Public*, pg. 165
BADGER METER, INC.; *U.S. Public*, pg. 164
BADGER METER INDUSTRIAL DIV.—Badger Meter, Inc.; *U.S. Public*, pg. 165
BAUMANN FEDERN AG; *Int'l*, pg. 171
BECK MANUFACTURING, INC.—Bitrek Corporation; *U.S. Private*, pg. 146
BETTIS CANADA LIMITED—Daniel Industries, Inc.; *U.S. Public*, pg. 483
BETTIS CORPORATION—Daniel Industries, Inc.; *U.S. Public*, pg. 482
BETTIS FRANCE—Daniel Industries, Inc.; *U.S. Public*, pg. 483
BETTIS UK LIMITED—Daniel Industries, Inc.; *U.S. Public*, pg. 483
BONNEY FORGE CORPORATION; *U.S. Private*, pg. 156
BORSIG KUGELHAHN GMBH—Deutsche Babcock AG; *Int'l*, pg. 400
ROBERT BOSCH FLUID POWER CORPORATION—Robert Bosch GmbH; *Int'l*, pg. 204
BOSTON WEATHERHEAD DIV.—Dana Corporation; *U.S. Public*, pg. 479
BRIDGEPORT FITTINGS, INC.; *U.S. Private*, pg. 168
BYRON VALVE FACILITY—Parker Hannifin Corporation; *U.S. Public*, pg. 1260
CMT ENGINEERING LTD.—Caparo Group Ltd.; *Int'l*, pg. 265
CAMERON; *U.S. Public*, pg. 298
CAPARO GROUP LTD.; *Int'l*, pg. 264
CAPARO INDUSTRIES PLC—Caparo Group Ltd.; *Int'l*, pg. 264
CAPITOL MANUFACTURING CO.—Harsco Corporation; *U.S. Public*, pg. 793
CASHCO, INC.; *U.S. Private*, pg. 218
CENTER LINE—Crane Co.; *U.S. Public*, pg. 457
CLEVITE DE MEXICO—Tenneco Inc.; *U.S. Public*, pg. 1577
CLOW VALVE DIV.—McWane, Inc.; *U.S. Private*, pg. 725
COLTEC HOLDINGS INC; *U.S. Public*, pg. 401
COMMERCIAL HYDRAULICS KEELAVITE, LTD.—Commercial Intertech Corp.; *U.S. Public*, pg. 411
COMMERCIAL HYDRAULICS PTY. LTD.—Commercial Intertech Corp.; *U.S. Public*, pg. 411
COMMERCIAL INTERTECH DO BRASIL LTDA.—Commercial Intertech Corp.; *U.S. Public*, pg. 411
COMMERCIAL INTERTECH LTD.—Commercial Intertech Corp.; *U.S. Public*, pg. 411
COMMERCIAL INTERTECH S.A.—Commercial Intertech Corp.; *U.S. Public*, pg. 411
CONBRACO INDUSTRIES-APOLLO DIVISION—Conbraco Industries Inc.; *U.S. Private*, pg. 261
CONBRACO INDUSTRIES INC.; *U.S. Private*, pg. 261
CONTINENTAL INDUSTRIES INC.—Handy & Harman; *U.S. Public*, pg. 780
CONTINENTAL MACHINES, INC.; *U.S. Private*, pg. 268
CONTROL COMPONENTS, INC.—IMI Plc; *Int'l*, pg. 646
COOK MANLEY—Dover Corporation; *U.S. Public*, pg. 521
CRANE AUSTRALIA PTY. LTD.—Crane Co.; *U.S. Public*, pg. 457
CRANE CANADA INC.—Crane Co.; *U.S. Public*, pg. 457
CRANE CO.; *U.S. Public*, pg. 456
CRANE LIMITED U.K.—Crane Co.; *U.S. Public*, pg. 458
CRANE RESISTOFLEX/INDUSTRIAL—Crane Co.; *U.S. Public*, pg. 457
CRANE VALVES/NORTH AMERICAN—Crane Co.; *U.S. Public*, pg. 457
CURTISS-WRIGHT CORP.; *U.S. Public*, pg. 469
DANIEL INDUSTRIES, INC.; *U.S. Public*, pg. 482
DANIEL VALVE COMPANY—Daniel Industries, Inc.; *U.S. Public*, pg. 483
DAVIES SHEPHARD PTY. LTD.—ABB Asea Brown Boveri (Holding) Ltd.; *Int'l*, pg. 2
DOVER DIVERSIFIED—Dover Corporation; *U.S. Public*, pg. 521
DRESSER INDUSTRIES, INC.; *U.S. Public*, pg. 528
DRESSER OIL TOOLS—Dresser Industries, Inc.; *U.S. Public*, pg. 528
DUFF-NORTON—Columbus McKinnon Corp.; *U.S. Public*, pg. 406
EG & G SEALOL EAGLE—EG & G, Inc.; *U.S. Public*, pg. 544
EG & G SEALOL ENGINEERED PRODUCTS DIVISION—EG & G, Inc.; *U.S. Public*, pg. 542
EG & G SEALOL-INDUSTRIAL DIVISION—EG & G, Inc.; *U.S. Public*, pg. 543
EG & G WRIGHT COMPONENTS—EG & G, Inc.; *U.S. Public*, pg. 542
EIS GROUP PLC; *Int'l*, pg. 426
EAGLE INDUSTRIES, INC.—Great American Management & Investment, Inc.; *U.S. Private*, pg. 473
EATON CORPORATION, DEFENSE VALVE AND ACTUATOR DIVISION—Eaton Corporation; *U.S. Public*, pg. 556
ELKHART PRODUCTS CORP.-PLUMBING DIVISION—Amcast Industrial Corporation; *U.S. Public*, pg. 63
EMCO LIMITED; *Int'l*, pg. 452
ENGINEER CONTROL INTL.; *U.S. Private*, pg. 376
EVERLASTING VALVE CO.—Armstrong International, Inc.; *U.S. Private*, pg. 83
EXPANSION VALVE DIVISION—Parker Hannifin Corporation; *U.S. Public*, pg. 1260
FIKE CORPORATION; *U.S. Private*, pg. 404
FIRE PROTECTION INDUSTRIES, INC.—Compagnie Generale Des Eaux; *Int'l*, pg. 321
FISHER CONTROLS INTERNATIONAL, INC.—Emerson Electric Co.; *U.S. Public*, pg. 573
FLAGG BRASS—Amcast Industrial Corporation; *U.S. Public*, pg. 63
FLOW CONTROL EQUIPMENT—Robbins & Myers, Inc.; *U.S. Public*, pg. 1393
FLUID CONNECTORS GROUP—Parker Hannifin Corporation; *U.S. Public*, pg. 1260
FLUID CONTROL DIVISION—FMC Corporation; *U.S. Public*, pg. 605
FORD METER BOX COMPANY; *U.S. Private*, pg. 418
FRANCE COMPRESSOR PRODUCTS DIVISION—Coltec Holdings Inc; *U.S. Public*, pg. 402
GALVESTON-HOUSTON COMPANY; *U.S. Private*, pg. 438
GESTRA GMBH; *Int'l*, pg. 549
GESTRA S.A.—GESTRA GmbH; *Int'l*, pg. 550
GESTRA (U.K.) LTD.—GESTRA GmbH; *Int'l*, pg. 550
GLYNWED PIPE SYSTEMS—Glynwed International PLC; *Int'l*, pg. 554
GRISWOLD INDUSTRIES, INC.; *U.S. Private*, pg. 482
GROUPE STRAFOR FACOM; *Int'l*, pg. 569
HARPER-WYMAN CO.—Oak Industries Inc.; *U.S. Public*, pg. 1209
HARSCO CORPORATION; *U.S. Public*, pg. 792
HAWS DRINKING FAUCET CO.; *U.S. Private*, pg. 512
HAYS FLUID CONTROLS-DIVISION OF ROMAC INDUSTRIES—Romac Industries, Inc.; *U.S. Private*, pg. 942
HAYWARD INDUSTRIAL PRODUCTS-STRAINER DIV.—Hayward Industries, Inc.; *U.S. Private*, pg. 513
HAYWARD INDUSTRIES, INC.; *U.S. Private*, pg. 513
HIGHFIELD MANUFACTURING CO.—BTR plc; *Int'l*, pg. 127
HOLSTEIN AND KAPPERT GMBH—Klockner-Werke AG; *Int'l*, pg. 737
HYDRAULIC VALVE DIV.—Commercial Intertech Corp.; *U.S. Public*, pg. 411
HYDRAULIC VALVE DIV.—Parker Hannifin Corporation; *U.S. Public*, pg. 1261
HYDRAULICS GROUP—Parker Hannifin Corporation; *U.S. Public*, pg. 1261
HYDRIL COMPANY; *U.S. Private*, pg. 551
HYDRO-STACK PRODUCTS—The Oilgear Company; *U.S. Public*, pg. 1215
HYUNDAI PRECISION & INDUSTRY CO., LTD.—Hyundai Motor Company; *Int'l*, pg. 642
IMI CASH VALVE, INC.—IMI Plc; *Int'l*, pg. 646
ITT FLUID HANDLING—ITT Industries, Inc.; *U.S. Public*, pg. 860
ITT HOFFMAN—ITT Industries, Inc.; *U.S. Public*, pg. 860
IDEAL FORGING CORPORATION; *U.S. Private*, pg. 557
IDEAL-STANDARD WABCO IND. E COM. LTDA—American Standard Inc.; *U.S. Public*, pg. 92
INSTRUMENTATION CONNECTORS DIV.—Parker Hannifin Corporation; *U.S. Public*, pg. 1261
INSTRUMENTATION VALVE DIVISION—Parker Hannifin Corporation; *U.S. Public*, pg. 1261
JOHNSON CONTROLS, INC.; *U.S. Public*, pg. 932
THE JOHNSON CORPORATION; *U.S. Private*, pg. 591
JOSAM COMPANY; *U.S. Private*, pg. 600
KSB AJAX PUMPS PTY. LTD.—KSB Aktiengesellschaft; *Int'l*, pg. 721
KSB AKTIENGESELLSCHAFT; *Int'l*, pg. 721
KSB A/S, RODOVRE—KSB Aktiengesellschaft; *Int'l*, pg. 721
N.V. KSB BELGIUM S.A.—KSB Aktiengesellschaft; *Int'l*, pg. 721
KSB BOMBAS E VALVULAS S.A.—KSB Aktiengesellschaft; *Int'l*, pg. 721
KSB BOMBAS HIDRAULICAS S.A.—KSB Aktiengesellschaft; *Int'l*, pg. 721
KSB ITALIA S.P.A.—KSB Aktiengesellschaft; *Int'l*, pg. 721
KSB LIMITED—KSB Aktiengesellschaft; *Int'l*, pg. 721
KSB LTD.—KSB Aktiengesellschaft; *Int'l*, pg. 721
KSB MEXICANA S.A. DE C.V.—KSB Aktiengesellschaft; *Int'l*, pg. 721
KSB MORCK AB—KSB Aktiengesellschaft; *Int'l*, pg. 721
KSB NEDERLANDER B.V.—KSB Aktiengesellschaft; *Int'l*, pg. 721
KSB OSTERREICH GES.MBH—KSB Aktiengesellschaft; *Int'l*, pg. 721
KSB POMPA—KSB Aktiengesellschaft; *Int'l*, pg. 721
KSB PUMPS ASIA PACIFIC PTE. LTD.—KSB Aktiengesellschaft; *Int'l*, pg. 721
KSB PUMPS CO. LTD.—KSB Aktiengesellschaft; *Int'l*, pg. 721
KSB PUMPS, INC.—KSB Aktiengesellschaft; *Int'l*, pg. 721
KSB PUMPS LIMITED, PUNE (BOMBAY)—KSB Aktiengesellschaft; *Int'l*, pg. 721
KSB PUMPY + ARMATURY SPOL. SR.O.—KSB Aktiengesellschaft; *Int'l*, pg. 721
KSB SZIVATTYU ES ARMATURA KFT.—KSB Aktiengesellschaft; *Int'l*, pg. 721
KSB TESMA AG—KSB Aktiengesellschaft; *Int'l*, pg. 721
KSB VENEZOLANA C.A.—KSB Aktiengesellschaft; *Int'l*, pg. 721
KSB ZURICH AG—KSB Aktiengesellschaft; *Int'l*, pg. 721
KEENEY MANUFACTURING CO.; *U.S. Private*, pg. 611
KENNEDY VALVE—McWane, Inc.; *U.S. Private*, pg. 725
KENT-TIEGHI S.P.A.—ABB Asea Brown Boveri (Holding) Ltd.; *Int'l*, pg. 3
KEYSTONE (CANADA) LTD.—Tyco International Ltd.; *U.S. Public*, pg. 1650
KEYSTONE DO BRASIL LTDA.—Tyco International Ltd.; *U.S. Public*, pg. 1650
KEYSTONE INTERNATIONAL, INC.—Tyco International Ltd.; *U.S. Public*, pg. 1650
KEYSTONE PACIFIC PTY. LTD.—Tyco International Ltd.; *U.S. Public*, pg. 1650
KEYSTONE SOUTHEAST ASIA PTY. LTD.—Tyco International Ltd.; *U.S. Public*, pg. 1650
KEYSTONE VALVE (EUROPA) B.V.—Tyco International Ltd.; *U.S. Public*, pg. 1650
KEYSTONE VALVE (KOREA) LTD.—Tyco International Ltd.; *U.S. Public*, pg. 1650
KEYSTONE VALVE (U.K.) LTD.—Tyco International Ltd.; *U.S. Public*, pg. 1650
KEYSTONE VALVES AND CONTROLS, INC.—Tyco International Ltd.; *U.S. Public*, pg. 1650
KOLTEK OY—Tetra Laval Group; *Int'l*, pg. 1379
THE MARMON GROUP, INC.; *U.S. Private*, pg. 706
MAROTTA SCIENTIFIC CONTROLS, INC.; *U.S. Private*, pg. 706
MARSH BELLOFRAM CORP.; *U.S. Private*, pg. 707
MARUBENI CORPORATION; *Int'l*, pg. 844
MASONEILAN NORTH AMERICAN OPERATIONS—Dresser Industries, Inc.; *U.S. Public*, pg. 528
MAXON CORPORATION; *U.S. Private*, pg. 716
N.V. MAXON INTERNATIONAL S.A.—Maxon Corporation; *U.S. Private*, pg. 717
A.Y. MCDONALD INDUSTRIES, INC.; *U.S. Private*, pg. 721
A.Y. MCDONALD MFG. CO.—A.Y. McDonald Industries, Inc.; *U.S. Private*, pg. 721
MCWANE CAST IRON PIPE CO.—McWane, Inc.; *U.S. Private*, pg. 725
GEORGE MELLER LTD.—Axel Johnson AB; *Int'l*, pg. 712
METALLGESELLSCHAFT AG; *Int'l*, pg. 860
MORRIS COUPLING CO.; *U.S. Private*, pg. 762
MUELLER STEAM SPECIALTY—United Dominion Industries, Ltd.; *U.S. Public*, pg. 1676
MURRAY TUBE—Senior Engineering Group, plc.; *Int'l*, pg. 1222
NELES-JAMESBURY CORP.—UPM-Kymmene Corporation; *Int'l*, pg. 1428
NIBCO, INC.; *U.S. Private*, pg. 798
NIPPON KEYSTONE CORPORATION—Tyco International Ltd.; *U.S. Public*, pg. 1650
NORGREN CO.—IMI Plc; *Int'l*, pg. 647
THE NORTH AMERICAN MANUFACTURING CO.; *U.S. Private*, pg. 803
OPW FUELING COMPONENTS—Dover Corporation; *U.S. Public*, pg. 521
OCEANEERING A/S—Oceaneering International, Inc.; *U.S. Public*, pg. 1211
OCEANEERING AUSTRALIA PTY. LTD.—Brambles Industries Limited; *Int'l*, pg. 211
OCEANEERING AUSTRALIA PTY. LTD.—Oceaneering International, Inc.; *U.S. Public*, pg. 1211
OCEANEERING PRODUCTION SYSTEMS—Oceaneering International, Inc.; *U.S. Public*, pg. 1211
ORBIT VALVE INTERNATIONAL, INC.; *U.S. Private*, pg. 819
PACIFIC VALVES—Crane Co.; *U.S. Public*, pg. 457
PARKER ENZED NEW ZEALAND PTY. LTD.—Parker Hannifin Corporation; *U.S. Public*, pg. 1261
PARKER ERMETO GMBH—Parker Hannifin Corporation; *U.S. Public*, pg. 1261
PARKER HANNIFIN CORPORATION; *U.S. Public*, pg. 1259
PARKER HANNIFIN CORPORATION—Parker Hannifin Corporation; *U.S. Public*, pg. 1263
PARKER HANNIFIN GMBH—Parker Hannifin Corporation; *U.S. Public*, pg. 1261
PARTEK OPERATION—Parker Hannifin Corporation; *U.S. Public*, pg. 1262
PATHWAY BELLOWS, INC.—Dover Corporation; *U.S. Public*, pg. 521
PEGLER-HATTERSLEY PLC—Tomkins PLC; *Int'l*, pg. 1395

PERRIN GMBH—Zimmermann & Jansen GmbH; *Int'l*, pg. 1528
PHILMAC PTY LIMITED—Glynwed International PLC; *Int'l*, pg. 555
PLEXCO/SPIROLITE—Chevron Corporation; *U.S. Public*, pg. 348
PNEUTRONICS DIV.—Parker Hannifin Corporation; *U.S. Public*, pg. 1262
PONT-A-MOUSSON SA—Saint-Gobain; *Int'l*, pg. 1176
THE WM. POWELL COMPANY; *U.S. Private*, pg. 877
HENRY PRATT CO.—Tyco International Ltd.; *U.S. Public*, pg. 1651
QUALITY CONTROL CORPORATION; *U.S. Private*, pg. 898
RP & C—Conbraco Industries Inc.; *U.S. Private*, pg. 261
RICHARDS INDUSTRIES, INC.; *U.S. Private*, pg. 929
ROBERT JAMES SALES INC.; *U.S. Private*, pg. 935
ROMAC INDUSTRIES, INC.; *U.S. Private*, pg. 942
SAINT-GOBAIN; *Int'l*, pg. 1170
SCHLUMBERGER INDUSTRIES—Schlumberger Limited; *U.S. Public*, pg. 1439
THE SHANE GROUP INC.; *U.S. Private*, pg. 989
THE SIAM PIPE INDUSTRY CO., LTD.—The Siam Cement Public Company Limited; *Int'l*, pg. 1238
SMITH METERS LTD.—Hanson PLC; *Int'l*, pg. 593
SMITH VALVE CORPORATION—Tyco International Ltd.; *U.S. Public*, pg. 1651
SNAP-TITE, INC.; *U.S. Private*, pg. 1010
SOLUS OCEANEERING (MALAYSIA) SDN. BHD.—Oceaneering International, Inc.; *U.S. Public*, pg. 1211
THE STARFLO CORPORATION—The Wm. Powell Company; *U.S. Private*, pg. 877
STERLING, INC.; *U.S. Private*, pg. 1041
STEWARTS & LLOYDS TRADING (PTY) LIMITED—Dorbyl Limited; *Int'l*, pg. 416
STOCKHAM VALVES & FITTINGS, INC.; *U.S. Private*, pg. 1043
STRAHMAN VALVES, INC.; *U.S. Private*, pg. 1046
SUNBEAM CORPORATION; *U.S. Public*, pg. 1533
SUPERIOR VALVE COMPANY—Amcast Industrial Corporation; *U.S. Public*, pg. 63
SWEPCO TUBE CORPORATION; *U.S. Private*, pg. 1058
T & S BRASS & BRONZE WORKS, INC.; *U.S. Private*, pg. 1061
TBV, INC.—Victaulic Company of America; *U.S. Private*, pg. 1138
TACTAIR FLUID CONTROLS CORP.—Young & Franklin, Inc.; *U.S. Private*, pg. 1196
TARGET ROCK CORP.—Curtiss-Wright Corp.; *U.S. Public*, pg. 470
TEDDINGTON CONTROLS LIMITED—SLD Holdings Ltd.; *Int'l*, pg. 1160
TEXAS METAL WORKS, INC.; *U.S. Private*, pg. 1078
TOKHEIM CORPORATION; *U.S. Public*, pg. 1620
TOTTORI SANYO ELECTRIC CO., LTD.—Sanyo Electric Co., Ltd.; *Int'l*, pg. 1191
TRANSLOGIC CORP.—Thyssen AG; *Int'l*, pg. 1387
TULSA MANUFACTURING PLANT—T.D. Williamson, Inc.; *U.S. Private*, pg. 1180
VALVULAS KEYSTONE DE MEXICO, S.A. DE C.V.—Tyco International Ltd.; *U.S. Public*, pg. 1650
VALVULES BARBARA S.A.—Saint-Gobain; *Int'l*, pg. 1176
VESTER CORPORATION—Arrowhead Holding Corporation; *U.S. Private*, pg. 86
VESUVIUS U.S.A.—Cookson Group plc; *Int'l*, pg. 329
VICTAULIC COMPANY OF AMERICA; *U.S. Private*, pg. 1138
VICTAULIC COMPANY OF CANADA LIMITED—Victaulic Company of America; *U.S. Private*, pg. 1138
VICTAULIC TOOL COMPANY—Victaulic Company of America; *U.S. Private*, pg. 1138
HENRY VOGT MACHINE CO.; *U.S. Private*, pg. 1143
THE WALWORTH COMPANY USA; *U.S. Private*, pg. 1149
WARD MANUFACTURING, INC.; *U.S. Private*, pg. 1149
WATSCO, INC.; *U.S. Public*, pg. 1745
WATTS INDUSTRIES, INC.; *U.S. Public*, pg. 1746
WATTS REGULATOR CO.—Watts Industries, Inc.; *U.S. Public*, pg. 1747
WEBSTER COMPANY, INC.—Danfoss A/S; *Int'l*, pg. 377
WESTERN ENTERPRISES DIV.—Berkshire Hathaway Inc.; *U.S. Public*, pg. 218
WILKINS-REGULATOR DIV.—Zurn Industries, Inc.; *U.S. Public*, pg. 1794
T.D. WILLIAMSON, INC.; *U.S. Private*, pg. 1179
T.D. WILLIAMSON S.A.—T.D. Williamson, Inc.; *U.S. Private*, pg. 1180
T.D. WILLIAMSON (U.K.) LTD.—T.D. Williamson, Inc.; *U.S. Private*, pg. 1180
WINROCK ENTERPRISES, INC.; *U.S. Private*, pg. 1183
WORCESTER CONTROLS CORP.—BTR plc; *Int'l*, pg. 128
XOMOX K.K.—Emerson Electric Co.; *U.S. Public*, pg. 578
XOMOX S.A. DE C.V.—Emerson Electric Co.; *U.S. Public*, pg. 578
XOMOX U.K. LIMITED—Emerson Electric Co.; *U.S. Public*, pg. 578
YARWAY CORPORATION—Tyco International Ltd.; *U.S. Public*, pg. 1650
YOUNG & FRANKLIN, INC.; *U.S. Private*, pg. 1196
ZIMMERMANN & JANSEN GMBH; *Int'l*, pg. 1528
ZIMMERMANN & JANSEN INC.—Zimmermann & Jansen GmbH; *Int'l*, pg. 1528
ZIMMERMANN & JANSEN S.A. (PTY.) LTD.—Zimmermann & Jansen GmbH; *Int'l*, pg. 1529

3495 — WIRE SPRINGS

ASSOCIATED SPRING—Barnes Group Inc.; *U.S. Public*, pg. 190
ASSOCIATED SPRING-ASIA—Barnes Group Inc.; *U.S. Public*, pg. 190
ASSOCIATED SPRING, LTD.—Barnes Group Inc.; *U.S. Public*, pg. 190
ASSOCIATED SPRING SPEC, LTD.—Barnes Group Inc.; *U.S. Public*, pg. 190
BARNES GROUP INC.; *U.S. Public*, pg. 189
BAUMANN FEDERN AG; *Int'l*, pg. 171
BAUMANN GMBH—Baumann Federn AG; *Int'l*, pg. 171
BAUMANN SPRING CO. (S) PTE. LTD.—Baumann Federn AG; *Int'l*, pg. 171
BAUMANN SPRINGS & PRESSINGS (UK) LTD.—Baumann Federn AG; *Int'l*, pg. 171
BAUMANN SPRINGS USA, INC.—Baumann Federn AG; *Int'l*, pg. 171
CALDWELL MANUFACTURING COMPANY; *U.S. Private*, pg. 200
CONNECTICUT SPRING & STAMPING CORPORATION; *U.S. Private*, pg. 263
EAGLE INDUSTRIES, INC.—Great American Management & Investment, Inc.; *U.S. Private*, pg. 473
EMTEC PRODUCTS CORPORATION—Kuhlman Corporation; *U.S. Public*, pg. 968
FLUID PRODUCT SALES DIV.—Dana Corporation; *U.S. Public*, pg. 479
GENERAL SPRING, INC.; *U.S. Private*, pg. 445
HEATH SPRING COMPANY LTD—Peterson American Corp.; *U.S. Private*, pg. 857
JOHNSON CONTROLS, INC.; *U.S. Public*, pg. 932
JOHNSON CONTROLS, INC.—Johnson Controls, Inc.; *U.S. Public*, pg. 932
LEAR CORPORATION; *U.S. Public*, pg. 981
LEE SPRING COMPANY—The Unimax Corporation; *U.S. Private*, pg. 1118
MATTHEW WARREN INC.—Harbour Group Ltd.; *U.S. Private*, pg. 500
MICHIGAN SPRING COMPANY—Precision Products Corporation; *U.S. Private*, pg. 880
NHK SPRING CO., LTD.; *Int'l*, pg. 901
NO-SAG FOAM PRODUCTS COMPANY—Leggett & Platt, Incorporated; *U.S. Public*, pg. 986
PECK SPRING COMPANY; *U.S. Private*, pg. 846
PETERSON AMERICAN CORP.; *U.S. Private*, pg. 857
PETERSON SPRING-KINGSVILLE PLANT—Peterson American Corp.; *U.S. Private*, pg. 857
PETERSON SPRING-WINDSOR PLANT—Peterson American Corp.; *U.S. Private*, pg. 857
PRECISION PRODUCTS CORPORATION; *U.S. Private*, pg. 879
PRODOTTI BAUMANN SPA—Baumann Federn AG; *Int'l*, pg. 171
RESORTES MECANICOS, S.A.—Barnes Group Inc.; *U.S. Public*, pg. 190
RESORTES Y PRODUCTOS METALICOS-QUERETARO PLANT—Peterson American Corp.; *U.S. Private*, pg. 857
SMALL PARTS, INC.; *U.S. Private*, pg. 1006
SPRING ENGINEERS OF HOUSTON LTD.—SEI Holding Corp.; *U.S. Private*, pg. 956
STEADLY COMPANY—Leggett & Platt, Incorporated; *U.S. Public*, pg. 986
STUMPP & SCHUELE DO BRASIL INDUSTRIA E COMERCIO LIMITADA—Barnes Group Inc.; *U.S. Public*, pg. 190
STYRIA FEDERN GES.M.B.H.—Voest-Alpine Stahl AG; *Int'l*, pg. 1470
TECHNITROL, INC.; *U.S. Public*, pg. 1564
THE TIMMS SPRING COMPANY—Precision Products Corporation; *U.S. Private*, pg. 880
THE TURNER & SEYMOUR MFG. COMPANY; *U.S. Private*, pg. 1109
WEBSTER SPRING CO., INC.—Leggett & Platt, Incorporated; *U.S. Public*, pg. 986

3496 — MISCELLANEOUS FABRICATED WIRE PRODUCTS

ACS INDUSTRIES, INC.; *U.S. Private*, pg. 3
ACS INTERNACIONAL S.A. DE C.V.—ACS Industries, Inc.; *U.S. Private*, pg. 4
ACS MISTERMESH—ACS Industries, Inc.; *U.S. Private*, pg. 4
ACCO BRANDS, INC.—Fortune Brands, Inc.; *U.S. Public*, pg. 674
ACCO WORLD CORPORATION—Fortune Brands, Inc.; *U.S. Public*, pg. 674
AMERICAN MILLIBAR DIV.—Okura & Co.; *Int'l*, pg. 1001
AMHERST METAL PRODUCTS, INC.—Brittany Corporation; *U.S. Private*, pg. 169
ANCHOR WIRE ROPE DIVISION—Okura & Co.; *Int'l*, pg. 1001
APACHE HOSE & BELTING COMPANY, INC.; *U.S. Private*, pg. 76
ARLEN METALS CORPORATION—The Arlen Corporation; *U.S. Public*, pg. 131
AUTOSWAGE PRODUCTS, INC.; *U.S. Private*, pg. 101
AVIS INDUSTRIAL CORPORATION; *U.S. Private*, pg. 102
AXIA INCORPORATED; *U.S. Private*, pg. 103
BICC BRAND-REX—BICC plc; *Int'l*, pg. 120
BAUMANN FEDERN AG; *Int'l*, pg. 171
BAUMANN GMBH—Baumann Federn AG; *Int'l*, pg. 171
BAUMANN SPRING CO. (S) PTE. LTD.—Baumann Federn AG; *Int'l*, pg. 171
BAUMANN SPRINGS & PRESSINGS (UK) LTD.—Baumann Federn AG; *Int'l*, pg. 171
WILLIAM BAYLEY/FOLGER ADAM SECURITY, INC.; *U.S. Private*, pg. 125
BELDEN INC.; *U.S. Public*, pg. 200
BERGEN CABLE TECHNOLOGIES, INC.—Matec Corporation; *U.S. Public*, pg. 1056
BOYE NEEDLE—Wm. E. Wright Limited Partnership; *U.S. Private*, pg. 1192
BRIDGEWATER RESOURCES CORPORATION; *U.S. Private*, pg. 168
BRIDON AMERICAN CORP.—Bridon PLC; *Int'l*, pg. 215
BRIDON PLC; *Int'l*, pg. 215
BRODERICK & BASCOM ROPE CO.—Amsted Industries Incorporated; *U.S. Private*, pg. 68
THE BROKEN HILL PROPRIETARY COMPANY LIMITED; *Int'l*, pg. 223
CCX, INC.; *U.S. Private*, pg. 193
CABLECRAFT INC.—Tuthill Corporation; *U.S. Private*, pg. 1110
CABLELINK, INCORPORATED—Robinson Nugent, Inc.; *U.S. Public*, pg. 1394
CANNON EQUIPMENT—IMI Plc; *Int'l*, pg. 646
CAROL CABLE COMPANY—Wassall Plc; *Int'l*, pg. 1487
CHICAGO RIVET & MACHINE COMPANY; *U.S. Public*, pg. 348
CLEANERS HANGER CO.; *U.S. Private*, pg. 245
SIGMUND COHN CORP.; *U.S. Private*, pg. 250
COLUMBUS MCKINNON CORP.; *U.S. Public*, pg. 405
CONNECTICUT SPRING & STAMPING CORPORATION; *U.S. Private*, pg. 263
CROWN PRODUCTS—Sommer Metalcraft Corporation; *U.S. Private*, pg. 1014
DAVIS WIRE CORP.—Pettibone Corporation; *U.S. Private*, pg. 859
DAYTON SUPERIOR CORPORATION—Ripplewood Holdings L.L.C.; *U.S. Private*, pg. 931
DELTA ENFIELD LTD.—Delta plc; *Int'l*, pg. 390
DOCAP (1985) CORPORATION—The Ivaco Group; *Int'l*, pg. 695
DOMINION SEAL LTD.—BTR plc; *Int'l*, pg. 129
DUDEK & BOCK SPRING MANUFACTURING COMPANY; *U.S. Private*, pg. 344
DURAND INC.—L & D Group; *U.S. Private*, pg. 638
EAGLE BUTTON CO., INC.; *U.S. Private*, pg. 354
EASTERN REGION—MMI Products, Inc.; *U.S. Private*, pg. 687
B. ELLIOTT PLC.; *Int'l*, pg. 448
ENIDINE INCORPORATED; *U.S. Private*, pg. 377
FKI INDUSTRIES. INC.—FKI Plc; *Int'l*, pg. 472
FATA EUROPEAN GROUP S.P.A.—FKI Plc; *Int'l*, pg. 474
FELLOWES MANUFACTURING CO.; *U.S. Private*, pg. 400
FROST WIRE PRODUCTS, LTD.—Stelco Inc.; *Int'l*, pg. 1299
GNWC WIRE, CABLE & NETWORK PRODUCTS—Communications Supply Corporation; *U.S. Private*, pg. 259
GS INDUSTRIES, INC.; *U.S. Private*, pg. 435
A.J. GERRARD AND COMPANY; *U.S. Private*, pg. 449
GILBERT & BENNETT MANUFACTURING COMPANY; *U.S. Private*, pg. 453
GLADDING BRAIDED PRODUCTS LLC—Crowe Rope Industries L.L.C.; *U.S. Private*, pg. 291
GUNNEBO A/S—Gunnebo Industrier AB; *Int'l*, pg. 578
GUNNEBO GMBH—Gunnebo Industrier AB; *Int'l*, pg. 578
GUNNEBO INDUSTRIER AB; *Int'l*, pg. 578
GUNNEBO LTD.—Gunnebo Industrier AB; *Int'l*, pg. 578
HALIFAX RACK & SCREW CUTTING CO., LTD.—B. Elliott plc.; *Int'l*, pg. 448
HANOVER WIRE CLOTH—CCX, Inc.; *U.S. Private*, pg. 193
HARFORD SYSTEMS, INC.—Lab Products, Inc.; *U.S. Private*, pg. 641
HEXCEL (LYON) S.A.—Hexcel Corporation; *U.S. Public*, pg. 824
HORIZON ENTERPRISES GROUP LLC; *U.S. Private*, pg. 539
HORIZON TECHNOLOGY GROUP LLC—Horizon Enterprises Group LLC; *U.S. Private*, pg. 539
HORIZON TECHNOLOGY GROUP - WYANDOTTE DIVISION—Horizon Enterprises Group LLC; *U.S. Private*, pg. 539
HYNES INDUSTRIES INC.; *U.S. Private*, pg. 552
HYSPAN PRECISION PRODUCTS, INC.; *U.S. Private*, pg. 552
HYUNDAI HEAVY INDUSTRIES CO., LTD.—Hyundai Motor Company; *Int'l*, pg. 641
HYUNDAI MOTOR COMPANY; *Int'l*, pg. 641
I.F.C. (FASTENERS) INC.—The Ivaco Group; *Int'l*, pg. 696
INSTEEL INDUSTRIES, INC.; *U.S. Public*, pg. 882
INSTEEL PANEL-MEX S.A. DE C.V.—Insteel Industries, Inc.; *U.S. Public*, pg. 882
INSTEEL WIRE PRODUCTS—Insteel Industries, Inc.; *U.S. Public*, pg. 882
THE IVACO GROUP; *Int'l*, pg. 695
KASPAR WIRE WORKS, INC.; *U.S. Private*, pg. 608
KEYSTONE STEEL & WIRE CO.—Keystone Consolidated Industries, Inc.; *U.S. Public*, pg. 955
KNAPE & VOGT CANADA INC.—Knape & Vogt Mfg. Co.; *U.S. Public*, pg. 963
LAB PRODUCTS, INC.; *U.S. Private*, pg. 641
LACLEDE CHAIN MANUFACTURING COMPANY—Laclede Steel Company; *U.S. Public*, pg. 974
LACLEDE CHAIN MANUFACTURING PLANT—Laclede Steel Company; *U.S. Public*, pg. 974
LAIDLAW CORPORATION; *U.S. Private*, pg. 642
LIFT-ALL CO., INC.; *U.S. Private*, pg. 667
LINDBERG CORPORATION; *U.S. Public*, pg. 999
LOZIER CORPORATION; *U.S. Private*, pg. 679
LUDLOW-SAYLOR INC.—Powerscreen International Plc; *Int'l*, pg. 1066
MMI PRODUCTS, INC.; *U.S. Private*, pg. 687
MATEC CORPORATION; *U.S. Public*, pg. 1056
METAL MANUFACTURES LIMITED—BICC plc; *Int'l*, pg. 120
METEX CORPORATION—United Capital Corp.; *U.S. Public*, pg. 1674
MICRO-MET L CORP.; *U.S. Private*, pg. 742
MIDCON CABLES CO.—Esterline Technologies Corporation; *U.S. Public*, pg. 594
MIDWEST REGION—MMI Products, Inc.; *U.S. Private*, pg. 687
MITSUBISHI CABLE INDUSTRIES, LTD.; *Int'l*, pg. 870
NASHVILLE WIRE PRODUCT CO.; *U.S. Private*, pg. 775
NATIONAL-STANDARD CO.; *U.S. Public*, pg. 1160
NELSEN STEEL & WIRE CO.; *U.S. Private*, pg. 790
NEW YORK WIRE CO.; *U.S. Private*, pg. 795
NEWELL CO.; *U.S. Public*, pg. 1176
NOMA INDUSTRIES LIMITED; *Int'l*, pg. 954
ORBEL CORPORATION; *U.S. Private*, pg. 819

PEERLESS CHAIN COMPANY—Peerless Industrial Group, Inc.; U.S. Public, pg. 1268
PEERLESS INDUSTRIAL GROUP, INC.; U.S. Public, pg. 1268
PETERSON AMERICAN CORP.; U.S. Private, pg. 857
THE PIERCE CO., INC.—Avis Industrial Corporation; U.S. Private, pg. 102
PIKE INDUSTRIES INC.—CRH, plc; Int'l, pg. 242
PORTLAND CHAIN MFG. CO.—Webster Industries Inc.; U.S. Private, pg. 1158
PREFORMED LINE PRODUCTS CANADA—Preformed Line Products; U.S. Public, pg. 1321
PREMIER METAL PRODUCTS CO.; U.S. Private, pg. 881
PRICE BROTHERS CO.; U.S. Private, pg. 883
PRODOTTI BAUMANN SPA—Baumann Federn AG; Int'l, pg. 171
PRYM-DRITZ CORPORATION—William Prym GmbH & Co. KG; Int'l, pg. 1499
RAYCHEM CORPORATION; U.S. Public, pg. 1362
RAYCHEM LTD.—Raychem Corporation; U.S. Public, pg. 1362
RAYCHEM N.V.—Raychem Corporation; U.S. Public, pg. 1362
RAYCHEM TECHNOLOGIAS—Raychem Corporation; U.S. Public, pg. 1363
RENCO GROUP; U.S. Private, pg. 922
ROBINSON NUGENT—Robinson Nugent, Inc.; U.S. Public, pg. 1395
ROCKBESTOS-SUPRENANT CABLE CORP.; U.S. Private, pg. 938
SMC SOUTH—Sommer Metalcraft Corporation; U.S. Private, pg. 1014
SANDVIK PROCESS SYSTEMS LTD.—Sandvik AB; Int'l, pg. 1187
SANDVIK STEEL CO.—Sandvik AB; Int'l, pg. 1185
SENCORP; U.S. Private, pg. 983
SENECA WIRE & MANUFACTURING CO.; U.S. Private, pg. 984
SHERMAN WIRE—Keystone Consolidated Industries, Inc.; U.S. Public, pg. 955
SHERMAN WIRE OF CALDWELL, INC.—Keystone Consolidated Industries, Inc.; U.S. Public, pg. 955
HOWARD SMITH SCREEN CO.—Halliburton Company; U.S. Public, pg. 776
SOMMER METALCRAFT CORPORATION; U.S. Private, pg. 1013
SOUTHWEST REGION—MMI Products, Inc.; U.S. Private, pg. 687
SPEEDRACK PRODUCTS GROUP, LTD.; U.S. Private, pg. 1024
STAENG LIMITED—Bowthorpe plc; Int'l, pg. 207
STANLEY FASTENING SYSTEMS—The Stanley Works; U.S. Public, pg. 1509
STORM PRODUCTS COMPANY, INC.; U.S. Private, pg. 1045
SUPER SAGLESS CORP.—Leggett & Platt, Incorporated; U.S. Public, pg. 986
TETKO, INC.; U.S. Private, pg. 1078
TIPPER TIE, INC.—Dover Corporation; U.S. Public, pg. 520
TITAN STEEL & WIRE CO., LTD.—Kobe Steel, Ltd.; Int'l, pg. 741
E.H. TITCHENER & COMPANY; U.S. Private, pg. 1089
TSUBAKIMOTO CHAIN CO.; Int'l, pg. 1425
TUTHILL CORPORATION; U.S. Private, pg. 1110
TYTON CORPORATION—Bowthorpe plc; Int'l, pg. 208
U.N.A. CORPORATION—Okura & Co.; Int'l, pg. 1001
UNITED CAPITAL CORP.; U.S. Public, pg. 1674
UNITED STEEL & WIRE CO.; U.S. Private, pg. 1126
VOEST-ALPINE AUSTRIA DRAHT GES.M.B.H.—Voest-Alpine Stahl AG; Int'l, pg. 1470
VOEST-ALPINE STAHL DONAWITZ GES.M.B.H.—Voest-Alpine Stahl AG; Int'l, pg. 1470
WEBSTER-PORTALLOY CHAINS, INC.—Webster Industries Inc.; U.S. Private, pg. 1158
WESTERN REGION—MMI Products, Inc.; U.S. Private, pg. 687
WILLIAM PRYM GMBH & CO. KG; Int'l, pg. 1499
WIRE ROPE CORPORATION OF AMERICA, INC.; U.S. Private, pg. 1184
G.F. WRIGHT STEEL & WIRE COMPANY; U.S. Private, pg. 1192
YORK PLANT—Cooper Industries, Inc.; U.S. Public, pg. 444

3497 — METAL FOIL & LEAF

CIRCUIT FOIL JAPAN, LTD.—Arbed S.A.; Int'l, pg. 80
CIRCUIT FOIL LUXEMBOURG S.A.—Arbed S.A.; Int'l, pg. 80
CIRCUIT FOIL USA INC.—Arbed S.A.; Int'l, pg. 80
DRI-PRINT FOILS INC.; U.S. Private, pg. 343
GOMAR MANUFACTURING CO., INC.—AlliedSignal Inc.; U.S. Public, pg. 51
GOULD ELECTRONICS INC.—Thermo Electron Corporation; U.S. Public, pg. 1591
HEXCEL, S.A.—Hexcel Corporation; U.S. Public, pg. 824
INDUSTRIAS GOMARIZ, S.A.—Reynolds Metals Company; U.S. Public, pg. 1387
JOHNSON MATTHEY INC.—Johnson Matthey Public Limited Company; Int'l, pg. 713
MACRISTY INDUSTRIES, INC.; U.S. Private, pg. 693
NYFFELER CORTI AG—Koninklijke Hoogovens N.V.; Int'l, pg. 755
PENNY PLATE, INC.; U.S. Private, pg. 850
RJR NABISCO HOLDINGS CORP.; U.S. Public, pg. 1354
REYNOLDS METALS COMPANY; U.S. Public, pg. 1385
JEFFERSON SMURFIT CORPORATION—Jefferson Smurfit Group p.l.c.; Int'l, pg. 1269
TENNECO PACKAGING—Tenneco Inc.; U.S. Public, pg. 1579
TENNECO SPECIALTY PRODUCTS—Tenneco Inc.; U.S. Public, pg. 1579

3498 — FABRICATED PIPE & FABRICATED PIPE FITTINGS

AC CORPORATION; U.S. Private, pg. 3
AMCAST INDUSTRIAL CORPORATION; U.S. Public, pg. 63
APEX SUPPLY CO., INC.; U.S. Private, pg. 77
ARIZONA GALVANIZING INC.—Aztec Manufacturing Co.; U.S. Public, pg. 159
AZTEC MANUFACTURING CO.; U.S. Public, pg. 159
BENT TUBE, INC.; U.S. Private, pg. 134
BOLIVAR STAMPING LTD.—Delta plc; Int'l, pg. 390
BRISTOL METALS, L.P.—Synalloy Corporation; U.S. Public, pg. 1548
BURNER SYSTEMS INTERNATIONAL, INC.—The Dyson-Kissner-Moran Corporation; U.S. Private, pg. 351
CAPITOL MANUFACTURING CO.—Harsco Corporation; U.S. Public, pg. 793
CERTAINTEED CORPORATION—Saint-Gobain; Int'l, pg. 1170
COFLEXIP S.A.; Int'l, pg. 304
COHART DE MEXICO, S.A. DE C.V.—Waxman Industries, Inc.; U.S. Public, pg. 1749
CONEX-SANBRA LTD.—Delta plc; Int'l, pg. 390
CONSOLIDATED PIPE & SUPPLY COMPANY; U.S. Private, pg. 266
CONTINENTAL INDUSTRIES INC.—Handy & Harman; U.S. Public, pg. 780
CROWLEY TUBING DIV.—Aztec Manufacturing Co.; U.S. Public, pg. 159
ELKHART PRODUCTS CORPORATION-INDUSTRIAL DIVISION—Amcast Industrial Corporation; U.S. Public, pg. 63
FARMERS MARINE COPPER WORKS—Four Winds Investment Corp.; U.S. Private, pg. 422
FERGUSON LYON CONKLIN & COMPANY INC.—Wolseley Plc.; Int'l, pg. 1512
L.B. FOSTER COMPANY; U.S. Public, pg. 675
L.B. FOSTER COMPANY-LANGFIELD YARD—L.B. Foster Company; U.S. Public, pg. 676
L.B. FOSTER COMPANY-PARKERSBURG PLANT—L.B. Foster Company; U.S. Public, pg. 676
GROUPE STRAFOR FACOM; Int'l, pg. 569
GULF COAST GALVANIZING INC.—Aztec Manufacturing Co.; U.S. Public, pg. 159
H & H TUBE & MANUFACTURING CO.; U.S. Private, pg. 489
HMI INDUSTRIES; U.S. Public, pg. 771
HARLAN ELECTRIC CO.—MYR Group Inc.; U.S. Public, pg. 1029
HART ENGINEERING CORPORATION; U.S. Private, pg. 507
HEWLETT PACKARD PRODUCT DIVISION—Hewlett-Packard Company; U.S. Public, pg. 816
INDUSTRIAL CONSTRUCTION, INC.; U.S. Private, pg. 560
K & G OF WISCONSIN, INC.; U.S. Private, pg. 602
KUBOTA CORP.; Int'l, pg. 762
KVAERNER INSTALLASJON, AGOTNES DIVISION—Kvaerner a.s.a.; Int'l, pg. 769
MFRI INC.; U.S. Public, pg. 1026
MACRISTY INDUSTRIES, INC.; U.S. Private, pg. 693
MARQUETTE COPPERSMITHING CO., INC.; U.S. Private, pg. 706
I.C. MOELLER A/S—ABB Asea Brown Boveri (Holding) Ltd.; Int'l, pg. 3
MUELLER INDUSTRIES, INC.; U.S. Public, pg. 1141
NT DOR-OMATIC; U.S. Private, pg. 771
PMC INDUSTRIES INC.; U.S. Private, pg. 827
PIEDMONT MECHANICAL, INC.; U.S. Private, pg. 865
PIPE FABRICATING & SUPPLY COMPANY; U.S. Private, pg. 867
PIPECO SERVICES; U.S. Private, pg. 867
PIPING DESIGN DIV.—Marquette Coppersmithing Co., Inc.; U.S. Private, pg. 706
PNEUMATIC DIV.—Parker Hannifin Corporation; U.S. Public, pg. 1264
POWER PIPING COMPANY—MYR Group Inc.; U.S. Public, pg. 1029
QUACKENBUSH CO. INC.; U.S. Private, pg. 897
SL INDUSTRIES, INC.; U.S. Public, pg. 1418
THE SPENCER TURBINE CO.; U.S. Private, pg. 1025
STANDCO INDUSTRIES, INC.; U.S. Private, pg. 1032
SULZER BINGHAM PUMPS INC.—Sulzer Ltd.; Int'l, pg. 1305
SYNALLOY CORPORATION; U.S. Public, pg. 1547
TUBULAR SERVICES, INC.; U.S. Private, pg. 1108
TYCO INTERNATIONAL LTD.; U.S. Public, pg. 1647
VICKERS INDUSTRIAL—Aeroquip-Vickers, Inc.; U.S. Public, pg. 24
VON ROLL AG DEPARTEMENT ARMATUREN—Von Roll AG; Int'l, pg. 1480

3499 — FABRICATED METAL PRODUCTS, NEC

A&A MANUFACTURING CO.; U.S. Private, pg. 1
A & S TRIBAL INDUSTRIES; U.S. Private, pg. 1
ACI CLOSURES—BTR plc; Int'l, pg. 128
ACI INTERNATIONAL LTD.—BTR plc; Int'l, pg. 128
ACI OPERATIONS PTY. LTD.—BTR plc; Int'l, pg. 128
ABRU ALUMINIUM LIMITED—Hepworth Plc; Int'l, pg. 615
ACME METALS INCORPORATED; U.S. Public, pg. 16
ACME PACKAGING CORPORATION—Acme Metals Incorporated; U.S. Public, pg. 16
ACROMETAL-BRAINERD—Acrometal Companies, Inc.; U.S. Private, pg. 14
ACROMETAL COMPANIES, INC.; U.S. Private, pg. 14
AERO MOTIVE (U.K.) LTD.—Woodhead Industries, Inc.; U.S. Public, pg. 1776
AEROCLO METAL PRODUCTS—Precision Valve Corporation; U.S. Private, pg. 880
AIRBORNE—Groupe Strafor Facom; Int'l, pg. 569
ALADDIN INDUSTRIES, INCORPORATED; U.S. Private, pg. 30
ALCO INDUSTRIES, INC.; U.S. Private, pg. 32
ALENITE L.P.; U.S. Private, pg. 33
ALLIED CHUCKER & ENGINEERING COMPANY; U.S. Private, pg. 38
ALLIED SECURITY, INTERNATIONAL; U.S. Private, pg. 41
ALLOY TECHNOLOGY INTERNATIONAL INC.; U.S. Private, pg. 42
AMERICAN SYSTEMS CORPORATION; U.S. Private, pg. 63
AMERICAN TANK & FABRICATING CO.; U.S. Private, pg. 63
AMERON PROTECTIVE LININGS DIVISION—Ameron International Corporation; U.S. Public, pg. 70
AMSTED INDUSTRIES INCORPORATED; U.S. Private, pg. 68
APPLIED POWER INC.; U.S. Public, pg. 124
APTARGROUP, INC.; U.S. Public, pg. 125
THE ARNOLD ENGINEERING COMPANY—SPS Technologies, Inc.; U.S. Public, pg. 1420
ARTRA GROUP INCORPORATED; U.S. Public, pg. 136
AUSTRAL BRONZE CRANE COPPER LIMITED—Crane Group Limited; Int'l, pg. 340
BABCOCK INDUSTRIEROHRLEITUNGSBAU GMBH—Deutsche Babcock AG; Int'l, pg. 399
BABCOCK ROHRLEITUNGSBAU GMBH—Deutsche Babcock AG; Int'l, pg. 399
BALDWIN HARDWARE CORPORATION—Masco Corporation; U.S. Public, pg. 1053
L.G. BALFOUR CO., INC.—Commemorative Brands, Inc.; U.S. Private, pg. 258
BARRY CONTROLS INDUSTRIAL/DEFENSE—Applied Power Inc.; U.S. Public, pg. 124
BARRY CONTROLS INTERNATIONAL GMBH—Applied Power Inc.; U.S. Public, pg. 125
BARTON HANDLING & STORAGE SYSTEMS LTD.—Caparo Group Ltd.; Int'l, pg. 264
BETTCHER MANUFACTURING CORP.—Brittany Corporation; U.S. Private, pg. 169
BOCK INDUSTRIES INC.—Caparo Group Ltd.; Int'l, pg. 265
BRUCE INDUSTRIES, INC.; U.S. Private, pg. 175
THE BUDD COMPANY—Thyssen AG; Int'l, pg. 1388
CCL INDUSTRIES, INC.; Int'l, pg. 238
CARADON (USA) INC.—Caradon Plc; Int'l, pg. 267
CARISTRAP INTERNATIONAL INC.; Int'l, pg. 271
CARLISLE COMPANIES INCORPORATED; U.S. Public, pg. 305
CARNAUDMETALBOX—Crown Cork & Seal Company, Inc.; U.S. Public, pg. 463
CHEMA BALCKE-DURR VERFAHRENSTECHNIK GMBH RUDISLEBEN—Deutsche Babcock AG; Int'l, pg. 399
CHICAGO WEST PULLMAN CORPORATION; U.S. Private, pg. 235
CHOCTAW, INC.; U.S. Private, pg. 238
CLARCOR, INC.; U.S. Public, pg. 381
CLARK DOOR CO., INC.; U.S. Private, pg. 242
J.L. CLARK TUBE DIV.—CLARCOR, Inc.; U.S. Public, pg. 382
CLIPPER BELT LACER COMPANY—Flexible Steel Lacing Company; U.S. Private, pg. 413
THE COLLAPSIBLE TUBE CO. LIMITED—Caradon Plc; Int'l, pg. 267
COLLIER-KEYWORTH COMPANY—Leggett & Platt, Incorporated; U.S. Public, pg. 985
COLOR COSMETICS GROUP—Crown Cork & Seal Company, Inc.; U.S. Public, pg. 464
COOK MANUFACTURING CORPORATION; U.S. Private, pg. 272
CRENLO, INC.; U.S. Private, pg. 288
CRES-COR; U.S. Private, pg. 288
CROWN CORK & SEAL COMPANY, INC.; U.S. Public, pg. 462
CRUCIBLE MATERIALS CORP.; U.S. Private, pg. 293
CURTISS-WRIGHT CORP.; U.S. Public, pg. 469
DCG PRECISION MANUFACTURING CORPORATION; U.S. Private, pg. 301
D.C.I., INC.; U.S. Private, pg. 301
DAMASCUS BISHOP TUBE CO.—Marcegaglia SpA; Int'l, pg. 842
DAY INDUSTRIES—Powers Fastening, Inc.; U.S. Private, pg. 878
DELREDO S.A. DE C.V.—General Motors Corporation; U.S. Public, pg. 721
DEUTSCHE BABCOCK S.A.—Deutsche Babcock AG; Int'l, pg. 398
DEXION (AUSTRALIA) PTY. LTD.—The Interlake Corporation; U.S. Public, pg. 893
DEXION GMBH—The Interlake Corporation; U.S. Public, pg. 893
DEXION GROUP PLC—The Interlake Corporation; U.S. Public, pg. 893
DEXION LTD.-STORAGE DIV.—The Interlake Corporation; U.S. Public, pg. 893
S.A. DEXION REDIRACK—The Interlake Corporation; U.S. Public, pg. 893
DEXTER MAGNETIC MATERIALS—The Dexter Corporation; U.S. Public, pg. 504
DIAMOND CHAIN COMPANY—Amsted Industries Incorporated; U.S. Private, pg. 68
DIEBOLD, INCORPORATED; U.S. Public, pg. 506
DOWTY TECMOLD—TI Group plc; Int'l, pg. 1338
DRIV-LOK, INC.; U.S. Private, pg. 343
DUTTON-LAINSON CO.; U.S. Private, pg. 350
DYCKERHOFF & WIDMANN AG; Int'l, pg. 423
DYNACAST—Coats Viyella plc; Int'l, pg. 300
E-Z LOK—TCI Aluminum; U.S. Private, pg. 1063
EG & G SEALOL-CALLISTO S.A.—EG & G, Inc.; U.S. Public, pg. 544
EAGLE INDUSTRY, LTD.—EG & G, Inc.; U.S. Public, pg. 544
ELECTRONIC SOLUTIONS—Zero Corporation; U.S. Public, pg. 1791
EMSON, INC.; U.S. Private, pg. 375

ENERGY ABSORPTION SYSTEMS, INC.—Quixote Corporation; *U.S. Public*, pg. 1353
ENERGY ABSORPTION SYSTEMS, INC.-PELL CITY—Quixote Corporation; *U.S. Public*, pg. 1353
ENERGY ABSORPTION SYSTEMS, INC.-ROCKLIN—Quixote Corporation; *U.S. Public*, pg. 1353
EVANS INDUSTRIES, INC.; *U.S. Private*, pg. 385
FATA EUROPEAN GROUP S.P.A.—FKI Plc; *Int'l*, pg. 474
FATALUMINIUM—FKI Plc; *Int'l*, pg. 474
FIELD EFFECTS, INC.—Intermagnetics General Corporation; *U.S. Public*, pg. 893
FIRE KING INTERNATIONAL, INC.; *U.S. Private*, pg. 406
FLENDER ENGINEERING & SERVICE ANTRIEBSTECHNIK GMBH—Deutsche Babcock AG; *Int'l*, pg. 400
FLEXIBLE STEEL LACING COMPANY; *U.S. Private*, pg. 413
FORE LINE SECURITY—Reeves Southeastern Corporation; *U.S. Private*, pg. 917
FORMFLO LIMITED—Caradon Plc; *Int'l*, pg. 267
L.B. FOSTER COMPANY; *U.S. Public*, pg. 675
L.B. FOSTER COMPANY-NILES PLANT—L.B. Foster Company; *U.S. Public*, pg. 676
L.B. FOSTER COMPANY-POMEROY PLANT—L.B. Foster Company; *U.S. Public*, pg. 676
FRIGOSCANDIA AB—FMC Corporation; *U.S. Public*, pg. 606
FRIGOSCANDIA FOOD PROCESS SYSTEMS S.A.—FMC Corporation; *U.S. Public*, pg. 607
G.E.-THORN LAMPS PRESSCAPS DIVISION—General Electric Company; *U.S. Public*, pg. 713
GARY STEEL CO., INC.—Primac Corp.; *U.S. Private*, pg. 884
GENERAL MACHINERY CO.—Alusuisse-Lonza Holding Ltd.; *Int'l*, pg. 68
A.J. GERRARD AND COMPANY; *U.S. Private*, pg. 449
GIBRALTAR STEEL CORP.; *U.S. Public*, pg. 742
GRAHAM CORPORATION; *U.S. Public*, pg. 757
GRAHAM MANUFACTURING CO., INC.—Graham Corporation; *U.S. Public*, pg. 757
GROUPE STRAFOR FACOM; *Int'l*, pg. 569
GRUPO IMSA S.A. DE C.V.; *Int'l*, pg. 575
HON INDUSTRIES INC.; *U.S. Public*, pg. 772
HANNAY REELS; *U.S. Private*, pg. 499
HARFORD SYSTEMS, INC.—Lab Products, Inc.; *U.S. Private*, pg. 641
HARRIS STEEL GROUP INC.; *Int'l*, pg. 597
HERFF JONES INC.; *U.S. Private*, pg. 523
HOOD & COMPANY—Groupe Usinor; *Int'l*, pg. 572
HOOGOVENS ALUMINIUM GEVELTECHNIEK BV—Koninklijke Hoogovens N.V.; *Int'l*, pg. 753
HORIZON TECHNOLOGY GROUP LLC—Horizon Enterprises Group LLC; *U.S. Private*, pg. 539
HUGHES-TREITLER MANUFACTURING CORPORATION; *U.S. Private*, pg. 547
D.M. HULL & CO. PTY. LTD.—Delta plc; *Int'l*, pg. 391
HUNTER DOUGLAS FABRICATION COMPANY—Hunter Douglas N.V.; *Int'l*, pg. 639
IPC-INTERNATIONAL PARTS CORP.—Whitman Corporation; *U.S. Public*, pg. 1766
ITW SIGNODE—Illinois Tool Works Inc.; *U.S. Public*, pg. 867
INDUSTRIAL COMPONENTS GROUP—BTR plc; *Int'l*, pg. 127
THE INTERLAKE CORPORATION; *U.S. Public*, pg. 892
IONICS, INCORPORATED; *U.S. Public*, pg. 912
JARKE CORPORATION; *U.S. Private*, pg. 583
JONATHAN MANUFACTURING CORP.; *U.S. Private*, pg. 595
K & G OF WISCONSIN, INC.; *U.S. Private*, pg. 602
K-T CORP.—Triumph Group, Inc.; *U.S. Public*, pg. 1640
KURT MANUFACTURING CO. INC.; *U.S. Private*, pg. 637
LAUBECK CORPORATION/CROSS; *U.S. Private*, pg. 652
CHARLES LEONARD, INC.; *U.S. Private*, pg. 660
LOUISVILLE LADDER DIV.—Emerson Electric Co.; *U.S. Public*, pg. 574
MACHIN & EWIN PTY. LTD.—Delta plc; *Int'l*, pg. 392
MACHINING ENTERPRISES INC.; *U.S. Private*, pg. 691
MARCEGAGLIA SPA; *Int'l*, pg. 841
MARDAKLEVS INDUSTRI AB—ACTIVE BioTech AB; *Int'l*, pg. 23
MAXCOR MANUFACTURING, INC.; *U.S. Private*, pg. 716
MCNALLY INDUSTRIES, INC.; *U.S. Private*, pg. 724
MEDICO INDUSTRIES, INC.; *U.S. Private*, pg. 728
METAL IMPROVEMENT CO.—Curtiss-Wright Corp.; *U.S. Public*, pg. 469
MOELLER PRODUCTS CO., INC.; *U.S. Private*, pg. 755
MOSLER INC.; *U.S. Private*, pg. 763
MOSSBERG INDUSTRIES, HUBBARD DIVISION—Mossberg Industries, Inc.; *U.S. Private*, pg. 764
MOSSBERG INDUSTRIES, INC.; *U.S. Private*, pg. 763
NORWALK POWDERED METALS, INC.; *U.S. Private*, pg. 808
R.S. OWENS; *U.S. Private*, pg. 824
PARK-OHIO INDUSTRIES, INC.; *U.S. Public*, pg. 1258
PEERLESS CHAIN COMPANY—Peerless Industrial Group, Inc.; *U.S. Public*, pg. 1268
PEERLESS INDUSTRIAL GROUP, INC.; *U.S. Public*, pg. 1268
PEERLESS MFG. CO.; *U.S. Public*, pg. 1268
PEERLESS TUBE COMPANY; *U.S. Public*, pg. 1269
PEERLESS TUBE CO. OF PUERTO RICO, INC.—Peerless Tube Company; *U.S. Public*, pg. 1269
PHELPS TOINTON INC.; *U.S. Private*, pg. 860
PNEUMAFIL CORPORATION; *U.S. Private*, pg. 873
POWERS FASTENING, INC.; *U.S. Private*, pg. 878
PRECISION VALVE CORPORATION; *U.S. Private*, pg. 880
THE PRESMET CORP.; *U.S. Private*, pg. 882
PRIMARY STEEL, INC.—Primac Corp.; *U.S. Private*, pg. 884
PRODUCTION MANAGEMENT COMPANIES, INC.; *U.S. Private*, pg. 888
PULLMAN INDUSTRIES, INC.; *U.S. Private*, pg. 894
PYRAMID MOULDINGS—TBG Management S.A.M.; *Int'l*, pg. 1335
PYRAMID SOUTHERN MOULDINGS—TBG Management S.A.M.; *Int'l*, pg. 1335
PYRAMID WESTERN MOULDINGS—TBG Management S.A.M.; *Int'l*, pg. 1335
PYRON METAL POWDERS, INC.—Zemex Corporation; *Int'l*, pg. 1524
QUAKER INDUSTRIES—Park-Ohio Industries, Inc.; *U.S. Public*, pg. 1259
QUIXOTE CORPORATION; *U.S. Public*, pg. 1353
RAWSON-KOENIG, INC.; *U.S. Public*, pg. 1362
RAYTECH CORPORATION; *U.S. Public*, pg. 1363
REGION GOTEBORG—ACTIVE BioTech AB; *Int'l*, pg. 23
REGION JONKOPING—ACTIVE BioTech AB; *Int'l*, pg. 23
REGION STOCKHOLM—ACTIVE BioTech AB; *Int'l*, pg. 23
REGION SUNDSVALL—ACTIVE BioTech AB; *Int'l*, pg. 23
RESOPAL GMBH—Premark International, Inc.; *U.S. Public*, pg. 1322
REYNOLDS EXTRUSION COMPANY—Reynolds Metals Company; *U.S. Public*, pg. 1387
REYNOLDS WHEELS S.P.A.—Reynolds Metals Company; *U.S. Public*, pg. 1387
RISDON CORPORATION—Crown Cork & Seal Company, Inc.; *U.S. Public*, pg. 463
ROSS TECHNOLOGY CORP.; *U.S. Private*, pg. 946
ROUSE THOMPSON & LLOYD LTD.—Delta plc; *Int'l*, pg. 391
ROYAL DEVELOPMENT CO., INC.—Furniture Brands International Inc.; *U.S. Public*, pg. 688
SCR DIVISION—Peerless Mfg. Co.; *U.S. Public*, pg. 1268
SPS TECHNOLOGIES, INC.; *U.S. Public*, pg. 1419
SARGENT & GREENLEAF, INC.; *U.S. Private*, pg. 965
SCHWAB CORP.; *U.S. Private*, pg. 974
SCHWEIZER AIRCRAFT CORPORATION; *U.S. Private*, pg. 975
SECURITY GROUP INC.; *U.S. Private*, pg. 981
SENTRY GROUP; *U.S. Private*, pg. 984
SIGMA-ALDRICH CORPORATION; *U.S. Public*, pg. 1471
SIMON LADDER TOWERS INC.—Simon Engineering plc; *Int'l*, pg. 1252
EVERETT SMITH GROUP, LTD.; *U.S. Private*, pg. 1007
SONESSON INDRETNING APS—ACTIVE BioTech AB; *Int'l*, pg. 23
SONESSON INREDNINGAR AB—ACTIVE BioTech AB; *Int'l*, pg. 23
SONOCO SPECIAL PRODUCTS GROUP—Sonoco Products Company; *U.S. Public*, pg. 1486
SPINCRAFT WISCONSIN—Standex International Corporation; *U.S. Public*, pg. 1506
SPIROL INTERNATIONAL CORP.; *U.S. Private*, pg. 1026
SPRAYING SYSTEMS CO.; *U.S. Private*, pg. 1026
SPRAYING SYSTEMS CO. FAR EAST—Spraying Systems Co.; *U.S. Private*, pg. 1027
SPRAYING SYSTEMS DEUTSCHLAND GMBH—Spraying Systems Co.; *U.S. Private*, pg. 1027
STAINLESS INCORPORATED; *U.S. Private*, pg. 1029
STEEL CEILINGS INC.—Airtite Contractors Inc.; *U.S. Private*, pg. 29
STEIN INC.—AGA AB; *Int'l*, pg. 13
STEMCO TRUCK PRODUCTS DIVISION—Coltec Holdings Inc; *U.S. Public*, pg. 402
SULZER BINGHAM PUMPS INC.—Sulzer Ltd.; *Int'l*, pg. 1305
SUMITOMO METAL INDUSTRIES, LTD.; *Int'l*, pg. 1315
SVEDALA INDUSTRIES INC.—Svedala Industri AB; *Int'l*, pg. 1325
TBG MANAGEMENT S.A.M.; *Int'l*, pg. 1335
TAMROCK CORP.; *Int'l*, pg. 1352
TELEDYNE WATER PIK—Allegheny Teledyne Incorporated; *U.S. Public*, pg. 44
TEMCO FIREPLACE PRODUCTS, INC.—Temtex Industries Inc.; *U.S. Public*, pg. 1576
THOMAS & SKINNER, INC.; *U.S. Private*, pg. 1082
TIME-MIST DIV.—Carpenter Technology Corporation; *U.S. Public*, pg. 308
TOSOH SMD, INC.—Tosoh Corporation; *Int'l*, pg. 1407
TOSOH SMD KOREA LTD.—Tosoh Corporation; *Int'l*, pg. 1408
TRANSCO INC.; *U.S. Private*, pg. 1096
TRANSCO PRODUCTS INC.—Transco Inc.; *U.S. Private*, pg. 1096
TRANTER, INC.—Dover Corporation; *U.S. Public*, pg. 521
TRICON INDUSTRIES, INC.; *U.S. Private*, pg. 1102
TRITON INDUSTRIES, INC.; *U.S. Private*, pg. 1104
TROPAR MFG. CO., INC.; *U.S. Private*, pg. 1105
TROPAR MFG. CO., INC.—Tropar Mfg. Co., Inc.; *U.S. Private*, pg. 1105
TRUE TEMPER SPORTS DIVISION—The Black & Decker Corporation; *U.S. Public*, pg. 233
TUTHILL CORPORATION; *U.S. Private*, pg. 1110
U.S. MANUFACTURING CORP.; *U.S. Private*, pg. 1125
UNITED STATES PIPE & FOUNDRY COMPANY, INC.—Walter Industries, Inc.; *U.S. Public*, pg. 1736
UNIVERSAL COMPOSITES-U.S.C.; *U.S. Private*, pg. 1126
UP-RIGHT, INC.; *U.S. Private*, pg. 1128
VACUUMSCHMELZE GMBH—Siemens AG; *Int'l*, pg. 1245
WASHINGTON SCIENTIFIC INDUSTRIES, INC.; *U.S. Public*, pg. 1744
WATERBURY COMPANIES, INC.-INDEPENDENCE DIV.—Carpenter Technology Corporation; *U.S. Public*, pg. 308
WEST FOOTSCRAY ENGINEERING WORKS PTY. LTD.—Delta plc; *Int'l*, pg. 392
WHEATON INC.—Alusuisse-Lonza Holding Ltd.; *Int'l*, pg. 67
WHITING METALS, INC.—Synalloy Corporation; *U.S. Public*, pg. 1548
WITT COMPANY; *U.S. Private*, pg. 1185
WOLVERINE VINYL SIDING—Saint-Gobain; *Int'l*, pg. 1171
XLM COMPANY—HON Industries Inc.; *U.S. Public*, pg. 772

3511 — STEAM, GAS, & HYDRAULIC TURBINES; & TURBINE GENERATOR SET UNITS

ABB ASEA BROWN BOVERI (HOLDING) LTD.; *Int'l*, pg. 1
ABB COMBUSTION ENGINEERING SYSTEMS—ABB Asea Brown Boveri (Holding) Ltd.; *Int'l*, pg. 3
ABB GENERATION AB—ABB Asea Brown Boveri (Holding) Ltd.; *Int'l*, pg. 7
ABB HYDRO POWER DIV.—ABB Asea Brown Boveri (Holding) Ltd.; *Int'l*, pg. 4
ABB POWER GENERATION INC.—ABB Asea Brown Boveri (Holding) Ltd.; *Int'l*, pg. 3
ABB STAL AB—ABB Asea Brown Boveri (Holding) Ltd.; *Int'l*, pg. 7
ABB STEAM POWER GENERATION COMPANY—ABB Asea Brown Boveri (Holding) Ltd.; *Int'l*, pg. 4
ALLIEDSIGNAL INC.; *U.S. Public*, pg. 49
ALLIEDSIGNAL LTD. TURBOCHARGERS—AlliedSignal Inc.; *U.S. Public*, pg. 53
ALLIEDSIGNAL TURBOCHARGERS, INC.—AlliedSignal Inc.; *U.S. Public*, pg. 53
ANSALDO COMPONENTI SRL—IRI Istituto Ricostruzione Industriale; *Int'l*, pg. 653
BJ SERVICES COMPANY; *U.S. Public*, pg. 161
BABCOCK & WILCOX ST COMPANY—McDermott International, Inc.; *U.S. Public*, pg. 1068
BELL-ESCHER WYSS LTD.—Sulzer Ltd.; *Int'l*, pg. 1305
THE BETHLEHEM CORPORATION; *U.S. Public*, pg. 225
JOHN BROWN ENGINEERING LIMITED—Kvaerner a.s.a.; *Int'l*, pg. 772
BRUSH ELECTRICAL MACHINES LTD.—BTR plc; *Int'l*, pg. 124
CATERPILLAR CAPITAL COMPANY, INC.—Caterpillar Inc.; *U.S. Public*, pg. 315
CATERPILLAR INC.; *U.S. Public*, pg. 315
COPPUS MURRAY GROUP, TUTHILL CORPORATION—Tuthill Corporation; *U.S. Private*, pg. 1110
DELTAK INC.—Jason Incorporated; *U.S. Public*, pg. 924
DEMAG DELAVAL TURBINE—Mannesmann A.G.; *Int'l*, pg. 837
DEUTSCHE BABCOCK ENERGIE-UND UMWELTTECHNIK AG—Deutsche Babcock AG; *Int'l*, pg. 398
DEUTZ AG; *Int'l*, pg. 407
DEUTZ CORPORATION—Deutz AG; *Int'l*, pg. 408
DONCASTERS PLC; *Int'l*, pg. 416
DRESSER INDUSTRIES, INC.; *U.S. Public*, pg. 528
DRESSER-RAND CO.—Ingersoll-Rand Company; *U.S. Public*, pg. 877
EG & G KT AEROFAB—EG & G, Inc.; *U.S. Public*, pg. 542
ELECTRO-MOTIVE DIVISION—General Motors Corporation; *U.S. Public*, pg. 719
ELLIOTT COMPANY; *U.S. Private*, pg. 373
EVANS INDUSTRIES, INC.; *U.S. Private*, pg. 385
FALKEMA AB; *Int'l*, pg. 477
FINMECCANICA S.P.A.—IRI Istituto Ricostruzione Industriale; *Int'l*, pg. 653
FREEDOM FORGE CORPORATION; *U.S. Private*, pg. 425
FUJI HEAVY INDUSTRIES, LTD., ENGINE & MACHINERY DIV.—Fuji Heavy Industries, Ltd.; *Int'l*, pg. 523
G.E. CANADA POWER SYSTEMS—General Electric Company; *U.S. Public*, pg. 713
G.E. POWER SYSTEMS—General Electric Company; *U.S. Public*, pg. 711
GEC ALSTHOM—Alcatel Alsthom Compagnie Generale D'Electricite; *Int'l*, pg. 52
GEC ALSTHOM N.V.—Alcatel Alsthom Compagnie Generale D'Electricite; *Int'l*, pg. 56
GHH BORSIG TURBOMASCHINEN GMBH—MAN Aktiengesellschaft; *Int'l*, pg. 824
GENERAL ELECTRIC DE MEXICO, S.A. DE C.V.—General Electric Company; *U.S. Public*, pg. 713
HITACHI, LTD.; *Int'l*, pg. 621
HITACHI POWER ENGINEERING CO., LTD.—Hitachi, Ltd.; *Int'l*, pg. 621
HOLLANDSCHE BETON GROEP NV; *Int'l*, pg. 630
HYUNDAI HEAVY INDUSTRIES CO., LTD.—Hyundai Motor Company; *Int'l*, pg. 641
ITT FLYGT AB—ITT Industries, Inc.; *U.S. Public*, pg. 860
INDUSTRIAL ACOUSTICS COMPANY S.C. INC.—Industrial Acoustics Company, Inc.; *U.S. Public*, pg. 875
INGERSOLL-DRESSER PUMP COMPANY—Dresser Industries, Inc.; *U.S. Public*, pg. 529
INGERSOLL-DRESSER PUMP COMPANY—Ingersoll-Rand Company; *U.S. Public*, pg. 877
INLAND DETROIT DIESEL ALLISON CO.; *U.S. Private*, pg. 564
INTEGRAL HYDRAULIK & CO.; *Int'l*, pg. 679
INTEGRAL TECHNOLOGIE GMBH—Integral Hydraulik & Co.; *Int'l*, pg. 679
KHD DEUTZ OF AMERICA CORPORATION—Deutz AG; *Int'l*, pg. 408
KATO ENGINEERING DIV.—Rockwell International Corporation; *U.S. Public*, pg. 1398
KRUPP MAK MASCHINENBAU GMBH—Fried. Krupp AG; *Int'l*, pg. 509
KUBOTA CORP.; *Int'l*, pg. 762
KUBOTA TRACTOR CORP. ENGINE DIVISION—Kubota Corp.; *Int'l*, pg. 762
KVAERNER BOVING (ANZ) PTY LTD—Kvaerner a.s.a.; *Int'l*, pg. 772
KVAERNER ENERGY, AGOTNES—Kvaerner a.s.a.; *Int'l*, pg. 767
KVAERNER ENERGY, DAMSGARD—Kvaerner a.s.a.; *Int'l*, pg. 767
KVAERNER ENERGY, SORUMSAND—Kvaerner a.s.a.; *Int'l*, pg. 767
KVAERNER HYDRO POWER, INC.—Kvaerner a.s.a.; *Int'l*, pg. 770
KVAERNER INC.—Kvaerner a.s.a.; *Int'l*, pg. 770
KVAERNER TURBIN AB—Kvaerner a.s.a.; *Int'l*, pg. 770
LIEBHERR-INTERNATIONAL AG; *Int'l*, pg. 807
MARINE & INDUSTRIAL ENGINES & SERVICE DIV.—General Electric Company; *U.S. Public*, pg. 710

MECHANICAL TECHNOLOGY INC.; *U.S. Public*, pg. 1077
MECHANICAL TECHNOLOGY INC.-TECHNOLOGY GRP.(LATHAM)—Mechanical Technology Inc.; *U.S. Public*, pg. 1077
MIKUNI ADEC.—Mikuni Corporation; *Int'l*, pg. 867
MITSUBISHI ELECTRIC CORPORATION; *Int'l*, pg. 872
MURRAY TURBOMACHINERY CORPORATION—Tuthill Corporation; *U.S. Private*, pg. 1110
NORTHROP GRUMMAN CORPORATION; *U.S. Public*, pg. 1197
NUOVO PIGNONE S.P.A.; *Int'l*, pg. 990
PALL INDUSTRIAL HYDRAULICS LTD.—Pall Corporation; *U.S. Public*, pg. 1254
PALL INDUSTRIE-HYDRAULIK GMBH—Pall Corporation; *U.S. Public*, pg. 1254
PETER BROTHERHOOD LTD.—Thermo Electron Corporation; *U.S. Public*, pg. 1596
PIGNONE ENGINEERING LTD.—Nuovo Pignone S.p.a.; *Int'l*, pg. 991
ROCKWELL INTERNATIONAL CORPORATION; *U.S. Public*, pg. 1397
ROLLS-ROYCE INDUSTRIES CANADA INC.—Rolls-Royce plc; *Int'l*, pg. 1127
SIEMENS POWER CORP.—Siemens AG; *Int'l*, pg. 1246
SOLAR TURBINES CANADA LTD.—Caterpillar Inc.; *U.S. Public*, pg. 317
SOLAR TURBINES S.A.—Caterpillar Inc.; *U.S. Public*, pg. 317
STEWART & STEVENSON SERVICES, INC.; *U.S. Public*, pg. 1517
STOLPER-FABRALLOY CO. LLC—Triumph Group, Inc.; *U.S. Public*, pg. 1640
SULZER-ESCHER WYSS AG—Sulzer Ltd.; *Int'l*, pg. 1305
SULZER INFORMATIK AG—Sulzer Ltd.; *Int'l*, pg. 1306
SULZER-WINTERTHUR GROUP—Sulzer Ltd.; *Int'l*, pg. 1307
TIC UNITED CORPORATION; *U.S. Private*, pg. 1063
THERM, INC.; *U.S. Private*, pg. 1079
THOMASSEN STEWART & STEVENSON INTERNATIONAL B.V.—Stewart & Stevenson Services, Inc.; *U.S. Public*, pg. 1518
TRAFALGAR HOUSE ENGINEERING—Kvaerner a.s.a.; *Int'l*, pg. 773
TURBINA SOLAR S.A. DE C.V.—Caterpillar Inc.; *U.S. Public*, pg. 316
TURBO TECHNOLOGIA DE REPARACIONES S.A. DE C.V.—Caterpillar Inc.; *U.S. Public*, pg. 316
U.S. TURBINE CORPORATION—Rolls-Royce plc; *Int'l*, pg. 1127
UNITED TECHNOLOGIES CORPORATION; *U.S. Public*, pg. 1689
VOEST-ALPINE INTERNATIONAL CORPORATION—Voest-Alpine Stahl AG; *Int'l*, pg. 1470
VOITH HYDRO, INC.—J.M. Voith, GmbH; *Int'l*, pg. 1473
J.M. VOITH AG—J.M. Voith, GmbH; *Int'l*, pg. 1473
J.M. VOITH, GMBH; *Int'l*, pg. 1472
VOITH S.A. MAQUINAS E EQUIPAMENTOS—J.M. Voith, GmbH; *Int'l*, pg. 1473
VOITH TOLOSA S.A.—J.M. Voith, GmbH; *Int'l*, pg. 1473
WESTINGHOUSE MOTOR COMPANY—CBS Corporation; *U.S. Public*, pg. 275
WOODWARD GOVERNOR ASIA-PACIFIC PTE. LTD.—Woodward Governor Company; *U.S. Public*, pg. 1776
WOODWARD GOVERNOR COMPANY; *U.S. Public*, pg. 1776
WOODWARD GOVERNOR GERMANY GMBH—Woodward Governor Company; *U.S. Public*, pg. 1777
WOODWARD GOVERNOR INDIA PVT. LTD.—Woodward Governor Company; *U.S. Public*, pg. 1777

3519 — INTERNAL COMBUSTION ENGINES, NEC

AMSTED INDUSTRIES INCORPORATED; *U.S. Private*, pg. 68
BOMBARDIER INC.; *Int'l*, pg. 199
ROBERT BOSCH CORPORATION—Robert Bosch GmbH; *Int'l*, pg. 204
BRIGGS & STRATTON CORPORATION; *U.S. Public*, pg. 252
BRUNSWICK CORPORATION; *U.S. Public*, pg. 265
BRUSH ELECTRICAL MACHINES LTD.—BTR plc; *Int'l*, pg. 124
BURGESS-NORTON MFG. CO.—Amsted Industries Incorporated; *U.S. Private*, pg. 68
CATERPILLAR INC.; *U.S. Public*, pg. 315
CHRYSLER CORPORATION; *U.S. Public*, pg. 352
COLTEC HOLDINGS INC; *U.S. Public*, pg. 401
CRUSADER MARINE ENGINES—Thermo Electron Corporation; *U.S. Public*, pg. 1591
CUMMINS ENGINE COMPANY, INC.; *U.S. Public*, pg. 467
CUMMINS INTERMOUNTAIN DIESEL; *U.S. Private*, pg. 295
CUMMINS NATURAL GAS ENGINES, INC.—Cummins Engine Company, Inc.; *U.S. Public*, pg. 468
DAEWOO HEAVY INDUSTRIES, LTD.—Daewoo Corporation; *Int'l*, pg. 357
DAIHATSU DIESEL MFG. CO., LTD.; *Int'l*, pg. 364
DANA CORPORATION; *U.S. Public*, pg. 479
DAYTON THERMAL PRODUCTS DIV.—Chrysler Corporation; *U.S. Public*, pg. 353
DEERE & COMPANY; *U.S. Public*, pg. 491
DEFIANCE PRECISION PRODUCTS, INC.—Defiance, Inc.; *U.S. Public*, pg. 493
DETROIT DIESEL CORP.—Penske Corporation; *U.S. Private*, pg. 850
DEUTZ AG; *Int'l*, pg. 407
DIESEL RECON—Cummins Engine Company, Inc.; *U.S. Public*, pg. 468
DIESEL RECON AUSTRALIA—Cummins Engine Company, Inc.; *U.S. Public*, pg. 469
DIESEL RECON UK—Cummins Engine Company, Inc.; *U.S. Public*, pg. 469
DOUGLAS PRODUCTS DIVISION—Tecumseh Products Company; *U.S. Public*, pg. 1565
DRESSER INDUSTRIES, INC.; *U.S. Public*, pg. 528
DUNLAP DIVISION—Tecumseh Products Company; *U.S. Public*, pg. 1565
ELECTRO-MOTIVE DIVISION—General Motors Corporation; *U.S. Public*, pg. 719
ENGINE AND GEAR SERVICE DIVISION—Tecumseh Products Company; *U.S. Public*, pg. 1565
EVANS INDUSTRIES, INC.; *U.S. Private*, pg. 385
FAIRBANKS MORSE ENGINE DIVISION—Coltec Holdings Inc; *U.S. Public*, pg. 401
FICHTEL & SACHS AG—Mannesmann A.G.; *Int'l*, pg. 835
FRANCAISE DE MECANIQUE—PSA Peugeot Citroen; *Int'l*, pg. 1021
FRANCAISE DE MECANIQUE—Renault; *Int'l*, pg. 1102
FUJI HEAVY INDUSTRIES, LTD., ENGINE & MACHINERY DIV.—Fuji Heavy Industries, Ltd.; *Int'l*, pg. 523
THE GENERAL ELECTRIC COMPANY OF MALAYSIA SDN. BHD.—The General Electric Company, p.l.c.; *Int'l*, pg. 546
GENERAL MOTORS CANADA DIESEL DIV.—General Motors Corporation; *U.S. Public*, pg. 722
GENEVA CORPORATION; *U.S. Private*, pg. 446
GOTAVERKEN MOTOR AB—Celsius AB; *Int'l*, pg. 276
HATHAWAY MOTION CONTROL DIVISION—Hathaway Corporation; *U.S. Public*, pg. 799
HOLSET ENGINEERING CO. LTD.—Cummins Engine Company, Inc.; *U.S. Public*, pg. 469
HONDA MOTOR CO., LTD.; *Int'l*, pg. 634
HYUNDAI MOTOR COMPANY; *Int'l*, pg. 641
ILLINOIS AUTO ELECTRIC CO.; *U.S. Private*, pg. 557
ILLINOIS AUTO ELECTRIC MIDWEST ENGINE WAREHOUSE DIV.—Illinois Auto Electric Co.; *U.S. Private*, pg. 558
INGERSOLL-RAND COMPANY; *U.S. Public*, pg. 876
IOCHPE-MAXION S.A.; *Int'l*, pg. 688
ISUZU ENGINE MANUFACTURING CO., (THAILAND) LTD.—Isuzu Motors Limited; *Int'l*, pg. 693
ISUZU TECHNICAL CENTER (THAILAND) CO., LTD.—Isuzu Motors Limited; *Int'l*, pg. 693
IVECO-FORD TRUCK LTD.—Fiat Auto SpA; *Int'l*, pg. 484
JACOBS VEHICLE EQUIPMENT COMPANY—Danaher Corporation; *U.S. Public*, pg. 481
JEUMONT-SCHNEIDER TRENFORMETEURS; *Int'l*, pg. 706
JOHNSON & TOWERS, INC.; *U.S. Private*, pg. 590
JOHNSON OUTBOARDS MARINE CORP.—Greenway Partners, L.P.; *U.S. Private*, pg. 478
KOHLER COMPANY; *U.S. Private*, pg. 630
KOHLER DE MEXICO, S.A. DE C.V.—Kohler Company; *U.S. Private*, pg. 631
KRUPP GERLACH COMPANY—Fried. Krupp AG; *Int'l*, pg. 508
KRUPP MAK MASCHINENBAU GMBH—Fried. Krupp AG; *Int'l*, pg. 509
KVAERNER ENERGY, SORUMSAND—Kvaerner a.s.a.; *Int'l*, pg. 767
KVAERNER KINCAID LTD.—Kvaerner a.s.a.; *Int'l*, pg. 772
KVAERNER KOREA LTD.—Kvaerner a.s.a.; *Int'l*, pg. 772
LAUSON ENGINE DIV.—Tecumseh Products Company; *U.S. Public*, pg. 1566
LIAONING LIEBHERR DIESEL ENGINE CO. LTD.—Liebherr-International AG; *Int'l*, pg. 807
LIEBHERR MACHINES BULLE S.A.—Liebherr-International AG; *Int'l*, pg. 808
LISTER-PETTER LTD.—BTR plc; *Int'l*, pg. 125
LUCASVARITY INC.—LucasVarity plc; *Int'l*, pg. 820
MAN B & W DIESEL AG—MAN Aktiengesellschaft; *Int'l*, pg. 824
MAN B & W DIESEL A/S—MAN Aktiengesellschaft; *Int'l*, pg. 824
MAN B & W JAPAN LTD.—MAN Aktiengesellschaft; *Int'l*, pg. 824
MAN B & W NORGE A/S—MAN Aktiengesellschaft; *Int'l*, pg. 824
MAN GHH (IRAN) SHERKATE SAHAMI KHASS—MAN Aktiengesellschaft; *Int'l*, pg. 824
MARINE & INDUSTRIAL PRODUCTS DIV.—Chrysler Corporation; *U.S. Public*, pg. 353
MARINE POWER AUSTRALIA, PTY. LTD.—Brunswick Corporation; *U.S. Public*, pg. 266
MARINE SYSTEMS, INC.-GULF COAST—Kirby Corporation; *U.S. Public*, pg. 961
MERCURY MARINE—Brunswick Corporation; *U.S. Public*, pg. 265
P.T. MESIN ISUZU INDONESIA—Isuzu Motors Limited; *Int'l*, pg. 693
P.T. MESIN ISUZU INDONESIA—General Motors Corporation; *U.S. Public*, pg. 724
METRA CORPORATION; *Int'l*, pg. 862
MIRRLEES BLACKSTONE (STOCKPORT) LTD.—BTR plc; *Int'l*, pg. 125
MITSUBISHI HEAVY INDUSTRIES LTD.; *Int'l*, pg. 873
MITSUI ENGINEERING & SHIPBUILDING CO., LTD.—Mitsui & Co., Ltd.; *Int'l*, pg. 878
MUSTANG TRACTOR & EQUIP. CO.; *U.S. Private*, pg. 768
NORTHROP GRUMMAN CORPORATION; *U.S. Public*, pg. 1197
OMC ANDREWS—Greenway Partners, L.P.; *U.S. Private*, pg. 478
OMC BURNSVILLE—Greenway Partners, L.P.; *U.S. Private*, pg. 478
OMC CALHOUN—Greenway Partners, L.P.; *U.S. Private*, pg. 478
OMC EL PASO—Greenway Partners, L.P.; *U.S. Private*, pg. 478
OMC MILWAUKEE—Greenway Partners, L.P.; *U.S. Private*, pg. 478
OMC SPRUCE PINE—Greenway Partners, L.P.; *U.S. Private*, pg. 478
ONAN CORPORATION—Cummins Engine Company, Inc.; *U.S. Public*, pg. 468
OUTBOARD MARINE CORPORATION—Greenway Partners, L.P.; *U.S. Private*, pg. 478
PSA PEUGEOT CITROEN; *Int'l*, pg. 1020
PENSKE CORPORATION; *U.S. Private*, pg. 850
SCHWITZER, INC.—Kuhlman Corporation; *U.S. Public*, pg. 968
SHINKO ENGINEERING CO., LTD.—Kobe Steel, Ltd.; *Int'l*, pg. 740
SSANGYONG BUSINESS GROUP; *Int'l*, pg. 1291
SSANGYONG HEAVY INDUSTRIES CO., LTD.—Ssangyong Business Group; *Int'l*, pg. 1292
STEWARTS & LLOYDS TRADING (PTY) LIMITED—Dorbyl Limited; *Int'l*, pg. 416
SUZUKI MARINA, HAMANAKO, CO., LTD.—Suzuki Motor Corporation; *Int'l*, pg. 1323
SUZUKI MOTOR CORPORATION; *Int'l*, pg. 1322
T A HOLDINGS LIMITED; *Int'l*, pg. 1334
TFX MARINE—Teleflex Incorporated; *U.S. Public*, pg. 1570
TECUMSEH EUROPA—Tecumseh Products Company; *U.S. Public*, pg. 1566
TECUMSEH PRODUCTS CO. ENGINE & TRANSMISSION GROUP—Tecumseh Products Company; *U.S. Public*, pg. 1566
TECUMSEH PRODUCTS COMPANY; *U.S. Public*, pg. 1565
THERMO ELECTRON CORPORATION; *U.S. Public*, pg. 1591
TRIPLE A SPECIALTY COMPANY; *U.S. Private*, pg. 1103
U.S. MARINE DIV.—Brunswick Corporation; *U.S. Public*, pg. 266
VM MOTORI S.P.A.—IRI Istituto Ricostruzione Industriale; *Int'l*, pg. 654
VARITY PERKINS—LucasVarity plc; *Int'l*, pg. 820
J.M. VOITH, GMBH; *Int'l*, pg. 1472
AB VOLVO PENTA—AB Volvo; *Int'l*, pg. 1476
WAUKESHA ENGINE DIVISION—Dresser Industries, Inc.; *U.S. Public*, pg. 528
WESTERBEKE CORPORATION; *U.S. Public*, pg. 1757
WINPOWER INC.—Dyna Technology Incorporated; *U.S. Private*, pg. 350
WOODWARD GOVERNOR COMPANY; *U.S. Public*, pg. 1776
YAMAHA MOTOR CO., LTD.—Yamaha Corporation; *Int'l*, pg. 1516
ZEXEL CORPORATION; *Int'l*, pg. 1528

3523 — FARM MACHINERY & EQUIPMENT

AG-CHEM EQUIPMENT CO., INC.; *U.S. Public*, pg. 6
AESCULAP AKTIENGESELLSCHAFT; *Int'l*, pg. 29
AGCO ARGENTINA S.A.; *Int'l*, pg. 30
AGCO CORPORATION; *U.S. Public*, pg. 28
AGCO INC.; *U.S. Private*, pg. 26
AGRICULTURAL EQUIPMENT DIV., J.I. CASE—Case Corporation; *U.S. Public*, pg. 311
AGROMAC INTERNATIONAL, INC.; *U.S. Private*, pg. 27
AGROTEC, WILLIAMS INC.—Williams Controls, Inc.; *U.S. Public*, pg. 1769
AGTEC INC.—Ag-Chem Equipment Co., Inc.; *U.S. Public*, pg. 6
ALAMO GROUP, INC.; *U.S. Public*, pg. 34
ALFA-LAVAL AG—Tetra Laval Group; *Int'l*, pg. 1380
ALFA-LAVAL AGRAR G.M.B.H.—Tetra Laval Group; *Int'l*, pg. 1377
ALFA LAVAL AGRI AB—Tetra Laval Group; *Int'l*, pg. 1378
ALFA-LAVAL FOOD ENGINEERING AB—Tetra Laval Group; *Int'l*, pg. 1378
ALFA-LAVAL INDIA LTD—Tetra Laval Group; *Int'l*, pg. 1380
ALFA LAVAL SEPARATION INC.—Tetra Laval Group; *Int'l*, pg. 1378
ALFA-LAVAL STALLTECHNIK G.M.B.H.—Tetra Laval Group; *Int'l*, pg. 1379
ALLIED PRODUCTS CORPORATION; *U.S. Public*, pg. 48
ANDIS COMPANY; *U.S. Private*, pg. 73
ARMATRON INTERNATIONAL, INC.; *U.S. Public*, pg. 131
ART'S-WAY MANUFACTURING CO., INC.; *U.S. Public*, pg. 136
AUSCO PRODUCTS, INC.—The Cypress Companies; *U.S. Private*, pg. 299
AUSTRALIAN NATIONAL INDUSTRIES LIMITED; *Int'l*, pg. 100
AUTOMATIC EQUIPMENT MFG. CO.; *U.S. Private*, pg. 101
BMB COMPANY—Alamo Group, Inc.; *U.S. Public*, pg. 35
BADGER FARM SYSTEMS, INC.—Miller-St. Nazianz, Inc.; *U.S. Private*, pg. 748
BEHLEN MFG. CO.; *U.S. Private*, pg. 130
BETA RAVEN INC.—Raven Industries, Inc.; *U.S. Public*, pg. 1361
BLUFFTON AGRI/INDUSTRIAL CORP. D/B/A BAIC—Farmatic Research, Inc.; *Int'l*, pg. 478
BLUMHARDT MANUFACTURING COMPANY—TIC United Corporation; *U.S. Private*, pg. 1063
BOMFORD TURNER LIMITED—Alamo Group, Inc.; *U.S. Public*, pg. 35
BONDIOLI & PAVESI S.P.A.; *Int'l*, pg. 201
BOU-MATIC—DEC International, Inc.; *U.S. Private*, pg. 301
BRILLION IRON WORKS, INC.—Johnstown America Industries; *U.S. Public*, pg. 933
BROWER EQUIPMENT—Hawkeye Steel Products, Inc.; *U.S. Private*, pg. 511
BUSH HOG DIVISION—Allied Products Corporation; *U.S. Public*, pg. 48
BYPY HYDRAULICS & TRANSMISSIONS LTD.—Bondioli & Pavesi S.p.A.; *Int'l*, pg. 201
CTB INTERNATIONAL CORP.; *U.S. Public*, pg. 284
THE CALKINS MANUFACTURING COMPANY; *U.S. Private*, pg. 201
CANNON EQUIPMENT—IMI Plc; *Int'l*, pg. 646
CARTER DAY INDUSTRIES (CANADA) LTD.—Carter Day International; *U.S. Private*, pg. 217
CASE CORPORATION; *U.S. Public*, pg. 311
CASE ENGINE HOLDING COMPANY, INC.—Case Corporation; *U.S. Public*, pg. 311

CASE FRANCE, S.A.—Tenneco Inc.; *U.S. Public*, pg. 1579
CASE FRANCE S.A.—Tenneco Inc.; *U.S. Public*, pg. 1579
CASE INTERNATIONAL—Tenneco Inc.; *U.S. Public*, pg. 1579
J.I. CASE SWEDEN AB—Tenneco Inc.; *U.S. Public*, pg. 1580
CASE POCLAIN GMBH & CO.—Tenneco Inc.; *U.S. Public*, pg. 1579
CASE TRACTEURS, S.A.—Tenneco Inc.; *U.S. Public*, pg. 1579
CASE TRAKTOREN GMBH—Tenneco Inc.; *U.S. Public*, pg. 1579
CASE TRAKTORI OY—Tenneco Inc.; *U.S. Public*, pg. 1579
CHORE-TIME CAGE SYSTEMS—CTB International Corp.; *U.S. Public*, pg. 285
CHORE-TIME EQUIPMENT—CTB International Corp.; *U.S. Public*, pg. 285
CONSTRUCCIONES AGROMETALICAS LEVANTE, S.A. (CALSA)—Tenneco Inc.; *U.S. Public*, pg. 1579
CONTINENTAL EAGLE CORPORATION; *U.S. Private*, pg. 267
CORN STATES HYBRID SERVICE, INC.—Monsanto Company; *U.S. Public*, pg. 1124
CRENLO, INC.; *U.S. Private*, pg. 288
CRUSTBUSTER, INC.; *U.S. Private*, pg. 293
DEC AG—DEC International, Inc.; *U.S. Private*, pg. 301
DEC INTERNATIONAL, INC.; *U.S. Private*, pg. 301
DMI, INC.; *U.S. Private*, pg. 305
DANI-TECH A/S—Bondioli & Pavesi S.p.A.; *Int'l*, pg. 201
DANUSER MACHINE CO.; *U.S. Private*, pg. 310
DEERE & COMPANY; *U.S. Public*, pg. 491
JOHN DEERE—Deere & Company; *U.S. Public*, pg. 492
DEERE MARKETING SERVICES, INC.—Deere & Company; *U.S. Public*, pg. 492
DEGELMAN INDUSTRIES LTD.; *Int'l*, pg. 388
DELAVAN COMMERCIAL PRODUCTS DIVISION—Coltec Holdings Inc; *U.S. Public*, pg. 401
DEMPSTER INDUSTRIES INC.; *U.S. Private*, pg. 324
DURBIN-DURCO—Columbus McKinnon Corp.; *U.S. Public*, pg. 406
DYER-LAUDERDALE FARMERS CO-OP—Tennessee Farmers Co-op; *U.S. Private*, pg. 1076
DYNAMICS CORPORATION OF AMERICA—CTS Corporation; *U.S. Public*, pg. 286
EAGLE ENGINEERING & MANUFACTURING, INC.—Dreison International, Inc.; *U.S. Private*, pg. 342
EQUIPOS AGRICOLAS ALFA-LAVAL S.A.—Tetra Laval Group; *Int'l*, pg. 1377
FMC CORPORATION; *U.S. Public*, pg. 604
FABDEC LTD.—DEC International, Inc.; *U.S. Private*, pg. 301
FABRIKEN ODIN AB—Tetra Laval Group; *Int'l*, pg. 1378
FARMATIC RESEARCH, INC.; *Int'l*, pg. 478
FARNAM COMPANIES, INC.; *U.S. Private*, pg. 396
FETERL MFG. CO.—United Dominion Industries, Ltd.; *U.S. Public*, pg. 1676
FIAT TRATTORI S.P.A.—Fiat Auto SpA; *Int'l*, pg. 481
FLEISCHER MANUFACTURING, INC.; *U.S. Private*, pg. 410
FLOW CONTROL DIVISION—Raven Industries, Inc.; *U.S. Public*, pg. 1361
GKN WALTERSCHEID GMBH—GKN plc; *Int'l*, pg. 535
GARDEN WAY, INC.; *U.S. Private*, pg. 440
GEHL COMPANY; *U.S. Public*, pg. 704
GENCOR INDUSTRIES, INC.; *U.S. Public*, pg. 705
GREAT PLAINS MANUFACTURING, INC.; *U.S. Private*, pg. 475
HCC INC.; *U.S. Private*, pg. 490
HAGIE MANUFACTURING CO.; *U.S. Private*, pg. 493
HARBOUR GROUP LTD.; *U.S. Private*, pg. 500
JAMES HARDIE INDUSTRIES LTD.; *Int'l*, pg. 596
JAMES HARDIE USA—James Hardie Industries Ltd.; *Int'l*, pg. 597
HAWKEYE STEEL PRODUCTS, INC.; *U.S. Private*, pg. 511
HEDLUND-MARTIN INC.—Gehl Company; *U.S. Public*, pg. 704
HELM RESOURCES INC.; *U.S. Public*, pg. 808
HERSCHEL ADAMS—Alamo Group, Inc.; *U.S. Public*, pg. 35
HIGHWAY EQUIPMENT COMPANY; *U.S. Private*, pg. 529
HINIKER COMPANY; *U.S. Private*, pg. 530
HOFFCO/COMET INDUSTRIES, INC.; *U.S. Private*, pg. 532
HOWARD MASCHINENFABRIK GMBH—Thrige-Titan Group; *Int'l*, pg. 1387
HOWARD S.A.—Thrige-Titan Group; *Int'l*, pg. 1387
H.D. HUDSON MANUFACTURING COMPANY; *U.S. Private*, pg. 545
ROBERT HUDSON (MACHINERY SALE & SERVICE) LTD.—Lonrho plc; *Int'l*, pg. 817
HUTCHINSON WIL-RICH MANUFACTURING CO.—TIC United Corporation; *U.S. Private*, pg. 1063
INDUSTRIAL DIV.—Federal Signal Corporation; *U.S. Public*, pg. 617
INTEGRATED TECHNICAL SYSTEMS (ITS)—Case Corporation; *U.S. Public*, pg. 311
IRRITOL SYSTEM—The Toro Company; *U.S. Public*, pg. 1624
J-STAR INDUSTRIES, INC.; *U.S. Private*, pg. 576
JACOBSEN TEXTRON—Textron Inc.; *U.S. Public*, pg. 1589
JONKOPINGS LANTMAN EK. FOR.; *Int'l*, pg. 714
KRAUSE PLOW CORP.; *U.S. Private*, pg. 635
KUBOTA CORP.; *Int'l*, pg. 762
LTR INDUSTRIES—Kimberly-Clark Corporation; *U.S. Public*, pg. 960
N.V. LAWN COMFORT S.A.—DSM N.V.; *Int'l*, pg. 355
LEMKEN TRI-AG LIMITED—Thrige-Titan Group; *Int'l*, pg. 1387
AB LIDINGO VERKSTADER—Tetra Laval Group; *Int'l*, pg. 1377
LINDSAY MANUFACTURING COMPANY; *U.S. Public*, pg. 999
LINDSAY TRANSPORTATION INC.—Lindsay Manufacturing Company; *U.S. Public*, pg. 1000
LONG MFG. NC, INC.; *U.S. Private*, pg. 674
LOR AL PRODUCTS INC—Ag-Chem Equipment Co., Inc.; *U.S. Public*, pg. 6
M&W—Alamo Group, Inc.; *U.S. Public*, pg. 35
MARINE & INDUSTRIAL PRODUCTS DIV.—Chrysler Corporation; *U.S. Public*, pg. 353
THE MARMON GROUP, INC.; *U.S. Private*, pg. 706
MARUBENI CORPORATION; *Int'l*, pg. 844
MILLER-ST. NAZIANZ, INC.; *U.S. Private*, pg. 748
MOORMAN'S INC.; *U.S. Private*, pg. 760
NANJING GOULDS PUMPS LIMITED—ITT Industries, Inc.; *U.S. Public*, pg. 861
NEBRASKA ENGINEERING CO.—TIC United Corporation; *U.S. Private*, pg. 1064
NEW HOLLAND LTD.—Fiat Auto SpA; *Int'l*, pg. 484
O.A. NEWTON & SON CO.; *U.S. Private*, pg. 797
NORDISK CASE A/S—Tenneco Inc.; *U.S. Public*, pg. 1580
NORDSTEN—Thrige-Titan Group; *Int'l*, pg. 1386
OMNIQUIP INTERNATIONAL, INC.—Harbour Group Ltd.; *U.S. Private*, pg. 500
AB OVERUMS BRUK—Electrolux, AB; *Int'l*, pg. 439
PAULS PLC—Harrisons & Crosfield plc; *Int'l*, pg. 598
POCLAIN DO BRASIL S.A.—Tenneco Inc.; *U.S. Public*, pg. 1580
POCLAIN HISPANA S.A.—Tenneco Inc.; *U.S. Public*, pg. 1580
PRYOR FOUNDRY, INC.—Case Corporation; *U.S. Public*, pg. 312
REINKE MANUFACTURING CO., INC.; *U.S. Private*, pg. 920
RENAULT; *Int'l*, pg. 1102
RICHARDTON MFG. CO.—United Dominion Industries, Ltd.; *U.S. Public*, pg. 1676
RITCHIE INDUSTRIES, INC.; *U.S. Private*, pg. 933
ROYER INDUSTRIES, INC.—Powerscreen International Plc; *Int'l*, pg. 1066
ROYER/MOGENSEN, INC.—Powerscreen International Plc; *Int'l*, pg. 1066
C.G. SARGENTS SONS—Aeroglide Corporation; *U.S. Private*, pg. 24
SAVILLE TRACTORS (BELFAST) LTD.—Lonrho plc; *Int'l*, pg. 817
THE SCOTTS COMPANY; *U.S. Public*, pg. 1446
SERVICE MOTOR CO.—Service Motor Company; *U.S. Private*, pg. 986
SERVICE MOTOR COMPANY; *U.S. Private*, pg. 986
SHENANDOAH MFG. CO. INC.; *U.S. Private*, pg. 992
THE SIAM KUBOTA INDUSTRY CO., LTD.—Kubota Corp.; *Int'l*, pg. 763
THE SIAM KUBOTA INDUSTRY CO., LTD.—The Siam Cement Public Company Limited; *Int'l*, pg. 1239
SIRMAC OFFICINE MECCANICHE SPA—Titan International, Inc.; *U.S. Public*, pg. 1619
A.O. SMITH CORPORATION; *U.S. Public*, pg. 1476
A.O. SMITH HARVESTORE PRODUCTS, INC.—A.O. Smith Corporation; *U.S. Public*, pg. 1477
SOUTH FRESH FARMS; *U.S. Private*, pg. 1014
SPICER OFF-HIGHWAY AXLE DIV.—Dana Corporation; *U.S. Public*, pg. 479
STEEL WHEELS, LTD.—Titan International, Inc.; *U.S. Public*, pg. 1619
STEIGER TRACTOR—Case Corporation; *U.S. Public*, pg. 311
STEVENS-LEE COMPANY; *U.S. Private*, pg. 1042
SUNFLOWER MFG. CO., INC.—United Dominion Industries, Ltd.; *U.S. Public*, pg. 1676
S.A. TENNECO BELGIUM (POCLAIN-MONROE-PETRO-TEX) N.V.—Tenneco Inc.; *U.S. Public*, pg. 1580
TENNECO INC.; *U.S. Public*, pg. 1577
THOMAS CONVEYOR COMPANY; *U.S. Private*, pg. 1082
THOMAS EQUIPMENT LIMITED—McCain Foods Limited; *Int'l*, pg. 850
THRIGE AGRO A/S—Thrige-Titan Group; *Int'l*, pg. 1386
THRIGE-TITAN GROUP; *Int'l*, pg. 1386
TITAN FRANCE SA—Titan International, Inc.; *U.S. Public*, pg. 1619
TITAN GERMANY GMBH—Titan International, Inc.; *U.S. Public*, pg. 1619
TITAN INTERNATIONAL, INC.; *U.S. Public*, pg. 1618
TITAN WHEEL CORPORATIO OF ILLINOIS—Titan International, Inc.; *U.S. Public*, pg. 1618
TOP AIR MANUFACTURING, INC.; *U.S. Public*, pg. 1621
THE TORO COMPANY; *U.S. Public*, pg. 1623
THE TORO COMPANY IRRIGATION PRODUCTS—The Toro Company; *U.S. Public*, pg. 1624
TRIUMPH MACHINE CO.—Alamo Group, Inc.; *U.S. Public*, pg. 35
TRUE TEMPER HARDWARE COMPANY—Huffy Corporation; *U.S. Public*, pg. 846
TYLER INDUSTRIES; *U.S. Private*, pg. 1112
UNIONTOOLS, INC.—Acorn Products, Inc.; *U.S. Public*, pg. 17
UNITED FARM TOOLS, INC.; *U.S. Private*, pg. 1122
UNIVERSAL COOPERATIVES, INC.; *U.S. Private*, pg. 1127
UNIVERSAL INDUSTRIAL PRODUCTS CO.—United Dominion Industries, Ltd.; *U.S. Public*, pg. 1677
UP-RIGHT, INC.; *U.S. Private*, pg. 1128
VACTOR MFG. INC.—Federal Signal Corporation; *U.S. Public*, pg. 617
VALMONT INDUSTRIES, INC.; *U.S. Public*, pg. 1706
VERMEER MANUFACTURING COMPANY; *U.S. Private*, pg. 1137
A/S VESTFROST—Electrolux, AB; *Int'l*, pg. 441
VIBRA SCREW INC.; *U.S. Private*, pg. 1138
WATVEARE LTD.—Lonrho plc; *Int'l*, pg. 817
WEATHER TEC CORPORATION; *U.S. Private*, pg. 1155
WESTMAC LTD.—Lonrho plc; *Int'l*, pg. 817
WIL-RICH NOBLE COMPANY—TIC United Corporation; *U.S. Private*, pg. 1064
WOOD EQUIPMENT COMPANY; *U.S. Private*, pg. 1186
WOODS EQUIPMENT COMPANY—Code, Hennessy & Simmons, Inc.; *U.S. Private*, pg. 249
WOODSTREAM CORPORATION—Ekco Group, Inc.; *U.S. Public*, pg. 566

3524 — LAWN & GARDEN TRACTORS & HOME LAWN & GARDEN EQUIPMENT

AIRCAP INDUSTRIES CORP.—MTD Products, Inc.; *U.S. Private*, pg. 688
AMERICAN HONDA MOTOR CO., INC.—Honda Motor Co., Ltd.; *Int'l*, pg. 634
ARITMOS AB—Proventus AB; *Int'l*, pg. 1072
BELMONT INDUSTRIES, INC.—RGP Holding, Inc.; *U.S. Private*, pg. 903
THE BLACK & DECKER CORPORATION; *U.S. Public*, pg. 233
BLOUNT, INC.—Blount International, Inc.; *U.S. Public*, pg. 238
BLOUNT INTERNATIONAL, INC.; *U.S. Public*, pg. 237
BUNTON DIVISION—Textron Inc.; *U.S. Public*, pg. 1589
CRUSTBUSTER, INC.; *U.S. Private*, pg. 293
DEERE & COMPANY; *U.S. Public*, pg. 491
THE DISSTON CO.—Kennametal Inc.; *U.S. Public*, pg. 950
DIXON INDUSTRIES, INC.—Blount International, Inc.; *U.S. Public*, pg. 238
ELECTROLUX, AB; *Int'l*, pg. 438
EXCEL INDUSTRIES, INC.; *U.S. Private*, pg. 387
FLANDRIA GARDEN N.V.—Proventus AB; *Int'l*, pg. 1072
FLOWTRON/GALAXIE DIVISION—Armatron International, Inc.; *U.S. Public*, pg. 131
FLYMO LTD.—Electrolux, AB; *Int'l*, pg. 444
FREDERICK MANUFACTURING CORPORATION—Blount International, Inc.; *U.S. Public*, pg. 238
FRIGIDAIRE HOME PRODUCTS—Electrolux, AB; *Int'l*, pg. 439
FRIGIDAIRE HOME PRODUCTS-SPECIALTY POWER EQUIPMENT—Electrolux, AB; *Int'l*, pg. 440
GARDEN WAY, INC.; *U.S. Private*, pg. 440
HCC INC.; *U.S. Private*, pg. 490
HAKO-WERKE GMBH & CO.; *Int'l*, pg. 587
HAVELLANDISCHE MASCHINENBAU GMBH—Hako-Werke GmbH & Co.; *Int'l*, pg. 587
HOFFCO/COMET INDUSTRIES, INC.; *U.S. Private*, pg. 532
HONDA MOTOR CO., LTD.; *Int'l*, pg. 634
HONDA POWER EQUIPMENT MANUFACTURING, INC.—Honda Motor Co., Ltd.; *Int'l*, pg. 635
INGERSOLL EQUIPMENT CO., INC.—Rothenberger Group GmbH; *Int'l*, pg. 1129
JACOBSEN TEXTRON—Textron Inc.; *U.S. Public*, pg. 1589
F. D. KEES POWER EQUIPMENT—Yazoo Power Equipment, LLC; *U.S. Private*, pg. 1195
LAWN-BOY INC.—The Toro Company; *U.S. Public*, pg. 1624
LESCO, INC.; *U.S. Public*, pg. 989
MTD PRODUCTS, INC.; *U.S. Private*, pg. 688
MTD PRODUCTS LIMITED—MTD Products, Inc.; *U.S. Private*, pg. 688
MATSUSHITA ELECTRIC WORKS, LTD.; *Int'l*, pg. 847
METROMEDIA INTERNATIONAL GROUP, INC.; *U.S. Public*, pg. 1102
THE MURRAY OHIO MFG. CO.—Tomkins PLC; *Int'l*, pg. 1397
NEW HOLLAND LTD.—Fiat Auto SpA; *Int'l*, pg. 484
ORBEX INC.—Blount International, Inc.; *U.S. Public*, pg. 238
PARK-OHIO INDUSTRIES, INC.; *U.S. Public*, pg. 1258
RGP HOLDING, INC.; *U.S. Private*, pg. 903
RANSOMES INC.—Ransomes Plc; *Int'l*, pg. 1088
RANSOMES PLC; *Int'l*, pg. 1087
ROTHENBERGER GROUP GMBH; *Int'l*, pg. 1127
SIMPLICITY MANUFACTURING, INC.; *U.S. Private*, pg. 1002
SNAPPER POWER EQUIPMENT—Metromedia International Group, Inc.; *U.S. Public*, pg. 1103
SPICER OFF-HIGHWAY AXLE DIV.—Dana Corporation; *U.S. Public*, pg. 479
STEINER TURF EQUIPMENT INC.—Ransomes Plc; *Int'l*, pg. 1088
SUNBEAM CORPORATION; *U.S. Public*, pg. 1533
SUPERIA N.V.—Proventus AB; *Int'l*, pg. 1072
THE TORO COMPANY; *U.S. Public*, pg. 1623
TORO KANSAS—The Toro Company; *U.S. Public*, pg. 1624
TORO-WHEEL HORSE—The Toro Company; *U.S. Public*, pg. 1624
TRUE TEMPER HARDWARE COMPANY—Huffy Corporation; *U.S. Public*, pg. 846
UNIONTOOLS, INC.—Acorn Products, Inc.; *U.S. Public*, pg. 17
WHITE CONSOLIDATED INDUSTRIES, INC.—Electrolux, AB; *Int'l*, pg. 439
YAZOO POWER EQUIPMENT, LLC; *U.S. Private*, pg. 1195

3531 — CONSTRUCTION MACHINERY & EQUIPMENT

ABG-FRANCE S.A.R.L.—Ingersoll-Rand Company; *U.S. Public*, pg. 877
ANI STRATA PRODUCTS—Australian National Industries Limited; *Int'l*, pg. 100
ANI WEAR RESISTANT PRODUCTS—Australian National Industries Limited; *Int'l*, pg. 100
APAC HOLDINGS, INC.—Ashland, Inc.; *U.S. Public*, pg. 139
ACCESS EQUIPMENT LTD.—Up-Right, Inc.; *U.S. Private*, pg. 1128
ALLIED CONSTRUCTION PRODUCTS, INC.—Pubco Corporation; *U.S. Public*, pg. 1339
ALLSPANN, ALLGEMEINE SPANNBETON GMBH—Dyckerhoff & Widmann AG; *Int'l*, pg. 423
ALTEC INDUSTRIES, INC.; *U.S. Private*, pg. 47
AMCLYDE ENGINEERED PRODUCTS CO., INC.—Halter Marine Group, Inc.; *U.S. Public*, pg. 778
AMCLYDE GULF COAST DIVISION—Halter Marine Group, Inc.; *U.S. Public*, pg. 778
AMERICAN FINANCIAL GROUP—American Financial Group; *U.S. Public*, pg. 75

AMQUIP (PROPRIETARY) LIMITED—Anglo American Corporation of South Africa Limited; *Int'l*, pg. 76
ANCRA INTERNATIONAL LLC; *U.S. Private*, pg. 71
ARNOLD MACHINERY COMPANY; *U.S. Private*, pg. 84
ASTEC, INC.—Astec Industries, Inc.; *U.S. Public*, pg. 141
ASTEC INDUSTRIES, INC.; *U.S. Public*, pg. 141
ASTRA VEICOLI INDUSTRIALI S.P.A.; *Int'l*, pg. 94
ATHEY PRODUCTS CORPORATION; *U.S. Public*, pg. 142
ATLAS COPCO AB; *Int'l*, pg. 95
ATLAS COPCO ACT—Atlas Copco AB; *Int'l*, pg. 96
ATLAS COPCO ROCKDRILLING EQUIPMENT—Atlas Copco AB; *Int'l*, pg. 96
ATLAS COPCO WAGNER INC.—Atlas Copco AB; *Int'l*, pg. 96
AUSCO PRODUCTS, INC.—The Cypress Companies; *U.S. Private*, pg. 299
AUTOMATIC EQUIPMENT MFG. CO.; *U.S. Private*, pg. 101
AVIS INDUSTRIAL CORPORATION; *U.S. Private*, pg. 102
BABCOCK JENKINS LTD.—FKI Plc; *Int'l*, pg. 472
BABCOCK SPRAYMIXER LTD—FKI Plc; *Int'l*, pg. 472
BABCOCK TRIPPLEJAY—Babcock International Group PLC; *Int'l*, pg. 131
BADGER EQUIPMENT CO.—Avis Industrial Corporation; *U.S. Private*, pg. 102
BALDERSON INC.—Caterpillar Inc.; *U.S. Public*, pg. 315
BARKO HYDRAULICS—Pettibone Corporation; *U.S. Private*, pg. 859
BEACON WINCH COMPANY—Beacon Group; *U.S. Private*, *pg. 126*
BEARDSLEY & PIPER, L.L.C.—Pettibone Corporation; *U.S. Private*, pg. 859
BERCO S.P.A.—Fried. Krupp AG; *Int'l*, pg. 511
BESSER COMPANY; *U.S. Private*, pg. 139
BIDWELL DIV.—CMI Corporation; *U.S. Public*, pg. 279
BLOUNT, INC. FORESTRY & INDUSTRIAL EQUIPMENT DIVISION—Blount International, Inc.; *U.S. Public*, pg. 238
BLOUNT INTERNATIONAL, INC.; *U.S. Public*, pg. 237
BLUFFTON AGRI/INDUSTRIAL CORP. D/B/A BAIC—Farmatic Research, Inc.; *Int'l*, pg. 478
BOLIDEN ALLIS AB—Trelleborg AB; *Int'l*, pg. 1423
BRETEC INC.—Tamrock Corp.; *Int'l*, pg. 1352
BRETEC OY—Tamrock Corp.; *Int'l*, pg. 1352
JERED BROWN BROTHERS INC.—Vickers PLC; *Int'l*, pg. 1468
BUCYRUS BLADES DE MEXICO—Esco Corporation; *U.S. Private*, pg. 383
BUCYRUS BLADES OF CANADA LTD.—Esco Corporation; *U.S. Private*, pg. 383
BUCYRUS INTERNATIONAL; *U.S. Private*, pg. 177
BULKLIFT A/S—Norsk Vekst ASA; *Int'l*, pg. 965
BUTTERLEY ENGINEERING LTD.—Haden Maclellan Holdings plc; *Int'l*, pg. 585
CAE MACHINERY LTD.—CAE Inc.; *Int'l*, pg. 237
CMI CORPORATION; *U.S. Public*, pg. 278
THE CADMAN COMPANIES—Heidelberger Zement A.G.; *Int'l*, pg. 605
CANADIAN KAWASAKI MOTORS INC.—Kawasaki Heavy Industries, Ltd.; *Int'l*, pg. 726
CAPITAL EQUIPMENT DIV.—Athey Products Corporation; *U.S. Public*, pg. 143
CASE CE DIV.-WAUSAU—Case Corporation; *U.S. Public*, pg. 311
CASE CE WICHITA DIV.—Case Corporation; *U.S. Public*, pg. 311
CASE CORPORATION; *U.S. Public*, pg. 311
CASE ENGINE HOLDING COMPANY, INC.—Case Corporation; *U.S. Public*, pg. 311
CASE FRANCE, S.A.—Tenneco Inc.; *U.S. Public*, pg. 1579
CASE FRANCE S.A.—Tenneco Inc.; *U.S. Public*, pg. 1579
J.I. CASE SWEDEN AB—Tenneco Inc.; *U.S. Public*, pg. 1580
CASE POCLAIN GMBH & CO.—Tenneco Inc.; *U.S. Public*, pg. 1579
CASE TRACTEURS, S.A.—Tenneco Inc.; *U.S. Public*, pg. 1579
CASE TRAKTOREN GMBH—Tenneco Inc.; *U.S. Public*, pg. 1579
CASE TRAKTORI OY—Tenneco Inc.; *U.S. Public*, pg. 1579
CATERPILLAR INC.; *U.S. Public*, pg. 315
CEDARAPIDS, INC.—Raytheon Company; *U.S. Public*, pg. 1365
CHARLES MACHINE WORKS, INC.; *U.S. Private*, pg. 230
CHICAGO WEST PULLMAN HEAVY INDUSTRIES—Chicago West Pullman Corporation; *U.S. Private*, pg. 236
CIMENTS FRANCAIS; *Int'l*, pg. 292
CLARK MATERIAL HANDLING COMPANY; *U.S. Private*, pg. 243
COMPANIA INGERSOLL ESPANOLA, S.A.—Ingersoll-Rand Company; *U.S. Public*, pg. 878
COMPONENTA INTERNATIONAL B.V.—Trelleborg AB; *Int'l*, pg. 1421
COMPONENTA VAGSTAL AB—Trelleborg AB; *Int'l*, pg. 1421
COMPONENTS DIV.—Case Corporation; *U.S. Public*, pg. 311
CONLEY FROG/SWITCH & FORGE CO.; *U.S. Private*, pg. 263
CONSTRUCCIONES AGROMETALICAS LEVANTE, S.A. (CALSA)—Tenneco Inc.; *U.S. Public*, pg. 1579
CONSTRUCTION EQUIPMENT DIV.—Case Corporation; *U.S. Public*, pg. 311
CRAFCO, INC.—Ergon, Inc.; *U.S. Private*, pg. 381
CRANE MANUFACTURING; *U.S. Private*, pg. 286
CRAWLER SYSTEMS—Fried. Krupp AG; *Int'l*, pg. 511
CRENLO, INC.; *U.S. Private*, pg. 288
CROWN HOLDINGS, INC.; *U.S. Private*, pg. 293
CROWN IRON WORKS COMPANY—Crown Holdings, Inc.; *U.S. Private*, pg. 293
CTR MANUFACTURING, INC.—Blount International, Inc.; *U.S. Public*, pg. 238
DAEWOO CORPORATION; *Int'l*, pg. 357
DAEWOO HEAVY INDUSTRIES, LTD.—Daewoo Corporation; *Int'l*, pg. 357
DANUSER MACHINE CO.; *U.S. Private*, pg. 310
DAVY INTERNATIONAL—Kvaerner a.s.a.; *Int'l*, pg. 773
DEERE & COMPANY; *U.S. Public*, pg. 491
JOHN DEERE DAVENPORT WORKS—Deere & Company; *U.S. Public*, pg. 492
JOHN DEERE DUBUQUE WORKS—Deere & Company; *U.S. Public*, pg. 492
DEGGENDORFER WERFT UND EISENBAU GMBH—MAN Aktiengesellschaft; *Int'l*, pg. 824
DEMIX BETON/AGREGATS—Holderbank Financiere Glaris Ltd.; *Int'l*, pg. 629
DEUTZ AG; *Int'l*, pg. 407
DOVATECH, LTD.—Dover Corporation; *U.S. Public*, pg. 520
DUTTON-LAINSON CO.; *U.S. Private*, pg. 350
DYNAPAC AB—Trelleborg AB; *Int'l*, pg. 1420
DYNAPAC CONCRETE EQUIPMENT AB—Trelleborg AB; *Int'l*, pg. 1420
DYNAPAC HEAVY EQUIPMENT AB—Trelleborg AB; *Int'l*, pg. 1420
DYNAPAC LIGHT EQUIPMENT AB—Trelleborg AB; *Int'l*, pg. 1420
DYNAPAC MFG. INC.—Trelleborg AB; *Int'l*, pg. 1420
DYNAPAC NORDEN AB—Trelleborg AB; *Int'l*, pg. 1420
EEI CORPORATION; *Int'l*, pg. 425
EAGER BEAVER; *U.S. Private*, pg. 354
EAGLE ENGINEERING & MANUFACTURING, INC.—Dreison International, Inc.; *U.S. Private*, pg. 342
EARTHMOVING EQUIPMENT DIV.—Esco Corporation; *U.S. Private*, pg. 383
ELJAY DIVISION—Raytheon Company; *U.S. Public*, pg. 1365
ELLICOTT MACHINE CORPORATION INTERNATIONAL; *U.S. Private*, pg. 372
ESCO CORPORATION; *U.S. Private*, pg. 382
ESCO, EUROPE S.A.—Esco Corporation; *U.S. Private*, pg. 383
ESCO, S.A.—Esco Corporation; *U.S. Private*, pg. 383
EUCLID HITACHI—Hitachi, Ltd.; *Int'l*, pg. 622
EUCLID HITACHI—AB Volvo; *Int'l*, pg. 1477
EVANS INDUSTRIES, INC.; *U.S. Private*, pg. 385
FLS INDUSTRIES A/S; *Int'l*, pg. 474
FMC ENERGY & TRANSPORTATION EQUIPMENT GROUP—FMC Corporation; *U.S. Public*, pg. 605
FERGUSON MANUFACTURING & EQUIPMENT COMPANY, INC.; *U.S. Private*, pg. 401
FERMEC HOLDINGS, LTD.—Case Corporation; *U.S. Public*, *pg. 312*
FIAT-ALLIS B.V.—Fiat Auto SpA; *Int'l*, pg. 483
FIAT AUTO SPA; *Int'l*, pg. 480
FIATGEOTECH S.P.A.—Fiat Auto SpA; *Int'l*, pg. 484
FINMECCANICA S.P.A.—IRI Istituto Ricostruzione Industriale; *Int'l*, pg. 653
FREEDOM FORGE CORPORATION; *U.S. Private*, pg. 425
FROG SWITCH & MANUFACTURING COMPANY; *U.S. Private*, pg. 429
GH HENSLEY INDUSTRIES, INC.—Galveston-Houston Company; *U.S. Private*, pg. 439
GIS MUNSTERS B.V.—Royal Begemann Group; *Int'l*, pg. 1133
GKN WHEELS—GKN plc; *Int'l*, pg. 535
GALVESTON-HOUSTON COMPANY; *U.S. Private*, pg. 438
GEHL COMPANY; *U.S. Public*, pg. 704
GEHL POWER PRODUCTS, INC.—Gehl Company; *U.S. Public*, pg. 704
GENCOR INDUSTRIES, INC.; *U.S. Public*, pg. 705
GLOUCESTER RAILWAY CARRIAGE & WAGON COMPANY LTD.—FKI Plc; *Int'l*, pg. 473
GOODMAN EQUIPMENT CORP.; *U.S. Private*, pg. 464
GROUPE GTM—Lyonnaise des Eaux S.A.; *Int'l*, pg. 823
GROVE EUROPE—Hanson PLC; *Int'l*, pg. 592
GROVE WORLDWIDE—Hanson PLC; *Int'l*, pg. 593
HALTEN GMBH & CO. KG—Franz Haniel & Cie, GmbH; *Int'l*, pg. 592
HANSON PLC; *Int'l*, pg. 592
HAWTHORNE LIFT SYSTEMS—Hawthorne Machinery Company; *U.S. Private*, pg. 513
HEDLUND-MARTIN INC.—Gehl Company; *U.S. Public*, pg. 704
HERCULES GRANDLAGGNING AB—NCC AB; *Int'l*, pg. 899
HIGHWAY EQUIPMENT COMPANY; *U.S. Private*, pg. 529
HITACHI CONSTRUCTION MACHINERY CO., LTD.—Hitachi, Ltd.; *Int'l*, pg. 621
HITACHI KIDEN KOGYO, LTD.—Hitachi, Ltd.; *Int'l*, pg. 621
HITACHI ZOSEN CORPORATION; *Int'l*, pg. 622
HOESCH ROTHE ERDE AG—Fried. Krupp AG; *Int'l*, pg. 509
HYUNDAI HEAVY INDUSTRIES CO., LTD.—Hyundai Motor Company; *Int'l*, pg. 641
INCENTIVE AB; *Int'l*, pg. 666
INGERSOLL-RAND AB—Ingersoll-Rand Company; *U.S. Public*, pg. 878
INGERSOLL-RAND COMPANY; *U.S. Public*, pg. 876
IOWA MOLD TOOLING CO., INC.—Intermet Corporation; *U.S. Public*, pg. 894
JEUMONT-SCHNEIDER TRENFORMETEURS; *Int'l*, pg. 706
JOHNSON ROSS CORPORATION—CMI Corporation; *U.S. Public*, pg. 279
KING FISHER, INC.—Seaman Timber Company, Inc.; *U.S. Private*, pg. 979
KLEIN TOOLS INC.; *U.S. Private*, pg. 625
KLOECKNER-WILHELMSBURGER GMBH—Klockner-Werke AG; *Int'l*, pg. 737
KOKOSING MATERIALS, INC.—Kokosing Construction Company, Inc.; *U.S. Private*, pg. 631
KOMATSU AMERICA INTERNATIONAL COMPANY—Komatsu Ltd.; *Int'l*, pg. 744
KOMATSU LTD.; *Int'l*, pg. 743
KOMATSU UK, LTD.—Komatsu Ltd.; *Int'l*, pg. 744
KRAUSE PLOW CORP.; *U.S. Private*, pg. 635
KRUPP INDUSTRIES INDIA LTD.—Fried. Krupp AG; *Int'l*, pg. 511
KRUPP MASCHINENTECHNIK GMBH—Fried. Krupp AG; *Int'l*, pg. 510
KRUPP MOBILKRANE GMBH—Fried. Krupp AG; *Int'l*, pg. 510
KRUPP POLYSIUS AG—Fried. Krupp AG; *Int'l*, pg. 512
KUBOTA CORP.; *Int'l*, pg. 762
KUMAGAI GUMI CO., LTD.; *Int'l*, pg. 763
KVAERNER-JOHN BROWN LTD.—Kvaerner a.s.a.; *Int'l*, pg. 773
LAFAYETTE PRECAST—Walters & Wolf; *U.S. Private*, pg. 1149
LE TOURNEAU, INC.—Rowan Companies, Inc.; *U.S. Public*, pg. 1410
LIAONING LIEBHERR HYDRAULIC EXCAVATOR CO. LTD.—Liebherr-International AG; *Int'l*, pg. 807
LIAONING LIEBHERR WHEEL LOADER CO. LTD.—Liebherr-International AG; *Int'l*, pg. 807
LIEBHERR BRASIL LTDA.—Liebherr-International AG; *Int'l*, *pg. 808*
LIEBHERR CONTAINER CRANES LTD.—Liebherr-International AG; *Int'l*, pg. 809
LIEBHERR-FRANCE S.A.—Liebherr-International AG; *Int'l*, pg. 808
LIEBHERR-HYDRAULIKBAGGER GMBH—Liebherr-International AG; *Int'l*, pg. 808
LIEBHERR INDUSTRIAS METALICAS, S.A.—Liebherr-International AG; *Int'l*, pg. 808
LIEBHERR-MISCHTECHNIK GMBH—Liebherr-International AG; *Int'l*, pg. 808
LIEBHERR-THAILAND CO., LTD.—Liebherr-International AG; *Int'l*, pg. 809
LIEBHERR-WERK BIBERACH GMBH—Liebherr-International AG; *Int'l*, pg. 808
LIEBHERR-WERK BISCHOFSHOFEN GMBH—Liebherr-International AG; *Int'l*, pg. 808
LIEBHERR-WERK EHINGEN GMBH—Liebherr-International AG; *Int'l*, pg. 808
LIEBHERR-WERK NENZING GMBH—Liebherr-International AG; *Int'l*, pg. 808
LIEBHERR-WERK TELFS GMBH—Liebherr-International AG; *Int'l*, pg. 808
LIGHTNIN MIXERS LIMITED—General Signal Corporation; *U.S. Public*, pg. 727
LONGWALL INTERNATIONAL LIMITED—Harnischfeger Industries, Inc.; *U.S. Public*, pg. 789
MAN AKTIENGESELLSCHAFT; *Int'l*, pg. 824
MAN GHH LOGISTICS GMBH—MAN Aktiengesellschaft; *Int'l*, pg. 824
MAN TECHNOLOGIE AG—MAN Aktiengesellschaft; *Int'l*, pg. 825
M.E. MACK VALVES PTY. LIMITED—Senior Engineering Group, plc.; *Int'l*, pg. 1222
MANITEX, INC.—The Manitowoc Company, Inc.; *U.S. Public*, pg. 1041
THE MANITOWOC COMPANY, INC.; *U.S. Public*, pg. 1040
MANITOWOC RE-MANUFACTURING, INC.—The Manitowoc Company, Inc.; *U.S. Public*, pg. 1041
MANNESMANN A.G.; *Int'l*, pg. 834
MANNESMANN DEMAG CORPORATION—Mannesmann A.G.; *Int'l*, pg. 837
MANNESMANN DEMAG FORDERTECHNIK AG—Mannesmann A.G.; *Int'l*, pg. 837
MANNESMANN DEMAG MATERIAL HANDLING LTD.—Mannesmann A.G.; *Int'l*, pg. 837
MANNESMANN DEMAG S.A.—Mannesmann A.G.; *Int'l*, pg. 837
MCNEILUS COMPANIES; *U.S. Private*, pg. 725
MELROE COMPANY—Ingersoll-Rand Company; *U.S. Public*, pg. 877
MI-JACK PRODUCTS, INC.; *U.S. Private*, pg. 740
MIKROPUL ENVIRONMENTAL SYSTEMS DIV.—Hosokawa Micron Corporation; *Int'l*, pg. 636
MINING EQUIPMENT DIVISION—Harnischfeger Industries, Inc.; *U.S. Public*, pg. 788
MINNESOTA POWER; *U.S. Public*, pg. 1116
MITSUBISHI HEAVY INDUSTRIES LTD.; *Int'l*, pg. 873
MITSUI CONCRETE INDUSTRIES CO., LTD.—Mitsui & Co., Ltd.; *Int'l*, pg. 877
MITSUI MATSUSHIMA CO., LTD.—Mitsui & Co., Ltd.; *Int'l*, pg. 877
MITSUI PRECON CO., LTD.—Mitsui & Co., Ltd.; *Int'l*, pg. 877
MUSTANG MANUFACTURING COMPANY, INC.—Gehl Company; *U.S. Public*, pg. 704
MUSTANG TRACTOR & EQUIP. CO.; *U.S. Private*, pg. 768
NATIONAL CRANE—Hanson PLC; *Int'l*, pg. 593
P.T. NATRA RAYA—Caterpillar Inc.; *U.S. Public*, pg. 317
NEW HOLLAND LTD.—Fiat Auto SpA; *Int'l*, pg. 484
NOKIA SOURCING, INC.—Oy Nokia Ab/Nokia Group; *Int'l*, pg. 953
NORCEM INDUSTRIER—Aker Raj Asa; *Int'l*, pg. 42
NORDBERG-READ, INC.—UPM-Kymmene Corporation; *Int'l*, pg. 1428
NORDISK CASE A/S—Tenneco Inc.; *U.S. Public*, pg. 1580
NYBRO SMIDE—Trelleborg AB; *Int'l*, pg. 1421
O&K ANTRIEBSTECHNIK GMBH, HATTINGEN WORKS—Fried. Krupp AG; *Int'l*, pg. 516
O&K ORENSTEIN & KOPPEL AKTIENGESELLSCHAFT—Fried. Krupp AG; *Int'l*, pg. 516
OTIS ENGINEERING INTERNATIONAL—Halliburton Company; *U.S. Public*, pg. 777
OTIS INTERNATIONAL, LTD.—Halliburton Company; *U.S. Public*, pg. 777
OTIS NIGERIA, LTD.—Halliburton Company; *U.S. Public*, pg. 777
PACCAR INC.; *U.S. Public*, pg. 1246
PACCAR WINCH DIVISION—Paccar Inc.; *U.S. Public*, pg. 1246
PACKAGING AND MATERIAL HANDLING EQUIPMENT DIV.—FMC Corporation; *U.S. Public*, pg. 606
PAPER CALMENSON & CO.; *U.S. Private*, pg. 837
PARK CORP.; *U.S. Private*, pg. 839
PETTIBONE CORPORATION; *U.S. Private*, pg. 859

PETTIBONE MICHIGAN DIV.—Pettibone Corporation; *U.S. Private*, pg. 860
POCLAIN DO BRASIL S.A.—Tenneco Inc.; *U.S. Public*, pg. 1580
POCLAIN HISPANA S.A.—Tenneco Inc.; *U.S. Public*, pg. 1580
PORTEC, INC.; *U.S. Public*, pg. 1317
PORTEC, INC.-CONSTRUCTION EQUIPMENT DIV.—Portec, Inc.; *U.S. Public*, pg. 1318
POWELL EQUIPMENT LTD.; *Int'l*, pg. 1066
PRECON AB—Scancem AB; *Int'l*, pg. 1199
QUEBEC & MARITIMES DIV. ST. LAWRENCE CEMENT—Holderbank Financiere Glaris Ltd.; *Int'l*, pg. 629
R.A. INDUSTRIES, INC.; *U.S. Private*, pg. 902
RACINE FEDERATED, INC.; *U.S. Private*, pg. 906
THE RADOS COMPANIES; *U.S. Private*, pg. 907
RAMMER DEUTSCHLAND GMBH—Tamrock Corp.; *Int'l*, pg. 1352
RAMMER INC.—Tamrock Corp.; *Int'l*, pg. 1352
RAMMER NORGE A/S—Tamrock Corp.; *Int'l*, pg. 1352
RAMMER OY—Tamrock Corp.; *Int'l*, pg. 1352
RAMMER OY JAPAN OFFICE—Tamrock Corp.; *Int'l*, pg. 1352
RAMMER SVENSKA AB—Tamrock Corp.; *Int'l*, pg. 1352
RAPID INDUSTRIES, INC.; *U.S. Private*, pg. 910
RAWSON-KOENIG, INC.; *U.S. Public*, pg. 1362
RAYTHEON COMPANY; *U.S. Public*, pg. 1364
REXWORKS INC.; *U.S. Private*, pg. 926
ROADTEC, INC.—Astec Industries, Inc.; *U.S. Public*, pg. 141
ROBOT POMPEN B.V.—Trelleborg AB; *Int'l*, pg. 1421
ROSCO MANUFACTURING CO.; *U.S. Private*, pg. 944
SIG SCHWEIZERSICHE INDUSTRIE-GESELLSCHAFT HOLDING AG; *Int'l*, pg. 1156
SLC S.A. INDUSTRIA E COMERCIO—Deere & Company; *U.S. Public*, pg. 493
ST. LAWRENCE CEMENT INC.—Holderbank Financiere Glaris Ltd.; *Int'l*, pg. 628
SANDVIK ROCK TOOLS SVENSKA FORSALJNINGS AB—Sandvik AB; *Int'l*, pg. 1185
SCHWING GMBH; *Int'l*, pg. 1211
SENIOR AUSTRALIA LIMITED—Senior Engineering Group, plc.; *Int'l*, pg. 1222
SENIOR ENGINEERING—Senior Engineering Group, plc.; *Int'l*, pg. 1222
SENIOR ENGINEERING COMPANY-USA—Senior Engineering Group, plc.; *Int'l*, pg. 1222
SENIOR ENGINEERING (PTY) LIMITED-SOUTH AFRICA—Senior Engineering Group, plc.; *Int'l*, pg. 1223
SENIOR THERMAL ENGINEERING LIMITED—Senior Engineering Group, plc.; *Int'l*, pg. 1221
SENIOR TIFT AUSTRALIA PTY LIMITED—Senior Engineering Group, plc.; *Int'l*, pg. 1223
SHIN CATERPILLAR MITSUBISHI LTD.—Caterpillar Inc.; *U.S. Public*, pg. 317
SHOWA AIRCRAFT INDUSTRY CO., LTD.—Mitsui & Co., Ltd.; *Int'l*, pg. 878
THE SIAM CEMENT PUBLIC COMPANY LIMITED; *Int'l*, pg. 1237
SIAM-HITACHI CONSTRUCTION MACHINERY CO., LTD.—The Siam Cement Public Company Limited; *Int'l*, pg. 1238
SIMON ACCESS (U.K.) LTD.—Simon Engineering plc; *Int'l*, pg. 1251
SIMON AERIALS INC.—Simon Engineering plc; *Int'l*, pg. 1252
SIMON AERIALS LTD.—Simon Engineering plc; *Int'l*, pg. 1252
SIMON-CELLA S.R.L.—Simon Engineering plc; *Int'l*, pg. 1252
SIMON-R O CORP.—Simon Engineering plc; *Int'l*, pg. 1252
SIMON-TELELECT INC.—Simon Engineering plc; *Int'l*, pg. 1252
F.L. SMIDTH & CO. A/S—FLS Industries A/S; *Int'l*, pg. 475
T.L. SMITH MACHINE; *U.S. Private*, pg. 1009
SNORKEL—Harbour Group Ltd.; *U.S. Private*, pg. 500
SOLAR TURBINES INCORPORATED—Caterpillar Inc.; *U.S. Public*, pg. 316
SPICER OFF-HIGHWAY AXLE DIV.—Dana Corporation; *U.S. Public*, pg. 479
SSANGYONG HEAVY INDUSTRIES CO., LTD.—Ssangyong Business Group; *Int'l*, pg. 1292
STAMLER CORPORATION—The Oldenburg Group Companies; *U.S. Private*, pg. 814
STANDARD HAVENS—Raytheon Company; *U.S. Public*, pg. 1365
STEIGER TRACTOR—Case Corporation; *U.S. Public*, pg. 311
SVEDALA INDUSTRI AB; *Int'l*, pg. 1323
TBG MANAGEMENT S.A.M.; *Int'l*, pg. 1335
TAMPO INDUSTRIES INC.—Trelleborg AB; *Int'l*, pg. 1420
TARMAC PLC; *Int'l*, pg. 1355
TARMAC TOPMIX LIMITED—Tarmac plc; *Int'l*, pg. 1355
TATA ENGINEERING & LOCOMOTIVE CO. LTD. (TELCO)—Daimler-Benz Aktiengesellschaft; *Int'l*, pg. 369
TATA ENGINEERING & LOCOMOTIVE CO. LTD. (TELCO)—The Tata Iron and Steel Co. Ltd.; *Int'l*, pg. 1356
TELEFLEX INCORPORATED; *U.S. Public*, pg. 1569
TELSMITH, INC.—Astec Industries, Inc.; *U.S. Public*, pg. 141
S.A. TENNECO BELGIUM (POCLAIN-MONROE-PETRO-TEX) N.V.—Tenneco Inc.; *U.S. Public*, pg. 1580
TENNECO EUROPE—Tenneco Inc.; *U.S. Public*, pg. 1580
TENNECO INC.; *U.S. Public*, pg. 1577
TEREX CORPORATION; *U.S. Public*, pg. 1581
THOMAS EQUIPMENT LIMITED—McCain Foods Limited; *Int'l*, pg. 850
TITAN INTERNATIONAL, INC.; *U.S. Public*, pg. 1618
TODD PACIFIC SHIPYARDS CORP.; *U.S. Public*, pg. 1619
TOKYO RYUKI SEIZO CO., LTD.—Ingersoll-Rand Company; *U.S. Public*, pg. 878
TRACTOR ENGINEERS LIMITED—Caterpillar Inc.; *U.S. Public*, pg. 317
TRAKTOR-ERSATZTEIL-GESELLSCHAFT MBH—Fried. Krupp AG; *Int'l*, pg. 511
TREMIX AB—Svedala Industri AB; *Int'l*, pg. 1324
TREMIX AB—Trelleborg AB; *Int'l*, pg. 1420
TRENCOR, INC.—Astec Industries, Inc.; *U.S. Public*, pg. 141
UDDEHOLM TOOLING AB—Voest-Alpine Stahl AG; *Int'l*, pg. 1471
UNITED DOMINION INDUSTRIES, LTD.; *U.S. Public*, pg. 1675
UNITIKA LTD.; *Int'l*, pg. 1444
UNIVERSAL BUILDERS SUPPLY, INC.; *U.S. Private*, pg. 1126
UNIVERSAL INDUSTRIAL PRODUCTS CO.—United Dominion Industries, Ltd.; *U.S. Public*, pg. 1677
UP-RIGHT, INC.; *U.S. Private*, pg. 1128
UPRIGHT—Up-Right, Inc.; *U.S. Private*, pg. 1128
VALK MANUFACTURING COMPANY; *U.S. Private*, pg. 1131
VIBCO INC.; *U.S. Private*, pg. 1138
VICKERS TRUCK EQUIPMENT—Arnold Machinery Company; *U.S. Private*, pg. 84
VIPAC VIBRATOR AB—Trelleborg AB; *Int'l*, pg. 1420
VOLVO CONSTRUCTION EQUIPMENT—AB Volvo; *Int'l*, pg. 1477
VOLVO EXCAVATORS AB—AB Volvo; *Int'l*, pg. 1477
VON ROLL AG DEPARTEMENT MASCHINEN & FORDERTECHN—Von Roll AG; *Int'l*, pg. 1480
WEATHERFORD—Weatherford Enterra Incorporated; *U.S. Public*, pg. 1749
WELLHEAD EQUIPMENT DIVISION—FMC Corporation; *U.S. Public*, pg. 605
WHITE CONSOLIDATED INDUSTRIES, INC.—Electrolux, AB; *Int'l*, pg. 439
WILLIAMS ADVANCED MATERIALS, INC.—Brush Wellman Inc.; *U.S. Public*, pg. 266
THE WYCO TOOL CO.—Racine Federated, Inc.; *U.S. Private*, pg. 906
XTEK, INC.; *U.S. Private*, pg. 1194
XUZHOU LIEBHERR CONCRETE MACHINERY CO. LTD.—Liebherr-International AG; *Int'l*, pg. 808
ZIMMERMAN HOLDINGS, INC.; *U.S. Private*, pg. 1206

3532 — MINING MACHINERY & EQUIPMENT, EXCEPT OIL & GAS FIELD MACHINERY EQUIPMENT

A & A ASSOCIATES—Zimmerman Holdings, Inc.; *U.S. Private*, pg. 1206
ANI MINERAL PROCESSING—Australian National Industries Limited; *Int'l*, pg. 100
ACRISON, INC.; *U.S. Private*, pg. 14
ALIMAK ELEVATOR COMPANY; *U.S. Private*, pg. 34
AMERICAN LONGWALL REBUILD INC.—Harnischfeger Industries, Inc.; *U.S. Public*, pg. 789
AMQUIP (PROPRIETARY) LIMITED—Anglo American Corporation of South Africa Limited; *Int'l*, pg. 76
ANSALDO INDUSTRIA S.P.A.—IRI Istituto Ricostruzione Industriale; *Int'l*, pg. 653
ARDCO/TRAVERSE LIFT—Pettibone Corporation; *U.S. Private*, pg. 859
ATLAS COPCO AB; *Int'l*, pg. 95
BAKER HUGHES MINING TOOLS, INC.—Baker Hughes Incorporated; *U.S. Public*, pg. 166
BAKER HUGHES PROCESS SYSTEMS COMPANY—Baker Hughes Incorporated; *U.S. Public*, pg. 166
BIJUR LUBRICATING CORPORATION; *U.S. Private*, pg. 143
BLUE TEE CORPORATION; *U.S. Private*, pg. 153
BOART LONGYEAR PTY. LTD.—Anglo American Corporation of South Africa Limited; *Int'l*, pg. 76
BOONVILLE MINING SERVICES, INC.—Bucyrus International; *U.S. Private*, pg. 177
BRETEC INC.—Tamrock Corp.; *Int'l*, pg. 1352
BRETEC OY—Tamrock Corp.; *Int'l*, pg. 1352
BRILLION IRON WORKS, INC.—Johnstown America Industries; *U.S. Public*, pg. 933
BUCYRUS (AFRICA) PROPRIETARY LTD.—Bucyrus International; *U.S. Private*, pg. 177
BUCYRUS (AUSTRALIA) PROPRIETARY LTD.—Bucyrus International; *U.S. Private*, pg. 177
BUCYRUS (BRASIL) LTDA.—Bucyrus International; *U.S. Private*, pg. 177
BUCYRUS CHILE LTDA.—Bucyrus International; *U.S. Private*, pg. 177
BUCYRUS-ERIE CO. OF CANADA LTD.—Bucyrus International; *U.S. Private*, pg. 177
BUCYRUS-EUROPE LTD.—Bucyrus International; *U.S. Private*, pg. 177
BUCYRUS INTERNATIONAL; *U.S. Private*, pg. 177
CASE INTERNATIONAL, AGR ENGINEERING—Tenneco Inc.; *U.S. Public*, pg. 1579
CELTITE INC.—Burmah Castrol plc; *Int'l*, pg. 234
CHARTER PLC; *Int'l*, pg. 280
CLINCH RIVER CORP.—Elgin National Industries, Inc.; *U.S. Private*, pg. 370
DAVY INTERNATIONAL—Kvaerner a.s.a.; *Int'l*, pg. 773
DENVER AUTOMETRICS—Svedala Industri AB; *Int'l*, pg. 1325
DENVER EQUIPMENT PTY., LTD.—Svedala Industri AB; *Int'l*, pg. 1326
DENVER PROCESS EQUIPMENT, LTD.—Svedala Industri AB; *Int'l*, pg. 1326
DINGS MAGNETIC CO.—Venturedyne, Ltd.; *U.S. Private*, pg. 1136
DOBSON PARK INDUSTRIES PLC—Harnischfeger Industries, Inc.; *U.S. Public*, pg. 789
DORR-OLIVER INCORPORATED—Mannesmann A.G.; *Int'l*, pg. 839
DRESSER INDUSTRIES, INC.; *U.S. Public*, pg. 528
ELGIN NATIONAL INDUSTRIES, INC.; *U.S. Private*, pg. 370
EXOLON-ESK COMPANY; *U.S. Public*, pg. 600
FKI INDUSTRIES, INC.—FKI Plc; *Int'l*, pg. 472
FLS MILJO A/S—FLS Industries A/S; *Int'l*, pg. 475
FANSTEEL VR/WESSON-LEXINGTON—Fansteel, Inc.; *U.S. Public*, pg. 612
J.H. FLETCHER & CO.; *U.S. Private*, pg. 412
FREEDOM FORGE CORPORATION; *U.S. Private*, pg. 425
FREIGHTLINER ENTERPRISE CORP.—Daimler-Benz Aktiengesellschaft; *Int'l*, pg. 368
FULLER COMPANY—FLS Industries A/S; *Int'l*, pg. 475
GENERAL SIGNAL CORPORATION; *U.S. Public*, pg. 726
GLOBAL INDUSTRIAL TECHNOLOGIES; *U.S. Public*, pg. 747
GOODMAN EQUIPMENT CORP.; *U.S. Private*, pg. 464
GREENFIELD INDUSTRIES INC.—Kennametal Inc.; *U.S. Public*, pg. 950
HARBERT CORPORATION; *U.S. Private*, pg. 500
HARBOUR GROUP LTD.; *U.S. Private*, pg. 500
HARNISCHFEGER INDUSTRIES, INC.; *U.S. Public*, pg. 788
HARTUNG, KUHN, & CO., MASCHINENFABRIK GMBH—Fried. Krupp AG; *Int'l*, pg. 511
HUBBELL LIGHTING INC.—Hubbell Incorporated; *U.S. Public*, pg. 844
HUMBOLDT WEDAG DIVISION—Deutz AG; *Int'l*, pg. 408
HUWOOD INTERNATIONAL—FKI Plc; *Int'l*, pg. 473
HUWOOD MINING SUPPORTS LIMITED—FKI Plc; *Int'l*, pg. 473
INCO LIMITED; *Int'l*, pg. 672
INGERSOLL-RAND (AUSTRALIA) PROPRIETARY LTD.—Ingersoll-Rand Company; *U.S. Public*, pg. 878
INGERSOLL-RAND COMPANY; *U.S. Public*, pg. 876
JOY MANUFACTURING COMPANY (AFRICA) (PTY) LTD. JOHANNESBURG PLANT—Harnischfeger Industries, Inc.; *U.S. Public*, pg. 789
JOY MANUFACTURING COMPANY (PTY) LTD., SYDNEY PLANT—Harnischfeger Industries, Inc.; *U.S. Public*, pg. 789
JOY MANUFACTURING COMPANY (UK) LTD., EAST KILBRIDE PLANT—Harnischfeger Industries, Inc.; *U.S. Public*, pg. 789
JOY MINING MACHINERY—Harnischfeger Industries, Inc.; *U.S. Public*, pg. 790
KHD DEUTZ OF AMERICA CORPORATION—Deutz AG; *Int'l*, pg. 408
KENNAMETAL INC.; *U.S. Public*, pg. 950
ING. G. KLEMM BOHRTECHNIK GMBH—Ingersoll-Rand Company; *U.S. Public*, pg. 878
KRUPP FORDERTECHNIK GMBH—Fried. Krupp AG; *Int'l*, pg. 511
KRUPP INDUSTRIES INDIA LTD.—Fried. Krupp AG; *Int'l*, pg. 511
KRUPP KOPPERS GMBH—Fried. Krupp AG; *Int'l*, pg. 511
KRUPP POLYSIUS AG—Fried. Krupp AG; *Int'l*, pg. 512
KVAERNER-JOHN BROWN LTD.—Kvaerner a.s.a.; *Int'l*, pg. 773
A.L. LEE CORP.—Salem Group, Inc.; *U.S. Private*, pg. 961
MAN TAKRAF FORDERTECHNIK GMBH—MAN Aktiengesellschaft; *Int'l*, pg. 824
MANNESMANN DEMAG CORPORATION—Mannesmann A.G.; *Int'l*, pg. 837
MANNESMANN DEMAG S.A.—Mannesmann A.G.; *Int'l*, pg. 837
MATERIAL HANDLING SYSTEMS DIV.—FMC Corporation; *U.S. Public*, pg. 605
MCLAUGHLIN MANUFACTURING COMPANY; *U.S. Private*, pg. 724
MCNALLY MANUFACTURING—Svedala Industri AB; *Int'l*, pg. 1326
METALL MINING CORPORATION—Metallgesellschaft AG; *Int'l*, pg. 862
MINE SAFETY APPLIANCES CO.; *U.S. Public*, pg. 1114
MINING AND CONSTRUCTION DIVISION—Kennametal Inc.; *U.S. Public*, pg. 950
MINING MACHINERY GROUP—Harnischfeger Industries, Inc.; *U.S. Public*, pg. 789
MINSERCO, INC.—Bucyrus International; *U.S. Private*, pg. 177
MORGANTOWN MACHINE & HYDRAULICS, INC.—Charter plc; *Int'l*, pg. 280
MORGARDSHAMMAR AB—Danielli & C. Officine Meccaniche S.p.A.; *Int'l*, pg. 378
NATIONAL MINE SERVICE, INC.—Charter plc; *Int'l*, pg. 280
NORRIS SCREEN & MFG., INC.—Elgin National Industries, Inc.; *U.S. Private*, pg. 370
NORTON INDUSTRIEPRODUKTE GMBH—Saint-Gobain; *Int'l*, pg. 1175
O&K ORENSTEIN & KOPPEL AKTIENGESELLSCHAFT—Fried. Krupp AG; *Int'l*, pg. 516
OUTOKUMPU MINTEC U.S.A., INC.—Outokumpu Oyj; *Int'l*, pg. 1017
OUTOKUMPU WENMEC OY—Outokumpu Oyj; *Int'l*, pg. 1017
PENNSYLVANIA CRUSHER CORP.; *U.S. Private*, pg. 850
PORTEC, INC.; *U.S. Public*, pg. 1317
PORTEC, INC.-CONSTRUCTION EQUIPMENT DIV.—Portec, Inc.; *U.S. Public*, pg. 1318
RAMMER OY—Tamrock Corp.; *Int'l*, pg. 1352
REEDRILL INC.—Svedala Industri AB; *Int'l*, pg. 1325
REXNORD CORPORATION—BTR plc; *Int'l*, pg. 127
SIG SCHWEIZERSICHE INDUSTRIE-GESELLSCHAFT HOLDING AG; *Int'l*, pg. 1156
SALEM CORPORATION—Salem Group, Inc.; *U.S. Private*, pg. 961
SANDVIK AB; *Int'l*, pg. 1185
SANDVIK GMBH—Sandvik AB; *Int'l*, pg. 1186
AB SANDVIK ROCK TOOLS—Sandvik AB; *Int'l*, pg. 1185
SANDVIK ROCK TOOLS, INC.—Sandvik AB; *Int'l*, pg. 1185
SANDVIK ROCK TOOLS SVENSKA FORSALJNINGS AB—Sandvik AB; *Int'l*, pg. 1185
SCREW CONVEYOR CORP.; *U.S. Private*, pg. 977
SIMPLICITY ENGINEERING, INC.—Powerscreen International Plc; *Int'l*, pg. 1066
EVERETT SMITH GROUP, LTD.; *U.S. Private*, pg. 1007

SMITH INTERNATIONAL, INC.; *U.S. Public*, pg. 1478
SPICER OFF-HIGHWAY AXLE DIV.—Dana Corporation; *U.S. Public*, pg. 479
STAMLER CORPORATION—The Oldenburg Group Companies; *U.S. Private*, pg. 814
SVEDALA INDUSTRIES INC.—Svedala Industri AB; *Int'l*, pg. 1325
SVEDALA PUMPS & PROCESS—Svedala Industri AB; *Int'l*, *pg. 1325*
TABOR MACHINE CO.—Elgin National Industries, Inc.; *U.S. Private*, pg. 371
TEREX CORPORATION; *U.S. Public*, pg. 1581
TOKYO RYUKI SEIZO CO., LTD.—Ingersoll-Rand Company; *U.S. Public*, pg. 878
TRIANGLE MINING EQUIPMENT CO. INC.—FKI Plc; *Int'l*, pg. 473
TRINITY DIFCO—Trinity Industries Inc.; *U.S. Public*, pg. 1639
TURULA WORKS INC.—Outokumpu Oyj; *Int'l*, pg. 1017
UNIROC AB—Atlas Copco AB; *Int'l*, pg. 96
VENTUREDYNE, LTD.; *U.S. Private*, pg. 1136
VOEST-ALPINE INTERNATIONAL CORPORATION—Voest-Alpine Stahl AG; *Int'l*, pg. 1470
WARN INDUSTRIES, INC.; *U.S. Private*, pg. 1150
XTEK/ARIZONA DIVISION—Xtek, Inc.; *U.S. Private*, pg. 1194
XTEK, INC.; *U.S. Private*, pg. 1194
ZIMMERMAN HOLDINGS, INC.; *U.S. Private*, pg. 1206

3533 — OIL & GAS FIELD MACHINERY & EQUIPMENT

ATLAS COPCO AB; *Int'l*, pg. 95
ATLAS COPCO ACT—Atlas Copco AB; *Int'l*, pg. 96
AZTEC MANUFACTURING CO.; *U.S. Public*, pg. 159
BS & B PROCESS SYSTEMS, INC.—International Systems & Controls Corp.; *U.S. Private*, pg. 572
BTR PAPER GROUP—BTR plc; *Int'l*, pg. 127
BAKER HUGHES DRILLING TECHNOLOGIES—Baker Hughes Incorporated; *U.S. Public*, pg. 166
BAKER HUGHES INCORPORATED; *U.S. Public*, pg. 165
BAKER HUGHES INTEQ—Baker Hughes Incorporated; *U.S. Public*, pg. 166
BAKER HUGHES PRODUCTION TOOLS, INC.—Baker Hughes Incorporated; *U.S. Public*, pg. 166
BAKER OIL TOOLS—Baker Hughes Incorporated; *U.S. Public*, pg. 167
BAROID DRILLING FLUIDS DIVISION—Dresser Industries, Inc.; *U.S. Public*, pg. 528
BESSER COMPANY; *U.S. Private*, pg. 139
BOLT RESEARCH DIVISION—Bolt Technology Corporation; *U.S. Public*, pg. 244
BOLT TECHNOLOGY CORPORATION; *U.S. Public*, pg. 244
BOWEN TOOLS—IRI International Corporation; *U.S. Public*, *pg. 858*
BROWN BROTHERS & COMPANY LTD.—Vickers PLC; *Int'l*, pg. 1466
THE BUSCHMAN CO.; *U.S. Private*, pg. 188
CAMCO INTERNATIONAL INC.; *U.S. Public*, pg. 297
CAMCO INTERNATIONAL INC.—Camco International Inc.; *U.S. Public*, pg. 298
CAMCO PRODUCTS & SERVICES COMPANY—Camco International Inc.; *U.S. Public*, pg. 298
CAMERON; *U.S. Public*, pg. 298
CENTRILIFT—Baker Hughes Incorporated; *U.S. Public*, pg. 167
CHRISTIANA COMPANIES, INC.; *U.S. Public*, pg. 352
COMPANIA HALLIBOURTON DE CEMENTACION—Halliburton Company; *U.S. Public*, pg. 776
COMPUTALOG LTD.; *Int'l*, pg. 325
CORE RESEARCH, INC.—Litton Industries, Inc.; *U.S. Public*, pg. 1003
DAVY INTERNATIONAL—Kvaerner a.s.a.; *Int'l*, pg. 773
DRESSER CANADA, INC.—Dresser Industries, Inc.; *U.S. Public*, pg. 529
DRESSER INDUSTRIES, INC.; *U.S. Public*, pg. 528
EVI, INC.; *U.S. Public*, pg. 547
ENERFLEX SYSTEMS LTD.—Toromont Industries Ltd.; *Int'l*, pg. 1400
EXPO PARTES S.A. DE C.V.—Varco International, Inc.; *U.S. Public*, pg. 1709
FMC CORPORATION; *U.S. Public*, pg. 604
FERRANTI SYSECA—Thomson S.A.; *Int'l*, pg. 1384
FLUID CONTROL DIVISION—FMC Corporation; *U.S. Public*, pg. 605
FOSTER WHEELER CORPORATION; *U.S. Public*, pg. 676
FREEDOM FORGE CORPORATION; *U.S. Private*, pg. 425
GKN WESTLAND AEROSPACE NORTH AMERICA INC.—GKN plc; *Int'l*, pg. 535
GALVESTON-HOUSTON COMPANY; *U.S. Private*, pg. 438
GROUPE GTM—Lyonnaise des Eaux S.A.; *Int'l*, pg. 823
HALLIBURTON COMPANY; *U.S. Public*, pg. 775
HALLIBURTON COMPANY GERMANY GMBH—Halliburton Company; *U.S. Public*, pg. 777
HALLIBURTON ENERGY SERVICES—Halliburton Company; *U.S. Public*, pg. 776
HALLIBURTON ENERGY SERVICES—Halliburton Company; *U.S. Public*, pg. 776
HALLIBURTON ENERGY SERVICES, INC.—Halliburton Company; *U.S. Public*, pg. 776
HALLIBURTON MFG. & SERVICES LTD.—Halliburton Company; *U.S. Public*, pg. 777
HOUSTON ENGINEERS—Wilson Industries Inc.; *U.S. Private*, pg. 1181
HUGHES CHRISTENSEN—Baker Hughes Incorporated; *U.S. Public*, pg. 166
HUGHES CHRISTENSEN CO.—Baker Hughes Incorporated; *U.S. Public*, pg. 166
HUGHES TOOL DO BRASIL EQUIPAMENTOS INDUSTRIAIS LTDA.—Baker Hughes Incorporated; *U.S. Public*, pg. 167
HUGHES TOOL COMPANY LIMITED—Baker Hughes Incorporated; *U.S. Public*, pg. 167
HUGHES TOOL COMPANY DE MEXICO, S.A. DE C.V.—Baker Hughes Incorporated; *U.S. Public*, pg. 167
HUGHES TOOL COMPANY S.A.C.I.F.I.—Baker Hughes Incorporated; *U.S. Public*, pg. 167
HUGHES TOOL S.A.F.—Baker Hughes Incorporated; *U.S. Public*, pg. 167
HURON MANUFACTURING DIV.—U.S. Industries, Inc.; *U.S. Public*, pg. 1684
HYDRIL COMPANY; *U.S. Private*, pg. 551
IRI INTERNATIONAL CORPORATION; *U.S. Public*, pg. 858
INDUSTRIAL COMPONENTS-GRAVENHAGE B.V.—Halliburton Company; *U.S. Public*, pg. 777
INDUSTRIAL ENERGY APPLICATIONS—IES Industries Inc.; *U.S. Public*, pg. 855
INGERSOLL-RAND CO., SOUTH AFRICA (PROPRIETARY) LTD.—Ingersoll-Rand Company; *U.S. Public*, pg. 878
INGERSOLL-RAND COMPANY; *U.S. Public*, pg. 876
INTERNATIONAL TOOL & SUPPLY, PLC; *Int'l*, pg. 684
KELSO OIL COMPANY; *U.S. Private*, pg. 613
KIMRAY, INC.; *U.S. Private*, pg. 620
KVAERNER EUREKA A/S, TRANBY—Kvaerner a.s.a.; *Int'l*, *pg. 766*
KVAERNER INSTALLASJON, AGOTNES DIVISION—Kvaerner a.s.a.; *Int'l*, pg. 769
KVAERNER-JOHN BROWN LTD.—Kvaerner a.s.a.; *Int'l*, pg. 773
LAWRENCE TECHNOLOGY—Camco International Inc.; *U.S. Public*, pg. 298
LAYNE CHRISTENSON CO.; *U.S. Public*, pg. 981
LONE STAR STEEL COMPANY—Lone Star Technologies, Inc.; *U.S. Public*, pg. 1012
LONE STAR TECHNOLOGIES, INC.; *U.S. Public*, pg. 1012
LUFKIN INDUSTRIES, INC.; *U.S. Public*, pg. 1019
M-I L.L.C.—Halliburton Company; *U.S. Public*, pg. 776
M-I L.L.C.—Smith International, Inc.; *U.S. Public*, pg. 1478
MARITIME PROTECTION A/S—Monsanto Company; *U.S. Public*, pg. 1125
MCCULLOUGH, AN ATLAS WIRELINE SERVICES OPERATION—Litton Industries, Inc.; *U.S. Public*, pg. 1004
MCNEILUS COMPANIES; *U.S. Private*, pg. 725
MITCHELL ENERGY & DEVELOPMENT CORP.; *U.S. Public*, pg. 1117
NAO, INC.; *U.S. Private*, pg. 771
NATIONAL-OILWELL/DRECO—National-Oilwell Inc.; *U.S. Public*, pg. 1158
NAITONAL-OILWELL/DRECO INC.—National-Oilwell Inc.; *U.S. Public*, pg. 1158
NATIONAL-OILWELL/DRECO RIG TECHNOLOGY & CONSTRUCTION—National-Oilwell Inc.; *U.S. Public*, pg. 1158
NATIONAL-OILWELL GRIFFITH OIL TOOL & TRUDRIL—National-Oilwell Inc.; *U.S. Public*, pg. 1158
NATIONAL-OILWELL INC.; *U.S. Public*, pg. 1158
NEWPARK RESOURCES, INC.; *U.S. Public*, pg. 1179
NORRIS—Dover Corporation; *U.S. Public*, pg. 521
NORRISEAL CONTROLS—Dover Corporation; *U.S. Public*, pg. 521
OIL DYNAMICS INC.—Franklin Electric Co., Inc.; *U.S. Public*, pg. 679
OTIS ENGINEERING INTERNATIONAL—Halliburton Company; *U.S. Public*, pg. 777
OTIS INTERNATIONAL, LTD.—Halliburton Company; *U.S. Public*, pg. 777
OTIS NIGERIA, LTD.—Halliburton Company; *U.S. Public*, pg. 777
PACCAR INC.; *U.S. Public*, pg. 1246
PARKER DRILLING COMPANY; *U.S. Public*, pg. 1259
PARKER TECHNOLOGY, INC.—Parker Drilling Company; *U.S. Public*, pg. 1259
PATTERSON-KELLEY COMPANY—Harsco Corporation; *U.S. Public*, pg. 793
PETRODYNE PRODUCTS—The Oilgear Company; *U.S. Public*, pg. 1215
REDA—Camco International Inc.; *U.S. Public*, pg. 298
REED TOOL COMPANY—Camco International Inc.; *U.S. Public*, pg. 298
REEDRILL INC.—Svedala Industri AB; *Int'l*, pg. 1325
SANDVIK AB; *Int'l*, pg. 1185
SANDVIK ASIA LTD.—Sandvik AB; *Int'l*, pg. 1187
SANDVIK K.K.—Sandvik AB; *Int'l*, pg. 1187
AB SANDVIK ROCK TOOLS—Sandvik AB; *Int'l*, pg. 1185
SCHLUMBERGER LIMITED; *U.S. Public*, pg. 1439
SCHLUMBERGER OILFIELD SERVICES—Schlumberger Limited; *U.S. Public*, pg. 1439
SECURITY/DBS DIVISION—Dresser Industries, Inc.; *U.S. Public*, pg. 528
HOWARD SMITH SCREEN CO.—Halliburton Company; *U.S. Public*, pg. 776
SMITH INTERNATIONAL, INC.; *U.S. Public*, pg. 1478
SPERRY-SUN DRILLING SERVICES DIVISION—Dresser Industries, Inc.; *U.S. Public*, pg. 528
STANDCO INDUSTRIES, INC.; *U.S. Private*, pg. 1032
STANDCO OILFIELD PRODUCTS DIV.—Standco Industries, Inc.; *U.S. Private*, pg. 1032
SULLIVAN SYSTEMS DIV.—Tetra Laval Group; *Int'l*, pg. 1379
SWIFT ENERGY COMPANY; *U.S. Public*, pg. 1543
TARO INDUSTRIES LIMITED—Trimac Corporation; *Int'l*, pg. 1424
TIMEC COMPANY; *U.S. Private*, pg. 1087
TRICO INDUSTRIES, INC.—Paccar Inc.; *U.S. Public*, pg. 1247
TULSA MANUFACTURING PLANT—T.D. Williamson, Inc.; *U.S. Private*, pg. 1180
UNITED AIR SPECIALISTS, INC.—CLARCOR, Inc.; *U.S. Public*, pg. 382
VARCO BEST PRODUCTS—Varco International, Inc.; *U.S. Public*, pg. 1709
VARCO BJ DRILLING SYSTEMS—Varco International, Inc.; *U.S. Public*, pg. 1709
VARCO BJ OIL TOOLS B.V.—Varco International, Inc.; *U.S. Public*, pg. 1709
VARCO INTERNATIONAL, INC.; *U.S. Public*, pg. 1709
VARCO (U.K.) LTD. DRILLING SYSTEMS—Varco International, Inc.; *U.S. Public*, pg. 1709
WEATHERFORD—Weatherford Enterra Incorporated; *U.S. Public*, pg. 1749
WEATHERFORD ENTERRA INCORPORATED; *U.S. Public*, pg. 1749
WEATHERFORD SAUDIA ARABIA LTD.—Weatherford Enterra Incorporated; *U.S. Public*, pg. 1750
WEATHERFORD U.K. LTD.—Weatherford Enterra Incorporated; *U.S. Public*, pg. 1750
WESTERN ATLAS LOGGING SERVICES—Western Atlas Inc.; *U.S. Public*, pg. 1757
T.D. WILLIAMSON, INC.; *U.S. Private*, pg. 1179
WILSON INDUSTRIES INC.; *U.S. Private*, pg. 1181
WOOD GROUP PRESSURE CONTROL; *U.S. Public*, pg. 1775

3534 — ELEVATORS & MOVING STAIRWAYS

ABM INDUSTRIES; *U.S. Public*, pg. 2
ACCESS INDUSTRIES; *U.S. Private*, pg. 11
ALIMAK ELEVATOR COMPANY; *U.S. Private*, pg. 34
ALIMAK ELEVATOR COMPANY—Alimak Elevator Company; *U.S. Private*, pg. 34
AMTECH ELEVATOR SERVICES—ABM Industries; *U.S. Public*, pg. 2
BECKWITH ELEVATOR CO.; *U.S. Private*, pg. 128
BORAL ACROW LTD. (NEW ZEALAND)—Boral Limited; *Int'l*, pg. 203
JERED BROWN BROTHERS INC.—Vickers PLC; *Int'l*, pg. 1468
CROW RIVER INDUSTRIES INCORPORATED—Mallinckrodt Inc.; *U.S. Public*, pg. 1040
DERLAN INDUSTRIES LIMITED; *Int'l*, pg. 395
DOVER CORPORATION; *U.S. Public*, pg. 520
DOVER CORP. (CANADA) LTD.—Dover Corporation; *U.S. Public*, pg. 522
DOVER CORPORATION (CANADA) LTD.-INDUSTRIAL DIV.—Dover Corporation; *U.S. Public*, pg. 522
DOVER CORPORATION (CANADA) LTD.-TURNBULL ELEVATOR DIV.—Dover Corporation; *U.S. Public*, pg. 522
DOVER ELEVATOR INTERNATIONAL, INC.—Dover Corporation; *U.S. Public*, pg. 521
DOVER ELEVATOR SYSTEMS, INC.—Dover Corporation; *U.S. Public*, pg. 521
ELEVADORES KONE SABIEM S.A. DE C.V.—Kone Corporation; *Int'l*, pg. 747
ELEVADORES OTIS, S.A. DE C.V.—United Technologies Corporation; *U.S. Public*, pg. 1691
ELEVADORES SCHINDLER SUWIS, S.A. DE C.V.—Schindler Holding AG; *Int'l*, pg. 1205
ESCO ELEVATOR CORP.; *U.S. Private*, pg. 383
HANKOOK OTIS ELEVATOR COMPANY—United Technologies Corporation; *U.S. Public*, pg. 1691
HAUENSTEIN & BURMEISTER, INC.; *U.S. Private*, pg. 510
KLECO CORP.; *U.S. Private*, pg. 625
KONE ASCENSORI S.P.A.—Kone Corporation; *Int'l*, pg. 747
KONE AUFZUG GMBH—Kone Corporation; *Int'l*, pg. 747
KONE AUFZUGWERKE—Kone Corporation; *Int'l*, pg. 747
KONE BELGIUM S.A.—Kone Corporation; *Int'l*, pg. 747
KONE CORPORATE OFFICE—Kone Corporation; *Int'l*, pg. 747
KONE CORPORATION; *Int'l*, pg. 746
KONE ELEVADORES LTDA.—Kone Corporation; *Int'l*, pg. 747
KONE ELEVATOR A/S—Kone Corporation; *Int'l*, pg. 747
KONE ELEVATOR GMBH—Kone Corporation; *Int'l*, pg. 748
KONE ELEVATOR INDIA LTD.—Kone Corporation; *Int'l*, pg. 748
KONE ELEVATOR PTE. LTD.—Kone Corporation; *Int'l*, pg. 747
KONE ELEVATORS (AUSTRALIA) PTY. LTD.—Kone Corporation; *Int'l*, pg. 748
KONE HISSAR AB—Kone Corporation; *Int'l*, pg. 747
KONE LIFTS LTD.—Kone Corporation; *Int'l*, pg. 747
KONE SOWITSCH AG—Kone Corporation; *Int'l*, pg. 748
LAGERQUIST CORPORATION—Dover Corporation; *U.S. Public*, pg. 521
MARRYAT & SCOTT EGYPT-S.A.—Kone Corporation; *Int'l*, *pg. 748*
MEMCO LIMITED—Halma p.l.c.; *Int'l*, pg. 589
MILLAR ELEVATOR INDUSTRIES, INC.—Schindler Holding AG; *Int'l*, pg. 1205
MITSUBISHI ELECTRIC CORPORATION; *Int'l*, pg. 872
MOLINE ACCESSORIES COMPANY—Kone Corporation; *Int'l*, pg. 746
MONTGOMERY ELEVATOR ARCHITECTURAL PRODUCTS DIVISION—Kone Corporation; *Int'l*, pg. 746
MONTGOMERY ELEVATOR CONTROLS DIVISION—Kone Corporation; *Int'l*, pg. 746
MONTGOMERY ELEVATOR DIVISION—Kone Corporation; *Int'l*, pg. 746
MONTGOMERY ESCALATOR DIVISION—Kone Corporation; *Int'l*, pg. 746
MONTGOMERY KONE INC.—Kone Corporation; *Int'l*, pg. 746
OTIS ELEVATOR COMPANY—United Technologies Corporation; *U.S. Public*, pg. 1690
OTIS ELEVATOR CO. PTY. LTD.—United Technologies Corporation; *U.S. Public*, pg. 1691
OTIS ELEVATOR PLC—United Technologies Corporation; *U.S. Public*, pg. 1691
OTIS GMBH—United Technologies Corporation; *U.S. Public*, pg. 1690
LEN OTIS LIFT—United Technologies Corporation; *U.S. Public*, pg. 1691
QUIPP, INC.; *U.S. Public*, pg. 1353
SABIEM S.R.L.—Kone Corporation; *Int'l*, pg. 748

SCHINDLER AUFZUGE AG—Schindler Holding AG; Int'l, pg. 1204
SHCHERBINKA OTIS LIFT—United Technologies Corporation; U.S. Public, pg. 1691
SOCIETE FRANCAISE DES ASCENSEURS KONE—Kone Corporation; Int'l, pg. 748
SOUND ELEVATOR—Dover Corporation; U.S. Public, pg. 521
STERLING MACHINERY CO., INC.—Kone Corporation; Int'l, pg. 746
TOSHIBA ELEVATOR & ESCALATOR SERVICE CO., LTD.—Toshiba Corporation; Int'l, pg. 1404
TYLER ELEVATOR PRODUCTS, INC.; U.S. Private, pg. 1112
U.S. ELEVATOR—Thyssen AG; Int'l, pg. 1387
UNITED TECHNOLOGIES CORPORATION; U.S. Public, pg. 1689
VAPOR—Westinghouse Air Brake Company; U.S. Public, pg. 1761
WHEEL TRONIC INC.—Snap-On Tools Corporation; U.S. Public, pg. 1481
ZARDOYA OTIS SA—United Technologies Corporation; U.S. Public, pg. 1691

3535 — CONVEYORS & CONVEYING EQUIPMENT

AC CORPORATION; U.S. Private, pg. 3
AEC, INC.—Harbour Group Ltd.; U.S. Private, pg. 500
AEC, INC.—Sterling, Inc.; U.S. Private, pg. 1041
AEC/WHITLOCK, INC.—Sterling, Inc.; U.S. Private, pg. 1041
ACCO SYSTEMS DIV.—FKI Plc; Int'l, pg. 472
AIRLINE EQUIPMENT DIV.—FMC Corporation; U.S. Public, pg. 605
ALVEY SYSTEMS, INC; U.S. Private, pg. 47
ALVEY OF MICHIGAN—Alvey Systems, Inc; U.S. Private, pg. 47
AMQUIP (PROPRIETARY) LIMITED—Anglo American Corporation of South Africa Limited; Int'l, pg. 76
ASHWORTH BROS., INC.; U.S. Private, pg. 89
ATHEY PRODUCTS CORPORATION; U.S. Public, pg. 142
BTR FARINGTON LTD.—BTR plc; Int'l, pg. 125
BABCOCK AFRICA (PTY) LTD.—Babcock International Group PLC; Int'l, pg. 131
BABCOCK CONSTRUCTION CONTRACTORS—Babcock International Group PLC; Int'l, pg. 131
BRIDON PLC; Int'l, pg. 215
BROCK MANUFACTURING—CTB International Corp.; U.S. Public, pg. 285
BUHLER INC.; U.S. Private, pg. 179
CCC CONVEYORS, INC.—The Dyson-Kissner-Moran Corporation; U.S. Private, pg. 351
CARRIER VIBRATING EQUIPMENT, INC.; U.S. Private, pg. 215
THE CHANTLAND COMPANY DIVISION—Magna International Inc.; Int'l, pg. 830
CLIPPER BELT LACER COMPANY—Flexible Steel Lacing Company; U.S. Private, pg. 413
CLYDESDALE JONES CO.—Caparo Group Ltd.; Int'l, pg. 265
COMPONENTA INTERNATIONAL B.V.—Trelleborg AB; Int'l, pg. 1421
CONSILIUM BULK - BABCOCK ATLANTA INC.—Babcock International Group PLC; Int'l, pg. 131
CONSILIUM BULK-BABCOCK, KVANUM AB—Babcock International Group PLC; Int'l, pg. 131
CONSILIUM BULK OY—Babcock International Group PLC; Int'l, pg. 131
CONSILIUM CMH-BABCOCK AB—Babcock International Group PLC; Int'l, pg. 131
CONSILIUM CLAUDIUS PETERS BABCOCK (HK) LTD—Babcock International Group PLC; Int'l, pg. 131
CONTINENTAL CONVEYOR & EQUIPMENT COMPANY—NESCO, Inc.; U.S. Private, pg. 791
COUNTEC RECYCLING SYSTEMS DIVISION—Portec, Inc.; U.S. Public, pg. 1318
DEUTSCHE BABCOCK AG; Int'l, pg. 398
DEUTSCHE BABCOCK TECHNOLOGIES, INC.—Deutsche Babcock AG; Int'l, pg. 401
DEXION (AUSTRALIA) PTY. LTD.—The Interlake Corporation; U.S. Public, pg. 893
DEXION GMBH—The Interlake Corporation; U.S. Public, pg. 893
DEXION GROUP PLC—The Interlake Corporation; U.S. Public, pg. 893
DEXION LTD.—The Interlake Corporation; U.S. Public, pg. 893
DORNER MANUFACTURING CORP.; U.S. Private, pg. 340
DURR AG; Int'l, pg. 421
DURR INDUSTRIES, INC.—Durr AG; Int'l, pg. 421
EICKHOFF CORPORATION—Gebr. Eickhoff Maschinenfabrik und Eisengiesserei mbH; Int'l, pg. 542
FKI INDUSTRIES, INC.—FKI Plc; Int'l, pg. 472
FMC MATERIAL HANDLING SYSTEMS DIVISION—FMC Corporation; U.S. Public, pg. 605
FATA PRODUCTION MACHINERY—FKI Plc; Int'l, pg. 474
FLEETWOOD SYSTEMS, INC.; U.S. Private, pg. 410
FROST INC.; U.S. Private, pg. 430
FULLER COMPANY—FLS Industries A/S; Int'l, pg. 475
FULLER COMPANY (CATASAUQUA)—FLS Industries A/S; Int'l, pg. 475
FULLER COMPANY (MANHEIM)—FLS Industries A/S; Int'l, pg. 475
GEBR. EICKHOFF MASCHINENFABRIK UND EISENGIESSEREI MBH; Int'l, pg. 542
GEORGIA DUCK & CORDAGE MILLS; U.S. Private, pg. 448
A.J. GERRARD AND COMPANY; U.S. Private, pg. 449
GIDDINGS & LEWIS, INC.—Thyssen AG; Int'l, pg. 1389
GILMAN—Thyssen AG; Int'l, pg. 1389
GURTEC GMBH & CO., KG—Tamrock Corp.; Int'l, pg. 1353
IDEA ENGINEERING & FABRICATING; U.S. Private, pg. 557
INTEGRATED MATERIAL HANDLING COMPANY—Tomkins PLC; Int'l, pg. 1397
THE INTERLAKE CORPORATION; U.S. Public, pg. 892
INTRALOX A/S—The Laitram Corporation; U.S. Private, pg. 643
INTRALOX, INC.—The Laitram Corporation; U.S. Private, pg. 643
JAGENBERG AG—Rheinmetall Group; Int'l, pg. 1108
JOHNSON ROSS CORPORATION—CMI Corporation; U.S. Public, pg. 279
KABELSCHLEPP AMERICA INC.—Kabelschlepp GmbH; Int'l, pg. 721
KABELSCHLEPP GMBH; Int'l, pg. 721
KEY HANDLING SYSTEMS, INC.; U.S. Private, pg. 618
KINGSTON-WARREN CORPORATION—Harvard Industries, Inc.; U.S. Public, pg. 796
KLOCKNER MASCHINEN - UND ANGLAGENBAU GMBH—Babcock International Group PLC; Int'l, pg. 131
KLOCKNER-WERKE AG; Int'l, pg. 736
GEORGE KOCH SONS, INC.; U.S. Private, pg. 628
KOPO AB—Tamrock Corp.; Int'l, pg. 1353
KRUPP FORDERTECHNIK GMBH—Fried. Krupp AG; Int'l, pg. 511
KRUPP INDUSTRIES INDIA LTD.—Fried. Krupp AG; Int'l, pg. 511
LAMB TECHNICON—UNOVA, Inc.; U.S. Public, pg. 1699
MAC EQUIPMENT INC.; U.S. Private, pg. 685
MACGREGOR (AUS) PTY. LTD.—Incentive AB; Int'l, pg. 670
MACGREGOR (BEL) N.V.—Incentive AB; Int'l, pg. 670
MACGREGOR (DNK) A/S—Incentive AB; Int'l, pg. 670
MACGREGOR (FRA) S.A.—Incentive AB; Int'l, pg. 670
MACGREGOR (GBR) LTD.—Incentive AB; Int'l, pg. 670
MACGREGOR (HKG), LTD.—Incentive AB; Int'l, pg. 671
MACGREGOR (ITA) S.P.A.—Incentive AB; Int'l, pg. 671
MACGREGOR (NLD) B.V.—Incentive AB; Int'l, pg. 671
MACGREGOR (PRT) LDA.—Incentive AB; Int'l, pg. 671
MACGREGOR (SGP) PTE. LTD.—Incentive AB; Int'l, pg. 671
MARTIN SPROCKET & GEAR, INC.; U.S. Private, pg. 709
MATERIALS HANDLING EQUIPMENT—Jervis B. Webb Company; U.S. Private, pg. 1156
MAYFRAN INTERNATIONAL, INC.—Tomkins PLC; Int'l, pg. 1397
MAYFRAN LIMBURG, B.V.—Tomkins PLC; Int'l, pg. 1398
MELROE COMPANY—Ingersoll-Rand Company; U.S. Public, pg. 877
MID-WEST CONVEYOR CO., INC.—Tomkins PLC; Int'l, pg. 1398
MITSUBISHI ELECTRIC CORPORATION; Int'l, pg. 872
MITSUBISHI HEAVY INDUSTRIES LTD.; Int'l, pg. 873
OVERHEAD CONVEYOR CO.; U.S. Private, pg. 822
PARKER HANNIFIN B.V.—Parker Hannifin Corporation; U.S. Public, pg. 1263
PARKER HANNIFIN DANMARK A/S—Parker Hannifin Corporation; U.S. Public, pg. 1263
PENTEK CORPORATION—The Dyson-Kissner-Moran Corporation; U.S. Private, pg. 352
PORTEC, INC.; U.S. Public, pg. 1317
PORTEC (U.K.) LTD.—Portec, Inc.; U.S. Public, pg. 1318
PRAB, INC.; U.S. Public, pg. 1319
PROK GROUP LTD.—Tamrock Corp.; Int'l, pg. 1353
QUIPP, INC.; U.S. Public, pg. 1353
RADAR COMPANIES, INC.—Harnischfeger Industries, Inc.; U.S. Public, pg. 789
RAPID INDUSTRIES, INC.; U.S. Private, pg. 910
RAPISTAN DEMAG CORP.—Mannesmann A.G.; Int'l, pg. 837
RENOLD, INC.—Renold PLC; Int'l, pg. 1104
RENOLD PLC; Int'l, pg. 1103
REXNORD CORPORATION—BTR plc; Int'l, pg. 127
ROXON KOMPONENTIT OY—Tamrock Corp.; Int'l, pg. 1353
SI HANDLING SYSTEMS, INC.; U.S. Public, pg. 1418
SANDVIK AB; Int'l, pg. 1185
SANDVIK PROCESS SYSTEMS GMBH—Sandvik AB; Int'l, pg. 1187
SANDVIK PROCESS SYSTEMS, INC.—Sandvik AB; Int'l, pg. 1185
SANDVIK SORTING SYSTEMS—Sandvik AB; Int'l, pg. 1186
SANTA ROSA STEEL FORMING, INC.; U.S. Private, pg. 965
SCHRADER BELLOWS DIVISION—Parker Hannifin Corporation; U.S. Public, pg. 1261
SCREW CONVEYOR CORP.; U.S. Private, pg. 977
SENIOR CONFLOW—Senior Engineering Group, plc.; Int'l, pg. 1220
SENIOR CONFLOW INC.—Senior Engineering Group, plc.; Int'l, pg. 1222
SENIOR CONTROL ENGINEERING LIMITED—Senior Engineering Group, plc.; Int'l, pg. 1220
SENIOR DAVIS DERBY—Senior Engineering Group, plc.; Int'l, pg. 1220
SENIOR ENTEX—Senior Engineering Group, plc.; Int'l, pg. 1220
SIMPLIMATIC ENGINEERING CO.—Crown Cork & Seal Company, Inc.; U.S. Public, pg. 463
THE SPENCER TURBINE CO.; U.S. Private, pg. 1025
STAMLER CORPORATION—The Oldenburg Group Companies; U.S. Private, pg. 814
STARCAN CORPORATION; Int'l, pg. 1297
STOCKER & YALE, INC.; U.S. Public, pg. 1518
SULZER PAPERTEC GMBH—Sulzer Ltd.; Int'l, pg. 1305
SYSTEMS & ELECTRONICS INC.—ESCO Electronics Corporation; U.S. Public, pg. 547
TCC INDUSTRIES; U.S. Public, pg. 1554
TOCCO, INC.—Park-Ohio Industries, Inc.; U.S. Public, pg. 1259
TOMKINS INDUSTRIES, INC.—Tomkins PLC; Int'l, pg. 1397
TRANSLOGIC CORP.—Thyssen AG; Int'l, pg. 1387
UNEX CONVEYING SYSTEMS, INC.; U.S. Private, pg. 1117
WALKER MAGNETICS GROUP, INC.; U.S. Private, pg. 1147
WARWICK FINSPA LIMITED—EIP Group plc; Int'l, pg. 426
WEBB HEAVY-DUTY ROLLER CONVEYOR SYSTEMS—Jervis B. Webb Company; U.S. Private, pg. 1156
JERVIS B. WEBB COMPANY; U.S. Private, pg. 1156
WEBB-TRIAX COMPANY—Jervis B. Webb Company; U.S. Private, pg. 1157
WEBSTER INDUSTRIES INC.; U.S. Private, pg. 1157
WEBSTER MFG. CO.—Webster Industries Inc.; U.S. Private, pg. 1158
WHITE SYSTEMS, INCORPORATED—Pinnacle Automation Inc.; U.S. Private, pg. 866
ZINIZ INC.; U.S. Private, pg. 1206

3536 — OVERHEAD TRAVELING CRANES, HOISTS & MONORAIL SYSTEMS

AAR ADVANCED STRUCTURES DIV.—AAR Corp.; U.S. Public, pg. 1
AAR CORP.; U.S. Public, pg. 1
AEC/WHITLOCK, INC.—Sterling, Inc.; U.S. Private, pg. 1041
ABELL-HOWE COMPANY; U.S. Private, pg. 10
AMCLYDE ENGINEERED PRODUCTS CO., INC.—Halter Marine Group, Inc.; U.S. Public, pg. 778
AMERICAN CRANE & EQUIPMENT CORP.; U.S. Private, pg. 52
AVIS INDUSTRIAL CORPORATION; U.S. Private, pg. 102
BABCOCK CONSTRUCTION CONTRACTORS—Babcock International Group PLC; Int'l, pg. 131
CM HOIST DIVISION—Columbus McKinnon Corp.; U.S. Public, pg. 405
CASE CORPORATION; U.S. Public, pg. 311
COLUMBUS MCKINNON CORP.; U.S. Public, pg. 405
CONSILIUM BULK - BABCOCK ATLANTA INC.—Babcock International Group PLC; Int'l, pg. 131
CONSILIUM BULK-BABCOCK, KVANUM AB—Babcock International Group PLC; Int'l, pg. 131
CONSILIUM BULK OY—Babcock International Group PLC; Int'l, pg. 131
CONSILIUM CMH-BABCOCK AB—Babcock International Group PLC; Int'l, pg. 131
CONSILIUM CLAUDIUS PETERS BABCOCK (HK) LTD—Babcock International Group PLC; Int'l, pg. 131
COOPER POWER TOOLS DIVISION—Cooper Industries, Inc.; U.S. Public, pg. 444
DURR AG; Int'l, pg. 421
DURR INDUSTRIES, INC.—Durr AG; Int'l, pg. 421
EDERER CRANES—Ederer Inc.; U.S. Private, pg. 363
EDERER INC.; U.S. Private, pg. 363
EDERER SERVICES, INC.—Ederer Inc.; U.S. Private, pg. 364
HARNISCHFEGER INDUSTRIES, INC.; U.S. Public, pg. 788
HARRINGTON HOISTS, INC.; U.S. Private, pg. 504
HEIL ENVIRONMENTAL INDUSTRIES—Dover Corporation; U.S. Public, pg. 520
HOLSTEIN AND KAPPERT GMBH—Klockner-Werke AG; Int'l, pg. 737
HYUNDAI HEAVY INDUSTRIES CO., LTD.—Hyundai Motor Company; Int'l, pg. 641
HYUNDAI MOTOR COMPANY; Int'l, pg. 641
IDEA ENGINEERING & FABRICATING; U.S. Private, pg. 557
INGERSOLL-RAND COMPANY; U.S. Public, pg. 876
INGERSOLL RAND TOOL & HOIST—Ingersoll-Rand Company; U.S. Public, pg. 877
JLG INDUSTRIES (AUSTRALIA) PTY. LIMITED—JLG Industries, Inc.; U.S. Public, pg. 918
JLG INDUSTRIES (UNITED KINGDOM) LIMITED—JLG Industries, Inc.; U.S. Public, pg. 918
JAGENBERG AG—Rheinmetall Group; Int'l, pg. 1108
JOY MANUFACTURING COMPANY (AFRICA) (PTY) LTD. JOHANNESBURG PLANT—Harnischfeger Industries, Inc.; U.S. Public, pg. 789
JOY MANUFACTURING COMPANY (PTY) LTD., SYDNEY PLANT—Harnischfeger Industries, Inc.; U.S. Public, pg. 789
KEY HANDLING SYSTEMS, INC.; U.S. Private, pg. 618
KLOCKNER MASCHINEN - UND ANGLAGENBAU GMBH—Babcock International Group PLC; Int'l, pg. 131
KLOCKNER-WERKE AG; Int'l, pg. 736
KRUPP MONTAGE- UND SERVICETECHNIK GMBH—Fried. Krupp AG; Int'l, pg. 516
KVAERNER BRUG (DEUTSCHLAND) GMBH—Kvaerner a.s.a.; Int'l, pg. 771
LIEBHERR-INTERNATIONAL AG; Int'l, pg. 807
LIFT TECH INTERNATIONAL—Columbus McKinnon Corp.; U.S. Public, pg. 406
MAN GHH LOGISTICS GMBH—MAN Aktiengesellschaft; Int'l, pg. 824
MACGREGOR (BEL) N.V.—Incentive AB; Int'l, pg. 670
MACGREGOR (DNK) A/S—Incentive AB; Int'l, pg. 670
MANNESMANN DEMAG CORPORATION—Mannesmann A.G.; Int'l, pg. 837
MANNESMANN DEMAG MATERIAL HANDLING LTD.—Mannesmann A.G.; Int'l, pg. 837
MANNESMANN DEMAG S.A.—Mannesmann A.G.; Int'l, pg. 837
MARINE TRAVELIFT, INC.; U.S. Private, pg. 703
MATERIAL HANDLING EQUIPMENT DIVISION—Harnischfeger Industries, Inc.; U.S. Public, pg. 788
META SERVICES INC.—Ederer Inc.; U.S. Private, pg. 363
MI-JACK PRODUCTS, INC.; U.S. Private, pg. 740
MODERN EQUIPMENT CO., INC.—Alco Industries, Inc.; U.S. Private, pg. 33
NORTHERN ENGINEERING CORP.—Crane Manufacturing; U.S. Private, pg. 286
PORTEC, INC.; U.S. Public, pg. 1317

POSITECH CORPORATION—Columbus McKinnon Corp.; *U.S. Public*, pg. 406
QUIPP, INC.; *U.S. Public*, pg. 1353
RAPID INDUSTRIES, INC.; *U.S. Private*, pg. 910
ROTARY LIFT—Dover Corporation; *U.S. Public*, pg. 521
SHEPARD NILES, INC.; *U.S. Private*, pg. 992
STAR CRANES—Ederer Inc.; *U.S. Private*, pg. 363
TRIBONETICS CO.—LSB Industries, Inc.; *U.S. Public*, pg. 971
UNIVERSAL BUILDERS SUPPLY, INC.; *U.S. Private*, pg. 1126
WASHINGTON CRANES—Ederer Inc.; *U.S. Private*, pg. 363
WHITING CORPORATION; *U.S. Private*, pg. 1173

3537 — INDUSTRIAL TRUCKS, TRACTORS, TRAILERS & STACKERS

ABB ROBOTICS AB—ABB Asea Brown Boveri (Holding) Ltd.; *Int'l*, pg. 7
ACCESS EQUIPMENT LTD.—Up-Right, Inc.; *U.S. Private*, pg. 1128
ACCO CHAIN & LIFTING PRODUCTS—FKI Plc; *Int'l*, pg. 473
ATHEY PRODUCTS CORPORATION; *U.S. Public*, pg. 142
AUTOLIFT INDUSTRIAL LIFT TRUCKS—Plymouth Industries, Inc.; *U.S. Private*, pg. 873
BT INDUSTRIES AB; *Int'l*, pg. 123
BAKER MATERIAL HANDLING CORP.—Linde AG; *Int'l*, pg. 810
BENFORD LIMITED—Powerscreen International Plc; *Int'l*, pg. 1066
BIG JOE MANUFACTURING CO.; *U.S. Private*, pg. 143
BLOUNT, INC.—Blount International, Inc.; *U.S. Public*, pg. 238
BLOUNT INTERNATIONAL, INC.; *U.S. Public*, pg. 237
BOMBARDIER INC.; *Int'l*, pg. 199
JERED BROWN BROTHERS INC.—Vickers PLC; *Int'l*, pg. 1468
BRUDI, INC.—Long Reach Holdings Inc.; *U.S. Private*, pg. 675
BURTMAN IRON WORKS, INC.; *U.S. Private*, pg. 188
CANNON EQUIPMENT—IMI Plc; *Int'l*, pg. 646
CAPACITY OF TEXAS, INC.—Collins Industries, Inc.; *U.S. Public*, pg. 400
CASCADE (AFRICA) PTY. LTD.—Cascade Corporation; *U.S. Public*, pg. 311
CASCADE (CANADA) INC.—Cascade Corporation; *U.S. Public*, pg. 311
CASCADE CORPORATION; *U.S. Public*, pg. 310
CASCADE (JAPAN) LTD.—Cascade Corporation; *U.S. Public*, pg. 311
CASCADE (U.K.) LTD.—Cascade Corporation; *U.S. Public*, pg. 311
CASE CORPORATION; *U.S. Public*, pg. 311
CATERPILLAR INC.; *U.S. Public*, pg. 315
CLARKLIFT OF MINNESOTA, INC.; *U.S. Private*, pg. 243
CLARKLIFT OF NORTH DAKOTA—Clarklift Of Minnesota, Inc.; *U.S. Private*, pg. 244
COMPONENTA TRANSPORT AB—Trelleborg AB; *Int'l*, pg. 1420
CONSILIUM BULK - BABCOCK ATLANTA INC.—Babcock International Group PLC; *Int'l*, pg. 131
CONSILIUM BULK-BABCOCK, KVANUM AB—Babcock International Group PLC; *Int'l*, pg. 131
CONSILIUM BULK OY—Babcock International Group PLC; *Int'l*, pg. 131
CONSILIUM CMH-BABCOCK AB—Babcock International Group PLC; *Int'l*, pg. 131
CONSILIUM CLAUDIUS PETERS BABCOCK (HK) LTD—Babcock International Group PLC; *Int'l*, pg. 131
CROWN EQUIPMENT CORPORATION; *U.S. Private*, pg. 292
DAEWOO CORPORATION; *Int'l*, pg. 357
JOHN DEERE DUBUQUE WORKS—Deere & Company; *U.S. Public*, pg. 492
DYNABILT PRODUCTS—Burtman Iron Works, Inc.; *U.S. Private*, pg. 188
ELWELL-PARKER LIMITED; *U.S. Private*, pg. 373
ELWELL-PARKER, INC.—Elwell-Parker Limited; *U.S. Private*, pg. 373
EQUIPOS DE ACUNA, S.A. DE C.V.—Eagle-Picher Industries, Inc.; *U.S. Private*, pg. 356
FAULTLESS NUTTING—FKI Plc; *Int'l*, pg. 473
FIAT AUTO SPA; *Int'l*, pg. 480
FORSS-PARATOR—Trelleborg AB; *Int'l*, pg. 1420
FREIGHTLINER TRUCK MFG. PLANT—Daimler-Benz Aktiengesellschaft; *Int'l*, pg. 368
GENERAL CABLE CO.—Wassall Plc; *Int'l*, pg. 1487
GROVE COLES FRANCE, S.A.—Hanson PLC; *Int'l*, pg. 594
GROVE COLES GMBH—Hanson PLC; *Int'l*, pg. 594
GUZZLER MANUFACTURING, INC.—Federal Signal Corporation; *U.S. Public*, pg. 616
HARBOUR GROUP LTD.; *U.S. Private*, pg. 500
HARNISCHFEGER INDUSTRIES, INC.; *U.S. Public*, pg. 788
HELM RESOURCES INC.; *U.S. Public*, pg. 808
HYDROLECTRIC LIFT TRUCKS INC.—Aluminum Company of America; *U.S. Public*, pg. 61
HYSTER EUROPE LTD.—NACCO Industries, Inc.; *U.S. Public*, pg. 1149
HYSTER (NI) LTD.—NACCO Industries, Inc.; *U.S. Public*, pg. 1150
INSTANT S.R.L.—Up-Right, Inc.; *U.S. Private*, pg. 1128
IOCHPE-MAXION S.A.; *Int'l*, pg. 688
IVECO MAGIRUS A/G—Fiat Auto SpA; *Int'l*, pg. 484
JLG INDUSTRIES, INC.; *U.S. Public*, pg. 918
K-D MANITOU, INC.—Manitou BF; *Int'l*, pg. 834
KALDNES HEAVY LIFT TRUCKS A/S—Norsk Vekst ASA; *Int'l*, pg. 965
KALMAR INDUSTRIES AB—Trelleborg AB; *Int'l*, pg. 1420
KALMAR LMV AB—Trelleborg AB; *Int'l*, pg. 1421
KENWORTH TRUCK COMPANY—Paccar Inc.; *U.S. Public*, pg. 1246
KLOCKNER MASCHINEN - UND ANGLAGENBAU GMBH—Babcock International Group PLC; *Int'l*, pg. 131
KRUPP FORDERTECHNIK GMBH—Fried. Krupp AG; *Int'l*, pg. 511
KVAERNER BRUG (DEUTSCHLAND) GMBH—Kvaerner a.s.a.; *Int'l*, pg. 771
LANSING LINDE LTD.—Linde AG; *Int'l*, pg. 810
LEVITON MFG. CO., INC.; *U.S. Private*, pg. 663
LIEBHERR-INTERNATIONAL AG; *Int'l*, pg. 807
LIFT-ALL CO., INC.; *U.S. Private*, pg. 667
LINDE AG; *Int'l*, pg. 810
LINDE AG WERKSGRUPPE GUELDNER ASCHAFFENBURG—Linde AG; *Int'l*, pg. 810
MAN GHH LOGISTICS GMBH—MAN Aktiengesellschaft; *Int'l*, pg. 824
MANITOU BF; *Int'l*, pg. 834
MANNESMANN DEMAG CORPORATION—Mannesmann A.G.; *Int'l*, pg. 837
MARINE TRAVELIFT, INC.; *U.S. Private*, pg. 703
MAXON COMPACTOR CORP.—Maxon Industries, Inc.; *U.S. Private*, pg. 717
MAXON INDUSTRIES, INC.; *U.S. Private*, pg. 717
MAXON REFUSE CHASSIS CORP.—Maxon Industries, Inc.; *U.S. Private*, pg. 717
MAYVILLE ENGINEERING CO., INC.; *U.S. Private*, pg. 718
MCNALLY WELLMAN—Svedala Industri AB; *Int'l*, pg. 1326
MELROE COMPANY—Ingersoll-Rand Company; *U.S. Public*, pg. 877
MITSUBISHI CATERPILLAR FORKLIFT AMERICA INC. (MCFA)—Caterpillar Inc.; *U.S. Public*, pg. 316
MITSUBISHI CATERPILLAR FORKLIFT AMERICA INC. (MCFA)—Mitsubishi Heavy Industries Ltd.; *Int'l*, pg. 874
MONNOYEUR SCA; *Int'l*, pg. 888
MORGAN TRAILER MANUFACTURING CO.; *U.S. Private*, pg. 761
MOTALA TANK—Trelleborg AB; *Int'l*, pg. 1420
MURATA MACHINERY, LTD.; *Int'l*, pg. 897
MUSTANG INDUSTRIAL EQUIPMENT CO.—Mustang Tractor & Equip. Co.; *U.S. Private*, pg. 769
MUSTANG MANUFACTURING COMPANY, INC.—Gehl Company; *U.S. Public*, pg. 704
NACCO INDUSTRIES, INC.; *U.S. Public*, pg. 1149
O.A. NEWTON & SON CO.; *U.S. Private*, pg. 797
NISSAN FORKLIFT CORPORATION, NORTH AMERICA—Nissan Motor Co., Ltd.; *Int'l*, pg. 944
O&K ORENSTEIN & KOPPEL AKTIENGESELLSCHAFT—Fried. Krupp AG; *Int'l*, pg. 516
OMNIQUIP INTERNATIONAL, INC.—Harbour Group Ltd.; *U.S. Private*, pg. 500
OSBY TVATTUTRUSININGAR AB—Electrolux, AB; *Int'l*, pg. 439
PETERBILT MOTORS CO.—Paccar Inc.; *U.S. Public*, pg. 1247
PETTIBONE CORPORATION; *U.S. Private*, pg. 859
PLYMOUTH INDUSTRIES, INC.; *U.S. Private*, pg. 873
PORTEC, INC.; *U.S. Public*, pg. 1317
POWERSCREEN INTERNATIONAL PLC; *Int'l*, pg. 1066
R.A. INDUSTRIES, INC.; *U.S. Private*, pg. 902
RAPID INDUSTRIES, INC.; *U.S. Private*, pg. 910
RAPISTAN DEMAG CORP.—Mannesmann A.G.; *Int'l*, pg. 837
THE RAYMOND CORPORATION—BT Industries AB; *Int'l*, pg. 123
RAYMOND INDUSTRIAL EQUIPMENT LTD.—BT Industries AB; *Int'l*, pg. 123
ROSS TECHNOLOGY CORP.; *U.S. Private*, pg. 946
JOHN RUSLING LTD.—Up-Right, Inc.; *U.S. Private*, pg. 1128
SLD SKIDHIRE LIMITED—SLD Holdings Ltd.; *Int'l*, pg. 1160
STILL GMBH—Linde AG; *Int'l*, pg. 811
SABANCI HOLDING A.S.; *Int'l*, pg. 1167
SHUTTLELIFT, INC.—Marine Travelift, Inc.; *U.S. Private*, pg. 703
SIMON AERIALS INC.—Simon Engineering plc; *Int'l*, pg. 1252
SYSTEMS & ELECTRONICS INC.—ESCO Electronics Corporation; *U.S. Public*, pg. 547
TAYLOR MACHINE WORKS, INC.; *U.S. Private*, pg. 1070
TEREX CORPORATION; *U.S. Public*, pg. 1581
TRANSPORTATION EQUIPMENT GROUP-NORTH AMERICA—Bombardier Inc.; *Int'l*, pg. 200
UNIVERSAL BUILDERS SUPPLY, INC.; *U.S. Private*, pg. 1126
UP-RIGHT (FAR EAST) LTD.—Up-Right, Inc.; *U.S. Private*, pg. 1128
UP-RIGHT (IRELAND) LTD.—Up-Right, Inc.; *U.S. Private*, pg. 1128
UP-RIGHT SCAFFOLDS LTD.—Up-Right, Inc.; *U.S. Private*, pg. 1128
VARITY DAYTON WALTHER—LucasVarity plc; *Int'l*, pg. 820
VECTUR ALUMINUMSTALLNINGAR—Up-Right, Inc.; *U.S. Private*, pg. 1128
VECTUR B.V.—Up-Right, Inc.; *U.S. Private*, pg. 1129
VECTUR GMBH—Up-Right, Inc.; *U.S. Private*, pg. 1129
VECTUR S.A.—Up-Right, Inc.; *U.S. Private*, pg. 1129
N.V. VECTUR S.A.—Up-Right, Inc.; *U.S. Private*, pg. 1129
VOEST-ALPINE SERVICES AND TECHNOLOGIES CORP.—Voest-Alpine Stahl AG; *Int'l*, pg. 1471
WAGNER FORDERTECHNIK GMBH & CO. KG—Linde AG; *Int'l*, pg. 811
WEBB-TRIAX COMPANY—Jervis B. Webb Company; *U.S. Private*, pg. 1157
ZIEMAN MANUFACTURING COMPANY; *U.S. Private*, pg. 1205

3541 — MACHINE TOOLS, METAL CUTTING TYPES

APV CHEMICAL MACHINERY LIMITED—Siebe plc; *Int'l*, pg. 1240
ABBOTT BALL COMPANY; *U.S. Private*, pg. 9
ALLIED CARBI-TECH, INC.; *U.S. Private*, pg. 38
ALLIED TOOL PRODUCTS INC.—Federal Signal Corporation; *U.S. Public*, pg. 617
APEX BROACH & MACHINE CO.; *U.S. Private*, pg. 77
AUTOCON TECHNOLOGIES, INC.—Hurco Companies, Inc.; *U.S. Public*, pg. 850
AVIS INDUSTRIAL CORPORATION; *U.S. Private*, pg. 102
BODINE ASSEMBLY AND TEST SYSTEMS; *U.S. Private*, pg. 154
ROBERT BOSCH AG—Robert Bosch GmbH; *Int'l*, pg. 205
ROBERT BOSCH CORPORATION—Robert Bosch GmbH; *Int'l*, pg. 204
BOSTON DIGITAL CORP.; *U.S. Private*, pg. 161
BRIDGEPORT MACHINES, INC.; *U.S. Public*, pg. 251
BROWN & SHARPE LIMITED—Brown & Sharpe Manufacturing Company; *U.S. Public*, pg. 260
BROWN & SHARPE MANUFACTURING COMPANY; *U.S. Public*, pg. 260
BRYANT GRINDER CORP.—Goldman Financial Group; *U.S. Private*, pg. 461
BUTLER NEWALL LIMITED-BUTLER MACHINE TOOL DIV.—B. Elliott plc.; *Int'l*, pg. 448
CHARMILLES TECHNOLOGIES CORP.—Georg Fischer Ltd.; *Int'l*, pg. 489
CHARMILLES TECHNOLOGIES SA—Georg Fischer Ltd.; *Int'l*, pg. 489
CINCINNATI INCORPORATED; *U.S. Private*, pg. 240
CINCINNATI MILACRON INC.; *U.S. Public*, pg. 368
CINCINNATI MILACRON INDUSTRIAL SYSTEMS DIVISION—Cincinnati Milacron Inc.; *U.S. Public*, pg. 368
CITY MACHINE TOOL & DIE COMPANY, INC.; *U.S. Private*, pg. 241
CLEVELAND PRECISION SYSTEMS GMBH—Danaher Corporation; *U.S. Public*, pg. 482
COLTEC HOLDINGS INC; *U.S. Public*, pg. 401
COMPONENTA TOOLS AB—Trelleborg AB; *Int'l*, pg. 1421
CONTAINER TOOLING CORPORATION—Federal Signal Corporation; *U.S. Public*, pg. 617
CONTINENTAL MACHINES, INC.; *U.S. Private*, pg. 268
JOHN CRANE LEMCO—TI Group plc; *Int'l*, pg. 1339
CRANKSHAFT MACHINE GROUP—Avis Industrial Corporation; *U.S. Private*, pg. 102
CURTIS-TOLEDO, INC.; *U.S. Private*, pg. 298
DAVENPORT MACHINE TOOL DIV.—Dover Corporation; *U.S. Public*, pg. 520
DERLAN INDUSTRIES LIMITED; *Int'l*, pg. 395
DURR AG; *Int'l*, pg. 421
DURR INDUSTRIES, INC.—Durr AG; *Int'l*, pg. 421
DURRIESSCHARMANN, AG—Metallgesellschaft AG; *Int'l*, pg. 860
ESAB AB—Charter plc; *Int'l*, pg. 281
ESAB GROUP (UK) LTD.—Charter plc; *Int'l*, pg. 282
ESAB-HANCOCK GMBH—Charter plc; *Int'l*, pg. 282
EFFICIENT ENGINEERING CO.; *U.S. Private*, pg. 365
B. ELLIOTT PLC.; *Int'l*, pg. 448
ENDURO-NIAGARA LTD.—J.H. Roberts Industries Inc.; *U.S. Private*, pg. 935
FLS MASKINTEKNIK A/S—FLS Industries A/S; *Int'l*, pg. 475
FMB S.A. - PRODUCTOS METALLURGICOS—Fiat Auto SpA; *Int'l*, pg. 483
FADAL ENGINEERING COMPANY, INC.—Thyssen AG; *Int'l*, pg. 1389
FATA PRODUCTION MACHINERY—FKI Plc; *Int'l*, pg. 474
FELLOWS CORPORATION—Goldman Financial Group; *U.S. Private*, pg. 461
FERGUSON MACHINE CO.—Crane Co.; *U.S. Public*, pg. 457
FIAT AUTO SPA; *Int'l*, pg. 480
FINCOMAU S.P.A.—Fiat Auto SpA; *Int'l*, pg. 482
GEORG FISCHER LTD.; *Int'l*, pg. 488
FREEDOM FORGE CORPORATION; *U.S. Private*, pg. 425
FRISCHMUTH & FREITAG GMBH—Rothenberger Group GmbH; *Int'l*, pg. 1128
GFI INC.—Kaufel Group Ltd.; *Int'l*, pg. 725
GARDNER ABRASIVES—UNOVA, Inc.; *U.S. Public*, pg. 1699
GARRYSON-INSLEY LTD.—B. Elliott plc.; *Int'l*, pg. 448
GIDDINGS & LEWIS, INC.—Thyssen AG; *Int'l*, pg. 1389
GIDDINGS & LEWIS LTD—Thyssen AG; *Int'l*, pg. 1389
THE GLEASON WORKS—Gleason Corporation; *U.S. Public*, pg. 746
GLEASON WORKS LTD.—Gleason Corporation; *U.S. Public*, pg. 746
GREENFIELD INDUSTRIES INC.—Kennametal Inc.; *U.S. Public*, pg. 950
HARDINGS, INC.; *U.S. Private*, pg. 502
HARIG GRINDERS—Bridgeport Machines, Inc.; *U.S. Public*, pg. 252
HECKERT CHEMNITZER WERZEUGMASCHINEN GMBH—Traub AG; *Int'l*, pg. 1419
HERMANN PFAUTER GMBH & CO.; *Int'l*, pg. 617
HERMLE AG—Traub AG; *Int'l*, pg. 1419
HERR-VOSS CORP.—Salem Group, Inc.; *U.S. Private*, pg. 961
HERR VOSS LTD.—Salem Group, Inc.; *U.S. Private*, pg. 962
HITACHI SEIKO, LTD.—Hitachi, Ltd.; *Int'l*, pg. 622
HITACHI ZOSEN METALMECANICA LTDA.—Nissho Iwai Corporation; *Int'l*, pg. 947
HONDA ENGINEERING CO., LTD.—Honda Motor Co., Ltd.; *Int'l*, pg. 634
S.E. HUFFMAN CORP.; *U.S. Private*, pg. 546
HURCO COMPANIES, INC.; *U.S. Public*, pg. 850
HURCO MANUFACTURING COMPANY—Hurco Companies, Inc.; *U.S. Public*, pg. 850
HUWOOD ELECTRIC LTD.—FKI Plc; *Int'l*, pg. 473
ISI NORGEN, INC.—IMI Plc; *Int'l*, pg. 646

IDEX CORPORATION; U.S. Public, pg. 862
INGERSOLL INTERNATIONAL INC.; U.S. Private, pg. 562
INGERSOLL MASCHINEN UND WERKZEUGE GMBH—Ingersoll International Inc.; U.S. Private, pg. 562
THE INGERSOLL MILLING MACHINE CO.—Ingersoll International Inc.; U.S. Private, pg. 562
ISCAR LTD.—IDB Holding Corporation; Int'l, pg. 644
JAGENBERG AG—Rheinmetall Group; Int'l, pg. 1108
KAMAN INDUSTRIAL TECHNOLOGIES CORP.—Kaman Corporation; U.S. Public, pg. 942
KARSTEN ENGINEERING CORP.—Karsten Manufacturing Corporation; U.S. Private, pg. 608
KASPER MACHINE COMPANY; U.S. Private, pg. 608
KAYEX CORP.—General Signal Corporation; U.S. Public, pg. 727
KENNAMETAL INC.; U.S. Public, pg. 950
KENNAMETAL METALWORKING SYSTEMS DIV.—Kennametal Inc.; U.S. Public, pg. 950
KINGSBURY CORPORATION; U.S. Private, pg. 621
KINGSBURY MACHINING CENTER, DIV.—Kingsbury Corporation; U.S. Private, pg. 622
KIRLOSKAR WARNER SWASEY LTD.—Thyssen AG; Int'l, pg. 1389
KNURLET TOOL CO.—Kasper Machine Company; U.S. Private, pg. 608
KOMATSU LTD.; Int'l, pg. 743
KOYO-MATTISON—Mattison Technologies, Inc.; U.S. Private, pg. 715
KROFAM INC.; U.S. Private, pg. 636
LANDIS—UNOVA, Inc.; U.S. Public, pg. 1699
LAPMASTER INTERNATIONAL LTD.—TI Group plc; Int'l, pg. 1338
LIDKOPING MACHINE TOOLS AB—AB SKF; Int'l, pg. 1157
LITTELL—MetalTech International PLC; Int'l, pg. 862
THE MACHINE TOOL GROUP—DeVlieg-Bullard Inc.; U.S. Public, pg. 503
B.V. MACHINEFABRIEK BREDA—Royal Begemann Group; Int'l, pg. 1133
MACHINEFABRIEK WERKLUST B.V.—Royal Begemann Group; Int'l, pg. 1133
MACHINING AND ASSEMBLY SYSTEMS—UNOVA, Inc.; U.S. Public, pg. 1699
MAKINO INC.—Makino Milling Machine Co. Ltd.; Int'l, pg. 831
MAKINO MILLING MACHINE CO. LTD.; Int'l, pg. 831
MANCHESTER TOOL COMPANY—Federal Signal Corporation; U.S. Public, pg. 617
MANCHESTER TOOL LIMITED, IRELAND—Federal Signal Corporation; U.S. Public, pg. 617
MASTERBLEND, INC.—Leggett & Platt, Incorporated; U.S. Public, pg. 986
MATTISON TECHNOLOGIES, INC.; U.S. Private, pg. 714
MCLEAN—Zero Corporation; U.S. Public, pg. 1791
MICRO-PRECISION OPERATIONS—Textron Inc.; U.S. Public, pg. 1589
MICROMATIC OPERATIONS (ANGOLA PLANT)—Textron Inc.; U.S. Public, pg. 1589
MICROMATIC TEXTRON—Textron Inc.; U.S. Public, pg. 1589
MIKRON AG NIDAU—Mikron Holding AG; Int'l, pg. 866
MIKRON BEIJING OFFICE—Mikron Holding AG; Int'l, pg. 867
MIKRON (BIRMINGHAM) LTD.—Mikron Holding AG; Int'l, pg. 867
MIKRON FRANCE SARL—Mikron Holding AG; Int'l, pg. 867
MIKRON HANNOVER GMBH—Mikron Holding AG; Int'l, pg. 867
MIKRON MACHINE TOOL ASIA PTE LTD—Mikron Holding AG; Int'l, pg. 867
MIKRON PAVIA S.R.L.—Mikron Holding AG; Int'l, pg. 867
MILL-LOG EQUIPMENT CO., INC.—Twin Disc, Incorporated; U.S. Public, pg. 1646
MONARCH CORTLAND DIV.—The Monarch Machine Tool Company; U.S. Public, pg. 1124
THE MONARCH MACHINE TOOL COMPANY; U.S. Public, pg. 1123
MONARCH WETKZENGMASCHINEN GMBH—The Monarch Machine Tool Company; U.S. Public, pg. 1124
MOORE TOOL COMPANY, INC.—The Producto Machine Co.; U.S. Private, pg. 889
MOTCH CORPORATION—Rothenberger Group GmbH; Int'l, pg. 1128
MURATA MACHINERY, LTD.; Int'l, pg. 897
NELMOR CO., INC.—Sterling, Inc.; U.S. Private, pg. 1041
NEWCOR, INC.; U.S. Public, pg. 1176
NIAGARA CUTTER, INC.; U.S. Private, pg. 798
NORITAKE CO., LIMITED; Int'l, pg. 958
NORTON INDUSTRIEPRODUKTE GMBH—Saint-Gobain; Int'l, pg. 1175
OKUMA AMERICA CORPORATION—Okuma Corporation; Int'l, pg. 1001
OKUMA CORPORATION; Int'l, pg. 1000
OLIVETTI SPA; Int'l, pg. 1002
OUTER DRIVE MANUFACTURING TECHNICAL CENTER—Chrysler Corporation; U.S. Public, pg. 353
PMC INDUSTRIES INC.; U.S. Private, pg. 827
PITTLER MASCHINENFABRIK AG—Rothenberger Group GmbH; Int'l, pg. 1128
PLASMA-THERM, INC.; U.S. Public, pg. 1308
PLASTIC ENGINEERED COMPONENTS INC.; U.S. Private, pg. 870
THE PRODUCTO MACHINE CO.; U.S. Private, pg. 889
PUSAN PRECISION INDUSTRIES, LTD.—Brother Industries, Ltd.; Int'l, pg. 230
QUALTERS & SMITH—Carclo Engineering Group plc; Int'l, pg. 268
R & B MACHINE TOOL CO.; U.S. Private, pg. 901
RMT TECHNOLOGY—Reynolds Machine Tool Corp.; U.S. Private, pg. 927
RENAULT; Int'l, pg. 1102
RENISHAW PLC; Int'l, pg. 1103
REYNOLDS MACHINE TOOL CORP.; U.S. Private, pg. 926
ROBOTIC VISION SYSTEMS, INC.; U.S. Public, pg. 1395
ROGERS TOOL WORKS, INC.—Kennametal Inc.; U.S. Public, pg. 950
SMT MACHINE COMPANY AB—Trelleborg AB; Int'l, pg. 1421
S.O.S. NEWALL—S.O.S. Newall Limited; Int'l, pg. 1166
S.O.S. NEWALL LIMITED; Int'l, pg. 1166
SALEM CORPORATION—Salem Group, Inc.; U.S. Private, pg. 961
SANDVIK COROMANT COMPANY—Sandvik AB; Int'l, pg. 1185
SANDVIK KOSTA GMBH—Sandvik AB; Int'l, pg. 1186
SCHIESS-METALNA GMBH—Metallgesellschaft AG; Int'l, pg. 860
SCOTCHMAN INDUSTRIES, INC.—Krofam Inc.; U.S. Private, pg. 636
SEDIN-SCHIESS—Metallgesellschaft AG; Int'l, pg. 860
SENECA FALLS TECHNOLOGY GROUP; U.S. Private, pg. 984
SETCO; U.S. Private, pg. 987
SHIN NIPPON KOKI CO. LTD.; Int'l, pg. 1234
SPEEDFAN INTERNATIONAL, INC.; U.S. Public, pg. 1497
STAMCO-DEPIEREUX GMBH—The Monarch Machine Tool Company; U.S. Public, pg. 1124
STAMCO DIV.—The Monarch Machine Tool Company; U.S. Public, pg. 1124
STAMCO (U.K.) LTD.—The Monarch Machine Tool Company; U.S. Public, pg. 1124
STANLEY HYDRAULIC TOOLS DIV.—The Stanley Works; U.S. Public, pg. 1509
STAR CUTTER CO.; U.S. Private, pg. 1034
STRIPPIT, INC.—IDEX Corporation; U.S. Public, pg. 862
SUMMIT EXPORT CORP.—LSB Industries, Inc.; U.S. Public, pg. 971
SUMMIT MACHINE TOOL MFG. CORP.—LSB Industries, Inc.; U.S. Public, pg. 971
SUMMIT MACHINERY CO.—LSB Industries, Inc.; U.S. Public, pg. 971
SUNNEN PRODUCTS COMPANY; U.S. Private, pg. 1053
TWC OF FLORIDA, INCORPORATED—The West Company, Incorporated; U.S. Public, pg. 1755
TAYLOR HOBSON PNEUMO—The Rank Group PLC; Int'l, pg. 1087
TEKSID ALUMINUM FOUNDRY—Fiat Auto SpA; Int'l, pg. 483
TEKSID S.P.A.—Fiat Auto SpA; Int'l, pg. 483
TOOLPRO—Kimball International, Inc.; U.S. Public, pg. 957
TORAY ENGINEERING CO., LTD.—Toray Industries, Inc.; Int'l, pg. 1399
TOSHIBA MACHINE CO., LTD.—Toshiba Corporation; Int'l, pg. 1404
TOSHIBA TUNGALOY CO., LTD.—Toshiba Corporation; Int'l, pg. 1405
TRAUB AG; Int'l, pg. 1419
TRAUB DREHMASCHINEN GMBH—Traub AG; Int'l, pg. 1419
TRAUB-GLORIA S.R.L.—Traub AG; Int'l, pg. 1419
TRAUB-HERMLE CORPORATION—Traub AG; Int'l, pg. 1419
TRAUBOMATIC IND. E COM. LTDA.—Traub AG; Int'l, pg. 1419
TULON CO.—Esterline Technologies Corporation; U.S. Public, pg. 594
UDDCOMB SWEDEN AB—Trelleborg AB; Int'l, pg. 1421
UNION WERKZEUGMASCHINENFABRIK GERA GMBH—Metallgesellschaft AG; Int'l, pg. 860
THE U.S. BAIRD CORPORATION; U.S. Private, pg. 1124
U.S. BROACH & MACHINE COMPANY—Avis Industrial Corporation; U.S. Private, pg. 102
UNIVERSAL PHOTONICS, INC.; U.S. Private, pg. 1127
USINE DE WECKER S.R.L.—Zimmermann & Jansen GmbH; Int'l, pg. 1529
VERMONT USA MACHINE TOOL GROUP—Goldman Financial Group; U.S. Private, pg. 461
J.M. VOITH, GMBH; Int'l, pg. 1472
WCI MACHINE TOOLS—Electrolux, AB; Int'l, pg. 440
WATERBURY FARREL TECHNOLOGIES—Goldman Financial Group; U.S. Private, pg. 461
WELDON MACHINE TOOL, INC.; U.S. Private, pg. 1161
WESTERN ATLAS INC.; U.S. Public, pg. 1757
WILTON CORPORATION; U.S. Private, pg. 1181
WISCONSIN AUTOMATED MACHINERY CORP.; U.S. Private, pg. 1184
WISCONSIN MACHINE AND TOOL CORPORATION; U.S. Private, pg. 1185

3542 — MACHINE TOOLS, METAL FORMING TYPES

A.T.I. TOOLS, INC.—Snap-On Tools Corporation; U.S. Public, pg. 1480
ABBEY ETNA MACHINE COMPANY; U.S. Private, pg. 9
ACME INDUSTRIAL COMPANY—Jergens Inc.; U.S. Private, pg. 586
ALCOA PACKAGING MACHINERY, INC.—Aluminum Company of America; U.S. Public, pg. 60
ALLIED PRODUCTS CORPORATION; U.S. Public, pg. 48
ARROW FASTENER CO., INC.; U.S. Private, pg. 85
ATLANTIC MACHINE TOOLS INC.—Haco N.V.; Int'l, pg. 585
AUTOCON TECHNOLOGIES, INC.—Hurco Companies, Inc.; U.S. Public, pg. 850
BABCOCK & WILCOX CO.—McDermott International, Inc.; U.S. Public, pg. 1068
BALTEC MASCHINENBAU AG—Feintool International Holding AG; Int'l, pg. 479
BLISS—CNB International, Inc.; U.S. Private, pg. 196
BOBST S.A.; Int'l, pg. 198
BOSAM S.A.—Bobst S.A.; Int'l, pg. 199
CNB INTERNATIONAL, INC.; U.S. Private, pg. 196
CHICAGO RIVET & MACHINE COMPANY; U.S. Public, pg. 348
CINCINNATI INCORPORATED; U.S. Private, pg. 240
CLEARING-NIAGARA—CNB International, Inc.; U.S. Private, pg. 196
CONNELL LIMITED PARTNERSHIP; U.S. Private, pg. 264
DAEWOO CORPORATION; Int'l, pg. 357
DEVLIEG-BULLARD INC.; U.S. Public, pg. 502
DEVLIEG-BULLARD SERVICES GROUP—DeVlieg-Bullard Inc.; U.S. Public, pg. 502
DEVLIEG-BULLARD TOOLING SYSTEMS DIVISION—DeVlieg-Bullard Inc.; U.S. Public, pg. 502
J. DIEFFENBACHER GMBH & CO.; Int'l, pg. 413
DIEFFENBACHER NORTH AMERICA—J. Dieffenbacher GmbH & Co.; Int'l, pg. 413
DREIS & KRUMP MANUFACTURING COMPANY; U.S. Private, pg. 342
DYNAMIC MATERIALS CORPORATION; U.S. Public, pg. 539
EAGLE INDUSTRIES, INC.—Great American Management & Investment, Inc.; U.S. Private, pg. 473
EATON INTERNATIONAL CORP.—Eaton Corporation; U.S. Public, pg. 558
EFFICIENT ENGINEERING CO.; U.S. Private, pg. 365
B. ELLIOTT PLC.; Int'l, pg. 448
ENSLEY TOOL CO. INC.—Rothenberger Group GmbH; Int'l, pg. 1129
ERIE PRESS SYSTEMS—EFCO Inc.; U.S. Private, pg. 353
ESTERLINE TECHNOLOGIES CORPORATION; U.S. Public, pg. 594
FEINTOOL AG LYSS—Feintool International Holding AG; Int'l, pg. 479
FEINTOOL CINCINNATI INC.—Feintool International Holding AG; Int'l, pg. 479
FEINTOOL ENGINEERING CO. LTD.—Feintool International Holding AG; Int'l, pg. 479
FEINTOOL EQUIPMENT CORP.—Feintool International Holding AG; Int'l, pg. 479
FEINTOOL INTERNATIONAL HOLDING AG; Int'l, pg. 479
FEINTOOL JAPAN CO. LTD.—Feintool International Holding AG; Int'l, pg. 479
FEINTOOL NEW YORK INC.—Feintool International Holding AG; Int'l, pg. 479
FEINTOOL U.S. OPERATIONS INC.—Feintool International Holding AG; Int'l, pg. 479
FENN MANUFACTURING CO.—United Dominion Industries, Ltd.; U.S. Public, pg. 1676
FINCOMAU S.P.A.—Fiat Auto SpA; Int'l, pg. 482
FLUID PRODUCT SALES DIV.—Dana Corporation; U.S. Public, pg. 479
FORGED PRODUCTS—The Cypress Companies; U.S. Private, pg. 299
GKN WESTLAND AEROSPACE NORTH AMERICA INC.—GKN plc; Int'l, pg. 535
GOUGLER INDUSTRIES, INC.; U.S. Private, pg. 466
HPM CORPORATION; U.S. Private, pg. 492
HACO N.V.; Int'l, pg. 585
HEIN-WERNER CORPORATION; U.S. Public, pg. 805
HESS ENGINEERING AG—Hess Engineering Inc.; U.S. Private, pg. 524
HESS ENGINEERING INC.; U.S. Private, pg. 524
HILTI AG; Int'l, pg. 619
HILTI INC.—Hilti AG; Int'l, pg. 620
HITACHI ZOSEN CORPORATION; Int'l, pg. 622
HURCO COMPANIES, INC.; U.S. Public, pg. 850
HURCO MANUFACTURING COMPANY—Hurco Companies, Inc.; U.S. Public, pg. 850
IPC-INTERNATIONAL PARTS CORP.—Whitman Corporation; U.S. Public, pg. 1766
ISI NORGEN, INC.—IMI Plc; Int'l, pg. 646
INSTA-PRO INTERNATIONAL, LTD.—Triple F, Inc.; U.S. Private, pg. 1104
IOWA PRECISION INDUSTRIES—Met-Coil Systems Corp.; U.S. Public, pg. 1100
KENNAMETAL HERTEL BELGIUM, S.A.—Kennametal Inc.; U.S. Public, pg. 951
KENNAMETAL INC.; U.S. Public, pg. 950
KLOECKNER-WILHELMSBURGER GMBH—Klockner-Werke AG; Int'l, pg. 737
LEXINGTON PRECISION CORPORATION; U.S. Public, pg. 991
LHOMME S.A.—Sonoco Products Company; U.S. Public, pg. 1487
LINDE AG; Int'l, pg. 810
MHIA MACHINE TOOL DIVISION—Mitsubishi Heavy Industries Ltd.; Int'l, pg. 874
B.V. MACHINEFABRIEK BREDA—Royal Begemann Group; Int'l, pg. 1133
MACHINEFABRIEK WERKLUST B.V.—Royal Begemann Group; Int'l, pg. 1133
MAKINO INC.—Makino Milling Machine Co. Ltd.; Int'l, pg. 831
MCNEIL & NRM., INC.; U.S. Private, pg. 725
MET-COIL LTD.—Met-Coil Systems Corp.; U.S. Public, pg. 1100
MET-COIL SYSTEMS CORP.; U.S. Public, pg. 1099
MILFORD FASTENING SYSTEMS; U.S. Private, pg. 745
MINING AND CONSTRUCTION DIVISION—Kennametal Inc.; U.S. Public, pg. 950
THE MINSTER MACHINE COMPANY; U.S. Private, pg. 751
MITEK, INC.—Rexam PLC; Int'l, pg. 1106
MITEK INDUSTRIES—Rexam PLC; Int'l, pg. 1106
MITSUI SEIKI KOGYO CO., LTD.—Mitsui & Co., Ltd.; Int'l, pg. 878
MONARCH CORTLAND DIV.—The Monarch Machine Tool Company; U.S. Public, pg. 1124
THE MONARCH MACHINE TOOL COMPANY; U.S. Public, pg. 1123
MONARCH WETKZENGMASCHINEN GMBH—The Monarch Machine Tool Company; U.S. Public, pg. 1124
MURATA MACHINERY, LTD.; Int'l, pg. 897
NATIONAL MACHINERY; U.S. Private, pg. 785
NOKIA SOURCING, INC.—Oy Nokia Ab/Nokia Group; Int'l, pg. 953
P/A INDUSTRIES, INC.; U.S. Private, pg. 825

PETERS MASCHINENFABRIK GMBH—Bobst S.A.; *Int'l, pg. 199*
PETTIBONE TIFFIN PARTS—Pettibone Corporation; *U.S. Private, pg. 860*
POWERMATIC—DeVlieg-Bullard Inc.; *U.S. Public, pg. 502*
AB PROFILA—Tetra Laval Group; *Int'l, pg. 1377*
PROGRESSIVE TOOL & INDUSTRIES CO.; *U.S. Private, pg. 890*
RING SCREW WORKS; *U.S. Private, pg. 931*
C.G. SARGENTS SONS—Aeroglide Corporation; *U.S. Private, pg. 24*
SCOTCHMAN INDUSTRIES, INC.—Krofam Inc.; *U.S. Private, pg. 636*
SEMTECH LTD.—Semtech Corporation; *U.S. Public, pg. 1456*
SENCO PRODUCTS, INC.—SENCORP; *U.S. Private, pg. 984*
SENECA FALLS TECHNOLOGY GROUP; *U.S. Private, pg. 984*
SIAM-HITACHI CONSTRUCTION MACHINERY CO., LTD.—The Siam Cement Public Company Limited; *Int'l, pg. 1238*
SMITHSTOWN LIGHT ENGINEERING LTD.—Molex Incorporated; *U.S. Public, pg. 1123*
SPEEDFAM CO LTD.—SpeedFan International, Inc.; *U.S. Public, pg. 1498*
SSANGYONG BUSINESS GROUP; *Int'l, pg. 1291*
SSANGYONG PRECISION INDUSTRY CO., LTD.—Ssangyong Business Group; *Int'l, pg. 1292*
STAMCO-DEPIEREUX GMBH—The Monarch Machine Tool Company; *U.S. Public, pg. 1124*
STAMCO DIV.—The Monarch Machine Tool Company; *U.S. Public, pg. 1124*
STAMCO (U.K.) LTD.—The Monarch Machine Tool Company; *U.S. Public, pg. 1124*
STERLING, INC.; *U.S. Private, pg. 1041*
SULZER, INC.—Sulzer Ltd.; *Int'l, pg. 1306*
SULZER METCO AG—Sulzer Ltd.; *Int'l, pg. 1307*
TAPCO INTERNATIONAL CORPORATION; *U.S. Private, pg. 1068*
TOYODA MACHINE WORKS, LTD.—Toyota Motor Corporation; *Int'l, pg. 1412*
TULIP CORPORATION; *U.S. Private, pg. 1109*
VERSON DIVISION—Allied Products Corporation; *U.S. Public, pg. 48*
WALTEC ENGINEERING—Emco Limited; *Int'l, pg. 453*
WATERBURY FARREL TECHNOLOGIES—Goldman Financial Group; *U.S. Private, pg. 461*
WATERBURY HEADERS, INC.—Seneca Falls Technology Group; *U.S. Private, pg. 984*
W.A. WHITNEY CO.—Esterline Technologies Corporation; *U.S. Public, pg. 594*
WILLIAMS, WHITE & CO.; *U.S. Private, pg. 1179*

3543 — INDUSTRIAL PATTERNS

DEERE & COMPANY; *U.S. Public, pg. 491*
G.D. PACKAGING MACHINERY INC.—G.D. S.p.A.; *Int'l, pg. 531*
G.D. S.P.A.; *Int'l, pg. 531*
NEENAH FOUNDRY COMPANY; *U.S. Private, pg. 790*
RELIABLE CASTINGS CORPORATION; *U.S. Private, pg. 920*
STOCKER & YALE, INC.; *U.S. Public, pg. 1518*
WHIPPS; *U.S. Private, pg. 1171*

3544 — SPECIAL DIES & TOOLS, DIE SETS, JIGS & FIXTURES & INDUSTRIAL MOLDS

ACI ENGINEERING—BTR plc; *Int'l, pg. 128*
ACTIVE TOOL & MANUFACTURING CO., INC.; *U.S. Private, pg. 16*
AETNA INDUSTRIES, INC.; *U.S. Private, pg. 25*
ANCHOR LAMINA INC.; *Int'l, pg. 75*
ANCHOR METAL PROCESSING—Anchor Tool & Die Company; *U.S. Private, pg. 71*
ANCHOR TOOL & DIE COMPANY; *U.S. Private, pg. 71*
ANSALDO INDUSTRIA S.P.A.—IRI Istituto Ricostruzione Industriale; *Int'l, pg. 653*
APEX BROACH & MACHINE CO.; *U.S. Private, pg. 77*
ATLAS TOOL INC.; *U.S. Private, pg. 97*
ATOLS TOOL AND MOLD CORP.; *U.S. Private, pg. 97*
B&B MOLDERS; *U.S. Private, pg. 105*
B.G. INDUSTRIES; *U.S. Private, pg. 106*
THE BARDEN CORPORATION—FAG Group; *Int'l, pg. 468*
BASSETT ROTARY TOOL CO.—Federal Signal Corporation; *U.S. Public, pg. 617*
BEACH MOLD & TOOL INC.; *U.S. Private, pg. 125*
ROBERT BOSCH CORPORATION—Robert Bosch GmbH; *Int'l, pg. 204*
BRUBAKER TOOL CORP.—Cincinnati Milacron Inc.; *U.S. Public, pg. 368*
CABLE DESIGN TECHNOLOGIES CORPORATION; *U.S. Public, pg. 287*
CAMBRIDGE INDUSTRIES, INC.—Cambridge Industries Inc.; *U.S. Private, pg. 202*
CAPTIVE PLASTICS; *U.S. Private, pg. 207*
CITY MACHINE TOOL & DIE COMPANY, INC.; *U.S. Private, pg. 241*
COATS & CLARK INC.—Coats Viyella plc; *Int'l, pg. 300*
COGNITRONICS CORPORATION; *U.S. Public, pg. 394*
CONDOR TOOL & DIE, INC.—Anchor Tool & Die Company; *U.S. Private, pg. 71*
CONNELL LIMITED PARTNERSHIP; *U.S. Private, pg. 264*
CONTAINER TOOLING CORPORATION—Federal Signal Corporation; *U.S. Public, pg. 617*
CRESCIVE DIE & TOOL, INC.; *U.S. Private, pg. 289*
D & H TOOL AND DIE—United States Ceramic Tile Co.; *U.S. Private, pg. 1124*
D-M-E COMPANY—Cincinnati Milacron Inc.; *U.S. Public, pg. 368*
DANLY DIE SET DIVISION—Connell Limited Partnership; *U.S. Private, pg. 264*
DAYTON PROGRESS CORPORATION—Federal Signal Corporation; *U.S. Public, pg. 617*
DIEBEL MANUFACTURING CO.; *U.S. Private, pg. 331*
DIEMAKERS, INC.; *U.S. Private, pg. 332*
DIGITRON TOOL CO., INC.; *U.S. Private, pg. 332*
DU PONT TAIWAN LIMITED-HSIEN PLANT—Du Pont (E.I. Du Pont De Nemours & Co.); *U.S. Public, pg. 533*
DUFFY TOOL & STAMPING, INC.—Brittany Corporation; *U.S. Private, pg. 169*
DYNACAST—Coats Viyella plc; *Int'l, pg. 300*
DYNAMIC METAL PRODUCTS COMPANY; *U.S. Private, pg. 350*
EOC FORMSYSTEM GMBH—Anchor Lamina Inc.; *Int'l, pg. 75*
EFFICIENT ENGINEERING CO.; *U.S. Private, pg. 365*
B. ELLIOTT PLC.; *Int'l, pg. 448*
ELTA PLASTICS LIMITED—Nifco Inc.; *Int'l, pg. 929*
EMTEC PRODUCTS CORPORATION—Kuhlman Corporation; *U.S. Public, pg. 968*
ESSEF CORPORATION; *U.S. Public, pg. 592*
FLAMBEAU CORPORATION; *U.S. Private, pg. 409*
FLUID PRODUCT SALES DIV.—Dana Corporation; *U.S. Public, pg. 479*
FRANKULIN TOOL & MFG. CO.—Wrought Washer Mfg., Inc.; *U.S. Private, pg. 1192*
GIDDINGS & LEWIS, INC.—Thyssen AG; *Int'l, pg. 1389*
GOUGLER INDUSTRIES, INC.; *U.S. Private, pg. 466*
GULDSMEDSHYTTE BRUKS AB—Sandvik AB; *Int'l, pg. 1185*
H S DIE & ENGINEERING, INC.; *U.S. Private, pg. 489*
HMI INDUSTRIES; *U.S. Public, pg. 771*
HPM CORPORATION; *U.S. Private, pg. 492*
HESS ENGINEERING INC.; *U.S. Private, pg. 524*
HI-P TOOL & DIE PTE. LTD.—Molex Incorporated; *U.S. Public, pg. 1122*
ILSCO; *U.S. Private, pg. 558*
INDEPENDENT TOOL & DIE—Oberg Industries Corp.; *U.S. Private, pg. 810*
INFATOOL—The Ivaco Group; *Int'l, pg. 696*
INTERSTATE ENGINEERING; *U.S. Private, pg. 573*
JAMESTOWN PERFORATORS INC.—Federal Signal Corporation; *U.S. Public, pg. 617*
JERGENS INC.; *U.S. Private, pg. 586*
KENNAMETAL HERTEL AG—Kennametal Inc.; *U.S. Public, pg. 951*
KENNAMETAL INC.; *U.S. Public, pg. 950*
KINGSLEY MACHINE CO.—Illinois Tool Works Inc.; *U.S. Public, pg. 866*
KIPP GROUP; *U.S. Private, pg. 623*
KLOECKNER-WILHELMSBURGER GMBH—Klockner-Werke AG; *Int'l, pg. 737*
LACEY MFG. CO.—FAG Group; *Int'l, pg. 468*
LAMINA INC.—Anchor Lamina Inc.; *Int'l, pg. 75*
MAGHIELSE TOOL CORPORATION; *U.S. Private, pg. 694*
MITCHELL CORPORATION OF OWOSSO; *U.S. Private, pg. 753*
MOORE TOOL COMPANY, INC.—The Producto Machine Co.; *U.S. Private, pg. 889*
MYERS INDUSTRIES, INC.; *U.S. Public, pg. 1143*
NATIONAL FORGE COMPANY; *U.S. Private, pg. 783*
NATIONAL TOOL & MANUFACTURING COMPANY; *U.S. Private, pg. 787*
NERADT TOOL & STAMPING COMPANY—Continental/Midland, Inc.; *U.S. Private, pg. 269*
NEWELL CO.; *U.S. Public, pg. 1176*
NIFCO INC.; *Int'l, pg. 928*
OBERG CARBIDE PUNCH & DIE—Oberg Industries Corp.; *U.S. Private, pg. 810*
OBERG INDUSTRIES CORP.; *U.S. Private, pg. 810*
OBERG MFG. CO.—Oberg Industries Corp.; *U.S. Private, pg. 810*
OUTER DRIVE MANUFACTURING TECHNICAL CENTER—Chrysler Corporation; *U.S. Public, pg. 353*
PEC MID WEST TECHNICAL CENTER—Plastic Engineered Components Inc.; *U.S. Private, pg. 871*
PEC MOARK—Plastic Engineered Components Inc.; *U.S. Private, pg. 871*
PHB TOOL & DIE—PHB Die Casting; *U.S. Private, pg. 826*
PMC INDUSTRIES INC.; *U.S. Private, pg. 827*
PTA CORPORATION; *U.S. Private, pg. 828*
PEMCO DIE CASTING CORPORATION; *U.S. Private, pg. 848*
PLASTOOLS LTD.—Delta plc; *Int'l, pg. 391*
PRIDGEON & CLAY, INC.; *U.S. Private, pg. 883*
PRODUCTO DIEMAKERS SUPPLIES LTD.—The Producto Machine Co.; *U.S. Private, pg. 889*
THE PRODUCTO MACHINE CO.; *U.S. Private, pg. 889*
PRODUCTO MACHINE CO. RING DIVISION—The Producto Machine Co.; *U.S. Private, pg. 889*
PROGRESSIVE TOOL & INDUSTRIES CO.; *U.S. Private, pg. 890*
PUNCHCRAFT COMPANY—Masco Corporation; *U.S. Public, pg. 1054*
RMT TECHNOLOGY—Reynolds Machine Tool Corp.; *U.S. Private, pg. 927*
THE RTZ CORPORATION PLC—Rio Tinto PLC; *Int'l, pg. 1118*
REYNOLDS MACHINE TOOL CORP.; *U.S. Private, pg. 926*
RING TECHNOLOGIES, INC.; *U.S. Private, pg. 931*
ROBERTSON TOOLING LTD.—B. Elliott plc.; *Int'l, pg. 449*
THOMAS ROBINSON GROUP PLC—Brunel Holdings Plc; *Int'l, pg. 231*
ROHM MECHATECH CO., LTD.—Rohm Co., Ltd.; *Int'l, pg. 1125*
SEVA—Saint-Gobain; *Int'l, pg. 1176*
SHOWPLA ASIA LIMITED; *Int'l, pg. 1237*
A.G. SIMPSON CO. LIMITED; *Int'l, pg. 1252*
SMITHSTOWN LIGHT ENGINEERING LTD.—Molex Incorporated; *U.S. Public, pg. 1123*
SOREL FORGE INC.—Slater Industries Inc.; *Int'l, pg. 1262*
STAHL SPECIALTY COMPANY; *U.S. Private, pg. 1029*
STOCKER & YALE, INC.; *U.S. Public, pg. 1518*
STRUCTURAL FOAM PLASTICS, INC.; *U.S. Private, pg. 1047*
SUPERIOR STEEL ACQUISITION CORPORATION—Anchor Lamina Inc.; *Int'l, pg. 75*
TARGET STAMPED PRODUCTS CORP.; *U.S. Private, pg. 1069*
THAI INTERNATIONAL DIE MAKING CO., LTD. (TDI)—Isuzu Motors Limited; *Int'l, pg. 693*
THOMAS & BETTS ELECTRONICS DIVISION—Thomas & Betts Corporation; *U.S. Public, pg. 1597*
TRIANGLE TOOL CO.—Plastek Group; *U.S. Private, pg. 870*
TRIPLE S PLASTICS, INC.; *U.S. Public, pg. 1639*
ULTRA TOOL & PLASTICS, INC.; *U.S. Private, pg. 1116*
WDS LIMITED—Ascot Holdings Plc; *Int'l, pg. 88*
WAGSTAFF INC.; *U.S. Private, pg. 1146*
WELDUN INTERNATIONAL, INC.—Robert Bosch GmbH; *Int'l, pg. 205*
THE WEST COMPANY (CUSTOM & SPECIALTY SERVICES) G.M.B.H—The West Company, Incorporated; *U.S. Public, pg. 1755*
THE WEST COMPANY (UK) LTD.—The West Company, Incorporated; *U.S. Public, pg. 1756*
WOODLAND MOLD & TOOL COMPANY—GP Strategies Corporation; *U.S. Public, pg. 694*
YORKTOWN TOOL & DIE CORPORATION; *U.S. Private, pg. 1196*

3545 — CUTTING TOOLS, MACHINE TOOL ACCESSORIES & MACHINISTS PRECISION MEASURING DEVICES

A&A MANUFACTURING CO.; *U.S. Private, pg. 1*
A.T.I. TOOLS, INC.—Snap-On Tools Corporation; *U.S. Public, pg. 1480*
AIR GAGE COMPANY—United Dominion Industries, Ltd.; *U.S. Public, pg. 1676*
AIRTRONICS CO.—Katy Industries, Inc.; *U.S. Public, pg. 944*
THE ALBIA DIVISION—Chicago Rivet & Machine Company; *U.S. Public, pg. 349*
AMADA CO., LTD.; *Int'l, pg. 70*
AMADA SCHIAVI S.R.L.—Amada Co., Ltd.; *Int'l, pg. 70*
AMERICAN TOOL COMPANIES, INC.; *U.S. Private, pg. 63*
AMPLEX/SGNIC—Saint-Gobain; *Int'l, pg. 1173*
APEX BROACH & MACHINE CO.; *U.S. Private, pg. 77*
APEX OPERATION—Cooper Industries, Inc.; *U.S. Public, pg. 444*
AVIS INDUSTRIAL CORPORATION; *U.S. Private, pg. 102*
B&D ELECTRODOMESTICOS LTDA.—The Black & Decker Corporation; *U.S. Public, pg. 234*
THE BOC GROUP INC. (DELAWARE)—The BOC Group plc; *Int'l, pg. 121*
BAIRNCO CORPORATION; *U.S. Public, pg. 165*
BARDONS & OLIVER, INC.; *U.S. Private, pg. 116*
BEEHIVE MACHINERY CO.—Weiler & Company, Inc.; *U.S. Private, pg. 1160*
BERTRAM & GRAF GMBH—Bairnco Corporation; *U.S. Public, pg. 165*
BIRKETT CUTMASTER LIMITED—Carclo Engineering Group plc; *Int'l, pg. 268*
BLACK & DECKER CANADA INC.—The Black & Decker Corporation; *U.S. Public, pg. 234*
THE BLACK & DECKER CORPORATION; *U.S. Public, pg. 233*
BLACK & DECKER DE ESPANA S.A.—The Black & Decker Corporation; *U.S. Public, pg. 234*
BLACK & DECKER (SWITZERLAND) S.A.—The Black & Decker Corporation; *U.S. Public, pg. 234*
BOHLER YBBSTALWERKE GES.M.B.H.—Voest-Alpine Stahl AG; *Int'l, pg. 1470*
BRIDGEPORT MACHINES, INC.; *U.S. Public, pg. 251*
BROOKE CUTTING TOOLS LTD.—Brooke Industrial Holdings Plc; *Int'l, pg. 228*
BROOKE INDUSTRIAL HOLDINGS PLC; *Int'l, pg. 228*
BROWN & SHARPE MANUFACTURING COMPANY; *U.S. Public, pg. 260*
BRUBAKER TOOL CORP.—Cincinnati Milacron Inc.; *U.S. Public, pg. 368*
CASIO ELECTRONICS CO., LTD.—Casio Computer Co., Ltd.; *Int'l, pg. 274*
THE CHALLENGE MACHINERY CO.; *U.S. Private, pg. 227*
CHICAGO RIVET & MACHINE COMPANY; *U.S. Public, pg. 348*
CHRISTENSEN GULF SERVICES (PRIVATE) LIMITED—Saint-Gobain; *Int'l, pg. 1174*
CHRISTENSEN PRODUCTS—Layne Christenson Co.; *U.S. Public, pg. 981*
CHRISTENSEN RODER ARGENTINA S.A.—Saint-Gobain; *Int'l, pg. 1174*
CHRISTENSEN RODER PRODUCTOS DIAMANTADOS LTDA.—Saint-Gobain; *Int'l, pg. 1174*
CHRISTENSEN SAUDI ARABIA LIMITED—Saint-Gobain; *Int'l, pg. 1174*
CLEVELAND TWIST DRILL CANADA LIMITED—Kennametal Inc.; *U.S. Public, pg. 950*
COGSDILL-NUNEATON, LTD.—Cogsdill Tool Products, Inc.; *U.S. Private, pg. 250*
COGSDILL TOOL PRODUCTS, INC.; *U.S. Private, pg. 250*
CONNOLLY TOOL & MACHINE CO.—Ennis Business Forms, Inc.; *U.S. Public, pg. 583*
CONTAINER TOOLING CORPORATION—Federal Signal Corporation; *U.S. Public, pg. 617*
CONTINENTAL MACHINES, INC.; *U.S. Private, pg. 268*
COOPER HAND TOOLS—Cooper Industries, Inc.; *U.S. Public, pg. 444*
COOPER INDUSTRIES, INC.; *U.S. Public, pg. 442*
COORDINATE MEASURING MACHINE DIV.—The L.S. Starrett Company; *U.S. Public, pg. 1511*
CRAFTS TECHNOLOGY, INC.—Carpenter Technology Corporation; *U.S. Public, pg. 307*
CRANE CO.; *U.S. Public, pg. 456*
CRANKSHAFT MACHINE GROUP—Avis Industrial Corporation; *U.S. Private, pg. 102*

DAEDAL DIVISION—Parker Hannifin Corporation; *U.S. Public*, pg. 1259
DAEWOO HEAVY INDUSTRIES, LTD.—Daewoo Corporation; *Int'l*, pg. 357
DEARBORN GAGE COMPANY; *U.S. Private*, pg. 319
DIAMOND PRODUCTIONS, INC.; *U.S. Private*, pg. 330
DISCO HI-TEC AMERICA INC.—Disco Corporation; *Int'l*, pg. 413
DOALL COMPANY; *U.S. Private*, pg. 337
DORMER TOOLS AB—Sandvik AB; *Int'l*, pg. 1185
DUMORE CORPORATION; *U.S. Private*, pg. 346
B. ELLIOTT PLC.; *Int'l*, pg. 448
EONIC INC.—Newcor, Inc.; *U.S. Public*, pg. 1176
ESTERLINE TECHNOLOGIES CORPORATION; *U.S. Public*, pg. 594
FADAL ENGINEERING COMPANY, INC.—Thyssen AG; *Int'l*, pg. 1389
FANSTEEL, INC.; *U.S. Public*, pg. 612
FANSTEEL VR/WESSON-PLANTSVILLE—Fansteel, Inc.; *U.S. Public*, pg. 612
FEDERAL PRODUCTS CO.—Esterline Technologies Corporation; *U.S. Public*, pg. 594
FEDERAL SIGNAL CORPORATION; *U.S. Public*, pg. 616
FERGUSON MACHINE CO.—Crane Co.; *U.S. Public*, pg. 457
FERGUSON MACHINE CO. S.A.—Crane Co.; *U.S. Public*, pg. 457
FORKARDT INTERNATIONAL GMBH—Wagon Industrial Holdings PLC; *Int'l*, pg. 1484
ABDULLA FOUAD-TESTRADE MIDDLE EAST—Abdulla Fouad Co. Ltd.; *Int'l*, pg. 502
CARL FREUDENBERG—Freudenberg & Company; *Int'l*, pg. 505
FREUDENBERG NOK—Freudenberg & Company; *Int'l*, pg. 507
GENERAL TOOLS MFG., CO. INC.; *U.S. Private*, pg. 445
GIDDINGS & LEWIS, INC.—Thyssen AG; *Int'l*, pg. 1389
GIDDINGS & LEWIS SHEFFIELD MEASUREMENT SYSTEMS—Thyssen AG; *Int'l*, pg. 1389
THE GLEASON WORKS—Gleason Corporation; *U.S. Public*, pg. 746
GREAT LAKES-EGLINTON—United Dominion Industries, Ltd.; *U.S. Public*, pg. 1676
GREENFIELD INDUSTRIES—Kennametal Inc.; *U.S. Public*, pg. 950
GREENFIELD INDUSTRIES INC.—Kennametal Inc.; *U.S. Public*, pg. 950
GROUND FLAT STOCK DIV.—The L.S. Starrett Company; *U.S. Public*, pg. 1511
HERRAMIENTAS CLEVELAND, S.A.—Kennametal Inc.; *U.S. Public*, pg. 950
HILTI AG; *Int'l*, pg. 619
HOUGEN MANUFACTURING INC.; *U.S. Private*, pg. 541
HUNGER DFE GMBH; *Int'l*, pg. 639
HYCALOG—Camco International Inc.; *U.S. Public*, pg. 298
IBM DANMARK-PRODUKT DISTRIBUTION SELSKAB A/S, DANISH DIV.—International Business Machines Corporation; *U.S. Public*, pg. 898
ISI NORGEN, INC.—IMI Plc; *Int'l*, pg. 646
ITW MICRO-POISE DIVISION—Illinois Tool Works Inc.; *U.S. Public*, pg. 865
INDUCTOTHERM INDUSTRIES, INC.; *U.S. Private*, pg. 560
INGERSOLL CUTTING TOOL CO.—Ingersoll International Inc.; *U.S. Private*, pg. 562
INGERSOLL MASCHINEN UND WERKZEUGE GMBH—Ingersoll International Inc.; *U.S. Private*, pg. 562
OY INTERNATIONAL BUSINESS MACHINES AB—International Business Machines Corporation; *U.S. Public*, pg. 898
JACOBS CHUCK MANUFACTURING—Danaher Corporation; *U.S. Public*, pg. 481
JACOBS VEHICLE EQUIPMENT COMPANY—Danaher Corporation; *U.S. Public*, pg. 481
KASCO CORPORATION—Bairnco Corporation; *U.S. Public*, pg. 165
KASPER MACHINE COMPANY; *U.S. Private*, pg. 608
KATY INDUSTRIES, INC.; *U.S. Public*, pg. 944
KEE CUTTERS—Masco Corporation; *U.S. Public*, pg. 1054
KENNAMETAL HERTEL AG—Kennametal Inc.; *U.S. Public*, pg. 951
KENNAMETAL HERTEL BELGIUM, S.A.—Kennametal Inc.; *U.S. Public*, pg. 951
KENNAMETAL INC.; *U.S. Public*, pg. 950
ABB KENT TAYLOR INC.—ABB Asea Brown Boveri (Holding) Ltd.; *Int'l*, pg. 4
KOBE STEEL, LTD.; *Int'l*, pg. 740
KONCOR INDUSTRIES DIV.—The Timken Company; *U.S. Public*, pg. 1617
KRAUTKRAMER-FOERSTER JAPAN CO., LTD.—Emerson Electric Co.; *U.S. Public*, pg. 577
KRAUTKRAMER G.M.B.H—Emerson Electric Co.; *U.S. Public*, pg. 577
KRUPP WIDIA GMBH—Fried. Krupp AG; *Int'l*, pg. 510
KURAKI COMPANY LTD.; *Int'l*, pg. 764
KURT MANUFACTURING CO. INC.; *U.S. Private*, pg. 637
KYOCERA CORPORATION; *Int'l*, pg. 775
KYOCERA INDUSTRIAL CERAMICS CORP.—Kyocera Corporation; *Int'l*, pg. 776
LK TOOL USA, INC.—TransTec Plc; *Int'l*, pg. 1418
LATROBE SPECIAL PRODUCTS DIV.—The Timken Company; *U.S. Public*, pg. 1617
LIEBHERR-AMERICA INC.—Liebherr-International AG; *Int'l*, pg. 808
LIEBHERR-VERZAHNTECHNIK GMBH—Liebherr-International AG; *Int'l*, pg. 808
M K DIAMOND PRODUCTS, INC.; *U.S. Private*, pg. 684
B.V. MACHINEFABRIEK BREDA—Royal Begemann Group; *Int'l*, pg. 1133
MACHINEFABRIEK WERKLUST B.V.—Royal Begemann Group; *Int'l*, pg. 1133
MAKINO INC.—Makino Milling Machine Co. Ltd.; *Int'l*, pg. 831
MASCHINENFABRIK LORENZ GMBH—Liebherr-International AG; *Int'l*, pg. 808
MCLAUGHLIN MANUFACTURING CO. OF S.C.—McLaughlin Manufacturing Company; *U.S. Private*, pg. 724
MCLEAN MIDWEST—Zero Corporation; *U.S. Public*, pg. 1791
THOMAS MERCER LTD.—Brown & Sharpe Manufacturing Company; *U.S. Public*, pg. 260
METAL & PIPELINE ENDURANCE LTD.—AMEC Plc; *Int'l*, pg. 16
METAL STAMPING EQUIP. DIV.—P/A Industries, Inc.; *U.S. Private*, pg. 825
MINING AND CONSTRUCTION DIVISION—Kennametal Inc.; *U.S. Public*, pg. 950
MONARCH CORTLAND DIV.—The Monarch Machine Tool Company; *U.S. Public*, pg. 1124
THE MONARCH MACHINE TOOL COMPANY; *U.S. Public*, pg. 1123
MONARCH WETKZENGMASCHINEN GMBH—The Monarch Machine Tool Company; *U.S. Public*, pg. 1124
MOORE TOOL COMPANY, INC.—The Producto Machine Co.; *U.S. Private*, pg. 889
MURATA MACHINERY, LTD.; *Int'l*, pg. 897
N E D CORP.; *U.S. Private*, pg. 771
NAITONAL-OILWELL/DRECO INC.—National-Oilwell Inc.; *U.S. Public*, pg. 1158
NATIONAL TWIST DRILL DIV.—Regal-Beloit Corporation; *U.S. Public*, pg. 1370
NEW YORK TWIST DRILL DIV.—Regal-Beloit Corporation; *U.S. Public*, pg. 1370
NORTH AMERICAN PRODUCTS CORP.; *U.S. Private*, pg. 803
NORTHERN TELECOM CANADA LIMITED, OUTSIDE PLANT DIV.—Northern Telecom Limited; *Int'l*, pg. 969
NORTON INDUSTRIEPRODUKTE GMBH—Saint-Gobain; *Int'l*, pg. 1175
OKUMA AMERICA CORPORATION—Okuma Corporation; *Int'l*, pg. 1001
P/A INDUSTRIES, INC.; *U.S. Private*, pg. 825
PMC INDUSTRIES INC.; *U.S. Private*, pg. 827
PAUMIER COMPANY INC.—The Cypress Companies; *U.S. Private*, pg. 300
POWELL DUFFRYN TOOLS LIMITED—Powell Duffryn PLC; *Int'l*, pg. 1066
POWERS FASTENING, INC.; *U.S. Private*, pg. 878
PRECISION TWIST DRILL CO.—Sandvik AB; *Int'l*, pg. 1185
PUSAN PRECISION INDUSTRIES, LTD.—Brother Industries, Ltd.; *Int'l*, pg. 230
RAMSEY TECHNOLOGY, INC.—Thermo Electron Corporation; *U.S. Public*, pg. 1592
REGAL-BELOIT CORPORATION; *U.S. Public*, pg. 1370
REGAL CUTTING TOOLS DIV.—Regal-Beloit Corporation; *U.S. Public*, pg. 1370
RENISHAW PLC; *Int'l*, pg. 1103
RESKA SPLINE PRODUCTS INC.—Masco Corporation; *U.S. Public*, pg. 1054
RICHARDS MICRO-TOOL, INC.—Masco Corporation; *U.S. Public*, pg. 1054
ROBERTSON TOOLING LTD.—B. Elliott plc.; *Int'l*, pg. 449
ROTHENBERGER GROUP GMBH; *Int'l*, pg. 1127
ROTHENBERGER PRODUCTIONS GMBH—Rothenberger Group GmbH; *Int'l*, pg. 1128
ROTHENBERGER USA, INC.—Rothenberger Group GmbH; *Int'l*, pg. 1129
RULE INDUSTRIES, INC.—Kennametal Inc.; *U.S. Public*, pg. 950
S & J INDUSTRIES—North American Products Corp.; *U.S. Private*, pg. 803
S-B POWER TOOL COMPANY—Robert Bosch GmbH; *Int'l*, pg. 205
SIG SCHWEIZERSICHE INDUSTRIE-GESELLSCHAFT HOLDING AG; *Int'l*, pg. 1156
AB SKF; *Int'l*, pg. 1156
SPS INTERNATIONAL LTD.—SPS Technologies, Inc.; *U.S. Public*, pg. 1420
SPS TECHNOLOGIES, INC.; *U.S. Public*, pg. 1419
SANDIACRE SCREW LTD.—Haden Maclellan Holdings plc; *Int'l*, pg. 585
SANDVIK AB; *Int'l*, pg. 1185
SANDVIK ASIA LTD.—Sandvik AB; *Int'l*, pg. 1187
AB SANDVIK COROMANT—Sandvik AB; *Int'l*, pg. 1185
SANDVIK COROMANT COMPANY—Sandvik AB; *Int'l*, pg. 1185
SANDVIK LATIN AMERICA, INC.—Sandvik AB; *Int'l*, pg. 1185
SANDVIK LTD.—Sandvik AB; *Int'l*, pg. 1186
AB SANDVIK METAL SAWS—Sandvik AB; *Int'l*, pg. 1185
SANDVIK TOBLER S.A.—Sandvik AB; *Int'l*, pg. 1187
SENECA FALLS TECHNOLOGY GROUP; *U.S. Private*, pg. 984
SETCO; *U.S. Private*, pg. 987
SHEFCUT TOOL & ENGINEERING LTD.—Cogsdill Tool Products, Inc.; *U.S. Private*, pg. 250
SIBEKA—Union Miniere; *Int'l*, pg. 1442
SIMONDS INDUSTRIES INC.; *U.S. Private*, pg. 1001
J.T. SLOCOMB COMPANY; *U.S. Private*, pg. 1006
SPLINE GAUGES LTD.—Danaher Corporation; *U.S. Public*, pg. 482
STAMCO-DEPIEREUX GMBH—The Monarch Machine Tool Company; *U.S. Public*, pg. 1124
STAMCO DIV.—The Monarch Machine Tool Company; *U.S. Public*, pg. 1124
STAMCO (U.K.) LTD.—The Monarch Machine Tool Company; *U.S. Public*, pg. 1124
STARRETT INDUSTRIAL E COMERCIO LTDA.—The L.S. Starrett Company; *U.S. Public*, pg. 1511
THE L.S. STARRETT COMPANY; *U.S. Public*, pg. 1511
L.S. STARRETT CO. LTD.—The L.S. Starrett Company; *U.S. Public*, pg. 1511
L.S. STARRETT COMPANY OF CANADA—The L.S. Starrett Company; *U.S. Public*, pg. 1511
SYSTEMATIC DRILL HEAD CO. LTD.—Haden Maclellan Holdings plc; *Int'l*, pg. 585
THE TATA IRON AND STEEL CO. LTD.; *Int'l*, pg. 1356
TATRY OFFICINA MECCANICA S.R.L.—The Black & Decker Corporation; *U.S. Public*, pg. 234
TAYLOR HOBSON PNEUMO—The Rank Group PLC; *Int'l*, pg. 1087
TOSOHAAS GMBH—Tosoh Corporation; *Int'l*, pg. 1408
TSUDAKOMA CORP.; *Int'l*, pg. 1425
THE U.S. BAIRD CORPORATION; *U.S. Private*, pg. 1124
VR/WESSON HYDRO CARBIDE—Fansteel, Inc.; *U.S. Public*, pg. 612
VR/WESSON HYDRO CARBIDE-GULFPORT—Fansteel, Inc.; *U.S. Public*, pg. 612
VERMONT AMERICAN TOOL CORP.—Emerson Electric Co.; *U.S. Public*, pg. 575
VLIER ENGINEERING—Applied Power Inc.; *U.S. Public*, pg. 124
WCI MACHINE TOOLS & SYSTEMS—Electrolux, AB; *Int'l*, pg. 440
WALDES TRUARC/INDUSTRIAL RETAINING RING—TransTechnology Corporation; *U.S. Public*, pg. 1632
WALKER MAGNETICS GROUP, INC.; *U.S. Private*, pg. 1147
O.S. WALKER CO. INC.—Walker Magnetics Group, Inc.; *U.S. Private*, pg. 1147
WEB PROCESSING EQUIP. DIV.—P/A Industries, Inc.; *U.S. Private*, pg. 825
WEBBER GAGE DIV.—The L.S. Starrett Company; *U.S. Public*, pg. 1511
WEIGH-TRONIX, INC.—Staveley Industries PLC; *Int'l*, pg. 1299
WEILER & COMPANY, INC.; *U.S. Private*, pg. 1160
WILTON CORPORATION; *U.S. Private*, pg. 1181
ZEPHYR MFG. CO.—Standun, Inc.; *U.S. Private*, pg. 1032

3546 — POWER DRIVEN HAND TOOLS

AMERICAN MACHINE & TOOL COMPANY, INC.; *U.S. Private*, pg. 58
ARNO-SKIL FERRAMENTAS ELECTRICAS LTDA.—Emerson Electric Co.; *U.S. Public*, pg. 575
ARO CORPORATION S.A.R.L.—Ingersoll-Rand Company; *U.S. Public*, pg. 877
ARO GMBH—Ingersoll-Rand Company; *U.S. Public*, pg. 877
N.V. ARO S.A.—Ingersoll-Rand Company; *U.S. Public*, pg. 877
ATLAS COPCO BEREMA AB—Atlas Copco AB; *Int'l*, pg. 96
ATLAS COPCO ELECTRIC TOOLS—Atlas Copco AB; *Int'l*, pg. 96
ATLAS COPCO INDUSTRIAL TOOLS & EQUIPMENT—Atlas Copco AB; *Int'l*, pg. 96
ATLAS COPCO NORTH AMERICA INC.—Atlas Copco AB; *Int'l*, pg. 96
ATLAS COPCO TOOLS INC.—Atlas Copco AB; *Int'l*, pg. 96
B&D ELECTRODOMESTICOS LTDA.—The Black & Decker Corporation; *U.S. Public*, pg. 234
BLACK & DECKER CANADA INC.—The Black & Decker Corporation; *U.S. Public*, pg. 234
THE BLACK & DECKER CORPORATION; *U.S. Public*, pg. 233
BLACK & DECKER DE ESPANA S.A.—The Black & Decker Corporation; *U.S. Public*, pg. 234
BLACK & DECKER (SWITZERLAND) S.A.—The Black & Decker Corporation; *U.S. Public*, pg. 234
ROBERT BOSCH GMBH; *Int'l*, pg. 203
CHERRY TEXTRON—Textron Inc.; *U.S. Public*, pg. 1589
CHICAGO PNEUMATIC TOOL COMPANY—Atlas Copco AB; *Int'l*, pg. 96
CONTINENTAL/MIDLAND, INC.; *U.S. Private*, pg. 268
COOPER POWER TOOLS DIVISION—Cooper Industries, Inc.; *U.S. Public*, pg. 444
DOM AG SICHERHEITSTECHNIK—The Black & Decker Corporation; *U.S. Public*, pg. 233
DOM S.A.R.L.—The Black & Decker Corporation; *U.S. Public*, pg. 233
DOM-SICHERHEITSTECHNIK GMBH & CO. KG—The Black & Decker Corporation; *U.S. Public*, pg. 233
DANIELS MANUFACTURING CORPORATION; *U.S. Private*, pg. 310
DESA INTERNATIONAL; *U.S. Private*, pg. 326
THE DISSTON CO.—Kennametal Inc.; *U.S. Public*, pg. 950
DOLMAR GMBH—Makita Corporation; *Int'l*, pg. 831
DOTCO—Cooper Industries, Inc.; *U.S. Public*, pg. 444
DREMEL—Emerson Electric Co.; *U.S. Public*, pg. 574
DUMORE CORPORATION; *U.S. Private*, pg. 346
DYNAPERT JAPAN LTD.—The Black & Decker Corporation; *U.S. Public*, pg. 233
FACOM—Groupe Strafor Facom; *Int'l*, pg. 570
FLORIDA PNEUMATIC MFG. CORP.—P & F Industries, Inc.; *U.S. Public*, pg. 1240
FRIGIDAIRE HOME PRODUCTS-SPECIALTY POWER EQUIPMENT—Electrolux, AB; *Int'l*, pg. 440
GRINDING MACHINE-U.K.—Litton Industries, Inc.; *U.S. Public*, pg. 1005
HILTI AG; *Int'l*, pg. 619
HITACHI KOKI CO., LTD.; *Int'l*, pg. 620
HOFFCO/COMET INDUSTRIES, INC.; *U.S. Private*, pg. 532
HOLMATRO, INC.—Holmatro Industrial & Rescue Equipment; *Int'l*, pg. 632
HOLMATRO INDUSTRIAL & RESCUE EQUIPMENT; *Int'l*, pg. 632
HOLZ-HER U.S. INC.—Karl M. Reich Maschinenfabrik GmbH; *Int'l*, pg. 1101
HOUGEN MANUFACTURING INC.; *U.S. Private*, pg. 541
HUSQVARNA FOREST & GARDEN PRODUCTS—Electrolux, AB; *Int'l*, pg. 440
HUTCHINS MANUFACTURING COMPANY; *U.S. Private*, pg. 550
ITW SIGNODE—Illinois Tool Works Inc.; *U.S. Public*, pg. 867
INGERSOLL-RAND CANADA, INC.—Ingersoll-Rand Company; *U.S. Public*, pg. 878
INGERSOLL-RAND COMPANY; *U.S. Public*, pg. 876

INGERSOLL-RAND GMBH—Ingersoll-Rand Company; *U.S. Public*, pg. 878
INGERSOLL RAND - POWER TOOL DIV.—Ingersoll-Rand Company; *U.S. Public*, pg. 877
INTERNATIONAL PIN—Continental/Midland, Inc.; *U.S. Private*, pg. 269
INTOOL ROTOR COMPANY; *U.S. Private*, pg. 574
IOWA MOLD TOOLING CO., INC.—Intermet Corporation; *U.S. Public*, pg. 894
MAKITA (AUSTRALIA) PTY. LTD.—Makita Corporation; *Int'l*, pg. 831
MAKITA BENELUX B.V.—Makita Corporation; *Int'l*, pg. 832
MAKITA CANADA INC.—Makita Corporation; *Int'l*, pg. 832
MAKITA (CHINA) CO., LTD.—Makita Corporation; *Int'l*, pg. 832
MAKITA CORPORATION; *Int'l*, pg. 831
MAKITA CORPORATION OF AMERICA—Makita Corporation; *Int'l*, pg. 831
MAKITA DO BRASIL FERRAMENTAS ELETRICAS LTDA.—Makita Corporation; *Int'l*, pg. 832
MAKITA FRANCE S.A.—Makita Corporation; *Int'l*, pg. 832
MAKITA MANUFACTURING EUROPE LTD.—Makita Corporation; *Int'l*, pg. 832
MAKITA MEXICO, S.A. DE C.V.—Makita Corporation; *Int'l*, pg. 832
MAKITA (NEW ZEALAND) LTD.—Makita Corporation; *Int'l*, pg. 832
MAKITA POWER TOOLS (H.K.) LTD.—Makita Corporation; *Int'l*, pg. 832
MAKITA, S.A.—Makita Corporation; *Int'l*, pg. 832
MAKITA SINGAPORE PTE. LTD.—Makita Corporation; *Int'l*, pg. 832
MAKITA SP. Z O.O.—Makita Corporation; *Int'l*, pg. 832
MAKITA S.P.A.—Makita Corporation; *Int'l*, pg. 832
MAKITA S.R.O.—Makita Corporation; *Int'l*, pg. 832
MAKITA (TAIWAN) LTD.—Makita Corporation; *Int'l*, pg. 832
MAKITA (U.K.) LTD.—Makita Corporation; *Int'l*, pg. 832
MAKITA U.S.A., INC.—Makita Corporation; *Int'l*, pg. 831
MAKITA WERKZEUG GMBH—Makita Corporation; *Int'l*, pg. 832
MANOIR INDUSTRIES—Groupe Strafor Facom; *Int'l*, pg. 570
MATSUSHITA ELECTRIC WORKS, LTD.; *Int'l*, pg. 847
MATTISON TECHNOLOGIES, INC.; *U.S. Private*, pg. 714
METABO CORPORATION; *U.S. Private*, pg. 734
MICROMATIC OPERATIONS (SWANNANOA PLANT)—Textron Inc.; *U.S. Public*, pg. 1590
MILWAUKEE ELECTRIC TOOL CORP.—Atlas Copco AB; *Int'l*, pg. 96
P & F INDUSTRIES, INC.; *U.S. Public*, pg. 1239
PARTNER INDUSTRIAL PRODUCTS INC.—Electrolux, AB; *Int'l*, pg. 440
PENTAIR, INC.; *U.S. Public*, pg. 1273
PFERD/AUGUST RUEGGEBERG; *Int'l*, pg. 1046
PORTER-CABLE CORPORATION—Pentair, Inc.; *U.S. Public*, pg. 1274
POWER TEAM DIVISION—SPX Corporation; *U.S. Public*, pg. 1421
KARL M. REICH MASCHINENFABRIK GMBH; *Int'l*, pg. 1101
REICH SPEZIALMASCHINEN GMBH—Karl M. Reich Maschinenfabrik GmbH; *Int'l*, pg. 1101
GEORGES RENOULT S.A.—Atlas Copco AB; *Int'l*, pg. 96
REPUBLIC FASTENER PRODUCTS CORP.; *U.S. Private*, pg. 923
RIDGE TOOL GMBH—Emerson Electric Co.; *U.S. Public*, pg. 577
RIDGID FERRAMENTAS E MAGUINAS, LTDA.—Emerson Electric Co.; *U.S. Public*, pg. 577
RIDGID VAERKTOJ A/S—Emerson Electric Co.; *U.S. Public*, pg. 577
ALBERT ROLLER GMBH & CO. KG; *Int'l*, pg. 1126
ROTHENBERGER PRODUCTIONS GMBH—Rothenberger Group GmbH; *Int'l*, pg. 1128
S-B POWER TOOL COMPANY—Robert Bosch GmbH; *Int'l*, pg. 205
SPX CORPORATION; *U.S. Public*, pg. 1420
SANDVIK GMBH—Sandvik AB; *Int'l*, pg. 1186
SANDVIK LATIN AMERICA, INC.—Sandvik AB; *Int'l*, pg. 1185
SANDVIK LTD.—Sandvik AB; *Int'l*, pg. 1186
SANDVIK WINDSOR CORP.—Sandvik AB; *Int'l*, pg. 1185
GEORGE T. SCHMIDT; *U.S. Private*, pg. 970
SCINTILLA AG—Robert Bosch GmbH; *Int'l*, pg. 206
SIOUX TOOLS, INC.—Snap-On Tools Corporation; *U.S. Public*, pg. 1480
SKILTOOLS DE MEXICO S.A. DE C.V.—Emerson Electric Co.; *U.S. Public*, pg. 578
SNAP-ON TOOLS CORPORATION; *U.S. Public*, pg. 1480
SPECIAL PRODUCTS DIV.—Emerson Electric Co.; *U.S. Public*, pg. 575
STANDUN, INC.; *U.S. Private*, pg. 1032
STANLEY AIR TOOLS DIV.—The Stanley Works; *U.S. Public*, pg. 1509
STANLEY HYDRAULIC TOOLS DIV.—The Stanley Works; *U.S. Public*, pg. 1509
STIHL EASTERN CANADA LTD.—Andreas Stihl; *Int'l*, pg. 1301
STIHL INC.—Andreas Stihl; *Int'l*, pg. 1301
TATRY OFFICINA MECCANICA S.R.L.—The Black & Decker Corporation; *U.S. Public*, pg. 234
VERMONT AMERICAN TOOL CORP.—Emerson Electric Co.; *U.S. Public*, pg. 575
WEN PRODUCTS, INC.; *U.S. Private*, pg. 1144
WESTERN FORGE DIV.—Emerson Electric Co.; *U.S. Public*, pg. 575
THE WYCO TOOL CO.—Racine Federated, Inc.; *U.S. Private*, pg. 906

3547 — ROLLING MILL MACHINERY & EQUIPMENT

ADDISON TUBE FORMING LIMITED—B. Elliott plc.; *Int'l*, pg. 448
AMPCO-PITTSBURGH CORPORATION; *U.S. Public*, pg. 103
BLISS-SALEM, INC.; *U.S. Private*, pg. 149
BRADBURY COMPANY, INC.; *U.S. Private*, pg. 163
CAPARO GROUP LTD.; *Int'l*, pg. 264
CAPARO INDUSTRIES PLC—Caparo Group Ltd.; *Int'l*, pg. 264
DANIELLI & C. OFFICINE MECCANICHE S.P.A.; *Int'l*, pg. 378
HEADER PRODUCTS INC.; *U.S. Private*, pg. 514
HEIDTMAN STEEL PRODUCTS, INC.; *U.S. Private*, pg. 519
HUNTER ENGINEERING CO., INC.—FKI Plc; *Int'l*, pg. 474
JONSEREDS GODSSKYDD AB—Electrolux, AB; *Int'l*, pg. 439
LOCKFORMER COMPANY—Met-Coil Systems Corp.; *U.S. Public*, pg. 1100
MORGAN CONSTRUCTION CO.; *U.S. Private*, pg. 761
MORGARDSHAMMAR AB—Danielli & C. Officine Meccaniche S.p.A.; *Int'l*, pg. 378
OUTOKUMPU CASTFORM OY—Outokumpu Oyj; *Int'l*, pg. 1017
ROUGE STEEL COMPANY; *U.S. Public*, pg. 1406
TIPPINS INCORPORATED; *U.S. Private*, pg. 1088
UNION ELECTRIC STEEL CORP.—Ampco-Pittsburgh Corporation; *U.S. Public*, pg. 103
UNION ELECTRIC STEEL N.V.—Ampco-Pittsburgh Corporation; *U.S. Public*, pg. 104
VOEST-ALPINE SERVICES AND TECHNOLOGIES CORP.—Voest-Alpine Stahl AG; *Int'l*, pg. 1471
WILDER DEEM, INC.; *U.S. Private*, pg. 1176
XTEK, INC.; *U.S. Private*, pg. 1194

3548 — ELECTRIC & GAS WELDING & SOLDERING EQUIPMENT

AGA GAS, INC.—AGA AB; *Int'l*, pg. 13
AFRICAN OXYGEN LTD.—The BOC Group plc; *Int'l*, pg. 121
AIR LIQUIDE AMERICA CORPORATION—Air Liquide S.A.; *Int'l*, pg. 37
AIRGAS, INC.; *U.S. Public*, pg. 33
AKTIESELIKABET ESAB—Charter plc; *Int'l*, pg. 281
ALLOY RODS KOREA CORPORATION—Charter plc; *Int'l*, pg. 281
AMBAC B.V.; *Int'l*, pg. 71
AMPCO METAL INCORPORATED; *U.S. Private*, pg. 67
ARMADA CORPORATION; *U.S. Private*, pg. 82
ASSOCIATED EQUIPMENT CO., INC.; *U.S. Private*, pg. 90
BOC GASES IRELAND LTD.—The BOC Group plc; *Int'l*, pg. 121
BOC GASES NEW ZEALAND LTD—The BOC Group plc; *Int'l*, pg. 121
THE BOC GROUP INC. (DELAWARE)—The BOC Group plc; *Int'l*, pg. 121
THE BOC GROUP PLC; *Int'l*, pg. 121
BOC INDIA LTD.—The BOC Group plc; *Int'l*, pg. 122
BOC PAKISTAN LTD.—The BOC Group plc; *Int'l*, pg. 122
BOC ZIMBABWE—The BOC Group plc; *Int'l*, pg. 122
BABCOCK WELDING PRODUCTS LIMITED—FKI Plc; *Int'l*, pg. 472
S.A. BERGIERS N.V.—Charter plc; *Int'l*, pg. 281
BERNZOMATIC—Newell Co.; *U.S. Public*, pg. 1177
CINTI FAB—Cincinnati Gear Company; *U.S. Private*, pg. 240
COGSDILL TOOL PRODUCTS, INC.; *U.S. Private*, pg. 250
DELTA WELDING EQUIPMENT LTD.—Delta plc; *Int'l*, pg. 390
DIMETRICS, INC.—Carpenter Technology Corporation; *U.S. Public*, pg. 308
DOVATECH, LTD.—Dover Corporation; *U.S. Public*, pg. 520
AS ESAB—Charter plc; *Int'l*, pg. 281
ESAB AB—Charter plc; *Int'l*, pg. 281
ESAB AG—Charter plc; *Int'l*, pg. 282
ESAB ASIA/PACIFIC PTE LTD.—Charter plc; *Int'l*, pg. 282
ESAB AUSTRALIA PTY. LTD.—Charter plc; *Int'l*, pg. 282
ESAB CONSUMABLES—Charter plc; *Int'l*, pg. 281
ESAB-CSEPEL KFT—Charter plc; *Int'l*, pg. 282
ESAB EQUIPMENT/AUTOMATION—Charter plc; *Int'l*, pg. 281
ESAB GES.M.B.H—Charter plc; *Int'l*, pg. 282
ESAB GMBH—Charter plc; *Int'l*, pg. 282
ESAB GROUP CANADA, INC.—Charter plc; *Int'l*, pg. 282
ESAB GROUP (UK) LTD.—Charter plc; *Int'l*, pg. 282
ESAB INDIA LTD.—Charter plc; *Int'l*, pg. 282
ESAB KFT—Charter plc; *Int'l*, pg. 282
ESAB LDA.—Charter plc; *Int'l*, pg. 282
ESAB MIDDLE EAST—Charter plc; *Int'l*, pg. 282
S.A. ESAB N.V.—Charter plc; *Int'l*, pg. 282
ESAB OY—Charter plc; *Int'l*, pg. 282
ESAB S.A. INDUSTRIA E COMERCIO—Charter plc; *Int'l*, pg. 282
ESAB SINGAPORE PTE. LTD.—Charter plc; *Int'l*, pg. 282
ESAB WELDING & CUTTING PRODUCTS—Charter plc; *Int'l*, pg. 281
ELECTRO-MATIC PRODUCTS INC.; *U.S. Private*, pg. 369
ELECTRON BEAM TECHNOLOGIES; *U.S. Private*, pg. 370
EMERSON JAPAN, LTD., FUSITE DIVISION—Emerson Electric Co.; *U.S. Public*, pg. 576
ERICO INTERNATIONAL; *U.S. Private*, pg. 381
PT ESABINDO PRATAMA—Charter plc; *Int'l*, pg. 282
FEMSA S.P.A.—Charter plc; *Int'l*, pg. 283
THE FIBRE-METAL PRODUCTS COMPANY; *U.S. Private*, pg. 402
FUSITE, B.V.—Emerson Electric Co.; *U.S. Public*, pg. 577
FUSITE JAPAN—Emerson Electric Co.; *U.S. Public*, pg. 577
GCE—AGA AB; *Int'l*, pg. 14
HARRIS EUROPA, S.P.A.—Emerson Electric Co.; *U.S. Public*, pg. 577
HOBART BROTHERS CO.—Illinois Tool Works Inc.; *U.S. Public*, pg. 866
HOECHST SPECIALTY PRODUCTS GROUP—Hoechst Aktiengesellschaft; *Int'l*, pg. 625
HOFLEY MANUFACTURING COMPANY; *U.S. Private*, pg. 532
HONG KONG OXYGEN & ACETYLENE CO. LTD.—The BOC Group plc; *Int'l*, pg. 122
ILLINOIS TOOL WORKS INC.; *U.S. Public*, pg. 865
INDUCTOTHERM INDUSTRIES, INC.; *U.S. Private*, pg. 560
INDUSTRIAL GASES LTD.—The BOC Group plc; *Int'l*, pg. 122
KEBE ERSATZTEILE GMBH—Charter plc; *Int'l*, pg. 283
KEEN COMPRESSED GAS CO.; *U.S. Private*, pg. 611
KEEN WELDING DIVISION—Keen Compressed Gas Co.; *U.S. Private*, pg. 611
KLOECKNER-WILHELMSBURGER GMBH—Klockner-Werke AG; *Int'l*, pg. 737
KOBE WELDING (SINGAPORE) PTE. LTD.—Kobe Steel, Ltd.; *Int'l*, pg. 741
L-TEC FRANCE SARL—Charter plc; *Int'l*, pg. 283
JOHN LAING PLC; *Int'l*, pg. 796
LAMB TECHNICON—Litton Industries, Inc.; *U.S. Public*, pg. 1004
LAMB TECHNICON UK—Litton Industries, Inc.; *U.S. Public*, pg. 1004
THE LINCOLN ELECTRIC CO. (FRANCE) S.A.—The Lincoln Electric Company; *U.S. Public*, pg. 996
THE LINCOLN ELECTRIC COMPANY; *U.S. Public*, pg. 996
THE LINCOLN ELECTRIC COMPANY (ASIA PACIFIC) PTE. LTD.—The Lincoln Electric Company; *U.S. Public*, pg. 996
THE LINCOLN ELECTRIC CO. AUSTRALIA PTY. LTD.—The Lincoln Electric Company; *U.S. Public*, pg. 996
THE LINCOLN ELECTRIC CO. OF CANADA LTD.—The Lincoln Electric Company; *U.S. Public*, pg. 997
LINCOLN ELECTRIC DO BRASIL—The Lincoln Electric Company; *U.S. Public*, pg. 997
LINCOLN ELECTRIC ITALIA SRL—The Lincoln Electric Company; *U.S. Public*, pg. 997
LINCOLN ELECTRIC MEXICANA S.A. DE C.V.—The Lincoln Electric Company; *U.S. Public*, pg. 997
LINCOLN ELECTRIC (U.K. LTD.)—The Lincoln Electric Company; *U.S. Public*, pg. 997
LINCOLN KD S.A.—The Lincoln Electric Company; *U.S. Public*, pg. 997
LINCOLN NORWELD AS—The Lincoln Electric Company; *U.S. Public*, pg. 997
LUCAS-MILHAUPT, INC.—Handy & Harman; *U.S. Public*, pg. 780
MALAYSIAN OXYGEN BERHAD—The BOC Group plc; *Int'l*, pg. 122
METCAL, INC.; *U.S. Private*, pg. 735
MORGAN CONSTRUCTION CO.; *U.S. Private*, pg. 761
NCH CORPORATION; *U.S. Public*, pg. 1145
NEDERMAN A/S—Charter plc; *Int'l*, pg. 283
NEDERMAN GMBH—Charter plc; *Int'l*, pg. 283
NEDERMAN IBERICA S.A.—Charter plc; *Int'l*, pg. 283
NEDERMAN INC.—Charter plc; *Int'l*, pg. 281
NEDERMAN LTD.—Charter plc; *Int'l*, pg. 283
AB PH. NEDERMAN & CO.—Charter plc; *Int'l*, pg. 281
NEWCOR BAY CITY DIVISION—Newcor, Inc.; *U.S. Public*, pg. 1176
NEWCOR, INC.; *U.S. Public*, pg. 1176
NIPPON BOC KK—The BOC Group plc; *Int'l*, pg. 122
POW CON—Illinois Tool Works Inc.; *U.S. Public*, pg. 867
RANSOME/TEMPIL—Air Liquide S.A.; *Int'l*, pg. 37
ROTHENBERGER-EXACT A/S—Rothenberger Group GmbH; *Int'l*, pg. 1129
ROTHENBERGER GROUP GMBH; *Int'l*, pg. 1127
ROTHENBERGER (IRELAND) LTD.—Rothenberger Group GmbH; *Int'l*, pg. 1129
H.A. SCHLATTER AG; *Int'l*, pg. 1205
SCIAKY, INC.—Phillips Service Industries, Inc.; *U.S. Private*, pg. 862
SCIAKY S.A.; *Int'l*, pg. 1211
SINGAPORE OXYGEN AIR LIQUIDE PTE LTD.—The BOC Group plc; *Int'l*, pg. 122
SOUTHERN CALIFORNIA AIR GAS—Airgas, Inc.; *U.S. Public*, pg. 33
STEELWELD FRANCE SARL—Ambac B.V.; *Int'l*, pg. 71
STEELWELD U.K.—Ambac B.V.; *Int'l*, pg. 71
STEWARTS & LLOYDS TRADING (PTY) LIMITED—Dorbyl Limited; *Int'l*, pg. 416
SYCAMORE PLANT—Cooper Industries, Inc.; *U.S. Public*, pg. 444
TALLEY INDUSTRIES, INC.—Carpenter Technology Corporation; *U.S. Public*, pg. 307
TECHALLOY CO., INC.—Groupe Usinor; *Int'l*, pg. 572
THAI KOBE WELDING CO., LTD.—Kobe Steel, Ltd.; *Int'l*, pg. 741
TRI-MARK INC.—Illinois Tool Works Inc.; *U.S. Public*, pg. 866
TRU-FIT PRODUCTS CORP.; *U.S. Private*, pg. 1107
U.S. INTEC, INC.—GAF Corporation; *U.S. Private*, pg. 433
WALL COLMONOY CORP.; *U.S. Private*, pg. 1148
WELDING PRODUCTS GROUP—National-Standard Co.; *U.S. Public*, pg. 1161
WELSCO INC.; *U.S. Private*, pg. 1161

3549 — METALWORKING MACHINERY, NEC

AGA GAS, INC.—AGA AB; *Int'l*, pg. 13
ABBEY ETNA MACHINE COMPANY; *U.S. Private*, pg. 9
AIR LIQUIDE AMERICA CORPORATION—Air Liquide S.A.; *Int'l*, pg. 37
APEX BROACH & MACHINE CO.; *U.S. Private*, pg. 77
AVDEL TEXTRON—Textron Inc.; *U.S. Public*, pg. 1590
THE BOC GROUP INC. (DELAWARE)—The BOC Group plc; *Int'l*, pg. 121

BALCRANK PRODUCTS—The General Chemical Group, Inc.; *U.S. Public*, pg. 707
BLISS-SALEM, INC.; *U.S. Private*, pg. 149
ROBERT BOSCH CORPORATION—Robert Bosch GmbH; *Int'l*, pg. 204
BRIDGEPORT MACHINES, INC.; *U.S. Public*, pg. 251
JAMES BURN INTL.—Standex International Corporation; *U.S. Public*, pg. 1506
CHAMP/PIK-A-NUT SERVICE LINE—Standard Motor Products Inc.; *U.S. Public*, pg. 1503
COLTEC HOLDINGS INC; *U.S. Public*, pg. 401
CONTINENTAL INDUSTRIES INC.—Handy & Harman; *U.S. Public*, pg. 780
COOPER POWER TOOLS DIVISION—Cooper Industries, Inc.; *U.S. Public*, pg. 444
CRANE CO.; *U.S. Public*, pg. 456
CROWN HOLDINGS, INC.; *U.S. Private*, pg. 293
CROWN IRON WORKS COMPANY—Crown Holdings, Inc.; *U.S. Private*, pg. 293
DANIELLI & C. OFFICINE MECCANICHE S.P.A.; *Int'l*, pg. 378
DOVATECH, LTD.—Dover Corporation; *U.S. Public*, pg. 520
EEI CORPORATION; *Int'l*, pg. 425
EFFICIENT ENGINEERING CO.; *U.S. Private*, pg. 365
THE ENTWISTLE COMPANY; *U.S. Private*, pg. 378
FADAL ENGINEERING COMPANY, INC.—Thyssen AG; *Int'l*, pg. 1389
GKN WESTLAND AEROSPACE NORTH AMERICA INC.—GKN plc; *Int'l*, pg. 535
GIDDINGS & LEWIS, INC.—Thyssen AG; *Int'l*, pg. 1389
GILMAN—Thyssen AG; *Int'l*, pg. 1389
HENNESSY INDUSTRIES, INC.—Danaher Corporation; *U.S. Public*, pg. 481
HESS ENGINEERING INC.; *U.S. Private*, pg. 524
THE HOLLAND HITCH COMPANY; *U.S. Private*, pg. 534
INGERSOLL MASCHINEN UND WERKZEUGE GMBH—Ingersoll International Inc.; *U.S. Private*, pg. 562
INGERSOLL-RAND COMPANY; *U.S. Public*, pg. 876
KINGSBURY ASSEMBLY MACHINE DIV.—Kingsbury Corporation; *U.S. Private*, pg. 622
KINGSBURY CORPORATION; *U.S. Private*, pg. 621
KINGSLEY MACHINE CO.—Illinois Tool Works Inc.; *U.S. Public*, pg. 866
KINGSTON-WARREN CORPORATION—Harvard Industries, Inc.; *U.S. Public*, pg. 796
LAMB TECHNICON—Litton Industries, Inc.; *U.S. Public*, pg. 1004
LAMB TECHNICON UK—Litton Industries, Inc.; *U.S. Public*, *pg. 1004*
LITTON SERVOTECHNIK—Litton Industries, Inc.; *U.S. Public*, pg. 1004
MESTEK, INC.; *U.S. Public*, pg. 1099
MIKRON CORP. MONROE—Mikron Holding AG; *Int'l*, pg. 866
MIKRON ROTTWEIL GMBH—Mikron Holding AG; *Int'l*, pg. 867
MIKRON SA AGNO—Mikron Holding AG; *Int'l*, pg. 866
MIKRON SA BOUDRY—Mikron Holding AG; *Int'l*, pg. 866
MIKRON SA MULHOUSE—Mikron Holding AG; *Int'l*, pg. 867
MIKRON SNC NERVIANO—Mikron Holding AG; *Int'l*, pg. 867
MIKRON S.R.L. LUINO—Mikron Holding AG; *Int'l*, pg. 867
MONARCH CORTLAND DIV.—The Monarch Machine Tool Company; *U.S. Public*, pg. 1124
THE MONARCH MACHINE TOOL COMPANY; *U.S. Public*, *pg. 1123*
MONARCH WETKZENGMASCHINEN GMBH—The Monarch Machine Tool Company; *U.S. Public*, pg. 1124
MOORE TOOL COMPANY, INC.—The Producto Machine Co.; *U.S. Private*, pg. 889
MORGARDSHAMMAR AB—Danielli & C. Officine Meccaniche S.p.A.; *Int'l*, pg. 378
NEW INGENIA SA—Mikron Holding AG; *Int'l*, pg. 866
NEWCOR, INC.; *U.S. Public*, pg. 1176
P/A INDUSTRIES, INC.; *U.S. Private*, pg. 825
PRAXAIR ESPANIA S.A.—Praxair Inc.; *U.S. Public*, pg. 1320
RAPPOLD, HERMANN & CO. GMBH—Viag AG; *Int'l*, pg. 1464
ROKOP CORPORATION; *U.S. Private*, pg. 941
SCHIAVI S.P.A.—Bobst S.A.; *Int'l*, pg. 199
SCIAKY S.A.; *Int'l*, pg. 1211
SENECA FALLS TECHNOLOGY GROUP; *U.S. Private*, pg. 984
STAMCO-DEPIEREUX GMBH—The Monarch Machine Tool Company; *U.S. Public*, pg. 1124
STAMCO DIV.—The Monarch Machine Tool Company; *U.S. Public*, pg. 1124
STAMCO (U.K.) LTD.—The Monarch Machine Tool Company; *U.S. Public*, pg. 1124
STANDARD LOCKNUT, INC.; *U.S. Private*, pg. 1031
STEEL TECHNOLOGIES INC.; *U.S. Public*, pg. 1513
THERMO ELECTRON CORPORATION; *U.S. Public*, pg. 1591
THOMAS ENGINEERING INC.; *U.S. Private*, pg. 1082
TIPPINS INCORPORATED; *U.S. Private*, pg. 1088
THE U.S. BAIRD CORPORATION; *U.S. Private*, pg. 1124
U.S. MANUFACTURING CORP.; *U.S. Private*, pg. 1125
J.M. VOITH, GMBH; *Int'l*, pg. 1472
WALKER MAGNETICS GROUP, INC.; *U.S. Private*, pg. 1147
WELDUN INTERNATIONAL, INC.—Robert Bosch GmbH; *Int'l*, pg. 205
WILTON CORPORATION; *U.S. Private*, pg. 1181
WIRE MACHINERY DIV.—FKI Plc; *Int'l*, pg. 473

3552 — TEXTILE MACHINERY

APV CREPACO, INC., DRYER DIV.—Siebe plc; *Int'l*, pg. 1240
APV GAULIN—Siebe plc; *Int'l*, pg. 1241
AMERICAN BARMAG CO.; *U.S. Private*, pg. 51
THE AMERICAN GROUP; *U.S. Private*, pg. 56
AMERICAN SAHM CORPORATION—Georg Sahm GmbH & Co. KG Maschinenfabrik; *Int'l*, pg. 1169
AMERICAN SUESSEN—Spindelfabrik Suessen; *Int'l*, pg. 1290
ASHWORTH BROS., INC.; *U.S. Private*, pg. 89
ASTEC INDUSTRIES, INC.; *U.S. Public*, pg. 141
BSL ENGINEERING LIMITED—Brammer plc; *Int'l*, pg. 212
BEHR SYSTEMS, INC.—Durr AG; *Int'l*, pg. 421
JOHN BROWN PLASTICS MACHINERY—Kvaerner a.s.a.; *Int'l*, pg. 773
CARCLO ENGINEERING GROUP PLC; *Int'l*, pg. 268
CLYDESDALE WALTON CO.—Caparo Group Ltd.; *Int'l*, pg. 265
DAY INTERNATIONAL TEXTILE PRODUCTS—American Industrial Partners; *U.S. Private*, pg. 56
DRAPER TEXMACO, INC.; *U.S. Private*, pg. 342
EEI CORPORATION; *Int'l*, pg. 425
EASTMAN WORLDWIDE; *U.S. Private*, pg. 358
ENGLISH CARD CLOTHING CO. LIMITED—Carclo Engineering Group plc; *Int'l*, pg. 268
ESTABLIS. PLATT FRERES S.A.—Carclo Engineering Group plc; *Int'l*, pg. 268
FAG AUSTRIA WAELZLAGER AG—FAG Group; *Int'l*, pg. 469
FAG GROUP; *Int'l*, pg. 468
GHM INDUSTRIES, INC.; *U.S. Private*, pg. 435
GASTON COUNTY DYEING MACHINE CO.; *U.S. Private*, pg. 441
GESSNER/MILLER CORPORATION—GHM Industries, Inc.; *U.S. Private*, pg. 435
W.L. GORE & ASSOCIATES, INC.; *U.S. Private*, pg. 465
HITACHI SEIKO, LTD.—Hitachi, Ltd.; *Int'l*, pg. 622
HOLLINGSWORTH SACO LOWELL CORPORATION, INC.; *U.S. Private*, pg. 535
HORSFALL & BICKHAM LIMITED—Carclo Engineering Group plc; *Int'l*, pg. 268
N.V. KAARDENFABRIEK "NEDERLAND"—Carclo Engineering Group plc; *Int'l*, pg. 268
KING COMPANY—United Dominion Industries, Ltd.; *U.S. Public*, pg. 1676
LAMONT HOLDINGS PLC; *Int'l*, pg. 797
LEESONA CORP.—Kvaerner a.s.a.; *Int'l*, pg. 774
LUWA BAHNSON, INC.; *U.S. Private*, pg. 682
MACPHERSON MEISTERGRAM, INC.—Willcox & Gibbs, Inc.; *U.S. Private*, pg. 1177
MAHLO AMERICA INC.—Mahlo GmbH & Co. KG; *Int'l*, pg. 830
MAHLO GMBH & CO. KG; *Int'l*, pg. 830
MARSHALL & WILLIAMS CO.; *U.S. Private*, pg. 708
MARUBENI CORPORATION; *Int'l*, pg. 844
MASCHINENFABRIK HOERAUF—Spindelfabrik Suessen; *Int'l*, pg. 1290
MORRISON BERKSHIRE INC.—Morrison Textile Machinery Co.; *U.S. Private*, pg. 762
MORRISON TEXTILE MACHINERY CO.; *U.S. Private*, pg. 762
MURATA MACHINERY, LTD.; *Int'l*, pg. 897
NISSAN TEXTILE MACHINERY CORP. IN U.S.A.—Nissan Motor Co., Ltd.; *Int'l*, pg. 945
NUOVO PIGNONE S.P.A.; *Int'l*, pg. 990
PNEUMAFIL CORPORATION; *U.S. Private*, pg. 873
THE ROWE CORPORATION; *U.S. Private*, pg. 948
AB SKF; *Int'l*, pg. 1156
SKF MFG. SINGAPORE (PTE.) LTD.—AB SKF; *Int'l*, pg. 1159
SKF TEXTILMASCHINEN-KOMPONENTEN GMBH—AB SKF; *Int'l*, pg. 1159
GEORG SAHM GMBH & CO. KG MASCHINENFABRIK; *Int'l*, pg. 1169
N. SCHLUMBERGER & CIE; *Int'l*, pg. 1206
SPEIZMAN INDUSTRIES, INC.; *U.S. Public*, pg. 1498
SPINDELFABRIK SUESSEN; *Int'l*, pg. 1290
SSANGYONG BUSINESS GROUP; *Int'l*, pg. 1291
WILHELM STAHLECKER GMBH—Spindelfabrik Suessen; *Int'l*, pg. 1290
SUESSEA MAQUIUAS S.A.—Spindelfabrik Suessen; *Int'l*, pg. 1291
SULZER IMMOBILIEN AG—Sulzer Ltd.; *Int'l*, pg. 1306
SULZER, INC.—Sulzer Ltd.; *Int'l*, pg. 1306
SULZER ITALIA S.P.A.—Sulzer Ltd.; *Int'l*, pg. 1306
SULZER RUTI GROUP—Sulzer Ltd.; *Int'l*, pg. 1307
SULZER RUTI INC.—Sulzer Ltd.; *Int'l*, pg. 1307
TAMROCK CORP.; *Int'l*, pg. 1352
TOYODA AUTOMATIC LOOM WORKS, LTD.—Toyota Motor Corporation; *Int'l*, pg. 1412
TSUDAKOMA CORP.; *Int'l*, pg. 1425
VALMET INC.- APPLETON DIVISION—Valmet Corporation; *Int'l*, pg. 1448
WEIGH-TRONIX—Staveley Industries PLC; *Int'l*, pg. 1299
WHITIN ROBERTS CO.—Damsmith Corp.; *U.S. Private*, pg. 309
WISCONSIN AUTOMATED MACHINERY CORP.; *U.S. Private*, pg. 1184
ZELLWEGER USTER AG—Hesta Tex AG; *Int'l*, pg. 618

3553 — WOODWORKING MACHINERY

ALBERTA OIL TOOL DIV.—Dover Corporation; *U.S. Public*, *pg. 522*
AMADA CO., LTD.; *Int'l*, pg. 70
AMADA SCHIAVI S.R.L.—Amada Co., Ltd.; *Int'l*, pg. 70
BABCOCK-BSH INC.—Deutsche Babcock AG; *Int'l*, pg. 399
THE BLACK & DECKER CORPORATION; *U.S. Public*, pg. 233
THE COE MANUFACTURING COMPANY; *U.S. Private*, pg. 249
THE COE MFG. LTD.—The Coe Manufacturing Company; *U.S. Private*, pg. 249
DELTA INTERNATIONAL MACHINERY—Pentair, Inc.; *U.S. Public*, pg. 1273
DELTA INTERNATIONAL MACHINERY CORP.—Pentair, Inc.; *U.S. Public*, pg. 1273
DELTA INTERNATIONAL MACHINERY CORP. (TUPELO)—Pentair, Inc.; *U.S. Public*, pg. 1273
DEUTSCHE BABCOCK AG; *Int'l*, pg. 398
DEUTSCHE BABCOCK TECHNOLOGIES, INC.—Deutsche Babcock AG; *Int'l*, pg. 401
DIEHL MACHINES—Katy Industries, Inc.; *U.S. Public*, pg. 944
DOVER CORPORATION; *U.S. Public*, pg. 520
ELECTROLUX CONSTRUCTOR—Electrolux, AB; *Int'l*, pg. 441
GUSTAV WAGNER MASCHINENFABRIK GMBH; *Int'l*, pg. 579
HIRSH COMPANY—Knape & Vogt Mfg. Co.; *U.S. Public*, pg. 963
KABUSHIKI KAISHA TMK—Makita Corporation; *Int'l*, pg. 831
LONDON LITHO ALUMINUM CO., INC.; *U.S. Private*, pg. 673
MATTISON TECHNOLOGIES, INC.; *U.S. Private*, pg. 714
PENTAIR, INC.; *U.S. Public*, pg. 1273
POOLE WOOD EQUIPMENT LTD.—Brunel Holdings Plc; *Int'l*, pg. 231
RAUMA LTD.—UPM-Kymmene Corporation; *Int'l*, pg. 1428
THOMAS ROBINSON GROUP PLC—Brunel Holdings Plc; *Int'l*, pg. 231
AB SANI-MASKINER—Cooper Industries, Inc.; *U.S. Public*, pg. 444
SHOPSMITH, INC.; *U.S. Public*, pg. 1467
SODERHAMNS VERKSTADER AB—Trelleborg AB; *Int'l*, pg. 1421
TIMESAVERS INC.; *U.S. Private*, pg. 1088
TITMAN TIP TOOLS—Brunel Holdings Plc; *Int'l*, pg. 231
VOEST-ALPINE INTERNATIONAL CORPORATION—Voest-Alpine Stahl AG; *Int'l*, pg. 1470
WACO JONSEREDS AB—Trelleborg AB; *Int'l*, pg. 1421
WADKIN PLC—Brunel Holdings Plc; *Int'l*, pg. 231
MICHAEL WEINIG AG; *Int'l*, pg. 1488
WILTON CORPORATION; *U.S. Private*, pg. 1181
WISCONSIN AUTOMATED MACHINERY CORP.; *U.S. Private*, pg. 1184

3554 — PAPER INDUSTRIES MACHINERY

ALBANY ENGINEERED SYSTEMS-CANADA—Thermo Electron Corporation; *U.S. Public*, pg. 1593
ALBANY INTERNATIONAL CANADA-PERTH—Albany International Corp.; *U.S. Public*, pg. 37
ALBANY INTERNATIONAL CORP.; *U.S. Public*, pg. 36
BABCOCK CONSTRUCTION CONTRACTORS—Babcock International Group PLC; *Int'l*, pg. 131
BELOIT CORPORATION—Harnischfeger Industries, Inc.; *U.S. Public*, pg. 789
BELOIT CORPORATION-BLACKHAWK PLANT—Harnischfeger Industries, Inc.; *U.S. Public*, pg. 789
BELOIT LENOX, DIV.—Harnischfeger Industries, Inc.; *U.S. Public*, pg. 789
BELOIT MANHATTAN INC.—Harnischfeger Industries, Inc.; *U.S. Public*, pg. 789
BUTLER AUTOMATIC, INC.; *U.S. Private*, pg. 189
CAE MACHINERY LTD.—CAE Inc.; *Int'l*, pg. 237
CPM—Gencor Industries, Inc.; *U.S. Public*, pg. 705
CAMERON ASHLEY—Cameron Ashley Building Products, Inc; *U.S. Public*, pg. 298
AB CELLECO—Tetra Laval Group; *Int'l*, pg. 1378
THE CHALLENGE MACHINERY CO.; *U.S. Private*, pg. 227
DERLAN INDUSTRIES LIMITED; *Int'l*, pg. 395
T.H. DIXON & CO. LTD.—Brunel Holdings Plc; *Int'l*, pg. 231
DORR-OLIVER INCORPORATED—Mannesmann A.G.; *Int'l*, *pg. 839*
DORRIES GMBH—J.M. Voith, GmbH; *Int'l*, pg. 1473
ENTERPRISES INTERNATIONAL INC.; *U.S. Private*, pg. 377
FMP-RAUMA COMPANY—UPM-Kymmene Corporation; *Int'l*, pg. 1428
GENERAL BINDING CORPORATION; *U.S. Public*, pg. 707
HARNISCHFEGER INDUSTRIES, INC.; *U.S. Public*, pg. 788
INGERSOLL-RAND COMPANY; *U.S. Public*, pg. 876
JAGENBERG AG—Rheinmetall Group; *Int'l*, pg. 1108
JAGENBERG, INC.—Rheinmetall Group; *Int'l*, pg. 1108
CURT G. JOA, INC.; *U.S. Private*, pg. 588
AXEL JOHNSON AB; *Int'l*, pg. 707
KRC (HEWITT) INC.—Scapa Group Plc; *Int'l*, pg. 1202
KLOCKNER-BARTELT, INC.—Klockner-Werke AG; *Int'l*, pg. 737
KLOCKNER ER-WE-PA—Klockner-Werke AG; *Int'l*, pg. 737
KVAERNER EUREKA A/S, TRANBY—Kvaerner a.s.a.; *Int'l*, *pg. 766*
MHI CORRUGATING MACHINERY COMPANY (MCMC)—Mitsubishi Heavy Industries Ltd.; *Int'l*, pg. 874
MACHINERY MANUFACTURING—Sonoco Products Company; *U.S. Public*, pg. 1486
MARK ANDY, INC.—Dover Corporation; *U.S. Public*, pg. 521
MIRAMICHI PULP & PAPER INC.—Repap Enterprises Inc.; *Int'l*, pg. 1104
OVALSTRAPPING INC.—Enterprises International Inc.; *U.S. Private*, pg. 378
PACKAGING AND MATERIAL HANDLING DIVISION—FMC Corporation; *U.S. Public*, pg. 606
REXAM INC.—Rexam PLC; *Int'l*, pg. 1106
REXAM MEDICAL PACKAGING—Rexam PLC; *Int'l*, pg. 1106
SANDUSKY INTERNATIONAL INC.; *U.S. Private*, pg. 964
SANDUSKY LIMITED—Sandusky International Inc.; *U.S. Private*, pg. 965
SCAPA GROUP PLC; *Int'l*, pg. 1202
SIMON-HOLDER LTD.—Simon Engineering plc; *Int'l*, pg. 1251
SULZER, INC.—Sulzer Ltd.; *Int'l*, pg. 1306
SULZER INFORMATIK AG—Sulzer Ltd.; *Int'l*, pg. 1306
SULZER ITALIA S.P.A.—Sulzer Ltd.; *Int'l*, pg. 1306

SUPERIOR MACHINE COMPANY OF SOUTH CAROLINA, INC.; U.S. Private, pg. 1055
SVEDALA PUMPS & PROCESS—Svedala Industri AB; Int'l, pg. 1325
THERMO ELECTRON (CANADA)—Thermo Electron Corporation; U.S. Public, pg. 1596
THERMO ELECTRON CORPORATION; U.S. Public, pg. 1591
THERMO ELECTRON WISCONSIN, INC.—Thermo Electron Corporation; U.S. Public, pg. 1593
THERMO FIBERTEK, INC.—Thermo Electron Corporation; U.S. Public, pg. 1593
TRISTAR INDUSTRIES LTD.—J.M. Voith, GmbH; Int'l, pg. 1473
UNITED PAPER MILLS LTD.—UPM-Kymmene Corporation; Int'l, pg. 1429
VALMET CORPORATION; Int'l, pg. 1447
VALMET-KARLSTAD AB—Valmet Corporation; Int'l, pg. 1448
VALMET-RAISIO OY—Valmet Corporation; Int'l, pg. 1448
VALMET-ROTOMEC S.P.A.—Valmet Corporation; Int'l, pg. 1449
VERATEC JAPAN, LTD.—International Paper Company; U.S. Public, pg. 906
VERATEC S.A.—International Paper Company; U.S. Public, pg. 906
VIDEOJET SYSTEMS INTERNATIONAL, INC.—The General Electric Company, p.l.c.; Int'l, pg. 545
VOITH INC.—J.M. Voith, GmbH; Int'l, pg. 1473
J.M. VOITH AG—J.M. Voith, GmbH; Int'l, pg. 1473
J.M. VOITH, GMBH; Int'l, pg. 1472
VOITH S.A. MAQUINAS E EQUIPAMENTOS—J.M. Voith, GmbH; Int'l, pg. 1473
VOITH TOLOSA S.A.—J.M. Voith, GmbH; Int'l, pg. 1473
THE WARD MACHINERY COMPANY; U.S. Private, pg. 1149
WINDMOELLER & HOELSCHER; Int'l, pg. 1510
WINTERBURN LTD.—Thermo Electron Corporation; U.S. Public, pg. 1596

3555 — PRINTING TRADES MACHINERY AND EQUIPMENT

AT INFORMATION PRODUCTS; U.S. Private, pg. 8
AGFA EPS DIVISION—Bayer AG; Int'l, pg. 172
ANCHOR INC.—International Paper Company; U.S. Public, pg. 903
ANO-COIL CORPORATION; U.S. Private, pg. 75
AUTOLOGIC INFORMATION INTERNATIONAL, INC.—Volt Information Sciences, Inc.; U.S. Public, pg. 1724
AUTOROLL MACHINE CO., LLC; U.S. Private, pg. 101
BALDWIN PRINTING CONTROLS LTD.—Baldwin Technology Company, Inc.; U.S. Public, pg. 170
BALDWIN TECHNOLOGY COMPANY, INC.; U.S. Public, pg. 169
BEACON GROUP; U.S. Private, pg. 126
BELMONT INDUSTRIES, INC.—RGP Holding, Inc.; U.S. Private, pg. 903
BERNAL DIVISION—Stevens International, Inc.; U.S. Public, pg. 1517
BOBST GROUP INC.—Bobst S.A.; Int'l, pg. 198
BOBST S.A.; Int'l, pg. 198
BOSAM S.A.—Bobst S.A.; Int'l, pg. 199
BUTLER AUTOMATIC, INC.; U.S. Private, pg. 189
CEDIGRAPH S.A.—Bobst S.A.; Int'l, pg. 198
CHECK TECHNOLOGY CORPORATION; U.S. Public, pg. 342
CONTAINER GRAPHICS CORPORATION; U.S. Private, pg. 267
COOKSON GROUP PLC; Int'l, pg. 328
DE LA RUE PLC; Int'l, pg. 386
DENNISON IMAGING SYSTEMS DIV.—Avery Dennison Corporation; U.S. Public, pg. 152
A.B. DICK COMPANY—NESCO, Inc.; U.S. Private, pg. 791
DIDDE CORPORATION; U.S. Private, pg. 331
DIDDE WEB PRESS—Didde Corporation; U.S. Private, pg. 331
EMHART INTERNATIONAL LTD.—The Black & Decker Corporation; U.S. Public, pg. 233
FAG S.A.—Bobst S.A.; Int'l, pg. 198
FERAG AG—WRH Walter Reist Holding AG; Int'l, pg. 1484
FERAG INC.—WRH Walter Reist Holding AG; Int'l, pg. 1484
FISHER GRAPHIC INDUSTRIES—Container Graphics Corporation; U.S. Private, pg. 267
G.E. HARRIS ENERGY CONTROL SYSTEMS, LLC—General Electric Company; U.S. Public, pg. 712
G.E. HARRIS ENERGY CONTROL SYSTEMS, LLC—Harris Corporation; U.S. Public, pg. 792
GOSS GRAPHIC SYSTEMS; U.S. Private, pg. 466
GOSS GRAPHIC SYSTEMS LTD.—Goss Graphic Systems; U.S. Private, pg. 466
GRAPHIC ENTERPRISES OF OHIO, INC.; U.S. Private, pg. 471
GRAPHLINE INC.; U.S. Private, pg. 471
HALM INDUSTRIES COMPANY, INCORPORATED; U.S. Private, pg. 496
HALM INDUSTRIES INTERNATIONAL—Halm Industries Company, Incorporated; U.S. Private, pg. 496
HEIDELBERG FINISHING SYSTEMS—Heidelberger Druckmaschinen A.G.; Int'l, pg. 604
HEIDELBERG GRAPHIC EQUIPMENT LTD.-HEIDELBERG AUSTRALIA—Heidelberger Druckmaschinen A.G.; Int'l, pg. 605
HEIDELBERG HARRIS S.A.—Heidelberger Druckmaschinen A.G.; Int'l, pg. 605
HEIDELBERG USA, INC.—Heidelberger Druckmaschinen A.G.; Int'l, pg. 604
HEIDELBERG WEB PRESS, INC.—Heidelberger Druckmaschinen A.G.; Int'l, pg. 604
HEIDELBERGER DRUCKMASCHINEN A.G.; Int'l, pg. 604
HESCO SUPPLY CO., INC.—The Hearst Corporation; U.S. Private, pg. 518
HOECHST SPECIALTY PRODUCTS GROUP—Hoechst Aktiengesellschaft; Int'l, pg. 625
ING. C. OLIVETTI & C.—Olivetti SpA; Int'l, pg. 1002
KALMAR INDUSTRIES AB—Trelleborg AB; Int'l, pg. 1420
KALMAR NOHAB AB—Trelleborg AB; Int'l, pg. 1421
KING PRESS CORPORATION—Publishers Equipment Corporation; U.S. Public, pg. 1341
KINGSLEY MACHINE CO.—Illinois Tool Works Inc.; U.S. Public, pg. 866
KOENIG & BAUER-ALBERT AG; Int'l, pg. 742
KOMORI CORPORATION; Int'l, pg. 745
LINOTYPE-HELL COMPANY—Heidelberger Druckmaschinen A.G.; Int'l, pg. 604
MAN ROLAND DRUCKMASCHINEN AKTIENGESELLSCHAFT—MAN Aktiengesellschaft; Int'l, pg. 825
MHI LITHOGRAPH PRINTING—Mitsubishi Heavy Industries Ltd.; Int'l, pg. 874
MAN ROLAND, INC.—MAN Aktiengesellschaft; Int'l, pg. 825
MARK ANDY, INC.—Dover Corporation; U.S. Public, pg. 521
MCCAIN BINDERY SYSTEMS, INC.; U.S. Private, pg. 719
METALLISED FILMS & PAPER, LTD.—Avery Dennison Corporation; U.S. Public, pg. 154
MULTIGRAPHICS INC.; U.S. Public, pg. 1141
NEW HERMES INCORPORATED; U.S. Private, pg. 793
OCE-U.S.A.—Oce-van der Grinten N.V.; Int'l, pg. 994
OLIVETTI SPA; Int'l, pg. 1002
PACKAGING AND MATERIAL HANDLING DIVISION—FMC Corporation; U.S. Public, pg. 606
PAMARCO TECHNOLOGIES, INC.; U.S. Private, pg. 835
PAXAR CORPORATION; U.S. Public, pg. 1266
POLYFIBRON TECHNOLOGIES CORP.; U.S. Private, pg. 875
PRESSTEK, INC.; U.S. Public, pg. 1324
PUBLISHERS EQUIPMENT CORPORATION; U.S. Public, pg. 1341
QUIPP, INC.; U.S. Public, pg. 1353
RGP HOLDING, INC.; U.S. Private, pg. 903
REXAM MEDICAL PACKAGING—Rexam PLC; Int'l, pg. 1106
ROCKWELL PMC/BAKER PERKINS—Siebe plc; Int'l, pg. 1240
RYOBI LTD.; Int'l, pg. 1151
SMC—Quad/Graphics, Inc.; U.S. Private, pg. 898
SEQUA CORPORATION; U.S. Public, pg. 1458
SERICOL INC.—Burmah Castrol plc; Int'l, pg. 235
SMYTH MANUFACTURING COMPANY—Beacon Group; U.S. Private, pg. 126
SOABAR G.M.B.H.—Avery Dennison Corporation; U.S. Public, pg. 154
SOABAR MARKING SYSTEMS LTD.—Avery Dennison Corporation; U.S. Public, pg. 154
SOABAR PRODUCTS GROUP—Avery Dennison Corporation; U.S. Public, pg. 153
SOABAR SYSTEMS (HONG KONG) LTD.—Avery Dennison Corporation; U.S. Public, pg. 154
STEVENS INTERNATIONAL, INC.; U.S. Public, pg. 1517
STEVENS SECURITY SYSTEMS—Stevens International, Inc.; U.S. Public, pg. 1517
SUMMIT GRAVURE LTD.—Forbo Holding SA; Int'l, pg. 498
THERMO ELECTRON CORPORATION; U.S. Public, pg. 1591
THERMO ELECTRON WISCONSIN, INC.—Thermo Electron Corporation; U.S. Public, pg. 1593
US REPROGRAPHICS, INC.—Wilco Reprographic, Inc.; U.S. Private, pg. 1176
VEB POLYGRAPH DRUCKMACHINENWERK PLANETA RADEBEUL; Int'l, pg. 1445
VALMET CORPORATION; Int'l, pg. 1447
VALMET-ROTOMEC S.P.A.—Valmet Corporation; Int'l, pg. 1449
VIDEOJET LTD.—The General Electric Company, p.l.c.; Int'l, pg. 546
WINDMOELLER & HOELSCHER; Int'l, pg. 1510
ZERAND DIVISION—Stevens International, Inc.; U.S. Public, pg. 1517

3556 — FOOD PRODUCTS MACHINERY

AC CORPORATION; U.S. Private, pg. 3
APV BAKER PLC—Siebe plc; Int'l, pg. 1240
APV CHEMICAL MACHINERY, INC., PROCESS SYSTEMS DIV.—Siebe plc; Int'l, pg. 1240
APV CREPACO, INC.—Siebe plc; Int'l, pg. 1240
APV DOUGLAS MACHINE CORP.—Siebe plc; Int'l, pg. 1240
APV GAULIN GMBH—Siebe plc; Int'l, pg. 1241
APV PASILAC—Siebe plc; Int'l, pg. 1240
APV PAVAILLER MONZIANI—Financiere Equipment S.A.; Int'l, pg. 485
APV ROSISTA GMBH—Siebe plc; Int'l, pg. 1241
APV U.K. PLC—Siebe plc; Int'l, pg. 1240
ACRISON, INC.; U.S. Private, pg. 14
AEROGLIDE AMERICAS INTERNATIONAL, INC.—Aeroglide Corporation; U.S. Private, pg. 24
ALFA-LAVAL AGRI, INC.—Tetra Laval Group; Int'l, pg. 1378
ALFA-LAVAL AGRI INTERNATIONAL AB—Tetra Laval Group; Int'l, pg. 1377
ALFA-LAVAL AGRI LTD—Tetra Laval Group; Int'l, pg. 1380
ALFA-LAVAL AGRI N.V.—Tetra Laval Group; Int'l, pg. 1379
ALFA-LAVAL AGRI SCANDINAVIA AB—Tetra Laval Group; Int'l, pg. 1377
ALFA-LAVAL AGRI SCANDINAVIA A/S—Tetra Laval Group; Int'l, pg. 1379
ALFA-LAVAL AGRI-SCANDINAVIA OY—Tetra Laval Group; Int'l, pg. 1379
ALFA-LAVAL FLOW EQUIPMENT—Tetra Laval Group; Int'l, pg. 1379
ALFA LAVAL INC.—Tetra Laval Group; Int'l, pg. 1378
ALFA-LAVAL S.A.—Tetra Laval Group; Int'l, pg. 1379
ALFA-LAVAL SEPARATION AB—Tetra Laval Group; Int'l, pg. 1378
ALLOY PRODUCTS CORP; U.S. Private, pg. 42
BKI—Standex International Corporation; U.S. Public, pg. 1506
BWI FORDS HOLMATIC—BWI Plc; Int'l, pg. 130
BWI KARTRIDG PAK—BWI Plc; Int'l, pg. 130
BAKER PERKINS (NZ) LIMITED—Siebe plc; Int'l, pg. 1240
BAKER PERKINS PROPRIETARY LIMITED—Siebe plc; Int'l, pg. 1240
BARRY-WEHMILLER COMPANY; U.S. Private, pg. 118
BERKEL INCORPORATED—The General Electric Company, p.l.c.; Int'l, pg. 545
BOBST GROUP INC.—Bobst S.A.; Int'l, pg. 198
BONGARD—Groupe Strafor Facom; Int'l, pg. 570
BONGARD GMBH—Groupe Strafor Facom; Int'l, pg. 570
BOU-MATIC—DEC International, Inc.; U.S. Private, pg. 301
CPM EUROPE B.V.—Gencor Industries, Inc.; U.S. Public, pg. 705
CPM/EUROPE LTD.—Gencor Industries, Inc.; U.S. Public, pg. 705
CARTER DAY INTERNATIONAL; U.S. Private, pg. 216
CASHIN SYSTEMS CORP.—Tetra Laval Group; Int'l, pg. 1378
CPM/PACIFIC PRIVATE LTD.—Gencor Industries, Inc.; U.S. Public, pg. 705
CUISINART INC.—Conair Corporation; U.S. Private, pg. 261
DEC AG—DEC International, Inc.; U.S. Private, pg. 301
DEC INTERNATIONAL, INC.; U.S. Private, pg. 301
DAWN FOOD PRODUCTS, INC.; U.S. Private, pg. 316
DEAN INDUSTRIES, INC.—Berisford plc; Int'l, pg. 188
DEDERT CORPORATION; U.S. Private, pg. 320
W.H. DICKINSON ENGINEERING LTD.—Brunel Holdings Plc; Int'l, pg. 231
DUPPS COMPANY; U.S. Private, pg. 348
DURAY/J.F. DUNCAN INDUSTRIES, INC.; U.S. Private, pg. 348
DURRIESSCHARMANN, AG—Metallgesellschaft AG; Int'l, pg. 860
ENGINEERING & MANUFACTURING DIV.—Siebe plc; Int'l, pg. 1240
ESMACH SPA—Groupe Strafor Facom; Int'l, pg. 570
FMC FOOD MACHINERY EUROPE, S.A.—FMC Corporation; U.S. Public, pg. 606
FMC FOOD MACHINERY FRANCE, S.A.—FMC Corporation; U.S. Public, pg. 606
FMC FOOD MACHINERY (ITALY) S.P.A.—FMC Corporation; U.S. Public, pg. 606
FMC S.P.A.—FMC Corporation; U.S. Public, pg. 606
FOOD PROCESSING SYSTEMS—FMC Corporation; U.S. Public, pg. 605
FORMAX, INC.—Tetra Laval Group; Int'l, pg. 1378
FRIGIDAIRE HOME PRODUCTS—Electrolux, AB; Int'l, pg. 439
GENCOR INDUSTRIES, INC.; U.S. Public, pg. 705
GENERAL SLICING/RED GOAT DISPOSERS—Standex International Corporation; U.S. Public, pg. 1506
THOMAS L. GREEN & CO., INC.; U.S. Private, pg. 477
GRINDMASTER CORPORATION; U.S. Private, pg. 482
GROUPE STRAFOR FACOM; Int'l, pg. 569
GUMACO INDUSTRIA E COMERCIO LTDA.—Gencor Industries, Inc.; U.S. Public, pg. 705
H&K AMERICA INC.—Klockner-Werke AG; Int'l, pg. 737
H&K MACHINES, INC.—Klockner-Werke AG; Int'l, pg. 737
OTTO HANSEL GMBH—Klockner-Werke AG; Int'l, pg. 737
HILLAND DAIRY COMPANY—Prairie Farms Dairy, Inc.; U.S. Private, pg. 879
HOLLYMATIC CORPORATION; U.S. Private, pg. 535
HOLSTEIN AND KAPPERT GMBH—Klockner-Werke AG; Int'l, pg. 737
HOSOKAWA MICRON CORPORATION; Int'l, pg. 635
O.G. HOYER A/S—Tetra Laval Group; Int'l, pg. 1378
INGERSOLL-RAND COMPANY; U.S. Public, pg. 876
JORDON COMMERCIAL REFRIGERATOR CO.; U.S. Private, pg. 599
KATY INDUSTRIES, INC.; U.S. Public, pg. 944
KOCH SUPPLIES INC.; U.S. Private, pg. 628
KRUPP INDUSTRIES INDIA LTD.—Fried. Krupp AG; Int'l, pg. 511
KRUPP MASCHINENTECHNIK GMBH—Fried. Krupp AG; Int'l, pg. 510
T.W. KUTTER, INC.—Tetra Laval Group; Int'l, pg. 1378
KYOTO MACHINERY CO. LTD.—Tetra Laval Group; Int'l, pg. 1380
LOISELET INTERNATIONAL S.A.—Groupe Strafor Facom; Int'l, pg. 570
MALLET & CO.; U.S. Private, pg. 698
MANUS (GREAT BRITAIN) LTD.—Tetra Laval Group; Int'l, pg. 1380
MARK S.R.L.—Tetra Laval Group; Int'l, pg. 1378
THE MIDDLEBY CORPORATION; U.S. Public, pg. 1109
MIDDLEBY MARSHALL/CTX—The Middleby Corporation; U.S. Public, pg. 1110
MINN-DAK GROWERS, LTD.; U.S. Private, pg. 750
NDS—Nestle S.A.; Int'l, pg. 918
NESTLE DAIRY SYSTEMS-PACKAGING/MACHINERY DIVISION—Nestle S.A.; Int'l, pg. 918
OWL AG LOGISTIK-SYSTEME—Georg Fischer Ltd.; Int'l, pg. 490
PARAMOUNT CITRUS ASSOCIATION—Roll International Corporation; U.S. Private, pg. 941
PAVAILLER EQUIPEMENT S.A.—Financiere Equipment S.A.; Int'l, pg. 485
PNEUMATIC SCALE CORPORATION—Barry-Wehmiller Company; U.S. Private, pg. 118
PREMARK FOOD EQUIPMENT GROUP—Premark International, Inc.; U.S. Public, pg. 1322
PURE PULSE TECHNOLOGIES, INC.—Maxwell Technologies, Inc.; U.S. Public, pg. 1062
QUALHEIM, INC.—CTS Corporation; U.S. Public, pg. 286
SALVIS AG—Brauerei Eichhof; Int'l, pg. 213
SCHMALBACH-LUBECA AG; Int'l, pg. 1206
SEITZ ENZINGER NOLL—Klockner-Werke AG; Int'l, pg. 737

SEQUA CAN MACHINERY-WEST COAST OPERATIONS—Sequa Corporation; *U.S. Public*, pg. 1458
SILVER-WEIBULL—Gencor Industries, Inc.; *U.S. Public*, pg. 705
SILVER-WEIBULL AB.—Gencor Industries, Inc.; *U.S. Public*, *pg. 705*
SOCIETA ALFA-LAVAL, S.P.A.—Tetra Laval Group; *Int'l*, pg. 1378
SOUTHBEND—The Middleby Corporation; *U.S. Public*, pg. 1110
SPECIALTY EQUIPMENT COMPANIES INC.; *U.S. Public*, pg. 1496
STANLEY KNIGHT CORPORATION; *U.S. Private*, pg. 1033
STEVENS-LEE COMPANY; *U.S. Private*, pg. 1042
SUB-ZERO FREEZER CO., INC.; *U.S. Private*, pg. 1048
TCC INDUSTRIES; *U.S. Public*, pg. 1554
TAYLOR COMPANY—Specialty Equipment Companies Inc.; *U.S. Public*, pg. 1496
TETRA-PAK PROCESSING SYSTEMS—Tetra Laval Group; *Int'l*, pg. 1379
TRIPLE F, INC.; *U.S. Private*, pg. 1104
UNIVERSAL DAIRY EQUIPMENT, INC.—Tetra Laval Group; *Int'l*, pg. 1379
URSCHEL LABS INCORPORATED; *U.S. Private*, pg. 1129
VULCAN-HART CORP.—Premark International, Inc.; *U.S. Public*, pg. 1322
WARING PRODUCTS—CTS Corporation; *U.S. Public*, pg. 286
WATERFORD CO-OPERATIVE DAIRY & TRADING SOCIETY LIMITED—Avonmore Waterford Group plc; *Int'l*, pg. 102
WEILER & COMPANY, INC.; *U.S. Private*, pg. 1160
WELBILT CORPORATION—Berisford plc; *Int'l*, pg. 188
WERK BAD KREUZNACH—Klockner-Werke AG; *Int'l*, pg. 737
WERNER & PFLEIDERER GMBH—Fried. Krupp AG; *Int'l*, pg. 510
WERNER & PFLEIDERER LEBENSMITTELTECHNIK GMBH—Fried. Krupp AG; *Int'l*, pg. 511
WEST AGRO, INC.-DES PLAINES—Tetra Laval Group; *Int'l*, pg. 1379

3559 — SPECIAL INDUSTRY MACHINERY, NEC

ABB ASEA BROWN BOVERI (HOLDING) LTD.; *Int'l*, pg. 1
ABB METALLURGY AB—ABB Asea Brown Boveri (Holding) Ltd.; *Int'l*, pg. 7
AE GOETZE AUTOMOTIVE—T & N Plc; *Int'l*, pg. 1334
AEC/APPLICATION AUTOMATION, INC.—Sterling, Inc.; *U.S. Private*, pg. 1041
AEC/APPLICATION ENGINEERING CORPORATION—Sterling, Inc.; *U.S. Private*, pg. 1041
AEC, INC.—Harbour Group Ltd.; *U.S. Private*, pg. 500
AEC, INC.—Sterling, Inc.; *U.S. Private*, pg. 1041
AEC/WHITLOCK, INC.—Sterling, Inc.; *U.S. Private*, pg. 1041
AG-CHEM EQUIPMENT CO., INC.; *U.S. Public*, pg. 6
AKO ARMATUREN - VERTRIEKS GMBH—Axel Johnson AB; *Int'l*, pg. 710
A.S.M. INDUSTRIES—Serfilco, Ltd.; *U.S. Private*, pg. 985
ACRISON, INC.; *U.S. Private*, pg. 14
ADMIRAL EQUIPMENT CO.—The Dow Chemical Company; *U.S. Public*, pg. 522
ADMIRAL HEINTZ, INC.—Myers Industries, Inc.; *U.S. Public*, pg. 1143
ADMIRAL HEINTZ, INC.—The Standard Products Company; *U.S. Public*, pg. 1504
AISIN SEIKI CO. LTD.; *Int'l*, pg. 39
AJAX METAL PROCESSING—Cold Heading Co.; *U.S. Private*, pg. 250
AKRON STANDARD DIVISION—Illinois Tool Works Inc.; *U.S. Public*, pg. 865
AKZO ELECTRONICS MATERIALS CO.—Akzo Nobel N.V.; *Int'l*, pg. 48
AKZO NOBEL INC.—Akzo Nobel N.V.; *Int'l*, pg. 47
ALAMO INDUSTRIAL GROUP; *U.S. Private*, pg. 31
ALAMO IRON WORKS—Alamo Industrial Group; *U.S. Private*, pg. 31
ALFA LAVAL AB—Tetra Laval Group; *Int'l*, pg. 1378
ALLEN-BRADLEY INDIA LIMITED—Rockwell International Corporation; *U.S. Public*, pg. 1398
ALLEN-BRADLEY S.R.L.—Rockwell International Corporation; *U.S. Public*, pg. 1399
ALLIANCE AUTOMATED; *U.S. Private*, pg. 38
ALLIEDSIGNAL AEROSPACE GMBH—AlliedSignal Inc.; *U.S. Public*, pg. 52
ALLIEDSIGNAL IRELAND LTD.—AlliedSignal Inc.; *U.S. Public*, pg. 53
ALLIEDSIGNAL TURBO S.A.—AlliedSignal Inc.; *U.S. Public*, *pg. 53*
ALLIEDSIGNAL TURBOCHARGERS, INC.—AlliedSignal Inc.; *U.S. Public*, pg. 53
ALTAIR CORPORATION; *U.S. Private*, pg. 46
ALTUS ENGINEERING (CORSHAM) LTD.—Delta plc; *Int'l*, pg. 390
AMANO CINCINNATI, INC.—Amano Corporation; *Int'l*, pg. 70
AMANO CINCINNATI INC.—Amano Corporation; *Int'l*, pg. 71
AMANO CORPORATION; *Int'l*, pg. 70
AMBAC B.V.; *Int'l*, pg. 71
AMETEK, INC.; *U.S. Public*, pg. 99
AMMCO TOOLS, INC.—Danaher Corporation; *U.S. Public*, pg. 480
ANCHOR CONTINENTAL INCORPORATED; *U.S. Private*, pg. 70
ANDAL CORP.; *U.S. Public*, pg. 111
APEX BROACH & MACHINE CO.; *U.S. Private*, pg. 77
APPLIED MATERIALS, INC.; *U.S. Public*, pg. 123
AQUA CHEM DIVISION—Imperial Chemical Industries PLC; *Int'l*, pg. 663
AQUA-CHEM INC.—Lyonnaise des Eaux S.A.; *Int'l*, pg. 824
ARJAY EQUIPMENT CORPORATION—RJR Nabisco Holdings Corp.; *U.S. Public*, pg. 1355
ARO FLUID PRODUCTS DIVISION—Ingersoll-Rand Company; *U.S. Public*, pg. 877
ASTEC INDUSTRIES, INC.; *U.S. Public*, pg. 141
ATLET AB; *Int'l*, pg. 97
ATLET FLURFORDERZUEGE GMBH—Atlet AB; *Int'l*, pg. 97
ATLET FRANCE S.A.—Atlet AB; *Int'l*, pg. 97
ATLET, INC.—Atlet AB; *Int'l*, pg. 97
ATLET LTD.—Atlet AB; *Int'l*, pg. 97
ATOCHEM CANADA INC.—Elf Aquitane; *Int'l*, pg. 446
AUTO JECTORS, INC.—Group Dekko; *U.S. Private*, pg. 484
AUTOMOTIVE SERVICE EQUIPMENT DIV.—FMC Corporation; *U.S. Public*, pg. 605
AVIMO GROUP LIMITED—Alvis plc; *Int'l*, pg. 70
AXIA INCORPORATED; *U.S. Private*, pg. 103
BOC COATING TECHNOLOGIES—The BOC Group plc; *Int'l*, pg. 121
BALCO, INC.—Snap-On Tools Corporation; *U.S. Public*, pg. 1480
BALZERS DUNNSCHICHT-KOMPONENTEN GMBH—Oerlikon-Buhrle Holding AG; *Int'l*, pg. 997
BALZERS LTD.—Oerlikon-Buhrle Holding AG; *Int'l*, pg. 997
S.A. BALZERS N.V.—Oerlikon-Buhrle Holding AG; *Int'l*, pg. 998
BALZERS S.A.—Oerlikon-Buhrle Holding AG; *Int'l*, pg. 997
BANANZA AIR MANAGEMENT SYSTEMS, INC.—Rapid Engineering Inc.; *U.S. Private*, pg. 910
BANDAG, INCORPORATED; *U.S. Public*, pg. 177
BARMAG MASCHINENFABRIK AG—Akzo Nobel N.V.; *Int'l*, *pg. 46*
BATTENFELD EXTRUSIONSTECHNIK GMBH—MAN Aktiengesellschaft; *Int'l*, pg. 825
BATTENFELD GLOUCESTER ENGINEERING CO. INC.; *U.S. Private*, pg. 123
BATTENFELD GLOUCESTER ENGINEERING CO., INC.—MAN Aktiengesellschaft; *Int'l*, pg. 825
BATTENFELD GMBH—MAN Aktiengesellschaft; *Int'l*, pg. 825
BATTENFELD KUNSTSTOFFMASCHINEN GES. M. B. H.—MAN Aktiengesellschaft; *Int'l*, pg. 826
BATTENFELD OF AMERICA—MAN Aktiengesellschaft; *Int'l*, pg. 825
BEE LINE COMPANY; *U.S. Private*, pg. 129
BERLIMED-PRODUCTOS QUIMICOS FARMACEULICOS E BIOLOGICOS LTDA.—Schering AG; *Int'l*, pg. 1204
BERNINA HOLDING AG; *Int'l*, pg. 189
BERNINA NAEHMASCHINENFABRIK AG—Bernina Holding AG; *Int'l*, pg. 189
BERWIND CORPORATION; *U.S. Private*, pg. 138
BESSER/APPCO—Besser Company; *U.S. Private*, pg. 139
BESSER CANADA, LTD.—Besser Company; *U.S. Private*, pg. 139
BESSER COMPANY; *U.S. Private*, pg. 139
THE BETHLEHEM CORPORATION; *U.S. Public*, pg. 225
BETZDEARBORN INC.; *U.S. Public*, pg. 226
BIRD-KATEMA—Baker Hughes Incorporated; *U.S. Public*, pg. 166
BIRKETT CUTMASTER LIMITED—Carclo Engineering Group plc; *Int'l*, pg. 268
THE BLACK & DECKER CORPORATION; *U.S. Public*, pg. 233
BLACKHAWK COLLISION REPAIR INC.—Hein-Werner Corporation; *U.S. Public*, pg. 805
BOU-MATIC—DEC International, Inc.; *U.S. Private*, pg. 301
BRAKE SUPPLY CO.—George Koch Sons, Inc.; *U.S. Private*, pg. 628
BROTHER INDUSTRIAL SEWING MACHINES DIV.—Brother Industries, Ltd.; *Int'l*, pg. 229
BROTHER INDUSTRIES, LTD.; *Int'l*, pg. 229
JOHN BROWN PLASTICS MACHINERY—Kvaerner a.s.a.; *Int'l*, pg. 773
BROWN MACHINE—Kvaerner a.s.a.; *Int'l*, pg. 774
BRUNNER & LAY, INC.; *U.S. Private*, pg. 176
BUHLER INC.; *U.S. Private*, pg. 179
BUSS AG—Georg Fischer Ltd.; *Int'l*, pg. 490
CAE SCREENPLATES INC.—CAE Inc.; *Int'l*, pg. 237
CMI CORPORATION; *U.S. Public*, pg. 278
CPAC EQUIPMENT DIVISION—CPAC, Inc.; *U.S. Public*, pg. 282
CTI CRYOGENICS DIV.—Helix Technology Corp.; *U.S. Public*, pg. 808
THE CARDWELL MACHINE COMPANY; *U.S. Private*, pg. 209
CARGILL DETROIT CORP.; *U.S. Private*, pg. 210
CARTER DAY INTERNATIONAL; *U.S. Private*, pg. 216
CARVER, INC.; *U.S. Private*, pg. 217
CEMENT EQUIPMENT COMPANY S.A.—FLS Industries A/S; *Int'l*, pg. 475
CHEMINEER, INC.—Robbins & Myers, Inc.; *U.S. Public*, pg. 1393
CINCINNATI MILACRON AUSTRIA AKTIENGESELLSCHAFT—Cincinnati Milacron Inc.; *U.S. Public*, pg. 368
CINCINNATI MILACRON B.V.—Cincinnati Milacron Inc.; *U.S. Public*, pg. 368
CINCINNATI MILACRON INC.; *U.S. Public*, pg. 368
CINCINNATI MILACRON PLASTICS MACHINERY GROUP—Cincinnati Milacron Inc.; *U.S. Public*, pg. 368
CLAUDIUS PETERS AG—Babcock International Group PLC; *Int'l*, pg. 131
COLTEC HOLDINGS INC; *U.S. Public*, pg. 401
COMADUR S.A.—SMH Swiss Corporation for Micro Electronics & Watchmaking Indus. Ltd.; *Int'l*, pg. 1161
COMAU PRODUCTIVITY SYSTEMS, INC.—Fiat Auto SpA; *Int'l*, pg. 483
COMAU S.P.A.—Fiat Auto SpA; *Int'l*, pg. 480
COMPUMOTOR DIVISION—Parker Hannifin Corporation; *U.S. Public*, pg. 1259
THE CONAIR GROUP, INC.; *U.S. Private*, pg. 261
CONTINENTAL EAGLE CORPORATION; *U.S. Private*, pg. 267
COURTAULDS AEROSPACE—Courtaulds plc; *Int'l*, pg. 339
CROMPTON & KNOWLES CORPORATION; *U.S. Public*, pg. 459
CROWN HOLDINGS, INC.; *U.S. Private*, pg. 293
CROWN IRON WORKS COMPANY—Crown Holdings, Inc.; *U.S. Private*, pg. 293
CRYCO TWENTY TWO, INC.—Tosoh Corporation; *Int'l*, pg. 1408
CUMBERLAND ENGINEERING—Kvaerner a.s.a.; *Int'l*, pg. 774
DMD—Dresser Industries, Inc.; *U.S. Public*, pg. 528
DAEHAN CHEMICAL MACHINERY MFG. CO., LTD.—Kobe Steel, Ltd.; *Int'l*, pg. 741
DAIDO HERR ENGINEERING—Salem Group, Inc.; *U.S. Private*, pg. 962
DAVIS ELECTRIC—Siebe plc; *Int'l*, pg. 1240
DAVIS STANDARD CORPORATION—Crompton & Knowles Corporation; *U.S. Public*, pg. 459
DERLAN INDUSTRIES LIMITED; *Int'l*, pg. 395
DETREX AUTOMATION DIV.—Detrex Corporation; *U.S. Public*, pg. 501
DETREX EQUIPMENT DIV.—Detrex Corporation; *U.S. Public*, pg. 501
W.H. DICKINSON ENGINEERING LTD.—Brunel Holdings Plc; *Int'l*, pg. 231
DOMINION MACHINERY CO. LTD.—Brunel Holdings Plc; *Int'l*, pg. 231
DORR-OLIVER INCORPORATED—Mannesmann A.G.; *Int'l*, *pg. 839*
DUPPS COMPANY; *U.S. Private*, pg. 348
DURCO GMBH ATOMAC DIVISION—Flowserve Corporation; *U.S. Public*, pg. 659
DURKOPP ADLER AG—FAG Group; *Int'l*, pg. 468
DURKOPP ADLER AUSTRIA GMBH—FAG Group; *Int'l*, pg. 469
DURKOPP ADLER CR S.R.O.—FAG Group; *Int'l*, pg. 469
DURKOPP ADLER FAR EAST LTD.—FAG Group; *Int'l*, pg. 469
DURKOPP ADLER FRANCE S.A.—FAG Group; *Int'l*, pg. 469
DURKOPP ADLER ITALIA S.R.L.—FAG Group; *Int'l*, pg. 469
DURKOPP ADLER POLSKA SPOLKA ZO.O.—FAG Group; *Int'l*, pg. 469
DURKOPP ADLER R. LTD.—FAG Group; *Int'l*, pg. 469
DURKOPP ADLER (UK) LTD.—FAG Group; *Int'l*, pg. 469
DURKOPP ADLER UKRAINE LTD.—FAG Group; *Int'l*, pg. 469
DURR AG; *Int'l*, pg. 421
DURR INDUSTRIES, INC.—Durr AG; *Int'l*, pg. 421
DYNAPERT INC.—Dover Corporation; *U.S. Public*, pg. 522
EPCO, INC.—Kvaerner a.s.a.; *Int'l*, pg. 773
EAGLE INDUSTRIES, INC.—Great American Management & Investment, Inc.; *U.S. Private*, pg. 473
EAGLE-PICHER INDUSTRIES, INC.; *U.S. Private*, pg. 355
EASTMAN WORLDWIDE; *U.S. Private*, pg. 358
EBARA CORPORATION; *Int'l*, pg. 431
EDELBROCK CORP.; *U.S. Public*, pg. 563
EDWARDS HIGH VACUUM, INTERNATIONAL—The BOC Group plc; *Int'l*, pg. 121
EFFICIENT ENGINEERING CO.; *U.S. Private*, pg. 365
ELECTROLUX, AB; *Int'l*, pg. 438
ELECTRONIC MEASUREMENTS, INC.—Berwind Corporation; *U.S. Private*, pg. 138
ELECTROVERT—Cookson Group plc; *Int'l*, pg. 328
ELITE SEWING MACHINE MFG. CO. LTD.—Aisin Seiki Co. Ltd.; *Int'l*, pg. 39
ELMA ELECTRONIC LTD.—Sulzer Ltd.; *Int'l*, pg. 1305
EMHART INTERNATIONAL LTD.—The Black & Decker Corporation; *U.S. Public*, pg. 233
ENTOLETER, INC.—Lynch Corporation; *U.S. Public*, pg. 1022
EQUIPMENT MANUFACTURING PLANT—Bandag, Incorporated; *U.S. Public*, pg. 177
ERIEZ MAGNETICS; *U.S. Private*, pg. 381
ESTERLINE TECHNOLOGIES CORPORATION; *U.S. Public*, pg. 594
EXCELLON AUTOMATION CO.—Esterline Technologies Corporation; *U.S. Public*, pg. 594
FAG GROUP; *Int'l*, pg. 468
FMC CORPORATION; *U.S. Public*, pg. 604
FMC FOOD MACHINERY GROUP—FMC Corporation; *U.S. Public*, pg. 605
FADAL ENGINEERING COMPANY, INC.—Thyssen AG; *Int'l*, pg. 1389
FAIRBANK BREARLEY—Carclo Engineering Group plc; *Int'l*, pg. 268
FARMERS MARINE COPPER WORKS—Four Winds Investment Corp.; *U.S. Private*, pg. 422
FARREL CORPORATION; *U.S. Public*, pg. 614
FARREL LTD.—Farrel Corporation; *U.S. Public*, pg. 614
FEED SCREWS DIV.—Ampco-Pittsburgh Corporation; *U.S. Public*, pg. 104
FERODO LTD.—T & N Plc; *Int'l*, pg. 1334
FERRO MSI—Ferro Corporation; *U.S. Public*, pg. 619
FISCHBEIN CO.—AXIA Incorporated; *U.S. Private*, pg. 103
GEORG FISCHER DISA, INC.—Georg Fischer Ltd.; *Int'l*, pg. 490
GEORG FISCHER LEICHTMETALL AG—Georg Fischer Ltd.; *Int'l*, pg. 490
GEORG FISCHER LTD.; *Int'l*, pg. 488
FISHER GAUGE LIMITED; *Int'l*, pg. 491
FISHERTECH—Fisher Gauge Limited; *Int'l*, pg. 491
FLEISSNER GMBH & CO. MASCHINENFABRIK; *Int'l*, pg. 493
FLOORDRESS REINIGUNGSGERATE GMBH—Henkel KGaA; *Int'l*, pg. 609
FLOTTWEG GMBH—Mannesmann A.G.; *Int'l*, pg. 836
FLOW ASIA—Flow International Corporation; *U.S. Public*, pg. 656
FLOW EUROPE—Flow International Corporation; *U.S. Public*, pg. 656
FLOW INTERNATIONAL CORPORATION; *U.S. Public*, pg. 656

FLOWSERVE CORPORATION; *U.S. Public*, pg. 658
FLUID MANAGEMENT, INC.—IDEX Corporation; *U.S. Public*, pg. 862
FOCKE & CO. (GMBH & CO.) VERPACKUNGSMASCHINER; *Int'l*, pg. 496
FOOD PROCESSING SYSTEMS—FMC Corporation; *U.S. Public*, pg. 605
FOSTER-MILLER, INC.; *U.S. Private*, pg. 421
FRIED. KRUPP AG; *Int'l*, pg. 507
FULLER COMPANY—FLS Industries A/S; *Int'l*, pg. 475
FULLER COMPANY (ALLENTOWN)—FLS Industries A/S; *Int'l*, pg. 475
FULLER-F.L. SMIDTH CANADA LIMITED—FLS Industries A/S; *Int'l*, pg. 475
FULLER-F.L. SMIDTH (PTY) LTD.—FLS Industries A/S; *Int'l*, pg. 475
FULLER-F.L. SMIDTH S.A.—FLS Industries A/S; *Int'l*, pg. 475
FULLER-K.C.P. LIMITED—FLS Industries A/S; *Int'l*, pg. 475
FULLER-F.L. SMIDTH (PACIFIC) PTY. LTD.—FLS Industries A/S; *Int'l*, pg. 475
GFG CORPORATION—Derlan Industries Limited; *Int'l*, pg. 395
GLS GESELLSCHAFT FUR LOGISTISCHEN SERVICE MBH—Mannesmann A.G.; *Int'l*, pg. 836
GASTON COUNTY DYEING MACHINE CO.; *U.S. Private*, pg. 441
GENCOR INDUSTRIES, INC.; *U.S. Public*, pg. 705
GENERAL DYNAMICS LAND SYSTEMS DIV.—General Dynamics Corporation; *U.S. Public*, pg. 709
GENUS INC.; *U.S. Public*, pg. 732
THE GLACIER METAL CO. LTD.—T & N Plc; *Int'l*, pg. 1334
GOODMAN EQUIPMENT CORP.; *U.S. Private*, pg. 464
GOTAVERKEN MILJO AB—Celsius AB; *Int'l*, pg. 276
GOUGLER INDUSTRIES, INC.; *U.S. Private*, pg. 466
GRANGES METALOCK AB—Electrolux, AB; *Int'l*, pg. 439
HMI INDUSTRIES; *U.S. Public*, pg. 771
HAMILTON DIVISION—Stevens International, Inc.; *U.S. Public*, pg. 1517
HANDLING SYSTEMS ENGINEERING; *U.S. Private*, pg. 499
OTTO HANSEL GMBH—Klockner-Werke AG; *Int'l*, pg. 737
HARBOUR GROUP LTD.; *U.S. Private*, pg. 500
HEATH CONSULTANTS INCORPORATED; *U.S. Private*, pg. 518
HEIN-WERNER CORPORATION; *U.S. Public*, pg. 805
HENNESSY/COATS DIVISION—Danaher Corporation; *U.S. Public*, pg. 481
HERMANN BERSTORFF MASCHINENBAU GMBH; *Int'l*, pg. 617
HERR-VOSS CORP.—Salem Group, Inc.; *U.S. Private*, pg. 961
HOLMATRO, INC.—Holmatro Industrial & Rescue Equipment; *Int'l*, pg. 632
HOLMATRO INDUSTRIAL & RESCUE EQUIPMENT; *Int'l*, pg. 632
HOLSTEIN AND KAPPERT GMBH—Klockner-Werke AG; *Int'l*, pg. 737
HOSOKAWA MICRON AUSTRALIA PTY. LTD.—Hosokawa Micron Corporation; *Int'l*, pg. 636
HOSOKAWA MICRON B.V.—Hosokawa Micron Corporation; *Int'l*, pg. 636
HOSOKAWA MICRON CORPORATION; *Int'l*, pg. 635
HOSOKAWA MICRON ESPANA S.A.—Hosokawa Micron Corporation; *Int'l*, pg. 636
HOSOKAWA MICRON INTERNATIONAL B.V.—Hosokawa Micron Corporation; *Int'l*, pg. 636
HOSOKAWA MICRON LTD.—Hosokawa Micron Corporation; *Int'l*, pg. 636
HOSOKAWA MIKROPUL GMBH—Hosokawa Micron Corporation; *Int'l*, pg. 636
HOUSTON FEARLESS 76 INC.; *U.S. Private*, pg. 542
HUELLER HILLE CORPORATION—Thyssen AG; *Int'l*, pg. 1387
HULL CORPORATION; *U.S. Private*, pg. 547
HURON - GRAFFENSTADEN S.A.—Fiat Auto SpA; *Int'l*, pg. 481
IDAB WAMAC INTERNATIONAL; *Int'l*, pg. 643
IDAB WAMAC PACIFIC LIMITED—IDAB Wamac International; *Int'l*, pg. 643
IRI ISTITUTO RICOSTRUZIONE INDUSTRIALE; *Int'l*, pg. 652
ISI NORGEN, INC.—IMI Plc; *Int'l*, pg. 646
ITW FINISHING SYSTEMS & PRODUCTS PTY. LTD.—Illinois Tool Works Inc.; *U.S. Public*, pg. 868
IDEX CORPORATION; *U.S. Public*, pg. 862
IMETAL; *Int'l*, pg. 661
S.A. INDUSTRIAS VOTORANTIM; *Int'l*, pg. 677
INDUSTRIE STAMPI E STAMPAGGIO LAMIERE BERTO-LAMET-IMPES S.P.A.—Fiat Auto SpA; *Int'l*, pg. 482
INTERNATIONAL SHOE MACHINE CORP.; *U.S. Private*, pg. 572
IONICS, INCORPORATED; *U.S. Public*, pg. 912
IONICS ITALBA S.P.A.—Ionics, Incorporated; *U.S. Public*, pg. 912
ITALIA S.P.A.—Ionics, Incorporated; *U.S. Public*, pg. 912
JANOME SEWING MACHINE CO., LTD.; *Int'l*, pg. 699
JOHNSON CONTROLS, INC.; *U.S. Public*, pg. 932
JOHNSON CONTROLS, INC.—Johnson Controls, Inc.; *U.S. Public*, pg. 932
R.A. JONES & CO. INC.; *U.S. Private*, pg. 597
KATY INDUSTRIES, INC.; *U.S. Public*, pg. 944
KEE SERVICES—Masco Corporation; *U.S. Public*, pg. 1054
KESTER SOLDER—Litton Industries, Inc.; *U.S. Public*, pg. 1004
KESTER SOLDER CO. OF CANADA LTD.—Litton Industries, Inc.; *U.S. Public*, pg. 1004
KETEMA, INC.—KTM Holdings Corp.; *U.S. Private*, pg. 604
KINGSBURY ASSEMBLY MACHINE DIV.—Kingsbury Corporation; *U.S. Private*, pg. 622
KINGSBURY CORPORATION; *U.S. Private*, pg. 621
KLOCKNER ER-WE-PA—Klockner-Werke AG; *Int'l*, pg. 737
KLOCKNER-WERKE AG; *Int'l*, pg. 736
KOBE STEEL, LTD.; *Int'l*, pg. 740
KOBELCO STEWART BOLLING INC.—Kobe Steel, Ltd.; *Int'l*, pg. 740
KOCH ENGINEERING COMPANY, INC.—Koch Industries, Incorporated; *U.S. Private*, pg. 628
GEORGE KOCH SONS, INC.; *U.S. Private*, pg. 628
KOKUSAI ELECTRIC CO., LTD.; *Int'l*, pg. 743
KOMLINE-SANDERSON ENGINEERING CORP.; *U.S. Private*, pg. 631
CARL GUSTAV KRAUSE GMBH—Fried. Krupp AG; *Int'l*, pg. 514
KRAUSS-MAFFEI AG—Mannesmann A.G.; *Int'l*, pg. 836
KRAUSS-MAFFEI AUTOMATIONSTECHNIK GMBH—Mannesmann A.G.; *Int'l*, pg. 836
KRAUSS-MAFFEI CHEMIOMECCANICA S.R.L.—Mannesmann A.G.; *Int'l*, pg. 836
KRAUSS-MAFFEI DIENSTLEISTUNG GMBH—Mannesmann A.G.; *Int'l*, pg. 836
KRAUSS-MAFFEI FRANCE S.A.R.L.—Mannesmann A.G.; *Int'l*, pg. 836
KRAUSS-MAFFEI KUNSTSTOFFTECHNIK GMBH—Mannesmann A.G.; *Int'l*, pg. 836
KRAUSS-MAFFEI (U.K.) LTD.—Mannesmann A.G.; *Int'l*, pg. 836
KRAUSS-MAFFEI WEHRTECHNIK GMBH—Mannesmann A.G.; *Int'l*, pg. 836
KRUPP CANADA INC.—Fried. Krupp AG; *Int'l*, pg. 511
KRUPP CORPOPLAST MASCHINENBAU GMBH—Fried. Krupp AG; *Int'l*, pg. 510
KRUPP GFT GESELLSCHAFT FUR ANLAGEN-, BAU- UND GLEISTECHNIK MBH—Fried. Krupp AG; *Int'l*, pg. 513
KRUPP HOESCH BERUFSBILDUNG GMBH—Fried. Krupp AG; *Int'l*, pg. 512
KRUPP KAUTEX MASCHINENBAU GMBH—Fried. Krupp AG; *Int'l*, pg. 510
KRUPP MASCHINENTECHNIK GMBH—Fried. Krupp AG; *Int'l*, pg. 510
KRUPP POLYSIUS AG—Fried. Krupp AG; *Int'l*, pg. 512
KRUPP STAHL WOHNUNGSBAU GMBH—Fried. Krupp AG; *Int'l*, pg. 512
KULICKE & SOFFA, AG—Kulicke & Soffa Industries, Inc.; *U.S. Public*, pg. 969
KULICKE & SOFFA INDUSTRIES, INC.; *U.S. Public*, pg. 968
LAITRAM MACHINERY INC.—The Laitram Corporation; *U.S. Private*, pg. 643
LAM RESEARCH CORPORATION; *U.S. Public*, pg. 975
LIBERTY MEXICANA S.A. DE C.V.—Aisin Seiki Co. Ltd.; *Int'l*, pg. 39
LITTLEFORD DAY INC.; *U.S. Private*, pg. 671
LITTON COMPONENTS PRIVATE LTD.—Litton Industries, Inc.; *U.S. Public*, pg. 1004
LYMAN—Senior Engineering Group, plc.; *Int'l*, pg. 1222
LYNCH CORPORATION; *U.S. Public*, pg. 1021
LYNCH MACHINERY, INC.—Lynch Corporation; *U.S. Public*, pg. 1022
MAN GHH CORP.—MAN Aktiengesellschaft; *Int'l*, pg. 824
MAN GUTEHOFFNUNGSHUETTE AG—MAN Aktiengesellschaft; *Int'l*, pg. 824
B.V. MACHINEFABRIEK SPAANS—FKI Plc; *Int'l*, pg. 472
M.E. MACK VALVES PTY. LIMITED—Senior Engineering Group, plc.; *Int'l*, pg. 1222
MACTAVISH MACHINE MANUFACTURING COMPANY; *U.S. Private*, pg. 693
MANNING & LEWIS ENGINEERING CO.; *U.S. Private*, pg. 700
MARION MACHINE COMPANY DIVISION—Superior Machine Company Of South Carolina, Inc.; *U.S. Private*, pg. 1055
MARKEM CORPORATION; *U.S. Private*, pg. 704
MARSHALL & WILLIAMS CO.; *U.S. Private*, pg. 708
MASCHINENFABRIK HENNECKE GMBH—Bayer AG; *Int'l*, pg. 172
MASTER APPLIANCE CORP.; *U.S. Private*, pg. 713
MATTHEWS INTERNATIONAL CORP.; *U.S. Public*, pg. 1059
MATTHEWS INTERNATIONAL MARKING SYSTEMS DIV.—Matthews International Corp.; *U.S. Public*, pg. 1059
MATTSON TECHNOLOGY, INC.; *U.S. Public*, pg. 1060
MCCLAIN INDUSTRIES, INC.; *U.S. Public*, pg. 1065
MCCLAIN OF GEORGIA, INC.—McClain Industries, Inc.; *U.S. Public*, pg. 1065
MCDERMOTT INTERNATIONAL, INC.; *U.S. Public*, pg. 1067
MECAKONE OY—Tamrock Corp.; *Int'l*, pg. 1353
MICRONYL-WEDCO S.A.—ICO, Inc.; *U.S. Public*, pg. 854
MID-WEST AUTOMATION SYSTEMS, INC.—DT Industries Inc.; *U.S. Public*, pg. 475
MINEBEA CO., LTD.; *Int'l*, pg. 867
MITSUI MIIKE ENGINEERING CORPORATION—Mitsui & Co., Ltd.; *Int'l*, pg. 878
MITSUI MIIKE MACHINERY CO., LTD.—Mitsui & Co., Ltd.; *Int'l*, pg. 878
MODERN EQUIPMENT CO., INC.—Alco Industries, Inc.; *U.S. Private*, pg. 33
MONSANTO ENVIRO-CHEM. SYSTEMS, INC.—Monsanto Company; *U.S. Public*, pg. 1125
MOTOROLA, INC.; *U.S. Public*, pg. 1136
MULTI-ARC INC.—Saurer AG; *Int'l*, pg. 1198
NAO, INC.; *U.S. Private*, pg. 771
NAPCO, INC.—Thermo Electron Corporation; *U.S. Public*, pg. 1592
NELMOR CO., INC.—Sterling, Inc.; *U.S. Private*, pg. 1041
NEW CASTLE INDUSTRIES, INC.—Ampco-Pittsburgh Corporation; *U.S. Public*, pg. 104
NEW ENGLAND CENTERLESS GRINDING—Delta plc; *Int'l*, pg. 391
O.A. NEWTON & SON CO.; *U.S. Private*, pg. 797
NIEDNER LIMITED—Wajax Limited; *Int'l*, pg. 1485
NIEMANN CHEMIE G.M.B.H.—Safety-Kleen Corp.; *U.S. Public*, pg. 1426
NIHON SCHERING K.K.—Schering AG; *Int'l*, pg. 1204
NIKON CORPORATION; *Int'l*, pg. 931
NIPPON HERR—Salem Group, Inc.; *U.S. Private*, pg. 962
NIPPON NOVELLUS KK—Novellus Systems, Inc.; *U.S. Public*, pg. 1204
NORDISKA BALZERS AB—Oerlikon-Buhrle Holding AG; *Int'l*, pg. 998
NORTON INDUSTRIEPRODUKTE GMBH—Saint-Gobain; *Int'l*, pg. 1175
NOVELLUS SYSTEMS, INC.; *U.S. Public*, pg. 1204
NOVELLUS SYSTEMS KOREA—Novellus Systems, Inc.; *U.S. Public*, pg. 1204
NOVELLUS SYSTEMS, LTD.—Novellus Systems, Inc.; *U.S. Public*, pg. 1204
OERLIKON-CONTRAVES PYROTEC AG—Oerlikon-Buhrle Holding AG; *Int'l*, pg. 998
OLIVETTI SPA; *Int'l*, pg. 1002
OTIS MERLA SYSTEMS—Halliburton Company; *U.S. Public*, pg. 776
OUTOKUMPU CASTFORM OY—Outokumpu Oyj; *Int'l*, pg. 1017
PACKAGE MACHINERY CO.; *U.S. Private*, pg. 832
PARKER HANNIFIN DO BRAZIL INDUSTRIA COMERCIO LTDA.—Parker Hannifin Corporation; *U.S. Public*, pg. 1263
PARKER HANNIFIN ESPANA S.A.—Parker Hannifin Corporation; *U.S. Public*, pg. 1263
PARKER HANNIFIN SA NV—Parker Hannifin Corporation; *U.S. Public*, pg. 1263
PARKER HANNIFIN SINGAPORE PTE. LTD.—Parker Hannifin Corporation; *U.S. Public*, pg. 1263
PARKER HANNIFIN (SWEDEN) AB—Parker Hannifin Corporation; *U.S. Public*, pg. 1263
PARKER HANNIFIN (U.K.) LTD. INSTRUMENTATION PRODUCTS DIV.—Parker Hannifin Corporation; *U.S. Public*, pg. 1264
PEGLER-HATTERSLEY PLC—Tomkins PLC; *Int'l*, pg. 1395
PENNSYLVANIA CRUSHER CORP.; *U.S. Private*, pg. 850
PERFECT EQUIPMENT CORP.—Berwind Corporation; *U.S. Private*, pg. 138
PERSEPTIVE BIOSYSTEMS, INC.—The Perkin-Elmer Corporation; *U.S. Public*, pg. 1279
PETTIBONE CORPORATION; *U.S. Private*, pg. 859
G.M. PFAFF AKTIENGESELLSCHAFT; *Int'l*, pg. 1046
PIPELINE INDUCTION HEAT LIMITED—Weatherford Enterra Incorporated; *U.S. Public*, pg. 1750
PLYMOUTH INDUSTRIES, INC.; *U.S. Private*, pg. 873
PNEUMAFIL CORPORATION; *U.S. Private*, pg. 873
PNEUMATIC DIVISION; INDUSTRIA E COMERCIO LTDA.—Parker Hannifin Corporation; *U.S. Public*, pg. 1264
POLYSIUS CORP.—Fried. Krupp AG; *Int'l*, pg. 512
L. POSSEHL & CO. MBH; *Int'l*, pg. 1063
POWER TEAM DIVISION—SPX Corporation; *U.S. Public*, pg. 1421
PREMIER MILL CORP.—Premier Mill Corp.; *U.S. Private*, pg. 881
QUALITY BEARING SERVICE OF NEVADA, INC.—Varlen Corporation; *U.S. Public*, pg. 1711
R. & H. SYSTEMS B.V.—Internatio-Muller N.V.; *Int'l*, pg. 680
R.A. INDUSTRIES, INC.; *U.S. Private*, pg. 902
R.F.A. GROUP LTD.—Brunel Holdings Plc; *Int'l*, pg. 231
RAILWAY EQUIPMENT EXPORT—Fried. Krupp AG; *Int'l*, pg. 513
RAPID ENGINEERING INC.; *U.S. Private*, pg. 910
REIFENHAUSER GMBH & CO. MASCHINENFABRIK; *Int'l*, pg. 1101
REIFENHAUSER IND. DE MAQUINAS LTDA.—Reifenhauser GmbH & Co. Maschinenfabrik; *Int'l*, pg. 1101
REPSOL S.A.; *Int'l*, pg. 1104
REXAM INC.—Rexam PLC; *Int'l*, pg. 1106
RICHMOND SCREW ANCHOR COMPANY—Ripplewood Holdings L.L.C.; *U.S. Private*, pg. 932
RIMOLDI DA AMAZONIA IND. E COM. LTDA.—Rimoldi Necchi S.R.L.; *Int'l*, pg. 1118
RIMOLDI NECCHI S.R.L.; *Int'l*, pg. 1117
RIMOLDI OF AMERICA INC.—Rimoldi Necchi S.R.L.; *Int'l*, pg. 1118
RO-SEARCH, INC.—Wellco Enterprises, Inc.; *U.S. Public*, pg. 1752
ROADTEC, INC.—Astec Industries, Inc.; *U.S. Public*, pg. 141
ROBBINS & MYERS, INC.; *U.S. Public*, pg. 1393
ROCKWELL AUTOMATION S.A.—Rockwell International Corporation; *U.S. Public*, pg. 1400
ROCKWELL INTERNATIONAL CORPORATION; *U.S. Public*, pg. 1397
ROCKWELL INTERNATIONAL S.A.—Rockwell International Corporation; *U.S. Public*, pg. 1401
ROXON AB—Tamrock Corp.; *Int'l*, pg. 1353
ROYER INDUSTRIES, INC.—Powerscreen International Plc; *Int'l*, pg. 1066
SMS SCHLOEMANN GMBH—MAN Aktiengesellschaft; *Int'l*, pg. 826
SPX CORPORATION; *U.S. Public*, pg. 1420
SVG TRACK SYSTEMS—Silicon Valley Group, Inc.; *U.S. Public*, pg. 1474
SAFETY-KLEEN CORP.; *U.S. Public*, pg. 1425
SALEM CORPORATION—Salem Group, Inc.; *U.S. Private*, pg. 961
SAMES ELECTROSTATIC, INC.—Binks Sames Corporation; *U.S. Public*, pg. 229
SASIB BEVERAGE & FOOD N.A., INC.—SASIB SpA; *Int'l*, pg. 1194
SCHERING ESPANA S. A.—Schering AG; *Int'l*, pg. 1204
SCHERING S.A.—Schering AG; *Int'l*, pg. 1204
SCHERING (SCHWEIZ) AG—Schering AG; *Int'l*, pg. 1204
SCHERING S.P.A.—Schering AG; *Int'l*, pg. 1204
SCHERING WIEN GES.M.B.H.—Schering AG; *Int'l*, pg. 1204
SCHRADER-BELLOWS PARKER S.A. DE C.V.—Parker Hannifin Corporation; *U.S. Public*, pg. 1261
SEBAGO, INC.; *U.S. Private*, pg. 980
SEIKO EPSON CORPORATION; *Int'l*, pg. 1219

SEMICONDUCTOR EQUIPMENT GROUP—Watkins-Johnson Company; U.S. Public, pg. 1745
SENIOR AUSTRALIA LIMITED—Senior Engineering Group, plc.; Int'l, pg. 1222
SENIOR COLMAN LIMITED—Senior Engineering Group, plc.; Int'l, pg. 1220
SENIOR CONFLOW—Senior Engineering Group, plc.; Int'l, pg. 1220
SENIOR CONFLOW INC.—Senior Engineering Group, plc.; Int'l, pg. 1222
SENIOR CONSTRUCTION SERVICES LIMITED—Senior Engineering Group, plc.; Int'l, pg. 1220
SENIOR CONTROL ENGINEERING LIMITED—Senior Engineering Group, plc.; Int'l, pg. 1220
SENIOR DAVIS DERBY—Senior Engineering Group, plc.; Int'l, pg. 1220
SENIOR ENGINEERING—Senior Engineering Group, plc.; Int'l, pg. 1222
SENIOR ENGINEERING COMPANY-USA—Senior Engineering Group, plc.; Int'l, pg. 1222
SENIOR ENGINEERING GROUP, PLC.; Int'l, pg. 1220
SENIOR ENGINEERING (PTY) LIMITED-SOUTH AFRICA—Senior Engineering Group, plc.; Int'l, pg. 1223
SENIOR ENTEX—Senior Engineering Group, plc.; Int'l, pg. 1220
SENIOR HARGREAVES LIMITED—Senior Engineering Group, plc.; Int'l, pg. 1221
SENIOR MODUCEL LIMITED—Senior Engineering Group, plc.; Int'l, pg. 1221
SENIOR PHOENIX RFS LIMITED—Senior Engineering Group, plc.; Int'l, pg. 1221
SENIOR THERMAL ENGINEERING LIMITED—Senior Engineering Group, plc.; Int'l, pg. 1221
SENIOR TIFT AUSTRALIA PTY LIMITED—Senior Engineering Group, plc.; Int'l, pg. 1223
SENIOR TIFT-VICTORIA—Senior Engineering Group, plc.; Int'l, pg. 1223
SERFILCO, LTD.; U.S. Private, pg. 985
SERVICE SOLUTION—SPX Corporation; U.S. Public, pg. 1421
SIFCO INDUSTRIES, INC.; U.S. Public, pg. 1470
SIFCO SELECTIVE PLATING—Sifco Industries, Inc.; U.S. Public, pg. 1471
SIGMA COATINGS B.V.—Petrofina S.A.; Int'l, pg. 1044
SIGNTECH USA, LTD.; U.S. Private, pg. 999
SILICON VALLEY GROUP, INC.; U.S. Public, pg. 1474
SKANSKA MASKIN AB—Skanska AB; Int'l, pg. 1261
SMITH & SMITH GLASS LTD.—International Paper Company; U.S. Public, pg. 904
SNAP-ON TOOLS CORPORATION; U.S. Public, pg. 1480
SNUGL MFG. CO. INC.—Berwind Corporation; U.S. Private, pg. 138
SOLITEC WAFER PROCESSING, INC.; U.S. Private, pg. 1013
SOMMER & MACA INDUSTRIES, INC.; U.S. Private, pg. 1013
SPADONE INC.; U.S. Private, pg. 1019
SPEEDFAM CORPORATION—SpeedFan International, Inc.; U.S. Public, pg. 1498
SPEEDFAM GMBH—SpeedFan International, Inc.; U.S. Public, pg. 1498
SPEEDFAM LIMITED—SpeedFan International, Inc.; U.S. Public, pg. 1498
SPEEDFAN INTERNATIONAL, INC.; U.S. Public, pg. 1497
SPICER OFF-HIGHWAY AXLE DIV.—Dana Corporation; U.S. Public, pg. 479
SPINNAKER INDUSTRIES, INC.—Lynch Corporation; U.S. Public, pg. 1022
SPIROL INTERNATIONAL CORP.; U.S. Private, pg. 1026
STANDARD CRESSALL LIMITED—Halma p.l.c.; Int'l, pg. 590
STEELWELD FRANCE SARL—Ambac B.V.; Int'l, pg. 71
STEELWELD U.K.—Ambac B.V.; Int'l, pg. 71
STERLING DAVIS STANDARD—Siebe plc; Int'l, pg. 1240
STERLING DAVIS STANDARD - BLOW MOLDING DIVISION—Crompton & Knowles Corporation; U.S. Public, pg. 459
STERLING, INC.; U.S. Private, pg. 1041
EDWIN B. STIMPSON COMPANY, INC.; U.S. Private, pg. 1043
STONE PACKAGING SYSTEMS, INC.—Stone Container Corporation; U.S. Public, pg. 1521
SULZER LTD.; Int'l, pg. 1305
SULZER PAPERTEC INC.—Sulzer Ltd.; Int'l, pg. 1305
SUMITOMO EATON NOVA CORPORATION—Eaton Corporation; U.S. Public, pg. 559
SWECO EUROPE S.A.—Emerson Electric Co.; U.S. Public, pg. 578
TCC INDUSTRIES; U.S. Public, pg. 1554
TE ENERGY SYSTEMS, INC.—Thermo Electron Corporation; U.S. Public, pg. 1592
TECO GENERATION INC.—Thermo Electron Corporation; U.S. Public, pg. 1592
TIFT SA—Senior Engineering Group, plc.; Int'l, pg. 1223
TAMROCK CORP.; Int'l, pg. 1352
TECHNIC INCORPORATED; U.S. Private, pg. 1071
TELEDYNE PORTLAND FORGE—Allegheny Teledyne Incorporated; U.S. Public, pg. 43
THERMO ELECTRON CORPORATION; U.S. Public, pg. 1591
THERMOTECH SYSTEMS CORPORATION—Gencor Industries, Inc.; U.S. Public, pg. 705
THOMAS ENGINEERING INC.; U.S. Private, pg. 1082
TOCCOA METAL TECHNOLOGIES, INC.; U.S. Private, pg. 1089
TRI-CAN INTERNATIONAL, LTD.—Lynch Corporation; U.S. Public, pg. 1022
TRION, INC.; U.S. Public, pg. 1639
UNION SPECIAL CORP.—Juki Corporation; Int'l, pg. 716
UNION SPECIAL G.M.B.H.—Juki Corporation; Int'l, pg. 717
UNION SPECIAL (UK) LTD.—Juki Corporation; Int'l, pg. 717
VDL GROEP BV; Int'l, pg. 1444
VG INSTRUMENTS PLC—Thermo Electron Corporation; U.S. Public, pg. 1595
VG SEMICON LTD.—Thermo Electron Corporation; U.S. Public, pg. 1595
VACUDYNE INC.—Altair Corporation; U.S. Private, pg. 46
VAN DORN DEMAG CORPORATION—Mannesmann A.G.; Int'l, pg. 837
VENTUREDYNE, LTD.; U.S. Private, pg. 1136
VEREINIGTE WEICHENBAU GMBH—Fried. Krupp AG; Int'l, pg. 513
WAH CHANG—Allegheny Teledyne Incorporated; U.S. Public, pg. 44
WAJAX LIMITED; Int'l, pg. 1484
WATERJET CUTTING SYSTEMS DIVISION—Ingersoll-Rand Company; U.S. Public, pg. 877
WATKINS-JOHNSON COMPANY; U.S. Public, pg. 1745
WATKINS-JOHNSON INTERNATIONAL—Watkins-Johnson Company; U.S. Public, pg. 1745
WEATHERFORD CANADA LTD.—Weatherford Enterra Incorporated; U.S. Public, pg. 1750
WEATHERFORD (U.K.) LIMITED—Weatherford Enterra Incorporated; U.S. Public, pg. 1750
WEDCO HOLLAND B.V.—ICO, Inc.; U.S. Public, pg. 854
WEDCO TECHNOLOGY—ICO, Inc.; U.S. Public, pg. 854
WEDCO TECHNOLOGY U.K. LTD.—ICO, Inc.; U.S. Public, pg. 854
WEDTECH INC.—ICO, Inc.; U.S. Public, pg. 854
WEISS GLASS TECHNOLOGIES, INC.—Tosoh Corporation; Int'l, pg. 1408
WEISS SCIENTIFIC GLASS BLOWING CO., INC.—Tosoh Corporation; Int'l, pg. 1408
WELLCO ENTERPRISES, INC.; U.S. Public, pg. 1752
WERNER & PFLEIDERER CORPORATION—Fried. Krupp AG; Int'l, pg. 511
WERNER & PFLEIDERER GMBH—Fried. Krupp AG; Int'l, pg. 510
WERNER & PFLEIDERER GUMMITECHNIK GMBH—Fried. Krupp AG; Int'l, pg. 510
WESTERN ATLAS INC.; U.S. Public, pg. 1757
WHIBCO, INC.; U.S. Private, pg. 1171
WHITING CORPORATION; U.S. Private, pg. 1173
WHITMIRE MICRO-GEN RESEARCH LABORATORIES INCORPORATED—S.C. Johnson & Son, Inc.; U.S. Private, pg. 592
WINDMOELLER & HOELSCHER; Int'l, pg. 1510
X-RITE, INCORPORATED; U.S. Public, pg. 1783
XTEK, INC.; U.S. Private, pg. 1194
XTEK CANADA, LTD.—Xtek, Inc.; U.S. Private, pg. 1194

3561 — PUMPS, AND PUMPING EQUIPMENT

ABB MASCHINENFABRIK MEYER AG—ABB Asea Brown Boveri (Holding) Ltd.; Int'l, pg. 1
ABS BELGIUM NV/SA—Cardo AB; Int'l, pg. 270
ABS BOMBAS LTDA—Cardo AB; Int'l, pg. 270
ABS INDUSTRIA DE BOMBAS CENTRIFUGES LTDA—Cardo AB; Int'l, pg. 270
ABS POMPE SRL—Cardo AB; Int'l, pg. 270
ABS POMPEN B.V.—Cardo AB; Int'l, pg. 270
ABS POMPES S.A.—Cardo AB; Int'l, pg. 270
ABS PRODUCTION S.A.R.L.—Cardo AB; Int'l, pg. 270
ABS PUMP AB—Cardo AB; Int'l, pg. 270
ABS PUMP AB, FAR EAST—Cardo AB; Int'l, pg. 270
ABS PUMP CENTER AG—Cardo AB; Int'l, pg. 270
ABS PUMPEN GES.M.B.H.—Cardo AB; Int'l, pg. 270
ABS PUMPER A/S—Cardo AB; Int'l, pg. 270
ABS PUMPS CORPORATION—Cardo AB; Int'l, pg. 270
ABS PUMPS INC.—Cardo AB; Int'l, pg. 270
ABS PUMPS LTD.—Cardo AB; Int'l, pg. 270
ABS PUMPUT OY—Cardo AB; Int'l, pg. 270
ABS SUBMERSIBLE DIVISION—Cardo AB; Int'l, pg. 270
AKO ARMATUREN - VERTRIEKS GMBH—Axel Johnson AB; Int'l, pg. 710
APV GAULIN—Siebe plc; Int'l, pg. 1241
APV GAULIN GMBH—Siebe plc; Int'l, pg. 1241
APV GAULIN INC.—Siebe plc; Int'l, pg. 1241
APV U.K. PLC—Siebe plc; Int'l, pg. 1240
A.S.M. INDUSTRIES—Serfilco, Ltd.; U.S. Private, pg. 985
AEROQUIP-VICKERS, INC.; U.S. Public, pg. 24
AGRICULTURAL MACHINERY DIV.—FMC Corporation; U.S. Public, pg. 605
A. AHLSTROM CORPORATION; Int'l, pg. 32
AHLSTROM MACHINERY LTD.—A. Ahlstrom Corporation; Int'l, pg. 35
AHLSTROM MACHINERY MANTTA PUMP FACTORY—A. Ahlstrom Corporation; Int'l, pg. 33
AHLSTROM MACHINERY PUMP INDUSTRY—A. Ahlstrom Corporation; Int'l, pg. 34
AHLSTROM MACHINERY PUMPS INC.—A. Ahlstrom Corporation; Int'l, pg. 33
AHLSTROM PROCESS EQUIPMENT INC. PUMP FACTORY—A. Ahlstrom Corporation; Int'l, pg. 34
ALFA-LAVAL CO. LTD.—Tetra Laval Group; Int'l, pg. 1380
ARO FLUID PRODUCTS DIVISION—Ingersoll-Rand Company; U.S. Public, pg. 877
ARO GMBH—Ingersoll-Rand Company; U.S. Public, pg. 877
N.V. ARO S.A.—Ingersoll-Rand Company; U.S. Public, pg. 877
ASSOCIATED FUEL PUMP SYSTEMS CORP.—Robert Bosch GmbH; Int'l, pg. 205
AURORA PUMP—General Signal Corporation; U.S. Public, pg. 726
BW/IP INTERNATIONAL, INC.—Flowserve Corporation; U.S. Public, pg. 658
BAKER HUGHES PROCESS SYSTEMS COMPANY—Baker Hughes Incorporated; U.S. Public, pg. 166
BARNES PUMPS, INC.—Crane Co.; U.S. Public, pg. 457
BELL-ESCHER WYSS LTD.—Sulzer Ltd.; Int'l, pg. 1305
BIJUR LUBRICATING CORPORATION; U.S. Private, pg. 143
BOMBAS GOULDS DE MEXICO, S.A. DE C.V.—ITT Industries, Inc.; U.S. Public, pg. 861
ROBERT BOSCH FLUID POWER CORPORATION—Robert Bosch GmbH; Int'l, pg. 204
BRAN & LUEBBE (G.B.) LTD.—Tetra Laval Group; Int'l, pg. 1380
BROWN & SHARPE MANUFACTURING COMPANY; U.S. Public, pg. 260
CGF INDUSTRIES; U.S. Private, pg. 194
CTI CRYOGENICS DIV.—Helix Technology Corp.; U.S. Public, pg. 808
CAMCO INTERNATIONAL INC.; U.S. Public, pg. 297
CAMCO INTERNATIONAL INC.—Camco International Inc.; U.S. Public, pg. 298
CARDO PUMP AB—Cardo AB; Int'l, pg. 270
J.C. CARTER COMPANY, INC.—Argo-Tech Corporation; U.S. Private, pg. 81
CAT PUMPS CORPORATION—Diversified Dynamics Corporation; U.S. Private, pg. 336
CAT PUMPS DEUTSCHLAND GMBH—Diversified Dynamics Corporation; U.S. Private, pg. 336
CAT PUMPS (UK) LTD.—Diversified Dynamics Corporation; U.S. Private, pg. 336
CHANDLER EVANS CONTROL SYSTEMS DIVISION—Coltec Holdings Inc; U.S. Public, pg. 401
CHEMPUMP—Crane Co.; U.S. Public, pg. 456
A.W. CHESTERTON COMPANY; U.S. Private, pg. 234
CHILTEM GROUP SAM—Alpha Omikron Limited; Int'l, pg. 65
CLIMATEMASTER CORP.—LSB Industries, Inc.; U.S. Public, pg. 970
COLTEC AUTOMOTIVE DIVISION—Coltec Holdings Inc; U.S. Public, pg. 401
COMMERCIAL HYDRAULICS KEELAVITE, LTD.—Commercial Intertech Corp.; U.S. Public, pg. 411
COMMERCIAL HYDRAULICS PTY. LTD.—Commercial Intertech Corp.; U.S. Public, pg. 411
COMMERCIAL INTERTECH DO BRASIL LTDA.—Commercial Intertech Corp.; U.S. Public, pg. 411
COMMERCIAL INTERTECH LTD.—Commercial Intertech Corp.; U.S. Public, pg. 411
COMMERCIAL INTERTECH S.A.—Commercial Intertech Corp.; U.S. Public, pg. 411
COMPONENTA BENELUX B.V.—Trelleborg AB; Int'l, pg. 1421
COMPONENTA INTERNATIONAL B.V.—Trelleborg AB; Int'l, pg. 1421
CONTINENTAL MACHINES, INC.; U.S. Private, pg. 268
CORKEN, INC.—IDEX Corporation; U.S. Public, pg. 862
CRANE AUSTRALIA PTY. LTD.—Crane Co.; U.S. Public, pg. 457
CRANE CO.; U.S. Public, pg. 456
CRANE DEMING PUMPS—Crane Co.; U.S. Public, pg. 457
CRANE LIMITED U.K.—Crane Co.; U.S. Public, pg. 458
CRANE PUMPS & SYSTEMS INC.—Crane Co.; U.S. Public, pg. 457
CROLL-REYNOLDS COMPANY, INC.; U.S. Private, pg. 290
DEMPSTER INDUSTRIES INC.; U.S. Private, pg. 324
DENVER EQUIPMENT PTY., LTD.—Svedala Industri AB; Int'l, pg. 1326
DENVER THOMAS, INC.—Svedala Industri AB; Int'l, pg. 1325
DIVERSIFIED DYNAMICS CORPORATION; U.S. Private, pg. 336
DORR-OLIVER INCORPORATED—Mannesmann A.G.; Int'l, pg. 839
DOSAPRO-MILTON ROY S.A.—Sundstrand Corporation; U.S. Public, pg. 1534
DOVER DIVERSIFIED—Dover Corporation; U.S. Public, pg. 521
DRESSER INDUSTRIES, INC.; U.S. Public, pg. 528
DRESSER OIL TOOLS—Dresser Industries, Inc.; U.S. Public, pg. 528
DRESSER VALVE & CONTROLS DIV.—Dresser Industries, Inc.; U.S. Public, pg. 528
DURCO B.V.—Flowserve Corporation; U.S. Public, pg. 659
S.A. DURCO EUROPE N.V.—Flowserve Corporation; U.S. Public, pg. 659
DURCO EUROPE S.R.L.—Flowserve Corporation; U.S. Public, pg. 659
DURCO PROCESS EQUIPMENT LTD.—Flowserve Corporation; U.S. Public, pg. 659
DURCO-VALTEK (ASIA PACIFIC) PTE. LTD.—Flowserve Corporation; U.S. Public, pg. 659
E.V. INTERNATIONAL, INC.—Greenwich Street Capital Partners, Inc.; U.S. Private, pg. 479
EAGLE INDUSTRIES, INC.—Great American Management & Investment, Inc.; U.S. Private, pg. 473
EATON CORPORATION, HYDRAULICS DIVISION—Eaton Corporation; U.S. Public, pg. 557
EATON HYDRAULICS LIMITED—Eaton Corporation; U.S. Public, pg. 558
EBARA ESPANA BOMBAS S.A.—Ebara Corporation; Int'l, pg. 432
P.T. EBARA INDONESIA—Ebara Corporation; Int'l, pg. 432
EDWARDS HIGH VACUUM, INTERNATIONAL—The BOC Group plc; Int'l, pg. 121
ENVIRONMENT/ONE CORPORATION; U.S. Public, pg. 586
EPOXYLITE CORPORATION-RESIN DIV.; U.S. Private, pg. 379
ESSEF CORPORATION; U.S. Public, pg. 592
FILL-RITE DIV.—Tuthill Corporation; U.S. Private, pg. 1111
FLECK CONTROLS—Pentair, Inc.; U.S. Public, pg. 1273
FLINT & WALLING INDUSTRIES, INC.—Masco Corporation; U.S. Public, pg. 1053
FLOJET CORPORATION; U.S. Private, pg. 414
FLOW ASIA—Flow International Corporation; U.S. Public, pg. 656
FLOW INTERNATIONAL CORPORATION; U.S. Public, pg. 656
FLOWSERVE CORPORATION; U.S. Public, pg. 658
FLOWSERVE CORPORATION—Flowserve Corporation; U.S. Public, pg. 658
FLOWSERVE DURIRON CANADA—Flowserve Corporation; U.S. Public, pg. 659

S.I.C. Index

FOSTER ELECTRIC CO. (TAIWAN), LTD.—Foster Electric Co., Ltd.; *Int'l*, pg. 500
FOSTER ELECTRIC (SINGAPORE) PTE. LTD.—Foster Electric Co., Ltd.; *Int'l*, pg. 500
GIW INDUSTRIES, INC.—KSB Aktiengesellschaft; *Int'l*, pg. 721
GARDNER DENVER MACHINERY INC.; *U.S. Public*, pg. 703
GENERAL SIGNAL CORPORATION; *U.S. Public*, pg. 726
THE GORMAN-RUPP COMPANY; *U.S. Public*, pg. 754
GORMAN-RUPP INDUSTRIES DIV.—The Gorman-Rupp Company; *U.S. Public*, pg. 754
THE GORMAN-RUPP INTERNATIONAL CO.—The Gorman-Rupp Company; *U.S. Public*, pg. 754
GORMAN-RUPP OF CANADA LTD.—The Gorman-Rupp Company; *U.S. Public*, pg. 754
GOULDS PUMPS, INCORPORATED—ITT Industries, Inc.; *U.S. Public*, pg. 860
GOULDS PUMPS (PHIL.) INC.—ITT Industries, Inc.; *U.S. Public*, pg. 861
GRACO CONTRACTOR EQUIPMENT DIV.—Graco Inc.; *U.S. Public*, pg. 757
GRAHAM MANUFACTURING CO., INC.—Graham Corporation; *U.S. Public*, pg. 757
GRAHAM PRECISION PUMPS LTD.—Graham Corporation; *U.S. Public*, pg. 757
GRAYMILLS CORP.; *U.S. Private*, pg. 473
GUSHER PUMPS, INC.; *U.S. Private*, pg. 488
HAMWORTHY ENGINEERING LIMITED—Powell Duffryn PLC; *Int'l*, pg. 1065
HAMWORTHY USA, INC.—Powell Duffryn PLC; *Int'l*, pg. 1066
HARLEY INDUSTRIES, INC.—Innovative Valve Technology, Inc.; *U.S. Public*, pg. 880
HARTELL DIV.—Sundstrand Corporation; *U.S. Public*, pg. 1534
HASKEL ENERGY SYSTEMS LTD.—Haskel International, Inc.; *U.S. Public*, pg. 798
HASKEL INTERNATIONAL, INC.; *U.S. Public*, pg. 798
HOLMATRO INDUSTRIAL & RESCUE EQUIPMENT; *Int'l*, pg. 632
HYDRAULICS GROUP—Parker Hannifin Corporation; *U.S. Public*, pg. 1261
HYDROMATIC PUMPS—General Signal Corporation; *U.S. Public*, pg. 726
HYPRO CORPORATION—WICOR, Inc.; *U.S. Public*, pg. 1767
IMO INDUSTRIES INC.; *U.S. Public*, pg. 856
IMO PUMP—IMO Industries Inc.; *U.S. Public*, pg. 857
IPT DIVISION—The Gorman-Rupp Company; *U.S. Public*, pg. 754
ITT A-C PUMP/ITT MARLOW—ITT Industries, Inc.; *U.S. Public*, pg. 860
ITT DOMESTIC PUMP—ITT Industries, Inc.; *U.S. Public*, pg. 860
ITT FLUID HANDLING—ITT Industries, Inc.; *U.S. Public*, pg. 860
ITT FLUID TECHNOLOGY CORPORATION—ITT Industries, Inc.; *U.S. Public*, pg. 860
ITT FLYGT AB—ITT Industries, Inc.; *U.S. Public*, pg. 860
ITT JABSCO—ITT Industries, Inc.; *U.S. Public*, pg. 860
ITW DYNATEC—Illinois Tool Works Inc.; *U.S. Public*, pg. 867
IBEX ENGINEERING CO. LTD.—Tetra Laval Group; *Int'l*, pg. 1380
IDEX CORPORATION; *U.S. Public*, pg. 862
INGERSOLL-RAND COMPANY; *U.S. Public*, pg. 876
INGERSOLL RAND TOOL & HOIST—Ingersoll-Rand Company; *U.S. Public*, pg. 877
IOWA MOLD TOOLING CO., INC.—Intermet Corporation; *U.S. Public*, pg. 894
JACUZZI BROS., JACUZZI, INC.—U.S. Industries, Inc.; *U.S. Public*, pg. 1684
JACUZZI, INC.—U.S. Industries, Inc.; *U.S. Public*, pg. 1684
JEUMONT-SCHNEIDER TRENFORMETEURS; *Int'l*, pg. 706
KSB AKTIENGESELLSCHAFT; *Int'l*, pg. 721
KSB INC.—KSB Aktiengesellschaft; *Int'l*, pg. 721
KINNEY VACUUM COMPANY—Tuthill Corporation; *U.S. Private*, pg. 1110
KOLTEK OY—Tetra Laval Group; *Int'l*, pg. 1379
KOMATSU LTD.; *Int'l*, pg. 743
KOMLINE-SANDERSON ENGINEERING CORP.; *U.S. Private*, pg. 631
LSB INDUSTRIES, INC.; *U.S. Public*, pg. 970
LAWRENCE PUMPS, INC.; *U.S. Private*, pg. 654
CHARLES S. LEWIS & CO., INC.—Weir Group PLC; *Int'l*, pg. 1489
LINCOLN INDUSTRIAL—Pentair, Inc.; *U.S. Public*, pg. 1273
LITTLE GIANT PUMP COMPANY—Tecumseh Products Company; *U.S. Public*, pg. 1566
LOWARA S.P.A—ITT Industries, Inc.; *U.S. Public*, pg. 861
MP PUMPS, INC.—Tecumseh Products Company; *U.S. Public*, pg. 1566
MPL PUMPS LTD—Tetra Laval Group; *Int'l*, pg. 1380
MANNESMANN A.G.; *Int'l*, pg. 834
MARCH MANUFACTURING INC.; *U.S. Private*, pg. 702
THE MARLEY COOLING TOWER CO.—United Dominion Industries, Ltd.; *U.S. Public*, pg. 1676
MARLEY PUMP—United Dominion Industries, Ltd.; *U.S. Public*, pg. 1676
MARSH BELLOFRAM CORP.; *U.S. Private*, pg. 707
MATRA-WERKE GMBH—Linde AG; *Int'l*, pg. 811
A.Y. MCDONALD INDUSTRIES, INC.; *U.S. Private*, pg. 721
A.Y. MCDONALD MFG. CO.—A.Y. McDonald Industries, Inc.; *U.S. Private*, pg. 721
MCNALLY INDUSTRIES, INC.; *U.S. Private*, pg. 724
GEORGE MELLER LTD.—Axel Johnson AB; *Int'l*, pg. 712
MET-PRO CORPORATION; *U.S. Public*, pg. 1100
MICROPUMP CORPORATION—IDEX Corporation; *U.S. Public*, pg. 862
MIKUNI CORPORATION; *Int'l*, pg. 867
MILTON ROY COMPANY—Sundstrand Corporation; *U.S. Public*, pg. 1534
MUNICIPAL BUSINESS UNIT—ITT Industries, Inc.; *U.S. Public*, pg. 861
F.E. MYERS—Pentair, Inc.; *U.S. Public*, pg. 1273
F.E. MYERS (CANADA) LTD./LTEE.—Pentair, Inc.; *U.S. Public*, pg. 1274
NETZSCH INCORPORATED; *U.S. Private*, pg. 792
NICHOLS PORTLAND DIV.—Parker Hannifin Corporation; *U.S. Public*, pg. 1260
NIHON-PALL LTD.—Pall Corporation; *U.S. Public*, pg. 1254
NUOVO PIGNONE S.P.A.; *Int'l*, pg. 990
PALL EUROPE LTD.—Pall Corporation; *U.S. Public*, pg. 1254
PARKER HANNIFIN SPA—Parker Hannifin Corporation; *U.S. Public*, pg. 1263
PARKER/ZENITH—Parker Hannifin Corporation; *U.S. Public*, pg. 1264
PATTERSON PUMP COMPANY—The Gorman-Rupp Company; *U.S. Public*, pg. 754
PEERLESS PUMP—TBG Management S.A.M.; *Int'l*, pg. 1335
PENTAIR, INC.; *U.S. Public*, pg. 1273
PHILIP INDUSTRIAL SERVICES GROUP—Philip Services Corp.; *Int'l*, pg. 1050
PNEUMAFIL CORPORATION; *U.S. Private*, pg. 873
PULLEN PUMPS DIVISION—Cardo AB; *Int'l*, pg. 271
PULSAFEEDER INC.—IDEX Corporation; *U.S. Public*, pg. 862
PUMPEX GMBH—Cardo AB; *Int'l*, pg. 271
PUMPEX INC.—Cardo AB; *Int'l*, pg. 270
PUMPEX S.A.R.L.—Cardo AB; *Int'l*, pg. 271
PUTZMEISTER, INC.; *U.S. Private*, pg. 896
R.A. INDUSTRIES, INC.; *U.S. Private*, pg. 902
REAGAN EQUIPMENT COMPANY, INC.; *U.S. Private*, pg. 913
RICHARDS INDUSTRIES, INC.; *U.S. Private*, pg. 929
RIMA AB—Cardo AB; *Int'l*, pg. 270
ROBBINS & MYERS, INC.; *U.S. Public*, pg. 1393
ROBOT POMPEN B.V.—Trelleborg AB; *Int'l*, pg. 1421
ROEHLEN INDUSTRIES PTY. LTD. PROCON PUMP DIV.—Standex International Corporation; *U.S. Public*, pg. 1507
ROLLEPAAL B.V.—Royal Dutch/Shell Group of Companies; *Int'l*, pg. 1136
ROPER INDUSTRIES, INC.; *U.S. Public*, pg. 1405
SLD PUMPS LIMITED—SLD Holdings Ltd.; *Int'l*, pg. 1160
SSP PUMPS LTD.—Tetra Laval Group; *Int'l*, pg. 1380
SANYO INDUSTRIES DEUTSCHLAND GMBH—Sanyo Electric Co., Ltd.; *Int'l*, pg. 1192
SAUER-SUNDSTRAND—Sauer Sundstrand Gmbh & Co.; *Int'l*, pg. 1198
SAUER-SUNDSTRAND COMPANY—Sauer Sundstrand Gmbh & Co.; *Int'l*, pg. 1198
SAUER SUNDSTRAND GMBH & CO.; *Int'l*, pg. 1198
SCHWING AMERICA INC.—Schwing Gmbh; *Int'l*, pg. 1211
SCHWING AMERICA, INC., SLUDGE PUMP DIV.—Schwing Gmbh; *Int'l*, pg. 1211
F.W. SCHWING GMBH—Schwing Gmbh; *Int'l*, pg. 1211
SCHWING GMBH; *Int'l*, pg. 1211
SELLERS CLEANING SYSTEMS—Crane Co.; *U.S. Public*, pg. 457
SERFILCO, LTD.; *U.S. Private*, pg. 985
STA-RITE INDUSTRIES, INC.—WICOR, Inc.; *U.S. Public*, pg. 1767
STA-RITE WATER SYSTEMS—WICOR, Inc.; *U.S. Public*, pg. 1767
STANDARD ALLOYS & MANUFACTURING—Blue Tee Corporation; *U.S. Private*, pg. 153
STANDEX INTERNATIONAL GMBH—Standex International Corporation; *U.S. Public*, pg. 1507
STANDEX INTERNATIONAL S.R.L. (PROCON DIVISION)—Standex International Corporation; *U.S. Public*, pg. 1508
STATE INDUSTRIES INC.; *U.S. Private*, pg. 1036
STERLING, INC.; *U.S. Private*, pg. 1041
STEWART WARNER CORP. OF CANADA, LTD.—BTR plc; *Int'l*, pg. 127
STRUCTURAL EUROPE—Essef Corporation; *U.S. Public*, pg. 593
SULZER BINGHAM PUMPS INC.—Sulzer Ltd.; *Int'l*, pg. 1305
SULZER BRASIL S.A.—Sulzer Ltd.; *Int'l*, pg. 1305
SULZER (UK) PUMPS LTD.—Sulzer Ltd.; *Int'l*, pg. 1306
SULZER WEISE GMBH—Sulzer Ltd.; *Int'l*, pg. 1306
SUMITOMO EATON HYDRAULICS CO. LTD.-HYDRAULICS DIV.—Eaton Corporation; *U.S. Public*, pg. 559
SUNDSTRAND CORPORATION; *U.S. Public*, pg. 1533
SUNDSTRAND INTERNATIONAL S.A.—Sundstrand Corporation; *U.S. Public*, pg. 1534
SUNSTRAND FLUID HANDLING—Sundstrand Corporation; *U.S. Public*, pg. 1534
SUNTEC INDUSTRIES INC.; *U.S. Private*, pg. 1054
SVANEHOJ INTERNATIONAL A/S—Powell Duffryn PLC; *Int'l*, pg. 1065
SVEDALA PUMPS & PROCESS—Svedala Industri AB; *Int'l*, pg. 1325
TBG SERVICES, INC.—TBG Management S.A.M.; *Int'l*, pg. 1335
TACO INCORPORATED; *U.S. Private*, pg. 1066
TARGET OILFIELD PIPE & SUPPLY COMPANY (TOPS)—Texas Pacific Group; *U.S. Private*, pg. 1078
TOKHEIM CORPORATION; *U.S. Public*, pg. 1620
TOTTORI SANYO ELECTRIC CO., LTD.—Sanyo Electric Co., Ltd.; *Int'l*, pg. 1191
TRI-CLOVER INC.—Tetra Laval Group; *Int'l*, pg. 1379
TRICO INDUSTRIES, INC.—Paccar Inc.; *U.S. Public*, pg. 1247
TUTHILL CORPORATION; *U.S. Private*, pg. 1110
TUTHILL PUMP—Tuthill Corporation; *U.S. Private*, pg. 1111
UNION PUMP COMPANY; *U.S. Private*, pg. 1119
VAPOR—Westinghouse Air Brake Company; *U.S. Public*, pg. 1761
VIKING PUMP, INC.—IDEX Corporation; *U.S. Public*, pg. 862
WAJAX LIMITED; *Int'l*, pg. 1484
WAJAX MANUFACTURING LIMITED—Wajax Limited; *Int'l*, pg. 1485
WARREN RUPP, INC.—IDEX Corporation; *U.S. Public*, pg. 862
WATER SYSTEMS GROUP—WICOR, Inc.; *U.S. Public*, pg. 1767
WATERJET CUTTING SYSTEMS DIVISION—Ingersoll-Rand Company; *U.S. Public*, pg. 877
WATEROUS COMPANY—American Cast Iron Pipe Co.; *U.S. Private*, pg. 52
WAUKESHA CHERRY-BURRELL—United Dominion Industries, Ltd.; *U.S. Public*, pg. 1677
WAUKESHA FOUNDRY INC.; *U.S. Private*, pg. 1154
WAYNE HOME EQUIPMENT DIV.—Berkshire Hathaway Inc.; *U.S. Public*, pg. 218
WEATHERFORD—Weatherford Enterra Incorporated; *U.S. Public*, pg. 1749
WEBSTER COMPANY, INC.—Danfoss A/S; *Int'l*, pg. 377
WEDA PUMP AB—Trelleborg AB; *Int'l*, pg. 1421
WEIR FLOWAY INC.—Weir Group PLC; *Int'l*, pg. 1489
WICOR, INC.; *U.S. Public*, pg. 1767
WILSON INDUSTRIES INC.; *U.S. Private*, pg. 1181
WINTHER & HEIDE'S EFTF. A/S—Dahl International AB; *Int'l*, pg. 359
ZENITH PUMPS DIV.—Parker Hannifin Corporation; *U.S. Public*, pg. 1261
ZOELLER CO.; *U.S. Private*, pg. 1207

3562 — BALL AND ROLLER BEARINGS

ABBOTT BALL COMPANY; *U.S. Private*, pg. 9
ACCURATE BUSHING CO., INC.; *U.S. Private*, pg. 11
AETNA BEARING COMPANY; *U.S. Private*, pg. 25
AMERICAN BEARING DIVISION, INC.—LSB Industries, Inc.; *U.S. Public*, pg. 970
AUSTRALIAN TIMKEN PROPRIETARY LTD.—The Timken Company; *U.S. Public*, pg. 1617
THE BARDEN CORPORATION—FAG Group; *Int'l*, pg. 468
THE BARDEN CORP., (U.K.) LTD.—FAG Group; *Int'l*, pg. 468
BARDEN PRECISION BEARINGS—FAG Group; *Int'l*, pg. 468
BEARING SERVICE COMPANY; *U.S. Private*, pg. 127
BOSTON GEAR—IMO Industries Inc.; *U.S. Public*, pg. 857
BRENCO, INC.—Varlen Corporation; *U.S. Public*, pg. 1710
BRITISH TIMKEN DIV.—The Timken Company; *U.S. Public*, pg. 1617
CANADIAN TIMKEN LTD.—The Timken Company; *U.S. Public*, pg. 1617
CLYDESDALE JONES CO.—Caparo Group Ltd.; *Int'l*, pg. 265
COOPER BEARINGS—Kaydon Corporation; *U.S. Public*, pg. 946
COOPER ROLLER BEARING CO., LTD.—Kaydon Corporation; *U.S. Public*, pg. 946
DODGE DIVISION—Rockwell International Corporation; *U.S. Public*, pg. 1398
EMERSON POWER TRANSMISSION CORPORATION—Emerson Electric Co.; *U.S. Public*, pg. 573
FAG AUSTRIA WAELZLAGER AG—FAG Group; *Int'l*, pg. 469
FAG BEARINGS CORPORATION—FAG Group; *Int'l*, pg. 469
FAG BEARINGS LIMITED—FAG Group; *Int'l*, pg. 469
FAG GROUP; *Int'l*, pg. 468
FAG ITALIA S.P.A.—FAG Group; *Int'l*, pg. 469
FAFNIR DIV. OF TORRINGTON CO.—Ingersoll-Rand Company; *U.S. Public*, pg. 877
FREEWAY CORPORATION; *U.S. Private*, pg. 426
GARLOCK BEARINGS DIVISION—Coltec Holdings Inc; *U.S. Public*, pg. 402
THE HOWDEN FAN CO.; *U.S. Private*, pg. 543
HUB CITY, INC.—Regal-Beloit Corporation; *U.S. Public*, pg. 1371
HUBER S.A.I.C.—AB SKF; *Int'l*, pg. 1157
HUTCHENSON SEAL CORPORATION; *U.S. Private*, pg. 550
INGERSOLL-RAND COMPANY; *U.S. Public*, pg. 876
JONATHAN MANUFACTURING CORP.; *U.S. Private*, pg. 595
KGM KUGELFABRIK GEBAUER GMBH—FAG Group; *Int'l*, pg. 468
KAMAN INDUSTRIAL TECHNOLOGIES CORP.—Kaman Corporation; *U.S. Public*, pg. 942
KAMATICS CORP.—Kaman Corporation; *U.S. Public*, pg. 942
KAYDON CORPORATION; *U.S. Public*, pg. 945
KAYDON CORPORATION, BEARINGS DIVISION—Kaydon Corporation; *U.S. Public*, pg. 946
KAYDON S.A. DE C.V.—Kaydon Corporation; *U.S. Public*, pg. 946
KENDALE INDUSTRIES, INC.; *U.S. Private*, pg. 614
KOREA HIGH PRECISION CO., LTD.—NSK Ltd.; *Int'l*, pg. 903
KOYO CORPORATION OF USA—Koyo Seiko Company, Ltd.; *Int'l*, pg. 760
KOYO CORPORATION OF USA, MANUFACTURING DIVISION—Koyo Seiko Company, Ltd.; *Int'l*, pg. 760
KOYO SEIKO COMPANY, LTD.; *Int'l*, pg. 760
KRUPP HOESCH STAHLEXPORT GMBH—Fried. Krupp AG; *Int'l*, pg. 515
L & S BEARING CO.—LSB Industries, Inc.; *U.S. Public*, pg. 970
LSB INDUSTRIES, INC.; *U.S. Public*, pg. 970
LACEY MFG. CO.—FAG Group; *Int'l*, pg. 468
MB MANUFACTURING—The Cypress Companies; *U.S. Private*, pg. 300
MPB CORPORATION—The Timken Company; *U.S. Public*, pg. 1617
MRC BEARINGS—AB SKF; *Int'l*, pg. 1157
MANNESMANN REXROTH GMBH—Mannesmann A.G.; *Int'l*, pg. 838

MCGILL MFG. CO. BEARING DIVISION—Emerson Electric Co.; *U.S. Public*, pg. 573
MCGILL MANUFACTURING COMPANY, INC.—Emerson Electric Co.; *U.S. Public*, pg. 573
MICHELL BEARINGS—Vickers PLC; *Int'l*, pg. 1467
MINEBEA CO., LTD.; *Int'l*, pg. 867
MORGAN CONSTRUCTION CO.; *U.S. Private*, pg. 761
NMB CORPORATION—Minebea Co., Ltd.; *Int'l*, pg. 868
NMB SINGAPORE LIMITED—Minebea Co., Ltd.; *Int'l*, pg. 868
NMB THAI LIMITED—Minebea Co., Ltd.; *Int'l*, pg. 868
NMB (U.K.) LIMITED—Minebea Co., Ltd.; *Int'l*, pg. 868
NN BALL & ROLLER, INC.; *U.S. Public*, pg. 1146
NSK-AKS PRECISION BALL EUROPE LTD.—NSK Ltd.; *Int'l*, pg. 903
NSK BEARINGS (THAILAND) CO., LTD.—NSK Ltd.; *Int'l*, pg. 903
NSK CORPORATION—NSK Ltd.; *Int'l*, pg. 903
NSK DO BRASIL INDUSTRIA E COMERCIO DE ROLAMENTOS LTDA.—NSK Ltd.; *Int'l*, pg. 904
NSK LTD.; *Int'l*, pg. 903
NSK-RHP AUSTRALIA PTY, LTD.—NSK Ltd.; *Int'l*, pg. 904
NSK-RHP FRANCE S.A.—NSK Ltd.; *Int'l*, pg. 904
NSK-RHP ITALIA S.P.A.—NSK Ltd.; *Int'l*, pg. 904
NSK-RHP NEDERLAND B.V.—NSK Ltd.; *Int'l*, pg. 904
NSK-RHP UK LIMITED—NSK Ltd.; *Int'l*, pg. 904
NSK RODAMIENTOS MEXICANA, S.A. DE C.V.—NSK Ltd.; *Int'l*, pg. 904
NSK SINGAPORE (PRIVATE) LTD.—NSK Ltd.; *Int'l*, pg. 904
NADELLA U.K. LIMITED—Ingersoll-Rand Company; *U.S. Public*, pg. 878
NADELLA WALZLAGER GMBH—Ingersoll-Rand Company; *U.S. Public*, pg. 878
NEW HAMPSHIRE BALL BEARINGS, INC.—Minebea Co., Ltd.; *Int'l*, pg. 868
NEW HAMPSHIRE BALL BEARINGS, PRECISION PRODUCTS GROUP—Minebea Co., Ltd.; *Int'l*, pg. 868
NICE SPECIALTY BEARINGS—AB SKF; *Int'l*, pg. 1157
NIHON TIMKEN K.K.—The Timken Company; *U.S. Public*, pg. 1617
PELMAC THAI LIMITED—Minebea Co., Ltd.; *Int'l*, pg. 868
PELMEC INDUSTRIES (PTE.) LIMITED—Minebea Co., Ltd.; *Int'l*, pg. 868
PIC DESIGN; *U.S. Private*, pg. 864
QUALITY BEARING SERVICE OF KENTUCKY, INC.—Varlen Corporation; *U.S. Public*, pg. 1711
QUALITY BEARING SERVICE OF MISSOURI, INC.—Varlen Corporation; *U.S. Public*, pg. 1711
QUALITY BEARING SERVICE OF NEVADA, INC.—Varlen Corporation; *U.S. Public*, pg. 1711
REXNORD CORPORATION—BTR plc; *Int'l*, pg. 127
ROLAMENTOS FAG LTDA.—FAG Group; *Int'l*, pg. 469
AB SKF; *Int'l*, pg. 1156
SKF ARGENTINA S.A.—AB SKF; *Int'l*, pg. 1158
SKF BEARING MFRS. PTY. LTD.—AB SKF; *Int'l*, pg. 1158
SKF BEARINGS INDIA LTD.—AB SKF; *Int'l*, pg. 1158
SKF CANADA LTD.—AB SKF; *Int'l*, pg. 1158
SKF CHILENA S.A.I.C.—AB SKF; *Int'l*, pg. 1158
SKF DE MEXICO, S.A. DE C.V.—AB SKF; *Int'l*, pg. 1158
SKF DO BRASIL LTDA.—AB SKF; *Int'l*, pg. 1158
SKF ESPANOLA S.A.—AB SKF; *Int'l*, pg. 1158
SKF FRANCE S.A.—AB SKF; *Int'l*, pg. 1158
SKF GMBH—AB SKF; *Int'l*, pg. 1158
SKF INDUSTRIE S.P.A.—AB SKF; *Int'l*, pg. 1158
SKF KOGELLAGERINDUSTRIE B.V.—AB SKF; *Int'l*, pg. 1159
SKF LINEARSYSTEME GMBH—AB SKF; *Int'l*, pg. 1159
SKF MEKAN AB—AB SKF; *Int'l*, pg. 1157
SKF NORGE A/S—AB SKF; *Int'l*, pg. 1159
SKF OSTERREICH AG—AB SKF; *Int'l*, pg. 1159
SKF PLAIN BEARINGS—AB SKF; *Int'l*, pg. 1157
SKF (SCHWEIZ)—AB SKF; *Int'l*, pg. 1159
SKF SPECIALTY PRODUCTS—AB SKF; *Int'l*, pg. 1157
SKF SVERIGE AB—AB SKF; *Int'l*, pg. 1157
SKF (U.K.) LTD.—AB SKF; *Int'l*, pg. 1159
SKF USA INC.—AB SKF; *Int'l*, pg. 1157
STOCK DRIVE PRODUCTS DIV.—Designatronics, Inc.; *U.S. Private*, pg. 327
TAIWAN NSK PRECISION CO. LTD.—NSK Ltd.; *Int'l*, pg. 904
TATA TIMKEN LIMITED—The Timken Company; *U.S. Public*, pg. 1617
TIMKEN ARGENTINA S.R.L.—The Timken Company; *U.S. Public*, pg. 1617
THE TIMKEN COMPANY; *U.S. Public*, pg. 1617
TIMKEN DE MEXICO, S.A. DE C.V.—The Timken Company; *U.S. Public*, pg. 1617
TIMKEN DO BRASIL S.A. COMERCIO E INDUSTRIA LIMITADA—The Timken Company; *U.S. Public*, pg. 1618
TIMKEN EUROPA GMBH—The Timken Company; *U.S. Public*, pg. 1618
TIMKEN FRANCE, SUCCURSALE DE THE TIMKEN CO.—The Timken Company; *U.S. Public*, pg. 1618
TIMKEN ITALIA S.R.L.—The Timken Company; *U.S. Public*, pg. 1618
TORRINGTON CO.-PRECISION COMPONENTS—Ingersoll-Rand Company; *U.S. Public*, pg. 877
THE TORRINGTON CO.—Ingersoll-Rand Company; *U.S. Public*, pg. 877
THE TORRINGTON COMPANY LIMITED—Ingersoll-Rand Company; *U.S. Public*, pg. 878
TORRINGTON GMBH—Ingersoll-Rand Company; *U.S. Public*, pg. 878
TRANSROL S.N.C.—AB SKF; *Int'l*, pg. 1160
VARLEN CORPORATION; *U.S. Public*, pg. 1710
WAUKESHA BEARINGS CORP.—Dover Corporation; *U.S. Public*, pg. 521
WINSTED PRECISION BALL CO.—FAG Group; *Int'l*, pg. 468

3563 — AIR & GAS COMPRESSORS

ABB TRALLFA ROBOT A/S—ABB Asea Brown Boveri (Holding) Ltd.; *Int'l*, pg. 8
ASF THOMAS—Thomas Industries Inc.; *U.S. Public*, pg. 1599
ACHESON INTERNATIONAL S.A.-EQUIPMENT DIV.—Acheson Industries, Inc.; *U.S. Private*, pg. 12
AIRTEC DIVISION—Atlas Copco AB; *Int'l*, pg. 96
ANDERSEN 2000 INC.—Crown Andersen Inc.; *U.S. Public*, pg. 462
ARIEL CORPORATION; *U.S. Private*, pg. 81
ATLAS COPCO AB; *Int'l*, pg. 95
ATLAS COPCO ACT—Atlas Copco AB; *Int'l*, pg. 96
ATLAS COPCO AIRPOWER N.V.—Atlas Copco AB; *Int'l*, pg. 96
ATLAS COPCO COMPRESSOR INTERNATIONAL—Atlas Copco AB; *Int'l*, pg. 96
ATLAS COPCO COMPRESSORS, INC.—Atlas Copco AB; *Int'l*, pg. 96
ATLAS COPCO COMPTEC INC.—Atlas Copco AB; *Int'l*, pg. 96
ATLAS COPCO NORTH AMERICA INC.—Atlas Copco AB; *Int'l*, pg. 96
ATOMI CORP.—Dugan Production Corp.; *U.S. Private*, pg. 345
BOC DO BRASIL LTDA.—The BOC Group plc; *Int'l*, pg. 121
BALZERS DUNNSCHICHT-KOMPONENTEN GMBH—Oerlikon-Buhrle Holding AG; *Int'l*, pg. 997
BALZERS LTD.—Oerlikon-Buhrle Holding AG; *Int'l*, pg. 997
S.A. BALZERS N.V.—Oerlikon-Buhrle Holding AG; *Int'l*, pg. 998
BALZERS S.A.—Oerlikon-Buhrle Holding AG; *Int'l*, pg. 997
BELLISS & MORCOM—Powell Duffryn PLC; *Int'l*, pg. 1065
BELLISS & MORCOM INDIA—Powell Duffryn PLC; *Int'l*, pg. 1065
BELLISS & MORCOM (USA) INC.—Powell Duffryn PLC; *Int'l*, pg. 1065
BINKS SAMES CORPORATION; *U.S. Public*, pg. 229
BRISTOL COMPRESSORS, INC.—York International Corporation; *U.S. Public*, pg. 1788
CAMPBELL HAUSFELD DIVISION OF SCOTT FETZER—Berkshire Hathaway Inc.; *U.S. Public*, pg. 217
CHAMPION PNEUMATIC MACHINERY CO., INC.; *U.S. Private*, pg. 228
CHICAGO PNEUMATIC TOOL COMPANY—Atlas Copco AB; *Int'l*, pg. 96
COLEMAN POWERMATE COMPRESSORS—MacAndrews & Forbes Holdings Inc.; *U.S. Private*, pg. 691
COLTEC HOLDINGS INC; *U.S. Public*, pg. 401
COMPANIA INGERSOLL ESPANOLA, S.A.—Ingersoll-Rand Company; *U.S. Public*, pg. 878
C. LEE COOK DIV.—Dover Corporation; *U.S. Public*, pg. 521
COPELAND CANADA, LTD.—Emerson Electric Co.; *U.S. Public*, pg. 576
CORKEN, INC.—IDEX Corporation; *U.S. Public*, pg. 862
CROLL-REYNOLDS COMPANY, INC.; *U.S. Private*, pg. 290
CROWN ANDERSEN INC.; *U.S. Public*, pg. 462
CURTIS-TOLEDO, INC.; *U.S. Private*, pg. 298
D.W.M COPELAND G.M.B.H.—Emerson Electric Co.; *U.S. Public*, pg. 576
DENCO LTD.—AMEC Plc; *Int'l*, pg. 16
DOLLINGER/TECHNOLAB—United Dominion Industries, Ltd.; *U.S. Public*, pg. 1676
DRESSER INDUSTRIES, INC.; *U.S. Public*, pg. 528
DRESSER-RAND CO.—Ingersoll-Rand Company; *U.S. Public*, pg. 877
EG & G ROTRON—EG & G, Inc.; *U.S. Public*, pg. 543
EIS GROUP PLC; *Int'l*, pg. 426
EDWARDS ALTO VUOTO SPA—The BOC Group plc; *Int'l*, pg. 122
EDWARDS HIGH VACUUM, INTERNATIONAL—The BOC Group plc; *Int'l*, pg. 121
EDWARDS HIGH VACUUM INTERNATIONAL—The BOC Group plc; *Int'l*, pg. 121
EDWARDS HOCHVAKUUM GMBH—The BOC Group plc; *Int'l*, pg. 122
ELLIOTT COMPANY; *U.S. Private*, pg. 373
EMPRESA BRASILEIRA DE COMPRESSORES S.A. (EMBRACO)—Whirlpool Corporation; *U.S. Public*, pg. 1765
FINMECCANICA S.P.A.—IRI Istituto Ricostruzione Industriale; *Int'l*, pg. 653
FULLER COMPANY—FLS Industries A/S; *Int'l*, pg. 475
FULLER COMPANY (MANHEIM)—FLS Industries A/S; *Int'l*, pg. 475
GARDNER DENVER MACHINERY INC.; *U.S. Public*, pg. 703
GARLOCK SEALING TECHNOLOGIES—Coltec Holdings Inc; *U.S. Public*, pg. 402
GRACO INC.; *U.S. Public*, pg. 756
GRAHAM CORPORATION; *U.S. Public*, pg. 757
HADEN DRYSYS LTD.—Haden Maclellan Holdings plc; *Int'l*, pg. 585
HADEN FRANCE S.A.—Haden Maclellan Holdings plc; *Int'l*, pg. 586
HADEN GMBH—Haden Maclellan Holdings plc; *Int'l*, pg. 586
HAMWORTHY COMPRESSOR SYSTEMS LIMITED—Powell Duffryn PLC; *Int'l*, pg. 1065
HAMWORTHY ENGINEERING LIMITED—Powell Duffryn PLC; *Int'l*, pg. 1065
HAMWORTHY USA, INC.—Powell Duffryn PLC; *Int'l*, pg. 1066
HARBOUR GROUP LTD.; *U.S. Private*, pg. 500
HARLEY INDUSTRIES, INC.—Innovative Valve Technology, Inc.; *U.S. Public*, pg. 880
HELIX TECHNOLOGY CORP.; *U.S. Public*, pg. 808
HOLSET ENGINEERING CO. INC.—Cummins Engine Company, Inc.; *U.S. Public*, pg. 468
HOWDEN GROUP CANADA LIMITED—Howden Group Plc; *Int'l*, pg. 636
HOWDEN GROUP PLC; *Int'l*, pg. 636
JAMES HOWDEN AMERICA INC.—Howden Group Plc; *Int'l*, pg. 636
IMI PLC; *Int'l*, pg. 646
ITW DYNATEC—Illinois Tool Works Inc.; *U.S. Public*, pg. 867
INGERSOLL-RAND AIR CENTERS—Ingersoll-Rand Company; *U.S. Public*, pg. 876
INGERSOLL-RAND (AUSTRALIA) PROPRIETARY LTD.—Ingersoll-Rand Company; *U.S. Public*, pg. 878
INGERSOLL-RAND CANADA, INC.—Ingersoll-Rand Company; *U.S. Public*, pg. 878
INGERSOLL-RAND CO., SOUTH AFRICA (PROPRIETARY) LTD.—Ingersoll-Rand Company; *U.S. Public*, pg. 878
INGERSOLL-RAND COMPANY; *U.S. Public*, pg. 876
IOWA MOLD TOOLING CO., INC.—Intermet Corporation; *U.S. Public*, pg. 894
JOSLYN CORPORATION—Danaher Corporation; *U.S. Public*, pg. 481
JOY MANUFACTURING COMPANY (UK) LTD., EAST KILBRIDE PLANT—Harnischfeger Industries, Inc.; *U.S. Public*, pg. 789
JUNG-PUMPEN GMBH—Masco Corporation; *U.S. Public*, pg. 1054
KROLL FAHRZEUGBAU GMBH—Rothenberger Group GmbH; *Int'l*, pg. 1128
LINCOLN GMBH—Pentair, Inc.; *U.S. Public*, pg. 1274
MAKO COMPRESSORS, INC.—Siebe plc; *Int'l*, pg. 1243
MANNESMANN DEMAG CORPORATION—Mannesmann A.G.; *Int'l*, pg. 837
MANNESMANN DEMAG FORDERTECHNIK AG—Mannesmann A.G.; *Int'l*, pg. 837
MAXCO, INC.; *U.S. Public*, pg. 1061
MELNOR INC.—O'Sullivan Corporation; *U.S. Public*, pg. 1234
MIDWEST PRODUCTS, INC.—Huntco Inc.; *U.S. Public*, pg. 849
MIKUNI ADEC.—Mikuni Corporation; *Int'l*, pg. 867
MONTAIR ANDERSEN B.V.—Crown Andersen Inc.; *U.S. Public*, pg. 462
NIJECT—Ingersoll-Rand Company; *U.S. Public*, pg. 877
NORDISKA BALZERS AB—Oerlikon-Buhrle Holding AG; *Int'l*, pg. 998
NORWALK CO., INC.; *U.S. Private*, pg. 807
NUOVO PIGNONE S.P.A.; *Int'l*, pg. 990
PAMCO—Stewart & Stevenson Services, Inc.; *U.S. Public*, pg. 1517
PIGNONE ENGINEERING LTD.—Nuovo Pignone S.p.a.; *Int'l*, pg. 991
PNEUMATIC PRODUCTS CORP.—United Dominion Industries, Ltd.; *U.S. Public*, pg. 1676
QUINCY COMPRESSOR DIVISION COLTEC INDUSTRIES—Coltec Holdings Inc; *U.S. Public*, pg. 402
ROOTS DIVISION—Dresser Industries, Inc.; *U.S. Public*, pg. 528
ROTOFLOW CORPORATION—Atlas Copco AB; *Int'l*, pg. 96
SCOTT SPECIALTY GASES; *U.S. Private*, pg. 977
SERMATECH SOUTHEAST—Teleflex Incorporated; *U.S. Public*, pg. 1570
SQUIRE-COGSWELL COMPANY; *U.S. Private*, pg. 1027
STOKES VACUUM INC.—EIS Group Plc; *Int'l*, pg. 426
SULLAIR CORPORATION—Sundstrand Corporation; *U.S. Public*, pg. 1534
SULZER-BURCKHARDT ENGINEERING WORKS LTD.—Sulzer Ltd.; *Int'l*, pg. 1307
SULZER (JAPAN) LTD.—Sulzer Ltd.; *Int'l*, pg. 1306
SULZER POMPES FRANCE S.A., MANTES-LA-JOLIE, FRANCE—Sulzer Ltd.; *Int'l*, pg. 1306
SULZER-WINTERTHUR GROUP—Sulzer Ltd.; *Int'l*, pg. 1307
SUNDSTRAND CORPORATION; *U.S. Public*, pg. 1533
SUNRISE MEDICAL RESPIRATORY PRODUCTS DIVISION—Sunrise Medical, Inc.; *U.S. Public*, pg. 1536
TAFA INCORPORATED—Illinois Tool Works Inc.; *U.S. Public*, pg. 866
TEXTRON COMPRESSOR COMPONENTS—Textron Inc.; *U.S. Public*, pg. 1590
THOMAS INDUSTRIES INC.; *U.S. Public*, pg. 1598
TIDEWATER COMPRESSION SERVICE, INC.—Tidewater Inc.; *U.S. Public*, pg. 1608
TITAN TOOL, INC.—Harbour Group Ltd.; *U.S. Private*, pg. 500
TOSHIBA COMPRESSOR (TAIWAN) CORP.—Toshiba Corporation; *Int'l*, pg. 1406
TOSHIBA CONSUMER PRODUCTS (THAILAND) CO., LTD.—Toshiba Corporation; *Int'l*, pg. 1406
TRIMAS CORPORATION—Masco Corporation; *U.S. Public*, pg. 1054
UNITED AIR SPECIALISTS, INC.—CLARCOR, Inc.; *U.S. Public*, pg. 382
WAGNER SPRAY TECH CORP.; *U.S. Private*, pg. 1146
WELCH/THOMAS VACUUM—Thomas Industries Inc.; *U.S. Public*, pg. 1599
WINTHER & HEIDE'S EFTF. A/S—Dahl International AB; *Int'l*, pg. 359

3564 — INDUSTRIAL & COMMERCIAL FANS & BLOWERS & AIR PURIFICATION EQUIPMENT

AAF-INTERNATIONAL—AAF McQuay, Inc.; *U.S. Private*, pg. 3
APL CORPORATION; *U.S. Private*, pg. 7
APV VENT-AXIA INC.—Siebe plc; *Int'l*, pg. 1241
ADTEC AB—Celsius AB; *Int'l*, pg. 276
ADVANCE ROSS CORPORATION—Cendant Corporation; *U.S. Public*, pg. 320
ADVANCE ROSS ELECTRONICS CORP.—Cendant Corporation; *U.S. Public*, pg. 320
ADVANCE ROSS STEEL CO.—Cendant Corporation; *U.S. Public*, pg. 320

AIR POLLUTION CONTROL—Air & Water Technologies Corporation; U.S. Public, pg. 29
AIRGUARD INDUSTRIES INC.—CLARCOR, Inc.; U.S. Public, pg. 382
AMER AIR FILTERS—AAF McQuay, Inc.; U.S. Private, pg. 3
AMERICAN AIR FILTERS—AAF McQuay, Inc.; U.S. Private, pg. 3
AMERICAN STANDARD INC.; U.S. Public, pg. 91
ANDERSEN 2000 INC.—Crown Andersen Inc.; U.S. Public, pg. 462
ASTEC INDUSTRIES, INC.; U.S. Public, pg. 141
AUBREY MANUFACTURING COMPANY—Nortek, Inc.; U.S. Public, pg. 1193
AUTOMATIC EQUIPMENT MFG. CO.; U.S. Private, pg. 101
BHA COMPANY, INC.—BHA Group Holdings Inc.; U.S. Public, pg. 161
BHA GROUP HOLDINGS INC.; U.S. Public, pg. 161
BHA INTERNATIONAL GMBH—BHA Group Holdings Inc.; U.S. Public, pg. 161
BAYLEY/FAN GROUP—Tomkins PLC; Int'l, pg. 1398
BECO ENGINEERING COMPANY; U.S. Private, pg. 129
BUHLER INC.; U.S. Private, pg. 179
CAPTIVE-AIRE SYSTEMS, INC.; U.S. Private, pg. 207
CARTER DAY INDUSTRIES (CANADA) LTD.—Carter Day International; U.S. Private, pg. 217
COMP-AIRE—Groupe Strafor Facom; Int'l, pg. 569
CONAIRE DIV.—Tomkins PLC; Int'l, pg. 1398
COPPUS MURRAY GROUP, TUTHILL CORPORATION—Tuthill Corporation; U.S. Private, pg. 1110
CORNING INCORPORATED; U.S. Public, pg. 448
CROLL-REYNOLDS COMPANY, INC.; U.S. Private, pg. 290
CROWN ANDERSEN INC.; U.S. Public, pg. 462
DCE GROUP—BTR plc; Int'l, pg. 125
DENCO LTD.—AMEC Plc; Int'l, pg. 16
DIAMOND POWER SPECIALTY CO.—McDermott International, Inc.; U.S. Public, pg. 1068
DIAMOND POWER SPECIALTY LTD.—FKI Plc; Int'l, pg. 472
DOVATECH, LTD.—Dover Corporation; U.S. Public, pg. 520
DURO DYNE CORPORATION; U.S. Private, pg. 349
DYNAMICS CORPORATION OF AMERICA—CTS Corporation; U.S. Public, pg. 286
EG & G ROTRON—EG & G, Inc.; U.S. Public, pg. 543
EG & G ROTRON INDUSTRIAL DIVISION—EG & G, Inc.; U.S. Public, pg. 543
EAGLE INDUSTRIES, INC.—Great American Management & Investment, Inc.; U.S. Private, pg. 473
ECLIPSE COMBUSTION, INC.—Eclipse Inc.; U.S. Private, pg. 360
ENVIRCO CORPORATION—Trion, Inc.; U.S. Public, pg. 1639
ENVIRONMENTAL ELEMENTS CORPORATION; U.S. Public, pg. 586
FARR COMPANY; U.S. Public, pg. 613
FARR FILTRATION, LTD.—Farr Company; U.S. Public, pg. 614
FARR INCORPORATED—Farr Company; U.S. Public, pg. 614
FASCO INDUSTRIES, INC.—BTR plc; Int'l, pg. 125
FINITE FILTER DIV.—Parker Hannifin Corporation; U.S. Public, pg. 1260
FLAKT, S.A. DE C.V.—ABB Asea Brown Boveri (Holding) Ltd.; Int'l, pg. 5
FLANDERS CORP.; U.S. Public, pg. 648
FLEETGUARD INC.—Cummins Engine Company, Inc.; U.S. Public, pg. 468
FLEETGUARD, INC.—Cummins Engine Company, Inc.; U.S. Public, pg. 468
FLEX-KLEEN CORPORATION—Air & Water Technologies Corporation; U.S. Public, pg. 29
FULLER COMPANY—FLS Industries A/S; Int'l, pg. 475
FULLER COMPANY (CATASAUQUA)—FLS Industries A/S; Int'l, pg. 475
GARDNER DENVER MACHINERY INC.; U.S. Public, pg. 703
GOTEK GMBH—Metallgesellschaft AG; Int'l, pg. 861
GRASEBY ANDERSEN LTD.—Smiths Industries plc; Int'l, pg. 1267
HALLIBURTON ENERGY SERVICES—Halliburton Company; U.S. Public, pg. 776
HILLIARD CORPORATION; U.S. Private, pg. 530
HOWDEN COMPRESSORS—Howden Group Plc; Int'l, pg. 636
THE HOWDEN FAN CO.; U.S. Private, pg. 543
HOWDEN GROUP CANADA LIMITED—Howden Group Plc; Int'l, pg. 636
HOWDEN GROUP PLC; Int'l, pg. 636
JAMES HOWDEN AMERICA INC.—Howden Group Plc; Int'l, pg. 636
HOWDEN SIROCCO, FLUID DRIVE DEPARTMENT—Howden Group Plc; Int'l, pg. 636
HOWDEN SIROCCO, INC.—Howden Group Plc; Int'l, pg. 636
IMC/A.K. FANS LTD.—Minebea Co., Ltd.; Int'l, pg. 868
ILLINOIS TOOL WORKS INC.; U.S. Public, pg. 865
INDUSTRIAL COMPONENTS GROUP—BTR plc; Int'l, pg. 127
INDUSTRIFILTER AB—Trelleborg AB; Int'l, pg. 1422
INDUSTRIVENTILATION PRODUKT AB—Skanska AB; Int'l, pg. 1260
ITEQ, INC.; U.S. Public, pg. 914
JOSLYN CORPORATION—Danaher Corporation; U.S. Public, pg. 481
JOY/GREEN FAN DIVISION—Harnischfeger Industries, Inc.; U.S. Public, pg. 789
JOY MINING MACHINERY—Harnischfeger Industries, Inc.; U.S. Public, pg. 789
KAYDON CORPORATION; U.S. Public, pg. 945
KAYDON CORPORATION, FILTRATION DIVISION—Kaydon Corporation; U.S. Public, pg. 946
KIEKENS B.V., AMSTERDAM—Internatio-Muller N.V.; Int'l, pg. 681
KING COMPANY—United Dominion Industries, Ltd.; U.S. Public, pg. 1676
LAKEWOOD ENGINEERING & MANUFACTURING CO.; U.S. Private, pg. 644
LAMB ELECTRIC DIV.—AMETEK, Inc.; U.S. Public, pg. 100
LAU DIV.—Tomkins PLC; Int'l, pg. 1398
MAN URANIT GRONAU GMBH—MAN Aktiengesellschaft; Int'l, pg. 825
MD PNEUMATICS—Tuthill Corporation; U.S. Private, pg. 1111
MIE, INC.—TRC Companies, Inc.; U.S. Public, pg. 1558
MARSHALL LABS INC.—Du Pont (E.I. Du Pont De Nemours & Co.); U.S. Public, pg. 531
MCLEAN ENGINEERING—Zero Corporation; U.S. Public, pg. 1791
MCLEAN MIDWEST—Zero Corporation; U.S. Public, pg. 1791
MESTEK, INC.; U.S. Public, pg. 1099
MET-PRO CORPORATION; U.S. Public, pg. 1100
MOLON MOTOR & COIL CORP.; U.S. Private, pg. 756
MONSANTO ENVIRO-CHEM. SYSTEMS, INC.—Monsanto Company; U.S. Public, pg. 1125
MONTAIR ANDERSEN B.V.—Crown Andersen Inc.; U.S. Public, pg. 462
NIDEC—Nippon Densan (NIDEC); Int'l, pg. 933
N.O.A. AIRSCREW HOWDEN INC.—Howden Group Plc; Int'l, pg. 636
NITTA-APITRON CO., LTD.—American Precision Industries Inc.; U.S. Public, pg. 90
NORDKLIMA LUFT-UND WARMETECHNIK GMBH—Senior Engineering Group, plc.; Int'l, pg. 1222
NORFI EXHAUST EXTRACTION SYSTEMS GMBH—Charter plc; Int'l, pg. 283
NORGREN CO.—IMI Plc; Int'l, pg. 647
THE NORTH AMERICAN MANUFACTURING CO.; U.S. Private, pg. 803
NUTONE, INC.—Williams Holdings Plc; Int'l, pg. 1499
PEACE INDUSTRIES INC.; U.S. Private, pg. 845
PNEUMAFIL CORPORATION; U.S. Private, pg. 873
PRECIPITAIR POLLUTION CONTROL—Cendant Corporation; U.S. Public, pg. 320
PRECIPTECH, INC.—BHA Group Holdings Inc.; U.S. Public, pg. 161
PRECISIONAIRE, INC.—Flanders Corp.; U.S. Public, pg. 648
REGAL WARE, INC.; U.S. Private, pg. 917
REVCOR, INC.; U.S. Private, pg. 925
ROOTS DIVISION—Dresser Industries, Inc.; U.S. Public, pg. 528
SENIOR ENGINEERING GROUP, PLC.; Int'l, pg. 1220
SIFAN SYSTEMS LIMITED—Smiths Industries plc; Int'l, pg. 1267
SIMCO—Illinois Tool Works Inc.; U.S. Public, pg. 865
THE SPENCER TURBINE CO.; U.S. Private, pg. 1025
SURCO PRODUCTS, INC.; U.S. Private, pg. 1056
SWARTWOUT INDUSTRIES—Tomkins PLC; Int'l, pg. 1398
TEMTROL, INC.—Nortek, Inc.; U.S. Public, pg. 1193
TOMKINS INDUSTRIES INC.—Tomkins PLC; Int'l, pg. 1397
THE TRANE COMPANY—American Standard Inc.; U.S. Public, pg. 92
THE TRANE COMPANY NORTH AMERICAN COMMERCIAL GROUP—American Standard Inc.; U.S. Public, pg. 92
TRION, INC.; U.S. Public, pg. 1639
TRION LTD.—Trion, Inc.; U.S. Public, pg. 1639
TURBO INDUSTRIES—Dreison International, Inc.; U.S. Private, pg. 342
TURBO-LUFTTECHNIK GMBH—Deutsche Babcock AG; Int'l, pg. 399
TUTHILL CORPORATION; U.S. Private, pg. 1110
UNITED AIR SPECIALISTS, INC.—CLARCOR, Inc.; U.S. Public, pg. 382
UNITED MCGILL CORP.; U.S. Private, pg. 1122
VENT-AXIA LTD.—Smiths Industries plc; Int'l, pg. 1267
VOKES LTD.—BTR plc; Int'l, pg. 125
WOLVERINE MASSACHUSETTS CORPORATION; U.S. Private, pg. 1186
XERXES CORPORATION; U.S. Private, pg. 1194

3565 — PACKAGING MACHINERY

ABC PACKAGING MACHINE CORP.; U.S. Private, pg. 3
APV BAKER INC.—Siebe plc; Int'l, pg. 1240
APV BAKER INC., FOOD MACHINERY DIV.—Siebe plc; Int'l, pg. 1240
APV DOUGLAS MACHINE CORP.—Siebe plc; Int'l, pg. 1240
ALFA-LAVAL AGRI SCANDINAVIA A/S—Tetra Laval Group; Int'l, pg. 1377
ALFA-LAVAL SEPARATION A/S—Tetra Laval Group; Int'l, pg. 1378
AVIOCART S.P.A.—The Mead Corporation; U.S. Public, pg. 1076
BWI FORDS HOLMATIC—BWI Plc; Int'l, pg. 130
BWI KARTRIDG PAK—BWI Plc; Int'l, pg. 130
BWI PLC; Int'l, pg. 130
BEDFORD INDUSTRIES, INC.; U.S. Private, pg. 129
BEMIS COMPANY, INC.; U.S. Public, pg. 210
BOBST GROUP INC.—Bobst S.A.; Int'l, pg. 198
BOSCH PACKAGING MACHINERY DIVISION—Robert Bosch GmbH; Int'l, pg. 204
ROBERT BOSCH CORPORATION—Robert Bosch GmbH; Int'l, pg. 204
JOHN BROWN PLASTICS MACHINERY—Kvaerner a.s.a.; Int'l, pg. 773
CMS GILBRETH PACKAGING SYSTEMS—IMPAXX, Inc.; U.S. Private, pg. 558
CADDY CORP. OF AMERICA; U.S. Private, pg. 198
CARISTRAP INTERNATIONAL INC.; Int'l, pg. 271
THE CHANTLAND COMPANY DIVISION—Magna International Inc.; Int'l, pg. 830
CHEMAP, INC.—Tetra Laval Group; Int'l, pg. 1378
CHRONOS RICHARDSON—Staveley Industries PLC; Int'l, pg. 1299
CITRUS MACHINERY ITALY, S.R.L.—FMC Corporation; U.S. Public, pg. 606
CLOUD CORPORATION; U.S. Private, pg. 247
CROLL-REYNOLDS COMPANY, INC.; U.S. Private, pg. 290
DEC ALKAR DIV.—DEC International, Inc.; U.S. Private, pg. 301
DIXIE UNION VERPACKUNGEN GMBH—Continental Can Co.; U.S. Public, pg. 440
EMHART (U.K.) LTD.—The Black & Decker Corporation; U.S. Public, pg. 234
EQUIPOS AGRICOLAS ALFA-LAVAL S.A.—Tetra Laval Group; Int'l, pg. 1377
ETIQUETAS INTERNACIONALES, INC.—Bacardi Limited; Int'l, pg. 132
FMC CORPORATION; U.S. Public, pg. 604
FMC PACKAGING MACHINERY, S.P.A.—FMC Corporation; U.S. Public, pg. 606
FABDEC LTD.—DEC International, Inc.; U.S. Private, pg. 301
FEDERAL INDUSTRIES, INC.—Standex International Corporation; U.S. Public, pg. 1506
FLEETWOOD SYSTEMS, INC.; U.S. Private, pg. 410
FLETCHER SMITH LTD.—Booker PLC; Int'l, pg. 202
FOMENTO ECONOMICO MEXICANO, S.A. DE CV; Int'l, pg. 496
FOOD PROCESSING SYSTEMS—FMC Corporation; U.S. Public, pg. 605
GHM INDUSTRIES, INC.; U.S. Private, pg. 435
GENERAL CIGAR HOLDINGS INC; U.S. Public, pg. 707
GERRARD-OVALSTRAPPING—Enterprises International Inc.; U.S. Private, pg. 378
HULL CORPORATION; U.S. Private, pg. 547
ICOMA PACKTECHNIK GMBH—Korsnas AB; Int'l, pg. 759
ITW MIMA, INC.—Illinois Tool Works Inc.; U.S. Public, pg. 866
IMPAXX, INC.; U.S. Private, pg. 558
KATY INDUSTRIES, INC.; U.S. Public, pg. 944
KLOCKNER-HOOPER PACKAGING MACHINERY—Klockner-Werke AG; Int'l, pg. 737
KLOECKNER PENTAPACK LTD.—Klockner-Werke AG; Int'l, pg. 737
KVAERNER-JOHN BROWN LTD.—Kvaerner a.s.a.; Int'l, pg. 773
LABEL-AIRE A/S—Label-Aire Inc.; U.S. Private, pg. 641
LABEL-AIRE INC.; U.S. Private, pg. 641
LAMB GRAYS HARBOR CO—Enterprises International Inc.; U.S. Private, pg. 378
LEPEL CORPORATION—Inductotherm Industries, Inc.; U.S. Private, pg. 560
LIQUI-BOX CORPORATION; U.S. Public, pg. 1000
LYNCH MACHINERY, INC.—Lynch Corporation; U.S. Public, pg. 1022
MARSH COMPANY; U.S. Private, pg. 707
MEAD EUROPE ENGINEERING, S.A.R.L.—The Mead Corporation; U.S. Public, pg. 1076
MEAD PACKAGING CHILE LIMITADA—The Mead Corporation; U.S. Public, pg. 1076
MEAD PACKAGING PROPRIETARY LTD.—The Mead Corporation; U.S. Public, pg. 1077
MERIDIAN MACHINE WORKS, INC.—Enterprises International Inc.; U.S. Private, pg. 378
MOJONNIER DE MEXICO, S DE R.L. DE C.V.—SASIB SpA; Int'l, pg. 1194
MOJONNIER DO BRASIL INDUSTRIA E COMMERCIO DE EQUIPAMENTOS LTDA.—SASIB SpA; Int'l, pg. 1194
NEW ENGLAND MACHINERY, INC.; U.S. Private, pg. 793
ORTMANN & HERBST GMBH—Siebe plc; Int'l, pg. 1240
OTTO HAENSEL EQUIPAMENTOS INDSTRIAIS LTDA.—Klockner-Werke AG; Int'l, pg. 737
P.S.I. DIVISION—Package Machinery Co.; U.S. Private, pg. 832
PACKAGE MACHINERY CO.; U.S. Private, pg. 832
PACKAGING AND MATERIAL HANDLING DIVISION—FMC Corporation; U.S. Public, pg. 606
PAXAR APPAREL IDENTIFICATION SYSTEMS—PAXAR Corporation; U.S. Public, pg. 1266
PETERS MACHINERY CO.—Katy Industries, Inc.; U.S. Public, pg. 944
PLASTEX EXTRUDERS INC., USA—Enterprises International Inc.; U.S. Private, pg. 378
PNEUMATIC SCALE-AKRON—Barry-Wehmiller Company; U.S. Private, pg. 118
PNEUMATIC SCALE CORPORATION—Barry-Wehmiller Company; U.S. Private, pg. 118
PNEUMATIC SCALE EUROPE—Barry-Wehmiller Company; U.S. Private, pg. 118
PRINTPAC-UEB CARTON GROUP—International Paper Company; U.S. Public, pg. 905
PRINTPAC-UEB CASE GROUP—International Paper Company; U.S. Public, pg. 905
PRODUCTS RESEARCH & CHEMICAL CORP., SEMCO DIVISION—Courtaulds plc; Int'l, pg. 339
PRYOR FOUNDRY, INC.—Case Corporation; U.S. Public, pg. 312
QUALHEIM, INC.—CTS Corporation; U.S. Public, pg. 286
REXAM MEDICAL PACKAGING—Rexam PLC; Int'l, pg. 1106
ROBERTS SYSTEMS, INC.—Derlan Industries Limited; Int'l, pg. 395
SASIB PACKAGING NORTH AMERICA—SASIB SpA; Int'l, pg. 1194
SALWASSER MANUFACTURING COMPANY, INC.; U.S. Private, pg. 963
SANI-MATIC SYSTEMS—DEC International, Inc.; U.S. Private, pg. 301
SASIB BEVERAGE & FOOD N.A., INC.—SASIB SpA; Int'l, pg. 1194
SASIB BEVERAGE UK LTD.—SASIB SpA; Int'l, pg. 1195
SASIB PACKAGING NORTH AMERICA—SASIB SpA; Int'l, pg. 1194
SASIB-WEST—SASIB SpA; Int'l, pg. 1194

SEALED AIR CORPORATION; *U.S. Public*, pg. 1450
SEPARATION TECHNOLOGIES INC.—Cummins Engine Company, Inc.; *U.S. Public*, pg. 468
STANDARD-KNAPP, INC.; *U.S. Private*, pg. 1031
SUPERIOR MACHINE SYSTEMS—Superior Label Systems, Inc.; *U.S. Private*, pg. 1055
SVEDALA PUMPS & PROCESS—Svedala Industri AB; *Int'l*, pg. 1325
T A HOLDINGS LIMITED; *Int'l*, pg. 1334
THOMAS ENGINEERING INC.; *U.S. Private*, pg. 1082
UNITED DOMINION INDUSTRIES, LTD.; *U.S. Public*, pg. 1675
U.S. BOTTLERS MACHINERY CO.; *U.S. Private*, pg. 1124
USINE DE WECKER S.R.L.—Zimmermann & Jansen GmbH; *Int'l*, pg. 1529
VENESTA INTERNATIONAL PACKAGING LIMITED—Caradon Plc; *Int'l*, pg. 267
VENESTA PACKAGING GROUP LTD.—Caradon Plc; *Int'l*, pg. 267
WARING PRODUCTS—CTS Corporation; *U.S. Public*, pg. 286
WELDOTRON CORPORATION; *U.S. Public*, pg. 1752
WELDOTRON DO BRASIL—Weldotron Corporation; *U.S. Public*, pg. 1752
WHITE CAP, INC.—Schmalbach-Lubeca AG; *Int'l*, pg. 1207
X-RITE, INCORPORATED; *U.S. Public*, pg. 1783
ZAZULA PROCESS EQUIP. LTD.—ABB Asea Brown Boveri (Holding) Ltd.; *Int'l*, pg. 6
ZIMMERMANN & JANSEN GMBH; *Int'l*, pg. 1528

3566 — SPEED CHANGERS, INDUSTRIAL HIGH SPEED DRIVES & GEARS

ABB FLEXIBLE AUTOMATION—ABB Asea Brown Boveri (Holding) Ltd.; *Int'l*, pg. 4
ALLING-LANDER—Regal-Beloit Corporation; *U.S. Public*, pg. 1370
ARROW GEAR COMPANY; *U.S. Private*, pg. 85
BHS-BAYER, BERG-, HUETTEN-, UND SALZWERKE AG—Viag AG; *Int'l*, pg. 1464
CGF INDUSTRIES; *U.S. Private*, pg. 194
CINCINNATI GEAR COMPANY; *U.S. Private*, pg. 240
CONE DRIVE TEXTRON—Textron Inc.; *U.S. Public*, pg. 1589
DANA CANADA INC.—Dana Corporation; *U.S. Public*, pg. 480
DANA CORPORATION; *U.S. Public*, pg. 479
DAVALL GROUP LTD.—EIS Group Plc; *Int'l*, pg. 426
DODGE DIVISION—Rockwell International Corporation; *U.S. Public*, pg. 1398
DUFF-NORTON—Columbus McKinnon Corp.; *U.S. Public*, pg. 406
DURST DIV.—Regal-Beloit Corporation; *U.S. Public*, pg. 1370
ELECTRA-GEAR DIV.—Regal-Beloit Corporation; *U.S. Public*, pg. 1370
EMERSON POWER TRANSMISSION CORPORATION—Emerson Electric Co.; *U.S. Public*, pg. 573
THE FALK CORPORATION—Sundstrand Corporation; *U.S. Public*, pg. 1534
A. FRIEDRICH FLENDER AG—Deutsche Babcock AG; *Int'l*, pg. 400
FLENDER CORPORATION—Deutsche Babcock AG; *Int'l*, pg. 400
BRAD FOOTE GEAR WORKS, INC.; *U.S. Private*, pg. 417
FOOTE-JONES/ILLINOIS GEAR—Regal-Beloit Corporation; *U.S. Public*, pg. 1370
FREEDOM FORGE CORPORATION; *U.S. Private*, pg. 425
FUNK MANUFACTURING CO.—Deere & Company; *U.S. Public*, pg. 492
GKN HARDY SPICER LTD.—GKN plc; *Int'l*, pg. 534
GEAR PRODUCTS INC.—Blount International, Inc.; *U.S. Public*, pg. 238
GRAHAM—Danfoss A/S; *Int'l*, pg. 377
GRAHAM TRANSMISSIONS INC/GRAHAM GEAR SYSTEMS, INC—Danfoss A/S; *Int'l*, pg. 377
GRANITE STATE MANUFACTURING CO.—Allard Industries; *U.S. Private*, pg. 36
GROSCHOPP & CO. GMBH EMW ELEKTROMOTOREN-FEINBAUWERK; *Int'l*, pg. 559
GROSCHOPP, INC.—Groschopp & Co. GmbH EMW Elektromotoren-Feinbauwerk; *Int'l*, pg. 559
GROVE GEAR DIV.—Regal-Beloit Corporation; *U.S. Public*, pg. 1370
P.C. HENDERSON LIMITED—Hepworth Plc; *Int'l*, pg. 615
HOFFCO/COMET INDUSTRIES, INC.; *U.S. Private*, pg. 532
HOLEC MACHINES & APPARATEN B.V.—Royal Begemann Group; *Int'l*, pg. 1133
THE HOWDEN FAN CO.; *U.S. Private*, pg. 543
HUB CITY, INC.—Regal-Beloit Corporation; *U.S. Public*, pg. 1371
IMO INDUSTRIES INC.; *U.S. Public*, pg. 856
ITW MAGNAFLUX—Illinois Tool Works Inc.; *U.S. Public*, pg. 866
JOHNSON GEAR—Arrow Gear Company; *U.S. Private*, pg. 85
KURT MANUFACTURING CO. INC.; *U.S. Private*, pg. 637
MANNESMANN REXROTH GMBH—Mannesmann A.G.; *Int'l*, pg. 838
MARTIN SPROCKET & GEAR, INC.; *U.S. Private*, pg. 709
MASTERGEAR DIVISION—Regal-Beloit Corporation; *U.S. Public*, pg. 1370
MIKI PULLEY CO., LTD.; *Int'l*, pg. 866
AB MIKRO-VERKTYG—Investor AB; *Int'l*, pg. 686
MOLON MOTOR & COIL CORP.; *U.S. Private*, pg. 756
NIIGATA CONVERTER CO., LTD.—Twin Disc, Incorporated; *U.S. Public*, pg. 1646
NUTTALL GEAR CORPORATION; *U.S. Private*, pg. 809
OHIO GEAR/RICHMOND GEAR - LIBERTY DIV.—Regal-Beloit Corporation; *U.S. Public*, pg. 1370
OVERTON GEAR & TOOL CORP.; *U.S. Private*, pg. 823
PIC DESIGN; *U.S. Private*, pg. 864
PITTSBURGH GEAR COMPANY—Brad Foote Gear Works, Inc.; *U.S. Private*, pg. 417
POWER TRANSMISSION INDUSTRIES DO BRASIL S.A.—Sundstrand Corporation; *U.S. Public*, pg. 1534
REEVES DIVISION—Rockwell International Corporation; *U.S. Public*, pg. 1398
REGAL-BELOIT CORPORATION; *U.S. Public*, pg. 1370
RENOLD, INC.—Renold PLC; *Int'l*, pg. 1104
RENOLD PLC; *Int'l*, pg. 1103
REULAND ELECTRIC COMPANY; *U.S. Private*, pg. 925
REXNORD CORPORATION—BTR plc; *Int'l*, pg. 127
SAUER-SUNDSTRAND—Sauer Sundstrand Gmbh & Co.; *Int'l*, pg. 1198
SAUER-SUNDSTRAND COMPANY—Sauer Sundstrand Gmbh & Co.; *Int'l*, pg. 1198
SAUER SUNDSTRAND GMBH & CO.; *Int'l*, pg. 1198
SIEMENS AG; *Int'l*, pg. 1244
SIEMENS RT.—Siemens AG; *Int'l*, pg. 1247
STERLING INSTRUMENT DIV.—Designatronics, Inc.; *U.S. Private*, pg. 327
STOCK DRIVE PRODUCTS DIV.—Designatronics, Inc.; *U.S. Private*, pg. 327
SUMITOMO HEAVY INDUSTRIES, LTD.; *Int'l*, pg. 1314
SUMITOMO MACHINERY CORP. OF AMERICA—Sumitomo Heavy Industries, Ltd.; *Int'l*, pg. 1314
TRANSTECHNOLOGY CORPORATION; *U.S. Public*, pg. 1632
TSUBAKIMOTO CHAIN CO.; *Int'l*, pg. 1425
TWIN DISC, INCORPORATED; *U.S. Public*, pg. 1646
TWIN DISC INTL., S.A.—Twin Disc, Incorporated; *U.S. Public*, pg. 1647
VALMET CORPORATION; *Int'l*, pg. 1447
W.G.C. CORP.—Zimmerman Holdings, Inc.; *U.S. Private*, pg. 1206
WARNER ELECTRIC INDUSTRIAL PRODUCTS DIVISION—Dana Corporation; *U.S. Public*, pg. 480
XTEK, INC.; *U.S. Private*, pg. 1194
ZERO-MAX, INC.—Miki Pulley Co., Ltd.; *Int'l*, pg. 866

3567 — INDUSTRIAL PROCESS FURNACES & OVENS

ABB POWER GENERATION INC.—ABB Asea Brown Boveri (Holding) Ltd.; *Int'l*, pg. 3
AICHELIN-STAHL, INC.—Stahl Specialty Company; *U.S. Private*, pg. 1029
AJAX MAGNETHERMIC CANADA LTD.—BBA Group plc; *Int'l*, pg. 113
AJAX MAGNETHERMIC CORP.—BBA Group plc; *Int'l*, pg. 113
AJAX MAGNETHERMIC U.K. LTD.—BBA Group plc; *Int'l*, pg. 113
AJAX SERVICES INC.—BBA Group plc; *Int'l*, pg. 113
ALLIANCE HEATER COMPANY—Watlow Electric Manufacturing Company; *U.S. Private*, pg. 1153
AMTROL INC.—The Cypress Group LLC; *U.S. Private*, pg. 300
ANDERSEN 2000 INC.—Crown Andersen Inc.; *U.S. Public*, pg. 462
ASTEC INDUSTRIES, INC.; *U.S. Public*, pg. 141
AUTOMATIC ASSEMBLY—Research, Incorporated; *U.S. Public*, pg. 1382
BBC BROWN BOVERI S.A. DE C.V.—ABB Asea Brown Boveri (Holding) Ltd.; *Int'l*, pg. 3
BTU ENGINEERING CORPORATION—BTU International, Inc.; *U.S. Public*, pg. 164
BTU INTERNATIONAL, INC.; *U.S. Public*, pg. 164
BALZERS DUNNSCHICHT-KOMPONENTEN GMBH—Oerlikon-Buhrle Holding AG; *Int'l*, pg. 997
BARD MFG. CO.; *U.S. Private*, pg. 116
BUSS-SMS GMBH VERFAHRENSTECHNIK—Georg Fischer Ltd.; *Int'l*, pg. 490
CHESTERFIELD INDUSTRIAL PARK, INC.—Watlow Electric Manufacturing Company; *U.S. Private*, pg. 1153
DESPATCH INDUSTRIES; *U.S. Private*, pg. 327
DETREX CORPORATION; *U.S. Public*, pg. 501
DIELECTRIC LABORATORIES—Dover Corporation; *U.S. Public*, pg. 521
DONLEE TECHNOLOGIES INC.; *U.S. Private*, pg. 339
DORR-OLIVER INCORPORATED—Mannesmann A.G.; *Int'l*, pg. 839
DRIVER-HARRIS COMPANY; *U.S. Public*, pg. 530
ECLIPSE INC.; *U.S. Private*, pg. 360
ELECTRIC FURNACE CO.; *U.S. Private*, pg. 367
ELECTRIC FURNACE GERMANY, GMBH—Electric Furnace Co.; *U.S. Private*, pg. 368
EPOXYLITE CORPORATION-EQUIPMENT DIV.—Epoxylite Corporation-Resin Div.; *U.S. Private*, pg. 379
FAIRBANK BREARLEY—Carclo Engineering Group plc; *Int'l*, pg. 268
FLINN & DREFFEIN ENGINEERING CO.; *U.S. Private*, pg. 413
FLINT MANUFACTURING CO.; *U.S. Private*, pg. 413
FOSTORIA INDUSTRIES, INC.; *U.S. Private*, pg. 421
FULLER COMPANY—FLS Industries A/S; *Int'l*, pg. 475
FUNDICIONES METALICAS, S.A.—Siebe plc; *Int'l*, pg. 1244
GENCOR INDUSTRIES, INC.; *U.S. Public*, pg. 705
GENERAL COMBUSTION CORPORATION—Gencor Industries, Inc.; *U.S. Public*, pg. 705
GENERAL COMBUSTION LTD.—Gencor Industries, Inc.; *U.S. Public*, pg. 705
GENERAL SIGNAL CORPORATION; *U.S. Public*, pg. 726
HADEN MACLELLAN HOLDINGS PLC; *Int'l*, pg. 585
HARROP INDUSTRIES, INC.; *U.S. Private*, pg. 506
HAUCK MFG. CO.; *U.S. Private*, pg. 510
C.I. HAYES, INC.; *U.S. Private*, pg. 513
HERAEUS QUARZGLAS GMBH—Heraeus Holding GmbH; *Int'l*, pg. 616
HOLMAN BOILER WORKS, INC.—Copes-Vulcan Inc.; *U.S. Private*, pg. 274
HOWDEN GROUP PLC; *Int'l*, pg. 636
IMETAL; *Int'l*, pg. 661
INDUCTOTHERM CORP.—Inductotherm Industries, Inc.; *U.S. Private*, pg. 560
INDUCTOTHERM INDUSTRIES, INC.; *U.S. Private*, pg. 560
THE INTERTECH GROUP INC.—BBA Group plc; *Int'l*, pg. 113
IPSEN CERAMICS—Ruhrgas Aktiengesellschaft; *Int'l*, pg. 1149
IPSEN INDUSTRIES INTERNATIONAL G.M.B.H.—Ruhrgas Aktiengesellschaft; *Int'l*, pg. 1149
IPSEN INDUSTRIES NORDISKA AB—Ruhrgas Aktiengesellschaft; *Int'l*, pg. 1149
IPSEN INTERNATIONAL, INC.—Ruhrgas Aktiengesellschaft; *Int'l*, pg. 1149
ITAM TECH ITALIMPLIANTI, INC.—IRI Istituto Ricostruzione Industriale; *Int'l*, pg. 655
JAPAN AJAX MAGNETHERMIC CO. LTD.—BBA Group plc; *Int'l*, pg. 113
JOY ENERGY SYSTEMS INC.—Harnischfeger Industries, Inc.; *U.S. Public*, pg. 789
KIEKENS B.V., AMSTERDAM—Internatio-Muller N.V.; *Int'l*, pg. 681
GEORGE KOCH SONS, INC.; *U.S. Private*, pg. 628
KOMLINE-SANDERSON ENGINEERING CORP.; *U.S. Private*, pg. 631
LAFARGE MATERIAUX DE SPECIALITES—Lafarge S.A.; *Int'l*, pg. 789
LEPEL CORPORATION—Inductotherm Industries, Inc.; *U.S. Private*, pg. 560
LINDBERG, A GENERAL SIGNAL COMPANY—General Signal Corporation; *U.S. Public*, pg. 727
MPH INDUSTRIES—General Signal Corporation; *U.S. Public*, pg. 726
MARTIN INDUSTRIES, INC. (AL); *U.S. Private*, pg. 709
MATRIX TECHNOLOGIES INC.; *U.S. Private*, pg. 714
METALLGESELLSCHAFT AG; *Int'l*, pg. 860
NAO, INC.; *U.S. Private*, pg. 771
NEW ZEALAND CONTROLS LTD.—Siebe plc; *Int'l*, pg. 1244
NIPPON SELAS CO., LTD.—Selas Corporation of America; *U.S. Public*, pg. 1455
NORDKLIMA LUFT-UND WARMETECHNIK GMBH—Senior Engineering Group, plc.; *Int'l*, pg. 1222
OILDYNE—Commercial Intertech Corp.; *U.S. Public*, pg. 411
OTTO JUNKER GMBH LAMMERSDORF; *Int'l*, pg. 1014
PACIFIC HEATER CORPORATION—Watlow Electric Manufacturing Company; *U.S. Private*, pg. 1153
PLASMA ENERGY CORPORATION—ChemFirst Inc.; *U.S. Public*, pg. 344
PRECISION S.A.—Siebe plc; *Int'l*, pg. 1244
QUALITY HEAT TREATMENT—Driver-Harris Company; *U.S. Public*, pg. 530
RAPID ENGINEERING INC.; *U.S. Private*, pg. 910
RAYCHEM CORPORATION; *U.S. Public*, pg. 1362
ROBERTSHAW CONTROLS NEW ZEALAND—Siebe plc; *Int'l*, pg. 1244
SVG THERMCO SYSTEMS—Silicon Valley Group, Inc.; *U.S. Public*, pg. 1474
SALEM CORPORATION—Salem Group, Inc.; *U.S. Private*, pg. 961
SALEM ENGINEERING CO., LTD.—Salem Group, Inc.; *U.S. Private*, pg. 962
SALEM ERECTORS—Salem Group, Inc.; *U.S. Private*, pg. 961
SALEM FURNACE CO.—Salem Group, Inc.; *U.S. Private*, pg. 961
SECO WARWICK CORPORATION; *U.S. Private*, pg. 980
SELAS CORPORATION OF AMERICA; *U.S. Public*, pg. 1454
SELAS ITALIANA, S.R.L.—Selas Corporation of America; *U.S. Public*, pg. 1455
SELAS S.A.—Selas Corporation of America; *U.S. Public*, pg. 1455
SELAS WAERMETECHNIK GMBH—Selas Corporation of America; *U.S. Public*, pg. 1455
SELKIRK METALBESTOS—Zurn Industries, Inc.; *U.S. Public*, pg. 1794
SEVERN FURNACES LIMITED—Instron Corporation; *U.S. Public*, pg. 883
SHENANDOAH MFG. CO. INC.; *U.S. Private*, pg. 992
SIEBE CONTROLS AUSTRALIA—Siebe plc; *Int'l*, pg. 1244
TAM CERAMICS INC.—Cookson Group plc; *Int'l*, pg. 329
TEMCO FIREPLACE PRODUCTS, INC.—Temtex Industries Inc.; *U.S. Public*, pg. 1576
THERMO ELECTRON CORPORATION; *U.S. Public*, pg. 1591
THERMO SOLUTIONS—Research, Incorporated; *U.S. Public*, pg. 1382
TOCCO, INC.—Park-Ohio Industries, Inc.; *U.S. Public*, pg. 1259
J.J. TOUREK CO.—Tuthill Corporation; *U.S. Private*, pg. 1111
UNITED INDUSTRIAL CORPORATION; *U.S. Public*, pg. 1679
WATLOW ELECTRIC MANUFACTURING COMPANY; *U.S. Private*, pg. 1153
WATLOW ELECTRIC MFG. CO. GMBH—Watlow Electric Manufacturing Company; *U.S. Private*, pg. 1153
WATLOW LIMITED—Watlow Electric Manufacturing Company; *U.S. Private*, pg. 1154
WESALEM COMPANY—Salem Group, Inc.; *U.S. Private*, pg. 962
WESTOFEN GMBH—Viag AG; *Int'l*, pg. 1466
WHITING CORPORATION; *U.S. Private*, pg. 1173
WIEGAND INDUSTRIAL-CHROMALOX—Emerson Electric Co.; *U.S. Public*, pg. 573
WOLVERINE MASSACHUSETTS CORPORATION; *U.S. Private*, pg. 1186
JOHN ZINK CO.—Koch Industries, Incorporated; *U.S. Private*, pg. 628
ZURN BALKE-DURR, INC.—Deutsche Babcock AG; *Int'l*, pg. 401

3568 — MECHANICAL POWER TRANSMISSION EQUIPMENT, NEC

ACCURATE BUSHING CO., INC.; *U.S. Private*, pg. 11
AEROSPACE BEARING SUPPORT, INC.—Banner Aerospace, Inc.; *U.S. Public*, pg. 187
AIRCRAFT BEARING CORP.—Banner Aerospace, Inc.; *U.S. Public*, pg. 187
AIRFLEX DIV. EATON CORP.—Eaton Corporation; *U.S. Public*, pg. 556
ALLIAGES FRITTES METAFRAM—Pechiney S.A.; *Int'l*, pg. 1028
AMSTED INDUSTRIES INCORPORATED; *U.S. Private*, pg. 68
AXSYS TECHNOLOGIES, INC.; *U.S. Public*, pg. 157
AYRA SERVICIO SA—GKN plc; *Int'l*, pg. 535
BORRI S.P.A.—General Signal Corporation; *U.S. Public*, pg. 727
BOSTON GEAR—IMO Industries Inc.; *U.S. Public*, pg. 857
FEODOR BURGMANN DICHTUNGSWERKE GMBH; *Int'l*, pg. 233
BURGMANN SEALS AMERICA, INC.—Feodor Burgmann Dichtungswerke GmbH; *Int'l*, pg. 233
CENTRIC CLUTCH CO.—Zurn Industries, Inc.; *U.S. Public*, pg. 1794
CHRYSLER DE MEXICO S.A.—Chrysler Corporation; *U.S. Public*, pg. 354
COLTEC HOLDINGS INC; *U.S. Public*, pg. 401
DAMPERS IBERICA, S.A.—Cummins Engine Company, Inc.; *U.S. Public*, pg. 469
DANA CANADA INC.—Dana Corporation; *U.S. Public*, pg. 480
DANSK UNI-CARDAN A/S—GKN plc; *Int'l*, pg. 535
DIAMOND CHAIN COMPANY—Amsted Industries Incorporated; *U.S. Private*, pg. 68
DINGS DYNAMICS CO.—Venturedyne, Ltd.; *U.S. Private*, pg. 1136
DYNAPOWER/STRATOPOWER—Aeroquip-Vickers, Inc.; *U.S. Public*, pg. 24
ECHLIN INC.; *U.S. Public*, pg. 560
EMERSON POWER TRANSMISSION CO.—Emerson Electric Co.; *U.S. Public*, pg. 573
EMERSON POWER TRANSMISSION CORPORATION—Emerson Electric Co.; *U.S. Public*, pg. 573
FLEXONICS EXPANSION JOINTS—Senior Engineering Group, plc.; *Int'l*, pg. 1222
FLUID CONTROL DIVISION—FMC Corporation; *U.S. Public*, pg. 605
GKN AYRA CARDAN SA—GKN plc; *Int'l*, pg. 535
GKN AYRA DUREX SA—GKN plc; *Int'l*, pg. 535
GKN BIRFIELD SPA—GKN plc; *Int'l*, pg. 535
GKN COMPONENTI FIRENZE SPA—GKN plc; *Int'l*, pg. 536
GKN DISTRIBUTION GMBH—GKN plc; *Int'l*, pg. 536
GKN DRIVESHAFTS LTD.—GKN plc; *Int'l*, pg. 534
GKN FLORANGE SARL—GKN plc; *Int'l*, pg. 536
GKN GELENKWELLENBAU GMBH—GKN plc; *Int'l*, pg. 536
GKN GELENKWELLENWERK KIEL GMBH—GKN plc; *Int'l*, pg. 536
GKN GELENKWELLENWERK MOSEL GMBH—GKN plc; *Int'l*, pg. 535
GKN GLAENZER CARDAN SA—GKN plc; *Int'l*, pg. 536
GKN GLAENZER SPICER SA—GKN plc; *Int'l*, pg. 536
GKN INDUGASA SA—GKN plc; *Int'l*, pg. 536
GKN NORDISKA KARDAN AB—GKN plc; *Int'l*, pg. 536
GKN REMANUFACTURING GMBH—GKN plc; *Int'l*, pg. 536
GKN RIBEMONT SARL—GKN plc; *Int'l*, pg. 536
GKN SERVICE-AUSTRIA GMBH—GKN plc; *Int'l*, pg. 536
GKN SERVICE GMBH—GKN plc; *Int'l*, pg. 536
GM POWERTRAIN GROUP—General Motors Corporation; *U.S. Public*, pg. 719
GEAR HEADQUARTERS INC.—Bearing Headquarters Co.; *U.S. Private*, pg. 127
GEMA VOLSTATIC INDUSTRIAL POWDER SYSTEMS (SWITZERLAND)—Illinois Tool Works Inc.; *U.S. Public*, pg. 868
GLAENZER-SEURRE NV/SA—GKN plc; *Int'l*, pg. 536
GLENCO SA—GKN plc; *Int'l*, pg. 536
GRIFFON CORP.; *U.S. Public*, pg. 766
HILLIARD CORPORATION; *U.S. Private*, pg. 530
HITACHI, LTD.; *Int'l*, pg. 621
HOLSET ENGINEERING CO. INC.—Cummins Engine Company, Inc.; *U.S. Public*, pg. 468
HOLSET ENGINEERING COMPANY LTD.—Cummins Engine Company, Inc.; *U.S. Public*, pg. 468
HUNGER DFE GMBH; *Int'l*, pg. 639
INERTIA DYNAMICS INC.—Rockwell International Corporation; *U.S. Public*, pg. 1398
INGERSOLL-RAND COMPANY; *U.S. Public*, pg. 876
ITALTRACTOR - CEPRANO PLANT—IRI Istituto Ricostruzione Industriale; *Int'l*, pg. 654
ITALTRACTOR ITM S.P.A.—IRI Istituto Ricostruzione Industriale; *Int'l*, pg. 654
JAPAN FAWICK CO., LTD.—Eaton Corporation; *U.S. Public*, pg. 559
KAYDON CORPORATION; *U.S. Public*, pg. 945
KAYDON CORPORATION, BEARINGS DIVISION—Kaydon Corporation; *U.S. Public*, pg. 946
KAYDON S.A. DE C.V.—Kaydon Corporation; *U.S. Public*, pg. 946
KINGSBURY, INC.; *U.S. Private*, pg. 622
LOHR & BROMKAMP GMBH—GKN plc; *Int'l*, pg. 536
LOVEJOY INC.; *U.S. Private*, pg. 677
MAGNUS METALS—Farley, Inc.; *U.S. Private*, pg. 394
MANNESMANN DEMAG CORPORATION—Mannesmann A.G.; *Int'l*, pg. 837
MANNESMANN DEMAG MATERIAL HANDLING LTD.—Mannesmann A.G.; *Int'l*, pg. 837
MANNESMANN DEMAG S.A.—Mannesmann A.G.; *Int'l*, pg. 837
MANNESMANN REXROTH GMBH—Mannesmann A.G.; *Int'l*, pg. 838
MARTIN SPROCKET & GEAR, INC.; *U.S. Private*, pg. 709
MELNOR INC.—O'Sullivan Corporation; *U.S. Public*, pg. 1234
MICHELL BEARINGS—Vickers PLC; *Int'l*, pg. 1467
P/M BEARING DIV.—Keystone Powdered Metal Company; *U.S. Private*, pg. 619
PARSONS CHAIN COMPANY LTD.—FKI Plc; *Int'l*, pg. 473
PARSONS CHAIN EUROPE SA—FKI Plc; *Int'l*, pg. 473
RELIANCE ELECTRIC COMPANY—Rockwell International Corporation; *U.S. Public*, pg. 1398
RENOLD, INC.—Renold PLC; *Int'l*, pg. 1104
RENOLD PLC; *Int'l*, pg. 1103
REXNORD CORPORATION—BTR plc; *Int'l*, pg. 127
ROCHESTER GEAR, INC.—Newcor, Inc.; *U.S. Public*, pg. 1176
SKF GLEITLAGER GMBH—AB SKF; *Int'l*, pg. 1158
SCHAFFNER-BEHREND AG—GKN plc; *Int'l*, pg. 536
SCHINDLER WAGGON AG—Schindler Holding AG; *Int'l*, pg. 1205
SOCIETE DE TRANSMISSIONS AUTOMATIQUES—Renault; *Int'l*, pg. 1102
STEMCO TRUCK PRODUCTS DIVISION—Coltec Holdings Inc; *U.S. Public*, pg. 402
STERLING INSTRUMENT DIV.—Designatronics, Inc.; *U.S. Private*, pg. 327
STEWARTS & LLOYDS TRADING (PTY) LIMITED—Dorbyl Limited; *Int'l*, pg. 416
STOCK DRIVE PRODUCTS DIV.—Designatronics, Inc.; *U.S. Private*, pg. 327
SUNDSTRAND CORPORATION; *U.S. Public*, pg. 1533
SUPERIOR LINKAGE DIVISION—Tuthill Corporation; *U.S. Private*, pg. 1111
TB WOOD'S CORPORATION; *U.S. Public*, pg. 1562
TECHNO DIV.—Designatronics, Inc.; *U.S. Private*, pg. 327
THE TORRINGTON CO.—Ingersoll-Rand Company; *U.S. Public*, pg. 877
TORRINGTON GMBH—Ingersoll-Rand Company; *U.S. Public*, pg. 878
J.J. TOUREK CO.—Tuthill Corporation; *U.S. Private*, pg. 1111
TSUBAKI, INC. - ENGINEERING CHAIN DIV.—Tsubakimoto Chain Co.; *Int'l*, pg. 1425
TSUBAKIMOTO CHAIN CO.; *Int'l*, pg. 1425
TWIN DISC, INCORPORATED; *U.S. Public*, pg. 1646
TWIN DISC INTL., S.A.—Twin Disc, Incorporated; *U.S. Public*, pg. 1647
UNI-CARDAN NORGE A/S—GKN plc; *Int'l*, pg. 536
U.S. TSUBAKI, INC.—Tsubakimoto Chain Co.; *Int'l*, pg. 1425
VAN GORP CORP.—Emerson Electric Co.; *U.S. Public*, pg. 573
WEASLER ENGINEERING INC.—Code, Hennessy & Simmons, Inc.; *U.S. Private*, pg. 249

3569 — GENERAL INDUSTRIAL MACHINERY & EQUIPMENT, NEC

AAR CORP.; *U.S. Public*, pg. 1
AAR POWER BOSS—AAR Corp.; *U.S. Public*, pg. 1
ABB ASEA BROWN BOVERI (HOLDING) LTD.; *Int'l*, pg. 1
ABB ASEA BROWN BOVERI PTY. LTD.—ABB Asea Brown Boveri (Holding) Ltd.; *Int'l*, pg. 2
ABB COMMERCIAL ENGINEERING CANADA—ABB Asea Brown Boveri (Holding) Ltd.; *Int'l*, pg. 5
APV BAKER LIMITED—Siebe plc; *Int'l*, pg. 1240
AVX FILTERS DIV.—Kyocera Corporation; *Int'l*, pg. 775
ACROMETAL COMPANIES, INC.; *U.S. Private*, pg. 14
R.P. ADAMS COMPANY, INC.; *U.S. Public*, pg. 19
ADEPT TECHNOLOGY, INC.; *U.S. Public*, pg. 19
ADTEC AB—Celsius AB; *Int'l*, pg. 276
ADVANCED ANIMATIONS, INC.—VSI Holdings, Inc.; *U.S. Public*, pg. 1703
AERO-MOTIVE COMPANY—Woodhead Industries, Inc.; *U.S. Public*, pg. 1776
AERO SYSTEMS ENGINEERING INC.—Celsius AB; *Int'l*, pg. 276
AEROQUIP CORPORATION—Aeroquip-Vickers, Inc.; *U.S. Public*, pg. 24
AHLSTROM A/S AHLSTROM MACHINERY—A. Ahlstrom Corporation; *Int'l*, pg. 34
AHLSTROM EQUIPAMENTOS LTDA.—A. Ahlstrom Corporation; *Int'l*, pg. 34
AHLSTROM-HANSSEN S.A.—A. Ahlstrom Corporation; *Int'l*, pg. 34
AHLSTROM MACHINERY AB—A. Ahlstrom Corporation; *Int'l*, pg. 34
AHLSTROM MACHINERY AB PROCESS EQUIPMENT—A. Ahlstrom Corporation; *Int'l*, pg. 34
AHLSTROM MACHINERY GMBH ECOMACHINERY—A. Ahlstrom Corporation; *Int'l*, pg. 35
AHLSTROM PULP & PAPER ENGINEERING S.A.—A. Ahlstrom Corporation; *Int'l*, pg. 35
AIR PRODUCTS AND CHEMICALS, INC.; *U.S. Public*, pg. 30
ALAMO INDUSTRIAL GROUP; *U.S. Private*, pg. 31
ALAMO IRON WORKS—Alamo Industrial Group; *U.S. Private*, pg. 31
ALCOA COMPOSITES, INC.—Aluminum Company of America; *U.S. Public*, pg. 60
ALFA-LAVAL AGRI, INC.—Tetra Laval Group; *Int'l*, pg. 1378
ALFA-LAVAL SEPARATION AB—Tetra Laval Group; *Int'l*, pg. 1378
ALFA-LAVAL SHARPLES—Tetra Laval Group; *Int'l*, pg. 1378
ALLIEDSIGNAL, AUTOMOTIVE AFTERMARKET—AlliedSignal Inc.; *U.S. Public*, pg. 51
ALLIEDSIGNAL FLUID SYSTEMS—AlliedSignal Inc.; *U.S. Public*, pg. 50
ALRO GROUP; *U.S. Private*, pg. 45
ALRO GROUP, CLEARWATER—Alro Group; *U.S. Private*, pg. 46
ALRO GROUP, KALAMAZOO—Alro Group; *U.S. Private*, pg. 46
ALRO GROUP, ORLANDO—Alro Group; *U.S. Private*, pg. 46
AMERICAN BALER CO.—Avis Industrial Corporation; *U.S. Private*, pg. 102
AMERICAN EAGLE—Federal Signal Corporation; *U.S. Public*, pg. 617
AMERICAN MACHINE & TOOL COMPANY, INC.; *U.S. Private*, pg. 58
AMETEK DENMARK—AMETEK, Inc.; *U.S. Public*, pg. 100
AMICON CANADA LTD.—Millipore Corporation; *U.S. Public*, pg. 1113
AMICON G.M.B.H.—Millipore Corporation; *U.S. Public*, pg. 1113
AMICON (H.K.) LTD.—Millipore Corporation; *U.S. Public*, pg. 1113
AMICON LTD.—Millipore Corporation; *U.S. Public*, pg. 1113
AMSTED INDUSTRIES INCORPORATED; *U.S. Private*, pg. 68
ARMSTRONG ENGINEERING LIMITED—Caparo Group Ltd.; *Int'l*, pg. 265
ARROW PNEUMATICS CO. INC.; *U.S. Private*, pg. 85
ASCOM HOLDING AG; *Int'l*, pg. 86
ATOCHEM CANADA INC.—Elf Aquitane; *Int'l*, pg. 446
AUSCO PRODUCTS, INC.—The Cypress Companies; *U.S. Private*, pg. 299
AUTOTROL CORPORATION—Osmonics, Inc.; *U.S. Public*, pg. 1234
AUTOTROL FRANCE, S.A.—Osmonics, Inc.; *U.S. Public*, pg. 1234
AVERY LABEL SYSTEMS LTD.—Avery Dennison Corporation; *U.S. Public*, pg. 153
AVIS INDUSTRIAL CORPORATION; *U.S. Private*, pg. 102
BALTIMORE AIRCOIL COMPANY—Amsted Industries Incorporated; *U.S. Private*, pg. 68
BARBER-COLMAN COMPANY—Siebe plc; *Int'l*, pg. 1242
BAYERN-CHEMIE GMBH—Daimler-Benz Aktiengesellschaft; *Int'l*, pg. 367
BETZDEARBORN INC.; *U.S. Public*, pg. 226
BIJUR LUBRICATING CORPORATION; *U.S. Private*, pg. 143
BIRD-KATEMA—Baker Hughes Incorporated; *U.S. Public*, pg. 166
BIRD MACHINE COMPANY—Baker Hughes Incorporated; *U.S. Public*, pg. 166
BIRD VINYL—Jannock Limited; *Int'l*, pg. 699
BLACKHAWK AUTOMOTIVE LIMITED—Hein-Werner Corporation; *U.S. Public*, pg. 805
BLACKHAWK GMBH—Hein-Werner Corporation; *U.S. Public*, pg. 805
BLACKHAWK ITALIA S.R.L.—Hein-Werner Corporation; *U.S. Public*, pg. 805
BLACKHAWK S.A.—Hein-Werner Corporation; *U.S. Public*, pg. 805
BOBST S.A.; *Int'l*, pg. 198
BOMBAS GOULDS DE MEXICO, S.A. DE C.V.—ITT Industries, Inc.; *U.S. Public*, pg. 861
ROBERT BOSCH CORPORATION—Robert Bosch GmbH; *Int'l*, pg. 204
BRANDT, INC.—De La Rue plc; *Int'l*, pg. 387
CRSS INC.—Tractebel; *Int'l*, pg. 1415
CAMERON ASHLEY—Cameron Ashley Building Products, Inc; *U.S. Public*, pg. 298
CAPTIVE-AIRE SYSTEMS, INC.; *U.S. Private*, pg. 207
CARISTRAP DE MEXICO S.A. DE C.V.—Caristrap International Inc.; *Int'l*, pg. 272
CEMENT EQUIPMENT COMPANY S.A.—FLS Industries A/S; *Int'l*, pg. 475
CENTRAL SPRINKLER COMPANY—Central Sprinkler Corporation; *U.S. Public*, pg. 327
CENTRAL SPRINKLER CORPORATION; *U.S. Public*, pg. 327
CENTRIFUGAL & MECHANICAL INDUSTRIES—Elgin National Industries, Inc.; *U.S. Private*, pg. 370
CHAMPION IGNITION PRODUCTS—Cooper Industries, Inc.; *U.S. Public*, pg. 442
CITIZEN WATCH COMPANY, LTD.; *Int'l*, pg. 293
COBURN OPTICAL INDUSTRIES INC.; *U.S. Private*, pg. 248
COMMERCIAL INTERTECH CORP.; *U.S. Public*, pg. 411
CONSTRUCTION MECANIQUE ET HYDRAULIQUE DE VENDEE—Jeumont-Schneider Trenformeteurs; *Int'l*, pg. 706
CONTINENTAL CONVEYOR & EQUIPMENT COMPANY—NESCO, Inc.; *U.S. Private*, pg. 791
COSCO FIRE PROTECTION INC.—Zurn Industries, Inc.; *U.S. Public*, pg. 1795
DANA CANADA INC.—Dana Corporation; *U.S. Public*, pg. 480
DANA CORPORATION; *U.S. Public*, pg. 479
DANFOSS FLUID POWER—Danfoss A/S; *Int'l*, pg. 377
DELL BALER—Carclo Engineering Group plc; *Int'l*, pg. 268
DENVER AUTOMETRICS—Svedala Industri AB; *Int'l*, pg. 1325
DESPATCH INDUSTRIES; *U.S. Private*, pg. 327
DICTAPHONE CORP.—Stonington Partners Inc.; *U.S. Private*, pg. 1045
DORR-OLIVER INCORPORATED—Mannesmann A.G.; *Int'l*, pg. 839
DUFF-NORTON—Columbus McKinnon Corp.; *U.S. Public*, pg. 406
DURO DYNE CORPORATION; *U.S. Private*, pg. 349
DURR AG; *Int'l*, pg. 421
DURR INDUSTRIES, INC.—Durr AG; *Int'l*, pg. 421
DURST DIV.—Regal-Beloit Corporation; *U.S. Public*, pg. 1370
EEI CORPORATION; *Int'l*, pg. 425
EFI CORPORATION—Racal Electronics Plc; *Int'l*, pg. 1082
EASTCO INDUSTRIAL SAFETY CORP.; *U.S. Public*, pg. 548
EBERLINE INSTRUMENT CORPORATION—Thermo Electron Corporation; *U.S. Public*, pg. 1593
ELECTROSTATIC TECHNOLOGY, INC.—Nordson Corporation; *U.S. Public*, pg. 1189
ENGINEERING SERVICE, INC.; *U.S. Private*, pg. 376

ENVIREX INC.—Aluminum Company of America; *U.S. Public*, pg. 61
ENVIRONMENTAL ELEMENTS CORPORATION; *U.S. Public*, pg. 586
ERIEZ MAGNETICS; *U.S. Private*, pg. 381
EVANA AUTOMATION SPECIALISTS; *U.S. Private*, pg. 384
EXACT EQUIPMENT CORPORATION; *U.S. Private*, pg. 387
FWD/SEAGRAVE FIRE APPARATUS, INC.; *U.S. Private*, pg. 390
FARR COMPANY; *U.S. Public*, pg. 613
FARR FILTRATION, LTD.—Farr Company; *U.S. Public*, pg. 614
FARR INCORPORATED—Farr Company; *U.S. Public*, pg. 614
FIGGIE INTERNATIONAL INC.; *U.S. Public*, pg. 622
FIKE CORPORATION; *U.S. Private*, pg. 404
FILMTEC CORPORATION—The Dow Chemical Company; *U.S. Public*, pg. 523
FILTERTEK INC.—ESCO Electronics Corporation; *U.S. Public*, pg. 546
FILTRATION GROUP—Parker Hannifin Corporation; *U.S. Public*, pg. 1260
FILTRATION SYSTEMS DIVISION—Aqua Care Systems Inc.; *U.S. Public*, pg. 126
FIRE PROTECTION INDUSTRIES, INC.—Compagnie Generale Des Eaux; *Int'l*, pg. 321
FIRETROL PROTECTION SYSTEMS, INC.—Zurn Industries, Inc.; *U.S. Public*, pg. 1795
FLEET INDUSTRIES—Magellan Aerospace Corporation; *Int'l*, pg. 829
FLEETGUARD INC.—Cummins Engine Company, Inc.; *U.S. Public*, pg. 468
FLEETGUARD, INC.—Cummins Engine Company, Inc.; *U.S. Public*, pg. 468
FLOWSERVE CORPORATION; *U.S. Public*, pg. 658
FORT BEND UTILITIES CO.—Imperial Holly Corporation; *U.S. Public*, pg. 872
FUJI HEAVY INDUSTRIES, LTD., ENGINE & MACHINERY DIV.—Fuji Heavy Industries, Ltd.; *Int'l*, pg. 523
FULLER-F.L. SMIDTH CANADA LIMITED—FLS Industries A/S; *Int'l*, pg. 475
FULLER-F.L. SMIDTH (PTY) LTD.—FLS Industries A/S; *Int'l*, pg. 475
FULLER-F.L. SMIDTH S.A.—FLS Industries A/S; *Int'l*, pg. 475
FULLER-K.C.P. LIMITED—FLS Industries A/S; *Int'l*, pg. 475
FULLER-F.L. SMIDTH (PACIFIC) PTY. LTD.—FLS Industries A/S; *Int'l*, pg. 475
GHM INDUSTRIES, INC.; *U.S. Private*, pg. 435
GENERAL CIGAR HOLDINGS INC; *U.S. Public*, pg. 707
GENERAL MANUFACTURING DIV.—FKI Plc; *Int'l*, pg. 472
GENERAL SIGNAL CORPORATION; *U.S. Public*, pg. 726
GITS MANUFACTURING COMPANY, INC.—Valley Forge Corporation; *U.S. Public*, pg. 1705
GLACIER VANDERVELL, INC.—T & N Plc; *Int'l*, pg. 1334
GOULDS PUMPS (PHIL.) INC.—ITT Industries, Inc.; *U.S. Public*, pg. 861
GREAT LAKES FILTER—Acme Mills Co. Inc.; *U.S. Private*, pg. 13
GRINNELL CORPORATION—Tyco International Ltd.; *U.S. Public*, pg. 1651
GRINNELL SISTEMAS DE PROTECCION CONTRA INCENDIO S.A. DE C.V.—Tyco International Ltd.; *U.S. Public*, pg. 1651
HADEN MACLELLAN HOLDINGS PLC; *Int'l*, pg. 585
THE HAMMERBLOW CORP.; *U.S. Private*, pg. 498
HANNAY REELS; *U.S. Private*, pg. 499
JAMES HARDIE INDUSTRIES LTD.; *Int'l*, pg. 596
HARLEY INDUSTRIES, INC.—Innovative Valve Technology, Inc.; *U.S. Public*, pg. 880
HARRIS WASTE MGMT. GROUP, INC.—FKI Plc; *Int'l*, pg. 473
HAYWARD S.A.—Hayward Industries, Inc.; *U.S. Private*, pg. 514
HEIN-WERNER CORPORATION; *U.S. Public*, pg. 805
HEINKEL INDUSTRIEZENTRIFUGEN GMBH & CO.; *Int'l*, pg. 608
HEIN-WERNER OF CANADA, LTD.—Hein-Werner Corporation; *U.S. Public*, pg. 805
HERMANN BERSTORFF MASCHINENBAU GMBH; *Int'l*, pg. 617
HICKHAM INDUSTRIES INC.—Sulzer Ltd.; *Int'l*, pg. 1305
HIGHFIELD MANUFACTURING CO.—BTR plc; *Int'l*, pg. 127
HISPANO-SUIZA S.A.—SNECMA - Societe Nationale d'Etude et de Construction de Moteurs d'Aviation; *Int'l*, pg. 1165
HOFFMAN ENGINEERING COMPANY—Pentair, Inc.; *U.S. Public*, pg. 1273
HUB CITY, INC.—Regal-Beloit Corporation; *U.S. Public*, pg. 1371
HYUNDAI MOTOR COMPANY; *Int'l*, pg. 641
IMI PLC; *Int'l*, pg. 646
IDEX CORPORATION; *U.S. Public*, pg. 862
IMTECH PROJECTS ZUIT B.V.—Internatio-Muller N.V.; *Int'l*, *pg. 681*
INCENTIVE AB; *Int'l*, pg. 666
INDUSTRIAL AMERICAS GROUP—Aeroquip-Vickers, Inc.; *U.S. Public*, pg. 24
INDUSTRIAL COMPONENTS GROUP—BTR plc; *Int'l*, pg. 127
THE INGERSOLL MILLING MACHINE CO.—Ingersoll International Inc.; *U.S. Private*, pg. 562
INNOVATIVE VALVE TECHNOLOGY, INC.; *U.S. Public*, pg. 880
IRRITOL SYSTEM—The Toro Company; *U.S. Public*, pg. 1624
JACUZZI (CHILE) S.A.—U.S. Industries, Inc.; *U.S. Public*, pg. 1684
JACUZZI DO BRASIL—U.S. Industries, Inc.; *U.S. Public*, pg. 1684
JACUZZI EUROPE, S.P.A.—U.S. Industries, Inc.; *U.S. Public*, pg. 1684
JACUZZI UNIVERSAL, S.A.—U.S. Industries, Inc.; *U.S. Public*, pg. 1684
JEUMONT-SCHNEIDER TRENFORMETEURS; *Int'l*, pg. 706
THE JOHNSON CORPORATION; *U.S. Private*, pg. 591
JOHNSON MATTHEY PUBLIC LIMITED COMPANY; *Int'l*, pg. 713
KHD DEUTZ OF AMERICA CORPORATION—Deutz AG; *Int'l*, pg. 408
KAMFAB AB—Kvaerner a.s.a.; *Int'l*, pg. 771
KAMYR AB—Kvaerner a.s.a.; *Int'l*, pg. 771
KAMYR DO BRASIL TECNICA DE CELULOSE LTDA.—Kvaerner a.s.a.; *Int'l*, pg. 771
KAMYR KK—Kvaerner a.s.a.; *Int'l*, pg. 771
KAWASAKI ROBOTICS (U.S.A.), INC.—Kawasaki Heavy Industries, Ltd.; *Int'l*, pg. 725
KAYDON CORPORATION; *U.S. Public*, pg. 945
KAYDON CORPORATION, FILTRATION DIVISION—Kaydon Corporation; *U.S. Public*, pg. 946
KETEMA, INC.—KTM Holdings Corp.; *U.S. Private*, pg. 604
WALTER KIDDE S.A. INDUSTRIA E COMERCIO—Hanson PLC; *Int'l*, pg. 594
KINGSBURY ASSEMBLY MACHINE DIV.—Kingsbury Corporation; *U.S. Private*, pg. 622
KINGSBURY CORPORATION; *U.S. Private*, pg. 621
KNIGHT EQUIPMENT INTERNATIONAL INC.—IDEX Corporation; *U.S. Public*, pg. 862
KOCH MEMBRANE SYSTEMS—Koch Industries, Incorporated; *U.S. Private*, pg. 628
KOMLINE-SANDERSON ENGINEERING CORP.; *U.S. Private*, pg. 631
KRAUSS-MAFFEI AG—Mannesmann A.G.; *Int'l*, pg. 836
KRAUSS-MAFFEI VERFAHRENSTECHNIK GMBH—Mannesmann A.G.; *Int'l*, pg. 836
KUBOTA CORP.; *Int'l*, pg. 762
KVAERNER BOVING LIMITED—Kvaerner a.s.a.; *Int'l*, pg. 772
KVAERNER ROSENBERG A.S.—Kvaerner a.s.a.; *Int'l*, pg. 769
LANTECH INC.; *U.S. Private*, pg. 650
LIGHTNIN MIXERS—General Signal Corporation; *U.S. Public*, pg. 726
LINCOLN GMBH—Pentair, Inc.; *U.S. Public*, pg. 1274
LINCOLN INDUSTRIAL—Pentair, Inc.; *U.S. Public*, pg. 1273
LUBECON SYSTEMS, INC.; *U.S. Private*, pg. 679
LUBRIQUIP, INC.—IDEX Corporation; *U.S. Public*, pg. 862
MACE PRODUCTS—Osmonics, Inc.; *U.S. Public*, pg. 1234
MACGREGOR GROUP—Incentive AB; *Int'l*, pg. 670
MACGREGOR (USA) INC.—Incentive AB; *Int'l*, pg. 670
MANNESMANN DEMAG CORPORATION—Mannesmann A.G.; *Int'l*, pg. 837
MANNESMANN DEMAG FORDERTECHNIK AG—Mannesmann A.G.; *Int'l*, pg. 837
MARION MANUFACTURING—Dreison International, Inc.; *U.S. Private*, pg. 342
MARK ANDY, INC.—Dover Corporation; *U.S. Public*, pg. 521
W.B. MCGUIRE CO.—Overhead Door Corporation; *U.S. Private*, pg. 823
MCNEIL (OHIO) CORPORATION—Pentair, Inc.; *U.S. Public*, *pg. 1273*
MET-PRO CORPORATION; *U.S. Public*, pg. 1100
METEOR AG—ABB Asea Brown Boveri (Holding) Ltd.; *Int'l*, *pg. 2*
METTLER-TOLEDO INC.—AEA Investors Inc.; *U.S. Private*, *pg. 4*
MILLIPORE CORPORATION; *U.S. Public*, pg. 1112
MILTON INDUSTRIES, INC.; *U.S. Private*, pg. 749
MODERN EQUIPMENT CO., INC.—Alco Industries, Inc.; *U.S. Private*, pg. 33
MONARCH MARKING SYSTEMS—PAXAR Corporation; *U.S. Public*, pg. 1266
MORGANTOWN MACHINE ANDERSON MAVOR—Charter plc; *Int'l*, pg. 281
MOUNTAINGATE ENGINEERING, INC.—Nordson Corporation; *U.S. Public*, pg. 1188
MUNROE, INC.; *U.S. Private*, pg. 767
NAO, INC.; *U.S. Private*, pg. 771
NASCO INTERNATIONAL, INC.—Geneve Corporation; *U.S. Private*, pg. 446
NESCO, INC.; *U.S. Private*, pg. 791
NESTE ALFA OY—Neste Oy; *Int'l*, pg. 914
NETZSCH INCORPORATED; *U.S. Private*, pg. 792
NEWCOR, INC.; *U.S. Public*, pg. 1176
NIHON MILLIPORE LTD.-YONEZAWA—Millipore Corporation; *U.S. Public*, pg. 1113
NORDSON CORPORATION; *U.S. Public*, pg. 1188
NORDSON SANG SAN ENGINEERING CO.—Nordson Corporation; *U.S. Public*, pg. 1190
NORDSON U.K., LTD.—Nordson Corporation; *U.S. Public*, pg. 1189
NORDSON WALCOM B.V.—Nordson Corporation; *U.S. Public*, pg. 1189
NORGREN CO.—IMI Plc; *Int'l*, pg. 647
OCEANEERING INTERNATIONAL, INC.; *U.S. Public*, pg. 1211
OLEAN ADVANCED PRODUCTS DIVISION—Kyocera Corporation; *Int'l*, pg. 775
OSMONICS ASIA/PACIFIC, LTD.—Osmonics, Inc.; *U.S. Public*, pg. 1234
OSMONICS ASIA/PACIFIC LTD.—Osmonics, Inc.; *U.S. Public*, pg. 1234
OSMONICS, INC.; *U.S. Public*, pg. 1233
OZONE RESEARCH & EQUIPMENT CORP.—Osmonics, Inc.; *U.S. Public*, pg. 1234
PTI TECHNOLGIES, INC.—ESCO Electronics Corporation; *U.S. Public*, pg. 546
PACKAGE MACHINERY CO.; *U.S. Private*, pg. 832
PALL CORPORATION; *U.S. Public*, pg. 1253
PALL ULTRAFINE FILTRATION COMPANY—Pall Corporation; *U.S. Public*, pg. 1254
PARKER HANNIFIN OY FINN FILTER DIVISION—Parker Hannifin Corporation; *U.S. Public*, pg. 1263
PEERLESS MFG. CO.; *U.S. Public*, pg. 1268
PENNZOIL COMPANY; *U.S. Public*, pg. 1272
PENTAIR, INC.; *U.S. Public*, pg. 1273
PEPCON SYSTEMS, INC.—American Pacific Corporation; *U.S. Public*, pg. 88
PERMEA, INC.—Air Products and Chemicals, Inc.; *U.S. Public*, pg. 31
PETERS MASCHINENFABRIK GMBH—Bobst S.A.; *Int'l*, pg. 199
PNEUMATIC PRODUCTS CORP.—United Dominion Industries, Ltd.; *U.S. Public*, pg. 1676
PRECIPITAIR POLLUTION CONTROL—Cendant Corporation; *U.S. Public*, pg. 320
PREMIER FARNELL PLC; *Int'l*, pg. 1068
PRESSURE PRODUCTS INDUSTRIES—Superior Group, Inc.; *U.S. Private*, pg. 1055
PROCESS FILTRATION DIV.—Parker Hannifin Corporation; *U.S. Public*, pg. 1260
PUROFLOW INCORPORATED; *U.S. Public*, pg. 1345
QUINCY COMPRESSOR DIVISION COLTEC INDUSTRIES—Coltec Holdings Inc; *U.S. Public*, pg. 402
R. & H. SYSTEMS B.V.—Internatio-Muller N.V.; *Int'l*, pg. 680
RACAL FILTER TECHNOLOGIES, INC.—Racal Electronics Plc; *Int'l*, pg. 1083
RELIABLE AUTOMATIC SPRINKLER CO., INC.; *U.S. Private*, pg. 920
REMMELE ENGINEERING, INC.; *U.S. Private*, pg. 921
REXAM INC.—Rexam PLC; *Int'l*, pg. 1106
ROBERTSHAW CONTROLS COMPANY—Siebe plc; *Int'l*, pg. 1243
ROCKWELL AUTOMATION—Rockwell International Corporation; *U.S. Public*, pg. 1397
RONNINGEN-PETTER DIV.—Dover Corporation; *U.S. Public*, pg. 521
ROYER INDUSTRIES, INC.—Powerscreen International Plc; *Int'l*, pg. 1066
SL INDUSTRIES, INC.; *U.S. Public*, pg. 1418
SNECMA - SOCIETE NATIONALE D'ETUDE ET DE CONSTRUCTION DE MOTEURS D'AVIATION; *Int'l*, pg. 1165
SPS TECHNOLOGIES, INC.; *U.S. Public*, pg. 1419
SPX CORPORATION; *U.S. Public*, pg. 1420
SAKO OY—Oy Nokia Ab/Nokia Group; *Int'l*, pg. 954
W.H. SALISBURY & COMPANY—Siebe plc; *Int'l*, pg. 1244
SASIB BEVERAGE & FOOD N.A., INC.—SASIB SpA; *Int'l*, pg. 1194
SCHROFF—Pentair, Inc.; *U.S. Public*, pg. 1274
SCOTT SPECIALTY GASES; *U.S. Private*, pg. 977
SEITZ ENZINGER NOLL—Klockner-Werke AG; *Int'l*, pg. 737
SELAS CORPORATION OF AMERICA; *U.S. Public*, pg. 1454
SENCORP; *U.S. Private*, pg. 983
SEPARATION TECHNOLOGIES INC.—Cummins Engine Company, Inc.; *U.S. Public*, pg. 468
SERFILCO, LTD.; *U.S. Private*, pg. 985
SERVICE SOLUTION—SPX Corporation; *U.S. Public*, pg. 1421
SIMON ACCESS (U.K.) LTD.—Simon Engineering plc; *Int'l*, pg. 1251
SIMON-DUPLEX INC.—Simon Engineering plc; *Int'l*, pg. 1252
SIMON ENGINEERING PLC; *Int'l*, pg. 1251
SIMPLIMATIC ENGINEERING CO.—Crown Cork & Seal Company, Inc.; *U.S. Public*, pg. 463
SLAUTTERBACK CORP.—Nordson Corporation; *U.S. Public*, pg. 1188
SMITH INDUSTRIES, INC.; *U.S. Private*, pg. 1008
JEFFERSON SMURFIT CORPORATION—Jefferson Smurfit Group p.l.c.; *Int'l*, pg. 1269
SNAP-TITE, INC.; *U.S. Private*, pg. 1010
SNORKEL—Harbour Group Ltd.; *U.S. Private*, pg. 500
SOCIETE D'APPLICATIONS GENERALES D'ELECTRICITE ET DE MECHANIQUE; *Int'l*, pg. 1273
SOUTHCO. INC.; *U.S. Private*, pg. 1014
SOUTHCO INTERNATIONAL—SouthCo. Inc.; *U.S. Private*, pg. 1015
THE SPENCER TURBINE CO.; *U.S. Private*, pg. 1025
SPIRE CORPORATION; *U.S. Public*, pg. 1499
SPOONER INDUSTRIES LTD.—Brunel Holdings Plc; *Int'l*, pg. 231
STANDARD-KNAPP, INC.; *U.S. Private*, pg. 1031
STOKES-MERRILL—Tetra Laval Group; *Int'l*, pg. 1379
STONE CONTAINER CORPORATION; *U.S. Public*, pg. 1520
STOREROOM SOLUTIONS INC.; *U.S. Private*, pg. 1045
SUPER EGO TOOLS S.A./ROTHENBERGER ESPANA—Rothenberger Group GmbH; *Int'l*, pg. 1129
SVEDALA PUMPS & PROCESS—Svedala Industri AB; *Int'l*, *pg. 1325*
SWECO—Emerson Electric Co.; *U.S. Public*, pg. 574
SWEQUIPOS, S.A.—Emerson Electric Co.; *U.S. Public*, pg. 578
TAC CONTROL AB—Incentive AB; *Int'l*, pg. 670
TECOMET INC.—Thermo Electron Corporation; *U.S. Public*, *pg. 1592*
TECOMET-TEMPE—Thermo Electron Corporation; *U.S. Public*, pg. 1592
TELSMITH, INC.—Astec Industries, Inc.; *U.S. Public*, pg. 141
TEMPLETON, KENLY & CO., INC.; *U.S. Private*, pg. 1075
TEREX CORPORATION; *U.S. Public*, pg. 1581
TEREX CRANES—Terex Corporation; *U.S. Public*, pg. 1581
THERMO ELECTRON (CANADA)—Thermo Electron Corporation; *U.S. Public*, pg. 1596
THERMO ENVIRONMENTAL INSTRUMENT INC.—Thermo Electron Corporation; *U.S. Public*, pg. 1593
THERMO PROCESS SYSTEMS INC./HOLCROFT—Thermo Electron Corporation; *U.S. Public*, pg. 1594
TOTAL WALTHER FEUERSCHUTZ GMBH—Tyco International Ltd.; *U.S. Public*, pg. 1651

TRINE MANUFACTURING CO.—IMPAXX, Inc.; *U.S. Private*, pg. 558
USECO—Litton Industries, Inc.; *U.S. Public*, pg. 1003
UNITED AIR SPECIALISTS, INC.—CLARCOR, Inc.; *U.S. Public*, pg. 382
UNITED INDUSTRIAL CORPORATION; *U.S. Public*, pg. 1679
U.S. DIVERS CO., INC.; *U.S. Private*, pg. 1125
U.S. FILTER CO., AMES—Aluminum Company of America; *U.S. Public*, pg. 61
USINES DEHOUSSE SA—SNECMA - Societe Nationale d'Etude et de Construction de Moteurs d'Aviation; *Int'l*, pg. 1166
VALMET AUTOMATION INC.—Valmet Corporation; *Int'l*, pg. 1449
VAPONICS INC.—Osmonics, Inc.; *U.S. Public*, pg. 1234
VEAM GMBH—Litton Industries, Inc.; *U.S. Public*, pg. 1005
VEAM S.A.—Litton Industries, Inc.; *U.S. Public*, pg. 1005
VELCON FILTERS, INC.; *U.S. Private*, pg. 1135
VIBCO INC.; *U.S. Private*, pg. 1138
WAYNE WIRE CLOTH PRODUCTS, INC.; *U.S. Private*, pg. 1155
WELDOTRON CORPORATION; *U.S. Public*, pg. 1752
WELDUN INTERNATIONAL, INC.—Robert Bosch GmbH; *Int'l*, pg. 205
WESTERN FILTER—Osmonics, Inc.; *U.S. Public*, pg. 1234
WESTERN STATES MACHINE COMPANY; *U.S. Private*, pg. 1168
WHATMAN PLC; *Int'l*, pg. 1498
WHITIN ROBERTS CO.—Damsmith Corp.; *U.S. Private*, pg. 309
WHITING CORPORATION; *U.S. Private*, pg. 1173
WILLIAMS PATENT CRUSHER AND PULVERIZER CO.; *U.S. Private*, pg. 1178
WILTON CORPORATION; *U.S. Private*, pg. 1181
WOODHEAD INDUSTRIES, INC.; *U.S. Public*, pg. 1776
WORMALD ANSUL U.K. LTD.—Tyco International Ltd.; *U.S. Public*, pg. 1651
WORMALD HOLDINGS U.K. LIMITED—Tyco International Ltd.; *U.S. Public*, pg. 1651
WORSHAM SPRINKLER COMPANY; *U.S. Private*, pg. 1191
WURZBURG, INC.; *U.S. Private*, pg. 1192
THE WYCO TOOL CO.—Racine Federated, Inc.; *U.S. Private*, pg. 906
YOUNGSTOWN MILLER CORP.—GHM Industries, Inc.; *U.S. Private*, pg. 435
ZENECA AB—Zeneca Group Plc; *Int'l*, pg. 1526
ZENECA HELLAS S.A.—Zeneca Group Plc; *Int'l*, pg. 1526
ZENECA OY—Zeneca Group Plc; *Int'l*, pg. 1527
ZENECA POLAND SP. Z.O.O.—Zeneca Group Plc; *Int'l*, pg. 1527
ZENECA ZIMBABWE (PRIVATE) LIMITED—Zeneca Group Plc; *Int'l*, pg. 1527

3571 — ELECTRONIC COMPUTERS

AMD CORPORATION—Advanced Micro Devices, Inc.; *U.S. Public*, pg. 21
AST RESEARCH INC.—Samsung Group; *Int'l*, pg. 1181
ACER/ALTOS COMPUTER SYSTEMS—Acer Incorporated; *Int'l*, pg. 22
ACER AMERICA CORPORATION—Acer Incorporated; *Int'l*, pg. 22
ACER INCORPORATED; *Int'l*, pg. 22
ACORN COMPUTERS LTD.—Olivetti SpA; *Int'l*, pg. 1002
ADRA SYSTEMS, INC.; *U.S. Private*, pg. 18
ADVANCED LOGIC RESEARCH, INC.—Gateway 2000; *U.S. Public*, pg. 703
ADVANCED MICRO, LTD.—Advanced Micro Devices, Inc.; *U.S. Public*, pg. 21
AFTONBLADET AB; *Int'l*, pg. 29
ALCATEL STC AUSTRALIA—Alcatel Alsthom Compagnie Generale D'Electricite; *Int'l*, pg. 56
ALPHA MICROSYSTEMS; *U.S. Public*, pg. 57
AMDAHL CORPORATION—Fujitsu Limited; *Int'l*, pg. 527
APPLE COMPUTER, INC.; *U.S. Public*, pg. 121
APPLIED TECHNOLOGY (GERMANY)—Litton Industries, Inc.; *U.S. Public*, pg. 1004
APPLIED TECHNOLOGY (UK)—Litton Industries, Inc.; *U.S. Public*, pg. 1004
APRICOT COMPUTERS—Mitsubishi Electric Corporation; *Int'l*, pg. 873
ASTRONAUTICS CORPORATION OF AMERICA; *U.S. Private*, pg. 93
AUTOMATION CONTROL—Thyssen AG; *Int'l*, pg. 1389
AUTOTOTE CORPORATION; *U.S. Public*, pg. 150
AYDIN CORPORATION; *U.S. Public*, pg. 158
BTG, INC.; *U.S. Public*, pg. 164
BARRISTER INFORMATION SYSTEMS CORPORATION; *U.S. Public*, pg. 192
BETACOM PLC; *Int'l*, pg. 193
BETZDEARBORN INC.; *U.S. Public*, pg. 226
BRITISH TELECOM TYMNET—British Telecommunications plc; *Int'l*, pg. 223
BULL ARGENTINA SACI—Compagnie des Machines Bull; *Int'l*, pg. 317
BULL CORPORATION OF JAPAN—Compagnie des Machines Bull; *Int'l*, pg. 318
BULL DEL URUGUAY S.A.—Compagnie des Machines Bull; *Int'l*, pg. 318
BULL FAR EAST PTE. LTD.—Compagnie des Machines Bull; *Int'l*, pg. 318
BULL PERIPHERALS GMBH—Compagnie des Machines Bull; *Int'l*, pg. 316
BULL S.A.—Compagnie des Machines Bull; *Int'l*, pg. 315
CAE ELEKTRONIK GMBH—CAE Inc.; *Int'l*, pg. 238
CII-HONEYWELL BULL CAMEROUN SARL—Compagnie des Machines Bull; *Int'l*, pg. 316
CNL BULL—Compagnie des Machines Bull; *Int'l*, pg. 318
CAMBEX CORPORATION; *U.S. Public*, pg. 296
CANON INC.; *Int'l*, pg. 261
CASIO COMPUTER CO., LTD.; *Int'l*, pg. 274
COMPAGNIE CII-HB INTERNATIONALE N.V.—Compagnie des Machines Bull; *Int'l*, pg. 319
COMPAGNIE DES MACHINES BULL; *Int'l*, pg. 315
COMPAGNIE IBM FRANCE, S.A—International Business Machines Corporation; *U.S. Public*, pg. 897
COMPAQ COMPUTER CORPORATION; *U.S. Public*, pg. 417
COMPUTER CITY—Tandy Corporation; *U.S. Public*, pg. 1560
CONVEX TECHNOLOGY CENTER - HEWLETT-PACKARD—Hewlett-Packard Company; *U.S. Public*, pg. 815
CRAY RESEARCH—Silicon Graphics, Inc.; *U.S. Public*, pg. 1473
CUBIX CORPORATION; *U.S. Private*, pg. 294
DBA SYSTEMS, INC.; *U.S. Public*, pg. 472
DAEWOO ELECTRONICS CO., LTD.—Daewoo Corporation; *Int'l*, pg. 357
DATA GENERAL CORPORATION; *U.S. Public*, pg. 485
DATA GENERAL LIMITED—Data General Corporation; *U.S. Public*, pg. 486
DATA GENERAL MANUFACTURING DIVISION—Data General Corporation; *U.S. Public*, pg. 485
DATARAM CORPORATION; *U.S. Public*, pg. 487
DATARAM INTERNATIONAL SALES CORP.—Dataram Corporation; *U.S. Public*, pg. 487
DATAWATCH CORPORATION; *U.S. Public*, pg. 488
DELL COMPUTER CORPORATION; *U.S. Public*, pg. 495
DESIGN CONCEPTS INTEGRATION, INC.—International Research & Evaluation; *U.S. Private*, pg. 572
DEVELOPMENT AND MANUFACTURING—Xerox Corporation; *U.S. Public*, pg. 1784
DIGITAL EQUIPMENT CORPORATION; *U.S. Public*, pg. 507
DYNATECH CORPORATION; *U.S. Public*, pg. 539
DYNATECH DATA COMMUNICATIONS LTD.—Thermo Electron Corporation; *U.S. Public*, pg. 1591
EM MICROELECTRONIC-MARIN S.A.—SMH Swiss Corporation for Micro Electronics & Watchmaking Indus. Ltd.; *Int'l*, pg. 1160
ENCORE COMPUTER CORPORATION; *U.S. Public*, pg. 580
EPSON AMERICA INC.—Seiko Epson Corporation; *Int'l*, pg. 1219
ERICSSON BUSINESS NETWORKS AB—Telefonaktiebolaget LM Ericsson; *Int'l*, pg. 1363
EUROBULL OVERSEAS N.V.—Compagnie des Machines Bull; *Int'l*, pg. 318
EVANS & SUTHERLAND COMPUTER CORPORATION; *U.S. Public*, pg. 595
EVEREX SYSTEMS INC.—Formosa Plastics Corporation; *Int'l*, pg. 498
FORMATION, INC.; *U.S. Private*, pg. 419
FOURTH GENERATION TECHNOLOGY INC.—Northrop Grumman Corporation; *U.S. Public*, pg. 1199
FRANKLIN ELECTRONIC PUBLISHERS, INC.; *U.S. Public*, pg. 679
FUJITSU BUSINESS COMMUNICATION SYSTEMS—Fujitsu Limited; *Int'l*, pg. 526
FUJITSU COMPUTER PRODUCTS OF AMERICA, INC.—Fujitsu Limited; *Int'l*, pg. 526
FUJITSU KIDEN LTD.—Fujitsu Limited; *Int'l*, pg. 526
FUJITSU LIMITED; *Int'l*, pg. 525
GATEFIELD CORPORATION; *U.S. Public*, pg. 703
GATEWAY 2000; *U.S. Public*, pg. 703
GOLDSTAR CO. LTD.—LG Group; *Int'l*, pg. 778
HEURIKON CORPORATION—Computer Products, Inc.; *U.S. Public*, pg. 422
HISPANO OLIVETTI OFFICE—Olivetti SpA; *Int'l*, pg. 1003
HITACHI ELECTRONICS ENGINEERING CO., LTD.—Hitachi, Ltd.; *Int'l*, pg. 621
HITACHI, LTD.; *Int'l*, pg. 621
HONEYWELL BULL AB—Compagnie des Machines Bull; *Int'l*, pg. 318
OY HONEYWELL BULL AB—Compagnie des Machines Bull; *Int'l*, pg. 318
HONEYWELL BULL AG—Compagnie des Machines Bull; *Int'l*, pg. 318
HONEYWELL BULL MADAGASCAR S.A.—Compagnie des Machines Bull; *Int'l*, pg. 318
HONEYWELL BULL MAROC S.A.—Compagnie des Machines Bull; *Int'l*, pg. 318
HONEYWELL BULL SAL—Compagnie des Machines Bull; *Int'l*, pg. 318
HYUNDAI ELECTRONICS AMERICA—Hyundai Motor Company; *Int'l*, pg. 641
I-BUS DIVISION—Maxwell Technologies, Inc.; *U.S. Public*, pg. 1062
ICL PLC—Fujitsu Limited; *Int'l*, pg. 528
IDEA COURIER, INC.—IDEA Corporation; *U.S. Private*, pg. 557
INCENTIVE AB; *Int'l*, pg. 666
INFORMATION SYSTEMS & NETWORK CORPORATION; *U.S. Private*, pg. 561
ING. C. OLIVETTI & C.—Olivetti SpA; *Int'l*, pg. 1002
INTEGRATED SYSTEMS ANALYSTS, INC.; *U.S. Private*, pg. 566
INTELLIGENT INSTRUMENTATION INC.—Burr-Brown Corporation; *U.S. Public*, pg. 270
INTERGRAPH CORPORATION; *U.S. Public*, pg. 890
INTERNATIO-MULLER N.V.; *Int'l*, pg. 680
INTERNATIONAL BUSINESS MACHINES A/S—International Business Machines Corporation; *U.S. Public*, pg. 898
INTERNATIONAL BUSINESS MACHINES CORPORATION; *U.S. Public*, pg. 895
INTERNATIONAL BUSINESS MACHINES OF BELGIUM S.A—International Business Machines Corporation; *U.S. Public*, pg. 898
INTERNATIONAL BUSINESS MACHINES, S.A.E.—International Business Machines Corporation; *U.S. Public*, pg. 898
INTERNATIONAL RESEARCH & EVALUATION; *U.S. Private*, pg. 571
INTERNATIONAL SHOE MACHINE CORP.; *U.S. Private*, pg. 572
ITRON INC.; *U.S. Public*, pg. 914
L.C.G. MALMBERG BV—VNU Verenigde Nederlandse Uitgeversbedrijven B.V.; *Int'l*, pg. 1445
LANDIS & GYR SYSTEMS, INC.—Landis & Staefa AG; *Int'l*, pg. 800
LITTON INDUSTRIES, INC.; *U.S. Public*, pg. 1002
LIUSKI INTERNATIONAL, INC.; *U.S. Public*, pg. 1005
LOGICON EAGLE TECHNOLOGY, INC.—Northrop Grumman Corporation; *U.S. Public*, pg. 1199
LOGICON, INC.—Northrop Grumman Corporation; *U.S. Public*, pg. 1198
LOGITECH INTERNATIONAL SA; *Int'l*, pg. 815
LOJACK CORPORATION; *U.S. Public*, pg. 1012
M/A-COM INC.—AMP Incorporated; *U.S. Public*, pg. 8
MIPS TECHNOLOGIES, INC.—Silicon Graphics, Inc.; *U.S. Public*, pg. 1473
MCBRIDE AND ASSOCIATES, INC.; *U.S. Private*, pg. 719
MEMOREX TELEX CORP.—Memorex Telex N.V.; *Int'l*, pg. 857
METRO AG; *Int'l*, pg. 863
MICRONICS COMPUTERS, INC.; *U.S. Public*, pg. 1106
MILTOPE GROUP, INC.; *U.S. Public*, pg. 1114
MODCOMP—CSP Inc.; *U.S. Public*, pg. 283
MOTOROLA, INC.; *U.S. Public*, pg. 1136
NCR CORPORATION; *U.S. Public*, pg. 1146
NEC CORPORATION; *Int'l*, pg. 899
NKK CORPORATION; *Int'l*, pg. 902
NEMATRON CORP.; *U.S. Private*, pg. 791
NORDIC BULL NET—Compagnie des Machines Bull; *Int'l*, pg. 318
NORTEC ELECTRONICS AB—Axel Johnson AB; *Int'l*, pg. 709
OLIVETTI NORTH AMERICA—Olivetti SpA; *Int'l*, pg. 1002
OLIVETTI SPA; *Int'l*, pg. 1002
OLIVETTI SYSTEMS & NETWORKS—Olivetti SpA; *Int'l*, pg. 1002
OMRON CORPORATION; *Int'l*, pg. 1005
PACKARD BELL NEC; *U.S. Private*, pg. 833
PACKARD BIOSCIENCE COMPANY; *U.S. Private*, pg. 833
PHOTOMATRIX CORPORATION; *U.S. Public*, pg. 1292
PINNACLE SYSTEMS, INC.; *U.S. Public*, pg. 1297
PRO-LOG CORPORATION; *U.S. Private*, pg. 887
PROXIMA CORPORATION; *U.S. Public*, pg. 1339
RACAL ELECTRONICS PLC; *Int'l*, pg. 1082
RADIX CORPORATION; *U.S. Private*, pg. 906
RADIX MICRO DEVICES, PLC—Radix Corporation; *U.S. Private*, pg. 907
SAGEM TERMINALS & TELECOMMUNICATIONS DIVISION—Societe d'Applications Generales d'Electricite et de Mechanique; *Int'l*, pg. 1273
SMH SWISS CORPORATION FOR MICRO ELECTRONICS & WATCHMAKING INDUS. LTD.; *Int'l*, pg. 1160
SAMSUNG GROUP; *Int'l*, pg. 1181
SANDERSON COMPUTERS LIMITED—Sanderson Technology Ltd.; *Int'l*, pg. 1184
SANDERSON COTSWOLD LIMITED—Sanderson Technology Ltd.; *Int'l*, pg. 1184
SANDERSON TECHNOLOGY LTD.; *Int'l*, pg. 1184
SHARP CORPORATION; *Int'l*, pg. 1228
SIEMENS NIXDORF INFORMATION SYSTEMS INC.—Siemens AG; *Int'l*, pg. 1245
SILICON GRAPHICS, INC.; *U.S. Public*, pg. 1473
SONY LOGISTICS SERVICE CO.—Sony Corporation; *Int'l*, pg. 1284
SQUARE D COMPANY—Schneider S.A.; *Int'l*, pg. 1208
STRATUS COMPUTER, INC.; *U.S. Public*, pg. 1524
STRATUS COMPUTER, LTD.—Stratus Computer, Inc.; *U.S. Public*, pg. 1524
STRATUS COMPUTER PTY, LTD.—Stratus Computer, Inc.; *U.S. Public*, pg. 1524
STRATUS COMPUTER S.A.—Stratus Computer, Inc.; *U.S. Public*, pg. 1524
STRATUS JAPAN CO. LTD.—Stratus Computer, Inc.; *U.S. Public*, pg. 1524
SUN MICROSYSTEMS FEDERAL INC.—Sun Microsystems, Inc.; *U.S. Public*, pg. 1531
SUN MICROSYSTEMS, R&D—Sun Microsystems, Inc.; *U.S. Public*, pg. 1531
TANDEM COMPUTERS A/S—COMPAQ Computer Corporation; *U.S. Public*, pg. 417
TANDEM NONSTOP PTY. LTD.—COMPAQ Computer Corporation; *U.S. Public*, pg. 418
TANDY CORPORATION; *U.S. Public*, pg. 1560
TANDY INTERNATIONAL ELECTRONICS, INC.—Tandy Corporation; *U.S. Public*, pg. 1560
TECMAR TECHNOLOGIES, INC.—Tecmar Technologies International, Inc.; *Int'l*, pg. 1361
TECMAR TECHNOLOGIES INTERNATIONAL, INC.; *Int'l*, pg. 1361
TELE-EKONOMI AB—Aftonbladet AB; *Int'l*, pg. 29
TELXON CORPORATION; *U.S. Public*, pg. 1573
TERMINAL DIVISION—Inkel USA Corporation; *U.S. Private*, pg. 563
TEXAS INSTRUMENTS INCORPORATED; *U.S. Public*, pg. 1585
TEXAS INSTRUMENTS INFORMATION TECHNOLOGY GROUP—Texas Instruments Incorporated; *U.S. Public*, pg. 1586
TEXAS INSTRUMENTS LIMITED—Texas Instruments Incorporated; *U.S. Public*, pg. 1586
TEXAS MICRO, INC.; *U.S. Public*, pg. 1586
THINKING MACHINES CORPORATION; *U.S. Private*, pg. 1081
TOKHEIM CORPORATION; *U.S. Public*, pg. 1620
TOSHIBA AMERICA INFORMATION SYSTEMS, INC.—Toshiba Corporation; *Int'l*, pg. 1405
TRANSICO INC., KEY PAD DIV.—Transico Incorporated; *U.S. Public*, pg. 1630
TRANSMARCO LIMITED; *Int'l*, pg. 1417
UNISYS CORPORATION; *U.S. Public*, pg. 1671
UNISYS MIDWEST—Unisys Corporation; *U.S. Public*, pg. 1671

U S WEST DEX—U S West Inc.; *U.S. Public*, pg. 1689
VERIFONE, INC.—Hewlett-Packard Company; *U.S. Public*, pg. 815
WANG AUSTRALIA PTY. LTD.—Wang Laboratories, Inc.; *U.S. Public*, pg. 1737
ZENITH DATA SYSTEMS—Compagnie des Machines Bull; *Int'l*, pg. 317

3572 — COMPUTER STORAGE DEVICES

ATL PRODUCTS, INC.—Odetics Inc.; *U.S. Public*, pg. 1212
ADVANCED MICRO DEVICES, INC.; *U.S. Public*, pg. 21
AMDAHL CORPORATION—Fujitsu Limited; *Int'l*, pg. 527
AMERIQUEST TECHNOLOGIES; *U.S. Public*, pg. 96
AMPEX CORPORATION; *U.S. Public*, pg. 104
APERTUS TECHNOLOGIES INCORPORATED; *U.S. Public*, pg. 119
APPLIED MAGNETICS CORPORATION; *U.S. Public*, pg. 123
BROTHER INDUSTRIES (USA) INC.—Brother Industries, Ltd.; *Int'l*, pg. 229
CAMBEX CORPORATION; *U.S. Public*, pg. 296
CIPRICO, INC.; *U.S. Public*, pg. 370
DRS AHEAD TECHNOLOGY, INC.—DRS Technologies, Inc.; *U.S. Public*, pg. 475
DATA GENERAL CORPORATION; *U.S. Public*, pg. 485
DATA GENERAL MANUFACTURING DIVISION—Data General Corporation; *U.S. Public*, pg. 485
DEXTER MAGNETIC MATERIALS—The Dexter Corporation; *U.S. Public*, pg. 504
DIGITAL EQUIPMENT CORPORATION; *U.S. Public*, pg. 507
ENCORE COMPUTER CORPORATION; *U.S. Public*, pg. 580
EXABYTE CORPORATION; *U.S. Public*, pg. 597
FKL DONG HWA LTD.—Fujitsu Limited; *Int'l*, pg. 528
FUJITSU BUSINESS COMMUNICATION SYSTEMS—Fujitsu Limited; *Int'l*, pg. 526
FUJITSU COMPUTER PRODUCTS OF AMERICA, INC.—Fujitsu Limited; *Int'l*, pg. 526
HMT TECHNOLOGY CORPORATION; *U.S. Public*, pg. 771
HTI EXPORT LTD.—Hutchinson Technology Inc.; *U.S. Public*, pg. 851
HARRIS SEMICONDUCTOR—Harris Corporation; *U.S. Public*, pg. 792
HUTCHINSON TECHNOLOGY ASIA—Hutchinson Technology Inc.; *U.S. Public*, pg. 851
HUTCHINSON TECHNOLOGY ASIA, INC.—Hutchinson Technology Inc.; *U.S. Public*, pg. 850
HUTCHINSON TECHNOLOGY INC.; *U.S. Public*, pg. 850
HUTCHINSON TECHNOLOGY INC., SIOUX FALLS—Hutchinson Technology Inc.; *U.S. Public*, pg. 851
INNOVEX, INC.; *U.S. Public*, pg. 880
INNOVEX PRECISION PRODUCTS—Innovex, Inc.; *U.S. Public*, pg. 880
INTERNATIONAL BUSINESS MACHINES CORPORATION; *U.S. Public*, pg. 895
INTERNATIONAL RESEARCH & EVALUATION; *U.S. Private*, pg. 571
IOMEGA CORPORATION; *U.S. Public*, pg. 912
IRVINE SENSORS CORPORATION; *U.S. Public*, pg. 913
KINGSTON TECHNOLOGY CORPORATION; *U.S. Private*, pg. 622
LEGACY STORAGE SYSTEMS CORP.; *Int'l*, pg. 805
LOGICON, INC.—Northrop Grumman Corporation; *U.S. Public*, pg. 1198
M4 DATA LTD.—Storage Technology Corporation; *U.S. Public*, pg. 1523
MAXOPTIX CORP.—Kubota Corp.; *Int'l*, pg. 762
MAXTOR CORPORATION—Hyundai Motor Company; *Int'l*, pg. 641
MCBRIDE AND ASSOCIATES, INC.; *U.S. Private*, pg. 719
MEMOREX TELEX CORP.—Memorex Telex N.V.; *Int'l*, pg. 857
MICROPOLIS CORPORATION; *U.S. Private*, pg. 742
MICROPOLIS CORPORATION (THAILAND) LTD.—Micropolis Corporation; *U.S. Private*, pg. 742
MICROPOLIS LIMITED—Micropolis Corporation; *U.S. Private*, pg. 742
MILTOPE GROUP, INC.; *U.S. Public*, pg. 1114
NAI TECHNOLOGIES, INC.; *U.S. Public*, pg. 1144
NCR CORPORATION; *U.S. Public*, pg. 1146
NEC SEMICONDUCTORS (MALAYSIA) SDN. BERHAD—NEC Corporation; *Int'l*, pg. 900
NEC TECHNOLOGIES, INC.—NEC Corporation; *Int'l*, pg. 900
NEC TECHNOLOGIES PHILIPPINES, INC.—NEC Corporation; *Int'l*, pg. 900
NASHUA CORPORATION; *U.S. Public*, pg. 1152
OPT INDUSTRIES, INC.—Torotel, Inc.; *U.S. Public*, pg. 1624
ODETICS INC.; *U.S. Public*, pg. 1212
PACKARD BELL NEC; *U.S. Private*, pg. 833
PHILIP LASER MAGNETIC STORAGE—Philips Electronics N.V.; *Int'l*, pg. 1054
THE PILOT CORPORATION; *Int'l*, pg. 1057
QUANTUM CORPORATION; *U.S. Public*, pg. 1350
RACET COMPUTES LIMITED—Kobe Steel, Ltd.; *Int'l*, pg. 740
REMMELE ENGINEERING, INC.; *U.S. Private*, pg. 921
SAMSUNG ELECTRON DEVICES CO., LTD.—Samsung Group; *Int'l*, pg. 1181
SANDERSON TECHNOLOGY LTD.; *Int'l*, pg. 1184
SEAGATE TECHNOLOGY (U.K.), LIMITED—Seagate Technology Inc.; *U.S. Public*, pg. 1450
SHARP ELECTRONICA ESPANA S.A. (BARCELONA)—Sharp Corporation; *Int'l*, pg. 1229
SHARP ELECTRONICS CORPORATION—Sharp Corporation; *Int'l*, pg. 1228
SHARP ELECTRONICS (EUROPE)—Sharp Corporation; *Int'l*, pg. 1230
SHARP ELECTRONICS (U.K.)—Sharp Corporation; *Int'l*, pg. 1230
SHARP INTERNATIONAL FINANCE (U.K.) PLC.—Sharp Corporation; *Int'l*, pg. 1230
SHARP LABORATORIES OF EUROPE, LTD.—Sharp Corporation; *Int'l*, pg. 1230
SHARP MANUFACTURING COMPANY OF U.K.—Sharp Corporation; *Int'l*, pg. 1230
SHARP PRECISION MANUFACTURING (U.K.) LTD.—Sharp Corporation; *Int'l*, pg. 1230
SHUGART CORPORATION; *U.S. Private*, pg. 997
THE STANDARD REGISTER COMPANY; *U.S. Public*, pg. 1505
STORAGE DIMENSIONS, INC.; *U.S. Public*, pg. 1522
STORAGE TECHNOLOGY CORPORATION; *U.S. Public*, pg. 1522
STORAGE TECHNOLOGY-PUERTO RICO—Storage Technology Corporation; *U.S. Public*, pg. 1523
STORAGETEK PERIPHERALS—Storage Technology Corporation; *U.S. Public*, pg. 1523
SYQUEST TECHNOLOGY, INC.; *U.S. Public*, pg. 1550
SYSTEMS ENGINEERING DIV.—Computer Sciences Corporation; *U.S. Public*, pg. 423
TAB PRODUCTS CO.; *U.S. Public*, pg. 1559
TANDY INTERNATIONAL ELECTRONICS, INC.—Tandy Corporation; *U.S. Public*, pg. 1560
TECMAR TECHNOLOGIES, INC.—Tecmar Technologies International, Inc.; *Int'l*, pg. 1361
TECMAR TECHNOLOGIES INTERNATIONAL, INC.; *Int'l*, pg. 1361
TOSHIBA AMERICA INFORMATION SYSTEMS, INC.—Toshiba Corporation; *Int'l*, pg. 1405
UNISYS CORPORATION; *U.S. Public*, pg. 1671
WESTERN DIGITAL CORPORATION; *U.S. Public*, pg. 1758
ZITEL CORPORATION; *U.S. Public*, pg. 1793

3575 — COMPUTER TERMINALS

ADVANCED INPUT DEVICES, INC.; *U.S. Private*, pg. 21
ALCATEL ISR—Alcatel Alsthom Compagnie Generale D'Electricite; *Int'l*, pg. 56
AMP INC. LYTEL DIVISION—AMP Incorporated; *U.S. Public*, pg. 8
ARK-LES CORPORATION; *U.S. Private*, pg. 82
AYDIN CORPORATION; *U.S. Public*, pg. 158
BMC INDUSTRIES, INC.; *U.S. Public*, pg. 162
BETACOM PLC; *Int'l*, pg. 193
BOX HILL SYSTEMS CORPORATION; *U.S. Public*, pg. 249
CHARLES RIVER DATA SYSTEMS, INC.; *U.S. Private*, pg. 230
COMPTEK RESEARCH, INC.; *U.S. Public*, pg. 419
CONTEC LIMITED PARTNERSHIP—Manhattan Partners L.P.; *U.S. Private*, pg. 699
CUBIX CORPORATION; *U.S. Private*, pg. 294
DAEWOO TELECOM CO., LTD.—Daewoo Corporation; *Int'l*, pg. 357
DATA GENERAL CORPORATION; *U.S. Public*, pg. 485
DATA GENERAL MANUFACTURING DIVISION—Data General Corporation; *U.S. Public*, pg. 485
DATAPOINT CORPORATION; *Int'l*, pg. 384
DELL COMPUTER CORPORATION; *U.S. Public*, pg. 495
DIGITAL EQUIPMENT CORPORATION; *U.S. Public*, pg. 507
DOTRONIX, INC.; *U.S. Public*, pg. 520
EATON IDT—Eaton Corporation; *U.S. Public*, pg. 558
ENCORE COMPUTER CORPORATION; *U.S. Public*, pg. 580
EPSON AMERICA INC.—Seiko Epson Corporation; *Int'l*, pg. 1219
EPSON PORTLAND INC.—Seiko Epson Corporation; *Int'l*, pg. 1219
EVANS & SUTHERLAND COMPUTER CORPORATION; *U.S. Public*, pg. 595
FUJITSU ESPANA, S.A.—Fujitsu Limited; *Int'l*, pg. 528
GE CAPITAL/IT SOLUTIONS—General Electric Company; *U.S. Public*, pg. 711
G.E. HARRIS ENERGY CONTROL SYSTEMS, LLC—General Electric Company; *U.S. Public*, pg. 712
G.E. HARRIS ENERGY CONTROL SYSTEMS, LLC—Harris Corporation; *U.S. Public*, pg. 792
GOLDSTAR CO. LTD.—LG Group; *Int'l*, pg. 778
HEWLETT PACKARD-BOISE—Hewlett-Packard Company; *U.S. Public*, pg. 816
HEWLETT-PACKARD COMPANY; *U.S. Public*, pg. 813
HITACHI TELECOM TECHNOLOGIES CO., LTD.—Hitachi, Ltd.; *Int'l*, pg. 622
IBM PERSONAL COMPUTER COMPANY—International Business Machines Corporation; *U.S. Public*, pg. 896
INDUSTRIAL ELECTRONIC ENGINEERS, INC.; *U.S. Private*, pg. 561
ING. C. OLIVETTI & C.—Olivetti SpA; *Int'l*, pg. 1002
INTERNATIONAL BUSINESS MACHINES CORPORATION; *U.S. Public*, pg. 895
INTERNATIONAL RESEARCH & EVALUATION; *U.S. Private*, pg. 571
JTS CORPORATION; *U.S. Public*, pg. 919
JUKI CORPORATION; *Int'l*, pg. 716
LXE INC.—Electromagnetic Sciences, Inc.; *U.S. Public*, pg. 569
LASERMASTER TECHNOLOGIES, INC.; *U.S. Public*, pg. 979
LITTON INDUSTRIES, INC.; *U.S. Public*, pg. 1002
MARK IV INDUSTRIES INC.; *U.S. Public*, pg. 1044
MEMOREX TELEX CORP.—Memorex Telex N.V.; *Int'l*, pg. 857
MICROS SYSTEMS INC.; *U.S. Public*, pg. 1106
MICROTOUCH SYSTEMS, INC.; *U.S. Public*, pg. 1108
MILTOPE GROUP, INC.; *U.S. Public*, pg. 1114
MITEL, INC.—Mitel Corporation; *Int'l*, pg. 870
MITSUBISHI ELECTRIC INDUSTRIAL CONTROL—Mitsubishi Electric Corporation; *Int'l*, pg. 872
NCR CORPORATION; *U.S. Public*, pg. 1146
NETWORK COMPUTING DEVICES, INC.; *U.S. Public*, pg. 1168
NOKIA TELECOMMUNICATIONS—Oy Nokia Ab/Nokia Group; *Int'l*, pg. 952
OLIVETTI NORTH AMERICA—Olivetti SpA; *Int'l*, pg. 1002
PACKARD BELL NEC; *U.S. Private*, pg. 833
PHILIPS INFORMATION SYSTEMS—Philips Electronics N.V.; *Int'l*, pg. 1055
PROGRESS CASTING GROUP, INC.; *U.S. Private*, pg. 890
RADIUS INC.; *U.S. Public*, pg. 1358
RANK XEROX AG—Xerox Corporation; *U.S. Public*, pg. 1785
SCI SYSTEMS, INC.; *U.S. Public*, pg. 1416
SCI (THAILAND) LTD.—SCI Systems, Inc.; *U.S. Public*, pg. 1417
SCI UK LTD.—SCI Systems, Inc.; *U.S. Public*, pg. 1417
SANDERSON INSIGHT LIMITED—Sanderson Technology Ltd.; *Int'l*, pg. 1184
SANDERSON TECHNOLOGY LTD.; *Int'l*, pg. 1184
SCANTRON CORPORATION—John H. Harland Company; *U.S. Public*, pg. 786
SEIKO INSTRUMENTS INC.; *Int'l*, pg. 1219
SHUGART CORPORATION; *U.S. Private*, pg. 997
SIEMENS PLC—Siemens AG; *Int'l*, pg. 1247
STRATUS COMPUTER, INC.; *U.S. Public*, pg. 1524
STRATUS COMPUTER PTY, LTD.—Stratus Computer, Inc.; *U.S. Public*, pg. 1524
STRATUS COMPUTER S.A.—Stratus Computer, Inc.; *U.S. Public*, pg. 1524
STRATUS JAPAN CO. LTD.—Stratus Computer, Inc.; *U.S. Public*, pg. 1524
SUN MICROSYSTEMS, INC.; *U.S. Public*, pg. 1531
SYMBOL TECHNOLOGIES, PORTABLE SYSTEMS DIVISION—Symbol Technologies, Inc.; *U.S. Public*, pg. 1546
TANDY INTERNATIONAL ELECTRONICS, INC.—Tandy Corporation; *U.S. Public*, pg. 1560
TEKGRAF, INC.; *U.S. Private*, pg. 1073
TEKTRONIX, INC.; *U.S. Public*, pg. 1567
TEXAS INSTRUMENTS INFORMATION TECHNOLOGY GROUP—Texas Instruments Incorporated; *U.S. Public*, pg. 1586
TEXAS INSTRUMENTS PRINTERS—Texas Instruments Incorporated; *U.S. Public*, pg. 1586
THRUSTMASTER, INC.; *U.S. Public*, pg. 1607
TOSHIBA AMERICA INFORMATION SYSTEMS, INC.—Toshiba Corporation; *Int'l*, pg. 1405
TOSHIBA EUROPE (I.E.) G.M.B.H.—Toshiba Corporation; *Int'l*, pg. 1406
TRANS-LUX CORPORATION; *U.S. Public*, pg. 1628
UNISYS CORPORATION; *U.S. Public*, pg. 1671
VERBATIM TAPE CORPORATION—Mitsubishi Corporation; *Int'l*, pg. 872
VERIFONE, INC.—Hewlett-Packard Company; *U.S. Public*, pg. 815

3577 — COMPUTER PERIPHERAL EQUIPMENT, NEC

AST RESEARCH INC.—Samsung Group; *Int'l*, pg. 1181
ACCU-SORT SYSTEMS, INC.; *U.S. Private*, pg. 11
ADVANCED DIGITAL SYSTEMS INC.—The Titan Corporation; *U.S. Public*, pg. 1618
ADVANCED MICRO DEVICES, INC.; *U.S. Public*, pg. 21
AISIN SEIKI CO. LTD.; *Int'l*, pg. 39
ALANTEC CORP.—FORE Systems, Inc.; *U.S. Public*, pg. 667
ALCATEL ALSTHOM COMPAGNIE GENERALE D'ELECTRICITE; *Int'l*, pg. 52
ALCATEL NETWORK SYSTEM, INC.—Alcatel Alsthom Compagnie Generale D'Electricite; *Int'l*, pg. 55
ALCATEL N.V.—Alcatel Alsthom Compagnie Generale D'Electricite; *Int'l*, pg. 55
ALLIEDSIGNAL AEROSPACE—AlliedSignal Inc.; *U.S. Public*, pg. 50
ALMO CORP.; *U.S. Private*, pg. 44
AMDAHL CORPORATION—Fujitsu Limited; *Int'l*, pg. 527
ANACOMP, INC.; *U.S. Public*, pg. 106
ANACOMP MAGNETICS, INC.—Anacomp, Inc.; *U.S. Public*, pg. 107
ANACOMP MAGNETICS WALES LTD.—Anacomp, Inc.; *U.S. Public*, pg. 107
ANALOGIC CORPORATION; *U.S. Public*, pg. 109
ANDOVER CONTROLS; *U.S. Private*, pg. 73
ANDOVER CONTROLS SECURITIES—Andover Controls; *U.S. Private*, pg. 73
ANRITSU CORPORATION; *Int'l*, pg. 77
APERTUS TECHNOLOGIES INCORPORATED; *U.S. Public*, pg. 119
APPLE COMPUTER, INC.; *U.S. Public*, pg. 121
APPLICATION SPECIFIC PRODUCTS GROUP—Philips Electronics N.V.; *Int'l*, pg. 1053
APPLICON INC.—Gores Technology Group; *U.S. Private*, pg. 465
APPLIED TECHNOLOGY—Litton Industries, Inc.; *U.S. Public*, pg. 1002
ASAHI OPTICAL CO., LTD.; *Int'l*, pg. 85
ASTEC INTERNATIONAL LIMITED; *Int'l*, pg. 92
ASTRO-MED, INC.; *U.S. Public*, pg. 141
AUSTRALIAN SUBMARINE CORPORATION—Celsius AB; *Int'l*, pg. 277
AUTODESK LTD.—Autodesk, Inc.; *U.S. Public*, pg. 149
AUTOLOGIC INFORMATION INTERNATIONAL, INC.—Volt Information Sciences, Inc.; *U.S. Public*, pg. 1724
AYDIN CORPORATION; *U.S. Public*, pg. 158
BADIX SYSTEMS INC.—Sulcus Computer Corp.; *U.S. Public*, pg. 1527
BANCTEC, INC.; *U.S. Public*, pg. 176
BANCTEC, INC.-ATLANTA—BancTec, Inc.; *U.S. Public*, pg. 177
BANCTEC, INC.-LOS ANGELES—BancTec, Inc.; *U.S. Public*, pg. 177

BANCTEC SERVICE CORP.—BancTec, Inc.; *U.S. Public*, pg. 177
BANCTEC TECHNOLOGIES—BancTec, Inc.; *U.S. Public*, pg. 177
BARRISTER INFORMATION SYSTEMS CORPORATION; *U.S. Public*, pg. 192
BAT OFFICE PRODUCTS—U.S. Office Products Company; *U.S. Public*, pg. 1686
BEIJING SANYO ELECTRONICS (SHEKOU) LTD.—Sanyo Electric Co., Ltd.; *Int'l*, pg. 1191
BELL INDUSTRIES, INC.; *U.S. Public*, pg. 204
BETACOM PLC; *Int'l*, pg. 193
BIO-LOGIC SYSTEMS CORP.; *U.S. Public*, pg. 230
BLACK BOX CORPORATION OF PA; *U.S. Public*, pg. 235
BLACK BOX CORPORATION OF PENNSYLVANIA—Black Box Corporation of PA; *U.S. Public*, pg. 235
BOSTON DIGITAL CORP.; *U.S. Private*, pg. 161
BOWMAR INSTRUMENT CORPORATION; *U.S. Public*, pg. 248
BREMSON DATA SYSTEMS, INC.—Eastman Kodak Company; *U.S. Public*, pg. 551
BROTHER INDUSTRIES, LTD.; *Int'l*, pg. 229
BULL ARGENTINA SACI—Compagnie des Machines Bull; *Int'l*, pg. 317
BULL DEL URUGUAY S.A.—Compagnie des Machines Bull; *Int'l*, pg. 318
BULL HN INFORMATION SYSTEMS INC.—Compagnie des Machines Bull; *Int'l*, pg. 316
BULL PERIPHERALS GMBH—Compagnie des Machines Bull; *Int'l*, pg. 316
BULL RUN CORPORATION; *U.S. Public*, pg. 267
BURR-BROWN CORPORATION; *U.S. Public*, pg. 270
CBM AMERICA CORP.; *U.S. Private*, pg. 192
CCA SYSTEMS, PTY. LTD.—COMPAQ Computer Corporation; *U.S. Public*, pg. 418
CD PRODUCTS, INC.; *U.S. Public*, pg. 276
CIE SYSTEMS—Itochu Corporation; *Int'l*, pg. 694
CMS ENHANCEMENTS, PTE. LTD.—Ameriquest Technologies; *U.S. Public*, pg. 96
CNL BULL—Compagnie des Machines Bull; *Int'l*, pg. 318
CNT FRANCE S.A.—Computer Network Technology Corporation; *U.S. Public*, pg. 421
CNT INTERNATIONAL—Computer Network Technology Corporation; *U.S. Public*, pg. 421
CRC; *Int'l*, pg. 241
CSP INC.; *U.S. Public*, pg. 283
CUC INTERNATIONAL, INC.—Cendant Corporation; *U.S. Public*, pg. 320
CALCOMP TECHNOLOGY, INC.—Lockheed Martin Corporation; *U.S. Public*, pg. 1007
CANON INC.; *Int'l*, pg. 261
CARROLL TOUCH, INC.—AMP Incorporated; *U.S. Public*, pg. 8
CBM AMERICA CORP.—CBM America Corp.; *U.S. Private*, pg. 192
CELSIUS AB; *Int'l*, pg. 276
CENDANT CORPORATION; *U.S. Public*, pg. 320
CHANGCHUN SANYO ELECTRONICS (SHEKOU) CO., LTD.—Sanyo Electric Co., Ltd.; *Int'l*, pg. 1191
CHATSWORTH DATA CORPORATION; *U.S. Private*, pg. 231
CHERASIA LIMITED—Cherry Electrical Products Corporation; *U.S. Public*, pg. 346
CHERRY AUSTRALIA PTY. LTD.—Cherry Electrical Products Corporation; *U.S. Public*, pg. 346
CHERRY ELECTRICAL PRODUCTS—Cherry Electrical Products Corporation; *U.S. Public*, pg. 346
CHERRY ELECTRICAL PRODUCTS CORPORATION; *U.S.* Public, pg. 346
CHERRY ELECTRICAL PRODUCTS, LTD.—Cherry Electrical Products Corporation; *U.S. Public*, pg. 346
CHERRY MIKROSCHALTER GMBH—Cherry Electrical Products Corporation; *U.S. Public*, pg. 346
CHERRY SARL—Cherry Electrical Products Corporation; *U.S. Public*, pg. 346
CHERRY SRO—Cherry Electrical Products Corporation; *U.S. Public*, pg. 346
CIMATRIX L.L.C.—Robotic Vision Systems, Inc.; *U.S. Public*, pg. 1395
CINET DANMARK A/S—Axel Johnson AB; *Int'l*, pg. 710
CINET PERIFERI A/S—Axel Johnson AB; *Int'l*, pg. 710
CISCO SYSTEMS, INC.; *U.S. Public*, pg. 375
CITIZEN WATCH COMPANY, LTD.; *Int'l*, pg. 293
COGNITRONICS CORPORATION; *U.S. Public*, pg. 394
COMPAGNIE CII-HB INTERNATIONALE N.V.—Compagnie des Machines Bull; *Int'l*, pg. 319
COMPAREX INFORMATIONSSYSTEME GMBH—BASF AG; *Int'l*, pg. 105
COMPSEE, INC.—McRae Industries, Inc.; *U.S. Public*, pg. 1073
COMPUTER NETWORK TECHNOLOGY CORPORATION; *U.S. Public*, pg. 421
COMPUTER OPTICAL PRODUCTS INC.—Hathaway Corporation; *U.S. Public*, pg. 799
COMPUTER PRODUCTS, INC.; *U.S. Public*, pg. 422
CONTROL MODULE, INC.; *U.S. Private*, pg. 271
CONVEX TECHNOLOGY CENTER - HEWLETT-PACKARD—Hewlett-Packard Company; *U.S. Public*, pg. 815
CROSFIELD ELECTRONICS LIMITED—Du Pont (E.I. Du Pont De Nemours & Co.); *U.S. Public*, pg. 532
CYBERGUARD CORPORATION; *U.S. Public*, pg. 470
DAEWOO ELECTRONICS CO., LTD.—Daewoo Corporation; *Int'l*, pg. 357
DALE ELECTRONICS, TECHRO—Vishay Intertechnology, Inc.; *U.S. Public*, pg. 1722
DANKA OFFICE IMAGING—Eastman Kodak Company; *U.S. Public*, pg. 551
DATA COMMAND SYSTEMS—Litton Industries, Inc.; *U.S. Public*, pg. 1002
DATA GENERAL CORPORATION; *U.S. Public*, pg. 485
DATA GENERAL GMBH—Data General Corporation; *U.S. Public*, pg. 486
DATA GENERAL MANUFACTURING DIVISION—Data General Corporation; *U.S. Public*, pg. 485
DATAMAX INTERNATIONAL CORPORATION; *U.S. Private*, pg. 313
DATAMETRICS CORPORATION; *U.S. Public*, pg. 487
DATAPOINT CORPORATION; *Int'l*, pg. 384
DATAPRODUCTS CORPORATION—Hitachi Koki Co., Ltd.; *Int'l*, pg. 620
DATAPRODUCTS (DUBLIN) LTD.—Hitachi Koki Co., Ltd.; *Int'l*, pg. 621
DATAPRODUCTS (HONG KONG), LTD.—Hitachi Koki Co., Ltd.; *Int'l*, pg. 621
DATAPRODUCTS NEW ENGLAND, INC.—Hitachi Koki Co., Ltd.; *Int'l*, pg. 621
DATASOUTH COMPUTER CORPORATION—Bull Run Corporation; *U.S. Public*, pg. 267
DATATROL TRANSACTION TERMINALS—DataCard Corporation; *U.S. Private*, pg. 312
DAYTON OPERATIONS—IDB Holding Corporation; *Int'l*, pg. 644
DE LA RUE CASH HANDLING PRODUCT GROUP—De La Rue plc; *Int'l*, pg. 387
DELFT INSTRUMENTS N.V.; *Int'l*, pg. 388
DELL COMPUTER S.A.—Dell Computer Corporation; *U.S. Public*, pg. 496
DELPHAX SYSTEMS—Avery Dennison Corporation; *U.S. Public*, pg. 153
DESKTOP GRAPHICS—Evans & Sutherland Computer Corporation; *U.S. Public*, pg. 596
DIAMOND MULTIMEDIA SYSTEMS, INC.; *U.S. Public*, pg. 505
DIGI INTERNATIONAL—Digi International Inc.; *U.S. Public*, pg. 507
DIGI INTERNATIONAL INC.; *U.S. Public*, pg. 506
DIGITAL COMPUTER CONTROLS, INC.—Data General Corporation; *U.S. Public*, pg. 485
DIGITAL EQUIPMENT CORPORATION; *U.S. Public*, pg. 507
DIGITAL HOUSE, LTD.—Emulex Corporation; *U.S. Public*, pg. 579
DIGITAL SOUND CORPORATION; *U.S. Public*, pg. 508
DU PONT PRINTING & PUBLISHING—Du Pont (E.I. Du Pont De Nemours & Co.); *U.S. Public*, pg. 531
DUKANE CORPORATION; *U.S. Private*, pg. 345
DYNATECH CORPORATION; *U.S. Public*, pg. 539
EG & G OPTOELECTRONICS RETICON—EG & G, Inc.; *U.S. Public*, pg. 543
EMC CORPORATION; *U.S. Public*, pg. 545
EDUCATION & ENTERTAINMENT—Evans & Sutherland Computer Corporation; *U.S. Public*, pg. 596
ELASTIMOLD CO.—Thomas & Betts Corporation; *U.S. Public*, pg. 1598
ELBIT COMPUTERS LTD.—IDB Holding Corporation; *Int'l*, pg. 644
ELDEEN MANUFACTURING CORPORATION—Recoton Corporation; *U.S. Public*, pg. 1369
ELECTRO-TEC CORP.—Kaydon Corporation; *U.S. Public*, pg. 946
ELECTROCOM AUTOMATION L.P.—Siemens AG; *Int'l*, pg. 1244
ELECTROSPACE SYSTEMS, INC.—Raytheon Company; *U.S. Public*, pg. 1365
EMULEX CARIBE INC.—Emulex Corporation; *U.S. Public*, pg. 579
EMULEX CORPORATION; *U.S. Public*, pg. 579
EPSON AMERICA INC.—Seiko Epson Corporation; *Int'l*, pg. 1219
EPSON CANADA LIMITED—Seiko Epson Corporation; *Int'l*, *pg. 1219*
EPSON MANUFACTURING LTD.—Seiko Epson Corporation; *Int'l*, pg. 1219
ESCOD INDUSTRIES—Insilco Corporation; *U.S. Public*, pg. 881
EUROBULL OVERSEAS N.V.—Compagnie des Machines Bull; *Int'l*, pg. 318
EVANS & SUTHERLAND COMPUTER CORPORATION; *U.S. Public*, pg. 595
EVEREX SYSTEMS INC.—Formosa Plastics Corporation; *Int'l*, pg. 498
FEDERAL INTEGRATED SYSTEMS CORP.—Electronic Data Systems Corporation; *U.S. Public*, pg. 570
FERROFLUIDICS CORPORATION; *U.S. Public*, pg. 620
FLEX-KEY CORPORATION—Astronics Corporation; *U.S. Public*, pg. 142
FRANKLIN ELECTRONIC PUBLISHERS, INC.; *U.S. Public*, *pg. 679*
FUJITSU COMPONENT (MALAYSIA) SDN. BHD.—Fujitsu Limited; *Int'l*, pg. 528
FUJITSU SYSTEMS OF AMERICA, INC.—Fujitsu Limited; *Int'l*, pg. 526
FUTABA CORPORATION; *Int'l*, pg. 531
FUTABA CORPORATION OF AMERICA—Futaba Corporation; *Int'l*, pg. 531
GDC FEDERAL SYSTEMS, INC.—General Datacomm Industries, Inc.; *U.S. Public*, pg. 708
G.E. HARRIS ENERGY CONTROL SYSTEMS, LLC—General Electric Company; *U.S. Public*, pg. 712
G.E. HARRIS ENERGY CONTROL SYSTEMS, LLC—Harris Corporation; *U.S. Public*, pg. 792
GTCO CORPORATION; *U.S. Private*, pg. 436
GTE INTERNETWORKING—GTE Corporation; *U.S. Public*, pg. 696
GENERAL AUTOMATION, INC.; *U.S. Public*, pg. 706
GENERAL SIGNAL NETWORKS—General Signal Corporation; *U.S. Public*, pg. 727
GENICOM CORPORATION; *U.S. Public*, pg. 729
GERBER SCIENTIFIC, INC.; *U.S. Public*, pg. 740
GESCHAFTSSTELLE BERLIN—Knurr AG; *Int'l*, pg. 739
GESCHAFTSSTELLE FRANKFURT—Knurr AG; *Int'l*, pg. 739
GESCHAFTSSTELLE HAMBURG—Knurr AG; *Int'l*, pg. 739
GESCHAFTSSTELLE HANNOVER—Knurr AG; *Int'l*, pg. 739
GESCHAFTSSTELLE NURNBERG—Knurr AG; *Int'l*, pg. 739
GESCHAFTSSTELLE STUTTGART—Knurr AG; *Int'l*, pg. 739
GLORY USA, INC.—Glory Ltd.; *Int'l*, pg. 554
GOLDSTAR CO. LTD.—LG Group; *Int'l*, pg. 778
GOVERNMENT AEROSPACE SYSTEMS DIVISION-ORLANDO OPERATIONS—Harris Corporation; *U.S. Public*, pg. 792
GRAPHLINE INC.; *U.S. Private*, pg. 471
GRIFFIN TECHNOLOGY INC., AMSEC DIV.—Diebold, Incorporated; *U.S. Public*, pg. 506
GRIFFIN TECHNOLOGY INCORPORATED—Diebold, Incorporated; *U.S. Public*, pg. 506
HEI, INC.; *U.S. Public*, pg. 770
HARMONIC LIGHTWAVES; *U.S. Public*, pg. 788
HARRIS SEMICONDUCTOR—Harris Corporation; *U.S. Public*, pg. 792
HARRIS SYSTEMS LTD.—Harris Corporation; *U.S. Public*, pg. 791
HATHAWAY CORPORATION; *U.S. Public*, pg. 798
HAYES CORPORATION, REGIONAL OFFICE—Hayes Corporation; *U.S. Public*, pg. 801
HEURIKON CORPORATION—Computer Products, Inc.; *U.S. Public*, pg. 422
HEWLETT PACKARD, RESEARCH & DEVELOPMENT—Hewlett-Packard Company; *U.S. Public*, pg. 816
HITACHI KOKI CO., LTD.; *Int'l*, pg. 620
HONEYWELL BULL AB—Compagnie des Machines Bull; *Int'l*, pg. 318
HONEYWELL BULL AE—Compagnie des Machines Bull; *Int'l*, pg. 318
HONEYWELL BULL AG—Compagnie des Machines Bull; *Int'l*, pg. 318
HONEYWELL LEEDS & NORTHRUP AUSTRALIA PTY. LTD.—Honeywell Inc.; *U.S. Public*, pg. 834
HUAGIANG SANYO ELECTRONICS CO., LTD.—Sanyo Electric Co., Ltd.; *Int'l*, pg. 1192
HYUNDAI ELECTRONICS AMERICA—Hyundai Motor Company; *Int'l*, pg. 641
HYUNDAI ELECTRONICS INDUSTRIES CO., LTD.—Hyundai Motor Company; *Int'l*, pg. 641
I-BUS DIVISION—Maxwell Technologies, Inc.; *U.S. Public*, pg. 1062
IBM WORLD TRADE AMERICAS/FAR EAST CORPORATION—International Business Machines Corporation; *U.S. Public*, pg. 896
IBM WORLD TRADE EUROPE/MIDDLE EAST/AFRICA CORP.—International Business Machines Corporation; *U.S. Public*, pg. 896
ICL, INC.—Fujitsu Limited; *Int'l*, pg. 529
ICL PLC—Fujitsu Limited; *Int'l*, pg. 528
ID SOLUTIONS—Intelligent Controls Inc.; *U.S. Private*, pg. 566
ICON INTERNATIONAL, INC.—Sanyo Electric Co., Ltd.; *Int'l*, pg. 1191
IDEA CORPORATION; *U.S. Private*, pg. 557
IDEA COURIER, INC.—IDEA Corporation; *U.S. Private*, pg. 557
IMAGING TECHNOLOGIES CORP.; *U.S. Public*, pg. 870
IN FOCUS SYSTEMS, INC.; *U.S. Public*, pg. 873
INDUSTRIAL ELECTRICAL PRODUCTS—Thomas & Betts Corporation; *U.S. Public*, pg. 1598
INDUSTRIAL ELECTRONIC ENGINEERS, INC.; *U.S. Private*, pg. 561
INFORMATION SYSTEMS CO.—Sony Corporation; *Int'l*, pg. 1281
INTEGRA TECHNOLOGIES CORP.; *U.S. Private*, pg. 565
INTEGRATION AND SYSTEMS PRODUCTS DIV.—Eastman Kodak Company; *U.S. Public*, pg. 555
INTELLIGENT CONTROLS INC.; *U.S. Private*, pg. 566
INTERGRAPH CORPORATION; *U.S. Public*, pg. 890
INTERMEC MEDIA PRODUCTS—UNOVA, Inc.; *U.S. Public*, *pg. 1699*
INTERMEC STRICHODE SYSTEME GMBH—Litton Industries, Inc.; *U.S. Public*, pg. 1004
INTERMEC SYSTEMS CORP.—Litton Industries, Inc.; *U.S. Public*, pg. 1005
INTERMEC TECHNOLOGIES CORPORATION—UNOVA, Inc.; *U.S. Public*, pg. 1699
INTERMEC UK LTD.—Litton Industries, Inc.; *U.S. Public*, pg. 1005
INTERNATIONAL BUSINESS MACHINES CORPORATION; *U.S. Public*, pg. 895
INTERNATIONAL RESEARCH & EVALUATION; *U.S. Private*, pg. 571
INTERPHASE CORPORATION; *U.S. Public*, pg. 908
INTERSTATE ELECTRONICS CORP.—Figgie International Inc.; *U.S. Public*, pg. 622
IRIS GRAPHICS INC.—IDB Holding Corporation; *Int'l*, pg. 644
JBA (HK) LTD.—Sulcus Computer Corp.; *U.S. Public*, pg. 1527
AXEL JOHNSON AB; *Int'l*, pg. 707
KEY TRONIC CORPORATION; *U.S. Public*, pg. 953
KINGSTON TECHNOLOGY CORPORATION; *U.S. Private*, pg. 622
KNURR AG; *Int'l*, pg. 739
KNURR AG—Knurr AG; *Int'l*, pg. 739
KNURR-ERCOTEC GMBH—Knurr AG; *Int'l*, pg. 739
KNURR-HEINZINGER ELECTRONIC GMBH—Knurr AG; *Int'l*, pg. 739
KNURR-INTERPLAST GMBH—Knurr AG; *Int'l*, pg. 739
KNURR-LOMMATEC GMBH & CO. KG—Knurr AG; *Int'l*, pg. 739
KNURR NEDERLAND B.V.—Knurr AG; *Int'l*, pg. 739
KNURR-NORGE AS—Knurr AG; *Int'l*, pg. 739
KNURR NV BELGIE—Knurr AG; *Int'l*, pg. 739
KNURR-SPECTRA (S.E.A.) PTE. LTD.—Knurr AG; *Int'l*, pg. 739
KNURR SVERIGE AB—Knurr AG; *Int'l*, pg. 739
KNURR-TAUNUS GMBH—Knurr AG; *Int'l*, pg. 739
KNURR (UK) LTD.—Knurr AG; *Int'l*, pg. 739
KNURR USA, INC.—Knurr AG; *Int'l*, pg. 739
KOCKUMS AB—Celsius AB; *Int'l*, pg. 277
KOCKUMS PACIFIC PTY LTD.—Celsius AB; *Int'l*, pg. 277

KONICA KOBE INDUSTRIAL CENTER—Konica Corporation; *Int'l*, pg. 748
KONICA TOKYO INDUSTRIAL CENTER HACHIOJI—Konica Corporation; *Int'l*, pg. 748
KYOCERA CORPORATION; *Int'l*, pg. 775
L.A. GAUGE CO.—Triumph Group, Inc.; *U.S. Public*, pg. 1640
LCS INDUSTRIES, INC.; *U.S. Public*, pg. 970
LANDMARK SYSTEMS INC.; *U.S. Private*, pg. 649
LANIER WORLDWIDE INC.—Harris Corporation; *U.S. Public*, pg. 791
LASERMASTER TECHNOLOGIES, INC.; *U.S. Public*, pg. 979
LEXMARK INTERNATIONAL GROUP, INC.; *U.S. Public*, pg. 991
LINEAR DIV.—Philips Electronics N.V.; *Int'l*, pg. 1054
LITTLE FALLS COLOR PRINT—Sullivan Paper Company; *U.S. Private*, pg. 1050
LITTON SYSTEMS CANADA LTD.—Litton Industries, Inc.; *U.S. Public*, pg. 1005
LLOYD CONTROLS, INC.; *U.S. Private*, pg. 672
LLOYD ELECTRIC APPARATUS CO.—Lloyd Controls, Inc.; *U.S. Private*, pg. 672
LOGICON, INC.—Northrop Grumman Corporation; *U.S. Public*, pg. 1198
LOGITECH INC.—Logitech International SA; *Int'l*, pg. 815
LOGITECH INTERNATIONAL SA; *Int'l*, pg. 815
M/A-COM INC.—AMP Incorporated; *U.S. Public*, pg. 8
MIPS TECHNOLOGIES, INC.—Silicon Graphics, Inc.; *U.S. Public*, pg. 1473
MTI TECHNOLOGY CORPORATION; *U.S. Public*, pg. 1028
MAGNETIC TECHNOLOGIES CORPORATION—SPS Technologies, Inc.; *U.S. Public*, pg. 1420
MATSUSHITA GRAPHIC COMMUNICATION SYSTEMS, INC.—Matsushita Electric Industrial Co., Ltd.; *Int'l*, pg. 846
MAXOPTIX CORP.—Kubota Corp.; *Int'l*, pg. 762
MCBRIDE AND ASSOCIATES, INC.; *U.S. Private*, pg. 719
MCLEAN ENGINEERING—Zero Corporation; *U.S. Public*, pg. 1791
MCRAE INDUSTRIES, INC.; *U.S. Public*, pg. 1073
MEDIA 100, INC.; *U.S. Public*, pg. 1079
MEIJI INFORMATION SYSTEM CENTER LTD.—Meiji Seika Kaisha, Ltd.; *Int'l*, pg. 855
MEMOREX TELEX CORP.—Memorex Telex N.V.; *Int'l*, pg. 857
MENTOR GRAPHICS CORPORATION; *U.S. Public*, pg. 1086
MERCURY COMPUTER SYSTEMS, INC.; *U.S. Private*, pg. 732
MERIDIAN COMMUNICATIONS SYSTEMS DIV.—Northern Telecom Limited; *Int'l*, pg. 970
METROLOGIC INSTRUMENTS, INC.; *U.S. Public*, pg. 1102
MICOM COMMUNICATIONS CORP.—Northern Telecom Limited; *Int'l*, pg. 969
MICROPROCESSOR & MICROCONTROLLER DIV.—Philips Electronics N.V.; *Int'l*, pg. 1054
MILTOPE GROUP, INC.; *U.S. Public*, pg. 1114
MITEK SYSTEMS, INC.—Mitek Systems, Inc.; *U.S. Public*, pg. 1118
MITSUBISHI ELECTRIC CORPORATION; *Int'l*, pg. 872
MITSUI KNOWLEDGE INDUSTRY CO., LTD.—Mitsui & Co., Ltd.; *Int'l*, pg. 878
MODINFORM—Olivetti SpA; *Int'l*, pg. 1002
MOLEX ELEKTRONIK GMBH—Molex Incorporated; *U.S. Public*, pg. 1122
MOORE INTELLIGENT IMAGING SYSTEMS PTY. LTD.—Moore Corporation Limited; *Int'l*, pg. 889
MULTIGRAPHICS INC.; *U.S. Public*, pg. 1141
MUTOH AMERICA INC.—Mutoh Industries Ltd.; *Int'l*, pg. 897
MUTOH BELGIUM N.V.—Mutoh Industries Ltd.; *Int'l*, pg. 897
MUTOH INDUSTRIES LTD.; *Int'l*, pg. 897
MYLEX CORPORATION; *U.S. Public*, pg. 1143
N BASE COMMUNICATIONS—MRV Communications, Inc.; *U.S. Public*, pg. 1027
NAI SYSTEMS DIVISION—NAI Technologies, Inc.; *U.S. Public*, pg. 1144
NAI TECHNOLOGIES, INC.; *U.S. Public*, pg. 1144
NCR CORPORATION; *U.S. Public*, pg. 1146
NEC CORPORATION; *Int'l*, pg. 899
NER HOLDINGS, INC.—Hargro Enterprises, Inc.; *U.S. Private*, pg. 502
NKK CORPORATION; *Int'l*, pg. 902
NORDX/CDT—Cable Design Technologies Corporation; *U.S. Public*, pg. 287
NATIONAL COMPUTER SYSTEMS; *U.S. Public*, pg. 1155
NATIONAL MICRONETICS, INC.—Tai-Il Media Co.; *Int'l*, pg. 1347
NETOPIA, INC.; *U.S. Public*, pg. 1168
NETWORK COMPUTING DEVICES, INC.; *U.S. Public*, pg. 1168
NETWORK EQUIPMENT TECHNOLOGIES, INC.; *U.S. Public*, pg. 1168
NETWORK POWER & LIGHT—Mylex Corporation; *U.S. Public*, pg. 1144
NETWORK SYSTEMS CORPORATION—Storage Technology Corporation; *U.S. Public*, pg. 1522
NEWCOM, INC.—Aura Systems, Inc.; *U.S. Public*, pg. 147
NEWMAX CO., LTD.—Tai-Il Media Co.; *Int'l*, pg. 1347
NICHIFU AMERICA, INC.—Nichifu Company Ltd.; *Int'l*, pg. 927
NICHIFU COMPANY LTD.; *Int'l*, pg. 927
NOKIA SOURCING, INC.—Oy Nokia Ab/Nokia Group; *Int'l*, pg. 953
NOKIA TELECOMMUNICATIONS—Oy Nokia Ab/Nokia Group; *Int'l*, pg. 952
NORDIC BULL NET—Compagnie des Machines Bull; *Int'l*, pg. 318
NORDISK ELEKTRONIK AB—Axel Johnson AB; *Int'l*, pg. 709
NORTEL—Northern Telecom Limited; *Int'l*, pg. 970
NORTHERN COMPUTERS INC.—American Trading and Production Corporation; *U.S. Private*, pg. 64
NORTHERN TELECOM CANADA LIMITED, BUSINESS PRODUCTS DIV.—Northern Telecom Limited; *Int'l*, pg. 969
NORTHERN TELECOM INC.—Northern Telecom Limited; *Int'l*, pg. 970
NOVELL, INC.; *U.S. Public*, pg. 1203
NVIEW CORPORATION; *U.S. Public*, pg. 1206
OCE HOLDING USA—Oce-van der Grinten N.V.; *Int'l*, pg. 994
OKI ELECTRIC INDUSTRY COMPANY, LTD.; *Int'l*, pg. 999
OKI (UK) LTD.—Oki Electric Industry Company, Ltd.; *Int'l*, pg. 999
OLIVETTI PERIPHERAL EQUIPMENT—Olivetti SpA; *Int'l*, pg. 1002
OLIVETTI SPA; *Int'l*, pg. 1002
OLSY NORTH AMERICA INC.—Olivetti SpA; *Int'l*, pg. 1002
OSICOM TECHNOLOGIES INC.—Osicom Technologies Inc.; *U.S. Public*, pg. 1233
PC SERVICE SOURCE, INC.; *U.S. Public*, pg. 1240
PFU LIMITED—Fujitsu Limited; *Int'l*, pg. 526
PACER INFOTEC INC.; *U.S. Private*, pg. 830
PALOMAR SYSTEMS, INC.—Electro Scientific Industries, Inc.; *U.S. Public*, pg. 569
PARADYNE; *U.S. Private*, pg. 838
PENNY & GILES COMPUTER PRODUCTS—Bowthorpe plc; *Int'l*, pg. 207
PERIPHONICS CORP.; *U.S. Public*, pg. 1278
PHILIPS INFORMATION SYSTEMS—Philips Electronics N.V.; *Int'l*, pg. 1055
PHILIPS SEMICONDUCTORS—Philips Electronics N.V.; *Int'l*, pg. 1054
THE PILOT CORPORATION; *Int'l*, pg. 1057
POLAROID MAG MEDIA—Polaroid Corporation; *U.S. Public*, pg. 1314
POSSO S.A.; *Int'l*, pg. 1064
PRINTER OPERATIONS-STORAGE TEK—Storage Technology Corporation; *U.S. Public*, pg. 1523
PRINTRONIX, AG—Printronix, Inc.; *U.S. Public*, pg. 1330
PRINTRONIX, INC.; *U.S. Public*, pg. 1329
PRO-LOG CORPORATION; *U.S. Private*, pg. 887
PROTEON, INC.; *U.S. Public*, pg. 1336
PROXIMA CORPORATION; *U.S. Public*, pg. 1339
QEI, INC.; *U.S. Private*, pg. 897
QMS, INC.; *U.S. Public*, pg. 1346
QUANTUM—Quantum Corporation; *U.S. Public*, pg. 1350
QUANTUM CORPORATION; *U.S. Public*, pg. 1350
RMI EDUCATIONAL SERVICES—Robertson Marketing Inc.; *U.S. Private*, pg. 936
RACAL-DATACOM—Racal Electronics Plc; *Int'l*, pg. 1083
RADIUS INC.; *U.S. Public*, pg. 1358
RANK XEROX AG—Xerox Corporation; *U.S. Public*, pg. 1785
RAYTHEON SEMICONDUCTOR-LA JOLLA—Raytheon Company; *U.S. Public*, pg. 1365
RECOTON CORPORATION; *U.S. Public*, pg. 1369
RHONE-POULENC SYSTEMES—Rhone-Poulenc S.A.; *Int'l*, pg. 1109
RICOH COMPANY, LTD.; *Int'l*, pg. 1114
RICOH CORPORATION—Ricoh Company, Ltd.; *Int'l*, pg. 1114
ROBERTSON MARKETING INC.; *U.S. Private*, pg. 936
ROCKWELL AUTOMATION—Rockwell International Corporation; *U.S. Public*, pg. 1397
ROCKWELL INTERNATIONAL CORPORATION; *U.S. Public*, pg. 1397
SBE, INC.; *U.S. Public*, pg. 1416
SCI SYSTEMS, INC.; *U.S. Public*, pg. 1416
SCI (THAILAND) LTD.—SCI Systems, Inc.; *U.S. Public*, pg. 1417
SCM MICROSYSTEMS, INC.; *U.S. Public*, pg. 1417
SFA DATACOMM INC.—SFA, Inc.; *U.S. Private*, pg. 956
SANDERS, A LOCKHEED MARTIN COMPANY—Lockheed Martin Corporation; *U.S. Public*, pg. 1008
SANYO SEMICONDUCTOR (SHEKOU) LTD.—Sanyo Electric Co., Ltd.; *Int'l*, pg. 1192
SCAN-OPTICS, INC.; *U.S. Public*, pg. 1436
SCANTRON CORPORATION—John H. Harland Company; *U.S. Public*, pg. 786
SCHLUMBERGER LIMITED; *U.S. Public*, pg. 1439
SCITEX AMERICA CORP.—IDB Holding Corporation; *Int'l*, pg. 644
SCITEX CORPORATION LTD.—IDB Holding Corporation; *Int'l*, pg. 644
SEAGATE CONTROL DATA—Seagate Technology Inc.; *U.S. Public*, pg. 1450
SEAGATE MAGNETICS—Seagate Technology Inc.; *U.S. Public*, pg. 1450
SEAGATE RECORDING MEDIA—Seagate Technology Inc.; *U.S. Public*, pg. 1450
SEAGATE TECHNOLOGY INC.; *U.S. Public*, pg. 1449
SEAGATE TECHNOLOGY (SINGAPORE) DEVELOPMENT CENTRE—Seagate Technology Inc.; *U.S. Public*, pg. 1450
SEAGATE TECHNOLOGY (SINGAPORE) PCB ASSEMBLY OPERATIONS—Seagate Technology Inc.; *U.S. Public*, pg. 1450
SEAGATE TECHNOLOGY (SINGAPORE) PTE. LTD.—Seagate Technology Inc.; *U.S. Public*, pg. 1450
SIEMENS NIXDORF INFORMATIONSSYSTEM AB, SOLNA (STOCKHOLM)—Siemens AG; *Int'l*, pg. 1247
SEMI-CUSTOM PRODUCTS DIV.—Philips Electronics N.V.; *Int'l*, pg. 1054
SHIZUOKA OKI ELECTRIC CO., LTD.—Oki Electric Industry Company, Ltd.; *Int'l*, pg. 999
SHUGART CORPORATION; *U.S. Private*, pg. 997
SIEMENS COMPONENTS (PTE) LTD.—Siemens AG; *Int'l*, pg. 1247
SIEMENS COMPONENTS SND. BHD.—Siemens AG; *Int'l*, pg. 1247
SIEMENS LTD.—Siemens AG; *Int'l*, pg. 1247
SIEMENS NIXDORF INFORMATICA S.P.A.—Siemens AG; *Int'l*, pg. 1245
SIEMENS NIXDORF INFORMATIESYSTEMEN BV—Siemens AG; *Int'l*, pg. 1245
SIEMENS NIXDORF INFORMATION SYSTEMS LTD.—Siemens AG; *Int'l*, pg. 1245
SIEMENS NIXDORF INFORMATION SYSTEMS S.A.—Siemens AG; *Int'l*, pg. 1245
SIEMENS-NIXDORF INFORMATIONSSYSTEME AG—Siemens AG; *Int'l*, pg. 1245
SIERRA SEMICONDUCTOR; *U.S. Public*, pg. 1470
SIGMA DESIGNS, INC.; *U.S. Public*, pg. 1472
SIMULATION DIVISION—Evans & Sutherland Computer Corporation; *U.S. Public*, pg. 596
SIXTEL—Olivetti SpA; *Int'l*, pg. 1002
SKY COMPUTERS, INC.—Analogic Corporation; *U.S. Public*, pg. 109
STANDARD MICROSYSTEMS CORP.; *U.S. Public*, pg. 1502
STEINHEIL OPTRONIK GMBH—British Aerospace p.l.c.; *Int'l*, pg. 218
STEWART STAMPING CORP.—Insilco Corporation; *U.S. Public*, pg. 881
STORAGE TECHNOLOGY LIMITED—Storage Technology Corporation; *U.S. Public*, pg. 1523
STORAGE TECHNOLOGY-PUERTO RICO—Storage Technology Corporation; *U.S. Public*, pg. 1523
SULCUS (AUSTRALIA)—Sulcus Computer Corp.; *U.S. Public*, pg. 1527
SULCUS COMPUTER CORP.; *U.S. Public*, pg. 1527
SULLIVAN PAPER COMPANY; *U.S. Private*, pg. 1050
SULPACO WEST—Sullivan Paper Company; *U.S. Private*, pg. 1050
SUN MICROSYSTEMS COMPUTER CORPORATION—Sun Microsystems, Inc.; *U.S. Public*, pg. 1531
SUN MICROSYSTEMS, INC.; *U.S. Public*, pg. 1531
SUN MICROSYSTEMS LABORATORIES, INC.—Sun Microsystems, Inc.; *U.S. Public*, pg. 1531
SUNSOFT—Sun Microsystems, Inc.; *U.S. Public*, pg. 1531
SYSTECH COMPUTER CORPORATION; *U.S. Private*, pg. 1061
SYSTEMS ENGINEERING DIV.—Computer Sciences Corporation; *U.S. Public*, pg. 423
TDK SYSTEMS DEVELOPMENT GROUP—TDK Corporation; *Int'l*, pg. 1336
TAB PRODUCTS CO.; *U.S. Public*, pg. 1559
TAB PRODUCTS EUROPA B.V.—Tab Products Co.; *U.S. Public*, pg. 1559
TAB PRODUCTS OF CANADA, LTD.—Tab Products Co.; *U.S. Public*, pg. 1559
TAI-IL MEDIA CO.; *Int'l*, pg. 1347
TANDY INTERNATIONAL ELECTRONICS, INC.—Tandy Corporation; *U.S. Public*, pg. 1560
TECHOTEL, AG—Sulcus Computer Corp.; *U.S. Public*, pg. 1527
TECMAR TECHNOLOGIES, INC.—Tecmar Technologies International, Inc.; *Int'l*, pg. 1361
TECMAR TECHNOLOGIES INTERNATIONAL, INC.; *Int'l*, pg. 1361
TECSINTER—Olivetti SpA; *Int'l*, pg. 1002
TEKTRONIX NEWSTAR, INC.—Tektronix, Inc.; *U.S. Public*, pg. 1567
TELEGENIX INC.; *U.S. Private*, pg. 1073
TELEVIDEO, INC.; *U.S. Public*, pg. 1572
TELOS CORPORATION; *U.S. Public*, pg. 1573
TELXON CORPORATION; *U.S. Public*, pg. 1573
TEXAS INSTRUMENTS INFORMATION TECHNOLOGY GROUP—Texas Instruments Incorporated; *U.S. Public*, pg. 1586
THOMAS & BETTS CORPORATION; *U.S. Public*, pg. 1597
3COM CORPORATION—3Com Corporation; *U.S. Public*, pg. 1604
THREE-FIVE SYSTEMS; *U.S. Public*, pg. 1604
TOSHIBA AMERICA INFORMATION SYSTEMS, INC.—Toshiba Corporation; *Int'l*, pg. 1405
TRACE MOUNTAIN PRODUCTS; *U.S. Private*, pg. 1095
TRANSICO INCORPORATED; *U.S. Public*, pg. 1630
TRANSICO INC., MEMBRANE SWITCH OPERATIONS—Transico Incorporated; *U.S. Public*, pg. 1631
TRIDEX CORPORATION; *U.S. Public*, pg. 1637
TRUEVISION, INC.; *U.S. Public*, pg. 1642
TRUEVISION, INC.—Truevision, Inc.; *U.S. Public*, pg. 1643
TSENG LABS; *U.S. Public*, pg. 1643
ULTIMATE TECHNOLOGY CORPORATION—Tridex Corporation; *U.S. Public*, pg. 1637
ULTRA ELECTRONICS COMMAND & CONTROL SYSTEMS—Ultra Electronics Holdings plc; *Int'l*, pg. 1431
ULTRA GMBH—Computer Network Technology Corporation; *U.S. Public*, pg. 421
UNISYS CORPORATION; *U.S. Public*, pg. 1671
VARITRONIC SYSTEMS, INC.—W.H. Brady Co.; *U.S. Public*, pg. 250
VERTEL; *U.S. Public*, pg. 1717
WEBER MARKING SYSTEMS, INC.; *U.S. Private*, pg. 1157
WESTERN DIGITAL CORPORATION; *U.S. Public*, pg. 1758
WESTERN DIGITAL DRIVE ENGINEERING INC.—Western Digital Corporation; *U.S. Public*, pg. 1758
WESTERN DIGITAL MEDIA INC.—Western Digital Corporation; *U.S. Public*, pg. 1758
WHITE PINE SOFTWARE; *U.S. Private*, pg. 1173
WHITTAKER COMMUNICATIONS, INC.—Whittaker Corporation; *U.S. Public*, pg. 1767
WYSE TECHNOLOGY INC.; *U.S. Private*, pg. 1194
XEROX CORPORATION; *U.S. Public*, pg. 1783
XEROX CUSTOM SYSTEMS DIVISION—Xerox Corporation; *U.S. Public*, pg. 1784
XEROX IMAGING SYSTEMS, INC.—Xerox Corporation; *U.S. Public*, pg. 1785
XEROX SPECIAL INFORMATION SYSTEMS—Xerox Corporation; *U.S. Public*, pg. 1784
XEROX SPECIAL MARKETS GROUP—Xerox Corporation; *U.S. Public*, pg. 1785
YAMAHA CORPORATION; *Int'l*, pg. 1515

ZENITH DATA SYSTEMS—Compagnie des Machines Bull; *Int'l*, pg. 317
ZITEL CORPORATION; *U.S. Public*, pg. 1793

3578 — CALCULATING & ACCOUNTING MACHINES, EXCEPT ELECTRONIC COMPUTERS

AMERICAN PAYMENT SYSTEMS, INC.—United Illuminating Company; *U.S. Public*, pg. 1678
BRANDT, INC.—De La Rue plc; *Int'l*, pg. 387
COMMLINK—Jack Henry & Associates, Inc.; *U.S. Public*, pg. 809
CUMMINS-ALLISON CORP.; *U.S. Private*, pg. 295
DE LA RUE CASH HANDLING PRODUCT GROUP—De La Rue plc; *Int'l*, pg. 387
DE LA RUE SYSTEMS SA—De La Rue plc; *Int'l*, pg. 387
DIEBOLD, INCORPORATED; *U.S. Public*, pg. 506
DIXIE-NARCO, INC.—Maytag Corporation; *U.S. Public*, pg. 1065
DRESSER INDUSTRIES WAYNE DIVISION—Dresser Industries, Inc.; *U.S. Public*, pg. 528
GARNY AG—De La Rue plc; *Int'l*, pg. 387
INTERBOLD—International Business Machines Corporation; *U.S. Public*, pg. 897
KYOCERA CORPORATION; *Int'l*, pg. 775
LEFEBURE, AREA NORTH—De La Rue plc; *Int'l*, pg. 387
LEFEBURE, AREA WEST—De La Rue plc; *Int'l*, pg. 387
LEFEBURE CORP.—De La Rue plc; *Int'l*, pg. 387
LEFEBURE, SOUTH—De La Rue plc; *Int'l*, pg. 387
MONROE SYSTEMS FOR BUSINESS, INC.; *U.S. Private*, pg. 757
NCR CORPORATION; *U.S. Public*, pg. 1146
OLIVETTI SPA; *Int'l*, pg. 1002
OMRON CORPORATION; *Int'l*, pg. 1005
ROYAL CONSUMER BUSINESS PRODUCTS—Olivetti SpA; *Int'l*, pg. 1002
SAGEM TERMINALS & TELECOMMUNICATIONS DIVISION—Societe d'Applications Generales d'Electricite et de Mechanique; *Int'l*, pg. 1273
SHARP CORPORATION; *Int'l*, pg. 1228
TA TRIUMPH-ADLER VERTRIEBS GMBH—Olivetti SpA; *Int'l*, pg. 1004
TIDEL ENGINEERING, INC.—Tidel Technologies, Inc.; *U.S. Public*, pg. 1608
TIDEL TECHNOLOGIES, INC.; *U.S. Public*, pg. 1608
TOKYO ELECTRIC CO., LTD.—Toshiba Corporation; *Int'l*, pg. 1403
TOTTORI SANYO ELECTRIC CO., LTD.—Sanyo Electric Co., Ltd.; *Int'l*, pg. 1191
VERIFONE, INC.—Hewlett-Packard Company; *U.S. Public*, pg. 815

3579 — OFFICE MACHINES, NEC

ACCO BRANDS, INC.—Fortune Brands, Inc.; *U.S. Public*, pg. 674
ACCO EUROPE PLC—Fortune Brands, Inc.; *U.S. Public*, pg. 674
ACCO-REXEL GROUP SERVICES PLC—Fortune Brands, Inc.; *U.S. Public*, pg. 674
ACCO WORLD CORPORATION—Fortune Brands, Inc.; *U.S. Public*, pg. 674
ACCU-TIME SYSTEM—Accu-Sort Systems, Inc.; *U.S. Private*, pg. 11
ALFA-LAVAL S.A.—Tetra Laval Group; *Int'l*, pg. 1380
AMBRASOFT INTERNATIONAL—Olivetti SpA; *Int'l*, pg. 1002
APERTUS TECHNOLOGIES INCORPORATED; *U.S. Public*, pg. 119
ARKWRIGHT, INC—Oce-van der Grinten N.V.; *Int'l*, pg. 994
ARROW FASTENER CO., INC.; *U.S. Private*, pg. 85
ARTIST GRAPHICS—Control Systems Inc.; *U.S. Private*, pg. 271
ASCOM AUTELCA AG—Ascom Holding AG; *Int'l*, pg. 86
ASCOM HASLER (JAPAN) LTD.—Ascom Holding AG; *Int'l*, pg. 87
ASCOM HOLDING AG; *Int'l*, pg. 86
AVERY DENNISON CORPORATION LABEL GROUP—Avery Dennison Corporation; *U.S. Public*, pg. 153
BASF JAPAN LTD.—BASF AG; *Int'l*, pg. 106
BALL AEROSPACE SYSTEMS DIVISION—Ball Corporation; *U.S. Public*, pg. 171
BAUM USA—Stahl GmbH & Co.; *Int'l*, pg. 1293
BELL & HOWELL DOCUMENT MANAGEMENT PRODUCTS COMPANY—Bell & Howell Holdings; *U.S. Public*, pg. 201
BELL & HOWELL GMBH—Bell & Howell Holdings; *U.S. Public*, pg. 201
BELL & HOWELL HOLDINGS; *U.S. Public*, pg. 201
BELL & HOWELL LTD., (UK) MAILHANDLING DIV.—Bell & Howell Holdings; *U.S. Public*, pg. 201
BRANDT, INC.—De La Rue plc; *Int'l*, pg. 387
BROTHER INDUSTRIES, LTD.; *Int'l*, pg. 229
BULL CORPORATION OF JAPAN—Compagnie des Machines Bull; *Int'l*, pg. 318
BULL FAR EAST PTE. LTD.—Compagnie des Machines Bull; *Int'l*, pg. 318
JAMES BURN BINDERS—Standex International Corporation; *U.S. Public*, pg. 1507
JAMES BURN INTERNATIONAL S.A.—Standex International Corporation; *U.S. Public*, pg. 1507
CII-HONEYWELL BULL CAMEROUN SARL—Compagnie des Machines Bull; *Int'l*, pg. 316
CASIO COMPUTER CO., LTD.; *Int'l*, pg. 274
CENTRAL PRODUCTS COMPANY, INC.—Lynch Corporation; *U.S. Public*, pg. 1022
CIAP S.A.—Oce-van der Grinten N.V.; *Int'l*, pg. 994
COMPAGNIE CII-HB INTERNATIONALE N.V.—Compagnie des Machines Bull; *Int'l*, pg. 319
COMPAGNIE DES MACHINES BULL; *Int'l*, pg. 315
CONTROL SYSTEMS INC.; *U.S. Private*, pg. 271
CORRPRO COMPANIES, INC.; *U.S. Public*, pg. 451
CREDIT CARD SENTINEL—Montgomery Ward & Co., Inc.; *U.S. Private*, pg. 759
CUMMINS-ALLISON CORP.; *U.S. Private*, pg. 295
CUTLER MANUFACTURING CORPORATION; *U.S. Private*, pg. 298
DATA GENERAL GMBH—Data General Corporation; *U.S. Public*, pg. 486
DATACARD-CLEVELAND—DataCard Corporation; *U.S. Private*, pg. 312
DATACARD CORPORATION; *U.S. Private*, pg. 312
DELTA TRADING CO. LTD.—Olivetti SpA; *Int'l*, pg. 1003
DESIGN SYSTEMS INC.—AGA AB; *Int'l*, pg. 13
DEVELOPMENT AND MANUFACTURING—Xerox Corporation; *U.S. Public*, pg. 1784
A.B. DICK COMPANY—NESCO, Inc.; *U.S. Private*, pg. 791
DICTAPHONE CANADA LTD.-LTEE.—Stonington Partners Inc.; *U.S. Private*, pg. 1045
DICTAPHONE CO. U.K. LTD.—Stonington Partners Inc.; *U.S. Private*, pg. 1045
DICTAPHONE CORP.—Stonington Partners Inc.; *U.S. Private*, pg. 1045
DICTAPHONE INTERNATIONAL AG—Stonington Partners Inc.; *U.S. Private*, pg. 1045
EASTMAN KODAK ADW INC.—Eastman Kodak Company; *U.S. Public*, pg. 555
ELECTROCOM AUTOMATION L.P.—Siemens AG; *Int'l*, pg. 1244
ESCALADE SPORTS; *U.S. Public*, pg. 591
ESSELTE AB; *Int'l*, pg. 459
FELLOWES MANUFACTURING CO.; *U.S. Private*, pg. 400
FICUT S.P.A.—Oce-van der Grinten N.V.; *Int'l*, pg. 994
FORTUNE BRANDS, INC.; *U.S. Public*, pg. 674
FRIDEN ALCATEL—Alcatel Alsthom Compagnie Generale D'Electricite; *Int'l*, pg. 55
FUJI XEROX COMPANY LTD.—Xerox Corporation; *U.S. Public*, pg. 1785
GBC/VELOBLIND—General Binding Corporation; *U.S. Public*, pg. 707
GENERAL BINDING CORPORATION; *U.S. Public*, pg. 707
GESTETNER CORPORATION—Ricoh Company, Ltd.; *Int'l*, pg. 1115
GLORY LTD.; *Int'l*, pg. 554
GLORY USA, INC.—Glory Ltd.; *Int'l*, pg. 554
GRADCO (JAPAN), LTD.—Gradco Systems, Inc.; *U.S. Public*, pg. 757
GRADCO SYSTEMS, INC.; *U.S. Public*, pg. 757
DON GRESSWELL LTD.—U.S. Office Products Company; *U.S. Public*, pg. 1687
HANIMEX PTY. LIMITED—Ricoh Company, Ltd.; *Int'l*, pg. 1115
HARRIS CORPORATION; *U.S. Public*, pg. 791
HEIDELBERG FINISHING SYSTEMS—Heidelberger Druckmaschinen A.G.; *Int'l*, pg. 604
HISPANO OLIVETTI OFFICE—Olivetti SpA; *Int'l*, pg. 1003
OY HONEYWELL BULL AB—Compagnie des Machines Bull; *Int'l*, pg. 318
HONEYWELL BULL MADAGASCAR S.A.—Compagnie des Machines Bull; *Int'l*, pg. 318
HONEYWELL BULL MAROC S.A.—Compagnie des Machines Bull; *Int'l*, pg. 318
HONEYWELL BULL SAL—Compagnie des Machines Bull; *Int'l*, pg. 318
HUNT CORPORATION; *U.S. Public*, pg. 848
HUNT INTERNATIONAL DIV.—Hunt Corporation; *U.S. Public*, pg. 849
IBM WORLD TRADE EUROPE/MIDDLE EAST/AFRICA CORP.—International Business Machines Corporation; *U.S. Public*, pg. 896
ICL PLC—Fujitsu Limited; *Int'l*, pg. 528
ISC SYSTEMS ASIA PACIFIC LTD.—Olivetti SpA; *Int'l*, pg. 1003
ILFORD INC.—International Paper Company; *U.S. Public*, pg. 904
INFORMATION PROCESSING PRODUCTS—Fellowes Manufacturing Co.; *U.S. Private*, pg. 400
ING. C. OLIVETTI & C.—Olivetti SpA; *Int'l*, pg. 1002
INTERNATIONAL BUSINESS MACHINES A/S—International Business Machines Corporation; *U.S. Public*, pg. 898
INTERNATIONAL BUSINESS MACHINES CORPORATION; *U.S. Public*, pg. 895
INTERNATIONAL BUSINESS MACHINES OF BELGIUM S.A—International Business Machines Corporation; *U.S. Public*, pg. 898
INTERNATIONAL BUSINESS MACHINES, S.A.E.—International Business Machines Corporation; *U.S. Public*, pg. 898
IOMEGA CORPORATION; *U.S. Public*, pg. 912
JUKI CORPORATION; *Int'l*, pg. 716
KONICA BUSINESS MACHINES EUROPE GMBH—Konica Corporation; *Int'l*, pg. 749
KONICA BUSINESS MACHINES USA, INC.—Konica Corporation; *Int'l*, pg. 748
KONICA CORPORATION; *Int'l*, pg. 748
KONICA TOKYO INDUSTRIAL CENTER HACHIOJI—Konica Corporation; *Int'l*, pg. 748
KYOCERA CORPORATION; *Int'l*, pg. 775
LANE INDUSTRIES, INC.; *U.S. Private*, pg. 649
LANIER WORLDWIDE INC.—Harris Corporation; *U.S. Public*, pg. 791
LEXMARK INTERNATIONAL GROUP, INC.; *U.S. Public*, pg. 991
MAGNETIC TECHNOLOGIES CORPORATION—SPS Technologies, Inc.; *U.S. Public*, pg. 1420
MASTER PRODUCTS MFG. CO.—James Crean PLC; *Int'l*, pg. 340
MECHANICAL TECHNOLOGY INC.-TECHNOLOGY GRP.(LATHAM)—Mechanical Technology Inc.; *U.S. Public*, pg. 1077
METO, USA—Esselte AB; *Int'l*, pg. 460
MITA COPYSTAR AMERICA INC.—Mita Industrial Company, Ltd.; *Int'l*, pg. 870
MODI OLIVETTI LTD.—Olivetti SpA; *Int'l*, pg. 1003
MONARCH MARKING SYSTEMS—PAXAR Corporation; *U.S. Public*, pg. 1266
MOORE BUSINESS EQUIPMENT DIV.—Moore Corporation Limited; *Int'l*, pg. 890
MOORE DOCUMENT SOLUTIONS—Moore Corporation Limited; *Int'l*, pg. 890
MOORE INTELLIGENT IMAGING SYSTEMS PTY. LTD.—Moore Corporation Limited; *Int'l*, pg. 889
NEW HAVEN MFG. CORP.; *U.S. Private*, pg. 793
NEWBOLD CORPORATION; *U.S. Private*, pg. 796
OCE-AUSTRALIA LIMITED—Oce-van der Grinten N.V.; *Int'l*, pg. 994
OCE-BRASIL COMERCIO E INDUSTRIA LTDA.—Oce-van der Grinten N.V.; *Int'l*, pg. 994
OCE-FRANCE S.A.—Oce-van der Grinten N.V.; *Int'l*, pg. 994
OCE GRAPHICS FRANCE S.A.—Oce-van der Grinten N.V.; *Int'l*, pg. 994
OCE HOLDING USA—Oce-van der Grinten N.V.; *Int'l*, pg. 994
OCE-ITALIA S.P.A.—Oce-van der Grinten N.V.; *Int'l*, pg. 994
OCE SVENSKA AB—Oce-van der Grinten N.V.; *Int'l*, pg. 995
OCE-U.S.A.—Oce-van der Grinten N.V.; *Int'l*, pg. 994
OCE USA, INC.—Oce-van der Grinten N.V.; *Int'l*, pg. 994
OCE-VAN DER GRINTEN N.V.; *Int'l*, pg. 993
OPD LTD. HONG KONG—Olivetti SpA; *Int'l*, pg. 1003
OLIVETTI SPA; *Int'l*, pg. 1002
PAMARCO TECHNOLOGIES, INC.; *U.S. Private*, pg. 835
PEACE INDUSTRIES INC.; *U.S. Private*, pg. 845
PHILIPS INFORMATION SYSTEMS—Philips Electronics N.V.; *Int'l*, pg. 1055
PITNEY BOWES INC.; *U.S. Public*, pg. 1303
PITNEY BOWES JAPAN—Pitney Bowes Inc.; *U.S. Public*, pg. 1304
POWER SHRED DIVISION—Fellowes Manufacturing Co.; *U.S. Private*, pg. 400
PRETEC PRECISIE TECHNIEK B.V.—Bell & Howell Holdings; *U.S. Public*, pg. 201
PRODUCTOS MAESTROS—James Crean PLC; *Int'l*, pg. 341
RANK XEROX AG—Xerox Corporation; *U.S. Public*, pg. 1785
RANK XEROX LIMITED—The Rank Group PLC; *Int'l*, pg. 1087
RANK XEROX LIMITED—Xerox Corporation; *U.S. Public*, pg. 1785
REPRES. OFF. INTERN. TRADE CENTER—Olivetti SpA; *Int'l*, pg. 1004
REXEL BUSINESS MACHINES LTD.—Fortune Brands, Inc.; *U.S. Public*, pg. 675
REXEL LIMITED—Fortune Brands, Inc.; *U.S. Public*, pg. 675
RICOH CALIFORNIA RESEARCH CENTER—Ricoh Company, Ltd.; *Int'l*, pg. 1114
RICOH COMPANY, LTD.; *Int'l*, pg. 1114
RICOH CORPORATION—Ricoh Company, Ltd.; *Int'l*, pg. 1114
RICOH ELECTRONICS, INC.—Ricoh Company, Ltd.; *Int'l*, pg. 1114
RING KING VISIBLES, INC.—Esselte AB; *Int'l*, pg. 460
ROYAL CONSUMER BUSINESS PRODUCTS—Olivetti SpA; *Int'l*, pg. 1002
SATAS - SOCIETE POUR L'AFFRANCHISSEMENT ET LE TIMBRAGE AUTOMATIQUES—Alcatel Alsthom Compagnie Generale D'Electricite; *Int'l*, pg. 54
SAVIN OF TAMPA BAY—Ricoh Company, Ltd.; *Int'l*, pg. 1114
SCANVEST OLIVETTI A/S—Olivetti SpA; *Int'l*, pg. 1004
SMITH CORONA CORP.; *U.S. Private*, pg. 1007
SMITH CORONA FINANCIAL DIVISION—Smith Corona Corp.; *U.S. Private*, pg. 1007
SPECTRA-PHYSICS SCANNING SYSTEMS INC.—Thermo Electron Corporation; *U.S. Public*, pg. 1594
STANDARD DUPLICATING MACHINES CORP.; *U.S. Private*, pg. 1031
THE STANDARD REGISTER COMPANY; *U.S. Public*, pg. 1505
SYSTEMS NORTHWEST—Ricoh Company, Ltd.; *Int'l*, pg. 1114
TAB PRODUCTS CO.; *U.S. Public*, pg. 1559
TAB PRODUCTS EUROPA B.V.—Tab Products Co.; *U.S. Public*, pg. 1559
TAB PRODUCTS OF CANADA, LTD.—Tab Products Co.; *U.S. Public*, pg. 1559
TICKETMASTER CORPORATION; *U.S. Private*, pg. 1084
TOSHIBA AMERICA INFORMATION SYSTEMS, INC.—Toshiba Corporation; *Int'l*, pg. 1405
TOTTORI SANYO ELECTRIC CO., LTD.—Sanyo Electric Co., Ltd.; *Int'l*, pg. 1191
TRANSLOGIC CORP.—Thyssen AG; *Int'l*, pg. 1387
TRIUMPH ADLER GROUP; *Int'l*, pg. 1424
TRIUMPH ADLER/ROYTYPE (UK) LTD.—Olivetti SpA; *Int'l*, pg. 1004
VIDEOJET SYSTEMS INTERNATIONAL, INC.—The General Electric Company, p.l.c.; *Int'l*, pg. 545
VOLUMATIC LIMITED—Halma p.l.c.; *Int'l*, pg. 590
WEBER MARKING SYSTEMS, INC.; *U.S. Private*, pg. 1157
XEROX CANADA LTD.—Xerox Corporation; *U.S. Public*, pg. 1785
XEROX CORPORATION; *U.S. Public*, pg. 1783
XEROX DOCUMENT PROCESSING—Xerox Corporation; *U.S. Public*, pg. 1784
XEROX SPECIAL INFORMATION SYSTEMS—Xerox Corporation; *U.S. Public*, pg. 1784
XEROX SPECIAL MARKETS GROUP—Xerox Corporation; *U.S. Public*, pg. 1785
XEROX TECHNIGRAPHIC PRODUCTS DIVISION—Xerox Corporation; *U.S. Public*, pg. 1784

3581 — AUTOMATIC VENDING MACHINES

ASSA ABLOY AB; Int'l, pg. 17
ASCOM AUTELCA AG—Ascom Holding AG; Int'l, pg. 86
ASCOM AUTOMATION INC.—Ascom Holding AG; Int'l, pg. 86
BUCYRUS BLADES INC.—Esco Corporation; U.S. Private, pg. 383
CAVALIER CORPORATION; U.S. Private, pg. 220
THE CORNELIUS COMPANY—IMI Plc; Int'l, pg. 646
CRANE CO.; U.S. Public, pg. 456
CRANE NATIONAL VENDORS CO., LTD.—Crane Co.; U.S. Public, pg. 456
DIXIE-NARCO, INC.—Maytag Corporation; U.S. Public, pg. 1065
GIANT AUTOMATIC MONEY SYSTEMS—Giant Food Inc.; U.S. Public, pg. 741
GLORY LTD.; Int'l, pg. 554
GOLD MEDAL PRODUCTS CO.; U.S. Private, pg. 459
GOLDSTAR CO. LTD.—LG Group; Int'l, pg. 778
GREENWALD INDUSTRIES, INC.—Publicker Industries Inc.; U.S. Public, pg. 1341
IMI CORNELIUS BRASIL—IMI Plc; Int'l, pg. 646
KASPAR WIRE WORKS, INC.; U.S. Private, pg. 608
MAYTAG CORPORATION; U.S. Public, pg. 1064
NRI IBERICA, S.A.—Crane Co.; U.S. Public, pg. 457
NATIONAL REJECTORS, INC., G.M.B.H.—Crane Co.; U.S. Public, pg. 456
NATIONAL VENDORS—Crane Co.; U.S. Public, pg. 457
ROWE INTERNATIONAL, INC.—RI Holdings; U.S. Private, pg. 904
SANDEN CORPORATION; Int'l, pg. 1184
SANYO ELECTRIC CO., LTD.; Int'l, pg. 1190
STAINLESS ICE-TAINER CO. (SITCO)—IMI Plc; Int'l, pg. 646
UMC INDUSTRIES, LTD.—Crane Co.; U.S. Public, pg. 457
THE VENDO COMPANY—Sanden Corporation; Int'l, pg. 1184
VENDO INTERNATIONAL DIV.—Sanden Corporation; Int'l, pg. 1184
VENDO (ITALY) S.P.A.—Sanden Corporation; Int'l, pg. 1184

3582 — COMMERCIAL LAUNDRY, DRY CLEANING & PRESSING MACHINES

BERMIL INDUSTRIES CORP.; U.S. Private, pg. 136
CHALLENGE INDUSTRIES—Electrolux, AB; Int'l, pg. 438
DETREX EQUIPMENT DIV.—Detrex Corporation; U.S. Public, pg. 501
DEXTER COMPANY; U.S. Private, pg. 329
ELECTROLUX-WASCATOR AB—Electrolux, AB; Int'l, pg. 439
MAYTAG COMPANY—Maytag Corporation; U.S. Public, pg. 1064
MAYTAG CORPORATION; U.S. Public, pg. 1064
MULTIMATIC CORPORATION; U.S. Private, pg. 767
PASSAT LAUNDRY SYSTEMS; U.S. Private, pg. 842
RAYTHEON APPLIANCES—Raytheon Company; U.S. Public, pg. 1366
REN-VASK A/S—Electrolux, AB; Int'l, pg. 441
SPICER OFF-HIGHWAY AXLE DIV.—Dana Corporation; U.S. Public, pg. 479
WHIRLPOOL CORPORATION; U.S. Public, pg. 1764

3585 — AIR CONDITIONING & WARM AIR HEATING EQUIPMENT & COMMERCIAL & INDUSTRIAL REFRIGERATION EQUIPMENT

AAF MCQUAY, INC.; U.S. Private, pg. 2
ABM INDUSTRIES; U.S. Public, pg. 2
AC CORPORATION; U.S. Private, pg. 3
APD CRYOGENICS INC.—Intermagnetics General Corporation; U.S. Public, pg. 894
API KATEMA INC.—American Precision Industries Inc.; U.S. Public, pg. 90
APL CORPORATION; U.S. Private, pg. 7
ACME REFRIGERATION OF BATON ROUGE INC.; U.S. Private, pg. 13
AEROFIN CORP.—Ampco-Pittsburgh Corporation; U.S. Public, pg. 103
AIR SYSTEMS LTD.—Tomkins PLC; Int'l, pg. 1398
AIRTEX—UIS, Inc.; U.S. Private, pg. 1113
AISIN SEIKI CO. LTD.; Int'l, pg. 39
AJAX MAGNETHERMIC CANADA LTD.—BBA Group plc; Int'l, pg. 113
AJAX MAGNETHERMIC CORP.—BBA Group plc; Int'l, pg. 113
AJAX MAGNETHERMIC U.K. LTD.—BBA Group plc; Int'l, pg. 113
ALADDIN INDUSTRIES PTY. LTD.—Aladdin Industries, Incorporated; U.S. Private, pg. 31
ALCO CONTROLS DIV.—Emerson Electric Co.; U.S. Public, pg. 572
ALFA-LAVAL THERMAL AB—Tetra Laval Group; Int'l, pg. 1378
AMERICAN STANDARD INC.; U.S. Public, pg. 91
AMERICOLD COMPRESSOR CO.—Electrolux, AB; Int'l, pg. 439
AMPCO-PITTSBURGH CORPORATION; U.S. Public, pg. 103
AMSTED INDUSTRIES INCORPORATED; U.S. Private, pg. 68
AMTROL INC.—The Cypress Group LLC; U.S. Private, pg. 300
APPLIED SYSTEMS—York International Corporation; U.S. Public, pg. 1788
AQUA-CHEM INC.—Lyonnaise des Eaux S.A.; Int'l, pg. 824
ARDCO, INC.; U.S. Private, pg. 80
ARMSTRONG AIR CONDITIONING INC.—Lennox International Inc.; U.S. Private, pg. 659
ARMSTRONG INTERNATIONAL, INC.; U.S. Private, pg. 83
ARROW FLUID POWER—Arrow Pneumatics Co. Inc.; U.S. Private, pg. 85
ARROW PNEUMATICS CO. INC.; U.S. Private, pg. 85
AUTOMOTIVE CONNECTORS DIV.—Parker Hannifin Corporation; U.S. Public, pg. 1260
AB BAHCO VENTILATION—ABB Asea Brown Boveri (Holding) Ltd.; Int'l, pg. 7
BARBEQUE KING—Standex International Corporation; U.S. Public, pg. 1507
BEUTLER HEATING & AIR CONDITIONING INC.; U.S. Private, pg. 141
BLISSFIELD MANUFACTURING COMPANY; U.S. Private, pg. 149
BONGARD—Groupe Strafor Facom; Int'l, pg. 570
BONLAND INDUSTRIES, INC.; U.S. Private, pg. 156
BOOTH/CRYSTAL TIPS—Scotsman Industries, Inc.; U.S. Public, pg. 1445
BOU-MATIC—DEC International, Inc.; U.S. Private, pg. 301
BRAN & LUEBBE G.M.B.H.—Tetra Laval Group; Int'l, pg. 1379
BURNHAM; U.S. Public, pg. 270
CIMCO REFRIGERATION—Toromont Industries Ltd.; Int'l, pg. 1400
CALSONIC CLIMATE CONTROL, INC.—Nissan Motor Co., Ltd.; Int'l, pg. 944
CALSONIC CORP.—Nissan Motor Co., Ltd.; Int'l, pg. 944
CALSONIC HARRISON CO., LTD.—General Motors Corporation; U.S. Public, pg. 724
CALSONIC MFG. CORP.—Nissan Motor Co., Ltd.; Int'l, pg. 944
CARLYLE COMPRESSOR CO., INC.—United Technologies Corporation; U.S. Public, pg. 1690
CARRIER AIR TERMINAL FACILITY—United Technologies Corporation; U.S. Public, pg. 1689
CARRIER CORP.—United Technologies Corporation; U.S. Public, pg. 1690
CARRIER CORP. TRANSICOLD DIVISION—United Technologies Corporation; U.S. Public, pg. 1689
CARRIER CORPORATION—United Technologies Corporation; U.S. Public, pg. 1689
CASTELMAC, S.P.A.—Scotsman Industries, Inc.; U.S. Public, pg. 1445
CENTRIA; U.S. Private, pg. 225
CERAMIC COOLING TOWER CO.—Amsted Industries Incorporated; U.S. Private, pg. 68
CHROMALOX, S.A.—Emerson Electric Co.; U.S. Public, pg. 576
CLEVELAND RANGE—Berisford plc; Int'l, pg. 188
COCHRANE, INC.—Crane Co.; U.S. Public, pg. 456
COLE ENGINEERING, INC.—Giant Food Inc.; U.S. Public, pg. 741
THE COLEMAN COMPANY, INC.—MacAndrews & Forbes Holdings Inc.; U.S. Private, pg. 690
COLUMBIA SPECIALTIES, INC.—Fedders Corp.; U.S. Public, pg. 615
COMMAIR MECHANICAL SERVICES—ABM Industries; U.S. Public, pg. 2
COMMERCIAL ENVIRONMENTAL SYSTEMS GROUP, INC.—Nortek, Inc.; U.S. Public, pg. 1193
COMPONENTES DELFA, C.A.—General Motors Corporation; U.S. Public, pg. 724
CONSOLIDATED INDUSTRIES CORP.—Berisford plc; Int'l, pg. 188
CONSTRUCTION SPECIALTIES, INC.; U.S. Private, pg. 266
CONTINENTAL MATERIALS CORPORATION; U.S. Public, pg. 441
CONVAIR COOLER CORP.; U.S. Private, pg. 271
COPELAND CANADA, LTD.—Emerson Electric Co.; U.S. Public, pg. 576
COPELAND CORPORATION—Emerson Electric Co.; U.S. Public, pg. 573
CORDLEY TEMPRITE—Elkay Manufacturing Company; U.S. Private, pg. 372
THE CORNELIUS COMPANY—IMI Plc; Int'l, pg. 646
D.W.M COPELAND G.M.B.H.—Emerson Electric Co.; U.S. Public, pg. 576
DAEWOO CORPORATION; Int'l, pg. 357
DAEWOO ELECTRONICS CO., LTD.—Daewoo Corporation; Int'l, pg. 357
DAIKIN INDUSTRIES, LTD.; Int'l, pg. 365
DANFOSS (PTY) LTD.—Danfoss A/S; Int'l, pg. 377
DATA AIRE, INC.—Construction Specialties, Inc.; U.S. Private, pg. 266
DELFIELD COMPANY—Scotsman Industries, Inc.; U.S. Public, pg. 1445
DELPHI HARRISON THERMAL SYSTEMS—General Motors Corporation; U.S. Public, pg. 719
DENCO LTD.—AMEC Plc; Int'l, pg. 16
DENSO SALES CALIFORNIA—Toyota Motor Corporation; Int'l, pg. 1412
DIAVIA S.P.A.—United Technologies Corporation; U.S. Public, pg. 1691
THE DOMETIC CORPORATION—Electrolux, AB; Int'l, pg. 440
DONLEE TECHNOLOGIES INC.; U.S. Private, pg. 339
DOVATECH, LTD.—Dover Corporation; U.S. Public, pg. 520
DYNAMICS CORPORATION OF AMERICA—CTS Corporation; U.S. Public, pg. 286
ECLIPSE-DUNGS CONTROLS, L.P.—Eclipse Inc.; U.S. Private, pg. 360
EDWARDS ENGINEERING CORPORATION; U.S. Private, pg. 365
ELECTROLUX COMMERCIAL REFRIGERATION AB—Electrolux, AB; Int'l, pg. 438
ELKAY MANUFACTURING COMPANY; U.S. Private, pg. 372
ELLIS & WATTS DIV.—CTS Corporation; U.S. Public, pg. 286
EMAIL LIMITED; Int'l, pg. 450
EMERSON ELECTRIC CO.; U.S. Public, pg. 572
EVANS TEMPCON INC.—APL Corporation; U.S. Private, pg. 7
EVCON INDUSTRIES, INC.—York International Corporation; U.S. Public, pg. 1788
FEDDERS CORP.; U.S. Public, pg. 614
FEDDERS INTERNATIONAL, INC.—Fedders Corp.; U.S. Public, pg. 614
FEDDERS NORTH AMERICA, INC.—Fedders Corp.; U.S. Public, pg. 614
FEVI-PROMAVENT—Jeumont-Schneider Trenformeteurs; Int'l, pg. 706
FLAKT AB—ABB Asea Brown Boveri (Holding) Ltd.; Int'l, pg. 7
FLORIDA HEAT PUMP—Harrow Industries; U.S. Private, pg. 506
FLUIDEX DIV.—Parker Hannifin Corporation; U.S. Public, pg. 1260
FORD ELECTRONICS & REFRIGERATION CORP.—Ford Motor Company; U.S. Public, pg. 664
FORD MOTOR COMPANY; U.S. Public, pg. 661
FOSTER REFRIGERATOR CORPORATION; U.S. Private, pg. 421
FOSTORIA INDUSTRIES, INC.; U.S. Private, pg. 421
FOUR SEASONS AIR CONDITIONING DIV.—Standard Motor Products Inc.; U.S. Public, pg. 1503
FRICK COMPANY—York International Corporation; U.S. Public, pg. 1788
FRIGID COIL WEST—York International Corporation; U.S. Public, pg. 1789
FRIGIDAIRE COMMERCIAL REFRIGERATION—Electrolux, AB; Int'l, pg. 439
FRIGIDAIRE HOME PRODUCTS—Electrolux, AB; Int'l, pg. 439
FRIGIDAIRE HOME PRODUCTS-HOME COMFORT PRODUCTS—Electrolux, AB; Int'l, pg. 440
FRIMONT, S.P.A.—Scotsman Industries, Inc.; U.S. Public, pg. 1445
PHILIP FRITZE & SONS, INC.; U.S. Private, pg. 429
G.E. APPLIANCES—General Electric Company; U.S. Public, pg. 710
GAMKO HOLDINGS—Specialty Equipment Companies Inc.; U.S. Public, pg. 1497
GENERAL CABLE CO.—Wassall Plc; Int'l, pg. 1487
GENERAL FILTERS, INC.; U.S. Private, pg. 444
GIBSON APPLIANCES—Electrolux, AB; Int'l, pg. 439
GOLDSTAR CO. LTD.—LG Group; Int'l, pg. 778
GOODMAN MANUFACTURING; U.S. Private, pg. 464
GOVERNAIR CORPORATION—Nortek, Inc.; U.S. Public, pg. 1193
GREAT BEAR SPRING COMPANY—Nestle S.A.; Int'l, pg. 919
GROUP MAINTENANCE AMERICA CORP.; U.S. Public, pg. 766
GUANGDONG SANYO AIR CONDITIONERS SYSTEM MANUFACTURING LTD.—Sanyo Electric Co., Ltd.; Int'l, pg. 1192
H & H REFRIGERATION LTD.—Pentland Group PLC; Int'l, pg. 1035
H M K ENTERPRISES, INC.; U.S. Private, pg. 489
HARFORD SYSTEMS, INC.—Lab Products, Inc.; U.S. Private, pg. 641
HARTEK BEVERAGE HANDLING GMBH—Scotsman Industries, Inc.; U.S. Public, pg. 1445
HEAT CONTROLLER, INC.; U.S. Private, pg. 518
HERRMIDIFIER CO., INC.—Trion, Inc.; U.S. Public, pg. 1639
HILL PHOENIX—Dover Corporation; U.S. Public, pg. 521
HITACHI OHIRA INDUSTRIAL CO., LTD.—Hitachi, Ltd.; Int'l, pg. 621
HOUSTON FEARLESS 76 INC.; U.S. Private, pg. 542
HOWDEN COMPRESSORS—Howden Group Plc; Int'l, pg. 636
HOWDEN FLUID SYSTEMS—Mark IV Industries Inc.; U.S. Public, pg. 1045
O.G. HOYER A/S—Tetra Laval Group; Int'l, pg. 1378
HUBBELL INCORPORATED; U.S. Public, pg. 844
HUSSMANN CORP.—Whitman Corporation; U.S. Public, pg. 1766
IMI CORNELIUS, INC. (IA)—IMI Plc; Int'l, pg. 646
IMI PLC; Int'l, pg. 646
IPAC, INC.; U.S. Private, pg. 555
IGLOO PRODUCTS CORPORATION—Brunswick Corporation; U.S. Public, pg. 265
INCENTIVE AB; Int'l, pg. 666
INDUSTRIAL COMPONENTS GROUP—BTR plc; Int'l, pg. 127
INDUSTRIAS KOLMEX, S.A.—MacAndrews & Forbes Holdings Inc.; U.S. Private, pg. 690
INTERMAGNETICS GENERAL CORPORATION; U.S. Public, pg. 893
INTERNATIONAL COLD STORAGE CO., INC.; U.S. Private, pg. 568
INTERNATIONAL COMFORT PRODUCTS; U.S. Public, pg. 898
INTERNATIONAL COMFORT PRODUCTS CORP.—International Comfort Products; U.S. Public, pg. 898
INTERNATIONAL DIVISION—Tecumseh Products Company; U.S. Public, pg. 1565
INTERNATIONAL ENVIRONMENTAL CORP.—LSB Industries, Inc.; U.S. Public, pg. 970
IPSEN INTERNATIONAL, INC.—Ruhrgas Aktiengesellschaft; Int'l, pg. 1149
ISOVEL INTERNATIONAL LTD.—Haden Maclellan Holdings plc; Int'l, pg. 585
JAPAN AJAX MAGNETHERMIC CO. LTD.—BBA Group plc; Int'l, pg. 113
JET SPRAY CORP.; U.S. Private, pg. 586
JET SPRAY INTERNATIONAL—Jet Spray Corp.; U.S. Private, pg. 587
JEUMONT-SCHNEIDER TRENFORMETEURS; Int'l, pg. 706
JEWETT INTERNATIONAL CORP.—Ruslander & Sons, Inc.; U.S. Private, pg. 952
THE JEWETT REFRIGERATOR CO., INC.—Ruslander & Sons, Inc.; U.S. Private, pg. 952

JUNG PUMPEN VERWALTUNGS GMBH—Masco Corporation; *U.S. Public*, pg. 1054
KHD DEUTZ OF AMERICA CORPORATION—Deutz AG; *Int'l*, pg. 408
KATHABAR INCORPORATED; *U.S. Private*, pg. 609
KECO INDUSTRY, INC.; *U.S. Private*, pg. 611
KEEPRITE INC—International Comfort Products; *U.S. Public*, pg. 898
KETEMA, INC.—KTM Holdings Corp.; *U.S. Private*, pg. 604
KIDRON INC.; *U.S. Private*, pg. 619
KILOHEAT LTD.—Masco Corporation; *U.S. Public*, pg. 1055
KIMMEL MOTZ REFRIGERATION CORP.—Toromont Industries Ltd.; *Int'l*, pg. 1400
KING SEELY THERMOS COMPANY—Eaton Corporation; *U.S. Public*, pg. 558
KLAXON SIGNALS LIMITED—Halma p.l.c.; *Int'l*, pg. 590
GEORGE KOCH SONS, INC.; *U.S. Private*, pg. 628
LEC REFRIGERATION PLC—Sime Darby Berhad; *Int'l*, pg. 1251
LSB INDUSTRIES, INC.; *U.S. Public*, pg. 970
LANDIS & STAEFA, INC.—Landis & Staefa AG; *Int'l*, pg. 800
LECTRODRYER DIV., AJAX MAGNETHERMIC CORP.—BBA Group plc; *Int'l*, pg. 113
LENNOX INDUSTRIES (CANADA) LTD.—Lennox International Inc.; *U.S. Private*, pg. 660
LENNOX INDUSTRIES INC.—Lennox International Inc.; *U.S. Private*, pg. 659
LENNOX INTERNATIONAL INC.; *U.S. Private*, pg. 659
LIEBERT CORPORATION—Emerson Electric Co.; *U.S. Public*, pg. 573
LIEBHERR-WERK LIENZ GMBH—Liebherr-International AG; *Int'l*, pg. 808
LINDE AG WERKSGRUPPE KALTE- U. EINRICHTUNGSTECHNIK—Linde AG; *Int'l*, pg. 810
LITTON SYSTEMS CANADA LTD.—Litton Industries, Inc.; *U.S. Public*, pg. 1005
LOISELET INTERNATIONAL S.A.—Groupe Strafor Facom; *Int'l*, pg. 570
LONRHO PLC; *Int'l*, pg. 817
L'UNITE HERMETIQUE S.A.—Tecumseh Products Company; *U.S. Public*, pg. 1566
MFRI INC.; *U.S. Public*, pg. 1026
MGR EQUIPMENT CORP.; *U.S. Private*, pg. 687
MHIA AIR-CONDITIONING & REFRIGERATION MACHINERY DIVISION—Mitsubishi Heavy Industries Ltd.; *Int'l*, pg. 874
M.E. MACK VALVES PTY. LIMITED—Senior Engineering Group, plc.; *Int'l*, pg. 1222
MAMMOTH, INC.—Nortek, Inc.; *U.S. Public*, pg. 1193
THE MANITOWOC COMPANY, INC.; *U.S. Public*, pg. 1040
MANITOWOC ICE, INC.—The Manitowoc Company, Inc.; *U.S. Public*, pg. 1041
MARINE AIR SYSTEMS, INC.—Taylor Made Group, Inc.; *U.S. Private*, pg. 1071
MARK IV INDUSTRIES INC.; *U.S. Public*, pg. 1044
MASTER-BILT PRODUCTS—Standex International Corporation; *U.S. Public*, pg. 1506
MATSUSHITA ELECTRIC INDUSTRIAL CO., LTD.; *Int'l*, pg. 846
MATSUSHITA REFRIGERATION INDUSTRIES (S) PTE. LTD.—Matsushita Electric Industrial Co., Ltd.; *Int'l*, pg. 847
MATSUSHITA SEIKO CO., LTD.—Matsushita Electric Industrial Co., Ltd.; *Int'l*, pg. 846
MCQUAY INT'L—AAF McQuay, Inc.; *U.S. Private*, pg. 3
MCQUAY INTERNATIONAL—AAF McQuay, Inc.; *U.S. Private*, pg. 3
MESTEK, INC.; *U.S. Public*, pg. 1099
MITSUBISHI ELECTRIC CORPORATION; *Int'l*, pg. 872
MITSUBISHI HEAVY INDUSTRIES LTD.; *Int'l*, pg. 873
AB CARL MUNTERS—Incentive AB; *Int'l*, pg. 669
AB CARL MUNTERS (SEA)—Incentive AB; *Int'l*, pg. 669
MUNTERS EUROFORM GMBH—Incentive AB; *Int'l*, pg. 669
MUNTERS GMBH—Incentive AB; *Int'l*, pg. 669
MUNTERS LTD.—Incentive AB; *Int'l*, pg. 669
MUNTERS NEDERLAND B.V.—Incentive AB; *Int'l*, pg. 669
MUNTERS S.A.—Incentive AB; *Int'l*, pg. 669
NAO, INC.; *U.S. Private*, pg. 771
N.O.A. AIRSCREW HOWDEN INC.—Howden Group Plc; *Int'l*, pg. 636
NIAGARA BLOWER COMPANY; *U.S. Private*, pg. 798
NORDYNE INC.—Nortek, Inc.; *U.S. Public*, pg. 1193
NORTEK, INC.; *U.S. Public*, pg. 1192
OASIS CORP.; *U.S. Private*, pg. 810
PALMER REFRIGERATION LTD.—Whitman Corporation; *U.S. Public*, pg. 1766
PARKER HANNIFIN ARGENTINA SAIC—Parker Hannifin Corporation; *U.S. Public*, pg. 1263
PARKER HANNIFIN A/S—Parker Hannifin Corporation; *U.S. Public*, pg. 1263
PARKER HANNIFIN CORPORATION; *U.S. Public*, pg. 1259
PATTERSON-KELLEY COMPANY—Harsco Corporation; *U.S. Public*, pg. 793
PHOENIX MANUFACTURING, INC.—Continental Materials Corporation; *U.S. Public*, pg. 441
PLANT CITY STEEL CO.—Harsco Corporation; *U.S. Public*, pg. 793
PNEUMAFIL CORPORATION; *U.S. Private*, pg. 873
PREMARK FOOD EQUIPMENT GROUP—Premark International, Inc.; *U.S. Public*, pg. 1322
PREMARK INTERNATIONAL, INC.; *U.S. Public*, pg. 1321
RANDELL—Dover Corporation; *U.S. Public*, pg. 520
REFRIGERATION HUSSMANN LTEE.—Whitman Corporation; *U.S. Public*, pg. 1766
ETS REINHARD RAFFEL GALVANISATION SARL—Ascot Holdings Plc; *Int'l*, pg. 88
REINHARD RAFFEL METALLWARENFABRIK GMBH—Ascot Holdings Plc; *Int'l*, pg. 88
REMCOR PRODUCTS CO.—IMI Plc; *Int'l*, pg. 646
RESEARCH PRODUCTS CORPORATION; *U.S. Private*, pg. 924
RHEEM AIR CONDITIONING DIV.—Paloma Industries Limited; *Int'l*, pg. 1022
RHEEM MANUFACTURING CO.—Paloma Industries Limited; *Int'l*, pg. 1022
RINNAI CORP.; *Int'l*, pg. 1118
RUSLANDER & SONS, INC.; *U.S. Private*, pg. 952
S & P COIL PRODUCTS LIMITED—Halma p.l.c.; *Int'l*, pg. 590
SAB IBERICA S.A.—Cardo AB; *Int'l*, pg. 271
SAB SISTEMI S.P.A.—Cardo AB; *Int'l*, pg. 271
SAB WABCO AB—Cardo AB; *Int'l*, pg. 271
SAB WABCO BENELUX—Cardo AB; *Int'l*, pg. 271
SAB WABCO ENGINEERING S.R.L.—Cardo AB; *Int'l*, pg. 271
SAB WABCO HOLDINGS B.V.—Cardo AB; *Int'l*, pg. 271
SAB WABCO LTD.—Cardo AB; *Int'l*, pg. 271
SAB WABCO N.V.—Cardo AB; *Int'l*, pg. 271
SAB WABCO S.A.—Cardo AB; *Int'l*, pg. 271
SAB WABCO S.P.A.—Cardo AB; *Int'l*, pg. 271
SS COILS LIMITED—Ascot Holdings Plc; *Int'l*, pg. 88
SANDEN CORPORATION; *Int'l*, pg. 1184
SANDEN INTERNATIONAL (U.S.A.), INC.—Sanden Corporation; *Int'l*, pg. 1184
SANISERV MANUFACTURING CORP.; *U.S. Private*, pg. 965
SANKI ENGINEERING CO., LTD.—Mitsui & Co., Ltd.; *Int'l*, pg. 877
SCOTSMAN ICE SYSTEMS—Scotsman Industries, Inc.; *U.S. Public*, pg. 1445
SCOTSMAN INDUSTRIES, INC.; *U.S. Public*, pg. 1444
SCOTTPOLAR CORPORATION—Toromont Industries Ltd.; *Int'l*, pg. 1400
SENIOR AUSTRALIA LIMITED—Senior Engineering Group, plc.; *Int'l*, pg. 1222
SENIOR ENGINEERING—Senior Engineering Group, plc.; *Int'l*, pg. 1222
SENIOR ENGINEERING COMPANY-USA—Senior Engineering Group, plc.; *Int'l*, pg. 1222
SENIOR ENGINEERING (PTY) LIMITED-SOUTH AFRICA—Senior Engineering Group, plc.; *Int'l*, pg. 1223
SENIOR THERMAL ENGINEERING LIMITED—Senior Engineering Group, plc.; *Int'l*, pg. 1221
SENIOR TIFT AUSTRALIA PTY LIMITED—Senior Engineering Group, plc.; *Int'l*, pg. 1223
SENIOR TIFT-QUEENSLAND—Senior Engineering Group, plc.; *Int'l*, pg. 1223
SERVICE CENTRALE VOOR KOELTECHNIEK B.V.—Internatio-Muller N.V.; *Int'l*, pg. 681
SEVERN FURNACES LIMITED—Instron Corporation; *U.S. Public*, pg. 883
SHANNON DIVISION—Tecumseh Products Company; *U.S. Public*, pg. 1566
THE SHANNON GROUP—The Manitowoc Company, Inc.; *U.S. Public*, pg. 1041
SHARP ELECTRONICA ESPANA S.A. (BARCELONA)—Sharp Corporation; *Int'l*, pg. 1229
SHARP ELECTRONICS CORPORATION—Sharp Corporation; *Int'l*, pg. 1228
SHARP ELECTRONICS (EUROPE)—Sharp Corporation; *Int'l*, pg. 1230
SHARP ELECTRONICS (U.K.)—Sharp Corporation; *Int'l*, pg. 1230
SHARP INTERNATIONAL FINANCE (U.K.) PLC.—Sharp Corporation; *Int'l*, pg. 1230
SHARP LABORATORIES OF EUROPE, LTD.—Sharp Corporation; *Int'l*, pg. 1230
SHARP MANUFACTURING COMPANY OF U.K.—Sharp Corporation; *Int'l*, pg. 1230
SHARP PRECISION MANUFACTURING (U.K.) LTD.—Sharp Corporation; *Int'l*, pg. 1230
SIEMENS A/S—Siemens AG; *Int'l*, pg. 1247
SLANT/FIN CORPORATION; *U.S. Private*, pg. 1005
SLANT-FIN, LTD./LTEE—Slant/Fin Corporation; *U.S. Private*, pg. 1005
SMITH ENGINEERING CO.—Haden Maclellan Holdings plc; *Int'l*, pg. 586
SMITHS INDUSTRIES PLC; *Int'l*, pg. 1266
SNAPPY AIR DISTRIBUTION PRODUCTS—Standex International Corporation; *U.S. Public*, pg. 1506
SOPRANO S.A.—Alcatel Alsthom Compagnie Generale D'Electricite; *Int'l*, pg. 53
STAINLESS ICE-TAINER CO. (SITCO)—IMI Plc; *Int'l*, pg. 646
STAL REFRIGERATION AB—ABB Asea Brown Boveri (Holding) Ltd.; *Int'l*, pg. 7
STANDARD MOTOR PRODUCTS INC.; *U.S. Public*, pg. 1503
STANDEX INTERNATIONAL CORPORATION; *U.S. Public*, pg. 1505
STANLEY KNIGHT CORPORATION; *U.S. Private*, pg. 1033
STEVENS-LEE COMPANY; *U.S. Private*, pg. 1042
SUECOBRAS INDUSTRIA E COMERCIO LTDA.—Cardo AB; *Int'l*, pg. 271
SULZER-ESCHER WYSS GMBH—Sulzer Ltd.; *Int'l*, pg. 1307
SULZER ITALIA S.P.A.—Sulzer Ltd.; *Int'l*, pg. 1306
SUNROC CORPORATION; *U.S. Private*, pg. 1053
T A HOLDINGS LIMITED; *Int'l*, pg. 1334
TA CONTROL A/S—Incentive AB; *Int'l*, pg. 670
TAC CONTROL AB—Incentive AB; *Int'l*, pg. 670
TAC CONTROL PTE. LTD.—Incentive AB; *Int'l*, pg. 670
TAC (UK) LTD.—Incentive AB; *Int'l*, pg. 670
TECUMSEH DIVISION—Tecumseh Products Company; *U.S. Public*, pg. 1566
TECUMSEH DO BRASIL—Tecumseh Products Company; *U.S. Public*, pg. 1566
TECUMSEH PRODUCTS COMPANY; *U.S. Public*, pg. 1565
TECUMSEH PRODUCTS CO. COMPRESSOR & REFRIGERATION GROUP OF DIVISIONS—Tecumseh Products Company; *U.S. Public*, pg. 1566
TECUMSEH PRODUCTS OF CANADA LTD.—Tecumseh Products Company; *U.S. Public*, pg. 1566
TEMCO FIREPLACE PRODUCTS, INC. (MANCHESTER)—Temtex Industries Inc.; *U.S. Public*, pg. 1576
TEMCO FIREPLACE PRODUCTS, INC. (PERRIS)—Temtex Industries Inc.; *U.S. Public*, pg. 1576
THERMO KING CORPORATION—Ingersoll-Rand Company; *U.S. Public*, pg. 877
THOMAS & BETTS REZNOR DIVISION—Thomas & Betts Corporation; *U.S. Public*, pg. 1598
TORIN ENGINEERED BLOWERS—BTR plc; *Int'l*, pg. 125
TOROMONT INDUSTRIES LTD.; *Int'l*, pg. 1400
TOROMONT PROCESS SYSTEMS INC.—Toromont Industries Ltd.; *Int'l*, pg. 1401
TOSHIBA HEATING APPLIANCES CO., LTD.—Toshiba Corporation; *Int'l*, pg. 1404
TRANE DO BRAZIL—American Standard Inc.; *U.S. Public*, pg. 92
THE TRANE COMPANY—American Standard Inc.; *U.S. Public*, pg. 92
TRANE CO. OF CANADA—American Standard Inc.; *U.S. Public*, pg. 92
THE TRANE COMPANY NORTH AMERICAN COMMERCIAL GROUP—American Standard Inc.; *U.S. Public*, pg. 92
THE TRANE COMPANY, UNITARY PRODUCTS GROUP—American Standard Inc.; *U.S. Public*, pg. 92
TRANE EUROPE—American Standard Inc.; *U.S. Public*, pg. 92
TRANE LTD.—American Standard Inc.; *U.S. Public*, pg. 92
UNIFLOW MANUFACTURING CO.; *U.S. Private*, pg. 1117
UNITARY PRODUCTS GROUP—York International Corporation; *U.S. Public*, pg. 1788
UNITED TECHNOLOGIES CORPORATION; *U.S. Public*, pg. 1689
VENTUREDYNE, LTD.; *U.S. Private*, pg. 1136
VILTER EXPORT CORP.—Vilter Manufacturing Corporation; *U.S. Private*, pg. 1141
VILTER MANUFACTURING CORPORATION; *U.S. Private*, pg. 1140
HENRY VOGT MACHINE CO.; *U.S. Private*, pg. 1143
WATSCO COMPONENTS, INC.—Watsco, Inc.; *U.S. Public*, pg. 1746
WELBILT CORPORATION—Berisford plc; *Int'l*, pg. 188
WESTINGHOUSE POWER SYSTEMS GROUP—CBS Corporation; *U.S. Public*, pg. 273
WHITE CONSOLIDATED INDUSTRIES, INC.—Electrolux, AB; *Int'l*, pg. 439
WHITLENGE DRINK EQUIPMENT LIMITED—Scotsman Industries, Inc.; *U.S. Public*, pg. 1445
WHITMAN CORPORATION; *U.S. Public*, pg. 1766
WICOR, INC.; *U.S. Public*, pg. 1767
YORK INTL./RECO—York International Corporation; *U.S. Public*, pg. 1789
ZERO CORPORATION; *U.S. Public*, pg. 1791

3586 — MEASURING & DISPENSING PUMPS

AKO ARMATUREN - VERTRIEKS GMBH—Axel Johnson AB; *Int'l*, pg. 710
ALEMITE CORPORATION—BTR plc; *Int'l*, pg. 127
ALFA-LAVAL S.A.—Tetra Laval Group; *Int'l*, pg. 1380
ALLIEDSIGNAL AEROSPACE—AlliedSignal Inc.; *U.S. Public*, pg. 50
AUTOMOTIVE ACCESSORY CO., LTD.—UIS, Inc.; *U.S. Private*, pg. 1113
BLACKMER PUMP/DOVER RESOURCES CO—Dover Corporation; *U.S. Public*, pg. 521
ROBERT BOSCH AG—Robert Bosch GmbH; *Int'l*, pg. 205
DOVER CORPORATION; *U.S. Public*, pg. 520
DOVER CORPORATION (CANADA) LTD.-INDUSTRIAL DIV.—Dover Corporation; *U.S. Public*, pg. 522
DOVER DIVERSIFIED—Dover Corporation; *U.S. Public*, pg. 521
DRESSER INDUSTRIES, INC.; *U.S. Public*, pg. 528
DRESSER INDUSTRIES WAYNE DIVISION—Dresser Industries, Inc.; *U.S. Public*, pg. 528
FILL-RITE DIV.—Tuthill Corporation; *U.S. Private*, pg. 1111
FILL-RITE DIVISION—Tuthill Corporation; *U.S. Private*, pg. 1110
FUJI HEAVY INDUSTRIES, LTD., ENGINE & MACHINERY DIV.—Fuji Heavy Industries, Ltd.; *Int'l*, pg. 523
GASBOY INTERNATIONAL, INC.—Tokheim Corporation; *U.S. Public*, pg. 1620
KOMLINE-SANDERSON ENGINEERING CORP.; *U.S. Private*, pg. 631
LINCOLN INDUSTRIAL—Pentair, Inc.; *U.S. Public*, pg. 1273
LUFKIN MACHINE CO. LTD.—Lufkin Industries, Inc.; *U.S. Public*, pg. 1019
GEORGE MELLER LTD.—Axel Johnson AB; *Int'l*, pg. 712
MONO PUMPS LTD.—Dresser Industries, Inc.; *U.S. Public*, pg. 529
NUOVO PIGNONE S.P.A.; *Int'l*, pg. 990
PEARCE INDUSTRIES INC.; *U.S. Private*, pg. 845
PENTAIR, INC.; *U.S. Public*, pg. 1273
PFEIFFER OF AMERICA, INC.—AptarGroup, Inc.; *U.S. Public*, pg. 125
SAR U.S.A. INCORPORATED—AptarGroup, Inc.; *U.S. Public*, pg. 125
SIHI PUMPS LTD.—SIHI GmbH & Co. KG; *Int'l*, pg. 1156
STANDEX (IRELAND) LTD.—Standex International Corporation; *U.S. Public*, pg. 1508
STEWART WARNER INSTRUMENTS CORPORATION; *U.S. Private*, pg. 1042
STEWART WARNER INSTRUMENTS CORPORATION—Stewart Warner Instruments Corporation; *U.S. Private*, pg. 1043
SUNTEC INDUSTRIES INC.; *U.S. Private*, pg. 1054
TOKHEIM & GASBOY OF CANADA LIMITED—Tokheim Corporation; *U.S. Public*, pg. 1620
TOKHEIM CORPORATION; *U.S. Public*, pg. 1620
TOKHEIM GMBH—Tokheim Corporation; *U.S. Public*, pg. 1620
TOKHEIM LTD.—Tokheim Corporation; *U.S. Public*, pg. 1620

TRIMAS CORPORATION—Masco Corporation; U.S. Public, pg. 1054
TUTHILL PUMP—Tuthill Corporation; U.S. Private, pg. 1111
VALOIS OF AMERICA, INC.—AptarGroup, Inc.; U.S. Public, pg. 125

3589 — SERVICE INDUSTRY MACHINES, NEC

ADAMATIC—Premark International, Inc.; U.S. Public, pg. 1322
ADVANCE MACHINE COMPANY—Nilfisk A/S; Int'l, pg. 932
AEROLYTE SYSTEMS; U.S. Private, pg. 24
ALADDIN INDUSTRIES, INCORPORATED; U.S. Private, pg. 30
ALADDIN SYNERGETICS, INC.—Aladdin Industries, Incorporated; U.S. Private, pg. 31
ALKOTA CLEANING SYSTEMS, INC.; U.S. Private, pg. 34
AMERICAN WYOTT CORPORATION—A.P. Wyott; U.S. Private, pg. 1193
AMETEK, INC.; U.S. Public, pg. 99
AQUA-CHEM INC.—Lyonnaise des Eaux S.A.; Int'l, pg. 824
AQUION; U.S. Private, pg. 78
ATHEY PRODUCTS-WASTE CONTROL DIV.—Athey Products Corporation; U.S. Public, pg. 143
BKI—Standex International Corporation; U.S. Public, pg. 1506
BARBEQUE KING—Standex International Corporation; U.S. Public, pg. 1507
BELSHAW BROTHERS, INC.—Berisford plc; Int'l, pg. 188
THE BETHLEHEM CORPORATION; U.S. Public, pg. 225
BISSELL INC.; U.S. Private, pg. 145
G.S. BLODGETT CORPORATION—Maytag Corporation; U.S. Public, pg. 1064
THE BLODGETT OVEN CO., INC.—Maytag Corporation; U.S. Public, pg. 1064
BREUER/TORNADO; U.S. Private, pg. 167
BRITA (USA), INC.—The Clorox Company; U.S. Public, pg. 387
BRUNER WATER TREATMENT SYSTEMS—Culligan International Company; U.S. Public, pg. 467
BUNN-O-MATIC CORPORATION; U.S. Private, pg. 180
CPAC, INC.; U.S. Public, pg. 282
CADDY CORP. OF AMERICA; U.S. Private, pg. 198
CANNON EQUIPMENT CO.—IMI Plc; Int'l, pg. 646
CAPITAL CONTROLS COMPANY INC.—Severn Trent Plc; Int'l, pg. 1226
CASTEX INCORPORATED—Tennant Company; U.S. Public, pg. 1577
CHIEF AGRI/INDUSTRIAL DIVISION—Chief Industries, Inc.; U.S. Private, pg. 236
CHIEF E-Z BREAKER, INC.—Chief Industries, Inc.; U.S. Private, pg. 236
CHIEF INDUSTRIES - AGRI/INDUSTRIAL PRODUCTS DIV.—Chief Industries, Inc.; U.S. Private, pg. 236
CHIEF INDUSTRIES, INC.; U.S. Private, pg. 236
CLOW VALVE DIV.—McWane, Inc.; U.S. Private, pg. 725
COCHRANE, INC.—Crane Co.; U.S. Public, pg. 456
COLUMBIAN ROPE COMPANY; U.S. Private, pg. 256
CONCORD EFS, INC.; U.S. Public, pg. 429
THE CORNELIUS COMPANY—IMI Plc; Int'l, pg. 646
CRANE CO.; U.S. Public, pg. 456
CRES-COR; U.S. Private, pg. 288
CULLIGAN—Culligan International Company; U.S. Public, pg. 467
CULLIGAN, C.I. DIV.—Culligan International Company; U.S. Public, pg. 467
CULLIGAN INTERNATIONAL COMPANY; U.S. Public, pg. 467
DAVCO DIV.—United States Filter Corporation; U.S. Public, pg. 1682
DAVIS PROCESS DIV.—United States Filter Corporation; U.S. Public, pg. 1682
DELFIELD COMPANY—Scotsman Industries, Inc.; U.S. Public, pg. 1445
DOVER CORPORATION; U.S. Public, pg. 520
DOVER DIVERSIFIED—Dover Corporation; U.S. Public, pg. 521
DUKE MANUFACTURING CO., INC.; U.S. Private, pg. 346
DURAY/J.F. DUNCAN INDUSTRIES, INC.; U.S. Private, pg. 348
EWU-AKTIENGESELLSCHAFT—Rubbermaid Incorporated; U.S. Public, pg. 1411
ECOLOGY SYSTEM DEPT.—Chief Industries, Inc.; U.S. Private, pg. 236
ELECTROLUX, AB; Int'l, pg. 438
ELECTROLUX A/S—Electrolux, AB; Int'l, pg. 441
ELECTROLUX CLEANING EQUIPMENT AB—Electrolux, AB; Int'l, pg. 438
ELECTROLUX CORPORATION; U.S. Private, pg. 369
ELECTROLUX ELMOTOR A/S—Electrolux, AB; Int'l, pg. 441
ELECTROLUX STORKOK AB—Electrolux, AB; Int'l, pg. 438
ELECTRONIC DISPLAY SYSTEMS (KALLEGO)—Chief Industries, Inc.; U.S. Private, pg. 236
ENERFAB INC.; U.S. Private, pg. 376
A/S ERNST VOSS FABRIK—Electrolux, AB; Int'l, pg. 441
EUROCLEAN CANADA INC.—Electrolux, AB; Int'l, pg. 441
EVERPURE INC.—Culligan International Company; U.S. Public, pg. 467
FEDERAL INDUSTRIES, INC.—Standex International Corporation; U.S. Public, pg. 1506
THE SCOTT FETZER COMPANY—Berkshire Hathaway Inc.; U.S. Public, pg. 217
FOSTER REFRIGERATOR CORPORATION; U.S. Private, pg. 421
FRIED. KRUPP AG; Int'l, pg. 507
THE FRYMASTER CORP.—Berisford plc; Int'l, pg. 188
FUJI ELECTRIC CO., LTD.; Int'l, pg. 522
GARLAND COMMERCIAL INDUSTRIES, INC.—Berisford plc; Int'l, pg. 188
GEBRUEDER KEMMER GMBH—Philipp Holzmann AG; Int'l, pg. 632
GENERAL IONICS—Ionics, Incorporated; U.S. Public, pg. 912
THE GENIE COMPANY—Overhead Door Corporation; U.S. Private, pg. 823
GROEN, A DOVER INDUSTRIES CO.—Dover Corporation; U.S. Public, pg. 521
HANNA-SHERMAN INTERNATIONAL, INC.; U.S. Private, pg. 499
HARBAUER GMBH & CO. KG—Philipp Holzmann AG; Int'l, pg. 632
HAYWARD INDUSTRIES, INC.; U.S. Private, pg. 513
HAYWARD POOL PRODUCTS, INC.—Hayward Industries, Inc.; U.S. Private, pg. 513
HEAT & CONTROL, INC.; U.S. Private, pg. 518
HEIL EUROPE—Dover Corporation; U.S. Public, pg. 521
HOBART CORPORATION—Premark International, Inc.; U.S. Public, pg. 1322
IKON OFFICE SOLUTIONS, INC.; U.S. Public, pg. 862
INDUSTRIAL COMPONENTS GROUP—BTR plc; Int'l, pg. 127
INDUSTRIAL DIV.—Federal Signal Corporation; U.S. Public, pg. 617
INSTITUTIONAL EQUIPMENT & INTERIORS, INC.—Piccadilly Cafeterias, Inc.; U.S. Public, pg. 1294
IONICS, INCORPORATED; U.S. Public, pg. 912
IONICS, INCORPORATED—Ionics, Incorporated; U.S. Public, pg. 912
IONICS ULTRAPURE WATER CORPORATION—Ionics, Incorporated; U.S. Public, pg. 912
JACKSON MSC; U.S. Private, pg. 579
JACUZZI (CHILE) S.A.—U.S. Industries, Inc.; U.S. Public, pg. 1684
JACUZZI DO BRASIL—U.S. Industries, Inc.; U.S. Public, pg. 1684
JACUZZI EUROPE, S.P.A.—U.S. Industries, Inc.; U.S. Public, pg. 1684
JACUZZI UNIVERSAL, S.A.—U.S. Industries, Inc.; U.S. Public, pg. 1684
THE KENT COMPANY—Electrolux, AB; Int'l, pg. 440
KIDRON INC.; U.S. Private, pg. 619
KIEKENS B.V., AMSTERDAM—Internatio-Muller N.V.; Int'l, pg. 681
KIRBY COMPANY—Berkshire Hathaway Inc.; U.S. Public, pg. 217
KNIGHT EQUIPMENT INTERNATIONAL INC.—IDEX Corporation; U.S. Public, pg. 862
KRAUSE PLOW CORP.; U.S. Private, pg. 635
KRUPP CANADA INC.—Fried. Krupp AG; Int'l, pg. 511
KRUPP GFT GESELLSCHAFT FUR ANLAGEN-, BAU- UND GLEISTECHNIK MBH—Fried. Krupp AG; Int'l, pg. 513
LANDA, INC.; U.S. Private, pg. 646
LINDSAY MANUFACTURING INC.; U.S. Private, pg. 668
LIQUI-DRI FOODS, INC.—The Quaker Oats Company; U.S. Public, pg. 1348
MAN-GILL CHEMICAL COMPANY; U.S. Private, pg. 699
MANITOWOC ICE, INC.—The Manitowoc Company, Inc.; U.S. Public, pg. 1041
THE MARLEY COOLING TOWER CO.—United Dominion Industries, Ltd.; U.S. Public, pg. 1676
MARTIN INDUSTRIES, INC. (AL); U.S. Private, pg. 709
MCALLEN PIPE & SUPPLY DIV.—United States Filter Corporation; U.S. Public, pg. 1682
MCNEIL (OHIO) CORPORATION—Pentair, Inc.; U.S. Public, pg. 1273
MERCO/SAVORY INC.—Berisford plc; Int'l, pg. 189
MICRONYL-WEDCO S.A.—ICO, Inc.; U.S. Public, pg. 854
MIDCO INTERNATIONAL INC.; U.S. Private, pg. 744
MILE HIGH EQUIPMENT CO.—Berisford plc; Int'l, pg. 189
MINUTEMAN INTERNATIONAL, INC.—Hako-Werke GmbH & Co.; Int'l, pg. 587
MONORAIL, INC.—Columbian Rope Company; U.S. Private, pg. 256
AB CARL MUNTERS—Incentive AB; Int'l, pg. 669
MUSKIN LEISURE PRODUCTS, INC.; U.S. Private, pg. 768
NATIONAL SAFETY ASSOCIATES; U.S. Private, pg. 786
THE NATIONAL SUPER SERVICE CO.; U.S. Private, pg. 787
NIECO CORPORATION; U.S. Private, pg. 799
NOBLES MFG. INC.; U.S. Private, pg. 800
NORTHLAND ALUMINUM PRODUCTS, INC.; U.S. Private, pg. 805
ORECK MANUFACTURING COMPANY—Oreck Corporation; U.S. Private, pg. 819
PAC-FAB, INC./EAST—Essef Corporation; U.S. Public, pg. 593
PALL CORPORATION; U.S. Public, pg. 1253
PARKER SWEEPER COMPANY—Hako-Werke GmbH & Co.; Int'l, pg. 587
PARKSON CORPORATION—Axel Johnson AB; Int'l, pg. 710
PERMA-FIX ENVIRONMENTAL SERVICES, INC.—Perma-Fix Environmental Services, Inc.; U.S. Public, pg. 1279
PETTIBONE CORPORATION; U.S. Private, pg. 859
PETWA CANADA LTD.—ABB Asea Brown Boveri (Holding) Ltd.; Int'l, pg. 6
PIONEER/ECLIPSE CORP.—Amano Corporation; Int'l, pg. 71
PITCO FRIALATOR INC.—Maytag Corporation; U.S. Public, pg. 1065
POLARIS POOL SYSTEMS, INC.; U.S. Private, pg. 873
PREMARK FOOD EQUIPMENT GROUP—Premark International, Inc.; U.S. Public, pg. 1322
PREMARK INTERNATIONAL, INC.; U.S. Public, pg. 1321
PROCON PRODUCTS—Standex International Corporation; U.S. Public, pg. 1506
PULLMAN/HOLT CORP.—White Mop Wringer Company; U.S. Private, pg. 1173
PURE SOLUTIONS—Ionics, Incorporated; U.S. Public, pg. 912
PUROFLOW INCORPORATED; U.S. Public, pg. 1345
QUALHEIM, INC.—CTS Corporation; U.S. Public, pg. 286
RAILWAY EQUIPMENT EXPORT—Fried. Krupp AG; Int'l, pg. 513
RAINSOFT WATER TREATMENT SYSTEMS—Aquion; U.S. Private, pg. 78
ROYER INDUSTRIES, INC.—Powerscreen International Plc; Int'l, pg. 1066
RYOBI MOTOR PRODUCTS—Ryobi Ltd.; Int'l, pg. 1151
SCIENTIFIC DUST COLLECTORS—Venturedyne, Ltd.; U.S. Private, pg. 1136
SOMAT CORPORATION—Premark International, Inc.; U.S. Public, pg. 1322
SPARTAN TOOL—Pettibone Corporation; U.S. Private, pg. 860
SPECIALTY EQUIPMENT COMPANIES INC.; U.S. Public, pg. 1496
THE SPENCER TURBINE CO.; U.S. Private, pg. 1025
SPICER OFF-HIGHWAY AXLE DIV.—Dana Corporation; U.S. Public, pg. 479
STANLEY KNIGHT CORPORATION; U.S. Private, pg. 1033
STANLEY STEEMER INTERNATIONAL, INC.; U.S. Private, pg. 1033
L. & C. STEINMUELLER GMBH—Philipp Holzmann AG; Int'l, pg. 633
STEVENS-LEE COMPANY; U.S. Private, pg. 1042
STRUCTURAL EUROPE—Essef Corporation; U.S. Public, pg. 593
TAYLOR-JETT DIV.—United States Filter Corporation; U.S. Public, pg. 1682
TELEDYNE LAARS/JANDY PRODUCTS—Allegheny Teledyne Incorporated; U.S. Public, pg. 43
TENNANT COMPANY; U.S. Public, pg. 1577
TENNANT HOLDING B.V.—Tennant Company; U.S. Public, pg. 1577
TENNANT MAINTENANCE SYSTEMS, LIMITED—Tennant Company; U.S. Public, pg. 1577
AB TOMAL—Tetra Laval Group; Int'l, pg. 1377
TOSHIBA CONSUMER PRODUCTS (U.K.) LIMITED—Toshiba Corporation; Int'l, pg. 1406
TUCHENHAGEN GMBH; Int'l, pg. 1426
TUCHENHAGEN NORTH AMERICA, INC.—Tuchenhagen GmbH; Int'l, pg. 1426
UMWELTSCHUTZ NORD GMBH & CO.—Philipp Holzmann AG; Int'l, pg. 633
UNITED SERVICE EQUIPMENT COMPANY—Standex International Corporation; U.S. Public, pg. 1507
U.S. FILTER—Aluminum Company of America; U.S. Public, pg. 61
U.S. FILTER CO., AMES—Aluminum Company of America; U.S. Public, pg. 61
UNITED STATES FILTER CORPORATION; U.S. Public, pg. 1681
U.S. FILTER/DAVIS WATER & WASTE INDUSTRIES, INC.—United States Filter Corporation; U.S. Public, pg. 1682
U.S. FILTER/PERMUTIT—United States Filter Corporation; U.S. Public, pg. 1682
USA WASTE SERVICES, INC.; U.S. Public, pg. 1686
VACTOR MFG. INC.—Federal Signal Corporation; U.S. Public, pg. 617
VEREINIGTE WEICHENBAU GMBH—Fried. Krupp AG; Int'l, pg. 513
AB VOLTA—Electrolux, AB; Int'l, pg. 439
VORWERK & CO.; Int'l, pg. 1480
WARING PRODUCTS—CTS Corporation; U.S. Public, pg. 286
WASTE KING—Masco Corporation; U.S. Public, pg. 1053
WATERWORKS EQUIPMENT CO. (WECO) DIV.—United States Filter Corporation; U.S. Public, pg. 1682
WEDCO HOLLAND B.V.—ICO, Inc.; U.S. Public, pg. 854
WEDCO TECHNOLOGY—ICO, Inc.; U.S. Public, pg. 854
WEDCO TECHNOLOGY U.K. LTD.—ICO, Inc.; U.S. Public, pg. 854
WEDTECH INC.—ICO, Inc.; U.S. Public, pg. 854
WELBILT CORPORATION—Berisford plc; Int'l, pg. 188
WHITE MOP WRINGER COMPANY; U.S. Private, pg. 1172
WICOR, INC.; U.S. Public, pg. 1767
WINDSOR INDUSTRIES, INC.; U.S. Private, pg. 1182
WOLF RANGE CO.—Premark International, Inc.; U.S. Public, pg. 1322
ZAZULA PROCESS EQUIP. LTD.—ABB Asea Brown Boveri (Holding) Ltd.; Int'l, pg. 6
ZENTOX CORP.; U.S. Private, pg. 1204

3592 — CARBURETORS, PISTONS, PISTON RINGS & VALVES

A E CLEVITE, INC.—T & N Plc; Int'l, pg. 1334
AE GOETZE-NORTH AMERICA—T & N Plc; Int'l, pg. 1334
AMSTED INDUSTRIES INCORPORATED; U.S. Private, pg. 68
AUTOFIELD ENGINEERS PRIVATE LTD.—Cummins Engine Company, Inc.; U.S. Public, pg. 469
BURGESS-NORTON MFG. CO.—Amsted Industries Incorporated; U.S. Private, pg. 68
CHILTEM GROUP SAM—Alpha Omikron Limited; Int'l, pg. 65
COLTEC HOLDINGS INC; U.S. Public, pg. 401
DEFONTAINE S.A.—Fried. Krupp AG; Int'l, pg. 509
DELPHI AUTOMOTIVE SYSTEMS—General Motors Corporation; U.S. Public, pg. 719
DELPHI CHASSIS SYSTEMS—General Motors Corporation; U.S. Public, pg. 719
DELPHI ENERGY & ENGINE MANAGEMENT SYSTEMS—General Motors Corporation; U.S. Public, pg. 719
DOVER DIVERSIFIED—Dover Corporation; U.S. Public, pg. 521
DRIVETRAIN SERVICE DIV.—Dana Corporation; U.S. Public, pg. 479
DUNLAP DIVISION—Tecumseh Products Company; U.S. Public, pg. 1565
EATON AUTOMOTIVE S.P.A. ENGINE COMPONENTS OPERATIONS—Eaton Corporation; U.S. Public, pg. 558

EATON CORPORATION DO BRASIL ENGINE COMPONENTS OPERATIONS—Eaton Corporation; U.S. Public, pg. 558
EATON CORPORATION, ENGINE COMPONENTS DIVISION—Eaton Corporation; U.S. Public, pg. 556
EATON EST S.P.A. ENGINE COMPONENTS OPERATIONS—Eaton Corporation; U.S. Public, pg. 558
FAIRBANKS MORSE ENGINE DIVISION—Coltec Holdings Inc; U.S. Public, pg. 401
FREEDOM FORGE CORPORATION; U.S. Private, pg. 425
GARLOCK VALVES & INDUSTRIAL PLASTICS—Coltec Holdings Inc; U.S. Public, pg. 402
GOETZE CORP. OF AMERICA—T & N Plc; Int'l, pg. 1335
AE GOETZE GMBH—T & N Plc; Int'l, pg. 1334
GROVER PISTON RING DIVISION—Furon Company; U.S. Public, pg. 689
HANNA CORPORATION—Chatwins Group, Inc.; U.S. Private, pg. 231
HASTINGS, INC.—Hastings Manufacturing Company; U.S. Public, pg. 798
HASTINGS MANUFACTURING COMPANY; U.S. Public, pg. 798
HOLLEY REPLACEMENT PARTS DIVISION—Coltec Holdings Inc; U.S. Public, pg. 402
IMPCO AIRSENSORS TECHNOLOGIES—AirSensors, Inc.; U.S. Public, pg. 34
KFW CANADA, INC.—TI Group plc; Int'l, pg. 1338
LUCAS INDUSTRIES INC.—LucasVarity plc; Int'l, pg. 820
MCCORD PAYEN—T & N Plc; Int'l, pg. 1335
MIKUNI CORPORATION; Int'l, pg. 867
NAF AB—Trelleborg AB; Int'l, pg. 1422
NIPPON PISTON RING CO., LTD.; Int'l, pg. 938
NITTAN VALVE COMPANY LTD.—Eaton Corporation; U.S. Public, pg. 559
NYLONCRAFT—Excel Industries, Inc.; U.S. Public, pg. 599
PACER INDUSTRIES, INC.—Echlin Inc.; U.S. Public, pg. 560
PERFECT CIRCLE PRODUCTS DIV.—Dana Corporation; U.S. Public, pg. 479
PRODUCTOS EATON LIVIA S.A. ENGINE COMPONENTS OPERATIONS—Eaton Corporation; U.S. Public, pg. 559
T & N INDUSTRIES, INC.—T & N Plc; Int'l, pg. 1334
TOMCO AUTO PRODUCTS, INC.; U.S. Private, pg. 1090
UNISIA JECS CORPORATION—Nissan Motor Co., Ltd.; Int'l, pg. 944
UNITED ENGINE & MACHINE COMPANY; U.S. Private, pg. 1121
VALVE DIVISION—TRW Inc.; U.S. Public, pg. 1559
WALBRO CORPORATION; U.S. Public, pg. 1733

3593 — FLUID POWER CYLINDERS & ACTUATORS

ALLIEDSIGNAL INC.; U.S. Public, pg. 49
APITECH—Applied Power Inc.; U.S. Public, pg. 124
APPLIED POWER INC.; U.S. Public, pg. 124
ATLAS CYLINDER—Parker Hannifin Corporation; U.S. Public, pg. 1261
ATLAS CYLINDERS—Parker Hannifin Corporation; U.S. Public, pg. 1261
AUTOMAX CONTROLS, INC.—Flowserve Corporation; U.S. Public, pg. 658
AUTOMAX, INC.—Flowserve Corporation; U.S. Public, pg. 658
AVIS INDUSTRIAL CORPORATION; U.S. Private, pg. 102
BIFFI ITALIA S.R.L.—Tyco International Ltd.; U.S. Public, pg. 1650
ROBERT BOSCH CORPORATION—Robert Bosch GmbH; Int'l, pg. 204
CGF INDUSTRIES; U.S. Private, pg. 194
CASCADE (U.K.) LTD.—Cascade Corporation; U.S. Public, pg. 311
CHANDLER EVANS CONTROL SYSTEMS DIVISION—Coltec Holdings Inc; U.S. Public, pg. 401
COMMERCIAL INTERTECH DISTRIBUTION SERVICES—Commercial Intertech Corp.; U.S. Public, pg. 411
CUSTOM HOISTS, INC.—Standex International Corporation; U.S. Public, pg. 1506
CYLINDER DIV., PARKER HANNIFIN PLC—Parker Hannifin Corporation; U.S. Public, pg. 1263
DENISON HYDRAULICS, INC.; U.S. Private, pg. 324
DOWTY AEROSPACE YAKIMA—TI Group plc; Int'l, pg. 1337
DRIVETRAIN SERVICE DIV.—Dana Corporation; U.S. Public, pg. 479
ENIDINE INCORPORATED; U.S. Private, pg. 377
GITS MANUFACTURING COMPANY, INC.—Valley Forge Corporation; U.S. Public, pg. 1705
HEIN-WERNER CORPORATION; U.S. Public, pg. 805
HUMPHREY PRODUCTS COMPANY; U.S. Private, pg. 547
HUNGER DFE GMBH; Int'l, pg. 639
HUNGER HYDRAULICS, LIMITED—Hunger DFE GmbH; Int'l, pg. 639
HYDRAULICS GROUP—Parker Hannifin Corporation; U.S. Public, pg. 1261
MARSH BELLOFRAM CORP.; U.S. Private, pg. 707
MATRA-WERKE GMBH—Linde AG; Int'l, pg. 811
MENASCO AEROSYSTEMS DIVISION—Coltec Holdings Inc; U.S. Public, pg. 402
MILLER FLUID POWER CORP.; U.S. Private, pg. 747
MILWAUKEE CYLINDER DIVISION—Applied Power Inc.; U.S. Public, pg. 124
THE OILGEAR COMPANY; U.S. Public, pg. 1215
OILGEAR GMBH—The Oilgear Company; U.S. Public, pg. 1215
OILGEAR/TOWLER AUSTRALIA PTY. LTD.—The Oilgear Company; U.S. Public, pg. 1215
OILGEAR TOWLER LTD.—The Oilgear Company; U.S. Public, pg. 1215
OILGEAR TOWLER LTD. (BEDFORD)—The Oilgear Company; U.S. Public, pg. 1215
OILGEAR TOWLER (LYON)—The Oilgear Company; U.S. Public, pg. 1215
OILGEAR TOWLER SA—The Oilgear Company; U.S. Public, pg. 1215
ORTMAN FLUID POWER DIVISION—Coltec Holdings Inc; U.S. Public, pg. 402
PARKER HANNIFIN (AUSTRALIA) (PTY.) LTD.—Parker Hannifin Corporation; U.S. Public, pg. 1263
POSITECH CORPORATION—Columbus McKinnon Corp.; U.S. Public, pg. 406
POWER-PACKER U.S.—Applied Power Inc.; U.S. Public, pg. 124
POWER TEAM DIVISION—SPX Corporation; U.S. Public, pg. 1421
SPX CORPORATION; U.S. Public, pg. 1420
SMITHS INDUSTRIES PLC; Int'l, pg. 1266
SNAP-TITE, INC.; U.S. Private, pg. 1010
STOCK DRIVE PRODUCTS DIV.—Designatronics, Inc.; U.S. Private, pg. 327
VALLEY FORGE CORPORATION; U.S. Public, pg. 1705
VALTEK INTERNATIONAL—Flowserve Corporation; U.S. Public, pg. 658
VICKERS, INCORPORATED—Aeroquip-Vickers, Inc.; U.S. Public, pg. 24
WATTS REGULATOR CO.—Watts Industries, Inc.; U.S. Public, pg. 1747
WILSON INDUSTRIES INC.; U.S. Private, pg. 1181

3594 — FLUID POWER PUMPS & MOTORS

ABB MASCHINENFABRIK MEYER AG—ABB Asea Brown Boveri (Holding) Ltd.; Int'l, pg. 1
AMW INDUSTRIES INC.—Crane Co.; U.S. Public, pg. 457
AEROSPACE-MARINE-DEFENSE GROUP—Aeroquip-Vickers, Inc.; U.S. Public, pg. 24
ALFA LAVAL INC.—Tetra Laval Group; Int'l, pg. 1378
ALLIEDSIGNAL INC.; U.S. Public, pg. 49
APITECH—Applied Power Inc.; U.S. Public, pg. 124
APPLIED POWER INC.; U.S. Public, pg. 124
ROBERT BOSCH CORPORATION—Robert Bosch GmbH; Int'l, pg. 204
CGF INDUSTRIES; U.S. Private, pg. 194
COMPUMOTOR DIVISION—Parker Hannifin Corporation; U.S. Public, pg. 1259
DANFOSS FLUID POWER—Danfoss A/S; Int'l, pg. 377
DENISON HYDRAULICS, INC.; U.S. Private, pg. 324
DOWTY AEROSPACE, WOLVERHAMPTON—TI Group plc; Int'l, pg. 1337
DRIVETRAIN SERVICE DIV.—Dana Corporation; U.S. Public, pg. 479
EDE - EMBRAER EQUIPMENT DIVISION—Embraer-Empresa Brasileira de Aeronautica S.A.; Int'l, pg. 452
EMPIRE HYDRAULIC SERVICE—Empire Southwest Co.; U.S. Private, pg. 374
FLEXIBOX GMBH—EIS Group Plc; Int'l, pg. 426
FLEXIBOX LTD.—EIS Group Plc; Int'l, pg. 426
FLOWSERVE CORPORATION—Flowserve Corporation; U.S. Public, pg. 658
FLUIDRIVE INC.; U.S. Private, pg. 415
FREMONT MFG.—The Oilgear Company; U.S. Public, pg. 1215
GRACO INC.; U.S. Public, pg. 756
HOWDEN FLUID SYSTEMS—Mark IV Industries Inc.; U.S. Public, pg. 1045
HYDRAULICS GROUP—Parker Hannifin Corporation; U.S. Public, pg. 1261
HYDURA PRODUCTS—The Oilgear Company; U.S. Public, pg. 1215
I.D.M. ELECTRONICS LTD.—Kaydon Corporation; U.S. Public, pg. 946
ITT FLUID TRANSFER DIVISION—ITT Industries, Inc.; U.S. Public, pg. 860
AXEL JOHNSON AB; Int'l, pg. 707
KAYDON CORPORATION; U.S. Public, pg. 945
KVAERNER EUREKA ESPANOLA S.A.—Kvaerner a.s.a.; Int'l, pg. 767
LINDE AG WERKSGRUPPE GUELDNER ASCHAFFENBURG—Linde AG; Int'l, pg. 810
NETZSCH INCORPORATED; U.S. Private, pg. 792
THE OILGEAR COMPANY; U.S. Public, pg. 1215
OILGEAR GMBH—The Oilgear Company; U.S. Public, pg. 1215
OILGEAR/TOWLER AUSTRALIA PTY. LTD.—The Oilgear Company; U.S. Public, pg. 1215
OILGEAR TOWLER LTD.—The Oilgear Company; U.S. Public, pg. 1215
OILGEAR TOWLER LTD. (BEDFORD)—The Oilgear Company; U.S. Public, pg. 1215
OILGEAR TOWLER (LYON)—The Oilgear Company; U.S. Public, pg. 1215
OILGEAR TOWLER SA—The Oilgear Company; U.S. Public, pg. 1215
PALL INDUSTRIAL HYDRAULICS LTD.—Pall Corporation; U.S. Public, pg. 1254
PALL INDUSTRIE-HYDRAULIK GMBH—Pall Corporation; U.S. Public, pg. 1254
PARKER HANNIFIN (AUSTRALIA) (PTY.) LTD.—Parker Hannifin Corporation; U.S. Public, pg. 1263
PARTEK OPERATION—Parker Hannifin Corporation; U.S. Public, pg. 1262
PEACOCK INC.—Weir Group PLC; Int'l, pg. 1489
PETRODYNE PRODUCTS—The Oilgear Company; U.S. Public, pg. 1215
PIRELLI JEROME INC.—Pirelli S.p.A.; Int'l, pg. 1059
POWER-PACKER ESPANA, S.A.—Applied Power Inc.; U.S. Public, pg. 125
POWER-PACKER EUROPA B.V.—Applied Power Inc.; U.S. Public, pg. 125
POWER-PACKER FRANCE—Applied Power Inc.; U.S. Public, pg. 125
POWER-PACKER U.S.—Applied Power Inc.; U.S. Public, pg. 124
POWER TEAM DIVISION—SPX Corporation; U.S. Public, pg. 1421
REULAND ELECTRIC COMPANY; U.S. Private, pg. 925
SIHI GMBH & CO. KG; Int'l, pg. 1156
SIHI INTERNATIONAL AG—SIHI GmbH & Co. KG; Int'l, pg. 1156
SIHI PUMPS INC.—SIHI GmbH & Co. KG; Int'l, pg. 1156
SPX CORPORATION; U.S. Public, pg. 1420
SAUER-SUNDSTRAND—Sauer Sundstrand Gmbh & Co.; Int'l, pg. 1198
SAUER-SUNDSTRAND COMPANY—Sauer Sundstrand Gmbh & Co.; Int'l, pg. 1198
SMITHS INDUSTRIES PLC; Int'l, pg. 1266
TOWLER PRODUCTS—The Oilgear Company; U.S. Public, pg. 1215
VICKERS, INCORPORATED—Aeroquip-Vickers, Inc.; U.S. Public, pg. 24
VICKERS INDUSTRIAL—Aeroquip-Vickers, Inc.; U.S. Public, pg. 24
VICKERS SYSTEMS—Aeroquip-Vickers, Inc.; U.S. Public, pg. 25
VICKERS SYSTEMS GMBH (AEROSPACE-MARINE-DEFENSE TRINOVA GMBH)—Aeroquip-Vickers, Inc.; U.S. Public, pg. 25
WHIPPS; U.S. Private, pg. 1171
WICOR, INC.; U.S. Public, pg. 1767

3596 — SCALES & BALANCES, EXCEPT LABORATORY

ASCOM HASLER MAILING SYSTEMS, INC.—Ascom Holding AG; Int'l, pg. 86
ASCOM HOLDING AG; Int'l, pg. 86
AUTOMATIC EQUIPMENT MFG. CO.; U.S. Private, pg. 101
BERKEL INCORPORATED—The General Electric Company, p.l.c.; Int'l, pg. 545
CMI WEIGHING EQUIPMENT DIVISION—CMI Corporation; U.S. Public, pg. 279
CARDINAL SCALE MANUFACTURING COMPANY; U.S. Private, pg. 209
DETECTO SCALE COMPANY—Cardinal Scale Manufacturing Company; U.S. Private, pg. 209
EDLUND COMPANY, INC.; U.S. Private, pg. 364
EXACT EQUIPMENT CORPORATION; U.S. Private, pg. 387
EXACT LEVEL—The L.S. Starrett Company; U.S. Public, pg. 1511
FERGUSON INTERNATIONAL, INC.; U.S. Private, pg. 401
GSE, INC.—United Dominion Industries, Ltd.; U.S. Public, pg. 1676
THE GENERAL ELECTRIC COMPANY, P.L.C.; Int'l, pg. 543
M/D TOTCO INSTRUMENTATION—Varco International, Inc.; U.S. Public, pg. 1709
POSSO S.A.; Int'l, pg. 1064
RELIANCE ELECTRIC COMPANY—Rockwell International Corporation; U.S. Public, pg. 1398
RICE LAKE WEIGHING SYSTEMS; U.S. Private, pg. 927
SIGNATURE BRANDS USA, INC.; U.S. Public, pg. 1472
TML METROLOGY CENTRE FOR BEDFORD—Brown & Sharpe Manufacturing Company; U.S. Public, pg. 260
TECHNITROL, INC.; U.S. Public, pg. 1564
TESA METROLOGY LIMITED—Brown & Sharpe Manufacturing Company; U.S. Public, pg. 260
TESA, S.A.—Brown & Sharpe Manufacturing Company; U.S. Public, pg. 260
THOMAS ENGINEERING INC.; U.S. Private, pg. 1082
WEIGH-TRONIX—Staveley Industries PLC; Int'l, pg. 1299
WEIGH-TRONIX, INC.—Staveley Industries PLC; Int'l, pg. 1299

3599 — INDUSTRIAL & COMMERCIAL MACHINERY & EQUIPMENT, NEC

A&A MANUFACTURING CO.; U.S. Private, pg. 1
ADK PRESSURE EQUIPMENT CORPORATION—Danaher Corporation; U.S. Public, pg. 481
AMF BAKERY SYSTEMS; U.S. Private, pg. 6
AEROCHEM, INC.—Ducommun Incorporated; U.S. Public, pg. 534
AEROCHEM, INC./EL MIRAGE—Ducommun Incorporated; U.S. Public, pg. 534
AEROLYTE SYSTEMS; U.S. Private, pg. 24
AGIE AG (FUR INDUSTRIELLE ELEKTRONIK)—Georg Fischer Ltd.; Int'l, pg. 488
AGIE U.S.A. LTD.—Georg Fischer Ltd.; Int'l, pg. 490
AIR-DRY CORPORATION OF AMERICA—Danaher Corporation; U.S. Public, pg. 481
AIRLINE EQUIPMENT DIV.—FMC Corporation; U.S. Public, pg. 605
ALCOA DEUTSCHLAND GMBH—Aluminum Company of America; U.S. Public, pg. 61
ALLIEDSIGNAL, AUTOMOTIVE AFTERMARKET—AlliedSignal Inc.; U.S. Public, pg. 51
ALLOMATIC PRODUCTS COMPANY—Raytech Corporation; U.S. Public, pg. 1363
ALLVAC—Allegheny Teledyne Incorporated; U.S. Public, pg. 43
ALPHA Q, INC.; U.S. Private, pg. 45
AMETEK, INC.; U.S. Public, pg. 99
ANAMET INC.; U.S. Private, pg. 70
ANCHOR TOOL & DIE COMPANY; U.S. Private, pg. 71
APPLIED POWER INC.; U.S. Public, pg. 124
AQUAPORE MOISTURE SYSTEMS, INC.—Powell Duffryn PLC; Int'l, pg. 1066
ARBURG, INC.; U.S. Private, pg. 79
ARITMOS AB—Proventus AB; Int'l, pg. 1072
ARO FLUID PRODUCTS DIVISION—Ingersoll-Rand Company; U.S. Public, pg. 877
ATKINSON; U.S. Public, pg. 143
AUTOCAM ACQUISITION, INC.—Autocam Corporation; U.S. Public, pg. 148
AUTOCAM CORPORATION; U.S. Public, pg. 148
AUTOCAM LASER TECHNOLOGIES, INC.—Autocam Corporation; U.S. Public, pg. 148

AUTOCAM-PAX, INC.—Autocam Corporation; *U.S. Public*, pg. 148
AUTOCAM SOUTH CAROLINA, INC.—Autocam Corporation; *U.S. Public*, pg. 148
AVIS INDUSTRIAL CORPORATION; *U.S. Private*, pg. 102
BC HYDROTILE MACHINERY CO.—International Pipe Machinery Corp.; *U.S. Private*, pg. 571
BT INDUSTRIES AB; *Int'l*, pg. 123
BWI KARTRIDG PAK—BWI Plc; *Int'l*, pg. 130
BARRY CONTROLS LTD.—Applied Power Inc.; *U.S. Public*, *pg. 125*
THE BLACK CLAWSON COMPANY; *U.S. Private*, pg. 147
BLACK CLAWSON CONVERTING MACHINERY COMPANY—The Black Clawson Company; *U.S. Private*, *pg. 147*
BLISS-SALEM, INC.; *U.S. Private*, pg. 149
BOLETTI F.B. S.R.L.—Fiat Auto SpA; *Int'l*, pg. 482
BOLLINGER SHIPYARDS, INC.; *U.S. Private*, pg. 155
JOHN BOUCHARD & SONS COMPANY; *U.S. Private*, pg. 161
BRADEN COMPANY—Jason Incorporated; *U.S. Public*, pg. 924
BRUNNER & LAY, INC.; *U.S. Private*, pg. 176
BUSS AG—Georg Fischer Ltd.; *Int'l*, pg. 490
BUSS-SMS GMBH VERFAHRENSTECHNIK—Georg Fischer Ltd.; *Int'l*, pg. 490
CRC INDUSTRIES, INC.—Berwind Corporation; *U.S. Private*, pg. 138
J.C. CARTER COMPANY, INC.—Argo-Tech Corporation; *U.S. Private*, pg. 81
CHARMILLES TECHNOLOGIES SA—Georg Fischer Ltd.; *Int'l*, pg. 489
CINCINNATI INCORPORATED; *U.S. Private*, pg. 240
COLTEC HOLDINGS INC; *U.S. Public*, pg. 401
COMMERCIAL INTERTECH CORP.; *U.S. Public*, pg. 411
COMMONWEALTH STEEL CO. LTD.—Australian National Industries Limited; *Int'l*, pg. 101
COMPAIR MAKO—Siebe plc; *Int'l*, pg. 1242
COMPOFLEX—Senior Engineering Group, plc.; *Int'l*, pg. 1221
COPES-VULCAN INC.; *U.S. Private*, pg. 274
CORPORATE ENGINEERING—Emerson Electric Co.; *U.S. Public*, pg. 575
DCG PRECISION MANUFACTURING CORPORATION; *U.S. Private*, pg. 301
DMD DRESSER MEASUREMENT OPERATION—Dresser Industries, Inc.; *U.S. Public*, pg. 528
DANA CORPORATION; *U.S. Public*, pg. 479
DEKORON DIVISION—Furon Company; *U.S. Public*, pg. 689
DELTA RESINS & REFRACTORIES, INC.; *U.S. Private*, pg. 323
THE DEXTER CORPORATION; *U.S. Public*, pg. 504
DONALDSON COMPANY, INC.; *U.S. Public*, pg. 517
DOVATECH, LTD.—Dover Corporation; *U.S. Public*, pg. 520
DOWTY AEROSPACE, WOLVERHAMPTON—TI Group plc; *Int'l*, pg. 1337
DUCOMMUN INCORPORATED; *U.S. Public*, pg. 533
DURHAM TUBE—Senior Engineering Group, plc.; *Int'l*, pg. 1221
JOHN DUSENBERY CO., INC.; *U.S. Private*, pg. 349
DYNAVAC—Tenney Environmental; *U.S. Private*, pg. 1076
EDLON PRODUCTS, INC.—Robbins & Myers, Inc.; *U.S. Public*, pg. 1393
EIMCO PROCESS EQUIPMENT CO.—Baker Hughes Incorporated; *U.S. Public*, pg. 166
ENERPAC B.V.—Applied Power Inc.; *U.S. Public*, pg. 125
ENERPAC U.S.—Applied Power Inc.; *U.S. Public*, pg. 124
ESSEX CORPORATION; *U.S. Public*, pg. 593
EXCEL SYSTEMS—Excel Industries, Inc.; *U.S. Public*, pg. 598
FAG AUSTRIA WAELZLAGER AG—FAG Group; *Int'l*, pg. 469
FLS MILJO A/S—FLS Industries A/S; *Int'l*, pg. 475
FMC CORPORATION; *U.S. Public*, pg. 604
FAIRBANKS MORSE ENGINE DIVISION—Coltec Holdings Inc; *U.S. Public*, pg. 401
FARMERS MARINE COPPER WORKS—Four Winds Investment Corp.; *U.S. Private*, pg. 422
FERGUSON MACHINE CO. S.A.—Crane Co.; *U.S. Public*, pg. 457
FIAT LUBRIFICANTI S.R.L.—Fiat Auto SpA; *Int'l*, pg. 482
FINITE FILTER DIV.—Parker Hannifin Corporation; *U.S. Public*, pg. 1260
FLAIR CORPORATION—United Dominion Industries, Ltd.; *U.S. Public*, pg. 1676
FLEXIBLE TECHNOLOGIES INC.—Smiths Industries plc; *Int'l*, pg. 1267
FLEXONICS HOSE—Senior Engineering Group, plc.; *Int'l*, pg. 1222
FLEXONICS OEM PRODUCTS—Senior Engineering Group, plc.; *Int'l*, pg. 1222
FLO-LINE FILTERS, INC.—Perry Equipment Corporation; *U.S. Private*, pg. 855
FLORIG EQUIPMENT COMPANY, INC.; *U.S. Private*, pg. 415
FRAM EUROPE LTD.—AlliedSignal Inc.; *U.S. Public*, pg. 53
GILARDINI S.P.A.—Fiat Auto SpA; *Int'l*, pg. 482
GOUGLER INDUSTRIES, INC.; *U.S. Private*, pg. 466
GRANITE STATE MANUFACTURING CO.—Allard Industries; *U.S. Private*, pg. 36
HANNA CORPORATION—Chatwins Group, Inc.; *U.S. Private*, pg. 231
HARMONY ENGINEERING CORPORATION; *U.S. Private*, pg. 503
HARRIS-KAYOT, INC.; *U.S. Private*, pg. 506
HIGHFIELD MANUFACTURING CO.—BTR plc; *Int'l*, pg. 127
HITACHI ZOSEN CORPORATION; *Int'l*, pg. 622
HUB CITY, INC.—Regal-Beloit Corporation; *U.S. Public*, pg. 1371
HYDRO-MILL CO.—Triumph Group, Inc.; *U.S. Public*, pg. 1640
HYOSUNG INDUSTRIES CO., LTD.—Hyosung Group; *Int'l*, pg. 640
IDAB WAMAC INTERNATIONAL; *Int'l*, pg. 643
ITT CANNON SEALECTRO—ITT Industries, Inc.; *U.S. Public*, pg. 859
ITW RAMSET/RED HEAD—Illinois Tool Works Inc.; *U.S. Public*, pg. 867
INDUSTRIAL COMPONENTS GROUP—BTR plc; *Int'l*, pg. 127
INDUSTRIAS TRATERH, S.A.—Senior Engineering Group, plc.; *Int'l*, pg. 1222
INTERNATIONAL PIPE MACHINERY CORP.; *U.S. Private*, *pg. 571*
JUSTRITE MFG. CO.—Federal Signal Corporation; *U.S. Public*, pg. 617
KAYDON CORPORATION; *U.S. Public*, pg. 945
KAYDON CORPORATION, FILTRATION DIVISION—Kaydon Corporation; *U.S. Public*, pg. 946
KINGSBURY MACHINING CENTER, DIV.—Kingsbury Corporation; *U.S. Private*, pg. 622
KOCH ENGINEERING CO., INC.—Koch Industries, Incorporated; *U.S. Private*, pg. 628
KOCH OTTO H. YORK CO., INC.—Koch Industries, Incorporated; *U.S. Private*, pg. 628
KRUPP HOESCH STAHLEXPORT GMBH—Fried. Krupp AG; *Int'l*, pg. 515
KRUPP ROBINS, INC.—Fried. Krupp AG; *Int'l*, pg. 511
LAMINAIRE CORPORATION—Thermo-Mizer Environmental Corp.; *U.S. Public*, pg. 1596
LEAR CORPORATION ITALIA S.P.A.—Lear Corporation; *U.S. Public*, pg. 982
LINDSAY MANUFACTURING COMPANY; *U.S. Public*, pg. 999
LINDSAY TRANSPORTATION INC.—Lindsay Manufacturing Company; *U.S. Public*, pg. 1000
LITTLEFORD DAY INC.; *U.S. Private*, pg. 671
LODAL, INC.; *U.S. Private*, pg. 672
LUCAS BODY SYSTEMS - NORTH AMERICA—LucasVarity plc; *Int'l*, pg. 820
MACDERMID SYSTEMS, INC.—MacDermid Incorporated; *U.S. Public*, pg. 1030
MARION MACHINE COMPANY DIVISION—Superior Machine Company Of South Carolina, Inc.; *U.S. Private*, pg. 1055
MARVIN ENGINEERING COMPANY, INC.; *U.S. Private*, pg. 710
MECANICA PESADA S.A.—MAN Aktiengesellschaft; *Int'l*, pg. 824
METAL TRADES, INC.; *U.S. Private*, pg. 734
MICHIGAN WHEEL CORPORATION; *U.S. Private*, pg. 741
MICRONYL-WEDCO S.A.—ICO, Inc.; *U.S. Public*, pg. 854
MIKRON HOLDING AG; *Int'l*, pg. 866
MILLER FLUID POWER CORP.; *U.S. Private*, pg. 747
MILWAUKEE CYLINDER DIVISION—Applied Power Inc.; *U.S. Public*, pg. 124
MORGANTOWN MACHINE & HYDRAULICS, INC.—Charter plc; *Int'l*, pg. 280
MOSLER INC.; *U.S. Private*, pg. 763
MOTEK ENGINEERING & MANUFACTURING COMPANY; *U.S. Private*, pg. 764
NASHVILLE MACHINE CO. INC.; *U.S. Private*, pg. 774
NATIONAL MINE SERVICE, INC.—Charter plc; *Int'l*, pg. 280
NESCO, INC.; *U.S. Private*, pg. 791
NIPPON DONALDSON LTD.—Donaldson Company, Inc.; *U.S. Public*, pg. 517
NITRO STEEL DIV.—Quanex Corporation; *U.S. Public*, pg. 1349
NORELEM S.A.—Applied Power Inc.; *U.S. Public*, pg. 125
OFI TECHNOLOGY, INC.—Iwerks Entertainment; *U.S. Public*, pg. 915
OHIO CRANKSHAFT DIV.—Park-Ohio Industries, Inc.; *U.S. Public*, pg. 1258
OLIVETTI SPA; *Int'l*, pg. 1002
ORIENTAL MOTOR CO., LTD.; *Int'l*, pg. 1008
PHB MACHINING DIVISION—PHB Die Casting; *U.S. Private*, pg. 826
PMC INDUSTRIES INC.; *U.S. Private*, pg. 827
PALL AEROSPACE—Pall Corporation; *U.S. Public*, pg. 1253
PALMER ENVIRONMENTAL LIMITED—Halma p.l.c.; *Int'l*, pg. 589
PANDROL JACKSON, INC.—Charter plc; *Int'l*, pg. 280
PARK-OHIO INDUSTRIES, INC.; *U.S. Public*, pg. 1258
PATHWAY BELLOWS, INC.—Dover Corporation; *U.S. Public*, pg. 521
PAXTON & VIERLING—Owen Industries, Inc.; *U.S. Private*, pg. 824
PENNZOIL PRODUCTS CO.—Pennzoil Company; *U.S. Public*, pg. 1272
PERRY EQUIPMENT CORPORATION; *U.S. Private*, pg. 855
PFAUDLER, INC.—Robbins & Myers, Inc.; *U.S. Public*, pg. 1393
PHOENIX STEEL TUBE—Senior Engineering Group, plc.; *Int'l*, pg. 1221
POLHEMUS INC.—Kaiser Aerospace & Electronics Corp.; *U.S. Private*, pg. 605
POWERFLEX—Senior Engineering Group, plc.; *Int'l*, pg. 1221
PRECISION DRAWN TUBE—Senior Engineering Group, plc.; *Int'l*, pg. 1222
PRECISION ROLL GRINDERS, INC.; *U.S. Private*, pg. 880
ROWO-ROHR-UND KANALREINIGUNGSGERATE GMBH—Rothenberger Group GmbH; *Int'l*, pg. 1128
THE RAYMOND CORPORATION—BT Industries AB; *Int'l*, pg. 123
REPUBLIC HOSE MANUFACTURING CO.—Trelleborg AB; *Int'l*, pg. 1423
REUTER MANUFACTURING INC.; *U.S. Public*, pg. 1383
RITE-HITE CORPORATION; *U.S. Private*, pg. 933
RITE-HITE DIVISION—Rite-Hite Corporation; *U.S. Private*, pg. 933
RITE-HITE DOOR DIVISION—Rite-Hite Corporation; *U.S. Private*, pg. 933
RITE-HITE FROMMELT DIVISION—Rite-Hite Corporation; *U.S. Private*, pg. 933
ROBERTSHAW TENNESSEE—Siebe plc; *Int'l*, pg. 1243
ROCKWELL INTERNATIONAL CORPORATION; *U.S. Public*, pg. 1397
ROLLEPAAL B.V.—Royal Dutch/Shell Group of Companies; *Int'l*, pg. 1136
ROLOCK, INC.; *U.S. Private*, pg. 942
SANDUSKY INTERNATIONAL INC.; *U.S. Private*, pg. 964
SANDUSKY LIMITED—Sandusky International Inc.; *U.S. Private*, pg. 965
SENIOR BIGWOOD LIMITED—Senior Engineering Group, plc.; *Int'l*, pg. 1220
SENIOR ENGINEERING PRODUCTS BUSINESS AREA—Senior Engineering Group, plc.; *Int'l*, pg. 1220
SENIOR ENGINEERING TIFT GMBH—Senior Engineering Group, plc.; *Int'l*, pg. 1223
SENIOR FLEXONICS INC.—Senior Engineering Group, plc.; *Int'l*, pg. 1222
SENIOR FLEXONICS LTD.—Senior Engineering Group, plc.; *Int'l*, pg. 1221
SENIOR FOSTER WHEELER CONSTRUCTION DIVISION—Senior Engineering Group, plc.; *Int'l*, pg. 1221
SENIOR FOSTER WHEELER INDUSTRIAL BOILER DIVISION—Senior Engineering Group, plc.; *Int'l*, pg. 1221
SENIOR FOSTER WHEELER POWER DIVISION—Senior Engineering Group, plc.; *Int'l*, pg. 1221
SENIOR GREEN ECONOMISER DIVISION—Senior Engineering Group, plc.; *Int'l*, pg. 1221
SENIOR HEAT TREATMENT LIMITED—Senior Engineering Group, plc.; *Int'l*, pg. 1221
SENIOR LUKE MATERIALS HANDLING DIVISION—Senior Engineering Group, plc.; *Int'l*, pg. 1221
SENIOR TIFT B.V.—Senior Engineering Group, plc.; *Int'l*, pg. 1223
SENIOR TIFT, INC.—Senior Engineering Group, plc.; *Int'l*, pg. 1222
SENIOR TIFT LIMITED—Senior Engineering Group, plc.; *Int'l*, pg. 1221
SENIOR TIFT PTE. LTD.—Senior Engineering Group, plc.; *Int'l*, pg. 1223
SENIOR TUBE LIMITED—Senior Engineering Group, plc.; *Int'l*, pg. 1221
SIFCO INDUSTRIES, INC.; *U.S. Public*, pg. 1470
SIMON ENGINEERING PLC; *Int'l*, pg. 1251
J.T. SLOCOMB COMPANY; *U.S. Private*, pg. 1006
SMITHS INDUSTRIES PLC; *Int'l*, pg. 1266
SOGEFI INDUSTRIA DE AUTOPECAS LTDA.—AlliedSignal Inc.; *U.S. Public*, pg. 53
SPEEDFAM CO LTD.—SpeedFan International, Inc.; *U.S. Public*, pg. 1498
SPHINX MANUFACTURING COMPANY, LTD.—AlliedSignal Inc.; *U.S. Public*, pg. 53
SPRING ENGINEERS OF HOUSTON LTD.—SEI Holding Corp.; *U.S. Private*, pg. 956
STEWART & STEVENSON POWER, INC.—Stewart & Stevenson Services, Inc.; *U.S. Public*, pg. 1518
STOCKER & YALE, INC.; *U.S. Public*, pg. 1518
STONE VICKERS—Vickers PLC; *Int'l*, pg. 1467
SULZER BINGHAM PUMPS INC.—Sulzer Ltd.; *Int'l*, pg. 1305
THE SUNBANK FAMILY OF COMPANIES, INC.—Danaher Corporation; *U.S. Public*, pg. 482
SUNBANK JOSLYN, INC.—Danaher Corporation; *U.S. Public*, pg. 482
SUPERIOR MACHINE COMPANY OF SOUTH CAROLINA, INC.; *U.S. Private*, pg. 1055
SUSPA COMPART AG; *Int'l*, pg. 1322
SUSPA, INC.—Suspa Compart AG; *Int'l*, pg. 1322
SVEDALA INDUSTRIES INC.—Svedala Industri AB; *Int'l*, pg. 1325
SYNFLEX DIVISION—Furon Company; *U.S. Public*, pg. 689
TBG MANAGEMENT S.A.M.; *Int'l*, pg. 1335
TP MANIPULATIONS—Senior Engineering Group, plc.; *Int'l*, *pg. 1222*
TELEDYNE CASTING SERVICE—Allegheny Teledyne Incorporated; *U.S. Public*, pg. 43
TENNEY ENVIRONMENTAL; *U.S. Private*, pg. 1076
THERMO BLACK CLAWSON, INC.—Thermo Electron Corporation; *U.S. Public*, pg. 1593
THERMO ELECTRON CORPORATION; *U.S. Public*, pg. 1591
TITEFLEX INDUSTRIAL AMERICAS—TI Group plc; *Int'l*, pg. 1340
TOCCO, INC.—Park-Ohio Industries, Inc.; *U.S. Public*, pg. 1259
TOWNSEND ENGINEERING CO.; *U.S. Private*, pg. 1094
TRACTOR MACHINING CO.—Empire Southwest Co.; *U.S. Private*, pg. 375
TUBE PRODUCTS—Senior Engineering Group, plc.; *Int'l*, pg. 1222
TURNER MACHINE COMPANY—Electric Furnace Co.; *U.S. Private*, pg. 368
TWIN DISC, INCORPORATED; *U.S. Public*, pg. 1646
TWIN DISC INTL., S.A.—Twin Disc, Incorporated; *U.S. Public*, pg. 1647
UNITED FILTERS, INC.—Perry Equipment Corporation; *U.S. Private*, pg. 855
UNITED FLEXIBLE—Senior Engineering Group, plc.; *Int'l*, pg. 1221
UNIVERSAL INDUSTRIAL PRODUCTS CO.—United Dominion Industries, Ltd.; *U.S. Public*, pg. 1677
VALMET AUTOMATION INC.—Valmet Corporation; *Int'l*, pg. 1449
VERIN S.A.—Suspa Compart AG; *Int'l*, pg. 1322
A/S VESTFROST—Electrolux, AB; *Int'l*, pg. 441
VICKERS ACTUATOR PRODUCTS—Aeroquip-Vickers, Inc.; *U.S. Public*, pg. 24
VON ROLL AG DEPARTEMENT MASCHINEN & FORDERTECHN—Von Roll AG; *Int'l*, pg. 1480

VOTAW PRECISION TECHNOLOGIES—Kaiser Aerospace & Electronics Corp.; *U.S. Private*, pg. 605
WATTS FLUIDAIR—Siebe plc; *Int'l*, pg. 1243
WEDCO HOLLAND B.V.—ICO, Inc.; *U.S. Public*, pg. 854
WEDCO TECHNOLOGY—ICO, Inc.; *U.S. Public*, pg. 854
WEDCO TECHNOLOGY U.K. LTD.—ICO, Inc.; *U.S. Public*, pg. 854
WEDTECH INC.—ICO, Inc.; *U.S. Public*, pg. 854
WERNER & PFLEIDERER GUMMITECHNIK GMBH—Fried. Krupp AG; *Int'l*, pg. 510
ZMP, INC.; *U.S. Private*, pg. 1203

3612 — POWER, DISTRIBUTION & SPECIALTY TRANSFORMERS

ABB ASEA BROWN BOVERI (HOLDING) LTD.; *Int'l*, pg. 1
ABB ATOM AB—ABB Asea Brown Boveri (Holding) Ltd.; *Int'l*, pg. 7
ABB FLEXIBLE AUTOMATION—ABB Asea Brown Boveri (Holding) Ltd.; *Int'l*, pg. 4
ABB IN CANADA—ABB Asea Brown Boveri (Holding) Ltd.; *Int'l*, pg. 7
ABB MOTORS AB—ABB Asea Brown Boveri (Holding) Ltd.; *Int'l*, pg. 7
ABB POWER GENERATION INC.—ABB Asea Brown Boveri (Holding) Ltd.; *Int'l*, pg. 3
ABB SECHERON S.A.—ABB Asea Brown Boveri (Holding) Ltd.; *Int'l*, pg. 1
ABB TRANSFORMERS AB—ABB Asea Brown Boveri (Holding) Ltd.; *Int'l*, pg. 7
AEG ELECTROCOM GMBH, KONSTANZ—Siemens AG; *Int'l*, pg. 1244
ABBOTT ELECTRONICS, INC.; *U.S. Private*, pg. 9
ACME ELECTRIC CORPORATION; *U.S. Public*, pg. 16
ADVANCE TRANSFORMER CO.—Philips Electronics N.V.; *Int'l*, pg. 1054
AICHI-EMERSON ELECTRIC CO.—Emerson Electric Co.; *U.S. Public*, pg. 578
AJAX MAGNETHERMIC CORP.—BBA Group plc; *Int'l*, pg. 113
ANSALDO COMPONENTI SRL—IRI Istituto Ricostruzione Industriale; *Int'l*, pg. 653
ARKANSAS ELECTRIC COOPERATIVES INC.; *U.S. Private*, pg. 82
AROMAT CORPORATION—Matsushita Electric Works, Ltd.; *Int'l*, pg. 847
AROMAT NORTHWESTERN SALES OFFICE—Matsushita Electric Works, Ltd.; *Int'l*, pg. 848
ASEA BROWN BOVERI INDUSTRIAL S.A.—ABB Asea Brown Boveri (Holding) Ltd.; *Int'l*, pg. 3
BCL MAGNETICS—Tempel Steel Company; *U.S. Private*, pg. 1075
BACHMANN INDUSTRIES, INC.; *U.S. Private*, pg. 109
BENTLY NEVADA CORPORATION; *U.S. Private*, pg. 134
BRUSH TRANSFORMERS LTD.—BTR plc; *Int'l*, pg. 124
BUSCH-JAEGER ELEKTRO GMBH—ABB Asea Brown Boveri (Holding) Ltd.; *Int'l*, pg. 2
CBS CORPORATION; *U.S. Public*, pg. 273
CANA INC.—Alcatel Alsthom Compagnie Generale D'Electricite; *Int'l*, pg. 55
CHALLENGER ELECTRICAL EQUIPMENT CORP.—Eaton Corporation; *U.S. Public*, pg. 558
CHLORIDE POWER ELECTRONICS INC.—Chloride Group PLC; *Int'l*, pg. 287
CIMELTA-JEUMONT—Jeumont-Schneider Trenformeteurs; *Int'l*, pg. 706
CIRCLE A.W. PRODUCTS, CO.—Sigma-Aldrich Corporation; *U.S. Public*, pg. 1471
J.M. CLARKE (ELECTRICAL ENGINEERS) LIMITED—B. Elliott plc.; *Int'l*, pg. 448
COILCRAFT, INC.; *U.S. Private*, pg. 250
COLTEC HOLDINGS INC; *U.S. Public*, pg. 401
COMPONENTS CORPORATION OF AMERICA; *U.S. Private*, pg. 259
CONTROL TRANSFORMER CORP.—BBA Group plc; *Int'l*, pg. 113
COOPER INDUSTRIES, INC.; *U.S. Public*, pg. 442
CYBEREX, INC.—Danaher Corporation; *U.S. Public*, pg. 481
DAMART S.A.; *Int'l*, pg. 376
DEL GLOBAL TECHNOLOGIES; *U.S. Public*, pg. 493
DELTA ELECTRICAL SYSTEMS LTD.—Delta plc; *Int'l*, pg. 390
EG & G OPTOELECTRONICS-COVINA—EG & G, Inc.; *U.S. Public*, pg. 543
ER-ELECTRIC A/S—ABB Asea Brown Boveri (Holding) Ltd.; *Int'l*, pg. 3
ELECTRIC RESEARCH AND MANUFACTURING COOPERATIVE, INC. (ERMCO)—Arkansas Electric Cooperatives Inc.; *U.S. Private*, pg. 82
ELECTRO-MATIC PRODUCTS INC.; *U.S. Private*, pg. 369
ELEKTRO-APPARATEBAU OLTEN AG; *Int'l*, pg. 444
B. ELLIOTT PLC.; *Int'l*, pg. 448
ENCO—Jeumont-Schneider Trenformeteurs; *Int'l*, pg. 706
ETITAS ELEKTRIK TECHIZATI—Jeumont-Schneider Trenformeteurs; *Int'l*, pg. 706
FSG HOLDING GMBH—Ruhrgas Aktiengesellschaft; *Int'l*, pg. 1148
FINMECCANICA S.P.A.—IRI Istituto Ricostruzione Industriale; *Int'l*, pg. 653
FOXBORO, S.A.—Siebe plc; *Int'l*, pg. 1243
FRANCE DIV.—Berkshire Hathaway Inc.; *U.S. Public*, pg. 217
FRANCE TRANSFO—Jeumont-Schneider Trenformeteurs; *Int'l*, pg. 706
G.E. POWER SYSTEMS—General Electric Company; *U.S. Public*, pg. 711
GEC ALSTHOM N.V.—Alcatel Alsthom Compagnie Generale D'Electricite; *Int'l*, pg. 56
GEC (NEW ZEALAND) LTD.—The General Electric Company, p.l.c.; *Int'l*, pg. 546
GEC ZIMBABWE (PVT) LTD.—The General Electric Company, p.l.c.; *Int'l*, pg. 546
GENERAL SIGNAL CORPORATION; *U.S. Public*, pg. 726
HAYES CORPORATION, REGIONAL OFFICE—Hayes Corporation; *U.S. Public*, pg. 801
HEVI-DUTY/DOWZER—General Signal Corporation; *U.S. Public*, pg. 726
HEVI-DUTY ELECTRIC—General Signal Corporation; *U.S. Public*, pg. 726
HIPOTRONICS, INC.—Hubbell Incorporated; *U.S. Public*, pg. 844
HOCHTEMPERATUR-REAKTORBAU GMBH—ABB Asea Brown Boveri (Holding) Ltd.; *Int'l*, pg. 2
HUGHES-PETERS, INC.; *U.S. Private*, pg. 546
HYUNDAI ELECTRICAL ENGINEERING CO., LTD.—Hyundai Motor Company; *Int'l*, pg. 641
JEUMONT-SCHNEIDER TRENFORMETEURS; *Int'l*, pg. 706
JOSLYN CORPORATION—Danaher Corporation; *U.S. Public*, pg. 481
KEARNEY-NATIONAL CANADA LTD.—The Dyson-Kissner-Moran Corporation; *U.S. Private*, pg. 351
KITASHIBA ELECTRIC CO., LTD.—Toshiba Corporation; *Int'l*, pg. 1403
KLOCKNER-MOELLER GMBH; *Int'l*, pg. 736
KUHLMAN CORPORATION; *U.S. Public*, pg. 968
KUHLMAN ELECTRIC CORPORATION—Kuhlman Corporation; *U.S. Public*, pg. 968
LAMBDA ELECTRONICS INC.—Siebe plc; *Int'l*, pg. 1241
LUMBERTON PLANT—Cooper Industries, Inc.; *U.S. Public*, pg. 443
MACOMB PLANT—Cooper Industries, Inc.; *U.S. Public*, pg. 443
MAGNETEK, INC.; *U.S. Public*, pg. 1037
MAGNETEK LIGHTING PRODUCTS GROUP—MagneTek, Inc.; *U.S. Public*, pg. 1037
MALLORY, INC.; *U.S. Private*, pg. 698
MATSUSHITA ELECTRIC WORKS, LTD.; *Int'l*, pg. 847
MITSUBISHI ELECTRIC CORPORATION; *Int'l*, pg. 872
MULTILIN—General Electric Company; *U.S. Public*, pg. 713
NORELCO CONSUMER PRODUCTS COMPANY—Philips Electronics N.V.; *Int'l*, pg. 1054
NORTH AMERICAN TRANSFORMER, INC.—Rockwell International Corporation; *U.S. Public*, pg. 1398
NUTONE, INC.—Williams Holdings Plc; *Int'l*, pg. 1499
OPT INDUSTRIES, INC.—Torotel, Inc.; *U.S. Public*, pg. 1624
OTTERMILL SWITCHGEAR LTD.—Northrop Grumman Corporation; *U.S. Public*, pg. 1198
PACIFIC DUNLOP LIMITED; *Int'l*, pg. 1021
PAMPUS VERMOGENSVERWALFUNGS GMBH & CO. KG.—Saint-Gobain; *Int'l*, pg. 1175
PILLAR ELECTRICAL PLC—Caradon Plc; *Int'l*, pg. 267
POWELL INDUSTRIES, INC.; *U.S. Public*, pg. 1319
POWER DESIGNS, INC.; *U.S. Private*, pg. 878
RAPID POWER TECHNOLOGIES, INC.; *U.S. Private*, pg. 910
RELM COMMUNICATIONS, INC.—Relm Wireless Corp.; *U.S. Public*, pg. 1376
RELM DEMAND SIDE MANAGEMENT SYSTEMS—Relm Wireless Corp.; *U.S. Public*, pg. 1376
SAE ENGINEERING, INC.; *U.S. Private*, pg. 955
SL INDUSTRIES, INC.; *U.S. Public*, pg. 1418
SCHOTT CORPORATION; *U.S. Private*, pg. 972
SEMTECH CORPUS CHRISTI—Semtech Corporation; *U.S. Public*, pg. 1456
SENMATEL—Jeumont-Schneider Trenformeteurs; *Int'l*, pg. 706
SHERMAN & REILLY, INC.; *U.S. Private*, pg. 993
SIEMENS PAKISTAN ENGINEERING CO. LTD.—Siemens AG; *Int'l*, pg. 1247
SIEMENS S.A.—Siemens AG; *Int'l*, pg. 1248
SIGNAL TRANSFORMER CO., INC.—Insilco Corporation; *U.S. Public*, pg. 881
SOMFY S.A.—Damart S.A.; *Int'l*, pg. 376
SPANG & COMPANY; *U.S. Private*, pg. 1020
SQUARE D CO.—Schneider S.A.; *Int'l*, pg. 1208
SQUARE D COMPANY—Schneider S.A.; *Int'l*, pg. 1208
SQUARE D CO.-TRANSFORMER BUS. DIV.—Schneider S.A.; *Int'l*, pg. 1208
STACOENERGY PRODUCTS CO.—Components Corporation Of America; *U.S. Private*, pg. 260
TECH-TRAN CORPORATION—Inductotherm Industries, Inc.; *U.S. Private*, pg. 560
TECHNITROL, INC.; *U.S. Public*, pg. 1564
TECHNOLOGY RESEARCH CORPORATION; *U.S. Public*, pg. 1564
TELEFLEX INCORPORATED; *U.S. Public*, pg. 1569
TEMPEL STEEL COMPANY; *U.S. Private*, pg. 1075
THOMAS & BETTS/AMERACE—Thomas & Betts Corporation; *U.S. Public*, pg. 1598
TRENCH ELECTRIC—BBA Group plc; *Int'l*, pg. 113
TRIPLE A SPECIALTY COMPANY; *U.S. Private*, pg. 1103
TURK ELEKTRIK ENDUSTRISI A.S.—Koc Holding A.S.; *Int'l*, pg. 741
UNITED TECHNOLOGIES CONTROL SYSTEMS—United Technologies Corporation; *U.S. Public*, pg. 1690
UNIVERSAL VOLTRONICS CORPORATION—Thermo Electron Corporation; *U.S. Public*, pg. 1596
WESTINGHOUSE CANADA INC.—CBS Corporation; *U.S. Public*, pg. 275
WESTINGHOUSE DO BRASIL S/A ELECTROMAR DIVISION—CBS Corporation; *U.S. Public*, pg. 275
WESTINGHOUSE DO BRASIL S/A MARINI E DAMINELLI DIVISION—CBS Corporation; *U.S. Public*, pg. 275

3613 — SWITCHGEAR & SWITCHBOARD APPARATUS

ABB CONTROL INC.—ABB Asea Brown Boveri (Holding) Ltd.; *Int'l*, pg. 4
ABB RELAYS AB—ABB Asea Brown Boveri (Holding) Ltd.; *Int'l*, pg. 7
ABB SACE LIMITADA—ABB Asea Brown Boveri (Holding) Ltd.; *Int'l*, pg. 7
ABB SACE S.P.A. COSTRUSIONI ELETTROMECCANICHE—ABB Asea Brown Boveri (Holding) Ltd.; *Int'l*, pg. 2
ABB SELFA AB—ABB Asea Brown Boveri (Holding) Ltd.; *Int'l*, pg. 7
ABB STOTZ-KONTAKT HELLAS S.A.—ABB Asea Brown Boveri (Holding) Ltd.; *Int'l*, pg. 2
ABB STOTZ-KONTAKT (PORTUGAL) LDA.—ABB Asea Brown Boveri (Holding) Ltd.; *Int'l*, pg. 2
ABB STOTZ-KONTAKT S.A.—ABB Asea Brown Boveri (Holding) Ltd.; *Int'l*, pg. 2
A.D. DATA SYSTEMS—PSC Inc.; *U.S. Public*, pg. 1246
ACCUDYNE CORPORATION—Alliant Techsystems; *U.S. Public*, pg. 47
ALCATEL CAVI, S.P.A.—Alcatel Alsthom Compagnie Generale D'Electricite; *Int'l*, pg. 55
ARMSTRONG ELECTRA LTD.—John Laing PLC; *Int'l*, pg. 796
ARMSTRONG INTERNATIONAL, INC.; *U.S. Private*, pg. 83
AROMAT CORPORATION—Matsushita Electric Works, Ltd.; *Int'l*, pg. 847
ASCO CONTROLS B.V.—Emerson Electric Co.; *U.S. Public*, pg. 575
ASCO G.M.B.H. & CO.—Emerson Electric Co.; *U.S. Public*, pg. 575
ASCO (JAPAN) CO. LIMITED—Emerson Electric Co.; *U.S. Public*, pg. 575
ASCO (UK)—Emerson Electric Co.; *U.S. Public*, pg. 575
ASCOMATICA S.A. DE C.V.—Emerson Electric Co.; *U.S. Public*, pg. 576
ASCOMATION PTY. LTD.—Emerson Electric Co.; *U.S. Public*, pg. 576
ASCOVAL INDUSTRIA E COMMERCIO LTDA.—Emerson Electric Co.; *U.S. Public*, pg. 576
ASEA BROWN BOVERI AKTIENGESELLSCHAFT—ABB Asea Brown Boveri (Holding) Ltd.; *Int'l*, pg. 2
ASEA BROWN BOVERI INDUSTRIAL S.A.—ABB Asea Brown Boveri (Holding) Ltd.; *Int'l*, pg. 3
ASEA BROWN BOVERI NEDERLAND B.V.—ABB Asea Brown Boveri (Holding) Ltd.; *Int'l*, pg. 2
ASEA BROWN BOVERI (S.E.A.) PTE. LTD.—ABB Asea Brown Boveri (Holding) Ltd.; *Int'l*, pg. 3
ASEA LIMITED—ABB Asea Brown Boveri (Holding) Ltd.; *Int'l*, pg. 8
BBC BROWN BOVERI S.A. DE C.V.—ABB Asea Brown Boveri (Holding) Ltd.; *Int'l*, pg. 3
BWD AUTOMOTIVE—Echlin Inc.; *U.S. Public*, pg. 560
N.G. BAILEY & CO. LTD.; *Int'l*, pg. 132
BANG & OLUFSEN A/S; *Int'l*, pg. 145
BILL SWITCHGEAR LTD.—Delta plc; *Int'l*, pg. 390
BOWTHORPE EMP LIMITED—Bowthorpe plc; *Int'l*, pg. 207
BURTON ELECTRICAL ENGINEERING—Wyle Laboratories, Inc.; *U.S. Private*, pg. 1193
BUSCH-JAEGER ELEKTRO GMBH—ABB Asea Brown Boveri (Holding) Ltd.; *Int'l*, pg. 2
BUSSMANN DIVISION—Cooper Industries, Inc.; *U.S. Public*, pg. 443
CBS CORPORATION; *U.S. Public*, pg. 273
COMSIP AUTOMATION BENELUX, S.A.—Alcatel Alsthom Compagnie Generale D'Electricite; *Int'l*, pg. 53
COMSIP LTD.—Alcatel Alsthom Compagnie Generale D'Electricite; *Int'l*, pg. 53
COMSIP NEDERLAND B.V.—Alcatel Alsthom Compagnie Generale D'Electricite; *Int'l*, pg. 53
CALOR-EMAG ELEKTRIZITATS-AKTIENGESELLSCHAFT—ABB Asea Brown Boveri (Holding) Ltd.; *Int'l*, pg. 2
CANADIAN PUREGAS EQUIPMENT LTD.—American Financial Group; *U.S. Public*, pg. 75
CANON BUSINESS MACHINES DE MEXICO S.A. DE C.V.—Canon Inc.; *Int'l*, pg. 262
CEGELEC—Alcatel Alsthom Compagnie Generale D'Electricite; *Int'l*, pg. 52
CELEGEC AUTOMATION—Alcatel Alsthom Compagnie Generale D'Electricite; *Int'l*, pg. 53
CIRCLE A.W. PRODUCTS, CO.—Sigma-Aldrich Corporation; *U.S. Public*, pg. 1471
C.P. CLARE CORPORATION; *U.S. Public*, pg. 382
COLE HERSEE COMPANY; *U.S. Private*, pg. 251
COMSIP AUTOMACION S.A.—Alcatel Alsthom Compagnie Generale D'Electricite; *Int'l*, pg. 53
CONTROLMATIC GMBH—Hepworth Plc; *Int'l*, pg. 615
COOPER INDUSTRIES, INC.; *U.S. Public*, pg. 442
COOPER POWER SYSTEMS—Cooper Industries, Inc.; *U.S. Public*, pg. 443
CORNELL DUBILIER ELECTRONICS—Kaplan Electronics; *U.S. Private*, pg. 607
CRABTREE ELECTRICAL INDUSTRIES LIMITED—Hanson PLC; *Int'l*, pg. 592
CROMPTON INSTRUMENTS LTD.—BTR plc; *Int'l*, pg. 125
CROUSE-HINDS (AUSTRALIA) PTY. LTD.—Cooper Industries, Inc.; *U.S. Public*, pg. 445
CUTLER HAMMER AUSTRALIA PTY. LTD.—Eaton Corporation; *U.S. Public*, pg. 558
CUTLER HAMMER MEXICANA, S.A.—Eaton Corporation; *U.S. Public*, pg. 558
CUTLER-HAMMER NEW ZEALAND LIMITED—Eaton Corporation; *U.S. Public*, pg. 558
CUTLER-HAMMER NIGERIA LIMITED—Eaton Corporation; *U.S. Public*, pg. 558
CYBEREX, INC.—Danaher Corporation; *U.S. Public*, pg. 481
DELTA PLC; *Int'l*, pg. 389
DYNAMICS CORPORATION OF AMERICA—CTS Corporation; *U.S. Public*, pg. 286
EB INSTALLASJON A/S—ABB Asea Brown Boveri (Holding) Ltd.; *Int'l*, pg. 3
EAGLE ELECTRIC MFG. CO., INC.; *U.S. Private*, pg. 354
EATON CONTROLES INDUSTRIALES, S.A.—Eaton Corporation; *U.S. Public*, pg. 558
EATON CONTROLS S.P.A—Eaton Corporation; *U.S. Public*, pg. 558
EATON CORPORATION; *U.S. Public*, pg. 555

EATON CORP. DIV.—Eaton Corporation; U.S. Public, pg. 556
EATON CORPORATION-HEINEMANN PRODUCTS, COMMERCIAL CONTROLS DIVISION—Eaton Corporation; U.S. Public, pg. 557
EATON CORPORATION, SPECIFIC INDUSTRY CONTROL DIVISION—Eaton Corporation; U.S. Public, pg. 557
EATON LIMITED COMMERCIAL & MILITARY CONTROLS OPERATIONS—Eaton Corporation; U.S. Public, pg. 559
EATON SVENSKA AB—Eaton Corporation; U.S. Public, pg. 559
EATON YALE LTD. INDUSTRIAL CONTROL DIVISION—Eaton Corporation; U.S. Public, pg. 559
EDISON FUSE GEAR—Cooper Industries, Inc.; U.S. Public, pg. 443
ELDON AB; Int'l, pg. 436
B. ELLIOTT PLC.; Int'l, pg. 448
ETIREX S.A.—Emerson Electric Co.; U.S. Public, pg. 577
EXIDE ELECTRONICS GROUP, INC.—BTR plc; Int'l, pg. 126
FAIRBANKS MORSE ENGINE DIVISION—Coltec Holdings Inc; U.S. Public, pg. 401
FASCO CONTROLS CORPORATION—BTR plc; Int'l, pg. 125
FUJITSU (SINGAPORE) PTE. LTD.—Fujitsu Limited; Int'l, pg. 528
G & H TECHNOLOGY, INC.—American Financial Group; U.S. Public, pg. 75
G.E. POWER SYSTEMS—General Electric Company; U.S. Public, pg. 711
GEC ALSTHOM N.V.—Alcatel Alsthom Compagnie Generale D'Electricite; Int'l, pg. 56
GEC ZIMBABWE (PVT) LTD.—The General Electric Company, p.l.c.; Int'l, pg. 546
GENERAL ELECTRIC COMPANY; U.S. Public, pg. 709
THE GENERAL ELECTRIC COMPANY, P.L.C.; Int'l, pg. 543
GHANA SANYO CO., LTD.—Sanyo Electric Co., Ltd.; Int'l, pg. 1192
GOLDSTAR ELECTRIC CO. LTD.—LG Group; Int'l, pg. 779
GOLDSTAR INSTRUMENT & ELECTRIC CO. LTD.—LG Group; Int'l, pg. 779
GOULD ELECTRONICS (CANADA) LTD., SHAWMUT DIV.—Thermo Electron Corporation; U.S. Public, pg. 1592
GOULD ELECTRONICS INC., SHAWMUT CIRCUIT PROTECTION DIVISION—Thermo Electron Corporation; U.S. Public, pg. 1592
GRUPO SIEMENS S.A. DE C.V.—Siemens AG; Int'l, pg. 1247
GUARANTEE ELECTRICAL COMPANY; U.S. Private, pg. 485
HAGER MODULAIRE S.A.—ABB Asea Brown Boveri (Holding) Ltd.; Int'l, pg. 3
HEINEMANN ELECTRIC CANADA LTD.—Eaton Corporation; U.S. Public, pg. 557
HEINEMANN ELECTRIC PTY. LTD.—Eaton Corporation; U.S. Public, pg. 557
HIROSE ELECTRIC CO., LTD.; Int'l, pg. 620
HITACHI, LTD.; Int'l, pg. 621
HONEYWELL INC.; U.S. Public, pg. 833
HONEYWELL'S MICRO SWITCH DIVISION—Honeywell Inc.; U.S. Public, pg. 834
HOUSTON FEARLESS 76 INC.; U.S. Private, pg. 542
HYOSUNG INDUSTRIES CO., LTD.—Hyosung Group; Int'l, pg. 640
HYUNDAI ELECTRICAL ENGINEERING CO., LTD.—Hyundai Motor Company; Int'l, pg. 641
ITT CANNON SWITCH PRODUCTS, INC.—ITT Industries, Inc.; U.S. Public, pg. 859
ITW BASIC SWITCH PRODUCTS—Illinois Tool Works Inc.; U.S. Public, pg. 866
ITW PANEL SWITCHES AND SYSTEMS—Illinois Tool Works Inc.; U.S. Public, pg. 866
IDAHO UTILITY PRODUCTS COMPANY—Idaho Power Company; U.S. Public, pg. 862
IMTECH PROJECTS ZUIT B.V.—Internatio-Muller N.V.; Int'l, pg. 681
JAPAN ENERGY CORPORATION; Int'l, pg. 702
JOHNSON CONTROLS, INC.; U.S. Public, pg. 932
JOSLYN CORPORATION—Danaher Corporation; U.S. Public, pg. 481
KEARNEY COMPANY—Cooper Industries, Inc.; U.S. Public, pg. 444
KIDDE SYSTEMS, INC.—Publicker Industries Inc.; U.S. Public, pg. 1341
KLOCKNER-MOELLER CORP.—Klockner-Moeller GmbH; Int'l, pg. 736
KLOCKNER-MOELLER GMBH; Int'l, pg. 736
KOHLER COMPANY; U.S. Private, pg. 630
LITTELFUSE B.V.—Littelfuse, Inc.; U.S. Public, pg. 1001
LITTELFUSE, INC.; U.S. Public, pg. 1001
LITTELFUSE LTD.—Littelfuse, Inc.; U.S. Public, pg. 1001
LITTELFUSE S.A. DE C.V.—Littelfuse, Inc.; U.S. Public, pg. 1001
LUCAS AFTERMARKET OPERATIONS—LucasVarity plc; Int'l, pg. 819
LUCAS-TVS LTD.—LucasVarity plc; Int'l, pg. 820
MARATHON EQUIPMENT COMPANY—Dover Corporation; U.S. Public, pg. 521
MASON ELECTRIC COMPANY—BTR plc; Int'l, pg. 127
MATSUSHITA ELECTRIC WORKS, LTD.; Int'l, pg. 847
MINARIK CORP; U.S. Private, pg. 749
NIFE GMBH STROMVERSORGUNGSSYSTEME—Alcatel Alsthom Compagnie Generale D'Electricite; Int'l, pg. 54
NIFE POWER SYSTEMS PTE LTD.—Alcatel Alsthom Compagnie Generale D'Electricite; Int'l, pg. 54
NIKKO DENKI SEISAKUSHO CO., LTD.—Oki Electric Industry Company, Ltd.; Int'l, pg. 999
O-Z/GEDNEY, NELSON FIRESTOP PRODUCTS—General Signal Corporation; U.S. Public, pg. 726
OTTERMILL SWITCHGEAR LTD.—Northrop Grumman Corporation; U.S. Public, pg. 1198
PACIFIC SCIENTIFIC COMPANY; U.S. Public, pg. 1250
PARADIGM TECHNOLOGY, INC.; U.S. Public, pg. 1256
PILLAR ELECTRICAL PLC—Caradon Plc; Int'l, pg. 267
POWELL ELECTRICAL MFG. CO.—Powell Industries, Inc.; U.S. Public, pg. 1319
POWELL INDUSTRIES, INC.; U.S. Public, pg. 1319
R. & H. SYSTEMS B.V.—Internatio-Muller N.V.; Int'l, pg. 680
REDCO, INC.—Jetronic Industries, Inc.; U.S. Public, pg. 926
THOMAS ROBINSON GROUP PLC—Brunel Holdings Plc; Int'l, pg. 231
ROMAN ELECTRIC COMPANY, INC.; U.S. Private, pg. 942
ROYAL BEGEMANN GROUP; Int'l, pg. 1133
S & C ELECTRIC CANADA LTD.—S & C Electric Company; U.S. Private, pg. 954
S & C ELECTRIC COMPANY; U.S. Private, pg. 954
SFA DATACOMM INC.—SFA, Inc.; U.S. Private, pg. 956
SPD TECHNOLOGIES; U.S. Private, pg. 957
SAHKOLAHTEENMAKI OY—ABB Asea Brown Boveri (Holding) Ltd.; Int'l, pg. 8
SCHLAGE LOCK COMPANY—Ingersoll-Rand Company; U.S. Public, pg. 876
SEMTECH CORPUS CHRISTI—Semtech Corporation; U.S. Public, pg. 1456
SHOGYO INTERNATIONAL CORPORATION; U.S. Private, pg. 996
SIEMENS A/S—Siemens AG; Int'l, pg. 1247
SIEMENS CANADA LTD.—Siemens AG; Int'l, pg. 1247
SIEMENS LTD.—Siemens AG; Int'l, pg. 1247
SIEMENS OSAKEYTIOE—Siemens AG; Int'l, pg. 1247
SIEMENS PAKISTAN ENGINEERING CO. LTD.—Siemens AG; Int'l, pg. 1247
SIEMENS PLC—Siemens AG; Int'l, pg. 1247
SIEMENS S.A.—Siemens AG; Int'l, pg. 1248
SOCIEDAD VENEZOLANA DE ELECTRIFICACION C.A. (SVECA)—ABB Asea Brown Boveri (Holding) Ltd.; Int'l, pg. 3
SPANG & COMPANY; U.S. Private, pg. 1020
SPRECHER ENERGIE AG—Alcatel Alsthom Compagnie Generale D'Electricite; Int'l, pg. 55
SQUARE D CO.—Schneider S.A.; Int'l, pg. 1208
SQUARE D COMPANY—Schneider S.A.; Int'l, pg. 1208
SWITCHCRAFT, INC.—Raytheon Company; U.S. Public, pg. 1366
SYNCHRO-START PRODUCTS, INC.—Knowles Electronics, Inc.; U.S. Private, pg. 627
TEMPO INSTRUMENT INC.—Bowthorpe plc; Int'l, pg. 208
THOMAS & BETTS/AMERACE—Thomas & Betts Corporation; U.S. Public, pg. 1598
3M; U.S. Public, pg. 1604
TRICON INDUSTRIES, INC.; U.S. Private, pg. 1102
TROQUELADOS ESPECIALES S.A. DE C.V.—ABB Asea Brown Boveri (Holding) Ltd.; Int'l, pg. 8
TURNER ELECTRIC CORPORATION—Valley Forge Corporation; U.S. Public, pg. 1705
VALLEY FORGE CORPORATION; U.S. Public, pg. 1705
WESSEL IND. LTD.—ABB Asea Brown Boveri (Holding) Ltd.; Int'l, pg. 3
WESTINGHOUSE ASIA CONTROLS CORP.—CBS Corporation; U.S. Public, pg. 273
WESTINGHOUSE CANADA INC.—CBS Corporation; U.S. Public, pg. 275
WESTINGHOUSE DO BRASIL S/A MARINI E DAMINELLI DIVISION—CBS Corporation; U.S. Public, pg. 275
WESTINGHOUSE POWER SYSTEMS GROUP—CBS Corporation; U.S. Public, pg. 273
WHIPP & BOURNE LTD.—FKI Plc; Int'l, pg. 473
YAMAKO ELECTRIC MANUFACTURE CO., LTD.—Oki Electric Industry Company, Ltd.; Int'l, pg. 999

3621 — MOTORS & GENERATORS

ABB ATOM AB—ABB Asea Brown Boveri (Holding) Ltd.; Int'l, pg. 7
ABB ELECTRO MECHANICS INC.—ABB Asea Brown Boveri (Holding) Ltd.; Int'l, pg. 3
ABB FLEXIBLE AUTOMATION—ABB Asea Brown Boveri (Holding) Ltd.; Int'l, pg. 4
ABB GENERATION AB—ABB Asea Brown Boveri (Holding) Ltd.; Int'l, pg. 7
ABB MOTORS AB—ABB Asea Brown Boveri (Holding) Ltd.; Int'l, pg. 7
ABB POWER LTD.—ABB Asea Brown Boveri (Holding) Ltd.; Int'l, pg. 2
ABB TECNOMASIO S.P.A.—ABB Asea Brown Boveri (Holding) Ltd.; Int'l, pg. 2
ABB TRACTION AB—ABB Asea Brown Boveri (Holding) Ltd.; Int'l, pg. 7
AC ROCHESTER OVERSEAS CORPORATION—General Motors Corporation; U.S. Public, pg. 722
AEG HAUSGERATE AG—Electrolux, AB; Int'l, pg. 442
API HAROWE—American Precision Industries Inc.; U.S. Public, pg. 90
AEROFLEX LABORATORIES INC.—Aeroflex Incorporated; U.S. Public, pg. 24
AEROSPACE-MARINE-DEFENSE GROUP—Aeroquip-Vickers, Inc.; U.S. Public, pg. 24
AMERICAN ELECTRONICS, INC.—AEI Holding Co., Inc.; U.S. Private, pg. 5
AMERICAN PRECISION INDUSTRIES INC.; U.S. Public, pg. 90
AMETEK G.M.B.H.—AMETEK, Inc.; U.S. Public, pg. 100
AMETEK, INC.; U.S. Public, pg. 99
AMETEK ITALIA—AMETEK, Inc.; U.S. Public, pg. 100
ANALOG DEVICES, SANTA CLARA—Analog Devices, Inc.; U.S. Public, pg. 108
ANSALDO TRANSPORTI-MILAN PLANT—IRI Istituto Ricostruzione Industriale; Int'l, pg. 653
ANSALDO TRANSPORTI SPA—IRI Istituto Ricostruzione Industriale; Int'l, pg. 653
ASEA S.A.—ABB Asea Brown Boveri (Holding) Ltd.; Int'l, pg. 8
AUXILEC, INC.—Thomson S.A.; Int'l, pg. 1383
AVIS INDUSTRIAL CORPORATION; U.S. Private, pg. 102
AXSYS TECHNOLOGIES, INC.; U.S. Public, pg. 157
B & B MOTOR & CONTROL CORPORATION; U.S. Private, pg. 105
BCL MAGNETICS—Tempel Steel Company; U.S. Private, pg. 1075
BEI SENSORS AND SYSTEMS COMPANY—BEI Technologies, Inc.; U.S. Public, pg. 160
BABCOCK & WILCOX CO.—McDermott International, Inc.; U.S. Public, pg. 1068
BALDOR ELECTRIC COMPANY; U.S. Public, pg. 168
BALDOR ELECTRIC COMPANY—Baldor Electric Company; U.S. Public, pg. 169
BARBER-COLMAN COMPANY—Siebe plc; Int'l, pg. 1242
BERKMANNS ANTRIEBE GMBH—Groschopp & Co. GmbH EMW Elektromotoren-Feinbauwerk; Int'l, pg. 559
BEST POWER; U.S. Private, pg. 140
BODINE ELECTRIC COMPANY; U.S. Private, pg. 154
ROBERT BOSCH CORPORATION—Robert Bosch GmbH; Int'l, pg. 204
BREEZE EASTERN—TransTechnology Corporation; U.S. Public, pg. 1632
BRUEL & KJAER MEASUREMENTS A/S—AGIV Group; Int'l, pg. 14
BRUSH ELECTRICAL MACHINES LTD.—BTR plc; Int'l, pg. 124
CBS CORPORATION; U.S. Public, pg. 273
CATERPILLAR INC.; U.S. Public, pg. 315
COLEMAN POWERMATE, INC.—MacAndrews & Forbes Holdings Inc.; U.S. Private, pg. 691
COLMAN MOTOR PRODUCTS, INC.—Siebe plc; Int'l, pg. 1242
COLMAN OEM, INC.—Siebe plc; Int'l, pg. 1242
COMPANIA DE MOTORES DOMESTICOS, S.A. DE C.V.—Emerson Electric Co.; U.S. Public, pg. 576
CONTEC LIMITED PARTNERSHIP—Manhattan Partners L.P.; U.S. Private, pg. 699
CONTINENTAL MACHINES, INC.; U.S. Private, pg. 268
CYBEREX, INC.—Danaher Corporation; U.S. Public, pg. 481
DELTEC CORPORATION—Fiskars Oy AB; Int'l, pg. 492
DOWTY AEROSPACE YAKIMA—TI Group plc; Int'l, pg. 1337
DYNAMICS CORPORATION OF AMERICA—CTS Corporation; U.S. Public, pg. 286
EG & G MISSOURI METALS—EG & G, Inc.; U.S. Public, pg. 544
EG & G ROTRON—EG & G, Inc.; U.S. Public, pg. 543
EASTERN AIR DEVICES, INC.; U.S. Private, pg. 357
EATON TECHNOLOGIES INC.—Eaton Corporation; U.S. Public, pg. 558
ELECTRA-GEAR DIV.—Regal-Beloit Corporation; U.S. Public, pg. 1370
ELECTRO-MECHANICAL INSTRUMENTS DIV.—AEI Holding Co., Inc.; U.S. Private, pg. 5
ELECTROMECHANICAL SYSTEMS, INC.—COMSAT Corporation; U.S. Public, pg. 424
ELGRO SP Z.O.O.—Groschopp & Co. GmbH EMW Elektromotoren-Feinbauwerk; Int'l, pg. 559
B. ELLIOTT PLC.; Int'l, pg. 448
ELOMETA CORPORATION—Treadwell Corporation; U.S. Private, pg. 1098
EMERSON ELECTRIC, C.A.—Emerson Electric Co.; U.S. Public, pg. 576
EMERSON ELECTRIC CO.; U.S. Public, pg. 572
EMERSON ELECTRIC (FRANCE) S.A.—Emerson Electric Co.; U.S. Public, pg. 576
EMERSON ELECTRIC IRELAND LIMITED—Emerson Electric Co.; U.S. Public, pg. 576
EMERSON MOTOR COMPANY—Emerson Electric Co.; U.S. Public, pg. 573
ETIREX S.A.—Emerson Electric Co.; U.S. Public, pg. 577
FASCO DC MOTORS—BTR plc; Int'l, pg. 125
FASCO INDUSTRIES, INC.—BTR plc; Int'l, pg. 125
FRANKLIN ELECTRIC CO., INC.; U.S. Public, pg. 679
FRANKLIN ELECTRIC EUROPA, GMBH—Franklin Electric Co., Inc.; U.S. Public, pg. 679
FRANKLIN ELECTRIC SOUTH AFRICA—Franklin Electric Co., Inc.; U.S. Public, pg. 679
G.E. CANADA, PETERBOROUGH—General Electric Company; U.S. Public, pg. 713
G.E. CAPITAL FLEET SERVICES—General Electric Company; U.S. Public, pg. 710
GEC ALSTHOM N.V.—Alcatel Alsthom Compagnie Generale D'Electricite; Int'l, pg. 56
GARDEN STATE CONVERTERS—Triangle Marketing Corp.; U.S. Private, pg. 1102
GENERAL DYNAMICS CORPORATION; U.S. Public, pg. 708
GENERAL ELECTRIC COMPANY; U.S. Public, pg. 709
THE GENERAL ELECTRIC COMPANY, P.L.C.; Int'l, pg. 543
GENERAL SIGNAL CORPORATION; U.S. Public, pg. 726
GOLDSTAR INSTRUMENT & ELECTRIC CO. LTD.—LG Group; Int'l, pg. 779
GROSCHOPP & CO. GMBH EMW ELEKTROMOTOREN-FEINBAUWERK; Int'l, pg. 559
GROSCHOPP, INC.—Groschopp & Co. GmbH EMW Elektromotoren-Feinbauwerk; Int'l, pg. 559
GRUPO SIEMENS S.A. DE C.V.—Siemens AG; Int'l, pg. 1247
HTL/KIN-TECH DIVISION—Pacific Scientific Company; U.S. Public, pg. 1250
HANSEN CORPORATION—Minebea Co., Ltd.; Int'l, pg. 868
HATHAWAY MOTION CONTROL DIVISION—Hathaway Corporation; U.S. Public, pg. 799
HAYDON SWITCH & INSTRUMENT, INC.; U.S. Private, pg. 513
HOBART BROTHERS CO.—Illinois Tool Works Inc.; U.S. Public, pg. 866
HOLEC MACHINES & APPARATEN B.V.—Royal Begemann Group; Int'l, pg. 1133
HOLSET ENGINEERING CO. LTD.—Cummins Engine Company, Inc.; U.S. Public, pg. 469
HONDA MOTOR CO., LTD.; Int'l, pg. 634

HOUSTON FEARLESS 76 INC.; *U.S. Private*, pg. 542
HURST MANUFACTURING—Emerson Electric Co.; *U.S. Public*, pg. 573
HYUNDAI ELECTRICAL ENGINEERING CO., LTD.—Hyundai Motor Company; *Int'l*, pg. 641
I.D.M. ELECTRONICS LTD.—Kaydon Corporation; *U.S. Public*, pg. 946
THE IMPERIAL ELECTRIC COMPANY—Jordan Industries, Inc.; *U.S. Private*, pg. 598
INDUCTOTHERM INDUSTRIES, INC.; *U.S. Private*, pg. 560
INDUSTRIAL DRIVES DIV.—Kollmorgen Corporation; *U.S. Public*, pg. 965
INLAND DETROIT DIESEL ALLISON CO.; *U.S. Private*, pg. 564
INLAND MOTOR DIV.—Kollmorgen Corporation; *U.S. Public*, pg. 965
INTERMATIC INC.; *U.S. Private*, pg. 567
JOHNSON WORLDWIDE ASSOCIATES, INC.; *U.S. Public*, *pg. 932*
KATO ENGINEERING DIV.—Rockwell International Corporation; *U.S. Public*, pg. 1398
KAWAMATA SEIKI CO., LTD.—Toshiba Corporation; *Int'l*, pg. 1403
KAWASAKI MOTORS CORP., U.S.A.—Kawasaki Heavy Industries, Ltd.; *Int'l*, pg. 725
KIRKWOOD INDUSTRIES, INC.; *U.S. Private*, pg. 623
KOHLER COMPANY; *U.S. Private*, pg. 630
KOHLER DE MEXICO, S.A. DE C.V.—Kohler Company; *U.S. Private*, pg. 631
KOLLMORGEN CORPORATION; *U.S. Public*, pg. 965
LAMB ELECTRIC DIV.—AMETEK, Inc.; *U.S. Public*, pg. 100
LAMBETH COMMUTATORS LTD.—Delta plc; *Int'l*, pg. 390
THE LINCOLN ELECTRIC CO. (FRANCE) S.A.—The Lincoln Electric Company; *U.S. Public*, pg. 996
THE LINCOLN ELECTRIC COMPANY; *U.S. Public*, pg. 996
THE LINCOLN ELECTRIC CO. AUSTRALIA PTY. LTD.—The Lincoln Electric Company; *U.S. Public*, pg. 996
THE LINCOLN ELECTRIC CO. OF CANADA LTD.—The Lincoln Electric Company; *U.S. Public*, pg. 997
LINCOLN ELECTRIC (U.K. LTD.)—The Lincoln Electric Company; *U.S. Public*, pg. 997
LITTON POLY-SCIENTIFIC—Litton Industries, Inc.; *U.S. Public*, pg. 1003
LOUIS ALLIS COMPANY; *U.S. Private*, pg. 677
MAGNEDYNE DIV.—Sierracin Corporation; *U.S. Private*, pg. 999
MAGNETEK, INC.; *U.S. Public*, pg. 1037
MANNESMANN DEMAG CORPORATION—Mannesmann A.G.; *Int'l*, pg. 837
MARATHON ELECTRIC, LIMA—Regal-Beloit Corporation; *U.S. Public*, pg. 1371
MARATHON ELECTRIC MANUFACTURING CORP.—Regal-Beloit Corporation; *U.S. Public*, pg. 1371
MATRA TRANSPORT—Lagardere Groupe; *Int'l*, pg. 793
MATSUSHITA ELECTRIC WORKS, LTD.; *Int'l*, pg. 847
MCLEAN ENGINEERING—Zero Corporation; *U.S. Public*, pg. 1791
MICROMOTORS GROSCHOPP IRELAND LTD.—Groschopp & Co. GmbH EMW Elektromotoren-Feinbauwerk; *Int'l*, pg. 559
MITSUBISHI ELECTRIC CORPORATION; *Int'l*, pg. 872
MOLON MOTOR & COIL CORP.; *U.S. Private*, pg. 756
MORGANITE INC.—Morgan Crucible Co. Plc; *Int'l*, pg. 893
MOTOR GROUP—Rockwell International Corporation; *U.S. Public*, pg. 1398
NIDEC—Nippon Densan (NIDEC); *Int'l*, pg. 933
NEW COLEMAN HOLDINGS INC.—MacAndrews & Forbes Holdings Inc.; *U.S. Private*, pg. 690
NOVA ELECTRIC MFG. CO.—Illinois Tool Works Inc.; *U.S. Public*, pg. 866
ONAN CORPORATION—Cummins Engine Company, Inc.; *U.S. Public*, pg. 468
PMI MOTION TECHNOLOGIES DIV.—Kollmorgen Corporation; *U.S. Public*, pg. 965
PACIFIC SCIENTIFIC COMPANY; *U.S. Public*, pg. 1250
PANDROL JACKSON, INC.—Charter plc; *Int'l*, pg. 280
PARAGON ELECTRIC CO., INC.—Siebe plc; *Int'l*, pg. 1243
PARKER KINETIC DESIGNS—Parker Drilling Company; *U.S. Public*, pg. 1259
PENN ENGINEERING & MANUFACTURING CORP.; *U.S. Public*, pg. 1269
PENTAIR, INC.; *U.S. Public*, pg. 1273
PHILIPS AUTOMOTIVE ELECTRONICS—Philips Electronics N.V.; *Int'l*, pg. 1054
PHILIPS ELECTRONICS N.V.; *Int'l*, pg. 1051
THE PIERCE CO., INC.—Avis Industrial Corporation; *U.S. Private*, pg. 102
THE PITTMAN COMPANY—Penn Engineering & Manufacturing Corp.; *U.S. Public*, pg. 1270
POLY-SCIENTIFIC DIV.—Litton Industries, Inc.; *U.S. Public*, pg. 1003
PRINTED MOTORS LTD.—B. Elliott plc.; *Int'l*, pg. 448
REAGAN EQUIPMENT COMPANY, INC.; *U.S. Private*, pg. 913
RELIABILITY INCORPORATED; *U.S. Public*, pg. 1373
RELIANCE ELECTRIC COMPANY—Rockwell International Corporation; *U.S. Public*, pg. 1398
REULAND ELECTRIC COMPANY; *U.S. Private*, pg. 925
M.H. RHODES, INC.; *U.S. Private*, pg. 927
ROLLS-ROYCE POWER ENGINEERING PLC—Rolls-Royce plc; *Int'l*, pg. 1127
SAB IBERICA S.A.—Cardo AB; *Int'l*, pg. 271
SAB SISTEMI S.P.A.—Cardo AB; *Int'l*, pg. 271
SAB WABCO AB—Cardo AB; *Int'l*, pg. 271
SAB WABCO BENELUX—Cardo AB; *Int'l*, pg. 271
SAB WABCO ENGINEERING S.R.L.—Cardo AB; *Int'l*, pg. 271
SAB WABCO HOLDINGS B.V.—Cardo AB; *Int'l*, pg. 271
SAB WABCO LTD.—Cardo AB; *Int'l*, pg. 271
SAB WABCO N.V.—Cardo AB; *Int'l*, pg. 271
SAB WABCO S.A.—Cardo AB; *Int'l*, pg. 271
SAB WABCO S.P.A.—Cardo AB; *Int'l*, pg. 271
SAE (INDIA) LTD.—ABB Asea Brown Boveri (Holding) Ltd.; *Int'l*, pg. 3
SAE-SOCIETA ANONIMA ELECTRIFICAZIONE S.P.A.—ABB Asea Brown Boveri (Holding) Ltd.; *Int'l*, pg. 3
SAFT—Alcatel Alsthom Compagnie Generale D'Electricite; *Int'l*, pg. 54
SL MONTEVIDEO TECHNOLOGY, INC.—SL Industries, Inc.; *U.S. Public*, pg. 1419
THE SCOTT MOTORS COMPANY—Jordan Industries, Inc.; *U.S. Private*, pg. 598
SHIBAURA ENGINEERING WORKS CO., LTD.—Toshiba Corporation; *Int'l*, pg. 1403
SIEMENS ENERGY & AUTOMATION INC.—Siemens AG; *Int'l*, pg. 1245
SIEMENS LTD.—Siemens AG; *Int'l*, pg. 1247
SIEMENS PAKISTAN ENGINEERING CO. LTD.—Siemens AG; *Int'l*, pg. 1247
SIEMENS S.A.—Siemens AG; *Int'l*, pg. 1248
SIEMENS TRANSPORTATION SYSTEMS, INC.—Siemens AG; *Int'l*, pg. 1246
SIERRACIN CORPORATION; *U.S. Private*, pg. 999
A.O. SMITH CORPORATION; *U.S. Public*, pg. 1476
A.O. SMITH/UPPCO, INC.—A.O. Smith Corporation; *U.S. Public*, pg. 1477
A.O. SMITH ELECTRIC MOTORS (IRELAND) LTD.—A.O. Smith Corporation; *U.S. Public*, pg. 1477
SOUTH HAVEN COIL INC.—Humphrey Products Company; *U.S. Private*, pg. 548
STEINER CO., INC.—Steiner Corporation; *U.S. Private*, pg. 1039
STERLING ELECTRIC, INC.; *U.S. Private*, pg. 1041
STEWART & STEVENSON SERVICES, INC.; *U.S. Public*, pg. 1517
SUECOBRAS INDUSTRIA E COMERCIO LTDA.—Cardo AB; *Int'l*, pg. 271
SUMITOMO HEAVY INDUSTRIES, LTD.; *Int'l*, pg. 1314
TECH SYSTEMS CORP.—Datron Incorporated; *U.S. Private*, pg. 313
TEMPEL STEEL COMPANY; *U.S. Private*, pg. 1075
TERMOSUD S.P.A.—IRI Istituto Ricostruzione Industriale; *Int'l*, pg. 653
THRIGE ELECTRIC—Thrige-Titan Group; *Int'l*, pg. 1387
THRIGE-TITAN GROUP; *Int'l*, pg. 1386
TOSHIBA INTERNATIONAL CORP. INDUSTRIAL DIV.—Toshiba Corporation; *Int'l*, pg. 1405
TOSHIBA INTERNATIONAL CORPORATION, UTILITY DIVISION—Toshiba Corporation; *Int'l*, pg. 1405
TREADWELL CORPORATION; *U.S. Private*, pg. 1098
TRENTON DIVISION—Tecumseh Products Company; *U.S. Public*, pg. 1566
U.S. ELECTRICAL MOTOR DIVISION—Emerson Electric Co.; *U.S. Public*, pg. 573
UNITED TECHNOLOGIES AUTOMOTIVE—United Technologies Corporation; *U.S. Public*, pg. 1691
UNITED TECHNOLOGIES CORPORATION; *U.S. Public*, pg. 1689
UNITED TECHNOLOGIES MOTOR SYSTEMS—United Technologies Corporation; *U.S. Public*, pg. 1690
VALEO-ELECTRONICAL SYSTEMS—CERUS - Compagnies Europeennes Reunies; *Int'l*, pg. 240
VANNER, INC.—B. Elliott plc.; *Int'l*, pg. 449
VERNITRON CONTROLS DIV.—Axsys Technologies, Inc.; *U.S. Public*, pg. 158
WAUKESHA ENGINE DIVISION—Dresser Industries, Inc.; *U.S. Public*, pg. 528
WESTCODE INC.—BTR plc; *Int'l*, pg. 127
WESTINGHOUSE POWER SYSTEMS GROUP—CBS Corporation; *U.S. Public*, pg. 273
WINCO—Dyna Technology Incorporated; *U.S. Private*, pg. 350
THE WING GROUP—Western Resources, Inc.; *U.S. Public*, *pg. 1760*
YAMAHA MOTOR CO., LTD.—Yamaha Corporation; *Int'l*, pg. 1516
ZEBCO—Brunswick Corporation; *U.S. Public*, pg. 265

3624 — CARBON & GRAPHITE PRODUCTS

ALLIANT TECHSYSTEMS (AEROSPACE DIVISION)—Alliant Techsystems; *U.S. Public*, pg. 47
ALUMINUM & CHEMIE ROTTERDAM B.V. - (ALUCHEMIE)—Alusuisse-Lonza Holding Ltd.; *Int'l*, pg. 68
AMERICAN CARBON INDUSTRIES—Morgan Crucible Co. Plc; *Int'l*, pg. 891
AMHERST METAL PRODUCTS, INC.—Brittany Corporation; *U.S. Private*, pg. 169
AMOCO PERFORMANCE PRODUCTS, INC.—Amoco Corporation; *U.S. Public*, pg. 102
THE CARBIDE/GRAPHITE GROUP, INC.; *U.S. Public*, pg. 304
CARBIDE PRODUCTS—The Carbide/Graphite Group, Inc.; *U.S. Public*, pg. 304
CARBONE-LORRAINE NORTH AMERICA—Pechiney S.A.; *Int'l*, pg. 1028
CARBONE OF AMERICA—Pechiney S.A.; *Int'l*, pg. 1028
CARBONE OF AMERICA, CARBON BRUSH DIV.—Pechiney S.A.; *Int'l*, pg. 1028
CARBONE OF AMERICA, GRAPHITE MATERIALS DIV.—Pechiney S.A.; *Int'l*, pg. 1028
CARBONE OF AMERICA (LCL) LTD.—Pechiney S.A.; *Int'l*, pg. 1028
CARBONE OF AMERICA, ULTRA CARBON DIV.—Pechiney S.A.; *Int'l*, pg. 1028
CEGRAM S.A.—Pechiney S.A.; *Int'l*, pg. 1030
ELDON AB; *Int'l*, pg. 436
ELECTRODES—The Carbide/Graphite Group, Inc.; *U.S. Public*, pg. 304
GENOSA—Pechiney S.A.; *Int'l*, pg. 1030
HELWIG CARBON PRODUCTS, INC.; *U.S. Private*, pg. 521
HOECHST SPECIALTY PRODUCTS GROUP—Hoechst Aktiengesellschaft; *Int'l*, pg. 625
HORSEHEAD INDUSTRIES, INC.; *U.S. Private*, pg. 540
I.D.M. ELECTRONICS LTD.—Kaydon Corporation; *U.S. Public*, pg. 946
IBIDEN CO., LTD.—Mitsui & Co., Ltd.; *Int'l*, pg. 878
KIRKWOOD INDUSTRIES, INC.; *U.S. Private*, pg. 623
LE CARBONE LORRAINE—Pechiney S.A.; *Int'l*, pg. 1028
MORGANITE CANADA CORPORATION—Morgan Crucible Co. Plc; *Int'l*, pg. 895
MORGANITE INC.—Morgan Crucible Co. Plc; *Int'l*, pg. 893
NATIONAL ELECTRICAL CARBON CORPORATION—Morgan Crucible Co. Plc; *Int'l*, pg. 891
PECHINEY S.A.; *Int'l*, pg. 1027
POCO GRAPHITE, INCORPORATED—Unocal Corporation; *U.S. Public*, pg. 1698
PURE CARBON COMPANY—Morgan Crucible Co. Plc; *Int'l*, *pg. 891*
SHOWA SAVOIE—Pechiney S.A.; *Int'l*, pg. 1032
SOCIETE DES ELECTRODES ET REFRACTAIRES "SAVOIE" (SERS)—Pechiney S.A.; *Int'l*, pg. 1028
SPLITFIRE, INC.—Old World Industries, Inc.; *U.S. Private*, pg. 814
STACKPOLE LTD.; *U.S. Private*, pg. 1028
STEELMARK-EAGLE & GLOBE—Australian National Industries Limited; *Int'l*, pg. 100
UCAR INTERNATIONAL INC.; *U.S. Public*, pg. 1662
UNOCAL CARBON & MINERALS—Unocal Corporation; *U.S. Public*, pg. 1698
ZOLTEK COMPANIES, INC.; *U.S. Public*, pg. 1794

3625 — RELAYS & INDUSTRIAL CONTROLS

AC CORPORATION; *U.S. Private*, pg. 3
ACCO CONTROLS—FKI Plc; *Int'l*, pg. 472
ADEPT TECHNOLOGY, INC.; *U.S. Public*, pg. 19
AEROSPACE-MARINE-DEFENSE GROUP—Aeroquip-Vickers, Inc.; *U.S. Public*, pg. 24
ALLEN-BRADLEY CANADA LIMITED—Rockwell International Corporation; *U.S. Public*, pg. 1398
ALLEN-BRADLEY DO BRASIL LTDA.—Rockwell International Corporation; *U.S. Public*, pg. 1398
ALLEN-BRADLEY PTY. LIMITED—Rockwell International Corporation; *U.S. Public*, pg. 1399
ALTAIR CORPORATION; *U.S. Private*, pg. 46
AMERICAN PRECISION INDUSTRIES INC.; *U.S. Public*, pg. 90
AROMAT CORPORATION—Matsushita Electric Works, Ltd.; *Int'l*, pg. 847
ASCO CONTROLS B.V.—Emerson Electric Co.; *U.S. Public*, *pg. 575*
ASCO G.M.B.H. & CO.—Emerson Electric Co.; *U.S. Public*, pg. 575
ASCO (JAPAN) CO. LIMITED—Emerson Electric Co.; *U.S. Public*, pg. 575
ASCO (UK)—Emerson Electric Co.; *U.S. Public*, pg. 575
ASCOLECTRIC LIMITED—Emerson Electric Co.; *U.S. Public*, pg. 575
ASCOMATICA S.A. DE C.V.—Emerson Electric Co.; *U.S. Public*, pg. 576
ASCOMATION PTY. LTD.—Emerson Electric Co.; *U.S. Public*, pg. 576
AUTOMATIC SIGNAL/EAGLE SIGNAL—Siemens AG; *Int'l*, pg. 1245
AUTOMATIC SWITCH CO.—Emerson Electric Co.; *U.S. Public*, pg. 573
AUTOMATIC TIMING & CONTROLS, INC.—Desco Corporation; *U.S. Private*, pg. 327
AUTOMATION CONTROL—Thyssen AG; *Int'l*, pg. 1389
AUXITROL S.A.—Esterline Technologies Corporation; *U.S. Public*, pg. 594
BEI SENSORS AND SYSTEMS COMPANY—BEI Technologies, Inc.; *U.S. Public*, pg. 160
BWP CONTROLS—FKI Plc; *Int'l*, pg. 472
BAKER-CAC, INC.—Baker Hughes Incorporated; *U.S. Public*, pg. 166
BALDOR ELECTRIC COMPANY; *U.S. Public*, pg. 168
BALDOR ELECTRIC COMPANY—Baldor Electric Company; *U.S. Public*, pg. 169
BANNER ENGINEERING CORP.; *U.S. Private*, pg. 114
BARBER-COLMAN COMPANY—Siebe plc; *Int'l*, pg. 1242
BASLER ELECTRIC COMPANY; *U.S. Private*, pg. 121
BENMAR MARINE ELECTRONICS, INC.; *U.S. Private*, pg. 133
A. BRADLEY PRESENCE SENSING—Rockwell International Corporation; *U.S. Public*, pg. 1397
ALLEN BRADLEY CREONICS—Rockwell International Corporation; *U.S. Public*, pg. 1397
BRUDI, INC.—Long Reach Holdings Inc.; *U.S. Private*, pg. 675
CBS CORPORATION; *U.S. Public*, pg. 273
CTS COMPONENTS TAIWAN, LTD.—CTS Corporation; *U.S. Public*, pg. 286
CTS OF CANADA, LTD.—CTS Corporation; *U.S. Public*, pg. 286
CTS SINGAPORE PTE., LTD.—CTS Corporation; *U.S. Public*, pg. 286
CAMCO CANADA—Emerson Electric Co.; *U.S. Public*, pg. 576
CAPRO, INC.—Teleflex Incorporated; *U.S. Public*, pg. 1569
CASI-RUSCO INC.; *U.S. Private*, pg. 218
CEGELEC DE MEXICO—Alcatel Alsthom Compagnie Generale D'Electricite; *Int'l*, pg. 53
CEGELEC ENTREPRISES, INC.—Alcatel Alsthom Compagnie Generale D'Electricite; *Int'l*, pg. 53
CEGELEC GMBH—Alcatel Alsthom Compagnie Generale D'Electricite; *Int'l*, pg. 53
CEGELEC (M) SDN BHD—Alcatel Alsthom Compagnie Generale D'Electricite; *Int'l*, pg. 53
CINCINNATI MILACRON INC.; *U.S. Public*, pg. 368
J.M. CLARKE (ELECTRICAL ENGINEERS) LIMITED—B. Elliott plc.; *Int'l*, pg. 448
COMPUTER PRODUCTS, INC.; *U.S. Public*, pg. 422
CONTROL TECHNIQUE LIMITED—Emerson Electric Co.; *U.S. Public*, pg. 576
COOPER INDUSTRIES, INC.; *U.S. Public*, pg. 442
CORNELL DUBILIER ELECTRONICS—Kaplan Electronics; *U.S. Private*, pg. 607

CRABTREE ELECTRICAL INDUSTRIES LIMITED—Hanson PLC; Int'l, pg. 592
CRAMER COMPANY—Owosso Corporation; U.S. Public, pg. 1238
CUSTOM CONTROL SENSORS, INC.; U.S. Private, pg. 298
CUSTOM SERVO MOTORS—MTS Systems Corporation; U.S. Public, pg. 1029
CUTLER-HAMMER EATON CORPORATION—Eaton Corporation; U.S. Public, pg. 556
CYBEREX, INC.—Danaher Corporation; U.S. Public, pg. 481
DAEWOO ELECTRIC MOTOR INDUSTRIES, LTD.—Daewoo Corporation; Int'l, pg. 357
DANA CORPORATION; U.S. Public, pg. 479
DEKKO HEATING TECHNOLOGIES, INC.—Group Dekko; U.S. Private, pg. 484
DELTRAN DIV.—American Precision Industries Inc.; U.S. Public, pg. 90
DERLAN INDUSTRIES LIMITED; Int'l, pg. 395
DESIGNATRONICS, INC.; U.S. Private, pg. 327
DIELECTRIC COMMUNICATIONS—General Signal Corporation; U.S. Public, pg. 727
DIMCO-GRAY COMPANY; U.S. Private, pg. 333
DORMEYER INDUSTRIES; U.S. Private, pg. 340
DYNAMICS RESEARCH CORPORATION; U.S. Public, pg. 539
EATON CORPORATION; U.S. Public, pg. 555
EATON CORPORATION, ELECTRIC DRIVES DIVISION—Eaton Corporation; U.S. Public, pg. 556
EATON CORPORATION, SPECIFIC INDUSTRY CONTROL DIVISION—Eaton Corporation; U.S. Public, pg. 557
EATON INTERNATIONAL CORP.—Eaton Corporation; U.S. Public, pg. 558
EATON LIMITED AEROSPACE & COMMERCIAL CONTROLS—Eaton Corporation; U.S. Public, pg. 559
EATON PTY. LTD. CONTROLS DIVISION—Eaton Corporation; U.S. Public, pg. 559
EATON S.A.M-CONTROLS DIV.-EUROPE—Eaton Corporation; U.S. Public, pg. 559
EATON YALE LTD.-CONTROLS DIVISION—Eaton Corporation; U.S. Public, pg. 559
ELECTRO-MATIC PRODUCTS INC.; U.S. Private, pg. 369
ELECTRONIC DRIVES AND CONTROLS; U.S. Private, pg. 370
EMERSON ELECTRIC CO.; U.S. Public, pg. 572
ENERGY DYNAMICS DIVISION—Pacific Scientific Company; U.S. Public, pg. 1250
EUROPEAN CABLES CONTROLS DIV.—FKI Plc; Int'l, pg. 472
FSSL LTD.—Kvaerner a.s.a.; Int'l, pg. 772
FAIRBANKS MORSE ENGINE DIVISION—Coltec Holdings Inc; U.S. Public, pg. 401
FANUC LTD.; Int'l, pg. 477
FANUC USA CORP.—Fanuc Ltd.; Int'l, pg. 477
FELSTED DIVISION—Furon Company; U.S. Public, pg. 689
FIMBEL DOOR CORPORATION; U.S. Private, pg. 404
FINCOR ELECTRONICS—IMO Industries Inc.; U.S. Public, pg. 857
GE FANUC AUTOMATION NORTH AMERICA, INC.—Fanuc Ltd.; Int'l, pg. 477
GEC INDUSTRIAL CONTROLS LTD.—Alcatel Alsthom Compagnie Generale D'Electricite; Int'l, pg. 53
THE GENERAL ELECTRIC COMPANY, P.L.C.; Int'l, pg. 543
GENICOM CORPORATION; U.S. Public, pg. 729
GHISALBA S.P.A.—Eaton Corporation; U.S. Public, pg. 559
GIDDINGS & LEWIS, INC.—Thyssen AG; Int'l, pg. 1389
GRUPO ECA S.A. DE C.V.—Eclipse Inc.; U.S. Private, pg. 361
HTL/KIN-TECH DIVISION—Pacific Scientific Company; U.S. Public, pg. 1250
HAMWORTHY PUMPS AND COMPRESSORS LIMITED—Powell Duffryn PLC; Int'l, pg. 1065
HAWKER DE HAVILLAND LTD.—BTR plc; Int'l, pg. 128
HOBBS CORPORATION—BTR plc; Int'l, pg. 127
HONEYWELL INC.; U.S. Public, pg. 833
HONEYWELL LEEDS & NORTHRUP AUSTRALIA PTY. LTD.—Honeywell Inc.; U.S. Public, pg. 834
HONEYWELL-MEASUREX CORPORATION—Honeywell Inc.; U.S. Public, pg. 833
HONEYWELL'S MICRO SWITCH DIVISION—Honeywell Inc.; U.S. Public, pg. 834
HORTON AUTOMATICS DIV.—Overhead Door Corporation; U.S. Private, pg. 823
HORTON AUTOMATICS, LTD.—Overhead Door Corporation; U.S. Private, pg. 823
HUBBELL INCORPORATED; U.S. Public, pg. 844
HUBBELL INDUSTRIAL CONTROLS, INC.—Hubbell Incorporated; U.S. Public, pg. 844
HURLETRON INC.—Altair Corporation; U.S. Private, pg. 46
HYOSUNG INDUSTRIES CO., LTD.—Hyosung Group; Int'l, pg. 640
I.D.M. ELECTRONICS LTD.—Kaydon Corporation; U.S. Public, pg. 946
ITT FLUID HANDLING—ITT Industries, Inc.; U.S. Public, pg. 860
THE IMPERIAL ELECTRIC COMPANY—Jordan Industries, Inc.; U.S. Private, pg. 598
INERTIA DYNAMICS INC.—Rockwell International Corporation; U.S. Public, pg. 1398
INTERMATIC INC.; U.S. Private, pg. 567
JAPAN AVIATION ELECTRONICS INDUSTRY, LTD.; Int'l, pg. 701
JAPAN SERVO CO., LTD.—Hitachi, Ltd.; Int'l, pg. 622
JOSLYN CORPORATION—Danaher Corporation; U.S. Public, pg. 481
JOSLYN JENNINGS CORPORATION—Danaher Corporation; U.S. Public, pg. 481
KAYDON CORPORATION; U.S. Public, pg. 945
KILLARK ELECTRIC MANUFACTURING CO.—Hubbell Incorporated; U.S. Public, pg. 844
KLOCKNER-MOELLER CORP.—Klockner-Moeller GmbH; Int'l, pg. 736
KLOCKNER-MOELLER GMBH; Int'l, pg. 736
KURT MANUFACTURING CO. INC.; U.S. Private, pg. 637
L&J TECHNOLOGIES; U.S. Private, pg. 638
LATSHAW ENTERPRISES, INC.; U.S. Public, pg. 979
LESLIE CONTROLS, INC.—Watts Industries, Inc.; U.S. Public, pg. 1746
LIEBERT CORPORATION—Emerson Electric Co.; U.S. Public, pg. 573
LIEBERT INTERNATIONAL B.V.—Emerson Electric Co.; U.S. Public, pg. 577
LIEBHERR-WERK NENZING GMBH—Liebherr-International AG; Int'l, pg. 808
LUCAS INDUSTRIES INC.—LucasVarity plc; Int'l, pg. 820
MAGNA INTERNATIONAL INC.; Int'l, pg. 829
MAGNETEK, INC.; U.S. Public, pg. 1037
MANDELLI INDUSTRIE S.P.A.; Int'l, pg. 834
MARLOW INDUSTRIES; U.S. Private, pg. 705
MATSUSHITA ELECTRIC WORKS, LTD.; Int'l, pg. 847
MCLEAN MIDWEST—Zero Corporation; U.S. Public, pg. 1791
MERTIK MAXITROL GMBH & CO., KG—Maxitrol Co.; U.S. Private, pg. 716
MINEBEA CO., LTD.; Int'l, pg. 867
MORSE CONTROLS—IMO Industries Inc.; U.S. Public, pg. 857
MOTOR GROUP—Rockwell International Corporation; U.S. Public, pg. 1398
MOTOROLA NORTEL—Motorola, Inc.; U.S. Public, pg. 1138
NMB (U.K.) LIMITED—Minebea Co., Ltd.; Int'l, pg. 868
NAMCO CONTROLS CORPORATION—Danaher Corporation; U.S. Public, pg. 482
O-Z/GEDNEY, NELSON FIRESTOP PRODUCTS—General Signal Corporation; U.S. Public, pg. 726
OAK INDUSTRIES INC.; U.S. Public, pg. 1209
OVERHEAD DOOR CORPORATION; U.S. Private, pg. 822
PARAGON ELECTRIC CO., INC.—Siebe plc; Int'l, pg. 1243
PASS & SEYMOUR/LEGRAND—LeGrand S.A.; Int'l, pg. 806
PHILIPS ELECTRONICS N.V.; Int'l, pg. 1051
POWELL ELECTRICAL MFG. CO.—Powell Industries, Inc.; U.S. Public, pg. 1319
POWELL INDUSTRIES, INC.; U.S. Public, pg. 1319
POWER DESIGNS, INC.; U.S. Private, pg. 878
RAMSEY TECHNOLOGY, INC.—Thermo Electron Corporation; U.S. Public, pg. 1592
RANCO INC.—Siebe plc; Int'l, pg. 1243
RAYTHEON MARINE—Raytheon Company; U.S. Public, pg. 1366
RAYTHEON SYSTEMS COMPANY ELECTRONICS SYSTEMS—Raytheon Company; U.S. Public, pg. 1365
RELIANCE ELECTRIC COMPANY—Rockwell International Corporation; U.S. Public, pg. 1398
RELIANCE MOTION CONTROL, INC.—Rockwell International Corporation; U.S. Public, pg. 1398
REULAND ELECTRIC COMPANY; U.S. Private, pg. 925
RHO SIGMA, INC.—Watsco, Inc.; U.S. Public, pg. 1746
M.H. RHODES, INC.; U.S. Private, pg. 927
ROCKWELL AUTOMATION B.V.—Rockwell International Corporation; U.S. Public, pg. 1399
ROCKWELL AUTOMATION LTD. U.K. DRIVE SYSTEMS—Rockwell International Corporation; U.S. Public, pg. 1400
ROCKWELL INTERNATIONAL CORPORATION; U.S. Public, pg. 1397
ROLTRA-MORSE S.P.A.—IMO Industries Inc.; U.S. Public, pg. 857
S & C ELECTRIC COMPANY; U.S. Private, pg. 954
SMC—Standard Microsystems Corp.; U.S. Public, pg. 1503
SCAN CONTROL SERVICES—Alcatel Alsthom Compagnie Generale D'Electricite; Int'l, pg. 53
SCHNEIDER AUTOMATION, INC.—Schneider S.A.; Int'l, pg. 1208
SCHNEIDER ELECTRIC S.A.—Schneider S.A.; Int'l, pg. 1207
SCHNEIDER S.A.; Int'l, pg. 1207
SCIAKY S.A.; Int'l, pg. 1211
THE SCOTT MOTORS COMPANY—Jordan Industries, Inc.; U.S. Private, pg. 598
SERVOTRONICS, INC.; U.S. Public, pg. 1462
SEVCON, INC.—Tech/Ops Sevcon, Inc.; U.S. Public, pg. 1563
SMITH METERS LTD.—Hanson PLC; Int'l, pg. 593
SOMFY SYSTEMS INC.—Damart S.A.; Int'l, pg. 376
SOUTHWESTERN INDUSTRIES, INC.; U.S. Private, pg. 1019
SPANG & COMPANY; U.S. Private, pg. 1020
SPANG POWER CONTROL—Spang & Company; U.S. Private, pg. 1020
SQUARE D AUTOMATION PRODUCTS—Schneider S.A.; Int'l, pg. 1208
SQUARE D CO.—Schneider S.A.; Int'l, pg. 1208
SQUARE D CO.- CONTROL PRODUCTS HQTRS.—Schneider S.A.; Int'l, pg. 1208
SQUARE D COMPANY—Schneider S.A.; Int'l, pg. 1208
SQUARE D COMPANY (DEUTSCHLAND) GMBH—Schneider S.A.; Int'l, pg. 1209
SQUARE D COMPANY ESPANA S.A.—Schneider S.A.; Int'l, pg. 1209
SQUARE D COMPANY ITALIA, S.P.A.—Schneider S.A.; Int'l, pg. 1209
SQUARE D SENECA PLANT—Schneider S.A.; Int'l, pg. 1208
TACO INCORPORATED; U.S. Private, pg. 1066
TECH DEVELOPMENT INC.—Siebe plc; Int'l, pg. 1242
TECH/OPS SEVCON, INC.; U.S. Public, pg. 1563
TELECHRON OF NORTH CAROLINA, INC.; U.S. Private, pg. 1073
TELEFLEX AUTOMOTIVE—Teleflex Incorporated; U.S. Public, pg. 1569
TELEFLEX (CANADA) LTD.—Teleflex Incorporated; U.S. Public, pg. 1570
TELEFLEX INCORPORATED; U.S. Public, pg. 1569
TELMA RETARDER DIVISION—Labinal SA; Int'l, pg. 786
THERMO ELECTRON LTD.—Thermo Electron Corporation; U.S. Public, pg. 1596
TIMEX CORPORATION; U.S. Private, pg. 1088
TORK ELECTRO SISTEMAS S.A. DE C.V.—Tork, Inc.; U.S. Private, pg. 1092
TORK, INC.; U.S. Private, pg. 1092
TRANSBULK, INC.—National Engineering & Contracting Co.; U.S. Private, pg. 782
TRIPLETT CORPORATION; U.S. Private, pg. 1104
THE UNIMAX CORPORATION; U.S. Private, pg. 1118
UNITECH PLC—Siebe plc; Int'l, pg. 1241
UNIVERSAL RELAY—Park Distributors, Inc.; U.S. Private, pg. 839
VEHICLE SYSTENIS DIVISION—Commercial Intertech Corp.; U.S. Public, pg. 411
VICKERS INC.—Aeroquip-Vickers, Inc.; U.S. Public, pg. 25
VICKERS TEDECO DIV.—Aeroquip-Vickers, Inc.; U.S. Public, pg. 25
VOLTEC—Sauer Industries, Inc.; U.S. Private, pg. 968
WALKER SYSTEMS, INC.—The Wiremold Company; U.S. Private, pg. 1184
WARD LEONARD ELECTRIC COMPANY, INC.—The Unimax Corporation; U.S. Private, pg. 1118
WARNER ELECTRIC INDUSTRIAL PRODUCTS DIVISION—Dana Corporation; U.S. Public, pg. 480
WARRICK CONTROLS, INC.—Danaher Corporation; U.S. Public, pg. 482
JERVIS B. WEBB COMPANY; U.S. Private, pg. 1156
WESCON PRODUCTS COMPANY—Latshaw Enterprises, Inc.; U.S. Public, pg. 979
XENTEK, INC.—Taiyo Yuden Company Ltd.; Int'l, pg. 1349
ZERO CORPORATION; U.S. Public, pg. 1791

3629 — ELECTRICAL INDUSTRIAL APPARATUS, NEC

ABB AB—ABB Asea Brown Boveri (Holding) Ltd.; Int'l, pg. 7
ABB CONTROL INC.—ABB Asea Brown Boveri (Holding) Ltd.; Int'l, pg. 4
ABB HAFO AB—ABB Asea Brown Boveri (Holding) Ltd.; Int'l, pg. 7
ABB PLAST AB—ABB Asea Brown Boveri (Holding) Ltd.; Int'l, pg. 7
AC CORPORATION; U.S. Private, pg. 3
ACX TECHNOLOGIES INC.; U.S. Public, pg. 3
ASC—Shizuki Electric Corporation; Int'l, pg. 1236
AVX CORP.—Kyocera Corporation; Int'l, pg. 775
ACME ELECTRIC CORPORATION; U.S. Public, pg. 16
ADVANCED CONTROLS, INC.; U.S. Private, pg. 21
ADVANCED DESIGN ELECTRONICS LIMITED—Chloride Group PLC; Int'l, pg. 287
AEROVOX INC.; U.S. Public, pg. 25
AMERICAN POWER CONVERSION CORPORATION; U.S. Public, pg. 89
AMERICAN TECHNICAL CERAMICS CORP.; U.S. Public, pg. 93
AMERICAN TECHNICAL CERAMICS (FLORIDA), INC.—American Technical Ceramics Corp.; U.S. Public, pg. 93
APPLICON INC.—Gores Technology Group; U.S. Private, pg. 465
ASCOM FRAKO GMBH—Ascom Holding AG; Int'l, pg. 87
ASCOVAL INDUSTRIA E COMMERCIO LTDA.—Emerson Electric Co.; U.S. Public, pg. 576
ASEA BICC CAPACITORS LTD.—ABB Asea Brown Boveri (Holding) Ltd.; Int'l, pg. 7
ASEA JUMET S.A.—ABB Asea Brown Boveri (Holding) Ltd.; Int'l, pg. 7
ASTEC AMERICA CORP.—Emerson Electric Co.; U.S. Public, pg. 573
ASTRONICS CORPORATION; U.S. Public, pg. 142
ATKINSON INDUSTRIES, INC.—Aztec Manufacturing Co.; U.S. Public, pg. 159
AULT INCORPORATED; U.S. Public, pg. 147
AZTEC MANUFACTURING CO.; U.S. Public, pg. 159
BMC INDUSTRIES, INC.; U.S. Public, pg. 162
BAKER PETROLITE CORPORATION—Baker Hughes Incorporated; U.S. Public, pg. 166
BALLANTYNE OF OMAHA, INC.—ARC International Corporation; Int'l, pg. 17
BEKO ELEKTRONIK A.S.—Koc Holding A.S.; Int'l, pg. 741
FRANK B. BLACK RESEARCH CENTER—Hubbell Incorporated; U.S. Public, pg. 844
BOWTHORPE (NZ) LIMITED—Bowthorpe plc; Int'l, pg. 208
C&D CHARTER POWER SYSTEMS; U.S. Public, pg. 271
CEGELEC—Alcatel Alsthom Compagnie Generale D'Electricite; Int'l, pg. 52
CHLORIDE ELECTRONICS LTD.—Chloride Group PLC; Int'l, pg. 287
CHLORIDE GROUP PLC; Int'l, pg. 287
CHLORIDE INDUSTRIAL BATTERIES LTD.—BTR plc; Int'l, pg. 125
CHLORIDE PORTUGAL LIMITADA—Chloride Group PLC; Int'l, pg. 287
CHLORIDE POWER ELECTRONICS PTY. LIMITED—Chloride Group PLC; Int'l, pg. 287
CHLORIDE POWER ELECTRONICS (THAILAND) LTD.—Chloride Group PLC; Int'l, pg. 287
COMPONENTS CORPORATION OF AMERICA; U.S. Private, pg. 259
COMPUTER PRODUCTS, INC.; U.S. Public, pg. 422
COMPUTER PRODUCTS, NATIONAL ACCOUNTS DIVISION—Computer Products, Inc.; U.S. Public, pg. 422
CONDOR D.C. POWER SUPPLIES INC.—SL Industries, Inc.; U.S. Public, pg. 1419
COOPER INDUSTRIES, INC.; U.S. Public, pg. 442
COPELAND CORPORATION—Emerson Electric Co.; U.S. Public, pg. 573
CROUSE-HINDS MOLDED PRODUCTS—Cooper Industries, Inc.; U.S. Public, pg. 444
DEL GLOBAL TECHNOLOGIES; U.S. Public, pg. 493
DESIGNATRONICS, INC.; U.S. Private, pg. 327
DORMEYER INDUSTRIES; U.S. Private, pg. 340

S.I.C. Index

DYNISCO, INC.—Berwind Corporation; *U.S. Private*, pg. 138
EG & G MANAGEMENT SYSTEMS INC.- ALBUQUERQUE OPERATIONS—EG & G, Inc.; *U.S. Public*, pg. 543
EG & G OPTOELECTRONICS-COVINA—EG & G, Inc.; *U.S. Public*, pg. 543
EG & G OPTOELECTRONICS-SALEM—EG & G, Inc.; *U.S. Public*, pg. 543
EG & G ROTRON—EG & G, Inc.; *U.S. Public*, pg. 543
ELECTRICAL PRODUCTS DIVISION—3M; *U.S. Public*, pg. 1605
ELECTRO METRICS, INC.; *U.S. Private*, pg. 369
ELECTRONICA CONDOR DE MEXICO, S.A.—SL Industries, Inc.; *U.S. Public*, pg. 1419
GB ELECTRICAL, INC.—Applied Power Inc.; *U.S. Public*, pg. 124
GENERAL SIGNAL CORPORATION; *U.S. Public*, pg. 726
HAYES CORPORATION, REGIONAL OFFICE—Hayes Corporation; *U.S. Public*, pg. 801
HOBART BROTHERS CO.—Illinois Tool Works Inc.; *U.S. Public*, pg. 866
HOLEC MACHINES & APPARATEN B.V.—Royal Begemann Group; *Int'l*, pg. 1133
HOLEC PROJECTS B.V.—Royal Begemann Group; *Int'l*, pg. 1133
HORSTMAN TIMERS & CONTROLS LIMITED—Clayhithe P.L.C.; *Int'l*, pg. 297
HUGHES-PETERS, INC.; *U.S. Private*, pg. 546
INTERNATIONAL POWER MACHINES CORPORATION—BTR plc; *Int'l*, pg. 126
JAPAN STORAGE BATTERY CO., LTD.; *Int'l*, pg. 702
JOSLYN CORPORATION—Danaher Corporation; *U.S. Public*, pg. 481
KAYENESS, INC.—Berwind Corporation; *U.S. Private*, pg. 138
KEARNEY-NATIONAL, INC.—The Dyson-Kissner-Moran Corporation; *U.S. Private*, pg. 351
KEMET CORPORATION; *U.S. Public*, pg. 949
KEMET DE MEXICO DE S.A. DE C.V.—Kemet Corporation; *U.S. Public*, pg. 949
KEMET ELECTRONICS ASIA LTD.—Kemet Corporation; *U.S. Public*, pg. 949
KEMET ELECTRONICS CORPORATION—Kemet Corporation; *U.S. Public*, pg. 949
KEMET ELECTRONICS SA—Kemet Corporation; *U.S. Public*, pg. 949
KLOCKNER-MOELLER GMBH; *Int'l*, pg. 736
LA MARCHE MFG. CO.; *U.S. Private*, pg. 640
LEACH INTERNATIONAL; *U.S. Private*, pg. 655
LIEBERT CORPORATION AUSTRALIA PTY. LTD.—Emerson Electric Co.; *U.S. Public*, pg. 577
LIEBERT FAR EAST LTD.—Emerson Electric Co.; *U.S. Public*, pg. 577
LIEBERT LTD.—Emerson Electric Co.; *U.S. Public*, pg. 577
LIEBERT MALAYSIA SDN. BHD.—Emerson Electric Co.; *U.S. Public*, pg. 577
LUCAS BODY SYSTEMS - NORTH AMERICA—LucasVarity plc; *Int'l*, pg. 820
M/A-COM, INC. COMPONENTS GROUP—AMP Incorporated; *U.S. Public*, pg. 8
MHIA TURBOCHARGER DIVISION—Mitsubishi Heavy Industries Ltd.; *Int'l*, pg. 874
MAGNETEK, INC.; *U.S. Public*, pg. 1037
MANDELLI INDUSTRIE S.P.A.; *Int'l*, pg. 834
MANNESMANN REXROTH GMBH—Mannesmann A.G.; *Int'l*, pg. 838
MATSUSHITA INDUSTRIAL EQUIP. CO., LTD.—Matsushita Electric Industrial Co., Ltd.; *Int'l*, pg. 846
MCHAL CORPORATION—Salem Group, Inc.; *U.S. Private*, pg. 961
MITSUBISHI ELECTRIC CORPORATION; *Int'l*, pg. 872
NITTO DENKO CORPORATION; *Int'l*, pg. 950
NORELCO CONSUMER PRODUCTS COMPANY—Philips Electronics N.V.; *Int'l*, pg. 1054
OPT INDUSTRIES, INC.—Torotel, Inc.; *U.S. Public*, pg. 1624
ONDULADORES DEL NORTE S.A.—Chloride Group PLC; *Int'l*, pg. 287
PACIFIC DUNLOP LIMITED; *Int'l*, pg. 1021
PETRECO BAKER HUGHES COMPANY—Baker Hughes Incorporated; *U.S. Public*, pg. 166
POWER CONVERSION ASIA-PACIFIC—Computer Products, Inc.; *U.S. Public*, pg. 422
POWER CONVERSION EUROPE—Computer Products, Inc.; *U.S. Public*, pg. 422
POWER DESIGNS, INC.; *U.S. Private*, pg. 878
RTP—Computer Products, Inc.; *U.S. Public*, pg. 422
RAPID POWER TECHNOLOGIES, INC.; *U.S. Private*, pg. 910
RICE LAKE WEIGHING SYSTEMS; *U.S. Private*, pg. 927
ROEDERSTEIN GMBH—Vishay Intertechnology, Inc.; *U.S. Public*, pg. 1722
SAIA AG—Williams Holdings Plc; *Int'l*, pg. 1500
SAIA-BURGESS ELECTRONICS GMBH—Williams Holdings Plc; *Int'l*, pg. 1501
SAIA-BURGESS GES.MBH—Williams Holdings Plc; *Int'l*, pg. 1501
SAIA-BURGESS SRL—Williams Holdings Plc; *Int'l*, pg. 1501
SALEM ELECTRIC COMPANY—Salem Group, Inc.; *U.S. Private*, pg. 961
SCHUMACHER ELECTRIC CORPORATION; *U.S. Private*, pg. 973
SHERMAN & REILLY, INC.; *U.S. Private*, pg. 993
SHIZUKI ELECTRIC CORPORATION; *Int'l*, pg. 1236
SILECTRON SPA—Chloride Group PLC; *Int'l*, pg. 287
SIMCO—Illinois Tool Works Inc.; *U.S. Public*, pg. 865
SOUTH HAVEN COIL INC.—Humphrey Products Company; *U.S. Private*, pg. 548
SPANG POWER CONTROL—Spang & Company; *U.S. Private*, pg. 1020
SPECTRUM CONTROL TECHNOLOGY INC.—Spectrum Control, Inc.; *U.S. Public*, pg. 1497
SQUARE D COMPANY—Schneider S.A.; *Int'l*, pg. 1208
STONERIDGE, INC.; *U.S. Private*, pg. 1044
TAKAGI CHOKOKU CO., LTD.; *Int'l*, pg. 1349
TECH-SYM CORPORATION; *U.S. Public*, pg. 1563
TECHSONIC INDUSTRIES, INC.—Teleflex Incorporated; *U.S. Public*, pg. 1570
TRIPLETT CORPORATION; *U.S. Private*, pg. 1104
U P SYSTEMS INC.—Chloride Group PLC; *Int'l*, pg. 287
UNIBUS, INC.—Powell Industries, Inc.; *U.S. Public*, pg. 1319
VANNER, INC.—B. Elliott plc.; *Int'l*, pg. 449
VARIAN ASSOCIATES, INC.; *U.S. Public*, pg. 1710
VICOR CORPORATION; *U.S. Public*, pg. 1719
VICTOR CORPORATION; *U.S. Private*, pg. 1138
WEST VIRGINIA ELECTRIC CORP.—Salem Group, Inc.; *U.S. Private*, pg. 962
WESTINGHOUSE ELECTRIC AUSTRALASIA LTD.-VICTORIA DIV.—CBS Corporation; *U.S. Public*, pg. 275
WHITTAKER POWER STORAGE DIVISION—Whittaker Corporation; *U.S. Public*, pg. 1767
WOLLARD AIRPORT EQUIPMENT CO.—Illinois Tool Works Inc.; *U.S. Public*, pg. 866
XEBEC CORPORATION; *U.S. Private*, pg. 1194

3631 — HOUSEHOLD COOKING EQUIPMENT

ARCELIK A.S.—Koc Holding A.S.; *Int'l*, pg. 741
BS CONTINENTAL S.A. UTILIDADES DOMESTICAS; *Int'l*, pg. 123
ROBERT BOSCH GMBH POWER TOOLS DIVISION—Robert Bosch GmbH; *Int'l*, pg. 204
BOSCH-SIEMENS HAUSGERAETE GMBH—Robert Bosch GmbH; *Int'l*, pg. 204
BOSCH-SIEMENS HAUSGERAETE GMBH—Siemens AG; *Int'l*, pg. 1245
W.C. BRADLEY CO.; *U.S. Private*, pg. 164
BRASTEMP S.A.—Whirlpool Corporation; *U.S. Public*, pg. 1765
CALOR S.A.—Groupe SEB; *Int'l*, pg. 568
CAMCO INC.—General Electric Company; *U.S. Public*, pg. 713
THE CANADIAN COLEMAN CO., LTD.—MacAndrews & Forbes Holdings Inc.; *U.S. Private*, pg. 691
THE CLIMATIC CORP.; *U.S. Private*, pg. 246
CONSUL S.A.—Whirlpool Corporation; *U.S. Public*, pg. 1765
CORBERO S.A.—Electrolux, AB; *Int'l*, pg. 443
DAEWOO ELECTRONICS CO., LTD.—Daewoo Corporation; *Int'l*, pg. 357
DOMAR S.A.—Electrolux, AB; *Int'l*, pg. 443
DREAMLAND APPLIANCES LIMITED—Newmond PLC; *Int'l*, pg. 925
ELECTROLUX, AB; *Int'l*, pg. 438
FRIGIDAIRE COMPANY RANGE PRODUCTS—Electrolux, AB; *Int'l*, pg. 439
THE GENERAL ELECTRIC COMPANY, P.L.C.; *Int'l*, pg. 543
GOLDSTAR CO. LTD.—LG Group; *Int'l*, pg. 778
GOLDSTAR OF AMERICA, INC.—LG Group; *Int'l*, pg. 779
GROUPE SEB; *Int'l*, pg. 568
GROUPE SEB DO BRASIL—Groupe SEB; *Int'l*, pg. 568
HICKORY SPECIALTIES, INC.—Bob Evans Farms, Inc.; *U.S. Public*, pg. 596
INGLIS LIMITED—Whirlpool Corporation; *U.S. Public*, pg. 1765
JENN-AIR—Maytag Corporation; *U.S. Public*, pg. 1064
LG GROUP INC.—LG Group; *Int'l*, pg. 779
MAYTAG COMPANY—Maytag Corporation; *U.S. Public*, pg. 1064
MAYTAG CORPORATION; *U.S. Public*, pg. 1064
MECO CORPORATION; *U.S. Private*, pg. 726
MIELE & CIE, GMBH; *Int'l*, pg. 865
MIRRO COMPANY—Newell Co.; *U.S. Public*, pg. 1177
MITSUBISHI ELECTRIC CORPORATION; *Int'l*, pg. 872
MOULINEX S.A.; *Int'l*, pg. 896
NATIONAL PRESTO INDUSTRIES, INC.; *U.S. Public*, pg. 1159
NEFF (UK) LIMITED; *Int'l*, pg. 912
NEWELL CO.; *U.S. Public*, pg. 1176
NORELCO CONSUMER PRODUCTS COMPANY—Philips Electronics N.V.; *Int'l*, pg. 1054
PARK-OHIO INDUSTRIES, INC.; *U.S. Public*, pg. 1258
PREMARK INTERNATIONAL, INC.; *U.S. Public*, pg. 1321
PRESTO MANUFACTURING COMPANY—National Presto Industries, Inc.; *U.S. Public*, pg. 1159
PRESTO PRODUCTS MANUFACTURING CO.—National Presto Industries, Inc.; *U.S. Public*, pg. 1159
PRIDE PRODUCTS, INC.; *U.S. Private*, pg. 883
RANCO INC.—Siebe plc; *Int'l*, pg. 1243
RINNAI CORP.; *Int'l*, pg. 1118
ROBESON APPLIANCE, INC.; *U.S. Public*, pg. 1394
ROPER CORPORATION—General Electric Company; *U.S. Public*, pg. 710
ROSIERES S.A.—Candy S.p.A.; *Int'l*, pg. 260
ROWENTA FRANCE S.A.—Groupe SEB; *Int'l*, pg. 569
ROWENTA WERKE—Groupe SEB; *Int'l*, pg. 569
SEB JAPAN CO. LTD.—Groupe SEB; *Int'l*, pg. 568
SEB S.A.—Groupe SEB; *Int'l*, pg. 569
SANYO ELECTRIC CO., LTD.; *Int'l*, pg. 1190
SHARP ELECTRONICA ESPANA S.A. (BARCELONA)—Sharp Corporation; *Int'l*, pg. 1229
SHARP ELECTRONICS CORPORATION—Sharp Corporation; *Int'l*, pg. 1228
SHARP ELECTRONICS (EUROPE)—Sharp Corporation; *Int'l*, pg. 1230
SHARP ELECTRONICS (U.K.)—Sharp Corporation; *Int'l*, pg. 1230
SHARP INTERNATIONAL FINANCE (U.K.) PLC.—Sharp Corporation; *Int'l*, pg. 1230
SHARP LABORATORIES OF EUROPE, LTD.—Sharp Corporation; *Int'l*, pg. 1230
SHARP MANUFACTURING COMPANY OF U.K.—Sharp Corporation; *Int'l*, pg. 1230
SHARP PRECISION MANUFACTURING (U.K.) LTD.—Sharp Corporation; *Int'l*, pg. 1230
STERNO, INC.—Colgate-Palmolive Company; *U.S. Public*, pg. 397
SUPREME/MIRRO—Newell Co.; *U.S. Public*, pg. 1178
T-FAL CORPORATION—Groupe SEB; *Int'l*, pg. 568
TATUNG COMPANY OF AMERICA—Tatung Corporation; *Int'l*, pg. 1357
TATUNG CORPORATION; *Int'l*, pg. 1357
TEFAL S.A.—Groupe SEB; *Int'l*, pg. 569
TEMCO FIREPLACE PRODUCTS, INC.—Temtex Industries Inc.; *U.S. Public*, pg. 1576
THE THERMOS COMPANY—Nippon Sanso Corporation; *Int'l*, pg. 938
VIKING RANGE CORP.; *U.S. Private*, pg. 1140
VITROMATIC, S.A. DE C.V.—Whirlpool Corporation; *U.S. Public*, pg. 1765
VOLLRATH-KEWAUNEE PLANT—The Vollrath Company, L.L.C.; *U.S. Private*, pg. 1143
WCI INTERNATIONAL COMPANY—Electrolux, AB; *Int'l*, pg. 440
WEBER-STEPHEN PRODUCTS CO.; *U.S. Private*, pg. 1157
THE WEST BEND CO.—Premark International, Inc.; *U.S. Public*, pg. 1322
WEST BEND/MEXICO—Premark International, Inc.; *U.S. Public*, pg. 1323
WHIRLPOOL CORPORATION; *U.S. Public*, pg. 1764
WHIRLPOOL DO BRAZIL S.A.—Whirlpool Corporation; *U.S. Public*, pg. 1765
WHIRLPOOL EUROPE B.V.—Whirlpool Corporation; *U.S. Public*, pg. 1765
WHITE CONSOLIDATED INDUSTRIES, INC.—Electrolux, AB; *Int'l*, pg. 439
WILLIAMS-SONOMA, INC.; *U.S. Public*, pg. 1770
WOLF RANGE CO.—Premark International, Inc.; *U.S. Public*, pg. 1322

3632 — HOUSEHOLD REFRIGERATORS & HOME & FARM FREEZERS

ARCELIK A.S.—Koc Holding A.S.; *Int'l*, pg. 741
ROBERT BOSCH GMBH POWER TOOLS DIVISION—Robert Bosch GmbH; *Int'l*, pg. 204
BOSCH-SIEMENS HAUSGERAETE GMBH—Robert Bosch GmbH; *Int'l*, pg. 204
BOSCH-SIEMENS HAUSGERAETE GMBH—Siemens AG; *Int'l*, pg. 1245
BRASTEMP S.A.—Whirlpool Corporation; *U.S. Public*, pg. 1765
CAMCO INC.—General Electric Company; *U.S. Public*, pg. 713
CASTELMAC, S.P.A.—Scotsman Industries, Inc.; *U.S. Public*, pg. 1445
CONSUL S.A.—Whirlpool Corporation; *U.S. Public*, pg. 1765
THE DOMETIC CORPORATION—Electrolux, AB; *Int'l*, pg. 440
ELECTROLUX, AB; *Int'l*, pg. 438
AB ELEKTRO HELIOS—Electrolux, AB; *Int'l*, pg. 438
EVERT LARSSON INDUSTRI AB—Electrolux, AB; *Int'l*, pg. 439
FRIGIDAIRE HOME PRODUCTS—Electrolux, AB; *Int'l*, pg. 439
FRIGIDAIRE HOME PRODUCTS-FREEZER PRODUCTS—Electrolux, AB; *Int'l*, pg. 440
FRIGIDAIRE HOME PRODUCTS-REFRIGERATOR PRODUCTS—Electrolux, AB; *Int'l*, pg. 440
FRIGOREX AG FUR KALTETECHNIK—Sulzer Ltd.; *Int'l*, pg. 1306
FRIMONT, S.P.A.—Scotsman Industries, Inc.; *U.S. Public*, pg. 1445
GENERAL ELECTRIC COMPANY; *U.S. Public*, pg. 709
THE GENERAL ELECTRIC COMPANY, P.L.C.; *Int'l*, pg. 543
GOLDSTAR CO. LTD.—LG Group; *Int'l*, pg. 778
HITACHI OHIRA INDUSTRIAL CO., LTD.—Hitachi, Ltd.; *Int'l*, pg. 621
HUSQVARNA AB—Electrolux, AB; *Int'l*, pg. 439
INGLIS LIMITED—Whirlpool Corporation; *U.S. Public*, pg. 1765
KELVINATOR APPLIANCES—Electrolux, AB; *Int'l*, pg. 440
KOREA SANYO ELECTRIC CO., LTD.—Sanyo Electric Co., Ltd.; *Int'l*, pg. 1192
KVAERNER EUREKA, ALESUND DIVISION—Kvaerner a.s.a.; *Int'l*, pg. 767
KVAERNER EUREKA, TROMSO DIVISION—Kvaerner a.s.a.; *Int'l*, pg. 767
LIEBHERR-HAUSGERATE GMBH—Liebherr-International AG; *Int'l*, pg. 808
LIEBHERR-WERK LIENZ GMBH—Liebherr-International AG; *Int'l*, pg. 808
LINDE AG WERKSGRUPPE KALTE- U. EINRICHTUNGSTECHNIK—Linde AG; *Int'l*, pg. 810
LITTELFUSE, INC.; *U.S. Public*, pg. 1001
MATSUSHITA ELECTRIC INDUSTRIAL CO., LTD.; *Int'l*, pg. 846
MATSUSHITA REFRIGERATION COMPANY—Matsushita Electric Industrial Co., Ltd.; *Int'l*, pg. 846
MAYTAG COMPANY—Maytag Corporation; *U.S. Public*, pg. 1064
MAYTAG CORPORATION; *U.S. Public*, pg. 1064
MAYTAG GALESBURG REFRIGERATION PRODUCTS—Maytag Corporation; *U.S. Public*, pg. 1064
MIELE & CIE, GMBH; *Int'l*, pg. 865
MITSUBISHI ELECTRIC CORPORATION; *Int'l*, pg. 872
NORCOLD—The Dyson-Kissner-Moran Corporation; *U.S. Private*, pg. 352
PRIDE PRODUCTS, INC.; *U.S. Private*, pg. 883
RANGAIRE INC.—Nortek, Inc.; *U.S. Public*, pg. 1193
ROBESON APPLIANCE, INC.; *U.S. Public*, pg. 1394
ROSIERES S.A.—Candy S.p.A.; *Int'l*, pg. 260
SAMSUNG ELECTRONICS CO., LTD.—Samsung Group; *Int'l*, pg. 1181
SANYO E & E CORPORATION—Sanyo Electric Co., Ltd.; *Int'l*, pg. 1191

SANYO ELECTRIC CO., LTD.; *Int'l*, pg. 1190
SCOTSMAN ICE SYSTEMS—Scotsman Industries, Inc.; *U.S. Public*, pg. 1445
SCOTSMAN INDUSTRIES, INC.; *U.S. Public*, pg. 1444
STEVENS-LEE COMPANY; *U.S. Private*, pg. 1042
TATUNG COMPANY OF AMERICA—Tatung Corporation; *Int'l*, pg. 1357
TATUNG CORPORATION; *Int'l*, pg. 1357
VITROMATIC, S.A. DE C.V.—Whirlpool Corporation; *U.S. Public*, pg. 1765
WCI INTERNATIONAL COMPANY—Electrolux, AB; *Int'l*, pg. 440
WHIRLPOOL CORPORATION; *U.S. Public*, pg. 1764
WHIRLPOOL DO BRAZIL S.A.—Whirlpool Corporation; *U.S. Public*, pg. 1765
WHIRLPOOL EUROPE B.V.—Whirlpool Corporation; *U.S. Public*, pg. 1765
WHITE CONSOLIDATED INDUSTRIES, INC.—Electrolux, AB; *Int'l*, pg. 439

3633 — HOUSEHOLD LAUNDRY EQUIPMENT

ARCELIK A.S.—Koc Holding A.S.; *Int'l*, pg. 741
BERNINA HOLDING AG; *Int'l*, pg. 189
ROBERT BOSCH GMBH POWER TOOLS DIVISION—Robert Bosch GmbH; *Int'l*, pg. 204
BOSCH-SIEMENS HAUSGERAETE GMBH—Robert Bosch GmbH; *Int'l*, pg. 204
BOSCH-SIEMENS HAUSGERAETE GMBH—Siemens AG; *Int'l*, pg. 1245
BRASTEMP S.A.—Whirlpool Corporation; *U.S. Public*, pg. 1765
CALOR S.A.—Groupe SEB; *Int'l*, pg. 568
CAMCO INC.—General Electric Company; *U.S. Public*, pg. 713
CONSUL S.A.—Whirlpool Corporation; *U.S. Public*, pg. 1765
ELECTROLUX SAN JOSE—Electrolux, AB; *Int'l*, pg. 442
FRIGIDAIRE HOME PRODUCTS-LAUNDRY PRODUCTS—Electrolux, AB; *Int'l*, pg. 440
G.E. APPLIANCES—General Electric Company; *U.S. Public*, pg. 710
GEC ZIMBABWE (PVT) LTD.—The General Electric Company, p.l.c.; *Int'l*, pg. 546
GOLDSTAR CO. LTD.—LG Group; *Int'l*, pg. 778
GROUPE SEB; *Int'l*, pg. 568
HOOVER MEXICANA S.A. DE C.V.—Maytag Corporation; *U.S. Public*, pg. 1065
INGLIS LIMITED—Whirlpool Corporation; *U.S. Public*, pg. 1765
MATSUSHITA ELECTRIC INDUSTRIAL CO., LTD.; *Int'l*, pg. 846
MAYTAG COMPANY—Maytag Corporation; *U.S. Public*, pg. 1064
MAYTAG CORPORATION; *U.S. Public*, pg. 1064
MIELE & CIE, GMBH; *Int'l*, pg. 865
PRIDE PRODUCTS, INC.; *U.S. Private*, pg. 883
RAYTHEON APPLIANCES—Raytheon Company; *U.S. Public*, pg. 1366
ROBERTSHAW CONTROLS COMPANY—Siebe plc; *Int'l*, pg. 1243
ROSIERES S.A.—Candy S.p.A.; *Int'l*, pg. 260
SAMSUNG ELECTRONICS CO., LTD.—Samsung Group; *Int'l*, pg. 1181
SANYO ELECTRIC CO., LTD.; *Int'l*, pg. 1190
SKETCHLEY RETAIL LTD.—Sketchley Plc; *Int'l*, pg. 1261
VITROMATIC, S.A. DE C.V.—Whirlpool Corporation; *U.S. Public*, pg. 1765
WCI INTERNATIONAL COMPANY—Electrolux, AB; *Int'l*, pg. 440
WHIRLPOOL CORPORATION; *U.S. Public*, pg. 1764
WHIRLPOOL DO BRAZIL S.A.—Whirlpool Corporation; *U.S. Public*, pg. 1765
WHIRLPOOL EUROPE B.V.—Whirlpool Corporation; *U.S. Public*, pg. 1765
WHITE CONSOLIDATED INDUSTRIES, INC.—Electrolux, AB; *Int'l*, pg. 439

3634 — ELECTRIC HOUSEWARES & FANS

ALUMITECH—Hayes Wheels International, Inc.; *U.S. Private*, pg. 513
ARCELIK A.S.—Koc Holding A.S.; *Int'l*, pg. 741
AUBREY MANUFACTURING COMPANY—Nortek, Inc.; *U.S. Public*, pg. 1193
BELSON PRODUCTS DIV.—Windmere-Durable Holdings; *U.S. Public*, pg. 1771
BEST S.P.A.—Nortek, Inc.; *U.S. Public*, pg. 1194
THE BLACK & DECKER CORPORATION; *U.S. Public*, pg. 233
BLACK & DECKER HOUSEHOLD PRODUCTS GROUP—The Black & Decker Corporation; *U.S. Public*, pg. 234
ROBERT BOSCH GMBH POWER TOOLS DIVISION—Robert Bosch GmbH; *Int'l*, pg. 204
BOSCH-SIEMENS HAUSGERAETE GMBH—Robert Bosch GmbH; *Int'l*, pg. 204
BOSCH-SIEMENS HAUSGERAETE GMBH—Siemens AG; *Int'l*, pg. 1245
BRASTEMP S.A.—Whirlpool Corporation; *U.S. Public*, pg. 1765
BRAUN AG—The Gillette Company; *U.S. Public*, pg. 744
BRAUN ESPANOLA, S.A.—The Gillette Company; *U.S. Public*, pg. 744
BRAUN IRELAND LTD.—The Gillette Company; *U.S. Public*, pg. 744
BRAUN ITALIA, S.R.L.—The Gillette Company; *U.S. Public*, pg. 744
BRAUN JAPAN K.K.—The Gillette Company; *U.S. Public*, pg. 744
BRAUN NEDERLAND B.V.—The Gillette Company; *U.S. Public*, pg. 744
BROAN LIMITED—Nortek, Inc.; *U.S. Public*, pg. 1194
BROAN MFG. CO., INC.—Nortek, Inc.; *U.S. Public*, pg. 1193
BROILMASTER DIVISION—Martin Industries, Inc. (AL); *U.S. Private*, pg. 709
BUNN-O-MATIC CORP. OF CANADA LTD.—Bunn-O-Matic Corporation; *U.S. Private*, pg. 181
BUTLER VENTAMATIC CORP.; *U.S. Private*, pg. 190
CADET MANUFACTURING COMPANY; *U.S. Private*, pg. 198
CALOR S.A.—Groupe SEB; *Int'l*, pg. 568
CALSONIC CLIMATE CONTROL, INC.—Nissan Motor Co., Ltd.; *Int'l*, pg. 944
CALSONIC CORP.—Nissan Motor Co., Ltd.; *Int'l*, pg. 944
CALSONIC MFG. CORP.—Nissan Motor Co., Ltd.; *Int'l*, pg. 944
CANTON SALES & STORAGE CO.—National Presto Industries, Inc.; *U.S. Public*, pg. 1159
A/S CARMEN CLAIROL—Bristol-Myers Squibb Company; *U.S. Public*, pg. 256
CASABLANCA FAN COMPANY—Hunter Fan Company; *U.S. Private*, pg. 549
CLAIROL, INC.—Bristol-Myers Squibb Company; *U.S. Public*, pg. 254
THE COLEMAN COMPANY, INC.—MacAndrews & Forbes Holdings Inc.; *U.S. Private*, pg. 690
COMPAGNIE FRANCAISE PHILIPS—Philips Electronics N.V.; *Int'l*, pg. 1055
COMPAGNIE HOBART, S.A.—Premark International, Inc.; *U.S. Public*, pg. 1322
CONAIR CORPORATION; *U.S. Private*, pg. 261
CONSUL S.A.—Whirlpool Corporation; *U.S. Public*, pg. 1765
DOM AG SICHERHEITSTECHNIK—The Black & Decker Corporation; *U.S. Public*, pg. 233
DOM S.A.R.L.—The Black & Decker Corporation; *U.S. Public*, pg. 233
DOM-SICHERHEITSTECHNIK GMBH & CO. KG—The Black & Decker Corporation; *U.S. Public*, pg. 233
DAEWOO ELECTRONICS CO., LTD.—Daewoo Corporation; *Int'l*, pg. 357
DART EUROPE S.A.—Premark International, Inc.; *U.S. Public*, pg. 1322
DEKKO HEATING TECHNOLOGIES, INC.—Group Dekko; *U.S. Private*, pg. 484
DELPHI ENERGY & ENGINE MANAGEMENT SYSTEMS—General Motors Corporation; *U.S. Public*, pg. 719
DIMPLEX NORTH AMERICA—The Glen Dimplex Group; *Int'l*, pg. 554
DOLAN NORTHWEST LLC; *U.S. Private*, pg. 338
DREAMLAND APPLIANCES LIMITED—Newmond PLC; *Int'l*, pg. 925
DYNAMICS CORPORATION OF AMERICA—CTS Corporation; *U.S. Public*, pg. 286
OY ELECTROLUX AB-ELEKTRO HELIOS—Electrolux, AB; *Int'l*, pg. 441
ELECTROLUX MECATRONIK AB—Electrolux, AB; *Int'l*, pg. 438
EMBASSY INDUSTRIES, INC.—P & F Industries, Inc.; *U.S. Public*, pg. 1240
EMERSON ELECTRIC CO.; *U.S. Public*, pg. 572
FASCO INDUSTRIES, INC.—BTR plc; *Int'l*, pg. 125
FRIGIDAIRE HOME PRODUCTS-HOME COMFORT PRODUCTS—Electrolux, AB; *Int'l*, pg. 440
GEC ZAMBIA LTD.—The General Electric Company, p.l.c.; *Int'l*, pg. 546
THE GENERAL ELECTRIC COMPANY, P.L.C.; *Int'l*, pg. 543
THE GILLETTE COMPANY; *U.S. Public*, pg. 743
GILLETTE DEUTSCHLAND G.M.B.H.—The Gillette Company; *U.S. Public*, pg. 744
GILLETTE ESPANOLA, S.A.—The Gillette Company; *U.S. Public*, pg. 744
GILLETTE FRANCE, S.A.—The Gillette Company; *U.S. Public*, pg. 744
GILLETTE UK LTD.—The Gillette Company; *U.S. Public*, pg. 745
THE GLEN DIMPLEX GROUP; *Int'l*, pg. 553
GOLDSTAR CO. LTD.—LG Group; *Int'l*, pg. 778
GROUPE SEB; *Int'l*, pg. 568
GROUPE SEB CR—Groupe SEB; *Int'l*, pg. 568
GROUPE SEB HUNGARY—Groupe SEB; *Int'l*, pg. 568
GROUPE SEB POLSKA—Groupe SEB; *Int'l*, pg. 568
GROUPE SEB SLOVENSKO—Groupe SEB; *Int'l*, pg. 568
HAMILTON BEACH/PROCTOR-SILEX, INC.—NACCO Industries, Inc.; *U.S. Public*, pg. 1149
HITACHI HEATING APPLIANCES CO., LTD.—Hitachi, Ltd.; *Int'l*, pg. 621
THE HOBART MANUFACTURING CO., LIMITED—Premark International, Inc.; *U.S. Public*, pg. 1322
THE HOWDEN FAN CO.; *U.S. Private*, pg. 543
HUNTER FAN COMPANY; *U.S. Private*, pg. 549
INGLIS LIMITED—Whirlpool Corporation; *U.S. Public*, pg. 1765
JACKSON SALES & STORAGE CO.—National Presto Industries, Inc.; *U.S. Public*, pg. 1159
KKW—The Glen Dimplex Group; *Int'l*, pg. 554
KAZ, INC.; *U.S. Private*, pg. 610
KENWOOD APPLIANCES PLC; *Int'l*, pg. 730
KENWOOD MANUFACTURING GMBH—Kenwood Appliances Plc; *Int'l*, pg. 730
KLAFS SAUNABAU GMBH & CO. KG MEDIZINISCHE TECHNIK; *Int'l*, pg. 736
KOREA SANYO ELECTRIC CO., LTD.—Sanyo Electric Co., Ltd.; *Int'l*, pg. 1192
LASKO METAL PRODUCTS, INC.; *U.S. Private*, pg. 652
MARLEY ELECTRIC HEATING COMPANY—United Dominion Industries, Ltd.; *U.S. Public*, pg. 1676
MARTIN GAS—Martin Industries, Inc. (AL); *U.S. Private*, pg. 709
MATSUSHITA ELECTRIC WORKS, LTD.; *Int'l*, pg. 847
MELITTA CANADA INC.—Melitta Unternehmensgruppe Bentz KG; *Int'l*, pg. 857
MELITTA NORTH AMERICA, INC.—Melitta Unternehmensgruppe Bentz KG; *Int'l*, pg. 857
MELITTA UNTERNEHMENSGRUPPE BENTZ KG; *Int'l*, pg. 856
MELITTA U.S.A., INC.—Melitta Unternehmensgruppe Bentz KG; *Int'l*, pg. 857
MERLONI ELETTRODOMESTICI S.P.A.; *Int'l*, pg. 860
THE METAL WARE CORP.; *U.S. Private*, pg. 734
MOULINEX S.A.; *Int'l*, pg. 896
NACCO INDUSTRIES, INC.; *U.S. Public*, pg. 1149
NATIONAL PRESTO INDUSTRIES, INC.; *U.S. Public*, pg. 1159
NORELCO CONSUMER PRODUCTS COMPANY—Philips Electronics N.V.; *Int'l*, pg. 1054
NORTEK, INC.; *U.S. Public*, pg. 1192
NUTONE, INC.—Williams Holdings Plc; *Int'l*, pg. 1499
OASIS CORP.; *U.S. Private*, pg. 810
PHILIPS AG—Philips Electronics N.V.; *Int'l*, pg. 1055
PHILIPS DO BRASIL-WALITA DIV.—Philips Electronics N.V.; *Int'l*, pg. 1055
PHILIPS DO BRAZIL LTDA.—Philips Electronics N.V.; *Int'l*, pg. 1055
PHILIPS ELECTRONICS NORTH AMERICA CORPORATION—Philips Electronics N.V.; *Int'l*, pg. 1053
PHILIPS ELECTRONICS N.V.; *Int'l*, pg. 1051
POLLENEX—The Rival Company; *U.S. Public*, pg. 1391
PREMARK CANADA INC.—Premark International, Inc.; *U.S. Public*, pg. 1323
PREMARK INTERNATIONAL, INC.; *U.S. Public*, pg. 1321
PRESTO MANUFACTURING COMPANY—National Presto Industries, Inc.; *U.S. Public*, pg. 1159
PRESTO PRODUCTS MANUFACTURING CO.—National Presto Industries, Inc.; *U.S. Public*, pg. 1159
PRIDE PRODUCTS, INC.; *U.S. Private*, pg. 883
PROCTOR SILEX CANADA, INC.—NACCO Industries, Inc.; *U.S. Public*, pg. 1150
PROCTOR-SILEX, MT. AIRY OPERATIONS—NACCO Industries, Inc.; *U.S. Public*, pg. 1149
PROCTOR-SILEX, S.A. DE C.V.—NACCO Industries, Inc.; *U.S. Public*, pg. 1150
PROCTOR-SILEX, SOUTHERN PINES OPERATIONS—NACCO Industries, Inc.; *U.S. Public*, pg. 1149
REGAL WARE, INC.; *U.S. Private*, pg. 917
REMINGTON PRODUCTS COMPANY, L.L.C.; *U.S. Private*, pg. 921
THE RIVAL COMPANY; *U.S. Public*, pg. 1391
ROBESON APPLIANCE, INC.; *U.S. Public*, pg. 1394
RONCO, INVENTIONS. LLC; *U.S. Private*, pg. 943
ROSIERES S.A.—Candy S.p.A.; *Int'l*, pg. 260
ROWENTA FRANCE S.A.—Groupe SEB; *Int'l*, pg. 569
ROWENTA WERKE—Groupe SEB; *Int'l*, pg. 569
SEB S.A.—Groupe SEB; *Int'l*, pg. 569
SANYO ELECTRIC CO., LTD.; *Int'l*, pg. 1190
SANYO HOME TECH CO., LTD.—Sanyo Electric Co., Ltd.; *Int'l*, pg. 1191
SANYO INDUSTRIES CANADA INC.—Sanyo Electric Co., Ltd.; *Int'l*, pg. 1192
SANYO INDUSTRIES (SINGAPORE) PRIVATE LIMITED—Sanyo Electric Co., Ltd.; *Int'l*, pg. 1192
SIGNATURE BRANDS USA, INC.; *U.S. Public*, pg. 1472
SLANT/FIN CORPORATION; *U.S. Private*, pg. 1005
SUNBEAM CORPORATION; *U.S. Public*, pg. 1533
SUNBEAM HOUSEHOLD PRODUCTS—Sunbeam Corporation; *U.S. Public*, pg. 1533
SUNBEAM MEXICANA S.A. DE C.V.—Sunbeam Corporation; *U.S. Public*, pg. 1533
SUNBEAM VICTA HOLDINGS LTD.—GUD Holdings Limited; *Int'l*, pg. 539
SURCO PRODUCTS, INC.; *U.S. Private*, pg. 1056
T-FAL DE MEXICO S.A. DE C.V.—Groupe SEB; *Int'l*, pg. 568
TATUNG COMPANY OF AMERICA—Tatung Corporation; *Int'l*, pg. 1357
TATUNG CORPORATION; *Int'l*, pg. 1357
TEFAL ROWENTA PORTUGAL—Groupe SEB; *Int'l*, pg. 568
TEFAL S.A.—Groupe SEB; *Int'l*, pg. 569
TELEDYNE WATER PIK—Allegheny Teledyne Incorporated; *U.S. Public*, pg. 44
TOASTMASTER, INC.; *U.S. Public*, pg. 1619
TOKYO ELECTRIC CO., LTD.—Toshiba Corporation; *Int'l*, pg. 1403
TOMKINS INDUSTRIES INC.—Tomkins PLC; *Int'l*, pg. 1397
TOTTORI SANYO ELECTRIC CO., LTD.—Sanyo Electric Co., Ltd.; *Int'l*, pg. 1191
VENMAR VENTILATION, INC.—Nortek, Inc.; *U.S. Public*, pg. 1194
WAHL CLIPPER CORP.; *U.S. Private*, pg. 1146
WARING PRODUCTS—CTS Corporation; *U.S. Public*, pg. 286
WAVERLY PRODUCTS CO.—The Rival Company; *U.S. Public*, pg. 1391
WELLA GROUP; *Int'l*, pg. 1489
WEST BEND OF CANADA LTD.—Premark International, Inc.; *U.S. Public*, pg. 1323
THE WEST BEND CO.—Premark International, Inc.; *U.S. Public*, pg. 1322
WINDMERE-DURABLE HOLDINGS; *U.S. Public*, pg. 1771

3635 — HOUSEHOLD VACUUM CLEANERS

ALFATEC SPA—Electrolux, AB; *Int'l*, pg. 442
BISSELL INC.; *U.S. Private*, pg. 145
THE BLACK & DECKER CORPORATION; *U.S. Public*, pg. 233
BRASTEMP S.A.—Whirlpool Corporation; *U.S. Public*, pg. 1765
CLAYTON INDUSTRIES CO.; *U.S. Private*, pg. 245
CLEVELAND WOOD PRODUCTS—Berkshire Hathaway Inc.; *U.S. Public*, pg. 217
CONSUL S.A.—Whirlpool Corporation; *U.S. Public*, pg. 1765
DOM S.A.R.L.—The Black & Decker Corporation; *U.S. Public*, pg. 233

DOM-SICHERHEITSTECHNIK GMBH & CO. KG—The Black & Decker Corporation; *U.S. Public*, pg. 233
DOUGLAS/QUIKUT—Berkshire Hathaway Inc.; *U.S. Public*, *pg. 217*
ELECTROLUX, AB; *Int'l*, pg. 438
C.A. ELECTROLUX—Electrolux, AB; *Int'l*, pg. 444
ELECTROLUX CORPORATION; *U.S. Private*, pg. 369
THE EUREKA COMPANY—Electrolux, AB; *Int'l*, pg. 440
THE SCOTT FETZER COMPANY—Berkshire Hathaway Inc.; *U.S. Public*, pg. 217
GOLDSTAR CO. LTD.—LG Group; *Int'l*, pg. 778
HMI INDUSTRIES; *U.S. Public*, pg. 771
HOOVER COMPANY—Maytag Corporation; *U.S. Public*, pg. 1065
INGLIS LIMITED—Whirlpool Corporation; *U.S. Public*, pg. 1765
INTERSTATE ENGINEERING; *U.S. Private*, pg. 573
JUVER INDUSTRIAL S.A. DE C.V.—Maytag Corporation; *U.S. Public*, pg. 1065
KIRBY COMPANY—Berkshire Hathaway Inc.; *U.S. Public*, pg. 217
KUWAIT SWEDISH CLEANING SERVICES CO. S.A.K.—Electrolux, AB; *Int'l*, pg. 443
LINDSAY MANUFACTURING INC.; *U.S. Private*, pg. 668
MATSUSHITA ELECTRIC INDUSTRIAL CO., LTD.; *Int'l*, pg. 846
MAYTAG CORPORATION; *U.S. Public*, pg. 1064
NATIONAL UNION ELECTRIC CORP.—Electrolux, AB; *Int'l*, *pg. 440*
NILFISK A/S; *Int'l*, pg. 932
ORECK CORPORATION; *U.S. Private*, pg. 819
ORECK MANUFACTURING COMPANY—Oreck Corporation; *U.S. Private*, pg. 819
PRIDE PRODUCTS, INC.; *U.S. Private*, pg. 883
REXAIR, INC.—U.S. Industries, Inc.; *U.S. Public*, pg. 1684
ROSIERES S.A.—Candy S.p.A.; *Int'l*, pg. 260
ROYAL APPLIANCE MFG. CO.; *U.S. Public*, pg. 1410
RYOBI MOTOR PRODUCTS—Ryobi Ltd.; *Int'l*, pg. 1151
SHARP ELECTRONICA ESPANA S.A. (BARCELONA)—Sharp Corporation; *Int'l*, pg. 1229
SHARP ELECTRONICS CORPORATION—Sharp Corporation; *Int'l*, pg. 1228
SHARP ELECTRONICS (EUROPE)—Sharp Corporation; *Int'l*, pg. 1230
SHARP ELECTRONICS (U.K.)—Sharp Corporation; *Int'l*, pg. 1230
SHARP INTERNATIONAL FINANCE (U.K.) PLC.—Sharp Corporation; *Int'l*, pg. 1230
SHARP LABORATORIES OF EUROPE, LTD.—Sharp Corporation; *Int'l*, pg. 1230
SHARP MANUFACTURING COMPANY OF U.K.—Sharp Corporation; *Int'l*, pg. 1230
SHARP PRECISION MANUFACTURING (U.K.) LTD.—Sharp Corporation; *Int'l*, pg. 1230
VITROMATIC, S.A. DE C.V.—Whirlpool Corporation; *U.S. Public*, pg. 1765
AB VOLTA—Electrolux, AB; *Int'l*, pg. 439
WHITE CONSOLIDATED INDUSTRIES, INC.—Electrolux, AB; *Int'l*, pg. 439
WHITE MOP WRINGER COMPANY; *U.S. Private*, pg. 1172

3639 — HOUSEHOLD APPLIANCES, NEC

AMF REECE INCORPORATED; *U.S. Private*, pg. 7
AERCO INTERNATIONAL INC.; *U.S. Private*, pg. 23
AISIN SEIKI CO. LTD.; *Int'l*, pg. 39
ANAHEIM MANUFACTURING COMPANY; *U.S. Private*, pg. 70
BASEL TRADING COMPANY LTD.; *Int'l*, pg. 169
BERNINA HOLDING AG; *Int'l*, pg. 189
ROBERT BOSCH GMBH POWER TOOLS DIVISION—Robert Bosch GmbH; *Int'l*, pg. 204
BOSCH-SIEMENS HAUSGERAETE GMBH—Robert Bosch GmbH; *Int'l*, pg. 204
BOSCH-SIEMENS HAUSGERAETE GMBH—Siemens AG; *Int'l*, pg. 1245
BRADFORD-WHITE CORPORATION; *U.S. Private*, pg. 164
BROAN MFG. CO., INC.—Nortek, Inc.; *U.S. Public*, pg. 1193
BROTHER INDUSTRIES, LTD.; *Int'l*, pg. 229
BROTHER U.K., LTD.—Brother Industries, Ltd.; *Int'l*, pg. 230
CAMCO INC.—General Electric Company; *U.S. Public*, pg. 713
CANDY S.P.A.; *Int'l*, pg. 259
COMPAGNIE HOBART, S.A.—Premark International, Inc.; *U.S. Public*, pg. 1322
DOM AG SICHERHEITSTECHNIK—The Black & Decker Corporation; *U.S. Public*, pg. 233
DOM S.A.R.L.—The Black & Decker Corporation; *U.S. Public*, pg. 233
DOM-SICHERHEITSTECHNIK GMBH & CO. KG—The Black & Decker Corporation; *U.S. Public*, pg. 233
DART EUROPE S.A.—Premark International, Inc.; *U.S. Public*, pg. 1322
DREAMLAND APPLIANCES LIMITED—Newmond PLC; *Int'l*, pg. 925
DUCHOSSOIS INDUSTRIES, INC.; *U.S. Private*, pg. 344
EATON GMBH CONTROLS DIV.-EUROPE—Eaton Corporation; *U.S. Public*, pg. 558
ELECTROLUX, AB; *Int'l*, pg. 438
C.A. ELECTROLUX—Electrolux, AB; *Int'l*, pg. 444
ELECTROLUX (JAPAN) LTD.—Electrolux, AB; *Int'l*, pg. 443
ELECTROLUX JORDAN TRADING COMPANY LTD.—Electrolux, AB; *Int'l*, pg. 443
ELECTROLUX SAN JOSE—Electrolux, AB; *Int'l*, pg. 442
ELITE SEWING MACHINE MFG. CO. LTD.—Aisin Seiki Co. Ltd.; *Int'l*, pg. 39
EVERT LARSSON INDUSTRI AB—Electrolux, AB; *Int'l*, pg. 439
AB FORMVERKTYG—Electrolux, AB; *Int'l*, pg. 439
FRIGIDAIRE COMPANY DISHWASHER PRODUCTS—Electrolux, AB; *Int'l*, pg. 439
FRIGIDAIRE HOME PRODUCTS-HOME COMFORT PRODUCTS—Electrolux, AB; *Int'l*, pg. 440
THE GENIE COMPANY—Overhead Door Corporation; *U.S. Private*, pg. 823
GRANGES AB—Electrolux, AB; *Int'l*, pg. 439
H M K ENTERPRISES, INC.; *U.S. Private*, pg. 489
THE HOBART MANUFACTURING CO., LIMITED—Premark International, Inc.; *U.S. Public*, pg. 1322
HOOVER CANADA INC.—Maytag Corporation; *U.S. Public*, pg. 1065
HUSQVARNA AB—Electrolux, AB; *Int'l*, pg. 439
IN-SINK-ERATOR—Emerson Electric Co.; *U.S. Public*, pg. 573
JANOME SEWING MACHINE CO., LTD.; *Int'l*, pg. 699
LIBERTY MEXICANA S.A. DE C.V.—Aisin Seiki Co. Ltd.; *Int'l*, pg. 39
LUSKIN'S, INC.; *U.S. Private*, pg. 681
MAYTAG COMPANY—Maytag Corporation; *U.S. Public*, pg. 1064
MAYTAG CORPORATION; *U.S. Public*, pg. 1064
MAYTAG INTERNATIONAL, INC.—Maytag Corporation; *U.S. Public*, pg. 1065
NEFF (UK) LIMITED; *Int'l*, pg. 912
NESCO LTD.—Electrolux, AB; *Int'l*, pg. 443
OSTER DE VENEZUELA S.A.—Sunbeam Corporation; *U.S. Public*, pg. 1533
PERSTORP FORM—Perstorp AB; *Int'l*, pg. 1037
PERSTORP FORM LTD.—Perstorp AB; *Int'l*, pg. 1038
PERSTORP FORM OY—Perstorp AB; *Int'l*, pg. 1038
PERSTORP PLASTIC SYSTEMS—Perstorp AB; *Int'l*, pg. 1037
PERSTORP S.A.-DIV. PERSTORP STAMP—Perstorp AB; *Int'l*, pg. 1038
PERSTORP XYTEC, INC.—Perstorp AB; *Int'l*, pg. 1037
G.M. PFAFF AKTIENGESELLSCHAFT; *Int'l*, pg. 1046
PHILIPS AG—Philips Electronics N.V.; *Int'l*, pg. 1055
PHILIPS DO BRASIL-WALITA DIV.—Philips Electronics N.V.; *Int'l*, pg. 1055
PHILIPS DO BRAZIL LTDA.—Philips Electronics N.V.; *Int'l*, pg. 1055
PREMARK CANADA INC.—Premark International, Inc.; *U.S. Public*, pg. 1323
PRIDE PRODUCTS, INC.; *U.S. Private*, pg. 883
REXEL, INC.—Rexel, S.A.; *Int'l*, pg. 1107
RHEEM MANUFACTURING CO.—Paloma Industries Limited; *Int'l*, pg. 1022
RHEEM WATER HEATER—Paloma Industries Limited; *Int'l*, *pg. 1022*
ROBESON APPLIANCE, INC.; *U.S. Public*, pg. 1394
ROTH CORPORATION—Trek Corporation; *U.S. Private*, pg. 1099
SCOTT & ENGLISH LIMITED—Haw Par Brothers International Limited; *Int'l*, pg. 603
SEMI-TECH CORPORATION; *Int'l*, pg. 1220
A.O. SMITH CORPORATION; *U.S. Public*, pg. 1476
A.O. SMITH-ENTERPRISES LTD.—A.O. Smith Corporation; *U.S. Public*, pg. 1477
SON CHIEF ELECTRICS, INC.; *U.S. Private*, pg. 1014
STATE INDUSTRIES INC.; *U.S. Private*, pg. 1036
SUNBEAM CORPORATION LTD.—GUD Holdings Limited; *Int'l*, pg. 539
SUNBEAM VICTA HOLDINGS LTD.—GUD Holdings Limited; *Int'l*, pg. 539
TAKARA STANDARD CO., LTD.—Takara Belmont Co., Ltd.; *Int'l*, pg. 1349
TEFAL ROWENTA PORTUGAL—Groupe SEB; *Int'l*, pg. 568
TELEDYNE WATER PIK—Allegheny Teledyne Incorporated; *U.S. Public*, pg. 44
THERMADOR—Masco Corporation; *U.S. Public*, pg. 1053
TOTTORI SANYO ELECTRIC CO., LTD.—Sanyo Electric Co., Ltd.; *Int'l*, pg. 1191
UNION SPECIAL (CANADA) LTD.—Juki Corporation; *Int'l*, pg. 716
UNIVEX CORPORATION; *U.S. Private*, pg. 1128
VITROMATIC, S.A. DE C.V.—Whirlpool Corporation; *U.S. Public*, pg. 1765
VORWERK & CO.; *Int'l*, pg. 1480
VORWERK & CO. ELEKTROWERKE KG.—Vorwerk & Co.; *Int'l*, pg. 1480
WHIRLPOOL CORPORATION; *U.S. Public*, pg. 1764
WHIRLPOOL DO BRAZIL S.A.—Whirlpool Corporation; *U.S. Public*, pg. 1765
WHIRLPOOL EUROPE B.V.—Whirlpool Corporation; *U.S. Public*, pg. 1765
WHITE CONSOLIDATED INDUSTRIES, INC.—Electrolux, AB; *Int'l*, pg. 439
WHITE MOP WRINGER COMPANY; *U.S. Private*, pg. 1172
ZANUSSI ELETTRODOMESTICI S.P.A.—Electrolux, AB; *Int'l*, pg. 442

3641 — ELECTRIC LAMP BULBS & TUBES

ARC INTERNATIONAL CORPORATION; *Int'l*, pg. 17
ASTRONICS CORPORATION; *U.S. Public*, pg. 142
BRUCE INDUSTRIES, INC.; *U.S. Private*, pg. 175
CANLYTE INCORPORATED—The Genlyte Group Incorporated; *U.S. Public*, pg. 730
CHADWICK-HELMUTH COMPANY, INC.; *U.S. Private*, pg. 227
COLE HERSEE COMPANY; *U.S. Private*, pg. 251
COMPAGNIE FRANCAISE PHILIPS—Philips Electronics N.V.; *Int'l*, pg. 1055
CROMPTON LIGHTING LTD.—BTR plc; *Int'l*, pg. 124
DURO-TEST CORPORATION—Duro-Lite International; *U.S. Private*, pg. 349
E-L PRODUCTS COMPANY—Astronics Corporation; *U.S. Public*, pg. 142
EG & G OPTOELECTRONICS-SALEM—EG & G, Inc.; *U.S. Public*, pg. 543
EATON CORPORATION, SEMI-CONDUCTOR—Eaton Corporation; *U.S. Public*, pg. 557
FASSON DE MEXICO, S.A.—Avery Dennison Corporation; *U.S. Public*, pg. 154
FUTABA CORPORATION; *Int'l*, pg. 531
G.E. LIGHTING DIVISION—General Electric Company; *U.S. Public*, pg. 710
G.E. LIGHTING EUROPE—General Electric Company; *U.S. Public*, pg. 713
G.E. LIGHTING (IRELAND) LTD.—General Electric Company; *U.S. Public*, pg. 713
G.E. LIGHTING LTD.—General Electric Company; *U.S. Public*, pg. 713
G.E. TUNGSTRAM CO.—General Electric Company; *U.S. Public*, pg. 713
GEC AUSTRALIA LTD.—The General Electric Company, p.l.c.; *Int'l*, pg. 546
GEC (NEW ZEALAND) LTD.—The General Electric Company, p.l.c.; *Int'l*, pg. 546
GENERAL ELECTRIC COMPANY; *U.S. Public*, pg. 709
HARRISON ELECTRIC CO., LTD.—Toshiba Corporation; *Int'l*, pg. 1402
LAVA WORLD INTERNATIONAL/HAGGERTY ENTERPRISES, INC.; *U.S. Private*, pg. 653
MATSUSHITA ELECTRIC WORKS, LTD.; *Int'l*, pg. 847
NORMAN ENTERPRISES, INC.—Photo Control Corporation; *U.S. Public*, pg. 1292
OPTICAL RADIATION CORPORATION—BEC Group, Inc.; *U.S. Public*, pg. 160
OSRAM ARGENTINA S.A.C.I.—Siemens AG; *Int'l*, pg. 1244
OSRAM DO BRASIL COMPANHIA DE LAMPADAS ELETRICAS S.A.—Siemens AG; *Int'l*, pg. 1244
OSRAM GMBH—Siemens AG; *Int'l*, pg. 1244
OSRAM LTD.—Siemens AG; *Int'l*, pg. 1244
OSRAM S.A.—Siemens AG; *Int'l*, pg. 1244
OSRAM SOCIETA RIUNITE OSRAM-EDISON-CLERICI S.P.A.—Siemens AG; *Int'l*, pg. 1244
OSRAM SYLVANIA INC.—Siemens AG; *Int'l*, pg. 1245
PHILIPS AG—Philips Electronics N.V.; *Int'l*, pg. 1055
PHILIPS DO BRAZIL LTDA.—Philips Electronics N.V.; *Int'l*, pg. 1055
PHILIPS ELECTRONICS LTD.—Philips Electronics N.V.; *Int'l*, pg. 1055
PHILIPS LIGHTING—Philips Electronics N.V.; *Int'l*, pg. 1055
PHILIPS LIGHTING LTD.—Philips Electronics N.V.; *Int'l*, pg. 1055
PHOTOGENIC MACHINE COMPANY, INC.; *U.S. Private*, pg. 864
PREFERRED PRODUCTS, INC.—SuperValu, Inc.; *U.S. Public*, pg. 1541
SPECTRONICS CORPORATION; *U.S. Private*, pg. 1024
TOKI ELECTRIC CO., LTD.—Toshiba Corporation; *Int'l*, pg. 1403
TOSHIBA SHOMEI PRECISION CORPORATION—Toshiba Corporation; *Int'l*, pg. 1404
UVP, INC.; *U.S. Private*, pg. 1115
ZENITH PRODUCTS CORP.—Masco Corporation; *U.S. Public*, pg. 1054

3643 — CURRENT-CARRYING WIRING DEVICES

ABB STOTZ-KONTAKT HELLAS S.A.—ABB Asea Brown Boveri (Holding) Ltd.; *Int'l*, pg. 2
ABB TRACTION INC.—ABB Asea Brown Boveri (Holding) Ltd.; *Int'l*, pg. 5
AMI GIBSON, INC.—Technitrol, Inc.; *U.S. Public*, pg. 1564
AMP INC. LYTEL DIVISION—AMP Incorporated; *U.S. Public*, pg. 8
AMP INC. LYTEL/NETCOM DIVISION—AMP Incorporated; *U.S. Public*, pg. 8
AMP INCORPORATED; *U.S. Public*, pg. 7
ACCORD CONTRACT SERVICES—Veba AG; *Int'l*, pg. 1458
ADVANCED METALLURGY, INC.—Technitrol, Inc.; *U.S. Public*, pg. 1564
AIM ELECTRONICS CORPORATION—Jordan Industries, Inc.; *U.S. Private*, pg. 598
AMARILLO PLANT—Cooper Industries, Inc.; *U.S. Public*, pg. 444
ANDERSON POWER PRODUCTS DIV.—High Voltage Engineering Corporation; *U.S. Private*, pg. 528
APPLETON ELECTRIC LTD.—Emerson Electric Co.; *U.S. Public*, pg. 575
APPLIED POWER INC.; *U.S. Public*, pg. 124
ARK LES CORP.—Ark-Les Corporation; *U.S. Private*, pg. 82
ARK-LES CORPORATION; *U.S. Private*, pg. 82
ARROW HART WIRING DEVICES—Cooper Industries, Inc.; *U.S. Public*, pg. 444
AVIS INDUSTRIAL CORPORATION; *U.S. Private*, pg. 102
AXSYS TECHNOLOGIES, INC.; *U.S. Public*, pg. 157
BIW CABLE MANUFACTURING PLANT—Draka Kabel B.V.; *Int'l*, pg. 417
BIW CABLE SYSTEMS-CONNECTOR SYSTEMS DIV.—Draka Kabel B.V.; *Int'l*, pg. 417
BIW CABLE SYSTEMS, INC.—Draka Kabel B.V.; *Int'l*, pg. 417
BARKSDALE, INC.—Crane Co.; *U.S. Public*, pg. 457
BEAU INTERCONNECT SYSTEMS—Axsys Technologies, Inc.; *U.S. Public*, pg. 157
BIRNBACH COMPANY, INC.—Bell Industries, Inc.; *U.S. Public*, pg. 207
BOHAIN JEUMONT CABLES—Jeumont-Schneider Trenformeteurs; *Int'l*, pg. 706
BRIDGEPORT FITTINGS, INC.; *U.S. Private*, pg. 168
BRYANT ELECTRICAL, INC.—Hubbell Incorporated; *U.S. Public*, pg. 844
BUCHANAN CONSTRUCTION PRODUCTS, INC.—Ideal Industries, Inc.; *U.S. Private*, pg. 557
BURTON ELECTRICAL ENGINEERING—Wyle Laboratories, Inc.; *U.S. Private*, pg. 1193
CAMBRIDGE PRODUCTS CORPORATION—Jordan Industries, Inc.; *U.S. Private*, pg. 598
CAPAX ELECTRISCHE APPARATENFABRIEK B.V.—Emerson Electric Co.; *U.S. Public*, pg. 576

CHERASIA LIMITED—Cherry Electrical Products Corporation; *U.S. Public*, pg. 346
CHERRY AUSTRALIA PTY. LTD.—Cherry Electrical Products Corporation; *U.S. Public*, pg. 346
CHERRY AUTOMOTIVE-JAPAN—Cherry Electrical Products Corporation; *U.S. Public*, pg. 346
CHERRY ELECTRICAL PRODUCTS—Cherry Electrical Products Corporation; *U.S. Public*, pg. 346
CHERRY ELECTRICAL PRODUCTS CORPORATION; *U.S.* Public, pg. 346
CHERRY ELECTRICAL PRODUCTS, LTD.—Cherry Electrical Products Corporation; *U.S. Public*, pg. 346
CHERRY MIKROSCHALTER GMBH—Cherry Electrical Products Corporation; *U.S. Public*, pg. 346
CHERRY SARL—Cherry Electrical Products Corporation; *U.S. Public*, pg. 346
CHERRY SRO—Cherry Electrical Products Corporation; *U.S. Public*, pg. 346
CIRCLE A.W. PRODUCTS, CO.—Sigma-Aldrich Corporation; *U.S. Public*, pg. 1471
COLE HERSEE COMPANY; *U.S. Private*, pg. 251
COMPAGNIE DES DISPOSITIFS SEMI-CONDUCTEURS WESTINGHOUSE—Jeumont-Schneider Trenformeteurs; *Int'l*, pg. 706
COMPAGNIE FRANCAISE PHILIPS—Philips Electronics N.V.; *Int'l*, pg. 1055
CONSTRUCTION & HOME IMPROVEMENT MARKETS DIVISION—3M; *U.S. Public*, pg. 1605
COOPER INDUSTRIES, INC.; *U.S. Public*, pg. 442
CROUSE-HINDS—Cooper Industries, Inc.; *U.S. Public*, pg. 444
CROUSE-HINDS (AUSTRALIA) PTY. LTD.—Cooper Industries, Inc.; *U.S. Public*, pg. 445
DEKKO AUTOMOTIVE TECHNOLOGIES IOWA ASSEMBLIES DIV.—Group Dekko; *U.S. Private*, pg. 484
DEKKO HEATING TECHNOLOGIES, INC.—Group Dekko; *U.S. Private*, pg. 484
DEUTSCH INDUSTRIAL PRODUCT DIVISION—The Deutsch Company; *U.S. Private*, pg. 328
EAGLE ELECTRIC MFG. CO., INC.; *U.S. Private*, pg. 354
EATON CORP., AEROSPACE & COMMERCIAL CONTROLS DIV.—Eaton Corporation; *U.S. Public*, pg. 557
EATON CORPORATION COMMERCIAL CONTROLS DIVISION—Eaton Corporation; *U.S. Public*, pg. 556
ELCO ELEKTRONIK GMBH—Kyocera Corporation; *Int'l*, pg. 775
ELCO INTERNATIONAL K.K.—Kyocera Corporation; *Int'l*, pg. 775
ELECTRICAL PRODUCTS DIVISION—3M; *U.S. Public*, pg. 1605
ELECTRONIC PRODUCTS DIVISION—3M; *U.S. Public*, pg. 1605
ELEKTRO-APPARATEBAU OLTEN AG; *Int'l*, pg. 444
AB ELEKTROKOPPAR—ABB Asea Brown Boveri (Holding) Ltd.; *Int'l*, pg. 7
EMERSON ELECTRIC, C.A.—Emerson Electric Co.; *U.S. Public*, pg. 576
EMERSON ELECTRIC (FRANCE) S.A.—Emerson Electric Co.; *U.S. Public*, pg. 576
ENFIELD WINDING WIRES LTD. (ENAMEL & TEXTILE)—Delta plc; *Int'l*, pg. 390
ERICO INTERNATIONAL; *U.S. Private*, pg. 381
EVERETT CHARLES TECHNOLOGIES; *U.S. Private*, pg. 386
FTZ INDUSTRIES, INC.—Ilsco; *U.S. Private*, pg. 558
FLECK MANUFACTURING INC.—Noma Industries Limited; *Int'l*, pg. 955
FRAMATOME CONNECTORS—Framatome SA; *Int'l*, pg. 503
FRAMATOME CONNECTORS BELGIUM N.V.—Framatome SA; *Int'l*, pg. 503
FRAMATOME CONNECTORS ESPANA S.A.—Framatome SA; *Int'l*, pg. 503
FRAMATOME CONNECTORS INTERNATIONAL—Framatome SA; *Int'l*, pg. 503
FRAMATOME CONNECTORS NEDERLAND B.V.—Framatome SA; *Int'l*, pg. 503
FRAMATOME CONNECTORS SCHWEIZ A.G.—Framatome SA; *Int'l*, pg. 503
FRAMATOME CONNECTORS S.P.A.—Framatome SA; *Int'l*, *pg. 503*
FRAMATOME CONNECTORS SWEDEN AB—Framatome SA; *Int'l*, pg. 503
FRAMATOME JAPAN, LTD.—Framatome SA; *Int'l*, pg. 503
FRAMATOME-MEXICO S.A. DE C.V.—Framatome SA; *Int'l*, *pg. 503*
FRAMATOME SA; *Int'l*, pg. 502
G.E. LIGHTING DIVISION—General Electric Company; *U.S.* Public, pg. 710
G.E. LIGHTING EUROPE—General Electric Company; *U.S. Public*, pg. 713
GEC AUSTRALIA LTD.—The General Electric Company, p.l.c.; *Int'l*, pg. 546
GEC (NEW ZEALAND) LTD.—The General Electric Company, p.l.c.; *Int'l*, pg. 546
GENERAL ELECTRIC COMPANY; *U.S. Public*, pg. 709
GLOBAL ATMOSPHERICS, INC.—Sankosha Corporation; *Int'l*, pg. 1189
GOULD ELECTRONICS INC., SHAWMUT CIRCUIT PROTECTION DIVISION—Thermo Electron Corporation; *U.S. Public*, pg. 1592
GROUP DEKKO; *U.S. Private*, pg. 484
HAYDON SWITCH & INSTRUMENT, INC.; *U.S. Private*, pg. 513
HIGH VOLTAGE ENGINEERING CORPORATION; *U.S. Private*, pg. 528
HIROSE CHERRY PRECISION COMPANY LTD.—Cherry Electrical Products Corporation; *U.S. Public*, pg. 346
HIVEC-IRELAND—High Voltage Engineering Corporation; *U.S. Private*, pg. 528
HOBBS CORPORATION—BTR plc; *Int'l*, pg. 127
HONEYWELL INC.; *U.S. Public*, pg. 833
ITT CANNON—ITT Industries, Inc.; *U.S. Public*, pg. 859
ITW SWITCHES—Illinois Tool Works Inc.; *U.S. Public*, pg. 867
IDEAL INDUSTRIES, INC.; *U.S. Private*, pg. 557
ILLINOIS TOOL WORKS INC.; *U.S. Public*, pg. 865
ILSCO; *U.S. Private*, pg. 558
INTERCONNECT PRODUCTS DIVISION—Methode Electronics Inc.; *U.S. Public*, pg. 1101
JAPAN AVIATION ELECTRONICS INDUSTRY, LTD.; *Int'l*, *pg. 701*
JEUMONT-SCHNEIDER TRENFORMETEURS; *Int'l*, pg. 706
JOHNSON MATTHEY INC.—Johnson Matthey Public Limited Company; *Int'l*, pg. 713
JOSLYN MANUFACTURING CO.—Danaher Corporation; *U.S. Public*, pg. 481
JOY MANUFACTURING COMPANY (PTY) LTD., SYDNEY PLANT—Harnischfeger Industries, Inc.; *U.S. Public*, pg. 789
KEARNEY COMPANY—Cooper Industries, Inc.; *U.S. Public*, *pg. 444*
THE LAMSON & SESSIONS CO.; *U.S. Public*, pg. 976
LAMSON & SESSIONS LTD.—The Lamson & Sessions Co.; *U.S. Public*, pg. 976
LEGRAND S.A.; *Int'l*, pg. 805
LEMO SA; *Int'l*, pg. 806
LEVIMEX DE BAJA CALIFORNIA S.A. DE C.V.—Leviton Mfg. Co., Inc.; *U.S. Private*, pg. 663
LEVITON—Leviton Mfg. Co., Inc.; *U.S. Private*, pg. 663
LEVITON MFG. CO., INC.; *U.S. Private*, pg. 663
LEX GROUP—Alcatel Alsthom Compagnie Generale D'Electricite; *Int'l*, pg. 53
MACLEAN-FOGG CO.; *U.S. Private*, pg. 692
MANUFACTURE LEVITON DU CANADA—Leviton Mfg. Co., Inc.; *U.S. Private*, pg. 663
MARATHON ELECTRIC MANUFACTURING CORP.—Regal-Beloit Corporation; *U.S. Public*, pg. 1371
MARATHON SPECIAL PRODS.—Regal-Beloit Corporation; *U.S. Public*, pg. 1371
MARINCO/AFI—Valley Forge Corporation; *U.S. Public*, pg. 1705
MASON METALS CO.—Standex International Corporation; *U.S. Public*, pg. 1506
MATSUSHITA ELECTRIC WORKS, LTD.; *Int'l*, pg. 847
MCGILL MANUFACTURING COMPANY, INC.—Emerson Electric Co.; *U.S. Public*, pg. 573
MCGILL MFG. CO., INC. ELECTRICAL DIVISION—Emerson Electric Co.; *U.S. Public*, pg. 573
METHODE ELECTRONICS EUROPE LIMITED—Methode Electronics Inc.; *U.S. Public*, pg. 1101
METHODE ELECTRONICS FAREAST PTE, LTD.—Methode Electronics Inc.; *U.S. Public*, pg. 1101
METHODE TECHNICAL COMPONENTS—Methode Electronics Inc.; *U.S. Public*, pg. 1101
MOLEX CARIBE—Molex Incorporated; *U.S. Public*, pg. 1122
NETWORK BUSS DIVISION—Methode Electronics Inc.; *U.S. Public*, pg. 1101
NIKKO DENKI SEISAKUSHO CO., LTD.—Oki Electric Industry Company, Ltd.; *Int'l*, pg. 999
NORTHERN TELECOM CANADA LIMITED—Northern Telecom Limited; *Int'l*, pg. 969
NORTHERN TELECOM CANADA LIMITED, OUTSIDE PLANT DIV.—Northern Telecom Limited; *Int'l*, pg. 969
OKI ELECTRIC CABLE CO., LTD.—Oki Electric Industry Company, Ltd.; *Int'l*, pg. 999
OSRAM DE MEXICO S.A. DE C.V.—Siemens AG; *Int'l*, pg. 1244
OSRAM-MELCO LTD.—Siemens AG; *Int'l*, pg. 1244
PLP PRODUTOS PARA LINHAS PROFORMADOS LTDA.—Preformed Line Products; *U.S. Public*, pg. 1321
PACIFIC ELECTRICORD CO.—Leviton Mfg. Co., Inc.; *U.S. Private*, pg. 663
PANDUIT CORP.; *U.S. Private*, pg. 836
PASS & SEYMOUR/LEGRAND—LeGrand S.A.; *Int'l*, pg. 806
PENT ASSEMBLIES, INC.—Group Dekko; *U.S. Private*, pg. 484
PENT PRODUCTS, INC.—Group Dekko; *U.S. Private*, pg. 484
PERKASIE INDUSTRIES CORPORATION; *U.S. Private*, pg. 854
PREFORMED LINE PRODUCTS; *U.S. Public*, pg. 1321
PREFORMED LINE PRODUCTS(GREAT BRITAIN) LTD.—Preformed Line Products; *U.S. Public*, pg. 1321
RAYCHEM CORPORATION; *U.S. Public*, pg. 1362
RAYCHEM GMBH—Raychem Corporation; *U.S. Public*, pg. 1362
RELTEC, INC.—RELTEC Corporation; *U.S. Private*, pg. 921
RESEARCH, INCORPORATED; *U.S. Public*, pg. 1382
ROWE INDUSTRIES—Carpenter Technology Corporation; *U.S. Public*, pg. 308
S & C ELECTRIC COMPANY; *U.S. Private*, pg. 954
SL AUBURN, INC.—Cooper Industries, Inc.; *U.S. Public*, pg. 443
SL INDUSTRIES, INC.; *U.S. Public*, pg. 1418
SHOGYO INTERNATIONAL CORPORATION; *U.S. Private*, *pg. 996*
SPECTRUM CONTROL, CONNECTING DEVICES DIV.—Spectrum Control, Inc.; *U.S. Public*, pg. 1497
SPECTRUM CONTROL, FILTER PRODUCTS GROUP—Spectrum Control, Inc.; *U.S. Public*, pg. 1497
SQUARE D COMPANY—Schneider S.A.; *Int'l*, pg. 1208
SQUARE D OXFORD PLANT—Schneider S.A.; *Int'l*, pg. 1208
STACOSWITCH, INC.—Components Corporation Of America; *U.S. Private*, pg. 260
EDWIN B. STIMPSON COMPANY, INC.; *U.S. Private*, pg. 1043
STIRLING CONNECTORS—ARC International Corporation; *Int'l*, pg. 17
STOCKO METALLWAREN FABRIKEN HENKELS & SOHN; *Int'l*, pg. 1301
STONERIDGE, INC.; *U.S. Private*, pg. 1044
STORM PRODUCTS COMPANY, INC.; *U.S. Private*, pg. 1045
THE SUNBANK FAMILY OF COMPANIES, INC.—Danaher Corporation; *U.S. Public*, pg. 482
SWITCHCRAFT DE MEXICO, S.A.—Raytheon Company; *U.S. Public*, pg. 1366
SWITCHCRAFT, INC.—Raytheon Company; *U.S. Public*, pg. 1366
SYSTEMES Y CONNEXIONES INTEGRADES S.A. DE C.V.—Noma Industries Limited; *Int'l*, pg. 955
TII DOMINICANA INC.—TII Industries, Inc.; *U.S. Public*, pg. 1556
TII INDUSTRIES, INC.; *U.S. Public*, pg. 1556
TVS CHERRY PRIVATE LIMITED—Cherry Electrical Products Corporation; *U.S. Public*, pg. 346
TECHNITROL, INC.; *U.S. Public*, pg. 1564
THOMAS & BETTS/AMERACE—Thomas & Betts Corporation; *U.S. Public*, pg. 1598
THOMAS & BETTS CARIBE, INC.—Thomas & Betts Corporation; *U.S. Public*, pg. 1598
THOMAS & BETTS CORPORATION; *U.S. Public*, pg. 1597
THOMAS & BETTS ELECTRONICS DIVISION—Thomas & Betts Corporation; *U.S. Public*, pg. 1597
THOMAS & BETTS GMBH—Thomas & Betts Corporation; *U.S. Public*, pg. 1598
THOMAS & BETTS LTD.—Thomas & Betts Corporation; *U.S. Public*, pg. 1598
THOMAS & BETTS MANUFACTURING LTD.—Thomas & Betts Corporation; *U.S. Public*, pg. 1598
THE TOBIN CORPORATION—Avis Industrial Corporation; *U.S. Private*, pg. 102
TOKI ELECTRIC CO., LTD.—Toshiba Corporation; *Int'l*, pg. 1403
USECO—Litton Industries, Inc.; *U.S. Public*, pg. 1003
VALLEY FORGE CORPORATION; *U.S. Public*, pg. 1705
WAGO CONTACT I.GR—Bowthorpe plc; *Int'l*, pg. 209
WAGO CONTACT SA—Bowthorpe plc; *Int'l*, pg. 209
WAGO CORPORATION—Bowthorpe plc; *Int'l*, pg. 209
WAGO KONTAKTTECHNIK GMBH—Bowthorpe plc; *Int'l*, pg. 209
WINCHESTER ELECTRONICS—Litton Industries, Inc.; *U.S.* Public, pg. 1003
THE WIREMOLD COMPANY; *U.S. Private*, pg. 1184
WOODHEAD CANADA LTD.—Woodhead Industries, Inc.; *U.S. Public*, pg. 1776
DANIEL WOODHEAD COMPANY—Woodhead Industries, Inc.; *U.S. Public*, pg. 1776
WOODHEAD DE MEXICO—Woodhead Industries, Inc.; *U.S.* Public, pg. 1776
WOODHEAD INDUSTRIES, INC.; *U.S. Public*, pg. 1776
ALOIS ZETTLER ELECKTROTECHNISCHE FABRIK GMBH; *Int'l*, pg. 1528

3644 — NONCURRENT-CARRYING WIRING DEVICES

ADALET DIV.—Berkshire Hathaway Inc.; *U.S. Public*, pg. 217
APPLETON ELECTRIC CO.—Emerson Electric Co.; *U.S. Public*, pg. 572
APPLETON ELECTRIC LTD.—Emerson Electric Co.; *U.S. Public*, pg. 575
ARTISAN ELECTRONICS CORPORATION—Morgan Crucible Co. Plc; *Int'l*, pg. 892
THE BENTLEY-HARRIS MANUFACTURING CO.—T & N Plc; *Int'l*, pg. 1334
THE BERGQUIST COMPANY; *U.S. Private*, pg. 135
BERGQUIST ITC, GMBH—The Bergquist Company; *U.S. Private*, pg. 135
BRIDGEPORT FITTINGS, INC.; *U.S. Private*, pg. 168
CAPAX ELECTRISCHE APPARATENFABRIEK B.V.—Emerson Electric Co.; *U.S. Public*, pg. 576
CAPITOL MANUFACTURING CO.—Harsco Corporation; *U.S. Public*, pg. 793
CHASE CORPORATION; *U.S. Public*, pg. 337
CONSTRUCTION & HOME IMPROVEMENT MARKETS DIVISION—3M; *U.S. Public*, pg. 1605
COOPER INDUSTRIES, INC.; *U.S. Public*, pg. 442
CROUSE-HINDS—Cooper Industries, Inc.; *U.S. Public*, pg. 444
EAGLE ELECTRIC MFG. CO., INC.; *U.S. Private*, pg. 354
EAST AFRICAN CABLES LTD.—Delta plc; *Int'l*, pg. 390
ELECTRICAL PRODUCTS DIVISION—3M; *U.S. Public*, pg. 1605
ELECTRONIC PRODUCTS DIVISION—3M; *U.S. Public*, pg. 1605
EMERSON ELECTRIC, C.A.—Emerson Electric Co.; *U.S. Public*, pg. 576
EMERSON ELECTRIC (FRANCE) S.A.—Emerson Electric Co.; *U.S. Public*, pg. 576
FLECK MANUFACTURING INC.—Noma Industries Limited; *Int'l*, pg. 955
FRAMATOME CONNECTORS—Framatome SA; *Int'l*, pg. 503
FRAMATOME JAPAN, LTD.—Framatome SA; *Int'l*, pg. 503
GENERAL CABLE CO.—Wassall Plc; *Int'l*, pg. 1487
GENERAL SIGNAL CORPORATION; *U.S. Public*, pg. 726
GOULD ELECTRONICS INC., SHAWMUT CIRCUIT PROTECTION DIVISION—Thermo Electron Corporation; *U.S. Public*, pg. 1592
HARSCO CORPORATION; *U.S. Public*, pg. 792
ICORE INTERNATIONAL INC.—Smiths Industries plc; *Int'l*, pg. 1268
ICORE INTERNATIONAL LIMITED—Smiths Industries plc; *Int'l*, pg. 1267
IDEAL INDUSTRIES, INC.; *U.S. Private*, pg. 557
INDUSTRIAL DIELECTRICS, INC.; *U.S. Private*, pg. 560
INSULATING MATERIALS, INC.; *U.S. Private*, pg. 565
JOSLYN MANUFACTURING CO.-HARDWARE DIV.—Danaher Corporation; *U.S. Public*, pg. 481
JOSLYN MANUFACTURING CO.-APPARATUS DIV.—Danaher Corporation; *U.S. Public*, pg. 481

KOPEX INTERNATIONAL LIMITED—Smiths Industries plc; Int'l, pg. 1267
THE LAMSON & SESSIONS CO.; U.S. Public, pg. 976
MACLEAN-FOGG CO.; U.S. Private, pg. 692
MACLEAN POWER SYSTEMS—Maclean-Fogg Co.; U.S. Private, pg. 692
MATSUSHITA ELECTRIC WORKS, LTD.; Int'l, pg. 847
MINERALLAC CO.; U.S. Private, pg. 750
MULBERRY METAL PRODUCTS, INC.; U.S. Private, pg. 766
NEER MANUFACTURING COMPANY INC.—General Signal Corporation; U.S. Public, pg. 727
O-Z/GEDNEY CO.—General Signal Corporation; U.S. Public, pg. 727
THE OHIO BRASS CO.—Hubbell Incorporated; U.S. Public, pg. 844
PANDUIT CORP.; U.S. Private, pg. 836
PASS & SEYMOUR/LEGRAND—LeGrand S.A.; Int'l, pg. 806
PREFORMED LINE PRODUCTS; U.S. Public, pg. 1321
PREFORMED LINE PRODUCTS CANADA—Preformed Line Products; U.S. Public, pg. 1321
RACO, INC.—Hubbell Incorporated; U.S. Public, pg. 845
RELIABLE/BETHEA POWER PRODUCTS INC.—Maclean-Fogg Co.; U.S. Private, pg. 692
RELTEC, INC.—RELTEC Corporation; U.S. Private, pg. 921
S & C ELECTRIC COMPANY; U.S. Private, pg. 954
SLACAN—Slater Industries Inc.; Int'l, pg. 1262
SQUARE D COMPANY—Schneider S.A.; Int'l, pg. 1208
SQUARE D OXFORD PLANT—Schneider S.A.; Int'l, pg. 1208
EDWIN B. STIMPSON COMPANY, INC.; U.S. Private, pg. 1043
SYSTEMES Y CONNEXIONES INTEGRADES S.A. DE C.V.—Noma Industries Limited; Int'l, pg. 955
TBG SERVICES, INC.—TBG Management S.A.M.; Int'l, pg. 1335
TII-DITEL—TII Industries, Inc.; U.S. Public, pg. 1556
TII DOMINICANA INC.—TII Industries, Inc.; U.S. Public, pg. 1556
TII INDUSTRIES, INC.; U.S. Public, pg. 1556
THOMAS & BETTS/AMERACE—Thomas & Betts Corporation; U.S. Public, pg. 1598
THOMAS & BETTS CORPORATION; U.S. Public, pg. 1597
VALMONT/ALS—Valmont Industries, Inc.; U.S. Public, pg. 1707
VALMONT INDUSTRIES, INC.; U.S. Public, pg. 1706
THE WIEGMANN COMPANY—Hubbell Incorporated; U.S. Public, pg. 845
THE WIREMOLD COMPANY; U.S. Private, pg. 1184

3645 — RESIDENTIAL ELECTRIC LIGHTING FIXTURES

ABOLITE LIGHTING INC.—LSI Industries, Inc.; U.S. Public, pg. 971
ADELPHIA LAMP & SHADE INC.; U.S. Private, pg. 17
AMERICAN FLUORESCENT CORPORATION; U.S. Private, pg. 54
APPLETON ELECTRIC LTD.—Emerson Electric Co.; U.S. Public, pg. 575
ARCHITECTURAL LANDSCAPE LIGHTING—Luxo A/S; Int'l, pg. 821
ARTESANIAS BAJA, S.A.—Hanson PLC; Int'l, pg. 594
ATKINSON INDUSTRIES, INC.—Aztec Manufacturing Co.; U.S. Public, pg. 159
AZTEC MANUFACTURING CO.; U.S. Public, pg. 159
BORENS AB—Luxo A/S; Int'l, pg. 821
BRILLIANT AG—Emess PLC; Int'l, pg. 453
BRILLIANT LIGHTING (AUSTRALIA)—Emess PLC; Int'l, pg. 453
BROWN JORDAN COMPANY; U.S. Private, pg. 174
BRUNSCHWIG & FILS, INC.; U.S. Private, pg. 176
COOPER LIGHTING DIVISION—Cooper Industries, Inc.; U.S. Public, pg. 443
CRESCENT GENLYTE—The Genlyte Group Incorporated; U.S. Public, pg. 730
CRESSWELL LIGHTING LIMITED—Emess PLC; Int'l, pg. 453
CRYSTAL CLEAR INDUSTRIES; U.S. Private, pg. 293
D'AC—Luxo A/S; Int'l, pg. 821
DANA LIGHTING, INC.—Catalina Lighting, Inc.; U.S. Public, pg. 314
ELITE LAMP, INC.; U.S. Private, pg. 371
EMESS LIGHTING INC.—Emess PLC; Int'l, pg. 453
EMESS PLC; Int'l, pg. 453
FKI PLC; Int'l, pg. 471
FANNER-PLP—Preformed Line Products; U.S. Public, pg. 1321
FASSON DE MEXICO, S.A.—Avery Dennison Corporation; U.S. Public, pg. 154
G.E. LIGHTING DIVISION—General Electric Company; U.S. Public, pg. 710
G.E. LIGHTING EUROPE—General Electric Company; U.S. Public, pg. 713
G.E. TOSHIBA LIGHTING CORPORATION—General Electric Company; U.S. Public, pg. 710
GEC ZIMBABWE (PVT) LTD.—The General Electric Company, p.l.c.; Int'l, pg. 546
GENERAL ELECTRIC COMPANY; U.S. Public, pg. 709
GENERAL ELECTRIC DE MEXICO, S.A. DE C.V.—General Electric Company; U.S. Public, pg. 713
GREENLEE LIGHTING INC.—LSI Industries, Inc.; U.S. Public, pg. 971
HALO LIGHTING—Cooper Industries, Inc.; U.S. Public, pg. 443
HAMILTON LAMP CORP.—RDM Sports Group; U.S. Public, pg. 1354
HIGH-LITES, INC.—Luxo A/S; Int'l, pg. 821
HINKLEY LIGHTING INC.; U.S. Private, pg. 530
HITACHI LIGHTING, LTD.—Hitachi, Ltd.; Int'l, pg. 621
HUBBELL LIGHTING INC.—Hubbell Incorporated; U.S. Public, pg. 844
IL INTERNATIONAL INC.; U.S. Public, pg. 855
IL USA, INC.—IL International Inc.; U.S. Public, pg. 856
IMI PLC; Int'l, pg. 646
ITALIANA LUCE S.R.L.—IL International Inc.; U.S. Public, pg. 856
JJI LIGHTING GROUP INC.—Luxo A/S; Int'l, pg. 821
JAC JACOBSEN ENTERPRISES, INC.—Luxo A/S; Int'l, pg. 821
JUNO LIGHTING, INC.; U.S. Public, pg. 935
KAMRO CHAMPION LIGHTING PRODUCTS INC.—Kaufel Group Ltd.; Int'l, pg. 725
KAMRO LIGHTING PRODUCTS LTD.—Kaufel Group Ltd.; Int'l, pg. 725
KAUFEL AMERICA INC.—Kaufel Group Ltd.; Int'l, pg. 725
KAUFEL GROUP LTD.; Int'l, pg. 724
GEORGE KOVACS LIGHTING, INC.; U.S. Private, pg. 634
LSI INDUSTRIES, INC.; U.S. Public, pg. 971
LSI INDUSTRIES, INC.—LSI Industries, Inc.; U.S. Public, pg. 971
LAWNWARE PRODUCTS, INC.; U.S. Private, pg. 653
L'ECLAIRAGE TECHNIQUE S.A.—Emess PLC; Int'l, pg. 453
LEDU INTERNATIONAL AB—Luxo A/S; Int'l, pg. 821
LIGHTCRAFT—Millstein Industries; U.S. Private, pg. 749
LIGHTING CORPORATION OF AMERICA—U.S. Industries, Inc.; U.S. Public, pg. 1684
LIGHTS OF AMERICA, INC.; U.S. Private, pg. 667
LITHONIA LIGHTING CO.—National Service Industries, Inc.; U.S. Public, pg. 1160
LUXO A/S; Int'l, pg. 821
MTD PRODUCTS, INC.; U.S. Private, pg. 688
MATSUSHITA ELECTRIC WORKS, LTD.; Int'l, pg. 847
A.Y. MCDONALD INDUSTRIES, INC.; U.S. Private, pg. 721
A.Y. MCDONALD SUPPLY CO. INC.—A.Y. McDonald Industries, Inc.; U.S. Private, pg. 721
METALUX LIGHTING—Cooper Industries, Inc.; U.S. Public, pg. 443
NATIONAL SERVICE INDUSTRIES, INC.; U.S. Public, pg. 1160
NESSEN LAMPS, INC.—Luxo A/S; Int'l, pg. 821
PHILADELPHIA SIGN COMPANY; U.S. Private, pg. 861
PHILIPS LIGHTING LTD.—Philips Electronics N.V.; Int'l, pg. 1055
POOLE LIGHTING LIMITED—Emess PLC; Int'l, pg. 453
PRESCOLITE MOLDCAST LIGHTING COMPANY—U.S. Industries, Inc.; U.S. Public, pg. 1684
PROGRESS LIGHTING—U.S. Industries, Inc.; U.S. Public, pg. 1684
PROGRESS LIGHTING CANADA—U.S. Industries, Inc.; U.S. Public, pg. 1684
QUALITY LIGHTING, INC.—Luxo A/S; Int'l, pg. 821
QUOIZEL INC.; U.S. Private, pg. 901
RANGAIRE INC.—Nortek, Inc.; U.S. Public, pg. 1193
THE RENOVATOR'S SUPPLY, INC.; U.S. Private, pg. 923
SELECTION LIGHTING INC.—Kaufel Group Ltd.; Int'l, pg. 725
SHOGYO INTERNATIONAL CORPORATION; U.S. Private, pg. 996
SPECIALTY LIGHTING—Luxo A/S; Int'l, pg. 821
THE STIFFEL COMPANY; U.S. Private, pg. 1043
THOMAS INDUSTRIES INC.; U.S. Public, pg. 1598
THOMAS LIGHTING-C&I ACCENT DIVISION—Thomas Industries Inc.; U.S. Public, pg. 1599
THOMAS LIGHTING-CANADIAN DIVISION—Thomas Industries Inc.; U.S. Public, pg. 1599
TOSHIBA ELECTRIC APPLIANCES CO., LTD.—Toshiba Corporation; Int'l, pg. 1404
TRIBORO ELECTRIC CO.; U.S. Private, pg. 1102
YMOS AG—Cockerill Sambre; Int'l, pg. 302

3646 — COMMERCIAL, INDUSTRIAL & INSTITUTIONAL ELECTRIC LIGHTING FIXTURES

ABM INDUSTRIES; U.S. Public, pg. 2
ABOLITE LIGHTING INC.—LSI Industries, Inc.; U.S. Public, pg. 971
ALKCO LIGHTING COMPANY—Luxo A/S; Int'l, pg. 821
AMERICAN FLUORESCENT CORPORATION; U.S. Private, pg. 54
AMTECH LIGHTING SERVICES CO.—ABM Industries; U.S. Public, pg. 2
ARCHITECTURAL LANDSCAPE LIGHTING—Luxo A/S; Int'l, pg. 821
ARENA LIGHTING LTD.; Int'l, pg. 80
ATLITE LIGHTING EQUIP, INC.—Cooper Industries, Inc.; U.S. Public, pg. 443
BROWN JORDAN COMPANY; U.S. Private, pg. 174
CANLYTE INCORPORATED—The Genlyte Group Incorporated; U.S. Public, pg. 730
CEAG SICHERHEITSTECHNIK GMBH—Cooper Industries, Inc.; U.S. Public, pg. 444
COLUMBIA LIGHTING, INC.—U.S. Industries, Inc.; U.S. Public, pg. 1684
COOPER INDUSTRIES, INC.; U.S. Public, pg. 442
COOPER LIGHTING DIVISION—Cooper Industries, Inc.; U.S. Public, pg. 443
CRESCENT GENLYTE—The Genlyte Group Incorporated; U.S. Public, pg. 730
CROUSE-HINDS—Cooper Industries, Inc.; U.S. Public, pg. 444
CUSTOM LIGHTS, INC.—Group Dekko; U.S. Private, pg. 484
D'AC—Luxo A/S; Int'l, pg. 821
DERLAN INDUSTRIES LIMITED; Int'l, pg. 395
DIAMOND FORECAST—The Genlyte Group Incorporated; U.S. Public, pg. 730
DUREL CORPORATION—Rogers Corporation; U.S. Public, pg. 1403
EDISON DIVISION—The Genlyte Group Incorporated; U.S. Public, pg. 730
EMERSON ELECTRIC CO.; U.S. Public, pg. 572
EMESS PLC; Int'l, pg. 453
FANNER-PLP—Preformed Line Products; U.S. Public, pg. 1321
FONTANA—The Genlyte Group Incorporated; U.S. Public, pg. 730
FOSTORIA INDUSTRIES, INC.; U.S. Private, pg. 421
G.E. LIGHTING DIVISION—General Electric Company; U.S. Public, pg. 710
G.E. LIGHTING EUROPE—General Electric Company; U.S. Public, pg. 713
G.E. TOSHIBA LIGHTING CORPORATION—General Electric Company; U.S. Public, pg. 710
GEC ZIMBABWE (PVT) LTD.—The General Electric Company, p.l.c.; Int'l, pg. 546
THE GENLYTE GROUP INCORPORATED; U.S. Public, pg. 729
GREENLEE LIGHTING INC.—LSI Industries, Inc.; U.S. Public, pg. 971
GUTH LIGHTING COMPANY—Luxo A/S; Int'l, pg. 821
HIGH-LITES, INC.—Luxo A/S; Int'l, pg. 821
HOLOPHANE, S.A. DE C.V.—McNeel International Corp.; U.S. Private, pg. 725
HOSPITALITY WORLDWIDE SERVICES, INC.; U.S. Public, pg. 841
INDY LIGHTING, INC.—Juno Lighting, Inc.; U.S. Public, pg. 935
JJI LIGHTING GROUP INC.—Luxo A/S; Int'l, pg. 821
JAC JACOBSEN ENTERPRISES, INC.—Luxo A/S; Int'l, pg. 821
JUNO LIGHTING, INC.; U.S. Public, pg. 935
JUNO LIGHTING LTD.—Juno Lighting, Inc.; U.S. Public, pg. 935
KAMRO CHAMPION LIGHTING PRODUCTS INC.—Kaufel Group Ltd.; Int'l, pg. 725
KAUFEL AMERICA INC.—Kaufel Group Ltd.; Int'l, pg. 725
KAUFEL GROUP LTD.; Int'l, pg. 724
LSI INDUSTRIES, INC.; U.S. Public, pg. 971
LSI INDUSTRIES, INC.—LSI Industries, Inc.; U.S. Public, pg. 971
LAM LIGHTING SYSTEMS INC.—Luxo A/S; Int'l, pg. 821
L'ECLAIRAGE TECHNIQUE S.A.—Emess PLC; Int'l, pg. 453
LEDU GMBH—Luxo A/S; Int'l, pg. 821
LEDU INTERNATIONAL AB—Luxo A/S; Int'l, pg. 821
LEDU LTD.—Luxo A/S; Int'l, pg. 821
LIGHTING CORPORATION OF AMERICA—U.S. Industries, Inc.; U.S. Public, pg. 1684
LIGHTOLIER—The Genlyte Group Incorporated; U.S. Public, pg. 730
LIGHTOLIER DIVISION—The Genlyte Group Incorporated; U.S. Public, pg. 730
LITECONTROL CORPORATION; U.S. Private, pg. 669
LITHONIA LIGHTING CO.—National Service Industries, Inc.; U.S. Public, pg. 1160
LUMEC, INC.—Thomas Industries Inc.; U.S. Public, pg. 1599
LUXO A/S; Int'l, pg. 821
MARK LIGHTING FIXTURE CO., INC.; U.S. Private, pg. 704
MARLIN LIGHTING LIMITED—Emess PLC; Int'l, pg. 453
A.Y. MCDONALD INDUSTRIES, INC.; U.S. Private, pg. 721
A.Y. MCDONALD SUPPLY CO. INC.—A.Y. McDonald Industries, Inc.; U.S. Private, pg. 721
NATIONAL SERVICE INDUSTRIES, INC.; U.S. Public, pg. 1160
NESSEN LAMPS, INC.—Luxo A/S; Int'l, pg. 821
PERKASIE INDUSTRIES CORPORATION; U.S. Private, pg. 854
PHILIPS LIGHTING LTD.—Philips Electronics N.V.; Int'l, pg. 1055
POOLE LIGHTING LIMITED—Emess PLC; Int'l, pg. 453
PRESCOLITE MOLDCAST LIGHTING COMPANY—U.S. Industries, Inc.; U.S. Public, pg. 1684
PROGRESS LIGHTING CANADA—U.S. Industries, Inc.; U.S. Public, pg. 1684
QUALITY LIGHTING, INC.—Luxo A/S; Int'l, pg. 821
RHC/SPACEMASTER CORPORATION; U.S. Private, pg. 904
RANGAIRE INC.—Nortek, Inc.; U.S. Public, pg. 1193
SAFT—Alcatel Alsthom Compagnie Generale D'Electricite; Int'l, pg. 54
SELECTION LIGHTING INC.—Kaufel Group Ltd.; Int'l, pg. 725
SPECIALTY LIGHTING—Luxo A/S; Int'l, pg. 821
STERNER LIGHTING SYSTEMS INCORPORATED; U.S. Private, pg. 1042
STONCO GENLYTE—The Genlyte Group Incorporated; U.S. Public, pg. 730
STRAND LIGHTING INC.—The Rank Group PLC; Int'l, pg. 1087
THOMAS & BETTS/AMERACE—Thomas & Betts Corporation; U.S. Public, pg. 1598
THOMAS INDUSTRIES INC.; U.S. Public, pg. 1598
THOMAS LIGHTING-C&I ACCENT DIVISION—Thomas Industries Inc.; U.S. Public, pg. 1599
THOMAS LIGHTING-C&I INDOOR DIVISON—Thomas Industries Inc.; U.S. Public, pg. 1599
THOMAS LIGHTING-C&I OUTDOOR DIVISION—Thomas Industries Inc.; U.S. Public, pg. 1599
THOMAS LIGHTING-CANADIAN DIVISION—Thomas Industries Inc.; U.S. Public, pg. 1599
THOMAS LIGHTING-MILAN OPERATIONS—Thomas Industries Inc.; U.S. Public, pg. 1599
THOMAS LIGHTING-SPARTA OPERS.—Thomas Industries Inc.; U.S. Public, pg. 1599
VICKSBURG PLANT—Cooper Industries, Inc.; U.S. Public, pg. 444
VISTA LIGHTING—Luxo A/S; Int'l, pg. 821
WENGER CORPORATION; U.S. Private, pg. 1162
WESTINGHOUSE ELECTRO-METALURGICA, C.A.—CBS Corporation; U.S. Public, pg. 275
H.E. WILLIAMS, INC.; U.S. Private, pg. 1178
THE WIREMOLD COMPANY; U.S. Private, pg. 1184
ZEP MANUFACTURING—National Service Industries, Inc.; U.S. Public, pg. 1160

3647 — VEHICULAR LIGHTING EQUIPMENT

ABB TRACTION INC.—ABB Asea Brown Boveri (Holding) Ltd.; *Int'l*, pg. 5
APPLIED TECHNOLOGY (UK)—Litton Industries, Inc.; *U.S. Public*, pg. 1004
BRITAX INTERNATIONAL PLC; *Int'l*, pg. 216
BRITAX (P.M.G.) LIMITED—Britax International plc; *Int'l*, pg. 216
BRITAX VEGA LIMITED—Britax International plc; *Int'l*, pg. 216
BRUCE INDUSTRIES, INC.; *U.S. Private*, pg. 175
BRYANT MANUFACTURING PTY LIMITED—Britax International plc; *Int'l*, pg. 217
BRYLITE PTY LIMITED—Britax International plc; *Int'l*, pg. 217
E-L PRODUCTS COMPANY—Astronics Corporation; *U.S. Public*, pg. 142
FLEXIBLE LAMPS LTD.—UIS, Inc.; *U.S. Private*, pg. 1113
G.E. LIGHTING DIVISION—General Electric Company; *U.S. Public*, pg. 710
G.E. LIGHTING EUROPE—General Electric Company; *U.S. Public*, pg. 713
GROTE INDUSTRIES; *U.S. Private*, pg. 483
HIABA PTY LIMITED—Britax International plc; *Int'l*, pg. 217
K-D LAMP COMPANY; *U.S. Private*, pg. 603
MARK IV INDUSTRIES INC.; *U.S. Public*, pg. 1044
PEREGRINE INCORPORATED; *U.S. Private*, pg. 852
SANYO INDUSTRIES (SINGAPORE) PRIVATE LIMITED—Sanyo Electric Co., Ltd.; *Int'l*, pg. 1192
SENALIZACION Y ACCESORIOS DEL AUTOMOVIL YORKA, S.A.—General Motors Corporation; *U.S. Public*, pg. 724
SUNG SAN COMPANY, LTD.—General Motors Corporation; *U.S. Public*, pg. 724
THOMAS & BETTS/AMERACE—Thomas & Betts Corporation; *U.S. Public*, pg. 1598
UNITY MANUFACTURING CO.; *U.S. Private*, pg. 1126
VALEO-LIGHTING—CERUS - Compagnies Europeennes Reunies; *Int'l*, pg. 240
WK MFG. COMPANY—K-D Lamp Company; *U.S. Private*, pg. 603
WAGNER LIGHTING PRODUCTS—Cooper Industries, Inc.; *U.S. Public*, pg. 442
WELDON, INC.—B. Elliott plc.; *Int'l*, pg. 449

3648 — LIGHTING EQUIPMENT, NEC

AMERICAN LOUVER CO.; *U.S. Private*, pg. 58
AMERON INTERNATIONAL CORPORATION; *U.S. Public*, pg. 98
AMERON POLE PRODUCTS & SYSTEMS—Ameron International Corporation; *U.S. Public*, pg. 99
APPLETON ELECTRIC LTD.—Emerson Electric Co.; *U.S. Public*, pg. 575
BRIGHT STAR INDUSTRIES, INC.—Publicker Industries Inc.; *U.S. Public*, pg. 1341
THE CANADIAN COLEMAN CO., LTD.—MacAndrews & Forbes Holdings Inc.; *U.S. Private*, pg. 691
CHLORIDE ELECTRONICS LTD.—Chloride Group PLC; *Int'l*, pg. 287
CHLORIDE GROUP PLC; *Int'l*, pg. 287
CHLORIDE POWER ELECTRONICS INC.—Chloride Group PLC; *Int'l*, pg. 287
COLUMBIA LIGHTING, INC.—U.S. Industries, Inc.; *U.S. Public*, pg. 1684
CONVERTER POWER, INC.—ILC Technology, Inc.; *U.S. Public*, pg. 856
COOPER INDUSTRIES, INC.; *U.S. Public*, pg. 442
COOPER LIGHTING DIVISION—Cooper Industries, Inc.; *U.S. Public*, pg. 443
CROUSE-HINDS (AUSTRALIA) PTY. LTD.—Cooper Industries, Inc.; *U.S. Public*, pg. 445
DUAL-LITE—General Signal Corporation; *U.S. Public*, pg. 726
DYNARAY INCORPORATED—Kaufel Group Ltd.; *Int'l*, pg. 725
EG & G OPTOELECTRONICS-SALEM—EG & G, Inc.; *U.S. Public*, pg. 543
EMERGENCY LIGHTING DIV.—General Signal Corporation; *U.S. Public*, pg. 726
EMERGI-LITE, INC.—Kaufel Group Ltd.; *Int'l*, pg. 725
EMERGI-LITE LANDMARK INC.—Kaufel Group Ltd.; *Int'l*, pg. 725
EMERGI-LITE SAFETY SYSTEMS LTD.—Kaufel Group Ltd.; *Int'l*, pg. 725
ESSEF CORPORATION; *U.S. Public*, pg. 592
EVEREADY DE MEXICO S.A. DE C.V.—Ralston Purina Company; *U.S. Public*, pg. 1360
FISHER PIERCE DIVISION—Pacific Scientific Company; *U.S. Public*, pg. 1250
G.E. TOSHIBA LIGHTING CORPORATION—General Electric Company; *U.S. Public*, pg. 710
HONEYWELL INC.; *U.S. Public*, pg. 833
ILC TECHNOLOGY, INC.; *U.S. Public*, pg. 856
INDUSTRIAS KOLMEX, S.A.—MacAndrews & Forbes Holdings Inc.; *U.S. Private*, pg. 690
JSB ELECTRICAL PLC—Emess PLC; *Int'l*, pg. 453
K2 INC.; *U.S. Public*, pg. 940
KAUFEL AMERICA INC.—Kaufel Group Ltd.; *Int'l*, pg. 725
KAUFEL GROUP LTD.; *Int'l*, pg. 724
KAUFEL INTERNATIONAL INC.—Kaufel Group Ltd.; *Int'l*, pg. 725
KOEHLER MANUFACTURING COMPANY—The Marmon Group, Inc.; *U.S. Private*, pg. 706
LIGHTALARMS ELECTRONICS CORPORATION—Kaufel Group Ltd.; *Int'l*, pg. 725
LUMACELL INC.—Kaufel Group Ltd.; *Int'l*, pg. 725
MARK IV INDUSTRIES INC.; *U.S. Public*, pg. 1044
MIAMI VALLEY LIGHTING, INC.—DPL Inc.; *U.S. Public*, pg. 474
NRD—Mark IV Industries Inc.; *U.S. Public*, pg. 1045
NEW COLEMAN HOLDINGS INC.—MacAndrews & Forbes Holdings Inc.; *U.S. Private*, pg. 690
NORTH AMERICAN RECREATION PRODUCTS COMPANY—MacAndrews & Forbes Holdings Inc.; *U.S. Private*, pg. 691
PACIFIC SCIENTIFIC COMPANY; *U.S. Public*, pg. 1250
PAN-ACC TRANSIT SYSTEMS INC.—Kaufel Group Ltd.; *Int'l*, pg. 725
PEERLESS LIGHTING CORP.; *U.S. Private*, pg. 847
PHILIPS LIGHTING LTD.—Philips Electronics N.V.; *Int'l*, pg. 1055
PLASKOLITE INC.; *U.S. Private*, pg. 870
PRECISION LAMP, INC.—ILC Technology, Inc.; *U.S. Public*, pg. 856
PRESCOLITE MOLDCAST LIGHTING COMPANY—U.S. Industries, Inc.; *U.S. Public*, pg. 1684
Q-ARC LIMITED—ILC Technology, Inc.; *U.S. Public*, pg. 856
RALSTON PURINA COMPANY; *U.S. Public*, pg. 1359
RAYOVAC CORPORATION; *U.S. Private*, pg. 912
READY-LITE MFG. LTD.—Kaufel Group Ltd.; *Int'l*, pg. 725
THE RENOVATOR'S SUPPLY, INC.; *U.S. Private*, pg. 923
ROSCO LABORATORIES, INC.; *U.S. Private*, pg. 944
SERMETO—Valmont Industries, Inc.; *U.S. Public*, pg. 1707
SHAKESPEARE COMPOSITES & ELECTRONICS—K2 Inc.; *U.S. Public*, pg. 940
THE SHANE GROUP INC.; *U.S. Private*, pg. 989
SPAR AEROSPACE LIMITED; *Int'l*, pg. 1287
SPECTRONICS CORPORATION; *U.S. Private*, pg. 1024
STERNER LIGHTING SYSTEMS INCORPORATED; *U.S. Private*, pg. 1042
STRAND LIGHTING INC.—The Rank Group PLC; *Int'l*, pg. 1087
STRAND LIGHTING LIMITED—The Rank Group PLC; *Int'l*, pg. 1087
STREAMLIGHT INC.; *U.S. Private*, pg. 1047
THOMAS & BETTS/AMERACE—Thomas & Betts Corporation; *U.S. Public*, pg. 1598
THOMAS INDUSTRIES INC.; *U.S. Public*, pg. 1598
TRACER PRODUCTS—Spectronics Corporation; *U.S. Private*, pg. 1024
20TH CENTURY PRODUCTS DIV.—Avery Dennison Corporation; *U.S. Public*, pg. 153
UVP, INC.; *U.S. Private*, pg. 1115
UNITY MANUFACTURING CO.; *U.S. Private*, pg. 1126
VALMONT INDUSTRIES, INC.; *U.S. Public*, pg. 1706
WENGER CORPORATION; *U.S. Private*, pg. 1162
WESTINGHOUSE ELECTRO-METALURGICA, C.A.—CBS Corporation; *U.S. Public*, pg. 275
WIDE-LITE—The Genlyte Group Incorporated; *U.S. Public*, pg. 730
THE WIREMOLD COMPANY; *U.S. Private*, pg. 1184
WISCONSIN PHARMACAL CO., INC.; *U.S. Private*, pg. 1185
WOODHEAD DE MEXICO—Woodhead Industries, Inc.; *U.S. Public*, pg. 1776
YUMEX/ILC—ILC Technology, Inc.; *U.S. Public*, pg. 856

3651 — HOUSEHOLD AUDIO & VIDEO EQUIPMENT

AKG ACOUSTICS—Harman International Industries, Inc.; *U.S. Public*, pg. 787
AIWA CO., LTD.—Sony Corporation; *Int'l*, pg. 1280
ALPINE ELECTRONICS OF AMERICA, INC.—Alps Electric Co., Ltd.; *Int'l*, pg. 65
ALTEC LANSING CORP.—Greenwich Street Capital Partners, Inc.; *U.S. Private*, pg. 479
ALTEC LANSING TECHNOLOGIES, INC.—Greenwich Street Capital Partners, Inc.; *U.S. Private*, pg. 479
AMERICAN TRADING AND PRODUCTION CORPORATION; *U.S. Private*, pg. 63
ASAHI KOGYO CO., LTD.—Hitachi, Ltd.; *Int'l*, pg. 621
ATLAS/SOUNDOLIER—American Trading and Production Corporation; *U.S. Private*, pg. 64
AUDAX INDUSTRIES, S.A.—Harman International Industries, Inc.; *U.S. Public*, pg. 787
AUDIOVOX CORPORATION; *U.S. Public*, pg. 147
AUTOCRAT SANYO HOLDING (N.Z.) LIMITED—Sanyo Electric Co., Ltd.; *Int'l*, pg. 1191
AUTOMATIC RADIO INTERNATIONAL—Armatron International, Inc.; *U.S. Public*, pg. 131
BGW SYSTEMS, INC.; *U.S. Private*, pg. 107
BANG & OLUFSEN A/S; *Int'l*, pg. 145
BOSCH-SIEMENS HAUSGERAETE GMBH—Robert Bosch GmbH; *Int'l*, pg. 204
BOSCH-SIEMENS HAUSGERAETE GMBH—Siemens AG; *Int'l*, pg. 1245
BOSE CORPORATION; *U.S. Private*, pg. 160
BOSE IRELAND—Bose Corporation; *U.S. Private*, pg. 161
BOSTON ACOUSTICS, INC.; *U.S. Public*, pg. 246
CALIBRON, INC.—Recoton Corporation; *U.S. Public*, pg. 1369
CARVER CORPORATION; *U.S. Public*, pg. 310
CASIO COMPUTER CO., LTD.; *Int'l*, pg. 274
CEDOSA—Thomson S.A.; *Int'l*, pg. 1384
CERWIN VEGA, INC.; *U.S. Private*, pg. 227
CETEC CORPORATION—Mark IV Industries Inc.; *U.S. Public*, pg. 1045
CHUGAI BOYEKI CO., LTD.; *Int'l*, pg. 290
CLARION CO., LTD.; *Int'l*, pg. 296
CLARION CORPORATION OF AMERICA—Clarion Co., Ltd.; *Int'l*, pg. 296
CLARION MANUFACTURING CORP. OF AMERICA—Clarion Co., Ltd.; *Int'l*, pg. 296
CLARION SALES CORPORATION—Clarion Co., Ltd.; *Int'l*, pg. 296
CONSUMER AUDIO PRODUCTS CO.—Sony Corporation; *Int'l*, pg. 1281
CONSUMER VIDEO PRODUCTS CO.—Sony Corporation; *Int'l*, pg. 1281
CORPORACION ELECTRONICA METROPOLITANA S.A.—Sanyo Electric Co., Ltd.; *Int'l*, pg. 1192
CROWN INTERNATIONAL, INC.; *U.S. Private*, pg. 293
DAEWOO ELECTRONICS CO., LTD.—Daewoo Corporation; *Int'l*, pg. 357
DELTRONICOS DE MATAMOROS S.A. DE C.V.—General Motors Corporation; *U.S. Public*, pg. 721
DISC MANUFACTURING CINRAM—Cinram Ltd.; *Int'l*, pg. 293
EMI GROUP PLC; *Int'l*, pg. 426
EMI-MANHATTAN RECORDS—EMI Group plc; *Int'l*, pg. 428
ELDEEN MANUFACTURING CORPORATION—Recoton Corporation; *U.S. Public*, pg. 1369
ELECTRO PARTES DE MATAMOROS, S.A. DE C.V.—Zenith Electronics Corp.; *U.S. Public*, pg. 1790
ELECTRO-VOICE, INC.—Greenwich Street Capital Partners, Inc.; *U.S. Private*, pg. 479
EMERSON RADIO CORP.; *U.S. Public*, pg. 578
THE ERTL COMPANY, INC—U.S. Industries, Inc.; *U.S. Public*, pg. 1684
ESQUIRE RADIO & ELECTRONICS INC.; *U.S. Private*, pg. 383
EUROTRON S.A.—Sanyo Electric Co., Ltd.; *Int'l*, pg. 1192
EVA-TONE INC.; *U.S. Private*, pg. 384
FAROUDJA, INC.; *U.S. Public*, pg. 613
FERGUSON LIMITED—Thomson S.A.; *Int'l*, pg. 1384
FOSTER ELECTRIC CO., LTD.; *Int'l*, pg. 500
FOSTER ELECTRIC (U.S.A.) INC.—Foster Electric Co., Ltd.; *Int'l*, pg. 500
FUJICONE—Recoton Corporation; *U.S. Public*, pg. 1369
FUJITSU LIMITED; *Int'l*, pg. 525
FUJITSU TEN LTD.—Fujitsu Limited; *Int'l*, pg. 526
FUNAI ELECTRIC CO., LTD.; *Int'l*, pg. 529
GP ELECTRONICS LIMITED—GP Batteries International Ltd.; *Int'l*, pg. 537
GENERAL MAGNETIC—Recoton Corporation; *U.S. Public*, pg. 1369
GO-VIDEO, INC.; *U.S. Public*, pg. 748
GOLD PEAK INDUSTRIES (HOLDINGS) LIMITED—GP Batteries International Ltd.; *Int'l*, pg. 537
GOLDSTAR CO. LTD.—LG Group; *Int'l*, pg. 778
GOLDSTAR OF AMERICA, INC.—LG Group; *Int'l*, pg. 779
GRANDETEL TECHNOLOGIES INC.; *Int'l*, pg. 556
HARMAN CONSUMER GROUP—Harman International Industries, Inc.; *U.S. Public*, pg. 787
HARMAN DEUTSCHLAND GMBH—Harman International Industries, Inc.; *U.S. Public*, pg. 787
HARMAN FRANCE—Harman International Industries, Inc.; *U.S. Public*, pg. 787
HARMAN INTERACTIVE GROUP—Harman International Industries, Inc.; *U.S. Public*, pg. 787
HARMAN INTERNATIONAL INDUSTRIES, INC.; *U.S. Public*, pg. 787
HARMAN JAPAN—Harman International Industries, Inc.; *U.S. Public*, pg. 787
HARMAN MOTIVE LTD—Harman International Industries, Inc.; *U.S. Public*, pg. 787
HITACHI CONSUMER PRODUCTS DE MEXICO—Hitachi, Ltd.; *Int'l*, pg. 622
HITACHI CONSUMER PRODUCTS OF AMERICA, INC.—Hitachi, Ltd.; *Int'l*, pg. 622
HITACHI HOME ELECTRONICS—Hitachi, Ltd.; *Int'l*, pg. 621
HITACHI TELEVISION (TAIWAN) LTD.—Hitachi, Ltd.; *Int'l*, pg. 622
HUGHES-JVC TECHNOLOGY CORP.—Matsushita Electric Industrial Co., Ltd.; *Int'l*, pg. 846
HUNTSVILLE ELECTRONICS DIV.—Chrysler Corporation; *U.S. Public*, pg. 353
IRI ISTITUTO RICOSTRUZIONE INDUSTRIALE; *Int'l*, pg. 652
IKEGAMI ELECTRONICS (U.S.A.), INC.—Ikegami Tsushinki Co., Ltd.; *Int'l*, pg. 660
INTERNATIONAL VIDEO PRODUCTS PTE. LTD.—Toshiba Corporation; *Int'l*, pg. 1405
JVC CANADA INC.—Matsushita Electric Industrial Co., Ltd.; *Int'l*, pg. 847
JVC COMPANY OF AMERICA—Matsushita Electric Industrial Co., Ltd.; *Int'l*, pg. 846
JVC DEUTSCHLAND GMBH—Matsushita Electric Industrial Co., Ltd.; *Int'l*, pg. 847
JVC DISC AMERICA, CO.—Matsushita Electric Industrial Co., Ltd.; *Int'l*, pg. 847
JVC INFORMATION PRODUCTS COMPANY OF AMERICA—Matsushita Electric Industrial Co., Ltd.; *Int'l*, pg. 847
JVC MAGNETS AMERICA, CO.—Matsushita Electric Industrial Co., Ltd.; *Int'l*, pg. 847
JVC MANUFACTURING COMPANY—Matsushita Electric Industrial Co., Ltd.; *Int'l*, pg. 847
JVC MANUFACTURING U.K. LTD.—Matsushita Electric Industrial Co., Ltd.; *Int'l*, pg. 847
JVC PROFESSIONAL PRODUCTS COMPANY—Matsushita Electric Industrial Co., Ltd.; *Int'l*, pg. 847
JVC PROFESSIONAL PRODUCTS (U.K.) LTD.—Matsushita Electric Industrial Co., Ltd.; *Int'l*, pg. 847
JVC SERVICE & ENGINEERING COMPANY OF AMERICA—Matsushita Electric Industrial Co., Ltd.; *Int'l*, pg. 847
JVC (U.K.) LTD.—Matsushita Electric Industrial Co., Ltd.; *Int'l*, pg. 847
KAIZUKA SANYO INDUSTRIES CO., LTD.—Sanyo Electric Co., Ltd.; *Int'l*, pg. 1191
KAMAN CORPORATION; *U.S. Public*, pg. 941
KENWOOD AGENCY CORPORATION—Kenwood Corporation; *Int'l*, pg. 730
KENWOOD & LEE ELECTRONICS, LTD.—Kenwood Corporation; *Int'l*, pg. 730
KENWOOD BUSINESS CORPORATION—Kenwood Corporation; *Int'l*, pg. 730
KENWOOD CORE CORPORATION—Kenwood Corporation; *Int'l*, pg. 730
KENWOOD CORPORATION; *Int'l*, pg. 730
KENWOOD ELECTRONICS AUSTRALIA PTY. LTD.—Kenwood Corporation; *Int'l*, pg. 730

KENWOOD ELECTRONICS CANADA INC.—Kenwood Corporation; *Int'l*, pg. 730
KENWOOD ELECTRONICS DEUTSCHLAND GMBH—Kenwood Corporation; *Int'l*, pg. 731
KENWOOD ELECTRONICS LATIN AMERICA S.A.—Kenwood Corporation; *Int'l*, pg. 731
KENWOOD ELECTRONICS SINGAPORE PTE. LTD.—Kenwood Corporation; *Int'l*, pg. 731
KENWOOD ENGINEERING CORPORATION—Kenwood Corporation; *Int'l*, pg. 730
KENWOOD KOMAGANE CORPORATION—Kenwood Corporation; *Int'l*, pg. 730
KENWOOD LINEAR S.P.A.—Kenwood Corporation; *Int'l*, pg. 731
KENWOOD NAGANO CORPORATION—Kenwood Corporation; *Int'l*, pg. 730
KENWOOD PERSONNEL CORPORATION—Kenwood Corporation; *Int'l*, pg. 730
KENWOOD SAITAMA CORPORATION—Kenwood Corporation; *Int'l*, pg. 730
KENWOOD USA—Kenwood Corporation; *Int'l*, pg. 730
KENWOOD YAMAGATA CORPORATION—Kenwood Corporation; *Int'l*, pg. 730
KLARK-TEKNIK PLC—Mark IV Industries Inc.; *U.S. Public*, pg. 1045
KLIPSCH, INC.; *U.S. Private*, pg. 626
KNOWLES ELECTRONICS, INC.; *U.S. Private*, pg. 627
KOREA SANYO ELECTRIC CO., LTD.—Sanyo Electric Co., Ltd.; *Int'l*, pg. 1192
KOSS CORPORATION; *U.S. Public*, pg. 966
KOSS EUROPE—Koss Corporation; *U.S. Public*, pg. 966
KOSS LTD.—Koss Corporation; *U.S. Public*, pg. 966
KRACO ENTERPRISES, INC.; *U.S. Private*, pg. 634
LG GROUP INC.—LG Group; *Int'l*, pg. 779
LONG'S ELECTRONICS, INC.; *U.S. Private*, pg. 675
LUWA AG—Hesta Tex AG; *Int'l*, pg. 617
LYDIG OF SCANDINAVIA A/S—Harman International Industries, Inc.; *U.S. Public*, pg. 787
MARK IV INDUSTRIES INC.; *U.S. Public*, pg. 1044
CURTIS MATHES CORPORATION—Curtis Mathes Holding Corp.; *U.S. Public*, pg. 1057
MATSUSHITA AVIONICS SYSTEMS—Matsushita Electric Industrial Co., Ltd.; *Int'l*, pg. 847
MATSUSHITA ELECTRIC CORPORATION OF AMERICA—Matsushita Electric Industrial Co., Ltd.; *Int'l*, pg. 847
MATSUSHITA ELECTRIC INDUSTRIAL CO., LTD.; *Int'l*, pg. 846
MATSUSHITA ELECTRIC (U.K.) LTD.—Matsushita Electric Industrial Co., Ltd.; *Int'l*, pg. 847
MATSUSHITA INDUSTRIAL DE BAJA CALIFORNIA, S.A.—Matsushita Electric Industrial Co., Ltd.; *Int'l*, pg. 847
MATSUSHITA INDUSTRIAL EQUIP. CO., LTD.—Matsushita Electric Industrial Co., Ltd.; *Int'l*, pg. 846
MATSUSHITA KOTOBUKI ELECTRONICS INDUSTRIES, LTD.—Matsushita Electric Industrial Co., Ltd.; *Int'l*, pg. 846
MATSUSHITA TELEVISION CO.—Matsushita Electric Industrial Co., Ltd.; *Int'l*, pg. 847
MINOLTA CO., LTD.; *Int'l*, pg. 869
MIRTONE—General Signal Corporation; *U.S. Public*, pg. 727
MITSUBISHI CONSUMER ELECTRONICS AMERICA—Mitsubishi Electric Corporation; *Int'l*, pg. 872
MITSUMI ELECTRIC CO., LTD.; *Int'l*, pg. 884
MITSUMI ELECTRONICS CORP.—Mitsumi Electric Co., Ltd.; *Int'l*, pg. 884
MOTOROLA DE MEXICO, S.A. DE C.V.—Motorola, Inc.; *U.S. Public*, pg. 1139
MULTIPLEX TECHNOLOGY, INC.—Valley Forge Corporation; *U.S. Public*, pg. 1705
NHT—Recoton Corporation; *U.S. Public*, pg. 1369
NADY SYSTEMS, INC.; *U.S. Private*, pg. 773
NAMCO LTD.; *Int'l*, pg. 905
NEUMANN (USA)—Sennheiser Electronic Corp.; *U.S. Private*, pg. 984
NOBLEX ARGENTINA S.A.C. E I.; *Int'l*, pg. 951
NOKIA AUDIO & ELECTRONICS AB—Oy Nokia Ab/Nokia Group; *Int'l*, pg. 954
NOKIA MOBILE PHONES CELLULAR DATA—Oy Nokia Ab/Nokia Group; *Int'l*, pg. 952
NOW HEAR THIS (NHT)—Recoton Corporation; *U.S. Public*, pg. 1369
ONKYO CORP.—Toshiba Corporation; *Int'l*, pg. 1403
OTARI, INC.; *Int'l*, pg. 1013
PEAVEY ELECTRONICS CORP.; *U.S. Private*, pg. 845
PENNY & GILES STUDIO EQUIPMENT LTD.—Bowthorpe plc; *Int'l*, pg. 207
PHASE LINEAR—Recoton Corporation; *U.S. Public*, pg. 1369
PHILIPS CONSUMER ELECTRONICS—Philips Electronics N.V.; *Int'l*, pg. 1054
PHILIPS ELECTRONICS LTD.—Philips Electronics N.V.; *Int'l*, pg. 1055
PIONEER ELECTRONIC CORPORATION; *Int'l*, pg. 1057
PIONEER ELECTRONICS MANUFACTURING NV—Pioneer Electronic Corporation; *Int'l*, pg. 1058
PIONEER ELECTRONICS (USA) INC.—Pioneer Electronic Corporation; *Int'l*, pg. 1058
POLK AUDIO, INC.; *U.S. Public*, pg. 1315
RECOTON AUTO CORPORATION—Recoton Corporation; *U.S. Public*, pg. 1369
RECOTON CORPORATION; *U.S. Public*, pg. 1369
ROWE INTERNATIONAL, INC.—RI Holdings; *U.S. Private*, pg. 904
SDI TECHNOLOGIES INC.; *U.S. Private*, pg. 956
SLM ELECTRONICS—St. Louis Music, Inc.; *U.S. Private*, pg. 961
SANMEX, S.A. DE C.V.—Sanyo Electric Co., Ltd.; *Int'l*, pg. 1192
SANYO ARMCO (KENYA) LIMITED—Sanyo Electric Co., Ltd.; *Int'l*, pg. 1192
SANYO ELECTRIC CO., LTD.; *Int'l*, pg. 1190
SANYO ELECTRONICS (SINGAPORE) PTE. LTD.—Sanyo Electric Co., Ltd.; *Int'l*, pg. 1192
SANYO ESPANA S.A.—Sanyo Electric Co., Ltd.; *Int'l*, pg. 1192
SANYO FISHER COMPANY—Sanyo Electric Co., Ltd.; *Int'l*, pg. 1191
SANYO INDUSTRIES CANADA INC.—Sanyo Electric Co., Ltd.; *Int'l*, pg. 1192
P.T. SANYO INDUSTRIES INDONESIA—Sanyo Electric Co., Ltd.; *Int'l*, pg. 1192
SANYO INDUSTRIES (SINGAPORE) PRIVATE LIMITED—Sanyo Electric Co., Ltd.; *Int'l*, pg. 1192
SANYO INDUSTRIES (U.K.) LIMITED—Sanyo Electric Co., Ltd.; *Int'l*, pg. 1192
SANYO VIDEO COMPONENTS (USA) CORPORATION—Sanyo Electric Co., Ltd.; *Int'l*, pg. 1191
SCOTT & ENGLISH LIMITED—Haw Par Brothers International Limited; *Int'l*, pg. 603
SEGA ENTERPRISES LTD.; *Int'l*, pg. 1218
SEGA OF AMERICA INC.—Sega Enterprises Ltd.; *Int'l*, pg. 1218
SEIKO EPSON CORPORATION; *Int'l*, pg. 1219
SEMI-TECH CORP.—Semi-Tech Corporation; *Int'l*, pg. 1220
SEMI-TECH CORPORATION; *Int'l*, pg. 1220
SENNHEISER ELECTRONIC CORP.; *U.S. Private*, pg. 984
SHARP CORPORATION; *Int'l*, pg. 1228
SHARP ELECTRONICA ESPANA S.A. (BARCELONA)—Sharp Corporation; *Int'l*, pg. 1229
SHARP ELECTRONICS CORPORATION—Sharp Corporation; *Int'l*, pg. 1228
SHARP ELECTRONICS (EUROPE)—Sharp Corporation; *Int'l*, pg. 1230
SHARP ELECTRONICS (U.K.)—Sharp Corporation; *Int'l*, pg. 1230
SHARP INTERNATIONAL FINANCE (U.K.) PLC.—Sharp Corporation; *Int'l*, pg. 1230
SHARP LABORATORIES OF EUROPE, LTD.—Sharp Corporation; *Int'l*, pg. 1230
SHARP MANUFACTURING COMPANY OF U.K.—Sharp Corporation; *Int'l*, pg. 1230
SHARP PRECISION MANUFACTURING (U.K.) LTD.—Sharp Corporation; *Int'l*, pg. 1230
SHINKO TELECOMMUNICATIONS CONSTRUCTION CO., LTD.—The Furukawa Electric Co., Ltd.; *Int'l*, pg. 530
SHOGYO INTERNATIONAL CORPORATION; *U.S. Private*, pg. 996
SHURE BROTHERS INCORPORATED; *U.S. Private*, pg. 997
SHURE ELECTRONICS OF AZ—Shure Brothers Incorporated; *U.S. Private*, pg. 997
THE SINGER COMPANY—Semi-Tech Corporation; *Int'l*, pg. 1220
SONY CORPORATION; *Int'l*, pg. 1280
SONY CORPORATION OF HONG KONG LTD.—Sony Corporation; *Int'l*, pg. 1284
SONY DEUTSCHLAND GMBH—Sony Corporation; *Int'l*, pg. 1284
SONY ELECTRONICS—Sony Corporation; *Int'l*, pg. 1281
SONY ENGINEERING & MANUFACTURING OF AMERICA—Sony Corporation; *Int'l*, pg. 1284
SONY IRELAND LTD.—Sony Corporation; *Int'l*, pg. 1284
SONY PROFESSIONAL PRODUCTS CO.—Sony Corporation; *Int'l*, pg. 1284
SONY (U.K.) LTD.—Sony Corporation; *Int'l*, pg. 1284
SONY VIDEO TAIWAN CO. LTD.—Sony Corporation; *Int'l*, pg. 1284
SONY-WEGA PRODUKTIONS GMBH—Sony Corporation; *Int'l*, pg. 1284
SOUNDCRAFT ELECTRONICS, LTD—Harman International Industries, Inc.; *U.S. Public*, pg. 787
SSANGYONG BUSINESS GROUP; *Int'l*, pg. 1291
TCE TELEVISION SINGAPORE PTE. LTD.—Thomson S.A.; *Int'l*, pg. 1384
TANDY CABINETS—Tandy Corporation; *U.S. Public*, pg. 1560
TANDY CORPORATION; *U.S. Public*, pg. 1560
TEAC CORPORATION; *Int'l*, pg. 1360
TEICHIKU RECORDS CO., LTD.—Matsushita Electric Industrial Co., Ltd.; *Int'l*, pg. 846
THOMSON MULTIMEDIA SA—Thomson S.A.; *Int'l*, pg. 1384
THOMSON S.A.; *Int'l*, pg. 1381
TOSHIBA AMERICA CONSUMER PRODUCTS, INC.—Toshiba Corporation; *Int'l*, pg. 1405
TOSHIBA AMERICA CONSUMER PRODUCTS MANUFACTURING DIV.—Toshiba Corporation; *Int'l*, pg. 1405
TOSHIBA AVE CO. LTD.—Toshiba Corporation; *Int'l*, pg. 1403
TOSHIBA CONSUMER PRODUCTS (U.K.) LIMITED—Toshiba Corporation; *Int'l*, pg. 1406
TOSHIBA CORPORATION; *Int'l*, pg. 1402
TOSHIBA DATA DYNAMICS PTE. LTD.—Toshiba Corporation; *Int'l*, pg. 1406
TOSHIBA SOUND SYSTEMS CORPORATION—Toshiba Corporation; *Int'l*, pg. 1405
TRACE ELLIOT LIMITED—Kaman Corporation; *U.S. Public*, pg. 942
TRIO-KENWOOD BRETAGNE S.A.—Kenwood Corporation; *Int'l*, pg. 731
TRIO-KENWOOD ELECTRONICS ENGINEERING (M) SDN. BHD.—Kenwood Corporation; *Int'l*, pg. 731
TRIO-KENWOOD EUROPE LTD.—Kenwood Corporation; *Int'l*, pg. 731
TRIO-KENWOOD FRANCE S.A.—Kenwood Corporation; *Int'l*, pg. 731
TRIO-KENWOOD SINGAPORE (PTE.) LTD.—Kenwood Corporation; *Int'l*, pg. 731
TRIO-KENWOOD U.K. LIMITED—Kenwood Corporation; *Int'l*, pg. 731
TRIO LABO CORPORATION—Kenwood Corporation; *Int'l*, pg. 730
TSUGARU TOSHIBA ONKYO CO., LTD.—Toshiba Corporation; *Int'l*, pg. 1405
ULTIMATE ELECTRONICS; *U.S. Public*, pg. 1662
UNITEL VIDEO, INC.; *U.S. Public*, pg. 1692
VICTOR COMPANY OF JAPAN, LTD.—Matsushita Electric Industrial Co., Ltd.; *Int'l*, pg. 846
WELLS-GARDNER ELECTRONICS CORP.; *U.S. Public*, pg. 1753
YAMAHA CORPORATION; *Int'l*, pg. 1515
ZENCO DE CHIHUAHUA, S.A. DE C.V.—Zenith Electronics Corp.; *U.S. Public*, pg. 1790
ZENITH ELECTRONICS CORP.; *U.S. Public*, pg. 1790
ZENITH ELECTRONICS CORP. OF TX—Zenith Electronics Corp.; *U.S. Public*, pg. 1790

3652 — PHONOGRAPH RECORDS & PRE-RECORDED AUDIO TAPES & DISCS

A&M RECORDS—Philips Electronics N.V.; *Int'l*, pg. 1052
ALL AMERICAN COMMUNICATIONS, INC.; *U.S. Public*, pg. 41
ARISTA RECORDS INC.—Bertelsmann AG; *Int'l*, pg. 192
ATLANTIC RECORDING CORPORATION—Time Warner Inc.; *U.S. Public*, pg. 1611
BASF ESPANOLA S.A.—BASF AG; *Int'l*, pg. 106
BMG ARIOLA MUSIC LTDA.—Bertelsmann AG; *Int'l*, pg. 192
BMG ARIOLA MUSICA S.P.A.—Bertelsmann AG; *Int'l*, pg. 192
BMG ARIOLA S.A. DE C.V. (MEXICO)—Bertelsmann AG; *Int'l*, pg. 192
BMG ARIOLA S.A. (FRANCE)—Bertelsmann AG; *Int'l*, pg. 192
BMG/MUSIC—Bertelsmann AG; *Int'l*, pg. 191
B.M.G. RECORDS—Thomson S.A.; *Int'l*, pg. 1383
BERTELSMANN INC.—Bertelsmann AG; *Int'l*, pg. 191
BERTELSMANN MUSIC GROUP—Bertelsmann AG; *Int'l*, pg. 191
BRENTWOOD BENSON PUBLISHING GROUP—Zomba Recording Corp.; *Int'l*, pg. 1529
BRENTWOOD LABEL GROUP—Zomba Recording Corp.; *Int'l*, pg. 1529
CAPITOL INDUSTRIES-EMI INC.—EMI Group plc; *Int'l*, pg. 427
CAPITOL RECORDS, INC.—EMI Group plc; *Int'l*, pg. 428
COMPAGNIE PHONOGRAPHIQUE FRANCAISE BARCLAY—Philips Electronics N.V.; *Int'l*, pg. 1053
DECCA INTERNATIONAL—Philips Electronics N.V.; *Int'l*, pg. 1053
THE DECCA RECORD CO. LTD.—Philips Electronics N.V.; *Int'l*, pg. 1053
DEUTSCHE GRAMMOPHON GESELLSCHAFT MBH—Philips Electronics N.V.; *Int'l*, pg. 1052
DIGITAL AUDIO DISC CORP.—Sony Corporation; *Int'l*, pg. 1284
DISCOS DE CENTRO AMERICA—Philips Electronics N.V.; *Int'l*, pg. 1052
WALT DISNEY MUSIC CO.—The Walt Disney Company; *U.S. Public*, pg. 513
EMC CORPORATION; *U.S. Public*, pg. 545
EMI GROUP PLC; *Int'l*, pg. 426
EMI MUSIC—EMI Group plc; *Int'l*, pg. 427
EMI RECORDS (UK), STUDIOS DIV.—EMI Group plc; *Int'l*, pg. 427
ELEKTRA ENTERTAINMENT—Time Warner Inc.; *U.S. Public*, pg. 1612
ENTERTAINMENT UK LTD.—Kingfisher plc; *Int'l*, pg. 733
FONOGRAM S.A.—Philips Electronics N.V.; *Int'l*, pg. 1052
GEFFEN RECORDS—The Seagram Company Ltd.; *Int'l*, pg. 1215
GOLDEN BOOKS FAMILY ENTERTAINMENT INC.; *U.S. Public*, pg. 749
GOLDEN BOOKS PUBLISHING—Golden Books Family Entertainment Inc.; *U.S. Public*, pg. 749
HARPER AUDIO—The News Corporation Limited; *Int'l*, pg. 926
HITACHI MAXELL, LTD.—Hitachi, Ltd.; *Int'l*, pg. 621
IMAGE ENTERTAINMENT, INC.; *U.S. Public*, pg. 870
IMPACT—Philips Electronics N.V.; *Int'l*, pg. 1052
INTERCORD TONGESELLSCHAFT MBH—EMI Group plc; *Int'l*, pg. 428
ISLAND ENTERTAINMENT GROUP, INC.—Philips Electronics N.V.; *Int'l*, pg. 1052
K-TEL DIRECT, INC.—K-Tel International, Inc.; *U.S. Public*, pg. 938
K-TEL INTERNATIONAL FINLAND O.Y.—K-Tel International, Inc.; *U.S. Public*, pg. 938
K-TEL INTERNATIONAL, INC.; *U.S. Public*, pg. 937
K-TEL INTERNATIONAL (USA) INC.—K-Tel International, Inc.; *U.S. Public*, pg. 938
K-TEL IRELAND LTD.—K-Tel International, Inc.; *U.S. Public*, pg. 938
KOSS CLASSICS LTD.—Koss Corporation; *U.S. Public*, pg. 966
LONDON RECORDS—Philips Electronics N.V.; *Int'l*, pg. 1052
LONGMAN FRANCE SA—Pearson plc; *Int'l*, pg. 1025
LONGMAN GROUP UK LTD.—Pearson plc; *Int'l*, pg. 1025
LONGMAN ITALIA SRL—Pearson plc; *Int'l*, pg. 1025
MATSUSHITA ELECTRIC CORPORATION OF AMERICA—Matsushita Electric Industrial Co., Ltd.; *Int'l*, pg. 847
MATSUSHITA ELECTRIC (U.K.) LTD.—Matsushita Electric Industrial Co., Ltd.; *Int'l*, pg. 847
MILLER INTL. SCHALLPLATTEN G.M.B.H.—The Seagram Company Ltd.; *Int'l*, pg. 1216
MITSUBISHI CONSUMER ELECTRONICS AMERICA—Mitsubishi Electric Corporation; *Int'l*, pg. 872
MOTOWN RECORD COMPANY, J.P.—Philips Electronics N.V.; *Int'l*, pg. 1052
NIGHTINGALE-CONANT CORP.; *U.S. Private*, pg. 799
NIPPON PHONOGRAM CO. LTD.—Philips Electronics N.V.; *Int'l*, pg. 1052
PHONOGRAM AG—Philips Electronics N.V.; *Int'l*, pg. 1052
PHONOGRAM B.V.—Philips Electronics N.V.; *Int'l*, pg. 1052
PHONOGRAM GMBH—Philips Electronics N.V.; *Int'l*, pg. 1052

PHONOGRAM INTERNATIONAL B.V.—Philips Electronics N.V.; *Int'l*, pg. 1052
PHONOGRAM LTD.—Philips Electronics N.V.; *Int'l*, pg. 1053
PHONOGRAM S.A.—Philips Electronics N.V.; *Int'l*, pg. 1052
PHONOGRAM S.A.I.C.—Philips Electronics N.V.; *Int'l*, pg. 1052
PIONEER ELECTRONIC CORPORATION; *Int'l*, pg. 1057
POLYDOR AB—Philips Electronics N.V.; *Int'l*, pg. 1052
POLYDOR B.V.—Philips Electronics N.V.; *Int'l*, pg. 1052
POLYDOR INC.—Philips Electronics N.V.; *Int'l*, pg. 1052
POLYDOR INTERNATIONAL GMBH—Philips Electronics N.V.; *Int'l*, pg. 1052
POLYDOR K.K.—Philips Electronics N.V.; *Int'l*, pg. 1052
POLYDOR LTD.—Philips Electronics N.V.; *Int'l*, pg. 1053
POLYDOR S.A.—Philips Electronics N.V.; *Int'l*, pg. 1053
POLYGRAM CLASSICS, INC.—Philips Electronics N.V.; *Int'l*, pg. 1052
POLYGRAM DISCHI S.P.A.—Philips Electronics N.V.; *Int'l*, pg. 1053
POLYGRAM DISCO S.A.—Philips Electronics N.V.; *Int'l*, pg. 1053
POLYGRAM DO BRAZIL—Philips Electronics N.V.; *Int'l*, pg. 1053
POLYGRAM HOLDING, INC.—Philips Electronics N.V.; *Int'l*, *pg. 1052*
POLYGRAM INC.—Philips Electronics N.V.; *Int'l*, pg. 1053
POLYGRAM INTERNATIONAL LTD.—Philips Electronics N.V.; *Int'l*, pg. 1053
POLYGRAM RECORD OPERATIONS LTD.—Philips Electronics N.V.; *Int'l*, pg. 1053
POLYGRAM RECORD SERVICE B.V.—Philips Electronics N.V.; *Int'l*, pg. 1052
POLYGRAM RECORD SERVICE GMBH—Philips Electronics N.V.; *Int'l*, pg. 1053
POLYGRAM RECORD SERVICE K.K.—Philips Electronics N.V.; *Int'l*, pg. 1053
POLYGRAM RECORD SERVICES GES. MBH—Philips Electronics N.V.; *Int'l*, pg. 1053
POLYGRAM RECORDS AB—Philips Electronics N.V.; *Int'l*, pg. 1053
POLYGRAM RECORDS, INC.—Philips Electronics N.V.; *Int'l*, pg. 1052
POLYGRAM RECORDS LTD.—Philips Electronics N.V.; *Int'l*, pg. 1053
POLYGRAM RECORDS PTY. LTD.—Philips Electronics N.V.; *Int'l*, pg. 1053
POLYGRAM RECORDS S.A.—Philips Electronics N.V.; *Int'l*, *pg. 1053*
POLYGRAM S.A. DE C.V.—Philips Electronics N.V.; *Int'l*, pg. 1053
POLYSTAR CO. LTD.—Philips Electronics N.V.; *Int'l*, pg. 1053
PROVIDENT MUSIC DISTRIBUTION—Zomba Recording Corp.; *Int'l*, pg. 1529
RCA RECORDS U.S.—Bertelsmann AG; *Int'l*, pg. 192
THE READER'S DIGEST ASSOCIATION, INC.; *U.S. Public*, pg. 1367
REUNION RECORDS—Zomba Recording Corp.; *Int'l*, pg. 1529
SCOTTI BROTHERS ENTERTAINMENT INDUSTRIES—All American Communications, Inc.; *U.S. Public*, pg. 41
SHAPE INC.; *U.S. Private*, pg. 990
SHAPE SOUTH, INC.—Shape Inc.; *U.S. Private*, pg. 990
SHEPARD'S—Reed Elsevier plc; *Int'l*, pg. 1095
SHEPARD'S—The Times Mirror Company; *U.S. Public*, pg. 1616
SIMON & SCHUSTER AUDIO—National Amusements, Inc.; *U.S. Private*, pg. 778
SONY CORPORATION; *Int'l*, pg. 1280
SONY CORPORATION OF HONG KONG LTD.—Sony Corporation; *Int'l*, pg. 1284
SONY MUSIC ENTERTAINMENT, INC.—Sony Corporation; *Int'l*, pg. 1281
SONY MUSIC ENTERTAINMENT (JAPAN) INC.—Sony Corporation; *Int'l*, pg. 1281
SONY MUSIC ENTERTAINMENT (UK) LIMITED—Sony Corporation; *Int'l*, pg. 1284
SONY MUSIC INTERNATIONAL LTD.—Sony Corporation; *Int'l*, pg. 1284
SONY (U.K.) LTD.—Sony Corporation; *Int'l*, pg. 1284
TEICHIKU RECORDS CO., LTD.—Matsushita Electric Industrial Co., Ltd.; *Int'l*, pg. 846
TIME WARNER INC.; *U.S. Public*, pg. 1610
UNIVERSAL STUDIOS, INC.—The Seagram Company Ltd.; *Int'l*, pg. 1215
UNIVERSAL STUDIOS MFG.—The Seagram Company Ltd.; *Int'l*, pg. 1216
VIRGIN RECORDS AMERICA INC.—EMI Group plc; *Int'l*, pg. 427
WEA CORP.—Time Warner Inc.; *U.S. Public*, pg. 1612
WEA MANUFACTURING—Time Warner Inc.; *U.S. Public*, pg. 1612
WARNER BROS. RECORDS, INC.—Time Warner Inc.; *U.S. Public*, pg. 1611
WARNER COMMUNICATIONS INC.—Time Warner Inc.; *U.S. Public*, pg. 1611
WARNER MUSIC GROUP, INC.—Time Warner Inc.; *U.S. Public*, pg. 1612
WARNER MUSIC INTERNATIONAL (EUROPE) LTD.—Time Warner Inc.; *U.S. Public*, pg. 1615
WORD, INCORPORATED—Gaylord Entertainment Co.; *U.S. Public*, pg. 704
ZOMBA GROUP OF COMPANIES—Zomba Recording Corp.; *Int'l*, pg. 1529
ZOMBA RECORDING CORP.; *Int'l*, pg. 1529
THE ZONDERVAN CORPORATION—The News Corporation Limited; *Int'l*, pg. 927

3661 — TELEPHONE & TELEGRAPH APPARATUS

ADC TELECOM CANADA INC.—ADC Telecommunications, Inc.; *U.S. Public*, pg. 4
ADC TELECOMMUNICATIONS, INC.; *U.S. Public*, pg. 4
ADC TELECOMUNICACIONES VENEZUELA, S.A.—ADC Telecommunications, Inc.; *U.S. Public*, pg. 4
ARC INTERNATIONAL CORPORATION; *Int'l*, pg. 17
AT&T BUSINESS COMMUNICATIONS SERVICES—AT&T Corporation; *U.S. Public*, pg. 10
AT&T CORPORATION; *U.S. Public*, pg. 10
ALCATEL—Alcatel Alsthom Compagnie Generale D'Electricite; *Int'l*, pg. 52
ALCATEL ALSTHOM COMPAGNIE GENERALE D'ELECTRICITE; *Int'l*, pg. 52
ALCATEL AUSTRIA A.G.—Alcatel Alsthom Compagnie Generale D'Electricite; *Int'l*, pg. 55
ALCATEL BUSINESS SYSTEMS (FRANCE)—Alcatel Alsthom Compagnie Generale D'Electricite; *Int'l*, pg. 55
ALCATEL CIT—Alcatel Alsthom Compagnie Generale D'Electricite; *Int'l*, pg. 55
ALCATEL CIT (S.A.); *Int'l*, pg. 56
ALCATEL FACE—Alcatel Alsthom Compagnie Generale D'Electricite; *Int'l*, pg. 55
ALCATEL INDETEL—Alcatel Alsthom Compagnie Generale D'Electricite; *Int'l*, pg. 56
ALCATEL ITS INC.—Alcatel Alsthom Compagnie Generale D'Electricite; *Int'l*, pg. 55
ALCATEL KIRK—Alcatel Alsthom Compagnie Generale D'Electricite; *Int'l*, pg. 56
ALCATEL NETHERLAND—Alcatel Alsthom Compagnie Generale D'Electricite; *Int'l*, pg. 55
ALCATEL NETWORK SYSTEMS, INC. (TX)—Alcatel Alsthom Compagnie Generale D'Electricite; *Int'l*, pg. 55
ALCATEL N.V.—Alcatel Alsthom Compagnie Generale D'Electricite; *Int'l*, pg. 55
ALCATEL PORTUGAL—Alcatel Alsthom Compagnie Generale D'Electricite; *Int'l*, pg. 56
ALCATEL STANDARD ELECTRICA, S.A—Telefonica de Espana, S.A.; *Int'l*, pg. 1372
ALCATEL STC AUSTRALIA—Alcatel Alsthom Compagnie Generale D'Electricite; *Int'l*, pg. 56
ALCATEL TELECOM—Alcatel Alsthom Compagnie Generale D'Electricite; *Int'l*, pg. 55
ALDEN ELECTRONICS, INC.—Platinum Equity Holdings, LLC; *U.S. Private*, pg. 872
ALENIA SPAZIO—IRI Istituto Ricostruzione Industriale; *Int'l*, *pg. 653*
ALIANT SYSTEMS INC.—Aliant Communications Inc.; *U.S. Public*, pg. 41
ALLTEL CORPORATION; *U.S. Public*, pg. 55
ALLTEL SUPPLY, INC.—ALLTEL Corporation; *U.S. Public*, pg. 55
AMECOM DIV.—Litton Industries, Inc.; *U.S. Public*, pg. 1002
AMERICAN PHONE CENTERS, INC.—Comdial Corporation; *U.S. Public*, pg. 407
AMERICAN TELECOMMUNICATIONS CORPORATION—Comdial Corporation; *U.S. Public*, pg. 407
AMERITECH INTERNATIONAL INC.—Ameritech Corporation; *U.S. Public*, pg. 98
ANDREW CORPORATION; *U.S. Public*, pg. 112
APPLIED DIGITAL ACCESS; *U.S. Public*, pg. 122
ARABTEL—Jeumont-Schneider Trenformeteurs; *Int'l*, pg. 706
ASCOM AUTELCA AG—Ascom Holding AG; *Int'l*, pg. 86
ASCOM HOLDING AG; *Int'l*, pg. 86
ASCOM HPF SA—Ascom Holding AG; *Int'l*, pg. 87
ASCOM SAFNAT SPA—Ascom Holding AG; *Int'l*, pg. 87
ASCOM ZELCOM AG—Ascom Holding AG; *Int'l*, pg. 86
AXIOM INC.; *U.S. Public*, pg. 157
BC TELECOM INC.—GTE Corporation; *U.S. Public*, pg. 697
BCE INC.; *Int'l*, pg. 114
BT (CBP) LIMITED—British Telecommunications plc; *Int'l*, pg. 222
BALL AEROSPACE SYSTEMS DIVISION—Ball Corporation; *U.S. Public*, pg. 171
BIO-LOGIC SYSTEMS CORP.; *U.S. Public*, pg. 230
BOGEN COMMUNICATIONS, INC.—Geotek Communications; *U.S. Public*, pg. 739
BOSCH TELECOM OFFENTLICHE VERMITTLUNGSTECHNIK GMBH—Robert Bosch GmbH; *Int'l*, pg. 204
BROTHER INDUSTRIES, LTD.; *Int'l*, pg. 229
BYTEX CORPORATION—Storage Technology Corporation; *U.S. Public*, pg. 1522
CSX TECHNOLOGY, INC.—CSX Corporation; *U.S. Public*, pg. 284
CXR TELCOM CORPORATION—Microtel International Inc.; *U.S. Public*, pg. 1108
CABLE SPINNING EQUIPMENT INC.; *U.S. Private*, pg. 197
CALIFORNIA MICROWAVE, INC.; *U.S. Public*, pg. 293
CENTIGRAM COMMUNICATIONS CORPORATION; *U.S. Public*, pg. 323
CINET DANMARK A/S—Axel Johnson AB; *Int'l*, pg. 710
COHERENT COMMUNICATIONS SYSTEMS CORP.—Safeguard Scientifics, Inc.; *U.S. Public*, pg. 1424
COMDIAL CORPORATION; *U.S. Public*, pg. 407
COMDIAL ENTERPRISE SYSTEMS, INC.—Comdial Corporation; *U.S. Public*, pg. 407
COMDIAL TELECOMMUNICATIONS INTERNATIONAL, INC.—Comdial Corporation; *U.S. Public*, pg. 407
COMMONWEALTH COMMUNICATIONS—RCN Corporation; *U.S. Public*, pg. 1354
COMMUNICATIONS SYSTEMS, INC.; *U.S. Public*, pg. 415
COMMUNICATIONS TECHNOLOGY (CANADA) LTD.—Danaher Corporation; *U.S. Public*, pg. 480
COMMUNICATIONS TECHNOLOGY CORPORATION—Danaher Corporation; *U.S. Public*, pg. 480
COMPAGNIE FRANCAISE PHILIPS—Philips Electronics N.V.; *Int'l*, pg. 1055
COMPANIA DOMINICANA DE TELEFONOS, C. POR A.—GTE Corporation; *U.S. Public*, pg. 697
COMPANIA ERICSSON DE CHILE S.A.—Telefonaktiebolaget LM Ericsson; *Int'l*, pg. 1365
COMPANIA ERICSSON S.A.—Telefonaktiebolaget LM Ericsson; *Int'l*, pg. 1365
COMPANIA ERICSSON S.A.C.I.—Telefonaktiebolaget LM Ericsson; *Int'l*, pg. 1365
COMVERSE TECHNOLOGY, INC.; *U.S. Public*, pg. 425
CONKLIN INSTRUMENT CORPORATION; *U.S. Private*, pg. 263
CONRAC DISPLAY PRODUCTS; *U.S. Private*, pg. 264
CORNING INCORPORATED; *U.S. Public*, pg. 448
COSMO COMMUNICATIONS CORPORATION; *U.S. Public*, *pg. 451*
CROSFIELD ELECTRONICS LIMITED—Du Pont (E.I. Du Pont De Nemours & Co.); *U.S. Public*, pg. 532
DIAX TELEKOMM A/S—Telefonaktiebolaget LM Ericsson; *Int'l*, pg. 1365
DMS-10 DIV.—Northern Telecom Limited; *Int'l*, pg. 969
DSC—DSC Communications Corporation; *U.S. Public*, pg. 475
DSC COMMUNICATIONS CORPORATION; *U.S. Public*, pg. 475
DACON ELECTRONICS PLC.—Cognitronics Corporation; *U.S. Public*, pg. 395
DAEWOO TELECOM CO., LTD.—Daewoo Corporation; *Int'l*, pg. 357
DANKA BUSINESS SYSTEMS—Danka Business Systems PLC; *Int'l*, pg. 379
DANKA BUSINESS SYSTEMS PLC; *Int'l*, pg. 379
DARCOM TECHNOLOGIES, INC.; *U.S. Private*, pg. 311
DATA FORTH—Burr-Brown Corporation; *U.S. Public*, pg. 270
DATAPOINT CORPORATION; *Int'l*, pg. 384
DAVEL COMMUNICATIONS GROUP, INC.; *U.S. Public*, pg. 488
DAVOX CORP.; *U.S. Public*, pg. 488
DIAMOND MULTIMEDIA SYSTEMS, INC.; *U.S. Public*, pg. 505
DU PONT PRINTING & PUBLISHING—Du Pont (E.I. Du Pont De Nemours & Co.); *U.S. Public*, pg. 531
DUKANE CANADA LTD.—Dukane Corporation; *U.S. Private*, pg. 346
DUKANE CORPORATION; *U.S. Private*, pg. 345
ECI TELECOM LTD.—IDB Holding Corporation; *Int'l*, pg. 643
ESL INC.—TRW Inc.; *U.S. Public*, pg. 1558
ELBIT COMPUTERS LTD.—IDB Holding Corporation; *Int'l*, pg. 644
ELECTRONIC TELE-COMMUNICATIONS, INC.; *U.S. Public*, pg. 570
ELECTROSPACE SYSTEMS, INC.—Raytheon Company; *U.S. Public*, pg. 1365
EMPRESA TECNOLOGICA ERICSSON S.A. DE C.V.—Telefonaktiebolaget LM Ericsson; *Int'l*, pg. 1366
ENTERPRISE GENERALE DE TELECOMMUNICATIONS—France Telecom; *Int'l*, pg. 503
ERICSSON AG—Telefonaktiebolaget LM Ericsson; *Int'l*, pg. 1366
ERICSSON BUSINESS NETWORKS AB—Telefonaktiebolaget LM Ericsson; *Int'l*, pg. 1363
ERICSSON COMMUNICATIONS (HONG KONG) LTD.—Telefonaktiebolaget LM Ericsson; *Int'l*, pg. 1366
ERICSSON COMMUNICATIONS (THAILAND) LTD.—Telefonaktiebolaget LM Ericsson; *Int'l*, pg. 1366
ERICSSON DE COSTA RICA—Telefonaktiebolaget LM Ericsson; *Int'l*, pg. 1366
ERICSSON GE MOBILE COMMUNICATIONS CANADA, INC.—Telefonaktiebolaget LM Ericsson; *Int'l*, pg. 1366
ERICSSON GE MOBILE COMMUNICATIONS INC.—Telefonaktiebolaget LM Ericsson; *Int'l*, pg. 1365
ERICSSON (HELLAS) TELECOMMUNICATIONS EQUIPMENT S.A.—Telefonaktiebolaget LM Ericsson; *Int'l*, pg. 1366
ERICSSON HOLDING A/S—Telefonaktiebolaget LM Ericsson; *Int'l*, pg. 1367
ERICSSON HOLDING NEDERLAND B.V.—Telefonaktiebolaget LM Ericsson; *Int'l*, pg. 1367
ERICSSON, INC.—Telefonaktiebolaget LM Ericsson; *Int'l*, pg. 1364
ERICSSON INDIA LTD.—Telefonaktiebolaget LM Ericsson; *Int'l*, pg. 1367
ERICSSON LTD.—Telefonaktiebolaget LM Ericsson; *Int'l*, pg. 1367
ERICSSON MOBILFUNK GMBH—Telefonaktiebolaget LM Ericsson; *Int'l*, pg. 1367
ERICSSON NORTH AMERICA, INC.—Telefonaktiebolaget LM Ericsson; *Int'l*, pg. 1364
ERICSSON S.A.—Telefonaktiebolaget LM Ericsson; *Int'l*, pg. 1367
ERICSSON SYSTEMS EXPERTISE LTD.—Telefonaktiebolaget LM Ericsson; *Int'l*, pg. 1367
ERICSSON TAIWAN LTD.—Telefonaktiebolaget LM Ericsson; *Int'l*, pg. 1367
ERICSSON TELECOM AB—Telefonaktiebolaget LM Ericsson; *Int'l*, pg. 1364
ERICSSON TELECOM A/S—Telefonaktiebolaget LM Ericsson; *Int'l*, pg. 1367
ERICSSON TELECOMMUNICATIE B.V.—Telefonaktiebolaget LM Ericsson; *Int'l*, pg. 1367
ERICSSON TELECOMUNICACIONES S.A.—Telefonaktiebolaget LM Ericsson; *Int'l*, pg. 1368
ERICSSON TELEKOMUNIKASYON A.S.—Telefonaktiebolaget LM Ericsson; *Int'l*, pg. 1368
ERICSSON TELEPHONE CORPORATION FAR EAST AB—Telefonaktiebolaget LM Ericsson; *Int'l*, pg. 1368
ERICSSON UTVECKLINGS AB—Telefonaktiebolaget LM Ericsson; *Int'l*, pg. 1364
EXECUTONE INFORMATION SYSTEMS, INC.; *U.S. Public*, *pg. 599*
THE FAIRCHILD CORPORATION; *U.S. Public*, pg. 610
FERRANTI AIR SYSTEMS LTD.—Datel Technologies Ltd.; *Int'l*, pg. 384
FUJITSU ESPANA, S.A.—Fujitsu Limited; *Int'l*, pg. 528
FUNAI ELECTRIC CO., LTD.; *Int'l*, pg. 529

GEC (NEW ZEALAND) LTD.—The General Electric Company, p.l.c.; *Int'l*, pg. 546
GEC ZIMBABWE (PVT) LTD.—The General Electric Company, p.l.c.; *Int'l*, pg. 546
GN GREAT NORDIC LTD.; *Int'l*, pg. 536
GAI-TRONICS CORPORATION—Salient 3 Communications, Inc.; *U.S. Public*, pg. 1430
GANDALF SYSTEMS CORPORATION—Gandalf Technologies Inc.; *Int'l*, pg. 540
GENERAL DATACOMM, INC.—General Datacomm Industries, Inc.; *U.S. Public*, pg. 708
GENERAL DATACOMM INDUSTRIES, INC.; *U.S. Public*, pg. 708
THE GENERAL ELECTRIC COMPANY, P.L.C.; *Int'l*, pg. 543
GENERAL ELECTRIC DE MEXICO, S.A. DE C.V.—General Electric Company; *U.S. Public*, pg. 713
GENERAL SIGNAL CORPORATION; *U.S. Public*, pg. 726
GOLDSTAR ELECTRIC CO. LTD.—LG Group; *Int'l*, pg. 779
HARRIS CORP., DIGITAL TELEPHONE SYSTEMS DIV.—Harris Corporation; *U.S. Public*, pg. 791
HARRIS CORPORATION; *U.S. Public*, pg. 791
HARRIS NETWORK SUPPORT SYSTEMS—Harris Corporation; *U.S. Public*, pg. 792
HAYES CORPORATION, REGIONAL OFFICE—Hayes Corporation; *U.S. Public*, pg. 801
HAYES MICROCOMPUTER PRODUCTS, INC.—Hayes Corporation; *U.S. Public*, pg. 801
HEURIKON CORPORATION—Computer Products, Inc.; *U.S. Public*, pg. 422
HUBBELL PREMISE WIRING, INC.—Hubbell Incorporated; *U.S. Public*, pg. 844
HUTCHISON TELEPHONE COMPANY LTD.—Motorola, Inc.; *U.S. Public*, pg. 1139
INTER-TEL, INCORPORATED; *U.S. Public*, pg. 888
INTER-TEL INTEGRATED SYSTEMS, INC.—Inter-Tel, Incorporated; *U.S. Public*, pg. 888
INTER-TEL NET SOLUTIONS—Inter-Tel, Incorporated; *U.S. Public*, pg. 888
INTERDIGITAL COMMUNICATIONS CORP.; *U.S. Public*, pg. 889
INTERNATIONAL BUSINESS MACHINES CORPORATION; *U.S. Public*, pg. 895
INTERNATIONAL MICROWAVE CORPORATION; *U.S. Private*, pg. 571
INTERVOICE, INC.; *U.S. Public*, pg. 910
INTERVOICE, INC.—InterVoice, Inc.; *U.S. Public*, pg. 910
JK LASERS DEUTSCHLAND GMBH—Sumitomo Heavy Industries, Ltd.; *Int'l*, pg. 1315
JEUMONT-SCHNEIDER TRENFORMETEURS; *Int'l*, pg. 706
JOSLYN SIERRA CORPORATION—Danaher Corporation; *U.S. Public*, pg. 482
KEUM KANG DEVELOPMENT INDUSTRIAL CO., LTD.—Hyundai Motor Company; *Int'l*, pg. 642
KONICA BUSINESS MACHINES USA, INC.—Konica Corporation; *Int'l*, pg. 748
KYOCERA CORPORATION; *Int'l*, pg. 775
LK PRODUCTS OY—Oy Nokia Ab/Nokia Group; *Int'l*, pg. 952
LM ERICSSON HOLDINGS LTD.—Telefonaktiebolaget LM Ericsson; *Int'l*, pg. 1368
LM ERICSSON INTERNATIONAL AB JAPAN—Telefonaktiebolaget LM Ericsson; *Int'l*, pg. 1368
LM ERICSSON INTERNATIONAL AB SINGAPORE—Telefonaktiebolaget LM Ericsson; *Int'l*, pg. 1369
LM ERICSSON (NIGERIA) LTD.—Telefonaktiebolaget LM Ericsson; *Int'l*, pg. 1369
LANDIS & STAEFA, INC.—Landis & Staefa AG; *Int'l*, pg. 800
LEVITON TELECOM—Leviton Mfg. Co., Inc.; *U.S. Private*, pg. 663
LOJACK CORPORATION; *U.S. Public*, pg. 1012
LONG ISLAND COMMUNICATIONS CORP.—Data General Corporation; *U.S. Public*, pg. 485
LORAIN PRODUCTS—RELTEC Corporation; *U.S. Private*, pg. 921
LUCENT TECHNOLOGIES—Lucent Technologies Inc.; *U.S. Public*, pg. 1017
LUCENT TECHNOLOGIES ENGINEERING RESEARCH CENTER—Lucent Technologies Inc.; *U.S. Public*, pg. 1018
LUCENT TECHNOLOGIES INC.; *U.S. Public*, pg. 1017
MARANTZ JAPAN INC.; *Int'l*, pg. 841
MCLEODUSA INCORPORATED; *U.S. Public*, pg. 1073
MEMOREX TELEX CORP.—Memorex Telex N.V.; *Int'l*, pg. 857
MICROTEL INTERNATIONAL INC.; *U.S. Public*, pg. 1108
MINOLTA CO., LTD.; *Int'l*, pg. 869
MITEL CORPORATION; *Int'l*, pg. 870
MITEL, INC.—Mitel Corporation; *Int'l*, pg. 870
MITEL TELECOM LIMITED—Mitel Corporation; *Int'l*, pg. 870
MOSCOM CORPORATION; *U.S. Public*, pg. 1136
MOTOMETER AG—Robert Bosch GmbH; *Int'l*, pg. 204
MOTOROLA, INC.; *U.S. Public*, pg. 1136
MURATA MACHINERY, LTD.; *Int'l*, pg. 897
N BASE COMMUNICATIONS—MRV Communications, Inc.; *U.S. Public*, pg. 1027
NEC AMERICA, INC.—NEC Corporation; *Int'l*, pg. 900
NEC AUSTRALIA PTY. LTD.—NEC Corporation; *Int'l*, pg. 901
NEC CORPORATION; *Int'l*, pg. 899
NEC DE MEXICO, S.A. DE C.V.—NEC Corporation; *Int'l*, pg. 901
NEC HOME ELECTRONICS (MALAYSIA) SDN. BHD.—NEC Corporation; *Int'l*, pg. 900
NATIONAL BAND THREE LTD.—Geotek Communications; *U.S. Public*, pg. 740
NEXTLEVEL SYSTEMS (JAPAN)—General Instrument Corporation; *U.S. Public*, pg. 716
NIPPON TELEGRAPH AND TELEPHONE CORPORATION; *Int'l*, pg. 940
OY NOKIA AB/NOKIA GROUP; *Int'l*, pg. 951
NOKIA AUDIO ELECTRONICS GMBH—Oy Nokia Ab/Nokia Group; *Int'l*, pg. 954
NOKIA CELLULAR SYSTEMS—Oy Nokia Ab/Nokia Group; *Int'l*, pg. 953
NOKIA (MALAYSIA) SDN. BHD.—Oy Nokia Ab/Nokia Group; *Int'l*, pg. 953
NOKIA MOBILE PHONES—Oy Nokia Ab/Nokia Group; *Int'l*, pg. 952
NOKIA MOBILE PHONES, INC.—Oy Nokia Ab/Nokia Group; *Int'l*, pg. 952
NOKIA MOBILE PHONES JAPAN K.K.—Oy Nokia Ab/Nokia Group; *Int'l*, pg. 952
NOKIA MOBILE PHONES MANUFACTURING (USA) LTD.—Oy Nokia Ab/Nokia Group; *Int'l*, pg. 952
NOKIA MOBILE PHONES R & D—Oy Nokia Ab/Nokia Group; *Int'l*, pg. 952
NOKIA MOBILE PHONES R & D CENTER—Oy Nokia Ab/Nokia Group; *Int'l*, pg. 952
NOKIA MOBILE PHONES (UK) LTD.—Oy Nokia Ab/Nokia Group; *Int'l*, pg. 952
NOKIA MOBILE PHONES UK SALES LTD.—Oy Nokia Ab/Nokia Group; *Int'l*, pg. 952
NOKIA NETWORK AND ACCESS SYSTEMS—Oy Nokia Ab/Nokia Group; *Int'l*, pg. 953
NOKIA PAGING—Oy Nokia Ab/Nokia Group; *Int'l*, pg. 952
NOKIA SOURCING, INC.—Oy Nokia Ab/Nokia Group; *Int'l*, pg. 953
NOKIA TELECOMMUNICATIONS—Oy Nokia Ab/Nokia Group; *Int'l*, pg. 952
NOKIA TELECOMMUNICATIONS LTD.—Oy Nokia Ab/Nokia Group; *Int'l*, pg. 953
NORTEL AUSTRALIA PTY. LIMITED—Northern Telecom Limited; *Int'l*, pg. 970
NORTEL CALA INC.—Northern Telecom Limited; *Int'l*, pg. 969
NORTEL DASA NETWORK SYSTEMS GMBH & CO. KG—Northern Telecom Limited; *Int'l*, pg. 970
NORTEL LIMITED—Northern Telecom Limited; *Int'l*, pg. 970
NORTH HILLS SIGNAL PROCESSING—Porta Systems Corp.; *U.S. Public*, pg. 1317
NORTHERN IRELAND LIMITED—Northern Telecom Limited; *Int'l*, pg. 970
NORTHERN TELECOM—Northern Telecom Limited; *Int'l*, pg. 970
NORTHERN TELECOM CANADA LIMITED—Northern Telecom Limited; *Int'l*, pg. 969
NORTHERN TELECOM INDUSTRIES SDN. BHD.—Northern Telecom Limited; *Int'l*, pg. 970
NORTHERN TELECOM (IRELAND) LIMITED—Northern Telecom Limited; *Int'l*, pg. 970
NORTHERN TELECOM JAPAN INC.—Northern Telecom Limited; *Int'l*, pg. 970
NORTHERN TELECOM LIMITED; *Int'l*, pg. 968
NORTHERN TELECOM - NATIONAL REPAIR & DISTRIBUTION CENTER—Northern Telecom Limited; *Int'l*, pg. 970
NORTHERN TELECOM SWITCHING NETWORKS—Northern Telecom Limited; *Int'l*, pg. 970
OCTEL MESSAGING DIVISION—Lucent Technologies Inc.; *U.S. Public*, pg. 1017
OKI ELECTRIC INDUSTRY COMPANY, LTD.; *Int'l*, pg. 999
OLTECO—Olivetti SpA; *Int'l*, pg. 1002
PACIFIC BELL—SBC Communications Inc.; *U.S. Public*, pg. 1416
PACIFIC TELESIS GROUP—SBC Communications Inc.; *U.S. Public*, pg. 1415
PAIRGAIN TECHNOLOGIES INC.; *U.S. Public*, pg. 1253
PHILIPS INDUSTRIE SA—Philips Electronics N.V.; *Int'l*, pg. 1055
PHILIPS INFORMATICA COMMUNICACIONES SA—Philips Electronics N.V.; *Int'l*, pg. 1055
PHILIPS KOMMUNIKATIONS INDUSTRIE AG—Philips Electronics N.V.; *Int'l*, pg. 1055
PHILNET ERICSSON INC.—Telefonaktiebolaget LM Ericsson; *Int'l*, pg. 1369
PICTURETEL; *U.S. Public*, pg. 1294
PITNEY BOWES INC.; *U.S. Public*, pg. 1303
PLANTRONICS INC.; *U.S. Public*, pg. 1308
PORTA SYSTEMS CORP.; *U.S. Public*, pg. 1317
PORTA SYSTEMS LIMITED—Porta Systems Corp.; *U.S. Public*, pg. 1317
PORTA SYSTEMS S.A. DE C.V.—Porta Systems Corp.; *U.S. Public*, pg. 1317
PRACTICAL PERIPHERALS—Hayes Corporation; *U.S. Public*, pg. 801
PREFORMED LINE PRODUCTS; *U.S. Public*, pg. 1321
PRISM SYSTEMS INC.—Northern Telecom Limited; *Int'l*, pg. 969
QUEBEC-TELEPHONE—GTE Corporation; *U.S. Public*, pg. 697
RACAL CANADA INC.—Racal Electronics Plc; *Int'l*, pg. 1083
RACAL-DATACOM—Racal Electronics Plc; *Int'l*, pg. 1083
RACAL ELECTRONICS PLC; *Int'l*, pg. 1082
RACAL INSTRUMENTS LTD.—Racal Electronics Plc; *Int'l*, pg. 1082
RELIANCE ELECTRIC COMPANY—Rockwell International Corporation; *U.S. Public*, pg. 1398
RELTEC CORPORATION; *U.S. Private*, pg. 921
RELTEC, INC.—RELTEC Corporation; *U.S. Private*, pg. 921
RELTEC SYSTEMS—RELTEC Corporation; *U.S. Private*, pg. 921
REMSDAQ LIMITED—DAQ Electronics Inc.; *U.S. Private*, pg. 300
ROCKEFELLER GROUP TELECOMMUNICATIONS SERVICES, INC.—Mitsubishi Estate Co., Ltd.; *Int'l*, pg. 873
SAIT-RADIOHOLLAND GROUP S.A.; *Int'l*, pg. 1151
SATAS - SOCIETE POUR L'AFFRANCHISSEMENT ET LE TIMBRAGE AUTOMATIQUES—Alcatel Alsthom Compagnie Generale D'Electricite; *Int'l*, pg. 54
SFA DATACOMM INC.—SFA, Inc.; *U.S. Private*, pg. 956
SIMCO ERICSSON LTD.—Telefonaktiebolaget LM Ericsson; *Int'l*, pg. 1370
SNET MOBILECOM, INC.—Southern New England Telecommunications Corporation; *U.S. Public*, pg. 1491
SNET MOBILITY, INC.—Southern New England Telecommunications Corporation; *U.S. Public*, pg. 1491
SNET SYSTEMS INC.—Southern New England Telecommunications Corporation; *U.S. Public*, pg. 1491
SAFEGUARD SCIENTIFICS, INC.; *U.S. Public*, pg. 1424
SAFETRAN SYSTEMS CORPORATION—BTR plc; *Int'l*, pg. 127
SALIENT 3 COMMUNICATIONS, INC.; *U.S. Public*, pg. 1429
SENCORE, INC.; *U.S. Private*, pg. 983
SHARE TECHNOLOGIES - FAIRCHILD—Tel-Save Holdings, Inc.; *U.S. Public*, pg. 1568
SHIZUOKA OKI ELECTRIC CO., LTD.—Oki Electric Industry Company, Ltd.; *Int'l*, pg. 999
SIEMENS AG; *Int'l*, pg. 1244
SIEMENS A/S—Siemens AG; *Int'l*, pg. 1247
SIEMENS BUSINESS COMMUNICATION SYSTEMS, INC.—Siemens AG; *Int'l*, pg. 1245
SIEMENS LTD.—Siemens AG; *Int'l*, pg. 1247
SIEMENS NEDERLAND N.V.—Siemens AG; *Int'l*, pg. 1247
SIEMENS OSAKEYTIOE—Siemens AG; *Int'l*, pg. 1247
SIEMENS SCHIEIZ AG—Siemens AG; *Int'l*, pg. 1248
SIEMENS TELECOMMUNICATION SYSTEMS LTD.—Siemens AG; *Int'l*, pg. 1248
SIMKO TICARET VE SANAYI A.S.—Siemens AG; *Int'l*, pg. 1248
SOCIEDADE ERICSSON DE PORTUGAL LDA.—Telefonaktiebolaget LM Ericsson; *Int'l*, pg. 1370
SOCIETE D'ETUDES ET DE CONSTRUCTIONS ELECTRONIQUES (SECRE)—Jeumont-Schneider Trenformeteurs; *Int'l*, pg. 706
SONY COMMUNICATIONS PRODUCTS CO.—Sony Corporation; *Int'l*, pg. 1281
THE SOUTHERN NEW ENGLAND TELEPHONE COMPANY—Southern New England Telecommunications Corporation; *U.S. Public*, pg. 1491
SPARTON CORPORATION; *U.S. Public*, pg. 1496
SPRINT NORTH SUPPLY—Sprint Corporation; *U.S. Public*, pg. 1501
STET SOCIETA FINANZIARIA TELEFONICA—IRI Istituto Ricostruzione Industriale; *Int'l*, pg. 655
STORAGETEK NETWORK SYSTEMS GROUP—Storage Technology Corporation; *U.S. Public*, pg. 1522
SUPERIOR TELECOMMUNICATIONS—The Alpine Group, Inc.; *U.S. Public*, pg. 58
SUTTLE APPARATUS CORPORATION—Communications Systems, Inc.; *U.S. Public*, pg. 416
SUTTLE CARIBE, INC.—Communications Systems, Inc.; *U.S. Public*, pg. 415
SUTTLE COSTA RICA S.A.—Communications Systems, Inc.; *U.S. Public*, pg. 416
SWITCHCRAFT, INC.—Raytheon Company; *U.S. Public*, pg. 1366
SYMMETRICOM, INC.; *U.S. Public*, pg. 1547
SYMPLEX COMMUNICATIONS CORP.; *U.S. Private*, pg. 1060
SYNTELLECT, INC.; *U.S. Public*, pg. 1550
TEL-CA-TELECOMMUNICAZIONI CALABRESE S.P.A.—Telefonaktiebolaget LM Ericsson; *Int'l*, pg. 1370
TII DOMINICANA INC.—TII Industries, Inc.; *U.S. Public*, pg. 1556
TII INDUSTRIES, INC.; *U.S. Public*, pg. 1556
TAIKO ELECTRIC WORK, LTD.—Oki Electric Industry Company, Ltd.; *Int'l*, pg. 999
TEKELEC, LTD.—Tekelec; *U.S. Public*, pg. 1566
TELCO SYSTEMS, INC.; *U.S. Public*, pg. 1568
TELECOM SOLUTIONS—SymmetriCom, Inc.; *U.S. Public*, pg. 1547
TELECOM SOLUTIONS (EUROPE) LIMITED—SymmetriCom, Inc.; *U.S. Public*, pg. 1547
TELECOM SOLUTIONS PUERTO RICO, INC.—SymmetriCom, Inc.; *U.S. Public*, pg. 1547
TELECOMUNICACIONES MARINAS, S.A. (TEMASA)—Telefonica de Espana, S.A.; *Int'l*, pg. 1372
TELEFONAKTIEBOLAGET LM ERICSSON; *Int'l*, pg. 1363
TELEFONICA DE ESPANA, S.A.; *Int'l*, pg. 1371
TELEFONOS ERICSSON C.A.—Telefonaktiebolaget LM Ericsson; *Int'l*, pg. 1371
TELEGLOBE, INC.; *Int'l*, pg. 1373
TELLABS OPERATIONS, INC.; *U.S. Public*, pg. 1572
TELLABS TEXAS INC.—Tellabs Operations, Inc.; *U.S. Public*, pg. 1573
TELUS MARKETING COMMUNICATIONS—Telus Corporation; *Int'l*, pg. 1374
3COM, LTD.—3Com Corporation; *U.S. Public*, pg. 1604
3M; *U.S. Public*, pg. 1604
TOHO ELECTRONICS CO., LTD.—Oki Electric Industry Company, Ltd.; *Int'l*, pg. 999
TONE COMMANDER SYSTEMS; *U.S. Private*, pg. 1090
TONG GUANG-NORTEL LIMITED LIABILITY COMPANY—Northern Telecom Limited; *Int'l*, pg. 970
TOSHIBA AMERICA INFORMATION SYSTEMS, INC.—Toshiba Corporation; *Int'l*, pg. 1405
TOSHIBA CORPORATION; *Int'l*, pg. 1402
TOSHIBA LOGISTIC SUPPORT CORPORATION—Toshiba Corporation; *Int'l*, pg. 1404
TRANSPORT SYSTEMS GROUP—ADC Telecommunications, Inc.; *U.S. Public*, pg. 4
V-BAND CORPORATION; *U.S. Public*, pg. 1701
VARI TRONICS COMPANY, INC.; *U.S. Private*, pg. 1134
VINDICATOR TECHNOLOGIES; *U.S. Private*, pg. 1141
WHEELOCK INC.; *U.S. Private*, pg. 1171
WHITTAKER COMMUNICATIONS, INC.—Whittaker Corporation; *U.S. Public*, pg. 1767
WIRELESS NETWORKS SKYLINE - NORTHERN TELECOM CANADA LIMITED—Northern Telecom Limited; *Int'l*, pg. 969
ZACK ELECTRONICS; *U.S. Private*, pg. 1203
ZOOM TELEPHONICS, INC.; *U.S. Public*, pg. 1794

3663 — RADIO & TELEVISION BROADCASTING & COMMUNICATIONS EQUIPMENT

A&E TELEVISION NETWORKS—The Hearst Corporation; *U.S. Private*, pg. 515
AEG SORTING SYSTEMS INC.—Siemens AG; *Int'l*, pg. 1244
ARC INTERNATIONAL CORPORATION; *Int'l*, pg. 17
AT&T CORPORATION; *U.S. Public*, pg. 10
AT&T WIRELESS SERVICES—AT&T Corporation; *U.S. Public*, pg. 11
AIRTOUCH COMMUNICATIONS, INC.; *U.S. Public*, pg. 34
AIRVISION—Philips Electronics N.V.; *Int'l*, pg. 1053
AISIN SEIKI CO. LTD.; *Int'l*, pg. 39
AL & ED'S AUTO SOUND CENTER; *U.S. Private*, pg. 30
ALARMNET/RADSCAN—Pittway Corporation; *U.S. Public*, pg. 1306
ALCATEL—Alcatel Alsthom Compagnie Generale D'Electricite; *Int'l*, pg. 52
ALCATEL ATFH—Alcatel Alsthom Compagnie Generale D'Electricite; *Int'l*, pg. 55
ALCATEL BUSINESS SYSTEMS (FRANCE)—Alcatel Alsthom Compagnie Generale D'Electricite; *Int'l*, pg. 55
ALCOA FUJIKURA LTD.—Aluminum Company of America; *U.S. Public*, pg. 60
ALCOA FUJIKURA LTD.—Fujikura Ltd.; *Int'l*, pg. 525
ALDEN ELECTRONICS, INC.—Platinum Equity Holdings, LLC; *U.S. Private*, pg. 872
ALENIA SPAZIO—IRI Istituto Ricostruzione Industriale; *Int'l*, *pg. 653*
ALLEN TELECOM INC.—Allen Telecom, Inc.; *U.S. Public*, pg. 45
ALPINE ELECTRONICS OF AMERICA, INC.—Alps Electric Co., Ltd.; *Int'l*, pg. 65
AMECOM DIV.—Litton Industries, Inc.; *U.S. Public*, pg. 1002
AMERICAN TRADING AND PRODUCTION CORPORATION; *U.S. Private*, pg. 63
ANAREN MICROWAVE INC.; *U.S. Public*, pg. 110
ANDREW ANTENNA CO. LTD.—Andrew Corporation; *U.S. Public*, pg. 113
ANDREW ANTENNAS—Andrew Corporation; *U.S. Public*, pg. 113
ANDREW CORPORATION; *U.S. Public*, pg. 112
ANRITSU CORPORATION; *Int'l*, pg. 77
ANTENNA PRODUCTS CORP.—Cabre Corp.; *U.S. Public*, pg. 289
ARTEL UTAH SCIENTIFIC, INC.—Artel Video Systems, Inc.; *U.S. Private*, pg. 86
ASCOM HPF SA—Ascom Holding AG; *Int'l*, pg. 87
ASCOM TATECO AB—Ascom Holding AG; *Int'l*, pg. 87
ASEA BROWN BOVERI LTD.—ABB Asea Brown Boveri (Holding) Ltd.; *Int'l*, pg. 2
AYDIN TELECOM DIVISION—Aydin Corporation; *U.S. Public*, pg. 158
AYDIN YAZILIM VE ELEKTRONIK SANAYII A.S. (AYES AS)—Aydin Corporation; *U.S. Public*, pg. 158
BR COMMUNICATIONS—TCI International Inc.; *U.S. Public*, pg. 1555
BALL AEROSPACE & TECHNOLOGIES CORP.—Ball Corporation; *U.S. Public*, pg. 171
BALL CORPORATION; *U.S. Public*, pg. 170
BANG & OLUFSEN A/S; *Int'l*, pg. 145
BLAUPUNKT-WERKE GMBH—Robert Bosch GmbH; *Int'l*, pg. 203
BLONDER-TONGUE LABORATORIES, INC.; *U.S. Public*, pg. 237
ROBERT BOSCH GMBH; *Int'l*, pg. 203
BRITISH AEROSPACE P.L.C.; *Int'l*, pg. 217
BROADBAND NETWORKS GROUP—General Instrument Corporation; *U.S. Public*, pg. 716
BROADCAST ELECTRONICS, INC.—Hoak Capital; *U.S. Private*, pg. 531
C-COR ELECTRONICS CANADA, INC.—C-COR Electronics, Inc.; *U.S. Public*, pg. 272
C-COR ELECTRONICS, INC.; *U.S. Public*, pg. 272
CBS CORPORATION; *U.S. Public*, pg. 273
CSA, LTD.—COMSAT Corporation; *U.S. Public*, pg. 424
CSC, HALIFAX—WIC Western International Communications Ltd.; *Int'l*, pg. 1482
CSC, OTTAWA—WIC Western International Communications Ltd.; *Int'l*, pg. 1482
CSC, SASKATOON—WIC Western International Communications Ltd.; *Int'l*, pg. 1482
CSC, VANCOUVER—WIC Western International Communications Ltd.; *Int'l*, pg. 1482
CT PAGING SDN. BHD.—Telefonaktiebolaget LM Ericsson; *Int'l*, pg. 1365
CT RADIOSET SDN. BHD.—Telefonaktiebolaget LM Ericsson; *Int'l*, pg. 1365
CALIFORNIA MICROWAVE, INC.; *U.S. Public*, pg. 293
CAMTEC ELECTRONIC LTD.—Telefonaktiebolaget LM Ericsson; *Int'l*, pg. 1365
CANADIAN SATELLITE COMMUNICATIONS INC.—WIC Western International Communications Ltd.; *Int'l*, pg. 1481
CANCOM—WIC Western International Communications Ltd.; *Int'l*, pg. 1482
CASCADE DESIGN AUTOMATION—Oki Electric Industry Company, Ltd.; *Int'l*, pg. 1000
CHANNEL MASTER; *U.S. Private*, pg. 228
CHYRON CORP.—Telefonica de Espana, S.A.; *Int'l*, pg. 1372
CINET PERIFERI A/S—Axel Johnson AB; *Int'l*, pg. 710
CLARION CORPORATION OF AMERICA—Clarion Co., Ltd.; *Int'l*, pg. 296
CLARION SALES CORPORATION—Clarion Co., Ltd.; *Int'l*, pg. 296
COHU, INC.; *U.S. Public*, pg. 396
COMARK COMMUNICATIONS, INC.—Thomson S.A.; *Int'l*, pg. 1383
COMPANIA CELULAR DE COLOMBIA COCELCO, S.A.—Telefonica de Espana, S.A.; *Int'l*, pg. 1373
COMPANIA ERICSSON DE CHILE S.A.—Telefonaktiebolaget LM Ericsson; *Int'l*, pg. 1365
COMPANIA ERICSSON S.A.—Telefonaktiebolaget LM Ericsson; *Int'l*, pg. 1365
COMPANIA ERICSSON S.A.C.I.—Telefonaktiebolaget LM Ericsson; *Int'l*, pg. 1365
COMSAT RSI—COMSAT Corporation; *U.S. Public*, pg. 424
COMSAT RSI, INC.—COMSAT Corporation; *U.S. Public*, pg. 424
COMSONICS, INC.; *U.S. Private*, pg. 260
COMTECH ANTENNA SYSTEMS, INC.—Comtech Telecommunications Corp.; *U.S. Public*, pg. 425
COMTECH COMMUNICATIONS CORP.—Comtech Telecommunications Corp.; *U.S. Public*, pg. 425
COMTECH PST CORP.—Comtech Telecommunications Corp.; *U.S. Public*, pg. 425
COMTECH SYSTEMS, INC.—Comtech Telecommunications Corp.; *U.S. Public*, pg. 425
COMTECH TELECOMMUNICATIONS CORP.; *U.S. Public*, pg. 425
COMVERSE NETWORK SYSTEMS—Comverse Technology, Inc.; *U.S. Public*, pg. 425
CONKLIN INSTRUMENT CORPORATION; *U.S. Private*, pg. 263
CONRAC DISPLAY PRODUCTS; *U.S. Private*, pg. 264
CONSOLIDATED COMMUNICATIONS MOBILE SERVICES, INC.—McLeodUSA Incorporated; *U.S. Public*, pg. 1073
CONSTEL S.A.—Telefonaktiebolaget LM Ericsson; *Int'l*, pg. 1365
CONTEC LIMITED PARTNERSHIP—Manhattan Partners L.P.; *U.S. Private*, pg. 699
CYLINK CORP.—Pittway Corporation; *U.S. Public*, pg. 1306
DBA SYSTEMS, INC.; *U.S. Public*, pg. 472
DIAX TELEKOMM A/S—Telefonaktiebolaget LM Ericsson; *Int'l*, pg. 1365
DOM-SICHERHEITSTECHNIK GMBH & CO. KG—The Black & Decker Corporation; *U.S. Public*, pg. 233
DPSA DEUTSCHE PERSONENSUCH-ANLAGEN GMBH—Telefonaktiebolaget LM Ericsson; *Int'l*, pg. 1365
DECIBEL PRODUCTS, INC.—Allen Telecom, Inc.; *U.S. Public*, pg. 46
DIAMOND ELECTRONICS, INC.—Ultrak Inc.; *U.S. Public*, pg. 1663
DIGITAL COURIER INTERNATIONAL INC.; *Int'l*, pg. 413
DIGITAL MICROWAVE CORPORATION; *U.S. Public*, pg. 508
DIRECTV INC.—General Motors Corporation; *U.S. Public*, pg. 720
DISTRIBUTION CONTROL SYSTEMS, INC. (DCS)—ESCO Electronics Corporation; *U.S. Public*, pg. 546
DORNE & MARGOLIN, INC.—United Capital Corp.; *U.S. Public*, pg. 1675
DORON PRECISION SYSTEMS, INC.; *U.S. Private*, pg. 341
DOTRONIX, INC.; *U.S. Public*, pg. 520
DYNATECH CORPORATION; *U.S. Public*, pg. 539
EAB DEUTSCHLAND INDUSTRIE-TV ANGLEN GMBH—Rothenberger Group GmbH; *Int'l*, pg. 1129
ENI; *U.S. Private*, pg. 354
EMCEE BROADCAST PRODUCTS, INC.; *U.S. Public*, pg. 570
EMPRESA TECNOLOGICA ERICSSON S.A. DE C.V.—Telefonaktiebolaget LM Ericsson; *Int'l*, pg. 1366
ENTERPRISE GENERALE DE TELECOMMUNICATIONS—France Telecom; *Int'l*, pg. 503
ERICSSON AG—Telefonaktiebolaget LM Ericsson; *Int'l*, pg. 1366
ERICSSON BUSINESS COMMUNICATIONS A/S—Telefonaktiebolaget LM Ericsson; *Int'l*, pg. 1366
ERICSSON BUSINESS COMMUNICATIONS GMBH—Telefonaktiebolaget LM Ericsson; *Int'l*, pg. 1366
ERICSSON BUSINESS COMMUNICATIONS LTD.—Telefonaktiebolaget LM Ericsson; *Int'l*, pg. 1366
ERICSSON BUSINESS SYSTEMS AB - WARSAW BRANCH OFFICE—Telefonaktiebolaget LM Ericsson; *Int'l*, pg. 1366
ERICSSON COMMUNICATIONS (HONG KONG) LTD.—Telefonaktiebolaget LM Ericsson; *Int'l*, pg. 1366
ERICSSON COMMUNICATIONS LTD.—Telefonaktiebolaget LM Ericsson; *Int'l*, pg. 1366
ERICSSON COMMUNICATIONS (THAILAND) LTD.—Telefonaktiebolaget LM Ericsson; *Int'l*, pg. 1366
ERICSSON DE COSTA RICA—Telefonaktiebolaget LM Ericsson; *Int'l*, pg. 1366
ERICSSON GE MOBILE COMMUNICATIONS HOLDING INC.—Telefonaktiebolaget LM Ericsson; *Int'l*, pg. 1365
ERICSSON GE MOBILE COMMUNICATIONS INC.—Telefonaktiebolaget LM Ericsson; *Int'l*, pg. 1365
ERICSSON (HELLAS) TELECOMMUNICATIONS EQUIPMENT S.A.—Telefonaktiebolaget LM Ericsson; *Int'l*, pg. 1366
ERICSSON HOLDING A/S—Telefonaktiebolaget LM Ericsson; *Int'l*, pg. 1367
ERICSSON HOLDING INTERNATIONAL B.V.—Telefonaktiebolaget LM Ericsson; *Int'l*, pg. 1367
ERICSSON HOLDING NEDERLAND B.V.—Telefonaktiebolaget LM Ericsson; *Int'l*, pg. 1367
ERICSSON INDIA LTD.—Telefonaktiebolaget LM Ericsson; *Int'l*, pg. 1367
ERICSSON LTD.—Telefonaktiebolaget LM Ericsson; *Int'l*, pg. 1367
ERICSSON MOBILE COMMUNICATIONS AB—Telefonaktiebolaget LM Ericsson; *Int'l*, pg. 1364
ERICSSON MOBILE DATA INC.—Telefonaktiebolaget LM Ericsson; *Int'l*, pg. 1365
ERICSSON MOBILE NETWORKS B.V.—Telefonaktiebolaget LM Ericsson; *Int'l*, pg. 1367
ERICSSON NORTH AMERICA, INC.—Telefonaktiebolaget LM Ericsson; *Int'l*, pg. 1364
ERICSSON PAGING SYSTEMS INC.—Telefonaktiebolaget LM Ericsson; *Int'l*, pg. 1365
ERICSSON PAGING SYSTEMS ZWEIGNIEDERLASSUNG DEUTSCHLAND—Telefonaktiebolaget LM Ericsson; *Int'l*, *pg. 1367*
ERICSSON RADIO SYSTEMER A/S—Telefonaktiebolaget LM Ericsson; *Int'l*, pg. 1367
ERICSSON RADIO SYSTEMS AB—Telefonaktiebolaget LM Ericsson; *Int'l*, pg. 1363
ERICSSON RADIO SYSTEMS A/S—Telefonaktiebolaget LM Ericsson; *Int'l*, pg. 1367
ERICSSON RADIO SYSTEMS B.V.—Telefonaktiebolaget LM Ericsson; *Int'l*, pg. 1367
ERICSSON RADIO SYSTEMS SVERIGE AB—Telefonaktiebolaget LM Ericsson; *Int'l*, pg. 1364
ERICSSON REDES S.A.—Telefonaktiebolaget LM Ericsson; *Int'l*, pg. 1367
ERICSSON S.A.—Telefonaktiebolaget LM Ericsson; *Int'l*, pg. 1367
ERICSSON SIELTE-INTERNATIONAL S.P.A.—Telefonaktiebolaget LM Ericsson; *Int'l*, pg. 1367
ERICSSON SISTEMAS AVANZADOS S.A.—Telefonaktiebolaget LM Ericsson; *Int'l*, pg. 1367
ERICSSON SUC. URUGUAY—Telefonaktiebolaget LM Ericsson; *Int'l*, pg. 1367
ERICSSON SYSTEMS EXPERTISE LTD.—Telefonaktiebolaget LM Ericsson; *Int'l*, pg. 1367
ERICSSON TAIWAN LTD.—Telefonaktiebolaget LM Ericsson; *Int'l*, pg. 1367
ERICSSON TELECOM A/S—Telefonaktiebolaget LM Ericsson; *Int'l*, pg. 1367
ERICSSON TELECOMMUNICATIE B.V.—Telefonaktiebolaget LM Ericsson; *Int'l*, pg. 1367
ERICSSON TELEKOM GMBH—Telefonaktiebolaget LM Ericsson; *Int'l*, pg. 1368
ERICSSON TELEKOMUNIKASYON A.S.—Telefonaktiebolaget LM Ericsson; *Int'l*, pg. 1368
ERICSSON TERMINALES MOVILES S.A.—Telefonaktiebolaget LM Ericsson; *Int'l*, pg. 1368
FIAR-FABBRICA ITALIANA APPARECCHIATURE RADIOELECTTRICHE S.P.A.—Telefonaktiebolaget LM Ericsson; *Int'l*, pg. 1368
FARADAY, INC.—Siemens AG; *Int'l*, pg. 1246
FAROUDJA, INC.; *U.S. Public*, pg. 613
FEDERAL SIGNAL CORPORATION; *U.S. Public*, pg. 616
FOREM S.P.A.—Allen Telecom, Inc.; *U.S. Public*, pg. 46
FUJIKURA AMERICA INC.—Fujikura Ltd.; *Int'l*, pg. 525
FUJIKURA LTD.; *Int'l*, pg. 525
FUJITSU ESPANA, S.A.—Fujitsu Limited; *Int'l*, pg. 528
FUJITSU LIMITED; *Int'l*, pg. 525
GMSI, INC.—Geotek Communications; *U.S. Public*, pg. 740
GENERAL INSTRUMENT CORPORATION; *U.S. Public*, pg. 716
GENERAL INSTRUMENT OF CANADA LTD.—General Instrument Corporation; *U.S. Public*, pg. 716
GENERAL KINETICS INCORPORATED; *U.S. Public*, pg. 716
GENERAL SIGNAL CORPORATION; *U.S. Public*, pg. 726
GIGA-TRONICS INCORPORATED; *U.S. Public*, pg. 742
GLENAYRE ELECTRONICS, INC.—Glenayre Technologies, Inc.; *U.S. Public*, pg. 747
GLENAYRE TECHNOLOGIES, INC.; *U.S. Public*, pg. 746
GOLDSTAR ELECTRIC CO. LTD.—LG Group; *Int'l*, pg. 779
GOLDSTAR PRECISION INDUSTRIES LTD.—LG Group; *Int'l*, pg. 779
GOLDSTAR TELECOMMUNICATIONS CO. LTD.—LG Group; *Int'l*, pg. 779
GYYR, INC.—Odetics Inc.; *U.S. Public*, pg. 1212
HAPAM-GOLDBACH B.V.—Internatio-Muller N.V.; *Int'l*, pg. 681
HARRIS BROADCAST DIVISION—Harris Corporation; *U.S. Public*, pg. 791
RICHARD HIRSCHMANN GMBH & CO.—Rheinmetall Group; *Int'l*, pg. 1108
RICHARD HIRSCHMANN OF AMERICA, INC.—Rheinmetall Group; *Int'l*, pg. 1108
HISPASAT, S.A.—Telefonica de Espana, S.A.; *Int'l*, pg. 1372
HITACHI DENSHI, LTD.—Hitachi, Ltd.; *Int'l*, pg. 621
HONEYWELL DEFENSE AVIONICS SYSTEMS—Honeywell Inc.; *U.S. Public*, pg. 834
HONEYWELL INC.; *U.S. Public*, pg. 833
HUBBELL PREMISE WIRING, INC.—Hubbell Incorporated; *U.S. Public*, pg. 844
IDB WORLDCOM—WorldCom, Inc.; *U.S. Public*, pg. 1779
IDB WORLDCOM, INC.—WorldCom, Inc.; *U.S. Public*, pg. 1779
IRI ISTITUTO RICOSTRUZIONE INDUSTRIALE; *Int'l*, pg. 652
ITT AEROSPACE/COMMUNICATIONS DIV.—ITT Industries, Inc.; *U.S. Public*, pg. 859
IKEGAMI TSUSHINKI CO., LTD.; *Int'l*, pg. 660
ITRON INC.; *U.S. Public*, pg. 914
JRC CANIDA, INC.; *U.S. Private*, pg. 578
JAVELIN SYSTEMS—Pittway Corporation; *U.S. Public*, pg. 1306
E.F. JOHNSON RADIO SYSTEMS—Transcrypt International; *U.S. Public*, pg. 1630
K2 INC.; *U.S. Public*, pg. 940
KAISER AEROSPACE & ELECTRONICS CORP.; *U.S. Private*, pg. 605
KENT-TIEGHI S.P.A.—ABB Asea Brown Boveri (Holding) Ltd.; *Int'l*, pg. 3
KEVLIN CORPORATION; *U.S. Public*, pg. 953
KOKUSAI ELECTRIC CO., LTD.; *Int'l*, pg. 743
KRACO ENTERPRISES, INC.; *U.S. Private*, pg. 634
KYSOR/MEDALLION—Kuhlman Corporation; *U.S. Public*, pg. 968
LM ERICSSON HOLDINGS LTD.—Telefonaktiebolaget LM Ericsson; *Int'l*, pg. 1368
LM ERICSSON INTERNATIONAL AB JAPAN—Telefonaktiebolaget LM Ericsson; *Int'l*, pg. 1368
LM ERICSSON INTERNATIONAL AB SINGAPORE—Telefonaktiebolaget LM Ericsson; *Int'l*, pg. 1369
LM ERICSSON (NIGERIA) LTD.—Telefonaktiebolaget LM Ericsson; *Int'l*, pg. 1369
LM ERICSSON PTY. LTD.—Telefonaktiebolaget LM Ericsson; *Int'l*, pg. 1369
LNR COMMUNICATIONS; *U.S. Private*, pg. 639

LXE INC.—Electromagnetic Sciences, Inc.; *U.S. Public*, pg. 569
LAMBDA ADVANCED ANALOG—Siebe plc; *Int'l*, pg. 1241
LAND MOBILE PRODUCTS SECTOR, MID ATLANTIC—Motorola, Inc.; *U.S. Public*, pg. 1137
LARSE CORPORATION—Axel Johnson AB; *Int'l*, pg. 710
LASER DIODE PRODUCTS—Morgan Crucible Co. Plc; *Int'l, pg. 892*
LECTRO PRODUCTS, INC.—BTR plc; *Int'l*, pg. 126
LICOM, INC.—V-Band Corporation; *U.S. Public*, pg. 1702
LOCKHEED MARTIN COMMAND & CONTROL SYSTEMS—Lockheed Martin Corporation; *U.S. Public*, pg. 1008
LOCKHEED MARTIN INFARED IMAGING SYSTEMS—Lockheed Martin Corporation; *U.S. Public*, pg. 1008
LOCKHEED MARTIN WESTERN DEVELOPMENT LABS—Lockheed Martin Corporation; *U.S. Public*, pg. 1009
LOCUS, INC.—Kaman Corporation; *U.S. Public*, pg. 942
LOJACK CORPORATION; *U.S. Public*, pg. 1012
LUCENT TECHNOLOGIES INC.; *U.S. Public*, pg. 1017
LUWA AG—Hesta Tex AG; *Int'l*, pg. 617
MLM DIVISION/ELECTRONICS GROUP—Israel Aircraft Industries Ltd.; *Int'l*, pg. 690
MAGNETIC AB—Telefonaktiebolaget LM Ericsson; *Int'l*, pg. 1364
MARK ANTENNA PRODUCTS, INC.—COMSAT Corporation; *U.S. Public*, pg. 424
MATH ASSOCIATES—General Microwave Corporation; *U.S. Public*, pg. 717
MATRA MARCONI SPACE—The General Electric Company, p.l.c.; *Int'l*, pg. 545
MATRA MARCONI SPACE UK LTD.—The General Electric Company, p.l.c.; *Int'l*, pg. 545
MATSUSHITA COMMUNICATION INDUSTRIAL CO., LTD.—Matsushita Electric Industrial Co., Ltd.; *Int'l*, pg. 846
MCBRIDE AND ASSOCIATES, INC.; *U.S. Private*, pg. 719
MEASUREMENT SCIENCE, INC.—The PBS&J Corporation; *U.S. Private*, pg. 826
MEGAHERTZ HOLDING INC.—3Com Corporation; *U.S. Public*, pg. 1604
MERET COMMUNICATIONS—Osicom Technologies Inc.; *U.S. Public*, pg. 1233
MICROFLECT COMPANY, INC.—Valmont Industries, Inc.; *U.S. Public*, pg. 1707
MICROWAVE DATA SYSTEMS, INC.—California Microwave, Inc.; *U.S. Public*, pg. 293
MILITARY AVIONICS DIVISION—Honeywell Inc.; *U.S. Public*, pg. 834
MITSUBISHI ELECTRIC CORPORATION; *Int'l*, pg. 872
MOOG SPACE PRODUCTS DIV.—Moog Incorporated; *U.S. Public*, pg. 1127
MOSLER INC.; *U.S. Private*, pg. 763
MOTOROLA, INC.; *U.S. Public*, pg. 1136
MULTIPLEX TECHNOLOGY, INC.—Valley Forge Corporation; *U.S. Public*, pg. 1705
MURATECH AMERICA, INC.—Murata Machinery, Ltd.; *Int'l, pg. 897*
N-LYNX ANDREW—Andrew Corporation; *U.S. Public*, pg. 112
NFT ERICSSON COMMUNICATIONS ANS—Telefonaktiebolaget LM Ericsson; *Int'l*, pg. 1369
NAPCO SECURITY SYSTEMS, INC.; *U.S. Public*, pg. 1151
NATIONAL MOBILE RADIO LIMITED—Motorola, Inc.; *U.S. Public*, pg. 1140
NETRIX, CORP.; *U.S. Private*, pg. 791
NEW BEDFORD PANORAMEX CORPORATION; *U.S. Private*, pg. 792
NEXTEL COMMUNICATIONS; *U.S. Public*, pg. 1180
N.V. NIRA COMMUNICATION SYSTEMS—Telefonaktiebolaget LM Ericsson; *Int'l*, pg. 1369
NOKIA CELLULAR SYSTEMS—Oy Nokia Ab/Nokia Group; *Int'l*, pg. 953
NOKIA DISPLAY PRODUCTS OY—Oy Nokia Ab/Nokia Group; *Int'l*, pg. 951
NOKIA SATELLITE SYSTEMS AB—Oy Nokia Ab/Nokia Group; *Int'l*, pg. 954
NOKIA TELECOMMUNICATIONS—Oy Nokia Ab/Nokia Group; *Int'l*, pg. 952
NORTEL AUSTRALIA PTY. LIMITED—Northern Telecom Limited; *Int'l*, pg. 970
NORTEL DASA NETWORK SYSTEMS GMBH & CO. KG—Northern Telecom Limited; *Int'l*, pg. 970
NORTHERN IRELAND LIMITED—Northern Telecom Limited; *Int'l*, pg. 970
NORTHERN TELECOM—Northern Telecom Limited; *Int'l*, pg. 970
NORTHERN TELECOM INDUSTRIES SDN. BHD.—Northern Telecom Limited; *Int'l*, pg. 970
NORTHERN TELECOM (IRELAND) LIMITED—Northern Telecom Limited; *Int'l*, pg. 970
NORTHERN TELECOM LIMITED; *Int'l*, pg. 968
NORTHERN TELECOM - NATIONAL REPAIR & DISTRIBUTION CENTER—Northern Telecom Limited; *Int'l*, pg. 970
ODETICS INC.; *U.S. Public*, pg. 1212
OKI TELECOM GROUP—Oki Electric Industry Company, Ltd.; *Int'l*, pg. 1000
OMNITRACS DIVISION—QUALCOMM; *U.S. Public*, pg. 1349
OMRON CORPORATION; *Int'l*, pg. 1005
ORBITAL SCIENCES CORPORATION; *U.S. Public*, pg. 1229
ORTEL CORPORATION; *U.S. Public*, pg. 1232
PHH CORPORATION—Cendant Corporation; *U.S. Public*, pg. 321
PARK AIR ELECTRONICS LTD.—Northrop Grumman Corporation; *U.S. Public*, pg. 1198
PHILNET ERICSSON INC.—Telefonaktiebolaget LM Ericsson; *Int'l*, pg. 1369
PICKER INTERNATIONAL CANADA INC.—The General Electric Company, p.l.c.; *Int'l*, pg. 545
PICO PRODUCTS, INC.; *U.S. Public*, pg. 1294
PITNEY BOWES INC.; *U.S. Public*, pg. 1303
C. PLATH—Litton Industries, Inc.; *U.S. Public*, pg. 1005
PRIMEDIA WORKPLACE LEARNING—Primedia Inc.; *U.S. Public*, pg. 1328
PRISM SYSTEMS INC.—Northern Telecom Limited; *Int'l*, pg. 969
PROXIM, INC.; *U.S. Public*, pg. 1338
PULSE COMMUNICATIONS, INC.—Hubbell Incorporated; *U.S. Public*, pg. 844
QEI, INC.; *U.S. Private*, pg. 897
R.X.D., INC.—Relm Wireless Corp.; *U.S. Public*, pg. 1376
RACAL CANADA INC.—Racal Electronics Plc; *Int'l*, pg. 1083
RACAL COMMUNICATIONS, INC.—Racal Electronics Plc; *Int'l*, pg. 1083
RACAL ELECTRONICS PLC; *Int'l*, pg. 1082
RADIOSYSTEM SWEDEN AB—Telefonaktiebolaget LM Ericsson; *Int'l*, pg. 1364
RANK CINTEL LTD.—The Rank Group PLC; *Int'l*, pg. 1087
RANTEC MICROWAVE AND ELECTRONICS, INC.—ESCO Electronics Corporation; *U.S. Public*, pg. 546
RAULAND-BORG CORPORATION; *U.S. Private*, pg. 911
RAYTHEON CANADA LIMITED—Raytheon Company; *U.S. Public*, pg. 1366
RAYTHEON E-SYSTEMS—Raytheon Company; *U.S. Public*, pg. 1365
RAYTHEON MARINE SALES & SERVICES CO.—Raytheon Company; *U.S. Public*, pg. 1366
RELM COMMUNICATIONS, INC.—Relm Wireless Corp.; *U.S. Public*, pg. 1376
RELM WIRELESS CORP.; *U.S. Public*, pg. 1376
REMSDAQ LIMITED—DAQ Electronics Inc.; *U.S. Private*, pg. 300
RICO GESELLSCHAFT FUR MICROELECTRONIK MBH—Rothenberger Group GmbH; *Int'l*, pg. 1129
ROCKWELL-COLLINS (U.K.) LTD.—Rockwell International Corporation; *U.S. Public*, pg. 1400
ROCKWELL INTERNATIONAL CORPORATION; *U.S. Public*, pg. 1397
ROTHENBERGER UMWELTTECHNIK GMBH—Rothenberger Group GmbH; *Int'l*, pg. 1128
SAGEM TERMINALS & TELECOMMUNICATIONS DIVISION—Societe d'Applications Generales d'Electricite et de Mechanique; *Int'l*, pg. 1273
SIMCO ERICSSON LTD.—Telefonaktiebolaget LM Ericsson; *Int'l*, pg. 1370
SITEL-SOCIETE INDUSTRIELLE ALGERIENNE DE TELECOMMUNICATIONS—Telefonaktiebolaget LM Ericsson; *Int'l*, pg. 1370
SSE TELECOM, INC.; *U.S. Public*, pg. 1421
STM WIRELESS, INC.; *U.S. Public*, pg. 1421
SAAB AUTOMATION AB—Investor AB; *Int'l*, pg. 686
SAAB SPACE AB—Investor AB; *Int'l*, pg. 687
SAGEM—Societe d'Applications Generales d'Electricite et de Mechanique; *Int'l*, pg. 1273
SAMSUNG ELECTRONICS CO., LTD.—Samsung Group; *Int'l*, pg. 1181
SATCOM INTERNATIONAL—British Aerospace p.l.c.; *Int'l*, pg. 218
SATCOM TECHNOLOGIES DIVISION—COMSAT Corporation; *U.S. Public*, pg. 424
SATELLITE DATA NETWORKS—General Instrument Corporation; *U.S. Public*, pg. 716
SATELLITE NETWORKS DIVISION—COMSAT Corporation; *U.S. Public*, pg. 424
SATELLITE TECHNICAL MANAGEMENT—SGS Societe Generale de Surveillance Holding S.A.; *Int'l*, pg. 1154
SAUDI ERICSSON COMMUNICATIONS CO. LTD.—Telefonaktiebolaget LM Ericsson; *Int'l*, pg. 1369
SCIENTIFIC-ATLANTA CANADA, INC.—Scientific-Atlanta, Inc.; *U.S. Public*, pg. 1443
SCIENTIFIC-ATLANTA, INC.; *U.S. Public*, pg. 1443
SCIENTIFIC COMMUNICATIONS, INC.—Andrew Corporation; *U.S. Public*, pg. 112
SECURE COMMUNICATIONS DIVISION—General Kinetics Incorporated; *U.S. Public*, pg. 717
SEMP TOSHIBA AMAZONAS S.A.—Toshiba Corporation; *Int'l*, pg. 1406
SENCORE, INC.; *U.S. Private*, pg. 983
SENTRY TECHNOLOGY CORP.; *U.S. Public*, pg. 1458
SETEMER, S.P.A.—Telefonaktiebolaget LM Ericsson; *Int'l*, pg. 1369
SIECOR CORPORATION—Corning Incorporated; *U.S. Public*, pg. 449
SIELTE, S.P.A.—Telefonaktiebolaget LM Ericsson; *Int'l*, pg. 1370
SIEMENS S.A.—Siemens AG; *Int'l*, pg. 1248
SISTEMAS ERICSSON S.A. DE C.V.—Telefonaktiebolaget LM Ericsson; *Int'l*, pg. 1370
SMARTRUNK SYSTEMS, INC.; *U.S. Private*, pg. 1006
SOCIEDADE ERICSSON DE PORTUGAL LDA.—Telefonaktiebolaget LM Ericsson; *Int'l*, pg. 1370
SOCIETE D'APPLICATIONS GENERALES D'ELECTRICITE ET DE MECHANIQUE; *Int'l*, pg. 1273
SONY DEUTSCHLAND GMBH—Sony Corporation; *Int'l*, pg. 1284
SONY TRANS COM SYSTEMS INC.—Sony Corporation; *Int'l*, pg. 1281
SOUNDCRAFT ELECTRONICS, LTD—Harman International Industries, Inc.; *U.S. Public*, pg. 787
STET SOCIETA FINANZIARIA TELEFONICA—IRI Istituto Ricostruzione Industriale; *Int'l*, pg. 655
STORNO LIMITED—Motorola, Inc.; *U.S. Public*, pg. 1140
STUDER—Harman International Industries, Inc.; *U.S. Public*, pg. 788
SUPERIOR TELECOMMUNICATIONS—The Alpine Group, Inc.; *U.S. Public*, pg. 58
SWEDISH ERICSSON COMPANY LTD.—Telefonaktiebolaget LM Ericsson; *Int'l*, pg. 1370
SWITCHCRAFT, INC.—Raytheon Company; *U.S. Public*, pg. 1366
SYSTEM PLANNING CORP.; *U.S. Private*, pg. 1061
SYSTEMS & ELECTRONICS INC.—ESCO Electronics Corporation; *U.S. Public*, pg. 547
TEL-CA-TELECOMMUNICAZIONI CALABRESE S.P.A.—Telefonaktiebolaget LM Ericsson; *Int'l*, pg. 1370
TII-DITEL—TII Industries, Inc.; *U.S. Public*, pg. 1556
TII DOMINICANA INC.—TII Industries, Inc.; *U.S. Public*, pg. 1556
TII INDUSTRIES, INC.; *U.S. Public*, pg. 1556
TRW INC.; *U.S. Public*, pg. 1558
TVT—Harris Corporation; *U.S. Public*, pg. 791
TALK-A-PHONE CO.; *U.S. Private*, pg. 1067
TECHNOLOGY FOR COMMUNICATIONS INTERNATIONAL—TCI International Inc.; *U.S. Public*, pg. 1555
TECHNOPHONE MANUFACTURING (H.K.) LTD.—Oy Nokia Ab/Nokia Group; *Int'l*, pg. 952
TELEFONAKTIEBOLAGET LM ERICSSON; *Int'l*, pg. 1363
TELEFONAKTIEBOLAGET LM ERICSSON BUREAUX TECHNIQUES D'ALGERIE—Telefonaktiebolaget LM Ericsson; *Int'l*, pg. 1370
TELEFONICA DE ESPANA, S.A.; *Int'l*, pg. 1371
TELEGENIX INC.; *U.S. Private*, pg. 1073
TELENORMA GMBH—Robert Bosch GmbH; *Int'l*, pg. 204
TELEQUIPOS, S.A.—Telefonaktiebolaget LM Ericsson; *Int'l, pg. 1371*
TELERIC PTY. LTD.—Telefonaktiebolaget LM Ericsson; *Int'l*, pg. 1371
TELUS MARKETING COMMUNICATIONS—Telus Corporation; *Int'l*, pg. 1374
THOMSON MULTIMEDIA SA—Thomson S.A.; *Int'l*, pg. 1384
THOMSON S.A.; *Int'l*, pg. 1381
TITAN LINKABIT—The Titan Corporation; *U.S. Public*, pg. 1618
TOM THUMB FOOD & PHARMACY—Randalls Food Markets, Inc.; *U.S. Private*, pg. 909
TONG GUANG-NORTEL LIMITED LIABILITY COMPANY—Northern Telecom Limited; *Int'l*, pg. 970
TOSHIBA AMERICA CONSUMER PRODUCTS, INC.—Toshiba Corporation; *Int'l*, pg. 1405
TOSHIBA AMERICA INFORMATION SYSTEMS, INC.—Toshiba Corporation; *Int'l*, pg. 1405
TOSHIBA CORPORATION; *Int'l*, pg. 1402
TOSHIBA LOGISTIC SUPPORT CORPORATION—Toshiba Corporation; *Int'l*, pg. 1404
TOSHIBA VISUAL-EQUIPMENT CORPORATION—Toshiba Corporation; *Int'l*, pg. 1405
TRANSCRYPT INTERNATIONAL; *U.S. Public*, pg. 1630
TURNKEY TECHNOLOGIES, INC.; *U.S. Private*, pg. 1110
UNR-ROHN DIV.—ROHN Industries, Inc.; *U.S. Public*, pg. 1404
UNIDEN CORPORATION; *Int'l*, pg. 1433
UNITED STATES SATELLITE BROADCASTING, CO.—Hubbard Broadcasting, Inc.; *U.S. Private*, pg. 544
VERTEX ANTENNENTECHNIK GMBH—Vertex Communications Corporation; *U.S. Public*, pg. 1718
VERTEX COMMUNICATIONS CORPORATION; *U.S. Public*, pg. 1717
VICON INDUSTRIES, INC.; *U.S. Public*, pg. 1719
VICON INDUSTRIES-SOUTHERN INC.—Vicon Industries, Inc.; *U.S. Public*, pg. 1719
VODAFONE GROUP PLC; *Int'l*, pg. 1469
WANDEL & GOLTERMANN TECHNOLOGIES, INC.—Wandel & Goltermann GmbH & Co., Elektronische Messtechnik; *Int'l*, pg. 1486
WARD PRODUCTS CORPORATION; *U.S. Private*, pg. 1149
WEGENER CORPORATION; *U.S. Public*, pg. 1751
WHEELOCK INC.; *U.S. Private*, pg. 1171
WIRELESS ONE NETWORK LP; *U.S. Private*, pg. 1184
WORLDCOM/IDB SYSTEMS—WorldCom, Inc.; *U.S. Public, pg. 1779*

3669 — COMMUNICATIONS EQUIPMENT, NEC

ABB REGIONAL PRODUCT CENTRE PTE. LTD.—ABB Asea Brown Boveri (Holding) Ltd.; *Int'l*, pg. 2
AC CORPORATION; *U.S. Private*, pg. 3
ADC TELECOM CANADA INC.—ADC Telecommunications, Inc.; *U.S. Public*, pg. 4
ADC TELECOMUNICACIONES VENEZUELA, S.A.—ADC Telecommunications, Inc.; *U.S. Public*, pg. 4
ADT PHONE & MODERN SECURITY—Tyco International Ltd.; *U.S. Public*, pg. 1649
AIL SYSTEMS INC.—Eaton Corporation; *U.S. Public*, pg. 556
AR DIVISION OF TELENEX—General Signal Corporation; *U.S. Public*, pg. 727
AT&T DATATEK INC.—AT&T Corporation; *U.S. Public*, pg. 10
ADEMCO MICROTECH LIMITED—Pittway Corporation; *U.S. Public*, pg. 1307
ADEMCO SENSOR COMPANY—Pittway Corporation; *U.S. Public*, pg. 1306
ADVANCED MICRO DEVICES, INC.; *U.S. Public*, pg. 21
AEROJET AZUSA OPERATIONS—GenCorp Inc.; *U.S. Public*, pg. 706
AIR TRAFFIC CONTROL SYSTEMS DIVISION—Harris Corporation; *U.S. Public*, pg. 792
AIRTRON—Litton Industries, Inc.; *U.S. Public*, pg. 1003
AIWA CO., LTD.—Sony Corporation; *Int'l*, pg. 1280
ALARM DEVICE MANUFACTURING COMPANY—Pittway Corporation; *U.S. Public*, pg. 1306
ALCATEL AUSTRIA A.G.—Alcatel Alsthom Compagnie Generale D'Electricite; *Int'l*, pg. 55
ALCATEL NETWORK SYSTEMS, INC. (TX)—Alcatel Alsthom Compagnie Generale D'Electricite; *Int'l*, pg. 55
ALCATEL STANDARD ELECTRICA, S.A—Telefonica de Espana, S.A.; *Int'l*, pg. 1372
ALCATEL TELECOM—Alcatel Alsthom Compagnie Generale D'Electricite; *Int'l*, pg. 55
ALENIA SISTEMI CIVILI—IRI Istituto Ricostruzione Industriale; *Int'l*, pg. 653
ALLIED RESEARCH CORPORATION; *U.S. Public*, pg. 48

ALLIEDSIGNAL AEROSPACE—AlliedSignal Inc.; U.S. Public, pg. 50
ALLIEDSIGNAL AIR TRANSPORT AVIONICS—AlliedSignal Inc.; U.S. Public, pg. 50
ALLIEDSIGNAL CONTROLS & ACCESSORIES—AlliedSignal Inc.; U.S. Public, pg. 50
ALLIEDSIGNAL (LTD.) SINGAPORE—AlliedSignal Inc.; U.S. Public, pg. 53
ALLIEDSIGNAL OCEAN SYSTEMS—AlliedSignal Inc.; U.S. Public, pg. 50
ALTEC LANSING CORP.—Greenwich Street Capital Partners, Inc.; U.S. Private, pg. 479
AMERICAN TRADING AND PRODUCTION CORPORATION; U.S. Private, pg. 63
ANDREA ELECTRONICS CORPORATION; U.S. Public, pg. 112
ANDREW CORPORATION; U.S. Public, pg. 112
ANDREW INTERNATIONAL CORP.—Andrew Corporation; U.S. Public, pg. 112
ANES SECURITY, INC.—Code-Alarm, Inc.; U.S. Public, pg. 394
ANSALDO TRANSPORTI-MILAN PLANT—IRI Istituto Ricostruzione Industriale; Int'l, pg. 653
ANSALDO TRANSPORTI SPA—IRI Istituto Ricostruzione Industriale; Int'l, pg. 653
ANTENNA PRODUCTS CORP.—Cabre Corp.; U.S. Public, pg. 289
ANTENNACRAFT CO.—Tandy Corporation; U.S. Public, pg. 1560
APEX—Pittway Corporation; U.S. Public, pg. 1306
APPLIED TECHNOLOGY—Litton Industries, Inc.; U.S. Public, pg. 1002
ASCEND COMMUNICATIONS, INC.; U.S. Public, pg. 138
ASCOM BUSINESS SYSTEMS AG—Ascom Holding AG; Int'l, pg. 86
ASCOM ERICSSON TRANSMISSION AG—Ascom Holding AG; Int'l, pg. 86
ASCOM ERICSSON TRANSMISSION AG—Telefonaktiebolaget LM Ericsson; Int'l, pg. 1364
ASCOM HASLER AG—Ascom Holding AG; Int'l, pg. 86
ASCOM HOLDING AG; Int'l, pg. 86
ASCOM TIMEPLEX—Ascom Holding AG; Int'l, pg. 86
ASTRO AEROSPACE CORP.—Spar Aerospace Limited; Int'l, pg. 1288
ASTRONAUTICS CORPORATION OF AMERICA; U.S. Private, pg. 93
ATALLA CORPORATION—COMPAQ Computer Corporation; U.S. Public, pg. 417
ATKINSON DYNAMICS COMPANY—Atkinson; U.S. Public, pg. 143
ATLAS/SOUNDOLIER—American Trading and Production Corporation; U.S. Private, pg. 64
ATTACHMATE; U.S. Private, pg. 98
AUDIBLE/VISIBLE & WATERFLOW DIVISION—Pittway Corporation; U.S. Public, pg. 1306
AUDIOVOX CORPORATION; U.S. Public, pg. 147
AVNET, INC.; U.S. Public, pg. 155
AYDIN CORPORATION; U.S. Public, pg. 158
AYDIN CORPORATION WEST—Aydin Corporation; U.S. Public, pg. 158
AYDIN DISPLAYS (EAST)—Aydin Corporation; U.S. Public, pg. 158
AYDIN VECTOR DIV.—Aydin Corporation; U.S. Public, pg. 158
BCE INC.; Int'l, pg. 114
BS & B SAFETY SYSTEMS—International Systems & Controls Corp.; U.S. Private, pg. 572
BALL SYSTEMS ENGINEERING OPERATIONS—Ball Corporation; U.S. Public, pg. 171
BASEL TRADING COMPANY LTD.; Int'l, pg. 169
BETZDEARBORN INC.; U.S. Public, pg. 226
BLACK BOX CORPORATION OF PENNSYLVANIA—Black Box Corporation of PA; U.S. Public, pg. 235
BYTEX CORPORATION—Storage Technology Corporation; U.S. Public, pg. 1522
CBS CORPORATION; U.S. Public, pg. 273
CVD INCORPORATED—Morton International Inc.; U.S. Public, pg. 1135
CXR TELCOM CORPORATION—Microtel International Inc.; U.S. Public, pg. 1108
CABLE CONSTRUCTORS, INC.; U.S. Private, pg. 197
CABLE PRODUCTOS DE CHIHUAHUA, S.A. DE C.V.—Zenith Electronics Corp.; U.S. Public, pg. 1790
CABLE SPINNING EQUIPMENT INC.; U.S. Private, pg. 197
CABLESA-INDUSTRIA DE COMPONENTES ELECTRICOS SOCIEDADE ANONIMA—General Motors Corporation; U.S. Public, pg. 721
CALIFORNIA MICROWAVE FOREIGN SALES CORPORATION—California Microwave, Inc.; U.S. Public, pg. 293
CAMTEC ELECTRONIC LTD.—Telefonaktiebolaget LM Ericsson; Int'l, pg. 1365
CELTE S.P.A.—Telefonaktiebolaget LM Ericsson; Int'l, pg. 1365
CERBERUS PYROTRONICS INC.—Siemens AG; Int'l, pg. 1246
CHANNEL MASTER; U.S. Private, pg. 228
CHAPMAN SECURITY SYSTEMS, INC.—Code-Alarm, Inc.; U.S. Public, pg. 394
CHECKPOINT SYSTEMS INC.; U.S. Public, pg. 343
CHLORIDE GROUP PLC; Int'l, pg. 287
CIRCLE SERVICE CO.—Andrew Corporation; U.S. Public, pg. 112
CIRMA ENTERPRISE—Alcatel Alsthom Compagnie Generale D'Electricite; Int'l, pg. 53
DAVID CLARK COMPANY INCORPORATED; U.S. Private, pg. 242
COASTCAST CORPORATION; U.S. Public, pg. 391
CODE-ALARM, INC.; U.S. Public, pg. 393
CODE ALARM SECURITY SYSTEMS—Code-Alarm, Inc.; U.S. Public, pg. 394
COHERENT COMMUNICATIONS SYSTEMS CORP.—Safeguard Scientifics, Inc.; U.S. Public, pg. 1424
COHU, INC.; U.S. Public, pg. 396
COMMUNICATION TECHNIQUES, INC.—Dover Corporation; U.S. Public, pg. 521
COMPAGNIE DE FAISCEAUX TUNISIAN INTERNATIONAL S.A.—General Motors Corporation; U.S. Public, pg. 723
COMPANIA ANONIMA ERICSSON—Telefonaktiebolaget LM Ericsson; Int'l, pg. 1365
COMPANIA ERICSSON DE CHILE S.A.—Telefonaktiebolaget LM Ericsson; Int'l, pg. 1365
COMPANIA ERICSSON S.A.—Telefonaktiebolaget LM Ericsson; Int'l, pg. 1365
COMPANIA ERICSSON S.A.C.I.—Telefonaktiebolaget LM Ericsson; Int'l, pg. 1365
COMPUTER SERVICE COMPANY—Steiny & Company, Inc.; U.S. Private, pg. 1040
COMSAT RSI, INC.—COMSAT Corporation; U.S. Public, pg. 424
COMSTREAM CORPORATION—Spar Aerospace Limited; Int'l, pg. 1288
COMTECH ANTENNA SYSTEMS, INC.—Comtech Telecommunications Corp.; U.S. Public, pg. 425
COMTECH COMMUNICATIONS CORP.—Comtech Telecommunications Corp.; U.S. Public, pg. 425
COMTECH PST CORP.—Comtech Telecommunications Corp.; U.S. Public, pg. 425
COMTECH SYSTEMS, INC.—Comtech Telecommunications Corp.; U.S. Public, pg. 425
COMTECH TELECOMMUNICATIONS CORP.; U.S. Public, pg. 425
CONDON TV SYSTEMS, INC.—Telephone and Data Systems, Inc.; U.S. Public, pg. 1571
CONDUCTORES LATINCASA S.A. DE C.V.—Telefonaktiebolaget LM Ericsson; Int'l, pg. 1365
CONEXIONADOS ELECTRICOS TARAZONA S.A.—General Motors Corporation; U.S. Public, pg. 724
CONRAC DISPLAY PRODUCTS; U.S. Private, pg. 264
CONTINENTAL ELECTRONICS CORPORATION—Tech-Sym Corporation; U.S. Public, pg. 1563
CONTROL LASER CORPORATION—Excel Technology, Inc.; U.S. Public, pg. 599
A.C. COSSOR ELECTRONICS, LIMITED—Raytheon Company; U.S. Public, pg. 1366
CUBIC COMMUNICATIONS—Cubic Corporation; U.S. Public, pg. 466
CUBIC CORPORATION; U.S. Public, pg. 466
DANIEL AUTOMATION COMPANY—Daniel Industries, Inc.; U.S. Public, pg. 483
DANSK SIGNAL INDUSTRI A/S—Telefonaktiebolaget LM Ericsson; Int'l, pg. 1365
DATA INDUSTRIAL CORPORATION—Datamarine International, Inc.; U.S. Public, pg. 487
DATAMARINE INTERNATIONAL, INC.; U.S. Public, pg. 486
DELTRONICOS DE MATAMOROS S.A. DE C.V.—General Motors Corporation; U.S. Public, pg. 721
DETECTOR ELECTRONICS CORPORATION—Williams Holdings Plc; Int'l, pg. 1500
DIEBOLD, INCORPORATED; U.S. Public, pg. 506
R.R. DONNELLEY & SONS COMPANY; U.S. Public, pg. 517
DUKANE CORPORATION; U.S. Private, pg. 345
EAB ELECTRONIC APPARATEBAU GMBH—Rothenberger Group GmbH; Int'l, pg. 1129
EDO CORPORATION; U.S. Public, pg. 541
EEV LTD.—The General Electric Company, p.l.c.; Int'l, pg. 543
EF DATA CORP.—California Microwave, Inc.; U.S. Public, pg. 293
EG & G ASTROPHYSICS—EG & G, Inc.; U.S. Public, pg. 543
EATON CORPORATION; U.S. Public, pg. 555
ECONOLITE CANADA, INC.—Econolite Control Products, Inc.; U.S. Private, pg. 362
ECONOLITE CONTROL PRODUCTS, INC.; U.S. Private, pg. 361
ELECTRO PARTES DE MATAMOROS, S.A. DE C.V.—Zenith Electronics Corp.; U.S. Public, pg. 1790
ELECTROCOM AUTOMATION L.P.—Siemens AG; Int'l, pg. 1244
ELECTRODYNAMICS, INC.—Carpenter Technology Corporation; U.S. Public, pg. 308
ELECTROHOME LTD.; Int'l, pg. 438
ELECTRONIC NAVIGATION INDUSTRIES—Emerson Electric Co.; U.S. Public, pg. 574
ELECTROSPACE SYSTEMS, INC.—Raytheon Company; U.S. Public, pg. 1365
ENGINEERING RESEARCH ASSOCIATES—Raytheon Company; U.S. Public, pg. 1365
ENTERPRISE ELECTRONICS CORP.—Tech-Sym Corporation; U.S. Public, pg. 1563
ERICON PACKARD ELECTRIC COMPONENTES S.A.—General Motors Corporation; U.S. Public, pg. 724
ERICSSON AG—Telefonaktiebolaget LM Ericsson; Int'l, pg. 1366
ERICSSON BUSINESS COMMUNICATIONS GMBH—Telefonaktiebolaget LM Ericsson; Int'l, pg. 1366
ERICSSON BUSINESS COMMUNICATIONS NV/SA—Telefonaktiebolaget LM Ericsson; Int'l, pg. 1366
ERICSSON BUSINESS NETWORKS AB—Telefonaktiebolaget LM Ericsson; Int'l, pg. 1363
ERICSSON COMMUNICATIONS, INC.—Telefonaktiebolaget LM Ericsson; Int'l, pg. 1366
ERICSSON DE COLOMBIA S.A.—Telefonaktiebolaget LM Ericsson; Int'l, pg. 1366
ERICSSON DE GUATEMALA, S.A.—Telefonaktiebolaget LM Ericsson; Int'l, pg. 1366
ERICSSON DO BRASIL COMERCIO E INDUSTRIA S.A.—Telefonaktiebolaget LM Ericsson; Int'l, pg. 1366
ERICSSON (HELLAS) TELECOMMUNICATIONS EQUIPMENT S.A.—Telefonaktiebolaget LM Ericsson; Int'l, pg. 1366
ERICSSON HOLDING A/S—Telefonaktiebolaget LM Ericsson; Int'l, pg. 1367
ERICSSON HOLDING INTERNATIONAL B.V.—Telefonaktiebolaget LM Ericsson; Int'l, pg. 1367
ERICSSON INDIA LTD.—Telefonaktiebolaget LM Ericsson; Int'l, pg. 1367
ERICSSON LTD.—Telefonaktiebolaget LM Ericsson; Int'l, pg. 1367
ERICSSON NORTH AMERICA, INC.—Telefonaktiebolaget LM Ericsson; Int'l, pg. 1364
ERICSSON REDES S.A.—Telefonaktiebolaget LM Ericsson; Int'l, pg. 1367
ERICSSON S.A.—Telefonaktiebolaget LM Ericsson; Int'l, pg. 1367
ERICSSON SIELTE-INTERNATIONAL S.P.A.—Telefonaktiebolaget LM Ericsson; Int'l, pg. 1367
ERICSSON SIGNAL SYSTEMS AB—Telefonaktiebolaget LM Ericsson; Int'l, pg. 1364
ERICSSON SUC. URUGUAY—Telefonaktiebolaget LM Ericsson; Int'l, pg. 1367
ERICSSON SYSTEMS EXPERTISE LTD.—Telefonaktiebolaget LM Ericsson; Int'l, pg. 1367
ERICSSON TAIWAN LTD.—Telefonaktiebolaget LM Ericsson; Int'l, pg. 1367
ERICSSON TELECOM AB—Telefonaktiebolaget LM Ericsson; Int'l, pg. 1364
ERICSSON TELECOMMUNICATIE B.V.—Telefonaktiebolaget LM Ericsson; Int'l, pg. 1367
ERICSSON TELECOMMUNICATIONS SDN BHD—Telefonaktiebolaget LM Ericsson; Int'l, pg. 1368
ERICSSON TELECOMUNICACIONES S.A.—Telefonaktiebolaget LM Ericsson; Int'l, pg. 1368
ERICSSON TELEKOM GMBH—Telefonaktiebolaget LM Ericsson; Int'l, pg. 1368
ERICSSON TELEKOMUNIKASYON A.S.—Telefonaktiebolaget LM Ericsson; Int'l, pg. 1368
ERICSSON TRAFFIC SYSTEMS AB—Telefonaktiebolaget LM Ericsson; Int'l, pg. 1364
AB ERIFON KOREA BRANCH—Telefonaktiebolaget LM Ericsson; Int'l, pg. 1368
ERITEL AB—Telefonaktiebolaget LM Ericsson; Int'l, pg. 1364
ESQUIRE RADIO & ELECTRONICS INC.; U.S. Private, pg. 383
EVERT LARSSON INDUSTRI AB—Electrolux, AB; Int'l, pg. 439
FRL, INC.—Cohu, Inc.; U.S. Public, pg. 396
FACOMEC S.A.—Telefonaktiebolaget LM Ericsson; Int'l, pg. 1368
FALCON SAFETY PRODUCTS INC.; U.S. Private, pg. 392
FALLS CHURCH DIV.—Raytheon Company; U.S. Public, pg. 1365
FARADAY, INC.—Siemens AG; Int'l, pg. 1246
FARINON CANADA LTD.—Harris Corporation; U.S. Public, pg. 791
FATME SOC. PER AZ—Telefonaktiebolaget LM Ericsson; Int'l, pg. 1368
FERGUSON LIMITED—Thomson S.A.; Int'l, pg. 1384
FIRE BURGLARY INSTRUMENTS, INC.—Pittway Corporation; U.S. Public, pg. 1306
FIRE CONTROLS INSTRUMENTS—Pittway Corporation; U.S. Public, pg. 1306
FIRE LITE ALARMS, INC./NOTIFIER CO.—Pittway Corporation; U.S. Public, pg. 1306
FIRST ALERT PROFESSIONAL—Pittway Corporation; U.S. Public, pg. 1306
FOREM S.P.A.—Allen Telecom, Inc.; U.S. Public, pg. 46
FUJITSU ESPANA, S.A.—Fujitsu Limited; Int'l, pg. 528
FYRNETICS, INC.—Williams Holdings Plc; Int'l, pg. 1499
GN NETCOM A/S—GN Great Nordic Ltd.; Int'l, pg. 537
GN NETTEST, TELECOM DIVISION—GN Great Nordic Ltd.; Int'l, pg. 536
GENERAL ELECTRIC COMPANY; U.S. Public, pg. 709
GENERAL KINETICS INCORPORATED; U.S. Public, pg. 716
GENERAL RAILWAY SIGNAL CORP.—SASIB SpA; Int'l, pg. 1194
GIGA-TRONICS INCORPORATED; U.S. Public, pg. 742
GOVERNMENT COMPONENTS DIVISION—AMP Incorporated; U.S. Public, pg. 8
GRINNELL CORPORATION—Tyco International Ltd.; U.S. Public, pg. 1651
GRINNELL SISTEMAS DE PROTECCION CONTRA INCENDIO S.A. DE C.V.—Tyco International Ltd.; U.S. Public, pg. 1651
GROUND SYSTEMS GROUP—Raytheon Company; U.S. Public, pg. 1364
GUARDIAN ALARM OF CLEVELAND—Guardian Alarm Co.; U.S. Private, pg. 485
GUIDANCE & CONTROL SYSTEMS—Litton Industries, Inc.; U.S. Public, pg. 1002
GUIDANCE & CONTROL SYSTEMS DIV.—Litton Industries, Inc.; U.S. Public, pg. 1002
HRB SYSTEMS—Raytheon Company; U.S. Public, pg. 1365
HARMON INDUSTRIES, INC.; U.S. Public, pg. 788
HARRIS CORP., RF COMMUNICATIONS GROUP MARKETING DIVISION—Harris Corporation; U.S. Public, pg. 792
HARRIS CORPORATION; U.S. Public, pg. 791
HENSCHEL CORP.—SPD Technologies; U.S. Private, pg. 957
HERLEY INDUSTRIES, INC.; U.S. Public, pg. 811
RICHARD HIRSCHMANN GMBH & CO.—Rheinmetall Group; Int'l, pg. 1108
RICHARD HIRSCHMANN OF AMERICA, INC.—Rheinmetall Group; Int'l, pg. 1108
HOCHIKI AMERICA CORPORATION—Hochiki Corporation; Int'l, pg. 623
HOCHIKI CORPORATION; Int'l, pg. 623
HOCHIKI EUROPE U.K. LTD.—Hochiki Corporation; Int'l, pg. 623
HONEYWELL INC.; U.S. Public, pg. 833
HUBBARD COMMUNICATIONS—Hubbard Broadcasting, Inc.; U.S. Private, pg. 544
HUBBELL PREMISE WIRING, INC.—Hubbell Incorporated; U.S. Public, pg. 844
HUGHES ELECTRONICS CORPORATION—General Motors Corporation; U.S. Public, pg. 720

ICI AEROSPACE—Imperial Chemical Industries PLC; *Int'l*, pg. 663
ITT AEROSPACE/COMMUNICATIONS DIV.—ITT Industries, Inc.; *U.S. Public*, pg. 859
ITT GILFILLAN—ITT Industries, Inc.; *U.S. Public*, pg. 859
IMTECH PROJECTS ZUIT B.V.—Internatio-Muller N.V.; *Int'l*, pg. 681
INDUSTRIAS DE TELECOMMUNICACION S.A. (INTELSA)—Telefonaktiebolaget LM Ericsson; *Int'l*, pg. 1368
INDUSTRIAS ELECTRICAS DE QUILMES—Telefonaktiebolaget LM Ericsson; *Int'l*, pg. 1368
INDUSTRIAS MERRIMAC INCORPORADA, S.A.—Merrimac Industries, Inc.; *U.S. Public*, pg. 1098
INFORMATION SYSTEMS & NETWORK CORPORATION; *U.S. Private*, pg. 561
INTELLICALL, INC.; *U.S. Public*, pg. 887
INTELLIGENCE, INFORMATION & AIRCRAFT INTEGRATION SYSTEMS—Raytheon Company; *U.S. Public*, pg. 1364
INTERACTIVE TECHNOLOGIES, INC.; *U.S. Public*, pg. 888
INTERCON SECURITY LIMITED—Jannock Limited; *Int'l*, pg. 699
INTERNATIONAL BUSINESS MACHINES CORPORATION; *U.S. Public*, pg. 895
INTERSTATE ELECTRONICS CORP.—Figgie International Inc.; *U.S. Public*, pg. 622
INTERSTATE ENGINEERING; *U.S. Private*, pg. 573
JANNOCK LIMITED; *Int'l*, pg. 698
JEUMONT-SCHNEIDER OF AMERICA—Jeumont-Schneider Trenformeteurs; *Int'l*, pg. 706
JEUMONT-SCHNEIDER TRENFORMETEURS; *Int'l*, pg. 706
KNOGO CANADA—Sentry Technology Corp.; *U.S. Public*, pg. 1458
KABELWERKE REINSHAGEN GMBH—General Motors Corporation; *U.S. Public*, pg. 723
KE-MASTER—Sunroc Corporation; *U.S. Private*, pg. 1053
KIDDE-GRAVINER LTD.—Williams Holdings Plc; *Int'l*, pg. 1500
KNOGO CARIBE, INC.—Sentry Technology Corp.; *U.S. Public*, pg. 1458
KNURR AG; *Int'l*, pg. 739
KNURR AG—Knurr AG; *Int'l*, pg. 739
KNURR-LOMMATEC GMBH & CO. KG—Knurr AG; *Int'l*, pg. 739
KNURR NEDERLAND B.V.—Knurr AG; *Int'l*, pg. 739
KNURR-NORGE AS—Knurr AG; *Int'l*, pg. 739
KNURR NV BELGIE—Knurr AG; *Int'l*, pg. 739
KNURR-SPECTRA (S.E.A.) PTE. LTD.—Knurr AG; *Int'l*, pg. 739
KNURR SVERIGE AB—Knurr AG; *Int'l*, pg. 739
KNURR (UK) LTD.—Knurr AG; *Int'l*, pg. 739
KODAK GRAPHICS IMAGING SYSTEMS DIVISION—Eastman Kodak Company; *U.S. Public*, pg. 551
KRACO ENTERPRISES, INC.; *U.S. Private*, pg. 634
L3 COMMUNICATIONS CONIC DIV.—L3 Communications; *U.S. Private*, pg. 638
L3 COMMUNICATIONS NARDA-MICROWAVE WEST DIV.—L3 Communications; *U.S. Private*, pg. 638
L3 COMMUNICATIONS NARDA-MICROWAVE DIV.—L3 Communications; *U.S. Private*, pg. 638
LFE TRAFFIC CONTROL—Mark IV Industries Inc.; *U.S. Public*, pg. 1045
OY LM ERICSSON AB—Telefonaktiebolaget LM Ericsson; *Int'l*, pg. 1368
LM ERICSSON A/S—Telefonaktiebolaget LM Ericsson; *Int'l*, pg. 1368
LM ERICSSON HOLDINGS LTD.—Telefonaktiebolaget LM Ericsson; *Int'l*, pg. 1368
LM ERICSSON INTERNATIONAL AB JAPAN—Telefonaktiebolaget LM Ericsson; *Int'l*, pg. 1368
LM ERICSSON INTERNATIONAL AB SINGAPORE—Telefonaktiebolaget LM Ericsson; *Int'l*, pg. 1369
LM ERICSSON LTD.—Telefonaktiebolaget LM Ericsson; *Int'l*, pg. 1369
LM ERICSSON (NIGERIA) LTD.—Telefonaktiebolaget LM Ericsson; *Int'l*, pg. 1369
LM ERICSSON PTY. LTD.—Telefonaktiebolaget LM Ericsson; *Int'l*, pg. 1369
L3 COMMUNICATIONS HYCOR DIV.—L3 Communications; *U.S. Private*, pg. 638
JOHN LAING PLC; *Int'l*, pg. 796
LARSE CORPORATION—Axel Johnson AB; *Int'l*, pg. 710
LASER SYSTEMS—Litton Industries, Inc.; *U.S. Public*, pg. 1002
LEX GROUP—Alcatel Alsthom Compagnie Generale D'Electricite; *Int'l*, pg. 53
LIFELINE SYSTEMS, INC.; *U.S. Public*, pg. 992
LINEAR CORPORATION—Nortek, Inc.; *U.S. Public*, pg. 1193
LITTON INDUSTRIES, INC.; *U.S. Public*, pg. 1002
LOCKHEED MARTIN COMMAND & CONTROL SYSTEMS—Lockheed Martin Corporation; *U.S. Public*, pg. 1008
LOCKHEED MARTIN CORPORATION; *U.S. Public*, pg. 1006
LOCKHEED MARTIN ELECTRO-OPTICAL SYSTEMS—Lockheed Martin Corporation; *U.S. Public*, pg. 1008
LOCKHEED MARTIN INFARED IMAGING SYSTEMS—Lockheed Martin Corporation; *U.S. Public*, pg. 1008
LORAL SPACE & COMMUNICATIONS; *U.S. Public*, pg. 1014
LUMONICS CORP.—Sumitomo Heavy Industries, Ltd.; *Int'l*, pg. 1315
LUMONICS INC.—Sumitomo Heavy Industries, Ltd.; *Int'l*, pg. 1314
LUWA AG—Hesta Tex AG; *Int'l*, pg. 617
M/A-COM INC.—AMP Incorporated; *U.S. Public*, pg. 8
M & S SYSTEMS, INC.—Nortek, Inc.; *U.S. Public*, pg. 1193
MET S.A.—Telefonaktiebolaget LM Ericsson; *Int'l*, pg. 1369
MPH & CMI—MPD, Inc.; *U.S. Private*, pg. 687
MACE SECURITY INTERNATIONAL, INC.; *U.S. Public*, pg. 1030
MALRITE COMMUNICATIONS GROUP, INC.; *U.S. Private*, pg. 698
MARCONI INSTRUMENTS LTD.—The General Electric Company, p.l.c.; *Int'l*, pg. 544
MARTIN MARIETTA ASTRONAUTICS—Lockheed Martin Corporation; *U.S. Public*, pg. 1007
MARTIN MARIETTA CANADA LTD.—Lockheed Martin Corporation; *U.S. Public*, pg. 1009
MARTIN MARIETTA ELECTRONICS & MISSILES—Lockheed Martin Corporation; *U.S. Public*, pg. 1007
MATSUSHITA ELECTRIC WORKS, LTD.; *Int'l*, pg. 847
MCBRIDE AND ASSOCIATES, INC.; *U.S. Private*, pg. 719
MERAT OPTICAL COMMUNICATIONS—Osicom Technologies Inc.; *U.S. Public*, pg. 1233
MERET COMMUNICATIONS—Osicom Technologies Inc.; *U.S. Public*, pg. 1233
MERRIMAC INDUSTRIES, INC.; *U.S. Public*, pg. 1098
METRIC SYSTEMS CORP.—Tech-Sym Corporation; *U.S. Public*, pg. 1563
MICOM COMMUNICATIONS CORP.—Northern Telecom Limited; *Int'l*, pg. 969
MICRODYNE CORPORATION; *U.S. Public*, pg. 1105
MICRODYNE CORP.—Microdyne Corporation; *U.S. Public*, pg. 1105
MICROLITE CORPORATION—Pittway Corporation; *U.S. Public*, pg. 1306
MICROTEL INTERNATIONAL INC.; *U.S. Public*, pg. 1108
MINIMAX GMBH—Preussag AG; *Int'l*, pg. 1069
MOORE CORPORATION LIMITED; *Int'l*, pg. 888
MOSLER INC.; *U.S. Private*, pg. 763
MOTOROLA CELLULAR SERVICE, INC. (ILLINOIS)—Motorola, Inc.; *U.S. Public*, pg. 1138
MOTOROLA GENERAL SYSTEMS GROUP—Motorola, Inc.; *U.S. Public*, pg. 1137
MOTOROLA GOVERNMENT ELECTRONICS GROUP—Motorola, Inc.; *U.S. Public*, pg. 1137
MOTOROLA, INC.; *U.S. Public*, pg. 1136
MOTOROLA ISRAEL INFORMATION SYSTEMS LTD.—Motorola, Inc.; *U.S. Public*, pg. 1139
MOTOROLA MILITARY & AEROSPACE ELECTRONICS, INC.—Motorola, Inc.; *U.S. Public*, pg. 1138
N-LYNX ANDREW—Andrew Corporation; *U.S. Public*, pg. 112
NASAM INTERNATIONAL, INCORPORATED—Banner Aerospace, Inc.; *U.S. Public*, pg. 187
NIPPON TELEGRAPH AND TELEPHONE CORPORATION; *Int'l*, pg. 940
NIRA AUSTRALIA PTY. LTD.—Telefonaktiebolaget LM Ericsson; *Int'l*, pg. 1369
N.V. NIRA COMMUNICATION SYSTEMS—Telefonaktiebolaget LM Ericsson; *Int'l*, pg. 1369
NIRA DEUTSCHLAND ZWEIGNIEDERLASSUNG DER NIRA INTERNATIONAL B.V.—Telefonaktiebolaget LM Ericsson; *Int'l*, pg. 1369
NIRA NEDERLAND B.V.—Telefonaktiebolaget LM Ericsson; *Int'l*, pg. 1369
NORTEK, INC.; *U.S. Public*, pg. 1192
NOTIFIER NETWORK TECHNOLOGIES COMPANY—Pittway Corporation; *U.S. Public*, pg. 1306
NOVAR ELECTRONICS; *U.S. Private*, pg. 808
ODETICS INC.; *U.S. Public*, pg. 1212
OKI ELECTRIC INDUSTRY COMPANY, LTD.; *Int'l*, pg. 999
ORIENTAL TELECOMMUNICATION COMPANY LTD.—Telefonaktiebolaget LM Ericsson; *Int'l*, pg. 1369
OSICOM TECHNOLOGIES INC.; *U.S. Public*, pg. 1233
OSICOM TECHNOLOGIES INC.—Osicom Technologies Inc.; *U.S. Public*, pg. 1233
PACKARD ELECTRIC VAS KFT—General Motors Corporation; *U.S. Public*, pg. 723
PANALARM PRODUCTS, AMETEK, INC.—AMETEK, Inc.; *U.S. Public*, pg. 100
PERWIRA ERICSSON SDN. BHD.—Telefonaktiebolaget LM Ericsson; *Int'l*, pg. 1369
PHILIPS INDUSTRIE SA—Philips Electronics N.V.; *Int'l*, pg. 1055
PHILIPS INFORMATICA COMMUNICACIONES SA—Philips Electronics N.V.; *Int'l*, pg. 1055
PHILIPS KOMMUNIKATIONS INDUSTRIE AG—Philips Electronics N.V.; *Int'l*, pg. 1055
PHILNET ERICSSON INC.—Telefonaktiebolaget LM Ericsson; *Int'l*, pg. 1369
PICTURETEL; *U.S. Public*, pg. 1294
PILKINGTON PLC; *Int'l*, pg. 1056
PITTWAY CORPORATION; *U.S. Public*, pg. 1305
PITTWAY TECNOLOGICA S.P.A.—Pittway Corporation; *U.S. Public*, pg. 1307
PREFORMED LINE PRODUCTS; *U.S. Public*, pg. 1321
R. & H. SYSTEMS B.V.—Internatio-Muller N.V.; *Int'l*, pg. 680
RTS SYSTEMS—Telex Communications, Inc.; *U.S. Private*, pg. 1074
RACAL-DATACOM—Racal Electronics Plc; *Int'l*, pg. 1083
RACAL ELECTRONICS PLC; *Int'l*, pg. 1082
RACAL RADIO LIMITED—Racal Electronics Plc; *Int'l*, pg. 1082
RADAR SYSTEMS—Raytheon Company; *U.S. Public*, pg. 1364
RADAR SYSTEMS GROUP—Raytheon Company; *U.S. Public*, pg. 1364
RADIONICS, INC.—Detection Systems, Inc.; *U.S. Public*, pg. 501
RAYTHEON SYSTEMS COMPANY ELECTRONICS SYSTEMS—Raytheon Company; *U.S. Public*, pg. 1365
REINSHAGEN ITALIA SRL.—General Motors Corporation; *U.S. Public*, pg. 723
REINSHAGEN TOURNAI S.A.—General Motors Corporation; *U.S. Public*, pg. 723
RELIANCE ELECTRIC COMPANY—Rockwell International Corporation; *U.S. Public*, pg. 1398
RELM COMMUNICATIONS, INC.—Relm Wireless Corp.; *U.S. Public*, pg. 1376
RELTEC CORPORATION; *U.S. Private*, pg. 921
REMMELE ENGINEERING, INC.; *U.S. Private*, pg. 921
REMSDAQ LIMITED—DAQ Electronics Inc.; *U.S. Private*, pg. 300
RESEARCH, INCORPORATED; *U.S. Public*, pg. 1382
ROCKWELL AUSTRALIA LIMITED—Rockwell International Corporation; *U.S. Public*, pg. 1399
ROCKWELL SALES & SUPPORT SERVICES—Rockwell International Corporation; *U.S. Public*, pg. 1402
ROHN INDUSTRIES, INC.; *U.S. Public*, pg. 1404
SAB IBERICA S.A.—Cardo AB; *Int'l*, pg. 271
SAB SISTEMI S.P.A.—Cardo AB; *Int'l*, pg. 271
SAB WABCO AB—Cardo AB; *Int'l*, pg. 271
SAB WABCO BENELUX—Cardo AB; *Int'l*, pg. 271
SAB WABCO ENGINEERING S.R.L.—Cardo AB; *Int'l*, pg. 271
SAB WABCO HOLDINGS B.V.—Cardo AB; *Int'l*, pg. 271
SAB WABCO LTD.—Cardo AB; *Int'l*, pg. 271
SAB WABCO N.V.—Cardo AB; *Int'l*, pg. 271
SAB WABCO S.A.—Cardo AB; *Int'l*, pg. 271
SAB WABCO S.P.A.—Cardo AB; *Int'l*, pg. 271
SCI SYSTEMS, INC.; *U.S. Public*, pg. 1416
SEA, INC.—Datamarine International, Inc.; *U.S. Public*, pg. 487
SIELTE PADANA S.P.A.—Telefonaktiebolaget LM Ericsson; *Int'l*, pg. 1370
SIMCO ERICSSON LTD.—Telefonaktiebolaget LM Ericsson; *Int'l*, pg. 1370
SITEL-SOCIETE INDUSTRIELLE ALGERIENNE DE TELECOMMUNICATIONS—Telefonaktiebolaget LM Ericsson; *Int'l*, pg. 1370
SLC TECHNOLOGIES—Berwind Corporation; *U.S. Private*, pg. 138
SAFETRAN SYSTEMS CORPORATION—BTR plc; *Int'l*, pg. 127
SANDERS, A LOCKHEED MARTIN COMPANY—Lockheed Martin Corporation; *U.S. Public*, pg. 1008
SANYO ELECTRIC (HONG KONG) LIMITED—Sanyo Electric Co., Ltd.; *Int'l*, pg. 1192
SASIB SPA; *Int'l*, pg. 1194
SATELLITE TECHNOLOGY GROUP—Uniden Corporation; *Int'l*, pg. 1433
SCARFINI S.P.A.—Telefonaktiebolaget LM Ericsson; *Int'l*, pg. 1369
SCHINDLER AUFZUGE AG—Schindler Holding AG; *Int'l*, pg. 1204
SCHLAGE LOCK COMPANY—Ingersoll-Rand Company; *U.S. Public*, pg. 876
SCIENTIFIC COMMUNICATIONS, INC.—Andrew Corporation; *U.S. Public*, pg. 112
SECURIPLEX INC.—SNC-Lavalin Group Inc.; *Int'l*, pg. 1162
SECURITY HOUSE—Pittway Corporation; *U.S. Public*, pg. 1307
SEMAFOR A/S—Telefonaktiebolaget LM Ericsson; *Int'l*, pg. 1369
SENTROL CONTROLS GROUP—Berwind Corporation; *U.S. Private*, pg. 139
SENTRY TECHNOLOGY CORP.; *U.S. Public*, pg. 1458
SERVO CORPORATION OF AMERICA; *U.S. Private*, pg. 987
SETEMER, S.P.A.—Telefonaktiebolaget LM Ericsson; *Int'l*, pg. 1369
SHAKESPEARE COMPOSITES & ELECTRONICS—K2 Inc.; *U.S. Public*, pg. 940
SICILIANA ELECTRONICA & TELECOMUNICAZIONI S.P.A.—Telefonaktiebolaget LM Ericsson; *Int'l*, pg. 1370
SIELTE, S.P.A.—Telefonaktiebolaget LM Ericsson; *Int'l*, pg. 1370
SIEMENS AG OESTERREICH—Siemens AG; *Int'l*, pg. 1247
SIEMENS LTD.—Siemens AG; *Int'l*, pg. 1247
SIERRACOM—Sierra Technologies Inc.; *U.S. Private*, pg. 999
SIMPLIMATIC ENGINEERING CO.—Crown Cork & Seal Company, Inc.; *U.S. Public*, pg. 463
SISTEMAS ERICSSON S.A. DE C.V.—Telefonaktiebolaget LM Ericsson; *Int'l*, pg. 1370
SKAGGS TELECOMMUNICATIONS SERVICES, INC.—American Stores Company; *U.S. Public*, pg. 93
SOCIETE D'ETUDES ET DE CONSTRUCTIONS ELECTRONIQUES (SECRE)—Jeumont-Schneider Trenformeteurs; *Int'l*, pg. 706
SONY CORPORATION; *Int'l*, pg. 1280
SONY CORPORATION OF HONG KONG LTD.—Sony Corporation; *Int'l*, pg. 1284
SONY (U.K.) LTD.—Sony Corporation; *Int'l*, pg. 1284
SPAR AEROSPACE LIMITED; *Int'l*, pg. 1287
SPAR APPLIED SYSTEMS—Spar Aerospace Limited; *Int'l*, pg. 1288
SPAR SATELLITE SYSTEMS—Spar Aerospace Limited; *Int'l*, pg. 1288
SPRINT NORTH SUPPLY—Sprint Corporation; *U.S. Public*, pg. 1501
SQUARE D COMPANY—Schneider S.A.; *Int'l*, pg. 1208
STANLEY ACCESS TECHNOLOGIES—The Stanley Works; *U.S. Public*, pg. 1509
STEWART-WARNER ELECTRONICS COMPANY—Herley Industries, Inc.; *U.S. Public*, pg. 811
STEWART WARNER INSTRUMENTS CORPORATION; *U.S. Private*, pg. 1042
STEWART WARNER INSTRUMENTS CORPORATION—Stewart Warner Instruments Corporation; *U.S. Private*, pg. 1043
SUECOBRAS INDUSTRIA E COMERCIO LTDA.—Cardo AB; *Int'l*, pg. 271
SUMMA FOUR, INC.; *U.S. Public*, pg. 1527
SUNROC CORPORATION; *U.S. Private*, pg. 1053
SUTTLE COSTA RICA S.A.—Communications Systems, Inc.; *U.S. Public*, pg. 416
SWEDISH ERICSSON COMPANY LTD.—Telefonaktiebolaget LM Ericsson; *Int'l*, pg. 1370
SWISSCOM; *Int'l*, pg. 1334
SYNTRON, INC.—Tech-Sym Corporation; *U.S. Public*, pg. 1563
SYSTEM SENSOR DIVISION—Pittway Corporation; *U.S. Public*, pg. 1306

SYSTEMS ENGINEERING DIV.—Computer Sciences Corporation; *U.S. Public*, pg. 423
SYSTEMS GROUP—AMP Incorporated; *U.S. Public*, pg. 8
TCE TELEVISION SINGAPORE PTE. LTD.—Thomson S.A.; *Int'l*, pg. 1384
TEL-CA-TELECOMMUNICAZIONI CALABRESE S.P.A.—Telefonaktiebolaget LM Ericsson; *Int'l*, pg. 1370
TII DOMINICANA INC.—TII Industries, Inc.; *U.S. Public*, pg. 1556
TII INDUSTRIES, INC.; *U.S. Public*, pg. 1556
TALK-A-PHONE CO.; *U.S. Private*, pg. 1067
TATUNG COMPANY OF AMERICA—Tatung Corporation; *Int'l*, pg. 1357
TATUNG CORPORATION; *Int'l*, pg. 1357
TAU-TRON—General Signal Corporation; *U.S. Public*, pg. 727
TEKTRONIX, INC.; *U.S. Public*, pg. 1567
TELECOMMUNICATIONS GROUP—Watkins-Johnson Company; *U.S. Public*, pg. 1745
TELECOMMUNICATIONS TECHNIQUES CORP.—Dynatech Corporation; *U.S. Public*, pg. 539
TELECOMPONENTES ERICSSON S.A. DE C.V.—Telefonaktiebolaget LM Ericsson; *Int'l*, pg. 1370
TELEDYNE BROWN ENGINEERING—Allegheny Teledyne Incorporated; *U.S. Public*, pg. 43
TELEDYNE CONTINENTAL MOTORS—Allegheny Teledyne Incorporated; *U.S. Public*, pg. 43
TELEDYNE ELECTRONIC TECHNOLOGIES—Allegheny Teledyne Incorporated; *U.S. Public*, pg. 43
TELEFONAKTIEBOLAGET LM ERICSSON; *Int'l*, pg. 1363
TELEFONAKTIEBOLAGET LM ERICSSON BUREAUX TECHNIQUES D'ALGERIE—Telefonaktiebolaget LM Ericsson; *Int'l*, pg. 1370
TELEGENIX INC.; *U.S. Private*, pg. 1073
TELEINDUSTRIA ERICSSON, S.A. DE C.V.—Telefonaktiebolaget LM Ericsson; *Int'l*, pg. 1371
TELEPHONICS CORP.—Griffon Corp.; *U.S. Public*, pg. 766
TELEQUIPOS, S.A.—Telefonaktiebolaget LM Ericsson; *Int'l*, pg. 1371
TELERIC PTY. LTD.—Telefonaktiebolaget LM Ericsson; *Int'l*, pg. 1371
TESSCO GROUP, INC.—Code-Alarm, Inc.; *U.S. Public*, pg. 394
THOMAS & BETTS CORPORATION; *U.S. Public*, pg. 1597
THOMSON CFS-BELGIUM—Thomson S.A.; *Int'l*, pg. 1385
THOMSON-CSF S.A.—Thomson S.A.; *Int'l*, pg. 1383
THOMSON-LGT (LABORATOIRE GENERALE DES TELECOMMUNICATIONS)—Thomson S.A.; *Int'l*, pg. 1385
THORN-ERICSSON TELECOMMUNICATIONS LIMITED—Telefonaktiebolaget LM Ericsson; *Int'l*, pg. 1370
3COM PERSONAL COMMUNICATIONS DIV.—3Com Corporation; *U.S. Public*, pg. 1604
3COM, S.A.—3Com Corporation; *U.S. Public*, pg. 1604
3M; *U.S. Public*, pg. 1604
TOSHIBA LIGHTING & TECHNOLOGY CORPORATION—Toshiba Corporation; *Int'l*, pg. 1404
TRAK MICROWAVE CORP.—Tech-Sym Corporation; *U.S. Public*, pg. 1563
TRANSPORT, INC.—Danaher Corporation; *U.S. Public*, pg. 482
TURNKEY TECHNOLOGIES, INC.; *U.S. Private*, pg. 1110
UNR-ROHN DIV.—ROHN Industries, Inc.; *U.S. Public*, pg. 1404
ULTRA ELECTRONICS HOLDINGS PLC; *Int'l*, pg. 1431
UNICABLES, S.A.—General Motors Corporation; *U.S. Public*, pg. 724
UNICAL S.P.A.—Telefonaktiebolaget LM Ericsson; *Int'l*, pg. 1371
UNICAN SECURITY SYSTEMS LTD.; *Int'l*, pg. 1432
UNITEL VIDEO, INC.; *U.S. Public*, pg. 1692
UNIVERSAL VOLTRONICS CORPORATION—Thermo Electron Corporation; *U.S. Public*, pg. 1596
VTEL CORPORATION; *U.S. Public*, pg. 1703
VTEL EUROPE, LTD.—VTEL Corporation; *U.S. Public*, pg. 1703
VOLT DELTA RESOURCES, INC.—Volt Information Sciences, Inc.; *U.S. Public*, pg. 1724
VULCAN INC.; *U.S. Private*, pg. 1144
WATKINS-JOHNSON COMPANY; *U.S. Public*, pg. 1745
WELLS FARGO ALARM SERVICES, INC.—Borg-Warner Security Corporation; *U.S. Public*, pg. 246
WESTERN DIGITAL CORPORATION; *U.S. Public*, pg. 1758
WHEELOCK INC.; *U.S. Private*, pg. 1171
WHITTAKER CORPORATION; *U.S. Public*, pg. 1766
THE WILLIAMS COMPANIES, INC.; *U.S. Public*, pg. 1769
WILLIAMS TELECOMMUNICATIONS SYSTEMS, INC.—The Williams Companies, Inc.; *U.S. Public*, pg. 1769
XI'AN SYSTEM SENSOR ELECTRONICS, LTD.—Pittway Corporation; *U.S. Public*, pg. 1307
ZERO CORPORATION; *U.S. Public*, pg. 1791

3671 — ELECTRON TUBES

ADFLEX SOLUTIONS, INC.; *U.S. Public*, pg. 20
APEX INTERNATIONAL, INC.—Video Display Corporation; *U.S. Public*, pg. 1720
BMG ARIOLA MUSIC LTDA.—Bertelsmann AG; *Int'l*, pg. 192
BMG ARIOLA S.A. DE C.V. (MEXICO)—Bertelsmann AG; *Int'l*, pg. 192
BMS, INC.—Cohu, Inc.; *U.S. Public*, pg. 396
BERTELSMANN MUSIC GROUP—Bertelsmann AG; *Int'l*, pg. 191
CLARKE ELECTRONICS—Video Display Corporation; *U.S. Public*, pg. 1720
COHU, INC.; *U.S. Public*, pg. 396
COMPUTER PRODUCTS DIVISION—Analog Devices, Inc.; *U.S. Public*, pg. 108
DIAMOND VISION, INC.—Mitsubishi Electric Corporation; *Int'l*, pg. 873
DOTRONIX, INC.; *U.S. Public*, pg. 520
DUNBAR SALES INC.—Video Display Corporation; *U.S. Public*, pg. 1720
EG & G HEIMANN OPTO. GMBH—EG & G, Inc.; *U.S. Public*, pg. 544
EG & G OPTOELECTRONICS-SALEM—EG & G, Inc.; *U.S. Public*, pg. 543
ABDULLA FOUAD IMPALLOY LTD. CO.—Abdulla Fouad Co. Ltd.; *Int'l*, pg. 502
HOKUTO ELECTRONICS CO., LTD.—Toshiba Corporation; *Int'l*, pg. 1402
LG GROUP INC.—LG Group; *Int'l*, pg. 779
MAGNAVIEW INC.—Video Display Corporation; *U.S. Public*, pg. 1720
MICROWAVE MATERIALS GROUP-MICROWAVE MATERIALS DIV.—Rogers Corporation; *U.S. Public*, pg. 1402
NEC SEMICONDUCTORS SINGAPORE PTE. LTD.—NEC Corporation; *Int'l*, pg. 900
NATIONAL ELECTRONICS MANUFACTURING DIVISION—Richardson Electronics, Ltd.; *U.S. Public*, pg. 1388
NORITAKE CO., LIMITED; *Int'l*, pg. 958
PHILIPS COMPONENTS-DISCRETE PRODUCTS DIVISION—Philips Electronics N.V.; *Int'l*, pg. 1054
PHILIPS DISPLAY COMPONENTS—Philips Electronics N.V.; *Int'l*, pg. 1055
PRODUCTOS ELECTRONICOS LAGUNA—Thomson S.A.; *Int'l*, pg. 1383
RANK BRIMAR LTD.—The Rank Group PLC; *Int'l*, pg. 1087
RICHARDSON ELECTRONICS, LTD.; *U.S. Public*, pg. 1387
ROBERTSHAW CONTROLS COMPANY—Siebe plc; *Int'l*, pg. 1243
SANMINA CORPORATION-SAN JOSE—Sanmina Corporation; *U.S. Public*, pg. 1431
SCHLUMBERGER LIMITED; *U.S. Public*, pg. 1439
SHINKO TELECOMMUNICATIONS CONSTRUCTION CO., LTD.—The Furukawa Electric Co., Ltd.; *Int'l*, pg. 530
SOLADYNE DIVISION—Merix Corporation; *U.S. Public*, pg. 1097
SONY DISPLAY SYSTEMS—Sony Corporation; *Int'l*, pg. 1284
TII DOMINICANA INC.—TII Industries, Inc.; *U.S. Public*, pg. 1556
TII INDUSTRIES, INC.; *U.S. Public*, pg. 1556
TELTRON TECHNOLOGIES, INC.—Video Display Corporation; *U.S. Public*, pg. 1720
THOMSON BAUELEMENTE GMBH—Thomson S.A.; *Int'l*, pg. 1385
TOKYO BANKIN INDUSTRIES CO., LTD.—Toshiba Corporation; *Int'l*, pg. 1403
TOSHIBA DISPLAY DEVICES (THAILAND) CO., LTD.—Toshiba Corporation; *Int'l*, pg. 1406
VIDEO DISPLAY CORPORATION; *U.S. Public*, pg. 1720
VIDEO DISPLAY CORPORATION LIMITED—Video Display Corporation; *U.S. Public*, pg. 1720
WESTINGHOUSE POWER SYSTEMS GROUP—CBS Corporation; *U.S. Public*, pg. 273
WHITTAKER ELECTRONIC SYSTEMS—Whittaker Corporation; *U.S. Public*, pg. 1767
ZENITH ELECTRONICS CORP.; *U.S. Public*, pg. 1790

3672 — PRINTED CIRCUIT BOARDS

ACCESS CORPORATION—Oce-van der Grinten N.V.; *Int'l*, pg. 994
ADELANTOS DE TECNOLOGIA S.A. DE C.V.—SCI Systems, Inc.; *U.S. Public*, pg. 1417
ALLIEDSIGNAL ENVIRONMENTAL CATALYSTS—AlliedSignal Inc.; *U.S. Public*, pg. 51
ALLIEDSIGNAL INC.; *U.S. Public*, pg. 49
ALTRON SYSTEMS CORPORATION—Altron Incorporated; *U.S. Public*, pg. 59
AMERICAN COMPUTER ASSEMBLY/COMPAS—AIM Safety Company Inc.; *Int'l*, pg. 36
ANALOG DEVICES—Analog Devices, Inc.; *U.S. Public*, pg. 108
ARBCO ELECTRONICS—Imperial Chemical Industries PLC; *Int'l*, pg. 664
BENCHMARK ELECTRONICS INC.; *U.S. Public*, pg. 210
BENCHMARK ELECTRONICS, INC.-WINONA DIVISION—Benchmark Electronics Inc.; *U.S. Public*, pg. 211
BOEING NORTH AMERICA, AUTONETICS ELECTRONICS SYS DIV.—The Boeing Company; *U.S. Public*, pg. 241
BUREAU OF ENGRAVING; *U.S. Private*, pg. 181
C.S.I.—Olivetti SpA; *Int'l*, pg. 1002
CTS CORPORATION-CONNECTOR DIVISION—CTS Corporation; *U.S. Public*, pg. 285
CIRCUIT SYSTEMS, INC.; *U.S. Public*, pg. 374
CIRCUIT-WISE, INC.; *U.S. Private*, pg. 240
COMPAQ COMPUTER ASIA PTE LTD.—COMPAQ Computer Corporation; *U.S. Public*, pg. 418
COMPAS ELECTRONICS, INC.—AIM Safety Company Inc.; *Int'l*, pg. 36
CUPLEX, INC.; *U.S. Private*, pg. 297
DDL ELECTRONICS, INC.; *U.S. Public*, pg. 473
DAKTRONICS, INC.; *U.S. Public*, pg. 478
DATA GENERAL CORPORATION—Data General Corporation; *U.S. Public*, pg. 485
DOVER CORPORATION; *U.S. Public*, pg. 520
DYNAMICS CORPORATION OF AMERICA—CTS Corporation; *U.S. Public*, pg. 286
ELECTRONIC PRODUCTS DIVISION—3M; *U.S. Public*, pg. 1605
ELMO SEMICONDUCTEURS SARL—Kimball International, Inc.; *U.S. Public*, pg. 958
ELMO SEMICONDUCTOR CORP.—Kimball International, Inc.; *U.S. Public*, pg. 957
ENTHONE-OMI, INC.—Asarco Incorporated; *U.S. Public*, pg. 138
EPEC, INC.; *U.S. Private*, pg. 379
FLEXIBLE CIRCUIT PRODUCTS DIVISION—Parlex Corporation; *U.S. Public*, pg. 1264
FUJIKURA LTD.; *Int'l*, pg. 525
GIDDINGS & LEWIS, INC.—Thyssen AG; *Int'l*, pg. 1389
GLASTEEL INDUSTRIAL LAMINATES—The Alpha Corporation Of Tennessee; *U.S. Private*, pg. 45
GRAPHIC RESEARCH, INC.—Methode Electronics Inc.; *U.S. Public*, pg. 1101
HADCO CORPORATION; *U.S. Public*, pg. 773
HADCO CORPORATION—Hadco Corporation; *U.S. Public*, pg. 773
HARRIS SEMICONDUCTOR—Harris Corporation; *U.S. Public*, pg. 792
HERLEY INDUSTRIES, INC.; *U.S. Public*, pg. 811
HEWLETT-PACKARD PUERTO RICO—Hewlett-Packard Company; *U.S. Public*, pg. 816
IDD CO., LTD.—Rohm Co., Ltd.; *Int'l*, pg. 1125
IEC ARAB ALABAMA OPERATIONS—IEC Electronics Corp.; *U.S. Public*, pg. 855
IEC EDINBURG, TEXAS—IEC Electronics Corp.; *U.S. Public*, pg. 855
IEC ELECTRONICS CORP.; *U.S. Public*, pg. 854
IRLANDUS CIRCUITS LIMITED—DDL Electronics, Inc.; *U.S. Public*, pg. 473
KIMBALL ELECTRONICS GROUP—Kimball International, Inc.; *U.S. Public*, pg. 957
KIMBALL INTERNATIONAL, INC.; *U.S. Public*, pg. 956
LITTON SYSTEMS, INC. ADVANCED CIRCUITRY DIV.—Litton Industries, Inc.; *U.S. Public*, pg. 1003
MARCON ELECTRONICS CO., LTD.—Toshiba Corporation; *Int'l*, pg. 1403
THE MARMON GROUP, INC.; *U.S. Private*, pg. 706
MERIX CORPORATION; *U.S. Public*, pg. 1096
METHODE ELECTRONICS INC.-EAST—Methode Electronics Inc.; *U.S. Public*, pg. 1101
MICRONICS COMPUTERS, INC.; *U.S. Public*, pg. 1106
NCR CORPORATION; *U.S. Public*, pg. 1146
NU VISIONS MANUFACTURING CORP.—Nu Horizons Electronics Corp.; *U.S. Public*, pg. 1205
ORBOTECH PACIFIC LTD.—Orbotech Ltd.; *Int'l*, pg. 1007
ORBOTECH S.A., EUROPE—Orbotech Ltd.; *Int'l*, pg. 1007
PARLEX CORPORATION; *U.S. Public*, pg. 1264
PATHETEK—Eastman Kodak Company; *U.S. Public*, pg. 551
PHILIPS CIRCUIT ASSEMBLIES—Philips Electronics N.V.; *Int'l*, pg. 1054
PHILWAY PRODUCTS, INC.; *U.S. Private*, pg. 862
PRINTED CIRCUIT CORPORATION; *U.S. Private*, pg. 886
PROTO SYSTEMS OF ATLANTA; *U.S. Private*, pg. 891
QMS CIRCUITS, INC.—QMS, Inc.; *U.S. Public*, pg. 1346
RAVEN INDUSTRIES, INC.; *U.S. Public*, pg. 1361
ROGERS CORPORATION; *U.S. Public*, pg. 1402
SAMSUNG ELECTRON DEVICES CO., LTD.—Samsung Group; *Int'l*, pg. 1181
SIGMATRON, INC.—Circuit Systems, Inc.; *U.S. Public*, pg. 374
SILICONE TECHNOLOGIES—Bairnco Corporation; *U.S. Public*, pg. 165
SOLECTRON CORPORATION; *U.S. Public*, pg. 1483
SPANG & COMPANY; *U.S. Private*, pg. 1020
SPARTON CORPORATION; *U.S. Public*, pg. 1496
SPARTON ELECTRONICS FLORIDA, INC.—Sparton Corporation; *U.S. Public*, pg. 1496
STAR CIRCUITS—Daktronics, Inc.; *U.S. Public*, pg. 478
STONERIDGE, INC.; *U.S. Private*, pg. 1044
TEKNECOMP—Olivetti SpA; *Int'l*, pg. 1002
TEMPE ELECTRONICS CENTER—Varian Associates, Inc.; *U.S. Public*, pg. 1710
TOSHIBA COMPONENTS CO., LTD.—Toshiba Corporation; *Int'l*, pg. 1403
TULON CO.—Esterline Technologies Corporation; *U.S. Public*, pg. 594
VLSI TECHNOLOGY GMBH—VLSI Technology, Inc.; *U.S. Public*, pg. 1703
VARIAN ASSOCIATES, INC.; *U.S. Public*, pg. 1710
VISHAY INTERTECHNOLOGY, INC.; *U.S. Public*, pg. 1721
WESTINGHOUSE POWER SYSTEMS GROUP—CBS Corporation; *U.S. Public*, pg. 273

3674 — SEMICONDUCTORS & RELATED DEVICES

ABB HAFO INC.—ABB Asea Brown Boveri (Holding) Ltd.; *Int'l*, pg. 4
ABB TRACTION AB—ABB Asea Brown Boveri (Holding) Ltd.; *Int'l*, pg. 7
AIL SYSTEMS INC.—Eaton Corporation; *U.S. Public*, pg. 556
AMD FAR EAST, LTD.—Advanced Micro Devices, Inc.; *U.S. Public*, pg. 21
AMD (U.K.) LTD.—Advanced Micro Devices, Inc.; *U.S. Public*, pg. 21
AMP INC. LYTEL DIVISION—AMP Incorporated; *U.S. Public*, pg. 8
ATMI, INC.; *U.S. Public*, pg. 12
AVX CORPORATION—Kyocera Corporation; *Int'l*, pg. 775
AVX LEADED PRODUCTS DIV.—Kyocera Corporation; *Int'l*, pg. 775
AVX LTD.—Kyocera Corporation; *Int'l*, pg. 776
ADAPTEC, INC.; *U.S. Public*, pg. 19
ADVANCED INFORMATION TECHNOLOGY CENTER—Toshiba Corporation; *Int'l*, pg. 1405
ADVANCED MICRO DEVICES, INC.; *U.S. Public*, pg. 21
ADVANCED MICRO DEVICES, SDN BHD—Advanced Micro Devices, Inc.; *U.S. Public*, pg. 21
ADVANTEST CORPORATION; *Int'l*, pg. 25
AEROFLEX LABORATORIES INC.—Aeroflex Incorporated; *U.S. Public*, pg. 24
AETRIUM INC.; *U.S. Public*, pg. 27
AKZO ELECTRONICS MATERIALS CO.—Akzo Nobel N.V.; *Int'l*, pg. 48
AKZO NOBEL INC.—Akzo Nobel N.V.; *Int'l*, pg. 47
ALCATEL ALSTHOM COMPAGNIE GENERALE D'ELECTRICITE; *Int'l*, pg. 52
ALCATEL N.V.—Alcatel Alsthom Compagnie Generale D'Electricite; *Int'l*, pg. 55

ALLEGRO MICROSYSTEMS INC.—Sanken Electric Co., Ltd.; *Int'l*, pg. 1188
ALLIANCE SEMICONDUCTOR CORP.; *U.S. Public*, pg. 47
ALPHA INDUSTRIES, INC.; *U.S. Public*, pg. 57
ALPINE ELECTRONICS, INC.—Alps Electric Co., Ltd.; *Int'l*, pg. 65
ALPS ELECTRIC CO., LTD.; *Int'l*, pg. 65
ALTEC ELECTRONICA DE CHIHUAHUA S. A. DE C. V.—Ford Motor Company; *U.S. Public*, pg. 665
ALTERA CORPORATION; *U.S. Public*, pg. 59
AMETEK, INC.; *U.S. Public*, pg. 99
AMKOR ELECTRONICS, INC.; *U.S. Private*, pg. 66
AMP INC. LYTEL DIVISION—AMP Incorporated; *U.S. Public*, pg. 8
AMPERIF CORPORATION—Storage Technology Corporation; *U.S. Public*, pg. 1523
ANALOG DEVICES—Analog Devices, Inc.; *U.S. Public*, pg. 108
ANALOG DEVICES, INC.; *U.S. Public*, pg. 107
ANALOG DEVICES NEDERLAND B.V.—Analog Devices, Inc.; *U.S. Public*, pg. 108
APPLICATION SPECIFIC PRODUCTS GROUP—Philips Electronics N.V.; *Int'l*, pg. 1053
APPLIED MATERIALS, INC.; *U.S. Public*, pg. 123
APPLIED TECHNOLOGY (GERMANY)—Litton Industries, Inc.; *U.S. Public*, pg. 1004
AQUIONICS INC.—Halma p.l.c.; *Int'l*, pg. 590
ATLAS WEATHERING DSET LABORATORIES—Atlas Electric Devices Co.; *U.S. Private*, pg. 96
AURORA ELECTRONICS, INC.; *U.S. Public*, pg. 147
AVNET, INC.; *U.S. Public*, pg. 155
AYDIN CORPORATION; *U.S. Public*, pg. 158
AYDIN ELECTRO-FAB DIV.—Aydin Corporation; *U.S. Public*, pg. 158
BMG MUSIC CANADA—Bertelsmann AG; *Int'l*, pg. 192
BPB INDUSTRIES PLC; *Int'l*, pg. 122
BAIRNCO CORPORATION; *U.S. Public*, pg. 165
BALZERS—Oerlikon-Buhrle Holding AG; *Int'l*, pg. 997
BECKMAN INDUSTRIAL CORPORATION—Emerson Electric Co.; *U.S. Public*, pg. 574
BERENDSEN PMC OY AB—Sophus Berendsen A/S; *Int'l*, pg. 1285
BOWMAR INSTRUMENT CORPORATION; *U.S. Public*, pg. 248
BURR-BROWN CORPORATION; *U.S. Public*, pg. 270
C-CUBE MICROSYSTEMS; *U.S. Public*, pg. 272
CAE ELEKTRONIK GMBH—CAE Inc.; *Int'l*, pg. 238
CTI CRYOGENICS DIV.—Helix Technology Corp.; *U.S. Public*, pg. 808
CALIFORNIA MICRO DEVICES; *U.S. Public*, pg. 293
CENTRONIC INC.—Morgan Crucible Co. Plc; *Int'l*, pg. 892
CHERRY ELECTRICAL PRODUCTS CORPORATION; *U.S. Public*, pg. 346
CHERRY SEMICONDUCTOR CORP.—Cherry Electrical Products Corporation; *U.S. Public*, pg. 346
CIRRUS LOGIC, INC.; *U.S. Public*, pg. 375
CLEARPOINT ENTERPRISES; *U.S. Private*, pg. 245
COHU, INC.; *U.S. Public*, pg. 396
COMPAGNIE FRANCAISE PHILIPS—Philips Electronics N.V.; *Int'l*, pg. 1055
COMPUTER PRODUCTS, NATIONAL ACCOUNTS DIVISION—Computer Products, Inc.; *U.S. Public*, pg. 422
CRANE CO.; *U.S. Public*, pg. 456
CYPRESS SEMICONDUCTOR CORPORATION; *U.S. Public*, pg. 470
CYRIX CORPORATION—National Semiconductor Corporation; *U.S. Public*, pg. 1160
DAEWOO TELECOM CO., LTD.—Daewoo Corporation; *Int'l*, pg. 357
DALLAS SEMICONDUCTOR CORPORATION; *U.S. Public*, pg. 478
DATA FORTH—Burr-Brown Corporation; *U.S. Public*, pg. 270
DATA GENERAL HONG KONG LTD.—Data General Corporation; *U.S. Public*, pg. 486
DELCO ELECTRONICS CORPORATION—General Motors Corporation; *U.S. Public*, pg. 720
DELCO SYSTEMS OPERATION—General Motors Corporation; *U.S. Public*, pg. 720
DELTA DESIGN, INC.—Cohu, Inc.; *U.S. Public*, pg. 396
DEVLIN ELECTRONICS LIMITED—Bowthorpe plc; *Int'l*, pg. 207
DIAMONAIR—Litton Industries, Inc.; *U.S. Public*, pg. 1003
DIGI INTERNATIONAL—Digi International Inc.; *U.S. Public*, pg. 507
DIGI INTERNATIONAL INC.; *U.S. Public*, pg. 506
DIGITAL EQUIPMENT CORPORATION; *U.S. Public*, pg. 507
DIODES INCORPORATED; *U.S. Public*, pg. 510
DISCO CORPORATION; *Int'l*, pg. 413
DU PONT PHOTOMASKS—Du Pont (E.I. Du Pont De Nemours & Co.); *U.S. Public*, pg. 531
EG & G HEIMANN OPTO. GMBH—EG & G, Inc.; *U.S. Public*, pg. 544
EG & G, INC.; *U.S. Public*, pg. 542
EG & G OPTOELECTRONICS MONTGOMERYVILLE—EG & G, Inc.; *U.S. Public*, pg. 543
EG & G OPTOELECTRONICS RETICON—EG & G, Inc.; *U.S. Public*, pg. 543
EG & G OPTOELECTRONICS-ST. LOUIS—EG & G, Inc.; *U.S. Public*, pg. 543
EMC CORPORATION; *U.S. Public*, pg. 545
EXAR JAPAN CORPORATION—EXAR Corporation; *U.S. Public*, pg. 598
EAGLE-PICHER INDUSTRIES, INC.; *U.S. Private*, pg. 355
EATON CORPORATION; *U.S. Public*, pg. 555
EATON CORPORATION, SEMI-CONDUCTOR—Eaton Corporation; *U.S. Public*, pg. 557
EDGE SEMICONDUCTOR—Semtech Corporation; *U.S. Public*, pg. 1456
ELCO CORPORATION—Kyocera Corporation; *Int'l*, pg. 775
ELECTRONIC PRODUCTS DIVISION—3M; *U.S. Public*, pg. 1605
ELMO SEMICONDUCTEURS SARL—Kimball International, Inc.; *U.S. Public*, pg. 958
ELMO SEMICONDUCTOR CORP.—Kimball International, Inc.; *U.S. Public*, pg. 957
ENERGY CONVERSION DEVICES, INC.; *U.S. Public*, pg. 581
ENTRON INDUSTRIES LIMITED PARTNERSHIP; *U.S. Private*, pg. 378
ERICSSON COMPONENTS AB—Telefonaktiebolaget LM Ericsson; *Int'l*, pg. 1363
ERICSSON COMPONENTS POWER DIVISION—Telefonaktiebolaget LM Ericsson; *Int'l*, pg. 1363
EXAR CORPORATION; *U.S. Public*, pg. 597
EXEL MICROELECTRONICS, INC.—Rohm Co., Ltd.; *Int'l*, pg. 1125
FEDERAL LABORATORIES—Mace Security International, Inc.; *U.S. Public*, pg. 1030
FERROFLUIDICS CORPORATION; *U.S. Public*, pg. 620
FLEXIBLE CIRCUIT PRODUCTS DIVISION—Parlex Corporation; *U.S. Public*, pg. 1264
GEC PLESSEY SEMICONDUCTORS—The General Electric Company, p.l.c.; *Int'l*, pg. 544
GASONICS INTERNATIONAL; *U.S. Public*, pg. 703
GATEFIELD CORPORATION; *U.S. Public*, pg. 703
GENERAL CABLE CO.—Wassall Plc; *Int'l*, pg. 1487
GENERAL INSTRUMENT CORPORATION; *U.S. Public*, pg. 716
GENERAL MICROCIRCUITS, INC.—Microsemi Corporation; *U.S. Public*, pg. 1107
GENERAL SEMICONDUCTOR, INC.; *U.S. Public*, pg. 726
GIGALEX CO., LTD.—Rohm Co., Ltd.; *Int'l*, pg. 1125
GOLDSTAR SEMICONDUCTOR LTD.—LG Group; *Int'l*, pg. 779
HEI, INC.; *U.S. Public*, pg. 770
HAMAOKA TOSHIBA ELECTRONICS CORP.—Toshiba Corporation; *Int'l*, pg. 1402
HANIMEX PTY. LIMITED—Ricoh Company, Ltd.; *Int'l*, pg. 1115
HANOVIA LIMITED—Halma p.l.c.; *Int'l*, pg. 589
HANYU SANYO ELECTRONICS CO., LTD.—Sanyo Electric Co., Ltd.; *Int'l*, pg. 1191
HARRIS CORPORATION; *U.S. Public*, pg. 791
HARRIS SEMICONDUCTOR—Harris Corporation; *U.S. Public*, pg. 792
HARRIS SEMICONDUCTOR MICROELECTRONICS CENTER—Harris Corporation; *U.S. Public*, pg. 792
HELIX TECHNOLOGY CORP.; *U.S. Public*, pg. 808
HERLEY INDUSTRIES, INC.; *U.S. Public*, pg. 811
HEWLETT-PACKARD COMPANY; *U.S. Public*, pg. 813
HEXFET AMERICA—International Rectifier Corporation; *U.S. Public*, pg. 906
HI-P TOOL & DIE PTE. LTD.—Molex Incorporated; *U.S. Public*, pg. 1122
RICHARD HIRSCHMANN OF AMERICA, INC.—Rheinmetall Group; *Int'l*, pg. 1108
HITACHI CHEMICAL CO., LTD.—Hitachi, Ltd.; *Int'l*, pg. 621
HITACHI, LTD.; *Int'l*, pg. 621
HITACHI SEMICONDUCTOR (AMERICA), INC.—Hitachi, Ltd.; *Int'l*, pg. 622
HOECHST SPECIALTY PRODUCTS GROUP—Hoechst Aktiengesellschaft; *Int'l*, pg. 625
HYUNDAI ELECTRONICS AMERICA—Hyundai Motor Company; *Int'l*, pg. 641
HYUNDAI ELECTRONICS INDUSTRIES CO., LTD.—Hyundai Motor Company; *Int'l*, pg. 641
ILC INDUSTRIES, INC.; *U.S. Private*, pg. 555
IPC CORPORATION LTD.; *Int'l*, pg. 651
ITT CANNON SEALECTRO—ITT Industries, Inc.; *U.S. Public*, pg. 859
ITT INDUSTRIES, INC.; *U.S. Public*, pg. 859
ITW SWITCHES-ASIA—Illinois Tool Works Inc.; *U.S. Public*, pg. 868
INFORMATION STORAGE DEVICES; *U.S. Public*, pg. 876
INTEGRATED DEVICE TECHNOLOGY, INC.; *U.S. Public*, pg. 884
INTEL CORPORATION; *U.S. Public*, pg. 886
INTEL CORPORATION U.K. LTD.—Intel Corporation; *U.S. Public*, pg. 887
INTERFACE ELECTRONICS CORPORATION; *U.S. Private*, pg. 567
INTERNATIONAL MICROCIRCUITS, INC.; *U.S. Private*, pg. 571
INTERNATIONAL MICROWAVE CORPORATION; *U.S. Private*, pg. 571
INTERNATIONAL RECTIFIER COMPANY (GREAT BRITAIN) LTD.—International Rectifier Corporation; *U.S. Public*, pg. 907
INTERNATIONAL RECTIFIER CORPORATION; *U.S. Public*, pg. 906
INTERNATIONAL RECTIFIER CORPORATION ITALIANA, S.P.A.—International Rectifier Corporation; *U.S. Public*, pg. 907
INTERPOINT—Crane Co.; *U.S. Public*, pg. 457
JEUMONT-SCHNEIDER TRENFORMETEURS; *Int'l*, pg. 706
E.F. JOHNSON RADIO SYSTEMS—Transcrypt International; *U.S. Public*, pg. 1630
KEITHLEY INSTRUMENTS, INC.; *U.S. Public*, pg. 946
KENT INSTRUMENTS PTY. LTD.—ABB Asea Brown Boveri (Holding) Ltd.; *Int'l*, pg. 2
KETEMA, INC.—KTM Holdings Corp.; *U.S. Private*, pg. 604
KITSUKI TOSHIBA ELECTRONICS CORPORATION—Toshiba Corporation; *Int'l*, pg. 1403
KODAK FEDERAL SYSTEMS DIVISION—Eastman Kodak Company; *U.S. Public*, pg. 555
KULICKE & SOFFA INDUSTRIES, INC.; *U.S. Public*, pg. 968
KULICKE & SOFFA (ISRAEL) LTD.—Kulicke & Soffa Industries, Inc.; *U.S. Public*, pg. 969
KULICKE & SOFFA (JAPAN), LTD.—Kulicke & Soffa Industries, Inc.; *U.S. Public*, pg. 969
KULICKE & SOFFA (ASIA), LTD.—Kulicke & Soffa Industries, Inc.; *U.S. Public*, pg. 969
KULITE SEMICONDUCTOR PRODUCTS, INC.; *U.S. Private*, pg. 636
KYOCERA AMERICA, INC.—Kyocera Corporation; *Int'l*, pg. 775
KYOCERA CORPORATION; *Int'l*, pg. 775
KYOCERA (HONG KONG), LTD.—Kyocera Corporation; *Int'l*, pg. 776
KYOCERA INTERNATIONAL, INC.—Kyocera Corporation; *Int'l*, pg. 775
LSI LOGIC CORP.; *U.S. Public*, pg. 971
LABARGE, INC.; *U.S. Public*, pg. 973
LAGARDERE GROUPE; *Int'l*, pg. 791
LAM RESEARCH CORPORATION; *U.S. Public*, pg. 975
LAMBDA ADVANCED ANALOG—Siebe plc; *Int'l*, pg. 1241
LASER DIODE PRODUCTS—Morgan Crucible Co. Plc; *Int'l*, pg. 892
LATTICE SEMICONDUCTOR CORPORATION; *U.S. Public*, pg. 979
LAWRENCE DIVISION—Aetrium Inc.; *U.S. Public*, pg. 27
LEACH INTERNATIONAL; *U.S. Private*, pg. 655
LINEAR TECHNOLOGY CORP.; *U.S. Public*, pg. 1000
LINFINITY MICROELECTRONICS INC.—SymmetriCom, Inc.; *U.S. Public*, pg. 1547
LOCKHEED MARTIN INFORMATION DISPLAY SYSTEMS—Lockheed Martin Corporation; *U.S. Public*, pg. 1008
LUCAS INDUSTRIES INC.—LucasVarity plc; *Int'l*, pg. 820
LUMONICS INC.—Sumitomo Heavy Industries, Ltd.; *Int'l*, pg. 1314
M/A-COM, INC. COMPONENTS GROUP—AMP Incorporated; *U.S. Public*, pg. 8
MIPS TECHNOLOGIES, INC.—Silicon Graphics, Inc.; *U.S. Public*, pg. 1473
MARTIN MARIETTA ELECTRONICS & MISSILES—Lockheed Martin Corporation; *U.S. Public*, pg. 1007
MATERIALS RESEARCH FRANCE—Sony Corporation; *Int'l*, pg. 1283
MATRA DATAVISION U.S.A.—Lagardere Groupe; *Int'l*, pg. 795
MATRA DESIGN SEMICONDUCTOR CORP.—Lagardere Groupe; *Int'l*, pg. 795
MATRA HARRIS SEMICONDUCTEURS—Lagardere Groupe; *Int'l*, pg. 793
MATSUSHITA ELECTRIC CORPORATION OF AMERICA—Matsushita Electric Industrial Co., Ltd.; *Int'l*, pg. 847
MATSUSHITA ELECTRIC (U.K.) LTD.—Matsushita Electric Industrial Co., Ltd.; *Int'l*, pg. 847
MAXIM INTEGRATED PRODUCTS, INC.; *U.S. Public*, pg. 1061
MAXWELL TECHNOLOGIES, INC.; *U.S. Public*, pg. 1061
MEMCOR TRUOHM—Ohmite Manufacturing Company; *U.S. Private*, pg. 813
MICRO NETWORKS CORP.—Sawgrass Electronics Group Inc.; *U.S. Private*, pg. 969
MICRON TECHNOLOGY INC.; *U.S. Public*, pg. 1105
MICRONICS COMPUTERS, INC.; *U.S. Public*, pg. 1106
MICROSEMI CORPORATION; *U.S. Public*, pg. 1107
MICROSEMI CORP.-COLORADO—Microsemi Corporation; *U.S. Public*, pg. 1107
MICROSEMI CORP.-SCOTTSDALE—Microsemi Corporation; *U.S. Public*, pg. 1107
MICROSEMI (H.K.) LTD.—Microsemi Corporation; *U.S. Public*, pg. 1107
MICROSEMI PPC, INC.—Microsemi Corporation; *U.S. Public*, pg. 1107
MICROSEMI RF PRODUCTS, INC.—Microsemi Corporation; *U.S. Public*, pg. 1107
MILITARY PRODUCTS DIV.—Philips Electronics N.V.; *Int'l*, pg. 1054
MITEL CORPORATION; *Int'l*, pg. 870
MITEL FAR EAST LTD.—Mitel Corporation; *Int'l*, pg. 870
MITEL SEMICONDUCTOR—Mitel Corporation; *Int'l*, pg. 870
MITEL SEMICONDUCTOR AB—Mitel Corporation; *Int'l*, pg. 870
MITSUBISHI MONSANTO CHEMICAL CO.—Monsanto Company; *U.S. Public*, pg. 1125
MITSUBISHI SEMICONDUCTOR AMERICA—Mitsubishi Electric Corporation; *Int'l*, pg. 872
MITSUBISHI SILICON AMERICA—Mitsubishi Materials Corp.; *Int'l*, pg. 875
MIYAZAKI OKI ELECTRIC CO., LTD.—Oki Electric Industry Company, Ltd.; *Int'l*, pg. 999
MONSANTO DO BRASIL LTDA. (MOBRA S.A.)—Monsanto Company; *U.S. Public*, pg. 1125
MOTOROLA AUTOMOTIVE & INDUSTRIAL ELECTRONICS GROUP—Motorola, Inc.; *U.S. Public*, pg. 1137
MOTOROLA GALVIN CENTER—Motorola, Inc.; *U.S. Public*, pg. 1138
MOTOROLA G.M.B.H.—Motorola, Inc.; *U.S. Public*, pg. 1139
MOTOROLA, INC.; *U.S. Public*, pg. 1136
MOTOROLA LIMITED—Motorola, Inc.; *U.S. Public*, pg. 1139
MOTOROLA MALAYSIA SDN. BHD.—Motorola, Inc.; *U.S. Public*, pg. 1140
MOTOROLA RADIUS—Motorola, Inc.; *U.S. Public*, pg. 1138
MOTOROLA SEMI CONDUCTEURS (SOCIETE)—Motorola, Inc.; *U.S. Public*, pg. 1140
MULTICHIP TECHNOLOGY—Cypress Semiconductor Corporation; *U.S. Public*, pg. 470
NCR CORPORATION; *U.S. Public*, pg. 1146
NEC CORPORATION; *Int'l*, pg. 899
NEC ELECTRONICS INC.—NEC Corporation; *Int'l*, pg. 900
NEC SEMICONDUCTORS IRELAND LIMITED—NEC Corporation; *Int'l*, pg. 900
NEC SEMICONDUCTORS (UK) LIMITED—NEC Corporation; *Int'l*, pg. 900
NAMCO CONTROLS GMBH—Danaher Corporation; *U.S. Public*, pg. 482
NATIONAL NUCLEAR CORPORATION—Thermo Electron Corporation; *U.S. Public*, pg. 1594
NATIONAL SEMICONDUCTOR CORPORATION; *U.S. Public*, pg. 1159

NEXTLEVEL SYSTEMS (HONG KONG)—General Instrument Corporation; *U.S. Public*, pg. 716
NEXTLEVEL SYSTEMS (JAPAN)—General Instrument Corporation; *U.S. Public*, pg. 716
NICHOLS RESEARCH CORPORATION; *U.S. Public*, pg. 1182
NIIGATA SANYO ELECTRONIC CO., LTD.—Sanyo Electric Co., Ltd.; *Int'l*, pg. 1191
NOGATA TOSHIBA ELECTRONICS CO.—Toshiba Corporation; *Int'l*, pg. 1403
NOK EG & G OPTOELECTRONICS CORPORATION—EG & G, Inc.; *U.S. Public*, pg. 544
NORTEC ELECTRONICS AB—Axel Johnson AB; *Int'l*, pg. 709
OERLIKON-BUHRLE HOLDING AG; *Int'l*, pg. 996
OKI ELECTRIC INDUSTRY COMPANY, LTD.; *Int'l*, pg. 999
OKI SEMICONDUCTOR GROUP—Oki Electric Industry Company, Ltd.; *Int'l*, pg. 1000
OKI (THAILAND) CO., LTD.—Oki Electric Industry Company, Ltd.; *Int'l*, pg. 1000
OKI UNISYS KAISHA, LTD.—Oki Electric Industry Company, Ltd.; *Int'l*, pg. 999
OLIVETTI SPA; *Int'l*, pg. 1002
OMRON CORPORATION; *Int'l*, pg. 1005
ONTRAK SYSTEMS, INC.—Lam Research Corporation; *U.S. Public*, pg. 975
OPTEK TECHNOLOGY, INC.; *U.S. Public*, pg. 1227
ORBIT SEMICONDUCTOR, INC.; *U.S. Private*, pg. 819
ORIEL INSTRUMENTS CORPORATION; *U.S. Private*, pg. 819
PANASONIC INDUSTRIAL U.K. LTD.—Matsushita Electric Industrial Co., Ltd.; *Int'l*, pg. 847
PERKINS CORPORATION—Sharp Corporation; *Int'l*, pg. 1229
PHILIPS COMPONENTS-DISCRETE PRODUCTS DIVISION—Philips Electronics N.V.; *Int'l*, pg. 1054
PHILIPS SEMICONDUCTORS—Philips Electronics N.V.; *Int'l*, pg. 1054
POLYFLON COMPANY—Crane Co.; *U.S. Public*, pg. 457
POWEREX INC.—Mitsubishi Electric Corporation; *Int'l*, pg. 873
QT OPTOELECTRONICS; *U.S. Private*, pg. 897
QUICKLOGIC CORPORATION; *U.S. Private*, pg. 901
RTI ELECTRONICS INC.—Selas Corporation of America; *U.S. Public*, pg. 1455
RTI EXPORT, INC. (BARBADOS)—Selas Corporation of America; *U.S. Public*, pg. 1455
RANCO INC.—Siebe plc; *Int'l*, pg. 1243
RAYTHEON COMPANY; *U.S. Public*, pg. 1364
RECTIFICADORES INTERNACIONALES, S.A.—International Rectifier Corporation; *U.S. Public*, pg. 907
RESISTANCE TECHNOLOGY INC.—Selas Corporation of America; *U.S. Public*, pg. 1455
RICHARDSON ELECTRONICS, LTD.; *U.S. Public*, pg. 1387
ROCKWELL AUTOMATION TECATE S.A. DE C.V.—Rockwell International Corporation; *U.S. Public*, pg. 1398
ROCKWELL SEMICONDUCTOR SYSTEMS PLC—Rockwell International Corporation; *U.S. Public*, pg. 1402
ROEDERSTEIN GMBH—Vishay Intertechnology, Inc.; *U.S. Public*, pg. 1722
ROHM APOLLO ELECTRONICS (THAILAND) CO., LTD.—Rohm Co., Ltd.; *Int'l*, pg. 1125
ROHM CO., LTD.; *Int'l*, pg. 1124
SEEQ TECHNOLOGY INC.; *U.S. Public*, pg. 1417
SEH AMERICA INC.—Shin-Etsu Chemical Co. ltd.; *Int'l*, pg. 1234
SGS-THOMSON MICROELECTRONICS, INC.—SGS Societe Generale de Surveillance Holding S.A.; *Int'l*, pg. 1153
SGS-THOMSON MICROELECTRONICS, INC.—Thomson S.A.; *Int'l*, pg. 1384
SAMSUNG ELECTRON DEVICES CO., LTD.—Samsung Group; *Int'l*, pg. 1181
SAMSUNG ELECTRONICS CO., LTD.—Samsung Group; *Int'l*, pg. 1181
SAMSUNG GROUP; *Int'l*, pg. 1181
SAMTEC INC.; *U.S. Private*, pg. 963
SAN DIEGO DIVISION—Aetrium Inc.; *U.S. Public*, pg. 27
SANKEN ELECTRIC CO., LTD.; *Int'l*, pg. 1188
SANYO ELECTRIC (HONG KONG) LIMITED—Sanyo Electric Co., Ltd.; *Int'l*, pg. 1192
SANYO ELECTRONIC (TAICHUNG) CO., LTD.—Sanyo Electric Co., Ltd.; *Int'l*, pg. 1192
SANYO VLSI ENGINEERING CO., LTD.—Sanyo Electric Co., Ltd.; *Int'l*, pg. 1191
SCHLUMBERGER LIMITED; *U.S. Public*, pg. 1439
SEMCON ELECTRONICS PVT. LTD.—Microsemi Corporation; *U.S. Public*, pg. 1107
SEMIKRON INTERNATIONAL, GMBH & CO. KG; *Int'l*, pg. 1220
SEMITOOL, INC.; *U.S. Public*, pg. 1456
SEMTECH CORPORATION; *U.S. Public*, pg. 1456
SEMTECH CORPUS CHRISTI—Semtech Corporation; *U.S. Public*, pg. 1456
SEMTECH LTD.—Semtech Corporation; *U.S. Public*, pg. 1456
SERTECH LABORATORIES, INC./SSI—Microsemi Corporation; *U.S. Public*, pg. 1107
SERVICIOS WESTINGHOUSE DE MEXICO, S.A. DE C.V.—CBS Corporation; *U.S. Public*, pg. 273
SHIN-ETSU CHEMICAL CO. LTD.; *Int'l*, pg. 1234
SHIN-ETSU HANDOTAI CO. LTD.—Shin-Etsu Chemical Co. ltd.; *Int'l*, pg. 1234
SHIZUOKA OKI ELECTRIC CO., LTD.—Oki Electric Industry Company, Ltd.; *Int'l*, pg. 999
SIEMENS AG; *Int'l*, pg. 1244
SIGNETICS THAILAND CO., LTD.—Philips Electronics N.V.; *Int'l*, pg. 1055
SILICON POWER CUBE CORPORATION; *U.S. Private*, pg. 1000
SILICON SYSTEMS, INC.—Texas Instruments Incorporated; *U.S. Public*, pg. 1585
SILICON VALLEY GROUP, INC.; *U.S. Public*, pg. 1474
SILICONIX (H.K.) LTD.—Daimler-Benz Aktiengesellschaft; *Int'l*, pg. 367
SILICONIX, INC.—Daimler-Benz Aktiengesellschaft; *Int'l*, pg. 367
SILICONIX LTD.—Daimler-Benz Aktiengesellschaft; *Int'l*, pg. 367
SILICONIX (TAIWAN)—Daimler-Benz Aktiengesellschaft; *Int'l*, pg. 367
SIMULATION DIVISION—Evans & Sutherland Computer Corporation; *U.S. Public*, pg. 596
SIPEX CORPORATION—Tractebel; *Int'l*, pg. 1415
SOLAREX CORPORATION—Amoco Corporation; *U.S. Public*, pg. 103
SOLID STATE DEVICES, INC.; *U.S. Private*, pg. 1012
SONY CORPORATION OF PANAMA—Sony Corporation; *Int'l*, pg. 1284
SONY MICROELECTRONICS—Sony Corporation; *Int'l*, pg. 1284
SORMEL—Lagardere Groupe; *Int'l*, pg. 793
SPARTON ELECTRONICS FLORIDA, INC.—Sparton Corporation; *U.S. Public*, pg. 1496
SPECTRA DIODE LABORATORIES—Xerox Corporation; *U.S. Public*, pg. 1785
SPECTRA-PHYSICS LASERPLANE INC.—Thermo Electron Corporation; *U.S. Public*, pg. 1594
SPECTRONICS CORPORATION; *U.S. Private*, pg. 1024
SQUARE D COMPANY—Schneider S.A.; *Int'l*, pg. 1208
STANDARD MICROSYSTEMS CORP.; *U.S. Public*, pg. 1502
STANDARD PRODUCTS GROUP—Philips Electronics N.V.; *Int'l*, pg. 1054
SUAREZ CORPORATION INDUSTRIES; *U.S. Private*, pg. 1048
SUMITOMO SITIX CORPORATION; *Int'l*, pg. 1317
SUMITOMO SITIX SILICON, INC.—Sumitomo Sitix Corporation; *Int'l*, pg. 1317
SUPERTEX, INC.; *U.S. Public*, pg. 1539
SYMMETRICOM, INC.; *U.S. Public*, pg. 1547
TAISIL ELECTRONIC MATERIALS CORPORATION—China Steel Corporation; *Int'l*, pg. 286
TAIYO YUDEN COMPANY LTD.; *Int'l*, pg. 1349
TAKETA TOSHIBA ELECTRONICS CORPORATION—Toshiba Corporation; *Int'l*, pg. 1403
TECSTAR INC.; *U.S. Private*, pg. 1072
TEKTRONIX, INC.; *U.S. Public*, pg. 1567
TELCOM SEMICONDUCTOR, INC.; *U.S. Public*, pg. 1569
TERMINAL DIVISION—Inkel USA Corporation; *U.S. Private*, pg. 563
TEXAS INSTRUMENTS ADC, SEMICONDUCTOR DIV.—Texas Instruments Incorporated; *U.S. Public*, pg. 1585
TEXAS INSTRUMENTS FACILITIES, SEMICONDUCTOR—Texas Instruments Incorporated; *U.S. Public*, pg. 1586
TEXAS INSTRUMENTS INCORPORATED; *U.S. Public*, pg. 1585
TEXAS INSTRUMENTS LMOS, CONSUMER PRODUCTS—Texas Instruments Incorporated; *U.S. Public*, pg. 1586
TEXAS INSTRUMENTS SEMICONDUCTOR GROUP—Texas Instruments Incorporated; *U.S. Public*, pg. 1586
TEXAS INSTRUMENTS SINGAPORE (PTE.) LTD.—Texas Instruments Incorporated; *U.S. Public*, pg. 1586
TEXTRON OPTOELECTRONICS—Textron Inc.; *U.S. Public*, pg. 1589
THERMALLOY, INC.—Bowthorpe plc; *Int'l*, pg. 208
THOMSON S.A.; *Int'l*, pg. 1381
THREE-FIVE SYSTEMS; *U.S. Public*, pg. 1604
3M; *U.S. Public*, pg. 1604
TOHOKU OKI ELECTRIC CO., LTD.—Oki Electric Industry Company, Ltd.; *Int'l*, pg. 999
TOHOKU SEMICONDUCTOR CORPORATION—Toshiba Corporation; *Int'l*, pg. 1403
TOKO AMERICA, INC.—Toko Inc.; *Int'l*, pg. 1393
TOKO INC.; *Int'l*, pg. 1393
TOKYO IC CO., LTD.—Sanyo Electric Co., Ltd.; *Int'l*, pg. 1191
TOSHIBA COMPONENTS CO., LTD.—Toshiba Corporation; *Int'l*, pg. 1403
TOSHIBA ELECTRONIC ENGINEERING CORPORATION—Toshiba Corporation; *Int'l*, pg. 1404
TOSHIBA ELECTRONICS MALAYSIA SDN. BHD.—Toshiba Corporation; *Int'l*, pg. 1406
TOSHIBA MICROELECTRONICS CORPORATION—Toshiba Corporation; *Int'l*, pg. 1404
TOSHIBA SEMICONDUCTOR G.M.B.H.—Toshiba Corporation; *Int'l*, pg. 1407
UNISYS SEMICONDUCTOR—Unisys Corporation; *U.S. Public*, pg. 1671
UNITRODE CORPORATION; *U.S. Public*, pg. 1694
VLSI TECHNOLOGY, INC.; *U.S. Public*, pg. 1703
VALOR ELECTRONICS, INC.—GTI Corporation; *U.S. Public*, pg. 768
VARIAN ASSOCIATES, INC.; *U.S. Public*, pg. 1710
VEEDER-ROOT COMPANY—Danaher Corporation; *U.S. Public*, pg. 482
VIKING SEMICONDUCTOR EQUIPMENT, INC.—Giga-Tronics Incorporated; *U.S. Public*, pg. 743
VISHAY INTERTECHNOLOGY, INC.; *U.S. Public*, pg. 1721
VITESSE SEMICONDUCTOR CORPORATION; *U.S. Public*, pg. 1723
WARATOKU STEEL CO., LTD.—Oki Electric Industry Company, Ltd.; *Int'l*, pg. 999
WESTINGHOUSE DO BRASIL S/A DIVISAO SERVICIOS INDUSTRIALES—CBS Corporation; *U.S. Public*, pg. 275
WHITE MICROELECTRONICS—Bowmar Instrument Corporation; *U.S. Public*, pg. 248
XETEL CORPORATION—Rohm Co., Ltd.; *Int'l*, pg. 1125
XICOR, INC.; *U.S. Public*, pg. 1785
XILINX, INC.; *U.S. Public*, pg. 1786

3675 — ELECTRONIC CAPACITORS

ABB CABLES AB—ABB Asea Brown Boveri (Holding) Ltd.; *Int'l*, pg. 7
AVX CONWAY PLANT—Kyocera Corporation; *Int'l*, pg. 775
AVX CORPORATION—Kyocera Corporation; *Int'l*, pg. 775
AVX LEADED PRODUCTS DIV.—Kyocera Corporation; *Int'l*, pg. 775
AVX LTD.—Kyocera Corporation; *Int'l*, pg. 776
AVX RALEIGH PLANT—Kyocera Corporation; *Int'l*, pg. 775
AVX TANTALUM DIV.—Kyocera Corporation; *Int'l*, pg. 775
AEROVOX INC.; *U.S. Public*, pg. 25
ALCATEL CIT (S.A.); *Int'l*, pg. 56
AMERICAN TECHNICAL CERAMICS CORP.; *U.S. Public*, pg. 93
ASEA HAGGLUNDS (U.K.) LTD.—ABB Asea Brown Boveri (Holding) Ltd.; *Int'l*, pg. 8
ASEA REGULADORES S.A. DE C.V.—ABB Asea Brown Boveri (Holding) Ltd.; *Int'l*, pg. 8
BHC AEROVOX LTD.—Aerovox Inc.; *U.S. Public*, pg. 26
CALIFORNIA MICRO DEVICES; *U.S. Public*, pg. 293
CEGELEC (M) SDN BHD—Alcatel Alsthom Compagnie Generale D'Electricite; *Int'l*, pg. 53
COOPER POWER SYSTEMS—Cooper Industries, Inc.; *U.S. Public*, pg. 443
CORNELL DUBILIER ELECTRONICS—Kaplan Electronics; *U.S. Private*, pg. 607
CORNING GMBH—Corning Incorporated; *U.S. Public*, pg. 449
CRANE CO.; *U.S. Public*, pg. 456
DEL GLOBAL TECHNOLOGIES; *U.S. Public*, pg. 493
ERICSSON COMPONENTS AB—Telefonaktiebolaget LM Ericsson; *Int'l*, pg. 1363
ERICSSON COMPONENTS POWER DIVISION—Telefonaktiebolaget LM Ericsson; *Int'l*, pg. 1363
GENERAL CABLE CO.—Wassall Plc; *Int'l*, pg. 1487
HUGHES-PETERS, INC.; *U.S. Private*, pg. 546
INDUCTOTHERM INDUSTRIES, INC.; *U.S. Private*, pg. 560
INTERFACE ELECTRONICS CORPORATION; *U.S. Private*, pg. 567
JOHANSON MANUFACTURING CORPORATION; *U.S. Private*, pg. 589
KCK CO., LTD.—Mitsubishi Materials Corp.; *Int'l*, pg. 875
KYOCERA CORPORATION; *Int'l*, pg. 775
MARCON ELECTRONICS CO., LTD.—Toshiba Corporation; *Int'l*, pg. 1403
MAXWELL TECHNOLOGIES, INC.; *U.S. Public*, pg. 1061
METHODE TECHNICAL COMPONENTS—Methode Electronics Inc.; *U.S. Public*, pg. 1101
MITSUMI ELECTRIC CO., LTD.; *Int'l*, pg. 884
MURATA ELECTRONICS NORTH AMERICA, INC.—Murata Manufacturing Co., Ltd.; *Int'l*, pg. 897
MURATA MANUFACTURING CO., LTD.; *Int'l*, pg. 897
N BASE COMMUNICATIONS—MRV Communications, Inc.; *U.S. Public*, pg. 1027
NEC SEMICONDUCTORS SINGAPORE PTE. LTD.—NEC Corporation; *Int'l*, pg. 900
OKI CERAMIC INDUSTRY CO., LTD.—Oki Electric Industry Company, Ltd.; *Int'l*, pg. 999
POLYFLON COMPANY—Crane Co.; *U.S. Public*, pg. 457
RFI CORP.—Del Global Technologies; *U.S. Public*, pg. 494
ROGERS CORPORATION; *U.S. Public*, pg. 1402
ROHM CO., LTD.; *Int'l*, pg. 1124
SALFORD ELECTRICAL INSTRUMENTS LTD.—The General Electric Company, p.l.c.; *Int'l*, pg. 545
SANKEN ELECTRIC U.S.A. CORP.—Sanken Electric Co., Ltd.; *Int'l*, pg. 1188
SCHLUMBERGER LIMITED; *U.S. Public*, pg. 1439
SHIZUKI ELECTRIC CORPORATION; *Int'l*, pg. 1236
SHURE BROTHERS INCORPORATED; *U.S. Private*, pg. 997
STANDEX ELECTRONICS (U.K.) LTD.—Standex International Corporation; *U.S. Public*, pg. 1507
TDK CORPORATION; *Int'l*, pg. 1336
THOMAS & BETTS CORPORATION; *U.S. Public*, pg. 1597
VITRAMON, INCORPORATED—Vishay Intertechnology, Inc.; *U.S. Public*, pg. 1722

3676 — ELECTRONIC RESISTORS

ANGSTROHM PRECISION, INC.—Vishay Intertechnology, Inc.; *U.S. Public*, pg. 1722
APOLLO ELECTRONICS CO., LTD.—Rohm Co., Ltd.; *Int'l*, pg. 1125
APPLIED SCIENCES DIVISION—Caddock Electronics, Inc.; *U.S. Private*, pg. 198
BECKMAN INDUSTRIAL CORPORATION—Emerson Electric Co.; *U.S. Public*, pg. 574
BOURNS, INC.; *U.S. Private*, pg. 161
BRADFORD ELECTRONIC INC.—Vishay Intertechnology, Inc.; *U.S. Public*, pg. 1722
CADDOCK ELECTRONICS EUROPE B.V.—Caddock Electronics, Inc.; *U.S. Private*, pg. 198
CALIFORNIA MICRO DEVICES; *U.S. Public*, pg. 293
CORNING GMBH—Corning Incorporated; *U.S. Public*, pg. 449
DRALORIC ELECTRONIC GMBH—Vishay Intertechnology, Inc.; *U.S. Public*, pg. 1722
ELECTRO-SCIENCE LABORATORIES, INC.; *U.S. Private*, pg. 369
ELECTRONICA DALE DE MEXICO S.A. DE C.V.—Vishay Intertechnology, Inc.; *U.S. Public*, pg. 1722
GEKA, S.A.—Vishay Intertechnology, Inc.; *U.S. Public*, pg. 1722
GRIFFON CORP.; *U.S. Public*, pg. 766
HAN RYUK ELECTRONICS CO., LTD.—Hokuriku Electric Industry Co., Ltd.; *Int'l*, pg. 628
HOKURIKU ELECTRIC INDUSTRY CO., LTD.; *Int'l*, pg. 627
HOKURIKU (MALAYSIA), SDN. BHD.—Hokuriku Electric Industry Co., Ltd.; *Int'l*, pg. 628
HUGHES-PETERS, INC.; *U.S. Private*, pg. 546
IPC POWER RESISTORS INTERNATIONAL INC.—Halma p.l.c.; *Int'l*, pg. 590
IPC RESISTORS INC.—Halma p.l.c.; *Int'l*, pg. 590
KYOCERA CORPORATION; *Int'l*, pg. 775
MEASUREMENTS GROUP, INC.—Vishay Intertechnology, Inc.; *U.S. Public*, pg. 1722

NARITA GIKEN CO., LTD.—Rohm Co., Ltd.; Int'l, pg. 1125
NIPPON VISHAY K.K.—Vishay Intertechnology, Inc.; U.S. Public, pg. 1722
OHMITE MANUFACTURING COMPANY; U.S. Private, pg. 813
POST GLOVER RESISTORS INC.—Halma p.l.c.; Int'l, pg. 590
REXCAN CIRCUITS INC.—Hokuriku Electric Industry Co., Ltd.; Int'l, pg. 628
ROCKWELL INTERNATIONAL CORPORATION; U.S. Public, pg. 1397
ROHM CO., LTD.; Int'l, pg. 1124
ROHM ELECTRONICS (TIANJIN) CO., LTD.—Rohm Co., Ltd.; Int'l, pg. 1125
ROHM FUKUOKA CO., LTD.—Rohm Co., Ltd.; Int'l, pg. 1125
ROHM LOGISTEC CO., LTD.—Rohm Co., Ltd.; Int'l, pg. 1125
ROHM-WAKO (KELANTAN) SDN. BHD.—Rohm Co., Ltd.; Int'l, pg. 1125
ROHM-WAKO (MALAYSIA) SDN. BHD.—Rohm Co., Ltd.; Int'l, pg. 1126
SFERNICE, S.A.—Vishay Intertechnology, Inc.; U.S. Public, pg. 1722
SOVCOR, SA—Vishay Intertechnology, Inc.; U.S. Public, pg. 1722
TAIWAN HOKURIKU CO., LTD.—Hokuriku Electric Industry Co., Ltd.; Int'l, pg. 628
THERMOMETRICS, INC.—Bowthorpe plc; Int'l, pg. 208
VERNITRON SENSOR SYSTEMS—Axsys Technologies, Inc.; U.S. Public, pg. 157
VISHAY INTERTECHNOLOGY, INC.; U.S. Public, pg. 1721

3677 — ELECTRONIC COILS, TRANSFORMERS & OTHER INDUCTORS

AFP TRANSFORMERS, INC.—United Capital Corp.; U.S. Public, pg. 1674
ACME ELECTRIC CORPORATION; U.S. Public, pg. 16
AEROVOX INC.; U.S. Public, pg. 25
AMERICAN PRECISION INDUSTRIES INC.; U.S. Public, pg. 90
AULT INCORPORATED; U.S. Public, pg. 147
AZTRONIC—Vishay Intertechnology, Inc.; U.S. Public, pg. 1722
BCL MAGNETICS—Tempel Steel Company; U.S. Private, pg. 1075
COILCRAFT, INC.; U.S. Private, pg. 250
COMPONENTS CORPORATION OF AMERICA; U.S. Private, pg. 259
COOPER POWER SYSTEMS—Cooper Industries, Inc.; U.S. Public, pg. 443
DELEVAN DIV.—American Precision Industries Inc.; U.S. Public, pg. 90
DELTEC CORPORATION—Fiskars Oy AB; Int'l, pg. 492
DETROIT COIL COMPANY; U.S. Private, pg. 328
DORMEYER INDUSTRIES; U.S. Private, pg. 340
EG & G OPTOELECTRONICS-SALEM—EG & G, Inc.; U.S. Public, pg. 543
ELECTRONIA DALE DE MEXICO S.A. DE C.V.—Vishay Intertechnology, Inc.; U.S. Public, pg. 1722
FRANCE TRANSFO—Jeumont-Schneider Trenformeteurs; Int'l, pg. 706
FREQUENCY ENGINEERING LABORATORIES; U.S. Private, pg. 427
HAYES CORPORATION, REGIONAL OFFICE—Hayes Corporation; U.S. Public, pg. 801
HUGHES-PETERS, INC.; U.S. Private, pg. 546
HYOSUNG INDUSTRIES CO., LTD.—Hyosung Group; Int'l, pg. 640
INTERNATIO-MULLER N.V.; Int'l, pg. 680
JEFFERS ELECTRONICS—Vishay Intertechnology, Inc.; U.S. Public, pg. 1722
H.W. JENCKS, INC.—Detroit Coil Company; U.S. Private, pg. 328
KLOCKNER-MOELLER GMBH; Int'l, pg. 736
KOREA TRANSFORMER CO. LTD.—Tabuchi Electric Co., Ltd.; Int'l, pg. 1346
LITTELFUSE, INC.; U.S. Public, pg. 1001
MAGNETEK, INC.; U.S. Public, pg. 1037
METEOR AG—ABB Asea Brown Boveri (Holding) Ltd.; Int'l, pg. 2
MICAFIL AG—ABB Asea Brown Boveri (Holding) Ltd.; Int'l, pg. 2
MITSUMI ELECTRIC CO., LTD.; Int'l, pg. 884
MITSUMI ELECTRONICS CORP.—Mitsumi Electric Co., Ltd.; Int'l, pg. 884
NYTRON INDUCTORS—Vishay Intertechnology, Inc.; U.S. Public, pg. 1722
OPT INDUSTRIES, INC.—Torotel, Inc.; U.S. Public, pg. 1624
ORTRONICS, INC.—LeGrand S.A.; Int'l, pg. 806
PREMIER METAL PRODUCTS CO.; U.S. Private, pg. 881
SCHOTT CORPORATION; U.S. Private, pg. 972
SCHUMACHER ELECTRIC CORPORATION; U.S. Private, pg. 973
SOSS OF SINGAPORE PTE. LTD.—United Dominion Industries, Ltd.; U.S. Public, pg. 1677
STACOENERGY PRODUCTS CO.—Components Corporation Of America; U.S. Private, pg. 260
TABUCHI ELECTRIC CO., LTD.; Int'l, pg. 1346
TABUCHI ELECTRIC DE MEXICO S.A. DE C.V.—Tabuchi Electric Co., Ltd.; Int'l, pg. 1346
TABUCHI ELECTRIC U.K. LTD.—Tabuchi Electric Co., Ltd.; Int'l, pg. 1346
TAMURA CORPORATION OF AMERICA; U.S. Private, pg. 1067
TECHNITROL, INC.; U.S. Public, pg. 1564
TEMPEL STEEL COMPANY; U.S. Private, pg. 1075
TOROTEL, INC.; U.S. Public, pg. 1624
TOROTEL PRODUCTS, INC.—Torotel, Inc.; U.S. Public, pg. 1624
TRANSISTOR DEVICES, INC.; U.S. Private, pg. 1097
VISHAY INTERTECHNOLOGY, INC.; U.S. Public, pg. 1721
WABASH MAGNETICS—The Dyson-Kissner-Moran Corporation; U.S. Private, pg. 351
WHITTAKER ELECTRONIC SYSTEMS—Whittaker Corporation; U.S. Public, pg. 1767

3678 — ELECTRONIC CONNECTORS

ADC TELECOMMUNICATIONS, INC.; U.S. Public, pg. 4
AMP INC. LYTEL DIVISION—AMP Incorporated; U.S. Public, pg. 8
AMP INCORPORATED; U.S. Public, pg. 7
AMP INDUSTRIAL DIV.—AMP Incorporated; U.S. Public, pg. 7
AMP SHANGHAI CONNECTOR, LTD.—AMP Incorporated; U.S. Public, pg. 9
ANDREW CORPORATION; U.S. Public, pg. 112
ANICOM—Anicom, Inc.; U.S. Public, pg. 115
ANICOM, INC.; U.S. Public, pg. 115
AUGAT, INC.—Thomas & Betts Corporation; U.S. Public, pg. 1597
AUGAT, LRC., COMMUNICATIONS DIVISION-HORSEHEADS PLANT—Thomas & Betts Corporation; U.S. Public, pg. 1598
AUSTRALIAN AMP PTY. LIMITED—AMP Incorporated; U.S. Public, pg. 9
AVNET, INC.; U.S. Public, pg. 155
BWD AUTOMOTIVE—Echlin Inc.; U.S. Public, pg. 560
BEAD INDUSTRIES INC.; U.S. Private, pg. 126
CTS CORPORATION-CONNECTOR DIVISION—CTS Corporation; U.S. Public, pg. 285
CABLEWAVE SYSTEMS; U.S. Private, pg. 197
COMATEL SRL—Siebe plc; Int'l, pg. 1241
CONNECTOR DIVISION AMERICA AND ASIA—Labinal SA; Int'l, pg. 786
CONNECTWARE, INC. LLC—AMP Incorporated; U.S. Public, pg. 8
DATAMATE DIVISION—Methode Electronics Inc.; U.S. Public, pg. 1101
DECOLLETAGE S.A. ST.-MAURICE—AMP Incorporated; U.S. Public, pg. 9
DOVER CORPORATION; U.S. Public, pg. 520
DU PONT TAIWAN LIMITED—Du Pont (E.I. Du Pont De Nemours & Co.); U.S. Public, pg. 533
ELASTOMERIC TECHNOLOGIES, INC.—Thomas & Betts Corporation; U.S. Public, pg. 1598
ELCO CORPORATION—Kyocera Corporation; Int'l, pg. 775
ELCO EURPOE GMBH—Textron Inc.; U.S. Public, pg. 1590
ELECTRICAL PRODUCTS DIVISION—3M; U.S. Public, pg. 1605
ELECTRO-MATIC PRODUCTS INC.; U.S. Private, pg. 369
ELECTROFORM S.A.—Thomas & Betts Corporation; U.S. Public, pg. 1598
ELECTRONIA DALE DE MEXICO S.A. DE C.V.—Vishay Intertechnology, Inc.; U.S. Public, pg. 1722
ELECTRONIC PRODUCTS DIVISION—3M; U.S. Public, pg. 1605
ELKAY ELECTRICAL—Smiths Industries plc; Int'l, pg. 1267
GLASSEAL PRODUCTS, INC.—HCC Industries; U.S. Private, pg. 490
HCC INDUSTRIES; U.S. Private, pg. 490
RICHARD HIRSCHMANN GMBH & CO.—Rheinmetall Group; Int'l, pg. 1108
RICHARD HIRSCHMANN OF AMERICA, INC.—Rheinmetall Group; Int'l, pg. 1108
HUGHES-PETERS, INC.; U.S. Private, pg. 546
HYPERTAC LIMITED—Smiths Industries plc; Int'l, pg. 1267
HYPERTRONICS CORPORATION—Smiths Industries plc; Int'l, pg. 1268
ICORE INTERNATIONAL INC.—Smiths Industries plc; Int'l, pg. 1268
E.F. JOHNSON RADIO SYSTEMS—Transcrypt International; U.S. Public, pg. 1630
LABARGE ELECTRONICS—LaBarge, Inc.; U.S. Public, pg. 973
LABARGE, INC.; U.S. Public, pg. 973
LABINAL SA; Int'l, pg. 785
M/A-COM LIMITED—AMP Incorporated; U.S. Public, pg. 8
MATRIX SCIENCE CORPORATION—AMP Incorporated; U.S. Public, pg. 8
METHODE ELECTRONICS INC.; U.S. Public, pg. 1101
MICROWAVE SIGNAL, INC.—AMP Incorporated; U.S. Public, pg. 8
MOLEX—Molex Incorporated; U.S. Public, pg. 1122
MOLEX CARIBE—Molex Incorporated; U.S. Public, pg. 1122
MOLEX ELETRONICA LTDA.—Molex Incorporated; U.S. Public, pg. 1122
MOLEX FIBER OPTIC INC.—Molex Incorporated; U.S. Public, pg. 1122
MOLEX INCORPORATED; U.S. Public, pg. 1121
MOLEX IRELAND LTD.—Molex Incorporated; U.S. Public, pg. 1122
MOLEX KOREA CO., LTD.—Molex Incorporated; U.S. Public, pg. 1122
MOLEX US INC.—Molex Incorporated; U.S. Public, pg. 1122
NEW ZEALAND AMP LTD.—AMP Incorporated; U.S. Public, pg. 9
PARLEX CORPORATION; U.S. Public, pg. 1264
PARLEX LAMINATED CABLE—Parlex Corporation; U.S. Public, pg. 1264
POSITRONIC INDUSTRIES, INC.; U.S. Private, pg. 876
PRONER COMATEL GMBH—Siebe plc; Int'l, pg. 1242
PYLE INC.—Kohlberg Kravis Roberts & Co.; U.S. Private, pg. 629
RAYCHEM CORPORATION; U.S. Public, pg. 1362
RAYLAN—AMP Incorporated; U.S. Public, pg. 8
ROBINSON NUGENT (EUROPE) B.V.—Robinson Nugent, Inc.; U.S. Public, pg. 1395
ROBINSON NUGENT, INC.; U.S. Public, pg. 1394
ROBINSON-NUGENT S.A.—Robinson Nugent, Inc.; U.S. Public, pg. 1395
ROBINSON NUGENT (SCOTLAND) LIMITED—Robinson Nugent, Inc.; U.S. Public, pg. 1395
ROCKWELL INTERNATIONAL CORPORATION; U.S. Public, pg. 1397
SAMTEC INC.; U.S. Private, pg. 963
SMITHS INDUSTRIES PLC; Int'l, pg. 1266
SQUARE D COMPANY—Schneider S.A.; Int'l, pg. 1208
STEWART CONNECTOR SYSTEMS, INC.—Insilco Corporation; U.S. Public, pg. 881
STONERIDGE, INC.; U.S. Private, pg. 1044
SWITCHCRAFT, INC.—Raytheon Company; U.S. Public, pg. 1366
TII DOMINICANA INC.—TII Industries, Inc.; U.S. Public, pg. 1556
TII INDUSTRIES, INC.; U.S. Public, pg. 1556
TALLEY INDUSTRIES, INC.—Carpenter Technology Corporation; U.S. Public, pg. 307
THOMAS & BETTS CORPORATION; U.S. Public, pg. 1597
3M; U.S. Public, pg. 1604
TRICON INDUSTRIES, INC.; U.S. Private, pg. 1102
ULTI-MATE, INC.—Molex Incorporated; U.S. Public, pg. 1122
UNITECH PLC—Siebe plc; Int'l, pg. 1241
VIKING ELECTRONICS, INC.—Wire-Pro Inc.; U.S. Private, pg. 1184
WELLS ELECTRONICS INC.—Siebe plc; Int'l, pg. 1241
WELLS JAPAN LTD.—Siebe plc; Int'l, pg. 1242
THE WHITAKER CORPORATION—AMP Incorporated; U.S. Public, pg. 8
WINCHESTER ELECTRONICS—Litton Industries, Inc.; U.S. Public, pg. 1003
ZETRONIC S.P.A.—Molex Incorporated; U.S. Public, pg. 1122

3679 — ELECTRONIC COMPONENTS, NEC

ABB CEAG POWER SUPPLIES INC.—ABB Asea Brown Boveri (Holding) Ltd.; Int'l, pg. 4
ABB DRIVES AB—ABB Asea Brown Boveri (Holding) Ltd.; Int'l, pg. 7
ACT MANUFACTURING; U.S. Public, pg. 3
ADC TELECOMMUNICATIONS, INC.; U.S. Public, pg. 4
AKG ACOUSTICS—Harman International Industries, Inc.; U.S. Public, pg. 787
AMP INCORPORATED; U.S. Public, pg. 7
AMP PACKAGING SYSTEMS, INC.—AMP Incorporated; U.S. Public, pg. 8
AP & T GMBH—Ferrofluidics Corporation; U.S. Public, pg. 620
API HAROWE—American Precision Industries Inc.; U.S. Public, pg. 90
ABBOTT ELECTRONICS, INC.; U.S. Private, pg. 9
ACESSORIOS ELECTRONICOS (BEL FUSE MACAO), LIMITADA—Bel Fuse Inc.; U.S. Public, pg. 200
ACME ELECTRIC CORPORATION; U.S. Public, pg. 16
ACTION MANUFACTURING CO.; U.S. Private, pg. 15
ACUSTAR, INC., ELECTRONICS GROUP—Chrysler Corporation; U.S. Public, pg. 353
ADVANCE CIRCUITS, INC.—Johnson Matthey Public Limited Company; Int'l, pg. 713
ADVANCE TRANSFORMER CO.—Philips Electronics N.V.; Int'l, pg. 1054
ADVANCED CIRCUIT DESIGN DIV.—Litton Industries, Inc.; U.S. Public, pg. 1003
ADVANCED CIRCUIT TECHNOLOGY; U.S. Private, pg. 21
ADVANCED ENERGY INDUSTRY; U.S. Public, pg. 20
ADVANCED MICRO DEVICES, INC.; U.S. Public, pg. 21
AEROFLEX INCORPORATED; U.S. Public, pg. 23
AEROFLEX LABORATORIES INC.—Aeroflex Incorporated; U.S. Public, pg. 24
AEROFLEX LINTEK CORP.—Aeroflex Incorporated; U.S. Public, pg. 24
AEROSPACE-MARINE-DEFENSE GROUP—Aeroquip-Vickers, Inc.; U.S. Public, pg. 24
AIR COMFORT PRODUCTS DIV.—Emerson Electric Co.; U.S. Public, pg. 572
AIR PRODUCTS A/S-GARDNER CRYOGENICS DIV.—Air Products and Chemicals, Inc.; U.S. Public, pg. 31
AIR PRODUCTS A/S PERMIA MARITIME DIV.—Air Products and Chemicals, Inc.; U.S. Public, pg. 31
AKZO ELECTRONICS MATERIALS CO.—Akzo Nobel N.V.; Int'l, pg. 48
AKZO NOBEL INC.—Akzo Nobel N.V.; Int'l, pg. 47
ALLEN-BRADLEY ENTERPRISE XIAMEN LTD.—Rockwell International Corporation; U.S. Public, pg. 1398
ALLEN-BRADLEY INDIA LIMITED—Rockwell International Corporation; U.S. Public, pg. 1398
ALLEN-BRADLEY S.R.L.—Rockwell International Corporation; U.S. Public, pg. 1399
ALLEN TELECOM, INC.; U.S. Public, pg. 45
ALLIEDSIGNAL COMMERCIAL AVIONIC SYSTEMS—AlliedSignal Inc.; U.S. Public, pg. 50
ALLIEDSIGNAL COMMERCIAL AVIONICS SYSTEMS—AlliedSignal Inc.; U.S. Public, pg. 50
ALLSOP, INC.; U.S. Private, pg. 44
ALPHA INDUSTRIES, INC.; U.S. Public, pg. 57
ALTAIR CORPORATION; U.S. Private, pg. 46
ALTEC ELECTRONICA DE CHIHUAHUA S. A. DE C. V.—Ford Motor Company; U.S. Public, pg. 665
ALTRON INCORPORATED; U.S. Public, pg. 59
AMERICABLE, INC.—ENStar, Inc.; U.S. Public, pg. 585
AMERICAN ELECTRONICS, INC.—AEI Holding Co., Inc.; U.S. Private, pg. 5
AMERICAN PRECISION INDUSTRIES INC.; U.S. Public, pg. 90
AMERICAN SYSTEMS CORPORATION; U.S. Private, pg. 63
AMETEK, INC.; U.S. Public, pg. 99
AMTECH CORPORATION; U.S. Public, pg. 105
AMTECH SYSTEMS CORPORATION—Amtech Corporation; U.S. Public, pg. 105
ANALOG DEVICES—Analog Devices, Inc.; U.S. Public, pg. 108

ANALOG DEVICES, INC.; U.S. Public, pg. 107
ANALOG DEVICES SEMICONDUCTOR—Analog Devices, Inc.; U.S. Public, pg. 108
ANAREN MICROWAVE INC.; U.S. Public, pg. 110
ANDREW CORPORATION; U.S. Public, pg. 112
ANTENNA PRODUCTS CORP.—Cabre Corp.; U.S. Public, pg. 289
APOLLO ELECTRONICS CO., LTD.—Rohm Co., Ltd.; Int'l, pg. 1125
APPLIANCE COMPONENTS LIMITED—Siebe plc; Int'l, pg. 1241
APPLIED MAGNETICS CORPORATION; U.S. Public, pg. 123
APPLIED MAGNETICS IRELAND, LTD.—Applied Magnetics Corporation; U.S. Public, pg. 123
APPLIED MAGNETICS KOREA, LTD.—Applied Magnetics Corporation; U.S. Public, pg. 123
APPLIED MAGNETICS (MALAYSIA) SDN. BHD.—Applied Magnetics Corporation; U.S. Public, pg. 123
APPLIED MATERIALS, INC.; U.S. Public, pg. 123
APPLIED SCIENCES DIVISION—Caddock Electronics, Inc.; U.S. Private, pg. 198
THE ARNOLD ENGINEERING COMPANY—SPS Technologies, Inc.; U.S. Public, pg. 1420
AROMAT CORPORATION—Matsushita Electric Works, Ltd.; Int'l, pg. 847
ATKINSON; U.S. Public, pg. 143
ATLANTIC GUEST, INC.—Valley Forge Corporation; U.S. Public, pg. 1705
ATLANTIC SCIENTIFIC CORPORATION—Bowthorpe plc; Int'l, pg. 208
ATLAS/SOUNDOLIER—American Trading and Production Corporation; U.S. Private, pg. 64
AUDIOVOX CORPORATION; U.S. Public, pg. 147
AUGAT, INC.—Thomas & Betts Corporation; U.S. Public, pg. 1597
AUGAT, INC., INTERCONNECTION PRODUCTS-SANFORD PLANT—Thomas & Betts Corporation; U.S. Public, pg. 1598
AUGAT LTD.—Thomas & Betts Corporation; U.S. Public, pg. 1598
AUGAT PTE. LTD.—Thomas & Betts Corporation; U.S. Public, pg. 1598
AURA SYSTEMS, INC.; U.S. Public, pg. 147
AUTOSWAGE PRODUCTS, INC.; U.S. Private, pg. 101
AUTRONICS CORPORATION—Bowthorpe plc; Int'l, pg. 208
AVEX ELECTRONICS, INC.—J.M. Huber Corporation; U.S. Private, pg. 545
AVIONICS—Lockheed Martin Corporation; U.S. Public, pg. 1008
AVIONICS & COMMUNICATIONS—Rockwell International Corporation; U.S. Public, pg. 1397
AVNET, INC.; U.S. Public, pg. 155
AXSYS TECHNOLOGIES, INC.; U.S. Public, pg. 157
AYDIN CORPORATION; U.S. Public, pg. 158
AYDIN EUROPE LTD.—Aydin Corporation; U.S. Public, pg. 158
AYDIN INTERNATIONAL U.K.—Aydin Corporation; U.S. Public, pg. 158
BCL MAGNETICS—Tempel Steel Company; U.S. Private, pg. 1075
BEI SENSORS AND SYSTEMS COMPANY—BEI Technologies, Inc.; U.S. Public, pg. 160
BICC BRAND-REX—BICC plc; Int'l, pg. 120
BKG FINISHING SYSTEMS, INC.—Illinois Tool Works Inc.; U.S. Public, pg. 865
BMC INDUSTRIES, INC.; U.S. Public, pg. 162
BOC AG—The BOC Group plc; Int'l, pg. 121
THE BOC GROUP PLC; Int'l, pg. 121
BOC INDIA LTD.—The BOC Group plc; Int'l, pg. 122
BOC PROCESS PLANTS LTD.—The BOC Group plc; Int'l, pg. 121
BWD AUTOMOTIVE—Echlin Inc.; U.S. Public, pg. 560
BAIRNCO CORPORATION; U.S. Public, pg. 165
BALL AEROSPACE SYSTEMS DIVISION—Ball Corporation; U.S. Public, pg. 171
BANG & OLUFSEN A/S; Int'l, pg. 145
BAUSCH & LOMB INCORPORATED; U.S. Public, pg. 194
BECKMAN INDUSTRIAL CORPORATION—Emerson Electric Co.; U.S. Public, pg. 574
BEL FUSE INC.; U.S. Public, pg. 200
BEL FUSE LTD.—Bel Fuse Inc.; U.S. Public, pg. 200
BELL INDUSTRIES, INC.; U.S. Public, pg. 204
BERG ELECTRONICS; U.S. Public, pg. 212
THE BERGQUIST COMPANY; U.S. Private, pg. 135
BERGQUIST ITC, GMBH—The Bergquist Company; U.S. Private, pg. 135
BIRTCHER—Zero Corporation; U.S. Public, pg. 1791
BOEING NORTH AMERICA, AUTONETICS ELECTRONIC SYSTEMS DIVISION—The Boeing Company; U.S. Public, pg. 241
BOEING NORTH AMERICA, TACTICAL SYSTEMS DIVISION—The Boeing Company; U.S. Public, pg. 241
BOURNS ELECTRONICS, LTD.—Bourns, Inc.; U.S. Private, pg. 161
BOURNS SENSORS & CONTROLS DIVISION—Bourns, Inc.; U.S. Private, pg. 161
BOWMAR INSTRUMENT CORPORATION; U.S. Public, pg. 248
BOWMAR TECHNOLOGIES—Bowmar Instrument Corporation; U.S. Public, pg. 248
BOWTHORPE PLC; Int'l, pg. 207
BRITISH AEROSPACE AUSTRALIA LIMITED—British Aerospace p.l.c.; Int'l, pg. 218
BUCKBEE-MEARS EUROPE GMBH—BMC Industries, Inc.; U.S. Public, pg. 162
BUD INDUSTRIES, INC.; U.S. Private, pg. 178
BURGESS GMBH—Williams Holdings Plc; Int'l, pg. 1500
BURGESS SAIA CO. INC.—Williams Holdings Plc; Int'l, pg. 1500
CSD, INC.—Philips Electronics N.V.; Int'l, pg. 1053
CTS CORPORATION; U.S. Public, pg. 285
CTS U.K., LTD.—CTS Corporation; U.S. Public, pg. 286
CABLETRON SYSTEMS, INC.; U.S. Public, pg. 288
CABLEWAVE SYSTEMS; U.S. Private, pg. 197
CADDOCK ELECTRONICS, INC.; U.S. Private, pg. 198
CADEC SYSTEMS INC.—Cummins Engine Company, Inc.; U.S. Public, pg. 468
CALCOR SPACE FACILITY, INC.; U.S. Private, pg. 200
CALIFORNIA MICROWAVE, INC.; U.S. Public, pg. 293
CARBONE-LORRAINE NORTH AMERICA—Pechiney S.A.; Int'l, pg. 1028
CARBONE OF AMERICA—Pechiney S.A.; Int'l, pg. 1028
CENTRAL DATA CORPORATION; U.S. Private, pg. 223
THE CHAMBERLAIN GROUP, INC.—Duchossois Industries, Inc.; U.S. Private, pg. 344
CHANNEL MASTER; U.S. Private, pg. 228
CHANNEL MASTER (UK) LIMITED—Channel Master; U.S. Private, pg. 228
CHANNEL TECHNOLOGIES, INC.; U.S. Private, pg. 228
CHART INDUSTRIES, INC.; U.S. Public, pg. 336
CHERRY AUTOMOTIVE-JAPAN—Cherry Electrical Products Corporation; U.S. Public, pg. 346
CHERRY ELECTRICAL PRODUCTS—Cherry Electrical Products Corporation; U.S. Public, pg. 346
CHERRY ELECTRICAL PRODUCTS CORPORATION; U.S. Public, pg. 346
CHERRY MIKROSCHALTER GMBH—Cherry Electrical Products Corporation; U.S. Public, pg. 346
CHRYSLER CORPORATION; U.S. Public, pg. 352
CIPRICO INTERTNATIONAL LTD.—Ciprico, Inc.; U.S. Public, pg. 370
DAVID CLARK COMPANY INCORPORATED; U.S. Private, pg. 242
COMATEL SRL—Siebe plc; Int'l, pg. 1241
COMMUNICATIONS INSTRUMENTS INC.; U.S. Private, pg. 259
COMPAS ELECTRONICS, INC.—AIM Safety Company Inc.; Int'l, pg. 36
COMPONENTS CORPORATION OF AMERICA; U.S. Private, pg. 259
COMPUTER PRODUCTS, NATIONAL ACCOUNTS DIVISION—Computer Products, Inc.; U.S. Public, pg. 422
COMSTRON DIVISION—Aeroflex Incorporated; U.S. Public, pg. 24
CONDOR D.C. POWER SUPPLIES INC.—SL Industries, Inc.; U.S. Public, pg. 1419
CONNECTOR DIVISION AMERICA AND ASIA—Labinal SA; Int'l, pg. 786
CONSUMER AUDIO PRODUCTS CO.—Sony Corporation; Int'l, pg. 1281
CONSUMER DISPLAY PRODUCTS CO.—Sony Corporation; Int'l, pg. 1281
CONSUMER VIDEO PRODUCTS CO.—Sony Corporation; Int'l, pg. 1281
CONTINENTAL CIRCUITS CORP.; U.S. Public, pg. 440
CORCOM, INC.; U.S. Public, pg. 446
CORNING GMBH—Corning Incorporated; U.S. Public, pg. 449
A.C. COSSOR ELECTRONICS, LIMITED—Raytheon Company; U.S. Public, pg. 1366
COUTANT ELECTRONIQUE SA—Siebe plc; Int'l, pg. 1241
COUTANT LAMBDA LIMITED—Siebe plc; Int'l, pg. 1241
CRYOSTAR FRANCE SA—The BOC Group plc; Int'l, pg. 122
CRYOTECHNOLOGIES SA—Thomson S.A.; Int'l, pg. 1383
DDL ELECTRONICS, INC.; U.S. Public, pg. 473
DDL ELECTRONICS LTD.—DDL Electronics, Inc.; U.S. Public, pg. 473
DOD ELECTRONICS CORPORATION—Harman International Industries, Inc.; U.S. Public, pg. 787
DALE ELECTRONICS, TEMPE DIV.—Vishay Intertechnology, Inc.; U.S. Public, pg. 1722
DATA IMAGES—Litton Industries, Inc.; U.S. Public, pg. 1004
DATA INSTRUMENTS, INC.; U.S. Private, pg. 312
DATAMATE DIVISION—Methode Electronics Inc.; U.S. Public, pg. 1101
DEL GLOBAL TECHNOLOGIES; U.S. Public, pg. 493
DELHI INDUSTRIES INC.—Russel Metals Inc.; Int'l, pg. 1150
DELPHI PACKARD ELECTRIC SYSTEMS—General Motors Corporation; U.S. Public, pg. 719
DERLAN INDUSTRIES LIMITED; Int'l, pg. 395
DETROIT COIL COMPANY; U.S. Private, pg. 328
DEXTER MAGNETIC MATERIALS—The Dexter Corporation; U.S. Public, pg. 504
DIALIGHT CORPORATION—The Roxboro Group PLC; Int'l, pg. 1130
DORNE & MARGOLIN, INC.—United Capital Corp.; U.S. Public, pg. 1675
DOUGLAS-RANDALL, INC.—Publicker Industries Inc.; U.S. Public, pg. 1341
DRAKA KABEL B.V.; Int'l, pg. 417
DU PONT DO BRASIL S.A.—Du Pont (E.I. Du Pont De Nemours & Co.); U.S. Public, pg. 532
DU PONT (SINGAPORE) ELECTRONICS PVT. LTD.—Du Pont (E.I. Du Pont De Nemours & Co.); U.S. Public, pg. 531
DUCOMMUN INCORPORATED; U.S. Public, pg. 533
DURAMETALLIC CORP.—Flowserve Corporation; U.S. Public, pg. 658
DYNAMICS CORPORATION OF AMERICA—CTS Corporation; U.S. Public, pg. 286
DYNAMICS RESEARCH CORPORATION; U.S. Public, pg. 539
DYNAPERT LIMITED—The Black & Decker Corporation; U.S. Public, pg. 234
DYNATECH CORPORATION; U.S. Public, pg. 539
EDO ACOUSTIC PRODUCTS—EDO Corporation; U.S. Public, pg. 542
EDO CORPORATION; U.S. Public, pg. 541
EDO MARINE & AIRCRAFT SYSTEMS—EDO Corporation; U.S. Public, pg. 542
EDO WESTERN CORPORATION—EDO Corporation; U.S. Public, pg. 542
EECO, SWITCH—Transico Incorporated; U.S. Public, pg. 1631
EG & G, INC.; U.S. Public, pg. 542
EG & G OPTOELECTRONICS-COVINA—EG & G, Inc.; U.S. Public, pg. 543
EG & G OPTOELECTRONICS-ST. LOUIS—EG & G, Inc.; U.S. Public, pg. 543
EG & G OPTOELECTRONICS-SALEM—EG & G, Inc.; U.S. Public, pg. 543
EASTMAN KODAK COMPANY; U.S. Public, pg. 550
EL. BO. MEC. THERMALLOY SRL.—Bowthorpe plc; Int'l, pg. 209
ELCO CORPORATION—Kyocera Corporation; Int'l, pg. 775
ELECTRO CORPORATION—BTR plc; Int'l, pg. 127
ELECTRO DYNAMICS CRYSTAL CORPORATION; U.S. Private, pg. 368
ELECTRO KINETICS DIV.—Pacific Scientific Company; U.S. Public, pg. 1250
ELECTRO MECHANICAL DESIGN SERVICES, INC.; U.S. Private, pg. 369
ELECTRO-MECHANICAL INSTRUMENTS DIV.—AEI Holding Co., Inc.; U.S. Private, pg. 5
ELECTRO OPTICAL IND.—Channel Technologies, Inc.; U.S. Private, pg. 228
ELECTRO PARTES DE MATAMOROS, S.A. DE C.V.—Zenith Electronics Corp.; U.S. Public, pg. 1790
ELECTRO-TEC CORP.—Kaydon Corporation; U.S. Public, pg. 946
ELECTROCOM AUTOMATION L.P.—Siemens AG; Int'l, pg. 1244
ELECTROID CO.; U.S. Private, pg. 369
ELECTROMAGNETIC SCIENCES, INC.; U.S. Public, pg. 569
ELECTRONIA DALE DE MEXICO S.A. DE C.V.—Vishay Intertechnology, Inc.; U.S. Public, pg. 1722
ELECTRONIC PRODUCTS DIVISION—3M; U.S. Public, pg. 1605
ELECTRONIC SOLUTIONS—Zero Corporation; U.S. Public, pg. 1791
ELECTRONICA PANTERA, S.A. DE C.V.—The JPM Company; U.S. Public, pg. 919
ELECTRONICS STAMPING CORP.; U.S. Private, pg. 370
ELEKTRO-APPARATEBAU OLTEN AG; Int'l, pg. 444
ELGAR CORPORATION—Harnischfeger Industries, Inc.; U.S. Public, pg. 789
ELMA ELECTRONIC INC.—Sulzer Ltd.; Int'l, pg. 1305
EMAIL LIMITED; Int'l, pg. 450
EMERSON & CUMING SPECIALTY POLYMERS—Unilever Plc; Int'l, pg. 1435
EMERSON ELECTRIC INDUS. CONTROLS LTD.—Emerson Electric Co.; U.S. Public, pg. 576
ENTRON INDUSTRIES LIMITED PARTNERSHIP; U.S. Private, pg. 378
ERICSSON COMPONENTS AB—Telefonaktiebolaget LM Ericsson; Int'l, pg. 1363
ERICSSON COMPONENTS A/S—Telefonaktiebolaget LM Ericsson; Int'l, pg. 1366
ERICSSON COMPONENTS EUROPE GMBH—Telefonaktiebolaget LM Ericsson; Int'l, pg. 1366
ERICSSON COMPONENTS S.R.L.—Telefonaktiebolaget LM Ericsson; Int'l, pg. 1366
ERICSSON COMPOSANTS S.A.—Telefonaktiebolaget LM Ericsson; Int'l, pg. 1366
ESPEY MFG. & ELECTRONICS CORP.; U.S. Public, pg. 592
ESTERLINE TECHNOLOGIES CORPORATION; U.S. Public, pg. 594
EXSIL, INC.—Laporte plc; Int'l, pg. 802
FARRAND CONTROLS—Ruhle Companies, Inc.; U.S. Private, pg. 951
FASCO CONTROLS CORPORATION—BTR plc; Int'l, pg. 125
FAWN INDUSTRIES, INC.; U.S. Private, pg. 397
FELDMUHLE KYOCERA EUROPA ELEKTRONISCHE—Kyocera Corporation; Int'l, pg. 776
FERRAZ CORPORATION—Pechiney S.A.; Int'l, pg. 1028
FISHER PIERCE DIVISION—Pacific Scientific Company; U.S. Public, pg. 1250
FLEXIBLE CIRCUIT PRODUCTS DIVISION—Parlex Corporation; U.S. Public, pg. 1264
FLUKE CORPORATION; U.S. Public, pg. 659
FORD MICROELECTRONICS, INC.—Ford Motor Company; U.S. Public, pg. 664
FREQUENCY ELECTRONICS, INC.; U.S. Public, pg. 681
FUJI ELECTROCHEMICAL CO., LTD.—Fujitsu Limited; Int'l, pg. 526
FUTABA CORPORATION; Int'l, pg. 531
FUTABA CORPORATION OF AMERICA—Futaba Corporation; Int'l, pg. 531
GKI ELECTRONIC ENCLOSURE DIVISION-JOHNSTOWN—General Kinetics Incorporated; U.S. Public, pg. 717
GKI ELECTRONIC ENCLOSURE DIVISION-ORLANDO—General Kinetics Incorporated; U.S. Public, pg. 717
GSE, INC.—United Dominion Industries, Ltd.; U.S. Public, pg. 1676
GAMMA-F CORPORATION—Vertex Communications Corporation; U.S. Public, pg. 1718
GANDALF CANADA LTD.—Gandalf Technologies Inc.; Int'l, pg. 540
GANDALF DIGITAL COMMUNICATIONS LTD.—Gandalf Technologies Inc.; Int'l, pg. 540
GANDALF INTERNATIONAL LTD.—Gandalf Technologies Inc.; Int'l, pg. 540
GANDALF NEDERLAND B.V.—Gandalf Technologies Inc.; Int'l, pg. 540
GANDALF S.A.—Gandalf Technologies Inc.; Int'l, pg. 541
GANDALF SYSTEMS CORPORATION—Gandalf Technologies Inc.; Int'l, pg. 540
GANDALF TECHNOLOGIES INC.; Int'l, pg. 540
GEKA, S.A.—Vishay Intertechnology, Inc.; U.S. Public, pg. 1722
GENERAL CABLE CO.—Wassall Plc; Int'l, pg. 1487

GENERAL DYNAMICS CORPORATION; *U.S. Public*, pg. 708
GENERAL KINETICS INCORPORATED; *U.S. Public*, pg. 716
GENERAL MICROCIRCUITS CORPORATION—General Microwave Corporation; *U.S. Public*, pg. 717
GENERAL MICROWAVE CORPORATION; *U.S. Public*, pg. 717
GENERAL POWER SYSTEMS, INC.—Components Corporation Of America; *U.S. Private*, pg. 260
GESCHAEFTSBEREICH DER ALLIEDSIGNAL (DEUTSCHLAND) GMBH (ENEVCO GERMANY)—AlliedSignal Inc.; *U.S. Public*, pg. 53
GIGA-TRONICS INCORPORATED; *U.S. Public*, pg. 742
W.L. GORE & ASSOCIATES, INC.; *U.S. Private*, pg. 465
GOULD ELECTRONICS GMBH FOIL DIVISION—Thermo Electron Corporation; *U.S. Public*, pg. 1592
GOULD ELECTRONICS INC.—Thermo Electron Corporation; *U.S. Public*, pg. 1591
GOULD ELECTRONICS INC., FIBER OPTICS—Thermo Electron Corporation; *U.S. Public*, pg. 1592
GOULD ELECTRONICS INC., FOIL DIVISION—Thermo Electron Corporation; *U.S. Public*, pg. 1592
GOULD ELECTRONICS LTD., FOIL DIV.—Thermo Electron Corporation; *U.S. Public*, pg. 1592
GRACE S.A.—W.R. Grace & Co.; *U.S. Public*, pg. 756
GRAYSON ELECTRONICS CORPORATION—Allen Telecom, Inc.; *U.S. Public*, pg. 46
GROUND SYSTEMS GROUP—Raytheon Company; *U.S. Public*, pg. 1364
GTI CORPORATION; *U.S. Public*, pg. 767
HCC INDUSTRIES; *U.S. Private*, pg. 490
H.E.S. INTERNATIONAL, INC.—Oak Industries Inc.; *U.S. Public*, pg. 1209
HAMLIN, INC.—Breed Technologies, Inc.; *U.S. Public*, pg. 251
HARMONY ENGINEERING CORPORATION; *U.S. Private*, pg. 503
HARRIS SEMICONDUCTOR—Harris Corporation; *U.S. Public*, pg. 792
HARVEY ELECTRONICS, INC.; *U.S. Public*, pg. 796
HATHAWAY CORPORATION; *U.S. Public*, pg. 798
HATHAWAY MOTORS & INSTRUMENTS DIVISION—Hathaway Corporation; *U.S. Public*, pg. 799
HEART INTERFACE CORPORATION—Valley Forge Corporation; *U.S. Public*, pg. 1705
HELICOFLEX CO.—Pechiney S.A.; *Int'l*, pg. 1028
HELIX TECHNOLOGY CORP.; *U.S. Public*, pg. 808
HERAEUS HOLDING GMBH; *Int'l*, pg. 615
HERAEUS INSTRUMENTS INC.—Heraeus Holding GmbH; *Int'l*, pg. 616
W.C. HERAEUS GMBH—Heraeus Holding GmbH; *Int'l*, pg. 616
HERLEY INDUSTRIES, INC.; *U.S. Public*, pg. 811
HERLEY-MDI—Herley Industries, Inc.; *U.S. Public*, pg. 811
HERON INDUSTRIES LIMITED—Russel Metals Inc.; *Int'l*, pg. 1150
HIGH VOLTAGE ENGINEERING CORPORATION; *U.S. Private*, pg. 528
HIMEJI TOSHIBA E.P. CORPORATION—Toshiba Corporation; *Int'l*, pg. 1402
RICHARD HIRSCHMANN GMBH & CO.—Rheinmetall Group; *Int'l*, pg. 1108
RICHARD HIRSCHMANN OF AMERICA, INC.—Rheinmetall Group; *Int'l*, pg. 1108
HITACHI CHEMICAL CO., LTD.—Hitachi, Ltd.; *Int'l*, pg. 621
HITACHI, LTD.; *Int'l*, pg. 621
HITACHI MAXELL, LTD.—Hitachi, Ltd.; *Int'l*, pg. 621
HONEYWELL INC.; *U.S. Public*, pg. 833
HONEYWELL LEEDS & NORTHRUP AUSTRALIA PTY. LTD.—Honeywell Inc.; *U.S. Public*, pg. 834
HOSIDEN CORPORATION; *Int'l*, pg. 635
J.M. HUBER CORPORATION; *U.S. Private*, pg. 544
HUGHES MICROELECTRONICS EUROPA ESPANA S.A.—General Motors Corporation; *U.S. Public*, pg. 725
HUGHES-PETERS, INC.; *U.S. Private*, pg. 546
HULL-THOMSON LIMITED—Russel Metals Inc.; *Int'l*, pg. 1150
HURLETRON INC.—Altair Corporation; *U.S. Private*, pg. 46
IPAC, INC.; *U.S. Private*, pg. 555
ITW NORWOOD MARKING SYSTEMS—Illinois Tool Works Inc.; *U.S. Public*, pg. 866
ITW PAKTRON—Illinois Tool Works Inc.; *U.S. Public*, pg. 866
ITW SCREEN PROCESS SPECIALIST, LTD.—Illinois Tool Works Inc.; *U.S. Public*, pg. 867
ITW WOODWORTH—Illinois Tool Works Inc.; *U.S. Public*, pg. 867
IBIDEN CO., LTD.—Mitsui & Co., Ltd.; *Int'l*, pg. 878
ICORE INTERNATIONAL INC.—Smiths Industries plc; *Int'l*, pg. 1268
IMATION CORPORATION; *U.S. Public*, pg. 870
INDUCTOTHERM INDUSTRIES, INC.; *U.S. Private*, pg. 560
INDUSTRIAL ELECTRONICS GROUP—Raytheon Company; *U.S. Public*, pg. 1364
INDUSTRIAS MERRIMAC INCORPORADA, S.A.—Merrimac Industries, Inc.; *U.S. Public*, pg. 1098
INTEGRATION AND SYSTEMS PRODUCTS DIV.—Eastman Kodak Company; *U.S. Public*, pg. 555
INTELLEDEX VISION PRODUCTS—Electro Scientific Industries, Inc.; *U.S. Public*, pg. 568
INTER-PAK ELECTRONICS—Litton Industries, Inc.; *U.S. Public*, pg. 1003
INTERMATIC INC.; *U.S. Private*, pg. 567
INTERNATIONAL ELECTRONIC RESEARCH CORP.—CTS Corporation; *U.S. Public*, pg. 286
INTERNATIONAL RECTIFIER CORPORATION; *U.S. Public*, pg. 906
ION IMPLANT SYSTEMS—Varian Associates, Inc.; *U.S. Public*, pg. 1710
IWATE TOSHIBA ELECTRONICS CO., LTD.—Toshiba Corporation; *Int'l*, pg. 1402
JCAIR, INC.—The B.F. Goodrich Company; *U.S. Public*, pg. 751
THE JPM COMPANY; *U.S. Public*, pg. 919
THE JPM COMPANY—The JPM Company; *U.S. Public*, pg. 919
JABIL CIRCUIT, INC.; *U.S. Public*, pg. 919
JAPAN ENERGY CORPORATION; *Int'l*, pg. 702
JAY-EL PRODUCTS, INC.—Ducommun Incorporated; *U.S. Public*, pg. 534
JOHANSON MANUFACTURING CORPORATION; *U.S. Private*, pg. 589
E.F. JOHNSON RADIO SYSTEMS—Transcrypt International; *U.S. Public*, pg. 1630
JOHNSON MATTHEY PUBLIC LIMITED COMPANY; *Int'l*, pg. 713
JOSLYN ELECTRONIC SYSTEMS CORPORATION—Danaher Corporation; *U.S. Public*, pg. 481
K&B MUNDELEIN INC.—Kirkwood Industries, Inc.; *U.S. Private*, pg. 623
K & L MICROWAVE DIV.—Dover Corporation; *U.S. Public*, pg. 521
K & M ELECTRONICS, INC.—Derlan Industries Limited; *Int'l*, pg. 395
KABELWERKE REINSHAGEN GMBH—General Motors Corporation; *U.S. Public*, pg. 723
KAGA TOSHIBA ELECTRONICS COMPANY—Toshiba Corporation; *Int'l*, pg. 1403
KAMAN INSTRUMENTATION CORP.—Kaman Corporation; *U.S. Public*, pg. 942
KAULT & BUX COMMUTATOR GMBH-HERRENBERG—Kirkwood Industries, Inc.; *U.S. Private*, pg. 623
KAYEX CORP.—General Signal Corporation; *U.S. Public*, pg. 727
KETEMA, INC.—KTM Holdings Corp.; *U.S. Private*, pg. 604
KEVLIN CORPORATION; *U.S. Public*, pg. 953
KIMBALL INTERNATIONAL, INC.; *U.S. Public*, pg. 956
KINSEKI, LTD.—Oki Electric Industry Company, Ltd.; *Int'l*, pg. 999
KIRKWOOD INDUSTRIES, INC.; *U.S. Private*, pg. 623
KODAK FEDERAL SYSTEMS DIVISION—Eastman Kodak Company; *U.S. Public*, pg. 555
KOREA TDK CO. LTD.—TDK Corporation; *Int'l*, pg. 1336
KORRY ELECTRONICS CO.—Esterline Technologies Corporation; *U.S. Public*, pg. 594
KYOCERA CORPORATION; *Int'l*, pg. 775
KYOCERA ELECTRONICS EUROPE GMBH—Kyocera Corporation; *Int'l*, pg. 776
KYOCERA ELECTRONICS U.K., LTD.—Kyocera Corporation; *Int'l*, pg. 776
KYOCERA (HONG KONG), LTD.—Kyocera Corporation; *Int'l*, pg. 776
KYOCERA INTERNATIONAL, INC.—Kyocera Corporation; *Int'l*, pg. 775
KYUSHU MATSUSHITA ELECTRIC CO. LTD.—Matsushita Electric Industrial Co., Ltd.; *Int'l*, pg. 846
L3 COMMUNICATIONS RANDTRON SYSTEMS—L3 Communications; *U.S. Private*, pg. 639
LCC S.A.—Thomson S.A.; *Int'l*, pg. 1384
LA MARCHE MFG. CO.; *U.S. Private*, pg. 640
LABARGE ELECTRONICS—LaBarge, Inc.; *U.S. Public*, pg. 973
LABARGE, INC.; *U.S. Public*, pg. 973
LAMBDA ELECTRONICA DE MEXICO, S.A.—Siebe plc; *Int'l*, pg. 1242
LAMBDA ELECTRONICS—Siebe plc; *Int'l*, pg. 1241
LAMBDA ELECTRONICS INC.—Siebe plc; *Int'l*, pg. 1241
LAMBDA-KOREA K.K.—Siebe plc; *Int'l*, pg. 1242
LAMBDA NOVATRONICS INC.—Siebe plc; *Int'l*, pg. 1241
LAMINAIRE CORPORATION—Thermo-Mizer Environmental Corp.; *U.S. Public*, pg. 1596
LANCE INDUSTRIES; *U.S. Private*, pg. 645
LEACH INTERNATIONAL; *U.S. Private*, pg. 655
LEWIS ENGINEERING COMPANY—Coltec Holdings Inc; *U.S. Public*, pg. 402
LIEBERT CORPORATION AUSTRALIA PTY. LTD.—Emerson Electric Co.; *U.S. Public*, pg. 577
LIEBERT FAR EAST LTD.—Emerson Electric Co.; *U.S. Public*, pg. 577
LIEBERT LTD.—Emerson Electric Co.; *U.S. Public*, pg. 577
LIEBERT MALAYSIA SDN. BHD.—Emerson Electric Co.; *U.S. Public*, pg. 577
LIGHT VALVE TECHNOLOGY—Eastman Kodak Company; *U.S. Public*, pg. 551
LITTELFUSE, INC.; *U.S. Public*, pg. 1001
LITTON SOLID STATE—Litton Industries, Inc.; *U.S. Public*, pg. 1003
LOCKHEED MARTIN MICROWAVE-FSI—Lockheed Martin Corporation; *U.S. Public*, pg. 1008
LORAL SPACE & COMMUNICATIONS; *U.S. Public*, pg. 1014
LUCAS BODY SYSTEMS—LucasVarity plc; *Int'l*, pg. 820
LUCAS BODY SYSTEMS - NORTH AMERICA—LucasVarity plc; *Int'l*, pg. 820
LUCAS INDUSTRIES INC.—LucasVarity plc; *Int'l*, pg. 820
LUCAS NOVASENSOR INC.—LucasVarity plc; *Int'l*, pg. 820
LUCENT TECHNOLOGIES—Lucent Technologies Inc.; *U.S. Public*, pg. 1017
LUWA AG—Hesta Tex AG; *Int'l*, pg. 617
LYALL ASSEMBLIES, INC.—Group Dekko; *U.S. Private*, pg. 484
M/A-COM EUROTECH—AMP Incorporated; *U.S. Public*, pg. 8
M/A-COM INC.—AMP Incorporated; *U.S. Public*, pg. 8
M-TRON INDUSTRIES, INC.—Lynch Corporation; *U.S. Public*, pg. 1022
MPD, INC.; *U.S. Private*, pg. 687
MAGNETIC METALS CORP.—Inductotherm Industries, Inc.; *U.S. Private*, pg. 560
MAGNETICS—Spang & Company; *U.S. Private*, pg. 1020
MARTIN MARIETTA ASTRONAUTICS—Lockheed Martin Corporation; *U.S. Public*, pg. 1007
MARTIN MARIETTA ELECTRONICS & MISSILES—Lockheed Martin Corporation; *U.S. Public*, pg. 1007
MATEC CORPORATION; *U.S. Public*, pg. 1056
MATSUSHITA ELECTRIC INDUSTRIAL CO., LTD.; *Int'l*, pg. 846
MATSUSHITA ELECTRIC COMPONENTS CO., LTD.—Matsushita Electric Industrial Co., Ltd.; *Int'l*, pg. 846
MAXIM INTEGRATED PRODUCTS, INC.; *U.S. Public*, pg. 1061
MAXWELL TECHNOLOGIES, INC.; *U.S. Public*, pg. 1061
MCBRIDE AND ASSOCIATES, INC.; *U.S. Private*, pg. 719
MCCOY ELECTRONICS CO.—Oak Industries Inc.; *U.S. Public*, pg. 1209
MCDONNELL AIRCRAFT & MISSILE SYSTEMS DIV.—The Boeing Company; *U.S. Public*, pg. 241
MEASUREMENTS GROUP, INC.—Vishay Intertechnology, Inc.; *U.S. Public*, pg. 1722
MEDTRONIC MICRO-REL—Medtronic, Inc.; *U.S. Public*, pg. 1083
MEMOREX TELEX GMBH—Memorex Telex N.V.; *Int'l*, pg. 857
MEMOREX TELEX N.V.; *Int'l*, pg. 857
MERITEX PLASTICS INDUSTRIES, INC.—Illinois Tool Works Inc.; *U.S. Public*, pg. 867
MERRIMAC INDUSTRIES, INC.; *U.S. Public*, pg. 1098
METCLAD S.A.—Park Electrochemical Corporation; *U.S. Public*, pg. 1258
METHODE ELECTRONICS INC.; *U.S. Public*, pg. 1101
METHODE TECHNICAL COMPONENTS—Methode Electronics Inc.; *U.S. Public*, pg. 1101
MICRO MEASUREMENTS DIV.—Vishay Intertechnology, Inc.; *U.S. Public*, pg. 1722
MICRON TECHNOLOGY INC.; *U.S. Public*, pg. 1105
MICROPHASE CORPORATION; *U.S. Private*, pg. 742
MICROSEMI CORPORATION; *U.S. Public*, pg. 1107
MILLENNIUM TECHNOLOGY SERVICES, INC.; *U.S. Private*, pg. 746
J.W. MILLER DIV.—Bell Industries, Inc.; *U.S. Public*, pg. 205
MINCO PRODUCTS, INC.; *U.S. Private*, pg. 749
MINELCO, INC.—Carpenter Technology Corporation; *U.S. Public*, pg. 308
MITSUMI ELECTRIC CO., LTD.; *Int'l*, pg. 884
MOLEX CARIBE—Molex Incorporated; *U.S. Public*, pg. 1122
MOLEX ELEKTRONIK GMBH—Molex Incorporated; *U.S. Public*, pg. 1122
MOLEX ELETRONICA LTDA.—Molex Incorporated; *U.S. Public*, pg. 1122
MOLEX INCORPORATED; *U.S. Public*, pg. 1121
MOLEX IRELAND LTD.—Molex Incorporated; *U.S. Public*, pg. 1122
MOLTO GES.M.B.H.—Williams Holdings Plc; *Int'l*, pg. 1501
MOLTO GMBH—Williams Holdings Plc; *Int'l*, pg. 1501
MORGAN MATROC INC.-ELECTRO CERAMICS DIVISION—Morgan Crucible Co. Plc; *Int'l*, pg. 893
MOTOROLA AUTOMOTIVE & INDUSTRIAL ELECTRONICS GROUP—Motorola, Inc.; *U.S. Public*, pg. 1137
MOTOROLA, INC.; *U.S. Public*, pg. 1136
MULTIPLEX TECHNOLOGY, INC.—Valley Forge Corporation; *U.S. Public*, pg. 1705
MURATA ELECTRONICS NORTH AMERICA, INC.—Murata Manufacturing Co., Ltd.; *Int'l*, pg. 897
MURATA MANUFACTURING CO., LTD.; *Int'l*, pg. 897
NEC AUSTRALIA PTY. LTD.—NEC Corporation; *Int'l*, pg. 901
NEC DE MEXICO, S.A. DE C.V.—NEC Corporation; *Int'l*, pg. 901
NEC ELECTRONICS SINGAPORE PTE. LTD.—NEC Corporation; *Int'l*, pg. 901
NEC SEMICONDUCTORS IRELAND LIMITED—NEC Corporation; *Int'l*, pg. 900
NEC SEMICONDUCTORS (UK) LIMITED—NEC Corporation; *Int'l*, pg. 900
NIDEC—Nippon Densan (NIDEC); *Int'l*, pg. 933
NATIONAL-ARNOLD MAGNETICS COMPANY—SPS Technologies, Inc.; *U.S. Public*, pg. 1420
NATIONAL SEMICONDUCTOR CORPORATION; *U.S. Public*, pg. 1159
NELCO FRANCE—Kirkwood Industries, Inc.; *U.S. Private*, pg. 623
NELCO INTERNATIONAL—Park Electrochemical Corporation; *U.S. Public*, pg. 1258
NELCO PRODUCTS, INC.—Park Electrochemical Corporation; *U.S. Public*, pg. 1258
NELCO TECHNOLOGY, INC.—Park Electrochemical Corporation; *U.S. Public*, pg. 1258
NEMIC-LAMBDA ISRAEL, LTD.—Siebe plc; *Int'l*, pg. 1241
NEMIC-LAMBDA KK—Siebe plc; *Int'l*, pg. 1242
NEMIC LAMBDA (M) SDN. BHD.—Siebe plc; *Int'l*, pg. 1242
NEMIC-LAMBDA PTE. LTD.—Siebe plc; *Int'l*, pg. 1242
NETWAVE TECHNOLOGIES, INC.—Technitrol, Inc.; *U.S. Public*, pg. 1564
NEUMANN (USA)—Sennheiser Electronic Corp.; *U.S. Private*, pg. 984
NEUWIESEN IMMOBILIEN AG—Sulzer Ltd.; *Int'l*, pg. 1305
NEW ENGLAND LAMINATES CO., INC.—Park Electrochemical Corporation; *U.S. Public*, pg. 1258
NEW ENGLAND LAMINATES (U.K.) LTD.—Park Electrochemical Corporation; *U.S. Public*, pg. 1258
NEW ENGLAND TECHNOLOGY GROUP, INC.; *U.S. Private*, pg. 793
NEXTLEVEL SYSTEMS (BELGIUM)—General Instrument Corporation; *U.S. Public*, pg. 716
NEXTLEVEL SYSTEMS (JAPAN)—General Instrument Corporation; *U.S. Public*, pg. 716
NIDEC POWER GENERAL—Nippon Densan (NIDEC); *Int'l*, pg. 933
NORDIC ELECTRONIC SYSTEMS A/S—Telefonaktiebolaget LM Ericsson; *Int'l*, pg. 1369
NORTECH SA—Siebe plc; *Int'l*, pg. 1242
NORTHERN TELECOM CANADA LIMITED—Northern Telecom Limited; *Int'l*, pg. 969
NVIEW CORPORATION; *U.S. Public*, pg. 1206
O/E/N INDIA LTD.—Oak Industries Inc.; *U.S. Public*, pg. 1209
OPT INDUSTRIES, INC.—Torotel, Inc.; *U.S. Public*, pg. 1624

OAK GRIGSBY—Oak Industries Inc.; *U.S. Public*, pg. 1209
OAK INDUSTRIES INC.; *U.S. Public*, pg. 1209
OERLIKON-BUHRLE HOLDING AG; *Int'l*, pg. 996
OHMITE MANUFACTURING COMPANY; *U.S. Private*, pg. 813
OMRON CORPORATION; *Int'l*, pg. 1005
OPTREX CORPORATION—Asahi Glass Co., Ltd.; *Int'l*, pg. 84
ORTRONICS, INC.—LeGrand S.A.; *Int'l*, pg. 806
OSICOM TECHNOLOGIES INC.—Osicom Technologies Inc.; *U.S. Public*, pg. 1233
OSILLATEK CORPORATION—Dover Corporation; *U.S. Public*, pg. 521
OTO-SONIC, INC.—Beltone Electronics Corporation; *U.S. Private*, pg. 132
OXFORD INSTRUMENTS-NUCLEAR MEASUREMENTS GROUP—Oxford Instruments plc; *Int'l*, pg. 1018
PACIFIC SCIENTIFIC COMPANY; *U.S. Public*, pg. 1250
PACKARD HUGHES INTERCONNECT—General Motors Corporation; *U.S. Public*, pg. 719
PARA SYSTEMS INC.—Components Corporation Of America; *U.S. Private*, pg. 260
PARK ELECTROCHEMICAL CORPORATION; *U.S. Public*, pg. 1258
PARLEX CORPORATION; *U.S. Public*, pg. 1264
PARTES DE TELEVISION DE REYNOSA S.A. DE C.V.—Zenith Electronics Corp.; *U.S. Public*, pg. 1790
PENT ASSEMBLIES, INC.—Group Dekko; *U.S. Private*, pg. 484
PENT PRODUCTS, INC.—Group Dekko; *U.S. Private*, pg. 484
THE PERKIN-ELMER CORPORATION; *U.S. Public*, pg. 1279
PHASE COMPONENTS LTD.—American Technical Ceramics Corp.; *U.S. Public*, pg. 93
PHILIPS COMPONENTS—Philips Electronics N.V.; *Int'l*, pg. 1054
PHILIPS COMPONENTS-DISCRETE PRODUCTS DIVISION—Philips Electronics N.V.; *Int'l*, pg. 1054
PHILIPS ELECTRONICS LTD.—Philips Electronics N.V.; *Int'l*, pg. 1055
PHILIPS LYS A/S—Philips Electronics N.V.; *Int'l*, pg. 1055
PHILIPS SEMICONDUCTORS—Philips Electronics N.V.; *Int'l*, pg. 1054
PITNEY BOWES INC.; *U.S. Public*, pg. 1303
PLAMEX, S.A. DE C.V.—Plantronics Inc.; *U.S. Public*, pg. 1308
PORTEC, INC.; *U.S. Public*, pg. 1317
PORTEC (U.K.) LTD.—Portec, Inc.; *U.S. Public*, pg. 1318
POWER-ONE, INC.; *U.S. Private*, pg. 878
POWER SYSTEMS INC.—Minebea Co., Ltd.; *Int'l*, pg. 868
PRECISION INTERCONNECT—AMP Incorporated; *U.S. Public*, pg. 8
PRECISION POWER DIV.—AEI Holding Co., Inc.; *U.S. Private*, pg. 5
PRECISION SYSTEMS, INC.; *U.S. Public*, pg. 1321
PREMIER METAL PRODUCTS CO.; *U.S. Private*, pg. 881
PROJECTS UNLIMITED, INC.; *U.S. Private*, pg. 890
PRONER COMATEL GMBH—Siebe plc; *Int'l*, pg. 1242
PULSE ENGINEERING, INC.—Technitrol, Inc.; *U.S. Public*, pg. 1564
PULSE SCIENCES, INC.—The Titan Corporation; *U.S. Public*, pg. 1618
QUAD SYSTEMS CORPORATION; *U.S. Private*, pg. 898
QUALIDYNE SYSTEMS INC.—Siebe plc; *Int'l*, pg. 1241
QUEROY S.A.—American Standard Inc.; *U.S. Public*, pg. 92
R. & H. SYSTEMS B.V.—Internatio-Muller N.V.; *Int'l*, pg. 680
RTI ELECTRONICS INC.—Selas Corporation of America; *U.S. Public*, pg. 1455
R.X.D., INC.—Relm Wireless Corp.; *U.S. Public*, pg. 1376
RACAL ELECTRONICS PLC; *Int'l*, pg. 1082
RANCO INC.—Siebe plc; *Int'l*, pg. 1243
RANTEC MICROWAVE AND ELECTRONICS, INC.—ESCO Electronics Corporation; *U.S. Public*, pg. 546
RAYTHEON E-SYSTEMS—Raytheon Company; *U.S. Public*, pg. 1365
READ-RITE CORPORATION; *U.S. Public*, pg. 1366
REDPOINT THERMALLOY LIMITED—Bowthorpe plc; *Int'l*, pg. 207
REEVES-HOFFMAN DIV.—CTS Corporation; *U.S. Public*, pg. 286
RELIABILITY INCORPORATED; *U.S. Public*, pg. 1373
RELM COMMUNICATIONS, INC.—Relm Wireless Corp.; *U.S. Public*, pg. 1376
REMEC, INC.; *U.S. Public*, pg. 1376
REPTRON ELECTRONICS, INC.; *U.S. Public*, pg. 1377
REVERE TRANSDUCERS BV—Harnischfeger Industries, Inc.; *U.S. Public*, pg. 790
REVERE TRANSDUCERS INC.—Harnischfeger Industries, Inc.; *U.S. Public*, pg. 790
RIBER; *Int'l*, pg. 1114
ROBINSON NUGENT, INC.; *U.S. Public*, pg. 1394
ROBINSON-NUGENT S.A.—Robinson Nugent, Inc.; *U.S. Public*, pg. 1395
ROCKWELL AUSTRALIA LIMITED—Rockwell International Corporation; *U.S. Public*, pg. 1399
ROCKWELL AUTOMACAO, LDA.—Rockwell International Corporation; *U.S. Public*, pg. 1399
ROCKWELL AUTOMATION—Rockwell International Corporation; *U.S. Public*, pg. 1397
ROCKWELL AUTOMATION GESMBH—Rockwell International Corporation; *U.S. Public*, pg. 1399
ROCKWELL AUTOMATION LIMITED—Rockwell International Corporation; *U.S. Public*, pg. 1399
ROCKWELL AUTOMATION (PROPRIETARY) LIMITED—Rockwell International Corporation; *U.S. Public*, pg. 1400
ROCKWELL AUTOMATION S.A.—Rockwell International Corporation; *U.S. Public*, pg. 1400
ROCKWELL CVC S.P.A.—Rockwell International Corporation; *U.S. Public*, pg. 1400
ROCKWELL INTERNATIONAL CORPORATION; *U.S. Public*, pg. 1397
ROCKWELL INTERNATIONAL OF CANADA SWITCHING SYSTEMS—Rockwell International Corporation; *U.S. Public*, pg. 1401
ROCKWELL SWITCHING SYSTEMS LIMITED—Rockwell International Corporation; *U.S. Public*, pg. 1402
ROGERS CORPORATION; *U.S. Public*, pg. 1402
ROGERS N.V.—Rogers Corporation; *U.S. Public*, pg. 1403
ROHM AMAGI CO., LTD.—Rohm Co., Ltd.; *Int'l*, pg. 1125
ROHM CO., LTD.; *Int'l*, pg. 1124
ROHM FUJI CO., LTD.—Rohm Co., Ltd.; *Int'l*, pg. 1125
ROHM LOGISTEC CO., LTD.—Rohm Co., Ltd.; *Int'l*, pg. 1125
RUHLE COMPANIES, INC.; *U.S. Private*, pg. 950
SAB ELECTRONIC DEVICES LTD.—Telefonaktiebolaget LM Ericsson; *Int'l*, pg. 1369
SAGEM ELECTRONICS AND INDUSTRY DIVISION—Societe d'Applications Generales d'Electricite et de Mechanique; *Int'l*, pg. 1273
SCI SYSTEMS, INC.; *U.S. Public*, pg. 1416
S.I. DE MEXICO S.A. DE C.V.—Standex International Corporation; *U.S. Public*, pg. 1507
SIELTE PADANA S.P.A.—Telefonaktiebolaget LM Ericsson; *Int'l*, pg. 1370
SL INDUSTRIES, INC.; *U.S. Public*, pg. 1418
SPD TECHNOLOGIES; *U.S. Private*, pg. 957
SPS TECHNOLOGIES, INC.; *U.S. Public*, pg. 1419
SVG THERMCO SYSTEMS—Silicon Valley Group, Inc.; *U.S. Public*, pg. 1474
SVG TRACK SYSTEMS—Silicon Valley Group, Inc.; *U.S. Public*, pg. 1474
SALFORD ELECTRICAL INSTRUMENTS LTD.—The General Electric Company, p.l.c.; *Int'l*, pg. 545
SANDERS, A LOCKHEED MARTIN COMPANY—Lockheed Martin Corporation; *U.S. Public*, pg. 1008
SARATOGA INDUSTRIES—Espey Mfg. & Electronics Corp.; *U.S. Public*, pg. 592
SCHLUMBERGER LIMITED; *U.S. Public*, pg. 1439
SCIENTIFIC-ATLANTA, INC.; *U.S. Public*, pg. 1443
SEABEAM INSTRUMENTS, INC.—Channel Technologies, Inc.; *U.S. Private*, pg. 228
SEAGATE TAPE TECHNOLOGIES, INC.—Seagate Technology Inc.; *U.S. Public*, pg. 1449
SEIKO EG & G CO. LTD.—EG & G, Inc.; *U.S. Public*, pg. 544
SEIKO INSTRUMENTS INC.; *Int'l*, pg. 1219
SEMICON ASSOCIATES—Ceradyne, Inc; *U.S. Public*, pg. 330
SEMTECH CORPORATION; *U.S. Public*, pg. 1456
SEMTECH LTD.—Semtech Corporation; *U.S. Public*, pg. 1456
SENNHEISER ELECTRONIC CORP.; *U.S. Private*, pg. 984
SENSORMATIC ELECTRONICS CORP. DE PUERTO RICO—Sensormatic Electronics Corporation; *U.S. Public*, pg. 1457
SFERNICE, S.A.—Vishay Intertechnology, Inc.; *U.S. Public*, pg. 1722
SHELDAHL, INC.; *U.S. Public*, pg. 1465
SHELDAHL INTL., INC.—Sheldahl, Inc.; *U.S. Public*, pg. 1465
SHOGYO INTERNATIONAL CORPORATION; *U.S. Private*, pg. 996
SHUR-LOK CORPORATION; *U.S. Private*, pg. 997
SICILIANA ELECTRONICA & TELECOMUNICAZIONI S.P.A.—Telefonaktiebolaget LM Ericsson; *Int'l*, pg. 1370
SIERRACOM—Sierra Technologies Inc.; *U.S. Private*, pg. 999
SOCIETE D'APPLICATIONS GENERALES D'ELECTRICITE ET DE MECHANIQUE; *Int'l*, pg. 1273
SOLADYNE DIVISION—Merix Corporation; *U.S. Public*, pg. 1097
SOLID STATE DEVICES, INC.; *U.S. Private*, pg. 1012
SONY CORPORATION; *Int'l*, pg. 1280
SONY CORPORATION OF HONG KONG LTD.—Sony Corporation; *Int'l*, pg. 1284
SONY ELECTRONICS—Sony Corporation; *Int'l*, pg. 1281
SONY PRECISION ENGINEERING CENTER (SINGAPORE) PTE. LTD.—Sony Corporation; *Int'l*, pg. 1284
SONY (U.K.) LTD.—Sony Corporation; *Int'l*, pg. 1284
SOVCOR, SA—Vishay Intertechnology, Inc.; *U.S. Public*, pg. 1722
SPANG & COMPANY; *U.S. Private*, pg. 1020
SPARTON ELECTRONICS FLORIDA, INC.—Sparton Corporation; *U.S. Public*, pg. 1496
SPARTON OF CANADA LTD.—Sparton Corporation; *U.S. Public*, pg. 1496
SPARTON TECHNOLOGY, INC.—Sparton Corporation; *U.S. Public*, pg. 1496
SPECTRUM CONTROL, INC.; *U.S. Public*, pg. 1497
SPIRE CORPORATION; *U.S. Public*, pg. 1499
SPRECHER + SCHUH AG—Rockwell International Corporation; *U.S. Public*, pg. 1402
SPRECHER & SCHUH VERKAUF AG—Rockwell International Corporation; *U.S. Public*, pg. 1402
SPRINT CORPORATION; *U.S. Public*, pg. 1500
SQUARE D CO.—Schneider S.A.; *Int'l*, pg. 1208
SQUARE D COMPANY—Schneider S.A.; *Int'l*, pg. 1208
SQUARE D COMPANY-ASSEMBLY OPERATIONS—Schneider S.A.; *Int'l*, pg. 1208
STACOSWITCH, INC.—Components Corporation Of America; *U.S. Private*, pg. 260
STANDEX ELECTRONICS—Standex International Corporation; *U.S. Public*, pg. 1507
STAVELEY/NDT TECHNOLOGIES INC.—Staveley Industries PLC; *Int'l*, pg. 1299
STAVELEY SENSORS DIVISION—Staveley Industries PLC; *Int'l*, pg. 1299
STONERIDGE, INC.; *U.S. Private*, pg. 1044
STORAGE TECHNOLOGY CORPORATION; *U.S. Public*, pg. 1522
STORAGE TECHNOLOGY LIMITED—Storage Technology Corporation; *U.S. Public*, pg. 1523
STORAGETEK NETWORK SYSTEMS GROUP—Storage Technology Corporation; *U.S. Public*, pg. 1522
SUMITOMO METAL MINING CO., LTD.; *Int'l*, pg. 1316
SUNDSTRAND CORPORATION; *U.S. Public*, pg. 1533
SUPERTEX, INC.; *U.S. Public*, pg. 1539
SWITCHCRAFT, INC.—Raytheon Company; *U.S. Public*, pg. 1366
SWITCHING SYSTEMS INTERNATIONAL—Bowthorpe plc; *Int'l*, pg. 208
SYSECA INC.—Thomson S.A.; *Int'l*, pg. 1384
SYSTEMS GROUP—AMP Incorporated; *U.S. Public*, pg. 8
SYSTRON DONNER-INERTIAL DIVISION—BEI Technologies, Inc.; *U.S. Public*, pg. 160
TDK CORPORATION; *Int'l*, pg. 1336
TDK CORPORATION OF AMERICA—TDK Corporation; *Int'l*, pg. 1336
TDK DE MEXICO S.A. DE C.V.—TDK Corporation; *Int'l*, pg. 1337
TDK DO BRASIL IND. E COM. LTDA.—TDK Corporation; *Int'l*, pg. 1336
TDK DO BRASIL SUZANO PLANT—TDK Corporation; *Int'l*, pg. 1337
TDK TAIWAN CORP.—TDK Corporation; *Int'l*, pg. 1337
TII DOMINICANA INC.—TII Industries, Inc.; *U.S. Public*, pg. 1556
TII INDUSTRIES, INC.; *U.S. Public*, pg. 1556
TECH/OPS SEVCON, INC.; *U.S. Public*, pg. 1563
TECHNITROL COMPONENT DIVISION—Technitrol, Inc.; *U.S. Public*, pg. 1564
TECHNITROL, INC.; *U.S. Public*, pg. 1564
TECHNOLOGY RESEARCH CORPORATION; *U.S. Public*, pg. 1564
TECKNIT INCORPORATED; *U.S. Private*, pg. 1072
TEDEA INC.—IDB Holding Corporation; *Int'l*, pg. 644
TEKTRONIX, INC.; *U.S. Public*, pg. 1567
TEKTRONIX-VIDEO & NETWORKING DIV., GRASS VALLEY PRODUCTS—Tektronix, Inc.; *U.S. Public*, pg. 1567
TELCOM SEMICONDUCTOR, INC.; *U.S. Public*, pg. 1569
TELEX COMMUNICATIONS, INC.; *U.S. Private*, pg. 1074
TELONIC BERKELEY, INC.; *U.S. Private*, pg. 1074
TEMPEL STEEL COMPANY; *U.S. Private*, pg. 1075
TEMPO INSTRUMENT INC.—Bowthorpe plc; *Int'l*, pg. 208
TERADYNE ASSEMBLY TEST/EAST DIVISION—Teradyne, Inc.; *U.S. Public*, pg. 1581
TERADYNE CIRCUITS OPERATION—Teradyne, Inc.; *U.S. Public*, pg. 1581
TERADYNE CONNECTION SYSTEMS, INC.—Teradyne, Inc.; *U.S. Public*, pg. 1581
TERADYNE, INC.; *U.S. Public*, pg. 1580
TERADYNE INDUSTRIAL/CONSUMER DIVISION—Teradyne, Inc.; *U.S. Public*, pg. 1581
TERADYNE SEMICONDUCTOR TEST DIVISION—Teradyne, Inc.; *U.S. Public*, pg. 1581
TEXAS INSTRUMENTS DEUTSCHLAND GMBH—Texas Instruments Incorporated; *U.S. Public*, pg. 1586
TEXAS INSTRUMENTS FRANCE SA—Texas Instruments Incorporated; *U.S. Public*, pg. 1586
TEXAS INSTRUMENTS INCORPORATED; *U.S. Public*, pg. 1585
TEXAS INSTRUMENTS ITALIA S.P.A.—Texas Instruments Incorporated; *U.S. Public*, pg. 1586
TEXAS INSTRUMENTS LIMITED—Texas Instruments Incorporated; *U.S. Public*, pg. 1586
TEXAS INSTRUMENTS SECURITY—Texas Instruments Incorporated; *U.S. Public*, pg. 1586
THERMALLOY LTD.—Bowthorpe plc; *Int'l*, pg. 209
THOMAS & BETTS CARIBE, INC.—Thomas & Betts Corporation; *U.S. Public*, pg. 1598
THOMAS & BETTS CORPORATION; *U.S. Public*, pg. 1597
THOMAS & SKINNER, INC.; *U.S. Private*, pg. 1082
THOMSON S.A.; *Int'l*, pg. 1381
THOMSON TELEVISION COMPONENTS FRANCE—Thomson S.A.; *Int'l*, pg. 1384
THREE-FIVE SYSTEMS; *U.S. Public*, pg. 1604
3M; *U.S. Public*, pg. 1604
THE TITAN CORPORATION; *U.S. Public*, pg. 1618
TOKHEIM CORPORATION; *U.S. Public*, pg. 1620
TOKYO ELECTRONIC INDUSTRY CO., LTD.—Toshiba Corporation; *Int'l*, pg. 1403
TOPFLIGHT CORP.; *U.S. Private*, pg. 1091
TOPPAN WEST, INC.—Toppan Printing Company, Ltd.; *Int'l*, pg. 1399
TOSHIBA CORPORATION; *Int'l*, pg. 1402
TOSHIBA ELECTRONIC SYSTEMS CO., LTD.—Toshiba Corporation; *Int'l*, pg. 1404
TOWER ELECTRONICS, INC.—Advanced Energy Industry; *U.S. Public*, pg. 20
TRACOR AEROSPACE ELECTRONICS SYSTEMS, INC.—Tracor, Inc.; *U.S. Public*, pg. 1627
TRANS-TECH, INC.—Alpha Industries, Inc.; *U.S. Public*, pg. 57
TRANSFORMIC ELECTRONICS LIMITED—Emess PLC; *Int'l*, pg. 453
TRANSICO INCORPORATED; *U.S. Public*, pg. 1630
TRANSISTOR DEVICES, INC.; *U.S. Private*, pg. 1097
TRANSPLANTATION & INDUSTRIAL PRODUCTS DIV.—Analog Devices, Inc.; *U.S. Public*, pg. 108
TRICON INDUSTRIES, INC.; *U.S. Private*, pg. 1102
TYCO BACKPLANES—Tyco International Ltd.; *U.S. Public*, pg. 1648
TYCO ENGINEERED SYSTEMS—Tyco International Ltd.; *U.S. Public*, pg. 1648
TYCO INTERNATIONAL LTD.; *U.S. Public*, pg. 1647
TYCO PRINTED CIRCUIT GROUP—Tyco International Ltd.; *U.S. Public*, pg. 1648
ULTRA ELECTRICS—Ultra Electronics Holdings plc; *Int'l*, pg. 1431
UNITECH PLC—Siebe plc; *Int'l*, pg. 1241
UNITED AIRCRAFT PRODUCTS—Parker Hannifin Corporation; *U.S. Public*, pg. 1262
UNITRODE CORPORATION; *U.S. Public*, pg. 1694
UNIVERSAL INSTRUMENTS CORPORATION—Dover Corporation; *U.S. Public*, pg. 522
UNIVERSAL VOLTRONICS CORPORATION—Thermo Electron Corporation; *U.S. Public*, pg. 1596
VALLEY FORGE CORPORATION; *U.S. Public*, pg. 1705

VALOR ELECTRONICS, INC.—GTI Corporation; *U.S. Public*, pg. 768
VALPEY-FISHER CORPORATION—Matec Corporation; *U.S. Public*, pg. 1056
VALPEY-FISHER FREQUENCY CONTROL DIV.—Matec Corporation; *U.S. Public*, pg. 1056
VALPEY-FISHER ULTRASOUND DIV.—Matec Corporation; *U.S. Public*, pg. 1056
VAPOR—Westinghouse Air Brake Company; *U.S. Public*, pg. 1761
VARI TRONICS COMPANY, INC.; *U.S. Private*, pg. 1134
VARIAN ASSOCIATES, INC.; *U.S. Public*, pg. 1710
VARIAN SPA—Varian Associates, Inc.; *U.S. Public*, pg. 1710
VARITRONIC SYSTEMS, INC.—W.H. Brady Co.; *U.S. Public*, pg. 250
VECTRON LABS, INC.—Dover Corporation; *U.S. Public*, pg. 522
VERNITRON CONTROLS DIV.—Axsys Technologies, Inc.; *U.S. Public*, pg. 158
VERNITRON SENSOR SYSTEMS—Axsys Technologies, Inc.; *U.S. Public*, pg. 157
VERTEX ANTENNENTECHNIK GMBH—Vertex Communications Corporation; *U.S. Public*, pg. 1718
VICOR CORPORATION; *U.S. Public*, pg. 1719
VIKING ELECTRONICS, INC.—Wire-Pro Inc.; *U.S. Private*, pg. 1184
VISHAY INSTRUMENTS DIV.—Vishay Intertechnology, Inc.; *U.S. Public*, pg. 1722
VISHAY INTERTECHNOLOGY, INC.; *U.S. Public*, pg. 1721
VISHAY RESISTOR PRODUCTS—Vishay Intertechnology, Inc.; *U.S. Public*, pg. 1722
VITRUS, INC.—Tecumseh Products Company; *U.S. Public*, pg. 1566
WABASH MAGNETICS—The Dyson-Kissner-Moran Corporation; *U.S. Private*, pg. 351
WAKO ELECTRIC CO., LTD.—Rohm Co., Ltd.; *Int'l*, pg. 1125
WALDOM ELECTRONICS, INC.—Katy Industries, Inc.; *U.S. Public*, pg. 944
WALKER EQUIPMENT CORP.—Plantronics Inc.; *U.S. Public*, pg. 1308
WARD PRODUCTS CORPORATION; *U.S. Private*, pg. 1149
WATERS INSTRUMENTS, INC.; *U.S. Public*, pg. 1745
WATKINS-JOHNSON COMPANY; *U.S. Public*, pg. 1745
WAUKESHA BEARINGS CORP.—Dover Corporation; *U.S. Public*, pg. 521
WEIR ELECTRONICS LIMITED—Siebe plc; *Int'l*, pg. 1241
WELLS-GARDNER ELECTRONICS CORP.; *U.S. Public*, pg. 1753
WESSEX ADVANCED SWITCHING PRODUCTS LTD.—Bowthorpe plc; *Int'l*, pg. 208
WESTINGHOUSE POWER SYSTEMS GROUP—CBS Corporation; *U.S. Public*, pg. 273
WHEELOCK INC.; *U.S. Private*, pg. 1171
WHITTAKER ELECTRONIC SYSTEMS—Whittaker Corporation; *U.S. Public*, pg. 1767
WIRELESS PRODUCTS GROUP—Watkins-Johnson Company; *U.S. Public*, pg. 1745
XEROX SPECIAL INFORMATION SYSTEMS—Xerox Corporation; *U.S. Public*, pg. 1784
XEROX SPECIAL MARKETS GROUP—Xerox Corporation; *U.S. Public*, pg. 1785
ZERO CORPORATION; *U.S. Public*, pg. 1791
ZERO PLASTICS—Zero Corporation; *U.S. Public*, pg. 1791
ALOIS ZETTLER ELECKTROTECHNISCHE FABRIK GMBH; *Int'l*, pg. 1528
ZWEIGNIEDERLASSUNG DER ROCKWELL INTERNATIONAL GMBH—Rockwell International Corporation; *U.S. Public*, pg. 1402

3691 — STORAGE BATTERIES

ALCATEL ALSTHOM COMPAGNIE GENERALE D'ELECTRICITE; *Int'l*, pg. 52
C&D CHARTER POWER SYSTEMS; *U.S. Public*, pg. 271
DURACELL DO BRASIL INDUSTRIA & COMERCIO LTDA.—The Gillette Company; *U.S. Public*, pg. 743
EATON CORP., SUPERCHARGER DIV.—Eaton Corporation; *U.S. Public*, pg. 556
ENERGIZER EVEREADY LTD.—Ralston Purina Company; *U.S. Public*, pg. 1360
ENERGY CONVERSION DEVICES, INC.; *U.S. Public*, pg. 581
EVEREADY DE MEXICO S.A. DE C.V.—Ralston Purina Company; *U.S. Public*, pg. 1360
FIAMM-GS—Fiamm S.p.A.; *Int'l*, pg. 480
FIAMM S.P.A.; *Int'l*, pg. 480
GRUPO IMSA S.A. DE C.V.; *Int'l*, pg. 575
HUBBELL, LTD.—Hubbell Incorporated; *U.S. Public*, pg. 845
JAPAN STORAGE BATTERY CO., LTD.; *Int'l*, pg. 702
JOHNSON CONTROLS, INC.; *U.S. Public*, pg. 932
K.W. POWER SOURCE—BTR plc; *Int'l*, pg. 127
LUCASVARITY PLC—LucasVarity plc; *Int'l*, pg. 819
MATSUSHITA BATTERY INDUSTRIAL CO., LTD.—Matsushita Electric Industrial Co., Ltd.; *Int'l*, pg. 846
MEDTRONIC PROMEON—Medtronic, Inc.; *U.S. Public*, pg. 1083
NIFE AB—Alcatel Alsthom Compagnie Generale D'Electricite; *Int'l*, pg. 53
NIFE ARGENTINA S.A.—Alcatel Alsthom Compagnie Generale D'Electricite; *Int'l*, pg. 54
NIFE A/S—Alcatel Alsthom Compagnie Generale D'Electricite; *Int'l*, pg. 54
NIFE AUSTRALIA PTY. LTD.—Alcatel Alsthom Compagnie Generale D'Electricite; *Int'l*, pg. 54
NIFE BRASIL SISTEMAS ELETRICOS LTDA.—Alcatel Alsthom Compagnie Generale D'Electricite; *Int'l*, pg. 54
NIFE B.V.—Alcatel Alsthom Compagnie Generale D'Electricite; *Int'l*, pg. 53
NIFE CORPORATION—Alcatel Alsthom Compagnie Generale D'Electricite; *Int'l*, pg. 54
NIFE ESPANA S.A.—Alcatel Alsthom Compagnie Generale D'Electricite; *Int'l*, pg. 53
NIFE FRANCE S.A.—Alcatel Alsthom Compagnie Generale D'Electricite; *Int'l*, pg. 53
NIFE GES.M.B.H.—Alcatel Alsthom Compagnie Generale D'Electricite; *Int'l*, pg. 53
NIFE FRANCE S.A.—Alcatel Alsthom Compagnie Generale D'Electricite; *Int'l*, pg. 54
NIFE ITALIA S.P.A.—Alcatel Alsthom Compagnie Generale D'Electricite; *Int'l*, pg. 54
NIFE POWER SYSTEMS LTD.—Alcatel Alsthom Compagnie Generale D'Electricite; *Int'l*, pg. 53
NIFE POWER SYSTEMS SDN. BHD.—Alcatel Alsthom Compagnie Generale D'Electricite; *Int'l*, pg. 54
NIFE SILCON LTD.—Alcatel Alsthom Compagnie Generale D'Electricite; *Int'l*, pg. 54
OFA-AKKUMULATOREN GES.M.B.H.—VARTA AG; *Int'l*, pg. 1452
OLDHAM CROMPTON BATTERIES LTD.—BTR plc; *Int'l*, pg. 125
OVONIC BATTERY COMPANY, INC.—Energy Conversion Devices, Inc.; *U.S. Public*, pg. 581
PACIFIC MARINE BATTERIES PTY. LTD.—VARTA AG; *Int'l*, pg. 1452
SAB NIFE OY—Alcatel Alsthom Compagnie Generale D'Electricite; *Int'l*, pg. 54
SAB NIFE (SUISSE) S.A.—Alcatel Alsthom Compagnie Generale D'Electricite; *Int'l*, pg. 54
SAFT—Alcatel Alsthom Compagnie Generale D'Electricite; *Int'l*, pg. 54
SAFT NIFE AB—Alcatel Alsthom Compagnie Generale D'Electricite; *Int'l*, pg. 54
SAFT AMERICA INC.—Alcatel Alsthom Compagnie Generale D'Electricite; *Int'l*, pg. 55
SAFT BATTERIES LTD.—Alcatel Alsthom Compagnie Generale D'Electricite; *Int'l*, pg. 55
SISTEMAS NIFE S.A. DE C.V.—Alcatel Alsthom Compagnie Generale D'Electricite; *Int'l*, pg. 54
STATRON AG—Alcatel Alsthom Compagnie Generale D'Electricite; *Int'l*, pg. 54
TOSHIBA BATTERY CO., LTD.—Toshiba Corporation; *Int'l*, pg. 1403
VB AUTOBATERIAS LDA.—VARTA AG; *Int'l*, pg. 1452
VB AUTOBATTERI AB—VARTA AG; *Int'l*, pg. 1452
VB AUTOBATTERIEN B.V.—VARTA AG; *Int'l*, pg. 1452
VB AUTOMOTIVE BATTERIES LTD.—VARTA AG; *Int'l*, pg. 1452
OY VB AUTONAKUT AB—VARTA AG; *Int'l*, pg. 1452
OY VARTA AB—VARTA AG; *Int'l*, pg. 1452
VARTA AG; *Int'l*, pg. 1451
VARTA AKU SPOL. SR.O.—VARTA AG; *Int'l*, pg. 1452
VARTA AUTOBATERIAS S.A.—VARTA AG; *Int'l*, pg. 1452
P.T. VARTA BATTERIES INDONESIA LTD.—VARTA AG; *Int'l*, pg. 1452
VARTA BATTERIES PTE. LTD.—VARTA AG; *Int'l*, pg. 1452
VARTA B.V.—VARTA AG; *Int'l*, pg. 1452
VARTA INDUSTRIEBATTERIE N.V. S.A.—VARTA AG; *Int'l*, pg. 1452
VARTA KERESKEDELMI ES SZOLGALTATO KFT.—VARTA AG; *Int'l*, pg. 1452
VARTA LTD.—VARTA AG; *Int'l*, pg. 1452
VARTA S.A.—VARTA AG; *Int'l*, pg. 1452
VARTA S.A. DE C.V.—VARTA AG; *Int'l*, pg. 1452
YARDNEY TECHNICAL PRODUCTS, INC.—Ener-Tek International Corporation; *U.S. Private*, pg. 376

3692 — PRIMARY BATTERIES, DRY & WET

ACCUDYNE CORPORATION—Alliant Techsystems; *U.S. Public*, pg. 47
ALCATEL ALSTHOM COMPAGNIE GENERALE D'ELECTRICITE; *Int'l*, pg. 52
ALUPOWER, INC.—Ener-Tek International Corporation; *U.S. Private*, pg. 376
BRIGHT STAR INDUSTRIES, INC.—Publicker Industries Inc.; *U.S. Public*, pg. 1341
C&D CHARTER POWER SYSTEMS; *U.S. Public*, pg. 271
DELKOR BATTERY COMPANY—General Motors Corporation; *U.S. Public*, pg. 724
DURACELL AG—The Gillette Company; *U.S. Public*, pg. 743
DURACELL AUSTRALIA PTY. LIMITED—The Gillette Company; *U.S. Public*, pg. 743
N.V. DURACELL BATTERIES, S.A.—The Gillette Company; *U.S. Public*, pg. 743
DURACELL BATTERY JAPAN, LTD.—The Gillette Company; *U.S. Public*, pg. 743
S.A. DURACELL BENELUX N.V.—The Gillette Company; *U.S. Public*, pg. 743
DURACELL CANADA INC.—The Gillette Company; *U.S. Public*, pg. 743
DURACELL DE MEXICO S.A. DE C.V.—The Gillette Company; *U.S. Public*, pg. 743
DURACELL INTERNATIONAL INC.—The Gillette Company; *U.S. Public*, pg. 743
DURACELL PRODUCTS CO.—The Gillette Company; *U.S. Public*, pg. 743
DURACELL (S.E.A.) PTE. LTD.—The Gillette Company; *U.S. Public*, pg. 744
DURACELL U.S.A.—The Gillette Company; *U.S. Public*, pg. 743
ENER-TEK INTERNATIONAL CORPORATION; *U.S. Private*, pg. 376
EVEREADY BATTERY CO.—Ralston Purina Company; *U.S. Public*, pg. 1360
EVEREADY DE MEXICO S.A. DE C.V.—Ralston Purina Company; *U.S. Public*, pg. 1360
EVEREADY SINGAPORE PTE. LTD.—Ralston Purina Company; *U.S. Public*, pg. 1360
EXIDE CORPORATION; *U.S. Public*, pg. 600
FIAMM-GS—Fiamm S.p.A.; *Int'l*, pg. 480
THE FURUKAWA BATTERY CO., LTD.—The Furukawa Electric Co., Ltd.; *Int'l*, pg. 530
G.E. LIGHTING DIVISION—General Electric Company; *U.S. Public*, pg. 710
GP BATTERIES INTERNATIONAL LTD.; *Int'l*, pg. 537
GOLD PEAK INDUSTRIES (HOLDINGS) LIMITED—GP Batteries International Ltd.; *Int'l*, pg. 537
GOLD PEAK INDUSTRIES (TAIWAN) LTD.—GP Batteries International Ltd.; *Int'l*, pg. 537
JOHNSON CONTROLS, INC.—Johnson Controls, Inc.; *U.S. Public*, pg. 932
JOHNSON CONTROLS, INC., BATTERY GROUP—Johnson Controls, Inc.; *U.S. Public*, pg. 932
LITHION, INC.—Ener-Tek International Corporation; *U.S. Private*, pg. 376
MSA (BRITAIN) LIMITED—Mine Safety Appliances Co.; *U.S. Public*, pg. 1114
MSA INDIA LIMITED—Mine Safety Appliances Co.; *U.S. Public*, pg. 1115
MATSUSHITA BATTERY INDUSTRIAL CO., LTD.—Matsushita Electric Industrial Co., Ltd.; *Int'l*, pg. 846
MINE SAFETY APPLIANCES CO.; *U.S. Public*, pg. 1114
MINE SAFETY APPLIANCES CO.—Mine Safety Appliances Co.; *U.S. Public*, pg. 1114
POWER CONVERSION, INC.—BTR plc; *Int'l*, pg. 127
RALSTON PURINA CANADA EVEREADY DIV.—Ralston Purina Company; *U.S. Public*, pg. 1360
RALSTON PURINA COMPANY; *U.S. Public*, pg. 1359
RAYOVAC CORPORATION; *U.S. Private*, pg. 912
RENATA SA—SMH Swiss Corporation for Micro Electronics & Watchmaking Indus. Ltd.; *Int'l*, pg. 1161
SAFT—Alcatel Alsthom Compagnie Generale D'Electricite; *Int'l*, pg. 54
SAFT AMERICA INC.—Alcatel Alsthom Compagnie Generale D'Electricite; *Int'l*, pg. 55
SAFT BATTERIES LTD.—Alcatel Alsthom Compagnie Generale D'Electricite; *Int'l*, pg. 55
SANYO ENERGY (U.S.A.) CORPORATION—Sanyo Electric Co., Ltd.; *Int'l*, pg. 1191
SYLVA INDUSTRIES LIMITED—GP Batteries International Ltd.; *Int'l*, pg. 537
TOSHIBA BATTERY CO., LTD.—Toshiba Corporation; *Int'l*, pg. 1403
VARTA BATTERIE AG—VARTA AG; *Int'l*, pg. 1452
YARDNEY TECHNICAL PRODUCTS, INC.—Ener-Tek International Corporation; *U.S. Private*, pg. 376
YUASA-EXIDE, INC.—Yuasa Corporation; *Int'l*, pg. 1522

3694 — ELECTRICAL EQUIPMENT FOR INTERNAL COMBUSTION ENGINES

ABB AB—ABB Asea Brown Boveri (Holding) Ltd.; *Int'l*, pg. 7
ABB FLEXIBLE AUTOMATION—ABB Asea Brown Boveri (Holding) Ltd.; *Int'l*, pg. 4
AC ROCHESTER OVERSEAS CORPORATION—General Motors Corporation; *U.S. Public*, pg. 722
ALLIEDSIGNAL AEROSPACE—AlliedSignal Inc.; *U.S. Public*, pg. 50
ALLIEDSIGNAL AEROSPACE SYSTEMS & EQUIPMENT—AlliedSignal Inc.; *U.S. Public*, pg. 50
ALLIEDSIGNAL COMMERCIAL AVIONIC SYSTEMS—AlliedSignal Inc.; *U.S. Public*, pg. 50
ALLIEDSIGNAL FILTERS & SPARK PLUGS—AlliedSignal Inc.; *U.S. Public*, pg. 51
ALLISON ENGINE COMPANY INC.—Rolls-Royce plc; *Int'l*, pg. 1127
ARROW AUTOMOTIVE INDUSTRIES, INC.; *U.S. Public*, pg. 133
ASAHI ELECTRIC MACHINERY CO., LTD.—The Furukawa Electric Co., Ltd.; *Int'l*, pg. 530
ASIA CABLE ENGINEERING CO., PTE. LTD. (ACECO)—The Furukawa Electric Co., Ltd.; *Int'l*, pg. 530
AUGAT, INC.—Thomas & Betts Corporation; *U.S. Public*, pg. 1597
AUGAT, INC., AUTOMOTIVE COMPONENTS DIVISION-BOYNE CITY—Thomas & Betts Corporation; *U.S. Public*, pg. 1598
AUGAT, INC., AUTOMOTIVE DIVISION—Thomas & Betts Corporation; *U.S. Public*, pg. 1598
AUGAT, INC., WIRING SYSTEMS—Thomas & Betts Corporation; *U.S. Public*, pg. 1598
AUGAT, INC., WIRING SYSTEMS & COMPONENTS GROUP—Thomas & Betts Corporation; *U.S. Public*, pg. 1598
AUTOMOTIVE CONTROLS CORP.—Echlin Inc.; *U.S. Public*, pg. 560
BANGKOK TELECOM CO., LTD. (BTC)—The Furukawa Electric Co., Ltd.; *Int'l*, pg. 531
BENDIX CONNECTOR, OPERATIONS—AlliedSignal Inc.; *U.S. Public*, pg. 51
BLUE STREAK-HYGRADE MOTOR PRODUCTS LTD.—Standard Motor Products Inc.; *U.S. Public*, pg. 1503
ROBERT BOSCH CORPORATION—Robert Bosch GmbH; *Int'l*, pg. 204
BUJIAS CHAMPION DE MEXICO, S.A. DE C.V.—Cooper Industries, Inc.; *U.S. Public*, pg. 444
CE SONORA S.A. DE C.V.—Cummins Engine Company, Inc.; *U.S. Public*, pg. 468
CHAMPION AVIATION PRODUCTS—Cooper Industries, Inc.; *U.S. Public*, pg. 443
CHAMPION IGNITION PRODUCTS—Cooper Industries, Inc.; *U.S. Public*, pg. 442
CHRYSLER CORPORATION; *U.S. Public*, pg. 352
CHRYSLER DE MEXICO S.A.—Chrysler Corporation; *U.S. Public*, pg. 354
COLE HERSEE COMPANY; *U.S. Private*, pg. 251
CONDUPHON INDUSTRIA, COMERCIO, REPRESENTACAO E SERVICOS LTDA.—The Furukawa Electric Co., Ltd.; *Int'l*, pg. 530
CONSOLIDATED ELECTRICAL DISTRIBUTORS; *U.S. Private*, pg. 265

CUMMINS ENGINE COMPANY, INC.—Cummins Engine Company, Inc.; *U.S. Public*, pg. 468
DAEWOO HEAVY INDUSTRIES, LTD.—Daewoo Corporation; *Int'l*, pg. 357
DANA CANADA INC.—Dana Corporation; *U.S. Public*, pg. 480
DELPHI CHASSIS SYSTEMS—General Motors Corporation; *U.S. Public*, pg. 719
DENSO SALES CALIFORNIA—Toyota Motor Corporation; *Int'l*, pg. 1412
DUNLAP DIVISION—Tecumseh Products Company; *U.S. Public*, pg. 1565
DYNACRAFT—Paccar Inc.; *U.S. Public*, pg. 1246
ECHLIN CANADA INC.—Echlin Inc.; *U.S. Public*, pg. 560
ECHLIN INC.; *U.S. Public*, pg. 560
ECHLIN-PONCE, INC.—Echlin Inc.; *U.S. Public*, pg. 560
EDELBROCK CORP.; *U.S. Public*, pg. 563
ELECSYS INC.; *U.S. Private*, pg. 367
F&B MANUFACTURING CO.; *U.S. Private*, pg. 388
FAIRBANKS MORSE ENGINE DIVISION—Coltec Holdings Inc; *U.S. Public*, pg. 401
FORD ELECTRONICA PORTUGUESA, LTD.—Ford Motor Company; *U.S. Public*, pg. 665
FORD ELECTRONICS MANUFACTURING CORPORATION—Ford Motor Company; *U.S. Public*, pg. 665
FURUKAWA ELECTRIC CABLES (MALAYSIA) SDN. BHD.—The Furukawa Electric Co., Ltd.; *Int'l*, pg. 530
FURUKAWA INDUSTRIAL S.A. PRODUTOS ELETRICOS (FISA)—The Furukawa Electric Co., Ltd.; *Int'l*, pg. 531
FURUKAWA SAUDI ARABIA, LTD. (FSA)—The Furukawa Electric Co., Ltd.; *Int'l*, pg. 531
HEATCRAFT INC.—Lennox International Inc.; *U.S. Private*, pg. 659
HESCO PARTS CORPORATION; *U.S. Private*, pg. 524
HORIZON AEROSPACE LLC; *U.S. Private*, pg. 538
IOWA INDUSTRIES INC.—Cooper Industries, Inc.; *U.S. Public*, pg. 442
KRAUSS-MAFFEI VERKEHRSTECHNIK GMBH—Mannesmann A.G.; *Int'l*, pg. 836
LAGARDERE GROUPE; *Int'l*, pg. 791
LEWIS ENGINEERING COMPANY—Coltec Holdings Inc; *U.S. Public*, pg. 402
LINDUSTRIES LTD.—Hanson PLC; *Int'l*, pg. 593
LODGE IGNITION LIMITED—Smiths Industries plc; *Int'l*, pg. 1267
LUCAS AEROSPACE POWER TRANSMISSION—LucasVarity plc; *Int'l*, pg. 820
LUCAS AFTERMARKET OPERATIONS—LucasVarity plc; *Int'l*, pg. 819
LUCAS INDUSTRIES INC.—LucasVarity plc; *Int'l*, pg. 820
LUCAS-TVS LTD.—LucasVarity plc; *Int'l*, pg. 820
MAGNETEK MOTORS & GENERATORS—MagneTek, Inc.; *U.S. Public*, pg. 1037
MALLORY, INC.; *U.S. Private*, pg. 698
MITSUBISHI ELECTRIC CORPORATION; *Int'l*, pg. 872
MITSUBISHI ELECTRIC MFG.—Mitsubishi Electric Corporation; *Int'l*, pg. 872
MOLEX ELEKTRONIK GMBH—Molex Incorporated; *U.S. Public*, pg. 1122
MOTOROLA, INC.; *U.S. Public*, pg. 1136
MR. GASKET INC.—Echlin Inc.; *U.S. Public*, pg. 560
NEWAGE INTERNATIONAL LTD.—Cummins Engine Company, Inc.; *U.S. Public*, pg. 469
PACIFIC TECHNOLOGY PRIVATE LTD.—Ssangyong Business Group; *Int'l*, pg. 1292
POWER DESIGNS, INC.; *U.S. Private*, pg. 878
RAYBRO ELECTRIC SUPPLIES—Consolidated Electrical Distributors; *U.S. Private*, pg. 265
SL AUBURN, INC.—Cooper Industries, Inc.; *U.S. Public*, pg. 443
SL INDUSTRIES, INC.; *U.S. Public*, pg. 1418
SAAB-SCANIA COMBITECH—Investor AB; *Int'l*, pg. 686
SHINSUNG PACKARD COMPANY, LTD.—General Motors Corporation; *U.S. Public*, pg. 724
SHOWA ELECTRIC WIRE & CABLE CO., LTD.—Toshiba Corporation; *Int'l*, pg. 1403
SOPRANO S.A.—Alcatel Alsthom Compagnie Generale D'Electricite; *Int'l*, pg. 53
SSANGYONG BUSINESS GROUP; *Int'l*, pg. 1291
STANDARD MOTOR PRODUCTS HONG KONG LIMITED—Standard Motor Products Inc.; *U.S. Public*, pg. 1503
STANDARD MOTOR PRODUCTS INC.; *U.S. Public*, pg. 1503
TELEFLEX INCORPORATED; *U.S. Public*, pg. 1569
P.T. TEMBAGA MULIA SEMANAN (TMS)—The Furukawa Electric Co., Ltd.; *Int'l*, pg. 531
TOSHIBA DALIAN CO. LTD.—Toshiba Corporation; *Int'l*, pg. 1406
TRANSICOIL, INC.—Horizon Aerospace LLC; *U.S. Private*, pg. 538
TRANSPO ELECTRONICS, INC.; *U.S. Private*, pg. 1097
TRIPLE A SPECIALTY COMPANY; *U.S. Private*, pg. 1103
UNITED TECHNOLOGIES AUTOMOTIVE—United Technologies Corporation; *U.S. Public*, pg. 1691
UNITED TECHNOLOGIES MOTOR SYSTEMS—United Technologies Corporation; *U.S. Public*, pg. 1690
WELLS MFG. CORP.—UIS, Inc.; *U.S. Private*, pg. 1113
WENCO INC.—Wendy's International Inc.; *U.S. Public*, pg. 1754
ZELLER CORP.; *U.S. Private*, pg. 1204

3695 — MAGNETIC & OPTICAL RECORDING MEDIA

AMPEX CORPORATION; *U.S. Public*, pg. 104
ANACOMP, INC.; *U.S. Public*, pg. 106
ANACOMP MAGNETICS, INC.—Anacomp, Inc.; *U.S. Public*, *pg. 107*
ASAHI KOMAG COMPANY LIMITED—Komag, Incorporated; *U.S. Public*, pg. 966
BASF S.A.—BASF AG; *Int'l*, pg. 107
COREL CORPORATION—Corel Corporation; *Int'l*, pg. 331
DATA GENERAL CORPORATION; *U.S. Public*, pg. 485
DATA I/O GMBH—Data I/O Corporation; *U.S. Public*, pg. 486
FUJI MAGNETICS GMBH—Fuji Photo Film Co., Ltd.; *Int'l*, pg. 524
FUJI PHOTO FILM CO., LTD.; *Int'l*, pg. 523
GRUPO VIDEO VISA S.A. DE C.V.; *Int'l*, pg. 577
HEWLETT-PACKARD COMPANY; *U.S. Public*, pg. 813
INTERNATIONAL BUSINESS MACHINES CORPORATION; *U.S. Public*, pg. 895
INTERNATIONAL RESEARCH & EVALUATION; *U.S. Private*, pg. 571
KAO CORPORATION; *Int'l*, pg. 717
KOMAG, INCORPORATED; *U.S. Public*, pg. 966
KOMAG MATERIAL TECHNOLOGY INC.—Komag, Incorporated; *U.S. Public*, pg. 966
KONICA CORPORATION; *Int'l*, pg. 748
MAXELL DE MEXICO S.A. DE C.V.—Hitachi, Ltd.; *Int'l*, pg. 621
MITSUBISHI CHEMICAL AMERICA, INC.—Mitsubishi Chemical Corporation; *Int'l*, pg. 871
NKK CORPORATION; *Int'l*, pg. 902
PHILIP LASER MAGNETIC STORAGE—Philips Electronics N.V.; *Int'l*, pg. 1054
PHILIPS & DUPONT OPTICAL COMPANY—Philips Electronics N.V.; *Int'l*, pg. 1055
RHONE-POULENC SYSTEMES—Rhone-Poulenc S.A.; *Int'l*, *pg. 1109*
SCANTRON CORPORATION—John H. Harland Company; *U.S. Public*, pg. 786
SCHLUMBERGER MALCO INC.—N. Schlumberger & Cie; *Int'l*, pg. 1206
TDK CORPORATION; *Int'l*, pg. 1336
VARITRONIC SYSTEMS, INC.—W.H. Brady Co.; *U.S. Public*, pg. 250

3699 — ELECTRICAL MACHINERY, EQUIPMENT & SUPPLIES, NEC

ABB PETERCEM S.A.—ABB Asea Brown Boveri (Holding) Ltd.; *Int'l*, pg. 2
ABB REGIONAL PRODUCT CENTRE PTE. LTD.—ABB Asea Brown Boveri (Holding) Ltd.; *Int'l*, pg. 2
ARI GROUP EUROPE—Tyco International Ltd.; *U.S. Public*, *pg. 1650*
AGUSTA S.P.A.; *Int'l*, pg. 32
A. AHLSTROM CORPORATION-STROMFORS WORKS—A. Ahlstrom Corporation; *Int'l*, pg. 32
AHLSTROMFORETAGEN SVENSKA AB—A. Ahlstrom Corporation; *Int'l*, pg. 33
AHLSTROMFORETAGEN SVENSKA AB-ELJO—A. Ahlstrom Corporation; *Int'l*, pg. 33
AJAX MAGNETHERMIC CORP.—BBA Group plc; *Int'l*, pg. 113
ALLIEDSIGNAL AEROSPATIALE CANADA INC.—AlliedSignal Inc.; *U.S. Public*, pg. 53
ALLISTER MANUFACTURING CO.—Relm Wireless Corp.; *U.S. Public*, pg. 1376
AMP INC. LYTEL DIVISION—AMP Incorporated; *U.S. Public*, pg. 8
ANALOG DEVICES, SANTA CLARA—Analog Devices, Inc.; *U.S. Public*, pg. 108
ANORAD CORPORATION; *U.S. Private*, pg. 75
APPLIED TECHNOLOGY (GERMANY)—Litton Industries, Inc.; *U.S. Public*, pg. 1004
APPLIED TECHNOLOGY (UK)—Litton Industries, Inc.; *U.S. Public*, pg. 1004
ATLANTIC AVIATION CORP.; *U.S. Private*, pg. 94
ATLANTIC GUEST, INC.—Valley Forge Corporation; *U.S. Public*, pg. 1705
AYDIN EUROPE LTD.—Aydin Corporation; *U.S. Public*, pg. 158
B&D ELECTRODOMESTICOS LTDA.—The Black & Decker Corporation; *U.S. Public*, pg. 234
BAILEY CONTROLS COMPANY—IRI Istituto Ricostruzione Industriale; *Int'l*, pg. 654
BARD MFG. CO.; *U.S. Private*, pg. 116
BENTLY NEVADA CORPORATION; *U.S. Private*, pg. 134
BERSON MILIEUTECHNIEK B.V.—Halma p.l.c.; *Int'l*, pg. 590
BLONDER-TONGUE LABORATORIES, INC.; *U.S. Public*, pg. 237
BOWDEN INDUSTRIES LIMITED—GP Batteries International Ltd.; *Int'l*, pg. 537
BRANSON (EUROPA) B.V.—Emerson Electric Co.; *U.S. Public*, pg. 576
BRANSON INTERNATIONAL PLASMA CORP.—Emerson Electric Co.; *U.S. Public*, pg. 574
BRANSON SONIC POWER, S.A.—Emerson Electric Co.; *U.S. Public*, pg. 576
BRANSON ULTRASONICS—Emerson Electric Co.; *U.S. Public*, pg. 574
BRANSON ULTRASONICS CORP.-PLASTICS JOINING DIV.—Emerson Electric Co.; *U.S. Public*, pg. 574
BRANSON ULTRASONICS CORP. - PRECISION CLEANING DIV.—Emerson Electric Co.; *U.S. Public*, pg. 574
BRANSON ULTRASUONI S.P.A.—Emerson Electric Co.; *U.S. Public*, pg. 576
BROTHER INDUSTRIES, LTD.; *Int'l*, pg. 229
CAE ELECTRONICS, LTD.—CAE Inc.; *Int'l*, pg. 237
CAE ELEKTRONIK GMBH—CAE Inc.; *Int'l*, pg. 238
CARCO ELECTRONICS; *U.S. Private*, pg. 208
CARLISLE COMPANIES INCORPORATED; *U.S. Public*, pg. 305
CARLON CHIMES CO.—The Lamson & Sessions Co.; *U.S. Public*, pg. 976
CASH FLOW, INC.—NationsBank Corporation; *U.S. Public*, pg. 1163
THE CHAMBERLAIN GROUP, INC.—Duchossois Industries, Inc.; *U.S. Private*, pg. 344
CIRCLE A.W. PRODUCTS, CO.—Sigma-Aldrich Corporation; *U.S. Public*, pg. 1471
COHERENT GMBH—Coherent, Inc.; *U.S. Public*, pg. 395
COHERENT, INC.; *U.S. Public*, pg. 395
COHERENT PACIFIC—Coherent, Inc.; *U.S. Public*, pg. 396
COHERENT S.A.—Coherent, Inc.; *U.S. Public*, pg. 396
COHERENT (U.K.) LTD.—Coherent, Inc.; *U.S. Public*, pg. 396
COMLINEAR CORPORATION—National Semiconductor Corporation; *U.S. Public*, pg. 1160
COMPAGNIE FRANCAISE PHILIPS—Philips Electronics N.V.; *Int'l*, pg. 1055
CONRAC DISPLAY PRODUCTS; *U.S. Private*, pg. 264
CONTROL LASER CORPORATION—Excel Technology, Inc.; *U.S. Public*, pg. 599
CRENLO, INC.; *U.S. Private*, pg. 288
CROUSE-HINDS—Cooper Industries, Inc.; *U.S. Public*, pg. 444
CRUISING EQUIPMENT COMPANY—Valley Forge Corporation; *U.S. Public*, pg. 1705
DAQ ELECTRONICS INC.; *U.S. Private*, pg. 300
DEL MAR AVIONICS; *U.S. Private*, pg. 321
DELTA-UNIBUS CORP.—Powell Industries, Inc.; *U.S. Public*, pg. 1319
DEPOSITION TECHNOLOGIES, INC.—Material Sciences Corporation; *U.S. Public*, pg. 1056
DETECTION SYSTEMS, INC.; *U.S. Public*, pg. 501
DETEX CORPORATION; *U.S. Private*, pg. 327
DRESSER INDUSTRIES WAYNE DIVISION—Dresser Industries, Inc.; *U.S. Public*, pg. 528
DUCHOSSOIS INDUSTRIES, INC.; *U.S. Private*, pg. 344
DUKANE CORPORATION; *U.S. Private*, pg. 345
E-L PRODUCTS COMPANY—Astronics Corporation; *U.S. Public*, pg. 142
EG & G ASTROPHYSICS—EG & G, Inc.; *U.S. Public*, pg. 543
EBTEC CORPORATION—TI Group plc; *Int'l*, pg. 1337
ELECTRICAL PRODUCTS DIVISION—3M; *U.S. Public*, pg. 1605
EMERSON JAPAN, LTD.—Emerson Electric Co.; *U.S. Public*, pg. 576
EMERSON JAPAN, LTD., FUSITE DIVISION—Emerson Electric Co.; *U.S. Public*, pg. 576
ETEC SYSTEMS, INC.; *U.S. Public*, pg. 594
EVCON INDUSTRIES, INC.—York International Corporation; *U.S. Public*, pg. 1788
EVERETT CHARLES TECHNOLOGIES; *U.S. Private*, pg. 386
EVERT LARSSON INDUSTRI AB—Electrolux, AB; *Int'l*, pg. 439
EXCEL TECHNOLOGY, INC.; *U.S. Public*, pg. 599
FIELD EFFECTS, INC.—Intermagnetics General Corporation; *U.S. Public*, pg. 893
FLIGHTSAFETY INTERNATIONAL INC.—Berkshire Hathaway Inc.; *U.S. Public*, pg. 218
AB FORMVERKTYG—Electrolux, AB; *Int'l*, pg. 439
FUSITE, B.V.—Emerson Electric Co.; *U.S. Public*, pg. 577
FUSITE JAPAN—Emerson Electric Co.; *U.S. Public*, pg. 577
G & W ELECTRIC CO.; *U.S. Private*, pg. 433
GENERAL SIGNAL CORPORATION; *U.S. Public*, pg. 726
THE GENIE COMPANY—Overhead Door Corporation; *U.S. Private*, pg. 823
GOODWAY TECHNOLOGIES CORPORATION; *U.S. Private*, pg. 464
GRANGES AB—Electrolux, AB; *Int'l*, pg. 439
HAKO-WERKE GMBH & CO.; *Int'l*, pg. 587
HAVELLANDISCHE MASCHINENBAU GMBH—Hako-Werke GmbH & Co.; *Int'l*, pg. 587
HORTON AUTOMATICS DIV.—Overhead Door Corporation; *U.S. Private*, pg. 823
HORTON AUTOMATICS, LTD.—Overhead Door Corporation; *U.S. Private*, pg. 823
THE HOTSY CORPORATION—Harbour Group Ltd.; *U.S. Private*, pg. 500
HUGHES-PETERS, INC.; *U.S. Private*, pg. 546
INTELLEDEX VISION PRODUCTS—Electro Scientific Industries, Inc.; *U.S. Public*, pg. 568
IWERKS ENTERTAINMENT—Iwerks Entertainment; *U.S. Public*, pg. 915
JETRONIC INDUSTRIES, INC.; *U.S. Public*, pg. 926
KENT INDUSTRIAL MEASUREMENTS LIMITED—ABB Asea Brown Boveri (Holding) Ltd.; *Int'l*, pg. 2
KERRY ULTRASONICS LIMITED—Halma p.l.c.; *Int'l*, pg. 589
KRAUTKRAMER-FOERSTER JAPAN CO., LTD.—Emerson Electric Co.; *U.S. Public*, pg. 577
KRAUTKRAMER G.M.B.H—Emerson Electric Co.; *U.S. Public*, pg. 577
L&R MANUFACTURING CO.; *U.S. Private*, pg. 638
LAMBDA PHYSIK GMBH—Coherent, Inc.; *U.S. Public*, pg. 396
LAMBDA PHYSIK JAPAN CO., LTD.—Coherent, Inc.; *U.S. Public*, pg. 396
LASAG AG—SMH Swiss Corporation for Micro Electronics & Watchmaking Indus. Ltd.; *Int'l*, pg. 1161
LINK-MILES LIMITED—Thomson S.A.; *Int'l*, pg. 1385
LOCKHEED MARTIN SOLARTRON SYSTEMS—Lockheed Martin Corporation; *U.S. Public*, pg. 1009
MLM DIVISION/ELECTRONICS GROUP—Israel Aircraft Industries Ltd.; *Int'l*, pg. 690
MARTIN DOOR MFG., INC.; *U.S. Private*, pg. 708
MATSUSHITA ELECTRIC WORKS, LTD.; *Int'l*, pg. 847
MAXWELL TECHNOLOGIES, INC.; *U.S. Public*, pg. 1061
MCKEE DOOR, INC.—American Buildings Co.; *U.S. Public*, pg. 69
METTLER-TOLEDO INC.—AEA Investors Inc.; *U.S. Private*, *pg. 4*
MICRO COMPONENT TECHNOLOGY INC.; *U.S. Public*, pg. 1104
MOORE-O-MATIC, INC.—Nortek, Inc.; *U.S. Public*, pg. 1193
MORSE CONTROLS LTD.—IMO Industries Inc.; *U.S. Public*, pg. 857
MR. CHRISTMAS INC.; *U.S. Private*, pg. 765

MULTI-CLEAN INC.—Hako-Werke GmbH & Co.; *Int'l*, pg. 587
NRD—Mark IV Industries Inc.; *U.S. Public*, pg. 1045
NT DOR-OMATIC; *U.S. Private*, pg. 771
NEWCOM, INC.—Aura Systems, Inc.; *U.S. Public*, pg. 147
NOMA INDUSTRIES LIMITED; *Int'l*, pg. 954
NOMA-INTERNATIONAL, INC.—Noma Industries Limited; *Int'l*, pg. 955
NORTEK, INC.; *U.S. Public*, pg. 1192
NORWESCO A/S—A. Ahlstrom Corporation; *Int'l*, pg. 33
OPT INDUSTRIES, INC.—Torotel, Inc.; *U.S. Public*, pg. 1624
OVERHEAD DOOR CORPORATION; *U.S. Private*, pg. 822
PLP PRODUTOS PARA LINHAS PROFORMADOS LTDA.—Preformed Line Products; *U.S. Public*, pg. 1321
PTR-PRECISION TECHNOLOGIES, INC.—Integral Hydraulik & Co.; *Int'l*, pg. 679
PENTAIR, INC.; *U.S. Public*, pg. 1273
PHILIPS DANMARK A/S—Philips Electronics N.V.; *Int'l*, pg. 1055
PHILIPS ELECTRONIC & ASSOCIATED INDUSTRIES, LTD.—Philips Electronics N.V.; *Int'l*, pg. 1055
PHILIPS INDUSTRIE SA—Philips Electronics N.V.; *Int'l*, pg. 1055
PHILIPS KISTAINDUSTRIER AB—Philips Electronics N.V.; *Int'l*, pg. 1055
PHILIPS NORDEN AB—Philips Electronics N.V.; *Int'l*, pg. 1055
PHILIPS NORRKOEPENGSINDUSTRIER AB—Philips Electronics N.V.; *Int'l*, pg. 1055
POWER SYSTEMS GROUP—Jetronic Industries, Inc.; *U.S. Public*, pg. 927
PRECISION ARC CO.—Smith Industries, Inc.; *U.S. Private*, pg. 1008
RFI SHIELDING LIMITED—Siebe plc; *Int'l*, pg. 1241
RAYNOR GARAGE DOORS; *U.S. Private*, pg. 912
RAYTHEON SYSTEMS CO.—Raytheon Company; *U.S. Public*, pg. 1364
REPUBLIC STORAGE SYSTEMS COMPANY INC.; *U.S. Private*, pg. 924
RETZLAFF INCORPORATED; *U.S. Private*, pg. 925
RITZ-C.INDUSTRIA E COMERCIO SA—Emerson Electric Co.; *U.S. Public*, pg. 577
ROLLS-ROYCE POWER ENGINEERING PLC—Rolls-Royce plc; *Int'l*, pg. 1127
ROTHENBERGER UMWELTTECHNIK GMBH—Rothenberger Group GmbH; *Int'l*, pg. 1128
SAB IBERICA S.A.—Cardo AB; *Int'l*, pg. 271
SAB SISTEMI S.P.A.—Cardo AB; *Int'l*, pg. 271
SAB WABCO AB—Cardo AB; *Int'l*, pg. 271
SAB WABCO BENELUX—Cardo AB; *Int'l*, pg. 271
SAB WABCO ENGINEERING S.R.L.—Cardo AB; *Int'l*, pg. 271
SAB WABCO HOLDINGS B.V.—Cardo AB; *Int'l*, pg. 271
SAB WABCO LTD.—Cardo AB; *Int'l*, pg. 271
SAB WABCO N.V.—Cardo AB; *Int'l*, pg. 271
SAB WABCO S.A.—Cardo AB; *Int'l*, pg. 271
SAB WABCO S.P.A.—Cardo AB; *Int'l*, pg. 271
SL INDUSTRIES, INC.; *U.S. Public*, pg. 1418
S.T. RESEARCH; *U.S. Private*, pg. 958
SARGENT & GREENLEAF, INC.; *U.S. Private*, pg. 965
SCHNEIDER ELECTRIC S.A.—Schneider S.A.; *Int'l*, pg. 1207
SCHNEIDER S.A.; *Int'l*, pg. 1207
SEALED AIR CORPORATION; *U.S. Public*, pg. 1450
SENIOR ENGINEERING GROUP, PLC.; *Int'l*, pg. 1220
SENSORMATIC ELECTRONICS CORPORATION; *U.S. Public*, pg. 1457
SENSORS & ELECTRONIC SYSTEMS—Raytheon Company; *U.S. Public*, pg. 1365
SIERRACOM—Sierra Technologies Inc.; *U.S. Private*, pg. 999
SIMULATION SYSTEMS DIVISION—Berkshire Hathaway Inc.; *U.S. Public*, pg. 218
SMITH INDUSTRIES, INC.; *U.S. Private*, pg. 1008
SOUTHWEST VACUUM DEVICES, INC.—Video Display Corporation; *U.S. Public*, pg. 1720
SPECTRA-PHYSICS LASERPLANE INC.—Thermo Electron Corporation; *U.S. Public*, pg. 1594
SPECTRUM TECHNOLOGIES LIMITED—British Aerospace p.l.c.; *Int'l*, pg. 218
STAVELEY SENSORS DIVISION—Staveley Industries PLC; *Int'l*, pg. 1299
SUECOBRAS INDUSTRIA E COMERCIO LTDA.—Cardo AB; *Int'l*, pg. 271
SUN MICRO STAMPING INC.—Sun Microsystems, Inc.; *U.S. Public*, pg. 1531
SURCO PRODUCTS, INC.; *U.S. Private*, pg. 1056
TECH-SYM CORPORATION; *U.S. Public*, pg. 1563
TEXAS INSTRUMENTS CONSUMER PRODUCTS DIV.—Texas Instruments Incorporated; *U.S. Public*, pg. 1586
TEXAS INSTRUMENTS GPL—Texas Instruments Incorporated; *U.S. Public*, pg. 1586
THOMAS ENGINEERING INC.; *U.S. Private*, pg. 1082
THOMSON TRAINING & SIMULATION—Thomson S.A.; *Int'l*, pg. 1384
3M; *U.S. Public*, pg. 1604
THE TITAN CORPORATION; *U.S. Public*, pg. 1618
TRIBORO ELECTRIC CO.; *U.S. Private*, pg. 1102
TRIPLE A SPECIALTY COMPANY; *U.S. Private*, pg. 1103
UNIBUS, INC.—Powell Industries, Inc.; *U.S. Public*, pg. 1319
UNICAN SECURITY SYSTEMS LTD.; *Int'l*, pg. 1432
UNIPHASE CORPORATION; *U.S. Public*, pg. 1670
VAPOR—Westinghouse Air Brake Company; *U.S. Public*, pg. 1761
VARI TRONICS COMPANY, INC.; *U.S. Private*, pg. 1134
VARIAN ASSOCIATES, INC.; *U.S. Public*, pg. 1710
VISUAL SIMULATION SYSTEMS DIVISION—Berkshire Hathaway Inc.; *U.S. Public*, pg. 218
VOLT INFORMATION SCIENCES, INC.; *U.S. Public*, pg. 1724
WICO; *U.S. Private*, pg. 1144
WANDEL & GOLTERMANN GMBH & CO., ELEKTRONISCHE MESSTECHNIK; *Int'l*, pg. 1485
WATERS INSTRUMENTS, INC.; *U.S. Public*, pg. 1745
XERTRONIX—Eastman Kodak Company; *U.S. Public*, pg. 551
YARDNEY TECHNICAL PRODUCTS, INC.—Ener-Tek International Corporation; *U.S. Private*, pg. 376
YUASA-IONICS CO., LTD.—Ionics, Incorporated; *U.S. Public*, pg. 912
ZEBRA TECHNOLOGIES CORPORATION; *U.S. Public*, pg. 1790

3711 — MOTOR VEHICLES & PASSENGER CAR BODIES

AM GENERAL CORPORATION—Renco Group; *U.S. Private*, pg. 922
ASC WEINSBERG KAROSSERIEWERKE WEINSBERG GMBH—ASC Incorporated; *U.S. Private*, pg. 8
ABCO MARKETS, INC.; *U.S. Private*, pg. 10
ADAM OPEL AG—General Motors Corporation; *U.S. Public*, pg. 721
ALFA LANCIA INDUSTRIALE S.P.A.—Fiat Auto SpA; *Int'l*, pg. 481
ALFA ROMEO E NISSAN AUTOVEICOLI S.P.A.—Fiat Auto SpA; *Int'l*, pg. 481
ALFA ROMEO VEICOLI COMM. E LAV MECC. S.P.A.—Fiat Auto SpA; *Int'l*, pg. 481
AMERICAN EAGLE—Federal Signal Corporation; *U.S. Public*, pg. 617
AMERICAN HONDA MOTOR CO., INC.—Honda Motor Co., Ltd.; *Int'l*, pg. 634
ANADOLU OTOMOTIV SANAYII VE TICARET A.S.—Isuzu Motors Limited; *Int'l*, pg. 692
ANAMBRA MOTOR MFG. CO. LTD.—Daimler-Benz Aktiengesellschaft; *Int'l*, pg. 368
ASTON MARTIN LAGONDA LIMITED—Ford Motor Company; *U.S. Public*, pg. 665
ATHEY PRODUCTS CORPORATION; *U.S. Public*, pg. 142
AUDI AG—Volkswagen AG; *Int'l*, pg. 1473
AUTOALLIANCE INTERNATIONAL INC.—Mazda Motor Corporation; *Int'l*, pg. 849
AUTOEUROPA AUTOMOVELS LDA.—Volkswagen AG; *Int'l*, pg. 1474
AUTOLATINA—Volkswagen AG; *Int'l*, pg. 1474
AUTOLATINA ARGENTINA S.A.—Volkswagen AG; *Int'l*, pg. 1475
AUTOMOBILES PEUGEOT S.A.—PSA Peugeot Citroen; *Int'l*, pg. 1020
AUTOMOTIVE ELECTRONIC CONTROL SYSTEMS, INC.—Robert Bosch GmbH; *Int'l*, pg. 205
AUTOMOTIVE MANUFACTURERS (MALAYSIA) SDN. BHD.—Isuzu Motors Limited; *Int'l*, pg. 692
AUTOMOTIVE REBUILDERS—Richmond Motor Company; *U.S. Private*, pg. 929
BMW MASCHINENFABRIK SPANDAU GMBH—Bayerische Motoren Werke Aktiengesellschaft; *Int'l*, pg. 177
BMW MOTOREN GES.M.B.H.—Bayerische Motoren Werke Aktiengesellschaft; *Int'l*, pg. 178
BMW MOTORRAD GMBH—Bayerische Motoren Werke Aktiengesellschaft; *Int'l*, pg. 177
BMW MOTORSPORT GMBH—Bayerische Motoren Werke Aktiengesellschaft; *Int'l*, pg. 177
BMW (SOUTH AFRICA) (PTY.) LTD.—Bayerische Motoren Werke Aktiengesellschaft; *Int'l*, pg. 178
BMW TECHNIK GMBH—Bayerische Motoren Werke Aktiengesellschaft; *Int'l*, pg. 177
BMY-WHEELED VEHICLES—Harsco Corporation; *U.S. Public*, pg. 793
BAYERISCHE MOTOREN WERKE AKTIENGESELLSCHAFT; *Int'l*, pg. 177
BEIJING BEILING SPECIAL AUTOMOBILE CO., LTD.—Isuzu Motors Limited; *Int'l*, pg. 692
AUGUST BILSTEIN GMBH & CO. KG—Fried. Krupp AG; *Int'l*, pg. 507
BILSTEIN CORPORATION OF AMERICA—Fried. Krupp AG; *Int'l*, pg. 507
BLUE BIRD CORPORATION; *U.S. Private*, pg. 151
BRITISH AEROSPACE P.L.C.; *Int'l*, pg. 217
BRUNINGHAUS SCHMIEDE GMBH—Fried. Krupp AG; *Int'l*, pg. 508
THE BUDD COMPANY—Thyssen AG; *Int'l*, pg. 1388
BUICK MOTOR DIV. GENERAL MOTORS CORP.—General Motors Corporation; *U.S. Public*, pg. 720
CAMI AUTOMOTIVE, INC.—General Motors Corporation; *U.S. Public*, pg. 722
CADILLAC MOTOR CAR DIVISION—General Motors Corporation; *U.S. Public*, pg. 720
CAMFORD AUTOMOTIVE SYSTEMS LTD.—Fried. Krupp AG; *Int'l*, pg. 507
CAMFORD DESIGN LTD.—Fried. Krupp AG; *Int'l*, pg. 507
CAMFORD PRESSINGS LTD.—Fried. Krupp AG; *Int'l*, pg. 507
CANADIAN KAWASAKI MOTORS INC.—Kawasaki Heavy Industries, Ltd.; *Int'l*, pg. 726
CANADIAN KENWORTH CO.—Paccar Inc.; *U.S. Public*, pg. 1247
CANLUBANG AUTOMOTIVE RESOURCES CORP.—Nissho Iwai Corporation; *Int'l*, pg. 947
CAR PRODUCT DEVELOPMENT—Ford Motor Company; *U.S. Public*, pg. 662
CHANCE INDUSTRIES, INC.; *U.S. Private*, pg. 228
CHEVROLET MOTOR DIV. GENERAL MOTORS CORP.—General Motors Corporation; *U.S. Public*, pg. 720
CHEVROLET, PONTIAC, GM OF CANADA GROUP—General Motors Corporation; *U.S. Public*, pg. 720
CHRYSLER ADVANCE MANUFACTURING OPERATIONS—Chrysler Corporation; *U.S. Public*, pg. 353
CHRYSLER CANADA LTD.—Chrysler Corporation; *U.S. Public*, pg. 354
CHRYSLER CORPORATION; *U.S. Public*, pg. 352
CHRYSLER DE MEXICO S.A.—Chrysler Corporation; *U.S. Public*, pg. 354
COLLINS INDUSTRIES, INC.; *U.S. Public*, pg. 399
COMMERCIAL VEHICLE DIV.—Champion Enterprises, Inc.; *U.S. Public*, pg. 333
CONSTRUCTORA VENEZOLANO DE VEHICULOS, C.A.—General Motors Corporation; *U.S. Public*, pg. 723
CRAIG SYSTEMS; *U.S. Private*, pg. 284
CRANE CARRIER COMPANY; *U.S. Private*, pg. 286
DAEWOO CORPORATION; *Int'l*, pg. 357
DAEWOO MOTOR COMPANY, LTD.—Daewoo Corporation; *Int'l*, pg. 357
DAIHATSU MOTOR CORPORATION, LTD.; *Int'l*, pg. 364
DAIHATSU-PHRANAKORN MOTOR CO., LTD.—Daihatsu Motor Corporation, Ltd.; *Int'l*, pg. 365
DAIMLER-BENZ AKTIENGESELLSCHAFT; *Int'l*, pg. 366
DESC, S.A. DE C.V.; *Int'l*, pg. 395
DEUTSCHE AUTOMOBILGESELLSCHAFT MBH—Volkswagen AG; *Int'l*, pg. 1473
DIAMOND STAR MOTORS—Mitsubishi Motors Corporation; *Int'l*, pg. 875
DITTMAN & NEUHAUS GMBH—Fried. Krupp AG; *Int'l*, pg. 508
DORBYL LIMITED; *Int'l*, pg. 416
DOUGLAS DYNAMICS, INC.—Armco Inc.; *U.S. Public*, pg. 131
G. DRAUZ GMBH & CO.—Fried. Krupp AG; *Int'l*, pg. 507
DRAUZ INGENIEURBETRIEB GMBH—Fried. Krupp AG; *Int'l*, pg. 508
DUTCHMEN MANUFACTURING, INC.—Thor Industries, Inc.; *U.S. Public*, pg. 1602
ELGIN SWEEPER COMPANY—Federal Signal Corporation; *U.S. Public*, pg. 617
EMERGENCY ONE, INC.—Federal Signal Corporation; *U.S. Public*, pg. 617
EVOBUS GMBH SETRA OMNIBUSSE—Daimler-Benz Aktiengesellschaft; *Int'l*, pg. 368
FAW-VOLKSWAGEN AUTOMOTIVE COMPANY CO. LTD.—Volkswagen AG; *Int'l*, pg. 1475
FWD/SEAGRAVE FIRE APPARATUS, INC.; *U.S. Private*, pg. 390
FEDERAL SIGNAL CORPORATION; *U.S. Public*, pg. 616
FIAT AUTO IRELAND LTD.—Fiat Auto SpA; *Int'l*, pg. 481
FIAT AUTO SPA; *Int'l*, pg. 480
FIAT AUTO S.P.A.—Fiat Auto SpA; *Int'l*, pg. 481
THE FLXIBLE CORP.—General Automotive Corporation; *U.S. Private*, pg. 444
FORD BODY & ASSEMBLY OPERATIONS—Ford Motor Company; *U.S. Public*, pg. 662
FORD ENGINE DIVISION—Ford Motor Company; *U.S. Public*, pg. 662
FORD ESPANA S.A.—Ford Motor Company; *U.S. Public*, pg. 665
HENRY FORD & SON, LIMITED—Ford Motor Company; *U.S. Public*, pg. 665
FORD LUSITANA—Ford Motor Company; *U.S. Public*, pg. 666
FORD MOTOR COMPANY; *U.S. Public*, pg. 661
FORD WERKE AG - GENK BRANCH—Ford Motor Company; *U.S. Public*, pg. 666
FOUR WIND INTERNATIONAL CORP.—Thor Industries, Inc.; *U.S. Public*, pg. 1602
FREIGHTLINER CORP.—Daimler-Benz Aktiengesellschaft; *Int'l*, pg. 368
FUDICKAR METALL GMBH—Fried. Krupp AG; *Int'l*, pg. 514
FUJI HEAVY INDUSTRIES, LTD.; *Int'l*, pg. 522
GENERAL AUTOMOTIVE CORPORATION; *U.S. Private*, pg. 443
GENERAL MOTORS CORPORATION; *U.S. Public*, pg. 718
GENERAL MOTORS EGYPT S.A.E.—Isuzu Motors Limited; *Int'l*, pg. 692
GENERAL MOTORS EGYPT S.A.E.—General Motors Corporation; *U.S. Public*, pg. 724
GERLACH-WERKE GMBH—Fried. Krupp AG; *Int'l*, pg. 508
P.T. GERMAN MOTOR MFG.—Daimler-Benz Aktiengesellschaft; *Int'l*, pg. 368
GROUP LOTUS LTD.—Proton; *Int'l*, pg. 1071
HALE PRODUCTS INC.—IDEX Corporation; *U.S. Public*, pg. 862
HARSCO CORPORATION; *U.S. Public*, pg. 792
HOESCH ARGENTINA S.A.I.Y.C.—Fried. Krupp AG; *Int'l*, pg. 508
HOESCH FEDERN GMBH—Fried. Krupp AG; *Int'l*, pg. 508
HOESCH INDUSTRIA DE MOLAS LTDA.—Fried. Krupp AG; *Int'l*, pg. 508
HOESCH INDUSTRIA ESPANOLA DE SUSPENSIONES S.A.—Fried. Krupp AG; *Int'l*, pg. 508
HOESCH SUSPENSIONES AUTOMOTRICES S.A. DE C.V.—Fried. Krupp AG; *Int'l*, pg. 508
HOESCH SUSPENSIONS INC.—Fried. Krupp AG; *Int'l*, pg. 508
HOESCH WOODHEAD LTD.—Fried. Krupp AG; *Int'l*, pg. 508
HOLZINDUSTRIE BRUCHSAL GMBH—Daimler-Benz Aktiengesellschaft; *Int'l*, pg. 368
HONDA AUSTRALIA PTY., LTD.—Honda Motor Co., Ltd.; *Int'l*, pg. 635
HONDA AUSTRIA G.M.B.H.—Honda Motor Co., Ltd.; *Int'l*, pg. 635
HONDA MOTOR CO., LTD.; *Int'l*, pg. 634
HONDA MOTOR DO BRASIL LTDA.—Honda Motor Co., Ltd.; *Int'l*, pg. 635
HONDA RACING CORPORATION—Honda Motor Co., Ltd.; *Int'l*, pg. 634
HONDA R&D CO., LTD.—Honda Motor Co., Ltd.; *Int'l*, pg. 634
WALTER HUNDHAUSEN GMBH & CO. KG—Fried. Krupp AG; *Int'l*, pg. 508
HYUNDAI MOTOR COMPANY; *Int'l*, pg. 641
HYUNDAI MOTOR COMPANY—Hyundai Motor Company; *Int'l*, pg. 641

IAV INGENIEURGESELLCHAFT FUR AGGREGATETECHNIK UND VERKEHRSFAHRZEUGE MBH—Volkswagen AG; *Int'l*, pg. 1473
IMPORMOL INDUSTRIA PORTUGUESA DE MOLAS S.A.—Fried. Krupp AG; *Int'l*, pg. 508
ISUZU MOTORS CO., (THAILAND) LTD.—Isuzu Motors Limited; *Int'l*, pg. 693
ISUZU MOTORS LIMITED; *Int'l*, pg. 692
ISUZU PILIPINAS CORPORATION—Isuzu Motors Limited; *Int'l*, pg. 693
IVECO B.V.—Fiat Auto SpA; *Int'l*, pg. 483
IVECO FIAT S.P.A.—Fiat Auto SpA; *Int'l*, pg. 484
IVECO FRANCE S.A.; *Int'l*, pg. 696
JAGUAR CARS LIMITED—Ford Motor Company; *U.S. Public*, pg. 666
JAYCO INC.; *U.S. Private*, pg. 583
JEEP—Chrysler Corporation; *U.S. Public*, pg. 353
JERR-DAN CORPORATION—Durakon Industries, Inc.; *U.S. Public*, pg. 537
KANTO AUTO WORKS, LTD.—Toyota Motor Corporation; *Int'l*, pg. 1412
GEO. W. KING LTD.—Fried. Krupp AG; *Int'l*, pg. 507
KRUPP BRUNINGHAUS GMBH—Fried. Krupp AG; *Int'l*, pg. 508
KRUPP GERLACH COMPANY—Fried. Krupp AG; *Int'l*, pg. 508
KRUPP METALURGICA CAMPO LIMPO LTDA.—Fried. Krupp AG; *Int'l*, pg. 508
LAGARDERE GROUPE; *Int'l*, pg. 791
LAND ROVER NORTH AMERICA—Bayerische Motoren Werke Aktiengesellschaft; *Int'l*, pg. 177
LODAL, INC.; *U.S. Private*, pg. 672
LUHN & PULVERMACHER—Fried. Krupp AG; *Int'l*, pg. 508
MAN AKTIENGESELLSCHAFT; *Int'l*, pg. 824
MAN AUTOMOTIVE (AUSTRALIA) PTY. LTD.—MAN Aktiengesellschaft; *Int'l*, pg. 825
MAN AUTOMOTIVE (SOUTH AFRICA) (PROPRIETARY) LTD.—MAN Aktiengesellschaft; *Int'l*, pg. 825
MTU MOTOREN-UND TURBINEN-UNION FRIEDRICHSHAFEN GMBH—Daimler-Benz Aktiengesellschaft; *Int'l*, pg. 367
MACK REMANUFACTURING CENTER—Renault; *Int'l*, pg. 1102
THE MARMON GROUP, INC.; *U.S. Private*, pg. 706
MASCHINENFABRIK ESSLINGEN AG—Daimler-Benz Aktiengesellschaft; *Int'l*, pg. 368
MATRA AUTOMOBILE—Lagardere Groupe; *Int'l*, pg. 792
MAVILOR S.A.—Fried. Krupp AG; *Int'l*, pg. 508
MAXON INDUSTRIES, INC.; *U.S. Private*, pg. 717
MERCEDES-BENZ ARGENTINA S.A.—Daimler-Benz Aktiengesellschaft; *Int'l*, pg. 368
MERCEDES-BENZ DO BRASIL S.A.—Daimler-Benz Aktiengesellschaft; *Int'l*, pg. 368
MERCEDES-BENZ ESPANA, S.A.—Daimler-Benz Aktiengesellschaft; *Int'l*, pg. 369
MERCEDES-BENZ MEXICO, S.A. DE C.V.—Daimler-Benz Aktiengesellschaft; *Int'l*, pg. 369
MITSUBISHI MOTORS CORPORATION; *Int'l*, pg. 875
MURE S.A.—Fried. Krupp AG; *Int'l*, pg. 508
NAW NUTZFAHRZEUGGESELLSCHAFT ARBON & WETZIKON AG—Daimler-Benz Aktiengesellschaft; *Int'l*, pg. 369
NATIONAL-OILWELL/DRECO—National-Oilwell Inc.; *U.S. Public*, pg. 1158
NAVISTAR INTERNATIONAL CORPORATION; *U.S. Public*, pg. 1167
NETHERLANDS CAR B.V.—Mitsubishi Motors Corporation; *Int'l*, pg. 876
NEW UNITED MOTOR MANUFACTURING INC.—Toyota Motor Corporation; *Int'l*, pg. 1413
NISSAN MEXICANA, S.A. DE C.V.—Nissan Motor Co., Ltd.; *Int'l*, pg. 945
NISSAN MOTOR CO., LTD.; *Int'l*, pg. 943
NISSAN MOTOR CORPORATION IN U.S.A.—Nissan Motor Co., Ltd.; *Int'l*, pg. 945
NISSAN MOTOR DEL PERU S.A.—Nissan Motor Co., Ltd.; *Int'l*, pg. 945
NISSAN MOTOR DEUTSCHLAND GMBH—Nissan Motor Co., Ltd.; *Int'l*, pg. 945
NISSAN MOTOR IBERICA S.A.—Nissan Motor Co., Ltd.; *Int'l*, pg. 945
NISSAN MOTOR MANUFACTURING CO. (AUSTRALIA) LTD.—Nissan Motor Co., Ltd.; *Int'l*, pg. 945
NISSAN MOTOR MFG. CORP., U.S.A.—Nissan Motor Co., Ltd.; *Int'l*, pg. 945
NISSAN MOTOR MANUFACTURING (UK) LTD.—Nissan Motor Co., Ltd.; *Int'l*, pg. 945
NISSAN SHATAI CO., LTD.—Nissan Motor Co., Ltd.; *Int'l*, pg. 944
OESTERREICHISCHE AUTOMOBILFABRIK—MAN Aktiengesellschaft; *Int'l*, pg. 825
OFFICINE A. MASERATI S.P.A.—Fiat Auto SpA; *Int'l*, pg. 482
OFFICINE ALFIERI MASERATI, SPA—Chrysler Corporation; *U.S. Public*, pg. 354
OLDSMOBILE DIV. GENERAL MOTORS CORP.—General Motors Corporation; *U.S. Public*, pg. 720
OMNIBUS BB TRANSPORTES, S.A.—General Motors Corporation; *U.S. Public*, pg. 723
OSHKOSH TRUCK CORPORATION; *U.S. Public*, pg. 1233
PSD HOLDINGS BHD.—Sime Darby Berhad; *Int'l*, pg. 1250
PACCAR AUSTRALIA PTY. LTD.—Paccar Inc.; *U.S. Public*, pg. 1247
PACCAR OF CANADA LTD.—Paccar Inc.; *U.S. Public*, pg. 1247
THE PANTHER CAR CO., LTD.—Ssangyong Business Group; *Int'l*, pg. 1292
PETERBILT OF CANADA—Paccar Inc.; *U.S. Public*, pg. 1247
PIERCE MANUFACTURING, INC.—Oshkosh Truck Corporation; *U.S. Public*, pg. 1233
PONTIAC-GMC DIVISION—General Motors Corporation; *U.S. Public*, pg. 720
PORSCHE AG; *Int'l*, pg. 1063
PRE-STAR LTD.—Fried. Krupp AG; *Int'l*, pg. 507
PRESS- UND STANZWERK AG—Fried. Krupp AG; *Int'l*, pg. 508
RAVO INTERNATIONAL—Federal Signal Corporation; *U.S. Public*, pg. 617
RENAULT; *Int'l*, pg. 1102
RENAULT V.I.—Renault; *Int'l*, pg. 1102
ROADTEC, INC.—Astec Industries, Inc.; *U.S. Public*, pg. 141
ROLLS-ROYCE MOTOR CARS LIMITED—Vickers PLC; *Int'l*, pg. 1467
ROVER GROUP LIMITED—Bayerische Motoren Werke Aktiengesellschaft; *Int'l*, pg. 178
SOFUNGE LTDA.—Daimler-Benz Aktiengesellschaft; *Int'l*, pg. 369
SAAB AUTOMOBILE AB—Investor AB; *Int'l*, pg. 687
SAAB AUTOMOBILE AB—General Motors Corporation; *U.S. Public*, pg. 725
SABANCI HOLDING A.S.; *Int'l*, pg. 1167
SALVADOR CAETANO I.M.V.T., S.A.R.L.—Toyota Motor Corporation; *Int'l*, pg. 1413
THE SATURN CORPORATION—General Motors Corporation; *U.S. Public*, pg. 721
SCANIA-BUSSAR AB—Investor AB; *Int'l*, pg. 687
SCANIA DIVISION—Investor AB; *Int'l*, pg. 687
SCOTT AVIATION—Figgie International Inc.; *U.S. Public*, pg. 622
SERVICE PARTS OPERATIONS—General Motors Corporation; *U.S. Public*, pg. 720
SHANGHAI-VOLKSWAGEN AUTOMOTIVE COMPANY LTD.—Volkswagen AG; *Int'l*, pg. 1475
SIME DARBY BERHAD; *Int'l*, pg. 1249
SITA—Lyonnaise des Eaux S.A.; *Int'l*, pg. 824
600 RACING INC.—Speedway Motorsports, Inc.; *U.S. Public*, pg. 1498
SKODA, AUTOMOBILOVA A.S.—Volkswagen AG; *Int'l*, pg. 1475
SOCIEDAD ESPANOLA DE AUTOMOVILES DE TURISME, S.A. (SEAT)—Volkswagen AG; *Int'l*, pg. 1475
SOMEFLOR SOCIETE MACANIQUE DE FLORANGE SA—Fried. Krupp AG; *Int'l*, pg. 508
SOUTH AFRICAN MOTOR CORPORATION PROPRIETARY LIMITED (SAMCOR)—Anglo American Corporation of South Africa Limited; *Int'l*, pg. 76
SSANGYONG BUSINESS GROUP; *Int'l*, pg. 1291
SSANGYONG MOTOR COMPANY—Ssangyong Business Group; *Int'l*, pg. 1292
SSANGYONG SINGAPORE PTE., LTD.—Ssangyong Business Group; *Int'l*, pg. 1291
STEWART & STEVENSON SERVICES, INC.; *U.S. Public*, pg. 1517
STEYR NUTZFAHRZEUGE AG—MAN Aktiengesellschaft; *Int'l*, pg. 825
N.V. SUBARU BENELUX S.A.—Mitsui & Co., Ltd.; *Int'l*, pg. 879
SUBARU-ISUZU AUTOMOTIVE, INC.—Fuji Heavy Industries, Ltd.; *Int'l*, pg. 523
SUBARU-ISUZU AUTOMOTIVE, INC.—Isuzu Motors Limited; *Int'l*, pg. 692
SUPERIOR EMERGENCY VEHICLES, LTD.—Federal Signal Corporation; *U.S. Public*, pg. 617
SUZUKI MOTOR CORPORATION; *Int'l*, pg. 1322
SWEDISH MOTOR ASSEMBLIES SDN. BHD.—AB Volvo; *Int'l*, pg. 1477
TAS TVORNICA AUTOMOBILA SARAJEVO—Volkswagen AG; *Int'l*, pg. 1475
TBG SERVICES, INC.—TBG Management S.A.M.; *Int'l*, pg. 1335
TIC UNITED CORPORATION; *U.S. Private*, pg. 1063
THAI-SWEDISH ASSEMBLY CO. LTD.—AB Volvo; *Int'l*, pg. 1476
THOR AMERICA—Thor Industries, Inc.; *U.S. Public*, pg. 1602
THOR INDUSTRIES, INC.; *U.S. Public*, pg. 1602
THOR WEST—Thor Industries, Inc.; *U.S. Public*, pg. 1602
TOOL & ENGINEERING CO.—Farley, Inc.; *U.S. Private*, pg. 394
TOYODA MACHINE WORKS, LTD.—Toyota Motor Corporation; *Int'l*, pg. 1412
TOYOTA AUTO BODY CO., LTD.—Toyota Motor Corporation; *Int'l*, pg. 1412
TOYOTA (GREAT BRITAIN) LIMITED—Toyota Motor Corporation; *Int'l*, pg. 1414
TOYOTA MOTOR CORPORATION; *Int'l*, pg. 1411
TOYOTASA A.S.—Sabanci Holding A.S.; *Int'l*, pg. 1168
TOYOTASA A.S.—Toyota Motor Corporation; *Int'l*, pg. 1414
TRIM DIVISION—Eagle-Picher Industries, Inc.; *U.S. Private*, pg. 355
UMW TOYOTA MOTOR SDN. BHN.—Toyota Motor Corporation; *Int'l*, pg. 1414
UTILIMASTER CORP.; *U.S. Private*, pg. 1130
UTSUNOMIYA MFG. DIV.—Fuji Heavy Industries, Ltd.; *Int'l*, pg. 522
V.A.G. VERTRIEBSZENTRUM WESER-EMS GMBH—Volkswagen AG; *Int'l*, pg. 1474
VW KRAFTWERK GMBH—Volkswagen AG; *Int'l*, pg. 1474
VW-VERSICHERUNGSVERMITTLUNGS-GMBH—Volkswagen AG; *Int'l*, pg. 1474
VW-WOHNUNGS GESELLSCHAFT MBH—Volkswagen AG; *Int'l*, pg. 1474
VALMET CORPORATION; *Int'l*, pg. 1447
VAUXHALL MOTORS LIMITED—General Motors Corporation; *U.S. Public*, pg. 724
VICKERS PLC; *Int'l*, pg. 1466
VOLKSWAGEN AG; *Int'l*, pg. 1473
VOLKSWAGEN BRATISLAVA SPOL. S.R.O.—Volkswagen AG; *Int'l*, pg. 1475
S.A. VOLKSWAGEN BRUXELLES N.V.—Volkswagen AG; *Int'l*, pg. 1475
VOLKSWAGEN CANADA, INC.—Volkswagen AG; *Int'l*, pg. 1475
VOLKSWAGEN DE MEXICO S.A. DE C.V.—Volkswagen AG; *Int'l*, pg. 1475
VOLKSWAGEN IFA PKW. GMBH.—Volkswagen AG; *Int'l*, pg. 1476
VOLKSWAGEN OF NIGERIA LTD.—Volkswagen AG; *Int'l*, pg. 1475
VOLKSWAGEN OF SOUTH AFRICA (PTY.) LTD.—Volkswagen AG; *Int'l*, pg. 1475
VOLKSWAGEN SACHSEN GMBH—Volkswagen AG; *Int'l*, pg. 1474
AB VOLVO; *Int'l*, pg. 1476
VOLVO AUTOMOBILES FRANCE S.A.—AB Volvo; *Int'l*, pg. 1477
VOLVO CAR CORPORATION—AB Volvo; *Int'l*, pg. 1476
VOLVO EUROPA CAR NV—AB Volvo; *Int'l*, pg. 1476
VOLVO ITALIA SPA—AB Volvo; *Int'l*, pg. 1476
VOLVO JAPAN CORPORATION—AB Volvo; *Int'l*, pg. 1476
VOTEX GMBH—Volkswagen AG; *Int'l*, pg. 1474
WALTER HUNDHAUSEN GMBH & CO KG—Fried. Krupp AG; *Int'l*, pg. 508
WESER-EMS VERTRIEBSGESELLSCHAFT MBH—Volkswagen AG; *Int'l*, pg. 1474
WEST JAPAN RAILWAY COMPANY; *Int'l*, pg. 1490
WHEELED COACH INDUSTRIES, INC.—Collins Industries, Inc.; *U.S. Public*, pg. 400
WILLENHALL MANUFACTURING—Caparo Group Ltd.; *Int'l*, pg. 265

3713 — TRUCK & BUS BODIES

A A CATER TRUCK MANUFACTURING COMPANY, INC.; *U.S. Private*, pg. 1
ALLEN TELECOM, INC.; *U.S. Public*, pg. 45
AMTRAN CORPORATION—Navistar International Corporation; *U.S. Public*, pg. 1167
BLUE BIRD CORPORATION; *U.S. Private*, pg. 151
BOLER COMPANY; *U.S. Private*, pg. 155
CENTENNIAL TRANSPORTATION INDUSTRIES, L.P.—Union City Body Company, L.P.; *U.S. Private*, pg. 1119
COLLINS BUS CORP.—Collins Industries, Inc.; *U.S. Public*, pg. 400
COLLINS INDUSTRIES, INC.; *U.S. Public*, pg. 399
CONSORCIO G. GRUPO DINA, S.A. DE C.V.; *Int'l*, pg. 326
CRENLO, INC.; *U.S. Private*, pg. 288
THE CROWN DIVISIONS—TransPro, Inc.; *U.S. Public*, pg. 1631
DAB-SILKEBORG A/S; *Int'l*, pg. 350
DAF TRUCKS N.V.—Paccar Inc.; *U.S. Public*, pg. 1247
DAEWOO CORPORATION; *Int'l*, pg. 357
DAIMLER-BENZ AKTIENGESELLSCHAFT; *Int'l*, pg. 366
DORBYL LIMITED; *Int'l*, pg. 416
DUTCHMEN MANUFACTURING, INC.—Thor Industries, Inc.; *U.S. Public*, pg. 1602
EL DORADO NATIONAL—Thor Industries, Inc.; *U.S. Public*, pg. 1602
FAHRZEUGWERKE NORD GMBH—MAN Aktiengesellschaft; *Int'l*, pg. 824
FLORIG EQUIPMENT COMPANY, INC.; *U.S. Private*, pg. 415
THE FLXIBLE CORP.—General Automotive Corporation; *U.S. Private*, pg. 444
FREIGHTLINER OF CANADA, LTD.—Daimler-Benz Aktiengesellschaft; *Int'l*, pg. 368
FUJI HEAVY INDUSTRIES, LTD.; *Int'l*, pg. 522
GENERAL COACH—Thor Industries, Inc.; *U.S. Public*, pg. 1602
GRUMMAN OLSON DIVISION—Northrop Grumman Corporation; *U.S. Public*, pg. 1198
HACKNEY AND SONS, INC.—Transportation Technologies, Inc.; *U.S. Private*, pg. 1097
HEIL ENVIRONMENTAL INDUSTRIES—Dover Corporation; *U.S. Public*, pg. 520
HEIL ENVIRONMENTAL INDUSTRIES (H.E.I.L.)—Dover Corporation; *U.S. Public*, pg. 520
HEIL STEEL FABRICATING, INC.—Dover Corporation; *U.S. Public*, pg. 521
HEIL TRAILER INTERNATIONAL—Dover Corporation; *U.S. Public*, pg. 520
HEIL WEST, INC.—Dover Corporation; *U.S. Public*, pg. 521
HINO MOTORS, LTD.; *Int'l*, pg. 620
HOLIDAY RAMBLER—Monaco Coach Corporation; *U.S. Public*, pg. 1123
HYUNDAI MOTOR COMPANY; *Int'l*, pg. 641
HYUNDAI MOTOR COMPANY—Hyundai Motor Company; *Int'l*, pg. 641
IOWA MOLD TOOLING CO., INC.—Intermet Corporation; *U.S. Public*, pg. 894
ISESAKI MFG. DIV.—Fuji Heavy Industries, Ltd.; *Int'l*, pg. 522
K-T CORP.—Triumph Group, Inc.; *U.S. Public*, pg. 1640
KALDNES HEAVY LIFT TRUCKS—Norsk Vekst ASA; *Int'l*, pg. 965
KALMAR INDUSTRIES AB—Trelleborg AB; *Int'l*, pg. 1420
KALMAR LAGAB AB—Trelleborg AB; *Int'l*, pg. 1421
KIDRON INC.; *U.S. Private*, pg. 619
LE TOURNEAU, INC.—Rowan Companies, Inc.; *U.S. Public*, pg. 1410
LEYLAND DAF LTD.—Paccar Inc.; *U.S. Public*, pg. 1247
MAN AUTOMOTIVE (AUSTRALIA) PTY. LTD.—MAN Aktiengesellschaft; *Int'l*, pg. 825
MAN KAMYON VE OTOBUES TICARET LTD. SIRKETI—MAN Aktiengesellschaft; *Int'l*, pg. 825
MAN NUTZFAHRZEUGE AG—MAN Aktiengesellschaft; *Int'l*, pg. 824
MACK CANADA INC.—Renault; *Int'l*, pg. 1103
MACK TRUCKS AUSTRALIA PTY. LTD.—Renault; *Int'l*, pg. 1103
MACK TRUCKS, INC.—Renault; *Int'l*, pg. 1102
MAXON INDUSTRIES, INC.; *U.S. Private*, pg. 717
MCCLAIN INDUSTRIES, INC.; *U.S. Public*, pg. 1065
MERITOR AUTOMOTIVE, INC.; *U.S. Public*, pg. 1096
MONACO COACH CORPORATION; *U.S. Public*, pg. 1123
MORGAN TRAILER MANUFACTURING CO.; *U.S. Private*, pg. 761

MOTOR COACH INDUSTRIES INTERNATIONAL, INC.—Consorcio G. Grupo Dina, S.A. de C.V.; *Int'l*, pg. 326
MOTOR COACH INDUSTRIES LTD.—Consorcio G. Grupo Dina, S.A. de C.V.; *Int'l*, pg. 326
NETHERLANDS CAR B.V.—Mitsubishi Motors Corporation; *Int'l*, pg. 876
NISSAN DIESEL MOTOR CO., LTD.—Nissan Motor Co., Ltd.; *Int'l*, pg. 944
NISSAN MOTOR CO., LTD.; *Int'l*, pg. 943
NISSAN MOTOR CORPORATION IN U.S.A.—Nissan Motor Co., Ltd.; *Int'l*, pg. 945
NISSAN MOTOR MFG. CORP., U.S.A.—Nissan Motor Co., Ltd.; *Int'l*, pg. 945
OSHKOSH TRUCK CORPORATION; *U.S. Public*, pg. 1233
PACCAR INC.; *U.S. Public*, pg. 1246
PEUGEOT AUTOMOBILE NIGERIA LTD.—PSA Peugeot Citroen; *Int'l*, pg. 1021
RAPID RAIL SYSTEMS—Dover Corporation; *U.S. Public*, pg. 521
RAWSON-KOENIG, INC.; *U.S. Public*, pg. 1362
READING BODY WORKS, INC.; *U.S. Private*, pg. 913
RENAULT; *Int'l*, pg. 1102
RIGGS INDUSTRIES, INC.; *U.S. Private*, pg. 930
ROCKWELL HEAVY VEHICLE SUSPENSION SYSTEMS COMPANY, INC.—Meritor Automotive, Inc.; *U.S. Public*, pg. 1096
ROLLALONG LIMITED—Hanson PLC; *Int'l*, pg. 593
SCANIA ARGENTINA S.A.—Investor AB; *Int'l*, pg. 687
SCANIA DO BRASIL LTDA—Investor AB; *Int'l*, pg. 687
SCANIA NEDERLAND B.V.—Investor AB; *Int'l*, pg. 687
SIME DARBY AUSTRALIA LIMITED—Sime Darby Berhad; *Int'l*, pg. 1251
SIMON LADDER TOWERS INC.—Simon Engineering plc; *Int'l*, pg. 1252
SISTEMA ARGOS S.A.; *Int'l*, pg. 1256
SOMERSET WELDING & STEEL, INC.—Riggs Industries, Inc.; *U.S. Private*, pg. 930
SPARTAN MOTORS, INC.; *U.S. Public*, pg. 1495
SSANGYONG MOTOR COMPANY—Ssangyong Business Group; *Int'l*, pg. 1292
STAHL DIV.—Berkshire Hathaway Inc.; *U.S. Public*, pg. 218
SUMITOMO-YALE CO., LTD.—NACCO Industries, Inc.; *U.S. Public*, pg. 1150
SUPREME CORPORATION—Supreme Industries, Inc.; *U.S. Public*, pg. 1542
SUPREME CORPORATION OF TEXAS—Supreme Industries, Inc.; *U.S. Public*, pg. 1542
SUPREME INDUSTRIES, INC.; *U.S. Public*, pg. 1541
SUPREME MIDATLANTIC CORPORATION—Supreme Industries, Inc.; *U.S. Public*, pg. 1542
SUPREME MURPHY CORP.—Supreme Industries, Inc.; *U.S. Public*, pg. 1542
SUPREME TRUCK BODIES OF CALIFORNIA, INC.—Supreme Industries, Inc.; *U.S. Public*, pg. 1542
TANK SERVICE, INC.—Dover Corporation; *U.S. Public*, pg. 521
THOMAS BUILT BUSES, INC.; *U.S. Private*, pg. 1082
THOR AMERICA—Thor Industries, Inc.; *U.S. Public*, pg. 1602
THOR INDUSTRIES, INC.; *U.S. Public*, pg. 1602
THOR WEST—Thor Industries, Inc.; *U.S. Public*, pg. 1602
TIMPTE INDUSTRIES, INC.; *U.S. Private*, pg. 1088
TRANSPORTATION MANUFACTURING CORPORATION—Consorcio G. Grupo Dina, S.A. de C.V.; *Int'l*, pg. 326
TRI-GLAS—Penda Corporation; *U.S. Private*, pg. 848
UNION CITY BODY COMPANY, L.P.; *U.S. Private*, pg. 1118
UTILIMASTER CORP.; *U.S. Private*, pg. 1130
VOLVO BUS CORPORATION—AB Volvo; *Int'l*, pg. 1476
VOLVO TRUCK CORPORATION—AB Volvo; *Int'l*, pg. 1477
VOLVO TRUCK NORTH AMERICA, INC.—AB Volvo; *Int'l*, pg. 1477
VOLVO TRUCKS (GREAT BRITAIN) LTD.—AB Volvo; *Int'l*, pg. 1478
WHEELED COACH INDUSTRIES, INC.—Collins Industries, Inc.; *U.S. Public*, pg. 400
YALE EUROPE MATERIALS HANDLING CORPORATION LTD.—NACCO Industries, Inc.; *U.S. Public*, pg. 1150

3714 — MOTOR VEHICLE PARTS & ACCESSORIES

A E CLEVITE, INC.—T & N Plc; *Int'l*, pg. 1334
ABB CONTROL INC.—ABB Asea Brown Boveri (Holding) Ltd.; *Int'l*, pg. 4
AC BAKONY KFT.—General Motors Corporation; *U.S. Public*, pg. 724
AC ROCHESTER CORPORATION—General Motors Corporation; *U.S. Public*, pg. 721
AC ROCHESTER DIVISION (GENNEVILLIERS)—General Motors Corporation; *U.S. Public*, pg. 724
AC ROCHESTER DIVISION (SAO PAULO)—General Motors Corporation; *U.S. Public*, pg. 721
AC ROCHESTER LUXEMBOURG S.A.—General Motors Corporation; *U.S. Public*, pg. 723
AC ROCHESTER OVERSEAS CORPORATION—General Motors Corporation; *U.S. Public*, pg. 722
ACG COMPONENTES, S.A.—General Motors Corporation; *U.S. Public*, pg. 724
AE GOETZE-NORTH AMERICA—T & N Plc; *Int'l*, pg. 1334
AP NORTH AMERICAN AFTERMARKET DIVISION—Charterhouse Group International, Inc.; *U.S. Private*, pg. 230
AP TECHNO GLASS COMPANY—Asahi Glass Co., Ltd.; *Int'l*, pg. 84
ASC INCORPORATED; *U.S. Private*, pg. 8
AVM INC.—Arvin Industries, Inc.; *U.S. Public*, pg. 137
ABEX FRICTION PRODUCTS—Cooper Industries, Inc.; *U.S. Public*, pg. 443
THE ACCESS WORKS, INC.—Fleet Engineers, Inc.; *U.S. Private*, pg. 410
ACCO CONTROLS INC.—FKI Plc; *Int'l*, pg. 472
ACCURIDE CORP.—Phelps Dodge Corporation; *U.S. Public*, pg. 1286
AEROMOTIVE SERVICES CO.—ASC Incorporated; *U.S. Private*, pg. 8
AEROQUIP INOAC COMPANY—Aeroquip-Vickers, Inc.; *U.S. Public*, pg. 24
AFTERMARKET PRODUCTION DIV.—Dana Corporation; *U.S. Public*, pg. 479
AHLSTROM FILTRATION, INC.-CHATTANOOGA MILL—A. Ahlstrom Corporation; *Int'l*, pg. 35
AHLSTROM INC.—A. Ahlstrom Corporation; *Int'l*, pg. 35
AICHI MACHINE INDUSTRY CO., LTD.—Nissan Motor Co., Ltd.; *Int'l*, pg. 943
AICHI STEEL WORKS, LTD.; *Int'l*, pg. 35
AIRSENSORS, INC.; *U.S. Public*, pg. 33
AIRTEX PRODUCTS—UIS, Inc.; *U.S. Private*, pg. 1113
AISIN SEIKI CO. LTD.; *Int'l*, pg. 39
AISIN U.S.A. MFG. INC.—Aisin Seiki Co. Ltd.; *Int'l*, pg. 39
AKSBONO BRAKE INDUSTRY CO., LTD.—AlliedSignal Inc.; *U.S. Public*, pg. 53
ALAMBRADOS AUTOMOTRICES, S.A. DE C.V.—General Motors Corporation; *U.S. Public*, pg. 721
ALAMBRADOS Y CIRCUITOS ELECTRICOS, S.A. DE C.V.—General Motors Corporation; *U.S. Public*, pg. 721
ALFA ROMEO VEICOLI COMM. E LAV MECC. S.P.A.—Fiat Auto SpA; *Int'l*, pg. 481
ALLEN TELECOM, INC.; *U.S. Public*, pg. 45
ALLIEDSIGNAL AFTERMARKET EUROPE S.A.—AlliedSignal Inc.; *U.S. Public*, pg. 53
ALLIEDSIGNAL, AUTOMOTIVE AFTERMARKET—AlliedSignal Inc.; *U.S. Public*, pg. 51
ALLIEDSIGNAL AUTOMOTIVE ITALIA S.P.A.—AlliedSignal Inc.; *U.S. Public*, pg. 53
ALLIEDSIGNAL AUTOMOTIVE ITALIA S.P.A., TURBOCOMPRESSORI GARRETT—AlliedSignal Inc.; *U.S. Public*, pg. 53
ALLIEDSIGNAL AUTOMOTIVE LTDA.—AlliedSignal Inc.; *U.S. Public*, pg. 52
ALLIEDSIGNAL AUTOMOTIVE LTDA-CAMPINAS PLANT—AlliedSignal Inc.; *U.S. Public*, pg. 53
ALLIEDSIGNAL AUTOMOTIVE PORTUGAL LTDA.—AlliedSignal Inc.; *U.S. Public*, pg. 53
ALLIEDSIGNAL BROMSBELAG GMBH—AlliedSignal Inc.; *U.S. Public*, pg. 52
ALLIEDSIGNAL CANADA INC., AUTOMOTIVE AFTERMARKET—AlliedSignal Inc.; *U.S. Public*, pg. 52
ALLIEDSIGNAL DE MEXICANO, S.A. DE C.V.—AlliedSignal Inc.; *U.S. Public*, pg. 54
ALLIEDSIGNAL FRANCE SPA—AlliedSignal Inc.; *U.S. Public*, pg. 54
ALLIEDSIGNAL INC.; *U.S. Public*, pg. 49
ALLIEDSIGNAL INC., ALLIEDSIGNAL AUTOMOTIVE—AlliedSignal Inc.; *U.S. Public*, pg. 51
ALLIEDSIGNAL-JIDOSHA KIKI CORPORATION—AlliedSignal Inc.; *U.S. Public*, pg. 51
ALLIEDSIGNAL LIMITED TRUCK BRAKE SYSTEMS—AlliedSignal Inc.; *U.S. Public*, pg. 54
ALLIEDSIGNAL MATERIAUX DE FRICTION S.A.—AlliedSignal Inc.; *U.S. Public*, pg. 54
ALLIEDSIGNAL TRUCK BRAKE SYSTEMS—AlliedSignal Inc.; *U.S. Public*, pg. 54
ALLIEDSIGNAL TURBOCHARGING & TRUCK BRAKE SYSTEMS—AlliedSignal Inc.; *U.S. Public*, pg. 51
ALLIEDSIGNAL TURBOS AUTOMATRICES, S.A. DE C.V.—AlliedSignal Inc.; *U.S. Public*, pg. 54
ALLISON CORPORATION; *U.S. Private*, pg. 41
ALLISON TRANSMISSION—General Motors Corporation; *U.S. Public*, pg. 719
ALLOMATIC PRODUCTS COMPANY—Raytech Corporation; *U.S. Public*, pg. 1363
ALVIS AEROSPACE & TRANSMISSIONS LIMITED—Alvis plc; *Int'l*, pg. 69
ALVIS LOGISTICS LIMITED—Alvis plc; *Int'l*, pg. 69
AMBAC INTERNATIONAL CORP.; *U.S. Private*, pg. 48
AMBRAKE CORPORATION—General Motors Corporation; *U.S. Public*, pg. 721
AMCAST AUTOMOTIVE-FREMONT PLANT—Amcast Industrial Corporation; *U.S. Public*, pg. 63
AMCAST AUTOMOTIVE-GAS CITY PLANT—Amcast Industrial Corporation; *U.S. Public*, pg. 63
AMERICAN AXLE & MANUFACTURING; *U.S. Private*, pg. 51
AMERICAN STANDARD INC.; *U.S. Public*, pg. 91
AMERICAN SUNROOF COMPANY—ASC Incorporated; *U.S. Private*, pg. 8
ANCO PRODUCTS—Cooper Industries, Inc.; *U.S. Public*, pg. 442
APEX MOTOR MFG. CORP.—Nissho Iwai Corporation; *Int'l*, pg. 947
ARALMEX, S.A. DE C.V.—General Motors Corporation; *U.S. Public*, pg. 724
ARMSTRONG AMORTIGUADORES S.A.—Caparo Group Ltd.; *Int'l*, pg. 265
ARMSTRONG PATENTS CO., LTD.—Caparo Group Ltd.; *Int'l*, pg. 265
ARVIN AUTOMOTIVE OF CANADA, LTD.—Arvin Industries, Inc.; *U.S. Public*, pg. 137
ARVIN INDUSTRIES, INC.; *U.S. Public*, pg. 136
ASAMAGIKEN CO., LTD.—Honda Motor Co., Ltd.; *Int'l*, pg. 634
ASIAN TRANSMISSION CORP.—Nissho Iwai Corporation; *Int'l*, pg. 947
ASPERA S.P.A.—Fiat Auto SpA; *Int'l*, pg. 480
ATKINSON; *U.S. Public*, pg. 143
ATLAS AUTOMOTIVE, INC.—General Automotive Corporation; *U.S. Private*, pg. 444
ATLAS CRANKSHAFT CORPORATION—Cummins Engine Company, Inc.; *U.S. Public*, pg. 468
ATLAS INC.—Cummins Engine Company, Inc.; *U.S. Public*, pg. 468
ATOMA INTERNATIONAL, INC.—Magna International Inc.; *Int'l*, pg. 829
ATSUGI MOTOR PARTS CO., LTD.—Nissan Motor Co., Ltd.; *Int'l*, pg. 944
AUBURN TECHNOLOGY, INC.—Bombardier Inc.; *Int'l*, pg. 200
AURA S.R.L.—General Motors Corporation; *U.S. Public*, pg. 721
AUTOLATINA—Volkswagen AG; *Int'l*, pg. 1474
AUTOLATINA ARGENTINA S.A.—Volkswagen AG; *Int'l*, pg. 1475
AUTOMATIC TIMING & CONTROLS—Desco Corporation; *U.S. Private*, pg. 327
AUTOMOBILES CITROEN—PSA Peugeot Citroen; *Int'l*, pg. 1020
AUTOMOBILES PEUGEOT S.A.—PSA Peugeot Citroen; *Int'l*, pg. 1020
AUTOMOTIVE ACCESSORY CO., LTD.—UIS, Inc.; *U.S. Private*, pg. 1113
AUTOMOTIVE DISTRIBUTION SALES DIV.—Dana Corporation; *U.S. Public*, pg. 479
AUTOMOTIVE ELECTRONIC CONTROL SYSTEMS, INC.—Robert Bosch GmbH; *Int'l*, pg. 205
AUTOMOTIVE MOULDING COMPANY—Guardian Industries Corp.; *U.S. Private*, pg. 485
AUTOMOTIVE PRODUCTS USA INC.—BBA Group plc; *Int'l*, pg. 113
AVIS INDUSTRIAL CORPORATION; *U.S. Private*, pg. 102
AXLES INDIA LIMITED—Eaton Corporation; *U.S. Public*, pg. 558
BBA FRICTION LTD.—BBA Group plc; *Int'l*, pg. 112
BTR PLC; *Int'l*, pg. 124
BALDWIN FILTERS—CLARCOR, Inc.; *U.S. Public*, pg. 381
BANDO CHEMICAL INDUSTRIES, LTD.; *Int'l*, pg. 145
BANDO MANUFACTURING OF AMERICA, INC.—Bando Chemical Industries, Ltd.; *Int'l*, pg. 145
BASEL TRADING COMPANY LTD.; *Int'l*, pg. 169
BASSANI MANUFACTURING; *U.S. Private*, pg. 122
BAUMANN FEDERN AG; *Int'l*, pg. 171
BAUMANN GMBH—Baumann Federn AG; *Int'l*, pg. 171
BAUMANN SPRINGS USA, INC.—Baumann Federn AG; *Int'l*, pg. 171
BELLETECH CORP.—Asahi Glass Co., Ltd.; *Int'l*, pg. 84
BENDIX DEUTSCHLAND G.M.B.H.—AlliedSignal Inc.; *U.S. Public*, pg. 54
BENDIX FRICTION MATERIALS DIVISION—AlliedSignal Inc.; *U.S. Public*, pg. 51
BENDIX MINTEX PTY., LTD.—AlliedSignal Inc.; *U.S. Public*, *pg. 54*
BEPCO, INC.; *U.S. Private*, pg. 134
BERRYMAN PRODUCTS, INC.; *U.S. Private*, pg. 138
BERWIND CORPORATION; *U.S. Private*, pg. 138
BESTOP, INC.—Magna International Inc.; *Int'l*, pg. 830
BINKLEY COMPANY—The Holland Hitch Company; *U.S. Private*, pg. 534
BLACKSTONE MFG. CO., INC.—Echlin Inc.; *U.S. Public*, pg. 560
BLOOMINGTON-NORMAL SEATING COMPANY—Magna International Inc.; *Int'l*, pg. 830
BLUE BIRD CORPORATION; *U.S. Private*, pg. 151
BONDO/MAR-HYDE CORPORATION—RPM, Inc.; *U.S. Public*, pg. 1357
BORLETTI CLIMATIZZAZIONE S.R.L.—Fiat Auto SpA; *Int'l*, *pg. 482*
BOSCH BRAKING SYSTEMS-NORTH AMERICA—Robert Bosch GmbH; *Int'l*, pg. 204
ROBERT BOSCH (AUSTRALIA) PTY LTD.—Robert Bosch GmbH; *Int'l*, pg. 205
ROBERT BOSCH CORPORATION—Robert Bosch GmbH; *Int'l*, pg. 204
ROBERT BOSCH GMBH; *Int'l*, pg. 203
ROBERT BOSCH LTD.—Robert Bosch GmbH; *Int'l*, pg. 205
BOWLES FLUIDICS CORPORATION; *U.S. Public*, pg. 248
BRAKES INDIA LTD.—LucasVarity plc; *Int'l*, pg. 820
BRIGGS & STRATTON CORPORATION; *U.S. Public*, pg. 252
BRITAX AUTOZUBEHOR GMBH—Britax International plc; *Int'l*, pg. 216
BRITAX (GECO) S.A.—Britax International plc; *Int'l*, pg. 216
BRITAX INTERNATIONAL PLC; *Int'l*, pg. 216
BROCKHOUSE FORGINGS LIMITED—EIP Group plc; *Int'l*, pg. 426
BRONSON SPECIALTIES, INC.—Solvay S.A.; *Int'l*, pg. 1277
JERED BROWN BROTHERS INC.—Vickers PLC; *Int'l*, pg. 1468
THE BUDD COMPANY—Thyssen AG; *Int'l*, pg. 1388
BUNDY NORTH AMERICA—TI Group plc; *Int'l*, pg. 1340
BUNDY VENEZOLANA C.A.—TI Group plc; *Int'l*, pg. 1342
CERUS - COMPAGNIES EUROPEENNES REUNIES; *Int'l*, pg. 240
CRC INDUSTRIES, INC.—Berwind Corporation; *U.S. Private*, pg. 138
CABLEADOS S.A. DE C.V.—General Motors Corporation; *U.S. Public*, pg. 721
CABLECRAFT INC.—Tuthill Corporation; *U.S. Private*, pg. 1110
CADEL DIV.—UAP, Inc.; *Int'l*, pg. 1426
CALHAC, INC.—Honda Motor Co., Ltd.; *Int'l*, pg. 634
CALSONIC CLIMATE CONTROL, INC.—Nissan Motor Co., Ltd.; *Int'l*, pg. 944
CALSONIC CORP.—Nissan Motor Co., Ltd.; *Int'l*, pg. 944
CALSONIC MFG. CORP.—Nissan Motor Co., Ltd.; *Int'l*, pg. 944
CALSONIC YOROZU CORPORATION—Nissan Motor Co., Ltd.; *Int'l*, pg. 944
CANADIAN AUTOPARTS TOYOTA, INC.—Toyota Motor Corporation; *Int'l*, pg. 1413
CANADIAN FABRICATED PRODUCTS—Chrysler Corporation; *U.S. Public*, pg. 354
CANANDAIGUA PLASTICS DIV.—Cambridge Industries Inc.; *U.S. Private*, pg. 202
CAPARO INDUSTRIES PLC.—Caparo Group Ltd.; *Int'l*, pg. 265
CAR PRODUCT DEVELOPMENT—Ford Motor Company; *U.S. Public*, pg. 662

CARBONE-LORRAINE NORTH AMERICA—Pechiney S.A.; *Int'l*, pg. 1028
CARBONE OF AMERICA—Pechiney S.A.; *Int'l*, pg. 1028
CARBONE OF AMERICA, COMMUTATION COMPONENTS DIV.—Pechiney S.A.; *Int'l*, pg. 1028
CARELLO S.P.A.—Fiat Auto SpA; *Int'l*, pg. 482
CARLISLE ENGINEERED PRODUCTS—Carlisle Companies Incorporated; *U.S. Public*, pg. 305
CAROLINA TANK CORP.—Kuhlman Corporation; *U.S. Public*, pg. 968
CARPLASTIC S.A. DE C.V.—Ford Motor Company; *U.S. Public*, pg. 665
CASCO PRODUCTS CORPORATION—Sequa Corporation; *U.S. Public*, pg. 1458
CAVIS S.R.L.—Fiat Auto SpA; *Int'l*, pg. 482
CELSIUS AB; *Int'l*, pg. 276
CHAMP/PIK-A-NUT SERVICE LINE—Standard Motor Products Inc.; *U.S. Public*, pg. 1503
CHAMPION IGNITION PRODUCTS—Cooper Industries, Inc.; *U.S. Public*, pg. 442
CHAMPION LABORATORIES, INC.—UIS, Inc.; *U.S. Private*, pg. 1113
CHAMPION PARTS (CANADA) LTD.—Champion Parts, Inc.; *U.S. Public*, pg. 335
CHAMPION PARTS, INC.; *U.S. Public*, pg. 334
CHANDLER PRODUCTS, INC.—Elgin National Industries, Inc.; *U.S. Private*, pg. 370
CHASSIS OVERSEAS CORP.—General Motors Corporation; *U.S. Public*, pg. 723
CHICAGO RAWHIDE—AB SKF; *Int'l*, pg. 1157
CHRYSLER CORPORATION; *U.S. Public*, pg. 352
CHRYSLER DE MEXICO S.A.—Chrysler Corporation; *U.S. Public*, pg. 354
CITROEN HISPANIA S.A.—PSA Peugeot Citroen; *Int'l*, pg. 1020
CLARCOR, INC.; *U.S. Public*, pg. 381
COACHMEN INDUSTRIES, INC.; *U.S. Public*, pg. 387
CODE-ALARM, INC.; *U.S. Public*, pg. 393
COFAP-ARVIN SISTEMAS DE EXAUSTAO LTDA.—Arvin Industries, Inc.; *U.S. Public*, pg. 137
COLTEC INDUSTRIES INC.—Coltec Holdings Inc; *U.S. Public*, pg. 401
COMMERCIAL STEERING DIVISION—TRW Inc.; *U.S. Public*, pg. 1558
COMPANIA NACIONAL DE DIRECCIONES AUTOMOTRICES, S.A. DE C.V.—General Motors Corporation; *U.S. Public*, pg. 724
COMPONENT OPERATIONS—Chrysler Corporation; *U.S. Public*, pg. 353
COMPONENTES MECANICOS DE MATAMOROS S.A. DE C.V.—General Motors Corporation; *U.S. Public*, pg. 721
CONDUCTORES COMPONENTES ELECTRICOS DE JUAREZ S.A. DE C.V.—General Motors Corporation; *U.S. Public*, pg. 721
CONNECTICUT DRIVE SHAFT, INC.; *U.S. Private*, pg. 263
CONSOLIDATED METCO, INC.—Varlen Corporation; *U.S. Public*, pg. 1710
CONTICO INTERNATIONAL, INC.; *U.S. Private*, pg. 267
COOK MANUFACTURING CORPORATION; *U.S. Private*, pg. 272
COOPER INDUSTRIES, INC.; *U.S. Public*, pg. 442
CORPORACION INDUSTRIAL SANLUIS; *Int'l*, pg. 332
COSWORTH ENGINEERING INC.—Vickers PLC; *Int'l*, pg. 1468
COSWORTH ENGINEERING LTD.—Vickers PLC; *Int'l*, pg. 1466
COSWORTH ENGINEERING, WELLINGBOROUGH PLANT—Vickers PLC; *Int'l*, pg. 1467
CROW RIVER INDUSTRIES INCORPORATED—Mallinckrodt Inc.; *U.S. Public*, pg. 1040
CUMMINS ENGINE COMPANY, INC.; *U.S. Public*, pg. 467
CUMMINS ENGINE COMPANY, INC.—Cummins Engine Company, Inc.; *U.S. Public*, pg. 468
CUMMINS NATURAL GAS ENGINES, INC.—Cummins Engine Company, Inc.; *U.S. Public*, pg. 468
THE CYPRESS COMPANIES; *U.S. Private*, pg. 299
D&A TECHNOLOGY—Asahi Glass Co., Ltd.; *Int'l*, pg. 85
DAF TRUCKS N.V.—Paccar Inc.; *U.S. Public*, pg. 1247
DCM MANUFACTURING, INC.—Dreison International, Inc.; *U.S. Private*, pg. 342
DG TRIM PRODUCTS DIV.—Indian Head Industries Inc.; *U.S. Private*, pg. 560
DHB-COMPONENTES AUTOMOTIVOS, S.A.—General Motors Corporation; *U.S. Public*, pg. 724
DAEWOO AUTOMOTIVE COMPONENTS, LTD.—Daewoo Corporation; *Int'l*, pg. 357
DAEWOO PRECISION INDUSTRIES, LTD.—Daewoo Corporation; *Int'l*, pg. 357
DAMPERS IBERICA, S.A.—Cummins Engine Company, Inc.; *U.S. Public*, pg. 469
DANA CANADA INC.—Dana Corporation; *U.S. Public*, pg. 480
DANA CORPORATION; *U.S. Public*, pg. 479
DANAHER CORPORATION; *U.S. Public*, pg. 480
DANFOSS FLUID POWER—Danfoss A/S; *Int'l*, pg. 377
DAYCO PRODUCTS INC.—Mark IV Industries Inc.; *U.S. Public*, pg. 1045
DAYTON PARTS, INC.—JPE, Inc.; *U.S. Public*, pg. 919
DAYTON THERMAL PRODUCTS DIV.—Chrysler Corporation; *U.S. Public*, pg. 353
DEALERS MANUFACTURING COMPANY; *U.S. Private*, pg. 318
DECOMA INTERNATIONAL INC.—Magna International Inc.; *Int'l*, pg. 829
DEE ZEE MFG., INC.—Lancaster Colony Corporation; *U.S. Public*, pg. 976
DEFIANCE, INC.; *U.S. Public*, pg. 493
DELCO MORAINE NDH DIVISION—General Motors Corporation; *U.S. Public*, pg. 724
DELCO PRODUCTS DIVISION—General Motors Corporation; *U.S. Public*, pg. 724
DELCO REMI-COMPONENTES ELECTRONICOS, LDA.—General Motors Corporation; *U.S. Public*, pg. 721
DELMEX DE JUAREZ S.A. DE C.V.—General Motors Corporation; *U.S. Public*, pg. 721
DELNOSA, S.A. DE C.V.—General Motors Corporation; *U.S. Public*, pg. 721
DELPHI HARRISON THERMAL SYSTEMS—General Motors Corporation; *U.S. Public*, pg. 719
DELPHI SAGINAW STEERING SYSTEMS—General Motors Corporation; *U.S. Public*, pg. 719
DENGYOSHA MACHINE WORKS CORPORATION—Toshiba Corporation; *Int'l*, pg. 1402
DENSHI GIKEN CO., LTD.—Honda Motor Co., Ltd.; *Int'l*, pg. 634
DETROIT AXLE DIV.—Chrysler Corporation; *U.S. Public*, pg. 353
DETROIT ELECTRO-COATINGS CO. LLC; *U.S. Private*, pg. 328
DEUER MANUFACTURING, INC.—Selas Corporation of America; *U.S. Public*, pg. 1455
DEUTZ AG; *Int'l*, pg. 407
DEXTER AXLE DIV.—Tomkins PLC; *Int'l*, pg. 1396
DIESEL RECON—Cummins Engine Company, Inc.; *U.S. Public*, pg. 468
DIGITRON TOOL CO., INC.; *U.S. Private*, pg. 332
DISTEX IND. INC.—Echlin Inc.; *U.S. Public*, pg. 560
THE DOMETIC CORPORATION—Electrolux, AB; *Int'l*, pg. 440
DOMINION CONTROLS COMPANY—FKI Plc; *Int'l*, pg. 473
DONNELLY CORPORATION; *U.S. Public*, pg. 519
DONNELLY MIRRORS, LIMITED—Donnelly Corporation; *U.S. Public*, pg. 519
DOUGLAS & LOMASON COMPANY—Magna International Inc.; *Int'l*, pg. 830
DOUGLAS Y LOMASON DE COAHUILA S.A. DE C.V.—Magna International Inc.; *Int'l*, pg. 830
DOUGLAS Y LOMASON DE MEXICO S.A. DE C.V.—Magna International Inc.; *Int'l*, pg. 830
DRIVETRAIN SERVICE DIV.—Dana Corporation; *U.S. Public*, pg. 479
DUNLITE POWER GENERATION PTY. LTD.—Cummins Engine Company, Inc.; *U.S. Public*, pg. 469
DUNLOP AUTOMOTIVE UK—BTR plc; *Int'l*, pg. 125
DURA AUTOMOTIVE SYSTEMS, INC.; *U.S. Public*, pg. 537
DYGERT SEATING—Flexsteel Industries, Inc.; *U.S. Public*, pg. 654
ECIA-EQUIPMENTS ET COMPOSANTS POUR L'INDUSTRIE AUTOMOBILE—PSA Peugeot Citroen; *Int'l*, pg. 1021
EIS BRAKE PARTS DIV.—Standard Motor Products Inc.; *U.S. Public*, pg. 1503
EAGLE-PICHER INDUSTRIES, INC.; *U.S. Private*, pg. 355
EAGLE-PICHER WOLVERINE GMBH—Eagle-Picher Industries, Inc.; *U.S. Private*, pg. 355
EATON CORPORATION; *U.S. Public*, pg. 555
EATON CORPORATION AUTOMOTIVE CONTROLS DIVISION—Eaton Corporation; *U.S. Public*, pg. 557
EATON CORPORATION DO BRAZIL TRANSMISSION OPERATIONS—Eaton Corporation; *U.S. Public*, pg. 558
EATON CORP., FLUID POWER DIV.—Eaton Corporation; *U.S. Public*, pg. 556
EATON CORPORATION, TORT CONTROL DIVISION—Eaton Corporation; *U.S. Public*, pg. 557
EATON EJES, S.A. DE C.V.—Eaton Corporation; *U.S. Public*, pg. 558
EATON ENGINE LIFTERS S.P.A.—Eaton Corporation; *U.S. Public*, pg. 558
EATON GMBH FLUID POWER OPERATIONS—Eaton Corporation; *U.S. Public*, pg. 558
EATON I.C.S.A AXLE & FOUNDRY DIVISIONS—Eaton Corporation; *U.S. Public*, pg. 558
EATON LIMITED AXLE OPERATIONS—Eaton Corporation; *U.S. Public*, pg. 559
EATON LIMITED COMMERCIAL & MILITARY CONTROLS OPERATIONS—Eaton Corporation; *U.S. Public*, pg. 559
EATON LIMITED FORGE DIVISION—Eaton Corporation; *U.S. Public*, pg. 559
EATON LIMITED TRANSMISSION DIVISION—Eaton Corporation; *U.S. Public*, pg. 559
EATON MANUFACTURERA, S.A. DE C.V.—Eaton Corporation; *U.S. Public*, pg. 559
EATON PTY. LTD.-TRUCK COMPONENTS OPERATIONS—Eaton Corporation; *U.S. Public*, pg. 559
EATON S.A. AXLE DIV.—Eaton Corporation; *U.S. Public*, pg. 559
EATON S.A. TRANSMISSION DIV.—Eaton Corporation; *U.S. Public*, pg. 559
EATON YALE LTD. ENGINEERED FASTENERS DIV.—Eaton Corporation; *U.S. Public*, pg. 559
EATON YALE LTD. SUSPENSION DIV.—Eaton Corporation; *U.S. Public*, pg. 559
ECHLIN CANADA INC.—Echlin Inc.; *U.S. Public*, pg. 560
ECHLIN CHARGER MFG. CO. (PTY.) LTD.—Echlin Inc.; *U.S. Public*, pg. 561
ECHLIN DE VENEZUELA, C.A.—Echlin Inc.; *U.S. Public*, pg. 561
ECHLIN DO BRASIL S.A.—Echlin Inc.; *U.S. Public*, pg. 561
ECHLIN INC.; *U.S. Public*, pg. 560
ECHLIN MEXICANA S.A. DE C.V.—Echlin Inc.; *U.S. Public*, pg. 561
EDGERTON FORGE, INC.—Avis Industrial Corporation; *U.S. Private*, pg. 102
EJEVEN S.A.—Eaton Corporation; *U.S. Public*, pg. 559
ELIXIR INDUSTRIES; *U.S. Private*, pg. 371
EMITEC INC.—GKN plc; *Int'l*, pg. 535
ENGINE CONTROL SYSTEMS, LTD.—The Lubrizol Corporation; *U.S. Public*, pg. 1016
ENGINEERED SINTERED COMPONENTS COMPANY—Eaton Corporation; *U.S. Public*, pg. 558
ENGINEERING CERAMIC TECHNOLOGIES, INC.—Cummins Engine Company, Inc.; *U.S. Public*, pg. 469
EONIC INC.—Newcor, Inc.; *U.S. Public*, pg. 1176
ERICSON PACKARD ELECTRIC COMPONENTES S.A.—General Motors Corporation; *U.S. Public*, pg. 724
ESTAMPACIONES NOROESTE S.A.—Caparo Group Ltd.; *Int'l*, pg. 265
ETABLISSEMENT ROBERT BELLANGER S.A.—Tenneco Inc.; *U.S. Public*, pg. 1579
EVANS INDUSTRIES, INC.; *U.S. Private*, pg. 385
EXCEL INDUSTRIES, INC.; *U.S. Public*, pg. 598
EXOR GROUP; *Int'l*, pg. 467
FAG GROUP; *Int'l*, pg. 468
FABBRICA ACCUMULATORI YORK S.P.A.—Fiat Auto SpA; *Int'l*, pg. 482
FANUC ROBOTICS NORTH AMERICA, INC.—Fanuc Ltd.; *Int'l*, pg. 477
FAUSTO CARELLO S.P.A.—Fiat Auto SpA; *Int'l*, pg. 482
FEDCO AUTOMOTIVE COMPONENTS COMPANY, INC.—Tomkins PLC; *Int'l*, pg. 1396
FEL-PRO INCORPORATED; *U.S. Private*, pg. 399
FELSTED DIVISION—Furon Company; *U.S. Public*, pg. 689
FENNER DRIVES; *U.S. Private*, pg. 400
FEY MFG. CO., INC.—Wedgestone Financial Inc.; *U.S. Public*, pg. 1751
FIAMM TECHNOLOGIES INC.—Fiamm S.p.A.; *Int'l*, pg. 480
FIAT AUTO S.P.A.—Fiat Auto SpA; *Int'l*, pg. 481
FIAT COMPONENTI AUTOVEICOLISTI S.P.A.—Fiat Auto SpA; *Int'l*, pg. 481
FIAT ENGINEERING S.P.A.—Fiat Auto SpA; *Int'l*, pg. 481
FIAT FERROVIARIA SAVIGLIANO S.P.A.—Fiat Auto SpA; *Int'l*, pg. 481
FIBRE GLASS-EVERCOAT COMPANY—Illinois Tool Works Inc.; *U.S. Public*, pg. 866
FICHTEL & SACHS AG—Mannesmann A.G.; *Int'l*, pg. 835
FICHTEL & SACHS INDUSTRIES, INC.—Mannesmann A.G.; *Int'l*, pg. 835
FILTRAN—SPX Corporation; *U.S. Public*, pg. 1421
FILTRATION GROUP—Parker Hannifin Corporation; *U.S. Public*, pg. 1260
FLECK MANUFACTURING INC.—Noma Industries Limited; *Int'l*, pg. 955
FLEET ENGINEERS, INC.; *U.S. Private*, pg. 410
FLEETGUARD INTERNATIONAL CORPORATION—Cummins Engine Company, Inc.; *U.S. Public*, pg. 469
FLEXIBLE LAMPS LTD.—UIS, Inc.; *U.S. Private*, pg. 1113
FLEXSTEEL INDUSTRIES, INC.; *U.S. Public*, pg. 653
FLUID CONNECTORS GROUP—Parker Hannifin Corporation; *U.S. Public*, pg. 1260
FLUID PRODUCT SALES DIV.—Dana Corporation; *U.S. Public*, pg. 479
FLUIDRIVE INC.; *U.S. Private*, pg. 415
THE FLXIBLE CORP.—General Automotive Corporation; *U.S. Private*, pg. 444
FORD BODY & ASSEMBLY OPERATIONS—Ford Motor Company; *U.S. Public*, pg. 662
FORD CLIMATE CONTROL DIVISION—Ford Motor Company; *U.S. Public*, pg. 662
FORD ELECTRONICA PORTUGUESA, LTD.—Ford Motor Company; *U.S. Public*, pg. 665
FORD ELECTRONICS DIVISION—Ford Motor Company; *U.S. Public*, pg. 662
FORD ELECTRONICS MANUFACTURING CORPORATION—Ford Motor Company; *U.S. Public*, pg. 665
FORD ENGINE DIVISION—Ford Motor Company; *U.S. Public*, pg. 662
FORD ENSITE INTERNATIONAL INC. (CANADIAN)—Ford Motor Company; *U.S. Public*, pg. 665
FORD ESPANA S.A.—Ford Motor Company; *U.S. Public*, pg. 665
FORD MOTOR COMPANY; *U.S. Public*, pg. 661
FORD WERKE AG - GENK BRANCH—Ford Motor Company; *U.S. Public*, pg. 666
FRAM EUROPE LTD.—AlliedSignal Inc.; *U.S. Public*, pg. 53
FRAM FILTER S.P.A.—AlliedSignal Inc.; *U.S. Public*, pg. 53
FREIGHTLINER CORP.—Daimler-Benz Aktiengesellschaft; *Int'l*, pg. 368
FREIOS VARGA S/A—LucasVarity plc; *Int'l*, pg. 820
FREMONT MFG. DIV.—Simpson Industries, Inc.; *U.S. Public*, pg. 1475
FRENOS LUSAC S.A. DE C.V.—Echlin Inc.; *U.S. Public*, pg. 561
FRESINBRA INDUS. S.A.—American Standard Inc.; *U.S. Public*, pg. 92
FREUDENBERG NOK—Freudenberg & Company; *Int'l*, pg. 507
FRICTION INC.—Echlin Inc.; *U.S. Public*, pg. 560
FUJI HEAVY INDUSTRIES, LTD., MITAKA PLANT—Fuji Heavy Industries, Ltd.; *Int'l*, pg. 523
FUJI HEAVY INDUSTRIES, LTD., NORTH PLANT—Fuji Heavy Industries, Ltd.; *Int'l*, pg. 523
FUJI HEAVY INDUSTRIES, LTD., OIZUMI PLANT—Fuji Heavy Industries, Ltd.; *Int'l*, pg. 523
FURON COMPANY; *U.S. Public*, pg. 688
FURON LTD.—Furon Company; *U.S. Public*, pg. 689
FURON S.A./N.V.—Furon Company; *U.S. Public*, pg. 689
THE G & O MANUFACTURING CO.—TransPro, Inc.; *U.S. Public*, pg. 1631
GKN AUTOMOTIVE INC.—GKN plc; *Int'l*, pg. 535
GKN AUTOMOTIVE INTERNATIONAL GMBH—GKN plc; *Int'l*, pg. 535
GKN DRIVELINE LTD.—GKN plc; *Int'l*, pg. 534
GKN PLC; *Int'l*, pg. 534
GKN SANKEY ENGINEERING PRODUCTS—GKN plc; *Int'l*, pg. 535
GKN SHEEPBRIDGE STOKES LTD.—GKN plc; *Int'l*, pg. 535
GKN WALTERSCHEID GMBH—GKN plc; *Int'l*, pg. 535
GKN WALTERSCHEID INC.—GKN plc; *Int'l*, pg. 536
GM POWERTRAIN GROUP—General Motors Corporation; *U.S. Public*, pg. 719
GVA MATERIALVERKSTADER AB—Celsius AB; *Int'l*, pg. 277
GABRIEL RIDE CONTROL PRODUCTS DIVISION HQ—Arvin Industries, Inc.; *U.S. Public*, pg. 137
GARLOCK BEARINGS DIVISION—Coltec Holdings Inc; *U.S. Public*, pg. 402
THE GATES CORPORATION—Tomkins PLC; *Int'l*, pg. 1396

GEAR HEADQUARTERS INC.—Bearing Headquarters Co.; *U.S. Private*, pg. 127
GENERAL AUTOMOTIVE CORPORATION; *U.S. Private*, pg. 443
GENERAL MOTORS CANADA COMPONENTS DIV.—General Motors Corporation; *U.S. Public*, pg. 722
GENERAL MOTORS CANADA ENGINE DIV.—General Motors Corporation; *U.S. Public*, pg. 722
GENERAL MOTORS CANADA TRANSMISSION DIV.—General Motors Corporation; *U.S. Public*, pg. 722
GENERAL MOTORS CORPORATION; *U.S. Public*, pg. 718
GENERAL MOTORS CORPORATION-AUTOMOTIVE COMPONENTS GRP. WORLDWIDE—General Motors Corporation; *U.S. Public*, pg. 719
GENERAL MOTORS DEL ECUADOR S.A.—General Motors Corporation; *U.S. Public*, pg. 722
GENERAL MOTORS EGYPT S.A.E.—Isuzu Motors Limited; *Int'l*, pg. 692
GENERAL MOTORS EGYPT S.A.E.—General Motors Corporation; *U.S. Public*, pg. 724
GENERAL MOTORS TURKIYE LIMITED SIRKETI—General Motors Corporation; *U.S. Public*, pg. 723
GENIE MECHANIQUE ZAIROSE, S.A.R.L—General Motors Corporation; *U.S. Public*, pg. 724
GENTEX CORPORATION; *U.S. Public*, pg. 731
GLACIER VANDERVELL, INC.—T & N Plc; *Int'l*, pg. 1334
GLADWIN MACHINE PRODUCTS DIV.—Simpson Industries, Inc.; *U.S. Public*, pg. 1475
GLASSMASTER COMPANY; *U.S. Public*, pg. 745
GLASSMASTER CONTROLS COMPANY, INC.—Glassmaster Company; *U.S. Public*, pg. 746
GO/DAN INDUSTRIES—TransPro, Inc.; *U.S. Public*, pg. 1631
GRANFORD MANUFACTURING, INC.—The Goodyear Tire & Rubber Company; *U.S. Public*, pg. 753
GRAU GMBH—Echlin Inc.; *U.S. Public*, pg. 561
GRAU LIMITED—Echlin Inc.; *U.S. Public*, pg. 561
GREENVILLE MFG. DIV.—Simpson Industries, Inc.; *U.S. Public*, pg. 1475
GRUPO CONDUMEX—Grupo Carso S.A. de C.V.; *Int'l*, pg. 572
GRUPO ECHLIN AUTOMOTRIZ—Echlin Inc.; *U.S. Public*, pg. 561
GUELPH PRODUCTS—Chrysler Corporation; *U.S. Public*, pg. 354
GUNITE CORPORATION—Johnstown America Industries; *U.S. Public*, pg. 933
GUSHER PUMPS, INC.; *U.S. Private*, pg. 488
HBD INDUSTRIES, INC.; *U.S. Private*, pg. 489
HADSYS, INC.—Honda Motor Co., Ltd.; *Int'l*, pg. 634
THE HAMMERBLOW CORP.; *U.S. Private*, pg. 498
HANDY & HARMAN; *U.S. Public*, pg. 780
HARMAN AUTOMOTIVE—Harvard Industries, Inc.; *U.S. Public*, pg. 796
HARMO INDUSTRIES, LTD.—Tenneco Inc.; *U.S. Public*, pg. 1579
HARRISON RADIATOR DIVISION—General Motors Corporation; *U.S. Public*, pg. 725
HARVARD INDUSTRIES, INC.; *U.S. Public*, pg. 796
HAYES BRAKE—The Cypress Companies; *U.S. Private*, pg. 299
HAYES-DANA FILTER, FITTING & GASKET DIV.—Dana Corporation; *U.S. Public*, pg. 480
HESCO PARTS CORPORATION; *U.S. Private*, pg. 524
HILLS PRECISION COMPONENTS LTD.—PSA Peugeot Citroen; *Int'l*, pg. 1021
HILLSDALE TOOL & MFG. CO.—Eagle-Picher Industries, Inc.; *U.S. Private*, pg. 355
HOBOURN AUTOMOTIVE LIMITED—Echlin Inc.; *U.S. Public*, pg. 561
HOBOURN-EATON STEERING LTD.—Eaton Corporation; *U.S. Public*, pg. 559
HOFFCO/COMET INDUSTRIES, INC.; *U.S. Private*, pg. 532
HOLDEN'S ENGINE PRODUCTS OVERSEAS CORPORATION—General Motors Corporation; *U.S. Public*, pg. 723
HOLLANDIA WEATHERSHIELDS LIMITED—Vermeulen Hollandia BV; *Int'l*, pg. 1463
HOLLEY REPLACEMENT PARTS DIVISION—Coltec Holdings Inc; *U.S. Public*, pg. 402
HOLMAN ENTERPRISES; *U.S. Private*, pg. 535
HOLSET BRAZIL—Cummins Engine Company, Inc.; *U.S. Public*, pg. 469
HOLSET ENGINEERING CO. INC.—Cummins Engine Company, Inc.; *U.S. Public*, pg. 468
HOLSET ENGINEERING CO. LTD.—Cummins Engine Company, Inc.; *U.S. Public*, pg. 469
HOLSET KOREA, LTD.—Cummins Engine Company, Inc.; *U.S. Public*, pg. 469
HONDA ACCESS CORP.—Honda Motor Co., Ltd.; *Int'l*, pg. 634
HONDA DE MEXICO, S.A. DE C.V.—Honda Motor Co., Ltd.; *Int'l*, pg. 635
HONDA FOUNDRY CO., LTD.—Honda Motor Co., Ltd.; *Int'l*, pg. 634
HONDA LOCK MFG., CO., LTD.—Honda Motor Co., Ltd.; *Int'l*, pg. 634
HONDA MOTOR CO., LTD.; *Int'l*, pg. 634
HOOKER INDUSTRIES; *U.S. Private*, pg. 538
HUNTING PLC; *Int'l*, pg. 640
HUNTSVILLE ELECTRONICS DIV.—Chrysler Corporation; *U.S. Public*, pg. 353
HURD LOCKS—Avis Industrial Corporation; *U.S. Private*, pg. 102
HYDRA-MATIC DIVISION—General Motors Corporation; *U.S. Public*, pg. 725
HYOSUNG ASC—ASC Incorporated; *U.S. Private*, pg. 8
HYUNDAI MOTOR SERVICE CO., LTD.—Hyundai Motor Company; *Int'l*, pg. 641
HYUNDAI PRECISION & INDUSTRY CO., LTD.—Hyundai Motor Company; *Int'l*, pg. 642
IBC VEHICLES LTD.—Isuzu Motors Limited; *Int'l*, pg. 693
IG AUTOTRIM, INC.—Rieter Holdings; *Int'l*, pg. 1117
IMO INDUSTRIES INC.; *U.S. Public*, pg. 856
IPC-INTERNATIONAL PARTS CORP.—Whitman Corporation; *U.S. Public*, pg. 1766
ITT AUTOMOTIVE, INC.—ITT Industries, Inc.; *U.S. Public*, pg. 859
ITT INDUSTRIES, INC.; *U.S. Public*, pg. 859
IKEDA BUSSAN CO., LTD.—Nissan Motor Co., Ltd.; *Int'l*, pg. 944
ILMOR ENGINEERING, LTD.—General Motors Corporation; *U.S. Public*, pg. 724
INDIAN HEAD INDUSTRIES INC.; *U.S. Private*, pg. 559
INDUSTRIE MAGNETI MARELLI S.R.L.—Fiat Auto SpA; *Int'l*, pg. 482
INDUSTRIE VERNICI ITALIANE S.R.L.—Fiat Auto SpA; *Int'l*, pg. 482
INDUSTRIES MECANIQUES MAGHREBINES—Isuzu Motors Limited; *Int'l*, pg. 693
INEMEX S.A. DE C.V.—Eaton Corporation; *U.S. Public*, pg. 559
INGERSOLL MACHINE AND TOOL DIVISION—The Ivaco Group; *Int'l*, pg. 695
INGERSOLL-RAND COMPANY; *U.S. Public*, pg. 876
INLAN-INDUSTRIA DE COMPONENTES MECANICOS, S.A.—General Motors Corporation; *U.S. Public*, pg. 723
INTERNATIONAL BRAKE INDUSTRIES, INC.—MascoTech, Inc.; *U.S. Public*, pg. 1055
IRVIN MANIFATTURE INDUSTRIALI S.P.A.—Hunting Plc; *Int'l*, pg. 640
ISUZU MOTORS LIMITED; *Int'l*, pg. 692
ITAPSA, S.A. DE C.V.—Echlin Inc.; *U.S. Public*, pg. 561
IVECO FIAT S.P.A.—Fiat Auto SpA; *Int'l*, pg. 484
IVECO FRANCE S.A.; *Int'l*, pg. 696
IVECO-UNIC S.A.—Fiat Auto SpA; *Int'l*, pg. 484
IZUMI MOTOR INDUSTRIES INC.; *Int'l*, pg. 696
JACOBS BRAKE DIVISION—Danaher Corporation; *U.S. Public*, pg. 481
JACOBS VEHICLE EQUIPMENT COMPANY—Danaher Corporation; *U.S. Public*, pg. 481
JAEGER S.A.—Fiat Auto SpA; *Int'l*, pg. 482
JANESVILLE PRODUCTS—Jason Incorporated; *U.S. Public*, pg. 924
JAPAN ELECTRONIC CONTROL SYSTEMS CO., LTD.—Nissan Motor Co., Ltd.; *Int'l*, pg. 944
JATCO CORPORATION—Nissan Motor Co., Ltd.; *Int'l*, pg. 944
JOSAM COMPANY; *U.S. Private*, pg. 600
JURID N.V. (S.A.)—AlliedSignal Inc.; *U.S. Public*, pg. 53
KYB CORPORATION OF AMERICA—Kayaba Industry Co., Ltd.; *Int'l*, pg. 727
KYB INDUSTRIES INC.—Kayaba Industry Co., Ltd.; *Int'l*, pg. 727
KANSEI CORP.—Nissan Motor Co., Ltd.; *Int'l*, pg. 944
KANTO AUTO WORKS, LTD.—Toyota Motor Corporation; *Int'l*, pg. 1412
KAYABA INDUSTRY CO., LTD.; *Int'l*, pg. 727
KENCO—Williams Controls, Inc.; *U.S. Public*, pg. 1769
KINETCO—Cummins Engine Company, Inc.; *U.S. Public*, pg. 468
KIRIU MACHINE MFG. CO., LTD.—Nissan Motor Co., Ltd.; *Int'l*, pg. 944
KLECO CORP.; *U.S. Private*, pg. 625
KNORR-BREMSE AG; *Int'l*, pg. 738
KNORR-BREMSE SYSTEME FUR NUTZFAHRZEUGE GMBH—Knorr-Bremse AG; *Int'l*, pg. 738
KOITO MANUFACTURING CO.; *Int'l*, pg. 743
KRACO ENTERPRISES, INC.; *U.S. Private*, pg. 634
KRAUSS-MAFFEI VERKEHRSTECHNIK GMBH—Mannesmann A.G.; *Int'l*, pg. 836
KYOCERA CORPORATION; *Int'l*, pg. 775
KYSOR COOLING SYSTEMS—Kuhlman Corporation; *U.S. Public*, pg. 968
KYSOR/MEDALLION—Kuhlman Corporation; *U.S. Public*, pg. 968
KYSOR/WESTRAN—Kuhlman Corporation; *U.S. Public*, pg. 968
LANCASTER COLONY AUTOMOTIVE GROUP—Lancaster Colony Corporation; *U.S. Public*, pg. 977
LANCASTER COLONY CANADA, INC.—Lancaster Colony Corporation; *U.S. Public*, pg. 977
LANCASTER COLONY CORPORATION; *U.S. Public*, pg. 976
LE TOURNEAU, INC.—Rowan Companies, Inc.; *U.S. Public*, pg. 1410
LEE INDUSTRIES—Fleet Engineers, Inc.; *U.S. Private*, pg. 410
LEYLAND DAF LTD.—Paccar Inc.; *U.S. Public*, pg. 1247
LINCOLN AUTOMOTIVE—Pentair, Inc.; *U.S. Public*, pg. 1273
LINCOLN CANADA LIMITED—Pentair, Inc.; *U.S. Public*, pg. 1274
LIPE LIMITED—Echlin Inc.; *U.S. Public*, pg. 561
LITTELFUSE, INC.; *U.S. Public*, pg. 1001
LONG MANUFACTURING, LTD.; *Int'l*, pg. 815
LONG MANUFACTURING LTD.—Long Manufacturing, Ltd.; *Int'l*, pg. 815
LONG MANUFACTURING LTD.-AFTERMARKET DIVISION—Long Manufacturing, Ltd.; *Int'l*, pg. 815
LOTUS CARS LTD.—Proton; *Int'l*, pg. 1071
LUBER-FINER, INC.—UIS, Inc.; *U.S. Private*, pg. 1113
LUBRIQUIP, INC.—IDEX Corporation; *U.S. Public*, pg. 862
LUCAS AFTERMARKET OPERATIONS—LucasVarity plc; *Int'l*, pg. 819
LUCAS BODY SYSTEMS - NORTH AMERICA—LucasVarity plc; *Int'l*, pg. 820
LUCAS DIESEL SYSTEMS—LucasVarity plc; *Int'l*, pg. 820
LUCAS INDUSTRIES INC.—LucasVarity plc; *Int'l*, pg. 820
LUCAS LIGHT VEHICLE BRAKING SYSTEMS—LucasVarity plc; *Int'l*, pg. 819
LUCAS SUMITOMO BRAKES INC.—LucasVarity plc; *Int'l*, pg. 819
LUCAS SUMITOMO BRAKES INC.—Sumitomo Electric Industries, Ltd.; *Int'l*, pg. 1313
LUCASVARITY INC.—LucasVarity plc; *Int'l*, pg. 820
LUCASVARITY PLC—LucasVarity plc; *Int'l*, pg. 819
LUND ACQUISITION CORP.—Lund International Holdings, Inc.; *U.S. Public*, pg. 1020
LUND INDUSTRIES INC.—Lund International Holdings, Inc.; *U.S. Public*, pg. 1020
LUND INTERNATIONAL HOLDINGS, INC.; *U.S. Public*, pg. 1020
LYDEX A/S—Tenneco Inc.; *U.S. Public*, pg. 1580
M&W—Alamo Group, Inc.; *U.S. Public*, pg. 35
MAN B & W DIESEL AG—MAN Aktiengesellschaft; *Int'l*, pg. 824
MAN B & W JAPAN LTD.—MAN Aktiengesellschaft; *Int'l*, pg. 824
MAN B & W NORGE A/S—MAN Aktiengesellschaft; *Int'l*, pg. 824
M.A.R.C.O.—Eagle-Picher Industries, Inc.; *U.S. Private*, pg. 355
MACLEAN-FOGG CO.; *U.S. Private*, pg. 692
MAGNA INTERNATIONAL INC.; *Int'l*, pg. 829
MAGNA LOMASON CORP.—Magna International Inc.; *Int'l*, pg. 830
MANGUM MFG. CO. OF MISSOURI, INC.—Allen Telecom, Inc.; *U.S. Public*, pg. 46
MANNESMANN A.G.; *Int'l*, pg. 834
MAR-HYDE CORPORATION—RPM, Inc.; *U.S. Public*, pg. 1357
MARELLI AUTRONICA S.P.A.—Fiat Auto SpA; *Int'l*, pg. 482
MAREMONT EXHAUST SYSTEM DIVISION—Arvin Industries, Inc.; *U.S. Public*, pg. 137
MAREMONT EXHAUST SYSTEMS PRODUCT DIVISION—Arvin Industries, Inc.; *U.S. Public*, pg. 137
MARK IV AUTOMOTIVE CANADA INC.—Mark IV Industries Inc.; *U.S. Public*, pg. 1045
THE MARMON GROUP, INC.; *U.S. Private*, pg. 706
MARVIN DE MEXICO, S.A. DE C.V.—Arvin Industries, Inc.; *U.S. Public*, pg. 137
MARWIL PRODUCTS COMPANY—Arvin Industries, Inc.; *U.S. Public*, pg. 137
MASCOTECH COATINGS—MascoTech, Inc.; *U.S. Public*, pg. 1055
MASTICO INDUSTRIES, LTD.—Rieter Holdings; *Int'l*, pg. 1117
MAZDA MOTOR CORPORATION; *Int'l*, pg. 849
MCCORD PAYEN INC.—T & N Plc; *Int'l*, pg. 1334
MCCORD WINN TEXTRON COMPANY—Textron Inc.; *U.S. Public*, pg. 1590
MEANS INDUSTRIES, INC.—Varlen Corporation; *U.S. Public*, pg. 1711
MECO USA INC.—L. Possehl & Co. mbH; *Int'l*, pg. 1064
MERCEDES-BENZ AG—Daimler-Benz Aktiengesellschaft; *Int'l*, pg. 368
MERITOR AUTOMOTIVE, INC.; *U.S. Public*, pg. 1096
MERITOR WABCO VEHICLE CONTROL SYSTEMS—Meritor Automotive, Inc.; *U.S. Public*, pg. 1096
METALASTIK VIBRATION CONTROL SYSTEMS—BTR plc; *Int'l*, pg. 126
METALLGESELLSCHAFT AG; *Int'l*, pg. 860
METALSA, S.A. DE C.V.—A.O. Smith Corporation; *U.S. Public*, pg. 1477
MICO INC.; *U.S. Private*, pg. 741
MID-SOUTH MANUFACTURING CO.—UIS, Inc.; *U.S. Private*, pg. 1113
MIDAS-INTERNATIONAL CORP.—Whitman Corporation; *U.S. Public*, pg. 1766
MIDLAND BRAKE, INC.—Echlin Inc.; *U.S. Public*, pg. 561
AB MIKRO-VERKTYG—Investor AB; *Int'l*, pg. 686
MIKUNI CORPORATION; *Int'l*, pg. 867
MITCHELL CORPORATION OF OWOSSO; *U.S. Private*, pg. 753
MITCHELL COTTS REMANUFACTURING LIMITED—Ascot Holdings Plc; *Int'l*, pg. 88
MODINE MANUFACTURING COMPANY; *U.S. Public*, pg. 1121
MOLEX ELEKTRONIK GMBH—Molex Incorporated; *U.S. Public*, pg. 1122
MONROE AUTO EQUIPMENT CO.—Tenneco Inc.; *U.S. Public*, pg. 1577
MONROE AUTO PECAS S.A.—Tenneco Inc.; *U.S. Public*, pg. 1580
MOOG AUTOMOTIVE, INC.—Cooper Industries, Inc.; *U.S. Public*, pg. 443
MORTON INTERNATIONAL INC.; *U.S. Public*, pg. 1134
MOTION CONTROL INDUSTRIES, INC.—Carlisle Companies Incorporated; *U.S. Public*, pg. 305
MOTOR INDUSTRIES CO. LTD.—Robert Bosch GmbH; *Int'l*, pg. 206
MR. GASKET INC.—Echlin Inc.; *U.S. Public*, pg. 560
NABCO LTD.—Kobe Steel, Ltd.; *Int'l*, pg. 740
NDC CO., LTD.—Nissan Motor Co., Ltd.; *Int'l*, pg. 944
NHK SPRING CO., LTD.; *Int'l*, pg. 901
NSK LTD.; *Int'l*, pg. 903
NASTECH CORP.—NSK Ltd.; *Int'l*, pg. 903
NAVISTAR INTERNATIONAL—Navistar International Corporation; *U.S. Public*, pg. 1167
NEAPCO, INC.—UIS, Inc.; *U.S. Private*, pg. 1113
NEW CASTLE CHASSIS SYSTEMS DIV.—Chrysler Corporation; *U.S. Public*, pg. 353
NEW PROCESS GEAR DIV.—Chrysler Corporation; *U.S. Public*, pg. 353
NEWAY ANCHORLOK INTERNATIONAL INC.; *U.S. Private*, pg. 796
NEWCOR, INC.; *U.S. Public*, pg. 1176
NIPPONDENSO CO., LTD.—Toyota Motor Corporation; *Int'l*, pg. 1412
NISSAN CANADA INC.—Nissan Motor Co., Ltd.; *Int'l*, pg. 945
NISSAN KOHKI CO., LTD.—Nissan Motor Co., Ltd.; *Int'l*, pg. 944
NISSAN MOTOR CO., LTD.; *Int'l*, pg. 943
NISSAN MOTOR CORPORATION IN U.S.A.—Nissan Motor Co., Ltd.; *Int'l*, pg. 945
NISSAN MOTOR MFG. CORP., U.S.A.—Nissan Motor Co., Ltd.; *Int'l*, pg. 945
NOBLE INTERNATIONAL LTD.; *U.S. Public*, pg. 1187

NORMALAIR-GARRETT MFG. AUSTRALIA—AlliedSignal Inc.; *U.S. Public*, pg. 53
NORSK HYDRO A.S; *Int'l*, pg. 959
NORTH AMERICAN PASSENGER CAR PLATFORMS—General Motors Corporation; *U.S. Public*, pg. 719
NORTHERN TUBE—Charterhouse Group International, Inc.; *U.S. Private*, pg. 230
NUCOR BEARING PRODUCTS, INC.—Nucor Corporation; *U.S. Public*, pg. 1206
NUCOR CORPORATION; *U.S. Public*, pg. 1205
OEA, INC.; *U.S. Public*, pg. 1206
OFFICINE A. MASERATI S.P.A.—Fiat Auto SpA; *Int'l*, pg. 482
OHIO STAR FORGE CO.—Daido Steel Co., Ltd.; *Int'l*, pg. 364
OILDYNE ASG GROUP—Commercial Intertech Corp.; *U.S. Public*, pg. 411
OLSONITE CORPORATION; *U.S. Private*, pg. 815
OMNIBUS BB TRANSPORTES, S.A.—General Motors Corporation; *U.S. Public*, pg. 723
OSHKOSH TRUCK CORPORATION; *U.S. Public*, pg. 1233
OVERHEAD DOOR CORPORATION; *U.S. Private*, pg. 822
OXFORD AUTOMOTIVE, INC.; *U.S. Private*, pg. 825
PSA PEUGEOT CITROEN; *Int'l*, pg. 1020
PACCAR INC.; *U.S. Public*, pg. 1246
PACKARD CTA PTY. LTD.—General Motors Corporation; *U.S. Public*, pg. 723
PACKARD ELEKTRIK SISTEMLERI LIMITED SIRKETI—General Motors Corporation; *U.S. Public*, pg. 723
PARISH DIV.—Dana Corporation; *U.S. Public*, pg. 479
PARKER HANNIFIN (AUSTRALIA) (PTY.) LTD.—Parker Hannifin Corporation; *U.S. Public*, pg. 1263
PARKER HANNIFIN INDUSTRIA E COMERCIO LTDA.—Parker Hannifin Corporation; *U.S. Public*, pg. 1260
PEREGRINE INCORPORATED; *U.S. Private*, pg. 852
PERFECT CIRCLE PRODUCTS DIV.—Dana Corporation; *U.S. Public*, pg. 479
PERFECT EQUIPMENT CORP.—Berwind Corporation; *U.S. Private*, pg. 138
PERFECTION AUTOMOTIVE PRODUCTS CORPORATION—Tenneco Inc.; *U.S. Public*, pg. 1577
PERSTORP COMPONENTS—Perstorp AB; *Int'l*, pg. 1040
PERSTORP S.A.-DIV. COMPONENTS FRANCE—Perstorp AB; *Int'l*, pg. 1040
THE PIERCE CO., INC.—Avis Industrial Corporation; *U.S. Private*, pg. 102
PIRELLI ARMSTRONG EXTRUDED PRODUCTS DIVISION—Pirelli S.p.A.; *Int'l*, pg. 1058
PLEWS/EDELMANN—Tomkins PLC; *Int'l*, pg. 1396
PONTIAC-GMC TRUCK DIVISION—General Motors Corporation; *U.S. Public*, pg. 720
PORSCHE AG; *Int'l*, pg. 1063
P.L. PORTER CO.; *U.S. Private*, pg. 876
POWERTRAIN DIV.—Renault; *Int'l*, pg. 1103
PRATTVILLE MFG., INC.—Echlin Inc.; *U.S. Public*, pg. 561
PRECISION FORMING FACILITY—GKN plc; *Int'l*, pg. 535
PRECISION UNIVERSAL JOINT CO.—Cooper Industries, Inc.; *U.S. Public*, pg. 443
PRIOR REMANUFACTURERS, INC.—The Cypress Companies; *U.S. Private*, pg. 300
PRODOTTI BAUMANN SPA—Baumann Federn AG; *Int'l*, pg. 171
PROMOTORA DE PARTES ELECTRICAS AUTOMOTRICES, S.A. DE C.V.—General Motors Corporation; *U.S. Public*, pg. 724
PYLON MANUFACTURING CORP.—MascoTech, Inc.; *U.S. Public*, pg. 1055
PYROINDUSTRIE S.A.—OEA, Inc.; *U.S. Public*, pg. 1207
QUADRASTAT CORP.—Adams Rite Manufacturing Co.; *U.S. Private*, pg. 17
QUINTON HAZELL PLC, COLWYN BAY—Echlin Inc.; *U.S. Public*, pg. 561
QUINTON HAZELL PLC, DUBLIN—Echlin Inc.; *U.S. Public*, pg. 561
QUINTON HAZELL PLC, LILLE—Echlin Inc.; *U.S. Public*, pg. 561
QUINTON HAZELL PLC, MILAN—Echlin Inc.; *U.S. Public*, pg. 561
QUINTON HAZELL PLC, NUNEATON—Echlin Inc.; *U.S. Public*, pg. 561
QUINTON HAZELL PLC, REDDITCH—Echlin Inc.; *U.S. Public*, pg. 561
R.A. SALES, INC.—Republic Automotive Parts, Inc.; *U.S. Public*, pg. 1377
RENK AKTIENGESELLSCHAFT—MAN Aktiengesellschaft; *Int'l*, pg. 825
ROR ROCKWELL B.V.—Rockwell International Corporation; *U.S. Public*, pg. 1399
ROR ROCKWELL ESPANA S.A.—Rockwell International Corporation; *U.S. Public*, pg. 1399
ROR ROCKWELL (IRELAND) LIMITED—Rockwell International Corporation; *U.S. Public*, pg. 1399
ROR ROCKWELL ITALIA S.R.L.—Rockwell International Corporation; *U.S. Public*, pg. 1399
ROR ROCKWELL LIMITED—Rockwell International Corporation; *U.S. Public*, pg. 1399
ROR ROCKWELL S.A.—Rockwell International Corporation; *U.S. Public*, pg. 1399
THE RTZ CORPORATION PLC—Rio Tinto PLC; *Int'l*, pg. 1118
RACOR DIVISION—Parker Hannifin Corporation; *U.S. Public*, pg. 1260
RANCO AUTOMOTIVE DIV.—Siebe plc; *Int'l*, pg. 1243
RANCO INC.—Siebe plc; *Int'l*, pg. 1243
RANDALL TEXTRON—Textron Inc.; *U.S. Public*, pg. 1590
RAYBESTOS/BRAKE PARTS INC.—Echlin Inc.; *U.S. Public*, pg. 560
RAYBESTOS INDUSTRIE-PRODUKTE GMBH—Raytech Corporation; *U.S. Public*, pg. 1364
RAYBESTOS PRODUCTS CO.—Raytech Corporation; *U.S. Public*, pg. 1363
RAYTECH CORPORATION; *U.S. Public*, pg. 1363
READING BODY WORKS, INC.; *U.S. Private*, pg. 913
RECARO NORTH AMERICA, INC.; *U.S. Private*, pg. 914
REDCO CORPORATION; *U.S. Private*, pg. 915
REDPATH INDUSTRIES LTD.—Tate & Lyle PLC; *Int'l*, pg. 1357
REINSHAGEN ITALIA SRL.—General Motors Corporation; *U.S. Public*, pg. 723
REINSHAGEN U.K.—General Motors Corporation; *U.S. Public*, pg. 723
RENAULT; *Int'l*, pg. 1102
REPUBLIC AUTOMOTIVE PARTS SALES, INC.—Republic Automotive Parts, Inc.; *U.S. Public*, pg. 1378
REYCO INDUSTRIES, INC.; *U.S. Private*, pg. 926
RHYTHM MOTOR PARTS MFG. CO., LTD.—Nissan Motor Co., Ltd.; *Int'l*, pg. 944
RIETER AUTOMOTIVE NORTH AMERICA INC—Rieter Holdings; *Int'l*, pg. 1117
RIKER PRODUCTS, INC.—The Cypress Companies; *U.S. Private*, pg. 300
RING SCREW WORKS; *U.S. Private*, pg. 931
RIO BRAVO ELECTRICOS, S.A. DE C.V.—General Motors Corporation; *U.S. Public*, pg. 724
ROCKWELL ARGENTINA S.A.—Rockwell International Corporation; *U.S. Public*, pg. 1399
ROCKWELL AUTOMOTIVE (U.K.) LTD.—Rockwell International Corporation; *U.S. Public*, pg. 1400
ROCKWELL CLUTCH COMPANY—Meritor Automotive, Inc.; *U.S. Public*, pg. 1096
ROCKWELL CVC S.P.A.—Rockwell International Corporation; *U.S. Public*, pg. 1400
ROCKWELL DO BRASIL LTDA.- FUMAGALLI WHEELS—Rockwell International Corporation; *U.S. Public*, pg. 1400
ROCKWELL DO BRAZIL LTDA.- BRASEIXOS DIVISION—Rockwell International Corporation; *U.S. Public*, pg. 1400
ROCKWELL HEAVY VEHICLE SUSPENSION SYSTEMS COMPANY, INC.—Meritor Automotive, Inc.; *U.S. Public*, pg. 1096
ROCKWELL INTERNATIONAL CORPORATION; *U.S. Public*, pg. 1397
ROCKWELL INTERNATIONAL GMBH—Rockwell International Corporation; *U.S. Public*, pg. 1401
ROCKWELL LVS - LIBEREC A.S.—Rockwell International Corporation; *U.S. Public*, pg. 1401
ROCKWELL MEXICANA, S.A. DE C.V.—Rockwell International Corporation; *U.S. Public*, pg. 1402
ROCKWELL STANDARD OF AUSTRALIA LTD.—Rockwell International Corporation; *U.S. Public*, pg. 1402
ROCKWELL SVI S.A.—Rockwell International Corporation; *U.S. Public*, pg. 1402
ROLERO OMEGA OPERATIONS—Cooper Industries, Inc.; *U.S. Public*, pg. 443
ROMEO RIM INC.—The Cypress Companies; *U.S. Private*, pg. 300
ROSS & CATHERALL CERAMICS LIMITED—Vickers PLC; *Int'l*, pg. 1467
RUBBER MOLDING DIVISION—Eagle-Picher Industries, Inc.; *U.S. Private*, pg. 355
RYOBI LTD.; *Int'l*, pg. 1151
SAGEM ALLUMAGE—Societe d'Applications Generales d'Electricite et de Mechanique; *Int'l*, pg. 1273
SKF MULTITEC—AB SKF; *Int'l*, pg. 1159
SPICA S.P.A.—Fiat Auto SpA; *Int'l*, pg. 481
SPX CORPORATION; *U.S. Public*, pg. 1420
STP CORPORATION—First Brands Corporation; *U.S. Public*, pg. 627
SACHS AUTOMOTIVE CORP.-NORTH AMERICAN OEM OPERATIONS—Mannesmann A.G.; *Int'l*, pg. 835
SACHS BOGE OF AMERICA—Mannesmann A.G.; *Int'l*, pg. 835
SAGAR-RICHARDS LIMITED—Ascot Holdings Plc; *Int'l*, pg. 88
SANDEN CORPORATION; *Int'l*, pg. 1184
SANDEN INTERNATIONAL (U.S.A.), INC.—Sanden Corporation; *Int'l*, pg. 1184
SAUER-SUNDSTRAND—Sauer Sundstrand Gmbh & Co.; *Int'l*, pg. 1198
SAUER-SUNDSTRAND COMPANY—Sauer Sundstrand Gmbh & Co.; *Int'l*, pg. 1198
SCHLEGEL WEST UNITY INC.—BTR plc; *Int'l*, pg. 128
SCHRADER BELLOWS DIVISION—Parker Hannifin Corporation; *U.S. Public*, pg. 1261
SCHWITZER, INC.—Kuhlman Corporation; *U.S. Public*, pg. 968
SEIBERT-OXIDERMO, INC.—Detrex Corporation; *U.S. Public*, pg. 502
THE SHANE GROUP INC.; *U.S. Private*, pg. 989
SHELLER-CLIFFORD LTD.—United Technologies Corporation; *U.S. Public*, pg. 1691
SHELTER PRODUCTS GROUP—Tomkins PLC; *Int'l*, pg. 1396
THE SIAM KUBOTA INDUSTRY CO., LTD.—Kubota Corp.; *Int'l*, pg. 763
THE SIAM KUBOTA INDUSTRY CO., LTD.—The Siam Cement Public Company Limited; *Int'l*, pg. 1239
SIAM LEMMERZ CO., LTD.—The Siam Cement Public Company Limited; *Int'l*, pg. 1238
SIAM TYRE CO., LTD.—The Siam Cement Public Company Limited; *Int'l*, pg. 1238
SIME DARBY AUSTRALIA LIMITED—Sime Darby Berhad; *Int'l*, pg. 1251
A.G. SIMPSON CO. LIMITED; *Int'l*, pg. 1252
SIMPSON INDUSTRIES, INC.; *U.S. Public*, pg. 1474
SIMPSON MFG. DIV.—Simpson Industries, Inc.; *U.S. Public*, pg. 1475
R.J. SIMPSON MFG. CO. (CANADA) LTD.—Simpson Industries, Inc.; *U.S. Public*, pg. 1475
SINTERING TECHNOLOGIES, INC.—Cummins Engine Company, Inc.; *U.S. Public*, pg. 468
SISTEMAS ELECTRICOS Y CONMUTADORES, S.A. DE C.V.—General Motors Corporation; *U.S. Public*, pg. 724
A.O. SMITH CORPORATION; *U.S. Public*, pg. 1476
SNUGL MFG. CO. INC.—Berwind Corporation; *U.S. Private*, *pg. 138*
SNYDER TANK CORP.; *U.S. Private*, pg. 1011
SOCIETE DE TRANSFORMATION DES MATIERES PLASTIQUES-S.T.M.P. S.A.—Solvay S.A.; *Int'l*, pg. 1279
SOCIETE FRANCO-SUEDOISE DE MOTEURS -PRV—AB Volvo; *Int'l*, pg. 1476
SOLEX S.A.—Fiat Auto SpA; *Int'l*, pg. 482
SOLVAY AUTOMOTIVE INC.—Solvay S.A.; *Int'l*, pg. 1277
SOMFY SYSTEMS INC.—Damart S.A.; *Int'l*, pg. 376
SOPLACHIM S.A.—Solvay S.A.; *Int'l*, pg. 1280
SOUTH AFRICAN MOTOR CORPORATION PROPRIETARY LIMITED (SAMCOR)—Anglo American Corporation of South Africa Limited; *Int'l*, pg. 76
SPARTON ENGINEERED PRODUCTS, INC.-FLORA GROUP—Sparton Corporation; *U.S. Public*, pg. 1496
SPEEDLINE S.P.A.—Amcast Industrial Corporation; *U.S. Public*, pg. 63
SPEEDY MUFFLER KING, INC.—Tenneco Inc.; *U.S. Public*, *pg. 1578*
SPHINX MANUFACTURING COMPANY, LTD.—AlliedSignal Inc.; *U.S. Public*, pg. 53
SPICER AXLE DIV.—Dana Corporation; *U.S. Public*, pg. 479
SPICER CLARK-HURTH—Dana Corporation; *U.S. Public*, pg. 479
SPICER DRIVESHAFT DIV.—Dana Corporation; *U.S. Public*, pg. 479
SPICER OFF-HIGHWAY AXLE DIV.—Dana Corporation; *U.S. Public*, pg. 479
SPICER TRAILER PRODUCTS DIV.—Dana Corporation; *U.S. Public*, pg. 479
SPRAGUE DEVICES, INC.—Echlin Inc.; *U.S. Public*, pg. 561
SPRECHER & SCHUH GMBH—Rockwell International Corporation; *U.S. Public*, pg. 1402
SSANGYONG PRECISION INDUSTRY CO., LTD.—Ssangyong Business Group; *Int'l*, pg. 1292
STANCO METAL PRODUCTS, INC.; *U.S. Private*, pg. 1030
STANDARD MOTOR PRODUCTS INC.; *U.S. Public*, pg. 1503
THE STANDARD PRODUCTS COMPANY; *U.S. Public*, pg. 1504
STANDARD-THOMSON CORPORATION—Tomkins PLC; *Int'l*, pg. 1396
STANRIC, INC.—Standard Motor Products Inc.; *U.S. Public*, *pg. 1503*
STANT CORPORATION—Tomkins PLC; *Int'l*, pg. 1396
AB STARLA-WERKEN—Tenneco Inc.; *U.S. Public*, pg. 1580
STEERING AND SUSPENSION DIVISION—Cooper Industries, Inc.; *U.S. Public*, pg. 443
STEERING WHEEL SYSTEMS NORTH AMERICA—TRW Inc.; *U.S. Public*, pg. 1558
STEMCO TRUCK PRODUCTS DIVISION—Coltec Holdings Inc; *U.S. Public*, pg. 402
STERLING, INC.; *U.S. Private*, pg. 1041
STEWART-WARNER ELECTRONICS COMPANY—Herley Industries, Inc.; *U.S. Public*, pg. 811
STEWART WARNER INSTRUMENTS CORPORATION; *U.S. Private*, pg. 1042
STEWART WARNER INSTRUMENTS CORPORATION—Stewart Warner Instruments Corporation; *U.S. Private*, pg. 1043
THE STOLLE CORPORATION—Aluminum Company of America; *U.S. Public*, pg. 61
STONERIDGE, INC.; *U.S. Private*, pg. 1044
STRATTEC SECURITIES CORPORATION; *U.S. Public*, pg. 1523
SUPERIOR INDUSTRIES-FAYETTEVILLE—Superior Industries International, Inc.; *U.S. Public*, pg. 1539
SUPERIOR INDUSTRIES INTERNATIONAL, INC.; *U.S. Public*, pg. 1539
SUPERIOR INDUSTRIES-MEMPHIS—Superior Industries International, Inc.; *U.S. Public*, pg. 1539
SUPERIOR INDUSTRIES-ROGERS—Superior Industries International, Inc.; *U.S. Public*, pg. 1539
SUPERIOR LINKAGE DIVISION—Tuthill Corporation; *U.S. Private*, pg. 1111
SUPERTRAPP INDUSTRIES—Dreison International, Inc.; *U.S. Private*, pg. 342
SUSPA COMPART AG; *Int'l*, pg. 1322
SUZUKI MOTOR CORPORATION; *Int'l*, pg. 1322
SUZUKI PARTS MANUFACTURING CO., LTD.—Suzuki Motor Corporation; *Int'l*, pg. 1323
SUZUKI SPECIAL PRODUCTS MANUFACTURING CO., LTD.—Suzuki Motor Corporation; *Int'l*, pg. 1323
SYNFLEX DIVISION—Furon Company; *U.S. Public*, pg. 689
SYSTEMES Y CONNEXIONES INTEGRADES S.A. DE C.V.—Noma Industries Limited; *Int'l*, pg. 955
SYSTEMS & ELECTRONICS INC.—ESCO Electronics Corporation; *U.S. Public*, pg. 547
SYTECH—Cummins Engine Company, Inc.; *U.S. Public*, pg. 468
T & N INDUSTRIES, INC.—T & N Plc; *Int'l*, pg. 1334
TBG SERVICES, INC.—TBG Management S.A.M.; *Int'l*, pg. 1335
TRW INC.; *U.S. Public*, pg. 1558
TRW STEERING, SUSPENSION & ENGINE GROUP—TRW Inc.; *U.S. Public*, pg. 1558
TRW VEHICLE SAFETY SYSTEMS INC.—TRW Inc.; *U.S. Public*, pg. 1559
TAKATTA INC.—Highland Industries Inc.; *U.S. Private*, pg. 528
TEKONSHA ENGINEERING CO.—Echlin Inc.; *U.S. Public*, pg. 560
TELEFLEX AUTOMOTIVE—Teleflex Incorporated; *U.S. Public*, pg. 1569
TELEFLEX INCORPORATED; *U.S. Public*, pg. 1569
TENNECO AUTOMOTIVE—Tenneco Inc.; *U.S. Public*, pg. 1577
TENNECO AUTOMOTIVE EUROPE, INC.—Tenneco Inc.; *U.S. Public*, pg. 1580
TENNECO INC.; *U.S. Public*, pg. 1577
TENNECO-WALKER (U.K.) LIMITED—Tenneco Inc.; *U.S. Public*, pg. 1580
TESMA INTERNATIONAL INC.—Magna International Inc.; *Int'l*, pg. 830

TEUTONIA GMBH & CO. KG—Britax International plc; *Int'l, pg. 217*
TEXAS INSTRUMENTS INCORPORATED; *U.S. Public*, pg. 1585
TEXAS INSTRUMENTS MATERIALS & CONTROLS GROUP—Texas Instruments Incorporated; *U.S. Public*, pg. 1586
TEXTRON AUTOMATIVE TRIM OPERATIONS—Textron Inc.; *U.S. Public*, pg. 1590
TEXTRON AUTOMOTIVE TRIM OPERATIONS—Textron Inc.; *U.S. Public*, pg. 1590
TEXTRON INC.; *U.S. Public*, pg. 1588
THERMAL COMPONENTS, INC.—Insilco Corporation; *U.S. Public*, pg. 881
3M; *U.S. Public*, pg. 1604
TIANJIN WIX FILTER CORP.—Dana Corporation; *U.S. Public*, pg. 480
TITAN INTERNATIONAL, INC.; *U.S. Public*, pg. 1618
TODCO—Overhead Door Corporation; *U.S. Private*, pg. 823
TOKHEIM CORPORATION; *U.S. Public*, pg. 1620
TOKICO LTD.; *Int'l*, pg. 1391
TOKICO (USA) INC.—Tokico Ltd.; *Int'l*, pg. 1391
TOKYO SOKUHAN CO., LTD.—Nissan Motor Co., Ltd.; *Int'l*, pg. 944
TOLEDO PRECISION MACHINING DIV.—Chrysler Corporation; *U.S. Public*, pg. 353
TOMKINS INDUSTRIES INC.—Tomkins PLC; *Int'l*, pg. 1397
THE TORRINGTON CO.—Ingersoll-Rand Company; *U.S. Public*, pg. 877
J.J. TOUREK CO.—Tuthill Corporation; *U.S. Private*, pg. 1111
TOYODA BOSHOFU CORPORATION—Toyota Motor Corporation; *Int'l*, pg. 1412
TOYOTA AUTO BODY CO., LTD.—Toyota Motor Corporation; *Int'l*, pg. 1412
TOYOTA AUTO BODY THAILAND CO., LTD.—Toyota Motor Corporation; *Int'l*, pg. 1414
TRAYER PRODUCTS, INC.; *U.S. Private*, pg. 1098
TRICO COMPONENTES, S.A.—Tomkins PLC; *Int'l*, pg. 1397
TRICO LTD.—Tomkins PLC; *Int'l*, pg. 1397
TRICO PRODUCTS CORPORATION—Tomkins PLC; *Int'l*, pg. 1397
TRICO PTY. LTD.—Tomkins PLC; *Int'l*, pg. 1397
TRICO TECHNOLOGIES CORPORATION—Tomkins PLC; *Int'l*, pg. 1397
TRIDON INC.—AT&T Corporation; *U.S. Public*, pg. 11
TRIM DIVISION—Eagle-Picher Industries, Inc.; *U.S. Private, pg. 355*
TROY OPERATIONS—Simpson Industries, Inc.; *U.S. Public, pg. 1475*
TRU-TURN CORPORATION—Hayes Wheels International, Inc.; *U.S. Private*, pg. 513
TRUCAST LTD.—Vickers PLC; *Int'l*, pg. 1467
TSUCHIYA MFG. CO., LTD.—Nissan Motor Co., Ltd.; *Int'l*, pg. 944
TURBOMOTORI INTERNAZIONALE S.P.A.—Fiat Auto SpA; *Int'l*, pg. 481
UAP, INC.; *Int'l*, pg. 1426
UIS, INC.; *U.S. Private*, pg. 1113
UTA HOLLAND PLANT—United Technologies Corporation; *U.S. Public*, pg. 1691
UNICABLES, S.A.—General Motors Corporation; *U.S. Public*, pg. 724
UNITED BRAKE SYSTEMS, INC.—Echlin Inc.; *U.S. Public*, pg. 561
U.S. AXLE, INC.; *U.S. Private*, pg. 1124
UNITED TECHNOLOGIES AUTOMOTIVE—United Technologies Corporation; *U.S. Public*, pg. 1691
UNITED TECHNOLOGIES CORPORATION; *U.S. Public*, pg. 1689
UNITED TECHNOLOGIES DIESEL SYSTEMS—United Technologies Corporation; *U.S. Public*, pg. 1690
URBA S.A. INDUSTRIA E COMERCIO DE AUTO PECAS—Echlin Inc.; *U.S. Public*, pg. 561
VALEO/ACUSTAR THERMAL SYSTEMS—Chrysler Corporation; *U.S. Public*, pg. 354
VALEO-CLUTCHES—CERUS - Compagnies Europeennes Reunies; *Int'l*, pg. 240
VALEO-ELECTRONICS—CERUS - Compagnies Europeennes Reunies; *Int'l*, pg. 240
VALEO-FRICTION MATERIALS—CERUS - Compagnies Europeennes Reunies; *Int'l*, pg. 240
VALEO RESEARCH SOOAL—CERUS - Compagnies Europeennes Reunies; *Int'l*, pg. 240
VANGUARDA COMPONENTES AUTOMOTIVOS, S.A.—General Motors Corporation; *U.S. Public*, pg. 722
VARITY KELSEY HAYES—LucasVarity plc; *Int'l*, pg. 820
VARLEN CORPORATION; *U.S. Public*, pg. 1710
VEGLIA BORLETTI S.R.L.—Fiat Auto SpA; *Int'l*, pg. 482
VENTURIAN CORP.; *U.S. Public*, pg. 1716
VERIN S.A.—Suspa Compart AG; *Int'l*, pg. 1322
VERMEULEN HOLLANDIA BV; *Int'l*, pg. 1463
VERNAY LABORATORIES, INC.; *U.S. Private*, pg. 1137
VESTIDURAS FRONTERIZAS, S.A. DE C.V.—General Motors Corporation; *U.S. Public*, pg. 724
VIBRATECH, INC.—IDEX Corporation; *U.S. Public*, pg. 862
VICKERS PLC; *Int'l*, pg. 1466
VICKERS PRECISION MACHINING—Vickers PLC; *Int'l*, pg. 1468
VICTOR PRODUCTS—Dana Corporation; *U.S. Public*, pg. 480
VOLKSWAGEN AG; *Int'l*, pg. 1473
VOLKSWAGEN IFA PKW. GMBH.—Volkswagen AG; *Int'l*, pg. 1476
VOLVO CAR COMPONENTS CORPORATION—AB Volvo; *Int'l*, pg. 1476
VOLVO PARTS CORP.—AB Volvo; *Int'l*, pg. 1476
VOLVO TRUCK COMPONENTS CORP.—AB Volvo; *Int'l*, pg. 1476
WAPSA AUTO-PECAS LIMITADA—Robert Bosch GmbH; *Int'l*, pg. 206
WABCO AUTOMOTIVE PODUCTS GROUP—American Standard Inc.; *U.S. Public*, pg. 92
WABCO FREINAGE DE VEHICULES S.A.—American Standard Inc.; *U.S. Public*, pg. 92
WABCO WESTINGHOUSE—American Standard Inc.; *U.S. Public*, pg. 92
WABCO WESTINGHOUSE AB—American Standard Inc.; *U.S. Public*, pg. 92
WABCO WESTINGHOUSE B.V.—American Standard Inc.; *U.S. Public*, pg. 92
WABCO WESTINGHOUSE EQUIPEMENTS FERROVIAIRES S.A.—American Standard Inc.; *U.S. Public*, pg. 92
WABCO WESTINGHOUSE FAHRZEUGBREMSEN G.M.B.H.—American Standard Inc.; *U.S. Public*, pg. 92
WABCO WESTINGHOUSE FRENI VEICOLI INDUSTRIALI S.P.A.—American Standard Inc.; *U.S. Public*, pg. 92
WABCO WESTINGHOUSE G.M.B.H.—American Standard Inc.; *U.S. Public*, pg. 92
WAGNER BRAKE SUBSIDIARY—Cooper Industries, Inc.; *U.S. Public*, pg. 443
WAGNER LIGHTING PRODUCTS—Cooper Industries, Inc.; *U.S. Public*, pg. 442
WALBRO AUTOMOTIVE CORP.—Walbro Corporation; *U.S. Public*, pg. 1733
WALBRO CORPORATION; *U.S. Public*, pg. 1733
WALKER DEUTSCHLAND GMBH—Tenneco Inc.; *U.S. Public*, pg. 1580
WALKER MANUFACTURING CO.—Tenneco Inc.; *U.S. Public*, pg. 1578
WARN INDUSTRIES, INC.; *U.S. Private*, pg. 1150
WEBER DO BRASIL INDUSTRIA E COMERCIO LTDA.—Fiat Auto SpA; *Int'l*, pg. 482
WEBER S.P.A.—Fiat Auto SpA; *Int'l*, pg. 483
WEBER S.R.L.—Fiat Auto SpA; *Int'l*, pg. 482
WEDGESTONE AUTOMOTIVE CORP.—Wedgestone Financial Inc.; *U.S. Public*, pg. 1751
WEDGESTONE FINANCIAL INC.; *U.S. Public*, pg. 1751
WELLINGTON MANUFACTURING, INC.—Rieter Holdings; *Int'l*, pg. 1117
WELLS MANUFACTURERA DE MEXICO S.A. DE C.V.—UIS, Inc.; *U.S. Private*, pg. 1113
WELLS MANUFACTURING CANADA LTD.—UIS, Inc.; *U.S. Private*, pg. 1113
WELLS MFG. CORP.—UIS, Inc.; *U.S. Private*, pg. 1113
WESTCON—Desco Corporation; *U.S. Private*, pg. 327
WEYBURN-BARTEL GMBH—T & N Plc; *Int'l*, pg. 1334
WEYBURN BARTEL, INC.—T & N Plc; *Int'l*, pg. 1334
WEYBURN-BARTEL LTD.—T & N Plc; *Int'l*, pg. 1334
WHITMAN CORPORATION; *U.S. Public*, pg. 1766
WILLENHALL MANUFACTURING—Caparo Group Ltd.; *Int'l, pg. 265*
WILLIAMS CONTROLS, INC.; *U.S. Public*, pg. 1769
THE W.W. WILLIAMS COMPANY; *U.S. Private*, pg. 1178
WINNEBAGO INDUSTRIES, INC.; *U.S. Public*, pg. 1772
WINNSBORO ASSEMBLY DIVISION—Renault; *Int'l*, pg. 1103
WINPOWER INC.—Dyna Technology Incorporated; *U.S. Private*, pg. 350
WIX DIV.—Dana Corporation; *U.S. Public*, pg. 479
WOLVERINE GASKET & MANUFACTURING CO.—Eagle-Picher Industries, Inc.; *U.S. Private*, pg. 355
WYNN'S INTERNATIONAL, INC.; *U.S. Public*, pg. 1782
XTRA CORPORATION; *U.S. Public*, pg. 1786
YOUNG RADIATOR COMPANY; *U.S. Private*, pg. 1201
ZF GREAT BRITAIN LTD.—ZF Friedrichshafen A.G.; *Int'l*, pg. 1522
ZELLER CORP.; *U.S. Private*, pg. 1204
ZEXEL ILLINOIS INC.—Zexel Corporation; *Int'l*, pg. 1528
ZEXEL INC.—Zexel Corporation; *Int'l*, pg. 1528

3715 — TRUCK TRAILERS

AJAX MANUFACTURING COMPANY, INC.—Standard Automotive Corporation; *U.S. Private*, pg. 1030
ALUMAX INC.; *U.S. Public*, pg. 59
BANKHEAD ENTERPRISES INC.; *U.S. Private*, pg. 114
CMI CORPORATION; *U.S. Public*, pg. 278
CMI LOAD KING TRAILER DIVISION—CMI Corporation; *U.S. Public*, pg. 279
C.R.A. HOLDINGS INC.—Stamford Capital; *U.S. Private*, pg. 1029
CARLISLE CONTAINER MANUFACTURING COMPANY—Carlisle Companies Incorporated; *U.S. Public*, pg. 305
CENTURY DOOR U.S.A. INC.—Premdor Inc.; *Int'l*, pg. 1067
COMPONENTA TRANSPORT AB—Trelleborg AB; *Int'l*, pg. 1420
CRAIG SYSTEMS; *U.S. Private*, pg. 284
CRANE CARRIER COMPANY; *U.S. Private*, pg. 286
DORSEY TRAILERS, INC.; *U.S. Public*, pg. 520
DORSEY TRAILERS, INC.—Dorsey Trailers, Inc.; *U.S. Public*, pg. 520
EAGER BEAVER; *U.S. Private*, pg. 354
ENGINEERING SYSTEMS CO.—Datron Incorporated; *U.S. Private*, pg. 313
FLORIG EQUIPMENT COMPANY, INC.; *U.S. Private*, pg. 415
FORSS-PARATOR—Trelleborg AB; *Int'l*, pg. 1420
FUJI HEAVY INDUSTRIES, LTD.; *Int'l*, pg. 522
GVA MATERIALVERKSTADER AB—Celsius AB; *Int'l*, pg. 277
HACKNEY AND SONS, INC.—Transportation Technologies, Inc.; *U.S. Private*, pg. 1097
INTERTRACTOR AMERICA CORPORATION—Wirten GmbH; *Int'l*, pg. 1511
INTERTRACTOR ZWEIGNIEDERLASSUNG DER WIRTGEN GMBH—Wirten GmbH; *Int'l*, pg. 1511
KENTUCKY MANUFACTURING CO.; *U.S. Private*, pg. 615
KIDRON INC.; *U.S. Private*, pg. 619
KIDRON, INC.—Transportation Technologies, Inc.; *U.S. Private*, pg. 1097
KOHLER INTERCONSULT—Trelleborg AB; *Int'l*, pg. 1420
LUFKIN INDUSTRIES, INC.; *U.S. Public*, pg. 1019
THE MARMON GROUP, INC.; *U.S. Private*, pg. 706
MITSUBISHI ELECTRIC CORPORATION; *Int'l*, pg. 872
MOTALA TANK—Trelleborg AB; *Int'l*, pg. 1420
OSHKOSH TRUCK CORPORATION; *U.S. Public*, pg. 1233
RIGGS INDUSTRIES, INC.; *U.S. Private*, pg. 930
SOMERSET WELDING & STEEL, INC.—Riggs Industries, Inc.; *U.S. Private*, pg. 930
STANDARD AUTOMOTIVE CORPORATION; *U.S. Private*, pg. 1030
STECO—Blue Tee Corporation; *U.S. Private*, pg. 153
STRICK CORP.—Xtra Corporation; *U.S. Public*, pg. 1787
SYSTEMS & ELECTRONICS INC.—ESCO Electronics Corporation; *U.S. Public*, pg. 547
SYSTEMS ASSEMBLY DIV.—Dana Corporation; *U.S. Public*, pg. 479
TIMPTE INDUSTRIES, INC.; *U.S. Private*, pg. 1088
UTILITY TRAILER MANUFACTURING CO.; *U.S. Private*, pg. 1130
WABASH NATIONAL CORP.; *U.S. Public*, pg. 1730
XTRA CORPORATION; *U.S. Public*, pg. 1786

3716 — MOTOR HOMES

ASC INCORPORATED; *U.S. Private*, pg. 8
FLEETWOOD ENTERPRISES, INC.; *U.S. Public*, pg. 650
FLEETWOOD MOTOR HOMES OF INDIANA, INC.-DECATUR PLANT—Fleetwood Enterprises, Inc.; *U.S. Public*, pg. 651
FLEETWOOD MOTOR HOMES OF CALIFORNIA, INC./CHICO—Fleetwood Enterprises, Inc.; *U.S. Public*, pg. 651
FLEETWOOD MOTOR HOMES OF CALIFORNIA, INC.-RIVERSIDE PLANT/VIA RICARDO—Fleetwood Enterprises, Inc.; *U.S. Public*, pg. 651
HOLIDAY RAMBLER—Monaco Coach Corporation; *U.S. Public*, pg. 1123
MONACO COACH CORPORATION; *U.S. Public*, pg. 1123
REXHALL INDUSTRIES, INC.; *U.S. Public*, pg. 1384
ROLLALONG LIMITED—Hanson PLC; *Int'l*, pg. 593
WINNEBAGO INDUSTRIES, INC.; *U.S. Public*, pg. 1772

3721 — AIRCRAFT

AERMACCHI S.P.A.—IRI Istituto Ricostruzione Industriale; *Int'l*, pg. 653
AEROSPACE PRODUCTS, INC.—AMETEK, Inc.; *U.S. Public*, pg. 100
AEROSPATIALE; *Int'l*, pg. 28
AGUSTA AEROSPACE CORPORATION—Agusta S.P.A.; *Int'l*, pg. 32
AGUSTA S.P.A.; *Int'l*, pg. 32
AIR HANSON LIMITED—Hanson PLC; *Int'l*, pg. 592
AIRBUS INDUSTRIE; *Int'l*, pg. 39
AIRCRAFT DIVISION/BEDEK AVIATION GROUP—Israel Aircraft Industries Ltd.; *Int'l*, pg. 690
AIRMATE—Day & Zimmermann, Inc.; *U.S. Private*, pg. 317
AKER STORD A.S.—Aker Raj Asa; *Int'l*, pg. 42
ALENIA—IRI Istituto Ricostruzione Industriale; *Int'l*, pg. 653
ALENIA AERONAUTICA—IRI Istituto Ricostruzione Industriale; *Int'l*, pg. 653
ALRASHID-ABETONG CO. LTD.—Scancem AB; *Int'l*, pg. 1199
AMERICAN EUROCOPTER CORP.—Aerospatiale; *Int'l*, pg. 29
AVIONS DIV.—Aerospatiale; *Int'l*, pg. 29
BELL—BCE Inc.; *Int'l*, pg. 115
BELL HELICOPTER TEXTRON—Textron Inc.; *U.S. Public*, pg. 1588
BOEING ADVANCED SYSTEMS—The Boeing Company; *U.S. Public*, pg. 240
BOEING BAO—The Boeing Company; *U.S. Public*, pg. 240
BOEING COMMERCIAL AIRPLANE GROUP—The Boeing Company; *U.S. Public*, pg. 240
THE BOEING COMPANY; *U.S. Public*, pg. 239
THE BOEING COMPANY CANADA LTD.—The Boeing Company; *U.S. Public*, pg. 242
BOEING DEFENSE & SPACE GROUP—The Boeing Company; *U.S. Public*, pg. 240
BOEING FABRICATION DIVISION—The Boeing Company; *U.S. Public*, pg. 240
BOEING HELICOPTER DIVISION—The Boeing Company; *U.S. Public*, pg. 241
BOEING HELICOPTERS—The Boeing Company; *U.S. Public*, pg. 241
BOEING INTERNATIONAL CORPORATION—The Boeing Company; *U.S. Public*, pg. 242
BOEING NORTH AMERICA, NORTH AMERICAN AIRCRAFT DIVISION—The Boeing Company; *U.S. Public*, pg. 241
BOEING OF PORTLAND—The Boeing Company; *U.S. Public*, pg. 240
BOMBARDIER INC. CANADAIR—Bombardier Inc.; *Int'l*, pg. 200
BOMBARDIER, LEARJET INC.—Bombardier Inc.; *Int'l*, pg. 200
BOMBARDIER REGIONAL AIRCRAFT DIVISION—The Boeing Company; *U.S. Public*, pg. 242
BRITISH AEROSPACE DEFENCE LIMITED (MILITARY AIRCRAFT)—British Aerospace p.l.c.; *Int'l*, pg. 217
BRITISH AEROSPACE P.L.C.; *Int'l*, pg. 217
THE CESSNA AIRCRAFT CO.—Textron Inc.; *U.S. Public*, pg. 1589
COMMODORE AVIATION—Israel Aircraft Industries Ltd.; *Int'l*, pg. 690
CONSTRUCCIONES AERONAUTICAS, S.A. (CASA)—Northrop Grumman Corporation; *U.S. Public*, pg. 1199
DAIMLER-BENZ AEROSPACE AG—Daimler-Benz Aktiengesellschaft; *Int'l*, pg. 367
DASSAULT AVIATION GROUP; *Int'l*, pg. 383
DASSAULT FALCON JET CORP.—Dassault Aviation Group; *Int'l*, pg. 383
DE HAVILLAND INC.—Bombardier Inc.; *Int'l*, pg. 200
DEUTSCHE AEROSPACE AIRBUS GMBH—Daimler-Benz Aktiengesellschaft; *Int'l*, pg. 367

EMBRAER-EMPRESA BRASILEIRA DE AERONAUTICA S.A.; *Int'l*, pg. 452
EUROCOPTER HOLDING S.A.—Aerospatiale; *Int'l*, pg. 29
EUROFIGHTER JAGDFLUGZEUG GMBH—British Aerospace p.l.c.; *Int'l*, pg. 218
EUROFIGHTER JAGDFLUGZEUG GMBH—Daimler-Benz Aktiengesellschaft; *Int'l*, pg. 367
EVERETT DIVISION—The Boeing Company; *U.S. Public*, pg. 240
FAIRCHILD AEROSPACE CORPORATION; *U.S. Private*, pg. 391
FAIRCHILD DORNIER USA—Fairchild Aerospace Corporation; *U.S. Private*, pg. 391
FIAT AVIAZIONE S.P.A.—Fiat Auto SpA; *Int'l*, pg. 481
FINMECCANICA S.P.A.—IRI Istituto Ricostruzione Industriale; *Int'l*, pg. 653
THE FLIGHT INTERNATIONAL GROUP, INC.; *U.S. Public*, *pg. 654*
FUJI HEAVY INDUSTRIES, LTD.; *Int'l*, pg. 522
GKN WESTLAND HELICOPTERS LIMITED—GKN plc; *Int'l*, *pg. 535*
GENERAL DYNAMICS CORPORATION; *U.S. Public*, pg. 708
GENERAL DYNAMICS INTERNATIONAL CORPORATION—General Dynamics Corporation; *U.S. Public*, pg. 709
GULFSTREAM AEROSPACE CORPORATION—Forstmann Little & Co.; *U.S. Private*, pg. 419
HSI AVIATION, INC.—Huntco Inc.; *U.S. Public*, pg. 849
HAWKER DE HAVILLAND LTD.—BTR plc; *Int'l*, pg. 128
HEAVYLIFT CARGO AIRLINES LIMITED—Kvaerner a.s.a.; *Int'l*, pg. 773
THE DEE HOWARD COMPANY; *U.S. Private*, pg. 542
INDUSTRIA AERONAUTICA NEIVA S.A.—Embraer-Empresa Brasileira de Aeronautica S.A.; *Int'l*, pg. 452
ISRAEL AIRCRAFT INDUSTRIES LTD.; *Int'l*, pg. 689
JETSTREAM AIRCRAFT LIMITED—British Aerospace p.l.c.; *Int'l*, pg. 217
KAMAN AEROSPACE CORP.—Kaman Corporation; *U.S. Public*, pg. 942
KAMAN CORPORATION; *U.S. Public*, pg. 941
KAWASAKI HEAVY INDUSTRIES, LTD.; *Int'l*, pg. 725
LAHAV DIVISION/MILITARY AIRCRAFT GROUP—Israel Aircraft Industries Ltd.; *Int'l*, pg. 690
LOCKHEED AERONAUTICAL SYSTEMS COMPANY—Lockheed Martin Corporation; *U.S. Public*, pg. 1007
LOCKHEED FORT WORTH COMPANY—Lockheed Martin Corporation; *U.S. Public*, pg. 1007
MALAT (UNMANNED AIR VEHICLES) DIVISION/MILITARY AIRCRAFT GROUP—Israel Aircraft Industries Ltd.; *Int'l*, pg. 690
MCDONNELL AIRCRAFT & MISSILE SYSTEMS DIV.—The Boeing Company; *U.S. Public*, pg. 241
MERCEDES-BENZ AG—Daimler-Benz Aktiengesellschaft; *Int'l*, pg. 368
METEOR CONSTRUZIONI AERONAUTICHE ED ELETTRONICHE S.P.A.—IRI Istituto Ricostruzione Industriale; *Int'l*, pg. 653
METEOR-GORIZIA PLANT—IRI Istituto Ricostruzione Industriale; *Int'l*, pg. 653
MILITARY AIRCRAFT GROUP—Israel Aircraft Industries Ltd.; *Int'l*, pg. 690
MOONEY AIRCRAFT CORPORATION; *U.S. Private*, pg. 759
NASAM INTERNATIONAL, INCORPORATED—Banner Aerospace, Inc.; *U.S. Public*, pg. 187
THE NEW PIPER AIRCRAFT, INC.; *U.S. Private*, pg. 794
NORTHROP GRUMMAN CORPORATION; *U.S. Public*, pg. 1197
PANAVIA AIRCRAFT GMBH—British Aerospace p.l.c.; *Int'l*, *pg. 218*
PANAVIA AIRCRAFT GMBH—Daimler-Benz Aktiengesellschaft; *Int'l*, pg. 367
PANAVIA AIRCRAFT GMBH—IRI Istituto Ricostruzione Industriale; *Int'l*, pg. 653
PARTENAVIA - CASORIA PLANT—IRI Istituto Ricostruzione Industriale; *Int'l*, pg. 653
PARTENAVIA CONSTRUZIONI AERONAUTICHE—IRI Istituto Ricostruzione Industriale; *Int'l*, pg. 653
PILATUS BRITTEN-NORMAN LTD.—Oerlikon-Buhrle Holding AG; *Int'l*, pg. 998
PILATUS FLUGZEUGWERKE AG—Oerlikon-Buhrle Holding AG; *Int'l*, pg. 998
RAVEN INDUSTRIES, INC.; *U.S. Public*, pg. 1361
RAYTHEON AIRCRAFT COMPANY—Raytheon Company; *U.S. Public*, pg. 1365
RAYTHEON COMPANY; *U.S. Public*, pg. 1364
RAYTHEON CORPORATE JETS, INC.—Raytheon Company; *U.S. Public*, pg. 1366
RAYTHEON E-SYSTEMS—Raytheon Company; *U.S. Public*, pg. 1365
ROBINSON HELICOPTER COMPANY; *U.S. Private*, pg. 936
ROCKWELL INTERNATIONAL CORPORATION; *U.S. Public*, pg. 1397
ROCKWELL INTERNATIONAL GMBH—Rockwell International Corporation; *U.S. Public*, pg. 1401
SECA (SOCIETE D'EXPLOITATION ET DE CONSTRUCTION AERONAUTIQUES)—Aerospatiale; *Int'l*, pg. 29
S.O.C.A.T.A.(SOCIETE DE CONSTRUCTION D'AVIONS DE TOURISMES ET D'AFFAIRES)—Aerospatiale; *Int'l*, pg. 29
SAAB AB—Investor AB; *Int'l*, pg. 686
SAAB AIRCRAFT DIVISION—Investor AB; *Int'l*, pg. 686
SCHWEIZER AIRCRAFT CORPORATION; *U.S. Private*, pg. 975
SEPECAT SA—British Aerospace p.l.c.; *Int'l*, pg. 218
777 PROGRAM—The Boeing Company; *U.S. Public*, pg. 240
737/757 PROGRAMS—The Boeing Company; *U.S. Public*, pg. 240
SHOWA AIRCRAFT INDUSTRY CO., LTD.—Mitsui & Co., Ltd.; *Int'l*, pg. 878
SIKORSKY AIRCRAFT—United Technologies Corporation; *U.S. Public*, pg. 1691
SOGERMA-SOCEA—Aerospatiale; *Int'l*, pg. 29
TEXTRON INC.; *U.S. Public*, pg. 1588
THERMAL ELECTRON TECH. CO.—Thermo Electron Corporation; *U.S. Public*, pg. 1593
UNITED TECHNOLOGIES CORPORATION; *U.S. Public*, pg. 1689
WHITEHALL CORPORATION; *U.S. Public*, pg. 1765

3724 — AIRCRAFT ENGINES & ENGINE PARTS

ACCURATE BUSHING CO., INC.; *U.S. Private*, pg. 11
AERMACCHI S.P.A.—IRI Istituto Ricostruzione Industriale; *Int'l*, pg. 653
AERO CORPORATION—Whitehall Corporation; *U.S. Public*, *pg. 1766*
AERONCA, INC.—Magellan Aerospace Corporation; *Int'l*, pg. 829
AEROSPACE PRODUCTS, INC.—AMETEK, Inc.; *U.S. Public*, pg. 100
AEROSPATIALE; *Int'l*, pg. 28
AIR & FUEL DIV.—Parker Hannifin Corporation; *U.S. Public*, *pg. 1262*
AIRCRAFT TECHNOLOGY, INC.—HEICO Corporation; *U.S. Public*, pg. 804
AIRFOIL TECHNOLOGIES INTERNATIONAL LLC—Teleflex Incorporated; *U.S. Public*, pg. 1569
ALCOA COMPOSITES, INC.—Aluminum Company of America; *U.S. Public*, pg. 60
ALENIA—IRI Istituto Ricostruzione Industriale; *Int'l*, pg. 653
ALFA ROMEO AVIO S.P.A.—Fiat Auto SpA; *Int'l*, pg. 481
ALLEN AUTOMOTIVE INTERNATIONAL (FRANCE) S.A.R.L.—AAR Corp.; *U.S. Public*, pg. 1
ALLIEDSIGNAL AEROSPACE LIMITED—AlliedSignal Inc.; *U.S. Public*, pg. 52
ALLIEDSIGNAL AEROSPACE SERVICE CORPORATION—AlliedSignal Inc.; *U.S. Public*, pg. 52
ALLIEDSIGNAL AEROSPACE—AlliedSignal Inc.; *U.S. Public*, pg. 50
ALLIEDSIGNAL CERAMIC COMPONENTS—AlliedSignal Inc.; *U.S. Public*, pg. 50
ALLIEDSIGNAL CONTROLS & ACCESSORIES—AlliedSignal Inc.; *U.S. Public*, pg. 50
ALLIEDSIGNAL ENGINES—AlliedSignal Inc.; *U.S. Public*, pg. 50
ALLIEDSIGNAL ENVIRONMENTAL CATALYSTS—AlliedSignal Inc.; *U.S. Public*, pg. 51
ALLIEDSIGNAL INC.; *U.S. Public*, pg. 49
AUTO-AIR COMPOSITES, INC.—Cade Industries, Inc.; *U.S. Public*, pg. 290
AVIALL, INC.—Aviall, Inc.; *U.S. Public*, pg. 154
B.H. AIRCRAFT CO., INC.; *U.S. Private*, pg. 107
BARNES GROUP AEROSPACE COMPONENTS—Barnes Group Inc.; *U.S. Public*, pg. 190
BARNES GROUP INC.; *U.S. Public*, pg. 189
BEACON GROUP—Beacon Group; *U.S. Private*, pg. 126
BOEING NORTH AMERICA, NORTH AMERICAN AIRCRAFT DIVISION—The Boeing Company; *U.S. Public*, pg. 241
BOEING SPOKANE—The Boeing Company; *U.S. Public*, pg. 241
CFE COMPANY—AlliedSignal Inc.; *U.S. Public*, pg. 51
CFM INTERNATIONAL INC.—SNECMA - Societe Nationale d'Etude et de Construction de Moteurs d'Aviation; *Int'l*, pg. 1166
CFM INTERNATIONAL SA—SNECMA - Societe Nationale d'Etude et de Construction de Moteurs d'Aviation; *Int'l*, pg. 1166
CALIFORNIA MANUFACTURING ENTERPRISES; *U.S. Private*, pg. 201
CHEM-TRONICS, INC.—The Interlake Corporation; *U.S. Public*, pg. 893
CHROMALLOY GAS TURBINE CORP.—Sequa Corporation; *U.S. Public*, pg. 1458
COLTEC PEABODY DIVISION—Coltec Holdings Inc; *U.S. Public*, pg. 402
CORSE COMPOSITES AERONAUTIQUES—SNECMA - Societe Nationale d'Etude et de Construction de Moteurs d'Aviation; *Int'l*, pg. 1166
DBS CO., LTD.—Briggs & Stratton Corporation; *U.S. Public*, *pg. 253*
DAC INTERNATIONAL, INC.—Banner Aerospace, Inc.; *U.S. Public*, pg. 187
DAIMLER-BENZ AEROSPACE AG—Daimler-Benz Aktiengesellschaft; *Int'l*, pg. 367
DALLAS AEROSPACE, INC.—Banner Aerospace, Inc.; *U.S. Public*, pg. 187
DELAVAN GAS TURBINE PRODUCTS DIVISION—Coltec Holdings Inc; *U.S. Public*, pg. 401
DELTA INDUSTRIES; *U.S. Private*, pg. 322
DERLAN INDUSTRIES LIMITED; *Int'l*, pg. 395
DONCASTERS PLC; *Int'l*, pg. 416
DOVER DIVERSIFIED—Dover Corporation; *U.S. Public*, pg. 521
DOWTY GROUP—TI Group plc; *Int'l*, pg. 1340
DUNLOP PRECISION RUBBER DIVISION—BTR plc; *Int'l*, pg. 125
DYNACRAFT—Paccar Inc.; *U.S. Public*, pg. 1246
EG & G AEROSPACE & ENGINEERED PRODUCTS—EG & G, Inc.; *U.S. Public*, pg. 542
EG & G KT AEROFAB—EG & G, Inc.; *U.S. Public*, pg. 542
EG & G MISSOURI METALS—EG & G, Inc.; *U.S. Public*, pg. 544
ELECTRO METHODS INC.; *U.S. Private*, pg. 369
ENGINES DIVISION/BEDEK AVIATION GROUP—Israel Aircraft Industries Ltd.; *Int'l*, pg. 690
ENGINS TACTIQUES DIV.—Aerospatiale; *Int'l*, pg. 29
FABRICATIONS MECANIQUES DE L'ATLANTIQUE (FAMAT SA)—SNECMA - Societe Nationale d'Etude et de Construction de Moteurs d'Aviation; *Int'l*, pg. 1166
FENN MANUFACTURING CO.—United Dominion Industries, Ltd.; *U.S. Public*, pg. 1676
FIAT AUTO S.P.A.—Fiat Auto SpA; *Int'l*, pg. 481
FINMECCANICA S.P.A.—IRI Istituto Ricostruzione Industriale; *Int'l*, pg. 653
FREEDOM FORGE CORPORATION; *U.S. Private*, pg. 425
FUEL SYSTEMS TEXTRON INC.—Textron Inc.; *U.S. Public*, *pg. 1589*
FUJI HEAVY INDUSTRIES, LTD.; *Int'l*, pg. 522
G.E. AIRCRAFT ENGINES—General Electric Company; *U.S. Public*, pg. 710
GKN WESTLAND INDUSTRIAL PRODUCTS LTD.—GKN plc; *Int'l*, pg. 535
GKN WESTLAND TECHNOLOGIES LIMITED—GKN plc; *Int'l*, pg. 535
GAS TURBINE FUEL SYSTEMS DIV.—Parker Hannifin Corporation; *U.S. Public*, pg. 1262
GAST MFG. CORP.; *U.S. Private*, pg. 440
GENERAL ELECTRIC COMPANY; *U.S. Public*, pg. 709
GENERAL MOTORS CORPORATION; *U.S. Public*, pg. 718
GEORGETOWN JET CENTER, INC.—Banner Aerospace, Inc.; *U.S. Public*, pg. 187
THE B.F. GOODRICH COMPANY; *U.S. Public*, pg. 751
GULL ELECTRONIC SYSTEMS DIV.—Parker Hannifin Corporation; *U.S. Public*, pg. 1262
GUNVER MANUFACTURING CO.; *U.S. Private*, pg. 488
HSC CONTROLS—Woodward Governor Company; *U.S. Public*, pg. 1776
HAWKER DE HAVILLAND LTD.—BTR plc; *Int'l*, pg. 128
HEICO AEROSPACE CORPORATION—HEICO Corporation; *U.S. Public*, pg. 804
HEICO CORPORATION; *U.S. Public*, pg. 804
HISPANO-SUIZA S.A.—SNECMA - Societe Nationale d'Etude et de Construction de Moteurs d'Aviation; *Int'l*, pg. 1165
HITCHCOCK INDUSTRIES, INC.; *U.S. Private*, pg. 531
HUGHES-TREITLER MANUFACTURING CORPORATION; *U.S. Private*, pg. 547
THE INTERLAKE CORPORATION; *U.S. Public*, pg. 892
INTERNATIONAL TURBINE ENGINE CORPORATION (ITEC)—AlliedSignal Inc.; *U.S. Public*, pg. 51
ISHIKAWAJIMA-HARIMA HEAVY INDUSTRIES CO., LTD.; *Int'l*, pg. 689
JET AVION CORPORATION—HEICO Corporation; *U.S. Public*, pg. 804
KAMAN AEROSPACE CORP.—Kaman Corporation; *U.S. Public*, pg. 942
KETEMA DIVISION—Senior Engineering Group, plc.; *Int'l*, pg. 1222
KETEMA, INC.—KTM Holdings Corp.; *U.S. Private*, pg. 604
KING FIFTH WHEEL CO.—TI Group plc; *Int'l*, pg. 1337
L.A. GAUGE CO.—Triumph Group, Inc.; *U.S. Public*, pg. 1640
LPI CORPORATION—HEICO Corporation; *U.S. Public*, pg. 804
LAGARDERE GROUPE; *Int'l*, pg. 791
LAVELLE COMPANY; *U.S. Private*, pg. 653
LEE COMPANY; *U.S. Private*, pg. 657
LIEBHERR-AEROSPACE LINDENBERG GMBH—Liebherr-International AG; *Int'l*, pg. 808
LIGHT HELICOPTER TURBINE ENGINE COMPANY (LHTEC)—AlliedSignal Inc.; *U.S. Public*, pg. 51
LUCAS AEROSPACE—LucasVarity plc; *Int'l*, pg. 819
LUCAS INDUSTRIES INC.—LucasVarity plc; *Int'l*, pg. 820
LUCASVARITY PLC—LucasVarity plc; *Int'l*, pg. 819
MTU MOTOREN-UND TURBINEN-UNION MUNCHEN GMBH—Daimler-Benz Aktiengesellschaft; *Int'l*, pg. 367
MENASCO AEROSPACE LTD.—Coltec Holdings Inc; *U.S. Public*, pg. 402
MERCEDES-BENZ AG—Daimler-Benz Aktiengesellschaft; *Int'l*, pg. 368
MICRODOT/RECOIL—KTI; *U.S. Public*, pg. 940
MIDDLETON AEROSPACE CORPORATION—BTR plc; *Int'l*, *pg. 124*
MIRRLEES BLACKSTONE (CANADA) LTD.—BTR plc; *Int'l*, *pg. 125*
NCI—TI Group plc; *Int'l*, pg. 1338
NICHOLS AIRCRAFT DIV.—Parker Hannifin Corporation; *U.S. Public*, pg. 1262
ORENDA (CANADA)—Hawker Siddeley Canada Inc.; *Int'l*, pg. 604
PACIFIC ELECTRO-DYNAMICS, INC.—Olin Corporation; *U.S. Public*, pg. 1219
PALL CORPORATION; *U.S. Public*, pg. 1253
PALMER MANUFACTURING COMPANY; *U.S. Private*, pg. 835
PILATUS FLUGZEUGWERKE AG—Oerlikon-Buhrle Holding AG; *Int'l*, pg. 998
PRATT & WHITNEY CANADA INC.—United Technologies Corporation; *U.S. Public*, pg. 1690
PROPULSION SYSTEMS DIVISION—The Boeing Company; *U.S. Public*, pg. 240
THE PURDY CORPORATION; *U.S. Private*, pg. 895
ROGERSON AIRCRAFT CORPORATION; *U.S. Private*, pg. 940
ROHR, INC.—The B.F. Goodrich Company; *U.S. Public*, pg. 751
ROLLS-ROYCE-COMMERCIAL AERO ENGINES LTD.—Rolls-Royce plc; *Int'l*, pg. 1127
SNECMA - SOCIETE NATIONALE D'ETUDE ET DE CONSTRUCTION DE MOTEURS D'AVIATION; *Int'l*, pg. 1165
SENSENICH PROPELLER MANUFACTURING CO., INC.—The Philadelphia Bourse, Inc.; *U.S. Private*, pg. 861
SEQUA CORPORATION; *U.S. Public*, pg. 1458
SIFCO CUSTOM MACHINING—Sifco Industries, Inc.; *U.S. Public*, pg. 1471
SIFCO INDUSTRIES, INC.; *U.S. Public*, pg. 1470
SIFCO TURBINE COMPONENTS, LTD.—Sifco Industries, Inc.; *U.S. Public*, pg. 1471
J.T. SLOCOMB COMPANY; *U.S. Private*, pg. 1006
SOCHATA—SNECMA - Societe Nationale d'Etude et de Construction de Moteurs d'Aviation; *Int'l*, pg. 1166
SPAR AEROSPACE LIMITED; *Int'l*, pg. 1287
SUNDSTRAND CORPORATION; *U.S. Public*, pg. 1533

SUNDSTRAND POWER SYSTEMS—Sundstrand Corporation; U.S. Public, pg. 1534
TI REYNOLDS RINGS LIMITED—TI Group plc; Int'l, pg. 1338
TECOMET-ALBUQUERQUE—Thermo Electron Corporation; U.S. Public, pg. 1592
TEXTRON INC.; U.S. Public, pg. 1588
THERM, INC.; U.S. Private, pg. 1079
TRI-MANUFACTURING—General Electric Company; U.S. Public, pg. 710
TRU-FORM—TI Group plc; Int'l, pg. 1338
TURBINE ENGINE COMPONENTS TEXTRON—Textron Inc.; U.S. Public, pg. 1588
UNISON INDUSTRIES; U.S. Private, pg. 1120
UNITED AIRCRAFT PRODUCTS—Parker Hannifin Corporation; U.S. Public, pg. 1262
UNITED TECHNOLOGIES CORPORATION; U.S. Public, pg. 1689
UNITED TECHNOLOGIES MICROELECTRONICS CENTER—United Technologies Corporation; U.S. Public, pg. 1690
VALLEY MANUFACTURING CORPORATION—TI Group plc; Int'l, pg. 1338
VICKERS AMD—Aeroquip-Vickers, Inc.; U.S. Public, pg. 25
VICKERS PLC; Int'l, pg. 1466
AB VOLVO; Int'l, pg. 1476
VOLVO AERO CORPORATION—AB Volvo; Int'l, pg. 1476
WALBAR INC.—Coltec Holdings Inc; U.S. Public, pg. 402
WALBAR OF ARIZONA, INC.—Coltec Holdings Inc; U.S. Public, pg. 402
WALL COLMONOY CORP.; U.S. Private, pg. 1148
WILLIAMS INTERNATIONAL; U.S. Private, pg. 1178
WINDSOR AIRMOTIVE—Barnes Group Inc.; U.S. Public, pg. 190
WINDSOR AIRMOTIVE ASIA PTE. LTD.—Barnes Group Inc.; U.S. Public, pg. 190
WINDSOR MANUFACTURING—Barnes Group Inc.; U.S. Public, pg. 190
WOODWARD GOVERNOR COMPANY; U.S. Public, pg. 1776
WORLD AEROSPACE CORPORATION; U.S. Private, pg. 1188
WYMAN-GORDON INVESTMENT CASTINGS, INC.—Wyman-Gordon; U.S. Public, pg. 1782

3728 — AIRCRAFT PARTS & AUXILIARY EQUIPMENT, NEC

AAI/ACL TECHNOLOGIES—United Industrial Corporation; U.S. Public, pg. 1679
AAR ENGINE COMPONENT SERVICES—AAR Corp.; U.S. Public, pg. 1
AAR TECHNICAL SERVICE CENTER—AAR Corp.; U.S. Public, pg. 1
ACR INDUSTRIES INC.; U.S. Private, pg. 3
AHF-DUCOMMUN INCORPORATED—Ducommun Incorporated; U.S. Public, pg. 534
AMPEP P.L.C.—AB SKF; Int'l, pg. 1157
ADAMS INDUSTRIES, INC.—Banner Aerospace, Inc.; U.S. Public, pg. 187
ADAMS RITE SABRE INTERNATIONAL—ZMP, Inc.; U.S. Private, pg. 1203
AEROFLEX INTERNATIONAL, INC.—Aeroflex Incorporated; U.S. Public, pg. 24
AEROFLEX LABORATORIES INC.—Aeroflex Incorporated; U.S. Public, pg. 24
AERONCA, INC.—Magellan Aerospace Corporation; Int'l, pg. 829
AEROQUIP-VICKERS, INC.; U.S. Public, pg. 24
AEROSPACE-MARINE-DEFENSE GROUP—Aeroquip-Vickers, Inc.; U.S. Public, pg. 24
AEROSPACE PRODUCTS, INC.—AMETEK, Inc.; U.S. Public, pg. 100
AIR CRUISERS CO.—Groupe Zodiac; Int'l, pg. 572
AIRCRAFT PRODUCTS COMPANY—B/E Aerospace, Inc.; U.S. Public, pg. 159
AIRCRAFT WHEEL & BRAKE DIV.—Parker Hannifin Corporation; U.S. Public, pg. 1262
ALCOA COMPOSITES, INC.—Aluminum Company of America; U.S. Public, pg. 60
ALENIA—IRI Istituto Ricostruzione Industriale; Int'l, pg. 653
ALENIA AERONAUTICA—IRI Istituto Ricostruzione Industriale; Int'l, pg. 653
ALLIEDSIGNAL AEROSPACE—AlliedSignal Inc.; U.S. Public, pg. 50
ALLIEDSIGNAL INC.; U.S. Public, pg. 49
AMERICAN AIRCRAFT PARTS MANUFACTURING CO.; U.S. Private, pg. 49
AMERICAN FUEL CELL & COATED FABRICS CO. (AMFUEL); U.S. Private, pg. 55
APEX PRECISION TECHNOLOGY INC.; U.S. Private, pg. 77
ARGO-TECH CORPORATION; U.S. Private, pg. 81
ASSOCIATED COMPANY, INC.; U.S. Private, pg. 89
ASTRONAUTICS CORPORATION OF AMERICA; U.S. Private, pg. 93
ATLANTIC AVIATION CORP.; U.S. Private, pg. 94
AUTO-AIR COMPOSITES, INC.—Cade Industries, Inc.; U.S. Public, pg. 290
AVIALL, INC.; U.S. Public, pg. 154
AVIALL, INC.—Aviall, Inc.; U.S. Public, pg. 154
AVICA INC.—Meggitt plc; Int'l, pg. 853
AVIONICS & COMMUNICATIONS—Rockwell International Corporation; U.S. Public, pg. 1397
AVIONS DE TRANSPORT REGIONAL - ATR—IRI Istituto Ricostruzione Industriale; Int'l, pg. 654
B/E AEROSPACE, INC.; U.S. Public, pg. 159
B/E AEROSPACE SEATING PRODUCTS GROUP—B/E Aerospace, Inc.; U.S. Public, pg. 159
BHS-BAYER, BERG-, HUETTEN-, UND SALZWERKE AG—Viag AG; Int'l, pg. 1464
BTR PLC; Int'l, pg. 124
BANNER AIRCRAFT INTERNATIONAL, INC.—Banner Aerospace, Inc.; U.S. Public, pg. 187
BARBER-COLMAN COMPANY—Siebe plc; Int'l, pg. 1242
BAVARIA KEYTRONIC TECHNOLOGIE GMBH—Rogerson Aircraft Corporation; U.S. Private, pg. 940
BEFAB-SAFELAND, LTD.—Datron Incorporated; U.S. Private, pg. 313
BERKSHIRE INDUSTRIES, INC.; U.S. Private, pg. 136
A. BIEDERMAN, INC.—Triumph Group, Inc.; U.S. Public, pg. 1640
THE BOEING COMPANY; U.S. Public, pg. 239
BOEING GEORGIA INC.—The Boeing Company; U.S. Public, pg. 241
BOEING LOUISIANA, INC.—The Boeing Company; U.S. Public, pg. 242
BOEING MILITARY AIRPLANES—The Boeing Company; U.S. Public, pg. 241
BOEING NORTH AMERICA, AUTONETICS ELECTRONIC SYSTEMS DIVISION—The Boeing Company; U.S. Public, pg. 241
BOEING NORTH AMERICA, NORTH AMERICAN AIRCRAFT DIVISION—The Boeing Company; U.S. Public, pg. 241
BOEING NORTH AMERICA, TACTICAL SYSTEMS DIVISION—The Boeing Company; U.S. Public, pg. 241
BOMBARDIER AEROSPACE—Bombardier Inc.; Int'l, pg. 200
BOMBARDIER INC.; Int'l, pg. 199
BOMBARDIER, LEARJET INC.—Bombardier Inc.; Int'l, pg. 200
BOMBARDIER REGIONAL AIRCRAFT DIVISION—The Boeing Company; U.S. Public, pg. 242
BOWMAR INSTRUMENT CORPORATION; U.S. Public, pg. 248
BREEZE EASTERN—TransTechnology Corporation; U.S. Public, pg. 1632
BRISTOL AEROSPACE LTD.—Rolls-Royce plc; Int'l, pg. 1127
BRITISH AEROSPACE AIRBUS LIMITED—British Aerospace p.l.c.; Int'l, pg. 217
BRUNNER ENGINEERING & MANUFACTURING, INC.; U.S. Private, pg. 176
BURBANK AIRCRAFT SUPPLY INC.—Banner Aerospace, Inc.; U.S. Public, pg. 187
CAE ELECTRONICS, LTD.—CAE Inc.; Int'l, pg. 237
CAE ELEKTRONIK GMBH—CAE Inc.; Int'l, pg. 238
CABLECRAFT INC.—Tuthill Corporation; U.S. Private, pg. 1110
CABLEWARE TECHNOLOGY DIV.—Loos & Co., Inc.; U.S. Private, pg. 675
CADE COMPOSITES, INC.—Cade Industries, Inc.; U.S. Public, pg. 290
CADE INDUSTRIES, INC.; U.S. Public, pg. 289
CALCOR SPACE FACILITY, INC.; U.S. Private, pg. 200
CALIFORNIA MANUFACTURING ENTERPRISES; U.S. Private, pg. 201
J.C. CARTER COMPANY, INC.—Argo-Tech Corporation; U.S. Private, pg. 81
THE CESSNA AIRCRAFT CO.—Textron Inc.; U.S. Public, pg. 1589
CHAMPION AVIATION PRODUCTS—Cooper Industries, Inc.; U.S. Public, pg. 443
CHEM-TRONICS, INC.—The Interlake Corporation; U.S. Public, pg. 893
CHROMALLOY GAS TURBINE CORP.—Sequa Corporation; U.S. Public, pg. 1458
COLTEC INDUSTRIES INC.—Coltec Holdings Inc; U.S. Public, pg. 401
COMPONENTS DIVISION/BEDEK AVIATION GROUP—Israel Aircraft Industries Ltd.; Int'l, pg. 690
CONTROL SYSTEMS DIV.-MILITARY—Parker Hannifin Corporation; U.S. Public, pg. 1262
CONTROL SYSTEMS DIVISION-COMMERCIAL—Parker Hannifin Corporation; U.S. Public, pg. 1262
CONVAIR DIV.—General Dynamics Corporation; U.S. Public, pg. 709
CORSE COMPOSITES AERONAUTIQUES—SNECMA - Societe Nationale d'Etude et de Construction de Moteurs d'Aviation; Int'l, pg. 1166
COX & COMPANY, INC.; U.S. Private, pg. 281
CRAIG SYSTEMS; U.S. Private, pg. 284
CRANE CO.; U.S. Public, pg. 456
CRANE LEAR ROMEC CORP.—Crane Co.; U.S. Public, pg. 457
CURTISS-WRIGHT CORP.; U.S. Public, pg. 469
CURTISS-WRIGHT FLIGHT SYSTEMS, INC.—Curtiss-Wright Corp.; U.S. Public, pg. 469
CUSTOMER SERVICES DIVISION—The Boeing Company; U.S. Public, pg. 240
DERLAN INDUSTRIES LIMITED; Int'l, pg. 395
THE DEUTSCH COMPANY; U.S. Private, pg. 328
DIGITRON TOOL CO., INC.; U.S. Private, pg. 332
DOVER DIVERSIFIED—Dover Corporation; U.S. Public, pg. 521
DOW UNITED TECHNOLOGIES—The Dow Chemical Company; U.S. Public, pg. 523
DOWTY AEROSPACE AVIATION SERVICES—TI Group plc; Int'l, pg. 1337
DOWTY AEROSPACE, ISLE OF MAN—TI Group plc; Int'l, pg. 1337
DOWTY AEROSPACE, LOS ANGELES—TI Group plc; Int'l, pg. 1337
DOWTY AEROSPACE, WOLVERHAMPTON—TI Group plc; Int'l, pg. 1337
DOWTY AEROSPACE YAKIMA—TI Group plc; Int'l, pg. 1337
DUCOMMUN INCORPORATED; U.S. Public, pg. 533
DUNLOP AVIATION DIV.—BTR plc; Int'l, pg. 125
DUNLOP PRECISION RUBBER DIVISION—BTR plc; Int'l, pg. 125
EDE - EMBRAER EQUIPMENT DIVISION—Embraer-Empresa Brasileira de Aeronautica S.A.; Int'l, pg. 452
EDO CORPORATION; U.S. Public, pg. 541
EDO FIBER SCIENCE—EDO Corporation; U.S. Public, pg. 542
EDO MARINE & AIRCRAFT SYSTEMS—EDO Corporation; U.S. Public, pg. 542
EFI CORPORATION—Racal Electronics Plc; Int'l, pg. 1082
EG & G AEROSPACE & ENGINEERED PRODUCTS—EG & G, Inc.; U.S. Public, pg. 542
EG & G WRIGHT COMPONENTS—EG & G, Inc.; U.S. Public, pg. 542
EIS GROUP PLC; Int'l, pg. 426
ELECTROSPACE SYSTEMS, INC.—Raytheon Company; U.S. Public, pg. 1365
ENGINEERING SYSTEMS CO.—Datron Incorporated; U.S. Private, pg. 313
FABER ENTERPRISES, INC.; U.S. Private, pg. 390
THE FAIRCHILD CORPORATION; U.S. Public, pg. 610
FINMECCANICA S.P.A.—IRI Istituto Ricostruzione Industriale; Int'l, pg. 653
FLEET INDUSTRIES—Magellan Aerospace Corporation; Int'l, pg. 829
FLUID CONNECTORS GROUP—Parker Hannifin Corporation; U.S. Public, pg. 1260
FLUID CONTROL DIVISION—FMC Corporation; U.S. Public, pg. 605
FREEDOM FORGE CORPORATION; U.S. Private, pg. 425
FUJI HEAVY INDUSTRIES, LTD.; Int'l, pg. 522
GEC ENGINEERING (ACCRINGTON) LTD.—The General Electric Company, p.l.c.; Int'l, pg. 544
GKN WESTLAND AEROSPACE LIMITED—GKN plc; Int'l, pg. 535
GKN WESTLAND AEROSPACE NORTH AMERICA INC.—GKN plc; Int'l, pg. 535
GKN WESTLAND INDUSTRIAL PRODUCTS LTD.—GKN plc; Int'l, pg. 535
GKN WESTLAND TECHNOLOGIES LIMITED—GKN plc; Int'l, pg. 535
GENERAL CABLE CO.—Wassall Plc; Int'l, pg. 1487
GENERAL DYNAMICS, ABILENE FACILITY—General Dynamics Corporation; U.S. Public, pg. 709
GENERAL DYNAMICS CORPORATION; U.S. Public, pg. 708
GENERAL DYNAMICS INTERNATIONAL CORPORATION—General Dynamics Corporation; U.S. Public, pg. 709
M.C. GILL CORPORATION; U.S. Private, pg. 453
BF GOODRICH AVIONIC SYSTEMS, INC.—The B.F. Goodrich Company; U.S. Public, pg. 751
THE B.F. GOODRICH COMPANY; U.S. Public, pg. 751
B.F. GOODRICH COMPONENT SERVICES, LTD.—The B.F. Goodrich Company; U.S. Public, pg. 752
HR TEXTRON—Textron Inc.; U.S. Public, pg. 1589
HTL/KIN-TECH DIVISION—Pacific Scientific Company; U.S. Public, pg. 1250
HAMILTON STANDARD—United Technologies Corporation; U.S. Public, pg. 1690
HARMONY ENGINEERING CORPORATION; U.S. Private, pg. 503
HAYDON SWITCH & INSTRUMENT, INC.; U.S. Private, pg. 513
HOUSTON FEARLESS 76 INC.; U.S. Private, pg. 542
THE DEE HOWARD COMPANY; U.S. Private, pg. 542
NOAH HOWDEN, INC.—Howden Group Plc; Int'l, pg. 636
HUGHES-TREITLER MANUFACTURING CORPORATION; U.S. Private, pg. 547
HYDRAULICS INTERNATIONAL, INC.; U.S. Private, pg. 551
HYDRO-AIRE—Crane Co.; U.S. Public, pg. 457
HYDRO-MILL CO.—Triumph Group, Inc.; U.S. Public, pg. 1640
IMC MAGNETICS CORP.—Minebea Co., Ltd.; Int'l, pg. 868
IMI PLC; Int'l, pg. 646
THE INTERLAKE CORPORATION; U.S. Public, pg. 892
ISCAR BLADES LTD.—IDB Holding Corporation; Int'l, pg. 644
JET ELECTRONICS & TECHNOLOGY, INC.—The B.F. Goodrich Company; U.S. Public, pg. 751
AXEL JOHNSON & CO. N.V. MARIN DIVISION—Axel Johnson AB; Int'l, pg. 711
K & F INDUSTRIES INC.; U.S. Private, pg. 602
KAISER AEROSPACE & ELECTRONICS CORP.; U.S. Private, pg. 605
KAMAN AEROSPACE CORP.—Kaman Corporation; U.S. Public, pg. 942
KAMAN CORPORATION; U.S. Public, pg. 941
KENT-TIEGHI S.P.A.—ABB Asea Brown Boveri (Holding) Ltd.; Int'l, pg. 3
KIDDE TECHNOLOGIES INC.—Williams Holdings Plc; Int'l, pg. 1500
KLECO CORP.; U.S. Private, pg. 625
KROPP FORGE CO.—TIC United Corporation; U.S. Private, pg. 1064
L&S MACHINE COMPANY, INC.—Axsys Technologies, Inc.; U.S. Public, pg. 157
LEE COMPANY; U.S. Private, pg. 657
LEWIS ENGINEERING COMPANY—Coltec Holdings Inc; U.S. Public, pg. 402
LIEBHERR-AEROSPACE TOULOUSE S.A.—Liebherr-International AG; Int'l, pg. 808
LITTON PRECISION GEAR DIV.—Litton Industries, Inc.; U.S. Public, pg. 1003
LOCKHEED AUSTIN DIVISION—Lockheed Martin Corporation; U.S. Public, pg. 1008
LOCKHEED MARTIN DEFENSE SYSTEMS—Lockheed Martin Corporation; U.S. Public, pg. 1008
LOCKHEED MARTIN SKUNK WORKS—Lockheed Martin Corporation; U.S. Public, pg. 1007
LOCKHEED MARTIN TACTICAL DEFENSE SYSTEMS (AKRON)—Lockheed Martin Corporation; U.S. Public, pg. 1009
LORAL SPACE & COMMUNICATIONS; U.S. Public, pg. 1014
LUCAS AEROSPACE CUSTOMER SUPPORT—LucasVarity plc; Int'l, pg. 819

LUCAS AIRCRAFT CARGO SYSTEMS—LucasVarity plc; *Int'l*, pg. 820
LUCAS INDUSTRIES INC.—LucasVarity plc; *Int'l*, pg. 820
MAGELLAN AEROSPACE CORPORATION; *Int'l*, pg. 829
MALAT (UNMANNED AIR VEHICLES) DIVISION/MILITARY AIRCRAFT GROUP—Israel Aircraft Industries Ltd.; *Int'l*, pg. 690
MARK IV INDUSTRIES INC.; *U.S. Public*, pg. 1044
MATERIEL DIVISION—The Boeing Company; *U.S. Public*, pg. 240
MCCAULEY PROPELLER SYSTEMS—Textron Inc.; *U.S. Public*, pg. 1589
MCDONNELL AIRCRAFT & MISSILE SYSTEMS DIV.—The Boeing Company; *U.S. Public*, pg. 241
MCWILLIAMS FORGE CO.; *U.S. Private*, pg. 725
MEGGITT AVIONICS—Meggitt plc; *Int'l*, pg. 853
MEGGITT AVIONICS INC.—Meggitt plc; *Int'l*, pg. 853
MEGGITT PLC; *Int'l*, pg. 853
MEGGITT USA, INC.—Meggitt plc; *Int'l*, pg. 853
MENASCO AEROSPACE LTD.—Coltec Holdings Inc; *U.S. Public*, pg. 402
MENASCO AEROSYSTEMS DIVISION—Coltec Holdings Inc; *U.S. Public*, pg. 402
MENASCO CALIFORNIA OPERATION—Coltec Holdings Inc; *U.S. Public*, pg. 402
MENASCO OVERHAUL DIVISION—Coltec Holdings Inc; *U.S. Public*, pg. 402
MESSIER-BUGATTI S.A.—SNECMA - Societe Nationale d'Etude et de Construction de Moteurs d'Aviation; *Int'l*, pg. 1165
AB MIKRO-VERKTYG—Investor AB; *Int'l*, pg. 686
MONITOR AEROSPACE CORPORATION; *U.S. Private*, pg. 757
MOOG AIRCRAFT CONTROLS DIV.—Moog Incorporated; *U.S. Public*, pg. 1127
MOOG ENGINE CONTROLS DIV.—Moog Incorporated; *U.S. Public*, pg. 1127
MOOG INCORPORATED; *U.S. Public*, pg. 1127
MOONEY AIRCRAFT CORPORATION; *U.S. Private*, pg. 759
NASAM INTERNATIONAL, INCORPORATED—Banner Aerospace, Inc.; *U.S. Public*, pg. 187
NAVCOM DEFENSE ELECTRONICS, INC.; *U.S. Private*, pg. 789
NICHOLS AIRCRAFT DIV.—Parker Hannifin Corporation; *U.S. Public*, pg. 1262
NIHON-PALL LTD.—Pall Corporation; *U.S. Public*, pg. 1254
NOBLES MFG. INC.; *U.S. Private*, pg. 800
NORTHROP GRUMMAN CORPORATION; *U.S. Public*, pg. 1197
OEA AEROSPACE, INC.—OEA, Inc.; *U.S. Public*, pg. 1207
OEA, INC.; *U.S. Public*, pg. 1206
OZONE INDUSTRIES INC.—BBA Group plc; *Int'l*, pg. 113
PACIFIC SCIENTIFIC COMPANY; *U.S. Public*, pg. 1250
PACIFIC SCIENTIFIC LTD.—Pacific Scientific Company; *U.S. Public*, pg. 1250
PALL AEROSPACE—Pall Corporation; *U.S. Public*, pg. 1253
PALL DEUTSCHLAND GMBH—Pall Corporation; *U.S. Public*, pg. 1254
PALL EUROPE LTD.—Pall Corporation; *U.S. Public*, pg. 1254
PARKER FLUID CONNECTORS DE MEXICO—Parker Hannifin Corporation; *U.S. Public*, pg. 1261
PARKER HANNIFIN (AUSTRALIA) (PTY.) LTD.—Parker Hannifin Corporation; *U.S. Public*, pg. 1263
PARKER HANNIFIN CORPORATION; *U.S. Public*, pg. 1259
PARKER HANNIFIN OY (FINLAND)—Parker Hannifin Corporation; *U.S. Public*, pg. 1263
PARKER HANNIFIN RAK S.A.—Parker Hannifin Corporation; *U.S. Public*, pg. 1261
PARKSON CORPORATOR—Axel Johnson AB; *Int'l*, pg. 711
PILATUS FLUGZEUGWERKE AG—Oerlikon-Buhrle Holding AG; *Int'l*, pg. 998
PNEUMATIC DIV.—Parker Hannifin Corporation; *U.S. Public*, pg. 1259
POLY-SCIENTIFIC DIV.—Litton Industries, Inc.; *U.S. Public*, pg. 1003
P.L. PORTER CO.; *U.S. Private*, pg. 876
PURITAN-BENNETT AERO SYSTEMS CO.—Mallinckrodt Inc.; *U.S. Public*, pg. 1040
RAYTHEON AIRCRAFT COMPANY—Raytheon Company; *U.S. Public*, pg. 1365
RAYTHEON E-SYSTEMS—Raytheon Company; *U.S. Public*, pg. 1365
RAYTHEON SYSTEMS MISSISSIPPI—Raytheon Company; *U.S. Public*, pg. 1365
ROCKFORD ACROMATIC PRODUCT CO.; *U.S. Private*, pg. 938
ROCKWELL DO BRASIL LTDA.—Rockwell International Corporation; *U.S. Public*, pg. 1400
ROCKWELL INTERNATIONAL CORPORATION; *U.S. Public*, pg. 1397
ROGERSON AIRCRAFT CORPORATION; *U.S. Private*, pg. 940
ROHR, INC.—The B.F. Goodrich Company; *U.S. Public*, pg. 751
ROLL FORMING CORPORATION; *U.S. Private*, pg. 941
ROLLS-ROYCE INDUSTRIES CANADA INC.—Rolls-Royce plc; *Int'l*, pg. 1127
RONSON AVIATION, INC.—Ronson Corporation; *U.S. Public*, pg. 1405
RONSON CORPORATION; *U.S. Public*, pg. 1405
ROONEY BROTHERS COMPANY; *U.S. Private*, pg. 943
SHL DIVISION/COMMERCIAL AIRCRAFT GROUP—Israel Aircraft Industries Ltd.; *Int'l*, pg. 690
SNECMA - SOCIETE NATIONALE D'ETUDE ET DE CONSTRUCTION DE MOTEURS D'AVIATION; *Int'l*, pg. 1165
SAMSUNG AEROSPACE INDUSTRIES, LTD.—Samsung Group; *Int'l*, pg. 1181
SARGENT CONTROLS—Dover Corporation; *U.S. Public*, pg. 521
SARGENT-FLETCHER INC.—Cobham plc; *Int'l*, pg. 301
SARMA—AB SKF; *Int'l*, pg. 1158
SCHRADER BELLOWS GMBH—Parker Hannifin Corporation; *U.S. Public*, pg. 1264
SCHWEIZER AIRCRAFT CORPORATION; *U.S. Private*, pg. 975
SCOTT AVIATION—Figgie International Inc.; *U.S. Public*, pg. 622
SEQUA CORPORATION; *U.S. Public*, pg. 1458
SERVOTRONICS, INC.; *U.S. Public*, pg. 1462
SIERRACIN CORPORATION; *U.S. Private*, pg. 999
SIFCO CUSTOM MACHINING—Sifco Industries, Inc.; *U.S. Public*, pg. 1471
SIFCO INDUSTRIES, INC.; *U.S. Public*, pg. 1470
SIFCO TURBINE COMPONENTS, LTD.—Sifco Industries, Inc.; *U.S. Public*, pg. 1471
SIMON AVIATION GROUND EQUIPMENT INC.—Simon Engineering plc; *Int'l*, pg. 1252
SMITHS INDUSTRIES AEROSPACE & DEFENSE SYSTEMS INC.-MALVERN—Smiths Industries plc; *Int'l*, pg. 1268
SMITHS INDUSTRIES PLC; *Int'l*, pg. 1266
SPAR AEROSPACE LIMITED; *Int'l*, pg. 1287
SPEEDRING, INC.—Axsys Technologies, Inc.; *U.S. Public*, pg. 158
SPEEDRING SYSTEMS, INC.—Axsys Technologies, Inc.; *U.S. Public*, pg. 158
SUNDSTRAND AEROSPACE ELECTRONICS—Sundstrand Corporation; *U.S. Public*, pg. 1533
SUNDSTRAND AEROSPACE GROUP OPERATION—Sundstrand Corporation; *U.S. Public*, pg. 1533
SUNDSTRAND AEROSPACE OPERATIONS—Sundstrand Corporation; *U.S. Public*, pg. 1533
SUNDSTRAND AVIATION MECHANICAL—Sundstrand Corporation; *U.S. Public*, pg. 1533
SUNDSTRAND AVIATION OPERATIONS—Sundstrand Corporation; *U.S. Public*, pg. 1533
SUNDSTRAND CORPORATION; *U.S. Public*, pg. 1533
SUNDSTRAND ELECTRIC POWER SYSTEMS—Sundstrand Corporation; *U.S. Public*, pg. 1533
SUNDSTRAND PACIFIC AEROSPACE (PTE) LTD.—Sundstrand Corporation; *U.S. Public*, pg. 1534
SWIFT-COR TOOL ENGINEERING; *U.S. Private*, pg. 1058
TSI HOLDINGS, INC.; *U.S. Private*, pg. 1066
TALLEY DEFENSE SYSTEMS, INC.—Carpenter Technology Corporation; *U.S. Public*, pg. 308
TALLEY INDUSTRIES, INC.—Carpenter Technology Corporation; *U.S. Public*, pg. 307
TELAIR INTERNATIONAL—Teleflex Incorporated; *U.S. Public*, pg. 1570
TELAIR INTERNATIONAL CARGO SYSTEMS—Teleflex Incorporated; *U.S. Public*, pg. 1570
TELEDYNE RYAN AERONAUTICAL—Allegheny Teledyne Incorporated; *U.S. Public*, pg. 43
TELEFLEX INCORPORATED; *U.S. Public*, pg. 1569
TEXTRON AUTOMOTIVE INTERIORS COMPANY—Textron Inc.; *U.S. Public*, pg. 1590
TEXTRON INC.; *U.S. Public*, pg. 1588
THOMSON S.A.; *Int'l*, pg. 1381
TRACOR FLIGHT SYSTEMS, INC.—Tracor, Inc.; *U.S. Public*, pg. 1627
TRANSTECHNOLOGY CORPORATION; *U.S. Public*, pg. 1632
TRIUMPH AIR REPAIR—Triumph Group, Inc.; *U.S. Public*, pg. 1640
TUTHILL CORPORATION; *U.S. Private*, pg. 1110
UNITED AIRCRAFT PRODUCTS—Parker Hannifin Corporation; *U.S. Public*, pg. 1262
UNITED TECHNOLOGIES CORPORATION; *U.S. Public*, pg. 1689
UNIVERSAL PROPULSION CO., INC.—Carpenter Technology Corporation; *U.S. Public*, pg. 308
VENTURIAN CORP.; *U.S. Public*, pg. 1716
VICKERS PLC; *Int'l*, pg. 1466
VICKERS TEDECO DIV.—Aeroquip-Vickers, Inc.; *U.S. Public*, pg. 25
WALBAR INC.—Coltec Holdings Inc; *U.S. Public*, pg. 402
WALL COLMONOY CORP.; *U.S. Private*, pg. 1148
WEBER AIRCRAFT, INC.—Groupe Zodiac; *Int'l*, pg. 572
WESTLAND SYSTEM ASSESSMENT LIMITED—GKN plc; *Int'l*, pg. 535
WHITTAKER CONTROLS, INC.—Whittaker Corporation; *U.S. Public*, pg. 1767
WHITTAKER CORPORATION; *U.S. Public*, pg. 1766
WOHLERT CORP.; *U.S. Private*, pg. 1185
WOODWARD GOVERNOR COMPANY; *U.S. Public*, pg. 1776
WYMAN-GORDON INVESTMENT CASTINGS, INC.—Wyman-Gordon; *U.S. Public*, pg. 1782
ZMP, INC.; *U.S. Private*, pg. 1203

3731 — SHIP BUILDING & REPAIRING

AESA ASTILLEROS ESPANOLES, S.A.—SEPI; *Int'l*, pg. 1223
ASTANDER - ASTILLEROS DE SANTANDER S.A.—SEPI; *Int'l*, pg. 1223
ASTANO - ASTILLEROS Y TALLERES DEL NOROESTE, S.A.—SEPI; *Int'l*, pg. 1223
AEROFLEX LABORATORIES INC.—Aeroflex Incorporated; *U.S. Public*, pg. 24
AKER ENGINEERING A.S. (AE)—Aker Raj Asa; *Int'l*, pg. 42
AKER OIL AND GAS TECHNOLOGY—Aker Raj Asa; *Int'l*, pg. 41
AMERICAN COMMERCIAL LINES INC.—CSX Corporation; *U.S. Public*, pg. 284
AMERICAN FINANCIAL GROUP—American Financial Group; *U.S. Public*, pg. 75
ASHEVILLE INDUSTRIES, INC.—Newport News Shipbuilding, Inc.; *U.S. Public*, pg. 1180
AUSTRALIAN SUBMARINE CORPORATION—Celsius AB; *Int'l*, pg. 277
AVONDALE GULFPORT MARINE INC.—Avondale Industries, Inc.; *U.S. Public*, pg. 157
AVONDALE INDUSTRIES, INC.; *U.S. Public*, pg. 156
AVONDALE INDUSTRIES INC. SHIPYARDS DIV.—Avondale Industries, Inc.; *U.S. Public*, pg. 157
BABCOCK INTERNATIONAL GROUP PLC; *Int'l*, pg. 130
BATH IRON WORKS CORPORATION—General Dynamics Corporation; *U.S. Public*, pg. 709
BAY SHIPBUILDING CO.—The Manitowoc Company, Inc.; *U.S. Public*, pg. 1041
BENDER SHIPBUILDING & REPAIR COMPANY, INC.; *U.S. Private*, pg. 132
BIRD-JOHNSON COMPANY—Axel Johnson AB; *Int'l*, pg. 709
BOLLINGER SHIPYARDS, INC.; *U.S. Private*, pg. 155
BROWN BROTHERS & COMPANY LTD.—Vickers PLC; *Int'l*, pg. 1466
CAMPBELL INDUSTRIES, INC.—Marine Construction & Design Co.; *U.S. Private*, pg. 703
CELSIUS AB; *Int'l*, pg. 276
CLEVELAND SHIPREPAIR COMPANY—The Manitowoc Company, Inc.; *U.S. Public*, pg. 1041
DAEWOO SHIPBUILDING & HEAVY MACHINERY, LTD.—Daewoo Corporation; *Int'l*, pg. 357
DAVIE INDUSTRIES INC.; *Int'l*, pg. 385
DEGGENDORFER WERFT UND EISENBAU GMBH—MAN Aktiengesellschaft; *Int'l*, pg. 824
DIESEL MARINE NORSHIPCO—Norfolk Shipbuilding & Drydock Corporation; *U.S. Private*, pg. 802
DORBYL LIMITED; *Int'l*, pg. 416
EEI-MARINE CORP.—EEI Corporation; *Int'l*, pg. 426
EVI, INC.; *U.S. Public*, pg. 547
EBASCO SERVICES SINGAPORE PTE. LTD.—Texas Utilities Company; *U.S. Public*, pg. 1587
FIBRE GLASS-EVERCOAT COMPANY—Illinois Tool Works Inc.; *U.S. Public*, pg. 866
GEC ALSTHOM—Alcatel Alsthom Compagnie Generale D'Electricite; *Int'l*, pg. 52
GENERAL DYNAMICS CORPORATION; *U.S. Public*, pg. 708
GENERAL DYNAMICS INTERNATIONAL CORPORATION—General Dynamics Corporation; *U.S. Public*, pg. 709
GENMAR HOLDINGS, INC.; *U.S. Private*, pg. 447
GOTAVERKEN ARENDAL AB—Celsius AB; *Int'l*, pg. 277
GOTAVERKEN CITYVARVET AB—Celsius AB; *Int'l*, pg. 277
HDW-NOBISKRUG GMBH—Preussag AG; *Int'l*, pg. 1069
HALTER MARINE GROUP, INC.; *U.S. Public*, pg. 778
HITACHI ZOSEN CORPORATION; *Int'l*, pg. 622
HOWALDTSWERKE-DEUTSCHE WERFT AG—Preussag AG; *Int'l*, pg. 1069
HYUNDAI HEAVY INDUSTRIES CO., LTD.—Hyundai Motor Company; *Int'l*, pg. 641
HYUNDAI MOTOR COMPANY; *Int'l*, pg. 641
INGALLS SHIPBUILDING—Litton Industries, Inc.; *U.S. Public*, pg. 1003
INTERNATIONAL MARINE CONSTRUCTION CO. S.A.K.—Nissho Iwai Corporation; *Int'l*, pg. 948
ISHIKAWAJIMA-HARIMA HEAVY INDUSTRIES CO., LTD.; *Int'l*, pg. 689
JULIANA CONSTRUCTORA GIJONESA, S.A.—SEPI; *Int'l*, pg. 1223
KALDNES INDUSTRI A/S—Norsk Vekst ASA; *Int'l*, pg. 965
KAMEWA AB—Vickers PLC; *Int'l*, pg. 1468
KARLSKRONAVARVET AB—Celsius AB; *Int'l*, pg. 277
KAWASAKI HEAVY INDUSTRIES, LTD.; *Int'l*, pg. 725
KAWASAKI KISEN KAISHA, LTD.; *Int'l*, pg. 726
KEPPEL-FELS LTD.—Keppel Corporation Limited; *Int'l*, pg. 731
KOCKUMS AB—Celsius AB; *Int'l*, pg. 277
KOCKUMS PACIFIC PTY LTD.—Celsius AB; *Int'l*, pg. 277
KOCKUMS SE ASIA PTE LTD.—Celsius AB; *Int'l*, pg. 277
KVAERNER DO BRASIL LTDA—Kvaerner a.s.a.; *Int'l*, pg. 767
KVAERNER EUREKA ESPANOLA S.A.—Kvaerner a.s.a.; *Int'l*, pg. 767
KVAERNER EUREKA, MOSS DIVISION—Kvaerner a.s.a.; *Int'l*, pg. 767
KVAERNER FJELLSTRAND A/S—Kvaerner a.s.a.; *Int'l*, pg. 768
KVAERNER FJELLSTRAND (S) PTE LTD.—Kvaerner a.s.a.; *Int'l*, pg. 771
KVAERNER GIBRALTER LTD.—Kvaerner a.s.a.; *Int'l*, pg. 772
KVAERNER GOVAN LTD.—Kvaerner a.s.a.; *Int'l*, pg. 772
KVAERNER KLEVEN FLORO A/S—Kvaerner a.s.a.; *Int'l*, pg. 769
KVAERNER KLEVEN FORDE A/S—Kvaerner a.s.a.; *Int'l*, pg. 769
KVAERNER KLEVEN LEIRVIK A/S—Kvaerner a.s.a.; *Int'l*, pg. 769
KVAERNER KLEVEN ULSTEINVIK A/S—Kvaerner a.s.a.; *Int'l*, pg. 769
KVAERNER MANDAL A/S—Kvaerner a.s.a.; *Int'l*, pg. 769
KVAERNER MASA-YARDS INC., HELSINKI NEW SHIPYARD—Kvaerner a.s.a.; *Int'l*, pg. 771
KVAERNER MASA-YARDS INC., TURKU NEW SHIPYARD—Kvaerner a.s.a.; *Int'l*, pg. 771
KVAERNER ROSENBERG A.S.—Kvaerner a.s.a.; *Int'l*, pg. 769
KVAERNER ROSENBERG NEWFOUNDLAND LTD.—Kvaerner a.s.a.; *Int'l*, pg. 768
KVAERNER SHIPS EQUIPMENT AB—Kvaerner a.s.a.; *Int'l*, pg. 771
AL LARSON BOAT SHOP, INC.; *U.S. Private*, pg. 652
LE TOURNEAU, INC.—Rowan Companies, Inc.; *U.S. Public*, pg. 1410
LITTON INDUSTRIES, INC.; *U.S. Public*, pg. 1002
LITTON SYSTEMS CANADA LTD.—Litton Industries, Inc.; *U.S. Public*, pg. 1005
THE MANITOWOC COMPANY, INC.; *U.S. Public*, pg. 1040

MARCO SEATTLE, INC.—Marine Construction & Design Co.; U.S. Private, pg. 703
MARINE CONSTRUCTION & DESIGN CO.; U.S. Private, pg. 703
MARINETTE MARINE CORPORATION; U.S. Private, pg. 703
MCDERMOTT INTERNATIONAL, INC.; U.S. Public, pg. 1067
METAL TRADES, INC.; U.S. Private, pg. 734
MICHELL BEARINGS—Vickers PLC; Int'l, pg. 1467
MITSUBISHI HEAVY INDUSTRIES LTD.; Int'l, pg. 873
MITSUI ENGINEERING & SHIPBUILDING CO., LTD.—Mitsui & Co., Ltd.; Int'l, pg. 878
NKK CORPORATION; Int'l, pg. 902
NATIONAL STEEL & SHIPBUILDING COMPANY; U.S. Private, pg. 787
NEWPORT NEWS INDUSTRIAL CORP.—Newport News Shipbuilding, Inc.; U.S. Public, pg. 1180
NEWPORT NEWS INDUSTRIAL CORP. OF OHIO—Newport News Shipbuilding, Inc.; U.S. Public, pg. 1180
NEWPORT NEWS OFFSHORE SYSTEMS CORP.—Newport News Shipbuilding, Inc.; U.S. Public, pg. 1180
NEWPORT NEWS REACTOR SERVICES, INC.—Newport News Shipbuilding, Inc.; U.S. Public, pg. 1180
NEWPORT NEWS SHIPBUILDING, INC.; U.S. Public, pg. 1179
NEWPORT NEWS TECHNICAL SERVICES, INC. (WISCONSIN)—Newport News Shipbuilding, Inc.; U.S. Public, pg. 1180
NORFOLK SHIPBUILDING & DRYDOCK CORPORATION; U.S. Private, pg. 802
OCEANEERING PRODUCTION SYSTEMS—Oceaneering International, Inc.; U.S. Public, pg. 1211
PACORD—SPD Technologies; U.S. Private, pg. 957
PETERSON BUILDERS, INC.; U.S. Private, pg. 857
PRODUCTION MANAGEMENT COMPANIES, INC.; U.S. Private, pg. 888
RECO TRANSPORTATION INC.—Vulcan Materials Company; U.S. Public, pg. 1726
RENOSA - REMOLCADORES DEL NOROESTE, S.A.—SEPI; Int'l, pg. 1223
RICHARDS (SHIPBUILDERS) LTD.—Tate & Lyle PLC; Int'l, pg. 1356
SAAB INSTRUMENTS—Investor AB; Int'l, pg. 686
SAMSUNG GROUP; Int'l, pg. 1181
WILHELM SANDER FERTIGUNG GMBH—KM-Europa Metal Aktiengesellschaft; Int'l, pg. 719
SCOTIA TRAWLER EQUIPMENT LIMITED—National Sea Products Limited; Int'l, pg. 909
SEA CONTAINERS ASIA PTE. LTD.—Sea Containers Ltd.; Int'l, pg. 1214
SEMBAWANG MARITIME LIMITED; Int'l, pg. 1219
SINGAPORE TECHNOLOGIES SHIPBUILDING & ENGINEERING LIMITED—Singapore Technologies Pte. Ltd.; Int'l, pg. 1253
SOUTHWEST MARINE, INC.—Carlyle Holding Corporation; U.S. Private, pg. 213
STONE VICKERS—Vickers PLC; Int'l, pg. 1467
SUMITOMO HEAVY INDUSTRIES, LTD.; Int'l, pg. 1314
TAMPA BAY SHIP BUILDING & REPAIR CO.; U.S. Private, pg. 1067
TENNECO INC.; U.S. Public, pg. 1577
TEXTRON MARINE & LAND SYSTEMS—Textron Inc.; U.S. Public, pg. 1589
TODD PACIFIC SHIPYARDS CORP.; U.S. Public, pg. 1619
TOLEDO SHIPREPAIR COMPANY—The Manitowoc Company, Inc.; U.S. Public, pg. 1041
TRINITY INDUSTRIES INC.; U.S. Public, pg. 1638
UNION NAVAL DE LEVANTE, S.A.; Int'l, pg. 1442
VOLVO PENTA U.K. LTD.—AB Volvo; Int'l, pg. 1478
YORKSHIRE MARINE CONTAINERS LTD.—Sea Containers Ltd.; Int'l, pg. 1214

3732 — BOAT BUILDING & REPAIRING

ALTRA MARINE PRODUCTS, INC.—Greenway Partners, L.P.; U.S. Private, pg. 479
ALUMACRAFT BOAT CO.—Timpte Industries, Inc.; U.S. Private, pg. 1088
AMBAR MARINE, INC.—The Beacon Group; U.S. Private, pg. 126
AMERICAN MARINE PTE. LTD.—GB Holdings; Int'l, pg. 531
BIC MARINE S.A.—Societe BIC S.A.; Int'l, pg. 1273
BLACK FIN YACHT CORPORATION; U.S. Private, pg. 147
BLUEWATER; U.S. Private, pg. 153
BOAT AMERICA CORP.; U.S. Private, pg. 153
BOLLINGER SHIPYARDS, INC.; U.S. Private, pg. 155
BOSTON WHALER, INC.—MacAndrews & Forbes Holdings Inc.; U.S. Private, pg. 689
BRAMCO, INC.—Greenway Partners, L.P.; U.S. Private, pg. 478
BRUNSWICK CORPORATION; U.S. Public, pg. 265
CANTIERI RIVA S.P.A.—Vickers PLC; Int'l, pg. 1468
CATALINA YACHTS, INC.; U.S. Private, pg. 219
CHAPARRAL BOATS—RPC Incorporated; U.S. Public, pg. 1356
THE COLEMAN COMPANY—MacAndrews & Forbes Holdings Inc.; U.S. Private, pg. 691
CRESTLINER, INC.—Genmar Holdings, Inc.; U.S. Private, pg. 447
DONZI MARINE CORPORATION—American Marine Holdings Inc.; U.S. Private, pg. 58
FOUNTAIN POWERBOAT INDUSTRIES, INC.; U.S. Public, pg. 678
FOUR WINNS, INC.—Greenway Partners, L.P.; U.S. Private, pg. 478
GB HOLDINGS; Int'l, pg. 531
GENMAR HOLDINGS, INC.; U.S. Private, pg. 447
GLASTRON BOATS—Genmar Holdings, Inc.; U.S. Private, pg. 447
GRAND BANKS YACHTS SDN. BHD.—GB Holdings; Int'l, pg. 531
HARRIS-KAYOT, INC.; U.S. Private, pg. 506
HATTERAS YACHTS—Genmar Holdings, Inc.; U.S. Private, pg. 447
HAWKER DE HAVILLAND LTD.—BTR plc; Int'l, pg. 128
HOBIE CAT COMPANY; U.S. Private, pg. 531
HUNTER MARINE CORPORATION; U.S. Private, pg. 549
HYDRA-SPORTS CORPORATION—Greenway Partners, L.P.; U.S. Private, pg. 478
KVAERNER A.S.A.; Int'l, pg. 766
LARSON BOATS—Genmar Holdings, Inc.; U.S. Private, pg. 447
LIPS UNITED B.V.; Int'l, pg. 812
CARL A. LOWE INDUSTRIES, INC.—Greenway Partners, L.P.; U.S. Private, pg. 478
LUHRS CORPORATION; U.S. Private, pg. 680
LUND BOATS—Genmar Holdings, Inc.; U.S. Private, pg. 447
MARINETTE MARINE CORPORATION; U.S. Private, pg. 703
MASTERCRAFT CORPORATION—Genmar Holdings, Inc.; U.S. Private, pg. 447
MID-ATLANTIC CORRECT CRAFT, INC.—Correct Craft, Inc.; U.S. Private, pg. 277
MID WEST CORRECT CRAFT, INC.—Correct Craft, Inc.; U.S. Private, pg. 277
OY NAUTOR AB—UPM-Kymmene Corporation; Int'l, pg. 1428
NEW COLEMAN HOLDINGS INC.—MacAndrews & Forbes Holdings Inc.; U.S. Private, pg. 690
NEW ENGLAND CORRECT CRAFT, INC.—Correct Craft, Inc.; U.S. Private, pg. 277
OLD TOWN CANOE—Johnson Worldwide Associates, Inc.; U.S. Public, pg. 933
OUTBOARD MARINE CORPORATION—Greenway Partners, L.P.; U.S. Private, pg. 478
PETERSON BUILDERS, INC.; U.S. Private, pg. 857
PRO-LINE BOATS—American Marine Holdings Inc.; U.S. Private, pg. 58
RPC INCORPORATED; U.S. Public, pg. 1356
REGAL MARINE INDUSTRIES INC.; U.S. Private, pg. 917
RYDS BATINDUSTRI AB—Greenway Partners, L.P.; U.S. Private, pg. 479
SEA NYMPH INC.—Greenway Partners, L.P.; U.S. Private, pg. 478
SEA RAY—Brunswick Corporation; U.S. Public, pg. 266
SOUTHEAST CORRECT CRAFT, INC.—Correct Craft, Inc.; U.S. Private, pg. 277
STRATOS BOAT COMPANY, LTD.—Greenway Partners, L.P.; U.S. Private, pg. 478
SUNBIRD BOAT CO., INC.—Greenway Partners, L.P.; U.S. Private, pg. 478
TIMPTE INDUSTRIES, INC.; U.S. Private, pg. 1088
U.S. MARINE DIV.—Brunswick Corporation; U.S. Public, pg. 266
VICKERS PLC; Int'l, pg. 1466
VIKING YACHT CO.; U.S. Private, pg. 1140
WELLCRAFT MARINE CORP.—Genmar Holdings, Inc.; U.S. Private, pg. 447
WEST COAST CORRECT CRAFT, INC.—Correct Craft, Inc.; U.S. Private, pg. 277
YAMAHA MOTOR CO., LTD.—Yamaha Corporation; Int'l, pg. 1516

3743 — RAILROAD EQUIPMENT

ABB-DAIMLER BENZ TRANSPORTATION (ADTRANZ)—ABB Asea Brown Boveri (Holding) Ltd.; Int'l, pg. 8
ABB-DAIMLER BENZ TRANSPORTATION (ADTRANZ)—Daimler-Benz Aktiengesellschaft; Int'l, pg. 369
ABB TRACTION INC.—ABB Asea Brown Boveri (Holding) Ltd.; Int'l, pg. 5
ABC RAIL COGIFER INDUSTRIES—ABC Rail Products Corp.; U.S. Public, pg. 2
ABC RAIL PRODUCTS CORP.; U.S. Public, pg. 2
ACF INDUSTRIES, INC.—Icahn & Co., Inc.; U.S. Private, pg. 556
ACIERIES DE PLOERMEL—Varlen Corporation; U.S. Public, pg. 1711
ADTRANS PITTSBURGH—Daimler-Benz Aktiengesellschaft; Int'l, pg. 369
AMERICAN RAILCAR INDUSTRIES—Icahn & Co., Inc.; U.S. Private, pg. 556
AMWAY CORPORATION; U.S. Private, pg. 69
BN DIVISION—Bombardier Inc.; Int'l, pg. 200
BADGER CRANE CO.—Avis Industrial Corporation; U.S. Private, pg. 102
BINKLEY COMPANY—The Holland Hitch Company; U.S. Private, pg. 534
BOMBARDIER INC.; Int'l, pg. 199
BOMBARDIER PRORAIL LTD.—Bombardier Inc.; Int'l, pg. 200
CADEL DIV.—UAP, Inc.; Int'l, pg. 1426
CAPACITY OF TEXAS, INC.—Collins Industries, Inc.; U.S. Public, pg. 400
CAREL FOUCHE INDUSTRIES (CFI)—Jeumont-Schneider Trenformeteurs; Int'l, pg. 706
CHICAGO WEST PULLMAN CORPORATION; U.S. Private, pg. 235
CHROME CRANKSHAFT COMPANY—Varlen Corporation; U.S. Public, pg. 1710
CLARCOR, INC.; U.S. Public, pg. 381
CLARK FILTER—CLARCOR, Inc.; U.S. Public, pg. 381
CONSTRUCTIONS FERROVIAIRES DU MANS (CFM)—Jeumont-Schneider Trenformeteurs; Int'l, pg. 706
CONSTRUZIONI FERROVIARIE DI COLLEFERRO S.P.A.—Fiat Auto SpA; Int'l, pg. 481
CURRAN GROUP, INC.; U.S. Private, pg. 297
DAEWOO HEAVY INDUSTRIES, LTD.—Daewoo Corporation; Int'l, pg. 357
DORBYL LIMITED; Int'l, pg. 416
DUCHOSSOIS INDUSTRIES, INC.; U.S. Private, pg. 344
EB INSTALLASJON A/S—ABB Asea Brown Boveri (Holding) Ltd.; Int'l, pg. 3
ELECTRO-MOTIVE DIVISION—General Motors Corporation; U.S. Public, pg. 719
FAIRBANKS MORSE ENGINE DIVISION—Coltec Holdings Inc; U.S. Public, pg. 401
FAIRMONT TAMPER—Harsco Corporation; U.S. Public, pg. 793
FIAT AUTO SPA; Int'l, pg. 480
FIAT FERROVIARIA S.P.A.—Fiat Auto SpA; Int'l, pg. 481
L.B. FOSTER COMPANY; U.S. Public, pg. 675
GEC ALSTHOM—Alcatel Alsthom Compagnie Generale D'Electricite; Int'l, pg. 52
GENERAL ELECTRIC CAPITAL RAILCAR SERVICES—General Electric Company; U.S. Public, pg. 712
GENERAL ELECTRIC COMPANY; U.S. Public, pg. 709
GENERAL ELECTRIC DE MEXICO, S.A. DE C.V.—General Electric Company; U.S. Public, pg. 713
GENERAL MOTORS CORPORATION; U.S. Public, pg. 718
H M K ENTERPRISES, INC.; U.S. Private, pg. 489
CARL HASSE & WREDE GMBH—Knorr-Bremse AG; Int'l, pg. 738
JEUMONT-SCHNEIDER TRENFORMETEURS; Int'l, pg. 706
KALMAR INDUSTRIES AB—Trelleborg AB; Int'l, pg. 1420
KALMAR NOHAB AB—Trelleborg AB; Int'l, pg. 1421
KALMAR VERKSTAD AB—Trelleborg AB; Int'l, pg. 1421
KARL GEORG BAHNTECHNIK G.M.B.H.—Varlen Corporation; U.S. Public, pg. 1711
KAWASAKI RAIL CAR, INC.—Kawasaki Heavy Industries, Ltd.; Int'l, pg. 725
KEYSTONE RAILWAY EQUIPMENT COMPANY—Varlen Corporation; U.S. Public, pg. 1711
KNORR-BRAKE AUSTRIALIA PTY. LIMITED—Knorr-Bremse AG; Int'l, pg. 738
KNORR-BREMSE AG; Int'l, pg. 738
KNORR-BREMSE ELECTRONIC GMBH—Knorr-Bremse AG; Int'l, pg. 738
KNORR-BREMSE S.A. (PTY.) LTD.—Knorr-Bremse AG; Int'l, pg. 738
KRAUSS-MAFFEI AG—Mannesmann A.G.; Int'l, pg. 836
KRAUSS-MAFFEI VERKEHRSTECHNIK GMBH—Mannesmann A.G.; Int'l, pg. 836
LIBERTY MEDICAL SUPPLY, INC.—PolyMedica Industries, Inc.; U.S. Public, pg. 1315
LUCAS INDUSTRIES INC.—LucasVarity plc; Int'l, pg. 820
MINER ENTERPRISES INC.; U.S. Private, pg. 749
MITSUBISHI HEAVY INDUSTRIES LTD.; Int'l, pg. 873
NORDCO, INC.—Oak Industries Inc.; U.S. Public, pg. 1209
PANDROL JACKSON, INC.—Charter plc; Int'l, pg. 280
PLYMOUTH INDUSTRIES, INC.; U.S. Private, pg. 873
PORTEC, INC.; U.S. Public, pg. 1317
PORTEC INC., RAILWAY MAINTENANCE PRODUCTS DIV.—Portec, Inc.; U.S. Public, pg. 1318
PORTEC LTD.—Portec, Inc.; U.S. Public, pg. 1318
PORTEC (U.K.) LTD.—Portec, Inc.; U.S. Public, pg. 1318
PRIME MANUFACTURING COMPANY—Varlen Corporation; U.S. Public, pg. 1711
SAB IBERICA S.A.—Cardo AB; Int'l, pg. 271
SAB SISTEMI S.P.A.—Cardo AB; Int'l, pg. 271
SAB WABCO AB—Cardo AB; Int'l, pg. 271
SAB WABCO BENELUX—Cardo AB; Int'l, pg. 271
SAB WABCO ENGINEERING S.R.L.—Cardo AB; Int'l, pg. 271
SAB WABCO HOLDINGS B.V.—Cardo AB; Int'l, pg. 271
SAB WABCO LTD.—Cardo AB; Int'l, pg. 271
SAB WABCO N.V.—Cardo AB; Int'l, pg. 271
SAB WABCO S.A.—Cardo AB; Int'l, pg. 271
SAB WABCO S.P.A.—Cardo AB; Int'l, pg. 271
SCHNEIDER JEUMONT RAIL—Jeumont-Schneider Trenformeteurs; Int'l, pg. 706
SLOAN VALVE COMPANY; U.S. Private, pg. 1006
SOCIETE ANF-INDUSTRIE S.A.—Bombardier Inc.; Int'l, pg. 201
SUECOBRAS INDUSTRIA E COMERCIO LTDA.—Cardo AB; Int'l, pg. 271
SULZER-WINTERTHUR GROUP—Sulzer Ltd.; Int'l, pg. 1307
SWISS LOCOMOTIVE AND MACHINE WORKS—Sulzer Ltd.; Int'l, pg. 1307
THRALL CAR MFG. CO.—Duchossois Industries, Inc.; U.S. Private, pg. 344
TRANSCO INC.; U.S. Private, pg. 1096
TRANSCO RAILWAY PRODUCTS INC.—Transco Inc.; U.S. Private, pg. 1096
TRANSPORTATION EQUIPMENT GROUP-NORTH AMERICA—Bombardier Inc.; Int'l, pg. 200
UAP, INC.; Int'l, pg. 1426
UNION SWITCH & SIGNAL INC.—Ansaldo Signal N.V.; Int'l, pg. 77
VAPOR—Westinghouse Air Brake Company; U.S. Public, pg. 1761
VARLEN CORPORATION; U.S. Public, pg. 1710
VIBRATECH, INC.—IDEX Corporation; U.S. Public, pg. 862
WABCO WESTINGHOUSE COMPAGNIA FRENI S.P.A.—American Standard Inc.; U.S. Public, pg. 92
WESTINGHOUSE AIR BRAKE COMPANY; U.S. Public, pg. 1760
WHITING CORPORATION; U.S. Private, pg. 1173
YSD INDUSTRIES; U.S. Private, pg. 1194

3751 — MOTORCYCLES, BICYCLES & PARTS

AMERICAN HONDA MOTOR CO., INC.—Honda Motor Co., Ltd.; Int'l, pg. 634
ARITMOS AB—Proventus AB; Int'l, pg. 1072
BAYERISCHE MOTOREN WERKE AKTIENGESELLSCHAFT; Int'l, pg. 177
BOMBARDIER-ROTAX GMBH MOTORENFABRIK—Bombardier Inc.; Int'l, pg. 200
BRIDGESTONE CYCLE CO., LTD.—Bridgestone Corporation; Int'l, pg. 213
BRIDGESTONE CYCLE (U.S.A.), INC.—Bridgestone Corporation; Int'l, pg. 213

BUELL MOTORCYCLE COMPANY—Harley-Davidson, Inc.; *U.S. Public*, pg. 786
CANNONDALE CORPORATION; *U.S. Public*, pg. 301
COLUMBIA MANUFACTURING INC.; *U.S. Private*, pg. 255
CYCLES EUROPE; *Int'l*, pg. 350
DERBY CYCLE CORPORATION—Derby International Corporation S.A.; *Int'l*, pg. 394
DERBY CYCLE WERKE GMBH—Derby International Corporation S.A.; *Int'l*, pg. 394
DERBY INDUSTRIES (PTY.) LTD.—Derby International Corporation S.A.; *Int'l*, pg. 394
DERBY INTERNATIONAL CORPORATION S.A.; *Int'l*, pg. 394
GT BICYCLES, INC.; *U.S. Public*, pg. 695
GENERAL SIGNAL CORPORATION; *U.S. Public*, pg. 726
HALFORDS, LTD.—The Boots Company PLC; *Int'l*, pg. 203
HARLEY-DAVIDSON, INC.; *U.S. Public*, pg. 786
HARLEY-DAVIDSON MOTOR COMPANY—Harley-Davidson, Inc.; *U.S. Public*, pg. 786
HEDSTROM CORPORATION—Hicks, Muse, Tate & Furst Inc.; *U.S. Private*, pg. 526
HONDA DE MEXICO, S.A. DE C.V.—Honda Motor Co., Ltd.; *Int'l*, pg. 635
HONDA MOTOR CO., LTD.; *Int'l*, pg. 634
HONDA R&D CO., LTD.—Honda Motor Co., Ltd.; *Int'l*, pg. 634
HOOKER INDUSTRIES; *U.S. Private*, pg. 538
HUFFY CORPORATION; *U.S. Public*, pg. 846
G. JOANNOU CYCLE CO. INC.; *U.S. Private*, pg. 588
KAWASAKI HEAVY INDUSTRIES, LTD.; *Int'l*, pg. 725
KAWASAKI MOTORS CORP., U.S.A.—Kawasaki Heavy Industries, Ltd.; *Int'l*, pg. 725
KAWASAKI MOTORS MANUFACTURING CORP., U.S.A.—Kawasaki Heavy Industries, Ltd.; *Int'l*, pg. 725
KEUM KANG DEVELOPMENT INDUSTRIAL CO., LTD.—Hyundai Motor Company; *Int'l*, pg. 642
KIMBERLY-CLARK CORPORATION; *U.S. Public*, pg. 958
KONINKLIJKE GAZELLE BV—Derby International Corporation S.A.; *Int'l*, pg. 394
LDI, LTD.; *U.S. Private*, pg. 639
MIYATA INDUSTRY CO., LTD.; *Int'l*, pg. 884
THE MURRAY OHIO MFG. CO.—Tomkins PLC; *Int'l*, pg. 1397
OFFICINE A. MASERATI S.P.A.—Fiat Auto SpA; *Int'l*, pg. 482
P.T. PABRIK ARAYA INDONESIA—Nissho Iwai Corporation; *Int'l*, pg. 949
RALEIGH INDUSTRIES LTD.—Derby International Corporation S.A.; *Int'l*, pg. 394
RALEIGH INDUSTRIES OF CANADA LTD.—Derby International Corporation S.A.; *Int'l*, pg. 394
ROADMASTER/BRUNSWICK—Brunswick Corporation; *U.S. Public*, pg. 265
ROSS BICYCLES USA LTD.; *U.S. Private*, pg. 946
SCHWINN CYCLING & FITNESS INC.—Schwinn Holdings; *U.S. Private*, pg. 975
SHIMANO INC.; *Int'l*, pg. 1232
STURMEY-ARCHER LIMITED—Derby International Corporation S.A.; *Int'l*, pg. 394
SUZUKI MOTOR CORPORATION; *Int'l*, pg. 1322
TREK BICYCLE CORPORATION—Trek Corporation; *U.S. Private*, pg. 1099
TUCKER-ROCKY DISTRIBUTING—LDI, Ltd.; *U.S. Private*, pg. 639
TUCKER ROCKY DISTRIBUTING—LDI, Ltd.; *U.S. Private*, pg. 639
VIGLEN TECHNOLOGY PLC; *Int'l*, pg. 1468
YAMAHA MOTOR CO., LTD.—Yamaha Corporation; *Int'l*, pg. 1516

3761 — GUIDED MISSILES & SPACE VEHICLES

THE BOEING COMPANY; *U.S. Public*, pg. 239
BOEING DEFENSE & SPACE GROUP—The Boeing Company; *U.S. Public*, pg. 240
BOEING MILITARY AIRPLANES—The Boeing Company; *U.S. Public*, pg. 241
BOEING NORTH AMERICA, NORTH AMERICAN AIRCRAFT DIVISION—The Boeing Company; *U.S. Public*, pg. 241
DORNIER GMBH—Daimler-Benz Aktiengesellschaft; *Int'l*, pg. 367
EUROMISSLE DYNAMICS GROUP—British Aerospace p.l.c.; *Int'l*, pg. 218
FREEDOM FORGE CORPORATION; *U.S. Private*, pg. 425
GENERAL DYNAMICS CORPORATION; *U.S. Public*, pg. 708
GENERAL DYNAMICS HARLINGEN—General Dynamics Corporation; *U.S. Public*, pg. 709
GENERAL DYNAMICS INTERNATIONAL CORPORATION—General Dynamics Corporation; *U.S. Public*, pg. 709
HARRIS SPACE SYSTEMS CORP.—Harris Corporation; *U.S. Public*, pg. 791
INTEGRATED SYSTEMS ANALYSTS, INC.; *U.S. Private*, pg. 566
IRVIN AEROSPACE CANADA LTD.—Hunting Plc; *Int'l*, pg. 640
IRVIN AEROSPACE LTD.—Hunting Plc; *Int'l*, pg. 640
IRVIN FALLSKARMS AB—Hunting Plc; *Int'l*, pg. 640
IRVIN MANIFATTURE INDUSTRIALI S.P.A.—Hunting Plc; *Int'l*, pg. 640
ISRAEL AIRCRAFT INDUSTRIES LTD.; *Int'l*, pg. 689
LAGARDERE GROUPE; *Int'l*, pg. 791
LOCKHEED MARTIN AERONUTRONIC—Lockheed Martin Corporation; *U.S. Public*, pg. 1008
LOCKHEED MARTIN AEROSTRUCTURE—Lockheed Martin Corporation; *U.S. Public*, pg. 1006
LOCKHEED MARTIN CORPORATION; *U.S. Public*, pg. 1006
LOCKHEED MARTIN MISSILES & SPACE—Lockheed Martin Corporation; *U.S. Public*, pg. 1008
MBT DIVISION/ELECTRONICS GROUP—Israel Aircraft Industries Ltd.; *Int'l*, pg. 690
MARTIN MARIETTA ASTRONAUTICS—Lockheed Martin Corporation; *U.S. Public*, pg. 1007
MARTIN MARIETTA ASTRONAUTICS SPACE SYSTEMS—Lockheed Martin Corporation; *U.S. Public*, pg. 1007
MARTIN MARIETTA ELECTRONICS & MISSILES—Lockheed Martin Corporation; *U.S. Public*, pg. 1007
MCDONNELL AIRCRAFT & MISSILE SYSTEMS DIV.—The Boeing Company; *U.S. Public*, pg. 241
MOOG SPACE PRODUCTS DIV.—Moog Incorporated; *U.S. Public*, pg. 1127
NORTHROP GRUMMAN CORPORATION; *U.S. Public*, pg. 1197
OERLIKON AEROSPACE, INC.—Oerlikon-Buhrle Holding AG; *Int'l*, pg. 998
OERLIKON LOGISTICS LTD.—Oerlikon-Buhrle Holding AG; *Int'l*, pg. 998
OERLIKON SINGAPORE PTE. LTD.—Oerlikon-Buhrle Holding AG; *Int'l*, pg. 998
ORBITAL SCIENCES CORPORATION; *U.S. Public*, pg. 1229
PACER INFOTEC INC.; *U.S. Private*, pg. 830
RHONE-POULENC INC.—Rhone-Poulenc S.A.; *Int'l*, pg. 1112
SNECMA - SOCIETE NATIONALE D'ETUDE ET DE CONSTRUCTION DE MOTEURS D'AVIATION; *Int'l*, pg. 1165
SRS TECHNOLOGIES; *U.S. Private*, pg. 958
SAAB AB—Investor AB; *Int'l*, pg. 686
SAAB MISSILES AB—Investor AB; *Int'l*, pg. 686
SAAB SPACE AB—Investor AB; *Int'l*, pg. 687
TRW INC.; *U.S. Public*, pg. 1558
UNITED SPACE BOOSTERS, INC.—United Technologies Corporation; *U.S. Public*, pg. 1690

3764 — GUIDED MISSILE & SPACE VEHICLE PROPULSION UNITS & PROPULSION UNIT PARTS

AEROJET—GenCorp Inc.; *U.S. Public*, pg. 706
ALENIA SPAZIO—IRI Istituto Ricostruzione Industriale; *Int'l*, pg. 653
ALLIANT TECHSYSTEMS (AEROSPACE DIVISION)—Alliant Techsystems; *U.S. Public*, pg. 47
ALLIANT TECHSYSTEMS-ROCKET CENTER—Alliant Techsystems; *U.S. Public*, pg. 47
AMERICAN FUEL CELL & COATED FABRICS CO. (AMFUEL); *U.S. Private*, pg. 55
ARC PROPULSION DIVISION—Sequa Corporation; *U.S. Public*, pg. 1458
ATLANTIC RESEARCH CORPORATION—Sequa Corporation; *U.S. Public*, pg. 1458
BOEING NORTH AMERICA, NORTH AMERICAN AIRCRAFT DIVISION—The Boeing Company; *U.S. Public*, pg. 241
BOEING NORTH AMERICA, ROCKETDYNE DIVISION—The Boeing Company; *U.S. Public*, pg. 241
BRITISH AEROSPACE P.L.C.; *Int'l*, pg. 217
CHEM-TRONICS, INC.—The Interlake Corporation; *U.S. Public*, pg. 893
DEFENSE & LAUNCH VEHICLES DIVISION—Thiokol Corporation; *U.S. Public*, pg. 1597
DORNIER GMBH—Daimler-Benz Aktiengesellschaft; *Int'l*, pg. 367
ELECTRO KINETICS DIV.—Pacific Scientific Company; *U.S. Public*, pg. 1250
ELKTON DLV OPERATIONS—Thiokol Corporation; *U.S. Public*, pg. 1597
EUROMISSLE DYNAMICS GROUP—British Aerospace p.l.c.; *Int'l*, pg. 218
GENCORP INC.; *U.S. Public*, pg. 705
HERCULES AEROSPACE ESPANA, S.A.—Hercules Incorporated; *U.S. Public*, pg. 810
HERCULES GMBH—Hercules Incorporated; *U.S. Public*, pg. 811
THE INTERLAKE CORPORATION; *U.S. Public*, pg. 892
KETEMA DIVISION—Senior Engineering Group, plc.; *Int'l*, pg. 1222
LAGARDERE GROUPE; *Int'l*, pg. 791
MBT DIVISION/ELECTRONICS GROUP—Israel Aircraft Industries Ltd.; *Int'l*, pg. 690
MARTIN MARIETTA ASTRONAUTICS—Lockheed Martin Corporation; *U.S. Public*, pg. 1007
MARTIN MARIETTA MANNED SPACE SYSTEMS—Lockheed Martin Corporation; *U.S. Public*, pg. 1007
MATRA DEFENSE—Lagardere Groupe; *Int'l*, pg. 793
MATRA ELECTRONIQUE—Lagardere Groupe; *Int'l*, pg. 793
MOOG AIRCRAFT CONTROLS DIV.—Moog Incorporated; *U.S. Public*, pg. 1127
MOOG INCORPORATED; *U.S. Public*, pg. 1127
MOOG MOTION SYSTEMS DIV.—Moog Incorporated; *U.S. Public*, pg. 1127
NIHON-PALL LTD.—Pall Corporation; *U.S. Public*, pg. 1254
OEA AEROSPACE, INC.—OEA, Inc.; *U.S. Public*, pg. 1207
OEA, INC.; *U.S. Public*, pg. 1206
PACIFIC SCIENTIFIC COMPANY; *U.S. Public*, pg. 1250
PILATUS FLUGZEUGWERKE AG—Oerlikon-Buhrle Holding AG; *Int'l*, pg. 998
PROFESSIONAL AVIATION ASSOCIATES, INC.—Banner Aerospace, Inc.; *U.S. Public*, pg. 187
ROHR, INC.—The B.F. Goodrich Company; *U.S. Public*, pg. 751
SAAB MISSILES AB—Investor AB; *Int'l*, pg. 686
SEQUA CORPORATION; *U.S. Public*, pg. 1458
SOLAIR, INC.—Banner Aerospace, Inc.; *U.S. Public*, pg. 187
TALLEY DEFENSE SYSTEMS, INC.—Carpenter Technology Corporation; *U.S. Public*, pg. 308
TALLEY INDUSTRIES, INC.—Carpenter Technology Corporation; *U.S. Public*, pg. 307
THERM, INC.; *U.S. Private*, pg. 1079
THIOKOL CORPORATION; *U.S. Public*, pg. 1596
THIOKOL SPACE OPERATIONS—Thiokol Corporation; *U.S. Public*, pg. 1597
UNITED TECHNOLOGIES, CHEMICAL SYSTEMS DIV.—United Technologies Corporation; *U.S. Public*, pg. 1690
UNITED TECHNOLOGIES CHEMICAL SYSTEMS DIVISION—United Technologies Corporation; *U.S. Public*, pg. 1690
UNITED TECHNOLOGIES CORPORATION; *U.S. Public*, pg. 1689
UNIVERSAL PROPULSION CO., INC.—Carpenter Technology Corporation; *U.S. Public*, pg. 308
WYMAN-GORDON INVESTMENT CASTINGS, INC.—Wyman-Gordon; *U.S. Public*, pg. 1782

3769 — GUIDED MISSILE & SPACE VEHICLE PARTS & AUXILIARY EQUIPMENT, NEC

AIL SYSTEMS INC.—Eaton Corporation; *U.S. Public*, pg. 556
A.T.I. TOOLS, INC.—Snap-On Tools Corporation; *U.S. Public*, pg. 1480
AEROFLEX INTERNATIONAL, INC.—Aeroflex Incorporated; *U.S. Public*, pg. 24
AEROFLEX LABORATORIES INC.—Aeroflex Incorporated; *U.S. Public*, pg. 24
AERONCA, INC.—Magellan Aerospace Corporation; *Int'l*, pg. 829
ALCOA COMPOSITES, INC.—Aluminum Company of America; *U.S. Public*, pg. 60
ALENIA SPAZIO—IRI Istituto Ricostruzione Industriale; *Int'l*, pg. 653
BARNES ENGINEERING—EDO Corporation; *U.S. Public*, pg. 542
THE BOEING COMPANY; *U.S. Public*, pg. 239
BOEING DEFENSE & SPACE GROUP—The Boeing Company; *U.S. Public*, pg. 240
BOMBARDIER AEROSPACE—Bombardier Inc.; *Int'l*, pg. 200
BOMBARDIER INC.; *Int'l*, pg. 199
CAE INC.; *Int'l*, pg. 237
COURTAULDS AEROSPACE—Courtaulds plc; *Int'l*, pg. 338
CURTISS-WRIGHT CORP.; *U.S. Public*, pg. 469
CURTISS-WRIGHT FLIGHT SYSTEMS, INC.—Curtiss-Wright Corp.; *U.S. Public*, pg. 469
THE DEUTSCH COMPANY; *U.S. Private*, pg. 328
DOWTY AEROSPACE, ISLE OF MAN—TI Group plc; *Int'l*, pg. 1337
DOWTY AEROSPACE, WOLVERHAMPTON—TI Group plc; *Int'l*, pg. 1337
DUCOMMUN INCORPORATED; *U.S. Public*, pg. 533
ELECTRO KINETICS DIV.—Pacific Scientific Company; *U.S. Public*, pg. 1250
ELECTRONICS & SYSTEMS INTEGRATION DIVISION—Northrop Grumman Corporation; *U.S. Public*, pg. 1198
FAG BEARINGS LIMITED—FAG Group; *Int'l*, pg. 469
FLEET INDUSTRIES—Magellan Aerospace Corporation; *Int'l*, pg. 829
GKN WESTLAND AEROSPACE NORTH AMERICA INC.—GKN plc; *Int'l*, pg. 535
GOULD ELECTRONICS INC.—Thermo Electron Corporation; *U.S. Public*, pg. 1591
HR TEXTRON—Textron Inc.; *U.S. Public*, pg. 1589
HARRIS SPACE SYSTEMS CORP.—Harris Corporation; *U.S. Public*, pg. 791
HUGHES-TREITLER MANUFACTURING CORPORATION; *U.S. Private*, pg. 547
INTERCONTINENTAL MFG. CO.—Datron Incorporated; *U.S. Private*, pg. 313
KAISER AEROSPACE & ELECTRONICS CORP.; *U.S. Private*, pg. 605
KAISER ELECTRO OPTICS—Kaiser Aerospace & Electronics Corp.; *U.S. Private*, pg. 605
KETEMA DIVISION—Senior Engineering Group, plc.; *Int'l*, pg. 1222
KETEMA, INC.—KTM Holdings Corp.; *U.S. Private*, pg. 604
LOCKHEED MARTIN AERONUTRONIC—Lockheed Martin Corporation; *U.S. Public*, pg. 1008
LOCKHEED MARTIN CORPORATION; *U.S. Public*, pg. 1006
LOCKHEED MARTIN FEDERAL SYSTEMS-GAITHERSBURG—Lockheed Martin Corporation; *U.S. Public*, pg. 1008
LOCKHEED SPACE OPERATIONS CO.—Lockheed Martin Corporation; *U.S. Public*, pg. 1009
LORAL SPACE & COMMUNICATIONS; *U.S. Public*, pg. 1014
LUCAS INDUSTRIES INC.—LucasVarity plc; *Int'l*, pg. 820
MBT DIVISION/ELECTRONICS GROUP—Israel Aircraft Industries Ltd.; *Int'l*, pg. 690
MAGELLAN AEROSPACE CORPORATION; *Int'l*, pg. 829
MARTIN MARIETTA ASTRONAUTICS—Lockheed Martin Corporation; *U.S. Public*, pg. 1007
MCDONNELL AIRCRAFT & MISSILE SYSTEMS DIV.—The Boeing Company; *U.S. Public*, pg. 241
NORMALAIR-GARRETT LTD.—AlliedSignal Inc.; *U.S. Public*, pg. 54
PACIFIC SCIENTIFIC COMPANY; *U.S. Public*, pg. 1250
PALL EUROPE LTD.—Pall Corporation; *U.S. Public*, pg. 1254
PALL ILFRACOMBE LTD.—Pall Corporation; *U.S. Public*, pg. 1254
PILATUS FLUGZEUGWERKE AG—Oerlikon-Buhrle Holding AG; *Int'l*, pg. 998
PRESSURE SYSTEMS, INC.; *U.S. Private*, pg. 882
PROGRAMMED COMPOSITES, INC.—Pressure Systems, Inc.; *U.S. Private*, pg. 882
REMMELE ENGINEERING, INC.; *U.S. Private*, pg. 921
SNECMA - SOCIETE NATIONALE D'ETUDE ET DE CONSTRUCTION DE MOTEURS D'AVIATION; *Int'l*, pg. 1165
SAAB MISSILES AB—Investor AB; *Int'l*, pg. 686
SAAB SPACE AB—Investor AB; *Int'l*, pg. 687
SERVOTRONICS, INC.; *U.S. Public*, pg. 1462

SNAP-ON TOOLS CORPORATION; U.S. Public, pg. 1480
SPACE SYSTEMS/LORAL, INC.—Loral Space & Communications; U.S. Public, pg. 1014
SPAR AEROSPACE LIMITED; Int'l, pg. 1287
STANFORD TELECOMMUNICATIONS; U.S. Public, pg. 1508
TECSTAR INC.; U.S. Private, pg. 1072
TELEFLEX INCORPORATED; U.S. Public, pg. 1569
UNITED DEFENSE L.P.—Carlyle Holding Corporation; U.S. Private, pg. 213
WYMAN-GORDON INVESTMENT CASTINGS, INC.—Wyman-Gordon; U.S. Public, pg. 1782

3792 — TRAVEL TRAILERS & CAMPERS

AAF INDUSTRIES PLC; Int'l, pg. 1
B & B HOMES CORPORATION; U.S. Private, pg. 105
COACHMEN AUTOMOTIVE—Coachmen Industries, Inc.; U.S. Public, pg. 388
COACHMEN INDUSTRIES, INC.; U.S. Public, pg. 387
COACHMEN RECREATIONAL VEHICLE COMPANY—Coachmen Industries, Inc.; U.S. Public, pg. 388
COACHMEN RECREATIONAL VEHICLE COMPANY OF GEORGIA—Coachmen Industries, Inc.; U.S. Public, pg. 388
THE COLEMAN COMPANY, INC.—MacAndrews & Forbes Holdings Inc.; U.S. Private, pg. 690
COUNTRY COACH, INC.—National R.V., Inc.; U.S. Public, pg. 1159
CREATIVE GROUP INC.; U.S. Private, pg. 287
FLEETWOOD CANADA LTD.—Fleetwood Enterprises, Inc.; U.S. Public, pg. 652
FLEETWOOD ENTERPRISES, INC.; U.S. Public, pg. 650
FLEETWOOD FOLDING TRAILERS, INC.—Fleetwood Enterprises, Inc.; U.S. Public, pg. 651
FLEETWOOD TRAVEL TRAILERS OF CALIFORNIA, INC.-RUBIDOUX—Fleetwood Enterprises, Inc.; U.S. Public, pg. 652
FRANK INDUSTRIES, INC.; U.S. Private, pg. 423
GEM TOP MFG., INC.; U.S. Private, pg. 443
GEORGIE BOY MANUFACTURING, INC.—Coachmen Industries, Inc.; U.S. Public, pg. 388
HOLIDAY RAMBLER—Monaco Coach Corporation; U.S. Public, pg. 1123
HOMETTE CORPORATION—Skyline Corporation; U.S. Public, pg. 1476
KING OF THE ROAD—Chief Industries, Inc.; U.S. Private, pg. 236
KIT MANUFACTURING COMPANY; U.S. Public, pg. 962
LANCE CAMPER MANUFACTURING CORPORATION; U.S. Private, pg. 645
LAYTON HOMES CORP.—Skyline Corporation; U.S. Public, pg. 1476
MARK III INDUSTRIES; U.S. Private, pg. 704
MITCHELL COACH MANUFACTURING; U.S. Private, pg. 753
MONACO COACH CORPORATION; U.S. Public, pg. 1123
MOTOR HOME SERVICE FACILITY-DECATUR, INDIANA—Fleetwood Enterprises, Inc.; U.S. Public, pg. 652
MOTOR HOME SERVICE FACILITY-RIVERSIDE, CALIFORNIA—Fleetwood Enterprises, Inc.; U.S. Public, pg. 652
NATIONAL R.V., INC.; U.S. Public, pg. 1159
PREMIER BUILDING GROUP—AAF Industries Plc; Int'l, pg. 1
R-4 KIT MFG. CO.—Kit Manufacturing Company; U.S. Public, pg. 962
R-2 KIT MFG. CO.—Kit Manufacturing Company; U.S. Public, pg. 962
RECREATIONAL VEHICLE DIV.—Kit Manufacturing Company; U.S. Public, pg. 962
ROLLALONG LIMITED—Hanson PLC; Int'l, pg. 593
SHASTA INDUSTRIES—Coachmen Industries, Inc.; U.S. Public, pg. 388
SKYLINE CORPORATION; U.S. Public, pg. 1476
SKYLINE HOMES, INC.—Skyline Corporation; U.S. Public, pg. 1476
SUNLINE COACH CO., INC.; U.S. Private, pg. 1053
TIFFIN MOTOR HOMES, INC.; U.S. Private, pg. 1086
TRAVELMASTER RECREATIONAL VEHICLES—Coachmen Industries, Inc.; U.S. Public, pg. 388
VIKING RECREATIONAL VEHICLES, INC.—Coachmen Industries, Inc.; U.S. Public, pg. 388
XPLORER MOTOR HOME DIV.—Frank Industries, Inc.; U.S. Private, pg. 423
ZIEMAN MANUFACTURING COMPANY; U.S. Private, pg. 1205

3795 — TANKS & TANK COMPONENTS

AEROFLEX INTERNATIONAL, INC.—Aeroflex Incorporated; U.S. Public, pg. 24
AEROFLEX LABORATORIES INC.—Aeroflex Incorporated; U.S. Public, pg. 24
ALFA-LAVAL INDUSTRIETECHNIK G.M.B.H.—Tetra Laval Group; Int'l, pg. 1379
ALFA-LAVAL LTD.—Tetra Laval Group; Int'l, pg. 1379
ALFA-LAVAL N.V.—Tetra Laval Group; Int'l, pg. 1380
ALLIEDSIGNAL AEROSPACE—AlliedSignal Inc.; U.S. Public, pg. 50
BMY CO.—Harsco Corporation; U.S. Public, pg. 793
COMBAT SYSTEMS DIVISION—Carlyle Holding Corporation; U.S. Private, pg. 213
FMC CORPORATION; U.S. Public, pg. 604
GENERAL DYNAMICS CORPORATION; U.S. Public, pg. 708
GENERAL DYNAMICS INTERNATIONAL CORPORATION—General Dynamics Corporation; U.S. Public, pg. 709
GENERAL DYNAMICS LAND SYSTEMS DIV.—General Dynamics Corporation; U.S. Public, pg. 709
HARSCO CORPORATION; U.S. Public, pg. 792
LKM GROUP A/S—Tetra Laval Group; Int'l, pg. 1379
MANSOUR GENERAL DYNAMICS LTD.—General Dynamics Corporation; U.S. Public, pg. 709
MASCOTECH TUBULAR PRODUCTS, INC.—MascoTech, Inc.; U.S. Public, pg. 1055
MOOG MOTION SYSTEMS DIV.—Moog Incorporated; U.S. Public, pg. 1127
RAMTA DIVISION/BEDEK AVIATION GROUP—Israel Aircraft Industries Ltd.; Int'l, pg. 690
ROTTERDAM VENTURES INC.—Galesi Group; U.S. Private, pg. 437
SHL DIVISION/COMMERCIAL AIRCRAFT GROUP—Israel Aircraft Industries Ltd.; Int'l, pg. 690
SIOUX MANUFACTURING CORP.; U.S. Private, pg. 1003
TARGET OILFIELD PIPE & SUPPLY COMPANY (TOPS)—Texas Pacific Group; U.S. Private, pg. 1078
TEXTRON INC.; U.S. Public, pg. 1588
VICKERS PLC; Int'l, pg. 1466
WAUKESHA CHERRY-BURRELL—United Dominion Industries, Ltd.; U.S. Public, pg. 1677

3799 — TRANSPORTATION EQUIPMENT, NEC

AMERICAN SYSTEMS CORPORATION; U.S. Private, pg. 63
AMES COMPANY—U.S. Industries, Inc.; U.S. Public, pg. 1683
ARCTIC CAT INC.; U.S. Public, pg. 128
ASEA TRUCK AB—ABB Asea Brown Boveri (Holding) Ltd.; Int'l, pg. 7
BOMBARDIER INC.; Int'l, pg. 199
BOMBARDIER MOTORIZED CONSUMER PRODUCTS GROUP—Bombardier Inc.; Int'l, pg. 200
BOMBARDIER-NORDTRAC OY—Bombardier Inc.; Int'l, pg. 200
BOMBARDIER-ROTAX GMBH MOTORENFABRIK—Bombardier Inc.; Int'l, pg. 200
THE CALKINS MANUFACTURING COMPANY; U.S. Private, pg. 201
THE COLEMAN COMPANY, INC.—MacAndrews & Forbes Holdings Inc.; U.S. Private, pg. 690
COLUMBIA PARCAR CORP.—Flambeau Corporation; U.S. Private, pg. 409
DRAW-TITE, INC.—Masco Corporation; U.S. Public, pg. 1054
E-Z-GO TEXTRON—Textron Inc.; U.S. Public, pg. 1589
E Z LOADER BOAT TRAILERS, INC.—E Z Loader Corporate; U.S. Private, pg. 353
FLAMBEAU CORPORATION; U.S. Private, pg. 409
HONDA MOTOR CO., LTD.; Int'l, pg. 634
INGERSOLL MACHINE AND TOOL DIVISION—The Ivaco Group; Int'l, pg. 695
KARTS INTERNATIONAL INC.; U.S. Public, pg. 944
KASSBOHRER NORTH AMERICA—Daimler-Benz Aktiengesellschaft; Int'l, pg. 368
KRAUSS-MAFFEI VERKEHRSTECHNIK GMBH—Mannesmann A.G.; Int'l, pg. 836
MINER ENTERPRISES INC.; U.S. Private, pg. 749
POLARIS INDUSTRIES, INC.; U.S. Public, pg. 1313
RANSOMES-CUSHMAN-RYAN—Ransomes Plc; Int'l, pg. 1088
REESE PRODUCTS, INC.—Masco Corporation; U.S. Public, pg. 1054
SPECIALTY EQUIPMENT COMPANIES INC.; U.S. Public, pg. 1496
SPICER OFF-HIGHWAY AXLE DIV.—Dana Corporation; U.S. Public, pg. 479
SPICER TRAILER PRODUCTS DIV.—Dana Corporation; U.S. Public, pg. 479
TRUE TEMPER HARDWARE COMPANY—Huffy Corporation; U.S. Public, pg. 846
YAMAHA MOTOR CO., LTD.—Yamaha Corporation; Int'l, pg. 1516

3812 — NAVIGATION, GUIDANCE, SEARCH & DETECTION SYSTEMS & INSTRUMENTS

A&M INSTRUMENTS INC.—BTR plc; Int'l, pg. 125
AAR ADVANCED STRUCTURES DIV.—AAR Corp.; U.S. Public, pg. 1
AAR ALLEN AIRMOTIVE, INC.—AAR Corp.; U.S. Public, pg. 1
AAR CORP.; U.S. Public, pg. 1
APSYS (AEROSPATIALE PROTECTION SYSTEMES)—Aerospatiale; Int'l, pg. 29
AERO PRODUCTS DIV.—Litton Industries, Inc.; U.S. Public, pg. 1002
AEROFLEX LABORATORIES INC.—Aeroflex Incorporated; U.S. Public, pg. 24
AEROSONIC CORPORATION; U.S. Public, pg. 25
AEROSPATIALE; Int'l, pg. 28
AIR TRAFFIC CONTROL SYSTEMS DIVISION—Harris Corporation; U.S. Public, pg. 792
AIRBORNE SYSTEMS INTEGRATION DIVISION—California Microwave, Inc.; U.S. Public, pg. 293
ALCATEL KIRK—Alcatel Alsthom Compagnie Generale D'Electricite; Int'l, pg. 56
ALDEN ELECTRONICS, INC.—Platinum Equity Holdings, LLC; U.S. Private, pg. 872
ALENIA—IRI Istituto Ricostruzione Industriale; Int'l, pg. 653
ALENIA SPAZIO—IRI Istituto Ricostruzione Industriale; Int'l, pg. 653
ALENIA SYSTEMI DIFESA—IRI Istituto Ricostruzione Industriale; Int'l, pg. 653
ALLARD INDUSTRIES; U.S. Private, pg. 36
ALLIANT TECHSYSTEMS; U.S. Public, pg. 47
ALLIEDSIGNAL AEROSPACE—AlliedSignal Inc.; U.S. Public, pg. 50
ALLIEDSIGNAL AEROSPACE CANADA, AEROMARINE—AlliedSignal Inc.; U.S. Public, pg. 53
ALLIEDSIGNAL AEROSPACE CANADA, ELECTRONIC SYSTEMS—AlliedSignal Inc.; U.S. Public, pg. 54
ALLIEDSIGNAL AEROSPACE CANADA OCEAN DEFENSE SYSTEMS—AlliedSignal Inc.; U.S. Public, pg. 53
ALLIEDSIGNAL AIRLINE SERVICES, ALLIED SIGNAL AEROSPACE CANADA—AlliedSignal Inc.; U.S. Public, pg. 53
ALLIEDSIGNAL COMMERCIAL AVIONIC SYSTEMS—AlliedSignal Inc.; U.S. Public, pg. 50
ALLIEDSIGNAL COMMERCIAL AVIONICS SYSTEMS—AlliedSignal Inc.; U.S. Public, pg. 50
ALLIEDSIGNAL GUIDANCE & CONTROL—AlliedSignal Inc.; U.S. Public, pg. 50
ALLIEDSIGNAL GUIDANCE & CONTROL SYSTEMS—AlliedSignal Inc.; U.S. Public, pg. 50
ALLIEDSIGNAL GUIDANCE SYSTEMS DIV.—AlliedSignal Inc.; U.S. Public, pg. 50
ALLIEDSIGNAL INC.; U.S. Public, pg. 49
ALLIEDSIGNAL OCEAN SYSTEMS—AlliedSignal Inc.; U.S. Public, pg. 50
AMECOM DIV.—Litton Industries, Inc.; U.S. Public, pg. 1002
AMETEK, INC.; U.S. Public, pg. 99
APPLIED BIOSYSTEMS—The Perkin-Elmer Corporation; U.S. Public, pg. 1279
APPLIED TECHNOLOGY—Litton Industries, Inc.; U.S. Public, pg. 1002
APPLIED TECHNOLOGY (GERMANY)—Litton Industries, Inc.; U.S. Public, pg. 1004
APPLIED TECHNOLOGY (UK)—Litton Industries, Inc.; U.S. Public, pg. 1004
ARGOSYSTEMS, INC.—The Boeing Company; U.S. Public, pg. 240
ARIZONA INSTRUMENT CORPORATION; U.S. Public, pg. 129
ASTRONAUTICS CORPORATION OF AMERICA; U.S. Private, pg. 93
AUTOMATIC POWER, INC.—Spectra-Physics AB; Int'l, pg. 1289
AVIONICS & COMMUNICATIONS—Rockwell International Corporation; U.S. Public, pg. 1397
B&D INSTRUMENTS AND AVIONICS, INC.—Bowthorpe plc; Int'l, pg. 208
BTR PLC; Int'l, pg. 124
BALL AEROSPACE & TECHNOLOGIES CORP.—Ball Corporation; U.S. Public, pg. 171
BALL CORPORATION; U.S. Public, pg. 170
BARNSTEAD/THERMOLYNE CORPORATION—Sybron International Corporation; U.S. Public, pg. 1545
BENCHMARK ELECTRONICS, INC.—Benchmark Electronics Inc.; U.S. Public, pg. 211
A. BIEDERMAN, INC.—Triumph Group, Inc.; U.S. Public, pg. 1640
BLUE M ELECTRIC CO.—General Signal Corporation; U.S. Public, pg. 726
BOEING AEROSPACE & ELECTRONICS, INC.—The Boeing Company; U.S. Public, pg. 240
BOEING AEROSPACE & ELECTRONICS, IRVING—The Boeing Company; U.S. Public, pg. 240
BOEING AEROSPACE & ELECTRONICS, OAK RIDGE—The Boeing Company; U.S. Public, pg. 240
THE BOEING COMPANY; U.S. Public, pg. 239
BOEING DEFENSE & SPACE GROUP—The Boeing Company; U.S. Public, pg. 240
BOEING ELECTRONICS, INC.—The Boeing Company; U.S. Public, pg. 240
BOEING NORTH AMERICA, AUTONETICS ELECTRONIC SYSTEMS DIVISION—The Boeing Company; U.S. Public, pg. 241
BOEING NORTH AMERICA, TACTICAL SYSTEMS DIVISION—The Boeing Company; U.S. Public, pg. 241
BRITISH AEROSPACE (SYSTEMS AND EQUIPMENT) LTD.—British Aerospace p.l.c.; Int'l, pg. 217
BROWN BROTHERS & COMPANY LTD.—Vickers PLC; Int'l, pg. 1466
CAE ELECTRONICS, LTD.—CAE Inc.; Int'l, pg. 237
CALIFORNIA MICROWAVE, INC.; U.S. Public, pg. 293
CELSIUS INVEST AB—Celsius AB; Int'l, pg. 276
CHANDLER EVANS CONTROL SYSTEMS DIVISION—Coltec Holdings Inc; U.S. Public, pg. 401
CHANNEL TECHNOLOGIES, INC.; U.S. Private, pg. 228
CLIMET INSTRUMENTS CO.—Venturedyne, Ltd.; U.S. Private, pg. 1136
COHERENT, INC.-AUBURN GROUP—Coherent, Inc.; U.S. Public, pg. 395
COMPONENTS DIVISION/BEDEK AVIATION GROUP—Israel Aircraft Industries Ltd.; Int'l, pg. 690
COMPUDYNE CORPORATION; U.S. Public, pg. 419
COMSAT RSI, INC.—COMSAT Corporation; U.S. Public, pg. 424
CONDOR PACIFIC INDUSTRIES, INC.; U.S. Private, pg. 262
CONTRAVES ADVANCED DEVICES, SDN. BHD.—Oerlikon-Buhrle Holding AG; Int'l, pg. 998
CONTROL LASER CORPORATION—Excel Technology, Inc.; U.S. Public, pg. 599
CUBIC CORPORATION; U.S. Public, pg. 466
DBA SYSTEMS, INC.; U.S. Public, pg. 472
DRS TECHNOLOGIES, INC.; U.S. Public, pg. 474
DATA CONTROL SYSTEMS—CompuDyne Corporation; U.S. Public, pg. 420
DAWSON GEOPHYSICAL COMPANY; U.S. Public, pg. 489
DECCA—Litton Industries, Inc.; U.S. Public, pg. 1003
DELFT INSTRUMENTS N.V.; Int'l, pg. 388
DERLAN INDUSTRIES LIMITED; Int'l, pg. 395
DIGICOURSE, INC.—The Laitram Corporation; U.S. Private, pg. 643
DORNE & MARGOLIN, INC.—United Capital Corp.; U.S. Public, pg. 1675
DUKANE CORPORATION; U.S. Private, pg. 345
DWYER INSTRUMENTS INC.; U.S. Private, pg. 350
EDO CORPORATION; U.S. Public, pg. 541
EDO MARINE & AIRCRAFT SYSTEMS—EDO Corporation; U.S. Public, pg. 542
ESCO ELECTRONICS CORPORATION; U.S. Public, pg. 546
EAGLE ELECTRONICS—Lowrance Electronics, Inc.; U.S. Public, pg. 1016

ELECTRODYNAMICS, INC.—Carpenter Technology Corporation; *U.S. Public*, pg. 308
ELECTROMAGNETIC SYSTEMS DIV.—Raytheon Company; *U.S. Public*, pg. 1364
ELECTRONIC PRINTING SYSTEMS—Eastman Kodak Company; *U.S. Public*, pg. 551
ELECTRONICS & SYSTEMS INTEGRATION DIVISION—Northrop Grumman Corporation; *U.S. Public*, pg. 1198
ELTA ELECTRONICS INDUSTRIES, LTD.—Israel Aircraft Industries Ltd.; *Int'l*, pg. 690
ERICSSON DEFENSE SYSTEMS PTY. LTD.—Telefonaktiebolaget LM Ericsson; *Int'l*, pg. 1366
ERICSSON RADAR ELECTRONICS AB—Telefonaktiebolaget LM Ericsson; *Int'l*, pg. 1363
ERISOFT AB—Telefonaktiebolaget LM Ericsson; *Int'l*, pg. 1364
ESCORT, INC.; *U.S. Private*, pg. 383
FFV AEROTECH AB—Celsius AB; *Int'l*, pg. 276
FKI PLC; *Int'l*, pg. 471
FMC CORPORATION; *U.S. Public*, pg. 604
FINNIGAN CORPORATION—Thermo Electron Corporation; *U.S. Public*, pg. 1591
THE FLIGHT DATA COMPANY LTD.—Bowthorpe plc; *Int'l*, pg. 207
FLIR SYSTEMS, INC.; *U.S. Public*, pg. 654
GDE SYSTEMS, INC.—Tracor, Inc.; *U.S. Public*, pg. 1627
GEC-MARCONI HAZELTINE CORPORATION—The General Electric Company, p.l.c.; *Int'l*, pg. 544
GKN WESTLAND AEROSPACE LIMITED—GKN plc; *Int'l*, pg. 535
GKN WESTLAND TECHNOLOGIES LIMITED—GKN plc; *Int'l*, pg. 535
GENERAL KINETICS INCORPORATED; *U.S. Public*, pg. 716
GERBER SCIENTIFIC, INC.; *U.S. Public*, pg. 740
GIGA-TRONICS INCORPORATED; *U.S. Public*, pg. 742
GOLDSTAR PRECISION INDUSTRIES LTD.—LG Group; *Int'l*, pg. 779
BF GOODRICH AVIONIC SYSTEMS, INC.—The B.F. Goodrich Company; *U.S. Public*, pg. 751
THE B.F. GOODRICH COMPANY; *U.S. Public*, pg. 751
GOULD INSTRUMENT SYSTEMS, S.A.—Thermo Electron Corporation; *U.S. Public*, pg. 1592
HRB SYSTEMS—Raytheon Company; *U.S. Public*, pg. 1365
HARRIS SPACE SYSTEMS CORP.—Harris Corporation; *U.S. Public*, pg. 791
HATHAWAY CORPORATION; *U.S. Public*, pg. 798
HAWKER INSTRUMENTS LTD.—BTR plc; *Int'l*, pg. 125
HAZELTINE OCEAN SYSTEMS—The General Electric Company, p.l.c.; *Int'l*, pg. 544
HEATH CONSULTANTS INCORPORATED; *U.S. Private*, pg. 518
HOLLANDSE SIGNAALAPPARATEN B.V.—Thomson S.A.; *Int'l*, pg. 1384
HONEYWELL DEFENSE AVIONICS SYSTEMS—Honeywell Inc.; *U.S. Public*, pg. 834
HONEYWELL INC.; *U.S. Public*, pg. 833
HUMPHREY, INC.—Remec, Inc.; *U.S. Public*, pg. 1376
HYDROSCIENCE, INC.; *U.S. Private*, pg. 552
INTERNATIONAL TRANSDUCER CORPORATION—Channel Technologies, Inc.; *U.S. Private*, pg. 228
INTERSPIRO INC.—Spectra-Physics AB; *Int'l*, pg. 1289
ISRAEL AIRCRAFT INDUSTRIES LTD.; *Int'l*, pg. 689
ITHACO INC.; *U.S. Private*, pg. 576
JAPAN AVIATION ELECTRONICS INDUSTRY, LTD.; *Int'l*, *pg. 701*
JET ELECTRONICS & TECHNOLOGY, INC.—The B.F. Goodrich Company; *U.S. Public*, pg. 751
KAMAN AEROSPACE CORP.—Kaman Corporation; *U.S. Public*, pg. 942
KEARFOTT GUIDANCE & NAVIGATION CORP.—Astronautics Corporation of America; *U.S. Private*, pg. 93
KEVLIN CORPORATION; *U.S. Public*, pg. 953
KIMBLE GLASS INC.—Viag AG; *Int'l*, pg. 1464
KODAK PATHE S.A.—Eastman Kodak Company; *U.S. Public*, pg. 554
KOLLMORGEN CORPORATION; *U.S. Public*, pg. 965
KRUPP ENGINEERING (AUSTRALIA) (PTY.) LTD.—Fried. Krupp AG; *Int'l*, pg. 511
KRUPP HOESCH STAHL UND METALL GMBH—Fried. Krupp AG; *Int'l*, pg. 514
KRUPP HOESCH STAHLEXPORT GMBH—Fried. Krupp AG; *Int'l*, pg. 515
L3 COMMUNICATIONS ADVANCED RECORDERS DIV.—L3 Communications; *U.S. Private*, pg. 638
LIEBHERR-AEROSPACE LINDENBERG GMBH—Liebherr-International AG; *Int'l*, pg. 808
LITEF (GMBH)—Litton Industries, Inc.; *U.S. Public*, pg. 1004
LITKOR LITTON KOREA LTD.—Litton Industries, Inc.; *U.S. Public*, pg. 1004
LITTON APPLIED TECHNOLOGY—Litton Industries, Inc.; *U.S. Public*, pg. 1003
LITTON AVIONICS SYSTEMS—Litton Industries, Inc.; *U.S. Public*, pg. 1005
LITTON INDUSTRIES, INC.; *U.S. Public*, pg. 1002
LITTON INSTRUMENTS & LIFE SUPPORT—Litton Industries, Inc.; *U.S. Public*, pg. 1003
LITTON ITALIA S.P.A.—Litton Industries, Inc.; *U.S. Public*, pg. 1004
LITTON SYSTEMS CANADA LTD. (NOVA SCOTIA)—Litton Industries, Inc.; *U.S. Public*, pg. 1005
LOCKHEED MARTIN ADVANCED PROJECTS—Lockheed Martin Corporation; *U.S. Public*, pg. 1008
LOCKHEED MARTIN AERONUTRONIC—Lockheed Martin Corporation; *U.S. Public*, pg. 1008
LOCKHEED MARTIN AIR TRAFFIC MANAGEMENT—Lockheed Martin Corporation; *U.S. Public*, pg. 1008
LOCKHEED MARTIN CORPORATION; *U.S. Public*, pg. 1006
LOCKHEED MARTIN-FAIRCHILD—Lockheed Martin Corporation; *U.S. Public*, pg. 1008
LOCKHEED MARTIN FAIRCHILD IMAGING SENSORS—Lockheed Martin Corporation; *U.S. Public*, pg. 1008
LOCKHEED MARTIN FAIRCHILD SYSTEMS—Lockheed Martin Corporation; *U.S. Public*, pg. 1008
LOCKHEED MARTIN FEDERAL SYSTEMS-OWEGO—Lockheed Martin Corporation; *U.S. Public*, pg. 1008
LOCKHEED MARTIN LIBRASCOPE—Lockheed Martin Corporation; *U.S. Public*, pg. 1008
LOCKHEED MARTIN SPACE & RANGE SYSTEMS—Lockheed Martin Corporation; *U.S. Public*, pg. 1009
LOCKHEED MARTIN TACTICAL DEFENSE SYSTEMS—Lockheed Martin Corporation; *U.S. Public*, pg. 1009
LOCKHEED MARTIN TACTICAL DEFENSE SYSTEMS (AKRON)—Lockheed Martin Corporation; *U.S. Public*, pg. 1009
LOCKHEED MARTIN TACTICAL DEFENSE SYSTEMS (ARIZONA)—Lockheed Martin Corporation; *U.S. Public*, pg. 1009
LOCKLEY MANUFACTURING DIVISION—The Entwistle Company; *U.S. Private*, pg. 378
LORAL SPACE & COMMUNICATIONS; *U.S. Public*, pg. 1014
LOWRANCE AUSTRALIA—Lowrance Electronics, Inc.; *U.S. Public*, pg. 1016
LOWRANCE ELECTRONICS, INC.; *U.S. Public*, pg. 1015
LUCAS INDUSTRIES INC.—LucasVarity plc; *Int'l*, pg. 820
MAN URANIT GRONAU GMBH—MAN Aktiengesellschaft; *Int'l*, pg. 825
MALAT (UNMANNED AIR VEHICLES) DIVISION/MILITARY AIRCRAFT GROUP—Israel Aircraft Industries Ltd.; *Int'l*, pg. 690
MAST MICROWAVE DIVISION—Kevlin Corporation; *U.S. Public*, pg. 953
MCCLAIN EASY PACK—McClain Industries, Inc.; *U.S. Public*, pg. 1065
MECHANICAL TECHNOLOGY INC.; *U.S. Public*, pg. 1077
MEGAPULSE, INC.; *U.S. Private*, pg. 729
METEX CORPORATION—United Capital Corp.; *U.S. Public*, *pg. 1674*
MILITARY AVIONICS DIVISION—Honeywell Inc.; *U.S. Public*, pg. 834
MONTEK DIV.—Raytheon Company; *U.S. Public*, pg. 1366
MOOG MOTION SYSTEMS DIV.—Moog Incorporated; *U.S. Public*, pg. 1127
NAI TECHNOLOGIES, INC.; *U.S. Public*, pg. 1144
NASAM INTERNATIONAL, INCORPORATED—Banner Aerospace, Inc.; *U.S. Public*, pg. 187
NATIONAL SYSTEMS & RESEARCH CO.; *U.S. Private*, pg. 787
NAVCOM DEFENSE ELECTRONICS, INC.; *U.S. Private*, pg. 789
NAVSTAR SYSTEMS LTD.—SymmetriCom, Inc.; *U.S. Public*, pg. 1547
NAVSYMM—SymmetriCom, Inc.; *U.S. Public*, pg. 1547
NICHOLS RESEARCH CORPORATION; *U.S. Public*, pg. 1182
NORMALAIR-GARRETT LTD.—AlliedSignal Inc.; *U.S. Public*, pg. 54
NORTHROP GRUMMAN CORPORATION; *U.S. Public*, pg. 1197
NUCLEAR MAGNETIC RESONANCE INSTRUMENTS—Varian Associates, Inc.; *U.S. Public*, pg. 1710
OERLIKON-CONTRAVES AG—Oerlikon-Buhrle Holding AG; *Int'l*, pg. 998
OERLIKON LOGISTICS LTD.—Oerlikon-Buhrle Holding AG; *Int'l*, pg. 998
PG TECHNOLOGY, LTD.—COMSAT Corporation; *U.S. Public*, pg. 424
PACER INFOTEC INC.; *U.S. Private*, pg. 830
PARK AIR ELECTRONICS LTD.—Northrop Grumman Corporation; *U.S. Public*, pg. 1198
PENNY & GILES AEROSPACE LTD.—Bowthorpe plc; *Int'l*, pg. 207
AB PHAROS MARINE LTD.—Spectra-Physics AB; *Int'l*, pg. 1290
PILKINGTON PLC; *Int'l*, pg. 1056
PROCESS EQUIPMENT—Sony Corporation; *Int'l*, pg. 1283
QUANTIC INDUSTRIES, INC.; *U.S. Private*, pg. 899
RACAL AVIONICS, INC.—Racal Electronics Plc; *Int'l*, pg. 1082
RACAL CANADA INC.—Racal Electronics Plc; *Int'l*, pg. 1083
RACAL ELECTRONICS PLC; *Int'l*, pg. 1082
RACAL NCS INC.—Racal Electronics Plc; *Int'l*, pg. 1083
RAMTA DIVISION/BEDEK AVIATION GROUP—Israel Aircraft Industries Ltd.; *Int'l*, pg. 690
RANTEC MICROWAVE AND ELECTRONICS, INC.—ESCO Electronics Corporation; *U.S. Public*, pg. 546
RAYTHEON—Raytheon Company; *U.S. Public*, pg. 1365
RAYTHEON COMPANY; *U.S. Public*, pg. 1364
RAYTHEON ELECTRONICS SYSTEMS—Raytheon Company; *U.S. Public*, pg. 1364
RAYTHEON SYSTEMS COMPANY—Raytheon Company; *U.S. Public*, pg. 1364
RAYTHEON SYSTEMS COMPANY ELECTRONICS SYSTEMS—Raytheon Company; *U.S. Public*, pg. 1365
RECON/OPTICAL, INC.; *U.S. Private*, pg. 914
REFLECTONE U.K. LTD.—British Aerospace p.l.c.; *Int'l*, pg. 218
RICHARDSON-VICKS, INC.—The Procter & Gamble Company; *U.S. Public*, pg. 1331
ROCKWELL-COLLINS (U.K.) LTD.—Rockwell International Corporation; *U.S. Public*, pg. 1400
ROCKWELL INTERNATIONAL CORPORATION; *U.S. Public*, pg. 1397
ROCKWELL SALES & SUPPORT SERVICES—Rockwell International Corporation; *U.S. Public*, pg. 1402
ROGERSON AIRCRAFT CORPORATION; *U.S. Private*, pg. 940
SAGEM NAVIGATION AND DEFENSE DIVISION—Societe d'Applications Generales d'Electricite et de Mechanique; *Int'l*, pg. 1273
SL INDUSTRIES, INC.; *U.S. Public*, pg. 1418
SL MONTEVIDEO TECHNOLOGY, INC.—SL Industries, Inc.; *U.S. Public*, pg. 1419
SLI INTERNATIONAL CORP.—Smiths Industries plc; *Int'l*, pg. 1268
SAAB INSTRUMENTS—Investor AB; *Int'l*, pg. 686
SAAB MARINE ELECTRONICS AB—Investor AB; *Int'l*, pg. 686
SAAB-SCANIA COMBITECH—Investor AB; *Int'l*, pg. 686
SAAB SPACE AB—Investor AB; *Int'l*, pg. 687
SAAB TRAINING SYSTEMS AB—Investor AB; *Int'l*, pg. 687
SANDERS, A LOCKHEED MARTIN COMPANY—Lockheed Martin Corporation; *U.S. Public*, pg. 1008
SANKI ENGINEERING CO., LTD.—Mitsui & Co., Ltd.; *Int'l*, pg. 877
SENSORS, INC.; *U.S. Private*, pg. 984
SENTRY TECHNOLOGY CORP.; *U.S. Public*, pg. 1458
SEXTANT AVIONIQUE—Aerospatiale; *Int'l*, pg. 29
THE SHERRILL CORP.—Custom Accessories Inc.; *U.S. Private*, pg. 298
SHIMADZU CORPORATION; *Int'l*, pg. 1232
SIERRACOM—Sierra Technologies Inc.; *U.S. Private*, pg. 999
SIMRAD NORGE AF; *Int'l*, pg. 1252
SMITHS INDUSTRIES AEROSPACE & DEFENSE SYSTEMS INC.-GRAND RAPIDS OPERATION—Smiths Industries plc; *Int'l*, pg. 1268
SMITHS INDUSTRIES PLC; *Int'l*, pg. 1266
SOCIETE D'APPLICATIONS GENERALES D'ELECTRICITE ET DE MECHANIQUE; *Int'l*, pg. 1273
SONATECH, INC.—Channel Technologies, Inc.; *U.S. Private*, pg. 229
SPAR APPLIED SYSTEMS—Spar Aerospace Limited; *Int'l*, pg. 1288
SPARTON CORPORATION; *U.S. Public*, pg. 1496
SPARTON ELECTRONICS FLORIDA, INC.—Sparton Corporation; *U.S. Public*, pg. 1496
SPARTON OF CANADA LTD.—Sparton Corporation; *U.S. Public*, pg. 1496
SPECTRA-PHYSICS AB; *Int'l*, pg. 1288
STOCKER & YALE, INC.; *U.S. Public*, pg. 1518
SYMMETRICOM, INC.; *U.S. Public*, pg. 1547
SYSTEM PLANNING CORP.; *U.S. Private*, pg. 1061
SYSTEMS & ELECTRONICS INC.—ESCO Electronics Corporation; *U.S. Public*, pg. 547
SYSTRON DONNER-INERTIAL DIVISION—BEI Technologies, Inc.; *U.S. Public*, pg. 160
TRW INC.; *U.S. Public*, pg. 1558
TALLEY INDUSTRIES, INC.—Carpenter Technology Corporation; *U.S. Public*, pg. 307
TAMAM DIVISION/ELECTRONICS GROUP—Israel Aircraft Industries Ltd.; *Int'l*, pg. 690
TECHNOLOGY INDUSTRIES SECTOR—General Signal Corporation; *U.S. Public*, pg. 727
TELECOM SOLUTIONS—SymmetriCom, Inc.; *U.S. Public*, pg. 1547
TENNEY ENVIRONMENTAL; *U.S. Private*, pg. 1076
TETRA TECH, INC.; *U.S. Public*, pg. 1582
THOMSON CFS-BELGIUM—Thomson S.A.; *Int'l*, pg. 1385
THOMSON S.A.; *Int'l*, pg. 1381
TRACOR AEROSPACE ELECTRONICS SYSTEMS, INC.—Tracor, Inc.; *U.S. Public*, pg. 1627
TRACOR AEROSPACE, INC.—Tracor, Inc.; *U.S. Public*, pg. 1627
TRACOR FLIGHT SYSTEMS, INC.—Tracor, Inc.; *U.S. Public*, pg. 1627
TREMETRICS, INC.—Thermo Electron Corporation; *U.S. Public*, pg. 1595
TRIMBLE NAVIGATION LIMITED; *U.S. Public*, pg. 1638
ULTRA ELECTRICS—Ultra Electronics Holdings plc; *Int'l*, pg. 1431
ULTRA ELECTRONICS HOLDINGS PLC; *Int'l*, pg. 1431
UNILASER—Aerospatiale; *Int'l*, pg. 29
UNITED CAPITAL CORP.; *U.S. Public*, pg. 1674
UNIVERSAL VOLTRONICS CORPORATION—Thermo Electron Corporation; *U.S. Public*, pg. 1596
VIBRATION MOUNTINGS & CONTROLS, INC.—Aeroflex Incorporated; *U.S. Public*, pg. 24
WATKINS-JOHNSON COMPANY; *U.S. Public*, pg. 1745
WEST INSTRUMENTS—Mark IV Industries Inc.; *U.S. Public*, pg. 1045
WHITTAKER ELECTRONIC SYSTEMS—Whittaker Corporation; *U.S. Public*, pg. 1767
WILCOX ELECTRIC, INC.—Thomson S.A.; *Int'l*, pg. 1384

3821 — LABORATORY APPARATUS & FURNITURE

APV CREPACO, INC., DRYER DIV.—Siebe plc; *Int'l*, pg. 1240
APV GAULIN—Siebe plc; *Int'l*, pg. 1241
AEROSPACE PRODUCTS, INC.—AMETEK, Inc.; *U.S. Public*, pg. 100
AMP INC. LYTEL DIVISION—AMP Incorporated; *U.S. Public*, pg. 8
BOC DO BRASIL LTDA.—The BOC Group plc; *Int'l*, pg. 121
BARNSTEAD/THERMOLYNE CORPORATION—Sybron International Corporation; *U.S. Public*, pg. 1545
BASIC AMERICAN MEDICAL PRODUCTS, INC.—Graham-Field Health Products, Inc.; *U.S. Public*, pg. 758
BECTON DICKINSON LABORATORY PRODUCTS-EUROPE—Becton Dickinson & Company; *U.S. Public*, pg. 200
BECTON DICKINSON PRIMARY CARE DIAGNOSTICS—Becton Dickinson & Company; *U.S. Public*, pg. 199
BIO-RAD LABORATORIES, GES.M.B.H.—Bio-Rad Laboratories, Inc.; *U.S. Public*, pg. 230
BIO-RAD LABORATORIES, INC.; *U.S. Public*, pg. 230
BIOSOL S.P.A.—Incentive AB; *Int'l*, pg. 667
BROOKFIELD ENGINEERING LABORATORIES, INC.; *U.S. Private*, pg. 171
BUEHLER, LIMITED—Emerson Electric Co.; *U.S. Public*, pg. 574
BUEHLER MET GMBH—Emerson Electric Co.; *U.S. Public*, *pg. 575*

BUEHLER U.K. LTD.—Emerson Electric Co.; *U.S. Public*, pg. 575
CVC PRODUCTS, INC.; *U.S. Private*, pg. 197
CARDINAL SCALE MANUFACTURING COMPANY; *U.S. Private*, pg. 209
CAROLINA BIOLOGICAL SUPPLY CO.; *U.S. Private*, pg. 213
COBE LABORATORIES, INC.—Incentive AB; *Int'l*, pg. 667
DESPATCH INDUSTRIES; *U.S. Private*, pg. 327
DETECTO SCALE COMPANY—Cardinal Scale Manufacturing Company; *U.S. Private*, pg. 209
EDWARDS ALTO VUOTO SPA—The BOC Group plc; *Int'l*, pg. 122
EDWARDS HOCHVAKUUM GMBH—The BOC Group plc; *Int'l*, pg. 122
EDWARDS JAPAN LTD.—The BOC Group plc; *Int'l*, pg. 122
ELKAY PRODUCTS, INC.; *U.S. Private*, pg. 372
FISHER SCIENTIFIC COMPANY—Thomas H. Lee Co.; *U.S. Private*, pg. 658
GAMBRO AB—Incentive AB; *Int'l*, pg. 666
GAMBRO DIALYSATOREN GMBH & CO KG—Incentive AB; *Int'l*, pg. 667
GAMBRO ENGSTROM AB—Incentive AB; *Int'l*, pg. 667
GAMBRO K.K.—Incentive AB; *Int'l*, pg. 668
GAMBRO LTD.—Incentive AB; *Int'l*, pg. 668
GAMBRO MEDICAL K.K.—Incentive AB; *Int'l*, pg. 668
GAMBRO N.V./S.A.—Incentive AB; *Int'l*, pg. 668
GAMBRO PTY LTD.—Incentive AB; *Int'l*, pg. 668
GAMBRO S.A.—Incentive AB; *Int'l*, pg. 668
GAMBRO SALES AB—Incentive AB; *Int'l*, pg. 668
GAMBRO S.P.A.—Incentive AB; *Int'l*, pg. 668
GAMBRO VERTRIEBSGESELLSCHAFT M.B.H.—Incentive AB; *Int'l*, pg. 668
GELMAN ITALY S.R.L.—Pall Corporation; *U.S. Public*, pg. 1253
GELMAN SCIENCES, LTD.—Pall Corporation; *U.S. Public*, pg. 1253
GELMAN SCIENCES PTY. LTD.—Pall Corporation; *U.S. Public*, pg. 1253
GETINGE INDUSTRIER AB; *Int'l*, pg. 551
GOULD INSTRUMENT SYSTEMS, INC.—Thermo Electron Corporation; *U.S. Public*, pg. 1592
HAEMONETICS CORPORATION; *U.S. Public*, pg. 773
HAMILTON CO., INC.; *U.S. Private*, pg. 497
HARROP INDUSTRIES, INC.; *U.S. Private*, pg. 506
HAVILAND ENTERPRISES; *U.S. Private*, pg. 511
HERAEUS QUARZGLAS GMBH—Heraeus Holding GmbH; *Int'l*, pg. 616
WALTER HERZOG G.M.B.H.—Varlen Corporation; *U.S. Public*, pg. 1711
HOGAMED S.A.—Incentive AB; *Int'l*, pg. 668
HOSPAL B.V.—Incentive AB; *Int'l*, pg. 668
HOSPAL-COBE RENAL N.V.—Incentive AB; *Int'l*, pg. 668
HOSPAL DASCO S.P.A.—Incentive AB; *Int'l*, pg. 668
HOSPAL-GAMBRO LIMITEE—Incentive AB; *Int'l*, pg. 668
HOSPAL INDUSTRIE S.A.—Incentive AB; *Int'l*, pg. 668
HOSPAL LTD.—Incentive AB; *Int'l*, pg. 668
HOSPAL MED TECH GMBH—Incentive AB; *Int'l*, pg. 668
HOSPAL S.A.—Incentive AB; *Int'l*, pg. 668
HOSPAL S.P.A.—Incentive AB; *Int'l*, pg. 668
ITW MAGNAFLUX—Illinois Tool Works Inc.; *U.S. Public*, pg. 866
JAMESTOWN METAL PRODUCTS, INC.—Brittany Corporation; *U.S. Private*, pg. 169
JEWETT INTERNATIONAL CORP.—Ruslander & Sons, Inc.; *U.S. Private*, pg. 952
THE JEWETT REFRIGERATOR CO., INC.—Ruslander & Sons, Inc.; *U.S. Private*, pg. 952
JOUAN, INC.; *U.S. Private*, pg. 601
KEWAUNEE SCIENTIFIC CORPORATION; *U.S. Public*, pg. 953
KVAERNER THUNE A/S—Kvaerner a.s.a.; *Int'l*, pg. 769
LAB CRAFTERS INC.—Aero Data Metal Crafters; *U.S. Private*, pg. 24
LABORATORY SUPPLY COMPANY—Laboratory Supply Company, Inc.; *U.S. Private*, pg. 642
LABORATORY SUPPLY COMPANY, INC.; *U.S. Private*, pg. 641
LIFE SCIENCE LABORATORIES LTD.—Thermo Electron Corporation; *U.S. Public*, pg. 1594
LIFE SCIENCES INTERNATIONAL (EUROPE) LIMITED—Thermo Electron Corporation; *U.S. Public*, pg. 1594
LIFE SCIENCES INTERNATIONAL PLC—Thermo Electron Corporation; *U.S. Public*, pg. 1594
LUMEX MEDICAL PRODUCTS—Graham-Field Health Products, Inc.; *U.S. Public*, pg. 758
MTN MEDIZINTECHNIK NEUBRANDENBURG GMBH I.G.—Incentive AB; *Int'l*, pg. 669
MEDICAL DATA INTELLIGENCE AB—Incentive AB; *Int'l*, pg. 667
MEDICAL LABORATORY AUTOMATION, INC.; *U.S. Private*, pg. 727
MILLIPORE CORPORATION; *U.S. Public*, pg. 1112
NESLAB INSTRUMENTS, INC.—Thermo Electron Corporation; *U.S. Public*, pg. 1595
NIHON MILLIPORE LTD.-YONEZAWA—Millipore Corporation; *U.S. Public*, pg. 1113
NOBLES MFG. INC.; *U.S. Private*, pg. 800
ORION RESEARCH INC.—Thermo Electron Corporation; *U.S. Public*, pg. 1592
PALL ULTRAFINE FILTRATION COMPANY—Pall Corporation; *U.S. Public*, pg. 1254
PERMA PURE INC.—Halma p.l.c.; *Int'l*, pg. 590
PERSTORP ANALYTICAL INC. DIVISION ALPKEM—Perstorp AB; *Int'l*, pg. 1039
PHARMACIA & UPJOHN BIOTECH INC.—Pharmacia & Upjohn, Inc.; *Int'l*, pg. 1047
PHIPPS & BIRD—McKesson Corporation; *U.S. Public*, pg. 1073
PRECISION SCIENTIFIC INC.—Jouan, Inc.; *U.S. Private*, pg. 601
RICE LAKE WEIGHING SYSTEMS; *U.S. Private*, pg. 927
SAVANT INSTRUMENTS INC.—Thermo Electron Corporation; *U.S. Public*, pg. 1595
SHANDON LIPSHAW INC.—Thermo Electron Corporation; *U.S. Public*, pg. 1595
SMITHKLINE BEECHAM CORPORATION—SmithKline Beecham plc; *Int'l*, pg. 1264
SPECIALTY EQUIPMENT COMPANIES INC.; *U.S. Public*, pg. 1496
SQUIRE-COGSWELL COMPANY; *U.S. Private*, pg. 1027
TECH-MET CANADA LTD.—Emerson Electric Co.; *U.S. Public*, pg. 575
TEGIMENTA AG—Roche Holding Ltd.; *Int'l*, pg. 1120
TENNEY ENVIRONMENTAL; *U.S. Private*, pg. 1076
THERMOTRON INDUSTRIES—Venturedyne, Ltd.; *U.S. Private*, pg. 1136
US STEEL TECHNICAL CENTER—USX Corporation; *U.S. Public*, pg. 1662
VARIAN ASSOCIATES, INC.; *U.S. Public*, pg. 1710
VARLEN CORPORATION; *U.S. Public*, pg. 1710
VARLEN INSTRUMENTS, INC.—Varlen Corporation; *U.S. Public*, pg. 1711
VAXJO ROSTFRITT AB—Getinge Industrier AB; *Int'l*, pg. 551
WALKER MAGNETICS GROUP, INC.; *U.S. Private*, pg. 1147
WHATMAN INC.—Whatman plc; *Int'l*, pg. 1498

3822 — AUTOMATIC CONTROLS FOR REGULATING RESIDENTIAL & COMMERCIAL ENVIRONMENTS & APPLIANCES

ABB MASCHINENFABRIK MEYER AG—ABB Asea Brown Boveri (Holding) Ltd.; *Int'l*, pg. 1
AC CORPORATION; *U.S. Private*, pg. 3
ACR GROUP; *U.S. Public*, pg. 3
AERCO INTERNATIONAL INC.; *U.S. Private*, pg. 23
AIRMASTER FAN CO.; *U.S. Private*, pg. 29
ALNOR INSTRUMENT COMPANY—TSI Incorporated; *U.S. Public*, pg. 1559
AMERICAN STANDARD INC.; *U.S. Public*, pg. 91
W.E. ANDERSON DIV.—Dwyer Instruments Inc.; *U.S. Private*, pg. 350
ANDOVER CONTROLS; *U.S. Private*, pg. 73
ANDOVER CONTROLS CORP.—BICC plc; *Int'l*, pg. 120
APOLLO FIRE DETECTORS LIMITED—Halma p.l.c.; *Int'l*, pg. 589
APPARECCHI DI CONTROLLO RANCO, S.R.L.—Siebe plc; *Int'l*, pg. 1243
ASCO (JAPAN) CO. LIMITED—Emerson Electric Co.; *U.S. Public*, pg. 575
ASCO (UK)—Emerson Electric Co.; *U.S. Public*, pg. 575
ASCOLECTRIC LIMITED—Emerson Electric Co.; *U.S. Public*, pg. 575
ASCOMATION PTY. LTD.—Emerson Electric Co.; *U.S. Public*, pg. 576
AUTOMATIC SIGNAL/EAGLE SIGNAL—Siemens AG; *Int'l*, pg. 1245
AUTOMATIC SWITCH CO.—Emerson Electric Co.; *U.S. Public*, pg. 573
AUTOMOTIVE & APPLIANCE CONTROLS DIV.—Eaton Corporation; *U.S. Public*, pg. 556
AZONIX INC.—Crane Co.; *U.S. Public*, pg. 457
BTR-MEASUREMENT & FLOW CONTROL DIVISION—BTR plc; *Int'l*, pg. 125
BADGER METER UTILITY DIV.—Badger Meter, Inc.; *U.S. Public*, pg. 165
BARBER-COLMAN COMPANY—Siebe plc; *Int'l*, pg. 1242
BARNSTEAD/THERMOLYNE CORPORATION—Sybron International Corporation; *U.S. Public*, pg. 1545
BERWIND CORPORATION; *U.S. Private*, pg. 138
CAM-STAT, INC.—Watsco, Inc.; *U.S. Public*, pg. 1746
CARRIER CORP. RCD—United Technologies Corporation; *U.S. Public*, pg. 1689
CELEGEC AUTOMATION PROJECTS INC.—Alcatel Alsthom Compagnie Generale D'Electricite; *Int'l*, pg. 53
CHROMALOX, S.A.—Emerson Electric Co.; *U.S. Public*, pg. 576
CLAYHITHE P.L.C.; *Int'l*, pg. 297
COMPAGNIE GENERALE DE GEOPHYSIQUE—CGG Group; *Int'l*, pg. 241
CONAX BUFFALO CORPORATION—IMI Plc; *Int'l*, pg. 646
CROWCON DETECTION INSTRUMENTS LIMITED—Halma p.l.c.; *Int'l*, pg. 589
CUSTOM CONTROL SENSORS, INC.; *U.S. Private*, pg. 298
DANFOSS A/S; *Int'l*, pg. 376
DANFOSS ELECTRONIC DRIVES—Danfoss A/S; *Int'l*, pg. 377
DEUTSCHE RANCO GMBH—Siebe plc; *Int'l*, pg. 1243
DICKINSON CONTROL SYSTEMS, LTD.—Brunel Holdings Plc; *Int'l*, pg. 231
DWYER INSTRUMENTS INC.; *U.S. Private*, pg. 350
DYNAMICS CORPORATION OF AMERICA—CTS Corporation; *U.S. Public*, pg. 286
EUA DAY—Eastern Utilities Associates; *U.S. Public*, pg. 549
EATON CORPORATION AUTOMOTIVE CONTROLS DIVISION—Eaton Corporation; *U.S. Public*, pg. 557
EDWARDS SYSTEMS TECH—General Signal Corporation; *U.S. Public*, pg. 726
ELECTRI-CORD MANUFACTURING CO.—Leucadia National Corporation; *U.S. Public*, pg. 990
ELECTROCATALYTIC, INC.; *U.S. Private*, pg. 369
ELLIS & WATTS DIV.—CTS Corporation; *U.S. Public*, pg. 286
ELMWOOD SENSORS, INC.—BTR plc; *Int'l*, pg. 125
EMERSON ELECTRIC GMBH—Emerson Electric Co.; *U.S. Public*, pg. 576
EMERSON ELECTRIC INDUS. CONTROLS, S.A.—Emerson Electric Co.; *U.S. Public*, pg. 576
EMERSON ELECTRIC IRELAND LIMITED—Emerson Electric Co.; *U.S. Public*, pg. 576
EMERSON ELECTRIC NEDERLAND B.V.—Emerson Electric Co.; *U.S. Public*, pg. 576
EMERSON ELECTRIC S.R.L.—Emerson Electric Co.; *U.S. Public*, pg. 576
EMERSON JAPAN, LTD.—Emerson Electric Co.; *U.S. Public*, pg. 576
EMTEK HEALTH CARE SYSTEMS, INC.—Motorola, Inc.; *U.S. Public*, pg. 1137
ERIE CONTROLS IBERICA S.A.—Siebe plc; *Int'l*, pg. 1241
ERIE MANUFACTURING CO.—Siebe plc; *Int'l*, pg. 1241
ERIE MANUFACTURING CO. (CANADA) LTD.—Siebe plc; *Int'l*, pg. 1241
FISONS INSTRUMENTS—Rhone-Poulenc S.A.; *Int'l*, pg. 1111
FOSTER-MILLER, INC.; *U.S. Private*, pg. 421
FREQUENCY ELECTRONICS, INC.; *U.S. Public*, pg. 681
GEC POWER INSTRUMENTATION & CONTROL LTD.—Alcatel Alsthom Compagnie Generale D'Electricite; *Int'l*, pg. 53
GOLDSTAR CO. LTD.—LG Group; *Int'l*, pg. 778
GRASEBY ANDERSEN LTD.—Smiths Industries plc; *Int'l*, pg. 1267
GRAYSON CONTROLS DIV.—Siebe plc; *Int'l*, pg. 1243
HANOVIA COLIGHT—ARC International Corporation; *Int'l*, pg. 17
HOBBS CORPORATION—BTR plc; *Int'l*, pg. 127
HONEYWELL INC.; *U.S. Public*, pg. 833
HORSTMAN TIMERS & CONTROLS LIMITED—Clayhithe P.L.C.; *Int'l*, pg. 297
HOSOKAWA MICRON LTD.—Hosokawa Micron Corporation; *Int'l*, pg. 636
IMI CORNELIUS, INC. (IA)—IMI Plc; *Int'l*, pg. 646
IRI ISTITUTO RICOSTRUZIONE INDUSTRIALE; *Int'l*, pg. 652
INTERNATIONAL RESEARCH & EVALUATION; *U.S. Private*, pg. 571
JAY INSTRUMENT & SPECIALTY CO.; *U.S. Private*, pg. 583
JOHNSON CONTROLS, INC.; *U.S. Public*, pg. 932
JOHNSON CONTROLS, INC., CONTROLS GROUP—Johnson Controls, Inc.; *U.S. Public*, pg. 932
JOHNSON CONTROLS INTERNATIONAL, INC.—Johnson Controls, Inc.; *U.S. Public*, pg. 932
JOHNSON YOKOGAWA CORPORATION—Yokogawa Electric Corporation; *Int'l*, pg. 1521
KENT INSTRUMENTS SOUTH AFRICA PTY. LTD.—ABB Asea Brown Boveri (Holding) Ltd.; *Int'l*, pg. 3
KVAERNER INCINERATION A/S—Kvaerner a.s.a.; *Int'l*, pg. 769
LABORTERAPICA-BRISTOL QUIMICA E FARMACEUTICA LTDA.—Bristol-Myers Squibb Company; *U.S. Public*, pg. 256
LANDIS & STAEFA AG; *Int'l*, pg. 800
LAROCHE AIR SYSTEMS INC.—LaRoche Industries Inc.; *U.S. Private*, pg. 652
LESLIE CONTROLS, INC.—Watts Industries, Inc.; *U.S. Public*, pg. 1746
LIEBERT CORPORATION—Emerson Electric Co.; *U.S. Public*, pg. 573
LIEBERT INTERNATIONAL B.V.—Emerson Electric Co.; *U.S. Public*, pg. 577
LOVE CONTROLS CORPORATION—Dwyer Instruments Inc.; *U.S. Private*, pg. 350
LUCAS BODY SYSTEMS—LucasVarity plc; *Int'l*, pg. 820
MIE, INC.—TRC Companies, Inc.; *U.S. Public*, pg. 1558
MALLORY, INC.; *U.S. Private*, pg. 698
MARK IV INDUSTRIES INC.; *U.S. Public*, pg. 1044
MAXITROL CO.; *U.S. Private*, pg. 716
MERCOID DIV.—Dwyer Instruments Inc.; *U.S. Private*, pg. 350
MERIAM INSTRUMENT—Berkshire Hathaway Inc.; *U.S. Public*, pg. 218
MIKUNI ADEC.—Mikuni Corporation; *Int'l*, pg. 867
MOTOROLA, INC.; *U.S. Public*, pg. 1136
NESLAB INSTRUMENTS, INC.—Thermo Electron Corporation; *U.S. Public*, pg. 1595
OAK INDUSTRIES INC.; *U.S. Public*, pg. 1209
OHKURA-ROSEMOUNT CO., LTD.—Emerson Electric Co.; *U.S. Public*, pg. 577
PAKTRONICS CONTROLS, INC.—Maxitrol Co.; *U.S. Private*, pg. 716
PATHWAY BELLOWS, INC.—Dover Corporation; *U.S. Public*, pg. 521
PERFECTION CORPORATION—Ruhrgas Aktiengesellschaft; *Int'l*, pg. 1149
POLITUBOS S.A.—Siebe plc; *Int'l*, pg. 1244
PROCESS CONTROLS SECTOR—General Signal Corporation; *U.S. Public*, pg. 726
PRODUCTION MANAGEMENT COMPANIES, INC.; *U.S. Private*, pg. 888
PROXIMITY CONTROLS CORP.—Dwyer Instruments Inc.; *U.S. Private*, pg. 350
RACAL ELECTRONICS PLC; *Int'l*, pg. 1082
RANCO CONTROLS CANADA, LTD.—Siebe plc; *Int'l*, pg. 1243
RANCO CONTROLS LTD.—Siebe plc; *Int'l*, pg. 1243
RANCO DE MEXICO, S.A. DE C.V.—Siebe plc; *Int'l*, pg. 1243
RANCO EUROPE PLYMOUTH UK—Siebe plc; *Int'l*, pg. 1243
RANCO FRANCE, S.R.L.—Siebe plc; *Int'l*, pg. 1243
RANCO INC.—Siebe plc; *Int'l*, pg. 1243
RANCO ITALIAN CONTROLS—Siebe plc; *Int'l*, pg. 1243
RANCO NORTH AMERICA—Siebe plc; *Int'l*, pg. 1243
REED NATIONAL COMPANY—Mestek, Inc.; *U.S. Public*, pg. 1099
REMINGTON PRODUCTS COMPANY, L.L.C.; *U.S. Private*, pg. 921
ROBERTSHAW CONTROLS (CANADA) INC.—Siebe plc; *Int'l*, pg. 1244
ROBERTSHAW DO BRASIL S.A.—Siebe plc; *Int'l*, pg. 1244
THOMAS ROBINSON GROUP PLC—Brunel Holdings Plc; *Int'l*, pg. 231
ROLOCK, INC.; *U.S. Private*, pg. 942

SMC ENVIRONMENTAL SERVICES GROUP INC.—Versar Inc.; *U.S. Public*, pg. 1717
SOR INC.; *U.S. Private*, pg. 957
SERCK CONTROLS LIMITED—Clayhithe P.L.C.; *Int'l*, pg. 297
SERVICE CENTRALE VOOR KOELTECHNIEK B.V.—Internatio-Muller N.V.; *Int'l*, pg. 681
SEVERN FURNACES LIMITED—Instron Corporation; *U.S. Public*, pg. 883
SLANT/FIN CORPORATION; *U.S. Private*, pg. 1005
SPORLAN VALVE COMPANY; *U.S. Private*, pg. 1026
STERLING, INC.; *U.S. Private*, pg. 1041
SUNBEAM CORPORATION; *U.S. Public*, pg. 1533
SYSTEM ONE CONTROL—Peoples Electric Contractor, Inc.; *U.S. Private*, pg. 851
SYSTEMS & SERVICES DIV.—Johnson Controls, Inc.; *U.S. Public*, pg. 932
TPS TECHNOLOGIES INC.—Thermo Electron Corporation; *U.S. Public*, pg. 1594
TSI INCORPORATED; *U.S. Public*, pg. 1559
TEDDINGTON CONTROLS LIMITED—SLD Holdings Ltd.; *Int'l*, pg. 1160
TEMPATRON LIMITED—Siebe plc; *Int'l*, pg. 1241
TEXAS INSTRUMENTS HOLLAND BV—Texas Instruments Incorporated; *U.S. Public*, pg. 1586
TEXAS INSTRUMENTS INCORPORATED; *U.S. Public*, pg. 1585
TEXAS INSTRUMENTS MATERIALS & CONTROLS GROUP—Texas Instruments Incorporated; *U.S. Public*, pg. 1586
THERM-O-DISC (CANADA) LIMITED—Emerson Electric Co.; *U.S. Public*, pg. 578
THERM-O-DISC INC.—Emerson Electric Co.; *U.S. Public*, pg. 573
TORK, INC.; *U.S. Private*, pg. 1092
TRANTER, INC.—Dover Corporation; *U.S. Public*, pg. 521
UNITED TECHNOLOGIES CORPORATION; *U.S. Public*, pg. 1689
VAPOR—Westinghouse Air Brake Company; *U.S. Public*, pg. 1761
WATLOW ELECTRIC MANUFACTURING COMPANY; *U.S. Private*, pg. 1153
WATSCO, INC.; *U.S. Public*, pg. 1745
WATTS INDUSTRIES, INC.; *U.S. Public*, pg. 1746
WATTS REGULATOR CO.—Watts Industries, Inc.; *U.S. Public*, pg. 1747
WHITE-RODGERS DIV., EMERSON ELECTRIC CO.—Emerson Electric Co.; *U.S. Public*, pg. 573
XKD CORPORATION; *U.S. Private*, pg. 1194
ZELLWEGER USTER AG—Hesta Tex AG; *Int'l*, pg. 618

3823 — INDUSTRIAL INSTRUMENTS FOR MEASUREMENT, DISPLAY & CONTROL OF PROCESS VARIABLES & RELATED PRODUCTS

ABB HV SWITCHGEAR AB—ABB Asea Brown Boveri (Holding) Ltd.; *Int'l*, pg. 7
ABB INC.—ABB Asea Brown Boveri (Holding) Ltd.; *Int'l*, pg. 3
ABB INDUSTRIAL SYSTEMS, INC.—ABB Asea Brown Boveri (Holding) Ltd.; *Int'l*, pg. 4
ABB KENT-TAYLOR LTD.—ABB Asea Brown Boveri (Holding) Ltd.; *Int'l*, pg. 7
ABB MASCHINENFABRIK MEYER AG—ABB Asea Brown Boveri (Holding) Ltd.; *Int'l*, pg. 1
ABB PROCESS ANALYTICS—ABB Asea Brown Boveri (Holding) Ltd.; *Int'l*, pg. 5
AC CORPORATION; *U.S. Private*, pg. 3
ACEC AUTOMATISME—Alcatel Alsthom Compagnie Generale D'Electricite; *Int'l*, pg. 54
ADS ENVIRONMENTAL SERVICES INC.—Axel Johnson AB; *Int'l*, pg. 709
AEC/APPLICATION ENGINEERING CORPORATION—Sterling, Inc.; *U.S. Private*, pg. 1041
AEC, INC.—Harbour Group Ltd.; *U.S. Private*, pg. 500
AEC, INC.—Sterling, Inc.; *U.S. Private*, pg. 1041
ARC INTERNATIONAL CORPORATION; *Int'l*, pg. 17
ACTION INSTRUMENTS, INC.; *U.S. Private*, pg. 15
AEROFLEX LABORATORIES INC.—Aeroflex Incorporated; *U.S. Public*, pg. 24
AEROSPACE PRODUCTS, INC.—AMETEK, Inc.; *U.S. Public*, pg. 100
AIR & WATER TECHNOLOGIES CORPORATION; *U.S. Public*, pg. 29
AIR TECHNIQUES, INC.; *U.S. Private*, pg. 28
ALBANY INTERNATIONAL CORP.; *U.S. Public*, pg. 36
ALFA-LAVAL THERMAL AB—Tetra Laval Group; *Int'l*, pg. 1378
ALLARD INDUSTRIES; *U.S. Private*, pg. 36
ALLIEDSIGNAL AEROSPACE—AlliedSignal Inc.; *U.S. Public*, pg. 50
ALLIEDSIGNAL CONTROLS & ACCESSORIES—AlliedSignal Inc.; *U.S. Public*, pg. 50
ALNOR INSTRUMENT COMPANY—TSI Incorporated; *U.S. Public*, pg. 1559
AMERICAN METER COMPANY—Ruhrgas Aktiengesellschaft; *Int'l*, pg. 1149
AMERICAN TECH MANUFACTURING CORPORATION—Halma p.l.c.; *Int'l*, pg. 590
AMETEK, INC.; *U.S. Public*, pg. 99
AMICON, INC.—Millipore Corporation; *U.S. Public*, pg. 1113
AMOT CONTROLS CORPORATION—Roper Industries, Inc.; *U.S. Public*, pg. 1405
ANALOG DEVICES, INC.; *U.S. Public*, pg. 107
ANALOGIC CORPORATION; *U.S. Public*, pg. 109
W.E. ANDERSON DIV.—Dwyer Instruments Inc.; *U.S. Private*, pg. 350
ANDROS INCORPORATED; *U.S. Private*, pg. 74
ANGAR SCIENTIFIC CO., INC.—Emerson Electric Co.; *U.S. Public*, pg. 574
ARO FLUID PRODUCTS DIVISION—Ingersoll-Rand Company; *U.S. Public*, pg. 877
ASCO (JAPAN) CO. LIMITED—Emerson Electric Co.; *U.S. Public*, pg. 575
ASCOMATION PTY. LTD.—Emerson Electric Co.; *U.S. Public*, pg. 576
AUTOCON INDUSTRIES INC.—Pearson plc; *Int'l*, pg. 1026
AUTOMATIC SIGNAL/EAGLE SIGNAL—Siemens AG; *Int'l*, pg. 1245
AUTOMATIC SWITCH CO.—Emerson Electric Co.; *U.S. Public*, pg. 573
AZONIX INC.—Crane Co.; *U.S. Public*, pg. 457
BEI SENSORS AND SYSTEMS COMPANY—BEI Technologies, Inc.; *U.S. Public*, pg. 160
BIF—General Signal Corporation; *U.S. Public*, pg. 726
BLH ELECTRONICS, INC.—Spectra-Physics AB; *Int'l*, pg. 1289
BTR-MEASUREMENT & FLOW CONTROL DIVISION—BTR plc; *Int'l*, pg. 125
BTR PLC; *Int'l*, pg. 124
BWI KARTRIDG PAK—BWI Plc; *Int'l*, pg. 130
BABCOCK & WILCOX DE MEXICO SA DE CV—FKI Plc; *Int'l*, pg. 474
BABCOCK AUSTRALIA HOLDINGS LTD.—FKI Plc; *Int'l*, pg. 474
BABCOCK-BRISTOL AB—FKI Plc; *Int'l*, pg. 473
BABCOCK BRISTOL AFRICA DIV.—FKI Plc; *Int'l*, pg. 474
BABCOCK HYDRO-PNEUMATICS LTD.—FKI Plc; *Int'l*, pg. 471
BABCOCK INTERNATIONAL GROUP PLC; *Int'l*, pg. 130
BABCOCK INTERNATIONAL (NZ) LTD.—FKI Plc; *Int'l*, pg. 474
BADGER METER EUROPE GMBH—Badger Meter, Inc.; *U.S. Public*, pg. 165
BADGER METER, INC.; *U.S. Public*, pg. 164
BADGER METER INDUSTRIAL DIV.—Badger Meter, Inc.; *U.S. Public*, pg. 165
BADGER METER, PMI—Badger Meter, Inc.; *U.S. Public*, pg. 165
BAILEY-FISCHER & PORTER B.V.—ELSAG Bailey Process Automation N.V.; *Int'l*, pg. 449
BAILEY, FISCHER & PORTER COMPANY—ELSAG Bailey Process Automation N.V.; *Int'l*, pg. 449
BAILEY MEXICO S.A. DE C.V.—ELSAG Bailey Process Automation N.V.; *Int'l*, pg. 449
BAILEY NETWORK MANAGEMENT—ELSAG Bailey Process Automation N.V.; *Int'l*, pg. 449
BALL AEROSPACE & TECHNOLOGIES CORP.—Ball Corporation; *U.S. Public*, pg. 171
BALL PRODUCTS, INC.—The Oilgear Company; *U.S. Public*, pg. 1215
BALLINGER SCHALTTECHNIK G.M.B.H.—Raytheon Company; *U.S. Public*, pg. 1366
BARBER-COLMAN COMPANY—Siebe plc; *Int'l*, pg. 1242
BARBER-COLMAN INDEV—Siebe plc; *Int'l*, pg. 1242
BECKMAN-IPD/DORIC—Emerson Electric Co.; *U.S. Public*, pg. 574
BENTLY NEVADA CORPORATION; *U.S. Private*, pg. 134
BERGER INSTRUMENTS—Chicago Steel Tape; *U.S. Private*, pg. 235
BETZDEARBORN INC.; *U.S. Public*, pg. 226
BINDICATOR COMPANY—Berwind Corporation; *U.S. Private*, pg. 138
BIO-CHEM VALVE INC.—Halma p.l.c.; *Int'l*, pg. 590
BLISS-SALEM, INC.; *U.S. Private*, pg. 149
BOHLIN INSTRUMENTS LTD.—Bowthorpe plc; *Int'l*, pg. 207
BOURNS PRESSURE PRODUCTS—Bourns, Inc.; *U.S. Private*, pg. 161
BOWTHORPE PLC; *Int'l*, pg. 207
BOWTHORPE THERMOMETRICS—Bowthorpe plc; *Int'l*, pg. 207
BRISTOL BABCOCK CANADA—FKI Plc; *Int'l*, pg. 473
BRISTOL BABCOCK, INC.—FKI Plc; *Int'l*, pg. 472
BRISTOL INSTRUMENTS DIV.—FKI Plc; *Int'l*, pg. 472
BROOKS INSTRUMENT—Emerson Electric Co.; *U.S. Public*, pg. 574
BROOKS INSTRUMENT B.V.—Emerson Electric Co.; *U.S. Public*, pg. 576
BROOKS INSTRUMENT (CANADA)—Emerson Electric Co.; *U.S. Public*, pg. 576
BROOKS INSTRUMENT (GERMANY)—Emerson Electric Co.; *U.S. Public*, pg. 576
BROOKS INSTRUMENT (JAPAN)—Emerson Electric Co.; *U.S. Public*, pg. 576
CAE INC.; *Int'l*, pg. 237
CEM CORPORATION; *U.S. Public*, pg. 277
CAPITAL CONTROLS COMPANY INC.—Severn Trent Plc; *Int'l*, pg. 1226
CAPP, INC.; *U.S. Private*, pg. 207
CARDINAL SYSTEMS—Tetra Laval Group; *Int'l*, pg. 1379
CASI-RUSCO EUROPE—CASI-RUSCO Inc.; *U.S. Private*, pg. 218
CEGELEC—Alcatel Alsthom Compagnie Generale D'Electricite; *Int'l*, pg. 52
CHROMATOGRAPHY SYSTEMS—Varian Associates, Inc.; *U.S. Public*, pg. 1710
CHRONOS RICHARDSON—Staveley Industries PLC; *Int'l*, pg. 1299
CHRONOS RICHARDSON LIMITED—Staveley Industries PLC; *Int'l*, pg. 1299
CHRYSLER CORPORATION; *U.S. Public*, pg. 352
CINCINNATI MILACRON INC.; *U.S. Public*, pg. 368
CIRCUIT WORKS—Liquid Controls LLC; *U.S. Private*, pg. 669
COLORADO DATA SYSTEMS INC.—Tektronix, Inc.; *U.S. Public*, pg. 1567
COMADUR S.A.—SMH Swiss Corporation for Micro Electronics & Watchmaking Industries Ltd.; *Int'l*, pg. 1161
COMPUTER PRODUCTS, INC.; *U.S. Public*, pg. 422
CONTRAVES GMBH—Oerlikon-Buhrle Holding AG; *Int'l*, pg. 998
COOK MANUFACTURING CORPORATION; *U.S. Private*, pg. 272
COOPER INSTRUMENT CORP.; *U.S. Private*, pg. 274
CROWCON INSTRUMENTS B.V.—Halma p.l.c.; *Int'l*, pg. 590
CUSTOM CONTROL SENSORS, INC.; *U.S. Private*, pg. 298
DAQ ELECTRONICS INC.; *U.S. Private*, pg. 300
DBA SYSTEMS, INC.; *U.S. Public*, pg. 472
DSP TECHNOLOGY INC.; *U.S. Public*, pg. 475
DANAHER CONTROLS—Danaher Corporation; *U.S. Public*, pg. 480
DANFOSS A/S; *Int'l*, pg. 376
DANIEL CANADA—Daniel Industries, Inc.; *U.S. Public*, pg. 483
DANIEL FLOW PRODUCTS, INC.—Daniel Industries, Inc.; *U.S. Public*, pg. 483
DANIEL INDUSTRIES, INC.; *U.S. Public*, pg. 482
DANIEL INDUSTRIES LTD.—Daniel Industries, Inc.; *U.S. Public*, pg. 483
DATACOLOR AG—Brauerei Eichhof; *Int'l*, pg. 213
DAYTRONIC CORPORATION—BTR plc; *Int'l*, pg. 126
DEGGENDORFER WERFT UND EISENBAU GMBH—MAN Aktiengesellschaft; *Int'l*, pg. 824
DELFT INSTRUMENTS N.V.; *Int'l*, pg. 388
DERLAN INDUSTRIES LIMITED; *Int'l*, pg. 395
DESCO CORPORATION; *U.S. Private*, pg. 326
DESKTOP GRAPHICS—Evans & Sutherland Computer Corporation; *U.S. Public*, pg. 596
DIGITAL EQUIPMENT CORPORATION; *U.S. Public*, pg. 507
DOVER DIVERSIFIED—Dover Corporation; *U.S. Public*, pg. 521
DRESSER INDUSTRIES, INC.; *U.S. Public*, pg. 528
DUKANE CORPORATION; *U.S. Private*, pg. 345
DWYER INSTRUMENTS INC.; *U.S. Private*, pg. 350
DYNALCO CONTROLS CORPORATION—Crane Co.; *U.S. Public*, pg. 457
DYNAMICS RESEARCH CORPORATION; *U.S. Public*, pg. 539
EG & G, INC.; *U.S. Public*, pg. 542
EG & G INSTRUMENTS-PROCESS MEASUREMENTS/CHANDLER—EG & G, Inc.; *U.S. Public*, pg. 543
ELXSI CORPORATION; *U.S. Public*, pg. 545
EAGLE CONVERTING INC.—Bradner Central Company; *U.S. Private*, pg. 165
ECLIPSE COMBUSTION & INDUSTRIAL EQUIPMENT—Eclipse Inc.; *U.S. Private*, pg. 361
ELECTROGLAS—General Signal Corporation; *U.S. Public*, pg. 727
B. ELLIOTT PLC.; *Int'l*, pg. 448
ELSAG BAILEY PTY LIMITED—ELSAG Bailey Process Automation N.V.; *Int'l*, pg. 449
EMERSON ELECTRIC CANADA LTD.—Emerson Electric Co.; *U.S. Public*, pg. 576
EMERSON ELECTRIC NEDERLAND B.V.—Emerson Electric Co.; *U.S. Public*, pg. 576
EMERSON ELECTRIC S.R.L.—Emerson Electric Co.; *U.S. Public*, pg. 576
EMERSON JAPAN, LTD.—Emerson Electric Co.; *U.S. Public*, pg. 576
ENERSTAT DIVISION- ERIE MANUFACTURING CO. (CANADA) LTD.—Siebe plc; *Int'l*, pg. 1241
ERIE CONTROLS EUROPE-NV—Siebe plc; *Int'l*, pg. 1241
ERIEZ MAGNETICS; *U.S. Private*, pg. 381
ESCA CORPORATION—Alcatel Alsthom Compagnie Generale D'Electricite; *Int'l*, pg. 53
EUROTHERM ANTRIEBSTECHNIK GMBH—Eurotherm plc; *Int'l*, pg. 466
EUROTHERM AUTOMATION SA—Eurotherm plc; *Int'l*, pg. 466
EUROTHERM CIRCUITS INC.—Eurotherm plc; *Int'l*, pg. 466
EUROTHERM CONTROLS INC.—Eurotherm plc; *Int'l*, pg. 466
EUROTHERM CONTROLS LTD.—Eurotherm plc; *Int'l*, pg. 466
EUROTHERM DRIVES INC.—Eurotherm plc; *Int'l*, pg. 466
EUROTHERM DRIVES LTD.—Eurotherm plc; *Int'l*, pg. 466
EUROTHERM DRIVES SPA—Eurotherm plc; *Int'l*, pg. 466
EUROTHERM GAUGING SYSTEMS INC.—Eurotherm plc; *Int'l*, pg. 466
EUROTHERM GAUGING SYSTEMS LTD.—Eurotherm plc; *Int'l*, pg. 466
EUROTHERM MESSDATENTECHNIK GMBH—Eurotherm plc; *Int'l*, pg. 466
EUROTHERM MESURES SA—Eurotherm plc; *Int'l*, pg. 466
EUROTHERM PLC; *Int'l*, pg. 465
EUROTHERM PROCESS AUTOMATION LTD.—Eurotherm plc; *Int'l*, pg. 466
EUROTHERM RECORDERS INC.—Eurotherm plc; *Int'l*, pg. 466
EUROTHERM RECORDERS LTD.—Eurotherm plc; *Int'l*, pg. 466
EUROTHERM REGLER GMBH—Eurotherm plc; *Int'l*, pg. 466
EUROTHERM SYSTEMES SA—Eurotherm plc; *Int'l*, pg. 466
EUROTHERM VITESSE VARIABLE SA—Eurotherm plc; *Int'l*, pg. 466
F&P HOLDING, INC.—ELSAG Bailey Process Automation N.V.; *Int'l*, pg. 449
FAG AUSTRIA WAELZLAGER AG—FAG Group; *Int'l*, pg. 469
FAG (UK) LIMITED—FAG Group; *Int'l*, pg. 469
FKI INDUSTRIES. INC.—FKI Plc; *Int'l*, pg. 472
FMC-SMITH METER CO.—FMC Corporation; *U.S. Public*, pg. 605
FENWAL ELECTRONICS, INC.—Publicker Industries Inc.; *U.S. Public*, pg. 1341
FERRANTI GMBH—Thomson S.A.; *Int'l*, pg. 1384
FESTO AG & CO.; *Int'l*, pg. 480
FESTO CORPORATION—Festo AG & Co.; *Int'l*, pg. 480
FIRE CONTROL INSTRUMENTS, INC.; *U.S. Private*, pg. 406
FISCHER & PORTER AB—ELSAG Bailey Process Automation N.V.; *Int'l*, pg. 449

FISCHER & PORTER (CANADA) LTD.—ELSAG Bailey Process Automation N.V.; *Int'l*, pg. 449
FISCHER & PORTER ITALIANA S.P.A.—ELSAG Bailey Process Automation N.V.; *Int'l*, pg. 449
FISCHER & PORTER LTD.—ELSAG Bailey Process Automation N.V.; *Int'l*, pg. 449
GEORG FISCHER LTD.; *Int'l*, pg. 488
FISHER CONTROLS INTERNATIONAL, INC.—Emerson Electric Co.; *U.S. Public*, pg. 573
FLINN & DREFFEIN ENGINEERING CO.; *U.S. Private*, pg. 413
FLIR SYSTEMS, INC.; *U.S. Public*, pg. 654
FLOW CONTROL DIVISION—Raven Industries, Inc.; *U.S. Public*, pg. 1361
FLUID CONSERVATION SYSTEMS INC.—Halma p.l.c.; *Int'l*, pg. 590
FLUIDISED COMBUSTION CONTRACTORS LTD.—FKI Plc; *Int'l*, pg. 472
FORD METER BOX COMPANY; *U.S. Private*, pg. 418
FORNEY CORPORATION—Williams Holdings Plc; *Int'l*, pg. 1500
FORTRESS INTERLOCKS LIMITED—Halma p.l.c.; *Int'l*, pg. 589
THE FOXBORO COMPANY—Siebe plc; *Int'l*, pg. 1243
FUTABA CORPORATION; *Int'l*, pg. 531
FUTABA CORPORATION OF AMERICA—Futaba Corporation; *Int'l*, pg. 531
G.E.-HITACHI HVB INC.—Hitachi, Ltd.; *Int'l*, pg. 622
GEC INDUSTRIAL CONTROLS LTD.—Alcatel Alsthom Compagnie Generale D'Electricite; *Int'l*, pg. 53
GASTON COUNTY DYEING MACHINE CO.; *U.S. Private*, pg. 441
GEMS SENSORS—Danaher Corporation; *U.S. Public*, pg. 481
GENCOR INDUSTRIES, INC.; *U.S. Public*, pg. 705
GENERAL SIGNAL CORPORATION; *U.S. Public*, pg. 726
GENERAL SIGNAL THINFILM COMPANY—General Signal Corporation; *U.S. Public*, pg. 727
GENERAL TOOLS MFG., CO. INC.; *U.S. Private*, pg. 445
GEOTRONICS OF NORTH AMERICA, INC.—Spectra-Physics AB; *Int'l*, pg. 1289
GESTRA S.A.—GESTRA GmbH; *Int'l*, pg. 550
GESTRA (U.K.) LTD.—GESTRA GmbH; *Int'l*, pg. 550
GOLDSTAR INSTRUMENT & ELECTRIC CO. LTD.—LG Group; *Int'l*, pg. 779
GOULD INSTRUMENT SYSTEMS, S.A.—Thermo Electron Corporation; *U.S. Public*, pg. 1592
GREAT LAKES-EGLINTON—United Dominion Industries, Ltd.; *U.S. Public*, pg. 1676
HALMA P.L.C.; *Int'l*, pg. 589
HAMWORTHY COMBUSTION SYSTEMS LIMITED—Powell Duffryn PLC; *Int'l*, pg. 1065
HAMWORTHY HEATING LIMITED—Powell Duffryn PLC; *Int'l*, pg. 1065
HARTMANN & BRAUN AG—Mannesmann A.G.; *Int'l*, pg. 835
HATHAWAY CORPORATION; *U.S. Public*, pg. 798
HATHAWAY MOTORS & INSTRUMENTS DIVISION—Hathaway Corporation; *U.S. Public*, pg. 799
HATHAWAY PROCESS INSTRUMENTATION—Hathaway Corporation; *U.S. Public*, pg. 799
HATHAWAY SYSTEMS CORPORATION—Hathaway Corporation; *U.S. Public*, pg. 799
HAUCK MFG. CO.; *U.S. Private*, pg. 510
HAWKE CABLE GLANDS—McKechnie PLC; *Int'l*, pg. 851
HEATH CONSULTANTS INCORPORATED; *U.S. Private*, pg. 518
WALTER HERZOG G.M.B.H.—Varlen Corporation; *U.S. Public*, pg. 1711
HIGH VOLTAGE ENGINEERING CORPORATION; *U.S. Private*, pg. 528
HOBBS CORPORATION—BTR plc; *Int'l*, pg. 127
HOLEC PROJECTS B.V.—Royal Begemann Group; *Int'l*, pg. 1133
HONEYWELL INC.; *U.S. Public*, pg. 833
HONEYWELL LEEDS & NORTHRUP AUSTRALIA PTY. LTD.—Honeywell Inc.; *U.S. Public*, pg. 834
HONEYWELL-MEASUREX CORPORATION—Honeywell Inc.; *U.S. Public*, pg. 833
HONEYWELL-MEASUREX PTY. LTD.—Honeywell Inc.; *U.S. Public*, pg. 834
HOWE SCALE—Staveley Industries PLC; *Int'l*, pg. 1299
J.M. HUBER CORPORATION; *U.S. Private*, pg. 544
HYER INDUSTRIES INC./THAYER SCALE; *U.S. Private*, pg. 552
ICL PLC—Fujitsu Limited; *Int'l*, pg. 528
IMI PLC; *Int'l*, pg. 646
ITT BARTON INSTRUMENTS—ITT Industries, Inc.; *U.S. Public*, pg. 860
ITT FLUID HANDLING—ITT Industries, Inc.; *U.S. Public*, pg. 860
INFRASTRUCTURE BUSINESS—Black & Veatch; *U.S. Private*, pg. 146
INGERSOLL-RAND GMBH—Ingersoll-Rand Company; *U.S. Public*, pg. 878
INGOLD MESSTECHNIK AG—Novartis AG; *Int'l*, pg. 972
INSTRUMENT DIVISION—Dresser Industries, Inc.; *U.S. Public*, pg. 528
INTERMATIC INC.; *U.S. Private*, pg. 567
INTERSPIRO INC.—Spectra-Physics AB; *Int'l*, pg. 1289
INTROTEK INTERNATIONAL—Magnetrol International; *U.S. Private*, pg. 696
IONICS, INCORPORATED; *U.S. Public*, pg. 912
ISCO ENVIRONMENTAL DIVISION—Isco, Inc.; *U.S. Public*, pg. 914
ISCO, INC.; *U.S. Public*, pg. 913
ISCO SEPARATION INSTRUMENTS DIVISION—Isco, Inc.; *U.S. Public*, pg. 914
JANUS ELEVATOR PRODUCTS INC.—Halma p.l.c.; *Int'l*, pg. 590
JAY INSTRUMENT & SPECIALTY CO.; *U.S. Private*, pg. 583
JEUMONT-SCHNEIDER TRENFORMETEURS; *Int'l*, pg. 706
JOHNSON CONTROLS, INC.; *U.S. Public*, pg. 932
JOHNSON MATTHEY INC.—Johnson Matthey Public Limited Company; *Int'l*, pg. 713
JOHNSON MATTHEY NOBLE METALS BUSINESS UNIT—Johnson Matthey Public Limited Company; *Int'l*, pg. 713
JOHNSON YOKOGAWA CORPORATION—Yokogawa Electric Corporation; *Int'l*, pg. 1521
K-TRON AMERICA, INC.—K-Tron International, Inc.; *U.S. Public*, pg. 938
K-TRON ELECTRONICS—K-Tron International, Inc.; *U.S. Public*, pg. 938
K-TRON FRANCE—K-Tron International, Inc.; *U.S. Public*, pg. 938
K-TRON INSTITUTE—K-Tron International, Inc.; *U.S. Public*, pg. 938
K-TRON INTERNATIONAL, INC.; *U.S. Public*, pg. 938
KAY RAY SENSALL INC.—Emerson Electric Co.; *U.S. Public*, pg. 574
KAYDON CORPORATION, FILTRATION DIVISION—Kaydon Corporation; *U.S. Public*, pg. 946
KAYE INSTRUMENTS, INC.—Bowthorpe plc; *Int'l*, pg. 208
KECK INSTRUMENTS, INC.—CILCORP Inc.; *U.S. Public*, pg. 367
KENT INDUSTRIAL MEASUREMENTS LIMITED—ABB Asea Brown Boveri (Holding) Ltd.; *Int'l*, pg. 2
KETEMA, INC.—KTM Holdings Corp.; *U.S. Private*, pg. 604
KIDDE-FENWAL, INC.—Williams Holdings Plc; *Int'l*, pg. 1500
KRAUTKRAMER-FOERSTER JAPAN CO., LTD.—Emerson Electric Co.; *U.S. Public*, pg. 577
KRAUTKRAMER G.M.B.H—Emerson Electric Co.; *U.S. Public*, pg. 577
KURT MANUFACTURING CO. INC.; *U.S. Private*, pg. 637
L3 COMMUNICATIONS TELEMETRY & INSTRUMENTATION DIV.—L3 Communications; *U.S. Private*, pg. 639
LFE INDUSTRIAL SYSTEMS CORPORATION—Mark IV Industries Inc.; *U.S. Public*, pg. 1045
LFE INSTRUMENTS—Danaher Corporation; *U.S. Public*, pg. 482
LAND INFRAROT GMBH—Land Instruments International Ltd.; *Int'l*, pg. 798
LAND INSTRUMENTS INTERNATIONAL, INC.—Land Instruments International Ltd.; *Int'l*, pg. 798
LAND INSTRUMENTS SARL—Land Instruments International Ltd.; *Int'l*, pg. 798
LAND INSTRUMENTS SRL—Land Instruments International Ltd.; *Int'l*, pg. 798
LAND KK—Land Instruments International Ltd.; *Int'l*, pg. 798
LEEDS & NORTHRUP LTD.—General Signal Corporation; *U.S. Public*, pg. 727
LEWIS ENGINEERING COMPANY—Coltec Holdings Inc; *U.S. Public*, pg. 402
LIEBERT CORPORATION—Emerson Electric Co.; *U.S. Public*, pg. 573
LIEBERT CORPORATION AUSTRALIA PTY. LTD.—Emerson Electric Co.; *U.S. Public*, pg. 577
LIEBERT FAR EAST LTD.—Emerson Electric Co.; *U.S. Public*, pg. 577
LIEBERT LTD.—Emerson Electric Co.; *U.S. Public*, pg. 577
LIEBERT MALAYSIA SDN. BHD.—Emerson Electric Co.; *U.S. Public*, pg. 577
LIQUID CONTROLS LLC; *U.S. Private*, pg. 669
LLOYD CONTROLS, INC.; *U.S. Private*, pg. 672
LLOYD INSTRUMENTS LTD.—AMETEK, Inc.; *U.S. Public*, pg. 100
LOVE CONTROLS CORPORATION—Dwyer Instruments Inc.; *U.S. Private*, pg. 350
LUCAS BODY SYSTEMS—LucasVarity plc; *Int'l*, pg. 820
LUCAS INDUSTRIES INC.—LucasVarity plc; *Int'l*, pg. 820
MFRI INC.; *U.S. Public*, pg. 1026
MPH & CMI—MPD, Inc.; *U.S. Private*, pg. 687
MTE-TURCK LTD.—B. Elliott plc.; *Int'l*, pg. 449
MTS SYSTEMS CORPORATION; *U.S. Public*, pg. 1028
M.E. MACK VALVES PTY. LIMITED—Senior Engineering Group, plc.; *Int'l*, pg. 1222
MAGNETIC ANALYSIS CORP.; *U.S. Private*, pg. 695
MAGNETROL INTERNATIONAL; *U.S. Private*, pg. 696
MARATHON MONITORS INCORPORATED—Halma p.l.c.; *Int'l*, pg. 590
MAROTTA SCIENTIFIC CONTROLS, INC.; *U.S. Private*, pg. 706
MATEC APPLIED SCIENCES, INC.—Matec Corporation; *U.S. Public*, pg. 1056
MATEC CORPORATION; *U.S. Public*, pg. 1056
MATEC INSTRUMENTS, INC.—Matec Corporation; *U.S. Public*, pg. 1056
MCCROMETER INC.—Danaher Corporation; *U.S. Public*, pg. 482
MCGILL MANUFACTURING COMPANY, INC.—Emerson Electric Co.; *U.S. Public*, pg. 573
MCGILL MFG. CO., INC. ELECTRICAL DIVISION—Emerson Electric Co.; *U.S. Public*, pg. 573
MEGGITT AVIONICS—Meggitt plc; *Int'l*, pg. 853
MEGGITT PLC; *Int'l*, pg. 853
MERCOID DIV.—Dwyer Instruments Inc.; *U.S. Private*, pg. 350
MERIAM INSTRUMENT—Berkshire Hathaway Inc.; *U.S. Public*, pg. 218
MESA LABORATORIES, INC.; *U.S. Public*, pg. 1099
MICRO MOTION INC.—Emerson Electric Co.; *U.S. Public*, pg. 574
MILLIPORE PROCESS DIV.—Millipore Corporation; *U.S. Public*, pg. 1112
MILLTRONICS—Russel Metals Inc.; *Int'l*, pg. 1150
MINCO PRODUCTS, INC.; *U.S. Private*, pg. 749
MOKON—Mark IV Industries Inc.; *U.S. Public*, pg. 1045
MONITOR LABS, INC.—Bowthorpe plc; *Int'l*, pg. 208
MONSANTO DO BRASIL LTDA. (MOBRA S.A.)—Monsanto Company; *U.S. Public*, pg. 1125
MONTEK DIV.—Raytheon Company; *U.S. Public*, pg. 1366
MOORE CONTROLS PVT. LIMITED—Moore Products Co.; *U.S. Public*, pg. 1128
MOORE PRODUCTS CO.; *U.S. Public*, pg. 1128
AB CARL MUNTERS—Incentive AB; *Int'l*, pg. 669
NANOMETRICS INCORPORATED; *U.S. Public*, pg. 1151
NAPCO EUROPE, LTD.—Thermo Electron Corporation; *U.S. Public*, pg. 1596
NEMATRON CORP.; *U.S. Private*, pg. 791
NIHON-PALL LTD.—Pall Corporation; *U.S. Public*, pg. 1254
NIPPON FISHER COMPANY, LTD.—Monsanto Company; *U.S. Public*, pg. 1126
NISHISHIBA ELECTRIC CO., LTD.—Toshiba Corporation; *Int'l*, pg. 1403
NORGREN CO.—IMI Plc; *Int'l*, pg. 647
NOVAR CONTROLS CORP.—Novar Electronics; *U.S. Private*, pg. 808
NUOVO PIGNONE S.P.A.; *Int'l*, pg. 990
OHKURA-ROSEMOUNT CO., LTD.—Emerson Electric Co.; *U.S. Public*, pg. 577
THE OILGEAR COMPANY; *U.S. Public*, pg. 1215
OPTIM ELECTRONICS CORPORATION—Bowthorpe plc; *Int'l*, pg. 208
ORION RESEARCH INC.—Thermo Electron Corporation; *U.S. Public*, pg. 1592
OUTOKUMPU MINTEC U.S.A., INC.—Outokumpu Oyj; *Int'l*, pg. 1017
PTC THERMISTOR DIV.—Bowthorpe plc; *Int'l*, pg. 208
PACIFIC SCIENTIFIC COMPANY; *U.S. Public*, pg. 1250
PALL DEUTSCHLAND GMBH—Pall Corporation; *U.S. Public*, pg. 1254
PALL EUROPE LTD.—Pall Corporation; *U.S. Public*, pg. 1254
PALL ILFRACOMBE LTD.—Pall Corporation; *U.S. Public*, pg. 1254
PANALARM PRODUCTS, AMETEK, INC.—AMETEK, Inc.; *U.S. Public*, pg. 100
PARAGON ELECTRIC CO., INC.—Siebe plc; *Int'l*, pg. 1243
PARKSON CORPORATION—Axel Johnson AB; *Int'l*, pg. 710
PARTLOW CORPORATION—Danaher Corporation; *U.S. Public*, pg. 482
PENNY & GILES POSITION SENSORS LTD.—Bowthorpe plc; *Int'l*, pg. 207
PENNY & GILES ELECTRONIC COMPONENTS LTD.—Bowthorpe plc; *Int'l*, pg. 207
PERSTORP ANALYTICAL INC.—Perstorp AB; *Int'l*, pg. 1039
PERSTORP ANALYTICAL INC. DIVISION ALPKEM—Perstorp AB; *Int'l*, pg. 1039
PETRECO BAKER HUGHES COMPANY—Baker Hughes Incorporated; *U.S. Public*, pg. 166
PHILIPS AUTOMOTIVE ELECTRONICS—Philips Electronics N.V.; *Int'l*, pg. 1054
PILLAR ELECTRICAL PLC—Caradon Plc; *Int'l*, pg. 267
POLYSIUS LTD.—Fried. Krupp AG; *Int'l*, pg. 512
POWER DEVELOPMENT—Bowthorpe plc; *Int'l*, pg. 207
POWERS PROCESS CONTROLS—Crane Co.; *U.S. Public*, pg. 457
PRATT & WHITNEY—Moore Products Co.; *U.S. Public*, pg. 1128
PRECISION SCIENTIFIC INC.—Jouan, Inc.; *U.S. Private*, pg. 601
PREFERRED INSTRUMENTS—Preferred Utilities Manufacturing Corp.; *U.S. Private*, pg. 881
PREFERRED UTILITIES MANUFACTURING CORP.; *U.S. Private*, pg. 881
PRINCETON GAMMA-TECH, INC.—Outokumpu Oyj; *Int'l*, pg. 1015
PROCESS CONTROL INSTRUMENTATION DIV.—FKI Plc; *Int'l*, pg. 473
PROCESS CONTROLS SECTOR—General Signal Corporation; *U.S. Public*, pg. 726
PROTIMETER PLC—Bowthorpe plc; *Int'l*, pg. 207
PROTIMETER ZWEIGNIEDERLASSUNG DER BOWTHORPE GMBH—Bowthorpe plc; *Int'l*, pg. 209
PROXIMITY CONTROLS CORP.—Dwyer Instruments Inc.; *U.S. Private*, pg. 350
QEI, INC.; *U.S. Private*, pg. 897
QUAD/GRAPHICS, INC.; *U.S. Private*, pg. 897
QUALITROL CORP.—Danaher Corporation; *U.S. Public*, pg. 482
QUANTIC INDUSTRIES, INC.; *U.S. Private*, pg. 899
THE RTZ CORPORATION PLC—Rio Tinto PLC; *Int'l*, pg. 1118
RACINE FEDERATED, INC.; *U.S. Private*, pg. 906
RAVEN INDUSTRIES, INC.; *U.S. Public*, pg. 1361
RAYTECH CORPORATION; *U.S. Public*, pg. 1363
RELA, INC.—Colorado MEDtech, Inc.; *U.S. Public*, pg. 401
RESEARCH, INCORPORATED; *U.S. Public*, pg. 1382
RHEOMETRIC SCIENTIFIC; *U.S. Public*, pg. 1387
RHEOMETRIC SCIENTIFIC, INC.—Rheometric Scientific; *U.S. Public*, pg. 1387
RHEOMETRICS SCIENTIFIC FAR EAST LTD.—Rheometric Scientific; *U.S. Public*, pg. 1387
RHO SIGMA, INC.—Watsco, Inc.; *U.S. Public*, pg. 1746
RICHARDS INDUSTRIES, INC.; *U.S. Private*, pg. 929
ROBERTSHAW CONTROLS COMPANY—Siebe plc; *Int'l*, pg. 1243
ROBERTSHAW TENNESSEE—Siebe plc; *Int'l*, pg. 1243
ROBICON—High Voltage Engineering Corporation; *U.S. Private*, pg. 528
ROBOTIC VISION SYSTEMS, INC.; *U.S. Public*, pg. 1395
ROSEMOUNT ANALYTICAL, INC.—Emerson Electric Co.; *U.S. Public*, pg. 574
ROSEMOUNT MEASUREMENT DIVISION—Emerson Electric Co.; *U.S. Public*, pg. 574
SAHA WOODALL-DUCKHAM (PRIVATE) LIMITED—FKI Plc; *Int'l*, pg. 472
SANDVIK AB; *Int'l*, pg. 1185
SANKI ENGINEERING CO., LTD.—Mitsui & Co., Ltd.; *Int'l*, pg. 877
SCHLUMBERGER LIMITED; *U.S. Public*, pg. 1439
SCHNEIDER ELECTRIC S.A.—Schneider S.A.; *Int'l*, pg. 1207
SCHNEIDER S.A.; *Int'l*, pg. 1207

SCHUTTE & KOERTING DIVISION—KTM Holdings Corp.; U.S. Private, pg. 604
SECHRIST INDUSTRIES, INC.; U.S. Private, pg. 980
SENIOR AUSTRALIA LIMITED—Senior Engineering Group, plc.; Int'l, pg. 1222
SENIOR ENGINEERING—Senior Engineering Group, plc.; Int'l, pg. 1222
SENIOR ENGINEERING COMPANY-USA—Senior Engineering Group, plc.; Int'l, pg. 1222
SENIOR ENGINEERING (PTY) LIMITED-SOUTH AFRICA—Senior Engineering Group, plc.; Int'l, pg. 1223
SENIOR TIFT AUSTRALIA PTY LIMITED—Senior Engineering Group, plc.; Int'l, pg. 1223
SENSALL, DIV. OF ROSEMOUNT, INC.—Emerson Electric Co.; U.S. Public, pg. 574
SENSODEC OY—Valmet Corporation; Int'l, pg. 1449
SENSORS DIVISION—MTS Systems Corporation; U.S. Public, pg. 1029
SENSORS & ELECTRONIC SYSTEMS—Raytheon Company; U.S. Public, pg. 1365
SERADYN, INC.—Mitsubishi Chemical Corporation; Int'l, pg. 871
SEVERN FURNACES LIMITED—Instron Corporation; U.S. Public, pg. 883
SHAPE SOUTH, INC.—Shape Inc.; U.S. Private, pg. 990
SHOGYO INTERNATIONAL CORPORATION; U.S. Private, pg. 996
SHOWA DENKO K.K.; Int'l, pg. 1236
SNAP-TITE, INC.; U.S. Private, pg. 1010
SPECTRA-PHYSICS AB; Int'l, pg. 1288
SPECTRA-TECH—Thermo Electron Corporation; U.S. Public, pg. 1593
SPECTROL ELECTRONICS CORPORATION—The Dyson-Kissner-Moran Corporation; U.S. Private, pg. 351
SPOTNAILS—Peace Industries Inc.; U.S. Private, pg. 845
SPRINGFIELD PRECISION INSTRUMENTS, INC.; U.S. Private, pg. 1027
SQUARE D COMPANY—Schneider S.A.; Int'l, pg. 1208
STAVELEY INDUSTRIES PLC; Int'l, pg. 1298
STAVELEY WEIGHING SYSTEMS CANADA, INC.—Staveley Industries PLC; Int'l, pg. 1299
STERIMATICS CORPORATION—Millipore Corporation; U.S. Public, pg. 1113
STERLING, INC.; U.S. Private, pg. 1041
STEWART WARNER INSTRUMENTS CORPORATION; U.S. Private, pg. 1042
STEWART WARNER INSTRUMENTS CORPORATION—Stewart Warner Instruments Corporation; U.S. Private, pg. 1043
STRAHMAN VALVES, INC.; U.S. Private, pg. 1046
STRUCTURAL EUROPE—Essef Corporation; U.S. Public, pg. 593
SULZER INFRA DEUTSCHLAND GMBH.—Sulzer Ltd.; Int'l, pg. 1306
SYMPLEX COMMUNICATIONS CORP.; U.S. Private, pg. 1060
TSI INCORPORATED; U.S. Public, pg. 1559
TAU-TRON—General Signal Corporation; U.S. Public, pg. 727
TECHNOLOGY INDUSTRIES SECTOR—General Signal Corporation; U.S. Public, pg. 727
TECHNOLOGY RESEARCH CORPORATION; U.S. Public, pg. 1564
TELEGAN GAS MONITORING LIMITED—Halma p.l.c.; Int'l, pg. 590
TERADYNE, INC.; U.S. Public, pg. 1580
TEST AND COLIBRATION INSTRUMENTS—AMETEK, Inc.; U.S. Public, pg. 100
THAMES SIDE-MAYWOOD LIMITED—Halma p.l.c.; Int'l, pg. 590
THERM-O-DISC INC.—Emerson Electric Co.; U.S. Public, pg. 573
THERMO ELECTRIC CO., INC.; U.S. Private, pg. 1080
THERMO ELECTRON CORPORATION; U.S. Public, pg. 1591
THERMON MANUFACTURING COMPANY; U.S. Private, pg. 1080
TIME WARNER INC.; U.S. Public, pg. 1610
TOKHEIM CORPORATION; U.S. Public, pg. 1620
TOSHIBA AUTOMATION CO., LTD.—Toshiba Corporation; Int'l, pg. 1403
TRADINCO INSTRUMENTEN-APPARATEN B.V.—Halma p.l.c.; Int'l, pg. 590
TRANSDYN CONTROLS, INC.—Powell Industries, Inc.; U.S. Public, pg. 1319
TRANSPORTATION GROUP—DSP Technology Inc.; U.S. Public, pg. 475
H.O. TRERICE COMPANY; U.S. Private, pg. 1099
TRI-CLOVER INC.—Tetra Laval Group; Int'l, pg. 1379
TRIPLETT CORPORATION; U.S. Private, pg. 1104
II-VI INCORPORATED; U.S. Public, pg. 1647
UNITECH INDUSTRIES, INC.; U.S. Public, pg. 1672
UNITED ELECTRONICS INDUSTRIES, INC.—United Technologies Corporation; U.S. Public, pg. 1690
UNITED SCIENCES INC.—Bowthorpe plc; Int'l, pg. 208
VG ELECTRONICS LTD.—Thermo Electron Corporation; U.S. Public, pg. 1595
VG INSTRUMENTS PLC—Thermo Electron Corporation; U.S. Public, pg. 1595
VALMET AUTOMATION INC.—Valmet Corporation; Int'l, pg. 1449
VALMET AUTOMATION INC.-CONTROL SYSTEMS—Valmet Corporation; Int'l, pg. 1449
VALMET AUTOMATION KAJAANI LTD.—Valmet Corporation; Int'l, pg. 1449
VARI TRONICS COMPANY, INC.; U.S. Private, pg. 1134
VARLEN CORPORATION; U.S. Public, pg. 1710
VARLEN INSTRUMENTS, INC.—Varlen Corporation; U.S. Public, pg. 1711
VEDA SYSTEMS, INCORPORATED—Veridian; U.S. Private, pg. 1136
WALKER MAGNETICS GROUP, INC.; U.S. Private, pg. 1147
WANSON CO. LTD.—FKI Plc; Int'l, pg. 472
WARNER AUDIO PUBLISHING—Time Warner Inc.; U.S. Public, pg. 1614
WATLOW ELECTRIC MANUFACTURING COMPANY; U.S. Private, pg. 1153
WATTS INDUSTRIES, INC.; U.S. Public, pg. 1746
WERNER & PFLEIDERER (U.K.) LTD.—Fried. Krupp AG; Int'l, pg. 511
WHESSOE PLC; Int'l, pg. 1498
WHESSOE SYSTEMS & CONTROLS LTD.—Whessoe Plc; Int'l, pg. 1498
WIEGAND INDUSTRIAL-CHROMALOX—Emerson Electric Co.; U.S. Public, pg. 573
YARWAY CORPORATION—Tyco International Ltd.; U.S. Public, pg. 1650
YOKOGAWA CORPORATION OF AMERICA—Yokogawa Electric Corporation; Int'l, pg. 1521
YOKOGAWA ELECTRIC CORPORATION; Int'l, pg. 1520
JOHN ZINK CO.—Koch Industries, Incorporated; U.S. Private, pg. 628

3824 — TOTALIZING FLUID METERS & COUNTING DEVICES

ABB ASEA BROWN BOVERI (HOLDING) LTD.; Int'l, pg. 1
ABB MASCHINENFABRIK MEYER AG—ABB Asea Brown Boveri (Holding) Ltd.; Int'l, pg. 1
AMERICAN METER COMPANY—Ruhrgas Aktiengesellschaft; Int'l, pg. 1149
ARGO INSTRUMENTS INC.—Mannesmann A.G.; Int'l, pg. 839
AUTOMATIC SIGNAL/EAGLE SIGNAL—Siemens AG; Int'l, pg. 1245
AUTOMATIC TIMING & CONTROLS, INC.—Desco Corporation; U.S. Private, pg. 327
BTR PLC; Int'l, pg. 124
BADGER METER DE MEXICO, S.A. DE C.V.—Badger Meter, Inc.; U.S. Public, pg. 165
BADGER METER, INC.; U.S. Public, pg. 164
BADGER METER INDUSTRIAL DIV.—Badger Meter, Inc.; U.S. Public, pg. 165
BADGER METER UTILITY DIV.—Badger Meter, Inc.; U.S. Public, pg. 165
BRAN & LUEBBE INC.—Tetra Laval Group; Int'l, pg. 1378
CASCADE CONTROLS, INC.—Synergism, Inc.; U.S. Private, pg. 1060
CHANDLER EVANS CONTROL SYSTEMS DIVISION—Coltec Holdings Inc; U.S. Public, pg. 401
CUTLER-HAMMER PRODUCTS—Eaton Corporation; U.S. Public, pg. 556
DMD DRESSER MEASUREMENT OPERATION—Dresser Industries, Inc.; U.S. Public, pg. 528
DANAHER CORPORATION—Danaher Corporation; U.S. Public, pg. 480
DANIEL INDUSTRIES, INC.; U.S. Public, pg. 482
DAVIES SHEPHARD PTY. LTD.—ABB Asea Brown Boveri (Holding) Ltd.; Int'l, pg. 2
DESCO CORPORATION; U.S. Private, pg. 326
DRESSER CANADA, INC.—Dresser Industries, Inc.; U.S. Public, pg. 529
DRESSER INDUSTRIES, INC.; U.S. Public, pg. 528
DWYER INSTRUMENTS INC.; U.S. Private, pg. 350
EG & G WALLAC OY—EG & G, Inc.; U.S. Public, pg. 544
B. ELLIOTT PLC.; Int'l, pg. 448
FMC-SMITH METER CO.—FMC Corporation; U.S. Public, pg. 605
FASCO CONTROLS CORPORATION—BTR plc; Int'l, pg. 125
GESELLSCHAFT FUR GEROTEBAU MBH—Hanson PLC; Int'l, pg. 594
HAYDON SWITCH & INSTRUMENT, INC.; U.S. Private, pg. 513
HAYS FLUID CONTROLS-DIVISION OF ROMAC INDUSTRIES—Romac Industries, Inc.; U.S. Private, pg. 942
HELICOID GAUGE DIV.—FKI Plc; Int'l, pg. 473
HONEYWELL INC.; U.S. Public, pg. 833
HONEYWELL'S MICRO SWITCH DIVISION—Honeywell Inc.; U.S. Public, pg. 834
ITT BARTON INSTRUMENTS—ITT Industries, Inc.; U.S. Public, pg. 860
INSTRUMENT DIVISION—Dresser Industries, Inc.; U.S. Public, pg. 528
ISCO ENVIRONMENTAL DIVISION—Isco, Inc.; U.S. Public, pg. 914
ISCO, INC.; U.S. Public, pg. 913
KENT INSTRUMENTS PTY. LTD.—ABB Asea Brown Boveri (Holding) Ltd.; Int'l, pg. 2
KENT METERS, INC.—ABB Asea Brown Boveri (Holding) Ltd.; Int'l, pg. 4
KENT METERS LTD.—ABB Asea Brown Boveri (Holding) Ltd.; Int'l, pg. 2
KENT METERS S.A. (PTY.) LTD.—ABB Asea Brown Boveri (Holding) Ltd.; Int'l, pg. 3
KETEMA, INC.—KTM Holdings Corp.; U.S. Private, pg. 604
KEX PRODUCTS, INC.—Berwind Corporation; U.S. Private, pg. 138
KVAERNER ENERGY, DAMSGARD—Kvaerner a.s.a.; Int'l, pg. 767
KYSOR/MEDALLION—Kuhlman Corporation; U.S. Public, pg. 968
LAGARDERE GROUPE; Int'l, pg. 791
LEFEBURE CORP.—De La Rue plc; Int'l, pg. 387
LEUPOLD & STEVENS, INC.; U.S. Private, pg. 662
MASONEILAN NORTH AMERICAN OPERATIONS—Dresser Industries, Inc.; U.S. Public, pg. 528
MINEBEA CO., LTD.; Int'l, pg. 867
MOOG INDUSTRIAL CONTROLS CORP.—Moog Incorporated; U.S. Public, pg. 1127
MOOG INTERNATIONAL GROUP—Moog Incorporated; U.S. Public, pg. 1127
MOOG TORRANCE—Moog Incorporated; U.S. Public, pg. 1127
MOTOROLA, INC.; U.S. Public, pg. 1136
NATIONAL CONTROLS CORPORATION—Cortec Group; U.S. Private, pg. 277
NUOVO PIGNONE S.P.A.; Int'l, pg. 990
THE OILGEAR COMPANY; U.S. Public, pg. 1215
OMRON CORPORATION; Int'l, pg. 1005
ONEOK TECHNOLOGY CO.—ONEOK Inc.; U.S. Public, pg. 1226
PROCHEM MIXING EQUIPMENT LTD.—Robbins & Myers, Inc.; U.S. Public, pg. 1393
PACIFIC SCIENTIFIC COMPANY; U.S. Public, pg. 1250
PENBERTHY DIV.—Axel Johnson AB; Int'l, pg. 711
PERFECT EQUIPMENT CORP.—Berwind Corporation; U.S. Private, pg. 138
PHILIPS AUTOMOTIVE ELECTRONICS—Philips Electronics N.V.; Int'l, pg. 1054
M.H. RHODES, INC.; U.S. Private, pg. 927
RICHARDS INDUSTRIES, INC.; U.S. Private, pg. 929
ROCKWELL INTERNATIONAL CORPORATION; U.S. Public, pg. 1397
SCHLUMBERGER INDUSTRIES—Schlumberger Limited; U.S. Public, pg. 1439
SCHLUMBERGER LIMITED; U.S. Public, pg. 1439
SUOMEN VESIMITTARIT OY—Oy Algol AB; Int'l, pg. 15
TOKHEIM CORPORATION; U.S. Public, pg. 1620
TOKHEIM GMBH—Tokheim Corporation; U.S. Public, pg. 1620
TOKHEIM LTD.—Tokheim Corporation; U.S. Public, pg. 1620
TRANSTECHNOLOGY CORPORATION; U.S. Public, pg. 1632

3825 — INSTRUMENTS FOR MEASURING & TESTING OF ELECTRICITY & ELECTRICAL SIGNALS

A&M INSTRUMENTS INC.—BTR plc; Int'l, pg. 125
AAI/ACL TECHNOLOGIES—United Industrial Corporation; U.S. Public, pg. 1679
ADC TELECOMMUNICATIONS, INC.; U.S. Public, pg. 4
AVO INTERNATIONAL; U.S. Private, pg. 9
AVO INTERNATIONAL—TBG Management S.A.M.; Int'l, pg. 1335
ACTION INSTRUMENTS, INC.; U.S. Private, pg. 15
ACTRON MANUFACTURING COMPANY; U.S. Private, pg. 16
ADTRAN, INC.; U.S. Public, pg. 20
AEROFLEX INCORPORATED; U.S. Public, pg. 23
AEROFLEX LINTEK CORP.—Aeroflex Incorporated; U.S. Public, pg. 24
AEROSPACE AVIONICS INC.—BTR plc; Int'l, pg. 126
AGEMA INFRARED SYSTEMS AB—Spectra-Physics AB; Int'l, pg. 1289
AGEMA INFRARED SYSTEMS LTD.—Spectra-Physics AB; Int'l, pg. 1289
ALBER ENGINEERING, INC.—BTR plc; Int'l, pg. 126
ALLARD INDUSTRIES; U.S. Private, pg. 36
ALLEN TELECOM, INC.; U.S. Public, pg. 45
ALLIEDSIGNAL AEROSPACE—AlliedSignal Inc.; U.S. Public, pg. 50
AMERICAN ELECTRONICS, INC.—AEI Holding Co., Inc.; U.S. Private, pg. 5
AMES CROSTA BABCOCK LTD.—FKI Plc; Int'l, pg. 471
AMPROBE INSTRUMENT—United Dominion Industries, Ltd.; U.S. Public, pg. 1676
ANALOG DEVICES, INC.; U.S. Public, pg. 107
ANALOGIC CORPORATION; U.S. Public, pg. 109
ANRITSU AMERICA, INC.-CENTRAL REGION—Anritsu Corporation; Int'l, pg. 77
ANRITSU AMERICA, INC.-WESTERN REGION—Anritsu Corporation; Int'l, pg. 77
ANRITSU CORPORATION; Int'l, pg. 77
ANRITSU ELEKTRONIK GMBH—Anritsu Corporation; Int'l, pg. 77
ANRITSU WILTRON—Anritsu Corporation; Int'l, pg. 77
ANSALDO INDUSTRIA S.P.A.—IRI Istituto Ricostruzione Industriale; Int'l, pg. 653
APPLIED MICROSYSTEMS CORPORATION; U.S. Public, pg. 123
ASEA BROWN BOVERI AG—ABB Asea Brown Boveri (Holding) Ltd.; Int'l, pg. 2
ASTRO-MED, INC.; U.S. Public, pg. 141
AUSTRON INC.—Datum Inc.; U.S. Public, pg. 488
AUXITROL S.A.—Esterline Technologies Corporation; U.S. Public, pg. 594
AXIOM INC.; U.S. Public, pg. 157
AXSYS TECHNOLOGIES, INC.; U.S. Public, pg. 157
BIF—General Signal Corporation; U.S. Public, pg. 726
BTR PLC; Int'l, pg. 124
BABCOCK & WILCOX DE MEXICO SA DE CV—FKI Plc; Int'l, pg. 474
BABCOCK ARGENTINA S.A.—FKI Plc; Int'l, pg. 473
BABCOCK AUSTRALIA HOLDINGS LTD.—FKI Plc; Int'l, pg. 474
BABCOCK DUIKER B.V.—FKI Plc; Int'l, pg. 472
BABCOCK INDUSTRIAL & ELECTRICAL PRODUCTS LTD.—FKI Plc; Int'l, pg. 472
BABCOCK INTERNATIONAL GROUP PLC; Int'l, pg. 130
BABCOCK INTERNATIONAL (NZ) LTD.—FKI Plc; Int'l, pg. 474
BABCOCK-MOXEY LTD.—FKI Plc; Int'l, pg. 472
BABCOCK POWER LIMITED-RESEARCH DIV.—FKI Plc; Int'l, pg. 472
BABCOCK POWER-PRODUCTION DIV.—FKI Plc; Int'l, pg. 472
BABCOCK ROBEY LIMITED—FKI Plc; Int'l, pg. 472
BABCOCK TRANSFORMERS LTD.—FKI Plc; Int'l, pg. 472
BABCOCK WOODALL-DUCKHAM LTD—FKI Plc; Int'l, pg. 472
BABCOCK WORSLEY LIMITED—FKI Plc; Int'l, pg. 472
BACH-SIMPSON LTD.—Katy Industries, Inc.; U.S. Public, pg. 944
BACH-SIMPSON (UK) LTD.—Katy Industries, Inc.; U.S. Public, pg. 944

BANCOMM—Datum Inc.; *U.S. Public*, pg. 488
BECKMAN INDUSTRIAL CORPORATION—Emerson Electric Co.; *U.S. Public*, pg. 574
BOURNS INTEGRATED TECHNOLOGIES DIVISION—Bourns, Inc.; *U.S. Private*, pg. 161
BOWTHORPE PLC; *Int'l*, pg. 207
BROADCAST ELECTRONICS, INC.—Hoak Capital; *U.S. Private*, pg. 531
CBS CORPORATION; *U.S. Public*, pg. 273
CEGELEC—Alcatel Alsthom Compagnie Generale D'Electricite; *Int'l*, pg. 52
CEGELEC DE MEXICO—Alcatel Alsthom Compagnie Generale D'Electricite; *Int'l*, pg. 53
CEGELEC ENTREPRISES, INC.—Alcatel Alsthom Compagnie Generale D'Electricite; *Int'l*, pg. 53
CEGELEC GMBH—Alcatel Alsthom Compagnie Generale D'Electricite; *Int'l*, pg. 53
CERPROBE CORPORATION; *U.S. Public*, pg. 332
CHEROKEE INTERNATIONAL LLC; *U.S. Private*, pg. 233
CHICAGO LASER SYSTEMS—Electro Scientific Industries, Inc.; *U.S. Public*, pg. 569
CIRMA ENTERPRISE—Alcatel Alsthom Compagnie Generale D'Electricite; *Int'l*, pg. 53
CLAROSTAT CENTERS & CONTROLS GROUP—BTR plc; *Int'l*, pg. 127
COMMERCIAL HYDRAULICS KEELAVITE, LTD.—Commercial Intertech Corp.; *U.S. Public*, pg. 411
COMPUDYNE CORPORATION; *U.S. Public*, pg. 419
COMSTRON DIVISION—Aeroflex Incorporated; *U.S. Public*, pg. 24
CORDIS, A JOHNSON & JOHNSON COMPANY EUROPA N.V.—Johnson & Johnson; *U.S. Public*, pg. 928
CROMPTON INSTRUMENTS LTD.—BTR plc; *Int'l*, pg. 125
CROMPTON MODUTEC INC.—BTR plc; *Int'l*, pg. 125
CYBER SYSTEMS, INC.; *U.S. Private*, pg. 299
DEI DIVISION—Alcatel Alsthom Compagnie Generale D'Electricite; *Int'l*, pg. 52
DSP TECHNOLOGY INC.; *U.S. Public*, pg. 475
DANFOSS A/S; *Int'l*, pg. 376
DATUM INC.; *U.S. Public*, pg. 488
DETEX CORPORATION; *U.S. Private*, pg. 327
DIAMOND POWER SPECIALTY CO.—McDermott International, Inc.; *U.S. Public*, pg. 1068
DOALL COMPANY; *U.S. Private*, pg. 337
DOBSON PARK INDUSTRIES PLC—Harnischfeger Industries, Inc.; *U.S. Public*, pg. 789
DORNE & MARGOLIN, INC.—United Capital Corp.; *U.S. Public*, pg. 1675
DRANETZ-BMI—WPT, Inc.; *U.S. Private*, pg. 1144
DYNAMICS RESEARCH CORPORATION; *U.S. Public*, pg. 539
DYNISCO GERATE G.M.B.H.—Berwind Corporation; *U.S. Private*, pg. 139
DYNISCO INSTRUMENT SARL.—Berwind Corporation; *U.S. Private*, pg. 139
DYNISCO (U.K.) LIMITED—Berwind Corporation; *U.S. Private*, pg. 139
EG & G INSTRUMENTS APPLIED RESEARCH—EG & G, Inc.; *U.S. Public*, pg. 543
EG & G INSTRUMENTS DIVISION—EG & G, Inc.; *U.S. Public*, pg. 544
EG & G MANAGEMENT SYSTEMS INC.- ALBUQUERQUE OPERATIONS—EG & G, Inc.; *U.S. Public*, pg. 543
EG & G RETICON—EG & G, Inc.; *U.S. Public*, pg. 544
ELE INTERNATIONAL, INC./SOILTEST—South West Water PLC; *Int'l*, pg. 1287
EMC TEST SYSTEM, L.P.—ESCO Electronics Corporation; *U.S. Public*, pg. 546
ENI POWER SYSTEMS—Emerson Electric Co.; *U.S. Public*, pg. 574
ENS GROUP—Alcatel Alsthom Compagnie Generale D'Electricite; *Int'l*, pg. 52
EDGCUMBE INSTRUMENTS LTD.—Bowthorpe plc; *Int'l*, pg. 207
ELBIT LTD.—IDB Holding Corporation; *Int'l*, pg. 644
ELECTRO METRICS, INC.; *U.S. Private*, pg. 369
ELECTRO-SCIENCE LABORATORIES, INC.; *U.S. Private*, pg. 369
ELECTRO SCIENTIFIC INDUSTRIES, INC.; *U.S. Public*, pg. 568
ELECTRODYNAMICS, INC.—Carpenter Technology Corporation; *U.S. Public*, pg. 308
ELO TOUCHSYSTEMS, INC.—Raychem Corporation; *U.S. Public*, pg. 1362
ELRON ELECTRONIC INDUSTRIES LTD.—IDB Holding Corporation; *Int'l*, pg. 644
ELSCINT LTD.; *Int'l*, pg. 450
ERIEZ MAGNETICS; *U.S. Private*, pg. 381
ESTERLINE TECHNOLOGIES CORPORATION; *U.S. Public*, pg. 594
EVERETT CHARLES TECHNOLOGIES; *U.S. Private*, pg. 386
FFV AEROTECH AB—Celsius AB; *Int'l*, pg. 276
FFV TEST SYSTEMS AB—Celsius AB; *Int'l*, pg. 277
FKI PLC; *Int'l*, pg. 471
FASCO CONTROLS CORPORATION—BTR plc; *Int'l*, pg. 125
FASCO SENSORS & CONTROLS DIVISION—BTR plc; *Int'l*, pg. 127
FERGUSON ELECTRIC EQUIPMENT CORPORATION—Ferguson Electric Construction Co., Inc.; *U.S. Private*, pg. 401
FLUKE CORPORATION; *U.S. Public*, pg. 659
FREQUENCY AND TIME SYSTEMS, INC.—Datum Inc.; *U.S. Public*, pg. 488
FREQUENCY ELECTRONICS, INC.; *U.S. Public*, pg. 681
FUJITSU MICROELECTRONICS, INC.—Fujitsu Limited; *Int'l*, pg. 527
GDE SYSTEMS, INC.—Tracor, Inc.; *U.S. Public*, pg. 1627
GEC ELECTRICAL PROJECTS LTD.—Alcatel Alsthom Compagnie Generale D'Electricite; *Int'l*, pg. 53
GN NETTEST, TELECOM DIVISION—GN Great Nordic Ltd.; *Int'l*, pg. 536
GENERAL ELECTRIC COMPANY; *U.S. Public*, pg. 709
GENERAL MICROCIRCUITS CORPORATION—General Microwave Corporation; *U.S. Public*, pg. 717
GENERAL MICROWAVE CORPORATION; *U.S. Public*, pg. 717
GENERAL SIGNAL CORPORATION; *U.S. Public*, pg. 726
GENRAD ELECTRONIC MANUFACTURING TESTS SYSTEMS—GenRad, Inc.; *U.S. Public*, pg. 731
GENRAD, INC.; *U.S. Public*, pg. 731
GEOTRONICS SCANDINAVIA AB—Spectra-Physics AB; *Int'l*, pg. 1289
GIGA-TRONICS INCORPORATED; *U.S. Public*, pg. 742
GOLDSTAR INSTRUMENT & ELECTRIC CO. LTD.—LG Group; *Int'l*, pg. 779
GOLDSTAR PRECISION INDUSTRIES LTD.—LG Group; *Int'l*, pg. 779
GOVERNMENT COMPONENTS DIVISION—AMP Incorporated; *U.S. Public*, pg. 8
HALMA P.L.C.; *Int'l*, pg. 589
HAMLIN, INC.—Breed Technologies, Inc.; *U.S. Public*, pg. 251
HARTMANN & BRAUN AG—Mannesmann A.G.; *Int'l*, pg. 835
HATHAWAY CORPORATION; *U.S. Public*, pg. 798
HATHAWAY MOTORS & INSTRUMENTS DIVISION—Hathaway Corporation; *U.S. Public*, pg. 799
HATHAWAY SYSTEMS NORTHWEST—Hathaway Corporation; *U.S. Public*, pg. 799
HAWKER INSTRUMENTS LTD.—BTR plc; *Int'l*, pg. 125
HAYES CORPORATION, REGIONAL OFFICE—Hayes Corporation; *U.S. Public*, pg. 801
HEKIMIAN LABORATORIES, INC.—Axel Johnson AB; *Int'l*, pg. 709
HEWLETT-PACKARD COMPANY; *U.S. Public*, pg. 813
HICKOK INCORPORATED; *U.S. Public*, pg. 825
HIPOTRONICS, INC.—Hubbell Incorporated; *U.S. Public*, pg. 844
HOLADAY INDUSTRIES, INC.—Bowthorpe plc; *Int'l*, pg. 208
HONEYWELL DEFENSE AVIONICS SYSTEMS—Honeywell Inc.; *U.S. Public*, pg. 834
HONEYWELL INC.; *U.S. Public*, pg. 833
HONEYWELL, INC.—Honeywell Inc.; *U.S. Public*, pg. 834
HOWELL INSTRUMENTS INC.; *U.S. Private*, pg. 543
HYDRIL COMPANY; *U.S. Private*, pg. 551
IVHS TECHNOLOGIES INC.—Eaton Corporation; *U.S. Public*, pg. 558
INCENTIVE AB; *Int'l*, pg. 666
INERTIA DYNAMICS INC.—Rockwell International Corporation; *U.S. Public*, pg. 1398
ISCO SEPARATION INSTRUMENTS DIVISION—Isco, Inc.; *U.S. Public*, pg. 914
JEOL, LTD.; *Int'l*, pg. 696
KLA TENCOR CORPORATION; *U.S. Public*, pg. 939
KAY RAY SENSALL INC.—Emerson Electric Co.; *U.S. Public*, pg. 574
KEITHLEY INSTRUMENTS, INC.; *U.S. Public*, pg. 946
KEITHLEY INSTRUMENTS INC.-RADIATION MEASUREMENTS DIV.—Keithley Instruments, Inc.; *U.S. Public*, pg. 946
KINETICSYSTEMS CORPORATION; *U.S. Private*, pg. 620
KONTRON MESSTECHNIK GMBH—Bayerische Motoren Werke Aktiengesellschaft; *Int'l*, pg. 177
KRATOS GROUP PLC/KRATOS ANALYTICAL LTD.—Shimadzu Corporation; *Int'l*, pg. 1232
KRUPP ENTWICKLUNGSZENTRUM GMBH—Fried. Krupp AG; *Int'l*, pg. 512
KRUPP HOESCH INTERNATIONAL GMBH—Fried. Krupp AG; *Int'l*, pg. 513
KUWANO ELECTRICAL INSTRUMENTS CO., LTD.—Oki Electric Industry Company, Ltd.; *Int'l*, pg. 999
LTX CORPORATION; *U.S. Public*, pg. 972
LAMBDA ELECTRONICS INC.—Siebe plc; *Int'l*, pg. 1241
LANDIS & STAEFA AG; *Int'l*, pg. 800
LANDIS & STAEFA, INC.—Landis & Staefa AG; *Int'l*, pg. 800
LANDIS & STAEFA INC.—Landis & Staefa AG; *Int'l*, pg. 800
LEADER INSTRUMENTS CORPORATION; *U.S. Private*, pg. 655
LINEAR DIVISION—LTX Corporation; *U.S. Public*, pg. 972
LOCUS, INC.—Kaman Corporation; *U.S. Public*, pg. 942
MALLORY, INC.; *U.S. Private*, pg. 698
MARCONI INSTRUMENTS LTD.—The General Electric Company, p.l.c.; *Int'l*, pg. 544
MARK IV INDUSTRIES INC.; *U.S. Public*, pg. 1044
MAROTTA SCIENTIFIC CONTROLS, INC.; *U.S. Private*, pg. 706
MEASUREMENTS GROUP, INC.—Vishay Intertechnology, Inc.; *U.S. Public*, pg. 1722
MECHANICAL TECHNOLOGY INC.; *U.S. Public*, pg. 1077
MEDIDORES BAILEY S.A.—FKI Plc; *Int'l*, pg. 474
METHODE ELECTRONICS INC.; *U.S. Public*, pg. 1101
MICRO COMPONENT TECHNOLOGY INC.; *U.S. Public*, pg. 1104
MICRO MEASUREMENTS DIV.—Vishay Intertechnology, Inc.; *U.S. Public*, pg. 1722
MICRO PROCESSOR SYSTEMS, INC.—Eaton Corporation; *U.S. Public*, pg. 558
MICROWAVE MEASUREMENT DIVISION—Anritsu Corporation; *Int'l*, pg. 77
MIKRONWERK GMBH—AB SKF; *Int'l*, pg. 1157
MILITARY AVIONICS DIVISION—Honeywell Inc.; *U.S. Public*, pg. 834
MILLIPORE TYLAN PRODUCTS—Millipore Corporation; *U.S. Public*, pg. 1112
MILTON INDUSTRIES, INC.; *U.S. Private*, pg. 749
MINELCO, INC.—Carpenter Technology Corporation; *U.S. Public*, pg. 308
MINING CONTROLS, INC.—Elgin National Industries, Inc.; *U.S. Private*, pg. 370
MONITOR PRODUCTS COMPANY INC.—Bowthorpe plc; *Int'l*, pg. 208
MONSANTO DO BRASIL LTDA. (MOBRA S.A.)—Monsanto Company; *U.S. Public*, pg. 1125
MOOG INDUSTRIAL CONTROLS CORP.—Moog Incorporated; *U.S. Public*, pg. 1127
MOOG INTERNATIONAL GROUP—Moog Incorporated; *U.S. Public*, pg. 1127
MOTOROLA, INC.; *U.S. Public*, pg. 1136
NEWPORT ELECTRONICS, INC.—OMEGA Engineering, Inc.; *U.S. Private*, pg. 816
NICOLET TEST & MEASUREMENT DIVISION—Thermo Electron Corporation; *U.S. Public*, pg. 1593
NIPPON FISHER COMPANY, LTD.—Monsanto Company; *U.S. Public*, pg. 1126
OAK INDUSTRIES INC.; *U.S. Public*, pg. 1209
ODETICS INC.; *U.S. Public*, pg. 1212
OKI ELECTRIC INDUSTRY COMPANY, LTD.; *Int'l*, pg. 999
OSCILLOQUARTZ SA—SMH Swiss Corporation for Micro Electronics & Watchmaking Indus. Ltd.; *Int'l*, pg. 1161
PG TECHNOLOGY, LTD.—COMSAT Corporation; *U.S. Public*, pg. 424
PACIFIC SCIENTIFIC COMPANY; *U.S. Public*, pg. 1250
PHONETICS, INC.; *U.S. Private*, pg. 863
POWERTV, INC.—Scientific-Atlanta, Inc.; *U.S. Public*, pg. 1443
PRESSURE SYSTEMS, INC.—The Roxboro Group PLC; *Int'l*, pg. 1130
PROCESS CONTROLS SECTOR—General Signal Corporation; *U.S. Public*, pg. 726
QUEST TECHNOLOGIES, INC.; *U.S. Private*, pg. 900
RACAL ELECTRONICS PLC; *Int'l*, pg. 1082
RACAL INSTRUMENTS, INC.—Racal Electronics Plc; *Int'l*, pg. 1083
RACAL RADAR DEFENCE—Racal Electronics Plc; *Int'l*, pg. 1082
RACAL RECORDERS INC.—Racal Electronics Plc; *Int'l*, pg. 1083
RAYTHEON—Raytheon Company; *U.S. Public*, pg. 1365
RECON/OPTICAL, INC.; *U.S. Private*, pg. 914
RELIABILITY INCORPORATED; *U.S. Public*, pg. 1373
RELTEC CORPORATION; *U.S. Private*, pg. 921
REVERE TRANSDUCERS BV—Harnischfeger Industries, Inc.; *U.S. Public*, pg. 790
REVERE TRANSDUCERS INC.—Harnischfeger Industries, Inc.; *U.S. Public*, pg. 790
ROHDE & SCHWARZ GMBH & CO. KG; *Int'l*, pg. 1124
ROHDE & SCHWARZ, INC.—Rohde & Schwarz GmbH & Co. KG; *Int'l*, pg. 1124
ROHDE & SCHWARZ MESSGERAETEBAU GMBH—Rohde & Schwarz GmbH & Co. KG; *Int'l*, pg. 1124
ROSEMOUNT ANALYTICAL, INC.—Emerson Electric Co.; *U.S. Public*, pg. 574
RUSKA INSTRUMENT CORPORATION; *U.S. Private*, pg. 952
SPX CORPORATION; *U.S. Public*, pg. 1420
SAFEGUARDS TECHNOLOGY, INC.—Sophus Berendsen A/S; *Int'l*, pg. 1286
SAHA WOODALL-DUCKHAM (PRIVATE) LIMITED—FKI Plc; *Int'l*, pg. 472
SCHLUMBERGER LIMITED; *U.S. Public*, pg. 1439
SCIENTIFIC-ATLANTA, INC.; *U.S. Public*, pg. 1443
SCITEC CORPORATION—Andros Incorporated; *U.S. Private*, pg. 74
SENIOR CONFLOW—Senior Engineering Group, plc.; *Int'l*, pg. 1220
SENIOR CONFLOW INC.—Senior Engineering Group, plc.; *Int'l*, pg. 1222
SENIOR CONTROL ENGINEERING LIMITED—Senior Engineering Group, plc.; *Int'l*, pg. 1220
SENIOR DAVIS DERBY—Senior Engineering Group, plc.; *Int'l*, pg. 1220
SENIOR ENTEX—Senior Engineering Group, plc.; *Int'l*, pg. 1220
SENIOR THERMAL ENGINEERING LIMITED—Senior Engineering Group, plc.; *Int'l*, pg. 1221
SENSYM INC.—BTR plc; *Int'l*, pg. 127
SERVICE SOLUTION—SPX Corporation; *U.S. Public*, pg. 1421
SERVO CORPORATION OF AMERICA; *U.S. Private*, pg. 987
SFERNICE, S.A.—Vishay Intertechnology, Inc.; *U.S. Public*, pg. 1722
SHAW INDUSTRIES LTD.; *Int'l*, pg. 1231
SHIMADZU (ASIA PACIFIC) PTE. LTD.—Shimadzu Corporation; *Int'l*, pg. 1232
SHIMADZU OCEANIA PTY. LTD.—Shimadzu Corporation; *Int'l*, pg. 1232
SHIZUOKA OKI ELECTRIC CO., LTD.—Oki Electric Industry Company, Ltd.; *Int'l*, pg. 999
SHUGART CORPORATION; *U.S. Private*, pg. 997
SIMPSON ELECTRIC CO.; *U.S. Private*, pg. 1002
SMITH METERS LTD.—Hanson PLC; *Int'l*, pg. 593
SNAP-ON TOOLS CORPORATION; *U.S. Public*, pg. 1480
SONY/TEKTRONIX CORPORATION—Tektronix, Inc.; *U.S. Public*, pg. 1568
SPECTRA-PHYSICS AB; *Int'l*, pg. 1288
SPECTRIS MESSTECHNIK GMBH—AGIV Group; *Int'l*, pg. 14
SPECTRIS TECHNOLOGIES, INC.—AGIV Group; *Int'l*, pg. 14
SPECTROL ELECTRONICS CORPORATION—The Dyson-Kissner-Moran Corporation; *U.S. Private*, pg. 351
SQUARE D CO.—Schneider S.A.; *Int'l*, pg. 1208
SQUARE D COMPANY—Schneider S.A.; *Int'l*, pg. 1208
STAVELEY/NDT TECHNOLOGIES INC.—Staveley Industries PLC; *Int'l*, pg. 1299
STERLING ELECTRONICS CORPORATION—Marshall Industries; *U.S. Public*, pg. 1051
STORAGETEK NETWORK SYSTEMS GROUP—Storage Technology Corporation; *U.S. Public*, pg. 1522
SUN ELECTRIC—Snap-On Tools Corporation; *U.S. Public*, pg. 1480
SUNBEAM CORPORATION; *U.S. Public*, pg. 1533
SWECO EUROPE S.A.—Emerson Electric Co.; *U.S. Public*, pg. 578
SYMMETRICOM, INC.; *U.S. Public*, pg. 1547

SYSTEMS & ELECTRONICS INC.—ESCO Electronics Corporation; U.S. Public, pg. 547
TRW SYSTEMS INTEGRATION GROUP—TRW Inc.; U.S. Public, pg. 1558
TAU-TRON—General Signal Corporation; U.S. Public, pg. 727
TECHNOLOGY RESEARCH CORPORATION; U.S. Public, pg. 1564
TECNOST-MAEL—Olivetti SpA; Int'l, pg. 1002
TEKELEC; U.S. Public, pg. 1566
TEKELEC, LTD.—Tekelec; U.S. Public, pg. 1566
TEKTRONIX, INC.; U.S. Public, pg. 1567
TELCOM SEMICONDUCTOR, INC.; U.S. Public, pg. 1569
TELDIX GMBH—Robert Bosch GmbH; Int'l, pg. 204
TELECOM SOLUTIONS PUERTO RICO, INC.—SymmetriCom, Inc.; U.S. Public, pg. 1547
TELECOMMUNICATIONS TECHNOLOGY—General Signal Corporation; U.S. Public, pg. 727
TELENEX—General Signal Corporation; U.S. Public, pg. 727
TEMPRESS—General Signal Corporation; U.S. Public, pg. 727
TERADYNE, INC.; U.S. Public, pg. 1580
TERADYNE TELECOMMUNICATIONS DIVISION—Teradyne, Inc.; U.S. Public, pg. 1581
THERMO SEPARATION PRODUCTS—Thermo Electron Corporation; U.S. Public, pg. 1594
TINIUS OLSEN TESTING MACHINE CO., INC.; U.S. Private, pg. 1088
TOHO ELECTRONICS CO., LTD.—Oki Electric Industry Company, Ltd.; Int'l, pg. 999
TOSHIBA CAMBRIDGE RESEARCH CENTRE LTD.—Toshiba Corporation; Int'l, pg. 1406
TOSHIBA SEMICONDUCTOR (THAILAND) CO., LTD.—Toshiba Corporation; Int'l, pg. 1407
TRACOR, INC.; U.S. Public, pg. 1627
TRANSISTOR DEVICES, INC.; U.S. Private, pg. 1097
TRANSPORTATION GROUP—DSP Technology Inc.; U.S. Public, pg. 475
TREMETRICS, INC.—Thermo Electron Corporation; U.S. Public, pg. 1595
TRIGON ADCOTECH; U.S. Private, pg. 1103
TRILLIUM DIGITAL DIVISION—LTX Corporation; U.S. Public, pg. 972
TRIPLE A SPECIALTY COMPANY; U.S. Private, pg. 1103
TRIPLETT CORPORATION; U.S. Private, pg. 1104
UNITED INDUSTRIAL CORPORATION; U.S. Public, pg. 1679
UNITED TECHNOLOGIES, NORDEN SYSTEMS LONG ISLAND—United Technologies Corporation; U.S. Public, pg. 1691
VARIAN ASSOCIATES, INC.; U.S. Public, pg. 1710
VISHAY INSTRUMENTS DIV.—Vishay Intertechnology, Inc.; U.S. Public, pg. 1722
VISHAY INTERTECHNOLOGY, INC.; U.S. Public, pg. 1721
WALKER NATIONAL, INC.—Walker Magnetics Group, Inc.; U.S. Private, pg. 1147
WALKER SCIENTIFIC—Walker Magnetics Group, Inc.; U.S. Private, pg. 1147
WANDEL & GOLTERMANN GMBH & CO., ELEKTRONISCHE MESSTECHNIK; Int'l, pg. 1485
WANDEL & GOLTERMANN INC.—Wandel & Goltermann GmbH & Co., Elektronische Messtechnik; Int'l, pg. 1486
WANDEL & GOLTERMANN TECHNOLOGIES, INC.—Wandel & Goltermann GmbH & Co., Elektronische Messtechnik; Int'l, pg. 1486
WATERS CORPORATION; U.S. Public, pg. 1745
WAVETEK CORPORATION; U.S. Private, pg. 1154
WESTRONICS, INC.—Thermo Electron Corporation; U.S. Public, pg. 1593
WHESSOE PLC; Int'l, pg. 1498
WHESSOE VAREC—Whessoe Plc; Int'l, pg. 1498
WILCOM PRODUCTS, INC.—NAI Technologies, Inc.; U.S. Public, pg. 1144
WILTRON COMPANY—Anritsu Corporation; Int'l, pg. 77
YOKOGAWA CORPORATION OF AMERICA—Yokogawa Electric Corporation; Int'l, pg. 1521
YOKOGAWA ELECTRIC CORPORATION; Int'l, pg. 1520
ZELLWEGER USTER AG—Hesta Tex AG; Int'l, pg. 618
ZETEC, INC.; U.S. Private, pg. 1205

3826 — LABORATORY ANALYTICAL INSTRUMENTS

ABBOTT LABORATORIES; U.S. Public, pg. 12
ADVANCED INSTRUMENTS, INC.; U.S. Private, pg. 22
AMERSHAM BUCHLER GMBH & CO. KG—Nycomed Amersham plc; Int'l, pg. 992
AMRAY, INC.; U.S. Private, pg. 67
ANALYTICAL DEVELOPMENT COMPANY LIMITED—Halma p.l.c.; Int'l, pg. 589
APPLIED RESEARCH LABS—Rhone-Poulenc S.A.; Int'l, pg. 1111
ASIA ELECTRONICS INC.—Toshiba Corporation; Int'l, pg. 1402
ATOS MEDICAL AB—Perstorp AB; Int'l, pg. 1036
BADGER METER, INC.; U.S. Public, pg. 164
BALZERS DUNNSCHICHT-KOMPONENTEN GMBH—Oerlikon-Buhrle Holding AG; Int'l, pg. 997
BECKMAN COULTER—Beckman Instruments, Inc.; U.S. Public, pg. 199
BECTON DICKINSON & COMPANY; U.S. Public, pg. 199
BECTON DICKINSON PRIMARY CARE DIAGNOSTICS—Becton Dickinson & Company; U.S. Public, pg. 199
BIO-RAD DIGILAB DIV.—Bio-Rad Laboratories, Inc.; U.S. Public, pg. 230
BIO-RAD S.P.D.—Bio-Rad Laboratories, Inc.; U.S. Public, pg. 230
BRINKMANN INSTRUMENTS, INC.; U.S. Private, pg. 169
BUEHLER, LIMITED—Emerson Electric Co.; U.S. Public, pg. 574
BUEHLER MET GMBH—Emerson Electric Co.; U.S. Public, pg. 575
BUEHLER U.K. LTD.—Emerson Electric Co.; U.S. Public, pg. 575
CIBA SPECIALTY CHEMICALS—Ciba Specialty Chemicals Holding Inc.; Int'l, pg. 291
DBA SYSTEMS, INC.; U.S. Public, pg. 472
DEGGENDORFER WERFT UND EISENBAU GMBH—MAN Aktiengesellschaft; Int'l, pg. 824
DIONEX CORPORATION; U.S. Public, pg. 510
DYNATECH CORPORATION; U.S. Public, pg. 539
DYNEX TECHNOLOGIES LTD. (U.K.)—Thermo Electron Corporation; U.S. Public, pg. 1591
E-C APPARATUS CORP.—Thermo Electron Corporation; U.S. Public, pg. 1595
EG & G INSTRUMENTS APPLIED RESEARCH—EG & G, Inc.; U.S. Public, pg. 543
EG & G OPTOELECTRONICS RETICON—EG & G, Inc.; U.S. Public, pg. 543
ESA, INC.; U.S. Private, pg. 354
ELSCINT LTD.; Int'l, pg. 450
EMBEDDED PERFORMANCE, INC.; U.S. Private, pg. 373
FORMA SCIENTIFIC INC.—Thermo Electron Corporation; U.S. Public, pg. 1595
GN NETTEST FIBER OPTIC DIVISION—GN Great Nordic Ltd.; Int'l, pg. 536
GALILEO CORP.; U.S. Public, pg. 698
HIAC/ROYCO DIVISION—Pacific Scientific Company; U.S. Public, pg. 1250
HAMILTON CO., INC.; U.S. Private, pg. 497
HARROP INDUSTRIES, INC.; U.S. Private, pg. 506
HARTMANN & BRAUN AG—Mannesmann A.G.; Int'l, pg. 835
HAVILAND ENTERPRISES; U.S. Private, pg. 511
HEWLETT PACKARD AVONDALE—Hewlett-Packard Company; U.S. Public, pg. 816
HITACHI INSTRUMENTS, INC.—Hitachi, Ltd.; Int'l, pg. 622
HOUSTON ATLAS—Thermo Electron Corporation; U.S. Public, pg. 1593
ISCO, INC.; U.S. Public, pg. 913
JEOL, LTD.; Int'l, pg. 696
JEAVONS ENGINEERING, LTD.—Ruhrgas Aktiengesellschaft; Int'l, pg. 1149
JOHNSON MATTHEY NOBLE METALS BUSINESS UNIT—Johnson Matthey Public Limited Company; Int'l, pg. 713
JOUAN, INC.; U.S. Private, pg. 601
KLA TENCOR CORPORATION; U.S. Public, pg. 939
KEVEX INSTRUMENTS—Thermo Electron Corporation; U.S. Public, pg. 1594
KONICA CORPORATION; Int'l, pg. 748
LABORATOIRES STAFFORD-MILLER S.A.R.L.—Block Drug Company, Inc.; U.S. Public, pg. 237
MICRO-CONTROLE S.A.—Newport Corporation; U.S. Public, pg. 1179
MICRON SEPARATIONS, INC.; U.S. Private, pg. 742
MICROSCIENCE LIMITED—Bio-Rad Laboratories, Inc.; U.S. Public, pg. 230
MILLIPORE ANALYTICAL DIV.—Millipore Corporation; U.S. Public, pg. 1112
MILLIPORE CORPORATION; U.S. Public, pg. 1112
MILLIPORE/PUERTO RICO—Millipore Corporation; U.S. Public, pg. 1112
NEWPORT CORPORATION; U.S. Public, pg. 1179
NICOLET ANALYTICAL—Thermo Electron Corporation; U.S. Public, pg. 1593
O.I. CORPORATION; U.S. Public, pg. 1208
OMNIFIT LTD.—Halma p.l.c.; Int'l, pg. 589
ORIEL INSTRUMENTS CORPORATION; U.S. Private, pg. 819
THE PERKIN-ELMER CORPORATION; U.S. Public, pg. 1279
PERKIN ELMER PHYSICAL ELECTRONICS DIV.—The Perkin-Elmer Corporation; U.S. Public, pg. 1279
PHARMACIA & UPJOHN BIOSYSTEMS AB—Pharmacia & Upjohn, Inc.; Int'l, pg. 1047
PHARMACIA & UPJOHN BIOTECH INC.—Pharmacia & Upjohn, Inc.; Int'l, pg. 1047
PHIPPS & BIRD—McKesson Corporation; U.S. Public, pg. 1073
PRINCETON GAMMA-TECH, INC.—Outokumpu Oyj; Int'l, pg. 1015
QUEST TECHNOLOGIES, INC.; U.S. Private, pg. 900
RADIOMETER ANALYTICAL S.A.—Radiometer A/S; Int'l, pg. 1084
RIBER; Int'l, pg. 1114
SCHLEICHER & SCHUELL GMBH; Int'l, pg. 1206
SCHLEICHER & SCHUELL, INC.—Schleicher & Schuell GmbH; Int'l, pg. 1206
SERADYN, INC.—Mitsubishi Chemical Corporation; Int'l, pg. 871
SHIMADZU CORPORATION; Int'l, pg. 1232
SPECTRONICS CORPORATION; U.S. Private, pg. 1024
SURFACE SCIENCE INSTRUMENTS—Rhone-Poulenc S.A.; Int'l, pg. 1111
TSI INCORPORATED, U.S. Public, pg. 1559
TECH-MET CANADA LTD.—Emerson Electric Co.; U.S. Public, pg. 575
THERMO ELECTRON CORPORATION; U.S. Public, pg. 1591
TOSHIBA AMERICA MRI INC.—Toshiba Corporation; Int'l, pg. 1405
TOYO CORPORATION; Int'l, pg. 1410
ULTRA ELECTRONICS MAGNETICS—Ultra Electronics Holdings plc; Int'l, pg. 1431
VG ANALYTICAL LTD.—Rhone-Poulenc S.A.; Int'l, pg. 1110
VG DATA SYSTEMS LTD.—Thermo Electron Corporation; U.S. Public, pg. 1595
VG ELEMENTAL LTD.—Rhone-Poulenc S.A.; Int'l, pg. 1110
VG GAS ANALYSIS SYSTEMS LTD.—Thermo Electron Corporation; U.S. Public, pg. 1595
VG INSTRUMENTS PLC—Thermo Electron Corporation; U.S. Public, pg. 1595
VG IONEX LTD.—Rhone-Poulenc S.A.; Int'l, pg. 1110
VG ISOTECH LTD.—Rhone-Poulenc S.A.; Int'l, pg. 1110
VG MASSLAB LTD.—Rhone-Poulenc S.A.; Int'l, pg. 1110
VG MICROSCOPES LTD.—Thermo Electron Corporation; U.S. Public, pg. 1595
VG MICROTECH LTD.—Thermo Electron Corporation; U.S. Public, pg. 1595
VG MICROTRACE LTD.—Rhone-Poulenc S.A.; Int'l, pg. 1111
VG QUADRUPOLES LTD.—Rhone-Poulenc S.A.; Int'l, pg. 1111
VG SCIENTIFIC LTD.—Thermo Electron Corporation; U.S. Public, pg. 1595
VG SPECIAL SYSTEMS LTD.—Thermo Electron Corporation; U.S. Public, pg. 1595
VG TRITECH LTD.—Rhone-Poulenc S.A.; Int'l, pg. 1111
VACUUM GENERATORS LTD.—Thermo Electron Corporation; U.S. Public, pg. 1595
VARIAN ASSOCIATES, INC.; U.S. Public, pg. 1710
WHATMAN INC.—Whatman plc; Int'l, pg. 1498
WHATMAN PLC; Int'l, pg. 1498
YSI INCORPORATED; U.S. Private, pg. 1195

3827 — OPTICAL INSTRUMENTS & LENSES

ANGENIEUX—Thomson S.A.; Int'l, pg. 1381
ANRITSU CORPORATION; Int'l, pg. 77
APPLIED BIOSYSTEMS—The Perkin-Elmer Corporation; U.S. Public, pg. 1279
ASAHI OPTICAL CO., LTD.; Int'l, pg. 85
BBGR SA—Essilor International Compagnie Generale d'Optique; Int'l, pg. 462
BASO PRECISION OPTICS—Eastman Kodak Company; U.S. Public, pg. 551
BAUSCH & LOMB INCORPORATED; U.S. Public, pg. 194
BAUSCH & LOMB PUERTO RICO, INC.—Bausch & Lomb Incorporated; U.S. Public, pg. 194
BAUSCH & LOMB U.K. LTD.—Bausch & Lomb Incorporated; U.S. Public, pg. 195
BAYER AG—Bayer AG; Int'l, pg. 172
BODENSEEWERK PERKIN-ELMER & CO. G.M.B.H.—The Perkin-Elmer Corporation; U.S. Public, pg. 1279
BUEHLER, LIMITED—Emerson Electric Co.; U.S. Public, pg. 574
CALUMET PHOTOGRAPHIC, INC.; U.S. Private, pg. 202
CANON INC.; Int'l, pg. 261
CHRISTIAN DALLOZ—Essilor International Compagnie Generale d'Optique; Int'l, pg. 462
CONTRAVES ADVANCED DEVICES, SDN. BHD.—Oerlikon-Buhrle Holding AG; Int'l, pg. 998
DRS PHOTRONICS, INC.—DRS Technologies, Inc.; U.S. Public, pg. 474
DRS TECHNOLOGIES, INC.; U.S. Public, pg. 474
DEUTSCHE SPEZIALGLAS AG—Carl-Zeiss-Stiftung; Int'l, pg. 1523
EDMUND SCIENTIFIC COMPANY; U.S. Private, pg. 364
ELECTRO OPTICAL DIV.—Kollmorgen Corporation; U.S. Public, pg. 965
ESSILOR IRELAND LTD.—Essilor International Compagnie Generale d'Optique; Int'l, pg. 462
ESSILOR LIMITED—Essilor International Compagnie Generale d'Optique; Int'l, pg. 462
EXCEL TECHNOLOGY, INC.; U.S. Public, pg. 599
FELLOWS CORPORATION—Goldman Financial Group; U.S. Private, pg. 461
GALILEO CORP.; U.S. Public, pg. 698
GENTEX GMBH—Gentex Corporation; U.S. Public, pg. 732
GERBER OPTICAL, INC.—Gerber Scientific, Inc.; U.S. Public, pg. 740
HARMONIC LIGHTWAVES; U.S. Public, pg. 788
HONEYWELL INC.; U.S. Public, pg. 833
HUGHES LEITZ OPTICAL TECHNOLOGIES, LTD.—General Motors Corporation; U.S. Public, pg. 722
J & L METROLOGY COMPANY, INC.—Goldman Financial Group; U.S. Private, pg. 461
KLA TENCOR CORPORATION; U.S. Public, pg. 939
KODAK AG—Eastman Kodak Company; U.S. Public, pg. 552
KODAK BERKELEY RESEARCH—Eastman Kodak Company; U.S. Public, pg. 555
KODAK KOREA LTD.—Eastman Kodak Company; U.S. Public, pg. 555
KODAK PATHE S.A.—Eastman Kodak Company; U.S. Public, pg. 554
KOLLMORGEN CORPORATION; U.S. Public, pg. 965
KONICA TOKYO INDUSTRIAL CENTER HACHIOJI—Konica Corporation; Int'l, pg. 748
L-ZOS OPTICS, LTD.; U.S. Private, pg. 639
LASER POWER CORPORATION; U.S. Private, pg. 652
LEUPOLD & STEVENS, INC.; U.S. Private, pg. 662
MMG DIVISION—Optical Coating Laboratory, Inc.; U.S. Public, pg. 1227
THE MARYLEBONE OPTICAL CO. LTD.—Dolland & Aitchison Ltd.; Int'l, pg. 414
MICRO-CONTROLE S.A.—Newport Corporation; U.S. Public, pg. 1179
MINOLTA CO., LTD.; Int'l, pg. 869
NANOMETRICS INCORPORATED; U.S. Public, pg. 1151
NANOQUEST DEFENCE PRODUCTS LIMITED—British Aerospace p.l.c.; Int'l, pg. 218
NEWPORT CORPORATION; U.S. Public, pg. 1179
NIKON CORPORATION; Int'l, pg. 931
OCLI OPTICAL COATINGS LTD.—Optical Coating Laboratory, Inc.; U.S. Public, pg. 1227
OPTICAL COATING LABORATORY, INC.; U.S. Public, pg. 1227
THE OPTICAL CORPORATION—Excel Technology, Inc.; U.S. Public, pg. 599
OPTICAL RADIATION CORPORATION—BEC Group, Inc.; U.S. Public, pg. 160
ORIEL INSTRUMENTS CORPORATION; U.S. Private, pg. 819
PENTAX CORPORATION—Asahi Optical Co., Ltd.; Int'l, pg. 85
PERKIN-ELMER LTD.—The Perkin-Elmer Corporation; U.S. Public, pg. 1279

PHOTOLASTIC DIVISION—Vishay Intertechnology, Inc.; U.S. Public, pg. 1722
PILKINGTON PLC; Int'l, pg. 1056
RAYTHEON OPTICAL SYSTEMS—Raytheon Company; U.S. Public, pg. 1364
RAYTHEON OPTICAL SYSTEMS, INCORPORATED—Raytheon Company; U.S. Public, pg. 1364
RECON/OPTICAL, INC.; U.S. Private, pg. 914
RELIANCE MEDICAL PRODUCTS, INC.; U.S. Private, pg. 921
SENSORS & ELECTRONIC SYSTEMS—Raytheon Company; U.S. Public, pg. 1365
SERADYN, INC.—Mitsubishi Chemical Corporation; Int'l, pg. 871
SERVO CORPORATION OF AMERICA; U.S. Private, pg. 987
SHIMADZU CORPORATION; Int'l, pg. 1232
SIMRAD OPTRONICS A/S—Kvaerner a.s.a.; Int'l, pg. 770
SLANT/FIN CORPORATION; U.S. Private, pg. 1005
SPECTRA-PHYSICS OPTICS CORP.—Thermo Electron Corporation; U.S. Public, pg. 1594
STOCKER & YALE, INC.; U.S. Public, pg. 1518
SWIFT INSTRUMENTS, INC.; U.S. Private, pg. 1058
SYSTEMS & ELECTRONICS INC.—ESCO Electronics Corporation; U.S. Public, pg. 547
TAIWAN GLASS INDUSTRY CORP.; Int'l, pg. 1348
TASCO SALES INC.—Rice, Sangalis, Toole & Wilson; U.S. Private, pg. 928
THERMO SEPARATION PRODUCTS—Thermo Electron Corporation; U.S. Public, pg. 1594
THOMSON-TRT DEFENSE—Thomson S.A.; Int'l, pg. 1383
TOPCON CORPORATION—Toshiba Corporation; Int'l, pg. 1403
U.S. PRECISION LENS INC.—Corning Incorporated; U.S. Public, pg. 448
UNIVERSAL OPTICAL INDUSTRIES, LTD.—Kyocera Corporation; Int'l, pg. 776
VERMONT USA MACHINE TOOL GROUP—Goldman Financial Group; U.S. Private, pg. 461
VIRGO OPTICS, INC.—II-VI Incorporated; U.S. Public, pg. 1647
VLOC—II-VI Incorporated; U.S. Public, pg. 1647
WHATMAN INC.—Whatman plc; Int'l, pg. 1498
DAVID WHITE, L.L.C.; U.S. Public, pg. 1765
DAVID WHITE, L.L.C.; U.S. Private, pg. 1765
YASHICA A.G.—Kyocera Corporation; Int'l, pg. 776
YASHICA DO BRASIL-EXPORTACAO E INDUSTRIA LTDA.—Kyocera Corporation; Int'l, pg. 776
YASHICA DO BRASIL-INDUSTRIA E COMERCIO LTDA.—Kyocera Corporation; Int'l, pg. 776
YASHICA HONG KONG CO., LTD.—Kyocera Corporation; Int'l, pg. 776
YASHICA KYOCERA GMBH—Kyocera Corporation; Int'l, pg. 776
CARL ZEISS—Carl-Zeiss-Stiftung; Int'l, pg. 1522
ZIPPO MANUFACTURING COMPANY; U.S. Private, pg. 1207

3829 — MEASURING & CONTROLLING DEVICES, NEC

AAI/ACL TECHNOLOGIES—United Industrial Corporation; U.S. Public, pg. 1679
ABB KABEL UND DRAHT GMBH—ABB Asea Brown Boveri (Holding) Ltd.; Int'l, pg. 2
ABB KENT PLC—ABB Asea Brown Boveri (Holding) Ltd.; Int'l, pg. 2
AGR INTERNATIONAL, INC.; U.S. Private, pg. 5
API-GETTYS CORPORATION—American Precision Industries Inc.; U.S. Public, pg. 90
AVO INTERNATIONAL; U.S. Private, pg. 9
AVO MULTI-AMP INSTITUTE—TBG Management S.A.M.; Int'l, pg. 1335
ADDISON TUBE FORMING LIMITED—B. Elliott plc.; Int'l, pg. 448
AEROFLEX LABORATORIES INC.—Aeroflex Incorporated; U.S. Public, pg. 24
AEROMETRICS, INC.—TSI Incorporated; U.S. Public, pg. 1559
AIM SAFETY COMPANY INC.; Int'l, pg. 36
AMERICAN SCIENCE & ENGINEERING, INC.; U.S. Public, pg. 90
AMES CROSTA BABCOCK LTD.—FKI Plc; Int'l, pg. 471
AMETEK, INC.; U.S. Public, pg. 99
AMSLER OTTO WOLPERT WERKE GMBH—Instron Corporation; U.S. Public, pg. 883
ANRITSU CORPORATION; Int'l, pg. 77
APPLIED AUTOMATION INC.—Mannesmann A.G.; Int'l, pg. 835
ASSOCIATED PROCESS CONTROLS; U.S. Private, pg. 92
ASTRO-MED, INC.; U.S. Public, pg. 141
ASTRONAUTICS CORPORATION OF AMERICA; U.S. Private, pg. 93
AVIONICS & COMMUNICATIONS—Rockwell International Corporation; U.S. Public, pg. 1397
BEI SENSORS AND SYSTEMS COMPANY—BEI Technologies, Inc.; U.S. Public, pg. 160
BWI INEX VISION SYSTEMS—BWI Plc; Int'l, pg. 130
BABCOCK ARGENTINA S.A.—FKI Plc; Int'l, pg. 473
BABCOCK AUSTRALIA HOLDINGS LTD.—FKI Plc; Int'l, pg. 474
BACHARACH INC.; U.S. Private, pg. 109
BALL AEROSPACE & TECHNOLOGIES CORP.—Ball Corporation; U.S. Public, pg. 171
BALL CORPORATION; U.S. Public, pg. 170
BALL TELECOMMUNICATION PRODUCTS DIVISION—Ball Corporation; U.S. Public, pg. 171
BARBER-COLMAN COMPANY—Siebe plc; Int'l, pg. 1242
BARKSDALE, INC.—Crane Co.; U.S. Public, pg. 457
BARRINGER TECHNOLOGIES INC.; U.S. Public, pg. 191
BAYER AG—Bayer AG; Int'l, pg. 172
BECKMAN INSTRUMENTS, INC.; U.S. Public, pg. 199
BENTLY NEVADA, AUSTRALIA—Bently Nevada Corporation; U.S. Private, pg. 134
BENTLY NEVADA GMBH—Bently Nevada Corporation; U.S. Private, pg. 134
BENTLY NEVADA (UK) LTD.—Bently Nevada Corporation; U.S. Private, pg. 134
BERLI JUCKER PUBLIC CO. LTD.—First Pacific Company Limited; Int'l, pg. 487
BOEING NORTH AMERICA, AUTONETICS ELECTRONIC SYSTEMS DIVISION—The Boeing Company; U.S. Public, pg. 241
BOEING NORTH AMERICA, TACTICAL SYSTEMS DIVISION—The Boeing Company; U.S. Public, pg. 241
ROBERT BOSCH ELETRONIK GMBH—Robert Bosch GmbH; Int'l, pg. 204
ROBERT BOSCH GMBH; Int'l, pg. 203
BRACCO S.P.A.; Int'l, pg. 209
BRAKE CABLES LTD—FKI Plc; Int'l, pg. 472
BREEZE INDUSTRIAL—TransTechnology Corporation; U.S. Public, pg. 1632
BRISTOL BABCOCK CANADA—FKI Plc; Int'l, pg. 473
BRITISH AEROSPACE AUSTRALIA LIMITED—British Aerospace p.l.c.; Int'l, pg. 218
BROOKFIELD ENGINEERING LABORATORIES, INC.; U.S. Private, pg. 171
BROWN & SHARPE LIMITED—Brown & Sharpe Manufacturing Company; U.S. Public, pg. 260
BROWN & SHARPE MANUFACTURING COMPANY; U.S. Public, pg. 260
BUEHLER MET GMBH—Emerson Electric Co.; U.S. Public, pg. 575
BUEHLER U.K. LTD.—Emerson Electric Co.; U.S. Public, pg. 575
CGA-HBS—Alcatel Alsthom Compagnie Generale D'Electricite; Int'l, pg. 53
CAMP—Alcatel Alsthom Compagnie Generale D'Electricite; Int'l, pg. 53
CAPINTEC INSTRUMENTS INC.—Capintec Inc.; U.S. Private, pg. 205
CAPP, INC.; U.S. Private, pg. 207
CERBERUS PYROTRONICS INC.—Siemens AG; Int'l, pg. 1246
CHADWICK-HELMUTH COMPANY, INC.; U.S. Private, pg. 227
CHICAGO STEEL TAPE; U.S. Private, pg. 235
CHILTEM GROUP SAM—Alpha Omikron Limited; Int'l, pg. 65
CHRONOS RICHARDSON—Staveley Industries PLC; Int'l, pg. 1299
CIRMA ENTERPRISE—Alcatel Alsthom Compagnie Generale D'Electricite; Int'l, pg. 53
COHU, INC.; U.S. Public, pg. 396
COMADUR S.A.—SMH Swiss Corporation for Micro Electronics & Watchmaking Indus. Ltd.; Int'l, pg. 1161
COMPUTATIONAL SYSTEMS INC.—Emerson Electric Co.; U.S. Public, pg. 572
CONTRAVES ADVANCED DEVICES, SDN. BHD.—Oerlikon-Buhrle Holding AG; Int'l, pg. 998
CONTROLE BAILEY DIVISION—Alcatel Alsthom Compagnie Generale D'Electricite; Int'l, pg. 52
COOPER INSTRUMENT CORP.; U.S. Private, pg. 274
DMD DRESSER MEASUREMENT OPERATION—Dresser Industries, Inc.; U.S. Public, pg. 528
DRS PHOTRONICS, INC.—DRS Technologies, Inc.; U.S. Public, pg. 474
DANIEL INDUSTRIES, INC.; U.S. Public, pg. 482
DATA I/O CORPORATION; U.S. Public, pg. 486
DATA INSTRUMENTS, INC.; U.S. Private, pg. 312
DEL MAR AVIONICS; U.S. Private, pg. 321
DELFT INSTRUMENTS FAR EAST, LTD.—Delft Instruments N.V.; Int'l, pg. 389
DELFT INSTRUMENTS N.V.; Int'l, pg. 388
DETECTORS, INC.—Media Recovery, Inc.; U.S. Private, pg. 727
DEXTER MAGNETIC MATERIALS—The Dexter Corporation; U.S. Public, pg. 504
DIAMOND POWER SPECIALTY CO.—McDermott International, Inc.; U.S. Public, pg. 1068
DU PONT NDT SYSTEMS INC.—Du Pont (E.I. Du Pont De Nemours & Co.); U.S. Public, pg. 531
DWYER INSTRUMENTS INC.; U.S. Private, pg. 350
DYNAMICS RESEARCH CORPORATION; U.S. Public, pg. 539
DYNATECH CORPORATION; U.S. Public, pg. 539
ECRM; U.S. Private, pg. 353
EG & G ASTROPHYSICS—EG & G, Inc.; U.S. Public, pg. 543
EG & G, INC.; U.S. Public, pg. 542
EG & G INSTRUMENTS—EG & G, Inc.; U.S. Public, pg. 543
EG & G INSTRUMENTS APPLIED RESEARCH—EG & G, Inc.; U.S. Public, pg. 543
EG & G INSTRUMENTS-PROCESS MEASUREMENTS/CHANDLER—EG & G, Inc.; U.S. Public, pg. 543
EG & G ORTEC—EG & G, Inc.; U.S. Public, pg. 543
EG & G WALLAC OY—EG & G, Inc.; U.S. Public, pg. 544
EATON CORPORATION, PRESSURE SENSORS DIVISION—Eaton Corporation; U.S. Public, pg. 557
EATON CORPORATION, SPECIALTIES DIVISION—Eaton Corporation; U.S. Public, pg. 557
ELECTRO METRICS, INC.; U.S. Private, pg. 369
ENERSTAT DIVISION- ERIE MANUFACTURING CO. (CANADA) LTD.—Siebe plc; Int'l, pg. 1241
ENRAF B.V.—Delft Instruments N.V.; Int'l, pg. 389
ENRAF SARL—Delft Instruments N.V.; Int'l, pg. 389
ERIE CONTROLS EUROPE-NV—Siebe plc; Int'l, pg. 1241
ERIE CONTROLS IBERICA S.A.—Siebe plc; Int'l, pg. 1241
ERIE MANUFACTURING CO.—Siebe plc; Int'l, pg. 1241
ERIE MANUFACTURING CO. (CANADA) LTD.—Siebe plc; Int'l, pg. 1241
ESCA CORPORATION—Alcatel Alsthom Compagnie Generale D'Electricite; Int'l, pg. 53
ESCORT, INC.; U.S. Private, pg. 383
EUROPEAN CABLES CONTROLS DIV.—FKI Plc; Int'l, pg. 472
FAG AUSTRIA WAELZLAGER AG—FAG Group; Int'l, pg. 469
FAG GROUP; Int'l, pg. 468
FAG (UK) LIMITED—FAG Group; Int'l, pg. 469
FMC-CROSBY VALVE, INC.—FMC Corporation; U.S. Public, pg. 605
FRL, INC.—Cohu, Inc.; U.S. Public, pg. 396
FALCON SAFETY PRODUCTS INC.; U.S. Private, pg. 392
FARO TECHNOLOGIES, INC.; U.S. Public, pg. 613
FASCO SENSORS & CONTROLS DIVISION—BTR plc; Int'l, pg. 127
FILL-RITE DIVISION—Tuthill Corporation; U.S. Private, pg. 1110
FLEX PRODUCTS, INC.—Optical Coating Laboratory, Inc.; U.S. Public, pg. 1227
FLUKE CORPORATION; U.S. Public, pg. 659
FOOD TECHNOLOGY CORPORATION—General Kinetics Incorporated; U.S. Public, pg. 717
FORD METER BOX COMPANY; U.S. Private, pg. 418
ABDULLA FOUAD-TESTRADE MIDDLE EAST—Abdulla Fouad Co. Ltd.; Int'l, pg. 502
FROUDE CONSINE—FKI Plc; Int'l, pg. 472
FROUDE CONSINE INC.—FKI Plc; Int'l, pg. 473
GFI-GENFARE—General Signal Corporation; U.S. Public, pg. 727
GN NETTEST FIBER OPTIC DIVISION—GN Great Nordic Ltd.; Int'l, pg. 536
GSE, INC.—United Dominion Industries, Ltd.; U.S. Public, pg. 1676
GAS EQUIPMENT COMPANY, INC.; U.S. Private, pg. 440
GAS TECH—Thermo Electron Corporation; U.S. Public, pg. 1593
GEKA, S.A.—Vishay Intertechnology, Inc.; U.S. Public, pg. 1722
GENERAL CABLE CO.—Wassall Plc; Int'l, pg. 1487
GENERAL KINETICS INCORPORATED; U.S. Public, pg. 716
GENERAL SCIENCES CORP.—Science Applications International Corp.; U.S. Private, pg. 976
GENRAD ELECTRONIC MANUFACTURING TESTS SYSTEMS—GenRad, Inc.; U.S. Public, pg. 731
GENRAD, INC.; U.S. Public, pg. 731
GEOPHYSICAL SURVEY SYSTEMS, INC.—OYO Corporation; Int'l, pg. 1019
GERBER SCIENTIFIC, INC.; U.S. Public, pg. 740
GIDDINGS & LEWIS SHEFFIELD MEASUREMENT SYSTEMS—Thyssen AG; Int'l, pg. 1389
GIGA-TRONICS INCORPORATED; U.S. Public, pg. 742
GOULD ELECTRONICS INC.—Thermo Electron Corporation; U.S. Public, pg. 1591
GOULD INSTRUMENT SYSTEMS, INC.—Thermo Electron Corporation; U.S. Public, pg. 1592
GOULD INSTRUMENT SYSTEMS, S.A.—Thermo Electron Corporation; U.S. Public, pg. 1592
GRANITE STATE MANUFACTURING CO.—Allard Industries; U.S. Private, pg. 36
GRANT GEOPHYSICAL INC.; U.S. Private, pg. 470
HACH COMPANY; U.S. Public, pg. 773
HANDAR, INC.—TSI Incorporated; U.S. Public, pg. 1559
HATHAWAY MOTORS & INSTRUMENTS DIVISION—Hathaway Corporation; U.S. Public, pg. 799
HEATH CONSULTANTS INCORPORATED; U.S. Private, pg. 518
HEWLETT-PACKARD COMPANY; U.S. Public, pg. 813
HONEYWELL DEFENSE AVIONICS SYSTEMS—Honeywell Inc.; U.S. Public, pg. 834
HONEYWELL INC.; U.S. Public, pg. 833
HYDRIL COMPANY; U.S. Private, pg. 551
IMO INDUSTRIES INC.; U.S. Public, pg. 856
IRD MECHANALYSIS, INC. (U.S.A.)—Harnischfeger Industries, Inc.; U.S. Public, pg. 789
IMAGE ACQUISITION PRODUCTS DIVISION—Eastman Kodak Company; U.S. Public, pg. 555
INCSTAR CORPORATION—Fiat Auto SpA; Int'l, pg. 483
INCSTAR LTD.—Fiat Auto SpA; Int'l, pg. 483
INPUT/OUTPUT, INC.; U.S. Public, pg. 880
INSTRON CORPORATION; U.S. Public, pg. 882
INSTRON S.A.—Instron Corporation; U.S. Public, pg. 883
INSTRUMENT DIVISION—Dresser Industries, Inc.; U.S. Public, pg. 528
INSTRUMENTOS BRISTOL S.A.—FKI Plc; Int'l, pg. 473
INTEGRATED PHOTOMATRIX LTD.—B. Elliott plc.; Int'l, pg. 448
ISCO, INC.; U.S. Public, pg. 913
JCAIR, INC.—The B.F. Goodrich Company; U.S. Public, pg. 751
JEUMONT-SCHNEIDER TRENFORMETEURS; Int'l, pg. 706
KVB—Air & Water Technologies Corporation; U.S. Public, pg. 29
KAMAN CORPORATION; U.S. Public, pg. 941
KAMAN INSTRUMENTATION CORP.—Kaman Corporation; U.S. Public, pg. 942
KIDDE TECHNOLOGIES INC. (WALTER KIDDE AEROSPACE)—Williams Holdings Plc; Int'l, pg. 1500
KINEMETRICS, INC.—OYO Corporation; Int'l, pg. 1019
KRAUTKRAMER-BRANSON, INC.—Emerson Electric Co.; U.S. Public, pg. 574
KRAUTKRAMER G.M.B.H—Emerson Electric Co.; U.S. Public, pg. 577
KULITE SEMICONDUCTOR PRODUCTS, INC.; U.S. Private, pg. 636
KVAERNER ENERGY, DAMSGARD—Kvaerner a.s.a.; Int'l, pg. 767
KYOCERA CORPORATION; Int'l, pg. 775
L.A.B. EQUIPMENT—Noonan Machine Co.; U.S. Private, pg. 801
LFE INSTRUMENTS—Danaher Corporation; U.S. Public, pg. 482
JOHN LAING PLC; Int'l, pg. 796
LAMBDA NOVATRONICS INC.—Siebe plc; Int'l, pg. 1241
LAZERDATA—BTR plc; Int'l, pg. 127

LEITZ MESSTECHNIK GMBH—Brown & Sharpe Manufacturing Company; *U.S. Public*, pg. 260
LEUPOLD & STEVENS, INC.; *U.S. Private*, pg. 662
LEWIS ENGINEERING COMPANY—Coltec Holdings Inc; *U.S. Public*, pg. 402
LIBERTY PRECISION INDUSTRIES; *U.S. Private*, pg. 666
LIEBERT CORPORATION—Emerson Electric Co.; *U.S. Public*, pg. 573
LIEBERT CORPORATION AUSTRALIA PTY. LTD.—Emerson Electric Co.; *U.S. Public*, pg. 577
LIEBERT FAR EAST LTD.—Emerson Electric Co.; *U.S. Public*, pg. 577
LIEBERT LTD.—Emerson Electric Co.; *U.S. Public*, pg. 577
LIEBERT MALAYSIA SDN. BHD.—Emerson Electric Co.; *U.S. Public*, pg. 577
LING ELECTRONICS INC.—Mechanical Technology Inc.; *U.S. Public*, pg. 1077
LITTON INSTRUMENTS & LIFE SUPPORT—Litton Industries, Inc.; *U.S. Public*, pg. 1003
LUCAS INDUSTRIES INC.—LucasVarity plc; *Int'l*, pg. 820
LUDWIG METROLOGIE, SA—Brown & Sharpe Manufacturing Company; *U.S. Public*, pg. 260
M & M PRECISION SYSTEMS CORPORATION—Danaher Corporation; *U.S. Public*, pg. 482
M&W—Alamo Group, Inc.; *U.S. Public*, pg. 35
MTS JAPAN LTD. (TOKYO)—MTS Systems Corporation; *U.S. Public*, pg. 1029
MTS SYSTEMS CORPORATION; *U.S. Public*, pg. 1028
MAGNETIC ANALYSIS CORP.; *U.S. Private*, pg. 695
MAGNETROL INTERNATIONAL; *U.S. Private*, pg. 696
MARSH COMPANY; *U.S. Private*, pg. 707
MARTIN MARIETTA ELECTRONICS & MISSILES—Lockheed Martin Corporation; *U.S. Public*, pg. 1007
MARTIN UNIVERSAL DESIGN, INC.; *U.S. Private*, pg. 709
MASONEILAN NORTH AMERICAN OPERATIONS—Dresser Industries, Inc.; *U.S. Public*, pg. 528
MATEC APPLIED SCIENCES, INC.—Matec Corporation; *U.S. Public*, pg. 1056
MATEC CORPORATION; *U.S. Public*, pg. 1056
MATEC INSTRUMENTS, INC.—Matec Corporation; *U.S. Public*, pg. 1056
MAXITROL CO.; *U.S. Private*, pg. 716
MEASUREMENTS GROUP, INC.—Vishay Intertechnology, Inc.; *U.S. Public*, pg. 1722
MEASURING SYSTEMS DIVISION—Brown & Sharpe Manufacturing Company; *U.S. Public*, pg. 260
MECHANICAL TECHNOLOGY INC.; *U.S. Public*, pg. 1077
MEFIAG NEDERLAND B.V.—Met-Pro Corporation; *U.S. Public*, pg. 1100
MEGGITT AVIONICS—Meggitt plc; *Int'l*, pg. 853
MEGGITT AVIONICS INC.—Meggitt plc; *Int'l*, pg. 853
MEGGITT PETROLEUM SYSTEMS (UK)—Meggitt plc; *Int'l*, *pg. 853*
MEGGITT PLC; *Int'l*, pg. 853
THOMAS MERCER LTD.—Brown & Sharpe Manufacturing Company; *U.S. Public*, pg. 260
METROLOGIC SOUTH CENTRAL REGION—Metrologic Instruments, Inc.; *U.S. Public*, pg. 1102
MICRO-CONTROLE S.A.—Newport Corporation; *U.S. Public*, pg. 1179
MICRO MEASUREMENTS DIV.—Vishay Intertechnology, Inc.; *U.S. Public*, pg. 1722
AB MIKRO-VERKTYG—Investor AB; *Int'l*, pg. 686
MILITARY AVIONICS DIVISION—Honeywell Inc.; *U.S. Public*, pg. 834
MILTON INDUSTRIES, INC.; *U.S. Private*, pg. 749
MINIATURE PRECISION COMPONENTS; *U.S. Private*, pg. 750
MODERN CONTROLS, INC.; *U.S. Public*, pg. 1120
MUTOH EUROPE GMBH—Mutoh Industries Ltd.; *Int'l*, pg. 897
MUTOH INDUSTRIES LTD.; *Int'l*, pg. 897
NANOMETRICS INCORPORATED; *U.S. Public*, pg. 1151
NATIONAL NUCLEAR CORPORATION—Thermo Electron Corporation; *U.S. Public*, pg. 1594
NEWPORT CORPORATION; *U.S. Public*, pg. 1179
NICOLET TEST & MEASUREMENT DIVISION—Thermo Electron Corporation; *U.S. Public*, pg. 1593
NOONAN MACHINE CO.; *U.S. Private*, pg. 801
NORD PHOTO ENGINEERING, INC.—Photo Control Corporation; *U.S. Public*, pg. 1292
NUTONE CANADA INC.—Williams Holdings Plc; *Int'l*, pg. 1499
OERLIKON-BUHRLE HOLDING AG; *Int'l*, pg. 996
OLDELFT CORP. OF AMERICA—Delft Instruments N.V.; *Int'l*, pg. 389
OLDELFT INTERNATIONAL TRADING CY. N.V.—Delft Instruments N.V.; *Int'l*, pg. 389
OLDELFT JAPAN LTD.—Delft Instruments N.V.; *Int'l*, pg. 389
OPTICAL COATING LABORATORY, INC.; *U.S. Public*, pg. 1227
ORTHO-KINETICS, INC.; *U.S. Private*, pg. 820
OUTOKUMPU MINTEC U.S.A., INC.—Outokumpu Oyj; *Int'l*, pg. 1017
OXFORD INSTRUMENTS-NUCLEAR MEASUREMENTS GROUP—Oxford Instruments plc; *Int'l*, pg. 1018
OYO CORPORATION; *Int'l*, pg. 1019
PACIFIC SCIENTIFIC COMPANY; *U.S. Public*, pg. 1250
PACKARD BIOSCIENCE—Packard BioScience Company; *U.S. Private*, pg. 833
PACKARD INSTRUMENT CO., INC.—Packard BioScience Company; *U.S. Private*, pg. 833
PEARLE VISION EXPRESS—Cole National Corporation; *U.S. Public*, pg. 397
PENTAX CORPORATION—Asahi Optical Co., Ltd.; *Int'l*, pg. 85
PHOTOLASTIC DIVISION—Vishay Intertechnology, Inc.; *U.S. Public*, pg. 1722
PRESSURE SYSTEMS, INC.—The Roxboro Group PLC; *Int'l*, pg. 1130
QUEST TECHNOLOGIES, INC.; *U.S. Private*, pg. 900
RENK AKTIENGESELLSCHAFT—MAN Aktiengesellschaft; *Int'l*, pg. 825
RACAL ELECTRONICS PLC; *Int'l*, pg. 1082
RACAL INSTRUMENTS, INC.—Racal Electronics Plc; *Int'l*, pg. 1083
RADIAN INTERNATIONAL LLC—The Dow Chemical Company; *U.S. Public*, pg. 522
RANCO INC.—Siebe plc; *Int'l*, pg. 1243
RANK TAYLOR HOBSON LIMITED—The Rank Group PLC; *Int'l*, pg. 1087
RAYMOND ENGINEERING—Kaman Corporation; *U.S. Public*, pg. 942
RELA, INC.—Colorado MEDtech, Inc.; *U.S. Public*, pg. 401
REVENUE COLLECTION GROUP—Cubic Corporation; *U.S. Public*, pg. 466
REVERE TRANSDUCERS BV—Harnischfeger Industries, Inc.; *U.S. Public*, pg. 790
REVERE TRANSDUCERS INC.—Harnischfeger Industries, Inc.; *U.S. Public*, pg. 790
RHEOMETRIC SCIENTIFIC; *U.S. Public*, pg. 1387
RHEOMETRIC SCIENTIFIC, INC.—Rheometric Scientific; *U.S. Public*, pg. 1387
RHEOMETRICS SCIENTIFIC FAR EAST LTD.—Rheometric Scientific; *U.S. Public*, pg. 1387
RIBER; *Int'l*, pg. 1114
ROBERTSHAW CONTROLS COMPANY—Siebe plc; *Int'l*, pg. 1243
P. ROCH, LTD.—Brown & Sharpe Manufacturing Company; *U.S. Public*, pg. 260
ROCHESTER GAUGES INC. OF TEXAS—Gas Equipment Company, Inc.; *U.S. Private*, pg. 440
ROSEMOUNT ANALYTICAL, INC.—Emerson Electric Co.; *U.S. Public*, pg. 574
ROSEMOUNT ANALYTICAL, UNILOC DIV.—Emerson Electric Co.; *U.S. Public*, pg. 574
SLI INTERNATIONAL CORP.—Smiths Industries plc; *Int'l*, pg. 1268
SLM IMMOBILIEN AG—Sulzer Ltd.; *Int'l*, pg. 1305
SAAB MARINE ELECTRONICS AB—Investor AB; *Int'l*, pg. 686
SAAB SYSTEMS, INC.—Investor AB; *Int'l*, pg. 687
SAAB TRAINING SYSTEMS AB—Investor AB; *Int'l*, pg. 687
SATEC SYSTEMS INC.; *U.S. Private*, pg. 967
SCHIAPPARELLI; *Int'l*, pg. 1204
SCHIAPPARELLI BIOSYSTEMS INC.—Schiapparelli; *Int'l*, pg. 1204
SCHLUMBERGER LIMITED; *U.S. Public*, pg. 1439
SCHUTTE & KOERTING DIVISION—KTM Holdings Corp.; *U.S. Private*, pg. 604
SENLSYS—BTR plc; *Int'l*, pg. 127
SENSYM INC.—BTR plc; *Int'l*, pg. 127
SEVERN FURNACES LIMITED—Instron Corporation; *U.S. Public*, pg. 883
SFERNICE, S.A.—Vishay Intertechnology, Inc.; *U.S. Public*, pg. 1722
THE SHERRILL CORP.—Custom Accessories Inc.; *U.S. Private*, pg. 298
SIMRAD OPTRONICS A/S—Kvaerner a.s.a.; *Int'l*, pg. 770
SINTECH DIVISION—MTS Systems Corporation; *U.S. Public*, pg. 1029
SLANT/FIN CORPORATION; *U.S. Private*, pg. 1005
SMITHKLINE BEECHAM CORPORATION—SmithKline Beecham plc; *Int'l*, pg. 1264
SMITHS INDUSTRIES PLC; *Int'l*, pg. 1266
SOPRANO S.A.—Alcatel Alsthom Compagnie Generale D'Electricite; *Int'l*, pg. 53
SOVCOR, SA—Vishay Intertechnology, Inc.; *U.S. Public*, pg. 1722
SPECTRA-PHYSICS AB; *Int'l*, pg. 1288
SPECTRA-PHYSICS LASERS, INC.—Thermo Electron Corporation; *U.S. Public*, pg. 1594
THE L.S. STARRETT COMPANY; *U.S. Public*, pg. 1511
STAVELEY INDUSTRIES PLC; *Int'l*, pg. 1298
STAVELEY/NDT TECHNOLOGIES INC.—Staveley Industries PLC; *Int'l*, pg. 1299
STAVELEY WEIGHING SYSTEMS CANADA, INC.—Staveley Industries PLC; *Int'l*, pg. 1299
STOCKER & YALE, INC.; *U.S. Public*, pg. 1518
STRAHMAN VALVES, INC.; *U.S. Private*, pg. 1046
STRAND LIGHTING LIMITED—The Rank Group PLC; *Int'l*, pg. 1087
SUN ELECTRIC—Snap-On Tools Corporation; *U.S. Public*, pg. 1480
SWIFT INSTRUMENTS, INC.; *U.S. Private*, pg. 1058
SYNTRON EUROPE LIMITED—Tech-Sym Corporation; *U.S. Public*, pg. 1563
SYSTRON DONNER-INERTIAL DIVISION—BEI Technologies, Inc.; *U.S. Public*, pg. 160
TGM DETECTORS INC.—Morgan Crucible Co. Plc; *Int'l*, pg. 892
TML METROLOGY CENTRE FOR BEDFORD—Brown & Sharpe Manufacturing Company; *U.S. Public*, pg. 260
TSI INCORPORATED; *U.S. Public*, pg. 1559
TECH-MET CANADA LTD.—Emerson Electric Co.; *U.S. Public*, pg. 575
TELEFLEX INCORPORATED; *U.S. Public*, pg. 1569
TEMPIL INC.—Associated Equipment Co., Inc.; *U.S. Private*, pg. 90
TESA LEITZ GMBH—Brown & Sharpe Manufacturing Company; *U.S. Public*, pg. 260
TESA METROLOGY LIMITED—Brown & Sharpe Manufacturing Company; *U.S. Public*, pg. 260
TESA, S.A.—Brown & Sharpe Manufacturing Company; *U.S. Public*, pg. 260
THERMO ELECTRON CORPORATION; *U.S. Public*, pg. 1591
THERMO ELECTRON LTD.—Thermo Electron Corporation; *U.S. Public*, pg. 1596
THERMO INSTRUMENT SYSTEMS (F.E.) LIMITED—Thermo Electron Corporation; *U.S. Public*, pg. 1596
THERMO INSTRUMENT SYSTEMS INC.—Thermo Electron Corporation; *U.S. Public*, pg. 1593
THERMO JARRELL ASH CORPORATION—Thermo Electron Corporation; *U.S. Public*, pg. 1594
THERMO MATERIALS—Ceradyne, Inc; *U.S. Public*, pg. 330
THERMO SEPARATION PRODUCTS—Thermo Electron Corporation; *U.S. Public*, pg. 1594
THOMSON-CSF S.A.—Thomson S.A.; *Int'l*, pg. 1383
3M; *U.S. Public*, pg. 1604
TIMEX CORPORATION; *U.S. Private*, pg. 1088
TRANSINSTRUMENTS—IMO Industries Inc.; *U.S. Public*, pg. 857
TRANSTECHNOLOGY CORPORATION; *U.S. Public*, pg. 1632
TRIMBLE NAVIGATION LIMITED; *U.S. Public*, pg. 1638
TRIPLETT CORPORATION; *U.S. Private*, pg. 1104
UDT SENSORS, INC.; *U.S. Private*, pg. 1112
ULTRA ELECTRONICS MAGNETICS—Ultra Electronics Holdings plc; *Int'l*, pg. 1431
UNITECH PLC—Siebe plc; *Int'l*, pg. 1241
VG INSTRUMENTS PLC—Thermo Electron Corporation; *U.S. Public*, pg. 1595
VARIAN AUSTRALIA PTY. LTD.—Varian Associates, Inc.; *U.S. Public*, pg. 1710
VENTUREDYNE, LTD.; *U.S. Private*, pg. 1136
VIBRO-METER CORP.; *U.S. Private*, pg. 1138
VISHAY INSTRUMENTS DIV.—Vishay Intertechnology, Inc.; *U.S. Public*, pg. 1722
VISHAY INTERTECHNOLOGY, INC.; *U.S. Public*, pg. 1721
WABASH MAGNETICS—The Dyson-Kissner-Moran Corporation; *U.S. Private*, pg. 351
WANDEL & GOLTERMANN GMBH & CO., ELEKTRONISCHE MESSTECHNIK; *Int'l*, pg. 1485
WANDEL & GOLTERMANN TECHNOLOGIES, INC.—Wandel & Goltermann GmbH & Co., Elektronische Messtechnik; *Int'l*, pg. 1486
WAVETEK CORPORATION; *U.S. Private*, pg. 1154
WELDING PRODUCTS GROUP—National-Standard Co.; *U.S. Public*, pg. 1161
WHIPPS; *U.S. Private*, pg. 1171
WILSON/SHORE INSTRUMENTS—Instron Corporation; *U.S. Public*, pg. 883
XETEX, INC.—Thermo Electron Corporation; *U.S. Public*, pg. 1594
CARL ZEISS—Carl-Zeiss-Stiftung; *Int'l*, pg. 1522
ZWICK/ROELL GROUP; *Int'l*, pg. 1532
ZYMARK CORPORATION—Berwind Corporation; *U.S. Private*, pg. 139

3841 — SURGICAL & MEDICAL INSTRUMENTS & APPARATUS

ADAC LABORATORIES INC.; *U.S. Public*, pg. 3
ABBOTT CRITICAL CARE SYSTEMS—Abbott Laboratories; *U.S. Public*, pg. 13
ABBOTT HOSPITALS INC.—Abbott Laboratories; *U.S. Public*, pg. 13
ABBOTT IRELAND LTD.—Abbott Laboratories; *U.S. Public*, *pg. 13*
ABBOTT LABORATORIES; *U.S. Public*, pg. 12
ABBOTT LABORATORIES—Abbott Laboratories; *U.S. Public*, pg. 13
ACME/CHASTON PUERTO RICO—GP Strategies Corporation; *U.S. Public*, pg. 694
ACME UNITED CORPORATION; *U.S. Public*, pg. 17
AEROS INSTRUMENTS, INC.—Squire-Cogswell Company; *U.S. Private*, pg. 1028
AIR-SHIELDS INC.—Vickers PLC; *Int'l*, pg. 1468
AKORN, INC.; *U.S. Public*, pg. 34
ALCON LABORATORIES, INC.—Nestle S.A.; *Int'l*, pg. 916
ALCON PHARMACEUTICALS LTD.—Nestle S.A.; *Int'l*, pg. 916
ALLEGIANCE HEALTHCARE CORP.—Allegiance Healthcare Corp.; *U.S. Public*, pg. 44
ALLEGIANCE HEALTHCARE INTERNATIONAL—Allegiance Healthcare Corp.; *U.S. Public*, pg. 45
ALLERGAN, INC.; *U.S. Public*, pg. 46
ALLIED HEALTHCARE PRODUCTS, INC.; *U.S. Public*, pg. 48
AMEDA AG—Hollister Incorporated; *U.S. Private*, pg. 535
AMERICAN HOME PRODUCTS CORPORATION; *U.S. Public*, pg. 79
AMERICAN SAFETY RAZOR COMPANY—The Jordan Company; *U.S. Private*, pg. 597
AMERSHAM BUCHLER GMBH & CO. KG—Nycomed Amersham plc; *Int'l*, pg. 992
AMICON CANADA LTD.—Millipore Corporation; *U.S. Public*, *pg. 1113*
AMICON G.M.B.H.—Millipore Corporation; *U.S. Public*, pg. 1113
AMICON (H.K.) LTD.—Millipore Corporation; *U.S. Public*, pg. 1113
AMICON IRELAND LIMITED—Millipore Corporation; *U.S. Public*, pg. 1113
AMICON LTD.—Millipore Corporation; *U.S. Public*, pg. 1113
ANGIODYNAMICS—E-Z-Em, Inc.; *U.S. Public*, pg. 540
ARROW INTERNATIONAL, INC.; *U.S. Public*, pg. 135
ASIA ELECTRONICS INC.—Toshiba Corporation; *Int'l*, pg. 1402
ASPEN LABORATORIES, INC.—Conmed Corporation; *U.S. Public*, pg. 431
ASTRA AB; *Int'l*, pg. 93
ASTRA TECH AB—Astra AB; *Int'l*, pg. 93
ASTRE CORPORATE GROUP; *U.S. Private*, pg. 93
ATOS MEDICAL AB—Perstorp AB; *Int'l*, pg. 1036
BEC GROUP, INC.; *U.S. Public*, pg. 160
BOC OHMEDA AB—The BOC Group plc; *Int'l*, pg. 122
BOC OHMEDA OY—The BOC Group plc; *Int'l*, pg. 122
BALLARD MEDICAL PRODUCTS; *U.S. Public*, pg. 171
BARD ACCESS SYSTEMS—C.R. Bard, Inc.; *U.S. Public*, pg. 189
C.R. BARD, INC.; *U.S. Public*, pg. 189
BARD DIAGNOSTIC SCIENCES—C.R. Bard, Inc.; *U.S. Public*, pg. 189
BARD INTERVENTIONAL PRODUCTS—C.R. Bard, Inc.; *U.S. Public*, pg. 189
BARD RADIOLOGY DIV.—C.R. Bard, Inc.; *U.S. Public*, pg. 189

W.A. BAUM COMPANY, INC.; *U.S. Private*, pg. 124
BAUSCH & LOMB INC.—Bausch & Lomb Incorporated; *U.S. Public*, pg. 194
BAUSCH & LOMB INCORPORATED; *U.S. Public*, pg. 194
BAXTER FENWAL DIVISION—Baxter International Inc.; *U.S. Public*, pg. 196
BAXTER HEALTHCARE CORPORATION—Baxter International Inc.; *U.S. Public*, pg. 196
BAXTER INTERNATIONAL INC.; *U.S. Public*, pg. 196
BAXTER NOVACOR DIVISION—Baxter International Inc.; *U.S. Public*, pg. 196
BAXTER RESEARCH MEDICAL, INC.—Baxter International Inc.; *U.S. Public*, pg. 196
BAYER AG—Bayer AG; *Int'l*, pg. 172
BAYER CORPORATION—Bayer AG; *Int'l*, pg. 172
BAYER CORPORATION/CONSUMER CARE DIVISION—Bayer AG; *Int'l*, pg. 173
BAYER CORPORATION/DIAGNOSTICS DIVISION—Bayer AG; *Int'l*, pg. 173
BECTON DICKINSON & CO., LTD.—Becton Dickinson & Company; *U.S. Public*, pg. 200
BECTON DICKINSON & CO., MASSACHUSETTS DIV.—Becton Dickinson & Company; *U.S. Public*, pg. 199
BECTON DICKINSON & COMPANY; *U.S. Public*, pg. 199
BECTON DICKINSON CANADA INC.—Becton Dickinson & Company; *U.S. Public*, pg. 200
BECTON DICKINSON CONSUMER PRODS.—Becton Dickinson & Company; *U.S. Public*, pg. 199
BECTON DICKINSON EUROPE—Becton Dickinson & Company; *U.S. Public*, pg. 200
BECTON DICKINSON IND. CIRURGICAS, S.A.—Becton Dickinson & Company; *U.S. Public*, pg. 200
BECTON DICKINSON INFUSION THERAPY, INC.—Becton Dickinson & Company; *U.S. Public*, pg. 199
BECTON DICKINSON LABWARE—Becton Dickinson & Company; *U.S. Public*, pg. 199
BECTON DICKINSON MEDICAL PRODUCTS-EUROPE—Becton Dickinson & Company; *U.S. Public*, pg. 200
BECTON DICKINSON MICROBIOLOGY SYSTEMS—Becton Dickinson & Company; *U.S. Public*, pg. 199
BECTON DICKINSON PRIMARY CARE DIAGNOSTICS—Becton Dickinson & Company; *U.S. Public*, pg. 199
BECTON DICKINSON VACUTAINER SYSTEMS—Becton Dickinson & Company; *U.S. Public*, pg. 199
BEHRINGWERKE AG—Hoechst Aktiengesellschaft; *Int'l*, pg. 624
BICOMP, S.A. DE C.V.—Emerson Electric Co.; *U.S. Public*, pg. 576
BIO-RAD LASERSHARP LTD.—Bio-Rad Laboratories, Inc.; *U.S. Public*, pg. 230
BIO-TEK INSTRUMENTS, INC.; *U.S. Private*, pg. 144
BIOMET DEUTSCHLAND GMBH—Biomet, Inc.; *U.S. Public*, *pg. 232*
BIOMET, INC.; *U.S. Public*, pg. 231
BIOMET LTD.—Biomet, Inc.; *U.S. Public*, pg. 232
BIOMET SPA—Biomet, Inc.; *U.S. Public*, pg. 232
BIOPLEX CORP.—Datascope Corp.; *U.S. Public*, pg. 487
BIOSOL S.P.A.—Incentive AB; *Int'l*, pg. 667
BIRD LIFE DESIGNS—Thermo Electron Corporation; *U.S. Public*, pg. 1591
BIRD PRODUCTS CORPORATION—Thermo Electron Corporation; *U.S. Public*, pg. 1591
BOEHRINGER MANNHEIM GMBH—Corange Limited; *Int'l*, pg. 331
BOEHRINGER MANNHEIM PHARM—Corange Limited; *Int'l*, pg. 331
BOSTON SCIENTIFIC CORP.; *U.S. Public*, pg. 247
BRISTOL-MYERS HEALTH CARE GROUP—Bristol-Myers Squibb Company; *U.S. Public*, pg. 253
BRISTOL-MYERS SQUIBB COMPANY; *U.S. Public*, pg. 253
BUZEN TOSHIBA ELECTRONICS CORPORATION—Toshiba Corporation; *Int'l*, pg. 1402
CABOT MEDICAL CORPORATION—Circon Corporation; *U.S. Public*, pg. 373
CAIRE, INC.—Minnesota Valley Engineering/Cryogenic Association; *U.S. Private*, pg. 751
CANTEL INDUSTRIES, INC.; *U.S. Public*, pg. 301
CARSTENS INC.; *U.S. Private*, pg. 216
CINCINNATI SUB-ZERO PRODUCTS, INC.; *U.S. Private*, pg. 240
CIRRUS DIAGNOSTICS INC.—Diagnostic Products Corporation; *U.S. Public*, pg. 505
COBE LABORATORIES, INC.—Incentive AB; *Int'l*, pg. 667
WARREN E. COLLINS, INC.; *U.S. Private*, pg. 253
COLORADO MEDTECH, INC.; *U.S. Public*, pg. 401
COLUMBIA MEDICAL, INC.—Utah Medical Products, Inc.; *U.S. Public*, pg. 1700
CONMED ANDOVER MEDICAL, INC.—Conmed Corporation; *U.S. Public*, pg. 431
CONMED CORPORATION; *U.S. Public*, pg. 431
CONVERTORS/CUSTOM STERILE—Allegiance Healthcare Corp.; *U.S. Public*, pg. 44
THE COOPER COMPANIES, INC.; *U.S. Public*, pg. 442
COOPERSURGICAL INC.—The Cooper Companies, Inc.; *U.S. Public*, pg. 442
CORANGE U.S. HOLDINGS, INC—Corange Limited; *Int'l*, pg. 331
CORDIS, A JOHNSON & JOHNSON COMPANY—Johnson & Johnson; *U.S. Public*, pg. 928
CORDIS, A JOHNSON & JOHNSON COMPANY EUROPA N.V.—Johnson & Johnson; *U.S. Public*, pg. 928
CORPORATE MARKETING AND SERVICES—C.R. Bard, Inc.; *U.S. Public*, pg. 189
CRITICARE SYSTEMS, INC.; *U.S. Public*, pg. 459
CRYSTAL BIOTECH, INC.—Matec Corporation; *U.S. Public*, *pg. 1056*
CUTTER BIOLOGICALS—Bayer AG; *Int'l*, pg. 174
CYANAMID OF GREAT BRITAIN LTD.—American Home Products Corporation; *U.S. Public*, pg. 81
DCG PRECISION MANUFACTURING CORPORATION; *U.S. Private*, pg. 301
DADE BEHRING—Bain Capital; *U.S. Private*, pg. 110
DADE BEHRING INC.—Bain Capital; *U.S. Private*, pg. 110
DADE BEHRING INC.—Hoechst Aktiengesellschaft; *Int'l*, pg. 626
DATASCOPE CARDIAC ASSIST DIVISION—Datascope Corp.; *U.S. Public*, pg. 487
DATASCOPE CORP.; *U.S. Public*, pg. 487
DAVOL INC.—C.R. Bard, Inc.; *U.S. Public*, pg. 189
DEL MAR AVIONICS; *U.S. Private*, pg. 321
DELFT INSTRUMENTS N.V.; *Int'l*, pg. 388
DEN-MAT CORPORATION; *U.S. Private*, pg. 324
DEPUY, INC.—Corange Limited; *Int'l*, pg. 331
DERLY, S.A.—Eli Lilly and Company; *U.S. Public*, pg. 993
DIAMEDIX CORPORATION—IVAX Corporation; *U.S. Public*, *pg. 914*
DIMEQ MEDIZINELECTRONIK GMBH—Delft Instruments N.V.; *Int'l*, pg. 389
DU PONT PHARMACEUTICALS—Du Pont (E.I. Du Pont De Nemours & Co.); *U.S. Public*, pg. 531
DYNATECH CORPORATION; *U.S. Public*, pg. 539
E FOR M CORP.—Marquette Medical Systems, Inc.; *U.S. Public*, pg. 1047
E-Z-EM CARIBE, INC.—E-Z-Em, Inc.; *U.S. Public*, pg. 540
E-Z-EM, INC.; *U.S. Public*, pg. 540
EVSCO PHARMACEUTICALS—IGI, Inc.; *U.S. Public*, pg. 855
ENRAF SARL—Delft Instruments N.V.; *Int'l*, pg. 389
ETHICON ENDO-SURGERY, INC.—Johnson & Johnson; *U.S. Public*, pg. 928
ETHNOR S.A.—Johnson & Johnson; *U.S. Public*, pg. 929
FISHER SCIENTIFIC INTERNATIONAL—Thomas H. Lee Co.; *U.S. Private*, pg. 658
FRESENIUS AG; *Int'l*, pg. 505
FRESENIUS MEDICAL CARE (NORTH AMERICA)—Fresenius AG; *Int'l*, pg. 505
GP STRATEGIES CORPORATION; *U.S. Public*, pg. 694
GAMBRO AB—Incentive AB; *Int'l*, pg. 666
GAMBRO DIALYSATOREN GMBH & CO KG—Incentive AB; *Int'l*, pg. 667
GAMBRO ENGSTROM AB—Incentive AB; *Int'l*, pg. 667
GAMBRO K.K.—Incentive AB; *Int'l*, pg. 668
GAMBRO LTD.—Incentive AB; *Int'l*, pg. 668
GAMBRO MEDICAL K.K.—Incentive AB; *Int'l*, pg. 668
GAMBRO N.V./S.A.—Incentive AB; *Int'l*, pg. 668
GAMBRO PTY LTD.—Incentive AB; *Int'l*, pg. 668
GAMBRO S.A.—Incentive AB; *Int'l*, pg. 668
GAMBRO SALES AB—Incentive AB; *Int'l*, pg. 668
GAMBRO S.P.A.—Incentive AB; *Int'l*, pg. 668
GAMBRO VERTRIEBSGESELLSCHAFT M.B.H.—Incentive AB; *Int'l*, pg. 668
GAYMAR INDUSTRIES, INC.; *U.S. Private*, pg. 442
GELMAN ITALY S.R.L.—Pall Corporation; *U.S. Public*, pg. 1253
GELMAN SCIENCES, INC.—Pall Corporation; *U.S. Public*, pg. 1253
GELMAN SCIENCES, LTD.—Pall Corporation; *U.S. Public*, pg. 1253
GELMAN SCIENCES PTY. LTD.—Pall Corporation; *U.S. Public*, pg. 1253
GEN-PROBE INC.—Chugai Pharmaceutical Co., Ltd.; *Int'l*, pg. 291
GESCO INTERNATIONAL—C.R. Bard, Inc.; *U.S. Public*, pg. 189
GETINGE/CASTLE INC.—Getinge Industrier AB; *Int'l*, pg. 551
GISH BIOMEDICAL, INC.; *U.S. Public*, pg. 745
W.L. GORE & ASSOCIATES, INC.; *U.S. Private*, pg. 465
GOULD ELECTRONICS INC.—Thermo Electron Corporation; *U.S. Public*, pg. 1591
GOULD INSTRUMENT SYSTEMS, S.A.—Thermo Electron Corporation; *U.S. Public*, pg. 1592
GUDEBROD, INC.; *U.S. Private*, pg. 486
GUIDANT CORPORATION-CARDIAC & VASCULAR SURGERY GROUP—Guidant Corporation; *U.S. Public*, pg. 768
GUIDANT CORPORATION-VASCULAR INTERVENTION GROUP—Guidant Corporation; *U.S. Public*, pg. 768
HELENA LABORATORIES CORPORATION; *U.S. Private*, pg. 519
HERAEUS MED GMBH—Heraeus Holding GmbH; *Int'l*, pg. 616
HILL-ROM COMPANY, INC.—Hillenbrand Industries, Inc.; *U.S. Public*, pg. 828
HILLENBRAND INDUSTRIES, INC.; *U.S. Public*, pg. 828
HOGAMED S.A.—Incentive AB; *Int'l*, pg. 668
HOLLISTER INCORPORATED; *U.S. Private*, pg. 535
HOSPAL B.V.—Incentive AB; *Int'l*, pg. 668
HOSPAL-COBE RENAL N.V.—Incentive AB; *Int'l*, pg. 668
HOSPAL DASCO S.P.A.—Incentive AB; *Int'l*, pg. 668
HOSPAL-GAMBRO LIMITEE—Incentive AB; *Int'l*, pg. 668
HOSPAL INDUSTRIE S.A.—Incentive AB; *Int'l*, pg. 668
HOSPAL LTD.—Incentive AB; *Int'l*, pg. 668
HOSPAL MED TECH GMBH—Incentive AB; *Int'l*, pg. 668
HOSPAL S.A.—Incentive AB; *Int'l*, pg. 668
HOSPAL S.P.A.—Incentive AB; *Int'l*, pg. 668
HUDSON, RCI; *U.S. Private*, pg. 546
HUTCHINSON TECHNOLOGY INC.; *U.S. Public*, pg. 850
IGI, INC.; *U.S. Public*, pg. 855
INAMED DEVELOPMENT COMPANY—Inamed Corporation; *U.S. Public*, pg. 873
INNOMEDICA—Innovex, Inc.; *U.S. Public*, pg. 880
INTERMEDICS S.A.—Sulzer Ltd.; *Int'l*, pg. 1307
INTERSPIRO INC.—Spectra-Physics AB; *Int'l*, pg. 1289
INTERVASCULAR GMBH—Datascope Corp.; *U.S. Public*, pg. 488
INTERVASCULAR, S.A.—Datascope Corp.; *U.S. Public*, pg. 488
INVACARE CORPORATION; *U.S. Public*, pg. 911
ISOMEDIX CORPORATION (CANADA)—Steris Corporation; *U.S. Public*, pg. 1515
ISOMEDIX INC.—Steris Corporation; *U.S. Public*, pg. 1515
JANSSEN-CILAG LTD.—Johnson & Johnson; *U.S. Public*, pg. 929
JEWETT INTERNATIONAL CORP.—Ruslander & Sons, Inc.; *U.S. Private*, pg. 952
THE JEWETT REFRIGERATOR CO., INC.—Ruslander & Sons, Inc.; *U.S. Private*, pg. 952
JOHNSON & JOHNSON; *U.S. Public*, pg. 927
JOHNSON & JOHNSON (EGYPT) S.A.E.—Johnson & Johnson; *U.S. Public*, pg. 930
P.T. JOHNSON & JOHNSON INDONESIA—Johnson & Johnson; *U.S. Public*, pg. 930
JOHNSON & JOHNSON PROFESSIONAL, INC.—Johnson & Johnson; *U.S. Public*, pg. 928
AXEL JOHNSON AB; *Int'l*, pg. 707
AXEL JOHNSON INSTRUMENT AB—Axel Johnson AB; *Int'l*, pg. 709
KEELER LIMITED—Halma p.l.c.; *Int'l*, pg. 589
KELSAR, S.A.—American Home Products Corporation; *U.S. Public*, pg. 81
THE KENDALL COMPANY—Tyco International Ltd.; *U.S. Public*, pg. 1647
KENDALL HEALTHCARE PRODUCTS COMPANY—Tyco International Ltd.; *U.S. Public*, pg. 1647
KIMBERLY-CLARK CORPORATION; *U.S. Public*, pg. 958
KIMBERLY-CLARK TECNOL—Kimberly-Clark Corporation; *U.S. Public*, pg. 959
KIPP GROUP; *U.S. Private*, pg. 623
KVAERNER THUNE A/S—Kvaerner a.s.a.; *Int'l*, pg. 769
LABORATORY SUPPLY COMPANY—Laboratory Supply Company, Inc.; *U.S. Private*, pg. 642
LABORATORY SUPPLY COMPANY, INC.; *U.S. Private*, pg. 641
LAKE REGION MANUFACTURING, INC.; *U.S. Private*, pg. 643
LEICA A.G.; *Int'l*, pg. 806
LEISEGANG MEDICAL, INC.—Galileo Corp.; *U.S. Public*, pg. 698
LEVTECH, INC.—Orthofix International N.V.; *Int'l*, pg. 1011
LIFE SCIENCES INTERNATIONAL PLC—Thermo Electron Corporation; *U.S. Public*, pg. 1594
LIFESCAN, INC.—Johnson & Johnson; *U.S. Public*, pg. 928
ELI LILLY AND COMPANY; *U.S. Public*, pg. 992
ELI LILLY Y COMPANIA DE VENEZUELA, S.A.—Eli Lilly and Company; *U.S. Public*, pg. 994
LITTON INDUSTRIES, INC.; *U.S. Public*, pg. 1002
LITTON INSTRUMENTS & LIFE SUPPORT—Litton Industries, Inc.; *U.S. Public*, pg. 1003
WALTER LORENZ SURGICAL, INC.—Biomet, Inc.; *U.S. Public*, pg. 231
LUMEX MEDICAL PRODUCTS—Graham-Field Health Products, Inc.; *U.S. Public*, pg. 758
MTN MEDIZINTECHNIK NEUBRANDENBURG GMBH I.G.—Incentive AB; *Int'l*, pg. 669
MALLINCKRODT AUSTRALIA PTY. LTD.—Mallinckrodt Inc.; *U.S. Public*, pg. 1040
MALLINCKRODT CANADA, INC.—Mallinckrodt Inc.; *U.S. Public*, pg. 1040
MALLINCKRODT MEDICAL—Mallinckrodt Inc.; *U.S. Public*, pg. 1040
MALLINCKRODT MEDICAL GMBH—Mallinckrodt Inc.; *U.S. Public*, pg. 1040
THE MARMON GROUP, INC.; *U.S. Private*, pg. 706
MEDASONICS, INC.—Settsu Corporation; *Int'l*, pg. 1225
MEDEX INC.—Furon Company; *U.S. Public*, pg. 689
MEDI-LAB A/S—Roche Holding Ltd.; *Int'l*, pg. 1121
MEDICA BV—Maxxim Medical, Inc.; *U.S. Public*, pg. 1063
MEDICAL ACTION INDUSTRIES INC.; *U.S. Public*, pg. 1079
MEDICAL DATA INTELLIGENCE AB—Incentive AB; *Int'l*, pg. 667
MEDICAL GRAPHICS CORP.; *U.S. Public*, pg. 1080
MEDICAL RESOURCES INC.; *U.S. Public*, pg. 1080
MEDICAL RUBBER AB—Perstorp AB; *Int'l*, pg. 1036
MEDICAL-SURGICAL DIVISION—3M; *U.S. Public*, pg. 1605
MEDICORE INC.; *U.S. Public*, pg. 1080
MEDLOG GMBH—Criticare Systems, Inc.; *U.S. Public*, pg. 459
MEDRAD, INC.—Schering AG; *Int'l*, pg. 1204
MEDTRONIC DLP—Medtronic, Inc.; *U.S. Public*, pg. 1083
MEDTRONIC HEART VALVE DIVISION—Medtronic, Inc.; *U.S. Public*, pg. 1083
MEDTRONIC, INC.; *U.S. Public*, pg. 1082
MEDTRONIC MED REL, INC.—Medtronic, Inc.; *U.S. Public*, *pg. 1083*
MEDTRONIC MILACA, INC.—Medtronic, Inc.; *U.S. Public*, pg. 1083
MEDTRONIC PUERTO RICO, INC.—Medtronic, Inc.; *U.S. Public*, pg. 1083
MEDTRONICS INC.—Medtronic, Inc.; *U.S. Public*, pg. 1083
MENNEN MEDICAL INC.—Mennen Medical Ltd.; *Int'l*, pg. 858
MENNEN MEDICAL LTD.; *Int'l*, pg. 858
MENTOR CORPORATION; *U.S. Public*, pg. 1086
MENTOR OPTHALMICS, INC.—Mentor Corporation; *U.S. Public*, pg. 1086
MERIDIAN MEDICAL TECHNOLOGY, INC.; *U.S. Public*, pg. 1095
MERIT MEDICAL SYSTEMS, INC.; *U.S. Public*, pg. 1096
MICROTEK MEDICAL, INC.—Isolyser Company, Inc.; *U.S. Public*, pg. 914
MILCARE, INC.—Herman Miller, Inc.; *U.S. Public*, pg. 1112
MINNESOTA VALLEY ENGINEERING/CRYOGENIC ASSOCIATION; *U.S. Private*, pg. 751
NELLCOR DE MEXICO, S.A. DE C.V.—Mallinckrodt Inc.; *U.S. Public*, pg. 1040
NELLCOR PURITAN BENNETT BELGIUM N.V./S.A.—Mallinckrodt Inc.; *U.S. Public*, pg. 1040
NELLCOR PURITAN BENNETT INCORPORATED—Mallinckrodt Inc.; *U.S. Public*, pg. 1039
NIHON MEDI-PHYSICS COMPANY LIMITED—Roche Holding Ltd.; *Int'l*, pg. 1121
NIHON MILLIPORE LTD.-YONEZAWA—Millipore Corporation; *U.S. Public*, pg. 1113
NOK EG & G OPTOELECTRONICS CORPORATION—EG & G, Inc.; *U.S. Public*, pg. 544
NOVAMETRIX MEDICAL SYSTEMS INC.; *U.S. Public*, pg. 1203

NOVEL BIOMEDICAL—Colorado MEDtech, Inc.; *U.S. Public*, pg. 401
OHMEDA BV—The BOC Group plc; *Int'l*, pg. 122
OHMEDA, INC.—The BOC Group plc; *Int'l*, pg. 121
OHMEDA LTD.—The BOC Group plc; *Int'l*, pg. 122
OHMEDA MEDICAL ENGINEERING—The BOC Group plc; *Int'l*, pg. 121
OLDELFT JAPAN LTD.—Delft Instruments N.V.; *Int'l*, pg. 389
OLDELFT VESTIGING LEEUWARDEN—Delft Instruments N.V.; *Int'l*, pg. 389
OMRON CORPORATION; *Int'l*, pg. 1005
ORGANON TEKNIKA CORP.—Akzo Nobel N.V.; *Int'l*, pg. 46
ORTHOFIX INC.—Orthofix International N.V.; *Int'l*, pg. 1011
ORTHOPLANT GMBH—Bristol-Myers Squibb Company; *U.S. Public*, pg. 256
PALL BIOMEDICAL PRODUCTS CORP.—Pall Corporation; *U.S. Public*, pg. 1254
PALL BIOMEDICAL PUERTO RICO—Pall Corporation; *U.S. Public*, pg. 1254
PALL BIOMEDIZIN GMBH—Pall Corporation; *U.S. Public*, pg. 1254
PALL CORPORATION; *U.S. Public*, pg. 1253
PALL EUROPE LTD.—Pall Corporation; *U.S. Public*, pg. 1254
PEGASUS INTERNATIONAL CORPORATION—Straube Regional Center LLC; *U.S. Private*, pg. 1046
PENTAX PRECISION INSTRUMENT CORP.—Asahi Optical Co., Ltd.; *Int'l*, pg. 85
PHARMACIA & UPJOHN BIOSYSTEMS AB—Pharmacia & Upjohn, Inc.; *Int'l*, pg. 1047
PHARMACIA & UPJOHN DELTEC, INC.—Pharmacia & Upjohn, Inc.; *Int'l*, pg. 1049
PHARMACIA & UPJOHN DIAGNOSTICS, INC.—Pharmacia & Upjohn, Inc.; *Int'l*, pg. 1048
PHARMACIA & UPJOHN, INC.; *Int'l*, pg. 1047
PHIPPS & BIRD—McKesson Corporation; *U.S. Public*, pg. 1073
PICKER INTERNATIONAL, INC.—The General Electric Company, p.l.c.; *Int'l*, pg. 545
PLASTOFILM INDUSTRIES, INC.—Ivex Packaging Corporation; *U.S. Public*, pg. 915
PROPPER MANUFACTURING CO., INC.; *U.S. Private*, pg. 891
PROTEK GROUP—Sulzer Ltd.; *Int'l*, pg. 1307
QUINTON INSTRUMENT COMPANY—American Home Products Corporation; *U.S. Public*, pg. 80
RADIOMETER A/S; *Int'l*, pg. 1083
RADIOMETER MEDICAL A/S—Radiometer A/S; *Int'l*, pg. 1083
REGENT-SHEFFIELD LTD.—McPherson's Limited; *Int'l*, pg. 852
RELIANCE MEDICAL PRODUCTS, INC.; *U.S. Private*, pg. 921
RICHARDSON-VICKS, INC.—The Procter & Gamble Company; *U.S. Public*, pg. 1331
S & W MEDICO TEKNIK A/S—Vickers PLC; *Int'l*, pg. 1468
SANKYO COMPANY LIMITED; *Int'l*, pg. 1189
SCHNEIDER (USA) INC.—Pfizer Inc.; *U.S. Public*, pg. 1284
SEARLE S.R.L; *Int'l*, pg. 1217
SERADYN, INC.—Mitsubishi Chemical Corporation; *Int'l*, pg. 871
SERATRONICS, INC.—Fresenius AG; *Int'l*, pg. 505
SHERWOOD-DAVIS & GECK—American Home Products Corporation; *U.S. Public*, pg. 80
SHIONOGI LILLY KABUSHIKI KAISHA—Eli Lilly and Company; *U.S. Public*, pg. 994
SIEMENS AG; *Int'l*, pg. 1244
SIEMENS MEDICAL SYSTEMS, INC.—Siemens AG; *Int'l*, pg. 1246
SIEMENS S.A.—Siemens AG; *Int'l*, pg. 1248
SIMS PORTEX INC.—Smiths Industries plc; *Int'l*, pg. 1268
SMITH & NEPHEW ENDOSCOPY—Smith & Nephew PLC; *Int'l*, pg. 1263
SMITH & NEPHEW ENT—Smith & Nephew PLC; *Int'l*, pg. 1263
SMITH & NEPHEW MEDICAL FABRICS—Smith & Nephew PLC; *Int'l*, pg. 1263
SMITH & NEPHEW PLC; *Int'l*, pg. 1263
SMITHS INDUSTRIES PLC; *Int'l*, pg. 1266
SORIN BIOMEDICA—Fiat Auto SpA; *Int'l*, pg. 483
SPACELABS MEDICAL, INC.; *U.S. Public*, pg. 1494
SPECTRIS MESSTECHNIK GMBH—AGIV Group; *Int'l*, pg. 14
SPECTRIS TECHNOLOGIES, INC.—AGIV Group; *Int'l*, pg. 14
SPENCO MEDICAL CORPORATION—SBS Enterprises Inc.; *U.S. Private*, pg. 955
SQUIBB SURGICARE LTD.—Bristol-Myers Squibb Company; *U.S. Public*, pg. 256
STACKHOUSE INC.—Thermo Electron Corporation; *U.S. Public*, pg. 1591
STORZ INSTRUMENT CO.—American Home Products Corporation; *U.S. Public*, pg. 79
STRYKER CORPORATION; *U.S. Public*, pg. 1525
STRYKER CORPORATION ENDOSCOPY—Stryker Corporation; *U.S. Public*, pg. 1526
SUMMIT TECHNOLOGY, INC.; *U.S. Public*, pg. 1528
SUMMIT TECHNOLOGY IRELAND—Summit Technology, Inc.; *U.S. Public*, pg. 1529
SURGICAL SPECIALTIES; *U.S. Private*, pg. 1056
SVENSKA BOC AB—The BOC Group plc; *Int'l*, pg. 122
TECA CORPORATION—Vickers PLC; *Int'l*, pg. 1468
TECHDYNE, INC.—Medicore Inc.; *U.S. Public*, pg. 1080
TERUMO MEDICAL CORPORATION—Terumo Corporation; *Int'l*, pg. 1376
THERAKOS, INC.—Johnson & Johnson; *U.S. Public*, pg. 929
THERMO ELECTRON CORPORATION; *U.S. Public*, pg. 1591
TOSHIBA CORPORATION; *Int'l*, pg. 1402
TRANSIDYNE GENERAL CORPORATION—Customedix Corporation; *U.S. Private*, pg. 298
USCI—C.R. Bard, Inc.; *U.S. Public*, pg. 189
UNILEVER N.V.—Unilever Plc; *Int'l*, pg. 1434
U.S. SURGICAL CORP.; *U.S. Public*, pg. 1687
UTAH MEDICAL PRODUCTS, INC.; *U.S. Public*, pg. 1700
UTAH MEDICAL PRODUCTS LTD.—Utah Medical Products, Inc.; *U.S. Public*, pg. 1700
UVEX SAFETY, INC.—Bacou S.A.; *Int'l*, pg. 132
VICKERS AIR-SHIELDS—Vickers PLC; *Int'l*, pg. 1467
VITAL SIGNS—Vital Signs, Inc.; *U.S. Public*, pg. 1723
VITAL SIGNS, INC.; *U.S. Public*, pg. 1723
WILLIAMS HEALTHCARE SYSTEMS—Standex International Corporation; *U.S. Public*, pg. 1507
CARL ZEISS—Carl-Zeiss-Stiftung; *Int'l*, pg. 1522
ZIMMER AUSTRALIA PTY. LIMITED—Bristol-Myers Squibb Company; *U.S. Public*, pg. 256
ZIMMER, INC.—Bristol-Myers Squibb Company; *U.S. Public*, *pg. 254*
ZIMMER INTERNATIONAL, S.A.—Bristol-Myers Squibb Company; *U.S. Public*, pg. 257
ZIMMER NEW ZEALAND LIMITED—Bristol-Myers Squibb Company; *U.S. Public*, pg. 257
ZIMMER PTE LTD.—Bristol-Myers Squibb Company; *U.S. Public*, pg. 257
ZIMMER S.A.—Bristol-Myers Squibb Company; *U.S. Public*, pg. 257

3842 — ORTHOPEDIC, PROSTHETIC & SURGICAL APPLIANCES & SUPPLIES

AAH MEDICAL—Franz Haniel & Cie, GmbH; *Int'l*, pg. 591
ABBOTT CRITICAL CARE SYSTEMS—Abbott Laboratories; *U.S. Public*, pg. 13
ABBOTT LABORATORIES—Abbott Laboratories; *U.S. Public*, pg. 13
ACME/CHASTON PUERTO RICO—GP Strategies Corporation; *U.S. Public*, pg. 694
ACORN ENGINEERING COMPANY; *U.S. Private*, pg. 14
AEARO COMPANY; *U.S. Private*, pg. 23
AESCULAP AKTIENGESELLSCHAFT; *Int'l*, pg. 29
AIRGAS, INC.; *U.S. Public*, pg. 33
ALARIS MEDICAL SYSTEMS, INC.—ALARIS Medical, Inc.; *U.S. Public*, pg. 35
ALBA-WALDENSIAN EXPORT CORP.—Alba-Waldensian, Inc.; *U.S. Public*, pg. 36
ALBA-WALDENSIAN, INC.; *U.S. Public*, pg. 35
ALIMED, INC.; *U.S. Private*, pg. 34
ALLEGIANCE HEALTHCARE CORP.—Allegiance Healthcare Corp.; *U.S. Public*, pg. 44
ALLEGIANCE HEALTHCARE INTERNATIONAL—Allegiance Healthcare Corp.; *U.S. Public*, pg. 45
ALLIED HEALTHCARE PRODUCTS, INC.; *U.S. Public*, pg. 48
ALLO PRO GMBH—Sulzer Ltd.; *Int'l*, pg. 1307
AMERICAL CORPORATION; *U.S. Private*, pg. 49
AMERICAN ALLSAFE CO.—NCH Corporation; *U.S. Public*, pg. 1145
AMERICAN OPTICAL CORPORATION; *U.S. Private*, pg. 60
AMERICAN WHITE CROSS—GP Strategies Corporation; *U.S. Public*, pg. 694
ANGIODYNAMICS—E-Z-Em, Inc.; *U.S. Public*, pg. 540
ANSELL INTERNATIONAL—Pacific Dunlop Limited; *Int'l*, pg. 1021
ARGOSY ELECTRONICS, INC.; *U.S. Private*, pg. 81
ARTHROTEK, INC.—Biomet, Inc.; *U.S. Public*, pg. 231
ASCOM HOLDING AG; *Int'l*, pg. 86
ASPEN LABORATORIES, INC.—Conmed Corporation; *U.S. Public*, pg. 431
ASTRA AB; *Int'l*, pg. 93
ASTRA TECH AB—Astra AB; *Int'l*, pg. 93
AUDIOTONE, INC.—Bausch & Lomb Incorporated; *U.S. Public*, pg. 194
AUERGESELLSCHAFT GMBH—Mine Safety Appliances Co.; *U.S. Public*, pg. 1114
BEI TECHNOLOGIES, INC.; *U.S. Public*, pg. 160
C.R. BARD, INC.; *U.S. Public*, pg. 189
BAUSCH & LOMB HEARING SYSTEMS DIVISION—Bausch & Lomb Incorporated; *U.S. Public*, pg. 194
BAUSCH & LOMB INCORPORATED; *U.S. Public*, pg. 194
BECTON DICKINSON & CO., LTD.—Becton Dickinson & Company; *U.S. Public*, pg. 200
BECTON DICKINSON & CO., MASSACHUSETTS DIV.—Becton Dickinson & Company; *U.S. Public*, pg. 199
BECTON DICKINSON & COMPANY; *U.S. Public*, pg. 199
BECTON DICKINSON CANADA INC.—Becton Dickinson & Company; *U.S. Public*, pg. 200
BECTON DICKINSON EUROPE—Becton Dickinson & Company; *U.S. Public*, pg. 200
BECTON DICKINSON LABORATORY PRODUCTS-EUROPE—Becton Dickinson & Company; *U.S. Public*, pg. 200
BECTON DICKINSON MEDICAL PRODUCTS-EUROPE—Becton Dickinson & Company; *U.S. Public*, pg. 200
BECTON DICKINSON MICROBIOLOGY SYSTEMS—Becton Dickinson & Company; *U.S. Public*, pg. 199
BECTON DICKINSON PRIMARY CARE DIAGNOSTICS—Becton Dickinson & Company; *U.S. Public*, pg. 199
BEHRINGWERKE AG—Hoechst Aktiengesellschaft; *Int'l*, pg. 624
BEIERSDORF, INC.—Beiersdorf Group; *Int'l*, pg. 182
BEIERSDORF JAPAN K.K.—Beiersdorf Group; *Int'l*, pg. 183
BELTONE ELECTRONICS CORPORATION; *U.S. Private*, pg. 132
BIO ENTERICS CORPORATION—Inamed Corporation; *U.S. Public*, pg. 873
BIOMET DEUTSCHLAND GMBH—Biomet, Inc.; *U.S. Public*, *pg. 232*
BIOMET, INC.; *U.S. Public*, pg. 231
BIOMET LTD.—Biomet, Inc.; *U.S. Public*, pg. 232
BIOMET SPA—Biomet, Inc.; *U.S. Public*, pg. 232
BIOPLEXUS CORPORATION—Inamed Corporation; *U.S. Public*, pg. 874
BIRD PRODUCTS CORPORATION—Thermo Electron Corporation; *U.S. Public*, pg. 1591
BIVONA INC.—L'Oreal S.A.; *Int'l*, pg. 818
BRISTOL-MYERS HEALTH CARE GROUP—Bristol-Myers Squibb Company; *U.S. Public*, pg. 253
BRISTOL-MYERS SQUIBB COMPANY; *U.S. Public*, pg. 253
E.D. BULLARD COMPANY; *U.S. Private*, pg. 180
CAMP HEALTHCARE—True Life; *Int'l*, pg. 1425
CARTERS (J&A) LTD.—Invacare Corporation; *U.S. Public*, pg. 911
CHAD THERAPEUTICS; *U.S. Public*, pg. 332
CHATTANOOGA GROUP, INC.; *U.S. Private*, pg. 231
CHICOPEE—BBA Group plc; *Int'l*, pg. 113
DAVID CLARK COMPANY INCORPORATED; *U.S. Private*, *pg. 242*
THE CLINIPAD CORPORATION; *U.S. Private*, pg. 246
COLLAGEN CORPORATION; *U.S. Public*, pg. 399
WARREN E. COLLINS, INC.; *U.S. Private*, pg. 253
COOPERSURGICAL INC.—The Cooper Companies, Inc.; *U.S. Public*, pg. 442
CORANGE U.S. HOLDINGS, INC—Corange Limited; *Int'l*, pg. 331
CROW RIVER INDUSTRIES INCORPORATED—Mallinckrodt Inc.; *U.S. Public*, pg. 1040
DAHLBERG, INC.—Bausch & Lomb Incorporated; *U.S. Public*, pg. 194
DAHLBERG SCIENCES, LTD.—Bausch & Lomb Incorporated; *U.S. Public*, pg. 194
DANEK MEDICAL INC.—Sofamor Danek Group, Inc.; *U.S. Public*, pg. 1482
DEPUY, INC.—Corange Limited; *Int'l*, pg. 331
DERLY, S.A.—Eli Lilly and Company; *U.S. Public*, pg. 993
DISPOSABLE SAFETY WEAR INC.—Eastco Industrial Safety Corp.; *U.S. Public*, pg. 548
DOW CORNING WRIGHT—The Dow Chemical Company; *U.S. Public*, pg. 523
DUNLOP MARINE SAFETY LTD.—BTR plc; *Int'l*, pg. 126
E-Z-EM, INC.; *U.S. Public*, pg. 540
EASTCO INDUSTRIAL SAFETY CORP.; *U.S. Public*, pg. 548
ETHICON G.M.B.H. & CO. KG—Johnson & Johnson; *U.S. Public*, pg. 929
ETHICON, INC.—Johnson & Johnson; *U.S. Public*, pg. 928
ETHICON S.P.A.—Johnson & Johnson; *U.S. Public*, pg. 929
ETHNOR S.A.—Johnson & Johnson; *U.S. Public*, pg. 929
EVEREST & JENNINGS DE MEXICO S.A. DE C.V.—Graham-Field Health Products, Inc.; *U.S. Public*, pg. 758
EVEREST & JENNINGS/GRAHAM-FIELD, CANADA—Graham-Field Health Products, Inc.; *U.S. Public*, pg. 758
EVEREST & JENNINGS, INC.—Graham-Field Health Products, Inc.; *U.S. Public*, pg. 758
THE FIBRE-METAL PRODUCTS COMPANY; *U.S. Private*, pg. 402
FILLAUER, INC.—Bergen Brunswig Corporation; *U.S. Public*, pg. 214
FIRELAND INDUSTRIES, INC.—Lakeland Industries, Inc.; *U.S. Public*, pg. 975
FIRST MEDICAL GROUP INC.; *U.S. Public*, pg. 636
FLOWMATRIX CORPORATION—Inamed Corporation; *U.S. Public*, pg. 874
FRESENIUS MEDICAL CARE, INC.—Fresenius AG; *Int'l*, pg. 505
FRESENIUS MEDICAL CARE (NORTH AMERICA)—Fresenius AG; *Int'l*, pg. 505
GN DANAVOX A/S—GN Great Nordic Ltd.; *Int'l*, pg. 537
GP STRATEGIES CORPORATION; *U.S. Public*, pg. 694
GERBER PRODUCTS DIVISION-BABY CARE—Novartis AG; *Int'l*, pg. 973
GETINGE/CASTLE INC.—Getinge Industrier AB; *Int'l*, pg. 551
GETINGE INDUSTRIER AB; *Int'l*, pg. 551
GUDEBROD, INC.; *U.S. Private*, pg. 486
HALL SURGICAL DIVISION—Bristol-Myers Squibb Company; *U.S. Public*, pg. 254
HIGHLAND INTERNATIONAL, INC.—Lakeland Industries, Inc.; *U.S. Public*, pg. 975
HILL-ROM COMPANY, INC.—Hillenbrand Industries, Inc.; *U.S. Public*, pg. 828
HOWMEDICA, INC.—Pfizer Inc.; *U.S. Public*, pg. 1282
HUDSON, RCI; *U.S. Private*, pg. 546
INAMED CORPORATION; *U.S. Public*, pg. 873
INAMED DEVELOPMENT COMPANY—Inamed Corporation; *U.S. Public*, pg. 873
INDUSTRIAS QUIRURGICAS DE LEVANTE, S.A.—Biomet, Inc.; *U.S. Public*, pg. 232
INTERMEDICS ORTHOPEDICS, INC.—Sulzer Ltd.; *Int'l*, pg. 1307
INTERMEDICS S.A.—Sulzer Ltd.; *Int'l*, pg. 1307
INTERVASCULAR, INC.—Datascope Corp.; *U.S. Public*, pg. 487
INVACARE CORPORATION; *U.S. Public*, pg. 911
JACUZZI CANADA—U.S. Industries, Inc.; *U.S. Public*, pg. 1684
JACUZZI (CHILE) S.A.—U.S. Industries, Inc.; *U.S. Public*, pg. 1684
JACUZZI DO BRASIL—U.S. Industries, Inc.; *U.S. Public*, pg. 1684
JACUZZI EUROPE, S.P.A.—U.S. Industries, Inc.; *U.S. Public*, pg. 1684
JACUZZI, INC.—U.S. Industries, Inc.; *U.S. Public*, pg. 1684
JACUZZI UNIVERSAL, S.A.—U.S. Industries, Inc.; *U.S. Public*, pg. 1684
JACUZZI WHIRLPOOL BATH INC.—U.S. Industries, Inc.; *U.S. Public*, pg. 1684
JOHNSON & JOHNSON; *U.S. Public*, pg. 927
JOHNSON & JOHNSON ASIA PACIFIC—Johnson & Johnson; *U.S. Public*, pg. 930
JOHNSON & JOHNSON CONSUMER PRODUCTS—Johnson & Johnson; *U.S. Public*, pg. 928
JOHNSON & JOHNSON (EGYPT) S.A.E.—Johnson & Johnson; *U.S. Public*, pg. 930
JOHNSON & JOHNSON LTDA.—Johnson & Johnson; *U.S. Public*, pg. 931

JOHNSON & JOHNSON MEDICAL, INC.—Johnson & Johnson; *U.S. Public*, pg. 928
JOHNSON & JOHNSON PROFESSIONAL, INC.—Johnson & Johnson; *U.S. Public*, pg. 928
JOHNSON & JOHNSON S.A. CONSUMER—Johnson & Johnson; *U.S. Public*, pg. 931
JOHNSON & JOHNSON SDN. BHD.—Johnson & Johnson; *U.S. Public*, pg. 931
KAPPLER EUROPE, LTD.—Kappler Safety Group, Inc.; *U.S. Private*, pg. 607
KAPPLER SAFETY GROUP, INC.; *U.S. Private*, pg. 607
KAPPLER USA—Kappler Safety Group, Inc.; *U.S. Private*, pg. 607
KAZ, INC.; *U.S. Private*, pg. 610
KEMIRA SAFETY LTD.—Kemira Oy; *Int'l*, pg. 729
THE KENDALL-BETHAM DIVISION—Tyco International Ltd.; *U.S. Public*, pg. 1647
THE KENDALL COMPANY—Tyco International Ltd.; *U.S. Public*, pg. 1647
KENDALL HEALTHCARE PRODUCTS COMPANY—Tyco International Ltd.; *U.S. Public*, pg. 1647
KIMBERLY-CLARK TECNOL—Kimberly-Clark Corporation; *U.S. Public*, pg. 959
KYOCERA CORPORATION; *Int'l*, pg. 775
L.A. GAUGE CO.—Triumph Group, Inc.; *U.S. Public*, pg. 1640
THE LANGER BIOMECHANICS GROUP, INC.; *U.S. Public*, pg. 978
THE LANGER BIOMECHANICS GROUP (UK) LTD.—The Langer Biomechanics Group, Inc.; *U.S. Public*, pg. 978
LIFESCAN CANADA LTD.—Johnson & Johnson; *U.S. Public*, pg. 931
ELI LILLY AND COMPANY; *U.S. Public*, pg. 992
LUMEX MEDICAL PRODUCTS—Graham-Field Health Products, Inc.; *U.S. Public*, pg. 758
MSA (AUSTRALIA) PTY. LTD.—Mine Safety Appliances Co.; *U.S. Public*, pg. 1114
MSA CANADA, INC.—Mine Safety Appliances Co.; *U.S. Public*, pg. 1114
MSA DE FRANCE—Mine Safety Appliances Co.; *U.S. Public*, pg. 1114
MSA DO BRASIL, LTDA.—Mine Safety Appliances Co.; *U.S. Public*, pg. 1115
MSA ITALIANA S.P.A.—Mine Safety Appliances Co.; *U.S. Public*, pg. 1115
MADDAK INC.—Bel-Art Products; *U.S. Private*, pg. 130
MCGHAN LIMITED—Inamed Corporation; *U.S. Public*, pg. 874
MCQUAY INT'L—AAF McQuay, Inc.; *U.S. Private*, pg. 3
MEADOX MEDICALS, INC.—Boston Scientific Corp.; *U.S. Public*, pg. 247
MEDIA RECOVERY INTL.—Media Recovery, Inc.; *U.S. Private*, pg. 727
MEDICAL ACTION INDUSTRIES INC.; *U.S. Public*, pg. 1079
MEDICAL-SURGICAL DIVISION—3M; *U.S. Public*, pg. 1605
MEDLINE INDUSTRIES, INC.; *U.S. Private*, pg. 728
MEDTRONIC BIO-MEDICUS—Medtronic, Inc.; *U.S. Public*, pg. 1083
MEDTRONIC CARBON IMPLANTS, INC.—Medtronic, Inc.; *U.S. Public*, pg. 1083
MEDTRONIC HEART VALVE DIVISION—Medtronic, Inc.; *U.S. Public*, pg. 1083
MEDTRONIC, INC.; *U.S. Public*, pg. 1082
MEDTRONIC PROMEON—Medtronic, Inc.; *U.S. Public*, pg. 1083
MEDTRONICS INC.—Medtronic, Inc.; *U.S. Public*, pg. 1083
MEGAS BEAUTY CARE, INC.; *U.S. Private*, pg. 729
MENTOR CORPORATION; *U.S. Public*, pg. 1086
MENTOR UROLOGY, INC.—Mentor Corporation; *U.S. Public*, pg. 1086
MERIDIAN INDUSTRIES, INC.; *U.S. Private*, pg. 732
MINE SAFETY APPLIANCES CO.; *U.S. Public*, pg. 1114
NORTH SAFETY PRODUCTS—Siebe plc; *Int'l*, pg. 1243
NORTH SAFETY PRODUCTS, HEALTH CARE DIVISION—Siebe plc; *Int'l*, pg. 1243
NORTH SAFETY PRODUCTS, SAFETY EQUIPMENT DIVISION—Siebe plc; *Int'l*, pg. 1243
NUEAR ELECTRONICS—Starkey Laboratories, Inc.; *U.S. Private*, pg. 1035
NUTRAMAX PRODUCTS, INC.; *U.S. Public*, pg. 1206
OHMEDA BV—The BOC Group plc; *Int'l*, pg. 122
OHMEDA, INC.—The BOC Group plc; *Int'l*, pg. 121
OHMEDA LTD.—The BOC Group plc; *Int'l*, pg. 122
ORGANON TEKNIKA BV—Akzo Nobel N.V.; *Int'l*, pg. 44
ORGANON TEKNIKA IRELAND LTD.—Akzo Nobel N.V.; *Int'l*, pg. 45
ORGANON TEKNIKA MEDIZINSCHE PRODUKTE GMBH—Akzo Nobel N.V.; *Int'l*, pg. 45
ORGANON TEKNIKA NV—Akzo Nobel N.V.; *Int'l*, pg. 45
ORTHO BIOTECH INC.—Johnson & Johnson; *U.S. Public*, pg. 929
ORTHO-KINETICS, INC.; *U.S. Private*, pg. 820
ORTHOFIX INC.—Orthofix International N.V.; *Int'l*, pg. 1011
ORTHOFIX INTERNATIONAL N.V.; *Int'l*, pg. 1011
ORTHOPLANT GMBH—Bristol-Myers Squibb Company; *U.S. Public*, pg. 256
OSTEONICS CORP.—Stryker Corporation; *U.S. Public*, pg. 1526
OTO-SONIC, INC.—Beltone Electronics Corporation; *U.S. Private*, pg. 132
PENNY & GILES DRIVES TECHNOLOGY LTD.—Bowthorpe plc; *Int'l*, pg. 207
POLLENEX—The Rival Company; *U.S. Public*, pg. 1391
POLYMEDICA INDUSTRIES, INC.; *U.S. Public*, pg. 1315
POLYMER TECHNOLOGIES—Maclean-Fogg Co.; *U.S. Private*, pg. 692
PROPPER MANUFACTURING CO., INC.; *U.S. Private*, pg. 891
PROTEK GROUP—Sulzer Ltd.; *Int'l*, pg. 1307
PUERTO RICO SAFETY EQUIPMENT CORPORATION—Eastco Industrial Safety Corp.; *U.S. Public*, pg. 548
QUEST MEDICAL, INC.; *U.S. Public*, pg. 1352
RACAL ELECTRONICS PLC; *Int'l*, pg. 1082
RACAL HEALTH & SAFETY, INC.—Racal Electronics Plc; *Int'l*, pg. 1083
RACAL PROTECTION CANADA—Racal Electronics Plc; *Int'l*, pg. 1083
RESOUND CORPORATION; *U.S. Public*, pg. 1382
RESPIRONICS (HK), LTD.—Respironics, Inc.; *U.S. Public*, pg. 1383
RESPIRONICS, INC.; *U.S. Public*, pg. 1383
RUSCH—Teleflex Incorporated; *U.S. Public*, pg. 1569
S & G IMPLANTS GMBH—Bristol-Myers Squibb Company; *U.S. Public*, pg. 256
SLM IMMOBILIEN AG—Sulzer Ltd.; *Int'l*, pg. 1305
ST. JUDE MEDICAL, INC.; *U.S. Public*, pg. 1427
ST. JUDE MEDICAL LTD.—St. Jude Medical, Inc.; *U.S. Public*, pg. 1428
ST. JUDE PUERTO RICO, INC.—St. Jude Medical, Inc.; *U.S. Public*, pg. 1428
SCHERER HEALTHCARE, INC.; *U.S. Public*, pg. 1437
SCHERING-PLOUGH CORPORATION; *U.S. Public*, pg. 1438
SCHERING-PLOUGH HEALTHCARE PRODUCTS—Schering-Plough Corporation; *U.S. Public*, pg. 1438
SCHOLL (UK) LTD.—Schering-Plough Corporation; *U.S. Public*, pg. 1439
SCHOLL U.S.A.—Schering-Plough Corporation; *U.S. Public*, pg. 1438
SCOTT AVIATION—Figgie International Inc.; *U.S. Public*, pg. 622
SECHRIST INDUSTRIES, INC.; *U.S. Private*, pg. 980
SELLSTROM MANUFACTURING CO.; *U.S. Private*, pg. 983
SIEBE NORTH INC.—Siebe plc; *Int'l*, pg. 1242
SIMMONS JUVENILE PRODUCTS; *U.S. Private*, pg. 1001
SIOUX MANUFACTURING CORP.; *U.S. Private*, pg. 1003
SMITH & NEPHEW DONJOY INC.—Smith & Nephew PLC; *Int'l*, pg. 1263
SMITH & NEPHEW ENDOSCOPY—Smith & Nephew PLC; *Int'l*, pg. 1263
SMITH & NEPHEW MEDICAL LTD.—Smith & Nephew PLC; *Int'l*, pg. 1263
SMITH LABORATORIES, INC.—Columbia/HCA Healthcare Corporation; *U.S. Public*, pg. 405
SOFAMOR DANEK GROUP, INC.; *U.S. Public*, pg. 1482
SOLON MANUFACTURING COMPANY; *U.S. Private*, pg. 1013
SOPUR MEDIZINTECHNIK GMBH—Sunrise Medical, Inc.; *U.S. Public*, pg. 1536
SPAN-AMERICA MEDICAL SYSTEMS INC.; *U.S. Public*, pg. 1495
STARKEY LABORATORIES, INC.; *U.S. Private*, pg. 1035
STERIS CORPORATION; *U.S. Public*, pg. 1515
STRYKER CORPORATION; *U.S. Public*, pg. 1525
SULZERMEDICA GROUP—Sulzer Ltd.; *Int'l*, pg. 1307
SULZERMEDICA USA INC.—Sulzer Ltd.; *Int'l*, pg. 1307
SUNRISE MEDICAL, INC.; *U.S. Public*, pg. 1535
SUNRISE MEDICAL MOBILITY PRODUCTS—Sunrise Medical, Inc.; *U.S. Public*, pg. 1536
SUPERIOR SURGICAL MFG. CO., INC.; *U.S. Public*, pg. 1539
SURGICAL APPLIANCE INDUSTRIES, INC.; *U.S. Private*, pg. 1056
SURGITEK—Bristol-Myers Squibb Company; *U.S. Public*, pg. 253
SVENSKA CELLULOSA AKTIEBOLAGET (SCA); *Int'l*, pg. 1326
TALLERES URIBARRI, S.L.—Sunrise Medical, Inc.; *U.S. Public*, pg. 1536
AB TEGMA—Mine Safety Appliances Co.; *U.S. Public*, pg. 1114
TERUMO CORPORATION; *Int'l*, pg. 1375
THERADYNE CORPORATION—Kurt Manufacturing Co. Inc.; *U.S. Private*, pg. 637
THERAKOS, INC.—Johnson & Johnson; *U.S. Public*, pg. 929
THERMO CARDIOSYSTEMS INC.—Thermo Electron Corporation; *U.S. Public*, pg. 1592
THERMO ELECTRON CORPORATION; *U.S. Public*, pg. 1591
3M; *U.S. Public*, pg. 1604
TORAY INDUSTRIES, INC.; *Int'l*, pg. 1399
UNILAND MFG. CO., INC.—Lakeland Industries, Inc.; *U.S. Public*, pg. 975
U.S. SAFETY; *U.S. Private*, pg. 1125
VAXJO ROSTFRITT AB—Getinge Industrier AB; *Int'l*, pg. 551
VICKERS AIR-SHIELDS—Vickers PLC; *Int'l*, pg. 1467
WARSAW ORTHOPEDIC INC.—Sofamor Danek Group, Inc.; *U.S. Public*, pg. 1482
WHITEHALL MANUFACTURING INC.—Acorn Engineering Company; *U.S. Private*, pg. 14
WORMALD HOLDINGS N.Z. LIMITED—Tyco International Ltd.; *U.S. Public*, pg. 1651
WRIGHT MEDICAL TECHNOLOGY; *U.S. Private*, pg. 1192
XOMED SURGICAL PRODUCTS—Bristol-Myers Squibb Company; *U.S. Public*, pg. 253
ZIMMER AUSTRALIA PTY. LIMITED—Bristol-Myers Squibb Company; *U.S. Public*, pg. 256
ZIMMER, INC.—Bristol-Myers Squibb Company; *U.S. Public*, pg. 254
ZIMMER INTERNATIONAL, S.A.—Bristol-Myers Squibb Company; *U.S. Public*, pg. 257
ZIMMER LIMITED—Bristol-Myers Squibb Company; *U.S. Public*, pg. 257
ZIMMER NEW ZEALAND LIMITED—Bristol-Myers Squibb Company; *U.S. Public*, pg. 257
ZIMMER PATIENT CARE SYSTEMS DIVISION—Bristol-Myers Squibb Company; *U.S. Public*, pg. 254
ZIMMER PTE LTD.—Bristol-Myers Squibb Company; *U.S. Public*, pg. 257

3843 — DENTAL EQUIPMENT & SUPPLIES

A-DEC, INC.; *U.S. Private*, pg. 2
AD PLASTICS LTD.—Dentsply International Inc.; *U.S. Public*, pg. 499
ACME/CHASTON PUERTO RICO—GP Strategies Corporation; *U.S. Public*, pg. 694
AMERICAN DENTAL TECHNOLOGIES; *U.S. Public*, pg. 70
ASH INSTRUMENTS DIVISION, DENTSPLY LTD.—Dentsply International Inc.; *U.S. Public*, pg. 499
BARNHARDT MANUFACTURING CO.; *U.S. Private*, pg. 116
BAUSCH & LOMB INCORPORATED; *U.S. Public*, pg. 194
BAYER AG—Bayer AG; *Int'l*, pg. 172
BAYER CORPORATION/CONSUMER CARE DIVISION—Bayer AG; *Int'l*, pg. 173
BELMONT INDUSTRIES, INC.—RGP Holding, Inc.; *U.S. Private*, pg. 903
BLOCK DRUG COMPANY, INC.; *U.S. Public*, pg. 236
BLOCK DRUG CORPORATION DENTAL PRODUCTS CO.—Block Drug Company, Inc.; *U.S. Public*, pg. 237
CALCITEK, INC.—Sulzer Ltd.; *Int'l*, pg. 1307
CERADYNE, INC; *U.S. Public*, pg. 330
COLE HERSEE COMPANY; *U.S. Private*, pg. 251
CUSTOMEDIX CORPORATION; *U.S. Private*, pg. 298
DAB DENTAL AB—Axel Johnson AB; *Int'l*, pg. 708
DAB ORTODONTI AB—Axel Johnson AB; *Int'l*, pg. 711
DEGUSSA CORP., DENTAL DEPT.—Degussa AG; *Int'l*, pg. 388
DENTAL PRODUCTS DIVISION—3M; *U.S. Public*, pg. 1605
DENTSPLY CERAMCO—Dentsply International Inc.; *U.S. Public*, pg. 499
DENTSPLY GMBH—Dentsply International Inc.; *U.S. Public*, pg. 499
DENTSPLY/IMPLANT DIVISION—Dentsply International Inc.; *U.S. Public*, pg. 499
DENTSPLY INDIA—Dentsply International Inc.; *U.S. Public*, pg. 499
DENTSPLY INTERNATIONAL INC.; *U.S. Public*, pg. 498
DETREY/DENTSPLY S.R.L.—Dentsply International Inc.; *U.S. Public*, pg. 500
GETINGE INDUSTRIER AB; *Int'l*, pg. 551
HAWS DRINKING FAUCET CO.; *U.S. Private*, pg. 512
INTERDENTAL AB—Axel Johnson AB; *Int'l*, pg. 708
JENERIC/PENTRON CORP.—Customedix Corporation; *U.S. Private*, pg. 298
JOHNSON & JOHNSON CONSUMER PRODUCTS—Johnson & Johnson; *U.S. Public*, pg. 928
AXEL JOHNSON AB; *Int'l*, pg. 707
AXEL JOHNSON DENTAL AB—Axel Johnson AB; *Int'l*, pg. 709
AXEL JOHNSON INSTRUMENT AB—Axel Johnson AB; *Int'l*, pg. 709
L&R MANUFACTURING CO.; *U.S. Private*, pg. 638
L.A. GAUGE CO.—Triumph Group, Inc.; *U.S. Public*, pg. 1640
MIDWEST DENTAL—Dentsply International Inc.; *U.S. Public*, pg. 499
NEY DENTAL INTERNATIONAL—Degussa AG; *Int'l*, pg. 388
THE J.M. NEY COMPANY—Andersen Group, Inc.; *U.S. Public*, pg. 111
ORAL-B LABORATORIES—The Gillette Company; *U.S. Public*, pg. 743
PATTERSON DENTAL CANADA INC.—Patterson Dental Company; *U.S. Public*, pg. 1265
PATTERSON DENTAL COMPANY; *U.S. Public*, pg. 1265
PATTERSON DENTAL SUPPLY, INC.—Patterson Dental Company; *U.S. Public*, pg. 1265
RGP HOLDING, INC.; *U.S. Private*, pg. 903
RANIR CORPORATION/DCP; *U.S. Private*, pg. 909
RANSOM & RANDOLPH DIVISION—Dentsply International Inc.; *U.S. Public*, pg. 499
RINN CORPORATION—Dentsply International Inc.; *U.S. Public*, pg. 499
SIEMENS MEDICAL SYSTEMS, INC.—Siemens AG; *Int'l*, pg. 1246
SULZERMEDICA USA INC.—Sulzer Ltd.; *Int'l*, pg. 1307
SVENSKA DENTALINSTRUMENT AB—Axel Johnson AB; *Int'l*, pg. 709
SYBRON DENTAL SPECIALTIES, INC.—Sybron International Corporation; *U.S. Public*, pg. 1545
3M UNITEK CORPORATION—3M; *U.S. Public*, pg. 1606
VAXJO ROSTFRITT AB—Getinge Industrier AB; *Int'l*, pg. 551

3844 — X-RAY APPARATUS, TUBES & EQUIPMENT

ADAC LABORATORIES INC.; *U.S. Public*, pg. 3
AFP IMAGING CORPORATION; *U.S. Public*, pg. 6
AMERICAN SCIENCE & ENGINEERING, INC.; *U.S. Public*, pg. 90
AMRAY, INC.; *U.S. Private*, pg. 67
BLOCK DRUG CORPORATION DENTAL PRODUCTS CO.—Block Drug Company, Inc.; *U.S. Public*, pg. 237
CARBOMEDICS, INC.—Sulzer Ltd.; *Int'l*, pg. 1307
COMPUTERIZED MEDICAL SYSTEMS, INC.; *U.S. Private*, pg. 260
COSTAIN PROCESS INC.—Costain Group PLC; *Int'l*, pg. 337
DEL GLOBAL TECHNOLOGIES; *U.S. Public*, pg. 493
DELFT INSTRUMENTS FAR EAST, LTD.—Delft Instruments N.V.; *Int'l*, pg. 389
DENTSPLY GENDEX DIVISION—Dentsply International Inc.; *U.S. Public*, pg. 499
EG & G ASTROPHYSICS—EG & G, Inc.; *U.S. Public*, pg. 543
EG & G HEIMANN OPTO. GMBH—EG & G, Inc.; *U.S. Public*, pg. 544
ELBIT LTD.—IDB Holding Corporation; *Int'l*, pg. 644
ELSCINT INC.—Elscint Ltd.; *Int'l*, pg. 450
ELSCINT LTD.; *Int'l*, pg. 450
ENRAF-NONIUS GMBH—Delft Instruments N.V.; *Int'l*, pg. 389

ENRAF-NONIUS LTD.—Delft Instruments N.V.; *Int'l*, pg. 389
FISCHER IMAGING AUSTRALIA PTY, LTD.—Fischer Imaging Corporation; *U.S. Public*, pg. 647
FISCHER IMAGING CORPORATION; *U.S. Public*, pg. 647
FISCHER IMAGING CORPORATION, RMS MANUFACTURING DIVISION—Fischer Imaging Corporation; *U.S. Public*, pg. 647
FISCHER IMAGING EUROPE—Fischer Imaging Corporation; *U.S. Public*, pg. 647
ABDULLA FOUAD-TESTRADE MIDDLE EAST—Abdulla Fouad Co. Ltd.; *Int'l*, pg. 502
GENDEX-DEL MEDICAL IMAGING CORP.—Del Global Technologies; *U.S. Public*, pg. 494
HITACHI MEDICAL CORPORATION—Hitachi, Ltd.; *Int'l*, pg. 621
HOLOGIC, INC.; *U.S. Public*, pg. 831
KEVEX INSTRUMENTS—Thermo Electron Corporation; *U.S. Public*, pg. 1594
KEVEX X-RAY—Thermo Electron Corporation; *U.S. Public*, pg. 1594
LUMENX COMPANY—Alltrista Corporation; *U.S. Public*, pg. 56
MEDI-LAB A/S—Roche Holding Ltd.; *Int'l*, pg. 1121
MEDICAL IMAGING SYSTEMS LIMITED—Halma p.l.c.; *Int'l*, pg. 589
MERIDIAN MEDICAL TECHNOLOGY, INC.; *U.S. Public*, pg. 1095
NICOLET TEST & MEASUREMENT DIVISION—Thermo Electron Corporation; *U.S. Public*, pg. 1593
NIHON MEDI-PHYSICS COMPANY LIMITED—Roche Holding Ltd.; *Int'l*, pg. 1121
NONIUS BV—Delft Instruments N.V.; *Int'l*, pg. 389
OEC MEDICAL SYSTEMS, INC.; *U.S. Public*, pg. 1207
OLDELFT B.V.—Delft Instruments N.V.; *Int'l*, pg. 389
OLDELFT CORP. OF AMERICA—Delft Instruments N.V.; *Int'l*, pg. 389
OLDELFT INTERNATIONAL TRADING CY. N.V.—Delft Instruments N.V.; *Int'l*, pg. 389
PICKER INTERNATIONAL GMBH—The General Electric Company, p.l.c.; *Int'l*, pg. 545
PICKER INTERNATIONAL, INC.—The General Electric Company, p.l.c.; *Int'l*, pg. 545
SCITEC CORPORATION—Andros Incorporated; *U.S. Private*, pg. 74
SHIMADZU CORPORATION; *Int'l*, pg. 1232
SONOTRON HOLDING AG—IDB Holding Corporation; *Int'l*, *pg. 644*
SPECTRONICS CORPORATION; *U.S. Private*, pg. 1024
3M; *U.S. Public*, pg. 1604
TOSHIBA MEDICAL SYSTEMS GMBH—Toshiba Corporation; *Int'l*, pg. 1407
TREX MEDICAL CORPORATION—Thermo Electron Corporation; *U.S. Public*, pg. 1595
II-VI INCORPORATED; *U.S. Public*, pg. 1647
VG INSTRUMENTS PLC—Thermo Electron Corporation; *U.S. Public*, pg. 1595
VARIAN ASSOCIATES, INC.; *U.S. Public*, pg. 1710
VINGMED SOUND A/S—IDB Holding Corporation; *Int'l*, pg. 644
XEROX MEDICAL SYSTEMS—Xerox Corporation; *U.S. Public*, pg. 1784

3845 — ELECTROMEDICAL & ELECTROTHERAPEUTIC APPARATUS

ADAC LABORATORIES INC.; *U.S. Public*, pg. 3
ATL ECHO ULTRASOUND—ATL Ultrasound, Inc.; *U.S. Public*, pg. 12
ATL ULTRASOUND, INC.; *U.S. Public*, pg. 11
ACUSON AB—Acuson Corporation; *U.S. Public*, pg. 18
ACUSON CORPORATION; *U.S. Public*, pg. 18
ACUSON LTD.—Acuson Corporation; *U.S. Public*, pg. 18
AIR-SHIELDS INC.—Vickers PLC; *Int'l*, pg. 1468
AKZO NOBEL INC.—Akzo Nobel N.V.; *Int'l*, pg. 47
AMERICAN HOME PRODUCTS CORPORATION; *U.S. Public*, pg. 79
ANALOGIC CORPORATION; *U.S. Public*, pg. 109
ANALOGIC SCIENTIFIC—Analogic Corporation; *U.S. Public*, *pg. 109*
APPLIED SUPER CONETICS, INC.—Toshiba Corporation; *Int'l*, pg. 1405
ASCOM HOLDING AG; *Int'l*, pg. 86
ASIA ELECTRONICS INC.—Toshiba Corporation; *Int'l*, pg. 1402
AUTOMATIC LIQUID PACKAGING, INC.; *U.S. Private*, pg. 101
BOC OHMEDA AB—The BOC Group plc; *Int'l*, pg. 122
BOC OHMEDA OY—The BOC Group plc; *Int'l*, pg. 122
BEHRINGWERKE AG—Hoechst Aktiengesellschaft; *Int'l*, pg. 624
BIO LOGIC SYSTEMS CORP.; *U.S. Public*, pg. 230
BIOMET DEUTSCHLAND GMBH—Biomet, Inc.; *U.S. Public*, *pg. 232*
BIOMET, INC.; *U.S. Public*, pg. 231
BIOMET LTD.—Biomet, Inc.; *U.S. Public*, pg. 232
BIOMET SPA—Biomet, Inc.; *U.S. Public*, pg. 232
BIOSOL S.P.A.—Incentive AB; *Int'l*, pg. 667
BRANSON ULTRASONICS—Emerson Electric Co.; *U.S. Public*, pg. 574
BRANSON ULTRASONICS CORP. - PRECISION CLEANING DIV.—Emerson Electric Co.; *U.S. Public*, pg. 574
BRISTOL-MYERS SQUIBB COMPANY; *U.S. Public*, pg. 253
BURDICK, INC.; *U.S. Private*, pg. 181
CAIRE, INC.—Minnesota Valley Engineering/Cryogenic Association; *U.S. Private*, pg. 751
CAMTRONICS LTD.—Analogic Corporation; *U.S. Public*, pg. 109
CANDELA CORPORATION; *U.S. Public*, pg. 300
CAPRIUS, INC.; *U.S. Public*, pg. 303
CARDIORHYTHM—Medtronic, Inc.; *U.S. Public*, pg. 1083
CIBA SPECIALTY CHEMICALS—Ciba Specialty Chemicals Holding Inc.; *Int'l*, pg. 291
CIRCON ACMI—Circon Corporation; *U.S. Public*, pg. 373
CIRCON CORPORATION; *U.S. Public*, pg. 373
CIRCON GMBH—Circon Corporation; *U.S. Public*, pg. 374
CIRCON VIDEO DIV.—Circon Corporation; *U.S. Public*, pg. 373
COBE LABORATORIES, INC.—Incentive AB; *Int'l*, pg. 667
COHERENT GMBH—Coherent, Inc.; *U.S. Public*, pg. 395
COHERENT, INC.; *U.S. Public*, pg. 395
COHERENT, INC.-MEDICAL GROUP—Coherent, Inc.; *U.S. Public*, pg. 395
COHERENT PACIFIC—Coherent, Inc.; *U.S. Public*, pg. 396
COHERENT S.A.—Coherent, Inc.; *U.S. Public*, pg. 396
COHERENT (U.K.) LTD.—Coherent, Inc.; *U.S. Public*, pg. 396
COLORADO MEDTECH, INC.; *U.S. Public*, pg. 401
CONMED CORPORATION; *U.S. Public*, pg. 431
CONTROL LASER CORPORATION—Excel Technology, Inc.; *U.S. Public*, pg. 599
DAIG CORPORATION—St. Jude Medical, Inc.; *U.S. Public*, pg. 1428
DATASCOPE PATIENT MONITORING DIVISION—Datascope Corp.; *U.S. Public*, pg. 487
DEL MAR AVIONICS; *U.S. Private*, pg. 321
DIASONICS ULTRA SOUND, INC.—IDB Holding Corporation; *Int'l*, pg. 644
DU PONT NDT SYSTEMS—Du Pont (E.I. Du Pont De Nemours & Co.); *U.S. Public*, pg. 531
DYNAMICS CORPORATION OF AMERICA—CTS Corporation; *U.S. Public*, pg. 286
DYNEX TECHNOLOGIES—Thermo Electron Corporation; *U.S. Public*, pg. 1591
E FOR M CORP.—Marquette Medical Systems, Inc.; *U.S. Public*, pg. 1047
EBI MEDICAL SYSTEMS, INC.—Biomet, Inc.; *U.S. Public*, pg. 231
EG & G INSTRUMENTS APPLIED RESEARCH—EG & G, Inc.; *U.S. Public*, pg. 543
EMPI, INC.; *U.S. Public*, pg. 545
ELBIT LTD.—IDB Holding Corporation; *Int'l*, pg. 644
ELECTRO-BIOLOGY, INC.—Biomet, Inc.; *U.S. Public*, pg. 231
ENDO-SERVICES S.A.R.L.—Olympus Optical Co., Ltd.; *Int'l*, *pg. 1005*
EXCEL TECHNOLOGY, INC.; *U.S. Public*, pg. 599
EXCORIM AB—Incentive AB; *Int'l*, pg. 667
FONAR CORPORATION; *U.S. Public*, pg. 661
G.E. MEDICAL SYSTEMS—General Electric Company; *U.S. Public*, pg. 710
GP STRATEGIES CORPORATION; *U.S. Public*, pg. 694
GAMBRO AB—Incentive AB; *Int'l*, pg. 666
GAMBRO AG—Incentive AB; *Int'l*, pg. 667
GAMBRO A/S—Incentive AB; *Int'l*, pg. 667
GAMBRO B.V.—Incentive AB; *Int'l*, pg. 667
GAMBRO DIALYSATOREN GMBH & CO KG—Incentive AB; *Int'l*, pg. 667
GAMBRO ENGSTROM AB—Incentive AB; *Int'l*, pg. 667
GAMBRO K.K.—Incentive AB; *Int'l*, pg. 668
GAMBRO LTD.—Incentive AB; *Int'l*, pg. 668
GAMBRO MEDICAL K.K.—Incentive AB; *Int'l*, pg. 668
GAMBRO N.V./S.A.—Incentive AB; *Int'l*, pg. 668
GAMBRO PTY LTD.—Incentive AB; *Int'l*, pg. 668
GAMBRO S.A.—Incentive AB; *Int'l*, pg. 668
GAMBRO SALES AB—Incentive AB; *Int'l*, pg. 668
GAMBRO S.P.A.—Incentive AB; *Int'l*, pg. 668
GAMBRO VERTRIEBSGESELLSCHAFT M.B.H.—Incentive AB; *Int'l*, pg. 668
GENERAL ELECTRIC COMPANY; *U.S. Public*, pg. 709
GETINGE/CASTLE INC.—Getinge Industrier AB; *Int'l*, pg. 551
GUIDANT CORPORATION-CARDIAC RHYTHM MANAGEMENT GROUP—Guidant Corporation; *U.S. Public*, pg. 768
HEWLETT-PACKARD COMPANY; *U.S. Public*, pg. 813
HITACHI MEDICAL CORPORATION—Hitachi, Ltd.; *Int'l*, pg. 621
HOGAMED S.A.—Incentive AB; *Int'l*, pg. 668
HOSPAL B.V.—Incentive AB; *Int'l*, pg. 668
HOSPAL-COBE RENAL N.V.—Incentive AB; *Int'l*, pg. 668
HOSPAL DASCO S.P.A.—Incentive AB; *Int'l*, pg. 668
HOSPAL-GAMBRO LIMITEE—Incentive AB; *Int'l*, pg. 668
HOSPAL INDUSTRIE S.A.—Incentive AB; *Int'l*, pg. 668
HOSPAL LTD.—Incentive AB; *Int'l*, pg. 668
HOSPAL MED TECH GMBH—Incentive AB; *Int'l*, pg. 668
HOSPAL S.A.—Incentive AB; *Int'l*, pg. 668
HOSPAL S.P.A.—Incentive AB; *Int'l*, pg. 668
INTERCARE TECHNOLOGIES, INC.—Criticare Systems, Inc.; *U.S. Public*, pg. 459
INTERMAGNETICS GENERAL CORPORATION; *U.S. Public*, pg. 893
INTERTRON—Standex International Corporation; *U.S. Public*, pg. 1507
JOHNSON & JOHNSON (EGYPT) S.A.E.—Johnson & Johnson; *U.S. Public*, pg. 930
P.T. JOHNSON & JOHNSON INDONESIA—Johnson & Johnson; *U.S. Public*, pg. 930
KODAK CLINICAL PRODUCTS DIVISION—Eastman Kodak Company; *U.S. Public*, pg. 551
KRUPP HOESCH STAHL UND METALL GMBH—Fried. Krupp AG; *Int'l*, pg. 514
KRUPP HOESCH STAHLEXPORT GMBH—Fried. Krupp AG; *Int'l*, pg. 515
LAMBDA PHYSIK—Coherent, Inc.; *U.S. Public*, pg. 395
LAMBDA PHYSIK GMBH—Coherent, Inc.; *U.S. Public*, pg. 396
LAMBDA PHYSIK JAPAN CO., LTD.—Coherent, Inc.; *U.S. Public*, pg. 396
LASAG AG—SMH Swiss Corporation for Micro Electronics & Watchmaking Indus. Ltd.; *Int'l*, pg. 1161
LASERSCOPE SURGICAL SYSTEMS; *U.S. Public*, pg. 979
LICAN MEDICAL PRODUCTS LTD.—Circon Corporation; *U.S. Public*, pg. 374
LIFESCAN CANADA LTD.—Johnson & Johnson; *U.S. Public*, pg. 931
ELI LILLY AND COMPANY; *U.S. Public*, pg. 992
LITTON INDUSTRIES, INC.; *U.S. Public*, pg. 1002
L'OREAL S.A.; *Int'l*, pg. 818
MTN MEDIZINTECHNIK NEUBRANDENBURG GMBH I.G.—Incentive AB; *Int'l*, pg. 669
MARQUETTE MEDICAL SYSTEMS, INC.; *U.S. Public*, pg. 1047
MAXWELL TECHNOLOGIES, INC.; *U.S. Public*, pg. 1061
MEDELEC LIMITED—Vickers PLC; *Int'l*, pg. 1467
MEDEX INC.—Furon Company; *U.S. Public*, pg. 689
MEDICAL DATA INTELLIGENCE AB—Incentive AB; *Int'l*, pg. 667
MEDICAL-SURGICAL DIVISION—3M; *U.S. Public*, pg. 1605
MEDICORE INC.; *U.S. Public*, pg. 1080
MEDSTONE INTERNATIONAL, INC.; *U.S. Public*, pg. 1082
MEDTRONIC BIO-MEDICUS—Medtronic, Inc.; *U.S. Public*, pg. 1083
MEDTRONIC, INC.; *U.S. Public*, pg. 1082
MEDTRONIC INTERVENTIONAL VASCULAR—Medtronic, Inc.; *U.S. Public*, pg. 1083
MEDTRONIC MILACA, INC.—Medtronic, Inc.; *U.S. Public*, pg. 1083
MEDTRONIC NEUROLOGICAL DIV.—Medtronic, Inc.; *U.S. Public*, pg. 1083
MEDTRONIC OF CANADA—Medtronic, Inc.; *U.S. Public*, pg. 1084
MEDTRONICS INC.—Medtronic, Inc.; *U.S. Public*, pg. 1083
MENNEN MEDICAL INC.—Mennen Medical Ltd.; *Int'l*, pg. 858
MESA LABORATORIES, INC.; *U.S. Public*, pg. 1099
MINNESOTA VALLEY ENGINEERING/CRYOGENIC ASSOCIATION; *U.S. Private*, pg. 751
NELLCOR DE MEXICO, S.A. DE C.V.—Mallinckrodt Inc.; *U.S. Public*, pg. 1040
NELLCOR PURITAN BENNETT BELGIUM N.V./S.A.—Mallinckrodt Inc.; *U.S. Public*, pg. 1040
NELLCOR PURITAN BENNETT INCORPORATED—Mallinckrodt Inc.; *U.S. Public*, pg. 1039
NOVEL BIOMEDICAL—Colorado MEDtech, Inc.; *U.S. Public*, pg. 401
OHMEDA LTD.—The BOC Group plc; *Int'l*, pg. 121
OLDELFT B.V.—Delft Instruments N.V.; *Int'l*, pg. 389
OLYMPUS DIAGNOSTICA GMBH—Olympus Optical Co., Ltd.; *Int'l*, pg. 1005
OLYMPUS OPTICAL CO., LTD.; *Int'l*, pg. 1004
ONCOLOGY SYSTEMS—Varian Associates, Inc.; *U.S. Public*, pg. 1710
OSTBY & BARTON CO.—Everett Charles Technologies; *U.S. Private*, pg. 386
PACING BUSINESS UNIT—Medtronic, Inc.; *U.S. Public*, pg. 1083
PALL BIOMEDICAL PUERTO RICO—Pall Corporation; *U.S. Public*, pg. 1254
PALL EUROPE LTD.—Pall Corporation; *U.S. Public*, pg. 1254
PALOMAR MEDICAL TECHNOLOGIES; *U.S. Public*, pg. 1255
PHARMACIA & UPJOHN, INC.; *Int'l*, pg. 1047
PHILIPS MEDICAL SYSTEMS NORTH AMERICA COMPANY—Philips Electronics N.V.; *Int'l*, pg. 1055
PHYSIO-CONTROL CORPORATION; *U.S. Public*, pg. 1294
PHYSIO-CONTROL S.A.R.L.—Physio-Control Corporation; *U.S. Public*, pg. 1294
PICKER INTERNATIONAL, INC.—The General Electric Company, p.l.c.; *Int'l*, pg. 545
PILKINGTON PLC; *Int'l*, pg. 1056
QC OPTICS, INC.; *U.S. Public*, pg. 1345
RADIOMETER AMERICA INC.—Radiometer A/S; *Int'l*, pg. 1083
RADIOMETER ANALYTICAL S.A.—Radiometer A/S; *Int'l*, pg. 1084
RESPIRONICS (HK), LTD.—Respironics, Inc.; *U.S. Public*, pg. 1383
RESPIRONICS, INC.; *U.S. Public*, pg. 1383
ST. JUDE MEDICAL, INC.; *U.S. Public*, pg. 1427
SHIMADZU SCIENTIFIC INSTRUMENTS, INC.—Shimadzu Corporation; *Int'l*, pg. 1232
SIEMENS AG; *Int'l*, pg. 1244
SIEMENS-ELEMA AB—Siemens AG; *Int'l*, pg. 1247
SIEMENS PAKISTAN ENGINEERING CO. LTD.—Siemens AG; *Int'l*, pg. 1247
SIEMENS S.A.—Siemens AG; *Int'l*, pg. 1248
STANDEX INTERNATIONAL CORPORATION; *U.S. Public*, *pg. 1505*
STAODYN INC.; *U.S. Public*, pg. 1509
SULZERMEDICA USA INC.—Sulzer Ltd.; *Int'l*, pg. 1307
SUMMIT TECHNOLOGY, INC.; *U.S. Public*, pg. 1528
SUMMIT TECHNOLOGY IRELAND—Summit Technology, Inc.; *U.S. Public*, pg. 1529
SUNRISE MEDICAL RESPIRATORY PRODUCTS DIVISION—Sunrise Medical, Inc.; *U.S. Public*, pg. 1530
SURGICAL LASER TECHNOLOGIES, INC.; *U.S. Public*, pg. 1542
SVENSKA BOC AB—The BOC Group plc; *Int'l*, pg. 122
TELEFLEX INCORPORATED; *U.S. Public*, pg. 1569
TELESENSORY CORPORATION; *U.S. Private*, pg. 1074
THERMEDICS INC.—Thermo Electron Corporation; *U.S. Public*, pg. 1592
THERMOTREX—Thermo Electron Corporation; *U.S. Public*, *pg. 1595*
3M; *U.S. Public*, pg. 1604
TOSHIBA AMERICA MRI INC.—Toshiba Corporation; *Int'l*, pg. 1405
ULTRA ELECTRONICS MAGNETICS—Ultra Electronics Holdings plc; *Int'l*, pg. 1431
VERNAY LABORATORIES, INC.; *U.S. Private*, pg. 1137
VICKERS AIR-SHIELDS—Vickers PLC; *Int'l*, pg. 1467
VICKERS PLC; *Int'l*, pg. 1466
VITAL SIGNS MN, INC.—Vital Signs, Inc.; *U.S. Public*, pg. 1723
WALKER MAGNETICS GROUP, INC.; *U.S. Private*, pg. 1147

WATERS INSTRUMENTS, INC.; *U.S. Public*, pg. 1745
XEROX MEDICAL SYSTEMS—Xerox Corporation; *U.S. Public*, pg. 1784
XEROX SPECIAL MARKETS GROUP—Xerox Corporation; *U.S. Public*, pg. 1785

3851 — OPHTHALMIC GOODS

ACME/CHASTON PUERTO RICO—GP Strategies Corporation; *U.S. Public*, pg. 694
AKORN MANUFACTURING, INC.—Akorn, Inc.; *U.S. Public*, pg. 34
ALCON LABORATORIES, INC.—Nestle S.A.; *Int'l*, pg. 916
ALCON PHARMA GMBH—Nestle S.A.; *Int'l*, pg. 918
ALCON PHARMACEUTICALS LTD.—Nestle S.A.; *Int'l*, pg. 916
ALLERGAN INC.—Allergan, Inc.; *U.S. Public*, pg. 46
AMERICAN ALLSAFE CO.—NCH Corporation; *U.S. Public*, pg. 1145
AMERICAN OPTICAL CORPORATION; *U.S. Private*, pg. 60
AVANT GARDE OPTICS INC.—Luxottica Group S.p.A.; *Int'l*, pg. 822
BEC GROUP, INC.; *U.S. Public*, pg. 160
BL INDUSTRIA OTICA, LTDA.—Bausch & Lomb Incorporated; *U.S. Public*, pg. 195
BMC INDUSTRIES, INC.; *U.S. Public*, pg. 162
BATAAN OPTICAL INC.—Essilor International Compagnie Generale d'Optique; *Int'l*, pg. 462
BAUSCH & LOMB INC.—Bausch & Lomb Incorporated; *U.S. Public*, pg. 194
BAUSCH & LOMB CONTACT LENS DIVISION-FL—Bausch & Lomb Incorporated; *U.S. Public*, pg. 194
BAUSCH & LOMB EYEWEAR DIVISION-MD—Bausch & Lomb Incorporated; *U.S. Public*, pg. 194
BAUSCH & LOMB EYEWEAR DIVISION-TX—Bausch & Lomb Incorporated; *U.S. Public*, pg. 194
BAUSCH & LOMB INCORPORATED; *U.S. Public*, pg. 194
BAUSCH & LOMB OPTICARE, INC.—Bausch & Lomb Incorporated; *U.S. Public*, pg. 194
BAUSCH & LOMB PERSONAL PRODUCTS DIVISION-SC—Bausch & Lomb Incorporated; *U.S. Public*, pg. 194
BAUSCH & LOMB PUERTO RICO, INC.—Bausch & Lomb Incorporated; *U.S. Public*, pg. 194
H.L. BOUTON COMPANY INC.; *U.S. Private*, pg. 162
CHIRON VISION—Chiron Corporation; *U.S. Public*, pg. 350
CIBA-GEIGY ARGENTINA S.A.I.C. Y F.—Novartis AG; *Int'l*, pg. 976
CIBA-GEIGY KOREA LTD.—Novartis AG; *Int'l*, pg. 977
CIBA-GEIGY PHARMACEUTICALS—Novartis AG; *Int'l*, pg. 978
CIBA SPECIALTY CHEMICALS—Ciba Specialty Chemicals Holding Inc.; *Int'l*, pg. 291
CIBA VISION—Novartis AG; *Int'l*, pg. 981
CIBA VISION AB—Novartis AG; *Int'l*, pg. 981
CIBA VISION AG—Novartis AG; *Int'l*, pg. 972
CIBA VISION AUSTRALIA PTY LIMITED—Novartis AG; *Int'l*, pg. 981
CIBA VISION AUSTRIA—Novartis AG; *Int'l*, pg. 981
S.A. CIBA VISION BENELUX NV—Novartis AG; *Int'l*, pg. 981
CIBA VISION CARE AUSTRALIA—Novartis AG; *Int'l*, pg. 981
CIBA-VISION CORPORATION—Novartis AG; *Int'l*, pg. 973
CIBA VISION DANMARK A/S—Novartis AG; *Int'l*, pg. 981
CIBA VISION FINLAND OY—Novartis AG; *Int'l*, pg. 981
CIBA VISION GMBH—Novartis AG; *Int'l*, pg. 981
CIBA VISION HOLDING AG—Novartis AG; *Int'l*, pg. 972
CIBA VISION KONTAKTLINSEN-PFLEGEMITTEL GMBH—Novartis AG; *Int'l*, pg. 981
CIBA VISION LENS CARE PRODUCTION LTD.—Novartis AG; *Int'l*, pg. 981
CIBA VISION MALAYSIA—Novartis AG; *Int'l*, pg. 981
CIBA VISION MANAGEMENT AG—Novartis AG; *Int'l*, pg. 972
CIBA VISION MANAGEMENT INC.—Novartis AG; *Int'l*, pg. 981
CIBA VISION NORGE A/S—Novartis AG; *Int'l*, pg. 981
CIBA VISION OPHTHALMICS—Novartis AG; *Int'l*, pg. 981
CIBA VISION S.A.—Novartis AG; *Int'l*, pg. 981
CIBA VISION (SINGAPORE) PTE LTD—Novartis AG; *Int'l*, pg. 981
CIBA VISION SRL—Novartis AG; *Int'l*, pg. 981
CIBA VISION STERILE MANUFACTURING LTD.—Novartis AG; *Int'l*, pg. 981
CIBA VISION TAIWAN CO LTD—Novartis AG; *Int'l*, pg. 981
CIBA VISION VERTRIEBS GMBH—Novartis AG; *Int'l*, pg. 981
THE COOPER COMPANIES, INC.; *U.S. Public*, pg. 442
CORNEALENT WAICON DE BRASIL INDUSTRIA E COMERCIO LTDA.—Bausch & Lomb Incorporated; *U.S. Public*, pg. 195
DELFT INSTRUMENTS N.V.; *Int'l*, pg. 388
DISPERSA AG—Novartis AG; *Int'l*, pg. 972
DISPERSA GMBH—Novartis AG; *Int'l*, pg. 982
DOLLAND & AITCHISON LTD.; *Int'l*, pg. 414
DOLLAND & AITCHISON - SOUTH EAST (LONDON) LTD.—Dolland & Aitchison Ltd.; *Int'l*, pg. 414
DOMILENZ—Essilor International Compagnie Generale d'Optique; *Int'l*, pg. 462
EASTCO INDUSTRIAL SAFETY CORP.; *U.S. Public*, pg. 548
ESSILOR INTERNATIONAL COMPAGNIE GENERALE D'OPTIQUE; *Int'l*, pg. 462
EYECARE (THAILAND) LIMITED—Novartis AG; *Int'l*, pg. 982
40 FORT EYE ASSOCIATES; *U.S. Private*, pg. 420
GENTEX CORPORATION; *U.S. Public*, pg. 731
GENTEX OPTICS, INC.—Essilor International Compagnie Generale d'Optique; *Int'l*, pg. 462
HAMBLIN CONTACT LENSES—Dolland & Aitchison Ltd.; *Int'l*, pg. 414
THE HILSINGER CO. L.P.; *U.S. Private*, pg. 530
INTERNATIONALE GAS APPARATUR A/S—Ruhrgas Aktiengesellschaft; *Int'l*, pg. 1149
JOHNSON & JOHNSON; *U.S. Public*, pg. 927
L-ZOS OPTICS, LTD.; *U.S. Private*, pg. 639
LA MECCANOPTICA LEONARDO S.P.A.—Luxottica Group S.p.A.; *Int'l*, pg. 822
LASERSIGHT INC.; *U.S. Public*, pg. 979
LOGO OF THE AMERICAS—Essilor International Compagnie Generale d'Optique; *Int'l*, pg. 462
LUXOTTICA BELGIUM N.V.—Luxottica Group S.p.A.; *Int'l*, pg. 822
LUXOTTICA CANADA INC.—Luxottica Group S.p.A.; *Int'l*, pg. 822
LUXOTTICA DO BRASIL LTDA.—Luxottica Group S.p.A.; *Int'l*, pg. 822
LUXOTTICA FASHION BRILLEN GMBH—Luxottica Group S.p.A.; *Int'l*, pg. 822
OY LUXOTTICA FINLAND AB—Luxottica Group S.p.A.; *Int'l*, pg. 822
LUXOTTICA FRANCE S.A.R.L.—Luxottica Group S.p.A.; *Int'l*, pg. 822
LUXOTTICA GROUP S.P.A.; *Int'l*, pg. 822
LUXOTTICA HELLAS AE—Luxottica Group S.p.A.; *Int'l*, pg. 822
LUXOTTICA IBERICA S.A.—Luxottica Group S.p.A.; *Int'l*, pg. 822
LUXOTTICA NEDERLAND B.V.—Luxottica Group S.p.A.; *Int'l*, pg. 822
LUXOTTICA PORTUGAL S.A.—Luxottica Group S.p.A.; *Int'l*, pg. 822
LUXOTTICA SWEDEN A.B.—Luxottica Group S.p.A.; *Int'l*, pg. 822
LUXOTTICA U.K. LTD.—Luxottica Group S.p.A.; *Int'l*, pg. 822
LUXOTTICA VERTRIEBSGESELLSHAFT MBH—Luxottica Group S.p.A.; *Int'l*, pg. 822
MXL INDUSTRIES, INC.—GP Strategies Corporation; *U.S. Public*, pg. 694
MADDEN & LAYMAN LIMITED—Bausch & Lomb Incorporated; *U.S. Public*, pg. 196
MARCHON EYEWEAR; *U.S. Private*, pg. 702
THE MARYLEBONE OPTICAL CO. LTD.—Dolland & Aitchison Ltd.; *Int'l*, pg. 414
MIRARI JAPAN LTD.—Luxottica Group S.p.A.; *Int'l*, pg. 822
MOVADO GROUP, INC.; *U.S. Public*, pg. 1140
NPDC-AS101, INC.—GP Strategies Corporation; *U.S. Public*, pg. 694
NIKON CORPORATION; *Int'l*, pg. 931
NOVARTIS—Novartis AG; *Int'l*, pg. 972
OPTICOS S.R.L.; *Int'l*, pg. 1007
OPTIMA INDUSTRIAL S.A. DE C.V.—Bausch & Lomb Incorporated; *U.S. Public*, pg. 196
OPTIMAXX INTERNATIONAL; *U.S. Private*, pg. 818
OPTISCHE WERKE G. RODENSTOCK; *Int'l*, pg. 1007
OUTLOOK EYEWEAR COMPANY—Bausch & Lomb Incorporated; *U.S. Public*, pg. 195
PHARM-ALLERGAN GMBH—Allergan, Inc.; *U.S. Public*, pg. 46
PHARMACIA & UPJOHN OPHTHALMICS—Pharmacia & Upjohn, Inc.; *Int'l*, pg. 1048
PILKINGTON PLC; *Int'l*, pg. 1056
POLYMER TECHNOLOGY CORPORATION—Bausch & Lomb Incorporated; *U.S. Public*, pg. 195
REVO, INC.—Bausch & Lomb Incorporated; *U.S. Public*, pg. 195
RICKY CONTACT LENS INC.—Novartis AG; *Int'l*, pg. 984
ROUSSEL UCLAF S.A.—Hoechst Aktiengesellschaft; *Int'l*, pg. 626
SCHERING-PLOUGH CORPORATION; *U.S. Public*, pg. 1438
SEIKO EPSON CORPORATION; *Int'l*, pg. 1219
SELLSTROM MANUFACTURING CO.; *U.S. Private*, pg. 983
SIGNATURE EYEWEAR, INC.; *U.S. Public*, pg. 1473
SILOR OPTICAL OF FLORIDA—Essilor International Compagnie Generale d'Optique; *Int'l*, pg. 462
STORZ INSTRUMENT CO.—American Home Products Corporation; *U.S. Public*, pg. 79
SUNSOFT CORPORATION—Essilor International Compagnie Generale d'Optique; *Int'l*, pg. 462
SWIFT INSTRUMENTS, INC.; *U.S. Private*, pg. 1058
SWISSCOLOR—Novartis AG; *Int'l*, pg. 986
THIN FILM TECHNOLOGY DIVISION—Bausch & Lomb Incorporated; *U.S. Public*, pg. 194
TORAY INDUSTRIES, INC.; *Int'l*, pg. 1399
UNION MEDICAL SUPPLY COMPANY—Novartis AG; *Int'l*, pg. 986
U.S. SAFETY; *U.S. Private*, pg. 1125
UVEX SAFETY, INC.—Bacou S.A.; *Int'l*, pg. 132
VISION-EASE LENS—BMC Industries, Inc.; *U.S. Public*, pg. 162
VISION-EASE LENS INC.—BMC Industries, Inc.; *U.S. Public*, pg. 162
VISTAKON JOHNSON & JOHNSON VISION PRODUCTS, INC.—Johnson & Johnson; *U.S. Public*, pg. 929
WGM SAFETY CORPORATION—Essilor International Compagnie Generale d'Optique; *Int'l*, pg. 462
WALMAN OPTICAL COMPANY; *U.S. Private*, pg. 1148
WESLEY-JESSEN—Bain Capital; *U.S. Private*, pg. 111
CARL ZEISS—Carl-Zeiss-Stiftung; *Int'l*, pg. 1522

3861 — PHOTOGRAPHIC EQUIPMENT & SUPPLIES

AFP IMAGING CORPORATION; *U.S. Public*, pg. 6
AIC INTERNATIONAL, INC.; *U.S. Private*, pg. 6
AMP INC. FLEXIBLE FILM SENSORS—AMP Incorporated; *U.S. Public*, pg. 7
ADEMCO LTD.—Hunt Corporation; *U.S. Public*, pg. 849
AGFA AG—Bayer AG; *Int'l*, pg. 172
AGFA EPS DIVISION—Bayer AG; *Int'l*, pg. 172
AGFA-GEVAERT AG—Bayer AG; *Int'l*, pg. 174
AGFA-GEVAERT ARGENTINA S.A.—Bayer AG; *Int'l*, pg. 174
AGFA-GEVAERT LIMITED—Bayer AG; *Int'l*, pg. 174
AGFA-GEVAERT N.V.—Bayer AG; *Int'l*, pg. 174
AGFA-GEVAERT S.A.—Bayer AG; *Int'l*, pg. 174
ALLIED DIAGNOSTIC IMAGING RESOURCES, INC.—CPAC, Inc.; *U.S. Public*, pg. 282
ANACOMP DO BRASIL LTDA.—Anacomp, Inc.; *U.S. Public*, pg. 107
ANACOMP (JAPAN) LTD.—Anacomp, Inc.; *U.S. Public*, pg. 107
ANITEC IMAGE INTERNATIONAL B.V.—International Paper Company; *U.S. Public*, pg. 904
ASAHI OPTICAL CO., LTD.; *Int'l*, pg. 85
ASAHI OPTICAL (INTERNATIONAL) LTD.—Asahi Optical Co., Ltd.; *Int'l*, pg. 85
ATOCHEM SERVICES INC.—Elf Aquitane; *Int'l*, pg. 445
AZON CORPORATION; *U.S. Private*, pg. 104
BALLANTYNE OF OMAHA, INC.—ARC International Corporation; *Int'l*, pg. 17
BAYER AG—Bayer AG; *Int'l*, pg. 172
BAYER ANTWERPEN N.V.—Bayer AG; *Int'l*, pg. 174
BAYER HISPANIA INDUSTRIAL, S.A.—Bayer AG; *Int'l*, pg. 175
BECTON DICKINSON & COMPANY; *U.S. Public*, pg. 199
BLU-RAY—Bidwell Industrial Group, Inc.; *U.S. Private*, pg. 142
ROBERT BOSCH AG—Robert Bosch GmbH; *Int'l*, pg. 205
BREMSON DATA SYSTEMS, INC.—Eastman Kodak Company; *U.S. Public*, pg. 551
CPAC, INC.; *U.S. Public*, pg. 282
CAMERZ PHOTO PRODUCTS—Photo Control Corporation; *U.S. Public*, pg. 1292
CANON BUSINESS MACHINES INC.—Canon Inc.; *Int'l*, pg. 261
CANON INC.; *Int'l*, pg. 261
CASTCRAFT INDUSTRIES, INC.; *U.S. Private*, pg. 219
CHEIL SYNTHETICS INC.—Samsung Group; *Int'l*, pg. 1181
CHINON INDUSTRIES INC.; *Int'l*, pg. 286
CINE MAGNETICS, INC.; *U.S. Private*, pg. 240
D/B CAMERAS MICROCHECK DIVISION—AEI Holding Co., Inc.; *U.S. Private*, pg. 5
DNP DENMARK A/S—Dai Nippon Printing Co., Ltd.; *Int'l*, pg. 363
DA-LITE SCREEN COMPANY, INC.; *U.S. Private*, pg. 306
DANKA BUSINESS SYSTEMS—Danka Business Systems PLC; *Int'l*, pg. 379
DANKA BUSINESS SYSTEMS PLC; *Int'l*, pg. 379
DANKA OFFICE IMAGING—Eastman Kodak Company; *U.S. Public*, pg. 551
DENTAL PRODUCTS DIVISION—3M; *U.S. Public*, pg. 1605
DIETZGEN CORPORATION; *U.S. Private*, pg. 332
DOLLANDS PHOTOGRAPHIC HOLDINGS LTD.—Dolland & Aitchison Ltd.; *Int'l*, pg. 414
DU PONT (E.I. DU PONT DE NEMOURS & CO.); *U.S. Public*, pg. 530
DUKANE CORPORATION; *U.S. Private*, pg. 345
DYNAMICS RESEARCH CORPORATION; *U.S. Public*, pg. 539
EG & G HEIMANN OPTO. GMBH—EG & G, Inc.; *U.S. Public*, pg. 544
EG & G OPTOELECTRONICS RETICON—EG & G, Inc.; *U.S. Public*, pg. 543
EG & G OPTOELECTRONICS-SALEM—EG & G, Inc.; *U.S. Public*, pg. 543
EASTMAN KODAK COMPANY DISTRIBUTION—Eastman Kodak Company; *U.S. Public*, pg. 555
EASTMAN KODAK KCD—Eastman Kodak Company; *U.S. Public*, pg. 555
ECTONA FIBRES LIMITED—Eastman Kodak Company; *U.S. Public*, pg. 552
ENERGY CONVERSION DEVICES, INC.; *U.S. Public*, pg. 581
FOTO INTERAMERICANA DE VENEZUELA S.A.—Eastman Kodak Company; *U.S. Public*, pg. 552
ABDULLA FOUAD-TESTRADE MIDDLE EAST—Abdulla Fouad Co. Ltd.; *Int'l*, pg. 502
FUJI HUNT PHOTOGRAPHIC CHEMICALS, INC.—Fuji Photo Film Co., Ltd.; *Int'l*, pg. 524
FUJI PHOTO FILM B.V.—Fuji Photo Film Co., Ltd.; *Int'l*, pg. 524
FUJI PHOTO FILM CO., LTD.; *Int'l*, pg. 523
FUJI XEROX COMPANY LTD.—Xerox Corporation; *U.S. Public*, pg. 1785
GENERAL CHEMICAL CORPORATION—The General Chemical Group, Inc.; *U.S. Public*, pg. 707
GRAPHLINE INC.; *U.S. Private*, pg. 471
GRIFFIN TECHNOLOGY INCORPORATED—Diebold, Incorporated; *U.S. Public*, pg. 506
HPS, INC.; *U.S. Private*, pg. 492
HAMAMATSU CORP.; *U.S. Private*, pg. 497
HANOVIA COLIGHT—ARC International Corporation; *Int'l*, pg. 17
HARGRO ENTERPRISES, INC.; *U.S. Private*, pg. 502
HOECHST SPECIALTY PRODUCTS GROUP—Hoechst Aktiengesellschaft; *Int'l*, pg. 625
HOUSTON FEARLESS 76 INC.; *U.S. Private*, pg. 542
INX INTERNATIONAL—Sumitomo Chemical Company, Ltd.; *Int'l*, pg. 1311
IKSELAH CORPORATION—Pubco Corporation; *U.S. Public*, pg. 1339
ILFORD ANITEC SA—International Paper Company; *U.S. Public*, pg. 906
ILFORD INC.—International Paper Company; *U.S. Public*, pg. 904
ILFORD LIMITED—International Paper Company; *U.S. Public*, pg. 905
ILFORD SA—International Paper Company; *U.S. Public*, pg. 906
IMAGE TECHNOLOGY CORPORATION—Olin Corporation; *U.S. Public*, pg. 1219
IMAGING PRODUCTS DIVISION—International Paper Company; *U.S. Public*, pg. 902

INDUSTRIA FOTOGRAFICA INTERAMERICANA S.A. DE C.V.—Eastman Kodak Company; *U.S. Public*, pg. 554
INTERNATIONAL BUSINESS MACHINES CORPORATION; *U.S. Public*, pg. 895
INTERNATIONAL POLAROID CORP.—Polaroid Corporation; *U.S. Public*, pg. 1313
J & R FILM / MOVIOLA DIGITAL CO.; *U.S. Private*, pg. 576
JAMIESON FILM COMPANY, INC.—Eastman Kodak Company; *U.S. Public*, pg. 551
KASEI VERBATIM CORPORATION—Eastman Kodak Company; *U.S. Public*, pg. 552
THE KENDALL COMPANY—Tyco International Ltd.; *U.S. Public*, pg. 1647
KLEER-VU PLASTICS CORP.—Kleer-Vu Plastics, Inc.; *U.S. Public*, pg. 962
KODAK AG—Eastman Kodak Company; *U.S. Public*, pg. 552
KODAK AMERICA, LTDA.—Eastman Kodak Company; *U.S.* Public, pg. 554
KODAK ARGENTINA S.A.I.C.—Eastman Kodak Company; *U.S. Public*, pg. 552
KODAK BRASILEIRA C.I.L.—Eastman Kodak Company; *U.S. Public*, pg. 552
KODAK BUSINESS IMAGING SYSTEMS DIVISION—Eastman Kodak Company; *U.S. Public*, pg. 555
KODAK CANADA INC.—Eastman Kodak Company; *U.S. Public*, pg. 553
KODAK GRAPHICS IMAGING SYSTEMS DIVISION—Eastman Kodak Company; *U.S. Public*, pg. 551
KODAK HEALTH SCIENCES DIVISION—Eastman Kodak Company; *U.S. Public*, pg. 551
KODAK ISRAEL—Eastman Kodak Company; *U.S. Public*, pg. 553
KODAK JAPAN INDUSTRIES LTD.—Eastman Kodak Company; *U.S. Public*, pg. 552
KODAK LIMITED—Eastman Kodak Company; *U.S. Public*, pg. 553
KODAK LIMITED-CHEMICAL DIVISION—Eastman Kodak Company; *U.S. Public*, pg. 553
KODAK MEXICANA SA DE C.V.—Eastman Kodak Company; *U.S. Public*, pg. 554
KODAK MOTION PICTURE & AUDIOVISUAL PRODUCTS DIVISION—Eastman Kodak Company; *U.S. Public*, pg. 555
KODAK PATHE S.A.—Eastman Kodak Company; *U.S. Public*, pg. 554
KODAK PHILIPPINES LTD.—Eastman Kodak Company; *U.S. Public*, pg. 554
KODAK PROFESSIONAL PHOTOGRAPHY DIVISION—Eastman Kodak Company; *U.S. Public*, pg. 555
KOLLMORGEN CORPORATION; *U.S. Public*, pg. 965
KONICA CORPORATION; *Int'l*, pg. 748
KONICA MANUFACTURING USA, INC.—Konica Corporation; *Int'l*, pg. 749
KONICA ODAWARA INDUSTRIAL CENTER—Konica Corporation; *Int'l*, pg. 748
KONICA TOKYO INDUSTRIAL CENTER HINO—Konica Corporation; *Int'l*, pg. 748
KREONITE, INC.; *U.S. Private*, pg. 635
KYOCERA CORPORATION; *Int'l*, pg. 775
LEICA A.G.; *Int'l*, pg. 806
LOGETRONICS CORPORATION—AFP Imaging Corporation; *U.S. Public*, pg. 6
LONDON LITHO ALUMINUM CO., INC.; *U.S. Private*, pg. 673
LUCHT, INC.—Northwestern Public Service; *U.S. Public*, pg. 1201
MACBETH DIV.—Kollmorgen Corporation; *U.S. Public*, pg. 965
MAGNASYNC MOVIOLA CORPORATION—J & R Film / Moviola Digital Co.; *U.S. Private*, pg. 576
THE MEAD CORPORATION; *U.S. Public*, pg. 1074
MICROMEDIA LIMITED—Bell & Howell Holdings; *U.S. Public*, pg. 201
MINOLTA CO., LTD.; *Int'l*, pg. 869
MITA INDUSTRIAL COMPANY, LTD.; *Int'l*, pg. 870
MORTON INTERNATIONAL LIMITED—Morton International Inc.; *U.S. Public*, pg. 1135
MOVIECAM-VOEST-ALPINE KINEMATOGRAPHISCHE GERATE GES.M.B.H.—Voest-Alpine Stahl AG; *Int'l*, pg. 1470
NASHUA CORPORATION; *U.S. Public*, pg. 1152
NIKON CORPORATION; *Int'l*, pg. 931
NISSHO IWAI CORPORATION; *Int'l*, pg. 946
NORD PHOTO ENGINEERING, INC.—Photo Control Corporation; *U.S. Public*, pg. 1292
NORMAN ENTERPRISES, INC.—Photo Control Corporation; *U.S. Public*, pg. 1292
NORTH SAFETY PRODUCTS, HEALTH CARE DIVISION—Siebe plc; *Int'l*, pg. 1243
NUARC COMPANY, INC.; *U.S. Private*, pg. 808
OLYMPUS OPTICAL CO., LTD.; *Int'l*, pg. 1004
PMC, INC.—Polaroid Corporation; *U.S. Public*, pg. 1313
PSC INC.; *U.S. Public*, pg. 1245
PATHE; *Int'l*, pg. 1024
PENTAX CORPORATION—Asahi Optical Co., Ltd.; *Int'l*, pg. 85
PHOTO CONTROL CORPORATION; *U.S. Public*, pg. 1292
PHOTO-ME INTERNATIONAL PLC; *Int'l*, pg. 1055
PHOTOGENIC MACHINE COMPANY, INC.; *U.S. Private*, pg. 864
PHOTRONICS, INC.; *U.S. Public*, pg. 1293
PINNACLE COATING & CONVERTING, INC.; *U.S. Private*, pg. 866
PITNEY BOWES INC.; *U.S. Public*, pg. 1303
PLANTA KODAK—Eastman Kodak Company; *U.S. Public*, pg. 554
PLASTIC REEL CORP. OF AMERICA; *U.S. Private*, pg. 871
POLAROID COPY SERVICES—Polaroid Corporation; *U.S. Public*, pg. 1313
POLAROID CORPORATION; *U.S. Public*, pg. 1313
POLAROID (NORGE) A/S—Polaroid Corporation; *U.S. Public*, pg. 1314
POLAROID SINGAPORE (PTE) LTD.—Polaroid Corporation; *U.S. Public*, pg. 1314
POLAROID (UK) LTD.—Polaroid Corporation; *U.S. Public*, pg. 1314
POLAROID (U.K.) LTD.-THE VALE—Polaroid Corporation; *U.S. Public*, pg. 1314
POLYCHROME CORP. DIV.—Dainippon Ink & Chemicals, Inc.; *Int'l*, pg. 370
POSSO S.A.; *Int'l*, pg. 1064
PRETEC PRECISIE TECHNIEK B.V.—Bell & Howell Holdings; *U.S. Public*, pg. 201
PROJECTA B.V.—Da-Lite Screen Company, Inc.; *U.S. Private*, pg. 306
RANK XEROX LIMITED—The Rank Group PLC; *Int'l*, pg. 1087
RANK XEROX LIMITED—Xerox Corporation; *U.S. Public*, pg. 1785
RECON/OPTICAL, INC.; *U.S. Private*, pg. 914
REXAM CUSTOM—Rexam PLC; *Int'l*, pg. 1107
REXAM INC.—Rexam PLC; *Int'l*, pg. 1106
RICOH COMPANY, LTD.; *Int'l*, pg. 1114
RICOH CORPORATION—Ricoh Company, Ltd.; *Int'l*, pg. 1114
RICOH ELECTRONICS, INC.—Ricoh Company, Ltd.; *Int'l*, pg. 1114
RIDGWAY'S, INC.—Wilco Reprographic, Inc.; *U.S. Private*, pg. 1176
SAAB AUTOMATION AB—Investor AB; *Int'l*, pg. 686
SEAL PRODUCTS INCORPORATED—Hunt Corporation; *U.S. Public*, pg. 849
SPECTRA-PHYSICS AB; *Int'l*, pg. 1288
STRAND LIGHTING LIMITED—The Rank Group PLC; *Int'l*, pg. 1087
TECHNICAL SPECIALTIES DIVISION—FiberMark Inc.; *U.S.* Public, pg. 620
TECHNICOLOR, INC.—Carlton Communications Plc; *Int'l*, pg. 272
TONER PRODUCT DIVISION—Toshiba Corporation; *Int'l*, pg. 1405
TRANSMARCO LIMITED; *Int'l*, pg. 1417
TRI-STAR PICTURES, INC.—Sony Corporation; *Int'l*, pg. 1282
UNITED SOLAR SYSTEMS CORP.—Energy Conversion Devices, Inc.; *U.S. Public*, pg. 581
VERBATIM DO AMAZONAS INDUSTRIAL LTD.—Eastman Kodak Company; *U.S. Public*, pg. 552
VIDEOLABS, INC.; *U.S. Public*, pg. 1720
WILCO REPROGRAPHIC, INC.; *U.S. Private*, pg. 1176
WINTHROP-ATKINS CO., INC.; *U.S. Private*, pg. 1183
X-RITE, INCORPORATED; *U.S. Public*, pg. 1783
XEROX CORPORATION; *U.S. Public*, pg. 1783
XEROX DIABLO SUPPLIES—Xerox Corporation; *U.S. Public*, pg. 1784
YRJ CORPORATION—Wilco Reprographic, Inc.; *U.S. Private*, pg. 1176
CARL ZEISS—Carl-Zeiss-Stiftung; *Int'l*, pg. 1522
ZONE VI STUDIOS, INC.—Calumet Photographic, Inc.; *U.S.* Private, pg. 202

3873 — WATCHES, CLOCKS, CLOCKWORK OPERATED DEVICES & PARTS

AMERICAN SIGN & MARKETING SERVICES, INC.—Plasti-Line, Inc.; *U.S. Public*, pg. 1309
BALDWIN PIANO & ORGAN COMPANY; *U.S. Public*, pg. 169
BAUME MERCIER, INC.; *U.S. Private*, pg. 124
BLANCPAIN S.A.—SMH Swiss Corporation for Micro Electronics & Watchmaking Indus. Ltd.; *Int'l*, pg. 1160
BULOVA CORPORATION—Loews Corporation; *U.S. Public*, *pg. 1010*
CASIO COMPUTER CO., LTD.; *Int'l*, pg. 274
CASSINA GEBR. KURTH AG—SMH Swiss Corporation for Micro Electronics & Watchmaking Indus. Ltd.; *Int'l*, pg. 1160
CITIZEN WATCH COMPANY, LTD.; *Int'l*, pg. 293
CLASSIC MOMENTS COMPANY—Loews Corporation; *U.S.* Public, pg. 1010
COMADUR S.A.—SMH Swiss Corporation for Micro Electronics & Watchmaking Indus. Ltd.; *Int'l*, pg. 1161
CONCORD WATCH COMPANY, S.A.—Movado Group, Inc.; *U.S. Public*, pg. 1140
COSMO COMMUNICATIONS CORPORATION; *U.S. Public*, *pg. 451*
CROTON WATCH COMPANY & NATIONWIDE TIME; *U.S.* Private, pg. 291
DAEWOO SANG SA—Daewoo Corporation; *Int'l*, pg. 357
DETEX CORPORATION; *U.S. Private*, pg. 327
DIANTUS WATCH SA—SMH Swiss Corporation for Micro Electronics & Watchmaking Indus. Ltd.; *Int'l*, pg. 1160
ETA S.A. FABRIQUES D'EBAUCHES—SMH Swiss Corporation for Micro Electronics & Watchmaking Indus. Ltd.; *Int'l*, pg. 1160
ELGIN WATCH COMPANY; *U.S. Private*, pg. 371
ENDURA SA—SMH Swiss Corporation for Micro Electronics & Watchmaking Indus. Ltd.; *Int'l*, pg. 1160
FKI PLC; *Int'l*, pg. 471
GENERAL TIME CORP.; *U.S. Private*, pg. 445
HATTORI OVERSEAS HONG KONG LTD.—Seiko Corporation; *Int'l*, pg. 1218
HAYDON SWITCH & INSTRUMENT, INC.; *U.S. Private*, pg. 513
HERMES INTERNATIONAL; *Int'l*, pg. 617
HUNTSVILLE ELECTRONICS DIV.—Chrysler Corporation; *U.S. Public*, pg. 353
JAEGER-LE COULTRE; *Int'l*, pg. 697
LOEWS CORPORATION; *U.S. Public*, pg. 1010
MATSUSHITA ELECTRIC WORKS, LTD.; *Int'l*, pg. 847
THOMAS MERCER CHRONOMETER LTD.—Brown & Sharpe Manufacturing Company; *U.S. Public*, pg. 260
MOVADO GROUP, INC.; *U.S. Public*, pg. 1140
MOVADO WATCH COMPANY, S.A.—Movado Group, Inc.; *U.S. Public*, pg. 1140
NINTENDO OF AMERICA—Nintendo Company, Ltd.; *Int'l*, pg. 932
NIVAROX-FAR S.A.—SMH Swiss Corporation for Micro Electronics & Watchmaking Indus. Ltd.; *Int'l*, pg. 1161
NOUVELLE LEMANIA S.A.; *Int'l*, pg. 971
OMEGA ELECTRONICS SA—SMH Swiss Corporation for Micro Electronics & Watchmaking Indus. Ltd.; *Int'l*, pg. 1161
OMEGA SA—SMH Swiss Corporation for Micro Electronics & Watchmaking Indus. Ltd.; *Int'l*, pg. 1160
PULASKI FURNITURE CORPORATION; *U.S. Public*, pg. 1342
M.H. RHODES, INC.; *U.S. Private*, pg. 927
RIDGEWAY CLOCK COMPANY—Pulaski Furniture Corporation; *U.S. Public*, pg. 1343
ROBERTSHAW CONTROLS COMPANY—Siebe plc; *Int'l*, pg. 1243
ROLEX WATCH CO. SA; *Int'l*, pg. 1126
ROLEX WATCH U.S.A., INC.—Rolex Watch Co. SA; *Int'l*, pg. 1126
GEORGES RUEDIN SA—SMH Swiss Corporation for Micro Electronics & Watchmaking Indus. Ltd.; *Int'l*, pg. 1160
SMH SWISS CORPORATION FOR MICRO ELECTRONICS & WATCHMAKING INDUS. LTD.; *Int'l*, pg. 1160
SMH (U.S.) INC.—SMH Swiss Corporation for Micro Electronics & Watchmaking Indus. Ltd.; *Int'l*, pg. 1161
MIDO G. SCHAEREN & CO., SA—SMH Swiss Corporation for Micro Electronics & Watchmaking Indus. Ltd.; *Int'l*, pg. 1161
SEIKO CORPORATION; *Int'l*, pg. 1218
SEIKO DEUTSCHLAND GMBH—Seiko Corporation; *Int'l*, pg. 1218
SEIKO EPSON CORPORATION; *Int'l*, pg. 1219
SEIKO FRANCE S.A.—Seiko Corporation; *Int'l*, pg. 1218
SEIKO HONG KONG LTD.—Seiko Corporation; *Int'l*, pg. 1218
SEIKO INSTRUMENTS INC.; *Int'l*, pg. 1219
SEIKO UK LIMITED—Seiko Corporation; *Int'l*, pg. 1218
SIGMA ELECTRONICS LIMITED—Hanson PLC; *Int'l*, pg. 595
SPARTUS (HK) LTD.—Hanson PLC; *Int'l*, pg. 595
STOCKER & YALE, INC.; *U.S. Public*, pg. 1518
SYRATECH CORPORATION; *U.S. Private*, pg. 1060
TELECHRON OF NORTH CAROLINA, INC.; *U.S. Private*, pg. 1073
TIFFANY & CO.; *U.S. Public*, pg. 1608
TIMEX CORPORATION; *U.S. Private*, pg. 1088
TOURNEAU INC.; *U.S. Private*, pg. 1093
TROPAR MFG. CO., INC.; *U.S. Private*, pg. 1105
WESTINGHOUSE INDUSTRIES & TECHNOLOGIES GROUP—CBS Corporation; *U.S. Public*, pg. 273
WITTNAUER INTERNATIONAL, INC.—CBS Corporation; *U.S. Public*, pg. 273

3911 — JEWELRY, PRECIOUS METAL

A&Z HAYWARD, INC.; *U.S. Private*, pg. 2
ANDIN INTERNATIONAL INC.; *U.S. Private*, pg. 73
ANJU JEWELRY LIMITED—Town & Country Corporation; *U.S. Public*, pg. 1625
L.G. BALFOUR CO., INC.—Commemorative Brands, Inc.; *U.S. Private*, pg. 258
B.A. BALLOU & CO. INC.; *U.S. Private*, pg. 112
BASEL TRADING COMPANY LTD.; *Int'l*, pg. 169
BULGARI SPA; *Int'l*, pg. 232
COMMEMORATIVE BRANDS, INC.; *U.S. Private*, pg. 258
DOWNEY DESIGNS INTERNATIONAL; *U.S. Private*, pg. 342
EXCELL MANUFACTURING COMPANY; *U.S. Private*, pg. 387
THE FRANKLIN MINT—Roll International Corporation; *U.S.* Private, pg. 941
GEORG JENSEN SILVERSMITHY LTD.—Royal Copenhagen A/S; *Int'l*, pg. 1134
GOLD LANCE, INC.—Town & Country Corporation; *U.S. Public*, pg. 1625
JABEL, INC.; *U.S. Private*, pg. 579
JEWELCOR COMPANIES; *U.S. Private*, pg. 587
JEWELMONT CORPORATION; *U.S. Private*, pg. 587
JOSTENS; *U.S. Public*, pg. 934
KYOCERA CORPORATION; *Int'l*, pg. 775
KYOCERA INTERNATIONAL, INC.—Kyocera Corporation; *Int'l*, pg. 775
LAZARE KAPLAN INTL., INC.; *U.S. Public*, pg. 981
LENOX BRANDS—Brown-Forman Corporation; *U.S. Public*, *pg. 261*
LENOX, INCORPORATED—Brown-Forman Corporation; *U.S. Public*, pg. 261
MAJORICA JEWELRY LTD.; *U.S. Private*, pg. 697
MICHAEL ANTHONY JEWELERS, INC.; *U.S. Public*, pg. 1103
MIKIMOTO (AMERICA) CO. LTD.—K. Mikimoto & Co., Ltd.; *Int'l*, pg. 866
K. MIKIMOTO & CO., LTD.; *Int'l*, pg. 866
THE NAPIER CO.; *U.S. Private*, pg. 774
OROAMERICA, INC.; *U.S. Public*, pg. 1232
THE PILOT CORPORATION; *Int'l*, pg. 1057
PLAINVILLE STOCK COMPANY, INC.; *U.S. Private*, pg. 868
RECOGNITION DIVISION—Jostens; *U.S. Public*, pg. 934
REED & BARTON CORPORATION; *U.S. Private*, pg. 916
ROLL INTERNATIONAL CORPORATION; *U.S. Private*, pg. 941
ROYAL COPENHAGEN A/S; *Int'l*, pg. 1134
SCHAAP & CITROEN—Vendex International N.V.; *Int'l*, pg. 1462
SCHOOL PRODUCTS GROUP—Jostens; *U.S. Public*, pg. 934
SWANK, INC.; *U.S. Public*, pg. 1543
TABAPACK, S.A.—Tabacalera, S.A.; *Int'l*, pg. 1346
TIFFANY & CO.; *U.S. Public*, pg. 1608

TIFFCO JEWELERY & CHAIN CRAFTS, INC.—Tiffany & Co.; *U.S. Public*, pg. 1609
TOWN & COUNTRY CORPORATION; *U.S. Public*, pg. 1625
TOWN & COUNTRY FINE JEWELRY GROUP, INC.—Town & Country Corporation; *U.S. Public*, pg. 1625
UNCAS MANUFACTURING COMPANY; *U.S. Private*, pg. 1116
WATERFORD WEDGWOOD UK PLC—Waterford Wedgwood Plc; *Int'l*, pg. 1487

3914 — SILVERWARE, PLATED WARE & STAINLESS STEEL WARE

AMERICAN SHEAR KNIVE CO.—Asko, Inc; *U.S. Private*, pg. 89
ASKO, INC; *U.S. Private*, pg. 89
BACCARAT (CIE DES CRISTALLERIES); *Int'l*, pg. 132
HENRY BIRKS & SONS (1993) INC.; *Int'l*, pg. 196
BULGARI SPA; *Int'l*, pg. 232
CKC—Asko, Inc; *U.S. Private*, pg. 89
CASSIDY'S LTD.; *Int'l*, pg. 275
DANSK INTERNATIONAL DESIGNS LTD.—Brown-Forman Corporation; *U.S. Public*, pg. 261
EKCO HOUSEWARES, INC.—Ekco Group, Inc.; *U.S. Public*, pg. 566
LEONARD FLORENCE ASSOCIATES—Syratech Corporation; *U.S. Private*, pg. 1061
FOTOBALL USA, INC.; *U.S. Public*, pg. 678
GEORG JENSEN SILVERSMITHY LTD.—Royal Copenhagen A/S; *Int'l*, pg. 1134
IMPERIAL SCHRADE CORP.; *U.S. Private*, pg. 559
JMP NEWCOR HOLDINGS INC.—Patra Ceramics Co., Ltd.; *Int'l*, pg. 1025
KIRK & MATZ LTD.; *U.S. Private*, pg. 623
LEACH & GARNER COMPANY; *U.S. Private*, pg. 655
LENOX BRANDS—Brown-Forman Corporation; *U.S. Public*, *pg. 261*
LIFETIME HOAN CORP.; *U.S. Public*, pg. 992
MCPHERSON'S LIMITED; *Int'l*, pg. 852
NORITAKE CO., LIMITED; *Int'l*, pg. 958
ONEIDA CANADA LTD.—Oneida Ltd.; *U.S. Public*, pg. 1226
ONEIDA LTD.; *U.S. Public*, pg. 1225
ONEIDA MEXICANA, S.A.—Oneida Ltd.; *U.S. Public*, pg. 1226
ONEIDA SILVERSMITHS DIV.—Oneida Ltd.; *U.S. Public*, pg. 1226
R.S. OWENS; *U.S. Private*, pg. 824
PARK-OHIO INDUSTRIES, INC.; *U.S. Public*, pg. 1258
THE PFALTZGRAFF CO.—The Pfaltzgraff Co.; *U.S. Private*, *pg. 860*
REED & BARTON CORPORATION; *U.S. Private*, pg. 916
STANLEY ROBERTS, INC.; *U.S. Private*, pg. 936
ROGERS, LUNT & BOWLEN CO.; *U.S. Private*, pg. 939
ROSENTHAL AG; *Int'l*, pg. 1127
ROYAL COPENHAGEN A/S; *Int'l*, pg. 1134
SALADMASTER; *U.S. Private*, pg. 961
SHEFFIELD SILVER CO.—Reed & Barton Corporation; *U.S. Private*, pg. 916
SYRATECH CORPORATION; *U.S. Private*, pg. 1060
TOWLE MANUFACTURING CORPORATION—Syratech Corporation; *U.S. Private*, pg. 1061

3915 — JEWELERS FINDINGS & MATERIALS & LAPIDARY WORK

B.A. BALLOU & CO. INC.; *U.S. Private*, pg. 112
DE BEERS CONSOLIDATED MINES LIMITED—Anglo American Corporation of South Africa Limited; *Int'l*, pg. 76
DE BEERS INDUSTRIAL DIAMOND DIVISION (PROPRIETARY) LIMITED—Anglo American Corporation of South Africa Limited; *Int'l*, pg. 77
GENERAL FINDINGS—Leach & Garner Company; *U.S. Private*, pg. 655
KYOCERA CORPORATION; *Int'l*, pg. 775
L&R MANUFACTURING CO.; *U.S. Private*, pg. 638
LEACH & GARNER COMPANY; *U.S. Private*, pg. 655
MYTTON'S LIMITED—Bristile Clay Tiles, Ltd.; *Int'l*, pg. 216
SIBEKA—Union Miniere; *Int'l*, pg. 1442
STERN-LEACH COMPANY—Cookson Group plc; *Int'l*, pg. 329

3931 — MUSICAL INSTRUMENTS

ALLEN ORGAN COMPANY; *U.S. Public*, pg. 45
BALDWIN PIANO & ORGAN COMPANY; *U.S. Public*, pg. 169
L. BOSENDORFER KLAVIERFABRIK GMBH—Kimball International, Inc.; *U.S. Public*, pg. 958
BOSENDORFER USA—Kimball International, Inc.; *U.S. Public*, pg. 957
BRIMMS INC.; *U.S. Private*, pg. 169
CASIO COMPUTER CO., LTD.; *Int'l*, pg. 274
ENSONIQ; *U.S. Private*, pg. 377
FENDER MUSICAL INSTRUMENTS; *U.S. Private*, pg. 400
GIBSON MUSICAL INSTRUMENTS, INC.; *U.S. Private*, pg. 451
GUILD MUSIC DIVISION—Fender Musical Instruments; *U.S. Private*, pg. 400
HAMER GUITARS—Kaman Corporation; *U.S. Public*, pg. 942
HOHNER/HSS INC.; *U.S. Private*, pg. 533
FRANK HOLTON CO.—G. Leblanc Corporation; *U.S. Private*, pg. 657
IRI ISTITUTO RICOSTRUZIONE INDUSTRIALE; *Int'l*, pg. 652
KAMAN CORPORATION; *U.S. Public*, pg. 941
KAMAN MUSIC CORP.—Kaman Corporation; *U.S. Public*, pg. 942
KAWAI AMERICA CORPORATION—Kawai Musical Instruments Mfg. Co., Ltd.; *Int'l*, pg. 725
KAWAI AMERICA MFG. INC.—Kawai Musical Instruments Mfg. Co., Ltd.; *Int'l*, pg. 725
KAWAI MUSICAL INSTRUMENTS MFG. CO., LTD.; *Int'l*, pg. 725
KEUM KANG DEVELOPMENT INDUSTRIAL CO., LTD.—Hyundai Motor Company; *Int'l*, pg. 642
KIMBALL INTERNATIONAL, INC.; *U.S. Public*, pg. 956
G. LEBLANC CORPORATION; *U.S. Private*, pg. 656
LUDWIG INDUSTRIES—Steinway Musical Instruments, Inc.; *U.S. Public*, pg. 1514
MARTIN BAND INSTRUMENT CO.—G. Leblanc Corporation; *U.S. Private*, pg. 657
MUSSER DIV.—Philips Electronics N.V.; *Int'l*, pg. 1054
OVATION INSTRUMENTS—Kaman Corporation; *U.S. Public*, pg. 942
ROCKY MOUNT INSTRUMENTS, INC.—Allen Organ Company; *U.S. Public*, pg. 45
SEIKO INSTRUMENTS INC.; *Int'l*, pg. 1219
THE SELMER CO., INC.—Steinway Musical Instruments, Inc.; *U.S. Public*, pg. 1514
THE WURLITZER COMPANY—Baldwin Piano & Organ Company; *U.S. Public*, pg. 169
YAMAHA CORPORATION; *Int'l*, pg. 1515
AVEDIS ZILDJIAN COMPANY; *U.S. Private*, pg. 1206

3942 — DOLLS & STUFFED TOYS

ACE NOVELTY COMPANY, INC.—Play by Play Toys & Novelties, Inc.; *U.S. Public*, pg. 1309
ACE NOVELTY FUN SERVICE DIVISION—Play by Play Toys & Novelties, Inc.; *U.S. Public*, pg. 1309
ANIMAL FAIR—Princess Soft Toys; *U.S. Private*, pg. 885
APPLAUSE INC.; *U.S. Private*, pg. 78
CENTURY PRODUCTS CO.; *U.S. Private*, pg. 226
COMMONWEALTH TOY & NOVELTY COMPANY; *U.S. Private*, pg. 258
THE FIRST YEARS INC.; *U.S. Public*, pg. 642
GALCO INTERNATIONAL TOYS, N.V.—Galoob Toys, Inc.; *U.S. Public*, pg. 698
GALOOB TOYS, INC.; *U.S. Public*, pg. 698
GOLDBERGER DOLL MFG. COMPANY, INC.; *U.S. Private*, *pg. 459*
IRWIN TOY LTD.; *Int'l*, pg. 688
MATTEL, INC.; *U.S. Public*, pg. 1057
PLAY BY PLAY TOYS & NOVELTIES, INC.; *U.S. Public*, pg. 1309
PRIDE PRODUCTS, INC.; *U.S. Private*, pg. 883
PRINCESS SOFT TOYS; *U.S. Private*, pg. 884
REMCO TOYS—JAKKS Pacific, Inc.; *U.S. Public*, pg. 923
TONKA CORPORATION—Hasbro, Inc.; *U.S. Public*, pg. 797
TOTSY MANUFACTURING COMPANY, INC.; *U.S. Private*, pg. 1093
TOY BIZ, INC.; *U.S. Public*, pg. 1625
THE TOY FACTORY—Pride Products, Inc.; *U.S. Private*, pg. 883
TYCO INDUSTRIES, INC.—Mattel, Inc.; *U.S. Public*, pg. 1058
TYCO TOYS, INC.—Mattel, Inc.; *U.S. Public*, pg. 1058
THE VERMONT TEDDY BEAR COMPANY, INC.; *U.S. Public*, pg. 1716

3944 — GAMES, TOYS & CHILDREN'S VEHICLES; EXCEPT DOLLS & BICYCLES

AG INDUSTRIES, INC.—AG Ajikawa Corporation; *Int'l*, pg. 40
ACCLAIM ENTERTAINMENT, INC.; *U.S. Public*, pg. 15
AMERICAN PLASTIC TOYS INC.; *U.S. Private*, pg. 60
AMLOID CORPORATION; *U.S. Private*, pg. 66
BANDAI CO., LTD.; *Int'l*, pg. 145
BAUSCH & LOMB INCORPORATED; *U.S. Public*, pg. 194
BENJAMIN SHERIDAN CO.—Crosman Corp.; *U.S. Private*, pg. 291
BINNEY & SMITH INC.—Hallmark Cards, Inc.; *U.S. Private*, *pg. 496*
BRITAINS PETITE INC.—Harnischfeger Industries, Inc.; *U.S. Public*, pg. 789
BRITAINS PETITE LTD.—Harnischfeger Industries, Inc.; *U.S. Public*, pg. 789
BRITAX INTERNATIONAL PLC; *Int'l*, pg. 216
CENTURY PRODUCTS CO.; *U.S. Private*, pg. 226
CHILDCRAFT EDUCATION CORPORATION—The Walt Disney Company; *U.S. Public*, pg. 513
COLORFORMS—Toy Biz, Inc.; *U.S. Public*, pg. 1625
CROSMAN CORP.; *U.S. Private*, pg. 291
DOBSON PARK INDUSTRIES PLC—Harnischfeger Industries, Inc.; *U.S. Public*, pg. 789
DUNCAN TOYS COMPANY—Flambeau Corporation; *U.S. Private*, pg. 409
DURANT ELECTRONICS, INC.—Strombecker Corporation; *U.S. Private*, pg. 1047
EMPIRE INDUSTRIES, INC.—Empire of Carolina, Inc.; *U.S. Public*, pg. 579
EMPIRE OF CAROLINA, INC.; *U.S. Public*, pg. 579
ERTL DE MEXICO—U.S. Industries, Inc.; *U.S. Public*, pg. 1684
ERTL U.K. LTD.—U.S. Industries, Inc.; *U.S. Public*, pg. 1684
ESQUIRE NOVELTY CO.—Strombecker Corporation; *U.S. Private*, pg. 1047
THE FIRST YEARS INC.; *U.S. Public*, pg. 642
FISHER-PRICE HOUSE—Mattel, Inc.; *U.S. Public*, pg. 1058
FISHER-PRICE, INC.—Mattel, Inc.; *U.S. Public*, pg. 1058
FISHER-PRICE SPIELWAREN GMBH—Mattel, Inc.; *U.S. Public*, pg. 1058
FLAMBEAU CORPORATION; *U.S. Private*, pg. 409
FLEXIBLE FLYER TOYS; *U.S. Private*, pg. 412
GALCO INTERNATIONAL TOYS, N.V.—Galoob Toys, Inc.; *U.S. Public*, pg. 698
GALOOB TOYS, INC.; *U.S. Public*, pg. 698
GEMSTAR INTERNATIONAL GROUP LIMITED; *U.S. Public*, pg. 705
GERBER PRODUCTS DIVISION-BABY CARE—Novartis AG; *Int'l*, pg. 973
GERRY BABY PRODUCTS COMPANY—Kohlberg Kravis Roberts & Co.; *U.S. Private*, pg. 629
GOLDBERGER DOLL MFG. COMPANY, INC.; *U.S. Private*, *pg. 459*
GOLDEN BOOKS PUBLISHING—Golden Books Family Entertainment Inc.; *U.S. Public*, pg. 749
HASBRO—Hasbro, Inc.; *U.S. Public*, pg. 797
HASBRO BRADLEY UK LIMITED—Hasbro, Inc.; *U.S. Public*, pg. 797
HASBRO CANADA INC.—Hasbro, Inc.; *U.S. Public*, pg. 797
HASBRO EUROPE UK LIMITED—Hasbro, Inc.; *U.S. Public*, *pg. 797*
HASBRO, INC.; *U.S. Public*, pg. 797
HASBRO INTERNATIONAL, INC.—Hasbro, Inc.; *U.S. Public*, pg. 797
HASBRO S.A.—Hasbro, Inc.; *U.S. Public*, pg. 797
HASBRO TOY DIVISION—Hasbro, Inc.; *U.S. Public*, pg. 797
HEDSTROM CANADA—Hicks, Muse, Tate & Furst Inc.; *U.S. Private*, pg. 526
HEDSTROM CORP.—Hicks, Muse, Tate & Furst Inc.; *U.S. Private*, pg. 526
HEDSTROM CORPORATION—Hicks, Muse, Tate & Furst Inc.; *U.S. Private*, pg. 526
HUTCH SPORTS USA, INC.—RDM Sports Group; *U.S. Public*, pg. 1354
IRWIN TOY LTD.; *Int'l*, pg. 688
JAKKS PACIFIC, INC.; *U.S. Public*, pg. 923
JAMES INDUSTRIES INC.; *U.S. Private*, pg. 580
JOY TOY, CO.—Strombecker Corporation; *U.S. Private*, pg. 1047
JUST TOYS—RGA and East End Accessories; *U.S. Private*, *pg. 903*
KENNER PARKER (AUSTRALIA) LTD.—Hasbro, Inc.; *U.S. Public*, pg. 797
KENNER PARKER EUROPE—Hasbro, Inc.; *U.S. Public*, pg. 797
KENNER PARKER (H.K.) LTD.—Hasbro, Inc.; *U.S. Public*, pg. 797
KENNER PARKER (N.Z.) LTD.—Hasbro, Inc.; *U.S. Public*, pg. 798
KENNER PARKER TOYS—Hasbro, Inc.; *U.S. Public*, pg. 798
KENNER PARKER TOYS INTERNATIONAL—Hasbro, Inc.; *U.S. Public*, pg. 798
KENNER PRODUCTS (CANADA) LIMITED—Hasbro, Inc.; *U.S. Public*, pg. 798
KEUM KANG DEVELOPMENT INDUSTRIAL CO., LTD.—Hyundai Motor Company; *Int'l*, pg. 642
KIDDE CONSUMER DURABLES CORP.—Hanson PLC; *Int'l*, pg. 594
KIDDE FRANCE—Hanson PLC; *Int'l*, pg. 594
LEGO SYSTEM A/S; *Int'l*, pg. 805
LEGO SYSTEMS, INC.—Lego System A/S; *Int'l*, pg. 805
LIFE-LIKE PRODUCTS, INC.; *U.S. Private*, pg. 666
LIONEL LLC; *U.S. Private*, pg. 669
LITTLE TIKES (CANADA) INC.—Rubbermaid Incorporated; *U.S. Public*, pg. 1411
THE LITTLE TIKES COMPANY—Rubbermaid Incorporated; *U.S. Public*, pg. 1411
THE LITTLE TIKES COMPANY (IRELAND), LIMITED—Rubbermaid Incorporated; *U.S. Public*, pg. 1411
LOUISIANA GAMING MANAGEMENT, INC.; *U.S. Private*, pg. 677
MB FRANCE S.A.—Hasbro, Inc.; *U.S. Public*, pg. 798
MB INTERNATIONAL B.V.—Hasbro, Inc.; *U.S. Public*, pg. 798
MB IRELAND—Hasbro, Inc.; *U.S. Public*, pg. 798
MB ITALY S.R.L.—Hasbro, Inc.; *U.S. Public*, pg. 798
MB (SWITZERLAND) AG—Hasbro, Inc.; *U.S. Public*, pg. 798
MABAMEX S.A.—Mattel, Inc.; *U.S. Public*, pg. 1059
MATTEL GAMES/PUZZLES—Mattel, Inc.; *U.S. Public*, pg. 1058
MATTEL, INC.; *U.S. Public*, pg. 1057
MATTEL (MALAYSIA) SDN. BHD.—Mattel, Inc.; *U.S. Public*, *pg. 1059*
MATTEL T COMPANY LTD.—Mattel, Inc.; *U.S. Public*, pg. 1059
MATTEL TOYS MEXICO—Mattel, Inc.; *U.S. Public*, pg. 1058
MILTON BRADLEY COMPANY—Hasbro, Inc.; *U.S. Public*, pg. 797
MILTON BRADLEY GMBH—Hasbro, Inc.; *U.S. Public*, pg. 798
MILTON BRADLEY (N.Z.) LTD.—Hasbro, Inc.; *U.S. Public*, pg. 798
MODERN PUBLISHING—Unisystems, Inc.; *U.S. Private*, pg. 1120
MONTOI MATTEL TOYS—Mattel, Inc.; *U.S. Public*, pg. 1058
MONTOI S.A. DE C.V.—Mattel, Inc.; *U.S. Public*, pg. 1059
NINTENDO COMPANY, LTD.; *Int'l*, pg. 932
NINTENDO OF AMERICA—Nintendo Company, Ltd.; *Int'l*, pg. 932
THE OHIO ART COMPANY, INC.; *U.S. Public*, pg. 1214
PARKER BROTHERS—Hasbro, Inc.; *U.S. Public*, pg. 797
PATONS & BALDWINS LIMITED—Coats Viyella plc; *Int'l*, pg. 300
PLAID ENTERPRISES INC.—The Dyson-Kissner-Moran Corporation; *U.S. Private*, pg. 352
PLASTICOS MARATON, S.A.—Mattel, Inc.; *U.S. Public*, pg. 1059
PLAYMATES HOLDINGS LTD.; *Int'l*, pg. 1060
PLAYSKOOL, INC.—Hasbro, Inc.; *U.S. Public*, pg. 797
PRESSMAN TOY CORP.; *U.S. Private*, pg. 882
PRIDE PRODUCTS, INC.; *U.S. Private*, pg. 883
PROCESSED PLASTIC COMPANY; *U.S. Private*, pg. 888
RAPID MOUNTING & FINISHING CO.; *U.S. Private*, pg. 910
REVELL-MONOGRAM INC.; *U.S. Private*, pg. 926

ROAD CHAMPS, INC.—JAKKS Pacific, Inc.; *U.S. Public*, pg. 923
ROADMASTER/BRUNSWICK—Brunswick Corporation; *U.S. Public*, pg. 265
ROSE ART INDUSTRIES; *U.S. Private*, pg. 945
SPALDING & EVENFLO COMPANIES, INC.—Kohlberg Kravis Roberts & Co.; *U.S. Private*, pg. 629
SPANG & COMPANY; *U.S. Private*, pg. 1020
SPORTCRAFT LTD.; *U.S. Private*, pg. 1026
STEVEN MANUFACTURING CO.; *U.S. Private*, pg. 1042
STOCK MODEL PARTS DIV.—Designatronics, Inc.; *U.S. Private*, pg. 327
STROMBECKER CORPORATION; *U.S. Private*, pg. 1047
STRYDEL, INC.—The Ohio Art Company, Inc.; *U.S. Public*, pg. 1214
TSR, INC.—Wizards of the Coast; *U.S. Private*, pg. 1185
THE TESTOR CORPORATION—RPM, Inc.; *U.S. Public*, pg. 1358
TODAY'S KIDS—Spang & Company; *U.S. Private*, pg. 1020
TONKA CORPORATION—Hasbro, Inc.; *U.S. Public*, pg. 797
TONKA CORP.—Hasbro, Inc.; *U.S. Public*, pg. 798
TONKA PRODUCTS DIVISION—Hasbro, Inc.; *U.S. Public*, pg. 797
TOOTSIETOY DIVISION—Strombecker Corporation; *U.S. Private*, pg. 1047
TOY BIZ, INC.; *U.S. Public*, pg. 1625
THE TOY FACTORY—Pride Products, Inc.; *U.S. Private*, pg. 883
TOYMAX INTERNATIONAL INC.; *U.S. Public*, pg. 1626
TUPPERWARE CORPORATION; *U.S. Public*, pg. 1644
TYCO (HONG KONG) LTD.—Mattel, Inc.; *U.S. Public*, pg. 1059
TYCO INDUSTRIES, INC.—Mattel, Inc.; *U.S. Public*, pg. 1058
TYCO PRESCHOOL—Mattel, Inc.; *U.S. Public*, pg. 1058
TYCO TOYS, INC.—Mattel, Inc.; *U.S. Public*, pg. 1058
UNISYSTEMS, INC.; *U.S. Private*, pg. 1120
THE UNITED STATES PLAYING CARD COMPANY; *U.S. Private*, pg. 1125
VIEW-MASTER, INC.—Mattel, Inc.; *U.S. Public*, pg. 1058
VISIBLE IMPACT TARGETS—Crosman Corp.; *U.S. Private*, pg. 291
WHAM-O, INC.; *U.S. Private*, pg. 1170
WIZARDS OF THE COAST; *U.S. Private*, pg. 1185

3949 — SPORTING & ATHLETIC GOODS, NEC

AMF BOWLING WORLDWIDE; *U.S. Private*, pg. 6
ABU GARCIA INC.—Outdoor Technologies Group; *U.S. Private*, pg. 822
ABU GARCIA (UK) LTD.—Outdoor Technologies Group; *U.S. Private*, pg. 822
ACUSHNET COMPANY—Fortune Brands, Inc.; *U.S. Public*, pg. 675
ADIDAS AG; *Int'l*, pg. 24
AJAY LEISURE PRODUCTS, INC.—Ajay Sports Inc.; *U.S. Public*, pg. 34
AJAY SPORTS INC.; *U.S. Public*, pg. 34
ALL-AMERICAN CO.—Riddell Sports, Inc.; *U.S. Public*, pg. 1389
ALLSOP, INC.; *U.S. Private*, pg. 44
AMER GROUP LTD.; *Int'l*, pg. 72
AMERICAN RECREATION PRODUCTS, INC.—Kellwood Company; *U.S. Public*, pg. 948
ARITMOS AB—Proventus AB; *Int'l*, pg. 1072
TOMMY ARMOUR GOLF—U.S. Industries, Inc.; *U.S. Public*, pg. 1683
ARMSTRONG INTERNATIONAL, INC.; *U.S. Private*, pg. 83
THE ARNOLD PALMER GOLF COMPANY; *U.S. Public*, pg. 132
ATHLETIC TRAINING EQUIPMENT COMPANY, INC.—Sport Supply Group, Inc.; *U.S. Public*, pg. 1499
AUTOMOTIVE RACING DIVISION—Bell Sports Corp.; *U.S. Public*, pg. 207
BTR PLC; *Int'l*, pg. 124
BANGKOK ATHLETIC CO., LTD.—Bangkok Rubber Public Co., Ltd.; *Int'l*, pg. 146
BAUER SPORTS INC.—Nike, Inc.; *U.S. Public*, pg. 1184
BEAD INDUSTRIES INC.; *U.S. Private*, pg. 126
BELL SPORTS AUSTRALIA—Bell Sports Corp.; *U.S. Public*, pg. 207
BELL SPORTS CANADA—Bell Sports Corp.; *U.S. Public*, pg. 207
BELL SPORTS CORP.; *U.S. Public*, pg. 207
BERKLEY, INC.—Outdoor Technologies Group; *U.S. Private*, pg. 822
BIKE ATHLETIC CO.; *U.S. Private*, pg. 143
THE BLACK & DECKER CORPORATION; *U.S. Public*, pg. 233
BLUE FOX TACKLE CO.—Normark Corporation; *U.S. Private*, pg. 802
BOLLINGER INDUSTRIES INC.; *U.S. Public*, pg. 243
BOWLING PRODUCTS DIV.—Vulcan International Corporation; *U.S. Public*, pg. 1725
BRIMMS INC.; *U.S. Private*, pg. 169
BROWNING SA—Herstal S.A.; *Int'l*, pg. 617
BRUNSWICK BOWLING & BILLIARDS CORP.—Brunswick Corporation; *U.S. Public*, pg. 265
BRUNSWICK CORPORATION; *U.S. Public*, pg. 265
CADACO—Rapid Mounting & Finishing Co.; *U.S. Private*, pg. 910
CALLAWAY GOLF COMPANY; *U.S. Public*, pg. 294
CENTURY FENCE COMPANY; *U.S. Private*, pg. 226
CHAMPSSPORTS—Woolworth Corporation; *U.S. Public*, pg. 1777
CHATTANOOGA GROUP, INC.; *U.S. Private*, pg. 231
ROGER CLEVELAND GOLF COMPANY—Rossignol S.A.; *Int'l*, pg. 1127
COAST CAST CORPORATION S.A.—Coastcast Corporation; *U.S. Public*, pg. 391
COBRA GOLF INCORPORATED—Fortune Brands, Inc.; *U.S. Public*, pg. 675
THE COLEMAN COMPANY, INC.—MacAndrews & Forbes Holdings Inc.; *U.S. Private*, pg. 690
COMPUTROL, INC.—Armstrong International, Inc.; *U.S. Private*, pg. 83
THE COOK BATES DIVISION—London International Group plc; *Int'l*, pg. 815
CREATIVE PLAYTHINGS LTD.; *U.S. Private*, pg. 287
CROSMAN AIRGUNS—Crosman Corp.; *U.S. Private*, pg. 291
CYBEX INTERNATIONAL, INC.—U.M. Holding Limited; *U.S. Private*, pg. 1114
DACOR CORPORATION; *U.S. Private*, pg. 306
DELAIR GROUP, L.L.C.—Aluminum Shapes, LLC; *U.S. Private*, pg. 47
DOUGLAS/QUIKUT—Berkshire Hathaway Inc.; *U.S. Public*, pg. 217
DUDLEY SPORTS CO. DIVISION—Kohlberg Kravis Roberts & Co.; *U.S. Private*, pg. 629
E-Z-GO TEXTRON—Textron Inc.; *U.S. Public*, pg. 1589
ERO INDUSTRIES, INC.—Hicks, Muse, Tate & Furst Inc.; *U.S. Private*, pg. 526
EKTELON—Prince Sports Group Inc.; *U.S. Private*, pg. 884
ELMER'S WEIGHTS—Bollinger Industries Inc.; *U.S. Public*, pg. 243
ESCALADE SPORTS; *U.S. Public*, pg. 591
EURO-BELL S.A.—Bell Sports Corp.; *U.S. Public*, pg. 207
EVERLAST SPORTS MANUFACTURING CORP.—Everlast World Boxing Corp.; *U.S. Private*, pg. 386
EVERLAST WORLD BOXING CORP.; *U.S. Private*, pg. 386
EXCELSIOR INC.; *U.S. Private*, pg. 387
FIBRE GLASS-EVERCOAT COMPANY—Illinois Tool Works Inc.; *U.S. Public*, pg. 866
FIRST TEAM SPORTS INC.; *U.S. Public*, pg. 638
FLAMBEAU CORPORATION; *U.S. Private*, pg. 409
FLAMBEAU PRODUCTS CORP.—Flambeau Corporation; *U.S. Private*, pg. 409
FLEX-FAB—Flexfab Horizons International, Inc.; *U.S. Private*, pg. 412
FORTUNE BRANDS, INC.; *U.S. Public*, pg. 674
FRANKLIN SPORTS, INC.; *U.S. Private*, pg. 424
GAME TIME, INC.—Swing-N-Slide Corp.; *U.S. Public*, pg. 1543
GARED SPORTS INC.—Nixdorff Krein Industries Inc.; *U.S. Private*, pg. 799
GIRO SPORTS DESIGN, INC.—Bell Sports Corp.; *U.S. Public*, pg. 207
GLADDING BRAIDED PRODUCTS LLC—Crowe Rope Industries L.L.C.; *U.S. Private*, pg. 291
GUDEBROD, INC.; *U.S. Private*, pg. 486
HI PRODUCTS INC.—Hofmann Industries, Inc.; *U.S. Private*, pg. 533
HANSBERGER PRECISION GOLF INC.; *U.S. Private*, pg. 499
HARVARD SPORTS, INC.—Escalade Sports; *U.S. Public*, pg. 591
HEAD USA, INC.; *U.S. Private*, pg. 514
HEDSTROM CANADA—Hicks, Muse, Tate & Furst Inc.; *U.S. Private*, pg. 526
HILLERICH & BRADSBY CO.; *U.S. Private*, pg. 530
HOPPE'S A BRUNSWICK COMPANY—Brunswick Corporation; *U.S. Public*, pg. 266
HUFFY CORPORATION; *U.S. Public*, pg. 846
HUSSEY CORPORATION; *U.S. Private*, pg. 550
HUTCH SPORTS USA, INC.—RDM Sports Group; *U.S. Public*, pg. 1354
HYE PRECISION CO.—Amer Group Ltd.; *Int'l*, pg. 73
ICON HEALTH & FITNESS, INC.; *U.S. Private*, pg. 556
IRWIN SPORTS, INC.—Irwin Toy Ltd.; *Int'l*, pg. 688
IRWIN TOY LTD.; *Int'l*, pg. 688
JOHNSON WORLDWIDE ASSOCIATES, INC.; *U.S. Public*, pg. 932
K2 SKI-SPORT & MODE GMBH—K2 Inc.; *U.S. Public*, pg. 940
K2 BIKE—K2 Inc.; *U.S. Public*, pg. 940
K2 CORPORATION—K2 Inc.; *U.S. Public*, pg. 940
K2 INC.; *U.S. Public*, pg. 940
KARSTEN MANUFACTURING CORPORATION; *U.S. Private*, pg. 608
KELLWOOD COMPANY; *U.S. Public*, pg. 948
KLAFS SAUNABAU GMBH & CO. KG MEDIZINISCHE TECHNIK; *Int'l*, pg. 736
KOMBI, LTD.; *U.S. Private*, pg. 631
LIFETIME PRODUCTS INC.; *U.S. Private*, pg. 667
LYNX GOLF, INC.; *U.S. Private*, pg. 684
MSR—Recreational Equipment, Inc.; *U.S. Private*, pg. 914
MACGREGOR GOLF COMPANY—Amer Group Ltd.; *Int'l*, pg. 72
MACGREGOR GOLF HONG KONG LTD.—Amer Group Ltd.; *Int'l*, pg. 73
MACGREGOR GOLF UK, LTD.—Amer Group Ltd.; *Int'l*, pg. 73
MADSHUS A/S—K2 Inc.; *U.S. Public*, pg. 940
MARTIN REELS, A DIVISION OF ZEBCO—Brunswick Corporation; *U.S. Public*, pg. 265
MASTERCRAFT BOAT COMPANY—MacAndrews & Forbes Holdings Inc.; *U.S. Private*, pg. 689
MATTEL POWER WHEELS—Mattel, Inc.; *U.S. Public*, pg. 1058
MEI HOY SPORTS CO. LTD.—Mizuno Corporation; *Int'l*, pg. 885
MEPPS S.A.—Sheldons' Inc.; *U.S. Private*, pg. 992
MIRACLE RECREATION EQUIPMENT COMPANY; *U.S. Private*, pg. 752
MISTER TWISTER—Sheldons' Inc.; *U.S. Private*, pg. 992
MITRE SPORTS (U.S.)—Pentland Group PLC; *Int'l*, pg. 1036
MIZUNO CORPORATION; *Int'l*, pg. 884
MIZUNO GOLF COMPANY—Mizuno Corporation; *Int'l*, pg. 885
MIZUNO USA, INC.—Mizuno Corporation; *Int'l*, pg. 885
THE MURRAY OHIO MFG. CO.—Tomkins PLC; *Int'l*, pg. 1397
MUSKIN LEISURE PRODUCTS, INC.; *U.S. Private*, pg. 768
MYO-TECH ELECTRONICS—Bollinger Industries Inc.; *U.S. Public*, pg. 244
N.B.F. BOLLINGER INDUSTRIES—Bollinger Industries Inc.; *U.S. Public*, pg. 243
NAUTILUS INTERNATIONAL—Delta Woodside Industries, Inc.; *U.S. Public*, pg. 498
NEW ERA CAP. CO.; *U.S. Private*, pg. 793
NICKLAUS GOLF COMPANY, L.C.; *U.S. Private*, pg. 799
NISSEN TRAMPOLINE AG—Hanson PLC; *Int'l*, pg. 595
NIXDORFF KREIN INDUSTRIES INC.; *U.S. Private*, pg. 799
NORDICTRACK, INC.—CML Group, Inc.; *U.S. Public*, pg. 279
NORMARK CORPORATION; *U.S. Private*, pg. 802
NORTHWESTERN GOLF COMPANY; *U.S. Private*, pg. 806
O'BRIEN INTERNATIONAL, INC.—MacAndrews & Forbes Holdings Inc.; *U.S. Private*, pg. 689
OPTICOS S.R.L.; *Int'l*, pg. 1007
ORBEX INC.—Blount International, Inc.; *U.S. Public*, pg. 238
THE ORIOLES, INC.; *U.S. Private*, pg. 819
THE ORVIS COMPANY, INC.; *U.S. Private*, pg. 820
OUTDOOR TECHNOLOGIES GROUP; *U.S. Private*, pg. 822
PARAMOUNT FITNESS CORP.; *U.S. Private*, pg. 838
PENGUIN INDUSTRIES, INC.; *U.S. Private*, pg. 849
PENN RACQUET SPORTS—GenCorp Inc.; *U.S. Public*, pg. 706
PENTLAND GROUP PLC; *Int'l*, pg. 1035
PLANET EARTH PRODUCTS—K2 Inc.; *U.S. Public*, pg. 940
PONY U.S.A.—Pentland Group PLC; *Int'l*, pg. 1036
PRECOR, INC.—Premark International, Inc.; *U.S. Public*, pg. 1322
PRINCE SPORTS GROUP INC.; *U.S. Private*, pg. 884
PRO-SELECT—Northwestern Golf Company; *U.S. Private*, pg. 806
PROFESSIONAL GOLF COMPANY SDN. BHD.—Sime Darby Berhad; *Int'l*, pg. 1250
RDM SPORTS GROUP; *U.S. Public*, pg. 1354
RAM GOLF CORPORATION; *U.S. Private*, pg. 908
RAWLINGS COSTA RICA—Rawlings Sporting Goods Company; *U.S. Public*, pg. 1362
RAWLINGS SPORTING GOODS COMPANY; *U.S. Public*, pg. 1361
REAL DE TENNIS S.A. DE C.V.—Proventus AB; *Int'l*, pg. 1072
RIDDELL SPORTS, INC.; *U.S. Public*, pg. 1389
RIDDELL SPORTS, INC.—Riddell Sports, Inc.; *U.S. Public*, pg. 1389
ROADMASTER/BRUNSWICK—Brunswick Corporation; *U.S. Public*, pg. 265
ROLLER DERBY SKATE CORP.; *U.S. Private*, pg. 941
ROLLERBLADE, INC.; *U.S. Private*, pg. 941
ROSSIGNOL S.A.; *Int'l*, pg. 1127
ROSSIGNOL SC S.P.A.—Rossignol S.A.; *Int'l*, pg. 1127
ROSSIGNOL SKI CO.—Rossignol S.A.; *Int'l*, pg. 1127
RYOBI LTD.; *Int'l*, pg. 1151
SALOMON S.A.; *Int'l*, pg. 1181
SCOTT SPORTS GROUP; *U.S. Private*, pg. 977
SHAKESPEARE (AUSTRALIA) PTY. LTD.—K2 Inc.; *U.S. Public*, pg. 940
SHAKESPEARE COMPANY UNITED KINGDOM—K2 Inc.; *U.S. Public*, pg. 940
SHAKESPEARE FISHING TACKLE—K2 Inc.; *U.S. Public*, pg. 940
SHAKESPEARE HENGELSPORT B.V.—K2 Inc.; *U.S. Public*, pg. 940
SHAKESPEARE (HONG KONG) LTD.—K2 Inc.; *U.S. Public*, pg. 940
THE SHANE GROUP INC.; *U.S. Private*, pg. 989
THE SHELBURNE CORPORATION; *U.S. Private*, pg. 991
SHELDONS' INC.; *U.S. Private*, pg. 992
SHIMANO INC.; *Int'l*, pg. 1232
SKEETER PRODUCTS, INC.—MacAndrews & Forbes Holdings Inc.; *U.S. Private*, pg. 689
SKIS DYNASTAR S.A.—Rossignol S.A.; *Int'l*, pg. 1127
SKIS ROSSIGNOL DE ESPANA S.A.—Rossignol S.A.; *Int'l*, pg. 1127
SONIFORM, INC.—MacAndrews & Forbes Holdings Inc.; *U.S. Private*, pg. 689
SPALDING & EVENFLO COMPANIES, INC.—Kohlberg Kravis Roberts & Co.; *U.S. Private*, pg. 629
SPORT SUPPLY GROUP, INC.; *U.S. Public*, pg. 1499
SPORTCRAFT LTD.; *U.S. Private*, pg. 1026
STEARNS MANUFACTURING COMPANY—K2 Inc.; *U.S. Public*, pg. 940
TAYLOR MADE GOLF CO. INC.—Salomon S.A.; *Int'l*, pg. 1181
TAYLOR MADE (GREAT BRITAIN) LTD.—Salomon S.A.; *Int'l*, pg. 1181
TIEDEMANNS - JOH.H.ANDRESEN ANS; *Int'l*, pg. 1389
TRETORN AB—Proventus AB; *Int'l*, pg. 1072
TRETORN SPORT LTD.—Proventus AB; *Int'l*, pg. 1072
TRUE TEMPER SPORTS DIVISION—The Black & Decker Corporation; *U.S. Public*, pg. 233
U.M. HOLDING LIMITED; *U.S. Private*, pg. 1113
U.S. DIVERS CO., INC.; *U.S. Private*, pg. 1125
VOIT SPORTS, INC.; *U.S. Private*, pg. 1143
VULCAN BRUNSWICK BOWLING PIN COMPANY—Brunswick Corporation; *U.S. Public*, pg. 266
VULCAN BRUNSWICK BOWLING PIN COMPANY—Vulcan International Corporation; *U.S. Public*, pg. 1725
VULCAN INTERNATIONAL CORPORATION; *U.S. Public*, pg. 1725
WELLINGTON INDUSTRIES INC.; *U.S. Private*, pg. 1161
WILSON SPORTING GOODS CO.—Amer Group Ltd.; *Int'l*, pg. 73
WOODSTREAM CORPORATION—Ekco Group, Inc.; *U.S. Public*, pg. 566
YAMAHA CORPORATION; *Int'l*, pg. 1515
YONEX CO., LTD.; *Int'l*, pg. 1522
YORK BARBELL CO., INC.; *U.S. Private*, pg. 1196
ZEBCO—Brunswick Corporation; *U.S. Public*, pg. 265

ZIPPO MANUFACTURING COMPANY; U.S. Private, pg. 1207
ZURN INDUSTRIES, INC.; U.S. Public, pg. 1794

3951 — PENS, MECHANICAL PENCILS & PARTS

ATX INTERNATIONAL, INC.—A.T. Cross Co.; U.S. Public, pg. 461
ATX MARKETING CO.—A.T. Cross Co.; U.S. Public, pg. 461
BALLOGRAF BIC AB—Societe BIC S.A.; Int'l, pg. 1273
BEROL CORP.—Newell Co.; U.S. Public, pg. 1178
BEROL CORPORATION—Newell Co.; U.S. Public, pg. 1178
BIC ASSEMBLAGE S.A.R.L.—Societe BIC S.A.; Int'l, pg. 1273
BIC CORPORATION—Societe BIC S.A.; Int'l, pg. 1273
BIC DE GUATEMALA—Societe BIC S.A.; Int'l, pg. 1273
BIC INC.—Societe BIC S.A.; Int'l, pg. 1273
BIRO BIC LTD.—Societe BIC S.A.; Int'l, pg. 1273
CONTE S.A.—Societe BIC S.A.; Int'l, pg. 1273
A.T. CROSS CO.; U.S. Public, pg. 460
DIXON TICONDEROGA COMPANY; U.S. Public, pg. 514
DIXON TICONDEROGA INC.—Dixon Ticonderoga Company; U.S. Public, pg. 515
DIXON WEAREVER INC.—Dixon Ticonderoga Company; U.S. Public, pg. 515
DRI MARK PRODUCTS, INC.; U.S. Private, pg. 342
EMPIRE BEROL U.S.A.—Newell Co.; U.S. Public, pg. 1178
EVERSHARP PEN CO.; U.S. Private, pg. 386
GILLETTE CO.-PARKER PEN USA—The Gillette Company; U.S. Public, pg. 745
THE GILLETTE COMPANY; U.S. Public, pg. 743
GILLETTE DO BRASIL & CIA—The Gillette Company; U.S. Public, pg. 744
GILLETTE GROUP ITALY S.R.L.—The Gillette Company; U.S. Public, pg. 745
GILLETTE (PHILIPPINES), INC.—The Gillette Company; U.S. Public, pg. 745
GILLETTE SOUTH AFRICA LIMITED—The Gillette Company; U.S. Public, pg. 745
GOLDEN BOOKS FAMILY ENTERTAINMENT INC.; U.S. Public, pg. 749
HUNT CORPORATION; U.S. Public, pg. 848
KOH-I-NOOR, INC.; U.S. Private, pg. 629
NO SABE FALLAR S.A.—Societe BIC S.A.; Int'l, pg. 1273
PARKER PEN (AUSTRALIA) PTY. LTD.—The Gillette Company; U.S. Public, pg. 745
PARKER PEN CANADA LIMITED—The Gillette Company; U.S. Public, pg. 745
PARKER PEN PLC—The Gillette Company; U.S. Public, pg. 745
PENTECH INTERNATIONAL, INC.; U.S. Public, pg. 1274
PENTEL CO., LTD.; Int'l, pg. 1035
PENTEL OF AMERICA, LTD.—Pentel Co., Ltd.; Int'l, pg. 1035
THE PILOT CORPORATION; Int'l, pg. 1057
THE PILOT CORPORATION OF AMERICA—The Pilot Corporation; Int'l, pg. 1057
THE PILOT PEN CORP. OF AMERICA—The Pilot Corporation; Int'l, pg. 1057
SANFORD BEROC CORP.—Newell Co.; U.S. Public, pg. 1178
SANFORD CORPORATION—Newell Co.; U.S. Public, pg. 1178
SCRIPTO-TOKAI CORP.; U.S. Private, pg. 977
SHEAFFER INC.—Gefinor S.A. Luxembourg; Int'l, pg. 542
SOCIETE BIC S.A.; Int'l, pg. 1272
STATIONERY PRODUCTS DIVISION—The Gillette Company; U.S. Public, pg. 744
UNIC S.A.—Societe BIC S.A.; Int'l, pg. 1273
WATERMAN S.A.—The Gillette Company; U.S. Public, pg. 745
ZIPPO MANUFACTURING COMPANY; U.S. Private, pg. 1207

3952 — LEAD PENCILS, CRAYONS, & ARTISTS' MATERIALS

AARON BROTHERS, INC.—Michaels Stores, Inc.; U.S. Public, pg. 1104
BADGER AIR BRUSH COMPANY; U.S. Private, pg. 110
BEROL CORP.—Newell Co.; U.S. Public, pg. 1178
BEROL CORPORATION—Newell Co.; U.S. Public, pg. 1178
BINNEY & SMITH INC.—Hallmark Cards, Inc.; U.S. Private, pg. 496
BUTLER CAPITAL CORP.; U.S. Private, pg. 190
CARLYLE INDUSTRIES, INC.—Noel Group, Inc.; U.S. Public, pg. 1187
CRAYOLA PRODUCTS DIV.—Hallmark Cards, Inc.; U.S. Private, pg. 496
CUMBERLAND GRAPHICS LTD.—Fortune Brands, Inc.; U.S. Public, pg. 674
DA-LITE SCREEN COMPANY, INC.; U.S. Private, pg. 306
DAY-GLO COLOR CORP.—RPM, Inc.; U.S. Public, pg. 1357
DIXON TICONDEROGA COMPANY; U.S. Public, pg. 514
DIXON TICONDEROGA COMPANY—Dixon Ticonderoga Company; U.S. Public, pg. 515
DIXON TICONDEROGA INC.—Dixon Ticonderoga Company; U.S. Public, pg. 515
EMPIRE BEROL U.S.A.—Newell Co.; U.S. Public, pg. 1178
GILLETTE CO.-PARKER PEN USA—The Gillette Company; U.S. Public, pg. 745
HALLMARK ART PRODUCTS & INTERNATIONAL DIV.—Hallmark Cards, Inc.; U.S. Private, pg. 496
HALLMARK CARDS, INC.; U.S. Private, pg. 495
HALLMARK EDUCATIONAL PRODUCTS DIV.—Hallmark Cards, Inc.; U.S. Private, pg. 496
HUNT CORPORATION; U.S. Public, pg. 848
KOH-I-NOOR, INC.; U.S. Private, pg. 629
NASCO MODESTO—Geneve Corporation; U.S. Private, pg. 446
NORTHEASTERN GRAPHIC SUPPLY, INC.; U.S. Private, pg. 805
PARKER PEN PLC—The Gillette Company; U.S. Public, pg. 745
PENTECH INTERNATIONAL, INC.; U.S. Public, pg. 1274
PENTEL CO., LTD.; Int'l, pg. 1035
PENTEL OF AMERICA, LTD.—Pentel Co., Ltd.; Int'l, pg. 1035
PROJECTA B.V.—Da-Lite Screen Company, Inc.; U.S. Private, pg. 306
QUARTET MANUFACTURING CO.—General Binding Corporation; U.S. Public, pg. 707
ROSE ART INDUSTRIES; U.S. Private, pg. 945
SANFORD CORPORATION—Newell Co.; U.S. Public, pg. 1178
SCRIPTO-TOKAI CORP.; U.S. Private, pg. 977
STATIONERY PRODUCTS DIVISION—The Gillette Company; U.S. Public, pg. 744
TIME WARNER INC.; U.S. Public, pg. 1610
TRANSILWRAP COMPANY, INC.; U.S. Private, pg. 1097
TRI-CHEM, INC.; U.S. Private, pg. 1100

3953 — MARKING DEVICES

ACCO-REXEL GROUP SERVICES PLC—Fortune Brands, Inc.; U.S. Public, pg. 674
AMERICAN MARKING SYSTEMS; U.S. Private, pg. 58
ANCHOR CONTINENTAL INCORPORATED; U.S. Private, pg. 70
BEROL CORPORATION—Newell Co.; U.S. Public, pg. 1178
W.H. BRADY CO.; U.S. Public, pg. 250
CONSOLIDATED SCREEN-MAKERS, INC.—The Dyson-Kissner-Moran Corporation; U.S. Private, pg. 351
COSCO INDUSTRIES; U.S. Private, pg. 277
DIAGRAPH CORPORATION; U.S. Private, pg. 330
GRAPHIC CONTROLS CORPORATION; U.S. Private, pg. 470
ILLINOIS TOOL WORKS INC.; U.S. Public, pg. 865
MATTHEWS CANADA LTD.—Matthews International Corp.; U.S. Public, pg. 1060
MATTHEY BEYRAND & CIE S.A.—Johnson Matthey Public Limited Company; Int'l, pg. 714
THE MEYERCORD COMPANY—Illinois Tool Works Inc.; U.S. Public, pg. 867
P-T TEMPLET COMPANY—NCH Corporation; U.S. Public, pg. 1145
PANNIER CORPORATION; U.S. Private, pg. 837
PARKER SEAL DE BAJA, S.A. DE C.V.—Parker Hannifin Corporation; U.S. Public, pg. 1262
PITNEY BOWES INC.; U.S. Public, pg. 1303
PRECISION DYNAMICS CORPORATION; U.S. Private, pg. 879
SANFORD CORPORATION—Newell Co.; U.S. Public, pg. 1178
THOMAS & BETTS CORPORATION; U.S. Public, pg. 1597
3M; U.S. Public, pg. 1604
WEBER MARKING SYSTEMS, INC.; U.S. Private, pg. 1157

3955 — CARBON PAPER & INKED RIBBONS

AHLSTROM PAPER AG—A. Ahlstrom Corporation; Int'l, pg. 35
ASPEN IMAGING INTERNATIONAL, INC.—Pubco Corporation; U.S. Public, pg. 1339
BAROUH EATON ALLEN CORPORATION; U.S. Private, pg. 117
CAPITAL IMAGING; U.S. Private, pg. 206
CRANE & CO., INC.; U.S. Private, pg. 286
DATAPRODUCTS CORPORATION—Hitachi Koki Co., Ltd.; Int'l, pg. 620
DATAPRODUCTS (DUBLIN) LTD.—Hitachi Koki Co., Ltd.; Int'l, pg. 621
DATAPRODUCTS SUPPLIES DIV.—Hitachi Koki Co., Ltd.; Int'l, pg. 621
FRYETECH, INC.; U.S. Private, pg. 430
HARGRO ENTERPRISES, INC.; U.S. Private, pg. 502
INTERNATIONAL BUSINESS MACHINES CORPORATION; U.S. Public, pg. 895
KO-REC-TYPE—Barouh Eaton Allen Corporation; U.S. Private, pg. 117
LEXMARK FRANCE—Lexmark International Group, Inc.; U.S. Public, pg. 991
THE MEAD CORPORATION; U.S. Public, pg. 1074
MELLON CORPORATION; U.S. Private, pg. 730
NCR CORPORATION; U.S. Public, pg. 1146
NU-KOTE INTERNATIONAL; U.S. Public, pg. 1205
OLIVETTI SUPPLIES, INC.—Olivetti SpA; Int'l, pg. 1002
REXAM DSI—Rexam PLC; Int'l, pg. 1106
RICOH ELECTRONICS, INC.—Ricoh Company, Ltd.; Int'l, pg. 1114
RITTENHOUSE INC.; U.S. Private, pg. 933
STUART HALL CO., INC.—Newell Co.; U.S. Public, pg. 1178
WEBER MARKING SYSTEMS, INC.; U.S. Private, pg. 1157

3961 — COSTUME JEWELRY & COSTUME NOVELTIES, EXCEPT PRECIOUS METAL

ARLINGTON, LTD.—Avon Products, Inc.; U.S. Public, pg. 156
ARTRA GROUP INCORPORATED; U.S. Public, pg. 136
AVON PRODUCTS, INC.; U.S. Public, pg. 155
L.G. BALFOUR CO., INC.—Commemorative Brands, Inc.; U.S. Private, pg. 258
DARLENE JEWELRY MANUFACTURING COMPANY; U.S. Private, pg. 311
ERI LABORATORIES—Inverness Corp.; U.S. Private, pg. 574
HERFF JONES INC.; U.S. Private, pg. 523
INVERNESS CORP.; U.S. Private, pg. 574
INVERNESS FRANCE—Inverness Corp.; U.S. Private, pg. 574
INVERNESS UK LTD.—Inverness Corp.; U.S. Private, pg. 574
K&M ASSOCIATES—American Biltrite Inc.; U.S. Public, pg. 69
MARVELLA INC.—The Monet Group, Inc.; U.S. Private, pg. 757
MEIJI JEWELRY—Meiji Seika Kaisha, Ltd.; Int'l, pg. 855
THE MONET GROUP, INC.; U.S. Private, pg. 757
MONET JEWELERS—The Monet Group, Inc.; U.S. Private, pg. 757
THE NAPIER CO.; U.S. Private, pg. 774
PERFECT PEARL COMPANY, INC.; U.S. Private, pg. 852
THE PILOT CORPORATION; Int'l, pg. 1057
RICHTON INTERNATIONAL CORPORATION; U.S. Public, pg. 1389
SWANK, INC.; U.S. Public, pg. 1543
VICTORIA CREATIONS, INC.; U.S. Private, pg. 1139

3965 — FASTENERS, BUTTONS, NEEDLES & PINS

ANCRA INTERNATIONAL LLC; U.S. Private, pg. 71
BLUMENTHAL/LANSING COMPANY—Noel Group, Inc.; U.S. Public, pg. 1187
BOYE NEEDLE—Wm. E. Wright Limited Partnership; U.S. Private, pg. 1192
CALDWELL BUTTON COMPANY—Empire of Carolina, Inc.; U.S. Public, pg. 579
CARLYLE INDUSTRIES, INC.—Noel Group, Inc.; U.S. Public, pg. 1187
COATS & CLARK INC.—Coats Viyella plc; Int'l, pg. 300
COMMONWEALTH INDUSTRIES—Masco Corporation; U.S. Public, pg. 1054
EAGLE BUTTON CO., INC.; U.S. Private, pg. 354
EMHART INTERNATIONAL LTD.—The Black & Decker Corporation; U.S. Public, pg. 233
EMPIRE OF CAROLINA, INC.; U.S. Public, pg. 579
FASTENAL COMPANY; U.S. Public, pg. 614
ILLINOIS TOOL WORKS INC.; U.S. Public, pg. 865
ITOCHU BUILDING PRODUCTS CO., INC.—Itochu Corporation; Int'l, pg. 694
MONOGRAM AEROSPACE FASTENERS, INC.—Masco Corporation; U.S. Public, pg. 1054
NORTH & JUDD; U.S. Private, pg. 804
NUCOR CORPORATION; U.S. Public, pg. 1205
NUCOR FASTENERS—Nucor Corporation; U.S. Public, pg. 1205
PSM INTERNATIONAL—McKechnie PLC; Int'l, pg. 852
PRYM-DRITZ CORPORATION—William Prym GmbH & Co. KG; Int'l, pg. 1499
REPUBLIC FASTENER PRODUCTS CORP.; U.S. Private, pg. 923
SEAC LIMITED—Halma p.l.c.; Int'l, pg. 590
EDWIN B. STIMPSON COMPANY, INC.; U.S. Private, pg. 1043
STOCKO CORP.—Stocko Metallwaren Fabriken Henkels & Sohn; Int'l, pg. 1301
STOCKO METALLWAREN FABRIKEN HENKELS & SOHN; Int'l, pg. 1301
TALLEY INDUSTRIES, INC.—Carpenter Technology Corporation; U.S. Public, pg. 307
3M; U.S. Public, pg. 1604
TRANSTECHNOLOGY CORPORATION; U.S. Public, pg. 1632
UNIVERSAL FASTENERS INC.—YKK Corporation; Int'l, pg. 1515
VELCRO CANADA INC.—Velcro Industries N.V.; Int'l, pg. 1462
VELCRO INDUSTRIES N.V.; Int'l, pg. 1462
VELCRO LAMINATES INC.—Velcro Industries N.V.; Int'l, pg. 1462
VELCRO USA INC.—Velcro Industries N.V.; Int'l, pg. 1462
VELCROMEX S.A. DE C.V.—Velcro Industries N.V.; Int'l, pg. 1462
WATERBURY COMPANIES, INC.—Carpenter Technology Corporation; U.S. Public, pg. 308
WATERBURY COMPANIES, INC.-METAL & BUTTON DIV.—Carpenter Technology Corporation; U.S. Public, pg. 308
WILLIAM PRYM GMBH & CO. KG; Int'l, pg. 1499
WM. E. WRIGHT LIMITED PARTNERSHIP; U.S. Private, pg. 1192
YKK CORPORATION; Int'l, pg. 1514
YKK (U.S.A.)—YKK Corporation; Int'l, pg. 1515
Y.K.K. (U.S.A.) INC.—YKK Corporation; Int'l, pg. 1515

3991 — BROOMS & BRUSHES

ATHEY PRODUCTS-SWEEPER DIV.—Athey Products Corporation; U.S. Public, pg. 143
BINNEY & SMITH INC.—Hallmark Cards, Inc.; U.S. Private, pg. 496
BRISTOL-MYERS SQUIBB COMPANY; U.S. Public, pg. 253
BRUSH RESEARCH MANUFACTURING COMPANY; U.S. Private, pg. 176
JOHN O. BUTLER CO.—Sunstar Inc.; Int'l, pg. 1320
COSMHOGAR, S.A.—Stanhome Inc.; U.S. Public, pg. 1508
DOUGLAS/QUIKUT—Berkshire Hathaway Inc.; U.S. Public, pg. 217
EKCO CLEANING, INC.—Ekco Group, Inc.; U.S. Public, pg. 566
EZ PAINTR CANADA—Newell Co.; U.S. Public, pg. 1178
EZ PAINTR CORP.—Newell Co.; U.S. Public, pg. 1177
EASY DAY MANUFACTURING COMPANY; U.S. Private, pg. 358
EKCO GROUP, INC.; U.S. Public, pg. 566
FELTON BRUSH INC.; U.S. Private, pg. 400
FLO-PAC CORPORATION; U.S. Private, pg. 414
FLO-PAC MIDWEST—Flo-Pac Corporation; U.S. Private, pg. 414

FLO-PAC PACIFIC—Flo-Pac Corporation; *U.S. Private*, pg. 414
FLO-PAC SOUTHEAST—Flo-Pac Corporation; *U.S. Private*, *pg. 414*
FLOQUIL-POLLY S COLOR CORP.—RPM, Inc.; *U.S. Public*, pg. 1357
FOAM PRO MANUFACTURING; *U.S. Private*, pg. 415
FRANKLIN BRUSH DIVISION—Crown Cork & Seal Company, Inc.; *U.S. Public*, pg. 463
THE FULLER BRUSH COMPANY—CPAC, Inc.; *U.S. Public*, *pg. 282*
JASON INCORPORATED; *U.S. Public*, pg. 923
JORDAN A/S; *Int'l*, pg. 714
KELLER-DORIAN GRAVEURS, DIV. OF ROEHLEN INDUSTRIES/EUROPE—Standex International Corporation; *U.S. Public*, pg. 1507
KIRKWOOD CARBON—Kirkwood Industries, Inc.; *U.S. Private*, pg. 623
LINZER PRODUCTS CORP.; *U.S. Private*, pg. 669
M & E MANUFACTURING CO.—Plastek Group; *U.S. Private*, pg. 870
MILL-ROSE COMPANY; *U.S. Private*, pg. 746
MURALO CO., INC.; *U.S. Private*, pg. 767
NEWELL CO.; *U.S. Public*, pg. 1176
OSBORN MANUFACTURING—Jason Incorporated; *U.S. Public*, pg. 924
PARKS PRODUCTS, INC.; *U.S. Private*, pg. 840
PLAYTEX PRODUCTS CORP.—Playtex Products Inc.; *U.S. Public*, pg. 1311
PLAYTEX PRODUCTS INC.; *U.S. Public*, pg. 1310
RANIR CORPORATION/DCP; *U.S. Private*, pg. 909
RUBBERMAID INCORPORATED; *U.S. Public*, pg. 1411
THE SHERWIN-WILLIAMS COMPANY; *U.S. Public*, pg. 1465
STANHOME INC.; *U.S. Public*, pg. 1508
STEINER CO., INC.—Steiner Corporation; *U.S. Private*, pg. 1039
SUNSTAR INC.; *Int'l*, pg. 1320
VENTURI INC.; *U.S. Private*, pg. 1136
WILTON CORPORATION; *U.S. Private*, pg. 1181
THE WOOSTER BRUSH COMPANY; *U.S. Private*, pg. 1188
WOOSTER MAGIKOTER WEST DIVISION—The Wooster Brush Company; *U.S. Private*, pg. 1188

3993 — SIGNS & ADVERTISING DISPLAYS

AMD INDUSTRIES INC.; *U.S. Private*, pg. 6
ADVERTISING DISPLAY CO.; *U.S. Private*, pg. 23
AMCO FOLDING CARTONS, INC.; *U.S. Private*, pg. 48
AMERICAN CONSUMER PRODUCTS—Vista 2000, Inc.; *U.S. Private*, pg. 1142
AMERICAN SIGN & MARKETING SERVICES, INC.—Plasti-Line, Inc.; *U.S. Public*, pg. 1309
ATLITE LIGHTING EQUIP, INC.—Cooper Industries, Inc.; *U.S. Public*, pg. 443
BUFKOR, INC.; *U.S. Private*, pg. 179
CGF INDUSTRIES; *U.S. Private*, pg. 194
CHICAGO SHOW PRINTING CO.; *U.S. Private*, pg. 235
COLE CONSUMER PRODUCTS—Vista 2000, Inc.; *U.S. Private*, pg. 1142
COSCO INDUSTRIES; *U.S. Private*, pg. 277
CUMMINGS INC.; *U.S. Private*, pg. 295
DAKTRONICS, INC.; *U.S. Public*, pg. 478
DAUMAN DISPLAYS, INC.—Continental Graphics Holdings, Inc.; *U.S. Private*, pg. 268
DUALITE INC.; *U.S. Private*, pg. 344
DUNLAP MANUFACTURING CO.—The Vernon Company; *U.S. Private*, pg. 1137
EVERBRITE, INC.; *U.S. Private*, pg. 386
FEDERAL SIGNAL CORPORATION; *U.S. Public*, pg. 616
FISCHBACH CORPORATION—American International Group, Inc.; *U.S. Public*, pg. 84
GHN—Everbrite, Inc.; *U.S. Private*, pg. 386
GEIGER BROTHERS; *U.S. Private*, pg. 442
A.J. GERRARD AND COMPANY; *U.S. Private*, pg. 449
GRAPHLINE INC.; *U.S. Private*, pg. 471
HALL SIGN, INC.; *U.S. Private*, pg. 495
W. HEATH & CO.—American International Group, Inc.; *U.S. Public*, pg. 84
INFINICOM; *U.S. Private*, pg. 561
LSI INDUSTRIES, INC.; *U.S. Public*, pg. 971
LA FRANCE CORPORATION; *U.S. Private*, pg. 640
LEWTAN INDUSTRIES CORP.; *U.S. Private*, pg. 666
LUMINATOR—Mark IV Industries Inc.; *U.S. Public*, pg. 1045
MARK IV INDUSTRIES INC.; *U.S. Public*, pg. 1044
MARKETING DISPLAYS INTERNATIONAL; *U.S. Private*, pg. 705
MEDIA NETWORKS INC.—Time Warner Inc.; *U.S. Public*, pg. 1612
MOUNT VERNON NEON—Everbrite, Inc.; *U.S. Private*, pg. 386
JACK NADEL, INC.; *U.S. Private*, pg. 773
OMEGA ELECTRONICS SA—SMH Swiss Corporation for Micro Electronics & Watchmaking Indus. Ltd.; *Int'l*, pg. 1161
PACIFIC HANDY CUTTER, INC.; *U.S. Private*, pg. 831
PANNIER CORPORATION; *U.S. Private*, pg. 837
PHILADELPHIA SIGN COMPANY; *U.S. Private*, pg. 861
PLASTI-LINE, INC.; *U.S. Public*, pg. 1308
RAPID MOUNTING & FINISHING CO.; *U.S. Private*, pg. 910
RENAISSANCE PUBLISHING CO., INC.—Bemrose Corporation; *Int'l*, pg. 185
SA-SO COMPANY; *U.S. Private*, pg. 955
SELECTO-FLASH, INC.; *U.S. Private*, pg. 982
SOUTHEAST REGION—Federal Signal Corporation; *U.S. Public*, pg. 617
SOUTHWEST REGION—Federal Signal Corporation; *U.S. Public*, pg. 617
TANDY SIGNS—Tandy Corporation; *U.S. Public*, pg. 1560
3M; *U.S. Public*, pg. 1604
TOPFLIGHT CORP.; *U.S. Private*, pg. 1091
TRANS-LUX CORPORATION; *U.S. Public*, pg. 1628
UNITED STATES NAME PLATE—La France Corporation; *U.S. Private*, pg. 640
THE VERNON COMPANY; *U.S. Private*, pg. 1137
VIAD CORP; *U.S. Public*, pg. 1718
VULCAN INC.; *U.S. Private*, pg. 1144
WENCO INC.—Wendy's International Inc.; *U.S. Public*, pg. 1754
WINTHROP-ATKINS CO., INC.; *U.S. Private*, pg. 1183
YOUNG ELECTRIC SIGN COMPANY; *U.S. Private*, pg. 1201

3995 — BURIAL CASKETS

AURORA CASKET COMPANY; *U.S. Private*, pg. 99
BATESVILLE CASKET COMPANY, INC.—Hillenbrand Industries, Inc.; *U.S. Public*, pg. 828
BROWN-SERVICE FUNERAL HOMES CO., INC.—Torchmark Corporation; *U.S. Public*, pg. 1622
CASKET SHELLS, INC.; *U.S. Private*, pg. 218
CLARK GRAVE VAULT CO.; *U.S. Private*, pg. 243
HILLENBRAND INDUSTRIES, INC.; *U.S. Public*, pg. 828
3M; *U.S. Public*, pg. 1604

3996 — LINOLEUM, ASPHALTED-FELT-BASE, & OTHER HARD SURFACE FLOOR COVERINGS, NEC

AMERICAN BILTRITE INC.; *U.S. Public*, pg. 68
ARMSTRONG-NYLEX PTY. LTD.—Armstrong World Industries, Inc.; *U.S. Public*, pg. 132
ARMSTRONG (SINGAPORE) PTE. LTD.—Armstrong World Industries, Inc.; *U.S. Public*, pg. 132
ARMSTRONG WORLD INDUSTRIES, INC.; *U.S. Public*, pg. 131
ARMSTRONG WORLD INDUSTRIES PTY. LTD.—Armstrong World Industries, Inc.; *U.S. Public*, pg. 132
ARMSTRONG WORLD INDUSTRIES, S.A.—Armstrong World Industries, Inc.; *U.S. Public*, pg. 132
CONGOLEUM CORPORATION—American Biltrite Inc.; *U.S. Public*, pg. 69
DOMCO INC.; *Int'l*, pg. 415
FORBO KROMMENIE B.V.—Forbo Holding SA; *Int'l*, pg. 497
FORBO-STAMOID AG—Forbo Holding SA; *Int'l*, pg. 497
FORMICA CORPORATION—BTR plc; *Int'l*, pg. 129
INARCO LIMITED—Armstrong World Industries, Inc.; *U.S. Public*, pg. 132
KENTILE OPERTING CO.; *U.S. Private*, pg. 615
MANNINGTON MILLS, INC.; *U.S. Private*, pg. 700
ROTH CORPORATION—Trek Corporation; *U.S. Private*, pg. 1099
3M; *U.S. Public*, pg. 1604

3999 — MANUFACTURING INDUSTRIES, NEC

AARON BROTHERS, INC.—Michaels Stores, Inc.; *U.S. Public*, pg. 1104
ADERANS CO., LTD.; *Int'l*, pg. 24
AESCULAP AKTIENGESELLSCHAFT; *Int'l*, pg. 29
ALLIANCE GAMING CORPORATION; *U.S. Public*, pg. 46
ALLOY PRODUCTS CORP; *U.S. Private*, pg. 42
ALPINE AKTIENGESELLSCHAFT—Hosokawa Micron Corporation; *Int'l*, pg. 636
ALPINE AMERICAN—Hosokawa Micron Corporation; *Int'l*, pg. 635
AMERICAN HOME ENTERTAINMENT—JAKKS Pacific, Inc.; *U.S. Public*, pg. 923
AMERICAN HOME IMPROVEMENT; *U.S. Private*, pg. 56
AMERICAN SPECIALTIES INC.; *U.S. Private*, pg. 62
ANDIS COMPANY; *U.S. Private*, pg. 73
ANSUL INCORPORATED—Tyco International Ltd.; *U.S. Public*, pg. 1648
ATARI GAMES CORPORATION—WMS Industries Inc.; *U.S. Public*, pg. 1727
AUTOSWAGE PRODUCTS, INC.; *U.S. Private*, pg. 101
BADGER FIRE PROTECTION INC.—Williams Holdings Plc; *Int'l*, pg. 1500
BAIRNCO CORPORATION; *U.S. Public*, pg. 165
L.G. BALFOUR CO., INC.—Commemorative Brands, Inc.; *U.S. Private*, pg. 258
BANTA HEALTHCARE PRODUCTS—Banta Corporation; *U.S. Public*, pg. 188
BARCREST LTD.—Bass PLC; *Int'l*, pg. 170
BASSANI MANUFACTURING; *U.S. Private*, pg. 122
THE W.E. BASSETT COMPANY; *U.S. Private*, pg. 122
BAZAAR & NOVELTY—Stuart Entertainment Inc.; *U.S. Public*, pg. 1526
BEAD INDUSTRIES INC.; *U.S. Private*, pg. 126
D.D. BEAN & SONS CO.; *U.S. Private*, pg. 126
BELVEDERE COMPANY—Smith Investment Company; *U.S. Private*, pg. 1008
BEPEX CORPORATION—Hosokawa Micron Corporation; *Int'l*, pg. 636
W.H. BRADY CO.; *U.S. Public*, pg. 250
BRIMMS INC.; *U.S. Private*, pg. 169
BUNZL EXTRUSION—Bunzl PLC; *Int'l*, pg. 232
BUNZL PLC; *Int'l*, pg. 232
BUTLER CAPITAL CORP.; *U.S. Private*, pg. 190
CC INDUSTRIES, INC.; *U.S. Private*, pg. 192
CANDLE CORPORATION OF AMERICA—Blyth Industries; *U.S. Public*, pg. 239
CANDLE-LITE, A LANCASTER COLONY CO.—Lancaster Colony Corporation; *U.S. Public*, pg. 976
CARSON PRODUCTS COMPANY; *U.S. Public*, pg. 309
CASINO ELECTRONICS, INC.—Alliance Gaming Corporation; *U.S. Public*, pg. 47
CELEBRITY INCORPORATED; *U.S. Public*, pg. 319
CENTRAL BEAUTY EQUIPMENT—Smith Investment Company; *U.S. Private*, pg. 1008
CERAMTEC NORTH AMERICA APPLICATIONS, INC.—Metallgesellschaft AG; *Int'l*, pg. 860
CERBERUS PYROTRONICS INC.—Siemens AG; *Int'l*, pg. 1246
CHANCE INDUSTRIES, INC.; *U.S. Private*, pg. 228
CHASE & SONS DIVISION—Chase Corporation; *U.S. Public*, pg. 337
CHASE & SONS-WEBSTER BRANCH—Chase Corporation; *U.S. Public*, pg. 337
CHASE CORPORATION; *U.S. Public*, pg. 337
CHEMISCHE FABRIK GRUNAU GMBH—Henkel KGaA; *Int'l*, pg. 609
CHEROKEE INC.; *U.S. Public*, pg. 345
CLAIROL, INC.—Bristol-Myers Squibb Company; *U.S. Public*, pg. 254
JOSLYN CLARK CONTROLS, INC.—Danaher Corporation; *U.S. Public*, pg. 481
THE CLOROX COMPANY; *U.S. Public*, pg. 386
CONSOLIDATED CIGAR CORPORATION—MacAndrews & Forbes Holdings Inc.; *U.S. Private*, pg. 690
CONTE S.A.—Societe BIC S.A.; *Int'l*, pg. 1273
COSCO INDUSTRIES; *U.S. Private*, pg. 277
CREATIVE PRODUCTIONS; *U.S. Private*, pg. 288
CRESSWELL LIGHTING LIMITED—Emess PLC; *Int'l*, pg. 453
W.W. CROSS, INC.—D.D. Bean & Sons Co.; *U.S. Private*, pg. 127
DELA—Groupe Strafor Facom; *Int'l*, pg. 570
DELAVAN COMMERCIAL PRODUCTS DIVISION—Coltec Holdings Inc; *U.S. Public*, pg. 401
DELAVAN GAS TURBINE PRODUCTS DIVISION—Coltec Holdings Inc; *U.S. Public*, pg. 401
DETAILS—Steelcase Inc.; *U.S. Private*, pg. 1038
DIAMOND BRANDS, INC.; *U.S. Private*, pg. 330
DIXON WEAREVER INC.—Dixon Ticonderoga Company; *U.S. Public*, pg. 515
DURACELL-DAIMON SVENSKA—The Gillette Company; *U.S. Public*, pg. 743
ELXSI CORPORATION; *U.S. Public*, pg. 545
ESAB TELE-COMP AB—Charter plc; *Int'l*, pg. 281
EZ INTERNATIONAL—Wm. E. Wright Limited Partnership; *U.S. Private*, pg. 1192
EDUCATIONAL INSIGHTS, INC.; *U.S. Public*, pg. 565
EMERY WATERHOUSE COMPANY; *U.S. Private*, pg. 373
EVANS RULE CO., INC.—The L.S. Starrett Company; *U.S. Public*, pg. 1511
FARNAM COMPANIES, INC.; *U.S. Private*, pg. 396
FIBER MATERIALS, INC.; *U.S. Private*, pg. 402
FILTER MEDIA—Hosokawa Micron Corporation; *Int'l*, pg. 636
FILTRONA RICHMOND COMPANY—Bunzl PLC; *Int'l*, pg. 232
FINKEL OUTDOOR PRODUCTS, INC.—Trace International Holdings, Inc.; *U.S. Private*, pg. 1094
THE FIRST REPUBLIC CORPORATION OF AMERICA; *U.S. Public*, pg. 637
FORCE 10 MARINE LTD.—Valley Forge Corporation; *U.S. Public*, pg. 1705
THE FRANKLIN MINT—Roll International Corporation; *U.S. Private*, pg. 941
GAF PREMIUM PRODUCTS, INC.—GAF Corporation; *U.S. Private*, pg. 433
GBC/VELOBLIND—General Binding Corporation; *U.S. Public*, pg. 707
GENERAL HOUSEWARES CORP.; *U.S. Public*, pg. 715
GENERAL SIGNAL CORPORATION; *U.S. Public*, pg. 726
GENERAL WIG MANUFACTURERS, INC.—MacAndrews & Forbes Holdings Inc.; *U.S. Private*, pg. 690
GHENT MANUFACTURING, INC.; *U.S. Private*, pg. 450
GIANT RESOURCE RECOVERY COMPANY (GRR!)—Giant Cement Holding Inc.; *U.S. Public*, pg. 741
GILLETTE DO BRASIL & CIA—The Gillette Company; *U.S. Public*, pg. 744
GLENDINNING MARINE PRODUCTS, INC.—Valley Forge Corporation; *U.S. Public*, pg. 1705
GOODY PRODUCTS, INC.—Newell Co.; *U.S. Public*, pg. 1177
HALLMARK CARDS, INC.; *U.S. Private*, pg. 495
HAMPSHIRE GROUP, LTD.; *U.S. Public*, pg. 778
HARTZ GROUP—The Hartz Mountain Corp.; *U.S. Private*, pg. 508
THE HARTZ MOUNTAIN CORP.; *U.S. Private*, pg. 508
HAZEN PAPER COMPANY; *U.S. Private*, pg. 514
THE HILSINGER CO. L.P.; *U.S. Private*, pg. 530
HITACHI MACHINERY & ENGINEERING, LTD.—Hitachi, Ltd.; *Int'l*, pg. 621
HOCHIKI CORPORATION; *Int'l*, pg. 623
HOSOKAWA MICRON INTERNATIONAL INC.—Hosokawa Micron Corporation; *Int'l*, pg. 635
HOSOKAWA MICRON POWDER SYSTEMS—Hosokawa Micron Corporation; *Int'l*, pg. 636
IGT NORTH AMERICA—International Game Technology; *U.S. Public*, pg. 900
ILC DOVER, INC.—ILC Industries, Inc.; *U.S. Private*, pg. 555
INTERNATIONAL GAME TECHNOLOGY; *U.S. Public*, pg. 900
INTERSTATE HIGHWAY SIGN—Mark IV Industries Inc.; *U.S. Public*, pg. 1045
JOSLYN CORPORATION—Danaher Corporation; *U.S. Public*, pg. 481
KIDDE-DEUGRA GMBH—Williams Holdings Plc; *Int'l*, pg. 1500
KIDDE DEXAERO S.A.—Williams Holdings Plc; *Int'l*, pg. 1500
KIDDE TECHNOLOGIES INC. (WALTER KIDDE AEROSPACE)—Williams Holdings Plc; *Int'l*, pg. 1500
WALTER KIDDE PORTABLE EQUIPMENT INC.—Williams Holdings Plc; *Int'l*, pg. 1500
KNOWSLEY SK LTD.—Internatio-Muller N.V.; *Int'l*, pg. 681
KOKEN MFG. CO. INC.—Takara Belmont Co., Ltd.; *Int'l*, pg. 1349
KRUG INTERNATIONAL CORP.; *U.S. Public*, pg. 967
LSI INDUSTRIES, INC.; *U.S. Public*, pg. 971
LA CROSS—Del Laboratories, Inc.; *U.S. Public*, pg. 494
LAIDLAW CORPORATION; *U.S. Private*, pg. 642

TONY LAMBERT COMPANY; *U.S. Private*, pg. 644
LANE LIMITED—Rothmans UK Holdings Limited; *Int'l*, pg. 1129
LAUGHTON & SONS, LTD.; *Int'l*, pg. 804
LEGO SYSTEM A/S; *Int'l*, pg. 805
LENOX, INCORPORATED—Brown-Forman Corporation; *U.S. Public*, pg. 261
LUFKIN—Cooper Industries, Inc.; *U.S. Public*, pg. 444
M & C SPECIALTIES COMPANY; *U.S. Private*, pg. 684
MADISON PLANT—Cooper Industries, Inc.; *U.S. Public*, pg. 444
MAGNAGRIP—Bidwell Industrial Group, Inc.; *U.S. Private*, pg. 142
MARBLE PRODUCTS DIV.—Takara Belmont Co., Ltd.; *Int'l*, *pg. 1349*
MARVELLA INC.—The Monet Group, Inc.; *U.S. Private*, pg. 757
MELE MANUFACTURING CO., INC.; *U.S. Private*, pg. 730
MENARDI-CRISWELL—Hosokawa Micron Corporation; *Int'l*, *pg. 636*
MENASHA CORP., MURFIN DIVISION—Menasha Corporation; *U.S. Private*, pg. 731
MIDWAY GAMES, INC.—WMS Industries Inc.; *U.S. Public*, pg. 1727
MIYATA INDUSTRY CO., LTD.; *Int'l*, pg. 884
MOBILE-TECH CORP.—Collins Industries, Inc.; *U.S. Public*, *pg. 400*
MONTEK DIV.—Raytheon Company; *U.S. Public*, pg. 1366
MORRIS MERCHANTS, INC.—Valley Resources, Inc.; *U.S. Public*, pg. 1706
MR. CHRISTMAS INC.; *U.S. Private*, pg. 765
NASCO INTERNATIONAL, INC.—Geneve Corporation; *U.S. Private*, pg. 446
NATIONAL BAND & TAG CO.; *U.S. Private*, pg. 780
NATIONAL MINE SERVICE, INC.—Charter plc; *Int'l*, pg. 280
NOBEL CONSUMER GOODS AB—Akzo Nobel N.V.; *Int'l*, pg. 48
NORDIA S.A.—Duni AB; *Int'l*, pg. 421
NORTHERN CROSS, LTD.—Barancorp; *U.S. Private*, pg. 115
PACKAGE SERVICE COMPANY, LLC.; *U.S. Private*, pg. 833
PANNIER CORPORATION; *U.S. Private*, pg. 837
PARTYLITE GIFTS, INC.—Blyth Industries; *U.S. Public*, pg. 239
PEERLESS UMBRELLA CO., INC.; *U.S. Private*, pg. 847
PHILLIES CIGAR COMPANY—Havatampa, Inc.; *U.S. Private*, pg. 510
PLAYFIELD INDUSTRIES INC.—TecSyn International, Inc.; *Int'l*, pg. 1362
POLYVISION CORP.; *U.S. Public*, pg. 1315
PRICE'S PATENT CANDLE CO. LTD.—Royal Dutch/Shell Group of Companies; *Int'l*, pg. 1139
PRO-LINE CORPORATION; *U.S. Private*, pg. 887
PROMETCOR INC.—Ronson Corporation; *U.S. Public*, pg. 1405
PRYM-DRITZ CORPORATION—William Prym GmbH & Co. KG; *Int'l*, pg. 1499
RAUCH INDUSTRIES, INC.—Syratech Corporation; *U.S. Private*, pg. 1061
RAVEN INDUSTRIES, INC.; *U.S. Public*, pg. 1361
RECLAMIZER—Steiner Corporation; *U.S. Private*, pg. 1039
REGIS CORPORATION; *U.S. Public*, pg. 1373
RENAISSANCE PUBLISHING CO., INC.—Bemrose Corporation; *Int'l*, pg. 185
RENNOC CORPORATION; *U.S. Private*, pg. 922
REPLOGLE GLOBES, INC.; *U.S. Private*, pg. 923
RISDON CORPORATION—Crown Cork & Seal Company, Inc.; *U.S. Public*, pg. 463
ROCHESTER MIDLAND CORPORATION; *U.S. Private*, pg. 937
RONSON CORPORATION; *U.S. Public*, pg. 1405
A.I. ROOT COMPANY; *U.S. Private*, pg. 944
ROSCO LABORATORIES, INC.; *U.S. Private*, pg. 944
ROYSTON LABORATORIES—Chase Corporation; *U.S. Public*, pg. 337
RUBBERMAID HOME PRODUCTS DIV.—Rubbermaid Incorporated; *U.S. Public*, pg. 1411
RUBBERMAID INCORPORATED; *U.S. Public*, pg. 1411
SAEL DECORS—Duni AB; *Int'l*, pg. 421
SALLY HAIR & BEAUTY—Alberto-Culver Company; *U.S. Public*, pg. 38
SAMSUNG SHIPBUILDING & HEAVY INDUSTRIES CO. LTD.—Samsung Group; *Int'l*, pg. 1183
SAVAL B.V., PRINSENBEEK—Internatio-Muller N.V.; *Int'l*, pg. 681
SCAN GLOBE A/S—Replogle Globes, Inc.; *U.S. Private*, pg. 923
SCOTT'S LIQUID GOLD-INC.; *U.S. Public*, pg. 1447
SCRIPTO-TOKAI CORP.; *U.S. Private*, pg. 977
SHAW CREATIONS, INC.; *U.S. Private*, pg. 990
SILUETT NORDIA AB—Duni AB; *Int'l*, pg. 421
SMITH MCDONALD CORP.; *U.S. Private*, pg. 1009
STABLER COMPANIES, INC.; *U.S. Private*, pg. 1028
STANDEX INTERNATIONAL CORPORATION; *U.S. Public*, *pg. 1505*
STAPO HOLLANDER INDUSTRIES; *U.S. Private*, pg. 1033
STARRETT INDUSTRIAL E COMERCIO LTDA.—The L.S. Starrett Company; *U.S. Public*, pg. 1511
STRIKE RITE MATCHES LTD.—D.D. Bean & Sons Co.; *U.S. Private*, pg. 127
STUART ENTERTAINMENT INC.; *U.S. Public*, pg. 1526
STUART HALL CO., INC.—Newell Co.; *U.S. Public*, pg. 1178
SUN HILL INDUSTRIES, INC.; *U.S. Private*, pg. 1051
SUPREME BEAUTY PRODUCTS—Johnson Publishing Company, Inc.; *U.S. Private*, pg. 592
SUTER EQUIPMENT LIMITED—Ascot Holdings Plc; *Int'l*, pg. 88
SWEDISH MATCH DO BRASIL S/A—Swedish Match S.A.; *Int'l*, pg. 1328
SWEDISH MATCH S.A.; *Int'l*, pg. 1328
TAKARA BELMONT CO., LTD.; *Int'l*, pg. 1349
TAYLOR MADE GROUP, INC.; *U.S. Private*, pg. 1070
TECSYN INTERNATIONAL, INC.; *Int'l*, pg. 1361
TOSHIBA BALLOTINE CO., LTD.—Toshiba Corporation; *Int'l*, pg. 1403
TOTES INCORPORATED—Bain Capital; *U.S. Private*, pg. 111
TYRI A/S—Duni AB; *Int'l*, pg. 421
UNITED COIN MACHINE CO.—Alliance Gaming Corporation; *U.S. Public*, pg. 47
UPRIGHT—Up-Right, Inc.; *U.S. Private*, pg. 1128
VALLEY FOREST RESOURCES CO.—Villaume Industries, Inc.; *U.S. Private*, pg. 1140
VENTURI INC.; *U.S. Private*, pg. 1136
WMS GAMES INC.—WMS Industries Inc.; *U.S. Public*, pg. 1727
WMS INDUSTRIES INC.; *U.S. Public*, pg. 1727
WAHL CLIPPER CORP.; *U.S. Private*, pg. 1146
ASHLEY F. WARD, INC.; *U.S. Private*, pg. 1149
WELLA GROUP; *Int'l*, pg. 1489
WELLINGTON INDUSTRIES INC.; *U.S. Private*, pg. 1161
WENGER CORPORATION; *U.S. Private*, pg. 1162
WILL & BAUMER INCORPORATED; *U.S. Private*, pg. 1176
WILLIAMS ELECTRONICS GAMES, INC.—WMS Industries Inc.; *U.S. Public*, pg. 1727
WINDMERE-DURABLE HOLDINGS; *U.S. Public*, pg. 1771
WINDSOR ART, INC.—Bentley International, Inc.; *U.S. Public*, pg. 212
WINSTAR GLOBAL PRODUCTS, INC.—Winstar Communications; *U.S. Public*, pg. 1772
WINTHROP-ATKINS CO., INC.; *U.S. Private*, pg. 1183
WORMALD HOLDINGS N.Z. LIMITED—Tyco International Ltd.; *U.S. Public*, pg. 1651
WORMALD SIGNALCO A/S—Tyco International Ltd.; *U.S. Public*, pg. 1651
ZIPPO MANUFACTURING COMPANY; *U.S. Private*, pg. 1207

4011 — RAILROADS, LINE-HAUL OPERATING

AT&L RAILROAD—Wheeler Brothers Grain Co.; *U.S. Private*, pg. 1171
THE ALABAMA GREAT SOUTHERN RAILROAD CO.—Norfolk Southern Corporation; *U.S. Public*, pg. 1191
AMADOR CENTRAL RAILROAD COMPANY—Georgia-Pacific Corporation; *U.S. Public*, pg. 736
AMTRAK-NATIONAL RAILROAD PASSENGER CORP.; *U.S. Private*, pg. 68
THE APACHE RAILWAY COMPANY—Stone Container Corporation; *U.S. Public*, pg. 1521
APALACHICOLA NORTHERN RR—St. Joe Corp.; *U.S. Public*, pg. 1427
ARROWOOD-SOUTHERN COMPANY—Norfolk Southern Corporation; *U.S. Public*, pg. 1190
ASHLEY, DREW & NORTHERN RAILWAY CO.—Georgia-Pacific Corporation; *U.S. Public*, pg. 736
THE ATLANTA & CHARLOTTE AIR LINE RAILWAY CO.—Norfolk Southern Corporation; *U.S. Public*, pg. 1191
ATLANTIC & EAST CAROLINA RAILWAY COMPANY—Norfolk Southern Corporation; *U.S. Public*, pg. 1191
BANGOR & AROOSTOOK RAILROAD CO.—Iron Road Railways Inc.; *U.S. Private*, pg. 575
BLUE ISLAND RAILROAD—Illinois Central Corporation; *U.S. Public*, pg. 865
BRITISH RAILWAYS BOARD; *Int'l*, pg. 220
BURLINGTON NORTHERN SANTA FE CORPORATION; *U.S. Public*, pg. 268
C & W RAILWAY CO.—Oregon Steel Mills Inc.; *U.S. Public*, *pg. 1230*
CGTX INC.—Hawker Siddeley Canada Inc.; *Int'l*, pg. 604
CSX CORPORATION; *U.S. Public*, pg. 284
CSX INTERMODAL, INC.—CSX Corporation; *U.S. Public*, pg. 284
CSX TECHNOLOGY—CSX Corporation; *U.S. Public*, pg. 284
CSX TRANSPORTATION, INC.—CSX Corporation; *U.S. Public*, pg. 284
CAMP LEJEUNE RAILROAD COMPANY—Norfolk Southern Corporation; *U.S. Public*, pg. 1191
CANADIAN AMERICAN RAILROAD COMPANY—Iron Road Railways Inc.; *U.S. Private*, pg. 575
CANADIAN NATIONAL RAILWAY COMPANY; *Int'l*, pg. 258
CANADIAN PACIFIC LIMITED; *Int'l*, pg. 258
CANADIAN PACIFIC RAILWAY—Canadian Pacific Limited; *Int'l*, pg. 258
CENTRAL CALIFORNIA TRACTION CO.—Union Pacific Corporation; *U.S. Public*, pg. 1668
CENTRAL OF GEORGIA RAILROAD COMPANY—Norfolk Southern Corporation; *U.S. Public*, pg. 1191
CENTRAL VERMONT RAILWAY, INC.—Canadian National Railway Company; *Int'l*, pg. 258
CHARLOTTE-SOUTHERN CORPORATION—Norfolk Southern Corporation; *U.S. Public*, pg. 1190
CHATTAHOOCHEE INDUSTRIAL RAILROAD—Georgia-Pacific Corporation; *U.S. Public*, pg. 736
CHESAPEAKE WESTERN RAILWAY—Norfolk Southern Corporation; *U.S. Public*, pg. 1191
CHICAGO INTERMODAL CO.—Illinois Central Corporation; *U.S. Public*, pg. 865
CHICAGO RAIL LINK—Broe Companies; *U.S. Private*, pg. 171
CHICAGO UNION STATION COMPANY—Amtrak-National Railroad Passenger Corp.; *U.S. Private*, pg. 69
CHICAGO WEST PULLMAN CORPORATION; *U.S. Private*, *pg. 235*
THE CINCINNATI, NEW ORLEANS & TEXAS PACIFIC RAILWAY CO.—Norfolk Southern Corporation; *U.S. Public*, pg. 1191
CONRAIL, INC.; *U.S. Public*, pg. 431
DEUTSCHE BAHN; *Int'l*, pg. 401
DULUTH & NORTHEASTERN RAILROAD CO.—Potlatch Corporation; *U.S. Public*, pg. 1318
DULUTH, WINNIPEG & PACIFIC RAILWAY CO.—Canadian National Railway Company; *Int'l*, pg. 258
ELBERTON SOUTHERN RAILWAY CO.—Norfolk Southern Corporation; *U.S. Public*, pg. 1191
EMONS RAILROAD GROUP, INC.—Emons Transportation Group, Inc.; *U.S. Public*, pg. 578
EMONS TRANSPORTATION GROUP, INC.; *U.S. Public*, pg. 578
FLORIDA EAST COAST INDUSTRIES INC.—St. Joe Corp.; *U.S. Public*, pg. 1427
FLORIDA EAST COAST RAILWAY CO.—St. Joe Corp.; *U.S. Public*, pg. 1427
FORDYCE & PRINCETON R.R. CO.—Georgia-Pacific Corporation; *U.S. Public*, pg. 736
GMO LAND COMPANY—Illinois Central Corporation; *U.S. Public*, pg. 865
THE GEORGIA MIDLAND RAILWAY CO.—Norfolk Southern Corporation; *U.S. Public*, pg. 1191
GEORGIA SOUTHERN & FLORIDA RAILWAY CO.—Norfolk Southern Corporation; *U.S. Public*, pg. 1191
GEORGIA WOODLANDS RAILROAD CO.—Broe Companies; *U.S. Private*, pg. 171
GRAND TRUNK CORPORATION (GTC)—Canadian National Railway Company; *Int'l*, pg. 258
GRAND TRUNK WESTERN RAILROAD, INC.—Canadian National Railway Company; *Int'l*, pg. 258
GRAYSONIA, NASHVILLE & ASHDOWN RAILROAD CO.—Holderbank Financiere Glaris Ltd.; *Int'l*, pg. 628
GUILFORD TRANSPORTATION INDUSTRIES INC.; *U.S. Private*, pg. 487
HIGH POINT, RANDLEMAN, ASHEBORO AND SOUTHERN RAILROAD CO.—Norfolk Southern Corporation; *U.S. Public*, pg. 1191
HOLLIS & EASTERN RAILROAD CO.—Republic Group Incorporated; *U.S. Public*, pg. 1378
HOLNAM INC. (WEST DIVISION)—Holderbank Financiere Glaris Ltd.; *Int'l*, pg. 628
IES INDUSTRIES INC.; *U.S. Public*, pg. 855
IES TRANSPORTATION, INC.—IES Industries Inc.; *U.S. Public*, pg. 855
ILLINOIS CENTRAL CORPORATION; *U.S. Public*, pg. 864
INTERSTATE RAILROAD CO.—Norfolk Southern Corporation; *U.S. Public*, pg. 1191
IOWA NORTHERN RAILROAD—Iron Road Railways Inc.; *U.S. Private*, pg. 575
JAMES TRANSPORTATION—Fort James Corporation; *U.S. Public*, pg. 672
KANSAS CITY SOUTHERN INDUSTRIES, INC.; *U.S. Public*, pg. 943
THE KANSAS CITY SOUTHERN RAILWAY CO.—Kansas City Southern Industries, Inc.; *U.S. Public*, pg. 944
KENSINGTON & EASTERN RAILROAD—Illinois Central Corporation; *U.S. Public*, pg. 865
LONE STAR STEEL COMPANY—Lone Star Technologies, Inc.; *U.S. Public*, pg. 1012
LOUISVILLE TRANSPORTATION—Interlock Industries, Inc.; *U.S. Private*, pg. 567
MANUFACTURERS' JUNCTION RAILROAD COMPANY—Broe Companies; *U.S. Private*, pg. 171
MARYLAND & PENNSYLVANIA RAILROAD—Emons Transportation Group, Inc.; *U.S. Public*, pg. 579
MEMPHIS & CHARLESTON RAILWAY CO.—Norfolk Southern Corporation; *U.S. Public*, pg. 1191
METALAIR LIMITED—Powell Duffryn PLC; *Int'l*, pg. 1065
METROPOLITANA MILANESE S.P.A.; *Int'l*, pg. 863
MINNESOTA, DAKOTA & WESTERN RAILWAY CO.—Boise Cascade Corporation; *U.S. Public*, pg. 243
MISSISSIPPI VALLEY CORP.—Illinois Central Corporation; *U.S. Public*, pg. 865
MOBILE & BIRMINGHAM RAILROAD CO.—Norfolk Southern Corporation; *U.S. Public*, pg. 1191
NEWBURGH & SOUTH SHORE RAILROAD COMPANY—Broe Companies; *U.S. Private*, pg. 171
NORFOLK AND PORTSMOUTH BELT LINE R.R. CO.—Norfolk Southern Corporation; *U.S. Public*, pg. 1191
NORFOLK AND WESTERN RAILWAY COMPANY—Norfolk Southern Corporation; *U.S. Public*, pg. 1191
NORFOLK SOUTHERN CORPORATION; *U.S. Public*, pg. 1190
NORFOLK SOUTHERN INDUSTRIAL DEVELOPMENT CORP.—Norfolk Southern Corporation; *U.S. Public*, pg. 1190
NORFOLK SOUTHERN PROPERTIES, INC.—Norfolk Southern Corporation; *U.S. Public*, pg. 1190
NORFOLK SOUTHERN RAILWAY COMPANY—Norfolk Southern Corporation; *U.S. Public*, pg. 1191
THE NORTH CAROLINA MIDLAND RAILROAD CO.—Norfolk Southern Corporation; *U.S. Public*, pg. 1191
NORTHWESTERN PACIFIC RAILROAD CO.—Union Pacific Corporation; *U.S. Public*, pg. 1668
PORTUGUESE RAILWAYS (CP); *Int'l*, pg. 1063
THE PRESCOTT & NORTHWESTERN RAILROAD CO.—Potlatch Corporation; *U.S. Public*, pg. 1318
PROVIDENCE AND WORCESTER RAILROAD COMPANY; *U.S. Public*, pg. 1336
THE ROBERVAL & SAGUENAY RAILWAY CO.—Alcan Aluminium Limited; *Int'l*, pg. 50
SNCF; *Int'l*, pg. 1163
ST. LAWRENCE & ATLANTIC RAILROAD—Emons Transportation Group, Inc.; *U.S. Public*, pg. 578
ST. LOUIS SOUTHWESTERN RAILWAY CO.—Union Pacific Corporation; *U.S. Public*, pg. 1668
ST. MARIES RIVER RAILROAD—Potlatch Corporation; *U.S. Public*, pg. 1318
SEABOARD CORPORATION; *U.S. Public*, pg. 1448
SEABOARD FLOUR CORPORATION—Seaboard Corporation; *U.S. Public*, pg. 1449
SOMERSET RAILROAD CORP.—New York State Electric & Gas Corporation; *U.S. Public*, pg. 1173
SOUTH CHICAGO RAILROAD COMPANY—Illinois Central Corporation; *U.S. Public*, pg. 865
THE SOUTH WESTERN RAIL ROAD CO.—Norfolk Southern Corporation; *U.S. Public*, pg. 1191

SOUTHERN PACIFIC RAIL CORPORATION—Union Pacific Corporation; U.S. Public, pg. 1668
SOUTHERN RAILWAY-CAROLINA DIV.—Norfolk Southern Corporation; U.S. Public, pg. 1191
SOUTHERN REGION COAL TRANSPORT, INC.—Norfolk Southern Corporation; U.S. Public, pg. 1191
STATE UNIVERSITY RAILROAD CO.—Norfolk Southern Corporation; U.S. Public, pg. 1191
SUNSET RAILWAY CO.—Union Pacific Corporation; U.S. Public, pg. 1668
TENNESSEE, ALABAMA & GEORGIA RAILWAY CO.—Norfolk Southern Corporation; U.S. Public, pg. 1191
TENNESSEE RAILWAY CO.—Norfolk Southern Corporation; U.S. Public, pg. 1191
TEXAS CENTRAL RAILROAD—Birdsong Corporation; U.S. Private, pg. 145
THE TOLEDO BELT RAILWAY CO.—Norfolk Southern Corporation; U.S. Public, pg. 1191
TRANSCO INC.; U.S. Private, pg. 1096
TRIPLE CROWN SERVICES, INC.—Norfolk Southern Corporation; U.S. Public, pg. 1192
UNION PACIFIC CORPORATION; U.S. Public, pg. 1667
UNION PACIFIC MOTOR FREIGHT—Union Pacific Corporation; U.S. Public, pg. 1668
UNION PACIFIC RAILROAD COMPANY—Union Pacific Corporation; U.S. Public, pg. 1668
VENICE SIMPLON-ORIENT-EXPRESS LTD.—Sea Containers Ltd.; Int'l, pg. 1213
VIRGINIA & SOUTHWESTERN RAILWAY CO.—Norfolk Southern Corporation; U.S. Public, pg. 1191
VISALIA ELECTRIC RAILROAD CO.—Union Pacific Corporation; U.S. Public, pg. 1668
WARREN & SALINE RIVER RAILROAD CO.—Potlatch Corporation; U.S. Public, pg. 1318
WASHINGTON TERMINAL COMPANY—Amtrak-National Railroad Passenger Corp.; U.S. Private, pg. 69
WATERLOO RAILWAY COMPANY—Illinois Central Corporation; U.S. Public, pg. 865
WHEELER BROTHERS GRAIN CO.; U.S. Private, pg. 1171
WILLAMETTE INDUSTRIES, INC.—Willamette Industries, Inc.; U.S. Public, pg. 1769
THE WINDSOR & HANTSPORT RAILWAY CO. LTD.—Iron Road Railways Inc.; U.S. Private, pg. 575
WISCONSIN & SOUTHERN RAILROAD CO.; U.S. Private, pg. 1184
WISCONSIN & SOUTHERN RAILROAD COMPANY—Wisconsin & Southern Railroad Co.; U.S. Private, pg. 1184
WISCONSIN CENTRAL TRANSPORTATION CORPORATION; U.S. Public, pg. 1772
YADKIN RAILROAD CO.—Norfolk Southern Corporation; U.S. Public, pg. 1191
YORKRAIL INC.—Emons Transportation Group, Inc.; U.S. Public, pg. 579

4013 — RAILROAD SWITCHING & TERMINAL ESTABLISHMENTS

ABB-DAIMLER BENZ TRANSPORTATION (ADTRANZ)—ABB Asea Brown Boveri (Holding) Ltd.; Int'l, pg. 8
ABB-DAIMLER BENZ TRANSPORTATION (ADTRANZ)—Daimler-Benz Aktiengesellschaft; Int'l, pg. 369
ADTRANS PITTSBURGH—Daimler-Benz Aktiengesellschaft; Int'l, pg. 369
ALBANY PORT RAILROAD CO.—Conrail, Inc.; U.S. Public, pg. 432
THE ALTON & SOUTHERN RAILWAY CO.—Union Pacific Corporation; U.S. Public, pg. 1668
THE BELT RAILWAY CO. OF CHICAGO—CSX Corporation; U.S. Public, pg. 284
THE BELT RAILWAY CO. OF CHICAGO—Conrail, Inc.; U.S. Public, pg. 432
THE BELT RAILWAY CO. OF CHICAGO—Illinois Central Corporation; U.S. Public, pg. 865
THE BELT RAILWAY CO. OF CHICAGO—Norfolk Southern Corporation; U.S. Public, pg. 1191
CGTX INC.—Hawker Siddeley Canada Inc.; Int'l, pg. 604
CHICAGO WEST PULLMAN & SOUTHERN RAILROAD—Broe Companies; U.S. Private, pg. 171
CHICAGO WEST PULLMAN CORPORATION; U.S. Private, pg. 235
CINERGY CORP.—Cinergy Corp.; U.S. Public, pg. 369
DALLAS TERMINAL RAILWAY AND UNION DEPOT CO.—Union Pacific Corporation; U.S. Public, pg. 1668
INDIANA HARBOR BELT RAILROAD CO.—Conrail, Inc.; U.S. Public, pg. 432
KANSAS CITY TERMINAL RAILWAY CO.—Union Pacific Corporation; U.S. Public, pg. 1668
PEORIA & PEKIN UNION RAILWAY CO.—Conrail, Inc.; U.S. Public, pg. 432
PITTSBURGH, CHARTIERS & YOUGHIOGHENY RAILWAY CO.—Conrail, Inc.; U.S. Public, pg. 432
PORTLAND TERMINAL RAILROAD CO.—Union Pacific Corporation; U.S. Public, pg. 1668
PORTLAND TRACTION CO.—Union Pacific Corporation; U.S. Public, pg. 1668
SOUTHERN RAIL TERMINALS, INC.—Norfolk Southern Corporation; U.S. Public, pg. 1191
SOUTHERN RAIL TERMINALS OF NORTH CAROLINA, INC.—Norfolk Southern Corporation; U.S. Public, pg. 1191
TERMINAL RAILROAD ASSOCIATION OF ST. LOUIS—Union Pacific Corporation; U.S. Public, pg. 1668

4111 — LOCAL & SUBURBAN TRANSIT

BRANDYWINE VALLEY RAILROAD COMPANY—Lukens Inc.; U.S. Public, pg. 1020
CENTRAL JAPAN RAILWAY COMPANY; Int'l, pg. 279
CENTRAL JAPAN RAILWAY COMPANY-SYDNEY OFFICE—Central Japan Railway Company; Int'l, pg. 279
EAST JAPAN RAILWAY COMPANY; Int'l, pg. 431
GREEN BUS LINES, INC.; U.S. Private, pg. 476
HANJIN TRANSPORTATION CO. LTD.—Hanjin Shipping Company Ltd.; Int'l, pg. 592
MTA LONG ISLAND RAIL ROAD—Metropolitan Transportation Authority; U.S. Private, pg. 739
MANHATTAN AND BRONX SURFACE TRANSIT OPERATING AUTHORITY—Metropolitan Transportation Authority; U.S. Private, pg. 739
METRA COMMUTER RAIL—Regional Transportation Authority (RTA); U.S. Private, pg. 919
METRA, COMMUTER RAIL SERVICE BOARD—Regional Transportation Authority (RTA); U.S. Private, pg. 919
METRO-NORTH COMMUTER RAILROAD COMPANY—Metropolitan Transportation Authority; U.S. Private, pg. 739
METROPOLITAN TRANSPORTATION AUTHORITY; U.S. Private, pg. 739
NJ TRANSIT; U.S. Private, pg. 794
NEW YORK CITY TRANSIT AUTHORITY—Metropolitan Transportation Authority; U.S. Private, pg. 739
NIAGARA FRONTIER TRANSPORTATION AUTHORITY; U.S. Private, pg. 798
ODAKYU ELECTRIC RAILWAY CO., LTD.; Int'l, pg. 996
AS OSLO SPORVEIER; Int'l, pg. 1012
OSTERREICHISCHEN BUNDESBAHNEN GMBH; Int'l, pg. 1012
RAIL EUROPE INC.—SNCF; Int'l, pg. 1165
REGIONAL TRANSPORTATION AUTHORITY (RTA); U.S. Private, pg. 918
ROBINSON BUS SERVICE; U.S. Private, pg. 936
RYDER SYSTEM, INC.; U.S. Public, pg. 1413
SNCF; Int'l, pg. 1163
SCANA CORPORATION; U.S. Public, pg. 1436
SCHWEIZERISCHE BUNDESBAHNEN - SBB AG; Int'l, pg. 1211
SORENOLIF SA—Accor S.A.; Int'l, pg. 21
SUPERSHUTTLE INC.; U.S. Private, pg. 1056
TOKYU CORPORATION; Int'l, pg. 1394
TRANSNET GROUP—Transnet Ltd.; Int'l, pg. 1418
TRIBOROUGH BRIDGE & TUNNEL AUTHORITY—Metropolitan Transportation Authority; U.S. Private, pg. 739
WEST JAPAN RAILWAY COMPANY; Int'l, pg. 1490

4119 — LOCAL PASSENGER TRANSPORTATION, NEC

BREWSTER TRANSPORT CO. LTD.—Viad Corp; U.S. Public, pg. 1719
CHICAGO TRANSIT AUTHORITY—Regional Transportation Authority (RTA); U.S. Private, pg. 919
CINCINNATI LIMOUSINE SERVICE INC.—Beechmont Investments Inc.; U.S. Private, pg. 129
DAV-EL WORLDWIDE; U.S. Private, pg. 314
EMKAY, INC.; U.S. Private, pg. 374
HUDSON GENERAL COACH LINES, INC.—Hudson General Corporation; U.S. Public, pg. 845
HUDSON GENERAL CORPORATION; U.S. Public, pg. 845
THE LOEWEN GROUP, INC.; Int'l, pg. 814
MEARS TRANSPORTATION GROUP; U.S. Private, pg. 726
PHH CORPORATION—Cendant Corporation; U.S. Public, pg. 321
PACE—Regional Transportation Authority (RTA); U.S. Private, pg. 919
REGIONAL TRANSPORTATION AUTHORITY (RTA); U.S. Private, pg. 918
RURAL METRO CORPORATION; U.S. Public, pg. 1412
SFZ TRANSPORTATION INC.—Berkshire Hathaway Inc.; U.S. Public, pg. 218

4121 — TAXICABS

GARVEY INDUSTRIES, INC.; U.S. Private, pg. 440
MEARS TRANSPORTATION GROUP; U.S. Private, pg. 726
YELLOW CAB CO.—Stamford Capital; U.S. Private, pg. 1030

4131 — INTERCITY & RURAL BUS TRANSPORTATION

BONANZA BUS LINES, INC.; U.S. Private, pg. 156
FLORIDA EAST COAST HIGHWAY DISPATCH CO.—St. Joe Corp.; U.S. Public, pg. 1427
GREYHOUND LINES, INC.; U.S. Public, pg. 765
GREYHOUND LINES OF CANADA LTD.; Int'l, pg. 559
PETER PAN BUS LINES, INC.; U.S. Private, pg. 856
TEXAS, NEW MEXICO & OKLAHOMA COACHES, INC.—Greyhound Lines, Inc.; U.S. Public, pg. 766
TOKYU CORPORATION; Int'l, pg. 1394
VERMONT TRANSIT CO., INC.—Greyhound Lines, Inc.; U.S. Public, pg. 766

4141 — LOCAL BUS CHARTER SERVICE

BLUE BIRD COACH LINES INC.; U.S. Private, pg. 150
DURHAM TRANSPORTATION, INC.; U.S. Private, pg. 348
DURHAM TRANSPORTATION INC.—Durham Transportation, Inc.; U.S. Private, pg. 348
LAIDLAW INC.—Canadian Pacific Limited; Int'l, pg. 259
ROBINSON BUS SERVICE; U.S. Private, pg. 936
SFZ TRANSPORTATION INC.—Berkshire Hathaway Inc.; U.S. Public, pg. 218
SOCANAV INC.; Int'l, pg. 1272

4142 — BUS CHARTER SERVICE, EXCEPT LOCAL

BLUE BIRD COACH LINES INC.; U.S. Private, pg. 150
FIRST GRAY LINE CORPORATION; U.S. Private, pg. 407
PETER PAN BUS LINES, INC.; U.S. Private, pg. 856

4151 — SCHOOL BUSES

CARPENTER INDUSTRIES, INC.; U.S. Private, pg. 215
CHARTERWAYS TRANSPORTATION LIMITED—Scott's Restaurants Inc.; Int'l, pg. 1213
DAY & ROSS INC.—McCain Foods Limited; Int'l, pg. 850
DURHAM TRANSPORTATION, INC.; U.S. Private, pg. 348
LAIDLAW INC.—Canadian Pacific Limited; Int'l, pg. 259
LAIDLAW TRANSIT, INC.—Canadian Pacific Limited; Int'l, pg. 259
LAIDLAW TRANSIT LIMITED—Canadian Pacific Limited; Int'l, pg. 259
NATIONAL SCHOOL BUS SERVICE—Scott's Restaurants Inc.; Int'l, pg. 1213
ROLL INTERNATIONAL CORPORATION; U.S. Private, pg. 941
RYDER SYSTEM, INC.; U.S. Public, pg. 1413
WOLFINGTON BODY COMPANY; U.S. Private, pg. 1186

4212 — LOCAL TRUCKING WITHOUT STORAGE

A-P-A TRANSPORT CORP.; U.S. Private, pg. 2
AAH DISTRIBUTION SERVICES LTD.—Franz Haniel & Cie, GmbH; Int'l, pg. 591
APL LIMITED—Neptune Orient Lines Ltd.; Int'l, pg. 912
AGGREGATE HAULERS INC.—Pioneer International Ltd.; Int'l, pg. 1058
AMERICAN WASTE SERVICES, INC.; U.S. Public, pg. 94
PAUL ARPIN VANLINES, INC.; U.S. Private, pg. 85
ARROW FREIGHT CORPORATION—Benguet Corporation; Int'l, pg. 186
ATLAS WORLD GROUP, INC.; U.S. Private, pg. 97
BTL AB; Int'l, pg. 123
BTL SWEDEN AB—BTL AB; Int'l, pg. 123
BW TRANSPORTATION SERVICES, INC.—Bindley Western Industries, Inc.; U.S. Public, pg. 228
BLACK HILLS TRUCKING CO.—True Companies; U.S. Private, pg. 1107
M. BRUENGER & CO., INC.; U.S. Private, pg. 175
BUILDERS TRANSPORT, INCORPORATED; U.S. Public, pg. 267
BUILDERS TRANSPORT OF TEXAS, INC.—Builders Transport, Incorporated; U.S. Public, pg. 267
CCG CORP.—Builders Transport, Incorporated; U.S. Public, pg. 267
CASSENS TRANSPORT COMPANY; U.S. Private, pg. 219
GIE CASTORAMA TRANSPORTS—Castorama Dubois Investissements S.C.A.; Int'l, pg. 276
CENTRAL FREIGHT LINES, INC.; U.S. Private, pg. 223
COLONIAL GAS COMPANY; U.S. Public, pg. 400
COMBITRANS OY—UPM-Kymmene Corporation; Int'l, pg. 1428
CONTAINER PORT GROUP—World Shipping, Inc.; U.S. Private, pg. 1191
CONTRACT FREIGHTERS, INC.; U.S. Private, pg. 270
CONTRANS CORPORATION; Int'l, pg. 328
CONWELL CORP.—Frozen Food Express Industries, Inc.; U.S. Public, pg. 685
CORPORATE EXPRESS DELIVERY SYSTEMS—Corporate Express, Inc.; U.S. Public, pg. 449
CORPORATE EXPRESS DELIVERY SYSTEMS SOUTHWEST, INC.—Corporate Express, Inc.; U.S. Public, pg. 449
CRETE CARRIER CORP.; U.S. Private, pg. 289
CROSBY & OVERTON, INC.; U.S. Private, pg. 290
DORCHESTER TRANSPORT SERVICES (LEE LINE COMMERCIALS)—Franz Haniel & Cie, GmbH; Int'l, pg. 591
FLANAGAN BROS. TRUCKING CO.—Pro-Fac Cooperative, Inc.; U.S. Private, pg. 887
FLORIDA EAST COAST DELIVERIES, INC.—St. Joe Corp.; U.S. Public, pg. 1427
FOOD HAULERS, INC.—Wakefern Food Corporation; U.S. Private, pg. 1146
G.E.O.S. FREIBERG INGENIEURGESELLSCHAFT MBH—Philipp Holzmann AG; Int'l, pg. 632
GRANTHAM ROAD SERVICES—Franz Haniel & Cie, GmbH; Int'l, pg. 591
GREAT FALLS NORTH AMERICAN, INC.—Norfolk Southern Corporation; U.S. Public, pg. 1191
GRIFFIN TRANSPORT SERVICES, INC.; U.S. Private, pg. 481
HAYES-ALBION—Harvard Industries, Inc.; U.S. Public, pg. 796
HEARTLAND EXPRESS, INC.; U.S. Public, pg. 803
HEARTLAND EXPRESS, INC., OF IOWA—Heartland Express, Inc.; U.S. Public, pg. 803
HUB FURNITURE STORE—Reliable Stores, Inc.; U.S. Private, pg. 921
J.B. HUNT TRANSPORT, INC.—J.B. Hunt Transport Services, Inc.; U.S. Public, pg. 849
J.B. HUNT TRANSPORT SERVICES, INC.; U.S. Public, pg. 849
INTERSTATE VAN LINES, INC.; U.S. Private, pg. 573
THE JAYDOR CORPORATION; U.S. Private, pg. 584
K & R EXPRESS SYSTEMS INC.; U.S. Private, pg. 602
KIMBERLY-CLARK INTEGRATED SERVICES CORP.—Kimberly-Clark Corporation; U.S. Public, pg. 959
KNIGHT-RIDDER, INC.; U.S. Public, pg. 963
L&P TRANSPORTATION CO.—Leggett & Platt, Incorporated; U.S. Public, pg. 986
LADD TRANSPORTATION, INC.—Ladd Furniture, Inc.; U.S. Public, pg. 974
LAKES & RIVERS TRANSFER DIV.—Jack Gray Transport, Inc.; U.S. Private, pg. 472
LILY TRANSPORTATION CORP.; U.S. Private, pg. 667
LOGISTICS SECTOR—Kimberly-Clark Corporation; U.S. Public, pg. 958
MAMMOET TRANSPORT DIV. B.V.—Royal Nedlloyd Group N.V.; Int'l, pg. 1144
MANUFACTURERS CONSOLIDATION SERVICE, INC.; U.S. Private, pg. 700

MARKS TRANSFER & STORAGE—The Fabri-Form Company; *U.S. Private*, pg. 390
MATERIAL TRANSPORT CO.—Ash Grove Cement Company; *U.S. Private*, pg. 88
MERCHANTS HOME DELIVERY SERVICE INC.—NFC plc; *Int'l*, pg. 901
MERCHANTS TRANSPORT OF HICKORY—Alex Lee, Inc.; *U.S. Private*, pg. 657
NACAL, INC.—Norfolk Southern Corporation; *U.S. Public*, pg. 1191
NFC PLC; *Int'l*, pg. 901
NAVTRANS CONTAINER LINES, INC.—Norfolk Southern Corporation; *U.S. Public*, pg. 1192
NISSAN RIKUSO CO., LTD.—Nissan Motor Co., Ltd.; *Int'l*, pg. 944
NORAM FORWARDING, INC.—Norfolk Southern Corporation; *U.S. Public*, pg. 1192
NORTH AMERICAN DISTRIBUTION SYSTEMS, INC.—Norfolk Southern Corporation; *U.S. Public*, pg. 1192
NORTH AMERICAN MOVING & STORAGE, INC.—Norfolk Southern Corporation; *U.S. Public*, pg. 1192
NORTH AMERICAN VAN LINES OF TEXAS, INC.—Norfolk Southern Corporation; *U.S. Public*, pg. 1192
NORTH SHORE MOVERS; *U.S. Private*, pg. 805
O'DONNELL-USEN FISHERIES CORP.—ConAgra, Inc.; *U.S. Public*, pg. 427
OVERLAND TRANSPORTATION SYSTEM, INC.—Vitran Corporation Inc.; *Int'l*, pg. 1469
P&O ROADTANKS LIMITED—The Peninsular and Oriental Steam Navigation Company; *Int'l*, pg. 1034
THE PENINSULAR AND ORIENTAL STEAM NAVIGATION COMPANY; *Int'l*, pg. 1032
PENSKE LOGISTICS—Penske Corporation; *U.S. Private*, pg. 851
RCLJ CONSTRUCTION, INC.—Republic Industries, Inc.; *U.S. Public*, pg. 1379
RHENANIA TRANSPORT GMBH—The Peninsular and Oriental Steam Navigation Company; *Int'l*, pg. 1033
JEFFERSON SMURFIT CORPORATION—Jefferson Smurfit Group p.l.c.; *Int'l*, pg. 1269
THE STANDARD PRODUCTS COMPANY; *U.S. Public*, pg. 1504
STAR TRANSPORTATION, INC.; *U.S. Private*, pg. 1035
STARVING STUDENTS, INC.; *U.S. Private*, pg. 1035
SUNFLOWER CARRIERS—Crete Carrier Corp.; *U.S. Private*, pg. 289
SUPERTRANSPORT—GIB Group; *Int'l*, pg. 533
TIC UNITED CORPORATION; *U.S. Private*, pg. 1063
TNT LIMITED; *Int'l*, pg. 1342
TNT PARTICIPACOES LTDA.—TNT Limited; *Int'l*, pg. 1343
TNT U.K. LIMITED—TNT Limited; *Int'l*, pg. 1343
TRR CARRIERS, INC.—Wakefern Food Corporation; *U.S. Private*, pg. 1146
TANDY TRANSPORTATION—Tandy Corporation; *U.S. Public*, pg. 1560
TRANSGAS INC.—Colonial Gas Company; *U.S. Public*, pg. 401
TRATEL—Ciments Francais; *Int'l*, pg. 292
TRINC COMPANY—The Ohio Art Company, Inc.; *U.S. Public*, pg. 1214
TRUE COMPANIES; *U.S. Private*, pg. 1107
UNIGROUP, INC.; *U.S. Private*, pg. 1117
UNION TRUCKING CO.—The Standard Products Company; *U.S. Public*, pg. 1505
UNITED VAN LINES, INC.—UniGroup, Inc.; *U.S. Private*, pg. 1117
WAMBACQ & PEETERS NV—Etablissements Delhaize Freres Et Cie "Le Lion" S.A.; *Int'l*, pg. 463
WASHINGTON AREA DISTRIBUTION CENTER—Reliable Stores, Inc.; *U.S. Private*, pg. 921
WATTS BROS. (A. SUTHRELL)—Franz Haniel & Cie, GmbH; *Int'l*, pg. 591
NELSON WESTERBERG, INC.; *U.S. Private*, pg. 1163
WHITE PASS SYSTEMS LTD.—Russel Metals Inc.; *Int'l*, pg. 1150

4213 — TRUCKING, EXCEPT LOCAL

A-P-A TRANSPORT CORP.; *U.S. Private*, pg. 2
AAH DISTRIBUTION SERVICES LTD.—Franz Haniel & Cie, GmbH; *Int'l*, pg. 591
ABC TRANSPORTATION CO.—American Buildings Co.; *U.S. Public*, pg. 69
ABF FREIGHT SYSTEM, INC.—Arkansas Best Corporation; *U.S. Public*, pg. 130
AM CAN—Frozen Food Express Industries, Inc.; *U.S. Public*, pg. 685
ANR FREIGHT SYSTEM, INC.—The Coastal Corporation; *U.S. Public*, pg. 389
ACME TRUCK LINE, INC.; *U.S. Private*, pg. 14
ADAMS RESOURCES & ENERGY, INC.; *U.S. Public*, pg. 18
ADVOCATE SERVICES, INC.—TruServ Corporation; *U.S. Private*, pg. 1108
AIR FRESH TRUCKING—Wilsey Bennett Co.; *U.S. Private*, pg. 1180
AIR PRO—Frozen Food Express Industries, Inc.; *U.S. Public*, pg. 685
ALASKA-WEST EXPRESS, INC.—Lynden Incorporated; *U.S. Private*, pg. 683
ALLIED AUTOMOTIVE GROUP—Allied Holdings, Inc.; *U.S. Public*, pg. 48
ALTERMAN TRANSPORT LINES, INC.; *U.S. Private*, pg. 47
AMERI-CO CARRIERS, INC.—AMCOL International Corp.; *U.S. Public*, pg. 63
AMERICAN EAGLE LINES—Frozen Food Express Industries, Inc.; *U.S. Public*, pg. 685
AMERICAN FREIGHTWAYS CORPORATION; *U.S. Public*, pg. 75
AMERICAN RED BALL TRANSIT CO. INC.—Atlas World Group, Inc.; *U.S. Private*, pg. 97
AMERITRUCK DISTRIBUTION CORPORATION; *U.S. Private*, pg. 65
AMERITRUCK REFRIGERATED TRANSPORT, INC.—Ameritruck Distribution Corporation; *U.S. Private*, pg. 66
ANDERSON TRUCKING SERVICE INC.; *U.S. Private*, pg. 72
ARCHER DANIELS MIDLAND COMPANY (ADM); *U.S. Public*, pg. 127
ARKANSAS BEST CORPORATION; *U.S. Public*, pg. 130
ARNOLD TRANSPORTATION SERVICES—Arnold Industries, Inc.; *U.S. Public*, pg. 132
PAUL ARPIN VANLINES, INC.; *U.S. Private*, pg. 85
ARROW FREIGHT CORPORATION—Benguet Corporation; *Int'l*, pg. 186
ASSOCIATED PETROLEUM CARRIERS; *U.S. Private*, pg. 92
ATLAS VAN LINES (CANADA) LTD.—Atlas World Group, Inc.; *U.S. Private*, pg. 97
ATLAS VAN LINES, INC.—Atlas World Group, Inc.; *U.S. Private*, pg. 97
AXIS GROUP—Allied Holdings, Inc.; *U.S. Public*, pg. 48
BCT, INC.—Boise Cascade Corporation; *U.S. Public*, pg. 243
BTL AB; *Int'l*, pg. 123
BTL SWEDEN AB—BTL AB; *Int'l*, pg. 123
BW TRANSPORTATION SERVICES, INC.—Bindley Western Industries, Inc.; *U.S. Public*, pg. 228
BERGER TRANSFER & STORAGE, INC.; *U.S. Private*, pg. 135
BLACK HILLS TRUCKING CO.—True Companies; *U.S. Private*, pg. 1107
BRAMBLES INTERNATIONAL FREIGHT PTY. LIMITED—Brambles Industries Limited; *Int'l*, pg. 211
M. BRUENGER & CO., INC.; *U.S. Private*, pg. 175
BUILDERS TRANSPORT, INCORPORATED; *U.S. Public*, pg. 267
BUILDERS TRANSPORT OF TEXAS, INC.—Builders Transport, Incorporated; *U.S. Public*, pg. 267
BURLINGTON MOTOR HOLDINGS INC.; *U.S. Private*, pg. 183
CCG CORP.—Builders Transport, Incorporated; *U.S. Public*, pg. 267
CMM TRANSPORTATION INC.—Abbott Laboratories; *U.S. Public*, pg. 13
CNF TRANSPORTATION INC.; *U.S. Public*, pg. 281
CABANO KINGSWAY TRANSPORT—Russel Metals Inc.; *Int'l*, pg. 1150
CALIBER SYSTEM, INC.—FDX Corporation; *U.S. Public*, pg. 604
CANADIAN FREIGHTWAYS LTD.—Consolidated Freightways Corp.; *U.S. Public*, pg. 435
CANNON EXPRESS CORP.—Cannon Express Inc.; *U.S. Public*, pg. 301
CANNON EXPRESS INC.; *U.S. Public*, pg. 301
CARRIAGE TRANSPORT, INC.—The Dixie Group, Inc.; *U.S. Public*, pg. 514
CASCADIA TRANSPORT—Lynden Incorporated; *U.S. Private*, pg. 683
CASSENS TRANSPORT COMPANY; *U.S. Private*, pg. 219
GIE CASTORAMA TRANSPORTS—Castorama Dubois Investissements S.C.A.; *Int'l*, pg. 276
CENTRAL TRANSPORT; *U.S. Private*, pg. 225
CHEMICAL LEAMAN CORPORATION; *U.S. Private*, pg. 233
COAST REFRIGERATED TRUCKING CO., INC.—Thorn Apple Valley, Inc.; *U.S. Public*, pg. 1603
THE COASTAL CORPORATION; *U.S. Public*, pg. 389
LESTER COGGINS TRUCKING; *U.S. Private*, pg. 250
COLONIAL GAS COMPANY; *U.S. Public*, pg. 400
CONSOLIDATED FREIGHTWAYS CORP.; *U.S. Public*, pg. 435
CONSOLIDATED SYSTEMS, INC.; *U.S. Private*, pg. 266
CONTAINER PORT GROUP—World Shipping, Inc.; *U.S. Private*, pg. 1191
COOK MOVING SYSTEMS, INC.; *U.S. Private*, pg. 272
CORCORAN TRUCKING COMPANY; *U.S. Private*, pg. 275
CRETE CARRIER CORP.; *U.S. Private*, pg. 289
CROWN MOVING & STORAGE INC.—Wheaton Van Lines, Inc.; *U.S. Private*, pg. 1171
DSI TRANSPORTS, INC.—Sophus Berendsen A/S; *Int'l*, pg. 1285
DAHLSTEN TRUCK LINE, INC.; *U.S. Private*, pg. 306
DALLAS MOVING SYSTEM INC.—Wheaton Van Lines, Inc.; *U.S. Private*, pg. 1171
DART TRANSIT COMPANY; *U.S. Private*, pg. 311
DEAD RIVER TRANSPORT—Dead River Company; *U.S. Private*, pg. 318
DEL MONTE FOODS; *U.S. Private*, pg. 321
DENVER MOVING & STORAGE CO.—Johnson Storage Moving Co; *U.S. Private*, pg. 594
DEWEY CORPORATION; *U.S. Private*, pg. 329
DIXIE EXPRESS, INC.—Torchmark Corporation; *U.S. Public*, pg. 1622
ACE DORAN HAULING & RIGGING COMPANY; *U.S. Private*, pg. 340
DORCHESTER TRANSPORT SERVICES (LEE LINE COMMERCIALS)—Franz Haniel & Cie, GmbH; *Int'l*, pg. 591
EMPIRE TRANSPORT—Empire Southwest Co.; *U.S. Private*, pg. 375
ENVIRONMENTAL SERVICES OF AMERICA, INC.—ERD Waste Corp.; *U.S. Public*, pg. 546
ERGON, INC.; *U.S. Private*, pg. 380
ERICKSON TRANSPORT CORPORATION; *U.S. Private*, pg. 381
ERIEVIEW CARTAGE, INC.—Alcan Aluminium Limited; *Int'l*, pg. 50
ESTES EXPRESS LINES, INC.; *U.S. Private*, pg. 384
FFE TRANSPORTATION SERVICES, INC.—Frozen Food Express Industries, Inc.; *U.S. Public*, pg. 685
THE FABRI-FORM COMPANY; *U.S. Private*, pg. 390
FEDERAL INDUSTRIES TRANSPORT GROUP—Russel Metals Inc.; *Int'l*, pg. 1150
FERNANDO ROQUE TISA—Royal Nedlloyd Group N.V.; *Int'l*, pg. 1145
A FIVE STAR FORWARDING, INC.—Norfolk Southern Corporation; *U.S. Public*, pg. 1191
FOOD CARRIER, INC.—Imperial Holly Corporation; *U.S. Public*, pg. 872
FOOD SERVICES OF AMERICA—Services Group of America; *U.S. Private*, pg. 987
FRANSEN TRANSPORT B.V.—Royal Nedlloyd Group N.V.; *Int'l*, pg. 1144
FRONTIER TRANSPORT CORPORATION—Vitran Corporation Inc.; *Int'l*, pg. 1469
FROZEN FOOD EXPRESS INDUSTRIES, INC.; *U.S. Public*, pg. 685
GLOBAL VAN LINES, INC.; *U.S. Private*, pg. 458
GOODALL TRANSPORTATION CO.—Trelleborg AB; *Int'l*, pg. 1423
GRACE LOGISTICS SERVICES—W.R. Grace & Co.; *U.S. Public*, pg. 755
GRANTHAM ROAD SERVICES—Franz Haniel & Cie, GmbH; *Int'l*, pg. 591
JACK GRAY TRANSPORT, INC.; *U.S. Private*, pg. 471
GRIFFIN TRANSPORT SERVICES, INC.; *U.S. Private*, pg. 481
GROENDYKE TRANSPORTS, INC.; *U.S. Private*, pg. 483
HT&T COMPANY, INC.—Buyco, Inc.; *U.S. Private*, pg. 190
HANIEL REEDEREI HOLDING GMBH—Franz Haniel & Cie, GmbH; *Int'l*, pg. 592
HAPAG-LLOYD (AMERICA), INC.—Hapag-Lloyd AG; *Int'l*, pg. 596
HAPAG-LLOYD TRANSPORT & SERVICE GMBH—Hapag-Lloyd AG; *Int'l*, pg. 596
HEARTLAND EXPRESS, INC.; *U.S. Public*, pg. 803
HEARTLAND EXPRESS, INC., OF IOWA—Heartland Express, Inc.; *U.S. Public*, pg. 803
JOE D. HUGHES, INC.—Halliburton Company; *U.S. Public*, pg. 776
J.B. HUNT TRANSPORT, INC.—J.B. Hunt Transport Services, Inc.; *U.S. Public*, pg. 849
J.B. HUNT TRANSPORT SERVICES, INC.; *U.S. Public*, pg. 849
INDIAN RIVER TRANSPORT CO.; *U.S. Private*, pg. 560
INTERNATIONAL AERO-SEA FORWARDERS, INC.—International Aero-Sea Forwarders, Ltd.; *Int'l*, pg. 683
INTERNATIONAL AERO-SEA FORWARDERS, LTD.; *Int'l*, pg. 682
INTERSTATE DISTRIBUTOR COMPANY; *U.S. Private*, pg. 573
INTERSTATE VAN LINES, INC.; *U.S. Private*, pg. 573
JEVIC TRANSPORTATION, INC.; *U.S. Public*, pg. 927
SHELBA D. JOHNSON TRUCKING; *U.S. Private*, pg. 594
JOHNSON STORAGE MOVING CO; *U.S. Private*, pg. 594
K & R EXPRESS SYSTEMS INC.; *U.S. Private*, pg. 602
KLLM TRANSPORT SERVICES, INC.; *U.S. Public*, pg. 939
KEYSTONE LINES—US 1 Industries Inc.; *U.S. Public*, pg. 1687
KIMBERLY-CLARK INTEGRATED SERVICES CORP.—Kimberly-Clark Corporation; *U.S. Public*, pg. 959
KNIGHT-RIDDER, INC.; *U.S. Public*, pg. 963
KUEHNE & NAGEL N.V.—Kuehne & Nagel International AG; *Int'l*, pg. 763
KYANITE MINING CORPORATION; *U.S. Private*, pg. 638
LTI, INC.—Lynden Incorporated; *U.S. Private*, pg. 683
LAND SPAN INC.—Watkins Associated Industries Inc.; *U.S. Private*, pg. 1153
LANDA MOTOR LINES—Kansas City Southern Industries, Inc.; *U.S. Public*, pg. 944
LANDSTAR HOLDING; *U.S. Public*, pg. 978
LEVCON, INC.—Manufacturers Consolidation Service, Inc.; *U.S. Private*, pg. 700
LIMITED DISTRIBUTION SERVICES—The Limited, Inc.; *U.S. Public*, pg. 995
LISA MOTOR LINES, INC.—Frozen Food Express Industries, Inc.; *U.S. Public*, pg. 685
LONE STAR CORRUGATED CONTAINER CORPORATION; *U.S. Private*, pg. 674
LYNCH CORPORATION; *U.S. Public*, pg. 1021
LYNDEN INCORPORATED; *U.S. Private*, pg. 683
M.S. CARRIERS, INC.; *U.S. Public*, pg. 1027
MAMMOET TRANSPORT DIV. B.V.—Royal Nedlloyd Group N.V.; *Int'l*, pg. 1144
MARK VII, INC.; *U.S. Public*, pg. 1046
MARKS TRANSFER & STORAGE—The Fabri-Form Company; *U.S. Private*, pg. 390
MARTEN TRANSPORT, LTD.; *U.S. Public*, pg. 1052
MATLACK (DE), INC.—Matlack Systems, Inc.; *U.S. Public*, pg. 1057
MATLACK SYSTEMS, INC.; *U.S. Public*, pg. 1057
MCCAIN FOODS LIMITED; *Int'l*, pg. 850
MCKENZIE TANK LINES, INC.; *U.S. Private*, pg. 723
MERCER TRANSPORTATION CO.; *U.S. Private*, pg. 732
MIDDLETON TRANSPORTATION CO.—Frozen Food Express Industries, Inc.; *U.S. Public*, pg. 685
MILKY WAY, INC.—Lynden Incorporated; *U.S. Private*, pg. 683
MILLER TRANSPORTERS, INC.—Dewey Corporation; *U.S. Private*, pg. 329
MONFORT, INC.—ConAgra, Inc.; *U.S. Public*, pg. 427
MORGAN DRIVE AWAY, INC.—Lynch Corporation; *U.S. Public*, pg. 1022
MOTORWAYS (1980) LIMITED—Russel Metals Inc.; *Int'l*, pg. 1150
MOUNT VERNON MILLS, INC.—R.B. Pamplin Corp.; *U.S. Private*, pg. 835
MOUNT VERNON MILLS, SMITH & WATERS, INC.—R.B. Pamplin Corp.; *U.S. Private*, pg. 835
F.W. MYERS & CO., INC.; *U.S. Private*, pg. 770
NFC PLC; *Int'l*, pg. 901
NW TRANSPORT SERVICE, INC.; *U.S. Private*, pg. 772
NATIONAL FOOD EXPRESS, INC.—Thorn Apple Valley, Inc.; *U.S. Public*, pg. 1603
NATIONAL TRANSPORT SERVICES CO.—Wakefern Food Corporation; *U.S. Private*, pg. 1146

NAVTRANS INTERNATIONAL FREIGHT FORWARDING, INC.—Norfolk Southern Corporation; *U.S. Public*, pg. 1192
NEW APPLE LINES, INC.; *U.S. Private*, pg. 792
NORFOLK SOUTHERN CORPORATION; *U.S. Public*, pg. 1190
NORTH AMERICAN VAN LINES CANADA LTD.—Norfolk Southern Corporation; *U.S. Public*, pg. 1192
NORTH AMERICAN VAN LINES, INC.—Norfolk Southern Corporation; *U.S. Public*, pg. 1191
NORTH AMERICAN VAN LINES LTD.—Norfolk Southern Corporation; *U.S. Public*, pg. 1192
NORTH SHORE MOVERS; *U.S. Private*, pg. 805
NORTHERN IRELAND TRAILERS—The Peninsular and Oriental Steam Navigation Company; *Int'l*, pg. 1033
OLD DOMINION FREIGHT LINE, INC.; *U.S. Public*, pg. 1216
OVERLAND TRANSPORTATION SYSTEM, INC.—Vitran Corporation Inc.; *Int'l*, pg. 1469
OVERNITE TRANSPORTATION CO.—Union Pacific Corporation; *U.S. Public*, pg. 1668
OZARK MOTOR LINES; *U.S. Private*, pg. 825
P&O EUROPEAN TRANSPORT SERVICES LTD.—The Peninsular and Oriental Steam Navigation Company; *Int'l*, pg. 1033
P&O ROADTANKS LIMITED—The Peninsular and Oriental Steam Navigation Company; *Int'l*, pg. 1034
PM TRANSPORT, INC.—Petroleum Marketers, Inc.; *U.S. Private*, pg. 859
PMT OF THE SOUTHWEST, INC.—Union Pacific Corporation; *U.S. Public*, pg. 1668
PST VANS, INC.; *U.S. Public*, pg. 1246
PACIFIC COAST BUILDING PRODUCTS INC.; *U.S. Private*, pg. 830
PACIFIC MOTOR TRANSPORT CO.—Union Pacific Corporation; *U.S. Public*, pg. 1668
PACIFIC MOTOR TRUCKING CO.—Union Pacific Corporation; *U.S. Public*, pg. 1668
PALMER MOVING & STORAGE CO.; *U.S. Private*, pg. 835
THE PENINSULAR AND ORIENTAL STEAM NAVIGATION COMPANY; *Int'l*, pg. 1032
PENSKE LOGISTICS—Penske Corporation; *U.S. Private*, pg. 851
PENSKE TRUCK LEASING COMPANY LP—Penske Corporation; *U.S. Private*, pg. 850
PERFORMANCE FOOD GROUP COMPANY; *U.S. Public*, pg. 1278
PETRON, INC.; *U.S. Private*, pg. 859
PIONEER EXPRESS INC.—Vitran Corporation Inc.; *Int'l*, pg. 1469
PLANES MOVING & STORAGE COMPANY OF COLUMBUS—Planes Moving And Storage, Inc.; *U.S. Private*, pg. 869
PLANES MOVING AND STORAGE, INC.; *U.S. Private*, pg. 869
PLANES MOVING & STORAGE OF DAYTON, INC.—Planes Moving And Storage, Inc.; *U.S. Private*, pg. 869
PLANES MOVING & STORAGE OF INDIANAPOLIS, INC.—Planes Moving And Storage, Inc.; *U.S. Private*, pg. 869
PLOOF TRUCK LINES, INC.; *U.S. Private*, pg. 872
PONY EXPRESS DELIVERY SERVICES, INC—Borg-Warner Security Corporation; *U.S. Public*, pg. 245
PRESTON TRUCKING COMPANY, INC.—Yellow Corporation; *U.S. Public*, pg. 1788
RPS INC.—FDX Corporation; *U.S. Public*, pg. 604
RED BALL CORPORATION—Atlas World Group, Inc.; *U.S. Private*, pg. 97
RHENANIA TRANSPORT GMBH—The Peninsular and Oriental Steam Navigation Company; *Int'l*, pg. 1033
RITEWAY TRUCKING—Quexco Incorporated; *U.S. Private*, pg. 900
ROADWAY EXPRESS, INC.; *U.S. Public*, pg. 1392
ROBERTS EXPRESS, INC.—FDX Corporation; *U.S. Public*, pg. 604
ROBERTS TRADING CORP.—Canandaigua Wine Company, Inc.; *U.S. Public*, pg. 300
ROCKVILLE FABRICS CORPORATION; *U.S. Private*, pg. 938
ROCOR TRANSPORTATION COMPANIES INC.; *U.S. Private*, pg. 938
RUSSEL METALS INC.; *Int'l*, pg. 1149
RYDER SYSTEM, INC.; *U.S. Public*, pg. 1413
SAIA MOTOR FREIGHT LINES—Yellow Corporation; *U.S. Public*, pg. 1788
SAVANNAH FOODS & INDUSTRIES, INC.—Imperial Holly Corporation; *U.S. Public*, pg. 872
SCHNEIDER NATIONAL, INC.; *U.S. Private*, pg. 971
SERVICES GROUP OF AMERICA; *U.S. Private*, pg. 987
SKYWAY FREIGHT SYSTEMS, INC.; *U.S. Private*, pg. 1005
SOUTHEASTERN FREIGHT LINES, INC.; *U.S. Private*, pg. 1015
SOUTHERN REGION MOTOR TRANSPORT, INC.—Norfolk Southern Corporation; *U.S. Public*, pg. 1101
STACEY MOVING & STORAGE—Planes Moving And Storage, Inc.; *U.S. Private*, pg. 869
STATEWIDE TRANSPORT, INC.—Vulcan Materials Company; *U.S. Public*, pg. 1726
STEWART & STEVENSON TRANSPORTATION, INC.—Stewart & Stevenson Services, Inc.; *U.S. Public*, pg. 1518
STONECUTTER TRUCKING CO.—Stonecutter Mills Corp.; *U.S. Private*, pg. 1044
THE SUDDATH COMPANIES; *U.S. Private*, pg. 1049
SUNFLOWER CARRIERS—Crete Carrier Corp.; *U.S. Private*, pg. 289
SUPERTRANSPORT—GIB Group; *Int'l*, pg. 533
SWIFT TRANSPORTATION CO.; *U.S. Public*, pg. 1543
TANDY TRANSPORTATION—Tandy Corporation; *U.S. Public*, pg. 1560
TEXAS TRANSPORTATION CO.—S & P Company; *U.S. Private*, pg. 954
THORN APPLE VALLEY-TRANSPORTATION DIVISION—Thorn Apple Valley, Inc.; *U.S. Public*, pg. 1603
A THREE RIVERS FORWARDING, INC.—Norfolk Southern Corporation; *U.S. Public*, pg. 1191
TIFFIN MOTOR HOMES, INC.; *U.S. Private*, pg. 1086
TRANSAMERICA CORPORATION; *U.S. Public*, pg. 1629
TRANSGAS INC.—Colonial Gas Company; *U.S. Public*, pg. 401
TRANSPORT DEVELOPMENT GROUP PLC; *Int'l*, pg. 1418
TRANSPORT USA, INC.—The Coastal Corporation; *U.S. Public*, pg. 389
TRANSUS INTERMODAL L.L.C.; *U.S. Private*, pg. 1097
TRATEL—Ciments Francais; *Int'l*, pg. 292
TRI-LINE EXPRESSWAYS LTD.—Russel Metals Inc.; *Int'l*, pg. 1150
TRI-STATE MOTOR TRANSIT CO.; *U.S. Private*, pg. 1101
TRINITY TRANSPORTATION, INC.—Trinity Industries Inc.; *U.S. Public*, pg. 1639
TRUE COMPANIES; *U.S. Private*, pg. 1107
UNIGROUP, INC.; *U.S. Private*, pg. 1117
UNION PACIFIC CORPORATION; *U.S. Public*, pg. 1667
US 1 INDUSTRIES INC.; *U.S. Public*, pg. 1687
UNITED VAN LINES, INC.—UniGroup, Inc.; *U.S. Private*, pg. 1117
UNIVERSAL TRANSPORT OPERATIONS PTY. LTD.—M.I.M. Holdings Ltd.; *Int'l*, pg. 827
VALLERIE'S TRANSPORT SERVICE, INC.; *U.S. Private*, pg. 1131
VIKING FREIGHT SYSTEM, INC.—FDX Corporation; *U.S. Public*, pg. 604
VULCAN MATERIALS COMPANY; *U.S. Public*, pg. 1725
WAMBACQ & PEETERS NV—Etablissements Delhaize Freres Et Cie "Le Lion" S.A.; *Int'l*, pg. 463
WANATAH TRUCKING CO.—Vulcan Materials Company; *U.S. Public*, pg. 1726
WARD TRUCKING CORP.; *U.S. Private*, pg. 1149
WATTS BROS. (A. SUTHRELL)—Franz Haniel & Cie, GmbH; *Int'l*, pg. 591
WERNER ENTERPRISES, INC.; *U.S. Public*, pg. 1754
NELSON WESTERBERG, INC.; *U.S. Private*, pg. 1163
WESTEX, INC.—Yellow Corporation; *U.S. Public*, pg. 1788
WHEATON VAN LINES, INC.; *U.S. Private*, pg. 1171
WHITE PASS SYSTEMS LTD.—Russel Metals Inc.; *Int'l*, pg. 1150
WILSEY BENNETT CO.; *U.S. Private*, pg. 1180
WILSON USA INC.—BTL AB; *Int'l*, pg. 124
YELLOW CORPORATION; *U.S. Public*, pg. 1788
YELLOW FREIGHT SYSTEM, INC.—Yellow Corporation; *U.S. Public*, pg. 1788
YOKOHAMA TRANSPORTATION CO., LTD.—Nissan Motor Co., Ltd.; *Int'l*, pg. 944
YUKON ALASKA TRANSPORT LTD.—Lynden Incorporated; *U.S. Private*, pg. 684

4214 — LOCAL TRUCKING WITH STORAGE

A & B-HAWAII, INC.—Alexander & Baldwin, Inc.; *U.S. Public*, pg. 39
AAH DISTRIBUTION SERVICES LTD.—Franz Haniel & Cie, GmbH; *Int'l*, pg. 591
ALEXANDER & BALDWIN, INC.; *U.S. Public*, pg. 39
AMERCO; *U.S. Private*, pg. 48
BTL AB; *Int'l*, pg. 123
BTL SWEDEN AB—BTL AB; *Int'l*, pg. 123
BERGER TRANSFER & STORAGE, INC.; *U.S. Private*, pg. 135
BURNHAM—Investcorp International; *Int'l*, pg. 686
GIE CASTORAMA TRANSPORTS—Castorama Dubois Investissements S.C.A.; *Int'l*, pg. 276
CITY STORAGE & TRANSFER, INC.—Norfolk Southern Corporation; *U.S. Public*, pg. 1191
COLIN BOOTH LTD.—Simon Engineering plc; *Int'l*, pg. 1251
CONTINENTAL PAPER & SUPPLY CO.; *U.S. Private*, pg. 269
COOK MOVING SYSTEMS, INC.; *U.S. Private*, pg. 272
CROWN LANCE ITALIA SRL—Bolliger, Inc.; *U.S. Private*, pg. 155
DENVER MOVING & STORAGE CO.—Johnson Storage Moving Co; *U.S. Private*, pg. 594
LOUIS DREYFUS CORPORATION; *U.S. Private*, pg. 342
GLOBAL MOVING & STORAGE, INC.—Global Van Lines, Inc.; *U.S. Private*, pg. 458
GLOBAL MOVING SYSTEMS, INC.—Global Van Lines, Inc.; *U.S. Private*, pg. 458
GLOBAL VAN & STORAGE CO.—Global Van Lines, Inc.; *U.S. Private*, pg. 458
HOT SHOT DELIVERY INC.; *U.S. Private*, pg. 541
INTERAMERICAN-STAR GROUP—Zuercher Lagerhaus AG; *Int'l*, pg. 1529
INTERSTATE VAN LINES, INC.; *U.S. Private*, pg. 573
JOHNSON STORAGE MOVING CO; *U.S. Private*, pg. 594
K & R EXPRESS SYSTEMS INC.; *U.S. Private*, pg. 602
KAHULUI TRUCKING & STORAGE, INC.—Alexander & Baldwin, Inc.; *U.S. Public*, pg. 39
NFC PLC; *Int'l*, pg. 901
NATIONAL CARRIERS, INC.—Farmland Industries, Inc.; *U.S. Private*, pg. 396
NATIONAL VAN LINES, INC.; *U.S. Private*, pg. 788
NISSAN RIKUSO CO., LTD.—Nissan Motor Co., Ltd.; *Int'l*, pg. 944
NORTH AMERICAN VAN LINES CANADA LTD.—Norfolk Southern Corporation; *U.S. Public*, pg. 1192
NORTH AMERICAN VAN LINES LTD.—Norfolk Southern Corporation; *U.S. Public*, pg. 1192
NORTH SHORE MOVERS; *U.S. Private*, pg. 805
PALMER MOVING & STORAGE CO.; *U.S. Private*, pg. 835
PENSKE LOGISTICS—Penske Corporation; *U.S. Private*, pg. 851
PLANES MOVING & STORAGE COMPANY OF COLUMBUS—Planes Moving And Storage, Inc.; *U.S. Private*, pg. 869
PLANES MOVING AND STORAGE, INC.; *U.S. Private*, pg. 869
PLANES MOVING & STORAGE OF DAYTON, INC.—Planes Moving And Storage, Inc.; *U.S. Private*, pg. 869
PLANES MOVING & STORAGE OF INDIANAPOLIS, INC.—Planes Moving And Storage, Inc.; *U.S. Private*, pg. 869
RELOCATION MANAGEMENT SYSTEMS, INC.—Norfolk Southern Corporation; *U.S. Public*, pg. 1192
STACEY MOVING & STORAGE—Planes Moving And Storage, Inc.; *U.S. Private*, pg. 869
THE SUDDATH COMPANIES; *U.S. Private*, pg. 1049
TRATEL—Ciments Francais; *Int'l*, pg. 292
U.C. MOVING SERVICES, INC.—Global Van Lines, Inc.; *U.S. Private*, pg. 458
UETA, INC.—BAA plc; *Int'l*, pg. 103
WATTS BROS. (A. SUTHRELL)—Franz Haniel & Cie, GmbH; *Int'l*, pg. 591
WILLIAMS EQUIPMENT CORPORATION—Williams Industries, Inc.; *U.S. Public*, pg. 1770

4215 — COURIER SERVICES, EXCEPT BY AIR

BRAMBLES TRANSPORT (FREIGHT FORWARDING) DIVISION—Brambles Industries Limited; *Int'l*, pg. 211
CALIBER SYSTEM, INC.—FDX Corporation; *U.S. Public*, pg. 604
COURIER DISPATCH DIVISION—Corporate Express, Inc.; *U.S. Public*, pg. 450
DAY & ROSS INC.—McCain Foods Limited; *Int'l*, pg. 850
DEPENDABLE COURIER—Corporate Express, Inc.; *U.S. Public*, pg. 450
EMS KURIERPOST GMBH—Deutsche Post AG; *Int'l*, pg. 407
ITW HI-CONE—Illinois Tool Works Inc.; *U.S. Public*, pg. 866
KYODOH HAISOH CO., LTD.—Matsuya Company Ltd.; *Int'l*, pg. 848
MEARS TRANSPORTATION GROUP; *U.S. Private*, pg. 726
MIDWEST COAST TRANSPORT L.P.; *U.S. Private*, pg. 744
MONSON TRUCKING, INC.; *U.S. Private*, pg. 758
PONY EXPRESS DELIVERY SERVICES, INC—Borg-Warner Security Corporation; *U.S. Public*, pg. 245
TNT LIMITED; *Int'l*, pg. 1342
UNITED PARCEL SERVICE OF AMERICA, INC.; *U.S. Private*, pg. 1123
UNITED TRANSNET, INC.—Corporate Express, Inc.; *U.S. Public*, pg. 449

4221 — FARM PRODUCT WAREHOUSING & STORAGE

AGRICULTURAL WAREHOUSING—Hydro/Kirby Agri Service, Inc.; *U.S. Private*, pg. 552
THE ANDERSONS WHITE PIGEON TERMINAL—The Andersons Incorporated; *U.S. Public*, pg. 111
ARCHER DANIELS MIDLAND COMPANY (ADM); *U.S. Public*, pg. 127
CALWEST COMPRESS & WAREHOUSE CO., INC.—Itochu Corporation; *Int'l*, pg. 694
CHICKASHA COTTON OIL CO.—Tomen Corporation; *Int'l*, pg. 1395
COLUSA ELEVATOR CO.; *U.S. Private*, pg. 257
CONAGRA TRADING & PROCESSING COMPANIES—ConAgra, Inc.; *U.S. Public*, pg. 428
LOUIS DREYFUS CORPORATION; *U.S. Private*, pg. 342
EDMONSON WHEAT GROWERS, INC.; *U.S. Private*, pg. 364
ESSEX GRAIN PRODUCTS, INC.; *U.S. Private*, pg. 383
FARMLAND INDUSTRIES, INC.; *U.S. Private*, pg. 395
FARMWAY CO-OP INC.; *U.S. Private*, pg. 396
FRIONA INDUSTRIES, L.P.; *U.S. Private*, pg. 429
GARVEY INTERNATIONAL, INC.—Garvey Industries, Inc.; *U.S. Private*, pg. 440
GOODPASTURE, INC.; *U.S. Private*, pg. 464
GRAIN SYSTEMS DIVISION—Butler Manufacturing Company; *U.S. Public*, pg. 271
HT&T COMPANY, INC.—Buyco, Inc.; *U.S. Private*, pg. 190
LA SALLE COUNTY FARM SUPPLY; *U.S. Private*, pg. 640
LEHNKERING MONTAN TRANSPORT AG—Metallgesellschaft AG; *Int'l*, pg. 862
LEHNKERING MONTAN TRANSPORT AG—Preussag AG; *Int'l*, pg. 1069
MFA INCORPORATED; *U.S. Private*, pg. 686
MID-KANSAS CO-OP ASSOCIATION; *U.S. Private*, pg. 743
ORANGE GROVE CO-OPERATIVE; *U.S. Private*, pg. 818
PLAINS COTTON CO-OP ASSOCIATION; *U.S. Private*, pg. 868
PRODUCERS CO-OP ASSOCIATION, INC.; *U.S. Private*, pg. 888
RAY-CARROLL COUNTY GRAIN CO-OP; *U.S. Private*, pg. 911
SEABOARD CORPORATION; *U.S. Public*, pg. 1448
SEABOARD FLOUR CORPORATION—Seaboard Corporation; *U.S. Public*, pg. 1449
SMOOT GRAIN CO., INC.—Archer Daniels Midland Company (ADM); *U.S. Public*, pg. 128
STAPLE COTTON COOPERATIVE ASSOCIATION; *U.S. Private*, pg. 1033
SUNMAC HAWAII, LTD.—Sunkist Growers, Inc.; *U.S. Private*, pg. 1053
TATE & LYLE PLC; *Int'l*, pg. 1356
WALLA WALLA GRAIN GROWERS, INC.; *U.S. Private*, pg. 1148
WHEELER BROS. GRAIN CO.—Wheeler Brothers Grain Co.; *U.S. Private*, pg. 1171
WINDSOR SHADE TOBACCO COMPANY, INC.; *U.S. Private*, pg. 1182
WOLCOTT & LINCOLN, INC.; *U.S. Private*, pg. 1185

4222 — REFRIGERATED WAREHOUSING & STORAGE

ALFORD REFRIGERATED WAREHOUSE, INC.; *U.S. Private*, pg. 33
BURRIS FOODS, INC.; *U.S. Private*, pg. 188

CALIFORNIA FARM PRODUCTS—J.M. Smucker Company; *U.S. Public*, pg. 1480
CEALCO C.A.—FMC Corporation; *U.S. Public*, pg. 606
CORY BROTHERS SHIPPING LIMITED—Powell Duffryn PLC; *Int'l*, pg. 1065
DFC TRANSPORTATION CO.—Dean Foods Company; *U.S. Public*, pg. 490
EXEL LOGISTICS—NFC plc; *Int'l*, pg. 901
FRIGOSCANDIA AB—FMC Corporation; *U.S. Public*, pg. 606
FRIGOSCANDIA A/S—FMC Corporation; *U.S. Public*, pg. 606
FRIGOSCANDIA GMBH—FMC Corporation; *U.S. Public*, pg. 607
FRIGOSCANDIA LTD.—FMC Corporation; *U.S. Public*, pg. 607
FRIGOSCANDIA SVENSKA AB—FMC Corporation; *U.S. Public*, pg. 606
GELAZUR S.A.—ConAgra, Inc.; *U.S. Public*, pg. 429
KLLM TRANSPORT SERVICES, INC.; *U.S. Public*, pg. 939
KVAERNER EUREKA, ALESUND DIVISION—Kvaerner a.s.a.; *Int'l*, pg. 767
KVAERNER EUREKA INC.—Kvaerner a.s.a.; *Int'l*, pg. 770
KVAERNER EUREKA, TROMSO DIVISION—Kvaerner a.s.a.; *Int'l*, pg. 767
LANGS COLD STORAGE DIV.—The Oshawa Group Limited; *Int'l*, pg. 1012
MCCAIN FOODS LIMITED; *Int'l*, pg. 850
NFC PLC; *Int'l*, pg. 901
P&O AUSTRALIA LTD.—The Peninsular and Oriental Steam Navigation Company; *Int'l*, pg. 1035
PERFORMANCE FOOD GROUP COMPANY; *U.S. Public*, pg. 1278
PLYMOUTH CREAMERIES, INC.; *U.S. Private*, pg. 872
PREFERRED PUBLIC STORAGE CO.—Certified Grocers of California; *U.S. Private*, pg. 227
PUBLIX SUPER MARKETS, INC.—Publix Supermarkets Inc.; *U.S. Private*, pg. 894
QUALITY FOODS INC.; *U.S. Private*, pg. 898
REALCOLD STORAGE—Spiegel Meats, Inc.; *U.S. Private*, pg. 1025
SOCIETE ANONYME MEDITERRANEENE DE SALAISONS—ConAgra, Inc.; *U.S. Public*, pg. 429
STONE & WEBSTER, INCORPORATED; *U.S. Public*, pg. 1519
URS LOGISTICS; *U.S. Private*, pg. 1114
WIENER-KUHLHAUS FRIGOSCANDIA GES.M.B.H.—FMC Corporation; *U.S. Public*, pg. 607

4225 — GENERAL WAREHOUSING & STORAGE

AAH DISTRIBUTION SERVICES LTD.—Franz Haniel & Cie, GmbH; *Int'l*, pg. 591
ALFORD REFRIGERATED WAREHOUSE, INC.; *U.S. Private*, pg. 33
AMERIFORD INTL. CORP.—Thyssen AG; *Int'l*, pg. 1388
AMMEX WAREHOUSE COMPANY, INC.—BAA plc; *Int'l*, pg. 103
ARNOLD TRANSPORTATION SERVICES—Arnold Industries, Inc.; *U.S. Public*, pg. 132
BATANGAS BAY TERMINAL, INC.—Nissho Iwai Corporation; *Int'l*, pg. 947
BEKINS DISTRIBUTION SERVICES CO.—Hospitality Worldwide Services, Inc.; *U.S. Public*, pg. 841
BERGER TRANSFER & STORAGE, INC.; *U.S. Private*, pg. 135
BINGO EXPRESS CO., LTD.—Nippon Express Co., Ltd.; *Int'l*, pg. 934
BOSCH SALES GROUP—Robert Bosch GmbH; *Int'l*, pg. 205
BURNHAM—Investcorp International; *Int'l*, pg. 686
BUTLER'S WAREHOUSING & DISTRIBUTION LTD.—The Peninsular and Oriental Steam Navigation Company; *Int'l*, pg. 1033
CWT DISTRIBUTION LIMITED; *Int'l*, pg. 246
CANADIAN MINI-WAREHOUSE PROPERTIES, LTD.—Public Storage, Inc.; *U.S. Public*, pg. 1341
CARTER-WALLACE LIMITED (UNITED KINGDOM)—Carter-Wallace, Inc.; *U.S. Public*, pg. 310
CIRCLE FREIGHT INTERNATIONAL—Circle International Group, Inc.; *U.S. Public*, pg. 370
CIRCLE FREIGHT INTERNATIONAL (U.S.A.)—Circle International Group, Inc.; *U.S. Public*, pg. 370
CIRCLE INTERNATIONAL—Circle International Group, Inc.; *U.S. Public*, pg. 371
CIRCLE INTERNATIONAL GROUP, INC.; *U.S. Public*, pg. 370
CITY STORAGE & TRANSFER, INC.—Norfolk Southern Corporation; *U.S. Public*, pg. 1191
CLAIRSON INTERNATIONAL CORP.—Emerson Electric Co.; *U.S. Public*, pg. 575
DSC LOGISTICS, INC.; *U.S. Private*, pg. 306
DELTA CONSOLIDATED INDUSTRIES, INC.—Danaher Corporation; *U.S. Public*, pg. 481
DICKURSBY FARG AB—Kemira Oy; *Int'l*, pg. 729
DOUBLE H WEST SHOE WHOLESALE—Berkshire Hathaway Inc.; *U.S. Public*, pg. 217
DUNEARN DISTRIBUTION SERVICES PRIVATE LIMITED—Sime Darby Berhad; *Int'l*, pg. 1250
EDISON PARKING PROPERTIES, LLC; *U.S. Private*, pg. 364
EMERALD WAREHOUSE & DISTRIBUTION SERVICES—Mail-Well Inc.; *U.S. Public*, pg. 1038
GATX CORPORATION; *U.S. Public*, pg. 690
GATX LOGISTICS, INC.—GATX Corporation; *U.S. Public*, pg. 691
GATX LOGISTICS, INC.-FLORIDA—GATX Corporation; *U.S. Public*, pg. 691
GATX LOGISTICS, INC.-GEORGIA—GATX Corporation; *U.S. Public*, pg. 691
GATX LOGISTICS, INC.-GEORGIA (NORPACK)—GATX Corporation; *U.S. Public*, pg. 691
GATX LOGISTICS, INC.-ILLINOIS—GATX Corporation; *U.S. Public*, pg. 691
GATX LOGISTICS, INC.-MISSOURI—GATX Corporation; *U.S. Public*, pg. 691
GATX LOGISTICS, INC.-UTAH—GATX Corporation; *U.S. Public*, pg. 692
GATX LOGISTICS, INC.-WASHINGTON—GATX Corporation; *U.S. Public*, pg. 692
GATX LOGISTICS NORPACK, INC.—GATX Corporation; *U.S. Public*, pg. 691
GENCO DISTRIBUTING DIV.—Genovese Drug Stores, Inc.; *U.S. Public*, pg. 730
GENOVESE DRUG STORES, INC.; *U.S. Public*, pg. 730
GIANT FOOD INC.; *U.S. Public*, pg. 741
GILCREST STORAGE—The Fred W. Albrecht Grocery Co.; *U.S. Private*, pg. 32
GROCERS GENERAL MERCHANDISE CO.—Certified Grocers of California; *U.S. Private*, pg. 227
HELM, INC.; *U.S. Private*, pg. 520
HUMBERSIDE HOLDINGS LTD—Powell Duffryn PLC; *Int'l*, pg. 1065
HYDROSHIP A/S—Norsk Hydro a.s; *Int'l*, pg. 960
INGRAM MERCHANDISING SERVICE INC.—Ingram Industries Inc.; *U.S. Private*, pg. 563
INTERAMERICAN-STAR GROUP—Zuercher Lagerhaus AG; *Int'l*, pg. 1529
THE JAYDOR CORPORATION; *U.S. Private*, pg. 584
KALAG LAGERHAUS-UND SPEDITIONS GES. MBH—The Peninsular and Oriental Steam Navigation Company; *Int'l*, pg. 1033
MEITO WAREHOUSE CO., LTD.—Meiji Seika Kaisha, Ltd.; *Int'l*, pg. 855
METRO AG; *Int'l*, pg. 863
MITSUBISHI CORPORATION; *Int'l*, pg. 871
MITSUBISHI INTERNATIONAL CORPORATION—Mitsubishi Corporation; *Int'l*, pg. 871
MITSUBISHI LOGISTICS CORP.; *Int'l*, pg. 874
THE MITSUI WAREHOUSE CO., LTD.—Mitsui & Co., Ltd.; *Int'l*, pg. 878
MITSUI WHARF CO., LTD.—Mitsui & Co., Ltd.; *Int'l*, pg. 878
MONTGOMERY ELEVATOR PARTS DISTRIBUTION CENTER—Kone Corporation; *Int'l*, pg. 746
MOUNT JACKSON PRESS, INC.—Perry Graphic Communications, Inc.; *U.S. Private*, pg. 855
F.W. MYERS & CO., INC.; *U.S. Private*, pg. 770
NFC PLC; *Int'l*, pg. 901
NIM CO., LTD.—Nissho Iwai Corporation; *Int'l*, pg. 948
NEDLLOYD DISTRICENTERS INTERNATIONAL—Royal Nedlloyd Group N.V.; *Int'l*, pg. 1144
NIPPON TRUCK CO., LTD.—Nippon Express Co., Ltd.; *Int'l*, pg. 934
ON-GUARD MINI-STORAGE INC.—Cambridge Shopping Centres Limited; *Int'l*, pg. 253
OVERNITE TRANSPORTATION CO.—Union Pacific Corporation; *U.S. Public*, pg. 1668
P&O EUROPEAN TRANSPORT SERVICES LTD.—The Peninsular and Oriental Steam Navigation Company; *Int'l*, pg. 1033
PETERSEN ALUMINUM CORPORATION; *U.S. Private*, pg. 856
POWELL DUFFRYN SHIPPING LTD.—Powell Duffryn PLC; *Int'l*, pg. 1065
POWELL DUFFRYN STORAGE LIMITED—Powell Duffryn PLC; *Int'l*, pg. 1065
PREFERRED PUBLIC STORAGE CO.—Certified Grocers of California; *U.S. Private*, pg. 227
PUBLIC STORAGE, INC.; *U.S. Public*, pg. 1340
PUBLISHER RESOURCES INC.—Ingram Industries Inc.; *U.S. Private*, pg. 563
QUIK N TASTY FOODS—QuikTrip Corporation; *U.S. Private*, pg. 901
RHENANIA ALLGEMEINE SPEDITIONS-GESELLSCHAFT MIT BESCHRANKTER HAFTUNG—The Peninsular and Oriental Steam Navigation Company; *Int'l*, pg. 1033
RHENANIA CONTAINER GMBH—The Peninsular and Oriental Steam Navigation Company; *Int'l*, pg. 1033
RHENANIA MUNCHENER LAGERHAUS-UND TRANSPORT-GES.MBH—The Peninsular and Oriental Steam Navigation Company; *Int'l*, pg. 1033
RHENANIA-SAAR SPEDITIONS-GMBH—The Peninsular and Oriental Steam Navigation Company; *Int'l*, pg. 1033
RHENANIA SCHIFFAHRTS-UND SPEDITIONS-GESELLSCHAFT MBH—The Peninsular and Oriental Steam Navigation Company; *Int'l*, pg. 1033
RHENANIA TRANSPORT GMBH—The Peninsular and Oriental Steam Navigation Company; *Int'l*, pg. 1033
RHENANIA UMSCHLAG UND LAGEREI GMBH—The Peninsular and Oriental Steam Navigation Company; *Int'l*, pg. 1034
RHENANIA WORMSER LAGERHAUS-UND SPEDITIONS-AG—The Peninsular and Oriental Steam Navigation Company; *Int'l*, pg. 1034
ROTTERDAM INDUSTRIAL PARK—Galesi Group; *U.S. Private*, pg. 437
ROTTERDAM VENTURES INC.—Galesi Group; *U.S. Private*, pg. 437
RUTHERFORD WAREHOUSE CORP.—Stonecutter Mills Corp.; *U.S. Private*, pg. 1044
SAVANNAH FOODS & INDUSTRIES, INC.—Imperial Holly Corporation; *U.S. Public*, pg. 872
SCOTIA INDUSTRIAL PARK, INC.—Galesi Group; *U.S. Private*, pg. 438
SCOTIAMOCATTA—The Bank of Nova Scotia; *Int'l*, pg. 156
SCOTT PACKING & WAREHOUSING LIMITED (SCOTLAND)—The Peninsular and Oriental Steam Navigation Company; *Int'l*, pg. 1034
SECURESPACE INC.—Cambridge Shopping Centres Limited; *Int'l*, pg. 253
SENTINEL SELF-STORAGE CORPORATION—Cambridge Shopping Centres Limited; *Int'l*, pg. 253
SOCIETE ANONYME MEDITERRANEENE DE SALAISONS—ConAgra, Inc.; *U.S. Public*, pg. 429
SOUTHEASTERN BONDED WAREHOUSES, INC.—GATX Corporation; *U.S. Public*, pg. 691
SOUTHERN PACIFIC WAREHOUSE CO.—Union Pacific Corporation; *U.S. Public*, pg. 1668
THE STANDARD PRODUCTS COMPANY; *U.S. Public*, pg. 1504
STAPLE COTTON COOPERATIVE ASSOCIATION/ITTA BENA—Staple Cotton Cooperative Association; *U.S. Private*, pg. 1033
STARVING STUDENTS, INC.; *U.S. Private*, pg. 1035
TLC—Christiana Companies, Inc.; *U.S. Public*, pg. 352
TLC GROUP, INC.—Christiana Companies, Inc.; *U.S. Public*, pg. 352
TATE & LYLE PLC; *Int'l*, pg. 1356
TENNESSEE BOOK COMPANY—Ingram Industries Inc.; *U.S. Private*, pg. 563
TOSHIBA LOGISTICS CORPORATION—Toshiba Corporation; *Int'l*, pg. 1404
UETA, INC.—BAA plc; *Int'l*, pg. 103
ULTRAMAR DIAMOND SHAMROCK CORPORATION; *U.S. Public*, pg. 1663
UNIT LOGISTICS INC.—GATX Corporation; *U.S. Public*, pg. 691
UNIT MULTI-PACK, INC.—GATX Corporation; *U.S. Public*, pg. 691
USA PETROLEUM CORPORATION; *U.S. Private*, pg. 1125
WAGNER FORDERTECHNIK GMBH & CO. KG—Linde AG; *Int'l*, pg. 811
WAREX-JESSUP, INC.—Giant Food Inc.; *U.S. Public*, pg. 741
WESTBORN SERVICE CENTER, INC.—The Standard Products Company; *U.S. Public*, pg. 1505
WHEATON INC.—Alusuisse-Lonza Holding Ltd.; *Int'l*, pg. 67
WILMOR WAREHOUSE & SHIPPING CO., INC.—The Hearst Corporation; *U.S. Private*, pg. 516
ZUERCHER LAGERHAUS AG; *Int'l*, pg. 1529

4226 — SPECIAL WAREHOUSING & STORAGE, NEC

A & B-HAWAII, INC.—Alexander & Baldwin, Inc.; *U.S. Public*, pg. 39
ALEXANDER & BALDWIN, INC.; *U.S. Public*, pg. 39
ALGOL CENTRAL STORAGE DEPOT—Oy Algol AB; *Int'l*, pg. 15
AVONMOUTH TERMINAL—GATX Corporation; *U.S. Public*, pg. 692
BARCELONA TERMINAL—GATX Corporation; *U.S. Public*, pg. 692
BELFAST TERMINAL—GATX Corporation; *U.S. Public*, pg. 692
BILBAO TERMINAL—GATX Corporation; *U.S. Public*, pg. 693
BRAMBLES MARINE SERVICES PTY. LTD.—Brambles Industries Limited; *Int'l*, pg. 211
BRAMBLES RECORD MANAGEMENT—Brambles Industries Limited; *Int'l*, pg. 211
BRAMBLES SECURITIES SERVICES LIMITED—Brambles Industries Limited; *Int'l*, pg. 211
BRAMBLES TRANSPORT (FREIGHT FORWARDING) DIVISION—Brambles Industries Limited; *Int'l*, pg. 211
BUCKEYE TANK TERMINALS L.P.—Buckeye Partners, L.P.; *U.S. Public*, pg. 266
BURNHAM—Investcorp International; *Int'l*, pg. 686
CGTX INC.—Hawker Siddeley Canada Inc.; *Int'l*, pg. 604
CENEX, INC.; *U.S. Private*, pg. 221
CIRCLE FREIGHT INTERNATIONAL (U.S.A.)—Circle International Group, Inc.; *U.S. Public*, pg. 370
CIRCLE INTERNATIONAL—Circle International Group, Inc.; *U.S. Public*, pg. 371
CIRCLE INTERNATIONAL GROUP, INC.; *U.S. Public*, pg. 370
COMMERCIAL COLD STORAGE, INC.—Stone & Webster, Incorporated; *U.S. Public*, pg. 1519
COMMERCIAL RECORD CENTER—Nelson Westerberg, Inc.; *U.S. Private*, pg. 1164
CONSOLIDATED WOOL SERVICES PTY. LTD.—Brambles Industries Limited; *Int'l*, pg. 211
CROWLEY MARITIME CORPORATION; *U.S. Private*, pg. 292
CURACAO OIL TERMINAL—Royal Dutch/Shell Group of Companies; *Int'l*, pg. 1141
EDINBURGH TERMINAL—GATX Corporation; *U.S. Public*, pg. 692
EXEL LOGISTICS—NFC plc; *Int'l*, pg. 901
FAIRFIELD PURCHASING & DESIGN, INC.—Fairfield Communities, Inc.; *U.S. Public*, pg. 611
FEDERAL COMPRESS & WAREHOUSE COMPANY, INC.; *U.S. Private*, pg. 398
FRANCESCO PARISI S.P.A.; *Int'l*, pg. 504
GATX CORPORATION; *U.S. Public*, pg. 690
GATX PRIVATE LTD.—GATX Corporation; *U.S. Public*, pg. 693
GATX TERMINALS CORPORATION—GATX Corporation; *U.S. Public*, pg. 692
GATX TERMINALS LTD.—GATX Corporation; *U.S. Public*, pg. 693
GATX TERMINALS (PTE.) LTD.—GATX Corporation; *U.S. Public*, pg. 693
GAMATEX N.V—GATX Corporation; *U.S. Public*, pg. 692
GENERAL AMERICAN TRANSPORTATION CORPORATION—GATX Corporation; *U.S. Public*, pg. 692
GLASGOW TERMINAL—GATX Corporation; *U.S. Public*, pg. 693
GRAYS TERMINAL—GATX Corporation; *U.S. Public*, pg. 693
HYDROSHIP A/S—Norsk Hydro a.s; *Int'l*, pg. 960
THE IMPEX GROUP LIMITED—Goldman Financial Group; *U.S. Private*, pg. 461
INGRAM PERIODICALS INC.—Ingram Industries Inc.; *U.S. Private*, pg. 563
INTERNATIO-MULLER N.V.; *Int'l*, pg. 680

INTERNATIONAL-MATEX TANK TERMINALS—Koninklijke Van Ommeren NV; *Int'l*, pg. 758
INTERNATIONAL MATEX TANK TERMINALS, BAYONNE—Koninklijke Van Ommeren NV; *Int'l*, pg. 758
KAHULUI TRUCKING & STORAGE, INC.—Alexander & Baldwin, Inc.; *U.S. Public*, pg. 39
KAWASAKI TERMINAL—GATX Corporation; *U.S. Public*, pg. 693
KINARK CORPORATION; *U.S. Public*, pg. 960
LAKE RIVER CORPORATION—Kinark Corporation; *U.S. Public*, pg. 961
LEHNKERING MONTAN TRANSPORT AG—Metallgesellschaft AG; *Int'l*, pg. 862
LEHNKERING MONTAN TRANSPORT AG—Preussag AG; *Int'l*, pg. 1069
LIPSCHUTZ BROTHERS INC—BAA plc; *Int'l*, pg. 103
MACRISTY INDUSTRIES, INC.; *U.S. Private*, pg. 693
MORTON SALT—Morton International Inc.; *U.S. Public*, pg. 1135
MULLER-THOMSEN ANTWERPEN—Internatio-Muller N.V.; *Int'l*, pg. 682
F.W. MYERS & CO., INC.; *U.S. Private*, pg. 770
NFC PLC; *Int'l*, pg. 901
NECKAR-GETREIDE UND FUTTERMITTEL SPEDITIONS GESELLSCHAFT MBH—The Peninsular and Oriental Steam Navigation Company; *Int'l*, pg. 1033
NIPPON CHEMICAL HANDLING—GATX Corporation; *U.S. Public*, pg. 693
NIPPON GATX CO., LTD.—GATX Corporation; *U.S. Public*, pg. 693
P&O AUSTRALIA LTD.—The Peninsular and Oriental Steam Navigation Company; *Int'l*, pg. 1035
FRANCESCO PARISI G.M.B.H.—Francesco Parisi S.p.A.; *Int'l*, pg. 504
FRANCESCO PARISI S.P.A.—Francesco Parisi S.p.A.; *Int'l*, pg. 504
PAULSBORO TERMINAL—GATX Corporation; *U.S. Public*, pg. 692
PHILADELPHIA TERMINAL—GATX Corporation; *U.S. Public*, pg. 692
PRECISION STEEL WAREHOUSE, INC.—Berkshire Hathaway Inc.; *U.S. Public*, pg. 217
RHENANIA ALLGEMEINE SPEDITIONS-GESELLSCHAFT MIT BESCHRANKTER HAFTUNG—The Peninsular and Oriental Steam Navigation Company; *Int'l*, pg. 1033
RHENANIA CONTAINER GMBH—The Peninsular and Oriental Steam Navigation Company; *Int'l*, pg. 1033
RHENANIA SCHIFFAHRTS-UND SPEDITIONS-GESELLSCHAFT MBH—The Peninsular and Oriental Steam Navigation Company; *Int'l*, pg. 1033
RHENANIA UMSCHLAG UND LAGEREI GMBH—The Peninsular and Oriental Steam Navigation Company; *Int'l*, pg. 1034
RICHMOND TERMINAL—GATX Corporation; *U.S. Public*, pg. 692
RUNCORN TERMINAL—GATX Corporation; *U.S. Public*, pg. 693
SMDDMS, INC.—The Reader's Digest Association, Inc.; *U.S. Public*, pg. 1368
SHOWA GATX COMPANY, LTD.—GATX Corporation; *U.S. Public*, pg. 693
SPONTEX, INC.—Total S.A.; *Int'l*, pg. 1409
STATEN ISLAND TERMINAL—GATX Corporation; *U.S. Public*, pg. 692
SUPPORT TERMINAL SERVICES, INC.—Kaneb Services, Inc.; *U.S. Public*, pg. 942
TLC—Christiana Companies, Inc.; *U.S. Public*, pg. 352
TLC GROUP, INC.—Christiana Companies, Inc.; *U.S. Public*, pg. 352
TAMPA PUMP STATION—GATX Corporation; *U.S. Public*, pg. 692
TAMPERE SALES OFFICE & STORAGE DEPOT—Oy Algol AB; *Int'l*, pg. 15
TANKSTORE PTE LTD.—GATX Corporation; *U.S. Public*, pg. 693
TARRAGONA TERMINAL—GATX Corporation; *U.S. Public*, pg. 693
TEES STORAGE COMPANY LIMITED—GATX Corporation; *U.S. Public*, pg. 693
TENNSCO CORPORATION; *U.S. Private*, pg. 1077
TERMINALS PORTUARIAS, S.A.—GATX Corporation; *U.S. Public*, pg. 693
TRUE COMPANIES; *U.S. Private*, pg. 1107
VALENCIA TERMINAL—GATX Corporation; *U.S. Public*, pg. 693
VICTORY PACKAGING; *U.S. Private*, pg. 1139
NELSON WESTERBERG, INC.; *U.S. Private*, pg. 1163
WYMONDHAM OIL STORAGE COMPANY LIMITED—GATX Corporation; *U.S. Public*, pg. 693

4231 — TERMINAL & JOINT TERMINAL MAINTENANCE FACILITIES FOR MOTOR FREIGHT TRANSPORTATION

ARGO TERMINAL CO.—GLS Corporation; *U.S. Private*, pg. 435
CANADIAN PACIFIC LIMITED; *Int'l*, pg. 258
GIE CASTORAMA TRANSPORTS—Castorama Dubois Investissements S.C.A.; *Int'l*, pg. 276
DFC TRANSPORTATION CO.—Dean Foods Company; *U.S. Public*, pg. 490
GREAT LAKES TERMINAL & TRANSPORT OF PENNSYLVANIA—GLS Corporation; *U.S. Private*, pg. 435
HAPAG-LLOYD (AMERICA), INC.—Hapag-Lloyd AG; *Int'l*, pg. 596
HAPAG-LLOYD TRANSPORT & SERVICE GMBH—Hapag-Lloyd AG; *Int'l*, pg. 596
LOGISTICS SECTOR—Kimberly-Clark Corporation; *U.S. Public*, pg. 958
MILLER TRANSPORTERS, INC.—Dewey Corporation; *U.S. Private*, pg. 329
NFC PLC; *Int'l*, pg. 901
RENNIES GROUP LIMITED—Anglo American Corporation of South Africa Limited; *Int'l*, pg. 76

4412 — DEEP SEA FREIGHT TRANSPORTATION-FOREIGN

APL LIMITED—Neptune Orient Lines Ltd.; *Int'l*, pg. 912
ALCAN (BERMUDA) LTD.—Alcan Aluminium Limited; *Int'l*, pg. 50
ALCOA STEAMSHIP CO., INC.—Aluminum Company of America; *U.S. Public*, pg. 61
AMERICAN OVERSEAS MARINE CORP.—General Dynamics Corporation; *U.S. Public*, pg. 709
ARCO MARINE, INCORPORATED—Atlantic Richfield Company; *U.S. Public*, pg. 144
AZTEC TRADING COMPANY, S.A.—Georgia-Pacific Corporation; *U.S. Public*, pg. 736
BIRDSALL, INC.—NICOR Inc.; *U.S. Public*, pg. 1182
BURMAH LNG SHIPPING, INC.—Burmah Castrol plc; *Int'l*, pg. 235
BURMAH MOL TRANSPORT LIMITED—Burmah Castrol plc; *Int'l*, pg. 235
BURMAH OIL TANKERS LTD.—Burmah Castrol plc; *Int'l*, pg. 235
BURMAH TRANSPORT HOLDINGS LTD.—Burmah Castrol plc; *Int'l*, pg. 235
CFS NEW ZEALAND LTD.—Circle International Group, Inc.; *U.S. Public*, pg. 372
CSX CORPORATION; *U.S. Public*, pg. 284
CSX INTERMODAL, INC.—CSX Corporation; *U.S. Public*, pg. 284
CANADIAN PACIFIC LIMITED; *Int'l*, pg. 258
CENTRAL GULF LINES, INC.—International Shipholding Corporation; *U.S. Public*, pg. 907
CHEVRON SHIPPING CO.—Chevron Corporation; *U.S. Public*, pg. 348
CIRCLE AIRFREIGHT INTERNATIONAL KOREA—Circle International Group, Inc.; *U.S. Public*, pg. 372
CIRCLE AIRFREIGHT INTL. (TAIWAN) LTD.—Circle International Group, Inc.; *U.S. Public*, pg. 372
CIRCLE FREIGHT INTERNATIONAL LLC—Circle International Group, Inc.; *U.S. Public*, pg. 372
CIRCLE FREIGHT INTERNATIONAL (SAUDI ARABIA) LTD.—Circle International Group, Inc.; *U.S. Public*, pg. 373
CIRCLE INTERNATIONAL—Circle International Group, Inc.; *U.S. Public*, pg. 371
CIRCLE INTERNATIONAL GROUP, INC.; *U.S. Public*, pg. 370
CIRCLE INTERNATIONAL (N.Z.) LTD.—Circle International Group, Inc.; *U.S. Public*, pg. 373
CIRCLE LEMAN AIR FREIGHT—Circle International Group, Inc.; *U.S. Public*, pg. 373
COASTWISE TRADING COMPANY, INC.—Amoco Corporation; *U.S. Public*, pg. 103
COMPAGNIE GENERALE MARITIME—Compagnie Generale Maritime et Financiere; *Int'l*, pg. 322
COMPAGNIE GENERALE MARITIME ET FINANCIERE; *Int'l*, pg. 322
CON-CARRIERS LTD.—Circle International Group, Inc.; *U.S. Public*, pg. 373
CORY BROTHERS SHIPPING LIMITED—Powell Duffryn PLC; *Int'l*, pg. 1065
COSTA CONTAINER LINES S.P.A.; *Int'l*, pg. 336
DENNISON TRANSOCEANIC CORPORATION—Avery Dennison Corporation; *U.S. Public*, pg. 154
THE EAST ASIATIC COMPANY LTD. A/S; *Int'l*, pg. 430
ELBE TRANSPORT G.M.B.H.—Unilever Plc; *Int'l*, pg. 1436
ESSO INTERNATIONAL SHIPPING (BAHAMAS) CO. LIMITED—Exxon Corporation; *U.S. Public*, pg. 601
EXXON COMPANY INTERNATIONAL—Exxon Corporation; *U.S. Public*, pg. 601
FAIRFIELD MAXWELL LTD.; *U.S. Private*, pg. 391
FARRELL LINES INCORPORATED; *U.S. Private*, pg. 397
FOREST LINES INC.—International Shipholding Corporation; *U.S. Public*, pg. 907
FOUAD TRAVEL & CARGO AGENCY—Abdulla Fouad Co. Ltd.; *Int'l*, pg. 502
FUJI KISEN KAISHA, LTD.—Mitsui & Co., Ltd.; *Int'l*, pg. 878
GENERAL ENGINEERS LIMITED—IDB Holding Corporation; *Int'l*, pg. 645
MAX GRUENHUT, GMBH & CO.—Circle International Group, Inc.; *U.S. Public*, pg. 373
MAX GRUENHUT INTERNATIONAL CANADA INC—Circle International Group, Inc.; *U.S. Public*, pg. 373
GULFMARK OFFSHORE INC.; *U.S. Public*, pg. 769
HANJIN CO., LTD.—Hanjin Shipping Company Ltd.; *Int'l*, pg. 592
HANJIN SHIPPING COMPANY LTD.; *Int'l*, pg. 592
HARPER FREIGHT INTERNATIONAL (SWEDEN) AB—Circle International Group, Inc.; *U.S. Public*, pg. 373
HAWAII INDEPENDENT REFINERY—The Broken Hill Proprietary Company Limited; *Int'l*, pg. 225
HYDROSHIP A/S—Norsk Hydro a.s; *Int'l*, pg. 960
HYUNDAI MERCHANT MARINE CO., LTD.—Hyundai Motor Company; *Int'l*, pg. 641
I-SPED INTERNATIONALE SPEDITION GMBH—Korf-Transport-GmbH; *Int'l*, pg. 759
IMPERIAL OIL LIMITED—Exxon Corporation; *U.S. Public*, pg. 602
INTERNATIO-MULLER N.V.; *Int'l*, pg. 680
INTERNATIONAL AERO-SEA FORWARDERS, INC.—International Aero-Sea Forwarders, Ltd.; *Int'l*, pg. 683
INTERNATIONAL AERO-SEA FORWARDERS, LTD.; *Int'l*, pg. 682
INTERNATIONAL SHIPHOLDING CORPORATION; *U.S. Public*, pg. 907
ITALIA DI NAVIGAZIONE S.P.A.—IRI Istituto Ricostruzione Industriale; *Int'l*, pg. 653
ITALIAN LINE—IRI Istituto Ricostruzione Industriale; *Int'l*, pg. 653
IVARAN AGENCIES INC.—A/S Ivaran Rederi; *Int'l*, pg. 696
A/S IVARAN REDERI; *Int'l*, pg. 696
KNSM-KROONBURGH B.V.—Royal Nedlloyd Group N.V.; *Int'l*, pg. 1144
KENTSHIPS—Tate & Lyle PLC; *Int'l*, pg. 1356
KORF-TRANSPORT-FRANCE S.A.R.L—Korf-Transport-GmbH; *Int'l*, pg. 759
KORF-TRANSPORT-GMBH; *Int'l*, pg. 758
KORF TRANSPORT GMBH—Korf-Transport-GmbH; *Int'l*, pg. 758
KUEHNE & NAGEL N.V.—Kuehne & Nagel International AG; *Int'l*, pg. 763
KUWAIT OIL TANKER COMPANY K.S.C.—Kuwait Petroleum Corporation; *Int'l*, pg. 765
KVAERNER A.S.A.; *Int'l*, pg. 766
LACHMAR—Duke Energy Corporation; *U.S. Public*, pg. 535
LEHNKERING MONTAN TRANSPORT AG—Metallgesellschaft AG; *Int'l*, pg. 862
LEHNKERING MONTAN TRANSPORT AG—Preussag AG; *Int'l*, pg. 1069
MARINE TRANSPORT LINES, INC.; *U.S. Private*, pg. 703
METALLGESELLSCHAFT AG; *Int'l*, pg. 860
MINEMET AUSTRALIA PTY. LTD.—Imetal; *Int'l*, pg. 661
MINEMET HOLDING—Imetal; *Int'l*, pg. 661
MINEMET ITALIA—Imetal; *Int'l*, pg. 661
MINEMET S.A.—Imetal; *Int'l*, pg. 661
MITSUI O.S.K. LINES, LTD.—Mitsui & Co., Ltd.; *Int'l*, pg. 878
MORMAC MARINE TRANSPORT, INC.; *U.S. Private*, pg. 762
F.W. MYERS & CO., INC.; *U.S. Private*, pg. 770
NYK LINE (NORTH AMERICA) INC.—Nippon Yusen K.K.; *Int'l*, pg. 941
NEBAM NEDERLANDSE BEVRACHTING EN AGENTUUR MAATSCHAPPIJ—Koninklijke Hoogovens N.V.; *Int'l*, pg. 754
NEDLLOYD BULK B.V.—Royal Nedlloyd Group N.V.; *Int'l*, pg. 1144
NICOR INC.; *U.S. Public*, pg. 1182
NIPPON YUSEN K.K.; *Int'l*, pg. 941
NISSHO IWAI PANAMA INTERNATIONAL S.A.—Nissho Iwai Corporation; *Int'l*, pg. 948
NORVAL, INC.—Scancem AB; *Int'l*, pg. 1201
OBERLANDER RECYCLING TECHNIK GMBH—Fried. Krupp AG; *Int'l*, pg. 513
OFFSHORE LOGISTICS INTERNATIONAL, INC.—Offshore Logistics, Inc.; *U.S. Public*, pg. 1213
OVERSEAS SHIPHOLDING GROUP, INC.; *U.S. Public*, pg. 1236
P&O BULK CARRIERS LTD. (BERMUDA)—The Peninsular and Oriental Steam Navigation Company; *Int'l*, pg. 1033
THE PENINSULAR AND ORIENTAL STEAM NAVIGATION COMPANY; *Int'l*, pg. 1032
RENNIES GROUP LIMITED—Anglo American Corporation of South Africa Limited; *Int'l*, pg. 76
ROYAL NEDLLOYD GROUP N.V.; *Int'l*, pg. 1143
S.B.T.N.V.—Unilever Plc; *Int'l*, pg. 1438
DIETER SCHEEL GMBH—Korf-Transport-GmbH; *Int'l*, pg. 759
SEA-LAND SERVICE, INC.—CSX Corporation; *U.S. Public*, pg. 284
SEA RIVER MARITIME, INC.—Exxon Corporation; *U.S. Public*, pg. 601
SHELL SEMPAKU—Royal Dutch/Shell Group of Companies; *Int'l*, pg. 1140
SHELL TANKERS B.V.—Royal Dutch/Shell Group of Companies; *Int'l*, pg. 1135
SNAM S.P.A.—ENI S.p.A.; *Int'l*, pg. 428
SOCANAV INC.; *Int'l*, pg. 1272
SOMOCAR S.P.A.—Coeclerici Group; *Int'l*, pg. 303
SSANGYONG BUSINESS GROUP; *Int'l*, pg. 1291
SSANGYONG SHIPPING CO. LTD.—Ssangyong Business Group; *Int'l*, pg. 1292
STENA LINE AB; *Int'l*, pg. 1300
TAIWAN MARKETING & TRANSPORTATION DIV.—Chinese Petroleum Corporation; *Int'l*, pg. 286
THAI OCEAN TRANSPORTATION—Royal Dutch/Shell Group of Companies; *Int'l*, pg. 1140
TOTAL TRANSPORT MARITIME—Total S.A.; *Int'l*, pg. 1409
TRANSPORTACION MARITIMA MEXICANA S.A. DE C.V.; *Int'l*, pg. 1418
UCAMAR SHIPPING & TRANSPORTATION CO.—Halliburton Company; *U.S. Public*, pg. 777
VILLAGE TRANSPORT CORP.—The Progressive Corporation; *U.S. Public*, pg. 1335
WATERMAN STEAMSHIP CORPORATION—International Shipholding Corporation; *U.S. Public*, pg. 907
WESTERN NAVIGATION GLOBAL LTD.—Circle International Group, Inc.; *U.S. Public*, pg. 373
WESTERN NAVIGATIONAL GLOBAL LIMITED—Circle International Group, Inc.; *U.S. Public*, pg. 373
WESTWOOD SHIPPING LINES—Weyerhaeuser Company; *U.S. Public*, pg. 1764

4424 — DEEP SEA FREIGHT TRANSPORTATION-DOMESTIC

ALASKA MARINE LINES, INC.—Lynden Incorporated; *U.S. Private*, pg. 683
ALEXANDER & BALDWIN, INC.; *U.S. Public*, pg. 39
BTL AB; *Int'l*, pg. 123
BRAMBLES CONTAINER SERVICES—Brambles Industries Limited; *Int'l*, pg. 211
BRAMBLES SHIPPING—Brambles Industries Limited; *Int'l*, pg. 211
CARGILL; *U.S. Private*, pg. 210
COASTAL TUG & BARGE, INC.—The Coastal Corporation; *U.S. Public*, pg. 390
DET NORSKE VERITAS; *Int'l*, pg. 396
GUARDIAN TRANSPORTATION CORP.—Guardian Industries Corp.; *U.S. Private*, pg. 485
INTERNATIO-MULLER N.V.; *Int'l*, pg. 680
KVAERNER A.S.A.; *Int'l*, pg. 766

LEHNKERING MONTAN TRANSPORT AG—Metallgesellschaft AG; Int'l, pg. 862
LEHNKERING MONTAN TRANSPORT AG—Preussag AG; Int'l, pg. 1069
LYNDEN INCORPORATED; U.S. Private, pg. 683
MARINE TRANSPORT LINES, INC.; U.S. Private, pg. 703
MATSON NAVIGATION COMPANY, INC.—Alexander & Baldwin, Inc.; U.S. Public, pg. 39
MITSUI LIQUEFIED GAS CO., LTD.—Mitsui & Co., Ltd.; Int'l, pg. 877
NIPPON EXPRESS CO., LTD.; Int'l, pg. 933
NIPPON SHIPPING CO., LTD.—Nippon Express Co., Ltd.; Int'l, pg. 934
P&O ROADWAYS LTD.—The Peninsular and Oriental Steam Navigation Company; Int'l, pg. 1034
POINT MARINE, INC.—Tidewater Inc.; U.S. Public, pg. 1608
SOCANAV INC.; Int'l, pg. 1272
SSANGYONG BUSINESS GROUP; Int'l, pg. 1291
SSANGYONG SHIPPING CO. LTD.—Ssangyong Business Group; Int'l, pg. 1292
STENA LINE AB; Int'l, pg. 1300
STENA LINE LIMITED—Stena Line AB; Int'l, pg. 1300
SUN COMPANY, INC.; U.S. Public, pg. 1530
TOTAL TRANSPORT MARITIME—Total S.A.; Int'l, pg. 1409
TOTEM RESOURCES CORPORATION; U.S. Private, pg. 1092
UNION AIR TRANSPORT GMBH—Union-Transport Corporation; U.S. Private, pg. 1120
UNITED TRANSPORT SERVICES PTY. LTD.—Brambles Industries Limited; Int'l, pg. 211
UNITED TRANSPORT (WA) PTY. LTD.—Brambles Industries Limited; Int'l, pg. 211
WESTAR GROUP LTD.; Int'l, pg. 1491
WESTWOOD SHIPPING LINES—Weyerhaeuser Company; U.S. Public, pg. 1764
THE WHITE PASS & YUKON CORP. LIMITED—Russel Metals Inc.; Int'l, pg. 1150

4432 — GREAT LAKES FREIGHT TRANSPORTATION

AMERICAN STEAMSHIP COMPANY—GATX Corporation; U.S. Public, pg. 690
CEMENT TRANSIT CO.—Medusa Corporation; U.S. Public, pg. 1084
GATX CORPORATION; U.S. Public, pg. 690
GREAT LAKES COAL AND DOCK COMPANY—Ashland, Inc.; U.S. Public, pg. 139
HANNA MARINE SERVICES—M.A. Hanna Company; U.S. Public, pg. 781
MARINE TRANSPORTATION—Oglebay Norton Company; U.S. Public, pg. 1213
MEDUSA CORPORATION; U.S. Public, pg. 1084
OGLEBAY NORTON COMPANY; U.S. Public, pg. 1213
SOCANAV INC.; Int'l, pg. 1272

4449 — FREIGHT TRANSPORTATION-WATER, NEC

ADAMS RESOURCES & ENERGY, INC.; U.S. Public, pg. 18
AMERICAN COMMERCIAL LINES INC.—CSX Corporation; U.S. Public, pg. 284
AMERICAN RIVER TRANSPORTATION CO.—Archer Daniels Midland Company (ADM); U.S. Public, pg. 128
ARCHER DANIELS MIDLAND COMPANY (ADM); U.S. Public, pg. 127
AUSTRALIAN NATIONAL INDUSTRIES LIMITED; Int'l, pg. 100
BAYOU CITY BARGE LINES—Adams Resources & Energy, Inc.; U.S. Public, pg. 19
BRENT TRANSPORTATION CO.—Kirby Corporation; U.S. Public, pg. 961
CSX CORPORATION; U.S. Public, pg. 284
CSX INTERMODAL, INC.—CSX Corporation; U.S. Public, pg. 284
CARGILL; U.S. Private, pg. 210
CONTAINER PORT GROUP—World Shipping, Inc.; U.S. Private, pg. 1191
DIXIE BULK TRANSPORT, INC.—Kirby Corporation; U.S. Public, pg. 962
DIXIE CARRIERS, INC.—Kirby Corporation; U.S. Public, pg. 962
DIXIE MARINE, INC.—Kirby Corporation; U.S. Public, pg. 962
EASTERN ENTERPRISES; U.S. Public, pg. 548
ERGON, INC.; U.S. Private, pg. 380
FOSS MARITIME CO.—Totem Resources Corporation; U.S. Private, pg. 1092
FRANCESCO PARISI GES.M.B.H.—Francesco Parisi S.p.A.; Int'l, pg. 504
FRANCESCO PARISI S.A.G.L.—Francesco Parisi S.p.A.; Int'l, pg. 504
FRANCESCO PARISI S.P.A.; Int'l, pg. 504
GARNAC GRAIN CO., INC.—Norfoods, Inc.; U.S. Private, pg. 802
GRUPO PROTEXA S.A. DE C.V.; Int'l, pg. 576
IKON OFFICE SOLUTIONS, INC.; U.S. Public, pg. 862
INGRAM INDUSTRIES INC.; U.S. Private, pg. 562
KIRBY CORPORATION; U.S. Public, pg. 961
KVAERNER FJELLSTRAND SHIPPING A/S—Kvaerner a.s.a.; Int'l, pg. 768
LAMBERT'S POINT BARGE COMPANY, INC.—Norfolk Southern Corporation; U.S. Public, pg. 1190
LEHNKERING MONTAN TRANSPORT AG—Metallgesellschaft AG; Int'l, pg. 862
LEHNKERING MONTAN TRANSPORT AG—Preussag AG; Int'l, pg. 1069
M/G TRANSPORTATION SERVICES, INC.—The Midland Company; U.S. Public, pg. 1111
THE MIDLAND COMPANY; U.S. Public, pg. 1110
MIDLAND ENTERPRISES INC.—Eastern Enterprises; U.S. Public, pg. 549
NEPTUNE ORIENT LINES LTD.; Int'l, pg. 912
NIPPON SHIPPING CO., LTD.—Nippon Express Co., Ltd.; Int'l, pg. 934
NOORDZEE VEERDIENSTEN B.V.—Royal Nedlloyd Group N.V.; Int'l, pg. 1145
THE OHIO RIVER COMPANY—Eastern Enterprises; U.S. Public, pg. 549
ORGULF TRANSPORT CO.—Eastern Enterprises; U.S. Public, pg. 549
FRANCESCO PARISI G.M.B.H.—Francesco Parisi S.p.A.; Int'l, pg. 504
FRANCESCO PARISI S.P.A.—Francesco Parisi S.p.A.; Int'l, pg. 504
RECO TRANSPORTATION INC.—Vulcan Materials Company; U.S. Public, pg. 1726
RED CIRCLE TRANSPORT CO.—Eastern Enterprises; U.S. Public, pg. 549
RHENANIA UMSCHLAG UND LAGEREI GMBH—The Peninsular and Oriental Steam Navigation Company; Int'l, pg. 1034
ROYAL NEDLLOYD GROUP N.V.; Int'l, pg. 1143
TECO TRANSPORT & TRADE CORP.—TECO Energy, Inc.; U.S. Public, pg. 1565
TRANSAMMONIA INC.; U.S. Private, pg. 1096
TWIN RIVERS TOWING CO.—Du Pont (E.I. Du Pont De Nemours & Co.); U.S. Public, pg. 531
VAN GEND & LOOS B.V.—Royal Nedlloyd Group N.V.; Int'l, pg. 1145

4481 — PASSENGER TRANSPORTATION-DEEP SEA

CANBERRA CRUISES LTD.—The Peninsular and Oriental Steam Navigation Company; Int'l, pg. 1033
CARNIVAL CORPORATION; U.S. Public, pg. 306
CELEBRITY CRUISES, INC.—Royal Caribbean Cruises Ltd.; U.S. Public, pg. 1410
COMMODORE HOLDINGS; U.S. Public, pg. 414
COSTA CRUISE LINES, N.V.; U.S. Private, pg. 278
CRUISE HOLDINGS LTD.; U.S. Private, pg. 293
CRYSTAL CRUISES, INC.—Nippon Yusen K.K.; Int'l, pg. 941
CUNARD LINE LTD.—Kvaerner a.s.a.; Int'l, pg. 773
GREYHOUND LEISURE SERVICES, INC.—Viad Corp; U.S. Public, pg. 1718
HOLLAND AMERICA LINE WESTOURS—Carnival Corporation; U.S. Public, pg. 306
NIPPON YUSEN K.K.; Int'l, pg. 941
NORWEGIAN CRUISE LINE; U.S. Private, pg. 808
P&O CRUISES LIMITED—The Peninsular and Oriental Steam Navigation Company; Int'l, pg. 1033
P&O LINES LTD.—The Peninsular and Oriental Steam Navigation Company; Int'l, pg. 1034
THE PENINSULAR AND ORIENTAL STEAM NAVIGATION COMPANY; Int'l, pg. 1032
PREMIER CRUISES—Cruise Holdings Ltd.; U.S. Private, pg. 293
PRINCESS CRUISE LINES—The Peninsular and Oriental Steam Navigation Company; Int'l, pg. 1035
ROYAL OLYMPIC CRUISES; U.S. Public, pg. 1411
SPIRIT CRUISES, INC.—Sodexho S.A.; Int'l, pg. 1274
STENA LINE AB; Int'l, pg. 1300
SWAN HELLENIC LTD.—The Peninsular and Oriental Steam Navigation Company; Int'l, pg. 1035

4482 — FERRIES

THE CEDAR POINT TRANSPORTATION CO.—Cedar Fair, L.P.; U.S. Public, pg. 319
NORTH SEA FERRIES LTD.—The Peninsular and Oriental Steam Navigation Company; Int'l, pg. 1035
P&O EUROPEAN FERRIES LTD.—The Peninsular and Oriental Steam Navigation Company; Int'l, pg. 1033
P&O EUROPEAN TRANSPORT SERVICES LTD.—The Peninsular and Oriental Steam Navigation Company; Int'l, pg. 1033
P&O SCOTTISH FERRIES LTD.—The Peninsular and Oriental Steam Navigation Company; Int'l, pg. 1034
PANDORO LTD.—The Peninsular and Oriental Steam Navigation Company; Int'l, pg. 1034
THE PENINSULAR AND ORIENTAL STEAM NAVIGATION COMPANY; Int'l, pg. 1032
SEA CONTAINERS LTD.; Int'l, pg. 1213
STENA LINE AB; Int'l, pg. 1300
STENA LINE LIMITED—Stena Line AB; Int'l, pg. 1300
WEST JAPAN RAILWAY COMPANY; Int'l, pg. 1490

4489 — WATER TRANSPORTATION-PASSENGER, NEC

AMERICAN CLASSIC VOYAGERS COMPANY—Equity Group Investments; U.S. Private, pg. 380
DANZAS VOYAGES—Danzas Holding Ltd.; Int'l, pg. 383
INGRAM MATERIALS CO.—Ingram Industries Inc.; U.S. Private, pg. 563
KONINKLIJKE VAN OMMEREN NV; Int'l, pg. 758
NIPPON SHIPPING CO., LTD.—Nippon Express Co., Ltd.; Int'l, pg. 934

4491 — MARINE CARGO HANDLING

A & B-HAWAII, INC.—Alexander & Baldwin, Inc.; U.S. Public, pg. 39
APL LIMITED—Neptune Orient Lines Ltd.; Int'l, pg. 912
ALEXANDER & BALDWIN, INC.; U.S. Public, pg. 39
AMERICAN OVERSEAS MARINE CORP.—General Dynamics Corporation; U.S. Public, pg. 709
ARCHER DANIELS MIDLAND COMPANY (ADM); U.S. Public, pg. 127
BTL AB; Int'l, pg. 123
CFS NEW ZEALAND LTD.—Circle International Group, Inc.; U.S. Public, pg. 372
CANADA MARITIME LIMITED—Canadian Pacific Limited; Int'l, pg. 259
CASTLE CEMENT LTD. (PORT OF BRISTOL)—Scancem AB; Int'l, pg. 1201
CHICAGO BOAT YARD, INC.—CFB Industries, Inc.; U.S. Private, pg. 194
CIRCLE AIRFREIGHT INTERNATIONAL KOREA—Circle International Group, Inc.; U.S. Public, pg. 372
CIRCLE AIRFREIGHT INTL. (TAIWAN) LTD.—Circle International Group, Inc.; U.S. Public, pg. 372
CIRCLE FREIGHT INTERNATIONAL LLC—Circle International Group, Inc.; U.S. Public, pg. 372
CIRCLE FREIGHT INTERNATIONAL (SAUDI ARABIA) LTD.—Circle International Group, Inc.; U.S. Public, pg. 373
CIRCLE INTERNATIONAL—Circle International Group, Inc.; U.S. Public, pg. 371
CIRCLE INTERNATIONAL GROUP, INC.; U.S. Public, pg. 370
CIRCLE INTERNATIONAL (N.Z.) LTD.—Circle International Group, Inc.; U.S. Public, pg. 373
COASTAL FUEL TERMINALS, INC.—The Coastal Corporation; U.S. Public, pg. 390
COASTAL TUG & BARGE, INC.—The Coastal Corporation; U.S. Public, pg. 390
COLUMBIA GRAIN, INC.—Marubeni Corporation; Int'l, pg. 845
COMBINED TERMINALS AMSTERDAM V.O.F.—Royal Nedlloyd Group N.V.; Int'l, pg. 1144
CON-CARRIERS LTD.—Circle International Group, Inc.; U.S. Public, pg. 373
CONSOLIDATED WOOL SERVICES PTY. LTD.—Brambles Industries Limited; Int'l, pg. 211
CROWLEY MARITIME CORPORATION; U.S. Private, pg. 292
ELECTRIC FUEL CORP.—Florida Progress Corporation; U.S. Public, pg. 655
ENSO NORD TRANSPORTGESELLSCHAFT MBH—Enso Oyj; Int'l, pg. 457
S.A. ENSO N.V. ENSO WEST—Enso Oyj; Int'l, pg. 457
EUROPE COMBINED TERMINALS B.V.—Internatio-Muller N.V.; Int'l, pg. 682
EUROPE COMBINED TERMINALS B.V.—Royal Nedlloyd Group N.V.; Int'l, pg. 1145
FARRELL LINES INCORPORATED; U.S. Private, pg. 397
FERRYMASTERS LIMITED—The Peninsular and Oriental Steam Navigation Company; Int'l, pg. 1033
FLORIDA PROGRESS CORPORATION; U.S. Public, pg. 655
FORT JAMES WESTERN TRANSPORTATION—Fort James Corporation; U.S. Public, pg. 672
FOSS MARITIME CO.—Totem Resources Corporation; U.S. Private, pg. 1092
FURNESS NORTH AMERICA INC.—Furness BV; Int'l, pg. 530
MAX GRUENHUT INTERNATIONAL CANADA INC—Circle International Group, Inc.; U.S. Public, pg. 373
HANJIN SHIPPING COMPANY LTD.; Int'l, pg. 592
HANJIN TRANSPORTATION CO. LTD.—Hanjin Shipping Company Ltd.; Int'l, pg. 592
M.A. HANNA COMPANY; U.S. Public, pg. 780
HARPER FREIGHT INTERNATIONAL (SWEDEN) AB—Circle International Group, Inc.; U.S. Public, pg. 373
HAWAIIAN TUG & BARGE CORP.—Hawaiian Electric Industries, Inc.; U.S. Public, pg. 800
HUMBERSIDE HOLDINGS LTD—Powell Duffryn PLC; Int'l, pg. 1065
INTERNATIONAL AERO-SEA FORWARDERS, INC.—International Aero-Sea Forwarders, Ltd.; Int'l, pg. 683
INTERNATIONAL AERO-SEA FORWARDERS, LTD.; Int'l, pg. 682
JOHORE MINING & STEVEDORING CO.—Alcan Aluminium Limited; Int'l, pg. 52
KILLINGHOLME WHARFAGE CO. LTD.—Simon Engineering plc; Int'l, pg. 1251
KUEHNE & NAGEL N.V.—Kuehne & Nagel International AG; Int'l, pg. 763
KUWAIT OIL TANKER COMPANY K.S.C.—Kuwait Petroleum Corporation; Int'l, pg. 765
LAMBERT'S POINT DOCKS, INC.—Norfolk Southern Corporation; U.S. Public, pg. 1190
LANCHILE AIRLINES; U.S. Private, pg. 645
LEHNKERING MONTAN TRANSPORT AG—Metallgesellschaft AG; Int'l, pg. 862
LEHNKERING MONTAN TRANSPORT AG—Preussag AG; Int'l, pg. 1069
MARINE PORT TERMINALS INC.—Koninklijke Van Ommeren NV; Int'l, pg. 758
MARITIMA SERVICES—Internatio-Muller N.V.; Int'l, pg. 682
MARITREND, INC.—Vectura Group, Inc.; U.S. Private, pg. 1135
MATSON NAVIGATION COMPANY, INC.—Alexander & Baldwin, Inc.; U.S. Public, pg. 39
MATSON TERMINALS, INC.—Alexander & Baldwin, Inc.; U.S. Public, pg. 40
MITSUBISHI LOGISTICS CORP.; Int'l, pg. 874
MITSUI WHARF CO., LTD.—Mitsui & Co., Ltd.; Int'l, pg. 878
MULLER-THOMSEN ANTWERPEN—Internatio-Muller N.V.; Int'l, pg. 682
WM. H. MULLER & CO. BREMEN/HAMBURG—Internatio-Muller N.V.; Int'l, pg. 682
F.W. MYERS & CO., INC.; U.S. Private, pg. 770
NASSAU TERMINALS—Koninklijke Van Ommeren NV; Int'l, pg. 758
NIPPON SHIPPING CO., LTD.—Nippon Express Co., Ltd.; Int'l, pg. 934
NIPPON YUSEN K.K.; Int'l, pg. 941
NORTH KILLINGHOLME CARGO TERMINAL—Simon Engineering plc; Int'l, pg. 1251

P&O HARBOURS LTD.—The Peninsular and Oriental Steam Navigation Company; *Int'l*, pg. 1034
THE PENINSULAR AND ORIENTAL STEAM NAVIGATION COMPANY; *Int'l*, pg. 1032
RENNIES GROUP LIMITED—Anglo American Corporation of South Africa Limited; *Int'l*, pg. 76
SNCF; *Int'l*, pg. 1163
SEA CONTAINERS LTD.; *Int'l*, pg. 1213
SEA-LAND ORIENT LTD.—CSX Corporation; *U.S. Public*, pg. 284
SEAFORTH MARITIME LIMITED—Halliburton Company; *U.S. Public*, pg. 776
SEAWHEEL LTD.—Sophus Berendsen A/S; *Int'l*, pg. 1285
SHELL ARGENTINA DE PETROLEO—Royal Dutch/Shell Group of Companies; *Int'l*, pg. 1141
SHELL SEMPAKU—Royal Dutch/Shell Group of Companies; *Int'l*, pg. 1140
STEVEDORING SERVICES OF AMERICA; *U.S. Private*, pg. 1042
STRACHAN SHIPPING CO.; *U.S. Private*, pg. 1045
SUMITRANS CORPORATION—Sumitomo Corporation; *Int'l*, *pg. 1312*
SUTTON BRIDGE WHARFAGE CO. LTD.—Simon Engineering plc; *Int'l*, pg. 1251
TECO TRANSPORT & TRADE CORP.—TECO Energy, Inc.; *U.S. Public*, pg. 1565
TNT LIMITED; *Int'l*, pg. 1342
TEXAS TANK SHIP AGENCY, INC.—The Coastal Corporation; *U.S. Public*, pg. 390
THAI OCEAN TRANSPORTATION—Royal Dutch/Shell Group of Companies; *Int'l*, pg. 1140
THUNDER BAY TERMINALS LTD.—Russel Metals Inc.; *Int'l*, pg. 1150
TRANSPORTACION MARITIMA MEXICANA S.A. DE C.V.; *Int'l*, pg. 1418
TYSON FOODS, INC.; *U.S. Public*, pg. 1652
UNITED INTERNATIONAL FERRY FREIGHT LTD.—Sophus Berendsen A/S; *Int'l*, pg. 1285
UNITED TRANSPORT CONTAINERS LTD.—Sophus Berendsen A/S; *Int'l*, pg. 1285
VANCOUVER ISLAND STEVEDORING CO. LTD.—MacMillan Bloedel Limited; *Int'l*, pg. 828
VECTURA GROUP, INC.; *U.S. Private*, pg. 1135
WESTERN TOWING COMPANY—Kirby Corporation; *U.S. Public*, pg. 961
YOUNG BROTHERS, LTD.—Hawaiian Electric Industries, Inc.; *U.S. Public*, pg. 800
ZEPHYR INC.; *U.S. Private*, pg. 1204

4492 — TOWING & TUGBOAT SERVICES

BERING MARINE CORPORATION—Lynden Incorporated; *U.S. Private*, pg. 683
CROWLEY MARITIME CORPORATION; *U.S. Private*, pg. 292
CURTIS BAY TOWING COMPANY OF VIRGINIA—Moran Transporation Company; *U.S. Private*, pg. 760
J. FENWICK & CO. PTY. LTD.—Brambles Industries Limited; *Int'l*, pg. 211
FLORIDA TOWING COMPANY—Moran Transporation Company; *U.S. Private*, pg. 760
FORT JAMES WESTERN TRANSPORTATION—Fort James Corporation; *U.S. Public*, pg. 672
THE GUTTMAN GROUP; *U.S. Private*, pg. 488
HAMPTON ROADS LAND CO., LTD—Moran Transporation Company; *U.S. Private*, pg. 760
HVIDE MARINE INCORPORATED; *U.S. Public*, pg. 851
INGRAM BARGE COMPANY—Ingram Industries Inc.; *U.S. Private*, pg. 563
JAKOBSON SHIPYARD, INC—Moran Transporation Company; *U.S. Private*, pg. 760
JAMES TRANSPORTATION—Fort James Corporation; *U.S.* Public, pg. 672
LEHNKERING MONTAN TRANSPORT AG—Metallgesellschaft AG; *Int'l*, pg. 862
LEHNKERING MONTAN TRANSPORT AG—Preussag AG; *Int'l*, pg. 1069
M/G TRANSPORTATION SERVICES, INC.—The Midland Company; *U.S. Public*, pg. 1111
MORAN BARGE CORPORATION—Moran Transporation Company; *U.S. Private*, pg. 760
MORAN BULK CORPORATION—Moran Transporation Company; *U.S. Private*, pg. 760
MORAN INSURANCE COMPANY LIMITED—Moran Transporation Company; *U.S. Private*, pg. 760
MORAN SERVICES CORPORATION—Moran Transporation Company; *U.S. Private*, pg. 760
MORAN SHIPYARD CORPORATION—Moran Transporation Company; *U.S. Private*, pg. 761
MORAN TOWING CORPORATION—Moran Transporation Company; *U.S. Private*, pg. 760
MORAN TOWING OF DELAWARE, INC—Moran Transporation Company; *U.S. Private*, pg. 760
MORAN TOWING OF TEXAS CORPORATION—Moran Transporation Company; *U.S. Private*, pg. 761
NATIONAL MARINE, INC.—Vectura Group, Inc.; *U.S. Private*, pg. 1135
NORTH WESTERN SHIPPING AND TOWAGE COMPANY PTY. LTD.—Brambles Industries Limited; *Int'l*, pg. 211
PETROLEUM TRANSPORTATION CORPORATION—Moran Transporation Company; *U.S. Private*, pg. 761
PORTSMOUTH NAVIGATION CORPORATION—Moran Transporation Company; *U.S. Private*, pg. 761
SEABOARD BARGE CORPORATION—Moran Transporation Company; *U.S. Private*, pg. 761
SEMBAWANG MARITIME LIMITED; *Int'l*, pg. 1219
TPT TRANSPORTATION COMPANY—Kirby Corporation; *U.S. Public*, pg. 962
TWIN RIVERS TOWING CO.—Du Pont (E.I. Du Pont De Nemours & Co.); *U.S. Public*, pg. 531
VECTURA GROUP, INC.; *U.S. Private*, pg. 1135

4493 — MARINAS

AMERICAN BUREAU OF SHIPPING; *U.S. Private*, pg. 51
COSCOL MARINE CORP.—The Coastal Corporation; *U.S. Public*, pg. 390
HYUNDAI MERCHANT MARINE CO., LTD.—Hyundai Motor Company; *Int'l*, pg. 641
HYUNDAI MIPO DOCKYARD CO., LTD.—Hyundai Motor Company; *Int'l*, pg. 641
INCHON IRON & STEEL CO., LTD.—Hyundai Motor Company; *Int'l*, pg. 642
AL LARSON BOAT SHOP, INC.; *U.S. Private*, pg. 652
NIPPON SHIPPING CO., LTD.—Nippon Express Co., Ltd.; *Int'l*, pg. 934
PICK'S COVE MARINA—Pickering Inc.; *U.S. Private*, pg. 865
TWIN RIVERS TOWING CO.—Du Pont (E.I. Du Pont De Nemours & Co.); *U.S. Public*, pg. 531
WINSCHERMANN BERLIN GMBH—Saarbergwerke Aktiengesellschaft; *Int'l*, pg. 1167

4499 — WATER TRANSPORTATION SERVICES, NEC

APL LIMITED—Neptune Orient Lines Ltd.; *Int'l*, pg. 912
AMERICAN BUREAU OF SHIPPING; *U.S. Private*, pg. 51
AMERICAN OVERSEAS MARINE CORP.—General Dynamics Corporation; *U.S. Public*, pg. 709
AUSTRALIAN NATIONAL INDUSTRIES LIMITED; *Int'l*, pg. 100
CONTAINER CARE INTERNATIONAL; *U.S. Private*, pg. 266
CONTAINER CARE INTERNATIONAL—Container Care International; *U.S. Private*, pg. 267
CROSBY & OVERTON, INC.; *U.S. Private*, pg. 290
CURTIS BAY TOWING COMPANY OF VIRGINIA—Moran Transporation Company; *U.S. Private*, pg. 760
DET NORSKE VERITAS; *Int'l*, pg. 396
DICOP—Petrobras - Petroleo Brasileiro S.A.; *Int'l*, pg. 1043
FLORIDA TOWING COMPANY—Moran Transporation Company; *U.S. Private*, pg. 760
FRONAPE—Petrobras - Petroleo Brasileiro S.A.; *Int'l*, pg. 1043
FUGRO GROUP COMPANIES; *U.S. Private*, pg. 430
HAMPTON ROADS LAND CO., LTD—Moran Transporation Company; *U.S. Private*, pg. 760
HOVERSPEED LTD.—Sea Containers Ltd.; *Int'l*, pg. 1214
JAKOBSON SHIPYARD, INC—Moran Transporation Company; *U.S. Private*, pg. 760
KINGCOME NAVIGATION COMPANY LTD.—MacMillan Bloedel Limited; *Int'l*, pg. 828
LEHNKERING MONTAN TRANSPORT AG—Metallgesellschaft AG; *Int'l*, pg. 862
LEHNKERING MONTAN TRANSPORT AG—Preussag AG; *Int'l*, pg. 1069
MTI LEASING, LTD.—Marine Travelift, Inc.; *U.S. Private*, pg. 703
THE MCARTHUR SHIPPING & AGENCY COMPANY PTY. LTD.—Brambles Industries Limited; *Int'l*, pg. 211
MORAN BARGE CORPORATION—Moran Transporation Company; *U.S. Private*, pg. 760
MORAN BULK CORPORATION—Moran Transporation Company; *U.S. Private*, pg. 760
MORAN INSURANCE COMPANY LIMITED—Moran Transporation Company; *U.S. Private*, pg. 760
MORAN SERVICES CORPORATION—Moran Transporation Company; *U.S. Private*, pg. 760
MORAN SHIPYARD CORPORATION—Moran Transporation Company; *U.S. Private*, pg. 761
MORAN TOWING CORPORATION—Moran Transporation Company; *U.S. Private*, pg. 760
MORAN TOWING OF DELAWARE, INC—Moran Transporation Company; *U.S. Private*, pg. 760
MORAN TOWING OF TEXAS CORPORATION—Moran Transporation Company; *U.S. Private*, pg. 761
NEDLLOYD FLEET SERVICES—Royal Nedlloyd Group N.V.; *Int'l*, pg. 1145
NIPPON KAIJI KYOKAI; *Int'l*, pg. 934
OFFSHORE LOGISTICS CARIBBEAN, S.A.—Offshore Logistics, Inc.; *U.S. Public*, pg. 1213
OFFSHORE LOGISTICS FAR EAST (PTE) LTD.—Offshore Logistics, Inc.; *U.S. Public*, pg. 1213
OFFSHORE LOGISTICS, INC.; *U.S. Public*, pg. 1212
OFFSHORE LOGISTICS SERVICES, INC.—Offshore Logistics, Inc.; *U.S. Public*, pg. 1213
THE PENINSULAR AND ORIENTAL STEAM NAVIGATION COMPANY; *Int'l*, pg. 1032
PETROLEUM TRANSPORTATION CORPORATION—Moran Transporation Company; *U.S. Private*, pg. 761
PORTSMOUTH NAVIGATION CORPORATION—Moran Transporation Company, *U.S. Private*, pg. 761
SEA CONTAINERS ASIA PTE. LTD.—Sea Containers Ltd.; *Int'l*, pg. 1214
SEA CONTAINERS LTD.; *Int'l*, pg. 1213
SEABOARD BARGE CORPORATION—Moran Transporation Company; *U.S. Private*, pg. 761
SEAFARER BOAT CORPORATION—Tidewater Inc.; *U.S. Public*, pg. 1608
SEAFORTH MARITIME LIMITED—Halliburton Company; *U.S. Public*, pg. 776
SEMBAWANG MARITIME LIMITED; *Int'l*, pg. 1219
TIDEWATER INC.; *U.S. Public*, pg. 1608
TIDEWATER MARINE, INC.—Tidewater Inc.; *U.S. Public*, pg. 1608
TIDEWATER MARINE INTERNATIONAL, INC.—Tidewater Inc.; *U.S. Public*, pg. 1608
TIDEWATER MARINE SERVICE, INC.—Tidewater Inc.; *U.S.* Public, pg. 1608
TIDEWATER MARINE WESTERN, INC.—Tidewater Inc.; *U.S. Public*, pg. 1608
TIDEWATER OFFSHORE SERVICES, INC.—Tidewater Inc.; *U.S. Public*, pg. 1608
TIDEX (MALAYSIA) SDN. BHD.—Tidewater Inc.; *U.S. Public*, pg. 1608
TIDEX NIGERIA LTD.—Tidewater Inc.; *U.S. Public*, pg. 1608
TWENTY GRAND OFFSHORE—Tidewater Inc.; *U.S. Public*, *pg. 1608*
WIGHTLINK LTD.—Sea Containers Ltd.; *Int'l*, pg. 1214

4512 — AIR TRANSPORTATION, SCHEDULED

ABX AIR, INC.—Airborne Freight Corporation; *U.S. Public*, pg. 33
AMR CORPORATION; *U.S. Public*, pg. 9
AER LINGUS; *Int'l*, pg. 28
AER LINGUS—Aer Lingus; *Int'l*, pg. 28
AERO PERU—Aero Peru Corporation; *U.S. Private*, pg. 24
AERO PERU CORPORATION; *U.S. Private*, pg. 24
AERO TRASPORTI ITALIANI - A.T.I. S.P.A.—IRI Istituto Ricostruzione Industriale; *Int'l*, pg. 652
AEROLINEAS ARGENTINAS—Grupo Iberia; *Int'l*, pg. 575
AEROMEXICO—Corporacion Internacional de Aviacion (CINTRA); *Int'l*, pg. 332
AIR ALLIANCE—Air Canada; *Int'l*, pg. 36
AIR BC—Air Canada; *Int'l*, pg. 36
AIR CANADA; *Int'l*, pg. 36
AIR CANADA—Air Canada; *Int'l*, pg. 36
AIR CHARTER—Groupe Air France; *Int'l*, pg. 560
AIR FRANCE—Groupe Air France; *Int'l*, pg. 560
AIR FRANCE (MID ATLANTIC REGION)—Groupe Air France; *Int'l*, pg. 560
AIR FRANCE (NORTH CENTRAL)—Groupe Air France; *Int'l*, pg. 560
AIR FRANCE (NORTHEAST REGION)—Groupe Air France; *Int'l*, pg. 560
AIR FRANCE (SOUTHEASTERN REGION)—Groupe Air France; *Int'l*, pg. 561
AIR FRANCE (U.S. PACIFIC REGION)—Groupe Air France; *Int'l*, pg. 561
AIR FRANCE (U.S. REGION)—Groupe Air France; *Int'l*, pg. 561
AIR GUADELOUPE—Groupe Air France; *Int'l*, pg. 561
AIR INDIA; *Int'l*, pg. 37
AIR JAMAICA LTD.; *U.S. Private*, pg. 28
AIR MALTA CO. LTD.; *Int'l*, pg. 37
AIR MIDWEST, INC.—Mesa Air Group; *U.S. Public*, pg. 1099
AIR NELSON—Air New Zealand Ltd.; *Int'l*, pg. 38
AIR NEW ZEALAND LTD.; *Int'l*, pg. 38
AIR NEW ZEALAND LTD. (U.S.A.)—Air New Zealand Ltd.; *Int'l*, pg. 38
AIR NOVA—Air Canada; *Int'l*, pg. 36
AIR ONTARIO—Air Canada; *Int'l*, pg. 36
AIR UK LTD.; *Int'l*, pg. 38
AIR WIS SERVICES, INC.—UAL Corporation; *U.S. Public*, pg. 1653
AIRBORNE FREIGHT CORPORATION; *U.S. Public*, pg. 32
ALASKA AIR GROUP, INC.; *U.S. Public*, pg. 35
ALASKA AIRLINES, INC.—Alaska Air Group, Inc.; *U.S. Public*, pg. 35
ALIGAME S.P.A.—IRI Istituto Ricostruzione Industriale; *Int'l*, *pg. 652*
ALINORD S.P.A.—Bastogi-S.p.A.; *Int'l*, pg. 170
ALITALIA—IRI Istituto Ricostruzione Industriale; *Int'l*, pg. 652
ALITALIA AIRLINES—IRI Istituto Ricostruzione Industriale; *Int'l*, pg. 652
ALITALIA LINEE AEREE ITALIANE S.P.A.—IRI Istituto Ricostruzione Industriale; *Int'l*, pg. 652
ALL NIPPON AIRWAYS CO. LTD.; *Int'l*, pg. 57
ALLEGHENY AIRLINES, INC.—US Airways Group, Inc.; *U.S. Public*, pg. 1680
ALOHA AIRGROUP, INC.; *U.S. Private*, pg. 44
AMERICA WEST AIRLINES, INC.—America West Holdings Corporation; *U.S. Public*, pg. 67
AMERICA WEST HOLDINGS CORPORATION; *U.S. Public*, *pg. 66*
AMERICAN AIRLINES CARGO—AMR Corporation; *U.S. Public*, pg. 9
AMERICAN AIRLINES, INC.—AMR Corporation; *U.S. Public*, pg. 9
AMERICAN INTERNATIONAL AIRWAYS; *U.S. Private*, pg. 57
AMERICAN TRANS AIR EXECUJET, INC.—Amtran, Inc.; *U.S. Public*, pg. 106
AMERICAN TRANS AIR, INC.—Amtran, Inc.; *U.S. Public*, pg. 106
AMTRAN, INC.; *U.S. Public*, pg. 106
ANSETT TRANSPORT INDUSTRIES LTD.—The News Corporation Limited; *Int'l*, pg. 925
ASIANA AIRLINES; *U.S. Private*, pg. 89
ATLANTIC SOUTHEAST AIRLINES INC.; *U.S. Public*, pg. 144
AUSTRIAN AIRLINES—Austrian Airlines; *Int'l*, pg. 101
AVIACO—Grupo Iberia; *Int'l*, pg. 574
AVIATECA; *Int'l*, pg. 102
BASTOGI-S.P.A.; *Int'l*, pg. 170
BINTER CANARIAS—Grupo Iberia; *Int'l*, pg. 574
BRITANNIA AIRWAYS LTD.—The Thomson Corporation; *U.S. Public*, pg. 1601
BRITISH AIRWAYS—British Airways PLC; *Int'l*, pg. 219
BRITISH AIRWAYS PLC; *Int'l*, pg. 218
CCAIR, INC.; *U.S. Public*, pg. 276
CVG AVIATION—Comair Holdings, Inc.; *U.S. Public*, pg. 406
CAMEROON AIRLINES—Groupe Air France; *Int'l*, pg. 561
CANADIAN AIRLINES CORPORATION; *Int'l*, pg. 255
CHINA AIRLINES LTD.; *Int'l*, pg. 284
COMAIR HOLDINGS, INC.; *U.S. Public*, pg. 406
COMAIR, INC.—Comair Holdings, Inc.; *U.S. Public*, pg. 406
CONDOR FLUGDIENST GMBH—Deutsche Lufthansa AG; *Int'l*, pg. 407
CONTINENTAL AIRLINE HOLDINGS, INC.—Scandinavian Airlines System (SAS); *Int'l*, pg. 1202

S.I.C. Index

CONTINENTAL AIRLINES; *U.S. Public*, pg. 439
CONTINENTAL EXPRESS—Continental Airlines; *U.S. Public*, pg. 439
DELTA AIR LINES, INC.; *U.S. Public*, pg. 497
DELTA AIR TRANSPORT N.V.—Sabena; *Int'l*, pg. 1168
DEUTSCHE LUFTHANSA AG; *Int'l*, pg. 407
ERA AVIATION, INC.—Rowan Companies, Inc.; *U.S. Public*, *pg. 1410*
EAGLE AVIATION LTD.—Air New Zealand Ltd.; *Int'l*, pg. 38
EL AL AIRLINES LTD.; *Int'l*, pg. 435
EL AL ISRAEL AIRLINES, LTD.—El Al Airlines Ltd.; *Int'l*, pg. 435
EMPIRE AIRLINES; *U.S. Private*, pg. 374
EVERGREEN INTERNATIONAL AVIATION, INC.; *U.S. Private*, pg. 386
FDX CORPORATION; *U.S. Public*, pg. 603
FINNAIR—FinnAir Oy; *Int'l*, pg. 485
FINNAIR OY; *Int'l*, pg. 485
GRAND HOLDINGS, INC.; *U.S. Private*, pg. 468
GROUPE AIR FRANCE; *Int'l*, pg. 559
GRUPO IBERIA; *Int'l*, pg. 574
HAWAIIAN AIRLINES, INC.—Hawaiian Airlines, Inc.; *U.S. Public*, pg. 799
HORIZON AIR INDUSTRIES—Alaska Air Group, Inc.; *U.S. Public*, pg. 35
HOTPAC RESERVATIONS (NZ) LTD.—Air New Zealand Ltd.; *Int'l*, pg. 38
HYATT AIR, INC.—Hyatt Corporation; *U.S. Private*, pg. 551
IBERIA—Grupo Iberia; *Int'l*, pg. 574
IBERIA CARGO—Grupo Iberia; *Int'l*, pg. 574
IBERIA - SPAIN—Grupo Iberia; *Int'l*, pg. 575
ICELANDAIR; *Int'l*, pg. 658
ICELANDAIR—Icelandair; *Int'l*, pg. 658
INTERNATIONAL AERO-SEA FORWARDERS, INC.—International Aero-Sea Forwarders, Ltd.; *Int'l*, pg. 683
INTERNATIONAL AERO-SEA FORWARDERS, LTD.; *Int'l*, pg. 682
ISLAND AIR—Aloha Airgroup, Inc.; *U.S. Private*, pg. 44
JAPAN AIRLINES—Japan Airlines Company, Ltd.; *Int'l*, pg. 700
JAPAN AIRLINES AMERICAN REGION—Japan Airlines Company, Ltd.; *Int'l*, pg. 700
JAPAN AIRLINES COMPANY, LTD.; *Int'l*, pg. 699
JARDINE MATHESON HOLDINGS LIMITED; *Int'l*, pg. 703
JETSET TRAVEL AND TECHNOLOGY HOLDINGS PTY. LTD.—Air New Zealand Ltd.; *Int'l*, pg. 38
KLM CITYHOPPER—KLM Royal Dutch Airlines; *Int'l*, pg. 719
KLM/ERA HELICOPTERS—KLM Royal Dutch Airlines; *Int'l*, *pg. 719*
KLM ROYAL DUTCH AIRLINES; *Int'l*, pg. 719
KOREAN AIRLINES CO., LTD.; *Int'l*, pg. 758
KUWAIT AIRWAYS, CANADA—Kuwait Airways Corp.; *Int'l*, pg. 764
KUWAIT AIRWAYS CORP.; *Int'l*, pg. 764
LEP PROFIT INTERNATIONAL, INC.—International Logistics Limited; *U.S. Private*, pg. 571
LANCHILE AIRLINES; *U.S. Private*, pg. 645
LOT POLISH AIRLINES SA—Polskie Linie Lotnicze LOT S.A.; *Int'l*, pg. 1062
LUFTHANSA CARGO AG—Deutsche Lufthansa AG; *Int'l*, pg. 407
LUFTHANSA CITYLINE GMBH—Deutsche Lufthansa AG; *Int'l*, pg. 407
MALEV HUNGARIAN AIRLINES, PLC.; *Int'l*, pg. 833
MALEV HUNGARIAN AIRLINES, U.S. OFFICE—Malev Hungarian Airlines, Plc.; *Int'l*, pg. 834
MANDARIN AIRLINES—China Airlines Ltd.; *Int'l*, pg. 284
MARTINAIR HOLLAND—KLM Royal Dutch Airlines; *Int'l*, pg. 719
MARTINAIR HOLLAND—Royal Nedlloyd Group N.V.; *Int'l*, pg. 1145
MESA AIR GROUP; *U.S. Public*, pg. 1098
MESABA AVIATION, INC.—Mesaba Holdings, Inc.; *U.S. Public*, pg. 1099
MEXICANA AIRLINES—Corporacion Internacional de Aviacion (CINTRA); *Int'l*, pg. 332
MEXICANA DE AVIACION S.A. DE C.V.—Corporacion Internacional de Aviacion (CINTRA); *Int'l*, pg. 332
MIDWEST EXPRESS AIRLINES, INC.—Midwest Express Holdings, Inc.; *U.S. Public*, pg. 1111
MIDWEST EXPRESS HOLDINGS, INC.; *U.S. Public*, pg. 1111
MITSUI AIR & SEA SERVICE CO., LTD.—Mitsui & Co., Ltd.; *Int'l*, pg. 878
THE MOUNT COOK GROUP LIMITED—Air New Zealand Ltd.; *Int'l*, pg. 38
F.W. MYERS & CO., INC.; *U.S. Private*, pg. 770
NIPPON EXPRESS CO., LTD.; *Int'l*, pg. 933
NORTHWEST AIRLINES CORP.; *U.S. Public*, pg. 1199
NORTHWEST AIRLINES, INC.—Northwest Airlines Corp.; *U.S. Public*, pg. 1200
NORTHWEST TERRITORIAL AIRWAYS LTD.—Air Canada; *Int'l*, pg. 36
OFFSHORE LOGISTICS, INC.; *U.S. Public*, pg. 1212
OLYMPIC AIRWAYS—Olympic Airways, S.A.; *Int'l*, pg. 1004
OLYMPIC AIRWAYS, S.A.; *Int'l*, pg. 1004
PSA AIRLINES, INC.—US Airways Group, Inc.; *U.S. Public*, pg. 1680
PAKISTAN INTERNATIONAL AIRLINES CORPORATION; *Int'l*, pg. 1021
PANALPINA LTD.—Panalpina Welttransport (Holding) AG; *Int'l*, pg. 1022
PANALPINA WELTTRANSPORT GMBH—Panalpina Welttransport (Holding) AG; *Int'l*, pg. 1023
PHILIPPINE AIRLINES, INC.; *Int'l*, pg. 1050
PIEDMONT AIRLINES, INC.—US Airways Group, Inc.; *U.S. Public*, pg. 1680
POLSKIE LINIE LOTNICZE LOT S.A.; *Int'l*, pg. 1062
QANTAS AIRWAYS LTD.; *Int'l*, pg. 1074
QANTAS AIRWAYS LTD.—Qantas Airways Ltd.; *Int'l*, pg. 1075
ROYAL NEDLLOYD GROUP N.V.; *Int'l*, pg. 1143
SAS AIRLINE—Scandinavian Airlines System (SAS); *Int'l*, pg. 1201
SABENA; *Int'l*, pg. 1168
SCANDINAVIAN AIRLINES SYSTEM (SAS); *Int'l*, pg. 1201
SCENIC AIRLINES INC.—SkyWest Inc.; *U.S. Public*, pg. 1476
SILK AIR—Temasek Holdings Pte. Ltd.; *Int'l*, pg. 1374
SIMMONS AIRLINES—AMR Corporation; *U.S. Public*, pg. 9
SIMMONS AMERICAN EAGLE AIRLINES—AMR Corporation; *U.S. Public*, pg. 10
SINGAPORE AIRLINES—Temasek Holdings Pte. Ltd.; *Int'l*, pg. 1374
SINGAPORE AIRLINES LTD.—Temasek Holdings Pte. Ltd.; *Int'l*, pg. 1374
SKYWEST AIRLINES, INC.—SkyWest Inc.; *U.S. Public*, pg. 1476
SOCIETA ITALIANA SERVIZI AEREI MEDITERRANEI S.I.S.A.M. S.P.A.—IRI Istituto Ricostruzione Industriale; *Int'l*, pg. 652
SOUTHWEST AIRLINES CO.; *U.S. Public*, pg. 1493
SUMITRANS CORPORATION—Sumitomo Corporation; *Int'l*, *pg. 1312*
THE SWISSAIR GROUP; *Int'l*, pg. 1333
TACA INTERNATIONAL AIRLINES, S. A.; *Int'l*, pg. 1346
TAP AIR PORTUGAL—Transportes Aereos Portugueses; *Int'l*, pg. 1418
TEMASEK HOLDINGS PTE. LTD.; *Int'l*, pg. 1374
THAI AIRWAYS INTERNATIONAL LTD.; *Int'l*, pg. 1381
TRADEWINDS PTE. LTD.—Temasek Holdings Pte. Ltd.; *Int'l*, pg. 1374
TRANS WORLD AIRLINES, INC.; *U.S. Public*, pg. 1629
TRANSBRASIL AIRLINES, INC.—Transbrasil S.A. Linhas Aereas; *Int'l*, pg. 1416
TRANSBRASIL S.A. LINHAS AEREAS; *Int'l*, pg. 1416
TRANSPORTES AEREOS PORTUGUESES; *Int'l*, pg. 1418
UAL CORPORATION; *U.S. Public*, pg. 1652
U.S.S. SEKO WORLDWIDE; *U.S. Private*, pg. 1115
UNION AIR TRANSPORT GMBH—Union-Transport Corporation; *U.S. Private*, pg. 1120
UNITED AIR LINES, INC.—UAL Corporation; *U.S. Public*, pg. 1653
US AIRWAYS GROUP, INC.; *U.S. Public*, pg. 1680
US AIRWAYS, INC.—US Airways Group, Inc.; *U.S. Public*, pg. 1680
US AIRWAYS SHUTTLE; *U.S. Private*, pg. 1124
VARIG BRAZILIAN AIRLINES—Varig Brazilian Airlines S.A.; *Int'l*, pg. 1451
VARIG BRAZILIAN AIRLINES S.A.; *Int'l*, pg. 1451
VIACAO AEREA SAO PAULO S.A. (VASP); *Int'l*, pg. 1464
VIVA—Grupo Iberia; *Int'l*, pg. 575
WESTAIR COMMUTER AIRLINES, INC.—Mesa Air Group; *U.S. Public*, pg. 1099
WORLD AIRWAYS, INC.—WorldCorp, Inc.; *U.S. Public*, pg. 1780
WORLDCORP, INC.; *U.S. Public*, pg. 1779

4513 — AIR COURIER SERVICES

AIR CANADA; *Int'l*, pg. 36
AIR COURIER DISPATCH—Corporate Express, Inc.; *U.S. Public*, pg. 450
AIRBORNE FREIGHT CORPORATION; *U.S. Public*, pg. 32
AIRSHOW—Dynatech Corporation; *U.S. Public*, pg. 539
BRINK'S, INC.—The Pittston Company; *U.S. Public*, pg. 1305
CITY POSTAL, INC.; *U.S. Private*, pg. 241
DHL WORLDWIDE EXPRESS; *U.S. Private*, pg. 301
DANZAS A.E.—Danzas Holding Ltd.; *Int'l*, pg. 382
DANZAS ARGENTINA S.A.—Danzas Holding Ltd.; *Int'l*, pg. 382
DANZAS B.V.—Danzas Holding Ltd.; *Int'l*, pg. 382
DANZAS (CANADA) LTD.—Danzas Holding Ltd.; *Int'l*, pg. 382
DANZAS CHILE S.A.—Danzas Holding Ltd.; *Int'l*, pg. 382
DANZAS CORPORATION—Danzas Holding Ltd.; *Int'l*, pg. 382
DANZAS FREIGHT (H.K.) LTD.—Danzas Holding Ltd.; *Int'l*, pg. 382
DANZAS HOLDING GMBH—Danzas Holding Ltd.; *Int'l*, pg. 382
DANZAS HOLDING LTD.; *Int'l*, pg. 382
DANZAS K.K.—Danzas Holding Ltd.; *Int'l*, pg. 382
DANZAS LDA—Danzas Holding Ltd.; *Int'l*, pg. 382
DANZAS LTDA—Danzas Holding Ltd.; *Int'l*, pg. 382
DANZAS N.V.—Danzas Holding Ltd.; *Int'l*, pg. 382
DANZAS PTY. LTD.—Danzas Holding Ltd.; *Int'l*, pg. 382
DANZAS SA—Danzas Holding Ltd.; *Int'l*, pg. 382
DANZAS S.A.—Danzas Holding Ltd.; *Int'l*, pg. 382
DANZAS (SINGAPORE) PTE LTD.—Danzas Holding Ltd.; *Int'l*, pg. 382
DANZAS S.P.A.—Danzas Holding Ltd.; *Int'l*, pg. 383
DANZAS TAIWAN LTD.—Danzas Holding Ltd.; *Int'l*, pg. 383
DANZAS (UK) LTD—Danzas Holding Ltd.; *Int'l*, pg. 383
C.A. DANZAS VENEZOLANA—Danzas Holding Ltd.; *Int'l*, pg. 383
DANZASMEX S.A.—Danzas Holding Ltd.; *Int'l*, pg. 383
DAY & ROSS INC.—McCain Foods Limited; *Int'l*, pg. 850
DYNAMEX EXPRESS—Air Canada; *Int'l*, pg. 36
EMS KURIERPOST GMBH—Deutsche Post AG; *Int'l*, pg. 407
FDX CORPORATION; *U.S. Public*, pg. 603
FEDERAL EXPRESS AVIATION SERVICES INC.—FDX Corporation; *U.S. Public*, pg. 604
FEDERAL EXPRESS CANADA LTD.—FDX Corporation; *U.S. Public*, pg. 604
FEDERAL EXPRESS INTERNATIONAL, INC.—FDX Corporation; *U.S. Public*, pg. 604
FEDERAL EXPRESS LEASING CORP.—FDX Corporation; *U.S. Public*, pg. 604
FEDERAL EXPRESS LOGISTICS, INC.—FDX Corporation; *U.S. Public*, pg. 604
FEDERAL EXPRESS REDEVELOPMENT CORP.—FDX Corporation; *U.S. Public*, pg. 604
FEDEX CUSTOMS BROKERAGE CORP.—FDX Corporation; *U.S. Public*, pg. 604
FEDEX INTERNATIONAL TRANSMISSION CORP.—FDX Corporation; *U.S. Public*, pg. 604
THE FLIGHT INTERNATIONAL GROUP, INC.; *U.S. Public*, *pg. 654*
ITW HI-CONE—Illinois Tool Works Inc.; *U.S. Public*, pg. 866
INTERNATIONAL AERO-SEA FORWARDERS, INC.—International Aero-Sea Forwarders, Ltd.; *Int'l*, pg. 683
INTERNATIONAL AERO-SEA FORWARDERS, LTD.; *Int'l*, pg. 682
KOA HOLDINGS; *U.S. Private*, pg. 603
MFA MISR FREIGHT AGENCIES S.A.R.L.—Danzas Holding Ltd.; *Int'l*, pg. 383
MID PACIFIC AIR CORPORATION—KOA Holdings; *U.S. Private*, pg. 603
MORAN TOWING OF MARYLAND—Moran Transporation Company; *U.S. Private*, pg. 761
PCL COURIER HOLDINGS INC.—Air Canada; *Int'l*, pg. 36
PIEDMONT AIRLINES, INC.—US Airways Group, Inc.; *U.S. Public*, pg. 1680
PILOT AIR FREIGHT CORP.; *U.S. Private*, pg. 865
ROYAL MAIL—The Post Office; *Int'l*, pg. 1064
ROYAL NEDLLOYD GROUP N.V.; *Int'l*, pg. 1143
SKY COURIER—Airborne Freight Corporation; *U.S. Public*, pg. 33
SKYWAY FREIGHT SYSTEMS, INC.; *U.S. Private*, pg. 1005
SODEXI—Groupe Air France; *Int'l*, pg. 560
SONIC COURIERS OF ARIZONA, INC.—United Parcel Service of America, Inc.; *U.S. Private*, pg. 1123
TNT LIMITED; *Int'l*, pg. 1342
U.S.S. SEKO WORLDWIDE; *U.S. Private*, pg. 1115
UNITED PARCEL SERVICE OF AMERICA, INC.; *U.S. Private*, pg. 1123
US AIRWAYS, INC.—US Airways Group, Inc.; *U.S. Public*, pg. 1680
UNITED TRANSNET, INC.—Corporate Express, Inc.; *U.S. Public*, pg. 449

4522 — AIR TRANSPORTATION, NON-SCHEDULED

AAR CORP.; *U.S. Public*, pg. 1
AER TURAS TEO—Aer Lingus; *Int'l*, pg. 28
AER LINGUS; *Int'l*, pg. 28
AIR CANADA VACATIONS INC.—Air Canada; *Int'l*, pg. 36
AIR UK LTD.; *Int'l*, pg. 38
AIR UK (LEISURE) LTD.—Air UK Ltd.; *Int'l*, pg. 39
ATLANTIC AVIATION CORP.; *U.S. Private*, pg. 94
BAX GLOBAL—The Pittston Company; *U.S. Public*, pg. 1305
BUSINESS AIR—Horizon Enterprises Group LLC; *U.S. Private*, pg. 539
CARIBE EXPRESS; *U.S. Private*, pg. 211
CIRCLE FREIGHT INTERNATIONAL—Circle International Group, Inc.; *U.S. Public*, pg. 370
CIRCLE FREIGHT INTERNATIONAL (U.S.A.)—Circle International Group, Inc.; *U.S. Public*, pg. 370
CIRCLE INTERNATIONAL—Circle International Group, Inc.; *U.S. Public*, pg. 372
CIRCLE INTERNATIONAL GROUP, INC.; *U.S. Public*, pg. 370
CUTTER AVIATION ALBUQUERQUE, INC; *U.S. Private*, pg. 298
DAY & ROSS INC.—McCain Foods Limited; *Int'l*, pg. 850
ERA AVIATION, INC.—Rowan Companies, Inc.; *U.S. Public*, *pg. 1410*
ECUAVIA ORIENTE S.A.—Petroleum Helicopters, Inc.; *U.S. Public*, pg. 1281
EVANGELINE AIRMOTIVE, INC.—Petroleum Helicopters, Inc.; *U.S. Public*, pg. 1281
EVERGREEN INTERNATIONAL AVIATION, INC.; *U.S. Private*, pg. 386
EXECUTIVE JET AVIATION, INC.; *U.S. Private*, pg. 388
THE FLIGHT INTERNATIONAL GROUP, INC.; *U.S. Public*, *pg. 654*
FLIGHT INTERNATIONAL, INC.—The Flight International Group, Inc.; *U.S. Public*, pg. 654
FOREST INDUSTRIES FLYING TANKERS LIMITED—MacMillan Bloedel Limited; *Int'l*, pg. 828
FRANCESCO PARISI GES.M.B.H.—Francesco Parisi S.p.A.; *Int'l*, pg. 504
FRANCESCO PARISI S.A.G.L.—Francesco Parisi S.p.A.; *Int'l*, pg. 504
FRANCESCO PARISI S.P.A.; *Int'l*, pg. 504
GRAND HOLDINGS, INC.; *U.S. Private*, pg. 468
MAX GRUENHUT INTERNATIONAL, INC.—Circle International Group, Inc.; *U.S. Public*, pg. 372
MAX GRUENHUT INTERNATIONAL INC. USA—Circle International Group, Inc.; *U.S. Public*, pg. 372
HORIZON ENTERPRISES GROUP LLC; *U.S. Private*, pg. 539
ICELANDAIR; *Int'l*, pg. 658
ICELANDAIR—Icelandair; *Int'l*, pg. 658
MALEV HUNGARIAN AIRLINES, PLC.; *Int'l*, pg. 833
MATAC CARGO LTD.—Air Canada; *Int'l*, pg. 36
MIAMI VALLEY CTC, INC.—DPL Inc.; *U.S. Public*, pg. 474
NETWORK AIR MEDICAL SYSTEMS, INC.—Conseco Inc.; *U.S. Public*, pg. 433
OFFSHORE LOGISTICS, INC.; *U.S. Public*, pg. 1212
OMNIFLIGHT HELICOPTERS, INC.—Omniflight, Inc.; *U.S. Private*, pg. 817
FRANCESCO PARISI G.M.B.H.—Francesco Parisi S.p.A.; *Int'l*, pg. 504
FRANCESCO PARISI S.P.A.—Francesco Parisi S.p.A.; *Int'l*, *pg. 504*
PETROLEUM HELICOPTERS, INC.; *U.S. Public*, pg. 1281
THE PITTSTON COMPANY; *U.S. Public*, pg. 1305
RALEIGH ENTERPRISES, INC.; *U.S. Private*, pg. 907
ROWAN COMPANIES, INC.; *U.S. Public*, pg. 1409
SCANDINAVIAN AIRLINES SYSTEM (SAS); *Int'l*, pg. 1201

SCANDINAVIAN LEISURE GROUP A.B.—Airtours Plc; Int'l, pg. 39
SCENIC AIRLINES INC.—SkyWest Inc.; U.S. Public, pg. 1476
SOBELAIR S.A.—Sabena; Int'l, pg. 1168
TRADEWINDS PTE. LTD.—Temasek Holdings Pte. Ltd.; Int'l, pg. 1374
UAL CORPORATION; U.S. Public, pg. 1652
US AIRWAYS GROUP, INC.; U.S. Public, pg. 1680
ZANTOP INTERNATIONAL AIRLINES, INC.; U.S. Private, pg. 1204

4581 — AIRPORTS, FLYING FIELDS & AIRPORT TERMINAL SERVICES

AAR ALLEN AIRMOTIVE, INC.—AAR Corp.; U.S. Public, pg. 1
AAR AVIATION SERVICES U.K.—AAR Corp.; U.S. Public, pg. 1
AAR CORP.; U.S. Public, pg. 1
AAR ENGINE COMPONENT SERVICES—AAR Corp.; U.S. Public, pg. 1
AAR LANDING GEAR CENTER—AAR Corp.; U.S. Public, pg. 1
AAR OKLAHOMA—AAR Corp.; U.S. Public, pg. 1
AAR PACIFIC PTE. LTD.—AAR Corp.; U.S. Public, pg. 1
AAR TECHNICAL SERVICE CENTER—AAR Corp.; U.S. Public, pg. 1
AMR SERVICES CORPORATION—AMR Corporation; U.S. Public, pg. 9
ATA S.P.A.—Bastogi-S.p.A.; Int'l, pg. 170
AERO ELECTRONICS INCORPORATED—Memphis Group, Inc.; U.S. Private, pg. 731
AERO SYSTEMS AVIATION CORP.; U.S. Private, pg. 24
AEROPLEX OF CENTRAL EUROPE LTD.—Malev Hungarian Airlines, Plc.; Int'l, pg. 834
AEROPORTI DI-ROMA-SOCIETA PER LA GESTIONE DEL AEROPORTUALE DELLA CAPITALE—IRI Istituto Ricostruzione Industriale; Int'l, pg. 652
AEROSERVICES J.T. INC.—Hudson General Corporation; U.S. Public, pg. 845
AEROSPACE TECHNOLOGY—DynCorp; U.S. Private, pg. 351
AEROTHRUST CORP.—Celsius AB; Int'l, pg. 276
AIR UK LTD.; Int'l, pg. 38
AIR UK ENGINEERING LTD.—Air UK Ltd.; Int'l, pg. 39
AIRCRAFT DIVISION/BEDEK AVIATION GROUP—Israel Aircraft Industries Ltd.; Int'l, pg. 690
AIRCRAFT SERVICE INTERNATIONAL GROUP—Viad Corp; U.S. Public, pg. 1719
AIRKAMAN OF JACKSONVILLE, INC.—Kaman Corporation; U.S. Public, pg. 942
AIRPORT GROUP INTERNATIONAL, INC.—Lockheed Martin Corporation; U.S. Public, pg. 1009
AVIA RADIO A/S—AAR Corp.; U.S. Public, pg. 2
AVIALL, INC.—Aviall, Inc.; U.S. Public, pg. 154
AVIATION PRODUCT SUPPORT INC.—Teleflex Incorporated; U.S. Public, pg. 1569
BAA PLC; Int'l, pg. 103
BEDEK AVIATION GROUP (IAI)—Israel Aircraft Industries Ltd.; Int'l, pg. 690
BOEING TECHNICAL OPERATIONS, INC.—The Boeing Company; U.S. Public, pg. 242
BRITISH AEROSPACE (LIVERPOOL AIRPORT) LIMITED—British Aerospace p.l.c.; Int'l, pg. 217
CFS NEW ZEALAND LTD.—Circle International Group, Inc.; U.S. Public, pg. 372
CVG AVIATION—Comair Holdings, Inc.; U.S. Public, pg. 406
CELSIUS AB; Int'l, pg. 276
CELSIUS INVEST AB—Celsius AB; Int'l, pg. 276
CIRCLE AIRFREIGHT INTERNATIONAL DE MEXICO S.A. DE C.V.—Circle International Group, Inc.; U.S. Public, pg. 372
CIRCLE AIRFREIGHT INTERNATIONAL KOREA—Circle International Group, Inc.; U.S. Public, pg. 372
CIRCLE AIRFREIGHT INTL. (TAIWAN) LTD.—Circle International Group, Inc.; U.S. Public, pg. 372
CIRCLE AIRFREIGHT INTL. (THAILAND) LTD.—Circle International Group, Inc.; U.S. Public, pg. 372
CIRCLE ESPANA S.A.—Circle International Group, Inc.; U.S. Public, pg. 372
CIRCLE FREIGHT INTERNATIONAL AGENCIA CHILENA—Circle International Group, Inc.; U.S. Public, pg. 372
CIRCLE FREIGHT INTERNATIONAL ARGENTINA S.A.—Circle International Group, Inc.; U.S. Public, pg. 372
CIRCLE FREIGHT INTERNATIONAL INDIA PVT. LTD.—Circle International Group, Inc.; U.S. Public, pg. 372
P.T. CIRCLE FREIGHT INTERNATIONAL INDONESIA—Circle International Group, Inc.; U.S. Public, pg. 372
CIRCLE FREIGHT INTERNATIONAL ITALIA-EUROLEVANT SRL—Circle International Group, Inc.; U.S. Public, pg. 372
CIRCLE FREIGHT INTERNATIONAL LLC—Circle International Group, Inc.; U.S. Public, pg. 372
CIRCLE FREIGHT INTERNATIONAL (PORTUGAL) LTDA.—Circle International Group, Inc.; U.S. Public, pg. 373
CIRCLE FREIGHT INTERNATIONAL (SAUDI ARABIA) LTD.—Circle International Group, Inc.; U.S. Public, pg. 373
CIRCLE FREIGHT INTERNATIONAL (U.S.A.)—Circle International Group, Inc.; U.S. Public, pg. 370
CIRCLE FREIGHT VENEZUELA S.A.—Circle International Group, Inc.; U.S. Public, pg. 373
CIRCLE INTERNATIONAL—Circle International Group, Inc.; U.S. Public, pg. 372
CIRCLE INTERNATIONAL GROUP, INC.; U.S. Public, pg. 370
CIRCLE INTERNATIONAL (N.Z.) LTD.—Circle International Group, Inc.; U.S. Public, pg. 373
CIRCLE LEMAN AIR FREIGHT—Circle International Group, Inc.; U.S. Public, pg. 373
CIRCLE ZIEGLER S.A. AIRFREIGHT—Circle International Group, Inc.; U.S. Public, pg. 373
COMAIR HOLDINGS, INC.; U.S. Public, pg. 406
COMAIR, INC.—Comair Holdings, Inc.; U.S. Public, pg. 406
COMAIR SERVICES, INC.—Comair Holdings, Inc.; U.S. Public, pg. 406
COMPONENTS DIVISION/BEDEK AVIATION GROUP—Israel Aircraft Industries Ltd.; Int'l, pg. 690
CUTTER AVIATION ALBUQUERQUE, INC; U.S. Private, pg. 298
DFI/INFLIGHT, INC.—BAA plc; Int'l, pg. 103
DALFORT AEROSPACE—Singapore Technologies Pte. Ltd.; Int'l, pg. 1253
DOWTY AEROSPACE AVIATION SERVICES—TI Group plc; Int'l, pg. 1337
ENGINES DIVISION/BEDEK AVIATION GROUP—Israel Aircraft Industries Ltd.; Int'l, pg. 690
EVERGREEN INTERNATIONAL AVIATION, INC.; U.S. Private, pg. 386
FFV AEROTECH AB—Celsius AB; Int'l, pg. 276
FFV AEROTECH INC.—Celsius AB; Int'l, pg. 276
FLIGHT INTERNATIONAL AVIATION, INC.—The Flight International Group, Inc.; U.S. Public, pg. 654
THE FLIGHT INTERNATIONAL GROUP, INC.; U.S. Public, pg. 654
FOKKER AIRCRAFT SERVICES B.V.—Stork N.V.; Int'l, pg. 1304
FOUAD TRAVEL & CARGO AGENCY—Abdulla Fouad Co. Ltd.; Int'l, pg. 502
FRANCESCO PARISI GES.M.B.H.—Francesco Parisi S.p.A.; Int'l, pg. 504
FRANCESCO PARISI S.A.G.L.—Francesco Parisi S.p.A.; Int'l, pg. 504
FRANCESCO PARISI S.P.A.; Int'l, pg. 504
G.E. (U.S.A.) AVIATION SERVICE OPERATION PTE. LTD.—General Electric Company; U.S. Public, pg. 713
THE B.F. GOODRICH COMPANY; U.S. Public, pg. 751
B.F. GOODRICH COMPONENT SERVICES, LTD.—The B.F. Goodrich Company; U.S. Public, pg. 752
GREENWICH AIR SERVICES—General Electric Company; U.S. Public, pg. 710
MAX GRUENHUT CHILE—Circle International Group, Inc.; U.S. Public, pg. 373
MAX GRUENHUT INTERNATIONAL CANADA INC—Circle International Group, Inc.; U.S. Public, pg. 373
MAX GRUENHUT INTERNATIONAL, INC.—Circle International Group, Inc.; U.S. Public, pg. 372
MAX GRUENHUT INTERNATIONAL INC. USA—Circle International Group, Inc.; U.S. Public, pg. 372
HARPER FREIGHT INTERNATIONAL—Circle International Group, Inc.; U.S. Public, pg. 373
HARPER FREIGHT INTERNATIONAL (SWEDEN) AB—Circle International Group, Inc.; U.S. Public, pg. 373
HAWKER DE HAVILLAND LTD.—BTR plc; Int'l, pg. 128
HAWTHORNE CORP.; U.S. Private, pg. 512
HONG KONG AIR TERMINAL SERVICES LTD.—Jardine Matheson Holdings Limited; Int'l, pg. 705
HUDSON AVIATION SERVICES INC., CALIFORNIA—Hudson General Corporation; U.S. Public, pg. 845
HUDSON AVIATION SERVICES INC., DELAWARE—Hudson General Corporation; U.S. Public, pg. 845
HUDSON GENERAL AVIATION SERVICES INC.—Hudson General Corporation; U.S. Public, pg. 846
HUDSON GENERAL CORPORATION; U.S. Public, pg. 845
INNOTECH AVIATION INDUSTRIES LTD.—Air Canada; Int'l, pg. 36
JARDINE MATHESON HOLDINGS LIMITED; Int'l, pg. 703
K-C AVIATION INC.—Kimberly-Clark Corporation; U.S. Public, pg. 959
KIMBERLY-CLARK CORPORATION; U.S. Public, pg. 958
LIVERPOOL AIRPORT PUBLIC LIMITED COMPANY—British Aerospace p.l.c.; Int'l, pg. 217
LIVINGSTON INTERNATIONAL FREIGHT—Circle International Group, Inc.; U.S. Public, pg. 373
LIVINGSTON INTERNATIONAL FREIGHT BELGIUM—Circle International Group, Inc.; U.S. Public, pg. 373
LOCKHEED AEROMOD CENTER, INC.—Lockheed Martin Corporation; U.S. Public, pg. 1007
LOCKHEED AIRCRAFT (ASIA) LTD.—Lockheed Martin Corporation; U.S. Public, pg. 1009
LOCKHEED CANADA—Lockheed Martin Corporation; U.S. Public, pg. 1009
LOCKHEED CORPORATION (INTERNATIONAL) S.A.—Lockheed Martin Corporation; U.S. Public, pg. 1009
LOCKHEED MIDDLE EAST SERVICES—Lockheed Martin Corporation; U.S. Public, pg. 1010
LOCKHEED SUPPORT SYSTEMS, INC.—Lockheed Martin Corporation; U.S. Public, pg. 1009
MATA (HELICOPTERS) DIVISION/MILITARY AIRCRAFT GROUP—Israel Aircraft Industries Ltd.; Int'l, pg. 690
MERCURY AIR CARGO—Mercury Air Group Inc.; U.S. Public, pg. 1093
MERCURY AIR CENTER—Mercury Air Group Inc.; U.S. Public, pg. 1093
MERCURY AIR GROUP INC.; U.S. Public, pg. 1092
MERCURY REFUELING, INC.—Mercury Air Group Inc.; U.S. Public, pg. 1093
MIDCOAST AVIATION, INC.—Sabreliner Corporation; U.S. Private, pg. 959
NORTHWEST AEROSPACE TRAINING CORPORATION—Northwest Airlines Corp.; U.S. Public, pg. 1200
NORTHWEST AIRCRAFT INC.—Northwest Airlines Corp.; U.S. Public, pg. 1200
OFFICINE AERONAVALI VENEZIA S.P.A.—IRI Istituto Ricostruzione Industriale; Int'l, pg. 653
OGDEN AVIATION SERVICES—Ogden Corporation; U.S. Public, pg. 1213
OGDEN CORPORATION; U.S. Public, pg. 1213
FRANCESCO PARISI G.M.B.H.—Francesco Parisi S.p.A.; Int'l, pg. 504
FRANCESCO PARISI S.P.A.—Francesco Parisi S.p.A.; Int'l, pg. 504
PENINSULAR AVIATION SERVICES—Royal Dutch/Shell Group of Companies; Int'l, pg. 1141
PILATUS FLUGZEUGWERKE AG—Oerlikon-Buhrle Holding AG; Int'l, pg. 998
PILLAR ENGINEERING LTD.—Caradon Plc; Int'l, pg. 267
PORT OF OAKLAND; U.S. Private, pg. 876
PRECISION STANDARD, INC.; U.S. Public, pg. 1321
PRIMARK CORPORATION; U.S. Public, pg. 1325
PRINCEVILLE CORPORATION; U.S. Private, pg. 885
RACO, INC.—Hubbell Incorporated; U.S. Public, pg. 845
ROHR AERO SERVICES, INC.—The B.F. Goodrich Company; U.S. Public, pg. 751
ROHR AERO SERVICES-ASIA—The B.F. Goodrich Company; U.S. Public, pg. 752
SATS APRON SERVICES PTE., LTD.—Temasek Holdings Pte. Ltd.; Int'l, pg. 1374
SATS PASSENGER SERVICES PTE. LTD.—Temasek Holdings Pte. Ltd.; Int'l, pg. 1374
S.W. AIRFREIGHT—Circle International Group, Inc.; U.S. Public, pg. 373
SABRELINER CORPORATION; U.S. Private, pg. 959
SABRETECH, INC.—Sabreliner Corporation; U.S. Private, pg. 959
SCANDINAVIAN AIRLINES SYSTEM (SAS); Int'l, pg. 1201
SENECA FLIGHT OPER.—Seneca Foods Corporation; U.S. Public, pg. 1456
SERV-AIR, INC.—Raytheon Company; U.S. Public, pg. 1366
SIGNATURE FLIGHT SUPPORT—BBA Group plc; Int'l, pg. 114
SINGAPORE AIRPORT TERMINAL SERVICES—Temasek Holdings Pte. Ltd.; Int'l, pg. 1374
SINGAPORE ENGINE OVERHAUL CENTRE (PTE.) LTD.—Temasek Holdings Pte. Ltd.; Int'l, pg. 1374
SPAR AVIATION SERVICES—Spar Aerospace Limited; Int'l, pg. 1288
TRAMCO INC.—The B.F. Goodrich Company; U.S. Public, pg. 752
TRIAD INTERNATIONAL MAINTENANCE CORPORATION—Primark Corporation; U.S. Public, pg. 1325
UAL CORPORATION; U.S. Public, pg. 1652
UNC ACCESSORY SERVICES—General Electric Company; U.S. Public, pg. 710
VIAD CORP; U.S. Public, pg. 1718

4612 — CRUDE PETROLEUM PIPE LINES

AEC PIPELINES—Alberta Energy Company, Ltd.; Int'l, pg. 48
ADRIA-WIEN PIPELINE—Royal Dutch/Shell Group of Companies; Int'l, pg. 1138
ALASKA PIPELINE CO.—Seagull Energy Corporation; U.S. Public, pg. 1450
ALBERTA ENERGY COMPANY, LTD.; Int'l, pg. 48
ALBERTA OIL SANDS PIPELINE LTD.—Alberta Energy Company, Ltd.; Int'l, pg. 48
ALYESKA PIPELINE SERVICE COMPANY; U.S. Private, pg. 47
AMOCO CORPORATION; U.S. Public, pg. 101
AMOCO PIPELINE CO.—Amoco Corporation; U.S. Public, pg. 102
BC GAS INC.; Int'l, pg. 114
BP AMERICA INC.—The British Petroleum Company P.L.C.; Int'l, pg. 220
BP INTERNATIONAL LTD.—The British Petroleum Company P.L.C.; Int'l, pg. 220
BP OIL PIPELINE COMPANY—The British Petroleum Company P.L.C.; Int'l, pg. 220
BP PIPELINES (ALASKA) INC.—The British Petroleum Company P.L.C.; Int'l, pg. 220
BELLE FOURCHE PIPELINE CO.—True Companies; U.S. Private, pg. 1107
THE BRITISH PETROLEUM COMPANY P.L.C.; Int'l, pg. 219
BRITISH PIPELINE AGENCY—Royal Dutch/Shell Group of Companies; Int'l, pg. 1139
CNG PRODUCING CO.—Consolidated Natural Gas Company; U.S. Public, pg. 435
CHINESE PETROLEUM CORPORATION; Int'l, pg. 286
CITGO PIPELINE COMPANY—Petroleos de Venezuela S.A.; Int'l, pg. 1045
THE COASTAL CORPORATION; U.S. Public, pg. 389
CROWN-RANCHO PIPE LINE CORP.—Crown Central Petroleum Corporation; U.S. Public, pg. 462
ENRON OIL TRADING & TRANSPORTATION CO.—Enron Corp.; U.S. Public, pg. 584
ENSTAR NATURAL GAS CO.—Seagull Energy Corporation; U.S. Public, pg. 1450
EXXON CORPORATION; U.S. Public, pg. 601
EXXON PIPELINE COMPANY—Exxon Corporation; U.S. Public, pg. 601
FIRST PHILIPPINE INDUSTRIAL CORP.—Royal Dutch/Shell Group of Companies; Int'l, pg. 1140
HOUSTON CONTRACTING COMPANY-ALASKA, LTD.—Arctic Slope Regional Corporation; U.S. Private, pg. 80
IPL INTERNATIONAL—IPL Energy Inc.; Int'l, pg. 652
INTERPROVINCIAL PIPE LINE INC.—IPL Energy Inc.; Int'l, pg. 652
INTERPROVINCIAL PIPE LINE (NW) LTD.—IPL Energy Inc.; Int'l, pg. 652
INTERSTATE ENERGY CO.—PP&L Resources; U.S. Public, pg. 1244
KOCH INDUSTRIES, INCORPORATED; U.S. Private, pg. 628
KUWAIT PETROLEUM CORPORATION; Int'l, pg. 764
LAKEHEAD PIPE LINE CO., INC.—IPL Energy Inc.; Int'l, pg. 652
LOUISIANA NEVADA TRANSIT CO.—Holderbank Financiere Glaris Ltd.; Int'l, pg. 628
MANNESMANN ANLAGENBAU AG—Mannesmann A.G.; Int'l, pg. 836
MARATHON ASHLAND PETROLEUM LLC—Ashland, Inc.; U.S. Public, pg. 139

MARATHON ASHLAND PETROLEUM LLC—USX Corporation; *U.S. Public*, pg. 1662
MARATHON OIL U.K., LTD.—USX Corporation; *U.S. Public, pg. 1662*
MOBIL PIPE LINE COMPANY—Mobil Oil Corporation; *U.S. Public*, pg. 1118
MURPHY OIL CO., LTD.—Murphy Oil Corporation; *U.S. Public*, pg. 1142
MURPHY OIL CORPORATION; *U.S. Public*, pg. 1141
NATCHIQ, INC.—Arctic Slope Regional Corporation; *U.S. Private*, pg. 80
NORTHROCK RESOURCES LTD.; *Int'l*, pg. 970
PHILLIPS GAS SUPPLY CORPORATION—Phillips Petroleum Company; *U.S. Public*, pg. 1291
PHILLIPS PETROLEUM COMPANY; *U.S. Public*, pg. 1290
PHILLIPS PIPE LINE COMPANY—Phillips Petroleum Company; *U.S. Public*, pg. 1291
PIPELINE SUD-EUROPEEN—Royal Dutch/Shell Group of Companies; *Int'l*, pg. 1138
ROTTERDAM-RIJN PIJPLEIDING—Royal Dutch/Shell Group of Companies; *Int'l*, pg. 1135
ROYAL DUTCH/SHELL GROUP OF COMPANIES; *Int'l*, pg. 1135
SHELL OIL COMPANY—Royal Dutch/Shell Group of Companies; *Int'l*, pg. 1136
SNAM S.P.A.—ENI S.p.A.; *Int'l*, pg. 428
SUN COMPANY, INC.; *U.S. Public*, pg. 1530
TEXACO INC.; *U.S. Public*, pg. 1582
TOTAL CRUDE OIL TRANSPORT, INC.—Ultramar Diamond Shamrock Corporation; *U.S. Public*, pg. 1663
TOTAL PIPELINE CORPORATION—Ultramar Diamond Shamrock Corporation; *U.S. Public*, pg. 1663
TRANS MOUNTAIN OIL PIPE LINE CORP.—BC Gas Inc.; *Int'l*, pg. 114
TRANS MOUNTAIN PIPELINE COMPANY LTD.—BC Gas Inc.; *Int'l*, pg. 114
TRUE COMPANIES; *U.S. Private*, pg. 1107
VANGUARD ENERGY CORP.; *U.S. Private*, pg. 1133
VENGAS PIPELINE COMPANY—Stone & Webster, Incorporated; *U.S. Public*, pg. 1519

4613 — REFINED PETROLEUM PIPE LINES

ADRIA-WIEN PIPELINE—Royal Dutch/Shell Group of Companies; *Int'l*, pg. 1138
AIRFORCE PIPELINE INC.—Norfolk Southern Corporation; *U.S. Public*, pg. 1191
ALBERTA ENERGY COMPANY, LTD.; *Int'l*, pg. 48
AMOCO CANADA RESOURCES LTD.—Amoco Corporation; *U.S. Public*, pg. 103
AMOCO CORPORATION; *U.S. Public*, pg. 101
AMOCO OIL COMPANY—Amoco Corporation; *U.S. Public*, pg. 102
AMOCO PIPELINE CO.—Amoco Corporation; *U.S. Public*, pg. 102
ATLANTIC RICHFIELD COMPANY; *U.S. Public*, pg. 144
BP AMERICA INC.—The British Petroleum Company P.L.C.; *Int'l*, pg. 220
BP INTERNATIONAL LTD.—The British Petroleum Company P.L.C.; *Int'l*, pg. 220
BP PIPELINES (ALASKA) INC.—The British Petroleum Company P.L.C.; *Int'l*, pg. 220
BADGER PIPE LINE CO.—Texaco Inc.; *U.S. Public*, pg. 1584
BELLE FOURCHE PIPELINE CO.—True Companies; *U.S. Private*, pg. 1107
THE BRITISH PETROLEUM COMPANY P.L.C.; *Int'l*, pg. 219
BRITISH PIPELINE AGENCY—Royal Dutch/Shell Group of Companies; *Int'l*, pg. 1139
BUCKEYE PARTNERS, L.P.; *U.S. Public*, pg. 266
BUCKEYE PIPE LINE COMPANY, L.P.—Buckeye Partners, L.P.; *U.S. Public*, pg. 266
CALNEV PIPELINE COMPANY—GATX Corporation; *U.S. Public*, pg. 692
CENTRAL FLORIDA PIPELINE CORP.—GATX Corporation; *U.S. Public*, pg. 692
CHINESE PETROLEUM CORPORATION; *Int'l*, pg. 286
THE COASTAL CORPORATION; *U.S. Public*, pg. 389
COLONIAL PIPELINE CO.—Texaco Inc.; *U.S. Public*, pg. 1584
COLONIAL PIPELINE COMPANY; *U.S. Private*, pg. 254
ENRON CORP.; *U.S. Public*, pg. 584
EVERGLADES PIPE LINE COMPANY, L.P.—Buckeye Partners, L.P.; *U.S. Public*, pg. 266
EXPLORER PIPELINE CO.—Texaco Inc.; *U.S. Public*, pg. 1584
EXXON CHEMICAL LIMITED—Exxon Corporation; *U.S. Public*, pg. 602
EXXON CORPORATION; *U.S. Public*, pg. 601
EXXON PIPELINE COMPANY—Exxon Corporation; *U.S. Public*, pg. 601
FIRST PHILIPPINE INDUSTRIAL CORP.—Royal Dutch/Shell Group of Companies; *Int'l*, pg. 1140
GATX CORPORATION; *U.S. Public*, pg. 690
GATX TERMINALS CORPORATION—GATX Corporation; *U.S. Public*, pg. 692
GENERAL AMERICAN TRANSPORTATION CORPORATION—GATX Corporation; *U.S. Public*, pg. 692
HOUSTON CONTRACTING COMPANY-ALASKA, LTD.—Arctic Slope Regional Corporation; *U.S. Private*, pg. 80
INTERSTATE ENERGY CO.—PP&L Resources; *U.S. Public*, pg. 1244
KANEB PIPE LINE CO.—Kaneb Services, Inc.; *U.S. Public*, pg. 942
KANEB PIPE LINE PARTNERS, L.P.—Kaneb Services, Inc.; *U.S. Public*, pg. 942
KANEB SERVICES, INC.; *U.S. Public*, pg. 942
KAW PIPELINE CO.—Texaco Inc.; *U.S. Public*, pg. 1584
KOCH INDUSTRIES, INCORPORATED; *U.S. Private*, pg. 628
KUWAIT PETROLEUM CORPORATION; *Int'l*, pg. 764
LL&E PIPELINE CORP.—Burlington Resources Inc.; *U.S. Public*, pg. 269
LAUREL PIPE LINE COMPANY, L.P.—Buckeye Partners, L.P.; *U.S. Public*, pg. 267
LOS ANGELES MARINE TERMINAL—GATX Corporation; *U.S. Public*, pg. 692
MAPCO INC.; *U.S. Public*, pg. 1042
MAPCO NATURAL GAS LIQUIDS INC.—Mapco Inc.; *U.S. Public*, pg. 1042
MARATHON ASHLAND PETROLEUM LLC—Ashland, Inc.; *U.S. Public*, pg. 139
MARATHON ASHLAND PETROLEUM LLC—USX Corporation; *U.S. Public*, pg. 1662
NATIONAL PIPE LINE CO.—Park-Ohio Industries, Inc.; *U.S. Public*, pg. 1259
NAVAJO PIPELINE CO.—Holly Corporation; *U.S. Public*, pg. 830
OLYMPIC PIPE LINE CO.—Texaco Inc.; *U.S. Public*, pg. 1584
PETROCHEMICAL INDUSTRIES COMPANY K.S.C.—Kuwait Petroleum Corporation; *Int'l*, pg. 765
PHILLIPS PETROLEUM COMPANY; *U.S. Public*, pg. 1290
PIPELINE SUD-EUROPEEN—Royal Dutch/Shell Group of Companies; *Int'l*, pg. 1138
THE PIPELINES OF PUERTO RICO, INC.—Texaco Inc.; *U.S. Public*, pg. 1584
ROTTERDAM-RIJN PIJPLEIDING—Royal Dutch/Shell Group of Companies; *Int'l*, pg. 1135
ROYAL DUTCH/SHELL GROUP OF COMPANIES; *Int'l*, pg. 1135
SHELL PIPE LINE CORP.—Royal Dutch/Shell Group of Companies; *Int'l*, pg. 1136
SNAM S.P.A.—ENI S.p.A.; *Int'l*, pg. 428
SOUTHWEST FLORIDA PIPELINE CORP.—GATX Corporation; *U.S. Public*, pg. 692
STANDARD PIPE LINE CO.—Chevron Corporation; *U.S. Public*, pg. 348
SUN COMPANY, INC.; *U.S. Public*, pg. 1530
SUNCOR INC.; *Int'l*, pg. 1320
TAIWAN MARKETING & TRANSPORTATION DIV.—Chinese Petroleum Corporation; *Int'l*, pg. 286
TEXACO INC.; *U.S. Public*, pg. 1582
TEXAS EASTERN PRODUCTS PIPELINE COMPANY, L.P.—Duke Energy Corporation; *U.S. Public*, pg. 535
TEXAS-NEW MEXICO PIPE LINE CO.—Texaco Inc.; *U.S. Public*, pg. 1584
TEXAS UTILITIES FUEL CO.—Texas Utilities Company; *U.S. Public*, pg. 1588
TOTAL PIPELINE CORPORATION—Ultramar Diamond Shamrock Corporation; *U.S. Public*, pg. 1663
TRANS-OHIO PIPELINE CO.—Duke Energy Corporation; *U.S. Public*, pg. 535
TRUE COMPANIES; *U.S. Private*, pg. 1107
VENTURE PIPELINE COMPANY—Stone & Webster, Incorporated; *U.S. Public*, pg. 1519
THE WILLIAMS COMPANIES, INC.; *U.S. Public*, pg. 1769
WILLIAMS PIPE LINE CO.—The Williams Companies, Inc.; *U.S. Public*, pg. 1769
WOLVERINE PIPE LINE CO.—Texaco Inc.; *U.S. Public*, pg. 1584

4619 — PIPE LINES, NEC

AMERON INTERNATIONAL CORPORATION; *U.S. Public*, pg. 98
BP PIPELINES (ALASKA) INC.—The British Petroleum Company P.L.C.; *Int'l*, pg. 220
BURLINGTON NORTHERN SANTA FE CORPORATION; *U.S. Public*, pg. 268
CROWN CENTRAL PIPE LINE CO.—Crown Central Petroleum Corporation; *U.S. Public*, pg. 462
ENERGYLINE CORPORATION—Rochester Gas And Electric Corporation; *U.S. Public*, pg. 1396
GIFFORD-HILL-AMERICAN, INC.—Ameron International Corporation; *U.S. Public*, pg. 99
HUSKY OIL LTD.; *Int'l*, pg. 640
HUSKY OIL OPERATIONS LTD.—Husky Oil Ltd.; *Int'l*, pg. 640
INTERPROVINCIAL PIPE LINE INC.—IPL Energy Inc.; *Int'l*, pg. 652
IPEX—The Ivaco Group; *Int'l*, pg. 695
LAKEHEAD PIPE LINE CO., INC.—IPL Energy Inc.; *Int'l*, pg. 652
MARSHLAND ENERGY, INC.—Borden, Inc.; *U.S. Private*, pg. 158
NESTE OY; *Int'l*, pg. 912
PACIFIC INTERSTATE MOJAVE COMPANY—Pacific Enterprises; *U.S. Public*, pg. 1249
PACIFIC INTERSTATE OFFSHORE COMPANY—Pacific Enterprises; *U.S. Public*, pg. 1249
PACIFIC OFFSHORE PIPELINE COMPANY—Pacific Enterprises; *U.S. Public*, pg. 1249
PLANTATION PIPE LINE CO.—Chevron Corporation; *U.S. Public*, pg. 348
RPC INCORPORATED; *U.S. Public*, pg. 1356
SUEDWESTDEUTSCHE ROHRLEITUNGSBAU GMBH—Hochtief AG; *Int'l*, pg. 623

4724 — TRAVEL AGENCIES

ADVENTURE TOURS USA, INC.; *U.S. Private*, pg. 22
AFRIQUE ASSISTANCE—Corporacion MAPFRE, Compania Internacional de Reaseguros, S.A.; *Int'l*, pg. 334
AIRTOURS PLC; *Int'l*, pg. 39
ALL NIPPON AIRWAYS CO. LTD.; *Int'l*, pg. 57
ALL NIPPON TRAVEL SERVICE INC.—All Nippon Airways Co. Ltd.; *Int'l*, pg. 57
AMBASSADAIR TRAVEL CLUB, INC.—Amtran, Inc.; *U.S. Public*, pg. 106
AMBER TRAVEL, INC.—Amtran, Inc.; *U.S. Public*, pg. 106
AMERICAN EXPRESS COMPANY; *U.S. Public*, pg. 73
AMERICAN EXPRESS SERVICE EUROPE LTD.—American Express Company; *U.S. Public*, pg. 74
ANNTAYLOR TRAVEL, INC.—AnnTaylor Stores Corporation; *U.S. Public*, pg. 116
APPLE VACATIONS WEST INC.; *U.S. Private*, pg. 78
ARRINGTON TRAVEL CENTER INC.; *U.S. Private*, pg. 85
ASBURY PARK PRESS, INC.—Gannett Company, Inc.; *U.S. Public*, pg. 699
ATCO GROUP CO.; *Int'l*, pg. 95
ATLAS WORLD-CLASS TRAVEL—Atlas World Group, Inc.; *U.S. Private*, pg. 97
BTI AMERICAS, INC.; *U.S. Private*, pg. 108
BAVARIA LLOYD REISEBURO GMBH—Bayerische Motoren Werke Aktiengesellschaft; *Int'l*, pg. 177
BRASIL ASISTENCIA—Corporacion MAPFRE, Compania Internacional de Reaseguros, S.A.; *Int'l*, pg. 334
CUC TRAVEL SERVICES INC.—Cendant Corporation; *U.S. Public*, pg. 320
CARLSON COMPANIES, INC.; *U.S. Private*, pg. 211
CENTRE COURT TRAVEL—Western Gas Resources, Inc.; *U.S. Public*, pg. 1758
CLUB VIDA AGENCIA DE VIAJES, S.A.—Corporacion MAPFRE, Compania Internacional de Reaseguros, S.A.; *Int'l*, pg. 334
COMPANIA DE ASISTENCIA DE LOS ANDES, S.A.—Corporacion MAPFRE, Compania Internacional de Reaseguros, S.A.; *Int'l*, pg. 334
COOP SWITZERLAND; *Int'l*, pg. 329
CORNING ENTERPRISES INC.—Corning Incorporated; *U.S. Public*, pg. 448
CORPORATE TRAVEL SERVICES; *U.S. Private*, pg. 276
CRUISES ONLY INC.; *U.S. Private*, pg. 293
DAIWA BUSINESS TOURIST CO. LTD.—Daiwa Securities Co. Ltd.; *Int'l*, pg. 374
DALLAS GLOBAL TRAVEL—Dallas Gold & Silver Exchange, Inc.; *U.S. Public*, pg. 478
DANZAS HOLDING LTD.; *Int'l*, pg. 382
WALT DISNEY TRAVEL CO., INC.—The Walt Disney Company; *U.S. Public*, pg. 513
E.M.I. TRAVEL CENTER, INC.—Encore Marketing International, Inc.; *U.S. Public*, pg. 580
EUROP ASSISTANCE—Assicurazioni Generali S.p.A.; *Int'l*, pg. 91
EUROPA CRUISES CORPORATION; *U.S. Public*, pg. 595
EUROSOS—Corporacion MAPFRE, Compania Internacional de Reaseguros, S.A.; *Int'l*, pg. 334
FAIRWAYS AND SWINFORD (TRAVEL) LTD.—Sea Containers Ltd.; *Int'l*, pg. 1214
FEDERAL ASSIST—Corporacion MAPFRE, Compania Internacional de Reaseguros, S.A.; *Int'l*, pg. 334
FINLAND TRAVEL BUREAU LTD.—FinnAir Oy; *Int'l*, pg. 485
FIRST TRAVELCORP INC.; *U.S. Private*, pg. 408
FITUR S.P.A.—Fiat Auto SpA; *Int'l*, pg. 482
FOREST LAKE TRAVEL SERVICE, INC.—The Seibels Bruce Group, Inc.; *U.S. Public*, pg. 1454
FOUAD TRAVEL & CARGO AGENCY—Abdulla Fouad Co. Ltd.; *Int'l*, pg. 502
FRANCE ASSISTANCE—Corporacion MAPFRE, Compania Internacional de Reaseguros, S.A.; *Int'l*, pg. 334
FRANK CONSOLIDATED ENTERPRISES INC.; *U.S. Private*, pg. 423
FRIENDLY HOLIDAYS INC.; *U.S. Private*, pg. 428
FUGAZY INTERNATIONAL CORPORATION; *U.S. Private*, pg. 430
GENERAL TRAVEL SERVICES, INC.—Washington Mutual Inc.; *U.S. Public*, pg. 1742
GULF ASIA TRAVEL CORPORATION—EEI Corporation; *Int'l*, pg. 426
GULF ASSIST E.C.—Corporacion MAPFRE, Compania Internacional de Reaseguros, S.A.; *Int'l*, pg. 334
HAPAG-LLOYD AG; *Int'l*, pg. 596
HAPAG-LLOYD REISEBURO GMBH—Hapag-Lloyd AG; *Int'l*, pg. 596
HOLIDAY HOUSE, INC.—Washington Mutual Inc.; *U.S. Public*, pg. 1742
HOME SHOPPING NETWORK, INC.—USA Networks, Inc.; *U.S. Public*, pg. 1685
HOTELPLAN INTERNATIONAL TRAVEL ORGANIZATION AG—Migros; *Int'l*, pg. 865
HUMBERSIDE HOLDINGS LTD—Powell Duffryn PLC; *Int'l*, pg. 1065
IBEROASISTENCIA ARGENTINA, S.A.—Corporacion MAPFRE, Compania Internacional de Reaseguros, S.A.; *Int'l*, pg. 334
IBEROASISTENCIA PORTUGAL—Corporacion MAPFRE, Compania Internacional de Reaseguros, S.A.; *Int'l*, pg. 334
IBEROASISTENCIA, S.A.—Corporacion MAPFRE, Compania Internacional de Reaseguros, S.A.; *Int'l*, pg. 334
INDUSTRIE-RING SACH-UND VERSICHERUNGS-VERMITTLUNGSGESELLSCHAFT MBH—Saarbergwerke Aktiengesellschaft; *Int'l*, pg. 1166
INTERNATIONAL AERO-SEA FORWARDERS, INC.—International Aero-Sea Forwarders, Ltd.; *Int'l*, pg. 683
INTERNATIONAL AERO-SEA FORWARDERS, LTD.; *Int'l*, pg. 682
INTERNATIONAL TRAVEL ASSOCIATES CORP.—ITA Group Inc.; *U.S. Private*, pg. 555
IRELAND ASSISTANCE LTD.—Corporacion MAPFRE, Compania Internacional de Reaseguros, S.A.; *Int'l*, pg. 334
ITALIATOUR S.P.A.—IRI Istituto Ricostruzione Industriale; *Int'l*, pg. 652
JET TOURS—Groupe Air France; *Int'l*, pg. 560
JEWELCOR TRAVEL SERVICES, INC.—Jewelcor Companies; *U.S. Private*, pg. 587
KAWAGUCHI TRAVEL SERVICES, INC.—Washington Mutual Inc.; *U.S. Public*, pg. 1742
P. LAWSON TRAVEL, LTD.—Carlson Companies, Inc.; *U.S. Private*, pg. 212
LUNN POLY LTD.—The Thomson Corporation; *U.S. Public, pg. 1601*
MARITZ TRAVEL CO.—Maritz Inc.; *U.S. Private*, pg. 704

MARTINAIR HOLLAND—KLM Royal Dutch Airlines; Int'l, pg. 719
MATSUYA TRAVEL SERVICE—Matsuya Company Ltd.; Int'l, pg. 848
MEDIA GENERAL, INC.; U.S. Public, pg. 1077
MEIKA KOSAN CO., LTD.—Meiji Seika Kaisha, Ltd.; Int'l, pg. 855
MEXICO ASISTENCIA, S.A.—Corporacion MAPFRE, Compania Internacional de Reaseguros, S.A.; Int'l, pg. 334
MITSUI AIR & SEA SERVICE CO., LTD.—Mitsui & Co., Ltd.; Int'l, pg. 878
MONTEITH TRAVEL SERVICES LTD—George Wimpey PLC; Int'l, pg. 1510
MUTUAL TRAVEL, INC.—Washington Mutual Inc.; U.S. Public, pg. 1742
NATIONAL LEISURE GROUP—Cendant Corporation; U.S. Public, pg. 320
NEW FRONTIERS—Nouvelles Frontieres; Int'l, pg. 971
NIPPON EXPRESS TOURS (EUROPE) LTD.—Nippon Express Co., Ltd.; Int'l, pg. 934
NOEL OLSON GROUP; U.S. Private, pg. 800
NOUVELLES FRONTIERES; Int'l, pg. 971
OBAYASHI CORPORATION; Int'l, pg. 995
OMEGA WORLD TRAVEL, INC.; U.S. Private, pg. 816
PASSPORT TRAVEL, INC.; U.S. Private, pg. 842
PELLA TRAVEL INC.—ITA Group Inc.; U.S. Private, pg. 555
PORTLAND HOLIDAYS LTD.—The Thomson Corporation; U.S. Public, pg. 1602
PROFESSIONAL/FIRST TRAVELCORP—First Travelcorp Inc.; U.S. Private, pg. 408
PROFESSIONAL TRAVEL INC.—First Travelcorp Inc.; U.S. Private, pg. 408
QUALITY INCENTIVE & TRAVEL—Fleming Companies, Inc.; U.S. Public, pg. 653
RCI TRAVEL—Cendant Corporation; U.S. Public, pg. 322
ROMINGER REISEBUERO GMBH; Int'l, pg. 1127
ROYAL TOURIST, LTD.—Sanyo Electric Co., Ltd.; Int'l, pg. 1191
S.E.A.V.T. SA—Accor S.A.; Int'l, pg. 20
SMI CO., LTD.—Sanyo Electric Co., Ltd.; Int'l, pg. 1191
SANYO TOURIST SALES CO., LTD.—Sanyo Electric Co., Ltd.; Int'l, pg. 1191
SCANDINAVIAN AIRLINES SYSTEM (SAS); Int'l, pg. 1201
SIGMA-SOCIETA ITALIANA GESTIONE SISTEMA MULTI ACCESSO—IRI Istituto Ricostruzione Industriale; Int'l, pg. 652
SIGNATURE TRAVEL, INC.—Washington Mutual Inc.; U.S. Public, pg. 1742
SOCIETA ITALIANA SERVIZI AEREI MEDITERRANEI S.I.S.A.M. S.P.A.—IRI Istituto Ricostruzione Industriale; Int'l, pg. 652
SODETIF—Groupe Air France; Int'l, pg. 560
SUR ASISTENCIA—Corporacion MAPFRE, Compania Internacional de Reaseguros, S.A.; Int'l, pg. 334
TNT VACATIONS; U.S. Private, pg. 1065
THOMSON HOLIDAYS LTD.—The Thomson Corporation; U.S. Public, pg. 1602
THOMSON TOUR OPERATIONS LTD.—The Thomson Corporation; U.S. Public, pg. 1601
TOSHIBA TOURIST CORPORATION—Toshiba Corporation; Int'l, pg. 1405
TRAVELSTRENGTH LIMITED—Commonwealth Bank Group; Int'l, pg. 313
USAA (UNITED SERVICES AUTOMOBILE ASSOCIATION); U.S. Private, pg. 1114
UNIVERSAL STUDIOS RECREATION SERVICES GROUP—The Seagram Company Ltd.; Int'l, pg. 1216
VENEASISTENCIA C.A.—Corporacion MAPFRE, Compania Internacional de Reaseguros, S.A.; Int'l, pg. 334
YAMAICHI WORLD TOURIST INC.—Yamaichi Securities Co., Ltd.; Int'l, pg. 1517
YOUR MAN TOURS, INC.; U.S. Private, pg. 1202

4725 — TOUR OPERATORS

AIR CANADA VACATIONS INC.—Air Canada; Int'l, pg. 36
AIRTOURS PLC; Int'l, pg. 39
AMBER TOURS, INC.—Amtran, Inc.; U.S. Public, pg. 106
AMERICAN SIGHTSEEING INTERNATIONAL; U.S. Private, pg. 61
BRITISH AIRWAYS HOLIDAYS LTD.—British Airways PLC; Int'l, pg. 219
CALEDONIAN AIRWAYS LTD—British Airways PLC; Int'l, pg. 219
CAREFREE CAMPING LIMITED—Eurocamp Plc; Int'l, pg. 465
CARLSON COMPANIES, INC.; U.S. Private, pg. 211
CLUB MED—Club Mediterranee SA; Int'l, pg. 298
CLUB MED SALES, INC.—Club Mediterranee SA; Int'l, pg. 298
TED COOK TOURS ISLANDS IN THE SUN—Accor S.A.; Int'l, pg. 21
EUROCAMP PLC; Int'l, pg. 464
EUROCAMP TRAVEL LIMITED—Eurocamp Plc; Int'l, pg. 465
EUROP ASSISTANCE—Assicurazioni Generali S.p.A.; Int'l, pg. 91
GENERAL TOURS INC.; U.S. Private, pg. 445
GLOBUS & COSMOS; U.S. Private, pg. 458
GRUPO POSADAS S.A. DE C.V.; Int'l, pg. 576
HAMBURGER ABENDBLATT/DIE WELT REISEBURO GMBH—Axel Springer Verlag AG; Int'l, pg. 102
HOLLAND AMERICA LINE WESTOURS—Carnival Corporation; U.S. Public, pg. 306
JAPAN TRAVEL BUREAU INTERNATIONAL, INC.; U.S. Private, pg. 582
MTI VACATIONS, INC.; U.S. Private, pg. 688
MARITZ TRAVEL CO.—Maritz Inc.; U.S. Private, pg. 704
P&O AUSTRALIA LTD.—The Peninsular and Oriental Steam Navigation Company; Int'l, pg. 1035
REGENCY CRUISES INC.; U.S. Private, pg. 918
REGENCY MARITIME CORP./REGSUN HOLDING CORP., LTD—Regency Cruises Inc.; U.S. Private, pg. 918
ROYAL CARIBBEAN CRUISES LTD.; U.S. Public, pg. 1410
SCANDINAVIAN AIRLINES SYSTEM (SAS); Int'l, pg. 1201
SCANDINAVIAN LEISURE GROUP A.B.—Airtours Plc; Int'l, pg. 39
SINGAPORE TOURIST PROMOTION BOARD; Int'l, pg. 1253
SINGAPORE TOURIST PROMOTION BOARD - CHICAGO—Singapore Tourist Promotion Board; Int'l, pg. 1254
SINOCHEM INTERNATIONAL PETROLEUM CO. LTD.; Int'l, pg. 1254
TRASE-MILLER—MTI Vacations, Inc.; U.S. Private, pg. 688
TUNDRA TOURS, INC.—Arctic Slope Regional Corporation; U.S. Private, pg. 80

4729 — ARRANGEMENT OF PASSENGER TRANSPORTATION, NEC

ALL NIPPON AIRWAYS-NEW YORK—All Nippon Airways Co. Ltd.; Int'l, pg. 57
BRITRAIL TRAVEL INTERNATIONAL INC.—SNCF; Int'l, pg. 1165
BUSINESS TRAVEL MANAGEMENT, INC.—Mary Kay Corporation; U.S. Private, pg. 711
CUC INTERNATIONAL, INC.—Cendant Corporation; U.S. Public, pg. 320
CENDANT CORPORATION; U.S. Public, pg. 320
CENTRAL PARKING CORP.; U.S. Public, pg. 326
COLORADO PLAINS MEDICAL CENTER—Brim, Inc.; U.S. Private, pg. 169
EUROP ASSISTANCE—Assicurazioni Generali S.p.A.; Int'l, pg. 91
GENERAL HOSPITAL—Brim, Inc.; U.S. Private, pg. 169
HONGKONG AND SHANGHAI THOMAS COOK LTD.—HSBC Holdings plc; Int'l, pg. 583
KLM ROYAL DUTCH AIRLINES; Int'l, pg. 719
MARITZ INC.; U.S. Private, pg. 703
ORIENT-EXPRESS HOTELS INC.—Sea Containers Ltd.; Int'l, pg. 1213
PARMELEE TRANSPORTATION CO.—Stamford Capital; U.S. Private, pg. 1030
SPIRIT CRUISES, INC.—Sodexho S.A.; Int'l, pg. 1274
THE SWISSAIR GROUP; Int'l, pg. 1333
TRADEWINDS PTE. LTD.—Temasek Holdings Pte. Ltd.; Int'l, pg. 1374
WORLDWIDE ASSISTANCE SERVICES INC.—Assicurazioni Generali S.p.A.; Int'l, pg. 90

4731 — ARRANGEMENT OF TRANSPORTATION OF FREIGHT & CARGO

A & B-HAWAII, INC.—Alexander & Baldwin, Inc.; U.S. Public, pg. 39
AEI AUSTRALIA PTY. LTD.—Air Express International Corporation; U.S. Public, pg. 30
AEI ITALY—Air Express International Corporation; U.S. Public, pg. 30
AEI OCEAN SERVICES—Air Express International Corporation; U.S. Public, pg. 30
A.I. OCEAN; Int'l, pg. 14
AJC INTERNATIONAL, INC.; U.S. Private, pg. 6
APL LAND TRANSPORT SERVICE INC.—Neptune Orient Lines Ltd.; Int'l, pg. 912
APL LIMITED—Neptune Orient Lines Ltd.; Int'l, pg. 912
AIR EXPRESS INTL. AGENCY, INC.—Air Express International Corporation; U.S. Public, pg. 30
AIR EXPRESS INTERNATIONAL CORPORATION; U.S. Public, pg. 30
AIR EXPRESS INTERNATIONAL (PVT) LTD.—Air Express International Corporation; U.S. Public, pg. 30
AIR EXPRESS INTERNATIONAL (S.A.) (PTY), LTD.—Air Express International Corporation; U.S. Public, pg. 30
AIR EXPRESS INTERNATIONAL SINGAPORE (PTE.) LTD.—Air Express International Corporation; U.S. Public, pg. 30
AIR EXPRESS INTL. USA, INC.—Air Express International Corporation; U.S. Public, pg. 30
AIRBORNE FREIGHT CORPORATION; U.S. Public, pg. 32
ALBA FORWARDING CO., INC.; U.S. Private, pg. 32
ALEXANDER & BALDWIN, INC.; U.S. Public, pg. 39
ALL NIPPON MANAGEMENT SERVICE INC.—All Nippon Airways Co. Ltd.; Int'l, pg. 57
ALLIED VAN LINES, INC.—NFC plc; Int'l, pg. 901
ALLIEDSIGNAL TRANSPORTATION INC.—AlliedSignal Inc.; U.S. Public, pg. 51
AMERFORD FRANCE S.A.—Thyssen AG; Int'l, pg. 1388
AMERFORD INTERNATIONAL CORPORATION—Thyssen AG; Int'l, pg. 1388
AMERFORD INTL. NEDERLAND B.V.—Thyssen AG; Int'l, pg. 1388
AMERFORD INTL. (PTY) LTD.—Thyssen AG; Int'l, pg. 1388
AMERFORD INTL. (U.K.) LTD.—Thyssen AG; Int'l, pg. 1388
AMERICAN CONSOLIDATION SERVICES LTD.—Neptune Orient Lines Ltd.; Int'l, pg. 912
AMERICAN PRESIDENT LINES, CANADA, LTD.—Neptune Orient Lines Ltd.; Int'l, pg. 912
AMERICAN PRESIDENT LINES, DELAWARE, LTD.—Neptune Orient Lines Ltd.; Int'l, pg. 912
AMERICAN RED BALL INTERNATIONAL, INC.—Atlas World Group, Inc.; U.S. Private, pg. 97
AMERIFORD INTL. CORP.—Thyssen AG; Int'l, pg. 1388
ASSOCIATED GLOBAL SYSTEMS; U.S. Private, pg. 90
AVEYRON EXPRESS—SNCF; Int'l, pg. 1163
BAX GLOBAL—The Pittston Company; U.S. Public, pg. 1305
BOC DISTRIBUTION SERVICES LTD.—The BOC Group plc; Int'l, pg. 121
BAYSIDE TRAFFIC SERVICES OF MARYLAND—Giant Food Inc.; U.S. Public, pg. 741
BERNIS—SNCF; Int'l, pg. 1163
BEVRACHTINGSKANTOOR TWENTHE-RIJN BV—Akzo Nobel N.V.; Int'l, pg. 43
BINGO EXPRESS CO., LTD.—Nippon Express Co., Ltd.; Int'l, pg. 934
BOLLIGER, INC.; U.S. Private, pg. 155
BRAMBLES INDUSTRIES LIMITED; Int'l, pg. 210
BRAMBLES INDUSTRIES (N.Z.) LTD.—Brambles Industries Limited; Int'l, pg. 212
BRAMBLES INTERNATIONAL FREIGHT PTY. LIMITED—Brambles Industries Limited; Int'l, pg. 211
BRAMBLES MARINE SERVICES PTY. LTD.—Brambles Industries Limited; Int'l, pg. 211
BRAMBLES SEACARGO—Brambles Industries Limited; Int'l, pg. 211
BRAMBLES TRANSPORT (FREIGHT FORWARDING) DIVISION—Brambles Industries Limited; Int'l, pg. 211
BRINK'S, INC.—The Pittston Company; U.S. Public, pg. 1305
BRITISH AIRWAYS CARGO—British Airways PLC; Int'l, pg. 219
CFS NEW ZEALAND LTD.—Circle International Group, Inc.; U.S. Public, pg. 372
CITRA—SNCF; Int'l, pg. 1163
C.J. TOWER INC.—The McGraw-Hill Companies; U.S. Public, pg. 1071
CNF TRANSPORTATION INC.; U.S. Public, pg. 281
CALBERSON—SNCF; Int'l, pg. 1163
CALBERSON DANZAS—SNCF; Int'l, pg. 1163
CALBERSON FREIGHT NETWORK DIVISION—SNCF; Int'l, pg. 1163
CALBERSON INTERNATIONAL—SNCF; Int'l, pg. 1163
CALBERSON INTERNATIONAL STRASBOURG—SNCF; Int'l, pg. 1163
CALBERSON PICARDIE—SNCF; Int'l, pg. 1163
CALVEL—SNCF; Int'l, pg. 1163
CANADIAN FREIGHTWAYS LTD.—Consolidated Freightways Corp.; U.S. Public, pg. 435
CANADIAN PACIFIC LIMITED; Int'l, pg. 258
CAREWOOD TRANSPORT LTD.—SNCF; Int'l, pg. 1165
W.G. CARROLL, INC.—The McGraw-Hill Companies; U.S. Public, pg. 1071
CASTELAZO & ASSOCIATES—The McGraw-Hill Companies; U.S. Public, pg. 1071
CHATHAM TOWING COMPANY, INC.—Colonial Oil Industries; U.S. Private, pg. 254
CHAVENEAU BERNIS—SNCF; Int'l, pg. 1163
CHINA ECOTEK CORPORATION—China Steel Corporation; Int'l, pg. 285
CIRCLE AIRFREIGHT INTERNATIONAL DE MEXICO S.A. DE C.V.—Circle International Group, Inc.; U.S. Public, pg. 372
CIRCLE AIRFREIGHT INTERNATIONAL KOREA—Circle International Group, Inc.; U.S. Public, pg. 372
CIRCLE AIRFREIGHT INTL. (TAIWAN) LTD.—Circle International Group, Inc.; U.S. Public, pg. 372
CIRCLE AIRFREIGHT INTL. (THAILAND) LTD.—Circle International Group, Inc.; U.S. Public, pg. 372
CIRCLE-ATS AG—Circle International Group, Inc.; U.S. Public, pg. 372
CIRCLE ESPANA S.A.—Circle International Group, Inc.; U.S. Public, pg. 372
CIRCLE FREIGHT INTERNATIONAL—Circle International Group, Inc.; U.S. Public, pg. 370
CIRCLE FREIGHT INTERNATIONAL AGENCIA CHILENA—Circle International Group, Inc.; U.S. Public, pg. 372
CIRCLE FREIGHT INTERNATIONAL ARGENTINA S.A.—Circle International Group, Inc.; U.S. Public, pg. 372
CIRCLE FREIGHT INTERNATIONAL INDIA PVT. LTD.—Circle International Group, Inc.; U.S. Public, pg. 372
P.T. CIRCLE FREIGHT INTERNATIONAL INDONESIA—Circle International Group, Inc.; U.S. Public, pg. 372
CIRCLE FREIGHT INTERNATIONAL ITALIA-EUROLEVANT SRL—Circle International Group, Inc.; U.S. Public, pg. 372
CIRCLE FREIGHT INTERNATIONAL LLC—Circle International Group, Inc.; U.S. Public, pg. 372
CIRCLE FREIGHT INTERNATIONAL (PHILIPPINES) LTD.—Circle International Group, Inc.; U.S. Public, pg. 373
CIRCLE FREIGHT INTERNATIONAL (PORTUGAL) LTDA.—Circle International Group, Inc.; U.S. Public, pg. 373
CIRCLE FREIGHT INTERNATIONAL (SAUDI ARABIA) LTD.—Circle International Group, Inc.; U.S. Public, pg. 373
CIRCLE FREIGHT INTERNATIONAL (U.S.A.)—Circle International Group, Inc.; U.S. Public, pg. 370
CIRCLE FREIGHT INTERNATIONAL USA—Circle International Group, Inc.; U.S. Public, pg. 370
CIRCLE FREIGHT VENEZUELA S.A.—Circle International Group, Inc.; U.S. Public, pg. 373
CIRCLE INTERNATIONAL—Circle International Group, Inc.; U.S. Public, pg. 371
CIRCLE INTERNATIONAL GROUP, INC.; U.S. Public, pg. 370
CIRCLE INTERNATIONAL (N.Z.) LTD.—Circle International Group, Inc.; U.S. Public, pg. 373
CIRCLE LEMAN AIR FREIGHT—Circle International Group, Inc.; U.S. Public, pg. 373
CIRCLE ZIEGLER S.A. AIRFREIGHT—Circle International Group, Inc.; U.S. Public, pg. 373
COLONIAL MARINE INDUSTRIES, INC.—Colonial Oil Industries; U.S. Private, pg. 254
CON-WAY CENTRAL EXPRESS, INC.—CNF Transportation Inc.; U.S. Public, pg. 281
CON-WAY SOUTHERN EXPRESS, INC.—CNF Transportation Inc.; U.S. Public, pg. 281
CON-WAY WESTERN EXPRESS, INC.—CNF Transportation Inc.; U.S. Public, pg. 281
CONRAIL DIRECT—Conrail, Inc.; U.S. Public, pg. 432
CONSOLIDATED FREIGHTWAYS CORP.; U.S. Public, pg. 435

S.I.C. Index

CORSE SUD EXPRESS—SNCF; *Int'l*, pg. 1163
CORY BROTHERS SHIPPING LIMITED—Powell Duffryn PLC; *Int'l*, pg. 1065
DSI TRANSPORTS—Sophus Berendsen A/S; *Int'l*, pg. 1285
DACHSER GMBH & CO.; *Int'l*, pg. 356
DACHSER TRANSPORT OF AMERICA INC.—Dachser GmbH & Co.; *Int'l*, pg. 357
DAMCO MARITIME (HK) LTD.—Royal Nedlloyd Group N.V.; *Int'l*, pg. 1144
DANZAS—SNCF; *Int'l*, pg. 1163
DANZAS A.E.—Danzas Holding Ltd.; *Int'l*, pg. 382
DANZAS ARGENTINA S.A.—Danzas Holding Ltd.; *Int'l*, pg. 382
DANZAS B.V.—Danzas Holding Ltd.; *Int'l*, pg. 382
DANZAS (CANADA) LTD.—Danzas Holding Ltd.; *Int'l*, pg. 382
DANZAS CHILE S.A.—Danzas Holding Ltd.; *Int'l*, pg. 382
DANZAS CORPORATION—Danzas Holding Ltd.; *Int'l*, pg. 382
DANZAS FREIGHT (H.K.) LTD.—Danzas Holding Ltd.; *Int'l*, pg. 382
DANZAS HOLDING LTD.; *Int'l*, pg. 382
DANZAS K.K.—Danzas Holding Ltd.; *Int'l*, pg. 382
DANZAS LDA—Danzas Holding Ltd.; *Int'l*, pg. 382
DANZAS LTDA—Danzas Holding Ltd.; *Int'l*, pg. 382
DANZAS N.V.—Danzas Holding Ltd.; *Int'l*, pg. 382
DANZAS PTY. LTD.—Danzas Holding Ltd.; *Int'l*, pg. 382
DANZAS SA—Danzas Holding Ltd.; *Int'l*, pg. 382
DANZAS S.A.—Danzas Holding Ltd.; *Int'l*, pg. 382
DANZAS (SINGAPORE) PTE LTD.—Danzas Holding Ltd.; *Int'l*, pg. 382
DANZAS S.P.A.—Danzas Holding Ltd.; *Int'l*, pg. 383
DANZAS TAIWAN LTD.—Danzas Holding Ltd.; *Int'l*, pg. 383
DANZAS (UK) LTD.—Danzas Holding Ltd.; *Int'l*, pg. 383
C.A. DANZAS VENEZOLANA—Danzas Holding Ltd.; *Int'l*, pg. 383
DANZASMEX S.A.—Danzas Holding Ltd.; *Int'l*, pg. 383
DELTA AIR LINES, INC.; *U.S. Public*, pg. 497
A.N. DERINGER, INC.; *U.S. Private*, pg. 326
DEUTSCHE POSTCONSULT—Deutsche Post AG; *Int'l*, pg. 407
DIVERSIFIED PARCELS FREIGHT DIVISION—SNCF; *Int'l*, pg. 1163
DORCHESTER TRANSPORT SERVICES (LEE LINE COMMERCIALS)—Franz Haniel & Cie, GmbH; *Int'l*, pg. 591
DUPONT-BEDU—SNCF; *Int'l*, pg. 1163
DUSOLIER—SNCF; *Int'l*, pg. 1163
DUVERGER—SNCF; *Int'l*, pg. 1163
EECO, SWITCH—Transico Incorporated; *U.S. Public*, pg. 1631
EAGLE USA AIRFREIGHT; *U.S. Public*, pg. 547
EMERY WORLDWIDE—CNF Transportation Inc.; *U.S. Public*, pg. 281
EMONS INDUSTRIES, INC.—Emons Transportation Group, Inc.; *U.S. Public*, pg. 578
EMONS TRANSPORTATION GROUP, INC.; *U.S. Public*, pg. 578
ERSA—SNCF; *Int'l*, pg. 1164
EXPEDITORS INTERNATIONAL OCEAN, INC.—Expeditors International of Washington, Inc.; *U.S. Public*, pg. 600
EXPEDITORS INTERNATIONAL OF WASHINGTON, INC.; *U.S. Public*, pg. 600
FAIRFIELD MAXWELL LTD.; *U.S. Private*, pg. 391
FARRELL LINES INCORPORATED; *U.S. Private*, pg. 397
FERON DE CLEBSATTEL—SNCF; *Int'l*, pg. 1165
FERRE EXPORT CORP.—Puerto Rican Cement Co., Inc.; *U.S. Public*, pg. 1342
FERRY MOUGIN—SNCF; *Int'l*, pg. 1164
FLAGEUL—SNCF; *Int'l*, pg. 1164
FLORIDA EXPRESS CARRIER INC.—St. Joe Corp.; *U.S. Public*, pg. 1427
FORT JAMES WESTERN TRANSPORTATION—Fort James Corporation; *U.S. Public*, pg. 672
FOUAD TRAVEL & CARGO AGENCY—Abdulla Fouad Co. Ltd.; *Int'l*, pg. 502
FRANCESCO PARISI GES.M.B.H.—Francesco Parisi S.p.A.; *Int'l*, pg. 504
FRANCESCO PARISI S.A.G.L.—Francesco Parisi S.p.A.; *Int'l*, pg. 504
FRANCESCO PARISI S.P.A.; *Int'l*, pg. 504
FRITZ AIR FREIGHT—Fritz Companies, Inc.; *U.S. Public*, pg. 683
FRITZ COMPANIES, INC.; *U.S. Public*, pg. 683
GD EXPRESS WORLDWIDE NV—TNT Limited; *Int'l*, pg. 1343
GKN FREIGHT SERVICES LTD.—GKN plc; *Int'l*, pg. 534
GALLE—SNCF; *Int'l*, pg. 1164
GATOR FREIGHTWAYS, INC.; *U.S. Private*, pg. 441
GEODIS; *Int'l*, pg. 549
GOLDEN EAGLE GROUP, INC.; *U.S. Public*, pg. 749
GRACE REMOVALS—Brambles Industries Limited; *Int'l*, pg. 211
GRANTHAM ROAD SERVICES—Franz Haniel & Cie, GmbH; *Int'l*, pg. 591
GRIFFIN TRANSPORT SERVICES, INC.; *U.S. Private*, pg. 481
MAX GRUENHUT CHILE—Circle International Group, Inc.; *U.S. Public*, pg. 373
MAX GRUENHUT, GMBH & CO.—Circle International Group, Inc.; *U.S. Public*, pg. 373
MAX GRUENHUT INTERNATIONAL CANADA INC—Circle International Group, Inc.; *U.S. Public*, pg. 373
MAX GRUENHUT INTERNATIONAL, INC.—Circle International Group, Inc.; *U.S. Public*, pg. 372
MAX GRUENHUT INTERNATIONAL INC. USA—Circle International Group, Inc.; *U.S. Public*, pg. 372
MAX GRUNHUT GMBH—The Peninsular and Oriental Steam Navigation Company; *Int'l*, pg. 1033
HII—Alcatel Alsthom Compagnie Generale D'Electricite; *Int'l*, pg. 53
HSBC SHIPBROKERS LIMITED—HSBC Holdings plc; *Int'l*, pg. 583
HANIEL REEDEREI HOLDING GMBH—Franz Haniel & Cie, GmbH; *Int'l*, pg. 592
HANJIN SHIPPING COMPANY LTD.; *Int'l*, pg. 592
HANJIN TRANSPORTATION CO. LTD.—Hanjin Shipping Company Ltd.; *Int'l*, pg. 592
HAPAG-LLOYD AG; *Int'l*, pg. 596
HAPAG-LLOYD (AMERICA), INC.—Hapag-Lloyd AG; *Int'l*, pg. 596
HAPAG-LLOYD FLUGGESELLSCHAFT MBH—Hapag-Lloyd AG; *Int'l*, pg. 596
HARPER FREIGHT INTERNATIONAL—Circle International Group, Inc.; *U.S. Public*, pg. 373
HARPER FREIGHT INTERNATIONAL (SWEDEN) AB—Circle International Group, Inc.; *U.S. Public*, pg. 373
HAUTE-PROVENCE EXPRESS—SNCF; *Int'l*, pg. 1164
HEAVYLIFT CARGO AIRLINES LIMITED—Kvaerner a.s.a.; *Int'l*, pg. 773
HERMANN LUDWIG GMBH & CO.—SNCF; *Int'l*, pg. 1165
HICKS & ASSOCIATES INC.—Science Applications International Corp.; *U.S. Private*, pg. 976
G.D. HOLMES LIMITED—Laporte plc; *Int'l*, pg. 802
HONGKONG AND SHANGHAI THOMAS COOK LTD.—HSBC Holdings plc; *Int'l*, pg. 583
HUMBERSIDE HOLDINGS LTD—Powell Duffryn PLC; *Int'l*, pg. 1065
I-SPED INTERNATIONALE SPEDITION GMBH—Korf-Transport-GmbH; *Int'l*, pg. 759
INDUSTRIE-RING SACH-UND VERSICHERUNGS-VERMITTLUNGSGESELLSCHAFT MBH—Saarbergwerke Aktiengesellschaft; *Int'l*, pg. 1166
INTERNATIO-MULLER N.V.; *Int'l*, pg. 680
INTERNATIONAL AERO-SEA FORWARDERS, INC.—International Aero-Sea Forwarders, Ltd.; *Int'l*, pg. 683
INTERNATIONAL AERO-SEA FORWARDERS, LTD.; *Int'l*, pg. 682
JAMES TRANSPORTATION—Fort James Corporation; *U.S. Public*, pg. 672
JET CHANDLER INTERNATIONAL—Groupe Air France; *Int'l*, pg. 560
KLM ROYAL DUTCH AIRLINES; *Int'l*, pg. 719
KALAG LAGERHAUS-UND SPEDITIONS GES. MBH—The Peninsular and Oriental Steam Navigation Company; *Int'l*, pg. 1033
KENAN TRANSPORT COMPANY; *U.S. Public*, pg. 949
KILLINGHOLME WHARFAGE CO. LTD.—Simon Engineering plc; *Int'l*, pg. 1251
KINTETSU INTERMODAL (U.S.A.), INC.—Kintetsu World Express, Inc.; *Int'l*, pg. 735
KINTETSU WORLD EXPRESS, INC.; *Int'l*, pg. 734
KINTETSU WORLD EXPRESS (U.S.A.), INC.—Kintetsu World Express, Inc.; *Int'l*, pg. 734
KONINKLIJKE VAN OMMEREN NV; *Int'l*, pg. 758
KORF-TRANSPORT-FRANCE S.A.R.L—Korf-Transport-GmbH; *Int'l*, pg. 759
KORF-TRANSPORT-GMBH; *Int'l*, pg. 758
KORF TRANSPORT GMBH—Korf-Transport-GmbH; *Int'l*, pg. 758
KUEHNE & NAGEL INTERNATIONAL AG; *Int'l*, pg. 763
KVAERNER A.S.A.; *Int'l*, pg. 766
LEP INTERNATIONAL INC.—International Logistics Limited; *U.S. Private*, pg. 571
LEP PROFIT INTERNATIONAL, INC.—International Logistics Limited; *U.S. Private*, pg. 571
LABLANC—SNCF; *Int'l*, pg. 1164
LACASSAGNE—SNCF; *Int'l*, pg. 1164
LAIDLAW TRANSIT—Canadian Pacific Limited; *Int'l*, pg. 259
LEHNKERING MONTAN TRANSPORT AG—Metallgesellschaft AG; *Int'l*, pg. 862
LEHNKERING MONTAN TRANSPORT AG—Preussag AG; *Int'l*, pg. 1069
LIFEROCA—SNCF; *Int'l*, pg. 1164
LIVINGSTON INTERNATIONAL FREIGHT—Circle International Group, Inc.; *U.S. Public*, pg. 373
LIVINGSTON INTERNATIONAL FREIGHT BELGIUM—Circle International Group, Inc.; *U.S. Public*, pg. 373
LYNDEN AIR FREIGHT, INC.—Lynden Incorporated; *U.S. Private*, pg. 683
LYNDEN FORWARDING, INC.—Lynden Incorporated; *U.S. Private*, pg. 684
MFA MISR FREIGHT AGENCIES S.A.R.L.—Danzas Holding Ltd.; *Int'l*, pg. 383
MACKINNON MACKENZIE & CO. OF PAKISTAN (PRIVATE) LTD.—The Peninsular and Oriental Steam Navigation Company; *Int'l*, pg. 1035
MANUFACTURERS CONSOLIDATION SERVICE, INC.; *U.S. Private*, pg. 700
MARITIMA SERVICES—Internatio-Muller N.V.; *Int'l*, pg. 682
MAUREL & CALBERSON MONTPELLIER—SNCF; *Int'l*, pg. 1164
METRAILLE—SNCF; *Int'l*, pg. 1164
J.R. MICHAELS, INC.—Circle International Group, Inc.; *U.S. Public*, pg. 372
MILNE & CRAIGHEAD CUSTOMS BROKERS, INC.—Consolidated Freightways Corp.; *U.S. Public*, pg. 435
MITRANS CORPORATION—Mitsubishi Logistics Corp.; *Int'l*, pg. 874
MITSUBISHI LOGISTICS CORP.; *Int'l*, pg. 874
THE MITSUI WAREHOUSE CO., LTD.—Mitsui & Co., Ltd.; *Int'l*, pg. 878
MITSUI WHARF CO., LTD.—Mitsui & Co., Ltd.; *Int'l*, pg. 878
MORVAN PARIS—SNCF; *Int'l*, pg. 1164
MOVEMENTS INTERNATIONAL MOVERS (NSW) PTY. LTD.—Brambles Industries Limited; *Int'l*, pg. 211
MULLER LINER AGENCIES N.V., ANTWERP—Internatio-Muller N.V.; *Int'l*, pg. 682
MULLER-THOMSEN ANTWERPEN—Internatio-Muller N.V.; *Int'l*, pg. 682
WM. H. MULLER & CO. NEDERLAND B.V.—Internatio-Muller N.V.; *Int'l*, pg. 682
F.W. MYERS & CO., INC.; *U.S. Private*, pg. 770
NS TRANSPORTATION BROKERAGE CORPORATION—Norfolk Southern Corporation; *U.S. Public*, pg. 1190
NATIONWIDE FREIGHT SERVICES, INC.—AMCOL International Corp.; *U.S. Public*, pg. 64
NEBAM NEDERLANDSE BEVRACHTING EN AGENTUUR MAATSCHAPPIJ—Koninklijke Hoogovens N.V.; *Int'l*, pg. 754
NEDLLOYD DISTRICENTERS INTERNATIONAL—Royal Nedlloyd Group N.V.; *Int'l*, pg. 1144
NEDLLOYD LINES B.V.—Royal Nedlloyd Group N.V.; *Int'l*, pg. 1145
NEPTUNE ORIENT LINES LTD.; *Int'l*, pg. 912
NIPPON EXPRESS CO., LTD.; *Int'l*, pg. 933
NIPPON SHIPPING CO., LTD.—Nippon Express Co., Ltd.; *Int'l*, pg. 934
NIPPON TRUCK CO., LTD.—Nippon Express Co., Ltd.; *Int'l*, pg. 934
NITTSU KIKO UNYU CO., LTD.—Nippon Express Co., Ltd.; *Int'l*, pg. 934
NORTH AMERICAN FORWARDING, INC.—Norfolk Southern Corporation; *U.S. Public*, pg. 1192
NORTH KILLINGHOLME CARGO TERMINAL—Simon Engineering plc; *Int'l*, pg. 1251
NOVA TRADING—Thyssen AG; *Int'l*, pg. 1389
OBERLANDER RECYCLING TECHNIK GMBH—Fried. Krupp AG; *Int'l*, pg. 513
OPERATIONS UNLIMITED, INC.—St. Joe Corp.; *U.S. Public*, pg. 1427
OVERSLAGBEDRIJF DE IJBUNKER BV—Akzo Nobel N.V.; *Int'l*, pg. 43
P&O (NEW ZEALAND) LTD.—The Peninsular and Oriental Steam Navigation Company; *Int'l*, pg. 1035
P.A.Y.S.E.N., S.A. DE C.V.—BASF AG; *Int'l*, pg. 109
PANALPINA, INC.—Panalpina Welttransport (Holding) AG; *Int'l*, pg. 1022
PANALPINA WELTTRANSPORT (HOLDING) AG; *Int'l*, pg. 1022
FRANCESCO PARISI G.M.B.H.—Francesco Parisi S.p.A.; *Int'l*, pg. 504
FRANCESCO PARISI S.P.A.—Francesco Parisi S.p.A.; *Int'l*, pg. 504
PATTERSON TRUCK LINE, INC.—RPC Incorporated; *U.S. Public*, pg. 1356
PENTLAND SHIPPING SERVICES, LTD.—Pentland Group PLC; *Int'l*, pg. 1035
PERDUE TRANSPORTATION INC.—Perdue Farms Incorporated; *U.S. Private*, pg. 852
PIEDMONT AIRLINES, INC.—US Airways Group, Inc.; *U.S. Public*, pg. 1680
THE PITTSTON COMPANY; *U.S. Public*, pg. 1305
POWELL DUFFRYN SHIPPING LTD.—Powell Duffryn PLC; *Int'l*, pg. 1065
PUICOUYOUL—SNCF; *Int'l*, pg. 1164
RPC INCORPORATED; *U.S. Public*, pg. 1356
RUG-RHEINISCHE UMSCHLAG-GESELLSCHAFT MBH—The Peninsular and Oriental Steam Navigation Company; *Int'l*, pg. 1033
RANDY INTERNATIONAL; *U.S. Private*, pg. 909
RED BALL FORWARDERS, INC.—Atlas World Group, Inc.; *U.S. Private*, pg. 97
REGIONAL & LOCAL EXPRESS PARCELS DIVISION—SNCF; *Int'l*, pg. 1163
RELIANCE TRANSPORT CO.—CalMat Co.; *U.S. Public*, pg. 296
RHENANIA ALLGEMEINE SPEDITIONS-GESELLSCHAFT MIT BESCHRANKTER HAFTUNG—The Peninsular and Oriental Steam Navigation Company; *Int'l*, pg. 1033
RHENANIA COMPAGNIE EUROPEENNE DE TRANSPORTS ET D'AFFRETEMENT S.A.R.L.—The Peninsular and Oriental Steam Navigation Company; *Int'l*, pg. 1034
RHENANIA COMPAGNIE EUROPEENNE DE TRANSPORTS ET D'AFFRETEMENT—The Peninsular and Oriental Steam Navigation Company; *Int'l*, pg. 1034
RHENANIA-FRIEDRICH KRAUSS SPEDITIONS GES. MBH—The Peninsular and Oriental Steam Navigation Company; *Int'l*, pg. 1033
RHENANIA INTERNATIONAL TRANSPORT SERVICES PTE. LTD.—The Peninsular and Oriental Steam Navigation Company; *Int'l*, pg. 1034
RHENANIA INTERNATIONAL TRANSPORT SERVICES (H.K.) LIMITED—The Peninsular and Oriental Steam Navigation Company; *Int'l*, pg. 1034
RHENANIA MUNCHENER LAGERHAUS-UND TRANSPORT-GES.MBH—The Peninsular and Oriental Steam Navigation Company; *Int'l*, pg. 1033
RHENANIA-SAAR SPEDITIONS-GMBH—The Peninsular and Oriental Steam Navigation Company; *Int'l*, pg. 1033
RHENANIA SCHIFFAHRTS-UND SPEDITIONS-GESELLSCHAFT MBH—The Peninsular and Oriental Steam Navigation Company; *Int'l*, pg. 1033
RHENANIA TRANSPORT B.V.—The Peninsular and Oriental Steam Navigation Company; *Int'l*, pg. 1034
RHENANIA TRANSPORT GMBH—The Peninsular and Oriental Steam Navigation Company; *Int'l*, pg. 1033
RHENANIA UMSCHLAG UND LAGEREI GMBH—The Peninsular and Oriental Steam Navigation Company; *Int'l*, pg. 1033
RHENANIA WORMSER LAGERHAUS-UND SPEDITIONS-AG—The Peninsular and Oriental Steam Navigation Company; *Int'l*, pg. 1034
RHENUS TRANSPORT INTERNATIONAL CORP.—Veba AG; *Int'l*, pg. 1460
RHENUS-WEICHELT AG—Veba AG; *Int'l*, pg. 1459
ROAD SYSTEMS, INC—CNF Transportation Inc.; *U.S. Public*, pg. 281
ROAD TRANSPORT, WAREHOUSING & DISTRIBUTION DIVISION—SNCF; *Int'l*, pg. 1163
C.H. ROBINSON CO.; *U.S. Public*, pg. 1394
ROYAL NEDLLOYD GROUP N.V.; *Int'l*, pg. 1143
ROYNEAU—SNCF; *Int'l*, pg. 1164
S.F.T.C.—SNCF; *Int'l*, pg. 1165
SNT CALBERSON—SNCF; *Int'l*, pg. 1164
SNT CALBERSON AGEN—SNCF; *Int'l*, pg. 1164
SNT CALBERSON ARRAS—SNCF; *Int'l*, pg. 1164
SNT CALBERSON AVIGNON—SNCF; *Int'l*, pg. 1164

SNT NOYON—SNCF; *Int'l*, pg. 1164
SNTR CALBERSON—SNCF; *Int'l*, pg. 1164
SNTR CALBERSON DIJON—SNCF; *Int'l*, pg. 1164
SNTR CALBERSON LA-ROCHE-SUR-YON—SNCF; *Int'l*, pg. 1164
SNTR CALBERSON MARSEILLE—SNCF; *Int'l*, pg. 1164
SNTR CALBERSON NANTES—SNCF; *Int'l*, pg. 1164
SNTR CALBERSON NICE—SNCF; *Int'l*, pg. 1164
SNTR CALBERSON NIEVRE—SNCF; *Int'l*, pg. 1164
SNTR CALBERSON NIMES—SNCF; *Int'l*, pg. 1164
SNTR CALBERSON ORLEANS—SNCF; *Int'l*, pg. 1164
SNTR CALBERSON PARIS—SNCF; *Int'l*, pg. 1164
SNTR CALBERSON ROANNE—SNCF; *Int'l*, pg. 1164
SNTR CALBERSON ROUEN—SNCF; *Int'l*, pg. 1164
SNTR CALBERSON ST. ETIENNE—SNCF; *Int'l*, pg. 1164
SNTR CALBERSON TOULON—SNCF; *Int'l*, pg. 1164
SNTR CALBERSON VALENCE—SNCF; *Int'l*, pg. 1164
S.W. AIRFREIGHT—Circle International Group, Inc.; *U.S. Public*, pg. 373
ST. JOHANN LAGERHAUS & SCHIFFAHRTS-GESELLSCHAFT—Coop Switzerland; *Int'l*, pg. 330
ST. LOUIS REFRIGERATOR CAR COMPANY—Anheuser-Busch Companies, Inc.; *U.S. Public*, pg. 114
SAINT MARYS RAILROAD CO.—Gilman Investment Company, Inc.; *U.S. Private*, pg. 454
SAND-UND KIES-KONTOR GESELLSCHAFT MIT BESCHRANKTER HAFTUNG—The Peninsular and Oriental Steam Navigation Company; *Int'l*, pg. 1034
DIETER SCHEEL GMBH—Korf-Transport-GmbH; *Int'l*, pg. 759
SCHENKER EUROCARGO AG—Veba AG; *Int'l*, pg. 1459
SCHENKER INTERNATIONAL AG—Veba AG; *Int'l*, pg. 1459
SCHENKERS INTERNATIONAL FORWARDERS, INC.—Veba AG; *Int'l*, pg. 1459
SIME DARBY HONG KONG LIMITED—Sime Darby Berhad; *Int'l*, pg. 1251
SOBOTRAM—SNCF; *Int'l*, pg. 1164
SODETAIR—Groupe Air France; *Int'l*, pg. 560
SODETRANS—SNCF; *Int'l*, pg. 1165
SOMOCAR S.P.A.—Coeclerici Group; *Int'l*, pg. 303
SOTRAB—SNCF; *Int'l*, pg. 1165
SPEEDBIRD EXPRESS—British Airways PLC; *Int'l*, pg. 219
SSANGYONG BUSINESS GROUP; *Int'l*, pg. 1291
SSANGYONG SHIPPING CO. LTD.—Ssangyong Business Group; *Int'l*, pg. 1292
STEUART INVESTMENT COMPANY; *U.S. Private*, pg. 1042
STOLT-NIELSEN S.A.; *Int'l*, pg. 1301
STONE & WEBSTER CIVIL & TRANSPORTATION SERVICES, INC.—Stone & Webster, Incorporated; *U.S. Public*, pg. 1519
SURFACE FREIGHT CORP.—Air Express International Corporation; *U.S. Public*, pg. 30
SUTTON BRIDGE WHARFAGE CO. LTD.—Simon Engineering plc; *Int'l*, pg. 1251
SUZUKI TRANSPORTATION AND PACKAGING CO., LTD.—Suzuki Motor Corporation; *Int'l*, pg. 1323
TNT AUSTRALIA PTY. LIMITED—TNT Limited; *Int'l*, pg. 1343
TNT HOLDING GMBH—TNT Limited; *Int'l*, pg. 1343
TNT LIMITED; *Int'l*, pg. 1342
TNT LOGISTICS ASIA PTE LTD.—TNT Limited; *Int'l*, pg. 1343
TNT LOGISTICS NORTH AMERICA—TNT Limited; *Int'l*, pg. 1343
TNT LOGISTICS UK—TNT Limited; *Int'l*, pg. 1343
TNT NEW ZEALAND LIMITED—TNT Limited; *Int'l*, pg. 1343
TNT NORTH AMERICA AND CANADA INC.—TNT Limited; *Int'l*, pg. 1343
TNT PARTICIPACOES LTDA.—TNT Limited; *Int'l*, pg. 1343
TNT TRACO S.P.A.—TNT Limited; *Int'l*, pg. 1343
TNT U.K. LIMITED—TNT Limited; *Int'l*, pg. 1343
TAYLOR RENTAL—TruServ Corporation; *U.S. Private*, pg. 1108
THYSSEN HANIEL LOGISTIC GMBH—Thyssen AG; *Int'l*, pg. 1388
THYSSEN HANIEL LOGISTIC INTERNATIONAL GMBH—Thyssen AG; *Int'l*, pg. 1388
THYSSEN HANIEL LOGISTICS—Thyssen AG; *Int'l*, pg. 1388
TOWER GROUP INTERNATIONAL—The McGraw-Hill Companies; *U.S. Public*, pg. 1071
TRANSAMERICA CORPORATION; *U.S. Public*, pg. 1629
TRANSPORTATION SERVICES DIVISION—The Sherwin-Williams Company; *U.S. Public*, pg. 1466
TRANSPORTS BERNIS—SNCF; *Int'l*, pg. 1165
TRANSPORTS MOULINOIS—SNCF; *Int'l*, pg. 1165
TRANSPORTS RAPIDES LOZERIENS—SNCF; *Int'l*, pg. 1165
TRANSPORTS VIROLLE—SNCF; *Int'l*, pg. 1165
TRANSQUERCY—SNCF; *Int'l*, pg. 1165
TRIPLE CROWN SERVICES COMPANY—Conrail, Inc.; *U.S. Public*, pg. 432
UNIGATE PLC; *Int'l*, pg. 1433
UNILEVER EXPORT LTD.—Unilever Plc; *Int'l*, pg. 1434
UNION AIR TRANSPORT GMBH—Union-Transport Corporation; *U.S. Private*, pg. 1120
UNION-TRANSPORT CORPORATION; *U.S. Private*, pg. 1119
UNISPED SPEDITION UND TRANSPORTGESELLSCHAFT MBH—Saarbergwerke Aktiengesellschaft; *Int'l*, pg. 1167
UNITED TRANSPORT CONTAINERS LTD.—Sophus Berendsen A/S; *Int'l*, pg. 1285
UNIVERSAL TRANSPORT GMBH—The Peninsular and Oriental Steam Navigation Company; *Int'l*, pg. 1034
V.A.G. TRANSPORT GMBH CO. DHG—Volkswagen AG; *Int'l*, pg. 1473
VAN OMMEREN SHIPPING, INC.—Koninklijke Van Ommeren NV; *Int'l*, pg. 758
VAUGHAN TRANSPORT (AUSTRALIA) PTY. LTD.—Brambles Industries Limited; *Int'l*, pg. 211
VEBA AG; *Int'l*, pg. 1454
VELLAVE DE TRANSPORTS—SNCF; *Int'l*, pg. 1165
VERKEHRSBETRIEBE PEINE-SALZGITTER GMBH—Preussag AG; *Int'l*, pg. 1070
VIROLLE—SNCF; *Int'l*, pg. 1165
VITRAN CORPORATION INC.; *Int'l*, pg. 1469
WALBAUM—SNCF; *Int'l*, pg. 1165
WESTERN NAVIGATION GLOBAL LTD.—Circle International Group, Inc.; *U.S. Public*, pg. 373
WORLD SHIPPING, INC.; *U.S. Private*, pg. 1190
YOKOHAMA TRANSPORTATION CO., LTD.—Nissan Motor Co., Ltd.; *Int'l*, pg. 944
YOSEMITE EXPRESS CO.—Save Mart Supermarkets; *U.S. Private*, pg. 968
DANIEL F. YOUNG, INC.; *U.S. Private*, pg. 1200
ZENTRANS, INC.—Zenith Electronics Corp.; *U.S. Public*, pg. 1790
ZUERCHER LAGERHAUS AG; *Int'l*, pg. 1529

4741 — RENTAL OF RAILROAD CARS

ACF INDUSTRIES, INC.—Icahn & Co., Inc.; *U.S. Private*, pg. 556
AMERICAN RAILCAR INDUSTRIES—Icahn & Co., Inc.; *U.S. Private*, pg. 556
ARCHER DANIELS MIDLAND COMPANY (ADM); *U.S. Public*, pg. 127
BRAMBLES EUROPE S.A.—Brambles Industries Limited; *Int'l*, pg. 212
BRAMBLES INDUSTRIES LIMITED; *Int'l*, pg. 210
BURLINGTON NORTHERN SANTA FE CORPORATION; *U.S. Public*, pg. 268
CAIB-AUSTRIA OEVA GMBH—Brambles Industries Limited; *Int'l*, pg. 212
C.A.I.B./EVA NEDERLAND B.V.—Brambles Industries Limited; *Int'l*, pg. 212
CAIB UK LIMITED—Brambles Industries Limited; *Int'l*, pg. 212
CGTX, INC.—GATX Corporation; *U.S. Public*, pg. 693
DUCHOSSOIS INDUSTRIES, INC.; *U.S. Private*, pg. 344
EISENBAHN-TRANSPORTMITTEL AG—Brambles Industries Limited; *Int'l*, pg. 212
EMONS INDUSTRIES, INC.—Emons Transportation Group, Inc.; *U.S. Public*, pg. 578
EMONS LOGISTICS SERVICES INC.—Emons Transportation Group, Inc.; *U.S. Public*, pg. 578
GATX CORPORATION; *U.S. Public*, pg. 690
GENERAL AMERICAN TRANSPORTATION CORPORATION—GATX Corporation; *U.S. Public*, pg. 692
GENERAL ELECTRIC CAPITAL RAILCAR SERVICES—General Electric Company; *U.S. Public*, pg. 712
LAKE ERIE DOCK CO.—Norfolk Southern Corporation; *U.S. Public*, pg. 1191
THE MARMON GROUP, INC.; *U.S. Private*, pg. 706
PLM INTERNATIONAL, INC.; *U.S. Public*, pg. 1241
PLM RAILCAR MANAGEMENT SERVICES, INC.—PLM International, Inc.; *U.S. Public*, pg. 1241
SOCIEDAD DE ALMACENAJE Y TRANSPORTES S.A.—Brambles Industries Limited; *Int'l*, pg. 212
TTX CO.; *U.S. Private*, pg. 1066
TRANSAMERICA LEASING INC.—Transamerica Corporation; *U.S. Public*, pg. 1630
TRANSPORTATION CORP. OF AMERICA—Duchossois Industries, Inc.; *U.S. Private*, pg. 344
TRINITY INDUSTRIES INC.; *U.S. Public*, pg. 1638
TRINITY LEASING—Trinity Industries Inc.; *U.S. Public*, pg. 1639
TRINITY RAILCAR LEASING—Trinity Industries Inc.; *U.S. Public*, pg. 1639

4783 — PACKING & CRATING

AMERICAN CONSOLIDATION SERVICES LTD.—Neptune Orient Lines Ltd.; *Int'l*, pg. 912
CFS NEW ZEALAND LTD.—Circle International Group, Inc.; *U.S. Public*, pg. 372
CALAVO GROWERS OF CALIFORNIA; *U.S. Private*, pg. 199
CIRCLE AIRFREIGHT INTERNATIONAL DE MEXICO S.A. DE C.V.—Circle International Group, Inc.; *U.S. Public*, pg. 372
CIRCLE AIRFREIGHT INTERNATIONAL KOREA—Circle International Group, Inc.; *U.S. Public*, pg. 372
CIRCLE AIRFREIGHT INTL. (TAIWAN) LTD.—Circle International Group, Inc.; *U.S. Public*, pg. 372
CIRCLE FREIGHT INTERNATIONAL—Circle International Group, Inc.; *U.S. Public*, pg. 370
CIRCLE FREIGHT INTERNATIONAL LLC—Circle International Group, Inc.; *U.S. Public*, pg. 372
CIRCLE FREIGHT INTERNATIONAL (SAUDI ARABIA) LTD.—Circle International Group, Inc.; *U.S. Public*, pg. 373
CIRCLE FREIGHT INTERNATIONAL (U.S.A.)—Circle International Group, Inc.; *U.S. Public*, pg. 370
CIRCLE INTERNATIONAL—Circle International Group, Inc.; *U.S. Public*, pg. 371
CIRCLE INTERNATIONAL GROUP, INC.; *U.S. Public*, pg. 370
CIRCLE INTERNATIONAL (N.Z.) LTD.—Circle International Group, Inc.; *U.S. Public*, pg. 373
CON-CARRIERS LTD.—Circle International Group, Inc.; *U.S. Public*, pg. 373
FRITZ AIR FREIGHT—Fritz Companies, Inc.; *U.S. Public*, pg. 683
MAX GRUENHUT, GMBH & CO.—Circle International Group, Inc.; *U.S. Public*, pg. 373
MAX GRUENHUT INTERNATIONAL CANADA INC—Circle International Group, Inc.; *U.S. Public*, pg. 373
MAX GRUENHUT INTERNATIONAL, INC.—Circle International Group, Inc.; *U.S. Public*, pg. 372
MAX GRUENHUT INTERNATIONAL INC. USA—Circle International Group, Inc.; *U.S. Public*, pg. 372
HARPER FREIGHT INTERNATIONAL—Circle International Group, Inc.; *U.S. Public*, pg. 373
HARPER FREIGHT INTERNATIONAL (SWEDEN) AB—Circle International Group, Inc.; *U.S. Public*, pg. 373
KONINKLIJKE VAN OMMEREN NV; *Int'l*, pg. 758
MAGNET WORLD TRAVEL LTD.—The General Electric Company, p.l.c.; *Int'l*, pg. 544
MEAD PACKAGING CHILE LIMITADA—The Mead Corporation; *U.S. Public*, pg. 1076
SUNMAC HAWAII, LTD.—Sunkist Growers, Inc.; *U.S. Private*, pg. 1053
WESTERN NAVIGATION GLOBAL LTD.—Circle International Group, Inc.; *U.S. Public*, pg. 373

4785 — INSPECTION & WEIGHING SERVICES FOR MOTOR VEHICLE TRANSPORTATION

CALEB BRETT USA INC.—Inchcape PLC; *Int'l*, pg. 671
GOODKIND & O'DEA, INC.—Dewberry & Davis; *U.S. Private*, pg. 329
MASSMAN CONSTRUCTION COMPANY; *U.S. Private*, pg. 713
MERCHANTS DESPATCH TRANSP. CO.—Conrail, Inc.; *U.S. Public*, pg. 432
OIL-DRI TRANSPORTATION CO.—Oil-Dri Corporation of America; *U.S. Public*, pg. 1215
PATTERSON TRUCK LINE, INC.—RPC Incorporated; *U.S. Public*, pg. 1356
TRIBOROUGH BRIDGE & TUNNEL AUTHORITY—Metropolitan Transportation Authority; *U.S. Private*, pg. 739

4789 — TRANSPORTATION SERVICES, NEC

APL LIMITED—Neptune Orient Lines Ltd.; *Int'l*, pg. 912
ARIANESPACE, INC.—Arianespace SA; *Int'l*, pg. 81
ARIANESPACE KOUROU—Arianespace SA; *Int'l*, pg. 81
ARIANESPACE SA; *Int'l*, pg. 81
ARKANSAS & MEMPHIS RAILWAY BRIDGE AND TERMINAL CO.—Union Pacific Corporation; *U.S. Public*, pg. 1668
B.I. TRANSPORTATION, INC.—Burlington Industries, Inc.; *U.S. Public*, pg. 268
BRAMBLES BULK HAULAGE—Brambles Industries Limited; *Int'l*, pg. 211
BRAMBLES MANFORD—Brambles Industries Limited; *Int'l*, pg. 211
CIRCLE FREIGHT INTERNATIONAL—Circle International Group, Inc.; *U.S. Public*, pg. 370
CIRCLE FREIGHT INTERNATIONAL (U.S.A.)—Circle International Group, Inc.; *U.S. Public*, pg. 370
CIRCLE INTERNATIONAL—Circle International Group, Inc.; *U.S. Public*, pg. 371
CIRCLE INTERNATIONAL GROUP, INC.; *U.S. Public*, pg. 370
COMDATA SAUNDERS INCORPORATED—Ceridian Corporation; *U.S. Public*, pg. 331
CONSOLIDATED CARGO CARRIERS—Consolidated Systems, Inc.; *U.S. Private*, pg. 266
EMONS TRANSPORTATION GROUP, INC.; *U.S. Public*, pg. 578
FRITZ AIR FREIGHT—Fritz Companies, Inc.; *U.S. Public*, pg. 683
GENERAL ELECTRIC RAILCAR REPAIR SERVICES CORP.—General Electric Company; *U.S. Public*, pg. 712
GRACE EXPRESS—Brambles Industries Limited; *Int'l*, pg. 211
GRACE REMOVALS—Brambles Industries Limited; *Int'l*, pg. 211
GRACE (WA) PTY. LIMITED—Brambles Industries Limited; *Int'l*, pg. 211
GULF MARINE FAR EAST PTE. LTD.—Gulfmark Offshore Inc.; *U.S. Public*, pg. 769
GULF OFFSHORE DO BRASIL—Gulfmark Offshore Inc.; *U.S. Public*, pg. 769
GULF OFFSHORE MARINE—Gulfmark Offshore Inc.; *U.S. Public*, pg. 769
GULF OFFSHORE MARINE INTERNATIONAL, INC.—Gulfmark Offshore Inc.; *U.S. Public*, pg. 769
GULF OFFSHORE N.S. LTD.—Gulfmark Offshore Inc.; *U.S. Public*, pg. 769
HARPEN AG; *Int'l*, pg. 597
INAGUA TRANSPORTS, INC.—Morton International Inc.; *U.S. Public*, pg. 1135
KENAN TRANSPORT COMPANY; *U.S. Public*, pg. 949
KIMBALL FLIGHT OPERATIONS—Kimball International, Inc.; *U.S. Public*, pg. 957
KIMBALL INTERNATIONAL, INC.; *U.S. Public*, pg. 956
KONINKLIJKE VAN OMMEREN NV; *Int'l*, pg. 758
MLT VACATIONS, INC.—Northwest Airlines Corp.; *U.S. Public*, pg. 1200
MANUFACTURERS RAILWAY COMPANY—Anheuser-Busch Companies, Inc.; *U.S. Public*, pg. 114
MIDWEST ENERGY RESOURCES CO.—DTE Energy Company; *U.S. Public*, pg. 476
NEWFOUNDLAND CAPITAL CORPORATION LIMITED; *Int'l*, pg. 924
THE OGDEN UNION RAILWAY AND DEPOT CO.—Union Pacific Corporation; *U.S. Public*, pg. 1668
P.A.M. TRANSPORT, INC.; *U.S. Private*, pg. 825
PHH CORPORATION—Cendant Corporation; *U.S. Public*, pg. 321
PACIFIC NUCLEAR TRANSPORT LTD.—Nissho Iwai Corporation; *Int'l*, pg. 949
PANDROL JACKSON, INC.—Charter plc; *Int'l*, pg. 280
PORT WARATAH COAL SERVICES PTY. LTD.—Nissho Iwai Corporation; *Int'l*, pg. 949
PROLER INTERNATIONAL CORP.—Schnitzer Steel Industries, Inc.; *U.S. Public*, pg. 1440
RUG-RHEINISCHE UMSCHLAG-GESELLSCHAFT MBH—The Peninsular and Oriental Steam Navigation Company; *Int'l*, pg. 1033

RHENANIA UMSCHLAG UND LAGEREI GMBH—The Peninsular and Oriental Steam Navigation Company; Int'l, pg. 1034
RIVERTON TRUCKERS, INC.—Gohmann Asphalt & Construction Inc.; U.S. Private, pg. 459
ROLLINS LOGISTICS INC.—Rollins Truck Leasing Corp.; U.S. Public, pg. 1405
SEAWAY IMPORTING COMPANY—Pamida Holdings Corporation; U.S. Public, pg. 1255
SOUTHERN ILLINOIS AND MISSOURI BRIDGE CO.—Union Pacific Corporation; U.S. Public, pg. 1668
STONE & WEBSTER CIVIL & TRANSPORTATION SERVICES, INC.—Stone & Webster, Incorporated; U.S. Public, pg. 1519
THYSSEN HANDELSUNION AG—Thyssen AG; Int'l, pg. 1388
TRANSCO INC.; U.S. Private, pg. 1096
UNITED TANKERS SERVICES PTY. LIMITED—Brambles Industries Limited; Int'l, pg. 211
WILLAMETTE INDUSTRIES, INC.—Willamette Industries, Inc.; U.S. Public, pg. 1769
YAMATO TRANSPORT CO., LTD.; Int'l, pg. 1519

4812 — RADIO TELEPHONE COMMUNICATIONS

AMT—Oy Nokia Ab/Nokia Group; Int'l, pg. 954
AT&T WIRELESS SERVICES—AT&T Corporation; U.S. Public, pg. 11
AIRTOUCH CELLULAR—AirTouch Communications, Inc.; U.S. Public, pg. 34
AIRTOUCH CELLULAR - WESTERN REGION—AirTouch Communications, Inc.; U.S. Public, pg. 34
AIRTOUCH PAGING—AirTouch Communications, Inc.; U.S. Public, pg. 34
ALIANT COMMUNICATIONS CO.—Aliant Communications Inc.; U.S. Public, pg. 40
ALLTEL ALABAMA—ALLTEL Corporation; U.S. Public, pg. 55
ALLTEL ARKANSAS, INC.—ALLTEL Corporation; U.S. Public, pg. 55
ALLTEL CAROLINA, INC.—ALLTEL Corporation; U.S. Public, pg. 55
ALLTEL CORPORATION; U.S. Public, pg. 55
ALLTEL FLORIDA, INC.—ALLTEL Corporation; U.S. Public, pg. 56
ALLTEL GEORGIA, INC.—ALLTEL Corporation; U.S. Public, pg. 56
ALLTEL KENTUCKY, INC.—ALLTEL Corporation; U.S. Public, pg. 56
ALLTEL MISSISSIPPI, INC.—ALLTEL Corporation; U.S. Public, pg. 56
ALLTEL MISSOURI, INC.—ALLTEL Corporation; U.S. Public, pg. 56
ALLTEL MOBILE COMMUNICATIONS, INC.—ALLTEL Corporation; U.S. Public, pg. 56
ALLTEL NEW YORK, INC.—ALLTEL Corporation; U.S. Public, pg. 56
ALLTEL OHIO, INC.—ALLTEL Corporation; U.S. Public, pg. 56
ALLTEL OKLAHOMA, INC.—ALLTEL Corporation; U.S. Public, pg. 56
ALLTEL PENNSYLVANIA, INC.—ALLTEL Corporation; U.S. Public, pg. 56
ALLTEL SERVICES, INC.—ALLTEL Corporation; U.S. Public, pg. 56
ALLTEL SOUTH CAROLINA, INC.—ALLTEL Corporation; U.S. Public, pg. 56
ALLTEL TENNESSEE, INC.—Citizens Utilities Company; U.S. Public, pg. 380
ALLTEL TEXAS, INC.—ALLTEL Corporation; U.S. Public, pg. 56
ALPHAPAGE—France Telecom; Int'l, pg. 503
AMERITECH—Ameritech Corporation; U.S. Public, pg. 97
AMERITECH CELLULAR AND PAGING SERVICES—Ameritech Corporation; U.S. Public, pg. 98
AMERITECH CORP.—Ameritech Corporation; U.S. Public, pg. 98
AMERITECH CORPORATION; U.S. Public, pg. 97
AMERITECH INFORMATION SYSTEMS INC.—Ameritech Corporation; U.S. Public, pg. 98
AMERITECH PHONE COMPANY—Ameritech Corporation; U.S. Public, pg. 98
AMERITECH—Ameritech Corporation; U.S. Public, pg. 97
ATLANTIC CELLULAR TELEPHONE CORP.—Vanguard Cellular Systems, Inc.; U.S. Public, pg. 1708
BCE INC.; Int'l, pg. 114
BCE MOBILE COMMUNICATIONS INC.—BCE Inc.; Int'l, pg. 115
BT (HONG KONG) LIMITED—British Telecommunications plc; Int'l, pg. 223
BELIZE TELECOMMUNICATIONS LIMITED—British Telecommunications plc; Int'l, pg. 223
BELL ATLANTIC ADMINISTRATIVE SERVICES, INC.—Bell Atlantic Corporation; U.S. Public, pg. 202
BELL ATLANTIC-MD—Bell Atlantic Corporation; U.S. Public, pg. 202
BELL ATLANTIC-NJ—Bell Atlantic Corporation; U.S. Public, pg. 202
BELL ATLANTIC-PA—Bell Atlantic Corporation; U.S. Public, pg. 203
BELL ATLANTIC-VA—Bell Atlantic Corporation; U.S. Public, pg. 203
BELL ATLANTIC VENTURES XX, INC.—Bell Atlantic Corporation; U.S. Public, pg. 203
BELL ATLANTIC-WASHINGTON, D.C., INC.—Bell Atlantic Corporation; U.S. Public, pg. 203
BELL ATLANTIC-WV—Bell Atlantic Corporation; U.S. Public, pg. 203
BELL MOBILITY CELLULAR INC.—BCE Inc.; Int'l, pg. 115
BELL MOBILITY PAGING INC.—BCE Inc.; Int'l, pg. 115
BELL MOBILITY RADIO INC.—BCE Inc.; Int'l, pg. 115
BELLSOUTH CORPORATION; U.S. Public, pg. 207
BINGHAMTON CEL TEL CO.—Vanguard Cellular Systems, Inc.; U.S. Public, pg. 1708
BRITISH TELECOMMUNICATIONS PLC; Int'l, pg. 222
BROOKVILLE TELEPHONE COMPANY—ALLTEL Corporation; U.S. Public, pg. 56
BRUNCOR, INC.; Int'l, pg. 230
CABLE & WIRELESS COMMUNICATIONS INC.—Cable and Wireless plc; Int'l, pg. 247
CABLE AND WIRELESS PLC; Int'l, pg. 247
CALL CONNECTIONS LIMITED—British Telecommunications plc; Int'l, pg. 222
CANTEL PAGING—Rogers Communications, Inc.; Int'l, pg. 1123
CELLULAR ONE ALBANY TELEPHONE COMPANY—SBC Communications Inc.; U.S. Public, pg. 1415
CELLULAR ONE BUFFALO—SBC Communications Inc.; U.S. Public, pg. 1415
CELLULAR ONE GENESEE TELEPHONE COMPANY—SBC Communications Inc.; U.S. Public, pg. 1415
CENTENNIAL CELLULAR CORP.—Century Communications Corp.; U.S. Public, pg. 329
CENTURY CELLULARNET—Century Telephone Enterprises, Inc.; U.S. Public, pg. 330
CENTURY CELLULARNET FOR EAU CLAIRE MSA, INC.—Century Telephone Enterprises, Inc.; U.S. Public, pg. 330
CENTURY CELLULARNET FOR LACROSSE MSA, INC.—Century Telephone Enterprises, Inc.; U.S. Public, pg. 330
CENTURY COMMUNICATIONS CORP.; U.S. Public, pg. 329
CHECKPOINT COMMUNICATIONS—Rogers Communications, Inc.; Int'l, pg. 1123
CITIZENS COMMUNICATIONS SERVICES, INC.—Citizens Utilities Company; U.S. Public, pg. 380
CITIZENS TELECOMMUNICATIONS—Citizens Utilities Company; U.S. Public, pg. 380
CITIZENS UTILITIES COMPANY; U.S. Public, pg. 379
CITIZENS UTILITIES COMPANY OF CALIFORNIA—Citizens Utilities Company; U.S. Public, pg. 380
COMCAST CELLULAR COMMUNICATIONS, INC.—Comcast Corporation; U.S. Public, pg. 407
COMMNET CELLULAR INC.; U.S. Public, pg. 414
COMMONWEALTH TELEPHONE CO.—Commonwealth Telephone Enterprises, Inc.; U.S. Public, pg. 415
COMMUNICATIONS MACLEAN HUNTER INC.—Rogers Communications, Inc.; Int'l, pg. 1123
COMPANIA GESTORA DE SERVICIO MENSATEL, S.A.—Telefonica de Espana, S.A.; Int'l, pg. 1372
COMUNICACIONES MTEL, S.A. DE C.V.—Mobile Telecommunications Technologies Corp.; U.S. Public, pg. 1120
DEUTSCHE POST AG; Int'l, pg. 407
EATELCORP INC.; U.S. Private, pg. 358
FLORALA TELEPHONE CO.—St. Joe Corp.; U.S. Public, pg. 1427
FONE AMERICA, INC.; U.S. Public, pg. 661
FRANCE TELECOM; Int'l, pg. 503
FRONTIER CORPORATION; U.S. Public, pg. 683
GTE ALASKA INCORPORATED—GTE Corporation; U.S. Public, pg. 697
GTE CALIFORNIA INCORPORATED—GTE Corporation; U.S. Public, pg. 697
GTE FLORIDA INCORPORATED—GTE Corporation; U.S. Public, pg. 697
GTE HAWAIIAN TELEPHONE COMPANY INCORPORATED—GTE Corporation; U.S. Public, pg. 697
GTE NORTHWEST INCORPORATED—GTE Corporation; U.S. Public, pg. 697
GTE SOUTHWEST INCORPORATED—GTE Corporation; U.S. Public, pg. 697
GIBRALTAR TELECOMMUNICATIONS INTERNATIONAL LIMITED—British Telecommunications plc; Int'l, pg. 223
GREAT SOUTHWEST TELEPHONE CORP.—ALLTEL Corporation; U.S. Public, pg. 56
GRUPO IUSACELL SA DE CV—Bell Atlantic Corporation; U.S. Public, pg. 204
HEINS TELEPHONE COMPANY—ALLTEL Corporation; U.S. Public, pg. 56
HONG KONG TELECOMMUNICATIONS LIMITED—Cable and Wireless plc; Int'l, pg. 247
HONG KONG TELEPHONE COMPANY LTD.—Cable and Wireless plc; Int'l, pg. 247
HUTCHISON PAGING HOLDINGS LTD.—Motorola, Inc.; U.S. Public, pg. 1139
HUTCHISON TELEPHONE COMPANY LTD.—Motorola, Inc.; U.S. Public, pg. 1139
IXC COMMUNICATIONS, INC.; U.S. Private, pg. 556
INDIANA BELL TELEPHONE COMPANY, INC.—Ameritech Corporation; U.S. Public, pg. 98
INTERTEL, INC.—Bell Atlantic Corporation; U.S. Public, pg. 203
LAGARDERE GROUPE; Int'l, pg. 791
LIN CELLULAR GROUP—AT&T Corporation; U.S. Public, pg. 11
MCI INTERNATIONAL INC.—MCI Communications Corp.; U.S. Public, pg. 1024
MTEL INTERNATIONAL—Mobile Telecommunications Technologies Corp.; U.S. Public, pg. 1120
MTEL INTERNATIONAL (TOKYO)—Mobile Telecommunications Technologies Corp.; U.S. Public, pg. 1120
MANX TELECOM LIMITED—British Telecommunications plc; Int'l, pg. 223
MCBRIDE AND ASSOCIATES, INC.; U.S. Private, pg. 719
METROCALL, INC.; U.S. Public, pg. 1102
METROMEDIA INTERNATIONAL GROUP, INC.; U.S. Public, pg. 1102
MILLICOM INTERNATIONAL CELLULAR SA; Int'l, pg. 867
MINITEL USA—France Telecom; Int'l, pg. 504
MOBILE COMMUNICATIONS CORPORATION OF AMERICA—MobileComm; U.S. Public, pg. 1120
MOBILE TELECOMMUNICATIONS TECHNOLOGIES CORP.; U.S. Public, pg. 1120
MOUNTAIN STATE TELEPHONE CO.—Citizens Utilities Company; U.S. Public, pg. 380
THE NEW BRUNSWICK TELEPHONE COMPANY, LIMITED (NBTEL)—Bruncor, Inc.; Int'l, pg. 230
NIPPON TELEGRAPH AND TELEPHONE CORPORATION; Int'l, pg. 940
NOKIA MOBILE PHONES—Oy Nokia Ab/Nokia Group; Int'l, pg. 952
NOKIA MOBILE PHONES AB—Oy Nokia Ab/Nokia Group; Int'l, pg. 952
NORSTAN CANADA INC.—Norstan, Inc.; U.S. Public, pg. 1192
NORSTAN COMMUNICATIONS, INC.—Norstan, Inc.; U.S. Public, pg. 1192
NORSTAN, INC.; U.S. Public, pg. 1192
NORTEL FRANCE S.A.—Lagardere Groupe; Int'l, pg. 793
NYNEX NETWORK SYSTEMS COMPANY—Bell Atlantic Corporation; U.S. Public, pg. 204
ORANGE COUNTY CELLULAR TELEPHONE CORP.—Vanguard Cellular Systems, Inc.; U.S. Public, pg. 1708
PACIFIC TELECOM CELLULAR, INC.—PacifiCorp; U.S. Public, pg. 1252
PACIFIC TELESIS GROUP—SBC Communications Inc.; U.S. Public, pg. 1415
PAGING NETWORK, INC.; U.S. Public, pg. 1252
PENNSYLVANIA CELLULAR TELEPHONE CORP.—Vanguard Cellular Systems, Inc.; U.S. Public, pg. 1708
PRICELLULAR CORPORATION; U.S. Public, pg. 1324
PRIME MATRIX WIRELESS COMMUNICATIONS; U.S. Private, pg. 884
ROGERS CANTEL MOBILE COMMUNICATIONS INC.—Rogers Communications, Inc.; Int'l, pg. 1122
ROLM RESALE SYSTEMS—Norstan, Inc.; U.S. Public, pg. 1192
SNET PAGING, INC.—Southern New England Telecommunications Corporation; U.S. Public, pg. 1491
ST. JOE COMMUNICATIONS, INC.—St. Joe Corp.; U.S. Public, pg. 1427
ST. JOE TELEPHONE & TELEGRAPH COMPANY—St. Joe Corp.; U.S. Public, pg. 1427
SKYTEL CORP.—Mobile Telecommunications Technologies Corp.; U.S. Public, pg. 1120
SOUTHERN NEW ENGLAND TELECOMMUNICATIONS CORPORATION; U.S. Public, pg. 1490
STORNO CELLULAR SERVICES LTD.—Motorola, Inc.; U.S. Public, pg. 1140
TMC COMPANY LTD.—Oy Nokia Ab/Nokia Group; Int'l, pg. 952
TSM (TELECOM SYSTEMES MOBILES)—France Telecom; Int'l, pg. 503
TEL-SAVE HOLDINGS, INC.; U.S. Public, pg. 1568
TELECOM ITALIA MOBILE—Telecom Italia S.p.A.; Int'l, pg. 1363
TELECOM SECURICOR CELLULAR RADIO LIMITED—British Telecommunications plc; Int'l, pg. 222
TELUS CORPORATION; Int'l, pg. 1374
TELUS MOBILITY—Telus Corporation; Int'l, pg. 1374
TRANSPAC—France Telecom; Int'l, pg. 503
UNITED STATES CELLULAR CORPORATION—Telephone and Data Systems, Inc.; U.S. Public, pg. 1572
U S WEST COMMUNICATIONS FEDERAL SERVICES INC.—U S West Inc.; U.S. Public, pg. 1689
U S WEST INC.; U.S. Public, pg. 1688
UNIVERSAL TELEPHONE, INC.—Century Telephone Enterprises, Inc.; U.S. Public, pg. 330
VANGUARD BINGHAMTON, INC.—Vanguard Cellular Systems, Inc.; U.S. Public, pg. 1708
VANGUARD CELLULAR SYSTEMS, INC.; U.S. Public, pg. 1707
VANGUARD CELLULAR SYSTEMS OF SOUTH CAROLINA, INC.—Vanguard Cellular Systems, Inc.; U.S. Public, pg. 1708
WEST VIRGINIA CELLULAR TELEPHONE CORP.—Vanguard Cellular Systems, Inc.; U.S. Public, pg. 1708
WESTERN FLORIDA CELLULAR TELEPHONE CORP.—Vanguard Cellular Systems, Inc.; U.S. Public, pg. 1708

4813 — TELEPHONE COMMUNICATIONS, EXCEPT RADIO TELEPHONE

ACC CORP.; U.S. Public, pg. 2
ACC LONG DISTANCE, LTD.—ACC Corp.; U.S. Public, pg. 3
ACC LONG DISTANCE U.K. LTD.—ACC Corp.; U.S. Public, pg. 3
ACC TELECOM—ACC Corp.; U.S. Public, pg. 3
ALC COMMUNICATIONS—IXC Communications, Inc.; U.S. Private, pg. 556
AT&T ALASCOM—AT&T Corporation; U.S. Public, pg. 10
AT&T BUSINESS COMMUNICATIONS SERVICES—AT&T Corporation; U.S. Public, pg. 10
AT&T CORPORATION; U.S. Public, pg. 10
ADAMSVILLE TELEPHONE CO.—Century Telephone Enterprises, Inc.; U.S. Public, pg. 329
AERONAUTICAL RADIO, INC.—Arinc Inc. (Consolidated); U.S. Private, pg. 81
AIRTOUCH CABLE—AirTouch Communications, Inc.; U.S. Public, pg. 34
AIRTOUCH INTERNATIONAL—AirTouch Communications, Inc.; U.S. Public, pg. 34
ALBACOM SPA—British Telecommunications plc; Int'l, pg. 223
ALIANT COMMUNICATIONS CO.—Aliant Communications Inc.; U.S. Public, pg. 40
ALIANT COMMUNICATIONS INC.; U.S. Public, pg. 40
ALLTEL CORPORATION; U.S. Public, pg. 55
ALLTEL MISSOURI, INC.—ALLTEL Corporation; U.S. Public, pg. 56
AMERITECH—Ameritech Corporation; U.S. Public, pg. 97
AMERITECH COMMUNICATIONS, INC.—Ameritech Corporation; U.S. Public, pg. 98
AMERITECH CONSUMER SERVICES—Ameritech Corporation; U.S. Public, pg. 98

AMERITECH CORPORATION; *U.S. Public*, pg. 97
AMERITECH CUSTOM BUSINESS SERVICES—Ameritech Corporation; *U.S. Public*, pg. 98
AMERITECH ENHANCED BUSINESS SERVICES—Ameritech Corporation; *U.S. Public*, pg. 98
AMERITECH SMALL BUSINESS SERVICES—Ameritech Corporation; *U.S. Public*, pg. 98
AMPER, S.A.—Telefonica de Espana, S.A.; *Int'l*, pg. 1372
AMWAY CORPORATION; *U.S. Private*, pg. 69
CIA. ARGENTINA DE TELEFONOS, S.A.—Telefonaktiebolaget LM Ericsson; *Int'l*, pg. 1365
ATCOM, INC.; *U.S. Private*, pg. 94
ATLANTIC WEST B.V.—Bell Atlantic Corporation; *U.S. Public*, pg. 203
BCE INC.; *Int'l*, pg. 114
BT AUSTRALASIA PTY LIMITED—British Telecommunications plc; *Int'l*, pg. 223
BT COMMUNICATIONS MANAGEMENT LIMITED—British Telecommunications plc; *Int'l*, pg. 222
BT (HONG KONG) LIMITED—British Telecommunications plc; *Int'l*, pg. 223
BT NORTH AMERICA, INC.—British Telecommunications plc; *Int'l*, pg. 223
BELL ATLANTIC—Bell Atlantic Corporation; *U.S. Public*, pg. 202
BELL ATLANTIC AUSTRALIA PTY LIMITED—Bell Atlantic Corporation; *U.S. Public*, pg. 204
BELL ATLANTIC CORPORATION; *U.S. Public*, pg. 201
BELL ATLANTIC-DE—Bell Atlantic Corporation; *U.S. Public*, *pg. 202*
BELL ATLANTIC EUROPE S.A.—Bell Atlantic Corporation; *U.S. Public*, pg. 204
BELL ATLANTIC NETWORK SERVICES, INC.—Bell Atlantic Corporation; *U.S. Public*, pg. 202
BELL ATLANTIC NEW ENGLAND—Bell Atlantic Corporation; *U.S. Public*, pg. 202
BELL ATLANTICOM SYSTEMS, INC.—Bell Atlantic Corporation; *U.S. Public*, pg. 203
BELL CANADA—BCE Inc.; *Int'l*, pg. 115
BELLSOUTH CORPORATION; *U.S. Public*, pg. 207
BELLSOUTH TELECOMMUNICATIONS, INC.—BellSouth Corporation; *U.S. Public*, pg. 209
BELMONT TELEPHONE COMPANY—Lynch Corporation; *U.S. Public*, pg. 1022
BRETTON WOODS TELEPHONE COMPANY—Lynch Corporation; *U.S. Public*, pg. 1021
BRITE HOLDING AG—Brite Voice Systems, Inc.; *U.S. Public*, pg. 257
BRITE VOICE SYSTEMS—Brite Voice Systems, Inc.; *U.S. Public*, pg. 257
BRITE VOICE SYSTEMS EUROPE—Brite Voice Systems, Inc.; *U.S. Public*, pg. 257
BRITE VOICE SYSTEMS GROUP, LTD.—Brite Voice Systems, Inc.; *U.S. Public*, pg. 257
BRITE VOICE SYSTEMS, INC.; *U.S. Public*, pg. 257
BRITE VOICE SYSTEMS, INC.—Brite Voice Systems, Inc.; *U.S. Public*, pg. 257
BRITISH TELECOMMUNICATIONS PLC; *Int'l*, pg. 222
BRUNCOR, INC.; *Int'l*, pg. 230
BUTLER INTERNATIONAL, INC.; *U.S. Public*, pg. 270
CABLE & WIRELESS COMMUNICATIONS INC.-TEXAS—Cable and Wireless plc; *Int'l*, pg. 247
CABLE & WIRELESS MANAGEMENT SERVICES—Cable and Wireless plc; *Int'l*, pg. 247
CABLEDATA INTERNATIONAL, LTD.—USCS International, Inc.; *U.S. Public*, pg. 1659
CARIFONE—Peoples Telephone Company, Inc.; *U.S. Public*, pg. 1275
CASCADE AUTOVON CO.—PacifiCorp; *U.S. Public*, pg. 1252
CASIO PHONE-MATE, INC.—Casio Computer Co., Ltd.; *Int'l*, pg. 274
CELLNET SOLUTIONS LIMITED—British Telecommunications plc; *Int'l*, pg. 222
CENTURY AREA LONG LINES INC.—Century Telephone Enterprises, Inc.; *U.S. Public*, pg. 330
CENTURY TELEPHONE COMPANY—Century Telephone Enterprises, Inc.; *U.S. Public*, pg. 329
CENTURY TELEPHONE CO. OF COLORADO—Century Telephone Enterprises, Inc.; *U.S. Public*, pg. 330
CENTURY TELEPHONE CO. OF NORTHERN WISCONSIN—Century Telephone Enterprises, Inc.; *U.S. Public*, pg. 330
CENTURY TELEPHONE ENTERPRISES, INC.; *U.S. Public*, *pg. 329*
CENTURY TELEPHONE OF IDAHO, INC.—Century Telephone Enterprises, Inc.; *U.S. Public*, pg. 329
CENTURY TELEPHONE OF MICHIGAN, INC.—Century Telephone Enterprises, Inc.; *U.S. Public*, pg. 329
CENTURY TELEPHONE OF WISCONSIN, INC.—Century Telephone Enterprises, Inc.; *U.S. Public*, pg. 329
CENTURY TELEPHONE, REGION IV—Century Telephone Enterprises, Inc.; *U.S. Public*, pg. 329
CINCINNATI BELL LONG DISTANCE INC.—Cincinnati Bell Telephone; *U.S. Public*, pg. 367
CINCINNATI BELL TELEPHONE; *U.S. Public*, pg. 367
CINCINNATI BELL TELEPHONE COMPANY—Cincinnati Bell Telephone; *U.S. Public*, pg. 367
CITIZENS TELECOMMUNICATIONS—Citizens Utilities Company; *U.S. Public*, pg. 380
CITIZENS UTILITIES COMPANY; *U.S. Public*, pg. 379
CITIZENS UTILITIES COMPANY—Citizens Utilities Company; *U.S. Public*, pg. 380
CITIZENS UTILITIES COMPANY OF CALIFORNIA—Citizens Utilities Company; *U.S. Public*, pg. 380
CLAIBORNE TELEPHONE CO.—Century Telephone Enterprises, Inc.; *U.S. Public*, pg. 330
CLEAR COMMUNICATIONS LIMITED—British Telecommunications plc; *Int'l*, pg. 223
COMMONWEALTH COMMUNICATIONS—RCN Corporation; *U.S. Public*, pg. 1354
COMMONWEALTH TELEPHONE ENTERPRISES, INC.; *U.S. Public*, pg. 415
CONCERT COMMUNICATIONS COMPANY—British Telecommunications plc; *Int'l*, pg. 223
CONFERTECH INTERNATIONAL—Frontier Corporation; *U.S. Public*, pg. 683
CONSOLIDATED COMMUNICATIONS—McLeodUSA Incorporated; *U.S. Public*, pg. 1073
CUBA CITY TELEPHONE EXCHANGE CO.—Lynch Corporation; *U.S. Public*, pg. 1022
DELTA COUNTY TELE-COMM, INC.—Telephone and Data Systems, Inc.; *U.S. Public*, pg. 1571
DEUTSCHE POST AG; *Int'l*, pg. 407
ELECTRA COMMUNICATIONS—IXC Communications, Inc.; *U.S. Private*, pg. 556
EXCEL COMMUNICATIONS, INC.; *U.S. Public*, pg. 598
FCR (FRANCE CABLES ET RADIO)—France Telecom; *Int'l*, pg. 503
THE FAIRCHILD CORPORATION; *U.S. Public*, pg. 610
FARMERS TELEPHONE CO-OP; *U.S. Private*, pg. 395
FONE AMERICA, INC.; *U.S. Public*, pg. 661
FORESTVILLE TELEPHONE, INC.—Century Telephone Enterprises, Inc.; *U.S. Public*, pg. 330
FRANCE TELECOM; *Int'l*, pg. 503
FRONTEL COMMUNICATIONS SERVICES—Frontier Corporation; *U.S. Public*, pg. 684
FRONTIER CORPORATION; *U.S. Public*, pg. 683
GTE CORPORATION; *U.S. Public*, pg. 696
GTE SUPPLY—GTE Corporation; *U.S. Public*, pg. 697
GEM STATE UTILITIES CORPORATION—PacifiCorp; *U.S. Public*, pg. 1252
GENERAL COMMUNICATION, INC.; *U.S. Public*, pg. 708
GIBRALTAR TELECOMMUNICATIONS INTERNATIONAL LIMITED—British Telecommunications plc; *Int'l*, pg. 223
GIBRALTAR TELEPHONE COMPANY—Bell Atlantic Corporation; *U.S. Public*, pg. 204
GOSHEN TELEPHONE COMPANY, INC.—Telephone and Data Systems, Inc.; *U.S. Public*, pg. 1571
GRANDETEL TECHNOLOGIES INC.; *Int'l*, pg. 556
GULF TELEPHONE CO.—St. Joe Corp.; *U.S. Public*, pg. 1427
HAVILAND TELEPHONE COMPANY, INC.—Lynch Corporation; *U.S. Public*, pg. 1021
HONG KONG TELECOM INTERNATIONAL LIMITED—Cable and Wireless plc; *Int'l*, pg. 247
HONG KONG TELECOMMUNICATIONS LIMITED—Cable and Wireless plc; *Int'l*, pg. 247
HONG KONG TELEPHONE COMPANY LTD.—Cable and Wireless plc; *Int'l*, pg. 247
IDB WORLDCOM—WorldCom, Inc.; *U.S. Public*, pg. 1779
IXC COMMUNICATIONS, INC.; *U.S. Private*, pg. 556
INFORMATION SYSTEMS & NETWORK CORPORATION; *U.S. Private*, pg. 561
INTELLICALL, INC.; *U.S. Public*, pg. 887
INTER-COMMUNITY TELEPHONE COMPANY—Lynch Corporation; *U.S. Public*, pg. 1022
INTER ISLAND TELEPHONE CO., INC.—PacifiCorp; *U.S. Public*, pg. 1252
INTER-TEL DATACOMM, INC.—Inter-Tel, Incorporated; *U.S. Public*, pg. 888
INTER-TEL, INCORPORATED; *U.S. Public*, pg. 888
INTER-TEL, INCORPORATED-NEW JERSEY—Inter-Tel, Incorporated; *U.S. Public*, pg. 888
INTER-TEL JAPAN, INC.—Inter-Tel, Incorporated; *U.S. Public*, pg. 888
INTER-TEL MIDWEST, INC.—Inter-Tel, Incorporated; *U.S. Public*, pg. 888
INTER-TEL TECHNOLOGIES, INC.—Inter-Tel, Incorporated; *U.S. Public*, pg. 888
J.B.N. FINANCE CORPORATION—Lynch Corporation; *U.S.* Public, pg. 1021
J.B.N. TELEPHONE CO.—Lynch Corporation; *U.S. Public*, pg. 1021
LDDS WORLDCOM—WorldCom, Inc.; *U.S. Public*, pg. 1779
LDDS/WORLDCOM COMMUNICATIONS—WorldCom, Inc.; *U.S. Public*, pg. 1779
LDDS WORLDCOM INC.—WorldCom, Inc.; *U.S. Public*, pg. 1779
LARSEN-READFIELD TELEPHONE COMPANY—Century Telephone Enterprises, Inc.; *U.S. Public*, pg. 330
LONG DISTANCE INTERNATIONAL—Sprint Corporation; *U.S. Public*, pg. 1501
LUCENT NETCARE MESSAGING SERVICES—Lucent Technologies Inc.; *U.S. Public*, pg. 1018
LUCENT TECHNOLOGIES INC.; *U.S. Public*, pg. 1017
LYNCH CORPORATION; *U.S. Public*, pg. 1021
LYNCH TELECOMMUNICATIONS CORPORATION—Lynch Corporation; *U.S. Public*, pg. 1022
LYNCH TELEPHONE CORPORATION—Lynch Corporation; *U.S. Public*, pg. 1022
MCI COMMUNICATIONS CORP.; *U.S. Public*, pg. 1023
MCI SYSTEMHOUSE—MCI Communications Corp.; *U.S. Public*, pg. 1024
MID-AMERICA TELEPHONE, INC.—Telephone and Data Systems, Inc.; *U.S. Public*, pg. 1571
MINITEL USA—France Telecom; *Int'l*, pg. 504
MONROE COUNTY TELEPHONE CO.—Century Telephone Enterprises, Inc.; *U.S. Public*, pg. 330
MONTANA POWER COMPANY; *U.S. Public*, pg. 1126
MUSTANG TELEPHONE CO.—Century Telephone Enterprises, Inc.; *U.S. Public*, pg. 329
MUTUAL SIGNAL CORPORATION OF MICHIGAN—IXC Communications, Inc.; *U.S. Private*, pg. 556
NATIONAL SYSTEMS & RESEARCH CO.; *U.S. Private*, pg. 787
NETWORK EQUIPMENT TECHNOLOGIES, INC.; *U.S. Public*, pg. 1168
NEVADA BELL—SBC Communications Inc.; *U.S. Public*, pg. 1416
THE NEW BRUNSWICK TELEPHONE COMPANY, LIMITED (NBTEL)—Bruncor, Inc.; *Int'l*, pg. 230
NEWBRIDGE NETWORKS CORPORATION; *Int'l*, pg. 923
NEWTEL COMMUNICATIONS—BCE Inc.; *Int'l*, pg. 115
NEWTEL ENTERPRISES LIMITED—BCE Inc.; *Int'l*, pg. 115
NIPPON TELEGRAPH AND TELEPHONE CORPORATION; *Int'l*, pg. 940
NOKIA TELECOMMUNICATIONS PARKTOWN OFFICE SUITES—Oy Nokia Ab/Nokia Group; *Int'l*, pg. 954
NORTHERN TELEPHONE LIMITED—BCE Inc.; *Int'l*, pg. 115
NORTHWESTEL INC.—BCE Inc.; *Int'l*, pg. 115
NORTHWESTERN TELEPHONE SYSTEMS, INC.—PacifiCorp; *U.S. Public*, pg. 1252
PTC CORRECTIONS—Peoples Telephone Company, Inc.; *U.S. Public*, pg. 1275
PTC SERVICES—Peoples Telephone Company, Inc.; *U.S. Public*, pg. 1275
PACIFIC BELL—SBC Communications Inc.; *U.S. Public*, pg. 1416
PACIFIC TELECOM, INC.—Century Telephone Enterprises, Inc.; *U.S. Public*, pg. 330
PACIFIC TELESIS GROUP—SBC Communications Inc.; *U.S. Public*, pg. 1415
PACIFICORP; *U.S. Public*, pg. 1251
PEOPLES TELEPHONE COMPANY, INC.; *U.S. Public*, pg. 1275
PROXIM, INC.; *U.S. Public*, pg. 1338
QST COMMUNICATIONS, INC.—CILCORP Inc.; *U.S. Public*, pg. 367
QUINCY TELEPHONE COMPANY—Telephone and Data Systems, Inc.; *U.S. Public*, pg. 1571
RCN CORPORATION; *U.S. Public*, pg. 1354
RCN LONG DISTANCE—RCN Corporation; *U.S. Public*, pg. 1354
ROCHESTER TELEPHONE CORP.—Frontier Corporation; *U.S. Public*, pg. 684
ROTTERDAM VENTURES INC.—Galesi Group; *U.S. Private*, pg. 437
SBC CABLECOMMS—SBC Communications Inc.; *U.S. Public*, pg. 1416
SBC COMMUNICATIONS INC.; *U.S. Public*, pg. 1415
ST. JOE COMMUNICATIONS, INC.—St. Joe Corp.; *U.S. Public*, pg. 1427
SCHNEIDER COMMUNICATIONS—Frontier Corporation; *U.S. Public*, pg. 684
SHARE TECHNOLOGIES - FAIRCHILD—Tel-Save Holdings, Inc.; *U.S. Public*, pg. 1568
SOLON SPRINGS TELEPHONE CO.—Century Telephone Enterprises, Inc.; *U.S. Public*, pg. 330
SOUTHWEST TELEPHONE SYSTEMS, INC.—Inter-Tel, Incorporated; *U.S. Public*, pg. 888
SOUTHWESTERN BELL TELEPHONE CO.—SBC Communications Inc.; *U.S. Public*, pg. 1416
SPRINT CORPORATION; *U.S. Public*, pg. 1500
SPRINT PARANET—Sprint Corporation; *U.S. Public*, pg. 1501
STARTEC GLOBAL COMMUNICATIONS CORPORATION; *U.S. Public*, pg. 1511
TCI/US WEST—TCI Communications, Inc.; *U.S. Public*, pg. 1555
TECHNOLOGY SERVICES—Sprint Corporation; *U.S. Public*, pg. 1501
TELEBEC LTEE—BCE Inc.; *Int'l*, pg. 116
TELEBRAS S.A.; *Int'l*, pg. 1362
TELEFONICA DE ESPANA, S.A.; *Int'l*, pg. 1371
TELEFONOS DE MEXICO S.A. DE C.V.; *Int'l*, pg. 1373
TELEGLOBE CANADA INC.—Teleglobe, Inc.; *Int'l*, pg. 1373
TELENORDIA A.B.—British Telecommunications plc; *Int'l*, pg. 223
TELEPHONE AND DATA SYSTEMS, INC.; *U.S. Public*, pg. 1570
TELEPHONE UTILITIES OF ALASKA, INC.—PacifiCorp; *U.S. Public*, pg. 1252
TELEPHONE UTILITIES OF EASTERN OREGON, INC.—PacifiCorp; *U.S. Public*, pg. 1252
TELEPHONE UTILITIES OF OREGON, INC.—PacifiCorp; *U.S. Public*, pg. 1252
TELEPHONE UTILITIES OF WASHINGTON, INC.—PacifiCorp; *U.S. Public*, pg. 1252
TELUS CORPORATION; *Int'l*, pg. 1374
TELUS MARKETING COMMUNICATIONS—Telus Corporation; *Int'l*, pg. 1374
TELUS MOBILITY—Telus Corporation; *Int'l*, pg. 1374
TETRAGENICS, INC.—Montana Power Company; *U.S. Public*, pg. 1127
TRI TOUCH AMERICA—Montana Power Company; *U.S. Public*, pg. 1127
TURKKABLO A.O.—Oy Nokia Ab/Nokia Group; *Int'l*, pg. 954
USLD COMMUNICATIONS CORP.—LCI International, Inc.; *U.S. Public*, pg. 969
U S WEST BUSINESS RESOURCES—U S West Inc.; *U.S. Public*, pg. 1689
U S WEST INC.; *U.S. Public*, pg. 1688
VESSEL MANAGEMENT SYSTEMS COMPANY—CSX Corporation; *U.S. Public*, pg. 284
VIAG INTERKOM GMBH & CO.—British Telecommunications plc; *Int'l*, pg. 223
VIDAR, INC.; *U.S. Private*, pg. 1139
VOLT DELTA RESOURCES, INC.—Volt Information Sciences, Inc.; *U.S. Public*, pg. 1724
VOLT INFORMATION SCIENCES, INC.; *U.S. Public*, pg. 1724
WATERWAY COMMUNICATIONS INC.—CSX Corporation; *U.S. Public*, pg. 284
WESTERN NEW MEXICO TELEPHONE CO.—Lynch Corporation; *U.S. Public*, pg. 1022
WHOLESALE SERVICES GROUP—Cable and Wireless plc; *Int'l*, pg. 247
WHOLESALE SERVICES GROUP—Sprint Corporation; *U.S.* Public, pg. 1501
THE WOODBURY TELEPHONE COMPANY—Southern New England Telecommunications Corporation; *U.S. Public*, pg. 1491
WORLDCOM, INC.; *U.S. Public*, pg. 1779

4822 — TELEGRAPH & OTHER MESSAGE COMMUNICATIONS

AT&T ALASCOM—AT&T Corporation; *U.S. Public*, pg. 10
AT&T STRATEGY & NEW SERVICE INNOVATIONS—AT&T Corporation; *U.S. Public*, pg. 11
AUSTRIAN POSTAL & TELEGRAPH ADMINISTRATION; *Int'l*, pg. 101
BCE INC.; *Int'l*, pg. 114
BELL & HOWELL GMBH—Bell & Howell Holdings; *U.S. Public*, pg. 201
BELL & HOWELL LTD., (UK) MAILHANDLING DIV.—Bell & Howell Holdings; *U.S. Public*, pg. 201
BELL CANADA—BCE Inc.; *Int'l*, pg. 115
BRITISH TELECOMMUNICATIONS PLC; *Int'l*, pg. 222
BRUNCOR, INC.; *Int'l*, pg. 230
CABLE AND WIRELESS PLC; *Int'l*, pg. 247
DANKA BUSINESS SYSTEMS—Danka Business Systems PLC; *Int'l*, pg. 379
DEUTSCHE POST AG; *Int'l*, pg. 407
DIGITAL SOUND CORPORATION; *U.S. Public*, pg. 508
FRANCE TELECOM; *Int'l*, pg. 503
GN GREAT NORTHERN TELEGRAPH COMPANY—GN Great Nordic Ltd.; *Int'l*, pg. 536
HONG KONG TELECOM INTERNATIONAL LIMITED—Cable and Wireless plc; *Int'l*, pg. 247
HONG KONG TELECOMMUNICATIONS LIMITED—Cable and Wireless plc; *Int'l*, pg. 247
HONG KONG TELEPHONE COMPANY LTD.—Cable and Wireless plc; *Int'l*, pg. 247
ITT INFORMATION SERVICES, INC.—Starwood Hotels & Resorts; *U.S. Public*, pg. 1512
JETPHONE LIMITED—British Telecommunications plc; *Int'l*, pg. 223
LAGARDERE GROUPE; *Int'l*, pg. 791
MCI COMMUNICATIONS CORP.; *U.S. Public*, pg. 1023
MCI INTERNATIONAL INC.—MCI Communications Corp.; *U.S. Public*, pg. 1024
MAIL BOXES ETC.—U.S. Office Products Company; *U.S. Public*, pg. 1687
MARITIME TELEGRAPH & TELEPHONE COMPANY, LTD.—BCE Inc.; *Int'l*, pg. 116
MINITEL USA—France Telecom; *Int'l*, pg. 504
THE NEW BRUNSWICK TELEPHONE COMPANY, LIMITED (NBTEL)—Bruncor, Inc.; *Int'l*, pg. 230
NIPPON TELEGRAPH AND TELEPHONE CORPORATION; *Int'l*, pg. 940
NORTEL FRANCE S.A.—Lagardere Groupe; *Int'l*, pg. 793
PACIFIC TELECOM, INC.—Century Telephone Enterprises, Inc.; *U.S. Public*, pg. 330
SECURITY GROUP INC.; *U.S. Private*, pg. 981
TELEFONICA DE ESPANA, S.A.; *Int'l*, pg. 1371
TELEGLOBE CANADA INC.—Teleglobe, Inc.; *Int'l*, pg. 1373
TRANSPAC—France Telecom; *Int'l*, pg. 503
U S WEST COMMUNICATIONS GROUP, INC.—U S West Inc.; *U.S. Public*, pg. 1689
WESTERN UNION INTERNATIONAL, INC.—MCI Communications Corp.; *U.S. Public*, pg. 1024

4832 — RADIO BROADCASTING STATIONS

ABC, INC—The Walt Disney Company; *U.S. Public*, pg. 511
ABC RADIO NETWORK, INC.—The Walt Disney Company; *U.S. Public*, pg. 512
AM106/CJAY RADIO—Rogers Communications, Inc.; *Int'l*, pg. 1123
THE ACKERLEY GROUP; *U.S. Public*, pg. 15
AGRINET FARM RADIO NETWORK—Ray Communications, Inc.; *U.S. Private*, pg. 911
THE APOGEE COMPANIES, INC.; *U.S. Private*, pg. 77
AUSTRALIAN RADIO NETWORK—Clear Channel Communications, Inc.; *U.S. Public*, pg. 386
BAY NETWORKS, INC.; *U.S. Public*, pg. 196
BLOOMBERG L.P.; *U.S. Private*, pg. 150
BLUE WATER BROADCASTING LIMITED—Rogers Communications, Inc.; *Int'l*, pg. 1123
BONNEVILLE INTERNATIONAL CORP.—Deseret Management Corporation; *U.S. Private*, pg. 327
BOOTH AMERICAN; *U.S. Private*, pg. 156
CBS—CBS Corporation; *U.S. Public*, pg. 273
CBS BROADCAST GROUP—CBS Corporation; *U.S. Public*, pg. 274
CBS BROADCAST SERVICES LTD.—CBS Corporation; *U.S. Public*, pg. 275
CBS CORPORATION; *U.S. Public*, pg. 273
CBS RADIO—CBS Corporation; *U.S. Public*, pg. 274
CBS RADIO DIV.—CBS Corporation; *U.S. Public*, pg. 274
CFAN-AM—Rogers Communications, Inc.; *Int'l*, pg. 1123
CFCO RADIO-AM—Rogers Communications, Inc.; *Int'l*, pg. 1123
CFCY-AM/CHLQ-FM—Rogers Communications, Inc.; *Int'l*, pg. 1124
CFNY-FM RADIO—Rogers Communications, Inc.; *Int'l*, pg. 1124
CHNS/CHFX RADIO—Maritime Broadcasting System Ltd.; *Int'l*, pg. 842
CHYM/CKGL RADIO—Rogers Communications, Inc.; *Int'l*, pg. 1124
CHYR RADIO-AM—Rogers Communications, Inc.; *Int'l*, pg. 1124
CIOK-FM RADIO—Rogers Communications, Inc.; *Int'l*, pg. 1124
CJCW-AM—Rogers Communications, Inc.; *Int'l*, pg. 1124
CKCW-AM/CFQM-FM—Rogers Communications, Inc.; *Int'l*, pg. 1124
CKDH RADIO-AM—Rogers Communications, Inc.; *Int'l*, pg. 1124
CKNB-AM—Rogers Communications, Inc.; *Int'l*, pg. 1124
CKNG-FM/CHED-AM RADIO—Rogers Communications, Inc.; *Int'l*, pg. 1124
CKTY/CFGX—Rogers Communications, Inc.; *Int'l*, pg. 1123
CKYC-AM RADIO—Rogers Communications, Inc.; *Int'l*, pg. 1124
CLT-UFA—Groupe Bruxelles Lambert S.A.; *Int'l*, pg. 561
CNBC—General Electric Company; *U.S. Public*, pg. 712
CSC, HALIFAX—WIC Western International Communications Ltd.; *Int'l*, pg. 1482
CSC, OTTAWA—WIC Western International Communications Ltd.; *Int'l*, pg. 1482
CSC, SASKATOON—WIC Western International Communications Ltd.; *Int'l*, pg. 1482
CSC, VANCOUVER—WIC Western International Communications Ltd.; *Int'l*, pg. 1482
CABLE AND WIRELESS PLC; *Int'l*, pg. 247
CANADIAN SATELLITE COMMUNICATIONS INC.—WIC Western International Communications Ltd.; *Int'l*, pg. 1481
CANCOM—WIC Western International Communications Ltd.; *Int'l*, pg. 1482
CAPITAL CITIES/ABC BROADCAST GROUP—The Walt Disney Company; *U.S. Public*, pg. 511
CAPITAL CITIES/ABC OWNED RADIO STATIONS—The Walt Disney Company; *U.S. Public*, pg. 512
CAPITAL CITIES/ABC RADIO—The Walt Disney Company; *U.S. Public*, pg. 512
CAPITOL BROADCASTING CO., INC.; *U.S. Private*, pg. 206
CHANCELLOR MEDIA CORPORATION; *U.S. Public*, pg. 335
CHANCELLOR RADIO BROADCASTING CO.—Chancellor Media Corporation; *U.S. Public*, pg. 335
CITADEL BROADCASTING CO.—Citadel Communications Corporation; *U.S. Private*, pg. 241
CITADEL COMMUNICATIONS CORPORATION; *U.S. Private*, pg. 241
CLEAR CHANNEL COMMUNICATIONS, INC.; *U.S. Public*, pg. 383
COX ENTERPRISES, INC.; *U.S. Private*, pg. 281
CURTIS MEDIA GROUP; *U.S. Private*, pg. 297
DATA GENERAL CORP. TRAVEL—Data General Corporation; *U.S. Public*, pg. 485
DUCHOSSOIS COMMUNICATIONS, INC.—Duchossois Industries, Inc.; *U.S. Private*, pg. 344
ENTERTAINMENT COMMUNICATIONS; *U.S. Private*, pg. 378
FISHER BROADCASTING INC.—Fisher Companies Inc.; *U.S. Public*, pg. 648
FORUM COMMUNICATIONS COMPANY; *U.S. Private*, pg. 420
FREEDOM COMMUNICATION INC.; *U.S. Private*, pg. 425
GACC HOLDING COMPANY—American Financial Group; *U.S. Public*, pg. 75
GCI BOSTON, INC.—Granum Communications; *U.S. Private*, pg. 470
GANNETT COMPANY, INC.; *U.S. Public*, pg. 698
GAYLORD BROADCASTING CO.—Gaylord Entertainment Co.; *U.S. Public*, pg. 704
GOLDEN WEST BASEBALL CLUB—Golden West Broadcasters; *U.S. Private*, pg. 461
GOLDEN WEST BROADCASTERS; *U.S. Private*, pg. 461
GRANUM COMMUNICATIONS; *U.S. Private*, pg. 470
GUARANTY CORPORATION; *U.S. Private*, pg. 485
HARRIS ENTERPRISES INC.; *U.S. Private*, pg. 505
HEARST-ARGYLE TELEVISION INCORPORATED—The Hearst Corporation; *U.S. Private*, pg. 516
THE HEARST CORPORATION; *U.S. Private*, pg. 515
HUBBARD BROADCASTING, INC.; *U.S. Private*, pg. 543
JACOR COMMUNICATIONS, INC.; *U.S. Public*, pg. 922
JEFFERSON-PILOT COMMUNICATIONS—Jefferson-Pilot Corporation; *U.S. Public*, pg. 925
JEFFERSON-PILOT CORPORATION; *U.S. Public*, pg. 925
JOHNSON PUBLISHING COMPANY, INC.; *U.S. Private*, pg. 591
JOURNAL BROADCAST GROUP, INC.—Journal Communications Inc.; *U.S. Private*, pg. 601
JOURNAL COMMUNICATIONS INC.; *U.S. Private*, pg. 601
KABC-AM RADIO, INC.—The Walt Disney Company; *U.S. Public*, pg. 512
KAJA-FM—Clear Channel Communications, Inc.; *U.S. Public*, pg. 384
KAKC-AM—Clear Channel Communications, Inc.; *U.S. Public*, pg. 384
KBXX-FM—Clear Channel Communications, Inc.; *U.S. Public*, pg. 384
KDDK-FM—Clear Channel Communications, Inc.; *U.S. Public*, pg. 384
KDKA-RADIO & KDKA-TV—CBS Corporation; *U.S. Public*, pg. 275
KEBC-AM—Clear Channel Communications, Inc.; *U.S. Public*, pg. 384
KEYI-FM—Clear Channel Communications, Inc.; *U.S. Public*, pg. 384
KFBK (AM) & KAER (FM) RADIO—Chancellor Media Corporation; *U.S. Public*, pg. 335
KFI, INC.—Cox Enterprises, Inc.; *U.S. Private*, pg. 282
KFON-AM—Clear Channel Communications, Inc.; *U.S. Public*, pg. 384
KFWB RADIO—CBS Corporation; *U.S. Public*, pg. 274
KFXX/KGON, INC.—Entertainment Communications; *U.S. Private*, pg. 378
KGO-AM RADIO, INC.—The Walt Disney Company; *U.S. Public*, pg. 512
KHEY-AM/FM—Clear Channel Communications, Inc.; *U.S. Public*, pg. 384
KHFI-FM—Clear Channel Communications, Inc.; *U.S. Public*, pg. 384
KHKS-FM—Chancellor Media Corporation; *U.S. Public*, pg. 335
KIKK AM/FM—CBS Corporation; *U.S. Public*, pg. 274
KILT AM/FM RADIO—CBS Corporation; *U.S. Public*, pg. 274
KIMN AM & KYGO FM—Jefferson-Pilot Corporation; *U.S. Public*, pg. 926
KJOJ-AM/FM—Clear Channel Communications, Inc.; *U.S. Public*, pg. 384
KJR-FM—New Century Media; *U.S. Private*, pg. 792
KJRH—The E.W. Scripps Company; *U.S. Public*, pg. 1448
KJYO-FM—Clear Channel Communications, Inc.; *U.S. Public*, pg. 384
KKBQ-AM-FM—Chancellor Media Corporation; *U.S. Public*, pg. 335
KKHK—Tribune Company; *U.S. Public*, pg. 1636
KKLT-FM—Pulitzer Publishing Company; *U.S. Public*, pg. 1344
KKND—Clear Channel Communications, Inc.; *U.S. Public*, pg. 384
KLOS-FM RADIO, INC.—The Walt Disney Company; *U.S. Public*, pg. 512
KMJQ-FM—Clear Channel Communications, Inc.; *U.S. Public*, pg. 384
KMOD-FM—Clear Channel Communications, Inc.; *U.S. Public*, pg. 384
KMVP-AM—Pulitzer Publishing Company; *U.S. Public*, pg. 1344
KNRX-FM—Clear Channel Communications, Inc.; *U.S. Public*, pg. 384
KOA-AM—Jacor Communications, Inc.; *U.S. Public*, pg. 922
KOAS-FM—Clear Channel Communications, Inc.; *U.S. Public*, pg. 384
KPEZ-FM—Clear Channel Communications, Inc.; *U.S. Public*, pg. 384
KPRC-AM—Clear Channel Communications, Inc.; *U.S. Public*, pg. 384
KPRR-FM—Clear Channel Communications, Inc.; *U.S. Public*, pg. 384
KQLL-AM/FM—Clear Channel Communications, Inc.; *U.S. Public*, pg. 384
KQRS, INC.—The Walt Disney Company; *U.S. Public*, pg. 512
KQXT RADIO—Clear Channel Communications, Inc.; *U.S. Public*, pg. 384
KRFX-FM—Jacor Communications, Inc.; *U.S. Public*, pg. 922
KSEV-AM—Clear Channel Communications, Inc.; *U.S. Public*, pg. 384
KSHB-TV—The E.W. Scripps Company; *U.S. Public*, pg. 1448
KSL RADIO—Deseret Management Corporation; *U.S. Private*, pg. 327
KSON AM & FM—Jefferson-Pilot Corporation; *U.S. Public*, pg. 926
KSTP-AM, INC.—Hubbard Broadcasting, Inc.; *U.S. Private*, pg. 544
KSTP-FM, INC.—Hubbard Broadcasting, Inc.; *U.S. Private*, pg. 544
KTAR-AM—Pulitzer Publishing Company; *U.S. Public*, pg. 1344
KTKR-AM—Clear Channel Communications, Inc.; *U.S. Public*, pg. 384
KTOK-AM—Clear Channel Communications, Inc.; *U.S. Public*, pg. 384
KTST-FM—Clear Channel Communications, Inc.; *U.S. Public*, pg. 384
KXXY-FM—Clear Channel Communications, Inc.; *U.S. Public*, pg. 384
KYW TV—CBS Corporation; *U.S. Public*, pg. 275
KANSAS CITY ROYALS RADIO NETWORK—Shivers Trading & Operating Co.; *U.S. Private*, pg. 995
KANSAS INFORMATION NETWORK—Shivers Trading & Operating Co.; *U.S. Private*, pg. 995
KEY RADIO LIMITED—Rogers Communications, Inc.; *Int'l*, pg. 1124
LANE INDUSTRIES, INC.; *U.S. Private*, pg. 649
MAC AMERICA COMMUNICATIONS, INC.; *U.S. Private*, pg. 685
MARITIME BROADCASTING SYSTEM LTD.; *Int'l*, pg. 842
MELODY RADIO—Hanson PLC; *Int'l*, pg. 593
MEYER BROADCASTING COMPANY; *U.S. Private*, pg. 739
MORRIS NEWSPAPER CORPORATION; *U.S. Private*, pg. 762
MULTIMEDIA RADIO, INC.—Gannett Company, Inc.; *U.S. Public*, pg. 699
NATIONAL AMUSEMENTS, INC.; *U.S. Private*, pg. 775
NEW CENTURY MEDIA; *U.S. Private*, pg. 792
NEW MEXICO BROADCASTING CO.—Lee Enterprises, Incorporated; *U.S. Public*, pg. 984
THE NEW YORK TIMES BROADCASTING SERVICE, INC.—The New York Times Company; *U.S. Public*, pg. 1173
THE NEW YORK TIMES COMPANY; *U.S. Public*, pg. 1173
OKLAHOMA PUBLISHING COMPANY; *U.S. Private*, pg. 813
PARTECH COMMUNICATIONS GROUP, INC.—Tropic Communications Inc.; *U.S. Public*, pg. 1641
PRESS COMMUNICATIONS, LLC; *U.S. Private*, pg. 882
PULITZER PUBLISHING COMPANY; *U.S. Public*, pg. 1343
RADIO FRANCE; *Int'l*, pg. 1083
THE RADIO NETWORK—Clear Channel Communications, Inc.; *U.S. Public*, pg. 386
RADIO ONE INC.; *U.S. Private*, pg. 906
RADIO ONE OF MARYLAND—Radio One Inc.; *U.S. Private*, pg. 906
RADIO STATIONS WFLS FM & WYSK-AM-FM—The Free Lance-Star Publishing Co.; *U.S. Private*, pg. 425
RAY COMMUNICATIONS, INC.; *U.S. Private*, pg. 911
RAY SPORTS NETWORK—Ray Communications, Inc.; *U.S. Private*, pg. 911
READING EAGLE COMPANY; *U.S. Private*, pg. 913
RICH PRODUCTS CORP.; *U.S. Private*, pg. 928
ROGERS CFAC-AM—Rogers Communications, Inc.; *Int'l*, pg. 1123
ROGERS CFGP-AM—Rogers Communications, Inc.; *Int'l*, pg. 1123
ROGERS CFTR-AM—Rogers Communications, Inc.; *Int'l*, pg. 1123
ROGERS CHFI-FM—Rogers Communications, Inc.; *Int'l*, pg. 1123
ROGERS CJVI-AM—Rogers Communications, Inc.; *Int'l*, pg. 1123

ROGERS CKKS-FM—Rogers Communications, Inc.; *Int'l*, pg. 1123
ROGERS CKWX-AM—Rogers Communications, Inc.; *Int'l*, pg. 1123
SFX BROADCASTING INCORPORATED; *U.S. Public*, pg. 1417
SARKES TARZIAN; *U.S. Private*, pg. 966
SCHURZ COMMUNICATIONS, INC.; *U.S. Private*, pg. 973
SCRIPPS HOWARD BROADCASTING CO.—The E.W. Scripps Company; *U.S. Public*, pg. 1448
SUSQUEHANNA RADIO CORP.—The Pfaltzgraff Co.; *U.S. Private*, pg. 860
TELEDIFFUSION DE FRANCE—France Telecom; *Int'l*, pg. 503
TELEMEDIA INC.; *Int'l*, pg. 1373
TELEMUNDO GROUP, INC.; *U.S. Public*, pg. 1570
TRIBUNE BROADCASTING COMPANY—Tribune Company; *U.S. Public*, pg. 1636
TRIBUNE COMPANY; *U.S. Public*, pg. 1635
TRIBUNE DENVER RADIO, INC.—Tribune Company; *U.S. Public*, pg. 1636
UNION GAS LIMITED—Westcoast Energy Inc.; *Int'l*, pg. 1492
UNITED BROADCASTING L.P.; *U.S. Private*, pg. 1121
VIACOM BROADCASTING INC.—National Amusements, Inc.; *U.S. Private*, pg. 778
VIACOM ENTERPRISES CANADA LTD.—National Amusements, Inc.; *U.S. Private*, pg. 779
VIACOM INTERNATIONAL INC.—National Amusements, Inc.; *U.S. Private*, pg. 778
W1310/CKBY RADIO—Rogers Communications, Inc.; *Int'l*, pg. 1124
WABC-AM RADIO, INC.—The Walt Disney Company; *U.S. Public*, pg. 512
WAMZ-FM—Clear Channel Communications, Inc.; *U.S. Public*, pg. 384
WARQ—Clear Channel Communications, Inc.; *U.S. Public*, pg. 384
WAXY (FM)—Jefferson-Pilot Corporation; *U.S. Public*, pg. 925
WBAL-AM—The Hearst Corporation; *U.S. Private*, pg. 516
WBAL DIVISION—The Hearst Corporation; *U.S. Private*, pg. 516
WBAP-KSCS RADIO, INC.—The Walt Disney Company; *U.S. Public*, pg. 512
WBBB—Curtis Media Group; *U.S. Private*, pg. 297
WBCT-FM—Clear Channel Communications, Inc.; *U.S. Public*, pg. 384
WBGG-FM—Clear Channel Communications, Inc.; *U.S. Public*, pg. 384
WBIR, INC.—Gannett Company, Inc.; *U.S. Public*, pg. 702
WBT AM & WBCY FM—Jefferson-Pilot Corporation; *U.S. Public*, pg. 926
WBZ RADIO & WBZ-TV—CBS Corporation; *U.S. Public*, pg. 275
WCKG, INC.—CBS Corporation; *U.S. Public*, pg. 274
WCKT—Clear Channel Communications, Inc.; *U.S. Public*, pg. 384
WCPS—Curtis Media Group; *U.S. Private*, pg. 297
WDEF AM/FM—Media General, Inc.; *U.S. Public*, pg. 1078
WDIA-AM—Clear Channel Communications, Inc.; *U.S. Public*, pg. 384
WEBN-FM—Jacor Communications, Inc.; *U.S. Public*, pg. 922
WEGR—Clear Channel Communications, Inc.; *U.S. Public*, pg. 384
WELI-AM—Clear Channel Communications, Inc.; *U.S. Public*, pg. 384
WENZ-FM—Clear Channel Communications, Inc.; *U.S. Public*, pg. 385
WERE—Clear Channel Communications, Inc.; *U.S. Public*, pg. 385
WFLA-AM—Jacor Communications, Inc.; *U.S. Public*, pg. 922
WFLZ-FM—Jacor Communications, Inc.; *U.S. Public*, pg. 922
WGBR—Curtis Media Group; *U.S. Private*, pg. 297
WGCI-AM/FM—Chancellor Media Corporation; *U.S. Public*, pg. 335
WGN RADIO—Tribune Company; *U.S. Public*, pg. 1636
WGST-AM—Jacor Communications, Inc.; *U.S. Public*, pg. 923
WHAS-AM—Clear Channel Communications, Inc.; *U.S. Public*, pg. 385
WHIO, INC.—Cox Enterprises, Inc.; *U.S. Private*, pg. 282
WHYI-FM—Clear Channel Communications, Inc.; *U.S. Public*, pg. 385
WHYN—Clear Channel Communications, Inc.; *U.S. Public*, pg. 385
WINS RADIO—CBS Corporation; *U.S. Public*, pg. 274
WIOD, INC.—Clear Channel Communications, Inc.; *U.S. Public*, pg. 385
WISN-AM—SFX Broadcasting Incorporated; *U.S. Public*, pg. 1418
WISN DIVISION—The Hearst Corporation; *U.S. Private*, pg. 516
WIYY-FM—The Hearst Corporation; *U.S. Private*, pg. 516
WJCD-FM—Clear Channel Communications, Inc.; *U.S. Public*, pg. 385
WJR-AM—The Walt Disney Company; *U.S. Public*, pg. 512
WKCI-FM—Clear Channel Communications, Inc.; *U.S. Public*, pg. 385
WKHX-AM/WKHX-FM—The Walt Disney Company; *U.S. Public*, pg. 512
WKKV-FM—Clear Channel Communications, Inc.; *U.S. Public*, pg. 385
WKTC—Curtis Media Group; *U.S. Private*, pg. 297
WKY-AM—Clear Channel Communications, Inc.; *U.S. Public*, pg. 385
WLKY-AM—Pulitzer Publishing Company; *U.S. Public*, pg. 1344
WLS-FM RADIO, INC.—The Walt Disney Company; *U.S. Public*, pg. 512
WLS, INC.—The Walt Disney Company; *U.S. Public*, pg. 512
WLTQ-FM—SFX Broadcasting Incorporated; *U.S. Public*, pg. 1418
WLW-AM—Jacor Communications, Inc.; *U.S. Public*, pg. 922
WMAL, INC.—The Walt Disney Company; *U.S. Public*, pg. 512
WMAZ-WAYS RADIO—Gannett Company, Inc.; *U.S. Public*, pg. 699
WMTX-AM—Clear Channel Communications, Inc.; *U.S. Public*, pg. 385
WMTX-FM—Clear Channel Communications, Inc.; *U.S. Public*, pg. 385
WMYK-FM—Clear Channel Communications, Inc.; *U.S. Public*, pg. 385
WMYU-FM—Jacor Communications, Inc.; *U.S. Public*, pg. 923
WNCX—Clear Channel Communications, Inc.; *U.S. Public*, pg. 385
WNOE—Clear Channel Communications, Inc.; *U.S. Public*, pg. 385
WNWS (AM) & WLYF (FM)—Jefferson-Pilot Corporation; *U.S. Public*, pg. 926
WOAI-AM—Clear Channel Communications, Inc.; *U.S. Public*, pg. 385
WODT-AM—Clear Channel Communications, Inc.; *U.S. Public*, pg. 385
WOOD-AM/FM—Clear Channel Communications, Inc.; *U.S. Public*, pg. 385
WOWI-FM—Clear Channel Communications, Inc.; *U.S. Public*, pg. 385
WPCH-FM—Jacor Communications, Inc.; *U.S. Public*, pg. 923
WPCM—Curtis Media Group; *U.S. Private*, pg. 298
WPIX, INC.—Tribune Company; *U.S. Public*, pg. 1636
WPLJ-FM RADIO, INC.—The Walt Disney Company; *U.S. Public*, pg. 512
WPLT-FM—The Walt Disney Company; *U.S. Public*, pg. 512
WPTF—Curtis Media Group; *U.S. Private*, pg. 298
WQDR—Curtis Media Group; *U.S. Private*, pg. 298
WQIK-AM—Jacor Communications, Inc.; *U.S. Public*, pg. 923
WQIK-FM—Jacor Communications, Inc.; *U.S. Public*, pg. 923
WQQK-FM—Clear Channel Communications, Inc.; *U.S. Public*, pg. 385
WQUE-FM—Clear Channel Communications, Inc.; *U.S. Public*, pg. 385
WQXI-WSTR—Jefferson-Pilot Corporation; *U.S. Public*, pg. 926
WQXR/FM, WQEW/AM—The New York Times Company; *U.S. Public*, pg. 1174
WRAW-AM—Clear Channel Communications, Inc.; *U.S. Public*, pg. 385
WRBQ-AM—Clear Channel Communications, Inc.; *U.S. Public*, pg. 385
WRBQ-FM—Clear Channel Communications, Inc.; *U.S. Public*, pg. 385
WREC—Clear Channel Communications, Inc.; *U.S. Public*, pg. 385
WRFY-FM—Clear Channel Communications, Inc.; *U.S. Public*, pg. 385
WRNL-FM—Clear Channel Communications, Inc.; *U.S. Public*, pg. 385
WRQX-FM—The Walt Disney Company; *U.S. Public*, pg. 512
WRVA-AM—Clear Channel Communications, Inc.; *U.S. Public*, pg. 385
WRVQ-FM—Clear Channel Communications, Inc.; *U.S. Public*, pg. 385
WRXL-FM—Clear Channel Communications, Inc.; *U.S. Public*, pg. 385
WRXQ—Clear Channel Communications, Inc.; *U.S. Public*, pg. 385
WSB, INC.—Cox Enterprises, Inc.; *U.S. Private*, pg. 282
WSJS—Clear Channel Communications, Inc.; *U.S. Public*, pg. 385
WSVY-FM—Clear Channel Communications, Inc.; *U.S. Public*, pg. 385
WTAE-AM—SFX Broadcasting Incorporated; *U.S. Public*, pg. 1418
WTAE DIVISION—The Hearst Corporation; *U.S. Private*, pg. 516
WTQR—Clear Channel Communications, Inc.; *U.S. Public*, pg. 385
WTVR-AM/FM—Clear Channel Communications, Inc.; *U.S. Public*, pg. 385
WVTY-FM—SFX Broadcasting Incorporated; *U.S. Public*, pg. 1418
WWBB—Clear Channel Communications, Inc.; *U.S. Public*, pg. 385
WWDM—Clear Channel Communications, Inc.; *U.S. Public*, pg. 385
WWRM, INC.—Cox Enterprises, Inc.; *U.S. Private*, pg. 282
WWRX—Clear Channel Communications, Inc.; *U.S. Public*, pg. 385
WXII-AM—Pulitzer Publishing Company; *U.S. Public*, pg. 1344
WXRA—Clear Channel Communications, Inc.; *U.S. Public*, pg. 385
WXRM—Clear Channel Communications, Inc.; *U.S. Public*, pg. 385
WYLD-AM/FM—Clear Channel Communications, Inc.; *U.S. Public*, pg. 386
WEHCO MEDIA, INC.; *U.S. Private*, pg. 1159

4833 — TELEVISION BROADCASTING STATIONS

ABC, INC—The Walt Disney Company; *U.S. Public*, pg. 511
ABC NEWS & SPORTS—The Walt Disney Company; *U.S. Public*, pg. 511
ABC TELEVISION NETWORK—The Walt Disney Company; *U.S. Public*, pg. 511
ABC TELEVISION NETWORK GROUP—The Walt Disney Company; *U.S. Public*, pg. 511
AT&T WIRELESS SERVICES—AT&T Corporation; *U.S. Public*, pg. 11
AV EUROMEDIA GESELLSCHAFT FUR AUDIOVISION MBH—Georg von Holtzbrinck GmbH; *Int'l*, pg. 1478
AVE GESELLSCHAFT FUR FERNSEHPRODUKTION MBH—Georg von Holtzbrinck GmbH; *Int'l*, pg. 1478
AVE GESELLSCHAFT FUR HORFUNKBETEILIGUNGEN MBH—Georg von Holtzbrinck GmbH; *Int'l*, pg. 1478
THE ACKERLEY GROUP; *U.S. Public*, pg. 15
AFLAC INCORPORATED; *U.S. Public*, pg. 28
ALLBRITTON COMMUNICATIONS COMPANY—Perpetual Corporation; *U.S. Private*, pg. 854
ALLBRITTON JACKSONVILLE, INC—Perpetual Corporation; *U.S. Private*, pg. 854
AMERICAN SAVANNAH BROADCASTING CO.—Raycom Media, Inc.; *U.S. Private*, pg. 912
AMERICA'S STORE—USA Networks, Inc.; *U.S. Public*, pg. 1685
ANIMAL PLANET—Discovery Communications, Inc.; *U.S. Private*, pg. 334
ARIZONA SPORTS PROGRAMMING NETWORK—Cox Communications, Inc.; *U.S. Public*, pg. 455
BBS ONTARIO INCORPORATED—Baton Broadcasting Incorporated; *Int'l*, pg. 171
BBS SASKATCHEWAN INCORPORATED—Baton Broadcasting Incorporated; *Int'l*, pg. 171
BHC COMMUNICATIONS, INC.—Chris-Craft Industries, Inc.; *U.S. Public*, pg. 352
BATON BROADCASTING INCORPORATED; *Int'l*, pg. 170
A.H. BELO CORPORATION; *U.S. Public*, pg. 209
BERTELSMANN AG; *Int'l*, pg. 189
BLACK ENTERTAINMENT TELEVISION HOLDINGS INC.; *U.S. Public*, pg. 235
BLADE COMMUNICATIONS, INC.; *U.S. Private*, pg. 147
BONNEVILLE INTERNATIONAL CORP.—Deseret Management Corporation; *U.S. Private*, pg. 327
BRAVO NETWORK—Cablevision Systems Corporation; *U.S. Public*, pg. 288
BROADCAST OPERATIONS & ENGINEERING—The Walt Disney Company; *U.S. Public*, pg. 511
CBS—CBS Corporation; *U.S. Public*, pg. 273
CBS AFFILIATE RELATIONS DIVISION—CBS Corporation; *U.S. Public*, pg. 274
CBS BROADCAST GROUP—CBS Corporation; *U.S. Public*, pg. 274
CBS BROADCAST SERVICES LTD.—CBS Corporation; *U.S. Public*, pg. 275
CBS CORPORATION; *U.S. Public*, pg. 273
CBS ENTERTAINMENT—CBS Corporation; *U.S. Public*, pg. 274
CBS NEWS—CBS Corporation; *U.S. Public*, pg. 274
CBS SPORTS DIV.—CBS Corporation; *U.S. Public*, pg. 274
CBS TELEVISION NETWORK—CBS Corporation; *U.S. Public*, pg. 274
CBS TELEVISION STATIONS DIV.—CBS Corporation; *U.S. Public*, pg. 275
CFCF INC.; *Int'l*, pg. 240
CFQC-TV—Baton Broadcasting Incorporated; *Int'l*, pg. 171
CFTO-TV—Baton Broadcasting Incorporated; *Int'l*, pg. 171
CHBX/CJIC-TV—Baton Broadcasting Incorporated; *Int'l*, pg. 171
CHRO-TV—Baton Broadcasting Incorporated; *Int'l*, pg. 171
CICI/CKNC-TV—Baton Broadcasting Incorporated; *Int'l*, pg. 171
CJOH-TV—Baton Broadcasting Incorporated; *Int'l*, pg. 171
CKBI/CIPA-TV, PRINCE ALBERT—Baton Broadcasting Incorporated; *Int'l*, pg. 171
CKCK-TV—Baton Broadcasting Incorporated; *Int'l*, pg. 171
CKCO-TV—Electrohome Ltd.; *Int'l*, pg. 438
CKNY/CHNB-TV—Baton Broadcasting Incorporated; *Int'l*, pg. 171
CKOS/CICC TV—Baton Broadcasting Incorporated; *Int'l*, pg. 171
CLT-UFA—Groupe Bruxelles Lambert S.A.; *Int'l*, pg. 561
CLTV NEWS—Tribune Company; *U.S. Public*, pg. 1635
CNBC—General Electric Company; *U.S. Public*, pg. 712
CNN (CABLE NEWS NETWORK)—Time Warner Inc.; *U.S. Public*, pg. 1614
CNN HEADLINE NEWS—Time Warner Inc.; *U.S. Public*, pg. 1614
CNN RADIO—Time Warner Inc.; *U.S. Public*, pg. 1614
CSC, HALIFAX—WIC Western International Communications Ltd.; *Int'l*, pg. 1482
CSC, OTTAWA—WIC Western International Communications Ltd.; *Int'l*, pg. 1482
CSC, SASKATOON—WIC Western International Communications Ltd.; *Int'l*, pg. 1482
CSC, VANCOUVER—WIC Western International Communications Ltd.; *Int'l*, pg. 1482
CANADIAN SATELLITE COMMUNICATIONS INC.—WIC Western International Communications Ltd.; *Int'l*, pg. 1481
CANCOM—WIC Western International Communications Ltd.; *Int'l*, pg. 1482
CAPITAL CITIES/ABC BROADCAST GROUP—The Walt Disney Company; *U.S. Public*, pg. 511
CAPITAL CITIES/ABC OWNED TELEVISION STATIONS—The Walt Disney Company; *U.S. Public*, pg. 512
CAPITOL BROADCASTING CO., INC.; *U.S. Private*, pg. 206
THE CARTOON NETWORK—Time Warner Inc.; *U.S. Public*, pg. 1614
CHANNEL 1—Lagardere Groupe; *Int'l*, pg. 792
CHANNEL ONE COMMUNICATIONS—Primedia Inc.; *U.S. Public*, pg. 1328
CHARLESTON TELEVISION, INC.—Media General, Inc.; *U.S. Public*, pg. 1078
CHRIS-CRAFT INDUSTRIES, INC.; *U.S. Public*, pg. 351
CITO/CFCL-TV—Baton Broadcasting Incorporated; *Int'l*, pg. 171

CLEAR CHANNEL COMMUNICATIONS, INC.; *U.S. Public*, pg. 383
CLEAR CHANNEL TELEVISION, INC.—Clear Channel Communications, Inc.; *U.S. Public*, pg. 383
COMCAST CABLE COMMUNICATIONS, INC.—Comcast Corporation; *U.S. Public*, pg. 407
COMCAST CORPORATION; *U.S. Public*, pg. 406
CORONET COMMUNICATIONS—Lynch Corporation; *U.S. Public*, pg. 1021
COSMOS BROADCASTING CORP.—Liberty Corporation; *U.S. Public*, pg. 992
COX ENTERPRISES, INC.; *U.S. Private*, pg. 281
DISCOVERY COMMUNICATIONS, INC.; *U.S. Private*, pg. 334
DIVERSIFIED COMMUNICATIONS; *U.S. Private*, pg. 336
DUCHOSSOIS COMMUNICATIONS, INC.—Duchossois Industries, Inc.; *U.S. Private*, pg. 344
ELECTROHOME LTD.; *Int'l*, pg. 438
F & F PRODUCTIONS, INC.—Hubbard Broadcasting, Inc.; *U.S. Private*, pg. 544
FISHER BROADCASTING INC.—Fisher Companies Inc.; *U.S. Public*, pg. 648
FISHER COMPANIES INC.; *U.S. Public*, pg. 647
FORUM COMMUNICATIONS COMPANY; *U.S. Private*, pg. 420
FOX NET—The News Corporation Limited; *Int'l*, pg. 926
FOX TELEVISION STATIONS INC.—The News Corporation Limited; *Int'l*, pg. 926
FREEDOM COMMUNICATION INC.; *U.S. Private*, pg. 425
GACC HOLDING COMPANY—American Financial Group; *U.S. Public*, pg. 75
GALAVISION—Chartwell Partners; *U.S. Private*, pg. 230
GANNETT COMPANY, INC.; *U.S. Public*, pg. 698
GUY GANNETT COMMUNICATIONS; *U.S. Private*, pg. 439
GATEWAY COMMUNICATIONS—Macromedia Incorporated; *U.S. Private*, pg. 693
GAYLORD BROADCASTING CO.—Gaylord Entertainment Co.; *U.S. Public*, pg. 704
GAYLORD ENTERTAINMENT CO.; *U.S. Public*, pg. 704
GENERAL ELECTRIC COMPANY; *U.S. Public*, pg. 709
GEORGIA TELEVISION COMPANY—Cox Enterprises, Inc.; *U.S. Private*, pg. 282
GRANITE BROADCASTING CORPORATION; *U.S. Public*, pg. 759
GRAY COMMUNICATIONS SYSTEMS, INC.; *U.S. Public*, pg. 759
HARRISBURG TELEVISION, INC—Perpetual Corporation; *U.S. Private*, pg. 854
HARTE-HANKS COMMUNICATIONS, INC.; *U.S. Public*, pg. 793
HARTE-HANKS TELEVISION, INC. (KENS-TV)—Harte-Hanks Communications, Inc.; *U.S. Public*, pg. 794
HEARST-ARGYLE TELEVISION INCORPORATED—The Hearst Corporation; *U.S. Private*, pg. 516
THE HEARST CORPORATION; *U.S. Private*, pg. 515
THE HISTORY CHANNEL—The Walt Disney Company; *U.S. Public*, pg. 512
IDAHO INDEPENDENT TELEVISION, INC.—Blade Communications, Inc.; *U.S. Private*, pg. 147
INDEPENDENCE TELEVISION CO.—Blade Communications, Inc.; *U.S. Private*, pg. 147
INDIANA BROADCASTING CO. (WANE)—AT&T Corporation; *U.S. Public*, pg. 11
INDIANA BROADCASTING CO. (WISH)—AT&T Corporation; *U.S. Public*, pg. 11
JEFFERSON-PILOT COMMUNICATIONS CO. OF VIRGINIA—Jefferson-Pilot Corporation; *U.S. Public*, pg. 926
JEFFERSON-PILOT CORPORATION; *U.S. Public*, pg. 925
JOHNSON PUBLISHING COMPANY, INC.; *U.S. Private*, pg. 591
JOURNAL BROADCAST GROUP, INC.—Journal Communications Inc.; *U.S. Private*, pg. 601
JOURNAL COMMUNICATIONS INC.; *U.S. Private*, pg. 601
KABC-TV—The Walt Disney Company; *U.S. Public*, pg. 512
KAIT-TV—Liberty Corporation; *U.S. Public*, pg. 992
KARE-TV—Gannett Company, Inc.; *U.S. Public*, pg. 702
KBAK-TV—Westwind Communications; *U.S. Private*, pg. 1170
KBHK TELEVISION, INC.—Chris-Craft Industries, Inc.; *U.S. Public*, pg. 352
KBIM-TV—Lee Enterprises, Incorporated; *U.S. Public*, pg. 984
KCBA-TV—The Ackerley Group; *U.S. Public*, pg. 16
KCBS-TV—CBS Corporation; *U.S. Public*, pg. 275
KCCI TELEVISION, INC.—Pulitzer Publishing Company; *U.S. Public*, pg. 1343
KCOP TELEVISION, INC.—Chris-Craft Industries, Inc.; *U.S. Public*, pg. 352
KCTV—Meredith Corporation; *U.S. Public*, pg. 1094
KDAF—The News Corporation Limited; *Int'l*, pg. 926
KDAF (WB)—Tribune Company; *U.S. Public*, pg. 1636
KDKA-RADIO & KDKA-TV—CBS Corporation; *U.S. Public*, pg. 275
KERO-TV—The McGraw-Hill Companies; *U.S. Public*, pg. 1070
KETV—Pulitzer Publishing Company; *U.S. Public*, pg. 1343
KFSM-TV—The New York Times Company; *U.S. Public*, pg. 1174
KFSN-TV—The Walt Disney Company; *U.S. Public*, pg. 512
KGAN-TV—Guy Gannett Communications; *U.S. Private*, pg. 439
KGET-TV—The Ackerley Group; *U.S. Public*, pg. 16
KGMB-TV—Lee Enterprises, Incorporated; *U.S. Public*, pg. 983
KGO TELEVISION, INC.—The Walt Disney Company; *U.S. Public*, pg. 512
KGTV—The McGraw-Hill Companies; *U.S. Public*, pg. 1070
KGUN-TV—Lee Enterprises, Incorporated; *U.S. Public*, pg. 983
KHON-TV—USA Networks, Inc.; *U.S. Public*, pg. 1685
KHOU-TV INC.—A.H. Belo Corporation; *U.S. Public*, pg. 209
KJRH—The E.W. Scripps Company; *U.S. Public*, pg. 1448
KKTV-TV—The Ackerley Group; *U.S. Public*, pg. 16
KLAS, INC.—Landmark Communications, Inc.; *U.S. Private*, pg. 647
KLRT-TV—Clear Channel Communications, Inc.; *U.S. Public*, pg. 384
KMBC DIVISION—The Hearst Corporation; *U.S. Private*, pg. 516
KMBC-TV—The Hearst Corporation; *U.S. Private*, pg. 516
KMGH-TV—The McGraw-Hill Companies; *U.S. Public*, pg. 1070
KMOL TELEVISION, INC.—Chris-Craft Industries, Inc.; *U.S. Public*, pg. 352
KMSP TELEVISION, INC.—Chris-Craft Industries, Inc.; *U.S. Public*, pg. 352
KMTV-3—Lee Enterprises, Incorporated; *U.S. Public*, pg. 983
KNXV-TV—The E.W. Scripps Company; *U.S. Public*, pg. 1448
KOAT-TV—Pulitzer Publishing Company; *U.S. Public*, pg. 1344
KOB-TV, INC.—Hubbard Broadcasting, Inc.; *U.S. Private*, pg. 544
KOIN-TV—Lee Enterprises, Incorporated; *U.S. Public*, pg. 983
KOKI-TV—Clear Channel Communications, Inc.; *U.S. Public*, pg. 384
KOLD-TV—Raycom Media, Inc.; *U.S. Private*, pg. 912
KOTV INC.—A.H. Belo Corporation; *U.S. Public*, pg. 209
KPHO-TV—Meredith Corporation; *U.S. Public*, pg. 1094
KPIX-TV—CBS Corporation; *U.S. Public*, pg. 275
KPLC-TV—Liberty Corporation; *U.S. Public*, pg. 992
KPNX-TV—Gannett Company, Inc.; *U.S. Public*, pg. 702
KPTV TELEVISION, INC.—Chris-Craft Industries, Inc.; *U.S. Public*, pg. 352
KRIV—The News Corporation Limited; *Int'l*, pg. 926
KRQE-TV—Lee Enterprises, Incorporated; *U.S. Public*, pg. 984
KSAS-TV—Clear Channel Communications, Inc.; *U.S. Public*, pg. 384
KSAX-TV—Hubbard Broadcasting, Inc.; *U.S. Private*, pg. 544
KSBW, INC.—FTSB Broadcasting; *U.S. Private*, pg. 389
KSDK, INC.—Gannett Company, Inc.; *U.S. Public*, pg. 702
KSFY-TV—Raycom Media, Inc.; *U.S. Private*, pg. 912
KSHB-TV—The E.W. Scripps Company; *U.S. Public*, pg. 1448
KSL-TV—Deseret Management Corporation; *U.S. Private*, pg. 327
KSNC—Lee Enterprises, Incorporated; *U.S. Public*, pg. 984
KSNK—Lee Enterprises, Incorporated; *U.S. Public*, pg. 984
KSNT-TV—Lee Enterprises, Incorporated; *U.S. Public*, pg. 983
KSNW-TV—Lee Enterprises, Incorporated; *U.S. Public*, pg. 983
KSTP-TV—Hubbard Broadcasting, Inc.; *U.S. Private*, pg. 544
KTLA, INC.—Tribune Company; *U.S. Public*, pg. 1636
KTRK TELEVISION, INC.—The Walt Disney Company; *U.S. Public*, pg. 512
KTTU-TV—Clear Channel Communications, Inc.; *U.S. Public*, pg. 384
KTTV—The News Corporation Limited; *Int'l*, pg. 926
KTVE, INC., CHANNEL 10—Gray Communications Systems, Inc.; *U.S. Public*, pg. 759
KTVU INC.—Cox Enterprises, Inc.; *U.S. Private*, pg. 282
KTVX TELEVISION, INC.—Chris-Craft Industries, Inc.; *U.S. Public*, pg. 352
KUSA-TV—Gannett Company, Inc.; *U.S. Public*, pg. 702
KUTP TELEVISION, INC.—Chris-Craft Industries, Inc.; *U.S. Public*, pg. 352
KVOS TELEVISION CORP.—The Ackerley Group; *U.S. Public*, pg. 16
KVUE-TV, INC.—Gannett Company, Inc.; *U.S. Public*, pg. 702
KVVU BROADCASTING CORPORATION—Meredith Corporation; *U.S. Public*, pg. 1094
KWGN INC.—Tribune Company; *U.S. Public*, pg. 1636
KWWL-TV—Raycom Media, Inc.; *U.S. Private*, pg. 912
KXAN—AT&T Corporation; *U.S. Public*, pg. 11
KXAS-TV—AT&T Corporation; *U.S. Public*, pg. 11
KXTV INC.—A.H. Belo Corporation; *U.S. Public*, pg. 209
KYW TV—CBS Corporation; *U.S. Public*, pg. 275
KATV, LLC—Perpetual Corporation; *U.S. Private*, pg. 854
KTUL, LLC—Perpetual Corporation; *U.S. Private*, pg. 854
LANDMARK COMMUNICATIONS, INC.; *U.S. Private*, pg. 647
LEE ENTERPRISES, INCORPORATED; *U.S. Public*, pg. 983
LIBERTY CORPORATION; *U.S. Public*, pg. 991
LIMA COMMUNICATIONS CORP.—Blade Communications, Inc.; *U.S. Private*, pg. 147
LIN CENTRAL BROADCASTING CORPORATION (WOTV)—AT&T Corporation; *U.S. Public*, pg. 11
LYNCH CORPORATION; *U.S. Public*, pg. 1021
LYNCH ENTERTAINMENT CORPORATION—Lynch Corporation; *U.S. Public*, pg. 1021
LYNCH ENTERTAINMENT CORPORATION II—Lynch Corporation; *U.S. Public*, pg. 1021
MAC AMERICA COMMUNICATIONS, INC.; *U.S. Private*, pg. 685
MTV FINLAND; *Int'l*, pg. 827
MTV NETWORKS—National Amusements, Inc.; *U.S. Private*, pg. 779
MACROMEDIA INCORPORATED; *U.S. Private*, pg. 693
MADISON SQUARE GARDEN NETWORK—Cablevision Systems Corporation; *U.S. Public*, pg. 288
MANUS PRESSE GMBH—Georg von Holtzbrinck GmbH; *Int'l*, pg. 1478
MCGRAW-HILL BROADCASTING CO., INC.—The McGraw-Hill Companies; *U.S. Public*, pg. 1070
THE MCGRAW-HILL COMPANIES; *U.S. Public*, pg. 1069
MEDIA GENERAL BROADCAST GROUP, INC.—Media General, Inc.; *U.S. Public*, pg. 1078
MEDIA GENERAL BROADCASTING, INC. (WJWB-TV)—Media General, Inc.; *U.S. Public*, pg. 1078
MEDIA GENERAL CABLE OF FAIRFAX COUNTY INC.—Media General, Inc.; *U.S. Public*, pg. 1078
MEDIA GENERAL CABLE OF FREDERICKSBURG, INC.—Media General, Inc.; *U.S. Public*, pg. 1078
MEDIA GENERAL, INC.; *U.S. Public*, pg. 1077
MEREDITH CORPORATION; *U.S. Public*, pg. 1094
MEYER BROADCASTING COMPANY; *U.S. Private*, pg. 739
MIAMI VALLEY BROADCASTING CORPORATION—Cox Enterprises, Inc.; *U.S. Private*, pg. 282
MORRIS NEWSPAPER CORPORATION; *U.S. Private*, pg. 762
MULTIMEDIA CABLEVISION, CO.—Gannett Company, Inc.; *U.S. Public*, pg. 699
NATIONAL AMUSEMENTS, INC.; *U.S. Private*, pg. 775
NATIONAL BROADCASTING CO., INC.—General Electric Company; *U.S. Public*, pg. 712
THE NEW YORK TIMES BROADCASTING SERVICE, INC.—The New York Times Company; *U.S. Public*, pg. 1173
THE NEW YORK TIMES COMPANY; *U.S. Public*, pg. 1173
THE NEW YORK TIMES COMPANY BROADCASTING GROUP—The New York Times Company; *U.S. Public*, pg. 1173
NEWS AMERICA PUBLISHING INC.—The News Corporation Limited; *Int'l*, pg. 925
THE NEWS CORPORATION LIMITED; *Int'l*, pg. 925
NEWS-PRESS & GAZETTE COMPANY; *U.S. Private*, pg. 797
NIHON KEIZAI SHIMBUN, INC.; *Int'l*, pg. 929
NIHON SHORTWAVE BROADCASTING CO., LTD.—Nihon Keizai Shimbun, Inc.; *Int'l*, pg. 929
OFFICE OF COMMUNICATIONS—The Walt Disney Company; *U.S. Public*, pg. 511
OKLAHOMA PUBLISHING COMPANY; *U.S. Private*, pg. 813
OWNED TELEVISION STATIONS—Blair Television; *U.S. Private*, pg. 148
PERPETUAL CORPORATION; *U.S. Private*, pg. 854
POST-NEWSWEEK CABLE DIVISION—The Washington Post Company; *U.S. Public*, pg. 1743
POST-NEWSWEEK STATIONS, CONNECTICUT, INC.—The Washington Post Company; *U.S. Public*, pg. 1743
POST-NEWSWEEK STATIONS, FLORIDA, INC.—The Washington Post Company; *U.S. Public*, pg. 1743
POST-NEWSWEEK STATIONS, MICHIGAN, INC.—The Washington Post Company; *U.S. Public*, pg. 1743
PRICE COMMUNICATIONS CORPORATION; *U.S. Public*, pg. 1324
PROVIDENCE JOURNAL-BULLETIN—A.H. Belo Corporation; *U.S. Public*, pg. 209
PULITZER PUBLISHING COMPANY; *U.S. Public*, pg. 1343
ROGERS COMMUNICATIONS, INC.; *Int'l*, pg. 1122
SF BROADCASTING COMPANIES—USA Networks, Inc.; *U.S. Public*, pg. 1685
SJL OF KANSAS CORP.—Lee Enterprises, Incorporated; *U.S. Public*, pg. 984
SARKES TARZIAN; *U.S. Private*, pg. 966
SCHURZ COMMUNICATIONS, INC.; *U.S. Private*, pg. 973
THE E.W. SCRIPPS COMPANY; *U.S. Public*, pg. 1447
SCRIPPS HOWARD BROADCASTING CO.—The E.W. Scripps Company; *U.S. Public*, pg. 1448
SIOUX VALLEY RURAL TELEVISION—Sioux Valley Southwestern Electric Association; *U.S. Private*, pg. 1004
SKY NETWORK TELEVISION LIMITED—Bell Atlantic Corporation; *U.S. Public*, pg. 204
STANDARD EXAMINER; *U.S. Private*, pg. 1031
SUPERSTATION INC.—Time Warner Inc.; *U.S. Public*, pg. 1615
TSN COMMUNICATIONS; *Int'l*, pg. 1343
TAMPA TELEVISION, INC.—Media General, Inc.; *U.S. Public*, pg. 1078
TARGET—Lee Enterprises, Incorporated; *U.S. Public*, pg. 984
TELEDIFFUSION DE FRANCE—France Telecom; *Int'l*, pg. 503
TELEGLOBE CANADA INC.—Teleglobe, Inc.; *Int'l*, pg. 1373
TELEMUNDO GROUP, INC.; *U.S. Public*, pg. 1570
TELEVISION TOKYO CHANNEL 12 LTD.—Nihon Keizai Shimbun, Inc.; *Int'l*, pg. 929
THAMES TELEVISION LTD.—Pearson plc; *Int'l*, pg. 1026
TOPEKA TELEVISION, CORP.—Lee Enterprises, Incorporated; *U.S. Public*, pg. 984
TRIBUNE BROADCASTING COMPANY—Tribune Company; *U.S. Public*, pg. 1636
TRIBUNE COMPANY; *U.S. Public*, pg. 1635
TRIBUNE REGIONAL PROGRAMMING INC.—Tribune Company; *U.S. Public*, pg. 1636
TURNER BROADCASTING SYSTEM INC.—Time Warner Inc.; *U.S. Public*, pg. 1614
TURNER NETWORK TELEVISION, INC.—Time Warner Inc.; *U.S. Public*, pg. 1615
TURNER PRIVATE NETWORKS—Time Warner Inc.; *U.S. Public*, pg. 1614
TV ALABAMA, INC.—Perpetual Corporation; *U.S. Private*, pg. 854
USA NETWORK CONTROL CENTER—USA Networks, Inc.; *U.S. Public*, pg. 1686
UNIVERSAL BELO PRODUCTIONS—A.H. Belo Corporation; *U.S. Public*, pg. 210
UNIVISION LTD. PARTNERSHIP—Chartwell Partners; *U.S. Private*, pg. 230
VIACOM BROADCASTING INC.—National Amusements, Inc.; *U.S. Private*, pg. 778
VIACOM ENTERPRISES CANADA LTD.—National Amusements, Inc.; *U.S. Private*, pg. 779
VIACOM INTERNATIONAL INC.—National Amusements, Inc.; *U.S. Private*, pg. 778
WABC T.V.—The Walt Disney Company; *U.S. Public*, pg. 512
WALA-TV—USA Networks, Inc.; *U.S. Public*, pg. 1685

WALB-TV, INC., CHANNEL 10—Gray Communications Systems, Inc.; *U.S. Public*, pg. 759
WAND TELEVISION, INC.—AT&T Corporation; *U.S. Public*, pg. 11
WAVE-TV—Liberty Corporation; *U.S. Public*, pg. 992
WAVY-TELEVISION, INC.—AT&T Corporation; *U.S. Public*, pg. 11
WAWS-TV—Clear Channel Communications, Inc.; *U.S. Public*, pg. 384
WBAL DIVISION—The Hearst Corporation; *U.S. Private*, pg. 516
WBAL-TV—The Hearst Corporation; *U.S. Private*, pg. 516
WBBM-TV—CBS Corporation; *U.S. Public*, pg. 275
WBIR, INC.—Gannett Company, Inc.; *U.S. Public*, pg. 702
WBMG-TV—Media General, Inc.; *U.S. Public*, pg. 1078
WBTV/WBT-AM & FM—Jefferson-Pilot Corporation; *U.S. Public*, pg. 926
WBZ RADIO & WBZ-TV—CBS Corporation; *U.S. Public*, pg. 275
WCAU-TV—General Electric Company; *U.S. Public*, pg. 712
WCBS-TV—CBS Corporation; *U.S. Public*, pg. 275
WCIV, LLC—Perpetual Corporation; *U.S. Private*, pg. 854
WCPO-TV—The E.W. Scripps Company; *U.S. Public*, pg. 1448
WCVB DIVISION—The Hearst Corporation; *U.S. Private*, pg. 516
WCVB-TV—The Hearst Corporation; *U.S. Private*, pg. 516
WDEF-TV—Media General, Inc.; *U.S. Public*, pg. 1078
WDIO-TV—Hubbard Broadcasting, Inc.; *U.S. Private*, pg. 544
WDIV-TV—The Washington Post Company; *U.S. Public*, pg. 1743
WDSU TELEVISION, INC.—Pulitzer Publishing Company; *U.S. Public*, pg. 1344
WDTN-TV—The Hearst Corporation; *U.S. Private*, pg. 516
WEWS-TV—The E.W. Scripps Company; *U.S. Public*, pg. 1448
WEYI, INC.—FTSB Broadcasting; *U.S. Private*, pg. 389
WFAA-TV—A.H. Belo Corporation; *U.S. Public*, pg. 209
WFIE-TV—Liberty Corporation; *U.S. Public*, pg. 992
WFLD INC.—The News Corporation Limited; *Int'l*, pg. 926
WFMY-TV—Gannett Company, Inc.; *U.S. Public*, pg. 702
WFOR-TV CHANNEL 4—CBS Corporation; *U.S. Public*, pg. 275
WFSB-TV—The Washington Post Company; *U.S. Public*, pg. 1743
WFTS-TV—The E.W. Scripps Company; *U.S. Public*, pg. 1448
WFTV, INC.—Cox Enterprises, Inc.; *U.S. Private*, pg. 282
WFXT-TV—The News Corporation Limited; *Int'l*, pg. 926
WGAL-TV—Pulitzer Publishing Company; *U.S. Public*, pg. 1344
WGGB-TV—Guy Gannett Communications; *U.S. Private*, pg. 439
WGME-TV—Guy Gannett Communications; *U.S. Private*, pg. 439
WGN-TV—Tribune Company; *U.S. Public*, pg. 1636
WGNO INC.—Tribune Company; *U.S. Public*, pg. 1636
WGNX, INC.—Tribune Company; *U.S. Public*, pg. 1636
WHBF—Lynch Corporation; *U.S. Public*, pg. 1021
WHLT—Media General, Inc.; *U.S. Public*, pg. 1078
WHNT-TV—The New York Times Company; *U.S. Public*, pg. 1174
WHP-TV—Clear Channel Communications, Inc.; *U.S. Public*, pg. 385
WICS-TV—Guy Gannett Communications; *U.S. Private*, pg. 439
WIS-TV—Liberty Corporation; *U.S. Public*, pg. 992
WISN-AM—SFX Broadcasting Incorporated; *U.S. Public*, pg. 1418
WISN DIVISION—The Hearst Corporation; *U.S. Private*, pg. 516
WISN-TV—The Hearst Corporation; *U.S. Private*, pg. 516
WIXT-TV—The Ackerley Group; *U.S. Public*, pg. 16
WJHG-TV, INC., CHANNEL 7—Gray Communications Systems, Inc.; *U.S. Public*, pg. 759
WJHL-TV—Media General, Inc.; *U.S. Public*, pg. 1078
WJLA-TV—Perpetual Corporation; *U.S. Private*, pg. 854
WJRT-TV—Lee Enterprises, Incorporated; *U.S. Public*, pg. 984
WJTV—Media General, Inc.; *U.S. Public*, pg. 1078
WJXT-TV—The Washington Post Company; *U.S. Public*, pg. 1743
WJZ-TV—CBS Corporation; *U.S. Public*, pg. 275
WKYC-TV—Gannett Company, Inc.; *U.S. Public*, pg. 702
WKYT-TV—Gray Communications Systems, Inc.; *U.S. Public*, pg. 759
WLFI-TV—Blade Communications, Inc.; *U.S. Private*, pg. 148
WLKY-TV—Pulitzer Publishing Company; *U.S. Public*, pg. 1344
WLS TELEVISION, INC.—The Walt Disney Company; *U.S. Public*, pg. 512
WLUK-TV—USA Networks, Inc.; *U.S. Public*, pg. 1685
WLVI-TV—Tribune Company; *U.S. Public*, pg. 1636
WMAR-TV—The E.W. Scripps Company; *U.S. Public*, pg. 1448
WNCT-TV—Media General, Inc.; *U.S. Public*, pg. 1078
WNEM-TV—Meredith Corporation; *U.S. Public*, pg. 1094
WNEP-TV—The New York Times Company; *U.S. Public*, pg. 1174
WNYW—The News Corporation Limited; *Int'l*, pg. 926
WOFL-TV—Meredith Corporation; *U.S. Public*, pg. 1094
WPHL-TV, INC.—Tribune Company; *U.S. Public*, pg. 1636
WPIX, INC.—Tribune Company; *U.S. Public*, pg. 1636
WPLG-TV—The Washington Post Company; *U.S. Public*, pg. 1743
WPMI-TV—Clear Channel Communications, Inc.; *U.S. Public*, pg. 385
WPRI-TV—Clear Channel Communications, Inc.; *U.S. Public*, pg. 385
WPTV—The E.W. Scripps Company; *U.S. Public*, pg. 1448
WPTY-TV—Clear Channel Communications, Inc.; *U.S. Public*, pg. 385
WPVI-TV—The Walt Disney Company; *U.S. Public*, pg. 512
WPXI INC.—Cox Enterprises, Inc.; *U.S. Private*, pg. 282
WQAD-TV—The New York Times Company; *U.S. Public*, pg. 1174
WREG-TV—The New York Times Company; *U.S. Public*, pg. 1174
WRGB-TV—Freedom Communication Inc.; *U.S. Private*, pg. 425
WROC, INC.—FTSB Broadcasting; *U.S. Private*, pg. 389
WRTV—The McGraw-Hill Companies; *U.S. Public*, pg. 1070
WSAZ-TV—Lee Enterprises, Incorporated; *U.S. Public*, pg. 984
WSET INCORPORATD—Perpetual Corporation; *U.S. Private*, pg. 854
WSFA-TV—Liberty Corporation; *U.S. Public*, pg. 992
WSLS-TV—Media General, Inc.; *U.S. Public*, pg. 1078
WSOC TELEVISION, INC.—Cox Enterprises, Inc.; *U.S. Private*, pg. 282
WSYM-TV—Journal Communications Inc.; *U.S. Private*, pg. 601
WTAE DIVISION—The Hearst Corporation; *U.S. Private*, pg. 516
WTAE-TV—The Hearst Corporation; *U.S. Private*, pg. 516
WTKR-TV—The New York Times Company; *U.S. Public*, pg. 1174
WTOL-TV—Liberty Corporation; *U.S. Public*, pg. 992
WTOV, INC.—FTSB Broadcasting; *U.S. Private*, pg. 390
WTTG—The News Corporation Limited; *Int'l*, pg. 926
WTTW (CHANNEL 11); *U.S. Private*, pg. 1145
WTVD-TV—The Walt Disney Company; *U.S. Public*, pg. 512
WTVF—Landmark Communications, Inc.; *U.S. Private*, pg. 647
WUSA-TV—Gannett Company, Inc.; *U.S. Public*, pg. 702
WUTR-TV—Media General, Inc.; *U.S. Public*, pg. 1078
WVEC-TV, INC.—A.H. Belo Corporation; *U.S. Public*, pg. 209
WVTM-TV, INC.—General Electric Company; *U.S. Public*, pg. 712
WVUE-TV—USA Networks, Inc.; *U.S. Public*, pg. 1685
WXIA-TV—Gannett Company, Inc.; *U.S. Public*, pg. 702
WXII-TV—Pulitzer Publishing Company; *U.S. Public*, pg. 1344
WXXA-TV—Clear Channel Communications, Inc.; *U.S. Public*, pg. 385
WXYZ TV - CHANNEL 7 OF DETROIT, INC.—The E.W. Scripps Company; *U.S. Public*, pg. 1448
WYFF-TV—Pulitzer Publishing Company; *U.S. Public*, pg. 1344
WYMT-TV—Gray Communications Systems, Inc.; *U.S. Public*, pg. 759
THE WASHINGTON POST COMPANY; *U.S. Public*, pg. 1742
WEHCO MEDIA, INC.; *U.S. Private*, pg. 1159
WESTWIND COMMUNICATIONS; *U.S. Private*, pg. 1170
RALPH C. WILSON ENTERPRISES; *U.S. Private*, pg. 1181

4841 — CABLE & OTHER PAY TELEVISION SERVICES

ABC, INC—The Walt Disney Company; *U.S. Public*, pg. 511
ALLEGAN COUNTY CABLEVISION INC.—Cable Michigan, Inc.; *U.S. Public*, pg. 287
AMERICAN TELECASTING, INC.; *U.S. Public*, pg. 93
AMERITECH NEW MEDIA—Ameritech Corporation; *U.S. Public*, pg. 98
ASCOM TELEMATIC AG—Ascom Holding AG; *Int'l*, pg. 86
BCE INC.; *Int'l*, pg. 114
BLACK ENTERTAINMENT TELEVISION HOLDINGS INC.; *U.S. Public*, pg. 235
BLADE COMMUNICATIONS, INC.; *U.S. Private*, pg. 147
CFCF INC.; *Int'l*, pg. 240
CSC, HALIFAX—WIC Western International Communications Ltd.; *Int'l*, pg. 1482
CSC, OTTAWA—WIC Western International Communications Ltd.; *Int'l*, pg. 1482
CSC, SASKATOON—WIC Western International Communications Ltd.; *Int'l*, pg. 1482
CSC, VANCOUVER—WIC Western International Communications Ltd.; *Int'l*, pg. 1482
CABLE MANAGEMENT CORP.—TCI Communications, Inc.; *U.S. Public*, pg. 1555
CABLE SERVICES GROUP—CSG Systems International, Inc.; *U.S. Public*, pg. 283
CABLEVISION—Cablevision Systems Corporation; *U.S. Public*, pg. 288
CABLEVISION SYSTEMS CORPORATION; *U.S. Public*, pg. 288
CANADIAN SATELLITE COMMUNICATIONS INC.—WIC Western International Communications Ltd.; *Int'l*, pg. 1481
CANCOM—WIC Western International Communications Ltd.; *Int'l*, pg. 1482
CAPITOL BROADCASTING CO., INC.; *U.S. Private*, pg. 206
CASCO CABLE TELEVISION INC.—The Pfaltzgraff Co.; *U.S. Private*, pg. 860
CENTURY COMMUNICATIONS CORP.; *U.S. Public*, pg. 329
CHARTER COMMUNICATIONS, INC.; *U.S. Private*, pg. 230
CHATTANOOGA CABLE T.V. COMPANY—The E.W. Scripps Company; *U.S. Public*, pg. 1447
COLDWATER CABLEVISION INC.—Cable Michigan, Inc.; *U.S. Public*, pg. 287
COMCAST CORPORATION; *U.S. Public*, pg. 406
COMMONWEALTH TELEPHONE ENTERPRISES, INC.; *U.S. Public*, pg. 415
COMSAT CORPORATION; *U.S. Public*, pg. 424
CONWAY CORPORATION; *U.S. Private*, pg. 272
COX CABLE UNIVERSITY CITY, INC.—Cox Communications, Inc.; *U.S. Public*, pg. 455
COX COMMUNICATIONS-NEW ORLEANS—Cox Communications, Inc.; *U.S. Public*, pg. 455
COX COMMUNICATIONS-SAN DIEGO—Cox Communications, Inc.; *U.S. Public*, pg. 455
COX ENTERPRISES, INC.; *U.S. Private*, pg. 281
DISCOVERY NETWORKS, INC.—Discovery Communications, Inc.; *U.S. Private*, pg. 334
THE DISNEY CHANNEL—The Walt Disney Company; *U.S. Public*, pg. 513
DIVERSIFIED COMMUNICATIONS; *U.S. Private*, pg. 336
ESPN, INC.—The Walt Disney Company; *U.S. Public*, pg. 512
EAST LANCASHIRE CABLEVISION LIMITED—Rogers Communications, Inc.; *Int'l*, pg. 1123
ERIE COUNTY CABLEVISION—Blade Communications, Inc.; *U.S. Private*, pg. 147
THE FAMILY CHANNEL INC.—WIC Western International Communications Ltd.; *Int'l*, pg. 1482
FOX BROADCASTING COMPANY (FBC)—The News Corporation Limited; *Int'l*, pg. 926
GARDEN STATE CABLE—Comcast Corporation; *U.S. Public*, pg. 407
GAYLORD ENTERTAINMENT CO.; *U.S. Public*, pg. 704
HBO FILM MANAGEMENT, INC.—Time Warner Inc.; *U.S. Public*, pg. 1612
HBO SATELLITES, INC.—Time Warner Inc.; *U.S. Public*, pg. 1612
THE HEARST CORPORATION; *U.S. Private*, pg. 515
HOLLINGER INC.; *Int'l*, pg. 630
HOME & GARDEN TELEVISION—The E.W. Scripps Company; *U.S. Public*, pg. 1447
JONES INTERCABLE, INC.—Jones International, Ltd.; *U.S. Private*, pg. 597
JONES INTERNATIONAL, LTD.; *U.S. Private*, pg. 597
JONES SPACELINK, LTD.—Jones International, Ltd.; *U.S. Private*, pg. 597
LAKE COUNTY CABLEVISION—The E.W. Scripps Company; *U.S. Public*, pg. 1448
LANDMARK COMMUNICATIONS, INC.; *U.S. Private*, pg. 647
LIBERTY MEDIA CORPORATION—TCI Communications, Inc.; *U.S. Public*, pg. 1555
LIFETIME TELEVISION/ABC—The Walt Disney Company; *U.S. Public*, pg. 512
LIFETIME TELEVISION/ABC—The Hearst Corporation; *U.S. Private*, pg. 516
LYONAISE COMMUNICATIONS—Lyonnaise des Eaux S.A.; *Int'l*, pg. 824
LYONNAISE DES EAUX S.A.; *Int'l*, pg. 822
MARCUS CABLE COMPANY, L.P.; *U.S. Private*, pg. 702
MEDIA GENERAL, INC.; *U.S. Public*, pg. 1077
MEDIAONE—U S West Inc.; *U.S. Public*, pg. 1688
MICHIGAN CA-TV COMPANY—Cable Michigan, Inc.; *U.S. Public*, pg. 287
NATIONAL AMUSEMENTS, INC.; *U.S. Private*, pg. 775
NATIONAL BROADCASTING CO., INC.—General Electric Company; *U.S. Public*, pg. 712
NICKELODEON/NICK AT NITE—National Amusements, Inc.; *U.S. Private*, pg. 779
NORTH DEKALB CABLE T.V. COMPANY—The E.W. Scripps Company; *U.S. Public*, pg. 1448
NYNEX NETWORK SYSTEMS COMPANY—Bell Atlantic Corporation; *U.S. Public*, pg. 204
PEOPLE'S CHOICE TV CORP.; *U.S. Public*, pg. 1274
PEOPLE'S CHOICE TV OF TUCSON, INC.—People's Choice TV Corp.; *U.S. Public*, pg. 1274
PHOENIX CABLE INCORPORATED—Phoenix American Incorporated; *U.S. Private*, pg. 862
PLAYBOY ENTERPRISES, INC.; *U.S. Public*, pg. 1309
RAINBOW PROGRAMMING HOLDINGS, INC.—Cablevision Systems Corporation; *U.S. Public*, pg. 288
RIVER RAISIN CABLEVISION INC.—Cable Michigan, Inc.; *U.S. Public*, pg. 287
ROGERS CABLE SYSTEMS—Rogers Communications, Inc.; *Int'l*, pg. 1123
ROGERS CABLE TV—Rogers Communications, Inc.; *Int'l*, pg. 1122
ROGERS CABLE TV-ALBERTA LIMITED—Rogers Communications, Inc.; *Int'l*, pg. 1122
ROGERS CABLE TV-BRANTFORD DIV.—Rogers Communications, Inc.; *Int'l*, pg. 1122
ROGERS CABLE TV-FRASER—Rogers Communications, Inc.; *Int'l*, pg. 1122
ROGERS CABLE TV-HAMILTON—Rogers Communications, Inc.; *Int'l*, pg. 1122
ROGERS CABLE TV-KITCHENER—Rogers Communications, Inc.; *Int'l*, pg. 1122
ROGERS CABLE TV-MISSISSAUGA DIV.—Rogers Communications, Inc.; *Int'l*, pg. 1122
ROGERS CABLE TV-NEWMARKET DIV.—Rogers Communications, Inc.; *Int'l*, pg. 1122
ROGERS CABLE TV-SURREY—Rogers Communications, Inc.; *Int'l*, pg. 1122
ROGERS CABLE TV-TORONTO DIV.—Rogers Communications, Inc.; *Int'l*, pg. 1122
ROGERS CABLE TV-VICTORIA—Rogers Communications, Inc.; *Int'l*, pg. 1122
SACRAMENTO CABLE—The E.W. Scripps Company; *U.S. Public*, pg. 1448
SCHURZ COMMUNICATIONS, INC.; *U.S. Private*, pg. 973
SCRIPPS HOWARD CABLE COMPANY—The E.W. Scripps Company; *U.S. Public*, pg. 1448
SCRIPPS HOWARD CABLE OF NORTHWEST GEORGIA—The E.W. Scripps Company; *U.S. Public*, pg. 1448
SCRIPPS HOWARD CABLE T.V. COMPANY—The E.W. Scripps Company; *U.S. Public*, pg. 1448
THE SPORTS NETWORK (TSN)—TSN Communications; *Int'l*, pg. 1343
SUN VALLEY CABLEVISION, INC.—TCA Cable TV, Inc.; *U.S. Public*, pg. 1553
TCA CABLE OF AMARILLO, INC.—TCA Cable TV, Inc.; *U.S. Public*, pg. 1553
TCA CABLE TV, INC.; *U.S. Public*, pg. 1553
TCA MANAGEMENT COMPANY—TCA Cable TV, Inc.; *U.S.* Public, pg. 1553

TCI CABLEVISION OF WASHINGTON—TCI Communications, Inc.; *U.S. Public*, pg. 1555
TCI COMMUNICATIONS, INC.; *U.S. Public*, pg. 1554
TCI/US WEST—TCI Communications, Inc.; *U.S. Public*, pg. 1555
TCI WEST—TCI Communications, Inc.; *U.S. Public*, pg. 1555
TELE-MUNCHEN FERNSEH GMBH & CO.; *Int'l*, pg. 1362
TELE SCRIPPS CABLE—The E.W. Scripps Company; *U.S. Public*, pg. 1448
TELECABLE ASSOCIATES, INC.—TCA Cable TV, Inc.; *U.S. Public*, pg. 1553
TELEFONICA SERVICIOS MULTIMEDIA, S.A.—Telefonica de Espana, S.A.; *Int'l*, pg. 1372
TELESERVICE CORPORATION OF AMERICA—TCA Cable TV, Inc.; *U.S. Public*, pg. 1553
TEXAS COMMUNITY ANTENNAS, INC.—TCA Cable TV, Inc.; *U.S. Public*, pg. 1553
TEXAS TELECABLE, INC.—TCA Cable TV, Inc.; *U.S. Public*, pg. 1553
THE TIME WARNER CABLE GROUP—Time Warner Inc.; *U.S. Public*, pg. 1610
TIME WARNER CABLE LIBERTY DIVISION—Time Warner Inc.; *U.S. Public*, pg. 1611
TIME WARNER INC.; *U.S. Public*, pg. 1610
THE TRAVEL CHANNEL—Landmark Communications, Inc.; *U.S. Private*, pg. 647
U S WEST INC.; *U.S. Public*, pg. 1688
VH-1/VIDEO HITS ONE—National Amusements, Inc.; *U.S. Private*, pg. 779
VIACOM ENTERPRISES CANADA LTD.—National Amusements, Inc.; *U.S. Private*, pg. 779
VIACOM INTERNATIONAL INC.—National Amusements, Inc.; *U.S. Private*, pg. 778
VIDEO SERVICE COMPANY—Cox Communications, Inc.; *U.S. Public*, pg. 455
THE WASHINGTON POST COMPANY; *U.S. Public*, pg. 1742
THE WEATHER CHANNEL—Landmark Communications, Inc.; *U.S. Private*, pg. 647
WEHCO MEDIA, INC.; *U.S. Private*, pg. 1159
WEHCO VIDEO INC.—Wehco Media, Inc.; *U.S. Private*, pg. 1159
WESTMINSTER CABLE COMPANY LIMITED—British Telecommunications plc; *Int'l*, pg. 222
WORLDVISION ENTERPRISES—National Amusements, Inc.; *U.S. Private*, pg. 776
WORLDVISION ENTERPRISES, INC.—National Amusements, Inc.; *U.S. Private*, pg. 776

4899 — COMMUNICATION SERVICES, NEC

AT&T WIRELESS SERVICES—AT&T Corporation; *U.S. Public*, pg. 11
ATC CABLEVISION OF SAN MARINO, INC.—Time Warner Inc.; *U.S. Public*, pg. 1610
ATC CABLEVISION OF SOUTH PASADENA, INC.—Time Warner Inc.; *U.S. Public*, pg. 1610
AV EUROMEDIA GESELLSCHAFT FUR AUDIOVISION MBH—Georg von Holtzbrinck GmbH; *Int'l*, pg. 1478
AVE GESELLSCHAFT FUR FERNSEHPRODUKTION MBH—Georg von Holtzbrinck GmbH; *Int'l*, pg. 1478
AVE GESELLSCHAFT FUR HORFUNKBETEILIGUNGEN MBH—Georg von Holtzbrinck GmbH; *Int'l*, pg. 1478
ALDEN ELECTRONICS, INC.—Platinum Equity Holdings, LLC; *U.S. Private*, pg. 872
ALIANT COMMUNICATIONS INC.; *U.S. Public*, pg. 40
ALLNEWSCO, INC.—Perpetual Corporation; *U.S. Private*, pg. 854
ALLTEL ANSWERING SERVICE, INC.—ALLTEL Corporation; *U.S. Public*, pg. 55
ALLTEL COMMUNICATIONS CORPORATION—ALLTEL Corporation; *U.S. Public*, pg. 55
ALLTEL CORPORATION; *U.S. Public*, pg. 55
ALLTEL SERVICE CORPORATION—ALLTEL Corporation; *U.S. Public*, pg. 56
AMERICAN CABLEVISION HOLDINGS, INC.—Time Warner Inc.; *U.S. Public*, pg. 1610
AMERICAN CABLEVISION OF KANSAS CITY, INC.—Time Warner Inc.; *U.S. Public*, pg. 1610
AMERICAN PAGING, INC.—Telephone and Data Systems, Inc.; *U.S. Public*, pg. 1570
AMERITECH CORPORATION; *U.S. Public*, pg. 97
ASCENT ENTERTAINMENT GROUP, INC.; *U.S. Public*, pg. 138
ASIA-PACIFIC SPACE & COMMUNICATION LIMITED—British Aerospace p.l.c.; *Int'l*, pg. 218
AUSTRIAN POSTAL & TELEGRAPH ADMINISTRATION; *Int'l*, pg. 101
BCE INC.; *Int'l*, pg. 114
BT (HONG KONG) LIMITED—British Telecommunications plc; *Int'l*, pg. 223
BAY NETWORKS, INC.; *U.S. Public*, pg. 196
BIRMINGHAM CABLE COMMUNICATIONS, INC.—Time Warner Inc.; *U.S. Public*, pg. 1610
BOOTH AMERICAN; *U.S. Private*, pg. 156
BOWDENS MEDIA MONITORING LIMITED—Rogers Communications, Inc.; *Int'l*, pg. 1124
BRITISH TELECOMMUNICATIONS PLC; *Int'l*, pg. 222
BROADCAST AND VIDEO ENTERPRISES DIV.—Landmark Communications, Inc.; *U.S. Private*, pg. 647
BUTLER FLEET SERVICES, INC.—Butler International, Inc.; *U.S. Public*, pg. 271
BUTLER TELECOM, INC.—Butler International, Inc.; *U.S. Public*, pg. 271
BUTLER UTILITIES SERVICES, INC.—Butler International, Inc.; *U.S. Public*, pg. 271
CBS CORPORATION; *U.S. Public*, pg. 273
CNBC—General Electric Company; *U.S. Public*, pg. 712
CABLE & WIRELESS (N.Y.) INC.—Cable and Wireless plc; *Int'l*, pg. 247
CABLEVISION OF DURHAM, INC.—Time Warner Inc.; *U.S. Public*, pg. 1610
CABLEVISION OF RALEIGH, INC.—Time Warner Inc.; *U.S. Public*, pg. 1610
CABLEVISION OF SHREVEPORT—Time Warner Inc.; *U.S. Public*, pg. 1610
CABLEVISION VII, INC.—TCI Communications, Inc.; *U.S. Public*, pg. 1555
CABLEVISION VI, INC.—TCI Communications, Inc.; *U.S. Public*, pg. 1555
CANADIAN AD-CHECK SERVICES INC.—Rogers Communications, Inc.; *Int'l*, pg. 1124
CANADIAN PRESS CLIPPING SERVICES—Rogers Communications, Inc.; *Int'l*, pg. 1124
CANTEL PAGING—Rogers Communications, Inc.; *Int'l*, pg. 1123
CENTURY CELLUNET, INC.—Century Telephone Enterprises, Inc.; *U.S. Public*, pg. 330
CENTURY TELEPHONE ENTERPRISES, INC.; *U.S. Public*, *pg. 329*
CHAMPAIGN-URBANA COMMUNICATIONS, INC.—Time Warner Inc.; *U.S. Public*, pg. 1610
COLORADO SPRINGS CABLEVISION, INC.—Time Warner Inc.; *U.S. Public*, pg. 1610
COMMUNICATIONS & CABLEVISION, INC.—Cable Michigan, Inc.; *U.S. Public*, pg. 287
COMMUNICORP, INC.—AFLAC Incorporated; *U.S. Public*, pg. 28
COMSAT CORPORATION; *U.S. Public*, pg. 424
COMSAT MOBILE COMMUNICATIONS—COMSAT Corporation; *U.S. Public*, pg. 424
COMSAT WORLD SYSTEMS—COMSAT Corporation; *U.S. Public*, pg. 424
COMSEARCH APPLIED TECHNOLOGY, INC.—Allen Telecom, Inc.; *U.S. Public*, pg. 46
COMVIDEO SYSTEMS, INC./N.J.—RCN Corporation; *U.S. Public*, pg. 1354
CONUS COMMUNICATION COMPANY LIMITED PARTNERSHIP—Hubbard Broadcasting, Inc.; *U.S. Private*, pg. 544
COX COMMUNICATIONS, INC.; *U.S. Public*, pg. 454
DATA TRANSMISSION NETWORK CORPORATION; *U.S. Public*, pg. 486
DENTSU INC.; *Int'l*, pg. 392
DOW JONES & COMPANY, INC.; *U.S. Public*, pg. 524
DYCOM INDUSTRIES, INC.; *U.S. Public*, pg. 538
EARTH STATION DIV.—Allen Telecom, Inc.; *U.S. Public*, pg. 46
EDWARDS & KELCEY CONSTRUCTION, INC.—Edwards and Kelcey, Inc.; *U.S. Private*, pg. 364
EDWARDS & KELCEY WIRELESS—Edwards and Kelcey, Inc.; *U.S. Private*, pg. 364
EUROPEAN TELECOMMUNICATIONS SATELLITE ORGANIZATION (EUTELSAT)—British Telecommunications plc; *Int'l*, pg. 223
FIRST DATA CORPORATION; *U.S. Public*, pg. 630
FLEET CALL OF UTAH, INC.—Nextel Communications; *U.S. Public*, pg. 1180
G.E. AMERICAN COMMUNICATIONS, INC.—General Electric Company; *U.S. Public*, pg. 711
G.E. SPACENET CORPORATION—General Electric Company; *U.S. Public*, pg. 711
GTE AIRFONE INCORPORATED—GTE Corporation; *U.S. Public*, pg. 696
GTE GOVERNMENT SYSTEMS CORPORATION—GTE Corporation; *U.S. Public*, pg. 696
GANDALF CANADA LTD.—Gandalf Technologies Inc.; *Int'l*, *pg. 540*
GANDALF DIGITAL COMMUNICATIONS LTD.—Gandalf Technologies Inc.; *Int'l*, pg. 540
GANDALF INTERNATIONAL LTD.—Gandalf Technologies Inc.; *Int'l*, pg. 540
GANDALF NEDERLAND B.V.—Gandalf Technologies Inc.; *Int'l*, pg. 540
GANDALF S.A.—Gandalf Technologies Inc.; *Int'l*, pg. 541
GANDALF SYSTEMS CORPORATION—Gandalf Technologies Inc.; *Int'l*, pg. 540
GANDALF TECHNOLOGIES INC.; *Int'l*, pg. 540
HEARST ENTERTAINMENT & SYNDICATION—The Hearst Corporation; *U.S. Private*, pg. 516
HENKELS & MCCOY, INC.; *U.S. Private*, pg. 522
HERITAGE CABLEVISION, INC.—TCI Communications, Inc.; *U.S. Public*, pg. 1555
HUGHES COMMUNICATIONS, INC.—General Motors Corporation; *U.S. Public*, pg. 721
HUGHES SPACE & COMMUNICATIONS GROUP—General Motors Corporation; *U.S. Public*, pg. 721
ITT FEDERAL SERVICES CORPORATION—ITT Industries, Inc.; *U.S. Public*, pg. 859
INDIANA DIGITAL ACCESS—Time Warner Inc.; *U.S. Public*, pg. 1610
INTERNATIONAL MARITIME SATELLITE ORGANISATION (INMARSAT)—British Telecommunications plc; *Int'l*, pg. 222
INTERNATIONAL RESEARCH & EVALUATION; *U.S. Private*, pg. 571
INTERNATIONAL TELECOMMUNICATIONS SATELLITE ORGANIZATION (INTELSAT)—British Telecommunications plc; *Int'l*, pg. 223
THE IRVINE COMPANY; *U.S. Private*, pg. 575
JOURNAL COMMUNICATIONS INC.; *U.S. Private*, pg. 601
KNIGHT-RIDDER, INC.; *U.S. Public*, pg. 963
LIFELINE SYSTEMS, INC.; *U.S. Public*, pg. 992
LOWER BUCKS CABLEVISION, INC.—Time Warner Inc.; *U.S. Public*, pg. 1611
MCI INTERNATIONAL INC.—MCI Communications Corp.; *U.S. Public*, pg. 1024
MCI TELECOMMUNICATIONS CORP.—MCI Communications Corp.; *U.S. Public*, pg. 1024
MPX SYSTEMS, INC.—SCANA Corporation; *U.S. Public*, pg. 1436
MACLEAN HUNTER MICROPUBLISHING—Rogers Communications, Inc.; *Int'l*, pg. 1124
MADISON SQUARE GARDEN CORPORATION—Cablevision Systems Corporation; *U.S. Public*, pg. 288
MALRITE COMMUNICATIONS GROUP, INC.; *U.S. Private*, *pg. 698*
MANUS PRESSE GMBH—Georg von Holtzbrinck GmbH; *Int'l*, pg. 1478
MARITIME TELEGRAPH & TELEPHONE COMPANY, LTD.—BCE Inc.; *Int'l*, pg. 116
MASTEC, INC.; *U.S. Public*, pg. 1055
MATERIALS RESEARCH FRANCE—Sony Corporation; *Int'l*, pg. 1283
MCCLATCHY NEWSPAPERS INC.; *U.S. Public*, pg. 1065
MICKELBERRY COMMUNICATIONS, INC.; *U.S. Private*, pg. 741
MOBILE COMMUNICATIONS CORPORATION OF AMERICA—MobileComm; *U.S. Public*, pg. 1120
MULTIMEDIA CABLEVISION, CO.—Gannett Company, Inc.; *U.S. Public*, pg. 699
NATIONAL BROADCASTING CO., INC.—General Electric Company; *U.S. Public*, pg. 712
NATIONAL REMOTE SENSING CENTRE LIMITED—The General Electric Company, p.l.c.; *Int'l*, pg. 545
NEWFOUNDLAND CAPITAL CORPORATION LIMITED; *Int'l*, pg. 924
NEWS-PRESS & GAZETTE COMPANY; *U.S. Private*, pg. 797
NORLIGHT TELECOMMUNICATIONS INC.—Journal Communications Inc.; *U.S. Private*, pg. 601
ORION NETWORK SYSTEMS INCORPORATED—British Aerospace p.l.c.; *Int'l*, pg. 218
PPV VENTURE PRODUCTIONS—Time Warner Inc.; *U.S. Public*, pg. 1610
PENN CENTRAL COMMUNICATIONS CORP.—Conrail, Inc.; *U.S. Public*, pg. 432
PHILLIPS COMMUNICATIONS, INC.—Phillips Petroleum Company; *U.S. Public*, pg. 1291
QUALCOMM; *U.S. Public*, pg. 1348
QUESTAR INFOCOMM—Questar Corporation; *U.S. Public*, pg. 1352
QUINTRON SYSTEMS, INC.; *U.S. Private*, pg. 901
RACAL-DATACOM—Racal Electronics Plc; *Int'l*, pg. 1083
RACAL-DATACOM LTD—Racal Electronics Plc; *Int'l*, pg. 1082
RACAL ELECTRONICS PLC; *Int'l*, pg. 1082
RAY SATELLITE NETWORK—Ray Communications, Inc.; *U.S. Private*, pg. 911
ROCKINGHAM-HAMLET CABLEVISION, INC.—Time Warner Inc.; *U.S. Public*, pg. 1610
ROCKINGHAM-HAMLET, INC.—Time Warner Inc.; *U.S. Public*, pg. 1610
ROGERS CABLE TV-BRAMPTON—Rogers Communications, Inc.; *Int'l*, pg. 1122
ROGERS CABLE TV-CORNWALL—Rogers Communications, Inc.; *Int'l*, pg. 1122
ROGERS CABLE TV-LONDON—Rogers Communications, Inc.; *Int'l*, pg. 1122
ROGERS CABLE TV-PINE RIDGE—Rogers Communications, Inc.; *Int'l*, pg. 1122
ROGERS CABLE TV-VANCOUVER—Rogers Communications, Inc.; *Int'l*, pg. 1122
ROGERS COMMUNICATIONS, INC.; *Int'l*, pg. 1122
SJL OF KANSAS CORP.—Lee Enterprises, Incorporated; *U.S. Public*, pg. 984
THE E.W. SCRIPPS COMPANY; *U.S. Public*, pg. 1447
SHARE TECHNOLOGIES - FAIRCHILD—Tel-Save Holdings, Inc.; *U.S. Public*, pg. 1568
SHOWTIME NETWORKS INC.—National Amusements, Inc.; *U.S. Private*, pg. 779
SHOWTIME SATELLITE NETWORKS, INC.—National Amusements, Inc.; *U.S. Private*, pg. 779
SHOWTIME/THE MOVIE CHANNEL INC. (U.K.)—National Amusements, Inc.; *U.S. Private*, pg. 779
STORAGETEK NETWORK SYSTEMS GROUP—Storage Technology Corporation; *U.S. Public*, pg. 1522
T-BAR, INC.—General Signal Corporation; *U.S. Public*, pg. 727
T-NETIX, INC.; *U.S. Public*, pg. 1553
TCI CABLEVISION OF DALLAS, INC.—TCI Communications, Inc.; *U.S. Public*, pg. 1555
TDS TELECOMMUNICATIONS CORPORATION—Telephone and Data Systems, Inc.; *U.S. Public*, pg. 1570
TWC CABLE PARTNERS—Cox Communications, Inc.; *U.S. Public*, pg. 455
TAR RIVER COMMUNICATIONS, INC.—Gannett Company, Inc.; *U.S. Public*, pg. 701
TELEGLOBE CANADA INC.—Teleglobe, Inc.; *Int'l*, pg. 1373
TELEPHONE AND DATA SYSTEMS, INC.; *U.S. Public*, pg. 1570
TELUS CORPORATION; *Int'l*, pg. 1374
TERRESTRIAL MICROWAVE SERVICES DIV.—Allen Telecom, Inc.; *U.S. Public*, pg. 46
3COM CORPORATION; *U.S. Public*, pg. 1603
TIME WARNER CABLE OF NEW YORK CITY—Time Warner Inc.; *U.S. Public*, pg. 1611
THE TITAN CORPORATION; *U.S. Public*, pg. 1618
TRACOR, INC.; *U.S. Public*, pg. 1627
TRIBUNE COMPANY; *U.S. Public*, pg. 1635
TURNER BROADCASTING SYSTEM INC.—Time Warner Inc.; *U.S. Public*, pg. 1614
TURNER ENTERTAINMENT COMPANY—Time Warner Inc.; *U.S. Public*, pg. 1615
TURNER HOME ENTERTAINMENT—Time Warner Inc.; *U.S. Public*, pg. 1615
TURNER NETWORK SALES—Time Warner Inc.; *U.S. Public*, pg. 1615
U.T.A. CABLE CORP.—Lennar Corporation; *U.S. Public*, pg. 989
UNITED STATES SATELLITE BROADCASTING, CO.—Hubbard Broadcasting, Inc.; *U.S. Private*, pg. 544
UNITED TELECOM SERVICES CO. LTD.—Telefonaktiebolaget LM Ericsson; *Int'l*, pg. 1371
VSI HOLDINGS, INC.; *U.S. Public*, pg. 1703
VALASSIS COMMUNICATIONS, INC.; *U.S. Public*, pg. 1704
VIACOM ENTERTAINMENT—National Amusements, Inc.; *U.S. Private*, pg. 778

VIACOM NETWORKS INC.—National Amusements, Inc.; *U.S. Private*, pg. 779
VIACOM SATELLITE NETWORKS INC.—National Amusements, Inc.; *U.S. Private*, pg. 779
VISTA CABLEVISION, INC.—Time Warner Inc.; *U.S. Public*, *pg. 1611*
WARNER CABLE COMMUNICATIONS, INC.—Time Warner Inc.; *U.S. Public*, pg. 1611
WARNER COMMUNICATIONS INC.—Time Warner Inc.; *U.S. Public*, pg. 1611
WEGENER CORPORATION; *U.S. Public*, pg. 1751
WENATCHEE MOUNTAINS, INC.—Time Warner Inc.; *U.S. Public*, pg. 1611
WESTERN UNION FINANCIAL SERVICES, INC.—First Data Corporation; *U.S. Public*, pg. 631
WOODWARD CABLE TV, INC.—Time Warner Inc.; *U.S. Public*, pg. 1611

4911 — ELECTRIC SERVICES

ABB ENERGY VENTURES INC.—ABB Asea Brown Boveri (Holding) Ltd.; *Int'l*, pg. 4
AEC POWER LTD.—Alberta Energy Company, Ltd.; *Int'l*, pg. 49
AEP GENERATING CO.—American Electric Power Company, Inc.; *U.S. Public*, pg. 72
AES CORPORATION; *U.S. Public*, pg. 5
APS—Pinnacle West Capital Corporation; *U.S. Public*, pg. 1297
AIKEN ELECTRIC COOPERATIVE INC.; *U.S. Private*, pg. 28
ALABAMA ELECTRIC COOPERATIVE, INC.; *U.S. Private*, pg. 30
ALABAMA POWER CO.—Southern Company; *U.S. Public*, pg. 1489
ALBERTA POWER LIMITED—ATCO Group Co.; *Int'l*, pg. 95
ALETSCH AG—Alusuisse-Lonza Holding Ltd.; *Int'l*, pg. 67
ALL AMERICAN SEMICONDUCTOR, INC.; *U.S. Public*, pg. 41
ALLEGHENY DEVELOPMENT CORP.—DQE Inc.; *U.S. Public*, pg. 474
ALLEGHENY POWER SYSTEM, INC.; *U.S. Public*, pg. 42
ALLTEL CORPORATION; *U.S. Public*, pg. 55
AMANA SOCIETY SERVICE CO.—Amana Society, Inc.; *U.S. Private*, pg. 48
AMERICAN ELECTRIC POWER COMPANY, INC.; *U.S. Public*, pg. 71
AMERICAN ELECTRIC POWER SERVICE CORP.—American Electric Power Company, Inc.; *U.S. Public*, pg. 72
ANOKA ELECTRIC COOPERATIVE; *U.S. Private*, pg. 75
APPALACHIAN POWER COMPANY—American Electric Power Company, Inc.; *U.S. Public*, pg. 72
ASSOCIATED ELECTRIC CO-OP INC.; *U.S. Private*, pg. 89
ATLANTIC GENERATION, INC.—Conectiv; *U.S. Public*, pg. 430
ATLAS ELECTRIC DEVICES CO.; *U.S. Private*, pg. 96
B.C. HYDRO; *Int'l*, pg. 114
BALTIMORE GAS AND ELECTRIC COMPANY; *U.S. Public*, pg. 172
BANGOR HYDRO-ELECTRIC COMPANY; *U.S. Public*, pg. 178
THE BARBADOS LIGHT & POWER CO. LTD.—Leucadia National Corporation; *U.S. Public*, pg. 990
BASIN ELECTRIC POWER COOPERATIVE; *U.S. Private*, pg. 121
BAYERNWERK AG—Viag AG; *Int'l*, pg. 1464
BLACK HILLS CORPORATION; *U.S. Public*, pg. 235
BLACK HILLS POWER & LIGHT COMPANY—Black Hills Corporation; *U.S. Public*, pg. 235
BLACKSTONE VALLEY ELECTRIC CO.—Eastern Utilities Associates; *U.S. Public*, pg. 549
BLUE RIDGE ELECTRIC COOPERATIVE INC.; *U.S. Private*, pg. 153
BLUE RIDGE ELECTRIC MEMBERSHIP CORP.; *U.S. Private*, pg. 153
BONNEVILLE PACIFIC CORPORATION; *U.S. Public*, pg. 244
BOSTON EDISON COMPANY; *U.S. Public*, pg. 247
BRAUNSCHWEIGISCHE KOHLEN-BERGWERKE AG—Veba AG; *Int'l*, pg. 1456
BRAZOS ELECTRIC POWER COOPERATIVE, INC.; *U.S. Private*, pg. 166
BROWNVILLE POWER COMPANY—Boise Cascade Corporation; *U.S. Public*, pg. 243
CRSS INC.—Tractebel; *Int'l*, pg. 1415
CU POWER INTERNATIONAL LTD.—ATCO Group Co.; *Int'l*, pg. 95
CAJUN ELECTRIC POWER CO-OP; *U.S. Private*, pg. 199
CALPINE CORPORATION; *U.S. Public*, pg. 296
CAMBRIDGE ELECTRIC LIGHT CO.—Commonwealth Energy System; *U.S. Public*, pg. 414
CANADIAN UTILITIES LIMITED—ATCO Group Co.; *Int'l*, pg. 95
CANAL ELECTRIC CO.—Commonwealth Energy System; *U.S. Public*, pg. 415
CARDINAL OPERATING CO.—American Electric Power Company, Inc.; *U.S. Public*, pg. 72
CAROLINA POWER & LIGHT COMPANY; *U.S. Public*, pg. 306
CENTRAL AND SOUTH WEST CORPORATION; *U.S. Public*, pg. 324
CENTRAL LINCOLN PEOPLE'S UTILITY DISTRICT; *U.S. Private*, pg. 223
CENTRAL LOUISIANA ELECTRIC COMPANY, INC.; *U.S. Public*, pg. 325
CENTRAL MAINE POWER COMPANY; *U.S. Public*, pg. 325
CENTRAL OPERATING CO.—American Electric Power Company, Inc.; *U.S. Public*, pg. 72
CENTRAL POWER AND LIGHT COMPANY—Central and South West Corporation; *U.S. Public*, pg. 324
CENTRAL VERMONT PUBLIC SERVICE CORPORATION; *U.S. Public*, pg. 327
CHOCTAW ELECTRIC CO-OP; *U.S. Private*, pg. 238
CHUBU ELECTRIC POWER CO., INC. (LONDON OFFICE)—Chubu Electric Power Company, Inc.; *Int'l*, pg. 290
CHUBU ELECTRIC POWER CO., INC. (WASHINGTON OFFICE)—Chubu Electric Power Company, Inc.; *Int'l*, pg. 290
CHUBU ELECTRIC POWER COMPANY, INC.; *Int'l*, pg. 290
THE CHUGOKU ELECTRIC POWER CO., INC.; *Int'l*, pg. 291
CINERGY—Cinergy Corp.; *U.S. Public*, pg. 369
CINERGY CORP.; *U.S. Public*, pg. 368
CINERGY INVESTMENTS, INC.—Cinergy Corp.; *U.S. Public*, pg. 369
CITIZENS UTILITIES COMPANY; *U.S. Public*, pg. 379
CITIZENS UTILITIES COMPANY—Citizens Utilities Company; *U.S. Public*, pg. 380
THE CLEVELAND ELECTRIC ILLUMINATING COMPANY—FirstEnergy Corp.; *U.S. Public*, pg. 645
THE COASTAL CORPORATION; *U.S. Public*, pg. 389
COLUMBUS SOUTHERN POWER COMPANY—American Electric Power Company, Inc.; *U.S. Public*, pg. 72
COMED—Unicom Corporation; *U.S. Public*, pg. 1664
COMMONWEALTH EDISON COMPANY OF INDIANA, INC.—Unicom Corporation; *U.S. Public*, pg. 1664
COMMONWEALTH ELECTRIC CO.—Commonwealth Energy System; *U.S. Public*, pg. 415
COMMONWEALTH ENERGY SYSTEM; *U.S. Public*, pg. 414
COMPAGNIE GENERALE DES EAUX; *Int'l*, pg. 321
CONCORD ELECTRIC COMPANY—Unitil Corporation; *U.S. Public*, pg. 1692
THE CONNECTICUT LIGHT & POWER CO.—Northeast Utilities; *U.S. Public*, pg. 1194
CONNECTICUT VALLEY ELECTRIC CO., INC.—Central Vermont Public Service Corporation; *U.S. Public*, pg. 328
CONNECTICUT YANKEE ATOMIC POWER CO.—Central Maine Power Company; *U.S. Public*, pg. 325
CONSOLIDATED EDISON COMPANY OF NEW YORK, INC.; *U.S. Public*, pg. 434
CONSOLIDATED WATER POWER CO.—Consolidated Papers, Inc.; *U.S. Public*, pg. 436
CONWAY CORPORATION; *U.S. Private*, pg. 272
COTTON ELECTRIC CO-OP; *U.S. Private*, pg. 278
CUBAN ELECTRIC CO.—Boise Cascade Corporation; *U.S. Public*, pg. 243
CYPRUS AMAX MINERALS COMPANY; *U.S. Public*, pg. 470
DPL INC.; *U.S. Public*, pg. 473
DQE INC.; *U.S. Public*, pg. 474
DTE ENERGY COMPANY; *U.S. Public*, pg. 475
DAIRYLAND POWER COOPERATIVE; *U.S. Private*, pg. 307
DAKOTA ELECTRIC ASSOCIATION; *U.S. Private*, pg. 308
DEEPWATER OPERATING CO.—Conectiv; *U.S. Public*, pg. 430
DELAWARE ELECTRIC CO-OP; *U.S. Private*, pg. 321
DIXIE ELECTRIC COOPERATIVE; *U.S. Private*, pg. 337
DUKE ENERGY CORPORATION; *U.S. Public*, pg. 534
DUKE POWER CO. MCGUIRE NUCLEAR—Duke Energy Corporation; *U.S. Public*, pg. 534
DUKE POWER OCONEE NUCLEAR STATION—Duke Energy Corporation; *U.S. Public*, pg. 534
DUQUESNE LIGHT COMPANY—DQE Inc.; *U.S. Public*, pg. 474
DUROFORM-J. FRITZ GMBH & CO KG—Alusuisse-Lonza Holding Ltd.; *Int'l*, pg. 68
ERAG ELEKTRIZITATSWERK RHEINAU AG—Alusuisse-Lonza Holding Ltd.; *Int'l*, pg. 67
ERE T DIVISION—Alcatel Alsthom Compagnie Generale D'Electricite; *Int'l*, pg. 52
ESI ENERGY, INC.—FPL Group, Inc.; *U.S. Public*, pg. 608
EUA CITIZENS CONSERVATION SERVICES, INC.—Eastern Utilities Associates; *U.S. Public*, pg. 549
EUA COGENEX CORPORATION—Eastern Utilities Associates; *U.S. Public*, pg. 549
EUA COGENEX WEST—Eastern Utilities Associates; *U.S. Public*, pg. 549
EUA OCEAN STATE CORPORATION—Eastern Utilities Associates; *U.S. Public*, pg. 549
EUA SERVICE CORPORATION—Eastern Utilities Associates; *U.S. Public*, pg. 549
EAST KENTUCKY POWER CO-OP; *U.S. Private*, pg. 356
EAST RIVER ELECTRIC COOPERATIVE; *U.S. Private*, pg. 357
EASTERN EDISON COMPANY—Eastern Utilities Associates; *U.S. Public*, pg. 550
EASTERN UTILITIES ASSOCIATES; *U.S. Public*, pg. 549
EBASINT INTERNATIONAL, INC.—Boise Cascade Corporation; *U.S. Public*, pg. 243
EDISON INTERNATIONAL; *U.S. Public*, pg. 564
EDISON SAULT ELECTRIC COMPANY—ESELCO, Inc.; *U.S. Public*, pg. 592
EDISON S.P.A.—Compart SpA; *Int'l*, pg. 324
EGAN COS.; *U.S. Private*, pg. 365
EGAN MCKAY ELECTRICAL CONTRACTORS—Egan Cos.; *U.S. Private*, pg. 366
EL PASO ELECTRIC COMPANY; *U.S. Public*, pg. 567
ELECTRABEL S.A.; *Int'l*, pg. 436
ELECTRIC ENERGY, INC.—Illinova Inc.; *U.S. Public*, pg. 870
ELECTRICITE DE FRANCE; *Int'l*, pg. 437
ELECTRICITE DE LA LIENNE SA-(LIENNE)—Alusuisse-Lonza Holding Ltd.; *Int'l*, pg. 67
ELEKTRIZITAETS-AKTIENGESELLSCHAFT MITTELDEUTSCHLAND—Veba AG; *Int'l*, pg. 1456
ELKEM ASA ENERGY—Elkem ASA; *Int'l*, pg. 447
ELKEM MANGAN SAUDA—Elkem ASA; *Int'l*, pg. 447
EMMETT POWER COMPANY—Boise Cascade Corporation; *U.S. Public*, pg. 243
THE EMPIRE DISTRICT ELECTRIC COMPANY; *U.S. Public*, pg. 579
EMPIRE ELECTRIC ASSOCIATION; *U.S. Private*, pg. 374
ENERGIEVERSORGUNG WESER-EMS AG—Veba AG; *Int'l*, pg. 1456
ENERGIS RESOURCES INCORPORATED—Public Service Enterprise Group Incorporated; *U.S. Public*, pg. 1340
ENERGY NATIONAL, INC.—PacifiCorp; *U.S. Public*, pg. 1252
ENTE NAZIONALE PER L'ENERGIA ELETTRICA SPA (ENEL); *Int'l*, pg. 458
ENTERGY ARKANSAS, INC.—Entergy Corporation; *U.S. Public*, pg. 586
ENTERGY CORPORATION; *U.S. Public*, pg. 585
ENTERGY LOUISIANA, INC.—Entergy Corporation; *U.S. Public*, pg. 586
ENTERGY MISSISSIPPI, INC.—Entergy Corporation; *U.S. Public*, pg. 586
ENTERGY NEW ORLEANS, INC.—Entergy Corporation; *U.S. Public*, pg. 586
ENTERGY OPERATIONS, INC.—Entergy Corporation; *U.S. Public*, pg. 586
ESELCO, INC.; *U.S. Public*, pg. 591
ESKOM; *Int'l*, pg. 459
EUROBAYERNWERK GMBH—Viag AG; *Int'l*, pg. 1464
EXETER & HAMPTON ELECTRIC CO.—Unitil Corporation; *U.S. Public*, pg. 1692
FPL GROUP, INC.; *U.S. Public*, pg. 608
FACILITY WORKS INC.—TNP Enterprises, Inc.; *U.S. Public*, *pg. 1557*
FAIRFIELD ELECTRIC COOPERATIVE; *U.S. Private*, pg. 391
FARM ELECTRIC SERVICES LTD.—Transalta Corporation; *Int'l*, pg. 1416
FERRANTI TECHNOLOGIES LTD.; *Int'l*, pg. 480
FIRST ELECTRIC COOPERATIVE, CORP.; *U.S. Private*, pg. 407
FIRSTENERGY CORP.; *U.S. Public*, pg. 644
FITCHBURG GAS AND ELECTRIC LIGHT CO.—Unitil Corporation; *U.S. Public*, pg. 1692
FLORIDA POWER & LIGHT COMPANY—FPL Group, Inc.; *U.S. Public*, pg. 608
FLORIDA POWER CORPORATION—Florida Progress Corporation; *U.S. Public*, pg. 655
FLORIDA PROGRESS CORPORATION; *U.S. Public*, pg. 655
FLORIDA PUBLIC UTILITIES COMPANY; *U.S. Public*, pg. 655
FORT BEND UTILITIES CO.—Imperial Holly Corporation; *U.S. Public*, pg. 872
FUJITSU DENSO LTD.—Fujitsu Limited; *Int'l*, pg. 526
G.E. POWER SYSTEMS—General Electric Company; *U.S. Public*, pg. 711
GEC ALSTHOM N.V.—Alcatel Alsthom Compagnie Generale D'Electricite; *Int'l*, pg. 56
GPU ENERGY—GPU, Inc.; *U.S. Public*, pg. 695
GPU, INC.; *U.S. Public*, pg. 695
GPU NUCLEAR CORP.—GPU, Inc.; *U.S. Public*, pg. 695
GARDEN CITY COMPLEX—Sunflower Electric Power Corporation; *U.S. Private*, pg. 1052
GEMEINSCHAFTSKERNKRAFTWERK GROHNDE GMBH—Veba AG; *Int'l*, pg. 1456
GEMEINSCHAFTSKRAFTWERK KIEL GMBH—Veba AG; *Int'l*, pg. 1456
GENERAL ELECTRIC COMPANY; *U.S. Public*, pg. 709
GEORGIA POWER CO.—Southern Company; *U.S. Public*, pg. 1490
GEORGIA TRANSMISSION CORPORATION; *U.S. Private*, pg. 448
GRANITE STATE ELECTRIC CO.—New England Electric System; *U.S. Public*, pg. 1171
GREAT LAKES POWER INC.—EdperBrascan Corporation; *Int'l*, pg. 433
GREEN MOUNTAIN POWER CORPORATION; *U.S. Public*, *pg. 761*
GROSSKRAFTWERK FRANKEN AG—Viag AG; *Int'l*, pg. 1464
GULF POWER COMPANY—Southern Company; *U.S. Public*, pg. 1490
HEI POWER CORP.—Hawaiian Electric Industries, Inc.; *U.S. Public*, pg. 800
HALIFAX CORPORATION; *U.S. Public*, pg. 775
HANNOVER-BRAUNSCHWEIGISCHE STROMVERSORGUNGS-AG—Veba AG; *Int'l*, pg. 1456
HARBOR ELECTRIC ENERGY COMPANY—Boston Edison Company; *U.S. Public*, pg. 247
HARPEN AG; *Int'l*, pg. 597
HAWAII ELECTRIC LIGHT CO., INC.—Hawaiian Electric Industries, Inc.; *U.S. Public*, pg. 800
HAWAIIAN ELECTRIC COMPANY, INC.—Hawaiian Electric Industries, Inc.; *U.S. Public*, pg. 800
HAWAIIAN ELECTRIC INDUSTRIES, INC.; *U.S. Public*, pg. 799
HEIZKRAFTWERK GLUCKSTADT GMBH—Veba AG; *Int'l*, pg. 1456
HOLCOMB STATION—Sunflower Electric Power Corporation; *U.S. Private*, pg. 1052
HOLY CROSS ELECTRIC ASSOCIATION, INC.; *U.S. Private*, pg. 536
HOLYOKE WATER POWER CO.—Northeast Utilities; *U.S. Public*, pg. 1195
HOUSTON INDUSTRIES ENERGY, INC.—Houston Industries Incorporated; *U.S. Public*, pg. 843
HOUSTON INDUSTRIES INCORPORATED; *U.S. Public*, pg. 842
HOUSTON LIGHTING & POWER COMPANY—Houston Industries Incorporated; *U.S. Public*, pg. 843
HYDRO ENERGY DEVELOPMENT CORP.—Puget Sound Energy, Inc.; *U.S. Public*, pg. 1342
IDA-WEST ENERGY COMPANY—Idaho Power Company; *U.S. Public*, pg. 862
IES INDUSTRIES INC.; *U.S. Public*, pg. 855
IES UTILITIES INC.—IES Industries Inc.; *U.S. Public*, pg. 855

IBERDROLA, S.A.; *Int'l*, pg. 657
IDAHO POWER COMPANY; *U.S. Public*, pg. 861
ILLINOIS POWER COMPANY—Illinova Inc.; *U.S. Public*, pg. 869
IMATRAN VOIMA OY; *Int'l*, pg. 660
INDIANA KENTUCKY ELECTRIC CORPORATION—Ohio Valley Electric Corporation; *U.S. Private*, pg. 813
INDIANA MICHIGAN POWER COMPANY—American Electric Power Company, Inc.; *U.S. Public*, pg. 72
INDIANAPOLIS POWER & LIGHT COMPANY—Ipalco Enterprises, Inc.; *U.S. Public*, pg. 913
INDUSTRIAL ENERGY APPLICATIONS—IES Industries Inc.; *U.S. Public*, pg. 855
INTERNATIONAL FALLS POWER COMPANY—Boise Cascade Corporation; *U.S. Public*, pg. 243
THE ISRAEL ELECTRIC CORPORATION LTD.; *Int'l*, pg. 690
JERSEY CENTRAL POWER & LIGHT CO.—GPU, Inc.; *U.S.* Public, pg. 695
KCS POWER MARKETING, INC.—KCS Energy Inc.; *U.S. Public*, pg. 939
KGE—Western Resources, Inc.; *U.S. Public*, pg. 1759
KPL—Western Resources, Inc.; *U.S. Public*, pg. 1759
KANELK TRANSMISSION CO. LTD.—Transalta Corporation; *Int'l*, pg. 1416
THE KANSAI ELECTRIC POWER CO., INC.; *Int'l*, pg. 722
KANSAS CITY POWER & LIGHT COMPANY; *U.S. Public*, pg. 943
KARSKAR ENERGI—Korsnas AB; *Int'l*, pg. 759
KAUAI ELECTRIC DIV.—Citizens Utilities Company; *U.S. Public*, pg. 380
KENTUCKY POWER CO.—American Electric Power Company, Inc.; *U.S. Public*, pg. 72
KENTUCKY UTILITIES COMPANY—KU Energy; *U.S. Public*, pg. 941
KERNKRAFTWERK BROKDORF GMBH—Veba AG; *Int'l*, pg. 1456
KERNKRAFTWERK BRUNSBUETTEL GMBH—Veba AG; *Int'l*, pg. 1457
KERNKRAFTWERK KRUMMEL GMBH—Veba AG; *Int'l*, pg. 1456
KERNKRAFTWERK STADE GMBH—Veba AG; *Int'l*, pg. 1456
KERNKRAFTWERK UNTERWESER GMBH—Veba AG; *Int'l*, pg. 1456
KINGSPORT POWER CO.—American Electric Power Company, Inc.; *U.S. Public*, pg. 72
KOREA ELECTRIC POWER CORPORATION (KEPCO); *Int'l*, pg. 758
KRAFTWERK EV3 1/S—Veba AG; *Int'l*, pg. 1457
KRAFTWERK KASSEL GMBH—Veba AG; *Int'l*, pg. 1456
KRAFTWERK MEHRUM GMBH—Veba AG; *Int'l*, pg. 1456
KRAFTWERK SCHKOPAU GMBH—Veba AG; *Int'l*, pg. 1460
KYUSHU ELECTRIC POWER CO., INC.; *Int'l*, pg. 778
LG & E ENERGY CORP.; *U.S. Public*, pg. 970
LG & E POWER SYSTEMS INC.—LG & E Energy Corp.; *U.S. Public*, pg. 970
LANDSVIRKJUN - THE NATIONAL POWER CO.; *Int'l*, pg. 801
LANSI-SUOMEN VOIMA OY—UPM-Kymmene Corporation; *Int'l*, pg. 1428
LECH-ELEKTRIZITATSWERKE AG; *Int'l*, pg. 805
LEX GROUP—Alcatel Alsthom Compagnie Generale D'Electricite; *Int'l*, pg. 53
LINCOLN ELECTRIC SYSTEMS; *U.S. Private*, pg. 668
LONG ISLAND LIGHTING COMPANY; *U.S. Public*, pg. 1013
LONZA AG—Alusuisse-Lonza Holding Ltd.; *Int'l*, pg. 67
LONZA BIOTEC SRO—Alusuisse-Lonza Holding Ltd.; *Int'l*, pg. 69
LONZA HONGKONG LTD.—Alusuisse-Lonza Holding Ltd.; *Int'l*, pg. 69
LONZA IBERICA S.A.—Alusuisse-Lonza Holding Ltd.; *Int'l*, pg. 69
LOUISVILLE GAS AND ELECTRIC COMPANY—LG & E Energy Corp.; *U.S. Public*, pg. 970
LYONNAISE DES EAUX S.A.; *Int'l*, pg. 822
MDU RESOURCES GROUP, INC.; *U.S. Public*, pg. 1025
MAINE AND NEW BRUNSWICK ELECTRICAL POWER COMPANY, LTD.—Maine Public Service Company; *U.S. Public*, pg. 1038
MAINE PUBLIC SERVICE COMPANY; *U.S. Public*, pg. 1038
MAINE YANKEE—Central Maine Power Company; *U.S. Public*, pg. 325
MAINE YANKEE ATOMIC POWER CO.—Maine Public Service Company; *U.S. Public*, pg. 1038
MANICOUAGAN POWER CO.—Reynolds Metals Company; *U.S. Public*, pg. 1387
MANITOBA HYDRO; *Int'l*, pg. 834
MASSACHUSETTS ELECTRIC CO.—New England Electric System; *U.S. Public*, pg. 1171
MAUI ELECTRIC CO., LTD.—Hawaiian Electric Industries, Inc.; *U.S. Public*, pg. 800
MENARD ELECTRIC COOPERATIVE; *U.S. Private*, pg. 731
METROPOLITAN EDISON CO.—GPU, Inc.; *U.S. Public*, pg. 695
MIAMI POWER CORP.—Cinergy Corp.; *U.S. Public*, pg. 369
MINNESOTA POWER; *U.S. Public*, pg. 1116
MINNKOTA POWER COOPERATIVE, INC.; *U.S. Private*, pg. 751
MISSISSIPPI POWER CO.—Southern Company; *U.S. Public*, pg. 1490
MISSOURI PUBLIC SERVICE—UtiliCorp United Inc.; *U.S. Public*, pg. 1701
MODELLKRAFTWERK VOELKLINGEN GMBH—Saarbergwerke Aktiengesellschaft; *Int'l*, pg. 1167
MOLDING COMPOUNDS SPA—Alusuisse-Lonza Holding Ltd.; *Int'l*, pg. 69
MONONGAHELA POWER CO.—Allegheny Power System, Inc.; *U.S. Public*, pg. 42
MONTANA-DAKOTA UTILITIES CO.—MDU Resources Group, Inc.; *U.S. Public*, pg. 1025
MONTAUP ELECTRIC CO.—Eastern Utilities Associates; *U.S. Public*, pg. 550
MOUNTAIN ENERGY, INC.—Green Mountain Power Corporation; *U.S. Public*, pg. 761
NSP-NORTH DEBATE REGION—Northern States Power Company; *U.S. Public*, pg. 1195
NSP-NORTHWEST AREA—Northern States Power Company; *U.S. Public*, pg. 1195
NSP-SIOUX FALLS REGION—Northern States Power Company; *U.S. Public*, pg. 1195
NSP-SOUTHEAST REGION—Northern States Power Company; *U.S. Public*, pg. 1195
A/S NAMDALENS TRAESLIPERI—Norske Skogindustrier A.S; *Int'l*, pg. 965
NANA REGIONAL CORPORATION, INC.; *U.S. Private*, pg. 774
NANTAHALA POWER AND LIGHT COMPANY—Duke Energy Corporation; *U.S. Public*, pg. 534
NARRAGANSETT ELECTRIC CO.—New England Electric System; *U.S. Public*, pg. 1171
NARRAGANSETT ENERGY RESOURCES COMPANY—New England Electric System; *U.S. Public*, pg. 1171
NATIONS ENERGY CORPORATION—UniSource Energy Corporation; *U.S. Public*, pg. 1670
NEBRASKA PUBLIC POWER DISTRICT; *U.S. Private*, pg. 789
NEVADA POWER COMPANY; *U.S. Public*, pg. 1169
NEW BRUNSWICK POWER CORPORATION; *Int'l*, pg. 923
NEW ENGLAND ELECTRIC TRANSMISSION CORP.—New England Electric System; *U.S. Public*, pg. 1171
NEW ENGLAND HYDRO-TRANSMISSION CORPORATION—New England Electric System; *U.S. Public*, pg. 1171
NEW ENGLAND HYDRO-TRANSMISSION ELECTRIC COMPANY, INC.—New England Electric System; *U.S. Public*, pg. 1171
NEW ENGLAND POWER CO.—New England Electric System; *U.S. Public*, pg. 1171
NEW ENGLAND POWER SERVICE CO.—New England Electric System; *U.S. Public*, pg. 1171
NEW YORK STATE ELECTRIC & GAS CORPORATION; *U.S. Public*, pg. 1173
NEWPORT ELECTRIC CORPORATION—Eastern Utilities Associates; *U.S. Public*, pg. 550
NIAGARA MOHAWK POWER CORPORATION; *U.S. Public*, pg. 1181
NODAK ELECTRIC CO-OP; *U.S. Private*, pg. 800
NORTH ATLANTIC ENERGY CORP.—Northeast Utilities; *U.S. Public*, pg. 1195
NORTH COAST ELECTRIC COMPANY; *U.S. Private*, pg. 804
NORTHEAST ENERGY MANAGEMENT—Eastern Utilities Associates; *U.S. Public*, pg. 549
NORTHEAST UTILITIES; *U.S. Public*, pg. 1194
NORTHWESTERN UTILITIES LIMITED—ATCO Group Co.; *Int'l*, pg. 95
NOVA SCOTIA POWER INC.; *Int'l*, pg. 971
NUOVO PIGNONE S.P.A.; *Int'l*, pg. 990
NYCOMED AMERSHAM—Nycomed Amersham plc; *Int'l*, pg. 993
NYCOMED PHARMA AS—Nycomed Amersham plc; *Int'l*, pg. 993
OES FUEL, INCORPORATED—FirstEnergy Corp.; *U.S. Public*, pg. 645
OGE ENERGY CORP.; *U.S. Public*, pg. 1207
OGLETHORPE POWER CORP.; *U.S. Private*, pg. 812
OHIO EDISON COMPANY—FirstEnergy Corp.; *U.S. Public*, pg. 645
OHIO EDISON CO.-SPRINGFIELD DIV.—FirstEnergy Corp.; *U.S. Public*, pg. 645
OHIO EDISON CO. WESTERN DIV.—FirstEnergy Corp.; *U.S. Public*, pg. 645
OHIO POWER COMPANY—American Electric Power Company, Inc.; *U.S. Public*, pg. 72
OHIO VALLEY ELECTRIC CORPORATION; *U.S. Private*, pg. 813
OMAHA PUBLIC POWER DISTRICT; *U.S. Private*, pg. 815
OPINAC ENERGY CORPORATION—Niagara Mohawk Power Corporation; *U.S. Public*, pg. 1181
ORANGE AND ROCKLAND UTILITIES, INC.; *U.S. Public*, pg. 1229
OTTER TAIL POWER COMPANY; *U.S. Public*, pg. 1234
PP&L RESOURCES; *U.S. Public*, pg. 1244
PSI POWER RESOURCE DEVELOPMENT, INC.—Cinergy Corp.; *U.S. Public*, pg. 369
PSI POWER RESOURCE OPERATIONS—Cinergy Corp.; *U.S. Public*, pg. 369
PACIFIC GENERATION COMPANY—PacifiCorp; *U.S. Public*, pg. 1252
PACIFIC POWER & LIGHT COMPANY—PacifiCorp; *U.S. Public*, pg. 1251
PACIFICORP; *U.S. Public*, pg. 1251
PEACE RIVER ELECTRIC COOPERATIVE, INC.; *U.S. Private*, pg. 845
PECO ENERGY COMPANY; *U.S. Public*, pg. 1268
PECO ENERGY POWER CO.—PECO Energy Company; *U.S. Public*, pg. 1268
PENNSYLVANIA POWER CO.—FirstEnergy Corp.; *U.S. Public*, pg. 645
PESAG AKTIENGESELLSCHAFT—Veba AG; *Int'l*, pg. 1456
PINNACLE WEST CAPITAL CORPORATION; *U.S. Public*, pg. 1297
PLAINS ELECTRIC GENERATION TRANSMISSION CO-OP, INC.; *U.S. Private*, pg. 868
PORTLAND GENERAL ELECTRIC CO.—Enron Corp.; *U.S. Public*, pg. 584
THE POTOMAC EDISON CO.—Allegheny Power System, Inc.; *U.S. Public*, pg. 42
POTOMAC ELECTRIC POWER COMPANY; *U.S. Public*, pg. 1318
POWELL ESCO COMPANY—Powell Industries, Inc.; *U.S. Public*, pg. 1319
PREUSSENELEKTRA AKTIENGESELLSCHAFT—Veba AG; *Int'l*, pg. 1456
PREUSSENELEKTRA WINDKRAFT NIEDERSACHSEN GMBH—Veba AG; *Int'l*, pg. 1456
PREUSSENELEKTRA WINDKRAFT SCHLESWIG-HOLSTEIN GMBH—Veba AG; *Int'l*, pg. 1456
PROVINZIALSAECHSISCHE ENERGIE-VERSORGUNGS GMBH—Veba AG; *Int'l*, pg. 1457
PUBLIC SERVICE COMPANY OF NEW HAMPSHIRE—Northeast Utilities; *U.S. Public*, pg. 1195
PUBLIC SERVICE COMPANY OF NEW MEXICO; *U.S. Public*, pg. 1339
PUBLIC SERVICE COMPANY OF OKLAHOMA—Central and South West Corporation; *U.S. Public*, pg. 324
PUBLIC SERVICE ENTERPRISE GROUP INCORPORATED; *U.S. Public*, pg. 1340
PUBLIC UTILITY DISTRICT NO. 2 OF GRANT COUNTY; *U.S. Private*, pg. 893
PUGET ENERGY INC.—Puget Sound Energy, Inc.; *U.S. Public*, pg. 1342
PUGET SOUND ENERGY, INC.; *U.S. Public*, pg. 1342
QST ENERGY, INC.—CILCORP Inc.; *U.S. Public*, pg. 367
QST ENTERPRISES INC.—CILCORP Inc.; *U.S. Public*, pg. 367
RWE-DEA AG—RWE AG; *Int'l*, pg. 1081
RED HILL COAL CO.—Kansas City Power & Light Company; *U.S. Public*, pg. 943
REGLAR SRL—Alusuisse-Lonza Holding Ltd.; *Int'l*, pg. 69
RESEARCH CENTER, INC.—United Illuminating Company; *U.S. Public*, pg. 1678
RESINMEC SPA—Alusuisse-Lonza Holding Ltd.; *Int'l*, pg. 69
ROANOKE VALLEY PLANT—LG & E Energy Corp.; *U.S. Public*, pg. 970
ROCHESTER GAS AND ELECTRIC CORPORATION; *U.S.* Public, pg. 1395
ROCKLAND ELECTRIC CO.—Orange and Rockland Utilities, Inc.; *U.S. Public*, pg. 1229
RURAL ELECTRIC CO-OP; *U.S. Private*, pg. 952
SAARBERG-FERNWAERME GMBH—Saarbergwerke Aktiengesellschaft; *Int'l*, pg. 1166
SAARBERGWERKE AKTIENGESELLSCHAFT; *Int'l*, pg. 1166
SAARLAENDISCHE KRAFTWERKSGESELLSCHAFT MBH—Saarbergwerke Aktiengesellschaft; *Int'l*, pg. 1167
SACRAMENTO MUNICIPAL UTILITY DISTRICT; *U.S. Private*, pg. 959
SAFE HARBOR WATER POWER CORP.—Baltimore Gas and Electric Company; *U.S. Public*, pg. 172
SAFE HARBOR WATER POWER CORP.—PP&L Resources; *U.S. Public*, pg. 1244
SASKPOWER; *Int'l*, pg. 1195
SAUDI AMERICAN GENERAL ELECTRIC—General Electric Company; *U.S. Public*, pg. 713
SAVANNAH ELECTRIC & POWER CO.—Southern Company; *U.S. Public*, pg. 1490
SCHLESWAG AKTIENGESELLSCHAFT—Veba AG; *Int'l*, pg. 1456
SEATTLE CITY LIGHT; *U.S. Private*, pg. 979
SIEMENS AG; *Int'l*, pg. 1244
SIMKO TICARET VE SANAYI A.S.—Siemens AG; *Int'l*, pg. 1248
SIOUX VALLEY SOUTHWESTERN ELECTRIC ASSOCIATION; *U.S. Private*, pg. 1004
SOUTH CAROLINA GENERATING CO., INC.—SCANA Corporation; *U.S. Public*, pg. 1436
SOUTH FLORIDA TEST SERVICE—Atlas Electric Devices Co.; *U.S. Private*, pg. 96
SOUTHERN CALIFORNIA EDISON COMPANY—Edison International; *U.S. Public*, pg. 564
SOUTHERN COMPANY; *U.S. Public*, pg. 1489
SOUTHERN ELECTRIC GENERATING CO.—Southern Company; *U.S. Public*, pg. 1490
SOUTHWESTERN ELECTRIC POWER CO.—Central and South West Corporation; *U.S. Public*, pg. 324
SOUTHWESTERN ELECTRIC SERVICE CO.—Texas Utilities Company; *U.S. Public*, pg. 1588
SOUTHWESTERN PUBLIC SERVICE COMPANY—New Century Energies, Inc.; *U.S. Public*, pg. 1170
STORA KOPPARBERGS BERGSLAGS AB; *Int'l*, pg. 1302
STORA POWER AB—Stora Kopparbergs Bergslags AB; *Int'l*, pg. 1303
THE STORMONT ELECTRIC LIGHT & POWER COMPANY LIMITED—Sun Life Assurance Company of Canada; *Int'l*, pg. 1319
SUN LIFE ASSURANCE COMPANY OF CANADA; *Int'l*, pg. 1318
SUNFLOWER ELECTRIC POWER CORPORATION; *U.S. Private*, pg. 1052
SUSQUEHANNA ELECTRIC CO.—PECO Energy Company; *U.S. Public*, pg. 1268
SUSQUEHANNA POWER CO.—PECO Energy Company; *U.S. Public*, pg. 1268
SYSTEM ENERGY RESOURCES, INC.—Entergy Corporation; *U.S. Public*, pg. 586
TNP ENTERPRISES, INC.; *U.S. Public*, pg. 1557
TNP ONE—TNP Enterprises, Inc.; *U.S. Public*, pg. 1557
TU ELECTRIC—Texas Utilities Company; *U.S. Public*, pg. 1588
TALLAPOOSA RIVER ELECTRIC CO-OP; *U.S. Private*, pg. 1067
TAMPA ELECTRIC CO.—TECO Energy, Inc.; *U.S. Public*, pg. 1565
TAPOCO, INC.—Aluminum Company of America; *U.S. Public*, pg. 61
TECO ENERGY, INC.; *U.S. Public*, pg. 1565
TENNESSEE VALLEY AUTHORITY; *U.S. Public*, pg. 1580
TEXAS GENERATING COMPANY—TNP Enterprises, Inc.; *U.S. Public*, pg. 1557
TEXAS-NEW MEXICO POWER CO.—TNP Enterprises, Inc.; *U.S. Public*, pg. 1557
TEXAS UTILITIES COMPANY; *U.S. Public*, pg. 1586
THERMO ELECTRON CORPORATION; *U.S. Public*, pg. 1591

THUGA AKTIENGESELLSCHAFT—Veba AG; Int'l, pg. 1456
TOHOKU ELECTRIC POWER CO., LTD.; Int'l, pg. 1390
THE TOKYO ELECTRIC POWER CO., INC.; Int'l, pg. 1394
THE TOLEDO EDISON COMPANY—FirstEnergy Corp.; U.S. Public, pg. 645
TRANSALTA CORPORATION; Int'l, pg. 1416
TRICO ELECTRIC CO-OP; U.S. Private, pg. 1102
TUCSON ELECTRIC POWER COMPANY—UniSource Energy Corporation; U.S. Public, pg. 1670
UGI CORPORATION; U.S. Public, pg. 1653
UBERLANDWERK LEINETAL GMBH—Veba AG; Int'l, pg. 1457
UBERLANDWERK NORD HANNOVER AG—Veba AG; Int'l, pg. 1457
UNITED ENERGY INTERNATIONAL, INC.—United Illuminating Company; U.S. Public, pg. 1678
UNITED ILLUMINATING COMPANY; U.S. Public, pg. 1678
UNITED POWER ASSOCIATION; U.S. Private, pg. 1123
UNITIL POWER CORPORATION—Unitil Corporation; U.S. Public, pg. 1692
UTAH POWER & LIGHT—PacifiCorp; U.S. Public, pg. 1251
UTILCO GROUP—UtiliCorp United Inc.; U.S. Public, pg. 1701
UTILICORP UNITED INC.; U.S. Public, pg. 1700
A/S VAN SEVEREN & CO. LTD.—Norske Skogindustrier A.S; Int'l, pg. 965
VATTENFALL AB; Int'l, pg. 1452
VEBA AG; Int'l, pg. 1454
VERMONT ELECTRIC POWER CO., INC.—Central Vermont Public Service Corporation; U.S. Public, pg. 328
VERMONT ENERGY RESOURCES, INC.—Green Mountain Power Corporation; U.S. Public, pg. 761
VERMONT YANKEE NUCLEAR POWER CORP.—Central Vermont Public Service Corporation; U.S. Public, pg. 328
VIRGINIA ELECTRIC AND POWER COMPANY—Dominion Resources, Inc.; U.S. Public, pg. 516
VOLKSWAGEN AG PREUSSENELEKTRA AG OHG—Veba AG; Int'l, pg. 1456
WPS LEASING, INC.—WPS Resources Corp.; U.S. Public, pg. 1728
THE WEST HARRISON GAS AND ELECTRIC CO.—Cinergy Corp.; U.S. Public, pg. 369
WEST KOOTENAY POWER—UtiliCorp United Inc.; U.S. Public, pg. 1701
WEST PENN POWER CO.—Allegheny Power System, Inc.; U.S. Public, pg. 42
WEST PLAINS ENERGY—UtiliCorp United Inc.; U.S. Public, pg. 1701
WEST TEXAS UTILITIES CO.—Central and South West Corporation; U.S. Public, pg. 324
WEST VIRGINIA POWER—UtiliCorp United Inc.; U.S. Public, pg. 1701
WESTERN COOPERATIVE ELECTRIC ASSOCIATION, INC.; U.S. Private, pg. 1165
WHEELING POWER COMPANY—American Electric Power Company, Inc.; U.S. Public, pg. 73
WINDMASTER NEDERLAND B.V.—Royal Begemann Group; Int'l, pg. 1134
WISCONSIN ELECTRIC POWER COMPANY—Wisconsin Energy Corporation; U.S. Public, pg. 1773
WISCONSIN ENERGY CORPORATION; U.S. Public, pg. 1773
WISCONSIN PUBLIC SERVICE CORPORATION—WPS Resources Corp.; U.S. Public, pg. 1728
WOLF CREEK NUCLEAR OPERATING CORP.—Kansas City Power & Light Company; U.S. Public, pg. 943
WOLF CREEK NUCLEAR OPERATING CORP.—Western Resources, Inc.; U.S. Public, pg. 1759
WOODRUFF ELECTRIC CO-OP; U.S. Private, pg. 1187
WYMO FUELS INC.—Kansas City Power & Light Company; U.S. Public, pg. 943
YADKIN, INC.—Aluminum Company of America; U.S. Public, pg. 61
YANKEE ATOMIC ELECTRIC CO.—Central Maine Power Company; U.S. Public, pg. 325
THE YUKON ELECTRICAL CO. LTD.—ATCO Group Co.; Int'l, pg. 95

4922 — NATURAL GAS TRANSMISSION

ANR PIPELINE CO.—The Coastal Corporation; U.S. Public, pg. 389
ANR STORAGE CO.—The Coastal Corporation; U.S. Public, pg. 389
ALGONQUIN GAS TRANSMISSION CORPORATION—Duke Energy Corporation; U.S. Public, pg. 534
AMOCO GAS COMPANY—Royal Dutch/Shell Group of Companies; Int'l, pg. 1136
ARKANSAS WESTERN PIPELINE COMPANY—Southwestern Energy Company; U.S. Public, pg. 1494
BC GAS INC.; Int'l, pg. 114
BG PLC; Int'l, pg. 118
BASIN PIPELINE CORP.—Energen Corporation; U.S. Public, pg. 581
CNG TRANSMISSION CORPORATION—Consolidated Natural Gas Company; U.S. Public, pg. 435
CANADIAN-MONTANA PIPELINE CO.—Montana Power Company; U.S. Public, pg. 1127
CENTRA GAS ALBERTA INC.—Westcoast Energy Inc.; Int'l, pg. 1492
CENTRA GAS BRITISH COLUMBIA INC.—Westcoast Energy Inc.; Int'l, pg. 1492
CENTRA GAS INC.—Westcoast Energy Inc.; Int'l, pg. 1492
CENTRA GAS MANITOBA INC.—Westcoast Energy Inc.; Int'l, pg. 1492
CENTRA GAS ONTARIO INC.—Westcoast Energy Inc.; Int'l, pg. 1492
CHANDELEUR PIPE LINE CO.—Chevron Corporation; U.S. Public, pg. 348
CHANNEL INDUSTRIES GAS CO.—Tenneco Inc.; U.S. Public, pg. 1579
CHESAPEAKE UTILITIES CORPORATION; U.S. Public, pg. 347
CHEVRON CORPORATION; U.S. Public, pg. 347
CHEVRON PIPE LINE COMPANY—Chevron Corporation; U.S. Public, pg. 348
CITIZENS GAS FUEL COMPANY—MCN Energy Group, Inc.; U.S. Public, pg. 1025
CITRUS CORP.—Enron Corp.; U.S. Public, pg. 585
CITRUS CORP.—Sonat Inc.; U.S. Public, pg. 1485
THE COASTAL CORPORATION; U.S. Public, pg. 389
COLORADO INTERSTATE GAS CO.—The Coastal Corporation; U.S. Public, pg. 390
COLUMBIA ENERGY GROUP; U.S. Public, pg. 402
COLUMBIA GAS TRANSMISSION CORP.—Columbia Energy Group; U.S. Public, pg. 403
COLUMBIA GULF TRANSMISSION CO.—Columbia Energy Group; U.S. Public, pg. 403
COMMONWEALTH ENERGY SYSTEM; U.S. Public, pg. 414
CORNERSTONE NATURAL GAS, INC.—El Paso Natural Gas Co.; U.S. Public, pg. 567
DELTRAN, INC.—Delta Natural Gas Company, Inc.; U.S. Public, pg. 497
DISTRIGAS CORP.—Cabot Corporation; U.S. Public, pg. 289
DUKE ENERGY CORPORATION; U.S. Public, pg. 534
DUKE ENERGY INTERNATIONAL, L.L.C.—Duke Energy Corporation; U.S. Public, pg. 534
ENI GAS SERVICES, INC.—CTG Resources, Inc.; U.S. Public, pg. 285
ET STORAGE COMPANY—Equitable Resources, Inc.; U.S. Public, pg. 590
EAST TENNESSEE NATURAL GAS CO.—El Paso Natural Gas Co.; U.S. Public, pg. 567
EASTERN SHORE NATURAL GAS COMPANY—Chesapeake Utilities Corporation; U.S. Public, pg. 347
EASTEX GAS TRANSMISSION CO.—El Paso Natural Gas Co.; U.S. Public, pg. 567
ENDEVCO PRODUCING CO.—El Paso Natural Gas Co.; U.S. Public, pg. 567
ENRON CORP.; U.S. Public, pg. 584
ENTERPRISE PRODUCTS COMPANY; U.S. Private, pg. 377
EQUITABLE PIPELINE COMPANY—Equitable Resources, Inc.; U.S. Public, pg. 590
EQUITABLE RESOURCES, INC.; U.S. Public, pg. 589
EQUITABLE STORAGE COMPANY—Equitable Resources, Inc.; U.S. Public, pg. 590
EQUITRANS, INC.—Equitable Resources, Inc.; U.S. Public, pg. 590
EXXON PIPELINE COMPANY—Exxon Corporation; U.S. Public, pg. 601
FLORIDA GAS TRANSMISSION CO.—Enron Corp.; U.S. Public, pg. 585
GRANITE STATE GAS TRANSMISSION, INC.—Bay State Gas Company; U.S. Public, pg. 197
GREAT LAKES GAS TRANSMISSION CO.—Transcanada Pipelines Limited; Int'l, pg. 1417
HAMPSHIRE GAS CO.—Washington Gas Light Co.; U.S. Public, pg. 1740
HARBERT CORPORATION; U.S. Private, pg. 500
HOPKINTON LNG CORP.—Commonwealth Energy System; U.S. Public, pg. 415
HOUSTON PIPE LINE CO.—Enron Corp.; U.S. Public, pg. 584
IRISH BULK LIQUID STORAGE LTD.—Simon Engineering plc; Int'l, pg. 1252
K N ENERGY, INC.; U.S. Public, pg. 937
KCS PIPELINE SYSTEMS, INC.—KCS Energy Inc.; U.S. Public, pg. 939
KENTUCKY WEST VIRGINIA GAS CO.—Equitable Resources, Inc.; U.S. Public, pg. 590
KIBO COMPRESSOR CORP.—Burk Royalty Co.; U.S. Private, pg. 183
LNG STORAGE INC.—Essex County Gas Company; U.S. Public, pg. 593
LACLEDE PIPELINE CO.—Laclede Gas Company; U.S. Public, pg. 974
LOUISIANA INTRASTATE GAS CORPORATION—Equitable Resources, Inc.; U.S. Public, pg. 590
MCN ENERGY GROUP, INC.; U.S. Public, pg. 1024
MDU RESOURCES GROUP, INC.; U.S. Public, pg. 1025
MGS STORAGE SERVICES, INC.—Mobile Gas Service Corp.; U.S. Public, pg. 1120
MGTC, INC.—Western Gas Resources, Inc.; U.S. Public, pg. 1758
MIGC, INC.—Western Gas Resources, Inc.; U.S. Public, pg. 1758
MANNESMANN ANLAGENBAU AG—Mannesmann A.G.; Int'l, pg. 836
MICHCON—MCN Energy Group, Inc.; U.S. Public, pg. 1025
MICHIGAN GAS STORAGE CO.—CMS Energy Corporation; U.S. Public, pg. 280
MIDCON CORP.—Occidental Petroleum Corporation; U.S. Public, pg. 1210
MIDCON TEXAS PIPELINE OPERATOR, INC.—Occidental Petroleum Corporation; U.S. Public, pg. 1210
MIDWESTERN GAS TRANSMISSION CO.—El Paso Natural Gas Co.; U.S. Public, pg. 567
MISSISSIPPI RIVER TRANSMISSION—Houston Industries Incorporated; U.S. Public, pg. 843
MITSUI LIQUEFIED GAS CO., LTD.—Mitsui & Co., Ltd.; Int'l, pg. 877
NGO DEVELOPMENT CORPORATION—National Gas & Oil Company; U.S. Public, pg. 1157
NATIONAL FUEL GAS SUPPLY CORP.—National Fuel Gas Company; U.S. Public, pg. 1156
NATIONAL GAS & OIL COMPANY; U.S. Public, pg. 1156
NATURAL GAS PIPELINE CO. AMERICA—Occidental Petroleum Corporation; U.S. Public, pg. 1210
NEDERLANDSE GASUNIE N.V.—Royal Dutch/Shell Group of Companies; Int'l, pg. 1135
N.V. NEDERLANDSE GASUNIE—Exxon Corporation; U.S. Public, pg. 602
NI-TEX, INC.—NIPSCO Industries, Inc.; U.S. Public, pg. 1185
NORA TRANSMISSION CO.—Equitable Resources, Inc.; U.S. Public, pg. 590
NORAM GAS TRANSMISSION—Houston Industries Incorporated; U.S. Public, pg. 843
NORTH CAROLINA NATURAL GAS CORPORATION; U.S. Public, pg. 1194
NORTHERN GAS COMPANY—K N Energy, Inc.; U.S. Public, pg. 937
NORTHERN NATURAL GAS CO.—Enron Corp.; U.S. Public, pg. 584
NORTHERN PLAINS NATURAL GAS CO.—Enron Corp.; U.S. Public, pg. 584
NORTHROCK RESOURCES LTD.; Int'l, pg. 970
NORTHWEST PIPELINE CORP.—The Williams Companies, Inc.; U.S. Public, pg. 1769
OGE ENERGY CORP.; U.S. Public, pg. 1207
ONG SAYRE STORAGE CO.—ONEOK Inc.; U.S. Public, pg. 1226
ONG TRANSMISSION COMPANY—ONEOK Inc.; U.S. Public, pg. 1226
OKLAHOMA NATURAL GAS COMPANY—ONEOK Inc.; U.S. Public, pg. 1226
ONEOK INC.; U.S. Public, pg. 1226
OSAKA GAS CO., LTD.; Int'l, pg. 1011
OSAKA GAS CO.-NEW YORK—Osaka Gas Co., Ltd.; Int'l, pg. 1012
PACIFIC INTERSTATE TRANSMISSION COMPANY—Pacific Enterprises; U.S. Public, pg. 1249
PACIFIC INTERSTATE TRANSMISSION COMPANY (ARCTIC)—Pacific Enterprises; U.S. Public, pg. 1249
PACIFIC NORTHERN GAS LTD.—Westcoast Energy Inc.; Int'l, pg. 1492
PAIUTE PIPELINE CO.—Southwest Gas Corporation; U.S. Public, pg. 1493
PARAMOUNT TRANSMISSION CORP.—Petroleum Development Corporation; U.S. Public, pg. 1281
PEACE RIVER TRANSMISSION CO., LTD.—BC Gas Inc.; Int'l, pg. 114
PETROLEUM DEVELOPMENT CORPORATION; U.S. Public, pg. 1280
PHILLIPS PETROLEUM COMPANY; U.S. Public, pg. 1290
PIEDMONT ENERGY COMPANY—Piedmont Natural Gas Co., Inc.; U.S. Public, pg. 1295
PIEDMONT INTRASTATE PIPELINE COMPANY—Piedmont Natural Gas Co., Inc.; U.S. Public, pg. 1295
PRODUCTION OPERATORS INC.—Camco International Inc.; U.S. Public, pg. 298
PUBLIC SERVICE ENTERPRISE GROUP INCORPORATED; U.S. Public, pg. 1340
QUESTAR CORPORATION; U.S. Public, pg. 1352
QUESTAR PIPELINE COMPANY—Questar Corporation; U.S. Public, pg. 1352
ST. CLAIR PIPELINES—Westcoast Energy Inc.; Int'l, pg. 1492
SEADRIFT PIPELINE CORP.—Union Carbide Corporation; U.S. Public, pg. 1667
SONAT INC.; U.S. Public, pg. 1484
SOUTHEASTERN MICHIGAN GAS ENTERPRISES, INC.; U.S. Public, pg. 1489
SOUTHERN NATURAL GAS COMPANY—Sonat Inc.; U.S. Public, pg. 1485
SOUTHWEST GAS CORPORATION; U.S. Public, pg. 1493
SOUTHWEST GAS TRANSMISSION COMPANY—Southwest Gas Corporation; U.S. Public, pg. 1493
SOUTHWESTERN ENERGY PIPELINE COMPANY—Southwestern Energy Company; U.S. Public, pg. 1494
STEUART INVESTMENT COMPANY; U.S. Private, pg. 1042
SUDPETROL A.G.—ENI S.p.A.; Int'l, pg. 429
TBG MANAGEMENT S.A.M.; Int'l, pg. 1335
TENNECO GAS PIPELINE GROUP—Tenneco Inc.; U.S. Public, pg. 1578
TENNESSEE GAS TRANSMISSION CO.—El Paso Natural Gas Co.; U.S. Public, pg. 567
TEXACO INC.; U.S. Public, pg. 1582
TEXAS EASTERN TRANSMISSION CORP.—Duke Energy Corporation; U.S. Public, pg. 535
TRANS AUSTRIA GASLEITUNG GMBH—ENI S.p.A.; Int'l, pg. 429
TRANS QUEBEC & MARITIMES PIPELINE—Transcanada Pipelines Limited; Int'l, pg. 1417
TRANSCANADA PIPELINES LIMITED; Int'l, pg. 1416
TRANSCONTINENTAL GAS PIPE LINE CORP.—The Williams Companies, Inc.; U.S. Public, pg. 1769
TRUNKLINE GAS CO.—Duke Energy Corporation; U.S. Public, pg. 534
UCAR PIPELINE, INC.—Union Carbide Corporation; U.S. Public, pg. 1667
USX CORPORATION; U.S. Public, pg. 1661
VELVA LIQUIDS LTD.—Simon Engineering plc; Int'l, pg. 1251
WESTCOAST ENERGY INC.; Int'l, pg. 1492
WESTGAS INTERSTATE, INC.—New Century Energies, Inc.; U.S. Public, pg. 1170
THE WILLIAMS COMPANIES, INC.; U.S. Public, pg. 1769
WILLIAMS NATURAL GAS COMPANY—The Williams Companies, Inc.; U.S. Public, pg. 1769
WILLISTON BASIN INTERSTATE PIPELINE COMPANY—MDU Resources Group, Inc.; U.S. Public, pg. 1026
YALE E KEY, INC.—Key Energy Group Inc.; U.S. Public, pg. 953
YORK RESEARCH CORPORATION; U.S. Public, pg. 1789

4923 — NATURAL GAS TRANSMISSION & DISTRIBUTION

ANR PIPELINE CO.—The Coastal Corporation; U.S. Public, pg. 389
ABU DHABI GAS INDUSTRIES—Royal Dutch/Shell Group of Companies; Int'l, pg. 1140
ACTION SUPPLY—Action Equipment; U.S. Private, pg. 15
ALABAMA TENNESSEE NATURAL GAS COMPANY—Midcoast Energy Resources, Inc.; U.S. Public, pg. 1109

AMERICAN OIL & GAS CORPORATION—K N Energy, Inc.; *U.S. Public*, pg. 937
APOLLO GAS CO.—USX Corporation; *U.S. Public*, pg. 1661
ARKANSAS WESTERN GAS CO.—Southwestern Energy Company; *U.S. Public*, pg. 1494
ATCO GAS SERVICES LTD.—ATCO Group Co.; *Int'l*, pg. 95
ATRION CORPORATION; *U.S. Public*, pg. 146
BC GAS INC.; *Int'l*, pg. 114
BRAZOS FUEL COMPANY INC.—Brazos Electric Power Cooperative, Inc.; *U.S. Private*, pg. 166
CABOT CORPORATION; *U.S. Public*, pg. 288
CANADIAN WESTERN NATURAL GAS COMPANY LIMITED—ATCO Group Co.; *Int'l*, pg. 95
CARNEGIE NATURAL GAS CO.—USX Corporation; *U.S. Public*, pg. 1661
CHINESE PETROLEUM CORPORATION; *Int'l*, pg. 286
CINERGY CORP.; *U.S. Public*, pg. 368
THE COASTAL CORPORATION; *U.S. Public*, pg. 389
COLUMBIA ENERGY GROUP; *U.S. Public*, pg. 402
COLUMBIA GAS SYSTEM SERVICE CORP.—Columbia Energy Group; *U.S. Public*, pg. 403
CONSOLIDATED NATURAL GAS COMPANY; *U.S. Public*, *pg. 435*
CORNERSTONE NATURAL GAS, INC.—El Paso Natural Gas Co.; *U.S. Public*, pg. 567
CORNERSTONE PIPELINE CO.—El Paso Natural Gas Co.; *U.S. Public*, pg. 567
DISTRIGAS OF MASSACHUSETTS CORPORATION—Cabot Corporation; *U.S. Public*, pg. 289
DISTRIGAZ SA SOC. DE DISTRIBUTION DU GAZ—Royal Dutch/Shell Group of Companies; *Int'l*, pg. 1138
THE EAST OHIO GAS CO.—Consolidated Natural Gas Company; *U.S. Public*, pg. 435
EL PASO ENERGY—El Paso Natural Gas Co.; *U.S. Public*, pg. 567
EL PASO NATURAL GAS CO.; *U.S. Public*, pg. 567
ENOGEX INC.—OGE Energy Corp.; *U.S. Public*, pg. 1207
ENRON ACESS—Enron Corp.; *U.S. Public*, pg. 584
ENSERCH CORPORATION—Texas Utilities Company; *U.S.* Public, pg. 1587
ENSERCH GAS CO.—Texas Utilities Company; *U.S. Public*, *pg. 1587*
ENTEX—Houston Industries Incorporated; *U.S. Public*, pg. 843
EQUITABLE RESOURCES, INC.; *U.S. Public*, pg. 589
EQUITABLE RESOURCES MARKETING COMPANY—Equitable Resources, Inc.; *U.S. Public*, pg. 590
FALL RIVER GAS COMPANY; *U.S. Public*, pg. 611
FIORENTINA GAS S.P.A.—ENI S.p.A.; *Int'l*, pg. 428
HADSON CORPORATION—Apache Corporation; *U.S. Public*, pg. 119
ITALGAS S.P.A.—ENI S.p.A.; *Int'l*, pg. 428
K N ENERGY, INC.; *U.S. Public*, pg. 937
K N GAS MARKETING, INC.—K N Energy, Inc.; *U.S. Public*, pg. 937
KEYSTONE PIPELINE SERVICES, INC.—Pennsylvania Enterprises Inc.; *U.S. Public*, pg. 1271
LGS PIPELINE, INC.—Citizens Utilities Company; *U.S. Public*, pg. 380
LONE STAR GAS CO.—Texas Utilities Company; *U.S. Public*, pg. 1587
LOUISIANA GAS SERVICE CO.—Citizens Utilities Company; *U.S. Public*, pg. 380
MG NATURAL GAS CORPORATION—Metallgesellschaft AG; *Int'l*, pg. 862
MID CONTINENT MARKET CENTER—Western Resources, Inc.; *U.S. Public*, pg. 1759
MIDCOAST ENERGY RESOURCES, INC.; *U.S. Public*, pg. 1109
MIDCOAST MARKETING COMPANY—Midcoast Energy Resources, Inc.; *U.S. Public*, pg. 1109
MISSISSIPPI VALLEY GAS CO.; *U.S. Private*, pg. 753
MITCHELL ENERGY & DEVELOPMENT CORP.; *U.S. Public*, pg. 1117
MOUNTAIN FUEL SUPPLY COMPANY—Questar Corporation; *U.S. Public*, pg. 1352
MOUNTAIN GAS REOURCES, INC.—Western Gas Resources, Inc.; *U.S. Public*, pg. 1758
NGO DEVELOPMENT CORPORATION—National Gas & Oil Company; *U.S. Public*, pg. 1157
NATIONAL GAS & OIL COMPANY; *U.S. Public*, pg. 1156
NATIONAL GAS & OIL CORP.—National Gas & Oil Company; *U.S. Public*, pg. 1157
NORAM ENERGY CORP.—Houston Industries Incorporated; *U.S. Public*, pg. 843
NORTHLAND UTILITIES (B.C.) LIMITED—ATCO Group Co.; *Int'l*, pg. 95
NORTHLAND UTILITIES ENTERPRISES LTD.—ATCO Group Co.; *Int'l*, pg. 95
NORTHLAND UTILITIES (NWT) LIMITED—ATCO Group Co.; *Int'l*, pg. 95
OSAKA GAS CO., LTD.; *Int'l*, pg. 1011
OSAKA GAS CO.-NEW YORK—Osaka Gas Co., Ltd.; *Int'l*, pg. 1012
PG&E CORPORATION; *U.S. Public*, pg. 1240
PG ENERGY, INC.—Pennsylvania Enterprises Inc.; *U.S. Public*, pg. 1271
PACIFIC INTERSTATE COMPANY—Pacific Enterprises; *U.S. Public*, pg. 1249
PACIFIC NORTHERN GAS LTD.—Westcoast Energy Inc.; *Int'l*, pg. 1492
PENNSYLVANIA ENTERPRISES INC.; *U.S. Public*, pg. 1271
PINNACLE GAS TREATING, INC.—Western Gas Resources, Inc.; *U.S. Public*, pg. 1758
PRODUCERS GAS SALES, INC.—National Gas & Oil Company; *U.S. Public*, pg. 1157
QUESTAR CORPORATION; *U.S. Public*, pg. 1352
ROCKY MOUNTAIN NATURAL GAS CO.—K N Energy, Inc.; *U.S. Public*, pg. 937
ROYAL DUTCH/SHELL GROUP OF COMPANIES; *Int'l*, pg. 1135
SAARBERG-FERNWAERME GMBH—Saarbergwerke Aktiengesellschaft; *Int'l*, pg. 1166
SCANA CORPORATION; *U.S. Public*, pg. 1436
SNAM S.P.A.—ENI S.p.A.; *Int'l*, pg. 428
SOUTH CAROLINA PIPELINE CORPORATION—SCANA Corporation; *U.S. Public*, pg. 1436
SOUTHERN CALIFORNIA GAS CO.—Pacific Enterprises; *U.S. Public*, pg. 1249
SOUTHERN UNION COMPANY; *U.S. Public*, pg. 1491
SOUTHWESTERN ENERGY COMPANY; *U.S. Public*, pg. 1494
SOUTHWESTERN GAS PIPELINE, INC.—Mitchell Energy & Development Corp.; *U.S. Public*, pg. 1117
TENNECO INC.; *U.S. Public*, pg. 1577
TENNESSEE RIVER INTRASTATE GAS COMPANY—Midcoast Energy Resources, Inc.; *U.S. Public*, pg. 1109
TIRRENIA GAS S.P.A.—ENI S.p.A.; *Int'l*, pg. 428
TRANSWESTERN PIPELINE CO.—Enron Corp.; *U.S. Public*, pg. 585
TRISTAR VENTURES CORPORATION—Columbia Energy Group; *U.S. Public*, pg. 403
UGI CORPORATION; *U.S. Public*, pg. 1653
UNIGAS—Westcoast Energy Inc.; *Int'l*, pg. 1492
UNION ENERGY INC.—Westcoast Energy Inc.; *Int'l*, pg. 1492
UNIT CORPORATION; *U.S. Public*, pg. 1672
VALERO ENERGY CORPORATION; *U.S. Public*, pg. 1704
VENEZIANA GAS S.P.A.—ENI S.p.A.; *Int'l*, pg. 428
WARRIOR BASIN GAS COMPANY—Atrion Corporation; *U.S. Public*, pg. 146
WESTANA GATHERING COMPANY—Duke Energy Corporation; *U.S. Public*, pg. 535
WESTANA GATHERING COMPANY—Western Gas Resources, Inc.; *U.S. Public*, pg. 1759
WESTERN GAS RESOURCES CANADA, INC.—Western Gas Resources, Inc.; *U.S. Public*, pg. 1759
WESTERN GAS RESOURCES, INC.; *U.S. Public*, pg. 1758
WESTERN GAS RESOURCES STORAGE, INC.—Western Gas Resources, Inc.; *U.S. Public*, pg. 1759
WESTERN GAS RESOURCES-LOUISIANA, INC.—Western Gas Resources, Inc.; *U.S. Public*, pg. 1758
WESTERN GAS RESOURCES-OKLAHOMA, INC.—Western Gas Resources, Inc.; *U.S. Public*, pg. 1758
WESTERN GAS RESOURCES-TEXAS, INC.—Western Gas Resources, Inc.; *U.S. Public*, pg. 1759
WICOR, INC.; *U.S. Public*, pg. 1767
WISCONSIN GAS COMPANY—WICOR, Inc.; *U.S. Public*, pg. 1767
YANKEE GAS SERVICES COMPANY—Yankee Energy System, Inc.; *U.S. Public*, pg. 1788
THE YUKON ELECTRICAL CO. LTD.—ATCO Group Co.; *Int'l*, pg. 95

4924 — NATURAL GAS DISTRIBUTION

AGL RESOURCES; *U.S. Public*, pg. 6
ANR PIPELINE CO.—The Coastal Corporation; *U.S. Public*, pg. 389
AGWAY ENERGY PRODUCTS (AEP)—Agway, Inc.; *U.S. Private*, pg. 27
ALABAMA GAS CORPORATION—Energen Corporation; *U.S. Public*, pg. 581
ARKLA—Houston Industries Incorporated; *U.S. Public*, pg. 843
ATMOS ENERGY CORPORATION; *U.S. Public*, pg. 145
BALTIMORE GAS AND ELECTRIC COMPANY; *U.S. Public*, pg. 172
BARRETT FUELS CORPORATION—Barrett Resources Corporation; *U.S. Public*, pg. 191
BATTLE CREEK GAS COMPANY—Southeastern Michigan Gas Enterprises, Inc.; *U.S. Public*, pg. 1489
BAY STATE GAS COMPANY; *U.S. Public*, pg. 196
THE BERKSHIRE GAS COMPANY; *U.S. Public*, pg. 216
BLUEFIELD GAS COMPANY—Roanoke Gas Company; *U.S. Public*, pg. 1393
BOSTON GAS COMPANY—Eastern Enterprises; *U.S. Public*, pg. 549
BREVARD DIV.—NUI Corporation; *U.S. Public*, pg. 1148
BRISTOL & WARREN GAS COMPANY—Valley Resources, Inc.; *U.S. Public*, pg. 1706
BROOKLYN UNION; *U.S. Public*, pg. 259
CG&E RESOURCE MARKETING, INC.—Cinergy Corp.; *U.S.* Public, pg. 369
CNG ENERGY SERVICES CORPORATION—Consolidated Natural Gas Company; *U.S. Public*, pg. 435
CANCARB GAS SERVICES LIMITED—Transcanada Pipelines Limited; *Int'l*, pg. 1417
CASCADE NATURAL GAS CORPORATION; *U.S. Public*, pg. 311
CELERON CORPORATION—The Goodyear Tire & Rubber Company; *U.S. Public*, pg. 753
CHESAPEAKE UTILITIES CORPORATION; *U.S. Public*, pg. 347
CILCORP INC.; *U.S. Public*, pg. 367
CINERGY CORP.—Cinergy Corp.; *U.S. Public*, pg. 369
CINERGY SERVICES, INC.—Cinergy Corp.; *U.S. Public*, pg. 369
CITIZENS GAS FUEL COMPANY—MCN Energy Group, Inc.; *U.S. Public*, pg. 1025
CITIZENS UTILITIES COMPANY; *U.S. Public*, pg. 379
CITIZENS UTILITIES COMPANY—Citizens Utilities Company; *U.S. Public*, pg. 380
CITY GAS COMPANY OF FLORIDA—NUI Corporation; *U.S. Public*, pg. 1147
CODY GAS DIVISION—Energy West Inc.; *U.S. Public*, pg. 581
COLONIAL GAS COMPANY; *U.S. Public*, pg. 400
COLUMBIA ENERGY GROUP; *U.S. Public*, pg. 402
COLUMBIA ENERGY SERVICES CORPORATION—Columbia Energy Group; *U.S. Public*, pg. 402
COLUMBIA GAS DISTRIBUTION COMPANIES—Columbia Energy Group; *U.S. Public*, pg. 402
COLUMBIA GAS OF KENTUCKY, INC.—Columbia Energy Group; *U.S. Public*, pg. 403
COLUMBIA GAS OF MARYLAND, INC.—Columbia Energy Group; *U.S. Public*, pg. 403
COLUMBIA GAS OF OHIO, INC.—Columbia Energy Group; *U.S. Public*, pg. 403
COLUMBIA GAS OF PENNSYLVANIA, INC.—Columbia Energy Group; *U.S. Public*, pg. 403
COMMONWEALTH ENERGY SYSTEM; *U.S. Public*, pg. 414
COMMONWEALTH GAS CO.—Commonwealth Energy System; *U.S. Public*, pg. 415
COMMONWEALTH GAS SERVICES, INC.—Columbia Energy Group; *U.S. Public*, pg. 403
CONNECTICUT ENERGY CORPORATION; *U.S. Public*, pg. 431
CONNECTICUT NATURAL GAS CORPORATION—CTG Resources, Inc.; *U.S. Public*, pg. 285
CONSOLIDATED EDISON COMPANY OF NEW YORK, INC.; *U.S. Public*, pg. 434
CONSTELLATION ENERGY SOURCE, INC.—Baltimore Gas and Electric Company; *U.S. Public*, pg. 172
DPL INC.; *U.S. Public*, pg. 473
DAYTON POWER & LIGHT CO.—DPL Inc.; *U.S. Public*, pg. 473
DELCHESTER OIL CO. INC.—Heating Oil Partners L.P.; *U.S. Private*, pg. 518
DELTA NATURAL GAS COMPANY, INC.; *U.S. Public*, pg. 497
DUKE ENERGY FIELD SERVICES, INC.—Duke Energy Corporation; *U.S. Public*, pg. 534
THE EAST OHIO GAS CO.—Consolidated Natural Gas Company; *U.S. Public*, pg. 435
EASTERN ENTERPRISES; *U.S. Public*, pg. 548
EASTEX ENERGY INC.—El Paso Natural Gas Co.; *U.S. Public*, pg. 567
ELECTRABEL S.A.; *Int'l*, pg. 436
ELIZABETHTOWN GAS CO.—NUI Corporation; *U.S. Public*, *pg. 1147*
ENERCOP GAS MARKETING—KCS Energy Inc.; *U.S. Public*, pg. 938
ENERGAS COMPANY—Atmos Energy Corporation; *U.S. Public*, pg. 145
ENERGEN CORPORATION; *U.S. Public*, pg. 581
ENERGIEVERSORGUNG WESER-EMS AG—Veba AG; *Int'l*, pg. 1456
ENERGY WEST INC.; *U.S. Public*, pg. 581
ENERGYLINE CORPORATION—Rochester Gas And Electric Corporation; *U.S. Public*, pg. 1396
ENERGYNORTH, INC.; *U.S. Public*, pg. 581
ENERGYNORTH NATURAL GAS, INC.—EnergyNorth, Inc.; *U.S. Public*, pg. 582
ENOVA CORP; *U.S. Public*, pg. 583
ENRON OPERATIONS CORP.—Enron Corp.; *U.S. Public*, pg. 584
ENSERCH CORPORATION—Texas Utilities Company; *U.S.* Public, pg. 1587
ENTERGY CORPORATION; *U.S. Public*, pg. 585
ENTERGY NEW ORLEANS, INC.—Entergy Corporation; *U.S. Public*, pg. 586
EQUITABLE GAS CO.—Equitable Resources, Inc.; *U.S. Public*, pg. 589
EQUITABLE RESOURCES MARKETING COMPANY—Equitable Resources, Inc.; *U.S. Public*, pg. 590
ESSEX COUNTY GAS COMPANY; *U.S. Public*, pg. 593
FALL RIVER GAS COMPANY; *U.S. Public*, pg. 611
FITCHBURG GAS AND ELECTRIC LIGHT CO.—Unitil Corporation; *U.S. Public*, pg. 1692
FLORIDA PUBLIC UTILITIES COMPANY; *U.S. Public*, pg. 655
FREDERICK GAS CO., INC.—Washington Gas Light Co.; *U.S. Public*, pg. 1740
GASELWEST—Electrabel S.A.; *Int'l*, pg. 437
GAZ METROPOLITAIN & COMPANY; *Int'l*, pg. 541
GAZNAT SA (GAZNAT)—Alusuisse-Lonza Holding Ltd.; *Int'l*, pg. 67
GAZODUC SA—Alusuisse-Lonza Holding Ltd.; *Int'l*, pg. 67
GREELEY GAS CO.—Atmos Energy Corporation; *U.S. Public*, pg. 145
HADSON CORPORATION—Apache Corporation; *U.S. Public*, pg. 119
HANNOVER-BRAUNSCHWEIGISCHE STROMVERSORGUNGS-AG—Veba AG; *Int'l*, pg. 1456
HARDIN COUNTY GAS COMPANY—Atrion Corporation; *U.S. Public*, pg. 146
HOPE GAS, INC.—Consolidated Natural Gas Company; *U.S. Public*, pg. 435
HOWELL GAS MANAGEMENT CO.—Howell Corporation; *U.S. Public*, pg. 844
IGAO—Electrabel S.A.; *Int'l*, pg. 437
IGH—Electrabel S.A.; *Int'l*, pg. 437
IGI RESOURCES, INC.—Intermountain Industries, Inc.; *U.S.* Private, pg. 568
IGEHO—Electrabel S.A.; *Int'l*, pg. 437
ILLINOIS POWER COMPANY—Illinova Inc.; *U.S. Public*, pg. 869
INDIANA GAS COMPANY, INC.—Indiana Energy, Inc.; *U.S.* Public, pg. 875
INTEREST—Electrabel S.A.; *Int'l*, pg. 437
INTERGEM—Electrabel S.A.; *Int'l*, pg. 437
INTERMOSANE—Electrabel S.A.; *Int'l*, pg. 437
INTERMOUNTAIN GAS CO.—Intermountain Industries, Inc.; *U.S. Private*, pg. 568
INTERMOUNTAIN INDUSTRIES, INC.; *U.S. Private*, pg. 568
IVEKA—Electrabel S.A.; *Int'l*, pg. 437
IVERLEK—Electrabel S.A.; *Int'l*, pg. 437
K N ENERGY, INC.; *U.S. Public*, pg. 937
KCS ENERGY INC.; *U.S. Public*, pg. 938
KCS ENERGY MARKETING INC.—KCS Energy Inc.; *U.S. Public*, pg. 938
KCS ENERGY MARKETING, INC.—KCS Energy Inc.; *U.S. Public*, pg. 939

KO TRANSMISSION COMPANY—Cinergy Corp.; *U.S. Public*, pg. 369
KANSAS PUBLIC SERVICE—UtiliCorp United Inc.; *U.S. Public*, pg. 1701
KINETICA LIMITED—Du Pont (E.I. Du Pont De Nemours & Co.); *U.S. Public*, pg. 533
KROMSCHRODER (U.K.) LTD.—Ruhrgas Aktiengesellschaft; *Int'l*, pg. 1149
KVAERNER HAVTOR (UK) LIMITED—Kvaerner a.s.a.; *Int'l*, *pg. 771*
LG & E ENERGY CORP.; *U.S. Public*, pg. 970
LACLEDE GAS COMPANY; *U.S. Public*, pg. 973
LAWRENCEBURG GAS CO.—Cinergy Corp.; *U.S. Public*, pg. 369
LOUISVILLE GAS AND ELECTRIC COMPANY—LG & E Energy Corp.; *U.S. Public*, pg. 970
LYKES ENERGY, INC.; *U.S. Private*, pg. 682
LYONNAISE DES EAUX S.A.; *Int'l*, pg. 822
MC2 INC.—Occidental Petroleum Corporation; *U.S. Public*, pg. 1210
MCN ENERGY GROUP, INC.; *U.S. Public*, pg. 1024
MDU RESOURCES GROUP, INC.; *U.S. Public*, pg. 1025
MICHCON—MCN Energy Group, Inc.; *U.S. Public*, pg. 1025
MICHIGAN GAS COMPANY—Southeastern Michigan Gas Enterprises, Inc.; *U.S. Public*, pg. 1489
MICHIGAN GAS UTILITIES—UtiliCorp United Inc.; *U.S. Public*, pg. 1701
MIDCON GAS SERVICES CORP.—Occidental Petroleum Corporation; *U.S. Public*, pg. 1210
MINNEGASCO—Houston Industries Incorporated; *U.S. Public*, pg. 843
MINNESOTA POWER; *U.S. Public*, pg. 1116
MISSISSIPPI ENERGIES, INC.—Mississippi Valley Gas Co.; *U.S. Private*, pg. 753
MISSOURI PUBLIC SERVICE—UtiliCorp United Inc.; *U.S. Public*, pg. 1701
MOBILE GAS SERVICE CORP.; *U.S. Public*, pg. 1120
MONTANA-DAKOTA UTILITIES CO.—MDU Resources Group, Inc.; *U.S. Public*, pg. 1025
MOUNTAIN IRON & SUPPLY COMPANY; *U.S. Private*, pg. 764
NGC CORPORATION; *U.S. Public*, pg. 1146
NUI CORPORATION; *U.S. Public*, pg. 1147
NATIONAL FUEL GAS COMPANY; *U.S. Public*, pg. 1156
NATIONAL FUEL GAS DISTRIBUTION CORP.—National Fuel Gas Company; *U.S. Public*, pg. 1156
NEW JERSEY NATURAL GAS CO.—New Jersey Resources Corporation; *U.S. Public*, pg. 1172
NEW JERSEY RESOURCES CORPORATION; *U.S. Public*, pg. 1172
NEW YORK STATE ELECTRIC & GAS CORPORATION; *U.S. Public*, pg. 1173
NIAGARA MOHAWK POWER CORPORATION; *U.S. Public*, pg. 1181
NICOR INC.; *U.S. Public*, pg. 1182
NICOR TECHNOLOGIES—NICOR Inc.; *U.S. Public*, pg. 1183
NORTH ATTLEBORO GAS COMPANY—Providence Energy Corporation; *U.S. Public*, pg. 1337
NORTH CANADIAN MARKETING—EdperBrascan Corporation; *Int'l*, pg. 434
NORTH CANADIAN POWER—EdperBrascan Corporation; *Int'l*, pg. 434
NORTH MISSISSIPPI NATURAL GAS CORPORATION—Atrion Corporation; *U.S. Public*, pg. 146
NORTH SHORE GAS CO.—Peoples Energy Corporation; *U.S. Public*, pg. 1275
NORTHERN ILLINOIS GAS COMPANY—NICOR Inc.; *U.S. Public*, pg. 1183
NORTHERN MINNESOTA UTILITIES—UtiliCorp United Inc.; *U.S. Public*, pg. 1701
NORTHERN UTILITIES, INC.—Bay State Gas Company; *U.S. Public*, pg. 197
NORTHWEST NATURAL GAS COMPANY; *U.S. Public*, pg. 1200
NORTHWESTERN PUBLIC SERVICE; *U.S. Public*, pg. 1200
OHIO GAS COMPANY; *U.S. Private*, pg. 812
OKLAHOMA NATURAL GAS COMPANY—ONEOK Inc.; *U.S. Public*, pg. 1226
ONEOK INC.; *U.S. Public*, pg. 1226
OSAKA GAS CO., LTD.; *Int'l*, pg. 1011
OSAKA GAS CO.-NEW YORK—Osaka Gas Co., Ltd.; *Int'l*, pg. 1012
PACIFIC ENTERPRISES; *U.S. Public*, pg. 1249
PACIFIC WESTERN RESOURCES CO.—Pacific Enterprises; *U.S. Public*, pg. 1249
PARAMOUNT NATURAL GAS COMPANY—Petroleum Development Corporation; *U.S. Public*, pg. 1280
PEOPLES ENERGY CORPORATION; *U.S. Public*, pg. 1274
THE PEOPLES GAS LIGHT & COKE CO.—Peoples Energy Corporation; *U.S. Public*, pg. 1275
PEOPLES GAS SYSTEM, INC.—TECO Energy, Inc.; *U.S. Public*, pg. 1565
THE PEOPLES NATURAL GAS CO.—Consolidated Natural Gas Company; *U.S. Public*, pg. 435
T.W. PHILLIPS GAS AND OIL CO.; *U.S. Private*, pg. 862
PIEDMONT NATURAL GAS CO., INC.; *U.S. Public*, pg. 1295
PLIGAS—Electrabel S.A.; *Int'l*, pg. 437
POCAHONTAS DEVELOPMENT CORPORATION—Norfolk Southern Corporation; *U.S. Public*, pg. 1192
PROVIDENCE ENERGY CORPORATION; *U.S. Public*, pg. 1337
PROVIDENCE GAS CO.—Providence Energy Corporation; *U.S. Public*, pg. 1337
PROVINZIALSAECHSISCHE ENERGIE-VERSORGUNGS GMBH—Veba AG; *Int'l*, pg. 1457
PUBLIC SERVICE COMPANY OF NEW MEXICO; *U.S. Public*, pg. 1339
PUBLIC SERVICE COMPANY OF NORTH CAROLINA, INC.; *U.S. Public*, pg. 1340
PUGET SOUND ENERGY, INC.; *U.S. Public*, pg. 1342
ROANOKE GAS COMPANY; *U.S. Public*, pg. 1392
ROCHESTER GAS AND ELECTRIC CORPORATION; *U.S. Public*, pg. 1395
RUHRGAS AG—Ruhrgas Aktiengesellschaft; *Int'l*, pg. 1149
SEMCO ENERGY SERVICES, INC.—Southeastern Michigan Gas Enterprises, Inc.; *U.S. Public*, pg. 1489
SAN DIEGO GAS & ELECTRIC COMPANY—Enova Corp; *U.S. Public*, pg. 584
SCHLESWAG AKTIENGESELLSCHAFT—Veba AG; *Int'l*, pg. 1456
SHENANDOAH GAS CO.—Washington Gas Light Co.; *U.S. Public*, pg. 1741
SIBELGAZ—Electrabel S.A.; *Int'l*, pg. 437
SIGCORP, INC.; *U.S. Public*, pg. 1471
SIMOGEL—Electrabel S.A.; *Int'l*, pg. 437
SNAM S.P.A.—ENI S.p.A.; *Int'l*, pg. 428
SOUTH COUNTY GAS COMPANY—Providence Energy Corporation; *U.S. Public*, pg. 1337
SOUTH JERSEY INDUSTRIES, INC.; *U.S. Public*, pg. 1488
SOUTHEASTERN MICHIGAN GAS COMPANY—Southeastern Michigan Gas Enterprises, Inc.; *U.S. Public*, pg. 1489
SOUTHERN CALIFORNIA AIR GAS—Airgas, Inc.; *U.S. Public*, pg. 33
THE SOUTHERN CONNECTICUT GAS COMPANY—Connecticut Energy Corporation; *U.S. Public*, pg. 431
SOUTHERN UNION COMPANY; *U.S. Public*, pg. 1491
SOUTHERN UNION GAS CO.—Southern Union Company; *U.S. Public*, pg. 1491
SOUTHWEST GAS CORPORATION; *U.S. Public*, pg. 1493
STAR GAS CORPORATION—Petroleum Heat & Power Co.; *U.S. Public*, pg. 1281
TENNECO ALASKA, INC.—Tenneco Inc.; *U.S. Public*, pg. 1578
TENNESSEE TRAILBLAZER GAS CO.—El Paso Natural Gas Co.; *U.S. Public*, pg. 567
THUGA AKTIENGESELLSCHAFT—Veba AG; *Int'l*, pg. 1456
TORCO OIL CO.; *U.S. Private*, pg. 1092
TRANS LOUISIANA GAS CO.—Atmos Energy Corporation; *U.S. Public*, pg. 145
TRANSCONTINENTAL GAS PIPE LINE CORP.—The Williams Companies, Inc.; *U.S. Public*, pg. 1769
UCG ENERGY CORPORATION—Atmos Energy Corporation; *U.S. Public*, pg. 146
UGI CORPORATION; *U.S. Public*, pg. 1653
UNITED CITIES GAS COMPANY—Atmos Energy Corporation; *U.S. Public*, pg. 146
UNITED CITIES GAS CO., GA/SC DIV.—Atmos Energy Corporation; *U.S. Public*, pg. 146
UNITED CITIES GAS CO., IL/TN/MO DIV.—Atmos Energy Corporation; *U.S. Public*, pg. 146
UNITED CITIES GAS CO., KS/IA/MO DIV.—Atmos Energy Corporation; *U.S. Public*, pg. 146
UNITED CITIES GAS CO., VA/ETN DIV.—Atmos Energy Corporation; *U.S. Public*, pg. 146
UNITED GAS CO. LTD.—UtiliCorp United Inc.; *U.S. Public*, pg. 1701
UTILICORP UNITED INC.; *U.S. Public*, pg. 1700
VALLEY GAS CO.—Valley Resources, Inc.; *U.S. Public*, pg. 1706
VALLEY RESOURCES, INC.; *U.S. Public*, pg. 1706
VANGUARD ENERGY CORP.; *U.S. Private*, pg. 1133
VENTURE DISTRIBUTION COMPANY—Stone & Webster, Incorporated; *U.S. Public*, pg. 1519
VENTURE RESOURCES, INC.—Stone & Webster, Incorporated; *U.S. Public*, pg. 1519
VIRGINIA NATURAL GAS, INC.—Consolidated Natural Gas Company; *U.S. Public*, pg. 436
WASHINGTON GAS LIGHT CO.; *U.S. Public*, pg. 1740
WEST VIRGINIA POWER—UtiliCorp United Inc.; *U.S. Public*, pg. 1701
WESTERN KENTUCKY GAS CO.—Atmos Energy Corporation; *U.S. Public*, pg. 146
WISCONSIN ENERGY CORPORATION; *U.S. Public*, pg. 1773
WISCONSIN PUBLIC SERVICE CORPORATION—WPS Resources Corp.; *U.S. Public*, pg. 1728

4925 — MIXED, MANUFACTURED OR LIQUEFIED PETROLEUM GAS PRODUCTION AND/OR DISTRIBUTION

AIRGAS, INC.; *U.S. Public*, pg. 33
ALASKA PIPELINE CO.—Seagull Energy Corporation; *U.S. Public*, pg. 1450
ANADARKO PETROLEUM CORPORATION; *U.S. Public*, pg. 107
BALCRON OIL DIVISION—Equitable Resources, Inc.; *U.S. Public*, pg. 589
BORAL GAS LIMITED—Boral Limited; *Int'l*, pg. 203
BORAL LIMITED; *Int'l*, pg. 203
CHINA STEEL CHEMICAL CORP.—China Steel Corporation; *Int'l*, pg. 286
CLARK REFINING & MARKETING INC.; *U.S. Private*, pg. 243
COLUMBIA ENERGY GROUP; *U.S. Public*, pg. 402
COLUMBIA LNG CORP.—Columbia Energy Group; *U.S. Public*, pg. 403
ENERCO, INC.—The Broken Hill Proprietary Company Limited; *Int'l*, pg. 225
ENERGYNORTH NATURAL GAS, INC.—EnergyNorth, Inc.; *U.S. Public*, pg. 582
ENERGYNORTH PROPANE, INC.—EnergyNorth, Inc.; *U.S. Public*, pg. 582
EQUITABLE RESOURCES, INC.; *U.S. Public*, pg. 589
EQUITECH DIVISION—Equitable Resources, Inc.; *U.S. Public*, pg. 590
FLORIDA PUBLIC UTILITIES COMPANY; *U.S. Public*, pg. 655
GASCO, INC.—The Broken Hill Proprietary Company Limited; *Int'l*, pg. 225
GLACIER GAS COMPANY—Montana Power Company; *U.S. Public*, pg. 1127
HONDO OIL & GAS COMPANY—Lonrho plc; *Int'l*, pg. 818
IGLOO POOL—Kvaerner a.s.a.; *Int'l*, pg. 766
KVAERNER MOSS TECHNOLOGY A.S.—Kvaerner a.s.a.; *Int'l*, pg. 769
MND ENERGY CORPORATION—Mitchell Energy & Development Corp.; *U.S. Public*, pg. 1117
MAPCO NATURAL GAS LIQUIDS INC.—Mapco Inc.; *U.S. Public*, pg. 1042
MESSER GRIESHEIM GMBH—Hoechst Aktiengesellschaft; *Int'l*, pg. 626
MIDCON GAS PRODUCTS CORP.—Occidental Petroleum Corporation; *U.S. Public*, pg. 1210
MITCHELL ENERGY & DEVELOPMENT CORP.; *U.S. Public*, pg. 1117
MOUNTAIN FUEL SUPPLY COMPANY—Questar Corporation; *U.S. Public*, pg. 1352
MOUNTAIN GAS REOURCES, INC.—Western Gas Resources, Inc.; *U.S. Public*, pg. 1758
NESTE OEL GMBH—Neste Oy; *Int'l*, pg. 915
PETROLEUM AUTHORITY OF THAILAND; *Int'l*, pg. 1046
PINNACLE GAS TREATING, INC.—Western Gas Resources, Inc.; *U.S. Public*, pg. 1758
PRODUCTION MANAGEMENT COMPANIES, INC.; *U.S. Private*, pg. 888
REPSOL BUTANO S.A.—Repsol S.A.; *Int'l*, pg. 1104
REPSOL S.A.; *Int'l*, pg. 1104
RESERVOIR TECHNOLOGY AND SIMULATION (GETEC)—Petrobras - Petroleo Brasileiro S.A.; *Int'l*, pg. 1042
SCANA ENERGY MARKETING INC.—SCANA Corporation; *U.S. Public*, pg. 1436
SCANA PETROLEUM RESOURCES, INC.—SCANA Corporation; *U.S. Public*, pg. 1436
SEAGULL ENERGY CORPORATION; *U.S. Public*, pg. 1450
SOUTH CAROLINA FUEL CO., INC.—SCANA Corporation; *U.S. Public*, pg. 1436
SOUTH JERSEY INDUSTRIES, INC.; *U.S. Public*, pg. 1488
SOUTHERN CALIFORNIA AIR GAS—Airgas, Inc.; *U.S. Public*, pg. 33
SWIFT ENERGY COMPANY; *U.S. Public*, pg. 1543
TEXAS UTILITIES FUEL CO.—Texas Utilities Company; *U.S. Public*, pg. 1588
TRUNKLINE LNG CO.—Duke Energy Corporation; *U.S. Public*, pg. 535
VANGUARD ENERGY CORP.; *U.S. Private*, pg. 1133
WESTANA GATHERING COMPANY—Duke Energy Corporation; *U.S. Public*, pg. 535
WESTANA GATHERING COMPANY—Western Gas Resources, Inc.; *U.S. Public*, pg. 1759
WESTCOAST ENERGY INC.; *Int'l*, pg. 1492
WESTERN GAS RESOURCES CANADA, INC.—Western Gas Resources, Inc.; *U.S. Public*, pg. 1759
WESTERN GAS RESOURCES, INC.; *U.S. Public*, pg. 1758
WESTERN GAS RESOURCES STORAGE, INC.—Western Gas Resources, Inc.; *U.S. Public*, pg. 1759
WESTERN GAS RESOURCES-LOUISIANA, INC.—Western Gas Resources, Inc.; *U.S. Public*, pg. 1758
WESTERN GAS RESOURCES-OKLAHOMA, INC.—Western Gas Resources, Inc.; *U.S. Public*, pg. 1758
WESTERN GAS RESOURCES-TEXAS, INC.—Western Gas Resources, Inc.; *U.S. Public*, pg. 1759

4931 — ELECTRIC & OTHER SERVICES COMBINED

APS—Pinnacle West Capital Corporation; *U.S. Public*, pg. 1297
ALLEGHENY GENERATING CO.—Allegheny Power System, Inc.; *U.S. Public*, pg. 42
AMEREN CORPORATION; *U.S. Public*, pg. 65
AMERENCIPS—Ameren Corporation; *U.S. Public*, pg. 65
AMERENUE—Ameren Corporation; *U.S. Public*, pg. 66
BALTIMORE GAS AND ELECTRIC COMPANY; *U.S. Public*, pg. 172
C H RESOURCES, INC.—Central Hudson Gas & Electric Corporation; *U.S. Public*, pg. 325
CMS ENERGY CORPORATION; *U.S. Public*, pg. 279
CENTRAL HUDSON COGENERATION, INC.—Central Hudson Gas & Electric Corporation; *U.S. Public*, pg. 325
CENTRAL HUDSON ENTERPRISES—Central Hudson Gas & Electric Corporation; *U.S. Public*, pg. 325
CENTRAL HUDSON GAS & ELECTRIC CORPORATION; *U.S. Public*, pg. 324
CENTRAL ILLINOIS LIGHT COMPANY—CILCORP Inc.; *U.S. Public*, pg. 367
CHEYENNE LIGHT, FUEL & POWER CO.—New Century Energies, Inc.; *U.S. Public*, pg. 1170
CILCO ENERGY CORP.—CILCORP Inc.; *U.S. Public*, pg. 367
CILCO EXPLORATION & DEVELOPMENT CO.—CILCORP Inc.; *U.S. Public*, pg. 367
CILCORP INC.; *U.S. Public*, pg. 367
CINERGY CORP.—Cinergy Corp.; *U.S. Public*, pg. 369
COMMUNITY ENERGY ALTERNATIVES INCORPORATED—Public Service Enterprise Group Incorporated; *U.S. Public*, pg. 1340
COMPAGNIE GENERALE DE CHAUFFE—Compagnie Generale Des Eaux; *Int'l*, pg. 321
COMPAGNIE GENERALE DES EAUX; *Int'l*, pg. 321
CONTINENTAL ENERGY SERVICES, INC.—Montana Power Company; *U.S. Public*, pg. 1127
DAYTON POWER & LIGHT CO.—DPL Inc.; *U.S. Public*, pg. 473
DELESTO BV—Akzo Nobel N.V.; *Int'l*, pg. 43
DELMARVA POWER & LIGHT COMPANY—Conectiv; *U.S. Public*, pg. 430
DOMINION RESOURCES, INC.; *U.S. Public*, pg. 516
E PRIME, INC.—New Century Energies, Inc.; *U.S. Public*, pg. 1170
ENERGY SYSTEMS GROUP, INC.—SIGCORP, Inc.; *U.S. Public*, pg. 1471
ENOVA CORP; *U.S. Public*, pg. 583
ENSERV, INC.—WPL Holdings, Inc.; *U.S. Public*, pg. 1728

ENTE NAZIONALE PER L'ENERGIA ELETTRICA SPA (ENEL); *Int'l*, pg. 458
ENTERGY GULF STATES, INC.—Entergy Corporation; *U.S. Public*, pg. 586
FPL GROUP, INC.; *U.S. Public*, pg. 608
FIRST MIDWEST AUTO PARK, INC.—Northern States Power Company; *U.S. Public*, pg. 1195
FITCHBURG GAS AND ELECTRIC LIGHT CO.—Unitil Corporation; *U.S. Public*, pg. 1692
FLORIDA PUBLIC UTILITIES COMPANY; *U.S. Public*, pg. 655
GPU ENERGY—GPU, Inc.; *U.S. Public*, pg. 695
GPU, INC.; *U.S. Public*, pg. 695
GREAT LAKES ENERGY CORP.—Madison Gas and Electric Company; *U.S. Public*, pg. 1033
GREENE POINT DEVELOPMENT CORP.—Central Hudson Gas & Electric Corporation; *U.S. Public*, pg. 325
HALIFAX CORPORATION; *U.S. Public*, pg. 775
HOLYOKE POWER AND ELECTRIC CO.—Northeast Utilities; *U.S. Public*, pg. 1195
IPC DEVELOPMENT CO.—Interstate Power Company; *U.S. Public*, pg. 910
INTERSTATE POWER COMPANY; *U.S. Public*, pg. 910
LAPAZ—Northern States Power Company; *U.S. Public*, pg. 1195
LEHIGH UTILITIES INC.—Minnesota Power; *U.S. Public*, pg. 1116
MADISON GAS AND ELECTRIC COMPANY; *U.S. Public*, pg. 1032
METROPOLITAN EDISON CO.—GPU, Inc.; *U.S. Public*, pg. 695
MINNESOTA POWER; *U.S. Public*, pg. 1116
MONTANA POWER COMPANY; *U.S. Public*, pg. 1126
NRG RESOURCE RECOVERY, INC.—Northern States Power Company; *U.S. Public*, pg. 1195
NEW YORK STATE ELECTRIC & GAS CORPORATION; *U.S. Public*, pg. 1173
NIPSCO INDUSTRIES, INC.; *U.S. Public*, pg. 1185
NORTH ATLANTIC ENERGY SERVICE CORP.—Northeast Utilities; *U.S. Public*, pg. 1195
NORTHEAST NUCLEAR ENERGY CO.—Northeast Utilities; *U.S. Public*, pg. 1195
NORTHEAST UTILITIES; *U.S. Public*, pg. 1194
NORTHERN INDIANA PUBLIC SERVICE COMPANY—NIPSCO Industries, Inc.; *U.S. Public*, pg. 1185
NORTHERN STATES POWER COMPANY; *U.S. Public*, pg. 1195
NORTHWESTERN PUBLIC SERVICE; *U.S. Public*, pg. 1200
OGE ENERGY CORP.; *U.S. Public*, pg. 1207
OGDEN CORPORATION; *U.S. Public*, pg. 1213
OGDEN ENERGY GROUP, INC.—Ogden Corporation; *U.S. Public*, pg. 1213
ONTARIO HYDRO; *Int'l*, pg. 1007
ORANGE AND ROCKLAND UTILITIES, INC.; *U.S. Public*, pg. 1229
PG&E CORPORATION; *U.S. Public*, pg. 1240
PECO ENERGY COMPANY; *U.S. Public*, pg. 1268
PHOENIX DEVELOPMENT CO., INC.—Central Hudson Gas & Electric Corporation; *U.S. Public*, pg. 325
PIKE COUNTY LIGHT & POWER CO.—Orange and Rockland Utilities, Inc.; *U.S. Public*, pg. 1229
PINNACLE WEST CAPITAL CORPORATION; *U.S. Public*, pg. 1297
PUBLIC SERVICE COMPANY OF COLORADO—New Century Energies, Inc.; *U.S. Public*, pg. 1170
PUBLIC SERVICE COMPANY OF NEW MEXICO; *U.S. Public*, pg. 1339
PUBLIC SERVICE ELECTRIC & GAS CO.—Public Service Enterprise Group Incorporated; *U.S. Public*, pg. 1340
PUBLIC SERVICE ENTERPRISE GROUP INCORPORATED; *U.S. Public*, pg. 1340
REEDY CREEK ENERGY SERVICES, INC.—The Walt Disney Company; *U.S. Public*, pg. 514
ROCHESTER GAS AND ELECTRIC CORPORATION; *U.S. Public*, pg. 1395
ST. JOSEPH LIGHT & POWER CO.; *U.S. Public*, pg. 1427
SALT RIVER PROJECT AGRICULTURAL IMPROVEMENT AND POWER DISTRICT; *U.S. Private*, pg. 962
SAN DIEGO GAS & ELECTRIC COMPANY—Enova Corp; *U.S. Public*, pg. 584
SCANA CORPORATION; *U.S. Public*, pg. 1436
SIERRA PACIFIC POWER CO.—Sierra Pacific Resources; *U.S. Public*, pg. 1470
SIGCORP, INC.; *U.S. Public*, pg. 1471
SITHE ENERGIES, INC.; *U.S. Private*, pg. 1004
SOUTH BELOIT WATER, GAS & ELECTRIC CO.—WPL Holdings, Inc.; *U.S. Public*, pg. 1728
SOUTHERN CALIFORNIA WATER COMPANY; *U.S. Public*, pg. 1489
SOUTHERN INDIANA GAS & ELECTRIC CO.—SIGCORP, Inc.; *U.S. Public*, pg. 1471
SOUTHERN INDIANA MINERALS, INC.—SIGCORP, Inc.; *U.S. Public*, pg. 1471
SOUTHERN INDIANA PROPERTIES, INC.—SIGCORP, Inc.; *U.S. Public*, pg. 1471
THE STORMONT ELECTRIC LIGHT & POWER COMPANY LIMITED—Sun Life Assurance Company of Canada; *Int'l*, pg. 1319
SUN LIFE ASSURANCE COMPANY OF CANADA; *Int'l*, pg. 1318
SUPERIOR WATER, LIGHT & POWER COMPANY—Minnesota Power; *U.S. Public*, pg. 1116
TECO POWER SERVICES, INC.—TECO Energy, Inc.; *U.S. Public*, pg. 1565
TRACTEBEL; *Int'l*, pg. 1414
UNION LIGHT, HEAT AND POWER CO.—Cinergy Corp.; *U.S. Public*, pg. 369
UTILICORP UNITED INC.; *U.S. Public*, pg. 1700
VIRGINIA ELECTRIC AND POWER COMPANY—Dominion Resources, Inc.; *U.S. Public*, pg. 516
WPL HOLDINGS, INC.; *U.S. Public*, pg. 1727
THE WASHINGTON WATER POWER COMPANY; *U.S. Public*, pg. 1744
WESTAR ENERGY—Western Resources, Inc.; *U.S. Public*, pg. 1759
WESTAR SECURITY—Western Resources, Inc.; *U.S. Public*, pg. 1760
WESTERN RESOURCES, INC.; *U.S. Public*, pg. 1759
WISCONSIN POWER & LIGHT COMPANY—WPL Holdings, Inc.; *U.S. Public*, pg. 1728
WISCONSIN RIVER POWER CO.—WPL Holdings, Inc.; *U.S. Public*, pg. 1728

4932 — GAS & OTHER SERVICES COMBINED

AGL ENERGY SERVICES, INC.—AGL Resources; *U.S. Public*, pg. 7
AMERICAN ENERGY MANAGEMENT—Madison Gas and Electric Company; *U.S. Public*, pg. 1033
BHP HAWAII, INC.—The Broken Hill Proprietary Company Limited; *Int'l*, pg. 225
CMS ENERGY CORPORATION; *U.S. Public*, pg. 279
CENTRAL ILLINOIS LIGHT COMPANY—CILCORP Inc.; *U.S. Public*, pg. 367
CENTRAL PLANTS, INC.—Pacific Enterprises; *U.S. Public*, pg. 1249
CILCO ENERGY CORP.—CILCORP Inc.; *U.S. Public*, pg. 367
CILCO EXPLORATION & DEVELOPMENT CO.—CILCORP Inc.; *U.S. Public*, pg. 367
CILCORP INC.; *U.S. Public*, pg. 367
CITIZENS GAS & COKE UTILITY; *U.S. Private*, pg. 241
COMPAGNIE GENERALE DES EAUX; *Int'l*, pg. 321
DMD DRESSER MEASUREMENT OPERATION—Dresser Industries, Inc.; *U.S. Public*, pg. 528
DELMARVA POWER & LIGHT COMPANY—Conectiv; *U.S. Public*, pg. 430
DUFF & PHELPS UTILITIES INCOME INC.; *U.S. Public*, pg. 534
E PRIME, INC.—New Century Energies, Inc.; *U.S. Public*, pg. 1170
FFP MARKETING COMPANY, INC.; *U.S. Public*, pg. 604
GAZ DE FRANCE; *Int'l*, pg. 541
GREAT LAKES ENERGY CORP.—Madison Gas and Electric Company; *U.S. Public*, pg. 1033
MCN ENERGY GROUP, INC.; *U.S. Public*, pg. 1024
MCN INVESTMENT—MCN Energy Group, Inc.; *U.S. Public*, pg. 1025
MADISON GAS AND ELECTRIC COMPANY; *U.S. Public*, pg. 1032
MIAMI VALLEY RESOURCES, INC.—DPL Inc.; *U.S. Public*, pg. 474
NATIONAL ENERGY MANAGEMENT LLC—Madison Gas and Electric Company; *U.S. Public*, pg. 1033
NEW YORK STATE ELECTRIC & GAS CORPORATION; *U.S. Public*, pg. 1173
NIPSCO INDUSTRIES, INC.; *U.S. Public*, pg. 1185
NORTH CANADIAN POWER—EdperBrascan Corporation; *Int'l*, pg. 434
NORTHERN INDIANA PUBLIC SERVICE COMPANY—NIPSCO Industries, Inc.; *U.S. Public*, pg. 1185
PRAXAIR INC.; *U.S. Public*, pg. 1319
RUHRGAS AKTIENGESELLSCHAFT; *Int'l*, pg. 1148
SAAR FERNGAS AG—Ruhrgas Aktiengesellschaft; *Int'l*, pg. 1148
SONAT ENERGY SERVICES COMPANY—Sonat Inc.; *U.S. Public*, pg. 1485
SONAT INC.; *U.S. Public*, pg. 1484
TOKYO GAS CO., LTD.; *Int'l*, pg. 1394
UGI CORPORATION; *U.S. Public*, pg. 1653
THE WILLIAMS COMPANIES, INC.; *U.S. Public*, pg. 1769

4939 — COMBINATION UTILITIES, NEC

PETER A. BASILE SONS INC.; *U.S. Private*, pg. 121
CRSS CAPITAL, INC.—Tractebel; *Int'l*, pg. 1415
CLAYTON GROUP, INC.; *U.S. Private*, pg. 244
CLEVELAND DISTRICT COOLING CORP.—Ipalco Enterprises, Inc.; *U.S. Public*, pg. 913
CLEVELAND THERMAL ENERGY CORPORATION—Ipalco Enterprises, Inc.; *U.S. Public*, pg. 913
COLUMBIA ATLANTIC TRADING CORPORATION—Columbia Energy Group; *U.S. Public*, pg. 402
COLUMBIA ENERGY GROUP; *U.S. Public*, pg. 402
CONSUMERS ENERGY—CMS Energy Corporation; *U.S. Public*, pg. 280
DELMARVA POWER & LIGHT COMPANY—Conectiv; *U.S. Public*, pg. 430
ELASCO AGENCY SALES, INC.—Hughes Supply, Inc.; *U.S. Public*, pg. 846
IMATRAN VOIMA OY; *Int'l*, pg. 660
IPALCO ENTERPRISES, INC.; *U.S. Public*, pg. 912
KNOXVILLE UTILITIES BOARD; *U.S. Private*, pg. 627
KRAFTWERK AEGINA AG (AEGINA)—Alusuisse-Lonza Holding Ltd.; *Int'l*, pg. 67
KRAFTWERK LOTSCHEN AG-(LOTSCHEN)—Alusuisse-Lonza Holding Ltd.; *Int'l*, pg. 67
KRAFTWERK RECKINGEN AG—Alusuisse-Lonza Holding Ltd.; *Int'l*, pg. 67
KRAFTWERKE GOUGRA AG-(GOUDRA)—Alusuisse-Lonza Holding Ltd.; *Int'l*, pg. 67
KRAFTWERKE MATTMARK AG—Alusuisse-Lonza Holding Ltd.; *Int'l*, pg. 67
LG & E ENERGY SYSTEMS INC.—LG & E Energy Corp.; *U.S. Public*, pg. 970
LA GLORIA OIL & GAS CO.—Crown Central Petroleum Corporation; *U.S. Public*, pg. 462
LONE STAR ENERGY CO.—Texas Utilities Company; *U.S. Public*, pg. 1587
MID-AMERICA ENERGY RESOURCES—Ipalco Enterprises, Inc.; *U.S. Public*, pg. 913
NRG GROUP, INC.—Northern States Power Company; *U.S. Public*, pg. 1195
PUBLIC SERVICE ENTERPRISE GROUP INCORPORATED; *U.S. Public*, pg. 1340
RKN RHEINKRAFTWERK NEUHAUSEN AG—Alusuisse-Lonza Holding Ltd.; *Int'l*, pg. 67
RHOWAG RHONEWERKE AG—Alusuisse-Lonza Holding Ltd.; *Int'l*, pg. 67
SALANFE SA—Alusuisse-Lonza Holding Ltd.; *Int'l*, pg. 67
SIERRA PACIFIC RESOURCES; *U.S. Public*, pg. 1470
TRIGEN ENERGY CORPORATION; *U.S. Public*, pg. 1637
UNITIL SERVICE CORPORATION—Unitil Corporation; *U.S. Public*, pg. 1693
WPS ENERGY SERVICES, INC.—WPS Resources Corp.; *U.S. Public*, pg. 1728
WPS POWER DEVELOPMENT, INC.—WPS Resources Corp.; *U.S. Public*, pg. 1728

4941 — WATER SUPPLY

AMANA SOCIETY SERVICE CO.—Amana Society, Inc.; *U.S. Private*, pg. 48
AMERICAN WATER WORKS COMPANY, INC.; *U.S. Public*, pg. 95
ANTELOPE VALLEY WATER COMPANY—Dominguez Services Corporation; *U.S. Public*, pg. 516
AQUARION COMPANY; *U.S. Public*, pg. 126
ARDEN WATER COMPANY—Dominguez Services Corporation; *U.S. Public*, pg. 516
ARTESIAN RESOURCES CORPORATION; *U.S. Public*, pg. 135
ARTESIAN WATER COMPANY, INC.—Artesian Resources Corporation; *U.S. Public*, pg. 135
AVATAR HOLDINGS INC.; *U.S. Public*, pg. 151
BATON ROUGE WATER WORKS COMPANY; *U.S. Private*, pg. 122
BLUE MOUNTAIN CONSOLIDATED WATER COMPANY—Citizens Utilities Company; *U.S. Public*, pg. 379
BLUEFIELD VALLEY WATER WORKS CO.—American Water Works Company, Inc.; *U.S. Public*, pg. 96
CVC OF OHIO—Citizens Utilities Company; *U.S. Public*, pg. 380
CALIFORNIA-AMERICAN WATER CO.—American Water Works Company, Inc.; *U.S. Public*, pg. 95
CALIFORNIA WATER SERVICE CO.; *U.S. Public*, pg. 294
CAMDEN/ROCKLAND DIVISION—Consumers Water Company; *U.S. Public*, pg. 438
CANDLEWICK DIVISION—Consumers Water Company; *U.S. Public*, pg. 438
CITIZENS UTILITIES COMPANY; *U.S. Public*, pg. 379
CITIZENS UTILITIES COMPANY—Citizens Utilities Company; *U.S. Public*, pg. 380
CITIZENS UTILITIES COMPANY OF CALIFORNIA—Citizens Utilities Company; *U.S. Public*, pg. 380
CITIZENS UTILITIES HOME WATER COMPANY—Citizens Utilities Company; *U.S. Public*, pg. 380
CITIZENS UTILITIES WATER COMPANY OF PENNSYLVANIA—Citizens Utilities Company; *U.S. Public*, pg. 380
CLOISTER PURE SPRING WATER CO., INC.; *U.S. Private*, pg. 247
COMPAGNIE GENERALE DES EAUX; *Int'l*, pg. 321
CONNECTICUT-AMERICAN WATER CO.—American Water Works Company, Inc.; *U.S. Public*, pg. 95
THE CONNECTICUT WATER COMPANY—Connecticut Water Service, Inc.; *U.S. Public*, pg. 431
CONNECTICUT WATER SERVICE, INC.; *U.S. Public*, pg. 431
CONSOLIDATED WATER CO.—Avatar Holdings Inc.; *U.S. Public*, pg. 151
CONSUMERS ILLINOIS WATER CO.—Consumers Water Company; *U.S. Public*, pg. 438
CONSUMERS MAINE WATER—Consumers Water Company; *U.S. Public*, pg. 438
CONSUMERS NEW HAMPSHIRE WATER CO.—Consumers Water Company; *U.S. Public*, pg. 438
CONSUMERS NEW JERSEY WATER COMPANY—Consumers Water Company; *U.S. Public*, pg. 438
CONSUMERS OHIO WATER COMPANY—Consumers Water Company; *U.S. Public*, pg. 438
CONSUMERS WATER COMPANY; *U.S. Public*, pg. 438
CONTINENTAL WATER COMPANY; *U.S. Private*, pg. 269
DOMINGUEZ WATER COMPANY—Dominguez Services Corporation; *U.S. Public*, pg. 516
E'TOWN CORPORATION; *U.S. Public*, pg. 540
ECO RESOURCES, INC.—Southwest Water Company; *U.S. Public*, pg. 1494
EAU ET FORCE—Lyonnaise des Eaux S.A.; *Int'l*, pg. 822
ELIZABETHTOWN WATER COMPANY—E'Town Corporation; *U.S. Public*, pg. 540
ELYO CORP.—Lyonnaise des Eaux S.A.; *Int'l*, pg. 823
FAIRBANKS MORSE ENGINE DIVISION—Coltec Holdings Inc; *U.S. Public*, pg. 401
FLORIDA CITIES WATER CO.—Avatar Holdings Inc.; *U.S. Public*, pg. 151
FLORIDA PUBLIC UTILITIES COMPANY; *U.S. Public*, pg. 655
FLOWING WELLS, INC.—Citizens Utilities Company; *U.S. Public*, pg. 380
GLEN ALSACE WATER COMPANY—Citizens Utilities Company; *U.S. Public*, pg. 380
GOODKIND & O'DEA, INC.—Dewberry & Davis; *U.S. Private*, pg. 329
GREENVILLE DIVISION—Consumers Water Company; *U.S. Public*, pg. 438
GUIGUES S.A.—Technip; *Int'l*, pg. 1361
THE HAMPTON WATER WORKS CO.—American Water Works Company, Inc.; *U.S. Public*, pg. 95
HARBOUR WATER CORPORATION—NIPSCO Industries, Inc.; *U.S. Public*, pg. 1185
HEATER UTILITIES, INCORPORATED—Minnesota Power; *U.S. Public*, pg. 1116
IWC RESOURCES CORPORATION—NIPSCO Industries, Inc.; *U.S. Public*, pg. 1185
ILLINOIS-AMERICAN WATER CO.—American Water Works Company, Inc.; *U.S. Public*, pg. 95

INDIANA-AMERICAN WATER CO., INC.—American Water Works Company, Inc.; *U.S. Public*, pg. 95
INDIANAPOLIS WATER COMPANY—NIPSCO Industries, Inc.; *U.S. Public*, pg. 1185
INDUSTRIAL WATER TREATMENT CO.—Air Liquide S.A.; *Int'l*, pg. 37
IOWA-AMERICAN WATER CO.—American Water Works Company, Inc.; *U.S. Public*, pg. 95
KAANAPALI WATER CORPORATION—JMB Realty Corporation; *U.S. Private*, pg. 578
KAUFMAN AND BROAD OF TEXAS, LTD.—Kaufman and Broad Home Corporation; *U.S. Public*, pg. 945
KENTUCKY-AMERICAN WATER CO.—American Water Works Company, Inc.; *U.S. Public*, pg. 95
KERNVILLE DOMESTIC WATER COMPANY—Dominguez Services Corporation; *U.S. Public*, pg. 516
LAKE HERITAGE UTILITIES, INC.—Citizens Utilities Company; *U.S. Public*, pg. 380
LONG ISLAND WATER CORPORATION; *U.S. Private*, pg. 674
LYONNAISE DES EAUX S.A.; *Int'l*, pg. 822
MCO PROPERTIES INC.—Maxxam Inc.; *U.S. Public*, pg. 1062
MAINE ELECTRIC POWER CO., INC.—Central Maine Power Company; *U.S. Public*, pg. 325
MARYLAND-AMERICAN WATER CO.—American Water Works Company, Inc.; *U.S. Public*, pg. 95
MASSACHUSETTS-AMERICAN WATER CO.—American Water Works Company, Inc.; *U.S. Public*, pg. 95
MICHIGAN-AMERICAN WATER COMPANY—American Water Works Company, Inc.; *U.S. Public*, pg. 95
MIDDLESEX WATER COMPANY; *U.S. Public*, pg. 1110
MILLINOCKET DIVISION—Consumers Water Company; *U.S. Public*, pg. 438
MINNESOTA POWER; *U.S. Public*, pg. 1116
MISSOURI-AMERICAN WATER CO.—American Water Works Company, Inc.; *U.S. Public*, pg. 95
MONTGOMERY WATSON—Montgomery Watson; *U.S. Private*, pg. 759
MOUNT HOLLY WATER CO.—E'Town Corporation; *U.S. Public*, pg. 540
NEW JERSEY-AMERICAN WATER CO.—American Water Works Company, Inc.; *U.S. Public*, pg. 95
NEW MEXICO-AMERICAN WATER CO.—American Water Works Company, Inc.; *U.S. Public*, pg. 95
NEW YORK-AMERICAN WATER CO., INC.—American Water Works Company, Inc.; *U.S. Public*, pg. 95
THE NEWELL COMPANY—The Homer Laughlin China Company; *U.S. Private*, pg. 653
NORTHERN DIVISION—Consumers Water Company; *U.S. Public*, pg. 438
OK TEDI MINING LIMITED—The Broken Hill Proprietary Company Limited; *Int'l*, pg. 228
OAK RUN UTILITIES—Consumers Water Company; *U.S. Public*, pg. 438
OGDEN CORPORATION; *U.S. Public*, pg. 1213
OHIO-AMERICAN WATER CO.—American Water Works Company, Inc.; *U.S. Public*, pg. 95
OHIO UTILITIES COMPANY—Citizens Utilities Company; *U.S. Public*, pg. 380
PACIFIC POWER & LIGHT COMPANY—PacifiCorp; *U.S. Public*, pg. 1251
PARADISE VALLEY WATER CO.—American Water Works Company, Inc.; *U.S. Public*, pg. 95
PARISH WATER COMPANY, INC.—Baton Rouge Water Works Company; *U.S. Private*, pg. 123
PENNSYLVANIA-AMERICAN WATER CO.—American Water Works Company, Inc.; *U.S. Public*, pg. 95
PHILADELPHIA SUBURBAN CORPORATION; *U.S. Public*, pg. 1287
PHILADELPHIA SUBURBAN WATER COMPANY—Philadelphia Suburban Corporation; *U.S. Public*, pg. 1287
PHIPPS & BIRD—McKesson Corporation; *U.S. Public*, pg. 1073
PRINCEVILLE UTILITIES COMPANY, INC.—Princeville Corporation; *U.S. Private*, pg. 885
REEDY CREEK ENERGY SERVICES, INC.—The Walt Disney Company; *U.S. Public*, pg. 514
ROARING CREEK DIVISION—Consumers Water Company; *U.S. Public*, pg. 439
SJW CORP.; *U.S. Public*, pg. 1418
SAARBERG-FERNWAERME GMBH—Saarbergwerke Aktiengesellschaft; *Int'l*, pg. 1166
THE SALISBURY WATER SUPPLY CO.—American Water Works Company, Inc.; *U.S. Public*, pg. 95
SAN JOSE WATER COMPANY—SJW Corp.; *U.S. Public*, pg. 1418
SHENANGO VALLEY WATER CO.—Consumers Water Company; *U.S. Public*, pg. 439
SKOWHEGAN DIVISION—Consumers Water Company; *U.S. Public*, pg. 438
SOUTH WEST WATER PLC; *Int'l*, pg. 1287
SOUTHERN CALIFORNIA WATER COMPANY; *U.S. Public*, pg. 1489
SOUTHWEST WATER COMPANY; *U.S. Public*, pg. 1494
THE SOUTHWOOD COMPANY—Artesian Resources Corporation; *U.S. Public*, pg. 136
THE SPRING GROVE WATER CO.—P.H. Glatfelter Company; *U.S. Public*, pg. 746
STRUTHERS DIVISION—Consumers Water Company; *U.S. Public*, pg. 439
SUBURBAN WATER SYSTEMS—Southwest Water Company; *U.S. Public*, pg. 1494
SUN CITY WATER COMPANY—Citizens Utilities Company; *U.S. Public*, pg. 380
SUN CITY WEST UTILITIES COMPANY—Citizens Utilities Company; *U.S. Public*, pg. 380
SUSQUEHANNA DIVISION—Consumers Water Company; *U.S. Public*, pg. 439
TECHNIP; *Int'l*, pg. 1360
TENNESSEE-AMERICAN WATER CO.—American Water Works Company, Inc.; *U.S. Public*, pg. 95
TIDEWATER UTILITIES, INC.—Middlesex Water Company; *U.S. Public*, pg. 1110
TUBAC VALLEY WATER COMPANY, INC.—Citizens Utilities Company; *U.S. Public*, pg. 380
THE UNION WATER-POWER CO.—Central Maine Power Company; *U.S. Public*, pg. 325
U.S. FILTER/POLYMETRICS—United States Filter Corporation; *U.S. Public*, pg. 1682
UNITED WATER NEW JERSEY, INC.—United Water Resources; *U.S. Public*, pg. 1692
UNITED WATER NEW YORK—United Water Resources; *U.S. Public*, pg. 1692
UNITED WATER RESOURCES; *U.S. Public*, pg. 1691
UNIVERSAL TELEPHONE, INC.—Century Telephone Enterprises, Inc.; *U.S. Public*, pg. 330
UNIVERSITY PARK DIVISION—Consumers Water Company; *U.S. Public*, pg. 438
VERMILION COUNTY DIVISION—Consumers Water Company; *U.S. Public*, pg. 438
VIRGINIA-AMERICAN WATER CO.—American Water Works Company, Inc.; *U.S. Public*, pg. 96
WATLINGTON WATERWORKS LIMITED—Ionics, Incorporated; *U.S. Public*, pg. 912
WEST VIRGINIA-AMERICAN WATER CO.—American Water Works Company, Inc.; *U.S. Public*, pg. 96
WOOLRICH, INC.; *U.S. Private*, pg. 1188
ZIONSVILLE WATER CORPORATION—NIPSCO Industries, Inc.; *U.S. Public*, pg. 1185

4952 — SEWERAGE SYSTEMS

ABB ENVIRONMENTAL SERVICES INC.—ABB Asea Brown Boveri (Holding) Ltd.; *Int'l*, pg. 4
AMERICAN WATER WORKS COMPANY, INC.; *U.S. Public*, pg. 95
AMERON INTERNATIONAL CORPORATION; *U.S. Public*, pg. 98
CVC OF OHIO—Citizens Utilities Company; *U.S. Public*, pg. 380
CAROLINA PUMP & SUPPLY CORP.—Hughes Supply, Inc.; *U.S. Public*, pg. 846
CHEMED CORPORATION; *U.S. Public*, pg. 343
CITIZENS UTILITIES COMPANY; *U.S. Public*, pg. 379
CITIZENS UTILITIES COMPANY—Citizens Utilities Company; *U.S. Public*, pg. 380
DEGREMONT INC.—Lyonnaise des Eaux S.A.; *Int'l*, pg. 822
FAIRBANKS MORSE ENGINE DIVISION—Coltec Holdings Inc; *U.S. Public*, pg. 401
FLORIDA CITIES WATER CO.—Avatar Holdings Inc.; *U.S. Public*, pg. 151
GIFFORD-HILL-AMERICAN, INC.—Ameron International Corporation; *U.S. Public*, pg. 99
HEATER UTILITIES, INCORPORATED—Minnesota Power; *U.S. Public*, pg. 1116
KAUFMAN AND BROAD OF TEXAS, LTD.—Kaufman and Broad Home Corporation; *U.S. Public*, pg. 945
NEW JERSEY-AMERICAN WATER CO.—American Water Works Company, Inc.; *U.S. Public*, pg. 95
THE NEWELL COMPANY—The Homer Laughlin China Company; *U.S. Private*, pg. 653
OGDEN CORPORATION; *U.S. Public*, pg. 1213
OHIO UTILITIES COMPANY—Citizens Utilities Company; *U.S. Public*, pg. 380
ROTO-ROOTER—Chemed Corporation; *U.S. Public*, pg. 344
SOUTH CHARLESTON SEWAGE TREATMENT CO.—Union Carbide Corporation; *U.S. Public*, pg. 1667
SUN CITY SEWER COMPANY—Citizens Utilities Company; *U.S. Public*, pg. 380
SUN CITY WATER COMPANY—Citizens Utilities Company; *U.S. Public*, pg. 380
SUN CITY WEST UTILITIES COMPANY—Citizens Utilities Company; *U.S. Public*, pg. 380

4953 — REFUSE SYSTEMS

ABB ENVIRONMENTAL SERVICES INC.—ABB Asea Brown Boveri (Holding) Ltd.; *Int'l*, pg. 4
ABB ENVIRONMENTAL SYSTEMS (ABBES)—ABB Asea Brown Boveri (Holding) Ltd.; *Int'l*, pg. 4
ADVANCED REMEDIATION INC. (ARM); *U.S. Private*, pg. 22
AIR PRODUCTS AND CHEMICALS, INC.; *U.S. Public*, pg. 30
ALLIED WASTE INDUSTRIES; *U.S. Public*, pg. 49
AMERICAN ECOLOGY CORPORATION; *U.S. Public*, pg. 71
AMNIR-RECYCLING INDUSTRIES LTD—American Israeli Paper Mills Ltd.; *Int'l*, pg. 75
AMREP SOLUTIONS, INC.—AMREP Corporation; *U.S. Public*, pg. 104
ANDERSON SOLID WASTE, INC.—Republic Industries, Inc.; *U.S. Public*, pg. 1379
ARTESIAN WASTEWATER MANAGEMENT INC.—Artesian Resources Corporation; *U.S. Public*, pg. 135
AUTOSHRED INC.—Allied Waste Industries; *U.S. Public*, pg. 49
BFI ACQUISITION, INC.—Browning-Ferris Industries, Inc.; *U.S. Public*, pg. 263
BFI AVIATION SERVICES, INC.—Browning-Ferris Industries, Inc.; *U.S. Public*, pg. 263
BFI ENERGY SYSTEMS, INC.—Browning-Ferris Industries, Inc.; *U.S. Public*, pg. 263
BFI WASTE SYSTEMS, INC.—Browning-Ferris Industries, Inc.; *U.S. Public*, pg. 263
BFI WASTE SYSTEMS OF INDIANA, INC.—Browning-Ferris Industries, Inc.; *U.S. Public*, pg. 263
JOSEPH BEHR & SONS INC.; *U.S. Private*, pg. 130
BOVAR INC.—Trimac Corporation; *Int'l*, pg. 1424
BRAMBLES INDUSTRIES LIMITED; *Int'l*, pg. 210
BRAMBLES (U.K.) LTD.—Brambles Industries Limited; *Int'l*, pg. 212
BRECKETT PTY. LIMITED—Brambles Industries Limited; *Int'l*, pg. 211
BRESLUBE DIVISION OF SAFETY-KLEEN CANADA INC.—Safety-Kleen Corp.; *U.S. Public*, pg. 1426
BROWN AND CALDWELL; *U.S. Private*, pg. 173
BROWNING-FERRIS, INC.—Browning-Ferris Industries, Inc.; *U.S. Public*, pg. 263
BROWNING-FERRIS INDUSTRIES CHEMICAL SERVICES, INC.—Browning-Ferris Industries, Inc.; *U.S. Public*, pg. 263
BROWNING-FERRIS INDUSTRIES, INC.; *U.S. Public*, pg. 262
BROWNING-FERRIS INDUSTRIES OF FLORIDA, INC.—Browning-Ferris Industries, Inc.; *U.S. Public*, pg. 263
CMI CORPORATION; *U.S. Public*, pg. 278
CMI ENERGY CONVERSION SYSTEMS, INC.—CMI Corporation; *U.S. Public*, pg. 279
CRX INC.—Allied Waste Industries; *U.S. Public*, pg. 49
CSC DISPOSAL AND LANDFILL, INC.—Republic Industries, Inc.; *U.S. Public*, pg. 1379
CASELLA WASTE SYSTEMS, INC.; *U.S. Public*, pg. 312
CECOS INTERNATIONAL, INC.—Browning-Ferris Industries, Inc.; *U.S. Public*, pg. 264
AB CENTRALSUG—Celsius AB; *Int'l*, pg. 276
CHAMBERS MEDICAL TECHNOLOGIES, INC.—USA Waste Services, Inc.; *U.S. Public*, pg. 1686
CHAMBERS USA WASTE, INC.—USA Waste Services, Inc.; *U.S. Public*, pg. 1686
CHEMFIX INTERNATIONAL, INC.—Advanced Remediation Inc. (ARM); *U.S. Private*, pg. 22
CHUCKS DISPOSAL COMPANY—Allied Waste Industries; *U.S. Public*, pg. 49
CLEAN HARBORS, INC.; *U.S. Public*, pg. 383
CLEANAWAY—Brambles Industries Limited; *Int'l*, pg. 211
CLEANAWAY LIMITED—Brambles Industries Limited; *Int'l*, pg. 212
CLEANAWAY LIMITED—GKN plc; *Int'l*, pg. 535
CLEVELAND CONTAINER SERVICE, INC.—Republic Industries, Inc.; *U.S. Public*, pg. 1379
COMET ENTERPRISES, INC.—Browning-Ferris Industries, Inc.; *U.S. Public*, pg. 264
CONVERSION SYSTEMS, INC.—EnviroSource, Inc.; *U.S. Public*, pg. 587
DAY & ZIMMERMANN SERVICES—Day & Zimmermann, Inc.; *U.S. Private*, pg. 317
DEUTSCHE BABCOCK ANLAGEN GMBH—Deutsche Babcock AG; *Int'l*, pg. 398
DEXT COMPANY—Scope Industries; *U.S. Public*, pg. 1444
DISPOSAL SPECIALISTS, INC.—Browning-Ferris Industries, Inc.; *U.S. Public*, pg. 264
DISPOSAL SYSTEMS, INC.—The GNI Group, Inc.; *U.S. Public*, pg. 694
DISPOSAL URBAN MAINTENANCE PROCESSION CO., INC.—Republic Industries, Inc.; *U.S. Public*, pg. 1380
DOMBROWSKI & HOLMES, INC.; *U.S. Private*, pg. 338
DOOLEY EQUIPMENT CORP.—Browning-Ferris Industries, Inc.; *U.S. Public*, pg. 264
EG & G DEFENSE MATERIALS DIVISION—EG & G, Inc.; *U.S. Public*, pg. 543
EG & G ENVIRONMENTAL, INC.—EG & G, Inc.; *U.S. Public*, pg. 543
ENSI, INC.—ERD Waste Corp.; *U.S. Public*, pg. 546
ERD WASTE CORP.; *U.S. Public*, pg. 546
ESI, INC.—Browning-Ferris Industries, Inc.; *U.S. Public*, pg. 264
EAGLE MOUNTAIN RECLAMATION, INC.—Kaiser Ventures, Inc.; *U.S. Public*, pg. 941
EASTERN ENVIRONMENTAL SERVICES, INC.; *U.S. Public*, pg. 549
ECOVA CORPORATION—Amoco Corporation; *U.S. Public*, pg. 103
EMCON; *U.S. Public*, pg. 571
ENVIRONMENTAL CONTROL INC.—Allied Waste Industries; *U.S. Public*, pg. 49
ENVIRONMENTAL DEVELOPMENT CORP.—Allied Waste Industries; *U.S. Public*, pg. 49
ENVIRONMENTAL SERVICES OF AMERICA, INC.—ERD Waste Corp.; *U.S. Public*, pg. 546
ENVIRONMENTAL SPECIALISTS, INC.—Republic Industries, Inc.; *U.S. Public*, pg. 1379
ENVIROSAFE SERVICES, INC.—EnviroSource, Inc.; *U.S. Public*, pg. 587
FIBRES INTERNATIONAL, INC.—Continental Paper Recycling LLC; *U.S. Private*, pg. 269
FLUOR DANIEL GTI, INC.—Fluor Corporation; *U.S. Public*, pg. 660
W.J. FLYTE CORPORATION—Allied Waste Industries; *U.S. Public*, pg. 49
FUGRO GROUP COMPANIES; *U.S. Private*, pg. 430
THE GNI GROUP, INC.; *U.S. Public*, pg. 693
GEESINK B.V.—Powell Duffryn PLC; *Int'l*, pg. 1066
THE B.F. GOODRICH COMPANY; *U.S. Public*, pg. 751
GUIGUES S.A.—Technip; *Int'l*, pg. 1361
HL-NIW, INC.—Browning-Ferris Industries, Inc.; *U.S. Public*, pg. 264
HALLIBURTON ENVIRONMENTAL TECHNOLOGIES, INC.—Halliburton Company; *U.S. Public*, pg. 776
HARZA ENVIRONMENTAL SERVICES, INC.—Harza Engineering Co.; *U.S. Private*, pg. 509
HORSEHEAD INDUSTRIES, INC.; *U.S. Private*, pg. 540
HORSEHEAD RESOURCE DEVELOPMENT COMPANY, INC.—Horsehead Industries, Inc.; *U.S. Private*, pg. 540
IT CORP.—International Technology Corporation; *U.S. Public*, pg. 908
INDOCO, INC.—Browning-Ferris Industries, Inc.; *U.S. Public*, pg. 264
INTERNATIONAL DISPOSAL CORP. OF CALIFORNIA—Browning-Ferris Industries, Inc.; *U.S. Public*, pg. 264
INTERNATIONAL DISPOSAL CORPORATION OF INDIANA—Browning-Ferris Industries, Inc.; *U.S. Public*, pg. 264
INTERNATIONAL EXPLORATION, INC.—ERD Waste Corp.; *U.S. Public*, pg. 546
THE INTERNATIONAL METALS RECLAMATION COMPANY, INC.—Inco Limited; *Int'l*, pg. 672
INTERNATIONAL RECOVERY CORP.; *U.S. Public*, pg. 906

IONICS, INCORPORATED; *U.S. Public*, pg. 912
ISLER'S REFUSE SERVICE, INC.—Browning-Ferris Industries, Inc.; *U.S. Public*, pg. 264
JEFFCO LAND RECLAMATION, INC.—Browning-Ferris Industries, Inc.; *U.S. Public*, pg. 264
KAISER EAGLE MOUNTAIN, INC.—Kaiser Ventures, Inc.; *U.S. Public*, pg. 941
KAISER VENTURES, INC.; *U.S. Public*, pg. 941
KAISER WASTE TREATMENT, INC.—Kaiser Ventures, Inc.; *U.S. Public*, pg. 941
KARAS TRUCKING CO., INC.—Browning-Ferris Industries, Inc.; *U.S. Public*, pg. 264
KIMMINS CORP.; *U.S. Public*, pg. 960
LOUIS KMITO & SON, INC.—Browning-Ferris Industries, Inc.; *U.S. Public*, pg. 264
KVAERNER INCINERATION A/S—Kvaerner a.s.a.; *Int'l*, pg. 769
LCS SERVICES, INC.—USA Waste Services, Inc.; *U.S. Public*, pg. 1686
LAIDLAW ENVIRONMENTAL SERVICES, INC.; *U.S. Public*, pg. 975
LAIDLAW INC.—Canadian Pacific Limited; *Int'l*, pg. 259
LANDFILL, INC.—Browning-Ferris Industries, Inc.; *U.S. Public*, pg. 264
LANHAM WASTE CONTROL, INC.—Browning-Ferris Industries, Inc.; *U.S. Public*, pg. 264
LAUGHLIN ENVIRONMENTAL, INC.—Republic Industries, Inc.; *U.S. Public*, pg. 1379
LEHNKERING MONTAN TRANSPORT AG—Metallgesellschaft AG; *Int'l*, pg. 862
LEHNKERING MONTAN TRANSPORT AG—Preussag AG; *Int'l*, pg. 1069
LEMONS WASTE SYSTEMS INC.—Allied Waste Industries; *U.S. Public*, pg. 49
LYONNAISE DES EAUX S.A.; *Int'l*, pg. 822
MERIDIAN ENVIRONMENTAL SERVICES, INC.—Meridian National Corporation; *U.S. Public*, pg. 1095
MERIDIAN NATIONAL CORPORATION; *U.S. Public*, pg. 1095
MIDWEST SANITATION, INC.—USA Waste Services, Inc.; *U.S. Public*, pg. 1686
MINNESOTA POWER; *U.S. Public*, pg. 1116
MONTANA POWER COMPANY; *U.S. Public*, pg. 1126
MONTGOMERY WATSON—Montgomery Watson; *U.S. Private*, pg. 759
NRG RESOURCE RECOVERY, INC.—Northern States Power Company; *U.S. Public*, pg. 1195
NAPCO, INC.—Thermo Electron Corporation; *U.S. Public*, pg. 1592
NATIONAL DISPOSAL SERVICE OF NEBRASKA, INC.—Browning-Ferris Industries, Inc.; *U.S. Public*, pg. 264
NATIONAL WASTE SERVICES INC.—Allied Waste Industries; *U.S. Public*, pg. 49
NEW SYSTECH CORPORATION—Lafarge S.A.; *Int'l*, pg. 788
NEWPARK ENVIRONMENTAL SERVICES, INC.—Newpark Resources, Inc.; *U.S. Public*, pg. 1179
NIAGARA LANDFILL, INC.—Browning-Ferris Industries, Inc.; *U.S. Public*, pg. 264
NIAGARA RECYCLING, INC.—Browning-Ferris Industries, Inc.; *U.S. Public*, pg. 264
NORCAL WASTE SYSTEMS; *U.S. Public*, pg. 1188
NORTHEAST ENVIRONMENTAL SERVICES, INC.—ERD Waste Corp.; *U.S. Public*, pg. 546
OHM CORPORATION; *U.S. Public*, pg. 1207
ORM BERGOLD CHEMIE GMBH & CO.—Safety-Kleen Corp.; *U.S. Public*, pg. 1426
OGDEN CORPORATION; *U.S. Public*, pg. 1213
OGDEN ENERGY GROUP, INC.—Ogden Corporation; *U.S. Public*, pg. 1213
OMNISOURCE CORPORATION; *U.S. Private*, pg. 817
PERMA-FIX ENVIRONMENTAL SERVICES, INC.—Perma-Fix Environmental Services, Inc.; *U.S. Public*, pg. 1279
PERMA-FIX OF DAYTON, INC.—Perma-Fix Environmental Services, Inc.; *U.S. Public*, pg. 1279
PERMA-FIX OF FT. LAUDERDALE, INC.—Perma-Fix Environmental Services, Inc.; *U.S. Public*, pg. 1279
PHILIP INDUSTRIAL SERVICES GROUP—Philip Services Corp.; *Int'l*, pg. 1050
PINE BEND LANDFILL, INC.—Browning-Ferris Industries, Inc.; *U.S. Public*, pg. 264
POPLAR BLUFF COMPANIES—Allied Waste Industries; *U.S. Public*, pg. 49
RECHEM INTERNATIONAL LTD—Shanks & McEwan Group Plc; *Int'l*, pg. 1228
RECOMP, INC.; *U.S. Private*, pg. 914
REMOVAL, INC.—Browning-Ferris Industries, Inc.; *U.S. Public*, pg. 264
REPUBLIC ENVIRONMENTAL RECYCLING (NEW JERSEY), INC.—Philip Services Corp.; *Int'l*, pg. 1050
REPUBLIC ENVIRONMENTAL SYSTEMS (CLEVELAND)—Republic Industries, Inc.; *U.S. Public*, pg. 1380
REPUBLIC ENVIRONMENTAL SYSTEMS, INC.—Philip Services Corp.; *Int'l*, pg. 1050
REPUBLIC ENVIRONMENTAL SYSTEMS (PENNSYLVANIA), INC.—Philip Services Corp.; *Int'l*, pg. 1050
REPUBLIC IMPERIAL AND EL CENTRO SANITATION SERVICE CO.—Republic Industries, Inc.; *U.S. Public*, pg. 1379
REPUBLIC INDUSTRIES, INC.; *U.S. Public*, pg. 1378
REPUBLIC/MALOY LANDFILL & SANITATION—Republic Industries, Inc.; *U.S. Public*, pg. 1379
RESEARCH ENVIRONMENTAL INDUSTRIES, INC.; *U.S. Private*, pg. 924
RESIDENTIAL SERVICE, INC.—Browning-Ferris Industries, Inc.; *U.S. Public*, pg. 264
RESOURCE TRANSPORTATION SERVICES, INC.—The GNI Group, Inc.; *U.S. Public*, pg. 694
RIEDEL-SMITH ENVIRONMENTAL SERVICES—Smith Environmental Technologies Corp.; *U.S. Public*, pg. 1478
RIEDEL WASTE DISPOSAL SYSTEMS—Smith Environmental Technologies Corp.; *U.S. Public*, pg. 1478
RIVER CITY REFUSE REMOVAL, INC.—Browning-Ferris Industries, Inc.; *U.S. Public*, pg. 264
SAARBERG-FERNWAERME GMBH—Saarbergwerke Aktiengesellschaft; *Int'l*, pg. 1166
SAFETY-KLEEN CANADA, LTD.—Safety-Kleen Corp.; *U.S. Public*, pg. 1426
SAFETY-KLEEN CORP.; *U.S. Public*, pg. 1425
SAFETY-KLEEN OIL RECOVERY CO.—Safety-Kleen Corp.; *U.S. Public*, pg. 1426
SAFETY-KLEEN U.K., LTD.—Safety-Kleen Corp.; *U.S. Public*, pg. 1426
SANCO INC.—Allied Waste Industries; *U.S. Public*, pg. 49
SANIFILL, INC.—USA Waste Services, Inc.; *U.S. Public*, pg. 1686
SCOPE INDUSTRIES; *U.S. Public*, pg. 1444
SCORI HOLDING—Ciments Francais; *Int'l*, pg. 292
SHANKS & MCEWAN GROUP PLC; *Int'l*, pg. 1228
SHANKS & MCEWAN (NORTHERN) LTD—Shanks & McEwan Group Plc; *Int'l*, pg. 1228
SHANKS & MCEWAN (SOUTHERN WASTE SERVICES) LTD—Shanks & McEwan Group Plc; *Int'l*, pg. 1228
SILVER STATE DISPOSAL SERVICE, INC.—Republic Industries, Inc.; *U.S. Public*, pg. 1380
SITA—Lyonnaise des Eaux S.A.; *Int'l*, pg. 824
SMITH ENVIRONMENTAL TECHNOLOGIES CORP.; *U.S. Public*, pg. 1477
SMITH ENVIRONMENTAL TECHNOLOGIES CORP.—Smith Environmental Technologies Corp.; *U.S. Public*, pg. 1477
SMITH TECHNOLOGIES CORP.—Smith Environmental Technologies Corp.; *U.S. Public*, pg. 1478
SPRINGFIELD RELAY SYSTEMS, INC.—Browning-Ferris Industries, Inc.; *U.S. Public*, pg. 264
SUPER SERVICES WASTE MANAGEMENT INC.—Allied Waste Industries; *U.S. Public*, pg. 49
T&W DISPOSAL CO.—Allied Waste Industries; *U.S. Public*, pg. 49
TPS TECHNOLOGIES INC.—Thermo Electron Corporation; *U.S. Public*, pg. 1594
TAY-BAN CORPORATION—Republic Industries, Inc.; *U.S. Public*, pg. 1380
TRANSALTA FLY ASH LTD.—Transalta Corporation; *Int'l*, pg. 1416
TRANSTEC ENVIRONMENTAL INC.—American Ecology Corporation; *U.S. Public*, pg. 71
TRIWASTE REDUCTION SERVICES INC.—Trimac Corporation; *Int'l*, pg. 1424
UPPER ROCK ISLAND COUNTY LANDFILL—Allied Waste Industries; *U.S. Public*, pg. 49
VARA INTERNATONAL—Calgon Carbon Corporation; *U.S. Public*, pg. 293
VON ROLL AG DEPARTEMENT UMWELTTECHNIK—Von Roll AG; *Int'l*, pg. 1480
WPI TRANSPORTATION, INC.—American Ecology Corporation; *U.S. Public*, pg. 71
WRR ENVIRONMENTAL SERVICES CO., INC.—The Ziegler Companies, Inc.; *U.S. Public*, pg. 1792
WABASH VALLEY LANDFILL COMPANY LTD.—Republic Industries, Inc.; *U.S. Public*, pg. 1380
WASTE DISPOSAL, INC.—Browning-Ferris Industries, Inc.; *U.S. Public*, pg. 264
WASTE HANDLING SYSTEMS, INC.—Republic Industries, Inc.; *U.S. Public*, pg. 1380
WASTE MANAGEMENT, INC.; *U.S. Public*, pg. 1744
WASTE MANAGEMENT INTERNATIONAL PLC—Waste Management, Inc.; *U.S. Public*, pg. 1745
WASTECO, INC.—Browning-Ferris Industries, Inc.; *U.S. Public*, pg. 264
WELLMAN, INC.; *U.S. Public*, pg. 1752
WELLMAN INTERNATIONAL LTD.—Wellman, Inc.; *U.S. Public*, pg. 1753
WEST ROXBURY CRUSHED STONE CO.—Browning-Ferris Industries, Inc.; *U.S. Public*, pg. 265
WESTERN WASTE INDUSTRIES—USA Waste Services, Inc.; *U.S. Public*, pg. 1686
WESTERN WASTE INDUSTRIES, INC. OF FLORIDA—USA Waste Services, Inc.; *U.S. Public*, pg. 1686
WESTOWNS DISPOSAL SYSTEMS, INC.—Browning-Ferris Industries, Inc.; *U.S. Public*, pg. 265
WEST VALLEY NUCLEAR SERVICES—CBS Corporation; *U.S. Public*, pg. 273
R.E. WOLFE ENTERPRISES OF EDINBURG—Republic Industries, Inc.; *U.S. Public*, pg. 1379
WOODLAKE SANITARY SERVICE, INC.—Browning-Ferris Industries, Inc.; *U.S. Public*, pg. 265
YOUNG ENVIRONMENTAL CLEAN UP—R.S. Young Excavating, Inc.; *U.S. Private*, pg. 1202
JOHN ZINK CO.—Koch Industries, Incorporated; *U.S. Private*, pg. 628

4959 — SANITARY SERVICES, NEC

AIR PRODUCTS REF-FUEL OF CONNECTICUT (S.E.), INC.—Air Products and Chemicals, Inc.; *U.S. Public*, pg. 31
AIR PRODUCTS REF-FUEL OF HEMPSTEAD, INC.—Air Products and Chemicals, Inc.; *U.S. Public*, pg. 31
BFI AVIATION SERVICES, INC.—Browning-Ferris Industries, Inc.; *U.S. Public*, pg. 263
BFI ENERGY SYSTEMS, INC.—Browning-Ferris Industries, Inc.; *U.S. Public*, pg. 263
BFI WASTE SYSTEMS, INC.—Browning-Ferris Industries, Inc.; *U.S. Public*, pg. 263
BFI WASTE SYSTEMS OF INDIANA, INC.—Browning-Ferris Industries, Inc.; *U.S. Public*, pg. 263
BROWNING-FERRIS INDUSTRIES, INC.; *U.S. Public*, pg. 262
CELSIUS AB; *Int'l*, pg. 276
CHEMISOLV—Serv-Tech, Inc.; *U.S. Public*, pg. 1460
HANDEX ENVIRONMENT INC.; *U.S. Private*, pg. 498
INTEGRATED WASTE SERVICES, INC.; *U.S. Public*, pg. 886
NEW SYSTECH CORPORATION—Lafarge S.A.; *Int'l*, pg. 788
OHM CORPORATION; *U.S. Public*, pg. 1207
OHM ENVIRONMENTAL RESOURCES MANAGEMENT CORP.—OHM Corporation; *U.S. Public*, pg. 1208
OIL MOP, INC.—The Beacon Group; *U.S. Private*, pg. 126
SERV-TECH EUROPE—Serv-Tech, Inc.; *U.S. Public*, pg. 1460
SOUTH WEST WATER PLC; *Int'l*, pg. 1287
TERMINAL TECHNOLOGIES, INC.—Serv-Tech, Inc.; *U.S. Public*, pg. 1460
THE VALLEY LINE COMPANY—CSX Corporation; *U.S. Public*, pg. 284

4961 — STEAM & AIR-CONDITIONING SUPPLY

ABB COMBUSTION ENGINEERING NUCLEAR POWER—ABB Asea Brown Boveri (Holding) Ltd.; *Int'l*, pg. 3
COM/ENERGY STEAM CO.—Commonwealth Energy System; *U.S. Public*, pg. 414
CALENERGY CO.; *U.S. Public*, pg. 292
COGENTRIX INCORPORATED; *U.S. Private*, pg. 249
COMMONWEALTH ENERGY SYSTEM; *U.S. Public*, pg. 414
CONNECTICUT NATURAL GAS CORPORATION—CTG Resources, Inc.; *U.S. Public*, pg. 285
CONSOLIDATED EDISON COMPANY OF NEW YORK, INC.; *U.S. Public*, pg. 434
DPL INC.; *U.S. Public*, pg. 473
DAYTON POWER & LIGHT CO.—DPL Inc.; *U.S. Public*, pg. 473
DOWNTOWN COGENERATION ASSOCIATES—CTG Resources, Inc.; *U.S. Public*, pg. 285
ENERGY NETWORKS, INC. (ENI)—CTG Resources, Inc.; *U.S. Public*, pg. 285
EQUITABLE GAS-ENERGY CO.—Equitable Resources, Inc.; *U.S. Public*, pg. 589
HARTFORD STEAM CO.—CTG Resources, Inc.; *U.S. Public*, pg. 285
INDIANAPOLIS POWER & LIGHT COMPANY—Ipalco Enterprises, Inc.; *U.S. Public*, pg. 913
LESLIE CONTROLS, INC.—Watts Industries, Inc.; *U.S. Public*, pg. 1746
MINNESOTA POWER; *U.S. Public*, pg. 1116
MONOCHEM, INC.—Borden, Inc.; *U.S. Private*, pg. 158
NRG THERMAL CORPORATION—Northern States Power Company; *U.S. Public*, pg. 1195
NORENCO CORP.—Northern States Power Company; *U.S. Public*, pg. 1195
PACIFIC POWER & LIGHT COMPANY—PacifiCorp; *U.S. Public*, pg. 1251
PAMECO CORP.; *U.S. Public*, pg. 1255
POWER SOURCES, INC.—ChemFirst Inc.; *U.S. Public*, pg. 344
THERMAL ENERGIES, INC.—United Illuminating Company; *U.S. Public*, pg. 1679
TRIGEN ENERGY CORPORATION; *U.S. Public*, pg. 1637
UNOCAL GEOTHERMAL OF INDONESIA LTD.—Unocal Corporation; *U.S. Public*, pg. 1698
WASHINGTON GAS LIGHT CO.; *U.S. Public*, pg. 1740

4971 — IRRIGATION SYSTEMS

ACQUEDOTTO DI DOMODOSSOLA S.P.A.—ENI S.p.A.; *Int'l*, pg. 428
ACQUEDOTTO DI SAVONA S.R.L.—ENI S.p.A.; *Int'l*, pg. 428
ACQUEDOTTO MONFERRATO S.P.A.—ENI S.p.A.; *Int'l*, pg. 428
ALEXANDER & BALDWIN, INC.; *U.S. Public*, pg. 39
AMERICAN GRANBY, INC.; *U.S. Private*, pg. 55
ANTELOPE VALLEY WATER COMPANY—Dominguez Services Corporation; *U.S. Public*, pg. 516
ARDEN WATER COMPANY—Dominguez Services Corporation; *U.S. Public*, pg. 516
CAROLINA PUMP & SUPPLY CORP.—Hughes Supply, Inc.; *U.S. Public*, pg. 846
DOMINGUEZ WATER COMPANY—Dominguez Services Corporation; *U.S. Public*, pg. 516
EAST MAUI IRRIGATION CO., LTD.—Alexander & Baldwin, Inc.; *U.S. Public*, pg. 39
GLACIER WATER SERVICES INC.; *U.S. Public*, pg. 745
KERNVILLE DOMESTIC WATER COMPANY—Dominguez Services Corporation; *U.S. Public*, pg. 516
PHILADELPHIA SUBURBAN WATER COMPANY—Philadelphia Suburban Corporation; *U.S. Public*, pg. 1287
SALT RIVER PROJECT AGRICULTURAL IMPROVEMENT AND POWER DISTRICT; *U.S. Private*, pg. 962
SOCIETA AZIONARIA PER LA CONDOTTA DI ACQUE POTABILI S.P.A.—ENI S.p.A.; *Int'l*, pg. 428
WAIAHOLE IRRIGATION CO., LTD.—JMB Realty Corporation; *U.S. Private*, pg. 578

5012 — WHOLESALE DISTRIBUTION OF AUTOMOBILES & OTHER MOTOR VEHICLES

ADT AUTOMOTIVE, INC.—Tyco International Ltd.; *U.S. Public*, pg. 1648
ADT TRUCK & EQUIPMENT AUCTIONS, INC.—Tyco International Ltd.; *U.S. Public*, pg. 1648
ADT LIMITED—Tyco International Ltd.; *U.S. Public*, pg. 1649
A.F.N. LTD.—Porsche AG; *Int'l*, pg. 1063
AM GENERAL CORPORATION—Renco Group; *U.S. Private*, pg. 922
ADESA PITTSBURGH AUTO AUCTION—Minnesota Power; *U.S. Public*, pg. 1116
ALBUQUERQUE AUTO AUCTION INC.—Tyco International Ltd.; *U.S. Public*, pg. 1648
ALFA ROMEO AUTO S.P.A.—Fiat Auto SpA; *Int'l*, pg. 481
ALFA ROMEO ESPANA—Fiat Auto SpA; *Int'l*, pg. 481
ALFA ROMEO VERTRIEBSGES M.B.H.—Fiat Auto SpA; *Int'l*, pg. 481

ALOHA AUTO AUCTION—Tyco International Ltd.; *U.S. Public*, pg. 1648
AMERICAN AUTO AUCTION, INC.—Cox Enterprises, Inc.; *U.S. Private*, pg. 282
AMERICAN HONDA MOTOR CO., INC.—Honda Motor Co., Ltd.; *Int'l*, pg. 634
AMERICAN HONDA MOTOR CO., INC. AUTOMOBILE SALES DIVISION—Honda Motor Co., Ltd.; *Int'l*, pg. 634
AMERICAN ISUZU MOTORS INC.—Isuzu Motors Limited; *Int'l*, pg. 692
AMERICAN LAND CRUISERS—Budget Group, Inc.; *U.S. Private*, pg. 178
AMERICAN SUZUKI MOTOR CORPORATION—Suzuki Motor Corporation; *Int'l*, pg. 1323
ANADOLU OTOMOTIV SANAYII VE TICARET A.S.—Isuzu Motors Limited; *Int'l*, pg. 692
ARCTIC CAT INC.; *U.S. Public*, pg. 128
ARENA AUTO AUCTION INC.—Tyco International Ltd.; *U.S. Public*, pg. 1648
ARIZONA AUCTION SERVICES, INC.—Cox Enterprises, Inc.; *U.S. Private*, pg. 282
ARIZONA AUTO AUCTION SERVICES—Cox Enterprises, Inc.; *U.S. Private*, pg. 282
ASIAN HONDA MOTOR CO., LTD.—Honda Motor Co., Ltd.; *Int'l*, pg. 635
ASTON MARTIN LAGONDA OF NORTH AMERICA, INC.—Ford Motor Company; *U.S. Public*, pg. 664
ASTON MARTIN SALES LIMITED—Ford Motor Company; *U.S. Public*, pg. 665
ATLANTA AUTO AUCTION, INC.—Cox Enterprises, Inc.; *U.S. Private*, pg. 282
ATLAS TERMINAL CO.—Atlas World Group, Inc.; *U.S. Private*, pg. 97
AUCTION TRANSPORT INC.—Tyco International Ltd.; *U.S. Public*, pg. 1648
AUDI OF AMERICA—Volkswagen AG; *Int'l*, pg. 1474
AUTO-BON OY (IMPORTS)—Amer Group Ltd.; *Int'l*, pg. 72
AUTOGERMA S.P.A.—Volkswagen AG; *Int'l*, pg. 1474
BMW AUSTRALIA LTD.—Bayerische Motoren Werke Aktiengesellschaft; *Int'l*, pg. 178
BMW AUSTRIA GESELLSCHAFT M.B.H.—Bayerische Motoren Werke Aktiengesellschaft; *Int'l*, pg. 178
BMW BELGIUM S.A./N.V.—Bayerische Motoren Werke Aktiengesellschaft; *Int'l*, pg. 178
BMW CANADA INC.—Bayerische Motoren Werke Aktiengesellschaft; *Int'l*, pg. 178
BMW FRANCE S.A.—Bayerische Motoren Werke Aktiengesellschaft; *Int'l*, pg. 178
BMW (GB) LTD.—Bayerische Motoren Werke Aktiengesellschaft; *Int'l*, pg. 178
BMW IBERICA S.A.—Bayerische Motoren Werke Aktiengesellschaft; *Int'l*, pg. 178
BMW ITALIA S.P.A.—Bayerische Motoren Werke Aktiengesellschaft; *Int'l*, pg. 178
BMW JAPAN CORP.—Bayerische Motoren Werke Aktiengesellschaft; *Int'l*, pg. 178
BMW MOTOREN GES.M.B.H.—Bayerische Motoren Werke Aktiengesellschaft; *Int'l*, pg. 178
BMW MOTORSPORT GMBH—Bayerische Motoren Werke Aktiengesellschaft; *Int'l*, pg. 177
BMW NEDERLAND B.V.—Bayerische Motoren Werke Aktiengesellschaft; *Int'l*, pg. 178
BMW NEW ZEALAND LTD.—Bayerische Motoren Werke Aktiengesellschaft; *Int'l*, pg. 178
BMW (SCHWEIZ) AG—Bayerische Motoren Werke Aktiengesellschaft; *Int'l*, pg. 178
BMW (SOUTH AFRICA) (PTY.) LTD.—Bayerische Motoren Werke Aktiengesellschaft; *Int'l*, pg. 178
BMW (US) HOLDING CORPORATION—Bayerische Motoren Werke Aktiengesellschaft; *Int'l*, pg. 177
BADGER TRUCK CENTER, INC.; *U.S. Private*, pg. 110
BALTIMORE-WASHINGTON AUTO EXCHANGE INC.—Tyco International Ltd.; *U.S. Public*, pg. 1648
JACK BARCLAY LTD.—Lonrho plc; *Int'l*, pg. 817
BAY CITIES AUTO AUCTION—Cox Enterprises, Inc.; *U.S. Private*, pg. 282
BAYERISCHE MOTOREN WERKE AKTIENGESELLSCHAFT; *Int'l*, pg. 177
BAYSIDE AUTO AUCTION OF TAMPA INC.—Tyco International Ltd.; *U.S. Public*, pg. 1648
BENELLI/MOTO GUZZI NORTH AMERICA—Fiat Auto SpA; *Int'l*, pg. 482
BIDDULPH AUTOMOTIVE GROUP; *U.S. Private*, pg. 142
BISHOP BROTHERS AUTO AUCTION—Cox Enterprises, Inc.; *U.S. Private*, pg. 282
BRITISH CAR AUCTION GROUP—Tyco International Ltd.; *U.S. Public*, pg. 1649
BUTLER AUTO AUCTION—Cox Enterprises, Inc.; *U.S. Private*, pg. 282
CFCI S.A.—Unilever Plc; *Int'l*, pg. 1436
CALIFORNIA AUTO DEALERS EXCHANGE, INC.—Cox Enterprises, Inc.; *U.S. Private*, pg. 282
CAMDEN MOTORS LTD.—Barclays Bank PLC; *Int'l*, pg. 165
CANADIAN AUTOPARTS TOYOTA, INC.—Toyota Motor Corporation; *Int'l*, pg. 1413
CANADIAN KAWASAKI MOTORS INC.—Kawasaki Heavy Industries, Ltd.; *Int'l*, pg. 726
CANLUBANG AUTOMOTIVE RESOURCES CORP.—Nissho Iwai Corporation; *Int'l*, pg. 947
CAPITAL AUTO AUCTION INC.—Tyco International Ltd.; *U.S. Public*, pg. 1648
CARCO INTERNATIONAL, INC.; *U.S. Private*, pg. 208
CASCADE EUROPE—Cascade Corporation; *U.S. Public*, pg. 311
CHRYSLER CANADA LTD.—Chrysler Corporation; *U.S. Public*, pg. 354
CHRYSLER CREDIT CORP.—Chrysler Corporation; *U.S. Public*, pg. 354
CHRYSLER/PLYMOUTH DIVISION—Chrysler Corporation; *U.S. Public*, pg. 353
CHRYSLER SALES GROUP—Chrysler Corporation; *U.S. Public*, pg. 353
CLANTON'S AUTO AUCTION—Cox Enterprises, Inc.; *U.S. Private*, pg. 282
CLEARWATER AUTO AUCTION INC.—Tyco International Ltd.; *U.S. Public*, pg. 1648
CLEVELAND BROTHERS EQUIPMENT CO., INC.; *U.S. Private*, pg. 245
COLORADO AUCTION SERVICES CORPORATION—Cox Enterprises, Inc.; *U.S. Private*, pg. 282
COLORADO SPRINGS AUTO AUCTION INC.—Tyco International Ltd.; *U.S. Public*, pg. 1648
COMPONENTA TRANSPORT AB—Trelleborg AB; *Int'l*, pg. 1420
CONSORCIO G. GRUPO DINA, S.A. DE C.V.; *Int'l*, pg. 326
CONVESCO VEHICLE SALES GMBH—General Motors Corporation; *U.S. Public*, pg. 724
COX ENTERPRISES, INC.; *U.S. Private*, pg. 281
CRUISE AMERICA, INC.—Budget Group, Inc.; *U.S. Private*, pg. 178
CYCLE & CARRIAGE INDUSTRIES (1986) PTE. LIMITED; *Int'l*, pg. 350
DAIHATSU AMERICA, INC.—Daihatsu Motor Corporation, Ltd.; *Int'l*, pg. 365
DAIHATSU AUSTRALIA PTY. LTD.—Daihatsu Motor Corporation, Ltd.; *Int'l*, pg. 365
DAIHATSU AUTOHANDELSGES M.B.H.—Daihatsu Motor Corporation, Ltd.; *Int'l*, pg. 365
DAIHATSU DEUTSCHLAND GMBH—Daihatsu Motor Corporation, Ltd.; *Int'l*, pg. 365
DAIHATSU HOLLAND B.V.—Daihatsu Motor Corporation, Ltd.; *Int'l*, pg. 365
DAIHATSU MALAYSIA SDN. BND.—Daihatsu Motor Corporation, Ltd.; *Int'l*, pg. 365
DAIHATSU MOTOR CORPORATION, LTD.; *Int'l*, pg. 364
DAIHATSU MOTOR (H.K.) LTD.—Daihatsu Motor Corporation, Ltd.; *Int'l*, pg. 365
DALLAS AUTO AUCTION INC.—Tyco International Ltd.; *U.S. Public*, pg. 1648
DEALERS AUTO AUCTION OF SANFORD, INC.—Tyco International Ltd.; *U.S. Public*, pg. 1649
DENVER AUTO AUCTION—Cox Enterprises, Inc.; *U.S. Private*, pg. 282
DISTRIBUIDORA TOYOTA CHILE LTDA.—Mitsui & Co., Ltd.; *Int'l*, pg. 879
DODGE CAR/TRUCK DIVISION—Chrysler Corporation; *U.S. Public*, pg. 353
DOONAN & SONS, INC.; *U.S. Private*, pg. 340
THE DOVERCOURT MOTOR CO. LTD.—Lonrho plc; *Int'l*, pg. 817
EATON CORPORATION, TRUCK COMPONENTS OPERATIONS-NORTH AMERICA—Eaton Corporation; *U.S. Public*, pg. 557
ELVINS EQUIPMENT SALES LIMITED—Wajax Limited; *Int'l*, pg. 1485
ERVINS GROUP—Acme Mills Co. Inc.; *U.S. Private*, pg. 13
FERRARI NORTH AMERICA, INC.—Fiat Auto SpA; *Int'l*, pg. 483
FIAT AUTO ESPANA S.A.—Fiat Auto SpA; *Int'l*, pg. 481
FIAT AUTO PORTUGUESA SA—Fiat Auto SpA; *Int'l*, pg. 481
FIAT AUTO S.P.A.—Fiat Auto SpA; *Int'l*, pg. 481
FIAT AUTO SUISSE SA—Fiat Auto SpA; *Int'l*, pg. 481
FIAT AUTO SVERIGE AB—Fiat Auto SpA; *Int'l*, pg. 481
FIAT AUTOMOBILE AG—Fiat Auto SpA; *Int'l*, pg. 481
FLORIDA AUTO AUCTION OF ORLANDO, INC.—Cox Enterprises, Inc.; *U.S. Private*, pg. 282
OY FORD AB—Ford Motor Company; *U.S. Public*, pg. 665
FORD DIVISION—Ford Motor Company; *U.S. Public*, pg. 662
FORD INTERNATIONAL EXPORT SALES (ASIA-PACIFIC REGION) INCORPORATED—Ford Motor Company; *U.S. Public*, pg. 664
FORD LUSITANA—Ford Motor Company; *U.S. Public*, pg. 666
FORD MOTOR COMPANY; *U.S. Public*, pg. 661
FORD MOTOR COMPANY A/S—Ford Motor Company; *U.S. Public*, pg. 666
FORD MOTOR CO. (SWITZERLAND) S.A.—Ford Motor Company; *U.S. Public*, pg. 666
FORD PERSONAL IMPORT EXPORT LTD.—Ford Motor Company; *U.S. Public*, pg. 666
FORD SALES COMPANY OF AUSTRALIA LIMITED—Ford Motor Company; *U.S. Public*, pg. 666
FORD SALES OPERATIONS—Ford Motor Company; *U.S. Public*, pg. 662
FORD TRUCK OPERATIONS—Ford Motor Company; *U.S. Public*, pg. 662
FORT WAYNE VEHICLE AUCTION INC.—Tyco International Ltd.; *U.S. Public*, pg. 1649
FORT WORTH AUTO AUCTION—Cox Enterprises, Inc.; *U.S. Private*, pg. 283
FRESNO AUTO DEALERS AUCTION—Cox Enterprises, Inc.; *U.S. Private*, pg. 282
GEFCO—PSA Peugeot Citroen; *Int'l*, pg. 1021
GM ALLISON JAPAN LIMITED—General Motors Corporation; *U.S. Public*, pg. 721
GENERAL COACH—Thor Industries, Inc.; *U.S. Public*, pg. 1602
GENERAL MOTORS CORPORATION; *U.S. Public*, pg. 718
GENERAL MOTORS HUNGARY—General Motors Corporation; *U.S. Public*, pg. 722
GENERAL MOTORS MARKETING SERVICES HELLAS AEE—General Motors Corporation; *U.S. Public*, pg. 722
GENERAL MOTORS TAIWAN, INC.—General Motors Corporation; *U.S. Public*, pg. 723
GENERAL MOTORS TURKIYE LIMITED SIRKETI—General Motors Corporation; *U.S. Public*, pg. 723
GENERAL MOTORS VENEZOLANA, C.A.—General Motors Corporation; *U.S. Public*, pg. 723
GEORGIA DEALERS AUTO AUCTION—Cox Enterprises, Inc.; *U.S. Private*, pg. 282
GLORY KAWASAKI MOTORS CO., LTD.—Nissho Iwai Corporation; *Int'l*, pg. 947
GOLDEN GATE AUTO AUCTION INC.—Tyco International Ltd.; *U.S. Public*, pg. 1649
GREAT LAKES PETERBILT, GMC; *U.S. Private*, pg. 475
GREATER CHICAGO AUTO AUCTION—Cox Enterprises, Inc.; *U.S. Private*, pg. 282
GREATER TAMPA BAY AUTO AUCTION—Cox Enterprises, Inc.; *U.S. Private*, pg. 282
GULF STATES TOYOTA, INC.; *U.S. Private*, pg. 488
HARRIS FORD, INC.; *U.S. Private*, pg. 506
HARRISONBURG AUTO AUCTION—Cox Enterprises, Inc.; *U.S. Private*, pg. 282
HEAVY MACHINES, INC.; *U.S. Private*, pg. 518
HINO DIESEL TRUCKS (U.S.A.), INC.—Hino Motors, Ltd.; *Int'l*, pg. 620
HOLAD HOLDING & ADMINISTRATION AG—Volkswagen AG; *Int'l*, pg. 1475
HONDA AUSTRALIA PTY., LTD.—Honda Motor Co., Ltd.; *Int'l*, pg. 635
HONDA AUSTRIA G.M.B.H.—Honda Motor Co., Ltd.; *Int'l*, pg. 635
HONDA AUTOMOBILI ITALIA S.P.A.—Honda Motor Co., Ltd.; *Int'l*, pg. 635
HONDA CANADA INC.—Honda Motor Co., Ltd.; *Int'l*, pg. 635
HONDA CLIO SHIN TOKYO CO., LTD.—Honda Motor Co., Ltd.; *Int'l*, pg. 634
HONDA DEUTSCHLAND GMBH—Honda Motor Co., Ltd.; *Int'l*, pg. 635
HONDA EUROPE N.V.—Honda Motor Co., Ltd.; *Int'l*, pg. 635
HONDA FRANCE S.A.—Honda Motor Co., Ltd.; *Int'l*, pg. 635
HONDA MOTOR DO BRASIL LTDA.—Honda Motor Co., Ltd.; *Int'l*, pg. 635
HONDA MOTOR EUROPE LTD.—Honda Motor Co., Ltd.; *Int'l*, pg. 635
HONDA NEDERLAND B.V.—Honda Motor Co., Ltd.; *Int'l*, pg. 635
HONDA RACING CORPORATION—Honda Motor Co., Ltd.; *Int'l*, pg. 634
HONDA TRADING CORP.—Honda Motor Co., Ltd.; *Int'l*, pg. 634
HUMBERSIDE HOLDINGS LTD—Powell Duffryn PLC; *Int'l*, pg. 1065
HYUNDAI AUTO CANADA INC.—Hyundai Motor Company; *Int'l*, pg. 641
HYUNDAI MOTOR AMERICA—Hyundai Motor Company; *Int'l*, pg. 641
HYUNDAI MOTOR AMERICA EASTERN REGIONAL OFFICE—Hyundai Motor Company; *Int'l*, pg. 641
HYUNDAI MOTOR AMERICA SOUTHERN REGIONAL OFFICE—Hyundai Motor Company; *Int'l*, pg. 641
HYUNDAI MOTOR AMERICA WESTERN REGIONAL OFFICE—Hyundai Motor Company; *Int'l*, pg. 641
HYUNDAI MOTOR COMPANY; *Int'l*, pg. 641
ITOCHU INDUSTRIAL MACHINERY, INC.—Itochu Corporation; *Int'l*, pg. 695
IMPERIAL AUTO AUCTION—Cox Enterprises, Inc.; *U.S. Private*, pg. 282
IMPERIAL SWEETNER DISTRIBUTORS, INC.—Imperial Holly Corporation; *U.S. Public*, pg. 872
P.T. INDOMOBIL SUZUKI INTERNATIONAL—Suzuki Motor Corporation; *Int'l*, pg. 1323
ISUZU-GENERAL MOTORS AUSTRALIA LTD.—Isuzu Motors Limited; *Int'l*, pg. 693
ISUZU-GENERAL MOTORS AUSTRALIA LTD.—General Motors Corporation; *U.S. Public*, pg. 725
IVECO TRUCKS OF NORTH AMERICA INC.—Fiat Auto SpA; *Int'l*, pg. 484
J&L TANK—Dover Corporation; *U.S. Public*, pg. 521
JM FAMILY ENTERPRISES INC.; *U.S. Private*, pg. 577
JAGUAR CANADA INC.—Ford Motor Company; *U.S. Public*, pg. 667
JEEP/EAGLE DIVISION—Chrysler Corporation; *U.S. Public*, pg. 353
KALMAR INC.—Trelleborg AB; *Int'l*, pg. 1421
KANSAS CITY AUTO AUCTION—Cox Enterprises, Inc.; *U.S. Private*, pg. 282
KASSBOHRER NORTH AMERICA—Daimler-Benz Aktiengesellschaft; *Int'l*, pg. 368
KOBELCO AMERICA INC.—Kobe Steel, Ltd.; *Int'l*, pg. 740
KORPIVAARA OY - FORKLIFTS—Amer Group Ltd.; *Int'l*, pg. 72
KORPIVAARA OY - TOYOTA GROUP—Amer Group Ltd.; *Int'l*, pg. 72
LB INDUSTRIES INC.; *U.S. Private*, pg. 639
LAKELAND AUTO AUCTION—Cox Enterprises, Inc.; *U.S. Private*, pg. 282
LAUDERDALE-MIAMI AUTO AUCTION INC.—Tyco International Ltd.; *U.S. Public*, pg. 1649
LINCOLN-MERCURY DIVISION—Ford Motor Company; *U.S. Public*, pg. 662
LOS ANGELES DEALERS AUTO AUCTIONS—Cox Enterprises, Inc.; *U.S. Private*, pg. 282
LOTUS CARS USA, INC.—Proton; *Int'l*, pg. 1071
MMC DANMARK A.S.—Mitsubishi Motors Corporation; *Int'l*, pg. 876
MMC SITTIPOL COMPANY, LTD.—Mitsubishi Motors Corporation; *Int'l*, pg. 876
MANHEIM AUCTIONS, INC.—Cox Enterprises, Inc.; *U.S. Private*, pg. 282
MANHEIM'S GREATER ORLANDO AUTO AUCTION—Cox Enterprises, Inc.; *U.S. Private*, pg. 282
MANHEIM'S OSHAWA DEALERS EXCHANGE—Cox Enterprises, Inc.; *U.S. Private*, pg. 283
MASEK DISTRIBUTING INC.; *U.S. Private*, pg. 711
MASERATI AUTOMOBILES, INCORPORATED—Fiat Auto SpA; *Int'l*, pg. 482
MCCOMBS AUTOMOTIVE; *U.S. Private*, pg. 720
MERCEDES-BENZ BELGIUM S.A./N.V.—Daimler-Benz Aktiengesellschaft; *Int'l*, pg. 368
MERCEDES-BENZ FRANCE S.A.—Daimler-Benz Aktiengesellschaft; *Int'l*, pg. 369
MERCEDES-BENZ OF NORTH AMERICA, INC.—Daimler-Benz Aktiengesellschaft; *Int'l*, pg. 368

MERCEDES-BENZ OF SOUTH AFRICA (PTY.) LTD.—Daimler-Benz Aktiengesellschaft; *Int'l*, pg. 369
MERCEDES-BENZ (UNITED KINGDOM) LTD.—Daimler-Benz Aktiengesellschaft; *Int'l*, pg. 369
METRO AUTO AUCTION OF KANSAS CITY, INC.—Tyco International Ltd.; *U.S. Public*, pg. 1649
METRO MILWAUKEE AUTO AUCTION—Cox Enterprises, Inc.; *U.S. Private*, pg. 282
MID-AMERICA AUTO AUCTION—Tyco International Ltd.; *U.S. Public*, pg. 1649
MID AMERICA INTERNATIONAL TRUCKS, INC.; *U.S. Private*, pg. 743
MIDWAY FORD TRUCK CENTER INC.; *U.S. Private*, pg. 744
MINNEAPOLIS AUTO AUCTION—Cox Enterprises, Inc.; *U.S. Private*, pg. 282
MISSISSIPPI AUTO AUCTION INC.—Tyco International Ltd.; *U.S. Public*, pg. 1649
MISSOURI AUCTION SERVICES CORP.—Cox Enterprises, Inc.; *U.S. Private*, pg. 282
MITSUBISHI FUSO TRUCK OF AMERICA, INC.—Mitsubishi Motors Corporation; *Int'l*, pg. 875
P.T. MITSUBISHI KRAMA YUDHA MOTORS & MANUFACTURING—Mitsubishi Motors Corporation; *Int'l*, *pg. 876*
MITSUBISHI MOTOR MARKETING RESEARCH EUROPE GMBH—Mitsubishi Motors Corporation; *Int'l*, pg. 876
MITSUBISHI MOTOR SALES OF AMERICA, INC.—Mitsubishi Motors Corporation; *Int'l*, pg. 875
MITSUBISHI MOTOR SALES OF CARIBBEAN INC.—Mitsubishi Motors Corporation; *Int'l*, pg. 876
MITSUBISHI MOTORS AMERICA, INC.—Mitsubishi Motors Corporation; *Int'l*, pg. 876
MITSUBISHI MOTORS AUSTRALIA LTD.—Mitsubishi Motors Corporation; *Int'l*, pg. 876
MITSUBISHI MOTORS DE PORTUGAL, S.A.—Mitsubishi Motors Corporation; *Int'l*, pg. 876
MITSUBISHI MOTORS NEW ZEALAND LTD.—Mitsubishi Motors Corporation; *Int'l*, pg. 876
MONNOYEUR SCA; *Int'l*, pg. 888
NAAO MARKETING—Ford Motor Company; *U.S. Public*, pg. 662
NAPCO INTERNATIONAL, INC.—Venturian Corp.; *U.S. Public*, pg. 1716
NASHVILLE AUTO AUCTION INC.—Tyco International Ltd.; *U.S. Public*, pg. 1649
NATIONAL AUTO DEALERS EXCHANGE—Cox Enterprises, Inc.; *U.S. Private*, pg. 282
NEWBURGH AUTO AUCTION—Cox Enterprises, Inc.; *U.S. Private*, pg. 282
NICHIMEN AMERICA, INC.—Nichimen Corporation; *Int'l*, pg. 927
NICHIMEN CORPORATION; *Int'l*, pg. 927
NIPPONDENSO (AUSTRALIA) PTY. LTD.—Toyota Motor Corporation; *Int'l*, pg. 1414
NISSAN CANADA INC.—Nissan Motor Co., Ltd.; *Int'l*, pg. 945
NISSAN MEXICANA, S.A. DE C.V.—Nissan Motor Co., Ltd.; *Int'l*, pg. 945
NISSAN MOTOR CO. (AUSTRALIA) PTY. LTD.—Nissan Motor Co., Ltd.; *Int'l*, pg. 945
NISSAN MOTOR CORPORATION IN HAWAII, LTD.—Nissan Motor Co., Ltd.; *Int'l*, pg. 945
NISSAN MOTOR CORPORATION IN U.S.A.—Nissan Motor Co., Ltd.; *Int'l*, pg. 945
NISSAN MOTOR DEL PERU S.A.—Nissan Motor Co., Ltd.; *Int'l*, pg. 945
NISSAN MOTOR DEUTSCHLAND GMBH—Nissan Motor Co., Ltd.; *Int'l*, pg. 945
NISSAN MOTOR IBERICA S.A.—Nissan Motor Co., Ltd.; *Int'l*, pg. 945
NISSAN MOTOR NEDERLAND B.V.—Nissan Motor Co., Ltd.; *Int'l*, pg. 945
NISSAN MOTOR (SCHWEIZ) AG—Nissan Motor Co., Ltd.; *Int'l*, pg. 945
NISSAN PRINCE MOTOR SALES CO., LTD.—Nissan Motor Co., Ltd.; *Int'l*, pg. 944
NISSAN TRADING CORP., USA—Nissan Motor Co., Ltd.; *Int'l*, pg. 945
NORTHSTAR AUTO AUCTION INC.—Tyco International Ltd.; *U.S. Public*, pg. 1649
OHIO AUTO AUCTION—Cox Enterprises, Inc.; *U.S. Private*, *pg. 283*
OMAHA AUTO AUCTION INC.—Tyco International Ltd.; *U.S. Public*, pg. 1649
PSA PEUGEOT CITROEN; *Int'l*, pg. 1020
PACCAR INTERNATIONAL—Paccar Inc.; *U.S. Public*, pg. 1246
PECK ROAD FORD TRUCK SALES; *U.S. Private*, pg. 846
PEUGEOT MOTOR CO. PLC—PSA Peugeot Citroen; *Int'l*, pg. 1021
PEUGEOT MOTORS OF AMERICA INC.—PSA Peugeot Citroen; *Int'l*, pg. 1020
PEUGEOT TALBOT ESPANA—PSA Peugeot Citroen; *Int'l*, pg. 1021
PHILIPPINE AUTOMOTIVE MANUFACTURING CORPORATION—Mitsubishi Motors Corporation; *Int'l*, pg. 876
PORSCHE AG; *Int'l*, pg. 1063
PORSCHE CARS GREAT BRITAIN LTD.—Porsche AG; *Int'l*, pg. 1063
PORSCHE CARS NORTH AMERICA, INC.—Porsche AG; *Int'l*, pg. 1063
PORSCHE ENTERPRISES INC.—Porsche AG; *Int'l*, pg. 1063
PORSCHE ESPANA S.A.—Porsche AG; *Int'l*, pg. 1063
PORSCHE ITALIA S.P.A PADOVA—Porsche AG; *Int'l*, pg. 1063
PORTLAND AUTO AUCTION—Cox Enterprises, Inc.; *U.S. Private*, pg. 283
PUGET SOUND AUTO AUCTION, INC.—Tyco International Ltd.; *U.S. Public*, pg. 1649
PULLIAM MOTOR COMPANY; *U.S. Private*, pg. 894
QINGLING MOTORS CO., LTD.—Isuzu Motors Limited; *Int'l*, pg. 693
RAYTECH CORPORATION; *U.S. Public*, pg. 1363
REGENT MOTORS LIMITED—Sime Darby Berhad; *Int'l*, pg. 1251
RENAULT ARGENTINA—Renault; *Int'l*, pg. 1103
RENCO GROUP; *U.S. Private*, pg. 922
RIHM MOTOR COMPANY; *U.S. Private*, pg. 931
ROUNDTREE AUTOMOTIVE GROUP; *U.S. Private*, pg. 947
SAAB CARS USA, INC.—Investor AB; *Int'l*, pg. 687
SAAB DANMARK A/S—Investor AB; *Int'l*, pg. 687
SAAB DEUTSCHLAND GMBH—Investor AB; *Int'l*, pg. 687
SAAB FRANCE S.A.—Investor AB; *Int'l*, pg. 687
SAAB GREAT BRITAIN LTD.—Investor AB; *Int'l*, pg. 687
SAAB NORGE A/S—Investor AB; *Int'l*, pg. 688
SAAB SWEDEN AB—Investor AB; *Int'l*, pg. 687
ST. LOUIS AUTO AUCTION—Cox Enterprises, Inc.; *U.S. Private*, pg. 283
ST. PETE AUTO AUCTION—Cox Enterprises, Inc.; *U.S. Private*, pg. 283
SALVADOR CAETANO I.M.V.T., S.A.R.L.—Toyota Motor Corporation; *Int'l*, pg. 1413
SAN ANTONIO AUTO AUCTION—Cox Enterprises, Inc.; *U.S. Private*, pg. 283
SAN DIEGO AUTO AUCTION INC.—Tyco International Ltd.; *U.S. Public*, pg. 1649
SAVAL N.V.—Internatio-Muller N.V.; *Int'l*, pg. 681
SAVILLES AUTO VILLAGE LTD.—Lonrho plc; *Int'l*, pg. 817
OY SCAN-AUTO AB—Investor AB; *Int'l*, pg. 686
OY SCAN-AUTO AB—Valmet Corporation; *Int'l*, pg. 1449
SCANIA AUSTRALIA PTY. LTD.—Investor AB; *Int'l*, pg. 687
SCANIA BELGIUM SA-NV—Investor AB; *Int'l*, pg. 687
SCANIA DANMARK A/S—Investor AB; *Int'l*, pg. 687
SCANIA DEUTSCHLAND GMBH—Investor AB; *Int'l*, pg. 687
SCANIA FRANCE S.A.—Investor AB; *Int'l*, pg. 687
SCANIA (GREAT BRITAIN) LTD.—Investor AB; *Int'l*, pg. 687
SCANIA OSTERREICH GES.M.B.H.—Investor AB; *Int'l*, pg. 687
SCANIA USA INC.—Investor AB; *Int'l*, pg. 687
SCANIA-VABIS DEL PERU S.A.—Investor AB; *Int'l*, pg. 687
SERVCO PACIFIC INC.; *U.S. Private*, pg. 986
SIME DARBY AUSTRALIA LIMITED—Sime Darby Berhad; *Int'l*, pg. 1251
SIME DARBY HONG KONG LIMITED—Sime Darby Berhad; *Int'l*, pg. 1251
SKYLINE PORT NEWARK FACILITY—Tyco International Ltd.; *U.S. Public*, pg. 1648
SOCIETE DE DISTRIBUTION ET D'EXPORTATION AUTOMOBILES - SODEXA—PSA Peugeot Citroen; *Int'l*, pg. 1020
SONAUTO S.A.—Porsche AG; *Int'l*, pg. 1063
SOUTH SEATTLE AUTO AUCTION—Cox Enterprises, Inc.; *U.S. Private*, pg. 283
SOUTHERN CALIFORNIA AUTO AUCTION—Cox Enterprises, Inc.; *U.S. Private*, pg. 282
SOUTHERN STATES VEHICLE AUCTION OF ATLANTA INC.—Tyco International Ltd.; *U.S. Public*, pg. 1649
SUBARU CENTRAL REGION, INC.—Fuji Heavy Industries, Ltd.; *Int'l*, pg. 523
SUBARU DISTRIBUTOR CORP.—Fuji Heavy Industries, Ltd.; *Int'l*, pg. 523
SUBARU MID-AMERICA, INC.—Fuji Heavy Industries, Ltd.; *Int'l*, pg. 523
SUBARU NORTHWEST REGION—Fuji Heavy Industries, Ltd.; *Int'l*, pg. 523
SUBARU OF AMERICA, INC.—Fuji Heavy Industries, Ltd.; *Int'l*, pg. 523
SUBARU OF AMERICA SOUTHEAST REGION—Fuji Heavy Industries, Ltd.; *Int'l*, pg. 523
SUBARU OF AMERICA WESTERN, INC.—Fuji Heavy Industries, Ltd.; *Int'l*, pg. 523
SUBARU OF NEW ENGLAND, INC.—Fuji Heavy Industries, Ltd.; *Int'l*, pg. 523
SUBARU SOUTHEAST REGION—Fuji Heavy Industries, Ltd.; *Int'l*, pg. 523
SUBARU SOUTHWEST REGION—Fuji Heavy Industries, Ltd.; *Int'l*, pg. 523
SUBARU WESTERN REGION—Fuji Heavy Industries, Ltd.; *Int'l*, pg. 523
SUZUKI MOTOR CORPORATION; *Int'l*, pg. 1322
DAVE SYVERSON LINCOLN MERCURY; *U.S. Private*, pg. 1061
TEREX TRUCKS—Terex Corporation; *U.S. Public*, pg. 1581
TEXAS AUTO AUCTION SERVICES, INC.—Cox Enterprises, Inc.; *U.S. Private*, pg. 283
TEXAS HOBBY AUTO AUCTION—Cox Enterprises, Inc.; *U.S. Private*, pg. 283
THAI SUZUKI MOTOR CO., LTD.—Suzuki Motor Corporation; *Int'l*, pg. 1323
THOR INDIANA, INC.—Thor Industries, Inc.; *U.S. Public*, pg. 1602
TOKYO SUBARU MOTORS CO., LTD.—Fuji Heavy Industries, Ltd.; *Int'l*, pg. 523
TOMEN TRANSPORTGERAETE GMBH—Toyota Motor Corporation; *Int'l*, pg. 1412
TORONTO AUTO AUCTION—Cox Enterprises, Inc.; *U.S. Private*, pg. 283
P.T. TOYOTA-ASTRA MOTOR—Toyota Motor Corporation; *Int'l*, pg. 1413
TOYOTA CANADA INC.—Toyota Motor Corporation; *Int'l*, pg. 1414
TOYOTA DEUTSCHLAND GMBH—Toyota Motor Corporation; *Int'l*, pg. 1413
TOYOTA (GREAT BRITAIN) LIMITED—Toyota Motor Corporation; *Int'l*, pg. 1414
TOYOTA MOTOR CORPORATE SERVICES OF NORTH AMERICA—Toyota Motor Corporation; *Int'l*, pg. 1412
TOYOTA MOTOR CORPORATION; *Int'l*, pg. 1411
TOYOTA MOTOR DISTRIBUTORS (IRELAND) LTD.—Toyota Motor Corporation; *Int'l*, pg. 1413
TOYOTA MOTOR SALES, U.S.A., INC.—Toyota Motor Corporation; *Int'l*, pg. 1412
TOYOTA MOTOR THAILAND CO., LTD.—Toyota Motor Corporation; *Int'l*, pg. 1414
TOYOTA NEW ZEALAND LTD.—Toyota Motor Corporation; *Int'l*, pg. 1414
TOYOTA NORGE A/S—Toyota Motor Corporation; *Int'l*, pg. 1414
TRACTORS MACHINERY INTERNATIONAL PTE. LTD.—Sime Darby Berhad; *Int'l*, pg. 1251
TRANSNATIONAL MOTORS INC.; *U.S. Private*, pg. 1097
TRI-CITY AUTO AUCTION, INC.—Tyco International Ltd.; *U.S. Public*, pg. 1649
TRI PETCH ISUZU SALES CO., LTD.—Isuzu Motors Limited; *Int'l*, pg. 693
TRI-STATE MACK INC; *U.S. Private*, pg. 1101
TRONCALLI MOTORS, INC.; *U.S. Private*, pg. 1104
TYCO INTERNATIONAL LTD.—Tyco International Ltd.; *U.S. Public*, pg. 1648
U-HAUL LEASING & SALES COMPANY—Amerco; *U.S. Private*, pg. 49
UTAH AUTO AUCTION—Cox Enterprises, Inc.; *U.S. Private*, pg. 283
V.A.G. FRANCE S.A.—Volkswagen AG; *Int'l*, pg. 1475
V.A.G. STOCKHOLM AB—Volkswagen AG; *Int'l*, pg. 1476
V.A.G. SYNKO GMBH—Volkswagen AG; *Int'l*, pg. 1473
V.A.G. SVERIGE AB—Volkswagen AG; *Int'l*, pg. 1474
VAUXHALL MOTORS LIMITED—General Motors Corporation; *U.S. Public*, pg. 724
VOLKSWAGEN AG; *Int'l*, pg. 1473
VOLKSWAGEN AUDI NIPPON K.K.—Volkswagen AG; *Int'l*, pg. 1475
VOLKSWAGEN OF AMERICA ADMINISTRATION CENTER WEST—Volkswagen AG; *Int'l*, pg. 1474
VOLKSWAGEN OF AMERICA, INC.—Volkswagen AG; *Int'l*, *pg. 1474*
AB VOLVO; *Int'l*, pg. 1476
VOLVO AUTOMATED SYSTEMS OF NORTH AMERICA—AB Volvo; *Int'l*, pg. 1477
VOLVO AUTOMOBILE (SCHWEIZ) AG—AB Volvo; *Int'l*, pg. 1477
VOLVO CANADIAN HOLDINGS LTD.—AB Volvo; *Int'l*, pg. 1477
VOLVO CAR ASIA (PTE) LTD.—AB Volvo; *Int'l*, pg. 1477
VOLVO CARS EUROPE MARKETING NV—AB Volvo; *Int'l*, pg. 1477
VOLVO CARS INTERCONTINENTAL AB—AB Volvo; *Int'l*, pg. 1476
VOLVO CARS OF NORTH AMERICA, INC.—AB Volvo; *Int'l*, pg. 1477
VOLVO DISTRIBUIDORA S.A.—AB Volvo; *Int'l*, pg. 1477
VOLVO ESPANA, S.A.—AB Volvo; *Int'l*, pg. 1477
VOLVO LASTVAGNER SVERIGE AB—AB Volvo; *Int'l*, pg. 1476
VOLVO NORGE A/S—AB Volvo; *Int'l*, pg. 1477
VOLVO NUTZFAHRZEUGE DEUTSCHLAND GMBH—AB Volvo; *Int'l*, pg. 1477
VOLVO PENTA INDUSTRY CORPORATION—AB Volvo; *Int'l*, pg. 1476
VOLVO PENTA LATINOAMERICA S.A.—AB Volvo; *Int'l*, pg. 1478
VOLVO PENTA NORDEN AB—AB Volvo; *Int'l*, pg. 1476
VOLVO PERSONVAGNAR NORDEN AB—AB Volvo; *Int'l*, pg. 1476
VOLVO SUDAMERICANA SACI—AB Volvo; *Int'l*, pg. 1478
VOLVO TRUCK NORTH AMERICA INC.—AB Volvo; *Int'l*, pg. 1477
VOLVO TRUCK NORTH AMERICA, INC.—AB Volvo; *Int'l*, pg. 1477
VOLVO TRUCKS (SCHWEIZ) AG—AB Volvo; *Int'l*, pg. 1478
VULCAN MATERIALS COMPANY; *U.S. Public*, pg. 1725
WAJAX LIMITED; *Int'l*, pg. 1484
W.W. WALLWORK, INC.; *U.S. Private*, pg. 1148
WEBB AUTOMOTIVE GROUP; *U.S. Private*, pg. 1156
WEST PALM BEACH AUTO AUCTION, INC.—Tyco International Ltd.; *U.S. Public*, pg. 1649
WINNEBAGO INDUSTRIES, INC.; *U.S. Public*, pg. 1772
WINNEBAGO INTERNATIONAL CORP.—Winnebago Industries, Inc.; *U.S. Public*, pg. 1772
WOLFINGTON BODY COMPANY; *U.S. Private*, pg. 1186
YORK TOYOTA CITY—Toyota Motor Corporation; *Int'l*, pg. 1413
ZIEGLER INC.; *U.S. Private*, pg. 1205

5013 — MOTOR VEHICLE SUPPLIES & NEW PARTS-WHOLESALE

A S H, INC.; *U.S. Private*, pg. 2
AEA INC./AUTO PARTS—Republic Automotive Parts, Inc.; *U.S. Public*, pg. 1377
AEA OF COLUMBIA—Republic Automotive Parts, Inc.; *U.S. Public*, pg. 1377
AEA OF RALEIGH—Republic Automotive Parts, Inc.; *U.S. Public*, pg. 1377
A.F.N. LTD.—Porsche AG; *Int'l*, pg. 1063
AGIP PETROLI—ENI S.p.A.; *Int'l*, pg. 428
APS HOLDING CORPORATION; *U.S. Public*, pg. 10
A.P.S., INC.—APS Holding Corporation; *U.S. Public*, pg. 10
ASC INCORPORATED; *U.S. Private*, pg. 8
AAMCO TRANSMISSIONS, INC.; *U.S. Private*, pg. 9
ACUSTAR, INC.—Chrysler Corporation; *U.S. Public*, pg. 353
AFTERMARKET PRODUCTION DIV.—Dana Corporation; *U.S. Public*, pg. 479
AID AUTO STORES, INC.; *U.S. Public*, pg. 29
AISIN EUROPE S.A.—Aisin Seiki Co. Ltd.; *Int'l*, pg. 39
AISIN WORLD CORP.-DETROIT—Aisin Seiki Co. Ltd.; *Int'l*, pg. 39
ALDEN AUTO PARTS WAREHOUSE, INC.; *U.S. Private*, pg. 33
ALEMITE GMBH—BTR plc; *Int'l*, pg. 127
ALFA ROMEO DISTRIBUTORS OF NORTH AMERICA—Fiat Auto SpA; *Int'l*, pg. 481

ALLIEDSIGNAL, AUTOMOTIVE AFTERMARKET—AlliedSignal Inc.; U.S. Public, pg. 51
ALLIEDSIGNAL CANADA INC., AUTOMOTIVE AFTERMARKET—AlliedSignal Inc.; U.S. Public, pg. 52
ALLIEDSIGNAL TURBOCHARGING & TRUCK BRAKE SYSTEMS—AlliedSignal Inc.; U.S. Public, pg. 53
ALLPARTS, INC.—JPE, Inc.; U.S. Public, pg. 919
ALVIS AEROSPACE & TRANSMISSIONS LIMITED—Alvis plc; Int'l, pg. 69
AMERICAN SUNROOF COMPANY—ASC Incorporated; U.S. Private, pg. 8
AMERICAN YAZAKI CORP., INC.—Yazaki Corporation; Int'l, pg. 1520
AMORTEX—Arvin Industries, Inc.; U.S. Public, pg. 137
ANDERSON WHOLESALE COMPANY; U.S. Private, pg. 73
APPLIED POWER INC.; U.S. Public, pg. 124
ARO FLUID PRODUCTS DIVISION—Ingersoll-Rand Company; U.S. Public, pg. 877
ARVIN INDUSTRIES, INC.; U.S. Public, pg. 136
ARVIN INTERNATIONAL, INC.—Arvin Industries, Inc.; U.S. Public, pg. 137
ASAHI GLASS AMERICA, INC.—Asahi Glass Co., Ltd.; Int'l, pg. 84
ATLAS COPCO INDUSTRIAL TOOLS & EQUIPMENT—Atlas Copco AB; Int'l, pg. 96
ATLAS SUPPLY COMPANY; U.S. Private, pg. 96
ATWOOD DISTRIBUTING, INC.; U.S. Private, pg. 98
AUDI OF AMERICA—Volkswagen AG; Int'l, pg. 1474
AUSTIN GROUP; U.S. Private, pg. 99
AUTO-BON OY (IMPORTS)—Amer Group Ltd.; Int'l, pg. 72
AUTOLIASONS FRANCE S.A.—Barnes Group Inc.; U.S. Public, pg. 190
AUTOMOBILE SPECIALTY CO.—ASC Incorporated; U.S. Private, pg. 8
AUTOMOTIVE AFTERMARKET, NORTH AMERICA—Mark IV Industries Inc.; U.S. Public, pg. 1045
AUTOMOTIVE DISTRIBUTION SALES DIV.—Dana Corporation; U.S. Public, pg. 479
AUTOMOTIVE SUPPLY ASSOCIATES, INC.; U.S. Private, pg. 101
BWD AUTOMOTIVE CORP.—Echlin Inc.; U.S. Public, pg. 560
BWD AUTOMOTIVE CORP. (INTERNATIONAL)—Echlin Inc.; U.S. Public, pg. 561
BADGER TRUCK CENTER, INC.; U.S. Private, pg. 110
BALCO, INC.—Snap-On Tools Corporation; U.S. Public, pg. 1480
BALE OF KENTUCKY, INC.; U.S. Private, pg. 112
BALKAMP, INC.—Genuine Parts Company; U.S. Public, pg. 732
BANDO AMERICA, INC.—Bando Chemical Industries, Ltd.; Int'l, pg. 145
BARNES GROUP INC.; U.S. Public, pg. 189
BASEL TRADING COMPANY LTD.; Int'l, pg. 169
BECK/ARNLEY WORLDPARTS CORP.—Echlin Inc.; U.S. Public, pg. 561
BELL INDUSTRIES, INC.; U.S. Public, pg. 204
BIG A AUTO PARTS—APS Holding Corporation; U.S. Public, pg. 10
BIG O TIRES INCORPORATED—TBC Corporation; U.S. Public, pg. 1553
BLUE STREAK-HYGRADE MOTOR PRODUCTS LTD.—Standard Motor Products Inc.; U.S. Public, pg. 1503
BONDO/MAR-HYDE CORPORATION—RPM, Inc.; U.S. Public, pg. 1357
BORG WARNER AUTOMOTIVE, INC.; U.S. Public, pg. 245
BOSCH AUTOMOTIVE GROUP—Robert Bosch GmbH; Int'l, pg. 204
ROBERT BOSCH AG—Robert Bosch GmbH; Int'l, pg. 205
ROBERT BOSCH ARGENTINA SA—Robert Bosch GmbH; Int'l, pg. 205
ROBERT BOSCH A/S—Robert Bosch GmbH; Int'l, pg. 205
ROBERT BOSCH CORPORATION—Robert Bosch GmbH; Int'l, pg. 204
BOSCH SALES GROUP—Robert Bosch GmbH; Int'l, pg. 205
BOWMAN DISTRIBUTION—Barnes Group Inc.; U.S. Public, pg. 190
BOWMAN DISTRIBUTION (CANADA) LTD.—Barnes Group Inc.; U.S. Public, pg. 190
BOWMAN DISTRIBUTION-EUROPE—Barnes Group Inc.; U.S. Public, pg. 190
CCI CORPORATION; U.S. Private, pg. 193
CALSONIC CLIMATE CONTROL, INC.—Nissan Motor Co., Ltd.; Int'l, pg. 944
CANTEX CORP.—BBA Group plc; Int'l, pg. 113
CARFEL, INC.; U.S. Private, pg. 210
CARQUEST CANADA LTD.—General Parts, Inc.; U.S. Private, pg. 445
CARQUEST CORPORATION; U.S. Private, pg. 215
CENEX, INC.; U.S. Private, pg. 221
CENTRAL ALL PRO—Republic Automotive Parts, Inc.; U.S. Public, pg. 1377
CENTRAL AUTOMOTIVE PRODUCTS, LTD.; Int'l, pg. 278
CHAMP/PIK A NUT SERVICE LINE—Standard Motor Products Inc.; U.S. Public, pg. 1503
CHIVAS PRODUCTS LTD.; U.S. Private, pg. 238
CHRYSLER SALES GROUP—Chrysler Corporation; U.S. Public, pg. 353
CITY MACHINE & WHEEL CO.—The Cypress Companies; U.S. Private, pg. 299
COACHMEN INDUSTRIES, INC.; U.S. Public, pg. 387
THE COAST DISTRIBUTION SYSTEM; U.S. Public, pg. 388
COAST RV, INC.—The Coast Distribution System; U.S. Public, pg. 388
CONSOLIDATED STORES CORP.; U.S. Public, pg. 437
COOLIDGE GLASS CO., INC.; U.S. Private, pg. 273
CUSTOM ACCESSORIES INC.; U.S. Private, pg. 298
THE CYPRESS COMPANIES; U.S. Private, pg. 299
DACCO, INC.—Jordan Industries, Inc.; U.S. Private, pg. 598
DANA CORPORATION; U.S. Public, pg. 479
DANA WORLD TRADE DIV.—Dana Corporation; U.S. Public, pg. 479
DARLING'S; U.S. Private, pg. 311
DART GROUP CORPORATION; U.S. Public, pg. 484
DISCOUNT AUTO PARTS, INC.; U.S. Public, pg. 510
DRIVE TRAIN INDUSTRIES; U.S. Private, pg. 343
DRIVETRAIN SERVICE DIV.—Dana Corporation; U.S. Public, pg. 479
DURALINER U.S.A.—Durakon Industries, Inc.; U.S. Public, pg. 537
DYNACRAFT—Paccar Inc.; U.S. Public, pg. 1246
EATON CORPORATION, U.S. ENGINE VALVE CORPORATION—Eaton Corporation; U.S. Public, pg. 557
ECHLIN INC.; U.S. Public, pg. 560
EDON MACHINE DIV.—Simpson Industries, Inc.; U.S. Public, pg. 1475
ELIXIR INDUSTRIES; U.S. Private, pg. 371
EXOR AMERICA—Exor Group; Int'l, pg. 467
EZON PRODUCTS, INC.; U.S. Private, pg. 388
FEDCO AUTOMOTIVE COMPONENTS COMPANY, INC.—Tomkins PLC; Int'l, pg. 1396
FEDERAL-MOGUL CORPORATION; U.S. Public, pg. 615
FEL-PRO INCORPORATED; U.S. Private, pg. 399
FINISHMASTER INC.—LDI, Ltd.; U.S. Private, pg. 639
FISHERIES SUPPLY COMPANY; U.S. Private, pg. 408
FLORIG EQUIPMENT COMPANY, INC.; U.S. Private, pg. 415
FLUID PRODUCT SALES DIV.—Dana Corporation; U.S. Public, pg. 479
OY FORD AB—Ford Motor Company; U.S. Public, pg. 665
FORD LUSITANA—Ford Motor Company; U.S. Public, pg. 666
FORD MOTOR COMPANY; U.S. Public, pg. 661
FORD MOTOR COMPANY A/S—Ford Motor Company; U.S. Public, pg. 666
FORD PARTS AND SERVICE DIV.—Ford Motor Company; U.S. Public, pg. 662
FORD PERSONAL IMPORT EXPORT LTD.—Ford Motor Company; U.S. Public, pg. 666
FORD SALES COMPANY OF AUSTRALIA LIMITED—Ford Motor Company; U.S. Public, pg. 666
FRAM EUROPE A.B.—AlliedSignal Inc.; U.S. Public, pg. 53
FREDERICK TRADING COMPANY—Distribution America; U.S. Private, pg. 335
FUJI HEAVY INDUSTRIES, LTD., OMIYA PARTS CENTER—Fuji Heavy Industries, Ltd.; Int'l, pg. 523
GKN DRIVETECH INC.—GKN plc; Int'l, pg. 535
GKN PLC; Int'l, pg. 534
GS BATTERY (U.S.A.), INC.—Japan Storage Battery Co., Ltd.; Int'l, pg. 702
GATE PETROLEUM COMPANY; U.S. Private, pg. 441
GENERAL MOTORS ACCEPTANCE CORPORATION (GMAC)—General Motors Corporation; U.S. Public, pg. 719
GENERAL PARTS, INC.; U.S. Private, pg. 445
GENUINE PARTS COMPANY; U.S. Public, pg. 732
GENUINE PARTS LTD.—Genuine Parts Company; U.S. Public, pg. 732
J. GERBER & CO. INC.—Gerber International Inc.; U.S. Private, pg. 449
THE GLASS DEPOT, INC.—Apogee Enterprises, Inc.; U.S. Public, pg. 120
GLEASON CORPORATION SALES—Gleason Corporation; U.S. Public, pg. 746
GLOBAL MOTOR SPORT GROUP, INC.; U.S. Public, pg. 748
GLOBE-AMERADA GLASS COMPANY; U.S. Private, pg. 458
GOLD EAGLE COMPANY; U.S. Private, pg. 459
HAHN AUTOMOTIVE WAREHOUSE, INC.; U.S. Public, pg. 774
HARMON GLASS COMPANY—Apogee Enterprises, Inc.; U.S. Public, pg. 120
HARMON GLASS OF FLORIDA, INC.—Apogee Enterprises, Inc.; U.S. Public, pg. 120
HAYES-DANA SERVICE PARTS DIV.—Dana Corporation; U.S. Public, pg. 480
HENNESSY INDUSTRIES, INC.—Danaher Corporation; U.S. Public, pg. 481
THE HERCULES TIRE & RUBBER COMPANY; U.S. Private, pg. 523
HERRAMIENTAS SNAP-ON DE MEXICO, S.A.—Snap-On Tools Corporation; U.S. Public, pg. 1481
HESCO PARTS CORPORATION; U.S. Private, pg. 524
HONDA NORTH AMERICA INC.—Honda Motor Co., Ltd.; Int'l, pg. 635
HONDA PARTS SALES CO., LTD.—Honda Motor Co., Ltd.; Int'l, pg. 634
HYOSUNG GROUP; Int'l, pg. 640
IDEAL DIVISION—Tomkins PLC; Int'l, pg. 1396
INDUSTRIAL DISTRIBUTION AND OEM, NORTH AMERICA—Mark IV Industries Inc.; U.S. Public, pg. 1045
INTERMARK WORLD PRODUCTS, LTD.; U.S. Private, pg. 567
INTERNATIONAL RADIATOR SERVICES LTD.—BTR plc; Int'l, pg. 126
INTERSTATE GLASS CO. INC.—Apogee Enterprises, Inc.; U.S. Public, pg. 120
ISUZU MOTORS AMERICA INC.—Isuzu Motors Limited; Int'l, pg. 692
JAGUAR CANADA INC.—Ford Motor Company; U.S. Public, pg. 667
JAGUAR CARS—Ford Motor Company; U.S. Public, pg. 664
KS WINSTON LTD.—Metallgesellschaft AG; Int'l, pg. 861
KALI-CHEMIE AKTIENGESELLSCHAFT—Solvay S.A.; Int'l, pg. 1278
KEMIRA KATALYSAFOREN GMBH—Kemira Oy; Int'l, pg. 729
KEYSTONE AUTOMOTIVE INDUSTRIES, INC.; U.S. Public, pg. 955
J. KORBER & COMPANY; U.S. Private, pg. 632
KORPIVAARA OY - TOYOTA GROUP—Amer Group Ltd.; Int'l, pg. 72
LDI AUTO PAINT—LDI, Ltd.; U.S. Private, pg. 639
LARAMIE TIRE DISTRIBUTORS INC.—Sumitomo Corporation; Int'l, pg. 1312
LAWSON PRODUCTS, INC.; U.S. Public, pg. 980
LAWSON PRODUCTS LTD.—Lawson Products, Inc.; U.S. Public, pg. 980
LUCAS FRANCE SA—LucasVarity plc; Int'l, pg. 820
LUCAS INDUSTRIES INC.—LucasVarity plc; Int'l, pg. 820
LUFKIN INDUSTRIES, INC.; U.S. Public, pg. 1019
MANNING EQUIPMENT, INC.; U.S. Private, pg. 700
MAREMONT EXHAUST SYSTEMS PRODUCT DIVISION—Arvin Industries, Inc.; U.S. Public, pg. 137
MASEK DISTRIBUTING INC.; U.S. Private, pg. 711
MATCO TOOLS—Danaher Corporation; U.S. Public, pg. 482
MEINEKE DISCOUNT MUFFLER SHOPS, INC.—GKN plc; Int'l, pg. 535
MIDWAY FORD TRUCK CENTER INC.; U.S. Private, pg. 744
MIDWEST AUTO PARTS DISTRIBUTORS, INC.; U.S. Private, pg. 744
MIDWEST TIRE & MUFFLER, INC.; U.S. Private, pg. 745
MIGHTY DISTRIBUTING SYSTEM; U.S. Private, pg. 745
MIKUNI CORPORATION; Int'l, pg. 867
MIKUNI SHOKO CORP.—Mikuni Corporation; Int'l, pg. 867
MITSUBISHI ENGINE NORTH AMERICA INC. (MENA)—Mitsubishi Heavy Industries Ltd.; Int'l, pg. 874
MOBIL OIL CORPORATION; U.S. Public, pg. 1118
MOLIN AUTO PARTS INC.; U.S. Private, pg. 756
MOOG AUTOMOTIVE, INC.—Cooper Industries, Inc.; U.S. Public, pg. 443
MOTION & CONTROL SALES DIV.—Parker Hannifin Corporation; U.S. Public, pg. 1261
MOTION INDUSTRIES (CANADA), INC.—Genuine Parts Company; U.S. Public, pg. 732
MYERS TIRE SUPPLY COMPANY—Myers Industries, Inc.; U.S. Public, pg. 1143
NHK INTERNATIONAL CORP.—NHK Spring Co., Ltd.; Int'l, pg. 902
NAPCO INTERNATIONAL, INC.—Venturian Corp.; U.S. Public, pg. 1716
NATIONAL DYNAMICS—Sperry Owens, Inc.; U.S. Private, pg. 1025
NATIONAL TYRE SERVICE LTD.—Continental AG; Int'l, pg. 328
NICHIMEN AMERICA, INC.—Nichimen Corporation; Int'l, pg. 927
NICHIMEN CORPORATION; Int'l, pg. 927
NISSAN MOTOR CORPORATION IN HAWAII, LTD.—Nissan Motor Co., Ltd.; Int'l, pg. 945
NISSAN MOTOR PARTS CENTRE (EUROPE) B.V.—Nissan Motor Co., Ltd.; Int'l, pg. 945
NISSAN PRINCE MOTOR SALES CO., LTD.—Nissan Motor Co., Ltd.; Int'l, pg. 944
NISSAN TRADING CO., LTD.—Nissan Motor Co., Ltd.; Int'l, pg. 944
OKABE COMPANY LIMITED; Int'l, pg. 999
OMEGA ENVIRONMENTAL INC.—Omega Environmental Inc.; U.S. Public, pg. 1222
O'REILLY AUTOMOTIVE INC.; U.S. Public, pg. 1230
OZARK AUTOMOTIVE DISTRIBUTORS, INC.—O'Reilly Automotive Inc.; U.S. Public, pg. 1230
PGA MOTORS—Lex Service PLC; Int'l, pg. 807
PACCAR AUTOMOTIVE INC.—Paccar Inc.; U.S. Public, pg. 1247
PACCAR INC.; U.S. Public, pg. 1246
PACCAR PARTS—Paccar Inc.; U.S. Public, pg. 1246
PACIFIC DISTRIBUTION—Pacific Dunlop Limited; Int'l, pg. 1021
PEARCE INDUSTRIES INC.; U.S. Private, pg. 845
PEGASUS INTERNATIONAL CORPORATION—Straube Regional Center LLC; U.S. Private, pg. 1046
PETER PAN BUS LINES, INC.; U.S. Private, pg. 856
PIEBURG AG—Rheinmetall Group; Int'l, pg. 1108
PORSCHE AG; Int'l, pg. 1063
PORSCHE CARS GREAT BRITAIN LTD.—Porsche AG; Int'l, pg. 1063
PORSCHE ESPANA S.A.—Porsche AG; Int'l, pg. 1063
PORSCHE ITALIA S.P.A PADOVA—Porsche AG; Int'l, pg. 1063
THE PROTECTOR CORPORATION; U.S. Private, pg. 891
QUAKER CITY MOTOR PARTS COMPANY; U.S. Private, pg. 898
QUAKER STATE CORPORATION; U.S. Public, pg. 1348
R.A. SALES, INC.—Republic Automotive Parts, Inc.; U.S. Public, pg. 1377
THE RTZ CORPORATION PLC—Rio Tinto PLC; Int'l, pg. 1118
THE RAO GROUP INC.; U.S. Private, pg. 910
REPUBLIC AUTOMOTIVE-AEA DIVISION—Republic Automotive Parts, Inc.; U.S. Public, pg. 1377
REPUBLIC AUTOMOTIVE PARTS, INC.; U.S. Public, pg. 1377
REPUBLIC AUTOMOTIVE PARTS SALES, INC.—Republic Automotive Parts, Inc.; U.S. Public, pg. 1378
ROBBINS AUTO PARTS, INC.; U.S. Private, pg. 934
RODEFELD CO., INC.; U.S. Private, pg. 939
ROUNDTREE AUTOMOTIVE GROUP; U.S. Private, pg. 947
RUPP AUTOMOTIVE—Republic Automotive Parts, Inc.; U.S. Public, pg. 1378
SF SERVICES; U.S. Private, pg. 956
SAAB AUTOMOBILE AB—Investor AB; Int'l, pg. 687
SAAB AUTOMOBILE AB—General Motors Corporation; U.S. Public, pg. 725
SANEL AUTO PARTS CO.—Automotive Supply Associates, Inc.; U.S. Private, pg. 101
OY SCAN-AUTO AB—Investor AB; Int'l, pg. 686
OY SCAN-AUTO AB—Valmet Corporation; Int'l, pg. 1449
SELTEC SELECTIVE TECHNOLOGY INC.—Zexel Corporation; Int'l, pg. 1528
SERVICE PARTS SUPPLY DIV.—Case Corporation; U.S. Public, pg. 311
SIAM FURUKAWA CO., LTD.—The Siam Cement Public Company Limited; Int'l, pg. 1238

SIAM TYRE CO., LTD.—The Siam Cement Public Company Limited; *Int'l*, pg. 1238
SIEMENS AUTOMOTIVE CORPORATION—Siemens AG; *Int'l*, pg. 1245
SIERRA INC.—Echlin Inc.; *U.S. Public*, pg. 560
SNAP-ON TOOLS CORPORATION; *U.S. Public*, pg. 1480
SNAP-ON TOOLS, GMBH—Snap-On Tools Corporation; *U.S. Public*, pg. 1481
SNAP-ON TOOLS INTERNATIONAL, LTD. (MIDDLE EAST/AFRICA DIVISION)—Snap-On Tools Corporation; *U.S. Public*, pg. 1481
SNAP-ON TOOLS LIMITED—Snap-On Tools Corporation; *U.S. Public*, pg. 1481
SOMERSET WELDING & STEEL, INC.—Riggs Industries, Inc.; *U.S. Private*, pg. 930
SONAUTO S.A.—Porsche AG; *Int'l*, pg. 1063
SPARTAN OIL CORP.; *U.S. Private*, pg. 1021
SPERRY OWENS, INC.; *U.S. Private*, pg. 1025
SPICER TRAILER PRODUCTS DIV.—Dana Corporation; *U.S. Public*, pg. 479
STANDARD MOTOR PRODUCTS HONG KONG LIMITED—Standard Motor Products Inc.; *U.S. Public*, pg. 1503
STANDARD MOTOR PRODUCTS INC.; *U.S. Public*, pg. 1503
STANDARD-THOMSON CORPORATION—Tomkins PLC; *Int'l*, pg. 1396
STANT MANUFACTURING INC.—Tomkins PLC; *Int'l*, pg. 1397
STAR SALES CO., INC.; *U.S. Private*, pg. 1035
STRAFCO, INC.; *U.S. Private*, pg. 1046
STURGIS IRON & METAL COMPANY, INC.; *U.S. Private*, pg. 1048
SUBARU MID-AMERICA, INC.—Fuji Heavy Industries, Ltd.; *Int'l*, pg. 523
SUBARU NORTHWEST REGION—Fuji Heavy Industries, Ltd.; *Int'l*, pg. 523
SUBARU OF AMERICA, INC.—Fuji Heavy Industries, Ltd.; *Int'l*, pg. 523
SUBARU OF AMERICA SOUTHEAST REGION—Fuji Heavy Industries, Ltd.; *Int'l*, pg. 523
SUBARU SOUTHEAST REGION—Fuji Heavy Industries, Ltd.; *Int'l*, pg. 523
SUBARU SOUTHWEST REGION—Fuji Heavy Industries, Ltd.; *Int'l*, pg. 523
SUBARU WESTERN REGION—Fuji Heavy Industries, Ltd.; *Int'l*, pg. 523
SUNTESTER (AUSTRALIA) PTY. LTD.—Snap-On Tools Corporation; *U.S. Public*, pg. 1481
TBC CORPORATION; *U.S. Public*, pg. 1553
TCG INTERNATIONAL INC.; *Int'l*, pg. 1336
TANK SERVICE CO.—Chemical Leaman Corporation; *U.S. Private*, pg. 233
TOKICO (USA) INC.—Tokico Ltd.; *Int'l*, pg. 1391
TOKYO SUBARU MOTORS CO., LTD.—Fuji Heavy Industries, Ltd.; *Int'l*, pg. 523
TRACTORS MACHINERY INTERNATIONAL PTE. LTD.—Sime Darby Berhad; *Int'l*, pg. 1251
TRAILER WHEEL & FRAME COMPANY; *U.S. Private*, pg. 1095
TRAK AUTO CORPORATION—Dart Group Corporation; *U.S. Public*, pg. 484
TRANSNATIONAL MOTORS INC.; *U.S. Private*, pg. 1097
TRANSPO ELECTRONICS, INC.; *U.S. Private*, pg. 1097
TREDIT TIRE & WHEEL CO.—The Cypress Companies; *U.S. Private*, pg. 300
TRONCALLI MOTORS, INC.; *U.S. Private*, pg. 1104
UAP, INC.; *Int'l*, pg. 1426
UIS EXPORT CORPORATION—UIS, Inc.; *U.S. Private*, pg. 1113
UNIPART GROUP LIMITED—British Aerospace p.l.c.; *Int'l*, pg. 218
UNIVERSAL FLEET—Rocor Transportation Companies Inc.; *U.S. Private*, pg. 939
VEHICLE SPARES LTD.—Metallgesellschaft AG; *Int'l*, pg. 861
VOLKSWAGEN OF AMERICA, INC.—Volkswagen AG; *Int'l*, pg. 1474
AB VOLVO; *Int'l*, pg. 1476
VOLVO NORGE A/S—AB Volvo; *Int'l*, pg. 1477
VOLVO NORTH AMERICA PARTS OPERATIONS DIV.—AB Volvo; *Int'l*, pg. 1477
VON HOUSEN MOTORS; *U.S. Private*, pg. 1143
W.W. WALLWORK, INC.; *U.S. Private*, pg. 1148
CARL WEISSMAN & SONS, INC.; *U.S. Private*, pg. 1160
WELLS MANUFACTURING CANADA LTD.—UIS, Inc.; *U.S. Private*, pg. 1113
WESTERN AUTO SUPPLY COMPANY—Sears, Roebuck and Co.; *U.S. Public*, pg. 1452
WESTLIE MOTOR COMPANY; *U.S. Private*, pg. 1169
BUFF WHELAN CHEVROLET & GEO, INC.; *U.S. Private*, pg. 1171
WYNN'S AUSTRALIA, PTY. LIMITED—Wynn's International, Inc.; *U.S. Public*, pg. 1782
WYNN'S AUTOMOTIVE FRANCE—Wynn's International, Inc.; *U.S. Public*, pg. 1783
WYNN'S BELGIUM N.V.—Wynn's International, Inc.; *U.S. Public*, pg. 1782
WYNN'S CANADA, LTD.—Wynn's International, Inc.; *U.S. Public*, pg. 1783
WYNN'S DEUTSCHLAND, GMBH—Wynn's International, Inc.; *U.S. Public*, pg. 1783
WYNN'S FRANCE, S.A.—Wynn's International, Inc.; *U.S. Public*, pg. 1783
WYNN'S FRICTION PROOFING DE MEXICO, S.A. DE C.V.—Wynn's International, Inc.; *U.S. Public*, pg. 1783
YAZAKI CORPORATION; *Int'l*, pg. 1520

5014 — TIRES & TUBES-WHOLESALE

A K H COMPANY, INC.; *U.S. Private*, pg. 2
ALLIED OIL & SUPPLY, INC.; *U.S. Private*, pg. 39
ATLAS SUPPLY COMPANY; *U.S. Private*, pg. 96
AUSTIN GROUP; *U.S. Private*, pg. 99
BALE OF KENTUCKY, INC.; *U.S. Private*, pg. 112
BANDAG AG—Bandag, Incorporated; *U.S. Public*, pg. 178
BANDAG DE MEXICO S.A. DE C.V.—Bandag, Incorporated; *U.S. Public*, pg. 178
BELL GAS, INC.; *U.S. Private*, pg. 131
BELLE TIRE DISTRIBUTOR INC.; *U.S. Private*, pg. 132
BIG O TIRES INCORPORATED—TBC Corporation; *U.S. Public*, pg. 1553
BRIDGESTONE/FIRESTONE INC. RETAIL OPERATIONS—Bridgestone Corporation; *Int'l*, pg. 213
BURRIS FOODS, INC.; *U.S. Private*, pg. 188
CAMPBELL OIL CO.; *U.S. Private*, pg. 204
CAPITAL TIRE, INC.; *U.S. Private*, pg. 206
COMPANHIA GOODYEAR DO BRASIL PRODUTOS DE BORRACHA—The Goodyear Tire & Rubber Company; *U.S. Public*, pg. 753
COMPANIA ANONIMA GOODYEAR DE VENEZUELA—The Goodyear Tire & Rubber Company; *U.S. Public*, pg. 753
COMPANIA GOODYEAR DEL PERU, S.A.—The Goodyear Tire & Rubber Company; *U.S. Public*, pg. 753
COMPANIA HULERA GOODYEAR-OXO SOCIEDAD ANONIMA—The Goodyear Tire & Rubber Company; *U.S. Public*, pg. 753
DAYTON TIRE COMPANY—Bridgestone Corporation; *Int'l*, pg. 213
DES MOINES TIRE—Rott-Keller Supply Co.; *U.S. Private*, pg. 947
DEUTSCHE GOODYEAR GMBH—The Goodyear Tire & Rubber Company; *U.S. Public*, pg. 753
EL DORADO TIRE CO.—Sumitomo Corporation; *Int'l*, pg. 1312
FATE DO BRASIL LTDA.—Fate S.A.; *Int'l*, pg. 478
FENWICK KALMAR SA—Trelleborg AB; *Int'l*, pg. 1421
FREE SERVICE TIRE COMPANY, INC.; *U.S. Private*, pg. 425
GANIN TIRE CO., INC.; *U.S. Private*, pg. 439
GENERAL TIRE INTL. CO.—Continental AG; *Int'l*, pg. 327
GENERAL TYRE EAST AFRICA LTD.—Continental AG; *Int'l*, pg. 327
GOODYEAR (SWITZERLAND) S.A.—The Goodyear Tire & Rubber Company; *U.S. Public*, pg. 753
GRAN INDUSTRIA DE NEUMATICOS CENTROAMERICANA, S.A.—The Goodyear Tire & Rubber Company; *U.S. Public*, pg. 753
GROSSENBURG IMPLEMENTS, INCORPORATED; *U.S. Private*, pg. 483
GUMMIWERKE FULDA—The Goodyear Tire & Rubber Company; *U.S. Public*, pg. 753
J.H. HEAFNER CO. INC.; *U.S. Private*, pg. 514
HORIZON DISTRIBUTION INC.; *U.S. Private*, pg. 539
KALMAR INDUSTRIES AB—Trelleborg AB; *Int'l*, pg. 1420
KALMAR KOCKUM A/S—Trelleborg AB; *Int'l*, pg. 1421
KALMAR KOCKUM FRANCE SA—Trelleborg AB; *Int'l*, pg. 1421
KALMAR KOCKUM GMBH—Trelleborg AB; *Int'l*, pg. 1421
KALMAR KOCKUM LTD.—Trelleborg AB; *Int'l*, pg. 1421
OY KALMAR LMV—Trelleborg AB; *Int'l*, pg. 1421
KALMAR LMV A/S—Trelleborg AB; *Int'l*, pg. 1421
KALMAR LMV EAST ASIA PTE. LTD.—Trelleborg AB; *Int'l*, pg. 1421
KENT SUSSEX TIRE SERVICE—Service Tire Truck Centers, Inc.; *U.S. Private*, pg. 987
LARAMIE TIRE DISTRIBUTORS INC.—Sumitomo Corporation; *Int'l*, pg. 1312
CARLOS R. LEFFLER INC.; *U.S. Private*, pg. 658
MICHELIN INDUSTRIA E COMERCIO S/A—Compagnie Generale des Etablissements Michelin; *Int'l*, pg. 322
MICHELIN KOREA TIRE COMPANY LIMITED—Compagnie Generale des Etablissements Michelin; *Int'l*, pg. 322
MICHELIN NORTH AMERICA (CANADA) INC.—Compagnie Generale des Etablissements Michelin; *Int'l*, pg. 322
MIDWEST TIRE & MUFFLER, INC.; *U.S. Private*, pg. 745
MITSUBISHI CORPORATION; *Int'l*, pg. 871
NAPCO INTERNATIONAL, INC.—Venturian Corp.; *U.S. Public*, pg. 1716
NATIONAL TYRE SERVICE LTD.—Continental AG; *Int'l*, pg. 328
NEUMATICOS GOODYEAR SA—The Goodyear Tire & Rubber Company; *U.S. Public*, pg. 753
NICHIMEN AMERICA, INC.—Nichimen Corporation; *Int'l*, pg. 927
NICHIMEN CORPORATION; *Int'l*, pg. 927
NORSK MICHELIN GUMMI A/S—Compagnie Generale des Etablissements Michelin; *Int'l*, pg. 322
PARRISH TIRE COMPANY, INC.; *U.S. Private*, pg. 840
THE RAO GROUP INC.; *U.S. Private*, pg. 910
REDBURN TIRE COMPANY; *U.S. Private*, pg. 915
REYNOLDS TIRE & RUBBER—Ganin Tire Co., Inc.; *U.S. Private*, pg. 439
ROTT-KELLER SUPPLY CO.; *U.S. Private*, pg. 947
SF SERVICES; *U.S. Private*, pg. 956
SPARTAN OIL CORP.; *U.S. Private*, pg. 1021
SUMITOMO CANADA LTD.—Sumitomo Corporation; *Int'l*, pg. 1312
SUMITOMO CORPORATION; *Int'l*, pg. 1312
SUMITOMO CORPORATION OF AMERICA—Sumitomo Corporation; *Int'l*, pg. 1312
TOYO TIRE (U.S.A.) CORPORATION—Toyo Tire & Rubber Co., Ltd.; *Int'l*, pg. 1411
TREADWAY CORPORATION—Sumitomo Corporation; *Int'l*, pg. 1312
TREDIT TIRE & WHEEL CO.—The Cypress Companies; *U.S. Private*, pg. 300
VAKUUM VULK, INC. U.S.—Bandag, Incorporated; *U.S. Public*, pg. 177
YOKOHAMA TIRE CORP.—The Yokohama Rubber Co., Ltd.; *Int'l*, pg. 1521
YOKOHAMA TIRE CORPORATION—The Yokohama Rubber Co., Ltd.; *Int'l*, pg. 1521
YOUNGSTOWN TIRE & SUPPLY COMPANY—Ziegler Tire & Supply Company, Inc.; *U.S. Private*, pg. 1205
ZIEGLER TIRE & SUPPLY COMPANY, INC.; *U.S. Private*, pg. 1205

5015 — MOTOR VEHICLE PARTS, USED-WHOLESALE & RETAIL

AC ROCHESTER PRODUCTS AUSTRIA GES.M.B.H—General Motors Corporation; *U.S. Public*, pg. 723
ACKLANDS LIMITED; *Int'l*, pg. 23
ALLEN TELECOM, INC.; *U.S. Public*, pg. 45
ALLIEDSIGNAL INC.; *U.S. Public*, pg. 49
ASTON MARTIN LAGONDA OF NORTH AMERICA, INC.—Ford Motor Company; *U.S. Public*, pg. 664
EMBOTELLADORES DEL VALLE DE ANAHUAC S.A. DE C.V.; *Int'l*, pg. 452
FOREST CITY AUTO PARTS—Tyler Corporation; *U.S. Public*, pg. 1652
FREDERICK TRADING COMPANY—Distribution America; *U.S. Private*, pg. 335
GM POWERTRAIN GROUP—General Motors Corporation; *U.S. Public*, pg. 719
JAGUAR CARS—Ford Motor Company; *U.S. Public*, pg. 664
PACKARD ELECTRIC BURGENLAND GES.M.B.H.—General Motors Corporation; *U.S. Public*, pg. 723
R&B, INC.; *U.S. Public*, pg. 1354
RAYBESTOS AFTERMARKET PRODUCTS CO.—Raytech Corporation; *U.S. Public*, pg. 1363
REPUBLIC AUTOMOTIVE-AEA DIVISION—Republic Automotive Parts, Inc.; *U.S. Public*, pg. 1377
ROBERTSON'S AUTO SALVAGE; *U.S. Private*, pg. 936
SOCIETE FRANCAISE DES AMORTISSEURS DE CARBON S.A.—General Motors Corporation; *U.S. Public*, pg. 725
SPROTT OIL CO., INC.; *U.S. Private*, pg. 1027
TRACTORS MACHINERY INTERNATIONAL PTE. LTD.—Sime Darby Berhad; *Int'l*, pg. 1251

5021 — FURNITURE-WHOLESALE

AF SISTEMAS SA—Groupe Strafor Facom; *Int'l*, pg. 569
AMERICAN FURNITURE COMPANY; *U.S. Private*, pg. 55
AVON WORKSHOP FICKS REED; *U.S. Private*, pg. 102
BKM ENTERPRISES, INC.; *U.S. Private*, pg. 107
W.S. BADCOCK CORPORATION; *U.S. Private*, pg. 109
BRUNSCHWIG & FILS, INC.; *U.S. Private*, pg. 176
BUTLER CAPITAL CORP.; *U.S. Private*, pg. 190
CAROLINA MILLS, INC.; *U.S. Private*, pg. 214
CLESTRA GMBH—Groupe Strafor Facom; *Int'l*, pg. 570
CLESTRA HAUSERMAN A.G.—Groupe Strafor Facom; *Int'l*, pg. 570
CLESTRA HAUSERMAN BELGIUM—Groupe Strafor Facom; *Int'l*, pg. 570
CLESTRA HAUSERMAN B.V.—Groupe Strafor Facom; *Int'l*, pg. 570
CLESTRA HAUSERMAN OVERSEAS—Groupe Strafor Facom; *Int'l*, pg. 570
CLESTRA HAUSERMAN SCANDINAVIA—Groupe Strafor Facom; *Int'l*, pg. 570
CLESTRA SRL—Groupe Strafor Facom; *Int'l*, pg. 570
CONTRACT INTERIORS INC.; *U.S. Private*, pg. 270
DANCKER, SELLEW & DOUGLAS, INC.; *U.S. Private*, pg. 309
DECORATIVE CRAFTS, INC.; *U.S. Private*, pg. 320
DEVIMCO—Accor S.A.; *Int'l*, pg. 20
DEVIMCO LTD.—Accor S.A.; *Int'l*, pg. 21
EDWARD DON & COMPANY; *U.S. Private*, pg. 339
DOUBLEDAY BROS. & CO.—Standex International Corporation; *U.S. Public*, pg. 1506
EATON OFFICE SUPPLY CO., INC.; *U.S. Private*, pg. 358
EBSCO INDUSTRIES, INC.; *U.S. Private*, pg. 358
ENVIRONETX; *U.S. Private*, pg. 378
FALCON PRODUCTS, INC.; *U.S. Public*, pg. 611
THE FIRST YEARS INC.; *U.S. Public*, pg. 642
FRAENKEL COMPANY; *U.S. Private*, pg. 423
FURNITURE BRANDS INTERNATIONAL INC.; *U.S. Public*, pg. 688
FURNITURE CONSULTANTS—U.S. Office Products Company; *U.S. Public*, pg. 1686
GENERAL MARBLE CORPORATION—Leucadia National Corporation; *U.S. Public*, pg. 990
GENERAL OFFICE ENVIRONMENTS INC.; *U.S. Private*, pg. 445
GOLDSMITHS, INC.; *U.S. Private*, pg. 462
GOODMANS, INC.; *U.S. Private*, pg. 464
HON EXPORT LIMITED—HON Industries Inc.; *U.S. Public*, pg. 772
HAGEMEYER N.V.—First Pacific Company Limited; *Int'l*, pg. 487
HALI-BUROMOBEL VERTRIEBS GESMBH; *Int'l*, pg. 589
HARPERS SALES—Kimball International, Inc.; *U.S. Public*, pg. 957
HAUENSTEIN & BURMEISTER, INC.; *U.S. Private*, pg. 510
HAWORTH U.K. LTD.—Haworth, Inc.; *U.S. Private*, pg. 512
HILTON EQUIPMENT CORP.—Hilton Hotels Corporation; *U.S. Public*, pg. 829
HUNT CANADA—Hunt Corporation; *U.S. Public*, pg. 849
HUSSEY PRODUCTS CO.—Hussey Corporation; *U.S. Private*, pg. 550
HYOSUNG GROUP; *Int'l*, pg. 640
IAC INDUSTRIES; *U.S. Private*, pg. 553
INTEX CORP.; *U.S. Private*, pg. 574
SHELBA D. JOHNSON TRUCKING; *U.S. Private*, pg. 594
JOYCE INTERNATIONAL, INC.; *U.S. Private*, pg. 602
KIMBALL LODGING GROUP—Kimball International, Inc.; *U.S. Public*, pg. 957
KIMBALL OFFICE FURNITURE CO.—Kimball International, Inc.; *U.S. Public*, pg. 957
KIMBALL U.K., INC.—Kimball International, Inc.; *U.S. Public*, pg. 958
KINGSDOWN, INC.; *U.S. Private*, pg. 622
MARTIN INDUSTRIES, INC. (AL); *U.S. Private*, pg. 709
HERMAN MILLER BV—Herman Miller, Inc.; *U.S. Public*, pg. 1112
HERMAN MILLER DEUTSCHLAND INC.—Herman Miller, Inc.; *U.S. Public*, pg. 1112

HERMAN MILLER ET CIE—Herman Miller, Inc.; U.S. Public, pg. 1112
MINEBEA CO., LTD.; Int'l, pg. 867
NATIONAL BEDDING CO.—National Bedding Co.; U.S. Private, pg. 780
NATIONAL OFFICE FURNITURE CO.—Kimball International, Inc.; U.S. Public, pg. 957
OFFICE DEPOT—Office Depot Inc.; U.S. Public, pg. 1212
OFFICE EQUIPMENT COMPANY OF CHICAGO; U.S. Private, pg. 812
PEABODY OFFICE FURNITURE CORPORATION; U.S. Private, pg. 844
A. POMERANTZ & COMPANY; U.S. Private, pg. 875
PORTFOLIO INTERIORS BY J.C. PENNEY—JC Penney Company, Inc.; U.S. Public, pg. 917
L. POWELL CO., INC.; U.S. Private, pg. 877
PRINT-O-STAT, INC.—Pace Resources, Inc.; U.S. Private, pg. 830
RENT-A-CENTER, INC.—Thorn plc; Int'l, pg. 1385
S-N BEDDING CO. INC.—Silentnight Holdings Plc; Int'l, pg. 1249
SACKNER-SOUTH DIV.—Jason Incorporated; U.S. Public, pg. 924
SACKNER-SOUTHEAST DIV.—Jason Incorporated; U.S. Public, pg. 924
SACKNER-WEST DIV.—Jason Incorporated; U.S. Public, pg. 924
SCHOENECKERS, INC.; U.S. Private, pg. 971
SERVCO PACIFIC INC.; U.S. Private, pg. 986
SHELBY WILLIAMS INDUSTRIES, INC.; U.S. Public, pg. 1464
SKINNER CORP.; U.S. Private, pg. 1005
STEELCASE STRAFOR AG—Groupe Strafor Facom; Int'l, pg. 569
STEELCASE STRAFOR (UK) LTD.—Groupe Strafor Facom; Int'l, pg. 569
TAB SALES CORP. (INTERNATIONAL)—Tab Products Co.; U.S. Public, pg. 1559
UNITED STATIONERS INC.; U.S. Public, pg. 1689
WANG'S INTERNATIONAL, INC.; U.S. Private, pg. 1149
WAREHOUSE HOME FURNISHINGS DISTRIBUTOR; U.S. Private, pg. 1150
WASSERSTROM COMPANY; U.S. Private, pg. 1152

5023 — HOME FURNISHINGS-WHOLESALE

AGG - SA ALUSUISSE GUY GEISLER NV—Alusuisse-Lonza Holding Ltd.; Int'l, pg. 68
ACCOR S.A.; Int'l, pg. 20
ALLEGA LTD.-(ALLEGA)—Alusuisse-Lonza Holding Ltd.; Int'l, pg. 67
ALLISON-ERWIN CO. INC.; U.S. Private, pg. 41
ALUMINUM COMPANY OF AMERICA; U.S. Public, pg. 60
AMERICAN FURNITURE COMPANY; U.S. Private, pg. 55
ANCHOR HOCKING CANADA DIV.—Newell Co.; U.S. Public, pg. 1178
ANDERSON WHOLESALE COMPANY; U.S. Private, pg. 73
ARIZONA WHOLESALE SUPPLY COMPANY; U.S. Private, pg. 82
ARMSTRONG (JAPAN) K.K.—Armstrong World Industries, Inc.; U.S. Public, pg. 132
ARMSTRONG (SINGAPORE) PTE. LTD.—Armstrong World Industries, Inc.; U.S. Public, pg. 132
ARMSTRONG WORLD INDUSTRIES PTY. LTD.—Armstrong World Industries, Inc.; U.S. Public, pg. 132
ARMSTRONG WORLD INDUSTRIES, S.A.—Armstrong World Industries, Inc.; U.S. Public, pg. 132
ARMSTRONG WORLD INDUSTRIES (SCHWEIZ) AG—Armstrong World Industries, Inc.; U.S. Public, pg. 132
ASAHI GLASS AMERICA, INC.—Asahi Glass Co., Ltd.; Int'l, pg. 84
BKM ENTERPRISES, INC.; U.S. Private, pg. 107
BACCARAT (CIE DES CRISTALLERIES); Int'l, pg. 132
BACCARAT, INC.—Baccarat (Cie des Cristalleries); Int'l, pg. 132
BALTIC LINEN COMPANY, INC.; U.S. Private, pg. 113
BEAULIEU GROUP; U.S. Private, pg. 127
BENMARK PTE. LTD.—F. J. Benjamin Holdings Ltd.; Int'l, pg. 187
BENNETT BROTHERS, INC.; U.S. Private, pg. 133
BENNETT BROTHERS, INC.—Bennett Brothers, Inc.; U.S. Private, pg. 133
BERNINA OF AMERICA INC.—Bernina Holding AG; Int'l, pg. 189
WILLIAM M. BIRD & CO., INC.; U.S. Private, pg. 145
THE BOMBAY COMPANY, INC.; U.S. Public, pg. 244
C&C ASSOCIATES—Couristan Inc.; U.S. Private, pg. 279
CAIN & BULTMAN; U.S. Private, pg. 199
CAMERON ASHLEY BUILDING PRODUCTS, INC; U.S. Public, pg. 298
CATALINA LIGHTING, INC.; U.S. Public, pg. 314
CELANESE CANADA TEXTILE GROUP—Hoechst Aktiengesellschaft; Int'l, pg. 625
CHEMIE LINZ FRANCE S.A.R.L.—DSM N.V.; Int'l, pg. 356
CHEMIE LINZ UK LTD.—DSM N.V.; Int'l, pg. 356
COLE PAPERS INC.; U.S. Private, pg. 251
CORNING CANADA INC.—Corning Incorporated; U.S. Public, pg. 448
CORNING TRADING (SINGAPORE) PTE. LTD.—Corning Incorporated; U.S. Public, pg. 448
COURI CARPET CO.—Couristan Inc.; U.S. Private, pg. 279
COURI-MURAD & CO.—Couristan Inc.; U.S. Private, pg. 279
COURISTAN INC.; U.S. Private, pg. 279
CROWN CRAFTS HOME FURNISHINGS, INC.—Crown Crafts, Inc.; U.S. Public, pg. 465
CROWN CRAFTS HOME FURNISHINGS OF ILLINOIS, INC.—Crown Crafts, Inc.; U.S. Public, pg. 465
CROWN CRAFTS, INC.; U.S. Public, pg. 465
D.J. TABLEWARE, INC.—Oneida Ltd.; U.S. Public, pg. 1226
DARBY GROUP OF COS.; U.S. Private, pg. 311
DEVIMCO—Accor S.A.; Int'l, pg. 20
DEVIMCO LTD.—Accor S.A.; Int'l, pg. 21
EBELING & REUSS COMPANY; U.S. Private, pg. 358
EKCO CANADA, INC.—Ekco Group, Inc.; U.S. Public, pg. 566
EKCO GROUP, INC.; U.S. Public, pg. 566
ETHAN ALLEN INTERIORS INC.; U.S. Public, pg. 595
FARGO GLASS & PAINT CO—Fargo Glass & Paint Company; U.S. Private, pg. 393
FARGO GLASS & PAINT CO.—Fargo Glass & Paint Company; U.S. Private, pg. 393
FARGO GLASS & PAINT COMPANY; U.S. Private, pg. 393
FITZ & FLOYD; U.S. Private, pg. 409
FORBO A/S—Forbo Holding SA; Int'l, pg. 497
FORBO INDUSTRIES INC.—Forbo Holding SA; Int'l, pg. 497
FORBO KROMMENIE B.V.—Forbo Holding SA; Int'l, pg. 497
FORBO KROMMENIE S.A.—Forbo Holding SA; Int'l, pg. 497
FORBO WALLCOVERINGS INC.—Forbo Holding SA; Int'l, pg. 497
GENERAL FELT INDUSTRIES, INC.—Trace International Holdings, Inc.; U.S. Private, pg. 1094
GENERAL MARBLE CORPORATION—Leucadia National Corporation; U.S. Public, pg. 990
GRUPO CARSO S.A. DE C.V.; Int'l, pg. 572
HAMBURG BROTHERS; U.S. Private, pg. 497
HAYWIN TEXTILE PRODUCTS, INC.; U.S. Private, pg. 514
HOME INTERIORS & GIFTS, INC.; U.S. Private, pg. 536
HORIZON CARPET—Mohawk Industries, Inc.; U.S. Public, pg. 1121
HUNTER DOUGLAS, INC.—Hunter Douglas N.V.; Int'l, pg. 639
INARCO LIMITED—Armstrong World Industries, Inc.; U.S. Public, pg. 132
JMP NEWCOR INTERNATIONAL INC.—Patra Ceramics Co., Ltd.; Int'l, pg. 1025
KELLER BUILDING PRODUCTS OF CHARLOTTE, INC.; U.S. Private, pg. 612
KELLER LADDERS INC.—U.S. Industries, Inc.; U.S. Public, pg. 1684
THE KRUSE COMPANY; U.S. Private, pg. 636
LALIQUE NORTH AMERICA—Lalique S.A.; Int'l, pg. 797
JACK LENOR LARSEN, INC.; U.S. Private, pg. 652
LAURA ASHLEY (USA) INC.—Laura Ashley Holdings Plc; Int'l, pg. 804
GEO. H. LEHLEITNER & CO., INC.; U.S. Private, pg. 659
LUCKY-GOLDSTAR INTERNATIONAL (AMERICA)—LG Group; Int'l, pg. 779
LUCKY GOLDSTAR INTERNATIONAL AMERICA, INC.—LG Group; Int'l, pg. 779
MCSWAIN CARPETS INC.; U.S. Private, pg. 725
MECO DEVELOPMENT LIMITED; Int'l, pg. 852
METALLICA S.A.—Alusuisse-Lonza Holding Ltd.; Int'l, pg. 67
N COR LTD.—Corning Incorporated; U.S. Public, pg. 449
NATIONAL BRANDS, INC.; U.S. Private, pg. 780
NEVCO HOUSEWARES, INC.—Publicker Industries Inc.; U.S. Public, pg. 1341
NEWELL INDUSTRIES CANADA, INC.—Newell Co.; U.S. Public, pg. 1178
NORITAKE CO., INC.—Noritake Co., Limited; Int'l, pg. 959
NORITAKE CO., INC.-TABLE TOP DIVISION—Noritake Co., Limited; Int'l, pg. 959
ONEIDA FOODSERVICE DIVISION—Oneida Ltd.; U.S. Public, pg. 1226
ONEIDA LTD.; U.S. Public, pg. 1225
ONEIDA SILVERSMITHS LIMITED—Oneida Ltd.; U.S. Public, pg. 1226
ORDERS DISTRIBUTING CO.; U.S. Private, pg. 819
OSTROW TEXTILE CO., INC.; U.S. Private, pg. 821
THE PAMPERED CHEF, LTD.; U.S. Private, pg. 835
PERFECT FIT INDUSTRIES, INC.; U.S. Private, pg. 852
PERFORMANCE PRODUCTS DIVISION—Springs Industries, Inc.; U.S. Public, pg. 1500
PORTFOLIO INTERIORS BY J.C. PENNEY—JC Penney Company, Inc.; U.S. Public, pg. 917
PUBLICKER INDUSTRIES INC.; U.S. Public, pg. 1341
Q.V.F. GLASTECHNIK GMBH—Corning Incorporated; U.S. Public, pg. 449
RENA-WARE DISTRIBUTORS INC.; U.S. Private, pg. 922
RIGHT IDEAS INC.; U.S. Private, pg. 930
ROBERDS, INC.; U.S. Public, pg. 1393
ROBERTSON FACTORIES, INC.; U.S. Private, pg. 936
ROBESON APPLIANCES—Robeson Appliance, Inc.; U.S. Public, pg. 1394
ROBESON SALES CORPORATION—Robeson Appliance, Inc.; U.S. Public, pg. 1394
ROSENTHAL U.S.A. LIMITED—Rosenthal AG; Int'l, pg. 1127
THE ROYAL CHINA & PORCELAIN COMPANIES INC.; U.S. Private, pg. 948
ROYAL COPENHAGEN & GEORG JENSEN PTY. LTD.—Royal Copenhagen A/S; Int'l, pg. 1135
ROYAL COPENHAGEN A/S; Int'l, pg. 1134
ROYAL COPENHAGEN GMBH—Royal Copenhagen A/S; Int'l, pg. 1135
ROYAL COPENHAGEN HAWAII, INC.—Royal Copenhagen A/S; Int'l, pg. 1134
ROYAL COPENHAGEN LTD.—Royal Copenhagen A/S; Int'l, pg. 1135
ROYAL COPENHAGEN NORGE A/S—Royal Copenhagen A/S; Int'l, pg. 1135
ROYAL COPENHAGEN PORCELAIN CORPORATION—Royal Copenhagen A/S; Int'l, pg. 1134
ROYAL COPENHAGEN SVENSKA AB—Royal Copenhagen A/S; Int'l, pg. 1135
ROYAL COPENHAGEN (TAIWAN) LTD.—Royal Copenhagen A/S; Int'l, pg. 1135
ROYAL DOULTON USA INC.—Royal Doulton Plc.; Int'l, pg. 1135
ROYAL WATERBEDS; U.S. Private, pg. 949
SALEM CARPET MILLS, INC.—Shaw Industries, Inc.; U.S. Public, pg. 1464
SCHOENECKERS, INC.; U.S. Private, pg. 971
F. SCHUMACHER & CO.; U.S. Private, pg. 973
SUPERIOR DRAPERY COMPANY; U.S. Private, pg. 1054
TECSYN INTERNATIONAL, INC.; Int'l, pg. 1361
THUNDERBIRD STEEL CORPORATION—Cameron Ashley Building Products, Inc; U.S. Public, pg. 298
TRUSERV CORPORATION; U.S. Private, pg. 1108
UNITED STATIONERS INC.; U.S. Public, pg. 1689
VG EMBALLAGE—Saint-Gobain; Int'l, pg. 1171
VILLEROY & BOCH TABLEWARE, LTD.—Villeroy & Boch AG; Int'l, pg. 1468
WATERFORD CRYSTAL GALLERY LTD.—Waterford Wedgwood Plc; Int'l, pg. 1487
WATERFORD WEDGWOOD PLC; Int'l, pg. 1487
WAVERLY FABRICS—F. Schumacher & Co.; U.S. Private, pg. 973
WEDGWOOD U.S.A.—Waterford Wedgwood Plc; Int'l, pg. 1487
WEST UNION CORPORATION; U.S. Private, pg. 1163
WESTGATE FABRICS, INC.; U.S. Private, pg. 1169
WILLITTS DESIGN; U.S. Private, pg. 1180
WILTON INDUSTRIES, INC.; U.S. Private, pg. 1181
WORLD TABLEWARE, INC.—Pilkington Plc; Int'l, pg. 1056

5031 — LUMBER, PLYWOOD, MILLWORK, WOOD PANELS-WHOLESALE

A.F. & D. MACKAY LTD.—Norske Skogindustrier A.S; Int'l, pg. 966
AETNA PLYWOOD, INC.; U.S. Private, pg. 25
ALAMO FOREST PRODUCTS, INC.—Vaughan & Sons, Inc.; U.S. Private, pg. 1135
ALL PRO WINDOW SUPPLY, INC.; U.S. Private, pg. 35
ALLIED PLYWOOD CORP.; U.S. Private, pg. 40
ALLIED PLYWOOD CORPORATION—Nortek, Inc.; U.S. Public, pg. 1193
AMERICAN INTERNATIONAL FOREST PRODUCTS, INC.—Forest City Enterprises, Inc.; U.S. Public, pg. 669
ANCO TRAE A/S—UPM-Kymmene Corporation; Int'l, pg. 1429
ANDERSON LUMBER COMPANY; U.S. Private, pg. 72
ANTHONY FOREST PRODUCTS CO., INC.; U.S. Private, pg. 76
ARCHITECTURAL WALL SYSTEMS, LLC—Fidelity Investments (FMR Corp.); U.S. Private, pg. 403
BIFP, INC.—Forest City Enterprises, Inc.; U.S. Public, pg. 669
BMC WEST—GAF Corporation; U.S. Private, pg. 433
BABCOCK LUMBER COMPANY; U.S. Private, pg. 108
BALFOUR TIMBER LTD.—Canfor Corporation; Int'l, pg. 260
BALTEK FOREIGN SALES CORPORATION—Baltek Corporation; U.S. Public, pg. 172
BALTEK LTD.—Baltek Corporation; U.S. Public, pg. 172
BALTEK S.A.—Baltek Corporation; U.S. Public, pg. 172
E.C. BARTON & COMPANY; U.S. Private, pg. 119
BATEMAN BROTHERS LUMBER CO., INC.; U.S. Private, pg. 122
BAY INDUSTRIES INC.; U.S. Private, pg. 124
BOISE CASCADE BUILDING MATERIALS DISTRIBUTION DIV.—Boise Cascade Corporation; U.S. Public, pg. 243
BOISE CASCADE CORPORATION; U.S. Public, pg. 242
BOISE CASCADE SALES LTD.—Boise Cascade Corporation; U.S. Public, pg. 243
BRIDGEWATER RESOURCES CORPORATION; U.S. Private, pg. 168
BROWER COMPANY—Bay Industries Inc.; U.S. Private, pg. 124
BUCKEYE PACIFIC CORP., INC.—Forest City Enterprises, Inc.; U.S. Public, pg. 669
BUILDER MARTS OF AMERICA, INC.; U.S. Private, pg. 179
CDF NORTHEAST—Cameron Ashley Building Products, Inc; U.S. Public, pg. 298
CALCASIEU LUMBER COMPANY; U.S. Private, pg. 200
CALIFORNIA PANEL & VENEER COMPANY; U.S. Private, pg. 201
CANADIAN TRANSPORT COMPANY—Northern Navigation International Inc.; U.S. Private, pg. 805
CANFOR U.S.A., BELLINGHAM DIVISION—Canfor Corporation; Int'l, pg. 260
CANFOR U.S.A. CORPORATION—Canfor Corporation; Int'l, pg. 260
CANUSA WOOD PRODUCTS LTD.—Meyer International PLC; Int'l, pg. 864
CAROLINA BUILDERS CORPORATION—Wolseley Plc.; Int'l, pg. 1512
CARTER-JONES COMPANIES, INC.; U.S. Private, pg. 217
CASCADE EMPIRE CORPORATION—Forest City Enterprises, Inc.; U.S. Public, pg. 669
CERTAINTEED CORPORATION—Saint-Gobain; Int'l, pg. 1170
CHEMAIUS SAWMILL DIVISION—MacMillan Bloedel Limited; Int'l, pg. 828
CHICHIBU ONODA CEMENT CORPORATION; Int'l, pg. 284
COLUMBIA LUMBER & MANUFACTURING CO.; U.S. Private, pg. 255
S.A. COMPTOIR FINLANDAIS N.V.—Enso Oyj; Int'l, pg. 457
CONSOLIDATED WHOLESALE LUMBER CO.—Calcasieu Lumber Company; U.S. Private, pg. 200
COOP SWITZERLAND; Int'l, pg. 329
COPAP—Enso Oyj; Int'l, pg. 457
COPELAND LUMBER YARD, INC.; U.S. Private, pg. 274
COUNTRYMARK COOPERATIVE, INC.; U.S. Private, pg. 279
COX WOOD PRESERVING CO.; U.S. Private, pg. 283
CRESTLINE DISTRIBUTION FACILITY—Nortek, Inc.; U.S. Public, pg. 1193
CYTEC FIBERITE EUROPE GMBH—Cytec Industries Inc.; U.S. Public, pg. 471
DAVIES MOLDING CO.—Pettibone Corporation; U.S. Private, pg. 859
DE BOO BEHEER B.V.—Scancem AB; Int'l, pg. 1200

DIAMOND HILL PLYWOOD COMPANY—Darlington Veneer Company; *U.S. Private*, pg. 311
DIXIE BUILDING SUPPLIES, INC.—Walter Industries, Inc.; *U.S. Public*, pg. 1736
DYKE INDUSTRY, INC.; *U.S. Private*, pg. 350
ENSO DANMARK A/S—Enso Oyj; *Int'l*, pg. 457
ENSO (DEUTSCHLAND) GMBH—Enso Oyj; *Int'l*, pg. 457
ENSO-EUROCAN-BUMJIN CO. LTD.—Enso Oyj; *Int'l*, pg. 457
ENSO IBERICA S.A.—Enso Oyj; *Int'l*, pg. 457
ENSO MARKETING CO. LTD.—Enso Oyj; *Int'l*, pg. 457
ENSO OYJ; *Int'l*, pg. 455
ENSO TRADING AB—Enso Oyj; *Int'l*, pg. 457
EUROC TRADE AB—Scancem AB; *Int'l*, pg. 1199
FINGERLE LUMBER CO.; *U.S. Private*, pg. 405
FINS VERKOOPKANTOOR—Enso Oyj; *Int'l*, pg. 458
FLETCHER MERCHANTS LIMITED—Fletcher Challenge Limited; *Int'l*, pg. 495
FLORENCE CORPORATION; *U.S. Private*, pg. 414
FOREST CITY CONTRACT LUMBER, INC.—Forest City Enterprises, Inc.; *U.S. Public*, pg. 668
FOREST CITY ENTERPRISES, INC.; *U.S. Public*, pg. 667
FOREST CITY TRADING GROUP, INC.—Forest City Enterprises, Inc.; *U.S. Public*, pg. 669
FOREST PRODUCTS S.A.—Enso Oyj; *Int'l*, pg. 458
FORT WORTH LUMBER COMPANY; *U.S. Private*, pg. 419
FOUAD & TOUFIC FADEL & CO.—Enso Oyj; *Int'l*, pg. 458
FOXWORTH-GALBRAITH LUMBER CO.; *U.S. Private*, pg. 423
FRANK PAXTON LUMBER COMPANY—Jeld-Wen, Inc.; *U.S. Private*, pg. 585
FURMAN LUMBER COMPANY INC.—Furman Lumber Company, Inc.; *U.S. Private*, pg. 431
FUTTER LUMBER CORPORATION; *U.S. Private*, pg. 432
GANAHL LUMBER COMPANY; *U.S. Private*, pg. 433
GEORGIA-PACIFIC BUILDING MATERIALS SALES, LTD.—Georgia-Pacific Corporation; *U.S. Public*, pg. 739
GEORGIA-PACIFIC S.A.—Georgia-Pacific Corporation; *U.S. Public*, pg. 739
GOLDEN STATE FLOORING—J.E. Higgins Lumber Co.; *U.S. Private*, pg. 527
GOLDENBERG GROUP, INC.—Nortek, Inc.; *U.S. Public*, pg. 1193
GREAT PLAINS COMPANIES, INC.; *U.S. Private*, pg. 475
GRUPO CARSO S.A. DE C.V.; *Int'l*, pg. 572
HANCOCK LUMBER, INC.; *U.S. Private*, pg. 498
HANKINS LUMBER COMPANY, INC.; *U.S. Private*, pg. 499
ELOF HANSSON INC.—Elof Hansson AB; *Int'l*, pg. 595
HANWA AMERICAN CORP.—Hanwa Co., Ltd.; *Int'l*, pg. 595
HANWA AMERICAN CORP., SEATTLE BRANCH—Hanwa Co., Ltd.; *Int'l*, pg. 595
JAMES HARDIE USA—James Hardie Industries Ltd.; *Int'l*, pg. 597
HIGGINS FRESNO OPERATIONS—J.E. Higgins Lumber Co.; *U.S. Private*, pg. 527
J.E. HIGGINS LUMBER COMPANY—J.E. Higgins Lumber Co.; *U.S. Private*, pg. 527
J.E. HIGGINS LUMBER CO.; *U.S. Private*, pg. 527
HIGGINS LUMBER PURCHASING—J.E. Higgins Lumber Co.; *U.S. Private*, pg. 527
HIGGINS MONTEREY BAY OPERATIONS—J.E. Higgins Lumber Co.; *U.S. Private*, pg. 527
HILL-BEHAN LUMBER COMPANY; *U.S. Private*, pg. 529
HOBOKEN WOOD FLOORING CORPORATION; *U.S. Private*, pg. 532
HOLBROOK LUMBER COMPANY; *U.S. Private*, pg. 533
HOLDERNESS SUPPLIES; *U.S. Private*, pg. 534
HUGHES SUPPLY, INC.; *U.S. Public*, pg. 846
HUNTER DOUGLAS HOLDINGS LTD.—Hunter Douglas N.V.; *Int'l*, pg. 640
HUNTER DOUGLAS LTD.—Hunter Douglas N.V.; *Int'l*, pg. 640
HURD MILLWORK COMPANY, INC.—UIS, Inc.; *U.S. Private*, pg. 1113
INCA PRESSWOOD PALLETS, LTD.—Inka Paletten GmbH; *Int'l*, pg. 678
IBSTOCK PLC; *Int'l*, pg. 658
INKA PALETTEN GMBH; *Int'l*, pg. 678
INTERLAKE PAPERS, INC.—Consolidated Papers, Inc.; *U.S. Public*, pg. 436
JEWSON LTD.—Meyer International PLC; *Int'l*, pg. 864
JONES LUMBER—Jeld-Wen, Inc.; *U.S. Private*, pg. 585
KAIBAB INDUSTRIES; *U.S. Private*, pg. 605
KAUFMAN AND BROAD OF TEXAS, LTD.—Kaufman and Broad Home Corporation; *U.S. Public*, pg. 945
KAUKAS NEDERLAND B.V.—UPM-Kymmene Corporation; *Int'l*, pg. 1429
KELLER LADDERS INC.—U.S. Industries, Inc.; *U.S. Public*, pg. 1684
KENTUCKY INDIANA LUMBER CO. INC.; *U.S. Private*, pg. 615
KOHLBECHER & CO. GMBH—Saarbergwerke Aktiengesellschaft; *Int'l*, pg. 1166
LUMBERMENS MERCHANDISING CORPORATION; *U.S. Private*, pg. 680
MB PAPER—MacMillan Bloedel Limited; *Int'l*, pg. 829
MBS HOLDING, INC.; *U.S. Private*, pg. 685
MACMILLAN BLOEDEL (ASIA) LIMITED—MacMillan Bloedel Limited; *Int'l*, pg. 829
MACMILLAN BLOEDEL BUILDING MATERIALS - WESTERN REGION—MacMillan Bloedel Limited; *Int'l*, pg. 828
MACMILLAN BLOEDEL LIMITED; *Int'l*, pg. 828
MACMILLAN BLOEDEL LIMITED - ALBERNI PACIFIC DIV.—MacMillan Bloedel Limited; *Int'l*, pg. 828
MACMILLAN BLOEDEL LIMITED, BUILDING MATERIALS - ALBERNI REGION—MacMillan Bloedel Limited; *Int'l*, pg. 828
MAINE POTATO GROWERS, INC.; *U.S. Private*, pg. 697
MAKI CORPORATION; *U.S. Private*, pg. 697
MAKI HOME CENTER, INC.—Maki Corporation; *U.S. Private*, pg. 698
MAYFIELD BUILDING SUPPLY CO.—MBS Holding, Inc.; *U.S. Private*, pg. 686
MCEWEN LUMBER COMPANY—International Paper Company; *U.S. Public*, pg. 903
J. GIBSON MCILVAIN CO.; *U.S. Private*, pg. 722
MCLEAN-THOMAS INC.; *U.S. Private*, pg. 724
MEYER FOREST PRODUCTS LTD—Meyer International PLC; *Int'l*, pg. 864
MEYER INTERNATIONAL PLC; *Int'l*, pg. 864
MID-AM BUILDING SUPPLY, INC.; *U.S. Private*, pg. 743
MINOT BUILDERS SUPPLY ASSOCIATION; *U.S. Private*, pg. 751
MITSUBISHI CORPORATION; *Int'l*, pg. 871
MITSUBISHI INTERNATIONAL CORPORATION—Mitsubishi Corporation; *Int'l*, pg. 871
MO OCH DOMSJO AB; *Int'l*, pg. 885
MODO SKOG AB—Mo och Domsjo AB; *Int'l*, pg. 887
MOLDED FIBER GLASS/WEST—Molded Fiber Glass Companies; *U.S. Private*, pg. 756
MONUMENTAL MILLWORK, INC.; *U.S. Private*, pg. 759
MOORE-HANDLEY, INC.; *U.S. Public*, pg. 1128
MORGAN DISTRIBUTION—Morgan Products Ltd.; *U.S. Public*, pg. 1132
NAMSENBYGG—Norske Skogindustrier A.S; *Int'l*, pg. 965
NATIONAL LUMBER CO.; *U.S. Private*, pg. 785
NOR HOLZ VERKAUFSGESELLSCHAFT—Norske Skogindustrier A.S; *Int'l*, pg. 966
NORTA TIMBER B.V.—Enso Oyj; *Int'l*, pg. 458
NORTH PACIFIC LUMBER COMPANY; *U.S. Private*, pg. 805
NORTHERN NAVIGATION INTERNATIONAL INC.; *U.S. Private*, pg. 805
OLYMPIC INDUSTRIES, INC.—Forest City Enterprises, Inc.; *U.S. Public*, pg. 670
ONODA NORTHWEST, INC.—Chichibu Onoda Cement Corporation; *Int'l*, pg. 284
P.S. INTERNATIONAL INC.; *U.S. Private*, pg. 827
PACESETTER CORPORATION; *U.S. Private*, pg. 830
PACIFIC LUMBER & SHIPPING CO.; *U.S. Private*, pg. 832
PATRICK INDUSTRIES INC.; *U.S. Public*, pg. 1264
PAXTON BEAUTIFUL WOODS—Jeld-Wen, Inc.; *U.S. Private*, pg. 585
FRANK PAXTON COMPANY—Jeld-Wen, Inc.; *U.S. Private*, pg. 585
FRANK PAXTON LUMBER COMPANY—Jeld-Wen, Inc.; *U.S. Private*, pg. 585
PENBERTHY LUMBER COMPANY; *U.S. Private*, pg. 848
PHILADELPHIA RESERVE SUPPLY COMPANY; *U.S. Private*, pg. 861
PIONEER PLASTICS CORPORATION; *U.S. Private*, pg. 867
PLYWOOD PLASTICS INC.; *U.S. Private*, pg. 873
ARTHUR A. POZZI CO., INC.; *U.S. Private*, pg. 878
PREDSTAVEITLSTVO FIRMY "ENSO"—Enso Oyj; *Int'l*, pg. 458
E.R. PROBYN LTD.; *Int'l*, pg. 1071
PROBYN LOG, LTD.—E.R. Probyn Ltd.; *Int'l*, pg. 1071
RLC INDUSTRIES CO.; *U.S. Private*, pg. 905
THE RTZ CORPORATION PLC—Rio Tinto PLC; *Int'l*, pg. 1118
REICO, INC.; *U.S. Private*, pg. 919
RESPATEX INTERNATIONAL LTD.—Norske Skogindustrier A.S; *Int'l*, pg. 967
REX LUMBER COMPANY; *U.S. Private*, pg. 926
RICHARDSON INDUSTRIES, INC.; *U.S. Private*, pg. 929
RICHMOND INTERNATIONAL FOREST PRODUCTS, INC.—Forest City Enterprises, Inc.; *U.S. Public*, pg. 669
RIEMEIER LUMBER COMPANY, INC.; *U.S. Private*, pg. 930
RIVERSIDE MILLWORK COMPANY, INC.; *U.S. Private*, pg. 934
ROBBINS MANUFACTURING COMPANY; *U.S. Private*, pg. 935
ROBINSON LUMBER COMPANY—Robinson Lumber & Export Company; *U.S. Private*, pg. 936
T.H. ROGERS LUMBER CO.; *U.S. Private*, pg. 940
ROSEBURG FOREST PRODUCTS CO.—RLC Industries Co.; *U.S. Private*, pg. 905
SCR, INC.; *U.S. Private*, pg. 955
SABBETH INDUSTRIES LTD; *U.S. Private*, pg. 959
SAGEBRUSH SALES COMPANY—Nortek, Inc.; *U.S. Public*, pg. 1193
SANDVIK BAHCO ARGENTINA S.A.C.EL.—Sandvik AB; *Int'l*, pg. 1187
SANFORD & HAWLEY, INC.; *U.S. Private*, pg. 965
SCANLAND AGENCIES LTD.—Norske Skogindustrier A.S; *Int'l*, pg. 967
SCHAUMAN B.V.—UPM-Kymmene Corporation; *Int'l*, pg. 1429
SCHAUMAN IBERICA S.A.—UPM-Kymmene Corporation; *Int'l*, pg. 1429
SCHAUMAN S.A.—UPM-Kymmene Corporation; *Int'l*, pg. 1429
SCHAUMAN (UK) LTD.—UPM-Kymmene Corporation; *Int'l*, pg. 1429
WILH. SCHAUMAN GMBH—UPM-Kymmene Corporation; *Int'l*, pg. 1429
SCHAUMAN WOOD AB—UPM-Kymmene Corporation; *Int'l*, pg. 1429
SCHAUMAN WOOD OY-ISTANBUL OFFICE—UPM-Kymmene Corporation; *Int'l*, pg. 1429
SCHAUMAN WOOD OY-REGIONAL OFFICE—UPM-Kymmene Corporation; *Int'l*, pg. 1429
SCHERER BROS. LUMBER COMPANY; *U.S. Private*, pg. 970
SCHUCK & SONS CONSTRUCTION CO.; *U.S. Private*, pg. 973
SCHUTTE LUMBER COMPANY; *U.S. Private*, pg. 973
SEABOARD INTERNATIONAL FOREST PRODUCTS, INC.—Forest City Enterprises, Inc.; *U.S. Public*, pg. 669
SEMAC INDUSTRIES INC.; *U.S. Private*, pg. 983
SHERWOOD LUMBER CORPORATION; *U.S. Private*, pg. 994
SIMPSON INVESTMENT CO.; *U.S. Private*, pg. 1003
SIMPSON TIMBER CO.—Simpson Investment Co.; *U.S. Private*, pg. 1003
KELLER SMITH SUPPLY, INC.; *U.S. Private*, pg. 1008
SNAVELY FOREST PRODUCTS, INC.; *U.S. Private*, pg. 1010
STANCOM HOME CENTER, INC.—Standard Commercial Corporation; *U.S. Public*, pg. 1502
H.A. STILES CO.—Saunders Brothers; *U.S. Private*, pg. 968
STONES, INC.; *U.S. Private*, pg. 1045
STORA TIMBER AB—Stora Kopparbergs Bergslags AB; *Int'l*, pg. 1303
SWANER HARDWOOD COMPANY, INC.; *U.S. Private*, pg. 1057
TSP INC.—Enso Oyj; *Int'l*, pg. 457
TAMPA INTL. FOREST PRODUCTS, INC.—Forest City Enterprises, Inc.; *U.S. Public*, pg. 669
TIMBER PRODUCTS COMPANY, LP; *U.S. Private*, pg. 1086
TRAVARU AB A. MOBERG & CO.—Scancem AB; *Int'l*, pg. 1199
TRAVARU AB A. THOMEE—Scancem AB; *Int'l*, pg. 1199
TREESOURCE, INC.—WTD Industries, Inc.; *U.S. Public*, pg. 1729
UNIVERSAL FOREST PRODUCTS, INC.; *U.S. Public*, pg. 1696
VAAGEN BROTHERS LUMBER, INC.; *U.S. Private*, pg. 1131
VALLEY FOREST RESOURCES CO.—Villaume Industries, Inc.; *U.S. Private*, pg. 1140
VAUGHAN & SONS, INC.; *U.S. Private*, pg. 1134
VIKING FOREST PRODUCTS, INC.—Forest City Enterprises, Inc.; *U.S. Public*, pg. 669
WEBB BUILDERS HARDWARE; *U.S. Private*, pg. 1156
WEST BUILDING MATERIALS; *U.S. Private*, pg. 1163
WESTERN INTL. FOREST PRODS., INC.—Forest City Enterprises, Inc.; *U.S. Public*, pg. 669
WEYERHAEUSER JAPAN LTD.—Weyerhaeuser Company; *U.S. Public*, pg. 1764
WEYERHAEUSER, S.A.—Weyerhaeuser Company; *U.S. Public*, pg. 1764
WILLAMETTE INDUSTRIES, INC.—Willamette Industries, Inc.; *U.S. Public*, pg. 1769
WILMER SERVICE LINE—The Reynolds and Reynolds Company; *U.S. Public*, pg. 1385
WING INDUSTRIES NORTH CENTRAL—Wing Industries, Inc.; *U.S. Private*, pg. 1183
WOODMARK LTD.—Norske Skogindustrier A.S; *Int'l*, pg. 967

5032 — BRICK, STONE & RELATED CONSTRUCTION MATERIALS-WHOLESALE

AAH BUILDERS SUPPLIES LIMITED—Franz Haniel & Cie, GmbH; *Int'l*, pg. 591
ARC CENTRAL—Hanson PLC; *Int'l*, pg. 592
ARC LIMITED—Hanson PLC; *Int'l*, pg. 592
ACME BRICK CO.—Justin Industries, Inc.; *U.S. Public*, pg. 936
AGGREGATE SUPPLY CO., LTD.—The Siam Cement Public Company Limited; *Int'l*, pg. 1237
AMERICAN STONE-MIX, INC.; *U.S. Private*, pg. 62
ASLAND S.A.—Lafarge S.A.; *Int'l*, pg. 790
BASS BLOCK & BUILDING SUPPLIES—Holderbank Financiere Glaris Ltd.; *Int'l*, pg. 629
BETAO LIZ S.A.—Lafarge S.A.; *Int'l*, pg. 790
BRASWELL SAND & GRAVEL COMPANY, INC.—Holderbank Financiere Glaris Ltd.; *Int'l*, pg. 628
BRISTILE CLAY TILES, LTD.; *Int'l*, pg. 216
CALCIA—Ciments Francais; *Int'l*, pg. 292
CAMERON ASHLEY BUILDING PRODUCTS, INC; *U.S. Public*, pg. 298
CANADIAN CEMENT LTD.—Medusa Corporation; *U.S. Public*, pg. 1084
CASTLE CEMENT LTD. (PORT OF BRISTOL)—Scancem AB; *Int'l*, pg. 1201
CEMENLAND S.A.—Lafarge S.A.; *Int'l*, pg. 790
CEMENTOS ASLAND S.A.—Lafarge S.A.; *Int'l*, pg. 790
CEMENTOS PEYLAND S.A.—Lafarge S.A.; *Int'l*, pg. 790
CHICHIBU ONODA CEMENT CORPORATION; *Int'l*, pg. 284
COLD SPRING GRANITE COMPANY; *U.S. Private*, pg. 250
DAL-TILE CORP.—Dal-Tile International; *U.S. Private*, pg. 308
DEMIX BETON/AGREGATS—Holderbank Financiere Glaris Ltd.; *Int'l*, pg. 629
DUTCHESS QUARRY & SUPPLY CO. INC.; *U.S. Private*, pg. 350
DYNAPAC GMBH—Trelleborg AB; *Int'l*, pg. 1420
EASTERN BULKCEM CO. LTD.—Scancem AB; *Int'l*, pg. 1201
ENCERATEC, INC.—Toshiba Corporation; *Int'l*, pg. 1405
EUROC BETONG & BALLAST AB—Scancem AB; *Int'l*, pg. 1200
H.G. FENTON MATERIAL COMPANY; *U.S. Private*, pg. 400
FLETCHER MERCHANTS LIMITED—Fletcher Challenge Limited; *Int'l*, pg. 495
FLORIDA TILE CERAMIC CENTERS, INC.—Premark International, Inc.; *U.S. Public*, pg. 1322
JOHN FYFE LTD.—Bardon Group PLC; *Int'l*, pg. 166
GILPATRICK CONSTRUCTION COMPANY, INC; *U.S. Private*, pg. 454
GROUPE BETON QUEBEC—Holderbank Financiere Glaris Ltd.; *Int'l*, pg. 629
E.P. HENRY CORPORATION; *U.S. Private*, pg. 522
HILLS MATERIALS CO.—Northwestern Engineering Co.; *U.S. Private*, pg. 806
HISPACEMENT S.A.—Lafarge S.A.; *Int'l*, pg. 790
INGRAM MATERIALS CO.—Ingram Industries Inc.; *U.S. Private*, pg. 563
INTERSTATE BRICK COMPANY—Pacific Coast Building Products Inc.; *U.S. Private*, pg. 830

LEHNKERING MONTAN TRANSPORT AG—Metallgesellschaft AG; *Int'l*, pg. 862
LEHNKERING MONTAN TRANSPORT AG—Preussag AG; *Int'l*, pg. 1069
MBS HOLDING, INC.; *U.S. Private*, pg. 685
MBT (MALAYSIA) SDM. BHD.—Viag AG; *Int'l*, pg. 1465
MBT (NEW ZEALAND) LTD.—Viag AG; *Int'l*, pg. 1465
MBT PORTUGAL LDA.—Viag AG; *Int'l*, pg. 1465
MBT (SINGAPORE) PTE. LTD.—Viag AG; *Int'l*, pg. 1465
MASTER BUILDERS INC.—Viag AG; *Int'l*, pg. 1465
MASTER BUILDERS SCANDINAVIA AB—Viag AG; *Int'l*, pg. 1465
MCLEAN-THOMAS INC.; *U.S. Private*, pg. 724
MEDUSA CORPORATION; *U.S. Public*, pg. 1084
MILES SAND & GRAVEL COMPANY; *U.S. Private*, pg. 745
JUAN MINETTI S.A.; *Int'l*, pg. 869
MONROC, INC.; *U.S. Public*, pg. 1124
OBAYASHI CORPORATION; *Int'l*, pg. 995
OLEN CORPORATION—Kokosing Construction Company, Inc.; *U.S. Private*, pg. 631
ORANGE COUNTY PLANT—Oglebay Norton Company; *U.S. Public*, pg. 1213
PERAK HANJUNG SINIEN SDN. BHD.—Korea Heavy Industries & Construction Co., Ltd.; *Int'l*, pg. 758
PERCHEM LTD.—Akzo Nobel N.V.; *Int'l*, pg. 47
PERCHEM SA—Akzo Nobel N.V.; *Int'l*, pg. 47
PERSTORP CHEMITEC—Perstorp AB; *Int'l*, pg. 1037
PETERBOROUGH QUARRIES LIMITED—Bardon Group PLC; *Int'l*, pg. 166
PETRICCA INDUSTRIES, INC.; *U.S. Private*, pg. 858
PLUESS-STAUFER AG; *Int'l*, pg. 1061
PORTCEMEN S.A.—Lafarge S.A.; *Int'l*, pg. 790
POZZOLITH BUSSAN CO. LTD.—Novartis AG; *Int'l*, pg. 983
QUEBEC & MARITIMES DIV. ST. LAWRENCE CEMENT—Holderbank Financiere Glaris Ltd.; *Int'l*, pg. 629
REDLAND AUSTRALIA LTD.—Redland PLC; *Int'l*, pg. 1092
REDLAND (DEUTSCHLAND) GMBH—Redland PLC; *Int'l*, pg. 1093
REDLAND GENSTAR STONE PRODUCTS COMPANY—Redland PLC; *Int'l*, pg. 1091
RIVERTON TRUCKERS, INC.—Gohmann Asphalt & Construction Inc.; *U.S. Private*, pg. 459
SCT CO., LTD.—The Siam Cement Public Company Limited; *Int'l*, pg. 1238
SABEMA MATERIAL AB—Scancem AB; *Int'l*, pg. 1199
ANN SACKS TILE & STONE, INC.—Kohler Company; *U.S. Private*, pg. 630
ST. LAWRENCE CEMENT INC.—Holderbank Financiere Glaris Ltd.; *Int'l*, pg. 628
SAMIN—Saint-Gobain; *Int'l*, pg. 1171
SANDVIK BAHCO ARGENTINA S.A.C.EL.—Sandvik AB; *Int'l*, pg. 1187
SANDVIK CANADA INC.—Sandvik AB; *Int'l*, pg. 1188
SANDVIK CHILE S.A.—Sandvik AB; *Int'l*, pg. 1187
SANDVIK COLOMBIA S.A.—Sandvik AB; *Int'l*, pg. 1188
SANDVIK DE MEXICO S.A. DE C.V.—Sandvik AB; *Int'l*, pg. 1188
SANDVIK DEL PERU S.A.—Sandvik AB; *Int'l*, pg. 1188
SANDVIK DO BRASIL S.A.—Sandvik AB; *Int'l*, pg. 1188
SANDVIK KENYA LTD.—Sandvik AB; *Int'l*, pg. 1187
SANDVIK KOREA LTD.—Sandvik AB; *Int'l*, pg. 1187
SANDVIK MALAYSIA SDN. BHD.—Sandvik AB; *Int'l*, pg. 1187
SANDVIK NEW ZEALAND LTD.—Sandvik AB; *Int'l*, pg. 1187
SANDVIK PHILIPPINES, INC.—Sandvik AB; *Int'l*, pg. 1187
SANDVIK (PTY.) LTD.—Sandvik AB; *Int'l*, pg. 1187
SANDVIK TAIWAN LTD.—Sandvik AB; *Int'l*, pg. 1187
SANDVIK VENEZUELA C.A.—Sandvik AB; *Int'l*, pg. 1188
SANITEC LTD. OY—Metra Corporation; *Int'l*, pg. 863
SCANSTONE GMBH—Scancem AB; *Int'l*, pg. 1199
THE SIAM GYPSUM INDUSTRY CO., LTD.—The Siam Cement Public Company Limited; *Int'l*, pg. 1238
SKANSKA PREFAB AB—Skanska AB; *Int'l*, pg. 1261
SOPLACAS LDA—Scancem AB; *Int'l*, pg. 1199
SSANGYONG CORPORATION—Ssangyong Business Group; *Int'l*, pg. 1291
SSANGYONG RESOURCES DEVELOPMENT CO., LTD.—Ssangyong Business Group; *Int'l*, pg. 1291
SYAR INDUSTRIES, INC.; *U.S. Private*, pg. 1059
TARMAC AMERICA, INC.—Tarmac plc; *Int'l*, pg. 1355
TECNOCRETO S.A. DE C.V.—Novartis AG; *Int'l*, pg. 986
THAI MASTER BUILDERS CO. LTD.—Novartis AG; *Int'l*, pg. 986
THUNDERBIRD STEEL CORPORATION—Cameron Ashley Building Products, Inc; *U.S. Public*, pg. 298
TILCON TOMASSO SERVICES INC.—Tilcon, Inc.; *U.S. Private*, pg. 1086
TOKUYAMA AMERICA INC.—Tokuyama Corporation; *Int'l*, pg. 1394
VULCAN MATERIALS COMPANY-MIDEAST DIV.—Vulcan Materials Company; *U.S. Public*, pg. 1725
WHIBCO, INC.; *U.S. Private*, pg. 1171

5033 — ROOFING, SIDING & INSULATION MATERIALS-WHOLESALE

AAH BUILDERS SUPPLIES LIMITED—Franz Haniel & Cie, GmbH; *Int'l*, pg. 591
AC & S INC.—Irex Corporation; *U.S. Public*, pg. 913
ALAMO FOREST PRODUCTS, INC.—Vaughan & Sons, Inc.; *U.S. Private*, pg. 1135
ALLIED BUILDING PRODUCTS CORPORATION; *U.S. Private*, pg. 38
CARTER HOLT HARVEY ROOFING USA, INC.—International Paper Company; *U.S. Public*, pg. 905
CELOTEX CORPORATION; *U.S. Private*, pg. 221
CHEMPOWER, INC.—American Eco Corporation; *Int'l*, pg. 74
COMFORT INC.—Jannock Limited; *Int'l*, pg. 698
FERGUSON LYON CONKLIN & COMPANY INC.—Wolseley Plc.; *Int'l*, pg. 1512
FOREST SIDING SUPPLY, INC.—Thermal Technology Industries; *U.S. Private*, pg. 1080
HARVEY INDUSTRIES, INC.; *U.S. Private*, pg. 508
INDUSTRIAL ACOUSTICS COMPANY GMBH—Industrial Acoustics Company, Inc.; *U.S. Public*, pg. 875
INTRA-ACOUSTICS COMPANY, LTD.—Industrial Acoustics Company, Inc.; *U.S. Public*, pg. 875
M M SYSTEMS CORPORATION; *U.S. Private*, pg. 685
MCLEAN-THOMAS INC.; *U.S. Private*, pg. 724
MOLDED FIBER GLASS/WEST—Molded Fiber Glass Companies; *U.S. Private*, pg. 756
MOLDED FIBER/NORTH CAROLINA—Molded Fiber Glass Companies; *U.S. Private*, pg. 756
MOY INSULATION LTD.—BPB Industries PLC; *Int'l*, pg. 123
PERFORMANCE CONTRACTING GROUP; *U.S. Private*, pg. 853
SANFORD & HAWLEY, INC.; *U.S. Private*, pg. 965
SCHULLER INTERNATIONAL, INC.—Johns Manville Corporation; *U.S. Public*, pg. 927
SIPLAST S.A.—Icopal a/s; *Int'l*, pg. 659
SPECIALTY PRODUCTS AND INSULATION COMPANY—Irex Corporation; *U.S. Public*, pg. 913
VAUGHAN & SONS, INC.; *U.S. Private*, pg. 1134

5039 — WHOLESALE CONSTRUCTION MATERIALS, NEC

AAH BUILDERS SUPPLIES LIMITED—Franz Haniel & Cie, GmbH; *Int'l*, pg. 591
ABC SUPPLY COMPANY, INC.; *U.S. Private*, pg. 3
AFG INDUSTRIES, INC.—Asahi Glass Co., Ltd.; *Int'l*, pg. 84
API GROUP INC.; *U.S. Private*, pg. 7
ACORN WINDOW SYSTEMS INC.; *U.S. Private*, pg. 14
ALASKAN COPPER COMPANIES; *U.S. Private*, pg. 31
ALL-AMERICAN SYSTEMS—NCI Building Systems, Inc.; *U.S. Public*, pg. 1146
ALL PRO WINDOW SUPPLY, INC.; *U.S. Private*, pg. 35
ALUMINUM COMPANY OF AMERICA; *U.S. Public*, pg. 60
AMERICAN FENCE & SECURITY COMPANY; *U.S. Private*, pg. 54
ANCHOR INDUSTRIES INC.; *U.S. Private*, pg. 71
ANCO INSULATIONS, INC.; *U.S. Private*, pg. 71
ARUNDEL SAND & GRAVEL CO.—Florida Rock Industries, Inc.; *U.S. Public*, pg. 656
ASAHI GLASS AMERICA, INC.—Asahi Glass Co., Ltd.; *Int'l*, pg. 84
ASHLAND-DAVIS COMPANY—Saint-Gobain; *Int'l*, pg. 1171
ASSOCIATED SAND & GRAVEL CO., INC.—CSR Limited; *Int'l*, pg. 245
ASSOCIATION SAND & GRAVEL—CSR Limited; *Int'l*, pg. 246
ATCO STRUCTURES INC.—ATCO Group Co.; *Int'l*, pg. 95
BMC WEST—GAF Corporation; *U.S. Private*, pg. 433
E.C. BARTON & COMPANY; *U.S. Private*, pg. 119
BEL-AIR FENCE BRANCH—The Ivaco Group; *Int'l*, pg. 695
BEL-AIR FENCE DIVISION—The Ivaco Group; *Int'l*, pg. 695
BENSON INDUSTRIES, INC.; *U.S. Private*, pg. 133
BERKS PRODUCTS CORPORATION; *U.S. Private*, pg. 136
WILLIAM M. BIRD & CO., INC.; *U.S. Private*, pg. 145
BLACK & CO.; *U.S. Private*, pg. 146
BORAL LIMITED; *Int'l*, pg. 203
BOURAS INDUSTRIES; *U.S. Private*, pg. 161
BRECKENRIDGE MATERIAL COMPANY; *U.S. Private*, pg. 166
BUILDER MARTS OF AMERICA, INC.; *U.S. Private*, pg. 179
BUILDING MATERIALS CORPORATION OF AMERICA—GAF Corporation; *U.S. Private*, pg. 433
BUILDING PLASTICS, INC.; *U.S. Private*, pg. 180
BUILDING PRODUCTS INC.; *U.S. Private*, pg. 180
CSR AMERICA INC.—CSR Limited; *Int'l*, pg. 245
CAMALLOY, INCORPORATED; *U.S. Private*, pg. 202
CAPITOL CITY STEEL CO.—Commercial Metals Company; *U.S. Public*, pg. 413
CAVALIER HOMES, INC.; *U.S. Public*, pg. 318
CEDIMAT S.A.—La Meridionale des Bois et Materiaux; *Int'l*, pg. 784
CHAPELLIER BOIS-MATERIAUX-QUINCAILLERIE—La Meridionale des Bois et Materiaux; *Int'l*, pg. 784
CHASE CANADA—Chase Corporation; *U.S. Public*, pg. 337
CIMATARN—La Meridionale des Bois et Materiaux; *Int'l*, pg. 784
COMPAIN BOIS ET MATERIAUX—La Meridionale des Bois et Materiaux; *Int'l*, pg. 784
COMPTOIR GENERAL DES GLACES (CGG)—Saint-Gobain; *Int'l*, pg. 1172
COMPTOIR NORMAND DE PRODUITS VERRIERS (CNPV)—Saint-Gobain; *Int'l*, pg. 1170
DELRIEU BOIS ET MATERIAUX—La Meridionale des Bois et Materiaux; *Int'l*, pg. 784
E.C.B. BROKERAGE—E.C. Barton & Company; *U.S. Private*, pg. 119
EPL PLANT & ACCESS—John Laing PLC; *Int'l*, pg. 796
EMERY WATERHOUSE COMPANY; *U.S. Private*, pg. 373
ENGINEERED PRODUCTS, INC.; *U.S. Private*, pg. 376
ESSROC CANADA—Ciments Francais; *Int'l*, pg. 292
EXPERT BOIS ET MATERIAUX—La Meridionale des Bois et Materiaux; *Int'l*, pg. 784
FARGO GLASS & PAINT COMPANY; *U.S. Private*, pg. 393
FINGERLE LUMBER CO.; *U.S. Private*, pg. 405
FISCHER COMPANIES; *U.S. Private*, pg. 408
FLORENCE CORPORATION; *U.S. Private*, pg. 414
FOURCO GLASS CO.—Asahi Glass Co., Ltd.; *Int'l*, pg. 84
FOXWORTH-GALBRAITH LUMBER CO.; *U.S. Private*, pg. 423
FREDERICK TRADING COMPANY—Distribution America; *U.S. Private*, pg. 335
FREUDENBERG BUILDING SYSTEMS INC.—Freudenberg & Company; *Int'l*, pg. 506
GALAMBA METALS, INC.—Galamet, Inc.; *U.S. Private*, pg. 437
GANAHL LUMBER COMPANY; *U.S. Private*, pg. 439
GERRER—Saint-Gobain; *Int'l*, pg. 1172
GLAVERBEL S.A.—Asahi Glass Co., Ltd.; *Int'l*, pg. 85
GRAVEY S.A.—La Meridionale des Bois et Materiaux; *Int'l*, pg. 784
HC&D DIV.—Ameron International Corporation; *U.S. Public*, pg. 99
HAHN SYSTEMS, INC.; *U.S. Private*, pg. 493
ELOF HANSSON INC.—Elof Hansson AB; *Int'l*, pg. 595
HARDWARE WHOLESALERS, INC.; *U.S. Private*, pg. 502
HILL-BEHAN LUMBER COMPANY; *U.S. Private*, pg. 529
HOLDERNESS SUPPLIES; *U.S. Private*, pg. 534
IMPO GLAZTILE—The Siam Cement Public Company Limited; *Int'l*, pg. 1239
INTREPID ENTERPRISES, INC.; *U.S. Private*, pg. 574
ISOVER S.A.—Saint-Gobain; *Int'l*, pg. 1176
JGC (U.S.A.), INC.—JGC Corporation; *Int'l*, pg. 697
JEWELL BUILDING SYSTEMS; *U.S. Private*, pg. 587
JOHNSON ACOUSTICAL & SUPPLY CO.; *U.S. Private*, pg. 590
P.J. KEATING COMPANY; *U.S. Private*, pg. 610
LA MERIDIONALE DES BOIS ET MATERIAUX; *Int'l*, pg. 784
LAFARGE CORPORATION—Lafarge S.A.; *Int'l*, pg. 788
LIMOUX OFFICE—La Meridionale des Bois et Materiaux; *Int'l*, pg. 784
LUCKY-GOLDSTAR INTERNATIONAL (AMERICA)—LG Group; *Int'l*, pg. 779
LUCKY GOLDSTAR INTERNATIONAL AMERICA, INC.—LG Group; *Int'l*, pg. 779
LUIGI FONTANA S.P.A.—Saint-Gobain; *Int'l*, pg. 1173
LUMBERMENS MERCHANDISING CORPORATION; *U.S. Private*, pg. 680
MAINE POTATO GROWERS, INC.; *U.S. Private*, pg. 697
MANVILLE CANADA INC.—Johns Manville Corporation; *U.S. Public*, pg. 927
MANVILLE DO BRASIL—Johns Manville Corporation; *U.S. Public*, pg. 927
MANVILLE JAPAN LTD.—Johns Manville Corporation; *U.S. Public*, pg. 927
MANVILLE MEXICANA S.A. DE C.V.—Johns Manville Corporation; *U.S. Public*, pg. 927
MANVILLE SALES CORPORATION—Johns Manville Corporation; *U.S. Public*, pg. 927
MASTER-HALCO, INC.—Itochu Corporation; *Int'l*, pg. 695
MCCOY'S BUILDING SUPPLY CENTERS; *U.S. Private*, pg. 720
MCLEAN-THOMAS INC.; *U.S. Private*, pg. 724
MEADOW STEEL PRODUCTS—Hanson PLC; *Int'l*, pg. 593
METALLIC BUILDING COMPANY—NCI Building Systems, Inc.; *U.S. Public*, pg. 1146
MIDWEST STEEL BUILDING COMPANY—NCI Building Systems, Inc.; *U.S. Public*, pg. 1146
MIROITERIES DE L'OUEST—Saint-Gobain; *Int'l*, pg. 1172
MODEL GLASS COMPANY; *U.S. Private*, pg. 754
MONARCH CEMENT CO.; *U.S. Public*, pg. 1123
NCI BUILDING SYSTEMS, INC.; *U.S. Public*, pg. 1145
NATIONAL GYPSUM COMPANY—Lafarge S.A.; *Int'l*, pg. 790
NEW ZEALAND FIBRE GLASS COMPANY-IMPORTED PRODUCTS DIVISION—International Paper Company; *U.S. Public*, pg. 904
NICHIMEN AMERICA, INC.—Nichimen Corporation; *Int'l*, pg. 927
NICHIMEN CORPORATION; *Int'l*, pg. 927
NITTETSU SHOJI CO., LTD.—Nippon Steel Corporation; *Int'l*, pg. 939
OKABE COMPANY, INC.—Okabe Company Limited; *Int'l*, pg. 999
O'KEEFFE'S, INC.; *U.S. Private*, pg. 813
OLLIER JACQUOT BOIS ET MATERIAUX—La Meridionale des Bois et Materiaux; *Int'l*, pg. 784
OWENS-CORNING FIBERGLAS DEUTSCHLAND G.M.B.H.—Owens Corning; *U.S. Public*, pg. 1237
OWENS-CORNING FIBERGLAS NORWAY AS—Owens Corning; *U.S. Public*, pg. 1237
P.S. INTERNATIONAL INC.; *U.S. Private*, pg. 827
PACESETTER CORPORATION; *U.S. Private*, pg. 830
PACIFIC COAST BUILDING PRODUCTS INC.; *U.S. Private*, pg. 830
R.B. PAMPLIN CORP.; *U.S. Private*, pg. 835
PHILADELPHIA RESERVE SUPPLY COMPANY; *U.S. Private*, pg. 861
PLYWOOD PLASTICS INC.; *U.S. Private*, pg. 873
PREMIER METAL PRODUCTS CO.; *U.S. Private*, pg. 881
PRUDENTIAL METAL SUPPLY CORP.; *U.S. Private*, pg. 893
PUGET SOUND ENERGY, INC.; *U.S. Public*, pg. 1342
RAYTECH CORPORATION; *U.S. Public*, pg. 1363
REDLAND, INC.—Redland PLC; *Int'l*, pg. 1091
REDLAND PLC; *Int'l*, pg. 1090
REDLAND STONE PRODUCTS CO.—Redland PLC; *Int'l*, pg. 1091
REEVES SOUTHEASTERN CORPORATION; *U.S. Private*, pg. 916
RIVER WOOD INTERNATIONAL CORP.—Johns Manville Corporation; *U.S. Public*, pg. 927
RIVER WOOD PRODUTOS FLORESTAIS LTDA.—Johns Manville Corporation; *U.S. Public*, pg. 927
ROCCO BUILDING SUPPLIES INC.—Rocco Inc.; *U.S. Private*, pg. 937
ROCCO INC.; *U.S. Private*, pg. 937
ROGERS GROUP INC.; *U.S. Private*, pg. 939
T.H. ROGERS LUMBER CO.; *U.S. Private*, pg. 940
ROOFING WHOLESALE CO., INC.; *U.S. Private*, pg. 943
SANFORD & HAWLEY, INC.; *U.S. Private*, pg. 965
SCANCEM INTERNATIONAL ANS—Scancem AB; *Int'l*, pg. 1201
SCHERER BROS. LUMBER COMPANY; *U.S. Private*, pg. 970
SCHULT HOMES CORPORATION—Schult Homes Corporation; *U.S. Public*, pg. 1442
SCHUTTE LUMBER COMPANY; *U.S. Private*, pg. 973

SHEFFIELD HARDWARE COMPANY—Distribution America; *U.S. Private*, pg. 335
KELLER SMITH SUPPLY, INC.; *U.S. Private*, pg. 1008
SOCIETE VERRIERE FRANCAISE (SVF)—Saint-Gobain; *Int'l*, pg. 1172
SOVEDYS—Saint-Gobain; *Int'l*, pg. 1172
SPACE MASTER INTERNATIONAL; *U.S. Private*, pg. 1019
SPECIALTY POLYMERS & CHEMICALS DIVISION—The B.F. Goodrich Company; *U.S. Public*, pg. 751
STANCOM HOME CENTER, INC.—Standard Commercial Corporation; *U.S. Public*, pg. 1502
STAR BUILDING SYSTEMS—Robertson-Ceco Corporation; *U.S. Public*, pg. 1394
STEEL SYSTEMS INC.—NCI Building Systems, Inc.; *U.S. Public*, pg. 1146
SUMITOMO CANADA LTD.—Sumitomo Corporation; *Int'l*, pg. 1312
SUNNILAND CORPORATION; *U.S. Private*, pg. 1053
TAPCO INTERNATIONAL CORPORATION; *U.S. Private*, pg. 1068
TECH-AEROFOAM PRODUCTS, INC.—Great American Industries, Inc.; *U.S. Private*, pg. 473
TILCON, INC.; *U.S. Private*, pg. 1086
TREMCO, INC.—RPM, Inc.; *U.S. Public*, pg. 1358
UAC INTERNATIONAL LTD.—Unilever Plc; *Int'l*, pg. 1434
UNION CRISTALERA—Saint-Gobain; *Int'l*, pg. 1176
UZES—La Meridionale des Bois et Materiaux; *Int'l*, pg. 784
VENDRES—La Meridionale des Bois et Materiaux; *Int'l*, pg. 784
WILLIAMS COMPANY OF ORLANDO, INC.; *U.S. Private*, pg. 1177

5043 — PHOTOGRAPHIC EQUIPMENT & SUPPLIES-WHOLESALE

AIC INTERNATIONAL, INC.; *U.S. Private*, pg. 6
A.M.P. TRANSPORTS—Lagardere Groupe; *Int'l*, pg. 795
AGFA COPAL INC.—Bayer AG; *Int'l*, pg. 173
AGFA-GEVAERT JAPAN, LTD.—Bayer AG; *Int'l*, pg. 174
AGFA-GEVAERT N.V.—Bayer AG; *Int'l*, pg. 174
ALLIED IMPEX CORP.—AIC International, Inc.; *U.S. Private*, *pg. 6*
ANSCO PHOTO-OPTICAL PRODUCTS CORP.—Haking Enterprises; *Int'l*, pg. 587
BAUSCH & LOMB INTERNATIONAL, INC.—Bausch & Lomb Incorporated; *U.S. Public*, pg. 195
BAUSCH & LOMB SVENSKA AB—Bausch & Lomb Incorporated; *U.S. Public*, pg. 195
BELL & HOWELL FRANCE S.A.—Bell & Howell Holdings; *U.S. Public*, pg. 201
BELL & HOWELL LTD.—Bell & Howell Holdings; *U.S. Public*, pg. 201
BENNETT BROTHERS, INC.; *U.S. Private*, pg. 133
BENNETT BROTHERS, INC.—Bennett Brothers, Inc.; *U.S. Private*, pg. 133
BLUMBERG COMMUNICATIONS INC.—Caribiner International, Inc.; *U.S. Public*, pg. 305
CM GRAPHICS—PrimeSource Corporation; *U.S. Public*, pg. 1329
CANON U.S.A., INC.—Canon Inc.; *Int'l*, pg. 262
CANTEL INDUSTRIES, INC.; *U.S. Public*, pg. 301
CARSEN GROUP INC.—Cantel Industries, Inc.; *U.S. Public*, *pg. 301*
CHILTEM GROUP SAM—Alpha Omikron Limited; *Int'l*, pg. 65
CONCORD CAMERA CORPORATION; *U.S. Public*, pg. 429
COSMICAR LENS DIV.—Asahi Optical Co., Ltd.; *Int'l*, pg. 85
DNP DENMARK A/S—Dai Nippon Printing Co., Ltd.; *Int'l*, pg. 363
DEAN'S PHOTO SERVICE; *U.S. Private*, pg. 319
DIXIE TYPE & SUPPLY CO., INC.—PrimeSource Corporation; *U.S. Public*, pg. 1329
FOTO INTERAMERICANA DE VENEZUELA S.A.—Eastman Kodak Company; *U.S. Public*, pg. 552
FUJI FILM ESPANA, S.A.—Fuji Photo Film Co., Ltd.; *Int'l*, pg. 524
FUJI GRAPHIC ARTS DIV.—Fuji Photo Film Co., Ltd.; *Int'l*, pg. 524
FUJI HUNT PHOTOGRAPHIC CHEMICALS, INC.—Fuji Photo Film Co., Ltd.; *Int'l*, pg. 524
FUJI INDUSTRIAL PHOTO PRODUCTS DIV.—Fuji Photo Film Co., Ltd.; *Int'l*, pg. 524
FUJI MEDICAL SYSTEMS USA, INC.—Fuji Photo Film Co., Ltd.; *Int'l*, pg. 524
FUJI MICROGRAPHICS DIV.—Fuji Photo Film Co., Ltd.; *Int'l*, pg. 524
FUJI PHOTO FILM B.V.—Fuji Photo Film Co., Ltd.; *Int'l*, pg. 524
FUJI PHOTO FILM CANADA, INC.—Fuji Photo Film Co., Ltd.; *Int'l*, pg. 524
FUJI PHOTO FILM CO., LTD.; *Int'l*, pg. 523
FUJI PHOTO FILM CO., LTD., BEIJING REPRESENTATIVE OFFICE—Fuji Photo Film Co., Ltd.; *Int'l*, pg. 524
FUJI PHOTO FILM CO., LTD., HONG KONG OFFICE—Fuji Photo Film Co., Ltd.; *Int'l*, pg. 525
FUJI PHOTO FILM CO., LTD., SEOUL OFFICE—Fuji Photo Film Co., Ltd.; *Int'l*, pg. 525
FUJI PHOTO FILM CO., LTD., SYDNEY OFFICE—Fuji Photo Film Co., Ltd.; *Int'l*, pg. 525
FUJI PHOTO FILM CO., LTD., TAIPEI OFFICE—Fuji Photo Film Co., Ltd.; *Int'l*, pg. 525
FUJI PHOTO FILM DO BRASIL LTDA.—Fuji Photo Film Co., Ltd.; *Int'l*, pg. 524
FUJI PHOTO FILM (EUROPE) GMBH—Fuji Photo Film Co., Ltd.; *Int'l*, pg. 524
FUJI PHOTO FILM HAWAII, INC.—Fuji Photo Film Co., Ltd.; *Int'l*, pg. 524
FUJI PHOTO FILM (MALAYSIA) SDN. BHD.—Fuji Photo Film Co., Ltd.; *Int'l*, pg. 524
FUJI PHOTO FILM (SINGAPORE) PTE. LTD.—Fuji Photo Film Co., Ltd.; *Int'l*, pg. 524
FUJI PHOTO FILM (THAILAND) LTD.—Fuji Photo Film Co., Ltd.; *Int'l*, pg. 525
FUJI PHOTO FILM (U.K.), LTD.—Fuji Photo Film Co., Ltd.; *Int'l*, pg. 524
FUJI PHOTO FILM U.S.A., INC.—Fuji Photo Film Co., Ltd.; *Int'l*, pg. 524
FUJI PHOTOGRAPHIC PRODUCTS DIV.—Fuji Photo Film Co., Ltd.; *Int'l*, pg. 524
GESTETNER HOLDINGS PLC—Ricoh Company, Ltd.; *Int'l*, pg. 1114
GRAPHIC ARTS SUPPLY DIVISION—Bell Industries, Inc.; *U.S. Public*, pg. 205
GRAPHLINE INC.; *U.S. Private*, pg. 471
HAGEMEYER N.V.—First Pacific Company Limited; *Int'l*, pg. 487
HANIMEX (FRANCE) S.A.—Ricoh Company, Ltd.; *Int'l*, pg. 1115
HANIMEX (NZ) LIMITED—Ricoh Company, Ltd.; *Int'l*, pg. 1116
HANIMEX VIVITAR (H.K.) LTD.—Plaza Create; *Int'l*, pg. 1061
HANIMEX VIVITAR JAPAN K.K.—Plaza Create; *Int'l*, pg. 1061
HARVEY HARRIS & CO. LTD.—Dolland & Aitchison Ltd.; *Int'l*, pg. 414
HASSELBLAD BELGIUM S.A. NV—Victor Hasselblad AB; *Int'l*, pg. 1468
HASSELBLAD FRANCE S.A.—Victor Hasselblad AB; *Int'l*, pg. 1468
HASSELBLAD (UK) LTD.—Victor Hasselblad AB; *Int'l*, pg. 1468
HASSELBLAD USA, INC.—Victor Hasselblad AB; *Int'l*, pg. 1468
HASSELBLAD VERTRIEBSGESELLSCHAFT M.B.H—Victor Hasselblad AB; *Int'l*, pg. 1468
INTERNATIONAL DIV., AM INTERNATIONAL—Multigraphics Inc.; *U.S. Public*, pg. 1141
INTERSTATE PHOTO SUPPLY CORP.—AIC International, Inc.; *U.S. Private*, pg. 6
JETCOM—PrimeSource Corporation; *U.S. Public*, pg. 1329
KODAK AG—Eastman Kodak Company; *U.S. Public*, pg. 552
KODAK ARGENTINA S.A.I.C.—Eastman Kodak Company; *U.S. Public*, pg. 552
KODAK (AUSTRALASIA) PTY. LTD.—Eastman Kodak Company; *U.S. Public*, pg. 552
KODAK BRASILEIRA C.I.L.—Eastman Kodak Company; *U.S. Public*, pg. 552
KODAK CANADA INC.—Eastman Kodak Company; *U.S. Public*, pg. 553
KODAK HALIFAX—Eastman Kodak Company; *U.S. Public*, pg. 553
KODAK KOREA LTD.—Eastman Kodak Company; *U.S. Public*, pg. 555
KODAK MEXICANA SA DE C.V.—Eastman Kodak Company; *U.S. Public*, pg. 554
KODAK NORGE A/S—Eastman Kodak Company; *U.S. Public*, pg. 554
KODAK OY—Eastman Kodak Company; *U.S. Public*, pg. 554
KODAK PATHE S.A.—Eastman Kodak Company; *U.S. Public*, pg. 554
KODAK S.A.—Eastman Kodak Company; *U.S. Public*, pg. 554
N.V. KODAK S.A.—Eastman Kodak Company; *U.S. Public*, pg. 554
KODAK (SINGAPORE) PTE. LIMITED—Eastman Kodak Company; *U.S. Public*, pg. 554
KODAK S.P.A.—Eastman Kodak Company; *U.S. Public*, pg. 554
KODAK (THAILAND) LTD.—Eastman Kodak Company; *U.S. Public*, pg. 555
KYOCERA INTERNATIONAL, INC.—Kyocera Corporation; *Int'l*, pg. 775
LOGETRONICS CORPORATION—AFP Imaging Corporation; *U.S. Public*, pg. 6
LONDON LITHO ALUMINUM CO., INC.; *U.S. Private*, pg. 673
LUCHT, INC.—Northwestern Public Service; *U.S. Public*, pg. 1201
THE MARBLE COMPANY—Blevins Inc.; *U.S. Private*, pg. 149
MATTHEWS STUDIO EQUIPMENT; *U.S. Public*, pg. 1060
MCBRIDE AND ASSOCIATES, INC.; *U.S. Private*, pg. 719
MOMENTUM—PrimeSource Corporation; *U.S. Public*, pg. 1329
NELSON PHOTO SUPPLIES; *U.S. Private*, pg. 791
NIKON INC.—Nikon Corporation; *Int'l*, pg. 931
NIPPON POLAROID K.K.—Polaroid Corporation; *U.S. Public*, pg. 1314
OAC INC.—Nissho Iwai Corporation; *Int'l*, pg. 947
OCE HOLDING USA—Oce-van der Grinten N.V.; *Int'l*, pg. 994
ONONDAGA LITHO SUPPLY CO., INC.—PrimeSource Corporation; *U.S. Public*, pg. 1329
PENTAX CANADA INC.—Asahi Optical Co., Ltd.; *Int'l*, pg. 85
PENTAX CANADA-VANCOUVER—Asahi Optical Co., Ltd.; *Int'l*, pg. 85
PENTAX TECHNOLOGIES CORP.—Asahi Optical Co., Ltd.; *Int'l*, pg. 85
PENTAX U.K. LTD.—Asahi Optical Co., Ltd.; *Int'l*, pg. 85
PHILLIPS & JACOBS/NORTH—PrimeSource Corporation; *U.S. Public*, pg. 1329
PHILLIPS & JACOBS/SOUTH—PrimeSource Corporation; *U.S. Public*, pg. 1329
PLAZA CREATE; *Int'l*, pg. 1060
POLAROID AB—Polaroid Corporation; *U.S. Public*, pg. 1314
POLAROID AG—Polaroid Corporation; *U.S. Public*, pg. 1314
POLAROID A.S.—Polaroid Corporation; *U.S. Public*, pg. 1314
POLAROID CARIBBEAN CORP.—Polaroid Corporation; *U.S. Public*, pg. 1313
PRIME SYSTEMS GROUP—PrimeSource Corporation; *U.S. Public*, pg. 1329
PRIMESOURCE CORPORATION; *U.S. Public*, pg. 1329
RICOH DEUTSCHLAND GMBH—Ricoh Company, Ltd.; *Int'l*, pg. 1116
RICOH ESPANA, S.A.—Ricoh Company, Ltd.; *Int'l*, pg. 1116
RICOH EUROPE B.V.—Ricoh Company, Ltd.; *Int'l*, pg. 1116
RICOH FRANCE S.A.—Ricoh Company, Ltd.; *Int'l*, pg. 1116
RICOH ITALIA S.P.A.—Ricoh Company, Ltd.; *Int'l*, pg. 1116
RICOH UK LTD.—Ricoh Company, Ltd.; *Int'l*, pg. 1116
SAARBACH—Lagardere Groupe; *Int'l*, pg. 796
SOLIGAR GMBH—AIC International, Inc.; *U.S. Private*, pg. 6
SOLIGOR U.S.A., INC.—AIC International, Inc.; *U.S. Private*, *pg. 6*
SON CINE OPTIQUE PHOTO S.A.—Olympus Optical Co., Ltd.; *Int'l*, pg. 1005
STRAND LIGHTING INC.—The Rank Group PLC; *Int'l*, pg. 1087
TK GRAY—PrimeSource Corporation; *U.S. Public*, pg. 1329
VICTOR HASSELBLAD AB; *Int'l*, pg. 1468
VIVITAR CANADA LIMITED—Ricoh Company, Ltd.; *Int'l*, pg. 1116
VIVITAR CORPORATION—Plaza Create; *Int'l*, pg. 1060
VIVITAR (EUROPE) LTD. HANIMEX-VIVITAR—Plaza Create; *Int'l*, pg. 1061
WILLOUGHBY'S; *U.S. Private*, pg. 1180
YASHICA HANDELSGESELLSCHAFT MBH—Kyocera Corporation; *Int'l*, pg. 776
YASHICA, INC.—Kyocera Corporation; *Int'l*, pg. 776
YOUNG-PHILLIPS SALES CO.; *U.S. Private*, pg. 1201

5044 — OFFICE EQUIPMENT-WHOLESALE

AMI GROUP, INC.; *U.S. Private*, pg. 7
ACCO-REXEL GROUP SERVICES PLC—Fortune Brands, Inc.; *U.S. Public*, pg. 674
APPLE COMPUTER INTERNATIONAL LTD.—Apple Computer, Inc.; *U.S. Public*, pg. 121
APPLE COMPUTER PTY. LTD.—Apple Computer, Inc.; *U.S. Public*, pg. 121
APPLE COMPUTER (SALES) LTD.—Apple Computer, Inc.; *U.S. Public*, pg. 121
ARROW/SCHWEBER ELECTRONICS—Arrow Electronics, Inc.; *U.S. Public*, pg. 133
BALTIMORE STATIONERY CO./TOTAL OFFICE; *U.S. Private*, pg. 113
BASEL TRADING COMPANY LTD.; *Int'l*, pg. 169
BAT OFFICE PRODUCTS—U.S. Office Products Company; *U.S. Public*, pg. 1686
BLIKMAN & SARTORIUS B.V.—Internatio-Muller N.V.; *Int'l*, pg. 682
CXR SA—Microtel International Inc.; *U.S. Public*, pg. 1108
CANON CANADA INC.—Canon Inc.; *Int'l*, pg. 262
CANON EUROPA N.V.—Canon Inc.; *Int'l*, pg. 262
CANON U.S.A., INC.—Canon Inc.; *Int'l*, pg. 262
CANON VIRGINIA, INC.—Canon Inc.; *Int'l*, pg. 261
CASIO, INC.—Casio Computer Co., Ltd.; *Int'l*, pg. 274
CHESHIRE—The General Electric Company, p.l.c.; *Int'l*, pg. 545
CHILTEM GROUP SAM—Alpha Omikron Limited; *Int'l*, pg. 65
COMDISCO CONTINUITY SERVICES—Comdisco, Inc.; *U.S. Public*, pg. 408
DACOR UK LIMITED—Fortune Brands, Inc.; *U.S. Public*, pg. 674
DANKA BUSINESS SYSTEMS—Danka Business Systems PLC; *Int'l*, pg. 379
DATAPOINT-DISC, INC.—Datapoint Corporation; *Int'l*, pg. 384
DATAPOINT S.A.—Datapoint Corporation; *Int'l*, pg. 384
DATAPOINT (SCHWEIZ) AG—Datapoint Corporation; *Int'l*, pg. 384
DATAPOINT (U.K.) LTD.—Datapoint Corporation; *Int'l*, pg. 384
DATAPRODUCTS GMBH—Hitachi Koki Co., Ltd.; *Int'l*, pg. 621
DATAPRODUCTS HANDELSGESELLSCHAFT M.B.H.—Hitachi Koki Co., Ltd.; *Int'l*, pg. 621
DATAPRODUCTS LTD.—Hitachi Koki Co., Ltd.; *Int'l*, pg. 621
A.B. DICK COMPANY OF CANADA, LTD.—NESCO, Inc.; *U.S. Private*, pg. 791
A.B. DICK HOLLAND B.V.—NESCO, Inc.; *U.S. Private*, pg. 791
A.B. DICK S.A.—NESCO, Inc.; *U.S. Private*, pg. 791
FAG INFORMATION SERVICES INC.—FAG Group; *Int'l*, pg. 469
FARMER BROTHERS COMPANY; *U.S. Public*, pg. 613
FIRST IMAGE MANAGEMENT CO.—First Data Corporation; *U.S. Public*, pg. 631
FORE LINE SECURITY—Reeves Southeastern Corporation; *U.S. Private*, pg. 917
FREIGHTLINER ENTERPRISE CORP.—Daimler-Benz Aktiengesellschaft; *Int'l*, pg. 368
FUNDING SERVICES INC.—Danka Business Systems PLC; *Int'l*, pg. 379
GBC/VELOBLIND—General Binding Corporation; *U.S. Public*, pg. 707
GDC FEDERAL SYSTEMS, INC.—General Datacomm Industries, Inc.; *U.S. Public*, pg. 708
GENERAL OFFICE ENVIRONMENTS INC.; *U.S. Private*, pg. 445
GESTETNER AB—Ricoh Company, Ltd.; *Int'l*, pg. 1115
GESTETNER A/S—Ricoh Company, Ltd.; *Int'l*, pg. 1115
GESTETNER AUSTRALASIA LIMITED—Ricoh Company, Ltd.; *Int'l*, pg. 1115
GESTETNER BANGLADESH LTD.—Ricoh Company, Ltd.; *Int'l*, pg. 1115
GESTETNER CHILE S.A.—Ricoh Company, Ltd.; *Int'l*, pg. 1115

GESTETNER CORPORATION—Ricoh Company, Ltd.; *Int'l*, pg. 1115
GESTETNER DO BRASIL, S.A. SISTEMAS REPROGRAPHICOS—Ricoh Company, Ltd.; *Int'l*, pg. 1115
GESTETNER HOLDINGS PLC—Ricoh Company, Ltd.; *Int'l*, pg. 1114
GESTETNER (ISRAEL) LIMITED—Ricoh Company, Ltd.; *Int'l*, pg. 1115
GESTETNER ITALIA SPA—Ricoh Company, Ltd.; *Int'l*, pg. 1115
GESTETNER LIMITED—Ricoh Company, Ltd.; *Int'l*, pg. 1115
GESTETNER MALAYSIA SDN BHD—Ricoh Company, Ltd.; *Int'l*, pg. 1115
GESTETNER OFFICE SYSTEMS NEW ZEALAND LIMITED—Ricoh Company, Ltd.; *Int'l*, pg. 1115
GESTETNER (PRIVATE) LIMITED—Ricoh Company, Ltd.; *Int'l*, pg. 1115
GESTETNER REGIONAL SERVICES INC. (USA)—Ricoh Company, Ltd.; *Int'l*, pg. 1115
GESTETNER S.A.—Ricoh Company, Ltd.; *Int'l*, pg. 1115
GESTETNER SECURITIES B.V.—Ricoh Company, Ltd.; *Int'l*, pg. 1115
GRIFFIN TECHNOLOGY INCORPORATED—Diebold, Incorporated; *U.S. Public*, pg. 506
HARRIS ITALIANA, INC.—Harris Corporation; *U.S. Public*, pg. 791
HARRIS SARL-SCIENTIFIC CALCULATIONS—Harris Corporation; *U.S. Public*, pg. 791
IBM ITALIA-DISTRIBUZIONE PRODOTTI S.R.L—International Business Machines Corporation; *U.S. Public*, pg. 897
IR INTERNATIONAL HOLDINGS, INC.—International Rectifier Corporation; *U.S. Public*, pg. 907
IKON OFFICE SOLUTIONS—Ikon Office Solutions, Inc.; *U.S. Public*, pg. 864
IKON OFFICE SOLUTIONS, INC.; *U.S. Public*, pg. 862
IKON OFFICE SYSTEMS—Ikon Office Solutions, Inc.; *U.S. Public*, pg. 864
INFINCOM—Ikon Office Solutions, Inc.; *U.S. Public*, pg. 864
INTERNATIONAL DIV., AM INTERNATIONAL—Multigraphics Inc.; *U.S. Public*, pg. 1141
INTERNATIONAL RECTIFIER FAR EAST COMPANY, LTD.—International Rectifier Corporation; *U.S. Public*, pg. 907
INTERNATIONAL RECTIFIER GMBH—International Rectifier Corporation; *U.S. Public*, pg. 907
INVINCIBLE OFFICE FURNITURE; *U.S. Private*, pg. 575
ITOCHU CORPORATION; *Int'l*, pg. 694
JS TELECOMMUNICATIONS S.A.—Jeumont-Schneider Trenformeteurs; *Int'l*, pg. 706
JOHN MENZIES PLC; *Int'l*, pg. 707
JOHN MENZIES (UK) LIMITED—John Menzies plc; *Int'l*, pg. 707
KODAK PATHE S.A.—Eastman Kodak Company; *U.S. Public*, pg. 554
KONICA ATHENS OFFICE—Konica Corporation; *Int'l*, pg. 749
KONICA BEIJING OFFICE—Konica Corporation; *Int'l*, pg. 749
KONICA BUREAUTIQUE S.A.—Konica Corporation; *Int'l*, pg. 749
KONICA BUSINESS MACHINES BELGIUM S.A./N.V—Konica Corporation; *Int'l*, pg. 749
KONICA BUSINESS MACHINES CANADA, LTD.—Konica Corporation; *Int'l*, pg. 749
KONICA BUSINESS MACHINES DEUTSCHLAND GMBH—Konica Corporation; *Int'l*, pg. 749
KONICA BUSINESS MACHINES (UK) LTD.—Konica Corporation; *Int'l*, pg. 749
KONICA (THAILAND) CO., LTD.—Konica Corporation; *Int'l*, pg. 749
LANCE INTERNATIONAL S.A.—Ricoh Company, Ltd.; *Int'l*, pg. 1116
LANIER WORLDWIDE, INC.-EUROPEAN DIVISION—Harris Corporation; *U.S. Public*, pg. 791
LINOTYPE-HELL COMPANY—Heidelberger Druckmaschinen A.G.; *Int'l*, pg. 604
MCS BUSINESS SOLUTIONS, INC.—Canon Inc.; *Int'l*, pg. 262
MARKETING AND CUSTOMER OPERATIONS—Xerox Corporation; *U.S. Public*, pg. 1784
MATSUSHITA ELECTRIC CORPORATION OF AMERICA—Matsushita Electric Industrial Co., Ltd.; *Int'l*, pg. 847
MCRAE GRAPHICS, INC.—McRae Industries, Inc.; *U.S. Public*, pg. 1074
MCRAE INDUSTRIES, INC.; *U.S. Public*, pg. 1073
MEMOREX TELEX (U.K.) LTD.—Memorex Telex N.V.; *Int'l*, pg. 858
A. MESSERLI AG—Oce-van der Grinten N.V.; *Int'l*, pg. 995
MICROAGE ENTERPRISES, INC.—MicroAge, Inc.; *U.S. Public*, pg. 1104
MICROAGE, INC.; *U.S. Public*, pg. 1104
MICROAGE INTERNATIONAL INC.—MicroAge, Inc.; *U.S. Public*, pg. 1104
MICROAGE SOLUTIONS, INC. (MAS)—MicroAge, Inc.; *U.S. Public*, pg. 1105
MICROSOURCE CORP.—MicroAge, Inc.; *U.S. Public*, pg. 1105
MIKUNI CORPORATION; *Int'l*, pg. 867
MIKUNI SHOKO CORP.—Mikuni Corporation; *Int'l*, pg. 867
MINNESOTA (3M) DE PORTUGAL, LDA.—3M; *U.S. Public*, pg. 1606
MITSUBISHI CORPORATION; *Int'l*, pg. 871
MITSUBISHI ELECTRIC AMERICA, INC.—Mitsubishi Electric Corporation; *Int'l*, pg. 872
MITSUBISHI ELECTRIC (UK) LTD.—Mitsubishi Electric Corporation; *Int'l*, pg. 873
MITSUBISHI ELECTRONICS AMERICA—Mitsubishi Electric Corporation; *Int'l*, pg. 872
NRG BELGIUM S.A.—Ricoh Company, Ltd.; *Int'l*, pg. 1116
NRG BENELUX B.V.—Ricoh Company, Ltd.; *Int'l*, pg. 1116
NRG COMUNICACIONES S.A.—Ricoh Company, Ltd.; *Int'l*, pg. 1116
NRG FRANCE S.A.—Ricoh Company, Ltd.; *Int'l*, pg. 1116
NRG GROUP LIMITED—Ricoh Company, Ltd.; *Int'l*, pg. 1114
NRG INTERNATIONAL LTD. (BERMUDA)—Ricoh Company, Ltd.; *Int'l*, pg. 1116
NRG ITALIA S.P.A.—Ricoh Company, Ltd.; *Int'l*, pg. 1116
NRG MEXICO S.A. DE C.V.—Ricoh Company, Ltd.; *Int'l*, pg. 1116
NRG OFFICE SYSTEMS GMBH—Ricoh Company, Ltd.; *Int'l*, pg. 1116
NEWBOLD CORPORATION; *U.S. Private*, pg. 796
NIPPON UNIVAC KAISHA, LTD.—Mitsui & Co., Ltd.; *Int'l*, pg. 879
NISSHO ELECTRONICS CORP.—Nissho Iwai Corporation; *Int'l*, pg. 946
NORTH SAFETY PRODUCTS SIEBE NORTH CANADA LTD.—Siebe plc; *Int'l*, pg. 1243
OCE-ASIA LTD.—Oce-van der Grinten N.V.; *Int'l*, pg. 994
OCE-BELGIUM N.V./S.A.—Oce-van der Grinten N.V.; *Int'l*, pg. 994
OCE-DANMARK AS—Oce-van der Grinten N.V.; *Int'l*, pg. 994
OCE-DEUTSCHLAND GMBH—Oce-van der Grinten N.V.; *Int'l*, pg. 994
OCE-ESPANA S.A.—Oce-van der Grinten N.V.; *Int'l*, pg. 994
OCE HOLDING USA—Oce-van der Grinten N.V.; *Int'l*, pg. 994
OCE-NORGE A/S—Oce-van der Grinten N.V.; *Int'l*, pg. 994
OCE OSTERREICH GES.M.B.H.—Oce-van der Grinten N.V.; *Int'l*, pg. 995
OCE USA, INC.—Oce-van der Grinten N.V.; *Int'l*, pg. 994
OFFICE AUTOMATION CORP.—Jeumont-Schneider Trenformeteurs; *Int'l*, pg. 706
OFFICE CONNECTION, INC.—U.S. Office Products Company; *U.S. Public*, pg. 1687
OMNI BUSINESS SYSTEMS, INC.—Ikon Office Solutions, Inc.; *U.S. Public*, pg. 864
OMRON BUSINESS SYSTEMS SINGAPORE PRIVATE LIMITED—Omron Corporation; *Int'l*, pg. 1005
PANASONIC BROADCAST SYSTEMS CO.—Matsushita Electric Industrial Co., Ltd.; *Int'l*, pg. 847
PHILIPS SPEECH PROCESSING—Philips Electronics N.V.; *Int'l*, pg. 1055
PITNEY BOWES INC.; *U.S. Public*, pg. 1303
RANK XEROX AG—Xerox Corporation; *U.S. Public*, pg. 1785
REX-ROTARY UK LIMITED—Ricoh Company, Ltd.; *Int'l*, pg. 1114
RICOH DEUTSCHLAND GMBH—Ricoh Company, Ltd.; *Int'l*, pg. 1116
RICOH ESPANA, S.A.—Ricoh Company, Ltd.; *Int'l*, pg. 1116
RICOH EUROPE B.V.—Ricoh Company, Ltd.; *Int'l*, pg. 1116
RICOH FRANCE S.A.—Ricoh Company, Ltd.; *Int'l*, pg. 1116
RICOH ITALIA S.P.A.—Ricoh Company, Ltd.; *Int'l*, pg. 1116
RICOH UK LTD.—Ricoh Company, Ltd.; *Int'l*, pg. 1116
SNC GEC COMPOSANTS ET CIE—The General Electric Company, p.l.c.; *Int'l*, pg. 546
SAGEM CORPORATION—Societe d'Applications Generales d'Electricite et de Mechanique; *Int'l*, pg. 1273
SANYO OFFICE AUTOMATION—Sanyo Electric Co., Ltd.; *Int'l*, pg. 1191
SAVIN CANADA INC.—Ricoh Company, Ltd.; *Int'l*, pg. 1116
SAVIN CORPORATION—Ricoh Company, Ltd.; *Int'l*, pg. 1114
SHARP ELECTRONICA ESPANA S.A. (BARCELONA)—Sharp Corporation; *Int'l*, pg. 1229
SHARP ELECTRONICS CORPORATION—Sharp Corporation; *Int'l*, pg. 1228
SHARP ELECTRONICS (EUROPE)—Sharp Corporation; *Int'l*, pg. 1230
SHARP ELECTRONICS (U.K.)—Sharp Corporation; *Int'l*, pg. 1230
SHARP INTERNATIONAL FINANCE (U.K.) PLC.—Sharp Corporation; *Int'l*, pg. 1230
SHARP LABORATORIES OF EUROPE, LTD.—Sharp Corporation; *Int'l*, pg. 1230
SHARP MANUFACTURING COMPANY OF U.K.—Sharp Corporation; *Int'l*, pg. 1230
SHARP PRECISION MANUFACTURING (U.K.) LTD.—Sharp Corporation; *Int'l*, pg. 1230
SIEMENS NIXDORF INFORMATION SYSTEMS INC.—Siemens AG; *Int'l*, pg. 1245
STORAGE TECHNOLOGY-PUERTO RICO—Storage Technology Corporation; *U.S. Public*, pg. 1523
TAB SALES CORP. (INTERNATIONAL)—Tab Products Co.; *U.S. Public*, pg. 1559
TEXAS COPY SYSTEMS, INC.—Ikon Office Solutions, Inc.; *U.S. Public*, pg. 864
TEXAS INSTRUMENTS (SWITZERLAND) AG—Texas Instruments Incorporated; *U.S. Public*, pg. 1586
3M A/S—3M; *U.S. Public*, pg. 1606
3M CANADA INC.—3M; *U.S. Public*, pg. 1606
TOSHIBA INFORMATION EQUIPMENT CO., LTD.—Toshiba Corporation; *Int'l*, pg. 1404
TOTTORI SANYO ELECTRIC CO., LTD.—Sanyo Electric Co., Ltd.; *Int'l*, pg. 1191
TWINLOCK (IRELAND) EXPORT LIMITED—Fortune Brands, Inc.; *U.S. Public*, pg. 675
UNISYS BELGIUM—Unisys Corporation; *U.S. Public*, pg. 1672
U.S. OFFICE PRODUCTS COMPANY; *U.S. Public*, pg. 1686
VENDO GMBH—Sanden Corporation; *Int'l*, pg. 1184
VENDO IBERIA, S.A.—Sanden Corporation; *Int'l*, pg. 1184
VENDO (ITALY) S.P.A.—Sanden Corporation; *Int'l*, pg. 1184
WESTERN DIGITAL HONG KONG LTD.—Western Digital Corporation; *U.S. Public*, pg. 1758
XEROX ARGENTINA I.C.S.A.—Xerox Corporation; *U.S. Public*, pg. 1785
XEROX BUSINESS SERVICES—Xerox Corporation; *U.S. Public*, pg. 1784
XEROX CANADA LTD.—Xerox Corporation; *U.S. Public*, pg. 1785
XEROX CORPORATION; *U.S. Public*, pg. 1783
XEROX DE CHILE S.A.—Xerox Corporation; *U.S. Public*, pg. 1785
XEROX SPECIAL MARKETS GROUP—Xerox Corporation; *U.S. Public*, pg. 1785
XEROX TECHNIGRAPHIC PRODUCTS DIVISION—Xerox Corporation; *U.S. Public*, pg. 1784
XEROX U.S. MARKETING GROUP—Xerox Corporation; *U.S. Public*, pg. 1784
YOUNG-PHILLIPS SALES CO.; *U.S. Private*, pg. 1201

5045 — COMPUTERS & COMPUTER PERIPHERAL EQUIPMENT & SOFTWARE-WHOLESALE

ALR INTERNATIONAL (PTE.) LTD.—Gateway 2000; *U.S. Public*, pg. 704
AMD FAR EAST, LTD.—Advanced Micro Devices, Inc.; *U.S. Public*, pg. 21
AMD GMBH—Advanced Micro Devices, Inc.; *U.S. Public*, pg. 21
AMD INTL. LTD.—Advanced Micro Devices, Inc.; *U.S. Public*, pg. 21
AST ASIA—Samsung Group; *Int'l*, pg. 1182
AST EUROPE LIMITED—Samsung Group; *Int'l*, pg. 1182
AST MIDDLE EAST LIMITED—Samsung Group; *Int'l*, pg. 1182
AST RESEARCH, INC.—Samsung Group; *Int'l*, pg. 1181
AST RESEARCH, INC.—Samsung Group; *Int'l*, pg. 1182
AST RESEARCH, INC.—Samsung Group; *Int'l*, pg. 1182
AST RESEARCH ITALIA S.R.L.—Samsung Group; *Int'l*, pg. 1182
AST RESEARCH SWITZERLAND S.A.—Samsung Group; *Int'l*, pg. 1182
AST SPAIN—Samsung Group; *Int'l*, pg. 1183
AST SWEDEN, AB—Samsung Group; *Int'l*, pg. 1183
AST TAIWAN LIMITED—Samsung Group; *Int'l*, pg. 1183
ACACIA TECHNOLOGIES—Computer Associates International, Inc.; *U.S. Public*, pg. 420
ACACIA TECHNOLOGIES ASIA—Computer Associates International, Inc.; *U.S. Public*, pg. 420
ACACIA TECHNOLOGIES AUSTRALIA/NEW ZEALAND—Computer Associates International, Inc.; *U.S. Public*, pg. 420
ACACIA TECHNOLOGIES UK/EUROPE—Computer Associates International, Inc.; *U.S. Public*, pg. 420
ACCLAIM ENTERTAINMENT GMBH—Acclaim Entertainment, Inc.; *U.S. Public*, pg. 15
ACCLAIM JAPAN, LTD.—Acclaim Entertainment, Inc.; *U.S. Public*, pg. 15
ACCPAC INTERNATIONAL—Computer Associates International, Inc.; *U.S. Public*, pg. 420
ACER AMERICA CORPORATION—Acer Incorporated; *Int'l*, pg. 22
ADOBE SYSTEMS CO. LIMITED—Adobe Systems Incorporated; *U.S. Public*, pg. 20
ADOBE SYSTEMS FRANCE—Adobe Systems Incorporated; *U.S. Public*, pg. 20
ADOBE SYSTEMS GMBH—Adobe Systems Incorporated; *U.S. Public*, pg. 20
ADOBE SYSTEMS LIMITED—Adobe Systems Incorporated; *U.S. Public*, pg. 20
ADOBE SYSTEMS NORDIC PB—Adobe Systems Incorporated; *U.S. Public*, pg. 20
ADOBE SYSTEMS UK LIMITED—Adobe Systems Incorporated; *U.S. Public*, pg. 20
ADVANCED LOGIC RESEARCH (DEUTSCHLAND) GMBH—Gateway 2000; *U.S. Public*, pg. 704
ADVANCED LOGIC RESEARCH, INC. (U.K.) LIMITED—Gateway 2000; *U.S. Public*, pg. 704
ADVANCED MICRO COMPUTERS EXPORT CORPORATION, INC.—Advanced Micro Devices, Inc.; *U.S. Public*, pg. 21
ADVANCED MICRO DEVICES AB—Advanced Micro Devices, Inc.; *U.S. Public*, pg. 21
ADVANCED MICRO DEVICES EXPORT CORPORATION—Advanced Micro Devices, Inc.; *U.S. Public*, pg. 21
ADVANCED MICRO DEVICES GMBH—Advanced Micro Devices, Inc.; *U.S. Public*, pg. 21
ADVANCED MICRO DEVICES, KK—Advanced Micro Devices, Inc.; *U.S. Public*, pg. 21
ADVANCED MICRO DEVICES (OVERSEAS CORP.)—Advanced Micro Devices, Inc.; *U.S. Public*, pg. 21
ADVANCED MICRO DEVICES OVERSEAS CORPORATION—Advanced Micro Devices, Inc.; *U.S. Public*, pg. 21
ADVANCED MICRO DEVICES, S.A.—Advanced Micro Devices, Inc.; *U.S. Public*, pg. 21
ADVANCED MICRO DEVICES S.P.A.—Advanced Micro Devices, Inc.; *U.S. Public*, pg. 21
ADVANCED MICRO DEVICES, (UK), LTD.—Advanced Micro Devices, Inc.; *U.S. Public*, pg. 21
ALIAS WAVEFRONT—Silicon Graphics, Inc.; *U.S. Public*, pg. 1474
ALLISON-ERWIN CO. INC.; *U.S. Private*, pg. 41
AMATI COMMUNICATIONS CORP.—Texas Instruments Incorporated; *U.S. Public*, pg. 1585
AMBASSADOR OFFICE EQUIPMENT, INC.—Canon Inc.; *Int'l*, pg. 262
AMDAHL CORPORATION—Fujitsu Limited; *Int'l*, pg. 527
ANACOMP, LTD.—Anacomp, Inc.; *U.S. Public*, pg. 107
ANACOMP MAGNETICS, INC.—Anacomp, Inc.; *U.S. Public*, pg. 107
ANACOMP S.A. (FRANCE)—Anacomp, Inc.; *U.S. Public*, pg. 107
ANALOG DEVICES AB—Analog Devices, Inc.; *U.S. Public*, pg. 108
ANALOG DEVICES INTERNATIONAL INC.—Analog Devices, Inc.; *U.S. Public*, pg. 108

ANALOG DEVICES LTD.—Analog Devices, Inc.; *U.S. Public*, pg. 108
ANALOG DEVICES LTD. - EASTERN SALES OFFICE—Analog Devices, Inc.; *U.S. Public*, pg. 108
ANALOG DEVICES SA—Analog Devices, Inc.; *U.S. Public*, pg. 108
ANALOG DEVICES SRL—Analog Devices, Inc.; *U.S. Public*, pg. 108
ANALOGIC LTD.—Analogic Corporation; *U.S. Public*, pg. 109
ANRITSU ELECTRONICA S.A.—Anritsu Corporation; *Int'l*, pg. 77
ANRITSU ELEKTRONIK GMBH—Anritsu Corporation; *Int'l*, pg. 77
ANRITSU EUROPE LTD.—Anritsu Corporation; *Int'l*, pg. 77
ANRITSU WILTRON—Anritsu Corporation; *Int'l*, pg. 77
APERTUS TECHNOLOGIES INCORPORATED; *U.S. Public*, pg. 119
ARROW COMMERCIAL SYSTEMS DIV.—Arrow Electronics, Inc.; *U.S. Public*, pg. 133
ARROW COMMERCIAL SYSTEMS GROUP—Arrow Electronics, Inc.; *U.S. Public*, pg. 133
ASAHI KOMAG COMPANY LIMITED—Komag, Incorporated; *U.S. Public*, pg. 966
AST RESEARCH, INC—Samsung Group; *Int'l*, pg. 1182
ASTRO BUSINESS SOLUTIONS, INC.—Canon Inc.; *Int'l*, pg. 262
AUTODESK AB—Autodesk, Inc.; *U.S. Public*, pg. 149
AUTODESK AG—Autodesk, Inc.; *U.S. Public*, pg. 149
AUTODESK AUSTRALIA PTY. LTD.—Autodesk, Inc.; *U.S. Public*, pg. 149
AUTODESK GESMBH—Autodesk, Inc.; *U.S. Public*, pg. 149
AUTODESK GMBH—Autodesk, Inc.; *U.S. Public*, pg. 149
AUTODESK LTD.—Autodesk, Inc.; *U.S. Public*, pg. 149
AUTODESK S.A.—Autodesk, Inc.; *U.S. Public*, pg. 149
AUTODESK S.A.R.L.—Autodesk, Inc.; *U.S. Public*, pg. 150
AUTODESK S.P.A.—Autodesk, Inc.; *U.S. Public*, pg. 150
THE BIS GROUP LIMITED—Bell Atlantic Corporation; *U.S. Public*, pg. 204
BTG, INC.; *U.S. Public*, pg. 164
BELL ATLANTIC TELEPRODUCTS CORP.—Bell Atlantic Corporation; *U.S. Public*, pg. 203
BLACK BOX CORPORATION OF PENNSYLVANIA—Black Box Corporation of PA; *U.S. Public*, pg. 235
BRAMMER PLC; *Int'l*, pg. 212
BRIGHT STAR TECHNOLOGY,INC.—Cendant Corporation; *U.S. Public*, pg. 321
BROTHER FRANCE S.A.—Brother Industries, Ltd.; *Int'l*, pg. 229
BROTHER INDUSTRIES (AUSTRALIA) PTY. LTD.—Brother Industries, Ltd.; *Int'l*, pg. 229
S.A. BROTHER INTERNATIONAL (BELGIUM) N.V.—Brother Industries, Ltd.; *Int'l*, pg. 229
BROTHER INTERNATIONAL CORPORATION (CANADA) LTD.—Brother Industries, Ltd.; *Int'l*, pg. 229
BROTHER INTERNATIONAL (PORTUGAL) DISTRIBUIDORES DE EQUIPAMENTOS ELECTRICOS LDA.—Brother Industries, Ltd.; *Int'l*, pg. 230
BROTHER INTERNATIONALE INDUSTRIEMASCHINEN G.M.B.H.—Brother Industries, Ltd.; *Int'l*, pg. 230
BROTHER NORGE A.S.—Brother Industries, Ltd.; *Int'l*, pg. 230
BROTHER (SCHWEIZ) A.G.—Brother Industries, Ltd.; *Int'l*, pg. 230
CBT SYSTEMS USA—CBT Systems USA Ltd.; *U.S. Public*, pg. 276
CBT SYSTEMS USA LTD.; *U.S. Public*, pg. 275
CCS DESKPRO COMPUTER AB—COMPAQ Computer Corporation; *U.S. Public*, pg. 418
CIE AMERICA, INC.—Itochu Corporation; *Int'l*, pg. 694
CANON CANADA INC.—Canon Inc.; *Int'l*, pg. 262
CASIO, INC.—Casio Computer Co., Ltd.; *Int'l*, pg. 274
CENTURY DATA SYSTEMS, INCORPORATED; *U.S. Private*, pg. 226
CIMATRIX LTD.—Robotic Vision Systems, Inc.; *U.S. Public*, pg. 1395
CIMATRIX NV/SA—Robotic Vision Systems, Inc.; *U.S. Public*, pg. 1395
CIMATRIX S.A.—Robotic Vision Systems, Inc.; *U.S. Public*, pg. 1395
CIMLINC INCORPORATED; *U.S. Private*, pg. 239
CINCINNATI BELL SUPPLY COMPANY—Cincinnati Bell Telephone; *U.S. Public*, pg. 367
COMARK; *U.S. Private*, pg. 257
COMDISCO, INC.; *U.S. Public*, pg. 407
COMPAQ COMPUTER GMBH—COMPAQ Computer Corporation; *U.S. Public*, pg. 418
COMPAQ COMPUTER HONG KONG LIMITED—COMPAQ Computer Corporation; *U.S. Public*, pg. 418
COMPAQ COMPUTER JAPAN KK—COMPAQ Computer Corporation; *U.S. Public*, pg. 418
COMPUCOM SYSTEMS, INC.—Safeguard Scientifics, Inc.; *U.S. Public*, pg. 1424
COMPUSA; *U.S. Public*, pg. 420
COMPUTER & ELECTRONIC DIVISION—Abdulla Fouad Co. Ltd.; *Int'l*, pg. 501
COMPUTER ASSOCIATES INTERNATIONAL, INC.—Computer Associates International, Inc.; *U.S. Public*, pg. 420
COMPUTER CENTER-CINCINNATI—Bell Industries, Inc.; *U.S. Public*, pg. 204
COMPUTER CENTER-INDIANAPOLIS—Bell Industries, Inc.; *U.S. Public*, pg. 204
COMPUTER CENTER-LOUISVILLE—Bell Industries, Inc.; *U.S. Public*, pg. 204
COMPUTER CENTER-MARYLAND—Bell Industries, Inc.; *U.S. Public*, pg. 204
COMPUTER CENTER-N. INDIANAPOLIS—Bell Industries, Inc.; *U.S. Public*, pg. 204
COMPUTER SALES INTERNATIONAL INC.; *U.S. Private*, pg. 260
COMPUTERS, ETC.—Storage Technology Corporation; *U.S. Public*, pg. 1522
COMPUTING DEVICES CO. LTD.—Ceridian Corporation; *U.S. Public*, pg. 331
CREATIVE COMPUTERS, INC.; *U.S. Public*, pg. 458
CREATIVE COMPUTERS, INC.—Creative Computers, Inc.; *U.S. Public*, pg. 458
D&H DISTRIBUTING COMPANY; *U.S. Private*, pg. 300
DTK COMPUTER INC.; *U.S. Private*, pg. 306
DAEWOO TELECOM CO. (NEWTON)—Daewoo Corporation; *Int'l*, pg. 357
DAISYTEK AUSTRALIA PTY. LTD.—Daisytek International Corporation; *U.S. Public*, pg. 477
DAISYTEK (CANADA) INC.—Daisytek International Corporation; *U.S. Public*, pg. 477
DAISYTEK INCORPORATED—Daisytek International Corporation; *U.S. Public*, pg. 477
DAISYTEK LATIN AMERICA—Daisytek International Corporation; *U.S. Public*, pg. 477
DAKCO DISTRIBUTORS, INC.; *U.S. Private*, pg. 308
DATA COMMUNICATIONS & NETWORKS—Northern Telecom Limited; *Int'l*, pg. 969
DATA GENERAL FRANCE SARL—Data General Corporation; *U.S. Public*, pg. 486
DATA GENERAL HONG KONG SALES & SERVICE, LTD.—Data General Corporation; *U.S. Public*, pg. 486
DATA GENERAL SALES & MARKETING DIVISION—Data General Corporation; *U.S. Public*, pg. 485
DATA I/O JAPAN CO., LTD.—Data I/O Corporation; *U.S. Public*, pg. 486
DATA TRANSLATION GMBH—Media 100, Inc.; *U.S. Public*, pg. 1079
DATA TRANSLATION LTD.—Media 100, Inc.; *U.S. Public*, pg. 1079
DATA TRANSLATION NETWORKING LIMITED—Media 100, Inc.; *U.S. Public*, pg. 1079
DATARAM CORPORATION; *U.S. Public*, pg. 487
DATARAM INTERNATIONAL SALES CORP.—Dataram Corporation; *U.S. Public*, pg. 487
DATATEAM DANMARK A/S—Axel Johnson AB; *Int'l*, pg. 710
DAVIDSON & ASSOCIATES, INC.—Cendant Corporation; *U.S. Public*, pg. 320
DELL COMPUTER CORPORATION; *U.S. Public*, pg. 495
DELL MARKETING CORPORATION—Dell Computer Corporation; *U.S. Public*, pg. 495
DIGITAL EQUIPMENT CORPORATION; *U.S. Public*, pg. 507
DISTRIBUPRO, INC.—Computer Associates International, Inc.; *U.S. Public*, pg. 420
DISTRIBUTED SYSTEMS DIVISION—Storage Technology Corporation; *U.S. Public*, pg. 1522
DISTRIBUTOREN INTERELKO A/S—Axel Johnson AB; *Int'l*, pg. 710
DYNETCOM—DynetCom; *Int'l*, pg. 425
DYNETCOM GMBH—DynetCom; *Int'l*, pg. 425
THE EAST ASIATIC COMPANY LTD. A/S; *Int'l*, pg. 430
ECONOCOM-USA INC.; *U.S. Private*, pg. 361
EDISA INFORMATICA S.A.—Hewlett-Packard Company; *U.S. Public*, pg. 817
ELGIN BROTHER INDUSTRIAL LTDA.—Brother Industries, Ltd.; *Int'l*, pg. 230
ENCORE COMPUTER GMBH—Encore Computer Corporation; *U.S. Public*, pg. 580
ENCORE COMPUTER ITALIA S.P.A.—Encore Computer Corporation; *U.S. Public*, pg. 580
ENCORE COMPUTER (UK) LTD.—Encore Computer Corporation; *U.S. Public*, pg. 580
ENCORE INFORMATIQUE LIMITEE—Encore Computer Corporation; *U.S. Public*, pg. 580
ENTEX INFORMATION SERVICES; *U.S. Private*, pg. 378
EPSON AUSTRALIA PTY. LTD. (E.A.L.)—Seiko Epson Corporation; *Int'l*, pg. 1219
EPSON CANADA LIMITED—Seiko Epson Corporation; *Int'l*, pg. 1219
EPSON DEUTSCHLAND GMBH (E.D.G.)—Seiko Epson Corporation; *Int'l*, pg. 1219
EPSON ELECTRONICS TRADING, LTD., TAIWAN BRANCH (E.T.T.)—Seiko Epson Corporation; *Int'l*, pg. 1219
EPSON FRANCE S.A. (E.F.S.)—Seiko Epson Corporation; *Int'l*, pg. 1219
EPSON HONG KONG LTD.—Seiko Epson Corporation; *Int'l*, pg. 1219
EPSON SINGAPORE PTE., LTD. (ESP)—Seiko Epson Corporation; *Int'l*, pg. 1219
EPSON (U.K.) LTD. (E.U.L.)—Seiko Epson Corporation; *Int'l*, pg. 1219
ERSKINE HOUSE GROUP PLC—Ikon Office Solutions, Inc.; *U.S. Public*, pg. 864
ESPRIT SYSTEMS, INC.; *U.S. Private*, pg. 383
EXCITE, INC.; *U.S. Public*, pg. 599
EXECUTIVE PRODUCTIVITY SYSTEMS, INC.; *U.S. Private*, pg. 388
FOLLETT SOFTWARE COMPANY—Follett Corporation; *U.S. Private*, pg. 417
ABDULLA FOUAD CO. LTD.; *Int'l*, pg. 501
FRANKLIN ELECTRONIC PUBLISHERS, INC.; *U.S. Public*, pg. 679
FUJITSU DEUTSCHLAND GMBH—Fujitsu Limited; *Int'l*, pg. 528
FUJITSU ESPANA, S.A.—Fujitsu Limited; *Int'l*, pg. 528
FUJITSU ICL AUSTRALIA PTY. LIMITED—Fujitsu Limited; *Int'l*, pg. 529
G.E. FANUC AUTOMATION CANADA—General Electric Company; *U.S. Public*, pg. 713
G.E. PLASTIC CANADA—General Electric Company; *U.S. Public*, pg. 713
GT INTERACTIVE SOFTWARE CORP.; *U.S. Public*, pg. 696
GTE INTERNETWORKING GMBH—GTE Corporation; *U.S. Public*, pg. 696
GANDALF S.A.—Gandalf Technologies Inc.; *Int'l*, pg. 541
GIGAMAX—Tai-Il Media Co.; *Int'l*, pg. 1347
GOLDSTAR CO. LTD.—LG Group; *Int'l*, pg. 778
GRADCO (JAPAN), LTD.—Gradco Systems, Inc.; *U.S. Public*, pg. 757
GRADCO SYSTEMS, INC.; *U.S. Public*, pg. 757
HBOC; *U.S. Public*, pg. 770
HAGEMEYER N.V.—First Pacific Company Limited; *Int'l*, pg. 487
HANDLEMAN COMPANY OF CANADA LTD.—Handleman Company; *U.S. Public*, pg. 780
HARRIS CORP. B.V.—Harris Corporation; *U.S. Public*, pg. 791
HARRIS GMBH—Harris Corporation; *U.S. Public*, pg. 791
HARRIS LANIER AUSTRALIA—Harris Corporation; *U.S. Public*, pg. 791
HARRIS SAUDI ARABIA LTD.—Harris Corporation; *U.S. Public*, pg. 791
HARRIS SYSTEMS LTD.—Harris Corporation; *U.S. Public*, pg. 791
HEWLETT-PACKARD GES.M.B.H.—Hewlett-Packard Company; *U.S. Public*, pg. 820
HEWLETT-PACKARD HELLAS—Hewlett-Packard Company; *U.S. Public*, pg. 820
HEWLETT-PACKARD ICELAND—Hewlett-Packard Company; *U.S. Public*, pg. 820
HEWLETT-PACKARD (N.Z.) LTD.—Hewlett-Packard Company; *U.S. Public*, pg. 821
HEWLETT-PACKARD OY—Hewlett-Packard Company; *U.S.* Public, pg. 821
HEWLETT-PACKARD POLSKA SP.Z.O.O.—Hewlett-Packard Company; *U.S. Public*, pg. 821
HEWLETT-PACKARD SALES (MALAYSIA) SDN. BHD.—Hewlett-Packard Company; *U.S. Public*, pg. 821
HEWLETT-PACKARD SINGAPORE PTE. LTD.—Hewlett-Packard Company; *U.S. Public*, pg. 822
HEWLETT-PACKARD SVERIGE AB—Hewlett-Packard Company; *U.S. Public*, pg. 822
HEWLETT-PACKARD TAIWAN LTD.—Hewlett-Packard Company; *U.S. Public*, pg. 822
HITACHI AMERICA, LTD.—Hitachi, Ltd.; *Int'l*, pg. 622
HITACHI DATA SYSTEMS CORPORATION—Hitachi, Ltd.; *Int'l*, pg. 622
HITACHI DATA SYSTEMS INC.—Hitachi, Ltd.; *Int'l*, pg. 622
HITACHI DATA SYSTEMS INC.—Sand Technology Systems; *Int'l*, pg. 1184
HOME ELECTRONICS CO., LTD.—The Siam Cement Public Company Limited; *Int'l*, pg. 1239
HONEYWELL INC.; *U.S. Public*, pg. 833
HONEYWELL-MEASUREX FOREIGN SALES CORPORATION—Honeywell Inc.; *U.S. Public*, pg. 833
HOWTEK, INC.; *U.S. Public*, pg. 844
IBM DISTRIBUTION AND SUPPORT, S.A.—International Business Machines Corporation; *U.S. Public*, pg. 897
IBM FRANCE DIFFUSION, S.A.—International Business Machines Corporation; *U.S. Public*, pg. 897
IBM ITALIA-DISTRIBUZIONE PRODOTTI S.R.L.—International Business Machines Corporation; *U.S. Public*, pg. 897
IBM NORGE PRODUKT DISTRIBUSJON A/S—International Business Machines Corporation; *U.S. Public*, pg. 898
IBM SVENSKA PRODUKT DISTRIBUTION AKTIEBOLAG—International Business Machines Corporation; *U.S. Public*, pg. 897
IBM THAILAND COMPANY LIMITED—International Business Machines Corporation; *U.S. Public*, pg. 897
IBM TRADE DEVELOPMENT, S.A.—International Business Machines Corporation; *U.S. Public*, pg. 897
IBM UNITED KINGDOM INTERNATIONAL PRODUCT SALES LIMITED—International Business Machines Corporation; *U.S. Public*, pg. 897
IBM UNITED KINGDOM PRODUCT SALES LIMITED—International Business Machines Corporation; *U.S. Public*, pg. 898
ICL (BELGIUM) S.A.—Fujitsu Limited; *Int'l*, pg. 529
ICL ESPANA INTERNATIONAL COMPUTERS S.A.—Fujitsu Limited; *Int'l*, pg. 529
ICL FINLAND OY—Fujitsu Limited; *Int'l*, pg. 529
ICL (FRANCE) INTERNATIONAL COMPUTERS—Fujitsu Limited; *Int'l*, pg. 529
ICL INTERNATIONAL COMPUTERS GMBH—Fujitsu Limited; *Int'l*, pg. 529
ICL ITALIA INTERNATIONAL COMPUTERS SPA—Fujitsu Limited; *Int'l*, pg. 529
ICL KENYA LIMITED—Fujitsu Limited; *Int'l*, pg. 529
ICL LUXEMBOURG S.A.—Fujitsu Limited; *Int'l*, pg. 529
ICL (MALAWI) LIMITED—Fujitsu Limited; *Int'l*, pg. 529
ICL NEDERLAND B.V.—Fujitsu Limited; *Int'l*, pg. 529
ICL SINGAPORE PRIVATE LIMITED—Fujitsu Limited; *Int'l*, pg. 529
ICL (SWITZERLAND) INTERNATIONAL COMPUTERS AG—Fujitsu Limited; *Int'l*, pg. 529
ICL ZAMBIA LIMITED—Fujitsu Limited; *Int'l*, pg. 529
ICL ZIMBABWE LIMITED—Fujitsu Limited; *Int'l*, pg. 529
IIS INTELLIGENT INFORMATION SYSTEMS LTD.; *Int'l*, pg. 645
IMAGING TECHNOLOGIES CORP.; *U.S. Public*, pg. 870
INACOM CORP.; *U.S. Public*, pg. 873
INDIANA RECORDS MANAGERS; *U.S. Private*, pg. 560
INFRESCO CORPORATION—Computer Associates International, Inc.; *U.S. Public*, pg. 420
INGRAM DISTRIBUTION GROUP INC.—Ingram Industries Inc.; *U.S. Private*, pg. 563
INGRAM ENTERTAINMENT INC.—Ingram Industries Inc.; *U.S. Private*, pg. 563
INGRAM MICRO INC.; *U.S. Public*, pg. 878
INLAND ASSOCIATES; *U.S. Private*, pg. 563
INTEGRATED SYSTEMS OPERATIONS—Xerox Corporation; *U.S. Public*, pg. 1784
INTEL AUSTRALIA PTY. LTD.—Intel Corporation; *U.S. Public*, pg. 887
INTEL CORPORATION ITALIA SPA—Intel Corporation; *U.S. Public*, pg. 887
INTEL CORPORATION S.A.R.L.—Intel Corporation; *U.S. Public*, pg. 887

INTEL CORPORATION U.K. LTD.—Intel Corporation; *U.S. Public*, pg. 887
INTEL DENMARK—Intel Corporation; *U.S. Public*, pg. 887
INTEL EUROPE—Intel Corporation; *U.S. Public*, pg. 887
INTEL FINLAND OY—Intel Corporation; *U.S. Public*, pg. 887
INTEL IBERIA S.A.—Intel Corporation; *U.S. Public*, pg. 887
INTEL JAPAN—Intel Corporation; *U.S. Public*, pg. 887
INTEL NORWAY—Intel Corporation; *U.S. Public*, pg. 887
INTEL SEMICONDUCTOR LTD.—Intel Corporation; *U.S. Public*, pg. 887
INTEL SINGAPORE LTD.—Intel Corporation; *U.S. Public*, pg. 887
INTEL SWEDEN—Intel Corporation; *U.S. Public*, pg. 887
INTEL SWITZERLAND—Intel Corporation; *U.S. Public*, pg. 887
INTEL TECHNOLOGY FAR EAST LTD.—Intel Corporation; *U.S. Public*, pg. 887
INTERGRAPH CORPORATION; *U.S. Public*, pg. 890
INTERGRAPH (DEUTSCHLAND) GMBH—Intergraph Corporation; *U.S. Public*, pg. 892
INTERGRAPH SERVICIOS DE VENEZUELA, C.A.—Intergraph Corporation; *U.S. Public*, pg. 891
INTERGRAPH SYSTEMS SOUTH-EAST ASIA (PTE.) LTD.—Intergraph Corporation; *U.S. Public*, pg. 891
INTERLEAF AUSTRALIA, PTY. LTD.—Interleaf, Inc.; *U.S. Public*, pg. 893
INTERLEAF FRANCE, S.A.—Interleaf, Inc.; *U.S. Public*, pg. 893
INTERLEAF GMBH—Interleaf, Inc.; *U.S. Public*, pg. 893
INTERLEAF JAPAN INC.—Interleaf, Inc.; *U.S. Public*, pg. 893
INTERLEAF UK, LTD.—Interleaf, Inc.; *U.S. Public*, pg. 893
INTERNATIONAL COMPUTERS HONG KONG LIMITED—Fujitsu Limited; *Int'l*, pg. 529
INTERNATIONAL COMPUTERS (MALAYSIA) SDN.BHD—Fujitsu Limited; *Int'l*, pg. 529
INTERNATIONAL COMPUTERS (NIGERIA) LIMITED—Fujitsu Limited; *Int'l*, pg. 529
INTERNATIONAL COMPUTERS (SOUTH AFRICA) (PROPRIETARY) LIMITED—Fujitsu Limited; *Int'l*, pg. 529
ITOCHU DIGITAL PRODUCTS, INC.—Itochu Corporation; *Int'l*, pg. 695
ITOCHU INTERNATIONAL INC.—Itochu Corporation; *Int'l*, pg. 694
JAPAN ENCORE COMPUTER, INC.—Encore Computer Corporation; *U.S. Public*, pg. 580
KHI (DALIAN) COMPUTER TECHNOLOGY CO., LTD.—Kawasaki Heavy Industries, Ltd.; *Int'l*, pg. 726
KANEBO, LTD.—Kanebo, Ltd.; *Int'l*, pg. 722
KOMAG, INCORPORATED; *U.S. Public*, pg. 966
KONAMI CORPORATION OF AMERICA INC.—Konami Co. Ltd.; *Int'l*, pg. 746
KYOCERA ELECTRONICS, INC.—Kyocera Corporation; *Int'l*, pg. 776
KYOCERA INTERNATIONAL, INC.—Kyocera Corporation; *Int'l*, pg. 775
LASERMASTER EXPORT CORPORATION—LaserMaster Technologies, Inc.; *U.S. Public*, pg. 979
LEXMARK AUSTRALIA—Lexmark International Group, Inc.; *U.S. Public*, pg. 991
LEXMARK CANADA INC.—Lexmark International Group, Inc.; *U.S. Public*, pg. 991
LITTON UK LTD.—Litton Industries, Inc.; *U.S. Public*, pg. 1005
LITTON WORLD TRADE CORPORATION—Litton Industries, Inc.; *U.S. Public*, pg. 1005
LIUSKI INTERNATIONAL, INC.; *U.S. Public*, pg. 1005
LIVINGSTON S.A.—Brammer plc; *Int'l*, pg. 212
LIVINGSTON UK LIMITED—Brammer plc; *Int'l*, pg. 212
LIVINGSTON U.K. LIMITED—Brammer plc; *Int'l*, pg. 212
LIVINGSTON UK LTD.—Brammer plc; *Int'l*, pg. 212
L.A. COMPUTER CENTER; *U.S. Private*, pg. 676
LOTUS DEVELOPMENT CORPORATION—International Business Machines Corporation; *U.S. Public*, pg. 896
LOTUS DEVELOPMENT LTD.—International Business Machines Corporation; *U.S. Public*, pg. 896
M.G. (SCANDANAVIA) AB—Mentor Graphics Corporation; *U.S. Public*, pg. 1087
MK GROUP—Computer Associates International, Inc.; *U.S. Public*, pg. 420
MTI SYSTEMS CORP.—Arrow Electronics, Inc.; *U.S. Public*, pg. 134
MTI SYSTEMS DIV.—Arrow Electronics, Inc.; *U.S. Public*, pg. 135
MACRO COMPUTER PRODUCTS INC.; *U.S. Private*, pg. 693
MAG INNOVISION CO., INC.; *U.S. Private*, pg. 694
MANCHESTER EQUIPMENT CO.; *U.S. Private*, pg. 699
MANTECH COMPUTER & EDUCATION AIDS—Abdulla Fouad Co. Ltd.; *Int'l*, pg. 502
MARKETING AND CUSTOMER OPERATIONS—Xerox Corporation; *U.S. Public*, pg. 1784
MATRA-HARRIS SEMICONDUCTEURS S.A.—Harris Corporation; *U.S. Public*, pg. 791
MCBRIDE AND ASSOCIATES, INC.; *U.S. Private*, pg. 719
MCRAE INDUSTRIES, INC.; *U.S. Public*, pg. 1073
MEMOREX TELEX CANADA INC.—Memorex Telex N.V.; *Int'l*, pg. 857
MENTOR GRAPHICS (FRANCE) SARL—Mentor Graphics Corporation; *U.S. Public*, pg. 1087
MENTOR GRAPHICS JAPAN CO., LTD.—Mentor Graphics Corporation; *U.S. Public*, pg. 1087
MENTOR GRAPHICS (KOREA)—Mentor Graphics Corporation; *U.S. Public*, pg. 1087
MERCURY INTERACTIVE CORP.; *U.S. Public*, pg. 1093
MERISEL, INC.; *U.S. Public*, pg. 1095
A. MESSERLI AG—Oce-van der Grinten N.V.; *Int'l*, pg. 995
MICOM COMMUNICATIONS CORP.—Northern Telecom Limited; *Int'l*, pg. 969
MICROAGE, INC.; *U.S. Public*, pg. 1104
MICROPOLIS CORP.—Micropolis Corporation; *U.S. Private*, pg. 742
MICROPOLIS GMBH—Micropolis Corporation; *U.S. Private*, pg. 742
MICROPOLIS S.A.R.L.—Micropolis Corporation; *U.S. Private*, pg. 743
MICROS-FIDELIO SOFTWARE DEUTSCHLAND GMBH—Micros Systems Inc.; *U.S. Public*, pg. 1106
MICROS SYSTEMS DEUTSCHLAND, GMBH—Micros Systems Inc.; *U.S. Public*, pg. 1107
MITEK SYSTEMS, INC.; *U.S. Public*, pg. 1117
MITSUBISHI ELECTRIC (UK) LTD.—Mitsubishi Electric Corporation; *Int'l*, pg. 873
MYKOTRONX—Rainbow Technologies, Inc.; *U.S. Public*, pg. 1359
NEC DEUTSCHLAND GMBH—NEC Corporation; *Int'l*, pg. 901
NEC HONG KONG LIMITED—NEC Corporation; *Int'l*, pg. 900
NEC SINGAPORE PTE. LTD.—NEC Corporation; *Int'l*, pg. 900
NEC (UK) LTD.—NEC Corporation; *Int'l*, pg. 901
NMI CORPORATION—NEC Corporation; *Int'l*, pg. 900
NOKO-NOKIA REPRESENTATIVE OFFICE—Oy Nokia Ab/Nokia Group; *Int'l*, pg. 953
NTT AMERICA, INC.—Nippon Telegraph and Telephone Corporation; *Int'l*, pg. 941
NABANCO—First Data Corporation; *U.S. Public*, pg. 631
NATIONAL BRANDS, INC.; *U.S. Private*, pg. 780
NATIONAL INSTRUMENTS CORP.; *U.S. Public*, pg. 1157
NATIONAL MICRONETICS, INC.—Tai-Il Media Co.; *Int'l*, pg. 1347
NETHAVEN—Computer Associates International, Inc.; *U.S. Public*, pg. 420
NETSCAPE COMMUNICATIONS CORP.; *U.S. Public*, pg. 1168
NETWORK SYSTEMS AUSTRIA GMBH—Storage Technology Corporation; *U.S. Public*, pg. 1522
NETWORK SYSTEMS LIMITED—Storage Technology Corporation; *U.S. Public*, pg. 1522
NICHIFU AMERICA, INC.—Nichifu Company Ltd.; *Int'l*, pg. 927
NICHIFU COMPANY LTD.; *Int'l*, pg. 927
NIHON MICROTEC RESEARCH—Mentor Graphics Corporation; *U.S. Public*, pg. 1087
NIHON SUN MICROSYSTEMS K.K.—Sun Microsystems, Inc.; *U.S. Public*, pg. 1531
NOKIA FRANCE S.A.—Oy Nokia Ab/Nokia Group; *Int'l*, pg. 954
NORTHERN TELECOM CANADA LIMITED, TELECOM SERVICES DIV.—Northern Telecom Limited; *Int'l*, pg. 969
OCE GRAPHICS SVENSKA AB—Oce-van der Grinten N.V.; *Int'l*, pg. 994
OCE GRAPHICS (U.K.) LIMITED—Oce-van der Grinten N.V.; *Int'l*, pg. 994
OCE-IRELAND LTD.—Oce-van der Grinten N.V.; *Int'l*, pg. 994
OBJECTIVE SYSTEMS INTEGRATORS, INC.; *U.S. Public*, pg. 1209
OKI ELECTRIC INDUSTRY CO., LTD.—Oki Electric Industry Company, Ltd.; *Int'l*, pg. 999
OKI EUROPE LTD.—Oki Electric Industry Company, Ltd.; *Int'l*, pg. 1000
OKI SYSTEMS (DANMARK) A.S.—Oki Electric Industry Company, Ltd.; *Int'l*, pg. 1000
OKI SYSTEMS (DEUTSCHLAND) GMBH—Oki Electric Industry Company, Ltd.; *Int'l*, pg. 1000
OKI SYSTEMS (HOLLAND) B.V.—Oki Electric Industry Company, Ltd.; *Int'l*, pg. 1000
OKI SYSTEMS (IRELAND) LTD.—Oki Electric Industry Company, Ltd.; *Int'l*, pg. 1000
OKI SYSTEMS (ITALIA) S.P.A.—Oki Electric Industry Company, Ltd.; *Int'l*, pg. 1000
OKI SYSTEMS (SWEDEN) AB—Oki Electric Industry Company, Ltd.; *Int'l*, pg. 1000
OKI SYSTEMS (UK) LTD.—Oki Electric Industry Company, Ltd.; *Int'l*, pg. 999
OKIDATA GROUP—Oki Electric Industry Company, Ltd.; *Int'l*, pg. 1000
ON TECHNOLOGY CORPORATION; *U.S. Public*, pg. 1225
ORCAD INC.; *U.S. Public*, pg. 1230
PNY TECHNOLOGIES, INC.; *U.S. Private*, pg. 827
PSI INTERNATIONAL—Storage Technology Corporation; *U.S. Public*, pg. 1522
PEIRCE-PHELPS, INC.; *U.S. Private*, pg. 847
PERIPHONICS VOICE PROCESSING SYSTEMS LTD.—Periphonics Corp.; *U.S. Public*, pg. 1279
PHYSICIAN COMPUTER NETWORK, INC.; *U.S. Public*, pg. 1293
PICTURETEL; *U.S. Public*, pg. 1294
PRINTRONIX, INC.; *U.S. Public*, pg. 1329
PROGRESS SOFTWARE CORPORATION; *U.S. Public*, pg. 1334
QMS INTERNATIONAL GMBH—QMS, Inc.; *U.S. Public*, pg. 1346
RMI EDUCATIONAL SERVICES—Robertson Marketing Inc.; *U.S. Private*, pg. 936
RADIO HOLLAND ELECTRONICS—SAIT-RadioHolland Group S.A.; *Int'l*, pg. 1151
RAINBOW TECHNOLOGIES, INC.; *U.S. Public*, pg. 1359
RANK XEROX AG—Xerox Corporation; *U.S. Public*, pg. 1785
RECOTON CANADA LTD.—Recoton Corporation; *U.S. Public*, pg. 1369
RECOTON CORPORATION; *U.S. Public*, pg. 1369
RETIX UNITED KINGDOM—Vertel; *U.S. Public*, pg. 1717
ROBERTSON MARKETING INC.; *U.S. Private*, pg. 936
ROSS SYSTEMS EUROPE N.V.—Ross Systems, Inc.; *U.S. Public*, pg. 1406
ROSS SYSTEMS FRANCE S.A.—Ross Systems, Inc.; *U.S. Public*, pg. 1406
ROSS SYSTEMS NEDERLAND B.V.—Ross Systems, Inc.; *U.S. Public*, pg. 1406
SKF CONDITION MONITORING INC.—AB SKF; *Int'l*, pg. 1157
SAFEGUARD SCIENTIFICS, INC.; *U.S. Public*, pg. 1424
SAGEM CORPORATION—Societe d'Applications Generales d'Electricite et de Mechanique; *Int'l*, pg. 1273
SAKATA INX USA CORP.—Sumitomo Chemical Company, Ltd.; *Int'l*, pg. 1311
SAMNA GMBH—International Business Machines Corporation; *U.S. Public*, pg. 896
SAMSUNG ELECTRONICS AMERICA, INC.—Samsung Group; *Int'l*, pg. 1183
SAMSUNG ELECTRONICS CO., LTD.—Samsung Group; *Int'l*, pg. 1183
SAMSUNG HEWLETT-PACKARD—Hewlett-Packard Company; *U.S. Public*, pg. 823
SAMSUNG PACIFIC INTERNATIONAL, INC.—Samsung Group; *Int'l*, pg. 1183
SAMSUNG SEMICONDUCTORS, INC.—Samsung Group; *Int'l*, pg. 1183
SAND TECHNOLOGY SYSTEMS; *Int'l*, pg. 1183
SANDERSON COMPUTERS HONG KONG LTD.—Sanderson Technology Ltd.; *Int'l*, pg. 1185
SANDERSON COMPUTERS NEW ZEALAND LTD.—Sanderson Technology Ltd.; *Int'l*, pg. 1185
SANDERSON COMPUTERS PTE. LTD.—Sanderson Technology Ltd.; *Int'l*, pg. 1185
SANDERSON COMPUTERS PTY. LTD.—Sanderson Technology Ltd.; *Int'l*, pg. 1185
SANYO OFFICE AUTOMATION—Sanyo Electric Co., Ltd.; *Int'l*, pg. 1191
SEAGATE SOFTWARE, INC.—Seagate Technology Inc.; *U.S. Public*, pg. 1449
SEAGATE TECHNOLOGY KOREA, INC.—Seagate Technology Inc.; *U.S. Public*, pg. 1450
SECURITY DYNAMICS TECHNOLOGIES; *U.S. Public*, pg. 1453
SIEMENS NIXDORF INFORMATIONSSYSTEME GES.M.B.H.—Siemens AG; *Int'l*, pg. 1245
SMART MODULAR TECHNOLOGIES; *U.S. Public*, pg. 1476
SOFTMART, INC.; *U.S. Private*, pg. 1012
SOFTWARE SPECTRUM, INC.; *U.S. Public*, pg. 1483
SORBUS EUROPE, LTD.—Bell Atlantic Corporation; *U.S. Public*, pg. 204
SOUTHERN ELECTRONICS CORPORATION; *U.S. Public*, pg. 1490
STANDARD MANIFOLD COMPANY, INC.; *U.S. Private*, pg. 1031
STORAGE TECHNOLOGY GMBH—Storage Technology Corporation; *U.S. Public*, pg. 1523
STORAGE TECHNOLOGY ITALIA S.P.A.—Storage Technology Corporation; *U.S. Public*, pg. 1523
STORAGE TECHNOLOGY OF JAPAN LTD.—Storage Technology Corporation; *U.S. Public*, pg. 1523
STORAGE TECHNOLOGY SWITZERLAND AG—Storage Technology Corporation; *U.S. Public*, pg. 1523
STORAGETEK CANADA, INC.—Storage Technology Corporation; *U.S. Public*, pg. 1523
STORAGETEK FRANCE, S.A.—Storage Technology Corporation; *U.S. Public*, pg. 1523
STRATUS COMPUTER, INC.; *U.S. Public*, pg. 1524
STRATUS COMPUTER, LTD.—Stratus Computer, Inc.; *U.S. Public*, pg. 1524
STRATUS COMPUTER PTY, LTD.—Stratus Computer, Inc.; *U.S. Public*, pg. 1524
STRATUS COMPUTER S.A.—Stratus Computer, Inc.; *U.S. Public*, pg. 1524
STRATUS JAPAN CO. LTD.—Stratus Computer, Inc.; *U.S. Public*, pg. 1524
STREAM INTERNATIONAL HOLDINGS INC.—R.R. Donnelley & Sons Company; *U.S. Public*, pg. 518
SUN DATA INC.; *U.S. Private*, pg. 1050
SUN MICROSYSTEMS AB—Sun Microsystems, Inc.; *U.S. Public*, pg. 1531
SUN MICROSYSTEMS OF AUSTRALIA PTY. LTD.—Sun Microsystems, Inc.; *U.S. Public*, pg. 1532
SUN MICROSYSTEMS OF CALIFORNIA—Sun Microsystems, Inc.; *U.S. Public*, pg. 1532
SUN MICROSYSTEMS OF CALIFORNIA LTD.—Sun Microsystems, Inc.; *U.S. Public*, pg. 1532
SUN MICROSYSTEMS OF CALIFORNIA (SERVICES) LTD.—Sun Microsystems, Inc.; *U.S. Public*, pg. 1532
SUN MICROSYSTEMS OF CANADA—Sun Microsystems, Inc.; *U.S. Public*, pg. 1532
SYMBOL TECHNOLOGIES CANADA INC.—Symbol Technologies, Inc.; *U.S. Public*, pg. 1546
SYMBOL TECHNOLOGIES INTERNATIONAL, INC.—Symbol Technologies, Inc.; *U.S. Public*, pg. 1546
SYMIX SYSTEMS, INC.; *U.S. Public*, pg. 1546
SYMIX SYSTEMS, INC.—Symix Systems, Inc.; *U.S. Public*, pg. 1547
SYMIX SYSTEMS INC.—Symix Systems, Inc.; *U.S. Public*, pg. 1547
SYMPLEX COMMUNICATIONS CORP.; *U.S. Private*, pg. 1060
SYNOPSYS, INC.; *U.S. Public*, pg. 1548
SYRACUSE SUPPLY COMPANY; *U.S. Private*, pg. 1060
TAI-IL MEDIA CO.; *Int'l*, pg. 1347
TAIWAN BROTHER INDUSTRIES, LTD.—Brother Industries, Ltd.; *Int'l*, pg. 230
TANDEM COMPUTERS CANADA LIMITED—COMPAQ Computer Corporation; *U.S. Public*, pg. 417
TECH DATA CORPORATION; *U.S. Public*, pg. 1562
TELTRONICS INC.; *U.S. Public*, pg. 1573
TELXON AUSTRALIA PTY. LIMITED—Telxon Corporation; *U.S. Public*, pg. 1573
N.V. TELXON BELGIUM S.A.—Telxon Corporation; *U.S. Public*, pg. 1574
TELXON CORPORATION; *U.S. Public*, pg. 1573
TELXON CORPORATION, SINGAPORE BRANCH—Telxon Corporation; *U.S. Public*, pg. 1574
TELXON FRANCE S.A.—Telxon Corporation; *U.S. Public*, pg. 1574
TELXON ITALIA S.R.L.—Telxon Corporation; *U.S. Public*, pg. 1574

TELXON LIMITED—Telxon Corporation; *U.S. Public*, pg. 1574
TEXAS INSTRUMENTS CONSUMER PRODUCTS DIV.—Texas Instruments Incorporated; *U.S. Public*, pg. 1586
TEXAS INSTRUMENTS INTERNATIONAL TRADE CORPORATION—Texas Instruments Incorporated; *U.S. Public*, pg. 1586
TEXAS INSTRUMENTS (SWITZERLAND) AG—Texas Instruments Incorporated; *U.S. Public*, pg. 1586
TIGER DIRECT, INC. (D/B/A TIGER SOFTWARE, INC.)—Global Direct Mail Corp; *U.S. Public*, pg. 747
TIMBERLINE SOFTWARE CORPORATION; *U.S. Public*, pg. 1609
TOSHIBA AMERICA INFORMATION SYSTEMS, INC.—Toshiba Corporation; *Int'l*, pg. 1405
TOSHIBA EUROPE (I.E.) G.M.B.H.—Toshiba Corporation; *Int'l*, pg. 1406
TOSHIBA INFORMATION SYSTEMS (JAPAN) CORPORATION—Toshiba Corporation; *Int'l*, pg. 1404
TOSOH USA, INC.—Tosoh Corporation; *Int'l*, pg. 1408
TOSOH USA, INC.-SAN FRANCISCO OFFICE—Tosoh Corporation; *Int'l*, pg. 1407
TRIVOLI SYSTEMS—International Business Machines Corporation; *U.S. Public*, pg. 896
TRIVOLI SYSTEMS INC.—International Business Machines Corporation; *U.S. Public*, pg. 896
UNISYS BELGIUM—Unisys Corporation; *U.S. Public*, pg. 1672
UTIMACO SAFEWARE AG; *Int'l*, pg. 1444
UTIMACO SAFEWARE, INC.—Utimaco Safeware AG; *Int'l*, pg. 1444
VERBATIM TAPE CORPORATION—Mitsubishi Corporation; *Int'l*, pg. 872
VERTEL; *U.S. Public*, pg. 1717
VICTOR TECHNOLOGY; *U.S. Private*, pg. 1139
THE VIRTUAL GROUP; *U.S. Private*, pg. 1141
WANG AUSTRALIA PTY. LTD.—Wang Laboratories, Inc.; *U.S. Public*, pg. 1737
WANG (UK) LIMITED—Wang Laboratories, Inc.; *U.S. Public*, pg. 1738
WESTERN DIGITAL HONG KONG LTD.—Western Digital Corporation; *U.S. Public*, pg. 1758
WESTERN DIGITAL SINGAPORE LTD.—Western Digital Corporation; *U.S. Public*, pg. 1758
WESTERN PACIFIC DATA SYSTEMS; *U.S. Private*, pg. 1168
RICHARD YOUNG OFFICE PRODUCTS, INC.—Corporate Express, Inc.; *U.S. Public*, pg. 450

5046 — COMMERCIAL EQUIPMENT-WHOLESALE, NEC

ABB COMBUSTION ENGINEERING BRASIL—ABB Asea Brown Boveri (Holding) Ltd.; *Int'l*, pg. 5
AVA; *U.S. Private*, pg. 8
J.W. ALLEN & COMPANY; *U.S. Private*, pg. 37
ALLSUPS CONVENIENCE STORES INC.; *U.S. Private*, pg. 44
AMERICAN ZETTLER INC.—Alois Zettler Elecktrotechnische Fabrik GmbH; *Int'l*, pg. 1528
ASSOCIATED BUSINESS PRODUCTS, INC.—Ikon Office Solutions, Inc.; *U.S. Public*, pg. 863
AVNET, INC.; *U.S. Public*, pg. 155
BAZAAR & NOVELTY—Stuart Entertainment Inc.; *U.S. Public*, pg. 1526
BELL ATLANTIC TELEPRODUCTS CORP.—Bell Atlantic Corporation; *U.S. Public*, pg. 203
BLOOMFIELD INDUSTRIES CANADA LTD.—Specialty Equipment Companies Inc.; *U.S. Public*, pg. 1497
BRINKMANN INSTRUMENTS (CANADA) LTD.—Brinkmann Instruments, Inc.; *U.S. Private*, pg. 169
CAVALIER CORPORATION; *U.S. Private*, pg. 220
CERTIFIED GROCERS OF CALIFORNIA; *U.S. Private*, pg. 226
CROUCH SUPPLY COMPANY, INC.; *U.S. Private*, pg. 291
CROWN CORK COORDINATION CENTER N.V.—Crown Cork & Seal Company, Inc.; *U.S. Public*, pg. 464
CUISINART INC.—Conair Corporation; *U.S. Private*, pg. 261
CURTIS EQUIPMENT CO., INC.—Hale-Halsell Company; *U.S. Private*, pg. 494
DAKTRONICS, INC.; *U.S. Public*, pg. 478
A.B. DICK COMPANY—NESCO, Inc.; *U.S. Private*, pg. 791
THE WILLIAM DIERICKX COMPANY—Ikon Office Solutions, Inc.; *U.S. Public*, pg. 863
EDWARD DON & COMPANY; *U.S. Private*, pg. 339
FOGA SYSTEMS—Foga System International AB; *Int'l*, pg. 496
GE CAPITAL/IT SOLUTIONS—General Electric Company; *U.S. Public*, pg. 711
H & H DISTRIBUTING COMPANY, INC.; *U.S. Private*, pg. 489
D.C. HEY COMPANY—Ikon Office Solutions, Inc.; *U.S. Public*, pg. 863
HILTON EQUIPMENT CORP.—Hilton Hotels Corporation; *U.S. Public*, pg. 829
HUBERT COMPANY; *U.S. Private*, pg. 545
HYOSUNG GROUP; *Int'l*, pg. 640
IKON OFFICE SOLUTIONS—Ikon Office Solutions, Inc.; *U.S. Public*, pg. 864
INFINCOM—Ikon Office Solutions, Inc.; *U.S. Public*, pg. 864
INTERNATIONAL CONTAINER SYSTEMS—Intertape Polymer Group Inc.; *Int'l*, pg. 685
INTERNATIONAL GAME TECHNOLOGY; *U.S. Public*, pg. 900
JP FOODSERVICE, INC.; *U.S. Public*, pg. 918
KARP'S BAKERY SUPPLY; *U.S. Private*, pg. 608
HAROLD LEONARD & COMPANY, INC.; *U.S. Private*, pg. 660
LEONE FOOD SERVICE CORP.—Clayton, Dubilier & Rice, Inc; *U.S. Private*, pg. 244
LIVINGSTON UK LIMITED—Brammer plc; *Int'l*, pg. 212
LIVINGSTON U.K. LIMITED—Brammer plc; *Int'l*, pg. 212
LOGICON GEODYNAMIC—Northrop Grumman Corporation; *U.S. Public*, pg. 1199
LOZIER CORPORATION; *U.S. Private*, pg. 679
MELITTA FOODSERVICE CORP.—Melitta Unternehmensgruppe Bentz KG; *Int'l*, pg. 857
MELITTA NORTH AMERICA, INC.—Melitta Unternehmensgruppe Bentz KG; *Int'l*, pg. 857
MINNESOTA VALLEY ENGINEERING/CRYOGENIC ASSOCIATION; *U.S. Private*, pg. 751
MODERNFOLD, INC.; *U.S. Private*, pg. 755
NATIONAL RESTAURANT SUPPLY COMPANY; *U.S. Private*, pg. 786
OVERHOLTZER CHURCH FURNITURE, INC.; *U.S. Private*, pg. 823
PARISI INC./ROYAL STORE FIXTURE; *U.S. Private*, pg. 839
REPUBLIC STORAGE SYSTEMS COMPANY INC.; *U.S. Private*, pg. 924
SERVICIO DE VENTA AUTOMATICA, S.A. (S.V.A.)—Tabacalera, S.A.; *Int'l*, pg. 1345
SPARTAN AUTOMATIC RETAILERS; *U.S. Private*, pg. 1020
STANDARD COMMUNICATIONS CORP.—Marantz Japan Inc.; *Int'l*, pg. 841
STANDARD INDUSTRIES, INC.; *U.S. Private*, pg. 1031
STANDARD RESTAURANT EQUIPMENT CO.—Standard Industries, Inc.; *U.S. Private*, pg. 1031
H.A. STILES CO.—Saunders Brothers; *U.S. Private*, pg. 968
STUART ENTERTAINMENT INC.; *U.S. Public*, pg. 1526
SUNBEAM CORPORATION (CANADA) LIMITED—Sunbeam Corporation; *U.S. Public*, pg. 1533
SUSPA FRANCE SARL—Suspa Compart AG; *Int'l*, pg. 1322
TDK ELECTRONICS CORPORATION—TDK Corporation; *Int'l*, pg. 1336
TEXAS COPY SYSTEMS, INC.—Ikon Office Solutions, Inc.; *U.S. Public*, pg. 864
3COM CORPORATION; *U.S. Public*, pg. 1603
WASSERSTROM COMPANY; *U.S. Private*, pg. 1152
WOOD COLONY MILLWORKS—Overholtzer Church Furniture, Inc.; *U.S. Private*, pg. 823

5047 — MEDICAL, DENTAL & HOSPITAL EQUIPMENT & SUPPLIES-WHOLESALE

ABBOTT S.A.—Abbott Laboratories; *U.S. Public*, pg. 14
ACUSON CORPORATION; *U.S. Public*, pg. 18
AESCULAP, INC.—Aesculap Aktiengesellschaft; *Int'l*, pg. 29
ALLEGIANCE HEALTHCARE CORP.; *U.S. Public*, pg. 44
ALLEGIANCE HEALTHCARE INTERNATIONAL—Allegiance Healthcare Corp.; *U.S. Public*, pg. 45
ALLIED HEALTHCARE PRODUCTS, INC.; *U.S. Public*, pg. 48
ANALOGIC LTD.—Analogic Corporation; *U.S. Public*, pg. 109
ANGIOGRAPHIC DEVICES—Thermo Electron Corporation; *U.S. Public*, pg. 1596
APPLIED RESEARCH LABORATORIES SA—Rhone-Poulenc S.A.; *Int'l*, pg. 1111
ARRHYTHMIA RESEARCH TECHNOLOGY, INC.; *U.S. Public*, pg. 133
ASIA ELECTRONICS INC.—Toshiba Corporation; *Int'l*, pg. 1402
ASTRA AB; *Int'l*, pg. 93
ASTRA CHEMICALS S.A.—Astra AB; *Int'l*, pg. 93
ASTRA DANMARK A/S—Astra AB; *Int'l*, pg. 93
ASTRA EXPORT & TRADING AB—Astra AB; *Int'l*, pg. 93
ASTRA FARMACEUTICI S.P.A.—Astra AB; *Int'l*, pg. 93
ASTRA GMBH—Astra AB; *Int'l*, pg. 93
ASTRA GES. M.B.H.—Astra AB; *Int'l*, pg. 93
ASTRA HELLAS S.A.—Astra AB; *Int'l*, pg. 93
ASTRA JAPAN—Astra AB; *Int'l*, pg. 94
ASTRA JAPAN—Fujisawa Pharmaceutical Co. Ltd.; *Int'l*, pg. 525
ASTRA JAPAN LTD.—Astra AB; *Int'l*, pg. 94
ASTRA LAKEMEDAL AB—Astra AB; *Int'l*, pg. 93
ASTRA PHARMACEUTICA AG—Astra AB; *Int'l*, pg. 94
ASTRA PHARMACEUTICALS (HK) LTD.—Astra AB; *Int'l*, pg. 94
ASTRA PHARMACEUTICALS (IRELAND) LTD.—Astra AB; *Int'l*, pg. 94
ASTRA PHARMACEUTICALS (MALAYSIA) SDN BHD.—Astra AB; *Int'l*, pg. 94
ASTRA PHARMACEUTICALS PTY. LTD.—Astra AB; *Int'l*, pg. 94
ASTRA PHARMACEUTICALS (SINGAPORE) PTE. LTD.—Astra AB; *Int'l*, pg. 94
ASTRA PHARMACEUTICALS (TAIWAN) LTD.—Astra AB; *Int'l*, pg. 94
ASTRA TECH AB—Astra AB; *Int'l*, pg. 93
AUTOMATIC LIQUID PACKAGING, INC.; *U.S. Private*, pg. 101
B&K ULTRASOUND A/S—Analogic Corporation; *U.S. Public*, pg. 109
BEI MEDICAL SYSTEMS COMPANY; *U.S. Private*, pg. 106
BEI TECHNOLOGIES, INC.; *U.S. Public*, pg. 160
C.R. BARD, INC.; *U.S. Public*, pg. 189
BAUSCH & LOMB (HONG KONG) LTD.—Bausch & Lomb Incorporated; *U.S. Public*, pg. 195
BAXTER FENWAL DIVISION—Baxter International Inc.; *U.S. Public*, pg. 196
BECTON DICKINSON & CO., MASSACHUSETTS DIV.—Becton Dickinson & Company; *U.S. Public*, pg. 199
BECTON DICKINSON & COMPANY; *U.S. Public*, pg. 199
BERGEN BRUNSWIG MEDICAL CORPORATION—Bergen Brunswig Corporation; *U.S. Public*, pg. 214
BERLI JUCKER PUBLIC CO. LTD.—First Pacific Company Limited; *Int'l*, pg. 487
BIO-LOGIC FSC INTERNATIONAL CORP.—Bio-Logic Systems Corp.; *U.S. Public*, pg. 230
BIO-RAD LABORATORIES BV—Bio-Rad Laboratories, Inc.; *U.S. Public*, pg. 230
BIO-RAD LABORATORIES LTD.—Bio-Rad Laboratories, Inc.; *U.S. Public*, pg. 230
BIO-RAD LABORATORIES PTY. LIMITED—Bio-Rad Laboratories, Inc.; *U.S. Public*, pg. 230
BIO-RAD PACIFIC—Bio-Rad Laboratories, Inc.; *U.S. Public*, pg. 230
BIOLOGIC 83 RESEARCH CORP.—Bio-Logic Systems Corp.; *U.S. Public*, pg. 230
BIOMET, INC.; *U.S. Public*, pg. 231
BIOWHITTAKER UK LTD.—Cambrex Corporation; *U.S. Public*, pg. 297
BIRD PRODUCTS CORPORATION—Thermo Electron Corporation; *U.S. Public*, pg. 1591
BRISTOL-MYERS EQUIBLE CANADA INC.—Bristol-Myers Squibb Company; *U.S. Public*, pg. 255
BRISTOL-MYERS HEALTH CARE GROUP—Bristol-Myers Squibb Company; *U.S. Public*, pg. 253
BUFFALO HOSPITAL SUPPLY CO., INC.; *U.S. Private*, pg. 179
COBE LABORATORIES PTY LTD.-MELBOURNE—Incentive AB; *Int'l*, pg. 667
COBE LABORATORIES PTY LTD.-SYDNEY—Incentive AB; *Int'l*, pg. 667
CAIRE, INC.—Minnesota Valley Engineering/Cryogenic Association; *U.S. Private*, pg. 751
CANDELA K.K.—Candela Corporation; *U.S. Public*, pg. 301
CANTEL INDUSTRIES, INC.; *U.S. Public*, pg. 301
CAPINTEC INC.; *U.S. Private*, pg. 205
CAPRIUS, INC.; *U.S. Public*, pg. 303
CAREMARK INTERNATIONAL INC—Medpartners Inc.; *U.S. Public*, pg. 1082
CARSEN GROUP INC.—Cantel Industries, Inc.; *U.S. Public*, pg. 301
COBE LABORATORIES, INC.—Incentive AB; *Int'l*, pg. 667
COMPUTERIZED MEDICAL SYSTEMS, INC.; *U.S. Private*, pg. 260
CONSOLIDATED MEDICAL EQUIPMENT INTERNATIONAL, INC.—Conmed Corporation; *U.S. Public*, pg. 431
CRITICARE SYSTEMS, INC.; *U.S. Public*, pg. 459
DDF DENTAL DEPOTET FLEX A/S—Axel Johnson AB; *Int'l*, pg. 710
DRS MEDICAL SYSTEMS—DRS Technologies, Inc.; *U.S. Public*, pg. 475
DADE BEHRING—Bain Capital; *U.S. Private*, pg. 110
DAHL INTERNATIONAL AB; *Int'l*, pg. 359
DANEK MEDICAL INC.—Sofamor Danek Group, Inc.; *U.S. Public*, pg. 1482
DARBY GROUP OF COS.; *U.S. Private*, pg. 311
DEGUSSA CORP., DENTAL DEPT.—Degussa AG; *Int'l*, pg. 388
DELFT INSTRUMENTS N.V.; *Int'l*, pg. 388
DENTSPLY ARGENTINA S.A.C.I.—Dentsply International Inc.; *U.S. Public*, pg. 499
DENTSPLY CANADA—Dentsply International Inc.; *U.S. Public*, pg. 499
DENTSPLY GMBH—Dentsply International Inc.; *U.S. Public*, pg. 499
DENTSPLY INTERNATIONAL INC.; *U.S. Public*, pg. 498
DETREY DENTSPLY AG—Dentsply International Inc.; *U.S. Public*, pg. 500
DETREY DENTSPLY S.A.—Dentsply International Inc.; *U.S. Public*, pg. 500
DETREY/DENTSPLY S.R.L.—Dentsply International Inc.; *U.S. Public*, pg. 500
DIASONICS PTY. LTD.—IDB Holding Corporation; *Int'l*, pg. 644
DIRECT DENTAL SUPPLY CO.—Patterson Dental Company; *U.S. Public*, pg. 1265
DRACO LAKEMEDEL AB/TIKA LAKEMEDEL AB—Astra AB; *Int'l*, pg. 93
DU PONT DE NEMOURS (BELGIUM) S.A.—Du Pont (E.I. Du Pont De Nemours & Co.); *U.S. Public*, pg. 532
DYNEX TECHNOLOGIES GMBH—Thermo Electron Corporation; *U.S. Public*, pg. 1591
DYNEX TECHNOLOGIES, INC.—Thermo Electron Corporation; *U.S. Public*, pg. 1591
E FOR M CORP.—Marquette Medical Systems, Inc.; *U.S. Public*, pg. 1047
E-Z-EM, INC.; *U.S. Public*, pg. 540
E-Z-EM LTD.—E-Z-Em, Inc.; *U.S. Public*, pg. 540
ELA MEDICAL INC.—L'Oreal S.A.; *Int'l*, pg. 818
ELECTRO SCIENTIFIC INDUSTRIES B.V.—Electro Scientific Industries, Inc.; *U.S. Public*, pg. 569
ELSCINT DE MEXICO S. DE R.L. DE C.V.—Elscint Ltd.; *Int'l*, pg. 450
ELSCINT INC.—Elscint Ltd.; *Int'l*, pg. 450
ELSCINT ITALIA S.R.L.—Elscint Ltd.; *Int'l*, pg. 450
ELSCINT LTD.; *Int'l*, pg. 450
ELSCINT NV/SA—Elscint Ltd.; *Int'l*, pg. 450
FSE PTY. LTD.—Rhone-Poulenc S.A.; *Int'l*, pg. 1111
FRESENIUS MEDICAL CARE, INC.—Fresenius AG; *Int'l*, pg. 505
FRESENIUS MEDICAL CARE (NORTH AMERICA)—Fresenius AG; *Int'l*, pg. 505
GE MEDICAL SYSTEMS ASIA LTD.—General Electric Company; *U.S. Public*, pg. 713
GAMBRO AB—Incentive AB; *Int'l*, pg. 666
GAMBRO AB OY—Incentive AB; *Int'l*, pg. 667
GAMBRO ENGSTROM AB—Incentive AB; *Int'l*, pg. 667
GAMBRO MEDICOTEKNIK A/S—Incentive AB; *Int'l*, pg. 668
GAMBRO PTY LTD.—Incentive AB; *Int'l*, pg. 668
GAMBRO SALES AB—Incentive AB; *Int'l*, pg. 667
GELMAN IRELAND LTD.—Pall Corporation; *U.S. Public*, pg. 1253
GELMAN ITALY S.R.L.—Pall Corporation; *U.S. Public*, pg. 1253
GELMAN SCIENCES (DEUTSCHLAND) GMBH—Pall Corporation; *U.S. Public*, pg. 1253
GELMAN SCIENCES, INC. (CANADA)—Pall Corporation; *U.S. Public*, pg. 1253
GELMAN SCIENCES JAPAN LIMITED—Pall Corporation; *U.S. Public*, pg. 1253

GELMAN SCIENCES PTY. LTD.—Pall Corporation; U.S. Public, pg. 1253
GELMAN SCIENCES S.A.—Pall Corporation; U.S. Public, pg. 1253
THE GENERAL ELECTRIC COMPANY OF HONG KONG LTD.—The General Electric Company, p.l.c.; Int'l, pg. 546
THE GENERAL ELECTRIC COMPANY, P.L.C.; Int'l, pg. 543
GENERAL MEDICAL CORP.—McKesson Corporation; U.S. Public, pg. 1073
GENETRACE SYSTEMS, INC.—SRI International; U.S. Private, pg. 958
GESCO INTERNATIONAL—C.R. Bard, Inc.; U.S. Public, pg. 189
GETAC INSTRUMENTEBAU GMBH—Rhone-Poulenc S.A.; Int'l, pg. 1111
GETINGE INTERNATIONAL INC.—Getinge Industrier AB; Int'l, pg. 551
GISH INTERNATIONAL, INC.—Gish Biomedical, Inc.; U.S. Public, pg. 745
GRUPO CARSO S.A. DE C.V.; Int'l, pg. 572
GUARDIAN PRODUCTS, INC.—Sunrise Medical, Inc.; U.S. Public, pg. 1535
GUIDANT CORPORATION; U.S. Public, pg. 768
GULF SOUTH MEDICAL SUPPLY—Physician Sales and Services Inc.; U.S. Public, pg. 1294
GULF SOUTH MEDICAL SUPPLY, INC.—Physician Sales and Services Inc.; U.S. Public, pg. 1294
HAGEMEYER N.V.—First Pacific Company Limited; Int'l, pg. 487
HALL SURGICAL DIVISION—Bristol-Myers Squibb Company; U.S. Public, pg. 254
HASSLE LAKEMEDEL AB—Astra AB; Int'l, pg. 93
HERAEUS/KULZER, INC. - DENTAL PRODUCTS DIV.—Heraeus Holding GmbH; Int'l, pg. 616
HOLLISTER MEDICAL SYSTEMS DIVISION—Hollister Incorporated; U.S. Private, pg. 535
HOWMEDICA G.M.B.H.—Pfizer Inc.; U.S. Public, pg. 1282
I-FLOW CORPORATION; U.S. Public, pg. 851
INAMED B.V.—Inamed Corporation; U.S. Public, pg. 874
INAMED LTD.—Inamed Corporation; U.S. Public, pg. 874
INAMED S.R.L.—Inamed Corporation; U.S. Public, pg. 874
INSTRUMENTARIUM IMAGING, INC.; U.S. Private, pg. 565
INTERNATIONAL COSMETICS CO., LTD.; Int'l, pg. 684
INTERVASCULAR GMBH—Datascope Corp.; U.S. Public, pg. 488
INTERVASCULAR, S.A.—Datascope Corp.; U.S. Public, pg. 488
INVACARE HEALTH CARE FURNISHINGS—Invacare Corporation; U.S. Public, pg. 911
ISOLYSER COMPANY, INC.; U.S. Public, pg. 914
JOERN'S SUNRISE MEDICAL—Sunrise Medical, Inc.; U.S. Public, pg. 1536
P.T. JOHNSON & JOHNSON INDONESIA—Johnson & Johnson; U.S. Public, pg. 930
KINRAY INC.; U.S. Private, pg. 622
KONICA MEDICAL CORPORATION—Konica Corporation; Int'l, pg. 749
KVAERNER THUNE A/S—Kvaerner a.s.a.; Int'l, pg. 769
LABORATORIES ASTRA FRANCE—Astra AB; Int'l, pg. 94
LABORATORIO ASTRA ESPANA, S.A.—Astra AB; Int'l, pg. 94
LEICA INC.—Leica A.G.; Int'l, pg. 806
ELI LILLY AND COMPANY; U.S. Public, pg. 992
ELI LILLY JAPAN K.K.—Eli Lilly and Company; U.S. Public, pg. 994
LIVINGSTON S.A.—Brammer plc; Int'l, pg. 212
LIVINGSTON U.K. LIMITED—Brammer plc; Int'l, pg. 212
LORAD CORPORATION—Thermo Electron Corporation; U.S. Public, pg. 1595
MDS INC.; Int'l, pg. 826
MSA DE CHILE LTDA.—Mine Safety Appliances Co.; U.S. Public, pg. 1114
MSA DE MEXICO, S.A. DE C.V.—Mine Safety Appliances Co.; U.S. Public, pg. 1114
MSA DEL PERU S.A.—Mine Safety Appliances Co.; U.S. Public, pg. 1115
MSA ESPAÑOLA, S.A.—Mine Safety Appliances Co.; U.S. Public, pg. 1115
MSA JAPAN LTD.—Mine Safety Appliances Co.; U.S. Public, pg. 1115
MSA S.E. ASIA PTE. LTD.—Mine Safety Appliances Co.; U.S. Public, pg. 1115
MSA SWITZERLAND LTD.—Mine Safety Appliances Co.; U.S. Public, pg. 1115
MSA ZIMBABWE (PVT.) LIMITED—Mine Safety Appliances Co.; U.S. Public, pg. 1115
MATEC CORPORATION; U.S. Public, pg. 1056
MAXXIM MEDICAL, INC.; U.S. Public, pg. 1063
MCKESSON HOME HEALTH CARE DIVISION—McKesson Corporation; U.S. Public, pg. 1073
MCKESSON MEDICAL SUPPLY—McKesson Corporation; U.S. Public, pg. 1073
MED-LAB SUPPLY COMPANY, INC.; U.S. Private, pg. 726
MEDCREST DIV.—Medline Industries, Inc.; U.S. Private, pg. 728
MEDELEC ESPANA S.A.—Vickers PLC; Int'l, pg. 1467
MEDELEC NORTHERN EUROPE—Vickers PLC; Int'l, pg. 1467
MEDICA BV—Maxxim Medical, Inc.; U.S. Public, pg. 1063
MEDICAL ACTION INDUSTRIES INC.; U.S. Public, pg. 1079
MEDICAL DATA INTELLIGENCE AB—Incentive AB; Int'l, pg. 667
MEDICAL INNOVATIONS CORP.—Ballard Medical Products; U.S. Public, pg. 171
MEDICAL SURGICAL SPECIALTIES, LTD.; U.S. Private, pg. 728
MEDTRONIC ASIA, LTD.—Medtronic, Inc.; U.S. Public, pg. 1083
MEDTRONIC EUROPE S.A./N.V.—Medtronic, Inc.; U.S. Public, pg. 1083
MEDTRONIC GMBH—Medtronic, Inc.; U.S. Public, pg. 1083
MEDTRONIC HEART VALVE DIVISION—Medtronic, Inc.; U.S. Public, pg. 1083
MEDTRONIC JAPAN CO., LTD.—Medtronic, Inc.; U.S. Public, pg. 1084
MEDTRONIC OF CANADA—Medtronic, Inc.; U.S. Public, pg. 1084
MENTOR CORPORATION; U.S. Public, pg. 1086
MESA LABORATORIES, INC.; U.S. Public, pg. 1099
MILLIPORE B.V.—Millipore Corporation; U.S. Public, pg. 1113
MINNESOTA NIGERIA LIMITED—3M; U.S. Public, pg. 1606
MOORE MEDICAL CORP.; U.S. Public, pg. 1128
NARCO MEDICAL SERVICES INC.—Vickers PLC; Int'l, pg. 1468
NELLCOR DE MEXICO, S.A. DE C.V.—Mallinckrodt Inc.; U.S. Public, pg. 1040
NELLCOR PURITAN BENNETT BELGIUM N.V./S.A.—Mallinckrodt Inc.; U.S. Public, pg. 1040
NELLCOR PURITAN BENNETT EUROPE B.V.—Mallinckrodt Inc.; U.S. Public, pg. 1040
NELLCOR PURITAN BENNETT FRANCE S.A.R.L.—Mallinckrodt Inc.; U.S. Public, pg. 1040
NELLCOR PURITAN BENNETT GMBH—Mallinckrodt Inc.; U.S. Public, pg. 1040
NELLCOR PURITAN BENNETT HK LTD.—Mallinckrodt Inc.; U.S. Public, pg. 1040
NELLCOR PURITAN BENNETT INCORPORATED—Mallinckrodt Inc.; U.S. Public, pg. 1039
NEXAIR—nexAir, LLC; U.S. Private, pg. 797
NEXAIR, LLC; U.S. Private, pg. 797
NICOLET INSTRUMENT GMBH—Thermo Electron Corporation; U.S. Public, pg. 1594
NICOLET INSTRUMENT S.A.R.L.—Thermo Electron Corporation; U.S. Public, pg. 1594
NICOLET JAPAN CORP.-OSAKA—Thermo Electron Corporation; U.S. Public, pg. 1594
NICOLET LIMITED—Thermo Electron Corporation; U.S. Public, pg. 1594
OEC MEDICAL SYSTEMS, INC.; U.S. Public, pg. 1207
OHMEDA LTD.—The BOC Group plc; Int'l, pg. 122
OHMEDA SA—The BOC Group plc; Int'l, pg. 122
OKI SYSTEMS (NORWAY) A/S—Oki Electric Industry Company, Ltd.; Int'l, pg. 1000
OLDELFT B.V.—Delft Instruments N.V.; Int'l, pg. 389
ORGANON TEKNIKA MEDIZINSCHE PRODUKTE GMBH—Akzo Nobel N.V.; Int'l, pg. 45
ORGANON TEKNIKA NEDERLAND BV—Akzo Nobel N.V.; Int'l, pg. 44
ORTHOFIX INC.—Orthofix International N.V.; Int'l, pg. 1011
OTSUKA ELECTRONICS (U.S.A.) INC.—Otsuka Pharmaceutical Co., Ltd.; Int'l, pg. 1013
OWENS & MINOR INC.; U.S. Public, pg. 1236
OXFORD INSTRUMENTS-MEDICAL SYSTEMS DIV.—Oxford Instruments plc; Int'l, pg. 1018
PSICOR, INC.—Baxter International Inc.; U.S. Public, pg. 196
PSS—Physician Sales and Services Inc.; U.S. Public, pg. 1294
PALL BIOMEDICAL FRANCE—Pall Corporation; U.S. Public, pg. 1254
PALL ITALIA S.R.L.—Pall Corporation; U.S. Public, pg. 1254
PATTERSON DENTAL COMPANY; U.S. Public, pg. 1265
PATTERSON DENTAL SUPPLY, INC.—Patterson Dental Company; U.S. Public, pg. 1265
PERFORMANCE MEDICAL GROUP; U.S. Private, pg. 853
PHYSICIAN SALES AND SERVICES INC.; U.S. Public, pg. 1293
PHYSICIAN SALES & SERVICES INC.—Physician Sales and Services Inc.; U.S. Public, pg. 1294
POLAR WARE COMPANY; U.S. Private, pg. 873
POLESTAR LABS, INC.; U.S. Private, pg. 874
PREMIER DENTAL PRODUCTS COMPANY; U.S. Private, pg. 881
PROPPER MANUFACTURING CO., INC.; U.S. Private, pg. 891
PROTOCOL SYSTEMS, INC.; U.S. Public, pg. 1336
PURITAN-BENNETT CANADA LTD.—Mallinckrodt Inc.; U.S. Public, pg. 1040
QUANTRONIX CORP.—Excel Technology, Inc.; U.S. Public, pg. 599
QUIDEL CORPORATION; U.S. Public, pg. 1352
QUINTON INSTRUMENT COMPANY—American Home Products Corporation; U.S. Public, pg. 80
RADIOMETER AMERICA INC.—Radiometer A/S; Int'l, pg. 1083
RADIOMETER DEUTSCHLAND GMBH—Radiometer A/S; Int'l, pg. 1084
RADIOMETER INTERNATIONAL A/S—Radiometer A/S; Int'l, pg. 1083
RADIOMETER K.K.—Radiometer A/S; Int'l, pg. 1084
RADIOMETER LTD.—Radiometer A/S; Int'l, pg. 1084
RADIOMETER MEDICAL A/S—Radiometer A/S; Int'l, pg. 1083
RADIOMETER NEDERLAND B.V.—Radiometer A/S; Int'l, pg. 1084
RADIOMETER PACIFIC LTD.—Radiometer A/S; Int'l, pg. 1084
RADIOMETER PACIFIC PTY. LTD.—Radiometer A/S; Int'l, pg. 1084
RADIOMETER RSCH GMBH—Radiometer A/S; Int'l, pg. 1084
RADIOMETER S.A.—Radiometer A/S; Int'l, pg. 1084
RADIOMETER TRADING K.K.—Radiometer A/S; Int'l, pg. 1084
RANCARE INC.—McKesson Corporation; U.S. Public, pg. 1073
RANSOM & RANDOLPH DIVISION—Dentsply International Inc.; U.S. Public, pg. 499
REXAM MEDICAL PACKAGING BRISTOL—Rexam PLC; Int'l, pg. 1106
S & W ELEKTROMEDIZIN GMBH—Vickers PLC; Int'l, pg. 1467
SCIEX, INC.—MDS Inc.; Int'l, pg. 827
HENRY SCHEIN, INC.; U.S. Public, pg. 1437
SELLES MEDICAL LIMITED—Alliance UniChem PLC; Int'l, pg. 58
SHIELD HEALTHCARE CENTERS—Kobayashi Pharmaceutical Co., Ltd.; Int'l, pg. 740
SIEMENS MEDICAL SYSTEMS, INC.—Siemens AG; Int'l, pg. 1246
SILVERMAN'S DENTAL SUPPLIES INC.—Axel Johnson AB; Int'l, pg. 710
DR. T.C. SMITH CO. INC.—Bergen Brunswig Corporation; U.S. Public, pg. 214
SONOTRON HOLDING AG—IDB Holding Corporation; Int'l, pg. 644
SOPUR MEDIZINTECHNIK GMBH—Sunrise Medical, Inc.; U.S. Public, pg. 1536
SORIN BIOMEDICA LTD.—Fiat Auto SpA; Int'l, pg. 483
SORIN BIOMEDICA OY—Fiat Auto SpA; Int'l, pg. 483
SQUIBB MEDICAL SYSTEMS EUROPA GMBH—Bristol-Myers Squibb Company; U.S. Public, pg. 256
STANDARD MEDICAL IMAGING, INC.; U.S. Private, pg. 1032
SUMITOMO 3M LIMITED—3M; U.S. Public, pg. 1606
SUNRISE MEDICAL CANADA INC.—Sunrise Medical, Inc.; U.S. Public, pg. 1536
SURGITEK—Bristol-Myers Squibb Company; U.S. Public, pg. 253
SYMBICOM AB—Astra AB; Int'l, pg. 93
TAYLOR HOME HEALTH INC.—Integrated Health Services, Inc.; U.S. Public, pg. 885
THERMO-MIZER ENVIRONMENTAL CORP.; U.S. Public, pg. 1596
P.T. 3M INDONESIA—3M; U.S. Public, pg. 1606
TOKUYAMA EUROPE GMBH—Tokuyama Corporation; Int'l, pg. 1394
TOSHIBA AMERICA MEDICAL SYSTEMS, INC.—Toshiba Corporation; Int'l, pg. 1405
TOSHIBA MEDICAL DO BRASIL LTDA.—Toshiba Corporation; Int'l, pg. 1407
TOSHIBA MEDICAL FRANCE S.A.—Toshiba Corporation; Int'l, pg. 1407
TOSHIBA MEDICAL SYSTEMS EUROPE B.V.—Toshiba Corporation; Int'l, pg. 1407
TOSOH MEDICS, INC.—Tosoh Corporation; Int'l, pg. 1407
TRUE LIFE; Int'l, pg. 1425
TUTA LABORATORIES (AUSTRALIA) PTY., LTD.—Otsuka Pharmaceutical Co., Ltd.; Int'l, pg. 1014
II-VI INCORPORATED; U.S. Public, pg. 1647
UTAH MEDICAL PRODUCTS, INC.; U.S. Public, pg. 1700
UTAH MEDICAL PRODUCTS LTD.—Utah Medical Products, Inc.; U.S. Public, pg. 1700
VWR SCIENTIFIC PRODUCTS; U.S. Public, pg. 1703
VICKER MEDICAL NEDERLANDS—Vickers PLC; Int'l, pg. 1467
VINGMED SOUND A/S—IDB Holding Corporation; Int'l, pg. 644
VITAL SIGNS—Vital Signs, Inc.; U.S. Public, pg. 1723
WEST INTERNATIONAL SALES CORPORATION—The West Company, Incorporated; U.S. Public, pg. 1755
XRE CORPORATION—Thermo Electron Corporation; U.S. Public, pg. 1595
XOMED SURGICAL PRODUCTS—Bristol-Myers Squibb Company; U.S. Public, pg. 253
YOSHITOMI-ASTRA LTD.—Astra AB; Int'l, pg. 94
YOUNG DENTAL MANUFACTURING; U.S. Private, pg. 1201
ZIMMER CHIRUGIE G.M.B.H.—Bristol-Myers Squibb Company; U.S. Public, pg. 256
ZIMMER, INC.—Bristol-Myers Squibb Company; U.S. Public, pg. 254
ZIMMER OF CANADA LIMITED—Bristol-Myers Squibb Company; U.S. Public, pg. 257
ZIMMER ORTHOPAEDIC IMPLANT DIVISION—Bristol-Myers Squibb Company; U.S. Public, pg. 254

5048 — OPTHALMIC GOODS-WHOLESALE

AMERICAN OPTICAL CORP.—American Optical Corporation; U.S. Private, pg. 60
BBGR SA—Essilor International Compagnie Generale d'Optique; Int'l, pg. 462
BAUSCH & LOMB INTERNATIONAL, INC.—Bausch & Lomb Incorporated; U.S. Public, pg. 195
BAUSCH & LOMB SVENSKA AB—Bausch & Lomb Incorporated; U.S. Public, pg. 195
CIBA-GEIGY SERVICES AG—Novartis AG; Int'l, pg. 979
THE COOPER COMPANIES, INC.; U.S. Public, pg. 442
DELFT INSTRUMENTS N.V.; Int'l, pg. 388
FLO-LITE OPTICAL CORP.—Essilor International Compagnie Generale d'Optique; Int'l, pg. 462
KYOCERA CANADA, INC.—Kyocera Corporation; Int'l, pg. 776
LEICA INC.—Leica A.G.; Int'l, pg. 806
LOGO OF THE AMERICAS—Essilor International Compagnie Generale d'Optique; Int'l, pg. 462
OPTISCHE WERKE G. RODENSTOCK; Int'l, pg. 1007
PENTAX U.K. LTD.—Asahi Optical Co., Ltd.; Int'l, pg. 85
PHOTOCENTRON INC.—Essilor International Compagnie Generale d'Optique; Int'l, pg. 462
PILKINGTON VISIONCARE—Pilkington Plc; Int'l, pg. 1056
RODENSTOCK USA, INC.—Optische Werke G. Rodenstock; Int'l, pg. 1007
SILOR OPTICAL INC.—Essilor International Compagnie Generale d'Optique; Int'l, pg. 462
TASCO SALES INC.—Rice, Sangalis, Toole & Wilson; U.S. Private, pg. 928
CARL ZEISS OPTICAL, INC.—Carl-Zeiss-Stiftung; Int'l, pg. 1523

5049 — PROFESSIONAL EQUIPMENT & SUPPLIES-WHOLESALE, NEC

ACCUCARE DIV.—Medline Industries, Inc.; U.S. Private, pg. 728

ACUSON CANADA, LTD.—Acuson Corporation; U.S. Public, pg. 18
ALLIEDSIGNAL INC., CHEMICAL INTERMEDIATES—AlliedSignal Inc.; U.S. Public, pg. 51
AQUILA BIOPHARMACEUTICALS, INC.; U.S. Public, pg. 126
AYDIN CONTROLS DIV.—Aydin Corporation; U.S. Public, pg. 158
BTR, INC.—BTR plc; Int'l, pg. 127
BTR MED/VET—BTR plc; Int'l, pg. 127
BALTIMORE STATIONERY CO./TOTAL OFFICE; U.S. Private, pg. 113
BATAAN OPTICAL INC.—Essilor International Compagnie Generale d'Optique; Int'l, pg. 462
BEL-ART PRODUCTS; U.S. Private, pg. 130
BIO-RAD SEMICONDUCTOR SYSTEMS DIV.—Bio-Rad Laboratories, Inc.; U.S. Public, pg. 230
BOREL & DUNNER, INC.—Brown & Sharpe Manufacturing Company; U.S. Public, pg. 260
BRAMMER PLC; Int'l, pg. 212
BRINKMANN INSTRUMENTS (CANADA) LTD.—Brinkmann Instruments, Inc.; U.S. Private, pg. 169
BRODART COMPANY; U.S. Private, pg. 170
BUEHLER, LIMITED—Emerson Electric Co.; U.S. Public, pg. 574
JOHN O. BUTLER COMPANY (CANADA)—Sunstar Inc.; Int'l, pg. 1320
JOHN O. BUTLER COMPANY (SWEDEN)—Sunstar Inc.; Int'l, pg. 1321
CADILLAC PLASTIC & CHEMICAL CO.—M.A. Hanna Company; U.S. Public, pg. 781
CANTEL INDUSTRIES, INC.; U.S. Public, pg. 301
CARSEN GROUP INC.—Cantel Industries, Inc.; U.S. Public, pg. 301
DAHL INTERNATIONAL AB; Int'l, pg. 359
DANSK INDUSTRI SYNDIKAT A/S; Int'l, pg. 381
DATASCOPE B.V.—Datascope Corp.; U.S. Public, pg. 488
DATASCOPE GMBH—Datascope Corp.; U.S. Public, pg. 488
DATASCOPE MEDICAL CO., LTD.—Datascope Corp.; U.S. Public, pg. 488
DATASCOPE SARL—Datascope Corp.; U.S. Public, pg. 488
DELFT INSTRUMENTS N.V.; Int'l, pg. 388
DENTSPLY ASH—Dentsply International Inc.; U.S. Public, pg. 499
DENTSPLY INTERNATIONAL INC.; U.S. Public, pg. 498
DERMAL MANAGEMENT SYS.—Medline Industries, Inc.; U.S. Private, pg. 728
DIETZGEN DE MEXICO S.A. DE C.V.—Dietzgen Corporation; U.S. Private, pg. 332
DYNACOR DIV.—Medline Industries, Inc.; U.S. Private, pg. 728
THE EAST ASIATIC COMPANY LTD. A/S; Int'l, pg. 430
EDMUND SCIENTIFIC COMPANY; U.S. Private, pg. 364
ELECTRO SCIENTIFIC INDUSTRIES GMBH—Electro Scientific Industries, Inc.; U.S. Public, pg. 569
ELECTRO SCIENTIFIC INDUSTRIES LTD.—Electro Scientific Industries, Inc.; U.S. Public, pg. 569
ELECTRO SCIENTIFIC INDUSTRIES SARL—Electro Scientific Industries, Inc.; U.S. Public, pg. 569
EQUIPAMENTOS CIENTIFICOS INSTRON LTD.—Instron Corporation; U.S. Public, pg. 883
EQUIPMENT SALES CO.—Esterline Technologies Corporation; U.S. Public, pg. 594
FINNIGAN MAT INSTITUTE—Thermo Electron Corporation; U.S. Public, pg. 1591
GEORG FISCHER DISA INC.—Dansk Industri Syndikat A/S; Int'l, pg. 382
GELMAN IRELAND LTD.—Pall Corporation; U.S. Public, pg. 1253
GELMAN SCIENCES (DEUTSCHLAND) GMBH—Pall Corporation; U.S. Public, pg. 1253
GELMAN SCIENCES, INC. (CANADA)—Pall Corporation; U.S. Public, pg. 1253
GELMAN SCIENCES JAPAN LIMITED—Pall Corporation; U.S. Public, pg. 1253
GELMAN SCIENCES S.A.—Pall Corporation; U.S. Public, pg. 1253
HACH INTERNATIONAL FOREIGN SALES CO., INC.—Hach Company; U.S. Public, pg. 773
HARTMANN & BRAUN AG—Mannesmann A.G.; Int'l, pg. 835
HITACHI INSTRUMENTS, INC.—Hitachi, Ltd.; Int'l, pg. 622
ITW HEARTLAND COMPONENTS—Illinois Tool Works Inc.; U.S. Public, pg. 866
INSTRON EXPORT CORP.—Instron Corporation; U.S. Public, pg. 882
INSTRON JAPAN CO., LTD.—Instron Corporation; U.S. Public, pg. 882
INSTRON S.A.—Instron Corporation; U.S. Public, pg. 883
JEOL (U.S.A.), INC.—JEOL, Ltd.; Int'l, pg. 697
JOHNSON & JOHNSON PRODUCTOS—Johnson & Johnson; U.S. Public, pg. 928
AXEL JOHNSON LAB SYSTEM A/S—Axel Johnson AB; Int'l, pg. 711
KEWAUNEE SCIENTIFIC CORPORATION; U.S. Public, pg. 953
LEICA INC.—Leica A.G.; Int'l, pg. 806
MARKS & MORGAN JEWELERS INC; U.S. Private, pg. 705
METTLER-TOLEDO, INC.—AEA Investors Inc.; U.S. Private, pg. 4
MICRO-CONTROLE ITALIA SRL—Newport Corporation; U.S. Public, pg. 1179
NEDCO (NEWPORT EUROPEAN DISTRIBUTION CO.)—Newport Corporation; U.S. Public, pg. 1179
NRG NUFUEL CO.—Telco Capital Corporation; U.S. Private, pg. 1073
NRG TECHNOLOGY, INC.—Telco Capital Corporation; U.S. Private, pg. 1073
NEW BRUNSWICK SCIENTIFIC BENELUX B.V.—New Brunswick Scientific Co., Inc.; U.S. Public, pg. 1170
NEW BRUNSWICK SCIENTIFIC GMBH—New Brunswick Scientific Co., Inc.; U.S. Public, pg. 1170
NEW BRUNSWICK SCIENTIFIC (UK) LTD.—New Brunswick Scientific Co., Inc.; U.S. Public, pg. 1170
NEWPORT B.V.—Newport Corporation; U.S. Public, pg. 1179
NEWPORT GMBH—Newport Corporation; U.S. Public, pg. 1179
NEWPORT INSTRUMENTS AG—Newport Corporation; U.S. Public, pg. 1179
NEWPORT INSTRUMENTS CANADA CORP.—Newport Corporation; U.S. Public, pg. 1179
NEWPORT LTD.—Newport Corporation; U.S. Public, pg. 1179
NICOLET INSTRUMENT GMBH—Thermo Electron Corporation; U.S. Public, pg. 1594
NICOLET INSTRUMENT S.A.R.L.—Thermo Electron Corporation; U.S. Public, pg. 1594
NICOLET JAPAN CORP.-OSAKA—Thermo Electron Corporation; U.S. Public, pg. 1594
NICOLET LIMITED—Thermo Electron Corporation; U.S. Public, pg. 1594
NIPPON DIONEX K.K.—Dionex Corporation; U.S. Public, pg. 510
NIPPON JARRELL-ASH COMPANY, LTD.—Thermo Electron Corporation; U.S. Public, pg. 1596
NOVAMETRIX MEDICAL SYSTEMS INC.; U.S. Public, pg. 1203
ORION RESEARCH FAR EAST INC.—Thermo Electron Corporation; U.S. Public, pg. 1592
OXFORD INSTRUMENTS PLC; Int'l, pg. 1018
OYANG ESI, INC.—Electro Scientific Industries, Inc.; U.S. Public, pg. 569
QUANTRONIX CORP.—Excel Technology, Inc.; U.S. Public, pg. 599
QUANTRONIX, GMBH—Excel Technology, Inc.; U.S. Public, pg. 599
QUEST MEDICAL, INC.; U.S. Public, pg. 1352
RADIO HOLLAND GROUP-SURVEY EQUIP.—SAIT-RadioHolland Group S.A.; Int'l, pg. 1151
RUSSELL PH LIMITED—Thermo Electron Corporation; U.S. Public, pg. 1592
SKF EQUIPEMENTS S.N.C.—AB SKF; Int'l, pg. 1158
SARGENT-WELCH SCIENTIFIC COMPANY—VWR Scientific Products; U.S. Public, pg. 1704
SEMCO INDUSTRIES INC.; U.S. Private, pg. 983
SHEER PRIDE LTD.—Lonrho plc; Int'l, pg. 817
SHIMADZU CORPORATION; Int'l, pg. 1232
SPAULDING COMPANY, INC.—Semco Industries Inc.; U.S. Private, pg. 983
STANDARD COMMUNICATIONS CORP.—Marantz Japan Inc.; Int'l, pg. 841
TAPETECH TOOL CO., INC.—AXIA Incorporated; U.S. Private, pg. 103
TASCO SALES INC.—Rice, Sangalis, Toole & Wilson; U.S. Private, pg. 928
THERMO INSTRUMENT SYSTEMS B.V.—Thermo Electron Corporation; U.S. Public, pg. 1596
THERMO INSTRUMENT SYSTEMS GMBH—Thermo Electron Corporation; U.S. Public, pg. 1596
TOKUYAMA AMERICA INC.—Tokuyama Corporation; Int'l, pg. 1394
TOSHIBA MEDICAL SYSTEMS CO., LTD.—Toshiba Corporation; Int'l, pg. 1404
TRIMBLE NAVIGATION EUROPE LTD.—Trimble Navigation Limited; U.S. Public, pg. 1638
TRIMBLE NAVIGATION JAPAN—Trimble Navigation Limited; U.S. Public, pg. 1638
TRIMBLE NAVIGATION LTD. DEUTSCHLAND—Trimble Navigation Limited; U.S. Public, pg. 1638
TRIMBLE NAVIGATION LTD., TEXAS—Trimble Navigation Limited; U.S. Public, pg. 1638
TRIMBLE NAVIGATION LTD., WASHINGTON, D.C.—Trimble Navigation Limited; U.S. Public, pg. 1638
VWR SCIENTIFIC PRODUCTS; U.S. Public, pg. 1703
VAN SON HOLLAND INK CORP. OF AMERICA; U.S. Private, pg. 1133
VAN SWAAY TRADING B.V.—Internatio-Muller N.V.; Int'l, pg. 681
WAVETEK CORPORATION; U.S. Private, pg. 1154
WHATMAN PLC; Int'l, pg. 1498
WILCO REPROGRAPHIC, INC.; U.S. Private, pg. 1176
YRJ CORPORATION—Wilco Reprographic, Inc.; U.S. Private, pg. 1176
CARL ZEISS OPTICAL, INC.—Carl-Zeiss-Stiftung; Int'l, pg. 1523

5051 — METALS SERVICE CENTERS & OFFICES

AG INDUSTRIES, INC.—AG Ajikawa Corporation; Int'l, pg. 40
OY ALGOL AB; Int'l, pg. 15
AMI METALS, INC.—Reliance Steel & Aluminum Co.; U.S. Public, pg. 1375
ATR WIRE & CABLE CO., INC.—Itochu Corporation; Int'l, pg. 694
ACEROS BOEHLER DEL PERU S.A.—Voest-Alpine Stahl AG; Int'l, pg. 1471
ACEROS BOEHLER S.A.—Voest-Alpine Stahl AG; Int'l, pg. 1471
ACIERS FRANCOSTEEL CANADA—Groupe Usinor; Int'l, pg. 572
ACOS PHOENIX-BOEHLER LTDA.—Voest-Alpine Stahl AG; Int'l, pg. 1471
ADVANCE STEEL CO.; U.S. Private, pg. 21
AFCO METALS, INC.—Inland Steel Industries, Inc.; U.S. Public, pg. 879
AFFIVAL INC.—Viag AG; Int'l, pg. 1465
AFFIVAL S.A.—Viag AG; Int'l, pg. 1466
AICHI STEEL WORKS, LTD.—Aichi Steel Works, Ltd.; Int'l, pg. 36
AKAGANE KAUIN SANGYO KABUSHIKI KAISHA—Benguet Corporation; Int'l, pg. 187
ALAMO INDUSTRIAL GROUP; U.S. Private, pg. 31
ALAMO IRON WORKS—Alamo Industrial Group; U.S. Private, pg. 31
ALASKAN COPPER COMPANIES; U.S. Private, pg. 31
ALCAN RECYCLING—Alcan Aluminium Limited; Int'l, pg. 50
ALCOA INTER-AMERICA CANADA LTD.—Aluminum Company of America; U.S. Public, pg. 62
ALCOA INTER-AMERICA, INC.—Aluminum Company of America; U.S. Public, pg. 60
ALCOA ITALIA S.P.A.—Aluminum Company of America; U.S. Public, pg. 62
ALCOA JAPAN LIMITED—Aluminum Company of America; U.S. Public, pg. 62
ALLEGHENY TELEDYNE INCORPORATED; U.S. Public, pg. 43
ALLIED BUILDING PRODUCTS CORPORATION; U.S. Private, pg. 38
ALRO GROUP; U.S. Private, pg. 45
ALRO GROUP, CLEARWATER—Alro Group; U.S. Private, pg. 46
ALRO GROUP, ORLANDO—Alro Group; U.S. Private, pg. 46
ALSTRIP EAST—Allegheny Teledyne Incorporated; U.S. Public, pg. 43
ALSTRIP, INC.—Allegheny Teledyne Incorporated; U.S. Public, pg. 43
ALSTRIP SOUTH—Allegheny Teledyne Incorporated; U.S. Public, pg. 43
ALUMINUM COMPANY OF AMERICA; U.S. Public, pg. 60
AMALGAMATED METAL CORPORATION PLC—Preussag AG; Int'l, pg. 1071
AMALGAMET, INC.—Preussag AG; Int'l, pg. 1071
AMCAN SPECIALTY STEELS—Carpenter Technology Corporation; U.S. Public, pg. 308
AMCAST AUTOMOTIVE—Amcast Industrial Corporation; U.S. Public, pg. 63
AMERICAN FINE WIRE CORP.—Kulicke & Soffa Industries, Inc.; U.S. Public, pg. 969
AMERICAN STEEL LLC—Reliance Steel & Aluminum Co.; U.S. Public, pg. 1375
AMERICAN STRIP STEEL INC.; U.S. Private, pg. 62
AMERICAN TANK & FABRICATING CO.; U.S. Private, pg. 63
AMPCO METAL LTD.—Ampco Metal Incorporated; U.S. Private, pg. 67
ANCHOR WIRE ROPE DIV.—Okura & Co.; Int'l, pg. 1001
ANGLO BLACKWELLS LTD.—Viag AG; Int'l, pg. 1465
ANGLO-SWISS ALUMINIUM COMPANY LTD.—Alusuisse-Lonza Holding Ltd.; Int'l, pg. 68
ARCHER PIPE & TUBE CO., INC.—Marubeni Corporation; Int'l, pg. 845
ARROW THOMPSON METALS—Thompson Steel Co., Inc.; U.S. Private, pg. 1083
ART IRON, INC.; U.S. Private, pg. 86
ASARCO INCORPORATED; U.S. Public, pg. 137
ASBURY CARBONS, INC.; U.S. Private, pg. 87
ASOMA CORPORATION; U.S. Private, pg. 89
ATKINSON; U.S. Public, pg. 143
ATLAS ALLOYS—Rio Algom Limited; Int'l, pg. 1118
AUSTRALIAN NATIONAL INDUSTRIES LIMITED; Int'l, pg. 100
AUTO BLANKERS—Kasle Steel Corporation; U.S. Private, pg. 608
AVESTA SHEFFIELD, INC.—British Steel Plc; Int'l, pg. 221
AZCON CORP.—Blue Tee Corporation; U.S. Private, pg. 153
B & K STEEL & SUPPLY, INC.; U.S. Private, pg. 105
BICC CABLES ASIA-PACIFIC PTE. LTD.—BICC plc; Int'l, pg. 120
I. BAHCALL STEEL & PIPE INC.—Russel Metals Inc.; Int'l, pg. 1150
BALDWIN INTERNATIONAL, INC.—Russel Metals Inc.; Int'l, pg. 1150
BALDWIN STEEL COMPANY—Duferco Steel Inc.; U.S. Private, pg. 345
BALDWIN STEEL COMPANY—Deutsche Babcock AG; Int'l, pg. 401
BEKAERT ASSOCIATES, INC.—N.V. Bekaert S.A.; Int'l, pg. 184
BEKAERT CORPORATION—N.V. Bekaert S.A.; Int'l, pg. 184
BENJAMIN METALS COMPANY; U.S. Private, pg. 133
BILLITON METALS, INC.—Royal Dutch/Shell Group of Companies; Int'l, pg. 1136
BING STEEL INC.; U.S. Private, pg. 144
BLEIM STEEL COMPANY—Marubeni Corporation; Int'l, pg. 845
BOHLER ACIERS SPECIAUX S.A.R.L.—Voest-Alpine Stahl AG; Int'l, pg. 1471
BOHLER AG—Voest-Alpine Stahl AG; Int'l, pg. 1471
BOHLER-UDDEHOLM CORP.—Voest-Alpine Stahl AG; Int'l, pg. 1471
BOLIDEN ORE & METALS—Trelleborg AB; Int'l, pg. 1422
BOWMAN & KEMP STEEL & SUPPLY COMPANY—B & K Steel & Supply, Inc.; U.S. Private, pg. 105
BRACONNOT—Royal Dutch/Shell Group of Companies; Int'l, pg. 1138
BRITISH STEEL CANADA INC.—British Steel Plc; Int'l, pg. 222
BRITISH STEEL GENERAL STEELS DIVISION—British Steel Plc; Int'l, pg. 220
BRITISH STEEL, INC.—British Steel Plc; Int'l, pg. 221
BRITISH STEEL PLC; Int'l, pg. 220
BRITISH STEEL SERVICE CENTRES LTD.—British Steel Plc; Int'l, pg. 221
BRODERNA EDSTRAND AB—Trelleborg AB; Int'l, pg. 1422
BRODRENE DAHL A/S—Dahl International AB; Int'l, pg. 359
BROWN-STRAUSS STEEL—Blue Tee Corporation; U.S. Private, pg. 153
BRUSH WELLMAN GMBH—Brush Wellman Inc.; U.S. Public, pg. 266
BRUSH WELLMAN (JAPAN) LTD.—Brush Wellman Inc.; U.S. Public, pg. 266

BRUSH WELLMAN LTD.—Brush Wellman Inc.; *U.S. Public, pg. 266*
CMC (AUSTRALIA) PTY. LIMITED—Commercial Metals Company; *U.S. Public*, pg. 413
CMC FAREAST LIMITED—Commercial Metals Company; *U.S. Public*, pg. 413
CMC INTERNATIONAL (S.E. ASIA) PTE. LIMITED—Commercial Metals Company; *U.S. Public*, pg. 413
CMT STEELS & SUPPLIES—Caparo Group Ltd.; *Int'l*, pg. 265
C.S. ALUMINIUM CORPORATION—China Steel Corporation; *Int'l*, pg. 285
C.S.I. CORPORACION SIDERURGIA INTEGRAL, S.A.—SEPI; *Int'l*, pg. 1224
CT&I CORP. OF WISCONSIN—Chicago Tube & Iron Co.; *U.S. Private*, pg. 235
CABVAL—Haynes International, Inc.; *U.S. Public*, pg. 801
CAMALLOY, INCORPORATED; *U.S. Private*, pg. 202
CAMBRIDGE-LEE (EUROPE) LTD.—Cambridge-Lee Industries, Inc.; *U.S. Private*, pg. 202
CAMBRIDGE STREET METAL CO.; *U.S. Private*, pg. 203
CAMBRIDGE-LEE CANADA LTD.—Cambridge-Lee Industries, Inc.; *U.S. Private*, pg. 202
CAMERON ASHLEY BUILDING PRODUCTS, INC; *U.S. Public*, pg. 298
CANADIAN ERECTORS LTD.; *Int'l*, pg. 256
CAPARO GROUP LTD.; *Int'l*, pg. 264
CAPARO INDUSTRIES PLC—Caparo Group Ltd.; *Int'l*, pg. 264
CAPARO STEEL STOCKHOLDERS LTD.—Caparo Group Ltd.; *Int'l*, pg. 265
CAROLINA STEEL CORPORATION; *U.S. Private*, pg. 214
CAROLINA STEEL-GREENVILLE PLANT—Carolina Steel Corporation; *U.S. Private*, pg. 214
CAROLINA STEEL SERVICE CENTER PLANT—Carolina Steel Corporation; *U.S. Private*, pg. 214
CARPENTER TECHNOLOGY CORPORATION; *U.S. Public, pg. 307*
CASTING MATERIALS DIVISION—Hickman, Williams & Co. Inc.; *U.S. Private*, pg. 525
A.M. CASTLE & CO.; *U.S. Public*, pg. 312
A.M. CASTLE & CO.—A.M. Castle & Co.; *U.S. Public*, pg. 313
A.M. CASTLE & CO. (CANADA), INC.—A.M. Castle & Co.; *U.S. Public*, pg. 313
CAVEXSA—Magellan International Trading; *U.S. Private*, pg. 694
CENTRAL PLAINS STEEL CO.—Owen Industries, Inc.; *U.S. Private*, pg. 824
CENTRAL STEEL & WIRE COMPANY; *U.S. Public*, pg. 327
CENTURY AMERICA CORPORATION; *U.S. Private*, pg. 225
CENTURY DOOR U.S.A. INC.—Premdor Inc.; *Int'l*, pg. 1067
CERRO MATOSO—Royal Dutch/Shell Group of Companies; *Int'l*, pg. 1141
CHICAGO TUBE & IRON CO.; *U.S. Private*, pg. 235
CHICAGO TUBE & IRON COMPANY OF MINNESOTA—Chicago Tube & Iron Co.; *U.S. Private*, pg. 235
CHICAGO WEST PULLMAN CORPORATION; *U.S. Private, pg. 235*
CHINA ECOTEK CORPORATION—China Steel Corporation; *Int'l*, pg. 285
CHINA STEEL GLOBAL TRADING CORPORATION—China Steel Corporation; *Int'l*, pg. 285
CHORI AMERICA, INC.—Chori Co., Ltd.; *Int'l*, pg. 288
CHORI CO., LTD.; *Int'l*, pg. 288
CLIFFORD METAL—Lapham-Hickey Steel Corp.; *U.S. Private*, pg. 651
MAX COCHIUS GMBH—Fried. Krupp AG; *Int'l*, pg. 514
COECLERICI GROUP; *Int'l*, pg. 303
COFLEXIP & SERVICES INC.—Coflexip S.A.; *Int'l*, pg. 304
COLUMBIA IRON & METAL CO.—Columbia National Group, Inc.; *U.S. Private*, pg. 256
COLUMBIA NATIONAL GROUP, INC.; *U.S. Private*, pg. 255
COLUMBUS PIPE & EQUIPMENT COMPANY; *U.S. Private*, pg. 257
COMALCO MINERALS & ALUMINA—Comalco Limited; *Int'l*, pg. 307
COMMERCIAL METALS COMPANY; *U.S. Public*, pg. 411
COMMERCIAL METALS (INTERNATIONAL) AG—Commercial Metals Company; *U.S. Public*, pg. 414
COMMONWEALTH METAL—Commercial Metals Company; *U.S. Public*, pg. 412
COMPAGNIE FRANCAISE DE L'ETAIN—Royal Dutch/Shell Group of Companies; *Int'l*, pg. 1138
CONSOLIDATED PIPE & SUPPLY COMPANY; *U.S. Private*, pg. 266
CONTECH CONSTRUCTION PRODUCTS INC.; *U.S. Private*, pg. 267
CONTRACTORS STEEL COMPANY; *U.S. Private*, pg. 270
COPCO STEEL CO.—Russel Metals Inc.; *Int'l*, pg. 1150
COPPER & BRASS SALES, INC.—Thyssen AG; *Int'l*, pg. 1389
CREST STEEL CORP.—Marubeni Corporation; *Int'l*, pg. 845
THE CRISPIN COMPANY; *U.S. Private*, pg. 290
CRUSTEEL LTD.—Crucible Materials Corp.; *U.S. Private*, pg. 293
DSI—British Steel Plc; *Int'l*, pg. 221
DYWIDAG SYSTEMS INTERNATIONAL, USA, INC., EASTERN DIV.—Dyckerhoff & Widmann AG; *Int'l*, pg. 424
DYWIDAG SYSTEMS INTERNATIONAL, USA, INC.—Dyckerhoff & Widmann AG; *Int'l*, pg. 424
DAHL INTERNATIONAL AB; *Int'l*, pg. 359
DATEC—Groupe Usinor; *Int'l*, pg. 571
DAVUM STAHL—Groupe Usinor; *Int'l*, pg. 572
DEECO INDUSTRIES; *U.S. Private*, pg. 320
DELTA STEEL INC.—Preussag AG; *Int'l*, pg. 1070
DEUTSCHE BABCOCK AG; *Int'l*, pg. 398
DIVERSIFIED STAINLESS STEEL OF CANADA—Carpenter Technology Corporation; *U.S. Public*, pg. 308
DRUMMOND MCCALL INC.—Russel Metals Inc.; *Int'l*, pg. 1150
DUBIN-CLARK & COMPANY; *U.S. Private*, pg. 344
DUFERCO STEEL INC.; *U.S. Private*, pg. 345
DUGGAN INDUSTRIES, INC.; *U.S. Private*, pg. 345
ESM II, INC.—Viag AG; *Int'l*, pg. 1465
EDGCOMB METALS—Groupe Usinor; *Int'l*, pg. 572
EISEN UND METALL GMBH—Fried. Krupp AG; *Int'l*, pg. 514
EISENMETALL GESELLSCHAFT MBH—Fried. Krupp AG; *Int'l*, pg. 514
ELCO INTERNATIONAL/SYNERGY DIVISION—Textron Inc.; *U.S. Public*, pg. 1590
ELECTROLUX CONSTRUCTOR AB—Electrolux, AB; *Int'l*, pg. 438
ELKEM DANMARK A/S—Elkem ASA; *Int'l*, pg. 447
ELKEM GMBH—Elkem ASA; *Int'l*, pg. 447
ELKEM INTERNATIONAL AS—Elkem ASA; *Int'l*, pg. 447
ELKEM LTD. - MATERIALS—Elkem ASA; *Int'l*, pg. 447
ELKEM REPRESENTATIVE OFFICE - HONG KONG—Elkem ASA; *Int'l*, pg. 447
ELKEM SALES & MARKETING SERVICE—Elkem ASA; *Int'l*, pg. 448
ELKEM S.A.R.L.—Elkem ASA; *Int'l*, pg. 447
ELKEM S.R.L.—Elkem ASA; *Int'l*, pg. 447
ELKEM SVERIGE—Elkem ASA; *Int'l*, pg. 447
B. ELLIOTT PLC.; *Int'l*, pg. 448
ENCO MATERIALS, INC.; *U.S. Private*, pg. 375
ENERGY & PROCESS CORP.—Wolseley Plc.; *Int'l*, pg. 1512
ENSAMBLE DE CABLES Y COMPONENTES, S.A. DE C.V.—General Motors Corporation; *U.S. Public*, pg. 721
ESCO INTERNATIONAL—Esco Corporation; *U.S. Private*, pg. 383
F&S INCORPORATED—Veba AG; *Int'l*, pg. 1458
FMC EUROPE NV—FMC Corporation; *U.S. Public*, pg. 606
FMC EUROPE, S.A./N.V.—FMC Corporation; *U.S. Public*, pg. 606
FMC HELLAS EPE—FMC Corporation; *U.S. Public*, pg. 606
FALCONBRIDGE DOMINICANA, C. POR A.—EdperBrascan Corporation; *Int'l*, pg. 434
FALCONBRIDGE EUROPE S.A.—EdperBrascan Corporation; *Int'l*, pg. 434
FALCONBRIDGE INTERNATIONAL LTD.—EdperBrascan Corporation; *Int'l*, pg. 434
FALCONBRIDGE INTERNATIONAL S.A.—EdperBrascan Corporation; *Int'l*, pg. 434
FALCONBRIDGE NIKKELVERK A/S—EdperBrascan Corporation; *Int'l*, pg. 434
FALCONBRIDGE U.S. INC.—EdperBrascan Corporation; *Int'l*, pg. 434
FEDERAL INDUSTRIES METALS GROUP—Russel Metals Inc.; *Int'l*, pg. 1150
FERALLOY CORP.—Preussag AG; *Int'l*, pg. 1070
FERALLOY NORTH AMERICAN STEEL CO. LTD. PARTNERSHIP—Preussag AG; *Int'l*, pg. 1070
FERGUSON ENTERPRISES, INC.—Wolseley Plc.; *Int'l*, pg. 1512
FERGUSON LYON CONKLIN & COMPANY INC.—Wolseley Plc.; *Int'l*, pg. 1512
FERRO UNION, INC., NORTHERN CALIFORNIA—Ferro Union, Inc.; *U.S. Private*, pg. 402
FERROLEGERINGAR AG—Metallurg, Inc.; *U.S. Private*, pg. 735
FERROSTAAL AKTIENGESELLSCHAFT—MAN Aktiengesellschaft; *Int'l*, pg. 824
FERS ET METAUX RECYCLES LTEE.—Stelco Inc.; *Int'l*, pg. 1299
FINNSTEEL INC.—Rautaruukki Oy; *Int'l*, pg. 1089
FLUOR CORPORATION; *U.S. Public*, pg. 659
FOARSA FORJAS Y ACEROS DE REINOSA, S.A.—SEPI; *Int'l*, pg. 1225
FORD STEEL CO., INC.; *U.S. Private*, pg. 418
L.B. FOSTER COMPANY; *U.S. Public*, pg. 675
L.B. FOSTER COMPANY-DORAVILLE YARD/COATED PIPE—L.B. Foster Company; *U.S. Public*, pg. 676
L.B. FOSTER COMPANY-LANGFIELD YARD—L.B. Foster Company; *U.S. Public*, pg. 676
L.B. FOSTER COMPANY-NILES PLANT—L.B. Foster Company; *U.S. Public*, pg. 676
L.B. FOSTER COMPANY-PARKERSBURG PLANT—L.B. Foster Company; *U.S. Public*, pg. 676
L.B. FOSTER COMPANY-SENECA YARD—L.B. Foster Company; *U.S. Public*, pg. 676
L.B. FOSTER COMPANY-STOCKTON YARD—L.B. Foster Company; *U.S. Public*, pg. 676
FRANCOSTEEL CORPORATION—Groupe Usinor; *Int'l*, pg. 572
HANS FRANKE NE-METALLHANDEL GMBH—Fried. Krupp AG; *Int'l*, pg. 514
FRIEDMAN INDUSTRIES, INC.; *U.S. Public*, pg. 682
FRITZ INDUSTRIES INC.; *U.S. Private*, pg. 429
FUCHS NE-METALLHANDEL GMBH—Fried. Krupp AG; *Int'l*, pg. 514
FUDICKAR METALL GMBH—Fried. Krupp AG; *Int'l*, pg. 514
FULLERTON METALS CO.; *U.S. Private*, pg. 431
FUNK ALUMINUM GMBH—Fried. Krupp AG; *Int'l*, pg. 514
GALEX METALL GMBH—Axel Johnson AB; *Int'l*, pg. 710
R.J. GALLAGHER CO.; *U.S. Private*, pg. 438
GARY STEEL CO., INC.—Primac Corp.; *U.S. Private*, pg. 884
GENERAL STEEL CORPORATION—Pitt-Des Moines, Inc.; *U.S. Public*, pg. 1305
GERBER INTERNATIONAL INC.; *U.S. Private*, pg. 448
J. GERBER & CO. INC.—Gerber International Inc.; *U.S. Private*, pg. 449
GIBBS WIRE & STEEL COMPANY, INC.; *U.S. Private*, pg. 451
GIBBS WIRE & STEEL COMPANY OF CANADA LTD.—Gibbs Wire & Steel Company, Inc.; *U.S. Private*, pg. 451
GIBRALTAR STEEL CORP.; *U.S. Public*, pg. 742
GRANT STEEL CORP.—Columbia National Group, Inc.; *U.S. Private*, pg. 256
GREAT WESTERN STEEL—Triumph Group, Inc.; *U.S. Public*, pg. 1640
GREEN BAY SUPPLY CO., INC.—Carpenter Technology Corporation; *U.S. Public*, pg. 307
GROUPACIER—Groupe Usinor; *Int'l*, pg. 571
GRUPO CARPENTER S.A. DE C.V.—Carpenter Technology Corporation; *U.S. Public*, pg. 308
GULF STATES STEEL, INC.; *U.S. Private*, pg. 488
H & D STEEL SERVICE, INC.; *U.S. Private*, pg. 489
H.S.C. CANADA INC.—Harris Chemical Group, Inc.; *U.S. Private*, pg. 505
HANWA CO., LTD.; *Int'l*, pg. 595
HARRIS STEEL CO.; *U.S. Private*, pg. 506
HICKMAN, WILLIAMS & CO. INC.; *U.S. Private*, pg. 525
HIRSCHFELD, INC.; *U.S. Private*, pg. 530
HIRSCHFELD STEEL COMPANY, INC.—Hirschfeld, Inc.; *U.S. Private*, pg. 531
HOOGOVENS ALUMINIUM CORP.—Koninklijke Hoogovens N.V.; *Int'l*, pg. 755
HOOGOVENS ALUMINIUM SIDAL GMBH—Koninklijke Hoogovens N.V.; *Int'l*, pg. 755
HOOGOVENS HANDEL BV—Koninklijke Hoogovens N.V.; *Int'l*, pg. 754
HOOGOVENS IJMUIDEN VERKOOPKANTOOR B.V.—Koninklijke Hoogovens N.V.; *Int'l*, pg. 754
HOOGOVENS STAALVERWERKING EN HANDEL BV—Koninklijke Hoogovens N.V.; *Int'l*, pg. 754
HOOGOVENS WAPENINGSSTAAL BV—Koninklijke Hoogovens N.V.; *Int'l*, pg. 754
HORSEHEAD RESOURCE DEVELOPMENT CO., INC.—Metallgesellschaft AG; *Int'l*, pg. 860
HUNTER DOUGLAS HOLDINGS LTD.—Hunter Douglas N.V.; *Int'l*, pg. 640
HUNTER DOUGLAS METALS—Hunter Douglas N.V.; *Int'l*, pg. 639
HY-ALLOY STEELS CO.—A.M. Castle & Co.; *U.S. Public*, pg. 313
HYOSUNG ALUMINUM CO., LTD.—Hyosung Group; *Int'l*, pg. 640
IMS—Groupe Usinor; *Int'l*, pg. 571
ITOCHU PIPE & TUBE, INC.—Itochu Corporation; *Int'l*, pg. 695
INCO EUROPE LIMITED—Inco Limited; *Int'l*, pg. 673
INCO LIMITED, JAPAN BRANCH—Inco Limited; *Int'l*, pg. 672
INCO PACIFIC SALES LIMITED—Inco Limited; *Int'l*, pg. 673
INDEPENDENT METALS; *U.S. Private*, pg. 559
INDEPENDENT METALS—Independent Metals; *U.S. Private*, pg. 559
INDUSTRIAL METALS OF THE SOUTH; *U.S. Private*, pg. 561
INDUSTRIAL STEEL & WIRE COMPANY; *U.S. Private*, pg. 561
INDUSTRIAS NACOBRE SA DE CV—Grupo Carso S.A. de C.V.; *Int'l*, pg. 572
INLAND STEEL PRODUCTS COMPANY—Inland Steel Industries, Inc.; *U.S. Public*, pg. 679
INTERNATIONAL NICKEL FRANCE S.A.—Inco Limited; *Int'l*, pg. 673
INTERNATIONAL NICKEL GBMH—Inco Limited; *Int'l*, pg. 673
INTERNATIONAL NICKEL SERVICES (U.K.) LIMITED—Inco Limited; *Int'l*, pg. 673
INTERSTATE STEEL CO. INC.—Groupe Usinor; *Int'l*, pg. 572
INTERSTATE STEEL SUPPLY COMPANY—Metals USA, Inc.; *U.S. Public*, pg. 1100
ITOCHU CORPORATION; *Int'l*, pg. 694
JANNOCK STEEL FABRICATING COMPANY—Jannock Limited; *Int'l*, pg. 698
JENKS (INMETCO)—Independent Metals; *U.S. Private*, pg. 559
AXEL JOHNSON AB; *Int'l*, pg. 707
JOHNSTOWN WIRE TECHNOLOGIES, INC.—Dubin-Clark & Company; *U.S. Private*, pg. 344
EARLE M. JORGENSEN COMPANY; *U.S. Private*, pg. 600
JOTUN CATHODIC PROTECTION A/S—Jotun A/S; *Int'l*, pg. 714
KME ROHSTOFF GMBH—KM-Europa Metal Aktiengesellschaft; *Int'l*, pg. 719
KAIBAB INDUSTRIES; *U.S. Private*, pg. 605
KAIBAB METALS, INC.—Kaibab Industries; *U.S. Private*, pg. 605
KASLE OF CANADA LTD—Kasle Steel Corporation; *U.S. Private*, pg. 608
KASLE STEEL CORPORATION; *U.S. Private*, pg. 608
KEN-MAC METALS, INC.—Thyssen AG; *Int'l*, pg. 1388
KENWAL PRODUCTS CORP.; *U.S. Private*, pg. 615
KLINE IRON & STEEL CO., INC.; *U.S. Private*, pg. 626
KOBE ALUMINA ASSOCIATES (AUSTRALIA) PTY. LTD.—Kobe Steel, Ltd.; *Int'l*, pg. 741
KOBE ALUMINA ASSOCIATES (AUSTRALIA) PTY. LTD.—Nissho Iwai Corporation; *Int'l*, pg. 946
KOBE DEVELOPMENT CORP.—Kobe Steel, Ltd.; *Int'l*, pg. 740
KOBE INTERNATIONAL (S) CO., PTE. LTD.—Kobe Steel, Ltd.; *Int'l*, pg. 741
KOBE STEEL EUROPE, LTD.—Kobe Steel, Ltd.; *Int'l*, pg. 741
CARL GUSTAV KRAUSE GMBH—Fried. Krupp AG; *Int'l*, pg. 514
KREHER STEEL CO., INC.; *U.S. Private*, pg. 635
KRUPP HOESCH METALLHANDEL GMBH—Fried. Krupp AG; *Int'l*, pg. 514
KRUPP WIDIA GMBH—Fried. Krupp AG; *Int'l*, pg. 510
LABARGE PIPE & STEEL COMPANY; *U.S. Private*, pg. 641
LAFAYETTE METAL SERVICE CORPORATION—Itochu Corporation; *Int'l*, pg. 695
LAFAYETTE STEEL—Olympic Steel Inc.; *U.S. Public*, pg. 1221
LANGENBERG KUPFER UND MESSINGWERKE GMBH—Olin Corporation; *U.S. Public*, pg. 1219

LAPHAM-HICKEY STEEL CORP.; *U.S. Private*, pg. 651
LAURA METAAL B.V.—Koninklijke Hoogovens N.V.; *Int'l*, pg. 754
LE NICKEL INC.—Imetal; *Int'l*, pg. 661
LONDON LITHO ALUMINUM CO., INC.; *U.S. Private*, pg. 673
LONGOMETAL—Groupe Usinor; *Int'l*, pg. 571
LONZA (UK) LTD.—Alusuisse-Lonza Holding Ltd.; *Int'l*, pg. 67
LOUISIANA UTILITIES SUPPLY COMPANY—Clayton Group, Inc.; *U.S. Private*, pg. 245
LUXFER USA LTD.—Alcan Aluminium Limited; *Int'l*, pg. 50
LYNCHBURG SERVICE CENTER—Carolina Steel Corporation; *U.S. Private*, pg. 214
M M SYSTEMS CORPORATION; *U.S. Private*, pg. 685
MNP CORP.; *U.S. Private*, pg. 687
MAISON MATHIEU—Groupe Usinor; *Int'l*, pg. 572
MANNESMANN A.G.; *Int'l*, pg. 834
MANNESMANN PIPE & STEEL CORP.—Mannesmann A.G.; *Int'l*, pg. 838
THE MARMON GROUP, INC.; *U.S. Private*, pg. 706
MARUBENI AMERICA CORPORATION—Marubeni Corporation; *Int'l*, pg. 844
MARUBENI AMERICA CORPORATION, DALLAS BRANCH—Marubeni Corporation; *Int'l*, pg. 844
MARUBENI AMERICA CORPORATION, DETROIT BRANCH—Marubeni Corporation; *Int'l*, pg. 844
MARUBENI AMERICA CORPORATION, PORTLAND BRANCH—Marubeni Corporation; *Int'l*, pg. 845
MARUBENI AMERICA CORPORATION, SAN FRANCISCO BRANCH—Marubeni Corporation; *Int'l*, pg. 845
MARUBENI AMERICAN CORPORATION, SEATTLE BRANCH—Marubeni Corporation; *Int'l*, pg. 845
MARUBENI CORPORATION; *Int'l*, pg. 844
MCJUNKIN CORPORATION; *U.S. Private*, pg. 722
MEIER METAL SERVICE CENTERS, INC.—Metals USA, Inc.; *U.S. Public*, pg. 1100
A.W. MENDENHALL CO., INC.; *U.S. Private*, pg. 731
MERCER COMPANY—Columbia National Group, Inc.; *U.S. Private*, pg. 256
MERIDIAN NATIONAL CORPORATION; *U.S. Public*, pg. 1095
METAL FAB CORPORATION—Flowserve Corporation; *U.S. Public*, pg. 658
METALCENTER, INC.—Reliance Steel & Aluminum Co.; *U.S. Public*, pg. 1375
METALLGESELLSCHAFT AG; *Int'l*, pg. 860
METALS USA, INC.; *U.S. Public*, pg. 1100
METALWEST LLC—O'Neal Steel Inc.; *U.S. Private*, pg. 817
METEX EXPORT CORP.—United Capital Corp.; *U.S. Public*, pg. 1675
METRON STEEL—Groupe Usinor; *Int'l*, pg. 572
METRON STEEL CORP.; *U.S. Private*, pg. 736
MINEMET HOLDING—Imetal; *Int'l*, pg. 661
MISSOURI VALLEY STEEL CO.—Owen Industries, Inc.; *U.S. Private*, pg. 824
MITCHEL & SCOTT MACHINE CO., INC.; *U.S. Private*, pg. 753
MITSIAM INTERNATIONAL, LTD.—Mitsui & Co., Ltd.; *Int'l*, pg. 880
MITSUBISHI CABLE AMERICA, INC.—Mitsubishi Cable Industries, Ltd.; *Int'l*, pg. 870
MITSUBISHI CORPORATION; *Int'l*, pg. 871
MITSUBISHI INTERNATIONAL CORPORATION—Mitsubishi Corporation; *Int'l*, pg. 871
MITSUBISHI MATERIALS—Mitsubishi Materials Corp.; *Int'l*, pg. 875
MITSUBISHI SILICON AMERICA-EASTERN REGIONAL SALES OFFICE—Mitsubishi Materials Corp.; *Int'l*, pg. 875
MITSUI & CO., LTD.; *Int'l*, pg. 877
MITSUI BRASILEIRA IMP. E EXP. LTDA.—Mitsui & Co., Ltd.; *Int'l*, pg. 882
MITSUI CHILENA COMMERCIAL LTDA.—Mitsui & Co., Ltd.; *Int'l*, pg. 882
MITSUI DE COLOMBIA S.A.—Mitsui & Co., Ltd.; *Int'l*, pg. 882
MITSUI DE MEXICO, S.A. DE C.V.—Mitsui & Co., Ltd.; *Int'l*, pg. 882
MITSUI DE VENEZUELA C.A.—Mitsui & Co., Ltd.; *Int'l*, pg. 882
MITSUI DEL ECUADOR S.A.—Mitsui & Co., Ltd.; *Int'l*, pg. 882
MITSUI DEL PERU S.A.—Mitsui & Co., Ltd.; *Int'l*, pg. 882
MONICO ALLOYS, INC.; *U.S. Private*, pg. 757
MULACH STEEL CORPORATION; *U.S. Private*, pg. 766
NI STEEL PRODUCTS CO., LTD.—Nissho Iwai Corporation; *Int'l*, pg. 946
NIK METAL CORP.—Nissho Iwai Corporation; *Int'l*, pg. 946
NKK AMERICA INC.—NKK Corporation; *Int'l*, pg. 902
NVW (USA) INC.—Koninklijke Hoogovens N.V.; *Int'l*, pg. 754
NASHVILLE STEEL CORP.; *U.S. Private*, pg. 775
NATIONAL MATERIAL LIMITED PARTNERSHIP—Tang Industries Inc.; *U.S. Private*, pg. 1068
NEILL-LAVIELLE SUPPLY CO.; *U.S. Private*, pg. 790
NICHIMEN AMERICA, INC.—Nichimen Corporation; *Int'l*, pg. 927
NICHIMEN CORPORATION; *Int'l*, pg. 927
NIFAST CORPORATION—Nissho Iwai Corporation; *Int'l*, pg. 947
NISSHO IWAI AUSTRALIA LTD.—Nissho Iwai Corporation; *Int'l*, pg. 948
NISSHO IWAI NONFERROUS METALS CORP.—Nissho Iwai Corporation; *Int'l*, pg. 947
NITTETSU SHOJI AMERICA, INC.—Nippon Steel Corporation; *Int'l*, pg. 939
NITTETSU SHOJI CO., LTD.—Nippon Steel Corporation; *Int'l*, pg. 939
NON FERROUS INTERNATIONAL CORP.—Mitsubishi Corporation; *Int'l*, pg. 872
NORSK HYDRO USA INC.—Norsk Hydro a.s; *Int'l*, pg. 961
NORTH STAR STEEL CO.—Cargill; *U.S. Private*, pg. 210
NORTHERN PLAINS STEEL CO.—Owen Industries, Inc.; *U.S. Private*, pg. 824
NORTHWEST PIPE FITTINGS, INC.; *U.S. Private*, pg. 806
NOZAL S.A.—Groupe Usinor; *Int'l*, pg. 570
OBERLANDER RECYCLING TECHNIK GMBH—Fried. Krupp AG; *Int'l*, pg. 513
OKAYA & CO. LTD.; *Int'l*, pg. 999
OKAYA (U.S.A.), INC.—Okaya & Co. Ltd.; *Int'l*, pg. 999
OLYMPIA INTERNATIONAL—Olympic Steel Inc.; *U.S. Public*, pg. 1221
OLYMPIC STEEL INC.; *U.S. Public*, pg. 1221
O'NEAL STEEL INC.; *U.S. Private*, pg. 817
THE ORE & CHEMICAL CORP.—Metallgesellschaft AG; *Int'l*, pg. 862
ORLEANS MATERIALS & EQUIPMENT CO., INC.; *U.S. Private*, pg. 820
ORTRONICS, INC.—LeGrand S.A.; *Int'l*, pg. 806
A.J. OSTER COMPANY—Olin Corporation; *U.S. Public*, pg. 1219
A.J. OSTER WEST, INC.—Olin Corporation; *U.S. Public*, pg. 1219
OSTER ALLOYS—Cookson Group plc; *Int'l*, pg. 329
OTTAWA RIVER STEEL CO.—Meridian National Corporation; *U.S. Public*, pg. 1095
OUTOKUMPU HARJAVALTA METALS OY—Outokumpu Oyj; *Int'l*, pg. 1016
OUTOKUMPU MINERA ESPANOLA S.A.—Outokumpu Oyj; *Int'l*, pg. 1016
OWEN INDUSTRIES, INC.; *U.S. Private*, pg. 824
PACESETTER STEEL SERVICE, INC.; *U.S. Private*, pg. 830
PACIFIC HIDE & FUR DEPOT; *U.S. Private*, pg. 831
PACIFIC METAL COMPANY; *U.S. Private*, pg. 832
PAXTON & VIERLING—Owen Industries, Inc.; *U.S. Private*, pg. 824
PHELPS DODGE SALES COMPANY—Phelps Dodge Corporation; *U.S. Public*, pg. 1287
PILLAR BUILDING PRODUCTS LTD.—Caradon Plc; *Int'l*, pg. 267
PIONEER ALUMINUM, INC.; *U.S. Private*, pg. 866
PIONEER METALS & TECHNOLOGY, INC.—The Pioneer Group, Inc.; *U.S. Public*, pg. 1298
PIRELLI CABLE, POWER DIV. SERVICE CENTER—Pirelli S.p.A.; *Int'l*, pg. 1059
PIRELLI S.P.A.; *Int'l*, pg. 1058
PITT-DES MOINES, INC.; *U.S. Public*, pg. 1304
PLATLUNA AB—Trelleborg AB; *Int'l*, pg. 1422
PLYMOUTH TUBE COMPANY; *U.S. Private*, pg. 873
POHANG STEEL AMERICA PTY., LTD (POSAM)—Pohang Iron & Steel Co., Ltd.; *Int'l*, pg. 1062
POSAM NEW YORK OFFICE—Pohang Iron & Steel Co., Ltd.; *Int'l*, pg. 1062
PRECISION SPECIALTY METALS, INC.—Dubin-Clark & Company; *U.S. Private*, pg. 344
PREUSSAG INTERNATIONAL STEEL CORP.—Preussag AG; *Int'l*, pg. 1070
PRIMARY STEEL, INC.—Primac Corp.; *U.S. Private*, pg. 884
PRODUCTOS TUBULARES, S.A.—SEPI; *Int'l*, pg. 1224
QUALITY COIL PROCESSING—Kasle Steel Corporation; *U.S. Private*, pg. 608
THE RTZ CORPORATION PLC—Rio Tinto PLC; *Int'l*, pg. 1118
JOS. RACKL & CO. GMBH—Fried. Krupp AG; *Int'l*, pg. 514
RAYTECH CORPORATION; *U.S. Public*, pg. 1363
RELIANCE STEEL & ALUMINUM CO.; *U.S. Public*, pg. 1375
RESEARCH-COTTRELL (BELGIUM) S.A.—Air & Water Technologies Corporation; *U.S. Public*, pg. 29
RESEARCH-COTTRELL (DEUTSCHLAND) G.M.B.H.—Air & Water Technologies Corporation; *U.S. Public*, pg. 29
RESEARCH-COTTRELL (FRANCE) S.A.—Air & Water Technologies Corporation; *U.S. Public*, pg. 30
REYNOLDS ALUMINUM RECYCLING CO.—Reynolds Metals Company; *U.S. Public*, pg. 1386
REYNOLDS ALUMINUM SUPPLY CO. DIV.—Reynolds Metals Company; *U.S. Public*, pg. 1386
REYNOLDS ALUMINUM SUPPLY COMPANY—Reynolds Metals Company; *U.S. Public*, pg. 1386
REYNOLDS METALS COMPANY; *U.S. Public*, pg. 1385
RIAU TIN MINING—Royal Dutch/Shell Group of Companies; *Int'l*, pg. 1139
RIDG-U-RAK, INC.; *U.S. Private*, pg. 930
ROBERT JAMES SALES INC.; *U.S. Private*, pg. 935
ROLLED ALLOYS/ATEK METALS DIVISION—Rolled Alloys, Inc.; *U.S. Private*, pg. 941
ROLLED ALLOYS, INC.; *U.S. Private*, pg. 941
ROLLED ALLOYS LTD.—Rolled Alloys, Inc.; *U.S. Private*, pg. 941
ROLLED STEEL PRODUCTS CORPORATION; *U.S. Private*, pg. 941
RUSSEL METALS INC.; *Int'l*, pg. 1149
JOSEPH T. RYERSON & SON, INC.—Inland Steel Industries, Inc.; *U.S. Public*, pg. 879
RYERSON TULL—Inland Steel Industries, Inc.; *U.S. Public*, pg. 879
SKW CANADA INC.—Viag AG; *Int'l*, pg. 1466
SKW EAST ASIA LTD.—Viag AG; *Int'l*, pg. 1466
SKW FRANCE S.A.—Viag AG; *Int'l*, pg. 1466
SKW METALS U.K. LTD., MOLYPRESS DIVISION—Viag AG; *Int'l*, pg. 1465
SKW STICKSTOFFWERKE PIESTERITZ GMBH—Viag AG; *Int'l*, pg. 1464
SKW TROSTBERG AKTIENGESELLSCHAFT—Viag AG; *Int'l*, pg. 1464
SLPM—Groupe Usinor; *Int'l*, pg. 571
SAARLUX BETEILIGUNG—Groupe Usinor; *Int'l*, pg. 572
SAARLUX GMBH—Groupe Usinor; *Int'l*, pg. 572
SAMSTEEL, INC.—Ferro Union, Inc.; *U.S. Private*, pg. 402
SAMSUNG ELECTRONICS NORTH AMERICA INC.—Samsung Group; *Int'l*, pg. 1183
SAMUEL SPECIALTY METALS; *U.S. Private*, pg. 964
SANDVIK CANADA INC.—Sandvik AB; *Int'l*, pg. 1188
SANDVIK CHILE S.A.—Sandvik AB; *Int'l*, pg. 1187
SANDVIK COLOMBIA S.A.—Sandvik AB; *Int'l*, pg. 1188
SANDVIK DE MEXICO S.A. DE C.V.—Sandvik AB; *Int'l*, pg. 1188
SANDVIK DEL PERU S.A.—Sandvik AB; *Int'l*, pg. 1188
SANDVIK DO BRASIL S.A.—Sandvik AB; *Int'l*, pg. 1188
SANDVIK KENYA LTD.—Sandvik AB; *Int'l*, pg. 1187
SANDVIK KOREA LTD.—Sandvik AB; *Int'l*, pg. 1187
SANDVIK MALAYSIA SDN. BHD.—Sandvik AB; *Int'l*, pg. 1187
SANDVIK NEW ZEALAND LTD.—Sandvik AB; *Int'l*, pg. 1187
SANDVIK PHILIPPINES, INC.—Sandvik AB; *Int'l*, pg. 1187
SANDVIK (PTY.) LTD.—Sandvik AB; *Int'l*, pg. 1187
SANDVIK TAIWAN LTD.—Sandvik AB; *Int'l*, pg. 1187
SANDVIK VENEZUELA C.A.—Sandvik AB; *Int'l*, pg. 1188
I.H. SCHLEZINGER, INC.—Worthington Industries, Inc.; *U.S. Public*, pg. 1780
SERVICE STEEL DIVISION—Van Pelt Corporation; *U.S. Private*, pg. 1133
SHELL BRASIL SA (PETROLEO)—Royal Dutch/Shell Group of Companies; *Int'l*, pg. 1141
SILTIN INDUSTRIES, INC.—DEECO Industries; *U.S. Private*, pg. 320
SINGAPORE ELECTRICAL STEEL SERVICES PRIVATE LTD.—Nissho Iwai Corporation; *Int'l*, pg. 949
J. SMITH & SONS (CLERKENWELL) LTD.—Delta plc; *Int'l*, pg. 391
SMITH PIPE & STEEL CO.; *U.S. Private*, pg. 1009
SMITH SPECIALTY METALS—Smith Pipe & Steel Co.; *U.S. Private*, pg. 1009
SOGEM—Union Miniere; *Int'l*, pg. 1442
SOUTHEASTERN METAL PROCESSING—Olympic Steel Inc.; *U.S. Public*, pg. 1221
SOUTHEASTERN STEEL COMPANY; *U.S. Private*, pg. 1015
SOUTHERN IRON & METAL CO.—Commercial Metals Company; *U.S. Public*, pg. 413
SOUTHERN RECLAMATION COMPANY—Reynolds Metals Company; *U.S. Public*, pg. 1386
SPANG & COMPANY; *U.S. Private*, pg. 1020
H.C. STARCK INC.—Bayer AG; *Int'l*, pg. 174
HERMANN C. STARCK, INC.—Bayer AG; *Int'l*, pg. 175
STEEL, INC.; *U.S. Private*, pg. 1037
STEEL SERVICE CENTER (MALAYSIA) S.B.—Nissho Iwai Corporation; *Int'l*, pg. 949
STELCO USA, INC.—Stelco Inc.; *Int'l*, pg. 1300
STIFAB PLAT AB—Trelleborg AB; *Int'l*, pg. 1422
STINNES CORPORATION—Veba AG; *Int'l*, pg. 1460
STOCKHOLMS BYGGPLAT—Trelleborg AB; *Int'l*, pg. 1422
STOLLBERG GMBH—Viag AG; *Int'l*, pg. 1465
STOLLBERG INC.—Viag AG; *Int'l*, pg. 1465
STUPP BROS, INC.; *U.S. Private*, pg. 1048
SUMIKIN BUSSAN CORPORATION; *Int'l*, pg. 1308
SUMITOMO CANADA LTD.—Sumitomo Corporation; *Int'l*, pg. 1312
SUMITOMO CORPORATION; *Int'l*, pg. 1312
SUMITOMO CORPORATION OF AMERICA—Sumitomo Corporation; *Int'l*, pg. 1312
SUMITOMO METAL MINING CO., LTD.; *Int'l*, pg. 1316
SUNKYONG INDUSTRIES CO.; *Int'l*, pg. 1320
SVENSKA VOEST-ALPINE AB—Voest-Alpine Stahl AG; *Int'l*, pg. 1472
SWEDISH RAIL SYSTEM SRS—Scancem AB; *Int'l*, pg. 1199
M. SWIFT & SONS INC.; *U.S. Private*, pg. 1059
TCI ALUMINUM; *U.S. Private*, pg. 1063
TALLEY INDUSTRIES, INC.—Carpenter Technology Corporation; *U.S. Public*, pg. 307
TAMPA BAY STEEL; *U.S. Private*, pg. 1067
TAMPA BAY STEEL—Tampa Bay Steel; *U.S. Private*, pg. 1067
A. TENENBAUM CO. INC.; *U.S. Private*, pg. 1076
TEXAS COLD FINISHED STEEL, INC.—Commercial Metals Company; *U.S. Public*, pg. 412
THAILAND SMELTING & REFINING, CO. LTD.—Royal Dutch/Shell Group of Companies; *Int'l*, pg. 1140
THOMAS PIPE & STEEL, INC.—Harvest Partners Inc.; *U.S. Private*, pg. 508
THOMPSON STEEL CO., INC.; *U.S. Private*, pg. 1083
THUNDERBIRD STEEL CORPORATION—Cameron Ashley Building Products, Inc; *U.S. Public*, pg. 298
THYSSEN AG; *Int'l*, pg. 1387
THYSSEN SPECIALTY STEELS, INC.—Thyssen AG; *Int'l*, pg. 1388
TIERNAY METALS; *U.S. Private*, pg. 1085
THE TITAN INDUSTRIAL CORP.; *U.S. Private*, pg. 1089
TOTTEN TUBES, INC.; *U.S. Private*, pg. 1093
TRADEARBED S.A.—Arbed S.A.; *Int'l*, pg. 79
TREFILARBED INC.—Arbed S.A.; *Int'l*, pg. 79
TREFILARBED LUXEMBOURG/SAARBRUCKEN S.A.R.L.—Arbed S.A.; *Int'l*, pg. 80
TRELLEBORG BUILDING & DISTRIBUTION DIV.—Trelleborg AB; *Int'l*, pg. 1421
TRIMIN ENTERPRISES, INC.; *Int'l*, pg. 1424
TRIUMPH INDUSTRIES—Triumph Group, Inc.; *U.S. Public*, pg. 1641
TUBE DIVISION—Olympic Steel Inc.; *U.S. Public*, pg. 1221
TUBETEC—Plymouth Tube Company; *U.S. Private*, pg. 873
TUBULAR STEEL INC.; *U.S. Private*, pg. 1108
J.M. TULL METALS CO., INC.—Inland Steel Industries, Inc.; *U.S. Public*, pg. 879
TURKU SALES OFFICE & STORAGE DEPOT—Oy Algol AB; *Int'l*, pg. 15
UBE INDUSTRIES (AMERICA) INC.—UBE Industries Ltd.; *Int'l*, pg. 1427
U.N. ALLOY STEEL DIV.—Okura & Co.; *Int'l*, pg. 1001
U.N. ALLOY STEEL SALES, INC.—Okura & Co.; *Int'l*, pg. 1001
U.N.A. CORPORATION—Okura & Co.; *Int'l*, pg. 1001
ULBRICH OF CALIFORNIA, INC.—Ulbrich Stainless Steels & Special Metals, Inc.; *U.S. Private*, pg. 1115
ULBRICH OF GEORGIA, INC.—Ulbrich Stainless Steels & Special Metals, Inc.; *U.S. Private*, pg. 1115

ULBRICH OF ILLINOIS, INC.—Ulbrich Stainless Steels & Special Metals, Inc.; *U.S. Private*, pg. 1115
UNIFIX (BELGIUM) S.A.—Brunel Holdings Plc; *Int'l*, pg. 232
U.S. STEEL INTERNATIONAL, INC.—USX Corporation; *U.S. Public*, pg. 1661
THE UNIVERSAL STEEL CO.—Columbia National Group, Inc.; *U.S. Private*, pg. 256
UNIVERSAL STEEL OF PENNSYLVANIA—Columbia National Group, Inc.; *U.S. Private*, pg. 256
UZES—La Meridionale des Bois et Materiaux; *Int'l*, pg. 784
VAASA SALES OFFICE—Oy Algol AB; *Int'l*, pg. 15
VALESUL ALUMINIO—Royal Dutch/Shell Group of Companies; *Int'l*, pg. 1142
VALOR—Groupe Usinor; *Int'l*, pg. 571
VAN LEEUWEN PIPE & TUBE OF THE SOUTHEAST, INC.—Van Leeuwen Pipe and Tube Group B.V.; *Int'l*, pg. 1450
VAN PELT CORPORATION; *U.S. Private*, pg. 1133
VENDRES—La Meridionale des Bois et Materiaux; *Int'l*, pg. 784
VESTER CORPORATION—Arrowhead Holding Corporation; *U.S. Private*, pg. 86
VICWEST STEEL SUPPLY—Jannock Limited; *Int'l*, pg. 698
VILLARES CORPORATION OF AMERICA—Acos Villares S.A.; *Int'l*, pg. 23
VILLARES STEEL INTERNATIONAL BV—Acos Villares S.A.; *Int'l*, pg. 23
VINCENT METALS DIVISION—Rio Algom Limited; *Int'l*, pg. 1118
VOEST-ALPINE (AUSTRALIA) PTY. LTD.—Voest-Alpine Stahl AG; *Int'l*, pg. 1472
VOEST-ALPINE HELLAS A.E.—Voest-Alpine Stahl AG; *Int'l*, pg. 1472
VOEST-ALPINE INTERNATIONAL CORPORATION—Voest-Alpine Stahl AG; *Int'l*, pg. 1470
VOEST-ALPINE INTERNATIONAL DE VENEZUELA C.A.—Voest-Alpine Stahl AG; *Int'l*, pg. 1472
VOEST-ALPINE NORGE A/S—Voest-Alpine Stahl AG; *Int'l*, pg. 1472
VOEST-ALPINE SAUDI ARABIA LTD.—Voest-Alpine Stahl AG; *Int'l*, pg. 1472
VOEST-ALPINE SOUTH AFRICA (PTY.) LTD.—Voest-Alpine Stahl AG; *Int'l*, pg. 1472
VOEST-ALPINE STAHLHANDEL AG—Voest-Alpine Stahl AG; *Int'l*, pg. 1470
WABUSH MINES—DoFasco, Inc.; *Int'l*, pg. 414
WALSALL CONDUITS LTD.—Arena Lighting Ltd.; *Int'l*, pg. 80
WASHINGTON SPECIALTY METALS—Lukens Inc.; *U.S. Public*, pg. 1020
WAYNE STEEL, INC.—Metals USA, Inc.; *U.S. Public*, pg. 1101
CARL WEISSMAN & SONS, INC.; *U.S. Private*, pg. 1160
WELDED TUBE—Australian National Industries Limited; *Int'l*, pg. 101
WESTDEUTSCHE MAX COCHIUS GMBH—Fried. Krupp AG; *Int'l*, pg. 514
WESTERN SPECIALTY CONTAINER—Independent Can Company; *U.S. Private*, pg. 559
WHITE STAR STEEL—Nashville Steel Corp.; *U.S. Private*, pg. 775
WILLIAMS & COMPANY, INC.—Superior Group, Inc.; *U.S. Private*, pg. 1055
WILLIAMS STEEL & HARDWARE COMPANY; *U.S. Private*, pg. 1178
WILSON SERVICE CENTER—Carolina Steel Corporation; *U.S. Private*, pg. 214
WINSTON STEEL PRODUCTS CO.; *U.S. Private*, pg. 1183
WIRTH LTD.—Russel Metals Inc.; *Int'l*, pg. 1150

5052 — COAL & OTHER MINERALS & ORES-WHOLESALE

ACI OPERATIONS PTY. LTD.—BTR plc; *Int'l*, pg. 128
ABBOT POINT BULKCOAL PTY. LTD—M.I.M. Holdings Ltd.; *Int'l*, pg. 827
AKAGANE KAUIN SANGYO KABUSHIKI KAISHA—Benguet Corporation; *Int'l*, pg. 187
ALLEY-CASSETTY COAL CO.; *U.S. Private*, pg. 37
AMALGAMATED METAL CORPORATION PLC—Preussag AG; *Int'l*, pg. 1071
APPLIED INDUSTRIAL MATERIALS CORPORATION—Walter Industries, Inc.; *U.S. Public*, pg. 1736
BILLITON METALS, INC.—Royal Dutch/Shell Group of Companies; *Int'l*, pg. 1136
BOLIDEN INTERMARKET AB—Trelleborg AB; *Int'l*, pg. 1422
BONIFACIUS KOHLE TRANSPORT UND HANDELSGESELLSCHAFT MBH & CO. KG—Veba AG; *Int'l*, pg. 1457
BRASILUX S.A.—Arbed S.A.; *Int'l*, pg. 79
CABOT CORPORATION; *U.S. Public*, pg. 288
CANNELTON INC.—Cyprus Amax Minerals Company; *U.S. Public*, pg. 471
CANNELTON INDUSTRIES, INC.—Cyprus Amax Minerals Company; *U.S. Public*, pg. 471
CAPE BRETON DEVELOPMENT CORPORATION; *Int'l*, pg. 265
CARBOTRADE INTERNATIONAL AB—Scancem AB; *Int'l*, pg. 1201
COAL VALLEY PROJECT—Alberta Energy Company, Ltd.; *Int'l*, pg. 49
COECLERICI GROUP; *Int'l*, pg. 303
CONSOL OF KENTUCKY, INC.—Du Pont (E.I. Du Pont De Nemours & Co.); *U.S. Public*, pg. 531
CYPRUS AMAX COAL SALES CORPORATION—Cyprus Amax Minerals Company; *U.S. Public*, pg. 471
CYPRUS AMAX MINERALS COMPANY; *U.S. Public*, pg. 470
ELECTRIC FUEL CORP.—Florida Progress Corporation; *U.S. Public*, pg. 655
FALCONBRIDGE DOMINICANA, C. POR A.—EdperBrascan Corporation; *Int'l*, pg. 434
FALCONBRIDGE EUROPE S.A.—EdperBrascan Corporation; *Int'l*, pg. 434
FALCONBRIDGE INTERNATIONAL LTD.—EdperBrascan Corporation; *Int'l*, pg. 434
FALCONBRIDGE NIKKELVERK A/S—EdperBrascan Corporation; *Int'l*, pg. 434
FLORIDA PROGRESS CORPORATION; *U.S. Public*, pg. 655
HICKMAN, WILLIAMS & CO. INC.; *U.S. Private*, pg. 525
HOKKAIDO COLLIERY & STEAMSHIP CO., LTD.—Mitsui & Co., Ltd.; *Int'l*, pg. 877
ITOCHU CORPORATION; *Int'l*, pg. 694
AXEL JOHNSON AB; *Int'l*, pg. 707
AXEL JOHNSON & CO. (SEA) PTE. LTD.—Axel Johnson AB; *Int'l*, pg. 711
AXEL JOHNSON ORE & METALS AB—Axel Johnson AB; *Int'l*, pg. 709
AXEL JOHNSON ORE & METALS, INC.—Axel Johnson AB; *Int'l*, pg. 710
KOHLE-KONTOR-SAAR GMBH—Saarbergwerke Aktiengesellschaft; *Int'l*, pg. 1167
KRONOS CANADA INC.—Contran Corporation; *U.S. Private*, pg. 271
LOGAN & KANAWHA COAL CO.; *U.S. Private*, pg. 672
A.T. MASSEY COAL COMPANY, INC.—Fluor Corporation; *U.S. Public*, pg. 660
MITSUI IRON ORE DEVELOPMENT PTY. LTD.—Mitsui & Co., Ltd.; *Int'l*, pg. 879
MITSUI MATSUSHIMA CO., LTD.—Mitsui & Co., Ltd.; *Int'l*, pg. 877
MITSUI MINING CO., LTD.—Mitsui & Co., Ltd.; *Int'l*, pg. 878
MONROC, INC.; *U.S. Public*, pg. 1124
MOUNT ISA MINES (COAL FINANCE) LIMITED—M.I.M. Holdings Ltd.; *Int'l*, pg. 827
NAPORANO IRON & METAL; *U.S. Private*, pg. 774
NICHIMEN AMERICA, INC.—Nichimen Corporation; *Int'l*, pg. 927
NICHIMEN CORPORATION; *Int'l*, pg. 927
NIPPON SILICA GLASS USA, INC.—Tosoh Corporation; *Int'l*, pg. 1407
NITTETSU SHOJI CO., LTD.—Nippon Steel Corporation; *Int'l*, pg. 939
NORTH COAL AB—Axel Johnson AB; *Int'l*, pg. 709
NORTH COAL, INC.—Axel Johnson AB; *Int'l*, pg. 709
OBERLANDER RECYCLING TECHNIK GMBH—Fried. Krupp AG; *Int'l*, pg. 513
THE ORE & CHEMICAL CORP.—Metallgesellschaft AG; *Int'l*, pg. 862
OREMCO INC.—Koninklijke Hoogovens N.V.; *Int'l*, pg. 754
PEABODY COALSALES COMPANY—Hanson PLC; *Int'l*, pg. 594
PEABODY HOLDING COMPANY, INC.—Hanson PLC; *Int'l*, pg. 594
POCAHONTAS DEVELOPMENT CORPORATION—Norfolk Southern Corporation; *U.S. Public*, pg. 1192
THE RTZ CORPORATION PLC—Rio Tinto PLC; *Int'l*, pg. 1118
RAAB KARCHER FRANCE S.A.—Veba AG; *Int'l*, pg. 1458
ROCHESTER & PITTSBURGH COAL COMPANY; *U.S. Public*, pg. 1395
ROCHESTER & PITTSBURGH COAL COMPANY (CANADA) LTD.—Rochester & Pittsburgh Coal Company; *U.S. Public*, pg. 1395
SAARBERG COAL AUSTRALIA PTY. LIMITED—Saarbergwerke Aktiengesellschaft; *Int'l*, pg. 1167
SALEN COAL AB—Scancem AB; *Int'l*, pg. 1201
SAMSUNG ELECTRONICS NORTH AMERICA INC.—Samsung Group; *Int'l*, pg. 1183
SASOL LIMITED; *Int'l*, pg. 1196
SID HARVEY INDUSTRIES; *U.S. Private*, pg. 998
H.C. STARCK INC.—Bayer AG; *Int'l*, pg. 174
HERMANN C. STARCK, INC.—Bayer AG; *Int'l*, pg. 175
STINNES CORPORATION—Veba AG; *Int'l*, pg. 1460
SUKAB INTERTRADE GESMBH—Axel Johnson AB; *Int'l*, pg. 712
SUMITOMO CORPORATION; *Int'l*, pg. 1312
SUMITOMO CORPORATION OF AMERICA—Sumitomo Corporation; *Int'l*, pg. 1312
USX CORPORATION; *U.S. Public*, pg. 1661
UNION DES COMBUSTIBLES "UNICO" S.A.—Veba AG; *Int'l*, pg. 1457
THE UNITED COMPANY; *U.S. Private*, pg. 1121
UNITED EASTERN COAL SALES CORP.—Rochester & Pittsburgh Coal Company; *U.S. Public*, pg. 1395
R.T. VANDERBILT COMPANY, INC.; *U.S. Private*, pg. 1133
VINCENT METALS DIVISION—Rio Algom Limited; *Int'l*, pg. 1118

5063 — ELECTRICAL APPARATUS & EQUIPMENT, WIRING SUPPLIES & CONSTRUCTION MATERIALS-WHOLESALE

ABB ASEA—ABB Asea Brown Boveri (Holding) Ltd.; *Int'l*, pg. 8
ABB ASEA SKANDIA AB—ABB Asea Brown Boveri (Holding) Ltd.; *Int'l*, pg. 7
ABB DISTRIBUTION AB—ABB Asea Brown Boveri (Holding) Ltd.; *Int'l*, pg. 7
ABB HYDRO POWER DIV.—ABB Asea Brown Boveri (Holding) Ltd.; *Int'l*, pg. 4
ABB IN CANADA—ABB Asea Brown Boveri (Holding) Ltd.; *Int'l*, pg. 7
ABB PETERCEM S.A.—ABB Asea Brown Boveri (Holding) Ltd.; *Int'l*, pg. 2
ABB STOTZ-KONTAKT HELLAS S.A.—ABB Asea Brown Boveri (Holding) Ltd.; *Int'l*, pg. 2
ABB TECNOMASIO S.P.A.—ABB Asea Brown Boveri (Holding) Ltd.; *Int'l*, pg. 2
ABC-ADEMCO SECURITY PRODUCTS—Pittway Corporation; *U.S. Public*, pg. 1306
ADI (ADEMCO DISTRIBUTION, INC.)—Pittway Corporation; *U.S. Public*, pg. 1306
ADI MEXICO—Pittway Corporation; *U.S. Public*, pg. 1307
ADT EUROPE—Tyco International Ltd.; *U.S. Public*, pg. 1649
ADT GREECE, S.A.—Tyco International Ltd.; *U.S. Public*, pg. 1649
ADT ITALIANA, S.P.A.—Tyco International Ltd.; *U.S. Public*, pg. 1649
ADT/PROEGUR, S.A.—Tyco International Ltd.; *U.S. Public*, pg. 1649
ADT SECURITY SERVICES, INC.—Tyco International Ltd.; *U.S. Public*, pg. 1649
ADT SECURITY SYSTEMS—Tyco International Ltd.; *U.S. Public*, pg. 1649
AEG SORTING SYSTEMS INC.—Siemens AG; *Int'l*, pg. 1244
ARC INTERNATIONAL CORPORATION; *Int'l*, pg. 17
ARI GROUP EUROPE—Tyco International Ltd.; *U.S. Public*, pg. 1650
ACTIVE ELECTRICAL SUPPLY COMPANY; *U.S. Private*, pg. 15
ADEMCO-ITALIA S.P.A.—Pittway Corporation; *U.S. Public*, pg. 1307
ADEMCO-SONTRIX (AUSTRALIA) PTY. LTD.—Pittway Corporation; *U.S. Public*, pg. 1307
ADEMCO-SONTRIX ESPANA, S.A.—Pittway Corporation; *U.S. Public*, pg. 1307
ADEMCO-SONTRIX (FAR EAST)—Pittway Corporation; *U.S. Public*, pg. 1307
ADI PUERTO RICO—Pittway Corporation; *U.S. Public*, pg. 1307
ALL-PHASE ELECTRIC SUPPLY CO.; *U.S. Private*, pg. 35
ALLTEL DISTRIBUTION, INC.—ALLTEL Corporation; *U.S. Public*, pg. 55
ALPHA WIRE COMPANY—Belden Inc.; *U.S. Public*, pg. 201
ALSTHOM-JEUMONT—Jeumont-Schneider Tranformeteurs; *Int'l*, pg. 706
AMERITECH CORPORATION; *U.S. Public*, pg. 97
ANDERSON WHOLESALE COMPANY; *U.S. Private*, pg. 73
ANESCO; *U.S. Private*, pg. 74
ANGELO BROTHERS CO.; *U.S. Private*, pg. 74
ANICOM, INC.; *U.S. Public*, pg. 115
ANIXTER CABLE TV—Anixter International; *U.S. Public*, pg. 115
ANIXTER INC.—Anixter International; *U.S. Public*, pg. 115
ANIXTER INTERNATIONAL; *U.S. Public*, pg. 115
APPLIED POWER INC.; *U.S. Public*, pg. 124
ARGO INTERNATIONAL CORP.—Delcal Enterprises, Inc.; *U.S. Private*, pg. 322
ARKANSAS ELECTRIC COOPERATIVES INC.; *U.S. Private*, pg. 82
ASCOM TELEMATIC AG—Ascom Holding AG; *Int'l*, pg. 86
ASEA BROWN BOVERI AKTIENGESELLSCHAFT MBH—ABB Asea Brown Boveri (Holding) Ltd.; *Int'l*, pg. 8
ASEA BROWN BOVERI LTD.—ABB Asea Brown Boveri (Holding) Ltd.; *Int'l*, pg. 8
ASEA BROWN BOVERI LTDA.—ABB Asea Brown Boveri (Holding) Ltd.; *Int'l*, pg. 8
ASEA BROWN BOVERI S.A.—ABB Asea Brown Boveri (Holding) Ltd.; *Int'l*, pg. 7
ASEA BROWN BOVERI SAKATI—ABB Asea Brown Boveri (Holding) Ltd.; *Int'l*, pg. 3
ASEA LIMITED—ABB Asea Brown Boveri (Holding) Ltd.; *Int'l*, pg. 8
ASEA S.A.—ABB Asea Brown Boveri (Holding) Ltd.; *Int'l*, pg. 8
ASEA SKANDIA A/S—ABB Asea Brown Boveri (Holding) Ltd.; *Int'l*, pg. 7
ASEA SKANDIA HAVEMANNS EI A/S—ABB Asea Brown Boveri (Holding) Ltd.; *Int'l*, pg. 7
ASEA SKANDIA OY—ABB Asea Brown Boveri (Holding) Ltd.; *Int'l*, pg. 7
ASSOCIATED INDUSTRIAL SUPPLY, INC.; *U.S. Private*, pg. 91
ASSOCIATED OF LOS ANGELES; *U.S. Private*, pg. 92
AVNET, INC.; *U.S. Public*, pg. 155
BBC BROWN BOVERI SAUDI ARABIA LTD.—ABB Asea Brown Boveri (Holding) Ltd.; *Int'l*, pg. 3
BTR, INC.—BTR plc; *Int'l*, pg. 127
BARNETT INC.—Waxman Industries, Inc.; *U.S. Public*, pg. 1749
BATTEY MACHINERY COMPANY; *U.S. Private*, pg. 123
BEARING HEADQUARTERS CO.; *U.S. Private*, pg. 127
BELL ATLANTIC MOBILE—Bell Atlantic Corporation; *U.S. Public*, pg. 202
BENTLY NEVADA CANADA LTD.—Bently Nevada Corporation; *U.S. Private*, pg. 134
BENTLY NEVADA EUROPA B.V.—Bently Nevada Corporation; *U.S. Private*, pg. 134
BENTLY NEVADA FRANCE S.A.R.L.—Bently Nevada Corporation; *U.S. Private*, pg. 134
BENTLY NEVADA SALES & SERVICE SINGAPORE PTE. LTD.—Bently Nevada Corporation; *U.S. Private*, pg. 134
BIRNBACH COMPANY, INC.—Bell Industries, Inc.; *U.S. Public*, pg. 207
BORDER STATES INDUSTRIES, INC.; *U.S. Private*, pg. 160
ROBERT BOSCH CORPORATION—Robert Bosch GmbH; *Int'l*, pg. 204
BOWTHORPE AUSTRALIA PTY. LTD.—Bowthorpe plc; *Int'l*, pg. 208
BOWTHORPE-HELLERMANN DISTRIBUTORS—Bowthorpe plc; *Int'l*, pg. 207
BOWTHORPE-HELLERMANN (PTY.) LTD.—Bowthorpe plc; *Int'l*, pg. 208
BRAID ELECTRIC COMPANY; *U.S. Private*, pg. 165
BRANCE KRACHY COMPANY, INC.; *U.S. Private*, pg. 165
BRANCH GROUP INC.; *U.S. Private*, pg. 165
BROWN BOVERI IRAN (PRIVATE JOINT STOCK COMPANY)—ABB Asea Brown Boveri (Holding) Ltd.; *Int'l*, pg. 3
BRUSH TRANSFORMERS LTD.—BTR plc; *Int'l*, pg. 124

BRYANT ELECTRIC SUPPLY COMPANY, INC.; *U.S. Private*, pg. 177
BUHRMAN-PHARR HARDWARE COMPANY; *U.S. Private*, pg. 179
BUILDER MARTS OF AMERICA, INC.; *U.S. Private*, pg. 179
CABLETEL COMMUNICATIONS INC.—ARC International Corporation; *Int'l*, pg. 17
CALTERM—Applied Power Inc.; *U.S. Public*, pg. 124
CAMERON & BARKLEY COMPANY; *U.S. Private*, pg. 203
CARTWRIGHT COMMUNICATIONS CO.—Tessco Technologies, Inc.; *U.S. Public*, pg. 1582
CATALINA LIGHTING CANADA—Catalina Lighting, Inc.; *U.S. Public*, pg. 314
CATALINA LIGHTING, INC.; *U.S. Public*, pg. 314
CENTRAL SUPPLY CO., INC.; *U.S. Private*, pg. 225
CHAMPION, INC.; *U.S. Private*, pg. 228
CHASE CANADA—Chase Corporation; *U.S. Public*, pg. 337
CHLORIDE FRANCE SA—Chloride Group PLC; *Int'l*, pg. 287
CINERGY INVESTMENTS, INC.—Cinergy Corp.; *U.S. Public*, pg. 369
CLEVELAND ELECTRIC CO.—Cleveland Group, Inc.; *U.S. Private*, pg. 246
CLEVELAND GROUP, INC.; *U.S. Private*, pg. 246
CLIPSAL ASIA LIMITED—GP Batteries International Ltd.; *Int'l*, pg. 537
COMMUNICATION CABLE, INC.—Kuhlman Corporation; *U.S. Public*, pg. 968
CONSOLIDATED ELECTRIC SUPPLY, INC.—Rexel, S.A.; *Int'l*, pg. 1107
CRESCENT ELECTRIC SUPPLY CO.; *U.S. Private*, pg. 289
CROMPTON METERMASTER INC.—BTR plc; *Int'l*, pg. 125
CRUM ELECTRIC SUPPLY CO., INC.; *U.S. Private*, pg. 293
CUMMINS MID-SOUTH, INC.; *U.S. Private*, pg. 295
DOM AG SICHERHEITSTECHNIK—The Black & Decker Corporation; *U.S. Public*, pg. 233
DSC—DSC Communications Corporation; *U.S. Public*, pg. 475
DANA LIGHTING, INC.—Catalina Lighting, Inc.; *U.S. Public*, *pg. 314*
DEALERS ELECTRICAL SUPPLY CO.; *U.S. Private*, pg. 318
DEKKO TECHNICAL CENTER—Group Dekko; *U.S. Private*, *pg. 484*
DELHI INDUSTRIES INC.—Russel Metals Inc.; *Int'l*, pg. 1150
DOUGLASTON ELECTRIC—Turtle & Hughes, Inc.; *U.S. Private*, pg. 1110
DUELLMAN ELECTRIC SUPPLY, INC.—Rexel, S.A.; *Int'l*, pg. 1107
DURACELL BATTERIES LIMITED—The Gillette Company; *U.S. Public*, pg. 743
DURACELL CHILE LTDA.—The Gillette Company; *U.S. Public*, pg. 743
DURACELL SCANDINAVIA APS—The Gillette Company; *U.S. Public*, pg. 744
DURO-TEST CANADA—Duro-Lite International; *U.S. Private*, pg. 349
DURO-TEST DE MEXICO, S.A.—Duro-Lite International; *U.S. Private*, pg. 349
DURO-TEST INTL. CORP.—Duro-Lite International; *U.S. Private*, pg. 349
EGA—Eldon AB; *Int'l*, pg. 436
EIS, INC.—Electrical Insulation Suppliers; *U.S. Private*, pg. 368
ESY EXPORT CO., INC.—Raytheon Company; *U.S. Public*, pg. 1365
EATON CORPORATION SINGAPORE REPRESENTATIVE OFFICE—Eaton Corporation; *U.S. Public*, pg. 558
EATON GMBH—Eaton Corporation; *U.S. Public*, pg. 558
EATON GMBH CONTROLS DIV.-EUROPE MARKETING CENTER—Eaton Corporation; *U.S. Public*, pg. 558
EATON INTERNATIONAL CORPORATION, KOREA—Eaton Corporation; *U.S. Public*, pg. 558
EATON JAPAN CO., LTD.—Eaton Corporation; *U.S. Public*, *pg. 558*
ELECTRIC COMPONENT OF PTE. LTD.—General Electric Company; *U.S. Public*, pg. 713
ELECTRIC PROTECTION SERVICES (EPS)—Tyco International Ltd.; *U.S. Public*, pg. 1650
ELECTRICAL EQUIPMENT COMPANY; *U.S. Private*, pg. 368
ELECTRICAL EQUIPMENT COMPANY—Electrical Equipment Company; *U.S. Private*, pg. 368
ELECTRICAL INSULATION SUPPLIERS; *U.S. Private*, pg. 368
ELECTRICAL WHOLESALE SUPPLY COMPANY, INC.; *U.S. Private*, pg. 368
ELECTRO-MATIC PRODUCTS INC.; *U.S. Private*, pg. 369
ELECTRO PROTECTION SERVICES/CEPS—Tyco International Ltd.; *U.S. Public*, pg. 1650
B. ELLIOTT PLC.; *Int'l*, pg. 448
EMERSON PACIFIC PTE. LTD.—Emerson Electric Co.; *U.S. Public*, pg. 576
EMPIRE POWER SYSTEMS—Empire Southwest Co.; *U.S. Private*, pg. 375
EMPIRE SOUTHWEST CO.; *U.S. Private*, pg. 374
ERICSSON COMPONENTS, INC.—Telefonaktiebolaget LM Ericsson; *Int'l*, pg. 1364
EVEREADY DE MEXICO S.A. DE C.V.—Ralston Purina Company; *U.S. Public*, pg. 1360
EVEREST ENCLOSURES—Applied Power Inc.; *U.S. Public*, *pg. 124*
FERGUSON ELECTRIC CONSTRUCTION CO., INC.; *U.S. Private*, pg. 401
THE SCOTT FETZER COMPANY—Berkshire Hathaway Inc.; *U.S. Public*, pg. 217
FIDUS INSTRUMENT CORP.—Bunzl PLC; *Int'l*, pg. 233
FIRST ALERT, INC.; *U.S. Private*, pg. 406
FLENDER-ATB-LOHER SYSTEMTECHNIK GMBH—Deutsche Babcock AG; *Int'l*, pg. 400
FORT BEND UTILITIES CO.—Imperial Holly Corporation; *U.S. Public*, pg. 872
FREDERICK TRADING COMPANY—Distribution America; *U.S. Private*, pg. 335
FRONTEC LOGISTICS CORPORATION—ATCO Group Co.; *Int'l*, pg. 95
FUJI/GE PTE LTD.—General Electric Company; *U.S. Public*, pg. 713
G.E. ASIA—General Electric Company; *U.S. Public*, pg. 713
G.E. LIGHTING (IRELAND) LTD.—General Electric Company; *U.S. Public*, pg. 713
G.E. LIGHTING LIMITED—General Electric Company; *U.S. Public*, pg. 713
G.E. TECHNICAL SERVICES—General Electric Company; *U.S. Public*, pg. 713
GEC COMPOSANTS S.A.—The General Electric Company, p.l.c.; *Int'l*, pg. 546
GEC DISTRIBUTORS (IRELAND) LTD.—The General Electric Company, p.l.c.; *Int'l*, pg. 546
GS ELECTRIC—General Signal Corporation; *U.S. Public*, pg. 726
THE GENERAL ELECTRIC COMPANY OF HONG KONG LTD.—The General Electric Company, p.l.c.; *Int'l*, pg. 546
THE GENERAL ELECTRIC COMPANY OF MALAYSIA SDN. BHD.—The General Electric Company, p.l.c.; *Int'l*, pg. 546
GENERAL ELECTRIC DO BRAZIL, S.A.—General Electric Company; *U.S. Public*, pg. 713
GENERAL ELECTRIC (USA) ASIA CO.—General Electric Company; *U.S. Public*, pg. 713
GENERAL RAILWAY SIGNAL CORP.—SASIB SpA; *Int'l*, pg. 1194
W.W. GRAINGER, INC.; *U.S. Public*, pg. 758
GRAYBAR ELECTRIC COMPANY, INC.; *U.S. Private*, pg. 472
GRAYBAR INTERNATIONAL, INC.—Graybar Electric Company, Inc.; *U.S. Private*, pg. 472
B. GRIMM—General Electric Company; *U.S. Public*, pg. 713
GRINNELL CANADA LTD.—Tyco International Ltd.; *U.S. Public*, pg. 1651
GRUPO CARSO S.A. DE C.V.; *Int'l*, pg. 572
HDW, INCORPORATED—Distribution America; *U.S. Private*, *pg. 335*
HSI INTERNATIONAL—Haydon Switch & Instrument, Inc.; *U.S. Private*, pg. 513
HWC DISTRIBUTION CORP.—ALLTEL Corporation; *U.S. Public*, pg. 55
HAGEMEYER N.V.—First Pacific Company Limited; *Int'l*, pg. 487
HARRISON ELECTRIC CO., LTD.—Toshiba Corporation; *Int'l*, pg. 1402
HELLERMANN IRELAND—Bowthorpe plc; *Int'l*, pg. 208
HERON INDUSTRIES LIMITED—Russel Metals Inc.; *Int'l*, pg. 1150
HIROSE ELECTRIC (U.S.A.), INC.—Hirose Electric Co., Ltd.; *Int'l*, pg. 620
HITACHI AMERICA, LTD.—Hitachi, Ltd.; *Int'l*, pg. 622
HUBBELL CANADA INC.—Hubbell Incorporated; *U.S. Public*, pg. 845
HUBBELL INCORPORATED; *U.S. Public*, pg. 844
HUBBELL, LTD.—Hubbell Incorporated; *U.S. Public*, pg. 845
HUBBELL PREMISE WIRING, INC.—Hubbell Incorporated; *U.S. Public*, pg. 844
HUGHES-PETERS, INC.; *U.S. Private*, pg. 546
HUGHES SUPPLY, INC.; *U.S. Public*, pg. 846
HULL-THOMSON LIMITED—Russel Metals Inc.; *Int'l*, pg. 1150
HYOSUNG INDUSTRIES CO., LTD.—Hyosung Group; *Int'l*, pg. 640
INDUSTRIAL ELECTRONIC ENGINEERS, INC.; *U.S. Private*, pg. 561
INTERNATIO-MULLER N.V.; *Int'l*, pg. 680
J & N WADE LIMITED—James Crean PLC; *Int'l*, pg. 341
JAE OREGON, INC.—Japan Aviation Electronics Industry, Ltd.; *Int'l*, pg. 701
JC DISTRIBUTION LIMITED—James Crean PLC; *Int'l*, pg. 340
JEUMONT-SCHNEIDER DO BRASIL—Jeumont-Schneider Trenformeteurs; *Int'l*, pg. 706
JEUMONT-SCHNEIDER QUEBEC INC.—Jeumont-Schneider Trenformeteurs; *Int'l*, pg. 706
JIRVA AB—Trelleborg AB; *Int'l*, pg. 1422
JOSLYN CANADA INC.—Danaher Corporation; *U.S. Public*, *pg. 482*
JUNO LIGHTING LTD.—Juno Lighting, Inc.; *U.S. Public*, pg. 935
KING WIRE INC.; *U.S. Private*, pg. 621
KRAUSS-MAFFEI AG—Mannesmann A.G.; *Int'l*, pg. 836
KRAUSS-MAFFEI CORP.—Mannesmann A.G.; *Int'l*, pg. 836
KRUPP HOESCH INFORMATIONSVERARBEITUNG GMBH—Fried. Krupp AG; *Int'l*, pg. 512
KVAERNER INC.—Kvaerner a.s.a.; *Int'l*, pg. 770
KVAERNER MOSS, INC.—Kvaerner a.s.a.; *Int'l*, pg. 770
LAPPIN ELECTRIC COMPANY—Consolidated Electrical Distributors; *U.S. Private*, pg. 265
J.H. LARSON ELECTRICAL COMPANY; *U.S. Private*, pg. 652
THE F.D. LAWRENCE ELECTRIC CO.; *U.S. Private*, pg. 654
LAWSON PRODUCTS, INC.; *U.S. Public*, pg. 980
LEVITON TELECOM—Leviton Mfg. Co., Inc.; *U.S. Private*, pg. 663
LINE EQUIPMENT SALES CO., INC.—Utilities Construction Co., Inc. Of South Carolina; *U.S. Private*, pg. 1130
LITTELFUSE AG—Littelfuse, Inc.; *U.S. Public*, pg. 1001
LUNALITE, INC.—The Toro Company; *U.S. Public*, pg. 1624
MIC TECHNOLOGY CORPORATION—Aeroflex Incorporated; *U.S. Public*, pg. 24
MADISON ELECTRIC CO.; *U.S. Private*, pg. 694
MAURICE ELECTRIC SUPPLY COMPANY; *U.S. Private*, pg. 715
MAXELL CORP. OF AMERICA—Hitachi, Ltd.; *Int'l*, pg. 621
MCDONALD EQUIPMENT CO.; *U.S. Private*, pg. 721
MCJUNKIN CORPORATION; *U.S. Private*, pg. 722
MCNAUGHTON-MCKAY ELECTRIC CO.; *U.S. Private*, pg. 724
MCNEEL INTERNATIONAL CORP.; *U.S. Private*, pg. 724
MEDAL DISTRIBUTING CO.—Waxman Industries, Inc.; *U.S. Public*, pg. 1748
MICAFIL AG—ABB Asea Brown Boveri (Holding) Ltd.; *Int'l*, pg. 2
MICROWAVE RADIO COMMUNICATIONS—California Microwave, Inc.; *U.S. Public*, pg. 294
MINARIK CORP; *U.S. Private*, pg. 749
MINEBEA CO., LTD.; *Int'l*, pg. 867
MINNESOTA ELECTRIC SUPPLY COMPANY; *U.S. Private*, pg. 750
MOORE ELECTRIC SUPPLY, INC.—Hughes Supply, Inc.; *U.S. Public*, pg. 847
MOORE-HANDLEY, INC.; *U.S. Public*, pg. 1128
REX MOORE ELECTRICAL CONTRACTORS & ENGINEERS; *U.S. Private*, pg. 760
MOSLER CANADA—American Standard Inc.; *U.S. Public*, pg. 92
MOTORES U. S. DE MEXICO, S.A.—Emerson Electric Co.; *U.S. Public*, pg. 577
MOTOROLA ELECTRONICA DE PUERTO RICO, INC.—Motorola, Inc.; *U.S. Public*, pg. 1138
NEC AMERICA, INC.—NEC Corporation; *Int'l*, pg. 900
NEC CORPORATION; *Int'l*, pg. 899
NIFE AB—Alcatel Alsthom Compagnie Generale D'Electricite; *Int'l*, pg. 52
NIFE A/S—Alcatel Alsthom Compagnie Generale D'Electricite; *Int'l*, pg. 54
NIFE AUSTRALIA PTY. LTD.—Alcatel Alsthom Compagnie Generale D'Electricite; *Int'l*, pg. 54
NIFE BRASIL SISTEMAS ELETRICOS LTDA.—Alcatel Alsthom Compagnie Generale D'Electricite; *Int'l*, pg. 54
NIFE B.V.—Alcatel Alsthom Compagnie Generale D'Electricite; *Int'l*, pg. 53
NIFE CORPORATION—Alcatel Alsthom Compagnie Generale D'Electricite; *Int'l*, pg. 54
NIFE ESPANA S.A.—Alcatel Alsthom Compagnie Generale D'Electricite; *Int'l*, pg. 53
NIFE FRANCE S.A.—Alcatel Alsthom Compagnie Generale D'Electricite; *Int'l*, pg. 53
NIFE GES.M.B.H.—Alcatel Alsthom Compagnie Generale D'Electricite; *Int'l*, pg. 53
NEW ENGLAND CONTROLS CORP.—Applied Power Inc.; *U.S. Public*, pg. 124
NIFE FRANCE S.A.—Alcatel Alsthom Compagnie Generale D'Electricite; *Int'l*, pg. 54
NIFE ITALIA S.P.A.—Alcatel Alsthom Compagnie Generale D'Electricite; *Int'l*, pg. 54
NIFE POWER SYSTEMS LTD.—Alcatel Alsthom Compagnie Generale D'Electricite; *Int'l*, pg. 53
NIFE POWER SYSTEMS SDN. BHD.—Alcatel Alsthom Compagnie Generale D'Electricite; *Int'l*, pg. 54
NIFE SILCON LTD.—Alcatel Alsthom Compagnie Generale D'Electricite; *Int'l*, pg. 54
NISHISHIBA ELECTRIC CO., LTD.—Toshiba Corporation; *Int'l*, pg. 1403
NISSAN FORKLIFT CORPORATION, NORTH AMERICA—Nissan Motor Co., Ltd.; *Int'l*, pg. 945
NOLAND COMPANY; *U.S. Public*, pg. 1187
NOLAND ELECTRICAL DIV.—Noland Company; *U.S. Public*, pg. 1187
NORDISK ELEKTRA AB—Axel Johnson AB; *Int'l*, pg. 709
NORTH ELECTRIC SUPPLY, INC.; *U.S. Private*, pg. 805
NORTHLAND ELECTRIC SUPPLY COMPANY; *U.S. Private*, pg. 806
NORTON GMBH—Saint-Gobain; *Int'l*, pg. 1175
NORTON S.A.—Saint-Gobain; *Int'l*, pg. 1175
NORTON S.A. INDUSTRIA E COMERCIO—Saint-Gobain; *Int'l*, pg. 1175
NORTON S.P.A.—Saint-Gobain; *Int'l*, pg. 1175
NOTIFIER AUSTRALIA—Pittway Corporation; *U.S. Public*, pg. 1307
NOTIFIER (BENELUX) S.A.—Pittway Corporation; *U.S. Public*, pg. 1307
NOTIFIER CANADA—Pittway Corporation; *U.S. Public*, pg. 1306
NOTIFIER DEUTSCHLAND GMBH—Pittway Corporation; *U.S. Public*, pg. 1307
NOTIFIER ESPANA S.A.—Pittway Corporation; *U.S. Public*, pg. 1307
NOTIFIER FAR EAST—Pittway Corporation; *U.S. Public*, pg. 1306
NOTIFIER ITALIA S.R.L.—Pittway Corporation; *U.S. Public*, pg. 1307
NOTIFIER LTD.—Pittway Corporation; *U.S. Public*, pg. 1307
NOTIFIER MIDDLE EAST—Pittway Corporation; *U.S. Public*, pg. 1307
PALMER ELECTRIC CO.; *U.S. Private*, pg. 834
PHILIPS BROADBAND NETWORKS—Philips Electronics N.V.; *Int'l*, pg. 1054
PILLAR ELECTRICAL PLC—Caradon Plc; *Int'l*, pg. 267
PILLAR ENGINEERING LTD.—Caradon Plc; *Int'l*, pg. 267
PIONEER-STANDARD ELECTRONICS, INC.; *U.S. Public*, pg. 1300
PIRELLI CABLE, POWER DIV. SERVICE CENTER—Pirelli S.p.A.; *Int'l*, pg. 1059
PITTWAY CORPORATION; *U.S. Public*, pg. 1305
PITTWAY CORP. OF CANADA—Pittway Corporation; *U.S. Public*, pg. 1307
PLOVER BLFC BRANCH—W.A. Roosevelt Co.; *U.S. Private*, pg. 943
PLYWOOD PLASTICS, INC.—Plywood Plastics Inc.; *U.S. Private*, pg. 873
POWELL ELECTRONICS INC.; *U.S. Private*, pg. 877
POWELL INDUSTRIES, INC.; *U.S. Public*, pg. 1319
POWER EQUIPMENT SUPPLY COMPANY—Cinergy Corp.; *U.S. Public*, pg. 369
PRESIDENT HOMES—Scherer Bros. Lumber Company; *U.S. Private*, pg. 970

PYRAMID ELECTRIC SUPPLY CO., INC.—Rexel, S.A.; Int'l, pg. 1108
RADIO-HOLLAND SECURITY SYSTEMS—SAIT-RadioHolland Group S.A.; Int'l, pg. 1151
RAYOVAC LIMITED—RAYOVAC Corporation; U.S. Private, pg. 912
REILY ELECTRICAL SUPPLY, INC.; U.S. Private, pg. 919
RELM COMMUNICATIONS, INC.—Relm Wireless Corp.; U.S. Public, pg. 1376
RELM DEMAND SIDE MANAGEMENT SYSTEMS—Relm Wireless Corp.; U.S. Public, pg. 1376
REVERE ELECTRIC SUPPLY CO.; U.S. Private, pg. 926
REXEL, INC.—Rexel, S.A.; Int'l, pg. 1107
W.A. ROOSEVELT CO.; U.S. Private, pg. 943
RUMSEY ELECTRIC COMPANY; U.S. Private, pg. 951
SAB NIFE OY—Alcatel Alsthom Compagnie Generale D'Electricite; Int'l, pg. 54
SAB NIFE (SUISSE) S.A.—Alcatel Alsthom Compagnie Generale D'Electricite; Int'l, pg. 54
SALCOMP OY—Oy Nokia Ab/Nokia Group; Int'l, pg. 951
SAVAL N.V.—Internatio-Muller N.V.; Int'l, pg. 681
OY SCAN-AUTO AB—Investor AB; Int'l, pg. 686
OY SCAN-AUTO AB—Valmet Corporation; Int'l, pg. 1449
SCHAEDLER BROTHERS, INC.; U.S. Private, pg. 969
SCHLEGEL CAROLINA DIV.—BTR plc; Int'l, pg. 128
SCHNEIDER ELECTRIC S.A.—Schneider S.A.; Int'l, pg. 1207
SCHNEIDER S.A.; Int'l, pg. 1207
SEGURIDAD MAPFRE, S.A.—Corporacion MAPFRE, Compania Internacional de Reaseguros, S.A.; Int'l, pg. 333
SHARE TECHNOLOGIES - FAIRCHILD—Tel-Save Holdings, Inc.; U.S. Public, pg. 1568
SHEALY ELECTRICAL WHOLESALERS; U.S. Private, pg. 991
SIEMENS ENERGY & AUTOMATION INC.—Siemens AG; Int'l, pg. 1245
SIEMENS LTD.—Siemens AG; Int'l, pg. 1247
SIMPLEX INTL. TIME EQUIP. CO. LTD. (CANADA)—Simplex Time Recorder Co.; U.S. Private, pg. 1002
SIMPLEX INTL. TIME EQUIP. PTY. LTD.—Simplex Time Recorder Co.; U.S. Private, pg. 1002
SISTEMAS NIFE S.A. DE C.V.—Alcatel Alsthom Compagnie Generale D'Electricite; Int'l, pg. 54
SONY SERVICE CO.—Sony Corporation; Int'l, pg. 1281
SOUTHERN ELECTRIC SUPPLY CO., INC.—Rexel, S.A.; Int'l, pg. 1107
SPRAY-TECH, INC.; U.S. Private, pg. 1026
SQUARE D CO.—Schneider S.A.; Int'l, pg. 1208
SQUARE D CO., CENTRAL DISTRIBUTION CTR.—Schneider S.A.; Int'l, pg. 1208
SQUARE D COMPANY SINGAPORE PTE. LTD.—Schneider S.A.; Int'l, pg. 1209
STACY EQUIPMENT CO.—Webster Industries Inc.; U.S. Private, pg. 1158
STATE ELECTRIC SUPPLY CO.; U.S. Private, pg. 1036
STATRON AG—Alcatel Alsthom Compagnie Generale D'Electricite; Int'l, pg. 54
STEINER ELECTRIC COMPANY; U.S. Private, pg. 1039
STUSSER ELECTRIC COMPANY—Consolidated Electrical Distributors; U.S. Private, pg. 265
SUD ELECTRA GMBH—Axel Johnson AB; Int'l, pg. 712
SUMMA FOUR LIMITED—Summa Four, Inc.; U.S. Public, pg. 1527
SUMMERS GROUP—Rexel, S.A.; Int'l, pg. 1108
SUNKYONG INDUSTRIES CO.; Int'l, pg. 1320
SUZUKI MOTOR CORPORATION; Int'l, pg. 1322
SYSTEM SENSOR CANADA—Pittway Corporation; U.S. Public, pg. 1307
SYSTEM SENSOR LTD.—Pittway Corporation; U.S. Public, pg. 1307
T & R ELECTRIC SUPPLY COMPANY, INC.; U.S. Private, pg. 1061
TVESCO, INC.; U.S. Private, pg. 1066
TAB ELECTRIC SUPPLY CO. INC.—Rumsey Electric Company; U.S. Private, pg. 951
TAIYO YUDEN COMPANY LTD.; Int'l, pg. 1349
TECOT ELECTRIC SUPPLY COMPANY—Rumsey Electric Company; U.S. Private, pg. 951
TERADYNE HONG KONG LIMITED—Teradyne, Inc.; U.S. Public, pg. 1581
TERADYNE, K.K.—Teradyne, Inc.; U.S. Public, pg. 1581
TESSCO TECHNOLOGIES, INC.; U.S. Public, pg. 1582
THOMAS & BETTS CORPORATION; U.S. Public, pg. 1597
TOKI ELECTRIC CO., LTD.—Toshiba Corporation; Int'l, pg. 1403
TOSHIBA INTERNATIONAL CORPORATION PTY., LTD.—Toshiba Corporation; Int'l, pg. 1406
TOSHIBA LIGHTING & TECHNOLOGY CORPORATION—Toshiba Corporation; Int'l, pg. 1404
TOSHIBA SHOMEI PRECISION CORPORATION—Toshiba Corporation; Int'l, pg. 1404
TRENCH ELECTRIC—BBA Group plc; Int'l, pg. 113
TRI-STATE ARMATURE & ELECTRIC WORKS; U.S. Private, pg. 1100
TRISTATE ELECTRICAL SUPPLY CO., INC.; U.S. Private, pg. 1104
TURNER SUPPLY COMPANY; U.S. Private, pg. 1110
TURTLE & HUGHES, INC.; U.S. Private, pg. 1110
UTILITIES CONSTRUCTION CO., INC. OF SOUTH CAROLINA; U.S. Private, pg. 1130
VARI-LITE INTERNATIONAL; U.S. Public, pg. 1709
VARTA BATTERIES INC.—VARTA AG; Int'l, pg. 1452
VEGAS ELECTRIC SUPPLY—Consolidated Electrical Distributors; U.S. Private, pg. 265
VISION CABLE TIES CO.—Applied Power Inc.; U.S. Public, pg. 124
WOC INC.—Waxman Industries, Inc.; U.S. Public, pg. 1748
WANDEL & GOLTERMANN & CO., ARGENTINA—Wandel & Goltermann GmbH & Co., Elektronische Messtechnik; Int'l, pg. 1486
WANDEL & GOLTERMANN FRANCE—Wandel & Goltermann GmbH & Co., Elektronische Messtechnik; Int'l, pg. 1486
WANDEL & GOLTERMANN GES.M.B.H—Wandel & Goltermann GmbH & Co., Elektronische Messtechnik; Int'l, pg. 1486
WANDEL & GOLTERMANN INC.—Wandel & Goltermann GmbH & Co., Elektronische Messtechnik; Int'l, pg. 1486
WANDEL & GOLTERMANN PTY. LTD.—Wandel & Goltermann GmbH & Co., Elektronische Messtechnik; Int'l, pg. 1486
WANDEL & GOLTERMANN S.A.—Wandel & Goltermann GmbH & Co., Elektronische Messtechnik; Int'l, pg. 1486
WANDEL & GOLTERMANN SALES LTD.—Wandel & Goltermann GmbH & Co., Elektronische Messtechnik; Int'l, pg. 1486
WARREN ELECTRIC GROUP; U.S. Private, pg. 1151
WATLOW TAIWAN—Watlow Electric Manufacturing Company; U.S. Private, pg. 1154
WATSON ELECTRIC—Warren Electric Group; U.S. Private, pg. 1151
WAXMAN USA INC.—Waxman Industries, Inc.; U.S. Public, pg. 1749
WEHLE ELECTRIC CO., INC.—Westburne Inc.; Int'l, pg. 1492
CARL WEISSMAN & SONS, INC.; U.S. Private, pg. 1160
WESCO DISTRIBUTION, INC.—Clayton, Dubilier & Rice, Inc; U.S. Private, pg. 244
WESTBURNE INC.; Int'l, pg. 1491
WHITE ELECTRICAL CONSTRUCTION CO.; U.S. Private, pg. 1172
WHOLESALE ELECTRIC DIVISION—Rexel, S.A.; Int'l, pg. 1108
WOODHEAD ASIA PTE. LTD.—Woodhead Industries, Inc.; U.S. Public, pg. 1776
WORMALD FIRE SYSTEMS AB—Tyco International Ltd.; U.S. Public, pg. 1650
WORMALD ITALIANA S.P.A.—Tyco International Ltd.; U.S. Public, pg. 1651

5064 — ELECTRICAL APPLIANCES, TELEVISION & RADIO SETS-WHOLESALE

AAH CONSUMER PRODUCTS LTD.—Franz Haniel & Cie, GmbH; Int'l, pg. 591
ADVENT LOUDSPEAKERS—Recoton Corporation; U.S. Public, pg. 1369
AIWA AMERICA, INC.—Sony Corporation; Int'l, pg. 1280
ALARON ASIA LTD.—Alaron Inc.; U.S. Private, pg. 31
ALARON INC.; U.S. Private, pg. 31
ALMO CORP.; U.S. Private, pg. 44
ARIZONA WHOLESALE SUPPLY COMPANY; U.S. Private, pg. 82
ASPERA S.R.L.—Whirlpool Corporation; U.S. Public, pg. 1765
BMG ARIOLA MUSICA S.P.A.—Bertelsmann AG; Int'l, pg. 192
BMG ARIOLA S.A. DE C.V. (MEXICO)—Bertelsmann AG; Int'l, pg. 192
BMG ARIOLA S.A. (FRANCE)—Bertelsmann AG; Int'l, pg. 192
BACARDI CORPORATION—Bacardi Limited; Int'l, pg. 131
OY BANG & OLUFSEN AB—Bang & Olufsen A/S; Int'l, pg. 146
S.A. BANG & OLUFSEN BELGIUM N.V.—Bang & Olufsen A/S; Int'l, pg. 146
BANG & OLUFSEN AG—Bang & Olufsen A/S; Int'l, pg. 146
BANG & OLUFSEN A/S; Int'l, pg. 145
BANG & OLUFSEN FRANCE S.A.—Bang & Olufsen A/S; Int'l, pg. 146
BANG & OLUFSEN GES. M.B.H.—Bang & Olufsen A/S; Int'l, pg. 146
BANG & OLUFSEN G.M.B.H.—Bang & Olufsen A/S; Int'l, pg. 146
BANG & OLUFSEN OF JAPAN LTD.—Bang & Olufsen A/S; Int'l, pg. 146
BANG & OLUFSEN SVENSKA AB—Bang & Olufsen A/S; Int'l, pg. 146
BANG & OLUFSEN UNITED KINGDOM LTD.—Bang & Olufsen A/S; Int'l, pg. 146
BENNETT BROTHERS, INC.; U.S. Private, pg. 133
BENNETT BROTHERS, INC.—Bennett Brothers, Inc.; U.S. Private, pg. 133
BERNINA OF AMERICA INC.—Bernina Holding AG; Int'l, pg. 189
BERTELSMANN MUSIC GROUP—Bertelsmann AG; Int'l, pg. 191
BISSELL LTD.—Bissell Inc.; U.S. Private, pg. 145
BLAGGE ENTERPRISES; U.S. Private, pg. 148
BLUFF CITY DISTRIBUTING CO., INC.; U.S. Private, pg. 153
ROBERT BOSCH GMBH POWER TOOLS DIVISION—Robert Bosch GmbH; Int'l, pg. 204
ROBERT BOSCH CORPORATION—Robert Bosch GmbH; Int'l, pg. 204
BOSCH-SIEMENS HAUSGERAETE GMBH—Robert Bosch GmbH; Int'l, pg. 204
BOSCH-SIEMENS HAUSGERAETE GMBH—Siemens AG; Int'l, pg. 1245
BOSE AG—Bose Corporation; U.S. Private, pg. 160
BOSE LTD.—Bose Corporation; U.S. Private, pg. 161
BOSE U.K., LTD.—Bose Corporation; U.S. Private, pg. 161
BRAUN CANADA LTD.—The Gillette Company; U.S. Public, pg. 744
BRAUN FRANCE S.A.—The Gillette Company; U.S. Public, pg. 744
BRAUN ITALIA, S.R.L.—The Gillette Company; U.S. Public, pg. 744
BRAUN, NORTH AMERICA—The Gillette Company; U.S. Public, pg. 743
BRAUN (U.K.) LTD.—The Gillette Company; U.S. Public, pg. 744
BROTHER FRANCE S.A.—Brother Industries, Ltd.; Int'l, pg. 229
BROTHER INDUSTRIES (AUSTRALIA) PTY. LTD.—Brother Industries, Ltd.; Int'l, pg. 229
S.A. BROTHER INTERNATIONAL (BELGIUM) N.V.—Brother Industries, Ltd.; Int'l, pg. 229
BROTHER INTERNATIONAL CORPORATION—Brother Industries, Ltd.; Int'l, pg. 229
BROTHER INTERNATIONAL CORPORATION (CANADA) LTD.—Brother Industries, Ltd.; Int'l, pg. 229
BROTHER INTERNATIONAL (PORTUGAL) DISTRIBUIDORES DE EQUIPAMENTOS ELECTRICOS LDA.—Brother Industries, Ltd.; Int'l, pg. 230
BROTHER INTERNATIONALE INDUSTRIEMASCHINEN G.M.B.H.—Brother Industries, Ltd.; Int'l, pg. 230
BROTHER NORGE A.S.—Brother Industries, Ltd.; Int'l, pg. 230
BROTHER (SCHWEIZ) A.G.—Brother Industries, Ltd.; Int'l, pg. 230
CAIN & BULTMAN; U.S. Private, pg. 199
CAMBRIDGE SOUNDWORKS, INC.; U.S. Private, pg. 202
CAPROFEM S.A.—Kingfisher plc; Int'l, pg. 734
CARRIER CORP. LATIN AMER OPERS—United Technologies Corporation; U.S. Public, pg. 1689
CASIO CANADA, LTD.—Casio Computer Co., Ltd.; Int'l, pg. 274
CLARICOM—Bain Capital; U.S. Private, pg. 111
THE CLIMATIC CORP.; U.S. Private, pg. 246
COBRA ELECTRONICS CORPORATION; U.S. Public, pg. 391
COBRA ELECTRONICS INTERNATIONAL (HONG KONG) LTD.—Cobra Electronics Corporation; U.S. Public, pg. 391
THE COLEMAN COMPANY, INC.—MacAndrews & Forbes Holdings Inc.; U.S. Private, pg. 690
COMPONENT PRODUCTS CO.—Sony Corporation; Int'l, pg. 1281
CONSUMER AUDIO PRODUCTS CO.—Sony Corporation; Int'l, pg. 1281
CONSUMER SALES PRODUCTS CO.—Sony Corporation; Int'l, pg. 1281
CONSUMER VIDEO PRODUCTS CO.—Sony Corporation; Int'l, pg. 1281
CONTINENTAL CONAIR, LTD.—Conair Corporation; U.S. Private, pg. 261
CRESCENT ELECTRIC SUPPLY CO.; U.S. Private, pg. 289
D&H DISTRIBUTING COMPANY; U.S. Private, pg. 300
DYD CO.—Bacardi Limited; Int'l, pg. 132
DIVERSIFIED GROUP—The Gillette Company; U.S. Public, pg. 743
DIXONS STORES GROUP (FAR EAST) LIMITED—Dixons Group plc; Int'l, pg. 414
EAST JAPAN TOSHIBA DISTRIBUTOR CORPORATION—Toshiba Corporation; Int'l, pg. 1402
ELECTRO BRAND, INC.; U.S. Private, pg. 368
ELECTRO-JACOBS, GUCO, HEIJMANS, ROVATO AND VALKENBERG—Vendex International N.V.; Int'l, pg. 1462
ELECTROLUX-WASCATOR A/S—Electrolux, AB; Int'l, pg. 441
ELGIN BROTHER INDUSTRIAL LTDA.—Brother Industries, Ltd.; Int'l, pg. 230
EMERSON RADIO CORP.; U.S. Public, pg. 578
EUROCLEAN CANADA INC.—Electrolux, AB; Int'l, pg. 441
FARGO GLASS & PAINT COMPANY; U.S. Private, pg. 393
FRIGOREX AG FUR KALTETECHNIK—Sulzer Ltd.; Int'l, pg. 1306
FUJI MAGNETIC PRODUCTS DIV.—Fuji Photo Film Co., Ltd.; Int'l, pg. 524
FUJITSU GENERAL AMERICA CORP.—Fujitsu Limited; Int'l, pg. 526
FUJITSU TEN CORP. OF AMERICA—Fujitsu Limited; Int'l, pg. 526
FUNAI CORPORATION—Funai Electric Co., Ltd.; Int'l, pg. 530
GEC COMPOSANTS S.A.—The General Electric Company, p.l.c.; Int'l, pg. 546
GAGGENAU USA CORPORATION; U.S. Private, pg. 437
GENERAL ELECTRIC (USA) ASIA CO.—General Electric Company; U.S. Public, pg. 713
GIBSON APPLIANCES—Electrolux, AB; Int'l, pg. 439
GREENLUX A/S—Electrolux, AB; Int'l, pg. 441
GROSSENBURG IMPLEMENTS, INCORPORATED; U.S. Private, pg. 483
HMI INCORPORATED—HMI Industries; U.S. Public, pg. 771
HARDWARE WHOLESALERS, INC.; U.S. Private, pg. 502
HARMAN AUDIO—Harman International Industries, Inc.; U.S. Public, pg. 787
HARMAN CONSUMER GROUP—Harman International Industries, Inc.; U.S. Public, pg. 787
HELEN OF TROY (CAYMAN) LTD.—Helen of Troy Corporation; U.S. Public, pg. 807
HELEN OF TROY, CONSUMER PRODUCTS DIV.—Helen of Troy Corporation; U.S. Public, pg. 807
HELEN OF TROY CORPORATION; U.S. Public, pg. 807
HELEN OF TROY (FAR EAST) LTD.—Helen of Troy Corporation; U.S. Public, pg. 807
HELEN OF TROY, PROFESSIONAL SALON DIV.—Helen of Troy Corporation; U.S. Public, pg. 807
HITACHI CONSUMER PRODUCTS OF AMERICA, INC.—Hitachi, Ltd.; Int'l, pg. 622
HITACHI HOME ELECTRONICS—Hitachi, Ltd.; Int'l, pg. 621
HITACHI HOME ELECTRONICS (AMERICA) INC.—Hitachi, Ltd.; Int'l, pg. 622
HITACHI HOME ELECTRONICS, EASTERN REGION—Hitachi, Ltd.; Int'l, pg. 622
HITACHI HOME ELECTRONICS, WESTERN REGION—Hitachi, Ltd.; Int'l, pg. 622
HITACHI SALES CORP.—Hitachi, Ltd.; Int'l, pg. 621
HOBART AG—Premark International, Inc.; U.S. Public, pg. 1322
HOOVER ELECTRICA PORTUGUESA LTDA.—Candy S.p.A.; Int'l, pg. 260
HUSQVARNA A/S—Electrolux, AB; Int'l, pg. 441

INKEL USA CORPORATION; *U.S. Private*, pg. 563
JANOME SEWING MACHINE CO., LTD.; *Int'l*, pg. 699
JOHNSON SUPPLY & EQUIPMENT CORP.; *U.S. Private*, pg. 594
JORDON COMMERCIAL REFRIGERATOR CO.; *U.S. Private*, pg. 599
KAIZUKA SANYO INDUSTRIES CO., LTD.—Sanyo Electric Co., Ltd.; *Int'l*, pg. 1191
KENWOOD A/S—Kenwood Appliances Plc; *Int'l*, pg. 730
KENWOOD (S.A.) (PTY.) LTD.—Kenwood Appliances Plc; *Int'l*, pg. 730
KJELLBERGS SUCCESSORS A/S—Axel Johnson AB; *Int'l*, pg. 712
KJELLBERGS SUCCESSORS B.V.—Axel Johnson AB; *Int'l*, pg. 712
KLAUS RADIO INC.; *U.S. Private*, pg. 625
GEO. H. LEHLEITNER & CO., INC.; *U.S. Private*, pg. 659
MELITTA HONG KONG LTD.—Melitta Unternehmensgruppe Bentz KG; *Int'l*, pg. 857
MELITTA MARKETING (H.K.) LTD.—Melitta Unternehmensgruppe Bentz KG; *Int'l*, pg. 857
MIELE APPLIANCES, INC.—Miele & Cie, GmbH; *Int'l*, pg. 865
MITSUBISHI CONSUMER ELECTRONICS AMERICA—Mitsubishi Electric Corporation; *Int'l*, pg. 872
MITSUBISHI ELECTRIC SALES AMERICA—Mitsubishi Electric Corporation; *Int'l*, pg. 872
MOULINEX CANADA LTD.—Moulinex S.A.; *Int'l*, pg. 896
NATIONAL BRANDS, INC.; *U.S. Private*, pg. 780
NEFF (UK) LIMITED; *Int'l*, pg. 912
NELSON & SMALL INC.; *U.S. Private*, pg. 790
THE NEW HOME SEWING MACHINE CO.—Janome Sewing Machine Co., Ltd.; *Int'l*, pg. 699
NICHIMEN AMERICA, INC.—Nichimen Corporation; *Int'l*, pg. 927
NICHIMEN CORPORATION; *Int'l*, pg. 927
NILFISK OF AMERICA INC.—Nilfisk A/S; *Int'l*, pg. 932
NOKIA FRANCE S.A.—Oy Nokia Ab/Nokia Group; *Int'l*, pg. 954
NOLAND COMPANY; *U.S. Public*, pg. 1187
OTARI CORPORATION—Otari, Inc.; *Int'l*, pg. 1013
PALMER ELECTRIC CO.; *U.S. Private*, pg. 834
PANASONIC BROADCAST & TELEVISION SYSTEMS COMPANY—Matsushita Electric Industrial Co., Ltd.; *Int'l*, pg. 847
PANASONIC DEUTSCHLAND GMBH—Matsushita Electric Industrial Co., Ltd.; *Int'l*, pg. 847
PARKS PRODUCTS, INC.; *U.S. Private*, pg. 840
PEIRCE-PHELPS, INC.; *U.S. Private*, pg. 847
PFAFF AMERICAN SALES CORP.—G.M. Pfaff Aktiengesellschaft; *Int'l*, pg. 1046
G.M. PFAFF AKTIENGESELLSCHAFT; *Int'l*, pg. 1046
PIONEER ELECTRONIC (EUROPE) NV—Pioneer Electronic Corporation; *Int'l*, pg. 1058
PIONEER ELECTRONICS (USA) INC.—Pioneer Electronic Corporation; *Int'l*, pg. 1058
POLLENEX—The Rival Company; *U.S. Public*, pg. 1391
PREMARK FOOD EQUIPMENT GROUP BELGIUM, N.V.—Premark International, Inc.; *U.S. Public*, pg. 1323
RADIO-HOLLAND AV SYSTEMS GROUP—SAIT-RadioHolland Group S.A.; *Int'l*, pg. 1151
RADIO HOLLAND ELECTRONICS—SAIT-RadioHolland Group S.A.; *Int'l*, pg. 1151
RENT-A-CENTER, INC.—Thorn plc; *Int'l*, pg. 1385
RIGHT IDEAS INC.; *U.S. Private*, pg. 930
RIMOLDI ESPANOLA S.A.—Rimoldi Necchi S.R.L.; *Int'l*, pg. 1118
RIMOLDI FRANCE S.A.—Rimoldi Necchi S.R.L.; *Int'l*, pg. 1118
RIMOLDI (GREAT BRITAIN) LTD.—Rimoldi Necchi S.R.L.; *Int'l*, pg. 1118
ROBESON APPLIANCES—Robeson Appliance, Inc.; *U.S. Public*, pg. 1394
ROBESON SALES CORPORATION—Robeson Appliance, Inc.; *U.S. Public*, pg. 1394
ROTT-KELLER SUPPLY CO.; *U.S. Private*, pg. 947
ROWENTA BELGIUM S.A.—Groupe SEB; *Int'l*, pg. 569
ROWENTA ITALIA S.P.A.—Groupe SEB; *Int'l*, pg. 569
ROWENTA NEDERLAND B.V.—Groupe SEB; *Int'l*, pg. 569
ROWENTA U.K. LTD.—Groupe SEB; *Int'l*, pg. 569
ROWENTA (USA), INC.—Groupe SEB; *Int'l*, pg. 569
ROWENTA-VERTRIEBSGESELLSCHAFT MBH—Groupe SEB; *Int'l*, pg. 569
SDI TECHNOLOGIES INC.; *U.S. Private*, pg. 956
SEB ASIA—Groupe SEB; *Int'l*, pg. 568
SABANCI HOLDING A.S.; *Int'l*, pg. 1167
SAMSUNG PACIFIC INTERNATIONAL, INC.—Samsung Group; *Int'l*, pg. 1183
SANYO BUSINESS SYSTEMS (HONG KONG) LIMITED—Sanyo Electric Co., Ltd.; *Int'l*, pg. 1192
SANYO CANADA INC.—Sanyo Electric Co., Ltd.; *Int'l*, pg. 1192
SANYO ELECTRIC TRADING CO., LTD.—Sanyo Electric Co., Ltd.; *Int'l*, pg. 1191
SANYO ELECTRONICS (HONG KONG) LIMITED—Sanyo Electric Co., Ltd.; *Int'l*, pg. 1192
SANYO E.T. CANADA INC.—Sanyo Electric Co., Ltd.; *Int'l*, pg. 1192
SANYO (EUROPE) INTERNATIONAL AG—Sanyo Electric Co., Ltd.; *Int'l*, pg. 1192
SANYO FISHER HOME APPLIANCE & CONSUMER PRODUCTS DIV.—Sanyo Electric Co., Ltd.; *Int'l*, pg. 1191
SANYO FISHER VERTRIEBS GMBH—Sanyo Electric Co., Ltd.; *Int'l*, pg. 1192
SANYO HOME TECH CO., LTD.—Sanyo Electric Co., Ltd.; *Int'l*, pg. 1191
SANYO ITALIANA S.P.A.—Sanyo Electric Co., Ltd.; *Int'l*, pg. 1192
SANYO LOGISTICS CORPORATION—Sanyo Electric Co., Ltd.; *Int'l*, pg. 1191
SANYO MALAYSIA SDN. BHD—Sanyo Electric Co., Ltd.; *Int'l*, pg. 1192
SANYO MARKETING CORPORATION—Sanyo Electric Co., Ltd.; *Int'l*, pg. 1192
SANYO NORTH AMERICAN CORPORATION—Sanyo Electric Co., Ltd.; *Int'l*, pg. 1191
SANYO SALES & SERVICE SDN. BHD.—Sanyo Electric Co., Ltd.; *Int'l*, pg. 1192
SANYO SEMICONDUCTOR (H.K.) CO., LTD.—Sanyo Electric Co., Ltd.; *Int'l*, pg. 1192
SANYO (THAILAND) CO., LTD.—Sanyo Electric Co., Ltd.; *Int'l*, pg. 1193
SANYO U.K. LIMITED—Sanyo Electric Co., Ltd.; *Int'l*, pg. 1193
SCHOENECKERS, INC.; *U.S. Private*, pg. 971
SCOTT & ENGLISH LIMITED—Haw Par Brothers International Limited; *Int'l*, pg. 603
SEMP TOSHIBA AMAZONAS S.A.—Toshiba Corporation; *Int'l*, pg. 1406
SERVCO PACIFIC INC.; *U.S. Private*, pg. 986
SHARP ELECTRONICS OF CANADA LTD.—Sharp Corporation; *Int'l*, pg. 1230
SKINNER CORP.; *U.S. Private*, pg. 1005
SMART ENERGY SERVICES, INC.—Central Vermont Public Service Corporation; *U.S. Public*, pg. 328
SOCIETE KENWOOD FRANCE—Kenwood Appliances Plc; *Int'l*, pg. 730
SONY CORPORATION; *Int'l*, pg. 1280
SONY CORPORATION OF HONG KONG LTD.—Sony Corporation; *Int'l*, pg. 1284
SONY ELECTRONICS—Sony Corporation; *Int'l*, pg. 1281
SONY INTERNATIONAL (SINGAPORE) PTE. LTD.—Sony Corporation; *Int'l*, pg. 1284
SONY SERVICE CO.—Sony Corporation; *Int'l*, pg. 1281
SONY SINGAPORE PTE. LTD.—Sony Corporation; *Int'l*, pg. 1284
SONY (U.K.) LTD.—Sony Corporation; *Int'l*, pg. 1284
SUES, YOUNG & BROWN INC.; *U.S. Private*, pg. 1049
SUMITOMO CORPORATION; *Int'l*, pg. 1312
SUMITOMO CORPORATION OF AMERICA—Sumitomo Corporation; *Int'l*, pg. 1312
T-FAL CANADA INC.—Groupe SEB; *Int'l*, pg. 568
TSC SHANNOCK CORPORATION; *Int'l*, pg. 1343
TACONY CORPORATION; *U.S. Private*, pg. 1066
TAIWAN BROTHER INDUSTRIES, LTD.—Brother Industries, Ltd.; *Int'l*, pg. 230
TANGENT INDUSTRIES LTD.—Esquire Radio & Electronics Inc.; *U.S. Private*, pg. 383
TATT SING SANYO ELECTRIC COMPANY LIMITED—Sanyo Electric Co., Ltd.; *Int'l*, pg. 1193
TEFAL BELGIUM—Groupe SEB; *Int'l*, pg. 568
TEFAL DANMARK A/S—Groupe SEB; *Int'l*, pg. 568
TEFAL DEUTSCHLAND GMBH—Groupe SEB; *Int'l*, pg. 569
TEFAL ESPANA SA—Groupe SEB; *Int'l*, pg. 568
TEFAL HANDELSGESELLSCHAFT MBH—Groupe SEB; *Int'l*, pg. 568
TEFAL ITALIA S.P.A.—Groupe SEB; *Int'l*, pg. 568
TEFAL NEDERLAND B.V.—Groupe SEB; *Int'l*, pg. 568
TEFAL ROWENTA PORTUGAL—Groupe SEB; *Int'l*, pg. 568
TEFAL UK LTD.—Groupe SEB; *Int'l*, pg. 569
TOSHIBA BUILDERS APPLIANCE CO., LTD.—Toshiba Corporation; *Int'l*, pg. 1403
TOSHIBA CHUBU CONSUMER ELECTRONICS CO., LTD.—Toshiba Corporation; *Int'l*, pg. 1403
TOSHIBA DE PANAMA, S.A.—Toshiba Corporation; *Int'l*, pg. 1406
TOSHIBA HAWAII, INC.—Toshiba Corporation; *Int'l*, pg. 1405
TOSHIBA HEATING APPLIANCES CO., LTD.—Toshiba Corporation; *Int'l*, pg. 1404
TOSHIBA KYUSHU CONSUMER ELECTRONICS CO., LTD.—Toshiba Corporation; *Int'l*, pg. 1404
TOSHIBA NISHI NIHON CONSUMER ELECTRONICS CO., LTD.—Toshiba Corporation; *Int'l*, pg. 1404
TOTTORI SANYO ELECTRIC CO., LTD.—Sanyo Electric Co., Ltd.; *Int'l*, pg. 1191
TRANE EUROPE—American Standard Inc.; *U.S. Public*, pg. 92
TRANE LTD.—American Standard Inc.; *U.S. Public*, pg. 92
TURK PHILIPS SANAYI A.S.—Philips Electronics N.V.; *Int'l*, pg. 1055
TURK PHILIPS SANAYI A.S.—Sabanci Holding A.S.; *Int'l*, pg. 1168
TURK PHILIPS TICARET A.S.—Philips Electronics N.V.; *Int'l*, pg. 1055
TURK PHILIPS TICARET A.S.—Sabanci Holding A.S.; *Int'l*, pg. 1168
VWS, INC.—Electrolux, AB; *Int'l*, pg. 440
VARILUX CORPORATION—Essilor International Compagnie Generale d'Optique; *Int'l*, pg. 462
VITROMATIC, S.A. DE C.V.—Whirlpool Corporation; *U.S. Public*, pg. 1765
VORWERK CONTEMPORA S.R.L.—Vorwerk & Co.; *Int'l*, pg. 1481
VORWERK ESPANA S.A.—Vorwerk & Co.; *Int'l*, pg. 1481
VORWERK FOLLETTO S.R.L.—Vorwerk & Co.; *Int'l*, pg. 1481
VORWERK GES.M.B.H.—Vorwerk & Co.; *Int'l*, pg. 1481
VORWERK NIPPON K. K.—Vorwerk & Co.; *Int'l*, pg. 1481
W & S DISTRIBUTORS, INC.—Bacardi Limited; *Int'l*, pg. 132
WARREN DISTRIBUTING CORP.; *U.S. Private*, pg. 1151
WARREN ELECTRIC GROUP; *U.S. Private*, pg. 1151
WATLOW FRANCE S.A.R.L.—Watlow Electric Manufacturing Company; *U.S. Private*, pg. 1154
WATSON ELECTRIC—Warren Electric Group; *U.S. Private*, pg. 1151
WEHLE ELECTRIC CO., INC.—Westburne Inc.; *Int'l*, pg. 1492
WESTINGHOUSE ELECTRIC AUSTRALASIA LTD.—CBS Corporation; *U.S. Public*, pg. 275
WHOLESALE ELECTRONIC SUPPLY; *U.S. Private*, pg. 1174
WILLIAMS DISTRIBUTING COMPANY; *U.S. Private*, pg. 1177
ZACK ELECTRONICS/TELE-COM PRODUCTS, INC.—Zack Electronics; *U.S. Private*, pg. 1203
THE ZAMOISKI CO.; *U.S. Private*, pg. 1203
ZENITH ELECTRONICS CORP.; *U.S. Public*, pg. 1790
ZENITH SALES CO. DIV.—Zenith Electronics Corp.; *U.S. Public*, pg. 1790

5065 — ELECTRONIC PARTS & EQUIPMENT-WHOLESALE

A & A INTERNATIONAL, INC.—Tandy Corporation; *U.S. Public*, pg. 1560
A & A INTERNATIONAL-SEOUL BRANCH—Tandy Corporation; *U.S. Public*, pg. 1561
A & A INTERNATIONAL-TAIPEI BRANCH—Tandy Corporation; *U.S. Public*, pg. 1561
A & A INTL. (YICHI-HK) LTD.—Tandy Corporation; *U.S. Public*, pg. 1561
A & A JAPAN LTD.—Tandy Corporation; *U.S. Public*, pg. 1561
AAH CONSUMER PRODUCTS LTD.—Franz Haniel & Cie, GmbH; *Int'l*, pg. 591
ARC INTERNATIONAL CORPORATION; *Int'l*, pg. 17
AST BEARINGS—Axsys Technologies, Inc.; *U.S. Public*, pg. 157
ATC INTERNATIONAL TECHNICAL CERAMICS, INC.—American Technical Ceramics Corp.; *U.S. Public*, pg. 93
ACCORD CONTRACT SERVICES—Veba AG; *Int'l*, pg. 1458
ACTION INSTRUMENTS (CHINA) LTD.—Action Instruments, Inc.; *U.S. Private*, pg. 15
ADAPTEC - CENTRAL REGION—Adaptec, Inc.; *U.S. Public*, pg. 19
ADAPTEC - CORPORATE HEADQUARTERS—Adaptec, Inc.; *U.S. Public*, pg. 19
ADAPTEC EUROPE, S.A.—Adaptec, Inc.; *U.S. Public*, pg. 19
ADAPTEC GMBH—Adaptec, Inc.; *U.S. Public*, pg. 19
ADAPTEC - MIDWESTERN REGION—Adaptec, Inc.; *U.S. Public*, pg. 19
ADAPTEC - NEW ENGLAND REGION—Adaptec, Inc.; *U.S. Public*, pg. 19
ADAPTEC - ROCKY MOUNTAIN REGION—Adaptec, Inc.; *U.S. Public*, pg. 19
ADAPTEC - SOUTHWESTERN REGION—Adaptec, Inc.; *U.S. Public*, pg. 19
ADVANCED PRODUCTS & SYSTEMS CORP.—Raytheon Company; *U.S. Public*, pg. 1365
AETRIUM-FSA—Aetrium Inc.; *U.S. Public*, pg. 27
AETRIUM INC.; *U.S. Public*, pg. 27
AIRCRAFT OF CANADA LTD.—Raytheon Company; *U.S. Public*, pg. 1365
AKZO ELECTRONICS MATERIALS CO.—Akzo Nobel N.V.; *Int'l*, pg. 48
ALLEGRO MICROSYSTEMS INC.—Sanken Electric Co., Ltd.; *Int'l*, pg. 1188
ALLIED BROADCAST EQUIPMENT, CANADA, LTD.—Harris Corporation; *U.S. Public*, pg. 791
ALLIEDSIGNAL GENERAL AVIATION AVIONICS—AlliedSignal Inc.; *U.S. Public*, pg. 52
ALLISON-ERWIN CO. INC.; *U.S. Private*, pg. 41
ALLTEL CORPORATION; *U.S. Public*, pg. 55
ALLTEL DISTRIBUTION, INC.—ALLTEL Corporation; *U.S. Public*, pg. 55
ALLTEL SUPPLY, INC.—ALLTEL Corporation; *U.S. Public*, pg. 55
ALPHA INDUSTRIES, USA, LTD.—Alpha Industries, Inc.; *U.S. Public*, pg. 57
AMERICABLE, INC.—ENStar, Inc.; *U.S. Public*, pg. 585
AMERICAN DYNAMICS—Sensormatic Electronics Corporation; *U.S. Public*, pg. 1457
AMERICAN NUCLEONICS CORP.—Eaton Corporation; *U.S. Public*, pg. 556
ANAREN MICROWAVE, LTD.—Anaren Microwave Inc.; *U.S. Public*, pg. 111
ANDREW AG—Andrew Corporation; *U.S. Public*, pg. 113
ANDREW CORPORATION (MEXICO) S.A. DE C.V.—Andrew Corporation; *U.S. Public*, pg. 113
ANDREW S.R.L.—Andrew Corporation; *U.S. Public*, pg. 113
ANRITSU ELECTRONICA S.A.—Anritsu Corporation; *Int'l*, pg. 77
ANRITSU ELEKTRONIK GMBH—Anritsu Corporation; *Int'l*, pg. 77
ANRITSU EUROPE LTD.—Anritsu Corporation; *Int'l*, pg. 77
ANRITSU WILTRON—Anritsu Corporation; *Int'l*, pg. 77
ANTENNES ANDREW S.A.R.L.—Andrew Corporation; *U.S. Public*, pg. 113
ANTHEM ELECTRONICS INC.—Arrow Electronics, Inc.; *U.S. Public*, pg. 134
ANTHEM TECHNOLOGY—Arrow Electronics, Inc.; *U.S. Public*, pg. 134
APPLICON INC.—Gores Technology Group; *U.S. Private*, pg. 465
APPLIED INNOVATION INC.; *U.S. Public*, pg. 123
APPLIED MATERIALS JAPAN, INC.—Applied Materials, Inc.; *U.S. Public*, pg. 123
ARGOSYSTEMS, INC.—The Boeing Company; *U.S. Public*, pg. 240
AROMAT CANADA INC.—Matsushita Electric Works, Ltd.; *Int'l*, pg. 848
AROMAT MID ATLANTIC SALES—Matsushita Electric Works, Ltd.; *Int'l*, pg. 848
AROMAT NEW ENGLAND SALES OFFICE—Matsushita Electric Works, Ltd.; *Int'l*, pg. 848
AROMAT NORTH CENTRAL SALES OFFICE—Matsushita Electric Works, Ltd.; *Int'l*, pg. 848
AROMAT NORTHWESTERN SALES OFFICE—Matsushita Electric Works, Ltd.; *Int'l*, pg. 848
AROMAT SOUTH CENTRAL SALES OFFICE—Matsushita Electric Works, Ltd.; *Int'l*, pg. 848
AROMAT SOUTHEAST SALES OFFICE—Matsushita Electric Works, Ltd.; *Int'l*, pg. 848
ARROW ELECTRONICS, INC.; *U.S. Public*, pg. 133

ARROW/SCHWEBER ELECTRONICS—Arrow Electronics, Inc.; *U.S. Public*, pg. 133
ARROW/SCHWEBER ELECTRONICS GROUP—Arrow Electronics, Inc.; *U.S. Public*, pg. 133
ASCEND COMMUNICATIONS, INC.; *U.S. Public*, pg. 138
ASCOM HASLER SA—Ascom Holding AG; *Int'l*, pg. 87
ASCOM TELETRON B.V.—Ascom Holding AG; *Int'l*, pg. 87
ASIA ELECTRONICS INC.—Toshiba Corporation; *Int'l*, pg. 1402
ASSOCIATED AIRCRAFT SUPPLY COMPANY; *U.S. Private*, pg. 89
ASTREX, INC.; *U.S. Public*, pg. 141
ATLAS/SOUNDOLIER—American Trading and Production Corporation; *U.S. Private*, pg. 64
AUGAT AG—Thomas & Betts Corporation; *U.S. Public*, pg. 1598
AUGAT ELECTRONICS INC.—Thomas & Betts Corporation; *U.S. Public*, pg. 1598
AUGAT GMBH—Thomas & Betts Corporation; *U.S. Public*, pg. 1598
AUGAT LTD.—Thomas & Betts Corporation; *U.S. Public*, pg. 1598
AUGAT PTE. LTD.—Thomas & Betts Corporation; *U.S. Public*, pg. 1598
AUGAT PTY LTD.—Thomas & Betts Corporation; *U.S. Public*, pg. 1598
AUGAT S.A.—Thomas & Betts Corporation; *U.S. Public*, pg. 1598
AUGAT SRL—Thomas & Betts Corporation; *U.S. Public*, pg. 1598
AURORA ELECTRONICS—Aurora Electronics, Inc.; *U.S. Public*, pg. 147
AVNET ACCESS LTD.—Avnet, Inc.; *U.S. Public*, pg. 155
AVNET COMPOSANTS AND AVNET TIME—Avnet, Inc.; *U.S. Public*, pg. 155
AVNET EMG SRL—Avnet, Inc.; *U.S. Public*, pg. 155
AVNET E2000 GMBH—Avnet, Inc.; *U.S. Public*, pg. 155
AVNET, INC.; *U.S. Public*, pg. 155
AVNET NORTEC AB—Avnet, Inc.; *U.S. Public*, pg. 155
AVNET VSI ELECTRONICS (AUSTRALIA) PTY. LTD.—Avnet, Inc.; *U.S. Public*, pg. 155
AVNET VSI ELECTRONICS (N.Z.) LTD.—Avnet, Inc.; *U.S. Public*, pg. 155
AXSYS TECHNOLOGIES, INC.; *U.S. Public*, pg. 157
BMC INDUSTRIES, INC.; *U.S. Public*, pg. 162
BMG/MUSIC—Bertelsmann AG; *Int'l*, pg. 191
B.M.G. RECORDS—Thomson S.A.; *Int'l*, pg. 1383
BAKER & TAYLOR, INC.; *U.S. Private*, pg. 111
BASEL TRADING COMPANY LTD.; *Int'l*, pg. 169
BELL & HOWELL LTD.—Bell & Howell Holdings; *U.S. Public*, pg. 201
BELL ATLANTIC INTERNATIONAL, INC.—Bell Atlantic Corporation; *U.S. Public*, pg. 202
BELL ATLANTIC PAGING—Bell Atlantic Corporation; *U.S. Public*, pg. 203
BELL INDUSTRIES, INC.; *U.S. Public*, pg. 204
THE BERGQUIST COMPANY; *U.S. Private*, pg. 135
BERGQUIST ITC, GMBH—The Bergquist Company; *U.S. Private*, pg. 135
BIRLA 3M LTD.—3M; *U.S. Public*, pg. 1606
BISCO INDUSTRIES, INC; *U.S. Private*, pg. 145
BLAGGE ENTERPRISES; *U.S. Private*, pg. 148
BORDER STATES INDUSTRIES, INC.; *U.S. Private*, pg. 160
BOSTON ACOUSTICS, INC.; *U.S. Public*, pg. 246
BOURNS AG & BOURNS (SCHWEIZ) AG—Bourns, Inc.; *U.S. Private*, pg. 161
BOURNS BENELUX B.V.—Bourns, Inc.; *U.S. Private*, pg. 161
BOURNS, GMBH—Bourns, Inc.; *U.S. Private*, pg. 161
BOURNS-OHMIC S.A.—Bourns, Inc.; *U.S. Private*, pg. 161
BRITE VOICE SYSTEMS—Brite Voice Systems, Inc.; *U.S. Public*, pg. 257
BROADCAST SUPPLY WORLDWIDE, INC.; *U.S. Private*, pg. 170
BROTHER INTERNATIONAL CORPORATION—Brother Industries, Ltd.; *Int'l*, pg. 229
BRYANT ELECTRIC SUPPLY COMPANY, INC.; *U.S. Private*, pg. 177
BURGESS-SAIA INC.—Williams Holdings Plc; *Int'l*, pg. 1500
BYTEX DATACOM LTD.—Storage Technology Corporation; *U.S. Public*, pg. 1522
C&L COMMUNICATIONS, INC.; *U.S. Private*, pg. 191
C-COR EUROPE, B.V.—C-COR Electronics, Inc.; *U.S. Public*, pg. 272
CIE AMERICA, INC.—Itochu Corporation; *Int'l*, pg. 694
CABLETEL COMMUNICATIONS INC.—ARC International Corporation; *Int'l*, pg. 17
CADILLAC ELECTRIC—Premier Farnell plc; *Int'l*, pg. 1068
CAMERA, INC.—Sensormatic Electronics Corporation; *U.S. Public*, pg. 1457
CAPP, INC.; *U.S. Private*, pg. 207
CAPSTONE ELECTRONICS CORP.—Arrow Electronics, Inc.; *U.S. Public*, pg. 134
CAR-LAC ELECTRONICS—Premier Farnell plc; *Int'l*, pg. 1068
CASIO COMPUTER CO., LTD.; *Int'l*, pg. 274
CASIO, INC.—Casio Computer Co., Ltd.; *Int'l*, pg. 274
CELLPHONE SALES LTD.—Telefonaktiebolaget LM Ericsson; *Int'l*, pg. 1365
CERAMTEC NORTH AMERICA APPLICATIONS, INC.—Metallgesellschaft AG; *Int'l*, pg. 860
CHARLESTON TOOL SERVICES—Cummins Engine Company, Inc.; *U.S. Public*, pg. 468
CHECKPOINT SYSTEMS INC.; *U.S. Public*, pg. 343
CHIP SUPPLY INC.; *U.S. Private*, pg. 237
CHRONOS RICHARDSON—Staveley Industries PLC; *Int'l*, pg. 1299
CIMLINC INCORPORATED; *U.S. Private*, pg. 239
CINCINNATI BELL SUPPLY COMPANY—Cincinnati Bell Telephone; *U.S. Public*, pg. 367
COBRA COMPONENTS—Park Distributors, Inc.; *U.S. Private*, pg. 839
COMMONWEALTH COMMUNICATIONS—RCN Corporation; *U.S. Public*, pg. 1354
COMPONENT PRODUCTS CO.—Sony Corporation; *Int'l*, pg. 1281
COMPUTER POWER SUPPORT GROUP—Emerson Electric Co.; *U.S. Public*, pg. 576
CONSOLIDATED STORES CORP.; *U.S. Public*, pg. 437
CONSUMER SALES PRODUCTS CO.—Sony Corporation; *Int'l*, pg. 1281
CRYSTAL SEMICONDUCTOR CORPORATION—Cirrus Logic, Inc.; *U.S. Public*, pg. 375
T.F. CUSHING, INC.—Astrex, Inc.; *U.S. Public*, pg. 141
DTC COMMUNICATIONS, INC.; *U.S. Private*, pg. 306
DX COMMUNICATIONS, INC.—Itochu Corporation; *Int'l*, pg. 694
DAEWOO INTERNATIONAL AMERICA CORP. - CHICAGO—Daewoo Corporation; *Int'l*, pg. 357
DAEWOO INTERNATIONAL AMERICA CORP. - NEW YORK—Daewoo Corporation; *Int'l*, pg. 357
DAEWOO TELECOM CO. (NEWTON)—Daewoo Corporation; *Int'l*, pg. 357
DALLAS SEMICONDUCTOR CORPORATION LTD.—Dallas Semiconductor Corporation; *U.S. Public*, pg. 478
DANFOSS INC.—Danfoss A/S; *Int'l*, pg. 377
DELCO-ELECTRONICS CUSTOMER SUPPORT—General Motors Corporation; *U.S. Public*, pg. 720
DIGIPHONIC SYSTEMS PTE. LTD.—Oki Electric Industry Company, Ltd.; *Int'l*, pg. 1000
DIGITAL MICROWAVE CORPORATION; *U.S. Public*, pg. 508
DIODES INCORPORATED; *U.S. Public*, pg. 510
DISCO HI-TEC AMERICA INC.—Disco Corporation; *Int'l*, pg. 413
DOTRONIX, INC.; *U.S. Public*, pg. 520
DOVER TECHNOLOGIES—Dover Corporation; *U.S. Public*, pg. 521
EAO SWITCH CORPORATION—Elektro-Apparatebau Olten AG; *Int'l*, pg. 444
EDD-ATLANTA—Bell Industries, Inc.; *U.S. Public*, pg. 204
EDD-HOUSTON—Bell Industries, Inc.; *U.S. Public*, pg. 205
EXAR JAPAN CORPORATION—EXAR Corporation; *U.S. Public*, pg. 598
EAGLE TECHNOLOGY—Microdyne Corporation; *U.S. Public*, pg. 1105
ECONOCOM-USA INC.; *U.S. Private*, pg. 361
ELCO NV-SA—Kyocera Corporation; *Int'l*, pg. 775
ELECTRO-JACOBS, GUCO, HEIJMANS, ROVATO AND VALKENBERG—Vendex International N.V.; *Int'l*, pg. 1462
ELECTRONIC DRIVES AND CONTROLS; *U.S. Private*, pg. 370
ELECTRONICA BASICA, S.A. (ELBASA)—Northrop Grumman Corporation; *U.S. Public*, pg. 1199
B. ELLIOTT PLC.; *Int'l*, pg. 448
EMERSON RADIO HONG KONG LTD.—Emerson Radio Corp.; *U.S. Public*, pg. 578
ENGEL & MEIER GMBH—SAIT-RadioHolland Group S.A.; *Int'l*, pg. 1152
THE ERICCSON CORPORATION—Telefonaktiebolaget LM Ericsson; *Int'l*, pg. 1364
ERICSSON BUSINESS COMMUNICATIONS, INC.—Telefonaktiebolaget LM Ericsson; *Int'l*, pg. 1364
ERICSSON COMPONENTS AB—Telefonaktiebolaget LM Ericsson; *Int'l*, pg. 1363
ERICSSON GE MOBILE COMMUNICATIONS DISTRIBUTION—Telefonaktiebolaget LM Ericsson; *Int'l*, pg. 1364
ERICSSON, INC.—Telefonaktiebolaget LM Ericsson; *Int'l*, pg. 1364
ERICSSON NETWORK SYSTEMS, INC.—Telefonaktiebolaget LM Ericsson; *Int'l*, pg. 1364
ERICSSON RADIO SYSTEMS—Telefonaktiebolaget LM Ericsson; *Int'l*, pg. 1365
EURODIS BYTECH ELECTRONICS LIMITED—Siemens AG; *Int'l*, pg. 1247
EURODIS ELECTRON PLC—Siemens AG; *Int'l*, pg. 1247
EURODIS HB ELECTRONICS LIMITED—Siemens AG; *Int'l*, pg. 1247
EXABYTE FSC LTD.—Exabyte Corporation; *U.S. Public*, pg. 597
EXABYTE SCOTLAND LIMITED—Exabyte Corporation; *U.S. Public*, pg. 597
EXAR CORPORATION; *U.S. Public*, pg. 597
EXECUTONE INFORMATION SYSTEMS, INC.; *U.S. Public*, pg. 599
FAR EASTERN ELECTRIC INDUSTRY CO., LTD.—Oki Electric Industry Company, Ltd.; *Int'l*, pg. 1000
FEDERAL SIGNAL CORPORATION, SIGNAL DIV.—Federal Signal Corporation; *U.S. Public*, pg. 616
FEDERAL SIGNAL INTERNATIONAL LTD.—Federal Signal Corporation; *U.S. Public*, pg. 616
FINNIGAN MAT AB—Thermo Electron Corporation; *U.S. Public*, pg. 1596
FLENDER-ATB-LOHER SYSTEMTECHNIK GMBH—Deutsche Babcock AG; *Int'l*, pg. 400
FLUKE CORPORATION; *U.S. Public*, pg. 659
FLUKE ELECTRONICS CANADA INC.—Fluke Corporation; *U.S. Public*, pg. 659
FLUKE, INC.—Fluke Corporation; *U.S. Public*, pg. 659
FLUKE INTERNATIONAL CORPORATION—Fluke Corporation; *U.S. Public*, pg. 659
FOLLETT CAMPUS RESOURCES—Follett Corporation; *U.S. Private*, pg. 417
FOSTER ELECTRIC (EUROPE) GMBH—Foster Electric Co., Ltd.; *Int'l*, pg. 500
FOSTER ELECTRIC (U.S.A.) INC.—Foster Electric Co., Ltd.; *Int'l*, pg. 500
ABDULLA FOUAD CO. LTD.; *Int'l*, pg. 501
FRED V. FOWLER COMPANY, INC.; *U.S. Private*, pg. 422
FOWLER TOOLS OF CANADA—Fred V. Fowler Company, Inc.; *U.S. Private*, pg. 422
FOX INTERNATIONAL LTD., INC.—Video Display Corporation; *U.S. Public*, pg. 1720
FREDERICK TRADING COMPANY—Distribution America; *U.S. Private*, pg. 335
FUJI COMPUTER MEDIA DIV.—Fuji Photo Film Co., Ltd.; *Int'l*, pg. 524
FUJI ELECTRIC CO., LTD.; *Int'l*, pg. 522
FUJI MAGNETICS GMBH—Fuji Photo Film Co., Ltd.; *Int'l*, pg. 524
FUJI PHOTO FILM CO., LTD.; *Int'l*, pg. 523
FUJI PHOTO FILM U.S.A., INC.—Fuji Photo Film Co., Ltd.; *Int'l*, pg. 524
FUJITSU BUSINESS SYSTEMS LTD.—Fujitsu Limited; *Int'l*, pg. 526
FUJITSU ESPANA, S.A.—Fujitsu Limited; *Int'l*, pg. 528
FUJITSU EUROPE LTD.—Fujitsu Limited; *Int'l*, pg. 528
FUJITSU ITALIA S.P.A.—Fujitsu Limited; *Int'l*, pg. 528
FUJITSU MIKROELEKTRONIK GMBH—Fujitsu Limited; *Int'l*, pg. 528
FUJITSU NORDIC AB—Fujitsu Limited; *Int'l*, pg. 528
FUJITSU (SINGAPORE) PTE. LTD.—Fujitsu Limited; *Int'l*, pg. 528
GDC FEDERAL SYSTEMS, INC.—General Datacomm Industries, Inc.; *U.S. Public*, pg. 708
G.E. SPACENET CORPORATION—General Electric Company; *U.S. Public*, pg. 711
GEC AUSTRALIA LTD.—The General Electric Company, p.l.c.; *Int'l*, pg. 546
GN GREAT NORDIC LTD.; *Int'l*, pg. 536
GN NETCOM A/S—GN Great Nordic Ltd.; *Int'l*, pg. 537
GN NETTEST, TELECOM DIVISION—GN Great Nordic Ltd.; *Int'l*, pg. 536
GANDALF CANADA LTD.—Gandalf Technologies Inc.; *Int'l*, pg. 540
GANDALF INTERNATIONAL LTD.—Gandalf Technologies Inc.; *Int'l*, pg. 540
GANDALF S.A.—Gandalf Technologies Inc.; *Int'l*, pg. 541
GANDALF SYSTEMS CORPORATION—Gandalf Technologies Inc.; *Int'l*, pg. 540
GENERAL DATACOMM INTL. CORP.—General Datacomm Industries, Inc.; *U.S. Public*, pg. 708
GENERAL DATACOMM LTD.—General Datacomm Industries, Inc.; *U.S. Public*, pg. 708
THE GENERAL ELECTRIC COMPANY, P.L.C.; *Int'l*, pg. 543
GENERAL ELECTRIC PHILIPPINES INC.—General Electric Company; *U.S. Public*, pg. 713
GENERAL ELECTRIC (USA) CHINA COMPANY, LTD.—General Electric Company; *U.S. Public*, pg. 713
GENERAL ELECTRIC (USA) CONSUMER ELECTRONICS (PTE) LTD.—General Electric Company; *U.S. Public*, pg. 714
GOULD INSTRUMENT SYSTEMS, S.A.—Thermo Electron Corporation; *U.S. Public*, pg. 1592
GRANDETEL TECHNOLOGIES INC.; *Int'l*, pg. 556
GRUPO SIEMENS S.A. DE C.V.—Siemens AG; *Int'l*, pg. 1247
HAGEMEYER N.V.—First Pacific Company Limited; *Int'l*, pg. 487
HAMAOKA TOSHIBA ELECTRONICS CORP.—Toshiba Corporation; *Int'l*, pg. 1402
HAMILTON HALLMARK—Avnet, Inc.; *U.S. Public*, pg. 155
HAMILTON HALLMARK (CANADA) LTD.—Avnet, Inc.; *U.S. Public*, pg. 155
HANDLEMAN COMPANY OF CANADA LTD.—Handleman Company; *U.S. Public*, pg. 780
HANYU SANYO ELECTRONICS CO., LTD.—Sanyo Electric Co., Ltd.; *Int'l*, pg. 1191
HARRIS SEMICONDUCTOR—Harris Corporation; *U.S. Public*, pg. 791
HAUENSTEIN & BURMEISTER, INC.; *U.S. Private*, pg. 510
HAYES MICROCOMPUTER PRODUCTS LTD.—Hayes Corporation; *U.S. Public*, pg. 801
HELLERMANN IRELAND—Bowthorpe plc; *Int'l*, pg. 208
HIMEJI TOSHIBA E.P. CORPORATION—Toshiba Corporation; *Int'l*, pg. 1402
HOECHST SPECIALTY PRODUCTS GROUP—Hoechst Aktiengesellschaft; *Int'l*, pg. 625
HOFFMAN PRODUCTS—Premier Farnell plc; *Int'l*, pg. 1068
HOKURIKU U.S.A. CO., LTD.—Hokuriku Electric Industry Co., Ltd.; *Int'l*, pg. 628
HONEYWELL LEEDS & NORTHRUP INTERNATIONAL—Honeywell Inc.; *U.S. Public*, pg. 834
HUGHES-PETERS, INC.; *U.S. Private*, pg. 546
HYUN DAI TERMINAL CO., LTD.—Molex Incorporated; *U.S. Public*, pg. 1122
ITT CANNON SEALECTRO—ITT Industries, Inc.; *U.S. Public*, pg. 859
INTERNATIONAL COMPONENTS CORPORATION; *U.S. Private*, pg. 569
INTERNATIONAL ELCO, A.P.S.—Kyocera Corporation; *Int'l*, pg. 775
INTERTAN INC.; *U.S. Public*, pg. 910
ISLAMBDA LTD.—Siebe plc; *Int'l*, pg. 1242
JAE ELECTRONICS, INC.—Japan Aviation Electronics Industry, Ltd.; *Int'l*, pg. 701
JAE OREGON, INC.—Japan Aviation Electronics Industry, Ltd.; *Int'l*, pg. 701
JACO ELECTRONICS, INC.; *U.S. Public*, pg. 920
JACO ELECTRONICS, INC.—Jaco Electronics, Inc.; *U.S. Public*, pg. 921
JAPAN ENERGY CORPORATION; *Int'l*, pg. 702
JOHNSON SUPPLY & EQUIPMENT CORP.; *U.S. Private*, pg. 594
JOSLYN FOREIGN SALES CORPORATION—Danaher Corporation; *U.S. Public*, pg. 481
KEITHLEY FOREIGN SALES CORP.—Keithley Instruments, Inc.; *U.S. Public*, pg. 947
KEITHLEY INSTRUMENTS, INC.; *U.S. Public*, pg. 946
KENT ELECTRONICS CORP.; *U.S. Public*, pg. 951
KENT PROCESS CONTROL LTD.—ABB Asea Brown Boveri (Holding) Ltd.; *Int'l*, pg. 2
KLAUS RADIO INC.; *U.S. Private*, pg. 625
KNOGO REGIONAL OFFICE-CHICAGO—Sentry Technology Corp.; *U.S. Public*, pg. 1458

KOKUSAI ELECTRIC CO., LTD. AMERICA—Kokusai Electric Co., Ltd.; *Int'l*, pg. 743
KOYO INTERNATIONAL INC. OF AMERICA—Koyo Seiko Company, Ltd.; *Int'l*, pg. 760
LABARGE ELECTRONICS—LaBarge, Inc.; *U.S. Public*, pg. 973
LABARGE, INC.; *U.S. Public*, pg. 973
LAMBDA ELECTRONICS—Siebe plc; *Int'l*, pg. 1241
LAMBDA ELECTRONICS GMBH—Siebe plc; *Int'l*, pg. 1242
LAMBDA ELECTRONIQUE SA—Siebe plc; *Int'l*, pg. 1242
LAND WIN ELECTRONIC CORPORATION—Molex Incorporated; *U.S. Public*, pg. 1123
LATTICE SEMICONDUCTOR CORPORATION; *U.S. Public*, *pg. 979*
LAWRENCE DIVISION—Aetrium Inc.; *U.S. Public*, pg. 27
LEMO U.S.A. INC.—Lemo SA; *Int'l*, pg. 806
LEX ELECTRONICS—Arrow Electronics, Inc.; *U.S. Public*, pg. 134
LONDON LITHO ALUMINUM CO., INC.; *U.S. Private*, pg. 673
LUCAS INDUSTRIES INC.—LucasVarity plc; *Int'l*, pg. 820
LUCENT TECHNOLOGIES INC.; *U.S. Public*, pg. 1017
LUCKY-GOLDSTAR INTERNATIONAL (AMERICA)—LG Group; *Int'l*, pg. 779
LUCKY GOLDSTAR INTERNATIONAL AMERICA, INC.—LG Group; *Int'l*, pg. 779
LUMONICS INC.—Sumitomo Heavy Industries, Ltd.; *Int'l*, pg. 1314
MCM ELECTRONICS INC.—Premier Farnell plc; *Int'l*, pg. 1068
MMC ELECTRONICS AMERICA INC.—Mitsubishi Materials Corp.; *Int'l*, pg. 875
MAGNACRAFT, STRUTHERS, DUNN, INC.; *U.S. Private*, pg. 695
MANTECH COMPUTER & EDUCATION AIDS—Abdulla Fouad Co. Ltd.; *Int'l*, pg. 502
MARSHALL INDUSTRIES; *U.S. Public*, pg. 1051
MARUBENI AMERICA CORPORATION—Marubeni Corporation; *Int'l*, pg. 844
MARUBENI INTERNATIONAL ELECTRONICS CORP.—Marubeni Corporation; *Int'l*, pg. 845
MATSUSHITA ELECTRIC CORPORATION OF AMERICA—Matsushita Electric Industrial Co., Ltd.; *Int'l*, pg. 847
MAXELL CORP. OF AMERICA—Hitachi, Ltd.; *Int'l*, pg. 621
METRIC SYSTEMS CORP.—Tech-Sym Corporation; *U.S. Public*, pg. 1563
MICRON EUROPE LTD.—Micron Technology Inc.; *U.S. Public*, pg. 1105
MILGRAY ELECTRONICS, INC.—Bell Industries, Inc.; *U.S. Public*, pg. 205
MILGRAY/MONTREAL—Bell Industries, Inc.; *U.S. Public*, pg. 207
MILGRAY/TORONTO, INC.—Bell Industries, Inc.; *U.S. Public*, pg. 207
MILGRAY/WESTERN CANADA—Bell Industries, Inc.; *U.S. Public*, pg. 207
MINNESOTA NIGERIA LIMITED—3M; *U.S. Public*, pg. 1606
MITSUBISHI CONSUMER ELECTRONICS AMERICA—Mitsubishi Electric Corporation; *Int'l*, pg. 872
MITSUBISHI ELECTRIC AMERICA, INC.—Mitsubishi Electric Corporation; *Int'l*, pg. 872
MITSUBISHI ELECTRIC SALES AMERICA—Mitsubishi Electric Corporation; *Int'l*, pg. 872
MITSUBISHI ELECTRIC (UK) LTD.—Mitsubishi Electric Corporation; *Int'l*, pg. 873
MITSUBISHI INTERNATIONAL CORPORATION—Mitsubishi Corporation; *Int'l*, pg. 871
MITSUBISHI MONSANTO CHEMICAL CO.—Monsanto Company; *U.S. Public*, pg. 1125
MITSUBISHI SILICON AMERICA-EASTERN REGIONAL SALES OFFICE—Mitsubishi Materials Corp.; *Int'l*, pg. 875
MITSUBISHI SILICON AMERICA-SOUTHWEST REGIONAL SALES OFFICE—Mitsubishi Materials Corp.; *Int'l*, pg. 875
MOLEX CHINA—Molex Incorporated; *U.S. Public*, pg. 1123
MOLEX ELECTRONICS LTD.—Molex Incorporated; *U.S. Public*, pg. 1122
MOLEX ELETTRONICA S.R.L.—Molex Incorporated; *U.S. Public*, pg. 1122
MOLEX FRANCE S.A.R.L.—Molex Incorporated; *U.S. Public*, pg. 1122
MOLEX GMBH—Molex Incorporated; *U.S. Public*, pg. 1122
MOLEX INDIA LTD.—Molex Incorporated; *U.S. Public*, pg. 1122
MOLEX (MALAYSIA) SND. BHD.—Molex Incorporated; *U.S. Public*, pg. 1122
MONSANTO DO BRASIL LTDA. (MOBRA S.A.)—Monsanto Company; *U.S. Public*, pg. 1125
MONSANTO ESPANA S.A.—Monsanto Company; *U.S. Public*, pg. 1125
MONSANTO JAPAN LTD.—Monsanto Company; *U.S. Public*, pg. 1126
MONSANTO P.L.C.—Monsanto Company; *U.S. Public*, pg. 1126
MONSANTO SINGAPORE COMPANY (PTE.) LTD.—Monsanto Company; *U.S. Public*, pg. 1126
MONSANTO (SUISSE) S.A.—Monsanto Company; *U.S. Public*, pg. 1126
MONSANTO THAILAND LTD.—Monsanto Company; *U.S. Public*, pg. 1126
MONSANTO (VENEZUELA) C.A.—Monsanto Company; *U.S. Public*, pg. 1126
MOTOR GROUP—Rockwell International Corporation; *U.S. Public*, pg. 1398
MOTOROLA AB—Motorola, Inc.; *U.S. Public*, pg. 1139
MOTOROLA AB COMMUNICATIONS GROUP—Motorola, Inc.; *U.S. Public*, pg. 1139
MOTOROLA AB INFORMATION SYSTEMS GROUP—Motorola, Inc.; *U.S. Public*, pg. 1139
MOTOROLA CANADA LTD./MOTOROLA CANADA LIMITEE—Motorola, Inc.; *U.S. Public*, pg. 1139
MOTOROLA CHINA, INC.—Motorola, Inc.; *U.S. Public*, pg. 1138
MOTOROLA COMMUNICATIONS INTERNATIONAL, INC.—Motorola, Inc.; *U.S. Public*, pg. 1138
MOTOROLA CVD, INC.—Motorola, Inc.; *U.S. Public*, pg. 1138
MOTOROLA DE PUERTO RICO, INC.—Motorola, Inc.; *U.S. Public*, pg. 1138
MOTOROLA ELECTRONICS PTE., LTD.—Motorola, Inc.; *U.S. Public*, pg. 1139
MOTOROLA INTERNATIONAL DEVELOPMENT CORP.—Motorola, Inc.; *U.S. Public*, pg. 1138
MOTOROLA INTERNATIONAL, INC.—Motorola, Inc.; *U.S. Public*, pg. 1138
MOTOROLA INTERNATIONAL SALES, INC.—Motorola, Inc.; *U.S. Public*, pg. 1138
MOTOROLA SINGAPORE PTE., LTD.—Motorola, Inc.; *U.S. Public*, pg. 1140
MURATECH AMERICA, INC.—Murata Machinery, Ltd.; *Int'l*, *pg. 897*
NAIS PRODUCTS SALES OFFICE—Matsushita Electric Works, Ltd.; *Int'l*, pg. 848
NEC BUSINESS COMMUNICATION SYSTEMS (EAST), INC.—NEC Corporation; *Int'l*, pg. 900
NEC BUSINESS COMMUNICATION SYSTEMS (WEST), INC.—NEC Corporation; *Int'l*, pg. 900
NEC CORPORATION; *Int'l*, pg. 899
NEC ELECTRONICS (EUROPE) GMBH—NEC Corporation; *Int'l*, pg. 901
NEC ELECTRONICS (FRANCE) S.A.—NEC Corporation; *Int'l*, pg. 901
NEC ELECTRONICS (GERMANY) GMBH—NEC Corporation; *Int'l*, pg. 901
NEC ELECTRONICS HONG KONG LIMITED—NEC Corporation; *Int'l*, pg. 901
NEC ELECTRONICS ITALIANA S.R.L.—NEC Corporation; *Int'l*, pg. 900
NEC EUROPE LTD.—NEC Corporation; *Int'l*, pg. 900
NEC TAIWAN LTD.—NEC Corporation; *Int'l*, pg. 900
NEC TECHNOLOGIES HONG KONG LIMITED—NEC Corporation; *Int'l*, pg. 900
NEC TECHNOLOGIES, INC.—NEC Corporation; *Int'l*, pg. 900
NEC TECHNOLOGIES PHILIPPINES, INC.—NEC Corporation; *Int'l*, pg. 900
NEC TECHNOLOGIES (UK) LTD.—NEC Corporation; *Int'l*, pg. 900
NI TUBULARS, INC.—Nissho Iwai Corporation; *Int'l*, pg. 947
NIC COMPONENTS CORP.—Nu Horizons Electronics Corp.; *U.S. Public*, pg. 1205
NOKO-NOKIA REPRESENTATIVE OFFICE—Oy Nokia Ab/Nokia Group; *Int'l*, pg. 953
NTT AMERICA, INC.—Nippon Telegraph and Telephone Corporation; *Int'l*, pg. 941
NAPCO INTERNATIONAL, INC.—Venturian Corp.; *U.S. Public*, pg. 1716
NATIONAL BRANDS, INC.; *U.S. Private*, pg. 780
NELCO PRODUCTS PTE. LTD.—Park Electrochemical Corporation; *U.S. Public*, pg. 1258
NELCO S.A.—Park Electrochemical Corporation; *U.S. Public*, pg. 1258
NEMIC-LAMBDA KK—Siebe plc; *Int'l*, pg. 1242
NEWARK ELECTRONICS CORPORATION—Premier Farnell plc; *Int'l*, pg. 1068
NEWEY & EYRE LTD.—BTR plc; *Int'l*, pg. 125
NICHIMEN AMERICA, INC.—Nichimen Corporation; *Int'l*, pg. 927
NICHIMEN CORPORATION; *Int'l*, pg. 927
NIHON EXABYTE K.K.—Exabyte Corporation; *U.S. Public*, pg. 597
NIHON VEECO K.K.—Veeco Instruments, Inc.; *U.S. Public*, pg. 1711
NIIGATA SANYO ELECTRONIC CO., LTD.—Sanyo Electric Co., Ltd.; *Int'l*, pg. 1191
NINTENDO OF AMERICA—Nintendo Company, Ltd.; *Int'l*, pg. 932
NOKIA JAPAN K.K. LTD.—Oy Nokia Ab/Nokia Group; *Int'l*, pg. 954
NOKIA MOBILE PHONES ITALIA S.R.L.—Oy Nokia Ab/Nokia Group; *Int'l*, pg. 952
NOKIA TELECOMMUNICATIONS LTD.—Oy Nokia Ab/Nokia Group; *Int'l*, pg. 953
NORDIC BAUMASCHINENHANDEL GMBH—Axel Johnson AB; *Int'l*, pg. 712
NORITAKE CO., INC.—Noritake Co., Limited; *Int'l*, pg. 959
NORITAKE CO., INC.-ELECTRONICS DIVISION—Noritake Co., Limited; *Int'l*, pg. 959
NORTEL CALA INC.—Northern Telecom Limited; *Int'l*, pg. 969
NORTEL COMMUNICATIONS—Northern Telecom Limited; *Int'l*, pg. 969
NORTEL COMMUNICATIONS—SBC Communications Inc.; *U.S. Public*, pg. 1416
NORTH AMERICAN CAPACITOR CO.; *U.S. Private*, pg. 803
NORTHERN TELECOM—Northern Telecom Limited; *Int'l*, pg. 970
NU HORIZONS ELECTRONICS CORP.; *U.S. Public*, pg. 1205
NU HORIZONS INTERNATIONAL CORP.—Nu Horizons Electronics Corp.; *U.S. Public*, pg. 1205
NU HORIZONS/MERIT ELECTRONICS CORP.—Nu Horizons Electronics Corp.; *U.S. Public*, pg. 1205
OKI ELECTRIC EUROPE GMBH—Oki Electric Industry Company, Ltd.; *Int'l*, pg. 1000
OKI ELECTRIC INDUSTRY CO., LTD.—Oki Electric Industry Company, Ltd.; *Int'l*, pg. 999
OKI ELECTRIC INDUSTRY COMPANY, LTD.; *Int'l*, pg. 999
OKI ELECTRONICS (HONG KONG) LTD.—Oki Electric Industry Company, Ltd.; *Int'l*, pg. 1000
OKI ELECTRONICS (HONG KONG) LTD.-SINGAPORE BRANCH—Oki Electric Industry Company, Ltd.; *Int'l*, pg. 1000
OKI ELECTRONICS (HONG KONG) LTD.-TAIPEI BRANCH—Oki Electric Industry Company, Ltd.; *Int'l*, pg. 1000
OKI ELECTRONICS (SINGAPORE) PTE LTD.—Oki Electric Industry Company, Ltd.; *Int'l*, pg. 1000
OKI (FRANCE) SARL—Oki Electric Industry Company, Ltd.; *Int'l*, pg. 1000
OKI SEMICONDUCTOR GROUP—Oki Electric Industry Company, Ltd.; *Int'l*, pg. 1000
OKI SEMICONDUCTOR (UK) LTD.—Oki Electric Industry Company, Ltd.; *Int'l*, pg. 1000
OKI TELECOM GROUP—Oki Electric Industry Company, Ltd.; *Int'l*, pg. 1000
OPTREX GLASS—Asahi Glass Co., Ltd.; *Int'l*, pg. 84
OPTREX GLASS—Mitsubishi Electric Corporation; *Int'l*, pg. 872
ORION INTL. SALES, INC.—Thermo Electron Corporation; *U.S. Public*, pg. 1592
ORION RESEARCH PUERTO RICO, INC.—Thermo Electron Corporation; *U.S. Public*, pg. 1592
PANASONIC CONSUMER ELECTRIC CO.—Matsushita Electric Industrial Co., Ltd.; *Int'l*, pg. 847
PANASONIC DEUTSCHLAND GMBH—Matsushita Electric Industrial Co., Ltd.; *Int'l*, pg. 847
PANASONIC INDUSTRIAL CO.—Matsushita Electric Industrial Co., Ltd.; *Int'l*, pg. 847
PARK DISTRIBUTORS, INC.; *U.S. Private*, pg. 839
PEAK TECHNOLOGIES GROUP, INC.—Moore Corporation Limited; *Int'l*, pg. 890
PEIRCE-PHELPS, INC.; *U.S. Private*, pg. 847
PENNY & GILES CONTROLS INC.—Bowthorpe plc; *Int'l*, pg. 208
PENNY & GILES INC.—Bowthorpe plc; *Int'l*, pg. 208
PHILIPS E.C.G.—Philips Electronics N.V.; *Int'l*, pg. 1054
PICO PRODUCTS, INC.; *U.S. Public*, pg. 1294
PICTURETEL CORPORATION-WORLD HEADQUARTERS—PictureTel; *U.S. Public*, pg. 1295
PICTURETEL INTERNATIONAL CORP.-ASIA PACIFIC/AMERICAS HEADQUARTERS—PictureTel; *U.S. Public*, pg. 1295
PIONEER NEW MEDIA TECHNOLOGIES; *U.S. Private*, pg. 866
PIONEER STANDARD CANADA INC.—Pioneer-Standard Electronics, Inc.; *U.S. Public*, pg. 1300
PIONEER-STANDARD ELECTRONICS, INC.; *U.S. Public*, pg. 1300
PIONEER STANDARD OF MARYLAND, INC.—Pioneer-Standard Electronics, Inc.; *U.S. Public*, pg. 1300
PLANTRONICS LTD.—Plantronics Inc.; *U.S. Public*, pg. 1308
PLAZA CREATE; *Int'l*, pg. 1060
POLAROID AG—Polaroid Corporation; *U.S. Public*, pg. 1314
POLAROID A.S.—Polaroid Corporation; *U.S. Public*, pg. 1314
POTENTIOMETER DIV.—Litton Industries, Inc.; *U.S. Public*, *pg. 1003*
POWELL ELECTRONICS INC.; *U.S. Private*, pg. 877
POWER & TELEPHONE SUPPLY COMPANY; *U.S. Private*, *pg. 877*
PREMIER ENERGY CORPORATION—Premier Farnell plc; *Int'l*, pg. 1068
PREMIER FARNELL—Premier Farnell plc; *Int'l*, pg. 1068
PREMIER FOREIGN SALES CORPORATION, INC.—Premier Farnell plc; *Int'l*, pg. 1068
PREMIER METAL PRODUCTS CO.; *U.S. Private*, pg. 881
PREMIERCO SERVICE CORP.—Premier Farnell plc; *Int'l*, pg. 1068
PROFESSIONAL INDUSTRIAL SALES—Hitachi, Ltd.; *Int'l*, pg. 622
PROGRESS INTERNATIONAL LIMITED—Astrex, Inc.; *U.S. Public*, pg. 141
PRONESTO—Investor AB; *Int'l*, pg. 687
RCA RECORDS U.S.—Bertelsmann AG; *Int'l*, pg. 192
RH COMMUNICATIONS (M) SDN BHD—SAIT-RadioHolland Group S.A.; *Int'l*, pg. 1152
RHG ARUBA—SAIT-RadioHolland Group S.A.; *Int'l*, pg. 1152
RHG CORPUS CHRISTI—SAIT-RadioHolland Group S.A.; *Int'l*, pg. 1151
RHG FISHING OFFICE HONG KONG—SAIT-RadioHolland Group S.A.; *Int'l*, pg. 1152
RHG FORT LAUDERDALE—SAIT-RadioHolland Group S.A.; *Int'l*, pg. 1151
RHG LONG BEACH—SAIT-RadioHolland Group S.A.; *Int'l*, pg. 1151
RHG MOBILE—SAIT-RadioHolland Group S.A.; *Int'l*, pg. 1151
RHG NEW ORLEANS—SAIT-RadioHolland Group S.A.; *Int'l*, pg. 1151
RHG NEW YORK—SAIT-RadioHolland Group S.A.; *Int'l*, pg. 1151
RHG NORFOLK/RH DEFENSE SYSTEMS INC.—SAIT-RadioHolland Group S.A.; *Int'l*, pg. 1151
RHG PANAMA CITY (FLORIDA)—SAIT-RadioHolland Group S.A.; *Int'l*, pg. 1151
RHG PORTLAND—SAIT-RadioHolland Group S.A.; *Int'l*, pg. 1151
RHG ST. MAARTEN—SAIT-RadioHolland Group S.A.; *Int'l*, pg. 1152
RHG SAN FRANCISCO—SAIT-RadioHolland Group S.A.; *Int'l*, pg. 1151
RHG SEATTLE—SAIT-RadioHolland Group S.A.; *Int'l*, pg. 1151
RHG YACHTING OFFICE HONG KONG—SAIT-RadioHolland Group S.A.; *Int'l*, pg. 1152
RS ELECTRONICS; *U.S. Private*, pg. 905
RS ELECTRONICS—RS Electronics; *U.S. Private*, pg. 905
R.X.D., INC.—Relm Wireless Corp.; *U.S. Public*, pg. 1376
RADIO-HOLLAND DE VENEZUELA S.A.—SAIT-RadioHolland Group S.A.; *Int'l*, pg. 1152
RADIO HOLLAND ELECTRONICS—SAIT-RadioHolland Group S.A.; *Int'l*, pg. 1151

RADIO HOLLAND GROUP CARRIBBEAN—SAIT-RadioHolland Group S.A.; Int'l, pg. 1152
RADIO HOLLAND GROUP-DEFENSE STAFF DIV.—SAIT-RadioHolland Group S.A.; Int'l, pg. 1151
RADIO HOLLAND GROUP-FISHERY EQUIP.—SAIT-RadioHolland Group S.A.; Int'l, pg. 1151
RADIO HOLLAND GROUP HEAD OFFICE-HOUSTON—SAIT-RadioHolland Group S.A.; Int'l, pg. 1152
RADIO-HOLLAND GROUP MIDDLE EAST—SAIT-RadioHolland Group S.A.; Int'l, pg. 1152
RADIO HOLLAND GROUP SINGAPORE—SAIT-RadioHolland Group S.A.; Int'l, pg. 1152
RADIO HOLLAND GROUP-SURVEY EQUIP.—SAIT-RadioHolland Group S.A.; Int'l, pg. 1151
RADIO-HOLLAND SECURITY SYSTEMS—SAIT-RadioHolland Group S.A.; Int'l, pg. 1151
RANK BRIMAR LTD.—The Rank Group PLC; Int'l, pg. 1087
THE RAO GROUP INC.; U.S. Private, pg. 910
RAULAND-BORG (CANADA) INC.—Rauland-Borg Corporation; U.S. Private, pg. 911
RAYTHEON SYSTEMS COMPANY—Raytheon Company; U.S. Public, pg. 1364
REAL WORLD; U.S. Private, pg. 913
RECOTON CANADA LTD.—Recoton Corporation; U.S. Public, pg. 1369
RECOTON CORPORATION; U.S. Public, pg. 1369
RELM COMMUNICATIONS, INC.—Relm Wireless Corp.; U.S. Public, pg. 1376
P.C. RICHARD & SON; U.S. Private, pg. 928
RICHARDSON ELECTRONICS, LTD.; U.S. Public, pg. 1387
RICHARDSON ELECTRONICS LTD.-CENTRAL—Richardson Electronics, Ltd.; U.S. Public, pg. 1388
RICHARDSON FRANC SNC—Richardson Electronics, Ltd.; U.S. Public, pg. 1388
RICHEY ELECTRONICS, INC.; U.S. Public, pg. 1388
ROBINSON-NUGENT GMBH—Robinson Nugent, Inc.; U.S. Public, pg. 1395
ROBOT RESEARCH, INC.—Sensormatic Electronics Corporation; U.S. Public, pg. 1457
ROGERS JAPAN INC.—Rogers Corporation; U.S. Public, pg. 1403
ROHDE & SCHWARZ, INC.—Rohde & Schwarz GmbH & Co. KG; Int'l, pg. 1124
ROHM APOLLO ELECTRONICS (THAILAND) CO., LTD.—Rohm Co., Ltd.; Int'l, pg. 1125
ROHM CO., LTD.; Int'l, pg. 1124
ROHM ELECTRONICS DALIAN CO., LTD.—Rohm Co., Ltd.; Int'l, pg. 1125
ROHM ELECTRONICS, EASTERN SALES DIV.—Rohm Co., Ltd.; Int'l, pg. 1125
ROHM ELECTRONICS GMBH—Rohm Co., Ltd.; Int'l, pg. 1125
ROHM ELECTRONICS (H.K.) CO., LTD.—Rohm Co., Ltd.; Int'l, pg. 1125
ROHM ELECTRONICS TAIWAN CO., LTD.—Rohm Co., Ltd.; Int'l, pg. 1125
ROHM ELECTRONICS (U.K.) LIMITED—Rohm Co., Ltd.; Int'l, pg. 1125
ROHM KOREA CORPORATION—Rohm Co., Ltd.; Int'l, pg. 1125
RONCO COMMUNICATIONS & ELECTRONICS INC.; U.S. Private, pg. 943
ROONEY BROTHERS COMPANY; U.S. Private, pg. 943
SAI DISTRIBUTORS—Sound Advice, Inc.; U.S. Public, pg. 1488
SEEQ TECHNOLOGY INC.; U.S. Public, pg. 1417
SABANCI HOLDING A.S.; Int'l, pg. 1167
SAGEM CORPORATION—Societe d'Applications Generales d'Electricite et de Mechanique; Int'l, pg. 1273
SAILTRON B.V.—SAIT-RadioHolland Group S.A.; Int'l, pg. 1151
SAKATA INX USA CORP.—Sumitomo Chemical Company, Ltd.; Int'l, pg. 1311
SAMSUNG ELECTRONICS AMERICA, INC.—Samsung Group; Int'l, pg. 1183
SAMSUNG ELECTRONICS CO., LTD.—Samsung Group; Int'l, pg. 1183
SAMSUNG SEMICONDUCTORS, INC.—Samsung Group; Int'l, pg. 1183
SAN DIEGO DIVISION—Aetrium Inc.; U.S. Public, pg. 27
SANKEN ELECTRIC U.S.A. CORP.—Sanken Electric Co., Ltd.; Int'l, pg. 1188
SANYO BUSINESS SYSTEMS (HONG KONG) LIMITED—Sanyo Electric Co., Ltd.; Int'l, pg. 1192
SANYO CANADA INC.—Sanyo Electric Co., Ltd.; Int'l, pg. 1192
SANYO ELECTRONICS (HONG KONG) LIMITED—Sanyo Electric Co., Ltd.; Int'l, pg. 1192
SANYO E.T. CANADA INC.—Sanyo Electric Co., Ltd.; Int'l, pg. 1192
SANYO (EUROPE) INTERNATIONAL AG—Sanyo Electric Co., Ltd.; Int'l, pg. 1192
SANYO FISHER VERTRIEBS GMBH—Sanyo Electric Co., Ltd.; Int'l, pg. 1192
SANYO ITALIANA S.P.A.—Sanyo Electric Co., Ltd.; Int'l, pg. 1192
SANYO LOGISTICS CORPORATION—Sanyo Electric Co., Ltd.; Int'l, pg. 1191
SANYO MALAYSIA SDN. BHD—Sanyo Electric Co., Ltd.; Int'l, pg. 1192
SANYO MARKETING CORPORATION—Sanyo Electric Co., Ltd.; Int'l, pg. 1192
SANYO NORTH AMERICAN CORPORATION—Sanyo Electric Co., Ltd.; Int'l, pg. 1191
SANYO SALES & SERVICE SDN. BHD.—Sanyo Electric Co., Ltd.; Int'l, pg. 1192
SANYO SEMICONDUCTOR CORPORATION—Sanyo Electric Co., Ltd.; Int'l, pg. 1191
SANYO SEMICONDUCTOR DISTRIBUTION (USA) CORPORATION—Sanyo Electric Co., Ltd.; Int'l, pg. 1191
SANYO SEMICONDUCTOR (H.K.) CO., LTD.—Sanyo Electric Co., Ltd.; Int'l, pg. 1192
SANYO (THAILAND) CO., LTD.—Sanyo Electric Co., Ltd.; Int'l, pg. 1193
SANYO U.K. LIMITED—Sanyo Electric Co., Ltd.; Int'l, pg. 1193
SANYO VLSI ENGINEERING CO., LTD.—Sanyo Electric Co., Ltd.; Int'l, pg. 1191
SCHNEIDER GROUP—Schneider S.A.; Int'l, pg. 1208
SCIENTIFIC ATLANTIC LIMITED—Scientific-Atlanta, Inc.; U.S. Public, pg. 1443
SEMICONDUCTOR PACKAGING MATERIALS CO., INC.; U.S. Public, pg. 1456
SENSORMATIC AG—Sensormatic Electronics Corporation; U.S. Public, pg. 1457
SENTRY TECHNOLOGY CORP.; U.S. Public, pg. 1458
SHARE TECHNOLOGIES - FAIRCHILD—Tel-Save Holdings, Inc.; U.S. Public, pg. 1568
SHARP ELECTRONICS (EUROPE) GMBH—Sharp Corporation; Int'l, pg. 1230
SHARP ELECTRONICS (U.K.) LTD.—Sharp Corporation; Int'l, pg. 1230
SHOKAI FAR EAST LTD.; U.S. Private, pg. 996
SIAM NEC CO., LTD.—The Siam Cement Public Company Limited; Int'l, pg. 1239
SID HARVEY INDUSTRIES; U.S. Private, pg. 998
SIEMENS A/S—Siemens AG; Int'l, pg. 1247
P.T. SIEMENS INDONESIA, JAKARTA—Siemens AG; Int'l, pg. 1247
SIEMENS K.K.—Siemens AG; Int'l, pg. 1247
SIEMENS LTD.—Siemens AG; Int'l, pg. 1247
SIEMENS LTD.-BEIJING, CHINA—Siemens AG; Int'l, pg. 1247
SIEMENS S.A.—Siemens AG; Int'l, pg. 1248
SILVERSTAR LTD., S.P.A.—Arrow Electronics, Inc.; U.S. Public, pg. 135
SIMRAD INC.—Simrad Norge AF; Int'l, pg. 1252
SLOAN TECHNOLOGY—Veeco Instruments, Inc.; U.S. Public, pg. 1711
SOMFY SYSTEMS INC.—Damart S.A.; Int'l, pg. 376
SONY (AUSTRALIA) PTY. LIMITED—Sony Corporation; Int'l, pg. 1283
SONY BROADCAST & COMMUNICATIONS LIMITED—Sony Corporation; Int'l, pg. 1283
SONY CORP.-PEOPLES REPUBLIC OF CHINA—Sony Corporation; Int'l, pg. 1283
SONY ELECTRONICS—Sony Corporation; Int'l, pg. 1281
SONY GES.M.B.H.—Sony Corporation; Int'l, pg. 1284
SONY INTERNATIONAL (SINGAPORE) PTE. LTD.—Sony Corporation; Int'l, pg. 1284
SONY LOGISTICS (SINGAPORE) PTE. LTD.—Sony Corporation; Int'l, pg. 1284
SONY MAGNETIC PRODUCTS CO.—Sony Corporation; Int'l, pg. 1281
SONY PRECISION ENGINEERING CENTER (SINGAPORE) PTE. LTD.—Sony Corporation; Int'l, pg. 1284
SONY SINGAPORE PTE. LTD.—Sony Corporation; Int'l, pg. 1284
SONY/TEKTRONIX CORPORATION—Tektronix, Inc.; U.S. Public, pg. 1568
SOUNDESIGN CORPORATION HONG KONG LTD.—SDI Technologies Inc.; U.S. Private, pg. 956
SOUNDESIGN CORPORATION JAPAN LTD.—SDI Technologies Inc.; U.S. Private, pg. 956
SOUTHERN ELECTRONICS CORPORATION; U.S. Public, pg. 1490
SPIRE INTERNATIONAL SALES CORPORATION—Spire Corporation; U.S. Public, pg. 1499
SPRINT NORTH SUPPLY—Sprint Corporation; U.S. Public, pg. 1501
SSANGYONG BUSINESS GROUP; Int'l, pg. 1291
STANDARD ELECTRONICS, INC.; U.S. Private, pg. 1031
STANDARD MARINE A/S—SAIT-RadioHolland Group S.A.; Int'l, pg. 1152
STEINER ELECTRIC COMPANY; U.S. Private, pg. 1039
STERLING ELECTRONICS—Marshall Industries; U.S. Public, pg. 1051
STERLING ELECTRONICS CORPORATION—Marshall Industries; U.S. Public, pg. 1051
STORAGE TECHNOLOGY DENMARK—Storage Technology Corporation; U.S. Public, pg. 1523
STORAGE TECHNOLOGY FINLAND—Storage Technology Corporation; U.S. Public, pg. 1523
STORAGE TECHNOLOGY NORWAY—Storage Technology Corporation; U.S. Public, pg. 1523
STORM PRODUCTS COMPANY, INC.; U.S. Private, pg. 1045
SUEZ ELECTRONICS S.A.E., ALEXANDRIA—SAIT-RadioHolland Group S.A.; Int'l, pg. 1152
SUMITOMO CANADA LTD.—Sumitomo Corporation; Int'l, pg. 1312
SUMITOMO CORPORATION; Int'l, pg. 1312
SUMITOMO CORPORATION OF AMERICA—Sumitomo Corporation; Int'l, pg. 1312
SUMITOMO 3M LIMITED—3M; U.S. Public, pg. 1606
SUMMA FOUR LIMITED—Summa Four, Inc.; U.S. Public, pg. 1527
SUNKYONG AMERICA, INC.—Sunkyong Industries Co.; Int'l, pg. 1320
SUNKYONG INDUSTRIES CO.; Int'l, pg. 1320
TCG INTERNATIONAL INC.; Int'l, pg. 1336
TDK (AUSTRALIA) PTY. LTD.—TDK Corporation; Int'l, pg. 1336
TDK CORPORATION; Int'l, pg. 1336
TDK DO BRASIL IND. E COM. LTDA.—TDK Corporation; Int'l, pg. 1336
TDK ELECTRONICS EUROPE GMBH—TDK Corporation; Int'l, pg. 1336
TDK HONG KONG CO., LTD.—TDK Corporation; Int'l, pg. 1337
TDK SINGAPORE (PTE.) LTD.—TDK Corporation; Int'l, pg. 1337
TDK TAIWAN CORP.—TDK Corporation; Int'l, pg. 1337
TDK UK LTD.—TDK Corporation; Int'l, pg. 1337
TPC WIRE & CABLE—Premier Farnell plc; Int'l, pg. 1068
TRW INC.; U.S. Public, pg. 1558
TABUCHI ELECTRIC COMPANY OF AMERICA—Tabuchi Electric Co., Ltd.; Int'l, pg. 1346
TANDEM COMPUTERS MCC—COMPAQ Computer Corporation; U.S. Public, pg. 417
TANDY CORPORATION; U.S. Public, pg. 1560
TANDY PACKAGING—Tandy Corporation; U.S. Public, pg. 1560
TATT SING SANYO ELECTRIC COMPANY LIMITED—Sanyo Electric Co., Ltd.; Int'l, pg. 1193
TEAL ELECTRONICS—SL Industries, Inc.; U.S. Public, pg. 1419
TECHNISH HANDELSKANTOOR LLOYD B.V.—AAR Corp.; U.S. Public, pg. 2
TECHNITROL INTERNATIONAL, INC.—Technitrol, Inc.; U.S. Public, pg. 1564
TECHNO MATSUYA CO., LTD.—Matsuya Company Ltd.; Int'l, pg. 848
TECHNOR PTY. LIMITED—Molex Incorporated; U.S. Public, pg. 1123
TECOM INDUSTRIES, INC.—Tech-Sym Corporation; U.S. Public, pg. 1563
TEKTRONIX CHINA LTD.—Tektronix, Inc.; U.S. Public, pg. 1567
TEKTRONIX HONG KONG LTD.—Tektronix, Inc.; U.S. Public, pg. 1567
TEKTRONIX SPA—Tektronix, Inc.; U.S. Public, pg. 1568
TELEINFORMATICA Y COMUNICACIONES, S.A.—Telefonica de Espana, S.A.; Int'l, pg. 1372
TELONIC BERKELEY, INC.; U.S. Private, pg. 1074
TEXAS INSTRUMENTS ASIA LTD.—Texas Instruments Incorporated; U.S. Public, pg. 1586
N.V. TEXAS INSTRUMENTS BELGIUM SA—Texas Instruments Incorporated; U.S. Public, pg. 1586
TEXAS INSTRUMENTS INTERNATIONAL TRADE CORPORATION—Texas Instruments Incorporated; U.S. Public, pg. 1586
TEXAS INSTRUMENTS JAPAN LTD.—Texas Instruments Incorporated; U.S. Public, pg. 1586
TEXAS INSTRUMENTS (SWITZERLAND) AG—Texas Instruments Incorporated; U.S. Public, pg. 1586
THOMSON BROADCAST SYSTEMS, INC.—Thomson S.A.; Int'l, pg. 1383
THOMSON COMPONENTS—Thomson S.A.; Int'l, pg. 1384
THOMSON-CSF, INC.—Thomson S.A.; Int'l, pg. 1384
THOMSON PASSIVE COMPONENTS CORP.—Thomson S.A.; Int'l, pg. 1384
THOMSON TUBES—Thomson S.A.; Int'l, pg. 1384
3COM CORPORATION—3Com Corporation; U.S. Public, pg. 1604
3COM, LTD.—3Com Corporation; U.S. Public, pg. 1604
3COM PERSONAL COMMUNICATIONS DIV.—3Com Corporation; U.S. Public, pg. 1604
3COM, S.A.—3Com Corporation; U.S. Public, pg. 1604
3M A/S—3M; U.S. Public, pg. 1606
P.T. 3M INDONESIA—3M; U.S. Public, pg. 1606
TIME ELECTRONICS—Avnet, Inc.; U.S. Public, pg. 155
TOKYO IC CO., LTD.—Sanyo Electric Co., Ltd.; Int'l, pg. 1191
TOSHIBA AMERICA ELECTRONIC COMPONENTS, INC.—Toshiba Corporation; Int'l, pg. 1405
TOSHIBA DE MEXICO, S.A. DE C.V.—Toshiba Corporation; Int'l, pg. 1406
TOSHIBA DEVICE CORPORATION—Toshiba Corporation; Int'l, pg. 1403
TOSHIBA ELECTRONICS ASIA (SINGAPORE) PTE. LTD.—Toshiba Corporation; Int'l, pg. 1406
TOSHIBA ELECTRONICS ESPANA S.A.—Toshiba Corporation; Int'l, pg. 1406
TOSHIBA ELECTRONICS EUROPE GMBH—Toshiba Corporation; Int'l, pg. 1406
TOSHIBA ELECTRONICS FRANCE S.A.R.L.—Toshiba Corporation; Int'l, pg. 1406
TOSHIBA ELECTRONICS (UK) LTD.—Toshiba Corporation; Int'l, pg. 1406
TOSHIBA LOGISTIC SUPPORT CORPORATION—Toshiba Corporation; Int'l, pg. 1404
TOSHIBA SOUND SYSTEMS CORPORATION—Toshiba Corporation; Int'l, pg. 1405
TRAK MICROWAVE CORP.—Tech-Sym Corporation; U.S. Public, pg. 1563
TRINKLE SALES, INC.; U.S. Private, pg. 1103
TURK PHILIPS AYDINLATMA SANAYI VE TICARET A.S.—Philips Electronics N.V.; Int'l, pg. 1055
TURK PHILIPS AYDINLATMA SANAYI VE TICARET A.S.—Sabanci Holding A.S.; Int'l, pg. 1168
UNIDEN AMERICA CORPORATION—Uniden Corporation; Int'l, pg. 1433
UNIDEN CORPORATION; Int'l, pg. 1433
UNITECH PLC—Siebe plc; Int'l, pg. 1241
VANCO INTERNATIONAL, INC.—Video Display Corporation; U.S. Public, pg. 1720
VARIAN KOREA LTD.—Varian Associates, Inc.; U.S. Public, pg. 1710
VARITRONIC SYSTEMS, INC.—W.H. Brady Co.; U.S. Public, pg. 250
VEECO GMBH—Veeco Instruments, Inc.; U.S. Public, pg. 1711
VEECO INSTRUMENTS LTD.—Veeco Instruments, Inc.; U.S. Public, pg. 1711
VISHAY INTERTECHNOLOGY, INC.; U.S. Public, pg. 1721
VIVITAR CORPORATION—Plaza Create; Int'l, pg. 1060
VORWERK & CO. THERMOMIX GMBH—Vorwerk & Co.; Int'l, pg. 1480
W & S DISTRIBUTORS, INC.—Bacardi Limited; Int'l, pg. 132
WAGO COMPANY OF JAPAN LIMITED—Bowthorpe plc; Int'l, pg. 209
WAGO CONTACT SARL—Bowthorpe plc; Int'l, pg. 209
WAGO KONTAKTTECHNIK GES MBH—Bowthorpe plc; Int'l, pg. 209
WAGO LIMITED—Bowthorpe plc; Int'l, pg. 209
WALKER & ASSOCIATES, INC.; U.S. Private, pg. 1147
WARREN ELECTRIC GROUP; U.S. Private, pg. 1151
WATSON ELECTRIC—Warren Electric Group; U.S. Private, pg. 1151

WEHLE ELECTRIC CO., INC.—Westburne Inc.; *Int'l*, pg. 1492
WESTBURNE INC.; *Int'l*, pg. 1491
WESTERN MICRO TECHNOLOGY, INC.; *U.S. Public*, pg. 1759
WHOLESALE ELECTRONIC SUPPLY; *U.S. Private*, pg. 1174
WILLIAMS TELECOMMUNICATIONS SYSTEMS, INC.—The Williams Companies, Inc.; *U.S. Public*, pg. 1769
WYLE ELECTRONICS—Veba AG; *Int'l*, pg. 1457
WYLE ELECTRONICS-SANTA CLARA—Veba AG; *Int'l*, pg. 1458
WYLE-GINSBURY ELECTRONICS—Veba AG; *Int'l*, pg. 1458
THE ZAMOISKI CO.; *U.S. Private*, pg. 1203
ZENITH ELECTRONICS CORP.; *U.S. Public*, pg. 1790
ZEUS COMPONENTS DIVISION - INTERNATIONAL SALES DIV.—Arrow Electronics, Inc.; *U.S. Public*, pg. 134

5072 — HARDWARE-WHOLESALE

ACE HARDWARE CORPORATION; *U.S. Private*, pg. 12
ADAMS RITE (EUROPE) LTD.—Adams Rite Manufacturing Co.; *U.S. Private*, pg. 17
ALASKA INDUSTRIAL HARDWARE INC.; *U.S. Private*, pg. 31
ALLMETAL SCREW PRODUCTS CORP.; *U.S. Private*, pg. 41
AMERICAN CONSUMER PRODUCTS—Vista 2000, Inc.; *U.S. Private*, pg. 1142
AMERICAN DETENTION SERVICES, INC.—Adtec Detention Systems; *U.S. Private*, pg. 18
AMERICAN SECURITY DISTRIBUTION; *U.S. Private*, pg. 61
ASSOCIATED INDUSTRIAL SUPPLY, INC.; *U.S. Private*, pg. 91
ATLANTIC HARDWARE & SUPPLY CO.—Colonial Commercial Corp.; *U.S. Public*, pg. 400
ATWOOD DISTRIBUTING, INC.; *U.S. Private*, pg. 98
B&D DE COSTA RICA, S.A.—The Black & Decker Corporation; *U.S. Public*, pg. 234
BARNES GROUP INC.; *U.S. Public*, pg. 189
BARNETT INC.—Waxman Industries, Inc.; *U.S. Public*, pg. 1749
BENSON INDUSTRIES, INC.; *U.S. Private*, pg. 133
BIFURCATED ENGINEERING FRANCE S.A.—Clayhithe P.L.C.; *Int'l*, pg. 297
BLACK & CO.; *U.S. Private*, pg. 146
BLACK & DECKER AB—The Black & Decker Corporation; *U.S. Public*, pg. 234
BLACK & DECKER (BELGIUM) N.V.—The Black & Decker Corporation; *U.S. Public*, pg. 234
BLACK & DECKER INTERNATIONAL CORP.—The Black & Decker Corporation; *U.S. Public*, pg. 234
BLACK & DECKER (NEDERLAND) B.V.—The Black & Decker Corporation; *U.S. Public*, pg. 234
BLACK & DECKER DE COLOMBIA S.A.—The Black & Decker Corporation; *U.S. Public*, pg. 234
BLACK & DECKER DE EL SALVADOR S.A. DE C.V.—The Black & Decker Corporation; *U.S. Public*, pg. 234
BLACK & DECKER HOLDINGS DE VENEZUELA, C.A.—The Black & Decker Corporation; *U.S. Public*, pg. 234
BLACK & DECKER HONG KONG LIMITED—The Black & Decker Corporation; *U.S. Public*, pg. 234
BLACK & DECKER HOUSEWARES (PTE.) LTD.—The Black & Decker Corporation; *U.S. Public*, pg. 234
BLACK & DECKER (NORGE) A/S—The Black & Decker Corporation; *U.S. Public*, pg. 234
BLACK & DECKER (OVERSEAS) A.G.—The Black & Decker Corporation; *U.S. Public*, pg. 234
BLACK & DECKER OY—The Black & Decker Corporation; *U.S. Public*, pg. 234
BLACK & DECKER WERKZEUGE VERTRIEBASGESELLSCHAFT M.B.H.—The Black & Decker Corporation; *U.S. Public*, pg. 234
BLOUNT EUROPE, S.A.—Blount International, Inc.; *U.S. Public*, pg. 238
BLOUNT GMBH—Blount International, Inc.; *U.S. Public*, pg. 239
BLOUNT JAPAN INC.—Blount International, Inc.; *U.S. Public*, pg. 239
BOWMAN DISTRIBUTION—Barnes Group Inc.; *U.S. Public*, *pg. 190*
BUCK & HICKMAN LIMITED—The Peninsular and Oriental Steam Navigation Company; *Int'l*, pg. 1032
BUHRMAN-PHARR HARDWARE COMPANY; *U.S. Private*, *pg. 179*
BULLDOG VSI—Newell Co.; *U.S. Public*, pg. 1176
CALIFORNIA HARDWARE COMPANY—Distribution America; *U.S. Private*, pg. 335
CARDER, INC.; *U.S. Private*, pg. 208
CAROLINA BUILDERS CORPORATION—Wolseley Plc.; *Int'l*, pg. 1512
CENEX, INC.; *U.S. Private*, pg. 221
CENTRAL STEEL & WIRE COMPANY; *U.S. Public*, pg. 327
CHARLESTON TOOL SERVICES—Cummins Engine Company, Inc.; *U.S. Public*, pg. 468
COMALCO-CHH ALUMINUM—International Paper Company; *U.S. Public*, pg. 905
CONSOLIDATED STORES CORP.; *U.S. Public*, pg. 437
DOM AG SICHERHEITSTECHNIK—The Black & Decker Corporation; *U.S. Public*, pg. 233
DAVIS PAINT COMPANY; *U.S. Private*, pg. 315
DECO PRODUCTS CO.; *U.S. Private*, pg. 320
DOUGLAS/QUIKUT—Berkshire Hathaway Inc.; *U.S. Public*, *pg. 217*
ELU MASKINER A/S—The Black & Decker Corporation; *U.S. Public*, pg. 234
EMERY WATERHOUSE COMPANY; *U.S. Private*, pg. 373
EUROC TRADE AB—Scancem AB; *Int'l*, pg. 1199
EVERBRIGHT FASTENERS LTD.—Haden Maclellan Holdings plc; *Int'l*, pg. 585
EXCELSIOR MANUFACTURING & SUPPLY CORP.; *U.S. Private*, pg. 387
FAR EAST POWER EQUIPMENT LIMITED—The Black & Decker Corporation; *U.S. Public*, pg. 234
FASTENAL COMPANY; *U.S. Public*, pg. 614
FINGERLE LUMBER CO.; *U.S. Private*, pg. 405
R.H. FORSCHNER DIVISION—Swiss Army Brands, Inc.; *U.S. Public*, pg. 1544
FREDERICK TRADING COMPANY—Distribution America; *U.S. Private*, pg. 335
R.J. GALLAGHER CO.; *U.S. Private*, pg. 438
GENERAL HARDWARE DISTRIBUTORS—Alaska Industrial Hardware Inc.; *U.S. Private*, pg. 31
GIBRALTAR LOCK CO. LTD.—Masco Corporation; *U.S. Public*, pg. 1054
GRAHAM BUILDERS MERCHANTS LIMITED—BTR plc; *Int'l*, pg. 124
W.W. GRAINGER, INC.; *U.S. Public*, pg. 758
GROCERS SUPPLY CO. INC.; *U.S. Private*, pg. 483
GROHE AMERICA, INC.—Friedrich Grohe Armaturenfabrik GmbH & Co.; *Int'l*, pg. 559
HDW, INCORPORATED—Distribution America; *U.S. Private*, *pg. 335*
HARCO—Banner Aerospace, Inc.; *U.S. Public*, pg. 187
HARDWARE WHOLESALERS, INC.; *U.S. Private*, pg. 502
HARTTUNG FASTENERS A/S—The Black & Decker Corporation; *U.S. Public*, pg. 233
HARTWELL CORPORATION—Western Sky Industries, Inc.; *U.S. Private*, pg. 1168
HATTON ET COOKSON S.A.—Unilever Plc; *Int'l*, pg. 1437
HEADS & THREADS—Alleghany Corporation; *U.S. Public*, pg. 42
HERITAGE CO-OP; *U.S. Private*, pg. 524
HILL-BEHAN LUMBER COMPANY; *U.S. Private*, pg. 529
ILCO UNICAN CORP.—Unican Security Systems Ltd.; *Int'l*, pg. 1432
ILCO UNICAN MEXICO S.A. DE C.V.—Unican Security Systems Ltd.; *Int'l*, pg. 1432
INDUSTRIAL FASTENERS LTD.—Haden Maclellan Holdings plc; *Int'l*, pg. 585
INTERMARK WORLD PRODUCTS, LTD.; *U.S. Private*, pg. 567
JIRVA AB—Trelleborg AB; *Int'l*, pg. 1422
KENNAMETAL AUSTRALIA PTY. LTD.—Kennametal Inc.; *U.S. Public*, pg. 951
KENNAMETAL HERTEL FRANCE, S.A.—Kennametal Inc.; *U.S. Public*, pg. 951
KENNAMETAL HERTEL NEDERLAND, B.V.—Kennametal Inc.; *U.S. Public*, pg. 951
KENNAMETAL HERTEL (SINGAPORE) PTE. LTD.—Kennametal Inc.; *U.S. Public*, pg. 951
KRUPP HOESCH INFORMATIONSVERARBEITUNG GMBH—Fried. Krupp AG; *Int'l*, pg. 512
THE KRUSE COMPANY; *U.S. Private*, pg. 636
LUX GMBH & CO. KG—OBI Bau-und Heimwerkermaerkte GmbH & Co. KG; *Int'l*, pg. 993
LUX INTERNATIONAL S.A.—OBI Bau-und Heimwerkermaerkte GmbH & Co. KG; *Int'l*, pg. 993
LUXTRONIC MASCHINEN GMBH—OBI Bau-und Heimwerkermaerkte GmbH & Co. KG; *Int'l*, pg. 993
MADISON GROCERY CO., INC.; *U.S. Private*, pg. 694
MAKITA U.S.A., INC.—Makita Corporation; *Int'l*, pg. 831
MAQUINAS Y HERRAMIENTAS BLACK & DECKER DE CHILE S.A.—The Black & Decker Corporation; *U.S. Public*, pg. 234
MCLAUGHLIN INDUSTRIAL DISTRIBUTORS, INC.; *U.S. Private*, pg. 724
MEDAL DISTRIBUTING CO.—Waxman Industries, Inc.; *U.S. Public*, pg. 1748
METRIC & MULTISTANDARD COMPONENTS; *U.S. Private*, pg. 736
MID-CONTINENT SCREW PRODUCTS CO.; *U.S. Private*, pg. 743
MONROE HARDWARE CO.—Distribution America; *U.S. Private*, pg. 335
NATIONAL-GENERAL SUPPLY, INC.—Carl Weissman & Sons, Inc.; *U.S. Private*, pg. 1160
NIFAST CORPORATION—Nissho Iwai Corporation; *Int'l*, pg. 947
NOLAND COMPANY; *U.S. Public*, pg. 1187
NORITAKE CO., INC.—Noritake Co., Limited; *Int'l*, pg. 959
ORGILL INC.; *U.S. Private*, pg. 819
PACIFIC HIDE & FUR DEPOT; *U.S. Private*, pg. 831
PRO GROUP, INC.; *U.S. Private*, pg. 887
RANCHERS SUPPLY COMPANY, INC.; *U.S. Private*, pg. 908
RAYMOND MERCHANDISE—Barnes Group Inc.; *U.S. Public*, pg. 190
REGENT-SHEFFIELD LTD.—McPherson's Limited; *Int'l*, pg. 852
REICO, INC.; *U.S. Private*, pg. 919
RICHMOND SCREW ANCHOR DIVISION—Ripplewood Holdings L.L.C.; *U.S. Private*, pg. 932
RIGHT IDEAS INC.; *U.S. Private*, pg. 930
ROCKFORD INTERNATIONAL GROUP—Rockford Products Corp.; *U.S. Private*, pg. 938
ROTHENBERGER WERKZEUGE MASCHINEN GMBH—Rothenberger Group GmbH; *Int'l*, pg. 1128
SAPA A/S—Electrolux, AB; *Int'l*, pg. 441
SKF MAINTENANCE PRODUCTS B.V.—AB SKF; *Int'l*, pg. 1159
SPS TECHNOLOGIES, INC.; *U.S. Public*, pg. 1419
SPS/UNBRAKO K.K.—SPS Technologies, Inc.; *U.S. Public*, *pg. 1420*
SANDVIK BAHCO ARGENTINA S.A.C.E.L.—Sandvik AB; *Int'l*, pg. 1187
SANDVIK CANADA INC.—Sandvik AB; *Int'l*, pg. 1188
SANDVIK CHILE S.A.—Sandvik AB; *Int'l*, pg. 1187
SANDVIK COLOMBIA S.A.—Sandvik AB; *Int'l*, pg. 1188
SANDVIK DE MEXICO S.A. DE C.V.—Sandvik AB; *Int'l*, pg. 1188
SANDVIK DEL PERU S.A.—Sandvik AB; *Int'l*, pg. 1188
SANDVIK DO BRASIL S.A.—Sandvik AB; *Int'l*, pg. 1188
SANDVIK HARD MATERIALS—Sandvik AB; *Int'l*, pg. 1186
SANDVIK KENYA LTD.—Sandvik AB; *Int'l*, pg. 1187
SANDVIK KOREA LTD.—Sandvik AB; *Int'l*, pg. 1187
SANDVIK MALAYSIA SDN. BHD.—Sandvik AB; *Int'l*, pg. 1187
SANDVIK NEW ZEALAND LTD.—Sandvik AB; *Int'l*, pg. 1187
SANDVIK PHILIPPINES, INC.—Sandvik AB; *Int'l*, pg. 1187
SANDVIK (PTY.) LTD.—Sandvik AB; *Int'l*, pg. 1187
SANDVIK SAWS & TOOLS CO.—Sandvik AB; *Int'l*, pg. 1185
SANDVIK TAIWAN LTD.—Sandvik AB; *Int'l*, pg. 1187
SANDVIK VENEZUELA C.A.—Sandvik AB; *Int'l*, pg. 1188
SECURITY GROUP INC.; *U.S. Private*, pg. 981
SERVICE SUPPLY CO. INC. OF INDIANA; *U.S. Private*, pg. 987
SHEFFIELD HARDWARE COMPANY—Distribution America; *U.S. Private*, pg. 335
ROBERT SKEELS & CO.—Wynn's International, Inc.; *U.S. Public*, pg. 1782
SKIL NEDERLAND B.V.—Emerson Electric Co.; *U.S. Public*, *pg. 577*
SNAP-ON TOOLS CORPORATION; *U.S. Public*, pg. 1480
SNYDER-DIAMOND; *U.S. Private*, pg. 1011
SOMMER & MACA INDUSTRIES, INC.; *U.S. Private*, pg. 1013
SOUTHTEC, INC.—SouthCo. Inc.; *U.S. Private*, pg. 1015
STANDARD SUPPLY & HARDWARE CO.; *U.S. Private*, pg. 1032
STANDCO CANADA, LTD.—SPS Technologies, Inc.; *U.S. Public*, pg. 1420
SVENSKA BLOUNT AB—Blount International, Inc.; *U.S. Public*, pg. 239
SWISS ARMY BRANDS, INC.; *U.S. Public*, pg. 1544
SWISS ARMY BRANDS LTD.—Swiss Army Brands, Inc.; *U.S. Public*, pg. 1544
TENNESSEE FARMERS CO-OP; *U.S. Private*, pg. 1076
THREE STATES SUPPLY CO., INC.—UIS, Inc.; *U.S. Private*, pg. 1113
THRUWAY FASTENERS INC.; *U.S. Private*, pg. 1084
TRUSERV CORPORATION; *U.S. Private*, pg. 1108
TUCKER GMBH—The Black & Decker Corporation; *U.S. Public*, pg. 234
TUCKER INDUSTRIES PTY. LTD.—The Black & Decker Corporation; *U.S. Public*, pg. 235
UNBRAKO MEXICANA, S.A. DE C.V.—SPS Technologies, Inc.; *U.S. Public*, pg. 1420
UNBRAKO PRODUCTS (SINGAPORE) PTE LTD.—SPS Technologies, Inc.; *U.S. Public*, pg. 1420
UNIFIX LTD.—Brunel Holdings Plc; *Int'l*, pg. 231
UNITED HARDWARE DISTRIBUTING CO.—Distribution America; *U.S. Private*, pg. 335
UNITED MARKETING (LEICESTER) LTD.—The Black & Decker Corporation; *U.S. Public*, pg. 234
VERMONT AMERICAN AUSTRALIA, LTD.—Emerson Electric Co.; *U.S. Public*, pg. 578
VERMONT AMERICAN CANADA, INC.—Emerson Electric Co.; *U.S. Public*, pg. 578
VERMONT AMERICAN TOOL GROUP—Emerson Electric Co.; *U.S. Public*, pg. 575
VERMONT GMBH—Emerson Electric Co.; *U.S. Public*, pg. 578
WOC INC.—Waxman Industries, Inc.; *U.S. Public*, pg. 1748
WAXMAN INDUSTRIES, INC.; *U.S. Public*, pg. 1748
WAXMAN USA INC.—Waxman Industries, Inc.; *U.S. Public*, pg. 1749
WEBB BUILDERS HARDWARE; *U.S. Private*, pg. 1156
CARL WEISSMAN & SONS, INC.; *U.S. Private*, pg. 1160
WEST UNION CORPORATION; *U.S. Private*, pg. 1163
WILLIAMS FASTENER & SUPPLY CO.—Williams Steel & Hardware Company; *U.S. Private*, pg. 1178
WILTON CORPORATION; *U.S. Private*, pg. 1181
WILTSHIRE CANADA, INC.—McPherson's Limited; *Int'l*, pg. 852
WOLSELEY PLC.; *Int'l*, pg. 1511
WYNN'S INTERNATIONAL, INC.; *U.S. Public*, pg. 1782

5074 — PLUMBING & HEATING EQUIPMENT & SUPPLIES-WHOLESALE

AHLSELL EL AB—Trelleborg AB; *Int'l*, pg. 1422
AHLSELL VVS AB—Trelleborg AB; *Int'l*, pg. 1422
APEX SUPPLY CO., INC.; *U.S. Private*, pg. 77
ARMATURTEKNIK I OSBY AB—Svedala Industri AB; *Int'l*, pg. 1323
ARMATURTEKNIK I OSBY AB—Trelleborg AB; *Int'l*, pg. 1419
ASSOCIATED EQUIPMENT COMPANY OF DELAWARE; *U.S. Private*, pg. 90
ATLANTIC PLUMBING SUPPLY COMPANY; *U.S. Private*, pg. 95
BPC DIVISION—Heywood Williams Group PLC; *Int'l*, pg. 618
BABCOCK-HITACHI K.K.—Hitachi, Ltd.; *Int'l*, pg. 621
BARNETT INC.—Waxman Industries, Inc.; *U.S. Public*, pg. 1749
BATTEY MACHINERY COMPANY; *U.S. Private*, pg. 123
BRODERNA EDSTRAND AB—Trelleborg AB; *Int'l*, pg. 1422
BUHRMAN-PHARR HARDWARE COMPANY; *U.S. Private*, *pg. 179*
BUILDER MARTS OF AMERICA, INC.; *U.S. Private*, pg. 179
CCTF—Emco Limited; *Int'l*, pg. 453
CALCASIEU LUMBER COMPANY; *U.S. Private*, pg. 200
CAPITAL PLUMBING & HEATING SUPPLY CO.—Granite Group Wholesale LLC; *U.S. Private*, pg. 469
CAPITAL PLUMBING & HEATING SUPPLY CO. INC.—Granite Group Wholesale LLC; *U.S. Private*, pg. 469
CAPITOL GROUP; *U.S. Private*, pg. 206
CENTRAL GOULET SUPPLY—Granite Group Wholesale LLC; *U.S. Private*, pg. 469
CENTRAL SUPPLY CO., INC.; *U.S. Private*, pg. 225

COLUMBIA PIPE & SUPPLY COMPANY; *U.S. Private, pg. 256*
COLUMBUS PIPE & EQUIPMENT COMPANY; *U.S. Private, pg. 257*
CONSOLIDATED PIPE & SUPPLY COMPANY; *U.S. Private, pg. 266*
CUSTOM PIPE & COUPLING CO.—Wolseley Plc.; *Int'l, pg. 1512*
DAHL INTERNATIONAL AB; *Int'l, pg. 359*
DELUXAIR INCORPORATED—Emco Limited; *Int'l, pg. 453*
DENGYOSHA MACHINE WORKS CORPORATION—Toshiba Corporation; *Int'l, pg. 1402*
DURCO-VALTEK (ASIA PACIFIC) PTE. LTD.—Flowserve Corporation; *U.S. Public, pg. 659*
ELECTRIC FURNACE FRANCE S.A.R.L.—Electric Furnace Co.; *U.S. Private, pg. 368*
ELJER PLUMBINGWARE—Zurn Industries, Inc.; *U.S. Public, pg. 1794*
ELSCINT (ASIA PACIFIC) LTD.—Elscint Ltd.; *Int'l, pg. 450*
ELSCINT (CANADA) LTD.—Elscint Ltd.; *Int'l, pg. 450*
ELSCINT FRANCE S.A.—Elscint Ltd.; *Int'l, pg. 450*
ELSCINT GMBH—Elscint Ltd.; *Int'l, pg. 450*
EMAIL LIMITED-BUILDING PRODUCTS GROUP—Email Limited; *Int'l, pg. 450*
EMCO DISTRIBUTION—Emco Limited; *Int'l, pg. 453*
EMCO DISTRIBUTION GROUP WESTERN REGION—Emco Limited; *Int'l, pg. 453*
EMCO LIMITED; *Int'l, pg. 452*
EMCO SUPPLY ATLANTIC DIVISION—Emco Limited; *Int'l, pg. 453*
EMCO SUPPLY CENTRAL REGION—Emco Limited; *Int'l, pg. 453*
EMCO SUPPLY EASTERN REGION—Emco Limited; *Int'l, pg. 453*
EXCELSIOR MANUFACTURING & SUPPLY CORP.; *U.S. Private, pg. 387*
FAMILIAN CORP.—Wolseley Plc.; *Int'l, pg. 1512*
FAMILIAN PIPE & SUPPLY CO.—Wolseley Plc.; *Int'l, pg. 1512*
FAMILIAN SOUTHWEST, INC.—Wolseley Plc.; *Int'l, pg. 1512*
FERGUSON ENTERPRISES, INC.—Wolseley Plc.; *Int'l, pg. 1512*
THE SCOTT FETZER COMPANY—Berkshire Hathaway Inc.; *U.S. Public, pg. 217*
FLOW EUROPE—Flow International Corporation; *U.S. Public, pg. 656*
FREDERICK TRADING COMPANY—Distribution America; *U.S. Private, pg. 335*
G&H PRODUCTS CORP.—Tetra Laval Group; *Int'l, pg. 1378*
GAGGENAU USA CORPORATION; *U.S. Private, pg. 437*
GOTAVERKEN ENERGY SYSTEMS INC.—Kvaerner a.s.a.; *Int'l, pg. 770*
GOTAVERKEN ENERGY SYSTEMS LTD.—Kvaerner a.s.a.; *Int'l, pg. 771*
GRAHAM BUILDERS MERCHANTS LIMITED—BTR plc; *Int'l, pg. 124*
W.W. GRAINGER, INC.; *U.S. Public, pg. 758*
GRANITE GROUP WHOLESALE LLC; *U.S. Private, pg. 469*
HDW, INCORPORATED—Distribution America; *U.S. Private, pg. 335*
HAJOCA CORP.; *U.S. Private, pg. 494*
HAMWORTHY COMBUSTION EQUIPMENT LIMITED—Powell Duffryn PLC; *Int'l, pg. 1065*
HARDWARE WHOLESALERS, INC.; *U.S. Private, pg. 502*
HAUCK MANUFACTURING COMPANY INC.—Ruhrgas Aktiengesellschaft; *Int'l, pg. 1149*
HERBALIFE INTERNATIONAL, S.A.-PORTUGAL—Herbalife International of America, Inc.; *U.S. Public, pg. 809*
HOLMAN BOILER WORKS, INC.—Copes-Vulcan Inc.; *U.S. Private, pg. 274*
HUGHES SUPPLY CORP.; *U.S. Private, pg. 547*
HUGHES SUPPLY, INC.; *U.S. Public, pg. 846*
HUMPHREY FLUID POWER LTD.—Humphrey Products Company; *U.S. Private, pg. 548*
IDEAL-STANDARD—American Standard Inc.; *U.S. Public, pg. 92*
INDECK POWER EQUIPMENT COMPANY; *U.S. Private, pg. 559*
INTERNATIONAL COMFORT PRODUCTS; *U.S. Public, pg. 898*
JACUZZI WHIRLPOOL BATH INC.—U.S. Industries, Inc.; *U.S. Public, pg. 1684*
JAMECO INDUSTRIES, INC.—Watts Industries, Inc.; *U.S. Public, pg. 1746*
JIRVA AB—Trelleborg AB; *Int'l, pg. 1422*
JUNKER INC.—Otto Junker GmbH Lammersdorf; *Int'l, pg. 1014*
KOHLER JAPAN K.K.—Kohler Company; *U.S. Private, pg. 631*
KOHLER LTD.—Kohler Company; *U.S. Private, pg. 631*
LANDA, INC.; *U.S. Private, pg. 646*
J.H. LARSON ELECTRICAL COMPANY; *U.S. Private, pg. 652*
LASALLE BRISTOL CORP.—Heywood Williams Group PLC; *Int'l, pg. 618*
LINCOLN PRODUCTS—Wolseley Plc.; *Int'l, pg. 1512*
MARTIN INDUSTRIES, INC. (AL); *U.S. Private, pg. 709*
MAXON COMBUSTION SYSTEMS, LTD.—Maxon Corporation; *U.S. Private, pg. 717*
MAXON GMBH—Maxon Corporation; *U.S. Private, pg. 717*
N.V. MAXON INTERNATIONAL S.A.—Maxon Corporation; *U.S. Private, pg. 717*
MAXON S.A.R.L.—Maxon Corporation; *U.S. Private, pg. 717*
MAY SUPPLY COMPANY, INC.—WLR Foods, Inc.; *U.S. Public, pg. 1727*
A.Y. MCDONALD INDUSTRIES, INC.; *U.S. Private, pg. 721*
A.Y. MCDONALD SUPPLY CO. INC.—A.Y. McDonald Industries, Inc.; *U.S. Private, pg. 721*
MEDAL DISTRIBUTING CO.—Waxman Industries, Inc.; *U.S. Public, pg. 1748*
MIURA BOILER CO. LTD.—Miura Co., Ltd.; *Int'l, pg. 884*
MIURA CO., LTD.; *Int'l, pg. 884*
MODERN CONCRETE SEPTIC TANK COMPANY; *U.S. Private, pg. 754*
MOLLENBERG-BETZ INC.; *U.S. Private, pg. 756*
MOORE-HANDLEY, INC.; *U.S. Public, pg. 1128*
MOUNTAIN STATES PIPE & SUPPLY COMPANY; *U.S. Private, pg. 764*
MUNROE, INC.; *U.S. Private, pg. 767*
MUTUAL MANUFACTURING & SUPPLY CO.; *U.S. Private, pg. 769*
NIBCO—NIBCO, Inc.; *U.S. Private, pg. 798*
NIBCO INC.—NIBCO, Inc.; *U.S. Private, pg. 798*
NOLAND COMPANY; *U.S. Public, pg. 1187*
NOLAND PLUMBING/HEATING DIV.—Noland Company; *U.S. Public, pg. 1187*
NORTHLAND ELECTRIC SUPPLY COMPANY; *U.S. Private, pg. 806*
NORTHWEST PIPE FITTINGS, INC.; *U.S. Private, pg. 806*
ONE STOP SUPPLY, INC.—Hughes Supply, Inc.; *U.S. Public, pg. 847*
PAINE SUPPLY OF JACKSON, INC.—Hughes Supply, Inc.; *U.S. Public, pg. 847*
PEIRCE-PHELPS, INC.; *U.S. Private, pg. 847*
PLUMBING SPECIALTIES & SUPPLIES, INC.—Wolseley Plc.; *Int'l, pg. 1512*
PRIMUS INC.; *U.S. Private, pg. 884*
PRODUTOS MEDICO HOSPITALARES ELSCINT LTDA.—Elscint Ltd.; *Int'l, pg. 450*
ROMAC INDUSTRIES, INC.; *U.S. Private, pg. 942*
W.A. ROOSEVELT CO.; *U.S. Private, pg. 943*
ROTHENBERGER WERKZEUGE MASCHINEN GMBH—Rothenberger Group GmbH; *Int'l, pg. 1128*
SANITEC LTD. OY—Metra Corporation; *Int'l, pg. 863*
SAUNDERS VALVE, INC.—Tetra Laval Group; *Int'l, pg. 1379*
J.A. SEXAUER, INC.—The Dyson-Kissner-Moran Corporation; *U.S. Private, pg. 352*
SHEFFIELD HARDWARE COMPANY—Distribution America; *U.S. Private, pg. 335*
SIERRA CRAFT, INC.—Wolseley Plc.; *Int'l, pg. 1512*
SLOAN FLUSHMATE—Sloan Valve Company; *U.S. Private, pg. 1006*
SLOAN VALVE COMPANY; *U.S. Private, pg. 1006*
SNYDER-DIAMOND; *U.S. Private, pg. 1011*
SPRAYING SYSTEMS CO. FAR EAST—Spraying Systems Co.; *U.S. Private, pg. 1027*
SPRAYING SYSTEMS DEUTSCHLAND GMBH—Spraying Systems Co.; *U.S. Private, pg. 1027*
STERLING SUPPLY COMPANY, INC.; *U.S. Private, pg. 1041*
TD INDUSTRIES INC.; *U.S. Private, pg. 1063*
TWI INTERNATIONAL, INC.—Waxman Industries, Inc.; *U.S. Public, pg. 1749*
TAIWAN TOTO CO., LTD.—Toto Ltd.; *Int'l, pg. 1410*
THERMO INDUSTRIES INC.; *U.S. Private, pg. 1080*
TITAN SALES CORP.—The Rival Company; *U.S. Public, pg. 1391*
TODD PIPE & SUPPLY GARDEN GROVE—Todd Pipe & Supply Hawthorne; *U.S. Private, pg. 1090*
TODD PIPE & SUPPLY HAWTHORNE; *U.S. Private, pg. 1090*
TOSHIBA ELECTRIC APPLIANCES CO., LTD.—Toshiba Corporation; *Int'l, pg. 1404*
TOTO (BEIJING) CO., LTD.—Toto Ltd.; *Int'l, pg. 1410*
USCO, INCORPORATED—Hughes Supply, Inc.; *U.S. Public, pg. 847*
VALLEY RESOURCES, INC.; *U.S. Public, pg. 1706*
VALTEK/AUSTRALIA—Flowserve Corporation; *U.S. Public, pg. 659*
VICTAULIC INTERNATIONAL—Victaulic Company of America; *U.S. Private, pg. 1138*
VICTAULIC TOOL COMPANY—Victaulic Company of America; *U.S. Private, pg. 1138*
WOC INC.—Waxman Industries, Inc.; *U.S. Public, pg. 1748*
WATTS INDUSTRIES (CANADA) INC.—Watts Industries, Inc.; *U.S. Public, pg. 1747*
WATTS INDUSTRIES EUROPE B.V.—Watts Industries, Inc.; *U.S. Public, pg. 1747*
WAXMAN INDUSTRIES, INC.; *U.S. Public, pg. 1748*
WAXMAN USA INC.—Waxman Industries, Inc.; *U.S. Public, pg. 1749*
CARL WEISSMAN & SONS, INC.; *U.S. Private, pg. 1160*
WESTBURNE INC.; *Int'l, pg. 1491*
WESTLUND INDUSTRIAL SUPPLY LTD.—Emco Limited; *Int'l, pg. 453*
WOLSELEY PLC.; *Int'l, pg. 1511*

5075 — WARM AIR HEATING & AIR CONDITIONING EQUIPMENT & SUPPLIES-WHOLESALE

ABB ENVIRONMENTAL SYSTEMS (UTILITIES)—ABB Asea Brown Boveri (Holding) Ltd.; *Int'l, pg. 4*
AHLSELL EL AB—Trelleborg AB; *Int'l, pg. 1422*
AHLSELL KYL AB—Trelleborg AB; *Int'l, pg. 1422*
AHLSELL VVS AB—Trelleborg AB; *Int'l, pg. 1422*
THE HARRY ALTER COMPANY—Temperature Equipment Corporation; *U.S. Private, pg. 1075*
AMANO CLEANTECH MALAYSIA SDN. BHD.—Amano Corporation; *Int'l, pg. 71*
APEX SUPPLY CO., INC.; *U.S. Private, pg. 77*
ARIZONA WHOLESALE SUPPLY COMPANY; *U.S. Private, pg. 82*
ASAHI/AMERICA, INC.; *U.S. Public, pg. 137*
ASSOCIATED EQUIPMENT COMPANY OF DELAWARE; *U.S. Private, pg. 90*
BHA COMPANY, INC.—BHA Group Holdings Inc.; *U.S. Public, pg. 161*
BHA GROUP HOLDINGS INC.; *U.S. Public, pg. 161*
BAKER DISTRIBUTING COMPANY—Watsco, Inc.; *U.S. Public, pg. 1746*
BERNER INTERNATIONAL CO. LTD.—Incentive AB; *Int'l, pg. 669*
BROWN BOVERI-YORK SUISSE—ABB Asea Brown Boveri (Holding) Ltd.; *Int'l, pg. 1*
BRYANT MUNGO DIVISION—Temperature Equipment Corporation; *U.S. Private, pg. 1075*
BURKE ENGINEERING COMPANY; *U.S. Private, pg. 183*
CADET MANUFACTURING COMPANY; *U.S. Private, pg. 198*
CANADIAN COLEMAN SUPPLY CO., INC.—MacAndrews & Forbes Holdings Inc.; *U.S. Private, pg. 691*
CAPITAL PLUMBING & HEATING SUPPLY CO.—Granite Group Wholesale LLC; *U.S. Private, pg. 469*
CAPITAL PLUMBING & HEATING SUPPLY CO. INC.—Granite Group Wholesale LLC; *U.S. Private, pg. 469*
CAPITOL GROUP; *U.S. Private, pg. 206*
CARRIER BUILDING SYSTEMS & SERVICES—United Technologies Corporation; *U.S. Public, pg. 1689*
CARRIER CANADA LTD.—United Technologies Corporation; *U.S. Public, pg. 1691*
CARRIER ONTARIO—United Technologies Corporation; *U.S. Public, pg. 1691*
CARRIER SINGAPORE (PTE.) LTD.—United Technologies Corporation; *U.S. Public, pg. 1691*
CENTRAL GOULET SUPPLY—Granite Group Wholesale LLC; *U.S. Private, pg. 469*
CENTRAL SUPPLY CO., INC.; *U.S. Private, pg. 225*
THE CLIMATIC CORP.; *U.S. Private, pg. 246*
DAEWOO INTERNATIONAL AMERICA CORP. - RIDGEFIELD—Daewoo Corporation; *Int'l, pg. 357*
DAHL INTERNATIONAL AB; *Int'l, pg. 359*
EXCELSIOR MANUFACTURING & SUPPLY CORP.; *U.S. Private, pg. 387*
FASTEC INDUSTRIAL; *U.S. Private, pg. 397*
FAYETTE TUBULAR PRODUCTS—Danaher Corporation; *U.S. Public, pg. 481*
FEDDERS ASIA PTE. LTD.—Fedders Corp.; *U.S. Public, pg. 615*
FERGUSON LYON CONKLIN & COMPANY INC.—Wolseley Plc.; *Int'l, pg. 1512*
FREDERICK TRADING COMPANY—Distribution America; *U.S. Private, pg. 335*
FROZEN FOOD EXPRESS INDUSTRIES, INC.; *U.S. Public, pg. 685*
GEC COMPOSANTS S.A.—The General Electric Company, p.l.c.; *Int'l, pg. 546*
GEMAIRE DISTRIBUTORS, INC.—Watsco, Inc.; *U.S. Public, pg. 1746*
GRAHAM BUILDERS MERCHANTS LIMITED—BTR plc; *Int'l, pg. 124*
W.W. GRAINGER, INC.; *U.S. Public, pg. 758*
GRANITE GROUP WHOLESALE LLC; *U.S. Private, pg. 469*
THE HABEGGER CORPORATION; *U.S. Private, pg. 492*
HADEN DRYSYS ENVIRONMENTAL LTD.—Haden Maclellan Holdings plc; *Int'l, pg. 585*
HAGEMEYER N.V.—First Pacific Company Limited; *Int'l, pg. 487*
HALMA P.L.C.; *Int'l, pg. 589*
HEATCRAFT INC.—Lennox International Inc.; *U.S. Private, pg. 659*
HEATING AND COOLING SUPPLY INC.—Watsco, Inc.; *U.S. Public, pg. 1746*
HEIGHTS HEATING & COOLING; *U.S. Private, pg. 519*
HUGHES SUPPLY, INC.; *U.S. Public, pg. 846*
JIRVA AB—Trelleborg AB; *Int'l, pg. 1422*
JOHNSON SUPPLY & EQUIPMENT CORP.; *U.S. Private, pg. 594*
GEORGE KOCH SONS, INC.; *U.S. Private, pg. 628*
A.Y. MCDONALD INDUSTRIES, INC.; *U.S. Private, pg. 721*
A.Y. MCDONALD SUPPLY CO. INC.—A.Y. McDonald Industries, Inc.; *U.S. Private, pg. 721*
MICRO-MET L CORP.; *U.S. Private, pg. 742*
MODINE MANUFACTURING COMPANY; *U.S. Public, pg. 1121*
MOLLENBERG-BETZ INC.; *U.S. Private, pg. 756*
MUTUAL MANUFACTURING & SUPPLY CO.; *U.S. Private, pg. 769*
NOLAND AIR CONDITIONING/REFRIGERATION DIV.—Noland Company; *U.S. Public, pg. 1187*
NOLAND COMPANY; *U.S. Public, pg. 1187*
PEIRCE-PHELPS, INC.; *U.S. Private, pg. 847*
PLOVER BLFC BRANCH—W.A. Roosevelt Co.; *U.S. Private, pg. 943*
REFRIGERATION AFTERMARKET DIVISION—Tecumseh Products Company; *U.S. Public, pg. 1566*
ROBERTSHAW CONTROLS COMPANY—Siebe plc; *Int'l, pg. 1243*
W.A. ROOSEVELT CO.; *U.S. Private, pg. 943*
SANYO AIRCONDITIONERS (SINGAPORE) PTE. LTD.—Sanyo Electric Co., Ltd.; *Int'l, pg. 1192*
SID HARVEY INDUSTRIES; *U.S. Private, pg. 998*
RUSSELL SIGLER INC.; *U.S. Private, pg. 999*
SQUIRE-COGSWELL COMPANY; *U.S. Private, pg. 1027*
SWARTWOUT INDUSTRIES—Tomkins PLC; *Int'l, pg. 1398*
TD INDUSTRIES INC.; *U.S. Private, pg. 1063*
TARRANT SERVICE, INC.; *U.S. Private, pg. 1069*
TEMPERATURE EQUIPMENT CORPORATION; *U.S. Private, pg. 1075*
THERMO INDUSTRIES INC.; *U.S. Private, pg. 1080*
UNI-LINE DIV.—Siebe plc; *Int'l, pg. 1243*
UNITARY PRODUCTS GROUP—York International Corporation; *U.S. Public, pg. 1788*
WATLOW LIMITED—Watlow Electric Manufacturing Company; *U.S. Private, pg. 1154*
WATLOW SINGAPORE PTE. LTD.—Watlow Electric Manufacturing Company; *U.S. Private, pg. 1154*
WATSCO, INC.; *U.S. Public, pg. 1745*
WHOLESALE HEATING SUPPLIES—Emco Limited; *Int'l, pg. 453*
YOUNG SUPPLY COMPANY; *U.S. Private, pg. 1202*

5078 — REFRIGERATION EQUIPMENT & SUPPLIES-WHOLESALE

ACME REFRIGERATION OF BATON ROUGE INC.; *U.S. Private*, pg. 13
AHLSELL KYL AB—Trelleborg AB; *Int'l*, pg. 1422
THE HARRY ALTER COMPANY—Temperature Equipment Corporation; *U.S. Private*, pg. 1075
AMERICAN EXCELSIOR COMPANY; *U.S. Private*, pg. 53
ARDCO, INC.; *U.S. Private*, pg. 80
AUSTRALIAN COLEMAN, INC.—MacAndrews & Forbes Holdings Inc.; *U.S. Private*, pg. 691
BAKER DISTRIBUTING COMPANY—Watsco, Inc.; *U.S. Public*, pg. 1746
BRAN & LUEBBE S.A.R.L.—Tetra Laval Group; *Int'l*, pg. 1380
BRAN & LUEBBE S.R.L.—Tetra Laval Group; *Int'l*, pg. 1380
BRYANT MUNGO DIVISION—Temperature Equipment Corporation; *U.S. Private*, pg. 1075
BURKE ENGINEERING COMPANY; *U.S. Private*, pg. 183
CALCASIEU LUMBER COMPANY; *U.S. Private*, pg. 200
COLEMAN JAPAN LTD.—MacAndrews & Forbes Holdings Inc.; *U.S. Private*, pg. 691
CUMMINS INTERMOUNTAIN DIESEL; *U.S. Private*, pg. 295
D&H DISTRIBUTING COMPANY; *U.S. Private*, pg. 300
DAWMEC LIMITED—Ascot Holdings Plc; *Int'l*, pg. 88
DEVIMCO—Accor S.A.; *Int'l*, pg. 20
DEVIMCO LTD.—Accor S.A.; *Int'l*, pg. 21
FASTEC INDUSTRIAL; *U.S. Private*, pg. 397
FILBERT CORP.—Vilter Manufacturing Corporation; *U.S. Private*, pg. 1140
GERBER INTERNATIONAL INC.; *U.S. Private*, pg. 448
J. GERBER & CO. INC.—Gerber International Inc.; *U.S. Private*, pg. 449
O.G. HOYER INC.—Tetra Laval Group; *Int'l*, pg. 1378
HUSSMANN CORP.—Whitman Corporation; *U.S. Public*, pg. 1766
ICEE-USA CORP.—J & J Snack Foods Corporation; *U.S. Public*, pg. 916
JOHNSON SUPPLY & EQUIPMENT CORP.; *U.S. Private*, pg. 594
JORDON COMMERCIAL REFRIGERATOR CO.; *U.S. Private*, pg. 599
KVAERNER EUREKA INC.—Kvaerner a.s.a.; *Int'l*, pg. 770
KVAERNER EUREKA ISLANDI—Kvaerner a.s.a.; *Int'l*, pg. 767
KYSOR/WARREN—Scotsman Industries, Inc.; *U.S. Public*, pg. 1445
MASEK DISTRIBUTING INC.; *U.S. Private*, pg. 711
MOLLENBERG-BETZ INC.; *U.S. Private*, pg. 756
NATIONWIDE REFRIGERATION SUPPLIES LIMITED—Ascot Holdings Plc; *Int'l*, pg. 88
NOLAND AIR CONDITIONING/REFRIGERATION DIV.—Noland Company; *U.S. Public*, pg. 1187
NOLAND COMPANY; *U.S. Public*, pg. 1187
PARISI INC./ROYAL STORE FIXTURE; *U.S. Private*, pg. 839
PLOVER BLFC BRANCH—W.A. Roosevelt Co.; *U.S. Private*, pg. 943
REFRIGERATION AFTERMARKET DIVISION—Tecumseh Products Company; *U.S. Public*, pg. 1566
REFRIGERATION SUPPLIES DISTRIBUTORS; *U.S. Private*, pg. 917
REVCO SCIENTIFIC—General Signal Corporation; *U.S. Public*, pg. 727
W.A. ROOSEVELT CO.; *U.S. Private*, pg. 943
SEAGRAM CANADA—The Seagram Company Ltd.; *Int'l*, pg. 1217
SUNDROP—Cadbury Schweppes p.l.c.; *Int'l*, pg. 248
TD INDUSTRIES INC.; *U.S. Private*, pg. 1063
TEMPERATURE EQUIPMENT CORPORATION; *U.S. Private*, pg. 1075
VICTORY REFRIGERATION CO. LC; *U.S. Private*, pg. 1139
VILTER MANUFACTURING CORPORATION; *U.S. Private*, pg. 1140
WESTBURNE INC.; *Int'l*, pg. 1491
WILLIAMS & COMPANY, INC.—Superior Group, Inc.; *U.S. Private*, pg. 1055
YOUNG SUPPLY COMPANY; *U.S. Private*, pg. 1202

5082 — CONSTRUCTION & MINING MACHINERY & EQUIPMENT, EXCEPT PETROLEUM-WHOLESALE

ACTION LIFT—Medico Industries, Inc.; *U.S. Private*, pg. 728
ALBAN TRACTOR CO. INC.; *U.S. Private*, pg. 32
ALLIED CONSTRUCTION PRODUCTS, INC.—Pubco Corporation; *U.S. Public*, pg. 1339
AMERICAN EQUIPMENT COMPANY, INC.—Fluor Corporation; *U.S. Public*, pg. 660
THE ARO CORPORATION—Ingersoll-Rand Company; *U.S. Public*, pg. 877
ASSOCIATED POWER, INC.; *U.S. Private*, pg. 92
ASTEC INDUSTRIES, INC.; *U.S. Public*, pg. 141
AUSTIN POWDER CO.; *U.S. Private*, pg. 100
B.T. EQUIPMENT CO., INC.—Gilbane Building Company; *U.S. Private*, pg. 453
BERRY COMPANIES, INC.; *U.S. Private*, pg. 137
BLACKWOOD HODGE (BELGIE) N.V.—Brunel Holdings Plc; *Int'l*, pg. 231
BLACKWOOD HODGE (ZAMBIA) LTD.—Brunel Holdings Plc; *Int'l*, pg. 231
BLOUNT U.K. LIMITED—Blount International, Inc.; *U.S. Public*, pg. 239
BOART INTERNATIONAL LIMITED—Anglo American Corporation of South Africa Limited; *Int'l*, pg. 76
BOART LONGYEAR B.V.—Anglo American Corporation of South Africa Limited; *Int'l*, pg. 76
BOART LONGYEAR INC.—Anglo American Corporation of South Africa Limited; *Int'l*, pg. 76
BOART LONGYEAR LIMITED—Anglo American Corporation of South Africa Limited; *Int'l*, pg. 76
BOART LONGYEAR LTD.—Anglo American Corporation of South Africa Limited; *Int'l*, pg. 76
BOART LONGYEAR S.A.—Anglo American Corporation of South Africa Limited; *Int'l*, pg. 76
BRUNEL HOLDINGS PLC; *Int'l*, pg. 230
THE BURKE CO.—Tridel Enterprises Inc.; *Int'l*, pg. 1423
CM HUMAN SERVICES CO. LTD.—Caterpillar Inc.; *U.S. Public*, pg. 317
CSR LIMITED; *Int'l*, pg. 245
CARLISLE CRANE CO—Carlisle Equipment Company; *U.S. Private*, pg. 211
CARLISLE EQUIPMENT CO—Carlisle Equipment Company; *U.S. Private*, pg. 211
CARLISLE EQUIPMENT COMPANY; *U.S. Private*, pg. 211
CAROLINA TRACTOR & EQUIPMENT CO.; *U.S. Private*, pg. 214
CATERPILLAR INC.; *U.S. Public*, pg. 315
CATERPILLAR MEXICO S.A. DE C.V.—Caterpillar Inc.; *U.S. Public*, pg. 316
CATERPILLAR (U.K.) LIMITED—Caterpillar Inc.; *U.S. Public*, pg. 317
W.C. CAYE & COMPANY, INC.; *U.S. Private*, pg. 220
CHAMPION, INC.; *U.S. Private*, pg. 228
CHARTER PLC; *Int'l*, pg. 280
CHOCTAW, INC.; *U.S. Private*, pg. 238
CLARK DISTRIBUTION SERVICES COMPANY—Ingersoll-Rand Company; *U.S. Public*, pg. 876
CLEVELAND BROTHERS EQUIPMENT CO., INC.; *U.S. Private*, pg. 245
CLOVERDALE EQUIPMENT CO.; *U.S. Private*, pg. 247
COECLERICI GROUP; *Int'l*, pg. 303
COMPONENTA BENELUX/BRANCH OFFICE BELGIUM—Trelleborg AB; *Int'l*, pg. 1421
COMPONENTA GJUTERIER AB—Trelleborg AB; *Int'l*, pg. 1419
COMPONENTA KRANLYFT AB—Trelleborg AB; *Int'l*, pg. 1419
COMPONENTA PARTS AB—Trelleborg AB; *Int'l*, pg. 1421
CONTRACTORS MACHINERY & EQUIPMENT—Hanson PLC; *Int'l*, pg. 594
CONTRACTORS SUPPLY COMPANY, INC.; *U.S. Private*, pg. 270
DAEWOO INTERNATIONAL AMERICA CORP. - RIDGEFIELD—Daewoo Corporation; *Int'l*, pg. 357
DAVIS MINING & MANUFACTURING; *U.S. Private*, pg. 315
DEAN OPERATIONS INC.; *U.S. Private*, pg. 318
DEUTZ AG; *Int'l*, pg. 407
THE DOSCO CORP.—BTR plc; *Int'l*, pg. 124
DYNAPAC A/S—Trelleborg AB; *Int'l*, pg. 1420
DYNAPAC CONSTRUCTION EQUIPMENT LTD.—Trelleborg AB; *Int'l*, pg. 1420
DYNAPAC EQUIPAMENTOS INDUSTRIAIS LTD.—Trelleborg AB; *Int'l*, pg. 1420
DYNAPAC FAR EAST LTD.—Trelleborg AB; *Int'l*, pg. 1420
DYNAPAC KENKI KK—Trelleborg AB; *Int'l*, pg. 1420
DYNAPAC LTD.—Trelleborg AB; *Int'l*, pg. 1420
DYNAPAC S.A.—Trelleborg AB; *Int'l*, pg. 1420
DYNAPAC S.P.A.—Trelleborg AB; *Int'l*, pg. 1420
DYNAPAC (UK) LTD.—Trelleborg AB; *Int'l*, pg. 1420
EICKHOFF CORPORATION—Gebr. Eickhoff Maschinenfabrik und Eisengiesserei mbH; *Int'l*, pg. 542
EMPIRE MACHINERY—Empire Southwest Co.; *U.S. Private*, pg. 374
EMPIRE SOUTHWEST CO.; *U.S. Private*, pg. 374
FMC EUROPE, S.A./N.V.—FMC Corporation; *U.S. Public*, pg. 606
FABICK & COMPANY—John Fabick Tractor Company; *U.S. Private*, pg. 390
FABICK BROTHERS EQUIPMENT—John Fabick Tractor Company; *U.S. Private*, pg. 390
JOHN FABICK TRACTOR COMPANY; *U.S. Private*, pg. 390
FABICK MACHINERY—John Fabick Tractor Company; *U.S. Private*, pg. 390
FASTENAL COMPANY; *U.S. Public*, pg. 614
FIATALLIS NORTH AMERICA, INC.—Fiat Auto SpA; *Int'l*, pg. 483
FOLEY HOLDING COMPANY, INC.; *U.S. Private*, pg. 416
FOLEY TRACTOR COMPANY, INC.—Foley Holding Company, Inc.; *U.S. Private*, pg. 416
L.B. FOSTER COMPANY; *U.S. Public*, pg. 675
FURNIVAL/STATE MACHINERY CO.—Komatsu Ltd.; *Int'l*, pg. 744
GILES & RANSOME, INC.; *U.S. Private*, pg. 453
GOODMAN EQUIPMENT CORP.; *U.S. Private*, pg. 464
GREENHAM TRADING LIMITED—Taylor Woodrow plc; *Int'l*, pg. 1358
GRESSER N.V.—Brunel Holdings Plc; *Int'l*, pg. 231
GROVE WORLDWIDE—Hanson PLC; *Int'l*, pg. 593
HANSON PLC; *Int'l*, pg. 592
HARNISCHFEGER INDUSTRIES, INC.; *U.S. Public*, pg. 788
HASPER EQUIPMENT CO.—Cloverdale Equipment Co.; *U.S. Private*, pg. 247
HASTINGS DEERING (SOLOMON ISLANDS) LIMITED—Sime Darby Berhad; *Int'l*, pg. 1250
HITACHI KENKI DYNAPAC KK—Trelleborg AB; *Int'l*, pg. 1420
HUTCHENSON SEAL CORPORATION; *U.S. Private*, pg. 550
I-R EQUIPMENT SALES—Ingersoll-Rand Company; *U.S. Public*, pg. 876
KATO CRANES (UK) LTD.—Trelleborg AB; *Int'l*, pg. 1420
KATO KRANER NORGE A/S—Trelleborg AB; *Int'l*, pg. 1420
KOCKUMS CANCAR CORP.—BTR plc; *Int'l*, pg. 124
KOMATSU AMERICA INTERNATIONAL COMPANY—Komatsu Ltd.; *Int'l*, pg. 744
AB KRANLYFT—Trelleborg AB; *Int'l*, pg. 1420
KUMAGAI GUMI CO., LTD.; *Int'l*, pg. 763
LETTS INDUSTRIES, INC.; *U.S. Private*, pg. 661
LIEBHERR-AMERICA INC.—Liebherr-International AG; *Int'l*, pg. 808
MEDICO INDUSTRIES, INC.; *U.S. Private*, pg. 728
MEYER INTERNATIONAL PLC; *Int'l*, pg. 864
MI-JACK PRODUCTS, INC.; *U.S. Private*, pg. 740
MICHIGAN CAT; *U.S. Private*, pg. 740
M.D. MOODY & SONS INC.; *U.S. Private*, pg. 759
JOHN MOWLEM & COMPANY PLC; *Int'l*, pg. 896
MULTIQUIP, INC.—Itochu Corporation; *Int'l*, pg. 695
MUSTANG TRACTOR & EQUIP. CO.; *U.S. Private*, pg. 768
NNG ENERGY SYSTEMS, INC.—Northwest Natural Gas Company; *U.S. Public*, pg. 1200
NATIONAL MINE SERVICE COMPANY, ALABAMA DIV.—Charter plc; *Int'l*, pg. 281
NATIONAL MINE SERVICE COMPANY, MT. VERNON DIV.—Charter plc; *Int'l*, pg. 281
NATIONAL MINE SERVICE, INC.—Charter plc; *Int'l*, pg. 280
NATIONAL-OILWELL/DRECO—National-Oilwell Inc.; *U.S. Public*, pg. 1158
NATIONAL-OILWELL/DRECO INDUSTRIAL—National-Oilwell Inc.; *U.S. Public*, pg. 1158
NATIONAL-OILWELL/DRECO RIG TECHNOLOGY & CONSTRUCTION—National-Oilwell Inc.; *U.S. Public*, pg. 1158
NAVISTAR INTERNATIONAL CORPORATION CANADA—Navistar International Corporation; *U.S. Public*, pg. 1167
NITTETSU SHOJI CO., LTD.—Nippon Steel Corporation; *Int'l*, pg. 939
NORTH CAROLINA EQUIPMENT CO.; *U.S. Private*, pg. 804
NORTH CENTRAL CRANE & EXCAVATOR SALES CORP.—The Manitowoc Company, Inc.; *U.S. Public*, pg. 1041
NORTON GMBH—Saint-Gobain; *Int'l*, pg. 1175
NORTON (NEW ZEALAND) LIMITED—Saint-Gobain; *Int'l*, pg. 1175
NORTON PTE. LTD.—Saint-Gobain; *Int'l*, pg. 1175
NORTON PTY. LTD.—Saint-Gobain; *Int'l*, pg. 1175
NORTON S.A.—Saint-Gobain; *Int'l*, pg. 1175
NORTON S.A. INDUSTRIA E COMERCIO—Saint-Gobain; *Int'l*, pg. 1175
NORTON S.A./N.V.—Saint-Gobain; *Int'l*, pg. 1175
NORTON SCANDINAVIA AB—Saint-Gobain; *Int'l*, pg. 1175
NORTON S.P.A.—Saint-Gobain; *Int'l*, pg. 1175
OHIO MACHINERY CO.; *U.S. Private*, pg. 812
OKABE COMPANY LIMITED; *Int'l*, pg. 999
OWSLEY & SONS, INC.; *U.S. Private*, pg. 824
PASCON LTD.—BTR plc; *Int'l*, pg. 124
PEARCE INDUSTRIES INC.; *U.S. Private*, pg. 845
H.O. PENN MACHINERY CO. INC.; *U.S. Private*, pg. 849
PETERSON TRACTOR COMPANY; *U.S. Private*, pg. 858
POLYPHASE CORPORATION; *U.S. Public*, pg. 1315
PUBCO CORPORATION; *U.S. Public*, pg. 1339
RICHMOND SCREW ANCHOR DIVISION—Ripplewood Holdings L.L.C.; *U.S. Private*, pg. 932
J.A. RIGGS TRACTOR CO.; *U.S. Private*, pg. 930
RISH EQUIPMENT COMPANY; *U.S. Private*, pg. 932
ROAD MACHINERY & SUPPLIES CO.; *U.S. Private*, pg. 934
ROAD MACHINERY COMPANY; *U.S. Private*, pg. 934
ROXON OY—Tamrock Corp.; *Int'l*, pg. 1353
RUSCON CORP.; *U.S. Private*, pg. 952
SGB CONSTRUCTION SERVICES, INC.—John Mowlem & Company plc; *Int'l*, pg. 896
SAUDI ELECTRO-MECHANICAL CONSTRUCTION CO. (PETCON)—Abdulla Fouad Co. Ltd.; *Int'l*, pg. 502
SHIN CATERPILLAR MITSUBISHI LTD.—Caterpillar Inc.; *U.S. Public*, pg. 317
SIME DARBY HONG KONG LIMITED—Sime Darby Berhad; *Int'l*, pg. 1251
L.B. SMITH, INC.; *U.S. Private*, pg. 1009
SOMERSET WELDING & STEEL, INC.—Riggs Industries, Inc.; *U.S. Private*, pg. 930
SOUTHERN GARDEN CITRUS PROCESSING—United States Sugar Corporation; *U.S. Private*, pg. 1126
STEPHENSON EQUIPMENT, INC.; *U.S. Private*, pg. 1040
SYRACUSE SUPPLY COMPANY; *U.S. Private*, pg. 1060
SYRACUSE SUPPLY CONSTRUCTION & EQUIPMENT DIVISION—Syracuse Supply Company; *U.S. Private*, pg. 1060
THOMPSON TRACTOR COMPANY; *U.S. Private*, pg. 1083
UBE INDUSTRIES LTD.; *Int'l*, pg. 1426
UP-RIGHT, INC.; *U.S. Private*, pg. 1128
VIBRATECHNIQUES STV—Trelleborg AB; *Int'l*, pg. 1420
WAJAX INDUSTRIES LIMITED—Wajax Limited; *Int'l*, pg. 1485
WHITE CAP INDUSTRIES, INC.; *U.S. Public*, pg. 1765
WYOMING MACHINERY COMPANY; *U.S. Private*, pg. 1193
ZIEGLER INC.; *U.S. Private*, pg. 1205
3UMMIT PERFORMANCE DIST. INC.—Oshkosh Truck Corporation; *U.S. Public*, pg. 1233

5083 — FARM & GARDEN MACHINERY & EQUIPMENT-WHOLESALE

AYP CANADA, INC.—Electrolux, AB; *Int'l*, pg. 440
AUTOTRACTOREXPORT; *Int'l*, pg. 101
B & W FARM CENTER—B&W Co-op, Inc.; *U.S. Private*, pg. 105
BAIC INTERNATIONAL—Farmatic Research, Inc.; *Int'l*, pg. 478
BHS-BAYER, BERG-, HUETTEN-, UND SALZWERKE AG—Viag AG; *Int'l*, pg. 1464
BELARUS MACHINERY, INC.—AutotractorExport; *Int'l*, pg. 101
BRIGGS & STRATTON CANADA INC.—Briggs & Stratton Corporation; *U.S. Public*, pg. 252
CFCI S.A.—Unilever Plc; *Int'l*, pg. 1436
CARCO INTERNATIONAL, INC.; *U.S. Private*, pg. 208

CENEX, INC.; *U.S. Private*, pg. 221
CENTURY SUPPLY CORP.—Richton International Corporation; *U.S. Public*, pg. 1389
CLEVELAND BROTHERS EQUIPMENT CO., INC.; *U.S. Private*, pg. 245
JOHN DEERE—Deere & Company; *U.S. Public*, pg. 492
A. DUDA & SONS INC.; *U.S. Private*, pg. 344
DUTTON-FORSHAW (LAND MACHINERY) LTD.—Lonrho plc; *Int'l*, pg. 817
EFFINGHAM-CLAY SERVICE CO.; *U.S. Private*, pg. 365
FMC CORPORATION; *U.S. Public*, pg. 604
FILIPINAS-ISEKI CORP.—Nissho Iwai Corporation; *Int'l*, pg. 947
FLOWTRON/GALAXIE DIVISION—Armatron International, Inc.; *U.S. Public*, pg. 131
FORD LUSITANA—Ford Motor Company; *U.S. Public*, pg. 666
GILES & RANSOME, INC.; *U.S. Private*, pg. 453
W.W. GRAINGER, INC.; *U.S. Public*, pg. 758
GRASSLAND EQUIPMENT & IRRIGATION CORP.; *U.S. Private*, pg. 471
GRINNELL SUPPLY SALES DIVISION—Tyco International Ltd.; *U.S. Public*, pg. 1648
GROSSENBURG IMPLEMENTS, INCORPORATED; *U.S. Private*, pg. 483
HAMILTON EQUIPMENT, INC.; *U.S. Private*, pg. 497
JAMES HARDIE INDUSTRIES LTD.; *Int'l*, pg. 596
HERITAGE CO-OP; *U.S. Private*, pg. 524
HERSCHEL ADAMS—Alamo Group, Inc.; *U.S. Public*, pg. 35
HOWARD—Thrige-Titan Group; *Int'l*, pg. 1387
HOWARD MASCHINENFABRIK GMBH—Thrige-Titan Group; *Int'l*, pg. 1387
HOWARD S.A.—Thrige-Titan Group; *Int'l*, pg. 1387
ILLINOIS AUTO ELECTRIC CO.; *U.S. Private*, pg. 557
IRRITOL SYSTEM—The Toro Company; *U.S. Public*, pg. 1624
KRUPP POLYSIUS AG—Fried. Krupp AG; *Int'l*, pg. 512
THE KRUSE COMPANY; *U.S. Private*, pg. 636
KUBOTA TRACTOR CORP.—Kubota Corp.; *Int'l*, pg. 762
LEMKEN TRI-AG LIMITED—Thrige-Titan Group; *Int'l*, pg. 1387
LONG EQUIPMENT CO.—Long MFG. NC, Inc.; *U.S. Private*, pg. 675
LONG MFG. NC, INC.; *U.S. Private*, pg. 674
MARUBENI AMERICA CORPORATION—Marubeni Corporation; *Int'l*, pg. 844
MASEK DISTRIBUTING INC.; *U.S. Private*, pg. 711
MIKUNI CORPORATION; *Int'l*, pg. 867
MIKUNI SHOKO CORP.—Mikuni Corporation; *Int'l*, pg. 867
MILLER-ST. NAZIANZ, INC.; *U.S. Private*, pg. 748
MONROE HARDWARE CO.—Distribution America; *U.S. Private*, pg. 335
MONTE VISTA CO-OP ASSOCIATION, INC.; *U.S. Private*, pg. 758
MUELLER INTERNATIONAL SALES CORP.—Paul Mueller Company; *U.S. Public*, pg. 1141
NORDSTEN—Thrige-Titan Group; *Int'l*, pg. 1386
NORGREN/LOS ANGELES—IMI Plc; *Int'l*, pg. 647
NORSE DAIRY SYSTEMS; *U.S. Private*, pg. 802
PETERSON TRACTOR COMPANY; *U.S. Private*, pg. 858
PURDEL, COOPERATIVE AGRO-ALIMENTAIRE; *Int'l*, pg. 1073
ROTT-KELLER SUPPLY CO.; *U.S. Private*, pg. 947
THE ROWE CORPORATION; *U.S. Private*, pg. 948
SF SERVICES; *U.S. Private*, pg. 956
SHEFFIELD HARDWARE COMPANY—Distribution America; *U.S. Private*, pg. 335
A.O. SMITH HARVESTORE PRODUCTS, INC.—A.O. Smith Corporation; *U.S. Public*, pg. 1477
STEIGER AUSTRALIA, LTD.—Tenneco Inc.; *U.S. Public*, pg. 1580
STEIGER TRACTOR—Case Corporation; *U.S. Public*, pg. 311
STIHL INC.—Andreas Stihl; *Int'l*, pg. 1301
TBG MANAGEMENT S.A.M.; *Int'l*, pg. 1335
TAYLOR, PEARSON & CARSON DIVISION—Acklands Limited; *Int'l*, pg. 23
THOMPSON TRACTOR COMPANY; *U.S. Private*, pg. 1083
TORO AUSTRALIA PTY. LTD.—The Toro Company; *U.S. Public*, pg. 1624
TRUSERV CORPORATION; *U.S. Private*, pg. 1108
UNIVERSAL COOPERATIVES, INC.; *U.S. Private*, pg. 1127
UP-RIGHT, INC.; *U.S. Private*, pg. 1128
VALMONT IRRIGATION DIVISION—Valmont Industries, Inc.; *U.S. Public*, pg. 1707
ZIEGLER INC.; *U.S. Private*, pg. 1205

5084 — INDUSTRIAL MACHINERY & EQUIPMENT-WHOLESALE

AAR CADILLAC MANUFACTURING DIV.—AAR Corp.; *U.S. Public*, pg. 1
AAR POWER BOSS—AAR Corp.; *U.S. Public*, pg. 1
ABB COMBUSTION ENGINEERING BRASIL—ABB Asea Brown Boveri (Holding) Ltd.; *Int'l*, pg. 5
ABB COMMERCIAL ENGINEERING CANADA—ABB Asea Brown Boveri (Holding) Ltd.; *Int'l*, pg. 5
ABB VETCO U.K. LTD.—ABB Asea Brown Boveri (Holding) Ltd.; *Int'l*, pg. 5
ABS PUMP AB, FAR EAST—Cardo AB; *Int'l*, pg. 270
ABS PUMPEN GES.M.B.H.—Cardo AB; *Int'l*, pg. 270
ABS PUMPER A/S—Cardo AB; *Int'l*, pg. 270
ABS PUMPUT OY—Cardo AB; *Int'l*, pg. 270
AGA GAS, INC.—AGA AB; *Int'l*, pg. 13
OY ALGOL AB; *Int'l*, pg. 15
AMRI NEDERLAND B.V.—KSB Aktiengesellschaft; *Int'l*, pg. 721
AMRI PTE. LTD.—KSB Aktiengesellschaft; *Int'l*, pg. 721
ACE TANK & EQUIPMENT CO.; *U.S. Private*, pg. 12
ACTION INSTRUMENTS (CHINA) LTD.—Action Instruments, Inc.; *U.S. Private*, pg. 15
ADDISON SAWS LIMITED—B. Elliott plc.; *Int'l*, pg. 448
ADDISON TUBE FORMING LIMITED—B. Elliott plc.; *Int'l*, pg. 448
ADMIRAL REMCO, INC.—The Standard Products Company; *U.S. Public*, pg. 1505
AEROGLIDE AMERICAS INTERNATIONAL, INC.—Aeroglide Corporation; *U.S. Private*, pg. 24
AGEMA DIRECT SALES AB—Spectra-Physics AB; *Int'l*, pg. 1289
AGEMA INFRARED SYSTEMS AB—Spectra-Physics AB; *Int'l*, pg. 1289
AGEMA INFRARED SYSTEMS GMBH—Spectra-Physics AB; *Int'l*, pg. 1289
AGEMA INFRARED SYSTEMS, INC.—Spectra-Physics AB; *Int'l*, pg. 1289
AGEMA INFRARED SYSTEMS LTD.—Spectra-Physics AB; *Int'l*, pg. 1289
AGEMA INFRARED SYSTEMS SRL—Spectra-Physics AB; *Int'l*, pg. 1289
AGIE U.S.A. LTD.—Georg Fischer Ltd.; *Int'l*, pg. 490
AGUADOR S.A.—KSB Aktiengesellschaft; *Int'l*, pg. 721
A. AHLSTROM GMBH—A. Ahlstrom Corporation; *Int'l*, pg. 34
AHLSTROM ANZ PTY LTD.—A. Ahlstrom Corporation; *Int'l*, pg. 34
AHLSTROM AQUAFLOW LTD.—A. Ahlstrom Corporation; *Int'l*, pg. 34
AHLSTROM A/S AHLSTROM MACHINERY—A. Ahlstrom Corporation; *Int'l*, pg. 34
AHLSTROM AUTOMATION OY—A. Ahlstrom Corporation; *Int'l*, pg. 34
AHLSTROM DAIICHI CO., LTD.—A. Ahlstrom Corporation; *Int'l*, pg. 34
AHLSTROM MACHINERY—A. Ahlstrom Corporation; *Int'l*, pg. 34
AHLSTROM MACHINERY CHEMICAL RECOVERY—A. Ahlstrom Corporation; *Int'l*, pg. 33
AHLSTROM MACHINERY MANTTA PUMP FACTORY—A. Ahlstrom Corporation; *Int'l*, pg. 33
AHLSTROM MACHINERY PUMP INDUSTRY—A. Ahlstrom Corporation; *Int'l*, pg. 34
AHLSTROM MACHINERY PUMP INDUSTRY AFTER SALES—A. Ahlstrom Corporation; *Int'l*, pg. 34
AHLSTROM MACHINERY PUMPS INC.—A. Ahlstrom Corporation; *Int'l*, pg. 33
AHLSTROM MACHINERY SALO WORKS—A. Ahlstrom Corporation; *Int'l*, pg. 34
AHLSTROM RECOVERY INC.—A. Ahlstrom Corporation; *Int'l*, pg. 34
AHLSTROM RECOVERY INC.-WESTERN REGION—A. Ahlstrom Corporation; *Int'l*, pg. 34
AIR POWER, INC.; *U.S. Private*, pg. 28
AIRGAS, INC.; *U.S. Public*, pg. 33
AISIN WORLD CORP. OF AMERICA—Aisin Seiki Co. Ltd.; *Int'l*, pg. 39
AJAX MAGNETHERMIC CORP.—BBA Group plc; *Int'l*, pg. 113
ALAMO INDUSTRIAL GROUP; *U.S. Private*, pg. 31
ALAMO IRON WORKS—Alamo Industrial Group; *U.S. Private*, pg. 31
ALBAN TRACTOR CO. INC.; *U.S. Private*, pg. 32
ALFA-LAVAL CHEDDAR SYSTEMS LTD.—Tetra Laval Group; *Int'l*, pg. 1380
ALGOA OIL & PIPELINE (PTY) LTD.—ABB Asea Brown Boveri (Holding) Ltd.; *Int'l*, pg. 5
AMADA ENGINEERING & SERVICE CO., INC.—Amada Co., Ltd.; *Int'l*, pg. 70
AMERICAN PFAUTER CORP.—Hermann Pfauter GmbH & Co.; *Int'l*, pg. 617
AMERICAN SAHM CORPORATION—Georg Sahm GmbH & Co. KG Maschinenfabrik; *Int'l*, pg. 1169
ANRITSU ELECTRONICA S.A.—Anritsu Corporation; *Int'l*, pg. 77
ANRITSU ELEKTRONIK GMBH—Anritsu Corporation; *Int'l*, pg. 77
ANRITSU EUROPE LTD.—Anritsu Corporation; *Int'l*, pg. 77
ANRITSU WILTRON—Anritsu Corporation; *Int'l*, pg. 77
APEX SUPPLY CO., INC.; *U.S. Private*, pg. 77
APPLIED POWER INC.; *U.S. Public*, pg. 124
ARGO INTERNATIONAL CORP.—Delcal Enterprises, Inc.; *U.S. Private*, pg. 322
ARIZONA ELEVATOR, INC.—Dover Corporation; *U.S. Public*, pg. 521
ARMATURTEKNIK I OSBY AB—Svedala Industri AB; *Int'l*, pg. 1323
ARMATURTEKNIK I OSBY AB—Trelleborg AB; *Int'l*, pg. 1419
ARMCO INC.; *U.S. Public*, pg. 131
ARO CORPORATION S.A.R.L.—Ingersoll-Rand Company; *U.S. Public*, pg. 877
N.V. ARO S.A.—Ingersoll-Rand Company; *U.S. Public*, pg. 877
ASAHI/AMERICA, INC.; *U.S. Public*, pg. 137
ASSOCIATED INDUSTRIAL SUPPLY, INC.; *U.S. Private*, pg. 91
ASSOCIATED POWER, INC.; *U.S. Private*, pg. 92
ASTRA VEICOLI INDUSTRIALI S.P.A.; *Int'l*, pg. 94
ATLAS COPCO COMPRESSOR CANADA—Atlas Copco AB; *Int'l*, pg. 96
ATLAS LIFT TRUCK RENTALS & SALES, INC.; *U.S. Private*, pg. 96
AUSTRALIAN OIL & GAS CORPORATION LIMITED; *Int'l*, pg. 101
AUTOMATIC LIQUID PACKAGING, INC.; *U.S. Private*, pg. 101
AUTOTROL CORPORATION—Osmonics, Inc.; *U.S. Public*, pg. 1234
AUTOTROL FRANCE, S.A.—Osmonics, Inc.; *U.S. Public*, pg. 1234
AVESTA SHEFFIELD, INC.—British Steel Plc; *Int'l*, pg. 221
AYLESBURY AUTOMATION LTD.—Clayhithe P.L.C.; *Int'l*, pg. 297
BAIC INTERNATIONAL—Farmatic Research, Inc.; *Int'l*, pg. 478
BMG ARIOLA MUSIC LTDA.—Bertelsmann AG; *Int'l*, pg. 192
BABCOCK AFRICA (PTY) LTD.—Babcock International Group PLC; *Int'l*, pg. 131
BABCOCK CLAUDIUS PETERS DIV.—FKI Plc; *Int'l*, pg. 474
BABCOCK CONSTRUCTION CONTRACTORS—Babcock International Group PLC; *Int'l*, pg. 131
BABCOCK MATERIALS HANDLING LTD.—Babcock International Group PLC; *Int'l*, pg. 131
BABCOCK TRIPPLEJAY—Babcock International Group PLC; *Int'l*, pg. 131
BAKER OIL TOOLS FAR EAST (PTY) LTD.—Baker Hughes Incorporated; *U.S. Public*, pg. 167
BAKER OIL TOOLS GMBH—Baker Hughes Incorporated; *U.S. Public*, pg. 167
BAKER OIL TOOLS OF CANADA, LTD.—Baker Hughes Incorporated; *U.S. Public*, pg. 167
BARMAG FAR EAST LTD.—Akzo Nobel N.V.; *Int'l*, pg. 45
BARRY CONTROLS LTD.—Applied Power Inc.; *U.S. Public*, pg. 125
BECKWITH MACHINERY COMPANY; *U.S. Private*, pg. 129
BERENDSEN PMC A/S—Sophus Berendsen A/S; *Int'l*, pg. 1284
BERINGER HYDRAULIK GMBH—Akzo Nobel N.V.; *Int'l*, pg. 46
BERNINA OF AMERICA INC.—Bernina Holding AG; *Int'l*, pg. 189
BERRY COMPANIES, INC.; *U.S. Private*, pg. 137
BERTELSMANN MUSIC GROUP—Bertelsmann AG; *Int'l*, pg. 191
BETHLEHEM INTL. SALES CORP.—The Bethlehem Corporation; *U.S. Public*, pg. 226
BINKS SAMES CORPORATION; *U.S. Public*, pg. 229
BLACK & CO.; *U.S. Private*, pg. 146
BLACK & DECKER (BELGIUM) N.V.—The Black & Decker Corporation; *U.S. Public*, pg. 234
BLACK & DECKER (NEDERLAND) B.V.—The Black & Decker Corporation; *U.S. Public*, pg. 234
BLODGETT INTERNATIONAL—Maytag Corporation; *U.S. Public*, pg. 1064
BLUE HAWK LTD.—BPB Industries PLC; *Int'l*, pg. 122
BOBST BENELUX N.V.—Bobst S.A.; *Int'l*, pg. 198
BOBST BRASIL LTDA.—Bobst S.A.; *Int'l*, pg. 198
BOBST CANADA, INC.—Bobst S.A.; *Int'l*, pg. 198
BOBST (FAR EAST) LTD.—Bobst S.A.; *Int'l*, pg. 198
BOBST GROUP INC.—Bobst S.A.; *Int'l*, pg. 198
BOBST ITALIANA SPA—Bobst S.A.; *Int'l*, pg. 199
BOBST JAPAN LTD.—Bobst S.A.; *Int'l*, pg. 199
BOBST S.A.; *Int'l*, pg. 198
BOLIDEN ALLIS AB—Trelleborg AB; *Int'l*, pg. 1423
BORAL ACROW LTD. (NEW ZEALAND)—Boral Limited; *Int'l*, pg. 203
ROBERT BOSCH CORPORATION—Robert Bosch GmbH; *Int'l*, pg. 204
BOSTIK INC.—Total S.A.; *Int'l*, pg. 1409
BOVAIRD SUPPLY CO.; *U.S. Private*, pg. 162
BOWEN TOOLS, LTD.—IRI International Corporation; *U.S. Public*, pg. 858
BRAMMER PLC; *Int'l*, pg. 212
BRIAN CONTROLS DIVISION—Axel Johnson AB; *Int'l*, pg. 711
BRIGGS WEAVER VINSON—Sammons Enterprises, Inc.; *U.S. Private*, pg. 963
BRONTO SKYLIFT OY AB—Federal Signal Corporation; *U.S. Public*, pg. 617
BROTHER INTERNATIONAL CORPORATION—Brother Industries, Ltd.; *Int'l*, pg. 229
JOHN BROWN PLASTICS MACHINERY—Kvaerner a.s.a.; *Int'l*, pg. 773
BRUCKNER MACHINE & TOOL CORP.; *U.S. Private*, pg. 175
BRUNNER & LAY, INC.; *U.S. Private*, pg. 176
BUFFALO TRUCK CENTER; *U.S. Private*, pg. 179
BUHLER INC.; *U.S. Private*, pg. 179
BUSS (AMERICA) INC.—Georg Fischer Ltd.; *Int'l*, pg. 490
BUSS (JAPAN) LTD.—Georg Fischer Ltd.; *Int'l*, pg. 490
BUSS S.R.L.—Georg Fischer Ltd.; *Int'l*, pg. 490
BUSS WAESCHLE LTD.—Georg Fischer Ltd.; *Int'l*, pg. 490
BUSS WAESCHLE SARL—Georg Fischer Ltd.; *Int'l*, pg. 490
BUTLER AUTOMATIC, INC.; *U.S. Private*, pg. 189
BUTLER NEWALL GMBH—B. Elliott plc.; *Int'l*, pg. 449
BUTTERLEY ENGINEERING LTD.—Haden Maclellan Holdings plc; *Int'l*, pg. 585
CFCI S.A.—Unilever Plc; *Int'l*, pg. 1436
CM HUMAN SERVICES CO. LTD.—Caterpillar Inc.; *U.S. Public*, pg. 317
CPAC, INC.; *U.S. Public*, pg. 282
CALORSTAT INDUSTRIES SA—Senior Engineering Group, plc.; *Int'l*, pg. 1222
CALSONIC YOROZU CORPORATION—Nissan Motor Co., Ltd.; *Int'l*, pg. 944
CALTROL, INC.; *U.S. Private*, pg. 201
CANADIAN HARDINGS MACHINE TOOLS LTD.—Hardings, Inc.; *U.S. Private*, pg. 502
CANADIAN KAWASAKI MOTORS INC.—Kawasaki Heavy Industries, Ltd.; *Int'l*, pg. 726
CARDINAL EG SAWS CORP.—Brooke Industrial Holdings Plc; *Int'l*, pg. 228
CAREY DIVISION—J. Fegely Inc.; *U.S. Private*, pg. 399
CAROLINA TRACTOR & EQUIPMENT CO.; *U.S. Private*, pg. 214
CARTER CHAMBERS SUPPLY, INC.; *U.S. Private*, pg. 216
CAT PUMPS AG—Diversified Dynamics Corporation; *U.S. Private*, pg. 336
CAT PUMPS INTERNATIONAL N.V.—Diversified Dynamics Corporation; *U.S. Private*, pg. 336
CATERPILLAR AMERICAS CO.—Caterpillar Inc.; *U.S. Public*, pg. 315
CATERPILLAR INC.; *U.S. Public*, pg. 315
CATERPILLAR INDUSTRIAL PRODUCTS, INC.—Caterpillar Inc.; *U.S. Public*, pg. 316

CATERPILLAR LOGISTICS SERVICES, INC.—Caterpillar Inc.; U.S. Public, pg. 316
CATERPILLAR (U.K.) LIMITED—Caterpillar Inc.; U.S. Public, pg. 317
CATERPILLAR WORLD TRADING CORPORATION—Caterpillar Inc.; U.S. Public, pg. 316
CELLECO HEDEMORA—Tetra Laval Group; Int'l, pg. 1378
CENTURY LEASING & LIQUIDATING, INC.—National Presto Industries, Inc.; U.S. Public, pg. 1159
CERAMIC COOLING TOWER CO.—Amsted Industries Incorporated; U.S. Private, pg. 68
THE CHALLENGE MACHINERY CO.; U.S. Private, pg. 227
CHARMILLES DEUTSCHLAND MASCHINEN GES. MBH—Georg Fischer Ltd.; Int'l, pg. 489
CHARMILLES TECHNOLOGIES (FRANCE) S.A.—Georg Fischer Ltd.; Int'l, pg. 489
CHARMILLES TECHNOLOGIES (ITALIA) SRL.—Georg Fischer Ltd.; Int'l, pg. 489
CHARMILLES TECHNOLOGIES (JAPAN) LTD.—Georg Fischer Ltd.; Int'l, pg. 489
CHICAGO MACHINE TOOL COMPANY; U.S. Private, pg. 235
CHUBB SINGAPORE PRIVATE LIMITED—Sime Darby Berhad; Int'l, pg. 1250
CINCINNATI MILACRON-CANADA LTD—Cincinnati Milacron Inc.; U.S. Public, pg. 368
CINCINNATI MILACRON S.R.L.—Cincinnati Milacron Inc.; U.S. Public, pg. 368
CLARK DETROIT-DIESEL ALLISON; U.S. Private, pg. 242
CLAUDIUS PETERS AG—Babcock International Group PLC; Int'l, pg. 131
CLAUDIUS PETERS (IBERICA) S.A.—Babcock International Group PLC; Int'l, pg. 131
CLAUDIUS PETERS INC.—Babcock International Group PLC; Int'l, pg. 131
CLAUDIUS PETERS S.A.—Babcock International Group PLC; Int'l, pg. 131
COECLERICI GROUP; Int'l, pg. 303
COMPAGNIE INGERSOLL-RAND S.A.—Ingersoll-Rand Company; U.S. Public, pg. 878
COMPONENTA BENELUX/BRANCH OFFICE BELGIUM—Trelleborg AB; Int'l, pg. 1421
COMPONENTA GJUTERIER AB—Trelleborg AB; Int'l, pg. 1419
COMPONENTA INTERNATIONAL INC.—Trelleborg AB; Int'l, pg. 1421
COMPONENTA PARTS AB—Trelleborg AB; Int'l, pg. 1421
CONE-BLANCHARD MACHINE COMPANY; U.S. Private, pg. 262
CONTINENTAL EAGLE VISALIA, CA—Continental Eagle Corporation; U.S. Private, pg. 267
CONTROL LASER CORPORATION—Excel Technology, Inc.; U.S. Public, pg. 599
THE COON-DE VISSER CO.; U.S. Private, pg. 273
CROWN IRON WORKS COMPANY—Crown Holdings, Inc.; U.S. Private, pg. 293
CUMMINS CUMBERLAND INC.; U.S. Private, pg. 295
CUMMINS INTERMOUNTAIN DIESEL; U.S. Private, pg. 295
CUMMINS MID-SOUTH, INC.; U.S. Private, pg. 295
CUMMINS SOUTHWEST INC.; U.S. Private, pg. 296
DAEWOO INTERNATIONAL AMERICA CORP. - RIDGEFIELD—Daewoo Corporation; Int'l, pg. 357
DAHL INTERNATIONAL AB; Int'l, pg. 359
DAI NIPPON SHOJI CO., LTD.—Dai Nippon Printing Co., Ltd.; Int'l, pg. 363
DAIHATSU DIESEL MFG. CO., LTD.; Int'l, pg. 364
DAIHATSU DIESEL (U.S.A.), INC.—Daihatsu Diesel Mfg. Co., Ltd.; Int'l, pg. 364
DAIHATSU DIESEL (U.S.A.), INC.—Nissho Iwai Corporation; Int'l, pg. 947
THE DAIRY FARM COMPANY, LIMITED—Jardine Matheson Holdings Limited; Int'l, pg. 703
DANFOSS ELECTRONIC DRIVES—Danfoss A/S; Int'l, pg. 377
DANIELLI OF AMERICA—Danielli & C. Officine Meccaniche S.p.A.; Int'l, pg. 378
DANSK INDUSTRI SYNDIKAT A/S; Int'l, pg. 381
DATAMARINE INTERNATIONAL AUSTRALIA PTY., LTD.—Datamarine International, Inc.; U.S. Public, pg. 487
DAVIS METER & SUPPLY DIV.—United States Filter Corporation; U.S. Public, pg. 1682
DAYTON PROGRESS INTL.—Federal Signal Corporation; U.S. Public, pg. 617
DAYTON PROGRESS OF JAPAN—Federal Signal Corporation; U.S. Public, pg. 617
DEERE & COMPANY; U.S. Public, pg. 491
JOHN DEERE INDUSTRIAL EQUIPMENT COMPANY—Deere & Company; U.S. Public, pg. 492
DELCAL ENTERPRISES, INC.; U.S. Private, pg. 322
DENGYOSHA MACHINE WORKS CORPORATION—Toshiba Corporation; Int'l, pg. 1402
DENNISON DATA SYSTEMS DIV.—Avery Dennison Corporation; U.S. Public, pg. 152
DEVILBISS RANSBURG BRAZIL—Illinois Tool Works Inc.; U.S. Public, pg. 867
DIE BETONKNACKER—Rothenberger Group GmbH; Int'l, pg. 1128
DIE BETONKNACKER GMBH—Rothenberger Group GmbH; Int'l, pg. 1128
ERNST W. DORN CO., INC.; U.S. Private, pg. 340
DUNCAN EQUIPMENT COMPANY; U.S. Private, pg. 346
DURAKUT INTERNATIONAL CORP.—Kobe Steel, Ltd.; Int'l, pg. 740
DURCO-VALTEK (ASIA PACIFIC) PTE. LTD.—Flowserve Corporation; U.S. Public, pg. 659
DURRIESSCHARMANN, AG—Metallgesellschaft AG; Int'l, pg. 860
DUTTON-LAINSON CO.; U.S. Private, pg. 350
DYNISCO GERATE G.M.B.H.—Berwind Corporation; U.S. Private, pg. 139
ER-WE-PA USA LTD.—Klockner-Werke AG; Int'l, pg. 737
ESAB HOLDING S.P.A.—Charter plc; Int'l, pg. 282
ESAB INTERNATIONAL AB—Charter plc; Int'l, pg. 281
ESAB SALDATURA S.P.A.—Charter plc; Int'l, pg. 282
ESAB SOLDADURA S.A.—Charter plc; Int'l, pg. 282
ESAB SVERIGE AB—Charter plc; Int'l, pg. 281
ESAB TECH AB—Charter plc; Int'l, pg. 281
EVI, INC.; U.S. Public, pg. 547
THE EAST ASIATIC COMPANY LTD. A/S; Int'l, pg. 430
ECLIPSE COMBUSTION, INC.—Eclipse Inc.; U.S. Private, pg. 360
ELEVADORES OTIS S/A—United Technologies Corporation; U.S. Public, pg. 1691
B. ELLIOTT PLC.; Int'l, pg. 448
ELLIOTT TURBOMACHINERY CANADA, INC.—Elliott Company; U.S. Private, pg. 373
ELLIOTT TURBOMACHINERY S.A.—Elliott Company; U.S. Private, pg. 373
ELVINS EQUIPMENT SALES LIMITED—Wajax Limited; Int'l, pg. 1485
EMBRACO NORTH AMERICA, INC.—Whirlpool Corporation; U.S. Public, pg. 1765
EMERSON EUROPA TRADING B.V.—Emerson Electric Co.; U.S. Public, pg. 576
EMERSON JAPAN, LTD.—Emerson Electric Co.; U.S. Public, pg. 576
EMPIRE POWER SYSTEMS—Empire Southwest Co.; U.S. Private, pg. 375
ENERPAC B.V.—Applied Power Inc.; U.S. Public, pg. 125
ENERPAC LTD.—Applied Power Inc.; U.S. Public, pg. 125
ENERPAC S.A.—Applied Power Inc.; U.S. Public, pg. 125
ENRAF-NONIUS TANK INVENTORY SYSTEMS INC.—Delft Instruments N.V.; Int'l, pg. 389
ENTERRA PETROLEUM EQUIPMENT GROUP, INC.—Weatherford Enterra Incorporated; U.S. Public, pg. 1749
OY ERHO AB—Oy Algol AB; Int'l, pg. 15
EXOTHERMICS-ECLIPSE, INC.—Eclipse Inc.; U.S. Private, pg. 360
FAG (UK) LIMITED—FAG Group; Int'l, pg. 469
FMC EUROPE NV—FMC Corporation; U.S. Public, pg. 606
FMC EUROPE, S.A./N.V.—FMC Corporation; U.S. Public, pg. 606
FMC HELLAS EPE—FMC Corporation; U.S. Public, pg. 606
FMC OF CANADA LIMITED—FMC Corporation; U.S. Public, pg. 606
FASTCUT TOOL CORPORATION—Cincinnati Milacron Inc.; U.S. Public, pg. 368
J. FEGELY INC.; U.S. Private, pg. 399
FICOMET S.A.R.L.—AXIA Incorporated; U.S. Private, pg. 103
FILARC WELDING INDUSTRIES B.V.—Charter plc; Int'l, pg. 283
FISAX—AXIA Incorporated; U.S. Private, pg. 103
FISCHBEIN CO.—AXIA Incorporated; U.S. Private, pg. 103
GEORG FISCHER DISA INC.—Dansk Industri Syndikat A/S; Int'l, pg. 382
FLEISSNER GMBH & CO. MASCHINENFABRIK; Int'l, pg. 493
FLETCHER SMITH LTD.—Booker PLC; Int'l, pg. 202
FLORI CORP.; U.S. Private, pg. 414
FLUOR CORPORATION; U.S. Public, pg. 659
FOCKE & CO., INC.—Focke & Co. (GmbH & Co.) Verpackungsmaschiner; Int'l, pg. 496
FOLEY HOLDING COMPANY, INC.; U.S. Private, pg. 416
FOLEY TRACTOR COMPANY, INC.—Foley Holding Company, Inc.; U.S. Private, pg. 416
FORASOL S.A.; Int'l, pg. 496
ABDULLA FOUAD-TESTRADE MIDDLE EAST—Abdulla Fouad Co. Ltd.; Int'l, pg. 502
FRED V. FOWLER COMPANY, INC.; U.S. Private, pg. 422
FOWLER TOOLS OF CANADA—Fred V. Fowler Company, Inc.; U.S. Private, pg. 422
FREEMAN MANUFACTURING & SUPPLY COMPANY; U.S. Private, pg. 426
FRIALATOR INTERNATIONAL—Maytag Corporation; U.S. Public, pg. 1065
FURNIVAL/STATE MACHINERY CO.—Komatsu Ltd.; Int'l, pg. 744
G&H PRODUCTS CORP.—Tetra Laval Group; Int'l, pg. 1378
G-NET CORPORATION; Int'l, pg. 531
G.E. INDUSTRIAL & POWER SYSTEMS SALES—General Electric Company; U.S. Public, pg. 711
GESTRA ESPANOLA S.A.—GESTRA GmbH; Int'l, pg. 550
GPD/EMBRACO NORTH AMERICA, INC.—Whirlpool Corporation; U.S. Public, pg. 1765
GSI EUROPE-IMPORT & EXPORT GMBH—Gunze Sangyo, Inc.; Int'l, pg. 579
GAS EQUIPMENT COMPANY, INC.; U.S. Private, pg. 440
GEMA VOLSTATIC INDUSTRIAL POWDER SYSTEMS (SWITZERLAND)—Illinois Tool Works Inc.; U.S. Public, pg. 868
THE GENERAL ELECTRIC COMPANY OF HONG KONG LTD.—The General Electric Company, p.l.c.; Int'l, pg. 546
THE GENERAL ELECTRIC COMPANY OF MALAYSIA SDN. BHD.—The General Electric Company, p.l.c.; Int'l, pg. 546
GERRARD SIGNODE PTE. LTD.—Illinois Tool Works Inc.; U.S. Public, pg. 868
GESTRA, INC.—GESTRA GmbH; Int'l, pg. 549
GESTRA PORTUGUESA VALVULAS LDA.—GESTRA GmbH; Int'l, pg. 550
GESTRA S.A.—GESTRA GmbH; Int'l, pg. 550
GESTRA (U.K.) LTD.—GESTRA GmbH; Int'l, pg. 550
GILES & RANSOME, INC.; U.S. Private, pg. 453
GLEASON CORPORATION SALES—Gleason Corporation; U.S. Public, pg. 746
GLEASON MILANO—Gleason Corporation; U.S. Public, pg. 746
GLOBE FASTENERS CORP.—Itochu Corporation; Int'l, pg. 694
GOMIYA USA, INC.—G-Net Corporation; Int'l, pg. 531
GOODMAN EQUIPMENT CORP.; U.S. Private, pg. 464
GOSIGER INC.; U.S. Private, pg. 466
GRACO CANADA INC.—Graco Inc.; U.S. Public, pg. 757
GRACO GMBH—Graco Inc.; U.S. Public, pg. 757
GRACO (HK) LIMITED—Graco Inc.; U.S. Public, pg. 757
GRACO HONG KONG LIMITED (TAIWAN LIAISON OFFICE)—Graco Inc.; U.S. Public, pg. 757
GRACO K.K.—Graco Inc.; U.S. Public, pg. 757
GRACO NORGE A.S.—Graco Inc.; U.S. Public, pg. 757
GRACO N.V.—Graco Inc.; U.S. Public, pg. 757
GRACO S.A.—Graco Inc.; U.S. Public, pg. 757
GRACO UK LIMITED—Graco Inc.; U.S. Public, pg. 757
W.W. GRAINGER, INC.; U.S. Public, pg. 758
P.T. GRAY INDONESIA—ABB Asea Brown Boveri (Holding) Ltd.; Int'l, pg. 5
GRAY SERVICE CO., A.G.—ABB Asea Brown Boveri (Holding) Ltd.; Int'l, pg. 5
GRAY TOOL CO. DE VENEZUELA CA.—ABB Asea Brown Boveri (Holding) Ltd.; Int'l, pg. 5
GRAY TOOL CO. (EUROPE)—ABB Asea Brown Boveri (Holding) Ltd.; Int'l, pg. 5
GRAY TOOL COMPANY—ABB Asea Brown Boveri (Holding) Ltd.; Int'l, pg. 5
GRAY TOOL CO. (EUROPE)—ABB Asea Brown Boveri (Holding) Ltd.; Int'l, pg. 5
GRAY TOOL CO. (NORWAY) A/S—ABB Asea Brown Boveri (Holding) Ltd.; Int'l, pg. 5
GRAY TOOL INTERNATIONAL—ABB Asea Brown Boveri (Holding) Ltd.; Int'l, pg. 6
GRAY TOOL INTERNATIONAL CORPORATION—ABB Asea Brown Boveri (Holding) Ltd.; Int'l, pg. 6
GRAY TOOL INTERNATIONAL, INC.—ABB Asea Brown Boveri (Holding) Ltd.; Int'l, pg. 6
GREAT WESTERN INDUSTRIAL MACHINERY CO.-GWIM—LSB Industries, Inc.; U.S. Public, pg. 970
GROCERS EQUIPMENT CO.—Certified Grocers of California; U.S. Private, pg. 227
HCC INDUSTRIES; U.S. Private, pg. 490
HK SYSTEMS, INC.; U.S. Private, pg. 491
HACH EUROPE, S.A./N.V.—Hach Company; U.S. Public, pg. 773
J. LEE HACKETT CO.; U.S. Private, pg. 492
HADEN DRYSYS GMBH—Haden Maclellan Holdings plc; Int'l, pg. 586
HADEN DRYSYS LTD.—Haden Maclellan Holdings plc; Int'l, pg. 585
HADEN FRANCE S.A.—Haden Maclellan Holdings plc; Int'l, pg. 586
HADEN GMBH—Haden Maclellan Holdings plc; Int'l, pg. 586
HADEN KING LIMITED—Haden Maclellan Holdings plc; Int'l, pg. 585
HADEN MACLELLAN HOLDINGS PLC; Int'l, pg. 585
HALLIDIE MACHINERY COMPANY, INC.; U.S. Private, pg. 495
HAMILTON EQUIPMENT, INC.; U.S. Private, pg. 497
HAMWORTHY ALLWEILLER LIMITED—Powell Duffryn PLC; Int'l, pg. 1065
HANWA CO., LTD.; Int'l, pg. 595
HARDINGS MACHINE TOOLS, LTD.—Hardings, Inc.; U.S. Private, pg. 502
HARLEY INDUSTRIES, INC.—Innovative Valve Technology, Inc.; U.S. Public, pg. 880
HART INDUSTRIAL SUPPLY CO.—LSB Industries, Inc.; U.S. Public, pg. 970
HASTINGS DEERING (SOLOMON ISLANDS) LIMITED—Sime Darby Berhad; Int'l, pg. 1250
HATTON ET COOKSON S.A.—Unilever Plc; Int'l, pg. 1437
HAVILAND ENTERPRISES; U.S. Private, pg. 511
HAWAIIAN PACIFIC ELEVATOR COMPANY—Dover Corporation; U.S. Public, pg. 521
HAWTHORNE LIFT SYSTEMS—Hawthorne Machinery Company; U.S. Private, pg. 513
HAWTHORNE MACHINERY COMPANY; U.S. Private, pg. 512
A HEALD LIMITED—Avonmore Waterford Group plc; Int'l, pg. 102
HEAVY MACHINES, INC.; U.S. Private, pg. 518
HERCULES ENGINE COMPANY; U.S. Private, pg. 523
HERMANN PFAUTER GMBH & CO.; Int'l, pg. 617
HERRAMIENTAS VARCO S.A.C.V.—Varco International, Inc.; U.S. Public, pg. 1709
HILTI LATIN AMERICA—Hilti AG; Int'l, pg. 620
HITACHI AMERICA, LTD.—Hitachi, Ltd.; Int'l, pg. 622
HITACHI KOKI U.S.A. LTD.—Hitachi Koki Co., Ltd.; Int'l, pg. 620
HOBART B.V.—Premark International, Inc.; U.S. Public, pg. 1322
HOBART GMBH—Premark International, Inc.; U.S. Public, pg. 1322
HOECHST MARION ROUSSEL, INC.—Hoechst Aktiengesellschaft; Int'l, pg. 624
HONEYWELL ASIA PACIFIC INC.—Honeywell Inc.; U.S. Public, pg. 834
HONEYWELL EUROPE S.A.—Honeywell Inc.; U.S. Public, pg. 834
THE HOWDEN FAN CO.; U.S. Private, pg. 543
HUGHES DAIRY LTD.—Avonmore Waterford Group plc; Int'l, pg. 102
HUGHES TOOL COMPANY, C.A.—Baker Hughes Incorporated; U.S. Public, pg. 167
HUSQVARNA VERTRIEBS GMBH—Electrolux, AB; Int'l, pg. 442
HY-TEK MATERIAL HANDLING, INC.; U.S. Private, pg. 550
HYOSUNG GROUP; Int'l, pg. 640
HYOSUNG INDUSTRIES CO., LTD.—Hyosung Group; Int'l, pg. 640
HYUNDAI CORP., U.S.A.—Hyundai Motor Company; Int'l, pg. 641
IDM CONTROLS; U.S. Private, pg. 554
IGA, INC. (INDEPENDENT GROCERS ALLIANCE); U.S. Private, pg. 555
IHI INC.—Ishikawajima-Harima Heavy Industries Co., Ltd.; Int'l, pg. 689
ITW FINISHING SYSTEMS & PRODUCTS-SOUTHERN EUROPE—Illinois Tool Works Inc.; U.S. Public, pg. 868

ITW OBERFLACHENTECHNK GMBH—Illinois Tool Works Inc.; *U.S. Public*, pg. 869
ILLINOIS AUTO ELECTRIC CO.; *U.S. Private*, pg. 557
IMPERIAL, INC.; *U.S. Private*, pg. 558
INDECK POWER EQUIPMENT COMPANY; *U.S. Private*, pg. 559
A/S INGENIOR GRAN—Dahl International AB; *Int'l*, pg. 359
INGERSOLL-RAND CO. (IRELAND) LTD.—Ingersoll-Rand Company; *U.S. Public*, pg. 878
INGERSOLL-RAND SALES CO., LTD.—Ingersoll-Rand Company; *U.S. Public*, pg. 877
INGERSOLL-RAND SALES COMPANY LIMITED UK—Ingersoll-Rand Company; *U.S. Public*, pg. 878
INLAND DETROIT DIESEL ALLISON CO.; *U.S. Private*, pg. 564
INTERNATIO (PTY.) LTD.—Internatio-Muller N.V.; *Int'l*, pg. 682
INTERNATIONAL DIV., AM INTERNATIONAL—Multigraphics Inc.; *U.S. Public*, pg. 1141
IRCON GMBH—Schneider S.A.; *Int'l*, pg. 1209
IRCON, LTD.—Schneider S.A.; *Int'l*, pg. 1209
IRCON PYROMETERS, INC.—Schneider S.A.; *Int'l*, pg. 1209
ISCO INSTRUMENTS (EUROPE) AG—Isco, Inc.; *U.S. Public*, pg. 914
ITALGESTRA S.R.L.—GESTRA GmbH; *Int'l*, pg. 550
ITALTRACTOR AMERICA INC.—IRI Istituto Ricostruzione Industriale; *Int'l*, pg. 654
JAY INSTRUMENT & SPECIALTY CO.; *U.S. Private*, pg. 583
JUKI ELECTRONICS CORP.—Juki Corporation; *Int'l*, pg. 716
JUKI LATIN AMERICA INC.—Juki Corporation; *Int'l*, pg. 716
JUKI UNION SPECIAL, INC.—Juki Corporation; *Int'l*, pg. 716
JUKI UNION SPECIAL INC.-ATLANTA OFFICE—Juki Corporation; *Int'l*, pg. 716
JUKI UNION SPECIAL, INC.-CALIFORNIA OFFICE—Juki Corporation; *Int'l*, pg. 716
JUSTIN INDUSTRIES, INC.; *U.S. Public*, pg. 936
KGM KUGELFABRIK GEBAUER GMBH—FAG Group; *Int'l*, pg. 468
KSB AJAX PUMPS PTY. LTD.—KSB Aktiengesellschaft; *Int'l*, pg. 721
KSB AKTIENGESELLSCHAFT; *Int'l*, pg. 721
KSB A/S, RODOVRE—KSB Aktiengesellschaft; *Int'l*, pg. 721
N.V. KSB BELGIUM S.A.—KSB Aktiengesellschaft; *Int'l*, pg. 721
KSB BOMBAS E VALVULAS S.A.—KSB Aktiengesellschaft; *Int'l*, pg. 721
KSB BOMBAS HIDRAULICAS S.A.—KSB Aktiengesellschaft; *Int'l*, pg. 721
KSB ITALIA S.P.A.—KSB Aktiengesellschaft; *Int'l*, pg. 721
KSB LIMITED—KSB Aktiengesellschaft; *Int'l*, pg. 721
KSB LTD.—KSB Aktiengesellschaft; *Int'l*, pg. 721
KSB MEXICANA S.A. DE C.V.—KSB Aktiengesellschaft; *Int'l*, pg. 721
KSB MORCK AB—KSB Aktiengesellschaft; *Int'l*, pg. 721
KSB NEDERLANDER B.V.—KSB Aktiengesellschaft; *Int'l*, pg. 721
KSB OSTERREICH GES.MBH—KSB Aktiengesellschaft; *Int'l*, pg. 721
KSB POMPA—KSB Aktiengesellschaft; *Int'l*, pg. 721
KSB PUMPS ASIA PACIFIC PTE. LTD.—KSB Aktiengesellschaft; *Int'l*, pg. 721
KSB PUMPS CO. LTD.—KSB Aktiengesellschaft; *Int'l*, pg. 721
KSB PUMPS, INC.—KSB Aktiengesellschaft; *Int'l*, pg. 721
KSB PUMPS LIMITED, PUNE (BOMBAY)—KSB Aktiengesellschaft; *Int'l*, pg. 721
KSB PUMPY + ARMATURY SPOL. SR.O.—KSB Aktiengesellschaft; *Int'l*, pg. 721
KSB SZIVATTYU ES ARMATURA KFT.—KSB Aktiengesellschaft; *Int'l*, pg. 721
KSB TESMA AG—KSB Aktiengesellschaft; *Int'l*, pg. 721
KSB VENEZOLANA C.A.—KSB Aktiengesellschaft; *Int'l*, pg. 721
KSB ZURICH AG—KSB Aktiengesellschaft; *Int'l*, pg. 721
KAMYR CHILE S A C EL—Kvaerner a.s.a.; *Int'l*, pg. 771
KAMYR KK—Kvaerner a.s.a.; *Int'l*, pg. 771
KAMYR OY—Kvaerner a.s.a.; *Int'l*, pg. 771
KAMYR PTY LTD.—Kvaerner a.s.a.; *Int'l*, pg. 771
KAMYR S.A.—Kvaerner a.s.a.; *Int'l*, pg. 771
P.T. KARYA YANSANTARA CAKTI—Charter plc; *Int'l*, pg. 283
KAWASAKI KIZAI CORPORATION—Toshiba Corporation; *Int'l*, pg. 1403
KENNEDY EQUIPMENT CO., INC.—Kennedy Tank & Manufacturing Co., Inc.; *U.S. Private*, pg. 614
KINGSBURY WORLD SALES—Kingsbury Corporation; *U.S. Private*, pg. 622
KIRLOSKAR CUMMINS LTD.—Cummins Engine Company, Inc.; *U.S. Public*, pg. 469
KOBE STEEL U.S.A. INC. (NEW YORK)—Kobe Steel, Ltd.; *Int'l*, pg. 740
KOCH SUPPLIES INC.; *U.S. Private*, pg. 628
KOMATSU AMERICA INDUSTRIES CORP.—Komatsu Ltd.; *Int'l*, pg. 744
KOMATSU AMERICA INTERNATIONAL COMPANY—Komatsu Ltd.; *Int'l*, pg. 744
KOMORI AMERICA CORPORATION—Komori Corporation; *Int'l*, pg. 745
KOMORI CANADA LTD.—Komori Corporation; *Int'l*, pg. 745
KOMORI-CHAMBON S.A.—Komori Corporation; *Int'l*, pg. 745
KRAUSS-MAFFEI AG—Mannesmann A.G.; *Int'l*, pg. 836
KRAUSS-MAFFEI CORP.—Mannesmann A.G.; *Int'l*, pg. 836
KRUPP CANADA INC.—Fried. Krupp AG; *Int'l*, pg. 511
KRUPP ENTWICKLUNGSZENTRUM GMBH—Fried. Krupp AG; *Int'l*, pg. 512
KRUPP WIDIA GMBH—Fried. Krupp AG; *Int'l*, pg. 510
KUBOTA AMERICA CORP.—Kubota Corp.; *Int'l*, pg. 762
KURAKI AMERICA CORP.—Kuraki Company Ltd.; *Int'l*, pg. 764
KURODA PRECISION INDUSTRIES LTD.; *Int'l*, pg. 764
KUSTERS CORPORATION; *U.S. Private*, pg. 637
KVAERNER BOVING (ANZ) PTY LTD—Kvaerner a.s.a.; *Int'l*, pg. 772
KVAERNER BOVING LIMITED—Kvaerner a.s.a.; *Int'l*, pg. 772
KVAERNER CHILE S.A.—Kvaerner a.s.a.; *Int'l*, pg. 771
KVAERNER ENERGY A.S. BUSINESS AREA HYDROPOWER—Kvaerner a.s.a.; *Int'l*, pg. 767
KVAERNER TURBIN AB—Kvaerner a.s.a.; *Int'l*, pg. 770
L-TEC DEUTSCHLAND GMBH—Charter plc; *Int'l*, pg. 283
LK LIMITED—TransTec Plc; *Int'l*, pg. 1418
LSB EUROPA LTD.—LSB Industries, Inc.; *U.S. Public*, pg. 971
LSB INDUSTRIES, INC.; *U.S. Public*, pg. 970
LTX CO., LTD.—LTX Corporation; *U.S. Public*, pg. 972
LTX INTERNATIONAL, INC.—LTX Corporation; *U.S. Public*, pg. 972
LAMB AG—Enterprises International Inc.; *U.S. Private*, pg. 378
LANTECH INC.; *U.S. Private*, pg. 650
LEADTEC SYSTEMS, INC.—Willcox & Gibbs, Inc.; *U.S. Private*, pg. 1177
LETTS INDUSTRIES, INC.; *U.S. Private*, pg. 661
LIBERTY PRECISION INDUSTRIES; *U.S. Private*, pg. 666
LINCOLN BIG THREE, INC.—Air Liquide S.A.; *Int'l*, pg. 37
LING ELECTRONICS LTD.—Mechanical Technology Inc.; *U.S. Public*, pg. 1077
LISTER-PETTER INC.—BTR plc; *Int'l*, pg. 127
LOGITECH LTD.—Radiometer A/S; *Int'l*, pg. 1084
LUCAS INDUSTRIES INC.—LucasVarity plc; *Int'l*, pg. 820
LUX GMBH & CO. KG—OBI Bau-und Heimwerkermaerkte GmbH & Co. KG; *Int'l*, pg. 993
LUX INTERNATIONAL S.A.—OBI Bau-und Heimwerkermaerkte GmbH & Co. KG; *Int'l*, pg. 993
LUXTRONIC MASCHINEN GMBH—OBI Bau-und Heimwerkermaerkte GmbH & Co. KG; *Int'l*, pg. 993
M/S FISCHBEIN PACKAGING (SINGAPORE) PTE. LTD.—AXIA Incorporated; *U.S. Private*, pg. 103
MB GROUP ENTERPRISES, INC.—Caradon Plc; *Int'l*, pg. 267
MCMC EUROPEAN OFFICE—Mitsubishi Heavy Industries Ltd.; *Int'l*, pg. 874
M/D TOTCO INSTRUMENTATION—Varco International, Inc.; *U.S. Public*, pg. 1709
MGI PUMPS, INC.—Tetra Laval Group; *Int'l*, pg. 1378
MHIA CHICAGO OFFICE—Mitsubishi Heavy Industries Ltd.; *Int'l*, pg. 874
MR SRL—Sony Corporation; *Int'l*, pg. 1283
MTE-TURCK LTD.—B. Elliott plc.; *Int'l*, pg. 449
MTS JAPAN LTD. (TOKYO)—MTS Systems Corporation; *U.S. Public*, pg. 1029
MTS SYSTEMS CHINA LTD.—MTS Systems Corporation; *U.S. Public*, pg. 1029
MTS SYSTEMS GMBH—MTS Systems Corporation; *U.S. Public*, pg. 1029
MTS SYSTEMS LTD. (UK)—MTS Systems Corporation; *U.S. Public*, pg. 1029
MTS SYSTEMS NORDEN AB—MTS Systems Corporation; *U.S. Public*, pg. 1029
MACE PRODUCTS—Osmonics, Inc.; *U.S. Public*, pg. 1234
MACHINERY SALES & SUPPLY CO.—LSB Industries, Inc.; *U.S. Public*, pg. 971
MANITOWOC EUROPE LTD.—The Manitowoc Company, Inc.; *U.S. Public*, pg. 1041
MANITOWOC INTERNATIONAL SALES CORP.—The Manitowoc Company, Inc.; *U.S. Public*, pg. 1041
MANITOWOC WESTERN COMPANY, INC.—The Manitowoc Company, Inc.; *U.S. Public*, pg. 1041
MARQUINARIAS INGERSOLL-RAND DE COLOMBIA S.A.—Ingersoll-Rand Company; *U.S. Public*, pg. 877
MARSHALL INDUSTRIES; *U.S. Public*, pg. 1051
MARUBENI AMERICA CORPORATION—Marubeni Corporation; *Int'l*, pg. 844
MARUBENI AMERICA CORPORATION, DALLAS BRANCH—Marubeni Corporation; *Int'l*, pg. 844
MARUBENI AMERICA CORPORATION, DETROIT BRANCH—Marubeni Corporation; *Int'l*, pg. 844
MARUBENI AMERICA CORPORATION, PORTLAND BRANCH—Marubeni Corporation; *Int'l*, pg. 845
MARUBENI AMERICAN CORPORATION, SEATTLE BRANCH—Marubeni Corporation; *Int'l*, pg. 845
MARUMOTO K.K. LTD.—Radiometer A/S; *Int'l*, pg. 1084
MASEK DISTRIBUTING INC.; *U.S. Private*, pg. 711
MATERIAL HANDLING EQUIPMENT CO.—Modern Group Ltd.; *U.S. Private*, pg. 754
MATERIALS HANDLING DIVISION—Oy Algol AB; *Int'l*, pg. 15
MATERIALS RESEARCH CORPORATION—Sony Corporation; *Int'l*, pg. 1283
MATERIALS RESEARCH GMBH—Sony Corporation; *Int'l*, pg. 1283
MATERIALS RESEARCH LTD.—Sony Corporation; *Int'l*, pg. 1283
MATERIALS RESEARCH S.A.—Sony Corporation; *Int'l*, pg. 1283
MATTHEWS INTERNATIONAL CORP.; *U.S. Public*, pg. 1059
MATTHEWS INTL. TRADING CORP.—Matthews International Corp.; *U.S. Public*, pg. 1060
MCJUNKIN CORPORATION; *U.S. Private*, pg. 722
MCMASTER CARR SUPPLY CO. INC.; *U.S. Private*, pg. 724
MEAD PACKAGING POLAND SP.Z O.O.—The Mead Corporation; *U.S. Public*, pg. 1076
MEDICO INDUSTRIES, INC.; *U.S. Private*, pg. 728
MERCEDES-BENZ FRANCE S.A.—Daimler-Benz Aktiengesellschaft; *Int'l*, pg. 369
METALLGESELLSCHAFT LTD.—Nissho Iwai Corporation; *Int'l*, pg. 948
METRIC & MULTISTANDARD COMPONENTS; *U.S. Private*, pg. 736
METTLER-TOLEDO B.V.—AEA Investors Inc.; *U.S. Private*, pg. 4
MI-JACK PRODUCTS, INC.; *U.S. Private*, pg. 740
MIAMI ELEVATOR—Dover Corporation; *U.S. Public*, pg. 521
MIKRON LTD. TOKYO—Mikron Holding AG; *Int'l*, pg. 867
MILLS MANUFACTURING TECHNOLOGY—Haden Maclellan Holdings plc; *Int'l*, pg. 585
MILTON ROY (BELGIUM) N.V.—Sundstrand Corporation; *U.S. Public*, pg. 1534
MILTON ROY (JAPAN) LTD.—Sundstrand Corporation; *U.S. Public*, pg. 1534
MINCE MASTER; *U.S. Private*, pg. 749
MINCO INTERNATIONAL AB—Trelleborg AB; *Int'l*, pg. 1423
MINUTEMAN INTERNATIONAL, INC.—Hako-Werke GmbH & Co.; *Int'l*, pg. 587
MITSIAM INTERNATIONAL, LTD.—Mitsui & Co., Ltd.; *Int'l*, pg. 880
MITSUBISHI CATERPILLAR FORKLIFT AMERICA INC. (MCFA)—Caterpillar Inc.; *U.S. Public*, pg. 316
MITSUBISHI CATERPILLAR FORKLIFT AMERICA INC. (MCFA)—Mitsubishi Heavy Industries Ltd.; *Int'l*, pg. 874
MITSUBISHI INTERNATIONAL CORPORATION—Mitsubishi Corporation; *Int'l*, pg. 871
MITSUI & CO., LTD.; *Int'l*, pg. 877
MITSUI BRASILEIRA IMP. E EXP. LTDA.—Mitsui & Co., Ltd.; *Int'l*, pg. 882
MITSUI CHILENA COMMERCIAL LTDA.—Mitsui & Co., Ltd.; *Int'l*, pg. 882
MITSUI DE COLOMBIA S.A.—Mitsui & Co., Ltd.; *Int'l*, pg. 882
MITSUI DE MEXICO, S.A. DE C.V.—Mitsui & Co., Ltd.; *Int'l*, pg. 882
MITSUI DE VENEZUELA C.A.—Mitsui & Co., Ltd.; *Int'l*, pg. 882
MITSUI DEL ECUADOR S.A.—Mitsui & Co., Ltd.; *Int'l*, pg. 882
MITSUI DEL PERU S.A.—Mitsui & Co., Ltd.; *Int'l*, pg. 882
MITSUI LEASING & DEVELOPMENT LTD.—Mitsui & Co., Ltd.; *Int'l*, pg. 878
MIYANO MACHINERY, INC.; *U.S. Private*, pg. 754
MOCON FSC CORPORATION—Modern Controls, Inc.; *U.S. Public*, pg. 1121
MODERN GROUP LTD.; *U.S. Private*, pg. 754
MODERN HILIFT EQUIPMENT CO.—Modern Group Ltd.; *U.S. Private*, pg. 755
MOORE CONTROLS PVT. LIMITED—Moore Products Co.; *U.S. Public*, pg. 1128
MOORE PRODUCTS DE MEXICO, S.A. DE C.V.—Moore Products Co.; *U.S. Public*, pg. 1129
MOORE SPECIAL TOOL AG—The Producto Machine Co.; *U.S. Private*, pg. 889
MORGARDSHAMMAR INC.—Danielli & C. Officine Meccaniche S.p.A.; *Int'l*, pg. 378
THE ROBERT E. MORRIS COMPANY; *U.S. Private*, pg. 762
MOTION & CONTROL SALES DIV.—Parker Hannifin Corporation; *U.S. Public*, pg. 1261
MUELLER INTERNATIONAL SALES CORP.—Paul Mueller Company; *U.S. Public*, pg. 1141
R.A. MUELLER, INC.; *U.S. Private*, pg. 766
MUNCK AUTOMATION TECHNOLOGY; *U.S. Private*, pg. 767
MUNROE, INC.; *U.S. Private*, pg. 767
MUNTERS INC.—Incentive AB; *Int'l*, pg. 669
MUNTERS TROCKNUNGS SERVICE GMBH—Incentive AB; *Int'l*, pg. 669
MURATA OF AMERICA, INC.—Murata Machinery, Ltd.; *Int'l*, pg. 897
NANJING GOULDS PUMPS LIMITED—ITT Industries, Inc.; *U.S. Public*, pg. 861
NANOMETRICS JAPAN LTD.—Nanometrics Incorporated; *U.S. Public*, pg. 1151
NASHVILLE MACHINE CO. INC.; *U.S. Private*, pg. 774
NATIONAL WELDERS SUPPLY CO. INC.; *U.S. Private*, pg. 788
NAVISTAR INTERNATIONAL CORPORATION CANADA—Navistar International Corporation; *U.S. Public*, pg. 1167
NEW ENGLAND NEWSPAPER SUPPLY COMPANY, INC.; *U.S. Private*, pg. 793
NEW ENGLAND TAP CORPORATION (NETCO)—Cincinnati Milacron Inc.; *U.S. Public*, pg. 368
NEW YORK REPRESENTATIVE OFFICE (ESNOR)—Petrobras - Petroleo Brasileiro S.A.; *Int'l*, pg. 1042
NEWCOR, INC.; *U.S. Public*, pg. 1176
NEXAIR—nexAir, LLC; *U.S. Private*, pg. 797
NEXAIR, LLC; *U.S. Private*, pg. 797
NICHIMEN AMERICA, INC.—Nichimen Corporation; *Int'l*, pg. 927
NICHIMEN CORPORATION; *Int'l*, pg. 927
NIHON MRC CO. LTD.—Sony Corporation; *Int'l*, pg. 1283
NIHON VEECO K.K.—Veeco Instruments, Inc.; *U.S. Public*, pg. 1711
NIPPON FISHER COMPANY, LTD.—Monsanto Company; *U.S. Public*, pg. 1126
NISSAN FORKLIFT CORPORATION, NORTH AMERICA—Nissan Motor Co., Ltd.; *Int'l*, pg. 945
NISSHO IWAI AUSTRALIA LTD.—Nissho Iwai Corporation; *Int'l*, pg. 948
NISSHO IWAI INDUSTRIAL MACHINERY INC.—Nissho Iwai Corporation; *Int'l*, pg. 946
NOBLEX ARGENTINA S.A.C. E I.; *Int'l*, pg. 951
NOLAND COMPANY; *U.S. Public*, pg. 1187
NORDSON CORPORATION; *U.S. Public*, pg. 1188
NORITAKE CO., INC.—Noritake Co., Limited; *Int'l*, pg. 959
NORITAKE CO., INC.-ABRASIVE DIVISION—Noritake Co., Limited; *Int'l*, pg. 959
NORTH CAROLINA EQUIPMENT CO.; *U.S. Private*, pg. 804
NORTH CENTRAL CRANE & EXCAVATOR SALES CORP.—The Manitowoc Company, Inc.; *U.S. Public*, pg. 1041
NORTHWEST PIPE FITTINGS, INC.; *U.S. Private*, pg. 806

OHIO TRANSMISSION CORPORATION; U.S. Private, pg. 813
OILGEAR GMBH—The Oilgear Company; U.S. Public, pg. 1215
OILGEAR SRL—The Oilgear Company; U.S. Public, pg. 1215
OKUMA AMERICA CORPORATION—Okuma Corporation; Int'l, pg. 1001
ORBOTECH INC.—Orbotech Ltd.; Int'l, pg. 1007
ORIENTAL MOTOR U.S.A. CORP.—Oriental Motor Co., Ltd.; Int'l, pg. 1008
OSMONICS ASIA/PACIFIC, LTD.—Osmonics, Inc.; U.S. Public, pg. 1234
OSMONICS ASIA/PACIFIC LTD.—Osmonics, Inc.; U.S. Public, pg. 1234
OSMONICS, INC.; U.S. Public, pg. 1233
OTIS CANADA INC.—United Technologies Corporation; U.S. Public, pg. 1691
OTIS HISS AB—United Technologies Corporation; U.S. Public, pg. 1691
OUTOKUMPU MINTEC CANADA LTD.—Outokumpu Oyj; Int'l, pg. 1017
OXARC INC.; U.S. Private, pg. 825
OZONE RESEARCH & EQUIPMENT CORP.—Osmonics, Inc.; U.S. Public, pg. 1234
PCC SPECIALTY PRODUCTS, INC.—Precision Castparts Corp.; U.S. Public, pg. 1321
PACIFIC SCIENTIFIC, GMBH—Pacific Scientific Company; U.S. Public, pg. 1250
LOUIS PADNOS IRON & METAL CO.; U.S. Private, pg. 834
PALL FRANCE S.A.—Pall Corporation; U.S. Public, pg. 1254
PALL ITALIA S.R.L.—Pall Corporation; U.S. Public, pg. 1254
PAMCO—Stewart & Stevenson Services, Inc.; U.S. Public, pg. 1517
PANASONIC FACTORY AUTOMATION CO.—Matsushita Electric Industrial Co., Ltd.; Int'l, pg. 847
FRANK PAXTON COMPANY—Jeld-Wen, Inc.; U.S. Private, pg. 585
PEARCE INDUSTRIES INC.; U.S. Private, pg. 845
PECO MFG. CO., INC.; U.S. Private, pg. 846
H.O. PENN MACHINERY CO. INC.; U.S. Private, pg. 849
PEREZ TRADING CO. INC.; U.S. Private, pg. 852
PERRY MACHINERY CORPORATION; U.S. Private, pg. 855
PETERSON TRACTOR COMPANY; U.S. Private, pg. 858
PETTIBONE CORPORATION; U.S. Private, pg. 859
G.M. PFAFF AKTIENGESELLSCHAFT; Int'l, pg. 1046
PFAFF-PEGASUS OF U.S.A.—G.M. Pfaff Aktiengesellschaft; Int'l, pg. 1046
PFERD, INC.—Pferd/August Rueggeberg; Int'l, pg. 1046
PHILLIPS SERVICE INDUSTRIES, INC.; U.S. Private, pg. 862
PINNACLE COATING & CONVERTING, INC.; U.S. Private, pg. 866
PRECISION INDUSTRIES; U.S. Private, pg. 879
PREMARK FOOD EQUIPMENT GROUP BELGIUM, N.V.—Premark International, Inc.; U.S. Public, pg. 1323
PREMIER DAIRIES (WEXFORD) LIMITED—Avonmore Waterford Group plc; Int'l, pg. 102
PRIME TECHNOLOGY IMPORTS, LTD.—Prime Technology, Inc.; U.S. Private, pg. 884
PRIME TECHNOLOGY, INC.; U.S. Private, pg. 884
PRIME TECHNOLOGY, INC.—Prime Technology, Inc.; U.S. Private, pg. 884
PROCESS EQUIPMENT—Sony Corporation; Int'l, pg. 1283
PUERTO RICAN CEMENT CO., INC.; U.S. Public, pg. 1341
QUANTRONIX CORP.—Excel Technology, Inc.; U.S. Public, pg. 599
RAILWAY EQUIPMENT EXPORT—Fried. Krupp AG; Int'l, pg. 513
RANK TAYLOR HOBSON LIMITED—The Rank Group PLC; Int'l, pg. 1087
RANSBURG INDUSTRIAL FINISHING—Illinois Tool Works Inc.; U.S. Public, pg. 869
RANSOME ENGINE—Giles & Ransome, Inc.; U.S. Private, pg. 453
THE RAYMOND EXPORT CORPORATION—BT Industries AB; Int'l, pg. 123
RECI INDUSTRI AB—Scancem AB; Int'l, pg. 1200
RECTOR CANADA LTD.—ABB Asea Brown Boveri (Holding) Ltd.; Int'l, pg. 6
RECTOR-GRAY, LTD.—ABB Asea Brown Boveri (Holding) Ltd.; Int'l, pg. 6
REIFENHAUSER LTD.—Reifenhauser GmbH & Co. Maschinenfabrik; Int'l, pg. 1101
REIFENHAUSER MASKINER A/S—Reifenhauser GmbH & Co. Maschinenfabrik; Int'l, pg. 1101
RELIABILITY INCORPORATED; U.S. Public, pg. 1373
RENISHAW INC.—Renishaw plc; Int'l, pg. 1103
REXEL, INC.—Rexel, S.A.; Int'l, pg. 1107
J.A. RIGGS TRACTOR CO.; U.S. Private, pg. 930
ROBINSON MILLING SYSTEMS B.V.—Brunel Holdings Plc; Int'l, pg. 231
ROBINSON MILLING SYSTEMS S.A.—Brunel Holdings Plc; Int'l, pg. 232
RODENSTOCK PRECISION OPTICS, INC.—Optische Werke G. Rodenstock; Int'l, pg. 1007
ROHDE & SCHWARZ ENGINEERING & SALES GMBH—Rohde & Schwarz GmbH & Co. KG; Int'l, pg. 1124
ROHDE & SCHWARZ VERTRIEBS GMBH—Rohde & Schwarz GmbH & Co. KG; Int'l, pg. 1124
ROHM MECHATECH PHILIPPINES, INC.—Rohm Co., Ltd.; Int'l, pg. 1125
ROLAMENTOS FAG LTDA.—FAG Group; Int'l, pg. 469
ROTHENBERGER AUSTRALIA PTY. LTD.—Rothenberger Group GmbH; Int'l, pg. 1129
ROTHENBERGER BENELUX BVBA—Rothenberger Group GmbH; Int'l, pg. 1129
ROTHENBERGER-EXACT A/S—Rothenberger Group GmbH; Int'l, pg. 1129
ROTHENBERGER FRANCE S.A.R.L.—Rothenberger Group GmbH; Int'l, pg. 1129
ROTHENBERGER (HELLAS) S.A.—Rothenberger Group GmbH; Int'l, pg. 1129
ROTHENBERGER (HUNGARY)—Rothenberger Group GmbH; Int'l, pg. 1129
ROTHENBERGER ITALIANA S.R.L.—Rothenberger Group GmbH; Int'l, pg. 1129
ROTHENBERGER NEDERLAND B.V.—Rothenberger Group GmbH; Int'l, pg. 1129
ROTHENBERGER (SCHWEIZ) AG—Rothenberger Group GmbH; Int'l, pg. 1129
ROTHENBERGER TOOLS CANADA INC.—Rothenberger Group GmbH; Int'l, pg. 1129
ROTHENBERGER TOOLS (FAR EAST) PTE LTD.—Rothenberger Group GmbH; Int'l, pg. 1129
ROTHENBERGER (UK) LTD.—Rothenberger Group GmbH; Int'l, pg. 1129
ROTHENBERGER WERKZEUG-UND MASCHINENHANDELSGESELLSCHAFT M.B.H.—Rothenberger Group GmbH; Int'l, pg. 1129
RUDEL MACHINERY COMPANY, INC.; U.S. Private, pg. 950
SISTO ARMATUREN S.A.—KSB Aktiengesellschaft; Int'l, pg. 721
SKF PRODUCTOS INDUSTRIALES S.A.—AB SKF; Int'l, pg. 1159
SNK AMERICA, INC.—Shin Nippon Koki Co. Ltd.; Int'l, pg. 1234
SPS TECHNOLOGIES, INC.; U.S. Public, pg. 1419
SAGEM CORPORATION—Societe d'Applications Generales d'Electricite et de Mechanique; Int'l, pg. 1273
GEORG SAHM SINGAPORE PTE. LTD.—Georg Sahm GmbH & Co. KG Maschinenfabrik; Int'l, pg. 1169
SALEM FOREIGN SALES CORP.—Salem Group, Inc.; U.S. Private, pg. 961
SAMMONS ENTERPRISES, INC.; U.S. Private, pg. 963
SANDVIK A/S—Sandvik AB; Int'l, pg. 1186
SANDVIK AUSTRALIA PTY. LTD.—Sandvik AB; Int'l, pg. 1187
SANDVIK BENELUX—Sandvik AB; Int'l, pg. 1186
SANDVIK BENELUX B.V.—Sandvik AB; Int'l, pg. 1185
SANDVIK COROMANT COMPANY—Sandvik AB; Int'l, pg. 1185
SANDVIK COROMANT SKANDINAVIEN AB—Sandvik AB; Int'l, pg. 1185
SANDVIK ESPANOLA S.A.—Sandvik AB; Int'l, pg. 1186
SANDVIK HARD MATERIALS—Sandvik AB; Int'l, pg. 1186
SANDVIK HONG KONG LTD.—Sandvik AB; Int'l, pg. 1187
SANDVIK IN AUSTRIA GES.M.B.H.—Sandvik AB; Int'l, pg. 1186
SANDVIK IRELAND LIMITED—Sandvik AB; Int'l, pg. 1186
SANDVIK ITALIA S.P.A.—Sandvik AB; Int'l, pg. 1186
SANDVIK NORGE A/S—Sandvik AB; Int'l, pg. 1186
SANDVIK PORTUGUESA LDA.—Sandvik AB; Int'l, pg. 1186
SANDVIK (PRIVATE) LTD.—Sandvik AB; Int'l, pg. 1187
SANDVIK PROCESS SYSTEMS B.V.—Sandvik AB; Int'l, pg. 1186
SANDVIK PROCESS SYSTEMS CANADA LTD.—Sandvik AB; Int'l, pg. 1188
SANDVIK PROCESS SYSTEMS GES.M.B.H.—Sandvik AB; Int'l, pg. 1187
SANDVIK PROCESS SYSTEMS S.A.—Sandvik AB; Int'l, pg. 1187
SANDVIK PROCESS SYSTEMS S.P.A.—Sandvik AB; Int'l, pg. 1187
SANDVIK S.A.—Sandvik AB; Int'l, pg. 1187
SANDVIK (SCHWEIZ) AG—Sandvik AB; Int'l, pg. 1187
AB SANDVIK SERVICE—Sandvik AB; Int'l, pg. 1185
SANDVIK SOUTH EAST ASIA LTD.—Sandvik AB; Int'l, pg. 1187
SANDVIK TICARET LTD. AS—Sandvik AB; Int'l, pg. 1187
SANDVIK (ZAMBIA) LTD.—Sandvik AB; Int'l, pg. 1187
SAVILLE TRACTORS LTD.—Lonrho plc; Int'l, pg. 817
SCANCEM FASTIGHETER AB—Scancem AB; Int'l, pg. 1200
SCHIESS-AMERICA CORP.—Metallgesellschaft AG; Int'l, pg. 860
SCHIESS-METALNA GMBH—Metallgesellschaft AG; Int'l, pg. 860
SCHIESS MOWEG GMBH—Metallgesellschaft AG; Int'l, pg. 860
SCHIESS (UK) LTD.—Metallgesellschaft AG; Int'l, pg. 860
SCHILLING COMPANIES, INC.; U.S. Private, pg. 970
H.A. SCHLATTER, INC.—H.A. Schlatter AG; Int'l, pg. 1206
N. SCHLUMBERGER & CIE; Int'l, pg. 1206
N. SCHLUMBERGER (USA) INC.—N. Schlumberger & Cie; Int'l, pg. 1206
SCIAKY GMBH—Sciaky S.A.; Int'l, pg. 1211
SEA OIL HOMCO LTD.—The Peninsular and Oriental Steam Navigation Company; Int'l, pg. 1034
SEELY EQUIPMENT & SUPPLY CO., INC.—Modern Group Ltd.; U.S. Private, pg. 755
WILLIAM R. SELWOOD LTD.—BTR plc; Int'l, pg. 124
SERVICE MOTOR COMPANY; U.S. Private, pg. 986
SHIMA AMERICAN CORP.—Shima Trading Co. Ltd.; Int'l, pg. 1232
SHIMA TRADING CO. LTD.; Int'l, pg. 1231
SHIN CATERPILLAR MITSUBISHI LTD.—Caterpillar Inc.; U.S. Public, pg. 317
THE SIAM KUBOTA INDUSTRY CO., LTD.—Kubota Corp.; Int'l, pg. 763
THE SIAM KUBOTA INDUSTRY CO., LTD.—The Siam Cement Public Company Limited; Int'l, pg. 1239
SID TOOL CO. INC.; U.S. Private, pg. 998
SIMCO JAPAN INC.—Illinois Tool Works Inc.; U.S. Public, pg. 869
SIMCO (NEDERLAND) B.V.—Illinois Tool Works Inc.; U.S. Public, pg. 869
SIME DARBY HONG KONG LIMITED—Sime Darby Berhad; Int'l, pg. 1251
SIMON ACCESS FAR EAST—Simon Engineering plc; Int'l, pg. 1252
SIMON AERIALS LTD.—Simon Engineering plc; Int'l, pg. 1252
SIMON-ATLANTICO INC.—Simon Engineering plc; Int'l, pg. 1252
SIMON-CELLA S.R.L.—Simon Engineering plc; Int'l, pg. 1252
SIMON ENGINEERING PLC; Int'l, pg. 1251
SIMON LADDER TOWERS INC.—Simon Engineering plc; Int'l, pg. 1252
SIMON-LIFT GMBH—Simon Engineering plc; Int'l, pg. 1252
SIMRAD OPTRONICS LTD.—Kvaerner a.s.a.; Int'l, pg. 770
SITA—Lyonnaise des Eaux S.A.; Int'l, pg. 824
SOGITEC—Dassault Aviation Group; Int'l, pg. 383
SOLAR TURBINES INTERNATIONAL COMPANY—Caterpillar Inc.; U.S. Public, pg. 316
SOLVAY PHARMA DEUTSCHLAND GMBH—Solvay S.A.; Int'l, pg. 1280
SONY/TEKTRONIX CORPORATION—Tektronix, Inc.; U.S. Public, pg. 1568
SOONER PIPE & SUPPLY CORP.; U.S. Private, pg. 1014
SOUTHERN PETROLEUM EQUIPMENT CO., INC.—Kennedy Tank & Manufacturing Co., Inc.; U.S. Private, pg. 614
SOUTHERN PUMP & TANK COMPANY; U.S. Private, pg. 1017
SPANTEK DIVISION—Upper Midwest Industries, Incorporated; U.S. Private, pg. 1129
SPHERE SUPPLY, INC.—Kuwait Petroleum Corporation; Int'l, pg. 765
SQUIRE-COGSWELL COMPANY; U.S. Private, pg. 1027
STA-RITE FOREIGN SALES CORPORATION—WICOR, Inc.; U.S. Public, pg. 1767
STANDARD COMMUNICATIONS CORP.—Marantz Japan Inc.; Int'l, pg. 841
STANDARD SUPPLY & HARDWARE CO.; U.S. Private, pg. 1032
STANDCO CANADA, LTD.—SPS Technologies, Inc.; U.S. Public, pg. 1420
STANDEX INTERNATIONAL S.R.L.—Standex International Corporation; U.S. Public, pg. 1507
STAVELEY/NDT TECHNOLOGIES INC.—Staveley Industries PLC; Int'l, pg. 1299
STEEL TANK & FABRICATING CORP.—Kennedy Tank & Manufacturing Co., Inc.; U.S. Private, pg. 615
STEWART & STEVENSON DE VENEZUELA, S.A.—Stewart & Stevenson Services, Inc.; U.S. Public, pg. 1518
STEWART & STEVENSON SERVICES, INC.; U.S. Public, pg. 1517
C. JIM STEWART & STEVENSON, INC.—Stewart & Stevenson Services, Inc.; U.S. Public, pg. 1517
STIHL INC.—Andreas Stihl; Int'l, pg. 1301
STIHL PARTS, INC.—Andreas Stihl; Int'l, pg. 1301
SULLAIR TAIWAN LTD.—Sundstrand Corporation; U.S. Public, pg. 1534
SULZER, INC.—Sulzer Ltd.; Int'l, pg. 1306
SULZER PLASMA TECHNIK, INC.—Sulzer Ltd.; Int'l, pg. 1307
SUMITOMO CORPORATION; Int'l, pg. 1312
SUMITOMO CORPORATION OF AMERICA—Sumitomo Corporation; Int'l, pg. 1312
SUNBRAND DIV.—Willcox & Gibbs, Inc.; U.S. Private, pg. 1177
SUNKYONG INDUSTRIES CO.; Int'l, pg. 1320
SUOMEN SANDVIK OY—Sandvik AB; Int'l, pg. 1187
SVANEHOJ INTERNATIONAL A/S—Powell Duffryn PLC; Int'l, pg. 1065
SVEDALA INDUSTRI AB; Int'l, pg. 1323
SVENSKA THAILAND LTD.—Sandvik AB; Int'l, pg. 1187
SYRACUSE SUPPLY COMPANY; U.S. Private, pg. 1060
TLC BEATRICE INTERNATIONAL HOLDINGS INC.; U.S. Private, pg. 1064
TSI GMBH—TSI Incorporated; U.S. Public, pg. 1559
TAMPERE SALES OFFICE & STORAGE DEPOT—Oy Algol AB; Int'l, pg. 15
TATA INC.—The Tata Iron and Steel Co. Ltd.; Int'l, pg. 1356
TAYLOR HOBSON PNEUMO—The Rank Group PLC; Int'l, pg. 1087
TEKMATEX, INC.—Marubeni Corporation; Int'l, pg. 845
TEKTRONIX CHINA LTD.—Tektronix, Inc.; U.S. Public, pg. 1567
TEKTRONIX HONG KONG LTD.—Tektronix, Inc.; U.S. Public, pg. 1567
TEKTRONIX SPA—Tektronix, Inc.; U.S. Public, pg. 1568
TENCARVA MACHINERY CO., INC.; U.S. Private, pg. 1075
TETRA-PAK PROCESSING SYSTEMS—Tetra Laval Group; Int'l, pg. 1379
TEXMAC, INC.—Itochu Corporation; Int'l, pg. 695
THERMO FIBERTEK, INC.—Thermo Electron Corporation; U.S. Public, pg. 1593
THERMON AUSTRALIA—Thermon Manufacturing Company; U.S. Private, pg. 1081
THOMPSON TRACTOR COMPANY; U.S. Private, pg. 1083
TITMAN GMBH.—Brunel Holdings Plc; Int'l, pg. 232
TOMEN (U.K.) PLC.—Tomen Corporation; Int'l, pg. 1395
TOSHIBA ELEVATOR SALES CORPORATION—Toshiba Corporation; Int'l, pg. 1404
TOSHIBA INTERNATIONAL CORPORATION, UTILITY DIVISION—Toshiba Corporation; Int'l, pg. 1405
TRADEWIND TECHNOLOGIES, INC.—Justin Industries, Inc.; U.S. Public, pg. 937
TRI-CLOVER CANADA—Tetra Laval Group; Int'l, pg. 1379
TRUMPF INC.; U.S. Private, pg. 1108
TUFIRA S.R.I.—Georg Fischer Ltd.; Int'l, pg. 490
TURKU SALES OFFICE & STORAGE DEPOT—Oy Algol AB; Int'l, pg. 15
TURNER SUPPLY COMPANY; U.S. Private, pg. 1110
UBE INDUSTRIES (AMERICA) INC.—UBE Industries Ltd.; Int'l, pg. 1427
UBE INDUSTRIES LTD.; Int'l, pg. 1426
UBE MACHINERY, INC.—UBE Industries Ltd.; Int'l, pg. 1427
UNION SPECIAL-BELGIUM—Juki Corporation; Int'l, pg. 716

UNION SPECIAL FAR EAST LTD.—Juki Corporation; *Int'l*, pg. 716
UNION SPECIAL-FRANCE, INC.—Juki Corporation; *Int'l*, pg. 717
UNION SPECIAL-JAPAN LTD.—Juki Corporation; *Int'l*, pg. 717
UNITED ENGINES, INC.; *U.S. Private*, pg. 1122
U.S. AMADA—Amada Co., Ltd.; *Int'l*, pg. 70
UNITY SEWING SUPPLY DIV.—Willcox & Gibbs, Inc.; *U.S. Private*, pg. 1177
UNIVERSAL INSTRUMENTS CORPORATION—Dover Corporation; *U.S. Public*, pg. 522
VALLEY DETROIT DIESEL ALLISON; *U.S. Private*, pg. 1132
VALLEY NATIONAL GASSES INC.; *U.S. Private*, pg. 1132
VALMET (ANZ) PTY. LTD.—Valmet Corporation; *Int'l*, pg. 1448
VALMET-BOUSTEAD PTY. LTD.—Valmet Corporation; *Int'l*, *pg. 1449*
VALMET PAPER MACHINERY (UK) LTD.—Valmet Corporation; *Int'l*, pg. 1448
VALMET SARL—Valmet Corporation; *Int'l*, pg. 1448
VALMET SERVICE GMBH—Valmet Corporation; *Int'l*, pg. 1449
VALTEK/AUSTRALIA—Flowserve Corporation; *U.S. Public*, pg. 659
VAPONICS INC.—Osmonics, Inc.; *U.S. Public*, pg. 1234
VAREL MANUFACTURING CO.; *U.S. Private*, pg. 1134
VEECO GMBH—Veeco Instruments, Inc.; *U.S. Public*, pg. 1711
VEECO INSTRUMENTS LTD.—Veeco Instruments, Inc.; *U.S. Public*, pg. 1711
VEREINIGTE WEICHENBAU GMBH—Fried. Krupp AG; *Int'l*, pg. 513
VERMONT AMERICAN CANADA, INC.—Emerson Electric Co.; *U.S. Public*, pg. 578
VERMONT AMERICAN TOOL GROUP—Emerson Electric Co.; *U.S. Public*, pg. 575
VERMONT GMBH—Emerson Electric Co.; *U.S. Public*, pg. 578
VICKERS SYSTEMS AB—Aeroquip-Vickers, Inc.; *U.S. Public*, pg. 25
VICKERS SYSTEMS LTD.—Aeroquip-Vickers, Inc.; *U.S. Public*, pg. 25
VICKERS SYSTEMS S.A.—Aeroquip-Vickers, Inc.; *U.S. Public*, pg. 25
VICKERS SYSTEMS SENDINIAN BERHAD—Aeroquip-Vickers, Inc.; *U.S. Public*, pg. 25
VINSON SUPPLY COMPANY—Sammons Enterprises, Inc.; *U.S. Private*, pg. 963
VIRGINIA MILK PRODUCTS LIMITED—Avonmore Waterford Group plc; *Int'l*, pg. 102
VOEST-ALPINE SERVICES AND TECHNOLOGIES CORP.-MATERIAL HANDLING EQUIPMENT—Voest-Alpine Stahl AG; *Int'l*, pg. 1471
VOLVO PENTA OF THE AMERICAS, INC.—AB Volvo; *Int'l*, *pg. 1477*
W & B REFRIGERATION SERVICE CO.—Frozen Food Express Industries, Inc.; *U.S. Public*, pg. 685
W-B SUPPLY CO.; *U.S. Private*, pg. 1144
WADKIN AGENCIES—Brunel Holdings Plc; *Int'l*, pg. 231
WAGNER SPRAY TECH CORP.; *U.S. Private*, pg. 1146
WALTER WERKZEUGE SALZBURG GES M.B.H. & CO.—Rothenberger Group GmbH; *Int'l*, pg. 1129
WARTSILA DIESEL INTERNATIONAL LTD. OY—Metra Corporation; *Int'l*, pg. 863
WATERFORD FOODS INC.—Avonmore Waterford Group plc; *Int'l*, pg. 102
WATEROUS DETROIT DIESEL-ALLISON INC.—Wajax Limited; *Int'l*, pg. 1485
WATLOW LIMITED—Watlow Electric Manufacturing Company; *U.S. Private*, pg. 1154
WATLOW SINGAPORE PTE. LTD.—Watlow Electric Manufacturing Company; *U.S. Private*, pg. 1154
WATLOW TAIWAN—Watlow Electric Manufacturing Company; *U.S. Private*, pg. 1154
WATSON ELECTRIC—Warren Electric Group; *U.S. Private*, pg. 1151
WEATHERFORD BIN HAMODAH—Weatherford Enterra Incorporated; *U.S. Public*, pg. 1750
WEATHERFORD ENTERRA INCORPORATED; *U.S. Public*, pg. 1749
WEATHERFORD OIL TOOL MIDDLE EAST LTD.—Weatherford Enterra Incorporated; *U.S. Public*, pg. 1750
JERVIS B. WEBB WORLDWIDE CO.—Jervis B. Webb Company; *U.S. Private*, pg. 1156
WELDUN INTERNATIONAL, INC.—Robert Bosch GmbH; *Int'l*, pg. 205
WELSCO INC.; *U.S. Private*, pg. 1161
WEST AGRO, INC.—Tetra Laval Group; *Int'l*, pg. 1379
WESTBURNE INC.; *Int'l*, pg. 1491
WESTERN ATLAS INC.; *U.S. Public*, pg. 1757
WESTERN FILTER—Osmonics, Inc.; *U.S. Public*, pg. 1234
THE WICKMAN CORP.; *U.S. Private*, pg. 1175
WILLCOX & GIBBS, INC.; *U.S. Private*, pg. 1177
WILLIAMS DETROIT DIESEL-ALLISON MIDWEST, INC.—The W.W. Williams Company; *U.S. Private*, pg. 1179
WILLIAMS DETROIT DIESEL-ALLISON S.E., INC.—The W.W. Williams Company; *U.S. Private*, pg. 1179
THE W.W. WILLIAMS COMPANY; *U.S. Private*, pg. 1178
WILSON INDUSTRIES INC.; *U.S. Private*, pg. 1181
WILTON CORPORATION; *U.S. Private*, pg. 1181
WINTERBURN LTD.—Thermo Electron Corporation; *U.S. Public*, pg. 1596
YAMATAKE-HONEYWELL COMPANY LTD.—Honeywell Inc.; *U.S. Public*, pg. 835
ZIEGLER INC.; *U.S. Private*, pg. 1205
ZIMA CORPORATION—Kusters Corporation; *U.S. Private*, pg. 637

5085 — INDUSTRIAL SUPPLIES-WHOLESALE

A-G SAFETY SALES, INC.—Tyco International Ltd.; *U.S. Public*, pg. 1650
AP & T LTD.—Ferrofluidics Corporation; *U.S. Public*, pg. 620
AST BEARINGS DIVISION—Axsys Technologies, Inc.; *U.S. Public*, pg. 157
ABRASIVES, INC.—Prime Technology, Inc.; *U.S. Private*, pg. 884
ACCO-REXEL GROUP SERVICES PLC—Fortune Brands, Inc.; *U.S. Public*, pg. 674
ACIERS FRANCOSTEEL CANADA—Groupe Usinor; *Int'l*, pg. 572
AEGIS, INC.—Olin Corporation; *U.S. Public*, pg. 1219
AEROQUIP MEXICANA S.A. DE C.V.—Aeroquip-Vickers, Inc.; *U.S. Public*, pg. 25
AHLSELL AB—Trelleborg AB; *Int'l*, pg. 1422
AIRLINE HYDRAULICS CORPORATION; *U.S. Private*, pg. 29
ALAMO INDUSTRIAL GROUP; *U.S. Private*, pg. 31
ALAMO IRON WORKS—Alamo Industrial Group; *U.S. Private*, pg. 31
ALATEC PRODUCTS, INC.; *U.S. Private*, pg. 31
ALLEN TELECOM, INC.; *U.S. Public*, pg. 45
ALRO INDUSTRIAL SUPPLY GROUP—Alro Group; *U.S. Private*, pg. 46
AMERICAN INTERNATIONAL CONTAINER, INC.; *U.S. Private*, pg. 57
AMERSHAM CORPORATION (AMERSHAM QSA)—Nycomed Amersham plc; *Int'l*, pg. 992
J.W. ANDERSSON MASKIN AB—Trelleborg AB; *Int'l*, pg. 1422
ANGLO-AUSTRIAN MAGNESITE, LTD.—RGP Holding, Inc.; *U.S. Private*, pg. 903
APACHE HOSE & BELTING COMPANY, INC.; *U.S. Private*, pg. 76
APPLIED INDUSTRIAL TECHNOLOGIES; *U.S. Public*, pg. 122
APPLIED INDUSTRIAL TECHNOLOGIES—Applied Industrial Technologies; *U.S. Public*, pg. 122
ARMSTRONG YORK PTY., LTD.—Caparo Group Ltd.; *Int'l*, pg. 265
ASSOCIATED INDUSTRIAL SUPPLY, INC.; *U.S. Private*, pg. 91
AUTOLIASONS FRANCE S.A.—Barnes Group Inc.; *U.S. Public*, pg. 190
AUTOTROL CORPORATION—Osmonics, Inc.; *U.S. Public*, pg. 1234
AUTOTROL FRANCE, S.A.—Osmonics, Inc.; *U.S. Public*, pg. 1234
BSL ENGINEERING LIMITED—Brammer plc; *Int'l*, pg. 212
BSL LIMITED—Brammer plc; *Int'l*, pg. 212
BARDEN CORPORATION GMBH—FAG Group; *Int'l*, pg. 468
BARDEN SARL—FAG Group; *Int'l*, pg. 468
BATTEY MACHINERY COMPANY; *U.S. Private*, pg. 123
BEARING DISTRIBUTORS, INC.; *U.S. Private*, pg. 127
BEARING HEADQUARTERS CO.; *U.S. Private*, pg. 127
BECKWITH MACHINERY COMPANY; *U.S. Private*, pg. 129
BERENDSEN FLUID POWER, INC.—Sophus Berendsen A/S; *Int'l*, pg. 1284
BERENDSEN PMC N.V./S.A.—Sophus Berendsen A/S; *Int'l*, pg. 1285
BERRY BEARING COMPANY—Genuine Parts Company; *U.S. Public*, pg. 732
BEST POWER; *U.S. Private*, pg. 140
BLACK & CO.; *U.S. Private*, pg. 146
JOHN BOUCHARD & SONS COMPANY; *U.S. Private*, pg. 161
W. BRAUN COMPANY; *U.S. Private*, pg. 166
W. BRAUN CO.—W. Braun Company; *U.S. Private*, pg. 166
W. BRAUN DISTRIBUTION CENTER—W. Braun Company; *U.S. Private*, pg. 166
W. BRAUN INTERNATIONAL—W. Braun Company; *U.S. Private*, pg. 166
BRIGGS WEAVER VINSON—Sammons Enterprises, Inc.; *U.S. Private*, pg. 963
BRUCKNER MACHINE & TOOL CORP.; *U.S. Private*, pg. 175
BRUENING BEARINGS, INC.—Applied Industrial Technologies; *U.S. Public*, pg. 122
BRYANT ELECTRIC SUPPLY COMPANY, INC.; *U.S. Private*, pg. 177
BUCK & HICKMAN LIMITED—The Peninsular and Oriental Steam Navigation Company; *Int'l*, pg. 1032
BURGMANN MALAYSIA SDN BHD—Feodor Burgmann Dichtungswerke GmbH; *Int'l*, pg. 233
BURGMANN SEALS AMERICA, INC.—Feodor Burgmann Dichtungswerke GmbH; *Int'l*, pg. 233
C&W REFRACTORIES, LTD.—CFB Industries, Inc.; *U.S. Private*, pg. 194
CALIFORNIA HARDWARE COMPANY—Distribution America; *U.S. Private*, pg. 335
THE CALKINS MANUFACTURING COMPANY; *U.S. Private*, pg. 201
CAMERON & BARKLEY COMPANY; *U.S. Private*, pg. 203
CAREY DIVISION—J. Fegely Inc.; *U.S. Private*, pg. 399
THE CARPENTER GROUP; *U.S. Private*, pg. 215
CARTER CHAMBERS SUPPLY, INC.; *U.S. Private*, pg. 216
CENTRAL SUPPLY CO., INC.; *U.S. Private*, pg. 225
CHEP AUSTRALIA—Brambles Industries Limited; *Int'l*, pg. 211
COLUMBIA PIPE & SUPPLY COMPANY; *U.S. Private*, pg. 256
COLUMBUS STEEL DRUM, INC.—Evans Industries, Inc.; *U.S. Private*, pg. 385
THE COON-DE VISSER CO.; *U.S. Private*, pg. 273
CORPAK INC.—Thermo Electron Corporation; *U.S. Public*, pg. 1592
COUNTY TOOL & ABRASIVE—Buck Knives, Inc.; *U.S. Private*, pg. 177
DANIELLI & C. FAR EAST—Danielli & C. Officine Meccaniche S.p.A.; *Int'l*, pg. 378
DAVCO EQUIPMENT, INC.—Flowserve Corporation; *U.S. Public*, pg. 658
DAYFLEX PLASTICS—Mark IV Industries Inc.; *U.S. Public*, pg. 1045
DE BEERS CENTENARY AG—Anglo American Corporation of South Africa Limited; *Int'l*, pg. 77
DE BEERS CENTRAL SELLING ORGANIZATION—Anglo American Corporation of South Africa Limited; *Int'l*, pg. 77
DE BEERS CONSOLIDATED MINES LIMITED—Anglo American Corporation of South Africa Limited; *Int'l*, pg. 76
DELCAL ENTERPRISES, INC.; *U.S. Private*, pg. 322
DENGYOSHA MACHINE WORKS CORPORATION—Toshiba Corporation; *Int'l*, pg. 1402
AB S.A. DES ROULEMENTS A BILLES SUEDOIS SKF—AB SKF; *Int'l*, pg. 1158
DEUTSCHE VAN RIETSCHOTEN & HOUWENS GMBH—Internatio-Muller N.V.; *Int'l*, pg. 682
DEWCO CHICAGO—Don E. Williams Co.; *U.S. Private*, pg. 1178
DEWCO MILWAUKEE SALES—Don E. Williams Co.; *U.S. Private*, pg. 1178
DEZURIK—General Signal Corporation; *U.S. Public*, pg. 726
DICALITE FRANCE, S.A.—RGP Holding, Inc.; *U.S. Private*, pg. 903
DICALITE SCANDINAVIA—RGP Holding, Inc.; *U.S. Private*, pg. 903
DICALITE TRADING, S.A.—RGP Holding, Inc.; *U.S. Private*, *pg. 903*
DIXIE BEARINGS, INC.—Applied Industrial Technologies; *U.S. Public*, pg. 122
DOALL COMPANY; *U.S. Private*, pg. 337
DOWTY POLYPAC SPA—TI Group plc; *Int'l*, pg. 1338
DOWTY SA—TI Group plc; *Int'l*, pg. 1338
DUNCAN EQUIPMENT COMPANY; *U.S. Private*, pg. 346
DURCO PROCESS EQUIPMENT LTD.—Flowserve Corporation; *U.S. Public*, pg. 659
DYNAPERT LIMITED—The Black & Decker Corporation; *U.S. Public*, pg. 234
B. ELLIOTT PLC.; *Int'l*, pg. 448
EMERY WATERHOUSE COMPANY; *U.S. Private*, pg. 373
EMHART AUSTRALIA PTY. LTD.—The Black & Decker Corporation; *U.S. Public*, pg. 234
EMHART INTERNATIONAL LTD.—The Black & Decker Corporation; *U.S. Public*, pg. 233
EMHART TEKNIK AB MACHINERY DIVISION—The Black & Decker Corporation; *U.S. Public*, pg. 233
ENERGY & PROCESS CORP.—Wolseley Plc.; *Int'l*, pg. 1512
ERVIN INDUSTRIES, INC.; *U.S. Private*, pg. 382
ESSELTE METO KIMBALL SYSTEMS—Esselte AB; *Int'l*, pg. 460
ETABLISSEMENTS RENE SALOMON—Saint-Gobain; *Int'l*, pg. 1171
FAG INTERAMERICANA AG—FAG Group; *Int'l*, pg. 469
FABREEKA INTERNATIONAL, INC.; *U.S. Private*, pg. 390
FABRICON PRODUCTS—Eagle-Picher Industries, Inc.; *U.S. Private*, pg. 355
J. FEGELY INC.; *U.S. Private*, pg. 399
FEL-PRO INCORPORATED; *U.S. Private*, pg. 399
FERGUSON ENTERPRISES, INC.—Wolseley Plc.; *Int'l*, pg. 1512
DR. C. OTTO FEUERFEST GMBH—Preussag AG; *Int'l*, pg. 1070
GEORG FISCHER AMASTEEL S.A.—Ervin Industries, Inc.; *U.S. Private*, pg. 382
FLOWSERVE DURIRON CANADA—Flowserve Corporation; *U.S. Public*, pg. 659
FLOWSERVE DURIRON CANADA INC.—Flowserve Corporation; *U.S. Public*, pg. 659
FRED V. FOWLER COMPANY, INC.; *U.S. Private*, pg. 422
FOWLER TOOLS OF CANADA—Fred V. Fowler Company, Inc.; *U.S. Private*, pg. 422
FREEMAN MANUFACTURING & SUPPLY COMPANY; *U.S. Private*, pg. 426
GESTRA ESPAÑOLA S.A.—GESTRA GmbH; *Int'l*, pg. 550
GSI EUROPE-IMPORT & EXPORT GMBH—Gunze Sangyo, Inc.; *Int'l*, pg. 579
GSI TRADING HONG KONG LIMITED—Gunze Sangyo, Inc.; *Int'l*, pg. 579
THE GAGE COMPANY; *U.S. Private*, pg. 437
R.J. GALLAGHER CO.; *U.S. Private*, pg. 438
GARLOCK BEARINGS DIVISION—Coltec Holdings Inc; *U.S. Public*, pg. 402
GEBR. EICKHOFF MASCHINENFABRIK UND EISENGIESSEREI MBH; *Int'l*, pg. 542
GENERAL BEARING CORP.; *U.S. Public*, pg. 706
GESTRA, INC.—GESTRA GmbH; *Int'l*, pg. 549
GESTRA PORTUGUESA VALVULAS LDA.—GESTRA GmbH; *Int'l*, pg. 550
GESTRA S.A.—GESTRA GmbH; *Int'l*, pg. 550
GESTRA (U.K.) LTD.—GESTRA GmbH; *Int'l*, pg. 550
GUNSAN EXPORTADORA E IMPORTADORA LTDA.—Gunze Sangyo, Inc.; *Int'l*, pg. 579
HDW, INCORPORATED—Distribution America; *U.S. Private*, *pg. 335*
HABISAT GLOBE INC.—Habisat Svergie AB; *Int'l*, pg. 585
HABISAT SVERGIE AB; *Int'l*, pg. 585
HAHN SYSTEMS, INC.; *U.S. Private*, pg. 493
HAJOCA CORP.; *U.S. Private*, pg. 494
HARLEY GAUGE & INSTRUMENT CO.—Innovative Valve Technology, Inc.; *U.S. Public*, pg. 880
HARTTUNG FASTENERS A/S—The Black & Decker Corporation; *U.S. Public*, pg. 233
HASKEL CONTROLS—Haskel International, Inc.; *U.S. Public*, pg. 798
HAVILAND ENTERPRISES; *U.S. Private*, pg. 511
HECTOR & C.O. A.B.—RGP Holding, Inc.; *U.S. Private*, pg. 904
HEINKEL FILTERING SYSTEMS INC.—Heinkel Industriezentrifugen GmbH & Co.; *Int'l*, pg. 609
HICKMAN, WILLIAMS & CO. INC.; *U.S. Private*, pg. 525
HILL-BEHAN LUMBER COMPANY; *U.S. Private*, pg. 529

S.I.C. Index

HITACHI AMERICA, LTD.—Hitachi, Ltd.; *Int'l*, pg. 622
HOECHST MARION ROUSSEL, INC.—Hoechst Aktiengesellschaft; *Int'l*, pg. 624
HOECHST SPECIALTY PRODUCTS GROUP—Hoechst Aktiengesellschaft; *Int'l*, pg. 625
HUGHES SUPPLY, INC.; *U.S. Public*, pg. 846
HYDROWA B.V.—Sophus Berendsen A/S; *Int'l*, pg. 1285
IBT, INC.; *U.S. Private*, pg. 553
ICI FRANCE SA—Imperial Chemical Industries PLC; *Int'l*, pg. 665
ICI OESTERREICH GMBH—Imperial Chemical Industries PLC; *Int'l*, pg. 665
ICI (PERU) S.A.—Imperial Chemical Industries PLC; *Int'l*, pg. 665
ICI (PHILIPPINES) INC.—Imperial Chemical Industries PLC; *Int'l*, pg. 665
ICI (SINGAPORE) PRIVATE LIMITED—Imperial Chemical Industries PLC; *Int'l*, pg. 665
ICI ZAMBIA LIMITED—Imperial Chemical Industries PLC; *Int'l*, pg. 665
ISS DARENAS INTERNATIONAL A/S—ISS-International Service System A/S; *Int'l*, pg. 656
ISS-INTERNATIONAL SERVICE SYSTEM A/S; *Int'l*, pg. 656
INDUSTRIAL DISTRIBUTION GROUP; *U.S. Public*, pg. 875
INDUSTRIAL RUBBER PRODUCTS COMPANY; *U.S. Private*, pg. 561
INGRAM PAPER COMPANY—International Paper Company; *U.S. Public*, pg. 904
INTERNATIONAL SHOE MACHINE CORP.; *U.S. Private*, pg. 572
ITALGESTRA S.R.L.—GESTRA GmbH; *Int'l*, pg. 550
JAPAN OXYGEN, INC.—Nippon Sanso Corporation; *Int'l*, pg. 938
JOHNSON ACOUSTICAL & SUPPLY CO.; *U.S. Private*, pg. 590
JOHNSON SUPPLY & EQUIPMENT CORP.; *U.S. Private*, pg. 594
KAMAN CORPORATION; *U.S. Public*, pg. 941
KAMAN INDUSTRIAL TECHNOLOGIES CORP.—Kaman Corporation; *U.S. Public*, pg. 942
KING BEARING, INC.—Applied Industrial Technologies; *U.S. Public*, pg. 122
KOYO CORPORATION OF USA, SALES DIVISION—Koyo Seiko Company, Ltd.; *Int'l*, pg. 760
THE KRUSE COMPANY; *U.S. Private*, pg. 636
LANTECH INC.; *U.S. Private*, pg. 650
LAWSON PRODUCTS, INC.; *U.S. Public*, pg. 980
LINATEX CORPORATION OF AMERICA—Harrisons & Crosfield plc; *Int'l*, pg. 599
LINDE HYDRAULICS CORPORATION—Linde AG; *Int'l*, pg. 810
K. LOEGAGER A/S—Martin Merkel GmbH & Co. KG; *Int'l*, pg. 859
LOGAN CORPORATION; *U.S. Private*, pg. 672
LUCAS INDUSTRIES INC.—LucasVarity plc; *Int'l*, pg. 820
LUFKIN INDUSTRIES, INC.; *U.S. Public*, pg. 1019
MCF CONTROLS INC.—IMI Plc; *Int'l*, pg. 647
MSC INDUSTRIAL SUPPLY CO.—Sid Tool Co. Inc.; *U.S. Private*, pg. 998
MACE PRODUCTS—Osmonics, Inc.; *U.S. Public*, pg. 1234
MAINLINE INDUSTRIAL DISTRIBUTORS, INC.—Applied Industrial Technologies; *U.S. Public*, pg. 123
EDWARD MARSDEN LIMITED—Imperial Chemical Industries PLC; *Int'l*, pg. 663
MARTIN MERKEL INC.—Martin Merkel GmbH & Co. KG; *Int'l*, pg. 859
MATERIALES INDUSTRIALES S.A.—RGP Holding, Inc.; *U.S. Private*, pg. 904
MCJUNKIN CORPORATION; *U.S. Private*, pg. 722
MCMASTER CARR SUPPLY CO. INC.; *U.S. Private*, pg. 724
MECOMB SINGAPORE LIMITED—Sime Darby Berhad; *Int'l*, pg. 1251
MERKEL KUNSTSTOFF GMBH—Martin Merkel GmbH & Co. KG; *Int'l*, pg. 859
MARTIN MERKEL DANMARK A/S—Martin Merkel GmbH & Co. KG; *Int'l*, pg. 859
MARTIN MERKEL FINLAND OY—Martin Merkel GmbH & Co. KG; *Int'l*, pg. 859
MARTIN MERKEL FRANCE-SARL—Martin Merkel GmbH & Co. KG; *Int'l*, pg. 860
MARTIN MERKEL GMBH & CO. KG; *Int'l*, pg. 859
MARTIN MERKEL-I.M.S.—Martin Merkel GmbH & Co. KG; *Int'l*, pg. 860
MARTIN MERKEL IRELAND LTD.—Martin Merkel GmbH & Co. KG; *Int'l*, pg. 860
MARTIN MERKEL ITALIA S.R.L.—Martin Merkel GmbH & Co. KG; *Int'l*, pg. 860
MARTIN MERKEL SVENSKA AB—Martin Merkel GmbH & Co. KG; *Int'l*, pg. 860
MARTIN MERKEL VERTRIEBSGESELLSCHAFT MBH—Martin Merkel GmbH & Co. KG; *Int'l*, pg. 860
METRIC & MULTISTANDARD COMPONENTS; *U.S. Private*, pg. 736
MICROFLECT COMPANY, INC.—Valmont Industries, Inc.; *U.S. Public*, pg. 1707
MINEBEA CO., LTD.; *Int'l*, pg. 867
MISSION SUPPLY CO.—Yellow Corporation; *U.S. Public*, pg. 1788
MITSUBISHI MONSANTO CHEMICAL CO.—Monsanto Company; *U.S. Public*, pg. 1125
MONSANTO DO BRASIL LTDA. (MOBRA S.A.)—Monsanto Company; *U.S. Public*, pg. 1125
MONSANTO ESPANA S.A.—Monsanto Company; *U.S. Public*, pg. 1125
MONSANTO SINGAPORE COMPANY (PTE.) LTD.—Monsanto Company; *U.S. Public*, pg. 1126
MONSANTO (SUISSE) S.A.—Monsanto Company; *U.S. Public*, pg. 1126
MONSANTO THAILAND LTD.—Monsanto Company; *U.S. Public*, pg. 1126
MONSANTO (VENEZUELA) C.A.—Monsanto Company; *U.S. Public*, pg. 1126
MOTION INDUSTRIES, INC.—Genuine Parts Company; *U.S. Public*, pg. 732
MYERS INDUSTRIES, INC.; *U.S. Public*, pg. 1143
NMB CORPORATION—Minebea Co., Ltd.; *Int'l*, pg. 868
NPR OF AMERICA INC.—Nippon Piston Ring Co., Ltd.; *Int'l*, pg. 938
NSK-RHP CANADA INC.—NSK Ltd.; *Int'l*, pg. 904
NSK-RHP DEUTSCHLAND G.M.B.H.—NSK Ltd.; *Int'l*, pg. 904
NATIONAL BEARINGS LIMITED—Wajax Limited; *Int'l*, pg. 1485
NEILL-LAVIELLE SUPPLY CO.; *U.S. Private*, pg. 790
NEMEF B.V.—The Black & Decker Corporation; *U.S. Public*, pg. 235
NIELSEN & BAINBRIDGE—Esselte AB; *Int'l*, pg. 460
NIPPON SILICA GLASS EUROPE LTD.—Tosoh Corporation; *Int'l*, pg. 1408
NIPPON SILICA GLASS USA, INC.—Tosoh Corporation; *Int'l*, pg. 1407
NOLAND INDUSTRIAL DIV.—Noland Company; *U.S. Public*, pg. 1187
NORGREN/DETROIT—IMI Plc; *Int'l*, pg. 647
NORTHWEST PIPE FITTINGS, INC.; *U.S. Private*, pg. 806
NORTON-ALCOA PROPPANTS—Saint-Gobain; *Int'l*, pg. 1174
NORTON EAST ASIA, INC.—Saint-Gobain; *Int'l*, pg. 1175
OSMONICS ASIA/PACIFIC, LTD.—Osmonics, Inc.; *U.S. Public*, pg. 1234
OSMONICS ASIA/PACIFIC LTD.—Osmonics, Inc.; *U.S. Public*, pg. 1234
OSMONICS, INC.; *U.S. Public*, pg. 1233
OZONE RESEARCH & EQUIPMENT CORP.—Osmonics, Inc.; *U.S. Public*, pg. 1234
PALL FLUID FILTRATION PTE. LTD.—Pall Corporation; *U.S. Public*, pg. 1254
PARK-OHIO INDUSTRIES, INC.; *U.S. Public*, pg. 1258
PARKER HANNIFIN ASIA PACIFIC CO., LTD.—Parker Hannifin Corporation; *U.S. Public*, pg. 1263
PARKER HANNIFIN (AUSTRALIA) (PTY.) LTD.—Parker Hannifin Corporation; *U.S. Public*, pg. 1263
PEGASUS INTERNATIONAL CORPORATION—Straube Regional Center LLC; *U.S. Private*, pg. 1046
PEGLER-HATTERSLEY PLC—Tomkins PLC; *Int'l*, pg. 1395
PERSINGERS, INC.; *U.S. Private*, pg. 855
PETRON, INC.; *U.S. Private*, pg. 859
PIPING RESOURCES—Bovaird Supply Co.; *U.S. Private*, pg. 162
POLI-TWINE CANADA (CALGARY)—TecSyn International, Inc.; *Int'l*, pg. 1362
POLI-TWINE SOUTHERN INC.—TecSyn International, Inc.; *Int'l*, pg. 1362
PRECISION INDUSTRIES; *U.S. Private*, pg. 879
PREMIER FARNELL—Premier Farnell plc; *Int'l*, pg. 1068
PRIOR GASKETS INC.—The Cypress Companies; *U.S. Private*, pg. 300
PRODUCTION TOOL SUPPLY CO.; *U.S. Private*, pg. 889
QUAKER STATE CORPORATION; *U.S. Public*, pg. 1348
RB&W CORPORATION—Park-Ohio Industries, Inc.; *U.S. Public*, pg. 1259
RFT S.P.A.—AB SKF; *Int'l*, pg. 1158
RADEX INTERNATIONAL S.A.—RGP Holding, Inc.; *U.S. Private*, pg. 904
RADEX-HERAKLITH INDUSTRIEBETEILIGUNGS, A.G.—RGP Holding, Inc.; *U.S. Private*, pg. 904
RANJIT CORPORATION; *U.S. Private*, pg. 909
REX SUPPLY COMPANY—Production Tool Supply Co.; *U.S. Private*, pg. 889
ROMAC INDUSTRIES, INC.; *U.S. Private*, pg. 942
ROTHENBERGER WERKZEUGE MASCHINEN GMBH—Rothenberger Group GmbH; *Int'l*, pg. 1128
RUBSON BENELUX S.A.—Henkel KGaA; *Int'l*, pg. 614
RYAN HERCO PRODUCTS CORP.; *U.S. Private*, pg. 953
SGD GLASS INC.—Saint-Gobain; *Int'l*, pg. 1171
OY SKF AB—AB SKF; *Int'l*, pg. 1158
SKF ABIDJAN S.A.R.L.—AB SKF; *Int'l*, pg. 1158
SKF AUSTRALIA PTY. LTD.—AB SKF; *Int'l*, pg. 1158
SKF BEARING SERVICES TAIWAN LTD.—AB SKF; *Int'l*, pg. 1158
SKF BELGIUM S.A.—AB SKF; *Int'l*, pg. 1158
SKF CHINA LTD.—AB SKF; *Int'l*, pg. 1158
SKF COLOMBIA S.A.—AB SKF; *Int'l*, pg. 1158
SKF DANMARK A/S—AB SKF; *Int'l*, pg. 1158
SKF DEL PERU S.A.—AB SKF; *Int'l*, pg. 1158
SKF FRANCE S.A.—AB SKF; *Int'l*, pg. 1158
SKF (HANOI)—AB SKF; *Int'l*, pg. 1158
SKF HELLAS S.A.—AB SKF; *Int'l*, pg. 1158
SKF (HO CHI MINH CITY)—AB SKF; *Int'l*, pg. 1158
SKF JAPAN LTD.—AB SKF; *Int'l*, pg. 1159
SKF KENYA LTD.—AB SKF; *Int'l*, pg. 1159
SKF LOZISKA A.S.—AB SKF; *Int'l*, pg. 1159
SKF MALAYSIA SDN. BHD.—AB SKF; *Int'l*, pg. 1159
SKF MULTITEC A/S—AB SKF; *Int'l*, pg. 1159
SKF NEDERLAND B.V.—AB SKF; *Int'l*, pg. 1159
SKF NEW ZEALAND LTD.—AB SKF; *Int'l*, pg. 1159
SKF PANAMA REGION—AB SKF; *Int'l*, pg. 1159
SKF PHILIPPINES INC.—AB SKF; *Int'l*, pg. 1160
SKF PORTUGAL ROLAMENTOS, LDA.—AB SKF; *Int'l*, pg. 1159
SKF SERVICES D.O.O.—AB SKF; *Int'l*, pg. 1159
SKF SINGAPORE—AB SKF; *Int'l*, pg. 1159
SKF SLEWING BEARINGS (RKS S.A)—AB SKF; *Int'l*, pg. 1159
SKF SOFIA—AB SKF; *Int'l*, pg. 1159
SKF SOUTH AFRICA (PTY.) LTD.—AB SKF; *Int'l*, pg. 1159
SKF SVED GOLYOSCSAPAGY RESZVENYTARSASAG—AB SKF; *Int'l*, pg. 1159
SKF (THAILAND) LTD.—AB SKF; *Int'l*, pg. 1159
SKF TRANSMISSION AB—AB SKF; *Int'l*, pg. 1157
SKF TURK SANAYI VE TICARET—AB SKF; *Int'l*, pg. 1159
SKF URUGUAY S.A.—AB SKF; *Int'l*, pg. 1159
SKF VENEZOLANA S.A.—AB SKF; *Int'l*, pg. 1159
SKF (ZAMBIA) LTD.—AB SKF; *Int'l*, pg. 1159
SKF (ZIMBABWE) (PVT.) LTD.—AB SKF; *Int'l*, pg. 1160
SMM SPINDEL AG—AB SKF; *Int'l*, pg. 1160
SEA CONTAINERS WEST INC.—Sea Containers Ltd.; *Int'l*, pg. 1214
SEALING DEVICES INC.; *U.S. Private*, pg. 978
SELAS CORPORATION OF AMERICA; *U.S. Public*, pg. 1454
SERVICE SUPPLY CO. INC. OF INDIANA; *U.S. Private*, pg. 987
SHIMA AMERICAN CORP.—Shima Trading Co. Ltd.; *Int'l*, pg. 1232
SHIMA TRADING CO. LTD.; *Int'l*, pg. 1231
SID TOOL CO. INC.; *U.S. Private*, pg. 998
SISTEMAS Y TECHNICAS DE SEGURIDAD, S.A.—The Black & Decker Corporation; *U.S. Public*, pg. 233
SNOWDEN RUBBER INDUSTRIES—Trelleborg AB; *Int'l*, pg. 1423
SOCAMIC STE. DE CAOUTCHOUC ET DE PRODUITS CHIMIQUES S.A.R.L.—Saarbergwerke Aktiengesellschaft; *Int'l*, pg. 1167
SOMERSET WELDING & STEEL, INC.—Riggs Industries, Inc.; *U.S. Private*, pg. 930
SOUTHERN PUMP & TANK COMPANY; *U.S. Private*, pg. 1017
STANDARD SUPPLY & HARDWARE CO.; *U.S. Private*, pg. 1032
STARCAN CORPORATION; *Int'l*, pg. 1297
STEYR WALZLAGER GES.M.B.H.—AB SKF; *Int'l*, pg. 1160
SUNDSVALLS VERKSTADER AB—The Black & Decker Corporation; *U.S. Public*, pg. 233
SUNRISE INDUSTRIAL AUTOMATION & DESIGN—IBT, Inc.; *U.S. Private*, pg. 553
SUSPA FRANCE SARL—Suspa Compart AG; *Int'l*, pg. 1322
SYRACUSE SUPPLY COMPANY; *U.S. Private*, pg. 1060
TATA INC.—The Tata Iron and Steel Co. Ltd.; *Int'l*, pg. 1356
TAYLOR & GOODMAN LTD.—Sophus Berendsen A/S; *Int'l*, pg. 1285
TAYLOR HOBSON PNEUMO—The Rank Group PLC; *Int'l*, pg. 1087
THRALL ENTERPRISES, INC.; *U.S. Private*, pg. 1084
3M CANADA INC.—3M; *U.S. Public*, pg. 1606
TOKYO PRINTING INK CORPORATION U.S.A—Tokyo Printing Ink Manufacturing Co., Ltd.; *Int'l*, pg. 1394
TOS GALANTA A.S.—Traub AG; *Int'l*, pg. 1419
TOSOH BELGIUM N.V.—Tosoh Corporation; *Int'l*, pg. 1408
TRAUB DREHMASCHINEN GMBH—Traub AG; *Int'l*, pg. 1419
TRELLEBORG INC.—Trelleborg AB; *Int'l*, pg. 1423
TRELLEBORG RUBBER & PLASTICS DIV.—Trelleborg AB; *Int'l*, pg. 1422
TRELLEX AB—Svedala Industri AB; *Int'l*, pg. 1324
TRELLEX AB—Trelleborg AB; *Int'l*, pg. 1423
TRICON INDUSTRIES, INC.; *U.S. Private*, pg. 1102
OY TULENKESTAVAAT TILIET, A.B.—RGP Holding, Inc.; *U.S. Private*, pg. 904
TWIN DISC (FAR EAST) LTD.—Twin Disc, Incorporated; *U.S. Public*, pg. 1646
TWIN DISC (PACIFIC) PTY. LTD.—Twin Disc, Incorporated; *U.S. Public*, pg. 1647
TWIN DISC (SOUTH AFRICA) (PTY.) LTD.—Twin Disc, Incorporated; *U.S. Public*, pg. 1647
VG EMBALLAGE—Saint-Gobain; *Int'l*, pg. 1171
VALLEN CORPORATION; *U.S. Public*, pg. 1705
VALLEN SAFETY SUPPLY COMPANY—Vallen Corporation; *U.S. Public*, pg. 1705
VALLEN SAFETY SUPPLY COMPANY, LTD.—Vallen Corporation; *U.S. Public*, pg. 1705
VALTEK/AUSTRALIA—Flowserve Corporation; *U.S. Public*, pg. 659
VALTEK AUSTRALIA/PERTH—Flowserve Corporation; *U.S. Public*, pg. 659
VALTEK CONTROLS, LTD.—Flowserve Corporation; *U.S. Public*, pg. 659
VALTEK NEW ZEALAND, LTD.—Flowserve Corporation; *U.S. Public*, pg. 659
VAN SON HOLLAND INK CORP. OF AMERICA; *U.S. Private*, pg. 1133
VAPONICS INC.—Osmonics, Inc.; *U.S. Public*, pg. 1234
VERMONT GMBH—Emerson Electric Co.; *U.S. Public*, pg. 578
VINSON SUPPLY COMPANY—Sammons Enterprises, Inc.; *U.S. Private*, pg. 963
VULCAN MATERIALS COMPANY; *U.S. Public*, pg. 1725
WEINIG INTL. GMBH—Michael Weinig AG; *Int'l*, pg. 1488
MICHAEL WEINIG AG; *Int'l*, pg. 1488
MICHAEL WEINIG, INC.—Michael Weinig AG; *Int'l*, pg. 1488
CARL WEISSMAN & SONS, INC.; *U.S. Private*, pg. 1160
WESTERN FILTER—Osmonics, Inc.; *U.S. Public*, pg. 1234
WHITE MOP WRINGER CO.—White Mop Wringer Company; *U.S. Private*, pg. 1173
DON E. WILLIAMS CO.; *U.S. Private*, pg. 1177
WILLIAMS STEEL & HARDWARE COMPANY; *U.S. Private*, pg. 1178
F.B. WRIGHT CO.; *U.S. Private*, pg. 1192
WYNN'S-PRECISION (CANADA) LTD.—Wynn's International, Inc.; *U.S. Public*, pg. 1783
WYNN'S-PRECISION (U.K.)LTD.—Wynn's International, Inc.; *U.S. Public*, pg. 1783
ZENECA AB—Zeneca Group Plc; *Int'l*, pg. 1526
ZENECA OY—Zeneca Group Plc; *Int'l*, pg. 1527
ZENECA POLAND SP. Z.O.O.—Zeneca Group Plc; *Int'l*, pg. 1527
ZENECA ZIMBABWE (PRIVATE) LIMITED—Zeneca Group Plc; *Int'l*, pg. 1527
ZUCKERMAN-HONICKMAN INC.; *U.S. Private*, pg. 1207

5087 — SERVICE ESTABLISHMENT EQUIPMENT & SUPPLIES-WHOLESALE

ABM INDUSTRIES; *U.S. Public*, pg. 2
APD CRYOGENICS—Intermagnetics General Corporation; *U.S. Public*, pg. 894

ALBERTO-CULVER COMPANY; *U.S. Public*, pg. 37
AMANO CLEANTECH MALAYSIA SDN. BHD.—Amano Corporation; *Int'l*, pg. 71
APPLIED POWER INC.; *U.S. Public*, pg. 124
AQUAPORE MOISTURE SYSTEMS, INC.—Powell Duffryn PLC; *Int'l*, pg. 1066
BRUNER WATER TREATMENT SYSTEMS—Culligan International Company; *U.S. Public*, pg. 467
CHEP AUSTRALIA—Brambles Industries Limited; *Int'l*, pg. 211
CONESTOGA CORPORATION; *U.S. Private*, pg. 262
CONTINENTAL PAPER & SUPPLY CO.; *U.S. Private*, pg. 269
L.N. CURTIS & SONS; *U.S. Private*, pg. 297
CUTLER MANUFACTURING CORPORATION; *U.S. Private*, pg. 298
DAYCON PRODUCTS COMPANY, INC.; *U.S. Private*, pg. 317
DEFENDER SERVICES, INC.; *U.S. Private*, pg. 320
EDWARD DON & COMPANY; *U.S. Private*, pg. 339
E-Z MART STORES, INC.; *U.S. Private*, pg. 353
ELECTROLUX CANADA—Electrolux Corporation; *U.S. Private*, pg. 370
THE SCOTT FETZER COMPANY—Berkshire Hathaway Inc.; *U.S. Public*, pg. 217
FORT PITT ACQUISITIONS, INC.; *U.S. Private*, pg. 419
S. FREEDMAN & SONS, INC.; *U.S. Private*, pg. 425
GRINNELL CANADA LTD.—Tyco International Ltd.; *U.S. Public*, pg. 1651
HOLOGIC, INC.; *U.S. Public*, pg. 831
INDUSTRIAL TOWEL & UNIFORM; *U.S. Private*, pg. 561
JP FOODSERVICE, INC.; *U.S. Public*, pg. 918
JACKSON PAPER COMPANY; *U.S. Private*, pg. 579
KELLERMEYER CO.; *U.S. Private*, pg. 612
KESTERSON FOOD COMPANY, INC.; *U.S. Private*, pg. 616
M.D. INDUSTRIES, INC.—Chris-Craft Industries, Inc.; *U.S. Public*, pg. 352
D.J. MEAD-HUBBS & HOWE—Sofco-Mead, Inc.; *U.S. Private*, pg. 1012
MERCURY DISTRIBUTING CO., INC.; *U.S. Private*, pg. 732
NATIONAL RESTAURANT SUPPLY COMPANY; *U.S. Private*, pg. 786
NEWELL PAPER CO. OF COLUMBUS—Jackson Paper Company; *U.S. Private*, pg. 579
NEWELL PAPER CO. OF MERIDIAN—Jackson Paper Company; *U.S. Private*, pg. 579
PACKAGING HOUSE NZFP LIMITED—International Paper Company; *U.S. Public*, pg. 905
PAPER ENTERPRISES, INC.; *U.S. Private*, pg. 837
PREMIER FARNELL—Premier Farnell plc; *Int'l*, pg. 1068
ROCHESTER-MIDLAND ICL—Rochester Midland Corporation; *U.S. Private*, pg. 937
SAFETY-KLEEN CORP.; *U.S. Public*, pg. 1425
SAFETYMASTER CORPORATION—Strategic Distribution Inc.; *U.S. Public*, pg. 1523
SALLY BEAUTY COMPANY, INC.—Alberto-Culver Company; *U.S. Public*, pg. 38
SCHNIEBER FINE FOODS, INC.; *U.S. Private*, pg. 971
SHELBY WILLIAMS TEXTILES—Shelby Williams Industries, Inc.; *U.S. Public*, pg. 1465
SOFCO-MEAD, INC.; *U.S. Private*, pg. 1012
SOREMAP HENKEL GV S.A.—Henkel KGaA; *Int'l*, pg. 614
SOUTHERN LEATHER CO., INC.; *U.S. Private*, pg. 1016
SYMTRON SYSTEMS, INC.—United Industrial Corporation; *U.S. Public*, pg. 1679
TAKARA BELMONT U.S.A., INC.—Takara Belmont Co., Ltd.; *Int'l*, pg. 1349
VALLEY SYSTEMS, INC.; *U.S. Public*, pg. 1706
WAJAX (AUSTRALASIA) PTY. LTD.—Wajax Limited; *Int'l*, pg. 1485
WAJAX PACIFIC FIRE EQUIPMENT INC.—Wajax Limited; *Int'l*, pg. 1485
WASSERSTROM COMPANY; *U.S. Private*, pg. 1152
WINDMERE-DURABLE HOLDINGS; *U.S. Public*, pg. 1771
WORMALD FIRE SYSTEMS AB—Tyco International Ltd.; *U.S. Public*, pg. 1650
WORMALD INTERNATIONAL (SCANDINAVIA) A/S—Tyco International Ltd.; *U.S. Public*, pg. 1651
WORMALD ITALIANA S.P.A.—Tyco International Ltd.; *U.S. Public*, pg. 1651

5088 — TRANSPORTATION EQUIPMENT & SUPPLIES, EXCEPT MOTOR VEHICLES-WHOLESALE

AAR AIRCRAFT TURBINE CENTER—AAR Corp.; *U.S. Public*, pg. 1
AAR ALLEN AIRCRAFT—AAR Corp.; *U.S. Public*, pg. 1
AAR CORP.; *U.S. Public*, pg. 1
AAR DEFENSE SYSTEMS—AAR Corp.; *U.S. Public*, pg. 1
AAR EUROPA—AAR Corp.; *U.S. Public*, pg. 1
AAR OKLAHOMA—AAR Corp.; *U.S. Public*, pg. 1
ABB TURBOCHARGER COMPANY—ABB Asea Brown Boveri (Holding) Ltd.; *Int'l*, pg. 5
ANR FREIGHT SYSTEM, INC.—The Coastal Corporation; *U.S. Public*, pg. 389
ADAMS INDUSTRIES, INC.—Banner Aerospace, Inc.; *U.S. Public*, pg. 187
ADAMS RITE SABRE INTERNATIONAL—ZMP, Inc.; *U.S. Private*, pg. 1203
AERO SYSTEMS AVIATION CORP.; *U.S. Private*, pg. 24
AGUSTA AEROSPACE CORPORATION—Agusta S.P.A.; *Int'l*, pg. 32
AGUSTA S.P.A.; *Int'l*, pg. 32
AIRBUS INDUSTRIE; *Int'l*, pg. 39
AIRBUS INDUSTRIE OF NORTH AMERICA, INC.—Airbus Industrie; *Int'l*, pg. 39
AIRLEASE LTD.; *U.S. Public*, pg. 33
AIRLEASE MANAGEMENT SERVICES, INC.—Airlease Ltd.; *U.S. Public*, pg. 33
ALLIEDSIGNAL AEROSPACE SERVICE CORPORATION—AlliedSignal Inc.; *U.S. Public*, pg. 52
ALLIEDSIGNAL AIRLINE SERVICES—AlliedSignal Inc.; *U.S. Public*, pg. 50
ALLIEDSIGNAL (AUSTRALIA) SALES LTD. FIBERS & CHEMICALS—AlliedSignal Inc.; *U.S. Public*, pg. 52
ALLIEDSIGNAL CHINA INC., ALLIEDSIGNAL AEROSPACE SERVICES CORPORATION—AlliedSignal Inc.; *U.S. Public*, pg. 52
ALLIEDSIGNAL EUROPE N.V.—AlliedSignal Inc.; *U.S. Public*, pg. 52
ALLIEDSIGNAL EUROPE S.A.—AlliedSignal Inc.; *U.S. Public*, pg. 52
ALLIEDSIGNAL INC. ASIA—AlliedSignal Inc.; *U.S. Public*, pg. 52
ALLIEDSIGNAL INTERNATIONAL, INC.—AlliedSignal Inc.; *U.S. Public*, pg. 52
AMRAIL—Jeumont-Schneider Trenformeteurs; *Int'l*, pg. 706
AMSTED INDUSTRIES INTERNATIONAL—Amsted Industries Incorporated; *U.S. Private*, pg. 68
ATLANTIC AVIATION CORP.; *U.S. Private*, pg. 94
AVIALL, INC.—Aviall, Inc.; *U.S. Public*, pg. 154
AVIATION SALES COMPANY; *U.S. Public*, pg. 154
AVIONS DE TRANSPORT REGIONAL - ATR—IRI Istituto Ricostruzione Industriale; *Int'l*, pg. 654
BAE-SEMA LIMITED—British Aerospace p.l.c.; *Int'l*, pg. 217
BTR, INC.—BTR plc; *Int'l*, pg. 127
BANNER AIRCRAFT INTERNATIONAL, INC.—Banner Aerospace, Inc.; *U.S. Public*, pg. 187
BOEING CHINA, INC.—The Boeing Company; *U.S. Public*, pg. 242
THE BOEING COMPANY—The Boeing Company; *U.S. Public*, pg. 242
BOEING JAPAN—The Boeing Company; *U.S. Public*, pg. 242
BOEING JAPAN, LTD.—The Boeing Company; *U.S. Public*, pg. 242
BOEING MIDDLE EAST LIMITED—The Boeing Company; *U.S. Public*, pg. 242
BOEING SERVICES, INC.—The Boeing Company; *U.S. Public*, pg. 242
THE BUDD COMPANY—Thyssen AG; *Int'l*, pg. 1388
BURBANK AIRCRAFT SUPPLY INC.—Banner Aerospace, Inc.; *U.S. Public*, pg. 187
CONSTRUCCIONES AERONAUTICAS, SA—The Boeing Company; *U.S. Public*, pg. 242
CURRAN GROUP, INC.; *U.S. Private*, pg. 297
DELCAL ENTERPRISES, INC.; *U.S. Private*, pg. 322
EAC-EMBRAER AIRCRAFT CORPORATION—Embraer-Empresa Brasileira de Aeronautica S.A.; *Int'l*, pg. 452
EAI-EMBRAER AVIATION INTERNATIONAL—Embraer-Empresa Brasileira de Aeronautica S.A.; *Int'l*, pg. 452
EATON CORPORATION, DEFENSE VALVE AND ACTUATOR DIVISION—Eaton Corporation; *U.S. Public*, pg. 556
FEDERAL APD, INC.—Federal Signal Corporation; *U.S. Public*, pg. 616
FISHERIES SUPPLY COMPANY; *U.S. Private*, pg. 408
THE FLIGHT INTERNATIONAL GROUP, INC.; *U.S. Public*, pg. 654
L.B. FOSTER COMPANY; *U.S. Public*, pg. 675
FRANCORAIL—Jeumont-Schneider Trenformeteurs; *Int'l*, pg. 706
GEFCO—PSA Peugeot Citroen; *Int'l*, pg. 1021
GENERAL DYNAMICS INTERNATIONAL CORPORATION—General Dynamics Corporation; *U.S. Public*, pg. 709
GENERAL ELECTRIC CAPITAL RAILCAR SERVICES—General Electric Company; *U.S. Public*, pg. 712
GENERAL ELECTRIC (USA) ASIA CO.—General Electric Company; *U.S. Public*, pg. 713
GENERAL ELECTRIC (USA) HERMETIC MOTOR OPERATION (PTE) LTD.—General Electric Company; *U.S. Public*, pg. 714
GENERATION METALS CORP.; *U.S. Private*, pg. 446
B.F. GOODRICH AEROSPACE—The B.F. Goodrich Company; *U.S. Public*, pg. 752
GULFSTREAM AEROSPACE CORPORATION—Forstmann Little & Co.; *U.S. Private*, pg. 419
HAWKER DE HAVILLAND LTD.—BTR plc; *Int'l*, pg. 128
HAWKER PACIFIC PTY. LTD.—BTR plc; *Int'l*, pg. 128
HAWTHORNE CORP.; *U.S. Private*, pg. 512
IHI INC.—Ishikawajima-Harima Heavy Industries Co., Ltd.; *Int'l*, pg. 689
ITOCHU AVIATION, INC.—Itochu Corporation; *Int'l*, pg. 694
INDUSTRIAL & TRANSPORTATION EQUIPMENT CO.—American Grain & Related Industries; *U.S. Private*, pg. 55
INTERLEASE TRADING CORP.—American International Group, Inc.; *U.S. Public*, pg. 85
INTERNATIONAL AIRLINE SUPPORT GROUP, INC.; *U.S. Public*, pg. 894
INTERNATIONAL LEASE FINANCE CORPORATION—American International Group, Inc.; *U.S. Public*, pg. 85
JAE ELECTRONICS, INC.—Japan Aviation Electronics Industry, Ltd.; *Int'l*, pg. 701
JEUMONT-SCHNEIDER DE MEXICO—Jeumont-Schneider Trenformeteurs; *Int'l*, pg. 706
JEUMONT-SCHNEIDER INDUSTRIAL SYSTEMS (JSIS)—Jeumont-Schneider Trenformeteurs; *Int'l*, pg. 706
JISTRAL—Jeumont-Schneider Trenformeteurs; *Int'l*, pg. 706
JOHNSON & TOWERS, INC.; *U.S. Private*, pg. 590
KVAERNER HONG KONG R O FOR KVAERNER SINGAPORE PTE LTD—Kvaerner a.s.a.; *Int'l*, pg. 772
MANSOUR GENERAL DYNAMICS LTD.—General Dynamics Corporation; *U.S. Public*, pg. 709
MASEK DISTRIBUTING INC.; *U.S. Private*, pg. 711
MATRIX AVIATION, INC.—Banner Aerospace, Inc.; *U.S. Public*, pg. 187
MEMPHIS GROUP, INC.; *U.S. Private*, pg. 730
MITSUBISHI CORPORATION; *Int'l*, pg. 871
MITSUBISHI INTERNATIONAL CORPORATION—Mitsubishi Corporation; *Int'l*, pg. 871
MOOG ENGINE CONTROLS DIV.—Moog Incorporated; *U.S. Public*, pg. 1127
MOONEY AIRCRAFT CORPORATION; *U.S. Private*, pg. 759
MOTION & CONTROL SALES DIV.—Parker Hannifin Corporation; *U.S. Public*, pg. 1261
NAPCO INTERNATIONAL, INC.—Venturian Corp.; *U.S. Public*, pg. 1716
NASAM INTERNATIONAL, INCORPORATED—Banner Aerospace, Inc.; *U.S. Public*, pg. 187
NIM-COR, INC.—Haden Maclellan Holdings plc; *Int'l*, pg. 586
NISSHO IWAI AEROSPACE (AMERICA) CORP.—Nissho Iwai Corporation; *Int'l*, pg. 947
NISSHO IWAI AEROSPACE CORP.—Nissho Iwai Corporation; *Int'l*, pg. 946
NOZAKI & COMPANY LTD.; *Int'l*, pg. 990
PACAERO—Banner Aerospace, Inc.; *U.S. Public*, pg. 187
PACCAR INTERNATIONAL—Paccar Inc.; *U.S. Public*, pg. 1246
PROFESSIONAL AVIATION ASSOCIATES, INC.—Banner Aerospace, Inc.; *U.S. Public*, pg. 187
RAYMOND TRANSPORTATION CORPORATION—BT Industries AB; *Int'l*, pg. 123
REAGAN EQUIPMENT COMPANY, INC.; *U.S. Private*, pg. 913
ROHR EUROPE—The B.F. Goodrich Company; *U.S. Public*, pg. 752
ROLLS-ROYCE INC.—Rolls-Royce plc; *Int'l*, pg. 1127
SAAB AIRCRAFT INTERNATIONAL LTD.—Investor AB; *Int'l*, pg. 687
SAAB AIRCRAFT OF AMERICA INC.—Investor AB; *Int'l*, pg. 687
SCHLEGEL BUILDING PRODUCTS DIV.—BTR plc; *Int'l*, pg. 128
SCHLEGEL CAROLINA DIV.—BTR plc; *Int'l*, pg. 128
SCHLEGEL NORTH AMERICAN AUTOMOTIVE OPERATIONS—BTR plc; *Int'l*, pg. 128
SENSENICH PROPELLER MANUFACTURING CO., INC.—The Philadelphia Bourse, Inc.; *U.S. Private*, pg. 861
SHIMADZU CORPORATION; *Int'l*, pg. 1232
SHIMADZU PRECISION INSTRUMENTS, INC.—Shimadzu Corporation; *Int'l*, pg. 1232
SIEMENS TRANSPORTATION SYSTEMS, INC.—Siemens AG; *Int'l*, pg. 1246
SINGAPORE BRITISH ENGINEERING PTE. LIMITED—British Aerospace p.l.c.; *Int'l*, pg. 218
SOLAIR, INC.—Banner Aerospace, Inc.; *U.S. Public*, pg. 187
SPAR AVIATION SERVICES—Spar Aerospace Limited; *Int'l*, pg. 1288
SUMITOMO CORPORATION; *Int'l*, pg. 1312
SUMITOMO CORPORATION OF AMERICA—Sumitomo Corporation; *Int'l*, pg. 1312
TIDEWATER OFFSHORE SERVICES, INC.—Tidewater Inc.; *U.S. Public*, pg. 1608
TRIUMPH GROUP, INC.; *U.S. Public*, pg. 1640
UNILASER—Aerospatiale; *Int'l*, pg. 29
VAN EIJLE B.V.—Internatio-Muller N.V.; *Int'l*, pg. 682
VOLVO AERO CORPORATION—AB Volvo; *Int'l*, pg. 1476

5091 — SPORTING & RECREATIONAL GOODS & SUPPLIES-WHOLESALE

ABU GARCIA PTY. LTD.—Outdoor Technologies Group; *U.S. Private*, pg. 822
ACUSHNET COMPANY—Fortune Brands, Inc.; *U.S. Public*, pg. 675
AJAY LEISURE PRODUCTS, INC.—Ajay Sports Inc.; *U.S. Public*, pg. 34
AMER GROUP LTD.; *Int'l*, pg. 72
AMERICAN CAMPER—Brunswick Corporation; *U.S. Public*, pg. 265
ANDERSON WHOLESALE COMPANY; *U.S. Private*, pg. 73
AQUA CHEM DIVISION—Imperial Chemical Industries PLC; *Int'l*, pg. 663
THE ARNOLD PALMER GOLF COMPANY; *U.S. Public*, pg. 132
THE AUSTAD COMPANY—Hanover Direct, Inc.; *U.S. Public*, pg. 782
AUSTRALIAN COLEMAN, INC.—MacAndrews & Forbes Holdings Inc.; *U.S. Private*, pg. 691
AVIVA SPORT, INC.—Mattel, Inc.; *U.S. Public*, pg. 1058
BASS PRO SHOPS, INC.; *U.S. Private*, pg. 122
BENNETT BROTHERS, INC.; *U.S. Private*, pg. 133
BENNETT BROTHERS, INC.—Bennett Brothers, Inc.; *U.S. Private*, pg. 133
BIC SPORT—Societe BIC S.A.; *Int'l*, pg. 1273
BILLIARDS DIV. OF BRUNSWICK—Brunswick Corporation; *U.S. Public*, pg. 265
BRUNSWICK GMBH—Brunswick Corporation; *U.S. Public*, pg. 266
BRUNSWICK INTERNATIONAL (CANADA) LIMITED Brunswick Corporation; *U.S. Public*, pg. 266
CAMPING WORLD, INC.; *U.S. Private*, pg. 204
CANSTAR APPAREL INC.—Nike, Inc.; *U.S. Public*, pg. 1184
CHRIS-CRAFT BOATS—Greenway Partners, L.P.; *U.S. Private*, pg. 478
COLEMAN JAPAN LTD.—MacAndrews & Forbes Holdings Inc.; *U.S. Private*, pg. 691
COLEMAN SPAS, INC.—MacAndrews & Forbes Holdings Inc.; *U.S. Private*, pg. 691
CONNELLY SKIS, INC.—Thyssen AG; *Int'l*, pg. 1388
CONSOLIDATED STORES CORP.; *U.S. Public*, pg. 437
CORTLAND LINE CO., INC.; *U.S. Private*, pg. 277
DAKCO DISTRIBUTORS, INC.; *U.S. Private*, pg. 308
DANA DESIGN—K2 Inc.; *U.S. Public*, pg. 940
DELAIR GROUP, L.L.C.—Aluminum Shapes, LLC; *U.S. Private*, pg. 47
DERBY CYCLE CORPORATION—Derby International Corporation S.A.; *Int'l*, pg. 394
ERO INDUSTRIES, INC.—Hicks, Muse, Tate & Furst Inc.; *U.S. Private*, pg. 526
EBSCO INDUSTRIES, INC.; *U.S. Private*, pg. 358

GANDER MOUNTAIN RETAIL—Holiday Companies; U.S. Private, pg. 534
GOLF SOPHISTICATES—Maruzen Company Limited; Int'l, pg. 846
HUFFY SPORTS COMPANY—Huffy Corporation; U.S. Public, pg. 846
HUNTER MARINE CORPORATION; U.S. Private, pg. 549
HUTCH SPORTS USA, INC.—RDM Sports Group; U.S. Public, pg. 1354
HYOSUNG GROUP; Int'l, pg. 640
INTEX CORP.; U.S. Private, pg. 574
K2 INC.; U.S. Public, pg. 940
M.W. KASCH COMPANY; U.S. Private, pg. 608
KELLWOOD COMPANY; U.S. Public, pg. 948
THE KRUSE COMPANY; U.S. Private, pg. 636
LILLYWHITES LTD.—Jeronimo Martins; Int'l, pg. 706
LITTLEFIELD, ADAMS & COMPANY; U.S. Public, pg. 1001
MACGREGOR GOLF (JAPAN) LTD.—Amer Group Ltd.; Int'l, pg. 73
MAINSHIP CORPORATION; U.S. Private, pg. 697
MARINCO/AFI—Valley Forge Corporation; U.S. Public, pg. 1705
MARUBENI AMERICA CORPORATION, SAN FRANCISCO BRANCH—Marubeni Corporation; Int'l, pg. 845
MARUBENI CORPORATION; Int'l, pg. 844
MATHEWS & BOUCHER; U.S. Private, pg. 714
MATTEL POWER WHEELS—Mattel, Inc.; U.S. Public, pg. 1058
SAMUEL MEISEL & COMPANY, INC.—BAA plc; Int'l, pg. 103
MITRE SPORTS (U.S.)—Pentland Group PLC; Int'l, pg. 1036
MIZUNO CORPORATION NIEDERLASSUNG DEUTSCHLAND—Mizuno Corporation; Int'l, pg. 885
MIZUNO (FRANCE) S.A.R.L.—Mizuno Corporation; Int'l, pg. 885
MIZUNO GOLF COMPANY—Mizuno Corporation; Int'l, pg. 885
MIZUNO (TAIWAN) CORPORATION—Mizuno Corporation; Int'l, pg. 885
MIZUNO (UK) LTD.—Mizuno Corporation; Int'l, pg. 885
MIZUNO USA, INC.—Mizuno Corporation; Int'l, pg. 885
NICKLAUS GOLF COMPANY, L.C.; U.S. Private, pg. 799
NIPPON BRUNSWICK CO., LTD.—Mitsui & Co., Ltd.; Int'l, pg. 879
NORTHLAND SPORTS INC.—Sportsman Supply; U.S. Private, pg. 1026
OUTDOOR TECHNOLOGIES - CANADA—Outdoor Technologies Group; U.S. Private, pg. 822
PELICAN PRODUCTS; U.S. Private, pg. 848
PLANET EARTH PRODUCTS—K2 Inc.; U.S. Public, pg. 940
PROFESSIONAL GOLF COMPANY SDN. BHD.—Sime Darby Berhad; Int'l, pg. 1250
QUEST JAPAN INC.—Jinwoong Inc.; Int'l, pg. 707
QUEST LEISURE PRODUCTS (AUST) PTY. LTD.—Jinwoong Inc.; Int'l, pg. 707
RAWLINGS CANADA—Rawlings Sporting Goods Company; U.S. Public, pg. 1362
RAWLINGS SPORTING GOODS COMPANY; U.S. Public, pg. 1361
ROLLERBLADE, INC.; U.S. Private, pg. 941
ROSSIGNOL S.A.; Int'l, pg. 1127
ROSSIGNOL SKI AG—Rossignol S.A.; Int'l, pg. 1127
ROSSIGNOL SKI CO.—Rossignol S.A.; Int'l, pg. 1127
ROSSIGNOL SKI DEUTSCHLAND GMBH—Rossignol S.A.; Int'l, pg. 1127
SALOMON-NORTH AMERICA INC.—Salomon S.A.; Int'l, pg. 1181
SALOMON SPORTS LTD.—Salomon S.A.; Int'l, pg. 1181
SCOTT U.S.A.—Scott Sports Group; U.S. Private, pg. 977
SHIMA AMERICAN CORP.—Shima Trading Co. Ltd.; Int'l, pg. 1232
SHIMA TRADING CO. LTD.; Int'l, pg. 1231
SHIMANO AMERICAN CORPORATION—Shimano Inc.; Int'l, pg. 1232
SHIMANO (EUROPA) GMBH—Shimano Inc.; Int'l, pg. 1233
SHIMANO (SINGAPORE) PTE. LTD.—Shimano Inc.; Int'l, pg. 1233
SIMMONS OUTDOOR CORPORATION—Blount International, Inc.; U.S. Public, pg. 238
SKIS DYNASTAR S.A.—Rossignol S.A.; Int'l, pg. 1127
SOWESTER LIMITED—Krug International Corp.; U.S. Public, pg. 968
SPORT MART, INC.; U.S. Public, pg. 1499
SPORT SUPPLY GROUP, INC.; U.S. Public, pg. 1499
SPORTSMAN SUPPLY; U.S. Private, pg. 1026
STANDARD COMMUNICATIONS CORP.—Marantz Japan Inc.; Int'l, pg. 841
SUPERIOR POOL PRODUCTS, INC.—Olin Corporation; U.S. Public, pg. 1219
SWISS ARMY BRANDS, INC.; U.S. Public, pg. 1544
TASCO SALES INC.—Rice, Sangalis, Toole & Wilson; U.S. Private, pg. 928
TREK BICYCLE CORPORATION—Trek Corporation; U.S. Private, pg. 1099
TRETORN A/S—Proventus AB; Int'l, pg. 1072
TRETORN FORSALJNINGS AB—Proventus AB; Int'l, pg. 1072
TRETORN GMBH—Proventus AB; Int'l, pg. 1072
TRETORN SPORT SALES LTD.—Proventus AB; Int'l, pg. 1072
UETA, INC.—BAA plc; Int'l, pg. 103
U.M. HOLDING LIMITED; U.S. Private, pg. 1113
VALLEY FORGE CORPORATION; U.S. Public, pg. 1705
VIKING YACHT CO.; U.S. Private, pg. 1140
WILSON FRANCE SARL—Amer Group Ltd.; Int'l, pg. 73
WILSON JAPAN, INC.—Amer Group Ltd.; Int'l, pg. 73
WILSON SPORTING GOODS ASIA, LTD.—Amer Group Ltd.; Int'l, pg. 73
WILSON SPORTING GOODS CO., LTD.—Amer Group Ltd.; Int'l, pg. 73
WILSON SPORTING GOODS GMBH—Amer Group Ltd.; Int'l, pg. 73
WILSON SPORTING GOODS (MALAYSIA) SDN. BHD.—Amer Group Ltd.; Int'l, pg. 73
WILSON SPORTS EQUIPMENT CANADA, INC.—Amer Group Ltd.; Int'l, pg. 73
WILSON SPORTS EQUIPMENT CANADA, LTD.—Amer Group Ltd.; Int'l, pg. 73
YONEX CORPORATION—Yonex Co., Ltd.; Int'l, pg. 1522

5092 — TOYS & HOBBY GOODS & SUPPLIES-WHOLESALE

ACE NOVELTY COMPANY, INC.—Play by Play Toys & Novelties, Inc.; U.S. Public, pg. 1309
ACE NOVELTY FUN SERVICE DIVISION—Play by Play Toys & Novelties, Inc.; U.S. Public, pg. 1309
ANDERSON WHOLESALE COMPANY; U.S. Private, pg. 73
APPLAUSE INC.; U.S. Private, pg. 78
BANDAI AMERICA, INC.—Bandai Co., Ltd.; Int'l, pg. 145
CSS INDUSTRIES, INC.; U.S. Public, pg. 283
CAP TOYS, INC.—Hasbro, Inc.; U.S. Public, pg. 797
CARDINAL INC.; U.S. Private, pg. 208
COMMONWEALTH TOY & NOVELTY COMPANY; U.S. Private, pg. 258
CONCORD MINIATURES—Cardinal Inc.; U.S. Private, pg. 209
CONSOLIDATED STORES CORP.; U.S. Public, pg. 437
DIMENSIONS INC.—Coats Viyella plc; Int'l, pg. 300
E-Z BOWZ, INC.; U.S. Private, pg. 352
THE FIRST YEARS INC.; U.S. Public, pg. 642
HAGEMEYER N.V.—First Pacific Company Limited; Int'l, pg. 487
HASBRO BRADLEY FAR EAST (1987) LTD.—Hasbro, Inc.; U.S. Public, pg. 797
HASBRO FOREIGN SALES CORP.—Hasbro, Inc.; U.S. Public, pg. 797
HASBRO, INC.; U.S. Public, pg. 797
HASBRO INTERNATIONAL, INC.—Hasbro, Inc.; U.S. Public, pg. 797
HASBRO-MB S.A.—Hasbro, Inc.; U.S. Public, pg. 797
HASBRO TOY DIVISION—Hasbro, Inc.; U.S. Public, pg. 797
INTEX CORP.; U.S. Private, pg. 574
JANLYNN CORPORATION; U.S. Private, pg. 582
JAYDON INCORPORATED; U.S. Private, pg. 584
JOHN MENZIES PLC; Int'l, pg. 707
JOHN MENZIES (UK) LIMITED—John Menzies plc; Int'l, pg. 707
M.W. KASCH COMPANY; U.S. Private, pg. 608
LEGO AG—Lego System A/S; Int'l, pg. 805
LEGO OVERSEAS A/S—Lego System A/S; Int'l, pg. 805
LIFE-LIKE PRODUCTS, INC.; U.S. Private, pg. 666
MB ESPANA, S.A.—Hasbro, Inc.; U.S. Public, pg. 798
MB (SWITZERLAND) AG—Hasbro, Inc.; U.S. Public, pg. 798
MATTEL GAMES/PUZZLES—Mattel, Inc.; U.S. Public, pg. 1058
MATTEL INTERNATIONAL LIMITED—Mattel, Inc.; U.S. Public, pg. 1058
MATTEL (K.L.) SDN. BHD. (MAYLAYSIA)—Mattel, Inc.; U.S. Public, pg. 1059
MECO DEVELOPMENT LIMITED; Int'l, pg. 852
SAMUEL MEISEL & COMPANY, INC.—BAA plc; Int'l, pg. 103
MILTON BRADLEY AUSTRALIA PTY. LTD.—Hasbro, Inc.; U.S. Public, pg. 798
MONARCH AVALON, INC.; U.S. Public, pg. 1123
NOODLE KIDOODLE INC.; U.S. Public, pg. 1188
THE PAPER MAGIC GROUP, INC.—CSS Industries, Inc.; U.S. Public, pg. 284
PAUL-SON GAMING CORPORATION; U.S. Public, pg. 1265
PLAYMATES TOYS INC.—Playmates Holdings Ltd.; Int'l, pg. 1060
REMCO TOYS—JAKKS Pacific, Inc.; U.S. Public, pg. 923
ROSE ART INDUSTRIES; U.S. Private, pg. 945
THE SCORE BOARD, INC.; U.S. Public, pg. 1444
STAR SALES CO., INC.; U.S. Private, pg. 1035
TSR, INC.—Wizards of the Coast; U.S. Private, pg. 1185
TIGER ELECTRONICS, INC.; U.S. Private, pg. 1086
TONKA CORP. PTY. LTD.—Hasbro, Inc.; U.S. Public, pg. 798
TOYS "R" US UNITED STATES—Toys "R" Us, Inc.; U.S. Public, pg. 1626
TYCO CANADA LTD.—Mattel, Inc.; U.S. Public, pg. 1059
TYCO PLAYTIME INC.—Mattel, Inc.; U.S. Public, pg. 1058
TYCO TOYS ESPANA—Mattel, Inc.; U.S. Public, pg. 1059
UETA, INC.—BAA plc; Int'l, pg. 103
UNICOVER CORPORATION; U.S. Private, pg. 1117
THE UNITED STATES PLAYING CARD COMPANY; U.S. Private, pg. 1125
WIZARDS OF THE COAST; U.S. Private, pg. 1185

5093 — SCRAP AND WASTE MATERIALS

AMALGAMATED METAL CORPORATION PLC—Preussag AG; Int'l, pg. 1071
AB ARV ANDERSON—Trelleborg AB; Int'l, pg. 1422
ARKANSAS ALUMINUM ALLOYS—A. Tenenbaum Co. Inc.; U.S. Private, pg. 1076
BAKERMET INC.—The Ivaco Group; Int'l, pg. 695
JOSEPH BEHR & SONS INC.; U.S. Private, pg. 130
CLOVER YARNS INC.; U.S. Private, pg. 247
LOUIS COHEN AND SONS, INC.—Medico Industries, Inc.; U.S. Private, pg. 728
COLONIAL METALS CO.; U.S. Private, pg. 253
COLUMBIA IRON & METAL CO.—Columbia National Group, Inc.; U.S. Private, pg. 256
COLUMBIA NATIONAL GROUP, INC.; U.S. Private, pg. 255
COMETALS CHINA, INC.—Commercial Metals Company; U.S. Public, pg. 414
COMMERCIAL METALS COMPANY; U.S. Public, pg. 411
COMMERCIAL METALS COMPANY—Commercial Metals Company; U.S. Public, pg. 413
CONNELL LIMITED PARTNERSHIP; U.S. Private, pg. 264
CONTINENTAL PAPER RECYCLING LLC; U.S. Private, pg. 269
DAVIDSONS WASTE PAPER—BPB Industries PLC; Int'l, pg. 123
DUGGAN INDUSTRIES, INC.; U.S. Private, pg. 345
FIRST RECOVERY—Ashland, Inc.; U.S. Public, pg. 139
GROSSMAN IRON & STEEL COMPANY; U.S. Private, pg. 483
HANWA AMERICAN CORP.—Hanwa Co., Ltd.; Int'l, pg. 595
HUGO NEU-PROLER CO.—Schnitzer Steel Industries, Inc.; U.S. Public, pg. 1440
ICD GROUP INTERNATIONAL INC.; U.S. Private, pg. 554
IL RETURPAPPER; Int'l, pg. 646
IL WASTEPAPER (UK) LTD—Danisco A/S; Int'l, pg. 378
DAVID JOSEPH CO.; U.S. Private, pg. 601
THE DAVID J. JOSEPH COMPANY—SHV Holdings N.V.; Int'l, pg. 1155
KALAMAZOO SCRAP & PROCESSING—Sturgis Iron & Metal Company, Inc.; U.S. Private, pg. 1048
KARCHMER IRON & METAL COMPANY—Commercial Metals Company; U.S. Public, pg. 413
KRUPP WIDIA GMBH—Fried. Krupp AG; Int'l, pg. 510
LOUISVILLE SCRAP MATERIAL CO., INC.; U.S. Private, pg. 677
LUNTZ CORPORATION; U.S. Private, pg. 681
MRI CORPORATION—Schnitzer Steel Industries, Inc.; U.S. Public, pg. 1440
SAMUEL MEISEL & COMPANY, INC.—BAA plc; Int'l, pg. 103
MERCER COMPANY—Columbia National Group, Inc.; U.S. Private, pg. 256
MONEY POINT DIAMOND CO.; U.S. Private, pg. 757
NICHIMEN AMERICA, INC.—Nichimen Corporation; Int'l, pg. 927
NICHIMEN CORPORATION; Int'l, pg. 927
NORTH PACIFIC LUMBER COMPANY; U.S. Private, pg. 805
OHIO VALLEY ALUMINUM COMPANY—Interlock Industries, Inc.; U.S. Private, pg. 567
OKAYA & CO. LTD.; Int'l, pg. 999
OMNISOURCE CORPORATION; U.S. Private, pg. 817
LOUIS PADNOS IRON & METAL CO.; U.S. Private, pg. 834
PADNOS-SUMMIT—Louis Padnos Iron & Metal Co.; U.S. Private, pg. 834
PAPER STOCK DEALERS, INC.—Sonoco Products Company; U.S. Public, pg. 1486
PERSTORP RAILITE S.A. DECORATIVE LAMINATE—Perstorp AB; Int'l, pg. 1038
MAYER POLLACK STEEL CORPORATION—The Pollock Corp.; U.S. Private, pg. 874
THE POLLOCK CORP.; U.S. Private, pg. 874
PROLER INTERNATIONAL CORP.—Schnitzer Steel Industries, Inc.; U.S. Public, pg. 1440
PROLERIDE TRANSPORT SYSTEMS, INC.—Schnitzer Steel Industries, Inc.; U.S. Public, pg. 1440
PROLERIZED NEW ENGLAND CO.—Schnitzer Steel Industries, Inc.; U.S. Public, pg. 1440
PROLERIZED SCHIABO-NEU CO.—Schnitzer Steel Industries, Inc.; U.S. Public, pg. 1440
RECLAIMERS, INC.—Philip Services Corp.; Int'l, pg. 1050
REPUBLIC ALLOYS, INC.; U.S. Private, pg. 923
S.D. RICHMAN SONS, INC.; U.S. Private, pg. 929
ROCK-TENN COMPANY; U.S. Public, pg. 1396
ROCK-TENN COMPANY, MILL DIVISION, INC.—Rock-Tenn Company; U.S. Public, pg. 1397
SHV HOLDINGS N.V.; Int'l, pg. 1154
SCHNITZER STEEL INDUSTRIES, INC.; U.S. Public, pg. 1439
SEWARD INC.; U.S. Private, pg. 988
JOSEPH SIMON & SONS, INC.; U.S. Private, pg. 1001
JEFFERSON SMURFIT CORPORATION—Jefferson Smurfit Group p.l.c.; Int'l, pg. 1269
JEFFERSON SMURFIT GROUP P.L.C.; Int'l, pg. 1269
SOUTH BEND SCRAP & PROCESSING—Sturgis Iron & Metal Company, Inc.; U.S. Private, pg. 1048
THE STOP & SHOP COMPANIES, INC.—Koninklijke Ahold NV; Int'l, pg. 750
STURGIS IRON & METAL COMPANY, INC.; U.S. Private, pg. 1048
STURGIS IRON & METAL, ELKHART METALS DIVISION—Sturgis Iron & Metal Company, Inc.; U.S. Private, pg. 1048
SVEDALA INDUSTRIES-UNIVERSAL ENGINEERING—Svedala Industri AB; Int'l, pg. 1326
A. TENENBAUM CO. INC.; U.S. Private, pg. 1076
THREE RIVERS IRON & METAL—Sturgis Iron & Metal Company, Inc.; U.S. Private, pg. 1048
UETA, INC.—BAA plc; Int'l, pg. 103
VEM ERZ UND STAHL GMBH—Internatio-Muller N.V.; Int'l, pg. 682
VOEST-ALPINE ROHSTOFFHANDEL GES.M.B.H.—Voest-Alpine Stahl AG; Int'l, pg. 1470
CARL WEISSMAN & SONS, INC.; U.S. Private, pg. 1160
ZENITH FINANCE & CONSTRUCTION CO.—Commercial Metals Company; U.S. Public, pg. 413

5094 — JEWELRY, WATCHES, PRECIOUS STONES & PRECIOUS METALS-WHOLESALE

A-MARK FINANCIAL; U.S. Private, pg. 2
ABN INTERNATIONAL DIAMOND DIVISION—ABN-AMRO Holding N.V.; Int'l, pg. 11
O.B. ALLAN JEWELLERS—Henry Birks & Sons (1993) Inc.; Int'l, pg. 197
ANAMINT—Anglo American Corporation of South Africa Limited; Int'l, pg. 76

ANGLO AMERICAN CORPORATION OF SOUTH AFRICA LIMITED (LONDON)—Anglo American Corporation of South Africa Limited; *Int'l*, pg. 77
ANTWERP DIAMOND DISTRIBUTORS INC.; *U.S. Private*, pg. 76
ARTRA GROUP INCORPORATED; *U.S. Public*, pg. 136
BMI PTE. LTD., SINGAPORE—F. J. Benjamin Holdings Ltd.; *Int'l*, pg. 187
JOSEPH BEHR & SONS INC.; *U.S. Private*, pg. 130
JAN BELL MARKETING INC.; *U.S. Public*, pg. 207
F.J. BENJAMIN FASHIONS (AUST) PTY. LTD.—F. J. Benjamin Holdings Ltd.; *Int'l*, pg. 187
F.J. BENJAMIN FASHIONS (HK) LTD.—F. J. Benjamin Holdings Ltd.; *Int'l*, pg. 187
F.J. BENJAMIN FASHIONS (M) SDN. BHD.—F. J. Benjamin Holdings Ltd.; *Int'l*, pg. 187
BENNETT BROTHERS, INC.; *U.S. Private*, pg. 133
BENNETT BROTHERS, INC.—Bennett Brothers, Inc.; *U.S. Private*, pg. 133
HENRY BIRKS & SONS (1993) INC.; *Int'l*, pg. 196
BULGARI CORPORATION OF AMERICA—Bulgari SPA; *Int'l*, pg. 232
BULOVA CORPORATION—Loews Corporation; *U.S. Public*, *pg. 1010*
BULOVA WATCH COMPANY LIMITED—Loews Corporation; *U.S. Public*, pg. 1011
CASIO CANADA, LTD.—Casio Computer Co., Ltd.; *Int'l*, pg. 274
CASIO, INC.—Casio Computer Co., Ltd.; *Int'l*, pg. 274
CITIZEN WATCH CO. OF AMERICA, INC.—Citizen Watch Company, Ltd.; *Int'l*, pg. 294
CONSOLIDATED STORES CORP.; *U.S. Public*, pg. 437
CONTINENTAL COIN CORPORATION; *U.S. Private*, pg. 267
COOKSON GROUP PLC; *Int'l*, pg. 328
D.J. TABLEWARE, INC.—Oneida Ltd.; *U.S. Public*, pg. 1226
DAIWA PRECIOUS METALS CO., LTD.—Daiwa Securities Co. Ltd.; *Int'l*, pg. 375
DE BEERS CENTENARY AG—Anglo American Corporation of South Africa Limited; *Int'l*, pg. 77
DE BEERS CENTRAL SELLING ORGANIZATION—Anglo American Corporation of South Africa Limited; *Int'l*, pg. 77
DESCO DE SCHULTHESS LTD.; *Int'l*, pg. 396
DOWNEY DESIGNS INTERNATIONAL; *U.S. Private*, pg. 342
EMPIRE DIAMOND CORPORATION; *U.S. Private*, pg. 374
ENGELHARD METALS AG—Engelhard Corporation; *U.S. Public*, pg. 582
ENGELHARD METALS LTD.—Engelhard Corporation; *U.S. Public*, pg. 582
M. FABRIKANT & SONS, INC.; *U.S. Private*, pg. 390
GEORG JENSEN S.A.R.L.—Royal Copenhagen A/S; *Int'l*, pg. 1134
GEORG JENSEN SILVER AB—Royal Copenhagen A/S; *Int'l*, pg. 1134
GEORG JENSEN SILVER LTD.—Royal Copenhagen A/S; *Int'l*, pg. 1134
GEORG JENSEN SILVER (NSW) PTY. LTD—Royal Copenhagen A/S; *Int'l*, pg. 1134
HAGEMEYER N.V.—First Pacific Company Limited; *Int'l*, pg. 487
IWI HOLDING LIMITED; *U.S. Public*, pg. 861
INVERNESS CORP.; *U.S. Private*, pg. 574
INVERNESS UK LTD.—Inverness Corp.; *U.S. Private*, pg. 574
JEWELCOR COMPANIES; *U.S. Private*, pg. 587
JEWELMONT CORPORATION; *U.S. Private*, pg. 587
JOHNSON MATTHEY PUBLIC LIMITED COMPANY; *Int'l*, pg. 713
MAX KAHAN INC.; *U.S. Private*, pg. 604
KNAR GOLD & SILVER EXCHANGE; *U.S. Private*, pg. 626
LAZARE KAPLAN BELGIUM N.V.—Lazare Kaplan Intl., Inc.; *U.S. Public*, pg. 981
LAZARE KAPLAN INTL., INC.; *U.S. Public*, pg. 981
LENOX BRANDS—Brown-Forman Corporation; *U.S. Public*, *pg. 261*
LENOX, INCORPORATED—Brown-Forman Corporation; *U.S. Public*, pg. 261
SAMUEL MEISEL & COMPANY, INC.—BAA plc; *Int'l*, pg. 103
K. MIKIMOTO & CO., LTD.; *Int'l*, pg. 866
HOWARD MILLER; *U.S. Private*, pg. 747
MONEX DEPOSIT CO.; *U.S. Private*, pg. 757
MOVADO GROUP, INC.; *U.S. Public*, pg. 1140
MOVADO GROUP INC.—Movado Group, Inc.; *U.S. Public*, pg. 1140
N.A. TRADING LTD.—Movado Group, Inc.; *U.S. Public*, pg. 1140
NINTENDO OF AMERICA—Nintendo Company, Ltd.; *Int'l*, pg. 932
ONEIDA FOODSERVICE DIVISION—Oneida Ltd.; *U.S. Public*, pg. 1226
ONEIDA LTD.; *U.S. Public*, pg. 1225
PRECIOUS METALS MANAGEMENT—Engelhard Corporation; *U.S. Public*, pg. 582
REPUBLIC NEW YORK CORPORATION; *U.S. Public*, pg. 1380
RIGHT IDEAS INC.; *U.S. Private*, pg. 930
ROLEX INDUSTRIES, INC.—Rolex Watch Co. SA; *Int'l*, pg. 1126
ROLEX WATCH U.S.A., INC.—Rolex Watch Co. SA; *Int'l*, pg. 1126
ROYAL COPENHAGEN & GEORG JENSEN PTY. LTD.—Royal Copenhagen A/S; *Int'l*, pg. 1135
ROYAL COPENHAGEN A/S; *Int'l*, pg. 1134
ROYAL COPENHAGEN HAWAII, INC.—Royal Copenhagen A/S; *Int'l*, pg. 1134
ROYAL COPENHAGEN (HONG KONG) LTD.—Royal Copenhagen A/S; *Int'l*, pg. 1135
ROYAL COPENHAGEN JAPAN LTD.—Royal Copenhagen A/S; *Int'l*, pg. 1135
ROYAL COPENHAGEN LTD.—Royal Copenhagen A/S; *Int'l*, pg. 1135
ROYAL COPENHAGEN NORGE A/S—Royal Copenhagen A/S; *Int'l*, pg. 1135
ROYAL COPENHAGEN SINGAPORE PTE. LTD.—Royal Copenhagen A/S; *Int'l*, pg. 1135
SMH BELGIUM SA—SMH Swiss Corporation for Micro Electronics & Watchmaking Indus. Ltd.; *Int'l*, pg. 1161
SCOTIAMOCATTA—The Bank of Nova Scotia; *Int'l*, pg. 156
SEIKO CANADA INC.—Seiko Corporation; *Int'l*, pg. 1218
SEIKO CORPORATION OF AMERICA—Seiko Corporation; *Int'l*, pg. 1218
SILVER TOWNE L.P.; *U.S. Private*, pg. 1000
SOUTHERN WATCH & CLOCK SUPPLIES LTD.—Lonrho plc; *Int'l*, pg. 817
SWATCH WATCH U.S.A.—SMH Swiss Corporation for Micro Electronics & Watchmaking Indus. Ltd.; *Int'l*, pg. 1161
SWISS ARMY BRANDS, INC.; *U.S. Public*, pg. 1544
SWISS ARMY BRANDS LTD.—Swiss Army Brands, Inc.; *U.S. Public*, pg. 1544
SWISS PRESTIGE, INC.—Jaeger-Le Coultre; *Int'l*, pg. 697
TIFFANY & CO.; *U.S. Public*, pg. 1608
UETA, INC.—BAA plc; *Int'l*, pg. 103
VAN CLEEF & ARPELS, INC.; *U.S. Private*, pg. 1132
WAL-MART JEWELRY DIV.—Wal-Mart Stores, Inc.; *U.S. Public*, pg. 1733
HARRY WINSTON, INC.; *U.S. Private*, pg. 1183
WORLD PACIFIC ULLENBERG CORP.—IWI Holding Limited; *U.S. Public*, pg. 861

5099 — WHOLESALE DURABLE GOODS, NEC

A&M RECORDS—Philips Electronics N.V.; *Int'l*, pg. 1052
ABITIBI-CONSOLIDATED PAPER SALES CORPORATION—Abitibi-Consolidated Inc.; *Int'l*, pg. 20
AKOM LTD.—Tultex Corporation; *U.S. Public*, pg. 1644
ALLMAC LUMBER LTD.—E.R. Probyn Ltd.; *Int'l*, pg. 1071
ANGLO AMERICAN CORPORATION OF SOUTH AFRICA LIMITED (LONDON)—Anglo American Corporation of South Africa Limited; *Int'l*, pg. 77
AUDIO CLUB OF NEW ZEALAND LTD.—Philips Electronics N.V.; *Int'l*, pg. 1052
AUSTIN POWDER CO.; *U.S. Private*, pg. 100
BEADLES LUMBER COMPANY, INC.; *U.S. Private*, pg. 126
P.T. BERNADI UTAMA SK—Internatio-Muller N.V.; *Int'l*, pg. 681
BLEVINS INC.; *U.S. Private*, pg. 149
BRENTWOOD BENSON PUBLISHING GROUP—Zomba Recording Corp.; *Int'l*, pg. 1529
BRIDGEWATER PAPER LIMITED—Abitibi-Consolidated Inc.; *Int'l*, pg. 20
BRITANNIA MUSIC CO. LTD.—Philips Electronics N.V.; *Int'l*, pg. 1052
BUCKA, SPIERO COMERCIO INDUSTRIA E IMPORTACAO LTDA./WALTER KIDDE S.A. INDUSTRIA E COMERCIO—Hanson PLC; *Int'l*, pg. 594
BURNS PHILP COMPANY OF SAN FRANCISCO—Burns, Philp & Company Limited; *Int'l*, pg. 236
CSR LIMITED; *Int'l*, pg. 245
CAMELOT MUSIC, INC.; *U.S. Private*, pg. 203
CAPITOL INDUSTRIES-EMI INC.—EMI Group plc; *Int'l*, pg. 427
CASIO CANADA, LTD.—Casio Computer Co., Ltd.; *Int'l*, pg. 274
CASIO, INC.—Casio Computer Co., Ltd.; *Int'l*, pg. 274
CLUBE DE SUCESSOS—Philips Electronics N.V.; *Int'l*, pg. 1052
COMPAGNIE PHONOGRAPHIQUE FRANCAISE BARCLAY—Philips Electronics N.V.; *Int'l*, pg. 1053
CRONATRON WELDING SYSTEMS, INC.—Lawson Products, Inc.; *U.S. Public*, pg. 980
CULP, INC.; *U.S. Public*, pg. 467
D&H DISTRIBUTING COMPANY; *U.S. Private*, pg. 300
D.I.A.L. DIFFUSION INTERNATIONALE D'ARTS ET LOISIRS S.A.—Philips Electronics N.V.; *Int'l*, pg. 1052
DE BEERS CONSOLIDATED MINES LIMITED—Anglo American Corporation of South Africa Limited; *Int'l*, pg. 76
DIAMOND HILL PLYWOOD COMPANY—Darlington Veneer Company; *U.S. Private*, pg. 311
A/S DIRECT—Philips Electronics N.V.; *Int'l*, pg. 1052
DISCOS DE CENTRO AMERICA—Philips Electronics N.V.; *Int'l*, pg. 1052
THE WALT DISNEY COMPANY (CANADA)—The Walt Disney Company; *U.S. Public*, pg. 514
DISPOSABLE SAFETY WEAR INC.—Eastco Industrial Safety Corp.; *U.S. Public*, pg. 548
DOMINION VERTRIEBS, G.M.B.H.—K-Tel International, Inc.; *U.S. Public*, pg. 938
EASTCO INDUSTRIAL SAFETY CORP.; *U.S. Public*, pg. 548
ELVY PTY. LTD.—Philips Electronics N.V.; *Int'l*, pg. 1052
ENESCO CORPORATION—Stanhome Inc.; *U.S. Public*, pg. 1508
ENESCO IMPORT, GMBH—Stanhome Inc.; *U.S. Public*, pg. 1508
ENSO AG—Enso Oyj; *Int'l*, pg. 457
EUROKASCO—Bairnco Corporation; *U.S. Public*, pg. 165
EVA-TONE INC.; *U.S. Private*, pg. 384
FONOGRAM S.A.—Philips Electronics N.V.; *Int'l*, pg. 1052
FUKADA-KIDDE CO., LTD.—Hanson PLC; *Int'l*, pg. 594
GAS ENERGIA S.P.A.—ENI S.p.A.; *Int'l*, pg. 428
GEORGIA-PACIFIC GMBH—Georgia-Pacific Corporation; *U.S. Public*, pg. 739
GEORGIA-PACIFIC INTERNATIONAL CORP.—Georgia-Pacific Corporation; *U.S. Public*, pg. 739
GRAMMOPHON SPEZIALHAUS SCHALLPLATTEN-EINZELHANDELS-GESELLSCHAFT MBH—Philips Electronics N.V.; *Int'l*, pg. 1052
GRINNELL CANADA LTD.—Tyco International Ltd.; *U.S. Public*, pg. 1651
H & C TIMBER & BUILDING SUPPLIES LTD.—Harrisons & Crosfield plc; *Int'l*, pg. 598
HACH EUROPE, S.A./N.V.—Hach Company; *U.S. Public*, pg. 773
HANDLEMAN COMPANY; *U.S. Public*, pg. 779
HANWA AMERICAN CORP.—Hanwa Co., Ltd.; *Int'l*, pg. 595
HANWA CO., LTD.; *Int'l*, pg. 595
HARCROS TIMBER AUSTRALIA PTY. LTD.—Harrisons & Crosfield plc; *Int'l*, pg. 599
HARDWARE WHOLESALERS, INC.; *U.S. Private*, pg. 502
HENSON TIMBER PRODUCTS CORP.—Stonecutter Mills Corp.; *U.S. Private*, pg. 1044
HOME COMPUTER SOFTWARE DIV.—Handleman Company; *U.S. Public*, pg. 779
HYOSUNG GROUP; *Int'l*, pg. 640
ICI FRANCE SA—Imperial Chemical Industries PLC; *Int'l*, pg. 665
ICI (PHILIPPINES) INC.—Imperial Chemical Industries PLC; *Int'l*, pg. 665
ICI (SINGAPORE) PRIVATE LIMITED—Imperial Chemical Industries PLC; *Int'l*, pg. 665
ICI (SWITZERLAND) AG—Imperial Chemical Industries PLC; *Int'l*, pg. 665
ICI ZAMBIA LIMITED—Imperial Chemical Industries PLC; *Int'l*, pg. 665
ITOCHU SHOE CO., INC.—Itochu Corporation; *Int'l*, pg. 695
IGGESUND TIMBER AB SCANDINAVIA—Mo och Domsjo AB; *Int'l*, pg. 886
IGGESUND TIMBER SALES LTD.—Mo och Domsjo AB; *Int'l*, pg. 886
IMPACT—Philips Electronics N.V.; *Int'l*, pg. 1052
P.T. INDONESIA TORAY SYNTHETICS—Mitsui & Co., Ltd.; *Int'l*, pg. 882
INGRAM LIBRARY SERVICES, INC.—Ingram Industries Inc.; *U.S. Private*, pg. 563
INMOBILIARIA TECHNICA INDUSTRIAL, S.A.—Baldwin Piano & Organ Company; *U.S. Public*, pg. 169
INTERNATIONAL LEARNING SYSTEMS (JAPAN) LTD.—Berlitz International, Inc.; *U.S. Public*, pg. 222
JACKPOT GAMING, INC.—Jackpot Enterprises, Inc.; *U.S. Public*, pg. 920
JAYDON INCORPORATED; *U.S. Private*, pg. 584
K-TEL DIRECT, INC.—K-Tel International, Inc.; *U.S. Public*, pg. 938
K-TEL ENTERTAINMENT (CAN) INC.—K-Tel International, Inc.; *U.S. Public*, pg. 938
K-TEL ENTERTAINMENT (U.K.) LTD.—K-Tel International, Inc.; *U.S. Public*, pg. 938
K-TEL INTERNATIONAL FINLAND O.Y.—K-Tel International, Inc.; *U.S. Public*, pg. 938
K-TEL INTERNATIONAL, INC.; *U.S. Public*, pg. 937
K-TEL INTERNATIONAL (USA) INC.—K-Tel International, Inc.; *U.S. Public*, pg. 938
K-TEL IRELAND LTD.—K-Tel International, Inc.; *U.S. Public*, pg. 938
KAMAN CORPORATION; *U.S. Public*, pg. 941
KAMAN MUSIC CORP.—Kaman Corporation; *U.S. Public*, pg. 942
KAWAI AMERICA CORPORATION—Kawai Musical Instruments Mfg. Co., Ltd.; *Int'l*, pg. 725
KAWAI MUSICAL INSTRUMENTS MFG. CO., LTD.; *Int'l*, pg. 725
KESKO LTD.; *Int'l*, pg. 732
THE WALTER KIDDE CO. LTD.—Hanson PLC; *Int'l*, pg. 593
KOREAN AMERICAN MUSICAL INSTRUMENT CORPORATION—Baldwin Piano & Organ Company; *U.S. Public*, pg. 169
LABATT FOOD SERVICE; *U.S. Private*, pg. 641
G. LEBLANC CORPORATION; *U.S. Private*, pg. 656
LES BOIS DE LA BALTIQUE SA—Mo och Domsjo AB; *Int'l*, *pg. 886*
LES BOIS DE LA BALTIQUE SA (ROCHEFORT)—Mo och Domsjo AB; *Int'l*, pg. 886
LONDON RECORDS—Philips Electronics N.V.; *Int'l*, pg. 1052
LOUIS VUITTON NORTH AMERICA, INC.—LVMH Moet Hennessy Louis Vuitton; *Int'l*, pg. 781
MATHER & PLATT WORMALD S.A.—Tyco International Ltd.; *U.S. Public*, pg. 1650
MICHAEL & CO (MICO) TONTRAGER VERTIEBS-GESELLSCHAFT MBH—Philips Electronics N.V.; *Int'l*, pg. 1052
MODO PAPER AG—Mo och Domsjo AB; *Int'l*, pg. 887
MODOCELL FRANCE S.A.R.L.—Mo och Domsjo AB; *Int'l*, pg. 887
MONZINO S.P.A.; *Int'l*, pg. 888
NATIONAL BOOK DISTRIBUTORS—Handleman Company; *U.S. Public*, pg. 780
NATIONAL WELDERS SUPPLY CO. INC.; *U.S. Private*, pg. 788
NIPPON PAPER INDUSTRIES COMPANY LIMITED VANCOUVER OFFICE—Nippon Paper Industries Company Limited; *Int'l*, pg. 938
NIPPON PHONOGRAM CO. LTD.—Philips Electronics N.V.; *Int'l*, pg. 1052
NISSHO IWAI AUSTRALIA LTD.—Nissho Iwai Corporation; *Int'l*, pg. 948
NOORD-EUROPESE HOUTIMPORT BV—Mo och Domsjo AB; *Int'l*, pg. 886
NORTH ARKANSAS WHOLESALE CO., INC.—Wal-Mart Stores, Inc.; *U.S. Public*, pg. 1733
NOVARTIS SEEDS, INC.—Novartis AG; *Int'l*, pg. 974
OAKITE PRODUCTS, INC.—Metallgesellschaft AG; *Int'l*, pg. 861
ORBEA ARGENTINA SOCIEDAD ANONIMA—Imperial Chemical Industries PLC; *Int'l*, pg. 665
ORR SAFETY COMPANY; *U.S. Private*, pg. 820
OSHMAN'S SPORTING GOODS, INC.; *U.S. Public*, pg. 1233
OVERHOLTZER CHURCH FURNITURE, INC.; *U.S. Private*, *pg. 823*
PACIFIC LUMBER & SHIPPING CO.; *U.S. Private*, pg. 832

PAUL-SON GAMING CORPORATION; *U.S. Public*, pg. 1265
PHONOGRAM AG—Philips Electronics N.V.; *Int'l*, pg. 1052
PHONOGRAM B.V.—Philips Electronics N.V.; *Int'l*, pg. 1052
PHONOGRAM GMBH—Philips Electronics N.V.; *Int'l*, pg. 1052
PHONOGRAM INTERNATIONAL B.V.—Philips Electronics N.V.; *Int'l*, pg. 1052
PHONOGRAM S.A.—Philips Electronics N.V.; *Int'l*, pg. 1052
PHONOGRAM S.A.I.C.—Philips Electronics N.V.; *Int'l*, pg. 1052
POCAHONTAS DEVELOPMENT CORPORATION—Norfolk Southern Corporation; *U.S. Public*, pg. 1192
POLARIS INDUSTRIES, INC.; *U.S. Public*, pg. 1313
POLYDOR AB—Philips Electronics N.V.; *Int'l*, pg. 1052
POLYDOR B.V.—Philips Electronics N.V.; *Int'l*, pg. 1052
POLYDOR INC.—Philips Electronics N.V.; *Int'l*, pg. 1052
POLYDOR INTERNATIONAL GMBH—Philips Electronics N.V.; *Int'l*, pg. 1052
POLYDOR K.K.—Philips Electronics N.V.; *Int'l*, pg. 1052
POLYDOR S.A.—Philips Electronics N.V.; *Int'l*, pg. 1053
POLYGRAM DIRECT MARKETING AND TRADING—Philips Electronics N.V.; *Int'l*, pg. 1053
POLYGRAM DIRECT MARKETING AUSTRALASIA—Philips Electronics N.V.; *Int'l*, pg. 1053
POLYGRAM DIRECT MARKETING SCANDINAVIA ORGANIZATION—Philips Electronics N.V.; *Int'l*, pg. 1053
POLYGRAM DISCHI S.P.A.—Philips Electronics N.V.; *Int'l*, pg. 1053
POLYGRAM DISCO S.A.—Philips Electronics N.V.; *Int'l*, pg. 1053
POLYGRAM DO BRAZIL—Philips Electronics N.V.; *Int'l*, pg. 1053
POLYGRAM INC.—Philips Electronics N.V.; *Int'l*, pg. 1053
POLYGRAM INTERNATIONAL LTD.—Philips Electronics N.V.; *Int'l*, pg. 1053
POLYGRAM N.V.—Philips Electronics N.V.; *Int'l*, pg. 1051
POLYGRAM RECORD SERVICE B.V.—Philips Electronics N.V.; *Int'l*, pg. 1052
POLYGRAM RECORD SERVICE GMBH—Philips Electronics N.V.; *Int'l*, pg. 1053
POLYGRAM RECORD SERVICE K.K.—Philips Electronics N.V.; *Int'l*, pg. 1053
POLYGRAM RECORD SERVICES GES. MBH—Philips Electronics N.V.; *Int'l*, pg. 1053
POLYGRAM RECORDS AB—Philips Electronics N.V.; *Int'l*, pg. 1053
POLYGRAM RECORDS, INC.—Philips Electronics N.V.; *Int'l*, pg. 1052
POLYGRAM RECORDS LTD.—Philips Electronics N.V.; *Int'l*, pg. 1053
POLYGRAM RECORDS PTY. LTD.—Philips Electronics N.V.; *Int'l*, pg. 1053
POLYGRAM RECORDS S.A.—Philips Electronics N.V.; *Int'l*, pg. 1053
POLYGRAM S.A. DE C.V.—Philips Electronics N.V.; *Int'l*, pg. 1053
POLYSTAR CO. LTD.—Philips Electronics N.V.; *Int'l*, pg. 1053
PRESTIGE AB (SCANDINAVIAN MUSIC CLUB)—Philips Electronics N.V.; *Int'l*, pg. 1053
PRO MUSICA MUSIK-UND KUNSTVERSAND GMBH—Philips Electronics N.V.; *Int'l*, pg. 1053
PUERTO RICO SAFETY CORPORATION—Eastco Industrial Safety Corp.; *U.S. Public*, pg. 548
RADICA USA LIMITED; *U.S. Private*, pg. 906
RAVENNA ARSENAL, INC.—Olin Corporation; *U.S. Public*, pg. 1219
RECORD RACK SCHALLPLATTEN VERTRIEBSGESELLSCHAFT MBH—Philips Electronics N.V.; *Int'l*, pg. 1053
RIGHT IDEAS INC.; *U.S. Private*, pg. 930
RINNAI AMERICA CORP.—Rinnai Corp.; *Int'l*, pg. 1118
SA-SO COMPANY; *U.S. Private*, pg. 955
SAS TRADING—Scandinavian Airlines System (SAS); *Int'l*, pg. 1202
ST. ANNE INDUSTRIES LTD.—Parsons & Whittemore, Inc.; *U.S. Private*, pg. 841
ST. ANNE PULP SALES CO. LTD.—Parsons & Whittemore, Inc.; *U.S. Private*, pg. 841
ST. LOUIS MUSIC, INC.; *U.S. Private*, pg. 960
SAVAL N.V.—Internatio-Muller N.V.; *Int'l*, pg. 681
SCANDINAVIAN AIRLINES SYSTEM (SAS); *Int'l*, pg. 1201
SCHLEGEL NORTH AMERICAN AUTOMOTIVE OPERATIONS—BTR plc; *Int'l*, pg. 128
THE SCORE BOARD, INC.; *U.S. Public*, pg. 1444
SERVCO PACIFIC INC.; *U.S. Private*, pg. 986
SKYWAY LUGGAGE CO.; *U.S. Private*, pg. 1005
STANHOME INC.; *U.S. Public*, pg. 1508
STAR VIDEO ENTERTAINMENT, L.P.—Valley Record Distributors, Inc.; *U.S. Private*, pg. 1132
TSC FILM DISTRIBUTION—TSC Shannock Corporation; *Int'l*, pg. 1343
TSC SHANNOCK CORPORATION; *Int'l*, pg. 1343
TSC SHANNOCK CORPORATION—TSC Shannock Corporation; *Int'l*, pg. 1343
TELEDYNE LAARS—Allegheny Teledyne Incorporated; *U.S. Public*, pg. 43
TORNE-JOTUN S.A.—Jotun A/S; *Int'l*, pg. 716
TRAX MUSIC VISION LTD.—TSC Shannock Corporation; *Int'l*, pg. 1343
UAC INTERNATIONAL LTD.—Unilever Plc; *Int'l*, pg. 1434
UNOCO—The Walt Disney Company; *U.S. Public*, pg. 514
VJ GROWERS, INC.; *U.S. Private*, pg. 1130
VV-AUTO OY—Kesko Ltd.; *Int'l*, pg. 732
VALLEN CORPORATION; *U.S. Public*, pg. 1705
VALLEY RECORD DISTRIBUTORS, INC.; *U.S. Private*, pg. 1132
VANPORT MANUFACTURING, INC.; *U.S. Private*, pg. 1134
VARIETY MUSIC CORP. S.A.—Philips Electronics N.V.; *Int'l*, pg. 1053
VIDEO TREASURES—Handleman Company; *U.S. Public*, pg. 780
VIKING ENTERTAINMENT—Handleman Company; *U.S. Public*, pg. 780
WOOD COLONY MILLWORKS—Overholtzer Church Furniture, Inc.; *U.S. Private*, pg. 823
WOOD EXPORT NEW ZEALAND (1986) LIMITED—International Paper Company; *U.S. Public*, pg. 905
WORMALD FIRE SYSTEMS AB—Tyco International Ltd.; *U.S. Public*, pg. 1650
THE ZAMOISKI CO.; *U.S. Private*, pg. 1203
ZENECA AB—Zeneca Group Plc; *Int'l*, pg. 1526
ZENECA HELLAS S.A.—Zeneca Group Plc; *Int'l*, pg. 1526
ZENECA OY—Zeneca Group Plc; *Int'l*, pg. 1527
ZENECA POLAND SP. Z.O.O.—Zeneca Group Plc; *Int'l*, pg. 1527
ZENECA ZIMBABWE (PRIVATE) LIMITED—Zeneca Group Plc; *Int'l*, pg. 1527
ZERO CORPORATION; *U.S. Public*, pg. 1791

5111 — PRINTING & WRITING PAPER-WHOLESALE

AARNE LAAKSONEN OY—Groupe Saint Louis; *Int'l*, pg. 568
AHLSTROM PAPER AG—A. Ahlstrom Corporation; *Int'l*, pg. 35
THE AILING & CORY COMPANY—Union Camp Corporation; *U.S. Public*, pg. 1666
ALCOR ENVELOPE CO.—Union Camp Corporation; *U.S. Public*, pg. 1666
THE ALLAN & GRAY CO.—Union Camp Corporation; *U.S. Public*, pg. 1666
ALTO PAPERS COMPANY—Bradner Central Company; *U.S. Private*, pg. 164
ARJO WIGGINS FINLAND HOLDINGS—Groupe Saint Louis; *Int'l*, pg. 567
ARJO WIGGINS INTERSERVICES S.A.—Groupe Saint Louis; *Int'l*, pg. 568
ATHENS PAPER CO. INC.; *U.S. Private*, pg. 94
ATHENS PAPER CO., INC.—Athens Paper Co. Inc.; *U.S. Private*, pg. 94
B.J. (N.Z.) LIMITED—International Paper Company; *U.S. Public*, pg. 905
BARTON NELSON EUROPE B.V.—Barton Nelson Inc.; *U.S. Private*, pg. 120
BARTON NELSON INC.; *U.S. Private*, pg. 120
BLEYCO PAPER CO. OF MICHIGAN—A.W. Mendenhall Co., Inc.; *U.S. Private*, pg. 731
BOISE CASCADE CORPORATION; *U.S. Public*, pg. 242
BOISE CASCADE OFFICE PRODUCTS CORPORATION—Boise Cascade Corporation; *U.S. Public*, pg. 243
BRADNER CENTRAL COMPANY; *U.S. Private*, pg. 164
BRADNER SMITH & CO.—Bradner Central Company; *U.S. Private*, pg. 164
BRODARD ET TAUPIN—Lagardere Groupe; *Int'l*, pg. 792
BUHRMANN-UBBENS PAPIER BV—N.V. Koninklijke KNP BT; *Int'l*, pg. 756
BUHRMANN-VROMEN VERPAKKING BV—N.V. Koninklijke KNP BT; *Int'l*, pg. 756
BUNZL DISTRIBUTION USA INC.—Bunzl PLC; *Int'l*, pg. 233
CS CARTIERA DEL NORD S.R.L.—Groupe Saint Louis; *Int'l*, pg. 567
CARTER RICE—International Paper Company; *U.S. Public*, pg. 903
CASTLE & OVERTON—Haindl Papier GmbH; *Int'l*, pg. 586
CENTRAL LEWMAR; *U.S. Private*, pg. 223
CENTRAL LEWMAR TRENTON DIVISION—Central Lewmar; *U.S. Private*, pg. 223
CENTRAL NATIONAL-GOTTESMAN INC.; *U.S. Private*, pg. 224
THE CINCINNATI CORDAGE & PAPER COMPANY; *U.S. Private*, pg. 239
A.T. CLAYTON & COMPANY, INC.; *U.S. Private*, pg. 244
COLE PAPERS INC.; *U.S. Private*, pg. 251
S.A. COMPTOIR FINLANDAIS N.V.—Enso Oyj; *Int'l*, pg. 457
COPAP—Enso Oyj; *Int'l*, pg. 457
DANKA BUSINESS SYSTEMS—Danka Business Systems PLC; *Int'l*, pg. 379
DEUTSCHMANN & ROELANTS BV—N.V. Koninklijke KNP BT; *Int'l*, pg. 756
DIAMETER PAPER CO.—Bradner Central Company; *U.S. Private*, pg. 165
DILLARD, A RESOURCENET INTERNATIONAL COMPANY—International Paper Company; *U.S. Public*, pg. 901
DIXON PAPER CO.—International Paper Company; *U.S. Public*, pg. 902
ENSO AG—Enso Oyj; *Int'l*, pg. 457
ENSO DANMARK A/S—Enso Oyj; *Int'l*, pg. 457
ENSO (DEUTSCHLAND) GMBH—Enso Oyj; *Int'l*, pg. 457
ENSO-EUROCAN-BUMJIN CO. LTD.—Enso Oyj; *Int'l*, pg. 457
ENSO-EUROCAN FAR EAST CO. LTD.—Enso Oyj; *Int'l*, pg. 457
ENSO-EUROCAN HONG KONG LTD.—Enso Oyj; *Int'l*, pg. 457
ENSO-EUROCAN SOUTH EAST ASIA PTE. LTD.—Enso Oyj; *Int'l*, pg. 457
ENSO FRANCE S.A.—Enso Oyj; *Int'l*, pg. 457
ENSO (HOLLAND) B.V.—Enso Oyj; *Int'l*, pg. 457
ENSO IBERICA S.A.—Enso Oyj; *Int'l*, pg. 457
ENSO INTERNATIONAL, INC.—Enso Oyj; *Int'l*, pg. 457
ENSO MARKETING CO. LTD.—Enso Oyj; *Int'l*, pg. 457
ENSO OYJ; *Int'l*, pg. 455
ENSO PORTUGAL LDA.—Enso Oyj; *Int'l*, pg. 457
ENSO PRESSE DRUCK VERTRIEB GMBH—Enso Oyj; *Int'l*, pg. 457
ENSO PUBLICATION PAPERS LIMITED—Enso Oyj; *Int'l*, pg. 457
EPACAR NV—N.V. Koninklijke KNP BT; *Int'l*, pg. 757
EUROFINN SERVICES—Enso Oyj; *Int'l*, pg. 458
FINS VERKOOPKANTOOR—Enso Oyj; *Int'l*, pg. 458
FIRST STATE PAPER, INC.—Central Lewmar; *U.S. Private*, pg. 223
FOUAD & TOUFIC FADEL & CO.—Enso Oyj; *Int'l*, pg. 458
FRASER PAPER LIMITED—EdperBrascan Corporation; *Int'l*, pg. 434
FUNDING SERVICES INC.—Danka Business Systems PLC; *Int'l*, pg. 379
THE GIBSON GROUP INC.; *U.S. Private*, pg. 451
GOULD MIDWEST, INC.—Stephen Gould Paper Co., Inc.; *U.S. Private*, pg. 467
GOULD PAPER CORPORATION OF NEW YORK, INC.—Stephen Gould Paper Co., Inc.; *U.S. Private*, pg. 467
GOULD PAPER INC/MIDHUDSON DIV.—Stephen Gould Paper Co., Inc.; *U.S. Private*, pg. 467
GOULD PAPER OF FLORIDA, INC.—Stephen Gould Paper Co., Inc.; *U.S. Private*, pg. 467
GOULD SOUTHERN—Stephen Gould Paper Co., Inc.; *U.S. Private*, pg. 467
STEPHEN GOULD OF INDIANA, INC.—Stephen Gould Paper Co., Inc.; *U.S. Private*, pg. 467
STEPHEN GOULD OF MICHIGAN, INC.—Stephen Gould Paper Co., Inc.; *U.S. Private*, pg. 467
STEPHEN GOULD OF OHIO, CORP.—Stephen Gould Paper Co., Inc.; *U.S. Private*, pg. 467
GRABNER PACIFIC CO.—Bradner Central Company; *U.S. Private*, pg. 165
GREAT NORTHERN PAPER, INC.—Bowater Incorporated; *U.S. Public*, pg. 248
GROUPE SAINT LOUIS; *Int'l*, pg. 567
ELOF HANSSON INC.—Elof Hansson AB; *Int'l*, pg. 595
HASELDONCKX SA—Groupe Saint Louis; *Int'l*, pg. 567
HENLEY PAPER COMPANY; *U.S. Private*, pg. 522
HOLMEN BELGIUM NV/SA—Mo och Domsjo AB; *Int'l*, pg. 885
HOLMEN ESPANA S.A. (MODO IBERICA SA)—Mo och Domsjo AB; *Int'l*, pg. 885
HOLMEN MD S.R.L.—Mo och Domsjo AB; *Int'l*, pg. 885
HOLMEN NEDERLAND B.V.—Mo och Domsjo AB; *Int'l*, pg. 885
HOLMEN PAPER AB—Mo och Domsjo AB; *Int'l*, pg. 885
HOLMEN PAPER LTD.—Mo och Domsjo AB; *Int'l*, pg. 885
HOLMEN PAPERS—Mo och Domsjo AB; *Int'l*, pg. 885
HOLMEN (SCHWEIZ) AG—Mo och Domsjo AB; *Int'l*, pg. 885
HOLMENS BRUK G.M.B.H.—Mo och Domsjo AB; *Int'l*, pg. 885
HORIZON PAPER CO., INC.; *U.S. Private*, pg. 539
HUDSON VALLEY PAPER COMPANY; *U.S. Private*, pg. 546
IBSTOCK PLC; *Int'l*, pg. 658
INGRAM PAPER COMPANY—International Paper Company; *U.S. Public*, pg. 904
JACKSON PAPER COMPANY; *U.S. Private*, pg. 579
KNP BELGIE NV—N.V. Koninklijke KNP BT; *Int'l*, pg. 757
KNP PRESS PAPER NV—N.V. Koninklijke KNP BT; *Int'l*, pg. 757
KIMBERLY-CLARK, WINSLOW—Kimberly-Clark Corporation; *U.S. Public*, pg. 958
KURTZ BROS., INC.; *U.S. Private*, pg. 637
LESLIE-MICHIGAN—International Paper Company; *U.S. Public*, pg. 903
LESLIE PAPER—International Paper Company; *U.S. Public*, pg. 903
LINDENMEYR MUNROE—Central National-Gottesman Inc.; *U.S. Private*, pg. 224
MD HOLMEN AUSTRALIA & NEW ZEALAND PTY. LTD.—Mo och Domsjo AB; *Int'l*, pg. 886
MD PAPER G.M.B.H.—Mo och Domsjo AB; *Int'l*, pg. 886
MAC PAPERS, INC.; *U.S. Private*, pg. 689
MARQUARDT & CO.—Central Lewmar; *U.S. Private*, pg. 223
F.A. MARSDEN LTD.—Georgia-Pacific Corporation; *U.S. Public*, pg. 739
THE MEAD CORPORATION; *U.S. Public*, pg. 1074
D.J. MEAD-HUBBS & HOWE—Sofco-Mead, Inc.; *U.S. Private*, pg. 1012
A.W. MENDENHALL CO., INC.; *U.S. Private*, pg. 731
MIDLAND PAPER CO.; *U.S. Private*, pg. 744
MITSUBISHI CORPORATION; *Int'l*, pg. 871
MO OCH DOMSJO AB; *Int'l*, pg. 885
MODO MERCHANTS AB—Mo och Domsjo AB; *Int'l*, pg. 886
MODO MERCHANTS LTD.—Mo och Domsjo AB; *Int'l*, pg. 886
MODO PAPER BENELUX BV—Mo och Domsjo AB; *Int'l*, pg. 887
MODO PAPER FRANCE—Mo och Domsjo AB; *Int'l*, pg. 887
MODO PAPER ITALIA SRL—Mo och Domsjo AB; *Int'l*, pg. 887
MODO PAPER LTD.—Mo och Domsjo AB; *Int'l*, pg. 887
MODO PAPER PSM—Mo och Domsjo AB; *Int'l*, pg. 887
MODO VAN GELDER—Mo och Domsjo AB; *Int'l*, pg. 886
MODOCELL ITALIA S.R.L.—Mo och Domsjo AB; *Int'l*, pg. 887
MODOCELL LTD.—Mo och Domsjo AB; *Int'l*, pg. 887
THE MUDGE PAPER CO.—International Paper Company; *U.S. Public*, pg. 902
NEW BROOK PAPER—Triangle Marketing Corp.; *U.S. Private*, pg. 1102
NEWELL PAPER CO. OF COLUMBUS—Jackson Paper Company; *U.S. Private*, pg. 579
NEWELL PAPER CO. OF MERIDIAN—Jackson Paper Company; *U.S. Private*, pg. 579
NORSKE SKOG PORTUGAL, LDA—Norske Skogindustrier A.S; *Int'l*, pg. 966
NORSKE SKOG SALES AS—Norske Skogindustrier A.S; *Int'l*, pg. 965
NORSKE SKOG TRADING FAR EAST PTE. LTD.—Norske Skogindustrier A.S; *Int'l*, pg. 966
PAPER AGENCIES (AUST.) PTY. LTD.—Enso Oyj; *Int'l*, pg. 458

PAPER AGENTS LTD.—Norske Skogindustrier A.S; *Int'l*, pg. 966
OY PAPERI-DAHLBERG AB—UPM-Kymmene Corporation; *Int'l*, pg. 1428
PAPETERIES DE MONTEVRAIN SA—Groupe Saint Louis; *Int'l*, pg. 567
PAPETERIES LIBERT BV—N.V. Koninklijke KNP BT; *Int'l*, pg. 756
BV PAPIERGROOTHANDEL V/H RIEM & HONIG—N.V. Koninklijke KNP BT; *Int'l*, pg. 756
PERKINS-GOODWIN CO. INC.—Haindl Papier GmbH; *Int'l*, pg. 586
PREDSTAVEITLSTVO FIRMY "ENSO"—Enso Oyj; *Int'l*, pg. 458
QUAIFE PAPERS, LTD.—Groupe Saint Louis; *Int'l*, pg. 567
QUALITY PARK PRODUCTS—Mail-Well Inc.; *U.S. Public*, pg. 1038
RESOURCE NET INTERNATIONAL—International Paper Company; *U.S. Public*, pg. 903
RESOURCENET INTERNATIONAL—International Paper Company; *U.S. Public*, pg. 903
S.F. RICHARDS CO.—Genuine Parts Company; *U.S. Public*, pg. 732
RIS PAPER COMPANY; *U.S. Private*, pg. 932
ROLLAND INC., DISTRIBUTION DIVISION—The Cascades Group; *Int'l*, pg. 273
ROTARY PAPER MANIFOLD CO.—Bradner Central Company; *U.S. Private*, pg. 165
SAMAB CIA. INDUSTRIA E COMERCIO DE PAPEL—Enso Oyj; *Int'l*, pg. 458
SCALDIA-BUHRMANN NV—N.V. Koninklijke KNP BT; *Int'l*, pg. 757
SEAMAN-PATRICK PAPER COMPANY; *U.S. Private*, pg. 979
SEATTLE PACKAGING CORPORATION; *U.S. Private*, pg. 980
W.H. SMITH GROUP PLC; *Int'l*, pg. 1264
SOCIETE MEDITERRANEENNE D'EMBALLAGES—International Paper Company; *U.S. Public*, pg. 906
SOCIETE NORMANDE DE CARTON ONDULE—International Paper Company; *U.S. Public*, pg. 906
SOCIETE ROANNAISE DES PAPIERS S.A.—Groupe Saint Louis; *Int'l*, pg. 567
SOMERSET MILL—Sappi Limited; *Int'l*, pg. 1193
STUART HALL CO., INC.—Newell Co.; *U.S. Public*, pg. 1178
SUNDAGARDAR LTD.—Norske Skogindustrier A.S; *Int'l*, pg. 966
SVENSKT PAPPER AB—Mo och Domsjo AB; *Int'l*, pg. 886
TSP INC.—Enso Oyj; *Int'l*, pg. 457
TRIANGLE MARKETING CORP.; *U.S. Private*, pg. 1102
TRICOM PAPER INTERNATIONAL B.V.—N.V. Koninklijke KNP BT; *Int'l*, pg. 756
UPM-KYMMENE CANADA—UPM-Kymmene Corporation; *Int'l*, pg. 1430
UPM-KYMMENE FRANCE S.A.—UPM-Kymmene Corporation; *Int'l*, pg. 1430
UPM-KYMMENE PAPIR A/S—UPM-Kymmene Corporation; *Int'l*, pg. 1430
UPM-KYMMENE UK PLC-NORTHERN OFFICE—UPM-Kymmene Corporation; *Int'l*, pg. 1431
UNISOURCE—Unisource Worldwide, Inc.; *U.S. Public*, pg. 1671
UNISOURCE (MIDWEST REGION)—Unisource Worldwide, Inc.; *U.S. Public*, pg. 1671
UNISOURCE (NORTH EAST)—Unisource Worldwide, Inc.; *U.S. Public*, pg. 1671
UNISOURCE (S.E. REGIONAL OFFICE)—Unisource Worldwide, Inc.; *U.S. Public*, pg. 1671
UNISOURCE (WEST REGION)—Unisource Worldwide, Inc.; *U.S. Public*, pg. 1671
UNISOURCE WORLDWIDE, INC.; *U.S. Public*, pg. 1670
UNITED STATIONERS INC.; *U.S. Public*, pg. 1689
UNITED STATIONERS SUPPLY CO.—United Stationers Inc.; *U.S. Public*, pg. 1689
VRG BELGIE NV—N.V. Koninklijke KNP BT; *Int'l*, pg. 757
Z.N. VALMAS & CO.—Enso Oyj; *Int'l*, pg. 458
WWF PAPER CORPORATION; *U.S. Private*, pg. 1145
S.D. WARREN CO.—Sappi Limited; *Int'l*, pg. 1193
WEBSOURCE—Unisource Worldwide, Inc.; *U.S. Public*, pg. 1671
WESTVACO ASIA, K.K.—Westvaco Corporation; *U.S. Public*, pg. 1762
WESTVACO CANADA, LTD.—Westvaco Corporation; *U.S. Public*, pg. 1762
WESTVACO EUROPE, S.A.—Westvaco Corporation; *U.S. Public*, pg. 1762
WESTVACO HONG KONG, LTD.—Westvaco Corporation; *U.S. Public*, pg. 1763
WESTVACO PACIFIC PTY. LTD.—Westvaco Corporation; *U.S. Public*, pg. 1763
WESTVACO WORLDWIDE DISTRIBUTION, S.A.—Westvaco Corporation; *U.S. Public*, pg. 1763
WEYERHAEUSER COMPANY; *U.S. Public*, pg. 1764
WIGGINS ARJO ITALIANA SRL—Groupe Saint Louis; *Int'l*, pg. 567
WIGGINS TEAPE (HONG KONG) LTD.—Groupe Saint Louis; *Int'l*, pg. 567
WIGGINS TEAPE PAPER LTD.—Groupe Saint Louis; *Int'l*, pg. 567
WORLDWIDE PAPER FACTORS INC.—Amcor Limited; *Int'l*, pg. 72
ZELLERBACH DIVISION—The Mead Corporation; *U.S. Public*, pg. 1075

5112 — STATIONERY & OFFICE SUPPLIES-WHOLESALE

AARNE LAAKSONEN OY—Groupe Saint Louis; *Int'l*, pg. 568
THE AILING & CORY COMPANY—Union Camp Corporation; *U.S. Public*, pg. 1666
ALDEN ELECTRONICS, INC.—Platinum Equity Holdings, LLC; *U.S. Private*, pg. 872
ALLIED OFFICE SUPPLIES; *U.S. Private*, pg. 39
AMES COLOR FILE DIVISION—Ames Safety Envelope Company, Inc.; *U.S. Private*, pg. 66
AMES SAFETY ENVELOPE COMPANY, INC.; *U.S. Private*, pg. 66
ANDERSON WHOLESALE COMPANY; *U.S. Private*, pg. 73
APPLAUSE INC.; *U.S. Private*, pg. 78
ARJO WIGGINS INTERSERVICES S.A.—Groupe Saint Louis; *Int'l*, pg. 568
ATAPCO CANADA, LTD.—American Trading and Production Corporation; *U.S. Private*, pg. 64
ATAPCO OFFICE PRODUCTS GROUP—American Trading and Production Corporation; *U.S. Private*, pg. 64
AZERTY INCORPORATED—Abitibi-Consolidated Inc.; *Int'l*, pg. 20
BT OFFICE PRODUCTS INTERNATIONAL, INC—N.V. Koninklijke KNP BT; *Int'l*, pg. 756
BT-U.S.A., INC.—N.V. Koninklijke KNP BT; *Int'l*, pg. 756
BVZ GMBH—N.V. Koninklijke KNP BT; *Int'l*, pg. 757
BALTIMORE STATIONERY CO./TOTAL OFFICE; *U.S. Private*, pg. 113
BAT OFFICE PRODUCTS—U.S. Office Products Company; *U.S. Public*, pg. 1686
BIC BENELUX S.A.—Societe BIC S.A.; *Int'l*, pg. 1273
BIC COMMERCIAL S.A.—Societe BIC S.A.; *Int'l*, pg. 1273
BIRLA 3M LTD.—3M; *U.S. Public*, pg. 1606
BOISE CASCADE CORPORATION; *U.S. Public*, pg. 242
BOISE CASCADE OFFICE PRODUCTS CORPORATION—Boise Cascade Corporation; *U.S. Public*, pg. 243
BRODART—Brodart Company; *U.S. Private*, pg. 170
BRODART COMPANY; *U.S. Private*, pg. 170
BUTLER CAPITAL CORP.; *U.S. Private*, pg. 190
CS CARTIERA DEL NORD S.R.L.—Groupe Saint Louis; *Int'l*, pg. 567
THE CAXTON PRINTERS LTD.; *U.S. Private*, pg. 220
CENTRAL LEWMAR; *U.S. Private*, pg. 223
CENTRAL LEWMAR TRENTON DIVISION—Central Lewmar; *U.S. Private*, pg. 223
CHAMPION INDUSTRIES; *U.S. Public*, pg. 333
CHESHIRE—The General Electric Company, p.l.c.; *Int'l*, pg. 545
CLASSIC GMBH—N.V. Koninklijke KNP BT; *Int'l*, pg. 757
COLUMBINE JDS SYSTEMS, INC.—Big Flower Press Holdings, Inc.; *U.S. Public*, pg. 228
S.A. COMPTOIR FINLANDAIS N.V.—Enso Oyj; *Int'l*, pg. 457
COPAP—Enso Oyj; *Int'l*, pg. 457
COPYGRAPHIC HARRIS LTD—N.V. Koninklijke KNP BT; *Int'l*, pg. 757
CORPORATE EXPRESS, INC.; *U.S. Public*, pg. 449
CORPORATE EXPRESS OFFICE PRODUCTS—Corporate Express, Inc.; *U.S. Public*, pg. 449
A.T. CROSS CO.; *U.S. Public*, pg. 460
A.T. CROSS EXPORT CO.—A.T. Cross Co.; *U.S. Public*, pg. 461
CURTIS 1000 EUROPE GMBH—American Business Products, Inc.; *U.S. Public*, pg. 70
DAISYTEK AUSTRALIA PTY. LTD.—Daisytek International Corporation; *U.S. Public*, pg. 477
DAISYTEK (CANADA) INC.—Daisytek International Corporation; *U.S. Public*, pg. 477
DAISYTEK INCORPORATED—Daisytek International Corporation; *U.S. Public*, pg. 477
DAISYTEK INTERNATIONAL CORPORATION; *U.S. Public*, pg. 477
DAISYTEK LATIN AMERICA—Daisytek International Corporation; *U.S. Public*, pg. 477
DATA BUSINESS FORMS—Data Business Forms Limited; *Int'l*, pg. 384
DATA BUSINESS FORMS LIMITED; *Int'l*, pg. 384
DAWN DISTRIBUTORS—Thomas Nelson Inc.; *U.S. Public*, pg. 1168
DIXON PAPER CO.—International Paper Company; *U.S. Public*, pg. 902
EPX; *U.S. Private*, pg. 354
EATON OFFICE SUPPLY CO., INC.; *U.S. Private*, pg. 358
ENSO AG—Enso Oyj; *Int'l*, pg. 457
ENSO DANMARK A/S—Enso Oyj; *Int'l*, pg. 457
ENSO (DEUTSCHLAND) GMBH—Enso Oyj; *Int'l*, pg. 457
ENSO-EUROCAN-BUMJIN CO. LTD.—Enso Oyj; *Int'l*, pg. 457
ENSO-EUROCAN FAR EAST CO. LTD.—Enso Oyj; *Int'l*, pg. 457
ENSO-EUROCAN HONG KONG LTD.—Enso Oyj; *Int'l*, pg. 457
ENSO-EUROCAN SOUTH EAST ASIA PTE. LTD.—Enso Oyj; *Int'l*, pg. 457
ENSO FRANCE S.A.—Enso Oyj; *Int'l*, pg. 457
ENSO (HOLLAND) B.V.—Enso Oyj; *Int'l*, pg. 457
ENSO IBERICA S.A.—Enso Oyj; *Int'l*, pg. 457
ENSO PORTUGAL LDA.—Enso Oyj; *Int'l*, pg. 457
ENSO PRESSE DRUCK VERTRIEB GMBH—Enso Oyj; *Int'l*, pg. 457
ESSELTE AB; *Int'l*, pg. 459
ESSELTE EUROPE—Esselte AB; *Int'l*, pg. 460
ESSELTE METO—Esselte AB; *Int'l*, pg. 460
ESSELTE METO AB—Esselte AB; *Int'l*, pg. 459
ESSELTE SVERIGE AB—Esselte AB; *Int'l*, pg. 459
EUROFINN SERVICES—Enso Oyj; *Int'l*, pg. 458
FINS VERKOOPKANTOOR—Enso Oyj; *Int'l*, pg. 458
FIRST DATA CORPORATION; *U.S. Public*, pg. 630
FORMS & SUPPLY, INC.; *U.S. Private*, pg. 419
FORMULARIOS Y PROCEDIMIENTOS MOORE S.A.—Moore Corporation Limited; *Int'l*, pg. 890
FORMULES D'AFFAIRES DATA—Data Business Forms Limited; *Int'l*, pg. 384
FOUAD & TOUFIC FADEL & CO.—Enso Oyj; *Int'l*, pg. 458
FRASER PAPER LIMITED—EdperBrascan Corporation; *Int'l*, pg. 434
GEHE AG—Franz Haniel & Cie, GmbH; *Int'l*, pg. 591
GIBSON GREETINGS INTERNATIONAL LIMITED—Gibson Greetings, Inc.; *U.S. Public*, pg. 742
GILLETTE DO BRASIL & CIA—The Gillette Company; *U.S. Public*, pg. 744
GILLETTE GROUP ITALY S.R.L.—The Gillette Company; *U.S. Public*, pg. 745
GILLETTE INDUSTRIES, LTD.—The Gillette Company; *U.S. Public*, pg. 745
GILLETTE SOUTH AFRICA LIMITED—The Gillette Company; *U.S. Public*, pg. 745
GILLETTE (SWITZERLAND) AG—The Gillette Company; *U.S. Public*, pg. 745
GRAFFITI OFFICE SUPPLIERS AND PAPER MARKETING LTD.—American Israeli Paper Mills Ltd.; *Int'l*, pg. 75
GROUPE SAINT LOUIS; *Int'l*, pg. 567
HAGEMEYER N.V.—First Pacific Company Limited; *Int'l*, pg. 487
ELOF HANSSON PAPER & BOARD, INC.—Elof Hansson AB; *Int'l*, pg. 595
HARTMANN & CIE GMBH & CO KG—N.V. Koninklijke KNP BT; *Int'l*, pg. 757
HASELDONCKX SA—Groupe Saint Louis; *Int'l*, pg. 567
JOHN HEATH & CO. LIMITED—American Trading and Production Corporation; *U.S. Private*, pg. 64
HENKEL-EYTESA S.A.—Henkel KGaA; *Int'l*, pg. 612
HERMES PRECISA AUSTRALIA PTY LTD.—HPI Holding S.A.; *Int'l*, pg. 579
HUDSON VALLEY PAPER COMPANY; *U.S. Private*, pg. 546
HUNT CANADA—Hunt Corporation; *U.S. Public*, pg. 849
HY-VEE FOOD STORES INCORPORATED; *U.S. Private*, pg. 550
INDIANA RECORDS MANAGERS; *U.S. Private*, pg. 560
KINGFISHER PLC; *Int'l*, pg. 733
KLEER-VU PLASTICS, INC.; *U.S. Public*, pg. 962
KURTZ BROS., INC.; *U.S. Private*, pg. 637
LADY BALTIMORE FOODS, INC.; *U.S. Public*, pg. 975
CHARLES LEONARD, INC.; *U.S. Private*, pg. 660
MARSH COMPANY; *U.S. Private*, pg. 707
MAXI-PAPIER MARKET GMBH—Staples, Inc.; *U.S. Public*, pg. 1510
MILLBANK ELECTRONICS GROUP LTD.—American Trading and Production Corporation; *U.S. Private*, pg. 64
MINNESOTA NIGERIA LIMITED—3M; *U.S. Public*, pg. 1606
MINNESOTA (3M) DE PORTUGAL, LDA.—3M; *U.S. Public*, pg. 1606
MO OCH DOMSJO AB; *Int'l*, pg. 885
MODO PAPER FRANCE—Mo och Domsjo AB; *Int'l*, pg. 887
MODO VAN GELDER—Mo och Domsjo AB; *Int'l*, pg. 886
MOORE BELGIUM NV—Moore Corporation Limited; *Int'l*, pg. 889
MOORE BUSINESS FORMS DE MEXICO S.A. DE C.V.—Moore Corporation Limited; *Int'l*, pg. 889
MOORE BUSINESS PRODUCTS & SERVICES DIVISIONS—Moore Corporation Limited; *Int'l*, pg. 890
MOORE GES.M.B.H.—Moore Corporation Limited; *Int'l*, pg. 889
MOORE-LITHOREX DIRECT MARKETING SERVICES N.V./S.A.—Moore Corporation Limited; *Int'l*, pg. 889
MULTIPLE PAKFOLD FORMS—Data Business Forms Limited; *Int'l*, pg. 384
NEBS BUSINESS FORMS LIMITED—New England Business Service, Inc.; *U.S. Public*, pg. 1171
NEBS BUSINESS STATIONERY—New England Business Service, Inc.; *U.S. Public*, pg. 1171
NEW YORK ENVELOPE CORP; *U.S. Private*, pg. 794
NEWELL CO.; *U.S. Public*, pg. 1176
NIELSEN DESIGN AB—Esselte AB; *Int'l*, pg. 459
OFFICE CONNECTION, INC.—U.S. Office Products Company; *U.S. Public*, pg. 1687
OFFICE DEPOT—Office Depot Inc.; *U.S. Public*, pg. 1212
OFFICEMAX; *U.S. Public*, pg. 1212
PAKFOLD BUSINESS FORMS—Data Business Forms Limited; *Int'l*, pg. 384
PAPER AGENCIES (AUST.) PTY. LTD.—Enso Oyj; *Int'l*, pg. 458
THE PAPER MAGIC GROUP, INC.—CSS Industries, Inc.; *U.S. Public*, pg. 284
PAPETERIES DE MONTEVRAIN SA—Groupe Saint Louis; *Int'l*, pg. 567
PARKER PEN CANADA LIMITED—The Gillette Company; *U.S. Public*, pg. 745
PARKER PEN JAPAN K.K.—The Gillette Company; *U.S. Public*, pg. 745
PENTECH INTERNATIONAL, INC.; *U.S. Public*, pg. 1274
PICK QUICK PAPERS, INC.—Central Lewmar; *U.S. Private*, pg. 223
PREDSTAVEITLSTVO FIRMY "ENSO"—Enso Oyj; *Int'l*, pg. 458
PUTNAM GRAPHIC INNOVATIONS, INC.—National Fiberstock Corporation; *U.S. Private*, pg. 782
QUAIFE PAPERS, LTD.—Groupe Saint Louis; *Int'l*, pg. 567
QUILL CORP.; *U.S. Private*, pg. 901
RANK XEROX AG—Xerox Corporation; *U.S. Public*, pg. 1785
RICCOBON & COMPANY, INC.; *U.S. Private*, pg. 927
P.C. RICHARD & SON; *U.S. Private*, pg. 928
ROYAL CONSUMER BUSINESS PRODUCTS—Olivetti SpA; *Int'l*, pg. 1002
THE RYTEX COMPANY—American Stationery Co., Inc.; *U.S. Private*, pg. 62
SAMAB CIA. INDUSTRIA E COMERCIO DE PAPEL—Enso Oyj; *Int'l*, pg. 458
SAVIN CORPORATION—Ricoh Company, Ltd.; *Int'l*, pg. 1114
SAVIN OF TAMPA BAY—Ricoh Company, Ltd.; *Int'l*, pg. 1114
SEALED AIR (FAR EAST) LTD.—Sealed Air Corporation; *U.S. Public*, pg. 1451
SEALED AIR JAPAN LTD.—Sealed Air Corporation; *U.S. Public*, pg. 1451
SEALED AIR (MALAYSIA) SDN BHD—Sealed Air Corporation; *U.S. Public*, pg. 1451
SEALED AIR (SINGAPORE) PTE. LTD.—Sealed Air Corporation; *U.S. Public*, pg. 1451

SEALED AIR (TAIWAN) LTD.—Sealed Air Corporation; *U.S. Public*, pg. 1451
SHEAFFER PEN CROWNMARK—Gefinor S.A. Luxembourg; *Int'l*, pg. 542
W.H. SMITH GROUP PLC; *Int'l*, pg. 1264
SMYTHSON OF BOND STREET—John Menzies plc; *Int'l*, pg. 707
SOCIETE ROANNAISE DES PAPIERS S.A.—Groupe Saint Louis; *Int'l*, pg. 567
STANDARD MANIFOLD COMPANY, INC.; *U.S. Private*, pg. 1031
STAPLES, INC.; *U.S. Public*, pg. 1509
STUART HALL CO., INC.—Newell Co.; *U.S. Public*, pg. 1178
SUMITOMO 3M LIMITED—3M; *U.S. Public*, pg. 1606
SYSTEMS NORTHWEST—Ricoh Company, Ltd.; *Int'l*, pg. 1114
P.T. 3M INDONESIA—3M; *U.S. Public*, pg. 1606
TOP FLIGHT, INC.; *U.S. Private*, pg. 1091
UPM-KYMMENE CANADA—UPM-Kymmene Corporation; *Int'l*, pg. 1430
UNISOURCE—Unisource Worldwide, Inc.; *U.S. Public*, pg. 1671
UNISOURCE (S.E. REGIONAL OFFICE)—Unisource Worldwide, Inc.; *U.S. Public*, pg. 1671
UNISOURCE WORLDWIDE, INC.; *U.S. Public*, pg. 1670
U.S. OFFICE PRODUCTS COMPANY; *U.S. Public*, pg. 1686
UNITED STATIONERS INC.; *U.S. Public*, pg. 1689
UNITED STATIONERS SUPPLY CO.—United Stationers Inc.; *U.S. Public*, pg. 1689
Z.N. VALMAS & CO.—Enso Oyj; *Int'l*, pg. 458
VALUE STATIONERY, INC.—American Pad and Paper Company; *U.S. Public*, pg. 89
VIKING DIRECT HOLDING CO.—Viking Office Products; *U.S. Public*, pg. 1721
VIKING DIRECT S.A.R.L.—Viking Office Products; *U.S. Public*, pg. 1721
VIKING OFFICE PRODUCTS; *U.S. Public*, pg. 1720
WALLACE COMPUTER SERVICES, INC.; *U.S. Public*, pg. 1735
WIGGINS ARJO ITALIANA SRL—Groupe Saint Louis; *Int'l*, pg. 567
WIGGINS TEAPE (HONG KONG) LTD.—Groupe Saint Louis; *Int'l*, pg. 567
WURTH BUROBEDARF & ORGANISATION GMBH—N.V. Koninklijke KNP BT; *Int'l*, pg. 758

5113 — INDUSTRIAL & PERSONAL SERVICE PAPER-WHOLESALE

AHLSTROM KOREA CO., LTD.—A. Ahlstrom Corporation; *Int'l*, pg. 35
AHLSTROM PAPER AG—A. Ahlstrom Corporation; *Int'l*, pg. 35
THE AILING & CORY COMPANY—Union Camp Corporation; *U.S. Public*, pg. 1666
AMERICAN PACKAGING CORPORATION; *U.S. Private*, pg. 60
AMERISERVE OF GRAND RAPIDS—Holberg Industries, Inc.; *U.S. Private*, pg. 533
AUTRON INCORPORATED—Marubeni Corporation; *Int'l*, pg. 845
BAGNASCO S.R.L.—Hollingsworth & Vose Co.; *U.S. Private*, pg. 535
BUNZL DISTRIBUTION USA INC.—Bunzl PLC; *Int'l*, pg. 233
BUNZL PACKAGING—Bunzl PLC; *Int'l*, pg. 233
BUNZL PACKAGING CONSULTANTS INC.—Bunzl PLC; *Int'l*, pg. 233
CDA DISTRIBUTORS—International Paper Company; *U.S. Public*, pg. 903
CAPITOL CONSOLIDATED—Bunzl PLC; *Int'l*, pg. 233
CARMEL CONTAINER SYSTEMS LTD.—American Israeli Paper Mills Ltd.; *Int'l*, pg. 75
CARTER RICE—International Paper Company; *U.S. Public*, pg. 903
CARTON DE COLUMBIA, S.A.—Jefferson Smurfit Group p.l.c.; *Int'l*, pg. 1271
CASE PAPER CO., INC.; *U.S. Private*, pg. 218
CENTRAL NATIONAL-GOTTESMAN INC.; *U.S. Private*, pg. 224
CENTRAL PRODUCTS COMPANY, INC.—Lynch Corporation; *U.S. Public*, pg. 1022
CHESAPEAKE PACKAGING CO./LEROY—Chesapeake Corporation; *U.S. Public*, pg. 346
CHESAPEAKE PACKAGING CO./MADISON—Chesapeake Corporation; *U.S. Public*, pg. 347
CHESAPEAKE PACKAGING CO./NORTH TONAWANDA—Chesapeake Corporation; *U.S. Public*, pg. 347
CHINA STEEL EXPRESS CORPORATION—China Steel Corporation; *Int'l*, pg. 285
CHISWICK TRADING INC.; *U.S. Private*, pg. 237
CLARK FOODSERVICE, INC.; *U.S. Private*, pg. 242
CLIFFORD PAPER INC.; *U.S. Private*, pg. 246
COLE PAPERS INC.; *U.S. Private*, pg. 251
S.A. COMPTOIR FINLANDAIS N.V.—Enso Oyj; *Int'l*, pg. 457
CONESTOGA CORPORATION; *U.S. Private*, pg. 262
CONTINENTAL PAPER & SUPPLY CO.; *U.S. Private*, pg. 269
COPAP—Enso Oyj; *Int'l*, pg. 457
CRESTAR FOOD PRODUCTS, INC.—H.J. Heinz Company; *U.S. Public*, pg. 805
DAKCO DISTRIBUTORS, INC.; *U.S. Private*, pg. 308
DENNISON TRADING HONG KONG LTD.—Avery Dennison Corporation; *U.S. Public*, pg. 153
DILLARD, A RESOURCENET INTERNATIONAL COMPANY—International Paper Company; *U.S. Public*, pg. 901
DIXON PAPER CO.—International Paper Company; *U.S. Public*, pg. 902
DONOHUE PAPER SALES CORPORATION—Quebecor Inc.; *Int'l*, pg. 1075
EAGLE-PICHER FAR EAST, INC.—Eagle-Picher Industries, Inc.; *U.S. Private*, pg. 355
EARP DISTRIBUTION CENTER; *U.S. Private*, pg. 356
EMPAQUES PONDEROSA SA—Empressa La Moderna SA de CV; *Int'l*, pg. 454
ENSO AG—Enso Oyj; *Int'l*, pg. 457
ENSO DANMARK A/S—Enso Oyj; *Int'l*, pg. 457
ENSO (DEUTSCHLAND) GMBH—Enso Oyj; *Int'l*, pg. 457
ENSO-EUROCAN FAR EAST CO. LTD.—Enso Oyj; *Int'l*, pg. 457
ENSO-EUROCAN HONG KONG LTD.—Enso Oyj; *Int'l*, pg. 457
ENSO-EUROCAN SOUTH EAST ASIA PTE. LTD.—Enso Oyj; *Int'l*, pg. 457
ENSO FRANCE S.A.—Enso Oyj; *Int'l*, pg. 457
ENSO (HOLLAND) B.V.—Enso Oyj; *Int'l*, pg. 457
ENSO IBERICA S.A.—Enso Oyj; *Int'l*, pg. 457
ENSO INTERNATIONAL, INC.—Enso Oyj; *Int'l*, pg. 457
ENSO MARKETING CO. LTD.—Enso Oyj; *Int'l*, pg. 457
ENSO OYJ; *Int'l*, pg. 455
ENSO PORTUGAL LDA.—Enso Oyj; *Int'l*, pg. 457
ENSO PRESSE DRUCK VERTRIEB GMBH—Enso Oyj; *Int'l*, pg. 457
ERNEST PAPER PRODUCTS, INC.; *U.S. Private*, pg. 381
EUROFINN SERVICES—Enso Oyj; *Int'l*, pg. 458
FIBREWEB INTERNATIONAL, LTD.—Gould Paper Corporation; *U.S. Private*, pg. 467
FILTERWERK MANN & HUMMEL GMBH; *Int'l*, pg. 484
FINS VERKOOPKANTOOR—Enso Oyj; *Int'l*, pg. 458
THE FONDA GROUP, INC.—Four M Corporation, Inc.; *U.S. Private*, pg. 421
FOUAD & TOUFIC FADEL & CO.—Enso Oyj; *Int'l*, pg. 458
FOUR M CORPORATION, INC.; *U.S. Private*, pg. 421
S. FREEDMAN & SONS, INC.; *U.S. Private*, pg. 425
GENCORP PRINTWORLD—GenCorp Inc.; *U.S. Public*, pg. 706
THE GIBSON GROUP INC.; *U.S. Private*, pg. 451
GORDON FOOD SERVICE INC.; *U.S. Private*, pg. 465
GRAFFITI OFFICE SUPPLIERS AND PAPER MARKETING LTD.—American Israeli Paper Mills Ltd.; *Int'l*, pg. 75
ELOF HANSSON INC.—Elof Hansson AB; *Int'l*, pg. 595
ELOF HANSSON PAPER & BOARD, INC.—Elof Hansson AB; *Int'l*, pg. 595
C.D. HAUPT PAPIER-UND PAPPENFABRIK GMBH & CO., K.G.—Jefferson Smurfit Group p.l.c.; *Int'l*, pg. 1271
HEARST ENTERPRISES DIVISION—The Hearst Corporation; *U.S. Private*, pg. 516
HENLEY PAPER COMPANY; *U.S. Private*, pg. 522
HOLLINGSWORTH & VOSE CO. U.K. LTD.—Hollingsworth & Vose Co.; *U.S. Private*, pg. 535
HOLLINGSWORTH & VOSE EUROPE NV—Hollingsworth & Vose Co.; *U.S. Private*, pg. 535
HOVOMEX S.A. DE C.V.—Hollingsworth & Vose Co.; *U.S. Private*, pg. 535
HUDSON VALLEY PAPER COMPANY; *U.S. Private*, pg. 546
IPI CORPORATION—International Paper Company; *U.S. Public*, pg. 906
IGGESUND AG—Mo och Domsjo AB; *Int'l*, pg. 886
IGGESUND BENELUX B.V.—Mo och Domsjo AB; *Int'l*, pg. 886
IGGESUND BENELUX N.V.—Mo och Domsjo AB; *Int'l*, pg. 886
IGGESUND BOARD SALES LTD. (WALTHAM ABBEY)—Mo och Domsjo AB; *Int'l*, pg. 886
IGGESUND PAPERBOARD AB—Mo och Domsjo AB; *Int'l*, pg. 886
INDUSTRIAL MATERIAL DISTRIBUTORS—International Paper Company; *U.S. Public*, pg. 903
INTERLAKE PAPERS, INC.—Consolidated Papers, Inc.; *U.S. Public*, pg. 436
INTERNATIONAL PAPER TAIWAN LTD.—International Paper Company; *U.S. Public*, pg. 905
JP FOODSERVICE, INC.; *U.S. Public*, pg. 918
JACKSON PAPER COMPANY; *U.S. Private*, pg. 579
JORDAN'S FOODS-CARIBOU DIVISION—Jordan's Meats; *U.S. Private*, pg. 599
KAISER WHOLESALE, INC.; *U.S. Private*, pg. 605
KELLERMEYER CO.; *U.S. Private*, pg. 612
KEYSTONE FOODS CORPORATION; *U.S. Private*, pg. 619
PERRY H. KOPLIK & SONS; *U.S. Private*, pg. 632
KORSNAS FRANCE S.A.—Korsnas AB; *Int'l*, pg. 759
KORSNAS GMBH—Korsnas AB; *Int'l*, pg. 759
KORSNAS SALES LTD.—Korsnas AB; *Int'l*, pg. 759
LEN S.A.—Henkel KGaA; *Int'l*, pg. 613
LEONE FOOD SERVICE CORP.—Clayton, Dubilier & Rice, Inc; *U.S. Private*, pg. 244
LESLIE PAPER—International Paper Company; *U.S. Public*, pg. 903
LIBERTY PAPER & BAG CO.—Bunzl PLC; *Int'l*, pg. 233
LONE STAR CORRUGATED CONTAINER CORPORATION; *U.S. Private*, pg. 674
M & C SPECIALTIES COMPANY; *U.S. Private*, pg. 684
M & C SPECIALTIES (IRELAND) LIMITED—M & C Specialties Company; *U.S. Private*, pg. 684
M & C REMCO TAPE PRODUCTS CO.—M & C Specialties Company; *U.S. Private*, pg. 684
MD HOLMEN AUSTRALIA & NEW ZEALAND PTY. LTD.—Mo och Domsjo AB; *Int'l*, pg. 886
MACMILLAN BLOEDEL LIMITED; *Int'l*, pg. 828
MACMILLAN BLOEDEL PULP & PAPER SALES LTD.—MacMillan Bloedel Limited; *Int'l*, pg. 829
MACTAC SCRANTON FACILITY—Bemis Company, Inc.; *U.S. Public*, pg. 210
MANVILLE CANADA INC.—Johns Manville Corporation; *U.S. Public*, pg. 927
MANVILLE DO BRASIL—Johns Manville Corporation; *U.S. Public*, pg. 927
MANVILLE JAPAN LTD.—Johns Manville Corporation; *U.S. Public*, pg. 927
MANVILLE MEXICANA S.A. DE C.V.—Johns Manville Corporation; *U.S. Public*, pg. 927
MARLI DE MEXICO S.A. DE C.V., MEXICO D.F.—Henkel KGaA; *Int'l*, pg. 613
F.A. MARSDEN LTD.—Georgia-Pacific Corporation; *U.S. Public*, pg. 739
THE MARTIN-BROWER COMPANY—Dalgety Plc; *Int'l*, pg. 376
MAYER MYERS PAPER COMPANY; *U.S. Private*, pg. 718
MEAD COATED BOARD EUROPE KARTONVERTRIEBS-A.G.—The Mead Corporation; *U.S. Public*, pg. 1076
THE MEAD CORPORATION; *U.S. Public*, pg. 1074
D.J. MEAD-HUBBS & HOWE—Sofco-Mead, Inc.; *U.S. Private*, pg. 1012
MISSION INDUSTRIES; *U.S. Private*, pg. 752
MITCHEL-LINCOLN PACKAGING; *Int'l*, pg. 870
MODO PAPER AB—Mo och Domsjo AB; *Int'l*, pg. 886
MODO PAPER AG—Mo och Domsjo AB; *Int'l*, pg. 887
MODO PAPER BENELUX BV—Mo och Domsjo AB; *Int'l*, pg. 887
MODO PAPER ITALIA SRL—Mo och Domsjo AB; *Int'l*, pg. 887
MODO PAPER LTD.—Mo och Domsjo AB; *Int'l*, pg. 887
MODO PAPER PSM—Mo och Domsjo AB; *Int'l*, pg. 887
MODOCELL FRANCE S.A.R.L.—Mo och Domsjo AB; *Int'l*, pg. 887
MODOCELL ITALIA S.R.L.—Mo och Domsjo AB; *Int'l*, pg. 887
MODOCELL LTD.—Mo och Domsjo AB; *Int'l*, pg. 887
MOSINEE PAPER INTERNATIONAL, INC.—Wausau-Mosinee Paper Corporation; *U.S. Public*, pg. 1747
MULTIWALL PACKAGING LIMITED—International Paper Company; *U.S. Public*, pg. 905
NDS—Nestle S.A.; *Int'l*, pg. 918
NATIONAL RESTAURANT SUPPLY COMPANY; *U.S. Private*, pg. 786
NETWORK SERVICES COMPANY; *U.S. Private*, pg. 791
NEWELL PAPER CO. OF COLUMBUS—Jackson Paper Company; *U.S. Private*, pg. 579
NEWELL PAPER CO. OF MERIDIAN—Jackson Paper Company; *U.S. Private*, pg. 579
NICHOLAS PAPER, INC.; *U.S. Private*, pg. 798
NIPPON PAPER INDUSTRIES COMPANY LIMITED; *Int'l*, pg. 937
NORSKE SKOG FRANCE SARL—Norske Skogindustrier A.S; *Int'l*, pg. 966
P.R. SOLO CUP, INC.—Solo Cup Company; *U.S. Private*, pg. 1013
PAPER AGENCIES (AUST.) PTY. LTD.—Enso Oyj; *Int'l*, pg. 458
PAPER ENTERPRISES, INC.; *U.S. Private*, pg. 837
PAPIER MALETTE—Malette Quebec, Inc.; *Int'l*, pg. 833
PEREZ TRADING CO. INC.; *U.S. Private*, pg. 852
PITNEY BOWES INC.; *U.S. Public*, pg. 1303
PREDSTAVEITLSTVO FIRMY "ENSO"—Enso Oyj; *Int'l*, pg. 458
PRINTPAC-UEB CASE GROUP—International Paper Company; *U.S. Public*, pg. 905
PROMO INDUSTRIE GV S.A.—Henkel KGaA; *Int'l*, pg. 613
QUALITY PARK PRODUCTS—Mail-Well Inc.; *U.S. Public*, pg. 1038
RESOURCE NET INTERNATIONAL—International Paper Company; *U.S. Public*, pg. 903
ROCHESTER MIDLAND CORPORATION; *U.S. Private*, pg. 937
SAMAB CIA. INDUSTRIA E COMERCIO DE PAPEL—Enso Oyj; *Int'l*, pg. 458
SCHNIEBER FINE FOODS, INC.; *U.S. Private*, pg. 971
SEALED AIR (FAR EAST) LTD.—Sealed Air Corporation; *U.S. Public*, pg. 1451
SEALED AIR JAPAN LTD.—Sealed Air Corporation; *U.S. Public*, pg. 1451
SEALED AIR (MALAYSIA) SDN BHD—Sealed Air Corporation; *U.S. Public*, pg. 1451
SEALED AIR (SINGAPORE) PTE. LTD.—Sealed Air Corporation; *U.S. Public*, pg. 1451
SEALED AIR (TAIWAN) LTD.—Sealed Air Corporation; *U.S. Public*, pg. 1451
SELECT ROBINSON INC.—The Cascades Group; *Int'l*, pg. 274
SETTSU USA—Settsu Corporation; *Int'l*, pg. 1225
SHIMA TRADING CO. LTD.; *Int'l*, pg. 1231
SHOREWOOD PACKAGING CORPORATION OF ALABAMA—Shorewood Packaging Corporation; *U.S. Public*, pg. 1468
SHOREWOOD PACKAGING CORPORATION OF CANADA, LTD.—Shorewood Packaging Corporation; *U.S. Public*, pg. 1468
SHOREWOOD PACKAGING OF CALIFORNIA, INC.—Shorewood Packaging Corporation; *U.S. Public*, pg. 1468
SMURFIT ESPANA, S.A.—Jefferson Smurfit Group p.l.c.; *Int'l*, pg. 1271
JEFFERSON SMURFIT ITALIA. S.R.L.—Jefferson Smurfit Group p.l.c.; *Int'l*, pg. 1271
SMURFIT MERCURIUS VERPAKKING B.V.—Jefferson Smurfit Group p.l.c.; *Int'l*, pg. 1271
SOCOFIDEX—The Procter & Gamble Company; *U.S. Public*, pg. 1333
SOFCO-MEAD, INC.; *U.S. Private*, pg. 1012
SOLO CUP COMPANY; *U.S. Private*, pg. 1013
STONE CONTAINER JAPAN COMPANY LIMITED—Stone Container Corporation; *U.S. Public*, pg. 1522
STORA CELL AB—Stora Kopparbergs Bergslags AB; *Int'l*, pg. 1303
SUKAB INTERTRADE GESMBH—Axel Johnson AB; *Int'l*, pg. 712
SUNCLIPSE, INC.—Amcor Limited; *Int'l*, pg. 72
TEKRA CORPORATION; *U.S. Private*, pg. 1073
TEMPO ROPARKO B.V.—The Procter & Gamble Company; *U.S. Public*, pg. 1333
TEMPO SANYS S.A.—The Procter & Gamble Company; *U.S. Public*, pg. 1333
TEMPO-VERTRIEBSGES FUR HYGIENISCHE ARTIKEL M.B.H—The Procter & Gamble Company; *U.S. Public*, pg. 1333

UPM-KYMMENE CANADA—UPM-Kymmene Corporation; *Int'l*, pg. 1430
UNGER COMPANY; *U.S. Private*, pg. 1117
UNISOURCE—Unisource Worldwide, Inc.; *U.S. Public*, pg. 1671
UNISOURCE (NORTH EAST)—Unisource Worldwide, Inc.; *U.S. Public*, pg. 1671
UNISOURCE (S.E. REGIONAL OFFICE)—Unisource Worldwide, Inc.; *U.S. Public*, pg. 1671
UNISOURCE (WEST REGION)—Unisource Worldwide, Inc.; *U.S. Public*, pg. 1671
UNISOURCE WORLDWIDE, INC.; *U.S. Public*, pg. 1670
VP-SCHICKEDANZ AG—The Procter & Gamble Company; *U.S. Public*, pg. 1333
Z.N. VALMAS & CO.—Enso Oyj; *Int'l*, pg. 458
WWF PAPER CORPORATION; *U.S. Private*, pg. 1145
WESTDEUTSCHE WELLPAPPENFABRIK GMBH—The Procter & Gamble Company; *U.S. Public*, pg. 1333
WEYERHAEUSER COMPANY; *U.S. Public*, pg. 1764
WINCHESTER CARTON CORP.—Rock-Tenn Company; *U.S. Public*, pg. 1397
WISAFOREST DEUTSCHLAND GMBH—UPM-Kymmene Corporation; *Int'l*, pg. 1429
WISAFOREST SVERIGE AB—UPM-Kymmene Corporation; *Int'l*, pg. 1429
WISAFOREST (UK) LTD.—UPM-Kymmene Corporation; *Int'l*, pg. 1429
WISAPAK MERTENS GMBH—UPM-Kymmene Corporation; *Int'l*, pg. 1430
WISAPAPER BENELUX B.V.—UPM-Kymmene Corporation; *Int'l*, pg. 1430
YAVNIR TRADING CO. LTD.—American Israeli Paper Mills Ltd.; *Int'l*, pg. 75
ZELLERBACH DIVISION—The Mead Corporation; *U.S. Public*, pg. 1075

5122 — DRUGS, DRUG PROPRIETARIES & DRUGGISTS' SUNDRIES-WHOLESALE

AAH MEDICAL—Franz Haniel & Cie, GmbH; *Int'l*, pg. 591
AAH PHARMACEUTICALS LIMITED—Franz Haniel & Cie, GmbH; *Int'l*, pg. 591
AAH PLC—Franz Haniel & Cie, GmbH; *Int'l*, pg. 591
OY ALGOL AB; *Int'l*, pg. 15
AM COSMETICS INC.; *U.S. Private*, pg. 6
AACIPHAR NV—Akzo Nobel N.V.; *Int'l*, pg. 44
ABBOTT LABORATORIES C.A.—Abbott Laboratories; *U.S. Public*, pg. 13
ABBOTT LABORATORIES-MOSCOW SALES OFFICE—Abbott Laboratories; *U.S. Public*, pg. 14
ABBOTT LABORATORIES NZ LTD.—Abbott Laboratories; *U.S. Public*, pg. 14
ABBOTT S.A.—Abbott Laboratories; *U.S. Public*, pg. 14
AFFILIATED FOODS, INC.; *U.S. Private*, pg. 25
AKZO NOBEL N.V.; *Int'l*, pg. 42
ALBERTO-CULVER COMPANY; *U.S. Public*, pg. 37
ALBERTO-CULVER (P.R.), INC.—Alberto-Culver Company; *U.S. Public*, pg. 38
THE FRED W. ALBRECHT GROCERY CO.; *U.S. Private*, pg. 32
ALCON JAPAN LTD.—Nestle S.A.; *Int'l*, pg. 918
ALFIN, INC.; *U.S. Public*, pg. 40
ALLEN & HANBURYS—Glaxo Wellcome plc; *Int'l*, pg. 552
ALLERGAN INC.—Allergan, Inc.; *U.S. Public*, pg. 46
ALLIANCE UNICHEM PLC; *Int'l*, pg. 57
ALLOU DISTRIBUTORS INC.—Allou Health & Beauty Care, Inc.; *U.S. Public*, pg. 55
ALLOU HEALTH & BEAUTY CARE, INC.; *U.S. Public*, pg. 55
ALLOU PERSONAL CARE CORP.—Allou Health & Beauty Care, Inc.; *U.S. Public*, pg. 55
ALRON CHEFARO KK—Akzo Nobel N.V.; *Int'l*, pg. 44
ALVA/AMCO PHARMACAL COMPANIES, INC.; *U.S. Private*, pg. 47
AMAFRUTAS S.A.—Novartis AG; *Int'l*, pg. 974
AMERICAN DRUG CORPORATION—American Home Products Corporation; *U.S. Public*, pg. 80
AMERISOURCE-BIRMINGHAM DIV.—AmeriSource Health Corp.; *U.S. Public*, pg. 96
AMERISOURCE HEALTH CORP.; *U.S. Public*, pg. 96
AMERSHAM AUSTRALIA PTY. LTD.—Nycomed Amersham plc; *Int'l*, pg. 992
AMERSHAM CANADA LIMITED—Nycomed Amersham plc; *Int'l*, pg. 992
AMERSHAM DENMARK APS—Nycomed Amersham plc; *Int'l*, pg. 993
AMERSHAM K.K.—Nycomed Amersham plc; *Int'l*, pg. 993
AMGEN B.V.—Amgen Inc.; *U.S. Public*, pg. 101
AMGEN CANADA INC.—Amgen Inc.; *U.S. Public*, pg. 101
AMGEN (EUROPE) AG—Amgen Inc.; *U.S. Public*, pg. 101
AMGEN GMBH—Amgen Inc.; *U.S. Public*, pg. 101
AMGEN INC.; *U.S. Public*, pg. 100
AMGEN INTERNATIONAL INC.—Amgen Inc.; *U.S. Public*, pg. 101
AMGEN LIMITED—Amgen Inc.; *U.S. Public*, pg. 101
AMGEN N.V.—Amgen Inc.; *U.S. Public*, pg. 101
AMGEN S.A.—Amgen Inc.; *U.S. Public*, pg. 101
AMGEN S.P.A.—Amgen Inc.; *U.S. Public*, pg. 101
ANDREWS GROUP, INCORPORATED—MacAndrews & Forbes Holdings Inc.; *U.S. Private*, pg. 689
ASIA PACIFIC RESIN CORPORATION—Novartis AG; *Int'l*, pg. 975
ASTRA AB; *Int'l*, pg. 93
ASTRA CHEMICALS S.A.—Astra AB; *Int'l*, pg. 93
ASTRA DANMARK A/S—Astra AB; *Int'l*, pg. 93
ASTRA DRACO AB—Astra AB; *Int'l*, pg. 93
ASTRA EXPORT & TRADING AB—Astra AB; *Int'l*, pg. 93
ASTRA FARMACEUTICI S.P.A.—Astra AB; *Int'l*, pg. 93
ASTRA GMBH—Astra AB; *Int'l*, pg. 93
ASTRA GES. M.B.H.—Astra AB; *Int'l*, pg. 93
ASTRA HELLAS S.A.—Astra AB; *Int'l*, pg. 93
ASTRA-IDL LTD.—Astra AB; *Int'l*, pg. 93
ASTRA JAPAN—Astra AB; *Int'l*, pg. 94
ASTRA JAPAN—Fujisawa Pharmaceutical Co. Ltd.; *Int'l*, pg. 525
ASTRA JAPAN LTD.—Astra AB; *Int'l*, pg. 94
ASTRA LAKEMEDEL AB—Astra AB; *Int'l*, pg. 93
ASTRA PHARMA INC.—Astra AB; *Int'l*, pg. 94
ASTRA PHARMACEUTICA AG—Astra AB; *Int'l*, pg. 94
ASTRA PHARMACEUTICA B.V.—Astra AB; *Int'l*, pg. 94
ASTRA PHARMACEUTICALS (HK) LTD.—Astra AB; *Int'l*, pg. 94
ASTRA PHARMACEUTICALS (IRELAND) LTD.—Astra AB; *Int'l*, pg. 94
ASTRA PHARMACEUTICALS LTD.—Astra AB; *Int'l*, pg. 94
ASTRA PHARMACEUTICALS (MALAYSIA) SDN BHD.—Astra AB; *Int'l*, pg. 94
ASTRA PHARMACEUTICALS (PHILIPPINES) INC.—Astra AB; *Int'l*, pg. 94
ASTRA PHARMACEUTICALS PTY. LTD.—Astra AB; *Int'l*, pg. 94
ASTRA PHARMACEUTICALS (SINGAPORE) PTE. LTD.—Astra AB; *Int'l*, pg. 94
ASTRA PHARMACEUTICALS (TAIWAN) LTD.—Astra AB; *Int'l*, pg. 94
ASTRA S.A. PRODUCTOS FARMACEUTICOS Y QUIMICOS—Astra AB; *Int'l*, pg. 94
ASTRA (THAI) LTD.—Astra AB; *Int'l*, pg. 94
ATLANTIC CHEMICAL CORPORATION LIMITED—Rhone-Poulenc S.A.; *Int'l*, pg. 1111
AUTOMATIC LIQUID PACKAGING, INC.; *U.S. Private*, pg. 101
AVATEX CORPORATION; *U.S. Public*, pg. 151
AYRTON SAUNDERS—Franz Haniel & Cie, GmbH; *Int'l*, pg. 591
THE B-M GROUP (PTY.) LTD.—Bristol-Myers Squibb Company; *U.S. Public*, pg. 255
BAKER CUMMINS, INC.—IVAX Corporation; *U.S. Public*, pg. 915
BASIC FOOD INTERNATIONAL INC.; *U.S. Private*, pg. 121
BAUSCH & LOMB (HONG KONG) LTD.—Bausch & Lomb Incorporated; *U.S. Public*, pg. 195
BAUSCH & LOMB INTERNATIONAL, INC.—Bausch & Lomb Incorporated; *U.S. Public*, pg. 195
BAUSCH & LOMB SVENSKA AB—Bausch & Lomb Incorporated; *U.S. Public*, pg. 195
BAXTER-HYLAND—Baxter International Inc.; *U.S. Public*, pg. 196
BAYER AG; *Int'l*, pg. 171
BEAUTY ENTERPRISES INC.; *U.S. Private*, pg. 128
BECTON DICKINSON & COMPANY; *U.S. Public*, pg. 199
BEHRINGWERKE AG—Hoechst Aktiengesellschaft; *Int'l*, pg. 624
BELCOSA DISTRIBUIDORA DE COSMETICOS LTDA.—Wella Group; *Int'l*, pg. 1489
BERGEN BRUNSWIG CORPORATION; *U.S. Public*, pg. 213
BERGEN BRUNSWIG DRUG COMPANY—Bergen Brunswig Corporation; *U.S. Public*, pg. 213
BERGEN BRUNSWIG MEDICAL CORPORATION—Bergen Brunswig Corporation; *U.S. Public*, pg. 214
BERLEX LABORATORIES INC.—Schering AG; *Int'l*, pg. 1204
BEUTLICH, L.P.; *U.S. Private*, pg. 141
BINDLEY WESTERN DRUG COMPANY—Bindley Western Industries, Inc.; *U.S. Public*, pg. 228
BINDLEY WESTERN INDUSTRIES, INC.; *U.S. Public*, pg. 228
BINDLEY WESTERN, TENNESSEE WHOLESALE DIVISION—Bindley Western Industries, Inc.; *U.S. Public*, pg. 229
BIO-RAD LABORATORIES PTY. LIMITED—Bio-Rad Laboratories, Inc.; *U.S. Public*, pg. 230
BIOGALENICA QUIMICA E FARMACEUTICA LTDA.—Novartis AG; *Int'l*, pg. 975
BISSELL LTD.—Bissell Inc.; *U.S. Private*, pg. 145
BLISTEX LIMITED—Blistex, Inc.; *U.S. Private*, pg. 149
THE BODY SHOP INTERNATIONAL; *Int'l*, pg. 199
BOEHRINGER INGELHEIM GMBH; *Int'l*, pg. 199
BOEHRINGER MANNHEIM JAPAN K.K.—Corange Limited; *Int'l*, pg. 331
BOEHRINGER MANNHEIM YAMANOUCHI K.K.—Corange Limited; *Int'l*, pg. 331
THE BOOTS COMPANY PLC; *Int'l*, pg. 202
BOOTS CONTRACT MANUFACTURING—The Boots Company PLC; *Int'l*, pg. 202
BOOTS HEALTHCARE INTERNATIONAL—The Boots Company PLC; *Int'l*, pg. 202
BRACCO DIAGNOSTICS, INC.—Bracco S.p.A.; *Int'l*, pg. 210
BRADLEY PHARMACEUTICALS; *U.S. Public*, pg. 249
GEORG A. BRENNER ARZNEIMITTEL-FABRIK GMBH—American Home Products Corporation; *U.S. Public*, pg. 80
BRISTOL-MYERS B.V.—Bristol-Myers Squibb Company; *U.S. Public*, pg. 255
BRISTOL-MYERS MARKETING SERVICES PTY. LTD.—Bristol-Myers Squibb Company; *U.S. Public*, pg. 255
BRISTOL-MYERS ONCOLOGY DIVISION—Bristol-Myers Squibb Company; *U.S. Public*, pg. 254
BRITISH PHARMACEUTICALS PTY. LTD.—Akzo Nobel N.V.; *Int'l*, pg. 44
JAMES BRUDNICK COMPANY—C.D. Smith Drug Company; *U.S. Private*, pg. 1007
DR. CHRISTIAN BRUNNENGRABER CHEMISCHE FABRIK GMBH—Novartis AG; *Int'l*, pg. 975
P.T. CANDRA SARI—Novartis AG; *Int'l*, pg. 975
CARDINAL HEALTH INC.; *U.S. Public*, pg. 304
CARRINGTON LABORATORIES, INC.; *U.S. Public*, pg. 309
CARTER-WALLACE DRUGS, INC.—Carter-Wallace, Inc.; *U.S. Public*, pg. 310
CARTER-WALLACE LIMITED (UNITED KINGDOM)—Carter-Wallace, Inc.; *U.S. Public*, pg. 310
CASTLEREAGH PHARMACEUTICALS—Franz Haniel & Cie, GmbH; *Int'l*, pg. 591
CHARLES OF THE RITZ GROUP LTD.—MacAndrews & Forbes Holdings Inc.; *U.S. Private*, pg. 689
CHATTEM (CANADA) INC.—Chattem, Inc.; *U.S. Public*, pg. 342
CHEFARO ESPANOLA SA—Akzo Nobel N.V.; *Int'l*, pg. 44
CHEFARO INTERNATIONAL B.V.—Akzo Nobel N.V.; *Int'l*, pg. 44
CHEFARO NV—Akzo Nobel N.V.; *Int'l*, pg. 44
CHEFARO PROPS LTD.—Akzo Nobel N.V.; *Int'l*, pg. 44
CHEIL CIBA-GEIGY CO, LTD—Novartis AG; *Int'l*, pg. 975
CHEMIE LINZ FRANCE S.A.R.L.—DSM N.V.; *Int'l*, pg. 356
CHEMO-TECHNISCHE MANUFACTURING, INC.—Wella Group; *Int'l*, pg. 1490
CHESEBROUGH POND'S—Unilever Plc; *Int'l*, pg. 1435
CHIRON CORPORATION—Chiron Corporation; *U.S. Public*, pg. 350
CHUGAI PHARMACEUTICAL CO., LTD.; *Int'l*, pg. 290
CIBA-GEIGY ARGENTINA S.A.I.C. Y F.—Novartis AG; *Int'l*, pg. 976
CIBA-GEIGY MAROC SA—Novartis AG; *Int'l*, pg. 978
CIBA-GEIGY (THAILAND) LTD.—Novartis AG; *Int'l*, pg. 980
CIBATUL LTD.—Novartis AG; *Int'l*, pg. 981
CILAG AG INTERNATIONAL—Johnson & Johnson; *U.S. Public*, pg. 929
CILAG DE MEXICO, S.A. DE C.V.—Johnson & Johnson; *U.S. Public*, pg. 929
CLAIROL DISTRIBUTION CENTER—Bristol-Myers Squibb Company; *U.S. Public*, pg. 255
CLAIROL, INC.—Bristol-Myers Squibb Company; *U.S. Public*, pg. 254
CLAIROL'S CONSUMER PRODUCTS DIVISION—Bristol-Myers Squibb Company; *U.S. Public*, pg. 254
COMPANIA SCHOLL S.A.—Scholl Plc; *Int'l*, pg. 1209
COMPAR—Antonio Puig SA; *Int'l*, pg. 1073
CONSOLIDATED COMPANIES INC. (CONCO); *U.S. Private*, pg. 265
CONSOLIDATED STORES CORP.; *U.S. Public*, pg. 437
CORANGE U.S. HOLDINGS, INC—Corange Limited; *Int'l*, pg. 331
COSMAIR, INC.—L'Oreal S.A.; *Int'l*, pg. 818
THE COSMETIC CENTER INC.—MacAndrews & Forbes Holdings Inc.; *U.S. Private*, pg. 689
COSMETIC PRODUCTS PTY, LTD.—Wella Group; *Int'l*, pg. 1490
COSMETICOS AVON, LTDA.—Avon Products, Inc.; *U.S. Public*, pg. 156
COSMETICOS AVON, S.A.C.I.—Avon Products, Inc.; *U.S. Public*, pg. 156
COSMETIQUES DE FRANCE PTE. LTD.—L'Oreal S.A.; *Int'l*, pg. 819
COSMITAL S.A.—Wella Group; *Int'l*, pg. 1490
THE JEAN COUTU GROUP (PJC) INC.; *Int'l*, pg. 340
CYANAMID DE COLUMBIA SA—American Home Products Corporation; *U.S. Public*, pg. 80
CYANAMID PERUANA SA—American Home Products Corporation; *U.S. Public*, pg. 81
CYANAMID PORTUGAL LTD.—American Home Products Corporation; *U.S. Public*, pg. 81
D & K HEALTHCARE RESOURCES DIVISION—D & K Healthcare Resources, Inc.; *U.S. Public*, pg. 472
D & K HEALTHCARE RESOURCES-LEXINGTON DIVISION—D & K Healthcare Resources, Inc.; *U.S. Public*, pg. 472
D & K HEALTHCARE RESOURCES-MINNEAPOLIS DIVISION—D & K Healthcare Resources, Inc.; *U.S. Public*, pg. 472
D.V.F. INC.—MacAndrews & Forbes Holdings Inc.; *U.S. Private*, pg. 690
DAKCO DISTRIBUTORS, INC.; *U.S. Private*, pg. 308
DAKOTA DRUG, INC.—Dakco Distributors, Inc.; *U.S. Private*, pg. 308
DARBY GROUP OF COS.; *U.S. Private*, pg. 311
DEL INTERNATIONAL—Del Laboratories, Inc.; *U.S. Public*, pg. 494
DEL LABORATORIES (CANADA) LTD.—Del Laboratories, Inc.; *U.S. Public*, pg. 494
DELTA BIOLOGICALS, S.R.L.—IVAX Corporation; *U.S. Public*, pg. 915
DEUTSCHE CHEFARO PHARMA GMBH—Akzo Nobel N.V.; *Int'l*, pg. 44
DIAGNOSTIC PRODUCTS CORPORATION; *U.S. Public*, pg. 505
DIAMEDIX CORPORATION—IVAX Corporation; *U.S. Public*, pg. 914
N.V. DIEETCENTRUM-WANDER S.A.—Novartis AG; *Int'l*, pg. 981
DIET CENTER WORLDWIDE, INC.—Physicians Weight Loss Centers, Inc.; *U.S. Private*, pg. 864
DIOSYNTH INTERNATIONAL BV—Akzo Nobel N.V.; *Int'l*, pg. 44
DIOSYNTH SCANDINAVIA—Akzo Nobel N.V.; *Int'l*, pg. 44
DIOSYNTH VERTRIEBSGESELLSCHAFT MBH—Akzo Nobel N.V.; *Int'l*, pg. 44
DIRECT SCRIPT—Oxford Health Plans Inc.; *U.S. Public*, pg. 1239
DISTRIBUIDORA DE PRODUCTOS SANDOZ S.A.—Novartis AG; *Int'l*, pg. 982
THE F. DOHMEN COMPANY; *U.S. Private*, pg. 338
F. DOHMEN COMPANY—The F. Dohmen Company; *U.S. Private*, pg. 338
DONG-MYUNG INDUSTRIAL CO., LTD.—Meiji Seika Kaisha, Ltd.; *Int'l*, pg. 856
DOW CHEMICAL AUSTRIA GESELLSCHAFT MBH—The Dow Chemical Company; *U.S. Public*, pg. 523
DOW CHEMICAL EXPORT S.A.—The Dow Chemical Company; *U.S. Public*, pg. 523
DR. SCHOLL'S SPA—Scholl Plc; *Int'l*, pg. 1209
DRACO LAKEMEDEL AB/TIKA LAKEMEDEL AB—Astra AB; *Int'l*, pg. 93
DRUG GUILD DIV.—Neuman Distributors, Inc.; *U.S. Public*, pg. 1169
DU PONT DE NEMOURS (BELGIUM) S.A.—Du Pont (E.I. Du Pont De Nemours & Co.); *U.S. Public*, pg. 532

DUPONT MERCK PHARM CO.—Merck & Co., Inc.; *U.S. Public*, pg. 1091
E-Z-EM, INC.; *U.S. Public*, pg. 540
EFFECTONA A/S—Wella Group; *Int'l*, pg. 1490
ELAN CORPORATION PLC; *Int'l*, pg. 435
ELAN PHARMA GMBH—Elan Corporation Plc; *Int'l*, pg. 436
ELAN PHARMA INC.—Elan Corporation Plc; *Int'l*, pg. 436
ELAN PHARMA PHILIPPINES, INC.—Elan Corporation Plc; *Int'l*, pg. 436
ELKINS-SINN, INC.-LEDERLE—American Home Products Corporation; *U.S. Public*, pg. 79
ENTERIC PRODUCTS, INC.—E-Z-Em, Inc.; *U.S. Public*, pg. 540
ENVIRONMENTAL FRAGRANCE TECHNOLOGIES, LTD.—MacAndrews & Forbes Holdings Inc.; *U.S. Private*, pg. 689
ETHNOR S.A.—Johnson & Johnson; *U.S. Public*, pg. 929
EURAND FRANCE S.A.—American Home Products Corporation; *U.S. Public*, pg. 81
EURAND INTERNATIONAL S.P.A.—American Home Products Corporation; *U.S. Public*, pg. 81
FAMILY PHARMACY GENERAL OFFICE—AmeriSource Health Corp.; *U.S. Public*, pg. 97
FERRO METAL & CHEMICAL CORPORATION LTD.—Philipp Brothers Chemicals, Inc.; *U.S. Private*, pg. 861
FERROSAN DANMARK A/S—Novo Nordisk A/S; *Int'l*, pg. 987
HERBERT FERRYMAN—Franz Haniel & Cie, GmbH; *Int'l*, pg. 591
FILA FITNESS LTD.—MacAndrews & Forbes Holdings Inc.; *U.S. Private*, pg. 690
FINE CARE CO. LTD.—Wella Group; *Int'l*, pg. 1490
FIRMENICH INCORPORATED—Firmenich S.A.; *Int'l*, pg. 486
FISONS AG—Rhone-Poulenc S.A.; *Int'l*, pg. 1111
FISONS A/S—Rhone-Poulenc S.A.; *Int'l*, pg. 1111
FISONS BV—Rhone-Poulenc S.A.; *Int'l*, pg. 1111
FISONS CORPORATION LIMITED—Rhone-Poulenc S.A.; *Int'l*, pg. 1111
FISONS FARMACEUTICI S.P.A.—Rhone-Poulenc S.A.; *Int'l*, *pg. 1111*
FISONS PTY. LIMITED—Rhone-Poulenc S.A.; *Int'l*, pg. 1111
FLORASYNTH GMBH—Bayer AG; *Int'l*, pg. 173
FLORASYNTH LIMITED—Bayer AG; *Int'l*, pg. 173
FLORASYNTH S.A. DE C.V.—Bayer AG; *Int'l*, pg. 174
FLORASYNTH SINGAPORE PTE LTD.—Bayer AG; *Int'l*, pg. 174
FOREVER LIVING PRODUCTS INTERNATIONAL, INC.; *U.S. Private*, pg. 418
FOURNEX N.V.—SmithKline Beecham plc; *Int'l*, pg. 1265
FRUEHLING COSMETICS CO. LTD.—Wella Group; *Int'l*, pg. 1490
FUJISAWA SYNTHELABO K.K.—L'Oreal S.A.; *Int'l*, pg. 818
FUJISAWA U.S.A.—Fujisawa Pharmaceutical Co. Ltd.; *Int'l*, pg. 525
FUJISAWA U.S.A. INC.—Fujisawa Pharmaceutical Co. Ltd.; *Int'l*, pg. 525
G.C. PHARMACEUTICAL (SINGAPORE) LTD.—The Green Cross Corporation; *Int'l*, pg. 558
GEHE AG—Franz Haniel & Cie, GmbH; *Int'l*, pg. 591
GP STRATEGIES CORPORATION; *U.S. Public*, pg. 694
GALENUS CHEMICALS GMBH—Corange Limited; *Int'l*, pg. 331
GALENUS MANNHEIM GMBH—Corange Limited; *Int'l*, pg. 331
GEMA S.A.—Novartis AG; *Int'l*, pg. 982
GEMINI SCIENCE, INC.—Kirin Brewery Co., Ltd.; *Int'l*, pg. 736
GENERAL DRUG CO.—C.D. Smith Drug Company; *U.S. Private*, pg. 1007
GENERAL MERCHANDISE DISTRIBUTORS, INC.—Fleming Companies, Inc.; *U.S. Public*, pg. 653
GENZYME B.V.—Genzyme Corporation; *U.S. Public*, pg. 733
GERMAPHARM GMBH, IMPORT, EXPORT SPEDITION—Schering AG; *Int'l*, pg. 1203
GILLETTE DO BRASIL & CIA—The Gillette Company; *U.S. Public*, pg. 744
GILLETTE GROUP ITALY S.R.L.—The Gillette Company; *U.S. Public*, pg. 745
GILLETTE INDUSTRIES, LTD.—The Gillette Company; *U.S.* Public, pg. 745
GILLETTE (JAPAN) INC.—The Gillette Company; *U.S. Public*, pg. 745
GILLETTE SOUTH AFRICA LIMITED—The Gillette Company; *U.S. Public*, pg. 745
GILLETTE (SWITZERLAND) AG—The Gillette Company; *U.S. Public*, pg. 745
GLAXO DANMARK A/S—Glaxo Wellcome plc; *Int'l*, pg. 553
GLAXO FAR EAST PTE. LTD.—Glaxo Wellcome plc; *Int'l*, pg. 553
GLAXO PHARMACEUTICALS—Glaxo Wellcome plc; *Int'l*, pg. 552
GLAXO PHARMACEUTICALS UK LTD.—Glaxo Wellcome plc; *Int'l*, pg. 552
GLAXO WELLCOME AB—Glaxo Wellcome plc; *Int'l*, pg. 553
GLAXO WELLCOME AUSTRALIA LTD.—Glaxo Wellcome plc; *Int'l*, pg. 553
GLAXO WELLCOME BELGIUM S.A.—Glaxo Wellcome plc; *Int'l*, pg. 553
GLAXO WELLCOME CHINA LTD.—Glaxo Wellcome plc; *Int'l*, pg. 553
GLAXO WELLCOME GMBH—Glaxo Wellcome plc; *Int'l*, pg. 553
GLAXO WELLCOME HONG KONG LTD.—Glaxo Wellcome plc; *Int'l*, pg. 553
GLAXO WELLCOME INC.—Glaxo Wellcome plc; *Int'l*, pg. 552
GLAXO WELLCOME PHARMA GMBH—Glaxo Wellcome plc; *Int'l*, pg. 553
GLAXO WELLCOME PLC; *Int'l*, pg. 552
GLAXO WELLCOME SINGAPORE PTE. LTD.—Glaxo Wellcome plc; *Int'l*, pg. 553
GOLDWELL COSMETICS (USA) INC.—Kao Corporation; *Int'l*, pg. 718
GOODY CANADA LIMITED—Newell Co.; *U.S. Public*, pg. 1177
J.E. GOOLD & COMPANY—Bindley Western Industries, Inc.; *U.S. Public*, pg. 229
GROCERS SUPPLY CO. INC.; *U.S. Private*, pg. 483
GRUPO CASA AUTREY; *Int'l*, pg. 573
GUERLAIN, INC.—LVMH Moet Hennessy Louis Vuitton; *Int'l*, pg. 780
GUEST INTERNATIONAL (CANADA) LTD.—Guest Supply, Inc.; *U.S. Public*, pg. 768
GUEST INTERNATIONAL (ENGLAND) LTD.—Guest Supply, Inc.; *U.S. Public*, pg. 768
GUEST INTERNATIONAL (NEW ZEALAND) LTD.—Guest Supply, Inc.; *U.S. Public*, pg. 768
GUEST SUPPLY, INC.; *U.S. Public*, pg. 768
HSN LIFEWAY HEALTH PRODUCTS, INC.—USA Networks, Inc.; *U.S. Public*, pg. 1685
HAGEMEYER N.V.—First Pacific Company Limited; *Int'l*, pg. 487
HALSTON ENTERPRISES, INC.—MacAndrews & Forbes Holdings Inc.; *U.S. Private*, pg. 690
HAN WHA PHARMA CO. LTD.—Akzo Nobel N.V.; *Int'l*, pg. 44
FRANZ HANIEL & CIE, GMBH; *Int'l*, pg. 591
HASSLE LAKEMEDEL AB—Astra AB; *Int'l*, pg. 93
HENKEL ARGENTINA S.A.—Henkel KGaA; *Int'l*, pg. 611
HENKEL CHEMICALS (CARIBBEAN) LTD.—Henkel KGaA; *Int'l*, pg. 614
HENKEL HELLAS, S.A.—Henkel KGaA; *Int'l*, pg. 612
HENKEL KENYA LTD.—Henkel KGaA; *Int'l*, pg. 613
HENKEL VENEZOLANA S.A.—Henkel KGaA; *Int'l*, pg. 614
HERBALIFE INTERNATIONAL OF AMERICA, INC.—Herbalife International of America, Inc.; *U.S. Public*, pg. 809
HERBALIFE (N.Z.) LIMITED—Herbalife International of America, Inc.; *U.S. Public*, pg. 809
HI-EISAI PHARMACEUTICALS, INC.—Eisai Co., Ltd.; *Int'l*, pg. 435
HICHEM DIAGNOSTICS B.V.—Elan Corporation Plc; *Int'l*, pg. 436
HICHEM DIAGNOSTICS, INC.—Elan Corporation Plc; *Int'l*, pg. 436
HILLCROSS PHARMACEUTICALS—Franz Haniel & Cie, GmbH; *Int'l*, pg. 591
HILLS PHARMACEUTICALS—Franz Haniel & Cie, GmbH; *Int'l*, pg. 591
HOECHST AUSTRALIA LTD.—Hoechst Aktiengesellschaft; *Int'l*, pg. 626
HOECHST MARION ROUSSEL AG—Hoechst Aktiengesellschaft; *Int'l*, pg. 624
HOECHST MARION ROUSSEL, INC.—Hoechst Aktiengesellschaft; *Int'l*, pg. 624
HOECHST MARION ROUSSEL NORTH AMERICA—Hoechst Aktiengesellschaft; *Int'l*, pg. 625
HOME SHOPPING NETWORK, INC.—USA Networks, Inc.; *U.S. Public*, pg. 1685
HORMOQUIMICA DE CHILE LTDA.—Akzo Nobel N.V.; *Int'l*, *pg. 44*
HOSPITAL MANAGEMENT & SUPPLIES LIMITED—Alliance UniChem PLC; *Int'l*, pg. 58
ICN PHARMACEUTICALS, INC.; *U.S. Public*, pg. 853
ICART S.A.—Carter-Wallace, Inc.; *U.S. Public*, pg. 310
INFAR (INDIA) LTD.—Akzo Nobel N.V.; *Int'l*, pg. 45
INGECOL—Novartis AG; *Int'l*, pg. 983
INTERCARE PRODUCTS LTD.—Novartis AG; *Int'l*, pg. 983
INTERCOSMETIC AB—Wella Group; *Int'l*, pg. 1490
INTERCOSMETIC (GREAT BRITAIN) LTD.—Wella Group; *Int'l*, pg. 1490
INTERCOSMETIC S.A.—Wella Group; *Int'l*, pg. 1490
INTERKOSMETIK GES.M.B.H.—Wella Group; *Int'l*, pg. 1490
INTERNATIONAL COSMETICS CO., LTD.; *Int'l*, pg. 684
INTERNATIONAL FLAVORS & FRAGRANCES I.F.F. (DEUTSCHLAND) GMBH—International Flavors & Fragrances, Inc.; *U.S. Public*, pg. 899
INTERPHARM BV—Internatio-Muller N.V.; *Int'l*, pg. 681
INTERVET MEXICO SA DE CV—Akzo Nobel N.V.; *Int'l*, pg. 45
INTERVET NEDERLAND BV—Akzo Nobel N.V.; *Int'l*, pg. 44
INTRAFIN S.A.—Bristol-Myers Squibb Company; *U.S. Public*, pg. 256
INVERNESS CORP.; *U.S. Private*, pg. 574
JC PENNEY COMPANY, INC.; *U.S. Public*, pg. 916
JMI-CANTON PHARMACEUTICALS, INC.—Jones Medical Industries Inc.; *U.S. Public*, pg. 934
JMI-PHOENIX LABORATORIES, INC.—Jones Medical Industries Inc.; *U.S. Public*, pg. 934
JANSSEN-CILAG AB—Johnson & Johnson; *U.S. Public*, pg. 929
JANSSEN/CILAG B.V.—Johnson & Johnson; *U.S. Public*, pg. 929
JANSSEN CILAG GMBH—Johnson & Johnson; *U.S. Public*, *pg. 929*
JANSSEN-CILAG K.K.—Johnson & Johnson; *U.S. Public*, pg. 929
JANSSEN-CILAG PHARMACEUTICA AG—Johnson & Johnson; *U.S. Public*, pg. 929
JANSSEN/CILAG PHARMACEUTICA GMBH—Johnson & Johnson; *U.S. Public*, pg. 929
JANSSEN/CILAG (PTY) LIMITED—Johnson & Johnson; *U.S. Public*, pg. 929
JANSSEN/CILAG S.A.C.I.—Johnson & Johnson; *U.S. Public*, pg. 929
JANSSEN PHARMACEUTICAL LTD.—Johnson & Johnson; *U.S. Public*, pg. 930
JAYDON INCORPORATED; *U.S. Private*, pg. 584
JOHNSON & JOHNSON GABA B.V.—Johnson & Johnson; *U.S. Public*, pg. 930
JOHNSON & JOHNSON/MERCK CONSUMER PHARMACEUTICALS CO.—Johnson & Johnson; *U.S. Public*, pg. 929
JOHNSON & JOHNSON/MERCK CONSUMER PHARMACEUTICALS CO.—Merck & Co., Inc.; *U.S. Public*, pg. 1091
JONES MEDICAL INDUSTRIES INC.; *U.S. Public*, pg. 933
KHR; *U.S. Private*, pg. 603
KV PHARMACEUTICAL COMPANY; *U.S. Public*, pg. 941
KANEBO COSMETICS OF HAWAII, INC.—Kanebo, Ltd.; *Int'l*, pg. 722
KANEBO, LTD.—Kanebo, Ltd.; *Int'l*, pg. 722
KARNEVAL COSMETIC CO., LTD.—Wella Group; *Int'l*, pg. 1490
KENDALL AUSTRALIA PTY. LTD.—Tyco International Ltd.; *U.S. Public*, pg. 1647
KENYA-SWISS CHEMICAL CO. LTD.—Novartis AG; *Int'l*, pg. 983
KING GROUP, INC.; *U.S. Private*, pg. 620
W.H. KING DRUG CO.—Bergen Brunswig Corporation; *U.S.* Public, pg. 214
KOSMOBEL AG HANDELSAKTIENGESELLSCHAFT FUR KOSMETIK UND FRISEURBEDARF—Wella Group; *Int'l*, pg. 1490
KYOWA HAKKO EUROPE GMBH—Kyowa Hakko Kogyo Company, Ltd.; *Int'l*, pg. 778
KYOWA HAKKO (H.K.) CO., LTD.—Kyowa Hakko Kogyo Company, Ltd.; *Int'l*, pg. 778
KYOWA HAKKO U.S.A., INC.—Kyowa Hakko Kogyo Company, Ltd.; *Int'l*, pg. 778
KYOWA HAKKO-WEST COAST OFFICE—Kyowa Hakko Kogyo Company, Ltd.; *Int'l*, pg. 778
KYTTA-WERK SAUTER GMBH—American Home Products Corporation; *U.S. Public*, pg. 81
L.P.B. INSTITUTO FARMACEUTICO S.P.A.—Novartis AG; *Int'l*, pg. 983
LABORATOIRE WELLCOME GLAXO S.A.—Glaxo Wellcome plc; *Int'l*, pg. 553
LABORATOIRES FISON SA—Rhone-Poulenc S.A.; *Int'l*, pg. 1111
LABORATOIRES PHARMACIA & UPJOHN SARL—Pharmacia & Upjohn, Inc.; *Int'l*, pg. 1049
LABORATOIRES SANDOZ S.A.R.L.—Novartis AG; *Int'l*, pg. 983
LABORATORIES ASTRA FRANCE—Astra AB; *Int'l*, pg. 94
LABORATORIO ASTRA ESPANA, S.A.—Astra AB; *Int'l*, pg. 94
LABORATORIO NORMAL PRODUCTOS FARMACEUTICOS, LDA.—Novartis AG; *Int'l*, pg. 983
LE SOLEIL S.A.—Henkel KGaA; *Int'l*, pg. 613
LEN S.A.—Henkel KGaA; *Int'l*, pg. 613
LEONARD WHOLESALE, INC.; *U.S. Private*, pg. 660
LIBAMEDI S.A.—American Home Products Corporation; *U.S. Public*, pg. 81
ELI LILLY AND COMPANY; *U.S. Public*, pg. 992
ELI LILLY BENELUX, S.A.—Eli Lilly and Company; *U.S. Public*, pg. 993
ELI LILLY INTERNATIONAL CORPORATION—Eli Lilly and Company; *U.S. Public*, pg. 993
ELI LILLY S.A.—Eli Lilly and Company; *U.S. Public*, pg. 994
LINTAPHARM AG—DSM N.V.; *Int'l*, pg. 356
LION HENKEL (HONGKONG) LTD.—Henkel KGaA; *Int'l*, pg. 614
LION HENKEL TAIWAN LTD.—Henkel KGaA; *Int'l*, pg. 614
LIPHA PHARMACEUTICALS—Lipha Chemicals S.A.; *Int'l*, pg. 812
LITEX A/S—FMC Corporation; *U.S. Public*, pg. 607
L'OREAL JAPAN LTD.—L'Oreal S.A.; *Int'l*, pg. 819
L'OREAL (UK) LIMITED—L'Oreal S.A.; *Int'l*, pg. 819
MGI PHARMA INC.; *U.S. Public*, pg. 1026
MSD SHARP & DOHME GMBH—Merck & Co., Inc.; *U.S. Public*, pg. 1092
MALLINCKRODT INC.; *U.S. Public*, pg. 1039
MALONE & HYDE, INC.-DRUG DISTRIBUTORS—Fleming Companies, Inc.; *U.S. Public*, pg. 653
MASON DISTRIBUTORS, INC.; *U.S. Private*, pg. 712
MAX FACTOR K.K.—The Procter & Gamble Company; *U.S.* Public, pg. 1331
MCKESSON CORPORATION; *U.S. Public*, pg. 1072
MCKESSON CORPORATION—McKesson Corporation; *U.S.* Public, pg. 1073
MCKESSON HOME HEALTH CARE DIVISION—McKesson Corporation; *U.S. Public*, pg. 1073
MCKESSON MEDICAL SUPPLY—McKesson Corporation; *U.S. Public*, pg. 1073
MCKESSON U.S. HEALTH CARE—McKesson Corporation; *U.S. Public*, pg. 1073
MEAD JOHNSON LABORATORIES—Bristol-Myers Squibb Company; *U.S. Public*, pg. 255
MEDCO CONTAINMENT SERVICES, INC.—Merck & Co., Inc.; *U.S. Public*, pg. 1091
MEDEVA PHARMACEUTICALS—Medeva PLC; *Int'l*, pg. 852
MEDI-MAIL, INC.; *U.S. Private*, pg. 726
MEDICAL MARKETING GROUP, INC.—Merck & Co., Inc.; *U.S. Public*, pg. 1091
MEDICAL SUPPLIES DIVISION—Abdulla Fouad Co. Ltd.; *Int'l*, pg. 502
MEDICORE INC.; *U.S. Public*, pg. 1080
P.T. MEIJI INDONESIAN PHARMACEUTICAL INDUSTRIES—Meiji Seika Kaisha, Ltd.; *Int'l*, pg. 856
MEIJI SEIKA KAISHA, LTD.; *Int'l*, pg. 855
MENLEY & JAMES LABORATORIES, INC.; *U.S. Public*, pg. 1086
MERCK & CO., INC.; *U.S. Public*, pg. 1090
MERCK FROSST CANADA INC.—Merck & Co., Inc.; *U.S. Public*, pg. 1092
MERCK MEDCO MANAGED CARE—Merck & Co., Inc.; *U.S. Public*, pg. 1091
MERCK SHARP & DOHME-CHIBRET A.G.—Merck & Co., Inc.; *U.S. Public*, pg. 1092
MERCK SHARP & DOHME-HOLLAND—Merck & Co., Inc.; *U.S. Public*, pg. 1092

MERCK SHARP & DOHME INTL.—Merck & Co., Inc.; *U.S. Public*, pg. 1092
MERCK SHARP & DOHME (SWEDEN) AB—Merck & Co., Inc.; *U.S. Public*, pg. 1092
MERCURY DISTRIBUTING CO., INC.; *U.S. Private*, pg. 732
MERIDIAN DIAGNOSTICS EUROPE S.R.L.—Meridian Diagnostics, Inc.; *U.S. Public*, pg. 1095
MENTHOLATUM PTY. LTD.—Rohto Pharmaceutical Co.; *Int'l*, pg. 1126
FRED MEYER STORES—Fred Meyer Incorporated; *U.S. Public*, pg. 1103
MARILYN MIGLIN, L.P.; *U.S. Private*, pg. 745
JOHN PAUL MITCHELL SYSTEMS; *U.S. Private*, pg. 753
MODERN HAIRDRESSING SUPPLIES (PTY) LTD.—Wella Group; *Int'l*, pg. 1490
MONARCH CROWN CORPORATION—Bristol-Myers Squibb Company; *U.S. Public*, pg. 254
MOORE MEDICAL CORP.; *U.S. Public*, pg. 1128
MUCH PHARMA—American Home Products Corporation; *U.S. Public*, pg. 81
NABI; *U.S. Public*, pg. 1148
NADRO S.A. DE C.V.—McKesson Corporation; *U.S. Public*, *pg. 1073*
NAGASE-CIBA LTD.—Novartis AG; *Int'l*, pg. 983
NATIONAL PHARMACIES, INC.—Merck & Co., Inc.; *U.S. Public*, pg. 1091
NATURE'S SUNSHINE DE MEXICO—Nature's Sunshine Products, Inc.; *U.S. Public*, pg. 1166
NATURE'S SUNSHINE PRODUCTS OF CANADA, LTD.—Nature's Sunshine Products, Inc.; *U.S. Public*, pg. 1167
NEUMAN DISTRIBUTORS, INC.; *U.S. Public*, pg. 1169
NEUTROGENA CORPORATION SARL—Johnson & Johnson; *U.S. Public*, pg. 928
NEW ENGLAND WHOLESALE DRUG COMPANY—Bindley Western Industries, Inc.; *U.S. Public*, pg. 229
NIPPON CENTOCOR, K.K.—Centocor, Inc.; *U.S. Public*, pg. 323
NIPPON GLAXO LTD.—Glaxo Wellcome plc; *Int'l*, pg. 553
NIPPON KAIJI KYOKAI—Nippon Kaiji Kyokai; *Int'l*, pg. 934
NORSK SCHERING A/S—Schering-Plough Corporation; *U.S. Public*, pg. 1439
NORTH CAROLINA MUTUAL WHOLESALE DRUG CO.; *U.S. Private*, pg. 804
NORTON HEALTHCARE LIMITED—IVAX Corporation; *U.S.* Public, pg. 915
NOURYPHARMA NEDERLAND B.V.—Akzo Nobel N.V.; *Int'l*, pg. 44
NU SKIN INTERNATIONAL; *U.S. Private*, pg. 808
OHMEDA LTD.—The BOC Group plc; *Int'l*, pg. 122
OMAHA VACCINE COMPANY—KHR; *U.S. Private*, pg. 603
ONDAL-FRANCE S.A.R.L.—Wella Group; *Int'l*, pg. 1490
ONDAWEL (G.B.) LTD.—Wella Group; *Int'l*, pg. 1490
ONDELLE S.A. (PTY.) LTD.—Wella Group; *Int'l*, pg. 1490
ORGANON (BANGLADESH) LTD.—Akzo Nobel N.V.; *Int'l*, pg. 45
LAB. ORGANON DO BRAZIL LTDA.—Akzo Nobel N.V.; *Int'l*, pg. 45
P.T. ORGANON INDONESIA—Akzo Nobel N.V.; *Int'l*, pg. 45
ORGANON MEXICANA SA—Akzo Nobel N.V.; *Int'l*, pg. 45
ORGANON NEDERLAND B.V.—Akzo Nobel N.V.; *Int'l*, pg. 44
ORGANON PAKISTAN (PRIVATE) LIMITED—Akzo Nobel N.V.; *Int'l*, pg. 45
ORGANON VENEZOLANA SA—Akzo Nobel N.V.; *Int'l*, pg. 45
OWENS & MINOR INC.; *U.S. Public*, pg. 1236
PSS—Physician Sales and Services Inc.; *U.S. Public*, pg. 1294
PACIFIC BEAUTY CARE PTE. LTD.—Wella Group; *Int'l*, pg. 1490
PACO RABANNE COMPAR—Antonio Puig SA; *Int'l*, pg. 1073
PARBEL INC.—L'Oreal S.A.; *Int'l*, pg. 818
PARFUMS GIVENCHY INC.—LVMH Moet Hennessy Louis Vuitton; *Int'l*, pg. 781
PARFUMS INTERNATIONAL LTD.—Unilever Plc; *Int'l*, pg. 1435
PARIS PRESENTS; *U.S. Private*, pg. 839
PARKE-DAVIS/ELAN LTD.—Elan Corporation Plc; *Int'l*, pg. 436
PELAGO MARKETING CORP. SDN. BHD.—Wella Group; *Int'l*, pg. 1490
PENWEST PHARM. CO.—Penford Corp.; *U.S. Public*, pg. 1269
PERRIGO OF TENNESSEE—L. Perrigo Company; *U.S. Public*, pg. 1280
PFIZER PRODUCTS PLC—Pfizer Inc.; *U.S. Public*, pg. 1282
PHARMACEUTICALS DIVISION—3M; *U.S. Public*, pg. 1605
OY PHARMACIA & UPJOHN AB—Pharmacia & Upjohn, Inc.; *Int'l*, pg. 1049
PHARMACIA & UPJOHN AS—Pharmacia & Upjohn, Inc.; *Int'l*, pg. 1049
PHARMACIA & UPJOHN A/S—Pharmacia & Upjohn, Inc.; *Int'l*, pg. 1049
PHARMACIA & UPJOHN (AUSTRALIA) PTY. LTD.—Pharmacia & Upjohn, Inc.; *Int'l*, pg. 1050
PHARMACIA & UPJOHN BIOTECH K.K.—Pharmacia & Upjohn, Inc.; *Int'l*, pg. 1048
PHARMACIA & UPJOHN CENTRAL AMERICAN MANAGEMENT COMPANY—Pharmacia & Upjohn, Inc.; *Int'l*, pg. 1048
PHARMACIA & UPJOHN COMPANY OF CANADA—Pharmacia & Upjohn, Inc.; *Int'l*, pg. 1049
PHARMACIA & UPJOHN FARMOQUIMICA, S.A.—Pharmacia & Upjohn, Inc.; *Int'l*, pg. 1049
PHARMACIA & UPJOHN GES.M.B.H.—Pharmacia & Upjohn, Inc.; *Int'l*, pg. 1050
PHARMACIA & UPJOHN GMBH—Pharmacia & Upjohn, Inc.; *Int'l*, pg. 1050
PHARMACIA & UPJOHN INTER-AMERICAN CORP.—Pharmacia & Upjohn, Inc.; *Int'l*, pg. 1048
PHARMACIA & UPJOHN INTER-AMERICAN CORPORATION-NEW ZEALAND—Pharmacia & Upjohn, Inc.; *Int'l*, pg. 1048
PHARMACIA & UPJOHN INTER-AMERICAN CORPORATION-PERU—Pharmacia & Upjohn, Inc.; *Int'l*, pg. 1048
PHARMACIA & UPJOHN INTER-AMERICAN CORPORATION-GREECE—Pharmacia & Upjohn, Inc.; *Int'l*, pg. 1048
PHARMACIA & UPJOHN INTL. INC.—Pharmacia & Upjohn, Inc.; *Int'l*, pg. 1048
PHARMACIA & UPJOHN LABORATORIES LIMITED—Pharmacia & Upjohn, Inc.; *Int'l*, pg. 1049
PHARMACIA & UPJOHN LTD.—Pharmacia & Upjohn, Inc.; *Int'l*, pg. 1050
PHARMACIA & UPJOHN NEDERLAND B.V.—Pharmacia & Upjohn, Inc.; *Int'l*, pg. 1050
PHARMACIA & UPJOHN (PROPRIETARY) LIMITED—Pharmacia & Upjohn, Inc.; *Int'l*, pg. 1049
PHARMACIA & UPJOHN PTY. LIMITED—Pharmacia & Upjohn, Inc.; *Int'l*, pg. 1049
PHARMACIA & UPJOHN S.A.—Pharmacia & Upjohn, Inc.; *Int'l*, pg. 1050
PHARMACIA & UPJOHN S.A.N.V.—Pharmacia & Upjohn, Inc.; *Int'l*, pg. 1050
PHARMAVITE CORP.; *U.S. Private*, pg. 860
PLAYTEX MARKETING CORPORATION—Playtex Products Inc.; *U.S. Public*, pg. 1311
PLOUGH (UK) LTD.—Schering-Plough Corporation; *U.S. Public*, pg. 1439
PLOUGH U.S.A.—Schering-Plough Corporation; *U.S. Public*, *pg. 1438*
POLAROME INTERNATIONAL; *U.S. Private*, pg. 874
PRESTIGE FRAGRANCE & COSMETICS, INC.—MacAndrews & Forbes Holdings Inc.; *U.S. Private*, pg. 690
PRESTIGE FRAGRANCES, LTD.—MacAndrews & Forbes Holdings Inc.; *U.S. Private*, pg. 690
PRESTIGE PERFUMES LTD.—MacAndrews & Forbes Holdings Inc.; *U.S. Private*, pg. 690
PROCTER & GAMBLE LAUNDRY CLEANING & PAPER PRODUCTS BENELUX—The Procter & Gamble Company; *U.S. Public*, pg. 1332
PRODUCTOS AVON DE GUATEMALA S.A.—Avon Products, Inc.; *U.S. Public*, pg. 156
PRODUCTOS AVON, S.A.—Avon Products, Inc.; *U.S. Public*, pg. 156
PRODUCTOS CIBA SA—Novartis AG; *Int'l*, pg. 983
PRODUCTOS COSMETICOS S.A.—Wella Group; *Int'l*, pg. 1490
PRODUCTOS ROCHE INTERAMERICANA S.A.—Roche Holding Ltd.; *Int'l*, pg. 1121
PRODUTOS SANDOZ LDA.—Novartis AG; *Int'l*, pg. 983
THE PROFESSIONAL PRODUCTS DIVISION—Bristol-Myers Squibb Company; *U.S. Public*, pg. 254
PROMO INDUSTRIE GV S.A.—Henkel KGaA; *Int'l*, pg. 613
ANTONIO PUIG SA; *Int'l*, pg. 1073
QUIMICA ESTEROIDAL SA DE CV—Akzo Nobel N.V.; *Int'l*, *pg. 45*
QUIMICA HENKEL CENTROAMERICANA DE EL SALVADOR S.A.—Henkel KGaA; *Int'l*, pg. 613
QUIMICA HENKEL CENTROAMERICANA DE HONDURAS S.A. DE C.V.—Henkel KGaA; *Int'l*, pg. 613
QUIMICA HENKEL CENTROAMERICANA S.A.—Henkel KGaA; *Int'l*, pg. 613
QUIMICA HENKEL S.A. DE C.V.—Henkel KGaA; *Int'l*, pg. 613
RADAR N.V.—Roche Holding Ltd.; *Int'l*, pg. 1121
RETI SA—Akzo Nobel N.V.; *Int'l*, pg. 45
REVLON INTERNATIONAL CORPORATION—MacAndrews & Forbes Holdings Inc.; *U.S. Private*, pg. 690
REVLON S.P.A.—MacAndrews & Forbes Holdings Inc.; *U.S. Private*, pg. 690
REXALL SUNDOWN INC.; *U.S. Public*, pg. 1384
RHONE-POULENC (ASIA)—Rhone-Poulenc S.A.; *Int'l*, pg. 1111
RHONE-POULENC JAPAN, LTD.—Rhone-Poulenc S.A.; *Int'l*, pg. 1113
RHONE-POULENC RORER—Rhone-Poulenc S.A.; *Int'l*, pg. 1111
RITA-ANN DISTRIBUTORS—AmeriSource Health Corp.; *U.S. Public*, pg. 97
ROBERTS LABORATORIES, INC.—Roberts Pharmaceutical Corporation; *U.S. Public*, pg. 1393
ROBERTS PHARMACEUTICAL CORPORATION; *U.S. Public*, pg. 1393
ROBERTS PHARMACEUTICAL OF CANADA—Roberts Pharmaceutical Corporation; *U.S. Public*, pg. 1394
A.H. ROBINS INTERNATIONAL, S.A.—American Home Products Corporation; *U.S. Public*, pg. 82
ROCHE A/S—Roche Holding Ltd.; *Int'l*, pg. 1121
ROCHE ECUADOR S.A.—Roche Holding Ltd.; *Int'l*, pg. 1121
P.T. ROCHE INDONESIA—Roche Holding Ltd.; *Int'l*, pg. 1121
ROCHE KOREA COMPANY LTD.—Roche Holding Ltd.; *Int'l*, pg. 1121
ROCHE NORGE A/S—Roche Holding Ltd.; *Int'l*, pg. 1121
ROCHE OY—Roche Holding Ltd.; *Int'l*, pg. 1121
ROCHE PRODUCTS LTD.—Roche Holding Ltd.; *Int'l*, pg. 1121
ROCHE PRODUCTS LTD. KOREA—Roche Holding Ltd.; *Int'l*, pg. 1122
ROCHE SINGAPORE PTE. LTD.—Roche Holding Ltd.; *Int'l*, *pg. 1122*
ROVIGYPT LTD.—Roche Holding Ltd.; *Int'l*, pg. 1122
RYDELLE LABORATORIES—S.C. Johnson & Son, Inc.; *U.S. Private*, pg. 592
SBS HOLDINGS, INC.; *U.S. Private*, pg. 955
SBS PHARMACEUTICALS—C.D. Smith Drug Company; *U.S. Private*, pg. 1007
SI/BAKER, INC.—SI Handling Systems, Inc.; *U.S. Public*, pg. 1418
ST. JUDE INTERNATIONAL SALES CORP.—St. Jude Medical, Inc.; *U.S. Public*, pg. 1428
SALLY BEAUTY COMPANY, INC.—Alberto-Culver Company; *U.S. Public*, pg. 38
SALVIA—Nestle S.A.; *Int'l*, pg. 922
SANDOZ A/S—Novartis AG; *Int'l*, pg. 984
P.T. SANDOZ-BIOCHEMIE FARMA INDONESIA—Novartis AG; *Int'l*, pg. 984
SANDOZ CANADA LTD.—Novartis AG; *Int'l*, pg. 984
SANDOZ COLOMBIANA S.A.—Novartis AG; *Int'l*, pg. 984
SANDOZ CORPORATION—Novartis AG; *Int'l*, pg. 974
SANDOZ DOMINICA, C. POR A.—Novartis AG; *Int'l*, pg. 984
SANDOZ DONGKOOK LTD.—Novartis AG; *Int'l*, pg. 984
SANDOZ FARMACEUTICA LTDA.—Novartis AG; *Int'l*, pg. 984
SANDOZ (HELLAS) S.A.C.I.—Novartis AG; *Int'l*, pg. 984
SANDOZ (INDIA) LTD.—Novartis AG; *Int'l*, pg. 984
SANDOZ KIMYA SANAYII LTD. SIRKETI—Novartis AG; *Int'l*, pg. 984
SANDOZ LATINOAMERICA S.A.—Novartis AG; *Int'l*, pg. 985
SANDOZ LATINOAMERICANA (ECUADOR) S.A.—Novartis AG; *Int'l*, pg. 985
SANDOZ LATINOAMERICANA (PANAMA) S.A.—Novartis AG; *Int'l*, pg. 985
SANDOZ OY—Novartis AG; *Int'l*, pg. 985
SANDOZ PERU S.A.—Novartis AG; *Int'l*, pg. 985
SANDOZ PHARMA LTD.—Novartis AG; *Int'l*, pg. 972
SANDOZ PHARMA S.A.E.—Novartis AG; *Int'l*, pg. 985
SANDOZ PHARMACEUTICALS LTD.—Novartis AG; *Int'l*, pg. 985
SANDOZ (PHILIPPINES) INC.—Novartis AG; *Int'l*, pg. 985
SANDOZ PRODOTTI FARMACEUTICI S.P.A.—Novartis AG; *Int'l*, pg. 985
SANDOZ PRODUCTS (IRELAND) LTD.—Novartis AG; *Int'l*, pg. 985
SANDOZ PRODUCTS LTD.—Novartis AG; *Int'l*, pg. 985
SANDOZ PRODUCTS (PTY.) LTD.—Novartis AG; *Int'l*, pg. 985
SANDOZ PRODUKTE (SCHWEIZ) AG—Novartis AG; *Int'l*, pg. 974
SANDOZ QUIMICA Y FARMACEUTICA S.A.—Novartis AG; *Int'l*, pg. 985
SANDOZ QUIMICO FARMACETICA CUBANA S.A.—Novartis AG; *Int'l*, pg. 985
SANDOZ S.A.—Novartis AG; *Int'l*, pg. 985
SANDOZ VERWALTUNGS G.M.B.H.—Novartis AG; *Int'l*, pg. 985
SANDOZ YAKUHIN K.K.—Novartis AG; *Int'l*, pg. 985
HENRY SCHEIN, INC.; *U.S. Public*, pg. 1437
SCHEIN PHARMACEUTICAL, INC.; *U.S. Private*, pg. 969
E. SCHEURICH PHARMWERK GMBH—American Home Products Corporation; *U.S. Public*, pg. 82
SCHOLL AG—Scholl Plc; *Int'l*, pg. 1209
SCHOLL (SVERIGE) SA—Scholl Plc; *Int'l*, pg. 1210
HANS SCHWARZKOPF GMBH—Henkel KGaA; *Int'l*, pg. 610
SERVIPHARM LTD.—Novartis AG; *Int'l*, pg. 972
SHISEIDO (AUSTRALIA) PTY. LIMITED—Shiseido Company Ltd.; *Int'l*, pg. 1235
SHISEIDO COSMETICI (ITALIA) S.P.A.—Shiseido Company Ltd.; *Int'l*, pg. 1235
SHISEIDO COSMETICS (AMERICA) LTD.—Shiseido Company Ltd.; *Int'l*, pg. 1235
SHISEIDO DEUTCHLAND GMBH—Shiseido Company Ltd.; *Int'l*, pg. 1235
SHISEIDO FRANCE S.A.—Shiseido Company Ltd.; *Int'l*, pg. 1235
SHISEIDO N.Z. LTD.—Shiseido Company Ltd.; *Int'l*, pg. 1235
SHISEIDO U.K. CO., LTD.—Shiseido Company Ltd.; *Int'l*, pg. 1236
SHOPPERS DRUG MART, LTD.—B.A.T Industries P.L.C.; *Int'l*, pg. 112
SMITH & NEPHEW CONSUMER PRODUCTS LTD.—Smith & Nephew PLC; *Int'l*, pg. 1263
C.D. SMITH DRUG COMPANY; *U.S. Private*, pg. 1007
J.M. SMITH CORP.; *U.S. Private*, pg. 1008
DR. T.C. SMITH CO. INC.—Bergen Brunswig Corporation; *U.S. Public*, pg. 214
SMITHKLINE BEECHAM CONSUMER BRANDS—SmithKline Beecham plc; *Int'l*, pg. 1264
SMITHKLINE BEECHAM FARMA B.V.—SmithKline Beecham plc; *Int'l*, pg. 1266
SMITHKLINE BEECHAM LABORATORIES—SmithKline Beecham plc; *Int'l*, pg. 1264
SMITHKLINE BEECHAM PHARMACEUTICALS—SmithKline Beecham plc; *Int'l*, pg. 1264
SMITHKLINE BEECHAM PHARMACEUTICALS, EUROPEAN DIVISION—SmithKline Beecham plc; *Int'l*, pg. 1264
SMITHKLINE BEECHAM PHARMACEUTICALS, INTERNATIONAL DIVISION—SmithKline Beecham plc; *Int'l*, pg. 1264
SMITHKLINE BEECHAM PHARMACEUTICALS (PTE.) LTD.—SmithKline Beecham plc; *Int'l*, pg. 1266
SMITHKLINE BEECHAM PRODUCTS WESTERN HEMISPHERE DIV., INTL.—SmithKline Beecham plc; *Int'l*, pg. 1264
SOCHIM COTE-D'IVOIRE SA—Novartis AG; *Int'l*, pg. 985
SOCIETE ZAIRO-SUISSE DE PRODUITS CHIMIQUES S.A.R.L.—Novartis AG; *Int'l*, pg. 986
SODIEMA S.A.—Novartis AG; *Int'l*, pg. 986
SOUTHERN BEAUTY ENTERPRISES—Beauty Enterprises Inc.; *U.S. Private*, pg. 128
SPECIAL SERVICES COMPANY—Bindley Western Industries, Inc.; *U.S. Public*, pg. 229
SQUIBB AG—Bristol-Myers Squibb Company; *U.S. Public*, pg. 256
SQUIBB (FAR EAST) LTD.—Bristol-Myers Squibb Company; *U.S. Public*, pg. 256
STAMFORD SUPERIOR DRUG CO., INC.—Bindley Western Industries, Inc.; *U.S. Public*, pg. 229

S.I.C. Index

STANHOME INC.; *U.S. Public*, pg. 1508
STAR SALES CO., INC.; *U.S. Private*, pg. 1035
SUOMEN ASTRA OY—Astra AB; *Int'l*, pg. 94
SUPERIOR WHOLESALE DRUG CO.—Bindley Western Industries, Inc.; *U.S. Public*, pg. 229
SWISS NIGERIAN CHEMICAL CO. LTD.—Novartis AG; *Int'l*, pg. 986
SWISSPHARMA S.A.E.—Novartis AG; *Int'l*, pg. 986
SYMBICOM AB—Astra AB; *Int'l*, pg. 93
SYNCOR INTERNATIONAL CORPORATION; *U.S. Public*, pg. 1548
SYNTHELABO PHARMACEUTICALS K.K.—L'Oreal S.A.; *Int'l*, pg. 818
SYNTHELABO S.A.—L'Oreal S.A.; *Int'l*, pg. 818
TWD BALTIMORE—Bindley Western Industries, Inc.; *U.S. Public*, pg. 229
TAISHO PHARMACEUTICAL CALIFORNIA INC.—Taisho Pharmaceutical Co., Ltd.; *Int'l*, pg. 1348
TAKEDA CHEMICAL INDUSTRIES, LTD.; *Int'l*, pg. 1350
TAKEDA USA INC.—Takeda Chemical Industries, Ltd.; *Int'l*, *pg. 1350*
TANABE U.S.A. INC.—Tanabe Seiyaku Co., Ltd.; *Int'l*, pg. 1354
THAI MEIJI PHARMACEUTICAL CO., LTD.—Meiji Seika Kaisha, Ltd.; *Int'l*, pg. 856
DR. RER. NAT. PETER THEISS NATURWAREN—Wella Group; *Int'l*, pg. 1489
THEON CO. LTD.—Del Laboratories, Inc.; *U.S. Public*, pg. 494
THIEMANN ARZNEIMITTEL GMBH—Akzo Nobel N.V.; *Int'l*, *pg. 45*
THOMPSON MEDICAL COMPANY, INC.; *U.S. Private*, pg. 1083
3M ZIMBABWE (PVT.) LTD.—3M; *U.S. Public*, pg. 1607
TIANJIN LIMING COSMETICS JOINT INDUSTRIAL CO.—Wella Group; *Int'l*, pg. 1490
TOSOHAAS COMPANY—Tosoh Corporation; *Int'l*, pg. 1408
TRANSKIMYA TICARET VE SANAYE A.S.—Wella Group; *Int'l*, pg. 1490
TRI-STATE WHOLESALE ASSOCIATED GROCERS, INC.; *U.S. Private*, pg. 1101
TRI TECH LABORATORIES, INC.; *U.S. Private*, pg. 1101
TRISTAR CORP.; *U.S. Public*, pg. 1640
TROPONWERKE GMBH & CO., KG—Bayer AG; *Int'l*, pg. 175
UBE INDUSTRIES (AMERICA) INC.—UBE Industries Ltd.; *Int'l*, pg. 1427
UBE INDUSTRIES LTD.; *Int'l*, pg. 1426
GEORGE UHE CO., INC.; *U.S. Private*, pg. 1115
UNI-BEAUTY LIMITED—Wella Group; *Int'l*, pg. 1490
VEMEDIA B.V.—Solvay S.A.; *Int'l*, pg. 1279
VESTRIC LTD.—Franz Haniel & Cie, GmbH; *Int'l*, pg. 592
VITAMIN WORLD—Nature's Bounty Inc.; *U.S. Public*, pg. 1166
WARNER-LAMBERT INTERNATIONAL OPERATIONS—Warner-Lambert Company; *U.S. Public*, pg. 1739
WARNER-LAMBERT VERKOOP B.V.—Warner-Lambert Company; *U.S. Public*, pg. 1740
WELLA (AUSTRALIA) COSMETIC SUPPLIERS PTY. LTD.—Wella Group; *Int'l*, pg. 1490
WELLA DUBLIN—Wella Group; *Int'l*, pg. 1490
WELLA GROUP; *Int'l*, pg. 1489
WELLA ITALIANA—Wella Group; *Int'l*, pg. 1490
WELLA PORTUGAL SOCIEDADE DE COSMETICOS LUSO-ALEMA LDA.—Wella Group; *Int'l*, pg. 1490
THE WEST COMPANY ITALIA S.R.L.—The West Company, Incorporated; *U.S. Public*, pg. 1756
WESTWOOD-SQUIBB PHARMACEUTICALS INC.—Bristol-Myers Squibb Company; *U.S. Public*, pg. 255
WHITEHALL LABORATORIES PTY. LIMITED—American Home Products Corporation; *U.S. Public*, pg. 82
WHITEHALL-ROBINS DE MEXICO, S.A. DE C.V.—American Home Products Corporation; *U.S. Public*, pg. 82
WHITEHALL-ROBINS INC.—American Home Products Corporation; *U.S. Public*, pg. 82
WINSTAR GLOBAL PRODUCTS, INC.—Winstar Communications; *U.S. Public*, pg. 1772
WYETH-AYERST INTERNATIONAL, INC.—American Home Products Corporation; *U.S. Public*, pg. 80
WYETH S.A.—American Home Products Corporation; *U.S. Public*, pg. 82
YOSHITOMI-ASTRA LTD.—Astra AB; *Int'l*, pg. 94
ZEE MEDICAL, INC.—McKesson Corporation; *U.S. Public*, pg. 1073
ZENECA AB—Zeneca Group Plc; *Int'l*, pg. 1526
ZENECA AG—Zeneca Group Plc; *Int'l*, pg. 1526
ZENECA OY—Zeneca Group Plc; *Int'l*, pg. 1527
ZENECA POLAND SP. Z.O.O.—Zeneca Group Plc; *Int'l*, pg. 1527
ZENECA ZIMBABWE (PRIVATE) LIMITED—Zeneca Group Plc; *Int'l*, pg. 1527
ZIMMER AUSTRALIA PTY. LIMITED—Bristol-Myers Squibb Company; *U.S. Public*, pg. 256
ZIMMER INTERNATIONAL, S.A.—Bristol-Myers Squibb Company; *U.S. Public*, pg. 257
ZYMA GMBH—Novartis AG; *Int'l*, pg. 986
ZYMA SA—Novartis AG; *Int'l*, pg. 972
ZYMA S.P.A—Novartis AG; *Int'l*, pg. 986

5131 — PIECE GOODS, NOTIONS & OTHER DRY GOODS-WHOLESALE

ANDERSON WHOLESALE COMPANY; *U.S. Private*, pg. 73
ARAMI FASER-VERTRIEB GMBH—Akzo Nobel N.V.; *Int'l*, pg. 46
ARAMI FRANCE SARL—Akzo Nobel N.V.; *Int'l*, pg. 45
ARAMI ITALIANA SRL—Akzo Nobel N.V.; *Int'l*, pg. 45
ARAMI UK LTD.—Akzo Nobel N.V.; *Int'l*, pg. 45
JOSHUA L. BAILY CO., INC.; *U.S. Private*, pg. 110
BALLANTYNE CASHMERE USA LTD.—Dawson International PLC; *Int'l*, pg. 386
BLUMENTHAL PRINT WORKS, INC.; *U.S. Private*, pg. 153
BRUNSCHWIG & FILS, INC.; *U.S. Private*, pg. 176
CFCI S.A.—Unilever Plc; *Int'l*, pg. 1436
CALICO PRINTERS ASSN. (U.S.A. LTD.)—Coats Viyella plc; *Int'l*, pg. 300
CHORI AMERICA, INC.—Chori Co., Ltd.; *Int'l*, pg. 288
CHORI CO., LTD.; *Int'l*, pg. 288
COATS & CLARK INC. (SALES OFFICE)—Coats Viyella plc; *Int'l*, pg. 300
CONCORD FABRICS INC.; *U.S. Public*, pg. 429
CONCORD FOREIGN SALES CORP., INC.—Concord Fabrics Inc.; *U.S. Public*, pg. 430
CONCORD HOUSE DIVISION—Concord Fabrics Inc.; *U.S. Public*, pg. 430
CONE MILLS CORPORATION; *U.S. Public*, pg. 430
CONTINENTAL CONAIR, LTD.—Conair Corporation; *U.S. Private*, pg. 261
CONTROLADORA COMERCIAL MEXICANA, S.A. DE C.V.; *Int'l*, pg. 328
DADE LEASE MANAGEMENT, INC.—Dollar General Corporation; *U.S. Public*, pg. 515
DESIGN/CRAFT FABRIC CORP.—RPM, Inc.; *U.S. Public*, pg. 1357
DOLGENCORP, INC.—Dollar General Corporation; *U.S. Public*, pg. 515
DOLLAR GENERAL CORPORATION; *U.S. Public*, pg. 515
THE EAST ASIATIC COMPANY LTD. A/S; *Int'l*, pg. 430
ENKA DANMARK A/S—Akzo Nobel N.V.; *Int'l*, pg. 46
ENKA FRANCE SARL—Akzo Nobel N.V.; *Int'l*, pg. 46
ENKA HELLAS LTD.—Akzo Nobel N.V.; *Int'l*, pg. 46
ENKA OSTERREICH HANDELSGESELLSCHAFT MBH—Akzo Nobel N.V.; *Int'l*, pg. 46
ENKA PORTUGUESA LDA—Akzo Nobel N.V.; *Int'l*, pg. 46
ENKA (SCHWEIZ) GMBH—Akzo Nobel N.V.; *Int'l*, pg. 46
ENKA SUOMI OY—Akzo Nobel N.V.; *Int'l*, pg. 46
ENKA SVERIGE AB—Akzo Nobel N.V.; *Int'l*, pg. 46
FAB INTERNATIONAL, LTD.—Fab Industries, Inc.; *U.S. Public*, pg. 603
GSI EUROPE-IMPORT & EXPORT GMBH—Gunze Sangyo, Inc.; *Int'l*, pg. 579
GSI EXIM AMERICA INC.—Gunze Sangyo, Inc.; *Int'l*, pg. 578
W. GAMBY & CO.; *U.S. Private*, pg. 439
GUNZE SANGYO, INC.; *Int'l*, pg. 578
HAMPTON PRINT WORKS, INC.; *U.S. Private*, pg. 498
HANCOCK FABRICS, INC.; *U.S. Public*, pg. 779
HARP'S FOOD STORES, INC.; *U.S. Private*, pg. 504
HARRISONS & CROSFIELD (N.Z.) LTD.—Harrisons & Crosfield plc; *Int'l*, pg. 599
HATEMA LTD.—Gamma Holding N.V.; *Int'l*, pg. 540
HATTON ET COOKSON S.A.—Unilever Plc; *Int'l*, pg. 1437
HELEN OF TROY, CONSUMER PRODUCTS DIV.—Helen of Troy Corporation; *U.S. Public*, pg. 807
HELEN OF TROY CORPORATION; *U.S. Public*, pg. 807
HELEN OF TROY (FAR EAST) LTD.—Helen of Troy Corporation; *U.S. Public*, pg. 807
HELEN OF TROY, PROFESSIONAL SALON DIV.—Helen of Troy Corporation; *U.S. Public*, pg. 807
HOF TEXTILES INC.—Neuebaum Woll-Spinnerei Und Weberei Hof A.G.; *Int'l*, pg. 923
THE JOHN JOHNSON CO.; *U.S. Private*, pg. 591
JACK LENOR LARSEN, INC.; *U.S. Private*, pg. 652
LEISURE ARTS, INC.—Time Warner Inc.; *U.S. Public*, pg. 1613
LEVEL EXPORT SALES CORP.; *U.S. Private*, pg. 662
MAHARAM; *U.S. Private*, pg. 696
MALDEN MILLS INDUSTRIES, INC.; *U.S. Private*, pg. 698
MARCUS BROTHERS TEXTILES, INC.; *U.S. Private*, pg. 702
MARK FABRICKS, INC.; *U.S. Private*, pg. 704
MARUBENI AMERICA CORPORATION, DALLAS BRANCH—Marubeni Corporation; *Int'l*, pg. 844
MARUBENI AMERICA CORPORATION, DETROIT BRANCH—Marubeni Corporation; *Int'l*, pg. 844
MARUBENI AMERICA CORPORATION, PORTLAND BRANCH—Marubeni Corporation; *Int'l*, pg. 845
MARUBENI AMERICA CORPORATION, SAN FRANCISCO BRANCH—Marubeni Corporation; *Int'l*, pg. 845
MARUBENI AMERICAN CORPORATION, SEATTLE BRANCH—Marubeni Corporation; *Int'l*, pg. 845
MARUBENI CORPORATION; *Int'l*, pg. 844
MINEBEA CO., LTD.; *Int'l*, pg. 867
MITSUBISHI CORPORATION; *Int'l*, pg. 871
MONSANTO (DEUTSCHLAND) GMBH—Monsanto Company; *U.S. Public*, pg. 1125
MONSANTO (VENEZUELA) C.A.—Monsanto Company; *U.S. Public*, pg. 1126
MOUNT VERNON MILLS, INC.—R.B. Pamplin Corp.; *U.S. Private*, pg. 835
MOUNT VERNON MILLS SALES CORP.—R.B. Pamplin Corp.; *U.S. Private*, pg. 836
PEM INTL. LTD.—Penn Engineering & Manufacturing Corp.; *U.S. Public*, pg. 1270
P.S. INTERNATIONAL INC.; *U.S. Private*, pg. 827
PAGO FABRICS, INC.—Itochu Corporation; *Int'l*, pg. 695
PAXAR DEUTSCHLAND GMBH—PAXAR Corporation; *U.S. Public*, pg. 1266
PAXAR ITALIA S.R.L.—PAXAR Corporation; *U.S. Public*, pg. 1267
PRINGLE OF SCOTLAND—Dawson International PLC; *Int'l*, *pg. 386*
QST FAR EAST LIMITED—QST Industries, Inc.; *U.S. Private*, pg. 897
QST INDUSTRIES, INC.; *U.S. Private*, pg. 897
ROCKVILLE FABRICS CORPORATION; *U.S. Private*, pg. 938
SCHOTTENSTEIN STORES CORPORATION; *U.S. Private*, *pg. 972*
F. SCHUMACHER & CO.; *U.S. Private*, pg. 973
STANLEY DRYING COMPANY—DEC International, Inc.; *U.S. Private*, pg. 301
STAR SALES CO., INC.; *U.S. Private*, pg. 1035
SUMITOMO CORPORATION; *Int'l*, pg. 1312
SUMITOMO CORPORATION OF AMERICA—Sumitomo Corporation; *Int'l*, pg. 1312
SUNKYONG AMERICA, INC.—Sunkyong Industries Co.; *Int'l*, pg. 1320
SUNKYONG INDUSTRIES CO.; *Int'l*, pg. 1320
TEXTILE IMPRESSIONS, INC.—Itochu Corporation; *Int'l*, pg. 695
TONG SHING INC.—Toray Industries, Inc.; *Int'l*, pg. 1400
TORAY DEUTSCHLAND GMBH—Toray Industries, Inc.; *Int'l*, pg. 1400
TORAY EUROPE LTD.—Toray Industries, Inc.; *Int'l*, pg. 1400
TORAY INDUSTRIES (H.K.) LTD.—Toray Industries, Inc.; *Int'l*, pg. 1400
TORAY INDUSTRIES (SINGAPORE) PTE. LTD.—Toray Industries, Inc.; *Int'l*, pg. 1400
TORAY ITALIA S.R.L.—Toray Industries, Inc.; *Int'l*, pg. 1400
TOYO BOSEKI (EUROPE) GMBH—Toyobo Co., Ltd.; *Int'l*, pg. 1411
TOYOBO AMERICA INC.—Toyobo Co., Ltd.; *Int'l*, pg. 1411
TOYOBO HONG KONG—Toyobo Co., Ltd.; *Int'l*, pg. 1411
VALUE CITY DEPARTMENT STORES, INC.—Schottenstein Stores Corporation; *U.S. Private*, pg. 972
VELCRO AUSTRALIA PTY. LTD.—Velcro Industries N.V.; *Int'l*, pg. 1462
WEILWOOD INDUSTRIES, INC.—Santee Print Works, Inc.; *U.S. Private*, pg. 965
WELLMAN BONDED FIBERS DIV.—Wellman, Inc.; *U.S. Public*, pg. 1753
WELLMAN FIBERS LTD.—Wellman, Inc.; *U.S. Public*, pg. 1753
WELLMAN, INC.; *U.S. Public*, pg. 1752
WELLMAN INTERNATIONAL GMBH—Wellman, Inc.; *U.S. Public*, pg. 1753
WELLMAN MAN-MADE FIBERS DIV.—Wellman, Inc.; *U.S. Public*, pg. 1752
WELLMAN NONWOVENS DIV.—Wellman, Inc.; *U.S. Public*, *pg. 1753*
FRANK W. WINNE & SON, INC.; *U.S. Private*, pg. 1183

5136 — MEN'S & BOYS CLOTHING & FURNISHINGS-WHOLESALE

ARC INTERNATIONAL CORPORATION; *Int'l*, pg. 17
AWI RETAIL—Alba-Waldensian, Inc.; *U.S. Public*, pg. 36
ACUSHNET COMPANY—Fortune Brands, Inc.; *U.S. Public*, pg. 675
ADIDAS SARRAGAN NORGE A/S—Adidas AG; *Int'l*, pg. 25
ALPHA SHIRT CO., INC.; *U.S. Private*, pg. 45
AMEREX USA, INC.; *U.S. Private*, pg. 49
AMERICAN CAMPER—Brunswick Corporation; *U.S. Public*, pg. 265
ARROW SHIRT COMPANY—Bidermann International S.A.; *Int'l*, pg. 194
AU BON MARCHE; *Int'l*, pg. 97
BAYER CLOTHING GROUP; *U.S. Private*, pg. 124
BEIJING DESCENTE CO., LTD.—Descente Ltd.; *Int'l*, pg. 396
BRODER BROS. CO.; *U.S. Private*, pg. 170
THE BUCKLE, INC.; *U.S. Public*, pg. 267
BUGLE BOY INDUSTRIES, INC.; *U.S. Private*, pg. 179
C S CRABLE SPORTSWEAR, INC.—The Midland Company; *U.S. Public*, pg. 1111
CALVIN KLEIN SPORT, INC.—Calvin Klein, Inc.; *U.S. Private*, pg. 202
CLIFTEX—Woolworth Corporation; *U.S. Public*, pg. 1777
DADE LEASE MANAGEMENT, INC.—Dollar General Corporation; *U.S. Public*, pg. 515
DAISY DE VENEZUELA C.A.—Fruit of the Loom, Inc.; *U.S. Public*, pg. 686
DESCENTE AMERICA INC.—Descente Ltd.; *Int'l*, pg. 395
DESCENTE CANADA INC.—Descente Ltd.; *Int'l*, pg. 396
DESCENTE LTD.; *Int'l*, pg. 395
DOCKERS BRAND—Levi Strauss & Co.; *U.S. Private*, pg. 663
DOLGENCORP, INC.—Dollar General Corporation; *U.S. Public*, pg. 515
DOLLAR GENERAL CORPORATION; *U.S. Public*, pg. 515
DON JUAN SPORTSWEAR, INC.—Marubeni Corporation; *Int'l*, pg. 845
DRAGON INTERNATIONAL—Bugle Boy Industries, Inc.; *U.S. Private*, pg. 179
FARAH (EXPORTS) IRELAND—Farah Incorporated; *U.S. Public*, pg. 613
FARAH INTERNATIONAL, INC.—Farah Incorporated; *U.S. Public*, pg. 613
FARAH SALES CORP.—Farah Incorporated; *U.S. Public*, pg. 613
FRED PERRY SPORTSWEAR LTD.—Hit Union Company Ltd.; *Int'l*, pg. 620
GILRICHCO, INC.; *U.S. Private*, pg. 454
GITANO FASHIONS LTD.—Fruit of the Loom, Inc.; *U.S. Public*, pg. 686
GITANO MEN'S DIVISION—Fruit of the Loom, Inc.; *U.S. Public*, pg. 686
HEYMAN CORPORATION; *U.S. Private*, pg. 524
HUGO BOSS FASHIONS INC.—Hugo Boss AG; *Int'l*, pg. 637
INTERNATIONAL COSMETICS CO., LTD.; *Int'l*, pg. 684
JOCKEY INTERNATIONAL, INC.; *U.S. Private*, pg. 588
JORDACHE ENTERPRISES, INC.; *U.S. Private*, pg. 597
K-SWISS EUROPE LTD.—K-Swiss Inc.; *U.S. Public*, pg. 937
K-SWISS INTERNATIONAL LTD.—K-Swiss Inc.; *U.S. Public*, pg. 937
KOSUGI SANGYO CO., LTD.; *Int'l*, pg. 759
LABELLE JARDINIERE—Au Bon Marche; *Int'l*, pg. 98
LOST ARROW CORPORATION; *U.S. Private*, pg. 676
LUCKY-GOLDSTAR INTERNATIONAL (AMERICA)—LG Group; *Int'l*, pg. 779
LUCKY GOLDSTAR INTERNATIONAL AMERICA, INC.—LG Group; *Int'l*, pg. 779
MARUBENI AMERICA CORPORATION—Marubeni Corporation; *Int'l*, pg. 844

MEMBERS ONLY BY EUROPE CRAFT—Aris Industries, Inc.; *U.S. Public*, pg. 129
THE MIDLAND COMPANY; *U.S. Public*, pg. 1110
MONROE G. MILSTEIN, INC.—Burlington Coat Factory Warehouse Corporation; *U.S. Public*, pg. 268
MITSUBISHI CORPORATION; *Int'l*, pg. 871
MIZUNO USA, INC.—Mizuno Corporation; *Int'l*, pg. 885
MOSS BROS GROUP PLC; *Int'l*, pg. 895
NANBU SEN-I KOGYO CO., LTD.—Kosugi Sangyo Co., Ltd.; *Int'l*, pg. 759
NAUTICA ENTERPRISES, INC.; *U.S. Public*, pg. 1167
OSHKOSH B'GOSH HOSIERY CO.—Heyman Corporation; *U.S. Private*, pg. 525
OSHKOSH B'GOSH, INC.-NEW YORK—OshKosh B'Gosh, Inc.; *U.S. Public*, pg. 1233
OXFORD PRODUCTS INTERNATIONAL LTD.—Oxford Industries, Inc.; *U.S. Public*, pg. 1239
PACIFIC TRAIL INC.—London Fog Industries, Inc.; *U.S. Private*, pg. 673
PATAGONIA—Lost Arrow Corporation; *U.S. Private*, pg. 677
PHILLIPS-VAN HEUSEN CORPORATION; *U.S. Public*, pg. 1291
PLAID CLOTHING COMPANY—Hartmarx Corporation; *U.S. Public*, pg. 796
POLO/RALPH LAUREN CORPORATION; *U.S. Private*, pg. 874
R & R UNIFORMS—Horace Small Apparel PLC; *Int'l*, pg. 635
RAM GRAPHICS, INC.; *U.S. Private*, pg. 908
RAWLINGS SPORTING GOODS COMPANY; *U.S. Public*, pg. 1361
RECREATIONAL EQUIPMENT, INC.; *U.S. Private*, pg. 914
RENFRO CORP.; *U.S. Private*, pg. 922
ROLANE FACTORY OUTLETS; *U.S. Private*, pg. 941
ROYTEX, INC.; *U.S. Private*, pg. 949
M. RUBIN & SONS INC.; *U.S. Private*, pg. 949
RUSSELL CORP. UK LIMITED—Russell Corporation; *U.S. Public*, pg. 1413
SAMSUNG AMERICA APPAREL SHOWROOM—Samsung Group; *Int'l*, pg. 1183
SARRAGAN BENELUX S.A.—Adidas AG; *Int'l*, pg. 25
SCHOOL APPAREL, INC.; *U.S. Private*, pg. 972
SCHOTTENSTEIN STORES CORPORATION; *U.S. Private*, *pg. 972*
SEATTLE PACIFIC INDUSTRIES, INC.; *U.S. Private*, pg. 980
SHELBY GROUP INTERNATIONAL, INC.; *U.S. Private*, pg. 991
SID HARVEY INDUSTRIES; *U.S. Private*, pg. 998
SOUTHERN APPAREL CORPORATION; *U.S. Private*, pg. 1015
SPORT OBERMEYER LTD., USA; *U.S. Private*, pg. 1026
SPORTS IMPRINTS/FUN WEAR—Littlefield, Adams & Company; *U.S. Public*, pg. 1002
SUNKYONG INDUSTRIES CO.; *Int'l*, pg. 1320
SUPERBA, INC.; *U.S. Private*, pg. 1054
SUPREME INTERNATIONAL CORP.; *U.S. Public*, pg. 1542
TOTES CANADA LTD.—Bain Capital; *U.S. Private*, pg. 111
TOTES U.K. LIMITED—Bain Capital; *U.S. Private*, pg. 111
TRAIN KOGYO CO., LTD.—Kosugi Sangyo Co., Ltd.; *Int'l*, pg. 759
TRU-FIT GLOVE & HEADWEAR DIV.—Heyman Corporation; *U.S. Private*, pg. 525
VF ASIA LIMITED—VF Corporation; *U.S. Public*, pg. 1702
VF INTERNATIONAL—VF Corporation; *U.S. Public*, pg. 1702
VALUE CITY DEPARTMENT STORES, INC.—Schottenstein Stores Corporation; *U.S. Private*, pg. 972
VALUE SLACKS, INC.—Farah Incorporated; *U.S. Public*, pg. 613
WARNACO INC.-INTERNATIONAL DIV.—Warnaco Inc.; *U.S. Public*, pg. 1738

5137 — WOMEN'S, CHILDREN'S, & INFANTS' CLOTHING & ACCESSORIES-WHOLESALE

ARC INTERNATIONAL CORPORATION; *Int'l*, pg. 17
ACCECONES RICCI U.S.A., INC.—Elf Aquitane; *Int'l*, pg. 445
ACCESSORY DESIGN GROUP, LTD.—Tandy Brands Accessories, Inc.; *U.S. Public*, pg. 1560
THE ACORN—Gilmore Bros., Inc.; *U.S. Private*, pg. 454
ADIDAS SARRAGAN NORGE A/S—Adidas AG; *Int'l*, pg. 25
AMEREX USA, INC.; *U.S. Private*, pg. 49
ARROW SHIRT COMPANY—Bidermann International S.A.; *Int'l*, pg. 194
AU BON MARCHE; *Int'l*, pg. 97
BALLY TRADING AG—Oerlikon-Buhrle Holding AG; *Int'l*, pg. 996
BELDOCH INDUSTRIES—Donnkenny, Inc.; *U.S. Public*, pg. 510
BELDOCH POPPER DIVISION—Donnkenny, Inc.; *U.S. Public*, pg. 520
BODY DRAMA (FAR EAST) LTD.—Niches, Inc.; *U.S. Public*, pg. 1182
BOSCARALE/TOM TOGS; *U.S. Private*, pg. 160
A.J. BRANDON—Kellwood Company; *U.S. Public*, pg. 948
BRODER BROS. CO.; *U.S. Private*, pg. 170
THE BUCKLE, INC.; *U.S. Public*, pg. 267
C S CRABLE SPORTSWEAR, INC.—The Midland Company; *U.S. Public*, pg. 1111
CALIFORNIA FASHION INDUSTRIES INC.; *U.S. Private*, pg. 200
CALVIN KLEIN SPORT, INC.—Calvin Klein, Inc.; *U.S. Private*, pg. 202
BERNARD CHAUS, INC.; *U.S. Public*, pg. 342
CLIFTEX—Woolworth Corporation; *U.S. Public*, pg. 1777
DADE LEASE MANAGEMENT, INC.—Dollar General Corporation; *U.S. Public*, pg. 515
DAISY DE VENEZUELA C.A.—Fruit of the Loom, Inc.; *U.S. Public*, pg. 686
DANCE FRANCE LTD.—Danskin Inc.; *U.S. Public*, pg. 483
DANIEL CARON SPORTSWEAR; *U.S. Private*, pg. 309
DESCENTE AMERICA INC.—Descente Ltd.; *Int'l*, pg. 395
DESCENTE LTD.; *Int'l*, pg. 395
DOCKERS BRAND—Levi Strauss & Co.; *U.S. Private*, pg. 663
DOLGENCORP, INC.—Dollar General Corporation; *U.S. Public*, pg. 515
DOLLAR GENERAL CORPORATION; *U.S. Public*, pg. 515
DON JUAN SPORTSWEAR, INC.—Marubeni Corporation; *Int'l*, pg. 845
EDELSON & SONS CORPORATION; *U.S. Private*, pg. 363
ESPRIT DE CORP.; *U.S. Private*, pg. 383
EVENFLO COMPANY, INC.—Kohlberg Kravis Roberts & Co.; *U.S. Private*, pg. 629
FCN CORPORATION—KOHAP Group; *Int'l*, pg. 742
FARAH INTERNATIONAL, INC.—Farah Incorporated; *U.S. Public*, pg. 613
FARAH SALES CORP.—Farah Incorporated; *U.S. Public*, pg. 613
THE FIRST YEARS INC.; *U.S. Public*, pg. 642
FORTUNE FASHION INC.; *U.S. Private*, pg. 419
FOSSIL INC.; *U.S. Private*, pg. 420
FRED PERRY SPORTSWEAR LTD.—Hit Union Company Ltd.; *Int'l*, pg. 620
THE GENERRA COMPANY; *U.S. Private*, pg. 446
GERBER PRODUCTS COMPANY OF PUERTO RICO, INC.—Novartis AG; *Int'l*, pg. 973
GILRICHCO, INC.; *U.S. Private*, pg. 454
GIRL'S DIVISION—Fruit of the Loom, Inc.; *U.S. Public*, pg. 686
GITANO FASHIONS LTD.—Fruit of the Loom, Inc.; *U.S. Public*, pg. 686
KENNETH GORDON IAG, INC.—Tom James Company; *U.S. Private*, pg. 581
H.K. INTERNATIONAL, INC.; *U.S. Private*, pg. 491
HAMPTON PRINT WORKS, INC.; *U.S. Private*, pg. 498
JOAN & DAVID HELPERN, INC.; *U.S. Private*, pg. 521
HEYMAN CORPORATION; *U.S. Private*, pg. 524
I.B. DIFFUSION, LP; *U.S. Private*, pg. 553
INTERNATIONAL COSMETICS CO., LTD.; *Int'l*, pg. 684
JACQUES MORET, INC.; *U.S. Private*, pg. 580
JONES APPAREL GROUP, INC. CANADA—Jones Apparel Group, Inc.; *U.S. Public*, pg. 933
JORDACHE ENTERPRISES, INC.; *U.S. Private*, pg. 597
K-SWISS EUROPE LTD.—K-Swiss Inc.; *U.S. Public*, pg. 937
K-SWISS INTERNATIONAL LTD.—K-Swiss Inc.; *U.S. Public*, pg. 937
KIRKSTONE COMPANY LTD.—Charming Shoppes, Inc.; *U.S. Public*, pg. 336
KOSUGI SANGYO CO., LTD.; *Int'l*, pg. 759
LAURA ASHLEY DISTRIBUTION BV—Laura Ashley Holdings Plc; *Int'l*, pg. 804
LILYETTE BRASSIERE CO.—Maidenform Worldwide; *U.S. Private*, pg. 697
LOST ARROW CORPORATION; *U.S. Private*, pg. 676
LOUIS VUITTON NORTH AMERICA, INC.—LVMH Moet Hennessy Louis Vuitton; *Int'l*, pg. 781
LUCKY-GOLDSTAR INTERNATIONAL (AMERICA)—LG Group; *Int'l*, pg. 779
LUCKY GOLDSTAR INTERNATIONAL AMERICA, INC.—LG Group; *Int'l*, pg. 779
M&S MODE—N.V. Koninklijke Bijenkorf Beheer KBB; *Int'l*, pg. 750
MARISA CHRISTINA INC.; *U.S. Public*, pg. 1044
MARUBENI AMERICA CORPORATION—Marubeni Corporation; *Int'l*, pg. 844
MAST INDUSTRIES—The Limited, Inc.; *U.S. Public*, pg. 996
THE MIDLAND COMPANY; *U.S. Public*, pg. 1110
MONROE G. MILSTEIN, INC.—Burlington Coat Factory Warehouse Corporation; *U.S. Public*, pg. 268
MITSUBISHI CORPORATION; *Int'l*, pg. 871
MIZUNO USA, INC.—Mizuno Corporation; *Int'l*, pg. 885
NANBU SEN-I KOGYO CO., LTD.—Kosugi Sangyo Co., Ltd.; *Int'l*, pg. 759
NATIONAL CORSET SUPPLY HOUSE; *U.S. Private*, pg. 781
NICHES, INC.; *U.S. Public*, pg. 1181
NICHIMEN AMERICA, INC.—Nichimen Corporation; *Int'l*, pg. 927
NICHIMEN CORPORATION; *Int'l*, pg. 927
NISSHO IWAI TEXTILE CO., LTD.—Nissho Iwai Corporation; *Int'l*, pg. 947
NITCHES (FAR EAST) LTD.—Niches, Inc.; *U.S. Public*, pg. 1182
OSHKOSH B'GOSH HOSIERY CO.—Heyman Corporation; *U.S. Private*, pg. 525
OSHKOSH B'GOSH, INC.-NEW YORK—OshKosh B'Gosh, Inc.; *U.S. Public*, pg. 1233
OXFORD COLLECTION—Oxford Industries, Inc.; *U.S. Public*, pg. 1239
OXFORD PRODUCTS INTERNATIONAL LTD.—Oxford Industries, Inc.; *U.S. Public*, pg. 1239
OXFORD SEPARATES—Oxford Industries, Inc.; *U.S. Public*, pg. 1239
PACIFIC TRAIL INC.—London Fog Industries, Inc.; *U.S. Private*, pg. 673
PATAGONIA—Lost Arrow Corporation; *U.S. Private*, pg. 677
PERRY MFG. CO.—Page Holdings, Inc.; *U.S. Private*, pg. 834
PIERRE CARDIN KNITS—Donnkenny, Inc.; *U.S. Public*, pg. 520
R & R UNIFORMS—Horace Small Apparel PLC; *Int'l*, pg. 635
RGA AND EAST END ACCESSORIES; *U.S. Private*, pg. 903
RECREATIONAL EQUIPMENT, INC.; *U.S. Private*, pg. 914
REGENT INTERNATIONAL; *U.S. Private*, pg. 918
RENFRO CORP.; *U.S. Private*, pg. 922
ST. JOHN KNITS; *U.S. Private*, pg. 960
SAMSUNG AMERICA APPAREL SHOWROOM—Samsung Group; *Int'l*, pg. 1183
SARRAGAN BENELUX S.A.—Adidas AG; *Int'l*, pg. 25
SCHOOL APPAREL, INC.; *U.S. Private*, pg. 972
SCHOTTENSTEIN STORES CORPORATION; *U.S. Private*, *pg. 972*
ROBERT SCOTT/DAVID BROOKS—Kellwood Company; *U.S. Public*, pg. 948
SEATTLE PACIFIC INDUSTRIES, INC.; *U.S. Private*, pg. 980
SEIBEL & STERN CORP.; *U.S. Private*, pg. 981
SHANE HANDBAGS—Jaclyn, Inc.; *U.S. Public*, pg. 920
SID HARVEY INDUSTRIES; *U.S. Private*, pg. 998
SPECIAL MARKETS (RTVCH)—Liz Claiborne, Inc.; *U.S. Public*, pg. 1006
SPORT OBERMEYER LTD., USA; *U.S. Private*, pg. 1026
SPORTS IMPRINTS/FUN WEAR—Littlefield, Adams & Company; *U.S. Public*, pg. 1002
SUNKYONG INDUSTRIES CO.; *Int'l*, pg. 1320
TOTES CANADA LTD.—Bain Capital; *U.S. Private*, pg. 111
TOTES U.K. LIMITED—Bain Capital; *U.S. Private*, pg. 111
TRAIN KOGYO CO., LTD.—Kosugi Sangyo Co., Ltd.; *Int'l*, pg. 759
TRU-FIT GLOVE & HEADWEAR DIV.—Heyman Corporation; *U.S. Private*, pg. 525
VF ASIA LIMITED—VF Corporation; *U.S. Public*, pg. 1702
VF INTERNATIONAL—VF Corporation; *U.S. Public*, pg. 1702
VALUE CITY DEPARTMENT STORES, INC.—Schottenstein Stores Corporation; *U.S. Private*, pg. 972
VARSITY SPIRIT CORPORATION—Riddell Sports, Inc.; *U.S. Public*, pg. 1389
WARNER'S AIGLON, S.A.—Warnaco Inc.; *U.S. Public*, pg. 1738
WARNER'S DE MEXICO, S.A. DE C.V.—Warnaco Inc.; *U.S. Public*, pg. 1738
WARNER'S (UNITED KINGDOM) LIMITED—Warnaco Inc.; *U.S. Public*, pg. 1738

5139 — FOOTWEAR-WHOLESALE

ACUSHNET COMPANY—Fortune Brands, Inc.; *U.S. Public*, pg. 675
ADIDAS AG; *Int'l*, pg. 24
ADIDAS SARRAGAN NORGE A/S—Adidas AG; *Int'l*, pg. 25
AGNEW GROUP—The Bentley Agnew Group Inc.; *Int'l*, pg. 187
ALLEN-EDMONDS SHOE CORP.; *U.S. Private*, pg. 36
AMALGAMATED SHOE CO. LTD.—Pentland Group PLC; *Int'l*, pg. 1035
AMERICAN CAMPER—Brunswick Corporation; *U.S. Public*, pg. 265
J. BAKER, INC.; *U.S. Public*, pg. 167
BALLY TRADING AG—Oerlikon-Buhrle Holding AG; *Int'l*, pg. 996
BALLY UK SALES LTD.—Oerlikon-Buhrle Holding AG; *Int'l*, *pg. 997*
BARIS SHOE COMPANY, INC.; *U.S. Private*, pg. 116
BARRY DISTRIBUTION OF SAN ANGELO—R.G. Barry Corporation; *U.S. Public*, pg. 192
R.G. BARRY CORPORATION; *U.S. Public*, pg. 192
THE BENTLEY AGNEW GROUP INC.; *Int'l*, pg. 187
BROWN GROUP, INC.; *U.S. Public*, pg. 262
BROWN SHOE CO. OF CANADA LTD.—Brown Group, Inc.; *U.S. Public*, pg. 262
C & J CLARK CANADA, LTD.—Clarks International; *Int'l*, pg. 297
CLARKS COS. N.A.—Clarks International; *Int'l*, pg. 297
COMPANIA SCHOLL S.A.—Scholl Plc; *Int'l*, pg. 1209
COWTOWN BOOT COMPANY; *U.S. Private*, pg. 281
CRADDOCK-TERRY INC.; *U.S. Private*, pg. 284
DIADORA AMERICA, INC.; *U.S. Private*, pg. 330
DR. SCHOLL'S SPA—Scholl Plc; *Int'l*, pg. 1209
E.J. FOOTWEAR CORP.—U.S. Industries, Inc.; *U.S. Public*, pg. 1684
FILA USA—Fila Sport S.p.A.; *Int'l*, pg. 484
FLEETFOOT LTD.—Pentland Group PLC; *Int'l*, pg. 1035
FORTUNE BRANDS, INC.; *U.S. Public*, pg. 674
FROLIC FOOTWEAR DIV.—Wolverine World Wide, Inc.; *U.S. Public*, pg. 1775
GATOR INDUSTRIES INC.; *U.S. Private*, pg. 441
GILRICHCO, INC.; *U.S. Private*, pg. 454
THE HARTSTONE GROUP PLC; *Int'l*, pg. 599
JOAN & DAVID HELPERN, INC.; *U.S. Private*, pg. 521
HUSH PUPPIES COMPANY—Wolverine World Wide, Inc.; *U.S. Public*, pg. 1775
INTERNATIONAL SEAWAY TRADING CORPORATION; *U.S. Private*, pg. 572
IPANEMA SHOE CORPORATION—Sumitomo Corporation; *Int'l*, pg. 1312
ITEMS INTERNATIONAL/AIRWALK, INC.; *U.S. Private*, pg. 576
JIMLAR CORPORATION; *U.S. Private*, pg. 587
JOHNSTON & MURPHY CO.—Genesco Inc.; *U.S. Public*, pg. 728
K-SWISS EUROPE LTD.—K-Swiss Inc.; *U.S. Public*, pg. 937
K-SWISS INTERNATIONAL LTD.—K-Swiss Inc.; *U.S. Public*, pg. 937
KAEPA INC.; *U.S. Private*, pg. 604
THE KEDS CORPORATION—The Stride Rite Corporation; *U.S. Public*, pg. 1525
GEO. E. KEITH COMPANY; *U.S. Private*, pg. 611
KEITH HIGHLANDERS SHOES—Geo. E. Keith Company; *U.S. Private*, pg. 612
LEHIGH SAFETY SHOE CO.—U.S. Industries, Inc.; *U.S. Public*, pg. 1684
LIVERPOOL SHOE CO. LTD.—Pentland Group PLC; *Int'l*, pg. 1035
MASSEY'S—Craddock-Terry Inc.; *U.S. Private*, pg. 284
MITRE SPORTS (U.S.)—Pentland Group PLC; *Int'l*, pg. 1036

MORSE SHOE, INC.—J. Baker, Inc.; *U.S. Public*, pg. 168
NEW BALANCE CANADA INC.—New Balance Athletic Shoe, Inc.; *U.S. Private*, pg. 792
NIKE CANADA LTD.—Nike, Inc.; *U.S. Public*, pg. 1184
NIKE FRANCE S.A.R.L.—Nike, Inc.; *U.S. Public*, pg. 1184
NIKE, INC.; *U.S. Public*, pg. 1184
NIKE INTERNATIONAL LTD.—Nike, Inc.; *U.S. Public*, pg. 1184
NIKE (U.K.) LIMITED—Nike, Inc.; *U.S. Public*, pg. 1184
NINE WEST GROUP, INC.; *U.S. Public*, pg. 1185
NUNN-BUSH SHOE CO.—Weyco Group, Inc.; *U.S. Public*, pg. 1763
PAGODA—Brown Group, Inc.; *U.S. Public*, pg. 262
PONY SPORTS UK LTD.—Pentland Group PLC; *Int'l*, pg. 1036
REEBOK INTERNATIONAL LTD.; *U.S. Public*, pg. 1369
SAMSUNG ELECTRONICS NORTH AMERICA INC.—Samsung Group; *Int'l*, pg. 1183
SARRAGAN BENELUX S.A.—Adidas AG; *Int'l*, pg. 25
SCHOLL PLC; *Int'l*, pg. 1209
SCHOLL (SVERIGE) SA—Scholl Plc; *Int'l*, pg. 1210
SCHOTTENSTEIN STORES CORPORATION; *U.S. Private*, pg. 972
SCHWARTZ & BENJAMIN, INC.; *U.S. Private*, pg. 974
JACK SCHWARTZ SHOES, INC.; *U.S. Private*, pg. 974
SIDNEY RICH & ASSOCIATES—Brown Group, Inc.; *U.S. Public*, pg. 262
SOUTHERN LEATHER CO., INC.; *U.S. Private*, pg. 1016
SPERRY TOP-SIDER, INC.—The Stride Rite Corporation; *U.S. Public*, pg. 1525
SPORTO CORP.; *U.S. Private*, pg. 1026
THE STRIDE RITE CORPORATION; *U.S. Public*, pg. 1524
TOBER INDUSTRIES, INC.; *U.S. Private*, pg. 1089
TOPLINE IMPORTS, INC.; *U.S. Private*, pg. 1091
VALUE CITY DEPARTMENT STORES, INC.—Schottenstein Stores Corporation; *U.S. Private*, pg. 972
WAL-MART SHOE DIV.—Wal-Mart Stores, Inc.; *U.S. Public*, pg. 1733
WEYCO GROUP, INC.; *U.S. Public*, pg. 1763
WOLVERINE BRAND DIV.—Wolverine World Wide, Inc.; *U.S. Public*, pg. 1775
WOLVERINE WORLD WIDE, INC.; *U.S. Public*, pg. 1775

5141 — GROCERIES, GENERAL LINE-WHOLESALE

A GREENHOUSE INC.—Koninklijke BolsWessanen nv; *Int'l*, pg. 752
AJC INTERNATIONAL, INC.; *U.S. Private*, pg. 6
AFFILIATED FOODS COOPERATIVE INC.; *U.S. Private*, pg. 25
AFFILIATED FOODS, INC.; *U.S. Private*, pg. 25
AFFILIATED FOODS SOUTHWEST; *U.S. Private*, pg. 26
THE FRED W. ALBRECHT GROCERY CO.; *U.S. Private*, pg. 32
ALLEN FOODS, INC.; *U.S. Private*, pg. 37
ALLOU DISTRIBUTORS INC.—Allou Health & Beauty Care, Inc.; *U.S. Public*, pg. 55
ALLOU HEALTH & BEAUTY CARE, INC.; *U.S. Public*, pg. 55
AMERICAN BEVERAGE CORP. INC.—Koninklijke BolsWessanen nv; *Int'l*, pg. 752
AMERICAN NATURAL SNACKS—Koninklijke BolsWessanen nv; *Int'l*, pg. 752
AMERICAN SEAWAY FOODS, INC.—Giant Eagle, Inc.; *U.S. Private*, pg. 451
AMERISERVE FOOD DISTRIBUTION, INC.—Holberg Industries, Inc.; *U.S. Private*, pg. 533
AMERISERVE OF GRAND RAPIDS—Holberg Industries, Inc.; *U.S. Private*, pg. 533
AMERISERVE OF NORCROSS—Holberg Industries, Inc.; *U.S. Private*, pg. 533
ANDERSON, CLAYTON & CO. S.A.—Unilever Plc; *Int'l*, pg. 1436
ANPING DISTRIBUTORS LTD.—Nestle S.A.; *Int'l*, pg. 918
ARROW-SYSCO FOOD SERVICES, INC.—Sysco Corporation; *U.S. Public*, pg. 1551
ASSOCIATED BRITISH FOODS PLC; *Int'l*, pg. 92
ASSOCIATED FOOD STORES INC.; *U.S. Private*, pg. 90
ASSOCIATED FOOD STORES, INC.; *U.S. Private*, pg. 90
ASSOCIATED GROCERS, INC.; *U.S. Private*, pg. 90
ASSOCIATED GROCERS OF NEW ENGLAND, INC.; *U.S. Private*, pg. 91
ASSOCIATED GROCERS OF THE SOUTH, INC.; *U.S. Private*, pg. 91
ASSOCIATED LEASE CORP.—Associated Grocers of New England, Inc.; *U.S. Private*, pg. 91
ASSOCIATED WHOLESALE GROCERS, INC.; *U.S. Private*, pg. 93
ASSOCIATED WHOLESALERS INC.; *U.S. Private*, pg. 93
ATALANTA CORPORATION; *U.S. Private*, pg. 93
ATALANTA (U.K.) LTD.—Atalanta Corporation; *U.S. Private*, pg. 94
ATLANTIC WHOLESALERS LTD.—George Weston Limited; *Int'l*, pg. 1495
AUDISIO INDUSTRIE ALUMENTARI SRL—CSM N.V.; *Int'l*, pg. 244
AWARD FOODS, INC.—Koninklijke BolsWessanen nv; *Int'l*, pg. 752
B & R FOODS—Performance Food Group Company; *U.S. Public*, pg. 1278
BMW; *U.S. Private*, pg. 107
BACON GROCERY CO., INC.—Jones Company, Inc.; *U.S. Private*, pg. 596
BALANCED FOODS, INC.—Koninklijke BolsWessanen nv; *Int'l*, pg. 752
BANNER WHOLESALE GROCERS, INC.; *U.S. Private*, pg. 114
BARABOO-SYSCO FOOD SERVICES, INC.—Sysco Corporation; *U.S. Public*, pg. 1550
BASIC AMERICAN FOODS; *U.S. Private*, pg. 121
BEAVER STREET FISHERIES, INC.; *U.S. Private*, pg. 128
BEEF DISTRIBUTORS, INC.—Keeners, Inc.; *U.S. Private*, pg. 611
BELL CARTER DISTRIBUTING—Bell-Carter Foods, Inc.; *U.S. Private*, pg. 131
BEST WHOLESALE CO., INC.—Old Fashion Foods, Inc.; *U.S. Private*, pg. 814
BIG SANDY WHOLESALE CO.—The H.T. Hackney Co.; *U.S. Private*, pg. 493
BOLANDS LIMITED—The Oshawa Group Limited; *Int'l*, pg. 1012
BOOKER PLC; *Int'l*, pg. 202
BOZZUTO'S INC.; *U.S. Public*, pg. 249
BRISTOL-MYERS PERUANA S.A.—Bristol-Myers Squibb Company; *U.S. Public*, pg. 255
BROOKSHIRE BROS., LTD.; *U.S. Private*, pg. 172
C & D DISTRIBUTING CO. INC.—Borden, Inc.; *U.S. Private*, pg. 158
C & S WHOLESALE GROCERY INC.; *U.S. Private*, pg. 192
CAINS FOODS, L.P.; *U.S. Private*, pg. 199
CASINO MODERNE MENU SYSTEME GMBH—Nestle S.A.; *Int'l*, pg. 919
CENTRAL GROCERS CO-OP; *U.S. Private*, pg. 223
CERTIFIED FOOD SERVICE OF GA., INC.—Sun City Industries, Inc.; *U.S. Public*, pg. 1529
CERTIFIED FOOD SERVICE OF PA, INC.—Sun City Industries, Inc.; *U.S. Public*, pg. 1529
CERTIFIED GROCERS MIDWEST, INC.; *U.S. Private*, pg. 226
CERTIFIED GROCERS OF CALIFORNIA; *U.S. Private*, pg. 226
CERTIFIED POULTRY & EGG CO., INC.—Sun City Industries, Inc.; *U.S. Public*, pg. 1529
CERTIFIED WHOLESALERS INC.—Associated Grocers of New England, Inc.; *U.S. Private*, pg. 91
CHEVY CHASE, INC.—Borden, Inc.; *U.S. Private*, pg. 158
THE CLOROX COMPANY; *U.S. Public*, pg. 386
COASTAL WHOLESALE, INC.; *U.S. Private*, pg. 248
COCHRAN/SYSCO FOOD SERVICES—Sysco Corporation; *U.S. Public*, pg. 1550
CODVILLE DISTRIBUTORS—The Oshawa Group Limited; *Int'l*, pg. 1012
COLIVITA USA, INC.; *U.S. Private*, pg. 252
COMPANIA INTERNACIONAL DE VENTAS, S.A.—Borden, Inc.; *U.S. Private*, pg. 159
CONNELL CO.; *U.S. Private*, pg. 264
CONSOLIDATED COMPANIES INC. (CONCO); *U.S. Private*, pg. 265
CUB FOODS STORES—SuperValu, Inc.; *U.S. Public*, pg. 1541
CULLUM DISTRIBUTION CENTER, INC.—Randalls Food Markets, Inc.; *U.S. Private*, pg. 909
DAHL SVERIGE—Dahl International AB; *Int'l*, pg. 359
DAHLSTEN TRUCK LINE, INC.; *U.S. Private*, pg. 306
DAIRY FARM INTERNATIONAL HOLDINGS LIMITED—Jardine Matheson Holdings Limited; *Int'l*, pg. 703
DEUTSCHE SB-KAUF AG—Metro AG; *Int'l*, pg. 863
DI GIORGIO CORPORATION; *U.S. Private*, pg. 330
DOMINO'S PIZZA DISTRIBUTION CORP.—Domino's Pizza Inc.; *U.S. Private*, pg. 339
DUSKIN USA, INC.—Duskin Co., Ltd.; *Int'l*, pg. 422
EFFEMS AG—Mars, Incorporated; *U.S. Private*, pg. 707
ETABLISSEMENTS DELHAIZE FRERES ET CIE "LE LION" S.A.; *Int'l*, pg. 462
FTI FOODTECH INTERNATIONAL INC.; *Int'l*, pg. 476
JAMES FERRERA & SONS, INC.; *U.S. Private*, pg. 401
FLEMING COMPANIES, INC.; *U.S. Public*, pg. 652
FLEMING COMPANY—Fleming Companies, Inc.; *U.S. Public*, pg. 653
FLEMING FOODS OF TENNESSEE, INC.—Fleming Companies, Inc.; *U.S. Public*, pg. 653
FOOD AND SNACK HOLDINGS (SINGAPORE)—Borden, Inc.; *U.S. Private*, pg. 159
FOOD 4 LESS, INC.—The Yucaipa Companies; *U.S. Private*, pg. 1202
FOOD SERVICES OF AMERICA—Services Group of America; *U.S. Private*, pg. 987
FOODBRANDS AMERICA, INC.—IBP, Inc.; *U.S. Public*, pg. 852
FOREVER LIVING PRODUCTS INTERNATIONAL, INC.; *U.S. Private*, pg. 418
4C FOODS CORPORATION; *U.S. Private*, pg. 421
FRENCH & BEAN—Associated Grocers of New England, Inc.; *U.S. Private*, pg. 91
FRESH AMERICA CORP.; *U.S. Public*, pg. 681
FRESH-LINE DISTRIBUTORS, INC.—Bozzuto's Inc.; *U.S. Public*, pg. 249
GSC ENTERPRISES, INC.; *U.S. Private*, pg. 436
GENERAL CIGAR HOLDINGS INC; *U.S. Public*, pg. 707
GENERAL MILLS, CONSUMER FOODS SALES DIV.—General Mills, Inc.; *U.S. Public*, pg. 718
GENERAL MILLS SALES, INC.—General Mills, Inc.; *U.S. Public*, pg. 718
GENERAL TRADING CO.; *U.S. Private*, pg. 445
GENUARDI FAMILY MARKETS INC.; *U.S. Private*, pg. 447
GERBER PRODUCTS COMPANY OF PUERTO RICO, INC.—Novartis AG; *Int'l*, pg. 973
GINSBERG'S INSTITUTIONAL FOODS, INC.; *U.S. Private*, pg. 455
GOLDEN STATE FOODS; *U.S. Private*, pg. 460
GOURMET FOODS, INC.—Koninklijke BolsWessanen nv; *Int'l*, pg. 752
GOURMET MENU-SERVICE GMBH & CO KG—Maresi Markenartikelvertrieb Aktiengesellschaft; *Int'l*, pg. 842
GOYA FOODS, INC.; *U.S. Private*, pg. 468
GRAND METROPOLITAN FOODSERVICE INC.—Diageo Plc; *Int'l*, pg. 408
B. GREEN & CO.; *U.S. Private*, pg. 476
AUTRY GREER & SONS, INC.; *U.S. Private*, pg. 479
GROCERS SPECIALTY CO.—Certified Grocers of California; *U.S. Private*, pg. 227
GROCERS SUPPLY CO. INC.; *U.S. Private*, pg. 483
GULF COAST FOOD SERVICE INC.—Sun City Industries, Inc.; *U.S. Public*, pg. 1529
H & H DISTRIBUTING COMPANY, INC.; *U.S. Private*, pg. 489
THE H.T. HACKNEY CO.; *U.S. Private*, pg. 493
HAGEMEYER N.V.—First Pacific Company Limited; *Int'l*, pg. 487
HALE-HALSELL COMPANY; *U.S. Private*, pg. 494
HALLSMITH-SYSCO FOOD SERVICES—Sysco Corporation; *U.S. Public*, pg. 1550
HARDIN'S-SYSCO FOOD SERVICES, INC.—Sysco Corporation; *U.S. Public*, pg. 1551
HARVEY ELECTRONICS, INC.; *U.S. Public*, pg. 796
HEAD DISTRIBUTING CO.; *U.S. Private*, pg. 514
H.J. HEINZ (BOTSWANA) (PROPRIETARY) LTD.—H.J. Heinz Company; *U.S. Public*, pg. 806
H.J. HEINZ COMPANY (IRELAND) LIMITED—H.J. Heinz Company; *U.S. Public*, pg. 806
H.J. HEINZ GMBH—H.J. Heinz Company; *U.S. Public*, pg. 806
H.J. HEINZ SARL—H.J. Heinz Company; *U.S. Public*, pg. 806
HI-PROFIT DISTRIBUTORS, INC.—Koninklijke BolsWessanen nv; *Int'l*, pg. 752
IRA HIGDON GROCERY, INC.; *U.S. Private*, pg. 527
HOLIDAY COMPANIES; *U.S. Private*, pg. 534
HONIG FOODS-B.V.—CSM N.V.; *Int'l*, pg. 244
HOUCHENS INDUSTRIES INC.; *U.S. Private*, pg. 541
HULMAN & COMPANY; *U.S. Private*, pg. 547
HUNT-WESSON GROCERY SALES DIVISION—ConAgra, Inc.; *U.S. Public*, pg. 428
HUNT-WESSON TOMATO PRODUCTS DIVISION—ConAgra, Inc.; *U.S. Public*, pg. 428
HY-VEE FOOD STORES INCORPORATED; *U.S. Private*, pg. 550
HYOSUNG GROUP; *Int'l*, pg. 640
PAUL INMAN ASSOCIATES INC.; *U.S. Private*, pg. 564
INSTITUTION FOOD HOUSE, INC.—Alex Lee, Inc.; *U.S. Private*, pg. 657
JENNY CRAIG, INC.; *U.S. Public*, pg. 926
JETRO CASH & CARRY—Jetro Holdings, Inc.; *U.S. Private*, pg. 587
JORDAN'S FOODS-CARIBOU DIVISION—Jordan's Meats; *U.S. Private*, pg. 599
JORDAN'S MEATS; *U.S. Private*, pg. 599
K-CASH & CARRY LTD.—Kesko Ltd.; *Int'l*, pg. 732
K-VA-T; *U.S. Private*, pg. 603
KF/KONSUM COOP GROUP; *Int'l*, pg. 718
KEENE DISTRIBUTORS—Koninklijke BolsWessanen nv; *Int'l*, pg. 752
KEENERS, INC.; *U.S. Private*, pg. 611
KELLY DOUGLAS & COMPANY LIMITED—George Weston Limited; *Int'l*, pg. 1495
KELLY DOUGLASS WESTFAIR FOODS LTD.—George Weston Limited; *Int'l*, pg. 1495
KEY FOOD STORES CO-OPERATIVE, INC.; *U.S. Private*, pg. 617
KIKKOMAN TRADING EUROPE GMBH—Kikkoman Corporation; *Int'l*, pg. 733
KING COTTON FOODS—Sara Lee Corporation; *U.S. Public*, pg. 1433
KINGSTON MARKETING CO.—Topco Associates, Inc.; *U.S. Private*, pg. 1091
KONINKLIJKE BOLSWESSANEN NV; *Int'l*, pg. 750
KRANTOR CORPORATION; *U.S. Public*, pg. 966
KRASDALE FOODS INC.; *U.S. Private*, pg. 635
LABATT FOOD SERVICE; *U.S. Private*, pg. 641
LACKMAN FOOD SERVICE; *U.S. Private*, pg. 642
LANECO, INC.—SuperValu, Inc.; *U.S. Public*, pg. 1541
LANKFORD-SYSCO FOOD SERVICES, INC.—Sysco Corporation; *U.S. Public*, pg. 1551
LEE GROCERY COMPANY; *U.S. Private*, pg. 657
LEONARD WHOLESALE, INC.; *U.S. Private*, pg. 660
LEONE FOOD SERVICE CORP.—Clayton, Dubilier & Rice, Inc.; *U.S. Private*, pg. 244
J.L. LESTER & SON, INC.; *U.S. Private*, pg. 660
KENNETH O. LESTER, INC.—Performance Food Group Company; *U.S. Public*, pg. 1278
LOBLAW COMPANIES LIMITED—George Weston Limited; *Int'l*, pg. 1495
LOEB INC.—Provigo Inc.; *Int'l*, pg. 1073
LOSURDO FOODS, INC.; *U.S. Private*, pg. 677
M & M RESTAURANT SUPPLY—Keystone Foods Corporation; *U.S. Private*, pg. 619
M M M SALES, INC.; *U.S. Private*, pg. 685
MADISON GROCERY CO., INC.; *U.S. Private*, pg. 694
MAINE/SYSCO, INC.—Sysco Corporation; *U.S. Public*, pg. 1551
MALONE & HYDE, INC.-GOODLETTSVILLE—Fleming Companies, Inc.; *U.S. Public*, pg. 653
MALONE & HYDE, INC.-SOUTHAVEN—Fleming Companies, Inc.; *U.S. Public*, pg. 653
MARESI MARKENARTIKELVERTRIEB AKTIENGESELLSCHAFT; *Int'l*, pg. 842
THE MARTIN-BROWER COMPANY—Dalgety Plc; *Int'l*, pg. 376
MARUBENI CORPORATION; *Int'l*, pg. 844
MAZO LERCH COMPANY, INC.—JP Foodservice, Inc.; *U.S. Public*, pg. 918
MCANALLY ENTERPRISES, INC.; *U.S. Private*, pg. 718
J.V. MCDANIEL LIMITED—James Crean PLC; *Int'l*, pg. 340
MCFARLING FOODS, INC.; *U.S. Private*, pg. 721
MCLANE COMPANY, INC.—Wal-Mart Stores, Inc.; *U.S. Public*, pg. 1733
MERCHANTS DISTRIBUTORS, INC.—Alex Lee, Inc.; *U.S. Private*, pg. 657
MERIT DISTRIBUTION SERVICES, INC.—Wal-Mart Stores, Inc.; *U.S. Public*, pg. 1733
MID-CENTRAL/SYSCO FOOD SERVICES, INC.—Sysco Corporation; *U.S. Public*, pg. 1551
MIDWEST NATURAL FOODS—Koninklijke BolsWessanen nv; *Int'l*, pg. 752
MIESEL/SYSCO FOOD SERVICE CO.—Sysco Corporation; *U.S. Public*, pg. 1551
MINYARD FOOD STORES, INC.; *U.S. Private*, pg. 752
MITSUBISHI CORPORATION; *Int'l*, pg. 871

MOWE TEIGWARENWERK GMBH—CSM N.V.; *Int'l*, pg. 244
NASH FINCH CO.—Nash Finch Company; *U.S. Public*, pg. 1152
NASH FINCH COMPANY; *U.S. Public*, pg. 1151
NATIONAL FOOD STORES, INC.; *U.S. Private*, pg. 783
NATIONAL GROCERS CO. LTD.—George Weston Limited; *Int'l*, pg. 1495
NESTLE SENEGAL—Nestle S.A.; *Int'l*, pg. 921
NESTLE WORLD TRADE CORPORATION—Nestle S.A.; *Int'l*, pg. 916
NISSHO IWAI DELICA CORP.—Nissho Iwai Corporation; *Int'l*, pg. 946
NISSHO IWAI FOODS CORP.—Nissho Iwai Corporation; *Int'l*, pg. 946
NOBEL/SYSCO FOOD SERVICE COMPANY-DENVER—Sysco Corporation; *U.S. Public*, pg. 1551
NORTHMAR DISTRIBUTORS—Silcorp Limited; *Int'l*, pg. 1249
NORTHWEST DIETETIC SUPPLY, INC.—Koninklijke BolsWessanen nv; *Int'l*, pg. 752
OBERLANDER RECYCLING TECHNIK GMBH—Fried. Krupp AG; *Int'l*, pg. 513
SYSCO FOOD SERVICES COMPANY—Sysco Corporation; *U.S. Public*, pg. 1551
ROBERT ORR-SYSCO FOOD SERVICES CO.—Sysco Corporation; *U.S. Public*, pg. 1551
THE OSHAWA GROUP LIMITED; *Int'l*, pg. 1012
OSTERREICHISCHE NESTLE GMBH—Nestle S.A.; *Int'l*, pg. 922
OSTERREICHISCHE UNILEVER GES. M.B.H.—Unilever Plc; *Int'l*, pg. 1438
P & C FOOD MARKETS, INC.—The Penn Traffic Company; *U.S. Public*, pg. 1270
P.S. INTERNATIONAL INC.; *U.S. Private*, pg. 827
PYA/MONARCH, INC.—Sara Lee Corporation; *U.S. Public*, pg. 1433
PEGLER-SYSCO FOOD SERVICES CO.—Sysco Corporation; *U.S. Public*, pg. 1550
THE PENN TRAFFIC COMPANY; *U.S. Public*, pg. 1270
PERFORMANCE FOOD GROUP COMPANY; *U.S. Public*, pg. 1278
PIGGLY WIGGLY CO.—Fleming Companies, Inc.; *U.S. Public*, pg. 653
POCAHONTAS FOODS, USA—Performance Food Group Company; *U.S. Public*, pg. 1278
PROFESSIONAL FOOD SYSTEMS—ConAgra, Inc.; *U.S. Public*, pg. 427
PROGRESSIVE DISTRIBUTORS, INC.—Hannaford Bros. Co.; *U.S. Public*, pg. 782
PROMODES SA; *Int'l*, pg. 1071
THE PROMOTION IN MOTION COMPANIES; *U.S. Private*, pg. 890
PROVIGO DISTRIBUTION—Provigo Inc.; *Int'l*, pg. 1073
PROVIGO INC.; *Int'l*, pg. 1072
PUBLIX SUPER MARKETS, INC.—Publix Supermarkets Inc.; *U.S. Private*, pg. 894
PUEBLO INTERNATIONAL, INC.-P.R. DIV.—Pueblo Xtra International, Inc.; *U.S. Private*, pg. 894
PUEBLO XTRA INTERNATIONAL, INC.; *U.S. Private*, pg. 894
PURAC AMERICA, INC.—CSM N.V.; *Int'l*, pg. 244
PURAC BIOCHEM (UK) LIMITED—CSM N.V.; *Int'l*, pg. 244
PURAC FAR EAST—CSM N.V.; *Int'l*, pg. 245
QUALITY FOODS INC.; *U.S. Private*, pg. 898
RCB BAKING COMPANY; *U.S. Public*, pg. 1354
C.B. RAGLAND COMPANY; *U.S. Private*, pg. 907
RICHARDS BROTHERS OF MOUNTAIN GROVE; *U.S. Private*, pg. 928
RICHFOOD HOLDINGS, INC.; *U.S. Public*, pg. 1388
RICHFOOD, INC.—Richfood Holdings, Inc.; *U.S. Public*, pg. 1389
RINI-REGO SUPERMARKETS, INC.—Giant Eagle, Inc.; *U.S. Private*, pg. 451
RISER FOODS, INC.—Giant Eagle, Inc.; *U.S. Private*, pg. 450
P.A. ROSS (FOOD BROKERS), LTD.—Koninklijke BolsWessanen nv; *Int'l*, pg. 753
ROUNDY'S, INC.; *U.S. Private*, pg. 948
ROUNDY'S, MILWAUKEE DIVISION—Roundy's, Inc.; *U.S. Private*, pg. 948
ROYAL FOODS DISTRIBUTORS, INC.—Fleming Companies, Inc.; *U.S. Public*, pg. 653
RYKOFF-SEXTON, INC.—JP Foodservice, Inc.; *U.S. Public*, pg. 918
SAFEWAY PLC; *Int'l*, pg. 1169
SAFEWAY SUPPLY, INC.—Safeway Inc.; *U.S. Public*, pg. 1426
SARATOGA BRANDS, INC.; *U.S. Public*, pg. 1435
SCHNIEBER FINE FOODS, INC.; *U.S. Private*, pg. 971
SCOTT NATIONAL—The Oshawa Group Limited; *Int'l*, pg. 1012
SEAWAY FOOD TOWN, INC.; *U.S. Public*, pg. 1452
SENNA NOHRUNPSMITTEL GMBH—Maresi Markenartikelvertrieb Aktiengesellschaft; *Int'l*, pg. 842
SERVICES GROUP OF AMERICA; *U.S. Private*, pg. 987
SHOP 'N SAVE WAREHOUSE FOODS, INC.—SuperValu, Inc.; *U.S. Public*, pg. 1541
SHOP-RITE BEVERAGES, INC.—Wakefern Food Corporation; *U.S. Private*, pg. 1146
SHOPPERS FOOD WAREHOUSE—Dart Group Corporation; *U.S. Public*, pg. 484
SHURFINE INTERNATIONAL, INC.; *U.S. Private*, pg. 997
SMELKINSON SYSCO FOOD SERVICES, INC.—Sysco Corporation; *U.S. Public*, pg. 1550
SNACK AMERICA; *U.S. Private*, pg. 1010
SOBEY INC.—Empire Company Limited; *Int'l*, pg. 454
SOCANAV INC.; *Int'l*, pg. 1272
SOCIETE POUR L'EXPORTATION DE PRODUITS NESTLE S.A.—Nestle S.A.; *Int'l*, pg. 922
SOUTH BEND PERISHABLES DIVISION—Roundy's, Inc.; *U.S. Private*, pg. 948
SPAR HANDELS AG; *Int'l*, pg. 1288
SPAR (UK) LTD.; *Int'l*, pg. 1288
SPARTAN STORES INC.; *U.S. Private*, pg. 1021
SPERBER-PETERMAN COMPANY—BMW; *U.S. Private*, pg. 107
SUMIKIN BUSSAN CORPORATION; *Int'l*, pg. 1308
SUN CITY INDUSTRIES, INC.; *U.S. Public*, pg. 1529
SUN RAY PRODUCTS, INC.—Koninklijke BolsWessanen nv; *Int'l*, pg. 752
SUPER DISCOUNT MARKETS, INC.—Etablissements Delhaize Freres Et Cie "Le Lion" S.A.; *Int'l*, pg. 463
SUPER FOOD SERVICES, INC.—Nash Finch Company; *U.S. Public*, pg. 1152
SUPERVALU, INC.; *U.S. Public*, pg. 1540
SWEET LIFE FOODS, INC.—SuperValu, Inc.; *U.S. Public*, pg. 1541
THE SYGMA NETWORK, INC.-DENVER CENTRAL—Sysco Corporation; *U.S. Public*, pg. 1551
SYSCO CORPORATION; *U.S. Public*, pg. 1550
SYSCO FOOD SERVICES-ALBANY—Sysco Corporation; *U.S. Public*, pg. 1551
SYSCO FOOD SERVICES CHICAGO, INC.—Sysco Corporation; *U.S. Public*, pg. 1551
SYSCO FOOD SERVICES OF ARIZONA, INC.—Sysco Corporation; *U.S. Public*, pg. 1551
SYSCO FOOD SERVICES OF ARKANSAS, INC.—Sysco Corporation; *U.S. Public*, pg. 1551
SYSCO FOOD SERVICES OF ATLANTA, INC.—Sysco Corporation; *U.S. Public*, pg. 1551
SYSCO FOOD SERVICES OF CHARLOTTE, INC.—Sysco Corporation; *U.S. Public*, pg. 1551
SYSCO FOOD SERVICES OF DALLAS—Sysco Corporation; *U.S. Public*, pg. 1551
SYSCO FOOD SERVICES OF GRAND RAPIDS, INC.—Sysco Corporation; *U.S. Public*, pg. 1551
SYSCO FOOD SERVICES OF HOUSTON, INC.—Sysco Corporation; *U.S. Public*, pg. 1551
SYSCO FOOD SERVICES OF SAN FRANCISCO, INC.—Sysco Corporation; *U.S. Public*, pg. 1552
SYSCO FOOD SERVICES-SAN ANTONIO, INC.—Sysco Corporation; *U.S. Public*, pg. 1552
SYSCO INTERMOUNTAIN FOOD SERVICES, INC.—Sysco Corporation; *U.S. Public*, pg. 1552
SYSCO/LOUISVILLE FOOD SERVICES CO.—Sysco Corporation; *U.S. Public*, pg. 1552
T.J. U.S. COMPANY—Nash Finch Company; *U.S. Public*, pg. 1152
TAV FOODS SERVICE—Thorn Apple Valley, Inc.; *U.S. Public*, pg. 1603
TLC BEATRICE INTERNATIONAL HOLDINGS INC.; *U.S. Private*, pg. 1064
TASTY BAKING COMPANY; *U.S. Public*, pg. 1561
TATA INC.—The Tata Iron and Steel Co. Ltd.; *Int'l*, pg. 1356
THOMAS & HOWARD CO.; *U.S. Private*, pg. 1081
THOMAS & HOWARD CO.—Thomas & Howard Co.; *U.S. Private*, pg. 1082
SYSCO FOOD SERVICES—Sysco Corporation; *U.S. Public*, pg. 1551
TOPCO ASSOCIATES, INC.; *U.S. Private*, pg. 1091
TOPS MARKETS, INC.—Koninklijke Ahold NV; *Int'l*, pg. 750
TRADING PORT, INC.; *U.S. Private*, pg. 1095
TREE OF LIFE, INC.—Koninklijke BolsWessanen nv; *Int'l*, pg. 752
J. TREFFILETTI & SONS, INC.; *U.S. Private*, pg. 1099
TRI-STATE WHOLESALE ASSOCIATED GROCERS, INC.; *U.S. Private*, pg. 1101
TRUCCHIS MARKETS; *U.S. Private*, pg. 1107
TUPMAN THURLOW CO. INC.; *U.S. Private*, pg. 1109
TWIN COUNTY GROCERS, INC.; *U.S. Private*, pg. 1111
URM STORES, INC.; *U.S. Private*, pg. 1114
THE UNCLE TOBY'S COMPANY LTD.—Goodman Fielder Limited; *Int'l*, pg. 555
UNI-DAN A/S—Unilever Plc; *Int'l*, pg. 1438
UNISOURCE (S.E. REGIONAL OFFICE)—Unisource Worldwide, Inc.; *U.S. Public*, pg. 1671
UNITED DAIRY FARMERS, INC.; *U.S. Private*, pg. 1121
VALLET FOOD SERV INC.; *U.S. Private*, pg. 1131
VALLEY ISLE PRODUCE, V.I.P. FOOD SERVICE; *U.S. Private*, pg. 1132
VALU-FOODS, INC.—Hale-Halsell Company; *U.S. Private*, pg. 494
WAKEFERN FOOD CORPORATION; *U.S. Private*, pg. 1146
WEIGHT WATCHERS INTERNATIONAL, INC.—H.J. Heinz Company; *U.S. Public*, pg. 806
WESTIN, INC.; *U.S. Private*, pg. 1169
WINN-DIXIE STORES, INC.; *U.S. Public*, pg. 1771
YOUNG'S HOLDINGS INC.; *U.S. Private*, pg. 1202

5142 — PACKAGED FROZEN FOODS-WHOLESALE

AFFILIATED FOODS COOPERATIVE INC.; *U.S. Private*, pg. 25
ALCOSA/SUNWISE—Hanover Foods Corporation; *U.S. Private*, pg. 499
ALIMENTOS FINDAS S.A. DE C.V.—Nestle S.A.; *Int'l*, pg. 918
AMERICAN FROZEN FOODS, INC.; *U.S. Private*, pg. 55
AMERICAN INSTITUTIONAL FOODS—AJC International, Inc.; *U.S. Private*, pg. 6
AMERISERVE OF GRAND RAPIDS—Holberg Industries, Inc.; *U.S. Private*, pg. 533
ARCTIC ALASKA FISHERIES CORPORATION—Tyson Foods, Inc.; *U.S. Public*, pg. 1652
BACARDI-MARTINI, USA, INC.; *U.S. Private*, pg. 109
BASIC FOOD INTERNATIONAL INC.; *U.S. Private*, pg. 121
BEAVER STREET FISHERIES, INC.; *U.S. Private*, pg. 128
BEEF DISTRIBUTORS, INC.—Keeners, Inc.; *U.S. Private*, pg. 611
BETA PLASTICS—Alpha Industries; *U.S. Private*, pg. 45
BRIDGFORD FOODS CORPORATION; *U.S. Public*, pg. 252
BURRIS FOODS, INC.; *U.S. Private*, pg. 188
C & S WHOLESALE GROCERY INC.; *U.S. Private*, pg. 192
CALAVO GROWERS OF CALIFORNIA; *U.S. Private*, pg. 199
CAMINO REAL FOODS, INC.—Nissin Food Products Co., Ltd.; *Int'l*, pg. 949
D. CANALE FOOD SERVICES, INC.; *U.S. Private*, pg. 204
CEDAR FARMS COMPANY, INC.; *U.S. Private*, pg. 221
CERTIFIED GROCERS MIDWEST, INC.; *U.S. Private*, pg. 226
CERTIFIED GROCERS OF CALIFORNIA; *U.S. Private*, pg. 226
CLOVER PRODUCE LIMITED—Empire Company Limited; *Int'l*, pg. 454
CONAGRA FROZEN FOODS—ConAgra, Inc.; *U.S. Public*, pg. 427
CONAGRA NISSUI INC.—ConAgra, Inc.; *U.S. Public*, pg. 429
CONNELL CO.; *U.S. Private*, pg. 264
CONSOLIDATED COMPANIES INC. (CONCO); *U.S. Private*, pg. 265
CROWN FOODS INC.; *U.S. Private*, pg. 292
DEAN FOODS VEGETABLE CO.—Dean Foods Company; *U.S. Public*, pg. 490
D'JESCO, INC.—AJC International, Inc.; *U.S. Private*, pg. 6
ESS-FOOD; *Int'l*, pg. 429
ESS-FOOD (H.K.) LTD.—ESS-Food; *Int'l*, pg. 429
ESS-FOOD HUNGARIA LLC—ESS-Food; *Int'l*, pg. 429
EARP DISTRIBUTION CENTER; *U.S. Private*, pg. 356
EDWARDS BAKING CO.; *U.S. Private*, pg. 365
EKOMAT SWEDEN AB—Nestle S.A.; *Int'l*, pg. 920
ELI'S CHEESE CAKE COMPANY; *U.S. Private*, pg. 371
ESKIMO EUROP S.A.R.L.—Eskimo Pie Corporation; *U.S. Public*, pg. 592
FAST FOOD MERCHANDISERS INC.—CKE Restaurants Inc.; *U.S. Public*, pg. 278
FLYING FOOD FARE, INC.; *U.S. Private*, pg. 415
FOOD SERVICES OF AMERICA—Services Group of America; *U.S. Private*, pg. 987
FRESH JUICE COMPANY; *U.S. Private*, pg. 427
GELAZUR S.A.—ConAgra, Inc.; *U.S. Public*, pg. 429
GENUARDI FAMILY MARKETS INC.; *U.S. Private*, pg. 447
GLOBAL FOOD CORPORATION—Basic Food International Inc.; *U.S. Private*, pg. 121
GOLDEN GEM GROWERS INC.; *U.S. Private*, pg. 460
GORDON FOOD SERVICE INC.; *U.S. Private*, pg. 465
HALE-HALSELL COMPANY; *U.S. Private*, pg. 494
HARKER'S DISTRIBUTION, INC.; *U.S. Private*, pg. 502
HAZELWOOD FARMS BAKERIES, INC.—SuperValu, Inc.; *U.S. Public*, pg. 1541
J. HELLMAN PRODUCE, INC.; *U.S. Private*, pg. 520
IRA HIGDON GROCERY, INC.; *U.S. Private*, pg. 527
HOSHO AMERICA INC.—Kibun Co. Ltd.; *Int'l*, pg. 733
ICEE-USA CORP.—J & J Snack Foods Corporation; *U.S. Public*, pg. 916
ITOHAM FOODS INC.; *Int'l*, pg. 695
J & J SNACK FOODS CORPORATION; *U.S. Public*, pg. 916
J & J SNACK FOODS SALES CORP.—J & J Snack Foods Corporation; *U.S. Public*, pg. 916
J & J SNACK FOODS TRANSPORT CORP.—J & J Snack Foods Corporation; *U.S. Public*, pg. 916
JORDAN'S FOODS-CARIBOU DIVISION—Jordan's Meats; *U.S. Private*, pg. 599
JORDAN'S MEATS; *U.S. Private*, pg. 599
KEENERS, INC.; *U.S. Private*, pg. 611
BEN E. KEITH COMPANY; *U.S. Private*, pg. 611
KESTERSON FOOD COMPANY, INC.; *U.S. Private*, pg. 616
KEYSTONE FOODS CORPORATION; *U.S. Private*, pg. 619
KING & PRINCE SEAFOOD CORPORATION; *U.S. Private*, pg. 620
KINGSTON MARKETING CO.—Topco Associates, Inc.; *U.S. Private*, pg. 1091
KYOKUYO AMERICA CORP.—Kyokuyo Co. Ltd.; *Int'l*, pg. 777
LADY BALTIMORE FOODS, INC.; *U.S. Public*, pg. 975
LANCASTER FOODS, INC.—Guest Services, Inc.; *U.S. Private*, pg. 487
LEE GROCERY COMPANY; *U.S. Private*, pg. 657
LEONE FOOD SERVICE CORP.—Clayton, Dubilier & Rice, Inc; *U.S. Private*, pg. 244
MADISON GROCERY CO., INC.; *U.S. Private*, pg. 694
MARUHA CORPORATION; *Int'l*, pg. 845
MCINERNEY-MILLER BROTHERS INC.; *U.S. Private*, pg. 722
MEIJI FROZEN DESSERT CORP.—Meiji Seika Kaisha, Ltd.; *Int'l*, pg. 855
MITSUBISHI CORPORATION; *Int'l*, pg. 871
NATIONAL SEA PRODUCTS LIMITED; *Int'l*, pg. 909
NESTLE S.A.; *Int'l*, pg. 915
NESTLE WORLD TRADE CORPORATION—Nestle S.A.; *Int'l*, pg. 916
NEW ENGLAND FROZEN FOODS, INC.; *U.S. Private*, pg. 793
NICHIMEN AMERICA, INC.—Nichimen Corporation; *Int'l*, pg. 927
NICHIMEN CORPORATION; *Int'l*, pg. 927
NICHIREI CORPORATION; *Int'l*, pg. 928
NIPPON SUISAN U.S.A.—Nippon Suisan Kaisha, Ltd.; *Int'l*, pg. 940
THE OSHAWA GROUP LIMITED; *Int'l*, pg. 1012
PARIS FOODS CORP.; *U.S. Private*, pg. 839
PETER'S SAVOURY PRODUCTS—Diageo Plc; *Int'l*, pg. 410
PIONEER SNACKS—Melody Foods, Inc.; *U.S. Private*, pg. 730
PROCORDIA FOOD AB—Orkla A.S.A.; *Int'l*, pg. 1011
RIVER RANCH SOUTHWEST, INC.; *U.S. Private*, pg. 934
ROBERTS FOODS, INC.; *U.S. Private*, pg. 935
ROMAN MEAL COMPANY; *U.S. Private*, pg. 942
RYMER INTERNATIONAL SEAFOOD INC.—Rymer Foods Inc.; *U.S. Public*, pg. 1414
SARA LEE CORPORATION; *U.S. Public*, pg. 1432
SCHNIEBER FINE FOODS, INC.; *U.S. Private*, pg. 971

SCOTT NATIONAL—The Oshawa Group Limited; *Int'l*, pg. 1012
SERVICES GROUP OF AMERICA; *U.S. Private*, pg. 987
SHAMROCK FOODS COMPANY; *U.S. Private*, pg. 989
SNOWCREST PACKERS LTD.—Nuburn Capital; *Int'l*, pg. 990
SOUTHERN FROZEN FOODS—Pro-Fac Cooperative, Inc.; *U.S. Private*, pg. 887
SPARTAN STORES INC.; *U.S. Private*, pg. 1021
SUMITOMO CORPORATION OF AMERICA—Sumitomo Corporation; *Int'l*, pg. 1312
TLC BEATRICE INTERNATIONAL HOLDINGS INC.; *U.S. Private*, pg. 1064
TOPCO ASSOCIATES, INC.; *U.S. Private*, pg. 1091
TOSHOKU AMERICA, INC.—Toshoku Ltd.; *Int'l*, pg. 1407
TOSHOKU LTD.; *Int'l*, pg. 1407
TRI-STATE WHOLESALE ASSOCIATED GROCERS, INC.; *U.S. Private*, pg. 1101
TROYER FOODS, INC.—Hillsdown Holdings Plc; *Int'l*, pg. 619
TUPMAN THURLOW CO. INC.; *U.S. Private*, pg. 1109
TWIN COUNTY GROCERS, INC.; *U.S. Private*, pg. 1111
TYSON FOODS, INC.; *U.S. Public*, pg. 1652
U.S. FOOD SERVICE—JP Foodservice, Inc.; *U.S. Public*, pg. 918
VALLEY ISLE PRODUCE, V.I.P. FOOD SERVICE; *U.S. Private*, pg. 1132
VAN DEN BERGH FOODS COMPANY—Unilever Plc; *Int'l*, pg. 1436
WEIS FOOD SERVICE—Weis Markets, Inc.; *U.S. Public*, pg. 1752
WEIS MARKETS, INC.; *U.S. Public*, pg. 1751
WESTERN ALASKA FISHERIES INC.—Maruha Corporation; *Int'l*, pg. 845
WHITE ROSE FROZEN FOOD—Di Giorgio Corporation; *U.S. Private*, pg. 330
WHITNEY INTERNATIONAL—Kyokuyo Co. Ltd.; *Int'l*, pg. 777

5143 — DAIRY PRODUCTS, EXCEPT DRIED OR CANNED-WHOLESALE

AFFILIATED FOODS COOPERATIVE INC.; *U.S. Private*, pg. 25
AFFILIATED FUNDING INC.—Affiliated Foods, Inc.; *U.S. Private*, pg. 25
AGRILINK FOODS, INC.—Pro-Fac Cooperative, Inc.; *U.S. Private*, pg. 887
AGROPUR; *Int'l*, pg. 31
ALPINE LACE BRANDS, INC.—Land O'Lakes, Inc.; *U.S. Private*, pg. 646
ALTA DENA INC.—Bongrain S.A.; *Int'l*, pg. 201
ANCHOR FOODS LIMITED—New Zealand Dairy Board; *Int'l*, pg. 923
ANDERSON ERICKSON DAIRY COMPANY; *U.S. Private*, pg. 72
ASTRO DAIRY PRODUCTS LTD.; *Int'l*, pg. 95
AURO TECH, INC.—International Flavors & Fragrances, Inc.; *U.S. Public*, pg. 899
AXELROD FOODS, INC.—Koninklijke BolsWessanen nv; *Int'l*, pg. 752
BC-USA—Bongrain S.A.; *Int'l*, pg. 201
BAARS KAAS B.V.—Koninklijke BolsWessanen nv; *Int'l*, pg. 752
BEATRICE CHEESE CO.—ConAgra, Inc.; *U.S. Public*, pg. 426
BEN & JERRY'S HOMEMADE INC.; *U.S. Public*, pg. 210
BONGRAIN CHEESE USA—Bongrain S.A.; *Int'l*, pg. 201
BONGRAIN S.A.; *Int'l*, pg. 201
BRESLER'S INDUSTRIES, INC.—Yogen Fruz Worldwide Inc.; *Int'l*, pg. 1520
C.F. BURGER CREAMERY COMPANY; *U.S. Private*, pg. 182
C & S WHOLESALE GROCERY INC.; *U.S. Private*, pg. 192
CABOT CREAMERY CO-OPERATIVE INC.—Agri-Mark, Inc.; *U.S. Private*, pg. 26
CALIFORNIA MILK PRODUCERS; *U.S. Private*, pg. 201
CEDAR FARMS COMPANY, INC.; *U.S. Private*, pg. 221
CERTIFIED FOOD SERVICE OF GA., INC.—Sun City Industries, Inc.; *U.S. Public*, pg. 1529
CERTIFIED FOOD SERVICE OF PA, INC.—Sun City Industries, Inc.; *U.S. Public*, pg. 1529
CERTIFIED GROCERS OF CALIFORNIA; *U.S. Private*, pg. 226
CERTIFIED POULTRY & EGG CO., INC.—Sun City Industries, Inc.; *U.S. Public*, pg. 1529
CHIPWICH INC.; *U.S. Private*, pg. 237
CROWLEY FOODS, INC.—Koninklijke BolsWessanen nv; *Int'l*, pg. 752
DAIRY FARMERS OF AMERICA, INC.; *U.S. Private*, pg. 307
DAIRY FRESH CORP.; *U.S. Private*, pg. 307
DAKOTA FARMS CHEESE, INC.—Land O'Lakes, Inc.; *U.S.* Private, pg. 646
DEAN FOODS—Dean Foods Company; *U.S. Public*, pg. 490
DEEP SOUTH PRODUCTS—Winn-Dixie Stores, Inc.; *U.S. Public*, pg. 1772
DETROIT CITY DAIRY, INC.; *U.S. Private*, pg. 328
DIXIE DAIRY COMPANY; *U.S. Private*, pg. 337
DREYER'S GRAND ICE CREAM, INC.; *U.S. Public*, pg. 529
DREYER'S NORTHERN CALIFORNIA REGION—Dreyer's Grand Ice Cream, Inc.; *U.S. Public*, pg. 529
DREYER'S ROCKY MOUNTAIN REGION—Dreyer's Grand Ice Cream, Inc.; *U.S. Public*, pg. 529
DREYER'S SOUTHERN CALIFORNIA REGION—Dreyer's Grand Ice Cream, Inc.; *U.S. Public*, pg. 529
EARP DISTRIBUTION CENTER; *U.S. Private*, pg. 356
EAST SMITHFIELD FARMS INC.—Bongrain S.A.; *Int'l*, pg. 201
EDY'S NORTHEAST REGION—Dreyer's Grand Ice Cream, Inc.; *U.S. Public*, pg. 529
EDY'S SOUTHEAST REGION—Dreyer's Grand Ice Cream, Inc.; *U.S. Public*, pg. 530
ELAN FOODS—Grotech Capital Group, Inc.; *U.S. Private*, pg. 484
ESKIMO PIE CORPORATION; *U.S. Public*, pg. 592
FARMLAND DAIRIES; *U.S. Private*, pg. 395
FIELDFRESH FARMS INC.—The Oshawa Group Limited; *Int'l*, pg. 1012
FRIENDSHIP DAIRIES, INC.; *U.S. Private*, pg. 429
FRIENDSHIP DAIRIES, INC.—Friendship Dairies, Inc.; *U.S. Private*, pg. 429
GARELICK FARMS, INC.—Suiza Foods Corporation; *U.S. Public*, pg. 1527
GOLD COAST MILK PTY. LTD.—Q.U.F. Industries Ltd.; *Int'l*, pg. 1074
GORDON FOOD SERVICE INC.; *U.S. Private*, pg. 465
THE GREAT ATLANTIC & PACIFIC TEA COMPANY, INC.—Tengelmann Warenhandelsgesellschaft; *Int'l*, pg. 1375
THE GREAT LAKES CHEESE CO.; *U.S. Private*, pg. 473
M.H. GREENEBAUM, INC.; *U.S. Private*, pg. 477
HALE-HALSELL COMPANY; *U.S. Private*, pg. 494
IRA HIGDON GROCERY, INC.; *U.S. Private*, pg. 527
HILAND DAIRY COMPANY—Prairie Farms Dairy, Inc.; *U.S. Private*, pg. 879
HOKKAIDO SNOW BRAND SALES CO., LTD.—Snow Brand Milk Products Co. Ltd.; *Int'l*, pg. 1272
HUNT-WESSON REFRIGERATED FOODS DIV.—ConAgra, Inc.; *U.S. Public*, pg. 426
I & K DISTRIBUTORS, INC.; *U.S. Private*, pg. 552
IBARAGI SNOW BRAND MILK CO., LTD.—Snow Brand Milk Products Co. Ltd.; *Int'l*, pg. 1272
INTEGRATED BRANDS INC.; *U.S. Public*, pg. 883
INTERNATIONAL DAIRY QUEEN, INC.—Berkshire Hathaway Inc.; *U.S. Public*, pg. 220
INTERNATIONAL MULTIFOODS CORPORATION; *U.S. Public*, pg. 900
JOHANNA FOODS INC.; *U.S. Private*, pg. 589
KEMPS FOODS, INC.—Koninklijke BolsWessanen nv; *Int'l*, pg. 752
LAND O'LAKES, INC.—Land O'Lakes, Inc.; *U.S. Private*, pg. 646
M & H DAIRY—Fleming Companies, Inc.; *U.S. Public*, pg. 653
MCT DAIRIES, INC.—Land O'Lakes, Inc.; *U.S. Private*, pg. 646
MD FOODS; *Int'l*, pg. 826
MAJOR SMITH INC.—Bongrain S.A.; *Int'l*, pg. 201
MAPLEHURST FARMS, INC.—Dean Foods Company; *U.S. Public*, pg. 490
MARYLAND & VIRGINIA MILK PRODUCERS COOPERATIVE ASSOCIATION, INC.; *U.S. Private*, pg. 711
MCARTHUR DAIRY, INC.—Dean Foods Company; *U.S. Public*, pg. 491
MEIJER WHOLESALE INC.—Meijer, Inc.; *U.S. Private*, pg. 729
MEIJI FROZEN DESSERT CORP.—Meiji Seika Kaisha, Ltd.; *Int'l*, pg. 855
MELODY FOODS, INC.; *U.S. Private*, pg. 730
METRO FOODS, INC.; *U.S. Private*, pg. 736
MICHIGAN MILK PRODUCERS ASSOCIATION; *U.S. Private*, pg. 741
MID-AMERICA DAIRYMEN, INC.; *U.S. Private*, pg. 743
MILK MARKETING INC.; *U.S. Private*, pg. 745
MITSUBISHI CORPORATION; *Int'l*, pg. 871
MORINAGA NUTRITIONAL FOODS EUROPE S.A.—Morinaga Milk Industry Co., Ltd.; *Int'l*, pg. 895
NATREL INC.—Agropur; *Int'l*, pg. 32
NESTLE PUERTO RICO, INC.—Nestle S.A.; *Int'l*, pg. 917
NESTLE WORLD TRADE CORPORATION—Nestle S.A.; *Int'l*, pg. 916
NEW ZEALAND MILK PRODUCTS (PACIFIC) LTD.—New Zealand Dairy Board; *Int'l*, pg. 923
NORTH CENTRAL AMPI, INC.; *U.S. Private*, pg. 804
THE OSHAWA GROUP LIMITED; *Int'l*, pg. 1012
THE PENN TRAFFIC COMPANY; *U.S. Public*, pg. 1270
PEVELY DAIRY COMPANY—Prairie Farms Dairy, Inc.; *U.S.* Private, pg. 879
PIONEER SNACKS—Melody Foods, Inc.; *U.S. Private*, pg. 730
PLYMOUTH CREAMERIES, INC.; *U.S. Private*, pg. 872
POLKA DOT DAIRY/TOM THUMB, INC.; *U.S. Private*, pg. 874
POLLIO DAIRY PRODUCTS—Philip Morris Companies Inc.; *U.S. Public*, pg. 1288
PRAIRIE FARMS DAIRY, INC.; *U.S. Private*, pg. 878
PRO-FAC COOPERATIVE, INC.; *U.S. Private*, pg. 887
Q.U.F. INDUSTRIES LTD.; *Int'l*, pg. 1074
Q.U.F. MILK MARKETING—Q.U.F. Industries Ltd.; *Int'l*, pg. 1074
REITER DAIRY, INC.—Dean Foods Company; *U.S. Public*, pg. 491
ROCKY MOUNTAIN COMPANY; *U.S. Private*, pg. 938
SODIAAL; *Int'l*, pg. 1166
SARGENTO FOODS INC.; *U.S. Private*, pg. 966
SCANGAS BROTHERS HOLDINGS, INC.; *U.S. Private*, pg. 969
SCHNEIDER FARMS DAIRY—Schneider's Dairy, Inc.; *U.S. Private*, pg. 971
SCHNEIDER'S DAIRY, INC.; *U.S. Private*, pg. 971
SCHWEIZERISCHE KASEUNION AG; *Int'l*, pg. 1211
SNOW BRAND MILK PRODUCTS CO. LTD.; *Int'l*, pg. 1271
SNOW BRAND ROLLY CO., LTD.—Snow Brand Milk Products Co. Ltd.; *Int'l*, pg. 1272
SNOW BRAND SHOJI CO., LTD.—Snow Brand Milk Products Co. Ltd.; *Int'l*, pg. 1272
SPARTAN STORES INC.; *U.S. Private*, pg. 1021
SUNGOLD DAIRIES PROPRIETARY LTD—Philip Morris Companies Inc.; *U.S. Public*, pg. 1290
SUNNYDALE FARMS; *U.S. Private*, pg. 1053
SWISSROSE INTERNATIONAL, INC.—ConAgra, Inc.; *U.S. Public*, pg. 426
SWITZERLAND CHEESE ASSOCIATION, INC.—Schweizerische Kaseunion AG; *Int'l*, pg. 1211
TLC BEATRICE INTERNATIONAL HOLDINGS INC.; *U.S. Private*, pg. 1064
TAIWAN MORINAGA NUTRITIONAL FOODS INC.—Morinaga Milk Industry Co., Ltd.; *Int'l*, pg. 895
TILLAMOOK COUNTY CREAMERY ASSN.; *U.S. Private*, pg. 1086
TOKYO SNOW BRAND SALES CO., LTD.—Snow Brand Milk Products Co. Ltd.; *Int'l*, pg. 1272
TOLEDO MILK PROCESSING, INC.—Seaway Food Town, Inc.; *U.S. Public*, pg. 1453
TRAUTH DAIRY INC.; *U.S. Private*, pg. 1098
TURNER HOLDING LLC; *U.S. Private*, pg. 1109
TWIN COUNTY GROCERS, INC.; *U.S. Private*, pg. 1111
UNIGATE PLC; *Int'l*, pg. 1433
UNITED DAIRY FARMERS, INC.; *U.S. Private*, pg. 1121
UNITED DAIRYMEN OF ARIZONA; *U.S. Private*, pg. 1121
UPSTATE MILK COOPERATIVES INC.; *U.S. Private*, pg. 1129
WEST LYNN CREAMERY, INC.—Scangas Brothers Holdings, Inc.; *U.S. Private*, pg. 969
WESTERN DAIRYMEN COOPERATIVE, INC.; *U.S. Private*, pg. 1165
WHITE ROSE DAIRY—Di Giorgio Corporation; *U.S. Private*, pg. 330
WHITE ROSE FROZEN FOOD—Di Giorgio Corporation; *U.S. Private*, pg. 330
YATSUGATAKE SNOW BRAND MILK CO., LTD.—Snow Brand Milk Products Co. Ltd.; *Int'l*, pg. 1272
YOGEN FRUZ WORLDWIDE INC.; *Int'l*, pg. 1520

5144 — POULTRY & POULTRY PRODUCTS-WHOLESALE

AJC INTERNATIONAL, INC.; *U.S. Private*, pg. 6
AFFILIATED FOODS COOPERATIVE INC.; *U.S. Private*, pg. 25
BEEF DISTRIBUTORS, INC.—Keeners, Inc.; *U.S. Private*, pg. 611
CAGLE'S INC.; *U.S. Public*, pg. 291
CARLISLE POULTRY & EGG ASSOCIATES—Sun City Industries, Inc.; *U.S. Public*, pg. 1529
CASE FOODS, INC.; *U.S. Private*, pg. 217
CEDAR FARMS COMPANY, INC.; *U.S. Private*, pg. 221
CERTIFIED FOOD SERVICE OF GA., INC.—Sun City Industries, Inc.; *U.S. Public*, pg. 1529
CERTIFIED FOOD SERVICE OF PA, INC.—Sun City Industries, Inc.; *U.S. Public*, pg. 1529
CERTIFIED POULTRY & EGG CO., INC.—Sun City Industries, Inc.; *U.S. Public*, pg. 1529
CITY MEATS & PROVISIONS CO.—Clayton, Dubilier & Rice, Inc; *U.S. Private*, pg. 244
CONAGRA POULTRY FOODSERVICE CO.—ConAgra, Inc.; *U.S. Public*, pg. 427
COUGLE COMMISSION COMPANY, INC.; *U.S. Private*, pg. 278
CROWN FOODS INC.; *U.S. Private*, pg. 292
DAY-LEE FOODS INC.—Nippon Meat Packers, Inc.; *Int'l*, pg. 936
LOUIS DREYFUS CORPORATION; *U.S. Private*, pg. 342
EGGLAND'S BEST, INC.; *U.S. Private*, pg. 366
KEENERS, INC.; *U.S. Private*, pg. 611
KEYSTONE FOODS CORPORATION; *U.S. Private*, pg. 619
LONGMONT FOODS—ConAgra, Inc.; *U.S. Public*, pg. 426
MAINE POTATO GROWERS, INC.; *U.S. Private*, pg. 697
MCCARTY FOODS, INC.—Tyson Foods, Inc.; *U.S. Public*, pg. 1652
MCINERNEY-MILLER BROTHERS INC.; *U.S. Private*, pg. 722
METRO FOODS, INC.; *U.S. Private*, pg. 736
NEARBY EGGS, INC.—Sun City Industries, Inc.; *U.S. Public*, pg. 1529
NORBEST, INC.; *U.S. Private*, pg. 801
NORTHWESTERN MEATS INC.; *U.S. Private*, pg. 807
NULAID FOODS; *U.S. Private*, pg. 809
PAPETTI HYGRADE EGG PRODUCTS—Michael Foods, Inc.; *U.S. Public*, pg. 1104
PILGRIM'S PRIDE CORPORATION; *U.S. Public*, pg. 1296
PLANTATION FOODS INC.; *U.S. Private*, pg. 869
ROCKY MOUNTAIN COMPANY; *U.S. Private*, pg. 938
SANDERSON FARMS, INC.; *U.S. Public*, pg. 1430
SHEPPARD FOODSERVICE, INC.—Sun City Industries, Inc.; *U.S. Public*, pg. 1529
SHERWOOD FOOD DISTRIBUTORS; *U.S. Private*, pg. 993
SHERWOOD FOODS—Sherwood Food Distributors; *U.S. Private*, pg. 994
SMITH FARMS, INC.; *U.S. Private*, pg. 1008
KEITH SMITH COMPANY; *U.S. Private*, pg. 1008
SPAFAS, INC.—Bausch & Lomb Incorporated; *U.S. Public*, pg. 195
SUN CITY EGG MARKETING, INC.—Sun City Industries, Inc.; *U.S. Public*, pg. 1529
SUN CITY INDUSTRIES, INC.; *U.S. Public*, pg. 1529
TATUM FARMS INT., INC.; *U.S. Private*, pg. 1069
TROYER FOODS, INC.—Hillsdown Holdings Plc; *Int'l*, pg. 619
TYSON EXPORT SALES, INC.—Tyson Foods, Inc.; *U.S. Public*, pg. 1652
TYSON FOODS, INC.—Tyson Foods, Inc.; *U.S. Public*, pg. 1652
VALLET FOOD SERV INC.; *U.S. Private*, pg. 1131

5145 — CONFECTIONERY-WHOLESALE

R.L. ALBERT & SON, INC.; *U.S. Private*, pg. 32
ANDERSON WHOLESALE COMPANY; *U.S. Private*, pg. 73
BEER NUTS, INC.; *U.S. Private*, pg. 130
BRACH & BROCK CONFECTIONS, INC.; *U.S. Private*, pg. 163
E.J. BRACH, INC.—Brach & Brock Confections, Inc.; *U.S. Private*, pg. 163
C & S WHOLESALE GROCERY INC.; *U.S. Private*, pg. 192

CADBURY INTERNATIONAL LIMITED—Cadbury Schweppes p.l.c.; *Int'l*, pg. 248
CAPE COD POTATO CHIP COMPANY; *U.S. Private*, pg. 205
COCA-COLA USA—The Coca-Cola Company; *U.S. Public*, pg. 392
COLIVITA USA, INC.; *U.S. Private*, pg. 252
COLUMBINA MEIJI S.A.—Meiji Seika Kaisha, Ltd.; *Int'l*, pg. 856
DAKCO DISTRIBUTORS, INC.; *U.S. Private*, pg. 308
DOHNAN SHOKUHIN CO., LTD.—Meiji Seika Kaisha, Ltd.; *Int'l*, pg. 855
ESKIMO EUROP S.A.R.L.—Eskimo Pie Corporation; *U.S. Public*, pg. 592
FAIRMONT SNACK GROUP, INC.; *U.S. Private*, pg. 392
FERRERO; *Int'l*, pg. 480
FERRERO INC.—Ferrero; *Int'l*, pg. 480
FERRERO U.S.A., INC.—Ferrero; *Int'l*, pg. 480
THE FOREIGN CANDY CO., INC.; *U.S. Private*, pg. 418
FRITZ CO. INC.; *U.S. Private*, pg. 429
GOLDEN ENTERPRISES INC.; *U.S. Public*, pg. 749
GROCERS SUPPLY CO. INC.; *U.S. Private*, pg. 483
GROCERY DIVISION—Grist Mill Company; *U.S. Public*, pg. 766
GRUPO CASA AUTREY; *Int'l*, pg. 573
H & H DISTRIBUTING COMPANY, INC.; *U.S. Private*, pg. 489
HAGEMEYER N.V.—First Pacific Company Limited; *Int'l*, pg. 487
HARMONY FOODS CORPORATION; *U.S. Private*, pg. 503
HERSHEY INTERNATIONAL—Hershey Foods Corporation; *U.S. Public*, pg. 812
INTERNATIONAL MULTIFOODS CORPORATION; *U.S. Public*, pg. 900
KAISER WHOLESALE, INC.; *U.S. Private*, pg. 605
LAYMAN CANDY COMPANY, INC.; *U.S. Private*, pg. 655
ALEX LEE, INC.; *U.S. Private*, pg. 657
MEIJI CHEWING GUM CO, LTD.—Meiji Seika Kaisha, Ltd.; *Int'l*, pg. 855
MEIJI SANGYO CO., LTD.—Meiji Seika Kaisha, Ltd.; *Int'l*, pg. 855
MEIJI SEIKA KAISHA, LTD.; *Int'l*, pg. 855
MEIJI SEIKA (SINGAPORE) PTE. LTD.—Meiji Seika Kaisha, Ltd.; *Int'l*, pg. 856
MEIJI SEIKA (U.S.A.) INC.—Meiji Seika Kaisha, Ltd.; *Int'l*, pg. 855
NESTLE PUERTO RICO, INC.—Nestle S.A.; *Int'l*, pg. 917
NESTLE WORLD TRADE CORPORATION—Nestle S.A.; *Int'l*, pg. 916
NORTHWEST TOBACCO & CANDY CO.; *U.S. Private*, pg. 806
NUT TREE PECAN COMPANY, INC.—Young Pecan Company (A Partnership); *U.S. Private*, pg. 1201
THE OSHAWA GROUP LIMITED; *Int'l*, pg. 1012
PINE STATE TRADING COMPANY; *U.S. Private*, pg. 865
THE PROMOTION IN MOTION COMPANIES; *U.S. Private*, pg. 890
RAGOLD, INC.—Ragolds Susswaren GmbH & Co.; *Int'l*, pg. 1084
RED BAND SUSSWAREN VERTRIEBS GMBH—CSM N.V.; *Int'l*, pg. 244
SATHERS INC.—Favorite Brands International, Inc.; *U.S. Private*, pg. 397
SMART & FINAL—Groupe Casino; *Int'l*, pg. 563
SOUTHCO DISTRIBUTING COMPANY; *U.S. Private*, pg. 1014
STORCK U.S.A., L.P.—Storck International GmbH; *Int'l*, pg. 1304
SUNMARK INC.—Nestle S.A.; *Int'l*, pg. 917
TLC BEATRICE INTERNATIONAL HOLDINGS INC.; *U.S. Private*, pg. 1064
TENNANT & RUTTLE DISTRIBUTION LIMITED—James Crean PLC; *Int'l*, pg. 340
TENNANT & RUTTLE LIMITED—James Crean PLC; *Int'l*, pg. 340
TOOTSIE ROLL OF CANADA, LTD.—Tootsie Roll Industries, Inc.; *U.S. Public*, pg. 1621
UTZ QUALITY FOODS, INC.; *U.S. Private*, pg. 1130
VSA, INC.—International Multifoods Corporation; *U.S. Public*, pg. 901
VAN MELLE-FRANCE S.A.—Van Melle N.V.; *Int'l*, pg. 1451
VAN MELLE NEDERLAND VERKOOP B. V.—Van Melle N.V.; *Int'l*, pg. 1451
VAN MELLE N.V.; *Int'l*, pg. 1450
N.V. VAN MELLE S.A.—Van Melle N.V.; *Int'l*, pg. 1451
VAN MELLE USA, INC.—Van Melle N.V.; *Int'l*, pg. 1451
WARNER CANDY COMPANY, INC.; *U.S. Private*, pg. 1150
WEAVER POPCORN COMPANY, INC.; *U.S. Private*, pg. 1156
WHOLESALE SUPPLY COMPANY, INC.; *U.S. Private*, pg. 1174
WORLD TRADE & MARKETING LTD.—Tootsie Roll Industries, Inc.; *U.S. Public*, pg. 1621
YOUNG PECAN COMPANY (A PARTNERSHIP); *U.S. Private*, pg. 1201
ZAO SHOKUHIN CO., LTD.—Meiji Seika Kaisha, Ltd.; *Int'l*, pg. 855

5146 — FISH & SEAFOODS-WHOLESALE

AJC INTERNATIONAL, INC.; *U.S. Private*, pg. 6
AMERICAN FOODS GROUP, INC.; *U.S. Private*, pg. 54
ARCTIC ALASKA FISHERIES CORPORATION—Tyson Foods, Inc.; *U.S. Public*, pg. 1652
ATALANTA CORPORATION; *U.S. Private*, pg. 93
ATALANTA (U.K.) LTD.—Atalanta Corporation; *U.S. Private*, pg. 94
BEAVER STREET FISHERIES, INC.; *U.S. Private*, pg. 128
BEEF DISTRIBUTORS, INC.—Keeners, Inc.; *U.S. Private*, pg. 611
CITY MEATS & PROVISIONS CO.—Clayton, Dubilier & Rice, Inc; *U.S. Private*, pg. 244
CLEARWATER FINE FOODS INC.; *Int'l*, pg. 297
CLEARWATER LOBSTER LIMITED—Clearwater Fine Foods Inc.; *Int'l*, pg. 297
CONAGRA SEAFOOD COMPANIES—ConAgra, Inc.; *U.S. Public*, pg. 427
CONAGRA SHRIMP COMPANY—ConAgra, Inc.; *U.S. Public*, pg. 427
CONNELL CO.; *U.S. Private*, pg. 264
DELTA PRIDE CATFISH, INC.; *U.S. Private*, pg. 322
E & G FOODS; *U.S. Private*, pg. 352
EMPRESS INTERNATIONAL LTD.; *U.S. Private*, pg. 375
FARMLAND NATIONAL BEEF PACKING COMPANY, L.P.—Farmland Industries, Inc.; *U.S. Private*, pg. 396
FRIONOR-PRODUKTER A/S—Frionor A/S; *Int'l*, pg. 516
HANWA AMERICAN CORP.—Hanwa Co., Ltd.; *Int'l*, pg. 595
HANWA AMERICAN CORP., SEATTLE BRANCH—Hanwa Co., Ltd.; *Int'l*, pg. 595
HANWA CO., LTD.; *Int'l*, pg. 595
KEENERS, INC.; *U.S. Private*, pg. 611
KESTERSON FOOD COMPANY, INC.; *U.S. Private*, pg. 616
KYOKUYO AMERICA CORP.—Kyokuyo Co. Ltd.; *Int'l*, pg. 777
LONGVA GROUP; *Int'l*, pg. 817
MCINERNEY-MILLER BROTHERS INC.; *U.S. Private*, pg. 722
NEW YORK REPRESENTATIVE OFFICE (ESNOR)—Petrobras - Petroleo Brasileiro S.A.; *Int'l*, pg. 1042
NICHIMEN AMERICA, INC.—Nichimen Corporation; *Int'l*, pg. 927
NICHIMEN CORPORATION; *Int'l*, pg. 927
NIPPON SUISAN U.S.A.—Nippon Suisan Kaisha, Ltd.; *Int'l*, pg. 940
NORTHWESTERN MEATS INC.; *U.S. Private*, pg. 807
PROCORDIA FOOD AB—Orkla A.S.A.; *Int'l*, pg. 1011
PURDEL, COOPERATIVE AGRO-ALIMENTAIRE; *Int'l*, pg. 1073
ROCKY MOUNTAIN COMPANY; *U.S. Private*, pg. 938
STEUART INVESTMENT COMPANY; *U.S. Private*, pg. 1042
SUMITOMO CORPORATION OF AMERICA—Sumitomo Corporation; *Int'l*, pg. 1312
TYSON FOODS, INC.; *U.S. Public*, pg. 1652
WHITNEY INTERNATIONAL—Kyokuyo Co. Ltd.; *Int'l*, pg. 777

5147 — MEATS & MEAT PRODUCTS-WHOLESALE

AJC INTERNATIONAL, INC.; *U.S. Private*, pg. 6
ABBYLAND FOODS, INC.; *U.S. Private*, pg. 10
ABBYLAND ILLINOIS, INC.—Abbyland Foods, Inc.; *U.S. Private*, pg. 10
AFFILIATED FOODS COOPERATIVE INC.; *U.S. Private*, pg. 25
AFFILIATED FOODS, INC.; *U.S. Private*, pg. 25
ASSOCIATED FOOD STORES, INC.; *U.S. Private*, pg. 90
BEEF DISTRIBUTORS, INC.—Keeners, Inc.; *U.S. Private*, pg. 611
BELL-GRUPPE—Coop Switzerland; *Int'l*, pg. 329
BINGHAMS COOKED MEATS LTD.—Northern Foods plc; *Int'l*, pg. 968
BLUE GRASS QUALITY MEATS; *U.S. Private*, pg. 152
BRIDGFORD DISTRIBUTING CO.—Bridgford Foods Corporation; *U.S. Public*, pg. 252
BRIDGFORD FOODS CORPORATION; *U.S. Public*, pg. 252
BROOKS PROVISIONS INC.; *U.S. Private*, pg. 172
BUTLER FOODS, INC.; *U.S. Private*, pg. 190
CAGLE'S INC.; *U.S. Public*, pg. 291
CEDAR FARMS COMPANY, INC.; *U.S. Private*, pg. 221
CERTIFIED GROCERS OF CALIFORNIA; *U.S. Private*, pg. 226
CHAMPION BOXED BEEF; *U.S. Private*, pg. 228
CHIPICO PICKLES—Vienna Sausage Mfg. Co.; *U.S. Private*, pg. 1140
CITY MEATS & PROVISIONS CO.—Clayton, Dubilier & Rice, Inc; *U.S. Private*, pg. 244
COLONIAL BEEF CO.; *U.S. Private*, pg. 253
COLORADO BOXED BEEF CO.; *U.S. Private*, pg. 254
CONAGRA ASIA-PACIFIC—ConAgra, Inc.; *U.S. Public*, pg. 429
CONNELL CO.; *U.S. Private*, pg. 264
CONSOLIDATED COMPANIES INC. (CONCO); *U.S. Private*, pg. 265
THE COPPS CORP.; *U.S. Private*, pg. 275
COUGLE COMMISSION COMPANY, INC.; *U.S. Private*, pg. 278
CROWN FOODS INC.; *U.S. Private*, pg. 292
DAY-LEE FOODS INC.—Nippon Meat Packers, Inc.; *Int'l*, pg. 936
DEEN WHOLESALE MEAT COMPANY, INC.; *U.S. Private*, pg. 320
LOUIS DREYFUS CORPORATION; *U.S. Private*, pg. 342
E & G FOODS; *U.S. Private*, pg. 352
ESS-FOOD; *Int'l*, pg. 429
ESS-FOOD (H.K.) LTD.—ESS-Food; *Int'l*, pg. 429
ESS-FOOD HUNGARIA LLC—ESS-Food; *Int'l*, pg. 429
EARP DISTRIBUTION CENTER; *U.S. Private*, pg. 356
ENTREE CORPORATION—Coyote Network Systems, Inc.; *U.S. Public*, pg. 455
FDL FOODS, INC.—Farmland Industries, Inc.; *U.S. Private*, pg. 396
FOODANE A/S—Vestjyske Slagterier; *Int'l*, pg. 1464
GENUARDI FAMILY MARKETS INC.; *U.S. Private*, pg. 447
GORDON FOOD SERVICE INC.; *U.S. Private*, pg. 465
HALE-HALSELL COMPANY; *U.S. Private*, pg. 494
IRA HIGDON GROCERY, INC.; *U.S. Private*, pg. 527
HORMEL FOODS CORP.; *U.S. Public*, pg. 840
HORMEL INTERNATIONAL CORPORATION—Hormel Foods Corp.; *U.S. Public*, pg. 840
IBP, INC.; *U.S. Public*, pg. 852
JORDAN'S FOODS-CARIBOU DIVISION—Jordan's Meats; *U.S. Private*, pg. 599
JORDAN'S MEATS; *U.S. Private*, pg. 599
SAM KANE BEEF PROCESSORS, INC.; *U.S. Private*, pg. 607
KEENERS, INC.; *U.S. Private*, pg. 611
A.C. KISSLING, INC.; *U.S. Private*, pg. 624
LANCE, INC.; *U.S. Public*, pg. 977
LEONARD & HARRAL PACKING CO.; *U.S. Private*, pg. 660
LEVONIAN BROTHERS INC.; *U.S. Private*, pg. 663
LINCOLN PROVISION, INC.; *U.S. Private*, pg. 668
MCINERNEY-MILLER BROTHERS INC.; *U.S. Private*, pg. 722
METRO FOODS, INC.; *U.S. Private*, pg. 736
ED MINIAT, INC.; *U.S. Private*, pg. 750
MITSUBISHI CORPORATION; *Int'l*, pg. 871
MONFORT, INC.—ConAgra, Inc.; *U.S. Public*, pg. 427
MULTIFOODS SPECIALTY DISTRIBUTION INC.—International Multifoods Corporation; *U.S. Public*, pg. 901
NATIONWIDE BEEF, INC.; *U.S. Private*, pg. 788
NEW ZEALAND LAMB CO., INC.; *U.S. Private*, pg. 796
NIPPON MEAT PACKERS, INC.; *Int'l*, pg. 936
NISSHO IWAI DELICA CORP.—Nissho Iwai Corporation; *Int'l*, pg. 946
NORTHWESTERN MEATS INC.; *U.S. Private*, pg. 807
OMAHA STEAKS; *U.S. Private*, pg. 815
ORLEANS INTERNATIONAL, INC.; *U.S. Private*, pg. 820
THE OSHAWA GROUP LIMITED; *Int'l*, pg. 1012
PENNINSULAR MEAT COMPANY, INC.; *U.S. Private*, pg. 850
QUALITY FOODS INC.; *U.S. Private*, pg. 898
ROCKY MOUNTAIN COMPANY; *U.S. Private*, pg. 938
RUSSER FOODS—Zemco Industries, Inc.; *U.S. Private*, pg. 1204
SARA LEE CORPORATION; *U.S. Public*, pg. 1432
SERVICE PACKING COMPANY-UNITED FOOD GROUP; *U.S. Private*, pg. 986
SHAMROCK FOODS COMPANY; *U.S. Private*, pg. 989
SHERWOOD FOOD DISTRIBUTORS; *U.S. Private*, pg. 993
SHERWOOD FOODS—Sherwood Food Distributors; *U.S. Private*, pg. 994
SMITHFIELD DIVISION—The Smithfield Companies, Inc.; *U.S. Public*, pg. 1479
SOCIETE ANONYME MEDITERRANEENE DE SALAISONS—ConAgra, Inc.; *U.S. Public*, pg. 429
SOUTHERN FOODS, INC.; *U.S. Private*, pg. 1016
SPARTAN STORES INC.; *U.S. Private*, pg. 1021
SPIEGEL MEATS, INC.; *U.S. Private*, pg. 1025
STAR FOOD PRODUCTS, INC.; *U.S. Private*, pg. 1034
STOCK YARDS PACKING CO., INC.; *U.S. Private*, pg. 1043
TENNESSEE DRESSED BEEF COMPANY; *U.S. Private*, pg. 1076
TWIN COUNTY GROCERS, INC.; *U.S. Private*, pg. 1111
VALLEY ISLE PRODUCE, V.I.P. FOOD SERVICE; *U.S. Private*, pg. 1132
VIENNA SAUSAGE MFG. CO.; *U.S. Private*, pg. 1139
WOLVERINE PACKING CO.; *U.S. Private*, pg. 1186
R.L. ZEIGLER CO. INC.; *U.S. Private*, pg. 1204
ZEMCO INDUSTRIES, INC.; *U.S. Private*, pg. 1204
ZOLL FOOD CORP.—ConAgra, Inc.; *U.S. Public*, pg. 426

5148 — FRESH FRUITS & VEGETABLES-WHOLESALE

AJC INTERNATIONAL, INC.; *U.S. Private*, pg. 6
AFFILIATED FOODS COOPERATIVE INC.; *U.S. Private*, pg. 25
AFFILIATED FOODS, INC.; *U.S. Private*, pg. 25
AGRINORTHWEST, INC.; *U.S. Private*, pg. 26
ARMSTRONG PRODUCE LTD.; *U.S. Private*, pg. 83
BANACOL MARKETING CORP.; *U.S. Private*, pg. 113
BASIC FOOD INTERNATIONAL INC.; *U.S. Private*, pg. 121
BEL AIR MARKETS—Raley's & Bel Air; *U.S. Private*, pg. 908
WM. BOLTHOUSE FARMS, INC.; *U.S. Private*, pg. 155
BOWEN BROTHERS FRUIT CO., INC.; *U.S. Private*, pg. 162
C. BREWER & COMPANY, LIMITED—Buyco, Inc.; *U.S. Private*, pg. 190
BROOKLYN BOTTLING CO. OF MILTON, NY; *U.S. Private*, pg. 171
CALAVO FOODS DE MEXICO, S.A. DE C.V.—Calavo Growers of California; *U.S. Private*, pg. 200
CALAVO GROWERS OF CALIFORNIA; *U.S. Private*, pg. 199
CHERRY CENTRAL COOPERATIVE; *U.S. Private*, pg. 233
CHESSWOOD PRODUCE LTD.—Tomkins PLC; *Int'l*, pg. 1396
CHIQUITA BANANA NORTH AMERICA—Chiquita Brands International, Inc.; *U.S. Public*, pg. 349
CHIQUITA BRANDS INTERNATIONAL, INC.; *U.S. Public*, pg. 349
CHRISTY'S MARKETS, INC.; *U.S. Private*, pg. 238
CLOVER PRODUCE LIMITED—Empire Company Limited; *Int'l*, pg. 454
CONSOLIDATED COMPANIES INC. (CONCO); *U.S. Private*, pg. 265
CREST FRUIT CO.—Standex International Corporation; *U.S. Public*, pg. 1506
DOLE FOOD COMPANY, INC.; *U.S. Public*, pg. 515
A. DUDA & SONS INC.; *U.S. Private*, pg. 344
FOOD SERVICES OF AMERICA—Services Group of America; *U.S. Private*, pg. 987
FRESH WESTERN INTERNATIONAL—The Albert Fisher Group PLC; *Int'l*, pg. 491
GLOBAL FOOD CORPORATION—Basic Food International Inc.; *U.S. Private*, pg. 121
GOLDEN GEM GROWERS INC.; *U.S. Private*, pg. 460
GORDON FOOD SERVICE INC.; *U.S. Private*, pg. 465
HAINES CITY CITRUS GROWERS ASSOCIATION; *U.S. Private*, pg. 494

HALE-HALSELL COMPANY; *U.S. Private*, pg. 494
HARTOG RAHIL FOODS, INC.; *U.S. Private*, pg. 508
J. HELLMAN PRODUCE, INC.; *U.S. Private*, pg. 520
V.B. HOOK & CO., INC.; *U.S. Private*, pg. 538
JORDAN'S FOODS-CARIBOU DIVISION—Jordan's Meats; *U.S. Private*, pg. 599
JORDAN'S MEATS; *U.S. Private*, pg. 599
BEN E. KEITH COMPANY; *U.S. Private*, pg. 611
LANCASTER FOODS, INC.—Guest Services, Inc.; *U.S. Private*, pg. 487
A. LEVY & J. ZENTNER CO.; *U.S. Private*, pg. 663
MAINE POTATO GROWERS, INC.; *U.S. Private*, pg. 697
MARTIN & BAYLEY INC.; *U.S. Private*, pg. 708
NASH DECAMP COMPANY—Nash Finch Company; *U.S. Public*, pg. 1152
OCEAN MIST FARMS CORP.; *U.S. Private*, pg. 811
THE ONTARIO PRODUCE CO.—The Oshawa Group Limited; *Int'l*, pg. 1012
PROCORDIA FOOD AB—Orkla A.S.A.; *Int'l*, pg. 1011
QUALITY FOODS INC.; *U.S. Private*, pg. 898
RIVER RANCH NORTHEAST, INC.; *U.S. Private*, pg. 934
C.H. ROBINSON CO.; *U.S. Public*, pg. 1394
ROCKY MOUNTAIN COMPANY; *U.S. Private*, pg. 938
SCHMIEDING ENTERPRISES INC.; *U.S. Private*, pg. 971
SERCA FOOD SERVICE-HICKESON DIV.—The Oshawa Group Limited; *Int'l*, pg. 1012
SERVICES GROUP OF AMERICA; *U.S. Private*, pg. 987
SPARTAN STORES INC.; *U.S. Private*, pg. 1021
STADELMAN FRUIT L.L.C.; *U.S. Private*, pg. 1028
THE STOP & SHOP COMPANIES, INC.—Koninklijke Ahold NV; *Int'l*, pg. 750
SUNKIST (FAR EAST) PROMOTION, LTD.—Sunkist Growers, Inc.; *U.S. Private*, pg. 1053
SUNKIST GROWERS, INC.; *U.S. Private*, pg. 1052
SUNKIST GROWERS, INC.-SOUTHERN DIVISION—Sunkist Growers, Inc.; *U.S. Private*, pg. 1052
SUNKIST GROWERS, INC.-WESTERN DIVISION—Sunkist Growers, Inc.; *U.S. Private*, pg. 1052
SUNKIST PACIFIC, LTD.—Sunkist Growers, Inc.; *U.S. Private*, pg. 1053
TROUT-BLUE CHELIAU, INC.; *U.S. Private*, pg. 1105
VALLET FOOD SERV INC.; *U.S. Private*, pg. 1131
VALLEY ISLE PRODUCE, V.I.P. FOOD SERVICE; *U.S. Private*, pg. 1132
WAILUKU AGRIBUSINESS CO., INC.—Buyco, Inc.; *U.S. Private*, pg. 191
WHOLE FOODS MARKET, INC.; *U.S. Public*, pg. 1767

5149 — GROCERIES AND RELATED PRODUCTS-WHOLESALE, NEC

AJC INTERNATIONAL, INC.; *U.S. Private*, pg. 6
AGROPUR; *Int'l*, pg. 31
AJINOMOTO U.S.A., INC.—Ajinomoto Company Inc.; *Int'l*, pg. 40
AKZO SALT LIMITED—Akzo Nobel N.V.; *Int'l*, pg. 43
AKZO ZOUT CHEMIE SVENSKA AB—Akzo Nobel N.V.; *Int'l*, pg. 44
R.L. ALBERT & SON, INC.; *U.S. Private*, pg. 32
ALL AMERICAN BOTTLING CORP.; *U.S. Private*, pg. 34
ALLIED YOUR COFFEE PARTNER—Allied Office Supplies; *U.S. Private*, pg. 39
THE AMALGAMATED SUGAR COMPANY LLC; *U.S. Private*, pg. 48
AMERICAN BREAD CO.—The Earthgrains Company; *U.S. Public*, pg. 547
AMFAC SUGAR AND AGRIBUSINESS, INC.—JMB Realty Corporation; *U.S. Private*, pg. 578
AMRION INC.—Whole Foods Market, Inc.; *U.S. Public*, pg. 1767
ANCHORAGE COLD STORAGE CO.—The Odom Corporation; *U.S. Private*, pg. 812
ARAMARK CORP.; *U.S. Private*, pg. 78
ARROW INDUSTRIES, INC.—ConAgra, Inc.; *U.S. Public*, pg. 426
ASSOCIATED FOOD STORES INC.; *U.S. Private*, pg. 90
AUSTIN QUALITY FOODS; *U.S. Private*, pg. 100
AWREY BAKERIES, INC.; *U.S. Private*, pg. 103
BACARDI CORPORATION—Bacardi Limited; *Int'l*, pg. 131
BACARDI-MARTINI CARIBBEAN CORPORATION—Bacardi Limited; *Int'l*, pg. 132
BACARDI-MARTINI, USA, INC.; *U.S. Private*, pg. 109
BAKERY & CONFECTIONARY DIVISION—Campbell Soup Company; *U.S. Public*, pg. 299
BASIC FOOD INTERNATIONAL INC.; *U.S. Private*, pg. 121
BAY STATE MILLING CO.; *U.S. Private*, pg. 124
BERRIEL VITTEL FRANCE—Nestle S.A.; *Int'l*, pg. 918
BERTOLLI USA, INC.—IRI Istituto Ricostruzione Industriale; *Int'l*, pg. 655
BEST FOODS SAUDI ARABIA CO. LTD.—Bestfoods; *U.S. Public*, pg. 225
BLUE LINE DISTRIBUTING—Little Caesar Enterprises, Inc.; *U.S. Private*, pg. 671
BOOTS HEALTHCARE INTERNATIONAL—The Boots Company PLC; *Int'l*, pg. 202
BORDEN, EXPORTS LIMITED—Borden, Inc.; *U.S. Private*, pg. 159
BOURY ENTERPRISES; *U.S. Private*, pg. 162
C. BREWER & COMPANY, LIMITED—Buyco, Inc.; *U.S. Private*, pg. 190
BRISTOL-MYERS PERUANA S.A.—Bristol-Myers Squibb Company; *U.S. Public*, pg. 255
BROOKLYN BOTTLING CO. OF MILTON, NY; *U.S. Private*, pg. 171
BRUCE FOODS CORP.; *U.S. Private*, pg. 175
BUCKEYE BISCUIT COMPANY—President Enterprises Corp.; *Int'l*, pg. 1069
BUSCH AGRICULTURAL RESOURCES, INC.—Anheuser-Busch Companies, Inc.; *U.S. Public*, pg. 114
BYRNES & KIEFER COMPANY; *U.S. Private*, pg. 191
CPC/AJI (SINGAPORE) PTE. LTD.—Bestfoods; *U.S. Public*, pg. 225
CPC EXPORT (AFRICA/MIDDLE EAST) AG—Bestfoods; *U.S. Public*, pg. 225
CADBURY BEVERAGES—Cadbury Schweppes p.l.c.; *Int'l*, pg. 248
CADBURY BEVERAGES NORTH AMERICA—Cadbury Schweppes p.l.c.; *Int'l*, pg. 248
CALAVO GROWERS OF CALIFORNIA; *U.S. Private*, pg. 199
CAMERICAN INTERNATIONAL—ConAgra, Inc.; *U.S. Public*, pg. 426
CAMPBELL JAPAN, INC.—Campbell Soup Company; *U.S. Public*, pg. 299
CAMPBELL SALES—Campbell Soup Company; *U.S. Public*, pg. 299
CAMPBELL SALES COMPANY—Campbell Soup Company; *U.S. Public*, pg. 299
CAMPBELL'S SOUPS (AUST.) PTY. LTD.—Campbell Soup Company; *U.S. Public*, pg. 299
CAPY U.S.A. INC.—Calpis Food Industry Co. Ltd.; *Int'l*, pg. 253
CARNEGIE HOLDING AB; *Int'l*, pg. 272
CARO PRODUCE & INSTITUTIONAL FOODS—Performance Food Group Company; *U.S. Public*, pg. 1278
CASE FOODS, INC.; *U.S. Private*, pg. 217
CEREAL WANDER—Novartis AG; *Int'l*, pg. 975
CERTIFIED GROCERS MIDWEST, INC.; *U.S. Private*, pg. 226
CERTIFIED GROCERS OF CALIFORNIA; *U.S. Private*, pg. 226
CHEESECAKE FACTORY INCORPORATED; *U.S. Public*, pg. 343
CHEIL FOODS & CHEMICALS INC.—Samsung Group; *Int'l*, pg. 1181
COCA-COLA BOTTLING CO. UNITED, INC.; *U.S. Private*, pg. 248
THE COCA-COLA COMPANY; *U.S. Public*, pg. 392
COMPACK DOUWE EGBERTS RT—Sara Lee Corporation; *U.S. Public*, pg. 1434
COMPANHIA EXPORTADORA DE MELACOS LTDA.—Tate & Lyle PLC; *Int'l*, pg. 1357
CONAGRA INTERNATIONAL—ConAgra, Inc.; *U.S. Public*, pg. 426
CONTADINA FRESH—Nestle S.A.; *Int'l*, pg. 918
COOKIE TREE INC.; *U.S. Private*, pg. 273
COOPER SMITH, INC.—The Earthgrains Company; *U.S. Public*, pg. 547
R.J. CORR NATURALS, INC.; *U.S. Private*, pg. 276
CRESTAR FOOD PRODUCTS, INC.—H.J. Heinz Company; *U.S. Public*, pg. 805
CROWN PRINCE, INC. (CA); *U.S. Private*, pg. 293
CRYSTAL GEYSER WATER COMPANY—Otsuka Pharmaceutical Co., Ltd.; *Int'l*, pg. 1013
CUISINE SOLUTIONS, INC.; *U.S. Public*, pg. 466
DANISH CREAMERY ASSOCIATION; *U.S. Private*, pg. 310
DAWN FOOD PRODUCTS, INC.; *U.S. Private*, pg. 316
DEAKTOR/SYSCO FOOD SERVICES CO.—Sysco Corporation; *U.S. Public*, pg. 1551
DEL MONTE FOODS; *U.S. Private*, pg. 321
DEVRO INTERNATIONAL PLC; *Int'l*, pg. 408
THE DIAL CORPORATION; *U.S. Public*, pg. 505
DIAMOND WALNUT GROWERS, INC.—Sun Diamond Growers of California; *U.S. Private*, pg. 1051
DIET CENTER WORLDWIDE, INC.—Physicians Weight Loss Centers, Inc.; *U.S. Private*, pg. 864
DISTRIBUTION AB DAGAB—Carnegie Holding AB; *Int'l*, pg. 272
DOHNAN SHOKUHIN CO., LTD.—Meiji Seika Kaisha, Ltd.; *Int'l*, pg. 855
DRAKE BAKERIES, INC.—Culinar Inc.; *Int'l*, pg. 349
EARP DISTRIBUTION CENTER; *U.S. Private*, pg. 356
THE EAST ASIATIC COMPANY LTD. A/S; *Int'l*, pg. 430
EBY-BROWN CO.; *U.S. Private*, pg. 359
ECKES AG; *Int'l*, pg. 432
EFFEMS AG—Mars, Incorporated; *U.S. Private*, pg. 707
EHIME KANZUME CO., LTD.—Meiji Seika Kaisha, Ltd.; *Int'l*, pg. 855
EMPIRE COMPANY LIMITED; *Int'l*, pg. 453
ESSEX GRAIN PRODUCTS, INC.; *U.S. Private*, pg. 383
EURYZA BV—CSM N.V.; *Int'l*, pg. 243
EURYZA INTERNATIONAL AG—CSM N.V.; *Int'l*, pg. 244
EURYZA REIS GMBH—CSM N.V.; *Int'l*, pg. 244
FERROSAN DANMARK A/S—Novo Nordisk A/S; *Int'l*, pg. 987
FERROSAN INTERNATIONAL A/S—Novo Nordisk A/S; *Int'l*, pg. 987
FLORASYNTH LIMITED—Bayer AG; *Int'l*, pg. 173
FLORASYNTH SINGAPORE PTE LTD.—Bayer AG; *Int'l*, pg. 174
FRANZ BAKERY—United States Bakery; *U.S. Private*, pg. 1124
GF INTERNATIONAL LIMITED—Goodman Fielder Limited; *Int'l*, pg. 555
GF PACIFIC EXPORTS (NZ) LTD.—Goodman Fielder Limited; *Int'l*, pg. 556
GFA BRANDS, INC.; *U.S. Private*, pg. 435
GATE CITY BEVERAGE DISTRIBUTORS; *U.S. Private*, pg. 441
GEEST PLC; *Int'l*, pg. 542
GILBEY'S OF IRELAND—Diageo Plc; *Int'l*, pg. 409
GIST-BROCADES BENELUX B.V.—Royal Gist-Brocades N.V.; *Int'l*, pg. 1143
GIST-BROCADES, LDA.—Royal Gist-Brocades N.V.; *Int'l*, pg. 1143
GLOBAL BEVERAGE CO.; *U.S. Private*, pg. 457
GLOBAL FOOD CORPORATION—Basic Food International Inc.; *U.S. Private*, pg. 121
GORDON FOOD SERVICE INC.; *U.S. Private*, pg. 465
GOYA FOODS, INC.; *U.S. Private*, pg. 468
GREAT BRANDS OF EUROPE—Danone Group; *Int'l*, pg. 381
GREAT WATERS OF FRANCE—Nestle S.A.; *Int'l*, pg. 919
GREEN GIANT COMPANY—Diageo Plc; *Int'l*, pg. 411
GROCERS BAKING CO.; *U.S. Private*, pg. 482
GROSVENOR MARKETING LTD.—Associated British Foods plc; *Int'l*, pg. 92
GRUPO INDUSTRIAL BIMBO S.A. DE C.V.; *Int'l*, pg. 575
HEG HOPFENEXTRAKTION GMBH—Viag AG; *Int'l*, pg. 1464
HSC EXPORT CORPORATION—Imperial Holly Corporation; *U.S. Public*, pg. 872
HALE BROTHERS, INC.—Performance Food Group Company; *U.S. Public*, pg. 1278
HANSA MELASSE HANDELS GMBH—Tate & Lyle PLC; *Int'l*, pg. 1357
HARMONY FOODS CORPORATION; *U.S. Private*, pg. 503
HARRISONS & CROSFIELD (CANADA) LTD.—Harrisons & Crosfield plc; *Int'l*, pg. 599
THE HARTZ MOUNTAIN CORP.; *U.S. Private*, pg. 508
HAZELNUT GROWERS OF OREGON—Sun Diamond Growers of California; *U.S. Private*, pg. 1051
HEINEKEN N.V.; *Int'l*, pg. 608
H.J. HEINZ (BOTSWANA) (PROPRIETARY) LTD.—H.J. Heinz Company; *U.S. Public*, pg. 806
H.J. HEINZ BRANCH BELGIUM—H.J. Heinz Company; *U.S. Public*, pg. 806
H.J. HEINZ COMPANY AUSTRALIA LTD.—H.J. Heinz Company; *U.S. Public*, pg. 807
H.J. HEINZ COMPANY (IRELAND) LIMITED—H.J. Heinz Company; *U.S. Public*, pg. 806
H.J. HEINZ GMBH—H.J. Heinz Company; *U.S. Public*, pg. 806
H.J. HEINZ SARL—H.J. Heinz Company; *U.S. Public*, pg. 806
HERBALIFE DOMINICANA, S.A.—Herbalife International of America, Inc.; *U.S. Public*, pg. 809
HERBALIFE INTERNATIONAL OF AMERICA, INC.; *U.S. Public*, pg. 809
HERBALIFE INTERNATIONAL OF AMERICA, INC.—Herbalife International of America, Inc.; *U.S. Public*, pg. 809
HERBALIFE ITALIA S.P.A.—Herbalife International of America, Inc.; *U.S. Public*, pg. 809
HERBALIFE (N.Z.) LIMITED—Herbalife International of America, Inc.; *U.S. Public*, pg. 809
HERBALIFE (UK) LIMITED—Herbalife International of America, Inc.; *U.S. Public*, pg. 809
HOKKAIDO COCA-COLA BOTTLING CO., LTD.—Dai Nippon Printing Co., Ltd.; *Int'l*, pg. 363
HOKKAIDO SNOW BRAND SALES CO., LTD.—Snow Brand Milk Products Co. Ltd.; *Int'l*, pg. 1272
HUBBARD MILLING COMPANY—Windy Hill Pet Food Co.; *U.S. Private*, pg. 1182
INDUSTRIAS DE MAIZ Y ALIMENTOS S.A.—Corn Products International, Inc.; *U.S. Public*, pg. 447
INGLES MARKETS, INCORPORATED; *U.S. Public*, pg. 878
INTERNATIONAL COSMETICS CO., LTD.; *Int'l*, pg. 684
INTERNATIONAL FLAVORS & FRAGRANCES (ESPANA) S.A.—International Flavors & Fragrances, Inc.; *U.S. Public*, pg. 899
INTERNATIONAL MULTIFOODS CORPORATION; *U.S. Public*, pg. 900
IONICS, INCORPORATED; *U.S. Public*, pg. 912
IONICS ULTRAPURE WATER CORPORATION—Ionics, Incorporated; *U.S. Public*, pg. 912
IRELAND COFFEE TEA, INC.—Chock Full O' Nuts Corporation; *U.S. Public*, pg. 351
IRELAND GOURMET SHOP—Chock Full O' Nuts Corporation; *U.S. Public*, pg. 351
ITOCHU CORPORATION; *Int'l*, pg. 694
J & J SNACK FOODS SALES CORP.—J & J Snack Foods Corporation; *U.S. Public*, pg. 916
J & J SNACK FOODS TRANSPORT CORP.—J & J Snack Foods Corporation; *U.S. Public*, pg. 916
JP FOODSERVICE, INC.; *U.S. Public*, pg. 918
KA-TEE-KA AG—Philip Morris Companies Inc.; *U.S. Public*, pg. 1288
M. KAMENSTEIN, INC.; *U.S. Private*, pg. 606
KELLOGG CANADA INC.—Kellogg Company; *U.S. Public*, pg. 947
KERN INDUSTRIES; *U.S. Private*, pg. 616
KERN'S BAKERIES, INCORPORATED—The Earthgrains Company; *U.S. Public*, pg. 547
KESTERSON FOOD COMPANY, INC.; *U.S. Private*, pg. 616
KNOTT'S BERRY FARM; *U.S. Private*, pg. 627
KONINKLIJKE BUNGE B.V.; *Int'l*, pg. 753
KRAFT JACOBS SUCHARD AG—Philip Morris Companies Inc.; *U.S. Public*, pg. 1288
LA HACIENDA S.A. DE C.V.—International Multifoods Corporation; *U.S. Public*, pg. 901
LA PREFERIDA, INC.; *U.S. Private*, pg. 640
LA TOURAINE COFFEE COMPANY—Chock Full O' Nuts Corporation; *U.S. Public*, pg. 351
LADY BALTIMORE FOODS, INC.; *U.S. Public*, pg. 975
LAND O'LAKES, INC.; *U.S. Private*, pg. 645
LEWIS BROTHERS BAKERIES, INC.; *U.S. Private*, pg. 665
MD FOODS; *Int'l*, pg. 826
MCCAIN ALIMENTARI (ITALIA) SRL—McCain Foods Limited; *Int'l*, pg. 850
MCCAIN FOODS (JAPAN) LIMITED—McCain Foods Limited; *Int'l*, pg. 850
MCCAIN GMBH (GERMANY)—McCain Foods Limited; *Int'l*, pg. 850
MCCORMICK (UK) PLC.—McCormick & Company, Incorporated; *U.S. Public*, pg. 1067
MCGLYNN BAKERIES INC.; *U.S. Private*, pg. 721
MEIJI TRADING CORP.—Meiji Seika Kaisha, Ltd.; *Int'l*, pg. 855
MELITTA A/S—Melitta Unternehmensgruppe Bentz KG; *Int'l*, pg. 857
MELITTA DO BRASIL INDUSTRIA E COMERCIO LTDA.—Melitta Unternehmensgruppe Bentz KG; *Int'l*, pg. 857
MELITTA FOODSERVICE CORP.—Melitta Unternehmensgruppe Bentz KG; *Int'l*, pg. 857
MELITTA HOUSE OF COFFEE PTY. LTD.—Melitta Unternehmensgruppe Bentz KG; *Int'l*, pg. 857

MELITTA NORTH AMERICA, INC.—Melitta Unternehmensgruppe Bentz KG; *Int'l*, pg. 857
MELITTA SOCIETE DE DISTRIBUTION BENTZ & CIE—Melitta Unternehmensgruppe Bentz KG; *Int'l*, pg. 857
MENEBA N.V.—Goodman Fielder Limited; *Int'l*, pg. 555
MILUPA COMPANY—Nutricia BV; *Int'l*, pg. 991
MITSIAM INTERNATIONAL, LTD.—Mitsui & Co., Ltd.; *Int'l*, pg. 880
MITSUBISHI FOODS (MC), INC.—Mitsubishi Corporation; *Int'l*, pg. 872
MITSUBISHI INTERNATIONAL CORPORATION—Mitsubishi Corporation; *Int'l*, pg. 871
MITSUI & CO., LTD.; *Int'l*, pg. 877
MITSUI BRASILEIRA IMP. E EXP. LTDA.—Mitsui & Co., Ltd.; *Int'l*, pg. 882
MITSUI CHILENA COMMERCIAL LTDA.—Mitsui & Co., Ltd.; *Int'l*, pg. 882
MITSUI DE COLOMBIA S.A.—Mitsui & Co., Ltd.; *Int'l*, pg. 882
MITSUI DE MEXICO, S.A. DE C.V.—Mitsui & Co., Ltd.; *Int'l*, pg. 882
MITSUI DE VENEZUELA C.A.—Mitsui & Co., Ltd.; *Int'l*, pg. 882
MITSUI DEL ECUADOR S.A.—Mitsui & Co., Ltd.; *Int'l*, pg. 882
MITSUI DEL PERU S.A.—Mitsui & Co., Ltd.; *Int'l*, pg. 882
MITSUI FOODS, INC.—Mitsui & Co., Ltd.; *Int'l*, pg. 879
MITSUI FOODS, INC., WESTERN DIV.—Mitsui & Co., Ltd.; *Int'l*, pg. 879
MITSUI SUGAR CO., LTD.—Mitsui & Co., Ltd.; *Int'l*, pg. 879
MOLINOS NACIONALES, C.A. (VENEZUELA)—International Multifoods Corporation; *U.S. Public*, pg. 901
THE MONARCH COMPANY, INC.; *U.S. Private*, pg. 756
MORINAGA MILK INDUSTRY CO., LTD.; *Int'l*, pg. 895
MOTT'S INC.—Cadbury Schweppes p.l.c.; *Int'l*, pg. 248
MOUNTAIN VALLEY SPRING COMPANY—Sammons Enterprises, Inc.; *U.S. Private*, pg. 963
MR. WRIGHT'S AMAZING COFFEE FACTORY; *U.S. Private*, pg. 765
MULTIFOOD INTERNATIONAL—Meiji Seika Kaisha, Ltd.; *Int'l*, pg. 855
MULTIFOODS SPECIALTY DISTRIBUTION INC.—International Multifoods Corporation; *U.S. Public*, pg. 901
MUTUAL TRADING CO., INC.; *U.S. Private*, pg. 770
NESTLE PANAMA S.A.—Nestle S.A.; *Int'l*, pg. 921
NESTLE PUERTO RICO, INC.—Nestle S.A.; *Int'l*, pg. 917
NESTLE S.A.; *Int'l*, pg. 915
NESTLE WORLD TRADE CORPORATION—Nestle S.A.; *Int'l*, pg. 916
NEW FOOD INGREDIENTS, LTD.—Newly Weds Foods Inc.; *U.S. Private*, pg. 797
NICHIMEN AMERICA, INC.—Nichimen Corporation; *Int'l*, pg. 927
NICHIMEN CORPORATION; *Int'l*, pg. 927
NIKO CO., LTD.—Mitsukoshi, Ltd.; *Int'l*, pg. 883
NISSHIN FLOUR MILLING CO., LTD.; *Int'l*, pg. 946
NORDISK MELASSE A/S—Tate & Lyle PLC; *Int'l*, pg. 1357
NORFOODS, INC.; *U.S. Private*, pg. 802
NORTH DAKOTA MILL & ELEVATOR ASSOCIATION; *U.S. Private*, pg. 804
THE ODOM CORPORATION; *U.S. Private*, pg. 811
OKAYAMAKEN SHOKUHIN CO., LTD.—Meiji Seika Kaisha, Ltd.; *Int'l*, pg. 855
ORANGINA INTERNATIONAL—Groupe Pernod Ricard; *Int'l*, pg. 567
OSTERREICHISCHE NESTLE GMBH—Nestle S.A.; *Int'l*, pg. 922
OTT FOOD PRODUCTS; *U.S. Private*, pg. 821
OVALTINE (WEST AFRICA) LTD.—Novartis AG; *Int'l*, pg. 983
PACIFIC FOODS, INC.; *U.S. Private*, pg. 831
PARECO G.I.E.—Bongrain S.A.; *Int'l*, pg. 201
PARMALAT CANADA LTD.—Parmalat S.p.A.; *Int'l*, pg. 1023
PEIRONE PRODUCE COMPANY—URM Stores, Inc.; *U.S. Private*, pg. 1114
PEPSI-COLA BOTTLING CO.; *U.S. Public*, pg. 1276
PEPSICO WORLD TRADING COMPANY (UK) LTD.—PepsiCo, Inc.; *U.S. Public*, pg. 1277
PERFECTION BAKERIES INC.; *U.S. Private*, pg. 852
PERFORMANCE FOOD GROUP COMPANY; *U.S. Public*, pg. 1278
THE PERRIER GROUP OF AMERICA—Nestle S.A.; *Int'l*, pg. 919
PERRIER GROUP OF CANADA LTD.—Nestle S.A.; *Int'l*, pg. 919
PERRIER UK LTD.—Nestle S.A.; *Int'l*, pg. 919
PETE'S BREWING COMPANY; *U.S. Public*, pg. 1280
POCAHONTAS FOODS, USA—Performance Food Group Company; *U.S. Public*, pg. 1278
POLAND SPRING CORPORATION—Nestle S.A.; *Int'l*, pg. 919
POLLIO DAIRY PRODUCTS—Philip Morris Companies Inc.; *U.S. Public*, pg. 1288
POLLIO DAIRY PRODUCTS COMPANY—Philip Morris Companies Inc.; *U.S. Public*, pg. 1288
PRESIDENT BAKING COMPANY—President Enterprises Corp.; *Int'l*, pg. 1069
PRESIDENT BAKING-LOUISVILLE—President Enterprises Corp.; *Int'l*, pg. 1069
PROCORDIA FOOD AB—Orkla A.S.A.; *Int'l*, pg. 1011
PRODUCERS RICE MILL INC.; *U.S. Private*, pg. 888
PRODUCTOS ALIMENTICIOS IMPERIAL, S.A.—Diageo Plc; *Int'l*, pg. 411
QUALITY FOOD OILS, INC.—Associated British Foods plc; *Int'l*, pg. 92
RCB BAKING COMPANY; *U.S. Public*, pg. 1354
RED STAR DE PUERTO RICO, S.A.—Universal Foods Corporation; *U.S. Public*, pg. 1696
RED WING CO. INC.—Tomkins PLC; *Int'l*, pg. 1398
REISMUHLE BRUNNEN AG—Coop Switzerland; *Int'l*, pg. 330
F.T. REYNOLDS COMPANY; *U.S. Private*, pg. 926
RICHHEIMER FOOD—Wechsler Coffee Corp.; *U.S. Private*, pg. 1158
ROBERTS FOODS, INC.; *U.S. Private*, pg. 935
ROBIN HOOD MULTIFOODS INC.—International Multifoods Corporation; *U.S. Public*, pg. 901
ROCKY MOUNTAIN COMPANY; *U.S. Private*, pg. 938
RONDE CORP.—Meiji Seika Kaisha, Ltd.; *Int'l*, pg. 855
RUSSELL STOVER CANDIES, INC.; *U.S. Private*, pg. 953
S&D COFFEE INC.; *U.S. Private*, pg. 954
SAMMONS ENTERPRISES, INC.; *U.S. Private*, pg. 963
SAN FRANCISCO FRENCH BREAD COMPANY—Interstate Bakeries Corporation; *U.S. Public*, pg. 909
SAN-J INTL. INC.—San-Jirushi; *Int'l*, pg. 1183
SANDOZ AB—Novartis AG; *Int'l*, pg. 984
SANDOZ-WANDER PHARMA AG—Novartis AG; *Int'l*, pg. 972
SCHNEEKOPPE GMBH—Eckes AG; *Int'l*, pg. 433
SCHULZE & BURCH BISCUIT COMPANY; *U.S. Private*, pg. 973
SCHWEPPES CANADA DIVISION—Cadbury Schweppes p.l.c.; *Int'l*, pg. 248
SCHWEPPES EUROPE LIMITED—Cadbury Schweppes p.l.c.; *Int'l*, pg. 248
SHAMROCK FOODS COMPANY; *U.S. Private*, pg. 989
SHOWA BUSSAN CO., LTD.—Snow Brand Milk Products Co. Ltd.; *Int'l*, pg. 1272
SIDWELL & COMPANY LTD.—SLD Holdings Ltd.; *Int'l*, pg. 1160
SIOUX HONEY ASSOCIATION; *U.S. Private*, pg. 1003
SKOKIE VALLEY BEVERAGE CO.; *U.S. Private*, pg. 1005
E.D. SMITH; *Int'l*, pg. 1263
SMITHKLINE BEECHAM CONSUMER BRANDS—SmithKline Beecham plc; *Int'l*, pg. 1264
SNOW BRAND MILK PRODUCTS CO. LTD.; *Int'l*, pg. 1271
SNOW BRAND SHOJI CO., LTD.—Snow Brand Milk Products Co. Ltd.; *Int'l*, pg. 1272
SNYDER BAKERY—United States Bakery; *U.S. Private*, pg. 1124
SNYDER'S OF HANOVER, INC.; *U.S. Private*, pg. 1011
SOCIEDADE PORTUGUESA DE PRODUTOS WANDER LDA.—Novartis AG; *Int'l*, pg. 985
SOCIETE EUROPEENNE DES MELASSES SA—Tate & Lyle PLC; *Int'l*, pg. 1357
SOCIETE EUROSUCRE S.N.C.—Generale Sucriere SNC; *Int'l*, pg. 549
SOCIETE GENERALE DE GRANDES SOURCES EAUX MINERALES—Nestle S.A.; *Int'l*, pg. 919
SOPRA S.A.—Philip Morris Companies Inc.; *U.S. Public*, pg. 1288
SPADEL SA; *Int'l*, pg. 1287
SPARKLETTS DRINKING WATER CORP.—McKesson Corporation; *U.S. Public*, pg. 1073
STANDARD FLOUR CO.—CSM N.V.; *Int'l*, pg. 244
STANSAND LIMITED—The Tetley Group Limited; *Int'l*, pg. 1377
THE STOP & SHOP COMPANIES, INC.—Koninklijke Ahold NV; *Int'l*, pg. 750
SUGAR FOODS CORP; *U.S. Private*, pg. 1049
SUMITOMO CANADA LTD.—Sumitomo Corporation; *Int'l*, pg. 1312
SUN DIAMOND GROWERS OF CALIFORNIA; *U.S. Private*, pg. 1051
SUPERIOR COFFEE AND FOODS—Sara Lee Corporation; *U.S. Public*, pg. 1434
SWAZILAND FRUIT CANNERS (PTY.) LTD.—Nestle S.A.; *Int'l*, pg. 922
E.A. SWEEN COMPANY; *U.S. Private*, pg. 1058
SYSCO CORPORATION; *U.S. Public*, pg. 1550
SYSCO FOOD SERVICES OF AUSTIN, INC.—Sysco Corporation; *U.S. Public*, pg. 1551
SYSCO FOOD SERVICES OF BEAUMONT, INC.—Sysco Corporation; *U.S. Public*, pg. 1551
TLC BEATRICE INTERNATIONAL HOLDINGS INC.; *U.S. Private*, pg. 1064
TAIWAN MORINAGA NUTRITIONAL FOODS INC.—Morinaga Milk Industry Co., Ltd.; *Int'l*, pg. 895
TAIYO SHOKUHIN CO., LTD.—Meiji Seika Kaisha, Ltd.; *Int'l*, pg. 855
TALOCA AG—Philip Morris Companies Inc.; *U.S. Public*, pg. 1288
TALOCA & CIA LTDA—Philip Morris Companies Inc.; *U.S. Public*, pg. 1289
TALOCA CAFE S/C LTDA.—Philip Morris Companies Inc.; *U.S. Public*, pg. 1289
TASTY BAKING COMPANY; *U.S. Public*, pg. 1561
TATE & LYLE INTERNATIONAL—Tate & Lyle PLC; *Int'l*, pg. 1356
TATE & LYLE PLC; *Int'l*, pg. 1356
TEEPAK, INC., ZURICH BRANCH—Devro International Plc; *Int'l*, pg. 408
TOKYO CALPIS BEVERAGES CO., LTD.—Calpis Food Industry Co. Ltd.; *Int'l*, pg. 253
TOKYO SNOW BRAND SALES CO., LTD.—Snow Brand Milk Products Co. Ltd.; *Int'l*, pg. 1272
TONE BROTHERS INC.—Burns, Philp & Company Limited; *Int'l*, pg. 237
TRANSINKO B.V.—Koninklijke BolsWessanen nv; *Int'l*, pg. 751
TRI-STATE WHOLESALE ASSOCIATED GROCERS, INC.; *U.S. Private*, pg. 1101
TRINIDAD/BENHAM CORP.; *U.S. Private*, pg. 1103
TROTTER SOFT PRETZELS, INC.—J & J Snack Foods Corporation; *U.S. Public*, pg. 916
TWIN COUNTY GROCERS, INC.; *U.S. Private*, pg. 1111
URM STORES, INC.; *U.S. Private*, pg. 1114
UNCLE B'S BAKERY, INC.; *U.S. Public*, pg. 1664
THE UNCLE TOBY'S COMPANY LTD.—Goodman Fielder Limited; *Int'l*, pg. 555
UNIFERM GMBH & CO.—Royal Gist-Brocades N.V.; *Int'l*, pg. 1143
UNITED BEVERAGES LIMITED—James Crean PLC; *Int'l*, pg. 340
UNITED MOLASSES COMPANY—Tate & Lyle PLC; *Int'l*, pg. 1356
UNITED STATES BAKERY; *U.S. Private*, pg. 1124
U.S. FOOD SERVICE—JP Foodservice, Inc.; *U.S. Public*, pg. 918
UNIVERSAL FOODS CORPORATION; *U.S. Public*, pg. 1695
UTZ QUALITY FOODS, INC.; *U.S. Private*, pg. 1130
UWAJIMA CANNING CO., LTD.—Meiji Seika Kaisha, Ltd.; *Int'l*, pg. 855
VALLET FOOD SERV INC.; *U.S. Private*, pg. 1131
VALLEY FIG GROWERS—Sun Diamond Growers of California; *U.S. Private*, pg. 1051
VAN DEN BERGH FOODS LTD.—Unilever Plc; *Int'l*, pg. 1434
VETERINARY COMPANIES OF AMERICA—Colgate-Palmolive Company; *U.S. Public*, pg. 397
VICOM PRODUCTION AND DISTRIBUTION CO.—Vicorp Restaurants, Inc.; *U.S. Public*, pg. 1719
JOSEPH VICTORI WINES, INC.; *U.S. Private*, pg. 1139
VIDA HERBAL SUPLEMENTOS ALIMENTICIOS, C.A. (VENEZUELA)—Herbalife International of America, Inc.; *U.S. Public*, pg. 809
C.J. VITNER CO.; *U.S. Private*, pg. 1142
WANDER GESELLSCHAFT M.B.H.—Novartis AG; *Int'l*, pg. 986
WANDER (PHILIPPINES) INC.—Novartis AG; *Int'l*, pg. 986
WANDER (PORTUGAL) ALIMENTOCAO LDA.—Novartis AG; *Int'l*, pg. 986
N.V. WANDER S.A.—Novartis AG; *Int'l*, pg. 986
WANDER (SINGAPORE) PTY. LTD.—Novartis AG; *Int'l*, pg. 986
WANDER S.P.A.—Novartis AG; *Int'l*, pg. 986
WARDS COVE PACKING COMPANY; *U.S. Private*, pg. 1149
WASA G.M.B.H.—Novartis AG; *Int'l*, pg. 986
WASABROD AB—Novartis AG; *Int'l*, pg. 986
WASABROD A/S—Novartis AG; *Int'l*, pg. 986
WECHSLER COFFEE CORP.; *U.S. Private*, pg. 1158
THE WEETABIX COMPANY, INC.—Weetabix Limited; *Int'l*, pg. 1488
WEETABIX LIMITED; *Int'l*, pg. 1488
WEETABIX OF CANADA (MFG.) LIMITED—Weetabix Limited; *Int'l*, pg. 1488
WESSANEN FLOUR INTERNATIONAL B.V.—Koninklijke BolsWessanen nv; *Int'l*, pg. 751
WESSON/PETER PAN FOODS CO.—ConAgra, Inc.; *U.S. Public*, pg. 428
WESTBRAE NATURAL, INC.—The Hain Food Group Inc.; *U.S. Public*, pg. 774
WESTCO FOOD SERVICE—CSM N.V.; *Int'l*, pg. 244
WESTCO PRODUCTS, INC.—CSM N.V.; *Int'l*, pg. 244
WESTCO PRODUCTS/SEATTLE—CSM N.V.; *Int'l*, pg. 244
WILLIAM'S BAKERY—United States Bakery; *U.S. Private*, pg. 1124
WILLS GROUP, INC.; *U.S. Private*, pg. 1180
WORLD FINER FOODS, INC.; *U.S. Private*, pg. 1190
WORLDWIDE FOODS, INC.—La Preferida, Inc.; *U.S. Private*, pg. 640
WYANDOT INC.; *U.S. Private*, pg. 1193
YAMAZAKI BAKING CO., LTD.; *Int'l*, pg. 1519
ZAO SHOKUHIN CO., LTD.—Meiji Seika Kaisha, Ltd.; *Int'l*, pg. 855
ZINK & TRIEST—A.M. Todd Company; *U.S. Private*, pg. 1090

5153 — GRAIN & FIELD BEANS-BUYING & MARKETING

ADM/GROWMARK—Archer Daniels Midland Company (ADM); *U.S. Public*, pg. 128
ADAIR FEED & GRAIN COMPANY; *U.S. Private*, pg. 16
AGRILAND COMPANY; *U.S. Private*, pg. 26
AGRILINK FOODS, INC.—Pro-Fac Cooperative, Inc.; *U.S. Private*, pg. 887
ALABAMA FARMERS CO-OP; *U.S. Private*, pg. 30
AMERICAN GRAIN & RELATED INDUSTRIES; *U.S. Private*, pg. 55
AMERICAN RICE INC.—Erly Industries, Inc.; *U.S. Public*, pg. 591
ARIZONA GRAINS INC.; *U.S. Private*, pg. 81
B&W CO-OP, INC.; *U.S. Private*, pg. 105
BADER & CO.; *U.S. Private*, pg. 110
BARTLETT AND COMPANY; *U.S. Private*, pg. 118
BERNARD MATTHEWS PLC; *Int'l*, pg. 189
BIG HORN CO-OP MARKETING ASSOCIATION; *U.S. Private*, pg. 143
BUSCH AGRICULTURAL RESOURCES, INC.—Anheuser-Busch Companies, Inc.; *U.S. Public*, pg. 114
CENTRAL STATES ENTERPRISES, INC.; *U.S. Private*, pg. 225
CHAMPAIGN LANDMARK, INC.; *U.S. Private*, pg. 227
CHINA NATIONAL CEREALS, OILS & FOODSTUFFS CORPORATION (COFCO); *Int'l*, pg. 285
COAST GRAIN COMPANY, INC.; *U.S. Private*, pg. 248
COLLINGWOOD GRAIN, INC.—Archer Daniels Midland Company (ADM); *U.S. Public*, pg. 128
COLUMBIA GRAIN, INC.—Marubeni Corporation; *Int'l*, pg. 845
COLUSA ELEVATOR CO.; *U.S. Private*, pg. 257
COMO GRAIN CO.—Tom Wade Co.; *U.S. Private*, pg. 1145
CONAGRA GRAIN COMPANIES—ConAgra, Inc.; *U.S. Public*, pg. 426
CONNELL CO.; *U.S. Private*, pg. 264
COUNTRYMARK COOPERATIVE, INC.; *U.S. Private*, pg. 279
DALGETY AGRICULTURE, LIMITED—Dalgety Plc; *Int'l*, pg. 376
DEBRUCE GRAIN INC.; *U.S. Private*, pg. 319
DEMETER, INC.—Archer Daniels Midland Company (ADM); *U.S. Public*, pg. 127
LOUIS DREYFUS CORPORATION; *U.S. Private*, pg. 342
DYER GRAIN CO.—Tom Wade Co.; *U.S. Private*, pg. 1145
EDMONSON WHEAT GROWERS, INC.; *U.S. Private*, pg. 364
EFFINGHAM-CLAY SERVICE CO.; *U.S. Private*, pg. 365

EQUITY SUPPLY COMPANY; *U.S. Private*, pg. 380
ESSEX GRAIN PRODUCTS, INC.; *U.S. Private*, pg. 383
EURYZA BV—CSM N.V.; *Int'l*, pg. 243
EURYZA INTERNATIONAL AG—CSM N.V.; *Int'l*, pg. 244
EURYZA REIS GMBH—CSM N.V.; *Int'l*, pg. 244
EXCEL CO-OP INC.; *U.S. Private*, pg. 387
FARBEST INC.—Countrymark Cooperative, Inc.; *U.S. Private*, pg. 279
FARMWAY CO-OP INC.; *U.S. Private*, pg. 396
FINAGRAIN, CIE COMMERCIALE AGRICOLE ET FINANCIERE S.A.—Continental Grain Company; *U.S. Private*, pg. 268
FINLEY FARMERS GRAIN & ELEVATOR COMPANY; *U.S. Private*, pg. 405
FRIONA INDUSTRIES, L.P.; *U.S. Private*, pg. 429
FRUEN OAT MILLING CO.—ConAgra, Inc.; *U.S. Public*, pg. 428
GARNAC GRAIN CO., INC.—Norfoods, Inc.; *U.S. Private*, pg. 802
GARVEY INDUSTRIES, INC.; *U.S. Private*, pg. 440
GARVEY INTERNATIONAL, INC.—Garvey Industries, Inc.; *U.S. Private*, pg. 440
GENERAL MILLS OPERATIONS, INC.—General Mills, Inc.; *U.S. Public*, pg. 718
GOODPASTURE, INC.; *U.S. Private*, pg. 464
GRAND PRAIRIE CO-OP, INC.; *U.S. Private*, pg. 468
GROWMARK, INC.; *U.S. Private*, pg. 484
HANEY SEED CO.—ConAgra, Inc.; *U.S. Public*, pg. 428
HARVEST STATES COOPERATIVES; *U.S. Private*, pg. 508
HERITAGE CO-OP; *U.S. Private*, pg. 524
HONEYMEAD PRODUCTS CO.; *U.S. Private*, pg. 537
HOPKINSVILLE ELEVATOR COMPANY, INC.; *U.S. Private*, pg. 538
INTERSTATE COMMODITIES INC.; *U.S. Private*, pg. 573
ITOCHU CORPORATION; *Int'l*, pg. 694
ITOCHU INTERNATIONAL INC.—Itochu Corporation; *Int'l*, pg. 694
JOHNSON COUNTY FARM BUREAU CO-OP; *U.S. Private*, pg. 591
KBC TRADING & PROCESSING—ConAgra, Inc.; *U.S. Public*, pg. 428
KELLEY BEAN CO., INC.; *U.S. Private*, pg. 612
KENTON GRAIN CO.—Tom Wade Co.; *U.S. Private*, pg. 1145
KINGFISHER CO-OP ELEVATOR ASSOCIATION; *U.S. Private*, pg. 621
KOKOMO GRAIN CO., INC.; *U.S. Private*, pg. 631
KONINKLIJKE BUNGE B.V.; *Int'l*, pg. 753
LA SALLE COUNTY FARM SUPPLY; *U.S. Private*, pg. 640
MFA INCORPORATED; *U.S. Private*, pg. 686
MAINE POTATO GROWERS, INC.; *U.S. Private*, pg. 697
MARUBENI AMERICA CORPORATION—Marubeni Corporation; *Int'l*, pg. 844
MARUBENI AMERICA CORPORATION, DALLAS BRANCH—Marubeni Corporation; *Int'l*, pg. 844
MARUBENI AMERICA CORPORATION, DETROIT BRANCH—Marubeni Corporation; *Int'l*, pg. 844
MARUBENI AMERICA CORPORATION, PORTLAND BRANCH—Marubeni Corporation; *Int'l*, pg. 845
MARUBENI AMERICAN CORPORATION, SEATTLE BRANCH—Marubeni Corporation; *Int'l*, pg. 845
MARUBENI CORPORATION; *Int'l*, pg. 844
MINNEAPOLIS MILLING—Archer Daniels Midland Company (ADM); *U.S. Public*, pg. 128
NEW COOPERATIVE INC.; *U.S. Private*, pg. 792
NICHIMEN AMERICA, INC.—Nichimen Corporation; *Int'l*, pg. 927
NICHIMEN CORPORATION; *Int'l*, pg. 927
NORFOODS, INC.; *U.S. Private*, pg. 802
NORTHEAST TEXAS FARMERS CO-OP; *U.S. Private*, pg. 805
BRUCE OAKLEY, INC.; *U.S. Private*, pg. 809
ORANGE GROVE CO-OPERATIVE; *U.S. Private*, pg. 818
OWENSBORO GRAIN CO., INC.; *U.S. Private*, pg. 824
PERRYTON EQUITY; *U.S. Private*, pg. 855
PILLSBURY GRAIN EXPORT, INC.—Diageo Plc; *Int'l*, pg. 411
PRO-FAC COOPERATIVE, INC.; *U.S. Private*, pg. 887
PRODUCERS CO-OP ASSOCIATION, INC.; *U.S. Private*, pg. 888
PRODUCERS RICE MILL INC.; *U.S. Private*, pg. 888
RANGEN, INC.; *U.S. Private*, pg. 909
REED GRAIN & BEAN COMPANY; *U.S. Private*, pg. 916
RICE GROWERS ASSOCIATION OF CALIFORNIA; *U.S. Private*, pg. 927
RUGBY FARMERS UNION ELEVATOR COMPANY; *U.S. Private*, pg. 950
SKW ITALIA S.R.L.—Viag AG; *Int'l*, pg. 1466
SKW NATURES INC.—Viag AG; *Int'l*, pg. 1465
SASKATCHEWAN WHEAT POOL; *Int'l*, pg. 1195
THE SCOULAR COMPANY; *U.S. Private*, pg. 977
SEABOARD CORPORATION; *U.S. Public*, pg. 1448
SEABOARD FLOUR CORPORATION—Seaboard Corporation; *U.S. Public*, pg. 1449
SEBASTIAN COTTON & GRAIN CORP.; *U.S. Private*, pg. 980
SHERLEY GRAIN COMPANY; *U.S. Private*, pg. 993
SIME DARBY HONG KONG LIMITED—Sime Darby Berhad; *Int'l*, pg. 1251
SIMONDS-SHIELDS-THEIS GRAIN CO.; *U.S. Private*, pg. 1001
SMOOT GRAIN CO., INC.—Archer Daniels Midland Company (ADM); *U.S. Public*, pg. 128
SOUTH CENTRAL CO-OP; *U.S. Private*, pg. 1014
SUMITOMO CORPORATION; *Int'l*, pg. 1312
TERMINAL GRAIN CORP.; *U.S. Private*, pg. 1077
TERRA INDUSTRIES, INC.; *U.S. Public*, pg. 1581
TERRA INTERNATIONAL—Terra Industries, Inc.; *U.S. Public*, pg. 1581
TERRAL SEED CO., INC.; *U.S. Private*, pg. 1077
TOBERMAN; *U.S. Private*, pg. 1089
TOSHOKU AMERICA, INC.—Toshoku Ltd.; *Int'l*, pg. 1407
TOSHOKU LTD.; *Int'l*, pg. 1407
TRINIDAD/BENHAM CORP.; *U.S. Private*, pg. 1103
VALLEY SEED CO.—Arizona Grains Inc.; *U.S. Private*, pg. 82
TOM WADE CO.; *U.S. Private*, pg. 1145
WAGNER MILLS INC.; *U.S. Private*, pg. 1146
WALLA WALLA GRAIN GROWERS, INC.; *U.S. Private*, pg. 1148
WEST CENTRAL COOPERATIVE; *U.S. Private*, pg. 1163
WESTERN GRAIN, INC.; *U.S. Private*, pg. 1165
WHEELER BROTHERS GRAIN CO.; *U.S. Private*, pg. 1171
WILLARD GRAIN & FEED, INC.; *U.S. Private*, pg. 1177
WOLCOTT & LINCOLN, INC.; *U.S. Private*, pg. 1185

5154 — LIVESTOCK-BUYING & MARKETING

BOCM SILCOCK LTD.—Unilever Plc; *Int'l*, pg. 1434
CHINA NATIONAL CEREALS, OILS & FOODSTUFFS CORPORATION (COFCO); *Int'l*, pg. 285
DEKALB SWINE BREEDERS, INC.—Dekalb Genetics Corporation; *U.S. Public*, pg. 493
EFFINGHAM-CLAY SERVICE CO.; *U.S. Private*, pg. 365
INTERSTATE PRODUCERS LIVESTOCK ASSOCIATION; *U.S. Private*, pg. 573
PRODUCERS LIVESTOCK; *U.S. Private*, pg. 888
ROSENS DIVERSIFIED, INC.; *U.S. Private*, pg. 945

5159 — FARM-PRODUCT RAW MATERIALS-BUYING & MARKETING, NEC

W.A. ADAMS, INC.—Standard Commercial Corporation; *U.S. Public*, pg. 1502
ALABAMA FARMERS CO-OP; *U.S. Private*, pg. 30
AMFAC SUGAR AND AGRIBUSINESS, INC.—JMB Realty Corporation; *U.S. Private*, pg. 578
ATCOT CORP., INC.—Coats Viyella plc; *Int'l*, pg. 300
BAKER COMMODITIES, INC.; *U.S. Private*, pg. 111
BALE OF KENTUCKY, INC.; *U.S. Private*, pg. 112
BAUMANN, HINDE & CO., LTD.—Lonrho plc; *Int'l*, pg. 817
BIRDSONG CORPORATION; *U.S. Private*, pg. 145
BLUE DIAMOND GROWERS; *U.S. Private*, pg. 152
CFCI S.A.—Unilever Plc; *Int'l*, pg. 1436
CALCOT, LTD.; *U.S. Private*, pg. 200
CALIFORNIA & HAWAIIAN SUGAR COMPANY INC.—Alexander & Baldwin, Inc.; *U.S. Public*, pg. 39
CASA EXPORT, LTD.—Universal Corporation; *U.S. Public*, pg. 1695
CASA EXPORT LIMITED—Universal Corporation; *U.S. Public*, pg. 1695
COMPANIA ESPANOLA DE TABACO EN RAMA, S.A.—Tabacalera, S.A.; *Int'l*, pg. 1346
COUNTRYMARK COOPERATIVE, INC.; *U.S. Private*, pg. 279
DAN RIVER COTTON CO., INC.—Dan River Inc.; *U.S. Public*, pg. 479
N.V. DELI-UNIVERSAL—Universal Corporation; *U.S. Public*, pg. 1695
DELTAFINA S.P.A.—Universal Corporation; *U.S. Public*, pg. 1695
DIMON, INCORPORATED; *U.S. Public*, pg. 509
DUNAVANT ENTERPRISES, INC.; *U.S. Private*, pg. 346
DUNNINGTON-BEACH TOBACCO CO.—Universal Corporation; *U.S. Public*, pg. 1694
K.R. EDWARDS LEAF TOBACCO CO., INC.—Universal Corporation; *U.S. Public*, pg. 1694
EQUITY SUPPLY COMPANY; *U.S. Private*, pg. 380
EXELKA S.A.—Standard Commercial Corporation; *U.S. Public*, pg. 1502
EXPORTADORA DE TABACOS TRANS-CONTINENTAL LTDA.—Standard Commercial Corporation; *U.S. Public*, pg. 1502
FARBEST INC.—Countrymark Cooperative, Inc.; *U.S. Private*, pg. 279
FARMERS INVESTMENT COMPANY, INC.—Bale Of Kentucky, Inc.; *U.S. Private*, pg. 112
FARMWAY CO-OP INC.; *U.S. Private*, pg. 396
GRETOBA, S.A.—Universal Corporation; *U.S. Public*, pg. 1695
HEAD DISTRIBUTING CO.; *U.S. Private*, pg. 514
HENKEL CANADA LTD.—Henkel KGaA; *Int'l*, pg. 612
HOHENBERG BROS. COMPANY—Cargill; *U.S. Private*, pg. 210
IMPERIAL TOBACCO LIMITED—B.A.T Industries P.L.C.; *Int'l*, pg. 112
ITOCHU COTTON, INC.—Itochu Corporation; *Int'l*, pg. 694
LANCASTER LEAF TOBACCO CO. OF PENNSYLVANIA—Universal Corporation; *U.S. Public*, pg. 1695
LATCO, INC.—Universal Corporation; *U.S. Public*, pg. 1695
LEAFCO TRADING GMBH—Standard Commercial Corporation; *U.S. Public*, pg. 1502
LOHMANN & COMPANY GMBH—Standard Commercial Corporation; *U.S. Public*, pg. 1502
MFA INCORPORATED; *U.S. Private*, pg. 686
MACLIN-ZIMMER MCGILL TOBACCO COMPANY, INC.—Universal Corporation; *U.S. Public*, pg. 1695
NICHIMEN AMERICA, INC.—Nichimen Corporation; *Int'l*, pg. 927
NICHIMEN CORPORATION; *Int'l*, pg. 927
NISSHO IWAI GENERAL MERCHANDISE CORP.—Nissho Iwai Corporation; *Int'l*, pg. 946
NOZAKI & COMPANY LTD.; *Int'l*, pg. 990
OBERLANDER RECYCLING TECHNIK GMBH—Fried. Krupp AG; *Int'l*, pg. 513
ORIENT LEAF TOBACCO CO., LTD.—Universal Corporation; *U.S. Public*, pg. 1695
ORIENTAL PROCESSORS & EXPORTERS OF KOREA, LTD.—Universal Corporation; *U.S. Public*, pg. 1695
OVERSEAS COMMODEX CORP.—Tiedemanns - Joh.H.Andresen ANS; *Int'l*, pg. 1390
PEIGNAGE DE LA TOSSEE—Standard Commercial Corporation; *U.S. Public*, pg. 1502
PLAINS COTTON CO-OP ASSOCIATION; *U.S. Private*, pg. 868
POTASH CORPORATION OF SASKATCHEWAN INC.; *Int'l*, pg. 1064
PROCORDIA FOOD AB—Orkla A.S.A.; *Int'l*, pg. 1011
SEBASTIAN COTTON & GRAIN CORP.; *U.S. Private*, pg. 980
SIAM TOBACCO EXPORT CORP. LTD.—Standard Commercial Corporation; *U.S. Public*, pg. 1502
SPIERER FRERES & CIE S.A.—Standard Commercial Corporation; *U.S. Public*, pg. 1502
SPIERER TUTUN IHRACAT SANAUI TICARET AS—Standard Commercial Corporation; *U.S. Public*, pg. 1502
STANCOM TOBACCO CO. (MALAWI) LTD.—Standard Commercial Corporation; *U.S. Public*, pg. 1502
STANCOM TOBACCO PACKERS (MALAWI) LTD.—Standard Commercial Corporation; *U.S. Public*, pg. 1502
STANDARD COMMERCIAL TOBACCO CO. OF CANADA LTD.—Standard Commercial Corporation; *U.S. Public*, pg. 1502
STANDARD COMMERCIAL TOBACCO CO. (U.K.) LTD.—Standard Commercial Corporation; *U.S. Public*, pg. 1502
STANDARD WOOL ARGENTINA S.A.—Standard Commercial Corporation; *U.S. Public*, pg. 1502
STANDARD WOOL (AUSTRALIA) PTY. LTD.—Standard Commercial Corporation; *U.S. Public*, pg. 1502
STANDARD WOOL (CHILE) S.A.—Standard Commercial Corporation; *U.S. Public*, pg. 1502
STANDARD WOOL FRANCE, SA—Standard Commercial Corporation; *U.S. Public*, pg. 1502
STANDARD WOOL, INC.—Standard Commercial Corporation; *U.S. Public*, pg. 1502
STANDARD WOOL (UK) LIMITED—Standard Commercial Corporation; *U.S. Public*, pg. 1502
STAPLE COTTON COOPERATIVE ASSOCIATION; *U.S. Private*, pg. 1033
SUMITOMO CORPORATION; *Int'l*, pg. 1312
SUMITOMO CORPORATION OF AMERICA—Sumitomo Corporation; *Int'l*, pg. 1312
TABACOS BRASILEIROS, LTDA.—Universal Corporation; *U.S. Public*, pg. 1695
TENTLER & CO., B.V.—Standard Commercial Corporation; *U.S. Public*, pg. 1502
THAI-AM TOBACCO LIMITED—Universal Corporation; *U.S. Public*, pg. 1695
TOBACCO PROCESSORS (ZIMBABWE) LTD.—Standard Commercial Corporation; *U.S. Public*, pg. 1502
TRANS-CONTINENTAL LEAF TOBACCO CO. (CENTRAL AFRICA) (PRIVATE) LTD.—Standard Commercial Corporation; *U.S. Public*, pg. 1502
TRANS-CONTINENTAL LEAF TOBACCO CORP.—Standard Commercial Corporation; *U.S. Public*, pg. 1502
TRANSHELLENIC TOBACCO S.A.—Standard Commercial Corporation; *U.S. Public*, pg. 1502
UNITED STATES TOBACCO COMPANY—UST Inc.; *U.S. Public*, pg. 1661
UNIVERSAL CORPORATION; *U.S. Public*, pg. 1694
UNIVERSAL LEAF EXPORT COMPANY, INC.—Universal Corporation; *U.S. Public*, pg. 1695
UNIVERSAL LEAF FAR-EAST, LTD.—Universal Corporation; *U.S. Public*, pg. 1695
UNIVERSAL LEAF SERVICES LTD.—Universal Corporation; *U.S. Public*, pg. 1695
UNIVERSAL LEAF TOBACCO COMPANY, INC.—Universal Corporation; *U.S. Public*, pg. 1694
UNIVERSAL LEAF (UK) LTD.—Universal Corporation; *U.S. Public*, pg. 1695
VIRGINIA TOBACCO CO., INC.—Universal Corporation; *U.S. Public*, pg. 1695
VIRSA, INC.—Universal Corporation; *U.S. Public*, pg. 1695
WEIL BROTHERS COTTON INC.; *U.S. Private*, pg. 1159
WELLENS & CO., INC.; *U.S. Private*, pg. 1161
WERKHOF GMBH—Standard Commercial Corporation; *U.S. Public*, pg. 1502
W.H. WINSTEAD COMPANY—Universal Corporation; *U.S. Public*, pg. 1695
WINSTON LEAF TOBACCO CO.—Universal Corporation; *U.S. Public*, pg. 1695
YOUNG PECAN COMPANY WEST, INC.—Young Pecan Company (A Partnership); *U.S. Private*, pg. 1201
ZIMLEAF HOLDINGS LIMITED—Universal Corporation; *U.S. Public*, pg. 1695

5162 — PLASTICS MATERIALS & BASIC FORMS & SHAPES-WHOLESALE

AEROSTAR INTERNATIONAL—Raven Industries, Inc.; *U.S. Public*, pg. 1361
AIN PLASTICS, INC.—Thyssen AG; *Int'l*, pg. 1388
AKZO PLASTICS B.V.—Akzo Nobel N.V.; *Int'l*, pg. 45
AKZO PLASTICS DANMARK A/S—Akzo Nobel N.V.; *Int'l*, pg. 45
AKZO PLASTICS GMBH—Akzo Nobel N.V.; *Int'l*, pg. 46
ALKOR MARKENHANDELS GMBH—Solvay S.A.; *Int'l*, pg. 1278
ALPHA INDUSTRIES; *U.S. Private*, pg. 45
AMARI PLASTICS PLC—Glynwed International PLC; *Int'l*, pg. 554
AMERICAN EXCELSIOR COMPANY; *U.S. Private*, pg. 53
AMOCO CHEMICALS FAR EAST, LTD.—Amoco Corporation; *U.S. Public*, pg. 103
AMOCO CHEMICALS PTY. LTD.—Amoco Corporation; *U.S. Public*, pg. 102
ARABIAN PLASTIC MANUFACTURING COMPANY—Georg Fischer Ltd.; *Int'l*, pg. 489
ARAMIDE MAATSCHAPPIJ VOF—Akzo Nobel N.V.; *Int'l*, pg. 45
ASHLAND, INC.; *U.S. Public*, pg. 138
BACHMANN INDUSTRIES, INC.; *U.S. Private*, pg. 109
BAKELITE AG—Ruetgers A.G.; *Int'l*, pg. 1148
BAYER JAPAN LTD.—Bayer AG; *Int'l*, pg. 174
BRENNTAG INTERCHEM, INC.—Veba AG; *Int'l*, pg. 1458
CADILLAC PLASTIC & CHEMICAL CO.—M.A. Hanna Company; *U.S. Public*, pg. 781

CAMERON ASHLEY BUILDING PRODUCTS, INC; *U.S. Public*, pg. 298
COLBOND BV—Akzo Nobel N.V.; *Int'l*, pg. 45
COMALLOY INTERNATIONAL COMPANY—A. Schulman, Inc.; *U.S. Public*, pg. 1441
CONESTOGA CORPORATION; *U.S. Private*, pg. 262
DSM N.V.; *Int'l*, pg. 352
DELTA RESINS & REFRACTORIES, INC.; *U.S. Private*, pg. 323
DUPERIAL 9 DE JULIO S.A.I.C.—Imperial Chemical Industries PLC; *Int'l*, pg. 664
DURCO FRANCE S.A.R.L.—Flowserve Corporation; *U.S. Public*, pg. 659
ETEX; *Int'l*, pg. 430
ELKAY PLASTICS CO., INC., STOCK SERVICE CENTER—Elkay Plastics Company, Inc.; *U.S. Private*, pg. 372
ENFIELD INDUSTRIAL CORP.—Glynwed International PLC; *Int'l*, pg. 554
G.E. PLASTICS-AMERICA—General Electric Company; *U.S. Public*, pg. 711
G.E. PLASTICS EUROPE—General Electric Company; *U.S. Public*, pg. 713
G.E. PLASTICS PACIFIC LTD.—General Electric Company; *U.S. Public*, pg. 713
GENERAL ELECTRIC PLASTICS GMBH—General Electric Company; *U.S. Public*, pg. 713
GENERAL ELECTRIC (USA) ASIA CO.—General Electric Company; *U.S. Public*, pg. 713
GENERAL LATEX & CHEMICAL CORPORATION; *U.S. Private*, pg. 444
HT TROPLAST—Ruetgers A.G.; *Int'l*, pg. 1148
M.A. HANNA COMPANY; *U.S. Public*, pg. 780
M.A. HANNA RESIN DISTRIBUTION—M.A. Hanna Company; *U.S. Public*, pg. 781
HELM RESOURCES INC.; *U.S. Public*, pg. 808
HENKEL-EYTESA S.A.—Henkel KGaA; *Int'l*, pg. 612
HOECHST SPECIALTY CHEMICALS GROUP—Hoechst Aktiengesellschaft; *Int'l*, pg. 624
HULS AMERICA INC., MIPLOM DIVISION—Veba AG; *Int'l*, pg. 1455
A.L. HYDE COMPANY—Danaher Corporation; *U.S. Public*, pg. 481
ICI FRANCE SA—Imperial Chemical Industries PLC; *Int'l*, pg. 665
ICI OESTERREICH GMBH—Imperial Chemical Industries PLC; *Int'l*, pg. 665
ICI (PERU) S.A.—Imperial Chemical Industries PLC; *Int'l*, pg. 665
ICI (PHILIPPINES) INC.—Imperial Chemical Industries PLC; *Int'l*, pg. 665
ICI (SINGAPORE) PRIVATE LIMITED—Imperial Chemical Industries PLC; *Int'l*, pg. 665
ICI (SWITZERLAND) AG—Imperial Chemical Industries PLC; *Int'l*, pg. 665
ICI ZAMBIA LIMITED—Imperial Chemical Industries PLC; *Int'l*, pg. 665
INDUSQUIMA S.A.—Henkel KGaA; *Int'l*, pg. 613
INTERNATIO (PTY.) LTD.—Internatio-Muller N.V.; *Int'l*, pg. 682
INTEX CORP.; *U.S. Private*, pg. 574
ISOLA WERKE AG—Ruetgers A.G.; *Int'l*, pg. 1148
KLOCKNER-PENTAPLAST OF CANADA, INC.—Klockner-Werke AG; *Int'l*, pg. 737
KOHAP GROUP; *Int'l*, pg. 742
KRUPP ENTWICKLUNGSZENTRUM GMBH—Fried. Krupp AG; *Int'l*, pg. 512
LANTECH INC.; *U.S. Private*, pg. 650
M.A. HANNA RESIN DISTRIBUTION—M.A. Hanna Company; *U.S. Public*, pg. 781
MARCO COLOR LABS, INC.; *U.S. Private*, pg. 702
A.W. MENDENHALL CO., INC.; *U.S. Private*, pg. 731
MEYER LAMINATES GEORGIA INC.—Meyer International PLC; *Int'l*, pg. 864
MEYER LAMINATES, INC.—Meyer International PLC; *Int'l*, pg. 864
MICROSI—Shin-Etsu Chemical Co. ltd.; *Int'l*, pg. 1234
MOLDED FIBER GLASS/WEST—Molded Fiber Glass Companies; *U.S. Private*, pg. 756
MOLDED FIBER/NORTH CAROLINA—Molded Fiber Glass Companies; *U.S. Private*, pg. 756
MYERS INDUSTRIES, INC.; *U.S. Public*, pg. 1143
PHB PLASTIC & RUBBER MOLDING DIVISION—PHB Die Casting; *U.S. Private*, pg. 826
PIONEER PLASTICS CORPORATION; *U.S. Private*, pg. 867
PLASTIC SALES DIV.—General Electric Company; *U.S. Public*, pg. 711
PLASTIGAGE CORPORATION; *U.S. Private*, pg. 871
PREMARK ITALIA SPA—Premark International, Inc.; *U.S. Public*, pg. 1323
RAPID INDUSTRIAL PLASTICS COMPANY; *U.S. Private*, pg. 910
REKO B.V.—DSM N.V.; *Int'l*, pg. 354
ROGERS JAPAN INC.—Rogers Corporation; *U.S. Public*, pg. 1403
ROVIN ROTTERDAMSE VINYLUNIE VOF—Akzo Nobel N.V.; *Int'l*, pg. 43
SABANCI HOLDING A.S.; *Int'l*, pg. 1167
SCHLEGEL LINING TECHNOLOGY, INC.—BTR plc; *Int'l*, pg. 128
A. SCHULMAN—A. Schulman, Inc.; *U.S. Public*, pg. 1441
A. SCHULMAN, INC.; *U.S. Public*, pg. 1441
A. SCHULMAN, INC.—A. Schulman, Inc.; *U.S. Public*, pg. 1441
P.T. STANDARD TOYO POLYMER—Tosoh Corporation; *Int'l*, pg. 1408
STRAUSS 9 DE JULIO S.A.I.C.—Imperial Chemical Industries PLC; *Int'l*, pg. 665
SUMITOMO CORPORATION; *Int'l*, pg. 1312
SUMITOMO CORPORATION OF AMERICA—Sumitomo Corporation; *Int'l*, pg. 1312
TEIJIN AMERICA, INC.—Teijin Limited; *Int'l*, pg. 1362
TEKRA CORPORATION; *U.S. Private*, pg. 1073
THUNDERBIRD STEEL CORPORATION—Cameron Ashley Building Products, Inc; *U.S. Public*, pg. 298
TOKUYAMA AMERICA INC.—Tokuyama Corporation; *Int'l*, pg. 1394
TOTAL PLASTIC INC.—A.M. Castle & Co.; *U.S. Public*, pg. 313
UNISOURCE (S.E. REGIONAL OFFICE)—Unisource Worldwide, Inc.; *U.S. Public*, pg. 1671
UNITED MARKETING (LEICESTER) LTD.—The Black & Decker Corporation; *U.S. Public*, pg. 234
VG EMBALLAGE—Saint-Gobain; *Int'l*, pg. 1171
WESTCHESTER PLASTICS—AMETEK, Inc.; *U.S. Public*, pg. 100
ZENECA AB—Zeneca Group Plc; *Int'l*, pg. 1526
ZENECA OY—Zeneca Group Plc; *Int'l*, pg. 1527
ZENECA POLAND SP. Z.O.O.—Zeneca Group Plc; *Int'l*, pg. 1527
ZENECA ZIMBABWE (PRIVATE) LIMITED—Zeneca Group Plc; *Int'l*, pg. 1527

5169 — CHEMICALS & ALLIED PRODUCTS-WHOLESALE, NEC

AAKO INC.—Makhteshim Chemical Works Ltd.; *Int'l*, pg. 830
OY ALGOL AB; *Int'l*, pg. 15
APCI (U.K.), INC.—Air Products and Chemicals, Inc.; *U.S. Public*, pg. 30
ACETO CORPORATION; *U.S. Public*, pg. 15
AEKYUNG & SHELL—Royal Dutch/Shell Group of Companies; *Int'l*, pg. 1140
AGRICUR-DEFENSIVOS AGRICOLAS LTD.—Makhteshim Chemical Works Ltd.; *Int'l*, pg. 830
AIR LIQUIDE CORPORATION BULK GASES DIVISION—Air Liquide S.A.; *Int'l*, pg. 37
AIR PRODUCTS S.A.—Air Products and Chemicals, Inc.; *U.S. Public*, pg. 32
AIR PRODUCTS WORLD TRADE, INC. C/O CHASE TRADE, INC.—Air Products and Chemicals, Inc.; *U.S. Public*, pg. 31
AJINOMOTO U.S.A., INC.—Ajinomoto Company Inc.; *Int'l*, pg. 40
AKROCHEM CORPORATION; *U.S. Private*, pg. 30
AKZO ZOUT CHEMIE DEUTSCHLAND GMBH—Akzo Nobel N.V.; *Int'l*, pg. 43
AKZO ZOUT CHEMIE FRANCE SARL—Akzo Nobel N.V.; *Int'l*, pg. 44
AKZO ZOUT CHEMIE SVENSKA AB—Akzo Nobel N.V.; *Int'l*, pg. 44
ALBEMARLE CORPORATION; *U.S. Public*, pg. 37
ALCO CHEMICAL—Unilever Plc; *Int'l*, pg. 1435
ALFA AGRICULTURAL SUPPLIES LTD.—Makhteshim Chemical Works Ltd.; *Int'l*, pg. 830
ALLIED COLLOIDS LTD.—Allied Colloids Group Plc.; *Int'l*, pg. 62
AMCAST INDUSTRIAL LTD.—Amcast Industrial Corporation; *U.S. Public*, pg. 63
AMERICO MANUFACTURING CO., INC.; *U.S. Private*, pg. 64
AMERSHAM LIFE SCIENCE, INC.—Nycomed Amersham plc; *Int'l*, pg. 992
AMOCO CHEMICAL BELGIUM N.V.—Amoco Corporation; *U.S. Public*, pg. 103
AMOCO CHEMICAL (UK) LTD.—Amoco Corporation; *U.S. Public*, pg. 103
AMOCO CHEMICALS FAR EAST, LTD.—Amoco Corporation; *U.S. Public*, pg. 103
AMOCO CHEMICALS PTY. LTD.—Amoco Corporation; *U.S. Public*, pg. 102
AMOCO FINA N.V.—Amoco Corporation; *U.S. Public*, pg. 102
AMOCO JAPAN LTD.—Amoco Corporation; *U.S. Public*, pg. 102
ANIKEM (PROPRIETARY) LTD.—Nalco Chemical Company; *U.S. Public*, pg. 1150
AQUACHLOR (PROPRIETARY) LIMITED—Olin Corporation; *U.S. Public*, pg. 1219
AQUILA BIOPHARMACEUTICALS, INC.; *U.S. Public*, pg. 126
ARKANSAS EASTMAN CO.—Eastman Chemical Company; *U.S. Public*, pg. 550
ASAHI GLASS AMERICA, INC.—Asahi Glass Co., Ltd.; *Int'l*, pg. 84
ASHLAND CHEMICAL—Ashland, Inc.; *U.S. Public*, pg. 139
ASHLAND, INC.; *U.S. Public*, pg. 138
BOC GASES (SAMOA) LTD.—The BOC Group plc; *Int'l*, pg. 121
BP AMERICA INC.—The British Petroleum Company P.L.C.; *Int'l*, pg. 220
BP AUSTRALIA LTD.—The British Petroleum Company P.L.C.; *Int'l*, pg. 220
BP CHEMICALS LTD.—The British Petroleum Company P.L.C.; *Int'l*, pg. 220
BP JAPAN KK—The British Petroleum Company P.L.C.; *Int'l*, pg. 220
BWK KRIEGLACH BAUWERKSTOFFE GES. M. B. H.—Viag AG; *Int'l*, pg. 1465
H.J. BAKER & BRO., INC.; *U.S. Private*, pg. 112
BASS—Novartis AG; *Int'l*, pg. 975
BAYER AG; *Int'l*, pg. 171
BAYER ANTWERPEN N.V.—Bayer AG; *Int'l*, pg. 174
BAYER CORPORATION—Bayer AG; *Int'l*, pg. 172
BEHRINGWERKE AG—Hoechst Aktiengesellschaft; *Int'l*, pg. 624
BELL FLAVORS & FRAGRANCES; *U.S. Private*, pg. 131
BELL INDUSTRIES, INC.; *U.S. Public*, pg. 204
BERNER LTD.; *Int'l*, pg. 189
BETTOR S.A.—Viag AG; *Int'l*, pg. 1465
BEVALOID AUSTRALIA (PTY) LTD.—Rhone-Poulenc S.A.; *Int'l*, pg. 1113
BIDDLE SAWYER CORPORATION; *U.S. Private*, pg. 142
BIOZYM GESELLSCHAFT M.B.H.—Novartis AG; *Int'l*, pg. 986
BIRLA 3M LTD.—3M; *U.S. Public*, pg. 1606
BLUE CROSS LABORATORIES; *U.S. Private*, pg. 152
BOAM CHEMICALS CO., INC.—MacAndrews & Forbes Holdings Inc.; *U.S. Private*, pg. 689
BOEHME CHEMIE GESELLSCHAFT MBH—Henkel KGaA; *Int'l*, pg. 609
C.F. BOEHRINGER & SOEHNE GMBH—Corange Limited; *Int'l*, pg. 331
BOEHRINGER MANNHEIM BIOCHEMICALS DIV.—Corange Limited; *Int'l*, pg. 331
BOREALIS S.A.—Neste Oy; *Int'l*, pg. 914
BRENNTAG INTERCHEM, INC.—Veba AG; *Int'l*, pg. 1458
C. BREWER & COMPANY, LIMITED—Buyco, Inc.; *U.S. Private*, pg. 190
BREWER ENVIRONMENTAL INDUSTRIES, LLC—Buyco, Inc.; *U.S. Private*, pg. 190
BRIDGEPORT BRASS CORPORATION—Olin Corporation; *U.S. Public*, pg. 1219
BRINER PAINT MANUFACTURING CO., INC.—RPM, Inc.; *U.S. Public*, pg. 1358
THE BRITISH PETROLEUM COMPANY P.L.C.; *Int'l*, pg. 219
BROWNING CHEMICAL CORPORATION; *U.S. Private*, pg. 175
BRUNEI SHELL MARKETING—Royal Dutch/Shell Group of Companies; *Int'l*, pg. 1139
BRYAN METALS, INC.—Olin Corporation; *U.S. Public*, pg. 1219
C & K COLOURS (H.K.) LIMITED—Crompton & Knowles Corporation; *U.S. Public*, pg. 460
CADILLAC PLASTIC—M.A. Hanna Company; *U.S. Public*, pg. 781
CALGON CARBON CANADA, INC.—Calgon Carbon Corporation; *U.S. Public*, pg. 293
CALGON FAR EAST CO. LTD.—Calgon Carbon Corporation; *U.S. Public*, pg. 293
CANADIAN ADHESIVES LTD.—Viag AG; *Int'l*, pg. 1466
CARBOLINE CO.—RPM, Inc.; *U.S. Public*, pg. 1357
CAROLINA EASTMAN CO.—Eastman Chemical Company; *U.S. Public*, pg. 550
P.J. CARROLL HOLDINGS P.L.C.—Rothmans UK Holdings Limited; *Int'l*, pg. 1130
CATALYST RESOURCES, INC—Mallinckrodt Inc.; *U.S. Public*, pg. 1039
CELANESE CANADA CHEMICALS & INDUSTRIAL PRODUCTS GROUP—Hoechst Aktiengesellschaft; *Int'l*, pg. 625
CENTRAL DE CERVEJAS, S.A.; *Int'l*, pg. 279
CHEMARKETING INTERNATIONAL, INC.—Bayer AG; *Int'l*, pg. 173
CHEMCENTRAL CORPORATION; *U.S. Private*, pg. 231
CHEMCENTRAL/PHILADELPHIA—CHEMCENTRAL Corporation; *U.S. Private*, pg. 232
CHEMDESIGN CORPORATION—Bayer AG; *Int'l*, pg. 173
CHEMIE LINZ FRANCE S.A.R.L.—DSM N.V.; *Int'l*, pg. 356
CHEMIE LINZ UK LTD.—DSM N.V.; *Int'l*, pg. 356
CHEMREX INC.—Viag AG; *Int'l*, pg. 1465
CHEMSERV INDUSTRIE SERVICE GES.M.B.H.—DSM N.V.; *Int'l*, pg. 356
CHINA AMERICAN PETROCHEMICAL CO., LTD.—Amoco Corporation; *U.S. Public*, pg. 102
CHINA STEEL CHEMICAL CORP.—China Steel Corporation; *Int'l*, pg. 286
CHLORURE DE VINYLE DE FOS—Royal Dutch/Shell Group of Companies; *Int'l*, pg. 1138
CHORI AMERICA, INC.—Chori Co., Ltd.; *Int'l*, pg. 288
CHORI CO., LTD.; *Int'l*, pg. 288
CIBA SPECIALTY CHEMICALS—Ciba Specialty Chemicals Holding Inc.; *Int'l*, pg. 291
COLLOIDS CANADA INC.—Rhone-Poulenc S.A.; *Int'l*, pg. 1113
COLORCON LTD.—Berwind Corporation; *U.S. Private*, pg. 139
COMPANIA DE PETROLEO SHELL DEL PERU SA—Royal Dutch/Shell Group of Companies; *Int'l*, pg. 1141
CROUCH SUPPLY COMPANY, INC.; *U.S. Private*, pg. 291
CUMBRIAN STORAGE LTD.—Simon Engineering plc; *Int'l*, pg. 1251
CURVER CONSUMER PRODUCTS LTD.—DSM N.V.; *Int'l*, pg. 353
DSM CHEMICALS NORTH AMERICA, INC.—DSM N.V.; *Int'l*, pg. 354
DSM HYDROCARBONS AMERICAS, INC.—DSM N.V.; *Int'l*, pg. 355
DSM RESINS BENELUX B.V.—DSM N.V.; *Int'l*, pg. 353
DSM RESINS B.V.—DSM N.V.; *Int'l*, pg. 353
DSM RESINS INTERNATIONAL B.V.—DSM N.V.; *Int'l*, pg. 353
DAICOLOR-POPE, INC.—Dainichiseika Colour & Chemicals Mfg. Co., Ltd.; *Int'l*, pg. 369
DAIHAN SWISS CHEMICAL CORPORATION—Ciba Specialty Chemicals Holding Inc.; *Int'l*, pg. 292
DAIICHI FINE CHEMICALS—Mitsui & Co., Ltd.; *Int'l*, pg. 879
DAP INC.—Wassall Plc; *Int'l*, pg. 1486
DEGUSSA AG; *Int'l*, pg. 388
DELGASCO, INC.—Delta Natural Gas Company, Inc.; *U.S. Public*, pg. 497
DELTA RESINS & REFRACTORIES, INC.; *U.S. Private*, pg. 323
DELTA RESOURCES, INC.—Delta Natural Gas Company, Inc.; *U.S. Public*, pg. 497
DENAK KK—Akzo Nobel N.V.; *Int'l*, pg. 44
DEUTSCHE ICI GMBH—Imperial Chemical Industries PLC; *Int'l*, pg. 664
DILLARD, A RESOURCENET INTERNATIONAL COMPANY—International Paper Company; *U.S. Public*, pg. 901
DINOL AUSTRALIA PTY. LTD.—Novartis AG; *Int'l*, pg. 981
DINOL FRANCE S.A.R.L.—Novartis AG; *Int'l*, pg. 981
DINOL INDUSTRIAL CANADA INC.—Novartis AG; *Int'l*, pg. 982
DINOL JAPAN—Novartis AG; *Int'l*, pg. 982
DINOL KOREA LTD.—Novartis AG; *Int'l*, pg. 982

DINOL NORGE A/S—Novartis AG; Int'l, pg. 982
DINOL OY—Novartis AG; Int'l, pg. 982
DINOL PROTECTOL LTD.—Novartis AG; Int'l, pg. 982
DINOL-SHROFF (INDIA) PVT. LTD.—Novartis AG; Int'l, pg. 982
DISTRIBUIDORA SHELL DE EL SALVADOR SA—Royal Dutch/Shell Group of Companies; Int'l, pg. 1141
DOBER CHEMICAL CORP.; U.S. Private, pg. 337
DOW CHEMICAL AUSTRIA GESELLSCHAFT MBH—The Dow Chemical Company; U.S. Public, pg. 523
DOW CHEMICAL EXPORT S.A.—The Dow Chemical Company; U.S. Public, pg. 523
DOW CHEMICAL INTERNATIONAL LTD.—The Dow Chemical Company; U.S. Public, pg. 523
DOW CHEMICAL JAPAN LTD.—The Dow Chemical Company; U.S. Public, pg. 523
DOW QUIMICA CHILENA S.A.—The Dow Chemical Company; U.S. Public, pg. 524
DOW SUOMI OY—The Dow Chemical Company; U.S. Public, pg. 524
DOW VENEZUELA CA—The Dow Chemical Company; U.S. Public, pg. 524
DOW VERTRIEBSGESELLSCHAFT M.B.H.—The Dow Chemical Company; U.S. Public, pg. 524
DOW VERTRIEBSGES.MBH—The Dow Chemical Company; U.S. Public, pg. 524
DREW INDUSTRIAL—Ashland, Inc.; U.S. Public, pg. 139
DU PONT ASIA PACIFIC LTD.—Du Pont (E.I. Du Pont De Nemours & Co.); U.S. Public, pg. 532
DU PONT (AUSTRALIA) LTD.—Du Pont (E.I. Du Pont De Nemours & Co.); U.S. Public, pg. 532
DU PONT DE NEMOURS (BELGIUM) S.A.—Du Pont (E.I. Du Pont De Nemours & Co.); U.S. Public, pg. 532
DU PONT DE NEMOURS (FRANCE) S.A.—Du Pont (E.I. Du Pont De Nemours & Co.); U.S. Public, pg. 532
DU PONT DE NEMOURS INTERNATIONAL S.A.—Du Pont (E.I. Du Pont De Nemours & Co.); U.S. Public, pg. 532
DU PONT FAR EAST INC.—Du Pont (E.I. Du Pont De Nemours & Co.); U.S. Public, pg. 532
DU PONT IBERICA S.A.—Du Pont (E.I. Du Pont De Nemours & Co.); U.S. Public, pg. 533
DU PONT (NEW ZEALAND) LTD.—Du Pont (E.I. Du Pont De Nemours & Co.); U.S. Public, pg. 533
DUPERIAL S.A.I.C.—Imperial Chemical Industries PLC; Int'l, pg. 664
DUSSEK CAMPBELL LTD.—Burmah Castrol plc; Int'l, pg. 236
DYNECOL, INC.—PVS Chemicals, Inc.; U.S. Private, pg. 828
ECP INCORPORATED—Daubert Industries, Inc.; U.S. Private, pg. 313
EMS-TOGO—Novartis AG; Int'l, pg. 981
EPPC POLYPLASTIC S.A.—The B.F. Goodrich Company; U.S. Public, pg. 752
EASTMAN KODAK COMPANY; U.S. Public, pg. 550
ECUATORIANA DE LUBRICANTES—Royal Dutch/Shell Group of Companies; Int'l, pg. 1141
ELECTROCLOR S.A.—Imperial Chemical Industries PLC; Int'l, pg. 664
ELF AQUITAINE, INC.—Elf Aquitane; Int'l, pg. 445
EMBECON (NEW ZEALAND) LIMITED—Novartis AG; Int'l, pg. 982
ENGLISH CHINA CLAYS PLC; Int'l, pg. 455
ESSEX CHEMICAL CORPORATION—The Dow Chemical Company; U.S. Public, pg. 523
ETABLISSEMENTS BEZ S.A.—Allied Colloids Group Plc.; Int'l, pg. 62
ETHYL CANADA, INC.—Ethyl Corporation; U.S. Public, pg. 595
EUROC TRADE AB—Scancem AB; Int'l, pg. 1199
EXPANDITE S.A.—Burmah Castrol plc; Int'l, pg. 236
FMC ARGENTINA, S.A. C.I., Y.F.—FMC Corporation; U.S. Public, pg. 606
FMC (AUSTRALIA) LIMITED—FMC Corporation; U.S. Public, pg. 606
FMC CAMEROON SARL—FMC Corporation; U.S. Public, pg. 606
FMC DO BRASIL, S.A.—FMC Corporation; U.S. Public, pg. 606
FMC EUROPE NV—FMC Corporation; U.S. Public, pg. 606
FMC EUROPE, S.A./N.V.—FMC Corporation; U.S. Public, pg. 606
FMC HELLAS EPE—FMC Corporation; U.S. Public, pg. 606
FMC INTERNATIONAL, A.G.—FMC Corporation; U.S. Public, pg. 606
FMC (IRELAND) LIMITED—FMC Corporation; U.S. Public, pg. 606
FALLEK CHEMICAL COMPANY (UK) LTD.—ICC Industries, Inc.; U.S. Private, pg. 553
FALLEK CHEMICAL S.A.—ICC Industries, Inc.; U.S. Private, pg. 553
FANCHEM, LTD.—PVS Chemicals, Inc.; U.S. Private, pg. 828
FASSON FRANCE S.A.R.L.—Avery Dennison Corporation; U.S. Public, pg. 154
FASSON PRODUTOS ADESIVOS LTDA.—Avery Dennison Corporation; U.S. Public, pg. 154
FASSON VERTRIEBS, AG—Avery Dennison Corporation; U.S. Public, pg. 154
FERRO METAL & CHEMICAL CORPORATION LTD.—Philipp Brothers Chemicals, Inc.; U.S. Private, pg. 861
FIRST CHEMICAL CORP.—ChemFirst Inc.; U.S. Public, pg. 344
GEORG FISCHER N.V.—Georg Fischer Ltd.; Int'l, pg. 489
FOOD & GAS, INC.; U.S. Private, pg. 417
FORMICA CANADA, INC.—BTR plc; Int'l, pg. 129
FORMICA VERTRIEBS GMBH—BTR plc; Int'l, pg. 130
FOSECO (SINGAPORE) PTE. LTD.—Burmah Castrol plc; Int'l, pg. 236
FREEDOM CHEMICAL COMPANY; U.S. Private, pg. 425
FREEDOM TEXTILES CHEMICALS CO.—Freedom Chemical Company; U.S. Private, pg. 425
H.B. FULLER COMPANY; U.S. Public, pg. 686
G.D. INTERNATIONAL, LTD.—Olin Corporation; U.S. Public, pg. 1219
GLS CORPORATION; U.S. Private, pg. 435
GALENUS CHEMICALS GMBH—Corange Limited; Int'l, pg. 331
GALENUS MANNHEIM GMBH—Corange Limited; Int'l, pg. 331
GEMISA S.A. DE C.V.—Henkel KGaA; Int'l, pg. 614
GENENCOR INTERNATIONAL, INC.—Cultor Ltd.; Int'l, pg. 349
GENERAL LATEX & CHEMICAL CORPORATION; U.S. Private, pg. 444
B.F. GOODRICH CHEMICAL DEUTSCHLAND GMBH—The B.F. Goodrich Company; U.S. Public, pg. 752
B.F. GOODRICH CHEMICAL EUROPE—The B.F. Goodrich Company; U.S. Public, pg. 752
B.F. GOODRICH CHEMICAL (FAR EAST) LTD.—The B.F. Goodrich Company; U.S. Public, pg. 752
GRACE ARGENTINA S.A.—W.R. Grace & Co.; U.S. Public, pg. 755
GRAPHIC ARTS SUPPLY DIVISION—Bell Industries, Inc.; U.S. Public, pg. 205
GRAPHITWERK KROPFMUEHL AG—Viag AG; Int'l, pg. 1464
GRIFFIN CORPORATION; U.S. Private, pg. 480
GRUPO CARSO S.A. DE C.V.; Int'l, pg. 572
GUATEMALTECA SHELL SA—Royal Dutch/Shell Group of Companies; Int'l, pg. 1141
HCI CHEMTECH; U.S. Private, pg. 490
HAGEMEYER N.V.—First Pacific Company Limited; Int'l, pg. 487
THE HALL CHEMICAL COMPANY—Goldman Financial Group; U.S. Private, pg. 461
HANNAFORD SEEDMASTER SERVICES AUSTRALIA (PTY) LTD.—Crompton & Knowles Corporation; U.S. Public, pg. 460
HARCROS CHEMICALS INC.—Harrisons & Crosfield plc; Int'l, pg. 598
HARRICROS CHEMICALS PTE. LTD.—Harrisons & Crosfield plc; Int'l, pg. 599
HARRISONS & CROSFIELD PLC; Int'l, pg. 598
HARRISONS & CROSFIELD (CANADA) LTD.—Harrisons & Crosfield plc; Int'l, pg. 599
HARWICK STANDARD DISTRIBUTION CORPORATION; U.S. Private, pg. 509
HAVILAND ENTERPRISES; U.S. Private, pg. 511
HAWKINS TERMINAL I—Hawkins Chemical, Inc.; U.S. Public, pg. 800
HEBRON S.A.—Otsuka Pharmaceutical Co., Ltd.; Int'l, pg. 1014
HENKEL ARGENTINA S.A.—Henkel KGaA; Int'l, pg. 611
HENKEL AUSTRALIA PTY. LTD.—Henkel KGaA; Int'l, pg. 611
HENKEL AUSTRIA GROUP—Henkel KGaA; Int'l, pg. 611
HENKEL BUDAPEST CHEMISCHE GESELLSCHAFT MBH—Henkel KGaA; Int'l, pg. 612
HENKEL CHEMICALS (CARIBBEAN) LTD.—Henkel KGaA; Int'l, pg. 614
HENKEL CHIMICA S.P.A.—Henkel KGaA; Int'l, pg. 612
HENKEL COLOMBIANA S.A.—Henkel KGaA; Int'l, pg. 612
HENKEL COMERCIAL S.A. DE C.V.—Henkel KGaA; Int'l, pg. 612
HENKEL-EYTESA S.A.—Henkel KGaA; Int'l, pg. 612
HENKEL HAKUSUI CORPORATION—Henkel KGaA; Int'l, pg. 612
HENKEL HELLAS—Henkel KGaA; Int'l, pg. 612
HENKEL HELLAS, S.A.—Henkel KGaA; Int'l, pg. 612
HENKEL INDUSTRIE AG—Henkel KGaA; Int'l, pg. 612
HENKEL ITALIANA S.P.A.—Henkel KGaA; Int'l, pg. 613
HENKEL KEMI AB—Henkel KGaA; Int'l, pg. 613
HENKEL KENYA LTD.—Henkel KGaA; Int'l, pg. 613
HENKEL KOREA LTD.—Henkel KGaA; Int'l, pg. 613
HENKEL NEDERLAND B.V.—Henkel KGaA; Int'l, pg. 613
HENKEL NEW ZEALAND LTD.—Henkel KGaA; Int'l, pg. 613
HENKEL NOPCO AB—Henkel KGaA; Int'l, pg. 613
HENKEL NOPCO OY—Henkel KGaA; Int'l, pg. 614
HENKEL NORGE A/S—Henkel KGaA; Int'l, pg. 613
HENKEL PHILIPPINES INC.—Henkel KGaA; Int'l, pg. 614
HENKEL PORTUGUESA PRODUCTOS QUIMICOS LDA.—Henkel KGaA; Int'l, pg. 613
HENKEL S/A. INDUSTRIAS QUIMICAS—Henkel KGaA; Int'l, pg. 613
HENKEL SINGAPORE PTE., LTD.—Henkel KGaA; Int'l, pg. 613
HENKEL SOUTH AFRICA (PTY.) LTD.—Henkel KGaA; Int'l, pg. 614
HENKEL SUD S.P.A.—Henkel KGaA; Int'l, pg. 613
HENKEL TAIWAN LTD.—Henkel KGaA; Int'l, pg. 613
HENKEL THAI LTD.—Henkel KGaA; Int'l, pg. 613
HENKEL VENEZOLANA S.A.—Henkel KGaA; Int'l, pg. 614
HENKEL ZIMBABWE (PVT) LTD.—Henkel KGaA; Int'l, pg. 613
WILL HENKO BV—Henkel KGaA; Int'l, pg. 614
HENKOMAR S.A.—Henkel KGaA; Int'l, pg. 614
HERCULES CANADA INC.—Hercules Incorporated; U.S. Public, pg. 810
HERITAGE MERCHANDISING CO., INC.—Pennzoil Company; U.S. Public, pg. 1272
HITACHI CHEMICAL CO. AMERICA LTD.—Hitachi, Ltd.; Int'l, pg. 622
HOECHST MARION ROUSSEL, INC.—Hoechst Aktiengesellschaft; Int'l, pg. 624
HOECHST SPECIALTY CHEMICALS GROUP—Hoechst Aktiengesellschaft; Int'l, pg. 624
HOECHST SPECIALTY PRODUCTS GROUP—Hoechst Aktiengesellschaft; Int'l, pg. 625
HOXAN AMERICA INCORPORATED—Daido Hoxan Inc.; Int'l, pg. 363
HUBBARD HALL INC.; U.S. Private, pg. 544
R.S. HUGHES CO., INC.; U.S. Private, pg. 547
R.S. HUGHES CO.—R.S. Hughes Co., Inc.; U.S. Private, pg. 547
HYDROLABS INC.—Allied Colloids Group Plc.; Int'l, pg. 62
ICC COMERCIO E INDUSTRIA LTDS.—ICC Industries, Inc.; U.S. Private, pg. 554
ICC HANDELS AG—ICC Industries, Inc.; U.S. Private, pg. 554
ICC (HONG KONG) LTD.—ICC Industries, Inc.; U.S. Private, pg. 554
ICC INDUSTRIES, B.V.—ICC Industries, Inc.; U.S. Private, pg. 554
ICD GROUP INTERNATIONAL INC.; U.S. Private, pg. 554
ICI FRANCE SA—Imperial Chemical Industries PLC; Int'l, pg. 665
ICI INDUSTRIAL CHEMICALS (MALAYSIA) SDN BHD—Imperial Chemical Industries PLC; Int'l, pg. 665
ICI NEW ZEALAND LIMITED—Imperial Chemical Industries PLC; Int'l, pg. 665
ICI OESTERREICH GMBH—Imperial Chemical Industries PLC; Int'l, pg. 665
ICI (PERU) S.A.—Imperial Chemical Industries PLC; Int'l, pg. 665
ICI (PHILIPPINES) INC.—Imperial Chemical Industries PLC; Int'l, pg. 665
ICI RESINS SA—Imperial Chemical Industries PLC; Int'l, pg. 665
ICI (SINGAPORE) PRIVATE LIMITED—Imperial Chemical Industries PLC; Int'l, pg. 665
ICI (SWITZERLAND) AG—Imperial Chemical Industries PLC; Int'l, pg. 665
ICI ZAMBIA LIMITED—Imperial Chemical Industries PLC; Int'l, pg. 665
ISK (EUROPE) S.A.—Ishihara Sangyo Kaisha, Ltd.; Int'l, pg. 689
ISS DARENAS INTERNATIONAL A/S—ISS-International Service System A/S; Int'l, pg. 656
ISS DARENAS LTD.—ISS-International Service System A/S; Int'l, pg. 657
IDEAL CHEMICAL & SUPPLY COMPANY; U.S. Private, pg. 557
IMMINGHAM STORAGE CO. LTD.—Simon Engineering plc; Int'l, pg. 1251
INDUSTRIAL DETERGENTS, LTD.—Henkel KGaA; Int'l, pg. 612
INTERENSCO N.V.—Internatio-Muller N.V.; Int'l, pg. 682
INTERNATIO MINERALS & CHEMICALS—Internatio-Muller N.V.; Int'l, pg. 682
INTERNATIO (PTY.) LTD.—Internatio-Muller N.V.; Int'l, pg. 682
INTERNATIONAL SPECIALTY PRODUCTS, INC.—ISP Holdings, Inc.; U.S. Public, pg. 858
IRAN HENKEL AG—Henkel KGaA; Int'l, pg. 613
IRANSEN ET SHELL—Royal Dutch/Shell Group of Companies; Int'l, pg. 1136
IRISH BULK LIQUID STORAGE LTD.—Simon Engineering plc; Int'l, pg. 1252
IRISH SHELL LTD.—Royal Dutch/Shell Group of Companies; Int'l, pg. 1138
ISHIHARA CORPORATION (U.S.A.)—Ishihara Sangyo Kaisha, Ltd.; Int'l, pg. 689
ITOCHU CORPORATION; Int'l, pg. 694
ITOCHU INTERNATIONAL INC.—Itochu Corporation; Int'l, pg. 694
J.U.L. SEILAZ AG—Henkel KGaA; Int'l, pg. 613
JARCHEM SPECIALTY CHEMICAL DIVISION—Jarchem Industries, Inc.; U.S. Private, pg. 583
JOTUN A/S; Int'l, pg. 714
JOTUN MIDEX AB—Jotun A/S; Int'l, pg. 715
JOTUN SVERIGE A.B.—Jotun A/S; Int'l, pg. 715
KEEN COMPRESSED GAS CO.; U.S. Private, pg. 611
KEMIRA KEMI (UK) LTD.—Kemira Oy; Int'l, pg. 728
KEMIRA MILJO A/S—Kemira Oy; Int'l, pg. 728
KEMIRA PAPER CHEMICALS CANADA, INC.—Kemira Oy; Int'l, pg. 728
KEMIRA SVENSKA AB—Kemira Oy; Int'l, pg. 729
KIMYATEKS DIS TICARET A.S.—Henkel KGaA; Int'l, pg. 614
KIWI BRANDS—Sara Lee Corporation; U.S. Public, pg. 1433
KONICA ATHENS OFFICE—Konica Corporation; Int'l, pg. 749
KONICA AUSTRALIA PTY.—Konica Corporation; Int'l, pg. 749
KONICA BEIJING OFFICE—Konica Corporation; Int'l, pg. 749
KONICA CANADA INC.—Konica Corporation; Int'l, pg. 749
KONICA EUROPE GMBH—Konica Corporation; Int'l, pg. 749
KONICA FRANCE S.A.—Konica Corporation; Int'l, pg. 749
KONICA GESELLSCHAFT MBH—Konica Corporation; Int'l, pg. 749
KONICA HONG KONG LTD.—Konica Corporation; Int'l, pg. 749
KONICA SINGAPORE PTE. LTD.—Konica Corporation; Int'l, pg. 749
KONICA (THAILAND) CO., LTD.—Konica Corporation; Int'l, pg. 749
KONICA UK LTD.—Konica Corporation; Int'l, pg. 749
KOSSACK CHEMIE GMBH—Henkel KGaA; Int'l, pg. 610
KRAUSS-MAFFEI AG—Mannesmann A.G.; Int'l, pg. 836
KRAUSS-MAFFEI CORP.—Mannesmann A.G.; Int'l, pg. 836
KRAZY GLUE INC.—Borden, Inc.; U.S. Private, pg. 158
KUBOTA GEORGE FISCHER LTD.—Georg Fischer Ltd.; Int'l, pg. 490
KYODO TDI LIMITED COMPANY—Olin Corporation; U.S. Public, pg. 1219
LAN-O-SHEEN, INC.; U.S. Private, pg. 645
P.T. LAUTAN OTSUKA CHEMICAL—Otsuka Pharmaceutical Co., Ltd.; Int'l, pg. 1014
LAWSON PRODUCTS, INC.; U.S. Public, pg. 980
LAWSON PRODUCTS LTD.—Lawson Products, Inc.; U.S. Public, pg. 980
LE SOLEIL S.A.—Henkel KGaA; Int'l, pg. 613
LEE PHARMACEUTICALS; U.S. Public, pg. 984
LEVER & KITCHEN PTY. LTD.—Unilever Plc; Int'l, pg. 1437
LEVER BROTHERS HOUSEHOLD PRODUCTS DIV.—Unilever Plc; Int'l, pg. 1436

LEVER BROTHERS INDUSTRIAL DIVISION—Unilever Plc; *Int'l*, pg. 1436
LION HENKEL CORPORATION—Henkel KGaA; *Int'l*, pg. 614
LIQUID AIR CORPORATION, PACKAGE GASES DIV.—Air Liquide S.A.; *Int'l*, pg. 37
LITEX A/S—FMC Corporation; *U.S. Public*, pg. 607
LOCTITE CORPORATION—Henkel KGaA; *Int'l*, pg. 611
LONDON LITHO ALUMINUM CO., INC.; *U.S. Private*, pg. 673
LUBRIZOL DE CHILE, LTDA.—The Lubrizol Corporation; *U.S. Public*, pg. 1016
LUBRIZOL GMBH—The Lubrizol Corporation; *U.S. Public*, pg. 1016
LUBRIZOL ITALIANA S.P.A.—The Lubrizol Corporation; *U.S. Public*, pg. 1016
LUBRIZOL JAPAN LTD.—The Lubrizol Corporation; *U.S. Public*, pg. 1016
LUBRIZOL LTD.—The Lubrizol Corporation; *U.S. Public*, pg. 1017
MBT DE VENEZUELA, C.A.—Viag AG; *Int'l*, pg. 1465
MBT (MALAYSIA) SDM. BHD.—Viag AG; *Int'l*, pg. 1465
MBT (NEW ZEALAND) LTD.—Viag AG; *Int'l*, pg. 1465
MBT PORTUGAL LDA.—Viag AG; *Int'l*, pg. 1465
MBT (SINGAPORE) PTE. LTD.—Viag AG; *Int'l*, pg. 1465
MFA INCORPORATED; *U.S. Private*, pg. 686
MACDERMID INCORPORATED; *U.S. Public*, pg. 1029
MAKHTESHIM-AGAN ESPANA S.L.—Makhteshim Chemical Works Ltd.; *Int'l*, pg. 830
MAKHTESHIM-AGAN FRANCE S.A.R.L.—Makhteshim Chemical Works Ltd.; *Int'l*, pg. 830
MAKHTESHIM AGAN OF NORTH AMERICA INC.—Makhteshim Chemical Works Ltd.; *Int'l*, pg. 830
MAKHTESHIM-AGAN ROMANIA S.R.L.—Makhteshim Chemical Works Ltd.; *Int'l*, pg. 831
MAKHTESHIM-AGAN (U.K.) LTD.—Makhteshim Chemical Works Ltd.; *Int'l*, pg. 831
MAKHTESHIM CHEMICAL WORKS LTD.; *Int'l*, pg. 830
MANCHEM INC.—Rhone-Poulenc S.A.; *Int'l*, pg. 1110
MARTIN GAS CORPORATION; *U.S. Private*, pg. 709
MARUBENI AMERICA CORPORATION, DALLAS BRANCH—Marubeni Corporation; *Int'l*, pg. 844
MARUBENI AMERICA CORPORATION, DETROIT BRANCH—Marubeni Corporation; *Int'l*, pg. 844
MARUBENI AMERICA CORPORATION, PORTLAND BRANCH—Marubeni Corporation; *Int'l*, pg. 845
MARUBENI AMERICAN CORPORATION, SEATTLE BRANCH—Marubeni Corporation; *Int'l*, pg. 845
MASTER BUILDERS MATERIALS LTD.—Viag AG; *Int'l*, pg. 1465
MAYS CHEMICAL COMPANY; *U.S. Private*, pg. 718
MERCK & CO., INC.; *U.S. Public*, pg. 1090
MERCK SHARP & DOHME-CHIBRET A.G.—Merck & Co., Inc.; *U.S. Public*, pg. 1092
MICROSI—Shin-Etsu Chemical Co. ltd.; *Int'l*, pg. 1234
MILCHEM DRILLING FLUIDS LTD.—Baker Hughes Incorporated; *U.S. Public*, pg. 167
MILCHEM FRANCE S.A.R.L.—Baker Hughes Incorporated; *U.S. Public*, pg. 167
MILCHEM GABON S.A.R.L.—Baker Hughes Incorporated; *U.S. Public*, pg. 167
P.T. MILCHEM INDONESIA—Baker Hughes Incorporated; *U.S. Public*, pg. 167
MILCHEM INTERNATIONAL LIMITED—Baker Hughes Incorporated; *U.S. Public*, pg. 167
MILCHEM VENEZUELA CORPORATION—Baker Hughes Incorporated; *U.S. Public*, pg. 167
MILCHEM WESTERN HEMISPHERE INC.—Baker Hughes Incorporated; *U.S. Public*, pg. 167
MINES ASSAY DIVISION—Acklands Limited; *Int'l*, pg. 23
MINNESOTA NIGERIA LIMITED—3M; *U.S. Public*, pg. 1606
MITSIAM INTERNATIONAL, LTD.—Mitsui & Co., Ltd.; *Int'l*, pg. 880
MITSUBISHI CHEMICAL AMERICA, INC.—Mitsubishi Chemical Corporation; *Int'l*, pg. 871
MITSUBISHI CHEMICAL (U.K.) PLC.—Mitsubishi Chemical Corporation; *Int'l*, pg. 871
MITSUBISHI CORPORATION; *Int'l*, pg. 871
MITSUBISHI INTERNATIONAL CORPORATION—Mitsubishi Corporation; *Int'l*, pg. 871
MITSUBISHI MONSANTO CHEMICAL CO.—Monsanto Company; *U.S. Public*, pg. 1125
MITSUBISHI RAYON AMERICA, INC.—Mitsubishi Rayon Co., Ltd.; *Int'l*, pg. 876
MITSUI & CO., LTD.; *Int'l*, pg. 877
MITSUI BRASILEIRA IMP. E EXP. LTDA.—Mitsui & Co., Ltd.; *Int'l*, pg. 882
MITSUI CHILENA COMMERCIAL LTDA.—Mitsui & Co., Ltd.; *Int'l*, pg. 882
MITSUI DE COLOMBIA S.A.—Mitsui & Co., Ltd.; *Int'l*, pg. 882
MITSUI DE MEXICO, S.A. DE C.V.—Mitsui & Co., Ltd., *Int'l*, pg. 882
MITSUI DE VENEZUELA C.A.—Mitsui & Co., Ltd.; *Int'l*, pg. 882
MITSUI DEL ECUADOR S.A.—Mitsui & Co., Ltd.; *Int'l*, pg. 882
MITSUI DEL PERU S.A.—Mitsui & Co., Ltd.; *Int'l*, pg. 882
MOBIL KABUSHIKI KAISHA—Mobil Oil Corporation; *U.S. Public*, pg. 1119
MOBIL OIL AUSTRIA A.G.—Mobil Oil Corporation; *U.S. Public*, pg. 1119
MOBIL OIL CORPORATION; *U.S. Public*, pg. 1118
MOBIL PHILIPPINES, INC.—Mobil Oil Corporation; *U.S. Public*, pg. 1119
MONSANTO B.V.—Monsanto Company; *U.S. Public*, pg. 1125
MONSANTO CANADA, INC.—Monsanto Company; *U.S. Public*, pg. 1125
MONSANTO DE COSTA RICA, S.A.—Monsanto Company; *U.S. Public*, pg. 1125
MONSANTO DO BRASIL LTDA. (MOBRA S.A.)—Monsanto Company; *U.S. Public*, pg. 1125
MONSANTO ESPANA S.A.—Monsanto Company; *U.S. Public*, pg. 1125
MONSANTO EXPORT LIMITED—Monsanto Company; *U.S. Public*, pg. 1125
MONSANTO FAR EAST LTD.—Monsanto Company; *U.S. Public*, pg. 1125
MONSANTO ITALIANA S.P.A.—Monsanto Company; *U.S. Public*, pg. 1125
MONSANTO JAPAN LTD.—Monsanto Company; *U.S. Public*, pg. 1126
MONSANTO P.L.C.—Monsanto Company; *U.S. Public*, pg. 1126
MONSANTO SINGAPORE COMPANY (PTE.) LTD.—Monsanto Company; *U.S. Public*, pg. 1126
MONSANTO SOUTH AFRICA (PTY.) LIMITED—Monsanto Company; *U.S. Public*, pg. 1126
MONSANTO (SUISSE) S.A.—Monsanto Company; *U.S. Public*, pg. 1126
MONSANTO THAILAND LTD.—Monsanto Company; *U.S. Public*, pg. 1126
MONSANTO (VENEZUELA) C.A.—Monsanto Company; *U.S. Public*, pg. 1126
MORTON INTERNATIONAL INC.; *U.S. Public*, pg. 1134
NCH CORPORATION; *U.S. Public*, pg. 1145
NCH CORPORATION KOREA—NCH Corporation; *U.S. Public*, pg. 1145
NCT HOLLAND B.V.—Neste Oy; *Int'l*, pg. 914
NCT HONG KONG LTD.—Neste Oy; *Int'l*, pg. 914
NCT NORDEN AB—Neste Oy; *Int'l*, pg. 915
NCT U.S.A. INC.—Neste Oy; *Int'l*, pg. 913
SOPHIE NERVAL S.A.—Henkel KGaA; *Int'l*, pg. 612
NESTE CHEMICALS (JAPAN) CO., LTD.—Neste Oy; *Int'l*, pg. 914
NESTE CHEMICALS SOUTH EAST ASIA LTD.—Neste Oy; *Int'l*, pg. 914
NESTE CHEMICALS UK LTD.—Neste Oy; *Int'l*, pg. 914
NESTE KEMI FORSALJNINGS AB—Neste Oy; *Int'l*, pg. 915
NESTE KJEMI A/S—Neste Oy; *Int'l*, pg. 915
NESTE OY, CHEMICALS—Neste Oy; *Int'l*, pg. 913
NESTE SVERIGE AB—Neste Oy; *Int'l*, pg. 915
NEW BRUNSWICK SCIENTIFIC CO., INC.—New Brunswick Scientific Co., Inc.; *U.S. Public*, pg. 1170
NEW YORK REPRESENTATIVE OFFICE (ESNOR)—Petrobras - Petroleo Brasileiro S.A.; *Int'l*, pg. 1042
NEXAIR—nexAir, LLC; *U.S. Private*, pg. 797
NEXAIR, LLC; *U.S. Private*, pg. 797
NEYNABER CHEMIE GMBH—Henkel KGaA; *Int'l*, pg. 610
NICHIMEN AMERICA, INC.—Nichimen Corporation; *Int'l*, pg. 927
NICHIMEN CORPORATION; *Int'l*, pg. 927
NIGU CHEMIE-BETEILIGUNGS GMBH—Viag AG; *Int'l*, pg. 1465
NIPPLA KASEI CO., LTD.—Nissho Iwai Corporation; *Int'l*, pg. 946
NISSHO IWAI CORPORATION; *Int'l*, pg. 946
NISSHO IWAI POLYMERS & PRODUCTS CORP.—Nissho Iwai Corporation; *Int'l*, pg. 947
NISSO MASTER BUILDERS CO. LTD.—Viag AG; *Int'l*, pg. 1466
NOPCO COLOMBIANA S.A.—Henkel KGaA; *Int'l*, pg. 614
NOPCO INDUSTRIAL S.A. DE C.V.—Henkel KGaA; *Int'l*, pg. 614
NOPCO ITALIANA SPA—Henkel KGaA; *Int'l*, pg. 612
NOPCO TRADING CORP.—Henkel KGaA; *Int'l*, pg. 613
NORDISK BYGGE KEMI A/S—Viag AG; *Int'l*, pg. 1466
NORIT N.V.; *Int'l*, pg. 958
NORSK HYDRO USA INC.—Norsk Hydro a.s; *Int'l*, pg. 961
NORTH AMERICAN SALT COMPANY—Harris Chemical Group, Inc.; *U.S. Private*, pg. 505
NOVO NORDISK A/S; *Int'l*, pg. 987
NOVO NORDISK BIOINDUSTRIALS, INC.—Novo Nordisk A/S; *Int'l*, pg. 987
OCG MICROELECTRONIC MATERIALS GMBH—Olin Corporation; *U.S. Public*, pg. 1219
OCG MICROELECTRONIC MATERIALS N.V.—Olin Corporation; *U.S. Public*, pg. 1220
OCG MICROELECTRONIC MATERIALS S.R.L.—Olin Corporation; *U.S. Public*, pg. 1220
OSCA—Great Lakes Chemical Corporation; *U.S. Public*, pg. 760
OAKITE PRODUCTS, INC.—Metallgesellschaft AG; *Int'l*, pg. 861
OIL-DRI S.A.—Oil-Dri Corporation of America; *U.S. Public*, pg. 1215
OLIN AUSTRALIA LIMITED—Olin Corporation; *U.S. Public*, pg. 1220
N.V. OLIN EUROPE S.A.—Olin Corporation; *U.S. Public*, pg. 1220
OLIN EXPORT TRADING CORPORATION—Olin Corporation; *U.S. Public*, pg. 1219
OLIN FAR EAST, LIMITED—Olin Corporation; *U.S. Public*, pg. 1219
OLIN GMBH—Olin Corporation; *U.S. Public*, pg. 1220
N.V. OLIN HUNT SPECIALTY PRODUCTS—Olin Corporation; *U.S. Public*, pg. 1220
OLIN HUNT SPECIALTY PRODUCTS S.R.L.—Olin Corporation; *U.S. Public*, pg. 1220
OLIN HUNT SUB. I CORP.—Olin Corporation; *U.S. Public*, pg. 1219
N.V. OLIN HUNT TRADING—Olin Corporation; *U.S. Public*, pg. 1220
OLIN INDUSTRIAL (HONG KONG) LIMITED—Olin Corporation; *U.S. Public*, pg. 1220
OLIN JAPAN, INC.—Olin Corporation; *U.S. Public*, pg. 1220
OLIN (PROPRIETARY) LIMITED—Olin Corporation; *U.S. Public*, pg. 1220
OLIN PTE., LTD., SINGAPORE—Olin Corporation; *U.S. Public*, pg. 1220
OLIN QUIMICA, S.A.—Olin Corporation; *U.S. Public*, pg. 1220
OLIN QUIMICA, S.A. DE C.V.—Olin Corporation; *U.S. Public*, pg. 1220
OLIN S.A.—Olin Corporation; *U.S. Public*, pg. 1220
OLIN UK LTD.—Olin Corporation; *U.S. Public*, pg. 1220
THE ORE & CHEMICAL CORP.—Metallgesellschaft AG; *Int'l*, pg. 862
ORR SAFETY COMPANY; *U.S. Private*, pg. 820
OXARC INC.; *U.S. Private*, pg. 825
PCI AUGSBURG GMBH—Viag AG; *Int'l*, pg. 1464
PD TERMINALS (PTY) LIMITED—Powell Duffryn PLC; *Int'l*, pg. 1065
PRS, INC.—CPAC, Inc.; *U.S. Public*, pg. 282
PVS CHEMICALS, INC.; *U.S. Private*, pg. 828
PVS-NOLWOOD CHEMICALS, INC.—PVS Chemicals, Inc.; *U.S. Private*, pg. 828
PAKISTAN BURMAH SHELL—Royal Dutch/Shell Group of Companies; *Int'l*, pg. 1140
PAN-ALBERTA GAS LTD.—Nova Corporation; *Int'l*, pg. 971
PARKER AMCHEM S.A. DE C.V.—Henkel KGaA; *Int'l*, pg. 614
PETROMALI-SHELL—Royal Dutch/Shell Group of Companies; *Int'l*, pg. 1136
PFIZER PRODUCTS PLC—Pfizer Inc.; *U.S. Public*, pg. 1282
PHARMA-WALDHOF GMBH—Corange Limited; *Int'l*, pg. 331
PHILLIPS PETROLEUM COMPANY; *U.S. Public*, pg. 1290
PLASTROM S.A.—Henkel KGaA; *Int'l*, pg. 612
POLYPURE RHONE-POULENC—Rhone-Poulenc S.A.; *Int'l*, pg. 1110
POREX CORP.—Synetic, Inc.; *U.S. Public*, pg. 1548
PRAEMIX WIRKSTOFF GMBH—Corange Limited; *Int'l*, pg. 331
PREMIER CHEMICAL CO., LTD.—Crompton & Knowles Corporation; *U.S. Public*, pg. 460
PREMIER INDUSTRIAL FRANCE S.A.R.L.—Premier Farnell plc; *Int'l*, pg. 1068
PROCTER & GAMBLE AUSTRIA GMBH—The Procter & Gamble Company; *U.S. Public*, pg. 1332
PROCTER & GAMBLE (SINGAPORE) PTE. LTD.—The Procter & Gamble Company; *U.S. Public*, pg. 1332
PRONOVA POLYMER LTD.—Norsk Hydro a.s; *Int'l*, pg. 961
QUAKER CHEMICAL CORPORATION; *U.S. Public*, pg. 1346
QUIMICA HARTING S.A.—Henkel KGaA; *Int'l*, pg. 614
QUIMICA HENKEL CENTROAMERICANA DE COSTA RICA S.A.—Henkel KGaA; *Int'l*, pg. 613
QUIMICA HENKEL CENTROAMERICANA DE EL SALVADOR S.A.—Henkel KGaA; *Int'l*, pg. 613
QUIMICA HENKEL CENTROAMERICANA DE HONDURAS S.A. DE C.V.—Henkel KGaA; *Int'l*, pg. 613
QUIMICA HENKEL CENTROAMERICANA S.A.—Henkel KGaA; *Int'l*, pg. 613
QUIMICA HENKEL S.A. DE C.V.—Henkel KGaA; *Int'l*, pg. 613
QUIMICA PARKER S.A. DE C.V.—Henkel KGaA; *Int'l*, pg. 614
QUIMICA S.A. DE C.V.—Henkel KGaA; *Int'l*, pg. 614
RAISIO, INC.—Raisio Group; *Int'l*, pg. 1086
RASCHIG CORP.—PMC, Inc.; *U.S. Private*, pg. 827
RECORDATI CORPORATION—Recordati Industria Chimica e Farmaceutica S.p.A.; *Int'l*, pg. 1090
REMTOX (CHEMICALS) LIMITED—Laporte plc; *Int'l*, pg. 802
REPSOL BUTANO S.A.—Repsol S.A.; *Int'l*, pg. 1104
REPSOL DERIVADOS—Repsol S.A.; *Int'l*, pg. 1104
REPSOL S.A.; *Int'l*, pg. 1104
REPUBLIC CHEMICAL COMPANY—Harwick Standard Distribution Corporation; *U.S. Private*, pg. 509
RHENANIA TRADING CORP.—Henkel KGaA; *Int'l*, pg. 613
RHODIACO INDUSTRIES QUIMICAS LTDA.—Amoco Corporation; *U.S. Public*, pg. 103
RHONE-POULENC CANADA, LTD.—Rhone-Poulenc S.A.; *Int'l*, pg. 1112
RIKA-HERCULES INC.—Hercules Incorporated; *U.S. Public*, pg. 811
RISING SUN—Royal Dutch/Shell Group of Companies; *Int'l*, pg. 1139
E.V. ROBERTS & ASSOCIATES, INC.; *U.S. Private*, pg. 935
ROHM & HAAS (UK) LTD.—Rohm and Haas Company; *U.S. Public*, pg. 1404
RUBSON IBERICA S.A.—Henkel KGaA; *Int'l*, pg. 612
RUBSON S.A.F.—Henkel KGaA; *Int'l*, pg. 614
SCM SPECIALTY CHEMICALS INC.—Hanson PLC; *Int'l*, pg. 594
SKW BAUWERKSTOFFE PIESTERITZ GMBH—Viag AG; *Int'l*, pg. 1465
SKW CHEMICALS CANADA INC.—Viag AG; *Int'l*, pg. 1466
SKW CHEMICALS INC.—Viag AG; *Int'l*, pg. 1465
SKW CHEMICALS UK LTD.—Viag AG; *Int'l*, pg. 1466
SKW CHEMIE - TECHNIK GMBH—Viag AG; *Int'l*, pg. 1465
SKW EAST ASIA LTD.—Viag AG; *Int'l*, pg. 1466
SKW ITALIA S.R.L.—Viag AG; *Int'l*, pg. 1466
SKW METALS & ALLOYS, INC.—Viag AG; *Int'l*, pg. 1465
SKW TROSTBERG AKTIENGESELLSCHAFT—Viag AG; *Int'l*, pg. 1464
SOCO CHEMICAL, INC.—Veba AG; *Int'l*, pg. 1458
SOCO-LYNCH CORP.—Veba AG; *Int'l*, pg. 1458
SAFETY-KLEEN CORP.; *U.S. Public*, pg. 1425
SALVIA—Nestle S.A.; *Int'l*, pg. 922
SAMSUNG PETROCHEMICAL CO. LTD.—Amoco Corporation; *U.S. Public*, pg. 102
SANDOZ AB—Novartis AG; *Int'l*, pg. 984
SANDOZ CHEMICALS PTE. LTD. SINGAPORE—Novartis AG; *Int'l*, pg. 984
SANDOZ HUNINGUE S.A.—Novartis AG; *Int'l*, pg. 984
SANDOZ INDUSTRIAL CHEMICALS LTD.—Novartis AG; *Int'l*, pg. 984
SANDOZ K.K.—Novartis AG; *Int'l*, pg. 984
SANDOZ-SODYECO LTD.—Novartis AG; *Int'l*, pg. 985
SANDOZ URUNLERI LTD.—Novartis AG; *Int'l*, pg. 985
SANITARIA MEXICANA S.A. DE C.V.—Henkel KGaA; *Int'l*, pg. 614
SCHELDE CHEMIE BRUNSBUTTEL GMBH—Bayer AG; *Int'l*, pg. 172

SCHWERMETALL HALBZEUGWERK GMBH & CO. KG—Olin Corporation; *U.S. Public*, pg. 1220
SEAL SANDS STORAGE LTD.—Simon Engineering plc; *Int'l*, pg. 1251
SENTRY POLYMERS, INC.—RPM, Inc.; *U.S. Public*, pg. 1357
OY SHELL AB—Royal Dutch/Shell Group of Companies; *Int'l*, pg. 1138
SHELL ANTILLES & GUIANAS LTD.—Royal Dutch/Shell Group of Companies; *Int'l*, pg. 1141
SHELL AUSTRIA AG—Royal Dutch/Shell Group of Companies; *Int'l*, pg. 1138
SHELL AVIATION GUINEA—Royal Dutch/Shell Group of Companies; *Int'l*, pg. 1136
SHELL BAHAMAS LTD.—Royal Dutch/Shell Group of Companies; *Int'l*, pg. 1141
SHELL BELIZE—Royal Dutch/Shell Group of Companies; *Int'l*, pg. 1141
SHELL BERMUDA—Royal Dutch/Shell Group of Companies; *Int'l*, pg. 1141
SHELL BRASIL SA (PETROLEO)—Royal Dutch/Shell Group of Companies; *Int'l*, pg. 1141
SHELL CHILE SA COMERCIAL E INDUSTRIAL—Royal Dutch/Shell Group of Companies; *Int'l*, pg. 1142
SHELL COLOMBIA SA—Royal Dutch/Shell Group of Companies; *Int'l*, pg. 1142
SHELL COMPANY (HELLAS) LTD.—Royal Dutch/Shell Group of Companies; *Int'l*, pg. 1138
SHELL CO. OF GIBRALTAR LTD.—Royal Dutch/Shell Group of Companies; *Int'l*, pg. 1138
SHELL COMPANY OF HONG KONG LTD.—Royal Dutch/Shell Group of Companies; *Int'l*, pg. 1139
SHELL COMPANY OF THAILAND LTD—Royal Dutch/Shell Group of Companies; *Int'l*, pg. 1140
SHELL COMPANY OF THE SUDAN LTD.—Royal Dutch/Shell Group of Companies; *Int'l*, pg. 1136
SHELL CYPRUS TRADING COMPANY LTD—Royal Dutch/Shell Group of Companies; *Int'l*, pg. 1140
SHELL DEVELOPMENTS (HK)—Royal Dutch/Shell Group of Companies; *Int'l*, pg. 1139
SHELL DISTRIBUTION CO., INC.—Royal Dutch/Shell Group of Companies; *Int'l*, pg. 1140
SHELL DJIBOUTI—Royal Dutch/Shell Group of Companies; *Int'l*, pg. 1137
SHELL EASTERN PETROLEUM (PTE) LTD.—Royal Dutch/Shell Group of Companies; *Int'l*, pg. 1140
SHELL ETHIOPIA LTD.—Royal Dutch/Shell Group of Companies; *Int'l*, pg. 1137
SHELL FIJI—Royal Dutch/Shell Group of Companies; *Int'l*, pg. 1137
SHELL GABON—Royal Dutch/Shell Group of Companies; *Int'l*, pg. 1137
SHELL GHANA SERVICES LTD.—Royal Dutch/Shell Group of Companies; *Int'l*, pg. 1137
SHELL HONDURAS SA—Royal Dutch/Shell Group of Companies; *Int'l*, pg. 1141
SHELL ITALIA SPA—Royal Dutch/Shell Group of Companies; *Int'l*, pg. 1138
SHELL JAPAN LTD.—Royal Dutch/Shell Group of Companies; *Int'l*, pg. 1139
SHELL KAGAKU K.K.—Royal Dutch/Shell Group of Companies; *Int'l*, pg. 1139
SHELL LUXEMBOURGEOISE SA—Royal Dutch/Shell Group of Companies; *Int'l*, pg. 1138
SHELL MALAYSIA TRADING—Royal Dutch/Shell Group of Companies; *Int'l*, pg. 1140
SHELL MARKETING BORNEO—Royal Dutch/Shell Group of Companies; *Int'l*, pg. 1140
SHELL MARKETS (MIDDLE EAST) LTD.—Royal Dutch/Shell Group of Companies; *Int'l*, pg. 1141
SHELL NEDERLANDSE ANTILLEN—Royal Dutch/Shell Group of Companies; *Int'l*, pg. 1141
SHELL NICARAGUA S.A.—Royal Dutch/Shell Group of Companies; *Int'l*, pg. 1141
SHELL NIGER—Royal Dutch/Shell Group of Companies; *Int'l*, pg. 1137
SHELL OIL BOTSWANA—Royal Dutch/Shell Group of Companies; *Int'l*, pg. 1136
SHELL PACIFIC ENTERPRISES LTD—Royal Dutch/Shell Group of Companies; *Int'l*, pg. 1140
SHELL (PACIFIC ISLANDS)—Royal Dutch/Shell Group of Companies; *Int'l*, pg. 1137
SHELL PAPUA NEW GUINEA PTY. LTD.—Royal Dutch/Shell Group of Companies; *Int'l*, pg. 1137
SHELL PARAGUAY LTD.—Royal Dutch/Shell Group of Companies; *Int'l*, pg. 1142
SHELL PORTUGUESA SA—Royal Dutch/Shell Group of Companies; *Int'l*, pg. 1139
SHELL (PUERTO RICO)—Royal Dutch/Shell Group of Companies; *Int'l*, pg. 1136
SHELL SEKIYU—Royal Dutch/Shell Group of Companies; *Int'l*, pg. 1140
SHELL SIERRA LEONE LTD.—Royal Dutch/Shell Group of Companies; *Int'l*, pg. 1137
SHELL TCHAD—Royal Dutch/Shell Group of Companies; *Int'l*, pg. 1137
SHELL TRADING (MIDDLE EAST)—Royal Dutch/Shell Group of Companies; *Int'l*, pg. 1141
SHELL UGANDA LTD.—Royal Dutch/Shell Group of Companies; *Int'l*, pg. 1137
SHELL URUGUAY LTD—Royal Dutch/Shell Group of Companies; *Int'l*, pg. 1142
SHIMA TRADING CO. LTD.; *Int'l*, pg. 1231
SHOWA DENKO AMERICA, INC.—Showa Denko K.K.; *Int'l*, *pg. 1237*
J.E. SIEBEL & SONS COMPANY INC.—Rhone-Poulenc S.A.; *Int'l*, pg. 1110
SIEGERT & CIE GMBH—Henkel KGaA; *Int'l*, pg. 610
SIMON ENGINEERING PLC; *Int'l*, pg. 1251
SINGAPORE OXYGEN AIR LIQUIDE PTE LTD.—The BOC Group plc; *Int'l*, pg. 122
SOCAMIC STE. DE CAOUTCHOUC ET DE PRODUITS CHIMIQUES S.A.R.L.—Saarbergwerke Aktiengesellschaft; *Int'l*, pg. 1167
SOCIEDADE PORTUGUESA DE DESENVOLVIMENTO-QUIMICO DE MONSANTO, LIMITADA—Monsanto Company; *U.S. Public*, pg. 1126
SOCIETE SHELL DE TUNISIE—Royal Dutch/Shell Group of Companies; *Int'l*, pg. 1137
SOCIETE SHELL DES ANTILLES ET DE LA GUYANE FRANCAISES—Royal Dutch/Shell Group of Companies; *Int'l*, pg. 1141
SOCIETE SHELL DU LAOS—Royal Dutch/Shell Group of Companies; *Int'l*, pg. 1140
SOCIETE SHELL DU MAROC—Royal Dutch/Shell Group of Companies; *Int'l*, pg. 1137
SOREMAP HENKEL GV S.A.—Henkel KGaA; *Int'l*, pg. 614
STAHL FRANCE S.A.R.L.—Zeneca Group Plc; *Int'l*, pg. 1526
H.C. STARCK INC.—Bayer AG; *Int'l*, pg. 174
HERMANN C. STARCK, INC.—Bayer AG; *Int'l*, pg. 175
STINNES CORPORATION—Veba AG; *Int'l*, pg. 1460
STORA BILLERUD PAPER S.A.—Stora Kopparbergs Bergslags AB; *Int'l*, pg. 1302
SUMITOMO BAYER URETHANE CO., LTD.—Bayer AG; *Int'l*, pg. 174
SUMITOMO CANADA LTD.—Sumitomo Corporation; *Int'l*, pg. 1312
SUMITOMO CHEMICAL AMERICA, INC.—Sumitomo Chemical Company, Ltd.; *Int'l*, pg. 1311
SUMITOMO CHEMICAL (U.K.) PLC—Sumitomo Chemical Company, Ltd.; *Int'l*, pg. 1312
SUMITOMO CORPORATION; *Int'l*, pg. 1312
SUMITOMO CORPORATION OF AMERICA—Sumitomo Corporation; *Int'l*, pg. 1312
SUMITOMO SEIKA CHEMICALS CO., LTD.—Sumitomo Chemical Company, Ltd.; *Int'l*, pg. 1311
SUMITOMO 3M LIMITED—3M; *U.S. Public*, pg. 1606
SUMMIT SPECIALTY CHEMICALS CORPORATION—Sumitomo Corporation; *Int'l*, pg. 1312
SUNKYONG AMERICA, INC.—Sunkyong Industries Co.; *Int'l*, pg. 1320
OY SUOMEN ALLIED COLLOIDS—Allied Colloids Group Plc.; *Int'l*, pg. 62
OY SUOMEN HENKEL AB—Henkel KGaA; *Int'l*, pg. 614
SUPERIOR OIL CO. INC.; *U.S. Private*, pg. 1055
TAIWAN MARKETING & TRANSPORTATION DIV.—Chinese Petroleum Corporation; *Int'l*, pg. 286
TAKEDA USA INC.—Takeda Chemical Industries, Ltd.; *Int'l*, *pg. 1350*
TAUBER OIL COMPANY; *U.S. Private*, pg. 1069
TEXACO INC.; *U.S. Public*, pg. 1582
TEXAS EASTMAN CO.—Eastman Chemical Company; *U.S. Public*, pg. 550
TEXAS PETRO CHEMICALS; *U.S. Private*, pg. 1078
THAI INDUSTRIAL GASSES PUBLIC CO. LTD.—The BOC Group plc; *Int'l*, pg. 122
THAI MASTER BUILDERS CO. LTD.—Novartis AG; *Int'l*, pg. 986
THOMPSON GMBH—Henkel KGaA; *Int'l*, pg. 610
3M A/S—3M; *U.S. Public*, pg. 1606
P.T. 3M INDONESIA—3M; *U.S. Public*, pg. 1606
3M ZIMBABWE (PVT.) LTD.—3M; *U.S. Public*, pg. 1607
TIDY CAR INTERNATIONAL, INC.—Ziebart International Corporation; *U.S. Private*, pg. 1205
TOGO ET SHELL—Royal Dutch/Shell Group of Companies; *Int'l*, pg. 1137
TOKUYAMA EUROPE GMBH—Tokuyama Corporation; *Int'l*, *pg. 1394*
TOSOH USA, INC.—Tosoh Corporation; *Int'l*, pg. 1408
TOSOH USA, INC.-SAN FRANCISCO OFFICE—Tosoh Corporation; *Int'l*, pg. 1407
TRAYLOR CHEMICAL & SUPPLY CO.; *U.S. Private*, pg. 1098
TROPONWERKE GMBH & CO., KG—Bayer AG; *Int'l*, pg. 175
TURYAG TURKLYE YAG VE MAMULATI A.S.—Henkel KGaA; *Int'l*, pg. 614
UBE INDUSTRIES (AMERICA) INC.—UBE Industries Ltd.; *Int'l*, pg. 1427
UCAR POLIMEROS Y QUIMICOS C.A.—Union Carbide Corporation; *U.S. Public*, pg. 1667
GEORGE UHE CO., INC.; *U.S. Private*, pg. 1115
UNION CARBIDE ARGENTINA S.A.I.C.S.—Union Carbide Corporation; *U.S. Public*, pg. 1667
UNION CARBIDE COMERCIAL C.A.—Union Carbide Corporation; *U.S. Public*, pg. 1667
UNIROYAL CHEMICAL COMPANY, INC. (SINGAPORE)—Crompton & Knowles Corporation; *U.S. Public*, pg. 460
UNISOURCE (S.E. REGIONAL OFFICE)—Unisource Worldwide, Inc.; *U.S. Public*, pg. 1671
UNITED CHEMICAL PRODUCTS—Mays Chemical Company; *U.S. Private*, pg. 718
UNITED LABORATORIES, INC.; *U.S. Private*, pg. 1122
UNITED MCGILL CORP.; *U.S. Private*, pg. 1122
UNIVAR EUROPE N.V.—Royal Pakhoed NV; *Int'l*, pg. 1147
UNIVERSAL FOODS CORPORATION; *U.S. Public*, pg. 1695
UTILISATION RATIONNELLE DES GAZ—Royal Dutch/Shell Group of Companies; *Int'l*, pg. 1138
VGF CORPORATION—Aceto Corporation; *U.S. Public*, pg. 15
VAN NEERBOS-PCI B.V.—Viag AG; *Int'l*, pg. 1466
VAN WATERS & ROGERS—Royal Pakhoed NV; *Int'l*, pg. 1147
VAN WATERS & ROGERS INC.—Royal Pakhoed NV; *Int'l*, pg. 1147
VAN WATERS & ROGERS LTD.—Royal Pakhoed NV; *Int'l*, *pg. 1147*
R.T. VANDERBILT COMPANY, INC.; *U.S. Private*, pg. 1133
VEBA AG; *Int'l*, pg. 1454
VELVA LIQUIDS LTD.—Simon Engineering plc; *Int'l*, pg. 1251
VENTRON DIV.—Morton International Inc.; *U.S. Public*, pg. 1135
WALTER INDUSTRIES, INC.; *U.S. Public*, pg. 1736
WARREN DISTRIBUTION, INC.; *U.S. Private*, pg. 1151
THE WEST COMPANY AUSTRALIA PTY. LTD.—The West Company, Incorporated; *U.S. Public*, pg. 1755
WEST PENETONE CORPORATION—Wechco, Inc.; *U.S. Private*, pg. 1158
WHITTAKER, CLARK & DANIELS, INC.; *U.S. Private*, pg. 1174
WILBUR-ELLIS COMPANY & CONNELL BROTHERS COMPANY; *U.S. Private*, pg. 1175
WITCO CORPORATION; *U.S. Public*, pg. 1773
YAPKIM YAPI KIMYA SANAYI A.S.—Viag AG; *Int'l*, pg. 1466
ZAIRE SHELL—Royal Dutch/Shell Group of Companies; *Int'l*, pg. 1137
ZENECA AB—Zeneca Group Plc; *Int'l*, pg. 1526
ZENECA HELLAS S.A.—Zeneca Group Plc; *Int'l*, pg. 1526
ZENECA OY—Zeneca Group Plc; *Int'l*, pg. 1527
ZENECA ZIMBABWE (PRIVATE) LIMITED—Zeneca Group Plc; *Int'l*, pg. 1527

5171 — PETROLEUM BULK STATIONS & TERMINALS-WHOLESALE

AMOCO OIL COMPANY—Amoco Corporation; *U.S. Public*, pg. 102
ARABIAN OIL COMPANY, LTD. (KUWAIT)—Arabian Oil Company, Ltd.; *Int'l*, pg. 78
ARABIAN OIL COMPANY, LTD. (NEW YORK)—Arabian Oil Company, Ltd.; *Int'l*, pg. 78
ARCO PRODUCTS CO.—Atlantic Richfield Company; *U.S. Public*, pg. 144
TRUMAN ARNOLD COMPANIES; *U.S. Private*, pg. 84
ATLANTIC RICHFIELD COMPANY; *U.S. Public*, pg. 144
BHP SOUTH PACIFIC, INC.—The Broken Hill Proprietary Company Limited; *Int'l*, pg. 225
BP INTERNATIONAL LTD.—The British Petroleum Company P.L.C.; *Int'l*, pg. 220
BALE OF KENTUCKY, INC.; *U.S. Private*, pg. 112
BAYSIDE FUEL OIL DEPOT CORP.; *U.S. Private*, pg. 125
BELL GAS, INC.; *U.S. Private*, pg. 131
BESCHE OIL COMPANY, INC.; *U.S. Private*, pg. 139
BIG HORN CO-OP MARKETING ASSOCIATION; *U.S. Private*, pg. 143
THE BRITISH PETROLEUM COMPANY P.L.C.; *Int'l*, pg. 219
BURMAH CASTROL TRADING, LTD.—Burmah Castrol plc; *Int'l*, pg. 234
CIECO (AMERICA), INC.—Itochu Corporation; *Int'l*, pg. 694
CAMPBELL OIL CO.; *U.S. Private*, pg. 204
THE COASTAL CORPORATION; *U.S. Public*, pg. 389
COASTAL OIL NEW ENGLAND, INC.—The Coastal Corporation; *U.S. Public*, pg. 390
COLAS EAST AFRICA—Royal Dutch/Shell Group of Companies; *Int'l*, pg. 1136
COLONIAL TERMINALS, INC.—Colonial Oil Industries; *U.S. Private*, pg. 254
CONDON OIL COMPANY, INC.; *U.S. Private*, pg. 262
COSBEL PETROLEUM CORP.—The Coastal Corporation; *U.S. Public*, pg. 390
DIXIE OIL COMPANY; *U.S. Private*, pg. 337
DU PONT (E.I. DU PONT DE NEMOURS & CO.); *U.S. Public*, pg. 530
ENGLEFIELD, INC.; *U.S. Private*, pg. 377
ENRON CORP.; *U.S. Public*, pg. 584
ERGON, INC.; *U.S. Private*, pg. 380
EXCEL CO-OP INC.; *U.S. Private*, pg. 387
FIRST MOUNT JOY CORPORATION; *U.S. Private*, pg. 407
GAL CORP.—Silcorp Limited; *Int'l*, pg. 1249
GETTY PETROLEUM MARKETING INC.; *U.S. Public*, pg. 740
GETTY TERMINALS, INC.—Getty Petroleum Marketing Inc.; *U.S. Public*, pg. 741
JACK GRIGGS INC.; *U.S. Private*, pg. 482
HCI CHEMTECH; *U.S. Private*, pg. 490
HARTFORD-WOOD RIVER TERMINAL—Piasa Motor Fuels Inc.; *U.S. Private*, pg. 864
HICKS OIL-HICKS GAS, INC.; *U.S. Private*, pg. 526
HIGH POINT OIL CO.; *U.S. Private*, pg. 528
ITT BARTON INSTRUMENTS—ITT Industries, Inc.; *U.S. Public*, pg. 860
ITOCHU INTERNATIONAL INC.—Itochu Corporation; *Int'l*, pg. 694
KOCH INDUSTRIES, INCORPORATED; *U.S. Private*, pg. 628
LA SALLE COUNTY FARM SUPPLY; *U.S. Private*, pg. 640
LEEMILTS PETROLEUM, INC.—Getty Petroleum Marketing Inc.; *U.S. Public*, pg. 741
CARLOS R. LEFFLER INC.; *U.S. Private*, pg. 658
LYON COUNTY CO-OP OIL CO.; *U.S. Private*, pg. 684
MAINE POTATO GROWERS, INC.; *U.S. Private*, pg. 697
MANSFIELD OIL COMPANY; *U.S. Private*, pg. 700
MAPCO NATURAL GAS LIQUIDS INC.—Mapco Inc.; *U.S. Public*, pg. 1042
MAPCO PETROLEUM INC.—Mapco Inc.; *U.S. Public*, pg. 1042
MARATHON ASHLAND PETROLEUM LLC—Ashland, Inc.; *U.S. Public*, pg. 139
MARATHON ASHLAND PETROLEUM LLC—USX Corporation; *U.S. Public*, pg. 1662
MARATHON ASHLAND PETROLEUM LLC RETAIN MARKETING—USX Corporation; *U.S. Public*, pg. 1662
MARUBENI CORPORATION; *Int'l*, pg. 844
MCCALL OIL & CHEMICAL CORP.; *U.S. Private*, pg. 719
MOBIL AMI, S.A.—Mobil Oil Corporation; *U.S. Public*, pg. 1119
MOBIL OIL CORPORATION; *U.S. Public*, pg. 1118
MURCO PETROLEUM LTD.—Murphy Oil Corporation; *U.S. Public*, pg. 1142
MURPHY OIL CORPORATION; *U.S. Public*, pg. 1141
MURPHY OIL USA, INC.—Murphy Oil Corporation; *U.S. Public*, pg. 1142
NORCEN ENERGY RESOURCES LIMITED—EdperBrascan Corporation; *Int'l*, pg. 434

A/S NORSKE SHELL—Royal Dutch/Shell Group of Companies; *Int'l*, pg. 1139
OLIVER OIL COMPANY, INC.; *U.S. Private*, pg. 815
PM PROPERTIES INC.—Petroleum Marketers, Inc.; *U.S. Private*, pg. 859
PACIFIC NORTHERN INC.; *U.S. Private*, pg. 832
PAKHOED USA INC.—Royal Pakhoed NV; *Int'l*, pg. 1147
PAKTANK INTERNATIONAL B.V.—Royal Pakhoed NV; *Int'l*, pg. 1147
THE PARMAN CORPORATION; *U.S. Private*, pg. 840
P.T. PETRO CORP.—Getty Petroleum Marketing Inc.; *U.S. Public*, pg. 741
PETROLEUM MARKETERS, INC.; *U.S. Private*, pg. 859
PETROLEUM PRODUCTS CORP.; *U.S. Private*, pg. 859
PHILLIPS PETROLEUM COMPANY; *U.S. Public*, pg. 1290
PHOENIX FUEL COMPANY, INC.; *U.S. Private*, pg. 863
PIASA MOTOR FUELS INC.; *U.S. Private*, pg. 864
PILIPINAS SHELL PETROLEUM CORPORATION—Royal Dutch/Shell Group of Companies; *Int'l*, pg. 1140
PUMPELLY OIL, INC.; *U.S. Private*, pg. 895
JOHN G. RATHBORNE—Royal Dutch/Shell Group of Companies; *Int'l*, pg. 1138
F.L. ROBERTS & CO. INC.; *U.S. Private*, pg. 935
ROYAL PAKHOED NV; *Int'l*, pg. 1147
RUSSELL PETROLEUM CORPORATION; *U.S. Private*, pg. 953
SHARP OIL COMPANY; *U.S. Private*, pg. 990
SHELL COMPANY OF WEST AFRICA LTD.—Royal Dutch/Shell Group of Companies; *Int'l*, pg. 1137
SHELL COTE D'IVOIRE—Royal Dutch/Shell Group of Companies; *Int'l*, pg. 1137
SHELL FRANCAISE—Royal Dutch/Shell Group of Companies; *Int'l*, pg. 1138
SHELL GABON—Royal Dutch/Shell Group of Companies; *Int'l*, pg. 1137
SHELL OIL LESOTHO (PTY.) LTD.—Royal Dutch/Shell Group of Companies; *Int'l*, pg. 1136
SHELL (SWITZERLAND)—Royal Dutch/Shell Group of Companies; *Int'l*, pg. 1139
SHOWA SHELL SEKIYU KK—Royal Dutch/Shell Group of Companies; *Int'l*, pg. 1140
SIMON ENGINEERING PLC; *Int'l*, pg. 1251
SOUTHERN STATES COOPERATIVE, INC.; *U.S. Private*, pg. 1017
SPARTAN OIL CORP.; *U.S. Private*, pg. 1021
STEUART INVESTMENT COMPANY; *U.S. Private*, pg. 1042
STONE & WEBSTER, INCORPORATED; *U.S. Public*, pg. 1519
SUN COMPANY, INC.; *U.S. Public*, pg. 1530
SUNCOR INC.; *Int'l*, pg. 1320
SUNOCO GROUP—Suncor Inc.; *Int'l*, pg. 1320
AB SVENSKA SHELL—Royal Dutch/Shell Group of Companies; *Int'l*, pg. 1139
TAYLOR OIL CO. INC.; *U.S. Private*, pg. 1071
TESORO PETROLEUM CORPORATION; *U.S. Public*, pg. 1581
TEXACO INC.; *U.S. Public*, pg. 1582
S.A. TEXACO PETROLEUM N.V.—Texaco Inc.; *U.S. Public*, pg. 1584
THORNHILL OIL COMPANY, INC.; *U.S. Private*, pg. 1084
TOTAL RAFFINAGE DISTRIBUTION S.A.—Total S.A.; *Int'l*, pg. 1409
TRANSMONTAIGNE—TransMontaigne Oil Company; *U.S. Public*, pg. 1631
TRUCK WORLD INC.; *U.S. Private*, pg. 1107
USX CORPORATION; *U.S. Public*, pg. 1661
WATERLOO SERVICE COMPANY; *U.S. Private*, pg. 1152
WESTERN PETROLEUM COMPANY; *U.S. Private*, pg. 1168
WESTERN STATES PETROLEUM INC.; *U.S. Private*, pg. 1169
THE WHITE PASS & YUKON CORP. LIMITED—Russel Metals Inc.; *Int'l*, pg. 1150
WORSLEY COMPANIES INC.; *U.S. Private*, pg. 1191
WYATT ENERGY INCORPORATED; *U.S. Private*, pg. 1193

5172 — PETROLEUM & PETROLEUM PRODUCTS WHOLESALERS, EXCEPT BULK STATIONS & TERMINALS

ADA CRUDE OIL COMPANY—Adams Resources & Energy, Inc.; *U.S. Public*, pg. 19
AFSC SIGNATURE FLIGHT SUPPORT—Japan Airlines Company, Ltd.; *Int'l*, pg. 700
AGIP DEUTSCHLAND AG—ENI S.p.A.; *Int'l*, pg. 428
AGIP (SUISSE) S.A.—ENI S.p.A.; *Int'l*, pg. 428
ACHESON COLLOIDEN B.V.—Acheson Industries, Inc.; *U.S. Private*, pg. 12
ACHESON FRANCE S.A.—Acheson Industries, Inc.; *U.S. Private*, pg. 12
ACHESON ITALIANA S.R.L.—Acheson Industries, Inc.; *U.S. Private*, pg. 12
ADAMS RESOURCES & ENERGY, INC.; *U.S. Public*, pg. 18
AERO OIL CORP.—Getty Petroleum Marketing Inc.; *U.S. Public*, pg. 741
AIRGAS, INC.; *U.S. Public*, pg. 33
AIRKAMAN OF JACKSONVILLE, INC.—Kaman Corporation; *U.S. Public*, pg. 942
ALABAMA OIL COMPANY—Spencer Companies Inc.; *U.S. Private*, pg. 1025
ALASKA LUBE AND FUEL—Arctic Slope Regional Corporation; *U.S. Private*, pg. 80
ALLIED OIL & SUPPLY, INC.; *U.S. Private*, pg. 39
AMAX ENERGY, INC.—Cyprus Amax Minerals Company; *U.S. Public*, pg. 470
AMOCO SUPPLY & TRADING COMPANY—Amoco Corporation; *U.S. Public*, pg. 103
AMOCO (U.K.) LTD.—Amoco Corporation; *U.S. Public*, pg. 103
ANADARKO MARKETING COMPANY—Anadarko Petroleum Corporation; *U.S. Public*, pg. 107
ANADARKO TRADING COMPANY—Anadarko Petroleum Corporation; *U.S. Public*, pg. 107
APEX OIL COMPANY, INC.; *U.S. Private*, pg. 77
APEX SERVICE STATIONS LIMITED—Burmah Castrol plc; *Int'l*, pg. 234
ARCO PRODUCTS CO.—Atlantic Richfield Company; *U.S. Public*, pg. 144
ASHLAND, INC.; *U.S. Public*, pg. 138
ASHLAND OIL INTL. LTD.—Ashland, Inc.; *U.S. Public*, pg. 139
ATLANTIC AVIATION CORP.; *U.S. Private*, pg. 94
AUSTIN GROUP; *U.S. Private*, pg. 99
BHP INTERNATIONAL LTD.—The Broken Hill Proprietary Company Limited; *Int'l*, pg. 225
BP NORTH AMERICA PETROLEUM INC.—The British Petroleum Company P.L.C.; *Int'l*, pg. 220
BELGIAN FUELLING AND SERVICES COMPANY—Sabena; *Int'l*, pg. 1168
BELGIAN SHELL, S.A.—Royal Dutch/Shell Group of Companies; *Int'l*, pg. 1138
BERRY OIL TRADING AND TRANSPORTATION—Berry Petroleum Company; *U.S. Public*, pg. 223
BRADFORD OIL COMPANY, INC.; *U.S. Private*, pg. 164
BREWER OIL CO.; *U.S. Private*, pg. 167
BRIAN CONTROLS—Weir Group PLC; *Int'l*, pg. 1489
BRIMA MINERALOL-VERTRIEBS-UNION GMBH—Veba AG; *Int'l*, pg. 1457
THE BRITISH PETROLEUM COMPANY P.L.C.; *Int'l*, pg. 219
BROWN EVANS DISTRIBUTING CO.; *U.S. Private*, pg. 174
BURMAH CASTROL IRELAND, LTD.—Burmah Castrol plc; *Int'l*, pg. 235
BURMAH CASTROL PLC; *Int'l*, pg. 234
BURMAH CASTROL TRADING, LTD.—Burmah Castrol plc; *Int'l*, pg. 234
BURMAH OIL AUSTRALIA LTD.—Burmah Castrol plc; *Int'l*, pg. 235
THE BURMAH OIL COMPANY (PAKISTAN TRADING) LIMITED—Burmah Castrol plc; *Int'l*, pg. 235
BURMAH OIL INDONESIA LIMITED—Burmah Castrol plc; *Int'l*, pg. 235
BURNS BROS. INC.; *U.S. Private*, pg. 187
CAMPBELL OIL CO.; *U.S. Private*, pg. 204
CARSE OIL CO. INC.; *U.S. Private*, pg. 216
CARTER COMPANIES; *U.S. Private*, pg. 216
CASEY CO.; *U.S. Private*, pg. 218
CASTLE OIL CORPORATION; *U.S. Private*, pg. 219
CASTROL AUSTRALIA PTY LTD.—Burmah Castrol plc; *Int'l*, pg. 235
CASTROL AUSTRIA GMBH—Burmah Castrol plc; *Int'l*, pg. 235
CASTROL BRASIL LIMITADA—Burmah Castrol plc; *Int'l*, pg. 235
CASTROL CANADA INC.—Burmah Castrol plc; *Int'l*, pg. 235
CASTROL CHILE SA—Burmah Castrol plc; *Int'l*, pg. 235
CASTROL CHINA LTD.—Burmah Castrol plc; *Int'l*, pg. 235
CASTROL DEL PERU SA—Burmah Castrol plc; *Int'l*, pg. 235
CASTROL FRANCE SA—Burmah Castrol plc; *Int'l*, pg. 235
CASTROL INC., SPECIALTY PRODUCTS DIV.—Burmah Castrol plc; *Int'l*, pg. 235
CASTROL KOREA LIMITED—Burmah Castrol plc; *Int'l*, pg. 236
CASTROL (MALAYSIA) SB—Burmah Castrol plc; *Int'l*, pg. 236
CASTROL NEDERLAND B.V.—Burmah Castrol plc; *Int'l*, pg. 236
CASTROL NORGE A/S—Burmah Castrol plc; *Int'l*, pg. 236
CASTROL NORTH AMERICA—Burmah Castrol plc; *Int'l*, pg. 235
CASTROL NV—Burmah Castrol plc; *Int'l*, pg. 236
CASTROL NZ LTD.—Burmah Castrol plc; *Int'l*, pg. 236
CASTROL (SWITZERLAND) AG—Burmah Castrol plc; *Int'l*, pg. 236
CASTROL (TAIWAN) LIMITED—Burmah Castrol plc; *Int'l*, pg. 236
CENEX, INC.; *U.S. Private*, pg. 221
CENTURY OILS (CANADA), INC.—Fuchs Petrolub AG Oel + Chemie; *Int'l*, pg. 518
CHAMPAIGN LANDMARK, INC.; *U.S. Private*, pg. 227
CHEMOIL; *U.S. Private*, pg. 233
CHEVRON INTERNATIONAL TRADING COMPANY-WEST AFRICA—Chevron Corporation; *U.S. Public*, pg. 348
CHINESE PETROLEUM CORPORATION; *Int'l*, pg. 286
THE COASTAL CORPORATION; *U.S. Public*, pg. 389
COASTAL FUELS MARKETING, INC.—The Coastal Corporation; *U.S. Public*, pg. 390
COASTAL OIL NEW YORK, INC.—The Coastal Corporation; *U.S. Public*, pg. 390
COASTAL PETROLEUM (FAR EAST) PTE LTD.—The Coastal Corporation; *U.S. Public*, pg. 390
COASTAL (ROTTERDAM) B.V.—The Coastal Corporation; *U.S. Public*, pg. 390
CODA ENERGY, INC.—Enron Corp.; *U.S. Public*, pg. 584
COLAS EAST AFRICA—Royal Dutch/Shell Group of Companies; *Int'l*, pg. 1136
COLONIAL OIL INDUSTRIES; *U.S. Private*, pg. 253
COMMANDER OIL CORPORATION; *U.S. Private*, pg. 257
CONDON OIL COMPANY, INC.; *U.S. Private*, pg. 262
CONOCO INC.—Du Pont (E.I. Du Pont De Nemours & Co.); *U.S. Public*, pg. 531
CONOCO IRELAND LTD.—Du Pont (E.I. Du Pont De Nemours & Co.); *U.S. Public*, pg. 531
CONOCO MINERALOEL GMBH—Du Pont (E.I. Du Pont De Nemours & Co.); *U.S. Public*, pg. 531
CONSOLIDATED MIDWEST, INC.; *U.S. Private*, pg. 265
CORAL OIL & GAS INC.; *U.S. Private*, pg. 275
COSMO OIL CO., LTD.; *Int'l*, pg. 335
COSMO OIL OF U.S.A. INC.—Cosmo Oil Co., Ltd.; *Int'l*, pg. 335
COWBOY OIL COMPANY; *U.S. Private*, pg. 280
THE CROWN OIL & GAS CO.—Crown Central Petroleum Corporation; *U.S. Public*, pg. 462
CUMBERLAND FARMS, INC.; *U.S. Private*, pg. 295
DAIGLE OIL CO.; *U.S. Private*, pg. 307
DEAD RIVER COMPANY; *U.S. Private*, pg. 318
DEAD RIVER PETROLEUM CO.—Dead River Company; *U.S. Private*, pg. 318
DISTRIBUIDORA SHELL DE EL SALVADOR SA—Royal Dutch/Shell Group of Companies; *Int'l*, pg. 1141
DISTRIBUTORS OIL COMPANY, INC.; *U.S. Private*, pg. 336
DISTRICT PETROLEUM PRODUCTS, INC.; *U.S. Private*, pg. 336
DOVER RESOURCES INC.—Dover Corporation; *U.S. Public*, pg. 521
DU PONT (E.I. DU PONT DE NEMOURS & CO.); *U.S. Public*, pg. 530
DU PONT SCANDINAVIA AB—Du Pont (E.I. Du Pont De Nemours & Co.); *U.S. Public*, pg. 533
DUROL OIL CO. (PTY.) LTD.—Burmah Castrol plc; *Int'l*, pg. 236
E-Z MART STORES, INC.; *U.S. Private*, pg. 353
ENI S.P.A.; *Int'l*, pg. 428
EDDINS-WALCHER COMPANY; *U.S. Private*, pg. 362
EFFINGHAM-CLAY SERVICE CO.; *U.S. Private*, pg. 365
ELF AQUITAINE, INC.—Elf Aquitane; *Int'l*, pg. 445
ELF FRANCE—Elf Aquitane; *Int'l*, pg. 445
ELF LUBRICANTS—Elf Aquitane; *Int'l*, pg. 445
ELF SUISSE S.A.—Elf Aquitane; *Int'l*, pg. 446
ELF TRADING, INC.—Elf Aquitane; *Int'l*, pg. 445
ENGLEFIELD, INC.; *U.S. Private*, pg. 377
ENRON CAPITAL & TRADE RESOURCES—Enron Corp.; *U.S. Public*, pg. 584
ENRON CORP.; *U.S. Public*, pg. 584
ESKIMOS, INC.—Arctic Slope Regional Corporation; *U.S. Private*, pg. 80
ESSO BRASILEIRA DE PETROLEO LIMITADA—Exxon Corporation; *U.S. Public*, pg. 602
ESSO EXPLORATION AND PRODUCTION UK LIMITED—Exxon Corporation; *U.S. Public*, pg. 602
ESSO MALAYSIA BERHAD—Exxon Corporation; *U.S. Public*, pg. 602
ESSO SEKIYU KABUSHIKI KAISHA—Exxon Corporation; *U.S. Public*, pg. 602
ESSO STANDARD THAILAND LTD.—Exxon Corporation; *U.S. Public*, pg. 602
ESSO TRADING COMPANY OF ABU DHABI—Exxon Corporation; *U.S. Public*, pg. 602
EXXON COMPANY, U.S.A.—Exxon Corporation; *U.S. Public*, pg. 601
FAIRFIELD MAXWELL LTD.; *U.S. Private*, pg. 391
FARM & HOME OIL COMPANY; *U.S. Private*, pg. 394
FARMLAND INDUSTRIES, INC.; *U.S. Private*, pg. 395
FERRELLGAS HOUSTON—Ferrellgas Partners, L.P.; *U.S. Public*, pg. 618
FINA CONGO S.A.R.L.—Petrofina S.A.; *Int'l*, pg. 1044
FINA, INC.—Petrofina S.A.; *Int'l*, pg. 1044
FINLEY FARMERS GRAIN & ELEVATOR COMPANY; *U.S. Private*, pg. 405
FLEISCHLI OIL COMPANY, INC.; *U.S. Private*, pg. 410
FLYING J. INC.; *U.S. Private*, pg. 415
FORD DISTRIBUIDORA DE PRODUTOS DE PETROLEO LTDA.—Ford Motor Company; *U.S. Public*, pg. 665
FRONTIER HOLDINGS INC.—Wainoco Oil Corporation; *U.S. Public*, pg. 1732
FRONTIER OIL CORPORATION—Wainoco Oil Corporation; *U.S. Public*, pg. 1732
FUEL SOUTH, INC.—Jones Company, Inc.; *U.S. Private*, pg. 596
GARY-WILLIAMS ENERGY CORPORATION; *U.S. Private*, pg. 440
GATE PETROLEUM COMPANY; *U.S. Private*, pg. 441
GENERAL SEKIYU K.K.—Exxon Corporation; *U.S. Public*, pg. 602
GETTY PETROLEUM MARKETING INC.; *U.S. Public*, pg. 740
GETTY TERMINALS, INC.—Getty Petroleum Marketing Inc.; *U.S. Public*, pg. 741
GIANT INDUSTRIES INC.; *U.S. Public*, pg. 741
GLOBAL PETROLEUM CORP.; *U.S. Private*, pg. 457
GREAT LAKES CARBON CORP.—Horsehead Industries, Inc.; *U.S. Private*, pg. 540
GREENWAY CO-OP SERVICE; *U.S. Private*, pg. 478
THE GUTTMAN GROUP; *U.S. Private*, pg. 488
THE H.T. HACKNEY CO.; *U.S. Private*, pg. 493
HEIN DE WINDT B.V.—Fuchs Petrolub AG Oel + Chemie; *Int'l*, pg. 517
HOLLINGSWORTH OIL CO. INC.; *U.S. Private*, pg. 535
HONOLULU FUELING FACILITIES CORP.—Japan Airlines Company, Ltd.; *Int'l*, pg. 700
HORIZON DISTRIBUTION INC.; *U.S. Private*, pg. 539
HORSEHEAD INDUSTRIES, INC.; *U.S. Private*, pg. 540
HUSKY OIL LTD.; *Int'l*, pg. 640
HUSKY OIL MKTG. COMPANY—Husky Oil Ltd.; *Int'l*, pg. 640
HUSKY OIL OPERATIONS LTD.—Husky Oil Ltd.; *Int'l*, pg. 640
ITOCHU INTERNATIONAL PETROLEUM CO., LTD.—Itochu Corporation; *Int'l*, pg. 695
INDUSTRIAL DISTRIBUTION GROUP; *U.S. Public*, pg. 875
INTERNATIONAL MARKETING & REFINING DIVISION—Mobil Oil Corporation; *U.S. Public*, pg. 1118
INTERNATIONAL PETROLEUM CORPORATION—International Recovery Corp.; *U.S. Public*, pg. 906
INTERNATIONAL RECOVERY CORP.; *U.S. Public*, pg. 906
JAPAN AIRLINES COMPANY, LTD.; *Int'l*, pg. 699
AXEL JOHNSON AB; *Int'l*, pg. 707
AXEL JOHNSON PETROLEUM AB—Axel Johnson AB; *Int'l*, pg. 709
GAY JOHNSON'S INC.; *U.S. Private*, pg. 595
JONES COMPANY, INC.; *U.S. Private*, pg. 596
KAIBAB INDUSTRIES; *U.S. Private*, pg. 605
KING FUELS INC.; *U.S. Private*, pg. 620
KNOX OIL OF TEXAS INC.; *U.S. Private*, pg. 627
KUWAIT NATIONAL PETROLEUM COMPANY K.S.C.—Kuwait Petroleum Corporation; *Int'l*, pg. 765

L & L OIL COMPANY, INC.; *U.S. Private*, pg. 638
LL&E PETROLEUM MARKETING, INC.—Royal Dutch/Shell Group of Companies; *Int'l*, pg. 1136
LEE-MOORE OIL CO., INC.; *U.S. Private*, pg. 657
LEEMILTS PETROLEUM, INC.—Getty Petroleum Marketing Inc.; *U.S. Public*, pg. 741
LEXINGTON CO-OP OIL CO.; *U.S. Private*, pg. 666
LUBRICANTES Y TAMBORES DEL ECUADOR, C.A.—Texaco Inc.; *U.S. Public*, pg. 1584
MDU RESOURCES GROUP, INC.; *U.S. Public*, pg. 1025
MAGELLAN PETROLEUM AUSTRALIA LTD.—Magellan Petroleum Corporation; *U.S. Public*, pg. 1037
MAGELLAN PETROLEUM CORPORATION; *U.S. Public*, pg. 1036
MAIN BROTHERS OIL COMPANY, INC.; *U.S. Private*, pg. 697
MAINE POTATO GROWERS, INC.; *U.S. Private*, pg. 697
MAJOR & CO. LTD.—Burmah Castrol plc; *Int'l*, pg. 234
MALICHA BRENNSTOFFHANDEL GMBH—Veba AG; *Int'l*, pg. 1457
MAPCO INC.; *U.S. Public*, pg. 1042
MARTIN GAS CORPORATION; *U.S. Private*, pg. 709
MAYTAG AIRCRAFT CORP.—Mercury Air Group Inc.; *U.S. Public*, pg. 1093
MCCALL OIL & CHEMICAL CORP.; *U.S. Private*, pg. 719
MEDITERRANEAN STANDARD OIL CO.—Exxon Corporation; *U.S. Public*, pg. 602
MEENAN OIL CO. L.P.; *U.S. Private*, pg. 729
METALLGESELLSCHAFT CORP.—Metallgesellschaft AG; *Int'l*, pg. 861
MID SOUTH SALES; *U.S. Private*, pg. 744
MIDWEST PETROLEUM CO.; *U.S. Private*, pg. 745
MILLER OIL CO., INC.; *U.S. Private*, pg. 747
MITSIAM INTERNATIONAL, LTD.—Mitsui & Co., Ltd.; *Int'l*, pg. 880
MITSUBISHI CORPORATION; *Int'l*, pg. 871
MITSUBISHI INTERNATIONAL CORPORATION—Mitsubishi Corporation; *Int'l*, pg. 871
MITSUI & CO., LTD.; *Int'l*, pg. 877
MITSUI BRASILEIRA IMP. E EXP. LTDA.—Mitsui & Co., Ltd.; *Int'l*, pg. 882
MITSUI CHILENA COMMERCIAL LTDA.—Mitsui & Co., Ltd.; *Int'l*, pg. 882
MITSUI DE COLOMBIA S.A.—Mitsui & Co., Ltd.; *Int'l*, pg. 882
MITSUI DE MEXICO, S.A. DE C.V.—Mitsui & Co., Ltd.; *Int'l*, pg. 882
MITSUI DE VENEZUELA C.A.—Mitsui & Co., Ltd.; *Int'l*, pg. 882
MITSUI DEL ECUADOR S.A.—Mitsui & Co., Ltd.; *Int'l*, pg. 882
MOBIL KABUSHIKI KAISHA—Mobil Oil Corporation; *U.S. Public*, pg. 1119
MOBIL OIL COMPANY, LTD.—Mobil Oil Corporation; *U.S. Public*, pg. 1119
MOBIL OIL ITALIANA SOCIETA PER AZIONI—Mobil Oil Corporation; *U.S. Public*, pg. 1119
MOBIL SOUTH, MARKETING & REFINING DIVISION—Mobil Oil Corporation; *U.S. Public*, pg. 1118
MOBILE OIL AB SWEDEN—Mobil Oil Corporation; *U.S. Public*, pg. 1119
MOCK RESOURCES, INC.—Wickland Corporation; *U.S. Private*, pg. 1175
MURPHY OIL CO., LTD.—Murphy Oil Corporation; *U.S. Public*, pg. 1142
MURPHY OIL TRADING CO. (EASTERN)—Murphy Oil Corporation; *U.S. Public*, pg. 1142
NEEB CORPORATION; *U.S. Private*, pg. 790
NEW YORK REPRESENTATIVE OFFICE (ESNOR)—Petrobras - Petroleo Brasileiro S.A.; *Int'l*, pg. 1042
NICHIMEN AMERICA, INC.—Nichimen Corporation; *Int'l*, pg. 927
NICHIMEN CORPORATION; *Int'l*, pg. 927
NISSHO IWAI GAS CO., LTD.—Nissho Iwai Corporation; *Int'l*, pg. 946
NISSHO IWAI PETROLEUM CORP.—Nissho Iwai Corporation; *Int'l*, pg. 947
NISSHO PROPANE SEKIYU CORP.—Nissho Iwai Corporation; *Int'l*, pg. 947
NORSK TEXACO A/S—Texaco Inc.; *U.S. Public*, pg. 1584
NORTHVILLE INDUSTRIES CORP.; *U.S. Private*, pg. 806
OBERLANDER RECYCLING TECHNIK GMBH—Fried. Krupp AG; *Int'l*, pg. 513
PDV AMERICA CORP.—Petroleos de Venezuela S.A.; *Int'l*, pg. 1045
PS TRADING, INC.—PS Group Holdings; *U.S. Public*, pg. 1245
PACE OIL CO., INC.; *U.S. Private*, pg. 829
PACIFIC FUEL TRADING CORPORATION—Japan Airlines Company, Ltd.; *Int'l*, pg. 700
PACIFIC NORTHERN INC.; *U.S. Private*, pg. 832
PEMEX—Petroleos Mexicanos; *Int'l*, pg. 1046
P.T. PETRO CORP.—Getty Petroleum Marketing Inc.; *U.S. Public*, pg. 741
PETRO-DIAMOND, INC.—Mitsubishi Corporation; *Int'l*, pg. 872
PETROCHEMICAL INDUSTRIES COMPANY K.S.C.—Kuwait Petroleum Corporation; *Int'l*, pg. 765
PETROFINA S.A.; *Int'l*, pg. 1043
PETROLEOS MEXICANOS; *Int'l*, pg. 1046
PETROLEUM TRADERS CORPORATION; *U.S. Private*, pg. 859
PHILLIPS PETROLEUM CHEMICALS S.A.—Phillips Petroleum Company; *U.S. Public*, pg. 1291
PHILLIPS PETROLEUM COMPANY; *U.S. Public*, pg. 1290
PIONEER OIL COMPANY INC.; *U.S. Private*, pg. 866
POUNDER EMULSIONS, LTD.—Husky Oil Ltd.; *Int'l*, pg. 640
PRAIRIELANDS ENERGY MARKETING, INC.—MDU Resources Group, Inc.; *U.S. Public*, pg. 1025
PRESTO FOOD STORES, INC.; *U.S. Private*, pg. 882
PRO-FAC COOPERATIVE, INC.; *U.S. Private*, pg. 887
PUGH OIL COMPANY; *U.S. Private*, pg. 894
PUMPELLY OIL, INC.; *U.S. Private*, pg. 895
QUAKER CHEMICAL CORPORATION; *U.S. Public*, pg. 1346
QUAKER STATE CORPORATION; *U.S. Public*, pg. 1348
QUAKER STATE INC.—Quaker State Corporation; *U.S. Public*, pg. 1348
QUAKER STATE JAPAN CO., LTD.—Quaker State Corporation; *U.S. Public*, pg. 1348
QUALITY PETROLEUM CORP.; *U.S. Private*, pg. 899
RAAB KARCHER AG—Veba AG; *Int'l*, pg. 1457
RACETRAC PETROLEUM, INC.; *U.S. Private*, pg. 906
REMOTE SERVICES, INC.—Dairy Mart Convenience Stores, Inc.; *U.S. Public*, pg. 477
REPSOL OIL INTERNATIONAL LIMITED—Repsol S.A.; *Int'l*, pg. 1105
REPSOL PETROLEO—Repsol S.A.; *Int'l*, pg. 1104
RISSER OIL CORP.; *U.S. Private*, pg. 932
F.L. ROBERTS & CO. INC.; *U.S. Private*, pg. 935
S&S-HARTWELL CO., INC.—Axel Johnson AB; *Int'l*, pg. 710
SF SERVICES; *U.S. Private*, pg. 956
SIPEC STE INTERNATIONALE DE PETROLE ET DE CHIMIE A R.L.—Saarbergwerke Aktiengesellschaft; *Int'l*, pg. 1167
SOCAP LTD ELF TRADING SA—Elf Aquitane; *Int'l*, pg. 445
SAARBERG BRENNSTOFFHANDEL GMBH—Saarbergwerke Aktiengesellschaft; *Int'l*, pg. 1167
SAARBERG HANDEL GMBH—Saarbergwerke Aktiengesellschaft; *Int'l*, pg. 1167
SERICOL SA—Burmah Castrol plc; *Int'l*, pg. 235
SHELL AEROCENTRE—Royal Dutch/Shell Group of Companies; *Int'l*, pg. 1138
SHELL ANTILLES—Royal Dutch/Shell Group of Companies; *Int'l*, pg. 1141
SHELL AVIATION SERVICE—Royal Dutch/Shell Group of Companies; *Int'l*, pg. 1139
SHELL BRASIL SA—Royal Dutch/Shell Group of Companies; *Int'l*, pg. 1141
SHELL CANADA PRODUCTS LTD.—Royal Dutch/Shell Group of Companies; *Int'l*, pg. 1138
SHELL COMPANY OF TURKEY LTD.—Royal Dutch/Shell Group of Companies; *Int'l*, pg. 1141
SHELL COTE D'IVOIRE—Royal Dutch/Shell Group of Companies; *Int'l*, pg. 1137
SHELL DE CABO VERDE—Royal Dutch/Shell Group of Companies; *Int'l*, pg. 1137
SHELL FRANCAISE—Royal Dutch/Shell Group of Companies; *Int'l*, pg. 1138
SHELL FUEL SUPPLIES—Royal Dutch/Shell Group of Companies; *Int'l*, pg. 1141
SHELL GABON—Royal Dutch/Shell Group of Companies; *Int'l*, pg. 1137
SHELL NEDERLAND VERKOOP MIJ B.V.—Royal Dutch/Shell Group of Companies; *Int'l*, pg. 1135
SHELL OF AALBORG—Royal Dutch/Shell Group of Companies; *Int'l*, pg. 1138
SHELL OF CASTLE DONINGTON—Royal Dutch/Shell Group of Companies; *Int'l*, pg. 1139
SHELL OF ESBJERG—Royal Dutch/Shell Group of Companies; *Int'l*, pg. 1138
SHELL OF GARDERMOEN—Royal Dutch/Shell Group of Companies; *Int'l*, pg. 1139
SHELL OF STJOERDAL—Royal Dutch/Shell Group of Companies; *Int'l*, pg. 1139
SHELL SURINAME VERKOOP MIJ NV—Royal Dutch/Shell Group of Companies; *Int'l*, pg. 1142
SHELL (SWITZERLAND)—Royal Dutch/Shell Group of Companies; *Int'l*, pg. 1139
SHELL UK LTD.—Royal Dutch/Shell Group of Companies; *Int'l*, pg. 1139
SHELL UK OIL (BIRMINGHAM)—Royal Dutch/Shell Group of Companies; *Int'l*, pg. 1139
SHELL UK OIL (STANDSTED)—Royal Dutch/Shell Group of Companies; *Int'l*, pg. 1139
SHIPLEY COMPANIES; *U.S. Private*, pg. 994
SHOWA SHELL SEKIYU KK—Royal Dutch/Shell Group of Companies; *Int'l*, pg. 1140
THE SICO COMPANY—First Mount Joy Corporation; *U.S. Private*, pg. 407
SOCIETE EUROPEENNE DES CARBURANTS S.A.—Du Pont (E.I. Du Pont De Nemours & Co.); *U.S. Public*, pg. 533
SOMERSET REFINERY INC.; *U.S. Private*, pg. 1013
SOURDOUGH FUEL, INC.—Arctic Slope Regional Corporation; *U.S. Private*, pg. 80
SOUTHERN STATES COOPERATIVE, INC.; *U.S. Private*, pg. 1017
SOUTHLAND OIL COMPANY; *U.S. Private*, pg. 1018
SPELLING ENTERTAINMENT GROUP, INC.—National Amusements, Inc.; *U.S. Private*, pg. 776
SPENCER COMPANIES INC.; *U.S. Private*, pg. 1024
SPRAGUE ENERGY CORP. NORTHEAST OPERATION—Axel Johnson AB; *Int'l*, pg. 710
SPRAUGE ENERGY CORP. SOUTHEAST OPERATIONS—Axel Johnson AB; *Int'l*, pg. 710
SPROTT OIL CO., INC.; *U.S. Private*, pg. 1027
STATE GAS & OIL COMPANY DIVISION—Uni-Marts, Inc.; *U.S. Public*, pg. 1664
STEUART INVESTMENT COMPANY; *U.S. Private*, pg. 1042
STINNES CORPORATION—Veba AG; *Int'l*, pg. 1460
STINNES INTEROIL INC.—Veba AG; *Int'l*, pg. 1459
J.D. STREETT & CO., INC.; *U.S. Private*, pg. 1047
SUDDEUTSCHE BRENNSTOFFHANDELSGESELLSCHAFT MBH—Saarbergwerke Aktiengesellschaft; *Int'l*, pg. 1167
SULLIVAN OIL COMPANY; *U.S. Private*, pg. 1050
SUMITOMO CORPORATION; *Int'l*, pg. 1312
SUMITOMO CORPORATION OF AMERICA—Sumitomo Corporation; *Int'l*, pg. 1312
SUN COMPANY, INC.; *U.S. Public*, pg. 1530
SUN REFINING & MARKETING CO. LUBES DIV.—Sun Company, Inc.; *U.S. Public*, pg. 1530
SUNCOR INC.; *Int'l*, pg. 1320
SUNKYONG INDUSTRIES CO.; *Int'l*, pg. 1320
SUNOCO GROUP—Suncor Inc.; *Int'l*, pg. 1320
SUPERIOR OIL CO. INC.; *U.S. Private*, pg. 1055
AB SVENSKA UNO-X—Burmah Castrol plc; *Int'l*, pg. 236
TAIWAN MARKETING & TRANSPORTATION DIV.—Chinese Petroleum Corporation; *Int'l*, pg. 286
TAUBER OIL COMPANY; *U.S. Private*, pg. 1069
TAURUS ENERGY CORP.—Enron Corp.; *U.S. Public*, pg. 584
TENNECO GAS MARKETING COMPANY—Tenneco Inc.; *U.S. Public*, pg. 1579
TENNESSEE FARMERS CO-OP; *U.S. Private*, pg. 1076
TESORO MARINE SERVICES—Tesoro Petroleum Corporation; *U.S. Public*, pg. 1582
TESORO PETROLEUM CORPORATION; *U.S. Public*, pg. 1581
TEXACO INC.; *U.S. Public*, pg. 1582
S.A. TEXACO PETROLEUM N.V.—Texaco Inc.; *U.S. Public*, pg. 1584
TEXAS PETRO CHEMICALS; *U.S. Private*, pg. 1078
TIME OIL COMPANY; *U.S. Private*, pg. 1086
TOMS SIERRA COMPANY; *U.S. Private*, pg. 1090
TONEN ENERGY INTERNATIONAL CORP.—Tonen Corporation; *Int'l*, pg. 1399
TORCO OIL CO.; *U.S. Private*, pg. 1092
TOSCO CORPORATION; *U.S. Public*, pg. 1624
TOTAL HOLDINGS (AUSTRALIA) PTY. LTD.—Total S.A.; *Int'l*, pg. 1409
TOTAL ITALIANA SRL.—Total S.A.; *Int'l*, pg. 1409
TOTAL OIL GREAT BRITAIN LTD.—Total S.A.; *Int'l*, pg. 1409
TOTAL OUTRE-MER—Total S.A.; *Int'l*, pg. 1409
TOTAL PETROLEUM CANADA LTD.—Total S.A.; *Int'l*, pg. 1409
TOTAL S.A.; *Int'l*, pg. 1408
TOTAL SOUTH AFRICA (PTY.) LTD.—Total S.A.; *Int'l*, pg. 1409
TOTALGAZ—Total S.A.; *Int'l*, pg. 1410
TRANSAMMONIA INC.; *U.S. Private*, pg. 1096
TRUE COMPANIES; *U.S. Private*, pg. 1107
UAL CORPORATION; *U.S. Public*, pg. 1652
UK PETROLEUM PRODUCTS LTD.—Powell Duffryn PLC; *Int'l*, pg. 1065
ULTRAMAR DIAMOND SHAMROCK CORPORATION; *U.S. Public*, pg. 1663
US AIRWAYS FUEL CORPORATION—US Airways Group, Inc.; *U.S. Public*, pg. 1680
VALERO MARKETING & SUPPLY COMPANY—Valero Energy Corporation; *U.S. Public*, pg. 1704
VALVOLINE COMPANY—Ashland, Inc.; *U.S. Public*, pg. 139
VEEDOL (CANADA) LTD.—Burmah Castrol plc; *Int'l*, pg. 236
VENGAS MARKETING COMPANY—Stone & Webster, Incorporated; *U.S. Public*, pg. 1519
VESCO OIL CORP.; *U.S. Private*, pg. 1138
WD-40 COMPANY (AUSTRALIA)—WD-40 Company; *U.S. Public*, pg. 1726
WD-40 COMPANY LTD.—WD-40 Company; *U.S. Public*, pg. 1726
WD-40 PRODUCTS (CANADA) LTD.—WD-40 Company; *U.S. Public*, pg. 1726
WARREN DISTRIBUTION, INC.; *U.S. Private*, pg. 1151
WARREN EQUITIES INC.; *U.S. Private*, pg. 1151
GEORGE E. WARREN CORPORATION; *U.S. Private*, pg. 1151
WESTERN PETROLEUM COMPANY; *U.S. Private*, pg. 1168
WEXPRO COMPANY—Questar Corporation; *U.S. Public*, pg. 1352
WICKLAND CORPORATION; *U.S. Private*, pg. 1174
WICKLAND INTERNATIONAL ASIA, LTD.—Wickland Corporation; *U.S. Private*, pg. 1175
WICKLAND OIL COMPANY, INC.—Wickland Corporation; *U.S. Private*, pg. 1175
WILLS GROUP, INC.; *U.S. Private*, pg. 1180
WILSHIRE OIL CO. OF TEXAS; *U.S. Public*, pg. 1770
WINSCHERMANN BERLIN GMBH—Saarbergwerke Aktiengesellschaft; *Int'l*, pg. 1167
WINSCHERMANN SUED GMBH—Saarbergwerke Aktiengesellschaft; *Int'l*, pg. 1167
WINSCHERMANN WEST GMBH—Saarbergwerke Aktiengesellschaft; *Int'l*, pg. 1167
WORLD FUEL SERVICES, INC.—International Recovery Corp.; *U.S. Public*, pg. 906
WORLD FUEL SERVICES OF FL—International Recovery Corp.; *U.S. Public*, pg. 906
WORLD OIL CORP.; *U.S. Private*, pg. 1190
YODER OIL COMPANY INC.; *U.S. Private*, pg. 1196

5181 — BEER & ALE-WHOLESALE

ALLIED DOMECQ BRASIL INDUSTRIA E COMERCIO LTDA.—Allied Domecq PLC; *Int'l*, pg. 63
ANHEUSER-BUSCH ASIA, INC.—Anheuser-Busch Companies, Inc.; *U.S. Public*, pg. 115
ANHEUSER-BUSCH COMPANIES, INC.; *U.S. Public*, pg. 113
ANHEUSER-BUSCH EUROPE, INC.—Anheuser-Busch Companies, Inc.; *U.S. Public*, pg. 115
ANHEUSER-BUSCH EUROPEAN TRADE LTD.—Anheuser-Busch Companies, Inc.; *U.S. Public*, pg. 115
ANHEUSER-BUSCH, INC.—Anheuser-Busch Companies, Inc.; *U.S. Public*, pg. 114
ANHEUSER-BUSCH INTERNATIONAL, INC.—Anheuser-Busch Companies, Inc.; *U.S. Public*, pg. 114
ASAHI BREWERIES U.S.A., INC.—Asahi Breweries Ltd.; *Int'l*, pg. 83
ATLANTA BEVERAGE CO.; *U.S. Private*, pg. 94
BACARDI-MARTINI CARIBBEAN CORPORATION—Bacardi Limited; *Int'l*, pg. 132
BARTON BEERS, LTD.—Canandaigua Wine Company, Inc.; *U.S. Public*, pg. 300
THE LEWIS BEAR COMPANY; *U.S. Private*, pg. 127

BEAUCHAMP DISTRIBUTING COMPANY; *U.S. Private*, pg. 127
BETTER BRANDS OF ATLANTA, INC.; *U.S. Private*, pg. 141
BRASSERIES ET LIMONADERIES DU BURUNDI "BRARUDI" S.A.R.L.—Heineken N.V.; *Int'l*, pg. 608
AUGUST A. BUSCH & CO. OF MASSACHUSETTS, INC.—Anheuser-Busch Companies, Inc.; *U.S. Public*, pg. 114
COCA-COLA NORTHERN NEW ENGLAND, INC.—Kirin Brewery Co., Ltd.; *Int'l*, pg. 736
CONSOLIDATED BEVERAGES, INC.; *U.S. Private*, pg. 264
ADOLPH COORS COMPANY; *U.S. Public*, pg. 445
COORS DISTRIBUTING CO.—Adolph Coors Company; *U.S. Public*, pg. 445
DRANKENHANDEL DE GRAAFSCHAP B.V.—Grolsch N.V.; *Int'l*, pg. 559
DRIBECK IMPORTERS, INC.; *U.S. Private*, pg. 343
ELDERS - QUEENSLAND—Foster's Brewing Group Limited; *Int'l*, pg. 501
EUROPEAN CELLARS LTD.—Whitbread PLC; *Int'l*, pg. 1499
GATE CITY BEVERAGE DISTRIBUTORS; *U.S. Private*, pg. 441
GENERAL WHOLESALE COMPANY, INC.; *U.S. Private*, pg. 445
GEORGIA CROWN DISTRIBUTING; *U.S. Private*, pg. 448
GLAZER'S WHOLESALE DRUG CO. INC.; *U.S. Private*, pg. 455
GOLDEN EAGLE DISTRIBUTORS, INC.; *U.S. Private*, pg. 460
GOLDEN EAGLE DISTRIBUTORS, INC.—Golden Eagle Distributors, Inc.; *U.S. Private*, pg. 460
GRANTHAM DISTRIBUTING COMPANY, INC.; *U.S. Private*, pg. 470
GREY EAGLE DISTRIBUTORS INC.; *U.S. Private*, pg. 480
GROLSCH IMPORTERS INC.—Grolsch N.V.; *Int'l*, pg. 559
GROLSCH N.V.; *Int'l*, pg. 559
GROLSCH (UK) LTD.—Grolsch N.V.; *Int'l*, pg. 559
GUINNESS IMPORT COMPANY—Diageo Plc; *Int'l*, pg. 412
HARTFORD DISTRIBUTORS INC.; *U.S. Private*, pg. 507
HAUS CRAMER GASTSTATTEN MANAGEMENT GMBH & CO. KG—Warsteiner Brauerei Haus Cramer GmbH & Co.; *Int'l*, pg. 1486
HEINEKEN N.V.; *Int'l*, pg. 608
HEINEKEN USA INC.—Heineken N.V.; *Int'l*, pg. 608
HENSLEY & CO.; *U.S. Private*, pg. 523
HIRAM WALKER—Allied Domecq PLC; *Int'l*, pg. 63
JOSEPH HUBER BREWING CO., INC.; *U.S. Private*, pg. 545
INTERNATIONAL DISTILLERS & VINTNERS LTD.—Diageo Plc; *Int'l*, pg. 409
INTERNATIONAL DISTILLERS JAPAN—Diageo Plc; *Int'l*, pg. 410
BEN E. KEITH COMPANY; *U.S. Private*, pg. 611
KIRIN USA, INC.—Kirin Brewery Co., Ltd.; *Int'l*, pg. 736
LATROBE BREWING CO.—Interbrew S.A.; *Int'l*, pg. 680
A. LEVY & J. ZENTNER CO.; *U.S. Private*, pg. 663
LIPSCHUTZ BROTHERS INC—BAA plc; *Int'l*, pg. 103
MCCORMICK (UK) PLC.—McCormick & Company, Incorporated; *U.S. Public*, pg. 1067
MILLER BRANDS OF PHOENIX—Philip Morris Companies Inc.; *U.S. Public*, pg. 1289
MOLSON BREWERIES—The Molson Companies Limited; *Int'l*, pg. 887
MOLSON BREWERIES U.S.A. INC.—Philip Morris Companies Inc.; *U.S. Public*, pg. 1289
MONTEBELLO BRANDS INC.; *U.S. Private*, pg. 758
BEN MYERSON CANDY COMPANY, INC.; *U.S. Private*, pg. 771
OLINDE HARDWARE & SUPPLY CO.; *U.S. Private*, pg. 814
PATERNO IMPORTS LIMITED; *U.S. Private*, pg. 843
PEARLSTINE DISTRIBUTORS INC.; *U.S. Private*, pg. 845
REPUBLIC BEVERAGE CO.—Block Distributing Company; *U.S. Private*, pg. 150
REPUBLIC BEVERAGE COMPANY—Block Distributing Company; *U.S. Private*, pg. 149
CLARE ROSE INC./CLARE ROSE OF NASSAU; *U.S. Private*, pg. 945
SAPPORO U.S.A., INC., NEW YORK—Sapporo Breweries Ltd.; *Int'l*, pg. 1193
SCOTTISH & COURAGE BEER DIV.—Scottish & Newcastle plc; *Int'l*, pg. 1212
SCOTTISH & COURAGE BEER PRODUCTION LIMITED—Scottish & Newcastle plc; *Int'l*, pg. 1212
SCOTTISH & NEWCASTLE IMPORTERS CO.—Scottish & Newcastle plc; *Int'l*, pg. 1212
SCOTTISH BREWERS LIMITED—Scottish & Newcastle plc; *Int'l*, pg. 1212
SHIEFFELIN SOMERSET CO.—Diageo Plc; *Int'l*, pg. 412
SUNTORY INTERNATIONAL CORP.—Suntory Ltd.; *Int'l*, pg. 1321
TRIANGLE DISTRIBUTING COMPANY; *U.S. Private*, pg. 1101
UNITED DISTRIBUTORS, INC.; *U.S. Private*, pg. 1121
VAUX GROUP PLC; *Int'l*, pg. 1453
WARSTEINER IMPORTERS AGENCY—Warsteiner Brauerei Haus Cramer GmbH & Co.; *Int'l*, pg. 1486
WHITBREAD PLC; *Int'l*, pg. 1498
WISDOM IMPORTS SALES CO. INC.—Interbrew S.A.; *Int'l*, pg. 679
THE ZAMOISKI CO.; *U.S. Private*, pg. 1203

5182 — WINES & DISTILLED ALCOHOLIC BEVERAGES-WHOLESALE

ADAMS WINE CO.; *U.S. Private*, pg. 17
ALLIED DOMECQ PLC; *Int'l*, pg. 62
ALLIED DOMECQ SPIRITS & WINE—Allied Domecq PLC; *Int'l*, pg. 63
ANDRES WINES (ALBERTA) LTD.—Andres Wines Ltd.; *Int'l*, pg. 76
ANDRES WINES (ATLANTIC) LTD.—Andres Wines Ltd.; *Int'l*, pg. 76
ANDRES WINES (B.C.) LTD.—Andres Wines Ltd.; *Int'l*, pg. 76
BEN ARNOLD CO., INC.; *U.S. Private*, pg. 83
ARTHUR TREACHER'S, INC.; *U.S. Public*, pg. 136
B & G WHOLESALERS, INC.; *U.S. Private*, pg. 105
BACARDI CORPORATION—Bacardi Limited; *Int'l*, pg. 131
BACARDI-MARTINI, USA, INC.; *U.S. Private*, pg. 109
R & A BAILEY & CO.—Diageo Plc; *Int'l*, pg. 409
BANFI VINTNERS; *U.S. Private*, pg. 113
BARTON BRANDS OF CALIFORNIA, INC.—Canandaigua Wine Company, Inc.; *U.S. Public*, pg. 300
BARTON BRANDS OF GEORGIA, INC.—Canandaigua Wine Company, Inc.; *U.S. Public*, pg. 300
BARTON DISTILLERS IMPORT CORP.—Canandaigua Wine Company, Inc.; *U.S. Public*, pg. 300
BARTON INCORPORATED—Canandaigua Wine Company, Inc.; *U.S. Public*, pg. 300
BEAUCHAMP DISTRIBUTING COMPANY; *U.S. Private*, pg. 127
BETTER BRANDS OF ATLANTA, INC.; *U.S. Private*, pg. 141
BETTERBRANDS, LTD.—Young's Holdings Inc.; *U.S. Private*, pg. 1202
BLOCK DISTRIBUTING COMPANY; *U.S. Private*, pg. 149
BOLS ROYAL DISTILLERIES—Koninklijke BolsWessanen nv; *Int'l*, pg. 751
BOULEVARD DISTILLERS AND IMPORTERS INC.—Groupe Pernod Ricard; *Int'l*, pg. 567
BOURBON WAREHOUSE RECEIPTS, INC.—Fortune Brands, Inc.; *U.S. Public*, pg. 675
CAMPBELL DISTILLERS LIMITED—Groupe Pernod Ricard; *Int'l*, pg. 567
CASTLETON BEVERAGE CORP.—Bacardi Limited; *Int'l*, pg. 132
CHARMER INDUSTRIES; *U.S. Private*, pg. 230
CHATHAM IMPORTS, INC.—Peerless Importers, Inc.; *U.S. Private*, pg. 847
CLICQUOT, INC.—LVMH Moet Hennessy Louis Vuitton; *Int'l*, pg. 781
COLONY LIQUOR DISTRIBUTORS, INC.; *U.S. Private*, pg. 254
CROFT & COMPANHIA LIMITADA—Diageo Plc; *Int'l*, pg. 409
DAHLSTEN TRUCK LINE, INC.; *U.S. Private*, pg. 306
DATEO IMPORT S.P.A.; *Int'l*, pg. 385
DOMECQ IMPORTERS INC.—Allied Domecq PLC; *Int'l*, pg. 63
ECKES AG; *Int'l*, pg. 432
EUROPEAN CELLARS LTD.—Whitbread PLC; *Int'l*, pg. 1499
FORMAN BROTHERS, INC.; *U.S. Private*, pg. 418
E. & J. GALLO WINERY; *U.S. Private*, pg. 438
GAULT DISTRIBUTORS INC.; *Int'l*, pg. 541
GENERAL WHOLESALE COMPANY, INC.; *U.S. Private*, pg. 445
GEORGIA CROWN DISTRIBUTING; *U.S. Private*, pg. 448
GILBEY CANADA INC.—Diageo Plc; *Int'l*, pg. 409
GILBEY'S OF IRELAND—Diageo Plc; *Int'l*, pg. 409
GLAZER'S WHOLESALE DRUG CO. INC.; *U.S. Private*, pg. 455
GLEN ELLEN WINERY; *U.S. Private*, pg. 455
GRANTHAM DISTRIBUTING COMPANY, INC.; *U.S. Private*, pg. 470
GROUPE PERNOD RICARD; *Int'l*, pg. 566
HAGEMEYER N.V.—First Pacific Company Limited; *Int'l*, pg. 487
HEUBLEIN, INC.—Diageo Plc; *Int'l*, pg. 410
C.G. HIBBERT LTD.—Allied Domecq PLC; *Int'l*, pg. 63
HIRAM WALKER—Allied Domecq PLC; *Int'l*, pg. 63
HIRAM WALKER & SONS LIMITED—Allied Domecq PLC; *Int'l*, pg. 63
THE HOUSE OF SEAGRAM—The Seagram Company Ltd.; *Int'l*, pg. 1217
IDV NORTH AMERICA—Diageo Plc; *Int'l*, pg. 411
IDV FRANCE—Diageo Plc; *Int'l*, pg. 410
IDV UK—Diageo Plc; *Int'l*, pg. 409
INTERAPPIA PUBLICITA S.P.A.—Koninklijke BolsWessanen nv; *Int'l*, pg. 751
INTERNATIONAL DISTILLERS & VINTNERS-EUROPE—Diageo Plc; *Int'l*, pg. 409
INTERNATIONAL DISTILLERS & VINTNERS LTD.—Diageo Plc; *Int'l*, pg. 409
INTERNATIONAL DISTILLERS JAPAN—Diageo Plc; *Int'l*, pg. 410
INTERNATIONAL DISTILLERS SOUTH ASIA—Diageo Plc; *Int'l*, pg. 410
CHARLES JACQUIN ET CIE, INC.; *U.S. Private*, pg. 580
JARDINE MATHESON HOLDINGS LIMITED; *Int'l*, pg. 703
THE JAYDOR CORPORATION; *U.S. Private*, pg. 584
JOHNSON BROTHERS WHOLESALE LIQUOR; *U.S. Private*, pg. 591
JUSTERINI & BROOKS LTD.—Diageo Plc; *Int'l*, pg. 409
LKI—Leonard Kreusch, Inc.; *U.S. Private*, pg. 635
LAIRD & COMPANY; *U.S. Private*, pg. 642
LES VINS ANDRES DU QUEBEC LTEE.—Andres Wines Ltd.; *Int'l*, pg. 76
A. LEVY & J. ZENTNER CO.; *U.S. Private*, pg. 663
LIPSCHUTZ BROTHERS INC—BAA plc; *Int'l*, pg. 103
MATTHEW CLARK TAUNTON, LTD.; *Int'l*, pg. 848
MEIJI SHOKUHIN CO., LTD.—Meiji Seika Kaisha, Ltd.; *Int'l*, pg. 855
SAMUEL MEISEL & COMPANY, INC.—BAA plc; *Int'l*, pg. 103
METAXA GREECE—Diageo Plc; *Int'l*, pg. 410
MONTEBELLO BRANDS INC.; *U.S. Private*, pg. 758
NWS INC.; *U.S. Private*, pg. 772
NATIONAL DISTRIBUTING CO., INC.; *U.S. Private*, pg. 781
NATIONAL DISTRIBUTING CO., INC.—National Distributing Co., Inc.; *U.S. Private*, pg. 781
NATIONAL DISTRIBUTORS—National Distributing Co., Inc.; *U.S. Private*, pg. 781
NATIONAL WINE & SPIRITS CORP.; *U.S. Private*, pg. 788
AUSTIN NICHOLS & CO. INC.—Groupe Pernod Ricard; *Int'l*, pg. 566
NUYENS LIQUOR IMPORTING, INC.—White Rock Distilleries Inc.; *U.S. Private*, pg. 1173
ORLANDO WYNDHAM—Groupe Pernod Ricard; *Int'l*, pg. 567
PR EUROPE—Groupe Pernod Ricard; *Int'l*, pg. 566
PACIFIC WINE CO.—Paterno Imports Limited; *U.S. Private*, pg. 843
PATERNO IMPORTS LIMITED; *U.S. Private*, pg. 843
PEARLSTINE DISTRIBUTORS INC.; *U.S. Private*, pg. 845
PEERLESS IMPORTERS, INC.; *U.S. Private*, pg. 847
PELLER WINES OF CALIFORNIA—Andres Wines Ltd.; *Int'l*, pg. 76
PENAFLOR S.A.; *Int'l*, pg. 1032
PINE STATE TRADING COMPANY; *U.S. Private*, pg. 865
R & R MARKETING; *U.S. Private*, pg. 902
A. RACKE GMBH; *Int'l*, pg. 1083
RACKE USA—A. Racke GmbH; *Int'l*, pg. 1083
REMY AMERIQUE INC.—Remy Cointreau; *Int'l*, pg. 1102
REMY COINTREAU; *Int'l*, pg. 1102
REPUBLIC BEVERAGE CO.—Block Distributing Company; *U.S. Private*, pg. 150
REPUBLIC BEVERAGE COMPANY—Block Distributing Company; *U.S. Private*, pg. 149
ROBERTSON & BAXTER LIMITED—The Highland Distilleries Company plc; *Int'l*, pg. 619
SAPPORO U.S.A., INC., NEW YORK—Sapporo Breweries Ltd.; *Int'l*, pg. 1193
SCHIEFFELIN & SOMERSET CO.—Diageo Plc; *Int'l*, pg. 412
SCHIEFFELIN & SOMERSET CO.—LVMH Moet Hennessy Louis Vuitton; *Int'l*, pg. 781
SCOTTISH & COURAGE BEER DIV.—Scottish & Newcastle plc; *Int'l*, pg. 1212
SEAGRAM ASIA PACIFIC/GLOBAL DUTY FREE—The Seagram Company Ltd.; *Int'l*, pg. 1217
THE SEAGRAM BEVERAGE GROUP—The Seagram Company Ltd.; *Int'l*, pg. 1217
SEAGRAM CHATEAU & ESTATE WINES CO.—The Seagram Company Ltd.; *Int'l*, pg. 1215
THE SEAGRAM CLASSICS WINE COMPANY—The Seagram Company Ltd.; *Int'l*, pg. 1215
THE SEAGRAM COMPANY LTD.; *Int'l*, pg. 1214
SEAGRAM EUROPE AND AFRICA—The Seagram Company Ltd.; *Int'l*, pg. 1217
SEAGRAM GLOBAL BRANDS—The Seagram Company Ltd.; *Int'l*, pg. 1217
JOSEPH E. SEAGRAM & SONS, INC.—The Seagram Company Ltd.; *Int'l*, pg. 1215
SEAGRAM LATIN AMERICA—The Seagram Company Ltd.; *Int'l*, pg. 1217
THE SEAGRAM SPIRITS AND WINE GROUP—The Seagram Company Ltd.; *Int'l*, pg. 1217
STAR INDUSTRIES INC.; *U.S. Private*, pg. 1034
TENNESSEE DICKEL DISTILLING CO.—Diageo Plc; *Int'l*, pg. 412
UNITED DISTILLERS UK PLC—Diageo Plc; *Int'l*, pg. 412
UNITED DISTILLERS USA, INC.—Diageo Plc; *Int'l*, pg. 412
UNITED DISTRIBUTORS, INC.; *U.S. Private*, pg. 1121
VANGUARD DIVISION—Nestle S.A.; *Int'l*, pg. 917
VAUX GROUP PLC; *Int'l*, pg. 1453
VERCOOPE-UNIAO DAS ADEGAS COOPERATIVAS DA REGIAO DOS VINHOA VERDES, U.C.R.L.; *Int'l*, pg. 1463
JOSEPH VICTORI WINES, INC.; *U.S. Private*, pg. 1139
M.S. WALKER, INC.; *U.S. Private*, pg. 1147
WAVERLY VINTNERS LIMITED—Scottish & Newcastle plc; *Int'l*, pg. 1212
WHITE ROCK DISTILLERIES INC.; *U.S. Private*, pg. 1173
FREDERICK WILDMAN & SONS LTD.; *U.S. Private*, pg. 1176
THE WINE GROUP; *U.S. Private*, pg. 1182
WINONA S.A.R.L.—Andres Wines Ltd.; *Int'l*, pg. 76
WORLD BRANDS DUTY FREE—Groupe Pernod Ricard; *Int'l*, pg. 567
YAMANASHI JOZO CO., LTD.—Meiji Seika Kaisha, Ltd.; *Int'l*, pg. 855
YOUNG'S HOLDINGS INC.; *U.S. Private*, pg. 1202
YOUNG'S MARKET COMPANY—Young's Holdings Inc.; *U.S. Private*, pg. 1202

5191 — FARM SUPPLIES-WHOLESALE

ADAIR FEED & GRAIN COMPANY; *U.S. Private*, pg. 16
AGRILAND COMPANY; *U.S. Private*, pg. 26
AGROLINZ INC.—DSM N.V.; *Int'l*, pg. 356
AGROSTAR A.G.—Novartis AG; *Int'l*, pg. 974
AGCO, INC.; *U.S. Private*, pg. 27
ALABAMA FARMERS CO-OP; *U.S. Private*, pg. 30
AMVAC CHEMICAL CORPORATION—American Vanguard Corporation; *U.S. Public*, pg. 94
THE ANDERSONS INCORPORATED; *U.S. Public*, pg. 111
ASGROW INTERNATIONAL CORP.—Pharmacia & Upjohn, Inc.; *Int'l*, pg. 1048
B&W CO-OP, INC.; *U.S. Private*, pg. 105
BAKER COMMODITIES, INC.; *U.S. Private*, pg. 111
BALL HORTICULTURAL COMPANY; *U.S. Private*, pg. 112
BALL SEED CO.—Ball Horticultural Company; *U.S. Private*, pg. 112
BIG HORN CO-OP MARKETING ASSOCIATION; *U.S. Private*, pg. 143
BREEDER'S SEEDS LTD.—Novartis AG; *Int'l*, pg. 975
C. BREWER & COMPANY, LIMITED—Buyco, Inc.; *U.S. Private*, pg. 190
GEORGE F. BROCKE & SONS, INC.; *U.S. Private*, pg. 170
CARDER, INC.; *U.S. Private*, pg. 208
CARGILL LTD.—Cargill; *U.S. Private*, pg. 210
CARGILL SEED DIV.—Cargill; *U.S. Private*, pg. 210
CENEX, INC.; *U.S. Private*, pg. 221
CHAMPAIGN LANDMARK, INC.; *U.S. Private*, pg. 227

CHAROEN SEEDS COMPANY LTD.—Dekalb Genetics Corporation; U.S. Public, pg. 493
CHEMI-TROL CHEMICAL CO.; U.S. Public, pg. 345
CHEMICAL COMPANY OF MALAYSIA BERHAD—Imperial Chemical Industries PLC; Int'l, pg. 664
CHEMIE LINZ FRANCE S.A.R.L.—DSM N.V.; Int'l, pg. 356
CHEMIE LINZ UK LTD.—DSM N.V.; Int'l, pg. 356
CHEMSERV INDUSTRIE SERVICE GES.M.B.H.—DSM N.V.; Int'l, pg. 356
CIBA-GEIGY (CHINA) LIMITED-GUANGZHOU BRANCH OFFICE—Novartis AG; Int'l, pg. 976
COUNTRYMARK COOPERATIVE, INC.; U.S. Private, pg. 279
DSM CHEMIE LINZ NORTH AMERICA INC.—DSM N.V.; Int'l, pg. 356
DALGETY AGRICULTURE, LIMITED—Dalgety Plc; Int'l, pg. 376
DEBRUCE GRAIN INC.; U.S. Private, pg. 319
DEKALB ARGENTINA, S.A.—Dekalb Genetics Corporation; U.S. Public, pg. 493
DEKALB CANADA INC.—Dekalb Genetics Corporation; U.S. Public, pg. 493
DEKALB ITALIA, S.P.A.—Dekalb Genetics Corporation; U.S. Public, pg. 493
DOW ELANCO—The Dow Chemical Company; U.S. Public, pg. 522
DU PONT ASIA PACIFIC LTD.—Du Pont (E.I. Du Pont De Nemours & Co.); U.S. Public, pg. 532
DU PONT DE NEMOURS (FRANCE) S.A.—Du Pont (E.I. Du Pont De Nemours & Co.); U.S. Public, pg. 532
EDMONSON WHEAT GROWERS, INC.; U.S. Private, pg. 364
EFFINGHAM-CLAY SERVICE CO.; U.S. Private, pg. 365
ELANCO PRODUCTS LIMITED—Eli Lilly and Company; U.S. Public, pg. 993
EMPREENDIMENTOS AGRICOLA PIONEER LTDA.—Pioneer Hi-Bred International, Inc.; U.S. Public, pg. 1299
EMSLAND-RAISIO CHEMIE GMBH—Raisio Group; Int'l, pg. 1086
ENTREPRISE MINIERE ET CHIMIQUE; Int'l, pg. 458
EXCEL CO-OP INC.; U.S. Private, pg. 387
FMC ARGENTINA, S.A. C.I., Y.F.—FMC Corporation; U.S. Public, pg. 606
FMC (AUSTRALIA) LIMITED—FMC Corporation; U.S. Public, pg. 606
FMC CAMEROON SARL—FMC Corporation; U.S. Public, pg. 606
FMC DO BRASIL, S.A.—FMC Corporation; U.S. Public, pg. 606
FMC EUROPE NV—FMC Corporation; U.S. Public, pg. 606
FMC EUROPE, S.A./N.V.—FMC Corporation; U.S. Public, pg. 606
FMC HELLAS EPE—FMC Corporation; U.S. Public, pg. 606
FMC INTERNATIONAL, A.G.—FMC Corporation; U.S. Public, pg. 606
FMC NEDERLAND B.V.—FMC Corporation; U.S. Public, pg. 606
FARMERS CO-OP MARKET INC.; U.S. Private, pg. 395
FARMWAY CO-OP INC.; U.S. Private, pg. 396
FINLEY FARMERS GRAIN & ELEVATOR COMPANY; U.S. Private, pg. 405
FISONS WESTERN CORPORATION—Rhone-Poulenc S.A.; Int'l, pg. 1111
FLORIDA FAVORITE FERTILIZER—Potash Corporation of Saskatchewan Inc.; Int'l, pg. 1064
FOUR-F NUTRITION—Tate & Lyle PLC; Int'l, pg. 1356
FREDERICK TRADING COMPANY—Distribution America; U.S. Private, pg. 335
FRIONA INDUSTRIES, L.P.; U.S. Private, pg. 429
GSC ENTERPRISES, INC.; U.S. Private, pg. 436
GEBRUDER DIPPE SAATZUCHT G.M.B.H.—Novartis AG; Int'l, pg. 982
GERBER AGRI INC.—Gerber International Inc.; U.S. Private, pg. 449
J. GERBER & CO. INC.—Gerber International Inc.; U.S. Private, pg. 449
GOLD KIST, INC.; U.S. Private, pg. 459
GRAND PRAIRIE CO-OP, INC.; U.S. Private, pg. 468
GREENWAY CO-OP SERVICE; U.S. Private, pg. 478
GRIFFIN CORPORATION; U.S. Private, pg. 480
GROW FORCE AUSTRALIA LIMITED—Imperial Chemical Industries PLC; Int'l, pg. 664
GROWMARK, INC.; U.S. Private, pg. 484
GRUPO AGROGEN S.A. DE C.V., MEXICO—Dekalb Genetics Corporation; U.S. Public, pg. 493
HERITAGE CO-OP; U.S. Private, pg. 524
HI-PRO ANIMAL HEALTH—Friona Industries, L.P.; U.S. Private, pg. 429
HI-PRO FEED—Friona Industries, L.P.; U.S. Private, pg. 429
HIBRIDOS PIONEER DE MEXICO S.A. DE C.V.—Pioneer Hi-Bred International, Inc.; U.S. Public, pg. 1299
HIBRIVEN HIBRIDOS VENEZOLANOS S.A.—Pioneer Hi-Bred International, Inc.; U.S. Public, pg. 1299
HILLESHOG AB—Novartis AG; Int'l, pg. 982
HOECHST MARION ROUSSEL, INC.—Hoechst Aktiengesellschaft; Int'l, pg. 624
HOFFMAN SEEDS, INC.—A.H. Hoffman, Inc.; U.S. Private, pg. 532
HOPKINSVILLE ELEVATOR COMPANY, INC.; U.S. Private, pg. 538
HYDRO AGRI NORTH AMERICA—Norsk Hydro a.s; Int'l, pg. 961
HYDRO/KIRBY AGRI SERVICE, INC.; U.S. Private, pg. 552
ICI AGROCHEMICALS (MALAYSIA) SDN BHD—Imperial Chemical Industries PLC; Int'l, pg. 664
ICI INDIA LIMITED—Imperial Chemical Industries PLC; Int'l, pg. 665
ICI (SINGAPORE) PRIVATE LIMITED—Imperial Chemical Industries PLC; Int'l, pg. 665
ICI ZAMBIA LIMITED—Imperial Chemical Industries PLC; Int'l, pg. 665
INCITEC LTD—Imperial Chemical Industries PLC; Int'l, pg. 665
INTERMOUNTAIN FARMERS ASSOCIATION; U.S. Private, pg. 568
INTERNATIONAL CHEMICAL COMPANY; U.S. Private, pg. 568
INTERSTATE COMMODITIES INC.; U.S. Private, pg. 573
INVESTIGACIONES PIONEER S DE R.L. DE C.V.—Pioneer Hi-Bred International, Inc.; U.S. Public, pg. 1299
JIFFY PRODUCTS OF AMERICA, INC.—Jiffy Products International Ltd.; Int'l, pg. 706
JOHNSON COUNTY FARM BUREAU CO-OP; U.S. Private, pg. 591
KEMIRA AGRO ROZENBURG B.V.—Kemira Oy; Int'l, pg. 729
KEMIRA S.A./N.V.—Kemira Oy; Int'l, pg. 728
KINGFISHER CO-OP ELEVATOR ASSOCIATION; U.S. Private, pg. 621
KONINKLIJKE ZAADTEELT EN ZAADHANDEL SLUIS EN GROOT B.V.—Novartis AG; Int'l, pg. 983
KOVA FERTILIZER INC.; U.S. Private, pg. 634
LA SALLE COUNTY FARM SUPPLY; U.S. Private, pg. 640
LAND O'LAKES, INC.; U.S. Private, pg. 645
LES GRAINES CAILLARD S.A.—Novartis AG; Int'l, pg. 983
LEXINGTON CO-OP OIL CO.; U.S. Private, pg. 666
LIVING EARTH TECHNOLOGY CO.—Republic Industries, Inc.; U.S. Public, pg. 1379
MFA INCORPORATED; U.S. Private, pg. 686
MISR PIONEER SEED CO. S.A.E.—Pioneer Hi-Bred International, Inc.; U.S. Public, pg. 1299
MAICES HIBRIDOS Y SEMILLAS SA—Novartis AG; Int'l, pg. 983
MAINE POTATO GROWERS, INC.; U.S. Private, pg. 697
MCCAIN FERTILIZERS LIMITED—McCain Foods Limited; Int'l, pg. 850
MITSUBISHI INTERNATIONAL CORPORATION—Mitsubishi Corporation; Int'l, pg. 871
MONSANTO B.V.—Monsanto Company; U.S. Public, pg. 1125
MONSANTO CANADA, INC.—Monsanto Company; U.S. Public, pg. 1125
MONSANTO CHEMICAL PRODUCTS HELLAS, E.P.E.—Monsanto Company; U.S. Public, pg. 1125
MONSANTO DE COSTA RICA, S.A.—Monsanto Company; U.S. Public, pg. 1125
MONSANTO ESPANA S.A.—Monsanto Company; U.S. Public, pg. 1125
MONSANTO IRELAND LTD.—Monsanto Company; U.S. Public, pg. 1125
MONSANTO JAPAN LTD.—Monsanto Company; U.S. Public, pg. 1126
MONSANTO PHILIPPINES INC.—Monsanto Company; U.S. Public, pg. 1126
MONSANTO P.L.C.—Monsanto Company; U.S. Public, pg. 1126
MONSANTO SINGAPORE COMPANY (PTE.) LTD.—Monsanto Company; U.S. Public, pg. 1126
MONSANTO SOUTH AFRICA (PTY.) LIMITED—Monsanto Company; U.S. Public, pg. 1126
MONSANTO (SUISSE) S.A.—Monsanto Company; U.S. Public, pg. 1126
MONSANTO THAILAND LTD.—Monsanto Company; U.S. Public, pg. 1126
MONSANTO (VENEZUELA) C.A.—Monsanto Company; U.S. Public, pg. 1126
MONTE VISTA CO-OP ASSOCIATION, INC.; U.S. Private, pg. 758
MYCOGEN CORPORATION; U.S. Public, pg. 1142
MYCOGEN SEEDS—Mycogen Corporation; U.S. Public, pg. 1142
NK LAWN & GARDEN—Novartis AG; Int'l, pg. 974
NEW COOPERATIVE INC.; U.S. Private, pg. 792
NIHON TOKUSHU NOYAKU SEIZO K.K.—Bayer AG; Int'l, pg. 174
NORTH PACIFIC LUMBER COMPANY; U.S. Private, pg. 805
NORTHEAST TEXAS FARMERS CO-OP; U.S. Private, pg. 805
NORTHRUP KING CO.—Novartis AG; Int'l, pg. 974
NORTHRUP KING PTY. LTD.—Novartis AG; Int'l, pg. 983
NORTHRUP KING SEEDS LTD.—Novartis AG; Int'l, pg. 983
NORTHRUP KING SEMENCES S.A.—Novartis AG; Int'l, pg. 983
NORTHRUP KING SEMENTI S.P.A.—Novartis AG; Int'l, pg. 983
NORTHRUP KING Y COMPANIA, S.A. DE C.V.—Novartis AG; Int'l, pg. 983
BRUCE OAKLEY, INC.; U.S. Private, pg. 809
PCS PHOSPHATE - AURORA—Potash Corporation of Saskatchewan Inc.; Int'l, pg. 1064
C.W. PANNEVIS ZAADTEELT EN ZAADHANDEL B.V.—Novartis AG; Int'l, pg. 975
PANNEVIS ZAADTEELT EN ZAADHANDEL N.V.—Novartis AG; Int'l, pg. 983
PFIZER PRODUCTS PLC—Pfizer Inc.; U.S. Public, pg. 1282
PIONEER AGRICULTURA LTDA.—Pioneer Hi-Bred International, Inc.; U.S. Public, pg. 1299
PIONEER ARGENTINA, S.A.—Pioneer Hi-Bred International, Inc.; U.S. Public, pg. 1299
PIONEER BIOGENE, PVT. LTD.—Pioneer Hi-Bred International, Inc.; U.S. Public, pg. 1299
G.I.E. PIONEER FRANCE—Pioneer Hi-Bred International, Inc.; U.S. Public, pg. 1299
PIONEER FRANCE MAIS S.A.—Pioneer Hi-Bred International, Inc.; U.S. Public, pg. 1299
PIONEER HI-BRED INTERNATIONAL, INC.; U.S. Public, pg. 1298
P.T. PIONEER HIBRIDA INDONESIA—Pioneer Hi-Bred International, Inc.; U.S. Public, pg. 1299
PIONEER INTERNATIONAL OPERATIONS DIVISION—Pioneer Hi-Bred International, Inc.; U.S. Public, pg. 1299
PIONEER OVERSEAS, GES.MBH.—Pioneer Hi-Bred International, Inc.; U.S. Public, pg. 1299
PIONEER SAATEN AG—Pioneer Hi-Bred International, Inc.; U.S. Public, pg. 1299
PIONEER SAATEN, GMBH—Pioneer Hi-Bred International, Inc.; U.S. Public, pg. 1299
PIONEER SEMENTES LTDA.—Pioneer Hi-Bred International, Inc.; U.S. Public, pg. 1299
PIONEER TOHUMCULUK A.S.—Pioneer Hi-Bred International, Inc.; U.S. Public, pg. 1299
PRODUCERS CO-OP ASSOCIATION, INC.; U.S. Private, pg. 888
PURDEL, COOPERATIVE AGRO-ALIMENTAIRE; Int'l, pg. 1073
PURINA KOREA INC.—Ralston Purina Company; U.S. Public, pg. 1360
RANCHERS SUPPLY COMPANY, INC.; U.S. Private, pg. 908
RAY-CARROLL COUNTY GRAIN CO-OP; U.S. Private, pg. 911
ROGERS N.K. SEED CO.—Novartis AG; Int'l, pg. 974
ROSENS DIVERSIFIED, INC.; U.S. Private, pg. 945
ROSENS, INC.—Rosens Diversified, Inc.; U.S. Private, pg. 945
RUGBY FARMERS UNION ELEVATOR COMPANY; U.S. Private, pg. 950
SCAC-FISONS SA—Rhone-Poulenc S.A.; Int'l, pg. 1111
SF SERVICES; U.S. Private, pg. 956
SAKATA SEED AMERICA, INC.—Sakata Seed Corporation; Int'l, pg. 1178
SAKATA SEED CORPORATION; Int'l, pg. 1178
SAKATA SEED EUROPE B.V.—Sakata Seed Corporation; Int'l, pg. 1178
SANDOZ AGRICOLA S.A. DE C.V.—Novartis AG; Int'l, pg. 984
SANDOZ B.V.—Novartis AG; Int'l, pg. 984
SANDOZ CORPORATION—Novartis AG; Int'l, pg. 974
SANDOZ-MAROC S.A.—Novartis AG; Int'l, pg. 985
THE SCOTTS COMPANY; U.S. Public, pg. 1446
SEMILLAS PIONEER CHILE LTDA.—Pioneer Hi-Bred International, Inc.; U.S. Public, pg. 1299
SERVICE GENETIQUES S.A.R.L.—Pioneer Hi-Bred International, Inc.; U.S. Public, pg. 1299
SHOWA DENKO AMERICA, INC.—Showa Denko K.K.; Int'l, pg. 1237
SLUIS & GROOT ITALIA S.P.A.—Novartis AG; Int'l, pg. 985
SNOW BRAND SEED CO., LTD.—Snow Brand Milk Products Co. Ltd.; Int'l, pg. 1272
SOCIEDADE PORTUGUESA DE DESENVOLVIMENTO-QUIMICO DE MONSANTO, LIMITADA—Monsanto Company; U.S. Public, pg. 1126
SOCKALB G.I.E. FRANCE—Dekalb Genetics Corporation; U.S. Public, pg. 493
SOUTH CENTRAL CO-OP; U.S. Private, pg. 1014
SOUTHCHEM; U.S. Private, pg. 1014
SOUTHERN AGRICULTURAL INSECTICIDES, INC.; U.S. Private, pg. 1015
SOUTHERN STATES COOPERATIVE, INC.; U.S. Private, pg. 1017
SPEEDLING INCORPORATED; U.S. Private, pg. 1024
STONEVILLE PEDIGREED SEED CO.—Monsanto Company; U.S. Public, pg. 1124
SUMITOMO CHEMICAL AMERICA, INC.—Sumitomo Chemical Company, Ltd.; Int'l, pg. 1311
SUNNILAND CORPORATION; U.S. Private, pg. 1053
TERMINAL GRAIN CORP.; U.S. Private, pg. 1077
TERRA INDUSTRIES, INC.; U.S. Public, pg. 1581
TERRA INTERNATIONAL—Terra Industries, Inc.; U.S. Public, pg. 1581
TERRAL SEED CO., INC.; U.S. Private, pg. 1077
TOBERMAN; U.S. Private, pg. 1089
TOSHOKU AMERICA, INC.—Toshoku Ltd.; Int'l, pg. 1407
TOSHOKU LTD.; Int'l, pg. 1407
TRANSAMMONIA AG—Transammonia Inc.; U.S. Private, pg. 1096
TRANSAMMONIA INC.; U.S. Private, pg. 1096
TRAYLOR CHEMICAL & SUPPLY CO.; U.S. Private, pg. 1098
UNIVERSAL COOPERATIVES, INC.; U.S. Private, pg. 1127
VALLEY SEED CO.—Arizona Grains Inc.; U.S. Private, pg. 82
VIGORO INDUSTRIES, SOUTHEAST DIVISION—IMC Global; U.S. Public, pg. 856
TOM WADE CO.; U.S. Private, pg. 1145
WATKINS INCORPORATED; U.S. Private, pg. 1153
WESTERN ASH COMPANY—Boral Limited; Int'l, pg. 203
WESTERN STATES PETROLEUM INC.; U.S. Private, pg. 1169
WHEELER BROS. GRAIN CO.—Wheeler Brothers Grain Co.; U.S. Private, pg. 1171
WILBUR-ELLIS AGRICULTURAL—Wilbur-Ellis Company & Connell Brothers Company; U.S. Private, pg. 1176
WILLARD GRAIN & FEED, INC.; U.S. Private, pg. 1177
ZAADUNIE B.V.—Novartis AG; Int'l, pg. 986
ZENECA AB—Zeneca Group Plc; Int'l, pg. 1526
ZENECA AGROCHEMICALS AND SEEDS—Zeneca Group Plc; Int'l, pg. 1524
ZENECA AGROCHEMICALS MAROC S.A.—Zeneca Group Plc; Int'l, pg. 1526
ZENECA COSTA RICA, S.A.—Zeneca Group Plc; Int'l, pg. 1526
ZENECA GROUP PLC; Int'l, pg. 1524
ZENECA OY—Zeneca Group Plc; Int'l, pg. 1527
ZENECA PANAMERICANA S.A.—BASF AG; Int'l, pg. 110
ZENECA PANAMERICANA S.A.—Zeneca Group Plc; Int'l, pg. 1527
ZENECA POLAND SP. Z.O.O.—Zeneca Group Plc; Int'l, pg. 1527
ZENECA ZIMBABWE (PRIVATE) LIMITED—Zeneca Group Plc; Int'l, pg. 1527
ZWAAN UND CO. SAMENZUCHT G.M.B.H.—Novartis AG; Int'l, pg. 986

5192 — BOOKS, PERIODICALS & NEWSPAPERS-WHOLESALE

ADDISON-WESLEY PUBLISHERS B.V.—Pearson plc; *Int'l*, pg. 1027
AKADEMIBOKHANDELSGRUPPEN—KF/Konsum Coop Group; *Int'l*, pg. 718
BANTAM BOOK CANADA INC.—Bertelsmann AG; *Int'l*, pg. 191
BARNES & NOBLE DIRECT—Barnes & Noble Inc.; *U.S. Public*, pg. 189
BELL & HOWELL LTD.—Bell & Howell Holdings; *U.S. Public*, pg. 201
BETTY CROCKER PRODUCTS—General Mills, Inc.; *U.S. Public*, pg. 718
BIBLIO DISTRIBUTION CTR.—University Press of America, Inc.; *U.S. Private*, pg. 1128
BOOKAZINE COMPANY, INC.; *U.S. Private*, pg. 156
BRODART COMPANY; *U.S. Private*, pg. 170
CHAPTERS INC.; *Int'l*, pg. 280
CORPORATE EXPRESS OFFICE PRODUCTS—Corporate Express, Inc.; *U.S. Public*, pg. 449
DIAMOND COMIC DISTRIBUTORS, INC.; *U.S. Private*, pg. 330
EASTERN NEWS DISTRIBUTORS, INC.—The Hearst Corporation; *U.S. Private*, pg. 517
EASTON PRESS BOOKS—MBI Inc.; *U.S. Private*, pg. 685
EDUCATIONAL DEVELOPMENT CORPORATION; *U.S. Public*, pg. 564
EX LIBRIS AG—Migros; *Int'l*, pg. 865
GROLIER LIMITED—Lagardere Groupe; *Int'l*, pg. 794
HADDON CRAFTSMEN, INC.—R.R. Donnelley & Sons Company; *U.S. Public*, pg. 518
HANDLEMAN COMPANY; *U.S. Public*, pg. 779
HUDSON COUNTY NEWS COMPANY; *U.S. Private*, pg. 545
INGRAM BOOK COMPANY—Ingram Industries Inc.; *U.S. Private*, pg. 563
INGRAM DISTRIBUTION GROUP INC.—Ingram Industries Inc.; *U.S. Private*, pg. 563
INTERNATIONAL CIRCULATION DISTRIBUTORS—The Hearst Corporation; *U.S. Private*, pg. 517
THE INTERNATIONAL PUBLISHING GROUP—Pearson plc; *Int'l*, pg. 1027
K & M PRODUCTS DIVISION—Avery Dennison Corporation; *U.S. Public*, pg. 152
KABLE NEWS CO., INC.—AMREP Corporation; *U.S. Public*, pg. 105
LAROUSSE-BELGIQUE—C.E.P. Communication Group; *Int'l*, pg. 240
EDITORIA LAROUSSE DO BRASIL—C.E.P. Communication Group; *Int'l*, pg. 240
EDICIONES LAROUSSE SA—C.E.P. Communication Group; *Int'l*, pg. 240
THE CHAS. LEVY COMPANY; *U.S. Private*, pg. 664
LUDINGTON NEWS CO. INC.; *U.S. Private*, pg. 679
MACMILLAN DISTRIBUTION LTD.—Georg von Holtzbrinck GmbH; *Int'l*, pg. 1479
MUNKSGAARD INTERNATIONAL BOOKSELLERS & PUBLISHERS LTD.—B.H. Blackwell Ltd.; *Int'l*, pg. 197
NATIONAL BOOK COMPANY INC.—W.W. Norton & Company, Inc.; *U.S. Private*, pg. 807
NATION'S BUSINESS; *U.S. Private*, pg. 788
NEBRASKA BOOK CO., INC.; *U.S. Private*, pg. 789
OXFORD UNIVERSITY PRESS, AUSTRALIA—Oxford University Press; *Int'l*, pg. 1019
OXFORD UNIVERSITY PRESS CANADA—Oxford University Press; *Int'l*, pg. 1019
OXFORD UNIVERSITY PRESS K.K.—Oxford University Press; *Int'l*, pg. 1019
OXFORD UNIVERSITY PRESS PTE. LTD.—Oxford University Press; *Int'l*, pg. 1019
PLENUM INTERNATIONAL SALES CORPORATION—Plenum Publishing Corporation; *U.S. Public*, pg. 1311
PRIMEDIA INC.—Primedia Inc.; *U.S. Public*, pg. 1328
RABEN & SJOGREN AB—KF/Konsum Coop Group; *Int'l*, pg. 718
SPRING ARBOR DISTRIBUTORS—Ingram Industries Inc.; *U.S. Private*, pg. 563
TIME DISTRIBUTION SERVICES—Time Warner Inc.; *U.S. Public*, pg. 1614
TIME-LIFE CUSTOMER SERVICE—Time Warner Inc.; *U.S. Public*, pg. 1613
URBAN & SCHWARZENBERG GMBH—Waverly, Inc.; *U.S. Public*, pg. 1748
VNU VERKOOPGROEP BV—VNU Verenigde Nederlandse Uitgeversbedrijven B.V.; *Int'l*, pg. 1445
WAVERLY, INC.; *U.S. Public*, pg. 1748
WAVERLY INTERNATIONAL—Waverly, Inc.; *U.S. Public*, pg. 1748
THE WORLD ALMANAC—Primedia Inc.; *U.S. Public*, pg. 1328

5193 — FLOWERS, NURSERY STOCK & FLORISTS' SUPPLIES-WHOLESALE

BALL HORTICULTURAL COMPANY; *U.S. Private*, pg. 112
BALL SEED CO.—Ball Horticultural Company; *U.S. Private*, pg. 112
BALL SUPERIOR LTD.—Ball Horticultural Company; *U.S. Private*, pg. 112
DWF OF GAYLORD—Denver Wholesale Florists Company; *U.S. Private*, pg. 326
DENVER WHOLESALE FLORISTS COMPANY; *U.S. Private*, pg. 326
DIMON, INCORPORATED; *U.S. Public*, pg. 509
EARL MAY SEED & NURSERY L.C.; *U.S. Private*, pg. 356
FLORIMEX WORLDWIDE GMBH—DIMON, Incorporated; *U.S. Public*, pg. 510
FLORIMEX WORLDWIDE, INC.—DIMON, Incorporated; *U.S. Public*, pg. 510
JIFFY PRODUCTS OF AMERICA, INC.—Jiffy Products International Ltd.; *Int'l*, pg. 706
LANCASTER FOODS, INC.—Guest Services, Inc.; *U.S. Private*, pg. 487
MID-WESTERN OF ALABAMA DIVISION—American Nursery Products, LLC; *U.S. Private*, pg. 60
MID-WESTERN NURSERY DIVISION—American Nursery Products, LLC; *U.S. Private*, pg. 60
MONROVIA NURSERY CO.; *U.S. Private*, pg. 757
NORTHLAND EVERGREENS, INC.—American Nursery Products, LLC; *U.S. Private*, pg. 60
NOVARTIS SEEDS, INC.—Novartis AG; *Int'l*, pg. 974
ORCHIDS ETC.—Yamanouchi Pharmaceutical Co. Ltd.; *Int'l*, pg. 1518
PETALS; *U.S. Private*, pg. 856
SAKATA SEED AMERICA, INC.—Sakata Seed Corporation; *Int'l*, pg. 1178
SAKATA SEED CORPORATION; *Int'l*, pg. 1178
SAKATA SEED EUROPE B.V.—Sakata Seed Corporation; *Int'l*, pg. 1178
STAR SALES CO., INC.; *U.S. Private*, pg. 1035
SUN BULB COMPANY, INC.; *U.S. Private*, pg. 1050
USA FLORAL PRODUCTS, INC.; *U.S. Public*, pg. 1685
ZAADUNIE B.V.—Novartis AG; *Int'l*, pg. 986

5194 — TOBACCO & TOBACCO PRODUCTS-WHOLESALE

B.A.T (DEUTSCHLAND) EXPORT GMBH—B.A.T Industries P.L.C.; *Int'l*, pg. 112
B.A.T INDUSTRIES P.L.C.; *Int'l*, pg. 110
B.A.T (SUISSE) SA—B.A.T Industries P.L.C.; *Int'l*, pg. 111
BRITISH AMERICAN TOBACCO CO. (HONG KONG) LTD.—B.A.T Industries P.L.C.; *Int'l*, pg. 111
BRITISH-AMERICAN TOBACCO CO. LTD.—B.A.T Industries P.L.C.; *Int'l*, pg. 111
BRITISH-AMERICAN TOBACCO CO. (SINGAPORE) LTD.—B.A.T Industries P.L.C.; *Int'l*, pg. 111
C & S WHOLESALE GROCERY INC.; *U.S. Private*, pg. 192
CIGARRERA LA MODERNA, SA DE CV—B.A.T Industries P.L.C.; *Int'l*, pg. 112
CLARENDON IMPORTS INC.—Rothmans UK Holdings Limited; *Int'l*, pg. 1130
COMPANIA GENERAL DE TABACOS DE FILIPINAS, S.A.—Tabacalera, S.A.; *Int'l*, pg. 1345
DAKCO DISTRIBUTORS, INC.; *U.S. Private*, pg. 308
FRITZ CO. INC.; *U.S. Private*, pg. 429
GALLAHER OVERSEAS LIMITED—Gallaher Limited; *Int'l*, pg. 539
GENERAL CIGAR COMPANY, INC.—General Cigar Holdings Inc; *U.S. Public*, pg. 708
GENERAL CIGAR HOLDINGS INC; *U.S. Public*, pg. 707
H & H DISTRIBUTING COMPANY, INC.; *U.S. Private*, pg. 489
HOUSE OF CRAVEN LTD.—Rothmans UK Holdings Limited; *Int'l*, pg. 1130
IMPERIAL TOBACCO LIMITED—B.A.T Industries P.L.C.; *Int'l*, pg. 112
JAPAN TOBACCO INC.; *Int'l*, pg. 703
THE JERSEY TOBACCO DISTRIBUTORS LTD.—B.A.T Industries P.L.C.; *Int'l*, pg. 111
LAYMAN CANDY COMPANY, INC.; *U.S. Private*, pg. 655
LEE GROCERY COMPANY; *U.S. Private*, pg. 657
LIPSCHUTZ BROTHERS INC—BAA plc; *Int'l*, pg. 103
LORILLARD TOBACCO COMPANY—Loews Corporation; *U.S. Public*, pg. 1011
SAMUEL MEISEL & COMPANY, INC.—BAA plc; *Int'l*, pg. 103
NATIONAL FOOD STORES, INC.; *U.S. Private*, pg. 783
NISSHO IWAI GENERAL MERCHANDISE CORP.—Nissho Iwai Corporation; *Int'l*, pg. 946
NORTHWEST TOBACCO & CANDY CO.; *U.S. Private*, pg. 806
PARK LANE TOBACCO COMPANY LTD.—Reemtsma Cigarettenfabriken GmbH, Hamburg; *Int'l*, pg. 1101
PHILIP MORRIS K.K.—Philip Morris Companies Inc.; *U.S. Public*, pg. 1290
PINE STATE TRADING COMPANY; *U.S. Private*, pg. 865
REEMTSMA HELLAS S.A.—Reemtsma Cigarettenfabriken GmbH, Hamburg; *Int'l*, pg. 1101
R.J. REYNOLDS (PORTUGAL) LIMITADA—RJR Nabisco Holdings Corp.; *U.S. Public*, pg. 1355
R.J. REYNOLDS TOBACCO B.V.—RJR Nabisco Holdings Corp.; *U.S. Public*, pg. 1355
R.J. REYNOLDS TOBACCO CO. (HONG KONG) LTD.—RJR Nabisco Holdings Corp.; *U.S. Public*, pg. 1355
ROTHMANS BENSON & HEDGES INC.—Rothmans UK Holdings Limited; *Int'l*, pg. 1130
ROTHMANS (UK) LTD.—Rothmans UK Holdings Limited; *Int'l*, pg. 1130
SARA LEE/DE—Sara Lee Corporation; *U.S. Public*, pg. 1434
SHOP-RITE CIGARETTES (CT)—Wakefern Food Corporation; *U.S. Private*, pg. 1146
SINGAPORE TOBACCO CO. (PRIVATE) CO.—B.A.T Industries P.L.C.; *Int'l*, pg. 111
SOUTHCO DISTRIBUTING COMPANY; *U.S. Private*, pg. 1014
SPEEDLING INCORPORATED; *U.S. Private*, pg. 1024
THE STOP & SHOP COMPANIES, INC.—Koninklijke Ahold NV; *Int'l*, pg. 750
SULLIVAN POWELL & COMPANY LTD.—Gallaher Limited; *Int'l*, pg. 539
SUPERMARKET CIGARETTE SALES, INC.—Jitney-Jungle Stores of America, Inc.; *U.S. Private*, pg. 588
TOBACCO EXPORTERS INTERNATIONAL (USA) LIMITED—Rothmans UK Holdings Limited; *Int'l*, pg. 1129
UNITED STATES TOBACCO COMPANY—UST Inc.; *U.S. Public*, pg. 1661
WEST PARK TOBACCO INC.—Reemtsma Cigarettenfabriken GmbH, Hamburg; *Int'l*, pg. 1101
WHOLESALE SUPPLY COMPANY, INC.; *U.S. Private*, pg. 1174

5198 — PAINTS, VARNISHES, & SUPPLIES-WHOLESALE

AKZO COATINGS INC.—Akzo Nobel N.V.; *Int'l*, pg. 46
AKZO COATINGS SA—Akzo Nobel N.V.; *Int'l*, pg. 43
AMERON (HONG KONG) LTD.—Ameron International Corporation; *U.S. Public*, pg. 99
WILLIAM M. BIRD & CO., INC.; *U.S. Private*, pg. 145
M.A. BRUDER & SONS, INCORPORATED; *U.S. Private*, pg. 175
BRUNSCHWIG & FILS, INC.; *U.S. Private*, pg. 176
BUILDER MARTS OF AMERICA, INC.; *U.S. Private*, pg. 179
CAMERON ASHLEY BUILDING PRODUCTS, INC; *U.S. Public*, pg. 298
CANADIAN TIRE CORPORATION LIMITED; *Int'l*, pg. 259
CHOKWANG JOTUN LTD.—Jotun A/S; *Int'l*, pg. 715
DICKURSBY FARG AB—Kemira Oy; *Int'l*, pg. 729
ERNST W. DORN CO., INC.; *U.S. Private*, pg. 340
DUNN-EDWARDS CORPORATION; *U.S. Private*, pg. 347
EMERY WATERHOUSE COMPANY; *U.S. Private*, pg. 373
FARGO GLASS & PAINT COMPANY; *U.S. Private*, pg. 393
FINGERLE LUMBER CO.; *U.S. Private*, pg. 405
FIVE STAR GROUP, INC.—GP Strategies Corporation; *U.S. Public*, pg. 694
FORBO KROMMENIE S.A.—Forbo Holding SA; *Int'l*, pg. 497
FREDERICK TRADING COMPANY—Distribution America; *U.S. Private*, pg. 335
GP STRATEGIES CORPORATION; *U.S. Public*, pg. 694
GENERAL PAINT LTD.—Williams Holdings Plc; *Int'l*, pg. 1501
HAMILTON EQUIPMENT, INC.; *U.S. Private*, pg. 497
HENKEL-EYTESA S.A.—Henkel KGaA; *Int'l*, pg. 612
HERBERTS GMBH—Hoechst Aktiengesellschaft; *Int'l*, pg. 625
IMPERIAL CHEMICAL INDUSTRIES PLC; *Int'l*, pg. 662
INTERNATIONAL PAINT EASTERN DIV.—Courtaulds plc; *Int'l*, pg. 339
INTERNATIONAL PAINT WESTERN DIV.—Courtaulds plc; *Int'l*, pg. 339
JOTUN A/S; *Int'l*, pg. 714
JOTUN-DANMARK A/S—Jotun A/S; *Int'l*, pg. 714
JOTUN DECORATIVE COATINGS LTD.—Jotun A/S; *Int'l*, pg. 715
JOTUN (DEUTSCHLAND) GMBH—Jotun A/S; *Int'l*, pg. 715
JOTUN FRANCE S.A.—Jotun A/S; *Int'l*, pg. 715
JOTUN HELLAS LTD.—Jotun A/S; *Int'l*, pg. 715
JOTUN-HENRY CLARK LTD.—Jotun A/S; *Int'l*, pg. 715
JOTUN ITALIA S.P.A.—Jotun A/S; *Int'l*, pg. 715
JOTUN NEDERLAND B.V.—Jotun A/S; *Int'l*, pg. 715
JOTUN NOF SINGAPORE PTE. LTD.—Jotun A/S; *Int'l*, pg. 715
JOTUN POLISAN BOYA TIC A.S.—Jotun A/S; *Int'l*, pg. 715
JOTUN POLYMER B.V.—Jotun A/S; *Int'l*, pg. 714
JOTUN PROTECTIVE COATINGS B.V.—Jotun A/S; *Int'l*, pg. 715
JOTUN-TINTAS MARITIMAS LDA.—Jotun A/S; *Int'l*, pg. 716
KANSAI PAINT (AMERICA), INC.—Kansai Paint Co., Ltd.; *Int'l*, pg. 723
KELLY-MOORE PAINT COMPANY, INC.; *U.S. Private*, pg. 613
KEMIRA PIGMENTS OY—Kemira Oy; *Int'l*, pg. 729
LEVIS B.V.—Akzo Nobel N.V.; *Int'l*, pg. 42
S.A. LEVIS—Akzo Nobel N.V.; *Int'l*, pg. 43
M.A.B. PAINTS—M.A. Bruder & Sons, Incorporated; *U.S. Private*, pg. 175
MAUTZ PAINT CO.; *U.S. Private*, pg. 715
MAXCO INC.-PAINTERS SUPPLY DIVISION—Maxco, Inc.; *U.S. Public*, pg. 1061
NOF JOTUN CO. LTD.—Jotun A/S; *Int'l*, pg. 716
NIPPON PAINT (AMERICA) CORP.—Nippon Paint Company Ltd.; *Int'l*, pg. 937
PEGASUS INTERNATIONAL CORPORATION—Straube Regional Center LLC; *U.S. Private*, pg. 1046
PERGAMENT HOME CENTERS, INC.; *U.S. Private*, pg. 853
PINTACASA—Corporacion Grupo Quimico, S.A.C.A.; *Int'l*, pg. 332
PREMIER COATINGS, INC.—Wattyl; *Int'l*, pg. 1488
PRESERVATIVE PAINT COMPANY—Kelly-Moore Paint Company, Inc.; *U.S. Private*, pg. 613
PROGRESS PAINT MFG. CO.; *U.S. Private*, pg. 890
E. RABINOWE & COMPANY, INC.—GP Strategies Corporation; *U.S. Public*, pg. 694
SANDOZ COLORQUIMICA LTDA.—Novartis AG; *Int'l*, pg. 984
SEABROOK WALLCOVERINGS, INC.; *U.S. Private*, pg. 978
SHEFFIELD HARDWARE COMPANY—Distribution America; *U.S. Private*, pg. 335
THE SHERWIN-WILLIAMS COMPANY; *U.S. Public*, pg. 1465
SICO INC.; *Int'l*, pg. 1239
SIMONIZ USA, INC.; *U.S. Private*, pg. 1001
STEEL PAINTS A/S—Jotun A/S; *Int'l*, pg. 715
THUNDERBIRD STEEL CORPORATION—Cameron Ashley Building Products, Inc; *U.S. Public*, pg. 298
THYBONY WALL COVERINGS CO.; *U.S. Private*, pg. 1084
TRU-TEST MFG. CO.—TruServ Corporation; *U.S. Private*, pg. 1108
WATTYL; *Int'l*, pg. 1488

5199 — NONDURABLE GOODS-WHOLESALE, NEC

ADDISON-WESLEY PUBLISHERS PTY. LTD.—Pearson plc; *Int'l*, pg. 1027
ADDISON-WESLEY (SINGAPORE) PVT. LTD.—Pearson plc; *Int'l*, pg. 1027
AIR SUPPLIES & CATERING CO. LTD.—Air Malta Co. Ltd.; *Int'l*, pg. 37

ALLEN-LEWIS MANUFACTURING CO., INC.—TCC Industries; *U.S. Public*, pg. 1554
AMERICAN CONSUMER PRODUCTS—Vista 2000, Inc.; *U.S. Private*, pg. 1142
AMERICAN FELT & FILTER; *U.S. Private*, pg. 54
AMOCO DEUTSCHLAND GMBH—Amoco Corporation; *U.S. Public*, pg. 103
AMOCO (U.K.) LTD.—Amoco Corporation; *U.S. Public*, pg. 103
AMREP CORPORATION; *U.S. Public*, pg. 104
AMWAY CORPORATION; *U.S. Private*, pg. 69
ARAMARK MAGAZINE & BOOK DIVISION, INC.—Aramark Corp.; *U.S. Private*, pg. 79
ARROW BUILDING CENTERS—Consolidated Lumber Co.; *U.S. Private*, pg. 265
ARROW INDUSTRIES, INC.—ConAgra, Inc.; *U.S. Public*, pg. 426
H.A. ASTLETT & CO. LTD.—Internatio-Muller N.V.; *Int'l*, pg. 682
BAKER & TAYLOR, INC.; *U.S. Private*, pg. 111
BARGAIN SUPPLY COMPANY; *U.S. Private*, pg. 116
BAZAAR & NOVELTY—Stuart Entertainment Inc.; *U.S. Public*, pg. 1526
BECKLEY CARDY GROUP—Butler Capital Corp.; *U.S. Private*, pg. 190
RUSS BERRIE AND COMPANY, INC.; *U.S. Public*, pg. 222
BIDDLE SAWYER CORPORATION; *U.S. Private*, pg. 142
BLACKWELL PUBLISHERS LTD.—B.H. Blackwell Ltd.; *Int'l*, pg. 197
BONTEX ITALIA S.R.L.—Georgia-Bonded Fibers, Inc.; *U.S. Public*, pg. 734
BRODART COMPANY; *U.S. Private*, pg. 170
BRODY CO. DIV.—Lancaster Colony Corporation; *U.S. Public*, pg. 976
JAMES BURN INTERNATIONAL AB—Standex International Corporation; *U.S. Public*, pg. 1507
JAMES BURN INTERNATIONAL GMBH—Standex International Corporation; *U.S. Public*, pg. 1507
BURNS PHILP COMPANY OF SAN FRANCISCO—Burns, Philp & Company Limited; *Int'l*, pg. 236
C.R.H INTERNATIONAL, INC.—Hills Stores Co.; *U.S. Public*, pg. 828
N.C. CAMERON & SONS, LTD.—Stanhome Inc.; *U.S. Public*, pg. 1508
CANTEL INDUSTRIES, INC.; *U.S. Public*, pg. 301
CARSEN GROUP INC.—Cantel Industries, Inc.; *U.S. Public*, pg. 301
CASTCRAFT INDUSTRIES, INC.; *U.S. Private*, pg. 219
CELEBRITY INCORPORATED; *U.S. Public*, pg. 319
CHADWICK-MILLER INC.—CMI Holding Corp.; *U.S. Private*, pg. 195
CHADWICK-MILLER INTL. LTD.—CMI Holding Corp.; *U.S. Private*, pg. 195
CLARK FOODSERVICE, INC.; *U.S. Private*, pg. 242
COLGATE-PALMOLIVE COMPANY; *U.S. Public*, pg. 397
P.F. COLLIER & SON LTD.—Editorial Planeta - DeAgostini, S.A.; *Int'l*, pg. 433
P.F. COLLIER LP—Editorial Planeta - DeAgostini, S.A.; *Int'l*, pg. 433
COLONY GLASS—Lancaster Colony Corporation; *U.S. Public*, pg. 976
CONSOLIDATED LUMBER CO.; *U.S. Private*, pg. 265
CUSTOM DECOR, INC.; *U.S. Private*, pg. 298
DNP (AMERICA), INC.—Dai Nippon Printing Co., Ltd.; *Int'l*, pg. 363
DAI NIPPON PRINTING CO. (AUSTRALIA) PTY. LTD.—Dai Nippon Printing Co., Ltd.; *Int'l*, pg. 363
DAI NIPPON PRINTING CO. (HONG KONG) LTD.—Dai Nippon Printing Co., Ltd.; *Int'l*, pg. 363
DAI NIPPON PRINTING CO. (SINGAPORE) PTE. LTD.—Dai Nippon Printing Co., Ltd.; *Int'l*, pg. 363
DAI NIPPON PRINTING CO. (UK) LTD.—Dai Nippon Printing Co., Ltd.; *Int'l*, pg. 363
DAI NIPPON PRINTING (EUROPA) GMBH—Dai Nippon Printing Co., Ltd.; *Int'l*, pg. 363
P.T. DAI NIPPON PRINTING INDONESIA—Dai Nippon Printing Co., Ltd.; *Int'l*, pg. 363
DAI NIPPON SHOJI CO., LTD.—Dai Nippon Printing Co., Ltd.; *Int'l*, pg. 363
DEITSCH PLASTIC EXPORT CO.—Deitsch Plastics Company; *U.S. Private*, pg. 321
DEWOLFE & FISKE INC.—CMI Holding Corp.; *U.S. Private*, pg. 195
DIAMOND BRANDS, INC.; *U.S. Private*, pg. 330
DOUBLEDAY CANADA LTD.—Bertelsmann AG; *Int'l*, pg. 192
DUPEY MANAGEMENT CORP.; *U.S. Private*, pg. 348
EARP DISTRIBUTION CENTER; *U.S. Private*, pg. 356
EBSCO INDUSTRIES, INC.; *U.S. Private*, pg. 358
ELKAY PLASTICS COMPANY, INC.; *U.S. Private*, pg. 372
ENESCO IMPORT, GMBH—Stanhome Inc.; *U.S. Public*, pg. 1508
ENESCO INTERNATIONAL (HONG KONG) LTD.—Stanhome Inc.; *U.S. Public*, pg. 1508
ENESCO LIMITED—Stanhome Inc.; *U.S. Public*, pg. 1508
FASSON IRELAND LTD.—Avery Dennison Corporation; *U.S. Public*, pg. 154
FASSON ITALIA S.P.A.—Avery Dennison Corporation; *U.S. Public*, pg. 154
FASSON (NEDERLAND) B.V.—Avery Dennison Corporation; *U.S. Public*, pg. 154
FASSON NORGE A/S—Avery Dennison Corporation; *U.S. Public*, pg. 154
FASSON PRODUCTS (PTY) LTD.—Avery Dennison Corporation; *U.S. Public*, pg. 154
FASSON-SANYO KOKUSAKU PULP CO. LTD.—Avery Dennison Corporation; *U.S. Public*, pg. 154
FAVORITE PRODUCTS CO.—Oil-Dri Corporation of America; *U.S. Public*, pg. 1215
FLEMING COMPANIES, INC.; *U.S. Public*, pg. 652
FOLLETT CAMPUS RESOURCES—Follett Corporation; *U.S. Private*, pg. 417
FOLLETT CORPORATION; *U.S. Private*, pg. 416
FOLLETT EDUCATIONAL SERVICES—Follett Corporation; *U.S. Private*, pg. 417
FOLLETT LIBRARY RESOURCES—Follett Corporation; *U.S. Private*, pg. 417
FORT WAYNE NEWSPAPER AGENCY—Knight-Ridder, Inc.; *U.S. Public*, pg. 964
GAILEY & ROBERTS LTD.—Unilever Plc; *Int'l*, pg. 1437
HA-LO INDUSTRIES, INC.; *U.S. Public*, pg. 773
HANWA CO., LTD.; *Int'l*, pg. 595
THE HARTZ MOUNTAIN CORP.; *U.S. Private*, pg. 508
HENKEL-EYTESA S.A.—Henkel KGaA; *Int'l*, pg. 612
HENKEL SOUTH AFRICA (PTY.) LTD.—Henkel KGaA; *Int'l*, pg. 614
HICKMAN, WILLIAMS & CO. INC.; *U.S. Private*, pg. 525
HICKORY SPECIALTIES, INC.—Bob Evans Farms, Inc.; *U.S. Public*, pg. 596
HOME COMPUTER SOFTWARE DIV.—Handleman Company; *U.S. Public*, pg. 779
HOUSTON FOODS COMPANY; *U.S. Private*, pg. 542
HULMAN & COMPANY; *U.S. Private*, pg. 547
HUNT CANADA—Hunt Corporation; *U.S. Public*, pg. 849
HYOSUNG GROUP; *Int'l*, pg. 640
IDEA MAN, INC.; *U.S. Private*, pg. 557
INGRAM INDUSTRIES INC.; *U.S. Private*, pg. 562
INTERNATIONAL FIBRE SALES, S.A.—The Mead Corporation; *U.S. Public*, pg. 1077
JAYDON INCORPORATED; *U.S. Private*, pg. 584
JOHN MENZIES PLC; *Int'l*, pg. 707
JOHN MENZIES (UK) LIMITED—John Menzies plc; *Int'l*, pg. 707
KALSEC, INC.—Kalamazoo Holdings, Inc.; *U.S. Private*, pg. 606
KANEBO, LTD.—Kanebo, Ltd.; *Int'l*, pg. 722
KAUTSCHUK-GESELLSCHAFT GMBH—Metallgesellschaft AG; *Int'l*, pg. 862
KIMFIBERS LTD.—Kimberly-Clark Corporation; *U.S. Public*, pg. 959
KMART FAR EAST LTD.—Kmart Corporation; *U.S. Public*, pg. 963
KOSS CLASSICS LTD.—Koss Corporation; *U.S. Public*, pg. 966
L & L NURSERY SUPPLY, INC.; *U.S. Private*, pg. 638
LANGSTON COMPANIES; *U.S. Private*, pg. 650
LAWSON PRODUCTS LTD.—Lawson Products, Inc.; *U.S. Public*, pg. 980
LEXICON PUBLICATIONS, INC.—Lagardere Groupe; *Int'l*, pg. 794
LINCOLN INDUSTRIES; *U.S. Private*, pg. 668
LONDON LITHO ALUMINUM CO., INC.; *U.S. Private*, pg. 673
MAIL ORDER BOOK SALES—Meredith Corporation; *U.S. Public*, pg. 1094
MARKETING CORP. OF AMERICA; *U.S. Private*, pg. 704
MCJUNKIN CORPORATION; *U.S. Private*, pg. 722
THE MEAD CORPORATION; *U.S. Public*, pg. 1074
MEAD PULP SALES, INC.—The Mead Corporation; *U.S. Public*, pg. 1074
MIDSOUTH ICE CO.—Spencer Companies Inc.; *U.S. Private*, pg. 1025
MILLER FREEMAN PLC—United News & Media plc; *Int'l*, pg. 1443
A. MINDEL & SON, INC.—Seton Company; *U.S. Private*, pg. 987
MITSIAM INTERNATIONAL, LTD.—Mitsui & Co., Ltd.; *Int'l*, pg. 880
MITSUBISHI RAYON AMERICA, INC.—Mitsubishi Rayon Co., Ltd.; *Int'l*, pg. 876
MITSUI & CO., LTD.; *Int'l*, pg. 877
MITSUI BRASILEIRA IMP. E EXP. LTDA.—Mitsui & Co., Ltd.; *Int'l*, pg. 882
MITSUI CHILENA COMMERCIAL LTDA.—Mitsui & Co., Ltd.; *Int'l*, pg. 882
MITSUI DE COLOMBIA S.A.—Mitsui & Co., Ltd.; *Int'l*, pg. 882
MITSUI DE MEXICO, S.A. DE C.V.—Mitsui & Co., Ltd.; *Int'l*, pg. 882
MITSUI DE VENEZUELA C.A.—Mitsui & Co., Ltd.; *Int'l*, pg. 882
MITSUI DEL ECUADOR S.A.—Mitsui & Co., Ltd.; *Int'l*, pg. 882
MITSUI DEL PERU S.A.—Mitsui & Co., Ltd.; *Int'l*, pg. 882
MUENCH-KREUZER CANDLE COMPANY; *U.S. Private*, pg. 766
JACK NADEL, INC.; *U.S. Private*, pg. 773
NATIONAL BOOK DISTRIBUTORS—Handleman Company; *U.S. Public*, pg. 780
THE NEW YORK TIMES COMPANY; *U.S. Public*, pg. 1173
NICHIMEN AMERICA, INC.—Nichimen Corporation; *Int'l*, pg. 927
NISSHO IWAI FIBER & YARN LTD.—Nissho Iwai Corporation; *Int'l*, pg. 946
NOVARTIS SEEDS, INC.—Novartis AG; *Int'l*, pg. 974
OIL-DRI CORPORATION OF AMERICA; *U.S. Public*, pg. 1214
OIL-DRI S.A.—Oil-Dri Corporation of America; *U.S. Public*, pg. 1215
OIL-DRI (U.K.) LTD.—Oil-Dri Corporation of America; *U.S. Public*, pg. 1215
OLD MERCHANDISE COMPANY—Spaghetti Warehouse, Inc.; *U.S. Public*, pg. 1495
OLINDE HARDWARE & SUPPLY CO.; *U.S. Private*, pg. 814
ORGANISATION DE VENTE DES PRODUITS FASSON S.A.R.L.—Avery Dennison Corporation; *U.S. Public*, pg. 154
PENNOCK; *U.S. Private*, pg. 850
PEREZ TRADING CO. INC.; *U.S. Private*, pg. 852
PERKINS-GOODWIN CO. INC.—Haindl Papier GmbH; *Int'l*, pg. 586
PRENTICE HALL CANADA, INC.—National Amusements, Inc.; *U.S. Private*, pg. 778
PRINCESS HOUSE, INC.—Colgate-Palmolive Company; *U.S. Public*, pg. 399
QINGDAO SSANGYONG APPAREL CO., LTD.—Ssangyong Business Group; *Int'l*, pg. 1291
READMORE PUBLICATIONS INC.—B.H. Blackwell Ltd.; *Int'l*, pg. 197
REXAM INC.—Rexam PLC; *Int'l*, pg. 1106
RYKOFF-SEXTON, INC.—JP Foodservice, Inc.; *U.S. Public*, pg. 918
SAFIC ALCAN & CIE S.A.—Metallgesellschaft AG; *Int'l*, pg. 862
SCHWAN'S SALES ENTERPRISES; *U.S. Private*, pg. 974
SETON COMPANY; *U.S. Private*, pg. 987
SIMON & SCHUSTER INTERNATIONAL & BUSINESS & PROFESSIONAL GROUP—National Amusements, Inc.; *U.S. Private*, pg. 778
SMITH ENTERPRISES; *U.S. Private*, pg. 1007
SOUTHERN LEATHER CO., INC.; *U.S. Private*, pg. 1016
SPARTAN STORES INC.; *U.S. Private*, pg. 1021
SPENCER COMPANIES INC.; *U.S. Private*, pg. 1024
SPINNERIN INC.; *U.S. Private*, pg. 1025
STANHOME INC.; *U.S. Public*, pg. 1508
STANHOME PANAMERICANA, C.A.—Stanhome Inc.; *U.S. Public*, pg. 1508
STANHOME S.P.A.—Stanhome Inc.; *U.S. Public*, pg. 1508
STUART ENTERTAINMENT INC.; *U.S. Public*, pg. 1526
SUNGLASS HUT INTERNATIONAL; *U.S. Public*, pg. 1535
SWINGSTER COMPANY—American Marketing Industries, Inc.; *U.S. Private*, pg. 58
TCC INDUSTRIES; *U.S. Public*, pg. 1554
TDS VENTURES, INC.—Time Warner Inc.; *U.S. Public*, pg. 1614
TEXTILE RUBBER & CHEMICAL COMPANY; *U.S. Private*, pg. 1079
TIEN WAH PRESS (PTE.) LTD.—Dai Nippon Printing Co., Ltd.; *Int'l*, pg. 363
P.T. TIGA MANUNGGAL SYNETHETIC INDUSTRIES—Mitsui & Co., Ltd.; *Int'l*, pg. 880
TRINIDAD/BENHAM CORP.; *U.S. Private*, pg. 1103
UAC INTERNATIONAL LTD.—Unilever Plc; *Int'l*, pg. 1434
GEORGE UHE CO., INC.; *U.S. Private*, pg. 1115
UNIBLEND SPINNERS, INC.; *U.S. Private*, pg. 1117
UNION PEN COMPANY; *U.S. Private*, pg. 1119
VJ GROWERS, INC.; *U.S. Private*, pg. 1130
VALLEY SEED CO.—Arizona Grains Inc.; *U.S. Private*, pg. 82
VICTORY PACKAGING; *U.S. Private*, pg. 1139
WANG'S INTERNATIONAL, INC.; *U.S. Private*, pg. 1149
WARNER CANDY COMPANY, INC.; *U.S. Private*, pg. 1150
WATERFORD CRYSTAL, INC.—Waterford Wedgwood Plc; *Int'l*, pg. 1487
WATERFORD CRYSTAL U.S.A.—Waterford Wedgwood Plc; *Int'l*, pg. 1487
WELLA NETHERLANDS N.V. VAN RAVENSBERG—Wella Group; *Int'l*, pg. 1490
WEST COAST LIQUIDATORS, INC.—Consolidated Stores Corp.; *U.S. Public*, pg. 437
WILHOLD INC.—American Greetings Corporation; *U.S. Public*, pg. 78
WILSONS THE LEATHER EXPERTS INC.; *U.S. Private*, pg. 1181
YOUNG-PHILLIPS SALES CO.; *U.S. Private*, pg. 1201

5211 — LUMBER & OTHER BUILDING MATERIALS DEALERS

ALAMO LUMBER COMPANY—Vaughan & Sons, Inc.; *U.S. Private*, pg. 1135
AMFAC, INC.—JMB Realty Corporation; *U.S. Private*, pg. 577
ANDERSON LUMBER COMPANY; *U.S. Private*, pg. 72
ARROW BUILDING CENTERS—Consolidated Lumber Co.; *U.S. Private*, pg. 265
ATLAS ROOFING CORP.; *U.S. Private*, pg. 96
BMC WEST—GAF Corporation; *U.S. Private*, pg. 433
E.C. BARTON & COMPANY; *U.S. Private*, pg. 119
BATSON-COOK COMPANY; *U.S. Private*, pg. 123
BEAVER LUMBER COMPANY LIMITED—The Molson Companies Limited; *Int'l*, pg. 887
BETHEL MILLS, INC.; *U.S. Private*, pg. 141
BETTER LIVING INC.; *U.S. Private*, pg. 141
BOEHMERS—Holderbank Financiere Glaris Ltd.; *Int'l*, pg. 629
BRASWELL SAND & GRAVEL COMPANY, INC.—Holderbank Financiere Glaris Ltd.; *Int'l*, pg. 628
BRAZOS POINT, INC.—Centex Corporation; *U.S. Public*, pg. 322
BRECKENRIDGE MATERIAL COMPANY; *U.S. Private*, pg. 166
BUILDERS SQUARE, INC.—Leonard Green & Partners; *U.S. Private*, pg. 477
CURT BULLOCK BUILDERS, INC.; *U.S. Private*, pg. 180
CB SARREGUEMINES—Castorama Dubois Investissements S.C.A.; *Int'l*, pg. 275
CSR AMERICA INC.—CSR Limited; *Int'l*, pg. 245
CALCASIEU LUMBER COMPANY; *U.S. Private*, pg. 200
CANWEL DISTRIBUTION LTD.—Canfor Corporation; *Int'l*, pg. 260
CARDO DOOR CONTINENTAL B.V.—Cardo AB; *Int'l*, pg. 269
CARDO DOOR INTERNATIONAL AG—Cardo AB; *Int'l*, pg. 269
CARDO DOOR PRODUCTION A/S—Cardo AB; *Int'l*, pg. 269
CARTER HOLT BUILDING SUPPLIES—International Paper Company; *U.S. Public*, pg. 905
CARTER HOLT HARVEY LIMITED—International Paper Company; *U.S. Public*, pg. 904
CARTER-JONES COMPANIES, INC.; *U.S. Private*, pg. 217
CASHWAY BUILDING CENTRES LTD.; *Int'l*, pg. 274
CASTORAMA BOURGES—Castorama Dubois Investissements S.C.A.; *Int'l*, pg. 275
CASTORAMA DIFFUSION—Castorama Dubois Investissements S.C.A.; *Int'l*, pg. 275

CASTORAMA ITALIA—Castorama Dubois Investissements S.C.A.; *Int'l*, pg. 276
CASTOWEST—Castorama Dubois Investissements S.C.A.; *Int'l*, pg. 275
W.C. CAYE & COMPANY, INC.; *U.S. Private*, pg. 220
CHICAGO FIRE BRICK CO.—CFB Industries, Inc.; *U.S. Private*, pg. 194
CHURCH & CHURCH INC.; *U.S. Private*, pg. 239
O.C. CLUSS LUMBER CO.; *U.S. Private*, pg. 248
O.C. CLUSS LUMBER CO.—O.C. Cluss Lumber Co.; *U.S. Private*, pg. 248
COLE HALL LUMBER CO.—Lumber Group Inc.; *U.S. Private*, pg. 680
COLUMBIA LUMBER & MANUFACTURING CO.; *U.S. Private*, pg. 255
COLWOOD CO., INC.—Columbia Lumber & Manufacturing Co.; *U.S. Private*, pg. 255
CONSOLIDATED LUMBER CO.; *U.S. Private*, pg. 265
CONTINENTAL LUMBER—Fleetwood Enterprises, Inc.; *U.S. Public*, pg. 651
COPELAND LUMBER YARD, INC.; *U.S. Private*, pg. 274
COX LUMBER CO.; *U.S. Private*, pg. 283
CRAFTY BEAVER HOME CENTER; *U.S. Private*, pg. 284
CRAWFORD DOOR AB—Cardo AB; *Int'l*, pg. 269
OY CRAWFORD DOOR AB—Cardo AB; *Int'l*, pg. 269
CRAWFORD DOOR A/S—Cardo AB; *Int'l*, pg. 269
CRAWFORD DOOR LTD.—Cardo AB; *Int'l*, pg. 269
S.A. CRAWFORD DOOR N.V.—Cardo AB; *Int'l*, pg. 269
CRAWFORD DOOR S.A.—Cardo AB; *Int'l*, pg. 269
CRAWFORD TOR GMBH—Cardo AB; *Int'l*, pg. 269
CURTIS LUMBER COMPANY; *U.S. Private*, pg. 297
CUSTOM LUMBER MFG. CO.—Lumber Group Inc.; *U.S. Private*, pg. 680
DEMCO INC.; *U.S. Private*, pg. 323
DENLINGER, INC.; *U.S. Private*, pg. 324
DUBOIS MATERIAUX—Castorama Dubois Investissements S.C.A.; *Int'l*, pg. 275
DUBOIS MATERIAUX RHONE ALPES—Castorama Dubois Investissements S.C.A.; *Int'l*, pg. 275
84 LUMBER COMPANY; *U.S. Private*, pg. 366
ELK SUPPLY COMPANY; *U.S. Private*, pg. 371
ELLIOTT GROUP LIMITED—The Davis Service Group Plc.; *Int'l*, pg. 385
FAIRFAX BUILDING SYSTEMS—Fairfax Lumber & Millwork Company Inc.; *U.S. Private*, pg. 391
FAIRFAX LUMBER & MILLWORK COMPANY INC.; *U.S. Private*, pg. 391
FALTEC PORTE A/S—Cardo AB; *Int'l*, pg. 269
FEDERATED-BLAIKIE LTD.—Barlow Ltd.; *Int'l*, pg. 167
FINGERLE LUMBER CO.; *U.S. Private*, pg. 405
FIRESTONE BUILDING PRODUCTS COMPANY—Bridgestone Corporation; *Int'l*, pg. 214
FOXWORTH-GALBRAITH LUMBER CO.; *U.S. Private*, pg. 423
FURMAN LUMBER COMPANY, INC.; *U.S. Private*, pg. 431
GIB GROUP; *Int'l*, pg. 532
GIEE BRICO INTERNATIONAL—GIB Group; *Int'l*, pg. 533
GANAHL LUMBER COMPANY; *U.S. Private*, pg. 439
THE GENERAL BUILDING SUPPLY COMPANY—Fidelity Investments (FMR Corp.); *U.S. Private*, pg. 403
GEORGIA-PACIFIC MID-CONTINENT WOOD PRODS. MFG. DIV.—Georgia-Pacific Corporation; *U.S. Public*, pg. 735
GREAT PLAINS COMPANIES, INC.; *U.S. Private*, pg. 475
GREEN FOREST LUMBER CORPORATION—MacMillan Bloedel Limited; *Int'l*, pg. 828
GROESBECK LUMBER & SUPPLY, INC.; *U.S. Private*, pg. 483
GROSSMAN'S, INC.—Jeld-Wen, Inc.; *U.S. Private*, pg. 585
GROUPE BETON QUEBEC—Holderbank Financiere Glaris Ltd.; *Int'l*, pg. 629
HANCOCK LUMBER, INC.; *U.S. Private*, pg. 498
FRANZ HANIEL & CIE, GMBH; *Int'l*, pg. 591
HERITAGE CO-OP; *U.S. Private*, pg. 524
HIGGINBOTHAM-BARTLETT CO.; *U.S. Private*, pg. 527
HILL-BEHAN LUMBER COMPANY; *U.S. Private*, pg. 529
EDWARD HINES LUMBER CO.; *U.S. Private*, pg. 530
HOLMQUIST GRAIN & LUMBER CO.; *U.S. Private*, pg. 535
HOMAN LUMBER MART, INC.; *U.S. Private*, pg. 536
THE HOME DEPOT, INC.; *U.S. Public*, pg. 831
IMPERIA BROS., INC.; *U.S. Private*, pg. 558
AB IWAN PAULSON—Scancem AB; *Int'l*, pg. 1199
AB JOH KOCK—Scancem AB; *Int'l*, pg. 1199
KELLER KITCHEN CABINETS; *U.S. Private*, pg. 612
KEVCO, INC.; *U.S. Public*, pg. 952
KMART CORPORATION; *U.S. Public*, pg. 963
L & W SUPPLY CORP.—USG Corporation; *U.S. Public*, pg. 1660
LAMPERT YARDS, INC.; *U.S. Private*, pg. 645
LANOGA CORPORATION; *U.S. Private*, pg. 650
JACOB LEVY & BROS., INC.; *U.S. Private*, pg. 664
LEXFORD RESIDENTIAL TRUST; *U.S. Public*, pg. 991
LOWE'S COMPANIES, INC.; *U.S. Public*, pg. 1015
LUMBER GROUP INC.; *U.S. Private*, pg. 680
LYMAN LUMBER COMPANY; *U.S. Private*, pg. 683
MACMILLAN BLOEDEL K. K.—MacMillan Bloedel Limited; *Int'l*, pg. 829
MAGNET LTD.—Berisford plc; *Int'l*, pg. 188
MAKI CORPORATION; *U.S. Private*, pg. 697
MAKI HOME CENTER, INC.—Maki Corporation; *U.S. Private*, pg. 698
MARVIN LUMBER & CEDAR COMPANY; *U.S. Private*, pg. 710
MEGADOOR INC.—Cardo AB; *Int'l*, pg. 269
MITSUI NORIN CO., LTD.—Mitsui & Co., Ltd.; *Int'l*, pg. 878
THE MOLSON COMPANIES LIMITED; *Int'l*, pg. 887
NATIONAL LUMBER CO.; *U.S. Private*, pg. 785
NICKERSON LUMBER COMPANY; *U.S. Private*, pg. 798
ORCHARD SUPPLY HARDWARE—Sears, Roebuck and Co.; *U.S. Public*, pg. 1452
ORIENTED STRANDBOARD PLANT—Georgia-Pacific Corporation; *U.S. Public*, pg. 737
PACIFIC COAST BUILDING PRODUCTS INC.; *U.S. Private*, pg. 830
PATRICK INDUSTRIES INC.; *U.S. Public*, pg. 1264
PATRICK METALS—Patrick Industries Inc.; *U.S. Public*, pg. 1265
THE PATY COMPANY; *U.S. Private*, pg. 844
FRANK PAXTON COMPANY—Jeld-Wen, Inc.; *U.S. Private*, pg. 585
PAYLESS CASHWAYS, INC.; *U.S. Public*, pg. 1267
PETER LUMBER COMPANY; *U.S. Private*, pg. 856
PIONEER PLASTICS CORPORATION; *U.S. Private*, pg. 867
E.R. PROBYN LTD.; *Int'l*, pg. 1071
QUEBEC & MARITIMES DIV. ST. LAWRENCE CEMENT—Holderbank Financiere Glaris Ltd.; *Int'l*, pg. 629
RANGER FOREST PRODUCTS LTD.—Alberta Energy Company, Ltd.; *Int'l*, pg. 49
REDLAND GRANULATS SA—Redland PLC; *Int'l*, pg. 1093
RESIDENTIAL SUPPORT SERVICES, INC.—John Wieland Homes Inc.; *U.S. Private*, pg. 1175
RHEINISCHE BAUSTOFFWERKE GMBH & CO. KG—Hochtief AG; *Int'l*, pg. 623
RICHARDSON INDUSTRIES, INC.; *U.S. Private*, pg. 929
RICHARDSON LUMBER CO.—Richardson Industries, Inc.; *U.S. Private*, pg. 929
RIEMEIER LUMBER COMPANY, INC.; *U.S. Private*, pg. 930
RINKER MATERIALS CORP.—CSR Limited; *Int'l*, pg. 246
RIVERSIDE MILLWORK COMPANY, INC.; *U.S. Private*, pg. 934
T.H. ROGERS LUMBER CO.; *U.S. Private*, pg. 940
ROONEY BROTHERS COMPANY; *U.S. Private*, pg. 943
ROPER BROS. LUMBER CO., INC.; *U.S. Private*, pg. 944
RUGG MANUFACTURING COMPANY; *U.S. Private*, pg. 950
J. SAINSBURY PLC; *Int'l*, pg. 1169
ST. LAWRENCE CEMENT INC.—Holderbank Financiere Glaris Ltd.; *Int'l*, pg. 628
SANFORD & HAWLEY, INC.; *U.S. Private*, pg. 965
SCHERER BROS. LUMBER COMPANY; *U.S. Private*, pg. 970
SCHOENEMAN BROTHERS COMPANY; *U.S. Private*, pg. 972
SCOTT LUMBER COMPANY; *U.S. Private*, pg. 977
SEIGLE'S HOME & BUILDING CENTERS; *U.S. Private*, pg. 981
SODEM—Castorama Dubois Investissements S.C.A.; *Int'l*, pg. 276
SOMERVILLE LUMBER & SUPPLY CO.—Payless Cashways, Inc.; *U.S. Public*, pg. 1268
SPERRHOLZ KOCH GMBH—Westag & Getalit AG; *Int'l*, pg. 1491
STAR LUMBER & SUPPLY COMPANY, INC.; *U.S. Private*, *pg. 1034*
STONES, INC.; *U.S. Private*, pg. 1045
STORA BUILDING PRODUCTS—Stora Kopparbergs Bergslags AB; *Int'l*, pg. 1303
STORA TIMBER AB—Stora Kopparbergs Bergslags AB; *Int'l*, pg. 1303
STROBER BROS., INC. BUILDING SUPPLY CENTERS—Fidelity Investments (FMR Corp.); *U.S. Private*, pg. 403
STROBER BUILDING SUPPLY CENTERS, INC.—Fidelity Investments (FMR Corp.); *U.S. Private*, pg. 403
STROBER KING BUILDING SUPPLY CENTERS, INC.—Fidelity Investments (FMR Corp.); *U.S. Private*, pg. 403
STROBER LONG ISLAND BUILDING MATERIALS CENTERS, INC.—Fidelity Investments (FMR Corp.); *U.S.* Private, pg. 403
STROBER NEW JERSEY BUILDING SUPPLY CENTERS, INC.—Fidelity Investments (FMR Corp.); *U.S. Private*, pg. 403
THE STROBER ORGANIZATION, INC.—Fidelity Investments (FMR Corp.); *U.S. Private*, pg. 403
SUPERIOR INDUSTRIES OF NEBRASKA, INC.; *U.S. Private*, pg. 1055
SURPLUS WAREHOUSE-TEMPLE—E.C. Barton & Company; *U.S. Private*, pg. 120
SURPLUS WAREHOUSE-LAKE CHARLES—E.C. Barton & Company; *U.S. Private*, pg. 119
SWEDOOR BAUELEMENTE GMBH—Stora Kopparbergs Bergslags AB; *Int'l*, pg. 1303
TEMBEC INC. PULP DIV.—Tembec Inc.; *Int'l*, pg. 1375
TEMPLE-INLAND INC.; *U.S. Public*, pg. 1574
TRAVARU AB A. THOMEE—Scancem AB; *Int'l*, pg. 1199
TRIANGLE BRASS MANUFACTURING; *U.S. Private*, pg. 1101
UAC INTERNATIONAL LTD.—Unilever Plc; *Int'l*, pg. 1434
UBE INDUSTRIES (AMERICA) INC.—UBE Industries Ltd.; *Int'l*, pg. 1427
UBE INDUSTRIES LTD.; *Int'l*, pg. 1426
UNITED DOMINION INDUSTRIES, LTD.; *U.S. Public*, pg. 1675
UNIVERSAL CORPORATION; *U.S. Public*, pg. 1694
UNIVERSAL INSULATION, INC.—Davenport Insulation, Inc; *U.S. Private*, pg. 314
VAUGHAN & SONS, INC.; *U.S. Private*, pg. 1134
VENDEX INTERNATIONAL N.V.; *Int'l*, pg. 1462
WALDO BROS. COMPANY; *U.S. Private*, pg. 1147
WEST BUILDING MATERIALS; *U.S. Private*, pg. 1163
WESTERN WOOD PRODS. MFG. DIV.—Georgia-Pacific Corporation; *U.S. Public*, pg. 736
WEYERHAEUSER COMPANY; *U.S. Public*, pg. 1764
WEYERHAEUSER FOREST PRODUCTS COMPANY—Weyerhaeuser Company; *U.S. Public*, pg. 1764
WHOLESALE WOOD PRODUCTS—Lumber Group Inc.; *U.S. Private*, pg. 680
WICKES INC.—Riverside Group, Inc.; *U.S. Public*, pg. 1391
WILLIAMS BROS.—Blue Circle Industries PLC; *Int'l*, pg. 198
WOLOHAN LUMBER CO.; *U.S. Public*, pg. 1774

5231 — PAINT, GLASS, & WALLPAPER STORES

A-OK DELAWARE INC.—GIB Group; *Int'l*, pg. 533
BEAVER LUMBER COMPANY LIMITED—The Molson Companies Limited; *Int'l*, pg. 887
M.A. BRUDER & SONS, INCORPORATED; *U.S. Private*, pg. 175
CARREFOUR COMMERCIO E INDUSTRIA—Carrefour; *Int'l*, pg. 272
CASTORAMA DUBOIS INVESTISSEMENTS S.C.A.; *Int'l*, pg. 275
CENTROS COMMERCIALES PRYCA—Carrefour; *Int'l*, pg. 273
COMPANIA SHERWIN-WILLIAMS, S.A. DE C.V.—The Sherwin-Williams Company; *U.S. Public*, pg. 1466
COSTCO WHOLESALE; *U.S. Public*, pg. 451
DUBOIS MATERIAUX—Castorama Dubois Investissements S.C.A.; *Int'l*, pg. 275
DUBOIS MATERIAUX RHONE ALPES—Castorama Dubois Investissements S.C.A.; *Int'l*, pg. 275
DURON, INC.; *U.S. Private*, pg. 349
FINGERLE LUMBER CO.; *U.S. Private*, pg. 405
FINNAREN & HALEY, INC.; *U.S. Private*, pg. 405
GIB GROUP; *Int'l*, pg. 532
GIEE BRICO INTERNATIONAL—GIB Group; *Int'l*, pg. 533
GROUPE BETON QUEBEC—Holderbank Financiere Glaris Ltd.; *Int'l*, pg. 629
GROW GROUP, INC.—Imperial Chemical Industries PLC; *Int'l*, pg. 663
HARMON GLASS COMPANY—Apogee Enterprises, Inc.; *U.S. Public*, pg. 120
KELLY-MOORE PAINT COMPANY, INC.; *U.S. Private*, pg. 613
KWAL-HOWELLS, INC.(DENVER)—Williams Holdings Plc; *Int'l*, pg. 1501
LAMPERT YARDS, INC.; *U.S. Private*, pg. 645
MAKI CORPORATION; *U.S. Private*, pg. 697
MAKI HOME CENTER, INC.—Maki Corporation; *U.S. Private*, pg. 698
MAUTZ PAINT CO.; *U.S. Private*, pg. 715
THE MOLSON COMPANIES LIMITED; *Int'l*, pg. 887
ORCHARD SUPPLY HARDWARE—Sears, Roebuck and Co.; *U.S. Public*, pg. 1452
PRESERVATIVE PAINT COMPANY—Kelly-Moore Paint Company, Inc.; *U.S. Private*, pg. 613
PRESICARRE CORP.—Carrefour; *Int'l*, pg. 273
J. SAINSBURY PLC; *Int'l*, pg. 1169
ST. CLAIR PAINT AND WALLPAPER CORPORATION; *Int'l*, pg. 1170
SEABROOK WALLCOVERINGS, INC.; *U.S. Private*, pg. 978
THE SHERWIN-WILLIAMS COMPANY; *U.S. Public*, pg. 1465
SHERWIN-WILLIAMS PAINT STORES GROUP—The Sherwin-Williams Company; *U.S. Public*, pg. 1466
SOUS GROUPE CASTORAMA—Castorama Dubois Investissements S.C.A.; *Int'l*, pg. 275
WALLPAPERS-TO-GO—Wicks 'n Sticks, Ltd; *U.S. Private*, pg. 1175
WELLBORN - DE CORP.—Dunn-Edwards Corporation; *U.S.* Private, pg. 347
ZYNOLYTE PRODUCTS COMPANY—Imperial Chemical Industries PLC; *Int'l*, pg. 663

5251 — HARDWARE STORES

ACO INC.; *U.S. Private*, pg. 3
ACE HARDWARE CORPORATION; *U.S. Private*, pg. 12
ALASKA INDUSTRIAL HARDWARE INC.; *U.S. Private*, pg. 31
ALL AMERICAN HOME CENTER; *U.S. Private*, pg. 34
W.E. AUBUCHON CO., INC.; *U.S. Private*, pg. 98
B & Q PLC—Kingfisher plc; *Int'l*, pg. 733
BEAVER LUMBER COMPANY LIMITED—The Molson Companies Limited; *Int'l*, pg. 887
BELWITH INTERNATIONAL DIV.—FKI Plc; *Int'l*, pg. 473
BERLAMONT—Castorama Dubois Investissements S.C.A.; *Int'l*, pg. 275
BLACK & CO.; *U.S. Private*, pg. 146
BRICOREV—Castorama Dubois Investissements S.C.A.; *Int'l*, pg. 275
BUHRMAN-PHARR HARDWARE COMPANY; *U.S. Private*, *pg. 179*
CB SARREGUEMINES—Castorama Dubois Investissements S.C.A.; *Int'l*, pg. 275
CARREFOUR; *Int'l*, pg. 272
CARREFOUR NEDERLAND B.V.—Carrefour; *Int'l*, pg. 273
CARTER HOLT BUILDING SUPPLIES—International Paper Company; *U.S. Public*, pg. 905
CARTER HOLT HARVEY LIMITED—International Paper Company; *U.S. Public*, pg. 904
CASTORAMA BOURGES—Castorama Dubois Investissements S.C.A.; *Int'l*, pg. 275
CASTORAMA ITALIA—Castorama Dubois Investissements S.C.A.; *Int'l*, pg. 276
CASTOWEST—Castorama Dubois Investissements S.C.A.; *Int'l*, pg. 275
CONSOLIDATED PIPE & SUPPLY COMPANY; *U.S. Private*, pg. 266
DISTRIBUTION AMERICA; *U.S. Private*, pg. 335
DO IT ALL—The Boots Company PLC; *Int'l*, pg. 203
DUBOIS MATERIAUX—Castorama Dubois Investissements S.C.A.; *Int'l*, pg. 275
DUBOIS MATERIAUX RHONE ALPES—Castorama Dubois Investissements S.C.A.; *Int'l*, pg. 275
FINGERLE LUMBER CO.; *U.S. Private*, pg. 405
GIB GROUP; *Int'l*, pg. 532
GIEE BRICO INTERNATIONAL—GIB Group; *Int'l*, pg. 533
HECHINGER COMPANY INVESTORS II, L.P.—Leonard Green & Partners; *U.S. Private*, pg. 477
HERITAGE CO-OP; *U.S. Private*, pg. 524
THE HOME DEPOT, INC.; *U.S. Public*, pg. 831

ILCO UNICAN AUSTRALIA (PTY.) LTD.—Unican Security Systems Ltd.; *Int'l*, pg. 1432
JARNIA AB—Bergman & Beving AB; *Int'l*, pg. 188
K-YHTIOT OY—Kesko Ltd.; *Int'l*, pg. 732
KINGFISHER PLC; *Int'l*, pg. 733
N.V. KONINKLIJKE BIJENKORF BEHEER KBB; *Int'l*, pg. 750
THE KRUSE COMPANY; *U.S. Private*, pg. 636
LEXFORD RESIDENTIAL TRUST; *U.S. Public*, pg. 991
LOWE'S COMPANIES, INC.; *U.S. Public*, pg. 1015
MAGNET LTD.—Berisford plc; *Int'l*, pg. 188
MAKITA KFT.—Makita Corporation; *Int'l*, pg. 832
S.A. MAKITA N.V.—Makita Corporation; *Int'l*, pg. 832
MAKITA WERKZEUG GESELLSCHAFT M.B.H.—Makita Corporation; *Int'l*, pg. 832
MARKET SWEDEN—Trelleborg AB; *Int'l*, pg. 1422
MARVIN LUMBER & CEDAR COMPANY; *U.S. Private*, pg. 710
MAURICE ELECTRIC SUPPLY COMPANY; *U.S. Private*, pg. 715
THE MOLSON COMPANIES LIMITED; *Int'l*, pg. 887
MORSE HARDWARE COMPANY; *U.S. Private*, pg. 763
NHD HARDWARE—ACO Inc.; *U.S. Private*, pg. 3
ORCHARD SUPPLY HARDWARE—Sears, Roebuck and Co.; *U.S. Public*, pg. 1452
THE PFH GROUP—N.V. Koninklijke Bijenkorf Beheer KBB; *Int'l*, pg. 750
PRAXIS DOE-HET-ZELF CENTER B.V.—N.V. Koninklijke Bijenkorf Beheer KBB; *Int'l*, pg. 750
RETAILNET B.V.—N.V. Koninklijke Bijenkorf Beheer KBB; *Int'l*, pg. 750
J. SAINSBURY PLC; *Int'l*, pg. 1169
SCHOENEMAN BROTHERS COMPANY; *U.S. Private*, pg. 972
SCOTT LUMBER COMPANY; *U.S. Private*, pg. 977
SEIGLE'S HOME & BUILDING CENTERS; *U.S. Private*, pg. 981
SEYMOUR MANUFACTURING COMPANY; *U.S. Private*, pg. 988
SNYDER-DIAMOND; *U.S. Private*, pg. 1011
SODEM—Castorama Dubois Investissements S.C.A.; *Int'l*, pg. 276
TOOL KING; *U.S. Private*, pg. 1091
TRACTOR SUPPLY CO.; *U.S. Public*, pg. 1627
UNITED PRODUCERS & CONSUMERS CO-OP; *U.S. Private*, pg. 1123
WESTLAKE HARDWARE, INC.; *U.S. Private*, pg. 1169

5261 — RETAIL NURSERIES, LAWN & GARDEN SUPPLY STORES

AGWAY RETAIL SERVICES—Agway, Inc.; *U.S. Private*, pg. 27
AIRCAP INDUSTRIES CORP.—MTD Products, Inc.; *U.S. Private*, pg. 688
AKI BRICOLAGE—GIB Group; *Int'l*, pg. 534
AMLINGS FLOWERLAND; *U.S. Private*, pg. 66
W.E. AUBUCHON CO., INC.; *U.S. Private*, pg. 98
B & Q PLC—Kingfisher plc; *Int'l*, pg. 733
BACHMAN'S, INC.; *U.S. Private*, pg. 109
BLITZ USA, INC.; *U.S. Private*, pg. 149
BRECKS—Foster & Gallagher, Inc.; *U.S. Private*, pg. 420
CASTORAMA DUBOIS INVESTISSEMENTS S.C.A.; *Int'l*, pg. 275
CONAGRA RETAIL COMPANIES—ConAgra, Inc.; *U.S. Public*, pg. 426
COPELAND LUMBER YARD, INC.; *U.S. Private*, pg. 274
COUNTRY GENERAL STORES—J.W. Childs Associates, L.P.; *U.S. Private*, pg. 237
EARL MAY SEED & NURSERY L.C.; *U.S. Private*, pg. 356
EDMONSON WHEAT GROWERS, INC.; *U.S. Private*, pg. 364
ENCORE GROUP, INC.—Encore Marketing International, Inc.; *U.S. Public*, pg. 580
ESPACE JARDIN—Castorama Dubois Investissements S.C.A.; *Int'l*, pg. 276
FARMWAY CO-OP INC.; *U.S. Private*, pg. 396
H.G. FENTON MATERIAL COMPANY; *U.S. Private*, pg. 400
FOSTER & GALLAGHER, INC.; *U.S. Private*, pg. 420
FRANCE JARDINERIES—Castorama Dubois Investissements S.C.A.; *Int'l*, pg. 276
FRANK'S NURSERY & CRAFTS, INC.—General Host Corporation; *U.S. Public*, pg. 715
GIB GROUP; *Int'l*, pg. 532
GIEE BRICO INTERNATIONAL—GIB Group; *Int'l*, pg. 533
GEBO DISTRIBUTING CO., INC.; *U.S. Private*, pg. 442
GENERAL CIGAR HOLDINGS INC; *U.S. Public*, pg. 707
GENERAL HOST CORPORATION; *U.S. Public*, pg. 715
IMPERIAL NURSERIES INC.—General Cigar Holdings Inc; *U.S. Public*, pg. 707
LOWE'S COMPANIES, INC.; *U.S. Public*, pg. 1015
MFA INCORPORATED; *U.S. Private*, pg. 686
NURSERYLAND GARDEN CENTERS—General Host Corporation; *U.S. Public*, pg. 715
BRUCE OAKLEY, INC.; *U.S. Private*, pg. 809
GEORGE W. PARK SEED CO., INC.; *U.S. Private*, pg. 839
PETALS; *U.S. Private*, pg. 856
QUALITY STORES INC.; *U.S. Private*, pg. 899
RAY-CARROLL COUNTY GRAIN CO-OP; *U.S. Private*, pg. 911
REGENT-SHEFFIELD LTD.—McPherson's Limited; *Int'l*, pg. 852
J. SAINSBURY PLC; *Int'l*, pg. 1169
SAKATA SEED AMERICA, INC.—Sakata Seed Corporation; *Int'l*, pg. 1178
SAKATA SEED CORPORATION; *Int'l*, pg. 1178
SAKATA SEED EUROPE B.V.—Sakata Seed Corporation; *Int'l*, pg. 1178
THE SCOTTS COMPANY; *U.S. Public*, pg. 1446
SMITH & HAWKEN—CML Group, Inc.; *U.S. Public*, pg. 279
SOUS GROUPE CASTORAMA—Castorama Dubois Investissements S.C.A.; *Int'l*, pg. 275
SOUTHERN STATES COOPERATIVE, INC.; *U.S. Private*, pg. 1017
SPRING HILL NURSERIES CO.—Foster & Gallagher, Inc.; *U.S. Private*, pg. 420
SUNBELT NURSERY GROUP INC.—General Host Corporation; *U.S. Public*, pg. 715
TIP TOP NURSERY—General Host Corporation; *U.S. Public*, pg. 715
VALLEY SEED CO.—Arizona Grains Inc.; *U.S. Private*, pg. 82
WHEELER BROS. GRAIN CO.—Wheeler Brothers Grain Co.; *U.S. Private*, pg. 1171
WOLFE NURSERY—General Host Corporation; *U.S. Public*, pg. 715

5271 — MOBILE HOME DEALERS

CMH HOMES, INC.—Clayton Homes, Inc.; *U.S. Public*, pg. 383
CLAYTON HOMES, INC.; *U.S. Public*, pg. 382
OAKWOOD HOMES CORPORATION; *U.S. Public*, pg. 1209
OAKWOOD MOBILE HOMES, INC.—Oakwood Homes Corporation; *U.S. Public*, pg. 1209
SCHULT HOMES CORPORATION—Schult Homes Corporation; *U.S. Public*, pg. 1442
STEENBERG HOMES, INC.; *U.S. Private*, pg. 1039

5311 — DEPARTMENT STORES

AHLENS AB—Axel Johnson AB; *Int'l*, pg. 708
ALEXANDER'S, INC.—Vornado Realty Trust; *U.S. Public*, pg. 1725
ALLDERS NUANCE—The Swissair Group; *Int'l*, pg. 1334
ALLENS OF HASTINGS, INC.; *U.S. Private*, pg. 37
AMES DEPARTMENT STORES, INC.; *U.S. Public*, pg. 99
ANCO TRANSPORTATION SERVICE, INC.—Stage Stores, Inc.; *U.S. Private*, pg. 1029
ARNOTTS PLC; *Int'l*, pg. 81
FREDERICK ATKINS; *U.S. Private*, pg. 94
AU BON MARCHE; *Int'l*, pg. 97
BJ'S WHOLESALE CLUB, INC.; *U.S. Public*, pg. 162
J. BACON & SONS—Mercantile Stores Company, Inc.; *U.S. Public*, pg. 1090
THE BAY—Hudson's Bay Company; *Int'l*, pg. 637
BAZAR DE L'HOTEL DE VILLE; *Int'l*, pg. 181
BAZARS ALENCONNAIS—Au Bon Marche; *Int'l*, pg. 97
BEALL'S, INC.; *U.S. Private*, pg. 126
BELK STORES SERVICES INC.; *U.S. Private*, pg. 131
BENTALLS PLC; *Int'l*, pg. 187
BERGDORF GOODMAN—Harcourt General, Inc.; *U.S. Public*, pg. 785
BIG BEAR STORES COMPANY—The Penn Traffic Company; *U.S. Public*, pg. 1270
BIGG'S HYPER SHOPPES, INC.—SuperValu, Inc.; *U.S. Public*, pg. 1541
BLOOMINGDALE'S—Federated Department Stores, Inc.; *U.S. Public*, pg. 617
THE BON MARCHE, INC.—Federated Department Stores, Inc.; *U.S. Public*, pg. 617
THE BON TON STORES, INC.; *U.S. Public*, pg. 244
BOSCOV'S DEPARTMENT STORE, INC.; *U.S. Private*, pg. 160
BOSTON STORE—Carson Pirie Scott & Co.; *U.S. Public*, pg. 309
BOYERS & CO. LIMITED—Arnotts plc; *Int'l*, pg. 81
BRADLEES INC.; *U.S. Public*, pg. 249
BURDINES—Federated Department Stores, Inc.; *U.S. Public*, pg. 618
THE BURTON GROUP PLC; *Int'l*, pg. 237
CARNEGIE HOLDING AB; *Int'l*, pg. 272
CARSON PIRIE SCOTT & CO.; *U.S. Public*, pg. 309
CARSON PIRIE SCOTT & COMPANY-DEPT. STORES DIV.—Carson Pirie Scott & Co.; *U.S. Public*, pg. 309
CASTNER KNOTT CO.—Mercantile Stores Company, Inc.; *U.S. Public*, pg. 1090
M.M. COHN CO., INC.—The Dunlap Company; *U.S. Private*, pg. 346
COLES MYER LTD.; *Int'l*, pg. 306
COOP SWITZERLAND; *Int'l*, pg. 329
CROWLEY, MILNER & COMPANY; *U.S. Public*, pg. 461
THE DAIEI, INC.; *Int'l*, pg. 364
DAYTON HUDSON CORPORATION; *U.S. Public*, pg. 489
DE BIJENKORF B.V.—N.V. Koninklijke Bijenkorf Beheer KBB; *Int'l*, pg. 750
DE LENDRECIE'S—Mercantile Stores Company, Inc.; *U.S. Public*, pg. 1090
THE DEPARTMENT STORE DIVISION OF DAYTON HUDSON CORPORATION—Dayton Hudson Corporation; *U.S. Public*, pg. 489
DEVON CAPITAL CORP.—Colonial Commercial Corp.; *U.S. Public*, pg. 400
DILLARD'S, INC.; *U.S. Public*, pg. 509
DUCKWALL-ALCO STORES, INC.; *U.S. Public*, pg. 533
THE DUNLAP COMPANY; *U.S. Private*, pg. 346
EL PUERTO DE LIVERPOOL S.A.; *Int'l*, pg. 435
THE ELDER-BEERMAN STORES CORP.; *U.S. Private*, pg. 367
EXPRESS 1 STOP—Sullivan Oil Company; *U.S. Private*, pg. 1050
FACTORY 2-U—Family Bargain Corporation; *U.S. Public*, pg. 612
FAMOUS-BARR—The May Department Stores Company; *U.S. Public*, pg. 1063
FEDCO, INC.; *U.S. Private*, pg. 398
FILENE'S—The May Department Stores Company; *U.S. Public*, pg. 1063
G.P. FITZGERALD & CO. LTD.—Harris Scarfe Holdings Limited; *Int'l*, pg. 597
FOLEY'S—The May Department Stores Company; *U.S. Public*, pg. 1063
FORTNUM & MASON PLC; *Int'l*, pg. 500
G.I. JOE'S INC.; *U.S. Private*, pg. 435
GIB GROUP; *Int'l*, pg. 532
GAYFERS—Mercantile Stores Company, Inc.; *U.S. Public*, pg. 1090
GILMORE BROS., INC.; *U.S. Private*, pg. 454
GLASS BLOCK—Mercantile Stores Company, Inc.; *U.S. Public*, pg. 1090
GOLDBLATT'S DEPARTMENT STORES—JG Industries, Inc.; *U.S. Public*, pg. 917
GOTTSCHALKS INC.; *U.S. Public*, pg. 754
GRUPO PALACIO DE HIERRO S.A. DE C.V.; *Int'l*, pg. 576
GRUPO SYR, S.A. DE C.V.; *Int'l*, pg. 576
HARCOURT GENERAL, INC.; *U.S. Public*, pg. 782
HARRIS SCARFE HOLDINGS LIMITED; *Int'l*, pg. 597
HARRIS SCARFE LTD.—Harris Scarfe Holdings Limited; *Int'l*, pg. 597
HECHT'S—The May Department Stores Company; *U.S. Public*, pg. 1063
HEMA B.V.—N.V. Koninklijke Bijenkorf Beheer KBB; *Int'l*, pg. 750
HENNESEYS—Mercantile Stores Company, Inc.; *U.S. Public*, pg. 1090
G.R. HERBERGER'S, INC.—Proffitt's, Inc.; *U.S. Public*, pg. 1333
HERTIE WAREN-UND KAUFHAUS GMBH—Karstadt Aktiengesellschaft; *Int'l*, pg. 724
THE HI-DAIEI TRADING CO., LTD.—The Daiei, Inc.; *Int'l*, pg. 364
HILLS STORES CO.; *U.S. Public*, pg. 828
HOME SHOPPING NETWORK, INC.—USA Networks, Inc.; *U.S. Public*, pg. 1685
HOMEBASE, INC.; *U.S. Public*, pg. 832
HUDSON'S BAY COMPANY; *Int'l*, pg. 637
HYPERMART USA—Wal-Mart Stores, Inc.; *U.S. Public*, pg. 1733
ITO-YOKADO CO., LTD.; *Int'l*, pg. 693
JC PENNEY COMPANY, INC.; *U.S. Public*, pg. 916
JG INDUSTRIES, INC.; *U.S. Public*, pg. 917
JOTSA, S.A. EMPRESSA CONSTRUCTOR—Philipp Holzmann AG; *Int'l*, pg. 634
THE JAEGER COMPANY'S SHOPS LTD.—Coats Viyella plc; *Int'l*, pg. 300
JAEGER SPORTSWEAR LTD.—Coats Viyella plc; *Int'l*, pg. 299
JELMOLI AG; *Int'l*, pg. 705
JONES & JONES, INC.; *U.S. Private*, pg. 596
DAVID JONES LIMITED; *Int'l*, pg. 714
THE JONES STORE CO.—Mercantile Stores Company, Inc.; *U.S. Public*, pg. 1090
JOSLINS—Mercantile Stores Company, Inc.; *U.S. Public*, pg. 1090
KF/KONSUM COOP GROUP; *Int'l*, pg. 718
KARSTADT AKTIENGESELLSCHAFT; *Int'l*, pg. 724
KAUFMANN'S—The May Department Stores Company; *U.S. Public*, pg. 1063
H. KESSLER & COMPANY; *U.S. Private*, pg. 616
KMART (CANADA) LTD.—Kmart Corporation; *U.S. Public*, pg. 963
KMART CORPORATION; *U.S. Public*, pg. 963
KOHL'S CORPORATION; *U.S. Public*, pg. 965
N.V. KONINKLIJKE BIJENKORF BEHEER KBB; *Int'l*, pg. 750
LADY ROSE DIV.—Masters, Inc.; *U.S. Private*, pg. 714
LEWIS DRUG, INC.; *U.S. Private*, pg. 665
LIBERTY HOUSE, INC.—JMB Realty Corporation; *U.S. Private*, pg. 578
LIBERTY PLC; *Int'l*, pg. 807
LIBERTY RETAIL LIMITED—Liberty PLC; *Int'l*, pg. 807
LION—Mercantile Stores Company, Inc.; *U.S. Public*, pg. 1090
LOEHMANN'S, INC.; *U.S. Public*, pg. 1010
LORD & TAYLOR—The May Department Stores Company; *U.S. Public*, pg. 1064
LORD BIBB DIV.—Masters, Inc.; *U.S. Private*, pg. 714
LOT$ OFF CORPORATION; *U.S. Public*, pg. 1014
LOTTE SHOPPING CO. LTD.—Lotte Company Ltd.; *Int'l*, pg. 819
M&S EXPORT (IRELAND) LIMITED—Marks & Spencer PLC; *Int'l*, pg. 843
MACY'S EAST—Federated Department Stores, Inc.; *U.S. Public*, pg. 618
MACY'S WEST—Federated Department Stores, Inc.; *U.S. Public*, pg. 618
MARKS & SPENCER CANADA INC.—Marks & Spencer PLC; *Int'l*, pg. 843
MARKS & SPENCER (FRANCE) S.A.—Marks & Spencer PLC; *Int'l*, pg. 843
MARKS & SPENCER PLC; *Int'l*, pg. 842
MARKS & SPENCER US HOLDINGS INC.—Marks & Spencer PLC; *Int'l*, pg. 843
MARSHALL FIELD—Dayton Hudson Corporation; *U.S. Public*, pg. 489
MASTERS, INC.; *U.S. Private*, pg. 714
MATSUYA ASAKUSA—Matsuya Company Ltd.; *Int'l*, pg. 848
MATSUYA COMPANY LTD.; *Int'l*, pg. 848
MATSUYA GINZA—Matsuya Company Ltd.; *Int'l*, pg. 848
MAUS FRERES S.A.; *Int'l*, pg. 849
THE MAY DEPARTMENT STORES COMPANY; *U.S. Public*, pg. 1063
MAY DEPARTMENT STORES INTERNATIONAL, INC.—The May Department Stores Company; *U.S. Public*, pg. 1064
MAY MERCHANDISING COMPANY—The May Department Stores Company; *U.S. Public*, pg. 1064
MCALPIN'S—Mercantile Stores Company, Inc.; *U.S. Public*, pg. 1090
MCRAE'S, INC.—Proffitt's, Inc.; *U.S. Public*, pg. 1333
MEIER & FRANK—The May Department Stores Company; *U.S. Public*, pg. 1064
MERCANTILE STORES COMPANY, INC.; *U.S. Public*, pg. 1089
MERVYN'S CALIFORNIA—Dayton Hudson Corporation; *U.S. Public*, pg. 489

FRED MEYER STORES—Fred Meyer Incorporated; *U.S. Public*, pg. 1103
MITSUKOSHI, LTD.; *Int'l*, pg. 883
MONTGOMERY WARD & CO., INC.; *U.S. Private*, pg. 758
MYCAL, CORP.; *Int'l*, pg. 897
NEHO VERSAND G.M.B.H.—The Seagram Company Ltd.; *Int'l*, pg. 1216
NAGOYA MITSUKOSHI, LTD.—Mitsukoshi, Ltd.; *Int'l*, pg. 883
NEIMAN MARCUS CO.—Harcourt General, Inc.; *U.S. Public*, pg. 785
THE NEIMAN-MARCUS GROUP, INC.—Harcourt General, Inc.; *U.S. Public*, pg. 784
NOPRI—GIB Group; *Int'l*, pg. 533
NORDISKA KOMPANIET (NK) AB—NCC AB; *Int'l*, pg. 899
NORDSTROM, INC.; *U.S. Public*, pg. 1190
PARISIAN, INC.—Proffitt's, Inc.; *U.S. Public*, pg. 1333
PEEBLES, INC.; *U.S. Private*, pg. 846
PEOPLES—Marks & Spencer PLC; *Int'l*, pg. 843
PHARMHOUSE, INC.; *U.S. Public*, pg. 1286
PRINTEMPS GINZA S.A.—The Daiei, Inc.; *Int'l*, pg. 364
PROFFITT'S, INC.; *U.S. Public*, pg. 1333
PROFFITT'S OF TRI-CITIES, INC.—Proffitt's, Inc.; *U.S. Public*, pg. 1334
QUALITY STORES INC.; *U.S. Private*, pg. 899
RICH'S/LAZARUS/GOLDSMITH'S—Federated Department Stores, Inc.; *U.S. Public*, pg. 618
ROBINSONS-MAY—The May Department Stores Company; *U.S. Public*, pg. 1064
ROSE'S STORES, INC.; *U.S. Public*, pg. 1405
ROSS STORES, INC.; *U.S. Public*, pg. 1405
SAM'S CLUBS DIV.—Wal-Mart Stores, Inc.; *U.S. Public*, pg. 1733
SAMSUNG GROUP; *Int'l*, pg. 1181
SCHOTTENSTEIN STORES CORPORATION; *U.S. Private*, pg. 972
SEARS LOGISTICS SERVICES—Sears, Roebuck and Co.; *U.S. Public*, pg. 1452
SEARS, ROEBUCK AND CO.; *U.S. Public*, pg. 1452
SEIYO, LTD.—The Saison Group; *Int'l*, pg. 1178
SERVCO PACIFIC INC.; *U.S. Private*, pg. 986
SHEPLERS, INC.; *U.S. Private*, pg. 993
SHOPKO STORES, INC.; *U.S. Public*, pg. 1467
THE SINCERE CO. LTD.; *Int'l*, pg. 1252
THE SINCERE COMPANY LTD. (KOWLOON BRANCH)—The Sincere Co. Ltd.; *Int'l*, pg. 1252
STAGE STORES, INC.; *U.S. Private*, pg. 1028
STEIN MART, INC.; *U.S. Public*, pg. 1514
STEINBACH STORES, INC.—Crowley, Milner & Company; *U.S. Public*, pg. 461
STEINBERG INC.—Socanav Inc.; *Int'l*, pg. 1272
STEKETEE PAUL & SONS COMPANY, INC.—The Dunlap Company; *U.S. Private*, pg. 346
STERN'S—Federated Department Stores, Inc.; *U.S. Public*, pg. 618
OY STOCKMANN AB; *Int'l*, pg. 1301
STONE & THOMAS; *U.S. Private*, pg. 1044
THE STOP & SHOP COMPANIES, INC.—Koninklijke Ahold NV; *Int'l*, pg. 750
SUPER CENTER WAREHOUSE CLUB, INC.—Wal-Mart Stores, Inc.; *U.S. Public*, pg. 1733
SUPERVALU, INC.; *U.S. Public*, pg. 1540
TAKASHIMAYA COMPANY, LIMITED; *Int'l*, pg. 1349
SUSAN TERRY DIV.—Masters, Inc.; *U.S. Private*, pg. 714
VALUE CITY DEPARTMENT STORES, INC.—Schottenstein Stores Corporation; *U.S. Private*, pg. 972
VENDEX INTERNATIONAL N.V.; *Int'l*, pg. 1462
VROOM & DREESMAN B.V.—Vendex International N.V.; *Int'l*, pg. 1463
WAL MART DISTRIBUTION CENTER—Wal-Mart Stores, Inc.; *U.S. Public*, pg. 1733
WAL-MART HOME/SEASONAL DIV.—Wal-Mart Stores, Inc.; *U.S. Public*, pg. 1733
WAL-MART JEWELRY DIV.—Wal-Mart Stores, Inc.; *U.S. Public*, pg. 1733
WAL-MART MERCHANDISING DIV.—Wal-Mart Stores, Inc.; *U.S. Public*, pg. 1733
WAL-MART STORES, INC.; *U.S. Public*, pg. 1732
WAL-MART DISTRIBUTION CENTER—Wal-Mart Stores, Inc.; *U.S. Public*, pg. 1733
WEARGUARD CORP.—Aramark Corp.; *U.S. Private*, pg. 79
WEINERS STORES, INC.; *U.S. Private*, pg. 1160
J.B. WHITE—Mercantile Stores Company, Inc.; *U.S. Public*, pg. 1090
WINNERS APPAREL LTD.—The TJX Companies, Inc.; *U.S. Public*, pg. 1557
F.W. WOOLWORTH CO. LIMITED, CANADA—Woolworth Corporation; *U.S. Public*, pg. 1778
WOOLWORTH MEXICANA, S.A. DE C.V.—Woolworth Corporation; *U.S. Public*, pg. 1778
WOOLWORTHS LIMITED—Industrial Equity Limited; *Int'l*, pg. 676
YOUNKERS, INC.—Proffitt's, Inc.; *U.S. Public*, pg. 1334
ZELLERS INC.—Hudson's Bay Company; *Int'l*, pg. 637
ZIONS CO-OPERATIVE MERCANTILE INSTITUTION; *U.S. Public*, pg. 1793

5331 — VARIETY STORES

THE FRED W. ALBRECHT GROCERY CO.; *U.S. Private*, pg. 32
ALLIED TIRE SALES; *U.S. Private*, pg. 41
BACHMAN'S, INC.; *U.S. Private*, pg. 109
BILL'S DOLLAR STORES, INC.; *U.S. Private*, pg. 144
CARREFOUR; *Int'l*, pg. 272
CARREFOUR NEDERLAND B.V.—Carrefour; *Int'l*, pg. 273
DAYTON HUDSON CORPORATION; *U.S. Public*, pg. 489
DUCKWALL-ALCO STORES, INC.; *U.S. Public*, pg. 533
FAMILY DOLLAR STORES, INC.; *U.S. Public*, pg. 612
FRED'S INC.; *U.S. Public*, pg. 680
GIBSON'S DISCOUNT CENTERS INC.; *U.S. Private*, pg. 452
KIJKSHOP/BEST-SELLERS—Vendex International N.V.; *Int'l*, pg. 1462
KINGFISHER PLC; *Int'l*, pg. 733
N.V. KONINKLIJKE BIJENKORF BEHEER KBB; *Int'l*, pg. 750
MAUI VARIETIES, LTD.; *U.S. Private*, pg. 715
MCCRORY CORPORATION; *U.S. Private*, pg. 720
FRED MEYER STORES—Fred Meyer Incorporated; *U.S. Public*, pg. 1103
PERRY BROTHERS, INC.; *U.S. Private*, pg. 854
OTTO REICHELT GMBH—SHV Holdings N.V.; *Int'l*, pg. 1156
SHV HOLDINGS N.V.; *Int'l*, pg. 1154
SIMAGO, S.A.—Jardine Matheson Holdings Limited; *Int'l*, pg. 704
SOCANAV INC.; *Int'l*, pg. 1272
STERNHEIMER BROTHERS INC.; *U.S. Private*, pg. 1042
SUPER CENTER WAREHOUSE CLUB, INC.—Wal-Mart Stores, Inc.; *U.S. Public*, pg. 1733
TARGET STORES—Dayton Hudson Corporation; *U.S. Public*, pg. 489
TESCO PLC; *Int'l*, pg. 1376
TESCO STORES LTD.—Tesco PLC; *Int'l*, pg. 1376
U.S. WOOLWORTH DIV.—Woolworth Corporation; *U.S. Public*, pg. 1778
VARIETY WHOLESALERS, INCORPORATED; *U.S. Private*, pg. 1134
VENTURE STORES, INC.; *U.S. Public*, pg. 1716
WAL-MART STORES, INC.; *U.S. Public*, pg. 1732
WOOLWORTH CORPORATION; *U.S. Public*, pg. 1777
F.W. WOOLWORTH CO.—Woolworth Corporation; *U.S. Public*, pg. 1777
F.W. WOOLWORTH CO. LIMITED, CANADA—Woolworth Corporation; *U.S. Public*, pg. 1778
F.W. WOOLWORTH GMBH CO. (GERMANY)—Woolworth Corporation; *U.S. Public*, pg. 1778
WOOLWORTHS PLC—Kingfisher plc; *Int'l*, pg. 734

5399 — MISCELLANEOUS GENERAL MERCHANDISE STORES

ADVANCE ROSS CORPORATION—Cendant Corporation; *U.S. Public*, pg. 320
ALIMENTATION COUCHE TARD INC.; *Int'l*, pg. 57
ASCO GENERAL SUPPLIES (FAR EAST) LTD.—Pentland Group PLC; *Int'l*, pg. 1036
ASSOCIATED FOOD STORES INC.; *U.S. Private*, pg. 90
ASTRUP DRUGS, INC.; *U.S. Private*, pg. 93
ATWOOD DISTRIBUTING, INC.; *U.S. Private*, pg. 98
BARGAIN SUPPLY COMPANY; *U.S. Private*, pg. 116
BENNETT BROTHERS, INC.; *U.S. Private*, pg. 133
BENNETT BROTHERS, INC.—Bennett Brothers, Inc.; *U.S. Private*, pg. 133
BERWICK BAY OIL CO. INC.; *U.S. Private*, pg. 138
BEST PRODUCTS CO., INC.—Shaykin & Company; *U.S. Private*, pg. 990
BIG DOG HOLDINGS INC.; *U.S. Public*, pg. 227
BRODART COMPANY; *U.S. Private*, pg. 170
CARREFOUR; *Int'l*, pg. 272
CARREFOUR COMMERCIO E INDUSTRIA—Carrefour; *Int'l*, pg. 272
CARREFOUR NEDERLAND B.V.—Carrefour; *Int'l*, pg. 273
CENTROS COMMERCIALES PRYCA—Carrefour; *Int'l*, pg. 273
COSTCO WHOLESALE; *U.S. Public*, pg. 451
CUMBERLAND FARMS, INC.; *U.S. Private*, pg. 295
DAIRY EXPORT CO., INC.—Darigold, Inc.; *U.S. Private*, pg. 311
EUROPE TAX-FREE SHOPPING LTD.—Cendant Corporation; *U.S. Public*, pg. 320
FILENE'S BASEMENT, INC.; *U.S. Public*, pg. 622
FUEL SOUTH, INC.—Jones Company, Inc.; *U.S. Private*, pg. 596
GRUPO CARSO S.A. DE C.V.; *Int'l*, pg. 572
HALLS MERCHANDISING INC.—Hallmark Cards, Inc.; *U.S. Private*, pg. 496
HAMILTON STORES, INC.; *U.S. Private*, pg. 497
IKE'S—Fleming Companies, Inc.; *U.S. Public*, pg. 653
INDUSTRIAL EQUITY LIMITED; *Int'l*, pg. 676
ITO-YOKADO CO., LTD.; *Int'l*, pg. 693
KMART CORPORATION; *U.S. Public*, pg. 963
KNOTT'S BERRY FARM; *U.S. Private*, pg. 627
LEWIS DRUG, INC.; *U.S. Private*, pg. 665
LINENS 'N THINGS, INC.; *U.S. Private*, pg. 668
L. LURIA & SON, INC.; *U.S. Public*, pg. 1020
MFA INCORPORATED; *U.S. Private*, pg. 686
MAC FRUGAL'S BARGAINS CLOSE-OUTS INC.—Consolidated Stores Corp.; *U.S. Public*, pg. 437
MEIJER, INC.; *U.S. Private*, pg. 729
PAMIDA HOLDINGS CORPORATION; *U.S. Public*, pg. 1255
PAMIDA, INC.—Pamida Holdings Corporation; *U.S. Public*, pg. 1255
THE PANTRY, INC.; *U.S. Private*, pg. 837
PENN-DANIELS, INC.—ShopKo Stores, Inc.; *U.S. Public*, pg. 1467
PERGAMENT HOME CENTERS, INC.; *U.S. Private*, pg. 853
PETROLEUM MARKETERS, INC.; *U.S. Private*, pg. 859
PRESICARRE CORP.—Carrefour; *Int'l*, pg. 273
QUIKTRIP CORPORATION; *U.S. Private*, pg. 901
RALEY'S & BEL AIR; *U.S. Private*, pg. 907
ROCKBOTTOM STORES, INC.; *U.S. Private*, pg. 938
SEARS CANADA, INC.—Sears, Roebuck and Co.; *U.S. Public*, pg. 1452
SEARS DE MEXICO—Grupo Carso S.A. de C.V.; *Int'l*, pg. 573
SEARS, ROEBUCK AND CO.; *U.S. Public*, pg. 1452
SERVICE MERCHANDISE COMPANY, INC.; *U.S. Public*, pg. 1461
SEVEN-ELEVEN JAPAN CO., LTD.—Ito-Yokado Co., Ltd.; *Int'l*, pg. 693
SPIEGEL, INC.; *U.S. Public*, pg. 1498
STACEY'S/J. K. GILL RETAIL STORES—Brodart Company; *U.S. Private*, pg. 170
TRACTOR SUPPLY CO.; *U.S. Public*, pg. 1627
UNI-MARTS, INC.; *U.S. Public*, pg. 1664
WANG'S INTERNATIONAL, INC.; *U.S. Private*, pg. 1149
WHITE HEN PANTRY, INC.; *U.S. Private*, pg. 1172
WOOLRICH, INC.; *U.S. Private*, pg. 1188
WOOLRICH STORE DIV.—Woolrich, Inc.; *U.S. Private*, pg. 1188
YODER OIL COMPANY INC.; *U.S. Private*, pg. 1196

5411 — GROCERY STORES

ABCO MARKETS, INC.; *U.S. Private*, pg. 10
ACME MARKETS—American Stores Company; *U.S. Public*, pg. 93
AEON GROUP; *Int'l*, pg. 28
ALBERTSON'S, INC.; *U.S. Public*, pg. 38
THE FRED W. ALBRECHT GROCERY CO.; *U.S. Private*, pg. 32
ALDI FOOD INC.; *U.S. Private*, pg. 33
ALIMENTOS HEINZ C.A.—H.J. Heinz Company; *U.S. Public*, pg. 806
ALLENS OF HASTINGS, INC.; *U.S. Private*, pg. 37
ALLSUPS CONVENIENCE STORES INC.; *U.S. Private*, pg. 44
AMERICAN CONSUMERS, INC.; *U.S. Public*, pg. 70
AMERICAN STORES COMPANY; *U.S. Public*, pg. 92
APPLETREE MARKETS; *U.S. Private*, pg. 78
ARDEN GROUP, INC.; *U.S. Public*, pg. 128
ARDEN-MAYFAIR, INC.—Arden Group, Inc.; *U.S. Public*, pg. 129
ASSOCIATED GROCERS, INC.; *U.S. Private*, pg. 90
AUCHAN S.A.; *Int'l*, pg. 98
AZTEX ENTERPRISES; *U.S. Private*, pg. 104
B&B CORPORATE HOLDINGS, INC.; *U.S. Private*, pg. 104
B & W STORMARKNADER AB—Axel Johnson AB; *Int'l*, pg. 708
BJ'S WHOLESALE CLUB, INC.; *U.S. Public*, pg. 162
BAINES MANAGEMENT CO.; *U.S. Private*, pg. 111
BAKER'S SUPERMARKETS, INC.—Fleming Companies, Inc.; *U.S. Public*, pg. 652
BASHAS; *U.S. Private*, pg. 120
BASISMARKT—Vendex International N.V.; *Int'l*, pg. 1463
BE-LO MARKETS INC.—Camellia Food Stores, Inc.; *U.S. Private*, pg. 203
BECKER MILK CO. LTD.; *Int'l*, pg. 182
BEL AIR MARKETS—Raley's & Bel Air; *U.S. Private*, pg. 908
BESCHE OIL COMPANY, INC.; *U.S. Private*, pg. 139
BI-LO INC.—Koninklijke Ahold NV; *Int'l*, pg. 749
BIG BEAR STORES COMPANY—The Penn Traffic Company; *U.S. Public*, pg. 1270
BIG V SUPERMARKETS, INC.; *U.S. Private*, pg. 143
BIG Y FOODS INC.; *U.S. Private*, pg. 143
BIGG'S HYPER SHOPPES, INC.—SuperValu, Inc.; *U.S. Public*, pg. 1541
BOLANDS LIMITED—The Oshawa Group Limited; *Int'l*, pg. 1012
BROOKSHIRE BROS., LTD.; *U.S. Private*, pg. 172
BROOKSHIRE GROCERY; *U.S. Private*, pg. 172
BRUNO'S INC.; *U.S. Public*, pg. 265
BRUNO'S INC.-GEORGIA—Bruno's Inc.; *U.S. Public*, pg. 265
BUCKEYE SPECIALTIES DIVISION—Seaway Food Town, Inc.; *U.S. Public*, pg. 1453
BURNSTAD BROTHERS, INC.; *U.S. Private*, pg. 187
BUTERA FINER FOODS INC.; *U.S. Private*, pg. 189
H.E. BUTT GROCERY CO.; *U.S. Private*, pg. 190
BUTTREY FOOD & DRUG COMPANY; *U.S. Public*, pg. 271
BYERLY'S INC.—Lund Food Holdings, Inc.; *U.S. Private*, pg. 680
C & K MARKET, INC.; *U.S. Private*, pg. 191
CAMELLIA FOOD STORES, INC.; *U.S. Private*, pg. 203
CANADA SAFEWAY LIMITED—Safeway Inc.; *U.S. Public*, pg. 1426
CARNEGIE HOLDING AB; *Int'l*, pg. 272
CARREFOUR; *Int'l*, pg. 272
CARREFOUR ARGENTINE S.A.—Carrefour; *Int'l*, pg. 272
CARREFOUR COMMERCIO E INDUSTRIA—Carrefour; *Int'l*, pg. 272
CARSE OIL CO. INC.; *U.S. Private*, pg. 216
CASA LEY S.A.—Safeway Inc.; *U.S. Public*, pg. 1426
CASEY'S GENERAL STORES, INC.; *U.S. Public*, pg. 312
CASH & CARRY GROCER INC.; *U.S. Private*, pg. 218
CENTROS COMMERCIALES PRYCA—Carrefour; *Int'l*, pg. 273
THE CIRCLE K COMPANY—Tosco Corporation; *U.S. Public*, pg. 1624
CLEMENS MARKETS INC.; *U.S. Private*, pg. 245
COCOS JAPAN—Kasumi Co., Ltd.; *Int'l*, pg. 724
CODVILLE DISTRIBUTORS—The Oshawa Group Limited; *Int'l*, pg. 1012
COMMUNITY CASH STORES; *U.S. Private*, pg. 259
CONSUMERS MARKETS INC.—Fleming Companies, Inc.; *U.S. Public*, pg. 653
CONVENIENCE PLUS PARTNERS LTD.; *U.S. Private*, pg. 271
CONVENIENT FOOD MART, INC.; *U.S. Private*, pg. 271
THE COPPS CORP.; *U.S. Private*, pg. 275
CORE-MARK INTERNATIONAL; *U.S. Private*, pg. 275
COSTCO WHOLESALE; *U.S. Public*, pg. 451
COVINGTON FOODS, INC.; *U.S. Private*, pg. 280
CROWN CENTRAL PETROLEUM CORPORATION; *U.S. Public*, pg. 462
CROWN GROCERS, INC.—Certified Grocers of California; *U.S. Private*, pg. 227
CRYSTAL FLASH PETROLEUM CORP.; *U.S. Private*, pg. 294
CUB FOODS STORES—SuperValu, Inc.; *U.S. Public*, pg. 1541

S.I.C. Index

CULCO, INC.—Randalls Food Markets, Inc.; *U.S. Private*, pg. 909
D & W FOOD CENTERS, INC.; *U.S. Private*, pg. 300
DAGMARKT—Vendex International N.V.; *Int'l*, pg. 1463
D'AGOSTINO SUPERMARKETS INC.; *U.S. Private*, pg. 306
DAIRY MART CONVENIENCE STORES, INC.; *U.S. Public*, pg. 476
DAIRY MART, INC.—Dairy Mart Convenience Stores, Inc.; *U.S. Public*, pg. 476
DAN'S SUPREME SUPER MARKETS INC.; *U.S. Private*, pg. 310
J.T. DAVENPORT & SONS, INC.; *U.S. Private*, pg. 314
JIMMY DAVIS ENTERPRISES, INC.; *U.S. Private*, pg. 315
DELCHAMPS, INC.—Jitney-Jungle Stores of America, Inc.; *U.S. Private*, pg. 588
DEMOULAS MARKET BASKET; *U.S. Private*, pg. 324
DEUTSCHE SB-KAUF AG—Metro AG; *Int'l*, pg. 863
DIERBERGS MARKETS INC.; *U.S. Private*, pg. 332
DILLON COMPANIES, INC.—The Kroger Co.; *U.S. Public*, pg. 967
DIXIELAND FOOD STORES INC.; *U.S. Private*, pg. 337
DOC FRANCOIS—Auchan S.A.; *Int'l*, pg. 98
DOCKS DE FRANCE S.A.—Auchan S.A.; *Int'l*, pg. 98
DOMINICK'S FINER FOODS—The Yucaipa Companies; *U.S. Private*, pg. 1202
DOMINION STORES—Tengelmann Warenhandelsgesellschaft; *Int'l*, pg. 1375
E-Z SERVE CONVENIENCE STORES, INC.—E-Z Serve Corp.; *U.S. Public*, pg. 540
E-Z SERVE CORP.; *U.S. Public*, pg. 540
EDA—Vendex International N.V.; *Int'l*, pg. 1463
EAGLE FOOD CENTERS, INC.; *U.S. Public*, pg. 547
ECONOMATS DU CENTRE—Auchan S.A.; *Int'l*, pg. 98
EDAH—Vendex International N.V.; *Int'l*, pg. 1463
EDWARDS SUPER FOOD STORES—Koninklijke Ahold NV; *Int'l*, pg. 749
EDWARDS SUPER FOOD STORES, LONG ISLAND DIV.—Koninklijke Ahold NV; *Int'l*, pg. 750
EMPIRE COMPANY LIMITED; *Int'l*, pg. 453
EMPRESS FOODS LTD.—Safeway Inc.; *U.S. Public*, pg. 1426
ENGLEFIELD, INC.; *U.S. Private*, pg. 377
ENTREPRENEUR, INC.—Worsley Companies Inc.; *U.S. Private*, pg. 1191
ERICKSON OIL PRODUCTS, INC.; *U.S. Private*, pg. 381
ERICKSON'S DIVERSIFIED CORP.; *U.S. Private*, pg. 381
ETABLISSEMENTS DELHAIZE FRERES ET CIE "LE LION" S.A.; *Int'l*, pg. 462
FFP MARKETING COMPANY, INC.; *U.S. Public*, pg. 604
FALLEY'S INC.—The Yucaipa Companies; *U.S. Private*, pg. 1202
FAREWAY STORES, INC.; *U.S. Private*, pg. 393
FARM FRESH, INC.—Richfood Holdings, Inc.; *U.S. Public*, pg. 1388
FARM STORES; *U.S. Private*, pg. 394
FARMER JACK SUPERMARKETS—Tengelmann Warenhandelsgesellschaft; *Int'l*, pg. 1375
FAST FARE, INC.—Crown Central Petroleum Corporation; *U.S. Public*, pg. 462
FIESTA MART INC.; *U.S. Private*, pg. 403
FINAST—Koninklijke Ahold NV; *Int'l*, pg. 750
FLEMING COMPANY—Fleming Companies, Inc.; *U.S. Public*, pg. 653
THE FOOD EMPORIUM—Tengelmann Warenhandelsgesellschaft; *Int'l*, pg. 1375
FOOD 4 LESS, INC.—The Yucaipa Companies; *U.S. Private*, pg. 1202
FOOD LION, INC.—Etablissements Delhaize Freres Et Cie "Le Lion" S.A.; *Int'l*, pg. 463
FOOD SERVICES OF AMERICA—Services Group of America; *U.S. Private*, pg. 987
FOOD TOWN SUPERMARKETS DIVISION—Seaway Food Town, Inc.; *U.S. Public*, pg. 1453
FOODARAMA SUPERMARKETS, INC.; *U.S. Public*, pg. 661
FORTINO'S SUPERMARKETS LTD.—George Weston Limited; *Int'l*, pg. 1495
FRANKLINS LIMITED—Jardine Matheson Holdings Limited; *Int'l*, pg. 703
FRESH FOOD, INC.; *U.S. Private*, pg. 427
FRESH MATSUYA CO., LTD.—Matsuya Company Ltd.; *Int'l*, pg. 848
FULMER SUPERMARKETS, INC.; *U.S. Private*, pg. 431
FURR'S SUPERMARKETS; *U.S. Private*, pg. 432
GB INTERNATIONAL—GIB Group; *Int'l*, pg. 534
SARL GB ZAIRE—GIB Group; *Int'l*, pg. 534
GES INC.; *U.S. Private*, pg. 434
GIB GROUP; *Int'l*, pg. 532
GS SOCIETA GENERALE SUPERMERCATI—Benetton Group S.p.A.; *Int'l*, pg. 186
GS SOCIETA GENERALE SUPERMERCATI—IRI Istituto Ricostruzione Industriale; *Int'l*, pg. 655
GELSON'S MARKETS—Arden Group, Inc.; *U.S. Public*, pg. 129
GENUARDI FAMILY MARKETS INC.; *U.S. Private*, pg. 447
GERLAND CORP.; *U.S. Private*, pg. 449
GETTY PETROLEUM MARKETING INC.; *U.S. Public*, pg. 740
GIANT EAGLE, INC.; *U.S. Private*, pg. 450
GIANT FOOD INC.; *U.S. Public*, pg. 741
GIANT FOOD STORES INC.—Koninklijke Ahold NV; *Int'l*, pg. 750
GIANT INDUSTRIES INC.; *U.S. Public*, pg. 741
GIANT OF CHERRY HILL, INC.—Giant Food Inc.; *U.S. Public*, pg. 741
GOLUB CORPORATION; *U.S. Private*, pg. 463
GORDY'S, INC.; *U.S. Private*, pg. 465
THE GRAND UNION COMPANY; *U.S. Public*, pg. 758
THE GREAT ATLANTIC & PACIFIC COMPANY OF CANADA LIMITED—Tengelmann Warenhandelsgesellschaft; *Int'l*, pg. 1375
THE GREAT ATLANTIC & PACIFIC TEA COMPANY, INC.—Tengelmann Warenhandelsgesellschaft; *Int'l*, pg. 1375
GREAT SCOTT FOOD MARKETS, INC.—James Ferrera & Sons, Inc.; *U.S. Private*, pg. 402
AUTRY GREER & SONS, INC.; *U.S. Private*, pg. 479
THE JOHN C. GROUB COMPANY INC.; *U.S. Private*, pg. 484
GRUPO GIGANTE S.A. DE C.V.; *Int'l*, pg. 574
HACKNEY PETROLEUM, INC.—The H.T. Hackney Co.; *U.S. Private*, pg. 493
HAGGEN, INC.; *U.S. Private*, pg. 493
HALE-HALSELL COMPANY; *U.S. Private*, pg. 494
HANNAFORD BROS. CO.; *U.S. Public*, pg. 781
HARMON CITY, INC.; *U.S. Private*, pg. 503
HARP'S FOOD STORES, INC.; *U.S. Private*, pg. 504
HARRIS TEETER, INC.—Ruddick Corporation; *U.S. Public*, pg. 1412
J.H. HARVEY COMPANY; *U.S. Private*, pg. 508
HAWKINS MARKETS—SuperValu, Inc.; *U.S. Public*, pg. 1540
ALBERT HEIJN B.V.—Koninklijke Ahold NV; *Int'l*, pg. 749
HEINEN'S INC.; *U.S. Private*, pg. 519
J.S. HEMKOPSKEDJAN AB—Carnegie Holding AB; *Int'l*, pg. 272
HERMANS GROEP B.V.—Tengelmann Warenhandelsgesellschaft; *Int'l*, pg. 1375
HI NABOR SUPERMARKET INC.; *U.S. Private*, pg. 525
HOLYOKE FOOD MART, INC.—Tengelmann Warenhandelsgesellschaft; *Int'l*, pg. 1375
HOMELAND STORES, INC.—Homeland Holding Corp.; *U.S. Public*, pg. 832
HONG KONG CONVENIENCE STORES LIMITED—Jardine Matheson Holdings Limited; *Int'l*, pg. 704
HOP-IN MICHIGAN, INC.—Silcorp Limited; *Int'l*, pg. 1249
HOUCHENS INDUSTRIES INC.; *U.S. Private*, pg. 541
HOUCHENS MARKETS—Houchens Industries Inc.; *U.S. Private*, pg. 541
HUB CITY FOODS—Fleming Companies, Inc.; *U.S. Public*, pg. 653
HUDON ET DEAUDELIN LTEE—The Oshawa Group Limited; *Int'l*, pg. 1012
HUGHES FAMILY MARKETS, INC.—Quality Food Centers, Inc.; *U.S. Public*, pg. 1349
HY-VEE FOOD STORES INCORPORATED; *U.S. Private*, pg. 550
ICA HANDLARNAS AB; *Int'l*, pg. 642
ICELAND FROZEN FOODS PLC.—Iceland Group plc; *Int'l*, pg. 658
ICELAND GROUP PLC; *Int'l*, pg. 658
INDUSTRIAL EQUITY LIMITED; *Int'l*, pg. 676
INGLES MARKETS, INCORPORATED; *U.S. Public*, pg. 878
INLAND EMPIRE DIVISION—Albertson's, Inc.; *U.S. Public*, pg. 38
INSERRA SHOPRITE; *U.S. Private*, pg. 565
INTERSTATE JITNEY JUNGLE STORES, INC.—Jitney-Jungle Stores of America, Inc.; *U.S. Private*, pg. 588
ITO-YOKADO CO., LTD.; *Int'l*, pg. 693
JARDINE MATHESON HOLDINGS LIMITED; *Int'l*, pg. 703
JERONIMO MARTINS; *Int'l*, pg. 705
JEWEL-OSCO—American Stores Company; *U.S. Public*, pg. 93
JEWEL OSCO SOUTHWEST, INC.—American Stores Company; *U.S. Public*, pg. 93
JITNEY-JUNGLE STORES OF AMERICA, INC.; *U.S. Private*, pg. 588
JONES COMPANY, INC.; *U.S. Private*, pg. 596
JUSCO USA, INC.—AEON Group; *Int'l*, pg. 28
KF/KONSUM COOP GROUP; *Int'l*, pg. 718
KAISER'S KAFFEE-GESCHAEFT AG—Tengelmann Warenhandelsgesellschaft; *Int'l*, pg. 1375
KASH N KARRY FOOD STORES, INC.—Etablissements Delhaize Freres Et Cie "Le Lion" S.A.; *Int'l*, pg. 463
KASUMI CO., LTD.; *Int'l*, pg. 724
KELLY DOUGLAS & COMPANY LIMITED—George Weston Limited; *Int'l*, pg. 1495
KENYON OIL COMPANY, INC.—Warren Equities Inc.; *U.S. Private*, pg. 1151
KING FUELS INC.; *U.S. Private*, pg. 620
KING KULLEN GROCERY CO., INC.; *U.S. Private*, pg. 621
KINGS SUPER MARKETS INC.—Marks & Spencer PLC; *Int'l*, pg. 843
KNECHTEL WHOLESALE GROCERS—The Oshawa Group Limited; *Int'l*, pg. 1012
KOHL'S FOOD STORES—Tengelmann Warenhandelsgesellschaft; *Int'l*, pg. 1375
KONINKLIJKE AHOLD NV; *Int'l*, pg. 749
KONMAR—Vendex International N.V.; *Int'l*, pg. 1463
KONSUM VEREIN ZURICH AG—Coop Switzerland; *Int'l*, pg. 330
THE KROGER CO.; *U.S. Public*, pg. 967
KWICKIE/FLASH FOODS, INC.—Jones Company, Inc.; *U.S. Private*, pg. 596
KWIK SAVE GROUP PLC—Jardine Matheson Holdings Limited; *Int'l*, pg. 704
KWIK TRIP INC.; *U.S. Private*, pg. 637
LA ROSA'S, INC.; *U.S. Private*, pg. 640
LA RUCHE PICARDE—Auchan S.A.; *Int'l*, pg. 98
LECLERC; *Int'l*, pg. 805
LECO INC.—Giant Food Inc.; *U.S. Public*, pg. 741
LIL'CHAMP/FOOD STORES INC.—The Pantry, Inc.; *U.S. Private*, pg. 837
LOBLAW COMPANIES LIMITED—George Weston Limited; *Int'l*, pg. 1495
LOBLAW SUPERMARKETS INC.—George Weston Limited; *Int'l*, pg. 1495
LOEWA WARENHANDEL GES.MBH—Tengelmann Warenhandelsgesellschaft; *Int'l*, pg. 1375
LOWE'S FOOD STORES, INC.—Alex Lee, Inc.; *U.S. Private*, pg. 657
LUCKY STORES NORTHERN CALIFORNIA DIVISION—American Stores Company; *U.S. Public*, pg. 93
LUCKY STORES SOUTHERN CALIFORNIA DIVISION—American Stores Company; *U.S. Public*, pg. 93
LUND FOOD HOLDINGS, INC.; *U.S. Private*, pg. 680
THE MAD BUTCHER, INC.; *U.S. Private*, pg. 693
MAKRO ATACADISTA S.A.—SHV Holdings N.V.; *Int'l*, pg. 1155
MAKRO AUTOSERVICIO MAYORISTA, S.A.—SHV Holdings N.V.; *Int'l*, pg. 1155
MAKRO AUTOSERVICO GROSSISTA, S.A.—SHV Holdings N.V.; *Int'l*, pg. 1155
MAKRO CASH AND CARRY WHOLESALE S.A.—SHV Holdings N.V.; *Int'l*, pg. 1155
MAKRO COMERCIALIZADORA S.A.—SHV Holdings N.V.; *Int'l*, pg. 1155
MAKRO INTERNATIONAL AG—SHV Holdings N.V.; *Int'l*, pg. 1155
MAKRO MOROCCO S.A.—SHV Holdings N.V.; *Int'l*, pg. 1155
MAKRO SELF SERVICE WHOLESALERS LTD.—SHV Holdings N.V.; *Int'l*, pg. 1156
MAKRO TAIWAN LTD.—SHV Holdings N.V.; *Int'l*, pg. 1156
MAKRO ZELFBEDIENINGSGROOTHANDEL C.V.—SHV Holdings N.V.; *Int'l*, pg. 1155
MALONE & HYDE, INC.-GOODLETTSVILLE—Fleming Companies, Inc.; *U.S. Public*, pg. 653
MALONE & HYDE, INC.-SOUTHAVEN—Fleming Companies, Inc.; *U.S. Public*, pg. 653
MARKS & SPENCER US HOLDINGS INC.—Marks & Spencer PLC; *Int'l*, pg. 843
MARS SUPER MARKETS, INC.; *U.S. Private*, pg. 707
MARSH SUPERMARKETS, INC.; *U.S. Public*, pg. 1049
MARTIN'S FOODS OF SOUTH BURLINGTON, INC.—Hannaford Bros. Co.; *U.S. Public*, pg. 782
MASTER-BILT PRODUCTS—Standex International Corporation; *U.S. Public*, pg. 1506
MAVERIK COUNTRY STORES, INC.; *U.S. Private*, pg. 715
MCLANE COMPANY, INC.—Wal-Mart Stores, Inc.; *U.S. Public*, pg. 1733
MEGAMARKETS, INC.—Fleming Companies, Inc.; *U.S. Public*, pg. 653
MEIJER, INC.; *U.S. Private*, pg. 729
JULIUS MEINL AG; *Int'l*, pg. 856
METRO AG; *Int'l*, pg. 863
FRED MEYER STORES—Fred Meyer Incorporated; *U.S. Public*, pg. 1103
MICHAEL FOODS, INC.; *U.S. Public*, pg. 1103
MID SOUTH SALES; *U.S. Private*, pg. 744
MIKE'S MART—Silcorp Limited; *Int'l*, pg. 1249
MINI MART, INC.—The Kroger Co.; *U.S. Public*, pg. 967
MINYARD FOOD STORES, INC.; *U.S. Private*, pg. 752
MITSUI MATSUSHIMA CO., LTD.—Mitsui & Co., Ltd.; *Int'l*, pg. 877
MOTO, INC.; *U.S. Private*, pg. 764
MURRY'S, INC.; *U.S. Private*, pg. 768
NASH FINCH COMPANY; *U.S. Public*, pg. 1151
NATIONAL FOOD STORES, INC.; *U.S. Private*, pg. 783
NEW ENGLAND FROZEN FOODS, INC.; *U.S. Private*, pg. 793
NEW LINDEN PRICE RITE, INC.—Foodarama Supermarkets, Inc.; *U.S. Public*, pg. 661
NOB HILL GENERAL STORE, INC.; *U.S. Private*, pg. 799
NOPRI—GIB Group; *Int'l*, pg. 533
NUR HIER GMBH—Borden, Inc.; *U.S. Private*, pg. 160
O'MALIA FOOD MARKETS INC.; *U.S. Private*, pg. 816
OMNI SUPERSTORES—The Yucaipa Companies; *U.S. Private*, pg. 1202
ORGANIZACION SORIANA S.A. DE C.V.; *Int'l*, pg. 1008
OSHAWA FOODS—The Oshawa Group Limited; *Int'l*, pg. 1012
THE OSHAWA GROUP LIMITED; *Int'l*, pg. 1012
P & C FOOD MARKETS, INC.—The Penn Traffic Company; *U.S. Public*, pg. 1270
THE PANTRY, INC.; *U.S. Private*, pg. 837
PARMART STORES—The Parman Corporation; *U.S. Private*, pg. 840
PATHMARK STORES INCORPORATED; *U.S. Private*, pg. 843
PAVILIONS—Safeway Inc.; *U.S. Public*, pg. 1426
PAY LESS SUPER MARKETS, INC.; *U.S. Private*, pg. 844
THE PENN TRAFFIC COMPANY; *U.S. Public*, pg. 1270
PIC N'PAY SUPERMARKETS, INC.; *U.S. Private*, pg. 864
PILOT CORPORATION; *U.S. Private*, pg. 865
PIONEER FOODS, INC.; *U.S. Private*, pg. 866
PLAID PANTRIES, INC.; *U.S. Private*, pg. 868
POLKA DOT DAIRY/TOM THUMB FOOD MARKETS—Polka Dot Dairy/Tom Thumb, Inc.; *U.S. Private*, pg. 874
PRESICARRE CORP.—Carrefour; *Int'l*, pg. 273
PRESTO FOOD STORES, INC.; *U.S. Private*, pg. 882
PRICE CHOPPER OPERATING CO., INC.—Golub Corporation; *U.S. Private*, pg. 463
PROVIGO INC.; *Int'l*, pg. 1072
PUBLIX SUPERMARKETS INC.; *U.S. Private*, pg. 893
PUEBLO INTERNATIONAL, INC.-P.R. DIV.—Pueblo Xtra International, Inc.; *U.S. Private*, pg. 894
PUNA PLANTATION HAWAII LTD.; *U.S. Private*, pg. 895
PURITAN MAID LTD.—Brake Bros plc; *Int'l*, pg. 210
PURITY WHOLESALE GROCERS; *U.S. Private*, pg. 896
QUALITY FOOD CENTERS, INC.; *U.S. Public*, pg. 1349
QUALITY MARKETS, INC.—The Penn Traffic Company; *U.S. Public*, pg. 1270
RACETRAC PETROLEUM, INC.; *U.S. Private*, pg. 906
RALEY'S & BEL AIR; *U.S. Private*, pg. 907
RALPHS GROCERY COMPANY—The Yucaipa Companies; *U.S. Private*, pg. 1202
RANDALL STORES, INC.; *U.S. Private*, pg. 909
RANDALLS FOOD MARKETS, INC.; *U.S. Private*, pg. 909
REAL HOLDING MANAGEMENT CORP.; *U.S. Private*, pg. 913
RED APPLE COMPANIES; *U.S. Private*, pg. 914
RED APPLE, INC.; *U.S. Private*, pg. 915
OTTO REICHELT GMBH—SHV Holdings N.V.; *Int'l*, pg. 1156
F.T. REYNOLDS COMPANY; *U.S. Private*, pg. 926
RICE FOOD MARKETS INC.; *U.S. Private*, pg. 927

RICHDALE DAIRY STORES, INC.—Scangas Brothers Holdings, Inc.; *U.S. Private*, pg. 969
RICHFOOD PENNSYLVANIA—Richfood Holdings, Inc.; *U.S. Public*, pg. 1389
RINI-REGO SUPERMARKETS, INC.—Giant Eagle, Inc.; *U.S. Private*, pg. 451
RISER FOODS, INC.—Giant Eagle, Inc.; *U.S. Private*, pg. 450
ROB—GIB Group; *Int'l*, pg. 533
F.L. ROBERTS & CO. INC.; *U.S. Private*, pg. 935
ROGERS MARKETS INC.; *U.S. Private*, pg. 940
ROSAUERS SUPERMARKETS, INC.; *U.S. Private*, pg. 944
ROYAL FARMS INC.; *U.S. Private*, pg. 948
RUDDICK CORPORATION; *U.S. Public*, pg. 1412
RUSSELL PETROLEUM CORPORATION; *U.S. Private*, pg. 953
SHV HOLDINGS N.V.; *Int'l*, pg. 1154
SHV MAKRO—SHV Holdings N.V.; *Int'l*, pg. 1155
SAFEWAY INC.; *U.S. Public*, pg. 1426
SAFEWAY PLC; *Int'l*, pg. 1169
SAFEWAY STORES PLC—Safeway PLC; *Int'l*, pg. 1169
J. SAINSBURY PLC; *Int'l*, pg. 1169
SAVACENTRE LIMITED—J. Sainsbury plc; *Int'l*, pg. 1170
SAVE-A-LOT—Houchens Industries Inc.; *U.S. Private*, pg. 541
SAVE MART SUPERMARKETS; *U.S. Private*, pg. 968
SCANGAS BROTHERS HOLDINGS, INC.; *U.S. Private*, pg. 969
SCHNUCK MARKETS, INC.; *U.S. Private*, pg. 971
SCHULTZ SAV-O STORES, INC.; *U.S. Public*, pg. 1442
BEN SCHWARTZ MARKET, INC.; *U.S. Private*, pg. 974
SCHWEGMANN GIANT SUPER MARKETS—Kohlberg & Company, LLC; *U.S. Private*, pg. 629
SCOTT'S FOOD STORES INC.—SuperValu, Inc.; *U.S. Public*, pg. 1541
SEAWAY FOOD TOWN, INC.; *U.S. Public*, pg. 1452
SEE'S CANDIES, INC.—Berkshire Hathaway Inc.; *U.S. Public*, pg. 221
SEESSEL HOLDINGS, INC.; *U.S. Private*, pg. 981
SENTRY MARKETS, INC.—Fleming Companies, Inc.; *U.S. Public*, pg. 653
SERVCO PACIFIC INC.; *U.S. Private*, pg. 986
SERVICES GROUP OF AMERICA; *U.S. Private*, pg. 987
7-ELEVEN STORES—Ito-Yokado Co., Ltd.; *Int'l*, pg. 693
SHAW COMMUNITY SUPERMARKET—Giant Food Inc.; *U.S. Public*, pg. 741
SHAW'S SUPERMARKETS, INC.—J. Sainsbury plc; *Int'l*, pg. 1170
SHEETZ, INC.; *U.S. Private*, pg. 991
SHERMS THUNDERBIRD MARKET; *U.S. Private*, pg. 993
SHOP RITE OF MALVERNE, INC.—Foodarama Supermarkets, Inc.; *U.S. Public*, pg. 661
SHOP-RITE SUPERMARKETS, INC.—Wakefern Food Corporation; *U.S. Private*, pg. 1146
SIAM MAKRO LTD.—SHV Holdings N.V.; *Int'l*, pg. 1156
SILCORP LIMITED; *Int'l*, pg. 1249
SITE OIL COMPANY OF MISSOURI; *U.S. Private*, pg. 1004
SMITH'S FOOD & DRUG CENTERS, INC.—Fred Meyer Incorporated; *U.S. Public*, pg. 1103
SO-LO-FOOD, INC.; *U.S. Private*, pg. 1011
SOBEY INC.—Empire Company Limited; *Int'l*, pg. 454
SOCANAV INC.; *Int'l*, pg. 1272
SOUTHLAND CORP.-BRITISH COLUMBIA DIVISION—Ito-Yokado Co., Ltd.; *Int'l*, pg. 694
SOUTHLAND CORP.-PRAIRIES DIVISION—Ito-Yokado Co., Ltd.; *Int'l*, pg. 694
THE SOUTHLAND CORPORATION—Ito-Yokado Co., Ltd.; *Int'l*, pg. 693
SPENCER COMPANIES INC.; *U.S. Private*, pg. 1024
STANLEY STORES, INC.; *U.S. Private*, pg. 1033
STAR MARKETS COMPANY, INC.; *U.S. Private*, pg. 1035
STATER BROS. INC.—Craig Corporation; *U.S. Public*, pg. 456
STEINBERG INC.—Socanav Inc.; *Int'l*, pg. 1272
STEWART'S ICE CREAM CO., INC.; *U.S. Private*, pg. 1043
THE STOP & SHOP COMPANIES, INC.—Koninklijke Ahold NV; *Int'l*, pg. 750
STOP IN FOOD STORES—Petroleum Marketers, Inc.; *U.S. Private*, pg. 859
SULLIVAN OIL COMPANY; *U.S. Private*, pg. 1050
SUPER DISCOUNT MARKETS, INC.—Etablissements Delhaize Freres Et Cie "Le Lion" S.A.; *Int'l*, pg. 463
SUPER FRESH COMPANY—Tengelmann Warenhandelsgesellschaft; *Int'l*, pg. 1375
SUPERMERCADOS MAYORISTAS MAKRA S.A.—SHV Holdings N.V.; *Int'l*, pg. 1156
SURE SAVE SUPER MARKET LTD.; *U.S. Private*, pg. 1056
THE SWISS COLONY, INC; *U.S. Private*, pg. 1059
TACT HOLDING; *U.S. Private*, pg. 1067
TENGELMANN WARENHANDELSGESELLSCHAFT; *Int'l*, pg. 1375
TER HUURNE—Koninklijke Ahold NV; *Int'l*, pg. 749
TERUYA BROS., LIMITED; *U.S. Private*, pg. 1077
THORNTON OIL CORP.; *U.S. Private*, pg. 1084
THRIFTWAY, INC.—Winn-Dixie Stores, Inc.; *U.S. Public*, pg. 1771
TIENDAS DE DESCUENTO SULTANA S.A. DE C.V.—Organizacion Soriana S.A. de C.V.; *Int'l*, pg. 1008
TIMES SUPER MARKET LTD.—Teruya Bros., Limited; *U.S. Private*, pg. 1078
TOM THUMB FOOD & PHARMACY—Randalls Food Markets, Inc.; *U.S. Private*, pg. 909
TOWN & COUNTRY SUPERMARKET; *U.S. Private*, pg. 1093
TOWN PUMP, INC.; *U.S. Private*, pg. 1093
TRADER JOE'S CO.—TACT Holding; *U.S. Private*, pg. 1067
TRADING PORT, INC.; *U.S. Private*, pg. 1095
TRAVEL PORTS OF AMERICA INC.; *U.S. Public*, pg. 1632
TREASURE ISLAND FOODMARTS INC.; *U.S. Private*, pg. 1098
TRITON MANUFACTURING, INC.; *U.S. Private*, pg. 1104
TRUCCHIS MARKETS; *U.S. Private*, pg. 1107
URM STORES, INC.; *U.S. Private*, pg. 1114
UKROP'S SUPER MARKETS; *U.S. Private*, pg. 1115
UNI-MARTS, INC.; *U.S. Public*, pg. 1664
UNITED DAIRY FARMERS, INC.; *U.S. Private*, pg. 1121
UNITED GROCERS INC.; *U.S. Private*, pg. 1122
UNITED SUPERMARKETS INC.; *U.S. Private*, pg. 1126
VALU DISCOUNT, INCORPORATED; *U.S. Private*, pg. 1132
VALU-FARE FOODS, INC.—Hale-Halsell Company; *U.S. Private*, pg. 494
VALU FOODS INC.—So-Lo-Food, Inc.; *U.S. Private*, pg. 1012
VENDEX INTERNATIONAL N.V.; *Int'l*, pg. 1462
VILLAGE PANTRIES, INC.—Marsh Supermarkets, Inc.; *U.S. Public*, pg. 1049
VILLAGE SUPER MARKET INC.; *U.S. Public*, pg. 1721
THE VONS COMPANIES, INC.—Safeway Inc.; *U.S. Public*, pg. 1426
WALDBAUM'S SUPERMARKETS, INC.—Tengelmann Warenhandelsgesellschaft; *Int'l*, pg. 1375
WAREMART INC.; *U.S. Private*, pg. 1150
WAREMART INC.—Waremart Inc.; *U.S. Private*, pg. 1150
WAWA, INC.; *U.S. Private*, pg. 1155
WEGMANS FOOD MARKETS, INC.; *U.S. Private*, pg. 1158
WEIS MARKETS, INC.; *U.S. Public*, pg. 1751
WELLCOME COMPANY LIMITED—Jardine Matheson Holdings Limited; *Int'l*, pg. 704
WELLCOME TAIWAN COMPANY LTD.—Jardine Matheson Holdings Limited; *Int'l*, pg. 704
WINN-DIXIE STORES, INC.; *U.S. Public*, pg. 1771
WOOLWORTHS (NEW ZEALAND) LTD.—Jardine Matheson Holdings Limited; *Int'l*, pg. 704
WORSLEY COMPANIES INC.; *U.S. Private*, pg. 1191
XTRA SUPER FOOD CENTERS, INC.—Pueblo Xtra International, Inc.; *U.S. Private*, pg. 894
YMR—Koninklijke Ahold NV; *Int'l*, pg. 750
YORK MART CO., LTD.—Ito-Yokado Co., Ltd.; *Int'l*, pg. 693
ZEHRMART INC.—George Weston Limited; *Int'l*, pg. 1495

5421 — MEAT & FISH MARKETS, INCLUDING FREEZER PROVISIONS

AMERICAN FROZEN FOODS, INC.; *U.S. Private*, pg. 55
BEL AIR MARKETS—Raley's & Bel Air; *U.S. Private*, pg. 908
CLEARWATER FINE FOODS INC.; *Int'l*, pg. 297
CROWN FOODS INC.; *U.S. Private*, pg. 292
FAREWAY STORES, INC.; *U.S. Private*, pg. 393
AB FRIONOR—Frionor A/S; *Int'l*, pg. 516
FRIONOR AG—Frionor A/S; *Int'l*, pg. 516
FRIONOR ASIA PACIFIC PTE. LTD.—Frionor A/S; *Int'l*, pg. 516
FRIONOR AUSTRALIA PTY. LTD.—Frionor A/S; *Int'l*, pg. 516
FRIONOR DANMARK A/S—Frionor A/S; *Int'l*, pg. 516
FRIONOR (ENGLAND) LTD.—Frionor A/S; *Int'l*, pg. 516
FRIONOR FRANCE SARL—Frionor A/S; *Int'l*, pg. 516
FRIONOR-PRODUKTER A/S—Frionor A/S; *Int'l*, pg. 516
FRIONOR (THAILAND) LTD.—Frionor A/S; *Int'l*, pg. 516
FRIONOR TIEFKUHL-PRODUKTE GMBH—Frionor A/S; *Int'l*, pg. 516
FRIONOR U.S.A. INC.—Frionor A/S; *Int'l*, pg. 516
GREEN ISLE LTD.—Northern Foods plc; *Int'l*, pg. 968
HICKORY FARMS CATALOGUES OF AMERICA, INC.—Hickory Farms, Inc.; *U.S. Private*, pg. 525
KOWALSKI SAUSAGE CO., INC.; *U.S. Private*, pg. 634
THE MAD BUTCHER, INC.; *U.S. Private*, pg. 693
OMAHA STEAKS; *U.S. Private*, pg. 815
PARMART STORES—The Parman Corporation; *U.S. Private*, pg. 840
PUBLIX SUPERMARKETS INC.; *U.S. Private*, pg. 893
ROTELLE, INC.—Richfood Holdings, Inc.; *U.S. Public*, pg. 1389
SEESSEL HOLDINGS, INC.; *U.S. Private*, pg. 981
STOCK YARDS PACKING CO., INC.; *U.S. Private*, pg. 1043

5431 — FRUIT STORES & VEGETABLE MARKETS

BLUE ANCHOR, INC.; *U.S. Private*, pg. 150
CROWN FOODS INC.; *U.S. Private*, pg. 292
GARGIULO INC.—Monsanto Company; *U.S. Public*, pg. 1124
RIVER RANCH NORTHEAST, INC.; *U.S. Private*, pg. 934
TWIN COUNTY GROCERS, INC.; *U.S. Private*, pg. 1111

5441 — CANDY, NUT & CONFECTIONERY STORES

ARCHIBALD CANDY COMPANY—The Jordan Company; *U.S. Private*, pg. 597
BERKSHIRE HATHAWAY INC.; *U.S. Public*, pg. 217
E-Z MART STORES, INC.; *U.S. Private*, pg. 353
FANNIE MAY CANDY SHOPS, INC.—The Jordan Company; *U.S. Private*, pg. 598
FAR-BEN S.A. DE C.V.; *Int'l*, pg. 478
HICKORY FARMS, INC.; *U.S. Private*, pg. 525
PACIFIC FOODS, INC.; *U.S. Private*, pg. 831
RUSSELL STOVER CANDIES, INC.; *U.S. Private*, pg. 953
SEE'S CANDY SHOPS, INC.—Berkshire Hathaway Inc.; *U.S. Public*, pg. 221

5451 — DAIRY PRODUCTS STORES

BRAUM ICE CREAM STORES INC.; *U.S. Private*, pg. 166
BROUGHTON FOODS COMPANY; *U.S. Public*, pg. 259
C.F. BURGER CREAMERY COMPANY; *U.S. Private*, pg. 182
COLONNA BROS., INC.; *U.S. Private*, pg. 254
COMPAGNIE LAITIERE BESNIER; *Int'l*, pg. 322
DAIRY EXPORT CO., INC.—Darigold, Inc.; *U.S. Private*, pg. 311
DAIRY MART CONVENIENCE STORES, INC.; *U.S. Public*, pg. 476
DIXIE DAIRY COMPANY; *U.S. Private*, pg. 337
HASTINGS CO-OP CREAMERY COMPANY; *U.S. Private*, pg. 510
MARYLAND & VIRGINIA MILK PRODUCERS COOPERATIVE ASSOCIATION, INC.; *U.S. Private*, pg. 711
MID-AMERICA DAIRYMEN, INC.; *U.S. Private*, pg. 743
NEW TAI MILK PRODUCTS CO. LTD.—New Zealand Dairy Board; *Int'l*, pg. 923
THE RESTAURANT COMPANY; *U.S. Private*, pg. 925
RICHDALE DAIRY STORES, INC.—Scangas Brothers Holdings, Inc.; *U.S. Private*, pg. 969
SCANGAS BROTHERS HOLDINGS, INC.; *U.S. Private*, pg. 969
THE SWISS COLONY, INC; *U.S. Private*, pg. 1059
TURNER HOLDING LLC; *U.S. Private*, pg. 1109
UPSTATE MILK COOPERATIVES INC.; *U.S. Private*, pg. 1129
WOMETCO DE PUERTO RICO INC.—Wometco Enterprises, Inc.; *U.S. Private*, pg. 1186
WOMETCO ENTERPRISES, INC.; *U.S. Private*, pg. 1186

5461 — RETAIL BAKERIES

AU BON PAIN CO., INC.; *U.S. Public*, pg. 146
AWREY BAKERIES, INC.; *U.S. Private*, pg. 103
BEL AIR MARKETS—Raley's & Bel Air; *U.S. Private*, pg. 908
BESS EATON DONUT FLOUR CO., INC.; *U.S. Private*, pg. 139
BYERLY'S INC.—Lund Food Holdings, Inc.; *U.S. Private*, pg. 680
DERST BAKING COMPANY, INC.; *U.S. Private*, pg. 326
KF/KONSUM COOP GROUP; *Int'l*, pg. 718
LUND FOOD HOLDINGS, INC.; *U.S. Private*, pg. 680
MRS. FIELDS' ORIGINAL COOKIES, INC.; *U.S. Private*, pg. 688
MCGLYNN BAKERIES INC.; *U.S. Private*, pg. 721
MISTER DONUT OF AMERICA, INC.—Allied Domecq PLC; *Int'l*, pg. 63
MRS. BAIRD'S BAKERIES, INC.; *U.S. Private*, pg. 765
THE PENN TRAFFIC COMPANY; *U.S. Public*, pg. 1270
PRESIDENT BAKING COMPANY—President Enterprises Corp.; *Int'l*, pg. 1069
PUBLIX SUPERMARKETS INC.; *U.S. Private*, pg. 893
SEAWAY FOOD TOWN, INC.; *U.S. Public*, pg. 1452
WINCHELL'S DONUT HOUSES, L.P.—Shato Holdings Ltd.; *Int'l*, pg. 1230
WINN-DIXIE STORES, INC.; *U.S. Public*, pg. 1771
YUM YUM DONUT SHOP, INC.; *U.S. Private*, pg. 1203

5499 — MISCELLANEOUS FOOD STORES

AMERICAN LANDMARK SPRINGS—Nestle S.A.; *Int'l*, pg. 919
AUSTRALIAN POULTRY LTD.—Goodman Fielder Limited; *Int'l*, pg. 555
BOOKER PLC; *Int'l*, pg. 202
CARR GOTTSTEIN FOODS; *U.S. Public*, pg. 308
CRYSTAL GEYSER; *U.S. Private*, pg. 294
THE DAIEI, INC.; *Int'l*, pg. 364
ETABLISSEMENTS DELHAIZE FRERES ET CIE "LE LION" S.A.; *Int'l*, pg. 462
GENERAL NUTRITION CENTERS—General Nutrition, Inc.; *U.S. Public*, pg. 725
GENERAL NUTRITION, INC.; *U.S. Public*, pg. 725
GREAT EARTH DISTRIBUTION—Evergood Products Corporation; *U.S. Private*, pg. 386
HICKORY FARMS, INC.; *U.S. Private*, pg. 525
INAGUA GENERAL STORE, LTD.—Morton International Inc.; *U.S. Public*, pg. 1135
FRED MEYER STORES—Fred Meyer Incorporated; *U.S. Public*, pg. 1103
MURRY'S, INC.; *U.S. Private*, pg. 768
OTT FOOD PRODUCTS; *U.S. Private*, pg. 821
PICK QUICK FOODS; *U.S. Private*, pg. 864
SAGE ENTERPRISES, INC.; *U.S. Private*, pg. 960
THE SECOND CUP—Cara Operations Limited; *Int'l*, pg. 266
SOMERFIELD STORES LTD.—Somerfield PLC; *Int'l*, pg. 1280
STARBUCKS COFFEE COMPANY; *U.S. Public*, pg. 1510
WESTERN BEEF, INC.; *U.S. Public*, pg. 1758
WHOLE FOODS MARKET, INC.; *U.S. Public*, pg. 1767

5511 — MOTOR VEHICLE DEALERS (NEW & USED CARS)

ASN INCORPORATED; *U.S. Private*, pg. 8
AGENCY CHRYSLER-PLYMOUTH, INC.—National Auto Credit Inc.; *U.S. Public*, pg. 1153
AGENCY FORD, INC.—National Auto Credit Inc.; *U.S. Public*, pg. 1153
ALL-STATE FORD TRUCK SALES—Hesco Parts Corporation; *U.S. Private*, pg. 524
AMADOR MOTORS—Prospect Motors, Inc.; *U.S. Private*, pg. 891
ANCIRA ENTERPRISES INC.; *U.S. Private*, pg. 71
DAYTON ANDREWS INC.; *U.S. Private*, pg. 74
ARROW CHEVROLET, INC.; *U.S. Private*, pg. 85
ASBURY AUTOMOTIVE GROUP; *U.S. Private*, pg. 87
AUTOMOBIELBEDRIJVEN HOOGENBOOM B.V.—Britax International plc; *Int'l*, pg. 216
AVIS FORD INC.; *U.S. Private*, pg. 101
B&M EQUIPMENT, INC.—Beaudry Ford, Inc.; *U.S. Private*, pg. 127
BANKSTON FORD OF FRISCO, LTD. CO.—Republic Industries, Inc.; *U.S. Public*, pg. 1379

S.I.C. Index

BANKSTON NISSAN IN IRVING, INC.—Republic Industries, Inc.; *U.S. Public*, pg. 1379
W.O. BANKSTON ENTERPRISES INC.—Republic Industries, Inc.; *U.S. Public*, pg. 1379
BAST CHEVROLET INC.; *U.S. Private*, pg. 122
BAUGHER CHEVROLET-BUICK INC.; *U.S. Private*, pg. 123
BEACH CITY CHEVROLET CO.; *U.S. Private*, pg. 125
BEAUDRY FORD, INC.; *U.S. Private*, pg. 127
BEECH ISUZU—Beechmont Investments Inc.; *U.S. Private*, pg. 129
BEECHMONT CHEVROLET, INC—Beechmont Investments Inc.; *U.S. Private*, pg. 129
BEECHMONT HYUNDAI—Beechmont Investments Inc.; *U.S. Private*, pg. 129
BEECHMONT INVESTMENTS INC.; *U.S. Private*, pg. 129
BENSON MOTORS CORPORATION; *U.S. Private*, pg. 134
BIDDULPH AUTOMOTIVE GROUP; *U.S. Private*, pg. 142
BILL HEARD OLDSMOBILE COMPANY—Bill Heard Enterprises, Inc.; *U.S. Private*, pg. 515
BILL WINK CHEVROLET; *U.S. Private*, pg. 144
BLACK CADILLAC OLDS, INC.; *U.S. Private*, pg. 146
BLUE GRASS CHRYSLER-PLYMOUTH INC.; *U.S. Private*, pg. 152
BRAMAN WORLD CAR CENTER; *U.S. Private*, pg. 165
BRISTOL STREET MOTORS LIMITED—Britax International plc; *Int'l*, pg. 216
BRITAX INTERNATIONAL PLC; *Int'l*, pg. 216
BROADWAY CHEVROLET; *U.S. Private*, pg. 170
BROWN & BROWN VENTURE GROUP, LLC; *U.S. Private*, pg. 172
BROWN AUTOMOTIVE GROUP; *U.S. Private*, pg. 173
BILL BROWN FORD INC.; *U.S. Private*, pg. 173
BROWN MOTORS; *U.S. Private*, pg. 174
BUERKLE BUICK-HONDA CO.; *U.S. Private*, pg. 178
BURNS, PHILP PACIFIC DIVISION—Burns, Philp & Company Limited; *Int'l*, pg. 237
BYERLY FORD-NISSAN INC.; *U.S. Private*, pg. 191
JACK BYRNE FORD & MERCURY, INC.; *U.S. Private*, pg. 191
CAMI AUTOMOTIVE, INC.—General Motors Corporation; *U.S. Public*, pg. 722
CAMINO REAL CHEVROLET & GEO; *U.S. Private*, pg. 203
CAPITOL CADILLAC, CORP.—Don Massey Cadillac Inc.; *U.S. Private*, pg. 712
CAPITOL CHEVROLET CADILLAC GEO SUBARU INC.; *U.S. Private*, pg. 206
CASSENS TRANSPORT COMPANY; *U.S. Private*, pg. 219
MIKE CASTRUCCI CHEVROLET; *U.S. Private*, pg. 219
JIM CAUSLEY PONTIAC GMC INC.; *U.S. Private*, pg. 220
CAVE CITY CHEVROLET—Don Massey Cadillac Inc.; *U.S. Private*, pg. 712
CERRITOS FORD, INC.; *U.S. Private*, pg. 226
HERB CHAMBERS COS.; *U.S. Private*, pg. 227
CHAMPION MOTORS (1975) PTE. LTD.—Inchcape PLC; *Int'l*, pg. 672
CHAPMAN AUTOMOTIVE GROUP INC.; *U.S. Private*, pg. 229
CHAPMAN MANAGEMENT GROUP; *U.S. Private*, pg. 229
CHASE CHEVROLET CO., INC.; *U.S. Private*, pg. 230
CHEMUNG FORD, INC.; *U.S. Private*, pg. 233
CHEVY CHASE CARS & GEO; *U.S. Private*, pg. 234
CHRYSLER CREDIT CORP.—Chrysler Corporation; *U.S. Public*, pg. 354
CLASSIC NISSAN—ASN Incorporated; *U.S. Private*, pg. 8
COGGIN AUTOMOTIVE GROUP; *U.S. Private*, pg. 250
COGGIN PONTIAC-GMC INC.—Coggin Automotive Group; *U.S. Private*, pg. 250
COLEMAN CADILLAC INC.; *U.S. Private*, pg. 251
COLEMAN OLDSMOBILE, INC.; *U.S. Private*, pg. 252
BILL COLLINS FORD INC.; *U.S. Private*, pg. 253
COLLINS OLDSMOBILE INC.; *U.S. Private*, pg. 253
COLONIAL DODGE, INC.; *U.S. Private*, pg. 253
COOPERATIVE MOTORS LTD.—Harris Scarfe Holdings Limited; *Int'l*, pg. 597
CORMIER CHEVROLET COMPANY, INC.; *U.S. Private*, pg. 276
COURTESY CHEVROLET & IMPORTS INC.; *U.S. Private*, pg. 279
CREST CADILLAC COMPANY; *U.S. Private*, pg. 289
CREST CADILLAC, INC.—Don Massey Cadillac Inc.; *U.S. Private*, pg. 712
CROSS MOTORS CORP.; *U.S. Private*, pg. 291
CROWN BUICK, INC.; *U.S. Private*, pg. 292
THE CURRY CORPORATION; *U.S. Private*, pg. 297
DAIMLER-BENZ AKTIENGESELLSCHAFT; *Int'l*, pg. 366
DALLAS PETERBILT, INC.; *U.S. Private*, pg. 309
DARCARS LTD.; *U.S. Private*, pg. 311
DARLING'S; *U.S. Private*, pg. 311
RUSS DARROW GROUP; *U.S. Private*, pg. 311
MIKE DAUGHERTY'S CHEVROLET GEO, INC.; *U.S. Private*, pg. 313
BUD DAVIS CADILLAC, INC.; *U.S. Private*, pg. 314
DAVIS-MOORE OLDSMOBILE, INC.; *U.S. Private*, pg. 315
DE NOOYER CHEVROLET INC.; *U.S. Private*, pg. 318
JACK DEMMER FORD, INC.; *U.S. Private*, pg. 323
DENNY MENHOLT FRONTIER CHEVROLET; *U.S. Private*, pg. 324
DIAMOND MOTORS INC.; *U.S. Private*, pg. 330
DODGE OF WINTER PARK; *U.S. Private*, pg. 337
A.K. DURNIN CHRYSLER PLYMOUTH, INC.; *U.S. Private*, pg. 348
EAGLE LINCOLN MERCURY INC.; *U.S. Private*, pg. 355
EARNHARDT'S MOTOR COMPANIES; *U.S. Private*, pg. 356
EASTSIDE LINCOLN MERCURY—Beechmont Investments Inc.; *U.S. Private*, pg. 129
STU EVANS LINCOLN-MERCURY INC.; *U.S. Private*, pg. 385
F.P.A., INC.; *U.S. Private*, pg. 389
FAIRWAY FORD, INC.; *U.S. Private*, pg. 392
FARMINGTON HILLS HOLDING COMPANY; *U.S. Private*, pg. 395
FAULKNER CADILLAC INC.; *U.S. Private*, pg. 397
FERMAN OLDSMOBILE; *U.S. Private*, pg. 401
STEVE FOLEY CADILLAC; *U.S. Private*, pg. 416
FORD ITALIANA S.P.A.—Ford Motor Company; *U.S. Public*, pg. 666
FORD MOTOR NORGE A/S—Ford Motor Company; *U.S. Public*, pg. 666
FOSTER PONTIAC, INC.; *U.S. Private*, pg. 421
FRANK CONSOLIDATED ENTERPRISES INC.; *U.S. Private*, pg. 423
JIM FRESARD PONTIAC BUICK, INC.; *U.S. Private*, pg. 427
FRIENDLY CHEVROLET CO. INC.; *U.S. Private*, pg. 428
LOU FUSZ AUTOMOTIVE NETWORK; *U.S. Private*, pg. 432
GALLES CHEVROLET; *U.S. Private*, pg. 438
GALPIN MOTORS; *U.S. Private*, pg. 438
GENERAL MOTORS ACCEPTANCE CORPORATION (GMAC)—General Motors Corporation; *U.S. Public*, pg. 719
GILLOGLY CHEVROLET & GEO, INC.; *U.S. Private*, pg. 454
GROUP 1 AUTOMOTIVE, INC.; *U.S. Public*, pg. 767
GULF STATES TOYOTA, INC.; *U.S. Private*, pg. 488
CURTIS C. GUNN, INC.; *U.S. Private*, pg. 488
GUNN PONTIAC GMC, INC.—Curtis C. Gunn, Inc.; *U.S. Private*, pg. 488
GURLEY MOTOR COMPANY; *U.S. Private*, pg. 488
H.B.L., INC.—Lantzsch-Andreas Enterprises, Inc.; *U.S. Private*, pg. 650
JERRY HAMM CHEVROLET INC.; *U.S. Private*, pg. 497
HARRIS FORD, INC.; *U.S. Private*, pg. 506
HARRIS SCARFE HOLDINGS LIMITED; *Int'l*, pg. 597
HATTON ET COOKSON S.A.—Unilever Plc; *Int'l*, pg. 1437
BILL HEARD ENTERPRISES, INC.; *U.S. Private*, pg. 515
HEINTZELMAN'S TRUCK CENTER INC.; *U.S. Private*, pg. 519
HENDRICK IMPORTS—Hendrick Automotive Group; *U.S. Private*, pg. 522
HITCHCOCK AUTOMOTIVE RESOURCES; *U.S. Private*, pg. 531
ROGER HOLLER CHEVROLET & GEO CO.; *U.S. Private*, pg. 534
HOLMAN ENTERPRISES; *U.S. Private*, pg. 535
HOLMES TUTTLE FORD, INC.; *U.S. Private*, pg. 535
HONDA EAST—Beechmont Investments Inc.; *U.S. Private*, pg. 129
HONDA INTERNATIONAL SALES CORP.—Honda Motor Co., Ltd.; *Int'l*, pg. 634
HUBACHER, CADILLAC & LANDROVER INC.; *U.S. Private*, pg. 543
HUBLER CHEVROLET INC.; *U.S. Private*, pg. 545
JIM HUDSON, PONTIAC, OLDSMOBILE GMC; *U.S. Private*, pg. 545
NEIL HUFFMAN NISSAN INC.; *U.S. Private*, pg. 546
NEIL HUFFMAN VOLKSWAGON MAZDA SUBURU—Neil Huffman Nissan Inc.; *U.S. Private*, pg. 546
CHUCK HUTTON CHEVROLET COMPANY; *U.S. Private*, pg. 550
INDUSTRIE-RING SACH-UND VERSICHERUNGS-VERMITTLUNGSGESELLSCHAFT MBH—Saarbergwerke Aktiengesellschaft; *Int'l*, pg. 1166
ISLAND LINCOLN-MERCURY; *U.S. Private*, pg. 576
JAGUAR CARS—Ford Motor Company; *U.S. Public*, pg. 664
JAMES CHEVROLET INC.; *U.S. Private*, pg. 580
JARDINE MATHESON HOLDINGS LIMITED; *Int'l*, pg. 703
JEFF WYLER BUICK, PONTIAC, INC.—Jeff Wyler Dealer Group, Inc.; *U.S. Private*, pg. 1193
JEFFERSON CHEVROLET CO.; *U.S. Private*, pg. 584
JEFFREY BUICK-NISSAN INC.; *U.S. Private*, pg. 585
JEROME-DUNCAN FORD; *U.S. Private*, pg. 586
FLETCHER JONES MANAGEMENT GROUP; *U.S. Private*, pg. 597
JORDAN MOTORS, INC.; *U.S. Private*, pg. 599
KEELER MOTOR CAR COMPANY, INC.; *U.S. Private*, pg. 611
KELLEY AUTOMOTIVE GROUP; *U.S. Private*, pg. 612
KENWORTH OF INDIANAPOLIS INC.; *U.S. Private*, pg. 615
KEY CADILLAC, INC.; *U.S. Private*, pg. 617
KEYES MOTORS, INC.; *U.S. Private*, pg. 618
KINGS TOYOTA SUZUKI; *U.S. Private*, pg. 621
KISSIMMEE TOYOTA INC.; *U.S. Private*, pg. 624
LB INDUSTRIES INC.; *U.S. Private*, pg. 639
LGC MANAGEMENT; *U.S. Private*, pg. 639
RAY LAETHEM PONTIAC-BUICK-GMC-TRUCK, INC.; *U.S. Private*, pg. 642
LANTZSCH-ANDREAS ENTERPRISES, INC.; *U.S. Private*, pg. 650
LARICHE CHEVROLET-CADILLAC—Lou LaRiche Chevrolet Inc.; *U.S. Private*, pg. 651
LOU LARICHE CHEVROLET INC.; *U.S. Private*, pg. 651
LARICHE TOYOTA-SUBARU—Lou LaRiche Chevrolet Inc.; *U.S. Private*, pg. 651
LESON CHEVROLET COMPANY, INC.; *U.S. Private*, pg. 660
LEX AUTOSALES—Lex Service PLC; *Int'l*, pg. 807
LIBERTYVILLE LINCOLN-MERCURY SALES, INC.; *U.S. Private*, pg. 666
LOCKHART CADILLAC INC.; *U.S. Private*, pg. 672
LOEBER MOTORS, INC.; *U.S. Private*, pg. 672
LOMBARD LINCOLN-MERCURY & LEASING, INC.; *U.S. Private*, pg. 673
LONRHO PLC; *Int'l*, pg. 817
JIM LUPIENT ENTERPRISES; *U.S. Private*, pg. 681
LUSTINE OLDSMOBILE & BUICK, INC.; *U.S. Private*, pg. 681
GUS MACHADO ENTERPRISES; *U.S. Private*, pg. 691
MARK CHEVROLET INC.; *U.S. Private*, pg. 704
MASSEY CADILLAC, INC.—Don Massey Cadillac Inc.; *U.S. Private*, pg. 713
MASSEY CHEVROLET GEO, INC.—Don Massey Cadillac Inc.; *U.S. Private*, pg. 713
DON MASSEY BUICK-PONTIAC—Don Massey Cadillac Inc.; *U.S. Private*, pg. 712
DON MASSEY CADILLAC INC.; *U.S. Private*, pg. 712
STERLING MCCALL TOYOTA GROUP; *U.S. Private*, pg. 719
MCCONNELL AUTOMOTIVE; *U.S. Private*, pg. 720
MCINERNEY INC.; *U.S. Private*, pg. 722
MCKEAN OLDSMOBILE COMPANY; *U.S. Private*, pg. 722
MCNAMARA PONTIAC ISUZU INC.; *U.S. Private*, pg. 724
MEADE GROUP, INC.; *U.S. Private*, pg. 725
DON MEALEY CHEVROLET INC.; *U.S. Private*, pg. 726
MELLOY BROS. ENTERPRISES; *U.S. Private*, pg. 730
MERCEDES-BENZ CANADA INC.—Daimler-Benz Aktiengesellschaft; *Int'l*, pg. 368
MERCEDES-BENZ ITALIA S.P.A.—Daimler-Benz Aktiengesellschaft; *Int'l*, pg. 369
MERCEDES-BENZ (SCHWEIZ) AG—Daimler-Benz Aktiengesellschaft; *Int'l*, pg. 369
MERCEDES-BENZ (UNITED KINGDOM) LTD.—Daimler-Benz Aktiengesellschaft; *Int'l*, pg. 369
MERCHANTS NISSAN—Merchants Rent A Car, Inc.; *U.S. Private*, pg. 732
MERCHANTS RENT A CAR, INC.; *U.S. Private*, pg. 732
METRO FORD INC.; *U.S. Private*, pg. 736
METRO FORD SALES, INC.; *U.S. Private*, pg. 736
MID AMERICA INTERNATIONAL TRUCKS, INC.; *U.S. Private*, pg. 743
MIDWAY FORD TRUCK CENTER INC.; *U.S. Private*, pg. 744
LARRY H. MILLER GROUP; *U.S. Private*, pg. 747
BOB MONTGOMERY CHEVROLET/HONDA; *U.S. Private*, pg. 758
MOOG AUTOMOTIVE, INC.—Cooper Industries, Inc.; *U.S. Public*, pg. 443
ART MORAN PONTIAC-GMC INC.; *U.S. Private*, pg. 760
MORITZ CADILLAC-BMW INC.; *U.S. Private*, pg. 761
ED MORSE AUTOMOTIVE GROUP; *U.S. Private*, pg. 763
ED MULLINAX FORD, INC.—Republic Industries, Inc.; *U.S. Public*, pg. 1379
NORTH PARK LINCOLN MERCURY INC.; *U.S. Private*, pg. 805
NORTHWAY MOTORCAR CORPORATION; *U.S. Private*, pg. 806
NUGGET MOTORS—Don Massey Cadillac Inc.; *U.S. Private*, pg. 713
#1 COCHRAN, INC.; *U.S. Private*, pg. 809
ROY O'BRIEN INC.; *U.S. Private*, pg. 810
OCEAN CHEVROLET, INC.; *U.S. Private*, pg. 810
ORANGE MOTOR COMPANY INC.; *U.S. Private*, pg. 818
OURISMAN CHEVROLET; *U.S. Private*, pg. 821
BUTCH OUSTALET FORD SAAB, INC.; *U.S. Private*, pg. 821
OVERSEAS MILITARY SALES CORPORATION; *U.S. Private*, pg. 823
PACIFICO AUTO GROUP; *U.S. Private*, pg. 832
ARNOLD PALMER CADILLAC INC.—Don Massey Cadillac Inc.; *U.S. Private*, pg. 713
PAR ENTERPRISES, INC.; *U.S. Private*, pg. 838
PARK MOTOR SALES COMPANY; *U.S. Private*, pg. 840
PARK PLACE MOTORCARS, LTD.; *U.S. Private*, pg. 840
PATSY'S, INC.; *U.S. Private*, pg. 843
PENSKE CORPORATION; *U.S. Private*, pg. 850
PERFORMANCE AUTOMOTIVE NETWORK; *U.S. Private*, pg. 853
PERFORMANCE CHEVROLET & GEO; *U.S. Private*, pg. 853
PETERSON MOTOR COMPANY; *U.S. Private*, pg. 857
POTAMKIN COMPANY; *U.S. Private*, pg. 876
POTAMKIN MANHATTAN—Potamkin Company; *U.S. Private*, pg. 876
POTAMKIN TOYOTA, INC.—Potamkin Company; *U.S. Private*, pg. 877
PRESTIGE FORD; *U.S. Private*, pg. 882
PROSPECT MOTORS, INC.; *U.S. Private*, pg. 891
PROSTROLLO MOTOR COMPANY; *U.S. Private*, pg. 891
PULLIAM MOTOR COMPANY; *U.S. Private*, pg. 894
QUALITY PONTIAC GMC BUICK; *U.S. Private*, pg. 899
QUALITY TOYOTA; *U.S. Private*, pg. 899
QUEBEDEAUX PONTIAC, INC.; *U.S. Private*, pg. 900
MEL RAPTON HONDA; *U.S. Private*, pg. 911
BILL RAY NISSAN, INC.; *U.S. Private*, pg. 911
GENE REED CHEVROLET—Trace International Holdings, Inc.; *U.S. Private*, pg. 1095
REED MOTORS, INC.; *U.S. Private*, pg. 916
REGENCY DODGE INC.; *U.S. Private*, pg. 918
REGENCY LINCOLN MERCURY, INC.; *U.S. Private*, pg. 918
RELIABLE CHEVROLET; *U.S. Private*, pg. 920
RICART FORD INC.; *U.S. Private*, pg. 927
RICHMOND LEASING—Richmond Motor Company; *U.S. Private*, pg. 929
RICHMOND MOTOR COMPANY; *U.S. Private*, pg. 929
RICO MOTOR COMPANY; *U.S. Private*, pg. 930
RINKE PONTIAC-GMC CO.; *U.S. Private*, pg. 931
THOMAS ROBINSON GROUP PLC—Brunel Holdings Plc; *Int'l*, pg. 231
BOB ROHRMAN AUTO GROUP; *U.S. Private*, pg. 940
ROSENTHAL AUTOMOTIVE ORGANIZATION; *U.S. Private*, pg. 946
ROSEVILLE CHRYSLER PLYMOUTH JEEP INC.; *U.S. Private*, pg. 946
JACK ROSS MOTORS INC.; *U.S. Private*, pg. 946
ROUNDTREE AUTOMOTIVE GROUP; *U.S. Private*, pg. 947
ROYAL JEEP EAGLE CHRYSLER PLYMOUTH, INC.; *U.S. Private*, pg. 948
ROYAL OAK FORD INC.; *U.S. Private*, pg. 948
ROYAL OLDSMOBILE MAZDA, INC.; *U.S. Private*, pg. 948
RUSSELL CHEVROLET COMPANY; *U.S. Private*, pg. 952
RYAN OLDSMOBILE; *U.S. Private*, pg. 953
SAAB CARS USA, INC.—Investor AB; *Int'l*, pg. 687
ALLEN SAMUELS CHEVROLET GEO; *U.S. Private*, pg. 964
SANDS MOTOR COMPANY, INC.; *U.S. Private*, pg. 964

SANSONE AUTO MALL; *U.S. Private*, pg. 965
SANTA MONICA FORD COMPANY; *U.S. Private*, pg. 965
SATURN OF FARMINGTON—Don Massey Cadillac Inc.; *U.S. Private*, pg. 713
SATURN OF GREENWOOD—Lockhart Cadillac Inc.; *U.S. Private*, pg. 672
MIKE SAVOIE CHEVROLET INC.; *U.S. Private*, pg. 968
RON SAXON FORD, INC.; *U.S. Private*, pg. 969
SCHILLING COMPANIES, INC.; *U.S. Private*, pg. 970
SCHILLING MOTORS, INC.—Schilling Companies, Inc.; *U.S. Private*, pg. 970
BOB SELLERS PONTIAC GMC TRUCK INC.; *U.S. Private*, pg. 983
DEAN SELLERS FORD INC.; *U.S. Private*, pg. 983
SELOVER BUICK, INC.; *U.S. Private*, pg. 983
SENATOR FORD; *U.S. Private*, pg. 983
SERVCO PACIFIC INC.; *U.S. Private*, pg. 986
SEWELL VILLAGE CADILLAC CO.; *U.S. Private*, pg. 988
L.B. SMITH, INC.; *U.S. Private*, pg. 1009
SMITH MOTORS, INC.; *U.S. Private*, pg. 1009
SOMERSET PONTIAC GMC INC.; *U.S. Private*, pg. 1013
SONIC AUTOMOTIVE, INC.; *U.S. Public*, pg. 1485
SOUTHERN CALIFORNIA AUTO GROUP; *U.S. Private*, pg. 1016
SOUTHGATE FORD INC.; *U.S. Private*, pg. 1018
P.T. STAR MOTORS INDONESIA—Daimler-Benz Aktiengesellschaft; *Int'l*, pg. 369
STEAKLEY CHEVROLET GEO SUBARU INC.; *U.S. Private*, pg. 1037
STERLING HEIGHTS DODGE, INC.; *U.S. Private*, pg. 1041
STILLMAN & HOAG, INC.; *U.S. Private*, pg. 1043
SUNRISE NISSAN OF ORANGE PARK; *U.S. Private*, pg. 1053
JAKE SWEENEY AUTOMOTIVE INC.; *U.S. Private*, pg. 1058
CHUCK SWIFT SALES & LEASING; *U.S. Private*, pg. 1058
SAM SWOPE AUTO GROUP, INC.; *U.S. Private*, pg. 1059
DAVE SYVERSON LINCOLN MERCURY; *U.S. Private*, pg. 1061
TAMAROFF BUICK INC.; *U.S. Private*, pg. 1067
TASHA; *U.S. Private*, pg. 1069
CHARLIE THOMAS DEALERSHIPS; *U.S. Private*, pg. 1082
THOMASON AUTO GROUP; *U.S. Private*, pg. 1083
THOMSON MACCONNELL CADILLAC, INC.; *U.S. Private*, pg. 1084
TORCO AUTOMOTIVE DIVISION—Torco Oil Co.; *U.S. Private*, pg. 1092
TORESCO ENTERPRISES; *U.S. Private*, pg. 1092
TORRANCE NISSAN, INC.—Republic Industries, Inc.; *U.S. Public*, pg. 1380
TOWN & COUNTRY FORD INC.; *U.S. Private*, pg. 1093
TOYOTA MOTOR DISTRIBUTORS (IRELAND) LTD.—Toyota Motor Corporation; *Int'l*, pg. 1413
TRACE INTERNATIONAL HOLDINGS, INC.; *U.S. Private*, pg. 1094
TRI-CITY OLDSMOBILE INC.; *U.S. Private*, pg. 1100
TRI-STATE MACK INC; *U.S. Private*, pg. 1101
TRONCALLI MOTORS, INC.; *U.S. Private*, pg. 1104
TROY MOTORS; *U.S. Private*, pg. 1106
TUNMORE OLDSMOBILE INC.; *U.S. Private*, pg. 1109
TUTTLE-CLICK AUTOMOBILE GROUP; *U.S. Private*, pg. 1111
UAC INTERNATIONAL LTD.—Unilever Plc; *Int'l*, pg. 1434
UNITED AUTO GROUP, INC.—Trace International Holdings, Inc.; *U.S. Private*, pg. 1095
V.T. INC.; *U.S. Private*, pg. 1131
VALLEY PONTIAC BUICK GMC, INC.; *U.S. Private*, pg. 1132
VANDERGRIFF CHEVROLET GEO; *U.S. Private*, pg. 1133
VILLAGE CAR COMPANY; *U.S. Private*, pg. 1140
VILLAGE FORD INC.; *U.S. Private*, pg. 1140
VOGLER MOTOR COMPANY, INC.; *U.S. Private*, pg. 1143
VOLKSWAGEN OF AMERICA, INC.—Volkswagen AG; *Int'l*, pg. 1474
VOLVO AND HONDA SALES & SERVICE; *U.S. Private*, pg. 1143
VON HOUSEN MOTORS; *U.S. Private*, pg. 1143
WALKER-JONES CHEVEROLET-BUICK-OLDSMOBILE INC.—Jones Company, Inc.; *U.S. Private*, pg. 596
W.W. WALLWORK, INC.; *U.S. Private*, pg. 1148
WALSER AUTOMOTIVE GROUP; *U.S. Private*, pg. 1148
WATKINS SYSTEM INC.; *U.S. Private*, pg. 1153
C. WEAVER CHEVROLET, INC.; *U.S. Private*, pg. 1156
WESTFALL GMC TRUCK INC.; *U.S. Private*, pg. 1169
WESTLIE MOTOR COMPANY; *U.S. Private*, pg. 1169
BUFF WHELAN CHEVROLET & GEO, INC.; *U.S. Private*, pg. 1171
WINTER VOLVO & LINCOLN MERCURY; *U.S. Private*, pg. 1183
WOODFIN PONTIAC-ISUZU; *U.S. Private*, pg. 1187
WOOLVERTON OLDSMOBILE-G.M.C. TRUCK, INC.; *U.S. Private*, pg. 1188
JEFF WYLER DEALER GROUP, INC.; *U.S. Private*, pg. 1193
YOUNG AUTOMOTIVE GROUP—Trace International Holdings, Inc.; *U.S. Private*, pg. 1095
HAROLD ZIEGLER FORD-ELKHART; *U.S. Private*, pg. 1205
ZUNG FU COMPANY LTD.—Jardine Matheson Holdings Limited; *Int'l*, pg. 704

5521 — MOTOR VEHICLE DEALERS (USED CARS ONLY)

JACK DEMMER FORD, INC.; *U.S. Private*, pg. 323
LEX AUTOSALES—Lex Service PLC; *Int'l*, pg. 807
RUSSELL CHEVROLET COMPANY; *U.S. Private*, pg. 952

5531 — AUTO & HOME SUPPLY STORES

A K H COMPANY, INC.; *U.S. Private*, pg. 2
A S H, INC.; *U.S. Private*, pg. 2
ADAP INC.; *U.S. Private*, pg. 4
A.P.S.—APS Holding Corporation; *U.S. Public*, pg. 10
AKI BRICOLAGE—GIB Group; *Int'l*, pg. 534
ALL PRO BUMPER TO BUMPER INC.; *U.S. Private*, pg. 35
AUSTIN GROUP; *U.S. Private*, pg. 99
AUTO 5—GIB Group; *Int'l*, pg. 533
AUTO GLASS SPECIALISTS; *U.S. Private*, pg. 100
AUTOMOTIVE SUPPLY ASSOCIATES, INC.; *U.S. Private*, pg. 101
AUTOZONE, INC.; *U.S. Public*, pg. 150
BANDAG NEW ZEALAND LTD.—Bandag, Incorporated; *U.S. Public*, pg. 178
BAUGHER CHEVROLET-BUICK INC.; *U.S. Private*, pg. 123
BEACH CITY CHEVROLET CO.; *U.S. Private*, pg. 125
BELLE TIRE DISTRIBUTOR INC.; *U.S. Private*, pg. 132
BROWN & BROWN VENTURE GROUP, LLC; *U.S. Private*, pg. 172
BURRIS FOODS, INC.; *U.S. Private*, pg. 188
C S K AUTO INC.—The Trump Group; *U.S. Private*, pg. 1108
CCI CORPORATION; *U.S. Private*, pg. 193
CAMECANICA, S.A.—Corporacion MAPFRE, Compania Internacional de Reaseguros, S.A.; *Int'l*, pg. 333
CANADIAN TIRE CORPORATION LIMITED; *Int'l*, pg. 259
CARQUEST CANADA LTD.—General Parts, Inc.; *U.S. Private*, pg. 445
CARQUEST CORP.—General Parts, Inc.; *U.S. Private*, pg. 445
CARQUEST CORPORATION; *U.S. Private*, pg. 215
CASTORAMA DUBOIS INVESTISSEMENTS S.C.A.; *Int'l*, pg. 275
COLEMAN CADILLAC INC.; *U.S. Private*, pg. 251
CONDERE CORPORATION; *U.S. Private*, pg. 262
DAYTON TIRE COMPANY—Bridgestone Corporation; *Int'l*, pg. 213
DISCOUNT TIRE; *U.S. Private*, pg. 334
EARNHARDT'S MOTOR COMPANIES; *U.S. Private*, pg. 356
4DAY TIRE STORES; *U.S. Private*, pg. 421
MARTY FRANICH AUTO CENTER; *U.S. Private*, pg. 423
FRIENDLY CHEVROLET CO. INC.; *U.S. Private*, pg. 428
GIB GROUP; *Int'l*, pg. 532
GANIN TIRE CO., INC.; *U.S. Private*, pg. 439
GEBO DISTRIBUTING CO., INC.; *U.S. Private*, pg. 442
GEM TOP MFG., INC.; *U.S. Private*, pg. 443
THE GOODYEAR TIRE & RUBBER COMPANY; *U.S. Public*, pg. 752
HALFORDS, LTD.—The Boots Company PLC; *Int'l*, pg. 203
HI/LO AUTOMOTIVE, INC.—O'Reilly Automotive Inc.; *U.S. Public*, pg. 1230
HONDA ACCESS CORP.—Honda Motor Co., Ltd.; *Int'l*, pg. 634
HONDA ACCESS SALES CORP.—Honda Motor Co., Ltd.; *Int'l*, pg. 634
HONDA MOTOR PARTS SERVICE CO., LTD.—Honda Motor Co., Ltd.; *Int'l*, pg. 634
GAY JOHNSON'S INC.; *U.S. Private*, pg. 595
J. KORBER & COMPANY; *U.S. Private*, pg. 632
LDI AUTO PAINT—LDI, Ltd.; *U.S. Private*, pg. 639
LESLIE METAL ARTS CO., INC.; *U.S. Private*, pg. 660
LUSTINE OLDSMOBILE & BUICK, INC.; *U.S. Private*, pg. 681
MCKENZIE TANK LINES, INC.; *U.S. Private*, pg. 723
MCNEILUS COMPANIES; *U.S. Private*, pg. 725
MID AMERICA INTERNATIONAL TRUCKS, INC.; *U.S. Private*, pg. 743
MOLIN AUTO PARTS INC.; *U.S. Private*, pg. 756
MURRAY'S DISCOUNT AUTO STORES; *U.S. Private*, pg. 768
NATIONAL TIRE & BATTERY—Sears, Roebuck and Co.; *U.S. Public*, pg. 1452
O'REILLY AUTOMOTIVE INC.; *U.S. Public*, pg. 1230
PACCAR AUTOMOTIVE INC.—Paccar Inc.; *U.S. Public*, pg. 1247
PARRISH TIRE COMPANY, INC.; *U.S. Private*, pg. 840
PATSY'S, INC.; *U.S. Private*, pg. 843
THE PEP BOYS-MANNY, MOE & JACK; *U.S. Public*, pg. 1276
THE PEP BOYS-MANNY, MOE & JACK OF CALIFORNIA—The Pep Boys-Manny, Moe & Jack; *U.S. Public*, pg. 1276
PEUGEOT-CITROEN MOTEURS (PCM)—PSA Peugeot Citroen; *Int'l*, pg. 1021
PIRELLI ATG VERTRIEBSGESELLSCHAFT M.B.H.—Pirelli S.p.A.; *Int'l*, pg. 1059
PIRELLI VERTRIEBS G.M.B.H.—Pirelli S.p.A.; *Int'l*, pg. 1059
QUAKER CITY MOTOR PARTS COMPANY; *U.S. Private*, pg. 898
BRAD RAGAN, INC.—The Goodyear Tire & Rubber Company; *U.S. Public*, pg. 753
REINALT-THOMAS CORP.; *U.S. Private*, pg. 919
RITE AID CORPORATION; *U.S. Public*, pg. 1390
ROBBINS AUTO PARTS, INC.; *U.S. Private*, pg. 934
ROUNDTREE AUTOMOTIVE GROUP; *U.S. Private*, pg. 947
RUSSELL CHEVROLET COMPANY; *U.S. Private*, pg. 952
SANEL AUTO PARTS CO.—Automotive Supply Associates, Inc.; *U.S. Private*, pg. 101
LES SCHWAB TIRE CENTERS; *U.S. Private*, pg. 974
SEARS AUTO CENTERS—Sears, Roebuck and Co.; *U.S. Public*, pg. 1452
SEARS TIRE GROUP—Sears, Roebuck and Co.; *U.S. Public*, pg. 1452
SELF AUTO—Castorama Dubois Investissements S.C.A.; *Int'l*, pg. 276
SERVICE MOTOR CO.—Service Motor Company; *U.S. Private*, pg. 986
SERVICE TIRE TRUCK CENTERS, INC.; *U.S. Private*, pg. 987
SOUS GROUPE CASTORAMA—Castorama Dubois Investissements S.C.A.; *Int'l*, pg. 275
SOUTH AFRICAN MOTOR CORPORATION PROPRIETARY LIMITED (SAMCOR)—Anglo American Corporation of South Africa Limited; *Int'l*, pg. 76
STRAFCO, INC.; *U.S. Private*, pg. 1046
STRAUSS DISCOUNT AUTO; *U.S. Private*, pg. 1046
TENNECO AUTOMOTIVE—Tenneco Inc.; *U.S. Public*, pg. 1577
THOMSON MACCONNELL CADILLAC, INC.; *U.S. Private*, pg. 1084
TIRE MILEAGE, INCORPORATED—Bandag, Incorporated; *U.S. Public*, pg. 177
TRACTOR SUPPLY CO.; *U.S. Public*, pg. 1627
TRAILER WHEEL & FRAME COMPANY; *U.S. Private*, pg. 1095
TRAK AUTO WEST, INC.—Dart Group Corporation; *U.S. Public*, pg. 484
TRONCALLI MOTORS, INC.; *U.S. Private*, pg. 1104
TYLER CORPORATION; *U.S. Public*, pg. 1651
ULTRAMAR DIAMOND SHAMROCK CORPORATION; *U.S. Public*, pg. 1663
VALEO DISTRIBUTION—CERUS - Compagnies Europeennes Reunies; *Int'l*, pg. 240
VASCOR—Neptune Orient Lines Ltd.; *Int'l*, pg. 912
VASCOR, LTD.—Neptune Orient Lines Ltd.; *Int'l*, pg. 912
VEHIDATA, S.A.—Corporacion MAPFRE, Compania Internacional de Reaseguros, S.A.; *Int'l*, pg. 334
VON HOUSEN MOTORS; *U.S. Private*, pg. 1143
W.W. WALLWORK, INC.; *U.S. Private*, pg. 1148
BUFF WHELAN CHEVROLET & GEO, INC.; *U.S. Private*, pg. 1171
WILLAMETTE SALES CO.—CNF Transportation Inc.; *U.S. Public*, pg. 281
WINSTON TIRE COMPANY—J.H. Heafner Co. Inc.; *U.S. Private*, pg. 514
ZIEBART INTERNATIONAL CORPORATION; *U.S. Private*, pg. 1205
ZIEGLER TIRE & SUPPLY COMPANY, INC.; *U.S. Private*, pg. 1205

5541 — GASOLINE SERVICE STATIONS

AGIP PETROLI—ENI S.p.A.; *Int'l*, pg. 428
ADAMS RESOURCES & ENERGY, INC.; *U.S. Public*, pg. 18
ALLSUPS CONVENIENCE STORES INC.; *U.S. Private*, pg. 44
AMOCO CORPORATION; *U.S. Public*, pg. 101
AMOCO OIL COMPANY—Amoco Corporation; *U.S. Public*, pg. 102
TRUMAN ARNOLD COMPANIES; *U.S. Private*, pg. 84
AUSTIN GROUP; *U.S. Private*, pg. 99
BP OIL CO.—The British Petroleum Company P.L.C.; *Int'l*, pg. 220
BELL GAS, INC.; *U.S. Private*, pg. 131
BESCHE OIL COMPANY, INC.; *U.S. Private*, pg. 139
BIG HORN CO-OP MARKETING ASSOCIATION; *U.S. Private*, pg. 143
BRADFORD OIL COMPANY, INC.; *U.S. Private*, pg. 164
CANADIAN TIRE CORPORATION LIMITED; *Int'l*, pg. 259
CAPITOL CHEVROLET CADILLAC GEO SUBARU INC.; *U.S. Private*, pg. 206
CARSE OIL CO. INC.; *U.S. Private*, pg. 216
CARTER COMPANIES; *U.S. Private*, pg. 216
CHEVRON CORPORATION; *U.S. Public*, pg. 347
THE CIRCLE K COMPANY—Tosco Corporation; *U.S. Public*, pg. 1624
THE COASTAL CORPORATION; *U.S. Public*, pg. 389
COASTAL REFINING & MARKETING—The Coastal Corporation; *U.S. Public*, pg. 390
CONDON OIL COMPANY, INC.; *U.S. Private*, pg. 262
COOP SWITZERLAND; *Int'l*, pg. 329
COWBOY OIL COMPANY; *U.S. Private*, pg. 280
CRANE DEFENSE SYSTEMS—Crane Co.; *U.S. Public*, pg. 456
CROWN CENTRAL PETROLEUM CORPORATION; *U.S. Public*, pg. 462
CROWN STATIONS, INC.—Crown Central Petroleum Corporation; *U.S. Public*, pg. 462
CRYSTAL FLASH PETROLEUM CORP.; *U.S. Private*, pg. 294
CUMBERLAND FARMS, INC.; *U.S. Private*, pg. 295
DAIGLE OIL CO.; *U.S. Private*, pg. 307
DAIRY MART CONVENIENCE STORES, INC.; *U.S. Public*, pg. 476
DAIRY MART, INC.—Dairy Mart Convenience Stores, Inc.; *U.S. Public*, pg. 476
JIMMY DAVIS ENTERPRISES, INC.; *U.S. Private*, pg. 315
DEAD RIVER COMPANY; *U.S. Private*, pg. 318
DIXIE OIL COMPANY; *U.S. Private*, pg. 337
E-Z SERVE CONVENIENCE STORES, INC.—E-Z Serve Corp.; *U.S. Public*, pg. 540
E-Z SERVE CORP.; *U.S. Public*, pg. 540
ELF FRANCE—Elf Aquitane; *Int'l*, pg. 445
ENGLEFIELD, INC.; *U.S. Private*, pg. 377
ENMARK STATIONS, INC.—Colonial Oil Industries; *U.S. Private*, pg. 254
EQUITY SUPPLY COMPANY; *U.S. Private*, pg. 380
ERICKSON OIL PRODUCTS, INC.; *U.S. Private*, pg. 381
EXXON CORPORATION; *U.S. Public*, pg. 601
FKG OIL COMPANY—Moto, Inc.; *U.S. Private*, pg. 764
FARM & HOME OIL COMPANY; *U.S. Private*, pg. 394
FARM STORES; *U.S. Private*, pg. 394
FARMWAY CO-OP INC.; *U.S. Private*, pg. 396
FIRST MOUNT JOY CORPORATION; *U.S. Private*, pg. 407
FISCA OIL CO., INC.; *U.S. Private*, pg. 408
FLYING J. INC.; *U.S. Private*, pg. 415
FOOD & GAS, INC.; *U.S. Private*, pg. 417
GATE PETROLEUM COMPANY; *U.S. Private*, pg. 441
GETTY PETROLEUM MARKETING INC.; *U.S. Public*, pg. 740
GETTY TERMINALS, INC.—Getty Petroleum Marketing Inc.; *U.S. Public*, pg. 741

S.I.C. Index

GIANT INDUSTRIES ARIZONA, INC.—Giant Industries Inc.; *U.S. Public*, pg. 742
GIANT INDUSTRIES INC.; *U.S. Public*, pg. 741
GREENWAY CO-OP SERVICE; *U.S. Private*, pg. 478
GULF OIL—Cumberland Farms, Inc.; *U.S. Private*, pg. 295
HICKS OIL-HICKS GAS, INC.; *U.S. Private*, pg. 526
HIGH POINT OIL CO.; *U.S. Private*, pg. 528
HOLIDAY COMPANIES; *U.S. Private*, pg. 534
HOLMQUIST GRAIN & LUMBER CO.; *U.S. Private*, pg. 535
HOP-IN MICHIGAN, INC.—Silcorp Limited; *Int'l*, pg. 1249
JONES COMPANY, INC.; *U.S. Private*, pg. 596
KING FUELS INC.; *U.S. Private*, pg. 620
KOCOLENE OIL CORP.; *U.S. Private*, pg. 629
KWICKIE/FLASH FOODS, INC.—Jones Company, Inc.; *U.S. Private*, pg. 596
LEEMILTS PETROLEUM, INC.—Getty Petroleum Marketing Inc.; *U.S. Public*, pg. 741
LEX AUTOCENTRES—Lex Service PLC; *Int'l*, pg. 807
LEX BODYCENTRES—Lex Service PLC; *Int'l*, pg. 807
LEX RETAIL GROUP—Lex Service PLC; *Int'l*, pg. 807
MANSFIELD OIL COMPANY; *U.S. Private*, pg. 700
MAPCO INC.; *U.S. Public*, pg. 1042
MAPCO PETROLEUM INC.—Mapco Inc.; *U.S. Public*, pg. 1042
MARATHON ASHLAND PETROLEUM LLC—Ashland, Inc.; *U.S. Public*, pg. 139
MARATHON ASHLAND PETROLEUM LLC—USX Corporation; *U.S. Public*, pg. 1662
MAVERIK COUNTRY STORES, INC.; *U.S. Private*, pg. 715
META OIL INC.—Fisca Oil Co., Inc.; *U.S. Private*, pg. 408
MID-KANSAS CO-OP ASSOCIATION; *U.S. Private*, pg. 743
MIDWEST PETROLEUM CO.; *U.S. Private*, pg. 745
MIKE'S MART—Silcorp Limited; *Int'l*, pg. 1249
MOCK RESOURCES, INC.—Wickland Corporation; *U.S. Private*, pg. 1175
MONTE VISTA CO-OP ASSOCIATION, INC.; *U.S. Private*, pg. 758
MOTO, INC.; *U.S. Private*, pg. 764
MURCO PETROLEUM LTD.—Murphy Oil Corporation; *U.S. Public*, pg. 1142
MURPHY OIL CO., LTD.—Murphy Oil Corporation; *U.S. Public*, pg. 1142
MURPHY OIL CORPORATION; *U.S. Public*, pg. 1141
MURPHY OIL USA, INC.—Murphy Oil Corporation; *U.S. Public*, pg. 1142
NELLA OIL COMPANY; *U.S. Private*, pg. 790
NORTHVILLE INDUSTRIES CORP.; *U.S. Private*, pg. 806
OK COOP AG—Coop Switzerland; *Int'l*, pg. 330
OLIVER OIL COMPANY, INC.; *U.S. Private*, pg. 815
PGA MOTORS—Lex Service PLC; *Int'l*, pg. 807
THE PARMAN CORPORATION; *U.S. Private*, pg. 840
PETRO-CANADA; *Int'l*, pg. 1041
P.T. PETRO CORP.—Getty Petroleum Marketing Inc.; *U.S. Public*, pg. 741
PHILLIPS PETROLEUM COMPANY; *U.S. Public*, pg. 1290
PIASA MOTOR FUELS INC.; *U.S. Private*, pg. 864
PILOT CORPORATION; *U.S. Private*, pg. 865
PIONEER OIL COMPANY INC.; *U.S. Private*, pg. 866
POLKA DOT DAIRY/TOM THUMB FOOD MARKETS—Polka Dot Dairy/Tom Thumb, Inc.; *U.S. Private*, pg. 874
PREEM PETROLEUM AB; *Int'l*, pg. 1066
PRESTIGE STATIONS INC.—Atlantic Richfield Company; *U.S. Public*, pg. 144
PRESTO FOOD STORES, INC.; *U.S. Private*, pg. 882
PRIDE OIL CO., INC.—Kelso Oil Company; *U.S. Private*, pg. 613
RACETRAC PETROLEUM, INC.; *U.S. Private*, pg. 906
RAY-CARROLL COUNTY GRAIN CO-OP; *U.S. Private*, pg. 911
RICHDALE DAIRY STORES, INC.—Scangas Brothers Holdings, Inc.; *U.S. Private*, pg. 969
F.L. ROBERTS & CO. INC.; *U.S. Private*, pg. 935
RUSSELL PETROLEUM CORPORATION; *U.S. Private*, pg. 953
J. SAINSBURY PLC; *Int'l*, pg. 1169
THE SICO COMPANY—First Mount Joy Corporation; *U.S. Private*, pg. 407
SILCORP LIMITED; *Int'l*, pg. 1249
SINCLAIR OIL CORP.; *U.S. Private*, pg. 1003
SITE OIL COMPANY OF MISSOURI; *U.S. Private*, pg. 1004
SPENCER COMPANIES INC.; *U.S. Private*, pg. 1024
J.D. STREETT & CO., INC.; *U.S. Private*, pg. 1047
TAYLOR OIL CO. INC.; *U.S. Private*, pg. 1071
THORNHILL OIL COMPANY, INC.; *U.S. Private*, pg. 1084
THORNTON OIL CORP.; *U.S. Private*, pg. 1084
TIME OIL COMPANY; *U.S. Private*, pg. 1086
TOWN PUMP, INC.; *U.S. Private*, pg. 1093
TRAVEL PORTS OF AMERICA INC.; *U.S. Public*, pg. 1632
TRITON MANUFACTURING, INC.; *U.S. Private*, pg. 1104
TRUCK WORLD INC.; *U.S. Private*, pg. 1107
USX CORPORATION; *U.S. Public*, pg. 1661
UNITED ACQUISITION CORPORATION—Red Apple Companies; *U.S. Private*, pg. 915
UNITED REFINING COMPANY—Red Apple Companies; *U.S. Private*, pg. 915
USA PETROLEUM CORPORATION; *U.S. Private*, pg. 1125
VALVOLINE INSTANT OIL CHANGE, INC.—Ashland, Inc.; *U.S. Public*, pg. 139
WESTERN STATES PETROLEUM INC.; *U.S. Private*, pg. 1169
WICKLAND CORPORATION; *U.S. Private*, pg. 1174
WICKLAND OIL COMPANY, INC.—Wickland Corporation; *U.S. Private*, pg. 1175
YODER OIL COMPANY INC.; *U.S. Private*, pg. 1196
YOUNGSTOWN TIRE & SUPPLY COMPANY—Ziegler Tire & Supply Company, Inc.; *U.S. Private*, pg. 1205

5551 — BOAT DEALERS

JAMES BLISS & CO., INC.—West Marine, Inc.; *U.S. Public*, pg. 1756
BILL COLLINS FORD INC.; *U.S. Private*, pg. 253
E & B MARINE INCORPORATED—West Marine, Inc.; *U.S. Public*, pg. 1756
E & B MARINE SUPPLY, INC.—West Marine, Inc.; *U.S. Public*, pg. 1756
FISHERIES SUPPLY COMPANY; *U.S. Private*, pg. 408
GENMAR HOLDINGS, INC.; *U.S. Private*, pg. 447
GOLDBERGS MARINE DISTRIBUTORS—West Marine, Inc.; *U.S. Public*, pg. 1756
KAWASAKI MOTORS CORP., U.S.A.—Kawasaki Heavy Industries, Ltd.; *Int'l*, pg. 725
MERCEDES-BENZ OF NORTH AMERICA, INC.—Daimler-Benz Aktiengesellschaft; *Int'l*, pg. 368
REX MARINE CENTER, INC.; *U.S. Private*, pg. 926
TOLLYCRAFT YACHT CORPORATION; *U.S. Public*, pg. 1620
WEST MARINE, INC.; *U.S. Public*, pg. 1756

5561 — RECREATIONAL VEHICLE DEALERS

MIKE DAUGHERTY'S CHEVROLET GEO, INC.; *U.S. Private*, pg. 313
DAVIS-MOORE OLDSMOBILE, INC.; *U.S. Private*, pg. 315
EARNHARDT'S MOTOR COMPANIES; *U.S. Private*, pg. 356
HOLIDAY RV SUPERSTORES, INC.; *U.S. Public*, pg. 829
HOLIDAY RV SUPERSTORES WEST, INC.—Holiday RV Superstores, Inc.; *U.S. Public*, pg. 830
LA MESA R V CENTER, INC.; *U.S. Private*, pg. 640
LANCE CAMPER MANUFACTURING CORPORATION; *U.S. Private*, pg. 645
LAZY DAYS R V CENTER, INC.; *U.S. Private*, pg. 655
RECREATIONAL PRODUCTS DIV.—Bell Industries, Inc.; *U.S. Public*, pg. 205
SHELTER COMPONENTS CORPORATION—Kevco, Inc.; *U.S. Public*, pg. 952

5571 — MOTORCYCLE DEALERS

AMERICAN HONDA MOTOR CO., INC.—Honda Motor Co., Ltd.; *Int'l*, pg. 634
AMERICAN HONDA MOTOR CO., INC. MOTORCYCLE DIVISION—Honda Motor Co., Ltd.; *Int'l*, pg. 634
KAWASAKI MOTORS CORP., U.S.A.—Kawasaki Heavy Industries, Ltd.; *Int'l*, pg. 725
ALLEN SAMUELS CHEVROLET GEO; *U.S. Private*, pg. 964

5599 — AUTOMOTIVE DEALERS, NEC

ALVIS-UNIPOWER LIMITED—Alvis plc; *Int'l*, pg. 69
ATHLETIC ATTIC RETAIL COMPANY—Just For Feet, Inc.; *U.S. Public*, pg. 936
AUTOMOTIVE EXPORT SUPPLIES LIMITED—Alvis plc; *Int'l*, pg. 70
CUTTER AVIATION ALBUQUERQUE, INC; *U.S. Private*, pg. 298
HAYES AXLE, INC.—The Cypress Companies; *U.S. Private*, pg. 299
HOLIDAY RV SUPERSTORES, INC.; *U.S. Public*, pg. 829
INNOTECH AVIATION INDUSTRIES LTD.—Air Canada; *Int'l*, pg. 36
ISRAEL AIRCRAFT INDUSTRIES INTERNATIONAL INC.—Israel Aircraft Industries Ltd.; *Int'l*, pg. 690
ITALIAN AEROSPACE INDUSTRIES—IRI Istituto Ricostruzione Industriale; *Int'l*, pg. 654
MARTIN INDUSTRIES, INC. (AL); *U.S. Private*, pg. 709
ALLEN SAMUELS CHEVROLET GEO; *U.S. Private*, pg. 964
OY SCAN-AUTO AB—Investor AB; *Int'l*, pg. 686
OY SCAN-AUTO AB—Valmet Corporation; *Int'l*, pg. 1449
TRAILER WHEEL & FRAME COMPANY; *U.S. Private*, pg. 1095
USA PETROLEUM CORPORATION; *U.S. Private*, pg. 1125

5611 — MEN'S & BOYS' CLOTHING & ACCESSORY STORES

AMERICAN EAGLES OUTFITTERS INC.; *U.S. Private*, pg. 53
AMICI—N.V. Koninklijke Bijenkorf Beheer KBB; *Int'l*, pg. 750
AUSTIN REED LIMITED—Hartmarx Corporation; *U.S. Public*, pg. 796
BHS PLC—Storehouse PLC; *Int'l*, pg. 1304
BARNEYS INC.; *U.S. Private*, pg. 116
GEOFFREY BEENE RETAIL—Phillips-Van Heusen Corporation; *U.S. Public*, pg. 1291
BENETTON GROUP S.P.A.; *Int'l*, pg. 186
BIGSBY & KRUTHERS COMPANIES; *U.S. Private*, pg. 143
BLAZER PLC—Moss Bros Group PLC; *Int'l*, pg. 896
BOB'S STORES, INC.—CVS Corp.; *U.S. Public*, pg. 287
BROOKS BROTHERS—Marks & Spencer PLC; *Int'l*, pg. 843
DICK BRUHN INCORPORATED; *U.S. Private*, pg. 175
BURBERRYS SHIRTS—Bidermann International S.A.; *Int'l*, pg. 194
THE BURTON GROUP PLC; *Int'l*, pg. 237
CHELSEA GROUP—Horizon Enterprises Group LLC; *U.S. Private*, pg. 539
CODA—Edison Brothers Stores, Inc.; *U.S. Public*, pg. 563
COHOES FASHIONS, INC.—Burlington Coat Factory Warehouse Corporation; *U.S. Public*, pg. 268
DESIGNS, INC.; *U.S. Public*, pg. 501
GERALD GROUP INC.; *U.S. Private*, pg. 448
GINGISS INTERNATIONAL; *U.S. Private*, pg. 455
GUESS ?, INC.; *U.S. Public*, pg. 768
HARCOURT GENERAL, INC.; *U.S. Public*, pg. 782
HORIZON ENTERPRISES GROUP LLC; *U.S. Private*, pg. 539
HORIZON INVESTMENT GROUP—Horizon Enterprises Group LLC; *U.S. Private*, pg. 539
HUGO BOSS FASHIONS INC.—Hugo Boss AG; *Int'l*, pg. 637
JAY JACOBS, INC.; *U.S. Public*, pg. 922
JACOBSON STORES INC.; *U.S. Public*, pg. 922
TOM JAMES OF ATLANTA, INC.—Tom James Company; *U.S. Private*, pg. 581
JEANS WEST, INC.—Edison Brothers Stores, Inc.; *U.S. Public*, pg. 563
KIEN—Vendex International N.V.; *Int'l*, pg. 1462
N.V. KONINKLIJKE BIJENKORF BEHEER KBB; *Int'l*, pg. 750
KREYMBORG—Vendex International N.V.; *Int'l*, pg. 1462
L.L. BEAN, INC.; *U.S. Private*, pg. 639
LANDS' END, INC.; *U.S. Public*, pg. 977
MARKS & SPENCER US HOLDINGS INC.—Marks & Spencer PLC; *Int'l*, pg. 843
MCCRORY CORPORATION; *U.S. Private*, pg. 720
MEN'S WEARHOUSE; *U.S. Public*, pg. 1086
HENRY MODELL & COMPANY, INC.; *U.S. Private*, pg. 754
MORLEY SHIRT COMPANY—HC Holdings; *U.S. Private*, pg. 490
OAKTREE—Edison Brothers Stores, Inc.; *U.S. Public*, pg. 564
ORGANIZACION ROBERTS S.A. DE C.V.—Hartmarx Corporation; *U.S. Public*, pg. 796
PHILLIPS-VAN HEUSEN CORPORATION; *U.S. Public*, pg. 1291
POLO/RALPH LAUREN CORPORATION; *U.S. Private*, pg. 874
REPP LTD. BIG AND TALL—Edison Brothers Stores, Inc.; *U.S. Public*, pg. 564
RETAILNET B.V.—N.V. Koninklijke Bijenkorf Beheer KBB; *Int'l*, pg. 750
THE RICHMAN BROTHERS CO.—Woolworth Corporation; *U.S. Public*, pg. 1777
J. RIGGINGS—Edison Brothers Stores, Inc.; *U.S. Public*, pg. 564
S & K FAMOUS BRANDS, INC.; *U.S. Public*, pg. 1414
MARK SHALE; *U.S. Private*, pg. 989
SYMS CORPORATION; *U.S. Public*, pg. 1547
T.J. MAXX—The TJX Companies, Inc.; *U.S. Public*, pg. 1557
THE TERRITORY AHEAD; *U.S. Private*, pg. 1077
TIE RACK PLC; *Int'l*, pg. 1389
TIE RACK TRADING LIMITED—Tie Rack plc; *Int'l*, pg. 1389
ULTIMO LTD.; *U.S. Private*, pg. 1116
URBAN OUTFITTERS, INC.; *U.S. Public*, pg. 1700
VALUE PRICED CLOTHING INC.—Men's Wearhouse; *U.S. Public*, pg. 1086
WINONA KNITS; *U.S. Private*, pg. 1183
WOOLWORTH CORPORATION; *U.S. Public*, pg. 1777

5621 — WOMEN'S CLOTHING STORES

A&E STORES, INC.; *U.S. Private*, pg. 1
ADDED DIMENSIONS—Catherines Stores Corporation; *U.S. Public*, pg. 318
ADLER MODEMARKTE GMBH—Metro AG; *Int'l*, pg. 863
AEON GROUP; *Int'l*, pg. 28
AMANDA FIELDING—JC Penney Company, Inc.; *U.S. Public*, pg. 917
AMICI—N.V. Koninklijke Bijenkorf Beheer KBB; *Int'l*, pg. 750
ANNTAYLOR, INC.—AnnTaylor Stores Corporation; *U.S. Public*, pg. 116
ANNTAYLOR STORES CORPORATION; *U.S. Public*, pg. 116
THE ANSWER—Catherines Stores Corporation; *U.S. Public*, pg. 318
ASHLEY SHOPS (IRELAND) LTD.—Laura Ashley Holdings Plc; *Int'l*, pg. 804
AUGUST MAX WOMAN—Casual Corner Group, Inc.; *U.S. Private*, pg. 219
BARNEYS INC.; *U.S. Private*, pg. 116
GEOFFREY BEENE RETAIL—Phillips-Van Heusen Corporation; *U.S. Public*, pg. 1291
BIG M, INC.; *U.S. Private*, pg. 143
BODY SHOP OF AMERICA; *U.S. Private*, pg. 154
BRAUNS FASHIONS CORPORATION; *U.S. Public*, pg. 251
BROOKS BROTHERS—Marks & Spencer PLC; *Int'l*, pg. 843
DICK BRUHN INCORPORATED; *U.S. Private*, pg. 175
THE BURTON GROUP PLC; *Int'l*, pg. 237
CACHE, INC.; *U.S. Public*, pg. 289
CASUAL CORNER GROUP, INC.; *U.S. Private*, pg. 219
CASUAL CORNER WOMAN—Casual Corner Group, Inc.; *U.S. Private*, pg. 219
CATHERINES STORES CORPORATION; *U.S. Public*, pg. 317
THE CATO CORPORATION; *U.S. Public*, pg. 318
CHARMING SHOPPES, INC.; *U.S. Public*, pg. 335
CHELSEA GROUP—Horizon Enterprises Group LLC; *U.S. Private*, pg. 539
CHEROKEE INC.; *U.S. Public*, pg. 345
CHICO'S FAS INC; *U.S. Public*, pg. 349
CLIFTEX—Woolworth Corporation; *U.S. Public*, pg. 1777
CLOTHESTIME STORES, INC.; *U.S. Public*, pg. 387
COHOES FASHIONS, INC.—Burlington Coat Factory Warehouse Corporation; *U.S. Public*, pg. 268
CONTEMPO CASUALS—The Wet Seal, Inc.; *U.S. Public*, pg. 1763
DEB SHOPS, INC.; *U.S. Public*, pg. 491
THE DRESS BARN, INC.; *U.S. Public*, pg. 528
DYLEX LIMITED; *Int'l*, pg. 425
EDISON BROTHERS STORES, INC.; *U.S. Public*, pg. 563
EVANS, INC.; *U.S. Public*, pg. 596
EXPRESS—The Limited, Inc.; *U.S. Public*, pg. 995
FASHION BUG—Charming Shoppes, Inc.; *U.S. Public*, pg. 336

FASHION BUG PLUS—Charming Shoppes, Inc.; *U.S. Public*, pg. 336
FASHION SHOP OF KENTUCKY INC.; *U.S. Private*, pg. 397
FIELDS STORES—Hudson's Bay Company; *Int'l*, pg. 637
FREDERICK'S OF HOLLYWOOD, INC.; *U.S. Private*, pg. 424
GANTOS INC.; *U.S. Public*, pg. 702
GANTOS, INC.—Gantos Inc.; *U.S. Public*, pg. 702
GOODY'S FAMILY CLOTHING, INC.; *U.S. Public*, pg. 753
GUESS ?, INC.; *U.S. Public*, pg. 768
HAMPSHIRE GROUP, LTD.; *U.S. Public*, pg. 778
HARCOURT GENERAL, INC.; *U.S. Public*, pg. 782
PAUL HARRIS STORES, INC.; *U.S. Public*, pg. 792
THE HE-RO GROUP, LTD.; *U.S. Public*, pg. 801
HIT OR MISS, INC.; *U.S. Private*, pg. 531
HORIZON INVESTMENT GROUP—Horizon Enterprises Group LLC; *U.S. Private*, pg. 539
JAY JACOBS, INC.; *U.S. Public*, pg. 922
JACOBSON STORES INC.; *U.S. Public*, pg. 922
TOM JAMES COMPANY; *U.S. Private*, pg. 580
KIEN—Vendex International N.V.; *Int'l*, pg. 1462
KINNEY SHOE CORPORATION—Woolworth Corporation; *U.S. Public*, pg. 1777
N.V. KONINKLIJKE BIJENKORF BEHEER KBB; *Int'l*, pg. 750
KORET OF CALIFORNIA, INC.; *U.S. Private*, pg. 632
KREYMBORG—Vendex International N.V.; *Int'l*, pg. 1462
L.L. BEAN, INC.; *U.S. Private*, pg. 639
LANE BRYANT—The Limited, Inc.; *U.S. Public*, pg. 995
GUY LAROCHE SA—Societe BIC S.A.; *Int'l*, pg. 1273
LAURA ASHLEY (AUSTRALIA) PTY LTD.—Laura Ashley Holdings Plc; *Int'l*, pg. 804
LAURA ASHLEY GMBH—Laura Ashley Holdings Plc; *Int'l*, pg. 804
LAURA ASHLEY LTD.—Laura Ashley Holdings Plc; *Int'l*, pg. 804
LAURA ASHLEY NV—Laura Ashley Holdings Plc; *Int'l*, pg. 804
LAURA ASHLEY SA—Laura Ashley Holdings Plc; *Int'l*, pg. 804
LAURA ASHLEY SHOPS LTD.—Laura Ashley Holdings Plc; *Int'l*, pg. 804
LAURA ASHLEY SRL—Laura Ashley Holdings Plc; *Int'l*, pg. 804
LAURA ASHLEY TRADING BV—Laura Ashley Holdings Plc; *Int'l*, pg. 804
LAURA ASHLEY (USA) INC.—Laura Ashley Holdings Plc; *Int'l*, pg. 804
LERNER NEW YORK—The Limited, Inc.; *U.S. Public*, pg. 995
LILLIE RUBIN FASHIONS INC.; *U.S. Private*, pg. 667
THE LIMITED, INC.; *U.S. Public*, pg. 995
LIMITED STORES—The Limited, Inc.; *U.S. Public*, pg. 996
METRO AG; *Int'l*, pg. 863
MITSUKOSHI (U.S.A.) INC.—Mitsukoshi, Ltd.; *Int'l*, pg. 883
MIXIT—JC Penney Company, Inc.; *U.S. Public*, pg. 917
NAMES FOR DAMES, INC.; *U.S. Private*, pg. 773
THE NEIMAN-MARCUS GROUP, INC.—Harcourt General, Inc.; *U.S. Public*, pg. 784
ONE PRICE CLOTHING OF PUERTO RICO, INC.—One Price Clothing Stores, Inc.; *U.S. Public*, pg. 1225
ONE PRICE CLOTHING STORES, INC.; *U.S. Public*, pg. 1225
PS...PLUS SIZES, PLUS SAVINGS—Catherines Stores Corporation; *U.S. Public*, pg. 318
PETITE SOPHISTICATE—Casual Corner Group, Inc.; *U.S. Private*, pg. 219
PETRIE RETAIL, INC.; *U.S. Private*, pg. 858
PIER 1 IMPORTS, INC.; *U.S. Public*, pg. 1295
PRENATAL B.V.—N.V. Koninklijke Bijenkorf Beheer KBB; *Int'l*, pg. 750
RETAILNET B.V.—N.V. Koninklijke Bijenkorf Beheer KBB; *Int'l*, pg. 750
RICHARD SHOPS HOLDINGS LTD.—Sears plc; *Int'l*, pg. 1217
THE RICHMAN BROTHERS CO.—Woolworth Corporation; *U.S. Public*, pg. 1777
SARMA-NOPRI GROUP—GIB Group; *Int'l*, pg. 533
MARK SHALE; *U.S. Private*, pg. 989
SHARPE DRY GOODS CO., INC.; *U.S. Private*, pg. 990
SHIRMAX LEASING LTD.; *Int'l*, pg. 1235
SHIRMAX RETAIL LTD.—Shirmax Leasing Ltd.; *Int'l*, pg. 1235
SIZE 5-7-9 SHOPS, INC.—Edison Brothers Stores, Inc.; *U.S. Public*, pg. 564
CLAUDIA STRATER—Vendex International N.V.; *Int'l*, pg. 1462
SUSIE'S DEALS; *U.S. Private*, pg. 1056
SYMS CORPORATION; *U.S. Public*, pg. 1547
T.J. MAXX—The TJX Companies, Inc.; *U.S. Public*, pg. 1557
THE TJX COMPANIES, INC.; *U.S. Public*, pg. 1556
TALBOTS—AEON Group; *Int'l*, pg. 28
THE TOG SHOP; *U.S. Private*, pg. 1090
TRUE TEMPER HARDWARE COMPANY—Huffy Corporation; *U.S. Public*, pg. 846
ULTIMO LTD.; *U.S. Private*, pg. 1116
UNITED RETAIL GROUP, INC.; *U.S. Public*, pg. 1679
URBAN OUTFITTERS, INC.; *U.S. Public*, pg. 1700
THE WEATHERVANE RETAIL CORP.; *U.S. Private*, pg. 1156
THE WET SEAL, INC.; *U.S. Public*, pg. 1763
WINDSOR FASHIONS; *U.S. Private*, pg. 1182
WINNERS APPAREL LTD.—The TJX Companies, Inc.; *U.S. Public*, pg. 1557
WINONA KNITS; *U.S. Private*, pg. 1183
WOOLWORTH CORPORATION; *U.S. Public*, pg. 1777
F.W. WOOLWORTH CO. LIMITED, CANADA—Woolworth Corporation; *U.S. Public*, pg. 1778

5632 — WOMEN'S ACCESSORY & SPECIALTY STORES

A&E STORES, INC.; *U.S. Private*, pg. 1
ANNTAYLOR, INC.—AnnTaylor Stores Corporation; *U.S. Public*, pg. 116
ANNTAYLOR STORES CORPORATION; *U.S. Public*, pg. 116
THE ANSWER—Catherines Stores Corporation; *U.S. Public*, *pg. 318*
BLACK & DECKER (BELGIUM) N.V.—The Black & Decker Corporation; *U.S. Public*, pg. 234
DICK BRUHN INCORPORATED; *U.S. Private*, pg. 175
CACHE, INC.; *U.S. Public*, pg. 289
CACIQUE—The Limited, Inc.; *U.S. Public*, pg. 995
CATHERINES STORES CORPORATION; *U.S. Public*, pg. 317
CLAIRE'S STORES INC.; *U.S. Public*, pg. 381
COHOES FASHIONS, INC.—Burlington Coat Factory Warehouse Corporation; *U.S. Public*, pg. 268
DEB SHOPS, INC.; *U.S. Public*, pg. 491
DENISE LINGERIE—House of Ronnie, Inc.; *U.S. Private*, pg. 542
EDISON BROTHERS STORES, INC.; *U.S. Public*, pg. 563
EVANS, INC.; *U.S. Public*, pg. 596
EVANS, INC. (MA)—Evans, Inc.; *U.S. Public*, pg. 596
G & G SHOPS, INC.—Petrie Retail, Inc.; *U.S. Private*, pg. 858
GATEWAY APPAREL, INC.; *U.S. Private*, pg. 441
JOAN & DAVID HELPERN, INC.; *U.S. Private*, pg. 521
HENRI BENDEL—The Limited, Inc.; *U.S. Public*, pg. 995
HEYMAN CORPORATION; *U.S. Private*, pg. 524
HOUSE OF RONNIE, INC.; *U.S. Private*, pg. 542
INTIMATE BRANDS, INC.—The Limited, Inc.; *U.S. Public*, pg. 995
LANDS' END, INC.; *U.S. Public*, pg. 977
LAURA ASHLEY LTD.—Laura Ashley Holdings Plc; *Int'l*, pg. 804
LAURA ASHLEY SHOPS LTD.—Laura Ashley Holdings Plc; *Int'l*, pg. 804
LAURA ASHLEY (USA) INC.—Laura Ashley Holdings Plc; *Int'l*, pg. 804
LIZ CLAIBORNE OUTLET DIVISION—Liz Claiborne, Inc.; *U.S. Public*, pg. 1006
ONE PRICE CLOTHING OF PUERTO RICO, INC.—One Price Clothing Stores, Inc.; *U.S. Public*, pg. 1225
ONE PRICE CLOTHING STORES, INC.; *U.S. Public*, pg. 1225
PS...PLUS SIZES, PLUS SAVINGS—Catherines Stores Corporation; *U.S. Public*, pg. 318
PACIFIC HIDE & FUR DEPOT; *U.S. Private*, pg. 831
PENN FASHIONS, INC.—Burlington Coat Factory Warehouse Corporation; *U.S. Public*, pg. 268
PETRIE RETAIL, INC.; *U.S. Private*, pg. 858
POLLACK CORPORATION; *U.S. Private*, pg. 874
POLO/RALPH LAUREN CORPORATION; *U.S. Private*, pg. 874
RAINBOW APPAREL DISTRIBUTION CENTER; *U.S. Private*, pg. 907
REITMANS (CANADA) LIMITED; *Int'l*, pg. 1102
REITMANS INC.—Reitmans (Canada) Limited; *Int'l*, pg. 1102
ROSENDORF/EVANS—Evans, Inc.; *U.S. Public*, pg. 597
SHARON SEZ, INC.—Burlington Coat Factory Warehouse Corporation; *U.S. Public*, pg. 268
CLAUDIA STRATER—Vendex International N.V.; *Int'l*, pg. 1462
SYMS CORPORATION; *U.S. Public*, pg. 1547
THE TERRITORY AHEAD; *U.S. Private*, pg. 1077
TIE RACK PLC; *Int'l*, pg. 1389
TIE RACK TRADING LIMITED—Tie Rack plc; *Int'l*, pg. 1389
TRIFARI JEWELERS—The Monet Group, Inc.; *U.S. Private*, *pg. 757*
U.S. WOOLWORTH DIV.—Woolworth Corporation; *U.S. Public*, pg. 1778
VICTORIA'S SECRET STORES—The Limited, Inc.; *U.S. Public*, pg. 995
WAL-MART MERCHANDISING DIV.—Wal-Mart Stores, Inc.; *U.S. Public*, pg. 1733
WILSONS THE LEATHER EXPERTS INC.; *U.S. Private*, pg. 1181
WINDSOR FASHIONS; *U.S. Private*, pg. 1182
WINKELMAN STORES, INC.—Petrie Retail, Inc.; *U.S. Private*, pg. 858
WOOLWORTH CORPORATION; *U.S. Public*, pg. 1777
F.W. WOOLWORTH CO.—Woolworth Corporation; *U.S. Public*, pg. 1777
F.W. WOOLWORTH GMBH CO. (GERMANY)—Woolworth Corporation; *U.S. Public*, pg. 1778

5641 — CHILDREN'S & INFANTS' WEAR STORES

BHS PLC—Storehouse PLC; *Int'l*, pg. 1304
BABYHALLEN B.V.—N.V. Koninklijke Bijenkorf Beheer KBB; *Int'l*, pg. 750
THE CHILDREN'S PLACE RETAIL STORES, INC.; *U.S. Private*, pg. 237
CHILDRENS WORLD—Storehouse PLC; *Int'l*, pg. 1304
CLIFTEX—Woolworth Corporation; *U.S. Public*, pg. 1777
FIELDS STORES—Hudson's Bay Company; *Int'l*, pg. 637
GYMBOREE CORPORATION; *U.S. Public*, pg. 770
HOLTZMAN'S LITTLE FOLK SHOP, INC.—Woolworth Corporation; *U.S. Public*, pg. 1777
KIDS "R" US—Toys "R" Us, Inc.; *U.S. Public*, pg. 1626
LAMONTS APPAREL, INC.; *U.S. Public*, pg. 975
LANDS' END, INC.; *U.S. Public*, pg. 977
LAURA ASHLEY (USA) INC.—Laura Ashley Holdings Plc; *Int'l*, pg. 804
MOTHERCARE WORLD UK LTD.—Storehouse PLC; *Int'l*, pg. 1304
PRENATAL B.V.—N.V. Koninklijke Bijenkorf Beheer KBB; *Int'l*, pg. 750
RETAILNET B.V.—N.V. Koninklijke Bijenkorf Beheer KBB; *Int'l*, pg. 750
STOREHOUSE PLC; *Int'l*, pg. 1304
SYMS CORPORATION; *U.S. Public*, pg. 1547
T.J. MAXX—The TJX Companies, Inc.; *U.S. Public*, pg. 1557
THE TERRITORY AHEAD; *U.S. Private*, pg. 1077
WOOLWORTH CORPORATION; *U.S. Public*, pg. 1777
F.W. WOOLWORTH CO. LIMITED, CANADA—Woolworth Corporation; *U.S. Public*, pg. 1778

5651 — FAMILY CLOTHING STORES

ABDALLA'S LAFAYETTE, INC.; *U.S. Private*, pg. 10
C.R. ANTHONY COMPANY—Stage Stores, Inc.; *U.S. Private*, pg. 1029
BICAPA-BJOERNKLAEDER AB—Sophus Berendsen A/S; *Int'l*, pg. 1285
BURLINGTON COAT FACTORY WAREHOUSE CORPORATION; *U.S. Public*, pg. 268
BURNSTAD BROTHERS, INC.; *U.S. Private*, pg. 187
CELANESE CANADA TEXTILE GROUP—Hoechst Aktiengesellschaft; *Int'l*, pg. 625
CONAGRA RETAIL COMPANIES—ConAgra, Inc.; *U.S. Public*, pg. 426
COUNTRY GENERAL STORES—J.W. Childs Associates, L.P.; *U.S. Private*, pg. 237
DAWAHARES, INC.; *U.S. Private*, pg. 316
DESIGNS, INC.; *U.S. Public*, pg. 501
THE DESIGNS/OLS PARTNERSHIP—Designs, Inc.; *U.S. Public*, pg. 501
GAPKIDS DIVISION—The Gap, Inc.; *U.S. Public*, pg. 702
GEBO DISTRIBUTING CO., INC.; *U.S. Private*, pg. 442
GENERAL TEXTILES; *U.S. Private*, pg. 445
ITO-YOKADO CO., LTD.; *Int'l*, pg. 693
LAMONTS APPAREL, INC.; *U.S. Public*, pg. 975
LANDS' END, INC.; *U.S. Public*, pg. 977
MARSHALLS, INC.—The TJX Companies, Inc.; *U.S. Public*, *pg. 1557*
NORDSTROM, INC.; *U.S. Public*, pg. 1190
OLD NAVY STORES—The Gap, Inc.; *U.S. Public*, pg. 703
SOUTHERN APPAREL CORPORATION; *U.S. Private*, pg. 1015
SPIEGEL, INC.; *U.S. Public*, pg. 1498
SYMS CORPORATION; *U.S. Public*, pg. 1547
THE TERRITORY AHEAD; *U.S. Private*, pg. 1077
UMBRO INTERNATIONAL, INC.; *U.S. Private*, pg. 1116
WINONA KNITS; *U.S. Private*, pg. 1183

5661 — SHOE STORES

ADLER SHOE SHOPS—Weyco Group, Inc.; *U.S. Public*, pg. 1764
AGNEW GROUP—The Bentley Agnew Group Inc.; *Int'l*, pg. 187
THE ATHLETE'S FOOT GROUP, INC.; *U.S. Private*, pg. 94
ATHLETIC ATTIC RETAIL COMPANY—Just For Feet, Inc.; *U.S. Public*, pg. 936
ATHLETIC EXPRESS—Woolworth Corporation; *U.S. Public*, *pg. 1777*
J. BAKER, INC.; *U.S. Public*, pg. 167
BAKERS/LEEDS SHOE STORES—Edison Brothers Stores, Inc.; *U.S. Public*, pg. 563
BALLY MANAGEMENT—Oerlikon-Buhrle Holding AG; *Int'l*, pg. 998
BASS RETAIL DIV.—Phillips-Van Heusen Corporation; *U.S. Public*, pg. 1291
BEE-GEE SHOE CORP.—The Elder-Beerman Stores Corp.; *U.S. Private*, pg. 367
THE BENTLEY AGNEW GROUP INC.; *Int'l*, pg. 187
BOB'S STORES, INC.—CVS Corp.; *U.S. Public*, pg. 287
BOSTONIAN SHOE CO.—Clarks International; *Int'l*, pg. 297
BOSTONIAN WHOLESALE DIVISION—Clarks International; *Int'l*, pg. 297
BROWN GROUP, INC.; *U.S. Public*, pg. 262
BROWN RETAIL DEVELOPMENT CO.—Brown Group, Inc.; *U.S. Public*, pg. 262
C & J CLARK AMERICA, INC.—Clarks International; *Int'l*, pg. 297
C & J CLARK DIRECT MARKETING DIVISION—Clarks International; *Int'l*, pg. 297
C & J CLARK RETAIL, INC.—Clarks International; *Int'l*, pg. 297
CHB CORP.; *U.S. Private*, pg. 194
CHAMPS—Woolworth Corporation; *U.S. Public*, pg. 1777
CHAMPSSPORTS—Woolworth Corporation; *U.S. Public*, pg. 1777
CHERNIN'S SHOE OUTLET—Chernin's Shoes, Inc.; *U.S. Private*, pg. 233
CHERNIN'S SHOES, INC.; *U.S. Private*, pg. 233
CHEYENNE OUTFITTERS, INC.; *U.S. Private*, pg. 234
CLARK SHOE CO.—Clarks International; *Int'l*, pg. 297
COWTOWN BOOT COMPANY; *U.S. Private*, pg. 281
DIANA—Coop Switzerland; *Int'l*, pg. 330
E.J. FOOTWEAR CORP.—U.S. Industries, Inc.; *U.S. Public*, pg. 1684
EDISON BROTHERS STORES, INC.; *U.S. Public*, pg. 563
THE ELDER-BEERMAN STORES CORP.; *U.S. Private*, pg. 367
FAMOUS FOOTWEAR—Brown Group, Inc.; *U.S. Public*, pg. 262
FLORSHEIM GROUP INC.; *U.S. Public*, pg. 656
FOOT LOCKER—Woolworth Corporation; *U.S. Public*, pg. 1777
FOOT LOCKER EUROPE B.V.—Woolworth Corporation; *U.S. Public*, pg. 1778
FOOTACTION USA—Footstar Inc.; *U.S. Public*, pg. 661
FOOTQUARTERS—Woolworth Corporation; *U.S. Public*, pg. 1777
FOOTSTAR INC.; *U.S. Public*, pg. 661

THE GENERAL SHOE WAREHOUSE—Genesco Inc.; U.S. Public, pg. 728
GENERAL TEXTILES; U.S. Private, pg. 445
GENESCO INC.; U.S. Public, pg. 728
GUCCI AMERICA INC.—Investcorp International; Int'l, pg. 686
HANOVER STORES—Clarks International; Int'l, pg. 297
JOAN & DAVID HELPERN, INC.; U.S. Private, pg. 521
HUSH PUPPIES RETAIL, INC.—Wolverine World Wide, Inc.; U.S. Public, pg. 1775
JOHNSTON & MURPHY RETAIL/WHOLESALE STORES—Genesco Inc.; U.S. Public, pg. 728
JUST FOR FEET, INC.; U.S. Public, pg. 935
KINNEY SHOE CORPORATION—Woolworth Corporation; U.S. Public, pg. 1777
KINNEY SHOES (AUSTRALIA), LTD.—Woolworth Corporation; U.S. Public, pg. 1778
L.L. BEAN, INC.; U.S. Private, pg. 639
LADY FOOTLOCKER—Woolworth Corporation; U.S. Public, pg. 1777
THE MAY DEPARTMENT STORES COMPANY; U.S. Public, pg. 1063
HENRY MODELL & COMPANY, INC.; U.S. Private, pg. 754
MORGAN-HAYES DIV.—Weyco Group, Inc.; U.S. Public, pg. 1764
MORSE SHOE, INC.—J. Baker, Inc.; U.S. Public, pg. 168
MORSE SHOE LEASED DIV.—J. Baker, Inc.; U.S. Public, pg. 168
NINE WEST GROUP, INC.; U.S. Public, pg. 1185
NORDSTROM, INC.; U.S. Public, pg. 1190
NUNN-BUSH SHOE CO.—Weyco Group, Inc.; U.S. Public, pg. 1763
PAYLESS SHOESOURCE, INC.; U.S. Public, pg. 1268
PIC'N PAY STORES, INC.; U.S. Private, pg. 864
JOHN REYER COMPANY; U.S. Private, pg. 926
SLJ RETAIL LLC; U.S. Private, pg. 957
SCHOLL PLC; Int'l, pg. 1209
SHOE PAVILION; U.S. Private, pg. 996
THE SHOE SHOW OF ROCKY MT., INC.; U.S. Private, pg. 996
SHONAC CORPORATION; U.S. Private, pg. 996
STRIDE RITE CHILDREN'S GROUP, INC.-RETAIL DIV.—The Stride Rite Corporation; U.S. Public, pg. 1525
THE STRIDE RITE CORPORATION; U.S. Public, pg. 1524
SYMS CORPORATION; U.S. Public, pg. 1547
TRACK 'N TRAIL; U.S. Public, pg. 1626
TRADEHOME SHOE STORES, INC.; U.S. Private, pg. 1095
TRANSMARCO LIMITED; Int'l, pg. 1417
WWW RETAIL, INC.—Wolverine World Wide, Inc.; U.S. Public, pg. 1775
THE WILD PAIR—Edison Brothers Stores, Inc.; U.S. Public, pg. 564
WOLVERINE WORLD WIDE, INC.; U.S. Public, pg. 1775
F.W. WOOLWORTH GMBH CO. (GERMANY)—Woolworth Corporation; U.S. Public, pg. 1778

5699 — MISCELLANEOUS APPAREL & ACCESSORY STORES

ACADEMY CORPORATION; U.S. Private, pg. 11
ALLDERS INTERNATIONAL (CANADA) LIMITED—Agra Inc.; Int'l, pg. 30
AMERICAN EAGLES OUTFITTERS INC.; U.S. Private, pg. 53
AMMEX TAX & DUTY FREE SHOPS—BAA plc; Int'l, pg. 103
AMMEX TAX & DUTY FREE SHOPS WEST, INC.—BAA plc; Int'l, pg. 103
ANGELICA CORPORATION; U.S. Public, pg. 113
ARCADIA SHOPS, INC.—Claire's Stores Inc.; U.S. Public, pg. 381
BANANA REPUBLIC—The Gap, Inc.; U.S. Public, pg. 702
CHAMPION PRODUCTS INC.—Sara Lee Corporation; U.S. Public, pg. 1433
CHEYENNE OUTFITTERS, INC.; U.S. Private, pg. 234
CLAIRE'S BOUTIQUES, INC.—Claire's Stores Inc.; U.S. Public, pg. 381
CUSTOM SHOP SHIRTMAKERS INC.—HC Holdings; U.S. Private, pg. 490
DUNHAM'S ATHLEISURE CORPORATION; U.S. Private, pg. 346
DUTY FREE INTERNATIONAL, INC.—BAA plc; Int'l, pg. 103
E & B MARINE INCORPORATED—West Marine, Inc.; U.S. Public, pg. 1756
FENTON HILL AMERICAN LIMITED—BAA plc; Int'l, pg. 103
GIB GROUP; Int'l, pg. 532
THE GAP, INC.; U.S. Public, pg. 702
GAP STORES DIVISION—The Gap, Inc.; U.S. Public, pg. 702
GATEWAY APPAREL, INC.; U.S. Private, pg. 441
GROSSENBURG IMPLEMENTS, INCORPORATED; U.S. Private, pg. 483
HUNTINGTON CLOTHIERS, INC.—HC Holdings; U.S. Private, pg. 490
JAZZERCISE, INC.; U.S. Private, pg. 584
LVMH MOET HENNESSY LOUIS VUITTON; Int'l, pg. 779
LENSCRAFTERS—Luxottica Group S.p.A.; Int'l, pg. 822
LIFE UNIFORM & SHOE SHOPS—Angelica Corporation; U.S. Public, pg. 113
LOEWE FASHIONS INCORPORATED—LVMH Moet Hennessy Louis Vuitton; Int'l, pg. 781
LOEWE HAWAII INC.—LVMH Moet Hennessy Louis Vuitton; Int'l, pg. 781
LOGO 7, INC.—Tultex Corporation; U.S. Public, pg. 1644
LOUIS VUITTON HAWAII—LVMH Moet Hennessy Louis Vuitton; Int'l, pg. 781
LUSKEYS WESTERN STORES, INC.; U.S. Private, pg. 681
NORCOSTCO, INC.; U.S. Private, pg. 801
PALAIS ROYAL—Stage Stores, Inc.; U.S. Private, pg. 1029
PAUL STUART, INC.; U.S. Private, pg. 844
PENDLETON WOOLEN MILLS, INC.; U.S. Private, pg. 848
R & R UNIFORMS—Horace Small Apparel PLC; Int'l, pg. 635
RECREATIONAL EQUIPMENT, INC.; U.S. Private, pg. 914
RETAIL STORES, INC.—VSI Holdings, Inc.; U.S. Public, pg. 1703
RYON'S SADDLE & RANCH SUPPLY—Luskeys Western Stores, Inc.; U.S. Private, pg. 681
I. SPIEWAK & SONS, INC.; U.S. Private, pg. 1025
SPORT OBERMEYER LTD., USA; U.S. Private, pg. 1026
THE SPORTS AUTHORITY INC.; U.S. Public, pg. 1499
THE SPORTS SECTION INC.—BAA plc; Int'l, pg. 103
STERLING VISION, INC.; U.S. Public, pg. 1516
SYMS CORPORATION; U.S. Public, pg. 1547
TEJAS WESTERN OUTLET—Luskeys Western Stores, Inc.; U.S. Private, pg. 681
UETA, INC.—BAA plc; Int'l, pg. 103
WEST MARINE, INC.; U.S. Public, pg. 1756

5712 — FURNITURE STORES

AARON RENTS, INC.; U.S. Public, pg. 12
AMERICAN FURNITURE COMPANY; U.S. Private, pg. 55
AMERICAN TV & APPLIANCE OF MADISON, INC.; U.S. Private, pg. 64
ARNOLDS INTERIORS, INC.—Huffman Koos; U.S. Private, pg. 546
ART VAN FURNITURE INC.; U.S. Private, pg. 86
AU BON MARCHE; Int'l, pg. 97
BKM ENTERPRISES, INC.; U.S. Private, pg. 107
W.S. BADCOCK CORPORATION; U.S. Private, pg. 109
J.D. BASSETT MFG. CO.—Bassett Furniture Industries, Incorporated; U.S. Public, pg. 193
BERKSHIRE HATHAWAY INC.; U.S. Public, pg. 217
CALIFORNIA CLOSET COMPANY, INC.—Williams-Sonoma, Inc.; U.S. Public, pg. 1770
COHEN FURNITURE COMPANY; U.S. Private, pg. 250
CONFORAMA—Au Bon Marche; Int'l, pg. 98
COPPEL S.A. DE C.V.; Int'l, pg. 330
DANTAS HOLDINGS LTD.—Jardine Matheson Holdings Limited; Int'l, pg. 704
DEARDEN'S; U.S. Private, pg. 319
DIAL A MATTRESS USA; U.S. Private, pg. 330
THE ELDER-BEERMAN STORES CORP.; U.S. Private, pg. 367
EUROMARKET DESIGNS, INC.; U.S. Private, pg. 384
FINGER FURNITURE COMPANY, INC.; U.S. Private, pg. 405
FURNITURE IN PARTS, INC.; U.S. Private, pg. 432
GABBERT'S, INC.; U.S. Private, pg. 437
GEM INDUSTRIES NE INC.—Gem Industries Finance Corporation; U.S. Private, pg. 442
GLOBE FURNITURE RENTALS; U.S. Private, pg. 458
GLOBE FURNITURE RENTALS—Globe Furniture Rentals; U.S. Private, pg. 458
GOLDSMITHS, INC.; U.S. Private, pg. 462
HABITAT GROUP—Ikea Holdings AB; Int'l, pg. 660
HAVERTY FURNITURE COMPANIES, INC.; U.S. Public, pg. 799
HEILIG-MEYERS COMPANY; U.S. Public, pg. 804
HEILIG MEYERS FURNITURE CO.—Heilig-Meyers Company; U.S. Public, pg. 804
HOMESTEAD HOUSE INC.; U.S. Private, pg. 537
HUB FURNITURE STORE—Reliable Stores, Inc.; U.S. Private, pg. 920
HUFFMAN KOOS; U.S. Private, pg. 546
IKEA NORTH AMERICA, INC.—Ikea Holdings AB; Int'l, pg. 660
IKEA SVENSKA AB—Ikea Holdings AB; Int'l, pg. 660
IKEA SVENSKA FORSALJNINGS AB—Ikea Holdings AB; Int'l, pg. 660
JARDINE MATHESON HOLDINGS LIMITED; Int'l, pg. 703
JENNIFER CONVERTIBLES INC.; U.S. Public, pg. 926
KALIN ENTERPRISES, INC.; U.S. Private, pg. 606
MORRIS KIRSCHMAN & COMPANY, INC.; U.S. Private, pg. 623
THE KLINE FURNITURE CO.—Reliable Stores, Inc.; U.S. Private, pg. 920
KRAUSE'S FURNITURE INC.; U.S. Public, pg. 967
KRAUSE'S SOFA FACTORY—Krause's Furniture Inc.; U.S. Public, pg. 967
LEVITZ FURNITURE CORPORATION—Levitz Furniture Incorporated; U.S. Public, pg. 990
LEVITZ FURNITURE INCORPORATED; U.S. Public, pg. 990
MFI FURNITURE CENTER PLC; Int'l, pg. 827
ED MARLING STORES, INC.; U.S. Private, pg. 705
MITY-LITE, INC.; U.S. Public, pg. 1118
NEBRASKA FURNITURE MART, INC.—Berkshire Hathaway Inc.; U.S. Public, pg. 221
OLINDE HARDWARE & SUPPLY CO.; U.S. Private, pg. 814
PIER 1 IMPORTS, INC.; U.S. Public, pg. 1295
RTG FURNITURE CORP.; U.S. Private, pg. 905
RAYMOUR AND FLANIGAN FURNITURE CO.; U.S. Private, pg. 912
RELIABLE STORES, INC.; U.S. Private, pg. 920
RHODES, INC.—Heilig-Meyers Company; U.S. Public, pg. 805
SEAMAN FURNITURE COMPANY, INC.; U.S. Public, pg. 1452
SERVCO PACIFIC INC.; U.S. Private, pg. 986
SHAPELL INDUSTRIES, INC.; U.S. Private, pg. 990
SKINNER CORP.; U.S. Private, pg. 1005
JOHN M. SMYTH CO.—Levitz Furniture Incorporated; U.S. Public, pg. 990
STAR FURNITURE COMPANY—Berkshire Hathaway Inc.; U.S. Public, pg. 221
STELAR INC.; U.S. Private, pg. 1040
STROUDS, INC.; U.S. Public, pg. 1525
SUSSEX GROUP, LTD.—JG Industries, Inc.; U.S. Public, pg. 918
V&D PROJECTINRICHTING—Vendex International N.V.; Int'l, pg. 1462
VENDEX INTERNATIONAL N.V.; Int'l, pg. 1462
D. WALDNER COMPANY, INC.; U.S. Private, pg. 1147
WAREHOUSE HOME FURNISHINGS DISTRIBUTOR; U.S. Private, pg. 1150
R.C. WILLEY HOME FURNISHINGS—Berkshire Hathaway Inc.; U.S. Public, pg. 221

5713 — FLOOR COVERING STORES

W.S. BADCOCK CORPORATION; U.S. Private, pg. 109
CARPETERIA, INC.; U.S. Private, pg. 215
CELANESE CANADA TEXTILE GROUP—Hoechst Aktiengesellschaft; Int'l, pg. 625
COLOR TILE, INC.—Investcorp International; Int'l, pg. 686
DESIGN CENTER—Del Webb Corporation; U.S. Public, pg. 495
EINSTEIN MOOMJY INC.; U.S. Private, pg. 366
GALLERY FURNITURE; U.S. Private, pg. 438
HEILIG MEYERS FURNITURE CO.—Heilig-Meyers Company; U.S. Public, pg. 804
IKEA SVENSKA FORSALJNINGS AB—Ikea Holdings AB; Int'l, pg. 660
MAUTZ PAINT CO.; U.S. Private, pg. 715
MCSWAIN CARPETS INC.; U.S. Private, pg. 725
NEW YORK CARPET WORLD—Shaw Industries, Inc.; U.S. Public, pg. 1464
OLSON RUG COMPANY; U.S. Private, pg. 815
ST. CLAIR PAINT AND WALLPAPER CORPORATION; Int'l, pg. 1170
STELAR INC.; U.S. Private, pg. 1040

5714 — DRAPERY, CURTAIN & UPHOLSTERY STORES

CALICO CORNERS—Everfast Inc.; U.S. Private, pg. 386
CHARLES CURTAIN COMPANY, INC.; U.S. Private, pg. 229
EVERFAST INC.; U.S. Private, pg. 386
MAUTZ PAINT CO.; U.S. Private, pg. 715

5719 — MISCELLANEOUS HOMEFURNISHING STORES

ACTIVE ELECTRICAL SUPPLY COMPANY; U.S. Private, pg. 15
ADRAY APPLIANCE & PHOTO CENTER, INC.; U.S. Private, pg. 18
W.E. AUBUCHON CO., INC.; U.S. Private, pg. 98
BHS PLC—Storehouse PLC; Int'l, pg. 1304
BEAVER LUMBER COMPANY LIMITED—The Molson Companies Limited; Int'l, pg. 887
BED BATH & BEYOND INC.; U.S. Public, pg. 200
BETTER LIVING INC.; U.S. Private, pg. 141
CARGO FURNITURE & ACCENTS—Tandycrafts, Inc.; U.S. Public, pg. 1561
CHARLES CURTAIN COMPANY, INC.; U.S. Private, pg. 229
DARWIN GLASS—BTR plc; Int'l, pg. 129
DE LAMPENIER—N.V. Koninklijke Bijenkorf Beheer KBB; Int'l, pg. 750
EFCO INC.; U.S. Private, pg. 353
EUROMARKET DESIGNS, INC.; U.S. Private, pg. 384
FINGER FURNITURE COMPANY, INC.; U.S. Private, pg. 405
FIRST BOWRING INSURANCE BROKERS HOLDINGS (PTY.) LTD.—First National Bank Holdings Limited; Int'l, pg. 487
FIRST NATIONAL ASSET MANAGEMENT & TRUST COMPANY (PTY) LTD.—First National Bank Holdings Limited; Int'l, pg. 487
FITZ & FLOYD; U.S. Private, pg. 409
FORTUNOFF; U.S. Private, pg. 420
GS INDUSTRIES, INC.; U.S. Private, pg. 435
GEBO DISTRIBUTING CO., INC.; U.S. Private, pg. 442
GEORG JENSEN SILVER—Royal Copenhagen A/S; Int'l, pg. 1134
HABITAT FRANCE SA—Ikea Holdings AB; Int'l, pg. 659
HAMMACHER, SCHLEMMER & CO., INC.; U.S. Private, pg. 497
HOLMEGAARDS GLASS—Royal Copenhagen A/S; Int'l, pg. 1134
HOME PRODUCTS INTERNATIONAL, INC.; U.S. Public, pg. 832
HOMEGOODS—The TJX Companies, Inc.; U.S. Public, pg. 1557
HOMESTEAD HOUSE INC.; U.S. Private, pg. 537
HORRIGAN AMERICAN INC.—ABN-AMRO Holding N.V.; Int'l, pg. 9
ILLUMS BOLIGHUS—Royal Copenhagen A/S; Int'l, pg. 1134
INTERNATIONAL CUTLERY, LTD; U.S. Private, pg. 569
M. KAMENSTEIN, INC.; U.S. Private, pg. 606
THE KITCHEN COLLECTION INC.—NACCO Industries, Inc.; U.S. Public, pg. 1149
KLEINSLEEP—Sleepy's The Mattress Professionals; U.S. Private, pg. 1006
LAPPIN ELECTRIC COMPANY—Consolidated Electrical Distributors; U.S. Private, pg. 265
LECHTERS, INC.; U.S. Public, pg. 983
LEGGETT AND PLATT INTERNATIONAL CORPORATION—Leggett & Platt, Incorporated; U.S. Public, pg. 986
LOWE'S COMPANIES, INC.; U.S. Public, pg. 1015
MAGEE CO.—Tandycrafts, Inc.; U.S. Public, pg. 1561
FRED MEYER STORES—Fred Meyer Incorporated; U.S. Public, pg. 1103
MINEBEA CO., LTD.; Int'l, pg. 867
NACCO INDUSTRIES, INC.; U.S. Public, pg. 1149
OLD AMERICA STORES; U.S. Public, pg. 1215
OSTROW TEXTILE CO., INC.; U.S. Private, pg. 821
PIER 1 IMPORTS, INC.; U.S. Public, pg. 1295

PLEJ'S LINEN SUPERMARKET—Ostrow Textile Co., Inc.; U.S. Private, pg. 821
REICO, INC.; U.S. Private, pg. 919
ROHM ELECTRONICS ASIA PTE. LTD., INVESTMENT DIV.—Rohm Co., Ltd.; Int'l, pg. 1125
ROYAL COPENHAGEN A/S; Int'l, pg. 1134
ROYAL COPENHAGEN PORCELAIN—Royal Copenhagen A/S; Int'l, pg. 1134
ROYAL COPENHAGEN PORCELAIN CORPORATION—Royal Copenhagen A/S; Int'l, pg. 1134
ROYAL COPENHAGEN RETAIL A/S—Royal Copenhagen A/S; Int'l, pg. 1134
THE SHARPER IMAGE; U.S. Public, pg. 1464
SLEEPY'S THE MATTRESS PROFESSIONALS; U.S. Private, pg. 1005
SPRINGS CANADA, LTD.—Springs Industries, Inc.; U.S. Public, pg. 1500
STROUDS, INC.; U.S. Public, pg. 1525
TRT HOLDINGS INC.; U.S. Private, pg. 1065
TANDYCRAFTS, INC.; U.S. Public, pg. 1561
THREE D DEPARTMENTS, INC.; U.S. Public, pg. 1604
TOSOH AMERICA, INC.—Tosoh Corporation; Int'l, pg. 1407
URBAN OUTFITTERS, INC.; U.S. Public, pg. 1700
WACCAMAW CORPORATION; U.S. Private, pg. 1145
WANG'S INTERNATIONAL, INC.; U.S. Private, pg. 1149
WATERFORD CRYSTAL, INC.—Waterford Wedgwood Plc; Int'l, pg. 1487
WEDGWOOD U.S.A.—Waterford Wedgwood Plc; Int'l, pg. 1487
WICKS 'N STICKS, LTD; U.S. Private, pg. 1175
WOOLWORTHS PLC—Kingfisher plc; Int'l, pg. 734

5722 — HOUSEHOLD APPLIANCE STORES

A B C APPLIANCE INC.; U.S. Private, pg. 2
AMF REECE INCORPORATED; U.S. Private, pg. 7
AARON RENTS, INC.; U.S. Public, pg. 12
ADRAY APPLIANCE & PHOTO CENTER, INC.; U.S. Private, pg. 18
AMERICAN FURNITURE COMPANY; U.S. Private, pg. 55
AMERICAN TV & APPLIANCE OF MADISON, INC.; U.S. Private, pg. 64
W.S. BADCOCK CORPORATION; U.S. Private, pg. 109
BEST BUY CO., INC.; U.S. Public, pg. 223
CIRCUIT CITY STORES, INC.; U.S. Public, pg. 374
COMET—Kingfisher plc; Int'l, pg. 733
DACEM S.A.R.L.—Kingfisher plc; Int'l, pg. 734
DARTY ALSACE LORRAINE—Kingfisher plc; Int'l, pg. 734
DARTY PROVINCE MEDITERRANNE—Kingfisher plc; Int'l, pg. 734
DARTY RHONE-ALPES—Kingfisher plc; Int'l, pg. 734
DEARDEN'S; U.S. Private, pg. 319
DIXONS STORES GROUP (FAR EAST) LIMITED—Dixons Group plc; Int'l, pg. 414
ELECTROLUX CORPORATION; U.S. Private, pg. 369
ELECTROLUX SVENSKA FORSALJNINGS AB—Electrolux, AB; Int'l, pg. 439
ESTABLISSEMENTS DARTY & FILS S.A.—Kingfisher plc; Int'l, pg. 734
FALL RIVER GAS APPLIANCE CO., INC.—Fall River Gas Company; U.S. Public, pg. 612
FILCO, INC.; U.S. Private, pg. 404
FRY'S ELECTRONICS, INC.; U.S. Private, pg. 430
GREGG APPLIANCES INC.; U.S. Private, pg. 479
GROSSENBURG IMPLEMENTS, INCORPORATED; U.S. Private, pg. 483
GRUPO ELEKTRA S.A. DE C.V.; Int'l, pg. 573
HEILIG-MEYERS COMPANY; U.S. Public, pg. 804
HEILIG MEYERS FURNITURE CO.—Heilig-Meyers Company; U.S. Public, pg. 804
HOUSE OF FABRICS, INC.; U.S. Public, pg. 842
HOWARDS TV & APPLIANCES, INC.; U.S. Private, pg. 543
HUSQVARNA SVENSKA FORSALJNINGS AB—Electrolux, AB; Int'l, pg. 439
IKEA SVENSKA FORSALJNINGS AB—Ikea Holdings AB; Int'l, pg. 660
JORDON COMMERCIAL REFRIGERATOR CO.; U.S. Private, pg. 599
JUKI UNION SPECIAL, INC.—Juki Corporation; Int'l, pg. 716
JUKI UNION SPECIAL INC.-ATLANTA OFFICE—Juki Corporation; Int'l, pg. 716
JUKI UNION SPECIAL, INC.-CALIFORNIA OFFICE—Juki Corporation; Int'l, pg. 716
KINGFISHER PLC; Int'l, pg. 733
MORRIS KIRSCHMAN & COMPANY, INC.; U.S. Private, pg. 623
LEC REFRIGERATION PLC—Sime Darby Berhad; Int'l, pg. 1251
LE GROUPE DARTY—Kingfisher plc; Int'l, pg. 734
LOWE'S COMPANIES, INC.; U.S. Public, pg. 1015
LYKES ENERGY, INC.; U.S. Private, pg. 682
MDR S.A.—Kingfisher plc; Int'l, pg. 734
ED MARLING STORES, INC.; U.S. Private, pg. 705
MARTA COOPERATIVE OF AMERICA INC.; U.S. Private, pg. 708
MASEK DISTRIBUTING INC.; U.S. Private, pg. 711
MIDWEST BOTTLE GAS COMPANY—Consolidated Midwest, Inc.; U.S. Private, pg. 266
MOLLENBERG-BETZ INC.; U.S. Private, pg. 756
PALMER ELECTRIC CO.; U.S. Private, pg. 834
PERSTORP RAILITE S.A. DECORATIVE LAMINATE—Perstorp AB; Int'l, pg. 1038
REMINGTON PRODUCTS COMPANY, L.L.C.; U.S. Private, pg. 921
SEMI-TECH CORPORATION; Int'l, pg. 1220
THAI TOSHIBA ELECTRIC INDUSTRIES CO., LTD.—Toshiba Corporation; Int'l, pg. 1406
TOSHIBA CHUO CONSUMER ELECTRONICS CO., LTD.—Toshiba Corporation; Int'l, pg. 1403
TOSHIBA CONTROL SYSTEM CORPORATION—Toshiba Corporation; Int'l, pg. 1403
TOSHIBA E & S HOKKAIDO CORPORATION—Toshiba Corporation; Int'l, pg. 1404
TOSHIBA ELECTRONICS ASIA, LTD.—Toshiba Corporation; Int'l, pg. 1406
TOSHIBA ELECTRONICS ITALIANA S.R.L.—Toshiba Corporation; Int'l, pg. 1406
TOSHIBA ELECTRONICS TAIWAN CORP.—Toshiba Corporation; Int'l, pg. 1406
TOSHIBA INTERNATIONAL (EUROPE) LTD.—Toshiba Corporation; Int'l, pg. 1406
TOSHIBA KN SYSTEM CO., LTD.—Toshiba Corporation; Int'l, pg. 1404
TOSHIBA SALES AND SERVICES SDN. BHD.—Toshiba Corporation; Int'l, pg. 1407
TOSHIBA THAILAND CO., LTD.—Toshiba Corporation; Int'l, pg. 1407
TOSHIBA (U.K.) LTD.—Toshiba Corporation; Int'l, pg. 1407
UNION SPECIAL CORP.—Juki Corporation; Int'l, pg. 716
VAMCO—Valley Resources, Inc.; U.S. Public, pg. 1706
R.C. WILLEY HOME FURNISHINGS—Berkshire Hathaway Inc.; U.S. Public, pg. 221

5731 — RADIO, TELEVISION & CONSUMER ELECTRONIC STORES

AARON RENTS, INC.; U.S. Public, pg. 12
AARON'S RENTAL PURCHASE—Aaron Rents, Inc.; U.S. Public, pg. 12
ADRAY APPLIANCE & PHOTO CENTER, INC.; U.S. Private, pg. 18
AUDIO KING CORPORATION—Ultimate Electronics; U.S. Public, pg. 1662
AUDIO KING MIDWEST—Ultimate Electronics; U.S. Public, pg. 1662
W.S. BADCOCK CORPORATION; U.S. Private, pg. 109
BEREL INDUSTRIES INC.; U.S. Private, pg. 135
BEST BUY CO., INC.; U.S. Public, pg. 223
CIRCUIT CITY STORES, INC.; U.S. Public, pg. 374
CURRYS GROUP PLC—Dixons Group plc; Int'l, pg. 414
DARTY ALSACE LORRAINE—Kingfisher plc; Int'l, pg. 734
DARTY PROVINCE MEDITERRANNE—Kingfisher plc; Int'l, pg. 734
DARTY RHONE-ALPES—Kingfisher plc; Int'l, pg. 734
DEARDEN'S; U.S. Private, pg. 319
DIXONS—Vendex International N.V.; Int'l, pg. 1462
DIXONS GROUP PLC; Int'l, pg. 413
DIXONS STORES GROUP (FAR EAST) LIMITED—Dixons Group plc; Int'l, pg. 414
DIXONS STORES GROUP LTD.—Dixons Group plc; Int'l, pg. 414
EROL'S INTERNET; U.S. Private, pg. 382
ESTABLISSEMENTS DARTY & FILS S.A.—Kingfisher plc; Int'l, pg. 734
THE GOOD GUYS, INC.; U.S. Public, pg. 750
GREGG APPLIANCES INC.; U.S. Private, pg. 479
GRUPO ELEKTRA S.A. DE C.V.; Int'l, pg. 573
HARRIS BROADCAST DIVISION—Harris Corporation; U.S. Public, pg. 791
HARVEY ELECTRONICS—Harvey Electronics, Inc.; U.S. Public, pg. 796
HARVEY ELECTRONICS, INC.; U.S. Public, pg. 796
HITACHI SALES CORP.—Hitachi, Ltd.; Int'l, pg. 621
HOWARDS TV & APPLIANCES, INC.; U.S. Private, pg. 543
INDUSTRIAL EQUITY LIMITED; Int'l, pg. 676
INTERTAN AUSTRALIA LTD.—InterTAN Inc.; U.S. Public, pg. 910
INTERTAN CANADA LTD.—InterTAN Inc.; U.S. Public, pg. 910
LE GROUPE DARTY—Kingfisher plc; Int'l, pg. 734
LOWE'S COMPANIES, INC.; U.S. Public, pg. 1015
MDR S.A.—Kingfisher plc; Int'l, pg. 734
MAGNOLIA HI-FI, INC.; U.S. Private, pg. 696
ED MARLING STORES, INC.; U.S. Private, pg. 705
CURTIS MATHES CORPORATION—Curtis Mathes Holding Corp.; U.S. Public, pg. 1057
NOBODY BEATS THE WIZ; U.S. Private, pg. 800
RADIO TV STEINER AG—Coop Switzerland; Int'l, pg. 330
RADIOSHACK—Tandy Corporation; U.S. Public, pg. 1560
REX STORES CORP.; U.S. Public, pg. 1384
SEMI-TECH CORPORATION; Int'l, pg. 1220
SERVCO PACIFIC INC.; U.S. Private, pg. 986
THE SHARPER IMAGE; U.S. Public, pg. 1464
SIXTH AVENUE ELECTRONICS CITY; U.S. Private, pg. 1004
SUN TV & APPLIANCES, INC.; U.S. Public, pg. 1532
TANDY CORPORATION; U.S. Public, pg. 1560
WEHLE ELECTRIC CO., INC.—Westburne Inc.; Int'l, pg. 1492
R.C. WILLEY HOME FURNISHINGS—Berkshire Hathaway Inc.; U.S. Public, pg. 221
WILLOUGHBY'S; U.S. Private, pg. 1180

5734 — COMPUTER & COMPUTER SOFTWARE STORES

ARMIN PLASTICS—Tyco International Ltd.; U.S. Public, pg. 1647
BABBAGE'S ETC. LLC; U.S. Private, pg. 108
BEST BUY CO., INC.; U.S. Public, pg. 223
CEM COMPUTERS LIMITED—Siemens AG; Int'l, pg. 1247
COMPUSA; U.S. Public, pg. 420
COMPUTER CITY—Tandy Corporation; U.S. Public, pg. 1560
THE COMPUTER PATCH OF JOPLIN—Shivers Trading & Operating Co.; U.S. Private, pg. 995
CONNECTING POINT COMPUTER SERVICES—Graphic Enterprises of Ohio, Inc.; U.S. Private, pg. 471
CREATIVE COMPUTERS, INC.—Creative Computers, Inc.; U.S. Public, pg. 458
DIXONS—Vendex International N.V.; Int'l, pg. 1462
DIXONS STORES GROUP (FAR EAST) LIMITED—Dixons Group plc; Int'l, pg. 414
EGGHEAD, INC.; U.S. Public, pg. 566
EL CAMINO RESOURCES, LTD.; U.S. Private, pg. 366
ENTEX INFORMATION SERVICES; U.S. Private, pg. 378
EXECUTIVE SOFTWARE; U.S. Private, pg. 388
FIRST COMPUTER CORPORATION; U.S. Private, pg. 406
GANDALF INTERNATIONAL LTD.—Gandalf Technologies Inc.; Int'l, pg. 540
GANDALF S.A.—Gandalf Technologies Inc.; Int'l, pg. 541
GIE GETTINOR—Castorama Dubois Investissements S.C.A.; Int'l, pg. 276
GRAMEX CORPORATION; U.S. Private, pg. 468
HEILIG-MEYERS COMPANY; U.S. Public, pg. 804
INACOM CORP.; U.S. Public, pg. 873
INDUSTRIAL EQUITY LIMITED; Int'l, pg. 676
INTELLIGENT ELECTRONICS, INC.; U.S. Public, pg. 887
INTERTAN AUSTRALIA LTD.—InterTAN Inc.; U.S. Public, pg. 910
INTERTAN CANADA LTD.—InterTAN Inc.; U.S. Public, pg. 910
JAPAN SYSTEMS CORPORATION—Toshiba Corporation; Int'l, pg. 1403
L.A. COMPUTER CENTER; U.S. Private, pg. 676
MICRO ELECTRONICS, INC.; U.S. Private, pg. 742
NATIONSCREDIT COMMERCIAL CORPORATION—NationsBank Corporation; U.S. Public, pg. 1165
NEW YORK SYSTEMS EXCHANGE CORP.—Syracuse Supply Company; U.S. Private, pg. 1060
PRINTRONIX, INC.; U.S. Public, pg. 1329
SODAL CORPORATION—GIB Group; Int'l, pg. 533
SUOMEN 3M OY—3M; U.S. Public, pg. 1606
TANDY CORPORATION; U.S. Public, pg. 1560
TOSHIBA (AUSTRALIA) PTY., LTD.—Toshiba Corporation; Int'l, pg. 1406
TOSHIBA INFORMATION SYSTEMS (U.K.) LTD.—Toshiba Corporation; Int'l, pg. 1406
TOSHIBA SYSTEMS (FRANCE) S.A.—Toshiba Corporation; Int'l, pg. 1407
VANSTAR CORPORATION; U.S. Public, pg. 1708
WESTWOOD COMPUTER CORPORATION; U.S. Private, pg. 1170
WILLOUGHBY'S; U.S. Private, pg. 1180

5735 — RECORD & PRERECORDED TAPE STORES

BMG/MUSIC—Bertelsmann AG; Int'l, pg. 191
B.M.G. RECORDS—Thomson S.A.; Int'l, pg. 1383
BLOCKBUSTER MUSIC—National Amusements, Inc.; U.S. Private, pg. 776
EASTON PRESS VIDEOS—MBI Inc.; U.S. Private, pg. 685
EROL'S INTERNET; U.S. Private, pg. 382
HMV LIMITED—EMI Group plc; Int'l, pg. 427
HARMONY HOUSE RECORDS & TAPES; U.S. Private, pg. 503
MCA RECORDS, INC.—The Seagram Company Ltd.; Int'l, pg. 1215
MSC TRADENAMES—Musicland Group Inc.; U.S. Public, pg. 1142
MTS, INC.; U.S. Private, pg. 688
MEDIA PLAY, INC.—Musicland Group Inc.; U.S. Public, pg. 1142
MUSICLAND GROUP INC.; U.S. Public, pg. 1142
THE MUSICLAND GROUP, INC.—Musicland Group Inc.; U.S. Public, pg. 1142
MUSICLAND RETAIL, INC.—Musicland Group Inc.; U.S. Public, pg. 1142
NIGHTINGALE-CONANT CORP.; U.S. Private, pg. 799
NOBODY BEATS THE WIZ; U.S. Private, pg. 800
ON CUE, INC.—Musicland Group Inc.; U.S. Public, pg. 1142
RCA RECORDS U.S.—Bertelsmann AG; Int'l, pg. 192
SERVCO PACIFIC INC.; U.S. Private, pg. 986
W.H. SMITH GROUP PLC; Int'l, pg. 1264
SODAL CORPORATION—GIB Group; Int'l, pg. 533
SPEC'S MUSIC, INC.; U.S. Public, pg. 1497
STRAWBERRIES INC.; U.S. Private, pg. 1046
TMG CARIBBEAN, INC.—Musicland Group Inc.; U.S. Public, pg. 1142
TMG UK DELAWARE, INC.—Musicland Group Inc.; U.S. Public, pg. 1142
TOWER RECORDS—MTS, Inc.; U.S. Private, pg. 688
TRANS WORLD ENTERTAINMENT CORPORATION; U.S. Public, pg. 1629
UNIVERSAL STUDIOS DISTRIBUTING CORP.—The Seagram Company Ltd.; Int'l, pg. 1216
VIDEO CITY INC.; U.S. Public, pg. 1719
WAXIE MAXIE QUALITY MUSIC CO.—Strawberries Inc.; U.S. Private, pg. 1047
WHEREHOUSE ENTERTAINMENT, INC.; U.S. Private, pg. 1171

5736 — MUSICAL INSTRUMENT STORES

FILCO, INC.; U.S. Private, pg. 404
G. LEBLANC CORPORATION; U.S. Private, pg. 656
PAUL A. SCHMITT MUSIC COMPANY; U.S. Private, pg. 971

5812 — EATING PLACES

A&W FOOD SERVICES OF CANADA INC.; Int'l, pg. 1
A&W RESTAURANTS, INC.; U.S. Private, pg. 1
A&W RESTAURANTS, INC.-CAROUSEL DIV.—A&W Restaurants, Inc.; U.S. Private, pg. 2
A TABLE MATSUYA CO., LTD.—Matsuya Company Ltd.; Int'l, pg. 848
A.S. MANAGEMENT CORPORATION; U.S. Private, pg. 7
ACAPULCO RESTAURANTS—Restaurant Associates Corporation; U.S. Private, pg. 925
ACCOR NORTH AMERICA—Accor S.A.; Int'l, pg. 21

ACCOR S.A.; *Int'l*, pg. 20
ACCORS HOTELS BELGIUM—Accor S.A.; *Int'l*, pg. 21
ADVANTICA RESTAURANT GROUP, INC.; *U.S. Public*, pg. 22
AIYA CO., LTD.—Skylark Co., Ltd.; *Int'l*, pg. 1262
ALL SEASONS SERVICES, INC.; *U.S. Private*, pg. 35
ALLIED DOMECQ RETAILING LIMITED—Allied Domecq PLC; *Int'l*, pg. 63
ALLTIMATE CATERING—Marsh Supermarkets, Inc.; *U.S. Public*, pg. 1049
AMBRIA—Lettuce Entertain You Enterprises, Inc.; *U.S. Private*, pg. 661
AMERICA—Ark Restaurants Corp.; *U.S. Public*, pg. 130
AMERICA CAFE—Ark Restaurants Corp.; *U.S. Public*, pg. 130
AN AMERICAN PLACE—Ark Restaurants Corp.; *U.S. Public*, pg. 130
AMERICAN RESTAURANT GROUP, INC.; *U.S. Private*, pg. 61
STUART ANDERSON'S BLACK ANGUS/CATTLE COMPANY RESTAURANTS—American Restaurant Group, Inc.; *U.S. Private*, pg. 61
ANDY'S RESTAURANTS INC.; *U.S. Private*, pg. 74
APPLE SOUTH, INC.; *U.S. Public*, pg. 121
APPLEBEE'S INTERNATIONAL, INC.; *U.S. Public*, pg. 122
ARAMARK CORP.; *U.S. Private*, pg. 78
ARAMARK HEALTHCARE SUPPORT SERVICES, INC.—Aramark Corp.; *U.S. Private*, pg. 79
ARAMARK SERVICES, PLC—Aramark Corp.; *U.S. Private*, pg. 79
ARAMARK SPORTS & ENTERTAINMENT SERVICES INC.—Aramark Corp.; *U.S. Private*, pg. 79
ARBY'S CANADA INC.—Triarc Companies, Inc.; *U.S. Public*, pg. 1635
ARITMOS AB—Proventus AB; *Int'l*, pg. 1072
ARK RESTAURANTS CORP.; *U.S. Public*, pg. 129
ASSOCIATED HOSTS, INC.—Brierley Investments Limited; *Int'l*, pg. 215
ASSOCIATED HOSTS OF CALIFORNIA—Brierley Investments Limited; *Int'l*, pg. 215
ASSOCIATED HOSTS OF INDIANA—Brierley Investments Limited; *Int'l*, pg. 215
ASSOCIATED HOSTS OF TEXAS, INC.—Brierley Investments Limited; *Int'l*, pg. 215
ATLANTA HILL RESTAURANT CORP.—Specialty Restaurants Corporation; *U.S. Private*, pg. 1023
ATLAS HOTELS, INC.; *U.S. Private*, pg. 96
AU BON PAIN CO., INC.; *U.S. Public*, pg. 146
AZTAR CORPORATION; *U.S. Public*, pg. 158
BR ASSOCIATES, INC.; *U.S. Private*, pg. 107
BAHAMA BREEZE—Darden Restaurants, Inc.; *U.S. Public*, pg. 484
BAKERS SQUARE RESTAURANTS—Vicorp Restaurants, Inc.; *U.S. Public*, pg. 1719
BAMIYAN CO., LTD.—Skylark Co., Ltd.; *Int'l*, pg. 1262
BASKIN-ROBBINS CANADA—Allied Domecq PLC; *Int'l*, pg. 63
BASS TAVERNS LTD.—Bass PLC; *Int'l*, pg. 170
BEETON RUMFORD LTD.—The Peninsular and Oriental Steam Navigation Company; *Int'l*, pg. 1032
BEN & JERRY'S HOMEMADE INC.; *U.S. Public*, pg. 210
BENIHANA, INC.; *U.S. Public*, pg. 211
BENIHANA NATIONAL CORP.—Benihana, Inc.; *U.S. Public*, pg. 212
BENIHANA OF BETHESDA CORP.—Benihana, Inc.; *U.S. Public*, pg. 212
BENIHANA SCHAUMBURG CORP.—Benihana, Inc.; *U.S. Public*, pg. 212
BENIHANA SUNRISE CORP.—Benihana, Inc.; *U.S. Public*, pg. 212
BENNIGAN'S—Metromedia Company; *U.S. Private*, pg. 736
BERKELEY MARINA RESTAURANT CORP.—Specialty Restaurants Corporation; *U.S. Private*, pg. 1022
BICKFORD'S FAMILY RESTAURANTS—ELXSI Corporation; *U.S. Public*, pg. 545
BICYCLE CLUB CASINO; *U.S. Private*, pg. 142
BIG SPLASH KENDALL CORP.—Benihana, Inc.; *U.S. Public*, pg. 212
BLACKEYED PEA RESTAURANTS INC.—DenAmerica Corp.; *U.S. Public*, pg. 498
BLIMPIE INTERNATIONAL, INC.; *U.S. Public*, pg. 236
BLIMPIE INTERNATIONAL, INC.—Blimpie International, Inc.; *U.S. Public*, pg. 236
BLUE BOAR CAFETERIA CO.; *U.S. Private*, pg. 151
BOARDWALK REGENCY CORPORATION—Starwood Hotels & Resorts; *U.S. Public*, pg. 1512
BODDIE-NOELL ENTERPRISES INC.; *U.S. Private*, pg. 154
BOJANGLES' RESTARAUNTS, INC.; *U.S. Private*, pg. 154
BOLS ROYAL DISTILLERIES—Koninklijke BolsWessanen nv; *Int'l*, pg. 751
BONANZA RESTAURANTS—Metromedia Company; *U.S. Private*, pg. 736
BOSTON CHICKEN, INC.; *U.S. Public*, pg. 247
BOURY ENTERPRISES; *U.S. Private*, pg. 162
BRAUM ICE CREAM STORES INC.; *U.S. Private*, pg. 166
BRESLER'S INDUSTRIES, INC.—Yogen Fruz Worldwide Inc.; *Int'l*, pg. 1520
BRIDGEMAN'S RESTAURANTS INC.; *U.S. Private*, pg. 167
BRIGHAM'S, INC.—Grotech Capital Group, Inc.; *U.S. Private*, pg. 483
BRINKER INTERNATIONAL, INC.; *U.S. Public*, pg. 253
BRITISH BAKERIES (MIDLANDS) LIMITED—Tomkins PLC; *Int'l*, pg. 1396
BRITISH BAKERIES (SCOTLAND) LIMITED—Tomkins PLC; *Int'l*, pg. 1396
BRYANT PARK GRILL—Ark Restaurants Corp.; *U.S. Public*, *pg. 130*
BUB CITY CRABSHACK & BAR-B-Q—Lettuce Entertain You Enterprises, Inc.; *U.S. Private*, pg. 661
BUFFALO WATERFRONT RESTAURANT CORP.—Specialty Restaurants Corporation; *U.S. Private*, pg. 1023
BUFFET MONTPARNASSE SA—Accor S.A.; *Int'l*, pg. 20
BUFFETS, INC.; *U.S. Public*, pg. 267
BURGER KING CORPORATION—Diageo Plc; *Int'l*, pg. 411
CA-1 SERVICES—Delaware North Companies, Inc.; *U.S. Private*, pg. 322
CKE RESTAURANTS INC.; *U.S. Public*, pg. 278
CAESARS WORLD, INC.—Starwood Hotels & Resorts; *U.S. Public*, pg. 1512
CAFE BA-BA-REEBA—Lettuce Entertain You Enterprises, Inc.; *U.S. Private*, pg. 661
CAFE ST-LOUIS—GIB Group; *Int'l*, pg. 534
CALIFORNIA PIZZA KITCHEN INC.—PepsiCo, Inc.; *U.S. Public*, pg. 1277
CAMPBELL CATERING LIMITED—Campbells/Bewley Group; *Int'l*, pg. 254
CANADIAN PACIFIC HOTELS & RESORTS INC.—Canadian Pacific Limited; *Int'l*, pg. 258
CANDLESTICK WATERFRONT REST. CORP.—Specialty Restaurants Corporation; *U.S. Private*, pg. 1022
CANTEEN CORPORATION—Compass Group plc; *Int'l*, pg. 324
CANYON ROADS—Ark Restaurants Corp.; *U.S. Public*, pg. 130
CAPTAIN D'S RESTAURANT—Shoney's, Inc.; *U.S. Public*, pg. 1467
CARA OPERATIONS LIMITED; *Int'l*, pg. 266
CARL'S JR.—CKE Restaurants Inc.; *U.S. Public*, pg. 278
CARLSON COMPANIES, INC.; *U.S. Private*, pg. 211
CARROLS CORPORATION; *U.S. Private*, pg. 216
CASA BONITA, INC.—CKE Restaurants Inc.; *U.S. Public*, pg. 278
CASA LUPITA—Famous Restaurants Inc.; *U.S. Private*, pg. 393
CASSANO'S INC.; *U.S. Private*, pg. 218
CASUDA CANYON RESTAURANT CORP.—Specialty Restaurants Corporation; *U.S. Private*, pg. 1022
CENTER CAFE—Ark Restaurants Corp.; *U.S. Public*, pg. 130
CERRAP—GIB Group; *Int'l*, pg. 534
CHARLIE BROWN'S & THE OFFICE RESTAURANT GROUP—Castle-Harlan, Inc.; *U.S. Private*, pg. 219
CHARLIO'S—National Restaurant Management, Inc.; *U.S. Private*, pg. 786
CHARTWELLS DINING SERVICES—Compass Group plc; *Int'l*, pg. 324
CHATTANOOGA CHOO-CHOO HOLIDAY INN; *U.S. Private*, pg. 231
CHECKERS DRIVE-IN RESTAURANTS, INC.; *U.S. Public*, pg. 342
CHEESECAKE FACTORY INCORPORATED; *U.S. Public*, pg. 343
CHEFS INTERNATIONAL, INC.; *U.S. Public*, pg. 343
CHI-CHI'S INC.—Family Restaurants, Inc.; *U.S. Private*, pg. 393
CHICK-FIL-A, INC.; *U.S. Private*, pg. 236
CHILI PEPPER OF ROCKY POINT, INC.—Specialty Restaurants Corporation; *U.S. Private*, pg. 1023
CHURCH'S CHICKEN, INC.—AFC Enterprises; *U.S. Private*, *pg. 5*
CHURRASCO STEAK-RESTAURANT GMBH—Whitbread PLC; *Int'l*, pg. 1499
DICK CLARK RESTAURANTS, INC.—Dick Clark Productions, Inc.; *U.S. Public*, pg. 382
P.J. CLARKE'S—Lettuce Entertain You Enterprises, Inc.; *U.S. Private*, pg. 661
COCO'S & CARROWS RESTAURANTS—Advantica Restaurant Group, Inc.; *U.S. Public*, pg. 23
COLORADO AIR RESTAURANT CORP.—Specialty Restaurants Corporation; *U.S. Private*, pg. 1023
COLUMBUS BAKERY—Ark Restaurants Corp.; *U.S. Public*, pg. 130
COMPASS GROUP-USA DIVISION—Compass Group plc; *Int'l*, pg. 324
CONSOLIDATED PRODUCTS, INC.; *U.S. Public*, pg. 436
CONSOLIDATED SPECIALTY RESTAURANT—Consolidated Products, Inc.; *U.S. Public*, pg. 436
CONTROLADORA COMERCIAL MEXICANA, S.A. DE C.V.; *Int'l*, pg. 328
COOKER RESTAURANT CORPORATION; *U.S. Public*, pg. 442
COUNTRY CLUB INN, INC.—Avatar Holdings Inc.; *U.S. Public*, pg. 151
COUNTRY KITCHEN INTERNATIONAL, INC.—Kitchen Investment Group; *U.S. Private*, pg. 624
COYOTE RESTAURANT CORP.—Specialty Restaurants Corporation; *U.S. Private*, pg. 1022
CRACKER BARREL OLD COUNTRY STORE, INC.; *U.S. Public*, pg. 455
DAIRY MART CONVENIENCE STORES, INC.; *U.S. Public*, *pg. 476*
DAIRY MART, INC.—Dairy Mart Convenience Stores, Inc.; *U.S. Public*, pg. 476
DAIRY QUEEN CORPORATE STORE—Berkshire Hathaway Inc.; *U.S. Public*, pg. 220
DARDEN RESTAURANTS, INC.; *U.S. Public*, pg. 483
DARIGOLD, INC.; *U.S. Private*, pg. 311
DAVCO RESTAURANTS INC.; *U.S. Public*, pg. 488
JIMMY DAVIS ENTERPRISES, INC.; *U.S. Private*, pg. 315
DEL REY RESTAURANT CORP.—Specialty Restaurants Corporation; *U.S. Private*, pg. 1022
DELAWARE NORTH COMPANIES, INC.; *U.S. Private*, pg. 321
DENAMERICA CORP.; *U.S. Public*, pg. 498
DENNY'S, INC.—Advantica Restaurant Group, Inc.; *U.S. Public*, pg. 23
DENNY'S JAPAN CO., LTD.—Ito-Yokado Co., Ltd.; *Int'l*, pg. 693
DENNY'S OF CANADA—Advantica Restaurant Group, Inc.; *U.S. Public*, pg. 23
DENVER BABY DOE'S REST. CORP.—Specialty Restaurants Corporation; *U.S. Private*, pg. 1023
DENVER FREEWAY RESTAURANT CORP.—Specialty Restaurants Corporation; *U.S. Private*, pg. 1023
DESERT PALACE, INC.—Starwood Hotels & Resorts; *U.S. Public*, pg. 1512
DIAGEO PLC; *Int'l*, pg. 408
DISTRIREST—GIB Group; *Int'l*, pg. 533
DOBBS INTERNATIONAL SERVICES, INC.—Viad Corp; *U.S. Public*, pg. 1718
DOMINO'S PIZZA INC.; *U.S. Private*, pg. 339
DON AND CHARLIE'S—Lettuce Entertain You Enterprises, Inc.; *U.S. Private*, pg. 661
DONUTS COMERCIO DE PRODUTOS ALIMENTICIOS, LTDA.—Allied Domecq PLC; *Int'l*, pg. 64
P.T. DUNKIN DO LESTARI—Allied Domecq PLC; *Int'l*, pg. 64
DUNKIN' DONUTS (BAHAMAS) LTD.—Allied Domecq PLC; *Int'l*, pg. 63
DUNKIN' DONUTS INCORPORATED—Allied Domecq PLC; *Int'l*, pg. 63
DUNKIN' DONUTS U.K. LIMITED—Allied Domecq PLC; *Int'l*, pg. 63
DUNKIN' DONUTS VENEZUELA—Allied Domecq PLC; *Int'l*, *pg. 63*
DUSKIN CO., LTD.; *Int'l*, pg. 422
ELXSI CORPORATION; *U.S. Public*, pg. 545
EAT N PARK RESTAURANTS; *U.S. Private*, pg. 358
EATERIES, INC.; *U.S. Public*, pg. 555
ECONOMATS DU CENTRE—Auchan S.A.; *Int'l*, pg. 98
EL CHICO RESTAURANTS, INC.—Cracken, Harkey, Street & Co., LLC; *U.S. Private*, pg. 283
EL PASO RESTAURANT CORP.—Specialty Restaurants Corporation; *U.S. Private*, pg. 1023
EL POLLO LOCO—Advantica Restaurant Group, Inc.; *U.S. Public*, pg. 23
EL RIO GRANDE—Ark Restaurants Corp.; *U.S. Public*, pg. 130
EL TORITO RESTAURANTS INC.—Family Restaurants, Inc.; *U.S. Private*, pg. 393
ELIAS BROTHERS RESTAURANTS, INC.; *U.S. Private*, pg. 371
ELLOREE FOODS, INC. (SOUTH CAROLINA)—WSMP, Inc.; *U.S. Public*, pg. 1729
ERNIE'S—Ark Restaurants Corp.; *U.S. Public*, pg. 130
ESTEVENON—GIB Group; *Int'l*, pg. 534
BOB EVANS FARMS, INC.; *U.S. Public*, pg. 596
EVERGREEN BUFFETS, INC.—Buffets, Inc.; *U.S. Public*, pg. 267
FMS MANAGEMENT SYSTEMS, INC.; *U.S. Private*, pg. 389
FAMIL CO., LTD.—Ito-Yokado Co., Ltd.; *Int'l*, pg. 693
FAMILY BUFFETS—GIB Group; *Int'l*, pg. 533
FAMILY INNS OF AMERICA, INC.; *U.S. Private*, pg. 392
FAMILY RESTAURANTS, INC.; *U.S. Private*, pg. 393
FAMOUS RESTAURANTS INC.; *U.S. Private*, pg. 393
FAST FOOD MERCHANDISERS INC.—CKE Restaurants Inc.; *U.S. Public*, pg. 278
FIESTA RESTAURANTS, INC.—Eateries, Inc.; *U.S. Public*, pg. 555
FIFTH QUARTER—Shoney's, Inc.; *U.S. Public*, pg. 1467
57TH FIGHTER GROUP OF ATLANTA, INC.—Specialty Restaurants Corporation; *U.S. Private*, pg. 1023
56TH FIGHTER GROUP OF LONG ISLAND, INC.—Specialty Restaurants Corporation; *U.S. Private*, pg. 1023
FITCH FOOD SERVICES LTD.—Booker PLC; *Int'l*, pg. 202
FIVE CROWNS—Lawry's Restaurants, Inc.; *U.S. Private*, pg. 654
FLANIGAN'S ENTERPRISES, INC.; *U.S. Public*, pg. 648
FLIK INTERNATIONAL—Compass Group plc; *Int'l*, pg. 324
FLO JAPON CO., LTD.—Skylark Co., Ltd.; *Int'l*, pg. 1262
FOOD LIFE—Lettuce Entertain You Enterprises, Inc.; *U.S. Private*, pg. 661
FOOD SERVICES DIVISION—Nestle S.A.; *Int'l*, pg. 917
FOODCORP LIMITED; *Int'l*, pg. 496
FOODMAKER, INC.; *U.S. Public*, pg. 661
FORTE (BERMUDA) LIMITED—Granada Group PLC; *Int'l*, pg. 556
FOSTERS FREEZE INTERNATIONAL, INC.; *U.S. Public*, pg. 677
FRANCE QUICK—GIB Group; *Int'l*, pg. 534
FREE TIME—GIB Group; *Int'l*, pg. 534
FRESH CHOICE, INC.; *U.S. Public*, pg. 682
FRIENDLY ICE CREAM CORP.; *U.S. Public*, pg. 682
FRISCH'S RESTAURANTS, INC.; *U.S. Public*, pg. 682
FUDDRUCKERS, INC.—Compass Group plc; *Int'l*, pg. 325
FURR'S/BISHOPS, INC.; *U.S. Public*, pg. 689
GF FOOD SERVICES—Goodman Fielder Limited; *Int'l*, pg. 555
GIB GROUP; *Int'l*, pg. 532
GALARDI GROUP, INC.; *U.S. Private*, pg. 437
GARCIA'S MEXICAN RESTAURANTS—Famous Restaurants Inc.; *U.S. Private*, pg. 393
GENERAL DE BAZAR—GIB Group; *Int'l*, pg. 534
GEORGIA WSMP, INC. (GEORGIA)—WSMP, Inc.; *U.S. Public*, pg. 1729
GINO'S EAST/ROLLING MEADOWS—Lettuce Entertain You Enterprises, Inc.; *U.S. Private*, pg. 661
GODFATHER'S PIZZA, INC.; *U.S. Private*, pg. 458
GOLDEN CORRAL CORPORATION—Investors Management Corp.; *U.S. Private*, pg. 575
GOLDEN DONUTS, INC.—Allied Domecq PLC; *Int'l*, pg. 63
GOLDEN DONUTS SBN. BHD.—Allied Domecq PLC; *Int'l*, pg. 63
GONZALEZ Y GONZALEZ—Ark Restaurants Corp.; *U.S. Public*, pg. 130
GRAND METROPOLITAN PLC—Diageo Plc; *Int'l*, pg. 408
GRANDY'S, INC.—American Restaurant Group, Inc.; *U.S. Private*, pg. 61
GREEN FOODS SERVICE CO., LTD.—Matsuya Company Ltd.; *Int'l*, pg. 848
GREENVILLE FOOD SYSTEMS, INC.—WSMP, Inc.; *U.S. Public*, pg. 1729
GRISANTI, INC.; *U.S. Private*, pg. 482
GROUND ROUND INC.; *U.S. Public*, pg. 766
GROUPE ACCOR OF CANADA INC.—Accor S.A.; *Int'l*, pg. 21
GROWTH MANAGEMENT CORP.—Family Inns of America, Inc.; *U.S. Private*, pg. 392

GUEST SERVICES, INC.; *U.S. Private*, pg. 486
H. SALT OF SOUTHERN CALIFORNIA, INC.; *U.S. Private, pg. 489*
HDS SERVICES; *U.S. Private*, pg. 490
HACIENDA HOTEL INC.—Santa Fe Gaming Corporation; *U.S. Public*, pg. 1432
HAKUSHIAN CO., LTD.—Skylark Co., Ltd.; *Int'l*, pg. 1262
HAMPTON INNS, INC.—Promus Hotel Corporation; *U.S. Public*, pg. 1335
HARDEE'S FOOD SYSTEMS, INC.—CKE Restaurants Inc.; *U.S. Public*, pg. 278
HARRIS FARMS, INC.; *U.S. Private*, pg. 505
HARRIS RANCH RESTAURANT—Harris Farms, Inc.; *U.S. Private*, pg. 506
HARRY'S BAR LTD.—Sea Containers Ltd.; *Int'l*, pg. 1213
HASSLOCHER ENTERPRISES, INC.; *U.S. Private*, pg. 510
HAT DANCE—Lettuce Entertain You Enterprises, Inc.; *U.S. Private*, pg. 661
HAWAII PIZZA HUT INC.—Jardine Matheson Holdings Limited; *Int'l*, pg. 704
HELMSLEY ENTERPRISES, INC.; *U.S. Private*, pg. 521
HELMSLEY-SPEAR INC.—Helmsley Enterprises, Inc.; *U.S. Private*, pg. 521
HIGH INDUSTRIES, INC.; *U.S. Private*, pg. 528
HILTON INTERNATIONAL (SWITZERLAND) AG—Ladbroke Group Plc; *Int'l*, pg. 788
HOLLY'S INC.; *U.S. Private*, pg. 535
HOST MARRIOTT SERVICES CORPORATION; *U.S. Public*, pg. 841
HOTEL CORPORATION OF AMERICA; *U.S. Private*, pg. 541
HOULIHAN'S RESTAURANT GROUP; *U.S. Public*, pg. 841
ICA MENY FORETAGEN AB—ICA Handlarnas AB; *Int'l*, pg. 643
ISS CATERING A.S.—ISS-International Service System A/S; *Int'l*, pg. 656
ISS-INTERNATIONAL SERVICE SYSTEM A/S; *Int'l*, pg. 656
ITT CORPORATION—Starwood Hotels & Resorts; *U.S. Public*, pg. 1512
IHOP CORP.; *U.S. Public*, pg. 862
IL FORNAIO AMERICA CORPORATION; *U.S. Public*, pg. 864
ILLINOIS FRUIT & PRODUCE CORP.—JP Foodservice, Inc.; *U.S. Public*, pg. 918
IMASCO LIMITED—B.A.T Industries P.L.C.; *Int'l*, pg. 112
INNCO MANAGEMENT CORP.—Family Inns of America, Inc.; *U.S. Private*, pg. 392
INNISBROOK/HILTON RESORT—Starwood Capital Group LLC; *U.S. Private*, pg. 1036
INTERNATIONAL DAIRY QUEEN, INC.—Berkshire Hathaway Inc.; *U.S. Public*, pg. 220
INTERNATIONAL DIVERSE FOODS—Levmark Capital Corporation; *U.S. Private*, pg. 663
INTERNATIONAL HOUSE OF PANCAKES, INC.—IHOP Corp.; *U.S. Public*, pg. 862
INTERNATIONAL IN-FLIGHT CATERING CO. LTD.—Japan Airlines Company, Ltd.; *Int'l*, pg. 700
IRELAND GOURMET SHOP—Chock Full O' Nuts Corporation; *U.S. Public*, pg. 351
ITALIAN FOOD MANUFACTURERS, INC.; *U.S. Private*, pg. 576
ITO-YOKADO CO., LTD.; *Int'l*, pg. 693
JRN, INC.; *U.S. Private*, pg. 578
JACKSONVILLE CRAWDADDY CORP.—Specialty Restaurants Corporation; *U.S. Private*, pg. 1023
JACMAR COMPANIES, INC.; *U.S. Private*, pg. 580
JAN-CO., INC.; *U.S. Private*, pg. 581
JAPAN AIRLINES COMPANY, LTD.; *Int'l*, pg. 699
JARDINE MATHESON (AUSTRALIA) LTD.—Jardine Matheson Holdings Limited; *Int'l*, pg. 705
JARDINE MATHESON DISTRIBUTORS LTD.—Jardine Matheson Holdings Limited; *Int'l*, pg. 705
JARDINE MATHESON HOLDINGS LIMITED; *Int'l*, pg. 703
JARDINE MATHESON VICTORIA LTD.—Jardine Matheson Holdings Limited; *Int'l*, pg. 705
W.B. JOHNSON PROPERTIES, LLC; *U.S. Private*, pg. 594
GAY JOHNSON'S INC.; *U.S. Private*, pg. 595
JONAS & CO., LTD.—Skylark Co., Ltd.; *Int'l*, pg. 1262
K.F.C. (N.Z.) LTD.—Tricon Global Restaurants, Inc.; *U.S. Public*, pg. 1637
CARL KARCHER ENTERPRISES, INC.—CKE Restaurants Inc.; *U.S. Public*, pg. 278
KEG RESTAURANTS U.S., INC.—Whitbread PLC; *Int'l*, pg. 1499
KENTUCKY FRIED CHICKEN CORPORATION (KFC)—Tricon Global Restaurants, Inc.; *U.S. Public*, pg. 1636
KETTLE RESTAURANTS; *U.S. Private*, pg. 617
KNOTT'S BERRY FARM; *U.S. Private*, pg. 627
KOO KOO ROO, INC.; *U.S. Public*, pg. 966
KRYSTAL COMPANY; *U.S. Private*, pg. 636
KUWAIT AVIATION SERVICES CO.—Kuwait Airways Corp.; *Int'l*, pg. 764
KYOTARU CO., LTD.; *Int'l*, pg. 777
KYOTARU RESTAURANT—Kyotaru Co., Ltd.; *Int'l*, pg. 777
LDB CORPORATION; *U.S. Private*, pg. 639
LDB FOOD SERVICES, INC.—LDB Corporation; *U.S. Private*, pg. 639
LA ROSA'S, INC.; *U.S. Private*, pg. 640
LA ROSE D'ANJOU—GIB Group; *Int'l*, pg. 534
LA RUCHE PICARDE—Auchan S.A.; *Int'l*, pg. 98
LAMP POST FRANCHISE CORPORATION; *U.S. Private*, pg. 644
LANDRY'S SEAFOOD RESTAURANTS INC.; *U.S. Public*, pg. 977
LARKEN INC.; *U.S. Private*, pg. 651
LAWRY'S RESTAURANTS, INC.; *U.S. Private*, pg. 654
LE PACTOLE—GIB Group; *Int'l*, pg. 534
LE PEEP'S GRILL INC.; *U.S. Private*, pg. 655
LEE'S FAMOUS RECIPE RESTAURANT—R.T.M. Winners; *U.S. Private*, pg. 906
LENOTRE—Accor S.A.; *Int'l*, pg. 20
LETTUCE ENTERTAIN YOU ENTERPRISES, INC.; *U.S. Private*, pg. 661
THE LEVY ORGANIZATION; *U.S. Private*, pg. 664
LEVY RESTAURANTS—The Levy Organization; *U.S. Private*, pg. 664
LITTLE CAESAR ENTERPRISES, INC.; *U.S. Private*, pg. 671
LONDON HOUSE—GIB Group; *Int'l*, pg. 534
LONG JOHN SILVER'S, INC.; *U.S. Private*, pg. 674
LOUISIANA COMMUNITY BAR & GRILL—Ark Restaurants Corp.; *U.S. Public*, pg. 130
LUBY'S CAFETERIAS, INC.; *U.S. Public*, pg. 1017
LUCKY INNS OF AMERICA, INC.—Family Inns of America, Inc.; *U.S. Private*, pg. 393
LUNCH GARDEN—GIB Group; *Int'l*, pg. 533
LUNDY ENTERPRISES, INC.; *U.S. Private*, pg. 681
LYON'S RESTAURANTS, INC.; *U.S. Private*, pg. 684
MAGGIANO'S LITTLE ITALY—Lettuce Entertain You Enterprises, Inc.; *U.S. Private*, pg. 661
MAJOR FOODS LTD.—Aramark Corp.; *U.S. Private*, pg. 79
MAMMA ILARDO'S CORP.; *U.S. Private*, pg. 699
THE MARCUS CORPORATION; *U.S. Public*, pg. 1044
MARCUS RESTAURANTS INC.—The Marcus Corporation; *U.S. Public*, pg. 1044
MARKETING CORP. OF AMERICA; *U.S. Private*, pg. 704
THE MARKETPLACE CAFE—Ark Restaurants Corp.; *U.S. Public*, pg. 130
MARRIOTT DISTRIBUTION SERVICES (MDS)—Marriott International, Inc.; *U.S. Public*, pg. 1048
MARRIOTT INTERNATIONAL, INC.; *U.S. Public*, pg. 1047
MARRIOTT MANAGEMENT SERVICES (MMS)—Marriott International, Inc.; *U.S. Public*, pg. 1048
MATTHEWS PRIME SIRLOIN, INC.—WSMP, Inc.; *U.S. Public*, pg. 1729
MAX & ERMA'S RESTAURANTS; *U.S. Public*, pg. 1060
MAXIM'S CATERERS LTD.—Jardine Matheson Holdings Limited; *Int'l*, pg. 704
MCDONALD'S CORPORATION; *U.S. Public*, pg. 1068
MCGUFFEY'S RESTAURANTS, INC.; *U.S. Private*, pg. 721
MCLANE FOOD SERVICE—Wal-Mart Stores, Inc.; *U.S. Public*, pg. 1733
MEDIEVAL TIMES DINNER & TOURNAMENT, INC.; *U.S. Private*, pg. 728
MELITTA CATERING PTY. LTD.—Melitta Unternehmensgruppe Bentz KG; *Int'l*, pg. 857
METROMEDIA STEAKHOUSES, INC.—Metromedia Company; *U.S. Private*, pg. 736
METROPOLITAN CAFE—Ark Restaurants Corp.; *U.S. Public*, pg. 130
MIAMI SUBS CORPORATION; *U.S. Public*, pg. 1103
MISSION HILLS RESTAURANT CORP.—Specialty Restaurants Corporation; *U.S. Private*, pg. 1022
MITSUI NORIN CO., LTD.—Mitsui & Co., Ltd.; *Int'l*, pg. 878
MITY NICE GRILL—Lettuce Entertain You Enterprises, Inc.; *U.S. Private*, pg. 661
MONTEREY'S ACQUISITION CORP.—Monterey's Acquisition Corporation; *U.S. Private*, pg. 758
MONTEREY'S ACQUISITION CORPORATION; *U.S. Private*, pg. 758
MORGAN'S FOODS, INC.; *U.S. Public*, pg. 1133
MORGAN'S RESTAURANTS OF OHIO, INC.—Morgan's Foods, Inc.; *U.S. Public*, pg. 1133
MORGAN'S RESTAURANTS OF PA., INC.—Morgan's Foods, Inc.; *U.S. Public*, pg. 1133
MORGAN'S WEIRTON FOODS, INC.—Morgan's Foods, Inc.; *U.S. Public*, pg. 1133
MORRISON RESTAURANTS, INC.; *U.S. Public*, pg. 1134
MORTON'S OF CHICAGO, INC.—Morton's Restaurant Group, Inc.; *U.S. Public*, pg. 1136
MORTON'S RESTAURANT GROUP, INC.; *U.S. Public*, pg. 1136
MR. GATTI'S, INC.—LDB Corporation; *U.S. Private*, pg. 639
MRS. WINNER'S CHICKEN & BISCUIT RESTAURANTS; *U.S. Private*, pg. 766
C.A. MUER CORP.; *U.S. Private*, pg. 766
NPC INTERNATIONAL, INC.; *U.S. Public*, pg. 1146
NAPLES FOODS, INC.—WSMP, Inc.; *U.S. Public*, pg. 1729
NATHAN'S FAMOUS INC.; *U.S. Public*, pg. 1152
NATIONAL RESTAURANT MANAGEMENT, INC.; *U.S. Private*, pg. 786
NEGOCE PIERRE—GIB Group; *Int'l*, pg. 534
NESTLE FOODSERVICE CANADA—Nestle S.A.; *Int'l*, pg. 922
NEW ORLEANS WATERFRONT REST. CORP.—Specialty Restaurants Corporation; *U.S. Private*, pg. 1023
NICE GARE—GIB Group; *Int'l*, pg. 534
NIKO CO., LTD.—Mitsukoshi, Ltd.; *Int'l*, pg. 883
94TH AERO SQUADRON OF COLUMBUS, INC.—Specialty Restaurants Corporation; *U.S. Private*, pg. 1023
NOBLE ROMAN'S INC.; *U.S. Public*, pg. 1187
NOPRI—GIB Group; *Int'l*, pg. 533
NORTH DENVER HILL CORP.—Specialty Restaurants Corporation; *U.S. Private*, pg. 1023
OAR BAR & GRILL—Ark Restaurants Corp.; *U.S. Public*, pg. 130
OBAYASHI CORPORATION; *Int'l*, pg. 995
OCEANS RACQUET CLUB, INC.—The Chubb Corporation; *U.S. Public*, pg. 355
O'CHARLEY'S INC.; *U.S. Public*, pg. 1211
OGDEN CORPORATION; *U.S. Public*, pg. 1213
OLD FASHION FOODS, INC.; *U.S. Private*, pg. 814
OLIVE GARDEN ITALIAN RESTAURANTS—Darden Restaurants, Inc.; *U.S. Public*, pg. 484
ORANGE HILL RESTAURANT CORP.—Specialty Restaurants Corporation; *U.S. Private*, pg. 1022
ORANGE JULIUS OF AMERICA—Berkshire Hathaway Inc.; *U.S. Public*, pg. 220
OUTBACK STEAKHOUSE INC.; *U.S. Public*, pg. 1235
P&O AUSTRALIA LTD.—The Peninsular and Oriental Steam Navigation Company; *Int'l*, pg. 1035
PMB ENTERPRISES WEST, INC.—Pancho's Mexican Buffet, Inc.; *U.S. Public*, pg. 1255
PAMEX OF TEXAS, INC.—Pancho's Mexican Buffet, Inc.; *U.S. Public*, pg. 1255
PANCHO'S MEXICAN BUFFET, INC.; *U.S. Public*, pg. 1255
PAPA GINO'S INC.; *U.S. Private*, pg. 837
PAPA JOHN'S INTERNATIONAL INC.; *U.S. Public*, pg. 1255
PARGO'S RESTAURANTS—Shoney's, Inc.; *U.S. Public*, pg. 1467
PEDUS FOOD SERVICES—Pedus Services, Inc.; *U.S. Private*, pg. 846
PEDUS SERVICES, INC.; *U.S. Private*, pg. 846
PEPPERONI GRILL—Eateries, Inc.; *U.S. Public*, pg. 555
PERFECT PIZZA LTD.—Scott's Restaurants Inc.; *Int'l*, pg. 1213
PERKINS FAMILY RESTAURANTS—The Restaurant Company; *U.S. Private*, pg. 925
PERRETTI—Ark Restaurants Corp.; *U.S. Public*, pg. 130
PETER PIPER, INC.—The Bank of Tokyo-Mitsubishi, Ltd.; *Int'l*, pg. 157
PICCADILLY CAFETERIAS, INC.; *U.S. Public*, pg. 1294
PICCADILLY RESTAURANTS, INC.—Piccadilly Cafeterias, Inc.; *U.S. Public*, pg. 1294
PINELLAS CRABCOOKER, INC.—Specialty Restaurants Corporation; *U.S. Private*, pg. 1023
PINELLAS FARMHOUSE, INC.—Specialty Restaurants Corporation; *U.S. Private*, pg. 1023
PIONEER HOTEL INC.—Santa Fe Gaming Corporation; *U.S. Public*, pg. 1432
PITTSBURGH STADIUM CONCESSIONS, INC.—Aramark Corp.; *U.S. Private*, pg. 79
PIZZA HAVEN INC.; *U.S. Private*, pg. 868
PIZZA HUT—Whitbread PLC; *Int'l*, pg. 1499
PIZZA HUT DIVISION—NPC International, Inc.; *U.S. Public*, pg. 1147
PIZZA HUT, INC.—Tricon Global Restaurants, Inc.; *U.S. Public*, pg. 1636
PIZZA HUT PROPERTIES PTY. LTD.—Tricon Global Restaurants, Inc.; *U.S. Public*, pg. 1637
PIZZA HUT (UK) LTD.—Whitbread PLC; *Int'l*, pg. 1499
PIZZA HUT (USSR)—Tricon Global Restaurants, Inc.; *U.S. Public*, pg. 1637
PIZZA INN, INC.; *U.S. Public*, pg. 1307
POLLO TROPICAL, INC.; *U.S. Public*, pg. 1315
PONDEROSA STEAKHOUSE—Metromedia Company; *U.S. Private*, pg. 736
PORTS O'CALL RESTAURANT CORP.—Specialty Restaurants Corporation; *U.S. Private*, pg. 1022
PRAIRIE FARMS DAIRY SUPPLY CORP.—Prairie Farms Dairy, Inc.; *U.S. Private*, pg. 879
PRIME HOSPITALITY CORP.; *U.S. Public*, pg. 1326
PRIME SIRLOIN, INC. (TENNESSEE)—WSMP, Inc.; *U.S. Public*, pg. 1729
PRO PORTION INDUSTRIES, INC.—Yogen Fruz Worldwide Inc.; *Int'l*, pg. 1520
PROFIT MANAGEMENT CORP.—Family Inns of America, Inc.; *U.S. Private*, pg. 393
QUALITY DINING INC.; *U.S. Public*, pg. 1349
QUICK INTERNATIONAL—GIB Group; *Int'l*, pg. 533
QUICK INTERNATIONAL DEVELOPMENT—GIB Group; *Int'l*, pg. 533
QUICK RESTAURANTS SA—GIB Group; *Int'l*, pg. 533
QUINCY FAMILY STEAK HOUSE—Advantica Restaurant Group, Inc.; *U.S. Public*, pg. 23
R.T.M. WINNERS; *U.S. Private*, pg. 906
RAGAZZIS, INC.—Investors Management Corp.; *U.S. Private*, pg. 575
RALLY'S HAMBURGERS, INC.; *U.S. Public*, pg. 1359
RAMADA EXPRESS—Aztar Corporation; *U.S. Public*, pg. 158
RAX RESTAURANTS; *U.S. Private*, pg. 911
RED LOBSTER USA—Darden Restaurants, Inc.; *U.S. Public*, pg. 484
RED ROBIN INTERNATIONAL INC.—Skylark Co., Ltd.; *Int'l*, pg. 1262
RESTAURA, INC.—Viad Corp; *U.S. Public*, pg. 1718
RESTAURANT ASSOCIATES CATERING—Restaurant Associates Corporation; *U.S. Private*, pg. 925
RESTAURANT ASSOCIATES CORPORATION; *U.S. Private*, pg. 924
THE RESTAURANT COMPANY; *U.S. Private*, pg. 925
RESTAURANT DEVELOPERS CORP.; *U.S. Private*, pg. 925
RESTAURANTS UNLIMITED; *U.S. Private*, pg. 925
RESTAURAP—GIB Group; *Int'l*, pg. 534
RESTEUROP—Accor S.A.; *Int'l*, pg. 20
F.L. ROBERTS & CO. INC.; *U.S. Private*, pg. 935
ROCK BOTTOM RESTAURANTS; *U.S. Public*, pg. 1396
ROCKY POINT VILLAGE CORP.—Specialty Restaurants Corporation; *U.S. Private*, pg. 1023
ROCKY ROCOCO CORPORATION; *U.S. Private*, pg. 938
KENNY ROGERS ROASTERS; *U.S. Private*, pg. 939
ROMACORP, INC.—NPC International, Inc.; *U.S. Public*, pg. 1147
ROSE'S STORES, INC.; *U.S. Public*, pg. 1405
ROY ROGERS RESTAURANTS—McDonald's Corporation; *U.S. Public*, pg. 1069
ROYAL GUEST, S.A.—Caja de Madrid Group; *Int'l*, pg. 252
RUBY TUESDAY, INC.; *U.S. Public*, pg. 1411
RUBY TUESDAY RESTAURANTS—Ruby Tuesday, Inc.; *U.S. Public*, pg. 1412
RUNWAY TWO FIVE CORPORATION—Specialty Restaurants Corporation; *U.S. Private*, pg. 1022
RYAN'S FAMILY STEAK HOUSES, INC.; *U.S. Public*, pg. 1413
SAS SERVICE PARTNER A/S—Scandinavian Airlines System (SAS); *Int'l*, pg. 1202
S.C. FOOD SERVICES (CANADA) INC.—Scott's Restaurants Inc.; *Int'l*, pg. 1213
S.E.P.—Accor S.A.; *Int'l*, pg. 20
S.P.R.B.—GIB Group; *Int'l*, pg. 534
SAINT AUGUSTINE FOODS, INC.—WSMP, Inc.; *U.S. Public*, pg. 1729
STE. EUROPEENNE DE RESTAURATION—Accor S.A.; *Int'l*, pg. 20
STE. RESTAURANTS DES NOUVEAUX SITES—Accor S.A.; *Int'l*, pg. 20
SANBORN HERMANOS—Grupo Carso S.A. de C.V.; *Int'l*, pg. 573

SANTA FE HOTEL INC.—Santa Fe Gaming Corporation; *U.S. Public*, pg. 1432
SANTA FE VALLEY, INC.—Santa Fe Gaming Corporation; *U.S. Public*, pg. 1432
SARIMMO—GIB Group; *Int'l*, pg. 533
SARMA-NOPRI GROUP—GIB Group; *Int'l*, pg. 533
SAVORY CO., LTD.—Matsuya Company Ltd.; *Int'l*, pg. 848
SBARRO, INC.; *U.S. Public*, pg. 1435
SCANDINAVIAN AIRLINES SYSTEM (SAS); *Int'l*, pg. 1201
SCHLOTZSKY'S, INC.; *U.S. Public*, pg. 1439
SCHNUCK MARKETS, INC.; *U.S. Private*, pg. 971
SCHWAN'S SALES ENTERPRISES; *U.S. Private*, pg. 974
SCOOZI—Lettuce Entertain You Enterprises, Inc.; *U.S. Private*, pg. 661
SCOTTISH & NEW CASTLE RETAIL—Scottish & Newcastle plc; *Int'l*, pg. 1212
SCOTT'S FOOD SERVICES INC.—Scott's Restaurants Inc.; *Int'l*, pg. 1213
SCOTT'S MANAGEMENT SERVICES INC.—Scott's Restaurants Inc.; *Int'l*, pg. 1213
SCOTT'S RESTAURANTS INC.; *Int'l*, pg. 1213
SEDRI—Accor S.A.; *Int'l*, pg. 20
SEED RESTAURANT GROUP, INC.; *U.S. Private*, pg. 981
SELECT RESTAURANTS, INC.; *U.S. Private*, pg. 982
SEQUOIA—Ark Restaurants Corp.; *U.S. Public*, pg. 130
SERARE—Accor S.A.; *Int'l*, pg. 20
SERVICE AMERICA CORPORATION; *U.S. Private*, pg. 986
SERVICEMASTER FOOD MANAGEMENT SERVICES—The ServiceMaster Company; *U.S. Public*, pg. 1462
SERVICO, INC.; *U.S. Public*, pg. 1462
SEVEN STARS, INC.—WSMP, Inc.; *U.S. Public*, pg. 1729
SHAKEY'S INCORPORATED; *U.S. Private*, pg. 989
SHATO HOLDINGS LTD.; *Int'l*, pg. 1230
SHAW'S DEERFIELD—Lettuce Entertain You Enterprises, Inc.; *U.S. Private*, pg. 661
SHOLODGE, INC.; *U.S. Public*, pg. 1467
SHONEY'S, INC.; *U.S. Public*, pg. 1467
SHOWBIZ PIZZA TIME, INC.; *U.S. Public*, pg. 1468
SHOWBOAT, INCORPORATED; *U.S. Public*, pg. 1469
SILCORP LIMITED; *Int'l*, pg. 1249
SILVER DOLLAR CITY, INC.; *U.S. Private*, pg. 1000
SIZZLER INTERNATIONAL, INC.; *U.S. Public*, pg. 1475
SIZZLER USA, INC.—Sizzler International, Inc.; *U.S. Public*, *pg. 1475*
SKYLARK CO., LTD.; *Int'l*, pg. 1262
SKYLINE CHILI, INC.; *U.S. Public*, pg. 1475
SMITH & SONS FOODS, INC.; *U.S. Private*, pg. 1006
B. SMITH'S—Ark Restaurants Corp.; *U.S. Public*, pg. 130
SMUGGLERS INN OF IL, INC.—Brierley Investments Limited; *Int'l*, pg. 216
SOCIETE DES PRODUITS NESTLE S.A.—Nestle S.A.; *Int'l*, *pg. 916*
SODEXHO S.A.; *Int'l*, pg. 1274
SODILY—GIB Group; *Int'l*, pg. 534
SONESTA INTERNATIONAL HOTELS CORPORATION; *U.S. Public*, pg. 1485
SONIC CORPORATION; *U.S. Public*, pg. 1485
SONIC INDUSTRIES, INC.—Sonic Corporation; *U.S. Public*, *pg. 1485*
SONIC RESTAURANTS, INC.—Sonic Corporation; *U.S. Public*, pg. 1485
SOUTH CAROLINA WSMP, INC. (SOUTH CAROLINA)—WSMP, Inc.; *U.S. Public*, pg. 1729
SOUTHERN HOSPITALITY CORPORATION—Davco Restaurants Inc.; *U.S. Public*, pg. 488
SPAGHETTI WAREHOUSE, INC.; *U.S. Public*, pg. 1495
SPECIALTY RESTAURANTS CORPORATION; *U.S. Private*, pg. 1022
SPIRES RESTAURANTS INC.; *U.S. Private*, pg. 1026
SPORTSERVICE CORPORATION—Delaware North Companies, Inc.; *U.S. Private*, pg. 322
STAR BUFFET, INC.—CKE Restaurants Inc.; *U.S. Public*, pg. 278
STEAK AND ALE RESTAURANTS—Metromedia Company; *U.S. Private*, pg. 736
STEAK 'N SHAKE, INC.—Consolidated Products, Inc.; *U.S. Public*, pg. 437
STEINBERG INC.—Socanav Inc.; *Int'l*, pg. 1272
STOCKTON RESTAURANT CORP.—Specialty Restaurants Corporation; *U.S. Private*, pg. 1022
STRAW HAT COOPERATIVE CORP.; *U.S. Private*, pg. 1046
SUMMIT FAMILY RESTAURANTS, INC.—CKE Restaurants Inc.; *U.S. Public*, pg. 278
SUMMIT FOOD SERVICE DISTRIBUTORS—Cara Operations Limited; *Int'l*, pg. 266
SUNSHINE WSMP, INC. (FLORIDA)—WSMP, Inc.; *U.S. Public*, pg. 1729
SWALLOW HOTELS LIMITED—Vaux Group Plc; *Int'l*, pg. 1454
SWENSEN'S ICE CREAM CO.—Integrated Brands Inc.; *U.S. Public*, pg. 883
THE SWISS COLONY, INC; *U.S. Private*, pg. 1059
THE SWISSAIR GROUP; *Int'l*, pg. 1333
SYBRA, INC.—Contran Corporation; *U.S. Private*, pg. 270
THE SYGMA NETWORK OF PENNSYLVANIA—Sysco Corporation; *U.S. Public*, pg. 1551
TCBY ENTERPRISES INC.; *U.S. Public*, pg. 1553
TGI FRIDAY'S, INC.—Carlson Companies, Inc.; *U.S. Private*, pg. 212
TACO ALOHA, INC.—Jardine Matheson Holdings Limited; *Int'l*, pg. 704
TACO BELL CORP.—Tricon Global Restaurants, Inc.; *U.S. Public*, pg. 1637
TACO CABANA; *U.S. Public*, pg. 1559
TACO JOHN'S INTERNATIONAL, INC.; *U.S. Private*, pg. 1066
TAM O'SHANTER INN—Lawry's Restaurants, Inc.; *U.S. Private*, pg. 654
TAMARRON DIVISION—Starwood Capital Group LLC; *U.S.* Private, pg. 1036
TASTEE FREEZ INTERNATIONAL INC.; *U.S. Private*, pg. 1069
THE TEAROOM IN UTICA SQUARE, INC.—Helmerich & Payne, Inc.; *U.S. Public*, pg. 808
TENNESSEE WSMP, INC. (TENNESSEE)—WSMP, Inc.; *U.S. Public*, pg. 1729
TEPPAN RESTAURANTS—Benihana, Inc.; *U.S. Public*, pg. 212
TIR A LOCQUES—GIB Group; *Int'l*, pg. 534
TOBY RESTAURANTS LTD.—Bass PLC; *Int'l*, pg. 170
TOWN PUMP, INC.; *U.S. Private*, pg. 1093
TRAPP FAMILY LODGE, INC.; *U.S. Private*, pg. 1098
TRAVEL PORTS OF AMERICA INC.; *U.S. Public*, pg. 1632
TREND LINE CORPORATION; *U.S. Private*, pg. 1099
TRIANGLE FOOD SERVICES CO.; *U.S. Private*, pg. 1102
TRIARC RESTAURANT GROUP—Triarc Companies, Inc.; *U.S. Public*, pg. 1635
TRICON GLOBAL RESTAURANTS, INC.; *U.S. Public*, pg. 1636
TROPICANA RESORT & CASINO—Aztar Corporation; *U.S. Public*, pg. 159
TUCCHETTI—Lettuce Entertain You Enterprises, Inc.; *U.S. Private*, pg. 661
TUCCI BENUCCH—Lettuce Entertain You Enterprises, Inc.; *U.S. Private*, pg. 661
TWIN CITY DINER—Lettuce Entertain You Enterprises, Inc.; *U.S. Private*, pg. 662
UAL CORPORATION; *U.S. Public*, pg. 1652
UNIQUE CASUAL RESTAURANTS, INC.—Compass Group plc; *Int'l*, pg. 324
UNITED ALLIANT FOOD SERVICE—Clayton, Dubilier & Rice, Inc; *U.S. Private*, pg. 244
U.S. WOOLWORTH DIV.—Woolworth Corporation; *U.S. Public*, pg. 1778
UNO RESTAURANT CORPORATION; *U.S. Public*, pg. 1698
VALLEY INNOVATIVE MANAGEMENT SERVICE—Trend Line Corporation; *U.S. Private*, pg. 1099
VAN NUYS AIRPORT RESTAURANT CORP.—Specialty Restaurants Corporation; *U.S. Private*, pg. 1022
VAUX GROUP PLC; *Int'l*, pg. 1453
VAUX INNS LTD.—Vaux Group Plc; *Int'l*, pg. 1454
VERDUGO RESTAURANT CORP.—Specialty Restaurants Corporation; *U.S. Private*, pg. 1022
VERSA SERVICES LTD.—Aramark Corp.; *U.S. Private*, pg. 79
VIAD CORP; *U.S. Public*, pg. 1718
VICORP RESTAURANTS, INC.; *U.S. Public*, pg. 1719
VICTORIA STATION INC.—A.S. Management Corporation; *U.S. Private*, pg. 8
VILLA SOUTH INC.—Thiele Kaolin Co.; *U.S. Private*, pg. 1081
VILLAGE INN RESTAURANTS—Vicorp Restaurants, Inc.; *U.S. Public*, pg. 1719
VIRGINIA WSMP, INC. (VIRGINIA)—WSMP, Inc.; *U.S. Public*, pg. 1729
WSMP, INC.; *U.S. Public*, pg. 1729
WAFFLE HOUSE, INCORPORATED; *U.S. Private*, pg. 1146
WALL STREET DELI, INC.; *U.S. Public*, pg. 1734
WALL STREET DELI, INC.—Wall Street Deli, Inc.; *U.S. Public*, pg. 1734
WALNUT CREEK RESTAURANT CORP.—Specialty Restaurants Corporation; *U.S. Private*, pg. 1022
WENDY'S INTERNATIONAL INC.; *U.S. Public*, pg. 1754
WENDY'S OF DENVER INC.—Wendy's International Inc.; *U.S. Public*, pg. 1754
WENDY'S OLD FASHIONED HAMBURGERS OF NEW YORK—Wendy's International Inc.; *U.S. Public*, pg. 1754
WENDY'S RESTAURANTS OF CANADA INC.—Wendy's International Inc.; *U.S. Public*, pg. 1754
WEST JAPAN RAILWAY COMPANY; *Int'l*, pg. 1490
WHATABURGER, INC.; *U.S. Private*, pg. 1170
WHITBREAD PLC; *Int'l*, pg. 1498
WHITBREAD RESTAURANTS & LEISURE—Whitbread PLC; *Int'l*, pg. 1498
WHITBREAD RESTAURANTS (AUSTRALIA) LTD.—Whitbread PLC; *Int'l*, pg. 1499
WHITE CASTLE SYSTEM, INC.; *U.S. Private*, pg. 1171
WOMETCO ENTERPRISES, INC.; *U.S. Private*, pg. 1186
WOMP'S RESTAURANT BAR & GRILL—The Seagram Company Ltd.; *Int'l*, pg. 1216
WOODY'S—Ark Restaurants Corp.; *U.S. Public*, pg. 130
WOOLWORTH CORPORATION; *U.S. Public*, pg. 1777
F.W. WOOLWORTH CO.—Woolworth Corporation; *U.S. Public*, pg. 1777
WYATT CAFETERIAS INC.—Triangle Food Services Co.; *U.S. Private*, pg. 1102
YANKEE WHALER COMPANY—Specialty Restaurants Corporation; *U.S. Private*, pg. 1023

5813 — DRINKING PLACES (ALCOHOLIC BEVERAGES)

ACAPULCO RESTAURANTS—Restaurant Associates Corporation; *U.S. Private*, pg. 925
AMERICA—Ark Restaurants Corp.; *U.S. Public*, pg. 130
AMERICA CAFE—Ark Restaurants Corp.; *U.S. Public*, pg. 130
ARK RESTAURANTS CORP.; *U.S. Public*, pg. 129
ASSOCIATED HOSTS OF INDIANA—Brierley Investments Limited; *Int'l*, pg. 215
BENIHANA, INC.; *U.S. Public*, pg. 211
BENIHANA NATIONAL CORP.—Benihana, Inc.; *U.S. Public*, *pg. 212*
BENIHANA OF BETHESDA CORP.—Benihana, Inc.; *U.S. Public*, pg. 212
BENIHANA SCHAUMBURG CORP.—Benihana, Inc.; *U.S. Public*, pg. 212
BENIHANA SUNRISE CORP.—Benihana, Inc.; *U.S. Public*, pg. 212
BIG SPLASH KENDALL CORP.—Benihana, Inc.; *U.S. Public*, pg. 212
THE BREWSKELLER—Ark Restaurants Corp.; *U.S. Public*, pg. 130
BRINKER INTERNATIONAL, INC.; *U.S. Public*, pg. 253
CNJ DISTRIBUTING; *U.S. Private*, pg. 196
CASA LUPITA—Famous Restaurants Inc.; *U.S. Private*, pg. 393
CHARLIE BROWN'S & THE OFFICE RESTAURANT GROUP—Castle-Harlan, Inc.; *U.S. Private*, pg. 219
CHATTANOOGA CHOO-CHOO HOLIDAY INN; *U.S. Private*, pg. 231
DIAGEO PLC; *Int'l*, pg. 408
EL RIO GRANDE—Ark Restaurants Corp.; *U.S. Public*, pg. 130
FAMILY RESTAURANTS, INC.; *U.S. Private*, pg. 393
FLANIGAN'S ENTERPRISES, INC.; *U.S. Public*, pg. 648
FLANIGAN'S MANAGEMENT SERVICES, INC.—Flanigan's Enterprises, Inc.; *U.S. Public*, pg. 648
GARCIA'S MEXICAN RESTAURANTS—Famous Restaurants Inc.; *U.S. Private*, pg. 393
GONZALEZ Y GONZALEZ—Ark Restaurants Corp.; *U.S. Public*, pg. 130
GRAND METROPOLITAN PLC—Diageo Plc; *Int'l*, pg. 408
HACIENDA HOTEL INC.—Santa Fe Gaming Corporation; *U.S. Public*, pg. 1432
HOULIHAN'S RESTAURANT GROUP; *U.S. Public*, pg. 841
INNISBROOK/HILTON RESORT—Starwood Capital Group LLC; *U.S. Private*, pg. 1036
W.B. JOHNSON PROPERTIES, LLC; *U.S. Private*, pg. 594
KYOTARU CO., LTD.; *Int'l*, pg. 777
LETTUCE ENTERTAIN YOU ENTERPRISES, INC.; *U.S. Private*, pg. 661
OAR BAR & GRILL—Ark Restaurants Corp.; *U.S. Public*, pg. 130
PIONEER HOTEL INC.—Santa Fe Gaming Corporation; *U.S. Public*, pg. 1432
PRIME HOSPITALITY CORP.; *U.S. Public*, pg. 1326
RESTAURANT ASSOCIATES CATERING—Restaurant Associates Corporation; *U.S. Private*, pg. 925
SANBORN HERMANOS—Grupo Carso S.A. de C.V.; *Int'l*, pg. 573
SANTA FE HOTEL INC.—Santa Fe Gaming Corporation; *U.S. Public*, pg. 1432
SANTA FE VALLEY, INC.—Santa Fe Gaming Corporation; *U.S. Public*, pg. 1432
SCOTTISH & NEW CASTLE RETAIL—Scottish & Newcastle plc; *Int'l*, pg. 1212
SCOTTISH & NEWCASTLE PLC; *Int'l*, pg. 1211
SCOTTISH BREWERS LIMITED—Scottish & Newcastle plc; *Int'l*, pg. 1212
SEVENTH STREET CORP.—Flanigan's Enterprises, Inc.; *U.S. Public*, pg. 648
SPAGHETTI WAREHOUSE, INC.; *U.S. Public*, pg. 1495
SPECIALTY RESTAURANTS CORPORATION; *U.S. Private*, pg. 1022
TAMARRON DIVISION—Starwood Capital Group LLC; *U.S.* Private, pg. 1036
TEPPAN RESTAURANTS—Benihana, Inc.; *U.S. Public*, pg. 212
THRESHER—Whitbread PLC; *Int'l*, pg. 1498
VAUX GROUP PLC; *Int'l*, pg. 1453
VAUX INNS LTD.—Vaux Group Plc; *Int'l*, pg. 1454
VIAD CORP; *U.S. Public*, pg. 1718
WHITBREAD BEER COMPANY—Whitbread PLC; *Int'l*, pg. 1498
WHITBREAD PLC; *Int'l*, pg. 1498

5912 — DRUG STORES & PROPRIETARY STORES

AAH PLC—Franz Haniel & Cie, GmbH; *Int'l*, pg. 591
AAH RETAIL PHARMACY LIMITED—Franz Haniel & Cie, GmbH; *Int'l*, pg. 591
THE FRED W. ALBRECHT GROCERY CO.; *U.S. Private*, pg. 32
ALLIED MERCANTILE COMPANY; *U.S. Private*, pg. 39
AMERICAN DRUG STORES INC.—American Stores Company; *U.S. Public*, pg. 93
AMERICAN STORES COMPANY; *U.S. Public*, pg. 92
ANDREWS GROUP, INCORPORATED—MacAndrews & Forbes Holdings Inc.; *U.S. Private*, pg. 689
ARBOR DRUGS, INC.; *U.S. Public*, pg. 126
ASTRUP DRUGS, INC.; *U.S. Private*, pg. 93
THE BARTELL DRUG COMPANY; *U.S. Private*, pg. 118
BEL AIR MARKETS—Raley's & Bel Air; *U.S. Private*, pg. 908
BELMEDCO PHARMACY—Vencor, Inc.; *U.S. Public*, pg. 1712
BIG V SUPERMARKETS, INC.; *U.S. Private*, pg. 143
BOOTS THE CHEMISTS—The Boots Company PLC; *Int'l*, pg. 203
BRUNO'S INC.; *U.S. Public*, pg. 265
BUTTREY FOOD & DRUG COMPANY; *U.S. Public*, pg. 271
CPC PHARMACY, INC.—Vencor, Inc.; *U.S. Public*, pg. 1712
CVS CORP.; *U.S. Public*, pg. 287
CARDINAL HEALTH INC.; *U.S. Public*, pg. 304
THE JEAN COUTU GROUP (PJC) INC.; *Int'l*, pg. 340
DISCOUNT DRUG MART INC.; *U.S. Private*, pg. 334
DRUG EMPORIUM, INC.; *U.S. Public*, pg. 530
DRUG EMPORIUM OF ARIZONA; *U.S. Private*, pg. 343
ECKERD CORPORATION—JC Penney Company, Inc.; *U.S. Public*, pg. 917
ECKERD DRUG CO.—JC Penney Company, Inc.; *U.S. Public*, pg. 917
EMPIRE COMPANY LIMITED; *Int'l*, pg. 453
ERICKSON'S DIVERSIFIED CORP.; *U.S. Private*, pg. 381
ETOS BV—Koninklijke Ahold NV; *Int'l*, pg. 749
EXTENDICARE (CANADA) INC.—Extendicare Inc.; *Int'l*, pg. 468
EXTENDICARE INC.; *Int'l*, pg. 468
FAR-BEN S.A. DE C.V.; *Int'l*, pg. 478
FLEMING COMPANY—Fleming Companies, Inc.; *U.S. Public*, pg. 653
GENOVESE DRUG STORES, INC.; *U.S. Public*, pg. 730

THE GREAT ATLANTIC & PACIFIC TEA COMPANY, INC.—Tengelmann Warenhandelsgesellschaft; *Int'l*, pg. 1375
HAGGEN, INC.; *U.S. Private*, pg. 493
HY-VEE FOOD STORES INCORPORATED; *U.S. Private*, pg. 550
IMASCO LIMITED—B.A.T Industries P.L.C.; *Int'l*, pg. 112
THE JEAN COUTU (PJC) USA INC.—The Jean Coutu Group (PJC) Inc.; *Int'l*, pg. 340
KAISER'S KAFFEE-GESCHAEFT AG—Tengelmann Warenhandelsgesellschaft; *Int'l*, pg. 1375
KASH N KARRY FOOD STORES, INC.—Etablissements Delhaize Freres Et Cie "Le Lion" S.A.; *Int'l*, pg. 463
KINGFISHER PLC; *Int'l*, pg. 733
LAWTONS DRUG STORES LIMITED—Empire Company Limited; *Int'l*, pg. 454
LEWIS DRUG, INC.; *U.S. Private*, pg. 665
LONGS DRUG STORES CORPORATION; *U.S. Public*, pg. 1013
MANNINGS RETAIL LIMITED—Jardine Matheson Holdings Limited; *Int'l*, pg. 704
MARSH SUPERMARKETS, INC.; *U.S. Public*, pg. 1049
MEDICINE SHOPPE INTERNATIONAL, INC.—Cardinal Health Inc.; *U.S. Public*, pg. 304
NATIONAL PHARMACIES, INC.—Merck & Co., Inc.; *U.S. Public*, pg. 1091
OMNICARE, INC.; *U.S. Public*, pg. 1223
OSCO DRUG—American Stores Company; *U.S. Public*, pg. 93
PAGES DRUGS—Randalls Food Markets, Inc.; *U.S. Private*, pg. 909
PAID PRESCRIPTIONS, INC.—Merck & Co., Inc.; *U.S. Public*, pg. 1091
PHAR-MOR, INC.; *U.S. Public*, pg. 1284
PHARMAPLUS DRUGMARTS LIMITED—The Oshawa Group Limited; *Int'l*, pg. 1012
PHARMHOUSE, INC.; *U.S. Public*, pg. 1286
PUBLIX SUPERMARKETS INC.; *U.S. Private*, pg. 893
RALEY'S & BEL AIR; *U.S. Private*, pg. 907
REAL HOLDING MANAGEMENT CORP.; *U.S. Private*, pg. 913
REGAL DRUGS, INC.—Foodarama Supermarkets, Inc.; *U.S. Public*, pg. 661
RITE AID CORPORATION; *U.S. Public*, pg. 1390
SCHNUCK MARKETS, INC.; *U.S. Private*, pg. 971
SENTRY DRUGS, INC.—Fleming Companies, Inc.; *U.S. Public*, pg. 653
SHOPPERS DRUG MART, LTD.—B.A.T Industries P.L.C.; *Int'l*, pg. 112
SMITH'S FOOD & DRUG CENTERS, INC.—Fred Meyer Incorporated; *U.S. Public*, pg. 1103
SNYDER'S DRUG STORES, INC.; *U.S. Private*, pg. 1011
STADTLANDER DRUG COMPANY, INC.—Counsel Corporation; *Int'l*, pg. 338
STAFFORD-MILLER INTL., INC.—Block Drug Company, Inc.; *U.S. Public*, pg. 237
SUPER D DRUG STORES—Stephen LaFrance Holdings, Inc.; *U.S. Private*, pg. 642
SUPERDRUG STORES PLC—Kingfisher plc; *Int'l*, pg. 734
THRIFTWAY, INC.—Winn-Dixie Stores, Inc.; *U.S. Public*, pg. 1771
TOM THUMB FOOD & PHARMACY—Randalls Food Markets, Inc.; *U.S. Private*, pg. 909
UNITED HEALTH, INC.—Extendicare Inc.; *Int'l*, pg. 468
VILLAGE PANTRIES, INC.—Marsh Supermarkets, Inc.; *U.S. Public*, pg. 1049
THE VONS COMPANIES, INC.—Safeway Inc.; *U.S. Public*, pg. 1426
WALGREEN CO.; *U.S. Public*, pg. 1733
WELLCOME TAIWAN COMPANY LTD.—Jardine Matheson Holdings Limited; *Int'l*, pg. 704
WINN-DIXIE STORES, INC.; *U.S. Public*, pg. 1771
WOOLWORTH CORPORATION; *U.S. Public*, pg. 1777

5921 — LIQUOR STORES

ALLIED DOMECQ RETAILING LIMITED—Allied Domecq PLC; *Int'l*, pg. 63
BIG Y FOODS INC.; *U.S. Private*, pg. 143
BOLS ROYAL DISTILLERIES—Koninklijke BolsWessanen nv; *Int'l*, pg. 751
BYERLY'S INC.—Lund Food Holdings, Inc.; *U.S. Private*, pg. 680
DELCHAMPS, INC.—Jitney-Jungle Stores of America, Inc.; *U.S. Private*, pg. 588
FLANIGAN'S ENTERPRISES, INC.; *U.S. Public*, pg. 648
FRESH SKYLARK CO., LTD.—Skylark Co., Ltd.; *Int'l*, pg. 1262
GALL & GALL—Koninklijke Ahold NV; *Int'l*, pg. 749
THE GREAT ATLANTIC & PACIFIC TEA COMPANY, INC.—Tengelmann Warenhandelsgesellschaft; *Int'l*, pg. 1375
KASH N KARRY FOOD STORES, INC.—Etablissements Delhaize Freres Et Cie "Le Lion" S.A.; *Int'l*, pg. 463
KWIK SAVE GROUP PLC—Jardine Matheson Holdings Limited; *Int'l*, pg. 704
LUND FOOD HOLDINGS, INC.; *U.S. Private*, pg. 680
MOTT'S HOLDINGS, INC.; *U.S. Private*, pg. 764
PIONEER FOODS, INC.; *U.S. Private*, pg. 866
A. RACKE GMBH; *Int'l*, pg. 1083
RALEY'S & BEL AIR; *U.S. Private*, pg. 907
RITE AID CORPORATION; *U.S. Public*, pg. 1390
SCOTTISH & COURAGE BREWERIES (SALES) LIMITED—Scottish & Newcastle plc; *Int'l*, pg. 1212
SCOTTISH & NEWCASTLE PLC; *Int'l*, pg. 1211
TACT HOLDING; *U.S. Private*, pg. 1067
THRESHER—Whitbread PLC; *Int'l*, pg. 1498
TRADER JOE'S CO.—TACT Holding; *U.S. Private*, pg. 1067
THE VICTORIA WINE COMPANY LIMITED—Allied Domecq PLC; *Int'l*, pg. 63
WHITBREAD PLC; *Int'l*, pg. 1498

5932 — USED MERCHANDISE STORES

FIRST CASH, INC.; *U.S. Public*, pg. 627
GLOBE FURNITURE RENTALS—Globe Furniture Rentals; *U.S. Private*, pg. 458
HARVEY & THOMPSON LTD.—Cash America International, Inc.; *U.S. Public*, pg. 312
HONDA INTERNATIONAL SALES CORP.—Honda Motor Co., Ltd.; *Int'l*, pg. 634
LIBERIA ARTE Y CULTURA, S.A.—Corporacion MAPFRE, Compania Internacional de Reaseguros, S.A.; *Int'l*, pg. 334
PAINE FURNITURE CO.; *U.S. Private*, pg. 834
ROYAL COPENHAGEN ANTIQUES—Royal Copenhagen A/S; *Int'l*, pg. 1134
SARAIVA S/A LIVREIROS EDITORES—Corporacion MAPFRE, Compania Internacional de Reaseguros, S.A.; *Int'l*, pg. 334

5941 — SPORTING GOODS & BICYCLE SHOPS

ABERCROMBIE & FITCH—The Limited, Inc.; *U.S. Public*, pg. 995
ACADEMY CORPORATION; *U.S. Private*, pg. 11
ALLIED SPORTING GOODS INC.; *U.S. Private*, pg. 41
THE ATHLETE'S FOOT GROUP, INC.; *U.S. Private*, pg. 94
BASS PRO SHOPS, INC.; *U.S. Private*, pg. 122
JAMES BLISS & CO., INC.—West Marine, Inc.; *U.S. Public*, pg. 1756
CML GROUP, INC.; *U.S. Public*, pg. 279
CAMPING WORLD, INC.; *U.S. Private*, pg. 204
CAMPMOR INC.; *U.S. Private*, pg. 204
CREATIVE PLAYTHINGS LTD.; *U.S. Private*, pg. 287
DISPORT—GIB Group; *Int'l*, pg. 534
DISPORT INTERNATIONAL—GIB Group; *Int'l*, pg. 533
DUNHAM'S ATHLEISURE CORPORATION; *U.S. Private*, pg. 346
E & B MARINE INCORPORATED—West Marine, Inc.; *U.S. Public*, pg. 1756
E & B MARINE SUPPLY, INC.—West Marine, Inc.; *U.S. Public*, pg. 1756
GT BICYCLES, INC.; *U.S. Public*, pg. 695
GALYAN'S TRADING CO.—The Limited, Inc.; *U.S. Public*, pg. 995
GANDER MOUNTAIN RETAIL—Holiday Companies; *U.S. Private*, pg. 534
GO SPORT—Kingfisher plc; *Int'l*, pg. 734
GOLDBERGS MARINE DISTRIBUTORS—West Marine, Inc.; *U.S. Public*, pg. 1756
GRAMEX CORPORATION; *U.S. Private*, pg. 468
JUMBO SPORTS INC.; *U.S. Public*, pg. 935
KINNEY SHOE CORPORATION—Woolworth Corporation; *U.S. Public*, pg. 1777
L.L. BEAN, INC.; *U.S. Private*, pg. 639
MITCHELL SPORTS SA—Johnson Worldwide Associates, Inc.; *U.S. Public*, pg. 933
MIZUNO CORPORATION; *Int'l*, pg. 884
MIZUNO CORPORATION (TOKYO HEAD OFFICE)—Mizuno Corporation; *Int'l*, pg. 885
HENRY MODELL & COMPANY, INC.; *U.S. Private*, pg. 754
OSHMAN'S SPORTING GOODS, INC.; *U.S. Public*, pg. 1233
PERRY SPORT—Vendex International N.V.; *Int'l*, pg. 1462
RAM GOLF UK—RAM Golf Corporation; *U.S. Private*, pg. 908
RECREATIONAL EQUIPMENT, INC.; *U.S. Private*, pg. 914
THE SHARPER IMAGE; *U.S. Public*, pg. 1464
SPORT OBERMEYER LTD., USA; *U.S. Private*, pg. 1026
THE SPORTS AUTHORITY INC.; *U.S. Public*, pg. 1499
SQUARE TWO GOLF INCORPORATED; *U.S. Public*, pg. 1501
TOYS "R" US, INC.; *U.S. Public*, pg. 1626
TREND-LINES INC.; *U.S. Private*, pg. 1099
WEST MARINE, INC.; *U.S. Public*, pg. 1756

5942 — BOOK STORES

AMAZON.COM, INC.; *U.S. Public*, pg. 62
B. DALTON BOOKSELLER, INC.—Barnes & Noble Inc.; *U.S. Public*, pg. 189
BARNES & NOBLE INC.; *U.S. Public*, pg. 189
THE BOOKPOINT (INDIA) PVT. LTD.—Pearson plc; *Int'l*, pg. 1026
BOOKS-A-MILLION, INC.; *U.S. Public*, pg. 244
BOOKS MANAGEMENT, INC.—Deb Shops, Inc.; *U.S. Public*, pg. 491
BOOKSTOP, INC.—Barnes & Noble Inc.; *U.S. Public*, pg. 189
BRODART COMPANY; *U.S. Private*, pg. 170
CHADWICK-MILLER INC.—CMI Holding Corp.; *U.S. Private*, pg. 195
CLUB SA—GIB Group; *Int'l*, pg. 533
CROWN BOOKS CORPORATION—Dart Group Corporation; *U.S. Public*, pg. 484
CROWN BOOKS EAST CORPORATION—Dart Group Corporation; *U.S. Public*, pg. 484
DART GROUP CORPORATION; *U.S. Public*, pg. 484
DEVELOPMENT ASSOCIATION, INC.—Tandycrafts, Inc.; *U.S. Public*, pg. 1561
DOUBLEDAY BOOK SHOPS, INC.—Barnes & Noble Inc.; *U.S. Public*, pg. 189
EDITIONS DU MONITEUR—C.E.P. Communication Group; *Int'l*, pg. 239
F.A.O. SCHWARZ—N.V. Koninklijke Bijenkorf Beheer KBB; *Int'l*, pg. 750
FOLLETT COLLEGE STORES CORP.—Follett Corporation; *U.S. Private*, pg. 417
FOLLETT CORPORATION; *U.S. Private*, pg. 416
GIB GROUP; *Int'l*, pg. 532
GROUPE DE LA CITE—Alcatel Alsthom Compagnie Generale D'Electricite; *Int'l*, pg. 53
HARCOURT BRACE & COMPANY - ELEMENTARY DIV.—Harcourt General, Inc.; *U.S. Public*, pg. 783
JOHN MENZIES PLC; *Int'l*, pg. 707
JOHN MENZIES (UK) LIMITED—John Menzies plc; *Int'l*, pg. 707
LAURIAT INC.—CMI Holding Corp.; *U.S. Private*, pg. 195
LINCOLN INDUSTRIES; *U.S. Private*, pg. 668
MSC TRADENAMES—Musicland Group Inc.; *U.S. Public*, pg. 1142
MTS, INC.; *U.S. Private*, pg. 688
MEDIA PLAY, INC.—Musicland Group Inc.; *U.S. Public*, pg. 1142
MUNKSGAARD INTERNATIONAL BOOKSELLERS & PUBLISHERS LTD.—B.H. Blackwell Ltd.; *Int'l*, pg. 197
THE MUSICLAND GROUP, INC.—Musicland Group Inc.; *U.S. Public*, pg. 1142
MUSICLAND RETAIL, INC.—Musicland Group Inc.; *U.S. Public*, pg. 1142
NEBRASKA BOOK CO., INC.; *U.S. Private*, pg. 789
ON CUE, INC.—Musicland Group Inc.; *U.S. Public*, pg. 1142
THE PENGUIN PUBLISHING CO. LTD.—Pearson plc; *Int'l*, pg. 1026
R.C.S. EDITORI S.P.A.; *Int'l*, pg. 1078
RITE AID CORPORATION; *U.S. Public*, pg. 1390
W.H. SMITH CANADA LTD.—Russel Metals Inc.; *Int'l*, pg. 1150
SODAL CORPORATION—GIB Group; *Int'l*, pg. 533
STACEY'S/J. K. GILL RETAIL STORES—Brodart Company; *U.S. Private*, pg. 170
UNIVERSITY BOOK STORE; *U.S. Private*, pg. 1127
VENDEX INTERNATIONAL N.V.; *Int'l*, pg. 1462
VERLAG KREMAYR UND SCHERIAU—Bertelsmann AG; *Int'l*, pg. 192
WALDEN BOOK COMPANY—Borders Group, Inc.; *U.S. Public*, pg. 245

5943 — STATIONERY STORES

BOISE CASCADE CORPORATION; *U.S. Public*, pg. 242
BOISE CASCADE OFFICE PRODUCTS CORPORATION—Boise Cascade Corporation; *U.S. Public*, pg. 243
BRODART COMPANY; *U.S. Private*, pg. 170
CLUB SA—GIB Group; *Int'l*, pg. 533
COBB REPROGRAPHICS & OFFICE SUPPLY—Wallace Computer Services, Inc.; *U.S. Public*, pg. 1735
S. FREEDMAN & SONS, INC.; *U.S. Private*, pg. 425
J.L. HAMMETT COMPANY; *U.S. Private*, pg. 498
INDIANA RECORDS MANAGERS; *U.S. Private*, pg. 560
KNOWLEDGE TREE INC.; *U.S. Private*, pg. 627
MCPAPER GMBH—Herlitz PBS Aktiengesellschaft; *Int'l*, pg. 616
OFFICE DEPOT—Office Depot Inc.; *U.S. Public*, pg. 1212
OFFICE DEPOT INC.; *U.S. Public*, pg. 1212
REYNOLDS AND REYNOLDS-BUSINESS FORMS DIVISION—The Reynolds and Reynolds Company; *U.S. Public*, pg. 1385
W.H. SMITH GROUP PLC; *Int'l*, pg. 1264
STACEY'S/J. K. GILL RETAIL STORES—Brodart Company; *U.S. Private*, pg. 170
STAPLES, INC.; *U.S. Public*, pg. 1509
STUART HALL CO., INC.—Newell Co.; *U.S. Public*, pg. 1178
TOP FLIGHT, INC.; *U.S. Private*, pg. 1091
U.S. WOOLWORTH DIV.—Woolworth Corporation; *U.S. Public*, pg. 1778
UNIVERSITY BOOK STORE; *U.S. Private*, pg. 1127
WILLIAMS & MACKIE—Russel Metals Inc.; *Int'l*, pg. 1150
WILLSON STATIONERS—Russel Metals Inc.; *Int'l*, pg. 1150
WOOLWORTH CORPORATION; *U.S. Public*, pg. 1777
F.W. WOOLWORTH CO.—Woolworth Corporation; *U.S. Public*, pg. 1777

5944 — JEWELRY STORES

A&Z HAYWARD, INC.; *U.S. Private*, pg. 2
ADRAY APPLIANCE & PHOTO CENTER, INC.; *U.S. Private*, pg. 18
ANJU JEWELRY LIMITED—Town & Country Corporation; *U.S. Public*, pg. 1625
B&L JEWELRY STORE—Reliable Stores, Inc.; *U.S. Private*, pg. 921
BARCLAY & SONS—Reliable Stores, Inc.; *U.S. Private*, pg. 921
BARLOW & EATON—Reliable Stores, Inc.; *U.S. Private*, pg. 921
BARRY'S JEWELERS, INC.; *U.S. Public*, pg. 192
HENRY BIRKS JEWELERS, INC.—Henry Birks & Sons (1993) Inc.; *Int'l*, pg. 197
BULGARI CORPORATION OF AMERICA—Bulgari SPA; *Int'l*, pg. 232
BULGARI SPA; *Int'l*, pg. 232
CARLYLE & CO. JEWELERS; *U.S. Private*, pg. 213
CASTLEBERG'S—Reliable Stores, Inc.; *U.S. Private*, pg. 921
CONTINENTAL COIN CORPORATION; *U.S. Private*, pg. 267
DALLAS GOLD & SILVER EXCHANGE, INC.; *U.S. Public*, pg. 478
DE VONS JEWELERS; *U.S. Private*, pg. 318
DEARDEN'S; *U.S. Private*, pg. 319
DOBBINS JEWLERS INC.—Zale Corporation; *U.S. Public*, pg. 1789
DOUCET, INC.—Henry Birks & Sons (1993) Inc.; *Int'l*, pg. 197
FOLAND'S JEWELRY BROKERS; *U.S. Private*, pg. 416
FORTUNOFF; *U.S. Private*, pg. 420
GORDON BROTHERS PARTNERS INC.; *U.S. Private*, pg. 465
HELZBERG'S DIAMOND SHOPS, INC.—Berkshire Hathaway Inc.; *U.S. Public*, pg. 220
HENEBRYS—Reliable Stores, Inc.; *U.S. Private*, pg. 921
ERNEST JONES (LONDON) LIMITED—Signet Group plc; *Int'l*, pg. 1248

LUIGI LUCARDI—Vendex International N.V.; *Int'l*, pg. 1462
L. LURIA & SON, INC.; *U.S. Public*, pg. 1020
MAPPINS JEWELERS—Peoples Jewellers Corporation; *Int'l*, pg. 1036
MEYER JEWELERS; *U.S. Private*, pg. 739
MORTON'S JEWELRY CO.—Reliable Stores, Inc.; *U.S. Private*, pg. 921
MOVADO GROUP INC.—Movado Group, Inc.; *U.S. Public*, pg. 1140
N.A. TRADING LTD.—Movado Group, Inc.; *U.S. Public*, pg. 1140
OSTERMAN'S INC.—Signet Group plc; *Int'l*, pg. 1248
PEOPLES JEWELLERS CORPORATION; *Int'l*, pg. 1036
PIERCING PAGODA, INC.; *U.S. Public*, pg. 1296
POLLACK CORPORATION; *U.S. Private*, pg. 874
REEDS JEWELERS, INC.; *U.S. Public*, pg. 1370
REEDS JEWELERS OF NORTH CAROLINA, INC.—Reeds Jewelers, Inc.; *U.S. Public*, pg. 1370
REGENT-SHEFFIELD LTD.—McPherson's Limited; *Int'l*, pg. 852
RELCO—Reliable Stores, Inc.; *U.S. Private*, pg. 921
RELIABLE STORES, INC.; *U.S. Private*, pg. 920
J.B. ROBINSON JEWELERS, INC.—Signet Group plc; *Int'l*, pg. 1248
ROYAL GOLD—Vendex International N.V.; *Int'l*, pg. 1462
S&N KATZ JEWELERS—Reliable Stores, Inc.; *U.S. Private*, pg. 921
SCOTT JEWELERS—Reliable Stores, Inc.; *U.S. Private*, pg. 921
SHREVE, CRUMP & LOW CO.—Henry Birks & Sons (1993) Inc.; *Int'l*, pg. 197
SIEBEL—Vendex International N.V.; *Int'l*, pg. 1462
SIGNET GROUP PLC; *Int'l*, pg. 1248
STERLING INC.—Signet Group plc; *Int'l*, pg. 1248
STERLING JEWELERS, INC.—Signet Group plc; *Int'l*, pg. 1248
SUMITOMO METAL MINING CO., LTD.; *Int'l*, pg. 1316
SWISSAM INC.—Movado Group, Inc.; *U.S. Public*, pg. 1140
TIFFANY & CO.—Tiffany & Co.; *U.S. Public*, pg. 1609
TIFFANY & CO. OF NEW YORK LIMITED—Tiffany & Co.; *U.S. Public*, pg. 1609
TIFFANY-FARAONE, S.P.A. (MILAN)—Tiffany & Co.; *U.S. Public*, pg. 1609
TOURNEAU INC.; *U.S. Private*, pg. 1093
VAN CLEEF & ARPELS, INC.; *U.S. Private*, pg. 1132
WEISS JEWELERS—Reliable Stores, Inc.; *U.S. Private*, pg. 921
WEST JEWEL INC.; *U.S. Private*, pg. 1163
THE WESTHALL CO.—Signet Group plc; *Int'l*, pg. 1248
HARRY WINSTON, INC.; *U.S. Private*, pg. 1183
ZALE CORPORATION; *U.S. Public*, pg. 1789
ZALE DELAWARE, INC.—Zale Corporation; *U.S. Public*, pg. 1789
ZALE PUERTO RICO INC.—Zale Corporation; *U.S. Public*, pg. 1789

5945 — HOBBY, TOY & GAME SHOPS

BABIES "R" US—Toys "R" Us, Inc.; *U.S. Public*, pg. 1626
CHILDRENS WORLD—Storehouse PLC; *Int'l*, pg. 1304
CHRISTIAENSEN—GIB Group; *Int'l*, pg. 534
CHRISTIAENSEN INTERNATIONAL—GIB Group; *Int'l*, pg. 533
CONAGRA RETAIL COMPANIES—ConAgra, Inc.; *U.S. Public*, pg. 426
EARLY LEARNING CENTRE—John Menzies plc; *Int'l*, pg. 707
F.A.O. SCHWARZ—N.V. Koninklijke Bijenkorf Beheer KBB; *Int'l*, pg. 750
GIB GROUP; *Int'l*, pg. 532
HEWLETT-PACKARD & CONTROL LTD.—Hewlett-Packard Company; *U.S. Public*, pg. 818
KAY-BEE TOY & HOBBY SHOPS, INC.—Consolidated Stores Corp.; *U.S. Public*, pg. 437
N.V. KONINKLIJKE BIJENKORF BEHEER KBB; *Int'l*, pg. 750
MANTECH CO., LTD.—Abdulla Fouad Co. Ltd.; *Int'l*, pg. 502
MICHAELS STORES, INC.; *U.S. Public*, pg. 1104
NOODLE KIDOODLE INC.; *U.S. Public*, pg. 1188
NORTHWEST FABRICS & CRAFTS—Hancock Fabrics, Inc.; *U.S. Public*, pg. 779
PLAID ENTERPRISES INC.—The Dyson-Kissner-Moran Corporation; *U.S. Private*, pg. 352
RETAILNET B.V.—N.V. Koninklijke Bijenkorf Beheer KBB; *Int'l*, pg. 750
TANDY CORPORATION; *U.S. Public*, pg. 1560
TONKA EUROPE, LIMITED—Hasbro, Inc.; *U.S. Public*, pg. 798
TOYS "R" US, INC.; *U.S. Public*, pg. 1626
TOYS "R" US INTERNATIONAL—Toys "R" Us, Inc.; *U.S. Public*, pg. 1626

5946 — CAMERA & PHOTOGRAPHIC SUPPLY STORES

ADRAY APPLIANCE & PHOTO CENTER, INC.; *U.S. Private*, pg. 18
BEST BUY CO., INC.; *U.S. Public*, pg. 223
C.O.F.E.C.—Lagardere Groupe; *Int'l*, pg. 792
DIXONS—Vendex International N.V.; *Int'l*, pg. 1462
FAR-BEN S.A. DE C.V.; *Int'l*, pg. 478
FILCO, INC.; *U.S. Private*, pg. 404
KYOCERA ELECTRONICS, INC.—Kyocera Corporation; *Int'l*, pg. 776
NELSON PHOTO SUPPLIES; *U.S. Private*, pg. 791
RADIO TV STEINER AG—Coop Switzerland; *Int'l*, pg. 330
WILLOUGHBY'S; *U.S. Private*, pg. 1180

5947 — GIFT, NOVELTY & SOUVENIR SHOPS

AERO-BOUTIQUE DE MEXICO S.A. DE C.V.—Lagardere Groupe; *Int'l*, pg. 796
AMERICAN GREETINGS CORPORATION; *U.S. Public*, pg. 77
AMMEX TAX & DUTY FREE SHOPS—BAA plc; *Int'l*, pg. 103
AMMEX TAX & DUTY FREE SHOPS WEST, INC.—BAA plc; *Int'l*, pg. 103
BRODART COMPANY; *U.S. Private*, pg. 170
BROOKSTONE COMPANY, INC.; *U.S. Public*, pg. 259
CA-1 SERVICES—Delaware North Companies, Inc.; *U.S. Private*, pg. 322
COLE NATIONAL CORPORATION; *U.S. Public*, pg. 396
CRACKER BARREL OLD COUNTRY STORE, INC.; *U.S. Public*, pg. 455
JIMMY DAVIS ENTERPRISES, INC.; *U.S. Private*, pg. 315
DELAWARE NORTH COMPANIES, INC.; *U.S. Private*, pg. 321
DUTY FREE INTERNATIONAL, INC.—BAA plc; *Int'l*, pg. 103
FABER, COE & GREGG, INC.; *U.S. Private*, pg. 390
FENTON HILL AMERICAN LIMITED—BAA plc; *Int'l*, pg. 103
FINE ART DEVELOPMENTS PLC; *Int'l*, pg. 485
GREYHOUND LEISURE SERVICES, INC.—Viad Corp; *U.S. Public*, pg. 1718
GUMP'S—Hanover Direct, Inc.; *U.S. Public*, pg. 782
HAMMACHER, SCHLEMMER & CO., INC.; *U.S. Private*, pg. 497
JUNORS—Russel Metals Inc.; *Int'l*, pg. 1150
KING GROUP, INC.; *U.S. Private*, pg. 620
THE NATURE COMPANY—Discovery Communications, Inc.; *U.S. Private*, pg. 334
OFFICE DEPOT—Office Depot Inc.; *U.S. Public*, pg. 1212
RENAISSANCE CENTER VENTURE—Ford Motor Company; *U.S. Public*, pg. 663
SANBORN HERMANOS—Grupo Carso S.A. de C.V.; *Int'l*, pg. 573
SILVER DOLLAR CITY, INC.; *U.S. Private*, pg. 1000
W.H. SMITH CANADA LTD.—Russel Metals Inc.; *Int'l*, pg. 1150
SPENCER GIFTS, INC.—The Seagram Company Ltd.; *Int'l*, pg. 1216
SUMMIT DIVISION—American Greetings Corporation; *U.S. Public*, pg. 78
THINGS REMEMBERED, INC.—Cole National Corporation; *U.S. Public*, pg. 397
TRAPP FAMILY LODGE, INC.; *U.S. Private*, pg. 1098
THE UCS GROUP—Lagardere Groupe; *Int'l*, pg. 792
VIAD CORP; *U.S. Public*, pg. 1718
WACCAMAW CORPORATION; *U.S. Private*, pg. 1145

5948 — LUGGAGE & LEATHER GOODS STORES

ADRAY APPLIANCE & PHOTO CENTER, INC.; *U.S. Private*, pg. 18
BENTLEY LEATHERS INC.—The Bentley Agnew Group Inc.; *Int'l*, pg. 187
COACH—Sara Lee Corporation; *U.S. Public*, pg. 1433
THE HARTSTONE GROUP PLC; *Int'l*, pg. 599
LOUIS VUITTON MALLETIER—LVMH Moet Hennessy Louis Vuitton; *Int'l*, pg. 781
THE SHARPER IMAGE; *U.S. Public*, pg. 1464
TANDY LEATHER CO.—Tandycrafts, Inc.; *U.S. Public*, pg. 1561

5949 — SEWING, NEEDLEWORK & PIECE GOODS STORES

CARON INTERNATIONAL—National Spinning Co., Inc.; *U.S. Private*, pg. 786
DYNO MERCHANDISE CORP.—ConAgra, Inc.; *U.S. Public*, *pg. 428*
FABRI-CENTERS OF AMERICA, INC.; *U.S. Public*, pg. 609
FABRIC KING—House of Fabrics, Inc.; *U.S. Public*, pg. 842
FABRICLAND, INC.—House of Fabrics, Inc.; *U.S. Public*, pg. 842
HANCOCK FABRICS, INC.; *U.S. Public*, pg. 779
HOUSE OF FABRICS, INC.; *U.S. Public*, pg. 842
LIBERTY PLC; *Int'l*, pg. 807
SO FRO FABRICS, INC.—House of Fabrics, Inc.; *U.S. Public*, pg. 842
WILLCOX & GIBBS, INC.; *U.S. Private*, pg. 1177

5961 — CATALOG & MAIL ORDER HOUSES

ABERCROMBIE & FITCH—The Limited, Inc.; *U.S. Public*, pg. 995
ADDRESSES UNLIMITED—Gannett Company, Inc.; *U.S. Public*, pg. 699
AMWAY CORPORATION; *U.S. Private*, pg. 69
ARTISTIC GREETINGS, INC.; *U.S. Public*, pg. 136
BMG/MUSIC—Bertelsmann AG; *Int'l*, pg. 191
B.M.G. RECORDS—Thomson S.A.; *Int'l*, pg. 1383
BARNES & NOBLE DIRECT—Barnes & Noble Inc.; *U.S. Public*, pg. 189
BASS PRO SHOPS, INC.; *U.S. Private*, pg. 122
BEAR CREEK CORPORATION—Yamanouchi Pharmaceutical Co. Ltd.; *Int'l*, pg. 1518
BERTELSMANN CLUB GMBH—Bertelsmann AG; *Int'l*, pg. 189
BLAIR CORPORATION; *U.S. Public*, pg. 236
JAMES BLISS & CO., INC.—West Marine, Inc.; *U.S. Public*, *pg. 1756*
BOOK OF THE MONTH CLUB—Time Warner Inc.; *U.S. Public*, pg. 1612
BRECKS—Foster & Gallagher, Inc.; *U.S. Private*, pg. 420
BROOKSTONE COMPANY, INC.; *U.S. Public*, pg. 259
BRYLANE L.P.—The Limited, Inc.; *U.S. Public*, pg. 996
W. ATLEE BURPEE CO.; *U.S. Private*, pg. 187
CDW COMPUTER CENTERS, INC.; *U.S. Public*, pg. 277
CML GROUP, INC.; *U.S. Public*, pg. 279
CSS INDUSTRIES, INC.; *U.S. Public*, pg. 283
CAMPMOR INC.; *U.S. Private*, pg. 204
CAREERTRACK INC.—TCI Communications, Inc.; *U.S. Public*, pg. 1555
CENTENNIAL TECHNOLOGIES, INC.; *U.S. Public*, pg. 322
CHADWICK'S OF BOSTON—The Limited, Inc.; *U.S. Public*, *pg. 996*
CHEYENNE OUTFITTERS, INC.; *U.S. Private*, pg. 234
CHILDCRAFT EDUCATION CORPORATION—The Walt Disney Company; *U.S. Public*, pg. 513
CHRONIMED INC.; *U.S. Public*, pg. 352
CIRCULO DE LECTORES S.A.—Bertelsmann AG; *Int'l*, pg. 192
CIRCULO DE LEITORES—Bertelsmann AG; *Int'l*, pg. 192
COLDWATER CREEK; *U.S. Public*, pg. 396
COLLIN STREET BAKERY; *U.S. Private*, pg. 252
COLUMBIA HOUSE MUSIC CLUB—Sony Corporation; *Int'l*, *pg. 1281*
COSMETIQUE, INC.; *U.S. Private*, pg. 277
CREATIVE COMPUTERS, INC.—Creative Computers, Inc.; *U.S. Public*, pg. 458
CREST FRUIT CO.—Standex International Corporation; *U.S. Public*, pg. 1506
CRITICS' CHOICE VIDEO, INC.—Playboy Enterprises, Inc.; *U.S. Public*, pg. 1310
CURRENT, INC.—Deluxe Corporation; *U.S. Public*, pg. 498
DM MANAGEMENT COMPANY; *U.S. Public*, pg. 473
DAMARK INTERNATIONAL, INC.; *U.S. Public*, pg. 478
DAMART S.A.; *Int'l*, pg. 376
DAMART SERVIPOSTE S.A.—Damart S.A.; *Int'l*, pg. 376
DAY-TIMERS, INC.—Fortune Brands, Inc.; *U.S. Public*, pg. 674
DAY-TIMERS OF CANADA, LIMITED—Fortune Brands, Inc.; *U.S. Public*, pg. 674
DELL COMPUTER CORPORATION; *U.S. Public*, pg. 495
DELL COMPUTER S.A.—Dell Computer Corporation; *U.S. Public*, pg. 496
DIRECT DENTAL SUPPLY CO.—Patterson Dental Company; *U.S. Public*, pg. 1265
DISTRIBUCION QUELLE, S.A. Y CIA SEC—Tabacalera, S.A.; *Int'l*, pg. 1346
DOUBLEDAY BOOK CLUB—Bertelsmann AG; *Int'l*, pg. 191
DOUBLEDAY DIRECT—Bertelsmann AG; *Int'l*, pg. 191
DOUBLEDAY PUBLISHING COMPANY—Bertelsmann AG; *Int'l*, pg. 191
E & B MARINE SUPPLY, INC.—West Marine, Inc.; *U.S. Public*, pg. 1756
EBG VERLAGS GMBH—Bertelsmann AG; *Int'l*, pg. 190
EASTON PRESS BOOKS—MBI Inc.; *U.S. Private*, pg. 685
EASTON PRESS VIDEOS—MBI Inc.; *U.S. Private*, pg. 685
EDDIE BAUER, INC.—Spiegel, Inc.; *U.S. Public*, pg. 1499
EDDIE BAUER MAIL ORDER DIVISION—Spiegel, Inc.; *U.S. Public*, pg. 1499
EDMUND SCIENTIFIC COMPANY; *U.S. Private*, pg. 364
ELLOS AB—ICA Handlarnas AB; *Int'l*, pg. 643
ENCORE CLUBS, INC.—Encore Marketing International, Inc.; *U.S. Public*, pg. 580
EX LIBRIS AG—Migros; *Int'l*, pg. 865
FIGI'S, INC.—Fingerhut Corp.; *U.S. Public*, pg. 623
FINE ART DEVELOPMENTS PLC; *Int'l*, pg. 485
FINGERHUT CORP.; *U.S. Public*, pg. 623
FLEXRX—Merck & Co., Inc.; *U.S. Public*, pg. 1091
FORTUNE PRODUCTS, INC.—Windmere-Durable Holdings; *U.S. Public*, pg. 1771
FOSTER & GALLAGHER, INC.; *U.S. Private*, pg. 420
FRANCE LOISIRS—C.E.P. Communication Group; *Int'l*, pg. 239
THE FRANKLIN MINT—Roll International Corporation; *U.S. Private*, pg. 941
FREDERICK'S OF HOLLYWOOD, INC.; *U.S. Private*, pg. 424
THE FULLER BRUSH COMPANY—CPAC, Inc.; *U.S. Public*, *pg. 282*
GEHE AG—Franz Haniel & Cie, GmbH; *Int'l*, pg. 591
GATEWAY 2000; *U.S. Public*, pg. 703
GLOBAL DIRECT MAIL CORP; *U.S. Public*, pg. 747
GOLDBERGS MARINE DISTRIBUTORS—West Marine, Inc.; *U.S. Public*, pg. 1756
GROLIER ENTERPRISES INC.—Lagardere Groupe; *Int'l*, pg. 794
GROLIER INTERNATIONAL, INC.—Lagardere Groupe; *Int'l*, *pg. 794*
GROLIER INTERSTATE, INC.—Lagardere Groupe; *Int'l*, pg. 794
GROLIER READING PROGRAMS, INC.—Lagardere Groupe; *Int'l*, pg. 794
GROLIER YEAR BOOK, INC.—Lagardere Groupe; *Int'l*, pg. 794
GROUPE DE LA CITE—Alcatel Alsthom Compagnie Generale D'Electricite; *Int'l*, pg. 53
HSN MAIL ORDER, INC.—USA Networks, Inc.; *U.S. Public*, *pg. 1685*
HSN TELECOMMUNICATIONS, INC.—USA Networks, Inc.; *U.S. Public*, pg. 1685
THE HAMILTON COLLECTION—Bradford Exchange Ltd.; *U.S. Private*, pg. 163
HAMMACHER, SCHLEMMER & CO., INC.; *U.S. Private*, pg. 497
HANDSOME REWARDS—Starcrest Products of California; *U.S. Private*, pg. 1035
HANOVER DIRECT, INC.; *U.S. Public*, pg. 782
HANOVER DIRECT PENNSYLVANIA, INC.—Hanover Direct, Inc.; *U.S. Public*, pg. 782
HARCOURT GENERAL, INC.; *U.S. Public*, pg. 782
HARRINGTON'S OF VERMONT, INC.; *U.S. Private*, pg. 504
HARRY AND DAVID—Yamanouchi Pharmaceutical Co. Ltd.; *Int'l*, pg. 1518
HEARTHSONG, INC.—Foster & Gallagher, Inc.; *U.S. Private*, pg. 421

HICKORY FARMS CATALOGUES OF AMERICA, INC.—Hickory Farms, Inc.; *U.S. Private*, pg. 525
HISTORY BOOK CLUB, INC.—Time Warner Inc.; *U.S. Public*, pg. 1612
HOLD EVERYTHING, INC.—Williams-Sonoma, Inc.; *U.S. Public*, pg. 1770
HOME SHOPPING NETWORK, INC.—USA Networks, Inc.; *U.S. Public*, pg. 1685
INDUSTRIAL BOOKSTORE—Manufacturers' News, Inc.; *U.S. Private*, pg. 701
INTERNATIONAL WINE ACCESSORIES, INC.; *U.S. Private*, pg. 572
J. CREW GROUP, INC.—Texas Pacific Group; *U.S. Private*, *pg. 1078*
JC PENNEY COMPANY, INC.; *U.S. Public*, pg. 916
JACKSON & PERKINS—Yamanouchi Pharmaceutical Co. Ltd.; *Int'l*, pg. 1518
JOHNNY APPLESEED'S, INC.; *U.S. Private*, pg. 590
JUNIOR DISCOUNT SERVICE AG,—Fotolabo S.A.; *Int'l*, pg. 501
L.L. BEAN, INC.; *U.S. Private*, pg. 639
LWI HOLDINGS INC.—Hanover Direct, Inc.; *U.S. Public*, pg. 782
LANDS' END, INC.; *U.S. Public*, pg. 977
LENOX COLLECTIONS—Brown-Forman Corporation; *U.S. Public*, pg. 261
LENOX, INCORPORATED—Brown-Forman Corporation; *U.S. Public*, pg. 261
THE LIMITED, INC.; *U.S. Public*, pg. 995
LITTLETON COIN CO., INC.; *U.S. Private*, pg. 671
MBI INC.; *U.S. Private*, pg. 685
MAIL MEDIA COMPANIES—The Stanley Works; *U.S. Public*, pg. 1509
B.A. MASON—Mason Shoe Mfg. Co.; *U.S. Private*, pg. 712
MASSEY'S—Craddock-Terry Inc.; *U.S. Private*, pg. 284
MARY MAXIM, INC.; *U.S. Private*, pg. 716
MCMASTER CARR SUPPLY CO. INC.; *U.S. Private*, pg. 724
MEDCO CONTAINMENT SERVICES, INC.—Merck & Co., Inc.; *U.S. Public*, pg. 1091
MEDI-MAIL, INC.; *U.S. Private*, pg. 726
MILES KIMBALL COMPANY; *U.S. Private*, pg. 745
MILITARY BOOK CLUB—Bertelsmann AG; *Int'l*, pg. 191
THE MONET GROUP, INC.; *U.S. Private*, pg. 757
MONET JEWELERS—The Monet Group, Inc.; *U.S. Private*, pg. 757
MONTGOMERY WARD DIRECT—Fingerhut Corp.; *U.S. Public*, pg. 623
MOORE BUSINESS PRODUCTS & SERVICES DIVISIONS—Moore Corporation Limited; *Int'l*, pg. 890
MOTHERS BACK ISSUES, INC.—Sussex Publishers, Inc.; *U.S. Private*, pg. 1056
MOTHER'S BOOKSHELF—Sussex Publishers, Inc.; *U.S. Private*, pg. 1056
MYSTERY GUILD—Bertelsmann AG; *Int'l*, pg. 191
MYSTIC STAMP COMPANY—Littleton Coin Co., Inc.; *U.S. Private*, pg. 671
NEBS BUSINESS FORMS LIMITED—New England Business Service, Inc.; *U.S. Public*, pg. 1171
NEBS BUSINESS STATIONERY—New England Business Service, Inc.; *U.S. Public*, pg. 1171
NASCO—Geneve Corporation; *U.S. Private*, pg. 446
NASCO INTERNATIONAL, INC.—Geneve Corporation; *U.S. Private*, pg. 446
NATIONAL PHARMACIES, INC.—Merck & Co., Inc.; *U.S. Public*, pg. 1091
THE NATURE COMPANY—Discovery Communications, Inc.; *U.S. Private*, pg. 334
NEWBRIDGE COMMUNICATIONS, INC.—Bertelsmann AG; *Int'l*, pg. 191
NEWPORT NEWS, INC.—Spiegel, Inc.; *U.S. Public*, pg. 1499
OMAHA STEAKS; *U.S. Private*, pg. 815
ORCHIDS ETC.—Yamanouchi Pharmaceutical Co. Ltd.; *Int'l*, pg. 1518
THE ORVIS COMPANY, INC.; *U.S. Private*, pg. 820
OSTERMANN PETERSEN BROS. LTD.—Scandinavian Airlines System (SAS); *Int'l*, pg. 1202
OTTO SUMISHO INC.—Otto Versand (GmbH & Co.); *Int'l*, pg. 1015
OTTO VERSAND (GMBH & CO.); *Int'l*, pg. 1014
PC CONNECTION, INC.; *U.S. Private*, pg. 826
GEORGE W. PARK SEED CO., INC.; *U.S. Private*, pg. 839
PETALS; *U.S. Private*, pg. 856
PITNEY BOWES INC.; *U.S. Public*, pg. 1303
PLAYBOY ENTERPRISES, INC.; *U.S. Public*, pg. 1309
PLAYBOY PREFERRED, INC.—Playboy Enterprises, Inc.; *U.S. Public*, pg. 1310
PLEASANT COMPANY; *U.S. Private*, pg. 872
POPULAR CLUB PLAN—Texas Pacific Group; *U.S. Private*, *pg. 1078*
POSTAL COMMEMORATIVE SOCIETY COLLECTION MBI Inc.; *U.S. Private*, pg. 685
POSTALMARKET; *Int'l*, pg. 1064
PUBCO CORPORATION; *U.S. Public*, pg. 1339
PUBLISHERS CLEARING HOUSE; *U.S. Private*, pg. 893
QVC, INC.; *U.S. Private*, pg. 897
QUELLE GROUP; *Int'l*, pg. 1078
QUILL CORP.; *U.S. Private*, pg. 901
RCA RECORDS U.S.—Bertelsmann AG; *Int'l*, pg. 192
RAPIDFORMS, INC.—New England Business Service, Inc.; *U.S. Public*, pg. 1171
REPLACEMENTS, LTD.; *U.S. Private*, pg. 923
RIGHT START, INC.; *U.S. Private*, pg. 930
SAKATA SEED AMERICA, INC.—Sakata Seed Corporation; *Int'l*, pg. 1178
SARA LEE DIRECT—Sara Lee Corporation; *U.S. Public*, pg. 1434
SCANDINAVIAN AIRLINES SYSTEM (SAS); *Int'l*, pg. 1201
SCIENCE FICTION BOOK CLUB—Bertelsmann AG; *Int'l*, pg. 191
SEARS CANADA, INC.—Sears, Roebuck and Co.; *U.S. Public*, pg. 1452
SERVICE MERCHANDISE COMPANY, INC.; *U.S. Public*, pg. 1461
THE SHARPER IMAGE; *U.S. Public*, pg. 1464
SHEPLERS, INC.; *U.S. Private*, pg. 993
SHILLCRAFT, INC.; *U.S. Private*, pg. 994
SIGNATURES—Starcrest Products of California; *U.S. Private*, pg. 1035
SILVER TOWNE L.P.; *U.S. Private*, pg. 1000
SOUTHERN PROGRESS CORPORATION—Time Warner Inc.; *U.S. Public*, pg. 1612
SPIEGEL, INC.; *U.S. Public*, pg. 1498
THE SPORTSMAN'S GUIDE, INC.; *U.S. Public*, pg. 1499
SPRING HILL NURSERIES CO.—Foster & Gallagher, Inc.; *U.S. Private*, pg. 420
STARCREST PRODUCTS OF CALIFORNIA; *U.S. Private*, pg. 1035
STOCK YARDS PACKING CO., INC.; *U.S. Private*, pg. 1043
STUDIO CARDS LTD.—Fine Art Developments plc; *Int'l*, pg. 485
THE SWISS COLONY, INC; *U.S. Private*, pg. 1059
THE TJX COMPANIES, INC.; *U.S. Public*, pg. 1556
TALBOTS—AEON Group; *Int'l*, pg. 28
TALBOTS, INC.—AEON Group; *Int'l*, pg. 28
TANDYCRAFTS, INC.; *U.S. Public*, pg. 1561
TEA DIRECT—Celestial Seasonings; *U.S. Public*, pg. 320
THE TERRITORY AHEAD; *U.S. Private*, pg. 1077
THIMBLE COLLECTORS CLUB COLLECTIONS—MBI Inc.; *U.S. Private*, pg. 685
TIGER DIRECT, INC.—Global Direct Mail Corp; *U.S. Public*, *pg. 747*
TIGER DIRECT, INC. (D/B/A TIGER SOFTWARE, INC.)—Global Direct Mail Corp; *U.S. Public*, pg. 747
THE TOG SHOP; *U.S. Private*, pg. 1090
THE TRUMPET CLUB—Bertelsmann AG; *Int'l*, pg. 191
TWEEDS, INC.—Hanover Direct, Inc.; *U.S. Public*, pg. 782
UNICOVER CORPORATION; *U.S. Private*, pg. 1117
VENDEX INTERNATIONAL N.V.; *Int'l*, pg. 1462
VERLAG KREMAYR UND SCHERIAU—Bertelsmann AG; *Int'l*, pg. 192
LILLIAN VERNON CORPORATION; *U.S. Public*, pg. 1716
VICTORIA'S SECRET CATALOG—The Limited, Inc.; *U.S. Public*, pg. 995
WALTER DRAKE, INC.—Foster & Gallagher, Inc.; *U.S. Private*, pg. 421
WILTON INDUSTRIES, INC.; *U.S. Private*, pg. 1181
WISSOTA TRADER LTD.—Mason Shoe Mfg. Co.; *U.S. Private*, pg. 712
WORD, INCORPORATED—Gaylord Entertainment Co.; *U.S. Public*, pg. 704
WORLD COLOR-CHICAGO DIV.—World Color Press, Inc.; *U.S. Public*, pg. 1778
WORLD COLOR PRESS, INC.; *U.S. Public*, pg. 1778
WORLDWIDE DIRECTORY PRODUCT SALES—SBC Communications Inc.; *U.S. Public*, pg. 1415

5962 — AUTOMATIC MERCHANDISING MACHINE OPERATORS

AVA; *U.S. Private*, pg. 8
AIM SERVICES CO., LTD.—Aramark Corp.; *U.S. Private*, pg. 79
ARAMARK CORP.; *U.S. Private*, pg. 78
AUTOMATIC SERVICE CO.—AVA; *U.S. Private*, pg. 8
CENTRAL COCA-COLA BOTTLING COMPANY, INC.; *U.S. Private*, pg. 222
MAJOR FOODS LTD.—Aramark Corp.; *U.S. Private*, pg. 79
PINE STATE VENDING—Pine State Trading Company; *U.S. Private*, pg. 865
E.V. ROBERTS & ASSOCIATES, INC.; *U.S. Private*, pg. 935
SERVICE AMERICA CORPORATION; *U.S. Private*, pg. 986
SODEXHO S.A.; *Int'l*, pg. 1274
TREND LINE CORPORATION; *U.S. Private*, pg. 1099
VALLEY INNOVATIVE MANAGEMENT SERVICE—Trend Line Corporation; *U.S. Private*, pg. 1099
VERSA SERVICES LTD.—Aramark Corp.; *U.S. Private*, pg. 79

5963 — DIRECT SELLING ESTABLISHMENTS

ALLTIMATE CATERING—Marsh Supermarkets, Inc.; *U.S. Public*, pg. 1049
AMWAY CORPORATION; *U.S. Private*, pg. 69
AVON PRODUCTS, INC.—Avon Products, Inc.; *U.S. Public*, *pg. 156*
B.R. GUEST, LTD.—Rich Products Corp.; *U.S. Private*, pg. 928
BEAUTICONTROL COSMETICS, INC.; *U.S. Public*, pg. 198
CALIFORNIA SCHOOL BOOK FAIRS, INC.—Scholastic Corporation; *U.S. Public*, pg. 1440
CARIBE GROLIER, INC.—Lagardere Groupe; *Int'l*, pg. 794
COMMUNITY NEWSDEALERS, INC.—The New York Times Company; *U.S. Public*, pg. 1175
DELAWARE NORTH COMPANIES, INC.; *U.S. Private*, pg. 321
EFFECTIVE MANAGEMENT SYSTEMS; *U.S. Public*, pg. 565
ELECTROLUX CORPORATION; *U.S. Private*, pg. 369
FIVE STAR FOODS INCORPORATED; *U.S. Private*, pg. 409
THE FULLER BRUSH COMPANY—CPAC, Inc.; *U.S. Public*, *pg. 282*
GIORGIO BEVERLY HILLS—The Procter & Gamble Company; *U.S. Public*, pg. 1331
GROLIER TELEMARKETING, INC.—Lagardere Groupe; *Int'l*, pg. 794
THE HEARST CORPORATION; *U.S. Private*, pg. 515
HOUSTON CHRONICLE—The Hearst Corporation; *U.S. Private*, pg. 517
INTERTAN U.K. LTD.—InterTAN Inc.; *U.S. Public*, pg. 910
IONICS, INCORPORATED; *U.S. Public*, pg. 912
MARSH COMPANY M.C.S.A.—Marsh Company; *U.S. Private*, pg. 708
MARY KAY CORPORATION; *U.S. Private*, pg. 710
MARY KAY, INC.—Mary Kay Corporation; *U.S. Private*, pg. 711
NATURALLY YOU—Southeastern Medequip, Inc.; *U.S. Private*, pg. 1015
NOUVELLES MESSAGERIES DE LA PRESSE PARISIENNE—Lagardere Groupe; *Int'l*, pg. 793
OLD FASHION FOODS, INC.; *U.S. Private*, pg. 814
PH. ORTH CO.—CSM N.V.; *Int'l*, pg. 244
PERIODICAL PUBLISHERS' SERVICE BUREAU, INC.—The Hearst Corporation; *U.S. Private*, pg. 517
RENA-WARE DISTRIBUTORS INC.; *U.S. Private*, pg. 922
SAN FRANCISCO NEWSPAPER AGENCY—Chronicle Publishing Co. Inc.; *U.S. Private*, pg. 239
SCHNEIDER CORP.; *Int'l*, pg. 1207
SCHOLASTIC BOOK FAIRS, INC.—Scholastic Corporation; *U.S. Public*, pg. 1440
SCHOLASTIC BOOK FAIRS, LTD.—Scholastic Corporation; *U.S. Public*, pg. 1440
SOCIETE D'AGENCES ET DE DIFFUSION—Lagardere Groupe; *Int'l*, pg. 793
SOUTHEASTERN MEDEQUIP, INC.; *U.S. Private*, pg. 1015
STANDARD COFFEE SERVICE—William B. Reily & Co., Inc.; *U.S. Private*, pg. 919
TUPPERWARE CORPORATION; *U.S. Public*, pg. 1644
U.S. DIRECT SELLING DIVISION—Avon Products, Inc.; *U.S. Public*, pg. 156
UPSTATE MILK COOPERATIVES INC.; *U.S. Private*, pg. 1129
VORWERK USA INC.—Vorwerk & Co.; *Int'l*, pg. 1481
WORLD BOOK DIRECT MARKETING—Berkshire Hathaway Inc.; *U.S. Public*, pg. 218

5983 — FUEL OIL DEALERS

AGWAY ENERGY PRODUCTS (AEP)—Agway, Inc.; *U.S. Private*, pg. 27
BAYSIDE FUEL OIL CORP.—Bayside Fuel Oil Depot Corp.; *U.S. Private*, pg. 125
BERKS PRODUCTS CORPORATION; *U.S. Private*, pg. 136
BESCHE OIL COMPANY, INC.; *U.S. Private*, pg. 139
BRADFORD OIL COMPANY, INC.; *U.S. Private*, pg. 164
BURKE FUEL & HEATING CO.—Meenan Oil Co. L.P.; *U.S. Private*, pg. 729
CHRISTY HALSEY OIL CO.—Meenan Oil Co. L.P.; *U.S. Private*, pg. 729
CLASHFERN HOLDINGS LIMITED—Avonmore Waterford Group plc; *Int'l*, pg. 102
COASTAL FUELS MARKETING, INC.—The Coastal Corporation; *U.S. Public*, pg. 390
COASTAL OIL NEW YORK, INC.—The Coastal Corporation; *U.S. Public*, pg. 390
COASTAL STATES PETROLEUM (U.K.) LIMITED—The Coastal Corporation; *U.S. Public*, pg. 391
COLONIAL OIL INDUSTRIES; *U.S. Private*, pg. 253
DAIGLE OIL CO.; *U.S. Private*, pg. 307
DEAD RIVER COMPANY; *U.S. Private*, pg. 318
DIRECT FUELS, L.P.—FFP Marketing Company, Inc.; *U.S. Public*, pg. 604
DISTRICT PETROLEUM PRODUCTS, INC.; *U.S. Private*, pg. 336
EFFRON FUEL OIL CO., INC.—Meenan Oil Co. L.P.; *U.S. Private*, pg. 729
FARM & HOME OIL COMPANY; *U.S. Private*, pg. 394
FIRST MOUNT JOY CORPORATION; *U.S. Private*, pg. 407
GATE PETROLEUM COMPANY; *U.S. Private*, pg. 441
GLOBAL PETROLEUM CORP.; *U.S. Private*, pg. 457
GAY JOHNSON'S INC.; *U.S. Private*, pg. 595
KING FUELS INC.; *U.S. Private*, pg. 620
KINGSTON OIL SUPPLY CORP.—Getty Petroleum Marketing Inc.; *U.S. Public*, pg. 741
CARLOS R. LEFFLER INC.; *U.S. Private*, pg. 658
LYON COUNTY CO-OP OIL CO.; *U.S. Private*, pg. 684
MAIN BROTHERS OIL COMPANY, INC.; *U.S. Private*, pg. 697
MEENAN OIL CO. L.P.; *U.S. Private*, pg. 729
MEENAN OIL/YOUNG SUPPLY CO.—Meenan Oil Co. L.P.; *U.S. Private*, pg. 729
MID-VALLEY OIL COMPANY, INC.—Warren Equities Inc.; *U.S. Private*, pg. 1151
MIDWEST BOTTLE GAS COMPANY—Consolidated Midwest, Inc.; *U.S. Private*, pg. 266
OLIVER OIL COMPANY, INC.; *U.S. Private*, pg. 815
PM PROPERTIES INC.—Petroleum Marketers, Inc.; *U.S. Private*, pg. 859
PETROLEUM HEAT & POWER CO.; *U.S. Public*, pg. 1281
PETROLEUM MARKETERS, INC.; *U.S. Private*, pg. 859
SHIPLEY COMPANIES; *U.S. Private*, pg. 994
THE SICO COMPANY—First Mount Joy Corporation; *U.S. Private*, pg. 407
SOUTHERN STATES COOPERATIVE, INC.; *U.S. Private*, pg. 1017
SPARTAN OIL CORP.; *U.S. Private*, pg. 1021
SPRAGUE ENERGY CORP. NORTHEAST OPERATION—Axel Johnson AB; *Int'l*, pg. 710
SPRAUGE ENERGY CORP. SOUTHEAST OPERATIONS—Axel Johnson AB; *Int'l*, pg. 710
STATE GAS & OIL COMPANY DIVISION—Uni-Marts, Inc.; *U.S. Public*, pg. 1664
ULTRAMAR DIAMOND SHAMROCK CORPORATION; *U.S. Public*, pg. 1663
YODER OIL COMPANY INC.; *U.S. Private*, pg. 1196

5984 — BOTTLED OR BULK LIQUIFIED PETROLEUM (LP) GAS DEALERS

AGWAY ENERGY PRODUCTS (AEP)—Agway, Inc.; *U.S. Private*, pg. 27
AGWAY, INC.; *U.S. Private*, pg. 27
ALL STAR GAS CORPORATION; *U.S. Private*, pg. 35

ALL STAR GAS, INC.—All Star Gas Corporation; *U.S. Private*, pg. 35
AMERIGAS, INC.—UGI Corporation; *U.S. Public*, pg. 1653
CALOR GROUP PLC—SHV Holdings N.V.; *Int'l*, pg. 1155
CHESAPEAKE UTILITIES CORPORATION; *U.S. Public*, pg. 347
COLUMBIA ENERGY GROUP; *U.S. Public*, pg. 402
COMMONWEALTH PROPANE, INC.—Columbia Energy Group; *U.S. Public*, pg. 403
COMPAGNIE DES GAZ DE PETROLE PRIMAGAZ S.A.—SHV Holdings N.V.; *Int'l*, pg. 1155
CONSOLIDATED MIDWEST, INC.; *U.S. Private*, pg. 265
COOP SWITZERLAND; *Int'l*, pg. 329
DEAD RIVER COMPANY; *U.S. Private*, pg. 318
ENRON CORP.; *U.S. Public*, pg. 584
ERGON, INC.; *U.S. Private*, pg. 380
FERRELLGAS PARTNERS, L.P.; *U.S. Public*, pg. 618
HANSON PLC; *Int'l*, pg. 592
HICKS OIL-HICKS GAS, INC.; *U.S. Private*, pg. 526
HIGHLAND PROPANE COMPANY—Roanoke Gas Company; *U.S. Public*, pg. 1393
JASPER COUNTY FARM BUREAU CO-OP ASSOCIATION, INC.; *U.S. Private*, pg. 583
GAY JOHNSON'S INC.; *U.S. Private*, pg. 595
KEEN COMPRESSED GAS CO.; *U.S. Private*, pg. 611
LA SALLE COUNTY FARM SUPPLY; *U.S. Private*, pg. 640
LYKES ENERGY, INC.; *U.S. Private*, pg. 682
MDU RESOURCES GROUP, INC.; *U.S. Public*, pg. 1025
MAPCO INC.; *U.S. Public*, pg. 1042
MAPCO NATURAL GAS LIQUIDS INC.—Mapco Inc.; *U.S. Public*, pg. 1042
MARATHON ASHLAND PETROLEUM LLC—Ashland, Inc.; *U.S. Public*, pg. 139
MARATHON ASHLAND PETROLEUM LLC—USX Corporation; *U.S. Public*, pg. 1662
MATHESON GAS PRODUCTS, INC.—Nippon Sanso Corporation; *Int'l*, pg. 938
MIDWEST BOTTLE GAS COMPANY—Consolidated Midwest, Inc.; *U.S. Private*, pg. 266
MINNESOTA POWER; *U.S. Public*, pg. 1116
NATIONAL PROPANE CORP.—Triarc Companies, Inc.; *U.S. Public*, pg. 1635
SHV HOLDINGS N.V.; *Int'l*, pg. 1154
SHARP ENERGY, INC.—Chesapeake Utilities Corporation; *U.S. Public*, pg. 347
SHARPGAS, INC.—Chesapeake Utilities Corporation; *U.S. Public*, pg. 347
SUBURBAN PROPANE GROUP, INC.—SCANA Corporation; *U.S. Public*, pg. 1436
TRIARC COMPANIES, INC.; *U.S. Public*, pg. 1634
VALLEY PROPANE, INC.—Valley Resources, Inc.; *U.S. Public*, pg. 1706
WYO L.P. GAS—Energy West Inc.; *U.S. Public*, pg. 581

5989 — FUEL DEALERS, NEC

ALLEY-CASSETTY COAL CO.; *U.S. Private*, pg. 37
FINA, INC.—Petrofina S.A.; *Int'l*, pg. 1044
INGRAM COAL COMPANY—Ingram Industries Inc.; *U.S. Private*, pg. 563
INTERNATIONAL CHEMICAL COMPANY; *U.S. Private*, pg. 568
MCCALL OIL & CHEMICAL CORP.; *U.S. Private*, pg. 719
POWELL DUFFRYN INTERNATIONAL FUELS LTD.—Powell Duffryn PLC; *Int'l*, pg. 1065
PUGH OIL COMPANY; *U.S. Private*, pg. 894

5992 — FLORISTS

AMLINGS FLOWERLAND; *U.S. Private*, pg. 66
CONROY'S FLOWERS—800-FLOWERS, Inc.; *U.S. Private*, pg. 366
DENVER WHOLESALE FLORISTS COMPANY; *U.S. Private*, pg. 326
800-FLOWERS, INC.; *U.S. Private*, pg. 366
FLORAFAX INTERNATIONAL, INC.; *U.S. Public*, pg. 654
FLOWERS USA; *U.S. Private*, pg. 415
TELEFLORA, LLC—Roll International Corporation; *U.S. Private*, pg. 941

5993 — TOBACCO STORES & STANDS

EXPORTADORA DE TABACO DE CEUTA Y MELILLA, S.A.—Tabacalera, S.A.; *Int'l*, pg. 1345
KAISER WHOLESALE, INC.; *U.S. Private*, pg. 605
THE UCS GROUP—Lagardere Groupe; *Int'l*, pg. 792

5994 — NEWS DEALERS & NEWSSTANDS

ARAMARK CORP.; *U.S. Private*, pg. 78
FABER, COE & GREGG, INC.; *U.S. Private*, pg. 390
GREYHOUND LEISURE SERVICES, INC.—Viad Corp; *U.S. Public*, pg. 1718
JOHN MENZIES PLC; *Int'l*, pg. 707
JOHN MENZIES RETAIL—John Menzies plc; *Int'l*, pg. 707
JOHN MENZIES (UK) LIMITED—John Menzies plc; *Int'l*, pg. 707
THE LEVY ORGANIZATION; *U.S. Private*, pg. 664

5995 — OPTICAL GOODS STORES

AVC/NU-VISION, INC.; *U.S. Private*, pg. 9
BMI PTE. LTD., SINGAPORE—F. J. Benjamin Holdings Ltd.; *Int'l*, pg. 187
BOOTS OPTICIANS—The Boots Company PLC; *Int'l*, pg. 202
BUTEN, DIVISION OF DURON—Duron, Inc.; *U.S. Private*, pg. 349
D.O.C. OPTICS CORPORATION; *U.S. Private*, pg. 305
DEERSKIN TRADING POST, INC.—Initio, Inc.; *U.S. Public*, pg. 879
DELFT INSTRUMENTS ELECTRO-OPTICS B.V.—Delft Instruments N.V.; *Int'l*, pg. 389
DOLLAND & AITCHISON SERVICES LTD.—Dolland & Aitchison Ltd.; *Int'l*, pg. 414
E & B MARINE INCORPORATED—West Marine, Inc.; *U.S. Public*, pg. 1756
FINISH LINE, INC.; *U.S. Public*, pg. 623
FOR EYES PLC—Dolland & Aitchison Ltd.; *Int'l*, pg. 414
FRANKE GMBH—Delft Instruments N.V.; *Int'l*, pg. 389
HAMBLIN OPTICAL SERVICES LTD.—Dolland & Aitchison Ltd.; *Int'l*, pg. 414
HORNER RAUSCH OPTICAL COMPANY EAST, INC.; *U.S. Private*, pg. 540
JC PENNEY COMPANY, INC.; *U.S. Public*, pg. 916
LITTLE SWITZERLAND, INC.; *U.S. Public*, pg. 1001
MIDWEST VISION CENTERS; *U.S. Private*, pg. 745
OIP N.V.—Delft Instruments N.V.; *Int'l*, pg. 389
OLDELFT ELECTRONIC INSTRUMENTS SRL—Delft Instruments N.V.; *Int'l*, pg. 389
PEARLE INC.—Cole National Corporation; *U.S. Public*, pg. 396
PEARLE VISION EXPRESS—Cole National Corporation; *U.S. Public*, pg. 397
PEARLE VISION, INC.—Cole National Corporation; *U.S. Public*, pg. 397
SOUND ADVICE, INC.; *U.S. Public*, pg. 1488
STROUDS, INC.; *U.S. Public*, pg. 1525
VISION CENTERS—GIB Group; *Int'l*, pg. 533

5999 — MISCELLANEOUS RETAIL STORES, NEC

AARON BROTHERS, INC.—Michaels Stores, Inc.; *U.S. Public*, pg. 1104
AGWAY RETAIL SERVICES—Agway, Inc.; *U.S. Private*, pg. 27
ALBERTO-CULVER COMPANY; *U.S. Public*, pg. 37
ALLIED SECURITY, INTERNATIONAL; *U.S. Private*, pg. 41
AMERICAN RETAIL GROUP; *U.S. Private*, pg. 61
AMILAND SA—Castorama Dubois Investissements S.C.A.; *Int'l*, pg. 275
AUGUST WEST SYSTEMS; *U.S. Private*, pg. 98
M.F. BANK & COMPANY, INC.; *U.S. Private*, pg. 113
BASEL TRADING COMPANY LTD.; *Int'l*, pg. 169
BAUSCH & LOMB HEARING SYSTEMS DIVISION—Bausch & Lomb Incorporated; *U.S. Public*, pg. 194
BEST BUY CO., INC.; *U.S. Public*, pg. 223
BIG J SUPER STORES, INC.—Jones Company, Inc.; *U.S. Private*, pg. 596
BLOCKBUSTER ENTERTAINMENT CORPORATION LIMITED (U.K.)—National Amusements, Inc.; *U.S. Private*, pg. 776
BLUE SEAL FEEDS, INC.—Varied Investments, Inc.; *U.S. Private*, pg. 1134
THE BODY SHOP—The Body Shop International; *Int'l*, pg. 199
THE BODY SHOP INTERNATIONAL; *Int'l*, pg. 199
BUSHNELL CORPORATION—Worldwide Sports & Recreation, Inc.; *U.S. Private*, pg. 1191
CPI CORP.; *U.S. Public*, pg. 283
CASWELL-MASSEY CO. LTD.; *U.S. Private*, pg. 219
COLE NATIONAL CORPORATION; *U.S. Public*, pg. 396
CONAGRA FEED CO.—ConAgra, Inc.; *U.S. Public*, pg. 428
CONAGRA TRADING & PROCESSING COMPANIES—ConAgra, Inc.; *U.S. Public*, pg. 428
THE COSMETIC CENTER INC.—MacAndrews & Forbes Holdings Inc.; *U.S. Private*, pg. 689
CUMMINS MID-SOUTH, INC.; *U.S. Private*, pg. 295
DAHLBERG, INC.—Bausch & Lomb Incorporated; *U.S. Public*, pg. 194
DAIRY QUEEN CANADA, INC.—Berkshire Hathaway Inc.; *U.S. Public*, pg. 220
DUPEY MANAGEMENT CORP.; *U.S. Private*, pg. 348
DUTY FREE INTERNATIONAL, INC.—BAA plc; *Int'l*, pg. 103
E & B MARINE INCORPORATED—West Marine, Inc.; *U.S. Public*, pg. 1756
E & B MARINE SUPPLY, INC.—West Marine, Inc.; *U.S. Public*, pg. 1756
EB5 CORPORATION; *U.S. Private*, pg. 353
ETABLISSEMENTS DELHAIZE FRERES ET CIE "LE LION" S.A.; *Int'l*, pg. 462
FAMILY BARGAIN CORPORATION; *U.S. Public*, pg. 612
FAR-BEN S.A. DE C.V.; *Int'l*, pg. 478
FARMERS CO-OP MARKET INC.; *U.S. Private*, pg. 395
WALLY FINDLAY GALLERIES, INC.—Wally Findlay Galleries International; *U.S. Private*, pg. 405
WALLY FINDLAY GALLERIES INTERNATIONAL; *U.S. Private*, pg. 405
FRAMES UNLIMITED INC.—Zimdar Enterprises/Frames Unlimited; *U.S. Private*, pg. 1206
GOLDBERGS MARINE DISTRIBUTORS—West Marine, Inc.; *U.S. Public*, pg. 1756
HEXCEL-FYFE COMPANY, INC.—Hexcel Corporation; *U.S. Public*, pg. 824
HOME SHOPPING CLUB, INC.—USA Networks, Inc.; *U.S. Public*, pg. 1685
HONG KONG TELECOM CSL LIMITED—Cable and Wireless plc; *Int'l*, pg. 247
I.D.Q. CANADA, INC.—Berkshire Hathaway Inc.; *U.S. Public*, pg. 220
IKON OFFICE SOLUTIONS, INC.; *U.S. Public*, pg. 862
INTERNATIONAL CUTLERY, LTD; *U.S. Private*, pg. 569
INTERNATIONAL DAIRY QUEEN, INC.—Berkshire Hathaway Inc.; *U.S. Public*, pg. 220
INTERNATIONAL THOROUGHBRED BREEDERS, INC.; *U.S. Public*, pg. 908
JASPER COUNTY FARM BUREAU CO-OP ASSOCIATION, INC.; *U.S. Private*, pg. 583
LENOX RETAIL—Brown-Forman Corporation; *U.S. Public*, pg. 261
MARTIN LAWRENCE LIMITED EDITIONS, INC.; *U.S. Private*, pg. 709
MARVIN LUMBER & CEDAR COMPANY; *U.S. Private*, pg. 710
MAUREXCO EXPORTERS—Maurice Electric Supply Company; *U.S. Private*, pg. 715
NORTH SAFETY PRODUCTS—Siebe plc; *Int'l*, pg. 1243
OFFICE DEPOT OFFICE SUPPLY WAREHOUSE—Office Depot Inc.; *U.S. Public*, pg. 1212
OFFICE PAVILION DIVISION (SLS. & MKTG. DIV.)—Herman Miller, Inc.; *U.S. Public*, pg. 1112
OLD AMERICA STORES; *U.S. Public*, pg. 1215
OLINDE HARDWARE & SUPPLY CO.; *U.S. Private*, pg. 814
ORLANE INSTITUT DE BEAUTE—Orlane; *Int'l*, pg. 1011
PADDOCK POOL CONSTRUCTION CO., INC.; *U.S. Private*, pg. 833
PETCARE PLUS, INC.; *U.S. Private*, pg. 856
PETS-N-SUCH INC.; *U.S. Private*, pg. 859
PET'S PLACE—Vendex International N.V.; *Int'l*, pg. 1463
PETSMART, INC.; *U.S. Public*, pg. 1281
SAS TRADING—Scandinavian Airlines System (SAS); *Int'l*, pg. 1202
SALLY BEAUTY COMPANY, INC.—Alberto-Culver Company; *U.S. Public*, pg. 38
SCANDINAVIAN AIRLINES SYSTEM (SAS); *Int'l*, pg. 1201
SEARS CANADA, INC.—Sears, Roebuck and Co.; *U.S. Public*, pg. 1452
SIR SPEEDY, INC.—Franchise Services, Inc.; *U.S. Private*, pg. 423
SUNGLASS HUT INTERNATIONAL; *U.S. Public*, pg. 1535
SUPERIOR AUCTIONEERS & MARKETING, INC.; *U.S. Private*, pg. 1054
TIE/COMMUNICATIONS, INC.; *U.S. Private*, pg. 1085
TODAY'S MAN, INC.; *U.S. Public*, pg. 1619
TONE BROTHERS INC.—Burns, Philp & Company Limited; *Int'l*, pg. 237
TUESDAY MORNING CORPORATION; *U.S. Public*, pg. 1644
UNI-BEAUTY LIMITED—Wella Group; *Int'l*, pg. 1490
UNICOVER CORPORATION; *U.S. Private*, pg. 1117
UNISOURCE—Unisource Worldwide, Inc.; *U.S. Public*, pg. 1671
UNITED PRODUCERS & CONSUMERS CO-OP; *U.S. Private*, pg. 1123
D. WALDNER COMPANY, INC.; *U.S. Private*, pg. 1147
WICKS 'N STICKS, LTD; *U.S. Private*, pg. 1175
WILLOUGHBY'S; *U.S. Private*, pg. 1180
THE W.B. WOOD COMPANY; *U.S. Private*, pg. 1186
ZIMDAR ENTERPRISES/FRAMES UNLIMITED; *U.S. Private*, pg. 1206

6011 — FEDERAL RESERVE BANKS

BANCO POPULAR DE PUERTO RICO; *U.S. Public*, pg. 175
BANPONCE CORPORATION—Banco Popular de Puerto Rico; *U.S. Public*, pg. 176
CITY NATIONAL CORPORATION; *U.S. Public*, pg. 380
FEDERAL RESERVE BANK OF DALLAS; *U.S. Private*, pg. 399
FIRST BANKS, INC.—First Banks America, Inc.; *U.S. Public*, pg. 626
FRANKLIN FIRST SAVINGS BANK—First Empire State Corporation; *U.S. Public*, pg. 632
GREAT WESTERN BANK—Washington Mutual Inc.; *U.S. Public*, pg. 1741
KEY BANK OF MAINE—Keycorp; *U.S. Public*, pg. 954
LAWRENCE SAVINGS BANK—Lawrence Savings Bank; *U.S. Public*, pg. 980
M & I MARSHALL & ILSLEY BANK—Marshall & Ilsley Corporation; *U.S. Public*, pg. 1050
OLD NATIONAL BANCORP; *U.S. Public*, pg. 1217
ONBANK—First Empire State Corporation; *U.S. Public*, pg. 632
ONBANK & TRUST CO.—First Empire State Corporation; *U.S. Public*, pg. 632
PENN SECURITY BANK AND TRUST CO.; *U.S. Public*, pg. 1270
UST CORPORATION; *U.S. Public*, pg. 1660
WILLIAMSPORT NATIONAL BANK—Susquehanna Bancshares, Inc.; *U.S. Public*, pg. 1543

6019 — CENTRAL RESERVE DEPOSITORY INSTITUTIONS, NEC

AMPLICON, INC.; *U.S. Public*, pg. 104

6021 — NATIONAL COMMERCIAL BANKS

ADVANTA NATIONAL BANK USA—Advanta Corp.; *U.S. Public*, pg. 22
AMCORE BANK N.A., NORTHWEST—Amcore Financial, Inc.; *U.S. Public*, pg. 64
AMCORE FINANCIAL, INC.; *U.S. Public*, pg. 64
AMERIANA BANK—Ameriana Bancorp; *U.S. Public*, pg. 66
AMERICAN INVESTMENT BANK, NA—Leucadia National Corporation; *U.S. Public*, pg. 990
AMERICAN NATIONAL BANK & TRUST CO. OF CHICAGO—First Chicago NBD Corporation; *U.S. Public*, pg. 628
AMERICAN NATIONAL BANK & TRUST OF CHICAGO—First Chicago NBD Corporation; *U.S. Public*, pg. 627
AMSOUTH BANK N.A.—AmSouth Bancorporation; *U.S. Public*, pg. 105
AMSOUTH OF TUSCALOOSA—AmSouth Bancorporation; *U.S. Public*, pg. 105
ARGENTARIA CORPORACION BANCARIA DE ESPANA, S.A.; *Int'l*, pg. 80
ASSOCIATED BANK, NATIONAL ASSOCIATION—Associated Banc-Corp; *U.S. Public*, pg. 140

ASSOCIATES NATIONAL BANK—Ford Motor Company; *U.S. Public*, pg. 663
ATLANTIC SAVINGS BANK FSB—Wachovia Corporation; *U.S. Public*, pg. 1730
AURORA NATIONAL BANK—GreatBanc, Inc.; *U.S. Public*, pg. 760
B & J OPERATIONS COMPANY, INC.—Huntington Bancshares Inc.; *U.S. Public*, pg. 850
BB&T CORPORATION; *U.S. Public*, pg. 159
BHF-BANK AG; *Int'l*, pg. 119
BNP-AK DRESDNER BANK A.S.—Dresdner Bank AG; *Int'l*, *pg. 420*
BNP-AK DRESDNER BANK A.S.—Sabanci Holding A.S.; *Int'l*, pg. 1167
BNY HOLDINGS (NEW JERSEY) CORP.—The Bank of New York Company, Inc.; *U.S. Public*, pg. 178
BOK FINANCIAL CORP.; *U.S. Public*, pg. 163
BANC ONE CORPORATION; *U.S. Public*, pg. 172
BANC ONE INDIANA CORPORATION—Banc One Corporation; *U.S. Public*, pg. 173
BANC ONE KENTUCKY CORPORATION—Banc One Corporation; *U.S. Public*, pg. 173
BANC ONE LEASING CO.—Banc One Corporation; *U.S. Public*, pg. 173
BANC ONE SERVICES CORPORATION—Banc One Corporation; *U.S. Public*, pg. 174
BANCO AMBROSIANO VENETO S.P.A.; *Int'l*, pg. 138
BANCO ESPANOL DE CREDITO SA—Banco Santander; *Int'l*, pg. 143
BANCO POPULAR—Banco Popular de Puerto Rico; *U.S. Public*, pg. 176
BANGKOK BANK OF COMMERCE LTD.; *Int'l*, pg. 146
BANGKOK BANK PUBLIC COMPANY LIMITED; *Int'l*, pg. 146
BANK LEUMI (LUXEMBOURG) S.A.—Bank Leumi le-Israel B.M.; *Int'l*, pg. 150
BANK OF AMERICA NT&SA—BankAmerica Corporation; *U.S. Public*, pg. 180
BANK OF HUNDRED—Huntington Bancshares Inc.; *U.S. Public*, pg. 850
BANK OF LAKE COUNTY, N.A.—Westamerica Bancorporation; *U.S. Public*, pg. 1756
THE BANK OF NEW YORK COMPANY, INC.; *U.S. Public*, pg. 178
BANK OF OKLAHOMA, N.A.—BOK Financial Corp.; *U.S. Public*, pg. 163
BANK OF PENNSYLVANIA—Allied Irish Banks, p.l.c.; *Int'l*, pg. 64
BANK OF SAN FRANCISCO—The San Francisco Co.; *U.S.* Public, pg. 1430
BANK ONE, ARIZONA, NA—Banc One Corporation; *U.S. Public*, pg. 173
BANK ONE, CHICAGO—Banc One Corporation; *U.S. Public*, pg. 173
BANK ONE, CINCINNATI—Banc One Corporation; *U.S. Public*, pg. 173
BANK ONE, COLORADO—Banc One Corporation; *U.S. Public*, pg. 173
BANK ONE, TEXAS CORP.—Banc One Corporation; *U.S. Public*, pg. 173
BANK ONE, WISCONSIN—Banc One Corporation; *U.S. Public*, pg. 174
BANKBOSTON CORPORATION; *U.S. Public*, pg. 183
BANKERS TRUST CO. OF FLORIDA, N.A.—Bankers Trust New York Corporation; *U.S. Public*, pg. 185
BANKNORTH GROUP INC.; *U.S. Public*, pg. 186
BANQUE D'HAWAII (VANUATU) LIMITED—Pacific Century Financial Corporation; *U.S. Public*, pg. 1248
BANQUE PARIBAS-CHICAGO—Compagnie Financiere de Paribas; *Int'l*, pg. 319
BANQUE PARIBAS-DALLAS—Compagnie Financiere de Paribas; *Int'l*, pg. 319
BANQUE PARIBAS-HOUSTON—Compagnie Financiere de Paribas; *Int'l*, pg. 319
BANQUE PARIBAS-LOS ANGELES—Compagnie Financiere de Paribas; *Int'l*, pg. 319
BANQUE PARIBAS-SAN FRANCISCO—Compagnie Financiere de Paribas; *Int'l*, pg. 319
BARNETT BANK OF SOUTHEAST GEORGIA, N.A.—NationsBank Corporation; *U.S. Public*, pg. 1162
BARNETT BANK OF SOUTHWEST GEORGIA—NationsBank Corporation; *U.S. Public*, pg. 1162
BARNETT BANKS, INC.—NationsBank Corporation; *U.S. Public*, pg. 1162
BAYBANK, N.A.—BankBoston Corporation; *U.S. Public*, pg. 184
BAYBANKS, INC.—BankBoston Corporation; *U.S. Public*, pg. 184
BENEFICIAL CORPORATION; *U.S. Public*, pg. 211
BENEFICIAL NATIONAL BANK—Beneficial Corporation; *U.S. Public*, pg. 211
BERLINER BANK AG—Bankgesellschaft Berlin; *Int'l*, pg. 159
BILL ACCEPTANCE CORPORATION LIMITED—Westpac Banking Corporation; *Int'l*, pg. 1496
BILL ACCEPTANCE CORPORATION LIMITED - VICTORIA—Westpac Banking Corporation; *Int'l*, pg. 1496
BOATMEN'S TRUST COMPANY, INC.—NationsBank Corporation; *U.S. Public*, pg. 1164
BOSTON TRADE BANK—BankBoston Corporation; *U.S. Public*, pg. 184
BRANCH BANKING & TRUST—BB&T Corporation; *U.S. Public*, pg. 160
BRENTON BANKS, INC.; *U.S. Public*, pg. 251
BROAD NATIONAL BANCORPORATION; *U.S. Public*, pg. 257
BROAD NATIONAL BANK—Broad National Bancorporation; *U.S. Public*, pg. 257
BROWN BROTHERS HARRIMAN TRUST CO. OF NEW YORK—Brown Brothers Harriman & Co.; *U.S. Private*, pg. 173
CALIFORNIA FEDERAL BANK—MacAndrews & Forbes Holdings Inc.; *U.S. Private*, pg. 690
CALIFORNIA STATE BANK-ANAHEIM—California State Bank; *U.S. Public*, pg. 294
CALIFORNIA STATE BANK-LAKE FOREST IRVINE—California State Bank; *U.S. Public*, pg. 294
CANADIAN WESTERN TRUST—Canadian Western Bank; *Int'l*, pg. 259
CAPITAL BANK, N.A.; *U.S. Private*, pg. 205
CAPITOLINE INVESTMENT SERVICES, INC.—Crestar Financial Corporation; *U.S. Public*, pg. 458
CHASE BANK OF FLORIDA, N.A.—The Chase Manhattan Corporation; *U.S. Public*, pg. 338
CHASE INVESTMENT BANK LIMITED—The Chase Manhattan Corporation; *U.S. Public*, pg. 339
THE CHASE MANHATTAN BANK—The Chase Manhattan Corporation; *U.S. Public*, pg. 338
THE CHASE MANHATTAN BANK (USA), NA—The Chase Manhattan Corporation; *U.S. Public*, pg. 338
THE CHASE MANHATTAN CORPORATION; *U.S. Public*, pg. 337
CHASE MANHATTAN, S.A.—The Chase Manhattan Corporation; *U.S. Public*, pg. 340
THE CHASE MANHATTAN TRUST CO. OF CALIFORNIA, N.A.—The Chase Manhattan Corporation; *U.S. Public*, pg. 338
THE CHIBA BANK, LTD.; *Int'l*, pg. 283
CITIBANK N.A.—Citicorp; *U.S. Public*, pg. 377
CITICORP; *U.S. Public*, pg. 376
CITIZENS BANK, GIBSON COUNTY REGION—CNB Bancshares, Inc.; *U.S. Public*, pg. 281
CITIZENS BANK OF NORTHWEST ARKANSAS—BOK Financial Corp.; *U.S. Public*, pg. 163
CITIZENS BANK, POSEY COUNTY REGION—CNB Bancshares, Inc.; *U.S. Public*, pg. 281
CITIZENS NATIONAL BANK OF LAKE GENEVA—Firstar Corporation; *U.S. Public*, pg. 643
CITIZENS NATIONAL BANK OF SOUTHERN PENNSYLVANIA—Susquehanna Bancshares, Inc.; *U.S. Public*, pg. 1542
THE CITIZENS NATIONAL BANK—Mercantile Bankshares Corporation; *U.S. Public*, pg. 1089
CITY NATIONAL BANK—City National Corporation; *U.S. Public*, pg. 381
CITY NATIONAL BANK OF BATON ROUGE—First Commerce Corporation; *U.S. Public*, pg. 629
COLORADO BUSINESS BANK—Colorado Business Bankshares, Inc.; *U.S. Private*, pg. 255
COLORADO BUSINESS BANKSHARES, INC.; *U.S. Private*, pg. 255
COLORADO NATIONAL BANK—U.S. Bancorp; *U.S. Public*, *pg. 1680*
COLORADO NATIONAL BANKSHARES, INC.—U.S. Bancorp; *U.S. Public*, pg. 1680
COMERICA BANK CALIFORNIA—Comerica Incorporated; *U.S. Public*, pg. 409
COMMERCE BANCSHARES, INC.; *U.S. Public*, pg. 409
COMMERCE BANK N.A.—Commerce Bancshares, Inc.; *U.S. Public*, pg. 409
COMMERCE BANK, N.A.—Commerce Bancshares, Inc.; *U.S. Public*, pg. 409
COMMERCIAL NATIONAL BANK OF BERWYN—Citizens Banking Corporation; *U.S. Public*, pg. 379
COMMUNITY BANK N.A.—Community Bank System, Inc.; *U.S. Public*, pg. 416
COMMUNITY BANK SYSTEM, INC.; *U.S. Public*, pg. 416
COMMUNITY FIRST BANK & TRUST—First Financial Bancorp; *U.S. Public*, pg. 633
COMMUNITY NATIONAL BANK—Community Bancorp; *U.S.* Public, pg. 416
COMPAGNIE FINANCIERE DE PARIBAS; *Int'l*, pg. 319
COMPASS BANCSHARES, INC.; *U.S. Public*, pg. 418
COMPASS BANK OF THE SOUTH, N.A.—Compass Bancshares, Inc.; *U.S. Public*, pg. 419
CONFEDERATION TRUST COMPANY—Confederation Life Insurance Company; *Int'l*, pg. 326
CORESTATES BANK—CoreStates Financial Corp.; *U.S. Public*, pg. 446
CORESTATES BANK, N.A.—CoreStates Financial Corp.; *U.S. Public*, pg. 446
CORESTATES BANK OF DELAWARE NA—CoreStates Financial Corp.; *U.S. Public*, pg. 447
CORESTATES CAPITAL CORP.—CoreStates Financial Corp.; *U.S. Public*, pg. 446
CORESTATES FINANCIAL CORP.; *U.S. Public*, pg. 446
CREDIT MUTUEL; *Int'l*, pg. 344
CREDIT SUISSE FIRST BOSTON—Credit Suisse Group; *Int'l*, pg. 345
CREGELUX SA—Banque Generale du Luxembourg SA; *Int'l*, pg. 162
CRESTAR BANK—Crestar Financial Corporation; *U.S. Public*, pg. 458
CRESTAR FINANCIAL CORPORATION; *U.S. Public*, pg. 458
CROSBIE & COMPANY INC.; *Int'l*, pg. 348
CULLEN/FROST BANKERS, INC.; *U.S. Public*, pg. 467
D & N BANK—D & N Financial Corporation; *U.S. Public*, pg. 472
DAUPHIN DEPOSIT BANK AND TRUST COMPANY—Allied Irish Banks, p.l.c.; *Int'l*, pg. 64
DEER PARK FEDERAL SAVINGS AND LOAN ASSOCIATION—Ameriana Bancorp; *U.S. Public*, pg. 66
DEN NORSKE BANK ASA; *Int'l*, pg. 392
DEPOSIT GUARANTY NATIONAL BANK—Deposit Guaranty Corp.; *U.S. Public*, pg. 500
DEPOSIT GUARANTY NATIONAL BANK OF LOUISIANA—Deposit Guaranty Corp.; *U.S. Public*, pg. 500
DRESDNER BANK AG; *Int'l*, pg. 417
EASTLAND NATIONAL BANK—First Financial Bankshares, Inc.; *U.S. Public*, pg. 633
EDEKA ZENTRALE AG; *Int'l*, pg. 433
EGYPTIAN BRITISH BANK S.A.E.—HSBC Holdings plc; *Int'l*, pg. 581
ELYRIA SAVINGS & TRUST NATIONAL BANK—FirstMerit Corporation; *U.S. Public*, pg. 646
EMPIRE NATIONAL BANK; *U.S. Private*, pg. 374
EQUATOR ADVISORY SERVICES LIMITED—HSBC Holdings plc; *Int'l*, pg. 580
EQUATOR HOLDINGS LTD.—HSBC Holdings plc; *Int'l*, pg. 580
EQUATOR LIMITED—HSBC Holdings plc; *Int'l*, pg. 580
EQUATOR TRADE SERVICES LIMITED—HSBC Holdings plc; *Int'l*, pg. 580
EUROPEAN INVESTMENT BANK; *Int'l*, pg. 465
EVANSTON BANK—GreatBanc, Inc.; *U.S. Public*, pg. 760
EXCHANGE BANK OF DUPAGE—ABN-AMRO Holding N.V.; *Int'l*, pg. 10
FARMERS AND MERCHANTS BANK AND TRUST—Susquehanna Bancshares, Inc.; *U.S. Public*, pg. 1542
FARMERS & MERCHANTS BANK OF CENTRAL CALIFORNIA; *U.S. Private*, pg. 394
FARMERS FIRST BANK—Susquehanna Bancshares, Inc.; *U.S. Public*, pg. 1542
FEDERATED BANK, S.S.B.—Firstar Corporation; *U.S. Public*, pg. 643
THE FIFTH THIRD BANK OF KENTUCKY—Fifth Third Bancorp; *U.S. Public*, pg. 621
THE FIFTH THIRD BANK OF NORTHWESTERN OHIO, NATIONAL ASSOCIATION—Fifth Third Bancorp; *U.S. Public*, pg. 622
THE FIFTH THIRD BANK OF WESTERN OHIO, NATIONAL ASSOCIATION—Fifth Third Bancorp; *U.S. Public*, pg. 622
FIRST AMERICAN FEDERAL SAVINGS BANK—First American Corporation; *U.S. Public*, pg. 624
FIRST AMERICAN METRO CORP.—First Union Corporation; *U.S. Public*, pg. 640
FIRST BANK NATIONAL ASSOCIATION—U.S. Bancorp; *U.S. Public*, pg. 1681
FIRST CHARTER CORPORATION; *U.S. Public*, pg. 627
FIRST CHARTER NATIONAL BANK—First Charter Corporation; *U.S. Public*, pg. 627
FIRST CHICAGO NBD CORPORATION; *U.S. Public*, pg. 627
FIRST COAST COMMUNITY BANK & TRUST—Synovus Financial Corp.; *U.S. Public*, pg. 1549
FIRST COMMERCIAL CORPORATION; *U.S. Public*, pg. 630
FIRST DEPOSIT NATIONAL BANK—Providian Financial Corporation; *U.S. Public*, pg. 1338
FIRST INTERNATIONAL BANCORP, INC.; *U.S. Public*, pg. 635
FIRST MARYLAND BANCORP—Allied Irish Banks, p.l.c.; *Int'l*, pg. 64
FIRST MARYLAND INTL. BANKING CORP.—Allied Irish Banks, p.l.c.; *Int'l*, pg. 64
FIRST MIDWEST BANK, N.A.—First Midwest Bancorp, Inc.; *U.S. Public*, pg. 636
FIRST NATIONAL BANK—Old National Bancorp; *U.S. Public*, pg. 1217
FIRST NATIONAL BANK IN CHICAGO HEIGHTS—GreatBanc, Inc.; *U.S. Public*, pg. 760
FIRST NATIONAL BANK IN CLEBURNE—First Financial Bankshares, Inc.; *U.S. Public*, pg. 633
FIRST NATIONAL BANK IN MASSILLON—FirstMerit Corporation; *U.S. Public*, pg. 646
FIRST NATIONAL BANK OF ABILENE—First Financial Bankshares, Inc.; *U.S. Public*, pg. 633
FIRST NATIONAL BANK OF BLUE ISLAND—Great Lakes Financial Resources, Inc.; *U.S. Private*, pg. 474
FIRST NATIONAL BANK OF CENTRAL ILLINOIS—Firstbank of Illinois Co.; *U.S. Public*, pg. 644
FIRST NATIONAL BANK OF CHICAGO—First Chicago NBD Corporation; *U.S. Public*, pg. 627
FIRST NATIONAL BANK OF CLIFTON FORGE—MainStreet BankGroup Incorporated; *U.S. Public*, pg. 1039
FIRST NATIONAL BANK OF COMMERCE—First Commerce Corporation; *U.S. Public*, pg. 629
FIRST NATIONAL BANK OF CROSSVILLE—Union Planters Corporation; *U.S. Public*, pg. 1669
FIRST NATIONAL BANK OF HUNTINGTON—Fort Wayne National Corporation; *U.S. Public*, pg. 674
FIRST NATIONAL BANK OF JENKS—Banc One Corporation; *U.S. Public*, pg. 174
THE FIRST NATIONAL BANK OF LAFAYETTE—First Commerce Corporation; *U.S. Public*, pg. 630
THE FIRST NATIONAL BANK OF LAKE CHARLES—First Commerce Corporation; *U.S. Public*, pg. 630
FIRST NATIONAL BANK OF MARYLAND—Allied Irish Banks, p.l.c.; *Int'l*, pg. 64
FIRST NATIONAL BANK OF OHIO—FirstMerit Corporation; *U.S. Public*, pg. 646
FIRST NATIONAL BANK OF PENNSYLVANIA—F.N.B. Corporation; *U.S. Public*, pg. 607
THE FIRST NATIONAL BANK OF ST. MARY'S—Mercantile Bankshares Corporation; *U.S. Public*, pg. 1089
FIRST NATIONAL BANK OF SWEETWATER—First Financial Bankshares, Inc.; *U.S. Public*, pg. 633
FIRST NATIONAL BANK OF WARSAW—Fort Wayne National Corporation; *U.S. Public*, pg. 674
FIRST OF AMERICA BANK CORPORATION; *U.S. Public*, pg. 636
FIRST OMNI BANK, N.A.—Allied Irish Banks, p.l.c.; *Int'l*, pg. 65
FIRST SECURITY CORPORATION; *U.S. Public*, pg. 637
FIRST STATE BANK N.A., ABILENE—Independent Bankshares, Inc.; *U.S. Public*, pg. 874
FIRST TENNESSEE BANK NATIONAL ASSOCIATION—First Tennessee National Corporation; *U.S. Public*, pg. 639
FIRST TENNESSEE NATIONAL CORPORATION; *U.S. Public*, pg. 638
FIRST UNION NATIONAL BANK OF CONNECTICUT—First Union Corporation; *U.S. Public*, pg. 640
FIRST UNION NATIONAL BANK OF FLORIDA—First Union Corporation; *U.S. Public*, pg. 640
FIRST UNION NATIONAL BANK OF MARYLAND—First Union Corporation; *U.S. Public*, pg. 640

FIRST UNION NATIONAL BANK OF NORTH CAROLINA—First Union Corporation; *U.S. Public*, pg. 640
FIRST UNION NATIONAL BANK OF SOUTH CAROLINA—First Union Corporation; *U.S. Public*, pg. 640
FIRST UNION NATIONAL BANK OF TENNESSEE—First Union Corporation; *U.S. Public*, pg. 640
FIRST UNION NATIONAL BANK OF VIRGINIA—First Union Corporation; *U.S. Public*, pg. 640
FIRST UNION NATIONAL BANK OF WASHINGTON—First Union Corporation; *U.S. Public*, pg. 640
FIRST WESTERN BANK, NATIONAL ASSOCIATION—First Western Bancorp, Inc.; *U.S. Public*, pg. 642
FIRST WISCONSIN TRUST COMPANY OF FLORIDA—Firstar Corporation; *U.S. Public*, pg. 643
FIRSTAR BANK OF MINNESOTA—Firstar Corporation; *U.S. Public*, pg. 643
FIRSTAR CORPORATION; *U.S. Public*, pg. 642
FIRSTBANK PUERTO RICO; *U.S. Public*, pg. 644
FLEET BANK, N.A.—Fleet Financial Group, Inc.; *U.S. Public*, pg. 649
FLEET BANK-NH—Fleet Financial Group, Inc.; *U.S. Public*, pg. 649
FLEET FINANCIAL GROUP, INC.; *U.S. Public*, pg. 648
FLEET NATIONAL BANK—Fleet Financial Group, Inc.; *U.S. Public*, pg. 649
FORT WAYNE NATIONAL BANK—Fort Wayne National Corporation; *U.S. Public*, pg. 674
FORT WAYNE NATIONAL CORPORATION; *U.S. Public*, pg. 673
FRANKLIN BANK—Franklin Resources, Inc.; *U.S. Public*, pg. 680
FROST NATIONAL BANK—Cullen/Frost Bankers, Inc.; *U.S. Public*, pg. 467
FULTON FINANCIAL CORP.; *U.S. Public*, pg. 687
GLEN FALLS NATIONAL BANK & TRUST COMPANY—Arrow Financial Corporation; *U.S. Public*, pg. 135
GRUPO BANCO EXTERIOR—Argentaria Corporacion Bancaria de Espana, S.A.; *Int'l*, pg. 80
GUYERZELLER BANK AG—HSBC Holdings plc; *Int'l*, pg. 582
HFC TRUST & SAVINGS LTD.—Household International, Inc.; *U.S. Public*, pg. 842
HSBC AMERICAS—HSBC Holdings plc; *Int'l*, pg. 580
HSBC INVESTMENT BANK ASIA LTD.—HSBC Holdings plc; *Int'l*, pg. 582
HSBC INVESTMENT BANK LIMITED—HSBC Holdings plc; *Int'l*, pg. 580
HSBC PRIVATE BANKING (C.I.) LIMITED—HSBC Holdings plc; *Int'l*, pg. 580
HSBC PRIVATE EQUITY EUROPE LIMITED—HSBC Holdings plc; *Int'l*, pg. 580
HSBC ROBERTS S.A.—HSBC Holdings plc; *Int'l*, pg. 583
HAMBURGER SPARKASSE; *Int'l*, pg. 590
HANG SENG BANK LIMITED—HSBC Holdings plc; *Int'l*, pg. 583
HANSON BANK LTD.—Hanson PLC; *Int'l*, pg. 592
HARRIS BANK BARRINGTON, N.A.—Bank of Montreal; *Int'l*, pg. 154
HARRIS BANK BATAVIA, N.A.—Bank of Montreal; *Int'l*, pg. 154
HARRIS BANK GLENCOE-NORTHBROOK, N.A.—Bank of Montreal; *Int'l*, pg. 154
HARRIS BANK HINSDALE N.A.—Bank of Montreal; *Int'l*, pg. 154
HARRIS BANK WILMETTE N.A.—Bank of Montreal; *Int'l*, pg. 154
HARRIS BANK WINNETKA N.A.—Bank of Montreal; *Int'l*, pg. 154
HARRIS BANKCORP, INC.—Bank of Montreal; *Int'l*, pg. 154
HIBERNIA CORPORATION; *U.S. Public*, pg. 825
HIBERNIA NATIONAL BANK—Hibernia Corporation; *U.S. Public*, pg. 825
HICKORY POINT BANK & TRUST—Archer Daniels Midland Company (ADM); *U.S. Public*, pg. 128
HIGH POINT FINANCIAL CORP.; *U.S. Public*, pg. 826
HONGKONG BANK MALAYSIA BERHAD—HSBC Holdings plc; *Int'l*, pg. 583
HONGKONGBANK OF AUSTRALIA LIMITED—HSBC Holdings plc; *Int'l*, pg. 583
HORIZON BANK—Horizon Bancorp; *U.S. Private*, pg. 539
HOUSEHOLD BANK, N.A.—Household International, Inc.; *U.S. Public*, pg. 842
HUNTINGTON BANCSHARES INC.; *U.S. Public*, pg. 849
HUNTINGTON BANCSHARES INDIANA, INC.—Huntington Bancshares Inc.; *U.S. Public*, pg. 850
HUNTINGTON BANCSHARES MICHIGAN, INC.—Huntington Bancshares Inc.; *U.S. Public*, pg. 850
HUNTINGTON NATIONAL BANK—Huntington Bancshares Inc.; *U.S. Public*, pg. 850
IBJ SCHRODER BANKING CORPORATION—The Industrial Bank of Japan, Limited; *Int'l*, pg. 675
ILLINOIS BANC ONE CORPORATION—Banc One Corporation; *U.S. Public*, pg. 174
IMPERIAL BANK—Imperial Bancorp; *U.S. Public*, pg. 871
INDEPENDENT BANK—Independent Bank Corporation; *U.S. Public*, pg. 874
INDEPENDENT BANK-SOUTH MICHIGAN—Independent Bank Corporation; *U.S. Public*, pg. 874
INDEPENDENT BANK-WEST MICHIGAN—Independent Bank Corporation; *U.S. Public*, pg. 874
INTERMOUNTAIN BANKSHARES OF COLORADO, INC.—Banc One Corporation; *U.S. Public*, pg. 173
JC PENNEY NATIONAL BANK—JC Penney Company, Inc.; *U.S. Public*, pg. 917
KEY BANK OF ALASKA—Keycorp; *U.S. Public*, pg. 954
KEY BANK OF UTAH—Keycorp; *U.S. Public*, pg. 954
KEY BANK OF VERMONT—Keycorp; *U.S. Public*, pg. 954
KEY BANK USA N.A.—Keycorp; *U.S. Public*, pg. 954
KEYCORP; *U.S. Public*, pg. 954
KEYSTONE HERITAGE GROUP, INC.—Fulton Financial Corp.; *U.S. Public*, pg. 687
KOCBANK A.S.—Koc Holding A.S.; *Int'l*, pg. 741
KREDIETBANK LONDON BRANCH—Kredietbank N.V.; *Int'l*, pg. 760
LANDESGIROKASSE BANK; *Int'l*, pg. 799
LASALLE BANK MADISON—ABN-AMRO Holding N.V.; *Int'l*, pg. 10
LASALLE BANK NORTHBROOK/VERNON HILLS—ABN-AMRO Holding N.V.; *Int'l*, pg. 10
LASALLE NATIONAL BANK—ABN-AMRO Holding N.V.; *Int'l*, pg. 10
LEBANON VALLEY FARMERS BANK—Fulton Financial Corp.; *U.S. Public*, pg. 688
LIBERTY BANK & TRUST OF OKLAHAOMA CITY—Banc One Corporation; *U.S. Public*, pg. 174
LIBERTY BANK & TRUST COMPANY OF OKLAHOMA CITY—Banc One Corporation; *U.S. Public*, pg. 174
LIBERTY BANK & TRUST COMPANY OF TULSA—Banc One Corporation; *U.S. Public*, pg. 174
THE LONG-TERM CREDIT BANK OF JAPAN, LIMITED; *Int'l*, pg. 815
M & I BANK—Marshall & Ilsley Corporation; *U.S. Public*, pg. 1050
M & I FIRST AMERICAN BANK—Marshall & Ilsley Corporation; *U.S. Public*, pg. 1050
M & I FIRST NATIONAL BANK—Marshall & Ilsley Corporation; *U.S. Public*, pg. 1050
M & I MID-STATE BANK—Marshall & Ilsley Corporation; *U.S. Public*, pg. 1050
MBNA AMERICA BANK N.A.—MBNA Corporation; *U.S. Public*, pg. 1023
MBNA CORPORATION; *U.S. Public*, pg. 1023
MBNA HALLMARK INFORMATION SYSTEMS—MBNA Corporation; *U.S. Public*, pg. 1023
MBNA MARKETING SYSTEMS, INC.—MBNA Corporation; *U.S. Public*, pg. 1023
MNC FINANCIAL, INC.—First Tennessee National Corporation; *U.S. Public*, pg. 639
MAGNA BANK—Magna Group, Inc.; *U.S. Public*, pg. 1037
MAGNA BANK, CARBONDALE REGION—Magna Group, Inc.; *U.S. Public*, pg. 1037
MAINSTREET TRUST COMPANY, N.A.—MainStreet BankGroup Incorporated; *U.S. Public*, pg. 1039
MANUFACTURERS BANK—The Sakura Bank, Limited; *Int'l*, pg. 1179
MARQUETTE BANCSHARES INC.; *U.S. Private*, pg. 706
MARQUIS INVESTMENTS—First Commerce Corporation; *U.S. Public*, pg. 629
MARSHALL & ILSLEY CORPORATION; *U.S. Public*, pg. 1049
MELLON BANK (DE) NATIONAL ASSOCIATION—Mellon Bank Corporation; *U.S. Public*, pg. 1085
MELLON BANK (MD)—Mellon Bank Corporation; *U.S. Public*, pg. 1085
MELLON BANK, N.A.—Mellon Bank Corporation; *U.S. Public*, pg. 1085
MELLON BANK, N.A.-COMMONWEALTH REGION—Mellon Bank Corporation; *U.S. Public*, pg. 1085
MELLON PSFS—Mellon Bank Corporation; *U.S. Public*, pg. 1085
MERCANTILE BANCORPORATION INC.; *U.S. Public*, pg. 1087
MERCANTILE BANK; *U.S. Private*, pg. 731
MERCANTILE BANK—Mercantile Bancorporation Inc.; *U.S. Public*, pg. 1087
MERCANTILE BANK OF IOWA—Mercantile Bancorporation Inc.; *U.S. Public*, pg. 1087
MERCANTILE BANK OF ST. LOUIS N.A.—Mercantile Bancorporation Inc.; *U.S. Public*, pg. 1087
MERCANTILE TRUST COMPANY N.A.—Mercantile Bancorporation Inc.; *U.S. Public*, pg. 1088
MERCHANTS NATIONAL BANK—Old National Bancorp; *U.S. Public*, pg. 1217
MICHIGAN NATIONAL BANK, N.A.—National Australia Bank Limited; *Int'l*, pg. 906
MICHIGAN NATIONAL CORPORATION—National Australia Bank Limited; *Int'l*, pg. 906
MIDLAND BANK INTERNATIONAL FINANCE CORPORATION LIMITED—HSBC Holdings plc; *Int'l*, pg. 580
MIDLAND HOLDING PARTICIPACAO, ADMINISTRACAO E REPRESENTACOES LIMITADA—HSBC Holdings plc; *Int'l*, pg. 580
MIDLANTIC BANK, N.A.—PNC Bank Corp.; *U.S. Public*, pg. 1242
THE MITSUBISHI TRUST AND BANKING CORPORATION; *Int'l*, pg. 876
J.P. MORGAN TRUST BANK LTD.—J.P. Morgan Co. Incorporated; *U.S. Public*, pg. 1131
MORGANFIELD NATIONAL BANK—Old National Bancorp; *U.S. Public*, pg. 1217
NBD BANK (INDIANA)—First Chicago NBD Corporation; *U.S. Public*, pg. 628
NBD BANK (MICHIGAN)—First Chicago NBD Corporation; *U.S. Public*, pg. 628
NBD BANK (OHIO)—First Chicago NBD Corporation; *U.S. Public*, pg. 628
NBD BANKING COMPANY—First Chicago NBD Corporation; *U.S. Public*, pg. 628
NBD BANKING COMPANY, NORTH—First Chicago NBD Corporation; *U.S. Public*, pg. 628
NBD BANKING COMPANY, NORTHEAST—First Chicago NBD Corporation; *U.S. Public*, pg. 628
NBD BANKING COMPANY, SOUTHWEST—First Chicago NBD Corporation; *U.S. Public*, pg. 628
NATIONAL BANK OF ARIZONA—Zions Bancorporation; *U.S. Public*, pg. 1793
NATIONAL BANK OF CANADA; *Int'l*, pg. 907
THE NATIONAL BANK OF FREDERICKSBURG—Mercantile Bankshares Corporation; *U.S. Public*, pg. 1089
NATIONAL BANK OF SOLOMON ISLANDS—Pacific Century Financial Corporation; *U.S. Public*, pg. 1248
THE NATIONAL BANK OF SOUTH CAROLINA—Synovus Financial Corp.; *U.S. Public*, pg. 1549
THE NATIONAL BANK OF SUSSEX COUNTY—High Point Financial Corp.; *U.S. Public*, pg. 826
NATIONAL BANK OF WALTON COUNTY—Synovus Financial Corp.; *U.S. Public*, pg. 1549
NATIONAL CITY BANK—National City Corporation; *U.S. Public*, pg. 1154
NATIONAL CITY TRUST COMPANY—National City Corporation; *U.S. Public*, pg. 1154
NATIONSBANK CORPORATION; *U.S. Public*, pg. 1162
NATIONSBANK OF ARKANSAS—NationsBank Corporation; *U.S. Public*, pg. 1164
NEVADA NATIONAL BANCORPORATION—BankAmerica Corporation; *U.S. Public*, pg. 181
NEW JERSEY NATIONAL BANK—CoreStates Financial Corp.; *U.S. Public*, pg. 447
NEWFOUNDLAND CAPITAL CORPORATION LIMITED; *Int'l*, pg. 924
NORD/LB LONDON—Norddeutsche Landesbank (NORD/LB); *Int'l*, pg. 958
NORD/LB NEW YORK—Norddeutsche Landesbank (NORD/LB); *Int'l*, pg. 958
NORDDEUTSCHE LANDESBANK (NORD/LB); *Int'l*, pg. 957
NORTH AMERICAN SALES—National Data Corporation; *U.S. Public*, pg. 1156
NORTHERN TRUST BANK OF ARIZONA, N.A.—Northern Trust Corporation; *U.S. Public*, pg. 1196
NORTHERN TRUST BANK OF FLORIDA, N.A.—Northern Trust Corporation; *U.S. Public*, pg. 1196
THE NORTHERN TRUST COMPANY—Northern Trust Corporation; *U.S. Public*, pg. 1197
NORWEST BANK EL PASO, N.A.—Norwest Corporation; *U.S. Public*, pg. 1201
NORWEST BANK ILLINOIS, N.A.—Norwest Corporation; *U.S. Public*, pg. 1202
NORWEST BANK MINNESOTA NORTH, N.A.—Norwest Corporation; *U.S. Public*, pg. 1202
NORWEST BANK NEBRASKA, N.A.—Norwest Corporation; *U.S. Public*, pg. 1202
NORWEST BANK SOUTH DAKOTA, N.A.—Norwest Corporation; *U.S. Public*, pg. 1203
NORWEST BANK WISCONSIN GREEN BAY N.A.—Norwest Corporation; *U.S. Public*, pg. 1203
NORWEST CORPORATION; *U.S. Public*, pg. 1201
OLD KENT FINANCIAL CORPORATION; *U.S. Public*, pg. 1216
OLD NATIONAL BANCORP; *U.S. Public*, pg. 1217
OLD NATIONAL BANK—Old National Bancorp; *U.S. Public*, pg. 1217
THE OLD PHOENIX NATIONAL BANK OF MEDINA—FirstMerit Corporation; *U.S. Public*, pg. 646
OMEGA FINANCIAL CORPORATION; *U.S. Public*, pg. 1222
PNC BANK—PNC Bank Corp.; *U.S. Public*, pg. 1242
PNC BANK, N.A.—PNC Bank Corp.; *U.S. Public*, pg. 1243
PNC BANK, NORTHERN KENTUCKY—PNC Bank Corp.; *U.S. Public*, pg. 1243
PNC BANK, OHIO NATIONAL ASSOC.—PNC Bank Corp.; *U.S. Public*, pg. 1243
PNC NATIONAL BANK—PNC Bank Corp.; *U.S. Public*, pg. 1243
PNC-NJ N.A.—PNC Bank Corp.; *U.S. Public*, pg. 1243
PNC TRUST COMPANY OF FLORIDA, N.A.—PNC Bank Corp.; *U.S. Public*, pg. 1244
PENNSYLVANIA NATIONAL BANK—Keystone Financial Inc.; *U.S. Public*, pg. 956
PEOPLES FEDERAL SAVINGS BANK—FirstMerit Corporation; *U.S. Public*, pg. 647
PEOPLES NATIONAL BANK—Old National Bancorp; *U.S. Public*, pg. 1217
PEOPLES NATIONAL BANK OF CENTRAL PENNSYLVANIA—Omega Financial Corporation; *U.S. Public*, pg. 1222
PEOPLES SAVINGS BANK OF ASHTABULA—FirstMerit Corporation; *U.S. Public*, pg. 647
PREMIER BANK N.A.—Banc One Corporation; *U.S. Public*, pg. 173
PRINCETON BANK & TRUST COMPANY NATIONAL ASSOCIATION—The Chase Manhattan Corporation; *U.S. Public*, pg. 338
THE PROVIDENT BANK—Provident Financial Group, Inc.; *U.S. Public*, pg. 1338
PROVIDENT COMMERCIAL GROUP, INC.—Provident Financial Group, Inc.; *U.S. Public*, pg. 1338
PROVIDIAN FINANCIAL CORPORATION; *U.S. Public*, pg. 1338
RABOBANK NEDERLAND; *Int'l*, pg. 1082
RAIFFEISEN ZENTRALBANK OSTERREICH; *Int'l*, pg. 1084
RAPIDES BANK & TRUST COMPANY OF ALEXANDRIA—First Commerce Corporation; *U.S. Public*, pg. 630
REGIONS BANK/ANNISTON—Regions Financial Corporation; *U.S. Public*, pg. 1371
REGIONS BANK/MOBILE—Regions Financial Corporation; *U.S. Public*, pg. 1372
REGIONS BANK/TALLADEGA COUNTY—Regions Financial Corporation; *U.S. Public*, pg. 1373
REPUBLIC INTERNATIONAL BANK OF NEW YORK—Republic New York Corporation; *U.S. Public*, pg. 1380
REPUBLIC NATIONAL BANK OF NEW YORK—Republic New York Corporation; *U.S. Public*, pg. 1380
REPUBLIC NEW YORK CORPORATION; *U.S. Public*, pg. 1380
REPUBLIC NEW YORK TRUST COMPANY OF FLORIDA, NATIONAL ASSOCIATION—Republic New York Corporation; *U.S. Public*, pg. 1381
RHODE ISLAND HOSPITAL TRUST NATIONAL BANK—BankBoston Corporation; *U.S. Public*, pg. 184
RIGGS A P BANK LIMITED—Riggs National Corporation; *U.S. Public*, pg. 1390
RIGGS BANK N.A.—Riggs National Corporation; *U.S. Public*, pg. 1390
THE RIGGS NATIONAL BANK OF MARYLAND—Riggs National Corporation; *U.S. Public*, pg. 1390

THE RIGGS NATIONAL BANK OF VIRGINIA—Riggs National Corporation; *U.S. Public*, pg. 1390
RIGGS NATIONAL CORPORATION; *U.S. Public*, pg. 1389
ROCKVILLE NATIONAL BANK—Old National Bancorp; *U.S. Public*, pg. 1217
THE RUSSELL NATIONAL BANK—Omega Financial Corporation; *U.S. Public*, pg. 1222
SABANCI HOLDING A.S.; *Int'l*, pg. 1167
SAFETY FUND NATIONAL BANK—CFX Bank; *U.S. Public*, pg. 278
SAN ANGELO NATIONAL BANK—First Financial Bankshares, Inc.; *U.S. Public*, pg. 633
SAN JOSE NATIONAL BANK—SJNB Financial Corp.; *U.S. Public*, pg. 1418
SECURITY PACIFIC BANK ALASKA, N.A.—BankAmerica Corporation; *U.S. Public*, pg. 180
SHIZUOKA BANK (EUROPE) S.A.—Shizuoka Bank, Ltd.; *Int'l*, pg. 1236
SHIZUOKA BANK, LTD.; *Int'l*, pg. 1236
SHIZUOKA FINANCE H.K. LIMITED—Shizuoka Bank, Ltd.; *Int'l*, pg. 1236
SIERRA WEST BANK—Sierra West Bancorp; *U.S. Public*, pg. 1470
SIME BANK BERHAD—Sime Darby Berhad; *Int'l*, pg. 1250
SMITHTOWN BANCORP, INC.; *U.S. Public*, pg. 1479
SOCIETY NATIONAL BANK—Keycorp; *U.S. Public*, pg. 954
SOUTHTRUST BANK, COVINGTON COUNTY—SouthTrust Corporation; *U.S. Public*, pg. 1491
SOUTHWEST NATIONAL BANK OF PENNSYLVANIA—Southwest National Corporation; *U.S. Public*, pg. 1493
SPRING GROVE NATIONAL BANK—Susquehanna Bancshares, Inc.; *U.S. Public*, pg. 1542
STAR BANK, N.A.—Starbanc Corporation; *U.S. Public*, pg. 1510
STARBANC CORPORATION; *U.S. Public*, pg. 1510
STATE STREET CORPORATION; *U.S. Public*, pg. 1513
SUDWESTLB; *Int'l*, pg. 1304
THE SUMITOMO TRUST & BANKING CO., LTD.; *Int'l*, pg. 1317
SUMMIT BANCORP; *U.S. Public*, pg. 1527
SUN BANK D/B/A WASTONTOWN NATIONAL BANK—Sun Bancorp, Inc.; *U.S. Public*, pg. 1529
SUNTRUST—SunTrust Banks, Inc.; *U.S. Public*, pg. 1537
SUNTRUST BANK, CENTRAL FLORIDA, N.A—SunTrust Banks, Inc.; *U.S. Public*, pg. 1537
SUNTRUST BANK, MIAMI, N.A.—SunTrust Banks, Inc.; *U.S. Public*, pg. 1537
SUNTRUST BANK, NORTH FLORIDA, N.A.—SunTrust Banks, Inc.; *U.S. Public*, pg. 1537
SUNTRUST BANKS, INC.; *U.S. Public*, pg. 1537
SUNTRUST BANKS OF GEORGIA, INC.—SunTrust Banks, Inc.; *U.S. Public*, pg. 1538
TEXAS COMMERCE BANK, N.A.—The Chase Manhattan Corporation; *U.S. Public*, pg. 339
TEXAS NATIONAL BANK—First Financial Bankshares, Inc.; *U.S. Public*, pg. 633
TRANS FINANCIAL, INC.; *U.S. Public*, pg. 1628
TRILON FINANCIAL CORP.—EdperBrascan Corporation; *Int'l*, pg. 434
TRINKAUS & BURKHARDT (INTERNATIONAL) S.A.—HSBC Holdings plc; *Int'l*, pg. 584
TRUST COMPANY OF GEORGIA—SunTrust Banks, Inc.; *U.S. Public*, pg. 1538
TRUSTCO BANK CORP., NY; *U.S. Public*, pg. 1643
TRUSTCO BANK, N.A.—TrustCo Bank Corp., NY; *U.S. Public*, pg. 1643
TRUSTCORP.—D.A. Davidson & Co.; *U.S. Private*, pg. 314
UMB BANK OF THE WEST, N.A.—UMB Financial Corporation; *U.S. Public*, pg. 1654
UMB COLUMBINE NATIONAL BANK—UMB Financial Corporation; *U.S. Public*, pg. 1654
UMB FINANCIAL CORPORATION; *U.S. Public*, pg. 1653
UNION PLANTERS BANK—Union Planters Corporation; *U.S. Public*, pg. 1669
UNION PLANTERS CORPORATION; *U.S. Public*, pg. 1668
UNITED BANKSHARES, INC.; *U.S. Public*, pg. 1674
US BANK—BankAmerica Corporation; *U.S. Public*, pg. 181
U.S. BANK OF WASHINGTON N.A.—U.S. Bancorp; *U.S. Public*, pg. 1681
UNITED STATES NATIONAL BANK—Cullen/Frost Bankers, Inc.; *U.S. Public*, pg. 467
UNITED STATES NATIONAL BANK OF OREGON—U.S. Bancorp; *U.S. Public*, pg. 1681
VALLEY NATIONAL BANK—Valley National Bancorp; *U.S. Public*, pg. 1705
VALLEY NATIONAL BANK OF CORTEZ—Zions Bancorporation; *U.S. Public*, pg. 1793
VEVAY DEPOSIT BANK—First Financial Bancorp; *U.S. Public*, pg. 633
WACHOVIA BANK—Wachovia Corporation; *U.S. Public*, pg. 1730
WACHOVIA BANK OF GEORGIA, N.A.—Wachovia Corporation; *U.S. Public*, pg. 1730
WACHOVIA BANK OF NORTH CAROLINA, N.A.—Wachovia Corporation; *U.S. Public*, pg. 1730
WACHOVIA BANK OF SOUTH CAROLINA, N.A.—Wachovia Corporation; *U.S. Public*, pg. 1730
WARDLEY INTERNATIONAL LIMITED—HSBC Holdings plc; *Int'l*, pg. 582
WEATHERFORD NATIONAL BANK—First Financial Bankshares, Inc.; *U.S. Public*, pg. 633
WELLS FARGO & COMPANY—Wells Fargo & Company; *U.S. Public*, pg. 1753
WELLS FARGO BANK, NATIONAL ASSN.—Wells Fargo & Company; *U.S. Public*, pg. 1753
WEST COAST BANCORP; *U.S. Public*, pg. 1755
WESTAMERICA BANK—Westamerica Bancorporation; *U.S. Public*, pg. 1756
WHITNEY NATIONAL BANK—Whitney Holding Corporation; *U.S. Public*, pg. 1766
WUESTENROT STAVEBNI SPORITELNA A.S.—Wuestenrot Holding GmbH; *Int'l*, pg. 1514
YAMAICHI TRUST & BANK, LTD.—Yamaichi Securities Co., Ltd.; *Int'l*, pg. 1517
YASUDA BANK AND TRUST COMPANY (U.S.A.)—The Yasuda Trust and Banking Co., Ltd.; *Int'l*, pg. 1520
THE YORK BANK AND TRUST COMPANY—Allied Irish Banks, p.l.c.; *Int'l*, pg. 65
YORKSHIRE BUILDING SOCIETY; *Int'l*, pg. 1522
ZIONS BANCORPORATION; *U.S. Public*, pg. 1792
ZIONS FIRST NATIONAL BANK—Zions Bancorporation; *U.S. Public*, pg. 1793

6022 — STATE COMMERCIAL BANKS & TRUST COMPANIES

AMERICAN EXPRESS FINANCIAL ADVISOR—American Express Company; *U.S. Public*, pg. 73
AMSOUTH BANK OF WALKER COUNTY—AmSouth Bancorporation; *U.S. Public*, pg. 105
ANCHOR FINANCIAL CORPORATION; *U.S. Public*, pg. 111
THE ANNAPOLIS BANKING & TRUST CO.—Mercantile Bankshares Corporation; *U.S. Public*, pg. 1088
ARCHER DANIELS MIDLAND COMPANY (ADM); *U.S. Public*, pg. 127
ASSOCIATED BANC-CORP; *U.S. Public*, pg. 140
ASSOCIATED BANK NORTH—Associated Banc-Corp; *U.S. Public*, pg. 140
ATLANTIC BANK—First Virginia Banks, Inc.; *U.S. Public*, pg. 642
THE AUBURN STATE BANK—Fort Wayne National Corporation; *U.S. Public*, pg. 674
BB&T OF SOUTH CAROLINA—BB&T Corporation; *U.S. Public*, pg. 160
B.M.J. FINANCIAL CORP.—Summit Bancorp; *U.S. Public*, pg. 1528
BALTIMORE TRUST COMPANY—Mercantile Bankshares Corporation; *U.S. Public*, pg. 1088
BANC ONE-NEWARK—Banc One Corporation; *U.S. Public*, pg. 173
BANK OF AGRICULTURE & COMMERCE; *U.S. Private*, pg. 114
BANK OF AMERICA—BankAmerica Corporation; *U.S. Public*, pg. 180
BANK OF AMERICA ILLINOIS—BankAmerica Corporation; *U.S. Public*, pg. 180
BANK OF CARROLL—MainStreet BankGroup Incorporated; *U.S. Public*, pg. 1038
BANK OF COWETA—Synovus Financial Corp.; *U.S. Public*, pg. 1549
BANK OF DWIGHT—Pontiac Bancorp, Inc.; *U.S. Public*, pg. 1316
BANK OF FERRUM—MainStreet BankGroup Incorporated; *U.S. Public*, pg. 1038
BANK OF HAWAII—Pacific Century Financial Corporation; *U.S. Public*, pg. 1248
BANK OF HAZLEHURST—Synovus Financial Corp.; *U.S. Public*, pg. 1549
BANK OF HOMEWOOD—Great Lakes Financial Resources, Inc.; *U.S. Private*, pg. 474
BANK OF MATTESON—Great Lakes Financial Resources, Inc.; *U.S. Private*, pg. 474
THE BANK OF MID-JERSEY—Summit Bancorp; *U.S. Public*, pg. 1528
BANK OF MISSISSIPPI—Bancorp South Inc.; *U.S. Public*, pg. 176
THE BANK OF NEW YORK (DELAWARE)—The Bank of New York Company, Inc.; *U.S. Public*, pg. 178
BANK OF NORTH DAKOTA; *U.S. Private*, pg. 114
BANK OF PENSACOLA—Synovus Financial Corp.; *U.S. Public*, pg. 1549
BANK OF PONTIAC—Pontiac Bancorp, Inc.; *U.S. Public*, pg. 1316
BANK OF SMITHTOWN; *U.S. Private*, pg. 114
BANK OF SOUTHERN MARYLAND—Mercantile Bankshares Corporation; *U.S. Public*, pg. 1088
BANK OF THE HUDSON—Poughkeepsie Financial Corp.; *U.S. Public*, pg. 1319
BANK OF THE WEST—Banque Nationale de Paris; *Int'l*, pg. 163
BANK OF UTAH; *U.S. Private*, pg. 114
BANK ONE, TEXAS CORP.—Banc One Corporation; *U.S. Public*, pg. 173
BANKERS TRUST COMPANY—Bankers Trust New York Corporation; *U.S. Public*, pg. 185
BANKERS TRUST (DELAWARE)—Bankers Trust New York Corporation; *U.S. Public*, pg. 185
BANKMANAGERS CORP.; *U.S. Private*, pg. 114
BAYBANKS, INC.—BankBoston Corporation; *U.S. Public*, pg. 184
BEECHWOOD INSURANCE AGENCY, INC.—Summit Bancorp; *U.S. Public*, pg. 1528
BENEFICIAL NATIONAL BANK—Beneficial Corporation; *U.S. Public*, pg. 211
BOSTON SAFE DEPOSIT & TRUST CO.—Mellon Bank Corporation; *U.S. Public*, pg. 1085
THE BRADFORD NATIONAL BANK OF GREENVILLE; *U.S. Private*, pg. 164
BREMER FINANCIAL CORPORATION; *U.S. Private*, pg. 167
BRENTON SAVINGS BANK, FSB—Brenton Banks, Inc.; *U.S. Public*, pg. 251
CB & T BANK OF MIDDLE GEORGIA—Synovus Financial Corp.; *U.S. Public*, pg. 1549
CB & T BANK OF RUSSELL COUNTY—Synovus Financial Corp.; *U.S. Public*, pg. 1549
CFX—CFX Bank; *U.S. Public*, pg. 278
CALIFORNIA STATE BANK; *U.S. Public*, pg. 294
CALVERT BANK & TRUST CO.—Mercantile Bankshares Corporation; *U.S. Public*, pg. 1088
CAROLINA FIRST BANK—Carolina First Corporation; *U.S. Public*, pg. 306
CENTAL CAROLINA BANK & TRUST COMPANY—CCB Financial Corporation; *U.S. Public*, pg. 276
CENTRAL BANK—Firstbank of Illinois Co.; *U.S. Public*, pg. 643
CENTRAL PACIFIC BANK—CPB Inc.; *U.S. Public*, pg. 283
CENTURA BANKS, INC.; *U.S. Public*, pg. 328
CHASE BANK OF ARIZONA—The Chase Manhattan Corporation; *U.S. Public*, pg. 338
CHASE BANK OF MARYLAND—The Chase Manhattan Corporation; *U.S. Public*, pg. 338
CHASE INSTITUTIONAL TRUST SYS.—The Chase Manhattan Corporation; *U.S. Public*, pg. 338
CHASE MANHATTAN BANK DELAWARE—The Chase Manhattan Corporation; *U.S. Public*, pg. 338
CHASE MANHATTAN BANK OF CONNECTICUT—The Chase Manhattan Corporation; *U.S. Public*, pg. 338
THE CHASE MANHATTAN CORPORATION; *U.S. Public*, pg. 337
CHELSEA STATE BANK; *U.S. Private*, pg. 231
CHEMICAL BANK & TRUST COMPANY—Chemical Financial Corporation; *U.S. Public*, pg. 345
CHEMICAL BANK CENTRAL—Chemical Financial Corporation; *U.S. Public*, pg. 345
CHEMICAL BANK MICHIGAN—Chemical Financial Corporation; *U.S. Public*, pg. 345
CHEMICAL BANK NORTH—Chemical Financial Corporation; *U.S. Public*, pg. 345
CHEMICAL BANK SOUTH—Chemical Financial Corporation; *U.S. Public*, pg. 345
CHEMICAL BANK WEST—Chemical Financial Corporation; *U.S. Public*, pg. 345
THE CHESTERTOWN BANK OF MARYLAND—Mercantile Bankshares Corporation; *U.S. Public*, pg. 1088
CHITTENDEN BANK—Chittenden Corporation; *U.S. Public*, pg. 351
CHITTENDEN CORPORATION; *U.S. Public*, pg. 350
CHURUBUSCO STATE BANK—Fort Wayne National Corporation; *U.S. Public*, pg. 674
CITIZENS BANK AND TRUST OF WEST GEORGIA—Synovus Financial Corp.; *U.S. Public*, pg. 1549
CITIZENS BANK OF JASPER—CNB Bancshares, Inc.; *U.S. Public*, pg. 280
CITIZENS BANK OF KENTUCKY—CNB Bancshares, Inc.; *U.S. Public*, pg. 280
CITIZENS BANK OF WESTERN INDIANA—CNB Bancshares, Inc.; *U.S. Public*, pg. 280
CITIZENS BANKING CORPORATION; *U.S. Public*, pg. 379
CITIZENS COMMERCIAL & SAVINGS BANK—Citizens Banking Corporation; *U.S. Public*, pg. 379
THE CITIZENS STATE BANK—Old National Bancorp; *U.S. Public*, pg. 1217
CITY NATIONAL CORPORATION; *U.S. Public*, pg. 380
CLINTON STATE BANK—Old National Bancorp; *U.S. Public*, pg. 1217
THE COASTAL BANK OF GEORGIA—Synovus Financial Corp.; *U.S. Public*, pg. 1549
COHUTTA BANKING COMPANY—Synovus Financial Corp.; *U.S. Public*, pg. 1549
COLE TAYLOR BANK—Taylor Capital Group; *U.S. Private*, pg. 1070
THE COLONIAL BANCGROUP, INC.; *U.S. Public*, pg. 400
COLONIAL BANK—The Colonial BancGroup, Inc.; *U.S. Public*, pg. 400
COLONIAL BANK—Firstbank of Illinois Co.; *U.S. Public*, pg. 643
COLUMBUS BANK AND TRUST COMPANY—Synovus Financial Corp.; *U.S. Public*, pg. 1549
COMERICA BANK MICHIGAN—Comerica Incorporated; *U.S. Public*, pg. 409
COMERICA INCORPORATED; *U.S. Public*, pg. 408
THE COMMERCIAL BANK; *U.S. Public*, pg. 410
COMMERCIAL BANK—Synovus Financial Corp.; *U.S. Public*, pg. 1549
COMMERCIAL BANK AND TRUST COMPANY OF TROUP COUNTY—Synovus Financial Corp.; *U.S. Public*, pg. 1549
COMMERCIAL NATIONAL BANK—Deposit Guaranty Corp.; *U.S. Public*, pg. 500
COMMUNITY BANK & TRUST OF S.E. ALABAMA—Synovus Financial Corp.; *U.S. Public*, pg. 1549
COMMUNITY FIRST BANKSHARES, INC.; *U.S. Public*, pg. 416
COMPASS BANK—Compass Bancshares, Inc.; *U.S. Public*, pg. 418
COMPASS BANK DALLAS—Compass Bancshares, Inc.; *U.S. Public*, pg. 419
COMPASS BANK HOUSTON—Compass Bancshares, Inc.; *U.S. Public*, pg. 419
CONCORD SAVINGS BANK—CFX Bank; *U.S. Public*, pg. 278
CONFEDERATION TRUST COMPANY—Confederation Life Insurance Company; *Int'l*, pg. 326
COUNTY BANKING & TRUST COMPANY—Mercantile Bankshares Corporation; *U.S. Public*, pg. 1089
CRESTAR FINANCIAL CORPORATION; *U.S. Public*, pg. 458
CUMMINS-ALLISON CORP.; *U.S. Private*, pg. 295
DEAN WITTER, DISCOVER & CO.—Morgan Stanley Dean Witter & Co.; *U.S. Public*, pg. 1132
DUBOIS COUNTY BANK—Old National Bancorp; *U.S. Public*, pg. 1217
THE EASTVILLE BANK—Mercantile Bankshares Corporation; *U.S. Public*, pg. 1089
ELLIOTT STATE BANK—Firstbank of Illinois Co.; *U.S. Public*, pg. 643
FARMERS & MERCHANTS BANK-EASTERN SHORE—Mercantile Bankshares Corporation; *U.S. Public*, pg. 1089
FARMERS AND MERCHANTS BANK OF CARLINVILLE—Firstbank of Illinois Co.; *U.S. Public*, pg. 644
FARMERS BANK & TRUST CO.—Old National Bancorp; *U.S. Public*, pg. 1217
FARMERS BANK OF MARYLAND—First Virginia Banks, Inc.; *U.S. Public*, pg. 641
FARMERS BANK & TRUST CO.—Old National Bancorp; *U.S. Public*, pg. 1217
THE FIDELITY BANK—Mercantile Bankshares Corporation; *U.S. Public*, pg. 1089

FIDUCIARY TRUST COMPANY INTERNATIONAL; *U.S. Public*, pg. 621
FIDUCIARY TRUST CO. OF NEW HAMPSHIRE—Torchmark Corporation; *U.S. Public*, pg. 1623
THE FIFTH THIRD BANK—Fifth Third Bancorp; *U.S. Public*, *pg. 622*
FIFTH THIRD BANK OF CENTRAL INDIANA—Fifth Third Bancorp; *U.S. Public*, pg. 621
THE FIFTH THIRD BANK OF COLUMBUS—Fifth Third Bancorp; *U.S. Public*, pg. 621
THE FIFTH THIRD BANK OF NORTHERN KENTUCKY—Fifth Third Bancorp; *U.S. Public*, pg. 621
THE FIFTH THIRD BANK OF SOUTHERN OHIO—Fifth Third Bancorp; *U.S. Public*, pg. 622
FIFTH-THIRD TRUST CO. & SAVINGS BANK, FSB—Fifth Third Bancorp; *U.S. Public*, pg. 622
FINANCIAL TRUST CORP—Keystone Financial Inc.; *U.S. Public*, pg. 956
FIRST BANK N.A.—U.S. Bancorp; *U.S. Public*, pg. 1680
FIRST BANK OF STUART—MainStreet BankGroup Incorporated; *U.S. Public*, pg. 1039
FIRST BANKS, INC.—First Banks America, Inc.; *U.S. Public*, pg. 626
FIRST CITIZENS BANC SHARES, INC.; *U.S. Public*, pg. 628
FIRST CITIZENS BANK & TRUST CO.—First Citizens Banc Shares, Inc.; *U.S. Public*, pg. 629
FIRST CITIZENS BANK OF HOHENWALD—Union Planters Corporation; *U.S. Public*, pg. 1669
FIRST COMMERCIAL BANK, N.A.—First Commercial Corporation; *U.S. Public*, pg. 630
FIRST COMMERCIAL CORPORATION; *U.S. Public*, pg. 630
FIRST COMMUNITY BANK—MainStreet BankGroup Incorporated; *U.S. Public*, pg. 1039
FIRST COMMUNITY BANK OF SALTVILLE—MainStreet BankGroup Incorporated; *U.S. Public*, pg. 1039
FIRST COMMUNITY BANK OF TIFTON—Synovus Financial Corp.; *U.S. Public*, pg. 1549
FIRST COUNTY BANK—F.N.B. Corporation; *U.S. Public*, pg. 607
FIRST FEDERAL SAVINGS & LOAN OF AMERICA—Pacific Century Financial Corporation; *U.S. Public*, pg. 1248
FIRST FEDERAL SAVINGS BANK LA CROSSE-MADISON—First Federal Capital Corp.; *U.S. Public*, pg. 632
FIRST GIBRALTAR BANK—BankAmerica Corporation; *U.S.* Public, pg. 181
FIRST HAWAIIAN BANK—First Hawaiian, Inc.; *U.S. Public*, pg. 634
FIRST HAWAIIAN, INC.; *U.S. Public*, pg. 634
FIRST NATIONAL BANK OF CENTRAL CALIFORNIA—Pacific Capital Bancorp; *U.S. Public*, pg. 1248
FIRST SECURITY BANK OF WYOMING—First Security Corporation; *U.S. Public*, pg. 637
FIRST SECURITY CORPORATION; *U.S. Public*, pg. 637
FIRST SIGNATURE BANK & TRUST CO.—John Hancock Mutual Life Insurance Company; *U.S. Private*, pg. 589
1ST SOURCE CORPORATION; *U.S. Public*, pg. 638
FIRST STATE BANK—Old National Bancorp; *U.S. Public*, pg. 1217
FIRST STATE BANK AND TRUST COMPANY—Synovus Financial Corp.; *U.S. Public*, pg. 1549
FIRST TRUST AND SAVINGS BANK OF TAYLORVILLE—Firstbank of Illinois Co.; *U.S. Public*, pg. 644
FIRST VANTAGE-TENNESSEE—First Virginia Banks, Inc.; *U.S. Public*, pg. 641
FIRST VERMONT BANK & TRUST COMPANY—Banknorth Group Inc.; *U.S. Public*, pg. 187
FIRST VIRGINIA BANK—First Virginia Banks, Inc.; *U.S. Public*, pg. 641
FIRST VIRGINIA BANK-COLONIAL—First Virginia Banks, Inc.; *U.S. Public*, pg. 641
FIRST VIRGINIA BANKS, INC.; *U.S. Public*, pg. 641
FIRST WESTERN TRUST SERVICES CO.—First Western Bancorp, Inc.; *U.S. Public*, pg. 642
FIRSTCITY FINANCIAL CORPORATION; *U.S. Public*, pg. 644
FLEET BANK—Fleet Financial Group, Inc.; *U.S. Public*, pg. 649
THE FOREST HILL STATE BANK—Mercantile Bankshares Corporation; *U.S. Public*, pg. 1089
FRANKLIN-LAMOILLE BANK—Banknorth Group Inc.; *U.S. Public*, pg. 187
FREDERICKTOWN BANK & TRUST CO.—Mercantile Bankshares Corporation; *U.S. Public*, pg. 1089
GIBSON COUNTY BANK—Old National Bancorp; *U.S. Public*, pg. 1217
GLENVIEW STATE BANK—Cummins-Allison Corp.; *U.S. Private*, pg. 295
GRAYLING STATE BANK—Citizens Banking Corporation; *U.S. Public*, pg. 379
GREAT LAKES FINANCIAL RESOURCES, INC.; *U.S. Private*, pg. 474
GROSSMONT BANK—Zions Bancorporation; *U.S. Public*, pg. 1793
HGC BANK—Bank of Montreal; *Int'l*, pg. 154
HANOVER BANK—MainStreet BankGroup Incorporated; *U.S. Public*, pg. 1039
HARRIS & BANK—Bank of Montreal; *Int'l*, pg. 154
HARRIS BANK ARGO—Bank of Montreal; *Int'l*, pg. 154
HARRIS BANK FRANKFORT—Bank of Montreal; *Int'l*, pg. 154
HARRIS BANK LIBERTYVILLE—Bank of Montreal; *Int'l*, pg. 154
HARRIS BANK NAPERVILLE—Bank of Montreal; *Int'l*, pg. 154
HARRIS BANK ST. CHARLES—Bank of Montreal; *Int'l*, pg. 154
HEREFORD STATE BANK—First Financial Bankshares, Inc.; *U.S. Public*, pg. 633
HUDSON UNITED BANK-CEDAR GROVE—Hubco, Inc.; *U.S. Public*, pg. 845
IMPERIAL BANK—Imperial Bancorp; *U.S. Public*, pg. 871
INTERCONTINENTAL BANK—NationsBank Corporation; *U.S. Public*, pg. 1162
ISRAEL DISCOUNT BANK OF NEW YORK—IDB Holding Corporation; *Int'l*, pg. 645
KEY BANK OF MAINE—Keycorp; *U.S. Public*, pg. 954
KEY BANK OF NEW YORK—Keycorp; *U.S. Public*, pg. 954
KEY BANK OF OREGON—Keycorp; *U.S. Public*, pg. 954
KEY BANK OF WASHINGTON—Keycorp; *U.S. Public*, pg. 954
KEYCORP; *U.S. Public*, pg. 954
KEYSTONE BANK—Keystone Financial Inc.; *U.S. Public*, pg. 956
LAKELAND FINANCIAL CORPORATION; *U.S. Public*, pg. 975
LAUREL BANK—BT Financial Corporation; *U.S. Public*, pg. 164
LAUREL TRUST COMPANY—BT Financial Corporation; *U.S. Public*, pg. 164
LAWRENCE SAVINGS BANK; *U.S. Public*, pg. 980
M & I BANK FOX VALLEY—Marshall & Ilsley Corporation; *U.S. Public*, pg. 1050
M & I BANK NORTHEAST—Marshall & Ilsley Corporation; *U.S. Public*, pg. 1050
M & I BANK SOUTHWEST—Marshall & Ilsley Corporation; *U.S. Public*, pg. 1050
M & I CENTRAL BANK & TRUST—Marshall & Ilsley Corporation; *U.S. Public*, pg. 1050
M & I CENTRAL STATE BANK—Marshall & Ilsley Corporation; *U.S. Public*, pg. 1050
M & I CITIZENS AMERICAN BANK—Marshall & Ilsley Corporation; *U.S. Public*, pg. 1050
M & I COMMUNITY STATE BANK—Marshall & Ilsley Corporation; *U.S. Public*, pg. 1050
M & I MERCHANTS BANK—Marshall & Ilsley Corporation; *U.S. Public*, pg. 1050
M & I NORTHERN BANK—Marshall & Ilsley Corporation; *U.S. Public*, pg. 1050
M & I THUNDERBIRD BANK—Marshall & Ilsley Corporation; *U.S. Public*, pg. 1050
M&T CREDIT CORPORATION—First Empire State Corporation; *U.S. Public*, pg. 631
M&T MORTGAGE CORP.—First Empire State Corporation; *U.S. Public*, pg. 631
MANUFACTURERS & TRADERS TRUST COMPANY—First Empire State Corporation; *U.S. Public*, pg. 631
MARQUETTE BANK ROCHESTER—Marquette Bancshares Inc.; *U.S. Private*, pg. 706
MARSHALL & ILSLEY CORPORATION; *U.S. Public*, pg. 1049
MELLON FIRST BUSINESS BANK—Mellon Bank Corporation; *U.S. Public*, pg. 1085
MELLON SECURITIES TRUST CO.—Mellon Bank Corporation; *U.S. Public*, pg. 1086
MERCANTILE BANCORPORATION INC.; *U.S. Public*, pg. 1087
MERCANTILE BANK OF JASPER COUNTY—Mercantile Bancorporation Inc.; *U.S. Public*, pg. 1088
MERCANTILE BANK OF LYON COUNTY—Mercantile Bancorporation Inc.; *U.S. Public*, pg. 1088
MERCANTILE BANK OF MAQUOKETA—Mercantile Bancorporation Inc.; *U.S. Public*, pg. 1088
MERCANTILE BANK OF MARSHALLTOWN—Mercantile Bancorporation Inc.; *U.S. Public*, pg. 1088
MERCANTILE BANK OF MOUNT AYR—Mercantile Bancorporation Inc.; *U.S. Public*, pg. 1088
MERCANTILE BANK OF ONAWA—Mercantile Bancorporation Inc.; *U.S. Public*, pg. 1088
MERCANTILE BANK OF TIPTON—Mercantile Bancorporation Inc.; *U.S. Public*, pg. 1088
MERCANTILE BANK OF VINTON—Mercantile Bancorporation Inc.; *U.S. Public*, pg. 1088
MERCANTILE BANK OF WASHINGTON COUNTY, N.A.—Mercantile Bancorporation Inc.; *U.S. Public*, pg. 1088
MERCANTILE INVESTMENT & TRUST SERVICES—Mercantile Bancorporation Inc.; *U.S. Public*, pg. 1088
MERCANTILE-SAFE DEPOSIT & TRUST CO.—Mercantile Bankshares Corporation; *U.S. Public*, pg. 1089
MICHIGAN NATIONAL CORPORATION—National Australia Bank Limited; *Int'l*, pg. 906
MID-STATE BANK—Keystone Financial Inc.; *U.S. Public*, pg. 956
MIDLANTIC BANK, N.A.—PNC Bank Corp.; *U.S. Public*, pg. 1242
MORGAN GUARANTY TRUST COMPANY OF NEW YORK—J.P. Morgan Co. Incorporated; *U.S. Public*, pg. 1129
J.P. MORGAN INVESTMENT MANAGEMENT INC.—J.P. Morgan Co. Incorporated; *U.S. Public*, pg. 1129
J.P. MORGAN CO. INCORPORATED; *U.S. Public*, pg. 1129
MORGAN STANLEY DEAN WITTER & CO.; *U.S. Public*, pg. 1132
NBC BANK, FSB (BELZONI)—National Commerce Bancorporation; *U.S. Public*, pg. 1155
NBC BANK, FSB (KNOXVILLE)—National Commerce Bancorporation; *U.S. Public*, pg. 1155
NAPA VALLEY BANK—Westamerica Bancorporation; *U.S. Public*, pg. 1756
NASHVILLE BANK OF COMMERCE—National Commerce Bancorporation; *U.S. Public*, pg. 1155
NATIONAL BANCORP OF ALASKA, INC.; *U.S. Public*, pg. 1153
NATIONAL BANK OF ALASKA—National Bancorp of Alaska, Inc.; *U.S. Public*, pg. 1153
NATIONAL BANK OF COMMERCE—National Commerce Bancorporation; *U.S. Public*, pg. 1155
NATIONAL PENN BANK—National Penn Bancshares, Inc.; *U.S. Public*, pg. 1159
NATIONSBANK WEST—NationsBank Corporation; *U.S. Public*, pg. 1164
NEVADA STATE BANK—Zions Bancorporation; *U.S. Public*, *pg. 1793*
NORTH AMERICAN SALES—National Data Corporation; *U.S. Public*, pg. 1156
NORTH FORK BANK—North Fork Bancorporation, Inc.; *U.S. Public*, pg. 1194
NORTHERN CENTRAL BANK—Keystone Financial Inc.; *U.S. Public*, pg. 956
NORTHERN TRUST BANK OF CALIFORNIA, N.A.—Northern Trust Corporation; *U.S. Public*, pg. 1196
NORTHERN TRUST BANK OF TEXAS, N.A.—Northern Trust Corporation; *U.S. Public*, pg. 1197
THE NORTHERN TRUST COMPANY—Northern Trust Corporation; *U.S. Public*, pg. 1197
NORTHERN TRUST CORPORATION; *U.S. Public*, pg. 1195
NORTHERN TRUST SECURITIES, INC.—Northern Trust Corporation; *U.S. Public*, pg. 1196
NORWEST BANK OF WISCONSIN—Norwest Corporation; *U.S. Public*, pg. 1202
ODELL STATE BANK—Pontiac Bancorp, Inc.; *U.S. Public*, pg. 1316
OLD KENT BANK—Old Kent Financial Corporation; *U.S. Public*, pg. 1216
OLD KENT BANK-CENTRAL—Old Kent Financial Corporation; *U.S. Public*, pg. 1216
OLD KENT BANK-GRAND TRAVERSE—Old Kent Financial Corporation; *U.S. Public*, pg. 1216
OLD KENT BANK-ILLINOIS—Old Kent Financial Corporation; *U.S. Public*, pg. 1216
OLD NATIONAL BANCORP; *U.S. Public*, pg. 1217
PNC BANK—PNC Bank Corp.; *U.S. Public*, pg. 1243
PNC BANK KENTUCKY, INC.—PNC Bank Corp.; *U.S. Public*, pg. 1243
PNC BANK NEW ENGLAND—PNC Bank Corp.; *U.S. Public*, pg. 1243
PNC BANK, SOUTH CENTRAL—PNC Bank Corp.; *U.S. Public*, pg. 1243
PNC MORTGAGE CORPORATION OF AMERICA—PNC Bank Corp.; *U.S. Public*, pg. 1243
PACIFIC CAPITAL BANCORP; *U.S. Public*, pg. 1247
PACIFIC CENTURY BANK—Pacific Century Financial Corporation; *U.S. Public*, pg. 1248
PACIFIC CENTURY FINANCIAL CORPORATION; *U.S. Public*, pg. 1248
PACIFIC ONE BANK—First Hawaiian, Inc.; *U.S. Public*, pg. 635
PALMER-AMERICAN NATIONAL BANK—Old National Bancorp; *U.S. Public*, pg. 1217
PENINSULA BANK—Mercantile Bankshares Corporation; *U.S. Public*, pg. 1089
PEOPLE'S BANK; *U.S. Public*, pg. 1274
PEOPLE'S BANK & TRUST CO.—Old National Bancorp; *U.S. Public*, pg. 1217
THE PEOPLES BANK OF MARYLAND—Mercantile Bankshares Corporation; *U.S. Public*, pg. 1089
PIEDMONT TRUST BANK—MainStreet BankGroup Incorporated; *U.S. Public*, pg. 1039
PITKIN COUNTY BANK & TRUST COMPANY—Zions Bancorporation; *U.S. Public*, pg. 1793
PORTSMOUTH SAVINGS BANK—CFX Bank; *U.S. Public*, pg. 278
POTOMAC VALLEY BANK—Mercantile Bankshares Corporation; *U.S. Public*, pg. 1089
THE PROVIDENT BANK—Provident Financial Group, Inc.; *U.S. Public*, pg. 1338
PROVIDENT BANK OF FLORIDA—Provident Financial Group, Inc.; *U.S. Public*, pg. 1338
THE PROVIDENT BANK OF KENTUCKY—Provident Financial Group, Inc.; *U.S. Public*, pg. 1338
PROVIDENT COMMERCIAL GROUP, INC.—Provident Financial Group, Inc.; *U.S. Public*, pg. 1338
PROVIDENT FINANCIAL GROUP, INC.; *U.S. Public*, pg. 1338
PULSE SAVINGS BANK—Pulse Bancorp, Inc.; *U.S. Public*, pg. 1344
THE QUINCY STATE BANK—Synovus Financial Corp.; *U.S. Public*, pg. 1549
REEVES BANK—F.N.B. Corporation; *U.S. Public*, pg. 607
REGIONS BANK/ALBERTVILLE/GUNTERSVILLE/ARAB—Regions Financial Corporation; *U.S. Public*, pg. 1371
REGIONS BANK/BLOUNT COUNTY—Regions Financial Corporation; *U.S. Public*, pg. 1372
REGIONS BANK/MONTGOMERY/ALEXANDER CITY—Regions Financial Corporation; *U.S. Public*, pg. 1372
REGIONS BANK/SHELBY COUNTY—Regions Financial Corporation; *U.S. Public*, pg. 1373
REGIONS BANK/SUMTER COUNTY—Regions Financial Corporation; *U.S. Public*, pg. 1373
REGIONS FINANCIAL CORPORATION; *U.S. Public*, pg. 1371
REPUBLIC NEW YORK TRUST COMPANY OF FLORIDA, NATIONAL ASSOCIATION—Republic New York Corporation; *U.S. Public*, pg. 1381
RIVER OAKS TRUST COMPANY—Compass Bancshares, Inc.; *U.S. Public*, pg. 419
ST. MICHAELS BANK—Mercantile Bankshares Corporation; *U.S. Public*, pg. 1089
SANTA MONICA BANK—Western Bancorp; *U.S. Public*, pg. 1757
SANWA BANK CALIFORNIA—The Sanwa Bank Limited; *Int'l*, pg. 1189
SEA ISLAND BANK—Synovus Financial Corp.; *U.S. Public*, pg. 1549
SECOND NATIONAL BANK OF BAY CITY—Citizens Banking Corporation; *U.S. Public*, pg. 379
SECOND NATIONAL BANK OF SAGINAW—Citizens Banking Corporation; *U.S. Public*, pg. 379
SECURITY BANK AND TRUST COMPANY—Synovus Financial Corp.; *U.S. Public*, pg. 1549
SECURITY BANK & TRUST CO.—Old National Bancorp; *U.S. Public*, pg. 1217
SECURITY PACIFIC BANK OREGON—BankAmerica Corporation; *U.S. Public*, pg. 182
SECURITY PACIFIC OREGON BANCORP—BankAmerica Corporation; *U.S. Public*, pg. 182
SECURITY PACIFIC STATE BANK—BankAmerica Corporation; *U.S. Public*, pg. 182

SHORELINE BANK—Shoreline Financial Corp.; *U.S. Public, pg. 1468*
SMITHTOWN BANCORP, INC.; *U.S. Public*, pg. 1479
SOCIETY NATIONAL BANK—Keycorp; *U.S. Public*, pg. 954
SOMERSET SAVINGS BANK; *U.S. Public*, pg. 1484
SONOMA VALLEY BANK; *U.S. Public*, pg. 1487
SOUTHERN CALIFORNIA BANK—Western Bancorp; *U.S. Public*, pg. 1758
SOUTHTRUST BANK, HARTSELLE—SouthTrust Corporation; *U.S. Public*, pg. 1491
SOUTHTRUST BANK, JASPER—SouthTrust Corporation; *U.S. Public*, pg. 1491
SOUTHTRUST BANK OF CENTRAL FLORIDA—SouthTrust Corporation; *U.S. Public*, pg. 1492
SOUTHTRUST LEASING, INC.—SouthTrust Corporation; *U.S. Public*, pg. 1492
SPARKS STATE BANK—Mercantile Bankshares Corporation; *U.S. Public*, pg. 1089
STATE BANK OF STANDISH—Citizens Banking Corporation; *U.S. Public*, pg. 379
STATE STREET BANK & TRUST CO.—State Street Corporation; *U.S. Public*, pg. 1513
STATE STREET CORPORATION; *U.S. Public*, pg. 1513
STEPHENVILLE BANK & TRUST CO.—First Financial Bankshares, Inc.; *U.S. Public*, pg. 633
SUMMIT BANCORP; *U.S. Public*, pg. 1527
SUMMIT BANK—Summit Bancorp; *U.S. Public*, pg. 1528
SUMTER BANK AND TRUST COMPANY—Synovus Financial Corp.; *U.S. Public*, pg. 1549
SUNTRUST—SunTrust Banks, Inc.; *U.S. Public*, pg. 1537
SUNTRUST BANK, ATLANTA—SunTrust Banks, Inc.; *U.S. Public*, pg. 1538
SUNTRUST BANK, EAST CENTRAL FLORIDA—SunTrust Banks, Inc.; *U.S. Public*, pg. 1537
SUNTRUST BANK, GULF COAST—SunTrust Banks, Inc.; *U.S. Public*, pg. 1537
SUNTRUST BANK, NATURE COAST—SunTrust Banks, Inc.; *U.S. Public*, pg. 1537
SUNTRUST BANK, NORTH CENTRAL FLORIDA—SunTrust Banks, Inc.; *U.S. Public*, pg. 1537
SUNTRUST BANK, WEST FLORIDA—SunTrust Banks, Inc.; *U.S. Public*, pg. 1538
SUNTRUST BANKS, INC.; *U.S. Public*, pg. 1537
SUNWEST BANK—West Coast Bancorp; *U.S. Public*, pg. 1755
SUNWEST BANK OF EL PASO—NationsBank Corporation; *U.S. Public*, pg. 1165
SWEDBANK; *Int'l*, pg. 1328
THE TALLAHASSEE STATE BANK—Synovus Financial Corp.; *U.S. Public*, pg. 1549
TAYLOR CAPITAL GROUP; *U.S. Private*, pg. 1070
TAYLOR CORPORATION; *U.S. Private*, pg. 1070
TRANS FINANCIAL, INC.; *U.S. Public*, pg. 1628
TRI-CITY BANK AND TRUST COMPANY—First Virginia Banks, Inc.; *U.S. Public*, pg. 642
THE TRUST COMPANY OF NEW JERSEY—The Trustcompany Bancorporation; *U.S. Public*, pg. 1643
THE TRUSTCOMPANY BANCORPORATION; *U.S. Public*, pg. 1643
UMB BANK COLORADO—UMB Financial Corporation; *U.S. Public*, pg. 1654
UMB FINANCIAL CORPORATION; *U.S. Public*, pg. 1653
UMB FIRST NATIONAL BANK—UMB Financial Corporation; *U.S. Public*, pg. 1654
UMB FIRST STATE BANK OF MORRISONVILLE—UMB Financial Corporation; *U.S. Public*, pg. 1654
UNION BANK OF CALIFORNIA—The Bank of Tokyo-Mitsubishi, Ltd.; *Int'l*, pg. 157
UNION PLANTERS BANK OF WEST TENNESSEE—Union Planters Corporation; *U.S. Public*, pg. 1669
UNION PLANTERS CORPORATION; *U.S. Public*, pg. 1668
UNITED SOUTHERN BANK—Union Planters Corporation; *U.S. Public*, pg. 1669
U.S. BANCORP; *U.S. Public*, pg. 1680
U.S. BANK OF IDAHO—U.S. Bancorp; *U.S. Public*, pg. 1681
U.S. BANK OF UTAH—U.S. Bancorp; *U.S. Public*, pg. 1681
U.S. TRUST CORPORATION; *U.S. Public*, pg. 1688
VALLEY AMERICAN BANK—Fort Wayne National Corporation; *U.S. Public*, pg. 674
VALLEY BANK & TRUST; *U.S. Private*, pg. 1132
VALLEY NATIONAL BANK—Valley National Bancorp; *U.S. Public*, pg. 1706
VANGUARD BANK & TRUST COMPANY—Synovus Financial Corp.; *U.S. Public*, pg. 1549
THE WASHINGTON TRUST COMPANY—Washington Trust Bancorp, Inc.; *U.S. Public*, pg. 1744
WESTERN BANCORP; *U.S. Public*, pg. 1757
WESTMINSTER BANK & TRUST CO. OF CARROLL COUNTY—Mercantile Bankshares Corporation; *U.S. Public*, pg. 1089
WHITNEY NATIONAL BANK—Whitney Holding Corporation; *U.S. Public*, pg. 1766
WINNETKA FINANCIAL CENTER—Northern Trust Corporation; *U.S. Public*, pg. 1197
YASUDA BANK AND TRUST COMPANY (U.S.A.)—The Yasuda Trust and Banking Co., Ltd.; *Int'l*, pg. 1520
THE YASUDA TRUST AND BANKING CO., LTD.; *Int'l*, pg. 1520
ZIONS BANCORPORATION; *U.S. Public*, pg. 1792

6029 — COMMERCIAL BANKS, NEC

BANCO EXTERIOR, S.A.—Argentaria Corporacion Bancaria de Espana, S.A.; *Int'l*, pg. 81
BANCO PROVINCIAL S.A. BANCO UNIVERSAL; *Int'l*, pg. 142
BANK BRUSSELS LAMBERT, SINGAPORE BRANCH—Bank Brussels Lambert; *Int'l*, pg. 148
BANK HAPOALIM B.M.—Bank Hapoalim; *Int'l*, pg. 149
BANK OF BOSTON CONNECTICUT—BankBoston Corporation; *U.S. Public*, pg. 184
BANK OF MONTREAL; *Int'l*, pg. 153
BANK ONE, KENTUCKY, NA—Banc One Corporation; *U.S. Public*, pg. 173
P.T. BANK SAKURA SWADHARMA—The Sakura Bank, Limited; *Int'l*, pg. 1180
BANQUE EUROPEENNE POUR L'AMERIQUE LATINE (BEAL) S.A.—Westdeutsche Landesbank Girozentrale; *Int'l*, pg. 1493
BANQUE NATIONALE DE PARIS; *Int'l*, pg. 163
THE BRITISH BANK OF THE MIDDLE EAST—HSBC Holdings plc; *Int'l*, pg. 579
BROWN BROTHERS HARRIMAN & CO.; *U.S. Private*, pg. 173
CITY NATIONAL BANK OF FORT SMITH—First United Bancshares, Inc.; *U.S. Public*, pg. 641
COMMERZBANK AG LONDON BRANCH—Commerzbank AG; *Int'l*, pg. 311
COMMERZBANK AG-COPENHAGEN REPRESENTATIVE OFFICE—Commerzbank AG; *Int'l*, pg. 311
DBS BANK LTD.; *Int'l*, pg. 350
FERRIER LULLIN & CIE SA; *Int'l*, pg. 480
FIRST AMERICAN BANK—Bremer Financial Corporation; *U.S. Private*, pg. 167
FIRST NATIONAL BANK OF EL DORADO—First United Bancshares, Inc.; *U.S. Public*, pg. 641
FIRST NATIONAL BANK OF MAGNOLIA—First United Bancshares, Inc.; *U.S. Public*, pg. 641
FIRST UNITED BANCSHARES, INC.; *U.S. Public*, pg. 641
FLORENCE DEPOSIT BANK—Banc One Corporation; *U.S. Public*, pg. 173
FOKUS BANK A/S; *Int'l*, pg. 496
KARL KAUERMAN NASSAUISCHE SPARKASSE; *Int'l*, pg. 724
KINCHENG-TOKYO FINANCE CO., LTD.—The Bank of Tokyo-Mitsubishi, Ltd.; *Int'l*, pg. 158
KOREA INTERNATIONAL MERCHANT BANK—Commerzbank AG; *Int'l*, pg. 312
LIBERTY NATIONAL BANK AND TRUST COMPANY OF INDIANA—Banc One Corporation; *U.S. Public*, pg. 173
LIBERTY NATIONAL BANK AND TRUST COMPANY OF CENTRAL KENTUCKY—Banc One Corporation; *U.S. Public*, pg. 173
LIBERTY NATIONAL BANK OF NORTHERN KENTUCKY—Banc One Corporation; *U.S. Public*, pg. 173
MERCHANT & PLANTERS BANK N.A. OF CAMDEN—First United Bancshares, Inc.; *U.S. Public*, pg. 641
MISR INTERNATIONAL BANK S.A.E.—The Sakura Bank, Limited; *Int'l*, pg. 1181
NDC MERCHANT BANK LTD.—DBS Bank Ltd.; *Int'l*, pg. 351
THE NANTO BANK, LTD.; *Int'l*, pg. 905
PEOPLES HERITAGE SAVINGS BANK—Peoples Heritage Financial Group, Inc.; *U.S. Public*, pg. 1275
POSTIPANKKI LTD.; *Int'l*, pg. 1064
PROGRESSIVE BANK, INC.; *U.S. Public*, pg. 1334
THE PROVIDENT BANK—Provident Financial Group, Inc.; *U.S. Public*, pg. 1338
THE SAKURA BANK (CANADA)—The Sakura Bank, Limited; *Int'l*, pg. 1180
SIAM CITY BANK PUBLIC COMPANY LIMITED; *Int'l*, pg. 1239
TOKYO-MITSUBISHI INTERNATIONAL (SINGAPORE) LTD.—The Bank of Tokyo-Mitsubishi, Ltd.; *Int'l*, pg. 158
TRUSTCO BANK, N.A.—TrustCo Bank Corp., NY; *U.S. Public*, pg. 1643
TURK SAKURA BANK A.S.—The Sakura Bank, Limited; *Int'l*, pg. 1180
WEST MERCHANT BANK LTD.—Westdeutsche Landesbank Girozentrale; *Int'l*, pg. 1493
WEST MERCHANT BANK LIMITED—Westdeutsche Landesbank Girozentrale; *Int'l*, pg. 1493
WESTLB EUROPA FINANZIARIA S.P.A.—Westdeutsche Landesbank Girozentrale; *Int'l*, pg. 1494
WESTPAC BANKING CORPORATION (COLUMBUS REPRESENTATIVE OFFICE)—Westpac Banking Corporation; *Int'l*, pg. 1496
WESTPAC BANKING CORPORATION (LOS ANGELES BRANCH)—Westpac Banking Corporation; *Int'l*, pg. 1496
WESTPAC BANKING CORPORATION (SAN FRANCISCO BRANCH)—Westpac Banking Corporation; *Int'l*, pg. 1496

6035 — SAVINGS INSTITUTIONS, FEDERALLY CHARTERED

H.F. AHMANSON & CO.; *U.S. Public*, pg. 29
AMERICAN SAVINGS BANK, F.S.B.—Hawaiian Electric Industries, Inc.; *U.S. Public*, pg. 800
AMSOUTH BANK—AmSouth Bancorporation; *U.S. Public*, pg. 105
ANDROSCOGGIN SAVINGS BANK; *U.S. Private*, pg. 74
BB&T SAVINGS BANK—BB&T Corporation; *U.S. Public*, pg. 100
BANCA DI ROMA; *Int'l*, pg. 135
BANCO BILBAO VIZCAYA, S.A.; *Int'l*, pg. 138
BANK OF BOSTON CONNECTICUT—BankBoston Corporation; *U.S. Public*, pg. 184
BAY VIEW BANK—Bay View Capital Corporation; *U.S. Public*, pg. 197
BAY VIEW CAPITAL CORPORATION; *U.S. Public*, pg. 197
BENEFICIAL CORPORATION; *U.S. Public*, pg. 211
BENEFICIAL SAVINGS BANK, FSB—Beneficial Corporation; *U.S. Public*, pg. 211
CALIFORNIA FEDERAL BANK—MacAndrews & Forbes Holdings Inc.; *U.S. Private*, pg. 690
CALIFORNIA NATIONAL BANK—The First Bank of Oak Park; *U.S. Private*, pg. 406
CANADIAN IMPERIAL BANK OF COMMERCE; *Int'l*, pg. 256
CENTURY BANCSHARES, INC.; *U.S. Public*, pg. 328
CHARTER ONE FINANCIAL, INC.; *U.S. Public*, pg. 336
CITICORP; *U.S. Public*, pg. 376
CITICORP SAVINGS, A FEDERAL SAVINGS & LOAN ASSN.—Citicorp; *U.S. Public*, pg. 378
CITIZENS FEDERAL BANK, F.S.B.—CitFed Bancorp, Inc.; *U.S. Public*, pg. 376
COAST FEDERAL BANK FSB—Coast Savings Financial, Inc.; *U.S. Public*, pg. 389
COLLECTIVE BANK—Summit Bancorp; *U.S. Public*, pg. 1528
COMMERCIAL FEDERAL BANK—Commercial Federal Corporation; *U.S. Public*, pg. 411
CONTINENTAL FEDERAL SAVING & LOAN—Banc One Corporation; *U.S. Public*, pg. 174
THE DIME SAVINGS BANK OF NEW YORK; *U.S. Public*, pg. 509
DOWNEY SAVINGS & LOAN ASSOCIATION, F.A.—Downey Financial Corp.; *U.S. Public*, pg. 526
FSF FINANCIAL CORP.; *U.S. Public*, pg. 608
FEDERAL SAVINGS BANK—Kemmons Wilson, Inc.; *U.S. Private*, pg. 614
THE FIRST BANK OF OAK PARK; *U.S. Private*, pg. 406
FIRST FEDERAL BANK OF CALIFORNIA, FSB—FirstFed Financial Corp.; *U.S. Public*, pg. 646
FIRST FEDERAL FSB—FSF Financial Corp.; *U.S. Public*, pg. 608
FIRST FEDERAL OF MICHIGAN—Charter One Financial, Inc.; *U.S. Public*, pg. 336
FIRST FEDERAL SAVINGS; *U.S. Public*, pg. 632
FIRST FEDERAL SAVINGS & LOAN ASSOCIATION OF CHARLESTON—First Financial Holdings, Inc.; *U.S. Public*, pg. 634
FIRST FINANCIAL BANK, FSB—Associated Banc-Corp; *U.S. Public*, pg. 140
FIRST FINANCIAL HOLDINGS, INC.; *U.S. Public*, pg. 634
FIRST INDIANA BANK, A FEDERAL SAVINGS BANK—The Somerset Group, Inc.; *U.S. Public*, pg. 1484
FIRST OF AMERICA BANK FLORIDA—First of America Bank Corporation; *U.S. Public*, pg. 636
FIRST OF AMERICA - FLORIDA—First of America Bank Corporation; *U.S. Public*, pg. 636
FIRSTFED FINANCIAL CORP.; *U.S. Public*, pg. 645
FLEET BANK NH—Fleet Financial Group, Inc.; *U.S. Public*, pg. 649
FRANKFURTER SPARKASSE; *Int'l*, pg. 504
GEORGIA FEDERAL BANK, FSB—First Union Corporation; *U.S. Public*, pg. 640
GLENDALE FEDERAL BANK, F.S.B.; *U.S. Public*, pg. 747
GREAT WESTERN FINANCIAL CORPORATION—Washington Mutual Inc.; *U.S. Public*, pg. 1741
GUARANTY F.S.B.—Temple-Inland Inc.; *U.S. Public*, pg. 1575
GULFCO INVESTMENT, INC.—Mercury Finance Co.; *U.S. Public*, pg. 1093
HAWAIIAN ELECTRIC INDUSTRIES, INC.; *U.S. Public*, pg. 799
HOME SAVINGS OF AMERICA, FSB—H.F. Ahmanson & Co.; *U.S. Public*, pg. 29
KEMMONS WILSON, INC.; *U.S. Private*, pg. 613
LSB INDUSTRIES, INC.; *U.S. Public*, pg. 970
LASALLE-TALMAN BANK—ABN-AMRO Holding N.V.; *Int'l*, pg. 11
LONG ISLAND BANCORP, INC.; *U.S. Public*, pg. 1013
MAGNA MORTGAGE—Union Planters Corporation; *U.S. Public*, pg. 1669
MONTICELLO BANK—The Monticello Companies, Inc.; *U.S. Private*, pg. 759
NBD BANK FSB—First Chicago NBD Corporation; *U.S. Public*, pg. 628
NATIONSBANK/MIAMI—NationsBank Corporation; *U.S. Public*, pg. 1162
PEOPLES FEDERAL SAVINGS & LOAN ASSOCIATION—First Financial Holdings, Inc.; *U.S. Public*, pg. 634
PEOPLES NATIONAL BANK—Old National Bancorp; *U.S. Public*, pg. 1217
PINNACLE BANK; *U.S. Public*, pg. 1297
PRIME BANCORP, INC.; *U.S. Public*, pg. 1326
PRIME BANK—Prime Bancorp, Inc.; *U.S. Public*, pg. 1326
REGENCY SAVINGS BANK—The First Bank of Oak Park; *U.S. Private*, pg. 406
ST. PAUL FEDERAL BANK FOR SAVINGS—St. Paul Bancorp, Inc.; *U.S. Public*, pg. 1428
THE SOMERSET GROUP, INC.; *U.S. Public*, pg. 1484
SOUTH TRUST BANK OF GEORGIA—SouthTrust Corporation; *U.S. Public*, pg. 1492
SOUTHERN PACIFIC BANK—Imperial Credit Industries, Inc.; *U.S. Public*, pg. 872
STADTSPARKASSE KOLN; *Int'l*, pg. 1293
STANDARD FEDERAL BANK—ABN-AMRO Holding N.V.; *Int'l*, pg. 10
STANDARD PACIFIC SAVINGS, F. A.—Standard Pacific Corp.; *U.S. Public*, pg. 1504
SUPERIOR FEDERAL BANK; *U.S. Private*, pg. 1054
TCF FINANCIAL CORP.; *U.S. Public*, pg. 1554
TEMPLE-INLAND FINANCIAL SERVICES, INC—Temple-Inland Inc.; *U.S. Public*, pg. 1575
TEXAS BANK N.A.—First Banks America, Inc.; *U.S. Public*, pg. 626
THE TROY SAVINGS BANK; *U.S. Private*, pg. 1106
VIRGINIA FIRST SAVINGS BANK, F.S.B.—Virginia First Financial Corp.; *U.S. Public*, pg. 1721
WSFS FINANCIAL CORPORATION; *U.S. Public*, pg. 1728
WASHINGTON FEDERAL SAVINGS; *U.S. Public*, pg. 1740
WASHINGTON MUTUAL FEDERAL SAVINGS BANK—Washington Mutual Inc.; *U.S. Public*, pg. 1742
WEBSTER BANK—Webster Financial Corporation; *U.S. Public*, pg. 1751
WESTERN FINANCIAL BANK—Westcorp; *U.S. Public*, pg. 1757
WESTERNBANK OF PUERTO RICO; *U.S. Public*, pg. 1760
WESTMINSTER CAPITAL INC.; *U.S. Public*, pg. 1761
WORLD SAVINGS & LOAN ASSOCIATION, FSLA—Golden West Financial Corporation; *U.S. Public*, pg. 750

6036 — SAVINGS INSTITUTIONS, NOT FEDERALLY CHARTERED

ASLK-CGER; *Int'l*, pg. 17
H.F. AHMANSON & CO.; *U.S. Public*, pg. 29
BB&T SAVINGS BANK, SSB—BB&T Corporation; *U.S. Public*, pg. 160
BRANFORD SAVINGS BANK; *U.S. Public*, pg. 250
BROOKLINE SAVINGS BANK; *U.S. Private*, pg. 171
CFX BANK; *U.S. Public*, pg. 277
CAISSE FRATERNELLE D'EPARGNE—Groupe GAN; *Int'l*, pg. 563
CARVER FEDERAL SAVINGS BANK; *U.S. Public*, pg. 310
CATSKILL SAVINGS BANK; *U.S. Public*, pg. 318
CENTRAL CAROLINA BANK—CCB Financial Corporation; *U.S. Public*, pg. 276
CLUB CORPORATION INTERNATIONAL; *U.S. Private*, pg. 247
EMIGRANT SAVINGS BANK; *U.S. Private*, pg. 373
FIRST INDEPENDENCE NATIONAL BANK; *U.S. Public*, pg. 635
FIRST MUTUAL OF BOSTON—BankBoston Corporation; *U.S. Public*, pg. 184
FIRST NORTHERN CAPITAL CORP.; *U.S. Public*, pg. 636
FIRST SECURITY BANK OF OREGON—First Security Corporation; *U.S. Public*, pg. 637
FLEET BANK NH—Fleet Financial Group, Inc.; *U.S. Public*, pg. 649
GIBRALTAR SAVINGS—BankAmerica Corporation; *U.S. Public*, pg. 181
THE GUARDIAN LIFE INSURANCE COMPANY OF AMERICA; *U.S. Private*, pg. 486
HELLER INTERNATIONAL; *U.S. Private*, pg. 520
HOUSEHOLD BANK F.S.B.—Household International, Inc.; *U.S. Public*, pg. 842
LIBERTY BANK—The Sanwa Bank Limited; *Int'l*, pg. 1189
LONDON LIFE INSURANCE GROUP—EdperBrascan Corporation; *Int'l*, pg. 435
M & I BANK S.S.B.—Marshall & Ilsley Corporation; *U.S. Public*, pg. 1050
MACANDREWS & FORBES HOLDINGS INC.; *U.S. Private*, pg. 689
THE METROPOLITAN SAVINGS BANK OF OHIO—F.N.B. Corporation; *U.S. Public*, pg. 608
MUTUAL SAVINGS & LOAN ASSOCIATION—Berkshire Hathaway Inc.; *U.S. Public*, pg. 217
NEW HAVEN SAVINGS BANK; *U.S. Private*, pg. 793
NORWEST BANK NEVADA, N.A.—Norwest Corporation; *U.S. Public*, pg. 1202
OSTERREICHISCHE POSTSPARKASSE AG; *Int'l*, pg. 1012
PAWLING SAVINGS BANK—Progressive Bank, Inc.; *U.S. Public*, pg. 1334
SANWA BANK CALIFORNIA—The Sanwa Bank Limited; *Int'l*, pg. 1189
SOCIETY NATIONAL BANK—Keycorp; *U.S. Public*, pg. 954
STERLING FINANCIAL CORPORATION; *U.S. Public*, pg. 1516
UNION BANK OF NORWAY; *Int'l*, pg. 1439
WASHINGTON MUTUAL INC.; *U.S. Public*, pg. 1741
WESCO FINANCIAL CORPORATION—Berkshire Hathaway Inc.; *U.S. Public*, pg. 217
WESTCORP; *U.S. Public*, pg. 1756

6061 — CREDIT UNIONS, FEDERALLY CHARTERED

AGAMERICA, FCB—Federal Farm Credit Banks Funding Corporation; *U.S. Private*, pg. 398
AGRIBANK, FCB—Federal Farm Credit Banks Funding Corporation; *U.S. Private*, pg. 398
CONFEDERATION DES CAISSES DES JARDINS; *Int'l*, pg. 325
CREDIOP-CREDITO PER LE IMPRESE E LE OPERE PUBBLICHE SPA; *Int'l*, pg. 341
FARM CREDIT LEASING SERVICES CORPORATION—Federal Farm Credit Banks Funding Corporation; *U.S. Private*, pg. 398
FEDERAL FARM CREDIT BANKS FUNDING CORPORATION; *U.S. Private*, pg. 398
JLW FINANCIAL MANAGEMENT SYSTEMS, INC.—AEGON N.V.; *Int'l*, pg. 28
NATIONAL AUSTRALIA BANK/GATX—GATX Corporation; *U.S. Public*, pg. 691
ST. PAUL BANK FOR COOPERATIVES—Federal Farm Credit Banks Funding Corporation; *U.S. Private*, pg. 398
TOWER LOAN OF MISSISSIPPI, INC.—Capitol Street Corp.; *U.S. Private*, pg. 207

6062 — CREDIT UNIONS, NOT FEDERALLY CHARTERED

LASALLE CRAGIN BANK—ABN-AMRO Holding N.V.; *Int'l*, pg. 10

6081 — BRANCHES & AGENCIES OF FOREIGN BANKS

ABN AMRO BANK, N.V. (SEATTLE)—ABN-AMRO Holding N.V.; *Int'l*, pg. 10
ABN-AMRO BANK (SVERIGE) AB—ABN-AMRO Holding N.V.; *Int'l*, pg. 11
ABN-AMRO HOLDING N.V.; *Int'l*, pg. 8
ABN-AMRO NORTH AMERICA INC., CHICAGO—ABN-AMRO Holding N.V.; *Int'l*, pg. 10
ABN (HEAD OFFICE)—ABN-AMRO Holding N.V.; *Int'l*, pg. 11
ABN (LUXEMBOURG) S.A.—ABN-AMRO Holding N.V.; *Int'l*, pg. 11
ABN, SUCURSAL EN ESPANA (BARCELONA)—ABN-AMRO Holding N.V.; *Int'l*, pg. 11
ABN, SUCURSAL EN ESPANA (MADRID)—ABN-AMRO Holding N.V.; *Int'l*, pg. 11
AIB CAPITAL MARKETS PLC—Allied Irish Banks, p.l.c.; *Int'l*, pg. 64
AIB SECURITIES SERVICES LTD.—Allied Irish Banks, p.l.c.; *Int'l*, pg. 64
ANZ BANK (GUERNSEY) LIMITED—Australia & New Zealand Banking Group Limited; *Int'l*, pg. 98
ANZ BANKING GROUP (NEW ZEALAND) LTD.—Australia & New Zealand Banking Group Limited; *Int'l*, pg. 98
ANZ GRINDLAYS BANK (JERSEY) LIMITED—Australia & New Zealand Banking Group Limited; *Int'l*, pg. 98
ANZ MCCAUGHAN (NZ) LIMITED—Australia & New Zealand Banking Group Limited; *Int'l*, pg. 99
ASB BANK LIMITED—Commonwealth Bank Group; *Int'l*, pg. 313
ABBEY NATIONAL PLC; *Int'l*, pg. 19
ALGEMENE BANK NEDERLAND N.V.—ABN-AMRO Holding N.V.; *Int'l*, pg. 9
KG ALLGEMEINE LEASING GMBH & CO.—Dresdner Bank AG; *Int'l*, pg. 418
ALLIED IRISH BANKS, P.L.C.; *Int'l*, pg. 64
ALTAE BANCO S.A.—Caja de Madrid Group; *Int'l*, pg. 251
AMERICAN EXPRESS BANK LTD.—American Express Company; *U.S. Public*, pg. 74
AMERICAN EXPRESS BANK (SWITZERLAND) S.A.—American Express Company; *U.S. Public*, pg. 74
AMERICAN SCANDINAVIAN BANKING CORPORATION—Merita Ltd.; *Int'l*, pg. 859
AMRO AUSTRALIA LTD.—ABN-AMRO Holding N.V.; *Int'l*, pg. 9
AMRO BANK OVERSEAS N.V.—ABN-AMRO Holding N.V.; *Int'l*, pg. 9
AMRO HANDELSBANK A.G.—ABN-AMRO Holding N.V.; *Int'l*, pg. 10
AMSTERDAM-ROTTERDAM BANK N.V.—ABN-AMRO Holding N.V.; *Int'l*, pg. 9
AMSTERDAM-ROTTERDAM BANK N.V. NEW YORK—ABN-AMRO Holding N.V.; *Int'l*, pg. 9
ANLAGE-UND KREDITBANK AKB, ZURICH—Bayerische Hypotheken-und Wechsel-Bank Aktiengesellschaft; *Int'l*, pg. 176
HENRY ANSBACHER HOLDING PLC—First National Bank Holdings Limited; *Int'l*, pg. 487
ANTWERPSE DIAMANTBANK N.V.—Bank Brussels Lambert; *Int'l*, pg. 147
ARRENDADORA COMERMEX S.A. DE C.V.—BankAmerica Corporation; *U.S. Public*, pg. 182
ASAHI BANK (DEUTSCHLAND) GMBH—The Asahi Bank, Ltd.; *Int'l*, pg. 83
THE ASAHI BANK, LTD.; *Int'l*, pg. 81
ASAHI BANK LONDON BRANCH—The Asahi Bank, Ltd.; *Int'l*, pg. 82
ASAHI BANK (NEDERLAND) N.V.—The Asahi Bank, Ltd.; *Int'l*, pg. 83
ASAHI BANK OF CALIFORNIA—The Asahi Bank, Ltd.; *Int'l*, pg. 82
ASAHI BANK (SCHWEIZ) AG—The Asahi Bank, Ltd.; *Int'l*, pg. 83
ASAHI FINANCE (U.K.) LTD.—The Asahi Bank, Ltd.; *Int'l*, pg. 83
ASAHI TRUST (NEDERLAND) B.V.—The Asahi Bank, Ltd.; *Int'l*, pg. 83
P.T. ASEAM INDONESIA—The Dai-Ichi Kangyo Bank, Limited; *Int'l*, pg. 362
ASEAMBANKERS MALAYSIA BERHAD—The Dai-Ichi Kangyo Bank, Limited; *Int'l*, pg. 362
ASSOCIATED MERCHANT BANK PTE. LTD.—The Royal Bank of Scotland plc; *Int'l*, pg. 1133
AUSSENHANDEL-FOERDERUNGSGESELLSCHAFT MBH—Commerzbank AG; *Int'l*, pg. 309
AUSTRALIA & NEW ZEALAND BANKING GROUP LIMITED BRAZIL—Australia & New Zealand Banking Group Limited; *Int'l*, pg. 99
B OF B (EUROPE) LIMITED—The Bank of Bermuda Limited; *Int'l*, pg. 151
BBL AUSTRALIA LIMITED—Bank Brussels Lambert; *Int'l*, pg. 148
BCI MER ROUGE—Banque Nationale de Paris; *Int'l*, pg. 163
BCN-BARCLAYS BANCO DE INVESTIMENTO S.A.—Barclays Bank PLC; *Int'l*, pg. 165
BDL BANCO DI LUGANO—Union Bank of Switzerland; *Int'l*, pg. 1439
BHF-BANK—BHF-BANK AG; *Int'l*, pg. 119
BHF-BANK AG; *Int'l*, pg. 119
BHF-BANK INTERNATIONAL S.A.—BHF-BANK AG; *Int'l*, pg. 119
BHF-BANK (JERSEY) LTD.—BHF-BANK AG; *Int'l*, pg. 119
BHF-BANK (SWITZERLAND) LTD.—BHF-BANK AG; *Int'l*, pg. 119
BHF FINANCE (NETHERLANDS) B.V.—BHF-BANK AG; *Int'l*, pg. 119
BMCI MOROCCO—Banque Nationale de Paris; *Int'l*, pg. 163
BNL CONSULTORIA E SERVICIOS LTDA.—Banca Nazionale del Lavoro Sj.A.; *Int'l*, pg. 136
BNL DE URUGUAY—Banca Nazionale del Lavoro Sj.A.; *Int'l*, pg. 136
BNL DISTRIBUIDORA DE TITULOS VAL. MOB. S.A.—Banca Nazionale del Lavoro Sj.A.; *Int'l*, pg. 136
BNP-AK DRESDNER BANK A.S.—Dresdner Bank AG; *Int'l*, pg. 420
BNP-AK DRESDNER BANK A.S.—Sabanci Holding A.S.; *Int'l*, pg. 1167
BNP ESPANA S.A.—Banque Nationale de Paris; *Int'l*, pg. 163
BNP FINANCE—Banque Nationale de Paris; *Int'l*, pg. 163
BNP (IRELAND) LTD.—Banque Nationale de Paris; *Int'l*, pg. 163
BNP LUXEMBOURG SA—Banque Nationale de Paris; *Int'l*, pg. 164
BNP PUBLIC LIMITED CO. (LONDON)—Banque Nationale de Paris; *Int'l*, pg. 164
BTM FINANCE AND SECURITIES (THAILAND) LTD.—The Bank of Tokyo-Mitsubishi, Ltd.; *Int'l*, pg. 157
BANCA AGRICOLA MANTOVANA SARL; *Int'l*, pg. 135
BANCA CANTRADE LUGANO SA—Union Bank of Switzerland; *Int'l*, pg. 1439
BANCA COMMERCIALE ITALIANA; *Int'l*, pg. 135
BANCA D'AMERICA E D'ITALIA S.P.A.—Deutsche Bank AG; *Int'l*, pg. 403
BANCA MARCH S.A.—Banca March S.A.; *Int'l*, pg. 136
BANCA MARCH S.A.; *Int'l*, pg. 136
BANCA MERCANTILE S.P.A.—La Fondiaria Assicurazioni S.p.A.; *Int'l*, pg. 784
BANCA MONTE PASCHI BELGIO—Bank Brussels Lambert; *Int'l*, pg. 147
BANCA NAZIONALE DEL LAVORO SJ.A.; *Int'l*, pg. 136
BANCA POPOLARE DI MILANO; *Int'l*, pg. 137
BANCA SERFIN, S.N.C.; *Int'l*, pg. 137
BANCO BANIF DE GESTION PRIVADA—Banco Central Hispanoamericano S.A.; *Int'l*, pg. 139
BANCO BNL DO BRASIL S.A.—Banca Nazionale del Lavoro Sj.A.; *Int'l*, pg. 137
BANCO BRADESCO S.A.; *Int'l*, pg. 139
BANCO CENTRAL CANADA—Banco Central Hispanoamericano S.A.; *Int'l*, pg. 140
BANCO CENTRAL CORP. (PUERTO RICO)—Banco Central Hispanoamericano S.A.; *Int'l*, pg. 139
BANCO CENTRAL HISPANOAMERICANO S.A.; *Int'l*, pg. 139
BANCO CHASE MANHATTAN, S.A.—The Chase Manhattan Corporation; *U.S. Public*, pg. 339
BANCO COMERCIAL TRANSATLANTICO, S.A. (BANCOTRANS) (BARCELONA)—Deutsche Bank AG; *Int'l*, pg. 403
BANCO COMERCIAL TRANSATLANTICO, S.A. (BANCOTRANS) (MADRID)—Deutsche Bank AG; *Int'l*, pg. 403
BANCO CREDIBANCO S.A.—The Bank of New York Company, Inc.; *U.S. Public*, pg. 179
BANCO DE ASUNCION—Banco Central Hispanoamericano S.A.; *Int'l*, pg. 140
BANCO DE COMERCIO E INDUSTRIA, S.A.—Banco Santander; *Int'l*, pg. 144
BANCO DE EXTREMADURA, S.A.—Caixa Geral de Depositos; *Int'l*, pg. 251
BANCO DE FORMENTO—Banco Central Hispanoamericano S.A.; *Int'l*, pg. 139
BANCO DE JEREZ—Banco Central Hispanoamericano S.A.; *Int'l*, pg. 139
BANCO DE MONTEVIDEO—Deutsche Bank AG; *Int'l*, pg. 403
BANCO DE VALENCIA—Banco Central Hispanoamericano S.A.; *Int'l*, pg. 139
BANCO DO BRASIL; *Int'l*, pg. 141
BANCO DO BRASIL S.A.-PARAGUAY—Banco do Brasil; *Int'l*, pg. 141
BANCO ESPIRITO SANTO E COMERCIAL DE LISBOA SA; *Int'l*, pg. 142
BANCO FINANCIAL PORTUGUES-BRAZIL—Caixa Geral de Depositos; *Int'l*, pg. 251
BANCO GALLEGO—Banco 21; *Int'l*, pg. 145
BANCO HISPANO DE INVESTIMENTO, S.A.—Banco Central Hispanoamericano S.A.; *Int'l*, pg. 140
BANCO INTERNACIONAL DE COLOMBIA, S.A.—Citicorp; *U.S. Public*, pg. 378
BANCO INTERNACIONAL DE COMERCIO—Banco Central Hispanoamericano S.A.; *Int'l*, pg. 139
BANCO ITAU S.A.; *Int'l*, pg. 142
BANCO ITAU S.A.—Banco Itau S.A.; *Int'l*, pg. 142
BANCO MERCANTIL DE TARRAGONA—Banco Central Hispanoamericano S.A.; *Int'l*, pg. 139
BANCO NACIONAL DE MEXICO, S.A. (BANAMEX)—Grupo Financiero Banamex/Accival, S.A. de C.V.; *Int'l*, pg. 574
BANCO NATWEST ESPANA SA—National Westminster Bank PLC; *Int'l*, pg. 911
BANCO POPULAR ARGENTINO—Banco Central Hispanoamericano S.A.; *Int'l*, pg. 140
BANCO QUILMES; *Int'l*, pg. 142
BANCO SANTANDER; *Int'l*, pg. 143
BANCO SANTANDER—Banco Santander; *Int'l*, pg. 143
BANCO STANDARD TOTTA DE MOCAMBIQUE, SARL—Standard Chartered Bank PLC; *Int'l*, pg. 1296
BANCO TOTTA & ACORES; *Int'l*, pg. 144
BANCOMER LONDON BRANCH—Bancomer, S.A.; *Int'l*, pg. 145
BANCOMER LOS ANGELES INTERNATIONAL BANKING BRANCH—Bancomer, S.A.; *Int'l*, pg. 145
BANCOMER, S.A.; *Int'l*, pg. 145
BANEXI (BANQUE POUR L'EXPANSION INDUSTRIELLE)—Banque Nationale de Paris; *Int'l*, pg. 163
BANK AUFINA—Union Bank of Switzerland; *Int'l*, pg. 1439
BANK BRUSSELS LAMBERT HONG KONG BRANCH—Bank Brussels Lambert; *Int'l*, pg. 148
BANK BRUSSELS LAMBERT - JAKARTA REPRESENTATIVE OFFICE—Bank Brussels Lambert; *Int'l*, pg. 148
BANK BRUSSELS LAMBERT, LONDON BRANCH—Bank Brussels Lambert; *Int'l*, pg. 147
BANK HAPOALIM; *Int'l*, pg. 149
BANK HAPOALIM B.M.—Bank Hapoalim; *Int'l*, pg. 149
BANK LEUMI LE-ISRAEL B.M.—Bank Leumi le-Israel B.M.; *Int'l*, pg. 150
BANK LEUMI LE-ISRAEL (SWITZERLAND)—Bank Leumi le-Israel B.M.; *Int'l*, pg. 150
BANK LEUMI (UK) P.L.C.—Bank Leumi le-Israel B.M.; *Int'l*, pg. 150
BANK LEUMI (UK) PLC—Bank Leumi le-Israel B.M.; *Int'l*, pg. 150
BANK MEES & HOPE NV—ABN-AMRO Holding N.V.; *Int'l*, pg. 9
BANK OF BERMUDA (CAYMAN) LIMITED—The Bank of Bermuda Limited; *Int'l*, pg. 151
BANK OF BERMUDA (GUERNSEY) LIMITED—The Bank of Bermuda Limited; *Int'l*, pg. 151

BANK OF BERMUDA (ISLE OF MAN) LIMITED—The Bank of Bermuda Limited; *Int'l*, pg. 151
THE BANK OF BERMUDA LIMITED; *Int'l*, pg. 150
BANK OF BERMUDA (LUXEMBOURG) S.A—The Bank of Bermuda Limited; *Int'l*, pg. 151
BANK OF BOSTON—BankBoston Corporation; *U.S. Public, pg. 184*
BANK OF BOSTON CANADA—BankBoston Corporation; *U.S. Public*, pg. 184
BANK OF BOSTON INTERNATIONAL—BankBoston Corporation; *U.S. Public*, pg. 184
BANK OF BOSTON OF THE PHILIPPINES—BankBoston Corporation; *U.S. Public*, pg. 184
BANK OF BOSTON S.A.—BankBoston Corporation; *U.S. Public*, pg. 185
BANK OF BOSTON TRUST CO. (BAHAMAS) LIMITED—BankBoston Corporation; *U.S. Public*, pg. 185
BANK OF HAWAII INTERNATIONAL CORPORATION, NEW YORK—Pacific Century Financial Corporation; *U.S.* Public, pg. 1248
BANK OF IRELAND; *Int'l*, pg. 152
BANK OF IRELAND (U.S.A.)—Bank of Ireland; *Int'l*, pg. 152
BANK OF MONTREAL - GERMANY—Bank of Montreal; *Int'l*, pg. 155
THE BANK OF NOVA SCOTIA—The Bank of Nova Scotia; *Int'l*, pg. 156
THE BANK OF TOKYO-MITSUBISHI (CANADA)—The Bank of Tokyo-Mitsubishi, Ltd.; *Int'l*, pg. 158
BANK OF TOKYO-MITSUBISHI (DEUTSCHLAND) AG—The Bank of Tokyo-Mitsubishi, Ltd.; *Int'l*, pg. 158
THE BANK OF TOKYO-MITSUBISHI (HOLLAND) N.V.—The Bank of Tokyo-Mitsubishi, Ltd.; *Int'l*, pg. 158
THE BANK OF TOKYO-MITSUBISHI, LTD.; *Int'l*, pg. 157
THE BANK OF TOKYO-MITSUBISHI, LTD.—The Bank of Tokyo-Mitsubishi, Ltd.; *Int'l*, pg. 157
BANK OF TOKYO-MITSUBISHI, LTD.—The Bank of Tokyo-Mitsubishi, Ltd.; *Int'l*, pg. 157
THE BANK OF TOKYO-MITSUBISHI, LTD. (HOUSTON AGENCY)—The Bank of Tokyo-Mitsubishi, Ltd.; *Int'l*, pg. 157
BANK OF TOKYO-MITSUBISHI LTD. (MIAMI AGENCY)—The Bank of Tokyo-Mitsubishi, Ltd.; *Int'l*, pg. 157
BANK OF TOKYO-MITSUBISHI LTD., PARIS BRANCH—The Bank of Tokyo-Mitsubishi, Ltd.; *Int'l*, pg. 158
BANK OF TOKYO-MITSUBISHI, LTD. (RIO DE JANIERO REPRESENTATIVE OFFICE)—The Bank of Tokyo-Mitsubishi, Ltd.; *Int'l*, pg. 158
BANK OF TOKYO-MITSUBISHI LTD., ZURICH REPRESENTATIVE OFFICE—The Bank of Tokyo-Mitsubishi, Ltd.; *Int'l*, pg. 158
THE BANK OF TOKYO-MITSUBISHI (LUXOMBOURG) S.A.—The Bank of Tokyo-Mitsubishi, Ltd.; *Int'l*, pg. 158
THE BANK OF TOKYO-MITSUBISHI (PANAMA BRANCH)—The Bank of Tokyo-Mitsubishi, Ltd.; *Int'l*, pg. 158
BANK OF TOKYO-MITSUBISHI TRUST COMPANY—The Bank of Tokyo-Mitsubishi, Ltd.; *Int'l*, pg. 157
BANK OF TOKYO-MITSUBISHI (UK) LIMITED—The Bank of Tokyo-Mitsubishi, Ltd.; *Int'l*, pg. 158
BANK OF TONGA—Pacific Century Financial Corporation; *U.S. Public*, pg. 1248
BANK OF YOKOHAMA SHANGHAI—Bank of Yokohama; *Int'l*, pg. 159
BANK ROHNER LTD.—Union Bank of Switzerland; *Int'l*, pg. 1439
BANKAMERICA TRUST & BANKING CORP. (BAHAMAS) LTD.—BankAmerica Corporation; *U.S. Public*, pg. 183
BANKAMERICA TRUST & BANKING CORP. (CAYMAN) LTD.—BankAmerica Corporation; *U.S. Public*, pg. 183
BANKERS TRUST AG—Bankers Trust New York Corporation; *U.S. Public*, pg. 185
BANKERS TRUST ASIA LIMITED—Bankers Trust New York Corporation; *U.S. Public*, pg. 185
BANKERS TRUST AUSTRALIA LIMITED—Bankers Trust New York Corporation; *U.S. Public*, pg. 185
BANKERS TRUST BANK OF CANADA—Bankers Trust New York Corporation; *U.S. Public*, pg. 186
BANKERS TRUST COMPANY—Bankers Trust New York Corporation; *U.S. Public*, pg. 186
BANKERS TRUST INTERNATIONAL (ASIA) LTD.—Bankers Trust New York Corporation; *U.S. Public*, pg. 186
BANKERS TRUST INTERNATIONAL LIMITED—Bankers Trust New York Corporation; *U.S. Public*, pg. 186
BANKERS TRUST INVESTMENT MANAGEMENT LTD.—Bankers Trust New York Corporation; *U.S. Public*, pg. 186
BANKHAUS GEBRUDER BETHMANN—Bayerische Vereinsbank Group; *Int'l*, pg. 179
BANQUE DE BOSTON S.A.—BankBoston Corporation; *U.S. Public*, pg. 185
BANQUE BRUXELLES LAMBERT FRANCE—Bank Brussels Lambert; *Int'l*, pg. 148
BANQUE CANTONALE VAUDOISE; *Int'l*, pg. 160
BANQUE CANTRADE LAUSANNE S.A.—Union Bank of Switzerland; *Int'l*, pg. 1439
BANQUE CANTRADE, ORMOND BURRUS SA—Union Bank of Switzerland; *Int'l*, pg. 1439
BANQUE COMMERCIALE DU BURUNDI SARL—Bank Brussels Lambert; *Int'l*, pg. 148
BANQUE COMMERCIALE DU RWANDA S.A.—Bank Brussels Lambert; *Int'l*, pg. 148
BANQUE CONTINENTALE DU LUXEMBOURG—Compagnie Financiere de Paribas; *Int'l*, pg. 319
BANQUE DE LUXEMBOURG—Deutsche Bank AG; *Int'l*, pg. 406
BANQUE DE NEUFLIZE, SCHLUMBERGER, MALLET—ABN-AMRO Holding N.V.; *Int'l*, pg. 12
BANQUE DE NOUVELLE CALEDONIE—Pacific Century Financial Corporation; *U.S. Public*, pg. 1248
BANQUE DE TAHITI—Pacific Century Financial Corporation; *U.S. Public*, pg. 1248
BANQUE DU CAIRE BARCLAYS INTL. BANK SAE—Barclays Bank PLC; *Int'l*, pg. 165
BANQUE FERRIER LULLIN (LUXEMBOURG) SA—Ferrier Lullin & Cie SA; *Int'l*, pg. 480
BANQUE FRANCAISE COMMERCIALE—Compagnie de Suez; *Int'l*, pg. 313
BANQUE GENERALE DU LUXEMBOURG SA—Banque Generale du Luxembourg SA; *Int'l*, pg. 162
BANQUE GENERALE DU LUXEMBOURG S.A.—Banque Generale du Luxembourg SA; *Int'l*, pg. 162
BANQUE GENERALE DU LUXEMBOURG (SUISSE) SA—Banque Generale du Luxembourg SA; *Int'l*, pg. 162
BANQUE INDOSUEZ—Compagnie de Suez; *Int'l*, pg. 313
BANQUE INTERNATIONALE A LUXEMBOURG S.A.—Banque Internationale a Luxembourg S.A.; *Int'l*, pg. 162
BANQUE INTERNATIONALE DE PLACEMENT S.A.—Dresdner Bank AG; *Int'l*, pg. 419
BANQUE KLEINWORT BENSON SA—Dresdner Bank AG; *Int'l*, pg. 420
BANQUE LEUMI FRANCE S.A.—Bank Leumi le-Israel B.M.; *Int'l*, pg. 150
BANQUE LEUMI FRANCE S.A.-STRASBOURG—Bank Leumi le-Israel B.M.; *Int'l*, pg. 150
BANQUE NAGELMACKERS SA—CoreStates Financial Corp.; *U.S. Public*, pg. 447
BANQUE NATIONALE DE PARIS; *Int'l*, pg. 163
BANQUE NATIONALE DE PARIS (CANADA)—Banque Nationale de Paris; *Int'l*, pg. 164
BANQUE NATIONALE DE PARIS-GUYANE—Banque Nationale de Paris; *Int'l*, pg. 164
BANQUE NATIONALE DE PARIS (PANAMA) SA—Banque Nationale de Paris; *Int'l*, pg. 164
BANQUE NATIONALE DE PARIS (SUISSE) S.A.—Banque Nationale de Paris; *Int'l*, pg. 164
BANQUE PIGUET & CIE S.A.—Banque Cantonale Vaudoise; *Int'l*, pg. 160
BANQUE POUR L'EUROPE S.A.-EUROPA BANK AG—Dresdner Bank AG; *Int'l*, pg. 419
BANQUE RIVAUD—Northern Trust Corporation; *U.S. Public*, pg. 1197
BANQUE SAINT DOMINIQUE—Credit Nationale; *Int'l*, pg. 344
BANQUE VEUVE MORIN-PONS—Dresdner Bank AG; *Int'l*, pg. 419
BARCLAYS BANK COMMERCIAL GROUP—Barclays Bank PLC; *Int'l*, pg. 165
BARCLAYS BANK FINANCE CO. (GUERNSEY) LTD.—Barclays Bank PLC; *Int'l*, pg. 165
BARCLAYS BANK FINANCE CO. (JERSEY) LTD.—Barclays Bank PLC; *Int'l*, pg. 165
BARCLAYS BANK OF CANADA—Barclays Bank PLC; *Int'l*, pg. 165
BARCLAYS BANK OF GHANA LTD.—Barclays Bank PLC; *Int'l*, pg. 165
BARCLAYS BANK OF KENYA LTD.—Barclays Bank PLC; *Int'l*, pg. 165
BARCLAYS BANK OF SIERRA LEONE LTD.—Barclays Bank PLC; *Int'l*, pg. 165
BARCLAYS BANK OF SWAZILAND LTD.—Barclays Bank PLC; *Int'l*, pg. 165
BARCLAYS BANK OF UGANDA LTD.—Barclays Bank PLC; *Int'l*, pg. 165
BARCLAYS BANK OF ZAMBIA LTD.—Barclays Bank PLC; *Int'l*, pg. 165
BARCLAYS BANK OF ZIMBABWE LTD.—Barclays Bank PLC; *Int'l*, pg. 165
BARCLAYS BANK PLC—Barclays Bank PLC; *Int'l*, pg. 165
BARCLAYS BANK SA—Barclays Bank PLC; *Int'l*, pg. 166
BARCLAYS BANK SA-MADRID—Barclays Bank PLC; *Int'l*, pg. 166
BARCLAYS BANK SZARL—Barclays Bank PLC; *Int'l*, pg. 166
BARCLAYS BANK TRUST CO. LTD.—Barclays Bank PLC; *Int'l*, pg. 164
BARCLAYS DISCOUNT BANK LTD.—Barclays Bank PLC; *Int'l*, pg. 166
BARCLAYS TRUST & BANKING COMPANY (JAPAN) LTD.—Barclays Bank PLC; *Int'l*, pg. 166
BARCLAYTRUST INVESTMENT SERVICES LTD.—Barclays Bank PLC; *Int'l*, pg. 166
BAYERISCHE HANDELSBANK AG—Bayerische Vereinsbank Group; *Int'l*, pg. 179
BAYERISCHE HYPOTHEKEN-UND WECHSEL-BANK AKTIENGESELLSCHAFT NEW YORK BRANCH—Bayerische Hypotheken-und Wechsel-Bank Aktiengesellschaft; *Int'l*, pg. 176
BAYERISCHE HYPOTHEKEN-UND WECHSEL-BANK AG (CAYMAN ISLANDS)—Bayerische Hypotheken-und Wechsel-Bank Aktiengesellschaft; *Int'l*, pg. 176
BAYERISCHE HYPOTHEKEN-UND WECHSEL-BANK AG (HONG KONG)—Bayerische Hypotheken-und Wechsel-Bank Aktiengesellschaft; *Int'l*, pg. 176
BAYERISCHE KAPITALANLAGEGESELLSCHAFT MBH—Bayerische Vereinsbank Group; *Int'l*, pg. 179
BAYERISCHE LANDESBANK; *Int'l*, pg. 176
BAYERISCHE VEREINSBANK AG—Bayerische Vereinsbank Group; *Int'l*, pg. 180
BAYERISCHE VEREINSBANK S.A. (BV FRANCE)—Bayerische Vereinsbank Group; *Int'l*, pg. 181
BAYERNHYPO FINANCE N.V.—Bayerische Hypotheken-und Wechsel-Bank Aktiengesellschaft; *Int'l*, pg. 176
BERMUDA TRUST (CAYMAN) LTD.—The Bank of Bermuda Limited; *Int'l*, pg. 151
BERMUDA TRUST (GUERNSEY) LIMITED—The Bank of Bermuda Limited; *Int'l*, pg. 151
BETEILIGUNGSGESELLSCHAFT FUR DIE DEUTSCHE WIRTSCHAFT GMBH—Dresdner Bank AG; *Int'l*, pg. 418
BRASILIAN AMERICAN MERCHANT BANK—Banco do Brasil; *Int'l*, pg. 142
BROWN BROTHERS HARRIMAN & CO.; *U.S. Private*, pg. 173
CB BANCSHARES, INC. (CITY BANK)—The Sakura Bank, Limited; *Int'l*, pg. 1179
CC-BANK, A.G.—Banco Santander; *Int'l*, pg. 144
CC BANQUE BELGIQUE—Banco Santander; *Int'l*, pg. 144
CCF LONDON—Credit Commercial de France; *Int'l*, pg. 342
CCF REPRESENTACAO E ASSESSORIA S/C LTDA.—Credit Commercial de France; *Int'l*, pg. 342
CIBC BANK AND TRUST COMPANY (CHANNEL ISLANDS) LIMITED—Canadian Imperial Bank of Commerce; *Int'l*, pg. 257
CIBC INC.—Canadian Imperial Bank of Commerce; *Int'l*, pg. 257
CIBC NEW ZEALAND LIMITED—Canadian Imperial Bank of Commerce; *Int'l*, pg. 258
CAIXA GERAL DE DEPOSITOS (FRANCE)—Caixa Geral de Depositos; *Int'l*, pg. 251
CALIFORNIA COMMERCE BANK—Grupo Financiero Banamex/Accival, S.A. de C.V.; *Int'l*, pg. 574
CANADIAN IMPERIAL BANK OF COMMERCE (CALIFORNIA)—Canadian Imperial Bank of Commerce; *Int'l*, pg. 257
CANADIAN IMPERIAL BANK OF COMMERCE (DEUTSCHLAND) AG—Canadian Imperial Bank of Commerce; *Int'l*, pg. 257
CANTRADE PRIVATE LTD.—Union Bank of Switzerland; *Int'l*, pg. 1439
CARIPLO FINANCE INC.—Cassa di Risparmio delle Provincie Lombarde SpA (CARIPLO); *Int'l*, pg. 275
CAYMADRID INTERNATIONAL LIMITED—Caja de Madrid Group; *Int'l*, pg. 252
CENTRO INTERNATIONALE HANDELSBANK AG (CENTROBANK)—Dresdner Bank AG; *Int'l*, pg. 420
CENTROBANCO (PANAMA), S.A.—Banco Central Hispanoamericano S.A.; *Int'l*, pg. 140
CHASE INVESTMENT BANK HOLDINGS LIMITED—The Chase Manhattan Corporation; *U.S. Public*, pg. 339
THE CHASE MANHATTAN BANK, N.A.—The Chase Manhattan Corporation; *U.S. Public*, pg. 340
THE CHASE MANHATTAN BANK OF CANADA—The Chase Manhattan Corporation; *U.S. Public*, pg. 340
CHASE MANHATTAN BANK (SWITZERLAND)—The Chase Manhattan Corporation; *U.S. Public*, pg. 340
CHASE MANHATTAN FINANCIAL SERVICES (HONG KONG) LTD.—The Chase Manhattan Corporation; *U.S. Public*, pg. 340
CHASE MANHATTAN GILTS LTD.—The Chase Manhattan Corporation; *U.S. Public*, pg. 339
CHASE MANHATTAN MILBANK, LTD.—The Chase Manhattan Corporation; *U.S. Public*, pg. 339
CHASE MANHATTAN OVERSEAS CORPORATION—The Chase Manhattan Corporation; *U.S. Public*, pg. 340
CHASE MANHATTAN TRADING S.A.—The Chase Manhattan Corporation; *U.S. Public*, pg. 340
CHASE MANHATTAN TRUST AND BANKING COMPANY (JAPAN) LIMITED—The Chase Manhattan Corporation; *U.S. Public*, pg. 340
CHASE MANHATTAN TRUST CAYMAN LTD.—The Chase Manhattan Corporation; *U.S. Public*, pg. 340
CHASE MANHATTAN TRUST COMPANY (HONG KONG) LTD.—The Chase Manhattan Corporation; *U.S. Public*, pg. 340
THE CHASE MANHATTAN TRUST CORPORATION LIMITED—The Chase Manhattan Corporation; *U.S. Public*, pg. 341
CHASE MANHATTAN TRUSTEES, LTD.—The Chase Manhattan Corporation; *U.S. Public*, pg. 339
CHASE NETTING (U.K.) LTD.—The Chase Manhattan Corporation; *U.S. Public*, pg. 341
CHEKIANG FIRST BANK LTD.—The Dai-Ichi Kangyo Bank, Limited; *Int'l*, pg. 361
CHEMICAL BANK (GUERNSEY) LIMITED—The Chase Manhattan Corporation; *U.S. Public*, pg. 341
CHEMICAL SECURITIES LIMITED—The Chase Manhattan Corporation; *U.S. Public*, pg. 341
CHINA UNIVERSAL LEASING CO., LTD.—The Sanwa Bank Limited; *Int'l*, pg. 1190
CHO HUNG BANK—Cho Hung Bank; *Int'l*, pg. 287
CHO HUNG BANK OF NEW YORK—Cho Hung Bank; *Int'l*, pg. 287
CHRISTIANIA BANK OG KREDITKASSE ASA; *Int'l*, pg. 289
THE CHUO TRUST & BANKING CO., LTD.; *Int'l*, pg. 291
CHUO TRUST ASIA LIMITED—The Chuo Trust & Banking Co., Ltd.; *Int'l*, pg. 291
CHUO TRUST INTERNATIONAL LIMITED—The Chuo Trust & Banking Co., Ltd.; *Int'l*, pg. 291
CITIBANK A.G.—Citicorp; *U.S. Public*, pg. 378
CITIBANK CANADA—Citicorp; *U.S. Public*, pg. 378
CITIBANK, N.A. BOGOTA—Citicorp; *U.S. Public*, pg. 378
CITIBANK OY—Citicorp; *U.S. Public*, pg. 378
CITIBANK SAVINGS—Citicorp; *U.S. Public*, pg. 378
CITIBANK (ZAIRE) S.A.R.L.—Citicorp; *U.S. Public*, pg. 379
CITICORP INTERNATIONAL BANK LTD.—Citicorp; *U.S. Public*, pg. 378
CITICORP INTERNATIONAL LIMITED—Citicorp; *U.S. Public*, pg. 378
CITICORP S.A.—Citicorp; *U.S. Public*, pg. 379
CITIZENS BANK OF MASSACHUSETTS—The Royal Bank of Scotland plc; *Int'l*, pg. 1132
CITIZENS SAVINGS BANK—The Royal Bank of Scotland plc; *Int'l*, pg. 1132
CLYDESDALE BANK PLC—National Australia Bank Limited; *Int'l*, pg. 906
COMMERCE INTERNATIONAL MERCHANT BANKERS BERHAD—The Sanwa Bank Limited; *Int'l*, pg. 1190
THE COMMERCIAL BANK OF CEYLON LIMITED—Standard Chartered Bank PLC; *Int'l*, pg. 1296
COMMERZBANK AG; *Int'l*, pg. 308
COMMERZBANK AG LONDON BRANCH—Commerzbank AG; *Int'l*, pg. 311
COMMONWEALTH BANK GROUP; *Int'l*, pg. 312
COMMONWEALTH BANK OF AUSTRALIA—Commonwealth Bank Group; *Int'l*, pg. 313
COMMONWEALTH DEVELOPMENT BANK—Commonwealth Bank Group; *Int'l*, pg. 313
COMPAGNIE DE SUEZ; *Int'l*, pg. 313
COUTTS & CO.—National Westminster Bank PLC; *Int'l*, pg. 910

CREDIT AGRICOLE (CNCA) U.S.A. (CHICAGO)—Credit Agricole; *Int'l*, pg. 341
CREDIT AGRICOLE (CNCA) U.S.A. (NEW YORK)—Credit Agricole; *Int'l*, pg. 341
CREDIT COMMERCIAL DE FRANCE; *Int'l*, pg. 341
CREDIT EUROPEEN—Bank Brussels Lambert; *Int'l*, pg. 148
CREDIT INDUSTRIEL ET COMMERCIAL—Compagnie de Suez; *Int'l*, pg. 313
CREDIT LYONNAIS CANADA—Credit Lyonnais S.A.; *Int'l*, pg. 344
CREDIT LYONNAIS S.A.; *Int'l*, pg. 343
CREDIT SUISSE FIRST BOSTON—Credit Suisse Group; *Int'l*, pg. 345
CREDIT SUISSE GROUP; *Int'l*, pg. 345
CREDITANSTALT A.S.—Creditanstalt-Bankverein; *Int'l*, pg. 348
CREDITANSTALT-BANKVEREIN; *Int'l*, pg. 346
CREDITANSTALT-BANKVEREIN, ATLANTA REPRESENTATIVE OFFICE—Creditanstalt-Bankverein; *Int'l*, pg. 347
CREDITANSTALT EXPORT FINANCE LTD.—Creditanstalt-Bankverein; *Int'l*, pg. 348
CREDITANSTALT FINANCE INC.- NEW YORK—Creditanstalt-Bankverein; *Int'l*, pg. 347
CREDITCAPITAL FINANCE CORP., LTD.—Union Bank of Switzerland; *Int'l*, pg. 1440
D & D TOLHURST LTD.—Canadian Imperial Bank of Commerce; *Int'l*, pg. 257
DB (BELGIUM) FINANCE S.A./N.V.—Deutsche Bank AG; *Int'l*, pg. 403
DB U.K. FINANCE P.L.C.—Deutsche Bank AG; *Int'l*, pg. 404
DG BANK-ATLANTA BRANCH—DG Bank; *Int'l*, pg. 352
DG BANK-LONDON BRANCH—DG Bank; *Int'l*, pg. 352
DG BANK-NEW YORK—DG Bank; *Int'l*, pg. 352
DG EUROPEAN SECURITIES CORPORATION—DG Bank; *Int'l*, pg. 352
DAI-ICHI KANGYO AUSTRALIA LIMITED—The Dai-Ichi Kangyo Bank, Limited; *Int'l*, pg. 361
THE DAI-ICHI KANGYO BANK, LIMITED; *Int'l*, pg. 359
DAI-ICHI KANGYO BANK, LTD.-NEW YORK—The Dai-Ichi Kangyo Bank, Limited; *Int'l*, pg. 359
THE DAISHI BANK, LTD.; *Int'l*, pg. 372
THE DAISHI BANK, LTD.—The Daishi Bank, Ltd.; *Int'l*, pg. 373
DAIWA BANK-LONDON—The Daiwa Bank Limited; *Int'l*, pg. 373
DAIWA EUROPE BANK PLC-DUBLIN BRANCH—Daiwa Securities Co. Ltd.; *Int'l*, pg. 375
DAIWA FINANCE AUSTRALIA LIMITED—The Daiwa Bank Limited; *Int'l*, pg. 373
DAIWA MERCHANT BANK (SINGAPORE) LIMITED—The Daiwa Bank Limited; *Int'l*, pg. 373
H. ALBERT DE BARY & CO. N.V. (AMSTERDAM)—Deutsche Bank AG; *Int'l*, pg. 404
DE SURINAAMSCHE BANK N.V.—ABN-AMRO Holding N.V.; *Int'l*, pg. 12
DEN NORSKE BANK AS, LONDON BRANCH—Den norske Bank ASA; *Int'l*, pg. 392
DEN NORSKE BANK AS, SINGAPORE BRANCH—Den norske Bank ASA; *Int'l*, pg. 392
DEN NORSKE BANK (LUXEMBOURG) S.A.—Den norske Bank ASA; *Int'l*, pg. 392
DEN NORSKE BANK, NEW YORK BRANCH—Den norske Bank ASA; *Int'l*, pg. 392
DEUTSCHE BANK AG; *Int'l*, pg. 401
DEUTSCHE BANK-KREDITBANK AG—Deutsche Bank AG; *Int'l*, pg. 402
DISKO FACTORING FINANZ GMBH—Dresdner Bank AG; *Int'l*, pg. 418
DRESDNER-ABD SECURITIES LTD.—Dresdner Bank AG; *Int'l*, pg. 419
DRESDNER ASSET MANAGEMENT IRELAND LTD.—Dresdner Bank AG; *Int'l*, pg. 419
DRESDNER BANK KREDITBANK AG—Dresdner Bank AG; *Int'l*, pg. 418
DRESDNER BAUSPAR AG—Dresdner Bank AG; *Int'l*, pg. 418
DRESDNER INTERNATIONAL FINANCE PLC—Dresdner Bank AG; *Int'l*, pg. 419
DRESDNER INTERNATIONAL FINANCIAL MARKETS (AUSTRALIA) LTD.—Dresdner Bank AG; *Int'l*, pg. 419
DRESDNER SECURITIES (ASIA) LTD.—Dresdner Bank AG; *Int'l*, pg. 420
DRESDNERBANK ASSET MANAGEMENT S.A.—Dresdner Bank AG; *Int'l*, pg. 420
EBC AMRO BANK LTD.—ABN-AMRO Holding N.V.; *Int'l*, pg. 10
EASTBRIDGE CAPITAL INC.—The Nippon Credit Bank, Ltd.; *Int'l*, pg. 933
EQUATOR BANK LIMITED—HSBC Holdings plc; *Int'l*, pg. 580
ERSTE BANK - NEW YORK BRANCH—Erste Bank der oesterreichischen Sparkassen AG; *Int'l*, pg. 459
EURO SYNERGIES MANAGEMENT SA—Bayerische Vereinsbank Group; *Int'l*, pg. 181
EURO SYNERGIES MANAGEMENT SA—Credit Nationale; *Int'l*, pg. 345
EUROFIP (MADRID)—Banque Nationale de Paris; *Int'l*, pg. 163
EUROPEAN AMERICAN BANK & TRUST CO.—ABN-AMRO Holding N.V.; *Int'l*, pg. 9
EUROPEAN BRAZILIAN BANK LTD.—BankAmerica Corporation; *U.S. Public*, pg. 183
THE EXPORT-IMPORT BANK OF KOREA; *Int'l*, pg. 467
FABC (NEW YORK) GRP.—Banque Nationale de Paris; *Int'l*, pg. 163
FPB BANK HOLDING COMPANY LIMITED—First Pacific Company Limited; *Int'l*, pg. 487
FAR EAST BANK AND TRUST COMPANY—The Sakura Bank, Limited; *Int'l*, pg. 1180
FERRIER LULLIN BANK & TRUST (BAHAMAS) LIMITED—Ferrier Lullin & Cie SA; *Int'l*, pg. 480
FINATA BANK N.V.—ABN-AMRO Holding N.V.; *Int'l*, pg. 9
FIRST BANK OF NIGERIA PLC—Standard Chartered Bank PLC; *Int'l*, pg. 1296
FIRST CHICAGO AUSTRALIA LTD.—First Chicago NBD Corporation; *U.S. Public*, pg. 628
THE FIRST NATIONAL BANK OF BOSTON (GUERNSEY) LIMITED—BankBoston Corporation; *U.S. Public*, pg. 185
FIRST PACIFIC BANK—First Pacific Company Limited; *Int'l*, pg. 487
FLEET BANK, N.A.—Fleet Financial Group, Inc.; *U.S. Public*, pg. 649
FRANKEN WKV BANK GMBH—Bayerische Vereinsbank Group; *Int'l*, pg. 179
THE FUJI BANK & TRUST CO.—The Fuji Bank, Limited; *Int'l*, pg. 519
FUJI BANK CANADA—The Fuji Bank, Limited; *Int'l*, pg. 521
FUJI BANK CANADA (MONTREAL BRANCH)—The Fuji Bank, Limited; *Int'l*, pg. 521
FUJI BANK (DEUTSCHLAND) AG—The Fuji Bank, Limited; *Int'l*, pg. 521
GENERALE BANK—Generale de Banque S.A.; *Int'l*, pg. 547
GRINDLAYS BAHRAIN BANK B.S.C. (C)—Australia & New Zealand Banking Group Limited; *Int'l*, pg. 100
GRONINGER INDUSTRIEELE CREDIET BANK N.V.—ABN-AMRO Holding N.V.; *Int'l*, pg. 9
HSBC INVESTMENT BANK ASIA HOLDINGS LIMITED—HSBC Holdings plc; *Int'l*, pg. 582
HABIB BANK LIMITED—Habib Bank Ltd.; *Int'l*, pg. 584
HANDELSBANK NATWEST—National Westminster Bank PLC; *Int'l*, pg. 911
HANDELSBANKEN MARKETS FRANCE S.A.—Svenska Handelsbanken; *Int'l*, pg. 1328
HANDELSBANKEN OSLO—Svenska Handelsbanken; *Int'l*, pg. 1327
HANG SENG BANK LTD.—HSBC Holdings plc; *Int'l*, pg. 583
HAPOALIM (LATIN AMERICA) S.A.—Bank Hapoalim; *Int'l*, pg. 150
HELABA LUXEMBOURG LANDESBANK HESSEN-THURINGEN INTERNATIONAL S.A.—Landesbank Hessen-Thuringen Girozentrale; *Int'l*, pg. 799
HESSE NEWMAN & CO.—Banca Nazionale del Lavoro Sj.A.; *Int'l*, pg. 137
THE HOKKAIDO TAKUSHOKU BANK, LTD.-LOS ANGELES AGENCY—The Hokkaido Takushoku Bank, Ltd.; *Int'l*, pg. 627
HOLANTSE BANK-UNI—ABN-AMRO Holding N.V.; *Int'l*, pg. 12
THE HONGKONG AND SHANGHAI BANKING CORPORATION LIMITED (HONGKONGBANK)—HSBC Holdings plc; *Int'l*, pg. 583
HYPO PROPERTY FINANCE—Bayerische Hypotheken-und Wechsel-Bank Aktiengesellschaft; *Int'l*, pg. 176
HYPO SECURITIES INC.—Bayerische Hypotheken-und Wechsel-Bank Aktiengesellschaft; *Int'l*, pg. 176
HYPO TRADE FINANCE LTD.—Bayerische Hypotheken-und Wechsel-Bank Aktiengesellschaft; *Int'l*, pg. 176
HYPOBANK INTERNATIONAL S.A.—Bayerische Hypotheken-und Wechsel-Bank Aktiengesellschaft; *Int'l*, pg. 176
HYPOSWISS (SWISS MORTGAGE & COMMERCIAL BANK)—Union Bank of Switzerland; *Int'l*, pg. 1440
HYPOTHEKENBANK IN HAMBURG AG—Dresdner Bank AG; *Int'l*, pg. 418
IBJ ASIA LIMITED—The Industrial Bank of Japan, Limited; *Int'l*, pg. 676
IBJ AUSTRALIA BANK LIMITED—The Industrial Bank of Japan, Limited; *Int'l*, pg. 676
IBJ AUSTRALIA CORPORATION LIMITED—The Industrial Bank of Japan, Limited; *Int'l*, pg. 676
IBJ AUSTRALIA NOMINEES LIMITED—The Industrial Bank of Japan, Limited; *Int'l*, pg. 676
P.T. IBJ INDONESIA BANK—The Industrial Bank of Japan, Limited; *Int'l*, pg. 676
IBJ INTERNATIONAL PLC—The Industrial Bank of Japan, Limited; *Int'l*, pg. 676
IBJ SCHRODER BANK & TRUST COMPANY—The Industrial Bank of Japan, Limited; *Int'l*, pg. 674
IBJ SCHRODER BANK & TRUST COMPANY (MIDTOWN BRANCH)—The Industrial Bank of Japan, Limited; *Int'l*, pg. 675
IBJ SCHRODER INTERNATIONAL BANK—The Industrial Bank of Japan, Limited; *Int'l*, pg. 675
ICBC (EUROPE) N.V.—The International Commercial Bank of China; *Int'l*, pg. 684
IDM BANK N.V.—ABN-AMRO Holding N.V.; *Int'l*, pg. 9
I.M.I.B.J. S.P.A.—The Industrial Bank of Japan, Limited; *Int'l*, pg. 676
ISS FINANS A/S—ISS-International Service System A/S; *Int'l*, pg. 656
IMPERIAL INTERNATIONAL BANK—Imperial Bancorp; *U.S. Public*, pg. 872
P.T. INDONESIA DAI-ICHI KANGYO BANK—The Dai-Ichi Kangyo Bank, Limited; *Int'l*, pg. 362
INDUSTRIAL BANK OF FINLAND LTD.—Merita Ltd.; *Int'l*, pg. 859
THE INDUSTRIAL BANK OF JAPAN, LIMITED; *Int'l*, pg. 674
INTERALLIANZ BANK ZURICH AG—The Nippon Credit Bank, Ltd.; *Int'l*, pg. 933
INTERNATIONAL BUSINESS DIVISION (TOYKO)—The Daiwa Bank Limited; *Int'l*, pg. 373
THE INTERNATIONAL COMMERCIAL BANK OF CHINA; *Int'l*, pg. 683
INTERNATIONALE BANK FUR AUSSENHANDEL, A.G.—CoreStates Financial Corp.; *U.S. Public*, pg. 447
IRISH INTERCONTINENTAL BANK, LTD.—Kredietbank N.V.; *Int'l*, pg. 761
IRISH LIFE HOMELOANS LTD.—Kredietbank N.V.; *Int'l*, pg. 761
THE ISLAMIC BANK OF BRUNEI BERHAD—The Dai-Ichi Kangyo Bank, Limited; *Int'l*, pg. 362
ISLE OF MAN BANK LIMITED—National Westminster Bank PLC; *Int'l*, pg. 910
JPM CORRETORA DE CAMBIO, TITULOS E VALORES MOBILIARIOS S.A. (RIO DE JANEIRO)—J.P. Morgan Co. Incorporated; *U.S. Public*, pg. 1130
JUGOBANKA BANKING GROUP; *Int'l*, pg. 716
KB FINANCIAL SERVICES (IRELAND) UNLTD.—Kredietbank N.V.; *Int'l*, pg. 761
KLEINWORT BENSON ARGENTINA SA—Dresdner Bank AG; *Int'l*, pg. 420
KLEINWORT BENSON ESPANA S.A.—Dresdner Bank AG; *Int'l*, pg. 420
KLEINWORT BENSON FRANCE SA—Dresdner Bank AG; *Int'l*, pg. 420
KLEINWORT BENSON INTERNATIONAL INC.—Dresdner Bank AG; *Int'l*, pg. 420
KLEINWORT BENSON LIMITED - HONG KONG BRANCH—Dresdner Bank AG; *Int'l*, pg. 420
KLEINWORT BENSON LTD.—Dresdner Bank AG; *Int'l*, pg. 420
KLEINWORT BENSON NORTH AMERICA INC.—Dresdner Bank AG; *Int'l*, pg. 420
THE KOREA INDUSTRIAL LEASING CO., LTD.—The Nippon Credit Bank, Ltd.; *Int'l*, pg. 933
KOREA INTERNATIONAL MERCHANT BANK—Commerzbank AG; *Int'l*, pg. 312
KREDIETBANK ATLANTA BRANCH—Kredietbank N.V.; *Int'l*, pg. 760
KREDIETBANK-BANKVEREIN AG—Kredietbank N.V.; *Int'l*, pg. 761
KREDIETBANK GRAND CAYMAN BRANCH—Kredietbank N.V.; *Int'l*, pg. 760
KREDIETBANK INTER-ALPHA REPRESENTATIVE OFFICE—Kredietbank N.V.; *Int'l*, pg. 760
KREDIETBANK INTERNATIONAL FINANCE N.V.—Kredietbank N.V.; *Int'l*, pg. 761
KREDIETBANK (NEDERLAND) N.V.—Kredietbank N.V.; *Int'l*, pg. 761
KREDIETBANK NEW YORK BRANCH—Kredietbank N.V.; *Int'l*, pg. 760
KREDIETBANK N.V.; *Int'l*, pg. 760
KREDIETBANK OFICINA DE REPRESENTACION—Kredietbank N.V.; *Int'l*, pg. 760
KREDIETBANK (SUISSE) S.A.—Kredietbank N.V.; *Int'l*, pg. 761
KREDIETFINANCE (U.K.) LTD.—Kredietbank N.V.; *Int'l*, pg. 761
LANDESBANK HESSEN-THURINGEN GIROZENTRALE; *Int'l*, pg. 798
LANDESBANK RHEINLAND-PFALZ; *Int'l*, pg. 799
LANDESBANK RHEINLAND PFALZ INTERNATIONAL S.A.—Landesbank Rheinland-Pfalz; *Int'l*, pg. 799
LASALLE BANK LAKE VIEW—ABN-AMRO Holding N.V.; *Int'l*, pg. 10
LASALLE BANK NORTHBROOK—ABN-AMRO Holding N.V.; *Int'l*, pg. 10
LASALLE BANK OF LISLE—ABN-AMRO Holding N.V.; *Int'l*, pg. 10
LASALLE BANK WESTMONT—ABN-AMRO Holding N.V.; *Int'l*, pg. 10
LASALLE NORTHWEST NATIONAL BANK—ABN-AMRO Holding N.V.; *Int'l*, pg. 10
LAVORO BANK A.G.—Banca Nazionale del Lavoro Sj.A.; *Int'l*, pg. 137
LEUMI LE-ISRAEL (LATIN AMERICA)—Bank Leumi le-Israel B.M.; *Int'l*, pg. 150
LIECHTENSTEIN GLOBAL TRUST LIMITED; *Int'l*, pg. 809
LLOYDS TSB GROUP PLC; *Int'l*, pg. 812
LOMBARD NATWEST COMMERCIAL SERVICES LIMITED—National Westminster Bank PLC; *Int'l*, pg. 910
LOMBARD NORTH CENTRAL PLC—National Westminster Bank PLC; *Int'l*, pg. 910
LOMBARD TRICITY FINANCE LIMITED—National Westminster Bank PLC; *Int'l*, pg. 910
LONG-TERM CREDIT BANK OF JAPAN, LIMITED - CHICAGO—The Long-Term Credit Bank of Japan, Limited; *Int'l*, pg. 816
LONG-TERM CREDIT BANK OF JAPAN, LIMITED - NEW YORK—The Long-Term Credit Bank of Japan, Limited; *Int'l*, pg. 816
LONG-TERM CREDIT BANK OF JAPAN, LTD. - LONDON BRANCH—The Long-Term Credit Bank of Japan, Limited; *Int'l*, pg. 816
MIL (FAR EAST) LIMITED—The Bank of Bermuda Limited; *Int'l*, pg. 151
MIL (UK) LIMITED—The Bank of Bermuda Limited; *Int'l*, pg. 151
MISR-AMERICA INTERNATIONAL BANK S.A.E.—BankAmerica Corporation; *U.S. Public*, pg. 183
MADRID LEASING CORPORATION, S.A.F., S.A.—Caja de Madrid Group; *Int'l*, pg. 251
MANAGEMENT INTERNATIONAL (GUERNSEY) LIMITED—The Bank of Bermuda Limited; *Int'l*, pg. 151
MANAGEMENT INTERNATIONAL (JERSEY) LTD.—The Bank of Bermuda Limited; *Int'l*, pg. 151
MANAGEMENT INTERNATIONAL (LUXEMBOURG) S.A.—The Bank of Bermuda Limited; *Int'l*, pg. 152
MELLON BANK CANADA—Mellon Bank Corporation; *U.S. Public*, pg. 1086
MERITA BANK LTD.—Merita Ltd.; *Int'l*, pg. 858
MERITA BANK LUXEMBOURG S.A.—Merita Ltd.; *Int'l*, pg. 859
MERITA CUSTOMER FINANCE LTD.—Merita Ltd.; *Int'l*, pg. 859
MERITA LTD.; *Int'l*, pg. 858
MERITA MERCHANT BANK SINGAPORE LTD.—Merita Ltd.; *Int'l*, pg. 859
MICHELL NBD LIMITED—First Chicago NBD Corporation; *U.S. Public*, pg. 628
MIDLAND BANK PLC—HSBC Holdings plc; *Int'l*, pg. 580
THE MITSUI TRUST AND BANKING COMPANY, LIMITED; *Int'l*, pg. 882
MITSUI TRUST BANK (EUROPE) S.A.—The Mitsui Trust and Banking Company, Limited; *Int'l*, pg. 883

MITSUI TRUST BANK (SWITZERLAND) LTD.—The Mitsui Trust and Banking Company, Limited; Int'l, pg. 883
MITSUI TRUST FINANCE (AUSTRALIA) LTD.—The Mitsui Trust and Banking Company, Limited; Int'l, pg. 883
MITSUI TRUST FINANCE (HONG KONG) LTD.—The Mitsui Trust and Banking Company, Limited; Int'l, pg. 883
SAMUEL MONTAGU & CO. LIMITED—HSBC Holdings plc; Int'l, pg. 580
MONTREAL TRUSTCO-PERSONAL SERVICES DIVISION—The Bank of Nova Scotia; Int'l, pg. 155
MORGAN GRENFELL GROUP PLC—Deutsche Bank AG; Int'l, pg. 405
MORGAN GUARANTY TRUST COMPANY—J.P. Morgan Co. Incorporated; U.S. Public, pg. 1130
J.P. MORGAN ARGENTINA SOCIEDAD DE BOLSA S.A.—J.P. Morgan Co. Incorporated; U.S. Public, pg. 1130
NBD BANK, CANADA—First Chicago NBD Corporation; U.S. Public, pg. 628
NCNB AUSTRALIA HOLDINGS LTD.—NationsBank Corporation; U.S. Public, pg. 1166
NCNB NATIONAL BANK, LONDON BRANCH—NationsBank Corporation; U.S. Public, pg. 1166
NACIONAL FINANCIERA—Nacional Financiera; Int'l, pg. 904
NATIONAL AUSTRALIA BANK LIMITED; Int'l, pg. 906
NATIONAL BANK OF MALAWI—Standard Chartered Bank PLC; Int'l, pg. 1296
NATIONAL BANK OF NEW ZEALAND LTD.—Lloyds TSB Group PLC; Int'l, pg. 814
NATIONAL BANK OF NEW ZEALAND SAVINGS BANK LTD.—Lloyds TSB Group PLC; Int'l, pg. 814
NATIONAL BANK OF PAKISTAN; Int'l, pg. 907
NATIONAL IRISH BANK LIMITED—National Australia Bank Limited; Int'l, pg. 906
NATIONAL WESTMINSTER BANK AG—National Westminster Bank PLC; Int'l, pg. 911
NATIONAL WESTMINSTER BANK FINANCE (CI) LIMITED—National Westminster Bank PLC; Int'l, pg. 911
NATIONAL WESTMINSTER BANK PLC; Int'l, pg. 910
NATIONAL WESTMINSTER BANK S.A.—National Westminster Bank PLC; Int'l, pg. 911
NATIONSBANK INTERNATIONAL—NationsBank Corporation; U.S. Public, pg. 1165
NATIONSBANK OVERSEAS CORP.—NationsBank Corporation; U.S. Public, pg. 1165
NATWEST EXPORT FINANCE LIMITED—National Westminster Bank PLC; Int'l, pg. 910
NATWEST INTERNATIONAL TRUST CORPORATION (CAYMAN) LIMITED—National Westminster Bank PLC; Int'l, pg. 911
NATWEST INTERNATIONAL TRUST CORPORATION (EUROPE) LIMITED—National Westminster Bank PLC; Int'l, pg. 911
NATWEST INTERNATIONAL TRUST HOLDINGS LIMITED—National Westminster Bank PLC; Int'l, pg. 911
NIGERIAN-AMERICAN MERCHANT BANK LTD—BankBoston Corporation; U.S. Public, pg. 185
NIPPON CREDIT BANK LTD., LOS ANGELES—The Nippon Credit Bank, Ltd.; Int'l, pg. 932
NIPPON CREDIT INTERNATIONAL LIMITED—The Nippon Credit Bank, Ltd.; Int'l, pg. 933
NIPPON CREDIT TRUST COMPANY—The Nippon Credit Bank, Ltd.; Int'l, pg. 933
NOMURA BANK (DEUTSCHLAND) GMBH—The Nomura Securities Co., Ltd.; Int'l, pg. 956
NOMURA BANK (LUXEMBOURG) S.A.—The Nomura Securities Co., Ltd.; Int'l, pg. 956
NOMURA BANK NEDERLAND N.V.—The Nomura Securities Co., Ltd.; Int'l, pg. 957
NOMURA BANK (SWITZERLAND) LTD.—The Nomura Securities Co., Ltd.; Int'l, pg. 957
NORTHERN BANK LIMITED—National Australia Bank Limited; Int'l, pg. 906
THE NORTHERN TRUST CO.—Northern Trust Corporation; U.S. Public, pg. 1197
ORCA BANK LTD.—Union Bank of Switzerland; Int'l, pg. 1440
PBZ PRIVATBANK ZURICH—Union Bank of Switzerland; Int'l, pg. 1440
PACIFIC COMMERCIAL BANK LIMITED—Pacific Century Financial Corporation; U.S. Public, pg. 1248
PANMURE GORDON BANKERS LTD.—NationsBank Corporation; U.S. Public, pg. 1166
PIERSON, HELDRING & PIERSON N.V.—ABN-AMRO Holding N.V.; Int'l, pg. 9
POST OFFICE BANK LIMITED—Australia & New Zealand Banking Group Limited; Int'l, pg. 100
P.T. PRIVATE DEVELOPMENT FINANCE COMPANY OF INDONESIA—The Nippon Credit Bank, Ltd.; Int'l, pg. 933
RBC DOMINION SECURITIES LTD.—Royal Bank of Canada; Int'l, pg. 1131
RBC FRANCE B.V.—Royal Bank of Canada; Int'l, pg. 1131
RNBNY BRANCH OFFICE-SINGAPORE—Republic New York Corporation; U.S. Public, pg. 1381
RNBNY BRANCH OFFICE-TOKYO—Republic New York Corporation; U.S. Public, pg. 1381
RNBNY REPRESENTATIVE OFFICE-TAIWAN—Republic New York Corporation; U.S. Public, pg. 1381
REPRESENTACION DEL DEUTSCHE BANK AG (CARACAS)—Deutsche Bank AG; Int'l, pg. 405
REPRESENTACION DEL DEUTSCHE BANK AG (SANTIAGO)—Deutsche Bank AG; Int'l, pg. 405
RIZAL COMMERCIAL BANKING CORPORATION—The Sanwa Bank Limited; Int'l, pg. 1190
ROYAL BANK OF CANADA AG—Royal Bank of Canada; Int'l, pg. 1131
ROYAL BANK OF CANADA (ASIA) LIMITED—Royal Bank of Canada; Int'l, pg. 1131
ROYAL BANK OF CANADA (CHANNEL ISLANDS) LIMITED—Royal Bank of Canada; Int'l, pg. 1131
THE ROYAL BANK OF SCOTLAND PLC; Int'l, pg. 1132
S.B. MERCHANT BANK (SINGAPORE) LIMITED—The Sumitomo Bank, Limited; Int'l, pg. 1309
SAEHAN MERCHANT BANKING CORPORATION—The Industrial Bank of Japan, Limited; Int'l, pg. 676
SAEHAN MERCHANT BANKING CORPORATION—The Long-Term Credit Bank of Japan, Limited; Int'l, pg. 817
THE SAKURA BANK—The Sakura Bank, Limited; Int'l, pg. 1179
THE SAKURA BANK, LIMITED; Int'l, pg. 1178
SANPAOLO-NEW YORK BRANCH—Istituto Bancario San Paolo Di Torino S.p.A.; Int'l, pg. 691
SANWA AUSTRALIA LIMITED—The Sanwa Bank Limited; Int'l, pg. 1190
SANWA BANK CANADA—The Sanwa Bank Limited; Int'l, pg. 1190
THE SANWA BANK LIMITED; Int'l, pg. 1189
SANWA BANK (SCHWEIZ) AG—The Sanwa Bank Limited; Int'l, pg. 1190
SANWA BUSINESS CREDIT CORPORATION—The Sanwa Bank Limited; Int'l, pg. 1189
SANWA INTERNATIONAL PLC—The Sanwa Bank Limited; Int'l, pg. 1190
SANWA SINGAPORE LIMITED—The Sanwa Bank Limited; Int'l, pg. 1190
THE SAUDI BRITISH BANK—HSBC Holdings plc; Int'l, pg. 583
SAUDI-SWISS BANK—Union Bank of Switzerland; Int'l, pg. 1440
SAVANNAH BANK OF NIGERIA LTD.—BankAmerica Corporation; U.S. Public, pg. 183
SCANDINAVISKA ENSKILDA BANKEN LONDON—Skandinaviska Enskilda Banken; Int'l, pg. 1259
OTTO SCHEURMANN BANK-KG—Dresdner Bank AG; Int'l, pg. 418
SCHWEIZERISCHE BANKGESELLSCHAFT (DEUTSCHLAND) AG—Union Bank of Switzerland; Int'l, pg. 1440
SEYCHELLES INTERNATIONAL MERCANTILE BANKING CORPORATION LIMITED—Standard Chartered Bank PLC; Int'l, pg. 1296
SHOKO CHUKIN BANK; Int'l, pg. 1236
SIMON AG—Bayerische Vereinsbank Group; Int'l, pg. 180
SKANDINAVISKA ENSKILDA BANKEN; Int'l, pg. 1258
SKANDINAVISKA ENSKILDA BANKEN—Skandinaviska Enskilda Banken; Int'l, pg. 1259
SKANDINAVISKA ENSKILDA BANKING, NEW YORK & CAYMAN ISLAND BRANCH—Skandinaviska Enskilda Banken; Int'l, pg. 1259
SOCIETE GENERALE; Int'l, pg. 1273
SOCIETE GENERALE—Societe Generale; Int'l, pg. 1273
STANDARD CHARTERED BANK PLC; Int'l, pg. 1294
STANDARD CHARTERED BANK (SWITZERLAND)—Standard Chartered Bank PLC; Int'l, pg. 1296
STATE BANK OF INDIA; Int'l, pg. 1297
STATE BANK OF INDIA (CANADA)—State Bank of India; Int'l, pg. 1297
STATE STREET CANADA, INC.—State Street Corporation; U.S. Public, pg. 1513
STATE STREET GLOBAL ADVISORS (U.K.) LIMITED—State Street Corporation; U.S. Public, pg. 1513
STATE STREET TRUST & BANKING COMPANY, LTD.—State Street Corporation; U.S. Public, pg. 1513
THE SUMITOMO BANK, LIMITED; Int'l, pg. 1308
SUMITOMO TRUST & BANKING (LUXEMBOURG) S.A.—The Sumitomo Trust & Banking Co., Ltd.; Int'l, pg. 1318
SUMITOMO TRUST INTERNATIONAL PLC.—The Sumitomo Trust & Banking Co., Ltd.; Int'l, pg. 1318
SVENSKA HANDELSBANKEN; Int'l, pg. 1327
SWISS BANK CORPORATION; Int'l, pg. 1329
TSB TRUST CO. LTD.—Lloyds TSB Group PLC; Int'l, pg. 813
TAKUGIN INTERNATIONAL (ASIA) LTD.—The Hokkaido Takushoku Bank, Ltd.; Int'l, pg. 627
TOKAI ASIA LIMITED—The Tokai Bank, Limited; Int'l, pg. 1391
TOKAI BANK EUROPE PLC—The Tokai Bank, Limited; Int'l, pg. 1391
THE TOKAI BANK, LIMITED; Int'l, pg. 1391
TOKAI BANK NEDERLAND N.V.—The Tokai Bank, Limited; Int'l, pg. 1391
THE TORONTO DOMINION BANK; Int'l, pg. 1401
TORONTO-DOMINION BANK (UNITED KINGDOM) LTD.—The Toronto Dominion Bank; Int'l, pg. 1401
TORONTO DOMINION-HONG KONG BRANCH—The Toronto Dominion Bank; Int'l, pg. 1401
TORONTO DOMINION JAPAN—The Toronto Dominion Bank; Int'l, pg. 1401
TORONTO DOMINION SECURITIES (U.S.A.) INC.—The Toronto Dominion Bank; Int'l, pg. 1401
TORONTO DOMINION (SOUTHEAST ASIA) LIMITED—The Toronto Dominion Bank; Int'l, pg. 1402
TORONTO DOMINION-TAIPEI BRANCH—The Toronto Dominion Bank; Int'l, pg. 1402
TORONTO-DOMINION (TEXAS), INC.—The Toronto Dominion Bank; Int'l, pg. 1401
TRUST CORPORATION OF CANADA—Royal Bank of Canada; Int'l, pg. 1131
UBCI (TUNISIA)—Banque Nationale de Paris; Int'l, pg. 163
UBS AUSTRALIA LTD.—Union Bank of Switzerland; Int'l, pg. 1440
UBS LIMITED—Union Bank of Switzerland; Int'l, pg. 1440
UBS PHILLIPS & DREW INTL. LTD.—Union Bank of Switzerland; Int'l, pg. 1440
UBS REPRESENTATIVE OFFICE—Union Bank of Switzerland; Int'l, pg. 1440
UBS SECURITIES LLC—Union Bank of Switzerland; Int'l, pg. 1440
UDC GROUP HOLDINGS LIMITED—Australia & New Zealand Banking Group Limited; Int'l, pg. 100
ULSTER BANK LIMITED—National Westminster Bank PLC; Int'l, pg. 911
ULSTER INVESTMENT BANK LIMITED—National Westminster Bank PLC; Int'l, pg. 912
UNIAO DE BANCOS BRASILEIROS (UNIBANCO) (BRAZIL)—Uniao de Bancos Brasileiros S.A. (Unibanco); Int'l, pg. 1431
UNION BANK OF SWITZERLAND; Int'l, pg. 1439
UNION BANK OF SWITZERLAND (CANADA)—Union Bank of Switzerland; Int'l, pg. 1441
UNION BANK OF SWITZERLAND (PANAMA) INC.—Union Bank of Switzerland; Int'l, pg. 1441
UNION DE BANQUES CONGOLAISES—Bank Brussels Lambert; Int'l, pg. 149
UNITED BANK FOR AFRICA, LTD.—Bankers Trust New York Corporation; U.S. Public, pg. 186
UNITED STATES TRUST CO. OF NEW YORK—U.S. Trust Corporation; U.S. Public, pg. 1688
F VAN LANSCHOT BANKIERS NV—National Westminster Bank PLC; Int'l, pg. 911
VEREINSBANK IN NUERNBERG AG—Bayerische Vereinsbank Group; Int'l, pg. 180
VON DER HEYDT-KERSTEN & SOEHNE—Commerzbank AG; Int'l, pg. 310
WAFABANK—Compagnie de Suez; Int'l, pg. 314
WARDLEY JAMES CAPEL CORPORATE FINANCE LTD.—HSBC Holdings plc; Int'l, pg. 584
WESTDEUTSCHE LANDESBANK GIROZENTRALE; Int'l, pg. 1492
WESTDEUTSCHE LANDESBANK GIROZENTRALE (WESTLB)—Westdeutsche Landesbank Girozentrale; Int'l, pg. 1492
WESTDEUTSCHE LANDESBANK MOSCOW—Westdeutsche Landesbank Girozentrale; Int'l, pg. 1494
WESTDEUTSCHE LANDESBANK (SCHWEIZ) AG—Westdeutsche Landesbank Girozentrale; Int'l, pg. 1494
WESTLB BIELEFELD BRANCH—Westdeutsche Landesbank Girozentrale; Int'l, pg. 1492
WILLIAMS DE BROE HOLDINGS LTD.—Bank Brussels Lambert; Int'l, pg. 148
WING HANG BANK LIMITED—The Bank of New York Company, Inc.; U.S. Public, pg. 179
YOKOHAMA ASIA LIMITED—Bank of Yokohama; Int'l, pg. 159
YORKSHIRE BANK—National Australia Bank Limited; Int'l, pg. 906

6082 — FOREIGN TRADE & INTERNATIONAL BANKING INSTITUTIONS

ABN-AMRO HOLDING N.V.; Int'l, pg. 8
AMERICAN EXPRESS BANK LTD.—American Express Company; U.S. Public, pg. 73
AMERICAN EXPRESS COMPANY; U.S. Public, pg. 73
ATLAS-VERMOEGENSVERWALTUNGS-GMBH—Commerzbank AG; Int'l, pg. 309
AUSTRALIA & NEW ZEALAND BANKING GROUP LIMITED; Int'l, pg. 98
BDL BANCO DI LUGANO—Union Bank of Switzerland; Int'l, pg. 1439
BHF-BANK AG; Int'l, pg. 119
BV-CONSULT—Bayerische Vereinsbank Group; Int'l, pg. 178
BV FINANCIAL (IRELAND) LTD.—Bayerische Vereinsbank Group; Int'l, pg. 180
BADEN-WURTTEMBERG BRANCH—IKB Deutsche Industriebank AG; Int'l, pg. 645
BANCA CANTRADE LUGANO SA—Union Bank of Switzerland; Int'l, pg. 1439
BANCA COMMERCIALE ITALIANA S.P.A.—IRI Istituto Ricostruzione Industriale; Int'l, pg. 652
BANCA MONTE DEI PASCHI DI SIENA S.P.A.; Int'l, pg. 136
BANCO BANIF DE GESTION PRIVADA—Banco Central Hispanoamericano S.A.; Int'l, pg. 139
BANCO CENTRAL CORP. (PUERTO RICO)—Banco Central Hispanoamericano S.A.; Int'l, pg. 139
BANCO CENTRAL HISPANOAMERICANO S.A.; Int'l, pg. 139
BANCO DE ASUNCION—Banco Central Hispanoamericano S.A.; Int'l, pg. 140
BANCO DE FORMENTO—Banco Central Hispanoamericano S.A.; Int'l, pg. 139
BANCO DE JEREZ—Banco Central Hispanoamericano S.A.; Int'l, pg. 139
BANCO DE LA PROVINCIA DE BUENOS AIRES; Int'l, pg. 140
BANCO DE TOKYO-MITSUBISHI BRASIL S/A—The Bank of Tokyo-Mitsubishi, Ltd.; Int'l, pg. 158
BANCO DE VALENCIA—Banco Central Hispanoamericano S.A.; Int'l, pg. 139
BANCO DI NAPOLI; Int'l, pg. 140
BANCO DI ROMA—IRI Istituto Ricostruzione Industriale; Int'l, pg. 652
BANCO DI SICILIA; Int'l, pg. 140
BANCO ESPIRITO SANTO E COMERCIAL DE LISBOA SA; Int'l, pg. 142
BANCO GALLEGO—Banco 21; Int'l, pg. 145
BANCO HISPANO DE INVESTIMENTO, S.A.—Banco Central Hispanoamericano S.A.; Int'l, pg. 140
BANCO INTERNACIONAL DE COMERCIO—Banco Central Hispanoamericano S.A.; Int'l, pg. 139
BANCO ITAU S.A.; Int'l, pg. 142
BANCO MAPFRE, S.A.—Corporacion MAPFRE, Compania Internacional de Reaseguros, S.A.; Int'l, pg. 332
BANCO MERCANTIL DE TARRAGONA—Banco Central Hispanoamericano S.A.; Int'l, pg. 139
BANCO NACIONAL DE MEXICO, S.A. (BANAMEX)—Grupo Financiero Banamex/Accival, S.A. de C.V.; Int'l, pg. 574
BANCO POPULAR ARGENTINO—Banco Central Hispanoamericano S.A.; Int'l, pg. 140
BANCOMER, S.A.; Int'l, pg. 145
BANK AUFINA—Union Bank of Switzerland; Int'l, pg. 1439
BANK BRUSSELS LAMBERT; Int'l, pg. 146
BANK LEUMI LE-ISRAEL B.M.; Int'l, pg. 150
BANK OF AMERICA—BankAmerica Corporation; U.S. Public, pg. 180
THE BANK OF BERMUDA LIMITED-HONG KONG BRANCH—The Bank of Bermuda Limited; Int'l, pg. 151

S.I.C. Index

BANK OF BERMUDA (NEW YORK) LIMITED—The Bank of Bermuda Limited; Int'l, pg. 151
BANK OF CHINA; Int'l, pg. 152
BANK OF COMMERCE TRINIDAD AND TOBAGO LIMITED—Canadian Imperial Bank of Commerce; Int'l, pg. 257
BANK OF COMMERCE TRUST COMPANY BARBADOS LIMITED—Canadian Imperial Bank of Commerce; Int'l, pg. 257
BANK OF MONTREAL GLOBAL, INC.—Bank of Montreal; Int'l, pg. 154
THE BANK OF NOVA SCOTIA; Int'l, pg. 155
BANK OF YOKOHAMA; Int'l, pg. 158
BANK ROHNER LTD.—Union Bank of Switzerland; Int'l, pg. 1439
BANKAMERICA INTERNATIONAL—BankAmerica Corporation; U.S. Public, pg. 181
BANKHAUS LOEBBECKE & CO.—Cassa di Risparmio delle Provincie Lombarde SpA (CARIPLO); Int'l, pg. 275
BANQUE BRUXELLES LAMBERT (SUISSE)—Bank Brussels Lambert; Int'l, pg. 148
BANQUE CANTRADE LAUSANNE S.A.—Union Bank of Switzerland; Int'l, pg. 1439
BANQUE CANTRADE, ORMOND BURRUS SA—Union Bank of Switzerland; Int'l, pg. 1439
BANQUE FRANCAISE DU COMMERCE EXTERIEUR; Int'l, pg. 160
BANQUE GENERALE DU LUXEMBOURG SA; Int'l, pg. 161
BANQUE HYDRO-ENERGIE—Lyonnaise des Eaux S.A.; Int'l, pg. 822
BANQUE INTERNATIONALE A LUXEMBOURG S.A.; Int'l, pg. 162
BANQUE INTERNATIONALE DE CREDIT ET DE GESTION MONACO—Bayerische Vereinsbank Group; Int'l, pg. 180
BANQUE SAINT DOMINIQUE—Credit Nationale; Int'l, pg. 344
BARCLAYS BANK PLC; Int'l, pg. 164
BAYERISCHE HYPOTHEKEN-UND WECHSEL-BANK AKTIENGESELLSCHAFT; Int'l, pg. 175
BAYERISCHE HYPOTHEKEN-UND WECHSEL-BANK AKTIENGESELLSCHAFT NEW YORK BRANCH—Bayerische Hypotheken-und Wechsel-Bank Aktiengesellschaft; Int'l, pg. 176
BAYERISCHE LANDESBANK; Int'l, pg. 176
BAYERISCHE VEREINSBANK AG—Bayerische Vereinsbank Group; Int'l, pg. 180
BAYERISCHE VEREINSBANK AG-LONDON BRANCH—Bayerische Vereinsbank Group; Int'l, pg. 181
BAYERISCHE VEREINSBANK GROUP; Int'l, pg. 178
CCF FOSTER-BRAITHWAITE—Credit Commercial de France; Int'l, pg. 342
CCF (LUXEMBOURG) S.A.—Credit Commercial de France; Int'l, pg. 342
CCF (MONACO) S.A.M.—Credit Commercial de France; Int'l, pg. 342
CIBC ASIA LIMITED—Canadian Imperial Bank of Commerce; Int'l, pg. 257
CIBC AUSTRALIA HOLDINGS LIMITED—Canadian Imperial Bank of Commerce; Int'l, pg. 257
CIBC AUSTRALIA LIMITED—Canadian Imperial Bank of Commerce; Int'l, pg. 257
CIBC FINANZ AG—Canadian Imperial Bank of Commerce; Int'l, pg. 257
CIBC HOLDINGS G.M.B.H.—Canadian Imperial Bank of Commerce; Int'l, pg. 257
CIBC JAMAICA LTD.—Canadian Imperial Bank of Commerce; Int'l, pg. 258
CIBC LIMITED—Canadian Imperial Bank of Commerce; Int'l, pg. 257
CAIXA GERAL DE DEPOSITOS; Int'l, pg. 250
CANADIAN IMPERIAL BANK OF COMMERCE; Int'l, pg. 256
CANTRADE PRIVATE LTD.—Union Bank of Switzerland; Int'l, pg. 1439
CASSA DI RISPARMIO DELLE PROVINCIE LOMBARDE SPA (CARIPLO); Int'l, pg. 274
CENTRAL-EUROPEAN INTERNATIONAL BANK LTD. (CIB)—Bayerische Vereinsbank Group; Int'l, pg. 181
CENTRAL-EUROPEAN INTERNATIONAL BANK LTD. (CIB)—The Long-Term Credit Bank of Japan, Limited; Int'l, pg. 816
CENTROBANCO (PANAMA), S.A.—Banco Central Hispanoamericano S.A.; Int'l, pg. 140
CHARTERHOUSE BANK LTD.—Credit Commercial de France; Int'l, pg. 342
CHASE BANK INTERNATIONAL—The Chase Manhattan Corporation; U.S. Public, pg. 338
CHASE MANHATTAN INVESTMENT HOLDINGS, INC.—The Chase Manhattan Corporation; U.S. Public, pg. 338
CHASE MANHATTAN OVERSEAS BANKING CORPORATION—The Chase Manhattan Corporation; U.S. Public, pg. 338
CHASE TRADE, INC.—The Chase Manhattan Corporation; U.S. Public, pg. 338
THE CHINESE AMERICAN BANK—The International Commercial Bank of China; Int'l, pg. 683
CHO HUNG BANK; Int'l, pg. 287
CITICORP INVESTMENT BANK (SINGAPORE) LTD.—Citicorp; U.S. Public, pg. 379
COMMERZBANK AKTIENGESELLSCHAFT CHICAGO BRANCH—Commerzbank AG; Int'l, pg. 310
CORESTATES BANK INTERNATIONAL—CoreStates Financial Corp.; U.S. Public, pg. 446
CORPORACION MAPFRE, COMPANIA INTERNACIONAL DE REASEGUROS, S.A.; Int'l, pg. 332
CREDIT AGRICOLE; Int'l, pg. 341
CREDIT LYONNAIS S.A.; Int'l, pg. 343
CREDIT SUISSE—Credit Suisse Group; Int'l, pg. 345
CREDITO ITALIANO—IRI Istituto Ricostruzione Industriale; Int'l, pg. 652
THE CYPRUS POPULAR BANK LTD.—HSBC Holdings plc; Int'l, pg. 581
DBS BANK LTD.; Int'l, pg. 350
DG BANK; Int'l, pg. 351
DAI-ICHI KANGYO BANK, LTD.-CHICAGO—The Dai-Ichi Kangyo Bank, Limited; Int'l, pg. 359
THE DAIWA BANK LIMITED; Int'l, pg. 373
DAIWA EUROPE BANK PLC—Daiwa Securities Co. Ltd.; Int'l, pg. 375
DELEGUE DE LA BAYERISCHE VEREINSBANK AUPRES DU CREDIT DU NORD—Bayerische Vereinsbank Group; Int'l, pg. 181
DEN NORSKE BANK ASA; Int'l, pg. 392
DEUTSCHE BANK AG; Int'l, pg. 401
DEUTSCHE GIROZENTRALE-DEUTSCHE KOMMUNALBANK; Int'l, pg. 406
DEUTSCHE GIROZENTRALE-DEUTSCHE KOMMUNALBANK (LUXEMBOURG)—Deutsche Girozentrale-Deutsche Kommunalbank; Int'l, pg. 406
DEUTSCHE GIROZENTRALE INTERNATIONAL S.A.—Deutsche Girozentrale-Deutsche Kommunalbank; Int'l, pg. 407
DIETER HASE BV—Bayerische Vereinsbank Group; Int'l, pg. 181
EGYPTIAN BRITISH BANK S.A.E.—HSBC Holdings plc; Int'l, pg. 581
THE EXPORT-IMPORT BANK OF KOREA; Int'l, pg. 467
FIRST FEDERAL SAVINGS & LOAN OF AMERICA—Pacific Century Financial Corporation; U.S. Public, pg. 1248
FIRSTAR EXPORT CREDIT LIMITED—Firstar Corporation; U.S. Public, pg. 643
FORD BANK AG—Ford Motor Company; U.S. Public, pg. 665
FORTIS; Int'l, pg. 498
FUJI BANK INTERNATIONAL, INC.—The Fuji Bank, Limited; Int'l, pg. 519
THE FUJI BANK, LIMITED; Int'l, pg. 519
FUJI BANK (LUXEMBOURG) S.A.—The Fuji Bank, Limited; Int'l, pg. 521
FUJI BANK (SCHWEIZ) AG—The Fuji Bank, Limited; Int'l, pg. 521
GENERALE DE BANQUE S.A.; Int'l, pg. 546
GULIO GALAVOTTI BV—Bayerische Vereinsbank Group; Int'l, pg. 181
HFC BANK PLC—Household International, Inc.; U.S. Public, pg. 842
HSBC AMERICAS—HSBC Holdings plc; Int'l, pg. 580
HABIB BANK LTD.; Int'l, pg. 584
HABIB NIGERIA BANK LTD.—Habib Bank Ltd.; Int'l, pg. 585
HANDELSFINANZ-CCF BANK—Credit Commercial de France; Int'l, pg. 343
HARRIS BANK INTERNATIONAL CORP.—Bank of Montreal; Int'l, pg. 154
HESSE, RHINELAND-PALATINATE & SAAR BRANCH—IKB Deutsche Industriebank AG; Int'l, pg. 645
THE HOKKAIDO TAKUSHOKU BANK, LTD.; Int'l, pg. 626
HONGKONG BANK OF CANADA—HSBC Holdings plc; Int'l, pg. 583
HYPO SECURITIES INC.—Bayerische Hypotheken-und Wechsel-Bank Aktiengesellschaft; Int'l, pg. 176
HYPOSWISS (SWISS MORTGAGE & COMMERCIAL BANK)—Union Bank of Switzerland; Int'l, pg. 1440
IKB DEUTSCHE INDUSTRIEBANK AG; Int'l, pg. 645
IKB LEASING BERLIN GMBH—IKB Deutsche Industriebank AG; Int'l, pg. 645
THE INDUSTRIAL BANK OF JAPAN, LIMITED (YOKOHAMA BRANCH)—The Industrial Bank of Japan, Limited; Int'l, pg. 674
INTERAMERICAN DEVELOPMENT BANK; U.S. Private, pg. 566
INTERNATIONAL COMMERCIAL BANK OF CATHAY—The International Commercial Bank of China; Int'l, pg. 684
INTERNATIONAL MOSKOW BANK—Bayerische Vereinsbank Group; Int'l, pg. 181
ISRAEL DISCOUNT BANK LTD.—IDB Holding Corporation; Int'l, pg. 645
ISTITUTO BANCARIO SAN PAOLO DI TORINO S.P.A.; Int'l, pg. 691
KREDIETBANK LONDON BRANCH—Kredietbank N.V.; Int'l, pg. 760
KREDIETBANK S.A. LUXEMBOURGEOISE—Kredietbank N.V.; Int'l, pg. 761
KWONG ON BANK, LIMITED—The Fuji Bank, Limited; Int'l, pg. 521
LGT BANK IN LIECHTENSTEIN AKTIENGESELLSCHAFT—Liechtenstein Global Trust Limited; Int'l, pg. 809
LAZARD BROTHERS & CO. LTD.—Pearson plc; Int'l, pg. 1026
LLOYDS BANK (AMERICAS) LTD.—Lloyds TSB Group PLC; Int'l, pg. 813
LLOYDS BANK (BELGIUM) S.A.—Lloyds TSB Group PLC; Int'l, pg. 813
LLOYDS BANK INTERNATIONAL LTD.—Lloyds TSB Group PLC; Int'l, pg. 813
LLOYDS BANK NZA LIMITED—Lloyds TSB Group PLC; Int'l, pg. 813
LLOYDS BANK SA—Lloyds TSB Group PLC; Int'l, pg. 813
LLOYDS INTERNATIONAL BANKING—Lloyds TSB Group PLC; Int'l, pg. 813
LLOYDS INTERNATIONAL LTD.—Lloyds TSB Group PLC; Int'l, pg. 813
LLOYDS MERCHANT BANK LTD.—Lloyds TSB Group PLC; Int'l, pg. 813
LLOYDS TSB GROUP PLC; Int'l, pg. 812
MASE WESTPAC AUSTRALIA LIMITED—Westpac Banking Corporation; Int'l, pg. 1496
MERITA BANK LTD.—Merita Ltd.; Int'l, pg. 858
MITSUI TRUST INTERNATIONAL LTD.—The Mitsui Trust and Banking Company, Limited; Int'l, pg. 883
NACIONAL FINANCIERA; Int'l, pg. 904
NACIONAL FINANCIERA—Nacional Financiera; Int'l, pg. 904
THE NANTO BANK, LTD.; Int'l, pg. 905
NATIONAL BANK OF GREECE S.A.; Int'l, pg. 907
NATIONSBANK (JAPAN)—NationsBank Corporation; U.S. Public, pg. 1166
THE NIPPON CREDIT BANK, LTD.; Int'l, pg. 932
NORDBANKEN AB; Int'l, pg. 957
THE NORINCHUKIN BANK; Int'l, pg. 958
THE NORTHERN TRUST INTERNATIONAL BANKING CORPORATION—Northern Trust Corporation; U.S. Public, pg. 1197
ORCA BANK LTD.—Union Bank of Switzerland; Int'l, pg. 1440
PBZ PRIVATBANK ZURICH—Union Bank of Switzerland; Int'l, pg. 1440
PNC INTERNATIONAL BANK—PNC Bank Corp.; U.S. Public, pg. 1243
PERWIRA HABIB BANK MALAYSIA BERHAD—Habib Bank Ltd.; Int'l, pg. 585
PRUDENTIAL ASIA CAPITAL LIMITED—The Prudential Insurance Company of America; U.S. Private, pg. 893
RNBNY BRANCH OFFICE-MILAN—Republic New York Corporation; U.S. Public, pg. 1381
RNBNY-BUENOS AIRES OFFICE—Republic New York Corporation; U.S. Public, pg. 1381
RNBNY REPRESENTATIVE OFFICE-LEBANON—Republic New York Corporation; U.S. Public, pg. 1381
RNBNY REPRESENTATIVE OFFICE-URUGUAY—Republic New York Corporation; U.S. Public, pg. 1381
REPUBLIC NATIONAL BANK OF NEW YORK (CANADA)—Republic New York Corporation; U.S. Public, pg. 1381
REPUBLIC NATIONAL BANK OF NEW YORK (CAYMAN) LIMITED—Republic New York Corporation; U.S. Public, pg. 1381
REPUBLIC NATIONAL BANK OF NEW YORK (GIBRALTAR) LTD.—Republic New York Corporation; U.S. Public, pg. 1381
REPUBLIC NATIONAL BANK OF NEW YORK (U.K.)—Republic New York Corporation; U.S. Public, pg. 1381
ROYAL BANK OF CANADA; Int'l, pg. 1131
THE SAKURA BANK, LIMITED; Int'l, pg. 1178
SAKURA FINANCE ASIA LTD.—The Sakura Bank, Limited; Int'l, pg. 1180
SAKURA FINANCE AUSTRALIA LIMITED—The Sakura Bank, Limited; Int'l, pg. 1180
SAKURA MERCHANT BANK (SINGAPORE) LTD.—The Sakura Bank, Limited; Int'l, pg. 1180
SANTANDER OVERSEAS BANK (PUERTO RICO)—Banco Santander; Int'l, pg. 143
THE SANWA BANK, LIMITED-TOKYO HEADQUARTERS—The Sanwa Bank Limited; Int'l, pg. 1189
SAUDI-SWISS BANK—Union Bank of Switzerland; Int'l, pg. 1440
SCHWEIZERISCHE BANKGESELLSCHAFT (DEUTSCHLAND) AG—Union Bank of Switzerland; Int'l, pg. 1440
SECURITY PACIFIC ASIAN BANK, LTD.—BankAmerica Corporation; U.S. Public, pg. 183
SECURITY PACIFIC BANK A.G.—BankAmerica Corporation; U.S. Public, pg. 183
SECURITY PACIFIC BANK CANADA—BankAmerica Corporation; U.S. Public, pg. 183
SECURITY PACIFIC HOARE GOVETT (HOLDINGS) LIMITED—BankAmerica Corporation; U.S. Public, pg. 183
SECURITY PACIFIC LIMITED—BankAmerica Corporation; U.S. Public, pg. 183
STANDARD CHARTERED BANK ZAMBIA LTD.—Standard Chartered Bank PLC; Int'l, pg. 1295
STANDARD CHARTERED BANK ZIMBABWE LIMITED—Standard Chartered Bank PLC; Int'l, pg. 1295
THE SUMITOMO TRUST & BANKING CO., LTD.; Int'l, pg. 1317
THE SUMITOMO TRUST & BANKING CO. (U.S.A.)—The Sumitomo Trust & Banking Co., Ltd.; Int'l, pg. 1317
SWISS BANK CORPORATION; Int'l, pg. 1329
TSB BANK SCOTLAND PLC—Lloyds TSB Group PLC; Int'l, pg. 813
THE TORONTO DOMINION BANK; Int'l, pg. 1401
TORONTO-DOMINION BANK (UNITED KINGDOM) LTD.—The Toronto Dominion Bank; Int'l, pg. 1401
UBS ASSET MANAGEMENT LONDON LTD.—Union Bank of Switzerland; Int'l, pg. 1440
UBS ASSET MANAGEMENT (UK) LTD.—Union Bank of Switzerland; Int'l, pg. 1440
UBS AUSTRALIA LTD.—Union Bank of Switzerland; Int'l, pg. 1440
UBS LIMITED—Union Bank of Switzerland; Int'l, pg. 1440
UBS PHILLIPS & DREW INTERNATIONAL INVESTMENT LTD.—Union Bank of Switzerland; Int'l, pg. 1440
UBS PHILLIPS & DREW INTL. LTD.—Union Bank of Switzerland; Int'l, pg. 1440
UBS REPRESENTATIVE OFFICE—Union Bank of Switzerland; Int'l, pg. 1440
UBS REPRESENTATIVE OFFICE LTD.—Union Bank of Switzerland; Int'l, pg. 1441
UBS SECURITIES LLC—Union Bank of Switzerland; Int'l, pg. 1440
UNIÃO DE BANCOS BRASILEIROS S.A. (UNIBANCO); Int'l, pg. 1431
UNION BANK OF SWITZERLAND; Int'l, pg. 1439
UNION BANK OF SWITZERLAND (PANAMA) INC.—Union Bank of Switzerland; Int'l, pg. 1441
UNION DE BANQUES SUISSES—Union Bank of Switzerland; Int'l, pg. 1441
UNION DE BANQUES SUISSES (LUXEMBOURG) S.A.—Union Bank of Switzerland; Int'l, pg. 1441
UTILX INTERNATIONAL PRODUCT SALES INC.—UTILX Corporation; U.S. Public, pg. 1701
VEREINS- UND WESTBANK AG—Bayerische Vereinsbank Group; Int'l, pg. 180
WACHOVIA INTERNATIONAL BANKING CORP.—Wachovia Corporation; U.S. Public, pg. 1730
WESTPAC BANK - PNG LIMITED—Westpac Banking Corporation; Int'l, pg. 1497
WESTPAC BANKING CORPORATION; Int'l, pg. 1495

WESTPAC - SOUTH AUSTRALIA—Westpac Banking Corporation; *Int'l*, pg. 1496
WIRTSCHAFTS-UND PRIVATBANK—Bayerische Vereinsbank Group; *Int'l*, pg. 181

6091 — NONDEPOSIT TRUST FACILITIES

ASSOCIATED TRUST COMPANY, INC.—Associated Banc-Corp; *U.S. Public*, pg. 140
BANK OF AMERICA ILLINOIS TRUST COMPANY OF FLORIDA, N.A.—BankAmerica Corporation; *U.S. Public*, pg. 181
BANK OF AMERICA ILLINOIS TRUST COMPANY OF FLORIDA, N.A. (SARASOTA BRANCH)—BankAmerica Corporation; *U.S. Public*, pg. 181
BANK OF BOSTON - FLORIDA, N.A.—BankBoston Corporation; *U.S. Public*, pg. 184
BANK OF COMMERCE TRUST COMPANY BARBADOS LIMITED—Canadian Imperial Bank of Commerce; *Int'l*, pg. 257
BANK OF MONTREAL TRUST COMPANY—Bank of Montreal; *Int'l*, pg. 154
BANK OF MONTREAL TRUST COMPANY (C.I.) LTD.—Bank of Montreal; *Int'l*, pg. 155
THE BANK OF NEW YORK TRUST COMPANY OF FLORIDA, N.A.—The Bank of New York Company, Inc.; *U.S. Public*, pg. 179
BANK ONE, OHIO TRUST COMPANY, N.A.—Banc One Corporation; *U.S. Public*, pg. 173
BANKAMERICA TRUST & BANKING CORP. (BAHAMAS) LTD.—BankAmerica Corporation; *U.S. Public*, pg. 183
BANKERS TRUST COMPANY OF CALIFORNIA, N.A.—Bankers Trust New York Corporation; *U.S. Public*, pg. 185
CIBC BANK AND TRUST COMPANY (CAYMAN) LIMITED—Canadian Imperial Bank of Commerce; *Int'l*, pg. 257
CIGNA SUPERANNUATION NOMINEES PTY LIMITED—Cigna Corp.; *U.S. Public*, pg. 364
CONTINENTAL AUXILIARY COMPANY TRUSTEE—BankAmerica Corporation; *U.S. Public*, pg. 181
FIRST AMERICAN TRUST COMPANY OF MINNESOTA—Bremer Financial Corporation; *U.S. Private*, pg. 167
FIRST MIDWEST TRUST COMPANY, N.A.—First Midwest Bancorp, Inc.; *U.S. Public*, pg. 636
FIRST TRUST COMPANY OF MONTANA, NATIONAL ASSOCIATION—U.S. Bancorp; *U.S. Public*, pg. 1681
FIRST TRUST COMPANY OF NORTH DAKOTA, NATIONAL ASSOCIATION—U.S. Bancorp; *U.S. Public*, pg. 1681
FIRST TRUST NATIONAL ASSOCIATION—U.S. Bancorp; *U.S. Public*, pg. 1681
FLEET TRUST CO. OF FLORIDA, N.A.—Fleet Financial Group, Inc.; *U.S. Public*, pg. 649
HARRIS TRUST BANK OF ARIZONA—Bank of Montreal; *Int'l*, pg. 155
HARRIS TRUST COMPANY OF CALIFORNIA—Bank of Montreal; *Int'l*, pg. 155
HARRIS TRUST COMPANY OF FLORIDA—Bank of Montreal; *Int'l*, pg. 155
HARRIS TRUST COMPANY OF NEW YORK—Bank of Montreal; *Int'l*, pg. 155
HOMEFED TRUST—Washington Mutual Inc.; *U.S. Public*, pg. 1742
THE HUNTINGTON INVESTMENT COMPANY—Huntington Bancshares Inc.; *U.S. Public*, pg. 850
THE HUNTINGTON TRUST COMPANY OF FLORIDA, N.A.—Huntington Bancshares Inc.; *U.S. Public*, pg. 850
KEY TRUST COMPANY—Keycorp; *U.S. Public*, pg. 954
KEY TRUST COMPANY OF ALASKA—Keycorp; *U.S. Public*, pg. 954
KEY TRUST COMPANY OF FLORIDA, NATIONAL ASSOCIATION—Keycorp; *U.S. Public*, pg. 954
KEY TRUST COMPANY OF MAINE—Keycorp; *U.S. Public*, pg. 954
KEY TRUST COMPANY OF THE NORTHWEST—Keycorp; *U.S. Public*, pg. 954
LGT TREUHAND AKTIENGESELLSCHAFT—Liechtenstein Global Trust Limited; *Int'l*, pg. 809
LANE INDUSTRIES, INC.; *U.S. Private*, pg. 649
M & I MARSHALL & ILSLEY TRUST COMPANY OF ARIZONA—Marshall & Ilsley Corporation; *U.S. Public*, pg. 1051
MARKS & SPENCER UNIT TRUST MANAGEMENT LIMITED—Marks & Spencer PLC; *Int'l*, pg. 843
MARSHALL & ILSLEY TRUST COMPANY—Marshall & Ilsley Corporation; *U.S. Public*, pg. 1051
MARSHALL & ILSLEY TRUST COMPANY OF FLORIDA—Marshall & Ilsley Corporation; *U.S. Public*, pg. 1051
NBD TRUST COMPANY OF FLORIDA N.A.—First Chicago NBD Corporation; *U.S. Public*, pg. 628
NATIONAL ASSET MANAGEMENT CORPORATION—National City Corporation; *U.S. Public*, pg. 1154
NATIONSBANK TRUST—NationsBank Corporation; *U.S. Public*, pg. 1165
C. PORTMANN—Commerzbank AG; *Int'l*, pg. 310
FRANK RUSSELL TRUST CO.—Frank Russell Company; *U.S. Private*, pg. 952
THE BANK OF NEW YORK TRUST COMPANY—The Bank of New York Company, Inc.; *U.S. Public*, pg. 179
VANGUARD REAL ESTATE FUND II—The Vanguard Group, Inc.; *U.S. Private*, pg. 1134
WELLINGTON TRUST COMPANY—BCE Inc.; *Int'l*, pg. 115

6099 — FUNCTIONS RELATED TO DEPOSITORY BANKING, NEC

ADVANTA CORP.; *U.S. Public*, pg. 22
AMERICAN EXPRESS COMPANY; *U.S. Public*, pg. 73
AMERICAN EXPRESS SERVICE EUROPE LTD.—American Express Company; *U.S. Public*, pg. 74
AMERICAN EXPRESS TRAVEL RELATED SERVICES CO., INC.—American Express Company; *U.S. Public*, pg. 73
ASAHI BANK BUSINESS SERVICE CO., LTD.—The Asahi Bank, Ltd.; *Int'l*, pg. 82
ASAHI BANK LOAN BUSINESS CO., LTD.—The Asahi Bank, Ltd.; *Int'l*, pg. 82
BA ATM, INC.—BankAmerica Corporation; *U.S. Public*, pg. 181
BB&T INTERNATIONAL—BB&T Corporation; *U.S. Public*, pg. 160
BDL BANCO DI LUGANO—Union Bank of Switzerland; *Int'l*, pg. 1439
BANCA CANTRADE LUGANO SA—Union Bank of Switzerland; *Int'l*, pg. 1439
BANCA MONTE DEI PASCHI DI SIENA S.P.A.; *Int'l*, pg. 136
BANCO BRADESCO S.A.; *Int'l*, pg. 139
BANCO CENTRAL CANADA—Banco Central Hispanoamericano S.A.; *Int'l*, pg. 140
BANCO CENTRAL HISPANOAMERICANO S.A.; *Int'l*, pg. 139
BANCO DE HONDURAS S.A.—Citicorp; *U.S. Public*, pg. 378
BANCO DE LA NACION ARGENTINA; *Int'l*, pg. 140
BANCO DE LA PROVINCIA DE BUENOS AIRES; *Int'l*, pg. 140
BANCO DI NAPOLI; *Int'l*, pg. 140
BANCO DI SICILIA; *Int'l*, pg. 140
BANCO DO BRASIL; *Int'l*, pg. 141
BANCO ITAU S.A.; *Int'l*, pg. 142
BANCO MAPFRE, S.A.—Corporacion MAPFRE, Compania Internacional de Reaseguros, S.A.; *Int'l*, pg. 332
BANCO NACIONAL DE MEXICO, S.A. (BANAMEX)—Grupo Financiero Banamex/Accival, S.A. de C.V.; *Int'l*, pg. 574
BANCO NORCHEM, S.A.—The Chase Manhattan Corporation; *U.S. Public*, pg. 339
BANCO POPULAR DE PUERTO RICO; *U.S. Public*, pg. 175
BANCOMER, S.A.; *Int'l*, pg. 145
BANEXI (BANQUE POUR L'EXPANSION INDUSTRIELLE)—Banque Nationale de Paris; *Int'l*, pg. 163
BANK AUFINA—Union Bank of Switzerland; *Int'l*, pg. 1439
BANK LEUMI LE-ISRAEL B.M.; *Int'l*, pg. 150
BANK LEUMI (UK) P.L.C.—Bank Leumi le-Israel B.M.; *Int'l*, pg. 150
BANK OF CHINA; *Int'l*, pg. 152
THE BANK OF NOVA SCOTIA; *Int'l*, pg. 155
THE BANK OF NOVA SCOTIA—The Bank of Nova Scotia; *Int'l*, pg. 156
BANK OF YOKOHAMA; *Int'l*, pg. 158
BANK ROHNER LTD.—Union Bank of Switzerland; *Int'l*, pg. 1439
BANKERS TRUST AG—Bankers Trust New York Corporation; *U.S. Public*, pg. 185
BANKERS TRUST ASIA LIMITED—Bankers Trust New York Corporation; *U.S. Public*, pg. 185
BANKERS TRUST AUSTRALIA LIMITED—Bankers Trust New York Corporation; *U.S. Public*, pg. 185
BANKERS TRUST BANK OF CANADA—Bankers Trust New York Corporation; *U.S. Public*, pg. 186
BANKERS TRUST COMPANY—Bankers Trust New York Corporation; *U.S. Public*, pg. 186
BANKERS TRUST INTERNATIONAL (ASIA) LTD.—Bankers Trust New York Corporation; *U.S. Public*, pg. 186
BANKNORTH GROUP INC.; *U.S. Public*, pg. 186
BANQUE CANTRADE LAUSANNE S.A.—Union Bank of Switzerland; *Int'l*, pg. 1439
BANQUE CANTRADE, ORMOND BURRUS SA—Union Bank of Switzerland; *Int'l*, pg. 1439
BANQUE PARIBAS-CHICAGO—Compagnie Financiere de Paribas; *Int'l*, pg. 319
BANQUE PARIBAS-DALLAS—Compagnie Financiere de Paribas; *Int'l*, pg. 319
BANQUE PARIBAS-HOUSTON—Compagnie Financiere de Paribas; *Int'l*, pg. 319
BANQUE PARIBAS-LOS ANGELES—Compagnie Financiere de Paribas; *Int'l*, pg. 319
BANQUE PARIBAS-SAN FRANCISCO—Compagnie Financiere de Paribas; *Int'l*, pg. 319
BAYERISCHE HYPOTHEKEN-UND WECHSEL-BANK AKTIENGESELLSCHAFT; *Int'l*, pg. 175
BAYERISCHE HYPOTHEKEN-UND WECHSEL-BANK AKTIENGESELLSCHAFT NEW YORK BRANCH—Bayerische Hypotheken-und Wechsel-Bank Aktiengesellschaft; *Int'l*, pg. 176
BROWN BROTHERS HARRIMAN & CO.; *U.S. Private*, pg. 173
CCF LONDON—Credit Commercial de France; *Int'l*, pg. 342
CANADIAN IMPERIAL BANK OF COMMERCE (NEW YORK)—Canadian Imperial Bank of Commerce; *Int'l*, pg. 257
CANTRADE PRIVATE LTD.—Union Bank of Switzerland; *Int'l*, pg. 1439
THE CARLYLE GROUP—Carlyle Holding Corporation; *U.S. Private*, pg. 213
CARLYLE HOLDING CORPORATION; *U.S. Private*, pg. 213
CASSA DI RISPARMIO DELLE PROVINCIE LOMBARDE SPA (CARIPLO); *Int'l*, pg. 274
CENTRAL CAROLINA BANK—CCB Financial Corporation; *U.S. Public*, pg. 276
CHELTENHAM & GLOUCESTER PLC; *Int'l*, pg. 283
CHEMBANK NOMINEES LIMITED—The Chase Manhattan Corporation; *U.S. Public*, pg. 341
CHEMICAL BANK PENSION PLAN TRUSTEE, LTD.—The Chase Manhattan Corporation; *U.S. Public*, pg. 341
CITIBANK (AUSTRIA) A.G.—Citicorp; *U.S. Public*, pg. 378
CITIBANK (CHANNEL ISLANDS) LTD.—Citicorp; *U.S. Public*, pg. 378
CITIBANK ESPANA S.A.—Citicorp; *U.S. Public*, pg. 378
CITIBANK-MAGHREB—Citicorp; *U.S. Public*, pg. 378
CITIBANK, N.A. LTD.—Citicorp; *U.S. Public*, pg. 378
CITIBANK, N.A. NIGER S.A.—Citicorp; *U.S. Public*, pg. 378
CITIBANK ZAMBIA LTD.—Citicorp; *U.S. Public*, pg. 378
CITICORP BANK (LUXEMBOURG) S.A.—Citicorp; *U.S. Public*, pg. 378
CITICORP BANK (SWITZERLAND) AG—Citicorp; *U.S. Public*, pg. 378
CITICORP INVESTMENT BANK LTD.—Citicorp; *U.S. Public*, pg. 379
CITIZENS FINANCIAL SERVICES CORPORATION—The Royal Bank of Scotland plc; *Int'l*, pg. 1132
THE CITIZENS SAVINGS BANK COMPANY—Rurban Financial Corp.; *U.S. Public*, pg. 1412
COMDATA CORPORATION—Ceridian Corporation; *U.S. Public*, pg. 331
COMPAGNIE FINANCIERE DE PARIBAS; *Int'l*, pg. 319
CONTINENTAL COIN CORPORATION; *U.S. Private*, pg. 267
CORPORATE CASH MANAGEMENT DIV.—Imperial Bancorp; *U.S. Public*, pg. 871
CREDIT COMMERCIAL DE FRANCE; *Int'l*, pg. 341
CREDIT LYONNAIS CANADA—Credit Lyonnais S.A.; *Int'l*, pg. 344
CREDIT LYONNAIS S.A.; *Int'l*, pg. 343
DG BANK; *Int'l*, pg. 351
DG BANK-ATLANTA BRANCH—DG Bank; *Int'l*, pg. 352
DG BANK-LONDON BRANCH—DG Bank; *Int'l*, pg. 352
DG BANK-NEW YORK—DG Bank; *Int'l*, pg. 352
DG EUROPEAN SECURITIES CORPORATION—DG Bank; *Int'l*, pg. 352
THE DAIWA BANK LIMITED; *Int'l*, pg. 373
DAIWA FINANCE AUSTRALIA LIMITED—The Daiwa Bank Limited; *Int'l*, pg. 373
DAIWA MERCHANT BANK (SINGAPORE) LIMITED—The Daiwa Bank Limited; *Int'l*, pg. 373
DELUXE CORPORATION; *U.S. Public*, pg. 498
DEUTSCHE BANK AG; *Int'l*, pg. 401
DRESDNER BANK AG; *Int'l*, pg. 417
ELECTRONIC TRANSACTION CORPORATION—Deluxe Corporation; *U.S. Public*, pg. 498
FFP FINANCIAL SERVICES, L.P.—FFP Marketing Company, Inc.; *U.S. Public*, pg. 604
FAMIBANK S.A.—Citicorp; *U.S. Public*, pg. 379
FERRIER LULLIN & CIE SA; *Int'l*, pg. 480
THE FIRST NATIONAL BANK OF OTTAWA—Rurban Financial Corp.; *U.S. Public*, pg. 1413
FIRST NATIONAL NIPPON SHINPAN CO., LTD.—Citicorp; *U.S. Public*, pg. 379
GARMENT CENTER REGION—Imperial Bancorp; *U.S. Public*, pg. 872
GENERALE BANK—Generale de Banque S.A.; *Int'l*, pg. 547
GENERALE DE BANQUE S.A.; *Int'l*, pg. 546
HILL SAMUEL INC.—Lloyds TSB Group PLC; *Int'l*, pg. 813
HILL SAMUEL INTERNATIONAL BANKING CORP.—Lloyds TSB Group PLC; *Int'l*, pg. 813
THE HOKKAIDO TAKUSHOKU BANK, LTD.; *Int'l*, pg. 626
THE LEWIS HORWITZ ORGANIZATION; *U.S. Private*, pg. 540
HYPO SECURITIES INC.—Bayerische Hypotheken-und Wechsel-Bank Aktiengesellschaft; *Int'l*, pg. 176
HYPOSWISS (SWISS MORTGAGE & COMMERCIAL BANK)—Union Bank of Switzerland; *Int'l*, pg. 1440
IDS TRUST CO.—American Express Company; *U.S. Public*, pg. 73
ILLINOIS BANC ONE SERVICES, INC.—Banc One Corporation; *U.S. Public*, pg. 174
IMPERIAL INTERNATIONAL BANK—Imperial Bancorp; *U.S. Public*, pg. 872
INTERNATIONAL BANKING DIV.—Imperial Bancorp; *U.S. Public*, pg. 872
KFW KREDITANSTALT FUR WIEDERAUFBAU; *Int'l*, pg. 718
KKB BANK KGAA—Citicorp; *U.S. Public*, pg. 379
LOMBARD AND ULSTER BANKING LIMITED—National Westminster Bank PLC; *Int'l*, pg. 911
LOMBARD AND ULSTER LIMITED—National Westminster Bank PLC; *Int'l*, pg. 910
LONG-TERM CREDIT BANK OF JAPAN, LIMITED - CHICAGO—The Long-Term Credit Bank of Japan, Limited; *Int'l*, pg. 816
LONG-TERM CREDIT BANK OF JAPAN, LTD. - LONDON BRANCH—The Long-Term Credit Bank of Japan, Limited; *Int'l*, pg. 816
MISR-AMERICA INTERNATIONAL BANK S.A.E.—BankAmerica Corporation; *U.S. Public*, pg. 183
MASE WESTPAC AUSTRALIA LIMITED—Westpac Banking Corporation; *Int'l*, pg. 1496
MASE WESTPAC HONG KONG LIMITED—Westpac Banking Corporation; *Int'l*, pg. 1497
MASE WESTPAC LIMITED—Westpac Banking Corporation; *Int'l*, pg. 1497
MASTERCARD INTERNATIONAL-CIRRUS BRAND—Mastercard International, Inc.; *U.S. Private*, pg. 714
MERRILL LYNCH BANK & TRUST CO.—Merrill Lynch & Co., Inc.; *U.S. Public*, pg. 1097
MERRILL LYNCH CAPITAL SERVICES, INC.—Merrill Lynch & Co., Inc.; *U.S. Public*, pg. 1097
MONTREAL TRUSTCO-CORPORATE SERVICES DIV.—The Bank of Nova Scotia; *Int'l*, pg. 155
MULTIBANCO INTERNACIONAL DE INVESTIMENTOS S.A. SAO PAULO HEAD OFFICE—BankAmerica Corporation; *U.S. Public*, pg. 183
P.T. MULTINATIONAL FINANCE CORPORATION—The Royal Bank of Scotland plc; *Int'l*, pg. 1133
NACIONAL FINANCIERA; *Int'l*, pg. 904
NACIONAL FINANCIERA—Nacional Financiera; *Int'l*, pg. 904
NATIONAL BANK OF GREECE S.A.; *Int'l*, pg. 907
NATIONAL CITY PROCESSING, INC.—National City Corporation; *U.S. Public*, pg. 1154
NATIONSBANK OF TEXAS NATIONAL MONEY ORDERS INC—NationsBank Corporation; *U.S. Public*, pg. 1163
NEW VALLEY CORPORATION; *U.S. Public*, pg. 1173
NIPPON CREDIT AUSTRALIA LIMITED—The Nippon Credit Bank, Ltd.; *Int'l*, pg. 933
THE NIPPON CREDIT BANK, LTD.; *Int'l*, pg. 932

NIPPON CREDIT INTERNATIONAL (HK) LIMITED—The Nippon Credit Bank, Ltd.; *Int'l*, pg. 933
NIPPON CREDIT (SCHWEIZ) AG—The Nippon Credit Bank, Ltd.; *Int'l*, pg. 933
NORDBANKEN AB; *Int'l*, pg. 957
ORCA BANK LTD.—Union Bank of Switzerland; *Int'l*, pg. 1440
PBZ PRIVATBANK ZURICH—Union Bank of Switzerland; *Int'l*, pg. 1440
PNC FINANCIAL SERVICES, INC.—PNC Bank Corp.; *U.S. Public*, pg. 1243
PNC FLORIDA, INC.—PNC Bank Corp.; *U.S. Public*, pg. 1243
PNC LEASING CORP.—PNC Bank Corp.; *U.S. Public*, pg. 1243
THE PEOPLES BANKING COMPANY—Rurban Financial Corp.; *U.S. Public*, pg. 1413
PRIME BANCORP, INC.; *U.S. Public*, pg. 1326
REPUBLIC NEW YORK CORPORATION; *U.S. Public*, pg. 1380
ROYAL BANK OF CANADA; *Int'l*, pg. 1131
THE ROYAL BANK OF SCOTLAND PLC; *Int'l*, pg. 1132
RURBAN FINANCIAL CORP.; *U.S. Public*, pg. 1412
THE SAKURA BANK, LIMITED; *Int'l*, pg. 1178
SAUDI AMERICAN BANK—Citicorp; *U.S. Public*, pg. 379
SAUDI-SWISS BANK—Union Bank of Switzerland; *Int'l*, pg. 1440
SAVANNAH BANK OF NIGERIA LTD.—BankAmerica Corporation; *U.S. Public*, pg. 183
SEATTLE-FIRST ASIA LTD.—BankAmerica Corporation; *U.S. Public*, pg. 183
THE STATE BANK AND TRUST COMPANY—Rurban Financial Corp.; *U.S. Public*, pg. 1413
SWISS BANK CORPORATION; *Int'l*, pg. 1329
THE TORONTO DOMINION BANK; *Int'l*, pg. 1401
TORONTO-DOMINION BANK (UNITED KINGDOM) LTD.—The Toronto Dominion Bank; *Int'l*, pg. 1401
TORONTO DOMINION SECURITIES (U.S.A.) INC.—The Toronto Dominion Bank; *Int'l*, pg. 1401
TRAVELERS EXPRESS COMPANY, INC.—Viad Corp; *U.S. Public*, pg. 1718
USAA (UNITED SERVICES AUTOMOBILE ASSOCIATION); *U.S. Private*, pg. 1114
ULSTER BANK COMMERCIAL SERVICES LIMITED—National Westminster Bank PLC; *Int'l*, pg. 911
ULSTER BANK COMMERCIAL SERVICES (NI) LIMITED—National Westminster Bank PLC; *Int'l*, pg. 911
ULSTER BANK GROUP TREASURY (INTERNATIONAL) LIMITED—National Westminster Bank PLC; *Int'l*, pg. 912
ULSTER BANK GROUP TREASURY LIMITED—National Westminster Bank PLC; *Int'l*, pg. 912
ULSTER BANK (ISLE OF MAN) LIMITED—National Westminster Bank PLC; *Int'l*, pg. 911
UNIAO DE BANCOS BRASILEIROS S.A. (UNIBANCO); *Int'l*, pg. 1431
UNIAO DE BANCOS BRASILEIROS (UNIBANCO) (BRAZIL)—Uniao de Bancos Brasileiros S.A. (Unibanco); *Int'l*, pg. 1431
UNION BANK OF SWITZERLAND; *Int'l*, pg. 1439
UNION BANK OF SWITZERLAND (CANADA)—Union Bank of Switzerland; *Int'l*, pg. 1441
UNITED BANK FOR AFRICA, LTD.—Bankers Trust New York Corporation; *U.S. Public*, pg. 186
U.S. BANK FINANCIAL SERVICES, INC.—U.S. Bancorp; *U.S. Public*, pg. 1681
WESTPAC BANK - PNG LIMITED—Westpac Banking Corporation; *Int'l*, pg. 1497
WESTPAC BANKING CORPORATION; *Int'l*, pg. 1495
WESTPAC - SOUTH AUSTRALIA—Westpac Banking Corporation; *Int'l*, pg. 1496
WILMINGTON SAVINGS FUND SOCIETY (FSB)—WSFS Financial Corporation; *U.S. Public*, pg. 1729

6111 — FEDERAL & FEDERALLY-SPONSORED CREDIT AGENCIES

ASSOCIATED BANC-CORP; *U.S. Public*, pg. 140
BANK ONE, COLORADO—Banc One Corporation; *U.S. Public*, pg. 173
FEDERAL HOME LOAN MORTGAGE CORPORATION; *U.S. Public*, pg. 615
FIDIS S.P.A.-FINANZIARIA DI SVILUPPO—Fiat Auto SpA; *Int'l*, pg. 482
FINANCIAL OPPORTUNITIES, INC.—Dairy Mart Convenience Stores, Inc.; *U.S. Public*, pg. 477
NORWEST FINANCIAL, INC.—Norwest Corporation; *U.S. Public*, pg. 1202
SASOL SYNTHETIC (OPERATING DIVISION)—Sasol Limited; *Int'l*, pg. 1197
SASOL TWO DIV.—Sasol Limited; *Int'l*, pg. 1197

6141 — PERSONAL CREDIT INSTITUTIONS

A.G.C. (FINANCE) LIMITED—Westpac Banking Corporation; *Int'l*, pg. 1496
AGC FINANCIAL (H.K.) LIMITED—Westpac Banking Corporation; *Int'l*, pg. 1497
A.G.C. (GENERAL FINANCE) LIMITED—Westpac Banking Corporation; *Int'l*, pg. 1496
A.G.C. (INDUSTRIAL) LIMITED—Westpac Banking Corporation; *Int'l*, pg. 1496
AMEV FINANCIERINGEN N.V.—Fortis; *Int'l*, pg. 499
AT&T CAPITAL CORPORATION—Newcourt Credit Group Inc.; *Int'l*, pg. 924
ADVANTA CORP.; *U.S. Public*, pg. 22
ADVANTA NATIONAL BANK USA—Advanta Corp.; *U.S. Public*, pg. 22
ALBANK B.V.—ABN-AMRO Holding N.V.; *Int'l*, pg. 9
ALBUQUERQUE CAPITAL MANAGEMENT, INC.—The Chase Manhattan Corporation; *U.S. Public*, pg. 337
ALCAN FINANCES B.V.—Alcan Aluminium Limited; *Int'l*, pg. 51
ALFA FINANCIAL CORPORATION—Alfa Corporation; *U.S. Public*, pg. 40
ALLIED PREMIUM FINANCE—Credit Suisse Group; *Int'l*, pg. 346
AMERICAN FAMILY FINANCIAL SERVICES, INC.—American Family Mutual Insurance Co.; *U.S. Private*, pg. 53
AMERICAN GENERAL CORPORATION; *U.S. Public*, pg. 76
AMERICAN GENERAL FINANCE, INC.—American General Corporation; *U.S. Public*, pg. 76
AMERICREDIT CORP.; *U.S. Public*, pg. 96
AMFAC, INC.—JMB Realty Corporation; *U.S. Private*, pg. 577
AMGRO, INC.—Allmerica Financial Corporation; *U.S. Public*, pg. 54
ASSOCIATES FINANCIAL SERVICES CORPORATION—Ford Motor Company; *U.S. Public*, pg. 663
ASTON MARTIN FINANCE LIMITED—Ford Motor Company; *U.S. Public*, pg. 665
AUSTRALIAN GUARANTEE CORPORATION LIMITED—Westpac Banking Corporation; *Int'l*, pg. 1496
AUSTRALIAN ROAD CREDIT LIMITED—Ford Motor Company; *U.S. Public*, pg. 665
AUTOLATINA BRASIL S.A.—Ford Motor Company; *U.S. Public*, pg. 665
AUTOLATINA FINANCIADORA S.A.-CREDITO, FINANCIAMENTO E INVESTIMENTOS—Ford Motor Company; *U.S. Public*, pg. 665
AUTOMOBILE PROTECTION CORPORATION-APCO; *U.S. Public*, pg. 150
AUTOMOTIVE FINANCE LIMITED—Ford Motor Company; *U.S. Public*, pg. 665
AVCO FINANCIAL SERVICES—Textron Inc.; *U.S. Public*, pg. 1589
BB&T OF SOUTH CAROLINA—BB&T Corporation; *U.S. Public*, pg. 160
BMW CREDIT CORP.—Bayerische Motoren Werke Aktiengesellschaft; *Int'l*, pg. 177
BPO FINANCE CORPORATION—Baldwin Piano & Organ Company; *U.S. Public*, pg. 169
BT PRIVATE CLIENTS GROUP—Bankers Trust New York Corporation; *U.S. Public*, pg. 185
BANC ONE FINANCIAL SERVICES, INC.—Banc One Corporation; *U.S. Public*, pg. 173
BANQUE PSA FINANCE HOLDING—PSA Peugeot Citroen; *Int'l*, pg. 1021
BARCLAYS FINANCIAL SERVICES CO. LTD.—Barclays Bank PLC; *Int'l*, pg. 164
BELL ATLANTIC CREDIT COMPANY—Bell Atlantic Corporation; *U.S. Public*, pg. 202
BENEFICIAL CANADA INC.—Beneficial Corporation; *U.S. Public*, pg. 211
BENEFICIAL CORPORATION; *U.S. Public*, pg. 211
BENEFICIAL CREDIT SERVICES, INC.—Beneficial Corporation; *U.S. Public*, pg. 211
BLAZER FINANCIAL SERVICES—Washington Mutual Inc.; *U.S. Public*, pg. 1741
BRENTON BANKS, INC.; *U.S. Public*, pg. 251
CIBC (HONG KONG) LIMITED—Canadian Imperial Bank of Commerce; *Int'l*, pg. 257
CMV CREDIET MAATSCHAPPIJ VENLO N.V. STEEGH ASSURANTIEN B.V.—ABN-AMRO Holding N.V.; *Int'l*, pg. 9
CNA FINANCIAL CORP.—Loews Corporation; *U.S. Public*, pg. 1010
CANADIAN ROAD CREDIT COMPANY, LIMITED—Ford Motor Company; *U.S. Public*, pg. 665
CAPITOL FINANCE GROUP, INC.—First Union Corporation; *U.S. Public*, pg. 640
CASH AMERICA INTERNATIONAL, INC.; *U.S. Public*, pg. 312
CATERPILLAR FINANCIAL SERVICES CORPORATION—Caterpillar Inc.; *U.S. Public*, pg. 315
CHASE AUTO FINANCE CORPORATION—The Chase Manhattan Corporation; *U.S. Public*, pg. 337
CHASE FINANCIAL MANAGEMENT CORP.—The Chase Manhattan Corporation; *U.S. Public*, pg. 338
CHASE FINANCIAL SERVICES CORP.—The Chase Manhattan Corporation; *U.S. Public*, pg. 338
THE CHASE MANHATTAN CORPORATION; *U.S. Public*, pg. 337
CHEMICAL ASIA LTD.—The Chase Manhattan Corporation; *U.S. Public*, pg. 341
CHRYSLER FINANCIAL CORPORATION—Chrysler Corporation; *U.S. Public*, pg. 354
CITICORP; *U.S. Public*, pg. 376
CITICORP MORTGAGE, INC.—Citicorp; *U.S. Public*, pg. 378
CITIZENS FINANCIAL SERVICES CORPORATION—The Royal Bank of Scotland plc; *Int'l*, pg. 1132
COMMERCIAL CREDIT COMPANY—Travelers Group; *U.S. Public*, pg. 1633
COMMERCIAL FEDERAL BANK—Commercial Federal Corporation; *U.S. Public*, pg. 411
COMPANIA DE FINANCIACION CASE, S.A.—Tenneco Inc.; *U.S. Public*, pg. 1579
CONTINENTAL COMMUNITY DEVELOPMENT CORP.—BankAmerica Corporation; *U.S. Public*, pg. 181
THE CONTINENTAL CORPORATION—Loews Corporation; *U.S. Public*, pg. 1011
CORESTATES FINANCIAL CORP.; *U.S. Public*, pg. 446
CREDIT FORD S.A.—Ford Motor Company; *U.S. Public*, pg. 666
DEAN WITTER, DISCOVER & CO.—Morgan Stanley Dean Witter & Co.; *U.S. Public*, pg. 1132
DEERE & COMPANY; *U.S. Public*, pg. 491
DEERE CREDIT, INC.—Deere & Company; *U.S. Public*, pg. 492
DEERE CREDIT SERVICES, INC.—Deere & Company; *U.S. Public*, pg. 492
JOHN DEERE CAPITAL CORPORATION—Deere & Company; *U.S. Public*, pg. 492
ECC FINANCIAL GROUP—Eaton Corporation; *U.S. Public*, pg. 558
EQUITABLE SAVINGS & LOAN ASSOCIATION; *U.S. Private*, pg. 380
ERSTE BANK DER OESTERREICHISCHEN SPARKASSEN AG; *Int'l*, pg. 459
ERSTE BANK - LONDON BRANCH—Erste Bank der oesterreichischen Sparkassen AG; *Int'l*, pg. 459
FAIRFIELD ACCEPTANCE CORPORATION—Fairfield Communities, Inc.; *U.S. Public*, pg. 611
FIAT CREDIT INTERNATIONAL S.R.L.—Fiat Auto SpA; *Int'l*, pg. 482
FIATSAVA S.P.A.—Fiat Auto SpA; *Int'l*, pg. 482
FINANCIERA FUSA, S.A.—Corporacion MAPFRE, Compania Internacional de Reaseguros, S.A.; *Int'l*, pg. 335
FINANSSKANDIC AB—Skandinaviska Enskilda Banken; *Int'l*, pg. 1259
FIRESIDE THRIFT—Unitrin, Inc.; *U.S. Public*, pg. 1694
FIRST CHICAGO CREDIT CORP.—First Chicago NBD Corporation; *U.S. Public*, pg. 628
FIRST LOUISIANA ACCEPTANCE CORP.—BankBoston Corporation; *U.S. Public*, pg. 184
FIRST MARYLAND BANCORP—Allied Irish Banks, p.l.c.; *Int'l*, pg. 64
FIRST MARYLAND CREDIT CORP.—Allied Irish Banks, p.l.c.; *Int'l*, pg. 64
FLEET FINANCE, INC.—Fleet Financial Group, Inc.; *U.S. Public*, pg. 650
FLEET FINANCIAL GROUP, INC.; *U.S. Public*, pg. 648
FLEMING FINANCE CORP.—Fleming Companies, Inc.; *U.S. Public*, pg. 653
FORAL SERVICE PROPRIETARY LIMITED—Ford Motor Company; *U.S. Public*, pg. 665
FORD AUTOMOTIVE LEASING LIMITED—Ford Motor Company; *U.S. Public*, pg. 665
FORD CREDIT A/S—Ford Motor Company; *U.S. Public*, pg. 666
FORD CREDIT AUSTRALIA LIMITED—Ford Motor Company; *U.S. Public*, pg. 665
FORD CREDIT CANADA LTD.—Ford Motor Company; *U.S. Public*, pg. 665
FORD CREDIT FUNDING PLC—Ford Motor Company; *U.S. Public*, pg. 665
FORD CREDIT N.V.—Ford Motor Company; *U.S. Public*, pg. 666
FORD FINANCIAL SERVICES INC.—Ford Motor Company; *U.S. Public*, pg. 663
FORD FINANCIAL TRUST LIMITED—Ford Motor Company; *U.S. Public*, pg. 666
FORD FLEET FINANCING LIMITED—Ford Motor Company; *U.S. Public*, pg. 666
HENRY FORD & SON (FINANCE) LIMITED—Ford Motor Company; *U.S. Public*, pg. 665
HENRY FORD & SON (SALES) LIMITED—Ford Motor Company; *U.S. Public*, pg. 665
FORD INVESTITIONS GMBH & CO. OHG—Ford Motor Company; *U.S. Public*, pg. 666
FORD ITALIANA S.P.A.—Ford Motor Company; *U.S. Public*, pg. 666
FORD LEASING S.A.—Ford Motor Company; *U.S. Public*, pg. 665
FORD MOTOR COMPANY; *U.S. Public*, pg. 661
FORD MOTOR CO. AKTIEBOLAG—Ford Motor Company; *U.S. Public*, pg. 666
FORD MOTOR CREDIT COMPANY—Ford Motor Company; *U.S. Public*, pg. 663
FORD MOTOR CREDIT COMPANY INTERNATIONAL—Ford Motor Company; *U.S. Public*, pg. 664
FORD MOTOR CREDIT COMPANY OF NEW ZEALAND LIMITED—Ford Motor Company; *U.S. Public*, pg. 663
FORD MOTOR NORGE A/S—Ford Motor Company; *U.S. Public*, pg. 666
FOREMOST CORPORATION OF AMERICA; *U.S. Public*, pg. 667
FOREMOST FINANCIAL SERVICES CORP.—Foremost Corporation of America; *U.S. Public*, pg. 667
FRUEHAUF FINANCE COMPANY—Ford Motor Company; *U.S. Public*, pg. 663
GPA GROUP PLC—Air Canada; *Int'l*, pg. 37
GENERAL ELECTRIC CAPITAL AVIATION SERVICES—General Electric Company; *U.S. Public*, pg. 712
GENERAL MOTORS ACCEPTANCE CORPORATION (GMAC)—General Motors Corporation; *U.S. Public*, pg. 719
GENERAL MOTORS ACCEPTANCE CORPORATION OF CANADA LIMITED—General Motors Corporation; *U.S. Public*, pg. 720
GOLDWAY LTD.—The Chase Manhattan Corporation; *U.S. Public*, pg. 341
HSBC AMERICAS—HSBC Holdings plc; *Int'l*, pg. 580
HARRIS BANKCORP, INC.—Bank of Montreal; *Int'l*, pg. 154
HARRISCORP FINANCE, INC.—Bank of Montreal; *Int'l*, pg. 155
HOUSEHOLD INTERNATIONAL, INC.; *U.S. Public*, pg. 842
THE HUNTINGTON ACCEPTANCE COMPANY—Huntington Bancshares Inc.; *U.S. Public*, pg. 850
HUNTINGTON BANCSHARES INC.; *U.S. Public*, pg. 849
IDS DEPOSIT CORP.—American Express Company; *U.S. Public*, pg. 73
INAC CORP.—Cigna Corp.; *U.S. Public*, pg. 366
INAC CORP. OF CALIFORNIA—Cigna Corp.; *U.S. Public*, pg. 366
ING GROEP N.V.; *Int'l*, pg. 647
LEUCADIA NATIONAL CORPORATION; *U.S. Public*, pg. 989
LIBERTY FINANCIAL SERVICES—Banc One Corporation; *U.S. Public*, pg. 173
LIBMAR SIX, INC.—The Chase Manhattan Corporation; *U.S. Public*, pg. 341
LOCKHEED FINANCE CORPORATION—Lockheed Martin Corporation; *U.S. Public*, pg. 1008

MARPAN ONE, INC.—The Chase Manhattan Corporation; *U.S. Public*, pg. 341
MARPAN TWO, INC.—The Chase Manhattan Corporation; *U.S. Public*, pg. 341
THE MAY DEPARTMENT STORES COMPANY; *U.S. Public*, pg. 1063
MENACREDIT—Kingfisher plc; *Int'l*, pg. 734
MERCEDES-BENZ CREDIT CORP.—Daimler-Benz Aktiengesellschaft; *Int'l*, pg. 368
MERCURY FINANCE CO.; *U.S. Public*, pg. 1093
MID-STATE HOMES, INC.—Walter Industries, Inc.; *U.S. Public*, pg. 1736
MONTREAL TRUSTCO-PERSONAL SERVICES DIVISION—The Bank of Nova Scotia; *Int'l*, pg. 155
MORGAN STANLEY DEAN WITTER & CO.; *U.S. Public*, pg. 1132
MOTOROLA CREDIT CORPORATION—Motorola, Inc.; *U.S. Public*, pg. 1138
MUENCHENER LEBENSVERSICHERUNG AG—Allianz Aktiengesellschaft; *Int'l*, pg. 61
NEC INDUSTRIES (UK) PLC.—NEC Corporation; *Int'l*, pg. 900
NNG FINANCIAL CORPORATION—Northwest Natural Gas Company; *U.S. Public*, pg. 1200
NATIONSBANK CREDIT CORPORATION—NationsBank Corporation; *U.S. Public*, pg. 1163
NESOTA CO.—The Minnesota Mutual Life Insurance Company; *U.S. Private*, pg. 750
NEW YORK FINANCIAL CORP.—Shepaug Corporation; *U.S. Private*, pg. 993
NISSAN CREDIT CORPORATION—Nissan Motor Co., Ltd.; *Int'l*, pg. 944
NISSAN MOTOR ACCEPTANCE CORP.—Nissan Motor Co., Ltd.; *Int'l*, pg. 945
ORIX ALPHA CORPORATION—Orix Corporation; *Int'l*, pg. 1008
ORIX CLUB CORPORATION—Orix Corporation; *Int'l*, pg. 1008
PSA INTERNATIONAL S.A.—PSA Peugeot Citroen; *Int'l*, pg. 1021
PSA PEUGEOT CITROEN; *Int'l*, pg. 1020
PACCAR FINANCIAL CORP.—Paccar Inc.; *U.S. Public*, pg. 1247
PAN AMERICAN FINANCE CORPORATION—Corporacion MAPFRE, Compania Internacional de Reaseguros, S.A.; *Int'l*, pg. 333
PEOPLES SECURITY FINANCE COMPANY, INC.—CNB Bancshares, Inc.; *U.S. Public*, pg. 280
PERSONAL FINANCE CO.—The Minnesota Mutual Life Insurance Company; *U.S. Private*, pg. 750
PERSONAL FINANCE CORP.—Bancorp South Inc.; *U.S. Public*, pg. 176
PHILCO FINANCE CORPORATION—Ford Motor Company; *U.S. Public*, pg. 663
PREMIUM SERVICE CORP.—The Seibels Bruce Group, Inc.; *U.S. Public*, pg. 1454
PROGRESSIVE PREMIUM BUDGET, INC.—The Progressive Corporation; *U.S. Public*, pg. 1335
REGENCY FINANCE COMPANY—F.N.B. Corporation; *U.S. Public*, pg. 607
ROCHESTER COMMUNITY SAVINGS BANK—Charter One Financial, Inc.; *U.S. Public*, pg. 336
SPS PAYMENT SYSTEMS, INC.—Morgan Stanley Dean Witter & Co.; *U.S. Public*, pg. 1132
SANYO ELECTRIC CREDIT CO. LTD.—Sanyo Electric Co., Ltd.; *Int'l*, pg. 1191
SAVAFINBUS S.P.A.—Fiat Auto SpA; *Int'l*, pg. 482
SECURITY LIFE OF DENVER REINSURANCE COMPANY—ING Groep N.V.; *Int'l*, pg. 648
SECURITY PACIFIC HOUSING SERVICES, INC.—BankAmerica Corporation; *U.S. Public*, pg. 182
SINGAPORE FACTORY DEVELOPMENT LTD.—DBS Bank Ltd.; *Int'l*, pg. 351
L.B. SMITH, INC.; *U.S. Private*, pg. 1009
STANDARD CHARTERED ASIA LIMITED—Standard Chartered Bank PLC; *Int'l*, pg. 1296
STANDARD CHARTERED ASIA (TAIWAN) LIMITED—Standard Chartered Bank PLC; *Int'l*, pg. 1296
STANDARD CHARTERED BANK, MERCHANT BANK SERVICES—Standard Chartered Bank PLC; *Int'l*, pg. 1296
STANDARD CHARTERED BANK, MERCHANT BANKING DIVISION—Standard Chartered Bank PLC; *Int'l*, pg. 1296
STANDARD CHARTERED FINANCIAL SERVICES LIMITED—Standard Chartered Bank PLC; *Int'l*, pg. 1296
STANDARD CHARTERED MERCHANT BANK ASIA LIMITED—Standard Chartered Bank PLC; *Int'l*, pg. 1296
STANDARD CHARTERED MERCHANT BANK ZIMBABWE LIMITED—Standard Chartered Bank PLC; *Int'l*, pg. 1296
P.T. STANDARD CHARTERED SECURITIES—Standard Chartered Bank PLC; *Int'l*, pg. 1296
STANDARD CHARTERED SECURITIES ASIA LIMITED—Standard Chartered Bank PLC; *Int'l*, pg. 1296
STANDARD CHARTERED THAILAND LIMITED—Standard Chartered Bank PLC; *Int'l*, pg. 1296
STEIGER TRACTOR—Case Corporation; *U.S. Public*, pg. 311
SUBARU FINANCIAL SERVICES, INC.—Fuji Heavy Industries, Ltd.; *Int'l*, pg. 523
SUMMIT BANCORP; *U.S. Public*, pg. 1527
TEXTRON INC.; *U.S. Public*, pg. 1588
TOYOTA MOTOR CREDIT CORP.—Toyota Motor Corporation; *Int'l*, pg. 1413
TRANS CANADA CREDIT CORPORATION—Norwest Corporation; *U.S. Public*, pg. 1202
TRANSAMERICA CORPORATION; *U.S. Public*, pg. 1629
TRANSAMERICA FINANCE GROUP, INC.—Transamerica Corporation; *U.S. Public*, pg. 1630
TRANSAMERICA LIFE COMPANIES—Transamerica Corporation; *U.S. Public*, pg. 1630
U-HAUL INTERNATIONAL, INC.—Amerco; *U.S. Private*, pg. 49
URM DEVELOPMENT CORP.—URM Stores, Inc.; *U.S. Private*, pg. 1114
UNISYS FINANCE CORPORATION—Unisys Corporation; *U.S. Public*, pg. 1671
UNITED AUTO GROUP, INC.—Trace International Holdings, Inc.; *U.S. Private*, pg. 1095
UNITED CONSUMER FINANCIAL SERVICES CO.—Berkshire Hathaway Inc.; *U.S. Public*, pg. 218
UNITED STATES REALTY & INVESTMENT CO.; *U.S. Private*, pg. 1125
V.A.G. FINANCEMENT S.A.—Volkswagen AG; *Int'l*, pg. 1475
VOLVO FINANCE NORTH AMERICA, INC.—AB Volvo; *Int'l*, pg. 1477
WFS FINANCIAL, INC.—Westcorp; *U.S. Public*, pg. 1757
WAY BO FINANCE LIMITED—HSBC Holdings plc; *Int'l*, pg. 584
WAY CHONG FINANCE LIMITED—HSBC Holdings plc; *Int'l*, pg. 584
WESTCORP; *U.S. Public*, pg. 1756
WESTERN FINANCIAL AUTO LOANS, INC.—Westcorp; *U.S. Public*, pg. 1757
WESTERN FINANCIAL BANK—Westcorp; *U.S. Public*, pg. 1757
WHIRLPOOL CORPORATION; *U.S. Public*, pg. 1764
WINNEBAGO ACCEPTANCE CORP.—Winnebago Industries, Inc.; *U.S. Public*, pg. 1772
WORLD BOOK FINANCE, INC.—Berkshire Hathaway Inc.; *U.S. Public*, pg. 218
WORLD BOOK FINANCIAL SERVICES—Berkshire Hathaway Inc.; *U.S. Public*, pg. 218
YAMAHA CREDIT CO., LTD.—Yamaha Corporation; *Int'l*, pg. 1515
YAMAHA PLANS CO., LTD.—Yamaha Corporation; *Int'l*, pg. 1516
ZIONS BANCORPORATION; *U.S. Public*, pg. 1792

6153 — SHORT-TERM BUSINESS CREDIT INSTITUTIONS, EXCEPT AGRICULTURAL

ABB FINANCIAL SERVICES INC.—ABB Asea Brown Boveri (Holding) Ltd.; *Int'l*, pg. 4
AFCO CREDIT CORP.—Mellon Bank Corporation; *U.S. Public*, pg. 1085
A.I. CREDIT CORP.—American International Group, Inc.; *U.S. Public*, pg. 85
ACACIA FINANCIAL CORPORATION—The Acacia Group - Acacia Life Insurance Co.; *U.S. Private*, pg. 11
ADVANTA BUSINESS SERVICES—Advanta Corp.; *U.S. Public*, pg. 22
ADVANTA CORP.; *U.S. Public*, pg. 22
AETNA INC.; *U.S. Public*, pg. 26
AGRISTOR CREDIT CORP.—A.O. Smith Corporation; *U.S. Public*, pg. 1477
AMERICA DO SUL LEASING S.A. ARRENDAMENTO MERCANTIL—The Fuji Bank, Limited; *Int'l*, pg. 521
AMERICAN EXPRESS COMPANY; *U.S. Public*, pg. 73
AMERICAN EXPRESS CREDIT CORPORATION—American Express Company; *U.S. Public*, pg. 74
AMERICAN EXPRESS SERVICE EUROPE LTD.—American Express Company; *U.S. Public*, pg. 74
AMOCO CREDIT CORPORATION—Amoco Corporation; *U.S. Public*, pg. 103
AMRESCO, INC.—Cravey, Green & Wahlen, Incorporated; *U.S. Private*, pg. 287
ASSOCIATES FINANCIAL SERVICES CORPORATION—Ford Motor Company; *U.S. Public*, pg. 663
BAI FACTORING S.P.A.—Deutsche Bank AG; *Int'l*, pg. 403
BHF-BANK AG; *Int'l*, pg. 119
BLE CAPITAL LIMITED—Westpac Banking Corporation; *Int'l*, pg. 1496
BACOT-ALLAIN S.A.—Swiss Bank Corporation; *Int'l*, pg. 1331
BANCA POPOLARE DI MILANO; *Int'l*, pg. 137
BANCBOSTON FINANCIAL CO.—BankBoston Corporation; *U.S. Public*, pg. 184
BANCO POPULAR DE PUERTO RICO; *U.S. Public*, pg. 175
BANCO SANTANDER; *Int'l*, pg. 143
BANK OF BOSTON CONNECTICUT—BankBoston Corporation; *U.S. Public*, pg. 184
BANK SBC WARBURG SODITIC AG—Swiss Bank Corporation; *Int'l*, pg. 1331
BANKBOSTON CORPORATION; *U.S. Public*, pg. 183
BANKNORTH GROUP INC.; *U.S. Public*, pg. 186
BANKSYS—Bank Brussels Lambert; *Int'l*, pg. 147
BANQUE DUMENIL-LEBLE—CERUS - Compagnies Europeennes Reunies; *Int'l*, pg. 240
BANQUE GENERALE DU LUXEMBOURG SA; *Int'l*, pg. 161
BANQUE INTERNATIONALE A LUXEMBOURG S.A.; *Int'l*, pg. 162
BANQUE SAINT DOMINIQUE—Credit Nationale; *Int'l*, pg. 344
BANSAFINA—Banco Santander; *Int'l*, pg. 143
BANSALEASING—Banco Santander; *Int'l*, pg. 143
BERWEIN WERTPAPIERHANDELS-UND BORSENMAKLER GMBH—Swiss Bank Corporation; *Int'l*, pg. 1331
BLAZER FINANCIAL SERVICES—Washington Mutual Inc.; *U.S. Public*, pg. 1741
BLUE RIDGE FINANCE CO., INC.—Carolina First Corporation; *U.S. Public*, pg. 306
BOSTON FACTORS OF CANADA, INC.—BankBoston Corporation; *U.S. Public*, pg. 185
BRASCAN BRAZIL—EdperBrascan Corporation; *Int'l*, pg. 435
BRUNCOR, INC.; *Int'l*, pg. 230
BUNTING WARBURG INC.—Swiss Bank Corporation; *Int'l*, pg. 1331
BUTTLE WILSON GROUP LTD.—Swiss Bank Corporation; *Int'l*, pg. 1331
CBS CORPORATION; *U.S. Public*, pg. 273
CES/CARD ESTABLISHMENT SERVICES INC.—First Data Corporation; *U.S. Public*, pg. 631
CIBC CAPITAL CORPORATION—Canadian Imperial Bank of Commerce; *Int'l*, pg. 257
CPS CREDIT CORP.—Carson Pirie Scott & Co.; *U.S. Public*, pg. 309
CRR INVESTMENTS, INC.—Conrail, Inc.; *U.S. Public*, pg. 432
CAMPBELL FINANCE CORP.—Campbell Soup Company; *U.S. Public*, pg. 299
CAPITAL ASSOCIATES, INC.; *U.S. Public*, pg. 302
CAPITAL ONE FINANCIAL CORPORATION; *U.S. Public*, pg. 302
CATERPILLAR FINANCIAL SERVICES CORPORATION—Caterpillar Inc.; *U.S. Public*, pg. 315
CENTURY BUSINESS CREDIT CORPORATION; *U.S. Private*, pg. 225
CHEVRON CAPITAL U.S.A. INC.—Chevron Corporation; *U.S. Public*, pg. 348
CHICAGO HOLDINGS, INC.; *U.S. Private*, pg. 234
CITICORP; *U.S. Public*, pg. 376
CITICORP ACCEPTANCE CO., INC.—Citicorp; *U.S. Public*, pg. 378
CITICORP BUSINESS CREDIT, INC.—Citicorp; *U.S. Public*, pg. 378
CITICORP INDUSTRIAL CREDIT, INC.—Citicorp; *U.S. Public*, pg. 378
CITIZENS FINANCIAL SERVICES CORPORATION—The Royal Bank of Scotland plc; *Int'l*, pg. 1132
CITIZENS LEASING CORPORATION—The Royal Bank of Scotland plc; *Int'l*, pg. 1132
CONCORD ASSETS GROUP; *U.S. Private*, pg. 261
CONGRESS FINANCIAL CORP.—CoreStates Financial Corp.; *U.S. Public*, pg. 447
THE CONTINENTAL CORPORATION—Loews Corporation; *U.S. Public*, pg. 1011
CORESTATES FINANCIAL CORP.; *U.S. Public*, pg. 446
CRAVEY, GREEN & WAHLEN, INCORPORATED; *U.S. Private*, pg. 287
CREDIT INSURANCE ASSOCIATION—Inchcape PLC; *Int'l*, pg. 671
CREDIT NATIONALE; *Int'l*, pg. 344
CREDIT SUISSE—Credit Suisse Group; *Int'l*, pg. 345
DBS FINANCE LTD.—DBS Bank Ltd.; *Int'l*, pg. 350
DATACARD CORPORATION—DataCard Corporation; *U.S. Private*, pg. 312
B.V. DE FACTORIJ, FACTORBEDRIJF ALGEMENE VAN DE BANK NEDERLAND—ABN-AMRO Holding N.V.; *Int'l*, pg. 9
DIAMOND SHAMROCK CREDIT CARD CENTER—Ultramar Diamond Shamrock Corporation; *U.S. Public*, pg. 1663
DIESEL TECHNOLOGY COMPANY—Robert Bosch GmbH; *Int'l*, pg. 205
DINERS CLUB INC.—Citicorp; *U.S. Public*, pg. 377
DINERS CLUB NORDIC A/S—Scandinavian Airlines System (SAS); *Int'l*, pg. 1202
DIXONS GROUP PLC; *Int'l*, pg. 413
EAGLEMARK FINANCIAL SERVICES, INC.—Harley-Davidson, Inc.; *U.S. Public*, pg. 786
THE EL-BEE CHARGIT CORP.—The Elder-Beerman Stores Corp.; *U.S. Private*, pg. 367
ENTERTAINMENT INDUSTRIES GROUP—Imperial Bancorp; *U.S. Public*, pg. 871
EQUITY FUND ADVISORS INC.; *U.S. Private*, pg. 380
EUROCARD AB, STOCKHOLM—Skandinaviska Enskilda Banken; *Int'l*, pg. 1259
EUROLEASE FACTOR SA—Banque Generale du Luxembourg SA; *Int'l*, pg. 162
EXPORT FINANCE CORPORATION OF CANADA LIMITED—Canadian Imperial Bank of Commerce; *Int'l*, pg. 257
FACTOFRANCE HELLER—Compagnie de Suez; *Int'l*, pg. 313
FINANCIAL OPPORTUNITIES, INC.—Dairy Mart Convenience Stores, Inc.; *U.S. Public*, pg. 477
FINANSSKANDIC AB—Skandinaviska Enskilda Banken; *Int'l*, pg. 1259
FIRST CONSOLIDATED HOLDINGS (PROPRIETARY) LIMITED—Anglo American Corporation of South Africa Limited; *Int'l*, pg. 77
FIRST HAWAIIAN CREDITCORP, INC.—First Hawaiian, Inc.; *U.S. Public*, pg. 635
FIRST MARYLAND BANCORP—Allied Irish Banks, p.l.c.; *Int'l*, pg. 64
FIRST USA, INC.—Banc One Corporation; *U.S. Public*, pg. 174
FLEET FINANCIAL GROUP, INC.; *U.S. Public*, pg. 648
THE FOOTHILL GROUP, INC.—Norwest Corporation; *U.S. Public*, pg. 1201
FORD MOTOR COMPANY; *U.S. Public*, pg. 661
FREMONT FINANCIAL CORPORATION—Fremont General Corporation; *U.S. Public*, pg. 681
GEFINOR S.A. LUXEMBOURG; *Int'l*, pg. 542
GENERAL ELECTRIC CAPITAL SERVICES, INC.—General Electric Company; *U.S. Public*, pg. 711
GENERAL MOTORS ACCEPTANCE CORPORATION OF CANADA LIMITED—General Motors Corporation; *U.S. Public*, pg. 720
GIBRALTAR CORP. OF AMERICA—Summit Bancorp; *U.S. Public*, pg. 1528
GREAT LAKES POWER INC.—EdperBrascan Corporation; *Int'l*, pg. 433
GRIMMER REALTY CO. INC.; *U.S. Private*, pg. 482
HCBECK; *U.S. Private*, pg. 490
HABIB BANK LTD.; *Int'l*, pg. 584
HANDELSBANKEN FINANS—Svenska Handelsbanken; *Int'l*, pg. 1327
HAWTHORNE CORP.; *U.S. Private*, pg. 512
HELLER FACTORING PORTUGUESA S.A.—The Fuji Bank, Limited; *Int'l*, pg. 521
HELLER FACTORING (SINGAPORE) LTD.—The Fuji Bank, Limited; *Int'l*, pg. 521
HOUSEHOLD BANK, N.A.—Household International, Inc.; *U.S. Public*, pg. 842

S.I.C. Index

HOUSEHOLD FINANCIAL CORPORATION LIMITED—Household International, Inc.; *U.S. Public*, pg. 842
HOUSEHOLD INTERNATIONAL, INC.; *U.S. Public*, pg. 842
HUDSON'S BAY COMPANY ACCEPTANCE LTD.—Hudson's Bay Company; *Int'l*, pg. 637
THE HUNTINGTON ACCEPTANCE COMPANY—Huntington Bancshares Inc.; *U.S. Public*, pg. 850
IBM CREDIT CORPORATION—International Business Machines Corporation; *U.S. Public*, pg. 896
INAC CORP.—Cigna Corp.; *U.S. Public*, pg. 366
INAC CORP. OF CALIFORNIA—Cigna Corp.; *U.S. Public*, pg. 366
ING GROEP N.V.; *Int'l*, pg. 647
IMPERIAL BANK—Imperial Bancorp; *U.S. Public*, pg. 871
IMPERIAL INTERNATIONAL BANK—Imperial Bancorp; *U.S. Public*, pg. 872
INSTITUT DE REESCOMPTE ET DE GARANTIE—Bank Brussels Lambert; *Int'l*, pg. 147
INTEGRATEC—Equifax Inc.; *U.S. Public*, pg. 588
INTERNATIONAL BANKING DIV.—Imperial Bancorp; *U.S. Public*, pg. 872
INTERNATIONAL FACTORS—Bank Brussels Lambert; *Int'l*, *pg. 147*
INTERNATIONAL FACTORS LIMITED—Lloyds TSB Group PLC; *Int'l*, pg. 813
INTERNATIONAL FACTORS NEDERLAND B.V.—ABN-AMRO Holding N.V.; *Int'l*, pg. 9
ISTITUTO BANCARIO SAN PAOLO DI TORINO S.P.A.; *Int'l*, pg. 691
JCB INTERNATIONAL CO., LTD.; *Int'l*, pg. 696
LB RHEINLAND PFALZ FINANCE B.V.—Landesbank Rheinland-Pfalz; *Int'l*, pg. 799
LSB INDUSTRIES, INC.; *U.S. Public*, pg. 970
LANDAU & HEYMAN INC.; *U.S. Private*, pg. 646
LANDESBANK RHEINLAND-PFALZ; *Int'l*, pg. 799
CYRUS J. LAWRENCE (UK) LIMITED—Deutsche Bank AG; *Int'l*, pg. 405
ALEX LAWRIE FACTORS LTD.—Lloyds TSB Group PLC; *Int'l*, pg. 813
LEHMAN COMMERCIAL PAPER INC.—Lehman Brothers Holdings Inc.; *U.S. Public*, pg. 987
LEUCADIA NATIONAL CORPORATION; *U.S. Public*, pg. 989
LYNDEN FINANCIAL SERVICES, INC.—Lynden Incorporated; *U.S. Private*, pg. 684
MASTERCARD INTERNATIONAL, INC.; *U.S. Private*, pg. 714
MERCANTILE BUSINESS CREDIT, INC.—Mercantile Bancorporation Inc.; *U.S. Public*, pg. 1087
MERRILL LYNCH CREDIT CORPORATION—Merrill Lynch & Co., Inc.; *U.S. Public*, pg. 1098
MIDLANTIC COMMERCIAL CO., INC.—PNC Bank Corp.; *U.S. Public*, pg. 1242
MORGAN GRENFELL (SCOTLAND) LIMITED—Deutsche Bank AG; *Int'l*, pg. 405
J.P. MORGAN CO. INCORPORATED; *U.S. Public*, pg. 1129
MULTIBANCO INTERNACIONAL DE INVESTIMENTOS S.A. SAO PAULO HEAD OFFICE—BankAmerica Corporation; *U.S. Public*, pg. 183
NMB HELLER N.V.—The Fuji Bank, Limited; *Int'l*, pg. 521
NTS—First Data Corporation; *U.S. Public*, pg. 631
NANTO CARD SERVICES CO., LTD.—The Nanto Bank, Ltd.; *Int'l*, pg. 905
NANTO DC CARD CO., LTD.—The Nanto Bank, Ltd.; *Int'l*, pg. 905
NOKIA FINANCE INTERNATIONAL B.V.—Oy Nokia Ab/Nokia Group; *Int'l*, pg. 954
NORWEST BUSINESS CREDIT, INC.—Norwest Corporation; *U.S. Public*, pg. 1202
NORWEST FINANCIAL BUSINESS CREDIT, INC.—Norwest Corporation; *U.S. Public*, pg. 1202
NOVUS SERVICES, INC.—Morgan Stanley Dean Witter & Co.; *U.S. Public*, pg. 1132
PNC CORP.—PNC Bank Corp.; *U.S. Public*, pg. 1243
PNC FUNDING CORP.—PNC Bank Corp.; *U.S. Public*, pg. 1243
P.S. COLORADO CREDIT CORP.—New Century Energies, Inc.; *U.S. Public*, pg. 1170
PARTNERSHIP PACIFIC LIMITED—Westpac Banking Corporation; *Int'l*, pg. 1496
PHILIPS CREDIT CORPORATION—Philips Electronics N.V.; *Int'l*, pg. 1055
POTTER WARBURG PTY. LTD.—Swiss Bank Corporation; *Int'l*, pg. 1331
REPUBLIC FACTORS CORP.—Republic New York Corporation; *U.S. Public*, pg. 1380
REPUBLIC NEW YORK CORPORATION; *U.S. Public*, pg. 1380
REUBEN ORGANIZATION; *U.S. Private*, pg. 925
RIUNIONE ADRIATICA DI SICURTA S.P.A.—Allianz Aktiengesellschaft; *Int'l*, pg. 61
ROCKY MOUNTAIN BANKCARD SYSTEM, INC.—U.S. Bancorp; *U.S. Public*, pg. 1680
ROYSCOT FINANCE GROUP PLC—The Royal Bank of Scotland plc; *Int'l*, pg. 1132
SBC BANQUE WARBURG—Swiss Bank Corporation; *Int'l*, pg. 1331
SBC WARBURG & CO. LTD.—Swiss Bank Corporation; *Int'l*, pg. 1331
SBC WARBURG DILLON READ—Swiss Bank Corporation; *Int'l*, pg. 1329
SBC WARBURG ESPANA S.A.—Swiss Bank Corporation; *Int'l*, pg. 1331
SBC WARBURG GROUP PLC—Swiss Bank Corporation; *Int'l*, pg. 1330
SANTANDER DE FACTORING—Banco Santander; *Int'l*, pg. 143
SANTANDER DE LEASING—Banco Santander; *Int'l*, pg. 143
SANTANDER INVESTMENT BANK—Banco Santander; *Int'l*, pg. 143
SCANDINAVIAN AIRLINES SYSTEM (SAS); *Int'l*, pg. 1201
SKANDINAVISKA ENSKILDA BANKEN; *Int'l*, pg. 1258
SOCIETY EQUIPMENT LEASING CORPORATION—Keycorp; *U.S. Public*, pg. 955
SOFIAS—Allianz Aktiengesellschaft; *Int'l*, pg. 62
SOUTHERN PACIFIC BANK—Imperial Credit Industries, Inc.; *U.S. Public*, pg. 872
SPATZ CENTERS INC.; *U.S. Private*, pg. 1021
TOSHIBA CREDIT CORP.—Toshiba Corporation; *Int'l*, pg. 1403
TOYOTA MOTOR CREDIT CORP.—Toyota Motor Corporation; *Int'l*, pg. 1413
TRILON FINANCIAL CORP.—EdperBrascan Corporation; *Int'l*, pg. 434
TRUST CORPORATION OF CANADA—Royal Bank of Canada; *Int'l*, pg. 1131
UNITED CREDIT CORP. & PATROIT FUNDING; *U.S. Private*, pg. 1121
VENDEX INTERNATIONAL N.V.; *Int'l*, pg. 1462
VISA U.S.A. INC.; *U.S. Private*, pg. 1141
WARBURG ASSET MANAGEMENT CANADA LTD.—Swiss Bank Corporation; *Int'l*, pg. 1331
WARBURG ASSET MANAGEMENT HONG KONG LTD.—Swiss Bank Corporation; *Int'l*, pg. 1331
WARBURG ASSET MANAGEMENT SINGAPORE PTE. LTD.—Swiss Bank Corporation; *Int'l*, pg. 1331
WARBURG INVESTMENT TRUST MANAGEMENT COMPANY LTD.—Swiss Bank Corporation; *Int'l*, pg. 1331
WESTDEUTSCHE LANDESBANK (SCHWEIZ) AG—Landesbank Rheinland-Pfalz; *Int'l*, pg. 799
WESTPAC FINANCE ASIA LIMITED—Westpac Banking Corporation; *Int'l*, pg. 1497
ZIEGLER FINANCING CORP.—The Ziegler Companies, Inc.; *U.S. Public*, pg. 1792

6159 — MISCELLANEOUS BUSINESS CREDIT INSTITUTIONS

ABB TREASURY CENTER (USA) INC.—ABB Asea Brown Boveri (Holding) Ltd.; *Int'l*, pg. 4
ABN AMRO CHICAGO CORP FINANCIAL SERVICES—ABN-AMRO Holding N.V.; *Int'l*, pg. 10
ABN AMRO CHICAGO CORPORATION—ABN-AMRO Holding N.V.; *Int'l*, pg. 10
ABN INTERNATIONAL FINANCIAL SERVICES CO.—ABN-AMRO Holding N.V.; *Int'l*, pg. 11
AIB CORPORATE FINANCE LTD.—Allied Irish Banks, p.l.c.; *Int'l*, pg. 64
AKF KREDITBANK GMBH. & CO.—Vorwerk & Co.; *Int'l*, pg. 1481
AMEV PRAKTIJKVOORZIENING N.V.—Fortis; *Int'l*, pg. 499
ANR FINANCE N.V.—The Coastal Corporation; *U.S. Public*, *pg. 391*
ARCA MERCHANT-ABK S.P.A.—Dresdner Bank AG; *Int'l*, pg. 420
AT ACCEPTANCE CORPORATION—Keycorp; *U.S. Public*, pg. 955
AT&T CORPORATION; *U.S. Public*, pg. 10
AT FINANCIAL CORPORATION—Keycorp; *U.S. Public*, pg. 955
ACACIA FINANCIAL CORPORATION—The Acacia Group - Acacia Life Insurance Co.; *U.S. Private*, pg. 11
AFFILIATED FIRST COLORADO LEASE COMPANY—Banc One Corporation; *U.S. Public*, pg. 173
AGRATRADE FINANCING, INC.—Gold Kist, Inc.; *U.S. Private*, pg. 459
AGRIGEST—Allianz Aktiengesellschaft; *Int'l*, pg. 61
AKTIEBOLAGET LM ERICSSON FINANS—Telefonaktiebolaget LM Ericsson; *Int'l*, pg. 1363
ALFA ROMEO INTERNATIONAL S.A.—Fiat Auto SpA; *Int'l*, *pg. 481*
ALICON BORMAEGLERSELKAB A/S—ABN-AMRO Holding N.V.; *Int'l*, pg. 12
ALLEGHANY CORPORATION; *U.S. Public*, pg. 42
KG ALLGEMEINE LEASING GMBH & CO.—Dresdner Bank AG; *Int'l*, pg. 418
ALLIANZ FINANCE B.V.—Allianz Aktiengesellschaft; *Int'l*, pg. 59
ALLIED CAPITAL ADVISORS, INC.—Allied Capital Corporation; *U.S. Public*, pg. 47
ALLIED CAPITAL CORPORATION; *U.S. Public*, pg. 47
ALLIED CAPITAL FINANCIAL CORPORATION—Allied Capital Corporation; *U.S. Public*, pg. 48
ALLIED CAPITAL LENDING CORPORATION—Allied Capital Corporation; *U.S. Public*, pg. 48
ALLIED DEVELOPMENT CORP.—Allied Capital Corporation; *U.S. Public*, pg. 48
ALLIED INVESTMENT CORP.—Allied Capital Corporation; *U.S. Public*, pg. 48
ALLTEL FINANCE CORPORATION—ALLTEL Corporation; *U.S. Public*, pg. 55
AMERICAN INTERNATIONAL GROUP, INC.; *U.S. Public*, pg. 83
AMERITECH CAPITAL SERVICES—Ameritech Corporation; *U.S. Public*, pg. 98
AMERITECH CORPORATION; *U.S. Public*, pg. 97
AMERITECH CREDIT CORPORATION—Ameritech Corporation; *U.S. Public*, pg. 98
AMOCO LEASING CORPORATION—Amoco Corporation; *U.S. Public*, pg. 102
AMRO BANK & FINANCE—ABN-AMRO Holding N.V.; *Int'l*, pg. 9
AMRO BEHEERS-MAATSCHAPPIJ N.V.—ABN-AMRO Holding N.V.; *Int'l*, pg. 9
AMRO FINANCE AND SECURITIES (ASIA) LTD.—ABN-AMRO Holding N.V.; *Int'l*, pg. 10
THE ANDEAN FUND, INC.—The Chase Manhattan Corporation; *U.S. Public*, pg. 338
ANGELES FUNDING CORPORATION—Angeles Housing Concepts; *U.S. Private*, pg. 74
ARMSTRONG VENTURES, INC.—Armstrong World Industries, Inc.; *U.S. Public*, pg. 132
ASAHIGIN GUARANTEE CO., LTD.—The Asahi Bank, Ltd.; *Int'l*, pg. 82
ASIA PACIFIC CAPITAL CORP., LIMITED—Citicorp; *U.S. Public*, pg. 378
ASIAN-AMERICAN MERCHANT BANK LTD.—The Dai-Ichi Kangyo Bank, Limited; *Int'l*, pg. 362
ASSOCIATED BANC-CORP; *U.S. Public*, pg. 140
ASSOCIATES COMMERCIAL CORPORATION—Ford Motor Company; *U.S. Public*, pg. 663
ASSOCIATES DIVERSIFIED INVESTMENTS LTD.—Ford Motor Company; *U.S. Public*, pg. 665
AUSTRALIAN GUARANTEE CORPORATION LIMITED—Westpac Banking Corporation; *Int'l*, pg. 1496
AUTOMAX FINANCE—Firstbank Puerto Rico; *U.S. Public*, pg. 644
AUTOMOTIVE FINANCIAL SERVICES, INC.—Chrysler Corporation; *U.S. Public*, pg. 354
AYUDHYA INVESTMENT AND TRUST PUBLIC CO., LTD.—The Sakura Bank, Limited; *Int'l*, pg. 1180
B.A.T INDUSTRIES P.L.C.; *Int'l*, pg. 110
B.A.T INTERNATIONAL FINANCE LTD.—B.A.T Industries P.L.C.; *Int'l*, pg. 111
BB&T LEASING CORP.—BB&T Corporation; *U.S. Public*, pg. 160
BB LEASING COMPANY LTD.—Banco do Brasil; *Int'l*, pg. 141
BBL CAPITAL MANAGEMENT CORPORATION—Bank Brussels Lambert; *Int'l*, pg. 147
BBL IRELAND—Bank Brussels Lambert; *Int'l*, pg. 148
BIL (FAR EAST HOLDINGS) LTD.—Brierley Investments Limited; *Int'l*, pg. 215
BMO FINANCIAL, INC.—Bank of Montreal; *Int'l*, pg. 154
BMW FINANCE N.V.—Bayerische Motoren Werke Aktiengesellschaft; *Int'l*, pg. 178
BMW LEASING CORP.—Bayerische Motoren Werke Aktiengesellschaft; *Int'l*, pg. 177
BMW OVERSEAS ENTERPRISES N.V.—Bayerische Motoren Werke Aktiengesellschaft; *Int'l*, pg. 178
BNU—Caixa Geral de Depositos; *Int'l*, pg. 250
BNY BROKERAGE, INC.—The Bank of New York Company, Inc.; *U.S. Public*, pg. 178
BNY FINANCIAL CORPORATION—The Bank of New York Company, Inc.; *U.S. Public*, pg. 178
BNY INFORMATION SERVICES, INC.—The Bank of New York Company, Inc.; *U.S. Public*, pg. 178
BRAC CREDIT CORP.—Budget Group, Inc.; *U.S. Private*, pg. 178
BRL LEASING (PTY) LTD.—Barlow Ltd.; *Int'l*, pg. 167
BT CAPITAL PARTNERS—Bankers Trust New York Corporation; *U.S. Public*, pg. 185
BT COMMERCIAL CORPORATION—Bankers Trust New York Corporation; *U.S. Public*, pg. 185
BT INVESTMENT MANAGERS, INC.—Bankers Trust New York Corporation; *U.S. Public*, pg. 185
BTM FINANZIARIA (ITALIA) S.P.A.—The Bank of Tokyo-Mitsubishi, Ltd.; *Int'l*, pg. 158
BANC ONE CORPORATION; *U.S. Public*, pg. 172
BANC ONE CREDIT CORPORATION—Banc One Corporation; *U.S. Public*, pg. 175
BANCA AGRICOLA MILANESE S.P.A.—Banca Popolare di Milano; *Int'l*, pg. 137
BANCA POPOLARE DI MILANO; *Int'l*, pg. 137
BANCBOSTON CAPITAL, INC.—BankBoston Corporation; *U.S. Public*, pg. 184
BANCBOSTON INVESTMENT INC.—BankBoston Corporation; *U.S. Public*, pg. 184
BANCO CREFISUL DE INVESTIMENTO, S.A.—Citicorp; *U.S. Public*, pg. 378
BANCO DE BOSTON—BankBoston Corporation; *U.S. Public*, pg. 184
BANGKOK SAKURA LEASING CO., LIMITED—The Sakura Bank, Limited; *Int'l*, pg. 1180
BANK CARD COMPANY—Bank Brussels Lambert; *Int'l*, pg. 147
BANK OF AMERICA AUTO LEASE CENTER—BankAmerica Corporation; *U.S. Public*, pg. 181
BANK OF AMERICA ILLINOIS—BankAmerica Corporation; *U.S. Public*, pg. 180
BANK OF BOSTON—BankBoston Corporation; *U.S. Public*, *pg. 184*
BANK OF BOSTON CONNECTICUT—BankBoston Corporation; *U.S. Public*, pg. 184
THE BANK OF NEW YORK—The Bank of New York Company, Inc.; *U.S. Public*, pg. 179
THE BANK OF NEW YORK COMPANY, INC.; *U.S. Public*, pg. 178
BANKAMERICA—BankAmerica Corporation; *U.S. Public*, pg. 181
BANKAMERICA FINANCIAL SERVICES SYSTEM, INC.—BankAmerica Corporation; *U.S. Public*, pg. 181
BANKERS LEASING CORP.—Citicorp; *U.S. Public*, pg. 377
BARCLAYS FINANCIAL SERVICES CO. LTD.—Barclays Bank PLC; *Int'l*, pg. 164
BARCLAYS UNICORN LTD.—Barclays Bank PLC; *Int'l*, pg. 165
BAZIMO—GIB Group; *Int'l*, pg. 533
BELL & HOWELL ACCEPTANCE CORPORATION—Bell & Howell Holdings; *U.S. Public*, pg. 201
BELL ATLANTIC FINANCIAL SERVICES—Bell Atlantic Corporation; *U.S. Public*, pg. 202
BELL ATLANTIC SYSTEMS LEASING INTERNATIONAL, INC.—Bell Atlantic Corporation; *U.S. Public*, pg. 203
BEXLEY FINANCE S.A.—Borden, Inc.; *U.S. Private*, pg. 159
BLACK HORSE FINANCIAL SERVICES LTD.—Lloyds TSB Group PLC; *Int'l*, pg. 813
BOEING CAPITAL CORP.—The Boeing Company; *U.S. Public*, pg. 240
BOWTHORPE BV—Bowthorpe plc; *Int'l*, pg. 208
BOWTHORPE GMBH—Bowthorpe plc; *Int'l*, pg. 208
BRADESCO LEASING S.A. ARRENDAMENTO MERCANTIL—Orix Corporation; *Int'l*, pg. 1009
BRISTOL-MYERS OVERSEAS FINANCE N.V.—Bristol-Myers Squibb Company; *U.S. Public*, pg. 255
BROWN & SHARPE INTL. CAPITAL CORP.—Brown & Sharpe Manufacturing Company; *U.S. Public*, pg. 260

P.T. BUMI DAYA-IBJ LEASING—The Industrial Bank of Japan, Limited; *Int'l*, pg. 676
BUTLER REAL ESTATE—Butler Manufacturing Company; *U.S. Public*, pg. 271
CBC-U.S.A INC.—The Chase Manhattan Corporation; *U.S. Public*, pg. 337
CBFC LIMITED—Commonwealth Bank Group; *Int'l*, pg. 313
CCF INTERNATIONAL FINANCE CORP.—Credit Commercial de France; *Int'l*, pg. 342
CCM FRAMLINGTON GROUP PLC—Credit Commercial de France; *Int'l*, pg. 342
CG PROJECTS, INC.—Conrail, Inc.; *U.S. Public*, pg. 432
CH MORTGAGE COMPANY—Continental Homes Holding Corp.; *U.S. Public*, pg. 441
CIBC AVIATION, INC.—Canadian Imperial Bank of Commerce; *Int'l*, pg. 257
CIBC FINANCE B.V.—Canadian Imperial Bank of Commerce; *Int'l*, pg. 257
CIC FINANCIAL—Loews Corporation; *U.S. Public*, pg. 1011
CII-HONEYWELL BULL FINANCE BV—Compagnie des Machines Bull; *Int'l*, pg. 318
CT FINANCIAL SERVICES, INC.—B.A.T Industries P.L.C.; *Int'l*, pg. 112
CAIXA PARTICIPACOES, SGPS. S.A.—Caixa Geral de Depositos; *Int'l*, pg. 250
CALIFIA COMPANY—Enova Corp; *U.S. Public*, pg. 584
CAMPBELL FINANCE CORP.—Campbell Soup Company; *U.S. Public*, pg. 299
CANADIAN IMPERIAL SERVICE CO.—Canadian Imperial Bank of Commerce; *Int'l*, pg. 257
CANADIAN MAAS RIVER INVESTMENT N.V.—MacMillan Bloedel Limited; *Int'l*, pg. 829
CANADIAN TIRE ACCEPTANCE LTD.—Canadian Tire Corporation Limited; *Int'l*, pg. 259
CANAGEX INVESTMENTS LIMITED—Desjardins-Laurentian Financial Corporation; *Int'l*, pg. 396
CANDEV FINANCIAL SERVICES LTD.—BCE Inc.; *Int'l*, pg. 115
CAPITOL FINANCE GROUP, INC.—First Union Corporation; *U.S. Public*, pg. 640
W.P. CAREY & CO., INC.; *U.S. Private*, pg. 209
CASCADE LAND LEASING CO.—Cascade Natural Gas Corporation; *U.S. Public*, pg. 311
J.I. CASE CREDIT CORP.—Case Corporation; *U.S. Public*, pg. 312
CATERPILLAR INC.; *U.S. Public*, pg. 315
CENTRAL CAROLINA BANK—CCB Financial Corporation; *U.S. Public*, pg. 276
CESSNA FINANCE CORP.—Textron Inc.; *U.S. Public*, pg. 1589
CHARGEX LTD./CHARGEX LTEE—Canadian Imperial Bank of Commerce; *Int'l*, pg. 257
CHARTERED TRUST PLC.—Standard Chartered Bank PLC; *Int'l*, pg. 1296
CHASE EDUCATION FINANCE—The Chase Manhattan Corporation; *U.S. Public*, pg. 338
CHASE EQUIPMENT LEASING, INC.—The Chase Manhattan Corporation; *U.S. Public*, pg. 338
CHASE MANHATTAN FINANCIAL CENTER, INC.—The Chase Manhattan Corporation; *U.S. Public*, pg. 338
CHASE MANHATTAN FINANCIAL SERVICES, INC.—The Chase Manhattan Corporation; *U.S. Public*, pg. 338
CHASE MANHATTAN OF UTAH—The Chase Manhattan Corporation; *U.S. Public*, pg. 338
CHASE MANHATTAN, S.A. DISTRIBUIDORA DE TITULOS E VALORES MOBILIARIOS—The Chase Manhattan Corporation; *U.S. Public*, pg. 340
CHASE TRADE FINANCE, LTD.—The Chase Manhattan Corporation; *U.S. Public*, pg. 339
CHASE U.S. CONSUMER SERVICES—The Chase Manhattan Corporation; *U.S. Public*, pg. 338
CHASEFIN-CHASE FINANZIARA, S.P.A.—The Chase Manhattan Corporation; *U.S. Public*, pg. 341
CHEVRON OIL FINANCE COMPANY—Chevron Corporation; *U.S. Public*, pg. 348
CHEVRON STATIONS, INC.—Chevron Corporation; *U.S. Public*, pg. 348
CHICAGO WEST PULLMAN FINANCIAL CORPORATION—Chicago West Pullman Corporation; *U.S. Private*, pg. 236
CHINA ORIENT LEASING CO., LTD.—Orix Corporation; *Int'l*, pg. 1009
CHINA UNITED INTERNATIONAL LEASING CO., LTD.—The Sakura Bank, Limited; *Int'l*, pg. 1180
CHRYSLER CAPITAL CORP.—Chrysler Corporation; *U.S. Public*, pg. 354
CHRYSLER COMERCIAL, S.A. DE C.V.—Chrysler Corporation; *U.S. Public*, pg. 354
CHRYSLER CREDIT CANADA LTD.—Chrysler Corporation; *U.S. Public*, pg. 354
CHRYSLER FINANCIAL CORPORATION—Chrysler Corporation; *U.S. Public*, pg. 354
CHRYSLER OVERSEAS CAPITAL CORPORATION—Chrysler Corporation; *U.S. Public*, pg. 354
CIRCLE BUSINESS CREDIT, INC.—Xerox Corporation; *U.S. Public*, pg. 1785
CITIBANK CREDITO, FINANCIAMENTO E INVESTIMENTO, S.A.—Citicorp; *U.S. Public*, pg. 378
CITICARD S.A. COMERCIAL FINANCIERA Y DE SERVICIOS—Citicorp; *U.S. Public*, pg. 378
CITICORP DEL-LEASE, INC.—Citicorp; *U.S. Public*, pg. 377
CITICORP GULF FINANCE LTD.—Citicorp; *U.S. Public*, pg. 378
CITICORP LEASING INC.—Citicorp; *U.S. Public*, pg. 377
CITICORP (USA), INC.—Citicorp; *U.S. Public*, pg. 377
CITICORP VENTURE CAPITAL LTD.—Citicorp; *U.S. Public*, pg. 377
COASTAL FINANCIAL B.V.—The Coastal Corporation; *U.S. Public*, pg. 390
COBANK—Federal Farm Credit Banks Funding Corporation; *U.S. Private*, pg. 398
COCA-COLA FINANCIAL CORPORATION—The Coca-Cola Company; *U.S. Public*, pg. 392
COLORADO BUSINESS LEASING, INC.—Colorado Business Bankshares, Inc.; *U.S. Private*, pg. 255
COLUMBIA WILLAMETTE LEASING, INC.—Enron Corp.; *U.S. Public*, pg. 585
COMERICA ACCEPTANCE CORPORATION—Comerica Incorporated; *U.S. Public*, pg. 409
COMMERCIAL FINANCIAL CORPORATION LIMITED—BCE Inc.; *Int'l*, pg. 115
COMMERCIAL UNION CAPITAL CORPORATION—Commercial Union plc; *Int'l*, pg. 308
COMMERCIALE FINANZIARIA S.P.A.—Fiat Auto SpA; *Int'l*, pg. 481
COMMERZBANK AG; *Int'l*, pg. 308
COMPAGNIE DE SUEZ; *Int'l*, pg. 313
COMPAGNIE FINANCIERE DE PARIBAS; *Int'l*, pg. 319
COMPANIA COLOMBIANA DE FINANCIAMENTOS, S.A.—Citicorp; *U.S. Public*, pg. 379
COMPASS INVESTMENT SERVICES—North Fork Bancorporation, Inc.; *U.S. Public*, pg. 1194
CONSOLIDATED ORIX LEASING AND FINANCE CORPORATION—Orix Corporation; *Int'l*, pg. 1009
THE COOPERATIVE FINANCE ASSN., INC.—Farmland Industries, Inc.; *U.S. Private*, pg. 396
COTTER ACCEPTANCE CO., INC.—TruServ Corporation; *U.S. Private*, pg. 1108
COUNCE FINANCE CORPORATION—Tenneco Inc.; *U.S. Public*, pg. 1578
CREDIT CORPORATION (MALAYSIA) BERHAD—Standard Chartered Bank PLC; *Int'l*, pg. 1297
CREDIT CORPORATION (SINGAPORE) LTD.—Standard Chartered Bank PLC; *Int'l*, pg. 1297
CREDITANSTALT-BANKVEREIN; *Int'l*, pg. 346
CREDITANSTALT FINANCE INC.- NEW YORK—Creditanstalt-Bankverein; *Int'l*, pg. 347
DKB DATA SERVICES (USA) INC.—The Dai-Ichi Kangyo Bank, Limited; *Int'l*, pg. 360
DVI, INC.; *U.S. Public*, pg. 476
P.T. DAI-ICHI KANGYO PANIN LEASING—The Dai-Ichi Kangyo Bank, Limited; *Int'l*, pg. 362
DAIMLER-BENZ AKTIENGESELLSCHAFT; *Int'l*, pg. 366
DAIMLER-BENZ INTERSERVICES (DEBIS) AG—Daimler-Benz Aktiengesellschaft; *Int'l*, pg. 367
DAIWA BANK (SCHWEIZ) AG—The Daiwa Bank Limited; *Int'l*, pg. 373
DAIWA FINANCE CO. LTD.—Daiwa Securities Co. Ltd.; *Int'l*, pg. 374
P.T. DAIWA LIPPO LEASING CORPORATION—The Daiwa Bank Limited; *Int'l*, pg. 374
DANA CORPORATION; *U.S. Public*, pg. 479
DATASCHALT GESELLSCHAFT FUR INDUSTRIELLE DATEN-MESS-UND ANTRIEBSTECHNIK MGH—FKI Plc; *Int'l*, pg. 473
CIA. DE SEGUROS AMERICA DO SUL YASUDA—The Fuji Bank, Limited; *Int'l*, pg. 521
DE SURINAAMSCHE BANK N.V.—ABN-AMRO Holding N.V.; *Int'l*, pg. 12
DEER PARK FEDERAL SAVINGS AND LOAN ASSOCIATION—Ameriana Bancorp; *U.S. Public*, pg. 66
DESAI CAPITAL MANAGEMENT INCORPORATED; *U.S. Private*, pg. 326
DEUTSCHE CREDIT CORPORATION—Deutsche Bank AG; *Int'l*, pg. 403
DIASONICS CREDIT CORPORATION—IDB Holding Corporation; *Int'l*, pg. 644
DIMELING, SCHREIBER & PARK; *U.S. Private*, pg. 333
DOMINION CAPITAL, INC.—Dominion Resources, Inc.; *U.S. Public*, pg. 516
DOMINION FINANCING, INC.—Dominion Resources, Inc.; *U.S. Public*, pg. 516
DOW CREDIT CORPORATION—The Dow Chemical Company; *U.S. Public*, pg. 522
THE DYSON-KISSNER-MORAN CORPORATION; *U.S. Private*, pg. 351
EAGLE ASSET MANAGEMENT, INC.—Raymond James Financial, Inc.; *U.S. Public*, pg. 923
EDISON CAPITAL—Edison International; *U.S. Public*, pg. 564
EDISON MISSION ENERGY—Edison International; *U.S. Public*, pg. 564
EL CHACO S.A. FINANCIERA—Citicorp; *U.S. Public*, pg. 379
ELDER'S FINANCE GROUP—Foster's Brewing Group Limited; *Int'l*, pg. 500
ELKHART CAPITAL CORPORATION—Schult Homes Corporation; *U.S. Public*, pg. 1442
ENERGY LAND, INCORPORATED—Minnesota Power; *U.S. Public*, pg. 1116
ENSERCH FINANCE N.V.—Texas Utilities Company; *U.S. Public*, pg. 1587
ERICSSON FINANZ AG—Telefonaktiebolaget LM Ericsson; *Int'l*, pg. 1366
ERIFIN SERVIZI FINANZIARI S.P.A.—Telefonaktiebolaget LM Ericsson; *Int'l*, pg. 1368
EUROPAY BELGIUM S.C.—Bank Brussels Lambert; *Int'l*, pg. 147
F. C. BANKS—Federal Farm Credit Banks Funding Corporation; *U.S. Private*, pg. 398
FHL LEASE HOLDING COMPANY, INC.—First Hawaiian, Inc.; *U.S. Public*, pg. 634
FMC FINANCE LIMITED—FMC Corporation; *U.S. Public*, pg. 606
FNCB FINANCIAL, LTD.—Citicorp; *U.S. Public*, pg. 379
FAMICREDIT—Citicorp; *U.S. Public*, pg. 379
FARM CREDIT BANK OF TEXAS—Federal Farm Credit Banks Funding Corporation; *U.S. Private*, pg. 398
FARM PLAN CORPORATION—Deere & Company; *U.S. Public*, pg. 492
FIAT USA INC.—Fiat Auto SpA; *Int'l*, pg. 483
FINANCIERE RYSSEN—Generale Sucriere SNC; *Int'l*, pg. 549
FININVEST—Compagnie de Suez; *Int'l*, pg. 313
FINSERVIZI S.P.A.—Bastogi-S.p.A.; *Int'l*, pg. 170
FIRST AMERICAN FIELD SERVICES—The First American Financial Corporation; *U.S. Public*, pg. 625
FIRST CHICAGO AUSTRALIA SECURITY LTD.—First Chicago NBD Corporation; *U.S. Public*, pg. 628
FIRST CHICAGO NBD CORPORATION; *U.S. Public*, pg. 627
FIRST CHURCH FINANCING CORPORATION—The Ziegler Companies, Inc.; *U.S. Public*, pg. 1792
FIRST FEDERAL FINANCE CORPORATION—Firstbank Puerto Rico; *U.S. Public*, pg. 644
FIRST FRANKLIN FINANCIAL CORP.; *U.S. Private*, pg. 407
FIRST HAWAIIAN CREDITCORP, INC.—First Hawaiian, Inc.; *U.S. Public*, pg. 635
FIRST HAWAIIAN LEASING, INC.—First Hawaiian, Inc.; *U.S. Public*, pg. 635
FIRST MARYLAND BANCORP—Allied Irish Banks, p.l.c.; *Int'l*, pg. 64
FIRST SECURITY BUSINESS INVESTMENT CORP.—First Security Corporation; *U.S. Public*, pg. 637
1ST SOURCE CAPITAL CORPORATION—1st Source Corporation; *U.S. Public*, pg. 638
FIRST SOURCE FINANCIAL, INC—Household International, Inc.; *U.S. Public*, pg. 842
FIRST UNITED SMALL BUSINESS INVESTMENT CO.—James Ferrera & Sons, Inc.; *U.S. Private*, pg. 402
FIRST VALLEY LEASING, INC.—Summit Bancorp; *U.S. Public*, pg. 1528
FIRSTCORP; *U.S. Private*, pg. 408
FLEET CAPITAL CORPORATION—Fleet Financial Group, Inc.; *U.S. Public*, pg. 649
FLEET LEASING DIVISION—Ford Motor Company; *U.S. Public*, pg. 663
FLEETWOOD CREDIT CORP.—Ford Motor Company; *U.S. Public*, pg. 663
FORD CREDIT AUSTRALIA WHOLESALE LIMITED—Ford Motor Company; *U.S. Public*, pg. 665
FORD MOTOR COMPANY; *U.S. Public*, pg. 661
FOREST CITY CREDIT CORPORATION—Forest City Enterprises, Inc.; *U.S. Public*, pg. 668
FORTIS; *Int'l*, pg. 498
FOSTER'S BREWING GROUP LIMITED; *Int'l*, pg. 500
FOUR-PHASE OVERSEAS CORP.—Motorola, Inc.; *U.S. Public*, pg. 1139
FREMONT FINANCIAL CORPORATION—Fremont General Corporation; *U.S. Public*, pg. 681
FRIONA AGRICULTURE CREDIT CORP.—Friona Industries, L.P.; *U.S. Private*, pg. 429
THE FUJI FUTURES (SINGAPORE) PTE., LIMITED—The Fuji Bank, Limited; *Int'l*, pg. 521
FUJI INTERNATIONAL FINANCE (AUSTRALIA) LIMITED—The Fuji Bank, Limited; *Int'l*, pg. 521
FUJI INTERNATIONAL FINANCE (HK) LIMITED—The Fuji Bank, Limited; *Int'l*, pg. 521
FUJI INTERNATIONAL FINANCE PLC—The Fuji Bank, Limited; *Int'l*, pg. 521
GATX CAPITAL CORPORATION—GATX Corporation; *U.S. Public*, pg. 690
GATX CORPORATION; *U.S. Public*, pg. 690
GATX FINANCE (UK) LTD.—GATX Corporation; *U.S. Public*, pg. 691
GATX FINANCIAL SERVICES—GATX Corporation; *U.S. Public*, pg. 690
GATX FINANCIAL SERVICES (AUSTRALIA) PTY. LIMITED—GATX Corporation; *U.S. Public*, pg. 691
GATX FINANCIAL SERVICES GMBH—GATX Corporation; *U.S. Public*, pg. 691
GATX LEASING (PACIFIC) LTD.—GATX Corporation; *U.S. Public*, pg. 691
GATX NATIONAL LEASING, LTD.—GATX Corporation; *U.S. Public*, pg. 691
G.E. CAPITAL COMMERCIAL REAL ESTATE FINANCING—General Electric Company; *U.S. Public*, pg. 712
GIB COORDINATION CENTER—GIB Group; *Int'l*, pg. 533
GAINS INVESTMENT CORPORATION—China Steel Corporation; *Int'l*, pg. 285
GATEWAY LAND PRIVATE LIMITED—Singapore Land Limited; *Int'l*, pg. 1253
GENERAL ELECTRIC CAPITAL SERVICES, INC.—General Electric Company; *U.S. Public*, pg. 711
GENERAL MOTORS ACCEPTANCE CORPORATION (GMAC)—General Motors Corporation; *U.S. Public*, pg. 719
GENESEE VENTURES, INC.—Genesee Corporation; *U.S. Public*, pg. 728
GEORGIA-PACIFIC FINANCE N.V.—Georgia-Pacific Corporation; *U.S. Public*, pg. 739
GERBER FINANCE CO.—Novartis AG; *Int'l*, pg. 973
GREAT LAKES PETERBILT, GMC; *U.S. Private*, pg. 475
GUINNESS YOKOHAMA LEASING LIMITED—Bank of Yokohama; *Int'l*, pg. 159
HSC SECURITIES CORPORATION—The Hallwood Group Incorporated; *U.S. Public*, pg. 778
THE HALLWOOD GROUP INCORPORATED; *U.S. Public*, pg. 777
HALLWOOD REALTY INVESTORS INC.—The Hallwood Group Incorporated; *U.S. Public*, pg. 778
HANDELSFINANZ-CCF BANK—Credit Commercial de France; *Int'l*, pg. 343
HARVEST PARTNERS INC.; *U.S. Private*, pg. 508
HELABA DUBLIN-LANDESBANK INTERNATIONAL—Landesbank Hessen-Thuringen Girozentrale; *Int'l*, pg. 799
HELIOS CAPITAL CORPORATION—Sun Company, Inc.; *U.S. Public*, pg. 1530
HELLER FINANCIAL, INC.—The Fuji Bank, Limited; *Int'l*, pg. 519
HERITAGE ASSET MANAGEMENT, INC.—Raymond James Financial, Inc.; *U.S. Public*, pg. 923
HICKS, MUSE, TATE & FURST INC.; *U.S. Private*, pg. 526
HILL SAMUEL INC.—Lloyds TSB Group PLC; *Int'l*, pg. 813
HOLLANDSE DISCONTERINGSMAATSCHAPPIJ MUNDUS N.V.—ABN-AMRO Holding N.V.; *Int'l*, pg. 9
HONDA FINANCE CO., LTD.—Honda Motor Co., Ltd.; *Int'l*, pg. 634
HONDA LEASING CORPORATION—Honda Motor Co., Ltd.; *Int'l*, pg. 634

HONEYWELL-MEASUREX (IRELAND) FINANCE UNLIMITED—Honeywell Inc.; *U.S. Public*, pg. 833
THE HOSPITAL TRUST LEASING CORPORATION—BankBoston Corporation; *U.S. Public*, pg. 184
HOUSEHOLD FINANCE CORPORATION—Household International, Inc.; *U.S. Public*, pg. 842
HOUSEHOLD FINANCIAL CORPORATION LIMITED—Household International, Inc.; *U.S. Public*, pg. 842
HOUSEHOLD INTERNATIONAL, INC.; *U.S. Public*, pg. 842
HOUSEHOLD RETAIL SERVICES, INC.—Household International, Inc.; *U.S. Public*, pg. 842
HUA TONG INTERNATIONAL LEASING CO., LTD.—The Sakura Bank, Limited; *Int'l*, pg. 1181
HUNTINGTON BANCSHARES INC.; *U.S. Public*, pg. 849
THE HUNTINGTON SERVICE COMPANY—Huntington Bancshares Inc.; *U.S. Public*, pg. 850
IBJ INTERNATIONAL PLC—The Industrial Bank of Japan, Limited; *Int'l*, pg. 676
IBJ SCHRODER LEASING CORPORATION—The Industrial Bank of Japan, Limited; *Int'l*, pg. 675
IDEAL HOMES PTE., LIMITED—Singapore Land Limited; *Int'l*, pg. 1253
IKON CAPITAL, INC.—Ikon Office Solutions, Inc.; *U.S. Public*, pg. 863
IKON OFFICE SOLUTIONS, INC.; *U.S. Public*, pg. 862
IMASCO LIMITED—B.A.T Industries P.L.C.; *Int'l*, pg. 112
IMBANK NOMINEES LIMITED—Canadian Imperial Bank of Commerce; *Int'l*, pg. 257
IMOLEASING—Caixa Geral de Depositos; *Int'l*, pg. 250
INCENTIVE CREDIT AB—Incentive AB; *Int'l*, pg. 670
INDUSTRIAL CREDIT COMPANY LTD.—Standard Chartered Bank PLC; *Int'l*, pg. 1297
INDUSTRIE-RING SACH-UND VERSICHERUNGS-VERMITTLUNGSGESELLSCHAFT MBH—Saarbergwerke Aktiengesellschaft; *Int'l*, pg. 1166
INFRASTRUCTURE LEASING & FINANCIAL SERVICES LIMITED—Orix Corporation; *Int'l*, pg. 1009
INTER LEASING MOROCCO—Banque Nationale de Paris; *Int'l*, pg. 163
P.T. INTER-PACIFIC BANK—The Sanwa Bank Limited; *Int'l*, pg. 1190
INTERNATIONAL CAPITAL EQUIPMENT LIMITED; *Int'l*, pg. 683
INTERPEX SERVICES PRIVATE LIMITED—Singapore Land Limited; *Int'l*, pg. 1253
INVESTMENT MANAGEMENT & RESEARCH, INC.—Raymond James Financial, Inc.; *U.S. Public*, pg. 923
INVESTMENT NETWORK, INC.—St. Paul Bancorp, Inc.; *U.S. Public*, pg. 1428
INVESTORS' FINANCE CORP.—Citicorp; *U.S. Public*, pg. 379
ISTITUTO BANCARIO SAN PAOLO DI TORINO S.P.A.; *Int'l*, pg. 691
IVARAN SHIPPING A/S—A/S Ivaran Rederi; *Int'l*, pg. 696
RAYMOND JAMES & ASSOCIATES, INC.—Raymond James Financial, Inc.; *U.S. Public*, pg. 923
RAYMOND JAMES PARTNERS, INC.—Raymond James Financial, Inc.; *U.S. Public*, pg. 923
RAYMOND JAMES REALTY ADVISORS, INC.—Raymond James Financial, Inc.; *U.S. Public*, pg. 923
JANEWAY PROPERTIES, INC.—Edison Parking Properties, LLC; *U.S. Private*, pg. 364
JAPAN ASSOCIATED FINANCE CO., LTD.—The Nomura Securities Co., Ltd.; *Int'l*, pg. 955
JOHN HANCOCK LEASING CORPORATION—John Hancock Mutual Life Insurance Company; *U.S. Private*, pg. 590
JOHNSON & JOHNSON FINANCE CORPORATION—Johnson & Johnson; *U.S. Public*, pg. 928
AXEL JOHNSON CREDIT AB—Axel Johnson AB; *Int'l*, pg. 708
EDWARD JONES; *U.S. Private*, pg. 597
KNP FINANCIERINGEN B.V.—N.V. Koninklijke KNP BT; *Int'l*, pg. 756
KLEINWORT BENSON CROSS FINANCING INCORPORATED—Dresdner Bank AG; *Int'l*, pg. 420
KLEINWORT BENSON DEUTSCHLAND GMBH—Dresdner Bank AG; *Int'l*, pg. 420
KLEINWORT BENSON IBERFOMENTO FUNCIONES & ADQUICISIONES S.A.—Dresdner Bank AG; *Int'l*, pg. 420
KOBE STEEL INTERNATIONAL (USA) INC.—Kobe Steel, Ltd.; *Int'l*, pg. 740
KOHAP-NEW YORK LIFE INSURANCE LTD.—KOHAP Group; *Int'l*, pg. 742
KOREA ORIX LEASE AND FINANCE LIMITED—Orix Corporation; *Int'l*, pg. 1009
KVAERNER INVEST A.S.—Kvaerner a.s.a.; *Int'l*, pg. 769
THE KYOEI LIFE INVESTMENT JERSEY CO., LTD.—The Kyoei Life Insurance Co., Ltd.; *Int'l*, pg. 777
KYOEI LIFE INVESTMENT LUXEMBOURG S/A—The Kyoei Life Insurance Co., Ltd.; *Int'l*, pg. 777
THE KYOEI-SEIMEI INVESTMENT CAYMAN CO., LTD.—The Kyoei Life Insurance Co., Ltd.; *Int'l*, pg. 777
AB LM ERICSSON FINANS—Telefonaktiebolaget LM Ericsson; *Int'l*, pg. 1364
LAMIC NV—Internatio-Muller N.V.; *Int'l*, pg. 682
LAMIFORMA S.A. DE C.V.—Henkel KGaA; *Int'l*, pg. 614
LANKA ORIX LEASING COMPANY LIMITED—Orix Corporation; *Int'l*, pg. 1009
LAURENTIAN BANK OF CANADA—Desjardins-Laurentian Financial Corporation; *Int'l*, pg. 396
LAURENTIAN FINANCIAL SERVICES—Desjardins-Laurentian Financial Corporation; *Int'l*, pg. 396
LEASING ANDINO S.A.—Orix Corporation; *Int'l*, pg. 1009
LEASING SOLUTIONS RECEIVABLES, INC.—Leasing Solutions, Inc.; *U.S. Public*, pg. 983
LEGACY MARKETING GROUP; *U.S. Private*, pg. 658
LEGAL & GENERAL FINANCE PLC—Legal & General Group PLC; *Int'l*, pg. 805
LEGAL & GENERAL FINANCIAL SERVICES LIMITED—Legal & General Group PLC; *Int'l*, pg. 805
LIBERTY FINANCIAL SERVICES—Banc One Corporation; *U.S. Public*, pg. 173
LINCOLN NATIONAL REALTY CORPORATION—Lincoln National Corporation; *U.S. Public*, pg. 998
LLOYDS BANK EXPORT FINANCE LTD.—Lloyds TSB Group PLC; *Int'l*, pg. 813
LLOYDS BANK FINANCE (ISLE OF MAN) LTD.—Lloyds TSB Group PLC; *Int'l*, pg. 813
LOCAPOR - COMPANHIA PORTUGUESA LOCACAO FINANCERIA MOBILIARIA, SA—Caixa Geral de Depositos; *Int'l*, pg. 250
LONHRO FINANCE PLC—Lonrho plc; *Int'l*, pg. 817
M & H FINANCIAL CORP.—Fleming Companies, Inc.; *U.S. Public*, pg. 653
M & I BROKERAGE SERVICES, INC.—Marshall & Ilsley Corporation; *U.S. Public*, pg. 1050
M & I VENTURES CORPORATION—Marshall & Ilsley Corporation; *U.S. Public*, pg. 1051
MBNA CONSUMER SERVICES, INC.—MBNA Corporation; *U.S. Public*, pg. 1023
MBT FINANCE INC.—Viag AG; *Int'l*, pg. 1465
MCI ACCEPTANCE CORP.—Consorcio G. Grupo Dina, S.A. de C.V.; *Int'l*, pg. 326
MAATSCHAPPIJ TOT FINANCIERING VAN BEDRIJFSPANDEN N.V.—ABN-AMRO Holding N.V.; *Int'l*, pg. 9
MACHINERY ACCEPTANCE CORPORATION—Stewart & Stevenson Services, Inc.; *U.S. Public*, pg. 1517
MACKAY-SHIELDS FINANCIAL CORP.—New York Life Insurance Company; *U.S. Private*, pg. 795
MAHCO, INC.—Mason & Hanger Corporation, Inc.; *U.S. Private*, pg. 711
MANULIFE FINANCIAL SYSTEMS (HONG KONG) LIMITED—Manulife Financial (The Manufacturers Life Insurance Company); *Int'l*, pg. 841
MARINE MIDLAND LEASING CORPORATION—HSBC Holdings plc; *Int'l*, pg. 581
MARKS & SPENCER FINANCE INC.—Marks & Spencer PLC; *Int'l*, pg. 843
MARKS & SPENCER FINANCE PLC—Marks & Spencer PLC; *Int'l*, pg. 842
MARKS & SPENCER PLC; *Int'l*, pg. 842
MARSHALL & ILSLEY CORPORATION; *U.S. Public*, pg. 1049
MEES & HOPE FINANZGESELLSCHAFT AG—ABN-AMRO Holding N.V.; *Int'l*, pg. 12
MELLON FINANCIAL SERVICES—Mellon Bank Corporation; *U.S. Public*, pg. 1085
MERCEDES-BENZ LEASING GMBH—Daimler-Benz Aktiengesellschaft; *Int'l*, pg. 368
MERIDIAN TECHNOLOGY LEASING SERVICES; *U.S. Private*, pg. 732
MERRILL LYNCH INSURANCE GROUP, INC.—Merrill Lynch & Co., Inc.; *U.S. Public*, pg. 1098
METALLGESELLSCHAFT EMERGING MARKETS, INC.—Metallgesellschaft AG; *Int'l*, pg. 862
METLIFE SECURITIES, INC.—Metropolitan Life Insurance Co.; *U.S. Private*, pg. 738
MID-AMERICA LEASING CORP.—Banc One Corporation; *U.S. Public*, pg. 175
MIZUNO FINANCE NETHERLANDS B.V.—Mizuno Corporation; *Int'l*, pg. 885
MONAVAL FINANZ AG—ABN-AMRO Holding N.V.; *Int'l*, pg. 12
MONSANTO FINANCE AG—Monsanto Company; *U.S. Public*, pg. 1125
MONSANTO GMBH—Monsanto Company; *U.S. Public*, pg. 1125
MONTREAL TRUSTCO-FINANCIAL OPERATIONS & CONTROL DIV.—The Bank of Nova Scotia; *Int'l*, pg. 155
J.P. MORGAN CANADA—J.P. Morgan Co. Incorporated; *U.S. Public*, pg. 1130
J.P. MORGAN CO. INCORPORATED; *U.S. Public*, pg. 1129
MORGAN STANLEY CAPITAL SERVICES INC.—Morgan Stanley Dean Witter & Co.; *U.S. Public*, pg. 1132
MULTI-CREDIT CORPORATION OF THAILAND LTD.—The Daiwa Bank Limited; *Int'l*, pg. 374
NBD LEASING, INC.—First Chicago NBD Corporation; *U.S. Public*, pg. 628
NCC FINANS—NCC AB; *Int'l*, pg. 899
NEC INDUSTRIES, INC.—NEC Corporation; *Int'l*, pg. 900
NANTO CREDIT GUARANTEE CO., LTD.—The Nanto Bank, Ltd.; *Int'l*, pg. 905
NATIONAL COMPUTER PRINT, INC.; *U.S. Private*, pg. 780
NATIONAL DATA CENTER—ING Groep N.V.; *Int'l*, pg. 648
NATIONALE BANK VOOR MIDDELLANG KREDIET N.V.—ABN-AMRO Holding N.V.; *Int'l*, pg. 9
NATIONALE MAATSCHAPPIJ VOOR VLIEGTUIGFINANCIERING B.V.—ABN-AMRO Holding N.V.; *Int'l*, pg. 9
NATIONALE TRUST MAATSCHAPPIJ (NEDERLANDSE ANTILLEN) N.V.—ABN-AMRO Holding N.V.; *Int'l*, pg. 10
NATIONALE TRUST MAATSCHAPPIJ N.V.—ABN-AMRO Holding N.V.; *Int'l*, pg. 9
NATIONSBANK REALTY SERVICES CORP.—NationsBank Corporation; *U.S. Public*, pg. 1164
NATIONSBANK SERVICES CORPORATION—NationsBank Corporation; *U.S. Public*, pg. 1164
NAVISTAR FINANCIAL CORPORATION—Navistar International Corporation; *U.S. Public*, pg. 1167
NEDERLANDSCHE TRUST-MAATSCHAPPIJ B.V.—ABN-AMRO Holding N.V.; *Int'l*, pg. 9
NESTLE CAPITAL CORPORATION—Nestle S.A.; *Int'l*, pg. 916
NETWORK SYSTEMS CREDIT CORP.—Storage Technology Corporation; *U.S. Public*, pg. 1522
NEW YORK CITY OFF-TRACK BETTING CORP.; *U.S. Private*, pg. 794
NEW YORK LIFE INSURANCE COMPANY; *U.S. Private*, pg. 794
NISSAY CREDIT CO., LTD.—Nippon Life Insurance Co.; *Int'l*, pg. 935
NOKIA FINANCE INTERNATIONAL B.V., GENEVA BRANCH—Oy Nokia Ab/Nokia Group; *Int'l*, pg. 954
NOMURA CAPITAL SERVICES, INC.—The Nomura Securities Co., Ltd.; *Int'l*, pg. 956
NOMURA FINANCE CO., LTD.—The Nomura Securities Co., Ltd.; *Int'l*, pg. 955
NOMURA OPTION INTERNATIONAL PLC—The Nomura Securities Co., Ltd.; *Int'l*, pg. 957
NOROESTE CHEMICAL S.A. ARRENDAMENTO MERCANTIL NORCHEM—The Chase Manhattan Corporation; *U.S. Public*, pg. 341
NORSTAN FINANCIAL SERVICES, INC.—Norstan, Inc.; *U.S. Public*, pg. 1192
NORSTAN, INC.; *U.S. Public*, pg. 1192
NORTHERN TELECOM FINANCE CORPORATION—Northern Telecom Limited; *Int'l*, pg. 969
NORTHERN TELECOM INTERNATIONAL FINANCE B.V.—Northern Telecom Limited; *Int'l*, pg. 970
NORWEST AGRICULTURAL CREDIT, INC.—Norwest Corporation; *U.S. Public*, pg. 1201
NORWEST ASIA LIMITED—Norwest Corporation; *U.S. Public*, pg. 1203
NORWEST FINANCIAL BUSINESS CREDIT, INC.—Norwest Corporation; *U.S. Public*, pg. 1202
NORWEST FINANCIAL COAST, INC.—Norwest Corporation; *U.S. Public*, pg. 1202
NORWEST FINANCIAL, INC.—Norwest Corporation; *U.S. Public*, pg. 1202
NORWEST FINANCIAL LEASING, INC.—Norwest Corporation; *U.S. Public*, pg. 1202
OCE-CREDIT CORPORATION—Oce-van der Grinten N.V.; *Int'l*, pg. 994
OCE HOLDING USA—Oce-van der Grinten N.V.; *Int'l*, pg. 994
OAKWOOD ACCEPTANCE CORP.—Oakwood Homes Corporation; *U.S. Public*, pg. 1209
OCASCO BUDGET, INC.—Ohio Casualty Corporation; *U.S. Public*, pg. 1214
OCCIDENTAL INTERNATIONAL FINANCE N.V.—Occidental Petroleum Corporation; *U.S. Public*, pg. 1210
OCCIDENTAL OVERSEAS FINANCE N.V.—Occidental Petroleum Corporation; *U.S. Public*, pg. 1210
OFFSHORE EQUITIES, INC.—The Chase Manhattan Corporation; *U.S. Public*, pg. 338
ORIX AUSTRALIA CORPORATION LIMITED—Orix Corporation; *Int'l*, pg. 1009
ORIX AVIATION SYSTEMS LIMITED—Orix Corporation; *Int'l*, pg. 1009
ORIX COMMERCIAL ALLIANCE CORPORATION—Orix Corporation; *Int'l*, pg. 1009
P.T. ORIX INDONESIA FINANCE—Orix Corporation; *Int'l*, pg. 1009
ORIX LEASING PAKISTAN LIMITED—Orix Corporation; *Int'l*, pg. 1010
ORIX LEASING SINGAPORE LIMITED—Orix Corporation; *Int'l*, pg. 1010
ORIX NEW ZEALAND (NZ) LIMITED—Orix Corporation; *Int'l*, pg. 1010
ORIX USA CORPORATION-LOS ANGELES—Orix Corporation; *Int'l*, pg. 1009
ORIX USA CORPORATION-NEW YORK—Orix Corporation; *Int'l*, pg. 1009
ORIX USA CORPORATION-SAN FRANCISCO—Orix Corporation; *Int'l*, pg. 1009
PLM FINANCIAL SERVICES, INC.—PLM International, Inc.; *U.S. Public*, pg. 1241
PMC CAPITAL INC.; *U.S. Public*, pg. 1242
PNC COMMERCIAL CORPORATION—PNC Bank Corp.; *U.S. Public*, pg. 1243
PNC INTERNATIONAL FINANCE, N.V.—PNC Bank Corp.; *U.S. Public*, pg. 1243
PNC LEASING CORP.—PNC Bank Corp.; *U.S. Public*, pg. 1243
PNC NATIONAL INVESTMENT CORPORATION—PNC Bank Corp.; *U.S. Public*, pg. 1243
PACCAR FINANCIAL LIMITED—Paccar Inc.; *U.S. Public*, pg. 1247
PACCAR FINANCIAL PTY, LTD.—Paccar Inc.; *U.S. Public*, pg. 1247
PACCAR FINANCIAL SERVICES LTD.—Paccar Inc.; *U.S. Public*, pg. 1247
PACCOM LEASING CORPORATION—PacifiCorp; *U.S. Public*, pg. 1252
PACIFICORP; *U.S. Public*, pg. 1251
PACIFICORP AVIATION (HOLDINGS), INC.—PacifiCorp; *U.S. Public*, pg. 1252
PACIFICORP CREDIT, INC.—PacifiCorp; *U.S. Public*, pg. 1252
PACIFICORP FINANCIAL SERVICES, INC.—PacifiCorp; *U.S. Public*, pg. 1252
PAINEWEBBER CAPITAL INC.—PaineWebber Group Incorporated; *U.S. Public*, pg. 1252
PAINEWEBBER PROPERTIES INCORPORATED—PaineWebber Group Incorporated; *U.S. Public*, pg. 1253
PANMURE GORDON & CO. LTD.—NationsBank Corporation; *U.S. Public*, pg. 1166
PARACORE COMPANY; *U.S. Private*, pg. 838
PARIBAS ASSET MANAGEMENT S.A.—Compagnie Financiere de Paribas; *Int'l*, pg. 321
PARIBAS FINANZIARIA SPA—Compagnie Financiere de Paribas; *Int'l*, pg. 321
PARIBAS SUISSE (BAHAMAS) LTD.—Compagnie Financiere de Paribas; *Int'l*, pg. 321
PARKLABREA FINANCE CORP.—Forest City Enterprises, Inc.; *U.S. Public*, pg. 669
PATIENCE REALTY CORPORATION—Providence Energy Corporation; *U.S. Public*, pg. 1337
PECHINEY BALE—Pechiney S.A.; *Int'l*, pg. 1031
P.T. PERJAHL LEASING INDONESIA—The Sakura Bank, Limited; *Int'l*, pg. 1181
PHILIP MORRIS CAPITAL CORPORATION—Philip Morris Companies Inc.; *U.S. Public*, pg. 1289
THE PHILIPPINE AMERICAN ACCIDENT INSURANCE CO., INC.—American International Group, Inc.; *U.S. Public*, pg. 85

THE PHILIPPINE AMERICAN MANAGEMENT & FINANCING CO., INC.—American International Group, Inc.; *U.S. Public*, pg. 85
PIERSON, HELDRING & PIERSON (CURACAO) N.V.—ABN-AMRO Holding N.V.; *Int'l*, pg. 10
PITNEY BOWES FINANCIAL SERVICES—Pitney Bowes Inc.; *U.S. Public*, pg. 1303
PITNEY BOWES INC.; *U.S. Public*, pg. 1303
PITNEY BOWES REAL ESTATE FINANCING CORPORATION—Pitney Bowes Inc.; *U.S. Public*, pg. 1303
PLANNING CORPORATION OF AMERICA—Raymond James Financial, Inc.; *U.S. Public*, pg. 923
POTHONIER SINGAPORE PTE LTD.—Singapore Land Limited; *Int'l*, pg. 1253
PREBETONG IBIZA S.A.—Lafarge S.A.; *Int'l*, pg. 790
PRESLEY RAC FINANCE CO., INC.—Pacific Enterprises; *U.S. Public*, pg. 1249
PRIMERICA BANK—Travelers Group; *U.S. Public*, pg. 1633
PROGRESSIVE CORP., FINANCIAL SERVICES DIV.—The Progressive Corporation; *U.S. Public*, pg. 1334
PRUDENTIAL AGRICULTURAL CREDIT, INC.—The Prudential Insurance Company of America; *U.S. Private*, pg. 892
PRUDENTIAL DEFINED CONTRIBUTION SERVICES—The Prudential Insurance Company of America; *U.S. Private*, pg. 892
RJ CREDIT PARTNERS—Raymond James Financial, Inc.; *U.S. Public*, pg. 923
RJ LEASING, INC.—Raymond James Financial, Inc.; *U.S. Public*, pg. 923
RJ PROPERTIES, INC.—Raymond James Financial, Inc.; *U.S. Public*, pg. 923
RJ REALTY, INC.—Raymond James Financial, Inc.; *U.S. Public*, pg. 923
RMA - LAND DEVELOPMENT PRIVATE LTD.—Singapore Land Limited; *Int'l*, pg. 1253
RALSTON PURINA OVERSEAS FINANCE N.V.—Ralston Purina Company; *U.S. Public*, pg. 1360
RANK ORLANDO, INC.—The Rank Group PLC; *Int'l*, pg. 1087
REDLAND FINANCE INC.—Redland PLC; *Int'l*, pg. 1091
REPUBLIC NEW YORK CORPORATION; *U.S. Public*, pg. 1380
REPUBLIC NEW YORK INVESTMENT CORP.—Republic New York Corporation; *U.S. Public*, pg. 1380
RESOURCE MONITORS, INC.—Providence Energy Corporation; *U.S. Public*, pg. 1337
THE REYNOLDS AND REYNOLDS COMPANY; *U.S. Public*, pg. 1384
ROHR CREDIT CORPORATION—The B.F. Goodrich Company; *U.S. Public*, pg. 751
THE ROUSE CO. FINANCIAL SERVICES, INC.—The Rouse Company; *U.S. Public*, pg. 1407
ROYAL BANK EXPORT FINANCE CO. LTD. (REFCO)—Royal Bank of Canada; *Int'l*, pg. 1131
ROYAL PREMIUM BUDGET, INC.—H.W. Kaufman Financial Group, Inc.; *U.S. Private*, pg. 609
ROYNAT—The Bank of Nova Scotia; *Int'l*, pg. 155
S-BETEILIGUNGSGESELLSCHAFT HESSEN- THURINGEN MBH—Landesbank Hessen-Thuringen Girozentrale; *Int'l*, *pg. 799*
S.L. BUILDING INVESTMENTS PTE LIMITED—Singapore Land Limited; *Int'l*, pg. 1253
S.L. CIVIC INVESTMENTS PTE LIMITED—Singapore Land Limited; *Int'l*, pg. 1253
S.L. EARN INVESTMENTS PTE LIMITED—Singapore Land Limited; *Int'l*, pg. 1253
S.L. HOME LOANS PTE LTD.—Singapore Land Limited; *Int'l*, pg. 1253
S.L. MANAGEMENT SERVICES PTE LIMITED—Singapore Land Limited; *Int'l*, pg. 1253
S.L. MARINA CENTRE DEVELOPMENT PRIVATE LIMITED—Singapore Land Limited; *Int'l*, pg. 1253
S.L. PRIME SECURITIES PTE LTD.—Singapore Land Limited; *Int'l*, pg. 1253
S.L. PROPERTIES LIMITED—Singapore Land Limited; *Int'l*, *pg. 1253*
S.L. REALTY SERVICES PTE LIMITED—Singapore Land Limited; *Int'l*, pg. 1253
SAS FINANCIAL SERVICES—Scandinavian Airlines System (SAS); *Int'l*, pg. 1201
SBC-ASSET MANAGEMENT INC.—SBC Communications Inc.; *U.S. Public*, pg. 1416
SBC WARBURG GROUP PLC—Swiss Bank Corporation; *Int'l*, pg. 1330
SKF TREASURY CENTRE—AB SKF; *Int'l*, pg. 1157
S.L. PRIME PROPERTIES PTE. LTD.—Singapore Land Limited; *Int'l*, pg. 1253
S.L. PRIME REALTY PTE. LTD.—Singapore Land Limited; *Int'l*, pg. 1253
SNET DIVERSIFIED GROUP, INC.—Southern New England Telecommunications Corporation; *U.S. Public*, pg. 1491
SOFITEC, SOCIETE FINANCIERE ET TECHNIQUE SA—Philipp Holzmann AG; *Int'l*, pg. 634
SAFECO CORPORATION; *U.S. Public*, pg. 1423
SAFECO CREDIT COMPANY, INC.—SAFECO Corporation; *U.S. Public*, pg. 1423
SAFECO PROPERTIES, INC.—SAFECO Corporation; *U.S. Public*, pg. 1423
ST. MICHAEL FINANCE LIMITED—Marks & Spencer PLC; *Int'l*, pg. 843
SAKURA FINANZ (DEUTSCHLAND) GMBH—The Sakura Bank, Limited; *Int'l*, pg. 1180
SANDOZ FINANCE N.V.—Novartis AG; *Int'l*, pg. 984
SANDOZ FINANCE SERVICES LTD.—Novartis AG; *Int'l*, pg. 984
SANDOZ NUTRITION FINANCE LTD.—Novartis AG; *Int'l*, pg. 985
SANDOZ OVERSEAS FINANCE LTD.—Novartis AG; *Int'l*, pg. 985
SANDOZ OVERSEAS N.V.—Novartis AG; *Int'l*, pg. 985
SANWA-DSP CREDIT LIMITED—The Sanwa Bank Limited; *Int'l*, pg. 1190
SANWA INTERNATIONAL FINANCE LIMITED—The Sanwa Bank Limited; *Int'l*, pg. 1190
SANYO ELECTRIC CREDIT CO. LTD.—Sanyo Electric Co., Ltd.; *Int'l*, pg. 1191
SAPAC CORP., LTD.—Roche Holding Ltd.; *Int'l*, pg. 1122
SAVIN CREDIT CORPORATION—Ricoh Company, Ltd.; *Int'l*, pg. 1114
SCANDINAVIAN AIRLINES SYSTEM (SAS); *Int'l*, pg. 1201
SECURITY GROUP INC.; *U.S. Private*, pg. 981
SECURITY PACIFIC EUROFINANCE, INC.—BankAmerica Corporation; *U.S. Public*, pg. 183
SECURITY PACIFIC HOUSING SERVICES, INC.—BankAmerica Corporation; *U.S. Public*, pg. 182
SECURITY PACIFIC INTERNATIONAL FINANCE, INC.—BankAmerica Corporation; *U.S. Public*, pg. 182
SECURITY PACIFIC SERVICES CORPORATION—BankAmerica Corporation; *U.S. Public*, pg. 182
SELMABIPIEMME LEASING SPA—Banca Popolare di Milano; *Int'l*, pg. 137
SENCORP; *U.S. Private*, pg. 983
SERVICE CORPORATION INTERNATIONAL; *U.S. Public*, pg. 1460
SHENTON HOLDINGS PRIVATE LIMITED—Singapore Land Limited; *Int'l*, pg. 1253
THE SIAM SANWA INDUSTRIAL CREDIT CO., LTD.—The Sanwa Bank Limited; *Int'l*, pg. 1190
A.O. SMITH CORPORATION; *U.S. Public*, pg. 1476
SOCIETE FONCIERE ET FINANCIERE DE LA VILLE-L'EVEGUE—Compagnie de Suez; *Int'l*, pg. 313
SOFIAS—Allianz Aktiengesellschaft; *Int'l*, pg. 62
SOGES-FIDUCEM S.A.—Bank Brussels Lambert; *Int'l*, pg. 147
SOTHEBY'S HOLDINGS INC.; *U.S. Public*, pg. 1487
SOUTH PACIFIC MERCHANT FINANCE LTD.—Lloyds TSB Group PLC; *Int'l*, pg. 814
SOUTHWESTERN FINANCIAL CORP.—Texas Industries, Inc.; *U.S. Public*, pg. 1585
SPIEGEL ACCEPTANCE CORPORATION—Spiegel, Inc.; *U.S. Public*, pg. 1499
SPONSOR'S PLAN ASSET MANAGEMENT, INC.—Lukens Inc.; *U.S. Public*, pg. 1020
STADTSPARKASSE MUNCHEN; *Int'l*, pg. 1293
STANDARD CHARTERED BANK (NEW YORK)—Standard Chartered Bank PLC; *Int'l*, pg. 1294
STANDARD CHARTERED FINANCE LIMITED—Standard Chartered Bank PLC; *Int'l*, pg. 1297
STANDARD CHARTERED FINANCE UGANDA LIMITED—Standard Chartered Bank PLC; *Int'l*, pg. 1297
STAPLE COTTON COOPERATIVE ASSOCIATION; *U.S. Private*, pg. 1033
STAPLE COTTON DISCOUNT CORPORATION—Staple Cotton Cooperative Association; *U.S. Private*, pg. 1033
STATIM FINANCE LIMITED—Franz Haniel & Cie, GmbH; *Int'l*, pg. 591
SUBARU CREDIT CORPORATION—Fuji Heavy Industries, Ltd.; *Int'l*, pg. 523
SUMMIT BANCORP; *U.S. Public*, pg. 1527
SUN COMPANY, INC.; *U.S. Public*, pg. 1530
SUN DATA INC.; *U.S. Private*, pg. 1050
T&W FINANCIAL CORPORATION; *U.S. Public*, pg. 1552
TCF FINANCIAL CORP.; *U.S. Public*, pg. 1554
TCV, INC.—Conrail, Inc.; *U.S. Public*, pg. 432
TSB HILL SAMUEL BANK HOLDING CO PLC—Lloyds TSB Group PLC; *Int'l*, pg. 813
TAKUGIN FINANCE INTERNATIONAL LTD.—The Hokkaido Takushoku Bank, Ltd.; *Int'l*, pg. 627
TATE & LYLE INTERNATIONAL FINANCE LIMITED—Tate & Lyle PLC; *Int'l*, pg. 1356
TAYLOR CAPITAL GROUP; *U.S. Private*, pg. 1070
TECO FINANCE, INC.—TECO Energy, Inc.; *U.S. Public*, pg. 1565
TEDDINGTON COMPANY LIMITED—Corning Incorporated; *U.S. Public*, pg. 449
TELEFONICA INTERNACIONAL DE ESPANA S.A.—Telefonica de Espana, S.A.; *Int'l*, pg. 1372
TELMARK, INC.—Agway, Inc.; *U.S. Private*, pg. 27
TEMPLE-INLAND INC.; *U.S. Public*, pg. 1574
TENNECO AVIATION LIMITED—Tenneco Inc.; *U.S. Public*, pg. 1580
TENNECO CREDIT CORP.—Tenneco Inc.; *U.S. Public*, pg. 1578
TENNECO FINANCIAL SERVICES, INC.—Tenneco Inc.; *U.S. Public*, pg. 1578
TENNECO INTERNATIONAL FINANCE LIMITED—Tenneco Inc.; *U.S. Public*, pg. 1580
TENNECO OCEAN METALS DEVELOPMENT CORP.—Tenneco Inc.; *U.S. Public*, pg. 1578
TENNECO PHOSPHATE, INC.—Tenneco Inc.; *U.S. Public*, pg. 1578
TENNECO SUDAN, INC.—Tenneco Inc.; *U.S. Public*, pg. 1578
TENNESSEE ARGENTINA, S.A.—Tenneco Inc.; *U.S. Public*, pg. 1578
TEXTRON FINANCIAL CORPORATION—Textron Inc.; *U.S. Public*, pg. 1590
THAI FUJI FINANCE AND SECURITIES COMPANY LTD.—The Fuji Bank, Limited; *Int'l*, pg. 521
ROBERT THOMAS SECURITIES, INC.—Raymond James Financial, Inc.; *U.S. Public*, pg. 923
THOMSON FINANCE LTD.—The Thomson Corporation; *U.S. Public*, pg. 1601
THOMSON FINANCIAL SERVICES—The Thomson Corporation; *U.S. Public*, pg. 1601
TIANJIN INTERNATIONAL LEASING CO., LTD.—The Sakura Bank, Limited; *Int'l*, pg. 1181
TOKYO-MITSUBISHI INTERNATIONAL (HK) LTD.—The Bank of Tokyo-Mitsubishi, Ltd.; *Int'l*, pg. 158
TOWN & COUNTRY BANK LTD.—Australia & New Zealand Banking Group Limited; *Int'l*, pg. 98
TOYOTA FINANCE AUSTRALIA LTD.—Toyota Motor Corporation; *Int'l*, pg. 1414
TRANS LEASING INTERNATIONAL INC.; *U.S. Public*, pg. 1628
TRANSAMERICA COMMERCIAL FINANCE CORP., INC.—Transamerica Corporation; *U.S. Public*, pg. 1630
TRANSPORTATION DIVISION—Ford Motor Company; *U.S. Public*, pg. 663
TRI-MASS., INC.—Tootsie Roll Industries, Inc.; *U.S. Public*, pg. 1621
TRIARCH CORPORATION LTD.—CoreStates Financial Corp.; *U.S. Public*, pg. 447
USX CREDIT—USX Corporation; *U.S. Public*, pg. 1661
UEBERSEEBANK AG—American International Group, Inc.; *U.S. Public*, pg. 85
UNION BANK OF CALIFORNIA—The Bank of Tokyo-Mitsubishi, Ltd.; *Int'l*, pg. 157
UNITED DOMINION INDUSTRIES, LTD.; *U.S. Public*, pg. 1675
UNITED ENERGY INTERNATIONAL, INC.—United Illuminating Company; *U.S. Public*, pg. 1678
UNITED FINANCIAL SERVICES, INC.—AEGON N.V.; *Int'l*, pg. 27
UNITED JERSEY LEASING COMPANY—Summit Bancorp; *U.S. Public*, pg. 1528
UNITED JERSEY VENTURE CAPITAL, INC.—Summit Bancorp; *U.S. Public*, pg. 1528
UNITED ORIX LEASING BERHAD—Orix Corporation; *Int'l*, pg. 1010
U.S. BANCORP LEASING & FINANCIAL—U.S. Bancorp; *U.S. Public*, pg. 1681
U S WEST INC.; *U.S. Public*, pg. 1688
UNIVERSAL STUDIOS NEW VENTURES, INC.—The Seagram Company Ltd.; *Int'l*, pg. 1216
UTILITY FINANCIAL CORP.—Southwest Gas Corporation; *U.S. Public*, pg. 1493
V.A.G. FINANCE LTD.—Lonrho plc; *Int'l*, pg. 817
VW FINANZ GMBH—Volkswagen AG; *Int'l*, pg. 1474
VALMONT FINANCIAL CORPORATION—Chancellor Corporation; *U.S. Public*, pg. 335
VOLKSWAGEN BANK GMBH—Volkswagen AG; *Int'l*, pg. 1474
VOLKSWAGEN INTL. FINANCE N.V.—Volkswagen AG; *Int'l*, pg. 1475
VOLKSWAGEN OVERSEAS FINANCE N.V.—Volkswagen AG; *Int'l*, pg. 1475
WTC INSURANCE CORP, LTD.—International Business Machines Corporation; *U.S. Public*, pg. 898
WAL-MART PROPERTIES, INC.—Wal-Mart Stores, Inc.; *U.S. Public*, pg. 1733
WELLINGTON TRUST COMPANY—BCE Inc.; *Int'l*, pg. 115
WESTDEUTSCHE LANDESBANK-BRUSSELS BRANCH—Westdeutsche Landesbank Girozentrale; *Int'l*, pg. 1493
WESTERN FARM CREDIT BANK—Federal Farm Credit Banks Funding Corporation; *U.S. Private*, pg. 398
WEYERHAEUSER FINANCIAL SERVICES, INC.—Weyerhaeuser Company; *U.S. Public*, pg. 1764
WHIRLPOOL FINANCIAL CORP.—Whirlpool Corporation; *U.S. Public*, pg. 1765
WILLIAMS SCOTSMAN GROUP, INC.—Scotsman Holding Inc.; *U.S. Private*, pg. 977
WINKELMAN STORES CREDIT CORP.—Petrie Retail, Inc.; *U.S. Private*, pg. 858
WINTZ COMPANIES; *U.S. Private*, pg. 1184
WORLD ACCEPTANCE CORPORATION; *U.S. Public*, pg. 1778
XEROX CANADA HOLDINGS INC.—Xerox Corporation; *U.S. Public*, pg. 1785
XEROX CREDIT CORPORATE FINANCE DIV.—Xerox Corporation; *U.S. Public*, pg. 1785
XEROX CREDIT CORPORATION—Xerox Corporation; *U.S. Public*, pg. 1785
XEROX INSTALLMENT SALES DIV.—Xerox Corporation; *U.S. Public*, pg. 1785
YAMAICHI FINANCE CO., LTD.—Yamaichi Securities Co., Ltd.; *Int'l*, pg. 1516
THE YELLOW RIVER INTERNATIONAL LEASING CO., LTD.—The Dai-Ichi Kangyo Bank, Limited; *Int'l*, pg. 362
THE YUCAIPA COMPANIES; *U.S. Private*, pg. 1202
Z-SEVEN FUND, INC.; *U.S. Public*, pg. 1789
ZIEGLER COLLATERALIZED SECURITIES, INC.—The Ziegler Companies, Inc.; *U.S. Public*, pg. 1792
ZIONS BANCORPORATION; *U.S. Public*, pg. 1792
ZIONS CREDIT CORPORATION—Zions Bancorporation; *U.S. Public*, pg. 1793

6162 — MORTGAGE BANKERS & LOAN CORRESPONDENTS

AMEV HYPOTHEEKBEDRIJF—Fortis; *Int'l*, pg. 499
AAMES FINANCIAL CORPORATION; *U.S. Public*, pg. 12
ABBEY NATIONAL PLC; *Int'l*, pg. 19
ADVANTA MORTGAGE CORP. USA—Advanta Corp.; *U.S. Public*, pg. 22
H.F. AHMANSON & CO.; *U.S. Public*, pg. 29
AHMANSON MORTGAGE COMPANY—H.F. Ahmanson & Co.; *U.S. Public*, pg. 29
AMERICAN GENERAL CORPORATION; *U.S. Public*, pg. 76
AMERISTAR FINANCIAL CORPORATION—Lennar Corporation; *U.S. Public*, pg. 987
AMPLICON, INC.; *U.S. Public*, pg. 104
AMREP FINANCIAL CORPORATION—AMREP Corporation; *U.S. Public*, pg. 105
AMRESCO, INC.—Cravey, Green & Wahlen, Incorporated; *U.S. Private*, pg. 287
AMWEST INSURANCE GROUP, INC.; *U.S. Public*, pg. 106
AMWEST SURETY INSURANCE COMPANY—Amwest Insurance Group, Inc.; *U.S. Public*, pg. 106
ASAHI BANK LOAN BUSINESS CO., LTD.—The Asahi Bank, Ltd.; *Int'l*, pg. 82
ASAHI BANK PROPERTY CO., LTD.—The Asahi Bank, Ltd.; *Int'l*, pg. 82
ASSOCIATED COMMERCIAL MORTGAGE, INC.—Associated Banc-Corp; *U.S. Public*, pg. 140
ASSOCIATED MORTGAGE, INC.—Associated Banc-Corp; *U.S. Public*, pg. 140

ASSOCIATES FIRST CAPITAL CORPORATION—Ford Motor Company; U.S. Public, pg. 662
ASSOCIATES NATIONAL MORTGAGE CORPORATION—Ford Motor Company; U.S. Public, pg. 663
ASSOCIATES REAL ESTATE FINANCIAL SERVICES COMPANY, INC.—Ford Motor Company; U.S. Public, pg. 663
AUTOMAX FINANCE—Firstbank Puerto Rico; U.S. Public, pg. 644
BA MORTGAGE & INTERNATIONAL REALTY CORP.—BankAmerica Corporation; U.S. Public, pg. 180
BB&T OF SOUTH CAROLINA—BB&T Corporation; U.S. Public, pg. 160
BHW BAUSPARKASSE AG; Int'l, pg. 120
BANC ONE CORPORATION; U.S. Public, pg. 172
BANC ONE MORTGAGE CORPORATION—Banc One Corporation; U.S. Public, pg. 175
BANCBOSTON REAL ESTATE CAPITOL CORPORATION—BankBoston Corporation; U.S. Public, pg. 184
BANK ONE, MORTGAGE COMPANY—Banc One Corporation; U.S. Public, pg. 174
BANKAMERICA SUTTER MORTGAGE CORPORATION—BankAmerica Corporation; U.S. Public, pg. 181
BANKNORTH MORTGAGE COMPANY—Banknorth Group Inc.; U.S. Public, pg. 187
BARCLAYS AMERICAN/MORTGAGE CORP.—Barclays Bank PLC; Int'l, pg. 165
BARNETT MORTGAGE COMPANY—NationsBank Corporation; U.S. Public, pg. 1162
BEAR STEARNS MORTGAGE CAPITAL CORPORATION—The Bear Stearns Companies Inc.; U.S. Public, pg. 198
BENEFICIAL CORPORATION; U.S. Public, pg. 211
BLUE RIDGE FINANCE CO., INC.—Carolina First Corporation; U.S. Public, pg. 306
BOATMEN'S MORTGAGE COMPANY—NationsBank Corporation; U.S. Public, pg. 1164
BOATMEN'S NATIONAL MORTGAGE INC.—NationsBank Corporation; U.S. Public, pg. 1165
BRENTON BANKS, INC.; U.S. Public, pg. 251
BRISTOL & WEST BUILDING SOCIETY; Int'l, pg. 216
CFX MORTGAGE, INC.—CFX Bank; U.S. Public, pg. 278
CIBC MORTGAGE CORPORATION—Canadian Imperial Bank of Commerce; Int'l, pg. 256
CIBC MORTGAGES PLC—Canadian Imperial Bank of Commerce; Int'l, pg. 257
CRS FINANCIAL SERVICES, INC.—Reliance Group Holdings, Inc.; U.S. Public, pg. 1374
CTX MORTGAGE CO., INC.—Centex Corporation; U.S. Public, pg. 323
CAISSE HYPOTHECAIRE DU LUXEMBOURG—Banque Internationale a Luxembourg S.A.; Int'l, pg. 162
CARLSBERG FINANCIAL CORP.; U.S. Private, pg. 211
CAROLINA FIRST MORTGAGE COMPANY—Carolina First Corporation; U.S. Public, pg. 306
CENTEX CORPORATION; U.S. Public, pg. 322
CHAMPION REALTY, INC.—Oriole Homes Corp.; U.S. Public, pg. 1231
CHASE HOME MORTGAGE CORPORATION—The Chase Manhattan Corporation; U.S. Public, pg. 338
CITFED MORTGAGE CORPORATION OF AMERICA—CitFed Bancorp, Inc.; U.S. Public, pg. 376
CITICORP CREDIT—Citicorp; U.S. Public, pg. 378
CITITRUST (BAHAMAS) LTD.—Citicorp; U.S. Public, pg. 379
CITITRUST (CAYMAN) LTD.—Citicorp; U.S. Public, pg. 379
CITY TRUST BANKING CORP.—Citicorp; U.S. Public, pg. 379
CLAYTON HOMES, INC.; U.S. Public, pg. 382
COLLECTIVE MORTGAGE SERVICES, INC.—Summit Bancorp; U.S. Public, pg. 1528
COLONIAL COMMERCIAL CORP.; U.S. Public, pg. 400
COLONIAL MORTGAGE COMPANY—The Colonial BancGroup, Inc.; U.S. Public, pg. 400
COMMERCIAL FEDERAL BANK—Commercial Federal Corporation; U.S. Public, pg. 411
CONSOLIDATED ACCEPTANCE CORP., INC.—Green Tree Financial Corporation; U.S. Public, pg. 762
CONTINENTAL MORTGAGE AND EQUITY TRUST; U.S. Public, pg. 441
COUNTRYWIDE FUNDING CORPORATION—Countrywide Home Loans Inc.; U.S. Public, pg. 453
COUNTRYWIDE HOME LOANS INC.; U.S. Public, pg. 452
COUNTRYWIDE SERVICING EXCHANGE—Countrywide Home Loans Inc.; U.S. Public, pg. 453
CRESTAR MORTGAGE CORPORATION—Crestar Financial Corporation; U.S. Public, pg. 458
CROSSMANN COMMUNITIES, INC.; U.S. Public, pg. 461
D & N MORTGAGE CORPORATION—D & N Financial Corporation; U.S. Public, pg. 472
D.C. BRANCH OFFICE—U.S. Home Corporation; U.S. Public, pg. 1683
DCA FINANCIAL CORP.—Lennar Corporation; U.S. Public, pg. 988
DANAHER CORPORATION; U.S. Public, pg. 480
DELTA LIFE CORPORATION—American Mutual Life Holding Co.; U.S. Private, pg. 59
DEPOSIT GUARANTY MORTGAGE CO.—Deposit Guaranty Corp.; U.S. Public, pg. 501
DERBYSHIRE BUILDING SOCIETY; Int'l, pg. 394
DEUTSCHE HYPOTHEKENBANK (ACTIEN-GESELLSCHAFT)—BHF-BANK AG; Int'l, pg. 119
DUNGEY & ASSOCIATES—FirstCity Financial Corporation; U.S. Public, pg. 644
ENTRUST HOME FINANCING—Long Island Bancorp, Inc.; U.S. Public, pg. 1013
EUROPAISCHE HYPOTHEKENBANK DER DEUTSCHEN BANK—Deutsche Bank AG; Int'l, pg. 405
F.C. HEDGED MORTGAGE CO.—Forest City Enterprises, Inc.; U.S. Public, pg. 668
FAR WEST INSURANCE COMPANY—Amwest Insurance Group, Inc.; U.S. Public, pg. 106
FARM CREDIT COUNCIL SERVICES—Federal Farm Credit Banks Funding Corporation; U.S. Private, pg. 398
FIRST CHICAGO NBD CORPORATION; U.S. Public, pg. 627
FIRST FEDERAL FINANCE CORPORATION—Firstbank Puerto Rico; U.S. Public, pg. 644
FIRST HAWAIIAN CREDITCORP, INC.—First Hawaiian, Inc.; U.S. Public, pg. 635
FIRST NATIONAL MORTGAGE CORPORATION—Allied Irish Banks, p.l.c.; Int'l, pg. 64
FIRST NH MORTGAGE CORP.—Bank of Ireland; Int'l, pg. 153
FIRST OF AMERICA COMMUNITY DEVELOPMENT CORPORATION—First of America Bank Corporation; U.S. Public, pg. 637
FIRST UNION HOME EQUITY CORPORATION—First Union Corporation; U.S. Public, pg. 640
FIRST UNION MORTGAGE CORPORATION—First Union Corporation; U.S. Public, pg. 640
FIRST UNION NATIONAL BANK OF FLORIDA—First Union Corporation; U.S. Public, pg. 640
FIRST VIRGINIA MORTGAGE COMPANY—First Virginia Banks, Inc.; U.S. Public, pg. 642
FIRSTAR MORTGAGE CORPORATION—Firstar Corporation; U.S. Public, pg. 643
FLEET MORTGAGE GROUP, INC.—Fleet Financial Group, Inc.; U.S. Public, pg. 650
FLEET REAL ESTATE, INC.—Fleet Financial Group, Inc.; U.S. Public, pg. 650
FONCIERE CASAMADRID—Caja de Madrid Group; Int'l, pg. 252
FORT MYERS BRANCH OFFICE—U.S. Home Corporation; U.S. Public, pg. 1683
G.E. CAPITAL MORTGAGE SERVICES—General Electric Company; U.S. Public, pg. 712
GMAC MORTGAGE CORPORATION—General Motors Corporation; U.S. Public, pg. 720
GMAC MORTGAGE CORPORATION OF IOWA—General Motors Corporation; U.S. Public, pg. 720
GMAC MORTGAGE CORPORATION OF PENNSYLVANIA—General Motors Corporation; U.S. Public, pg. 720
GARVEY INDUSTRIES, INC.; U.S. Private, pg. 440
GENERAL ELECTRIC CAPITAL SERVICES, INC.—General Electric Company; U.S. Public, pg. 711
GLOBE MORTGAGE AMERICA, LLC.; U.S. Private, pg. 458
SHELDON GOOD & CO.; U.S. Private, pg. 463
GREEN TREE ACCEPTANCE, INC.—Green Tree Financial Corporation; U.S. Public, pg. 762
GREEN TREE CONSUMER DISCOUNT COMPANY—Green Tree Financial Corporation; U.S. Public, pg. 763
GREEN TREE CREDIT CORP.—Green Tree Financial Corporation; U.S. Public, pg. 763
GREEN TREE FINANCE CORP.-ONE—Green Tree Financial Corporation; U.S. Public, pg. 763
GREEN TREE FINANCIAL CORPORATION; U.S. Public, pg. 761
GRUBB & ELLIS COMPANY; U.S. Public, pg. 767
GUARANTY CORPORATION; U.S. Private, pg. 485
GULF STATE MORTGAGE, INC.—The Royal Bank of Scotland plc; Int'l, pg. 1133
HFC BANK PLC—Household International, Inc.; U.S. Public, pg. 842
HARBOR FINANCIAL MORTGAGE CORP.—FirstCity Financial Corporation; U.S. Public, pg. 644
HARBOR FINANCIAL PROPERTY MANAGEMENT INC.—FirstCity Financial Corporation; U.S. Public, pg. 644
HARTGER & WILLARD MORTGAGE ASSOCIATES, INC.—Old Kent Financial Corporation; U.S. Public, pg. 1216
HELLER FINANCIAL, INC.—The Fuji Bank, Limited; Int'l, pg. 519
HIPOTEBANSA—Banco Santander; Int'l, pg. 143
HOMEAMERICAN MORTGAGE CORP.—M.D.C. Holdings, Inc.; U.S. Public, pg. 1025
HOMEBUYER'S MORTGAGE, INC.—Washington Homes, Inc.; U.S. Public, pg. 1741
HOMESIDE LENDING COMPANY—National Australia Bank Limited; Int'l, pg. 906
HOUSEHOLD BANK F.S.B.—Household International, Inc.; U.S. Public, pg. 842
HOUSEHOLD FINANCIAL CORPORATION LIMITED—Household International, Inc.; U.S. Public, pg. 842
HOUSEHOLD INTERNATIONAL, INC.; U.S. Public, pg. 842
HUNTINGTON INVESTMENT MANAGEMENT CO.—Huntington Bancshares Inc.; U.S. Public, pg. 850
THE HUNTINGTON MORTGAGE COMPANY—Huntington Bancshares Inc.; U.S. Public, pg. 850
INMC MORTGAGE HOLDINGS, INC.; U.S. Public, pg. 857
ILLINOIS BANC ONE MORTGAGE CORPORATION—Banc One Corporation; U.S. Public, pg. 174
IMPERIAL CREDIT INDUSTRIES, INC.; U.S. Public, pg. 872
INDIMAC, INC.—INMC Mortgage Holdings, Inc.; U.S. Public, pg. 857
INDIMAC MANUFACTURED HOUSING DIVISION—INMC Mortgage Holdings, Inc.; U.S. Public, pg. 857
ISTITUTO BANCARIO SAN PAOLO DI TORINO S.P.A.; Int'l, pg. 691
KALIN ENTERPRISES, INC.; U.S. Private, pg. 606
KAUFMAN AND BROAD HOME CORPORATION; U.S. Public, pg. 944
KAUFMAN AND BROAD MORTGAGE CO.—Kaufman and Broad Home Corporation; U.S. Public, pg. 945
J.I. KISLAK INC.; U.S. Private, pg. 624
J.I. KISLAK MORTGAGE SERVICE CORPORATION—J.I. Kislak Inc.; U.S. Private, pg. 624
KRAUS-ANDERSON MORTGAGE COMPANY—Kraus-Anderson Incorporated; U.S. Private, pg. 635
LATIMER & BUCK, INC.—Legg Mason, Inc.; U.S. Public, pg. 985
LEGAL & GENERAL MORTGAGE SERVICES LIMITED—Legal & General Group PLC; Int'l, pg. 805
LEXFORD RESIDENTIAL TRUST; U.S. Public, pg. 991
LIBERTY MORTGAGE CO.—Banc One Corporation; U.S. Public, pg. 174
LITCHFIELD FINANCIAL CORPORATION; U.S. Public, pg. 1001
M & I MORTGAGE CORP.—Marshall & Ilsley Corporation; U.S. Public, pg. 1051
M.D.C. HOLDINGS, INC.; U.S. Public, pg. 1025
MADRID HIPOTECARIA, S.C.H., S.A.—Caja de Madrid Group; Int'l, pg. 251
MARINE MIDLAND MORTGAGE (USA), INC.—HSBC Holdings plc; Int'l, pg. 581
MARINE MIDLAND REALTY CREDIT CORPORATION—HSBC Holdings plc; Int'l, pg. 581
MARSHALL & ILSLEY CORPORATION; U.S. Public, pg. 1049
MELLON MORTGAGE COMPANY—Mellon Bank Corporation; U.S. Public, pg. 1085
MERCANTILE MORTGAGE CORP.—Mercantile Bankshares Corporation; U.S. Public, pg. 1089
MERRILL LYNCH & CO., INC.; U.S. Public, pg. 1097
MERRILL LYNCH BANK & TRUST CO.—Merrill Lynch & Co., Inc.; U.S. Public, pg. 1097
MERRILL LYNCH, HUBBARD, INC.—Merrill Lynch & Co., Inc.; U.S. Public, pg. 1098
MID-STATES MORTGAGE CORP.—Seligman & Associates, Inc.; U.S. Private, pg. 982
MIDCOAST MORTGAGE CORPORATION; U.S. Private, pg. 744
MONTREAL TRUSTCO-FINANCIAL OPERATIONS & CONTROL DIV.—The Bank of Nova Scotia; Int'l, pg. 155
MONTREAL TRUSTCO-PERSONAL SERVICES DIVISION—The Bank of Nova Scotia; Int'l, pg. 155
MORGAN KEEGAN MORTGAGE COMPANY, INC.—Morgan Keegan, Inc.; U.S. Public, pg. 1131
MORGUARD INVESTMENTS LIMITED, TORONTO—Metropolitan Life Insurance Co.; U.S. Private, pg. 738
NBD MORTGAGE COMPANY—First Chicago NBD Corporation; U.S. Public, pg. 628
NBD MORTGAGE CORPORATION—First Chicago NBD Corporation; U.S. Public, pg. 628
NVR FINANCIAL SERVICES, INC.—NVR, Inc.; U.S. Public, pg. 1148
NVR, INC.; U.S. Public, pg. 1148
NVR MORTGAGE—NVR, Inc.; U.S. Public, pg. 1148
NATIONAL CITY MORTGAGE CO.—National City Corporation; U.S. Public, pg. 1154
NATIONAL WESTMINSTER HOME LOANS LIMITED—National Westminster Bank PLC; Int'l, pg. 910
NATIONSBANK EQUITY MORTGAGE CORPORATION—NationsBank Corporation; U.S. Public, pg. 1163
NATIONSBANK MORTGAGE CORPORATION—NationsBank Corporation; U.S. Public, pg. 1165
NATIONSBANK REALTY SERVICES CORP.—NationsBank Corporation; U.S. Public, pg. 1164
NEW ENGLAND LIFE MORTGAGE FUNDING CORP.—Metropolitan Life Insurance Co.; U.S. Private, pg. 738
NOMURA CAPITAL SERVICES, INC.—The Nomura Securities Co., Ltd.; Int'l, pg. 956
NOMURA MORTGAGE CAPITAL CORPORATION—The Nomura Securities Co., Ltd.; Int'l, pg. 956
NORTH COAST MORTGAGE, INC.—The Rottlund Company, Inc.; U.S. Public, pg. 1406
NORWEST MORTGAGE, INC.—Norwest Corporation; U.S. Public, pg. 1202
NYKREDIT; Int'l, pg. 993
ONE MORTGAGE CORPORATION—The Somerset Group, Inc.; U.S. Public, pg. 1484
ORIOLE ENTERPRISES, INC.—Oriole Homes Corp.; U.S. Public, pg. 1231
ORIOLE HOMES CORP.; U.S. Public, pg. 1230
ORLANDO BRANCH OFFICE—U.S. Home Corporation; U.S. Public, pg. 1683
PHH CORPORATION—Cendant Corporation; U.S. Public, pg. 321
PHH MORTGAGE SERVICES CORPORATION—Cendant Corporation; U.S. Public, pg. 321
PNC BANK MORTGAGE CENTER—PNC Bank Corp.; U.S. Public, pg. 1243
PNC REALTY MORTGAGE CO.—PNC Bank Corp.; U.S. Public, pg. 1243
PRESIDENTIAL REALTY CORPORATION; U.S. Public, pg. 1323
PRESLEY-HOME MAC FINANCE CO., INC.—Pacific Enterprises; U.S. Public, pg. 1249
THE PRUDENTIAL REALTY GROUP—The Prudential Insurance Company of America; U.S. Private, pg. 892
PULTE CORPORATION; U.S. Public, pg. 1344
PULTE FINANCIAL COMPANIES, INC.—Pulte Corporation; U.S. Public, pg. 1345
PULTE MORTGAGE CORPORATION—Pulte Corporation; U.S. Public, pg. 1345
RE SERVICES, INC.—Firstar Corporation; U.S. Public, pg. 643
REGIONS MORTGAGE, INC.—Regions Financial Corporation; U.S. Public, pg. 1373
REPUBLIC NEW YORK CORPORATION; U.S. Public, pg. 1380
REPUBLIC NEW YORK MORTGAGE CORPORATION—Republic New York Corporation; U.S. Public, pg. 1381
RHEINHYP RHEINISCHE HYPOTHEKENBANK—Commerzbank AG; Int'l, pg. 310
RICE PARK PROPERTIES—Green Tree Financial Corporation; U.S. Public, pg. 763
RICHTER-SCHROEDER COMPANY, INC.—Marshall & Ilsley Corporation; U.S. Public, pg. 1051
RIVERSIDE GROUP, INC.; U.S. Public, pg. 1391
ROCHESTER COMMUNITY SAVINGS BANK—Charter One Financial, Inc.; U.S. Public, pg. 336
THE RYLAND GROUP, INC.; U.S. Public, pg. 1414
SMC MORTGAGE CORP.—Lennar Corporation; U.S. Public, pg. 989
SACRAMENTO BRANCH OFFICE—U.S. Home Corporation; U.S. Public, pg. 1683
SHAPELL INDUSTRIES, INC.; U.S. Private, pg. 990
SOUTH FLORIDA RESIDENTIAL MORTGAGE CO.—Oriole Homes Corp.; U.S. Public, pg. 1231

SOUTHERN MORTGAGE ASSOCIATES, INC.—Colonial Commercial Corp.; *U.S. Public*, pg. 400
SOUTHERN MORTGAGE COMPANY, INC.—United Companies Financial Corporation; *U.S. Public*, pg. 1675
SOUTHTRUST MOBILE SERVICES—SouthTrust Corporation; *U.S. Public*, pg. 1492
SOUTHTRUST MORTGAGE CORP.—SouthTrust Corporation; *U.S. Public*, pg. 1492
STANDARD CHARTERED BANK PLC; *Int'l*, pg. 1294
STATE HOME MORTGAGE CORP.—Lennar Corporation; *U.S. Public*, pg. 989
SUEDDEUTSCHE BODENCREDITBANK AG—Bayerische Vereinsbank Group; *Int'l*, pg. 180
SUMMIT BANCORP; *U.S. Public*, pg. 1527
THE SUMMIT MORTGAGE COMPANY, INC.—Summit Bancorp; *U.S. Public*, pg. 1528
SUNTRUST—SunTrust Banks, Inc.; *U.S. Public*, pg. 1537
SUNTRUST BANKS, INC.; *U.S. Public*, pg. 1537
SUNTRUST BANKS OF GEORGIA, INC.—SunTrust Banks, Inc.; *U.S. Public*, pg. 1538
SUNTRUST MORTGAGE INC.—SunTrust Banks, Inc.; *U.S. Public*, pg. 1538
SUPERIOR BANK; *U.S. Private*, pg. 1054
TCF FINANCIAL SERVICES INC.—TCF Financial Corp.; *U.S. Public*, pg. 1554
TALMAN HOME MORTGAGE CORP. & TALMAN INSURANCE SERVICES, INC.—ABN-AMRO Holding N.V.; *Int'l*, pg. 11
TEMPLE-INLAND FINANCIAL SERVICES, INC—Temple-Inland Inc.; *U.S. Public*, pg. 1575
TEMPLE-INLAND INC.; *U.S. Public*, pg. 1574
TEMPLE-INLAND MORTGAGE CORPORATION—Temple-Inland Inc.; *U.S. Public*, pg. 1575
TRUST COMPANY OF GEORGIA—SunTrust Banks, Inc.; *U.S. Public*, pg. 1538
ULSTER BANK TRUST COMPANY—National Westminster Bank PLC; *Int'l*, pg. 911
U.S. HOME MORTGAGE CORPORATION—U.S. Home Corporation; *U.S. Public*, pg. 1683
USLIFE REAL ESTATE SERVICES CORP.—American General Corporation; *U.S. Public*, pg. 77
UNIVERSAL AMERICAN MORTGAGE COMPANY—Lennar Corporation; *U.S. Public*, pg. 989
UNIVEST FINANCIAL SERVICES, LLC; *U.S. Private*, pg. 1128
VANDERBILT MORTGAGE & FINANCE, INC.—Clayton Homes, Inc.; *U.S. Public*, pg. 383
VANFED MORTGAGE COMPANY—Washington Mutual Inc.; *U.S. Public*, pg. 1742
VIRGINIA FIRST MORTGAGE—Virginia First Financial Corp.; *U.S. Public*, pg. 1721
WACHOVIA MORTGAGE—Wachovia Corporation; *U.S. Public*, pg. 1731
WACHOVIA MORTGAGE CO.—Wachovia Corporation; *U.S. Public*, pg. 1731
WAYFOONG FINANCE LTD.—HSBC Holdings plc; *Int'l*, pg. 584
WELLINGTON TRUST COMPANY—BCE Inc.; *Int'l*, pg. 115
WESTMARK GROUP HOLDINGS INC.; *U.S. Public*, pg. 1761
WESTMARK MORTGAGE CORPORATION—Westmark Group Holdings Inc.; *U.S. Public*, pg. 1761
WEYERHAEUSER MORTGAGE COMPANY—Weyerhaeuser Company; *U.S. Public*, pg. 1764
WOODGATE CONSOLIDATED INCORPORATED—Green Tree Financial Corporation; *U.S. Public*, pg. 763
WOODGATE UTILITIES INCORPORATED—Green Tree Financial Corporation; *U.S. Public*, pg. 763
WUSTENROT HYPOTHEKENBANK AKTIENGESELLSCHAFT—Wuestenrot Holding GmbH; *Int'l*, pg. 1514
ZIONS BANCORPORATION; *U.S. Public*, pg. 1792
ZIONS MORTGAGE COMPANY—Zions Bancorporation; *U.S. Public*, pg. 1793

6163 — LOAN BROKERS

ACACIA FEDERAL MORTGAGE CORP.—The Acacia Group - Acacia Life Insurance Co.; *U.S. Private*, pg. 11
ACTION COMMODITIES CORPORATION—Tennessee Dressed Beef Company; *U.S. Private*, pg. 1076
ASAHI BANK LOAN BUSINESS CO., LTD.—The Asahi Bank, Ltd.; *Int'l*, pg. 82
ASAHI BANK PROPERTY CO., LTD.—The Asahi Bank, Ltd.; *Int'l*, pg. 82
ASSOCIATES FIRST CAPITAL CORPORATION—Ford Motor Company; *U.S. Public*, pg. 662
ASSUREX DEVELOPMENT CORPORATION—Cigna Corp.; *U.S. Public*, pg. 366
ATTIJARI CREDIT—Caja de Madrid Group; *Int'l*, pg. 252
AUTOMAX FINANCE—Firstbank Puerto Rico; *U.S. Public*, pg. 644
COLORADO NATIONAL BANKSHARES, INC.—U.S. Bancorp; *U.S. Public*, pg. 1680
CONTIFINANCIAL CORPORATION; *U.S. Public*, pg. 439
DIVERSIFIED BUSINESS CREDIT, INC.—National City Bancorp; *U.S. Public*, pg. 1154
FINANCE ONE PUBLIC COMPANY LIMITED; *Int'l*, pg. 484
FIRST FEDERAL FINANCE CORPORATION—Firstbank Puerto Rico; *U.S. Public*, pg. 644
GARMENT CENTER REGION—Imperial Bancorp; *U.S. Public*, pg. 872
GREEN TREE FINANCIAL CORPORATION; *U.S. Public*, pg. 761
HSBC AMERICAS—HSBC Holdings plc; *Int'l*, pg. 580
HSBC FINANCE (MALAYSIA) BERHAD—HSBC Holdings plc; *Int'l*, pg. 582
HAWK MANAGEMENT CORPORATION; *U.S. Private*, pg. 511
HIGHER EDUCATION LOAN PROGRAM OF KANSAS—Hawk Management Corporation; *U.S. Private*, pg. 511
HOUSEHOLD FINANCE CORPORATION—Household International, Inc.; *U.S. Public*, pg. 842
HUNTINGTON BANCSHARES INC.; *U.S. Public*, pg. 849
INDIMAC THIRD PARTY CONSTRUCTION LENDING DIVISION—INMC Mortgage Holdings, Inc.; *U.S. Public*, pg. 857
J.I. KISLAK INC.; *U.S. Private*, pg. 624
LIBERTY INVESTMENT SERVICES, INC.—Banc One Corporation; *U.S. Public*, pg. 173
MERCURY FINANCE CO.; *U.S. Public*, pg. 1093
MORTGAGE & FINANCE BERHAD—HSBC Holdings plc; *Int'l*, pg. 583
MORTGAGE SERVICE CORPORATION—F.N.B. Corporation; *U.S. Public*, pg. 607
NEWCOURT CREDIT GROUP INC.; *Int'l*, pg. 924
NEWCOURT FINANCIAL USA, INC.—Newcourt Credit Group Inc.; *Int'l*, pg. 924
POPULAR CONSUMER SERVICES, INC.—Banco Popular de Puerto Rico; *U.S. Public*, pg. 176
REGENCY GROUP INC.; *U.S. Private*, pg. 918
RELIANCE REALTY, INC.—The Chubb Corporation; *U.S. Public*, pg. 355
SPRING FINANCIAL SERVICES—Banco Popular de Puerto Rico; *U.S. Public*, pg. 176
TOPA EQUITIES LTD, INC.; *U.S. Private*, pg. 1091

6211 — SECURITY BROKERS, DEALERS & FLOTATION COMPANIES

AAL CAPITAL MANAGEMENT CORP.—Aid Association for Lutherans; *U.S. Private*, pg. 28
ABN AMRO CHICAGO CORP.—ABN-AMRO Holding N.V.; *Int'l*, pg. 10
ABN AMRO CHICAGO CORPORATION—ABN-AMRO Holding N.V.; *Int'l*, pg. 10
ABN-AMRO SECURITIES (USA) INC.—ABN-AMRO Holding N.V.; *Int'l*, pg. 11
AIB FINANCE & LEASING LTD.—Allied Irish Banks, p.l.c.; *Int'l*, pg. 64
ANZ MCCAUGHAN SECURITIES LIMITED—Australia & New Zealand Banking Group Limited; *Int'l*, pg. 98
ATE INVESTMENT, INC.—Conectiv; *U.S. Public*, pg. 430
AXA ASSET MANAGEMENT EUROPE—AXA-UAP; *Int'l*, pg. 18
AXA BANQUE—AXA-UAP; *Int'l*, pg. 18
AXA CREDIT—AXA-UAP; *Int'l*, pg. 18
GIE AXA GESTION DES ACTIFS—AXA-UAP; *Int'l*, pg. 18
AXA GESTION INTERESSEMENT—AXA-UAP; *Int'l*, pg. 18
ACADIAN ASSET MANAGEMENT—United Asset Management Corporation; *U.S. Public*, pg. 1672
ACCIONES Y VALORES DE MEXICO, S.A. DE C.V.—Grupo Financiero Banamex/Accival, S.A. de C.V.; *Int'l*, pg. 574
THE ADVEST GROUP, INC.; *U.S. Public*, pg. 23
ADVEST, INC.—The Advest Group, Inc.; *U.S. Public*, pg. 23
AETNA FINANCIAL SERVICES INC.—Aetna Inc.; *U.S. Public*, pg. 26
AFFILIATED FUND, INC.—Lord Abbett & Co.; *U.S. Private*, pg. 675
AIM EQUITY FUNDS, INC.—Invesco Group Asset Management Ltd.; *Int'l*, pg. 685
AIM FAMILY OF FUNDS—Invesco Group Asset Management Ltd.; *Int'l*, pg. 685
ALEXANDER & ALEXANDER SERVICES INC.—AON Corporation; *U.S. Public*, pg. 117
ALGEMENE PARTICIPATIEMAATSCHAPPIJ B.V.—ABN-AMRO Holding N.V.; *Int'l*, pg. 9
ALLEN & COMPANY INCORPORATED; *U.S. Private*, pg. 36
ALLIANCE CAPITAL MANAGEMENT CORP.—The Equitable Companies Incorporated; *U.S. Public*, pg. 589
ALLIANZ OF AMERICA, INC.—Allianz Aktiengesellschaft; *Int'l*, pg. 58
AMERICAN CENTURY INVESTMENTS—American Century Companies, Inc.; *U.S. Private*, pg. 52
AMERICAN ENTERPRISE INVESTMENT SERVICES, INC.—American Express Company; *U.S. Public*, pg. 73
AMERICAN EXPRESS FINANCIAL ADVISOR—American Express Company; *U.S. Public*, pg. 73
AMERICAN FUND ADVISORS, INC.; *U.S. Private*, pg. 55
AMERICAN GENERAL CORPORATION; *U.S. Public*, pg. 76
AMERICAN INDUSTRIAL PARTNERS; *U.S. Private*, pg. 56
AMRO EFFECTENBEWAARBEDRIJF N.V.—ABN-AMRO Holding N.V.; *Int'l*, pg. 9
AMSTERDAM DEPOSITARY CO. N.V.—ABN-AMRO Holding N.V.; *Int'l*, pg. 9
ARCHER DANIELS MIDLAND COMPANY (ADM); *U.S. Public*, pg. 127
ARNHOLD AND S. BLEICHROEDER, INC.; *U.S. Private*, pg. 83
AROS FONDKOMMISSION AB—ABB Asea Brown Boveri (Holding) Ltd.; *Int'l*, pg. 7
ASAHI SECURITIES CO., LTD.—The Asahi Bank, Ltd.; *Int'l*, pg. 82
ASIAN CAPITAL PARTNERS HOLDINGS LIMITED—Dresdner Bank AG; *Int'l*, pg. 420
ASSOCIATED FINANCIAL CENTER, LTD.—Associated Banc-Corp; *U.S. Public*, pg. 140
AUSTRALIA & NEW ZEALAND BANKING GROUP LIMITED; *Int'l*, pg. 98
AYMORE GROUP—ABN-AMRO Holding N.V.; *Int'l*, pg. 12
AYUDHYA INVESTMENT AND TRUST PUBLIC CO., LTD.—The Sakura Bank, Limited; *Int'l*, pg. 1180
BBL IRELAND—Bank Brussels Lambert; *Int'l*, pg. 148
BHC SECURITIES, INC.—Fiserv, Inc.; *U.S. Public*, pg. 647
BHF-BANK AG; *Int'l*, pg. 119
BHF SECURITIES CORP.—BHF-BANK AG; *Int'l*, pg. 119
BLFC SECURITIES CORPORATION—Citicorp; *U.S. Public*, pg. 377
BNB INVESTMENT CORPORATION—Broad National Bancorporation; *U.S. Public*, pg. 258
BSN S.A. SOCIEDAD DE VALORES Y BOLSA—Banco Santander; *Int'l*, pg. 143
BT ALEX. BROWN INC.—Bankers Trust New York Corporation; *U.S. Public*, pg. 185
BT BROKERAGE CORPORATION—Bankers Trust New York Corporation; *U.S. Public*, pg. 185
BT BROKERAGE (PHILIPPINES) INC.—Bankers Trust New York Corporation; *U.S. Public*, pg. 185
BV FINANCIAL MANAGEMENT GMBH—Bayerische Vereinsbank Group; *Int'l*, pg. 178
BAIN & COMPANY LTD. (TOKYO)—Deutsche Bank AG; *Int'l*, pg. 406
BAIN & COMPANY NEW ZEALAND LTD.—Deutsche Bank AG; *Int'l*, pg. 406
BAIN & COMPANY PTE. LTD. (SINGAPORE)—Deutsche Bank AG; *Int'l*, pg. 406
BAIN & COMPANY (SECURITIES) LTD.—Deutsche Bank AG; *Int'l*, pg. 406
BAIN SECURITIES, INC.—Deutsche Bank AG; *Int'l*, pg. 406
BAIRD, PATRICK & CO., INC.; *U.S. Private*, pg. 111
BANC ONE CORPORATION; *U.S. Public*, pg. 172
BANC ONE SECURITIES CORPORATION—Banc One Corporation; *U.S. Public*, pg. 175
BANCA FIDEURAN S.P.A.—Istituto Mobiliare Italiano; *Int'l*, pg. 692
BANCA JOVER—Credit Lyonnais S.A.; *Int'l*, pg. 344
BANCBOSTON BROKERAGE INC.—BankBoston Corporation; *U.S. Public*, pg. 184
BANCO CHASE MANHATTAN, S.A.—The Chase Manhattan Corporation; *U.S. Public*, pg. 339
BANCO DE BOSTON—BankBoston Corporation; *U.S. Public*, pg. 184
BANCO SANTANDER; *Int'l*, pg. 143
BANEXI INTERNATIONAL FINANCIAL SERVICES (NORTH AMERICA) CORP.—Banque Nationale de Paris; *Int'l*, pg. 163
BANK OF AMERICA PUBLIC FINANCE—BankAmerica Corporation; *U.S. Public*, pg. 181
BANK OF AMERICA-THE SEQUOR GROUP—BankAmerica Corporation; *U.S. Public*, pg. 181
BANK OF BOSTON—BankBoston Corporation; *U.S. Public*, pg. 184
BANK OF BOSTON LTD—BankBoston Corporation; *U.S. Public*, pg. 184
THE BANK OF NEW YORK CAPITAL MARKETS, LIMITED—The Bank of New York Company, Inc.; *U.S. Public*, pg. 179
BANK OF SAN FRANCISCO SECURITIES BROKERAGE—The San Francisco Co.; *U.S. Public*, pg. 1430
BANQUE GENERALE DU LUXEMBOURG SA; *Int'l*, pg. 161
BANQUE IBJ (FRANCE) S.A.—The Industrial Bank of Japan, Limited; *Int'l*, pg. 676
BANQUE INTERNATIONALE A LUXEMBOURG S.A.; *Int'l*, pg. 162
BARCLAYS STOCKBROKERS LTD.—Barclays Bank PLC; *Int'l*, pg. 165
BARNETT INVESTMENTS INC.—NationsBank Corporation; *U.S. Public*, pg. 1162
BARR BROTHERS & CO., INC.; *U.S. Private*, pg. 117
BARROW, HANLEY, MEWHINNEY & STRAUSS, INC.—United Asset Management Corporation; *U.S. Public*, pg. 1672
BARTLETT & CO.—Legg Mason, Inc.; *U.S. Public*, pg. 985
BAYERISCHE LANDESBANK; *Int'l*, pg. 176
THE BEAR STEARNS COMPANIES INC.; *U.S. Public*, pg. 197
F. BERGER & CO. B.V.—ABN-AMRO Holding N.V.; *Int'l*, pg. 9
BERKELEY FINANCIAL GROUP—John Hancock Mutual Life Insurance Company; *U.S. Private*, pg. 589
ARNOLD BERNHARD & CO.; *U.S. Private*, pg. 137
SANFORD C. BERNSTEIN & CO., INC.; *U.S. Private*, pg. 137
BERWEIN WERTPAPIERHANDELS-UND BORSENMAKLER GMBH—Swiss Bank Corporation; *Int'l*, pg. 1331
BICKER CAARTEN EN OBREEN N.V.—ABN-AMRO Holding N.V.; *Int'l*, pg. 9
WILLIAM BLAIR & COMPANY L.L.C.; *U.S. Private*, pg. 148
J.C. BRADFORD & CO.; *U.S. Private*, pg. 163
BRENTON BANKS, INC.; *U.S. Public*, pg. 251
THE BRIDGEFORD GROUP—The Industrial Bank of Japan, Limited; *Int'l*, pg. 674
BROWN & COMPANY SECURITIES CORPORATION—The Chase Manhattan Corporation; *U.S. Public*, pg. 337
BROWN BROTHERS HARRIMAN & CO.; *U.S. Private*, pg. 173
BRUNEL HOLDINGS PLC; *Int'l*, pg. 230
BULL, INC.—Science Applications International Corp.; *U.S. Private*, pg. 976
BUNTING WARBURG INC.—Swiss Bank Corporation; *Int'l*, pg. 1331
CCIC FINANCE LIMITED—The Industrial Bank of Japan, Limited; *Int'l*, pg. 676
CIBC INVESTMENT MANAGEMENT LIMITED—Canadian Imperial Bank of Commerce; *Int'l*, pg. 257
CIBC OPPENHEIMER CORP.—Canadian Imperial Bank of Commerce; *Int'l*, pg. 257
CIBC SECURITIES EUROPE LIMITED—Canadian Imperial Bank of Commerce; *Int'l*, pg. 257
CIBC SECURITIES, INC.—Canadian Imperial Bank of Commerce; *Int'l*, pg. 256
CIBC UNIT TRUST MANAGERS PLC—Canadian Imperial Bank of Commerce; *Int'l*, pg. 257
THE CIBC WOOD GUNDY CORPORATION—Canadian Imperial Bank of Commerce; *Int'l*, pg. 256
CIBC WOOD GUNDY INC.—Canadian Imperial Bank of Commerce; *Int'l*, pg. 256
CALVERT GROUP, LTD.—The Acacia Group - Acacia Life Insurance Co.; *U.S. Private*, pg. 11
CAMBIAR INVESTORS, INC.—United Asset Management Corporation; *U.S. Public*, pg. 1672
THE CAMPBELL GROUP, INC.—United Asset Management Corporation; *U.S. Public*, pg. 1672

CANADA LIFE MORTGAGE SERVICES LTD.—The Canada Life Assurance Company; Int'l, pg. 255
THE CANADA TRUST COMPANY—B.A.T Industries P.L.C.; Int'l, pg. 112
CANADA TRUSTCO MORTGAGE COMPANY—B.A.T Industries P.L.C.; Int'l, pg. 112
CAPITAL HOUSE INVESTMENT MANAGEMENT LIMITED—The Royal Bank of Scotland plc; Int'l, pg. 1132
CAPITOL STREET CORP.; U.S. Private, pg. 207
CARNEGIE HOLDING AB; Int'l, pg. 272
CARNEGIE INC.—Carnegie Holding AB; Int'l, pg. 272
CARNEGIE INTERNATIONAL LIMITED—Carnegie Holding AB; Int'l, pg. 272
CATERPILLAR INVESTMENT MANAGEMENT LTD.—Caterpillar Inc.; U.S. Public, pg. 316
CEMLAND INVESTMENT AG—Lafarge S.A.; Int'l, pg. 790
CENTRAL PENNSYLVANIA INVESTMENT CO.—Omega Financial Corporation; U.S. Public, pg. 1222
CHASE INVEST A/S—The Chase Manhattan Corporation; U.S. Public, pg. 339
CHASE INVESTMENT BANK HOLDINGS LIMITED—The Chase Manhattan Corporation; U.S. Public, pg. 339
CHASE INVESTMENT BANK LIMITED—The Chase Manhattan Corporation; U.S. Public, pg. 339
THE CHASE MANHATTAN BANK, N.A.—The Chase Manhattan Corporation; U.S. Public, pg. 340
THE CHASE MANHATTAN BANK OF CANADA—The Chase Manhattan Corporation; U.S. Public, pg. 340
CHASE MANHATTAN BANK (SWITZERLAND)—The Chase Manhattan Corporation; U.S. Public, pg. 340
CHASE MANHATTAN CAPITAL MARKETS (U.K.) LTD.—The Chase Manhattan Corporation; U.S. Public, pg. 339
CHASE MANHATTAN EQUITIES LIMITED—The Chase Manhattan Corporation; U.S. Public, pg. 339
CHASE MANHATTAN FINANCIAL SERVICES (HONG KONG) LTD.—The Chase Manhattan Corporation; U.S. Public, pg. 340
CHASE MANHATTAN FUTURES CORP.—The Chase Manhattan Corporation; U.S. Public, pg. 340
CHASE MANHATTAN FUTURES (U.K.)—The Chase Manhattan Corporation; U.S. Public, pg. 339
CHASE MANHATTAN GILTS LTD.—The Chase Manhattan Corporation; U.S. Public, pg. 339
CHASE MANHATTAN INVESTMENT SERVICES (HONG KONG) LTD.—The Chase Manhattan Corporation; U.S. Public, pg. 340
CHASE MANHATTAN MILBANK, LTD.—The Chase Manhattan Corporation; U.S. Public, pg. 339
CHASE MANHATTAN MORTGAGE CORPORATION—The Chase Manhattan Corporation; U.S. Public, pg. 338
CHASE MANHATTAN OVERSEAS CORPORATION—The Chase Manhattan Corporation; U.S. Public, pg. 340
CHASE MANHATTAN OVERSEAS FINANCE CORPORATION, N.V.—The Chase Manhattan Corporation; U.S. Public, pg. 340
CHASE MANHATTAN, S.A.—The Chase Manhattan Corporation; U.S. Public, pg. 340
CHASE MANHATTAN SECURITIES (JAPAN)—The Chase Manhattan Corporation; U.S. Public, pg. 340
CHASE MANHATTAN SECURITIES S.A.—The Chase Manhattan Corporation; U.S. Public, pg. 340
CHASE MANHATTAN TRADING S.A.—The Chase Manhattan Corporation; U.S. Public, pg. 340
CHASE MANHATTAN TRUST AND BANKING COMPANY (JAPAN) LIMITED—The Chase Manhattan Corporation; U.S. Public, pg. 340
CHASE MANHATTAN TRUST COMPANY (HONG KONG) LTD.—The Chase Manhattan Corporation; U.S. Public, pg. 340
THE CHASE MANHATTAN TRUST CORPORATION LIMITED—The Chase Manhattan Corporation; U.S. Public, pg. 341
CHASE MANHATTAN TRUSTEES, LTD.—The Chase Manhattan Corporation; U.S. Public, pg. 339
CHEMICAL INSURANCE COMPANY LIMITED—Novartis AG; Int'l, pg. 975
CHESAPEAKE INVESTMENT CO.—Chesapeake Utilities Corporation; U.S. Public, pg. 347
CHICAGO ASSET MANAGEMENT COMPANY—United Asset Management Corporation; U.S. Public, pg. 1672
CIBA-GEIGY INTERNATIONAL AG—Novartis AG; Int'l, pg. 972
CIGNA CAPITAL BROKERAGE, INC.—Cigna Corp.; U.S. Public, pg. 357
CIGNA LLOYDS INSURANCE COMPANY—Cigna Corp.; U.S. Public, pg. 365
CIGNA SECURITIES, INC.—Cigna Corp.; U.S. Public, pg. 360
CITICORP; U.S. Public, pg. 376
CITICORP NATIONAL SYSTEM—Citicorp; U.S. Public, pg. 378
CITICORP SCRIMGEOUR VICKERS—Citicorp; U.S. Public, pg. 379
CITICORP SECURITIES MARKETS, INC.—Citicorp; U.S. Public, pg. 377
CITICORP SELECT INVESTMENTS—Citicorp; U.S. Public, pg. 377
CLAYTON, DUBILIER & RICE, INC; U.S. Private, pg. 244
COAST BUSINESS CREDIT—Imperial Credit Industries, Inc.; U.S. Public, pg. 872
CODE, HENNESSY & SIMMONS, INC.; U.S. Private, pg. 249
COLONY MANAGEMENT SERVICES—Front Royal, Inc.; U.S. Private, pg. 430
COMMERCE INTERNATIONAL TRUST LIMITED—Canadian Imperial Bank of Commerce; Int'l, pg. 257
COMMERCE INVESTMENT CORPORATION—National Commerce Bancorporation; U.S. Public, pg. 1155
COMPAGNIE DES IMMEUBLES DES LA PLAINE MONCEAU—AXA-UAP; Int'l, pg. 18
COMPAGNIE FINANCIERE DE PARIS—AXA-UAP; Int'l, pg. 18
COOKE & BIELER, INC.—United Asset Management Corporation; U.S. Public, pg. 1673
COSMO SECURITIES CO., LTD.; Int'l, pg. 335
COUNTRYWIDE SECURITIES CORPORATION—Countrywide Home Loans Inc.; U.S. Public, pg. 453
COWEN & COMPANY; U.S. Private, pg. 280
CREDIT LYONNAIS BELGIUM—Credit Lyonnais S.A.; Int'l, pg. 344
CREDIT LYONNAIS CAPITAL MARKETS PLC—Credit Lyonnais S.A.; Int'l, pg. 344
CREDIT LYONNAIS ESPANA SA—Credit Lyonnais S.A.; Int'l, pg. 344
CREDIT LYONNAIS SUISSE SA—Credit Lyonnais S.A.; Int'l, pg. 344
CREDIT NATIONALE; Int'l, pg. 344
CREDIT SUISSE—Credit Suisse Group; Int'l, pg. 345
CREDIT SUISSE FIRST BOSTON, INC.—Credit Suisse Group; Int'l, pg. 345
CROWELL, WEEDON & CO.; U.S. Private, pg. 291
DB CAPITAL MARKETS (ASIA) LTD. (HONG KONG)—Deutsche Bank AG; Int'l, pg. 404
DBS SECURITIES SINGAPORE PTE. LTD.—DBS Bank Ltd.; Int'l, pg. 351
DKB ASIA LIMITED—The Dai-Ichi Kangyo Bank, Limited; Int'l, pg. 361
DKB INTERNATIONAL PUBLIC LIMITED COMPANY—The Dai-Ichi Kangyo Bank, Limited; Int'l, pg. 361
DKB INVESTMENT MANAGEMENT INTERNATIONAL LIMITED—The Dai-Ichi Kangyo Bank, Limited; Int'l, pg. 362
DKB SECURITIES CORPORATION—The Dai-Ichi Kangyo Bank, Limited; Int'l, pg. 360
DAEWOO SECURITIES CO., LTD.; Int'l, pg. 358
DAIN RAUSCHER CORPORATION; U.S. Public, pg. 476
DAIN RAUSCHER INCORPORATED—Dain Rauscher Corporation; U.S. Public, pg. 476
DAIWA EUROPE LIMITED—Daiwa Securities Co. Ltd.; Int'l, pg. 375
P.T. DAIWA INDONESIA SECURITIES—Daiwa Securities Co. Ltd.; Int'l, pg. 375
DAIWA MIDDLE EAST E.C.—Daiwa Securities Co. Ltd.; Int'l, pg. 375
DAIWA-MKB (HUNGARY) INVESTMENT AND SECURITIES CO. LTD.—Daiwa Securities Co. Ltd.; Int'l, pg. 376
DAIWA SECURITIES CO. LTD.; Int'l, pg. 374
DAIWA SINGAPORE LIMITED—Daiwa Securities Co. Ltd.; Int'l, pg. 376
DATASCOPE INVESTMENT CORP.—Datascope Corp.; U.S. Public, pg. 487
D.A. DAVIDSON & CO.; U.S. Private, pg. 314
DEAN WITTER, DISCOVER & CO.—Morgan Stanley Dean Witter & Co.; U.S. Public, pg. 1132
DEL-VEST INC.—PNC Bank Corp.; U.S. Public, pg. 1243
DEPOSIT GUARANTY INVESTMENTS, INC.—Deposit Guaranty Corp.; U.S. Public, pg. 501
DEUTSCHE ASSET MANAGEMENT G.M.B.H.—Deutsche Bank AG; Int'l, pg. 402
DEUTSCHE BANK CAPITAL CORPORATION—Deutsche Bank AG; Int'l, pg. 403
DEUTSCHE BANK DE INVESTIMENTO, S.A. (LISBON)—Deutsche Bank AG; Int'l, pg. 405
DEUTSCHE BANK GOVERNMENT SECURITIES, INC.—Deutsche Bank AG; Int'l, pg. 403
DEUTSCHE WAGNISFINANZIERUNGS-GESELLSCHAFT MBH—Bayerische Vereinsbank Group; Int'l, pg. 179
DEWEY SQUARE INVESTORS CORPORATION—United Asset Management Corporation; U.S. Public, pg. 1673
DOLPHIN & BRADBURY, INC.; U.S. Private, pg. 338
DOMINICK & DOMINICK FUTURES, INC.—Dominick & Dominick, Incorporated; U.S. Private, pg. 339
DOMINICK & DOMINICK, INCORPORATED; U.S. Private, pg. 338
DONALDSON, LUFKIN, & JENRETTE, INC.—The Equitable Companies Incorporated; U.S. Public, pg. 589
DORMAN & WILSON, INC.—Legg Mason, Inc.; U.S. Public, pg. 985
DRESDNER SECURITIES (USA) INC.—Dresdner Bank AG; Int'l, pg. 418
THE DREYFUS CORPORATION—Mellon Bank Corporation; U.S. Public, pg. 1085
DREYFUS SERVICE CORP.—Mellon Bank Corporation; U.S. Public, pg. 1085
DUNCANSON & HOLT—UNUM Corporation; U.S. Public, pg. 1699
EATON VANCE MANAGEMENT—Eaton Vance Corp.; U.S. Public, pg. 559
EDISON CAPITAL—Edison International; U.S. Public, pg. 564
A.G. EDWARDS & SONS, INC.—A.G. Edwards, Inc.; U.S. Public, pg. 565
A.G. EDWARDS TRUST COMPANY—A.G. Edwards, Inc.; U.S. Public, pg. 565
EQUITABLE FINANCIAL CONSULTANTS, INC.—The Equitable Companies Incorporated; U.S. Public, pg. 589
EQUITY SERVICES, INC.—National Life Insurance Company; U.S. Private, pg. 785
EVEREN SECURITIES, INC.; U.S. Public, pg. 597
EXECUTION SERVICES INCORPORATED—The Industrial Bank of Japan, Limited; Int'l, pg. 675
FFG INVESTMENTS, INC.—Firstbank of Illinois Co.; U.S. Public, pg. 644
FAHNESTOCK VINER HOLDINGS INC.; Int'l, pg. 476
FAR EAST BANK AND TRUST COMPANY—The Sakura Bank, Limited; Int'l, pg. 1180
FARMLAND SECURITIES CO.—Farmland Industries, Inc.; U.S. Private, pg. 396
FEDERAL NATIONAL MORTGAGE ASSOCIATION (FANNIE MAE); U.S. Public, pg. 615
FENCHURCH CAPITAL MANAGEMENT LIMITED—Dresdner Bank AG; Int'l, pg. 420
FERRIER LULLIN & CIE SA; Int'l, pg. 480
FIDUCIARY MANAGEMENT ASSOCIATES, INC.—United Asset Management Corporation; U.S. Public, pg. 1673
FINANCIAL AIMS CORPORATION—D.A. Davidson & Co.; U.S. Private, pg. 314
FINANCIAL NETWORK INVESTMENT CORP; U.S. Private, pg. 404
FIRST EMPIRE STATE CORPORATION; U.S. Public, pg. 631
FIRST MARATHON INC.; Int'l, pg. 486
FIRST MARATHON SECURITIES—First Marathon Inc.; Int'l, pg. 487
FIRST MARATHON SECURITIES LIMITED—First Marathon Inc.; Int'l, pg. 486
FIRST MARATHON (U.K.) LIMITED—First Marathon Inc.; Int'l, pg. 487
FIRST MARYLAND BROKERAGE CORPORATION—Allied Irish Banks, p.l.c.; Int'l, pg. 64
FIRST PACIFIC ADVISORS, INC.—United Asset Management Corporation; U.S. Public, pg. 1673
FIRST SECURITY INVESTOR SERVICES, INC.—First Security Corporation; U.S. Public, pg. 638
FIRST SOUTHWEST COMPANY; U.S. Private, pg. 407
FIRSTATE SERVICES, INC.—FSF Financial Corp.; U.S. Public, pg. 608
FLEET BROKERAGE SECURITIES CORP.—Fleet Financial Group, Inc.; U.S. Public, pg. 649
FLEET SECURITIES, INC.—Fleet Financial Group, Inc.; U.S. Public, pg. 650
FLEMING CAPITAL MANAGEMENT—Robert Fleming Holdings Ltd.; Int'l, pg. 493
ROBERT FLEMING HOLDINGS LTD.; Int'l, pg. 493
ROBERT FLEMING, INC.—Robert Fleming Holdings Ltd.; Int'l, pg. 493
FOLGER NOLAN FLEMING DOUGLAS; U.S. Private, pg. 416
FRANKLIN RESOURCES, INC.; U.S. Public, pg. 679
FREEDOM INVESTMENT—Fahnestock Viner Holdings Inc.; Int'l, pg. 476
FRONT ROYAL, INC.; U.S. Private, pg. 430
FURMAN SELZ HOLDING CORPORATION—Xerox Corporation; U.S. Public, pg. 1785
GEICO INVESTMENT SERVICES CO.—Berkshire Hathaway Inc.; U.S. Public, pg. 220
GESELLSCHAFT FUR WERTPAPIERANLAGEN MBH—Dresdner Bank AG; Int'l, pg. 418
GESTION ET PATRIMOINE—AXA-UAP; Int'l, pg. 19
GESTIONE FONDI INVESTIMENTO MILANO SPA—Banca Popolare di Milano; Int'l, pg. 137
GESTIRAS—Allianz Aktiengesellschaft; Int'l, pg. 61
GOLDMAN, SACHS & CO.; U.S. Private, pg. 462
GOLDMAN SACHS INTERNATIONAL LIMITED—Goldman, Sachs & Co.; U.S. Private, pg. 462
GOLDMAN SACHS (JAPAN) LTD.—Goldman, Sachs & Co.; U.S. Private, pg. 462
GOULD INVESTORS, L.P.; U.S. Private, pg. 466
GRADISON DIVISION—McDonald & Company Investments, Inc.; U.S. Public, pg. 1068
GREAT FINANCIAL BANK FSB; U.S. Private, pg. 473
LEONARD GREEN & PARTNERS; U.S. Private, pg. 477
GREEN LINE INVESTOR SERVICE—The Toronto Dominion Bank; Int'l, pg. 1401
GREENWICH CAPITAL MARKETS, INC.—National Westminster Bank PLC; Int'l, pg. 911
GRUPO FINANCIERO BANAMEX/ACCIVAL, S.A. DE C.V.; Int'l, pg. 574
GUARDIAN INVESTOR SERVICES CORP.—The Guardian Life Insurance Company of America; U.S. Private, pg. 486
GUINNESS MAHON HOLDINGS PLC—Bank of Yokohama; Int'l, pg. 159
HSBC CAPITAL LIMITED—HSBC Holdings plc; Int'l, pg. 582
HSBC CORPORATE FINANCE LIMITED—HSBC Holdings plc; Int'l, pg. 582
HSBC FINANCE & SECURITIES (THAILAND) LIMITED—HSBC Holdings plc; Int'l, pg. 582
HBSC FORFAITING ASIA PTE. LIMITED—HSBC Holdings plc; Int'l, pg. 582
HSBC FORFAITING LTD.—HSBC Holdings plc; Int'l, pg. 579
HSBC GREENWELL—HSBC Holdings plc; Int'l, pg. 580
HSBC HOLDINGS BV—HSBC Holdings plc; Int'l, pg. 582
HSBC INSURANCE HOLDINGS LIMITED—HSBC Holdings plc; Int'l, pg. 580
HSBC INTERNATIONAL TRADE FINANCE LTD—HSBC Holdings plc; Int'l, pg. 580
HSBC (KUALA LUMPUR) NOMINEES SDN BHD—HSBC Holdings plc; Int'l, pg. 582
HSBC MARKETS LIMITED—HSBC Holdings plc; Int'l, pg. 580
HSBC NOMINEES (JERSEY) LIMITED—HSBC Holdings plc; Int'l, pg. 580
HSBC SECURITIES, INC.—HSBC Holdings plc; Int'l, pg. 581
HSBC (SINGAPORE) NOMINEES PRIVATE LIMITED—HSBC Holdings plc; Int'l, pg. 583
HABIB BANK LTD.; Int'l, pg. 584
HAGLER, MASTROVITA & HEWITT, INC.—United Asset Management Corporation; U.S. Public, pg. 1673
HAMBRECHT & QUIST LLC.; U.S. Public, pg. 778
HAMILTON, ALLEN & ASSOCIATES, INC—United Asset Management Corporation; U.S. Public, pg. 1673
HANSON INVESTMENT MANAGEMENT COMPANY—United Asset Management Corporation; U.S. Public, pg. 1673
HANSON OVERSEAS FINANCE—Hanson PLC; Int'l, pg. 594
HARRIS INVESTORS DIRECT, INC.—Bank of Montreal; Int'l, pg. 154
HARRIS-NESBITT THOMSON SECURITIES, INC.—Bank of Montreal; Int'l, pg. 155
HARROWSTON CAPITAL CORPORATION—Harrowston Corporation; Int'l, pg. 599
HELLMAN, JORDAN MANAGEMENT COMPANY, INC.—United Asset Management Corporation; U.S. Public, pg. 1673

S.I.C. Index

HERITABLE GROUP, PLC—CoreStates Financial Corp.; *U.S. Public*, pg. 447
HOARE GOVETT LIMITED—BankAmerica Corporation; *U.S. Public*, pg. 183
HONGGROUP NOMINEES LIMITED—HSBC Holdings plc; *Int'l*, pg. 580
HOPPER SOLIDAY & CO., INC.—Allied Irish Banks, p.l.c.; *Int'l*, pg. 65
HOWARD WEIL LABOUISSE FRIEDRICHS, INC.—Legg Mason, Inc.; *U.S. Public*, pg. 985
HSBC JAMES CAPEL JAPAN LIMITED—HSBC Holdings plc; *Int'l*, pg. 582
IBJ AUSTRALIA BANK LIMITED—The Industrial Bank of Japan, Limited; *Int'l*, pg. 676
IBJ-CA CONSULT HANDELS-UND INVESTITIONSBERATUNGSGESELLSCHAFT M.B.H.—Creditanstalt-Bankverein; *Int'l*, pg. 347
IBJ-CA CONSULT HANDELS-UND INVESTITIONSBERATUNGSGESELLSCHAFT M.B.H.—The Industrial Bank of Japan, Limited; *Int'l*, pg. 676
IBJ INTERNATIONAL PLC—The Industrial Bank of Japan, Limited; *Int'l*, pg. 676
IBJ MERCHANT BANK (SINGAPORE) LIMITED—The Industrial Bank of Japan, Limited; *Int'l*, pg. 676
IBJ SCHRODER BANK & TRUST COMPANY (CAYMAN BRANCH)—The Industrial Bank of Japan, Limited; *Int'l*, pg. 675
IDS CERTIFICATE COMPANY—American Express Company; *U.S. Public*, pg. 73
IDS FINANCIAL SERVICES, INC.—American Express Company; *U.S. Public*, pg. 73
IFD—AXA-UAP; *Int'l*, pg. 19
IFG ASSET MANAGEMENT SERVICES, INC.—Dain Rauscher Corporation; *U.S. Public*, pg. 476
ING GROEP N.V.; *Int'l*, pg. 647
ICAHN & CO., INC.; *U.S. Private*, pg. 556
IMPERIAL INVESTMENTS LTD.—Hanson PLC; *Int'l*, pg. 593
INDEPENDENCE CAPITAL MANAGEMENT, INC.—The Penn Mutual Life Insurance Company; *U.S. Private*, pg. 849
INDEPENDENCE SQUARE PROPERTIES—The Penn Mutual Life Insurance Company; *U.S. Private*, pg. 849
INDUSTRIEBANK VON JAPAN (DEUTSCHLAND) AKTIENGESELLSCHAFT—The Industrial Bank of Japan, Limited; *Int'l*, pg. 676
INTERNATIONAL INVESTMENT MANAGEMENT GESELLSCHAFT S.A.—Deutsche Bank AG; *Int'l*, pg. 405
INTERNATIONAL MARINE UNDERWRITERS OF NEW ENGLAND, INC.—Xerox Corporation; *U.S. Public*, pg. 1784
INTERSECURITIES, INC.—AEGON N.V.; *Int'l*, pg. 27
INTERSTATE/JOHNSON LANE CORPORATION—Interstate/Johnson Lane, Inc.; *U.S. Public*, pg. 910
INTERSTATE/JOHNSON LANE, INC.; *U.S. Public*, pg. 909
INTERSTATE NATIONAL CORP.—Allianz Aktiengesellschaft; *Int'l*, pg. 59
INVERSIONES ARAUCARIA—Corporacion MAPFRE, Compania Internacional de Reaseguros, S.A.; *Int'l*, pg. 335
INVESCO CAPITAL MANAGEMENT—Invesco Group Asset Management Ltd.; *Int'l*, pg. 685
INVESCO GROUP ASSET MANAGEMENT LTD.; *Int'l*, pg. 685
INVESCO LTD.—Invesco Group Asset Management Ltd.; *Int'l*, pg. 685
INVESTCORP INTERNATIONAL; *Int'l*, pg. 686
INVESTMENT COUNSELORS OF MARYLAND, INC.—United Asset Management Corporation; *U.S. Public*, pg. 1673
INVESTMENT TECHNOLOGY GROUP, INC.—Jefferies Group, Inc.; *U.S. Public*, pg. 924
INVESTORS SERVICES GROUP—First Data Corporation; *U.S. Public*, pg. 631
ISTITUTO MOBILIARE ITALIANO; *Int'l*, pg. 692
JJC SPECIALIST CORP.—Fleet Financial Group, Inc.; *U.S. Public*, pg. 650
JPM CORRETORA DE CAMBIO, TITULOS E VALORES MOBILIARIOS S.A.—J.P. Morgan Co. Incorporated; *U.S. Public*, pg. 1130
JANNEY MONTGOMERY SCOTT INC.—The Penn Mutual Life Insurance Company; *U.S. Private*, pg. 849
JANUS CAPITAL CORPORATION—Kansas City Southern Industries, Inc.; *U.S. Public*, pg. 944
JAPAN SECURITIES FINANCE CO. LTD.; *Int'l*, pg. 702
JARAMIEL SOCIEDAD DE INVERSION MOBILIARIA S.A.—Corporacion MAPFRE, Compania Internacional de Reaseguros, S.A.; *Int'l*, pg. 334
JARDINE FLEMING HOLDINGS LTD.—Robert Fleming Holdings Ltd.; *Int'l*, pg. 494
JEFFERIES GROUP, INC.; *U.S. Public*, pg. 924
JEFFERIES INTERNATIONAL LIMITED—Jefferies Group, Inc.; *U.S. Public*, pg. 925
JEFFERSON-PILOT CORPORATION; *U.S. Public*, pg. 925
JEFFERSON-PILOT INVESTOR SERVICES, INC.—Jefferson-Pilot Corporation; *U.S. Public*, pg. 926
TOM JOHNSON INVESTMENT MANAGEMENT, INC.—United Asset Management Corporation; *U.S. Public*, pg. 1673
JOHNSTON, LEMON & CO. INC.; *U.S. Private*, pg. 595
EDWARD JONES; *U.S. Private*, pg. 597
JONES INVESTMENT CO., INC.—Jones Apparel Group, Inc.; *U.S. Public*, pg. 933
THE JORDAN COMPANY; *U.S. Private*, pg. 597
KAY HIAN PRIVATE LTD.—HSBC Holdings plc; *Int'l*, pg. 583
J.J. KENNY CO., INC.—The McGraw-Hill Companies; *U.S. Public*, pg. 1070
KEY INVESTMENTS, INC.—Keycorp; *U.S. Public*, pg. 954
KEYSTONE FINANCIAL INC.; *U.S. Public*, pg. 956
KEYSTONE GROUP INC.—Security Group Inc.; *U.S. Private*, pg. 981
KI PACIFIC ASSET MANAGEMENT—United Asset Management Corporation; *U.S. Public*, pg. 1674
KLEINWORT BENSON INC.—Dresdner Bank AG; *Int'l*, pg. 420
KLEINWORT BENSON INVESTMENT MANAGEMENT KK—Dresdner Bank AG; *Int'l*, pg. 420
KLEINWORT BENSON LTD.—Dresdner Bank AG; *Int'l*, pg. 420
KLEINWORT BENSON (U.S.A.) INC.—Dresdner Bank AG; *Int'l*, pg. 420
KOHLBERG KRAVIS ROBERTS & CO.; *U.S. Private*, pg. 629
LGS SECURITIES, INC.—Citizens Utilities Company; *U.S. Public*, pg. 380
LANDESBANK RHEINLAND-PFALZ; *Int'l*, pg. 799
AUBREY G. LANSTON & CO. INC.—The Industrial Bank of Japan, Limited; *Int'l*, pg. 675
C.J. LAWRENCE, MORGAN GRENFELL INC.—Deutsche Bank AG; *Int'l*, pg. 405
CYRUS J. LAWRENCE (UK) LIMITED—Deutsche Bank AG; *Int'l*, pg. 405
LAZARD FRERES & CO.—Pearson plc; *Int'l*, pg. 1027
LAZARD FRERES ET CIE—Pearson plc; *Int'l*, pg. 1027
LEGG MASON CAPITAL MANAGEMENT INC.—Legg Mason, Inc.; *U.S. Public*, pg. 985
LEGG MASON, INC.; *U.S. Public*, pg. 984
LEGG MASON WOOD WALKER, INCORPORATED—Legg Mason, Inc.; *U.S. Public*, pg. 985
LEHIGH SECURITIES CORPORATION—Summit Bancorp; *U.S. Public*, pg. 1528
LEHMAN BROTHERS—Lehman Brothers Holdings Inc.; *U.S. Public*, pg. 987
LIBERTY DISTRIBUTORS INC.—Liberty Mutual Insurance Co.; *U.S. Private*, pg. 666
LIBERTY FINANCIAL COMPANIES—Liberty Mutual Insurance Co.; *U.S. Private*, pg. 666
LINCOLN FINANCIAL ADVISORS—Lincoln National Corporation; *U.S. Public*, pg. 998
LORD ABBETT & CO.; *U.S. Private*, pg. 675
LYNCH CAPITAL CORPORATION—Lynch Corporation; *U.S. Public*, pg. 1021
M&T SECURITIES, INC.—First Empire State Corporation; *U.S. Public*, pg. 631
MML INVESTORS SERVICES, INC.—Massachusetts Mutual Life Insurance Co.; *U.S. Private*, pg. 712
MACKENZIE FINANCIAL CORPORATION; *Int'l*, pg. 828
MAISON LAZARD ET CIE—Pearson plc; *Int'l*, pg. 1027
MAPFRE INVERSION S.V., S.A.—Corporacion MAPFRE, Compania Internacional de Reaseguros, S.A.; *Int'l*, pg. 334
MARIANA PROPERTIES, INC.—Cigna Corp.; *U.S. Public*, pg. 365
MARINE MIDLAND SECURITIES, INC.—HSBC Holdings plc; *Int'l*, pg. 581
MARSHALLS FINANCE LIMITED—British Telecommunications plc; *Int'l*, pg. 222
MASE WESTPAC LIMITED—Westpac Banking Corporation; *Int'l*, pg. 1497
MCDONALD & COMPANY INVESTMENTS, INC.; *U.S. Public*, pg. 1068
MCGRAW-HILL SECURITIES TRADING, INC.—The McGraw-Hill Companies; *U.S. Public*, pg. 1071
C.S. MCKEE & COMPANY, INC.—United Asset Management Corporation; *U.S. Public*, pg. 1673
MCLEAN MCCARTHY LIMITED—Deutsche Bank AG; *Int'l*, pg. 405
MCRAE FINANCIAL AND LEASING DIV.—McRae Industries, Inc.; *U.S. Public*, pg. 1073
MEES & HOPE INVESTMENT MANAGEMENT LTD.—ABN-AMRO Holding N.V.; *Int'l*, pg. 12
MEES & HOPE SECURITIES HOLDINGS LTD.—ABN-AMRO Holding N.V.; *Int'l*, pg. 12
MEES & HOPE SECURITIES LTD.—ABN-AMRO Holding N.V.; *Int'l*, pg. 12
MEESCHAERT-ROUSSELLE—AXA-UAP; *Int'l*, pg. 19
MELLON EUROPE-LONDON—Mellon Bank Corporation; *U.S. Public*, pg. 1086
MERCANTILE INVESTMENT SERVICES, INC.—Mercantile Bancorporation Inc.; *U.S. Public*, pg. 1087
MERCK FINCK & CO.—Barclays Bank PLC; *Int'l*, pg. 166
MERRILL LYNCH & CO., INC.; *U.S. Public*, pg. 1097
MERRILL LYNCH CANADA INC.—Merrill Lynch & Co., Inc.; *U.S. Public*, pg. 1098
MERRILL LYNCH GOVERNMENT SECURITIES, INC.—Merrill Lynch & Co., Inc.; *U.S. Public*, pg. 1097
MERRILL LYNCH, PIERCE, FENNER & SMITH, INC.—Merrill Lynch & Co., Inc.; *U.S. Public*, pg. 1098
MESIROW FINANCIAL; *U.S. Private*, pg. 733
METALLBANK GMBH—Metallgesellschaft AG; *Int'l*, pg. 861
METALLGESELLSCHAFT SERVICES GMBH—Metallgesellschaft AG; *Int'l*, pg. 861
METALLGESELLSCHAFT TRADING CORP.—Metallgesellschaft AG; *Int'l*, pg. 862
METROPOLITAN LIFE INSURANCE CO.; *U.S. Private*, pg. 737
MIDLAND INTERNATIONAL TRADE SERVICES (USA) CORPORATION—HSBC Holdings plc; *Int'l*, pg. 581
MIDLAND WALWYN CAPITAL INC.—Midland Walwyn Inc.; *Int'l*, pg. 865
MIDLAND WALWYN INC.; *Int'l*, pg. 865
MINEMET AUSTRALIA PTY. LTD.—Imetal; *Int'l*, pg. 661
MINEMET HOLDING—Imetal; *Int'l*, pg. 661
MINEMET ITALIA—Imetal; *Int'l*, pg. 661
MINEMET S.A.—Imetal; *Int'l*, pg. 661
MISSISSIPPI VALLEY ADVISORS INC.—Mercantile Bancorporation Inc.; *U.S. Public*, pg. 1087
MONTAGU MANAGEMENT SERVICES (JERSEY) LIMITED—HSBC Holdings plc; *Int'l*, pg. 580
MONTAGU NOMINEES (JERSEY) LIMITED—HSBC Holdings plc; *Int'l*, pg. 580
MONTAUK—DQE Inc.; *U.S. Public*, pg. 474
MONTREAL TRUSTCO-CORPORATE SERVICES DIV.—The Bank of Nova Scotia; *Int'l*, pg. 155
MONTREAL TRUSTCO INVESTMENT MANAGEMENT SERVICES—The Bank of Nova Scotia; *Int'l*, pg. 155
MONTREAL TRUSTCO-PERSONAL SERVICES DIVISION—The Bank of Nova Scotia; *Int'l*, pg. 155
MONTRUSCO ASSOCIATES, INC.; *Int'l*, pg. 888
MONY SECURITIES CORP.—The Mutual Life Insurance Company of New York; *U.S. Private*, pg. 769
MORGAN ASSET MANAGEMENT, INC.—Morgan Keegan, Inc.; *U.S. Public*, pg. 1131
MORGAN GRENFELL & CO. LIMITED—Deutsche Bank AG; *Int'l*, pg. 405
MORGAN GRENFELL ASIA LIMITED (SINGAPORE)—Deutsche Bank AG; *Int'l*, pg. 406
MORGAN GRENFELL GROUP PLC—Deutsche Bank AG; *Int'l*, pg. 405
MORGAN GRENFELL JAPAN LIMITED—Deutsche Bank AG; *Int'l*, pg. 406
MORGAN GRENFELL (SCOTLAND) LIMITED—Deutsche Bank AG; *Int'l*, pg. 405
MORGAN GUARANTY TRUST COMPANY—J.P. Morgan Co. Incorporated; *U.S. Public*, pg. 1130
J.P. MORGAN FUTURES HONG KONG LTD.—J.P. Morgan Co. Incorporated; *U.S. Public*, pg. 1130
J.P. MORGAN INTERNATIONAL CAPITAL CORPORATION—J.P. Morgan Co. Incorporated; *U.S. Public*, pg. 1131
J.P. MORGAN INVESTIMENTOS E FINANCAS LTDA. (RIO DE JANEIRO)—J.P. Morgan Co. Incorporated; *U.S. Public*, pg. 1131
J.P. MORGAN INVESTIMENTOS E FINANCES LTDA.—J.P. Morgan Co. Incorporated; *U.S. Public*, pg. 1131
J.P. MORGAN INVESTMENT GMBH—J.P. Morgan Co. Incorporated; *U.S. Public*, pg. 1131
J.P. MORGAN INVESTMENT MANAGEMENT AUSTRALIA LTD.—J.P. Morgan Co. Incorporated; *U.S. Public*, pg. 1131
J.P. MORGAN SECURITIES ASIA LTD.—J.P. Morgan Co. Incorporated; *U.S. Public*, pg. 1131
J.P. MORGAN SECURITIES CANADA INC.—J.P. Morgan Co. Incorporated; *U.S. Public*, pg. 1131
J.P. MORGAN SECURITIES HONG KONG LTD.—J.P. Morgan Co. Incorporated; *U.S. Public*, pg. 1131
J.P. MORGAN SECURITIES LTD.—J.P. Morgan Co. Incorporated; *U.S. Public*, pg. 1131
MORGAN KEEGAN FUNDING CORP.—Morgan Keegan, Inc.; *U.S. Public*, pg. 1131
MORGAN KEEGAN, INC.; *U.S. Public*, pg. 1131
MORGAN KEEGAN MANAGED FUTURES, INC.—Morgan Keegan, Inc.; *U.S. Public*, pg. 1131
MORGAN STANLEY & CO. INCORPORATED—Morgan Stanley Dean Witter & Co.; *U.S. Public*, pg. 1132
MORGAN STANLEY CANADA LTD.—Morgan Stanley Dean Witter & Co.; *U.S. Public*, pg. 1133
MORGAN STANLEY CAPITAL GROUP INC.—Morgan Stanley Dean Witter & Co.; *U.S. Public*, pg. 1132
MORGAN STANLEY DEAN WITTER & CO.; *U.S. Public*, pg. 1132
MORGAN STANLEY GROUP INC.—Morgan Stanley Dean Witter & Co.; *U.S. Public*, pg. 1132
MORGAN STANLEY INTERNATIONAL—Morgan Stanley Dean Witter & Co.; *U.S. Public*, pg. 1133
MOUNT ISA INTERNATIONAL PTY. LTD.—M.I.M. Holdings Ltd.; *Int'l*, pg. 827
MOUNT ISA MINES (COAL FINANCE) LIMITED—M.I.M. Holdings Ltd.; *Int'l*, pg. 827
MULTIBANCO INTERNACIONAL DE INVESTIMENTOS S.A. SAO PAULO HEAD OFFICE—BankAmerica Corporation; *U.S. Public*, pg. 183
MURPHEY FAVRE, INC.—Washington Mutual Inc.; *U.S. Public*, pg. 1742
NBD BROKERAGE SERVICES, INC.—First Chicago NBD Corporation; *U.S. Public*, pg. 628
NBD SECURITIES, INC.—First Chicago NBD Corporation; *U.S. Public*, pg. 628
NBSC INVESTMENT CO.—High Point Financial Corp.; *U.S. Public*, pg. 826
NWL PROPERTIES, INC.—National Western Life Insurance Company; *U.S. Public*, pg. 1161
NWNL MANAGEMENT CORP.—ReliaStar Financial Corp.; *U.S. Public*, pg. 1375
NWQ INVESTMENT MANAGAEMENT COMPANY—United Asset Management Corporation; *U.S. Public*, pg. 1673
NATIONAL DISCOUNT BROKERS—The Sherwood Group, Inc.; *U.S. Public*, pg. 1467
NATIONAL LIFE INSURANCE COMPANY; *U.S. Private*, pg. 785
NATIONAL RURAL UTILITIES COOPERATIVE FINANCE CORPORATION; *U.S. Private*, pg. 786
NATIONSBANK CAPITAL MANAGEMENT CORPORATION—NationsBank Corporation; *U.S. Public*, pg. 1163
NATIONSBANK FUNDING CORPORATION—NationsBank Corporation; *U.S. Public*, pg. 1163
NATIONSBANK INVESTMENT CORPORATION—NationsBank Corporation; *U.S. Public*, pg. 1163
NATIONSBANK MONTGOMERY SECURITIES LLC—NationsBank Corporation; *U.S. Public*, pg. 1162
NATIONSBANK OF TEXAS NATIONAL VENTURES GROUP INC.—NationsBank Corporation; *U.S. Public*, pg. 1163
NATIONSBANK SECURITIES, INC.—NationsBank Corporation; *U.S. Public*, pg. 1165
NATWEST STOCKBROKERS LIMITED—National Westminster Bank PLC; *Int'l*, pg. 910
NELSON, BENSON & ZELLMER, INC.—United Asset Management Corporation; *U.S. Public*, pg. 1673
THE NESBITT THOMSON CORPORATION LIMITED—Bank of Montreal; *Int'l*, pg. 153
NEVITTS LIMITED—HSBC Holdings plc; *Int'l*, pg. 583
THE NEW ENGLAND—Metropolitan Life Insurance Co.; *U.S. Private*, pg. 737
NEW ENGLAND SECURITIES CORP.—Metropolitan Life Insurance Co.; *U.S. Private*, pg. 738

NYLIFE FUNDING INC.—New York Life Insurance Company; *U.S. Private*, pg. 795
NYLIFE SECURITIES INC.—New York Life Insurance Company; *U.S. Private*, pg. 795
W.H. NEWBOLD—Fahnestock Viner Holdings Inc.; *Int'l*, pg. 476
NIKKO EUROPE PLC—The Nikko Securities Co., Ltd.; *Int'l*, pg. 930
NIKKO INTERNATIONAL CAPITAL MANAGEMENT (U.K.) LTD.—The Nikko Securities Co., Ltd.; *Int'l*, pg. 930
NIKKO SECURITIES CO., CHICAGO—The Nikko Securities Co., Ltd.; *Int'l*, pg. 930
THE NIKKO SECURITIES CO. INTERNATIONAL INC.—The Nikko Securities Co., Ltd.; *Int'l*, pg. 930
NIKKO SECURITIES CO., LOS ANGELES—The Nikko Securities Co., Ltd.; *Int'l*, pg. 930
THE NIKKO SECURITIES CO., LTD.; *Int'l*, pg. 930
NISSAY ASSET MANAGEMENT CORPORATION—Nippon Life Insurance Co.; *Int'l*, pg. 935
NISSAY CAPITAL CO., LTD.—Nippon Life Insurance Co.; *Int'l*, pg. 935
NISSAY INVESTMENT CO., LTD.—Nippon Life Insurance Co.; *Int'l*, pg. 935
NISSAY MORTGAGE CO., LTD.—Nippon Life Insurance Co.; *Int'l*, pg. 935
NITTANY INVESTMENT CO.—Omega Financial Corporation; *U.S. Public*, pg. 1222
NOMURA AUSTRALIA LIMITED—The Nomura Securities Co., Ltd.; *Int'l*, pg. 956
NOMURA BANK INTERNATIONAL PLC—The Nomura Securities Co., Ltd.; *Int'l*, pg. 956
NOMURA CANADA INC.—The Nomura Securities Co., Ltd.; *Int'l*, pg. 957
NOMURA ESPANA SOCIEDAD DE VALORES, S.A.—The Nomura Securities Co., Ltd.; *Int'l*, pg. 957
NOMURA EUROPE PLC—The Nomura Securities Co., Ltd.; *Int'l*, pg. 957
NOMURA FUTURES (HONG KONG) LIMITED—The Nomura Securities Co., Ltd.; *Int'l*, pg. 957
NOMURA FUTURES (SINGAPORE) PTE. LTD.—The Nomura Securities Co., Ltd.; *Int'l*, pg. 957
NOMURA HOLDING AMERICA, INC.—The Nomura Securities Co., Ltd.; *Int'l*, pg. 956
P.T. NOMURA INDONESIA—The Nomura Securities Co., Ltd.; *Int'l*, pg. 957
NOMURA INTERNATIONAL (HONG KONG) LIMITED—The Nomura Securities Co., Ltd.; *Int'l*, pg. 957
NOMURA INTERNATIONAL PLC—The Nomura Securities Co., Ltd.; *Int'l*, pg. 957
NOMURA INTERNATIONAL TRUST COMPANY—The Nomura Securities Co., Ltd.; *Int'l*, pg. 956
NOMURA INVESTMENT BANKING (MIDDLE EAST) E.C.—The Nomura Securities Co., Ltd.; *Int'l*, pg. 957
NOMURA MORTGAGE FUND MANAGEMENT CORPORATION—The Nomura Securities Co., Ltd.; *Int'l*, pg. 956
THE NOMURA SECURITIES CO., LTD.; *Int'l*, pg. 955
NOMURA SECURITIES HONG KONG LIMITED—The Nomura Securities Co., Ltd.; *Int'l*, pg. 957
NOMURA SECURITIES INTERNATIONAL, INC.—The Nomura Securities Co., Ltd.; *Int'l*, pg. 956
NOMURA SINGAPORE LIMITED—The Nomura Securities Co., Ltd.; *Int'l*, pg. 957
NOMURA WASSERSTEIN PERELLA CO., LTD.—The Nomura Securities Co., Ltd.; *Int'l*, pg. 956
NORCHEM DISTRIBUIDORA DE TITULOS E VALORES MOBILIARIOS S.A.—The Chase Manhattan Corporation; *U.S. Public*, pg. 339
NORTHEAST PROPERTIES, INC.—Eaton Vance Corp.; *U.S. Public*, pg. 559
NORTHERN CAPITAL MANAGEMENT, INC.—United Asset Management Corporation; *U.S. Public*, pg. 1673
NORTHERN FUTURES CORPORATION—Northern Trust Corporation; *U.S. Public*, pg. 1196
THE NORTHERN TRUST COMPANY-CANADIAN REPRESENTATIVE OFFICE—Northern Trust Corporation; *U.S. Public*, pg. 1197
NORWEST INVESTMENT SERVICES, INC.—Norwest Corporation; *U.S. Public*, pg. 1202
THE JOHN NUVEEN COMPANY—The St. Paul Companies, Inc.; *U.S. Public*, pg. 1429
OKURA & CO.; *Int'l*, pg. 1001
OKURA & CO. (AMERICA) INC.—Okura & Co.; *Int'l*, pg. 1001
OLD KENT BROKERAGE SERVICES, INC.—Old Kent Financial Corporation; *U.S. Public*, pg. 1216
OMEGA FINANCIAL CORPORATION; *U.S. Public*, pg. 1222
ONBANCORP, INC.—First Empire State Corporation; *U.S. Public*, pg. 631
ONE INVESTMENT CORPORATION—The Somerset Group, Inc.; *U.S. Public*, pg. 1484
WILLIAM O'NEIL & CO., INC.; *U.S. Private*, pg. 817
ORD MINNETT GROUP—Westpac Banking Corporation; *Int'l*, pg. 1496
ORD MINNETT GROUP LIMITED—Westpac Banking Corporation; *Int'l*, pg. 1496
ORD O'CONNOR GRIEVE LIMITED—Westpac Banking Corporation; *Int'l*, pg. 1497
ORION CAPITAL CORPORATION; *U.S. Public*, pg. 1231
ORIX COMMODITIES CORPORATION—Orix Corporation; *Int'l*, pg. 1008
ORIX CORPORATE FINANCE LIMITED—Orix Corporation; *Int'l*, pg. 1009
ORIX CORPORATION; *Int'l*, pg. 1008
ORIX IRELAND LIMITED—Orix Corporation; *Int'l*, pg. 1009
ORIX SECURITIES CO., LTD.—Orix Corporation; *Int'l*, pg. 1009
OXBOW CORPORATION; *U.S. Private*, pg. 825
PDC SECURITIES, INC.—Petroleum Development Corporation; *U.S. Public*, pg. 1280
PEC ISRAEL ECONOMIC CORPORATION—IDB Holding Corporation; *Int'l*, pg. 644
PFS INVESTMENTS INC.—Travelers Group; *U.S. Public*, pg. 1633
PML SECURITIES CO.—Provident Mutual Life Insurance Co.; *U.S. Private*, pg. 892
PNC DISCOUNT BROKERAGE—PNC Bank Corp.; *U.S. Public*, pg. 1242
PNC NATIONAL INVESTMENT CORPORATION—PNC Bank Corp.; *U.S. Public*, pg. 1243
PNC SECURITIES CORP.—PNC Bank Corp.; *U.S. Public*, pg. 1244
PACIFIC MUTUAL DISTRIBUTORS—Pacific Life Insurance Company; *U.S. Private*, pg. 831
PAINEWEBBER GROUP INCORPORATED; *U.S. Public*, pg. 1252
PAINEWEBBER INCORPORATED—PaineWebber Group Incorporated; *U.S. Public*, pg. 1252
PAINEWEBBER INTERNATIONAL INC.—PaineWebber Group Incorporated; *U.S. Public*, pg. 1253
PEARSON, INC.—Pearson plc; *Int'l*, pg. 1026
PEARSON PLC; *Int'l*, pg. 1025
PELL, RUDMAN & COMPANY—United Asset Management Corporation; *U.S. Public*, pg. 1673
PENN VIRGINIA EQUITIES CORP.—Penn Virginia Corporation; *U.S. Public*, pg. 1271
PEOPLE'S SECURITIES INCORPORATED—People's Bank; *U.S. Public*, pg. 1274
PEREGRINE CAPITAL MANAGEMENT, INC.—Norwest Corporation; *U.S. Public*, pg. 1202
PETROLEUM DEVELOPMENT CORPORATION; *U.S. Public*, pg. 1280
PHIBRO DIVISION OF SALOMON INC.—Travelers Group; *U.S. Public*, pg. 1633
PHILLIPS HENDERSON WARD LIMITED—HSBC Holdings plc; *Int'l*, pg. 583
PHOENIX AMERICAN ALARM AFFILIATES, INC.—Phoenix American Incorporated; *U.S. Private*, pg. 862
PHOENIX SECURITIES, INC.—Phoenix American Incorporated; *U.S. Private*, pg. 863
PHOENIX SECURITIES LIMITED—Deutsche Bank AG; *Int'l*, pg. 405
PILKINGTON FINANCE LIMITED—Pilkington Plc; *Int'l*, pg. 1056
PIMCO ADVISORS; *U.S. Public*, pg. 1296
PIONEER ASSOCIATES INC.—The Pioneer Group, Inc.; *U.S. Public*, pg. 1298
PIONEER CAPITAL CORPORATION—The Pioneer Group, Inc.; *U.S. Public*, pg. 1298
PIONEER FUNDS DISTRIBUTOR, INC.—The Pioneer Group, Inc.; *U.S. Public*, pg. 1298
PIONEER FUNDS MARKETING GMBH—The Pioneer Group, Inc.; *U.S. Public*, pg. 1298
THE PIONEER GROUP, INC.; *U.S. Public*, pg. 1298
PIPER, JAFFRAY & HOPWOOD, INC.—Piper Jaffray Companies, Inc.; *U.S. Public*, pg. 1300
PIPER, JAFFRAY & HOPWOOD INCORPORATED, LONDON—Piper Jaffray Companies, Inc.; *U.S. Public*, pg. 1303
PIPER JAFFRAY COMPANIES, INC.; *U.S. Public*, pg. 1300
PIPER JAFFRAY INC.—Piper Jaffray Companies, Inc.; *U.S. Public*, pg. 1300
PIPER JAFFRAY, INC.—Piper Jaffray Companies, Inc.; *U.S.* Public, pg. 1303
PIPER TRUST COMPANY—Piper Jaffray Companies, Inc.; *U.S. Public*, pg. 1303
PREBETONG IBIZA S.A.—Lafarge S.A.; *Int'l*, pg. 790
PREMIER SECURITIES CORPORATION—Banc One Corporation; *U.S. Public*, pg. 173
T. ROWE PRICE ASSOCIATES, INC.; *U.S. Public*, pg. 1324
T. ROWE PRICE INVESTMENT SERVICES INC.—T. Rowe Price Associates, Inc.; *U.S. Public*, pg. 1324
PRIVATE INVESTMENT CO. FOR ASIA S.A.—Nissho Iwai Corporation; *Int'l*, pg. 949
PROVIDENT COMPANIES, INC.; *U.S. Public*, pg. 1337
PROVIDENT MUTUAL LIFE INSURANCE CO.; *U.S. Private*, pg. 891
THE PRUDENTIAL INSURANCE COMPANY OF AMERICA; *U.S. Private*, pg. 892
THE PRUDENTIAL INVESTMENT CORP.—The Prudential Insurance Company of America; *U.S. Private*, pg. 892
PRUDENTIAL SECURITIES INC.—The Prudential Insurance Company of America; *U.S. Private*, pg. 892
THE QUICK & REILLY GROUP INC.—Fleet Financial Group, Inc.; *U.S. Public*, pg. 650
QUICK & REILLY, INC.—Fleet Financial Group, Inc.; *U.S. Public*, pg. 650
RBC DOMINION SECURITIES LTD.—Royal Bank of Canada; *Int'l*, pg. 1131
REGIONS INVESTMENTS, INC.—Regions Financial Corporation; *U.S. Public*, pg. 1371
REPUBLIC NATIONAL BANK OF NEW YORK (CANADA)—Republic New York Corporation; *U.S. Public*, pg. 1381
REPUBLIC NEW YORK CORPORATION; *U.S. Public*, pg. 1380
REPUBLIC NEW YORK SECURITIES CORPORATION—Republic New York Corporation; *U.S. Public*, pg. 1381
RIADA & CO.—ABN-AMRO Holding N.V.; *Int'l*, pg. 12
RICE, HALL, JAMES & ASSOCIATES—United Asset Management Corporation; *U.S. Public*, pg. 1674
THE ROBINSON-HUMPHREY COMPANY, INC.—Travelers Group; *U.S. Public*, pg. 1633
ROCHESTER FUND MUNICIPALS; *U.S. Private*, pg. 937
RONEY & CO.; *U.S. Private*, pg. 943
ROTHSCHILD NORTH AMERICA INC.; *U.S. Private*, pg. 947
ROTHSCHILD/PELL, RUDMAN & CO., INC.—United Asset Management Corporation; *U.S. Public*, pg. 1674
ROWE & PITMAN LTD.—Swiss Bank Corporation; *Int'l*, pg. 1331
ROYAL ALLIANCE ASSOCIATES, INC.—SunAmerica Inc.; *U.S. Public*, pg. 1533
FRANK RUSSELL SECURITIES, INC.—Frank Russell Company; *U.S. Private*, pg. 952
S.L. DEVELOPMENT MANAGEMENT PTE LIMITED—Singapore Land Limited; *Int'l*, pg. 1253
SBC BANQUE WARBURG—Swiss Bank Corporation; *Int'l*, pg. 1331
SBC WARBURG & CO. LTD.—Swiss Bank Corporation; *Int'l*, pg. 1331
SBC WARBURG ASSET MANAGEMENT LUXEMBOURG S.A.—Swiss Bank Corporation; *Int'l*, pg. 1331
SBC WARBURG DILLON READ—Swiss Bank Corporation; *Int'l*, pg. 1329
SBC WARBURG DILLON READ INC.—Swiss Bank Corporation; *Int'l*, pg. 1329
SBC WARBURG ESPANA S.A.—Swiss Bank Corporation; *Int'l*, pg. 1331
SBC WARBURG GROUP PLC—Swiss Bank Corporation; *Int'l*, pg. 1330
SBC WARBURG ITALIA S.P.A.—Swiss Bank Corporation; *Int'l*, pg. 1331
SBC WARBURG SECURITIES (FAR EAST) LTD.—Swiss Bank Corporation; *Int'l*, pg. 1331
SBC WARBURG SECURITIES (JAPAN) INC.—Swiss Bank Corporation; *Int'l*, pg. 1331
SBC WARBURG SECURITIES LTD.—Swiss Bank Corporation; *Int'l*, pg. 1331
SBC WARBURG SECURITIES (SINGAPORE) PTE. LTD.—Swiss Bank Corporation; *Int'l*, pg. 1331
SPS—AXA-UAP; *Int'l*, pg. 19
SAFECO CORPORATION; *U.S. Public*, pg. 1423
SAFECO MUTUAL FUNDS—SAFECO Corporation; *U.S. Public*, pg. 1423
SAFECO SECURITIES, INC.—SAFECO Corporation; *U.S. Public*, pg. 1423
ST. JAMES'S PLACE CAPITAL PLC.; *Int'l*, pg. 1177
THE ST. PAUL COMPANIES, INC.; *U.S. Public*, pg. 1429
SAKURA FINANCE INTERNATIONAL LIMITED—The Sakura Bank, Limited; *Int'l*, pg. 1180
SAKURA SECURITIES—The Sakura Bank, Limited; *Int'l*, pg. 1179
SANWA SECURITIES (USA) CO., L.P.—The Sanwa Bank Limited; *Int'l*, pg. 1189
CHARLES SCHWAB & CO. INC.—The Charles Schwab Corporation; *U.S. Public*, pg. 1443
THE CHARLES SCHWAB CORPORATION; *U.S. Public*, pg. 1442
THE CHARLES SCHWAB TRUST COMPANY—The Charles Schwab Corporation; *U.S. Public*, pg. 1443
SCOTT & STRINGFELLOW FINANCIAL, INC.; *U.S. Public*, pg. 1445
SCOTT & STRINGFELLOW, INC.—Scott & Stringfellow Financial, Inc.; *U.S. Public*, pg. 1445
SECURITY PACIFIC INVESTMENTS, INC.—BankAmerica Corporation; *U.S. Public*, pg. 182
J. & W. SELIGMAN & CO.; *U.S. Private*, pg. 982
SHADFORTHS LIMITED—HSBC Holdings plc; *Int'l*, pg. 583
THE SHERWOOD GROUP, INC.; *U.S. Public*, pg. 1466
SHING KWAN REALTY (PTE) LIMITED—Singapore Land Limited; *Int'l*, pg. 1253
SIME UEP PROPERTIES BERHAD—Sime Darby Berhad; *Int'l*, pg. 1250
SIRACH CAPITAL MANAGEMENT, INC.—United Asset Management Corporation; *U.S. Public*, pg. 1674
SOCIETE CIVILE DE GESTION IMMOBILIERE—AXA-UAP; *Int'l*, pg. 19
SOCIETE GENERALE EQUITIES INTERNATIONAL—Societe Generale; *Int'l*, pg. 1274
SOGERAP—Elf Aquitane; *Int'l*, pg. 445
SPECIALTY FOODS INVESTMENT INL.—Worthington Foods Inc.; *U.S. Public*, pg. 1780
SPRING LANE ASSOCS., INC.—Eaton Vance Corp.; *U.S. Public*, pg. 559
SSANGYONG INVESTMENT & SECURITIES CO., LTD.—Ssangyong Business Group; *Int'l*, pg. 1292
STANDARD BROKERAGE SERVICES, INC.—ABN-AMRO Holding N.V.; *Int'l*, pg. 11
STANDARD CHARTERED EQUITOR GROUP LIMITED—Standard Chartered Bank PLC; *Int'l*, pg. 1296
STANDARD CHARTERED FINANCE (BRUNEI) BERHAD—Standard Chartered Bank PLC; *Int'l*, pg. 1297
STANDARD CHARTERED FINANCE ZIMBABWE LIMITED—Standard Chartered Bank PLC; *Int'l*, pg. 1297
STANDARD CHARTERED SECURITIES ASIA LIMITED—Standard Chartered Bank PLC; *Int'l*, pg. 1296
STANDARD CHARTERED SECURITIES INVESTMENT PTE LIMITED—Standard Chartered Bank PLC; *Int'l*, pg. 1296
STANDARD CHARTERED SECURITIES LIMITED—Standard Chartered Bank PLC; *Int'l*, pg. 1296
STANDARD FEDERAL BANK—ABN-AMRO Holding N.V.; *Int'l*, pg. 10
STATE STREET CORPORATION; *U.S. Public*, pg. 1513
STERLING CAPITAL MANAGEMENT COMPANY—United Asset Management Corporation; *U.S. Public*, pg. 1674
M.L. STERN & COMPANY, INC.; *U.S. Private*, pg. 1041
STIFEL FINANCIAL CORP.; *U.S. Public*, pg. 1518
SUMITOMO LIFE HONG KONG LIMITED—Sumitomo Life Insurance Company; *Int'l*, pg. 1315
SUMITOMO LIFE INTERNATIONAL (UK) LIMITED—Sumitomo Life Insurance Company; *Int'l*, pg. 1315
SUMITOMO LIFE REALTY (U.K.) LIMITED—Sumitomo Life Insurance Company; *Int'l*, pg. 1315
SUMMIT BANCORP; *U.S. Public*, pg. 1527
SUNAMERICA INC.; *U.S. Public*, pg. 1532
SUNAMERICA SECURITIES, INC.—SunAmerica Inc.; *U.S. Public*, pg. 1533
SUNBANK CAPITAL MANAGEMENT, N.A.—SunTrust Banks, Inc.; *U.S. Public*, pg. 1537
SUNTRUST SECURITIES, INC.—SunTrust Banks, Inc.; *U.S.* Public, pg. 1538
SYNOVUS SECURITIES, INC.—Synovus Financial Corp.; *U.S. Public*, pg. 1550
TNE FUNDING CORPORATION—Metropolitan Life Insurance Co.; *U.S. Private*, pg. 738
TNE INVESTMENT SERVICES CORP.—Metropolitan Life Insurance Co.; *U.S. Private*, pg. 737

TAKUGIN FINANCE INTERNATIONAL LTD.—The Hokkaido Takushoku Bank, Ltd.; *Int'l*, pg. 627
TENNECO CORPORATION—Tenneco Inc.; *U.S. Public*, pg. 1578
THAI INVESTMENT & SECURITIES CO. LTD.—The Dai-Ichi Kangyo Bank, Limited; *Int'l*, pg. 362
THOMPSON, SIEGEL & WALMSLEY, INC.—United Asset Management Corporation; *U.S. Public*, pg. 1674
TOKYO-MITSUBISHI INTERNATIONAL PLC—The Bank of Tokyo-Mitsubishi, Ltd.; *Int'l*, pg. 158
TOKYO-MITSUBISHI SECURITIES (U.S.A.), INC.—The Bank of Tokyo-Mitsubishi, Ltd.; *Int'l*, pg. 157
TOUCHE REMNANT HOLDINGS, LTD.—Henderson Administration Group PLC; *Int'l*, pg. 609
TRADESTAR INVESTMENTS, INC.—Fiserv, Inc.; *U.S. Public*, pg. 647
TRAVELERS GROUP; *U.S. Public*, pg. 1632
TRILON FINANCIAL CORP.—EdperBrascan Corporation; *Int'l*, pg. 434
TRUSCO CAPITAL MANAGEMENT—SunTrust Banks, Inc.; *U.S. Public*, pg. 1538
UGEFO—AXA-UAP; *Int'l*, pg. 19
USAA (UNITED SERVICES AUTOMOBILE ASSOCIATION); *U.S. Private*, pg. 1114
UNDERWRITERS & MANAGEMENT SERVICES INC.—Lincoln National Corporation; *U.S. Public*, pg. 998
UNION DES ASSURANCES FEDERALES—Credit Lyonnais S.A.; *Int'l*, pg. 344
UNITED ASSET MANAGEMENT CORPORATION; *U.S. Public*, pg. 1672
UNITED INVESTORS EQUITY SERVICES, INC.—Torchmark Corporation; *U.S. Public*, pg. 1623
UNITED JERSEY BANK SERVICES CO—Summit Bancorp; *U.S. Public*, pg. 1528
UNITED MISSOURI BROKERAGE SERVICES—UMB Financial Corporation; *U.S. Public*, pg. 1655
UNITED MISSOURI MORTGAGE COMPANY—UMB Financial Corporation; *U.S. Public*, pg. 1655
UNITED PULP & PAPER COMPANY LIMITED; *Int'l*, pg. 1444
U.S. BANCORP BROKERAGE—U.S. Bancorp; *U.S. Public*, pg. 1681
US BENEFITS INSURANCE SERVICES, INC.—Centris Group Inc.; *U.S. Public*, pg. 328
U.S. CLEARING CORP.—Fleet Financial Group, Inc.; *U.S. Public*, pg. 650
USLIFE EQUITY SALES CORP.—American General Corporation; *U.S. Public*, pg. 77
VALORCAT, AGENCIA DE VALORES, S.A.—Caixa d'Estalvis de Catalunya; *Int'l*, pg. 250
VALUE LINE, INC.—Arnold Bernhard & Co.; *U.S. Private*, pg. 137
VON DER HEYDT-KERSTEN & SOEHNE—Commerzbank AG; *Int'l*, pg. 310
W & D SECURITIES, INC.—Jefferies Group, Inc.; *U.S. Public*, pg. 925
WADDELL & REED, INC.—Torchmark Corporation; *U.S. Public*, pg. 1623
WADDELL & REED INVESTMENT MNGMT. CO.—Torchmark Corporation; *U.S. Public*, pg. 1623
WAKO SECURITIES (AMERICA), INC.—Wako Securities Co., Ltd.; *Int'l*, pg. 1485
WAKO SECURITIES CO., LTD.; *Int'l*, pg. 1485
WALNUT STREET SECURITIES, INC.—General American Life Insurance Co.; *U.S. Private*, pg. 443
WARBURG ASSET MANAGEMENT CANADA LTD.—Swiss Bank Corporation; *Int'l*, pg. 1331
WARBURG ASSET MANAGEMENT HONG KONG LTD.—Swiss Bank Corporation; *Int'l*, pg. 1331
WARBURG ASSET MANAGEMENT SINGAPORE PTE. LTD.—Swiss Bank Corporation; *Int'l*, pg. 1331
WARBURG INVESTMENT TRUST MANAGEMENT COMPANY LTD.—Swiss Bank Corporation; *Int'l*, pg. 1331
WARDLEY BROKING SERVICES PRIVATE LIMITED—HSBC Holdings plc; *Int'l*, pg. 584
WARDLEY FINANCIAL SERVICES LIMITED—HSBC Holdings plc; *Int'l*, pg. 584
WATERHOUSE INVESTOR SERVICES—The Toronto Dominion Bank; *Int'l*, pg. 1401
WEATHERLY SECURITIES CORP.—Weatherly Private Capital, Inc.; *U.S. Private*, pg. 1156
WESTERN ASSET MANAGEMENT—Legg Mason, Inc.; *U.S. Public*, pg. 985
WESTLB SECURITIES PACIFIC LTD.—Westdeutsche Landesbank Girozentrale; *Int'l*, pg. 1494
WHEAT FIRST BUTCHER SINGER, INC.—First Union Corporation; *U.S. Public*, pg. 640
WOODCHESTER INVESTMENTS PLC—General Electric Company; *U.S. Public*, pg. 712
YAMAICHI FINANCIAL SERVICES INC.—Yamaichi Securities Co., Ltd.; *Int'l*, pg. 1517
YAMAICHI INTERNATIONAL (AMERICA) INC.—Yamaichi Securities Co., Ltd.; *Int'l*, pg. 1517
YAMAICHI SECURITIES CO., LTD.; *Int'l*, pg. 1516
YAMAICHI TRUST & BANK, LTD.—Yamaichi Securities Co., Ltd.; *Int'l*, pg. 1517
THE YASUDA TRUST AND BANKING CO., LTD.; *Int'l*, pg. 1520
ZAHORIK CO., INC.—AEGON N.V.; *Int'l*, pg. 28
B.C. ZIEGLER & CO.—The Ziegler Companies, Inc.; *U.S. Public*, pg. 1792
ZIEGLER SECURITIES DIVISION—The Ziegler Companies, Inc.; *U.S. Public*, pg. 1792
ZIEGLER THRIFT TRADING, INC.—The Ziegler Companies, Inc.; *U.S. Public*, pg. 1792
ZIONS INVESTMENT SECURITIES, INC.—Zions Bancorporation; *U.S. Public*, pg. 1793
ZURICH KEMPER INVESTMENTS, INC.—Zurich Insurance Company; *Int'l*, pg. 1530

6221 — COMMODITY CONTRACTS BROKERS & DEALERS

ABN AMRO CHICAGO CORPORATION—ABN-AMRO Holding N.V.; *Int'l*, pg. 10
AMERICAN EXPRESS FINANCIAL ADVISOR—American Express Company; *U.S. Public*, pg. 73
AXTRADE AB—Axel Johnson AB; *Int'l*, pg. 708
BA FUTURES, INCORPORATED—BankAmerica Corporation; *U.S. Public*, pg. 180
BT FUTURES CORP.—Bankers Trust New York Corporation; *U.S. Public*, pg. 185
THE BEAR STEARNS COMPANIES INC.; *U.S. Public*, pg. 197
BOEHRINGER INGELHEIM PHARMACEUTICALS, INC.—Boehringer Ingelheim GmbH; *Int'l*, pg. 199
BROADCORT CAPITAL CORP.—Merrill Lynch & Co., Inc.; *U.S. Public*, pg. 1097
BROMAR INC.; *U.S. Private*, pg. 171
CIBC OPPENHEIMER CORP.—Canadian Imperial Bank of Commerce; *Int'l*, pg. 257
CHASE FUTURES & OPTIONS, INC.—The Chase Manhattan Corporation; *U.S. Public*, pg. 341
CIGNA RUN-OFF SERVICES, INC.—Cigna Corp.; *U.S. Public*, pg. 365
CONAGRA FEED INGREDIENT MERCHANDISING COMPANY—ConAgra, Inc.; *U.S. Public*, pg. 428
CONTINENTAL GRAIN COMPANY; *U.S. Private*, pg. 268
DBS TRADING PTE. LTD.—DBS Bank Ltd.; *Int'l*, pg. 351
DKB FINANCIAL FUTURES CORP.—The Dai-Ichi Kangyo Bank, Limited; *Int'l*, pg. 360
DKB FUTURES (SINGAPORE) PTE LTD.—The Dai-Ichi Kangyo Bank, Limited; *Int'l*, pg. 361
DEAN WITTER, DISCOVER & CO.—Morgan Stanley Dean Witter & Co.; *U.S. Public*, pg. 1132
DOMINICK & DOMINICK, INCORPORATED; *U.S. Private*, pg. 338
DUNAVANT COMMODITY CORP.—Dunavant Enterprises, Inc.; *U.S. Private*, pg. 346
A.G. EDWARDS & SONS, INC.—A.G. Edwards, Inc.; *U.S. Public*, pg. 565
A.G. EDWARDS TRUST COMPANY—A.G. Edwards, Inc.; *U.S. Public*, pg. 565
ELF AQUITAINE, INC.—Elf Aquitane; *Int'l*, pg. 445
FIRST CHICAGO FUTURES, INC.—First Chicago NBD Corporation; *U.S. Public*, pg. 628
FIRST MARYLAND ANNUITIES AGENCY CORPORATION—Allied Irish Banks, p.l.c.; *Int'l*, pg. 64
FIRST UNION BROKERAGE SERVICES, INC.—First Union Corporation; *U.S. Public*, pg. 640
FIRST UNION COMMERCIAL CORP.—First Union Corporation; *U.S. Public*, pg. 640
GOLDMAN, SACHS & CO.; *U.S. Private*, pg. 462
GOLDMAN SACHS (JAPAN) LTD.—Goldman, Sachs & Co.; *U.S. Private*, pg. 462
HARRIS FUTURES CORPORATION—Bank of Montreal; *Int'l*, pg. 154
HOWARD WEIL LABOUISSE FRIEDRICHS, INC.—Legg Mason, Inc.; *U.S. Public*, pg. 985
IBJ FUTURES PTE. LIMITED—The Industrial Bank of Japan, Limited; *Int'l*, pg. 676
IMA OF COLORADO INC.—Insurance Management Associates; *U.S. Private*, pg. 565
JOHNSON FRY HOLDINGS PLC; *Int'l*, pg. 713
KLEINWORT BENSON INVESTMENT MANAGEMENT AMERICAS INC.—Dresdner Bank AG; *Int'l*, pg. 420
LIT AMERICA INC.—BankAmerica Corporation; *U.S. Public*, *pg. 181*
MASE WESTPAC HONG KONG LIMITED—Westpac Banking Corporation; *Int'l*, pg. 1497
MERRILL LYNCH & CO., INC.; *U.S. Public*, pg. 1097
MERRILL LYNCH FUTURES INC.—Merrill Lynch & Co., Inc.; *U.S. Public*, pg. 1098
METALLGESELLSCHAFT CORP.—Metallgesellschaft AG; *Int'l*, pg. 861
MONTGOMERY TANK LINES, INC.—MTL Inc.; *U.S. Public*, *pg. 1028*
MORGAN FUTURES CORP.—J.P. Morgan Co. Incorporated; *U.S. Public*, pg. 1129
J.P. MORGAN INVESTMENT MANAGEMENT INC.—J.P. Morgan Co. Incorporated; *U.S. Public*, pg. 1131
MORGAN KEEGAN & COMPANY, INC.—Morgan Keegan, Inc.; *U.S. Public*, pg. 1131
MORGAN STANLEY DEAN WITTER & CO.; *U.S. Public*, pg. 1132
NATIONSBANK FUTURES CORPORATION—NationsBank Corporation; *U.S. Public*, pg. 1163
NORCHEM DISTRIBUIDORA DE TITULOS E VALORES MOBILIARIOS S.A.—The Chase Manhattan Corporation; *U.S. Public*, pg. 339
ORIX COMMODITIES CORPORATION—Orix Corporation; *Int'l*, pg. 1008
ORIX COMMODITIES SINGAPORE PTE LIMITED—Orix Corporation; *Int'l*, pg. 1009
P.S. INTERNATIONAL INC.; *U.S. Private*, pg. 827
PHIBRO DIVISION OF SALOMON INC.—Travelers Group; *U.S. Public*, pg. 1633
J.H. RAYNER (MINCING LANE) LIMITED—Berisford plc; *Int'l*, pg. 188
REFCO GROUP LTD.; *U.S. Private*, pg. 917
REFCO INC.—Refco Group Ltd.; *U.S. Private*, pg. 917
REPUBLIC NEW YORK CORPORATION; *U.S. Public*, pg. 1380
SBC WARBURG FUTURES & OPTIONS LTD.—Swiss Bank Corporation; *Int'l*, pg. 1331
SBC WARBURG GROUP PLC—Swiss Bank Corporation; *Int'l*, pg. 1330
SCOTIAMOCATTA—The Bank of Nova Scotia; *Int'l*, pg. 156
SHARPS PIXLEY BROKERS INCORPORATED—Deutsche Bank AG; *Int'l*, pg. 403
SHARPS PIXLEY INC.—Deutsche Bank AG; *Int'l*, pg. 403
SIME DARBY COMMODITIES INC.—Sime Darby Berhad; *Int'l*, pg. 1250
SIME DARBY COMMODITIES LIMITED—Sime Darby Berhad; *Int'l*, pg. 1250
SIME DARBY COMMODITY TRADING & PLANTATIONS DIVISION—Sime Darby Berhad; *Int'l*, pg. 1250
SIMONDS-SHIELDS-THEIS GRAIN CO.; *U.S. Private*, pg. 1001
SOGEM—Union Miniere; *Int'l*, pg. 1442
SOUTHTRUST SECURITIES INC.—SouthTrust Corporation; *U.S. Public*, pg. 1492
STOCKTON HOLDINGS LIMITED—Orix Corporation; *Int'l*, pg. 1010
VEBA AG; *Int'l*, pg. 1454
WOLCOTT & LINCOLN, INC.; *U.S. Private*, pg. 1185

6231 — SECURITY & COMMODITY EXCHANGES

ABN-AMRO SECURITIES (U.K.) LTD—ABN-AMRO Holding N.V.; *Int'l*, pg. 12
AMERICAN MONEY MANAGEMENT CORPORATION—American Financial Group; *U.S. Public*, pg. 74
THE AMERICAN STOCK EXCHANGE; *U.S. Private*, pg. 62
AMEX COMMODITIES CORPORATION—The American Stock Exchange; *U.S. Private*, pg. 62
THE BEAR STEARNS COMPANIES INC.; *U.S. Public*, pg. 197
BOSTON FINANCIAL DATA SERVICES, INC.—State Street Corporation; *U.S. Public*, pg. 1513
CHASE FUTURES & OPTIONS, INC.—The Chase Manhattan Corporation; *U.S. Public*, pg. 341
CHICAGO MERCANTILE EXCHANGE; *U.S. Private*, pg. 235
DCA OF NEVADA, INC.—Lennar Corporation; *U.S. Public*, pg. 988
NORCHEM DISTRIBUIDORA DE TITULOS E VALORES MOBILIARIOS S.A.—The Chase Manhattan Corporation; *U.S. Public*, pg. 339
OPTIONS CLEARING CORP.—The American Stock Exchange; *U.S. Private*, pg. 62
PRINCIPAL FINANCIAL SECURITIES—The Principal Financial Group; *U.S. Private*, pg. 885
SEMPRA ENERGY TRADING—Pacific Enterprises; *U.S. Public*, pg. 1249

6282 — INVESTMENT ADVICE

AAL CAPITAL MANAGEMENT CORP.—Aid Association for Lutherans; *U.S. Private*, pg. 28
ABB PROJECT & EXPORT FINANCE (USA) INC.—ABB Asea Brown Boveri (Holding) Ltd.; *Int'l*, pg. 4
AETNA CAPITAL MANAGEMENT INVESTMENT LIMITED—Aetna Inc.; *U.S. Public*, pg. 27
AETNA INVESTMENT MANAGEMENT (JAPAN), K.K.—Aetna Inc.; *U.S. Public*, pg. 27
ALLIANCE & LEICESTER BUILDING SOCIETY—Alliance Leicester Building Society; *Int'l*, pg. 57
ALLIANCE CAPITAL MANAGEMENT CORP.—The Equitable Companies Incorporated; *U.S. Public*, pg. 589
ALLIED CAPITAL CORPORATION; *U.S. Public*, pg. 47
AMCORE CAPITAL MANAGEMENT, INC.—Amcore Financial, Inc.; *U.S. Public*, pg. 64
AMERICAN CENTURY COMPANIES, INC.; *U.S. Private*, pg. 52
ARABIAN GULF INVESTMENTS (FAR EAST) LIMITED—HSBC Holdings plc; *Int'l*, pg. 581
AUTRANET, INC.—The Equitable Companies Incorporated; *U.S. Public*, pg. 589
BHF-BANK AG; *Int'l*, pg. 119
BHF TRUST MANAGEMENT GESELLSCHAFT FUR VERMOEGENSVERWALTUNG MBH—BHF-BANK AG; *Int'l*, pg. 119
BWC FINANCIAL CORP.; *U.S. Private*, pg. 108
BACK BAY ADVISORS, INC.—Metropolitan Life Insurance Co.; *U.S. Private*, pg. 737
BAIL EQUIPEMENT—Groupe GAN; *Int'l*, pg. 563
BAKER & MCKENZIE, ATTORNEYS AT LAW; *U.S. Private*, pg. 111
BANCO DE BOSTON—BankBoston Corporation; *U.S. Public*, pg. 184
BANCO SANTANDER; *Int'l*, pg. 143
BANK OF BOSTON—BankBoston Corporation; *U.S. Public*, *pg. 184*
BANKAMERICA CAPITAL CORP.—BankAmerica Corporation; *U.S. Public*, pg. 181
BANQUE BONNASSE—Groupe GAN; *Int'l*, pg. 563
BANQUE INTERNATIONALE A LUXEMBOURG S.A.; *Int'l*, pg. 162
BANQUE REGIONALE DE L'AIN—Groupe GAN; *Int'l*, pg. 563
BANQUE SCALBERT DUPONT—Groupe GAN; *Int'l*, pg. 563
BARCLAYS FINANCIAL SERVICES CO. LTD.—Barclays Bank PLC; *Int'l*, pg. 164
BARROW, HANLEY, MEWHINNEY & STRAUSS, INC.—United Asset Management Corporation; *U.S. Public*, pg. 1672
THE BEAR STEARNS COMPANIES INC.; *U.S. Public*, pg. 197
BELL CANADA INTERNATIONAL, INC.—BCE Inc.; *Int'l*, pg. 115
ALFRED BERG FONDKOMMISSION AB—ABN-AMRO Holding N.V.; *Int'l*, pg. 12
BERKLEY DEAN & COMPANY, INC.—W.R. Berkley Corporation; *U.S. Public*, pg. 216
SANFORD C. BERNSTEIN & CO., INC.; *U.S. Private*, pg. 137
WILLIAM BLAIR & COMPANY L.L.C.; *U.S. Private*, pg. 148
THE BOSTON COMPANY, INC.—Mellon Bank Corporation; *U.S. Public*, pg. 1085
BROOKS, MONTAGUE & ASSOCIATES, INC.—National Commerce Bancorporation; *U.S. Public*, pg. 1155
CIC PARIS—Groupe GAN; *Int'l*, pg. 564

CICM (IRELAND) LIMITED—Commerzbank AG; *Int'l*, pg. 309
THE CAPITAL GROUP COMPANIES INC.; *U.S. Private*, pg. 206
CARNEGIE HOLDING AB; *Int'l*, pg. 272
CENTRAL PENNSYLVANIA INVESTMENT CO.—Omega Financial Corporation; *U.S. Public*, pg. 1222
CHASE TRUST BANK—The Chase Manhattan Corporation; *U.S. Public*, pg. 341
CHICAGO ASSET MANAGEMENT COMPANY—United Asset Management Corporation; *U.S. Public*, pg. 1672
CHIEF FINANCIAL SERVICES—Chief Industries, Inc.; *U.S. Private*, pg. 236
CIGNA ADVISORY PARTNERS, INC.—Cigna Corp.; *U.S. Public*, pg. 357
CIGNA FINANCIAL FUTURES, INC.—Cigna Corp.; *U.S. Public*, pg. 357
CIGNA FUND MANAGERS LIMITED—Cigna Corp.; *U.S. Public*, pg. 357
CIGNA INTERNATIONAL INVESTMENT ADVISORS AUSTRALIA LIMITED—Cigna Corp.; *U.S. Public*, pg. 357
CIGNA INTERNATIONAL INVESTMENT ADVISORS, LTD.—Cigna Corp.; *U.S. Public*, pg. 357
CIGNA INVESTMENT ADVISORY COMPANY, INC.—Cigna Corp.; *U.S. Public*, pg. 357
CIGNA INVESTMENTS, INC.—Cigna Corp.; *U.S. Public*, pg. 357
CIGNA LEVERAGED CAPITAL FUND, INC.—Cigna Corp.; *U.S. Public*, pg. 357
CITIBANK CREDIT CARD MARKETING—Citicorp; *U.S. Public*, pg. 377
COMMERCE CAPITAL MANAGEMENT, INC.—National Commerce Bancorporation; *U.S. Public*, pg. 1155
COMMERZ FINANZ-MANAGEMENT GMBH—Commerzbank AG; *Int'l*, pg. 309
COMMERZ INTERNATIONAL CAPITAL MANAGEMENT GMBH—Commerzbank AG; *Int'l*, pg. 309
COMMERZBANK INVESTMENT MANAGEMENT GMBH—Commerzbank AG; *Int'l*, pg. 309
COMPASS GROUP, INC.—U.S. Bancorp; *U.S. Public*, pg. 1681
COMPOSITE RESEARCH & MANAGEMENT COMPANY—Washington Mutual Inc.; *U.S. Public*, pg. 1742
CONFED INVESTMENT COUNSELLING LIMITED—Confederation Life Insurance Company; *Int'l*, pg. 325
CONNECTICUT GENERAL PENSION SERVICES, INC.—Cigna Corp.; *U.S. Public*, pg. 362
CONSUMER MARKETING SERVICES, INC.—First Chicago NBD Corporation; *U.S. Public*, pg. 628
COOKE & BIELER, INC.—United Asset Management Corporation; *U.S. Public*, pg. 1673
COOPER VENTURES, INC.—Cooper Communities, Inc.; *U.S. Private*, pg. 274
CORESTATES CAPITAL MARKETS GROUP—CoreStates Financial Corp.; *U.S. Public*, pg. 446
CREDIT INDUSTRIEL D'ALSACE ET DE LORRAINE—Groupe GAN; *Int'l*, pg. 564
CREDIT INDUSTRIEL DE L'OUEST—Groupe GAN; *Int'l*, pg. 564
CREDIT INDUSTRIEL DE NORMANDIE—Groupe GAN; *Int'l*, pg. 564
CREDIT SUISSE—Credit Suisse Group; *Int'l*, pg. 345
AB CUSTODIA—Carnegie Holding AB; *Int'l*, pg. 272
DCA OF SAN FRANCISCO INC.—Lennar Corporation; *U.S. Public*, pg. 988
DLJ CAPITAL CORP.—The Equitable Companies Incorporated; *U.S. Public*, pg. 589
DAIWA INTERNATIONAL CAPITAL MANAGEMENT CO., LTD.—Daiwa Securities Co. Ltd.; *Int'l*, pg. 375
DANIELSON HOLDING CORPORATION; *U.S. Public*, pg. 483
DEAN WITTER, DISCOVER & CO.—Morgan Stanley Dean Witter & Co.; *U.S. Public*, pg. 1132
DELAWARE MANAGEMENT HOLDINGS, INC.—Lincoln National Corporation; *U.S. Public*, pg. 997
DIVAL—Allianz Aktiengesellschaft; *Int'l*, pg. 61
DONALDSON, LUFKIN, & JENRETTE, INC.—The Equitable Companies Incorporated; *U.S. Public*, pg. 589
DONALDSON, LUFKIN & JENRETTE SECURITIES CORP.—The Equitable Companies Incorporated; *U.S. Public*, pg. 589
DRAYCOTT PARTNERS, LTD.—Metropolitan Life Insurance Co.; *U.S. Private*, pg. 738
DREYFUS INVESTMENT SERVICES CORP.—Mellon Bank Corporation; *U.S. Public*, pg. 1085
EATON VANCE CORP.; *U.S. Public*, pg. 559
ELAN INVESTMENT SERVICES, INC.—Firstar Corporation; *U.S. Public*, pg. 643
ESANDA FINANCE CORPORATION LIMITED—Australia & New Zealand Banking Group Limited; *Int'l*, pg. 98
EURO MAKITA CORPORATION B.V.—Makita Corporation; *Int'l*, pg. 831
FTI-BANQUE FIDUCIARY TRUST—Fiduciary Trust Company International; *U.S. Public*, pg. 621
FAHNESTOCK VINER HOLDINGS INC.; *Int'l*, pg. 476
FEDERATION DES CAISSES POPULAIRES DESJARDINS; *Int'l*, pg. 479
FERRIER LULLIN & CIE SA; *Int'l*, pg. 480
FIDUCIARY MANAGEMENT ASSOCIATES, INC.—United Asset Management Corporation; *U.S. Public*, pg. 1673
FIDUCIARY TRUST COMPANY INTERNATIONAL; *U.S. Public*, pg. 621
FIDUCIARY TRUST INTERNATIONAL ASIA LIMITED—Fiduciary Trust Company International; *U.S. Public*, pg. 621
FIDUCIARY TRUST INTERNATIONAL LIMITED—Fiduciary Trust Company International; *U.S. Public*, pg. 621
FIDUCIARY TRUST INTERNATIONAL OF CALIFORNIA—Fiduciary Trust Company International; *U.S. Public*, pg. 621
FIDUCIARY TRUST INTERNATIONAL OF THE SOUTH—Fiduciary Trust Company International; *U.S. Public*, pg. 621
FINANCE ONE PUBLIC COMPANY LIMITED; *Int'l*, pg. 484
FIRST BANKS, INC.—First Banks America, Inc.; *U.S. Public*, pg. 626
FIRST CHICAGO INVESTMENT CORP.—First Chicago NBD Corporation; *U.S. Public*, pg. 628
FIRST CHICAGO LIMITED—First Chicago NBD Corporation; *U.S. Public*, pg. 628
FIRST MARATHON INC.; *Int'l*, pg. 486
FIRST MARATHON SECURITIES—First Marathon Inc.; *Int'l*, pg. 487
FIRST MARATHON SECURITIES LIMITED—First Marathon Inc.; *Int'l*, pg. 486
FIRST MARATHON (U.K.) LIMITED—First Marathon Inc.; *Int'l*, pg. 487
FIRST OF AMERICA TRUST COMPANY—First of America Bank Corporation; *U.S. Public*, pg. 637
FIRST SECURITY INVESTMENT MANAGEMENT, INC.—First Security Corporation; *U.S. Public*, pg. 638
FIRSTATE SERVICES, INC.—FSF Financial Corp.; *U.S. Public*, pg. 608
FLEET BANK, N.A.—Fleet Financial Group, Inc.; *U.S. Public*, pg. 649
FOLGER NOLAN FLEMING DOUGLAS; *U.S. Private*, pg. 416
FORD INTERNATIONAL SERVICES, INC.—Ford Motor Company; *U.S. Public*, pg. 664
FORD MOTOR CREDIT COMPANY INTERNATIONAL—Ford Motor Company; *U.S. Public*, pg. 664
FORT WASHINGTON INVESTMENT ADVISORS, INC.—The Western and Southern Life Insurance Company; *U.S. Private*, pg. 1164
FRANKFURT CONSULT GMBH—BHF-BANK AG; *Int'l*, pg. 119
FRANKLIN ADVISERS, INC.—Franklin Resources, Inc.; *U.S. Public*, pg. 680
FRANKLIN PORTFOLIO ASSOCIATES TRUST—Mellon Bank Corporation; *U.S. Public*, pg. 1085
FRANKLIN RESOURCES, INC.; *U.S. Public*, pg. 679
FRANKLIN/TEMPLETON DISTRIBUTORS, INC.—Franklin Resources, Inc.; *U.S. Public*, pg. 680
FRANKLIN TEMPLETON TRUST COMPANY—Franklin Resources, Inc.; *U.S. Public*, pg. 680
GREYSTONE REALTY CORPORATION—New York Life Insurance Company; *U.S. Private*, pg. 795
GUYERZELLER BANK AG—HSBC Holdings plc; *Int'l*, pg. 582
HD VEST FINANCIAL SERVICES; *U.S. Public*, pg. 770
HSBC ASSET MANAGEMENT AMERICAS, INC.—HSBC Holdings plc; *Int'l*, pg. 581
HSBC ASSET MANAGEMENT AMERICAS INC.—HSBC Holdings plc; *Int'l*, pg. 581
HSBC ASSET MANAGEMENT LIMITED—HSBC Holdings plc; *Int'l*, pg. 579
HSBC INVESTMENT FUNDS AUSTRALIA LIMITED—HSBC Holdings plc; *Int'l*, pg. 582
HSBC INVESTMENT SERVICES LIMITED—HSBC Holdings plc; *Int'l*, pg. 580
HSBC PRIVATE EQUITY MANAGEMENT LIMITED—HSBC Holdings plc; *Int'l*, pg. 583
HSBC UNIT TRUST MANAGEMENT LIMITED—HSBC Holdings plc; *Int'l*, pg. 580
HABIB BANK LTD.; *Int'l*, pg. 584
HAGLER, MASTROVITA & HEWITT, INC.—United Asset Management Corporation; *U.S. Public*, pg. 1673
HALIFAX PLC; *Int'l*, pg. 589
HAMILTON, ALLEN & ASSOCIATES, INC—United Asset Management Corporation; *U.S. Public*, pg. 1673
HANSON INVESTMENT MANAGEMENT COMPANY—United Asset Management Corporation; *U.S. Public*, pg. 1673
HARRIS INVESTMENT MANAGEMENT, INC.—Bank of Montreal; *Int'l*, pg. 154
HARRIS TRADING ADVISORY CORPORATION—Bank of Montreal; *Int'l*, pg. 154
HELLMAN, JORDAN MANAGEMENT COMPANY, INC.—United Asset Management Corporation; *U.S. Public*, pg. 1673
HENDERSON ADMINISTRATION GROUP PLC; *Int'l*, pg. 609
HONGKONGBANK OF AUSTRALIA LIMITED—HSBC Holdings plc; *Int'l*, pg. 583
HUHTAMAKI FINANCE B.V.—Huhtamaki Oy; *Int'l*, pg. 639
HUHTAMAKI FINANCE OY—Huhtamaki Oy; *Int'l*, pg. 638
IFS FINANCIAL SERVICES, INC.—The Western and Southern Life Insurance Company; *U.S. Private*, pg. 1165
IMOCASCAIS GESTAO MOBILIARIA E IMMOBILIARIA—Corporacion MAPFRE, Compania Internacional de Reaseguros, S.A.; *Int'l*, pg. 333
INCHCAPE FAMILY INVESTMENT—Inchcape PLC; *Int'l*, pg. 671
INDEPENDENCE INVESTMENT ASSOCIATES, INC.—John Hancock Mutual Life Insurance Company; *U.S. Private*, pg. 589
INVESCO CAPITAL MANAGEMENT—Invesco Group Asset Management Ltd.; *Int'l*, pg. 685
INVESCO FUNDS GROUP—Invesco Group Asset Management Ltd.; *Int'l*, pg. 685
INVESCO GROUP ASSET MANAGEMENT LTD.; *Int'l*, pg. 685
INVESTMENT COUNSELORS OF MARYLAND, INC.—United Asset Management Corporation; *U.S. Public*, pg. 1673
INVESTMENT MANAGEMENT CO. CHILE SA—HSBC Holdings plc; *Int'l*, pg. 583
JP INVESTMENT MANAGEMENT CO.—Jefferson-Pilot Corporation; *U.S. Public*, pg. 925
RAYMOND JAMES FINANCIAL, INC.; *U.S. Public*, pg. 923
JARDINE FLEMING HOLDINGS LTD.—Robert Fleming Holdings Ltd.; *Int'l*, pg. 494
JARDINE MATHESON HOLDINGS LIMITED; *Int'l*, pg. 703
JEFFERIES GROUP, INC.; *U.S. Public*, pg. 924
JEFFERIES INTERNATIONAL LIMITED—Jefferies Group, Inc.; *U.S. Public*, pg. 925
JEFFERSON-PILOT CORPORATION; *U.S. Public*, pg. 925
JOHN HANCOCK ADVISERS, INC.—John Hancock Mutual Life Insurance Company; *U.S. Private*, pg. 589
JOSEPH, LITTLEJOHN & LEVY; *U.S. Private*, pg. 601
KANSAS CITY SOUTHERN INDUSTRIES, INC.; *U.S. Public*, pg. 943
THE KYOEI LIFE AMERICA CO., LTD.—The Kyoei Life Insurance Co., Ltd.; *Int'l*, pg. 776
THE KYOEI LIFE EUROPE CO., LTD.—The Kyoei Life Insurance Co., Ltd.; *Int'l*, pg. 777
LBI FINANCE (HONG KONG) LTD.—Lloyds TSB Group PLC; *Int'l*, pg. 813
LAUREL CAPITAL ADVISORS—Mellon Bank Corporation; *U.S. Public*, pg. 1085
C.J. LAWRENCE, MORGAN GRENFELL INC.—Deutsche Bank AG; *Int'l*, pg. 405
CYRUS J. LAWRENCE (UK) LIMITED—Deutsche Bank AG; *Int'l*, pg. 405
LEE NATIONAL CORPORATION; *U.S. Private*, pg. 658
LEE, ROBINSON & STEINE, INC.—First American Corporation; *U.S. Public*, pg. 624
LLOYDS BANK (JERSEY) LTD.—Lloyds TSB Group PLC; *Int'l*, pg. 813
LLOYDS BOWMAKER FINANCE LTD—Lloyds TSB Group PLC; *Int'l*, pg. 813
LLOYDS EUROFINANCE NV—Lloyds TSB Group PLC; *Int'l*, pg. 813
LLOYDS LEASING LTD.—Lloyds TSB Group PLC; *Int'l*, pg. 813
LOOMIS, SAYLES & CO.—Metropolitan Life Insurance Co.; *U.S. Private*, pg. 737
LOWRY HILL INVESTMENT ADVISORS, INC.—Norwest Corporation; *U.S. Public*, pg. 1201
LYNCH & MAYER, INC.—Lincoln National Corporation; *U.S. Public*, pg. 998
LYONNAISE DE BANQUE—Groupe GAN; *Int'l*, pg. 565
M & I INVESTMENT MANAGEMENT CORP.—Marshall & Ilsley Corporation; *U.S. Public*, pg. 1051
MLC LIMITED—Lend Lease Corporation Limited; *Int'l*, pg. 806
MAFINA B.V.—Petrofina S.A.; *Int'l*, pg. 1044
MAISON LAZARD ET CIE—Pearson plc; *Int'l*, pg. 1027
MANULIFE FINANCIAL (THE MANUFACTURERS LIFE INSURANCE COMPANY); *Int'l*, pg. 840
MARINE MIDLAND BUSINESS LOANS, INC.—HSBC Holdings plc; *Int'l*, pg. 581
MARINE MIDLAND LEASING CORPORATION—HSBC Holdings plc; *Int'l*, pg. 581
MARLBOROUGH CAPITAL ADVISORS, INC.—Metropolitan Life Insurance Co.; *U.S. Private*, pg. 737
MAYTAG FINANCIAL SERVICES CORP.—Maytag Corporation; *U.S. Public*, pg. 1065
C.S. MCKEE & COMPANY, INC.—United Asset Management Corporation; *U.S. Public*, pg. 1673
MELLON BOND ASSOCIATES CORP.—Mellon Bank Corporation; *U.S. Public*, pg. 1085
MELLON CAPITAL MANAGEMENT CORPORATION (MFSC 1085
MELLON EQUITY ASSOCIATES CORP.—Mellon Bank Corporation; *U.S. Public*, pg. 1085
MERRILL LYNCH & CO., INC.; *U.S. Public*, pg. 1097
MERRILL LYNCH INVESTMENT MANAGEMENT, INC.—Merrill Lynch & Co., Inc.; *U.S. Public*, pg. 1098
MESIROW FINANCIAL; *U.S. Private*, pg. 733
METALLBANK CAPITAL CORPORATION—Metallgesellschaft AG; *Int'l*, pg. 861
MIDLAND BANK PLC—HSBC Holdings plc; *Int'l*, pg. 580
MIDLAND INTERNATIONAL FINANCIAL SERVICES (IRELAND) LIMITED—HSBC Holdings plc; *Int'l*, pg. 583
MIDLAND UNIT TRUST MANAGEMENT LIMITED—HSBC Holdings plc; *Int'l*, pg. 580
MIMLIC ASSET MANAGEMENT COMPANY—The Minnesota Mutual Life Insurance Company; *U.S. Private*, pg. 750
MITCHELL HUTCHINS ASSET MANAGEMENT INC.—PaineWebber Group Incorporated; *U.S. Public*, pg. 1253
MITCHELL HUTCHINS INSTITUTIONAL INVESTORS INC.—PaineWebber Group Incorporated; *U.S. Public*, pg. 1253
MITO S.P.A.—Fiat Auto SpA; *Int'l*, pg. 482
MONITOR CAPITAL ADVISORS INC.—New York Life Insurance Company; *U.S. Private*, pg. 795
MONTAUK—DQE Inc.; *U.S. Public*, pg. 474
MONY ADVISERS, INC.—The Mutual Life Insurance Company of New York; *U.S. Private*, pg. 769
MORGAN GRENFELL (SCOTLAND) LIMITED—Deutsche Bank AG; *Int'l*, pg. 405
MORGAN STANLEY DEAN WITTER & CO.; *U.S. Public*, pg. 1132
MURPHEY FAVRE SECURITIES SERVICES, INC.—Washington Mutual Inc.; *U.S. Public*, pg. 1742
NBD FINANCIAL SERVICES OF MICHIGAN, INC.—First Chicago NBD Corporation; *U.S. Public*, pg. 628
NBSC INVESTMENT ADVISORY SERVICES—High Point Financial Corp.; *U.S. Public*, pg. 826
NTC GROUP; *U.S. Private*, pg. 772
NANTO INVESTMENT MANAGEMENT CO., LTD.—The Nanto Bank, Ltd.; *Int'l*, pg. 905
NATIONAL & PROVINCIAL BUILDING SOCIETY; *Int'l*, pg. 906
NATIONAL LIFE INVESTMENT MANAGEMENT CO., INC.—National Life Insurance Company; *U.S. Private*, pg. 785
NATIONAL TRUST COMPANY—National Trustco Inc.; *Int'l*, pg. 910
NELSON, BENSON & ZELLMER, INC.—United Asset Management Corporation; *U.S. Public*, pg. 1673
THE NEW ENGLAND—Metropolitan Life Insurance Co.; *U.S. Private*, pg. 737
NEWBOLD'S ASSET MANAGEMENT INC.—United Asset Management Corporation; *U.S. Public*, pg. 1673
NEWPORT—Metropolitan Life Insurance Co.; *U.S. Private*, pg. 738
NIKKO INTERNATIONAL CAPITAL MANAGEMENT CO., LTD.—The Nikko Securities Co., Ltd.; *Int'l*, pg. 930

THE NIKKO SECURITIES CO., LTD.; *Int'l*, pg. 930
NIPPON STEEL U.S.A., INC.—Nippon Steel Corporation; *Int'l*, pg. 939
NITTANY INVESTMENT CO.—Omega Financial Corporation; *U.S. Public*, pg. 1222
NORTHERN CAPITAL MANAGEMENT, INC.—United Asset Management Corporation; *U.S. Public*, pg. 1673
NOVUS SERVICES, INC.—Morgan Stanley Dean Witter & Co.; *U.S. Public*, pg. 1132
OECHSLE INTERNATIONAL ADVISORS L.P.—Dresdner Bank AG; *Int'l*, pg. 418
OPPENHEIMER CAPITAL—Canadian Imperial Bank of Commerce; *Int'l*, pg. 257
OPPENHEIMER FUNDS, INC.—Massachusetts Mutual Life Insurance Co.; *U.S. Private*, pg. 712
ORD MINNETT GROUP—Westpac Banking Corporation; *Int'l*, pg. 1496
ORD MINNETT GROUP LIMITED—Westpac Banking Corporation; *Int'l*, pg. 1496
ORD O'CONNOR GRIEVE LIMITED—Westpac Banking Corporation; *Int'l*, pg. 1497
ORIX EUROPE LIMITED—Orix Corporation; *Int'l*, pg. 1009
PM REALTY ADVISORS INC.—Pacific Life Insurance Company; *U.S. Private*, pg. 831
PACIFIC CREST CAPITAL, INC.; *U.S. Public*, pg. 1248
PACKER SECURITY PATROL, INC.—Thorn Apple Valley, Inc.; *U.S. Public*, pg. 1603
PALUPE-COMERCIO, PARTICIPACAO E SERVICOS LTDA.—The Chase Manhattan Corporation; *U.S. Public*, pg. 341
PANAGORA ASSET MANAGMENT, INC.—Lehman Brothers Holdings Inc.; *U.S. Public*, pg. 987
PHILADELPHIA INTERNATIONAL INVESTMENT CORP.—CoreStates Financial Corp.; *U.S. Public*, pg. 447
PIMCO ADVISORS L.P.—Pacific Life Insurance Company; *U.S. Private*, pg. 832
PIONEER CAPITAL CORPORATION—The Pioneer Group, Inc.; *U.S. Public*, pg. 1298
PIONEER FUNDS MARKETING GMBH—The Pioneer Group, Inc.; *U.S. Public*, pg. 1298
THE PIONEER GROUP, INC.; *U.S. Public*, pg. 1298
PIONEER INTERNATIONAL CORPORATION—The Pioneer Group, Inc.; *U.S. Public*, pg. 1298
PIONEER INVESTMENTS CORPORATION—The Pioneer Group, Inc.; *U.S. Public*, pg. 1298
PIONEER PLANS CORPORATION—The Pioneer Group, Inc.; *U.S. Public*, pg. 1298
PIONEER SBIC CORP.—The Pioneer Group, Inc.; *U.S. Public*, pg. 1298
PIONEERING MANAGEMENT CORPORATION—The Pioneer Group, Inc.; *U.S. Public*, pg. 1298
PIONEERING SERVICES CORPORATION—The Pioneer Group, Inc.; *U.S. Public*, pg. 1298
PIPER CAPITAL MANAGEMENT, INCORPORATED—Piper Jaffray Companies, Inc.; *U.S. Public*, pg. 1303
THE PORTFOLIO GROUP, INC.—The Chase Manhattan Corporation; *U.S. Public*, pg. 338
POTTER WARBURG ASSET MANAGEMENT—Swiss Bank Corporation; *Int'l*, pg. 1331
POTTER WARBURG ASSET MANAGEMENT LTD.—Swiss Bank Corporation; *Int'l*, pg. 1331
POTTER WARBURG PTY. LTD.—Swiss Bank Corporation; *Int'l*, pg. 1331
PREMIER INVESTMENT ADVISORS, L.C.—Banc One Corporation; *U.S. Public*, pg. 173
PRESTON RIDGE FINANCIAL SERVICES CORPORATION—Washington Mutual Inc.; *U.S. Public*, pg. 1742
T. ROWE PRICE ASSOCIATES, INC.; *U.S. Public*, pg. 1324
T. ROWE PRICE INVESTMENT SERVICES INC.—T. Rowe Price Associates, Inc.; *U.S. Public*, pg. 1324
PROVIDENT MUTUAL LIFE INSURANCE CO.; *U.S. Private*, pg. 891
PUGET SOUND ENERGY CO.—Puget Sound Energy, Inc.; *U.S. Public*, pg. 1342
PUTNAM INVESTMENTS, INC.—Marsh & McLennan Companies, Inc.; *U.S. Public*, pg. 1049
QUALIVEST CAPITAL MANAGEMENT, INC.—U.S. Bancorp; *U.S. Public*, pg. 1681
RCM CAPITAL MANAGEMENT—Dresdner Bank AG; *Int'l*, pg. 418
RE/MAX INTERNATIONAL, INC.; *U.S. Private*, pg. 912
RICE, HALL, JAMES & ASSOCIATES—United Asset Management Corporation; *U.S. Public*, pg. 1674
RINCON SECURITIES, INC.—Dominion Resources, Inc.; *U.S. Public*, pg. 516
ROTHSCHILD ASSET MANAGEMENT INC.—Rothschild North America Inc.; *U.S. Private*, pg. 947
J. ROTHSCHILD INVESTMENT MANAGEMENT LIMITED—St. James's Place Capital plc.; *Int'l*, pg. 1178
ROTHSCHILD/PELL, RUDMAN & CO., INC.—United Asset Management Corporation; *U.S. Public*, pg. 1674
ROUSE CONTROLLERS DIV.—The Rouse Company; *U.S. Public*, pg. 1407
ROUSE FINANCE DIV.—The Rouse Company; *U.S. Public*, pg. 1407
FRANK RUSSELL COMPANY; *U.S. Private*, pg. 952
SBC WARBURG GROUP PLC—Swiss Bank Corporation; *Int'l*, pg. 1330
SBC WARBURG SECURITIES LTD.—Swiss Bank Corporation; *Int'l*, pg. 1331
SBCS COMPANY LIMITED—The Sakura Bank, Limited; *Int'l*, pg. 1181
SAFECO ASSET MANAGEMENT COMPANY—SAFECO Corporation; *U.S. Public*, pg. 1423
SAFECO CORPORATION; *U.S. Public*, pg. 1423
SAFECO SERVICES CO.—SAFECO Corporation; *U.S. Public*, pg. 1423
B.F. SAUL ADVISORY CO.—Saul Centers Inc.; *U.S. Public*, pg. 1435
SAVAFACTORING S.P.A.—Fiat Auto SpA; *Int'l*, pg. 482
SCOTT & STRINGFELLOW FINANCIAL, INC.; *U.S. Public*, pg. 1445
SCOTT & STRINGFELLOW, INC.—Scott & Stringfellow Financial, Inc.; *U.S. Public*, pg. 1445
SEDGWICK GROUP PLC; *Int'l*, pg. 1217
SEDGWICK NOBLE LOWNDES—Sedgwick Group plc; *Int'l*, pg. 1218
SEDGWICK NOBLE LOWNDES GROUP LIMITED—Sedgwick Group plc; *Int'l*, pg. 1218
SEDGWICK NOBLE LOWNDES LIMITED—Sedgwick Group plc; *Int'l*, pg. 1218
SENTINEL ADVISORS, INC.—National Life Insurance Company; *U.S. Private*, pg. 785
SHARED SERVICES DIVISION—Black & Veatch; *U.S. Private*, pg. 146
SILVER TOWNE L.P.; *U.S. Private*, pg. 1000
SIME BANK BERHAD—Sime Darby Berhad; *Int'l*, pg. 1250
SOCIETE BORDELAISE DE CIC—Groupe GAN; *Int'l*, pg. 565
SOCIETE NANCEIENNE VARIN-BERNIER—Groupe GAN; *Int'l*, pg. 565
SPECTRUM ASSET MANAGEMENT, INC.—United Asset Management Corporation; *U.S. Public*, pg. 1674
SSANGYONG BUSINESS GROUP; *Int'l*, pg. 1291
SSANGYONG INVESTMENT & SECURITIES CO., LTD.—Ssangyong Business Group; *Int'l*, pg. 1292
STATE STREET RESEARCH & MANAGEMENT COMPANY—Metropolitan Life Insurance Co.; *U.S. Private*, pg. 738
STERLING CAPITAL MANAGEMENT COMPANY—United Asset Management Corporation; *U.S. Public*, pg. 1674
STRATTON MANAGEMENT COMPANY; *U.S. Private*, pg. 1046
SUCCESS DEVELOPMENT INTERNATIONAL; *U.S. Private*, pg. 1048
SUMMIT BANCORP; *U.S. Public*, pg. 1527
SUN LIFE ASSURANCE COMPANY OF CANADA; *Int'l*, pg. 1318
SUN LIFE OF CANADA BENEFIT MANAGEMENT LIMITED—Sun Life Assurance Company of Canada; *Int'l*, pg. 1319
SUN LIFE OF CANADA INVESTMENT MANAGEMENT LIMITED—Sun Life Assurance Company of Canada; *Int'l*, pg. 1319
SUNAMERICA ASSET MANAGEMENT CORPORATION—SunAmerica Inc.; *U.S. Public*, pg. 1533
SUNGARD FINANCIAL SYSTEMS, INC.—SunGard Data Systems Inc.; *U.S. Public*, pg. 1534
SUNGARD TRADING SYSTEMS GROUP—SunGard Data Systems Inc.; *U.S. Public*, pg. 1535
TBC FINANCIAL SERVICES—Tasty Baking Company; *U.S. Public*, pg. 1561
TELEFONIA Y FINANZAS, S.A. (TELFISA)—Telefonica de Espana, S.A.; *Int'l*, pg. 1372
TELEFONICA NORTH AMERICA, INC.—Telefonica de Espana, S.A.; *Int'l*, pg. 1372
THOMPSON, SIEGEL & WALMSLEY, INC.—United Asset Management Corporation; *U.S. Public*, pg. 1674
TOKIO MARINE ASSET MANAGEMENT NEW YORK CO., LTD.—The Tokio Marine & Fire Insurance Company, Ltd.; *Int'l*, pg. 1392
THE TOKIO MARINE CAPITAL RESEARCH LIMITED—The Tokio Marine & Fire Insurance Company, Ltd.; *Int'l*, pg. 1393
THE TOKIO MARINE INTERNATIONAL FUND (LUXEMBOURG) S.A.—The Tokio Marine & Fire Insurance Company, Ltd.; *Int'l*, pg. 1393
TOKIO MARINE INVESTMENT SERVICES, LIMITED—The Tokio Marine & Fire Insurance Company, Ltd.; *Int'l*, pg. 1393
TORCHMARK INVESTMENT ADVISORY COMPANY, INC.—Torchmark Corporation; *U.S. Public*, pg. 1623
TRAINER WORTHAM & COMPANY INCORPORATED; *U.S. Private*, pg. 1095
TRANSAMERICA INVESTMENT SERVICES, INC.—Transamerica Corporation; *U.S. Public*, pg. 1630
TRIDENT FINANCIAL CORPORATION; *U.S. Private*, pg. 1103
TRINKAUS & BURKHARDT (INTERNATIONAL) S.A.—HSBC Holdings plc; *Int'l*, pg. 584
TRINKAUS CAPITAL MANAGEMENT—HSBC Holdings plc; *Int'l*, pg. 584
TULE HUB SERVICES CO.—Enron Corp.; *U.S. Public*, pg. 585
UAM INVESTMENT SERVICES, INC.—United Asset Management Corporation; *U.S. Public*, pg. 1674
U.B.R.—Groupe GAN; *Int'l*, pg. 565
UJB DISCOUNT BROKERAGE—Summit Bancorp; *U.S. Public*, pg. 1528
UJB INVESTOR SERVICES COMPANY—Summit Bancorp; *U.S. Public*, pg. 1528
USAA (UNITED SERVICES AUTOMOBILE ASSOCIATION); *U.S. Private*, pg. 1114
UNION BANK—The Bank of Tokyo-Mitsubishi, Ltd.; *Int'l*, pg. 157
UNION EUROPEENNE DE CIC—Groupe GAN; *Int'l*, pg. 565
UNITED ASSET MANAGEMENT CORPORATION; *U.S. Public*, pg. 1672
UNITED PLANNERS' FINANCIAL SERVICES OF AMERICA—Pacific Life Insurance Company; *U.S. Private*, pg. 831
USLIFE ADVISERS, INC.—American General Corporation; *U.S. Public*, pg. 77
U.S. TRUST CORPORATION; *U.S. Public*, pg. 1688
VALUE LINE, INC.—Arnold Bernhard & Co.; *U.S. Private*, pg. 137
VAN DEVENTER & HOCH—The Chase Manhattan Corporation; *U.S. Public*, pg. 339
VANFED INVESTMENT SERVICES, INC.—Washington Mutual Inc.; *U.S. Public*, pg. 1742
VANTAGE GLOBAL ADVISORS, INC.—Lincoln National Corporation; *U.S. Public*, pg. 998
VOLVO FINANCE S.A.—AB Volvo; *Int'l*, pg. 1476
VOLVO GROUP FINANCE SWEDEN AB—AB Volvo; *Int'l*, pg. 1476
WM FINANCIAL, INC.—Washington Mutual Inc.; *U.S. Public*, pg. 1742
WADDELL & REED ASSET MNGMT. CO.—Torchmark Corporation; *U.S. Public*, pg. 1623
WADDELL & REED SERVICES CO.—Torchmark Corporation; *U.S. Public*, pg. 1623
WARBURG ASSET MANAGEMENT ISLE OF MAN LTD.—Swiss Bank Corporation; *Int'l*, pg. 1331
WARBURG ASSET MANAGEMENT JAPAN LTD.—Swiss Bank Corporation; *Int'l*, pg. 1331
WARBURG ASSET MANAGEMENT JERSEY LTD.—Swiss Bank Corporation; *Int'l*, pg. 1331
WARRINGTON FINANCIAL SYSTEMS INC.—SunGard Data Systems Inc.; *U.S. Public*, pg. 1535
WASHINGTON SQUARE ADVISORS, INC.—ReliaStar Financial Corp.; *U.S. Public*, pg. 1376
WEISS GROUP.; *U.S. Private*, pg. 1160
THE WESTCAP CORPORATION—National Western Life Insurance Company; *U.S. Public*, pg. 1161
WESTCORP; *U.S. Public*, pg. 1756
WESTERN-SOUTHERN LIFE ASSURANCE CO.—The Western and Southern Life Insurance Company; *U.S. Private*, pg. 1164
WESTERN UNION FINANCIAL SERVICES, INC.—First Data Corporation; *U.S. Public*, pg. 631
WESTPAC FINANCIAL SERVICES GROUP LIMITED—Westpac Banking Corporation; *Int'l*, pg. 1496
WESTPEAK INVESTMENT ADVISORS, INC.—Metropolitan Life Insurance Co.; *U.S. Private*, pg. 738
WHITBREAD INVESTMENTS LTD.—Whitbread PLC; *Int'l*, pg. 1499
WOOD, STRUTHERS & WINTHROP MANAGEMENT CORP.—The Equitable Companies Incorporated; *U.S. Public*, pg. 589
WOOLWICH PLC; *Int'l*, pg. 1514
WUESTENROT FINANCE B.V.—Wuestenrot Holding GmbH; *Int'l*, pg. 1514
XEROX FINANCIAL SERVICES INC.—Xerox Corporation; *U.S. Public*, pg. 1784
YAMAICHI INTERNATIONAL (AMERICA) INC.—Yamaichi Securities Co., Ltd.; *Int'l*, pg. 1517
ZIEGLER ASSET MANAGEMENT, INC.—The Ziegler Companies, Inc.; *U.S. Public*, pg. 1792

6289 — SERVICES ALLIED WITH EXCHANGE OF SECURITIES OR COMMODITIES, NEC

AT&T AMERICAN TRANSTECH INC.—AT&T Corporation; *U.S. Public*, pg. 10
ANTHEM, INC.; *U.S. Private*, pg. 76
BNCI COMERCIAL EXPORTADORA LTDA.—The Chase Manhattan Corporation; *U.S. Public*, pg. 339
BANK OF AMERICA—BankAmerica Corporation; *U.S. Public*, pg. 180
THE BANK OF BERMUDA LIMITED-HONG KONG BRANCH—The Bank of Bermuda Limited; *Int'l*, pg. 151
BANK OF BERMUDA (NEW YORK) LIMITED—The Bank of Bermuda Limited; *Int'l*, pg. 151
BANKAMERICA REALTY SERVICES, INC.—BankAmerica Corporation; *U.S. Public*, pg. 181
BANKAMERICA TRUST CO. OF NEW YORK—BankAmerica Corporation; *U.S. Public*, pg. 181
CAMPBELL FINANCE CORP.—Campbell Soup Company; *U.S. Public*, pg. 299
CHASE AUTOMATED CLEARING HOUSE, INC.—The Chase Manhattan Corporation; *U.S. Public*, pg. 337
CHEMBANK DEPOSITORY NOMINEES, LTD.—The Chase Manhattan Corporation; *U.S. Public*, pg. 341
CITICORP; *U.S. Public*, pg. 376
CONSOLIDATED SHARE REGISTERS LIMITED—Anglo American Corporation of South Africa Limited; *Int'l*, pg. 77
CORESTATES FINANCIAL CORP.; *U.S. Public*, pg. 446
DBS FINANCE NOMINEES PTE. LTD.—DBS Bank Ltd.; *Int'l*, pg. 350
DBS INVESTMENT RESEARCH PTE. LTD.—DBS Bank Ltd.; *Int'l*, pg. 350
DBS TRUSTEE LTD.—DBS Bank Ltd.; *Int'l*, pg. 351
DKB FINANCIAL PRODUCTS, INC.—The Dai-Ichi Kangyo Bank, Limited; *Int'l*, pg. 360
DISCLOSURE INCORPORATED—Primark Corporation; *U.S. Public*, pg. 1325
DOW JONES MARKETS—Dow Jones & Company, Inc.; *U.S. Public*, pg. 525
DOW JONES TELERATE HOLDINGS, INC.—Dow Jones & Company, Inc.; *U.S. Public*, pg. 525
FEDERATION DES CAISSES POPULAIRES DESJARDINS; *Int'l*, pg. 479
THE FINANCIAL POST—Sun Media Corporation; *Int'l*, pg. 1320
FORD MOTOR COMPANY; *U.S. Public*, pg. 661
FRANKLIN RESOURCES, INC.; *U.S. Public*, pg. 679
FRANKLIN TEMPLETON INVESTOR SERVICES, INC.—Franklin Resources, Inc.; *U.S. Public*, pg. 680
HCBECK; *U.S. Private*, pg. 490
HSBC ASSET MANAGEMENT AMERICAS, INC.—HSBC Holdings plc; *Int'l*, pg. 581
HENKEL COORDINATION CENTER N.V., S.A.—Henkel KGaA; *Int'l*, pg. 612
INSTITUTIONAL BROKERS ESTIMATE SYSTEM INC. (IBIS)—Primark Corporation; *U.S. Public*, pg. 1325
INTERNATIONAL FACTORS (SINGAPORE) LTD.; *Int'l*, pg. 684
INVESTMENT ADVISERS, INC.—Lloyds TSB Group PLC; *Int'l*, pg. 813
JEFFERSON-PILOT CORPORATION; *U.S. Public*, pg. 925
KHI EUROPE FINANCE B.V.—Kawasaki Heavy Industries, Ltd.; *Int'l*, pg. 726
KEYSTONE BROKERAGE, INC.—Keystone Financial Inc.; *U.S. Public*, pg. 956
MARSH & MCLENNAN COMPANIES, INC.; *U.S. Public*, pg. 1048
THE MCGRAW-HILL COMPANIES; *U.S. Public*, pg. 1069

MONEX DEPOSIT CO.; *U.S. Private*, pg. 757
MONTREAL TRUSTCO-CORPORATE SERVICES DIV.—The Bank of Nova Scotia; *Int'l*, pg. 155
MONTREAL TRUSTCO INVESTMENT MANAGEMENT SERVICES—The Bank of Nova Scotia; *Int'l*, pg. 155
MOODY'S INVESTORS SERVICE LTD.—The Dun & Bradstreet Corporation; *U.S. Public*, pg. 537
MOODY'S JAPAN KK—The Dun & Bradstreet Corporation; *U.S. Public*, pg. 537
THE MUTUAL LIFE INSURANCE COMPANY OF NEW YORK; *U.S. Private*, pg. 769
NC COMERCIAL EXPORTADORA LTDA.—The Chase Manhattan Corporation; *U.S. Public*, pg. 339
OPTIONS CLEARING CORP.—The American Stock Exchange; *U.S. Private*, pg. 62
PB LEASING LTD.—Pitney Bowes Inc.; *U.S. Public*, pg. 1304
PEOPLE'S SECURITIES INCORPORATED—People's Bank; *U.S. Public*, pg. 1274
PHOENIX INVESTMENT COUNSEL INC.—Phoenix Home Life Mutual Insurance Company; *U.S. Private*, pg. 863
PREMIUM ADVANCE COMPANY—Robert F. Driver Co., Inc.; *U.S. Private*, pg. 343
PRIMARK CORPORATION; *U.S. Public*, pg. 1325
ROWE & PITMAN MONEY BROKING LTD.—Swiss Bank Corporation; *Int'l*, pg. 1331
SCOTT & STRINGFELLOW FINANCIAL, INC.; *U.S. Public*, pg. 1445
SCOTT & STRINGFELLOW, INC.—Scott & Stringfellow Financial, Inc.; *U.S. Public*, pg. 1445
SENTINEL ADMINISTRATIVE SERVICE CORPORATION—National Life Insurance Company; *U.S. Private*, pg. 785
STANDARD & POOR'S RATINGS SERVICES—The McGraw-Hill Companies; *U.S. Public*, pg. 1071
SUMMIT BANCORP; *U.S. Public*, pg. 1527
SUNGARD TRUST & SHAREHOLDER SYSTEMS GROUP—SunGard Data Systems Inc.; *U.S. Public*, pg. 1535
WORLDSCOPE/DISCLOSURE, LLC—Primark Corporation; *U.S. Public*, pg. 1325
YALE-CORBIN CANADA LIMITED—Williams Holdings Plc; *Int'l*, pg. 1499
YAMAICHI SECURITIES CO., LTD.; *Int'l*, pg. 1516

6311 — LIFE INSURANCE

AGC LIFE INSURANCE CO.—American General Corporation; *U.S. Public*, pg. 76
AGF ASSURANCES; *Int'l*, pg. 14
AIG LIFE INSURANCE COMPANY—American International Group, Inc.; *U.S. Public*, pg. 84
AMEV LEVENSVERZEKERING N.V.—Fortis; *Int'l*, pg. 499
AON REINSURANCE AGENCY, INC.—AON Corporation; *U.S. Public*, pg. 117
AON RISK SERVICES, INC.—AON Corporation; *U.S. Public*, pg. 117
AUSA HOLDING COMPANY—AEGON N.V.; *Int'l*, pg. 27
AUSA LIFE INSURANCE CO.—AEGON N.V.; *Int'l*, pg. 27
AXA ASSURANCES LUXEMBOURG—AXA-UAP; *Int'l*, pg. 19
AXA EQUITY & LAW LEVENSVERZEKERINGEN NV—AXA-UAP; *Int'l*, pg. 19
AXA RE ASIA—AXA-UAP; *Int'l*, pg. 19
AXA RE FRANCE—AXA-UAP; *Int'l*, pg. 18
AXA RE UNITED KINGDOM—AXA-UAP; *Int'l*, pg. 19
AXA RE UNITED STATES—AXA-UAP; *Int'l*, pg. 19
AXA-UAP; *Int'l*, pg. 18
AACHENER UND MUENCHENER LEBENSVERSICHERUNG—AMB Aachener und Muenchener Beteiligungs-AG; *Int'l*, pg. 15
THE ACACIA GROUP - ACACIA LIFE INSURANCE CO.; *U.S. Private*, pg. 10
ACACIA NATIONAL LIFE INS. CO.—The Acacia Group - Acacia Life Insurance Co.; *U.S. Private*, pg. 11
ACADEMY INSURANCE GROUP, INC.—AEGON N.V.; *Int'l*, pg. 27
ACADEMY LIFE INSURANCE CO.—AEGON N.V.; *Int'l*, pg. 27
ACCELERATION INSURANCE AGENCY, INC.—ACCEL International Corporation; *U.S. Public*, pg. 14
ACCELERATION INSURANCE AGENCY OF INDIANA, INC.—ACCEL International Corporation; *U.S. Public*, pg. 14
ACCELERATION LIFE INSURANCE AGENCY, INC.—ACCEL International Corporation; *U.S. Public*, pg. 14
ADRIATICA-SOCIEDAD ANONIMA DE SEGUROS Y REASEGUROS—Allianz Aktiengesellschaft; *Int'l*, pg. 61
ADVANTA INSURANCE COMPANIES—Advanta Corp.; *U.S. Public*, pg. 22
AEGON LEVENSVERZEKERING NV—AEGON N.V.; *Int'l*, pg. 25
AEGON NEDERLAND N.V.—AEGON N.V.; *Int'l*, pg. 26
AEGON N.V.; *Int'l*, pg. 25
AEGON USA, INC.—AEGON N.V.; *Int'l*, pg. 26
AETNA CANADA HOLDINGS LTD.—Aetna Inc.; *U.S. Public*, pg. 27
AETNA INC.; *U.S. Public*, pg. 26
AETNA INTERNATIONAL CHILE S.A.—Aetna Inc.; *U.S. Public*, pg. 27
AETNA LIFE INSURANCE AND ANNUITY CO.—Aetna Inc.; *U.S. Public*, pg. 26
AETNA LIFE INSURANCE COMPANY—Aetna Inc.; *U.S. Public*, pg. 26
AETNA LIFE INSURANCE CO. OF AMERICA (ALICA)—Aetna Inc.; *U.S. Public*, pg. 27
AETNA LIFE INSURANCE COMPANY OF ILLINOIS—Aetna Inc.; *U.S. Public*, pg. 26
AETNA UNIVERSAL INSURANCE SDN. BHD.—Aetna Inc.; *U.S. Public*, pg. 27
AFLAC INCORPORATED; *U.S. Public*, pg. 28
AFRICAN LIFE ASSURANCE COMPANY LIMITED—Anglo American Corporation of South Africa Limited; *Int'l*, pg. 77
AGRIPPINA LEBENSVERSICHERUNG AKTIENGESELLSCHAFT—Zurich Insurance Company; *Int'l*, pg. 1531
AID ASSOCIATION FOR LUTHERANS; *U.S. Private*, pg. 27
ALBANY LIFE ASSURANCE COMPANY LIMITED—The Canada Life Assurance Company; *Int'l*, pg. 255
JOHN ALDEN LIFE INSURANCE COMPANY—John Alden Financial Corporation; *U.S. Public*, pg. 39
ALFA CORPORATION; *U.S. Public*, pg. 40
ALFA LIFE INSURANCE CORP.—Alfa Corporation; *U.S. Public*, pg. 40
ALL AMERICAN LIFE INSURANCE CO.—American General Corporation; *U.S. Public*, pg. 77
ALLCITY INSURANCE CO., ROCHESTER—Leucadia National Corporation; *U.S. Public*, pg. 990
ALLCITY INSURANCE CO., ROCKVILLE CENTRE—Leucadia National Corporation; *U.S. Public*, pg. 990
ALLCITY INSURANCE CO., SCARSDALE—Leucadia National Corporation; *U.S. Public*, pg. 990
ALLEGIANCE LIFE INSURANCE COMPANY—Horace Mann Educators Corporation; *U.S. Public*, pg. 836
ALLIANZ LEBENSVERSICHERUNGS-AG—Allianz Aktiengesellschaft; *Int'l*, pg. 58
ALLIED MUTUAL INSURANCE COMPANY; *U.S. Private*, pg. 39
THE ALLSTATE CORPORATION; *U.S. Public*, pg. 55
AMERICA LATINA COMPANHIA DE SEGUROS—The Tokio Marine & Fire Insurance Company, Ltd.; *Int'l*, pg. 1392
AMERICAN-AMICABLE LIFE INSURANCE COMPANY OF TEXAS—PennCorp Financial Group, Inc.; *U.S. Public*, pg. 1271
AMERICAN ANNUITY GROUP—American Financial Group; *U.S. Public*, pg. 74
AMERICAN BANKERS INSURANCE CO. OF FLORIDA—American Bankers Insurance Group, Inc.; *U.S. Public*, pg. 67
AMERICAN BANKERS INSURANCE GROUP, INC.; *U.S. Public*, pg. 67
AMERICAN BANKERS LIFE ASSURANCE CO. OF FLORIDA—American Bankers Insurance Group, Inc.; *U.S. Public*, pg. 67
AMERICAN FAMILY LIFE ASSURANCE CO. OF COLUMBUS—AFLAC Incorporated; *U.S. Public*, pg. 28
AMERICAN FAMILY LIFE ASSURANCE COMPANY OF NEW YORK—AFLAC Incorporated; *U.S. Public*, pg. 28
AMERICAN FAMILY MUTUAL INSURANCE CO.; *U.S. Private*, pg. 53
AMERICAN FIDELITY CORP.; *U.S. Private*, pg. 54
AMERICAN FINANCIAL GROUP; *U.S. Public*, pg. 74
AMERICAN FOUNDATION LIFE INSURANCE COMPANY—Protective Life Corporation; *U.S. Public*, pg. 1336
THE AMERICAN FRANKLIN LIFE INSURANCE CO.—American General Corporation; *U.S. Public*, pg. 76
AMERICAN GENERAL CORPORATION; *U.S. Public*, pg. 76
AMERICAN GENERAL LIFE & ACCIDENT INSURANCE CO.—American General Corporation; *U.S. Public*, pg. 76
AMERICAN GENERAL LIFE INSURANCE COMPANY—American General Corporation; *U.S. Public*, pg. 76
AMERICAN GENERAL LIFE INSURANCE COMPANY OF NEW YORK—American General Corporation; *U.S. Public*, pg. 76
AMERICAN GENERAL LIFE INSURANCE COMPANY OF OKLAHOMA—American General Corporation; *U.S. Public*, pg. 76
AMERICAN HERITAGE LIFE INSURANCE CO.—American Heritage Life Investment Corp.; *U.S. Public*, pg. 79
AMERICAN HERITAGE LIFE INVESTMENT CORP.; *U.S. Public*, pg. 78
AMERICAN HOME ASSURANCE COMPANY NEW YORK, SWISS BRANCH—American International Group, Inc.; *U.S. Public*, pg. 85
AMERICAN INTERNATIONAL GROUP, INC.; *U.S. Public*, pg. 83
AMERICAN INTERNATIONAL LIFE ASSURANCE COMPANY OF NEW YORK—American International Group, Inc.; *U.S. Public*, pg. 84
AMERICAN INVESTORS LIFE INSURANCE COMPANY—American Mutual Life Holding Co.; *U.S. Private*, pg. 59
AMERICAN LIFE & CASUALTY INSURANCE CO.—Conseco Inc.; *U.S. Public*, pg. 433
AMERICAN LIFE INSURANCE CO., UK—American International Group, Inc.; *U.S. Public*, pg. 85
AMERICAN MUTUAL LIFE HOLDING CO.; *U.S. Private*, pg. 59
AMERICAN NATIONAL INSURANCE COMPANY; *U.S. Public*, pg. 87
AMERICAN NATIONAL LIFE INSURANCE CO. OF TEXAS—American National Insurance Company; *U.S. Public*, pg. 87
AMERICAN REPUBLIC INSURANCE CO.; *U.S. Private*, pg. 61
AMERICAN SECURITY GROUP—Fortis; *Int'l*, pg. 499
AMERICAN STATES LIFE INSURANCE CO.—Lincoln National Corporation; *U.S. Public*, pg. 997
AMERICAN TRAVELLERS CORPORATION—Conseco Inc.; *U.S. Public*, pg. 433
AMERICAN UNITED LIFE INSURANCE COMPANY; *U.S. Private*, pg. 64
AMERITAS LIFE INSURANCE CORP.; *U.S. Private*, pg. 65
AMERUS LIFE—American Mutual Life Holding Co.; *U.S. Private*, pg. 59
AMEX LIFE ASSURANCE CO.—General Electric Company; *U.S. Public*, pg. 712
AMVESTORS ACQUISITION SUBSIDIARY, INC.—American Mutual Life Holding Co.; *U.S. Private*, pg. 59
AMVESTORS FINANCIAL CORPORATION—American Mutual Life Holding Co.; *U.S. Private*, pg. 59
ANCHOR NATIONAL LIFE INSURANCE CO.—SunAmerica Inc.; *U.S. Public*, pg. 1533
ANSVAR AMERICA LIFE INSURANCE COMPANY—Preferred Risk Mutual Insurance; *U.S. Private*, pg. 880
ANTHEM HEALTH PLANS OF TEXAS—Anthem, Inc.; *U.S. Private*, pg. 76
ANTHEM, INC.; *U.S. Private*, pg. 76
THE ARAB-EASTERN INSURANCE COMPANY LIMITED E.C.—The Tokio Marine & Fire Insurance Company, Ltd.; *Int'l*, pg. 1392
ASAHI MUTUAL LIFE INSURANCE COMPANY; *Int'l*, pg. 85
ASCEND FINANCIAL SERVICES—The Minnesota Mutual Life Insurance Company; *U.S. Private*, pg. 750
ASSICURAZIONI GENERALI S.P.A.; *Int'l*, pg. 89
ASSOCIATES FINANCIAL LIFE INSURANCE COMPANY—Ford Motor Company; *U.S. Public*, pg. 663
ASSOCIATES FINANCIAL SERVICES CORPORATION—Ford Motor Company; *U.S. Public*, pg. 663
ASSOCIATES INSURANCE COMPANY—Ford Motor Company; *U.S. Public*, pg. 663
ASSOCIATES INSURANCE GROUP, INC.—Ford Motor Company; *U.S. Public*, pg. 663
ASSU-VIE—Groupe GAN; *Int'l*, pg. 563
ASSURANCE VIE DESJARDINS-LAURENTIENNE—Desjardins-Laurentian Financial Corporation; *Int'l*, pg. 396
ASSUREX—Groupe GAN; *Int'l*, pg. 564
ASTER INSURANCE LTD.—Harrah's Entertainment, Inc.; *U.S. Public*, pg. 790
P.T. ASURANSI JIWA DHARMALA MANULIFE—Manulife Financial (The Manufacturers Life Insurance Company); *Int'l*, pg. 841
ATLANTA LIFE INSURANCE COMPANY; *U.S. Private*, pg. 94
ATLANTIC AMERICAN CORPORATION; *U.S. Public*, pg. 143
ATLANTIC AMERICAN LIFE INSURANCE COMPANY—Atlantic American Corporation; *U.S. Public*, pg. 143
AUSTRALIA & NEW ZEALAND BANKING GROUP LIMITED; *Int'l*, pg. 98
AUSTRALIAN MUTUAL PROVIDENT; *Int'l*, pg. 100
AVCO FINANCIAL SERVICES—Textron Inc.; *U.S. Public*, pg. 1589
BA INSURANCE COMPANY, INC.—BankAmerica Corporation; *U.S. Public*, pg. 180
B.A.T INDUSTRIES P.L.C.; *Int'l*, pg. 110
BANC ONE LIFE INSURANCE CO.—Banc One Corporation; *U.S. Public*, pg. 175
BANK ONE, COLORADO—Banc One Corporation; *U.S. Public*, pg. 173
BANKERS AMERICAN LIFE ASSURANCE COMPANY—American Bankers Insurance Group, Inc.; *U.S. Public*, pg. 68
BANKERS FIDELITY LIFE INSURANCE COMPANY—Atlantic American Corporation; *U.S. Public*, pg. 143
BANKERS FINANCIAL LIFE INSURANCE COMPANY—AEGON N.V.; *Int'l*, pg. 27
BANKERS LIFE & CASUALTY COMPANY—Conseco Inc.; *U.S. Public*, pg. 433
BANKERS LIFE INSURANCE CO. OF NEW YORK—Indianapolis Life Insurance Co.; *U.S. Private*, pg. 560
BANKERS NATIONAL LIFE INSURANCE CO.—Conseco Inc.; *U.S. Public*, pg. 433
BANKERS SECURITY LIFE INSURANCE SOCIETY—ReliaStar Financial Corp.; *U.S. Public*, pg. 1375
BANNER LIFE INSURANCE CO.—Legal & General Group PLC; *Int'l*, pg. 805
BARCLAYS FINANCIAL SERVICES CO. LTD.—Barclays Bank PLC; *Int'l*, pg. 164
BARCLAYS LIFE ASSURANCE CO. LTD.—Barclays Bank PLC; *Int'l*, pg. 165
BELGIUM UNION DES ASSUREURS, BELGIQUE—La Fondiaria Assicurazioni S.p.A.; *Int'l*, pg. 784
BENEFICIAL CORPORATION; *U.S. Public*, pg. 211
BENEFICIAL LIFE INSURANCE—Deseret Management Corporation; *U.S. Private*, pg. 327
BERJAYA GENERAL INSURANCE SDN. BHD.—The Tokio Marine & Fire Insurance Company, Ltd.; *Int'l*, pg. 1392
BERKSHIRE LIFE INSURANCE COMPANY; *U.S. Private*, pg. 136
BILBAO COMPANIA ANONIMA DE SEGUROS Y REASEGUROS—Fortis; *Int'l*, pg. 499
BOSTON MUTUAL LIFE INSURANCE CO.; *U.S. Private*, pg. 161
BROOKS-SHETTLE CO.—Avemco Corporation; *U.S. Public*, pg. 152
CBI INSURANCE CO.—Commerce Bancshares, Inc.; *U.S. Public*, pg. 410
CGRM—AXA-UAP; *Int'l*, pg. 19
CNA FINANCIAL CORP.—Loews Corporation; *U.S. Public*, pg. 1010
CNL FINANCIAL CORP.; *U.S. Public*, pg. 281
CS LIFE—Credit Suisse Group; *Int'l*, pg. 345
CSE INSURANCE GROUP; *U.S. Private*, pg. 197
CAISSE FRATERNELLE VIE—Groupe GAN; *Int'l*, pg. 564
CAJA MADRID VIDA, S.A. DE SEGUROS Y REASEGUROS—Caja de Madrid Group; *Int'l*, pg. 251
CAJA REASEGURADORA DE ARGENTINA, S.A.—Corporacion MAPFRE, Compania Internacional de Reaseguros, S.A.; *Int'l*, pg. 335
CAJA REASEGURADORA DE CHILE, S.A.—Corporacion MAPFRE, Compania Internacional de Reaseguros, S.A.; *Int'l*, pg. 335
CALAMERICA LIFE INSURANCE CO.—SunAmerica Inc.; *U.S. Public*, pg. 1533
CALFARM INSURANCE AGENCY—Zenith National Insurance Corp.; *U.S. Public*, pg. 1791
CALFARM INSURANCE COMPANY—Zenith National Insurance Corp.; *U.S. Public*, pg. 1791
CANADA LIFE ASSURANCE (IRELAND) LTD.—The Canada Life Assurance Company; *Int'l*, pg. 255
CANADA LIFE INSURANCE COMPANY OF AMERICA—The Canada Life Assurance Company; *Int'l*, pg. 255
CANADA LIFE INVESTMENT MANAGEMENT LIMITED—The Canada Life Assurance Company; *Int'l*, pg. 255
CAPARO INSURANCE LTD.—Caparo Group Ltd.; *Int'l*, pg. 265

CAPITAL LIBERTY, L.P.—AEGON N.V.; *Int'l*, pg. 26
CARIBBEAN AMERICAN LIFE ASSURANCE COMPANY—American Bankers Insurance Group, Inc.; *U.S. Public*, pg. 67
CASIOPEA REASEGURADORA, S.A.—Telefonica de Espana, S.A.; *Int'l*, pg. 1371
CATHOLIC ORDER OF FORESTERS; *U.S. Private*, pg. 220
CENTRAL PENNSYLVANIA LIFE INSURANCE CO.—Omega Financial Corporation; *U.S. Public*, pg. 1222
CENTRAL UNITED LIFE INSURANCE CO.; *U.S. Private*, pg. 225
CENTURY CREDIT LIFE INSURANCE COMPANY—Bancorp South Inc.; *U.S. Public*, pg. 176
CENTURY EMPLOYERS LIFE ASSURANCE COMPANY LIMITED—Invesco Group Asset Management Ltd.; *Int'l*, pg. 685
CENTURY LIFE—Invesco Group Asset Management Ltd.; *Int'l*, pg. 685
CERTIFIED LIFE INSURANCE—Conseco Inc.; *U.S. Public*, pg. 433
CHARLESTON FINANCIAL SERVICES, INC.—First Financial Holdings, Inc.; *U.S. Public*, pg. 634
CHARTER NATIONAL LIFE INSURANCE CO.—Leucadia National Corporation; *U.S. Public*, pg. 990
CHEROKEE NATIONAL LIFE INSURANCE CO.—CNL Financial Corp.; *U.S. Public*, pg. 282
THE CHESAPEAKE LIFE INSURANCE CO.—United Insurance Companies, Inc.; *U.S. Public*, pg. 1679
CHRYSLER FINANCIAL CORPORATION—Chrysler Corporation; *U.S. Public*, pg. 354
CHRYSLER INSURANCE CO.—Chrysler Corporation; *U.S. Public*, pg. 354
CHRYSLER LIFE INSURANCE CO.—Chrysler Corporation; *U.S. Public*, pg. 354
CIGNA COMPANIA DE SEGUROS DE PANAMA S.A.—Cigna Corp.; *U.S. Public*, pg. 364
CIGNA CORP.; *U.S. Public*, pg. 356
CIGNA INSURANCE COMPANY (HELLAS) S.A.—Cigna Corp.; *U.S. Public*, pg. 364
CIGNA INTERNATIONAL REINSURANCE COMPANY LTD.—Cigna Corp.; *U.S. Public*, pg. 364
CIGNA LIFE INSURANCE AUSTRALIA LIMITED—Cigna Corp.; *U.S. Public*, pg. 364
CIGNA LIFE INSURANCE COMPANY—Cigna Corp.; *U.S. Public*, pg. 361
CIGNA LIFE INSURANCE COMPANY OF CANADA—Cigna Corp.; *U.S. Public*, pg. 362
CIGNA LIFE INSURANCE COMPANY OF EUROPE S.A.-N.V.—Cigna Corp.; *U.S. Public*, pg. 364
CIGNA RE CORPORATION—Cigna Corp.; *U.S. Public*, pg. 360
CIGNA REINSURANCE COMPANY S.A.-N.V.—Cigna Corp.; *U.S. Public*, pg. 365
CIGNA SEGURADORA S.A.—Cigna Corp.; *U.S. Public*, pg. 363
CIGNA SEGUROS DE COLOMBIA S.A.—Cigna Corp.; *U.S. Public*, pg. 363
CIGNA WORLDWIDE INSURANCE COMPANY—Cigna Corp.; *U.S. Public*, pg. 365
CINCINNATI FINANCIAL CORP.; *U.S. Public*, pg. 368
CINCINNATI LIFE INSURANCE CO.—Cincinnati Financial Corp.; *U.S. Public*, pg. 368
CLAYTON HOMES, INC.; *U.S. Public*, pg. 382
CLAYTON REINSURANCE, LTD.—The Reliable Life Insurance Company; *U.S. Public*, pg. 1374
COFASSUR VIE—Groupe GAN; *Int'l*, pg. 564
COLBOURNE INSURANCE CO. LTD.—The Coastal Corporation; *U.S. Public*, pg. 391
COLINA INSURANCE COMPANY LIMITED—Cigna Corp.; *U.S. Public*, pg. 363
COLONIAL COMPANIES, INC.—UNUM Corporation; *U.S. Public*, pg. 1699
COLONIAL LIFE & ACCIDENT INSURANCE CO.—UNUM Corporation; *U.S. Public*, pg. 1699
COLONIAL PENN GROUP, INC.—Leucadia National Corporation; *U.S. Public*, pg. 990
COLUMBIA UNIVERSAL LIFE INSURANCE COMPANY—American Heritage Life Investment Corp.; *U.S. Public*, pg. 79
COLUMBIAN LIFE INSURANCE COMPANY—Columbian Mutual Life Insurance Co.; *U.S. Private*, pg. 256
COLUMBIAN MUTUAL LIFE INSURANCE CO.; *U.S. Private*, pg. 256
COLUMBUS LIFE INSURANCE CO.—The Western and Southern Life Insurance Company; *U.S. Private*, pg. 1164
COMBINED INSURANCE COMPANY OF AMERICA—AON Corporation; *U.S. Public*, pg. 118
COMBINED INSURANCE COMPANY OF IRELAND LTD.—AON Corporation; *U.S. Public*, pg. 118
COMBINED LIFE INSURANCE CO. OF AUSTRALIA, LTD.—AON Corporation; *U.S. Public*, pg. 118
COMMERCIAL UNION CORPORATION—Commercial Union plc; *Int'l*, pg. 308
COMMERCIAL UNION LIFE ASSURANCE COMPANY OF CANADA—Commercial Union plc; *Int'l*, pg. 308
COMMERCIAL UNION LIFE INSURANCE COMPANY OF AMERICA—Commercial Union plc; *Int'l*, pg. 308
COMMERCIAL UNION PLC; *Int'l*, pg. 308
COMMODORE NATIONAL LIFE—CNL Financial Corp.; *U.S. Public*, pg. 282
COMPAGNIA EURPOEA D'ASSICURAZIONE—Allianz Aktiengesellschaft; *Int'l*, pg. 61
COMPAGNIE INTERNATIONALE D'ASSURANCES ET REASSURANCES (CIAR)—Corporacion MAPFRE, Compania Internacional de Reaseguros, S.A.; *Int'l*, pg. 335
A.S. COMPANHIA PORTUGUESA DE SEGUROS—La Fondiaria Assicurazioni S.p.A.; *Int'l*, pg. 784
COMPANION LIFE INSURANCE CO.—Mutual of Omaha Insurance Company; *U.S. Private*, pg. 770
CONCOMBER, LTD.—Unicom Corporation; *U.S. Public*, pg. 1664
CONCORD GENERAL LIFE INSURANCE COMPANY—American Heritage Life Investment Corp.; *U.S. Public*, pg. 79
CONFEDERATION LIFE INSURANCE AND ANNUITY COMPANY—Confederation Life Insurance Company; *Int'l*, pg. 326
CONFEDERATION LIFE INSURANCE COMPANY; *Int'l*, pg. 325
CONFEDERATION LIFE INSURANCE COMPANY (U.K.), LIMITED—Sun Life Assurance Company of Canada; *Int'l*, pg. 1319
CONGRESS LIFE INSURANCE COMPANY—Security American Financial Enterprises, Inc.; *U.S. Private*, pg. 980
CONNECTICUT GENERAL LIFE INSURANCE COMPANY—Cigna Corp.; *U.S. Public*, pg. 360
CONSECO INC.; *U.S. Public*, pg. 432
CONSTITUTION LIFE INSURANCE CO.—Southwestern Financial Corporation; *U.S. Private*, pg. 1018
CONSTITUTION REINSURANCE CORPORATION—Exor Group; *Int'l*, pg. 467
CONSUMERS CAR CARE CORPORATION—Consumers Financial Corporation; *U.S. Public*, pg. 438
CONSUMERS LIFE INSURANCE COMPANY—Consumers Financial Corporation; *U.S. Public*, pg. 438
CONSUMERS REINSURANCE COMPANY—Consumers Financial Corporation; *U.S. Public*, pg. 438
CONTINENTAL ASSURANCE COMPANY; *U.S. Private*, pg. 267
CONTINENTAL INTERNATIONAL LIFE INSURANCE CO.—UNUM Corporation; *U.S. Public*, pg. 1700
CONTINENTAL LIFE INSURANCE COMPANY—Conseco Inc.; *U.S. Public*, pg. 433
CONTINENTAL LIFE INSURANCE PLC—Loews Corporation; *U.S. Public*, pg. 1011
CONTINENTAL NATIONAL LIFE INSURANCE CO.—UNUM Corporation; *U.S. Public*, pg. 1700
COOP LEBENSVERSICHERUNGS GENOSSENSCHAFT—Coop Switzerland; *Int'l*, pg. 330
CORPORACION MAPFRE, COMPANIA INTERNACIONAL DE REASEGUROS, S.A.; *Int'l*, pg. 332
COUNTRY INVESTORS LIFE ASSURANCE COMPANY—Country Life Insurance Company; *U.S. Private*, pg. 279
COUNTRY LIFE INSURANCE COMPANY; *U.S. Private*, pg. 278
COVENTRY HEALTH & LIFE INSURANCE—Coventry Corporation; *U.S. Public*, pg. 454
CRITERION LIFE INSURANCE CO.—Berkshire Hathaway Inc.; *U.S. Public*, pg. 219
CROSS-COUNTRY LIFE INSURANCE COMPANY—AEGON N.V.; *Int'l*, pg. 27
CROWN AMERICA LIFE INSURANCE COMPANY—Extendicare Inc.; *Int'l*, pg. 468
CRUSADER COMPANY (GHANA) LIMITED—Cigna Corp.; *U.S. Public*, pg. 363
CUNA MUTUAL INSURANCE SOCIETY; *U.S. Private*, pg. 296
DAI-ICHI LIFE INSURANCE AGENCY EUROPE LIMITED—Dai-ichi Mutual Life Insurance Company; *Int'l*, pg. 362
DAI-ICHI LIFE INSURANCE AGENCY (U.S.A.) INC.—Dai-ichi Mutual Life Insurance Company; *Int'l*, pg. 362
DAI-ICHI LIFE INSURANCE AGENCY (U.S.A.), INC.-LOS ANGELES—Dai-ichi Mutual Life Insurance Company; *Int'l*, pg. 362
DAI-ICHI LIFE INTERNATIONAL (AUSTRALIA) LIMITED—Dai-ichi Mutual Life Insurance Company; *Int'l*, pg. 362
DAI-ICHI LIFE INTERNATIONAL (CANADA), INC.—Dai-ichi Mutual Life Insurance Company; *Int'l*, pg. 362
DAI-ICHI LIFE INTERNATIONAL (H.K.) LIMITED—Dai-ichi Mutual Life Insurance Company; *Int'l*, pg. 362
DAI-ICHI LIFE INTERNATIONAL (U.K.) LIMITED—Dai-ichi Mutual Life Insurance Company; *Int'l*, pg. 362
DAI-ICHI LIFE PROPERTY (LONDON) LIMITED—Dai-ichi Mutual Life Insurance Company; *Int'l*, pg. 363
DAI-ICHI MUTUAL LIFE INSURANCE COMPANY; *Int'l*, pg. 362
THE DAI-ICHI MUTUAL LIFE INSURANCE (OI OFFICE)—Dai-ichi Mutual Life Insurance Company; *Int'l*, pg. 362
DAI-ICHI SEIMEI AMERICA CORP.—Dai-ichi Mutual Life Insurance Company; *Int'l*, pg. 362
DE BES' INSURANCE LTD.—Weyerhaeuser Company; *U.S. Public*, pg. 1764
DEERE & COMPANY; *U.S. Public*, pg. 491
DELAWARE AMERICAN LIFE INSURANCE CO.—American International Group, Inc.; *U.S. Public*, pg. 84
DELTA LIFE & ANNUITY CO.—American Mutual Life Holding Co.; *U.S. Private*, pg. 59
DELTA LIFE CORPORATION—American Mutual Life Holding Co.; *U.S. Private*, pg. 59
DESJARDINS LAURENTIAN LIFE ASSURANCE—Desjardins-Laurentian Financial Corporation; *Int'l*, pg. 396
DIXIE NATIONAL LIFE INSURANCE COMPANY—Standard Management Corporation; *U.S. Public*, pg. 1502
DOMINION INSURANCE LTD.—La Fondiaria Assicurazioni S.p.A.; *Int'l*, pg. 784
DONGBU AETNA LIFE INSURANCE CO., LTD.—Aetna Inc.; *U.S. Public*, pg. 27
ROBERT F. DRIVER CO., INC.; *U.S. Private*, pg. 343
EMC INSURANCE GROUP, INC.; *U.S. Public*, pg. 545
EAGLE STAR VIE SA—B.A.T Industries P.L.C.; *Int'l*, pg. 112
838 INVESTMENT GROUP, INC.—WSFS Financial Corporation; *U.S. Public*, pg. 1729
ELAN LIFE INSURANCE COMPANY—Firstar Corporation; *U.S. Public*, pg. 643
EMPIRE INSURANCE GROUP—Leucadia National Corporation; *U.S. Public*, pg. 990
EMPIRE LIFE INSURANCE COMPANY—Washington Mutual Inc.; *U.S. Public*, pg. 1742
EMPRESA GUATEMALTICA CIGNA DE SEGUROS, SOCIEDAD ANONIMA—Cigna Corp.; *U.S. Public*, pg. 364
THE EQUITABLE COMPANIES INCORPORATED; *U.S. Public*, pg. 588
EQUITABLE LIFE INSURANCE COMPANY OF IOWA—ING Groep N.V.; *Int'l*, pg. 647
EQUITABLE OF IOWA COMPANIES—ING Groep N.V.; *Int'l*, pg. 647
ERIE FAMILY LIFE INSURANCE COMPANY; *U.S. Public*, pg. 590
ERIE INSURANCE GROUP—Erie Family Life Insurance Company; *U.S. Public*, pg. 591
FAIRLANE LIFE INSURANCE COMPANY—Ford Motor Company; *U.S. Public*, pg. 664
FAMILY SERVICE LIFE INSURANCE CO.—Torchmark Corporation; *U.S. Public*, pg. 1622
FARMERS AND TRADERS LIFE INSURANCE CO.; *U.S. Private*, pg. 394
FARMERS GROUP, INC.—B.A.T Industries P.L.C.; *Int'l*, pg. 110
FARMERS NEW WORLD LIFE INSURANCE CO.—B.A.T Industries P.L.C.; *Int'l*, pg. 110
FARMLAND INSURANCE AGENCY, INC.—Farmland Industries, Inc.; *U.S. Private*, pg. 396
FEDERAL KEMPER LIFE ASSURANCE COMPANY—Zurich Insurance Company; *Int'l*, pg. 1530
FIANZAS MONTERREY S.A.—Aetna Inc.; *U.S. Public*, pg. 27
FIDELITY & GUARANTY LIFE INSURANCE CO.—USF&G Corporation; *U.S. Public*, pg. 1659
FIDELITY MUTUAL LIFE INSURANCE CO.; *U.S. Private*, pg. 403
FINANCIAL INDUSTRIES CORP.; *U.S. Public*, pg. 622
FINANCIAL LIFE ASSURANCE CO. OF CANADA—American General Corporation; *U.S. Public*, pg. 77
FINANCIAL LIFE COMPANIES, INC.; *U.S. Private*, pg. 404
FINANCIAL LIFE INSURANCE CO. OF GEORGIA—Wachovia Corporation; *U.S. Public*, pg. 1730
FIRST COLONY LIFE INSURANCE CO.—General Electric Company; *U.S. Public*, pg. 711
FIRST COLORADO BANKSHARES INSURANCE CO.—Banc One Corporation; *U.S. Public*, pg. 173
FIRST EQUICOR LIFE INSURANCE COMPANY—Cigna Corp.; *U.S. Public*, pg. 361
FIRST PENN-PACIFIC LIFE INSURANCE CO.—Lincoln National Corporation; *U.S. Public*, pg. 998
FIRST-RE LIFE INSURANCE COMPANY—AEGON N.V.; *Int'l*, pg. 27
FIRST SOUTHEAST INSURANCE AGENCY—First Financial Holdings, Inc.; *U.S. Public*, pg. 634
FIRST SUNAMERICA LIFE INSURANCE COMPANY—SunAmerica Inc.; *U.S. Public*, pg. 1533
FIRST UNION INSURANCE GROUP, INC.—First Union Corporation; *U.S. Public*, pg. 640
FIRST UNITED AMERICAN LIFE INSURANCE COMPANY—Torchmark Corporation; *U.S. Public*, pg. 1623
FIRST UNUM LIFE INSURANCE COMPANY—UNUM Corporation; *U.S. Public*, pg. 1699
FIRST VALLEY LIFE INSURANCE COMPANY—Summit Bancorp; *U.S. Public*, pg. 1528
FIRST VIRGINIA LIFE INSURANCE COMPANY—First Virginia Banks, Inc.; *U.S. Public*, pg. 642
FLORIDA PROGRESS CORPORATION; *U.S. Public*, pg. 655
FLORISTS' MUTUAL INSURANCE CO.; *U.S. Private*, pg. 415
FORD LIFE INSURANCE COMPANY—SunAmerica Inc.; *U.S. Public*, pg. 1533
THE FORETHOUGHT GROUP, INC.—Hillenbrand Industries, Inc.; *U.S. Public*, pg. 828
FORTIS; *Int'l*, pg. 498
FORTIS BENEFITS INSURANCE COMPANY—Fortis; *Int'l*, pg. 499
FORTIS, INC.—Fortis; *Int'l*, pg. 499
FORTIS (U.K.) LIMITED—Fortis; *Int'l*, pg. 499
FOUNDATION HEALTH BENEFIT LIFE INSURANCE COMPANY—Foundation Health Systems, Inc.; *U.S. Public*, pg. 678
FOUNDATION INSURANCE COMPANY—Foundation Health Systems, Inc.; *U.S. Public*, pg. 678
FRANDISCO LIFE INSURANCE CO.—First Franklin Financial Corp.; *U.S. Private*, pg. 407
THE FRANKLIN LIFE INSURANCE COMPANY—American General Corporation; *U.S. Public*, pg. 76
FREMONT GENERAL CORPORATION; *U.S. Public*, pg. 681
FREMONT INDEMNITY CO./MEDICAL PROFESSIONAL LIAB. DIV.—Fremont General Corporation; *U.S. Public*, pg. 681
FREMONT LIFE INSURANCE CO.—Fremont General Corporation; *U.S. Public*, pg. 681
FRONT ROYAL INSURANCE COMPANY—Front Royal, Inc.; *U.S. Private*, pg. 430
FUKOKU MUTUAL LIFE INSURANCE COMPANY; *Int'l*, pg. 529
G & W LIFE INSURANCE CO.—Deposit Guaranty Corp.; *U.S. Public*, pg. 501
G.E. CAPITAL ASSURANCE—General Electric Company; *U.S. Public*, pg. 712
GAN ESPANA SEGUROS GENERALES Y VIDA—Groupe GAN; *Int'l*, pg. 564
GAN INTERNATIONAL—Groupe GAN; *Int'l*, pg. 564
GAN ITALIA VITA S.P.A.—Groupe GAN; *Int'l*, pg. 564
GAN LIFE AND PENSIONS PLC—Groupe GAN; *Int'l*, pg. 565
GAN PACIFIQUE VIE—Groupe GAN; *Int'l*, pg. 564
GAN PORTUGAL VIDA—Groupe GAN; *Int'l*, pg. 564
GAN VIE—Groupe GAN; *Int'l*, pg. 565
GAN VIE GUADELOUPE—Groupe GAN; *Int'l*, pg. 565
GAN VIE MARTINIQUE—Groupe GAN; *Int'l*, pg. 565
GEICO CORPORATION—Berkshire Hathaway Inc.; *U.S. Public*, pg. 219
GENERAL AMERICAN LIFE INSURANCE CO.; *U.S. Private*, pg. 443

GENEVA LIFE INSURANCE COMPANY—Zurich Insurance Company; *Int'l*, pg. 1529
GLOBE LIFE AND ACCIDENT INSURANCE CO.—Torchmark Corporation; *U.S. Public*, pg. 1622
GODWINS BOOKE & DICKENSON, INC.—AON Corporation; *U.S. Public*, pg. 118
GOLDEN STATE MUTUAL LIFE INSURANCE COMPANY; *U.S. Private*, pg. 461
GRANITE STATE INSURANCE CO.—American International Group, Inc.; *U.S. Public*, pg. 84
GREAT AMERICAN HOLDING CORPORATION—American Financial Group; *U.S. Public*, pg. 74
GREAT-WEST LIFE & ANNUITY INSURANCE CO.—The Great-West Life Assurance Company; *Int'l*, pg. 558
THE GREAT-WEST LIFE ASSURANCE COMPANY; *Int'l*, pg. 557
GREAT WESTERN CONSUMER FINANCE GROUP—Washington Mutual Inc.; *U.S. Public*, pg. 1741
GREEN TREE LIFE INSURANCE CO.—Green Tree Financial Corporation; *U.S. Public*, pg. 763
GROUP LIFE & HEALTH INSURANCE COMPANY—Blue Cross & Blue Shield of Texas, Inc.; *U.S. Private*, pg. 152
GROUPE DES ASSURANCES DE TUNISIE (GAT)—Groupe GAN; *Int'l*, pg. 565
GUARANTEE AMERICAN LIFE COMPANY—Guarantee Life Insurance Co.; *U.S. Public*, pg. 768
GUARANTEE LIFE INSURANCE CO.; *U.S. Public*, pg. 768
GUARANTY CORPORATION; *U.S. Private*, pg. 485
GUARDIAN BAILLIE GIFFORD, LTD.—The Guardian Life Insurance Company of America; *U.S. Private*, pg. 486
THE GUARDIAN INSURANCE & ANNUITY CO. (GIAC)—The Guardian Life Insurance Company of America; *U.S. Private*, pg. 486
THE GUARDIAN LIFE INSURANCE COMPANY OF AMERICA; *U.S. Private*, pg. 486
GUNES SIGORTA—Groupe GAN; *Int'l*, pg. 565
HSBC GIBBS LTD.—HSBC Holdings plc; *Int'l*, pg. 579
HSBC INSURANCE LIMITED—HSBC Holdings plc; *Int'l*, pg. 582
HADAR INSURANCE COMPANY LTD.—Groupe GAN; *Int'l*, pg. 565
HANDELSBANKEN LIV—Svenska Handelsbanken; *Int'l*, pg. 1327
HARLEYSVILLE GROUP; *U.S. Public*, pg. 786
HARLEYSVILLE LIFE INSURANCE CO.—Harleysville Group; *U.S. Public*, pg. 787
HARRIS LIFE INSURANCE COMPANY—Bank of Montreal; *Int'l*, pg. 154
THE HARTFORD FINANCIAL SERVICES GROUP INC.; *U.S. Public*, pg. 794
HARTFORD FIRE INSURANCE CO.—The Hartford Financial Services Group Inc.; *U.S. Public*, pg. 794
HARTFORD INSURANCE GROUP OF CANADA—The Hartford Financial Services Group Inc.; *U.S. Public*, pg. 794
THE HARTFORD LIFE INSURANCE COMPANY—The Hartford Financial Services Group Inc.; *U.S. Public*, pg. 794
HEALTH & LIFE INSURANCE CO. OF AMERICA—Conseco Inc.; *U.S. Public*, pg. 434
HIGH STATE/INVESTORS GUARANTY—B.A.T Industries P.L.C.; *Int'l*, pg. 110
HILB, ROGAL AND HAMILTON COMPANY; *U.S. Public*, pg. 826
HILLENBRAND INDUSTRIES, INC.; *U.S. Public*, pg. 828
THE HOLDEN GROUP—EdperBrascan Corporation; *Int'l*, pg. 435
HOME BENEFICIAL CORPORATION—American General Corporation; *U.S. Public*, pg. 76
HOME BENEFICIAL LIFE INSURANCE CO.—American General Corporation; *U.S. Public*, pg. 77
HOME OWNERS LIFE INSURANCE CO.—Old Republic International Corporation; *U.S. Public*, pg. 1218
THE HONGKONG AND SHANGHAI BANKING CORPORATION LIMITED (HONGKONGBANK)—HSBC Holdings plc; *Int'l*, pg. 583
HORACE MANN EDUCATORS CORPORATION; *U.S. Public*, pg. 835
HORACE MANN LIFE INSURANCE COMPANY—Horace Mann Educators Corporation; *U.S. Public*, pg. 836
HOUSEHOLD FINANCE CORPORATION—Household International, Inc.; *U.S. Public*, pg. 842
HOUSEHOLD FINANCIAL CORPORATION LIMITED—Household International, Inc.; *U.S. Public*, pg. 842
HOUSEHOLD RETAIL SERVICES, INC.—Household International, Inc.; *U.S. Public*, pg. 842
HUDSON LIFE REASSURANCE CORPORATION—Skandia Insurance Company Limited; *Int'l*, pg. 1257
THE HUNTINGTON NATIONAL LIFE INSURANCE COMPANY—Huntington Bancshares Inc.; *U.S. Public*, pg. 850
I.C.H. CORPORATION; *U.S. Public*, pg. 853
IDS LIFE INSURANCE CO. OF NEW YORK—American Express Company; *U.S. Public*, pg. 73
ILA FINANCIAL SERVICES, INC.—Franklin Resources, Inc.; *U.S. Public*, pg. 680
INA LIFE INSURANCE CO., LTD.—Cigna Corp.; *U.S. Public*, pg. 362
INA LIFE INSURANCE COMPANY OF NEW YORK—Cigna Corp.; *U.S. Public*, pg. 362
ING GROEP N.V.; *Int'l*, pg. 647
ING INVESTMENT MANAGEMENT INC.—ING Groep N.V.; *Int'l*, pg. 648
ING (U.S.) CAPITAL HOLDINGS—ING Groep N.V.; *Int'l*, pg. 648
ITT HARTFORD LIFE & ANNUITY INSURANCE CORPORATION—The Hartford Financial Services Group Inc.; *U.S. Public*, pg. 795
ILLINOIS BANC ONE INSURANCE SERVICES, INC.—Banc One Corporation; *U.S. Public*, pg. 174
ILLINOIS BANC ONE LIFE INSURANCE CO.—Banc One Corporation; *U.S. Public*, pg. 174
ILLINOIS NATIONAL INSURANCE CO.—American International Group, Inc.; *U.S. Public*, pg. 84
THE IMPERIAL LIFE ASSURANCE CO.—Desjardins-Laurentian Financial Corporation; *Int'l*, pg. 396
INAMEX S.A.—Cigna Corp.; *U.S. Public*, pg. 364
INLAND NATIONAL INS. CO.—American International Group, Inc.; *U.S. Public*, pg. 84
INTEC—AXA-UAP; *Int'l*, pg. 19
INTERNATIONAL LIFE INVESTORS INSURANCE COMPANY—AEGON N.V.; *Int'l*, pg. 27
INTERNCONTINENTAL LIFE CORP.—Financial Industries Corp.; *U.S. Public*, pg. 622
INVESCO GROUP ASSET MANAGEMENT LTD.; *Int'l*, pg. 685
INVESTORS FIDELITY LIFE ASSURANCE CORP.—Consumers Financial Corporation; *U.S. Public*, pg. 438
INVESTORS HERITAGE LIFE INSURANCE CO.—Kentucky Investors, Inc.; *U.S. Public*, pg. 952
INVESTORS INSURANCE CORP.—Investors Insurance Group, Inc.; *U.S. Public*, pg. 912
INVESTORS INSURANCE GROUP, INC.; *U.S. Public*, pg. 911
INVESTORS NATIONAL LIFE INSURANCE CO.—The Seibels Bruce Group, Inc.; *U.S. Public*, pg. 1454
IOWA FIDELITY LIFE INSURANCE CO.—AEGON N.V.; *Int'l*, pg. 27
J.C. PENNEY LIFE INSURANCE COMPANY—JC Penney Company, Inc.; *U.S. Public*, pg. 917
JC PENNEY REINSURANCE COMPANY—JC Penney Company, Inc.; *U.S. Public*, pg. 917
JACKSON NATIONAL LIFE INSURANCE COMPANY—Prudential Corporation PLC; *Int'l*, pg. 1073
JARDINE MATHESON HOLDINGS LIMITED; *Int'l*, pg. 703
JEFFERSON-PILOT CORPORATION; *U.S. Public*, pg. 925
JEFFERSON-PILOT LIFE INSURANCE CO.—Jefferson-Pilot Corporation; *U.S. Public*, pg. 926
JOHN HANCOCK MUTUAL LIFE INSURANCE COMPANY; *U.S. Private*, pg. 589
KMA INSURANCE AGENCY, INC.—Michigan Physicians Mutual Liability Inc.; *U.S. Private*, pg. 741
KANSAS CITY LIFE INSURANCE CO.; *U.S. Public*, pg. 942
KENTUCKY INVESTORS, INC.; *U.S. Public*, pg. 951
KENTUCKY MEDICAL INSURANCE COMPANY (KMIC)—Michigan Physicians Mutual Liability Inc.; *U.S. Private*, pg. 741
KEY BANK LIFE INSURANCE, LTD.—Keycorp; *U.S. Public*, pg. 954
KEYPORT LIFE INSURANCE COMPANY—Liberty Mutual Insurance Co.; *U.S. Private*, pg. 666
KEYSTONE HERITAGE GROUP, INC.—Fulton Financial Corp.; *U.S. Public*, pg. 687
KOLON-MET LIFE INSURANCE COMPANY LIMITED—Metropolitan Life Insurance Co.; *U.S. Private*, pg. 738
THE KYOEI LIFE INSURANCE CO., LTD.; *Int'l*, pg. 776
LTCB MERCHANT BANK (SINGAPORE) LIMITED—The Long-Term Credit Bank of Japan, Limited; *Int'l*, pg. 816
LA FONDIARIA ASSICURAZIONI S.P.A.; *Int'l*, pg. 784
LA FRANCO PENN LIFE COMPANIA DE SEGURES DE VIDA S.A.—PennCorp Financial Group, Inc.; *U.S. Public*, pg. 1271
LA RURAL DEL PARAGUAY S.A. , PARAGUAYA DE SEGUROS—The Tokio Marine & Fire Insurance Company, Ltd.; *Int'l*, pg. 1392
LA VITTORIA RIASSICURAZIONI—SCOR; *Int'l*, pg. 1152
LEGACY MARKETING GROUP; *U.S. Private*, pg. 658
LEGAL & GENERAL AMERICA, INC.—Legal & General Group PLC; *Int'l*, pg. 805
LEGAL & GENERAL ASSURANCE HOLDINGS (AUSTRALIA) LIMITED—Legal & General Group PLC; *Int'l*, pg. 805
LEGAL & GENERAL ASSURANCE SOCIETY LIMITED—Legal & General Group PLC; *Int'l*, pg. 805
LEGAL & GENERAL GROUP PLC; *Int'l*, pg. 805
LEGAL & GENERAL HOLDINGS (FRANCE) S.A.—Legal & General Group PLC; *Int'l*, pg. 805
LEUCADIA NATIONAL CORPORATION; *U.S. Public*, pg. 989
LIBERTY BANCORP, INC.—Banc One Corporation; *U.S. Public*, pg. 174
LIBERTY CORPORATION; *U.S. Public*, pg. 991
LIBERTY LIFE ASSURANCE COMPANY OF BOSTON—Liberty Mutual Insurance Co.; *U.S. Private*, pg. 666
LIBERTY LIFE INSURANCE COMPANY—Liberty Corporation; *U.S. Public*, pg. 992
LIBERTY NATIONAL LIFE INSURANCE CO.—Torchmark Corporation; *U.S. Public*, pg. 1622
LIFE INSURANCE COMPANY OF NORTH AMERICA—Cigna Corp.; *U.S. Public*, pg. 362
THE LIFE INSURANCE CO. OF VIRGINIA—General Electric Company; *U.S. Public*, pg. 712
LINCOLN AMERICAN LIFE INSURANCE CO.—Conseco Inc.; *U.S. Public*, pg. 433
LINCOLN ASSURANCE LIMITED—Lincoln National Corporation; *U.S. Public*, pg. 998
LINCOLN NATIONAL CORPORATION; *U.S. Public*, pg. 997
LINCOLN NATIONAL INTERMEDIARIES, INC.—Lincoln National Corporation; *U.S. Public*, pg. 998
THE LINCOLN NATIONAL LIFE INSURANCE CO.—Lincoln National Corporation; *U.S. Public*, pg. 998
L'ITALICA - DIVAL VITA—Allianz Aktiengesellschaft; *Int'l*, pg. 61
LIVSFORSIKRINGS-AKTIESELSKABET UTRECHT—Fortis; *Int'l*, pg. 499
LLOYDS ABBEY LIFE PLC—Lloyds TSB Group PLC; *Int'l*, pg. 813
THE LOEWEN GROUP, INC.; *Int'l*, pg. 814
LONDON LIFE INSURANCE GROUP—EdperBrascan Corporation; *Int'l*, pg. 435
LUTHERAN BROTHERHOOD; *U.S. Private*, pg. 681
LUXLIFE—Groupe GAN; *Int'l*, pg. 565
MBL LIFE ASSURANCE CORPORATION; *U.S. Private*, pg. 685
MBNA INSURANCE SERVICES—MBNA Corporation; *U.S. Public*, pg. 1023
MLIG, INC.—AEGON N.V.; *Int'l*, pg. 27
MMI COMPANIES, INC.; *U.S. Public*, pg. 1027
MSI INSURANCE COMPANIES; *U.S. Private*, pg. 688
MADISON NATIONAL LIFE INSURANCE CO., INC.—Geneve Corporation; *U.S. Private*, pg. 446
MAIN LIFE INSURANCE CO.—The Midland Company; *U.S. Public*, pg. 1111
MANAMERICA - TAIWAN BRANCH—Manulife Financial (The Manufacturers Life Insurance Company); *Int'l*, pg. 841
MANHATTAN LIFE INSURANCE COMPANY—The Union Central Life Insurance Co.; *U.S. Private*, pg. 1118
MANHATTAN NATIONAL LIFE INSURANCE COMPANY—Conseco Inc.; *U.S. Public*, pg. 434
THE MANUFACTURERS LIFE INSURANCE COMPANY OF AMERICA—Manulife Financial (The Manufacturers Life Insurance Company); *Int'l*, pg. 840
THE MANUFACTURERS LIFE INSURANCE COMPANY OF MICHIGAN—Manulife Financial (The Manufacturers Life Insurance Company); *Int'l*, pg. 840
THE MANUFACTURERS LIFE INSURANCE COMPANY (UK) LIMITED—Manulife Financial (The Manufacturers Life Insurance Company); *Int'l*, pg. 841
MANUFACTURERS LIFE SERVICES CANADA LIMITED—Manulife Financial (The Manufacturers Life Insurance Company); *Int'l*, pg. 840
THE MANUFACTURERS (PACIFIC ASIA) INSURANCE CO. LTD.—Manulife Financial (The Manufacturers Life Insurance Company); *Int'l*, pg. 841
MANULIFE FINANCIAL SYSTEMS (HONG KONG) LIMITED—Manulife Financial (The Manufacturers Life Insurance Company); *Int'l*, pg. 841
MANULIFE FINANCIAL (THE MANUFACTURERS LIFE INSURANCE COMPANY); *Int'l*, pg. 840
MANULIFE (INTERNATIONAL) LIMITED—Manulife Financial (The Manufacturers Life Insurance Company); *Int'l*, pg. 841
MANULIFE INVESTMENT HOLDINGS LIMITED—Manulife Financial (The Manufacturers Life Insurance Company); *Int'l*, pg. 840
MANULIFE - PHILIPPINES BRANCH—Manulife Financial (The Manufacturers Life Insurance Company); *Int'l*, pg. 841
MANULIFE (SINGAPORE) PTE. LTD.—Manulife Financial (The Manufacturers Life Insurance Company); *Int'l*, pg. 841
MAPFRE ASISTENCIA CIA. INTERNACIONAL DE SEGUROS Y REASEGUROS, S.A.—Corporacion MAPFRE, Compania Internacional de Reaseguros, S.A.; *Int'l*, pg. 334
MAPFRE CAUCION Y CREDITO CIA INTERNACIONAL DE SEGUROS Y REASEGUROS, S.A.—Corporacion MAPFRE, Compania Internacional de Reaseguros, S.A.; *Int'l*, pg. 335
MAPFRE GUANARTEME CIA. DE SEGUROS GENERALES Y REASEGUROS DE CANARIAS, S.A.—Corporacion MAPFRE, Compania Internacional de Reaseguros, S.A.; *Int'l*, pg. 333
MAPFRE INDUSTRIAL, S.A. DE SEGUROS—Corporacion MAPFRE, Compania Internacional de Reaseguros, S.A.; *Int'l*, pg. 333
MAPFRE RE CIA REASEGUROS, S.A.—Corporacion MAPFRE, Compania Internacional de Reaseguros, S.A.; *Int'l*, pg. 334
MAPFRE SEGUROS GENERALES CIA. DE SEGUROS Y REASEGUROS, S.A.—Corporacion MAPFRE, Compania Internacional de Reaseguros, S.A.; *Int'l*, pg. 332
MAPFRE VIDA, S.A. DE SEGUROS Y REASEGUROS SOBRE LA VIDA HUMANA—Corporacion MAPFRE, Compania Internacional de Reaseguros, S.A.; *Int'l*, pg. 334
MAPLUX REINSURANCE COMPANY LTD.—Corporacion MAPFRE, Compania Internacional de Reaseguros, S.A.; *Int'l*, pg. 335
MARITIME LIFE ASSURANCE CO.—John Hancock Mutual Life Insurance Company; *U.S. Private*, pg. 590
MARMID LIFE INSURANCE COMPANY—HSBC Holdings plc; *Int'l*, pg. 581
MASSACHUSETTS MUTUAL LIFE INSURANCE CO.; *U.S. Private*, pg. 712
MASSACHUSETTS MUTUAL LIFE INSURANCE COMPANY—Massachusetts Mutual Life Insurance Co.; *U.S. Private*, pg. 712
MCWANE, INC.; *U.S. Private*, pg. 725
MEIJI LIFE INSURANCE COMPANY; *Int'l*, pg. 854
MEMBER SERVICE LIFE INSURANCE CO.—Blue Cross and Blue Shield of Oklahoma; *U.S. Private*, pg. 152
MERCANTILE INSURANCE SERVICES, INC.—Mercantile Bancorporation Inc.; *U.S. Public*, pg. 1088
MERIT LIFE INSURANCE CO.—American General Corporation; *U.S. Public*, pg. 77
MERRILL LYNCH & CO., INC.; *U.S. Public*, pg. 1097
MERRILL LYNCH LIFE AGENCY INC.—Merrill Lynch & Co., Inc.; *U.S. Public*, pg. 1098
METROPOLITAN INSURANCE & ANNUITY CO.—Metropolitan Life Insurance Co.; *U.S. Private*, pg. 737
METROPOLITAN LIFE INSURANCE CO.; *U.S. Private*, pg. 737
METROPOLITAN TOWER LIFE INSURANCE CO.—Metropolitan Life Insurance Co.; *U.S. Private*, pg. 737
THE MIAMI VALLEY INSURANCE CO.—Starbanc Corporation; *U.S. Public*, pg. 1510
MICHIGAN PHYSICIANS MUTUAL LIABILITY INC.; *U.S. Private*, pg. 741
MID-AMERICA CREDIT LIFE ASSURANCE CO.—Banc One Corporation; *U.S. Public*, pg. 175
MID-CONTINENT LIFE INSURANCE COMPANY—Florida Progress Corporation; *U.S. Public*, pg. 655
MIDLAND LIFE INSURANCE CO.; *U.S. Private*, pg. 744
MIDLAND LIFE LIMITED—HSBC Holdings plc; *Int'l*, pg. 580
MIDLAND NATIONAL LIFE INSURANCE CO.—Sammons Enterprises, Inc.; *U.S. Private*, pg. 963
MIDLAND WALWYN INC.; *Int'l*, pg. 865

MIDLAND WALWYN INSURANCE SERVICES LIMITED—Midland Walwyn Inc.; *Int'l*, pg. 865
MINERVA VITA ASSICURAZIONI S.P.A.—Zurich Insurance Company; *Int'l*, pg. 1531
MINISTERS LIFE INSURANCE CO—The Minnesota Mutual Life Insurance Company; *U.S. Private*, pg. 750
MINISTERS LIFE RESOURCES—The Minnesota Mutual Life Insurance Company; *U.S. Private*, pg. 750
THE MINNESOTA MUTUAL LIFE INSURANCE COMPANY; *U.S. Private*, pg. 750
MITSUBISHI CORPORATION; *Int'l*, pg. 871
MITSUI MUTUAL LIFE INSURANCE COMPANY—Mitsui & Co., Ltd.; *Int'l*, pg. 878
MODERN AMERICAN LIFE INSURANCE COMPANY—I.C.H. Corporation; *U.S. Public*, pg. 853
MONUMENTAL GENERAL INSURANCE COMPANY—AEGON N.V.; *Int'l*, pg. 27
MONUMENTAL GENERAL INSURANCE GROUP, INC.—AEGON N.V.; *Int'l*, pg. 27
MONUMENTAL LIFE INSURANCE COMPANY—AEGON N.V.; *Int'l*, pg. 27
MOTORISTS LIFE INSURANCE COMPANY—Motorists Mutual Insurance Co.; *U.S. Private*, pg. 764
MT. HOOD LIFE INSURANCE, INC.—U.S. Bancorp; *U.S. Public*, pg. 1681
THE MUTUAL LIFE INSURANCE COMPANY OF NEW YORK; *U.S. Private*, pg. 769
MUTUAL OF AMERICA LIFE INSURANCE COMPANY; *U.S. Private*, pg. 769
NBD INSURANCE AGENCY, INC.—First Chicago NBD Corporation; *U.S. Public*, pg. 628
NBD LIFE INSURANCE COMPANY—First Chicago NBD Corporation; *U.S. Public*, pg. 628
NACOLAH HOLDING CORP. INC.—Sammons Enterprises, Inc.; *U.S. Private*, pg. 963
NAN SHAN LIFE INSURANCE COMPANY, LTD.—American International Group, Inc.; *U.S. Public*, pg. 85
NATIONAL-BEN FRANKLIN INSURANCE CO. OF ILLINOIS—Loews Corporation; *U.S. Public*, pg. 1011
NATIONAL BENEFIT LIFE INSURANCE CO.—Travelers Group; *U.S. Public*, pg. 1633
NATIONAL FIDELITY LIFE INSURANCE CO.—Conseco Inc.; *U.S. Public*, pg. 433
NATIONAL FINANCIAL INSURANCE COMPANY; *U.S. Private*, pg. 782
NATIONAL GENERAL INSURANCE COMPANY—General Motors Corporation; *U.S. Public*, pg. 720
NATIONAL GROUP LIFE INSURANCE COMPANY—Conseco Inc.; *U.S. Public*, pg. 433
NATIONAL GUARDIAN LIFE INSURANCE COMPANY; *U.S. Private*, pg. 784
NATIONAL LIBERTY CORPORATION—AEGON N.V.; *Int'l*, pg. 26
NATIONAL LIBERTY LIFE INSURANCE CO.—AEGON N.V.; *Int'l*, pg. 27
NATIONAL LIFE INSURANCE COMPANY; *U.S. Private*, pg. 785
THE NATIONAL MUTUAL LIFE ASSOCIATION OF AUSTRALIA LIMITED—National Mutual Holdings Limited; *Int'l*, pg. 909
NATIONAL OLD LINE INSURANCE CO.—AEGON N.V.; *Int'l*, pg. 27
NATIONAL PUBLIC SERVICE INS. CO.—American General Corporation; *U.S. Public*, pg. 77
NATIONAL TRAVELERS LIFE CO.; *U.S. Private*, pg. 787
NATIONAL WESTERN LIFE INSURANCE COMPANY; *U.S. Public*, pg. 1161
NATIONSBANK LIFE INSURANCE CO.—NationsBank Corporation; *U.S. Public*, pg. 1164
NATIONSBANK OF TEXAS NATIONAL LIFE INSURANCE CO.—NationsBank Corporation; *U.S. Public*, pg. 1163
NATIONWIDE LIFE INSURANCE CO.—Nationwide Insurance Enterprise; *U.S. Private*, pg. 789
NECKURA VERISCHERUNGS AG—Nationwide Insurance Enterprise; *U.S. Private*, pg. 789
THE NEW ENGLAND—Metropolitan Life Insurance Co.; *U.S. Private*, pg. 737
NEW ENGLAND LIFE INSURANCE CO—Metropolitan Life Insurance Co.; *U.S. Private*, pg. 738
NEW ENGLAND PENSION & ANNUITY CO.—Metropolitan Life Insurance Co.; *U.S. Private*, pg. 738
NEW YORK LIFE & HEALTH INSURANCE COMPANY—New York Life Insurance Company; *U.S. Private*, pg. 795
NYLIFE CARE—New York Life Insurance Company; *U.S. Private*, pg. 795
NEW YORK LIFE INSURANCE AND ANNUITY CORPORATION—New York Life Insurance Company; *U.S. Private*, pg. 795
NEW YORK LIFE INSURANCE COMPANY; *U.S. Private*, pg. 794
NYLIFE INSURANCE COMPANY OF ARIZONA—New York Life Insurance Company; *U.S. Private*, pg. 795
NEW YORK LIFE INSURANCE WORLDWIDE LTD.—New York Life Insurance Company; *U.S. Private*, pg. 795
NEW YORK LIFE (U.K.) LIMITED—New York Life Insurance Company; *U.S. Private*, pg. 795
NIPPON INSURANCE SERVICE CO., LTD.—Nippon Life Insurance Co.; *Int'l*, pg. 935
NIPPON LIFE INSURANCE CO.; *Int'l*, pg. 934
NISSAN MUTUAL LIFE INSURANCE COMPANY; *Int'l*, pg. 945
NISSAY OKINAWA KOGYO CO., LTD.—Nippon Life Insurance Co.; *Int'l*, pg. 935
NOBEL LLOYDS INSURANCE COMPANY—Nobel Insurance Limited; *Int'l*, pg. 951
NORTH CAROLINA MUTUAL LIFE INSURANCE CO.; *U.S. Private*, pg. 804
NORTH CENTRAL LIFE INSURANCE COMPANY—Financial Life Companies, Inc.; *U.S. Private*, pg. 404
NORTHERN LIFE INSURANCE COMPANY—ReliaStar Financial Corp.; *U.S. Public*, pg. 1375
NORTHWESTERN MUTUAL LIFE INSURANCE CO.; *U.S. Private*, pg. 807
NORTHWESTERN NATIONAL LIFE INSURANCE CO.—ReliaStar Financial Corp.; *U.S. Public*, pg. 1375
NORWICH UNION LIFE INSURANCE; *Int'l*, pg. 970
OHIO CASUALTY CORPORATION; *U.S. Public*, pg. 1214
OHIO STATE LIFE INSURANCE CO.—B.A.T Industries P.L.C.; *Int'l*, pg. 110
OLD AMERICAN INSURANCE CO.—Kansas City Life Insurance Co.; *U.S. Public*, pg. 943
OLD DOMINION LIFE INSURANCE CO.—Shenandoah Life Insurance Company; *U.S. Private*, pg. 992
OLD KENT FINANCIAL LIFE INSURANCE COMPANY—Old Kent Financial Corporation; *U.S. Public*, pg. 1217
THE OLD LINE LIFE INSURANCE CO. OF AMERICA—American General Corporation; *U.S. Public*, pg. 77
OLD REPUBLIC DEALER SERVICE CORPORATION—Old Republic International Corporation; *U.S. Public*, pg. 1218
OLD REPUBLIC INTERNATIONAL CORPORATION; *U.S. Public*, pg. 1218
OLD REPUBLIC LIFE INSURANCE CO. OF NEW YORK—Old Republic International Corporation; *U.S. Public*, pg. 1218
ORIX INSURANCE SERVICES CORPORATION—Orix Corporation; *Int'l*, pg. 1008
ORIX LIFE INSURANCE CORPORATION—Orix Corporation; *Int'l*, pg. 1009
OSAKA AGENCY OF NIPPON LIFE INSURANCE CO., LTD.—Nippon Life Insurance Co.; *Int'l*, pg. 935
PM GROUP LIFE INSURANCE COMPANY—Pacific Life Insurance Company; *U.S. Private*, pg. 831
PACIFIC GUARDIAN LIFE INSURANCE—Meiji Life Insurance Company; *Int'l*, pg. 854
PACIFIC INSURANCE CO.—Loews Corporation; *U.S. Public*, pg. 1011
PACIFIC LIFE INSURANCE COMPANY; *U.S. Private*, pg. 831
PACIFIC MEZZANINE INVESTORS—Pacific Life Insurance Company; *U.S. Private*, pg. 831
PACIFIC UNION ASSURANCE COMPANY—American International Group, Inc.; *U.S. Public*, pg. 84
PACIFICARE HEALTH SYSTEMS, INC.; *U.S. Public*, pg. 1250
PAN-AMERICAN LIFE INSURANCE COMPANY; *U.S. Private*, pg. 836
PAN-MALAYAN INSURANCE CORPORATION—The Tokio Marine & Fire Insurance Company, Ltd.; *Int'l*, pg. 1392
PARAGON LIFE INSURANCE CO.—General American Life Insurance Co.; *U.S. Private*, pg. 443
THE PAUL REVERE CORPORATION—Provident Companies, Inc.; *U.S. Public*, pg. 1338
PENN INSURANCE & ANNUITY CO.—The Penn Mutual Life Insurance Company; *U.S. Private*, pg. 850
THE PENN MUTUAL LIFE INSURANCE COMPANY; *U.S. Private*, pg. 849
PENN-OHIO LIFE INSURANCE COMPANY—F.N.B. Corporation; *U.S. Public*, pg. 607
PEOPLES SECURITY INSURANCE COMPANY—AEGON N.V.; *Int'l*, pg. 27
PEOPLE'S SECURITY LIFE INSURANCE—AEGON N.V.; *Int'l*, pg. 27
PHILAM LIFE HOLDING CO.—American International Group, Inc.; *U.S. Public*, pg. 85
THE PHILIPPINES AMERICAN ASSURANCE CO., INC.—American International Group, Inc.; *U.S. Public*, pg. 85
PHOENIX AMERICAN LIFE INS. CO.—Phoenix Home Life Mutual Insurance Company; *U.S. Private*, pg. 863
PHOENIX HOME LIFE MUTUAL INSURANCE COMPANY; *U.S. Private*, pg. 863
PHYSICIANS MUTUAL INSURANCE CO.; *U.S. Private*, pg. 864
PIONEER LIFE INSURANCE CO. OF ILLINOIS—Conseco Inc.; *U.S. Public*, pg. 434
PIONEER MUTUAL LIFE INSURANCE COMPANY; *U.S. Private*, pg. 866
PLUS LEBEN—Groupe GAN; *Int'l*, pg. 565
POE & BROWN, INC.; *U.S. Public*, pg. 1312
PREFERRED ABSTAINERS INSURANCE COMPAN—Preferred Risk Mutual Insurance; *U.S. Private*, pg. 880
PREFERRED RISK LIFE INSURANCE CO.—Preferred Risk Mutual Insurance; *U.S. Private*, pg. 880
PRESIDENTIAL LIFE CORPORATION; *U.S. Public*, pg. 1323
PREVINDUSTRIA—Allianz Aktiengesellschaft; *Int'l*, pg. 62
PRIMERICA LIFE INSURANCE COMPANY—Travelers Group; *U.S. Public*, pg. 1633
THE PRINCIPAL FINANCIAL GROUP; *U.S. Private*, pg. 885
PRINCIPAL MUTUAL LIFE INSURANCE CO.—The Principal Financial Group; *U.S. Private*, pg. 886
PROTECTIVE LIFE INSURANCE CO.—Protective Life Corporation; *U.S. Public*, pg. 1336
PROVIDENT COMPANIES, INC.; *U.S. Public*, pg. 1337
PROVIDENT LIFE AND CASUALTY INSURANCE CO.—Provident Companies, Inc.; *U.S. Public*, pg. 1338
PROVIDENT MUTUAL LIFE & ANNUITY COMPANY OF AMERICA—Provident Mutual Life Insurance Co.; *U.S. Private*, pg. 892
PROVIDENT MUTUAL LIFE INSURANCE CO.; *U.S. Private*, pg. 891
PROVIDIAN AGENCY GROUP—AEGON N.V.; *Int'l*, pg. 27
PROVIDIAN LIFE & HEALTH INSURANCE CO.—AEGON N.V.; *Int'l*, pg. 27
PRUDENTIAL ASSURANCE CO. LTD.—Prudential Corporation PLC; *Int'l*, pg. 1073
PRUDENTIAL CORPORATION PLC; *Int'l*, pg. 1073
THE PRUDENTIAL INSURANCE COMPANY OF AMERICA; *U.S. Private*, pg. 892
THE PRUDENTIAL LIFE INSURANCE COMPANY, LTD.—The Prudential Insurance Company of America; *U.S. Private*, pg. 893
THE PYRAMID LIFE INSURANCE CO.—Unitrin, Inc.; *U.S. Public*, pg. 1694
RIHT LIFE INSURANCE COMPANY—BankBoston Corporation; *U.S. Public*, pg. 184
REASEGURADORA HEMISFERICA, S.A.—Corporacion MAPFRE, Compania Internacional de Reaseguros, S.A.; *Int'l*, pg. 335
REGENCE LIFE & HEALTH INSURANCE CO.—Regence BlueCross BlueShield of Oregon; *U.S. Private*, pg. 918
THE RELIABLE LIFE INSURANCE COMPANY; *U.S. Public*, pg. 1374
RELIASTAR FINANCIAL CORP.; *U.S. Public*, pg. 1375
REPUBLIC VANGUARD (OF ARIZONA) INSURANCE CO.—Credit Suisse Group; *Int'l*, pg. 346
RESOLUTE GROUP, INC.—Berkshire Hathaway Inc.; *U.S. Public*, pg. 220
RESOLUTE MANAGEMENT CORP.—Berkshire Hathaway Inc.; *U.S. Public*, pg. 220
RESOLUTE MANAGEMENT CORPORATION—Berkshire Hathaway Inc.; *U.S. Public*, pg. 220
RIVERSIDE GROUP, INC.; *U.S. Public*, pg. 1391
ROLLINS BURDICK HUNTER (CAYMAN) LIMITED—AON Corporation; *U.S. Public*, pg. 119
ROYAL INSURANCE ATLANTIC REGIONAL CENTRE—Royal & Sun Alliance Insurance Group plc; *Int'l*, pg. 1131
ROYAL LIFE HOLDINGS LIMITED—Royal & Sun Alliance Insurance Group plc; *Int'l*, pg. 1130
ROYAL LIFE INSURANCE COMPANY OF AMERICA—Royal & Sun Alliance Insurance Group plc; *Int'l*, pg. 1131
ROYAL LIFE INSURANCE COMPANY OF CANADA—Royal & Sun Alliance Insurance Group plc; *Int'l*, pg. 1130
ROYAL LIFE INSURANCE COMPANY OF NEW YORK—Royal & Sun Alliance Insurance Group plc; *Int'l*, pg. 1131
ROYAL NEDERLAND LEVENSVERZEKERING N.V.—AMB Aachener und Muenchener Beteiligungs-AG; *Int'l*, pg. 16
RURBAN LIFE INSURANCE COMPANY—Rurban Financial Corp.; *U.S. Public*, pg. 1413
SCOR ASIA-PACIFIC PTE. LTD.—SCOR; *Int'l*, pg. 1152
SCOR CANADA REINSURANCE COMPANY—SCOR; *Int'l*, pg. 1152
SCOR DEUTSCHLAND—SCOR; *Int'l*, pg. 1153
SCOR VIE—SCOR; *Int'l*, pg. 1152
SABANCI HOLDING A.S.; *Int'l*, pg. 1167
SAFECO CORPORATION; *U.S. Public*, pg. 1423
SAFECO LIFE AND HEALTH INSURANCE COMPANIES—SAFECO Corporation; *U.S. Public*, pg. 1423
SAMMONS ENTERPRISES, INC.; *U.S. Private*, pg. 963
SAMSUNG LIFE INSURANCE CO. LTD.—Samsung Group; *Int'l*, pg. 1183
SCOTT & STRINGFELLOW FINANCIAL, INC.; *U.S. Public*, *pg. 1445*
SCOTTISH WIDOWS' FUND & LIFE ASSURANCE SOCIETY; *Int'l*, pg. 1212
SEAFIRST INSURANCE CORPORATION—BankAmerica Corporation; *U.S. Public*, pg. 181
SECURA INSURANCE COMPANIES—Migros; *Int'l*, pg. 866
SECURITY AMERICAN FINANCIAL ENTERPRISES, INC.; *U.S. Private*, pg. 980
SECURITY INDUSTRIAL INSURANCE CO., INC.—The Loewen Group, Inc.; *Int'l*, pg. 814
SECURITY LIFE INSURANCE COMPANY OF AMERICA—Security American Financial Enterprises, Inc.; *U.S. Private*, pg. 980
SECURITY MUTUAL LIFE INSURANCE CO. OF NEW YORK; *U.S. Private*, pg. 981
SEGUROS DE VIDA Y PENSIONES ANTARES, S.A.—Telefonica de Espana, S.A.; *Int'l*, pg. 1371
SEGUROS GENESIS, S.A.—Metropolitan Life Insurance Co.; *U.S. Private*, pg. 738
SEGUROS MONTERREY, S.A.—Aetna Inc.; *U.S. Public*, pg. 27
SEGUROS ORBITA S.A.—Fortis; *Int'l*, pg. 499
SENTRY INSURANCE, A MUTUAL COMPANY; *U.S. Private*, pg. 984
SERVCO INSURANCE AGENCY, INC.—Servco Pacific Inc.; *U.S. Private*, pg. 986
THE SHELBY INSURANCE COMPANIES—Vesta Insurance Group, Inc.; *U.S. Public*, pg. 1718
SHELTER MUTUAL INSURANCE COMPANY; *U.S. Private*, *pg. 992*
SHENANDOAH LIFE INSURANCE COMPANY; *U.S. Private*, pg. 992
SIERRA HEALTH AND LIFE INSURANCE COMPANY, INC.—Sierra Health Services, Inc.; *U.S. Public*, pg. 1469
SIERRA HEALTH SERVICES, INC.; *U.S. Public*, pg. 1469
THE SIGNATURE GROUP—Montgomery Ward & Co., Inc.; *U.S. Private*, pg. 758
SILVEY CORPORATION—General Accident Fire and Life Assurance Corporation p.l.c.; *Int'l*, pg. 543
SIME DARBY BERHAD; *Int'l*, pg. 1249
SIME DARBY BERHAD INSURANCE SERVICES DIVISION—Sime Darby Berhad; *Int'l*, pg. 1250
THE SINCERE CO. LTD.; *Int'l*, pg. 1252
THE SINCERE LIFE ASSURANCE CO. LTD.—The Sincere Co. Ltd.; *Int'l*, pg. 1252
SKANDIA CORREDURIA DE REASEGUROS SA—Skandia Insurance Company Limited; *Int'l*, pg. 1256
SKANDIA INSURANCE COMPANY LIMITED; *Int'l*, pg. 1256
SKANDIA LIFE ASSURANCE CO. LTD.—Skandia Insurance Company Limited; *Int'l*, pg. 1258
SKANDIA S.A.—Skandia Insurance Company Limited; *Int'l*, pg. 1256
SOCIEDAD GESTORA DE FUNDOS DE PENSOES SA—Groupe GAN; *Int'l*, pg. 565
SOCIETA ASSICURATRICE INDUSTRIALE SPA (SAI)—Groupe GAN; *Int'l*, pg. 565
SOUTHERN GUARANTY INSURANCE COMPANIES—Credit Suisse Group; *Int'l*, pg. 346
SOUTHERN LIFE AND HEALTH INSURANCE COMPANY—Geneve Corporation; *U.S. Private*, pg. 447
THE SOUTHERN LIFE ASSOCIATION LIMITED—Anglo American Corporation of South Africa Limited; *Int'l*, pg. 77

SOUTHTRUST INSURANCE AGENCY, INC.—SouthTrust Corporation; *U.S. Public*, pg. 1492
SOUTHTRUST LIFE INSURANCE CO.—SouthTrust Corporation; *U.S. Public*, pg. 1492
SOUTHWEST EQUITY LIFE INSURANCE CO.—AEGON N.V.; *Int'l*, pg. 27
SOUTHWESTERN LIFE INSURANCE COMPANY—Southwestern Financial Corporation; *U.S. Private*, pg. 1018
THE SRI MUANG INSURANCE CO., LTD.—The Tokio Marine & Fire Insurance Company, Ltd.; *Int'l*, pg. 1392
STANDARD CHARTERED BANK PLC; *Int'l*, pg. 1294
STANDARD INSURANCE CO.; *U.S. Private*, pg. 1031
STANDARD LIFE & ACCIDENT INSURANCE CO.—American National Insurance Company; *U.S. Public*, pg. 88
STANDARD LIFE ASSURANCE; *Int'l*, pg. 1297
STANDARD SECURITY LIFE INSURANCE COMPANY OF NEW YORK—Geneve Corporation; *U.S. Private*, pg. 446
STATE AUTO LIFE INSURANCE COMPANY—Financial Industries Corp.; *U.S. Public*, pg. 622
STATE FARM LIFE AND ACCIDENT ASSURANCE CO.—State Farm Mutual Automobile Insurance Company; *U.S.* Private, pg. 1036
STATE FARM LIFE INSURANCE CO.—State Farm Mutual Automobile Insurance Company; *U.S. Private*, pg. 1036
STATE FARM MUTUAL AUTOMOBILE INSURANCE COMPANY; *U.S. Private*, pg. 1036
SUMITOMO LIFE INSURANCE COMPANY; *Int'l*, pg. 1315
SUMMIT BANCORP; *U.S. Public*, pg. 1527
SUN LIFE AND PROVINCIAL HOLDINGS PLC; *Int'l*, pg. 1318
SUN LIFE ASSURANCE COMPANY OF CANADA; *Int'l*, pg. 1318
SUNAMERICA INC.; *U.S. Public*, pg. 1532
SUNAMERICA LIFE INSURANCE COMPANY—SunAmerica Inc.; *U.S. Public*, pg. 1533
SUNSET LIFE INSURANCE CO. OF AMERICA—Kansas City Life Insurance Co.; *U.S. Public*, pg. 943
SUPERIOR LIFE INSURANCE COMPANY—NationsBank Corporation; *U.S. Public*, pg. 1165
SUSQUE-BANCSHARES LIFE INSURANCE COMPANY—Susquehanna Bancshares, Inc.; *U.S. Public*, pg. 1542
THE SWISS LIFE/RENTENANSTALT GROUP; *Int'l*, pg. 1332
SWISS REINSURANCE COMPANY; *Int'l*, pg. 1332
T A HOLDINGS LIMITED; *Int'l*, pg. 1334
TCF FINANCIAL CORP.; *U.S. Public*, pg. 1554
THE TAIYO MUTUAL LIFE INSURANCE CO.; *Int'l*, pg. 1348
TAPIOLA-YHTIOT; *Int'l*, pg. 1354
TEACHERS INSURANCE AND ANNUITY ASSOCIATION; *U.S. Private*, pg. 1071
TEMPLE-INLAND MORTGAGE CORPORATION—Temple-Inland Inc.; *U.S. Public*, pg. 1575
TENNESSEE VALLEY LIFE INSURANCE CO.—NationsBank Corporation; *U.S. Public*, pg. 1163
TEXAS LIFE INSURANCE COMPANY—Metropolitan Life Insurance Co.; *U.S. Private*, pg. 738
TEXTRON INC.; *U.S. Public*, pg. 1588
THE TOKIO MARINE & FIRE INSURANCE COMPANY (U.K.) LIMITED—The Tokio Marine & Fire Insurance Company, Ltd.; *Int'l*, pg. 1393
THOMAS JEFFERSON LIFE INSURANCE CO.—USF&G Corporation; *U.S. Public*, pg. 1659
TIARA INSURANCE COMPANY—Crown Central Petroleum Corporation; *U.S. Public*, pg. 462
TICINO SOCIETA D'ASSICURAZZIONI SULA VITA—American International Group, Inc.; *U.S. Public*, pg. 85
TIME INSURANCE—Fortis; *Int'l*, pg. 499
TOHO MUTUAL LIFE INSURANCE COMPANY; *Int'l*, pg. 1390
THE TOKIO MARINE & FIRE INSURANCE COMPANY (U.K.) LIMITED—The Tokio Marine & Fire Insurance Company, Ltd.; *Int'l*, pg. 1392
TOKIO MARINE & FIRE INSURANCE COMPANY (U.K.) LIMITED—The Tokio Marine & Fire Insurance Company, Ltd.; *Int'l*, pg. 1392
THE TOKIO MARINE & FIRE INSURANCE COMPANY (U.K.) LIMITED—The Tokio Marine & Fire Insurance Company, Ltd.; *Int'l*, pg. 1392
THE TOKIO MARINE & FIRE INSURANCE COMPANY (SINGAPORE) PTE. LIMITED—The Tokio Marine & Fire Insurance Company, Ltd.; *Int'l*, pg. 1392
TOKIO MARINE DE VENEZUELA, C.A.—The Tokio Marine & Fire Insurance Company, Ltd.; *Int'l*, pg. 1393
THE TOKIO MARINE & FIRE INSURANCE COMPANY (U.K.) LIMITED—The Tokio Marine & Fire Insurance Company, Ltd.; *Int'l*, pg. 1392
TOKIO MARINE INTERNACIONAL SOCIEDAD ANONIMA—The Tokio Marine & Fire Insurance Company, Ltd.; *Int'l*, pg. 1393
TOKYO AGENCY OF NIPPON LIFE INSURANCE CO., LTD.—Nippon Life Insurance Co.; *Int'l*, pg. 935
TORCHMARK CORPORATION; *U.S. Public*, pg. 1622
TOWERS PERRIN; *U.S. Private*, pg. 1093
TRANSAMERICA CORPORATION; *U.S. Public*, pg. 1629
TRANSAMERICA LIFE COMPANIES—Transamerica Corporation; *U.S. Public*, pg. 1630
TRANSAMERICA LIFE INSURANCE CO.-CANADA—Transamerica Corporation; *U.S. Public*, pg. 1630
TRANSPORT LIFE INSURANCE CO.—Conseco Inc.; *U.S. Public*, pg. 433
TRAVELERS GROUP; *U.S. Public*, pg. 1632
THE TRAVELERS LIFE & ANNUITY CO.—Travelers Group; *U.S. Public*, pg. 1633
THE TRAVELERS LIFE INSURANCE CO.—Travelers Group; *U.S. Public*, pg. 1633
TRILON FINANCIAL CORP.—EdperBrascan Corporation; *Int'l*, pg. 434
TUREGUM INSURANCE COMPANY—Zurich Insurance Company; *Int'l*, pg. 1529
20TH CENTURY INDUSTRIES; *U.S. Public*, pg. 1646
20TH CENTURY INSURANCE CO.—20th Century Industries; *U.S. Public*, pg. 1646
21ST CENTURY CASUALTY CO.—20th Century Industries; *U.S. Public*, pg. 1646
TWINCO SERVICES, INC.—Twin County Grocers, Inc.; *U.S.* Private, pg. 1111
UBO VERZEKERINGEN—AEGON N.V.; *Int'l*, pg. 26
URM INSURANCE AGENCY—URM Stores, Inc.; *U.S. Private*, pg. 1114
USAA (UNITED SERVICES AUTOMOBILE ASSOCIATION); *U.S. Private*, pg. 1114
USF&G CORPORATION; *U.S. Public*, pg. 1659
USG ANNUITY & LIFE COMPANY—ING Groep N.V.; *Int'l*, pg. 647
ULLICO INC.; *U.S. Private*, pg. 1115
UNION BENEFIT LIFE INSURANCE CO.—Conseco Inc.; *U.S. Public*, pg. 434
THE UNION CENTRAL LIFE INSURANCE CO.; *U.S. Private*, pg. 1118
THE UNION LABOR LIFE INSURANCE CO.—ULLICO Inc.; *U.S. Private*, pg. 1116
UNION STANDARD OF AMERICA LIFE INSURANCE CO.—ULLICO Inc.; *U.S. Private*, pg. 1116
UNISEGUROS VIDA Y PENSIONES (UNIVYP)—Groupe GAN; *Int'l*, pg. 565
UNITED AMERICAN INSURANCE CO.—Torchmark Corporation; *U.S. Public*, pg. 1623
UNITED CASUALTY INSURANCE COMPANY OF AMERICA—Unitrin, Inc.; *U.S. Public*, pg. 1694
UNITED FAMILY LIFE INSURANCE CO.—Fortis; *Int'l*, pg. 499
UNITED FARM FAMILY LIFE INSURANCE CO.; *U.S. Private*, pg. 1122
UNITED GENERAL LIFE INSURANCE—Conseco Inc.; *U.S. Public*, pg. 433
UNITED INSURANCE COMPANIES, INC.; *U.S. Public*, pg. 1679
UNITED INSURANCE COMPANY OF AMERICA—Unitrin, Inc.; *U.S. Public*, pg. 1694
UNITED INSURANCE CORPORATION OF AMERICA—Unitrin, Inc.; *U.S. Public*, pg. 1694
UNITED INVESTORS LIFE INSURANCE CO.—Torchmark Corporation; *U.S. Public*, pg. 1623
UNITED JERSEY CREDIT LIFE INSURANCE COMPANY—Summit Bancorp; *U.S. Public*, pg. 1528
UNITED LIFE INSURANCE COMPANY—United Fire & Casualty Company; *U.S. Public*, pg. 1677
UNITED PRESIDENTIAL LIFE INSURANCE CO.—Conseco Inc.; *U.S. Public*, pg. 434
UNITED SERVICES LIFE INSURANCE CO.—ReliaStar Financial Corp.; *U.S. Public*, pg. 1376
USLIFE CORPORATION—American General Corporation; *U.S. Public*, pg. 77
THE UNITED STATES LIFE INS. CO. IN THE CITY OF NEW YORK—American General Corporation; *U.S. Public*, pg. 77
USLIFE INSURANCE SERVICES CORPORATION—American General Corporation; *U.S. Public*, pg. 77
UNITRIN, INC.; *U.S. Public*, pg. 1693
UNIVERSAL FIDELITY LIFE INSURANCE COMPANY; *U.S. Private*, pg. 1127
UNIVERSAL FINANCIAL SERVICES—Universal Life Insurance Company; *U.S. Private*, pg. 1127
UNIVERSAL LIFE INSURANCE COMPANY; *U.S. Private*, pg. 1127
UNIVERSAL UNDERWRITERS OF TEXAS—Zurich Insurance Company; *Int'l*, pg. 1530
UNUM CORPORATION; *U.S. Public*, pg. 1699
UNUM EUROPEAN HOLDING COMPANY LIMITED—UNUM Corporation; *U.S. Public*, pg. 1700
UNUM LIFE INSURANCE COMPANY OF AMERICA—UNUM Corporation; *U.S. Public*, pg. 1699
UTICA NATIONAL LIFE INSURANCE COMPANY—Utica Mutual Insurance Company; *U.S. Private*, pg. 1130
VALLEY FORGE LIFE INSURANCE COMPANY—Continental Assurance Company; *U.S. Private*, pg. 267
THE VARIABLE ANNUITY LIFE INSURANCE CO.—American General Corporation; *U.S. Public*, pg. 76
VASA BROUGHER, INC.—Eureko B.V.; *Int'l*, pg. 464
VETERANS LIFE INSURANCE CO.—AEGON N.V.; *Int'l*, pg. 26
VICTORY FINANCIAL GROUP, INC.; *U.S. Private*, pg. 1139
VISION FINANCIAL CORPORATION; *U.S. Private*, pg. 1141
VISTA LIFE INSURANCE COMPANY OF TEXAS—Ford Motor Company; *U.S. Public*, pg. 664
VOLKSFURSORGE DEUTSCHE LEBENSVERSICHERUNG AG—AMB Aachener und Muenchener Beteiligungs-AG; *Int'l*, pg. 16
VULCAN LIFE INSURANCE CO.—Conseco Inc.; *U.S. Public*, pg. 433
WM LIFE INSURANCE COMPANY—Washington Mutual Inc.; *U.S. Public*, pg. 1742
WASHINGTON MUTUAL LIFE INSURANCE SERVICES, INC.—Washington Mutual Inc.; *U.S. Public*, pg. 1742
WASHINGTON NATIONAL INSURANCE CO.—Conseco Inc.; *U.S. Public*, pg. 434
WASHINGTON NATIONAL LIFE INSURANCE CO. OF NEW YORK—Columbian Mutual Life Insurance Co.; *U.S.* Private, pg. 256
WEST COAST LIFE INSURANCE CO.—Protective Life Corporation; *U.S. Public*, pg. 1336
WESTCORP; *U.S. Public*, pg. 1756
THE WESTERN AND SOUTHERN LIFE INSURANCE COMPANY; *U.S. Private*, pg. 1164
WESTERN NATIONAL LIFE INSURANCE CO.—American General Corporation; *U.S. Public*, pg. 76
WESTERN PIONEER LIFE INSURANCE CO.—I.C.H. Corporation; *U.S. Public*, pg. 853
WESTERN RESERVE LIFE ASSURANCE CO. OF OHIO—AEGON N.V.; *Int'l*, pg. 27
WESTFIELD COMPANIES; *U.S. Private*, pg. 1169
WESTHRIFT LIFE INSURANCE COMPANY—Westcorp; *U.S. Public*, pg. 1757
WESTMARK MORTGAGE CORPORATION—Westmark Group Holdings Inc.; *U.S. Public*, pg. 1761
WESTPAC FINANCIAL SERVICES GROUP LIMITED—Westpac Banking Corporation; *Int'l*, pg. 1496
WESTPAC INSURANCE SERVICES (BROKERS) LIMITED—Westpac Banking Corporation; *Int'l*, pg. 1496
WESTPAC LIFE LIMITED—Westpac Banking Corporation; *Int'l*, pg. 1496
WIENER ALLIANZ LEBENSVERSICHERUNGS-AG—Allianz Aktiengesellschaft; *Int'l*, pg. 62
WILLIAM PENN LIFE INSURANCE CO. OF NEW YORK—Legal & General Group PLC; *Int'l*, pg. 805
WILLIS CORROON CORP.—Willis Corroon Group PLC; *Int'l*, pg. 1504
WINTERTHUR LEBENVERSICHERUNGS-GESELLSCHAFT—Credit Suisse Group; *Int'l*, pg. 345
WINTERTHUR U.S. HOLDINGS INC.—Credit Suisse Group; *Int'l*, pg. 345
WOODMEN ACCIDENT & LIFE CO.; *U.S. Private*, pg. 1187
THE WUPHOON INSURANCE COMPANY LIMITED—The Tokio Marine & Fire Insurance Company, Ltd.; *Int'l*, pg. 1393
YASUDA LIFE AMERICA CAPITAL MANAGEMENT, LTD.—Yasuda Mutual Life Insurance Co.; *Int'l*, pg. 1520
YASUDA MUTUAL LIFE INSURANCE CO.; *Int'l*, pg. 1519
YOUNG POONG MANULIFE INSURANCE COMPANY—Manulife Financial (The Manufacturers Life Insurance Company); *Int'l*, pg. 841
ZALE LIFE INSURANCE CO.—Zale Corporation; *U.S. Public*, pg. 1789
ZENITH NATIONAL INSURANCE CORP.; *U.S. Public*, pg. 1790
ZENITH VIE—Groupe GAN; *Int'l*, pg. 565
ZIONS BANCORPORATION; *U.S. Public*, pg. 1792
ZIONS LIFE INSURANCE CO.—Zions Bancorporation; *U.S.* Public, pg. 1793
ZURICH AMERICAN INSURANCE COMPANY OF ILLINOIS—Zurich Insurance Company; *Int'l*, pg. 1530
ZURICH AUSTRALIAN LIFE INSURANCE LIMITED—Zurich Insurance Company; *Int'l*, pg. 1531
ZURICH COMPAGNIE D'ASSURANCES SUR LA VIE—Zurich Insurance Company; *Int'l*, pg. 1529
ZURICH COMPANIA DE SEGUROS SOBRE LA VIDA—Zurich Insurance Company; *Int'l*, pg. 1529
ZURICH INSURANCE COMPANY; *Int'l*, pg. 1529
ZURICH LEBENVERSICHERUNGS-GESELLSCHAFT—Zurich Insurance Company; *Int'l*, pg. 1529
ZURICH LEVENSVERZEKERING-MAATSCHAPPIJ—Zurich Insurance Company; *Int'l*, pg. 1529
ZURICH LIFE INSURANCE CO. OF CANADA—Zurich Insurance Company; *Int'l*, pg. 1532
ZURICH LIFE INSURANCE COMPANY—Zurich Insurance Company; *Int'l*, pg. 1529
ZURICH LIFE INSURANCE COMPANY LTD.—Zurich Insurance Company; *Int'l*, pg. 1530
ZURICH LIFE INSURANCE COMPANY OF AMERICA—Zurich Insurance Company; *Int'l*, pg. 1530
ZURICH LIVSFORSIKRING—Zurich Insurance Company; *Int'l*, pg. 1530
ZURIGO COMPAGNIA DI ASSICURAZIONI SULLA VITA—Zurich Insurance Company; *Int'l*, pg. 1530

6321 — ACCIDENT & HEALTH INSURANCE

ABR INFORMATION SERVICES, INC.; *U.S. Public*, pg. 2
AFS INSURANCE SERVICES, INC.—Associated Food Stores Inc.; *U.S. Private*, pg. 90
AGF ASSURANCES; *Int'l*, pg. 14
AMEV GENERAL INSURANCE COMPANY LIMITED—Fortis; *Int'l*, pg. 499
AUSA HOLDING COMPANY—AEGON N.V.; *Int'l*, pg. 27
AXA-UAP; *Int'l*, pg. 18
ACADEMY INSURANCE GROUP, INC.—AEGON N.V.; *Int'l*, pg. 27
ACADEMY LIFE INSURANCE CO.—AEGON N.V.; *Int'l*, pg. 27
ACCELERATION LIFE INSURANCE AGENCY, INC.—ACCEL International Corporation; *U.S. Public*, pg. 14
ACCELERATION NATIONAL INSURANCE COMPANY—ACCEL International Corporation; *U.S. Public*, pg. 14
ADRIATIC LIFE LTD.—Allianz Aktiengesellschaft; *Int'l*, pg. 61
ADRIATICA DE SEGUROS C.A.—Allianz Aktiengesellschaft; *Int'l*, pg. 61
ADRIATICA-SOCIEDAD ANONIMA DE SEGUROS Y REASEGUROS—Allianz Aktiengesellschaft; *Int'l*, pg. 61
ADVANTA INSURANCE COMPANIES—Advanta Corp.; *U.S.* Public, pg. 22
AETNA INC.; *U.S. Public*, pg. 26
AETNA LIFE INSURANCE COMPANY—Aetna Inc.; *U.S. Public*, pg. 26
AETNA LIFE INSURANCE CO. OF AMERICA (ALICA)—Aetna Inc.; *U.S. Public*, pg. 27
AFLAC INCORPORATED; *U.S. Public*, pg. 28
AGRIPPINA RUCKVERSICHERUNG AKTIENGESELLSCHAFT—Zurich Insurance Company; *Int'l*, pg. 1531
AID ASSOCIATION FOR LUTHERANS; *U.S. Private*, pg. 27
AL WATANIYA—Groupe GAN; *Int'l*, pg. 564
ALASKA PACIFIC ASSURANCE COMPANY—Cigna Corp.; *U.S. Public*, pg. 366
JOHN ALDEN LIFE INSURANCE COMPANY—John Alden Financial Corporation; *U.S. Public*, pg. 39
ALFA CORPORATION; *U.S. Public*, pg. 40
ALLIED INSURANCE COMPANY—Cigna Corp.; *U.S. Public*, pg. 362
AMERICAN FAMILY LIFE ASSURANCE CO. OF COLUMBUS—AFLAC Incorporated; *U.S. Public*, pg. 28
AMERICAN FAMILY LIFE ASSURANCE COMPANY OF NEW YORK—AFLAC Incorporated; *U.S. Public*, pg. 28

AMERICAN FAMILY MUTUAL INSURANCE CO.; *U.S. Private*, pg. 53
AMERICAN FIDELITY CORP.; *U.S. Private*, pg. 54
AMERICAN GENERAL CORPORATION; *U.S. Public*, pg. 76
AMERICAN GENERAL LIFE & ACCIDENT INSURANCE CO.—American General Corporation; *U.S. Public*, pg. 76
AMERICAN HARDWARE MUTUAL INSURANCE CO.—Motorists Mutual Insurance Co.; *U.S. Private*, pg. 764
AMERICAN HERITAGE LIFE INSURANCE CO.—American Heritage Life Investment Corp.; *U.S. Public*, pg. 79
AMERICAN HERITAGE LIFE INVESTMENT CORP.; *U.S. Public*, pg. 78
AMERICAN INCOME HOLDING, INC.—Torchmark Corporation; *U.S. Public*, pg. 1622
AMERICAN MERCHANTS CASUALTY CO.—Motorists Mutual Insurance Co.; *U.S. Private*, pg. 764
AMERICAN NATIONAL INSURANCE COMPANY; *U.S. Public*, pg. 87
AMERICAN NATIONAL LIFE INSURANCE CO. OF TEXAS—American National Insurance Company; *U.S. Public*, pg. 87
AMERICAN REPUBLIC INSURANCE CO.; *U.S. Private*, pg. 61
AMERICAN SECURITY GROUP—Fortis; *Int'l*, pg. 499
AMERICAN TRAVELLERS CORPORATION—Conseco Inc.; *U.S. Public*, pg. 433
AMERICAN TRAVELLERS LIFE INSURANCE COMPANY—Conseco Inc.; *U.S. Public*, pg. 433
ANCON INSURANCE COMPANY, INC.—Exxon Corporation; *U.S. Public*, pg. 601
ANTHEM, INC.; *U.S. Private*, pg. 76
AON CORPORATION; *U.S. Public*, pg. 117
ASEGURADORA CUAUHTEMOC S.A.—Allianz Aktiengesellschaft; *Int'l*, pg. 61
ASSICURAZIONI GENERALI S.P.A.; *Int'l*, pg. 89
ASSOCIATED AVIATION, INC.—The Chubb Corporation; *U.S. Public*, pg. 355
ASSOCIATES FINANCIAL SERVICES CORPORATION—Ford Motor Company; *U.S. Public*, pg. 663
ASSOCIATES INSURANCE COMPANY—Ford Motor Company; *U.S. Public*, pg. 663
ASSOCIATES INSURANCE GROUP, INC.—Ford Motor Company; *U.S. Public*, pg. 663
ASSURANCE VIE DESJARDINS-LAURENTIENNE—Desjardins-Laurentian Financial Corporation; *Int'l*, pg. 396
ASSUREX—Groupe GAN; *Int'l*, pg. 564
ATLANTIC AMERICAN CORPORATION; *U.S. Public*, pg. 143
ATLANTIC AMERICAN LIFE INSURANCE COMPANY—Atlantic American Corporation; *U.S. Public*, pg. 143
ATLANTIC EMPLOYERS INSURANCE COMPANY—Cigna Corp.; *U.S. Public*, pg. 366
AUTO DIREKT VERSICHERUNGS AG—Nationwide Insurance Enterprise; *U.S. Private*, pg. 789
AVCO FINANCIAL SERVICES—Textron Inc.; *U.S. Public*, pg. 1589
AVCO INSURANCE SERVICES/BALBOA LIFE & CASUALTY—Textron Inc.; *U.S. Public*, pg. 1589
BANKERS FIDELITY LIFE INSURANCE COMPANY—Atlantic American Corporation; *U.S. Public*, pg. 143
BANKERS LIFE & CASUALTY COMPANY—Conseco Inc.; *U.S. Public*, pg. 433
BANKERS STANDARD FIRE & MARINE COMPANY—Cigna Corp.; *U.S. Public*, pg. 365
BANKERS STANDARD INSURANCE COMPANY—Cigna Corp.; *U.S. Public*, pg. 365
BANNER LIFE INSURANCE CO.—Legal & General Group PLC; *Int'l*, pg. 805
BARNETT BANKS SERVICES INSURANCE, INC.—NationsBank Corporation; *U.S. Public*, pg. 1162
BAUSCH & LOMB INSURANCE COMPANY—Bausch & Lomb Incorporated; *U.S. Public*, pg. 194
BENEFICIAL CORPORATION; *U.S. Public*, pg. 211
BILBAO COMPANIA ANONIMA DE SEGUROS Y REASEGUROS—Fortis; *Int'l*, pg. 499
E.W. BLANCH CAPITAL RISK SOLUTIONS, INC.—E.W. Blanch Holdings, Inc.; *U.S. Public*, pg. 236
E.W. BLANCH HOLDINGS, INC.; *U.S. Public*, pg. 236
BLUE CROSS & BLUE SHIELD OF ILLINOIS; *U.S. Private*, pg. 151
BLUE CROSS AND BLUE SHIELD OF MASSACHUSETTS; *U.S. Private*, pg. 151
BLUE CROSS & BLUE SHIELD OF MICHIGAN; *U.S. Private*, pg. 151
BLUE SHIELD OF CALIFORNIA; *U.S. Private*, pg. 153
BRITISH RESERVE—Allianz Aktiengesellschaft; *Int'l*, pg. 61
CFI INSURERS, LTD.—Sizzler International, Inc.; *U.S. Public*, pg. 1475
CNA FINANCIAL CORP.—Loews Corporation; *U.S. Public*, pg. 1010
CAJA DE MADRID DE SEGUROS GENERALES, S.A. DE SEGUROS Y REASEGUROS—Caja de Madrid Group; *Int'l*, pg. 251
CAJA SALUD, S.A. DE SEGUROS Y REASEGUROS—Caja de Madrid Group; *Int'l*, pg. 251
CALAMERICA LIFE INSURANCE CO.—SunAmerica Inc.; *U.S. Public*, pg. 1533
CALFARM INSURANCE COMPANY—Zenith National Insurance Corp.; *U.S. Public*, pg. 1791
THE CANADA LIFE ASSURANCE COMPANY; *Int'l*, pg. 254
CENTRAL KRANKENVERSICHERUNG AG—AMB Aachener und Muenchener Beteiligungs-AG; *Int'l*, pg. 15
CENTRAL RESERVE LIFE CORPORATION; *U.S. Public*, pg. 326
CENTRAL RESERVE LIFE OF NORTH AMERICA INSURANCE CO.—Central Reserve Life Corporation; *U.S. Public*, pg. 326
CENTRAL UNITED LIFE INSURANCE CO.; *U.S. Private*, pg. 225
CENTRE REINSURANCE REPRESENTATIVE LIMITED—Zurich Insurance Company; *Int'l*, pg. 1530
CENTURY INDEMNITY COMPANY—Cigna Corp.; *U.S. Public*, pg. 365
CENTURY LIFE INSURANCE LIMITED—Invesco Group Asset Management Ltd.; *Int'l*, pg. 685
CERTIFIED LIFE INSURANCE—Conseco Inc.; *U.S. Public*, pg. 433
CHARLESTON FINANCIAL SERVICES, INC.—First Financial Holdings, Inc.; *U.S. Public*, pg. 634
CHUBBHEALTH NEW YORK/NEW JERSEY—Cigna Corp.; *U.S. Public*, pg. 360
CIGNA BENEFITS PROCESSING IRELAND LTD.—Cigna Corp.; *U.S. Public*, pg. 358
CIGNA COMPANIA DE SEGUROS DE PANAMA S.A.—Cigna Corp.; *U.S. Public*, pg. 364
CIGNA CORP.; *U.S. Public*, pg. 356
CIGNA DENTAL HEALTH OF NEW JERSEY, INC.—Cigna Corp.; *U.S. Public*, pg. 358
CIGNA DENTAL HEALTH OF OHIO, INC.—Cigna Corp.; *U.S. Public*, pg. 358
CIGNA FIRE UNDERWRITERS INSURANCE COMPANY—Cigna Corp.; *U.S. Public*, pg. 365
CIGNA HEALTHCARE OF OKLAHOMA, INC.—Cigna Corp.; *U.S. Public*, pg. 360
CIGNA HEALTHCARE OF TENNESSEE, INC.—Cigna Corp.; *U.S. Public*, pg. 360
CIGNA HEALTHCARE OF UTAH, INC.—Cigna Corp.; *U.S. Public*, pg. 360
CIGNA HEALTHCARE OF VIRGINIA, INC.—Cigna Corp.; *U.S. Public*, pg. 360
CIGNA INSURANCE COMPANY—Cigna Corp.; *U.S. Public*, pg. 365
CIGNA INSURANCE COMPANY OF TEXAS—Cigna Corp.; *U.S. Public*, pg. 365
CIGNA INSURANCE NEW ZEALAND LIMITED—Cigna Corp.; *U.S. Public*, pg. 364
CIGNA LIFE INSURANCE COMPANY—Cigna Corp.; *U.S. Public*, pg. 361
CIGNA LIFE INSURANCE COMPANY OF CANADA—Cigna Corp.; *U.S. Public*, pg. 362
CIGNA PROPERTY & CASUALTY INSURANCE COMPANY—Cigna Corp.; *U.S. Public*, pg. 364
CIGNA RE CORPORATION—Cigna Corp.; *U.S. Public*, pg. 360
CIGNA REINSURANCE COMPANY S.A.-N.V.—Cigna Corp.; *U.S. Public*, pg. 365
CIGNA SPECIALTY INSURANCE COMPANY—Cigna Corp.; *U.S. Public*, pg. 366
CIGNASA SIGORTA A.S.—Cigna Corp.; *U.S. Public*, pg. 363
CIGNASA SIGORTA A.S.—Sabanci Holding A.S.; *Int'l*, pg. 1167
CINCINNATI FINANCIAL CORP.; *U.S. Public*, pg. 368
COLINA INSURANCE COMPANY LIMITED—Cigna Corp.; *U.S. Public*, pg. 363
COLONIAL COMPANIES, INC.—UNUM Corporation; *U.S. Public*, pg. 1699
COLONIAL LIFE & ACCIDENT INSURANCE CO.—UNUM Corporation; *U.S. Public*, pg. 1699
COLUMBIAN LIFE INSURANCE COMPANY—Columbian Mutual Life Insurance Co.; *U.S. Private*, pg. 256
COLUMBIAN MUTUAL LIFE INSURANCE CO.; *U.S. Private*, pg. 256
COMBINED INSURANCE COMPANY OF AMERICA—AON Corporation; *U.S. Public*, pg. 118
COMMERCIAL TRAVELERS MUTUAL INSURANCE COMPANY; *U.S. Private*, pg. 258
COMMERCIAL UNION PLC; *Int'l*, pg. 308
COMPAGNIA EURPOEA D'ASSICURAZIONE—Allianz Aktiengesellschaft; *Int'l*, pg. 61
COMPANHIA ADRIATICA DE SEGUROS GERAIS—Allianz Aktiengesellschaft; *Int'l*, pg. 61
COMPANIA ASEGURADORA ARGENTINA S.A.—Allianz Aktiengesellschaft; *Int'l*, pg. 61
CONCOMBER, LTD.—Unicom Corporation; *U.S. Public*, pg. 1664
CONFEDERATION LIFE INSURANCE COMPANY; *Int'l*, pg. 325
CONSECO INC.; *U.S. Public*, pg. 432
CONSTITUTION LIFE INSURANCE CO.—Southwestern Financial Corporation; *U.S. Private*, pg. 1018
CONSTITUTION REINSURANCE CORPORATION—Exor Group; *Int'l*, pg. 467
CONTINENTAL ASSURANCE COMPANY; *U.S. Private*, pg. 267
THE CONTINENTAL CORPORATION—Loews Corporation; *U.S. Public*, pg. 1011
THE CONTINENTAL INSURANCE CO.—Loews Corporation; *U.S. Public*, pg. 1011
CONTINENTAL LEBENSVERSICHERUNGSGESELLSCHAFT—Allianz Aktiengesellschaft; *Int'l*, pg. 61
CONTINENTALE ALLGEMINE VERSICHERUNGS-AG—Allianz Aktiengesellschaft; *Int'l*, pg. 61
CORPORACION MAPFRE, COMPANIA INTERNACIONAL DE REASEGUROS, S.A.; *Int'l*, pg. 332
COSMOS KRANKENVERSICHERUNG AG—AMB Aachener und Muenchener Beteiligungs-AG; *Int'l*, pg. 15
COUNTRY LIFE INSURANCE COMPANY; *U.S. Private*, pg. 278
CRESA ASEGURADORA Y REASEGURADORA IBERICA S.A.—Allianz Aktiengesellschaft; *Int'l*, pg. 61
CRITERION LIFE INSURANCE CO.—Berkshire Hathaway Inc.; *U.S. Public*, pg. 219
CUNA MUTUAL INSURANCE SOCIETY; *U.S. Private*, pg. 296
DE BES' INSURANCE LTD.—Weyerhaeuser Company; *U.S. Public*, pg. 1764
DEERE & COMPANY; *U.S. Public*, pg. 491
JOHN DEERE HEALTH CARE, INC.—Deere & Company; *U.S. Public*, pg. 492
DELAWARE REINSURANCE COMPANY—Cigna Corp.; *U.S. Public*, pg. 363
DELPHI FINANCIAL GROUP, INC.; *U.S. Public*, pg. 496
DESJARDINS-LAURENTIAN LIFE ASSURANCE—Desjardins-Laurentian Financial Corporation; *Int'l*, pg. 396
DIXIE NATIONAL LIFE INSURANCE COMPANY—Standard Management Corporation; *U.S. Public*, pg. 1502
DOMUS FORSIKRINGSAKTIESELSKABET A/S—Allianz Aktiengesellschaft; *Int'l*, pg. 61
ROBERT F. DRIVER CO., INC.; *U.S. Private*, pg. 343
EBP LIFE INSURNACE CO.—First Health Group Corp.; *U.S. Public*, pg. 635
EL SOL COMPANIA DE SEGUROS GENERALES—Allianz Aktiengesellschaft; *Int'l*, pg. 61
EMPIRE BLUE CROSS & BLUE SHIELD; *U.S. Private*, pg. 374
EMPLOYERS HEALTH INSURANCE COMPANY—Humana Inc.; *U.S. Public*, pg. 847
EMPRESA GUATEMALTICA CIGNA DE SEGUROS, SOCIEDAD ANONIMA—Cigna Corp.; *U.S. Public*, pg. 364
ERICSSON REINSURANCE S.A.—Telefonaktiebolaget LM Ericsson; *Int'l*, pg. 1367
EUROPA-GAN BIZTOSITO—Groupe GAN; *Int'l*, pg. 564
EVEREST REINSURANCE HOLDINGS; *U.S. Public*, pg. 597
FEDERATED MUTUAL INSURANCE COMPANY; *U.S. Private*, pg. 399
FIDELITY & GUARANTY LIFE INSURANCE CO.—USF&G Corporation; *U.S. Public*, pg. 1659
FINANCIAL LIFE COMPANIES, INC.; *U.S. Private*, pg. 404
FIRST EQUICOR LIFE INSURANCE COMPANY—Cigna Corp.; *U.S. Public*, pg. 361
FIRST SOUTHEAST INSURANCE AGENCY—First Financial Holdings, Inc.; *U.S. Public*, pg. 634
FIRST UNITED AMERICAN LIFE INSURANCE COMPANY—Torchmark Corporation; *U.S. Public*, pg. 1623
FIRST UNUM LIFE INSURANCE COMPANY—UNUM Corporation; *U.S. Public*, pg. 1699
FIRST VALLEY LIFE INSURANCE COMPANY—Summit Bancorp; *U.S. Public*, pg. 1528
FLORISTS' MUTUAL INSURANCE CO.; *U.S. Private*, pg. 415
FORTIS; *Int'l*, pg. 498
FORTIS BENEFITS INSURANCE COMPANY—Fortis; *Int'l*, pg. 499
FORTIS, INC.—Fortis; *Int'l*, pg. 499
FORTIS (U.K.) LIMITED—Fortis; *Int'l*, pg. 499
FOUNDATION HEALTH BENEFIT LIFE INSURANCE COMPANY—Foundation Health Systems, Inc.; *U.S. Public*, pg. 678
FOUNDATION INSURANCE COMPANY—Foundation Health Systems, Inc.; *U.S. Public*, pg. 678
FRANDISCO LIFE INSURANCE CO.—First Franklin Financial Corp.; *U.S. Private*, pg. 407
GAN CANADA INSURANCE COMPANY—Groupe GAN; *Int'l*, pg. 564
GAN CAPITALISATION—Groupe GAN; *Int'l*, pg. 564
THE GAN COMPANY OF CANADA LTD.—Groupe GAN; *Int'l*, pg. 564
GAN ESPANA SEGUROS GENERALES Y VIDA—Groupe GAN; *Int'l*, pg. 564
GAN GENERAL INSURANCE COMPANY—Groupe GAN; *Int'l*, pg. 564
GAN INCENDIE ACCIDENTS—Groupe GAN; *Int'l*, pg. 564
GAN INSURANCE COMPANY LIMITED—Groupe GAN; *Int'l*, pg. 565
GAN INTERNATIONAL—Groupe GAN; *Int'l*, pg. 564
GAN ITALIA S.P.A.—Groupe GAN; *Int'l*, pg. 564
GAN NATIONAL INSURANCE CO.—Groupe GAN; *Int'l*, pg. 564
GAN PACIFIQUE IARD—Groupe GAN; *Int'l*, pg. 564
GAN PACIFIQUE VIE—Groupe GAN; *Int'l*, pg. 564
GAN PORTUGAL SEGUROS—Groupe GAN; *Int'l*, pg. 564
GAN SANTE—Groupe GAN; *Int'l*, pg. 565
GAN UK PLC—Groupe GAN; *Int'l*, pg. 565
GAN VIE—Groupe GAN; *Int'l*, pg. 565
GENERAL ACCIDENT FIRE AND LIFE ASSURANCE CORPORATION P.L.C.; *Int'l*, pg. 542
GENERAL AMERICAN LIFE INSURANCE CO.; *U.S. Private*, pg. 443
GIBRALTAR CASUALTY CO.—The Prudential Insurance Company of America; *U.S. Private*, pg. 892
GLOBE LIFE AND ACCIDENT INSURANCE CO.—Torchmark Corporation; *U.S. Public*, pg. 1622
GODWINS BOOKE & DICKENSON, INC.—AON Corporation; *U.S. Public*, pg. 118
GOLDEN STATE MUTUAL LIFE INSURANCE COMPANY; *U.S. Private*, pg. 461
THE GREAT EASTERN LIFE ASSURANCE COMPANY LIMITED; *Int'l*, pg. 557
THE GREAT-WEST LIFE ASSURANCE COMPANY; *Int'l*, pg. 557
GROUP INSURANCE INC. OF LOUISIANA; *U.S. Private*, pg. 484
GROUPE DES ASSURANCES DE TUNISIE (GAT)—Groupe GAN; *Int'l*, pg. 565
GUARANTEE LIFE INSURANCE CO.; *U.S. Public*, pg. 768
THE GUARDIAN LIFE INSURANCE COMPANY OF AMERICA; *U.S. Private*, pg. 486
GUNES SIGORTA—Groupe GAN; *Int'l*, pg. 565
HSBC GIBBS LTD.—HSBC Holdings plc; *Int'l*, pg. 579
HSBC INSURANCE LIMITED—HSBC Holdings plc; *Int'l*, pg. 582
HADAR INSURANCE COMPANY LTD.—Groupe GAN; *Int'l*, pg. 565
HANG SENG LIFE LTD.—HSBC Holdings plc; *Int'l*, pg. 582
THE HARTFORD FINANCIAL SERVICES GROUP INC.; *U.S. Public*, pg. 794
HARTFORD FIRE INSURANCE CO.—The Hartford Financial Services Group Inc.; *U.S. Public*, pg. 794
HEALTH & LIFE INSURANCE CO. OF AMERICA—Conseco Inc.; *U.S. Public*, pg. 434
HEALTHSOURCE CONNECTICUT—Cigna Corp.; *U.S. Public*, pg. 360

HEALTHSOURCE GEORGIA—Cigna Corp.; *U.S. Public*, pg. 360
HEALTHSOURCE, INC.—Cigna Corp.; *U.S. Public*, pg. 360
HEALTHSOURCE KENTUCKY—Cigna Corp.; *U.S. Public*, pg. 360
HEALTHSOURCE NEW YORK—Cigna Corp.; *U.S. Public*, pg. 360
HILB, ROGAL AND HAMILTON COMPANY; *U.S. Public*, pg. 826
THE HOLDEN GROUP—EdperBrascan Corporation; *Int'l*, pg. 435
THE HONGKONG AND SHANGHAI BANKING CORPORATION LIMITED (HONGKONGBANK)—HSBC Holdings plc; *Int'l*, pg. 583
HUMANA HEALTH INSURANCE OF NEVADA, INC.—Humana Inc.; *U.S. Public*, pg. 847
HUMANA INC.; *U.S. Public*, pg. 847
IDS LIFE INSURANCE CO. OF NEW YORK—American Express Company; *U.S. Public*, pg. 73
ING GROEP N.V.; *Int'l*, pg. 647
ING INVESTMENT MANAGEMENT INC.—ING Groep N.V.; *Int'l*, pg. 648
ING (U.S.) CAPITAL HOLDINGS—ING Groep N.V.; *Int'l*, pg. 648
ING (U.S.) FINANCIAL SERVICES KK—ING Groep N.V.; *Int'l*, pg. 648
ILLINOIS BANC ONE LIFE INSURANCE CO.—Banc One Corporation; *U.S. Public*, pg. 174
ILLINOIS UNION INSURANCE COMPANY—Cigna Corp.; *U.S. Public*, pg. 365
THE IMPERIAL LIFE ASSURANCE CO.—Desjardins-Laurentian Financial Corporation; *Int'l*, pg. 396
INDEMNITY INSURANCE COMPANY OF NORTH AMERICA—Cigna Corp.; *U.S. Public*, pg. 366
INDUSTRIFORSIKRING A/S—Norsk Hydro a.s; *Int'l*, pg. 960
INSURANCE COMPANY OF NORTH AMERICA—Cigna Corp.; *U.S. Public*, pg. 366
INSURANCE COMPANY OF NORTH AMERICA (U.K.) LIMITED—Cigna Corp.; *U.S. Public*, pg. 363
INTERUNFALL LEASING—Allianz Aktiengesellschaft; *Int'l*, pg. 61
JAE SERVICES, LTD.—Japan Aviation Electronics Industry, Ltd.; *Int'l*, pg. 701
J.C. PENNEY LIFE INSURANCE COMPANY—JC Penney Company, Inc.; *U.S. Public*, pg. 917
JC PENNEY REINSURANCE COMPANY—JC Penney Company, Inc.; *U.S. Public*, pg. 917
JOHN HANCOCK MUTUAL LIFE INSURANCE COMPANY; *U.S. Private*, pg. 589
KMA INSURANCE AGENCY, INC.—Michigan Physicians Mutual Liability Inc.; *U.S. Private*, pg. 741
KENTUCKY MEDICAL INSURANCE COMPANY, HOSPITAL DIVISION—Michigan Physicians Mutual Liability Inc.; *U.S. Private*, pg. 741
KENTUCKY MEDICAL INSURANCE COMPANY (KMIC)—Michigan Physicians Mutual Liability Inc.; *U.S. Private*, pg. 741
KEYSTONE HERITAGE GROUP, INC.—Fulton Financial Corp.; *U.S. Public*, pg. 687
J.I. KISLAK AGENCY, INC.—J.I. Kislak Inc.; *U.S. Private*, pg. 624
LA FONDIARIA ASSICURAZIONI S.P.A.; *Int'l*, pg. 784
L'ALLIANCE AFRICAINE—Groupe GAN; *Int'l*, pg. 565
LAVORO & SICURTA—Allianz Aktiengesellschaft; *Int'l*, pg. 61
LEGAL & GENERAL AMERICA, INC.—Legal & General Group PLC; *Int'l*, pg. 805
LEGAL & GENERAL ASSURANCE HOLDINGS (AUSTRALIA) LIMITED—Legal & General Group PLC; *Int'l*, pg. 805
LEGAL & GENERAL GROUP PLC; *Int'l*, pg. 805
LIBERTY BANCORP, INC.—Banc One Corporation; *U.S. Public*, pg. 174
LIBERTY LIFE INSURANCE COMPANY—Liberty Corporation; *U.S. Public*, pg. 992
LIBERTY NATIONAL LIFE INSURANCE CO.—Torchmark Corporation; *U.S. Public*, pg. 1622
THE LIFE INSURANCE CO. OF VIRGINIA—General Electric Company; *U.S. Public*, pg. 712
LINCOLN NATIONAL CORPORATION; *U.S. Public*, pg. 997
L'ITALICA—Allianz Aktiengesellschaft; *Int'l*, pg. 61
LITTON CLIFTON PRECISION SOUTH—Litton Industries, Inc.; *U.S. Public*, pg. 1003
LONDON LIFE INSURANCE GROUP—EdperBrascan Corporation; *Int'l*, pg. 435
MBNA INSURANCE SERVICES—MBNA Corporation; *U.S. Public*, pg. 1023
MAIN LIFE INSURANCE CO.—The Midland Company; *U.S. Public*, pg. 1111
MARITIME LIFE ASSURANCE CO.—John Hancock Mutual Life Insurance Company; *U.S. Private*, pg. 590
MAXICARE HEALTH PLANS, INC.; *U.S. Public*, pg. 1061
MCWANE, INC.; *U.S. Private*, pg. 725
MEDICAL PROFESSIONAL LIABILITY AGENCY, LTD.—Frontier Insurance Group, Inc.; *U.S. Public*, pg. 685
MERCANTILE INSURANCE SERVICES, INC.—Mercantile Bancorporation Inc.; *U.S. Public*, pg. 1088
MERCHANTS GROUP, INC.; *U.S. Public*, pg. 1090
MERIT LIFE INSURANCE CO.—American General Corporation; *U.S. Public*, pg. 77
METROPOLITAN INSURANCE & ANNUITY COMPANY, TAIWAN BRANCH—Metropolitan Life Insurance Co.; *U.S. Private*, pg. 738
METROPOLITAN LIFE INSURANCE CO.; *U.S. Private*, pg. 737
MIAMI VALLEY INSURANCE CO.—DPL Inc.; *U.S. Public*, pg. 474
MID-AMERICA CREDIT LIFE ASSURANCE CO.—Banc One Corporation; *U.S. Public*, pg. 175
MID ATLANTIC MEDICAL SERVICES, INC.; *U.S. Public*, pg. 1109
MINISTERS LIFE RESOURCES—The Minnesota Mutual Life Insurance Company; *U.S. Private*, pg. 750
MITSUBISHI CORPORATION; *Int'l*, pg. 871
MONITOR LIFE INSURANCE COMPANY OF NEW YORK—Commercial Travelers Mutual Insurance Company; *U.S. Private*, pg. 258
MONUMENTAL GENERAL INSURANCE COMPANY—AEGON N.V.; *Int'l*, pg. 27
MONUMENTAL GENERAL INSURANCE GROUP, INC.—AEGON N.V.; *Int'l*, pg. 27
MOTORISTS LIFE INSURANCE COMPANY—Motorists Mutual Insurance Co.; *U.S. Private*, pg. 764
MOTORISTS MUTUAL INSURANCE CO.; *U.S. Private*, pg. 764
MUTUA ASSICURATRICE COTONI—Allianz Aktiengesellschaft; *Int'l*, pg. 62
THE MUTUAL LIFE INSURANCE COMPANY OF NEW YORK; *U.S. Private*, pg. 769
MUTUAL OF OMAHA INSURANCE COMPANY; *U.S. Private*, pg. 769
NBD CREDIT INSURANCE AGENCY, INC.—First Chicago NBD Corporation; *U.S. Public*, pg. 628
NBD INSURANCE AGENCY, INC.—First Chicago NBD Corporation; *U.S. Public*, pg. 628
NBD LIFE INSURANCE COMPANY—First Chicago NBD Corporation; *U.S. Public*, pg. 628
NWNL HEALTH MANAGEMENT CORP.—ReliaStar Financial Corp.; *U.S. Public*, pg. 1375
NATIONAL FINANCIAL INSURANCE COMPANY; *U.S. Private*, pg. 782
NATIONAL GENERAL INSURANCE COMPANY—General Motors Corporation; *U.S. Public*, pg. 720
NATIONAL GROUP LIFE INSURANCE COMPANY—Conseco Inc.; *U.S. Public*, pg. 433
NATIONAL LIFE INSURANCE COMPANY; *U.S. Private*, pg. 785
NATIONAL TRAVELERS LIFE CO.; *U.S. Private*, pg. 787
NATIONWIDE HMO, INC.—Nationwide Insurance Enterprise; *U.S. Private*, pg. 789
NATIONWIDE INSURANCE ENTERPRISE; *U.S. Private*, pg. 788
NECKURA VERISCHERUNGS AG—Nationwide Insurance Enterprise; *U.S. Private*, pg. 789
THE NEW ENGLAND—Metropolitan Life Insurance Co.; *U.S. Private*, pg. 737
NEW HAMPSHIRE INSURANCE GROUP—American International Group, Inc.; *U.S. Public*, pg. 84
NEW YORK LIFE & HEALTH INSURANCE COMPANY—New York Life Insurance Company; *U.S. Private*, pg. 795
NEW YORK LIFE INSURANCE AND ANNUITY CORPORATION—New York Life Insurance Company; *U.S. Private*, pg. 795
NEW YORK LIFE INSURANCE COMPANY; *U.S. Private*, pg. 794
NYLIFE INSURANCE COMPANY OF ARIZONA—New York Life Insurance Company; *U.S. Private*, pg. 795
NORDEUROPA FORSIKRINGSAKTIESELSKABET A/S—Allianz Aktiengesellschaft; *Int'l*, pg. 62
NORTHWESTERN NATIONAL LIFE INSURANCE CO.—ReliaStar Financial Corp.; *U.S. Public*, pg. 1375
ORION CAPITAL CORPORATION; *U.S. Public*, pg. 1231
OXFORD HEALTH INSURANCE, INC.—Oxford Health Plans Inc.; *U.S. Public*, pg. 1239
OXFORD HEALTH PLANS (FL), INC.—Oxford Health Plans Inc.; *U.S. Public*, pg. 1239
OXFORD HEALTH PLANS (IL), INC.—Oxford Health Plans Inc.; *U.S. Public*, pg. 1239
PACIFIC EMPLOYERS INSURANCE COMPANY—Cigna Corp.; *U.S. Public*, pg. 365
PACIFIC GUARDIAN LIFE INSURANCE—Meiji Life Insurance Company; *Int'l*, pg. 854
PACIFIC LIFE INSURANCE COMPANY; *U.S. Private*, pg. 831
PACIFIC MEZZANINE INVESTORS—Pacific Life Insurance Company; *U.S. Private*, pg. 831
PAN-AMERICAN LIFE INSURANCE COMPANY; *U.S. Private*, pg. 836
THE PAUL REVERE CORPORATION—Provident Companies, Inc.; *U.S. Public*, pg. 1338
PHOENIX HOME LIFE MUTUAL INSURANCE COMPANY; *U.S. Private*, pg. 863
PHYSICIAN CORPORATION OF AMERICA; *U.S. Public*, pg. 1293
PHYSICIAN PARTNERS OF NEW ENGLAND, INC.—Blue Cross and Blue Shield of Massachusetts; *U.S. Private*, pg. 151
PHYSICIANS MUTUAL INSURANCE CO.; *U.S. Private*, pg. 864
PIONEER CLAIM MANAGEMENT, INC.—Frontier Insurance Group, Inc.; *U.S. Public*, pg. 685
PLUS ALLGEMEINE—Groupe GAN; *Int'l*, pg. 565
PREFERRED RISK LIFE INSURANCE CO.—Preferred Risk Mutual Insurance; *U.S. Private*, pg. 880
PREVINDUSTRIA—Allianz Aktiengesellschaft; *Int'l*, pg. 62
PROVIDENT COMPANIES, INC.; *U.S. Public*, pg. 1337
PRUDENTIAL CORPORATION PLC; *Int'l*, pg. 1073
THE PRUDENTIAL INSURANCE COMPANY OF AMERICA; *U.S. Private*, pg. 892
THE PYRAMID LIFE INSURANCE CO.—Unitrin, Inc.; *U.S. Public*, pg. 1694
RIHT LIFE INSURANCE COMPANY—BankBoston Corporation; *U.S. Public*, pg. 184
THE RELIABLE LIFE INSURANCE COMPANY; *U.S. Public*, pg. 1374
REPUBLIC VANGUARD (OF ARIZONA) INSURANCE CO.—Credit Suisse Group; *Int'l*, pg. 346
RIUNIONE ADRIATICA DI SICURTA S.P.A.—Allianz Aktiengesellschaft; *Int'l*, pg. 61
ROYAL INSURANCE—Royal & Sun Alliance Insurance Group plc; *Int'l*, pg. 1130
SCOR REASSURANCE—SCOR; *Int'l*, pg. 1152
SABANCI HOLDING A.S.; *Int'l*, pg. 1167
SARK SIGORTA T.A.S. (RAS)—Allianz Aktiengesellschaft; *Int'l*, pg. 62
SECURA INSURANCE COMPANIES—Migros; *Int'l*, pg. 866
SECURITY AMERICAN FINANCIAL ENTERPRISES, INC.; *U.S. Private*, pg. 980
SECURITY LIFE INSURANCE COMPANY OF AMERICA—Security American Financial Enterprises, Inc.; *U.S. Private*, pg. 980
SECURITY MUTUAL LIFE INSURANCE CO. OF NEW YORK; *U.S. Private*, pg. 981
SEGURCAJA, CORREDURIA DE SEGUROS, S.A.—Caja de Madrid Group; *Int'l*, pg. 252
SEGUROS ORBITA S.A.—Fortis; *Int'l*, pg. 499
SENTRY INSURANCE, A MUTUAL COMPANY; *U.S. Private*, pg. 984
SHELTER MUTUAL INSURANCE COMPANY; *U.S. Private*, pg. 992
SIERRA HEALTH AND LIFE INSURANCE COMPANY, INC.—Sierra Health Services, Inc.; *U.S. Public*, pg. 1469
SILVEY CORPORATION—General Accident Fire and Life Assurance Corporation p.l.c.; *Int'l*, pg. 543
SIME DARBY BERHAD; *Int'l*, pg. 1249
SIME DARBY BERHAD INSURANCE SERVICES DIVISION—Sime Darby Berhad; *Int'l*, pg. 1250
SINGAPORE REINSURANCE CORPORATION LIMITED; *Int'l*, pg. 1253
SKANDIA INSURANCE COMPANY LIMITED; *Int'l*, pg. 1256
SOCAPI—Groupe GAN; *Int'l*, pg. 565
SOCIETA ASSICURATRICE INDUSTRIALE SPA (SAI)—Groupe GAN; *Int'l*, pg. 565
SOCIETE FRANCAISE DE PROTECTION JURIDIQUE (S.F.P.J.)—Groupe GAN; *Int'l*, pg. 565
STANDARD LIFE & ACCIDENT INSURANCE CO.—American National Insurance Company; *U.S. Public*, pg. 88
STATE VOLUNTEER MUTUAL INSURANCE CO.; *U.S. Private*, pg. 1037
SUMMIT BANCORP; *U.S. Public*, pg. 1527
TAPIOLA-YHTIOT; *Int'l*, pg. 1354
TENNESSEE INSURANCE CO.—Ingram Industries Inc.; *U.S. Private*, pg. 563
TEXTRON INC.; *U.S. Public*, pg. 1588
THOMAS JEFFERSON LIFE INSURANCE CO.—USF&G Corporation; *U.S. Public*, pg. 1659
TIME INSURANCE—Fortis; *Int'l*, pg. 499
TORCHMARK CORPORATION; *U.S. Public*, pg. 1622
TRANSAMERICA LIFE COMPANIES—Transamerica Corporation; *U.S. Public*, pg. 1630
TRILON FINANCIAL CORP.—EdperBrascan Corporation; *Int'l*, pg. 434
20TH CENTURY INDUSTRIES; *U.S. Public*, pg. 1646
TWINCO SERVICES, INC.—Twin County Grocers, Inc.; *U.S. Private*, pg. 1111
USF RE INSURANCE COMPANY—Centris Group Inc.; *U.S. Public*, pg. 328
ULLICO INC.; *U.S. Private*, pg. 1115
UNDERWRITERS REINSURANCE—Alleghany Corporation; *U.S. Public*, pg. 42
UNION BANKER INSURANCE CO.—Southwestern Financial Corporation; *U.S. Private*, pg. 1018
THE UNION CENTRAL LIFE INSURANCE CO.; *U.S. Private*, pg. 1118
THE UNION LABOR LIFE INSURANCE CO.—ULLICO Inc.; *U.S. Private*, pg. 1116
UNISEGUROS VIDA Y PENSIONES (UNIVYP)—Groupe GAN; *Int'l*, pg. 565
UNITED AMERICAN INSURANCE CO.—Torchmark Corporation; *U.S. Public*, pg. 1623
UNITED CASUALTY INSURANCE COMPANY OF AMERICA—Unitrin, Inc.; *U.S. Public*, pg. 1694
UNITED INSURANCE COMPANIES, INC.; *U.S. Public*, pg. 1679
UNITED INSURANCE COMPANY OF AMERICA—Unitrin, Inc.; *U.S. Public*, pg. 1694
UNITED JERSEY CREDIT LIFE INSURANCE COMPANY—Summit Bancorp; *U.S. Public*, pg. 1528
USLIFE CORPORATION—American General Corporation; *U.S. Public*, pg. 77
USLIFE INSURANCE SERVICES CORPORATION—American General Corporation; *U.S. Public*, pg. 77
UNITRIN, INC.; *U.S. Public*, pg. 1693
UNIVERSAL FIDELITY LIFE INSURANCE COMPANY; *U.S. Private*, pg. 1127
UNIVERSAL LIFE INSURANCE COMPANY; *U.S. Private*, pg. 1127
UNUM CORPORATION; *U.S. Public*, pg. 1699
UNUM EUROPEAN HOLDING COMPANY LIMITED—UNUM Corporation; *U.S. Public*, pg. 1700
UNUM JAPAN ACCIDENT INSURANCE COMPANY LIMITED—UNUM Corporation; *U.S. Public*, pg. 1700
UNUM LIMITED—UNUM Corporation; *U.S. Public*, pg. 1700
VALLEY FORGE LIFE INSURANCE COMPANY—Continental Assurance Company; *U.S. Private*, pg. 267
VASA BROUGHER, INC.—Eureko B.V.; *Int'l*, pg. 464
VOLKSFURSORGE KRANKENVERSICHERUNG AG—AMB Aachener und Muenchener Beteiligungs-AG; *Int'l*, pg. 16
VULCAN LIFE INSURANCE CO.—Conseco Inc.; *U.S. Public*, pg. 433
WASHINGTON MUTUAL LIFE INSURANCE SERVICES, INC.—Washington Mutual Inc.; *U.S. Public*, pg. 1742
WESTMARK MORTGAGE CORPORATION—Westmark Group Holdings Inc.; *U.S. Public*, pg. 1761
WESTMINSTER INSURANCE AGENCIES LIMITED—Groupe GAN; *Int'l*, pg. 565
WILLIS CORROON CORP.—Willis Corroon Group PLC; *Int'l*, pg. 1504
WINTERTHUR REINSURANCE CORPORATION OF AMERICA—Credit Suisse Group; *Int'l*, pg. 346
WINTERTHUR U.S. HOLDINGS INC.—Credit Suisse Group; *Int'l*, pg. 345
WOODMEN ACCIDENT & LIFE CO.; *U.S. Private*, pg. 1187
RODNEY D. YOUNG INSURANCE; *U.S. Private*, pg. 1202
ZENITH NATIONAL INSURANCE CORP.; *U.S. Public*, pg. 1790
ZENITH VIE—Groupe GAN; *Int'l*, pg. 565

6324 — HOSPITAL & MEDICAL SERVICE PLANS

ACCELERATED CLAIMS PROCESSING, INC.—Health Management Systems, Inc.; *U.S. Public*, pg. 802
ACCELERATION INSURANCE AGENCY OF INDIANA, INC.—ACCEL International Corporation; *U.S. Public*, pg. 14
ACCELERATION LIFE INSURANCE AGENCY, INC.—ACCEL International Corporation; *U.S. Public*, pg. 14
ACORDIA, INC.; *U.S. Private*, pg. 14
AETNA CANADA HOLDINGS LTD.—Aetna Inc.; *U.S. Public*, pg. 27
AETNA HEALTH (NEW ZEALAND) LIMITED—Aetna Inc.; *U.S. Public*, pg. 27
AETNA INC.; *U.S. Public*, pg. 26
AETNA UNIVERSAL INSURANCE SDN. BHD.—Aetna Inc.; *U.S. Public*, pg. 27
THE AFFORDABLE MEDICAL NETWORKS—First Health Group Corp.; *U.S. Public*, pg. 635
AMERICAN MEDICAL SECURITY HOLDINGS, INC.—United Wisconsin Services, Inc.; *U.S. Public*, pg. 1692
AMERITAS LIFE INSURANCE CORP.; *U.S. Private*, pg. 65
ANTHEM BLUE CROSS & BLUE SHIELD—Anthem, Inc.; *U.S. Private*, pg. 76
ANTHEM HEALTH COMPANIES—Anthem, Inc.; *U.S. Private*, pg. 76
ANTHEM, INC.; *U.S. Private*, pg. 76
ASSOCIATES INSURANCE GROUP, INC.—Ford Motor Company; *U.S. Public*, pg. 663
BANNER LIFE INSURANCE CO.—Legal & General Group PLC; *Int'l*, pg. 805
BENEFITAMERICA—UNUM Corporation; *U.S. Public*, pg. 1699
BLUE CROSS AND BLUE SHIELD ASSOCIATION; *U.S. Private*, pg. 151
BLUE CROSS AND BLUE SHIELD OF OKLAHOMA; *U.S. Private*, pg. 151
BLUE CROSS & BLUE SHIELD OF TEXAS, INC.; *U.S. Private*, pg. 152
BLUELINCS HMO—Blue Cross and Blue Shield of Oklahoma; *U.S. Private*, pg. 152
BRITISH RESERVE—Allianz Aktiengesellschaft; *Int'l*, pg. 61
CAJA DE MADRID DE SEGUROS GENERALES, S.A. DE SEGUROS Y REASEGUROS—Caja de Madrid Group; *Int'l*, pg. 251
CALFARM INSURANCE COMPANY—Zenith National Insurance Corp.; *U.S. Public*, pg. 1791
THE CANADA LIFE ASSURANCE COMPANY; *Int'l*, pg. 254
CARE AMERICA-SOUTHERN CA—Blue Shield of California; *U.S. Private*, pg. 153
CENTRO MEDICO DE CHEQUEOS DE MAPFRE VIDA—Corporacion MAPFRE, Compania Internacional de Reaseguros, S.A.; *Int'l*, pg. 334
CERTIFIED LIFE INSURANCE—Conseco Inc.; *U.S. Public*, pg. 433
CIGNA DENTAL CARE OF ILLINOIS, INC.—Cigna Corp.; *U.S. Public*, pg. 358
CIGNA DENTAL HEALTH PLAN OF NEW MEXICO, INC.—Cigna Corp.; *U.S. Public*, pg. 358
CIGNA DENTAL HEALTH PLAN OF NORTH CAROLINA, INC.—Cigna Corp.; *U.S. Public*, pg. 358
CIGNA HEALTH NETWORK, INC.—Cigna Corp.; *U.S. Public*, pg. 359
CIGNA HEALTHCARE MID-ATLANTIC, INC.—Cigna Corp.; *U.S. Public*, pg. 359
CIGNA HEALTHCARE OF NORTH CAROLINA, INC.—Cigna Corp.; *U.S. Public*, pg. 360
CIGNA HOSPITAL OF LOS ANGELES, INC.—Cigna Corp.; *U.S. Public*, pg. 360
COLONIAL COMPANIES, INC.—UNUM Corporation; *U.S. Public*, pg. 1699
COLUMBIA/HCA HEALTHCARE CORPORATION; *U.S. Public*, pg. 403
COMMERCIAL UNION PLC; *Int'l*, pg. 308
CORPORATE HEALTH ADMINISTRATORS, INC.—Aetna Inc.; *U.S. Public*, pg. 26
CORVEL CORPORATION; *U.S. Public*, pg. 451
COVENTRY CORPORATION; *U.S. Public*, pg. 454
DAI-ICHI SEIMEI AMERICA CORP.—Dai-ichi Mutual Life Insurance Company; *Int'l*, pg. 362
DEUTSCHE KRANKENVERSICHERUNG AG—Allianz Aktiengesellschaft; *Int'l*, pg. 58
DEUTSCHE KRANKENVERSICHERUNG AG—Munchener Ruckversicherungs-Gessellschaft; *Int'l*, pg. 897
EAST ASIA AETNA INSURANCE GROUP—Aetna Inc.; *U.S. Public*, pg. 27
FALLON COMMUNITY HEALTH PLAN; *U.S. Private*, pg. 392
FOUNDATION HEALTH, A CALIFORNIA HEALTH PLAN—Foundation Health Systems, Inc.; *U.S. Public*, pg. 678
FOUNDATION HEALTH FEDERAL SERVICES, INC.—Foundation Health Systems, Inc.; *U.S. Public*, pg. 678
FOUNDATION HEALTH SYSTEMS, INC.; *U.S. Public*, pg. 678
GALEN HOSPITAL ILLINOIS, INC.—Columbia/HCA Healthcare Corporation; *U.S. Public*, pg. 404
GROUP HEALTH PLAN, INC.—Coventry Corporation; *U.S. Public*, pg. 454
GROUP LIFE & HEALTH INSURANCE COMPANY—Blue Cross & Blue Shield of Texas, Inc.; *U.S. Private*, pg. 152
HEALTH MAINTENANCE OREGON—Regence BlueCross BlueShield of Oregon; *U.S. Private*, pg. 918
HEALTH MAINTENANCE ORGANIZATION OF NEW JERSEY, INC.—Aetna Inc.; *U.S. Public*, pg. 26
HEALTH PLAN OF NEVADA, INC.—Sierra Health Services, Inc.; *U.S. Public*, pg. 1469
HEALTHAMERICA OF CENTRAL PENNSYLVANIA—Coventry Corporation; *U.S. Public*, pg. 454
HEALTHAMERICA PENNSYLVANIA, INC.—Coventry Corporation; *U.S. Public*, pg. 454
HEALTHCARE USA—Coventry Corporation; *U.S. Public*, pg. 454
HUMAN AFFAIRS INTERNATIONAL INC.—Magellan Health Services, Inc.; *U.S. Public*, pg. 1036
HUMANA HEALTH CHICAGO, INC.—Humana Inc.; *U.S. Public*, pg. 847
HUMANA HEALTH PLAN OF TEXAS, INC.—Humana Inc.; *U.S. Public*, pg. 848
HUMANA INC.; *U.S. Public*, pg. 847
HUMANA WISCONSIN HEALTH ORGANIZATION INSURANCE CORPORATION—Humana Inc.; *U.S. Public*, pg. 848
ISS HOSPITAL SERVICE A/S—ISS-International Service System A/S; *Int'l*, pg. 656
INTEGRAMED AMERICA; *U.S. Public*, pg. 883
KAISER PERMANENTE; *U.S. Private*, pg. 605
KENTUCKY MEDICAL INSURANCE COMPANY, HOSPITAL DIVISION—Michigan Physicians Mutual Liability Inc.; *U.S. Private*, pg. 741
KENTUCKY MEDICAL INSURANCE COMPANY (KMIC)—Michigan Physicians Mutual Liability Inc.; *U.S. Private*, pg. 741
KYOEI S/A-CENTRO DE CHECK-UPS MEDICOS—The Kyoei Life Insurance Co., Ltd.; *Int'l*, pg. 777
LEGAL & GENERAL AMERICA, INC.—Legal & General Group PLC; *Int'l*, pg. 805
LEGAL & GENERAL ASSURANCE HOLDINGS (AUSTRALIA) LIMITED—Legal & General Group PLC; *Int'l*, pg. 805
LEGAL & GENERAL GROUP PLC; *Int'l*, pg. 805
LONDON LIFE INSURANCE GROUP—EdperBrascan Corporation; *Int'l*, pg. 435
LOVELACE HEALTH SYSTEMS, INC.—Cigna Corp.; *U.S. Public*, pg. 360
MEDCO CONTAINMENT SERVICES, INC.—Merck & Co., Inc.; *U.S. Public*, pg. 1091
METROPOLITAN LIFE INSURANCE CO.; *U.S. Private*, pg. 737
THE MULTICARE COMPANIES, INC.—Genesis Health Ventures, Inc.; *U.S. Public*, pg. 729
NATIONAL HEALTH PLANS—Tenet Healthcare Corporation; *U.S. Public*, pg. 1577
NATIONAL HOME HEALTH CARE CORP.; *U.S. Public*, pg. 1157
NATIONAL OLD LINE INSURANCE CO.—AEGON N.V.; *Int'l*, pg. 27
NETWORK EPO, INC.—Humana Inc.; *U.S. Public*, pg. 848
NYLIFE ADMINISTRATION CORP.—New York Life Insurance Company; *U.S. Private*, pg. 795
NEW YORK LIFE INSURANCE COMPANY; *U.S. Private*, pg. 794
OXFORD HEALTH PLANS INC.; *U.S. Public*, pg. 1238
PPP HC; *Int'l*, pg. 1020
PACIFICARE HEALTH SYSTEMS—PacifiCare Health Systems, Inc.; *U.S. Public*, pg. 1251
PACIFICARE HEALTH SYSTEMS, INC.; *U.S. Public*, pg. 1250
PACIFICARE OF CALIFORNIA—PacifiCare Health Systems, Inc.; *U.S. Public*, pg. 1251
PACIFICARE OF OREGON—PacifiCare Health Systems, Inc.; *U.S. Public*, pg. 1251
PACIFICARE OF TEXAS—PacifiCare Health Systems, Inc.; *U.S. Public*, pg. 1251
PACIFICARE OF WASHINGTON—PacifiCare Health Systems, Inc.; *U.S. Public*, pg. 1251
PREFERRED HEALTH NETWORK—Foundation Health Systems, Inc.; *U.S. Public*, pg. 678
PRIMECARE HEALTH PLAN, INC.—United HealthCare Corporation; *U.S. Public*, pg. 1678
THE PRINCIPAL FINANCIAL GROUP; *U.S. Private*, pg. 885
PRIVATE PATIENTS PLAN LIMITED—PPP hc; *Int'l*, pg. 1020
PROVIDENT COMPANIES, INC.; *U.S. Public*, pg. 1337
QUAL-MED, INC.—Foundation Health Systems, Inc.; *U.S. Public*, pg. 678
QUALMED PLANS FOR HEALTH-NEW MEXICO—Foundation Health Systems, Inc.; *U.S. Public*, pg. 678
QUALMED PLANS FOR HEALTH-OREGON—Foundation Health Systems, Inc.; *U.S. Public*, pg. 678
QUALMED PLANS FOR HEALTH-WASHINGTON—Foundation Health Systems, Inc.; *U.S. Public*, pg. 678
RIUNIONE ADRIATICA DI SICURTA S.P.A.—Allianz Aktiengesellschaft; *Int'l*, pg. 61
ROSS-LOOS HEALTH PLAN OF CALIFORNIA—Cigna Corp.; *U.S. Public*, pg. 359
SAFEGUARD HEALTH ENTERPRISES, INC.; *U.S. Public*, pg. 1424
SAFEGUARD HEALTH PLANS, INC.—Safeguard Health Enterprises, Inc.; *U.S. Public*, pg. 1424
SEGURCAJA, CORREDURIA DE SEGUROS, S.A.—Caja de Madrid Group; *Int'l*, pg. 252
SIERRA HEALTH SERVICES, INC.; *U.S. Public*, pg. 1469
SOUTHERN HEALTH SERVICES, INC.—Coventry Corporation; *U.S. Public*, pg. 454
TRANSAMERICA LIFE COMPANIES—Transamerica Corporation; *U.S. Public*, pg. 1630
TRIGON BLUE CROSS & BLUE SHIELD; *U.S. Public*, pg. 1637
TRILON FINANCIAL CORP.—EdperBrascan Corporation; *Int'l*, pg. 434
TWINCO SERVICES, INC.—Twin County Grocers, Inc.; *U.S. Private*, pg. 1111
UNITED HEALTHCARE CORPORATION; *U.S. Public*, pg. 1677
UNITED HEALTHCARE OF GEORGIA, INC.—United HealthCare Corporation; *U.S. Public*, pg. 1678
UNITED HEALTHCARE OF THE MIDLANDS, INC.—United HealthCare Corporation; *U.S. Public*, pg. 1678
UNITED HEALTHCARE OF UTAH—United HealthCare Corporation; *U.S. Public*, pg. 1678
UNITED HEALTHCARE PLANS OF NEW ENGLAND, INC.—United HealthCare Corporation; *U.S. Public*, pg. 1678
UNITED STATES HEALTH CARE SYSTEMS OF PENNSYLVANIA, INC.—Aetna Inc.; *U.S. Public*, pg. 26
U.S. HEALTH INSURANCE COMPANY—Aetna Inc.; *U.S. Public*, pg. 26
U.S. HEALTHCARE DENTAL PLAN, INC. (DELAWARE)—Aetna Inc.; *U.S. Public*, pg. 26
U.S. HEALTHCARE, INC.—Aetna Inc.; *U.S. Public*, pg. 26
U.S. HEALTHCARE, INC. (CONNECTICUT)—Aetna Inc.; *U.S. Public*, pg. 26
UNITED STATES PHYSICIANS CARE SYSTEMS, INC.—Aetna Inc.; *U.S. Public*, pg. 27
UNITED WISCONSIN SERVICES, INC.; *U.S. Public*, pg. 1692
UNUM CORPORATION; *U.S. Public*, pg. 1699
ZENITH NATIONAL INSURANCE CORP.; *U.S. Public*, pg. 1790

6331 — FIRE, MARINE & CASUALTY INSURANCE

AGF ASSURANCES; *Int'l*, pg. 14
AIG AVIATION, INC.—American International Group, Inc.; *U.S. Public*, pg. 85
AIU CANADA LTD.—American International Group, Inc.; *U.S. Public*, pg. 85
AIU INSURANCE COMPANY—American International Group, Inc.; *U.S. Public*, pg. 84
AMB AACHENER UND MUENCHENER BETEILIGUNGS-AG; *Int'l*, pg. 15
AXA-UAP; *Int'l*, pg. 18
AACHENER UND MUENCHENER VERSICHERUNG AKTIENGESELLSCHAFT—AMB Aachener und Muenchener Beteiligungs-AG; *Int'l*, pg. 15
ACCEL INTERNATIONAL CORPORATION; *U.S. Public*, pg. 14
ACCELERATION NATIONAL INSURANCE COMPANY—ACCEL International Corporation; *U.S. Public*, pg. 14
ACCEPTANCE INSURANCE CO., INC.; *U.S. Public*, pg. 14
ACCEPTANCE INSURANCE COMPANIES, INC.—Acceptance Insurance Co., Inc.; *U.S. Public*, pg. 15
ADDISON INSURANCE COMPANY—United Fire & Casualty Company; *U.S. Public*, pg. 1677
ADMIRAL INSURANCE COMPANY—W.R. Berkley Corporation; *U.S. Public*, pg. 216
ADRIATIC INSURANCE COMPANY OF CANADA—Allianz Aktiengesellschaft; *Int'l*, pg. 61
ADRIATIC LIFE LTD.—Allianz Aktiengesellschaft; *Int'l*, pg. 61
ADRIATICA DE SEGUROS C.A.—Allianz Aktiengesellschaft; *Int'l*, pg. 61
ADRIATICA-SOCIEDAD ANONIMA DE SEGUROS Y REASEGUROS—Allianz Aktiengesellschaft; *Int'l*, pg. 61
AEGON INSURANCE COMPANY (UK) LIMITED—AEGON N.V.; *Int'l*, pg. 28
AEGON NEVAK HOLDING B.V.—AEGON N.V.; *Int'l*, pg. 26
AEGON N.V.; *Int'l*, pg. 25
AEGON USA, INC.—AEGON N.V.; *Int'l*, pg. 26
AETNA INTERNATIONAL CHILE S.A.—Aetna Inc.; *U.S. Public*, pg. 27
AETNA UNIVERSAL INSURANCE SDN. BHD.—Aetna Inc.; *U.S. Public*, pg. 27
AFFILIATED FM INSURANCE CO.—Allendale Mutual Insurance Co.; *U.S. Private*, pg. 37
AGRICULTURAL INSURANCE COMPANY—American Financial Group; *U.S. Public*, pg. 74
AGRONAUT GREAT CENTRAL INSURANCE CO.—Argonaut Group, Inc.; *U.S. Public*, pg. 129
AGWAY INSURANCE CO.—Agway, Inc.; *U.S. Private*, pg. 27
ALASKA PACIFIC ASSURANCE COMPANY—Cigna Corp.; *U.S. Public*, pg. 366
ALEXANDER & ALEXANDER SERVICES INC.—AON Corporation; *U.S. Public*, pg. 117
ALFA CORPORATION; *U.S. Public*, pg. 40
ALFA GENERAL INSURANCE CORP.—Alfa Corporation; *U.S. Public*, pg. 40
ALFA INSURANCE CORP.—Alfa Corporation; *U.S. Public*, pg. 40
ALITALIA LINEE AEREE ITALIANE S.P.A.—IRI Istituto Ricostruzione Industriale; *Int'l*, pg. 652
ALLCITY INSURANCE CO.—Leucadia National Corporation; *U.S. Public*, pg. 990
ALLCITY INSURANCE CO., ROCHESTER—Leucadia National Corporation; *U.S. Public*, pg. 990
ALLCITY INSURANCE CO., ROCKVILLE CENTRE—Leucadia National Corporation; *U.S. Public*, pg. 990
ALLCITY INSURANCE CO., SCARSDALE—Leucadia National Corporation; *U.S. Public*, pg. 990
ALLEGIANCE INSURANCE COMPANY—Cigna Corp.; *U.S. Public*, pg. 362
ALLENDALE MUTUAL INSURANCE CO.; *U.S. Private*, pg. 37
ALLIANZ NEDERLAND N.V. (ROTTERDAM OFFICE)—Allianz Aktiengesellschaft; *Int'l*, pg. 60
ALLIANZ NEDERLAND N.V. (STOCK EXCHANGE OFFICE)—Allianz Aktiengesellschaft; *Int'l*, pg. 60
ALLIANZ VERSICHERUNG (SCHWEIZ) AG—Allianz Aktiengesellschaft; *Int'l*, pg. 60
ALLIED INSURANCE COMPANY—Cigna Corp.; *U.S. Public*, pg. 362
ALLIED MUTUAL INSURANCE COMPANY; *U.S. Private*, pg. 39
THE ALLSTATE CORPORATION; *U.S. Public*, pg. 55
ALPHA PROPERTY & CASUALTY INSURANCE CO.—Unitrin, Inc.; *U.S. Public*, pg. 1694
ALTE LEIPZIGER RUECKVERSICHERUNG AG—Alte Leipziger Versicherung Aktiengesellschaft; *Int'l*, pg. 66
ALTE LEIPZIGER VERSICHERUNG AKTIENGESELLSCHAFT; *Int'l*, pg. 66
AMERICA LATINA COMPANHIA DE SEGUROS—The Tokio Marine & Fire Insurance Company, Ltd.; *Int'l*, pg. 1392
AMERICAN AND FOREIGN INSURANCE CO.—Royal & Sun Alliance Insurance Group plc; *Int'l*, pg. 1130

AMERICAN AUTOMOBILE INSURANCE CO.—Allianz Aktiengesellschaft; *Int'l*, pg. 59
AMERICAN COUNTRY INSURANCE CO.—Stamford Capital; *U.S. Private*, pg. 1030
AMERICAN EAGLE GROUP, INC.; *U.S. Public*, pg. 71
AMERICAN EMPIRE SURPLUS LINES INSURANCE COMPANY—American Financial Group; *U.S. Public*, pg. 74
AMERICAN EXPRESS FINANCIAL ADVISOR—American Express Company; *U.S. Public*, pg. 73
AMERICAN FAMILY HOME INSURANCE CO.—The Midland Company; *U.S. Public*, pg. 1110
AMERICAN FAMILY MUTUAL INSURANCE CO.; *U.S. Private*, pg. 53
AMERICAN FEDERATION INSURANCE CO.—Foremost Corporation of America; *U.S. Public*, pg. 667
AMERICAN FINANCIAL GROUP; *U.S. Public*, pg. 74
AMERICAN FIRE & CASUALTY CO.—Ohio Casualty Corporation; *U.S. Public*, pg. 1214
AMERICAN FIRE & INDEMNITY CO.—American Indemnity Financial Corp.; *U.S. Public*, pg. 83
AMERICAN GENERAL LIFE & ACCIDENT INSURANCE CO.—American General Corporation; *U.S. Public*, pg. 76
AMERICAN HARDWARE MUTUAL INSURANCE CO.—Motorists Mutual Insurance Co.; *U.S. Private*, pg. 764
AMERICAN HOME ASSURANCE CO.—American International Group, Inc.; *U.S. Public*, pg. 84
AMERICAN HOME ASSURANCE COMPANY NEW YORK, SWISS BRANCH—American International Group, Inc.; *U.S. Public*, pg. 85
AMERICAN INDEMNITY COMPANY—American Indemnity Financial Corp.; *U.S. Public*, pg. 83
AMERICAN INDEMNITY FINANCIAL CORP.; *U.S. Public*, pg. 83
AMERICAN INTERNATIONAL ASSURANCE CO. LTD.—American International Group, Inc.; *U.S. Public*, pg. 85
AMERICAN INTERNATIONAL GROUP, INC.; *U.S. Public*, pg. 83
AMERICAN MERCHANTS CASUALTY CO.—Motorists Mutual Insurance Co.; *U.S. Private*, pg. 764
AMERICAN MODERN HOME INSURANCE CO.—The Midland Company; *U.S. Public*, pg. 1110
AMERICAN MODERN HOME INSURANCE GROUP—The Midland Company; *U.S. Public*, pg. 1110
AMERICAN MOTORISTS INSURANCE CO.—Kemper Insurance Companies; *U.S. Private*, pg. 614
AMERICAN NATIONAL FIRE INSURANCE COMPANY—American Financial Group; *U.S. Public*, pg. 74
AMERICAN NATIONAL GENERAL INSURANCE COMPANY—American National Insurance Company; *U.S. Public*, pg. 88
AMERICAN NATIONAL INSURANCE SERVICE CO.—American National Insurance Company; *U.S. Public*, pg. 88
AMERICAN NATIONAL PROPERTY & CASUALTY CO.—American National Insurance Company; *U.S. Public*, pg. 87
AMERICAN PROTECTION INSURANCE CO.—Kemper Insurance Companies; *U.S. Private*, pg. 614
AMERICAN RE-INSURANCE COMPANY—Munchener Ruckversicherungs-Gesellschaft; *Int'l*, pg. 897
AMERICAN RELIABLE INSURANCE COMPANY—American Bankers Insurance Group, Inc.; *U.S. Public*, pg. 67
THE AMERICAN ROAD INSURANCE COMPANY—Ford Motor Company; *U.S. Public*, pg. 664
AMERICAN STANDARD INSURANCE COMPANY OF WISCONSIN—American Family Mutual Insurance Co.; *U.S. Private*, pg. 53
AMERICAN STATES ECONOMY INSURANCE CO.—Lincoln National Corporation; *U.S. Public*, pg. 997
AMERICAN STATES INSURANCE COMPANIES—Lincoln National Corporation; *U.S. Public*, pg. 997
AMERICAN STATES INSURANCE CO. OF TEXAS—Lincoln National Corporation; *U.S. Public*, pg. 997
AMERICAN WEST INSURANCE COMPANY—W.R. Berkley Corporation; *U.S. Public*, pg. 216
AMICA MUTUAL INSURANCE CO.; *U.S. Private*, pg. 66
ANCON INSURANCE COMPANY, INC.—Exxon Corporation; *U.S. Public*, pg. 601
APPALACHIAN INSURANCE CO.—Allendale Mutual Insurance Co.; *U.S. Private*, pg. 37
ARABIA CIGNA INSURANCE COMPANY LIMITED E.C.—Cigna Corp.; *U.S. Public*, pg. 363
ARGENT INSURANCE CO. LIMITED—Johnson Matthey Public Limited Company; *Int'l*, pg. 714
ARGONAUT CO.—Argonaut Group, Inc.; *U.S. Public*, pg. 129
ARGONAUT GROUP, INC.; *U.S. Public*, pg. 129
ARGOS COMPANHIA DE SEGUROS—The Chubb Corporation; *U.S. Public*, pg. 355
ARKANSAS FARM BUREAU FEDERATION; *U.S. Private*, pg. 82
ASEGURADORA CUAUHTEMOC S.A.—Allianz Aktiengesellschaft; *Int'l*, pg. 61
ASSICURAZIONI GENERALI S.P.A.; *Int'l*, pg. 89
ASSOCIATES FINANCIAL SERVICES CORPORATION—Ford Motor Company; *U.S. Public*, pg. 663
ASSOCIATES INSURANCE COMPANY—Ford Motor Company; *U.S. Public*, pg. 663
ASSOCIATES INSURANCE GROUP, INC.—Ford Motor Company; *U.S. Public*, pg. 663
ASTER INSURANCE LTD.—Harrah's Entertainment, Inc.; *U.S. Public*, pg. 790
P.T. ASURANSI CIGNA INDONESIA—Cigna Corp.; *U.S. Public*, pg. 363
ATLANTA CASUALTY COMPANY—American Financial Group; *U.S. Public*, pg. 75
ATLANTIC AMERICAN CORPORATION; *U.S. Public*, pg. 143
ATLANTIC EMPLOYERS INSURANCE COMPANY—Cigna Corp.; *U.S. Public*, pg. 366
ATLANTIC MUTUAL COMPANIES; *U.S. Private*, pg. 95
AUTO-OWNERS INSURANCE; *U.S. Private*, pg. 100
AUTOMOBILE CLUB INSURANCE COMPANY—American Automobile Association; *U.S. Private*, pg. 51
AVEMCO INSURANCE CO.—Avemco Corporation; *U.S. Public*, pg. 152
BALDWIN & LYONS, INC.; *U.S. Public*, pg. 169
BANKERS STANDARD FIRE & MARINE COMPANY—Cigna Corp.; *U.S. Public*, pg. 365
BANKERS STANDARD INSURANCE COMPANY—Cigna Corp.; *U.S. Public*, pg. 365
BANNER LIFE INSURANCE CO.—Legal & General Group PLC; *Int'l*, pg. 805
BAYERISCHE VERSICHERUNGSBANK-AG—Allianz Aktiengesellschaft; *Int'l*, pg. 58
BELGIUM UNION DES ASSUREURS, BELGIQUE—La Fondiaria Assicurazioni S.p.A.; *Int'l*, pg. 784
BERKLEY RISK MANAGERS—W.R. Berkley Corporation; *U.S. Public*, pg. 215
BERKLEY RISK SERVICES, INC.—W.R. Berkley Corporation; *U.S. Public*, pg. 215
W.R. BERKLEY CORPORATION; *U.S. Public*, pg. 215
BERKSHIRE HATHAWAY INC.; *U.S. Public*, pg. 217
BIRMINGHAM FIRE INSURANCE CO. OF PENNSYLVANIA—American International Group, Inc.; *U.S. Public*, pg. 84
BITUMINOUS CASUALTY CORP.—Old Republic International Corporation; *U.S. Public*, pg. 1218
BOSTON OLD COLONY INSURANCE CO.—Loews Corporation; *U.S. Public*, pg. 1010
BRADSTOCK GROUP PLC; *Int'l*, pg. 210
BRITISH RESERVE—Allianz Aktiengesellschaft; *Int'l*, pg. 61
BUCKEYE UNION INSURANCE CO.—Loews Corporation; *U.S. Public*, pg. 1010
BURNS & WILCOX—H.W. Kaufman Financial Group, Inc.; *U.S. Private*, pg. 609
CFI INSURERS, LTD.—Sizzler International, Inc.; *U.S. Public*, pg. 1475
CNA FINANCIAL CORP.—Loews Corporation; *U.S. Public*, pg. 1010
CNL FINANCIAL CORP.; *U.S. Public*, pg. 281
CSE INSURANCE GROUP; *U.S. Private*, pg. 197
CALFARM INSURANCE AGENCY—Zenith National Insurance Corp.; *U.S. Public*, pg. 1791
CALFARM INSURANCE COMPANY—Zenith National Insurance Corp.; *U.S. Public*, pg. 1791
THE CAMDEN FIRE INSURANCE ASSN.—General Accident Fire and Life Assurance Corporation p.l.c.; *Int'l*, pg. 543
CANADA LIFE CASUALTY INSURANCE COMPANY—The Canada Life Assurance Company; *Int'l*, pg. 254
CAPARO INSURANCE LTD.—Caparo Group Ltd.; *Int'l*, pg. 265
CAPITOL COUNTY MUTUAL FIRE INSURANCE CO.—The Reliable Life Insurance Company; *U.S. Public*, pg. 1374
CAPITOL INDEMNITY CORPORATION—Capitol Indemnity Corporation; *U.S. Public*, pg. 302
CAPITOL SPECIALTY INSURANCE CORPORATION—Capitol Indemnity Corporation; *U.S. Public*, pg. 302
CAPSURE HOLDINGS CORP.; *U.S. Public*, pg. 303
CAROLINA CASUALTY INSURANCE COMPANY—W.R. Berkley Corporation; *U.S. Public*, pg. 216
CATAWBA INSURANCE CO.—The Seibels Bruce Group, Inc.; *U.S. Public*, pg. 1454
CENTRAL PROPERTY & CASUALTY INSURANCE COMPANY—Preferred Risk Mutual Insurance; *U.S. Private*, pg. 880
CENTURY INDEMNITY COMPANY—Cigna Corp.; *U.S. Public*, pg. 365
CENTURY REINSURANCE COMPANY—Cigna Corp.; *U.S. Public*, pg. 365
CHARLESTON FINANCIAL SERVICES, INC.—First Financial Holdings, Inc.; *U.S. Public*, pg. 634
THE CHARTER OAK FIRE INSURANCE CO.—Travelers Group; *U.S. Public*, pg. 1633
CHESAPEAKE INSURANCE DIVISION—W.R. Berkley Corporation; *U.S. Public*, pg. 215
CHRYSLER INSURANCE CO.—Chrysler Corporation; *U.S. Public*, pg. 354
THE CHUBB CORPORATION; *U.S. Public*, pg. 354
CHUBB CUSTOM INSURANCE COMPANY—The Chubb Corporation; *U.S. Public*, pg. 355
CHUBB INSURANCE COMPANY OF NEW JERSEY—The Chubb Corporation; *U.S. Public*, pg. 355
CHURCH MUTUAL INSURANCE CO.; *U.S. Private*, pg. 239
CIGNA COMPANIA DE SEGUROS (CHILE) S.A.—Cigna Corp.; *U.S. Public*, pg. 363
CIGNA CORP.; *U.S. Public*, pg. 356
CIGNA FIRE UNDERWRITERS INSURANCE COMPANY—Cigna Corp.; *U.S. Public*, pg. 365
CIGNA INSURANCE AUSTRALIA LIMITED—Cigna Corp.; *U.S. Public*, pg. 364
CIGNA INSURANCE COMPANY—Cigna Corp.; *U.S. Public*, pg. 365
CIGNA INSURANCE COMPANY OF CANADA—Cigna Corp.; *U.S. Public*, pg. 366
CIGNA INSURANCE COMPANY OF EUROPE, S.A.-N.V.—Cigna Corp.; *U.S. Public*, pg. 364
CIGNA INSURANCE COMPANY OF TEXAS—Cigna Corp.; *U.S. Public*, pg. 365
CIGNA INSURANCE COMPANY OF PUERTO RICO—Cigna Corp.; *U.S. Public*, pg. 364
CIGNA INSURANCE NEW ZEALAND LIMITED—Cigna Corp.; *U.S. Public*, pg. 364
CIGNA INTERNATIONAL REINSURANCE COMPANY LTD.—Cigna Corp.; *U.S. Public*, pg. 364
CIGNA PROPERTY & CASUALTY INSURANCE COMPANY—Cigna Corp.; *U.S. Public*, pg. 364
CIGNA REINSURANCE COMPANY—Cigna Corp.; *U.S. Public*, pg. 365
CIGNA REINSURANCE COMPANY S.A.-N.V.—Cigna Corp.; *U.S. Public*, pg. 365
CIGNA REINSURANCE NEW ZEALAND LIMITED—Cigna Corp.; *U.S. Public*, pg. 363
CIGNA SEGURADORA S.A.—Cigna Corp.; *U.S. Public*, pg. 363
CIGNA SEGUROS DE COLOMBIA S.A.—Cigna Corp.; *U.S. Public*, pg. 363
CIGNA SPECIALTY INSURANCE COMPANY—Cigna Corp.; *U.S. Public*, pg. 366
CIGNA WORLDWIDE INSURANCE COMPANY—Cigna Corp.; *U.S. Public*, pg. 365
CINCINNATI CASUALTY CO.—Cincinnati Financial Corp.; *U.S. Public*, pg. 368
CINCINNATI FINANCIAL CORP.; *U.S. Public*, pg. 368
CINCINNATI INDEMNITY COMPANY—Cincinnati Financial Corp.; *U.S. Public*, pg. 368
CINCINNATI INSURANCE CO.—Cincinnati Financial Corp.; *U.S. Public*, pg. 368
CITATION INSURANCE COMPANY—Citation Insurance Group; *U.S. Public*, pg. 376
CITATION INSURANCE GROUP; *U.S. Public*, pg. 376
CITATION NATIONAL INSURANCE COMPANY—Citation Insurance Group; *U.S. Public*, pg. 376
CITIZENS INSURANCE COMPANY OF AMERICA—Allmerica Financial Corporation; *U.S. Public*, pg. 54
CLAYTON HOMES, INC.; *U.S. Public*, pg. 382
CLERMONT SPECIALTY MANAGERS, LTD.—W.R. Berkley Corporation; *U.S. Public*, pg. 215
COLONIAL PENN GROUP, INC.—Leucadia National Corporation; *U.S. Public*, pg. 990
COLONIAL PENN INSURANCE CO.—General Electric Company; *U.S. Public*, pg. 712
COMMERCE & INDUSTRY INSURANCE CO.—American International Group, Inc.; *U.S. Public*, pg. 84
COMMERCE & INDUSTRY INSURANCE CO. OF CANADA—American International Group, Inc.; *U.S. Public*, pg. 85
COMMERCIAL UNION CORPORATION—Commercial Union plc; *Int'l*, pg. 308
COMMERCIAL UNION INSURANCE COMPANY—Commercial Union plc; *Int'l*, pg. 308
COMMERCIAL UNION PLC; *Int'l*, pg. 308
COMPAGNIA DI GENOVA—Allianz Aktiengesellschaft; *Int'l*, pg. 61
COMPAGNIE D'ASSURANCE DU QUEBEC—Royal & Sun Alliance Insurance Group plc; *Int'l*, pg. 1131
COMPANHIA ADRIATICA DE SEGUROS GERAIS—Allianz Aktiengesellschaft; *Int'l*, pg. 61
A.S. COMPANHIA PORTUGUESA DE SEGUROS—La Fondiaria Assicurazioni S.p.A.; *Int'l*, pg. 784
COMPANIA ASEGURADORA ARGENTINA S.A.—Allianz Aktiengesellschaft; *Int'l*, pg. 61
CONCOMBER, LTD.—Unicom Corporation; *U.S. Public*, pg. 1664
CONNECTICUT GENERAL FIRE & CASUALTY INSURANCE COMPANY—Cigna Corp.; *U.S. Public*, pg. 365
THE CONNECTICUT INDEMNITY CO.—Orion Capital Corporation; *U.S. Public*, pg. 1231
CONSECO LIFE OF NEW YORK—Conseco Inc.; *U.S. Public*, pg. 433
CONSECO RISK MANAGEMENT, INC.—Conseco Inc.; *U.S. Public*, pg. 433
CONSOLIDATED AMERICAN INSURANCE CO.—The Seibels Bruce Group, Inc.; *U.S. Public*, pg. 1454
CONTINENTAL AVIATION UNDERWRITERS, INC.—Reliance Group Holdings, Inc.; *U.S. Public*, pg. 1374
THE CONTINENTAL CORPORATION—Loews Corporation; *U.S. Public*, pg. 1011
CONTINENTAL DIVIDE INSURANCE CO.—Berkshire Hathaway Inc.; *U.S. Public*, pg. 221
THE CONTINENTAL INSURANCE CO.—Loews Corporation; *U.S. Public*, pg. 1011
CONTINENTAL LEBENSVERSICHERUNGSGESELLSCHAFT—Allianz Aktiengesellschaft; *Int'l*, pg. 61
CONTINENTAL WESTERN INSURANCE COMPANY—W.R. Berkley Corporation; *U.S. Public*, pg. 215
CONTINENTALE ALLGEMINE VERSICHERUNGS-AG—Allianz Aktiengesellschaft; *Int'l*, pg. 61
CORNHUSKER CASUALTY CO.—Berkshire Hathaway Inc.; *U.S. Public*, pg. 221
CORPORACION MAPFRE, COMPANIA INTERNACIONAL DE REASEGUROS, S.A.; *Int'l*, pg. 332
COSMOS VERSICHERUNG AG—AMB Aachener und Muenchener Beteiligungs-AG; *Int'l*, pg. 15
COUNTRY CASUALTY INSURANCE COMPANY—Country Life Insurance Company; *U.S. Private*, pg. 279
COUNTRY LIFE INSURANCE COMPANY; *U.S. Private*, pg. 278
COUNTRY MUTUAL INSURANCE COMPANY—Country Life Insurance Company; *U.S. Private*, pg. 279
COUNTRY MUTUAL NORTHWEST REGIONAL OFFICE—Country Life Insurance Company; *U.S. Private*, pg. 279
COUNTRY PREFERRED INSURANCE COMPANY—Country Life Insurance Company; *U.S. Private*, pg. 279
COUNTRYWIDE SERVICES CORP.—Nationwide Insurance Enterprise; *U.S. Private*, pg. 789
CRESA ASEGURADORA Y REASEGURADORA IBERICA S.A.—Allianz Aktiengesellschaft; *Int'l*, pg. 61
CRUM & FORSTER UNDERWRITERS CO. OF OHIO—Xerox Corporation; *U.S. Public*, pg. 1784
CRUM & FORSTER MANAGERS CORPORATION (NY)—Xerox Corporation; *U.S. Public*, pg. 1784
CRUSADER INSURANCE COMPANY OF AUSTRALIA LIMITED—Cigna Corp.; *U.S. Public*, pg. 364
DAIRYLAND COUNTY MUTUAL INSURANCE CO.—Sentry Insurance, A Mutual Company; *U.S. Private*, pg. 985
DAIRYLAND INSURANCE CO.—Sentry Insurance, A Mutual Company; *U.S. Private*, pg. 985
DELAWARE REINSURANCE COMPANY—Cigna Corp.; *U.S. Public*, pg. 363
DELVAG LUFTFAHRTVERSICHERUNGS-AG—Deutsche Lufthansa AG; *Int'l*, pg. 407
DESJARDINS LAURENTIAN LIFE ASSURANCE—Desjardins-Laurentian Financial Corporation; *Int'l*, pg. 396
DIXIE INSURANCE COMPANY—American Financial Group; *U.S. Public*, pg. 75

DODSON GROUP; *U.S. Private*, pg. 338
DOMINION INSURANCE LTD.—La Fondiaria Assicurazioni S.p.A.; *Int'l*, pg. 784
DOMUS FORSIKRINGSAKTIESELSKABET A/S—Allianz Aktiengesellschaft; *Int'l*, pg. 61
DONG BU INSURANCE CO.; *Int'l*, pg. 416
EMC INSURANCE COMPANIES—EMC Insurance Group, Inc.; *U.S. Public*, pg. 545
EMC INSURANCE GROUP, INC.; *U.S. Public*, pg. 545
EAST ASIA AETNA INSURANCE GROUP—Aetna Inc.; *U.S. Public*, pg. 27
EL SOL COMPANIA DE SEGUROS GENERALES—Allianz Aktiengesellschaft; *Int'l*, pg. 61
EMPIRE FIRE & MARINE INSURANCE CO.—Zurich Insurance Company; *Int'l*, pg. 1530
EMPIRE INSURANCE GROUP—Leucadia National Corporation; *U.S. Public*, pg. 990
EMPLOYERS INSURANCE OF WAUSAU—Nationwide Insurance Enterprise; *U.S. Private*, pg. 788
EMPLOYERS REINSURANCE CORP.—General Electric Company; *U.S. Public*, pg. 711
EMPRESA GUATEMALTICA CIGNA DE SEGUROS, SOCIEDAD ANONIMA—Cigna Corp.; *U.S. Public*, pg. 364
ENNIA CARIBE N.V.—AEGON N.V.; *Int'l*, pg. 28
ENRON CORP.; *U.S. Public*, pg. 584
EQUITY FIRE & CASUALTY INSURANCE COMPANY—Preferred Risk Mutual Insurance; *U.S. Private*, pg. 881
EVEREST INDEMNITY INSURANCE COMPANY—Everest Reinsurance Holdings; *U.S. Public*, pg. 597
EVEREST INSURANCE COMPANY OF CANADA—Everest Reinsurance Holdings; *U.S. Public*, pg. 597
EVEREST NATIONAL INSURANCE CO.—Everest Reinsurance Holdings; *U.S. Public*, pg. 597
EVEREST REINSURANCE CO.—Everest Reinsurance Holdings; *U.S. Public*, pg. 597
EVEREST REINSURANCE HOLDINGS; *U.S. Public*, pg. 597
EVEREST REINSURANCE, LTD.—Everest Reinsurance Holdings; *U.S. Public*, pg. 597
FARM BUREAU CASUALTY INSURANCE CO.—Arkansas Farm Bureau Federation; *U.S. Private*, pg. 82
FARM FAMILY CASUALTY INSURANCE CO.; *U.S. Private*, pg. 394
FEDERAL INSURANCE CO.—The Chubb Corporation; *U.S. Public*, pg. 355
FEDERATED MUTUAL INSURANCE COMPANY; *U.S. Private*, pg. 399
FIDELITY AND CASUALTY CO. OF NEW YORK—Loews Corporation; *U.S. Public*, pg. 1011
THE FIRE & CASUALTY CO. OF CONNECTICUT—Orion Capital Corporation; *U.S. Public*, pg. 1231
FIRE, EQUITY & GENERAL INSURANCE COMPANY LIMITED—Cigna Corp.; *U.S. Public*, pg. 363
FIREMAN'S FUND INDEMNITY CORPORATION—Allianz Aktiengesellschaft; *Int'l*, pg. 59
FIREMAN'S FUND INSURANCE COMPANY—Allianz Aktiengesellschaft; *Int'l*, pg. 58
FIREMEN'S INSURANCE CO. OF NEWARK, N.J.—Loews Corporation; *U.S. Public*, pg. 1011
FIREMEN'S INSURANCE COMPANY OF WASHINGTON, D.C.—W.R. Berkley Corporation; *U.S. Public*, pg. 215
FIRST INSURANCE CO. OF HAWAII, LTD.—Loews Corporation; *U.S. Public*, pg. 1011
FIRST NATIONAL INSURANCE CO. OF AMERICA—SAFECO Corporation; *U.S. Public*, pg. 1423
FIRST QUADRANT CORPORATION—Xerox Corporation; *U.S. Public*, pg. 1784
FIRST SOUTHEAST INSURANCE AGENCY—First Financial Holdings, Inc.; *U.S. Public*, pg. 634
FIRST VIRGINIA INSURANCE SERVICES, INC.—First Virginia Banks, Inc.; *U.S. Public*, pg. 642
FLEET INSURANCE MANAGEMENT, INC.—Norfolk Southern Corporation; *U.S. Public*, pg. 1191
FOREMOST CORPORATION OF AMERICA; *U.S. Public*, pg. 667
FOREMOST INSURANCE CO.—Foremost Corporation of America; *U.S. Public*, pg. 667
FOREMOST PROPERTY & CASUALTY INSURANCE COMPANY—Foremost Corporation of America; *U.S. Public*, pg. 667
FOREMOST SIGNATURE INSURANCE CO.—Foremost Corporation of America; *U.S. Public*, pg. 667
FORSAKRINGSAKTIEBOLAGET VOLVIA—AB Volvo; *Int'l*, pg. 1476
FRANDISCO PROPERTY & CASUALTY INSURANCE—First Franklin Financial Corp.; *U.S. Private*, pg. 407
FRANKFURTER VERSICHERUNGS-AG—Allianz Aktiengesellschaft; *Int'l*, pg. 58
FREMONT GENERAL CORPORATION; *U.S. Public*, pg. 681
FRONTIER INSURANCE GROUP, INC.; *U.S. Public*, pg. 684
FRONTIER PACIFIC INSURANCE COMPANY—Frontier Insurance Group, Inc.; *U.S. Public*, pg. 685
GEICO CASUALTY COMPANY—Berkshire Hathaway Inc.; *U.S. Public*, pg. 219
GEICO CORPORATION—Berkshire Hathaway Inc.; *U.S. Public*, pg. 219
GEICO GENERAL INSURANCE CO.—Berkshire Hathaway Inc.; *U.S. Public*, pg. 219
GEICO INDEMNITY COMPANY—Berkshire Hathaway Inc.; *U.S. Public*, pg. 220
GELLATLY HANKEY MARINE SERVICES—Inchcape PLC; *Int'l*, pg. 672
GENERAL ACCIDENT FIRE AND LIFE ASSURANCE CORPORATION P.L.C.; *Int'l*, pg. 542
GENERAL ACCIDENT INSURANCE—General Accident Fire and Life Assurance Corporation p.l.c.; *Int'l*, pg. 543
GENERAL ASSURANCE COMPANY—General Accident Fire and Life Assurance Corporation p.l.c.; *Int'l*, pg. 543
GENERAL ASSURANCE INSURANCE COMPANY OF NEW YORK—General Accident Fire and Life Assurance Corporation p.l.c.; *Int'l*, pg. 543
GENERAL CASUALTY COMPANY OF ILLINOIS—Credit Suisse Group; *Int'l*, pg. 346
GENERAL CASUALTY COMPANY OF WISCONSIN—Credit Suisse Group; *Int'l*, pg. 345
GENERAL ELECTRIC CAPITAL SERVICES, INC.—General Electric Company; *U.S. Public*, pg. 711
GENERAL INSURANCE CO. OF AMERICA—SAFECO Corporation; *U.S. Public*, pg. 1423
GENERAL RE EUROPE LIMITED—General Re Corporation; *U.S. Public*, pg. 726
GENERAL REINSURANCE CORP.—General Re Corporation; *U.S. Public*, pg. 725
GEORGIA CASUALTY & SURETY COMPANY—Atlantic American Corporation; *U.S. Public*, pg. 143
GLOBE INDEMNITY CO.—Royal & Sun Alliance Insurance Group plc; *Int'l*, pg. 1130
GLOBUS VERSICHERUNGS AG—Allianz Aktiengesellschaft; *Int'l*, pg. 58
GMAC INSURANCE HOLDINGS—General Motors Corporation; *U.S. Public*, pg. 719
GOLD CIRCLE INSURANCE CO.—The Great-West Life Assurance Company; *Int'l*, pg. 558
GOVERNMENT EMPLOYEES INSURANCE CO. (GEICO)—Berkshire Hathaway Inc.; *U.S. Public*, pg. 220
GRANITE STATE INSURANCE CO.—American International Group, Inc.; *U.S. Public*, pg. 84
GREAT AMERICAN HOLDING CORPORATION—American Financial Group; *U.S. Public*, pg. 74
GREAT AMERICAN INSURANCE COMPANY—American Financial Group; *U.S. Public*, pg. 74
THE GREAT EASTERN INSURANCE COMPANY—The Hartford Financial Services Group Inc.; *U.S. Public*, pg. 794
GREAT NORTHERN INSURANCE CO.—The Chubb Corporation; *U.S. Public*, pg. 355
GREAT OAKS INSURANCE COMPANY—Harleysville Group; *U.S. Public*, pg. 786
GREAT PACIFIC INSURANCE COMPANY—National Insurance Group; *U.S. Public*, pg. 1158
GREAT RIVER INSURANCE COMPANY—W.R. Berkley Corporation; *U.S. Public*, pg. 215
GREAT WEST CASUALTY COMPANY—Old Republic International Corporation; *U.S. Public*, pg. 1218
GREATER NEW YORK MUTUAL INSURANCE COMPANY; *U.S. Private*, pg. 476
GREENWICH INSURANCE COMPANY—NAC Re Corp.; *U.S. Public*, pg. 1144
GULF INSURANCE COMPANY—Travelers Group; *U.S. Public*, pg. 1633
HSBC GIBBS LTD.—HSBC Holdings plc; *Int'l*, pg. 579
HSBC INSURANCE LIMITED—HSBC Holdings plc; *Int'l*, pg. 582
HSN INSURANCE, INC.—USA Networks, Inc.; *U.S. Public*, pg. 1685
THE HANOVER INSURANCE COMPANY—Allmerica Financial Corporation; *U.S. Public*, pg. 54
HANOVER LLOYD'S INSURANCE COMPANY—Allmerica Financial Corporation; *U.S. Public*, pg. 54
HARLEYSVILLE ATLANTIC INSURANCE COMPANY—Harleysville Group; *U.S. Public*, pg. 786
HARLEYSVILLE-GARDEN STATE INSURANCE CO.—Harleysville Group; *U.S. Public*, pg. 787
HARLEYSVILLE GROUP; *U.S. Public*, pg. 786
HARLEYSVILLE INSURANCE COMPANY OF NEW JERSEY—Harleysville Group; *U.S. Public*, pg. 787
HARLEYSVILLE MUTUAL INSURANCE—Harleysville Group; *U.S. Public*, pg. 787
HARLEYSVILLE SERVICES INC—Harleysville Group; *U.S. Public*, pg. 787
HARTFORD FIRE INSURANCE CO.—The Hartford Financial Services Group Inc.; *U.S. Public*, pg. 794
THE HARTFORD FIRE INSURANCE COMPANY—The Hartford Financial Services Group Inc.; *U.S. Public*, pg. 794
HARTFORD INSURANCE GROUP OF CANADA—The Hartford Financial Services Group Inc.; *U.S. Public*, pg. 794
THE HARTFORD STEAM BOILER INSPECTION & INSURANCE CO.; *U.S. Public*, pg. 795
HAWKEYE-SECURITY INSURANCE CO.—General Accident Fire and Life Assurance Corporation p.l.c.; *Int'l*, pg. 543
HIGHLANDS INSURANCE CO.; *U.S. Public*, pg. 826
HILB, ROGAL AND HAMILTON COMPANY; *U.S. Public*, pg. 826
HOME SHOPPING NETWORK, INC.—USA Networks, Inc.; *U.S. Public*, pg. 1685
THE HONGKONG AND SHANGHAI BANKING CORPORATION LIMITED (HONGKONGBANK)—HSBC Holdings plc; *Int'l*, pg. 583
HONORIS COMPANIA DE SEGUROS DE VIDA S.A.—Cigna Corp.; *U.S. Public*, pg. 364
HOOSIER INSURANCE COMPANY—Credit Suisse Group, *Int'l*, pg. 346
HORACE MANN EDUCATORS CORPORATION; *U.S. Public*, pg. 835
HORACE MANN INSURANCE COMPANY—Horace Mann Educators Corporation; *U.S. Public*, pg. 836
HUDSON INSURANCE COMPANY—Skandia Insurance Company Limited; *Int'l*, pg. 1258
HUNTINGTON BANCSHARES INC.; *U.S. Public*, pg. 849
HURON INSURANCE CO.—Harleysville Group; *U.S. Public*, pg. 787
IDS PROPERTY CASUALTY INSURANCE COMPANY—American Express Company; *U.S. Public*, pg. 73
INA COUNTY MUTUAL INSURANCE COMPANY—Cigna Corp.; *U.S. Public*, pg. 366
ILLINOIS BANC ONE INSURANCE SERVICES, INC.—Banc One Corporation; *U.S. Public*, pg. 174
ILLINOIS NATIONAL INSURANCE CO.—American International Group, Inc.; *U.S. Public*, pg. 84
ILLINOIS UNION INSURANCE COMPANY—Cigna Corp.; *U.S. Public*, pg. 365
IMPERIAL CASUALTY & INDEMNITY CO.—Amoco Corporation; *U.S. Public*, pg. 103
THE IMPERIAL LIFE ASSURANCE CO.—Desjardins-Laurentian Financial Corporation; *Int'l*, pg. 396
INDEMNITY INSURANCE COMPANY OF NORTH AMERICA—Cigna Corp.; *U.S. Public*, pg. 366
INDIAN HARBOR INSURANCE COMPANY—NAC Re Corp.; *U.S. Public*, pg. 1144
INDIANA INSURANCE COMPANY—ING Groep N.V.; *Int'l*, pg. 648
INDUSTRIAL INDEMNITY INSURANCE SERVICES, INC.—Fremont General Corporation; *U.S. Public*, pg. 681
INDUSTRIFORSIKRING A/S—Norsk Hydro a.s; *Int'l*, pg. 960
INLAND NATIONAL INS. CO.—American International Group, Inc.; *U.S. Public*, pg. 84
THE INNOVATIVE COMPANY—The Seibels Bruce Group, Inc.; *U.S. Public*, pg. 1454
INSURANCE COMPANY OF GREATER NEW YORK—Greater New York Mutual Insurance Company; *U.S. Private*, pg. 476
INSURANCE COMPANY OF NORTH AMERICA—Cigna Corp.; *U.S. Public*, pg. 366
INSURANCE COMPANY OF NORTH AMERICA (U.K.) LIMITED—Cigna Corp.; *U.S. Public*, pg. 363
INSURANCE COMPANY OF OHIO—Meridian Insurance Group, Inc.; *U.S. Public*, pg. 1095
INSURANCE COMPANY OF THE STATE OF PENNSYLVANIA—American International Group, Inc.; *U.S. Public*, pg. 84
THE INSURANCE CORP. OF NEW YORK—Chartwell Re Corporation; *U.S. Public*, pg. 336
INTEGON CASUALTY INSURANCE COMPANY—General Motors Corporation; *U.S. Public*, pg. 720
INTEGON CORPORATION—General Motors Corporation; *U.S. Public*, pg. 719
INTEGON GENERAL INSURANCE CORPORATION—General Motors Corporation; *U.S. Public*, pg. 720
INTEGON INDEMNITY CORPORATION—General Motors Corporation; *U.S. Public*, pg. 720
INTEGON NATIONAL INSURANCE CO.—General Motors Corporation; *U.S. Public*, pg. 720
INTEGON PREFERRED INSURANCE COMPANY—General Motors Corporation; *U.S. Public*, pg. 720
INTEGON SPECIALTY INSURANCE COMPANY—General Motors Corporation; *U.S. Public*, pg. 720
INTEGRITY MUTUAL INSURANCE COMPANY; *U.S. Private*, pg. 566
INTERNATIONAL BUSINESS AND MERCANTILE REASSURANCE COMPANY—Old Republic International Corporation; *U.S. Public*, pg. 1218
INTERSTATE NATIONAL CORP.—Allianz Aktiengesellschaft; *Int'l*, pg. 59
INTERUNFALL LEASING—Allianz Aktiengesellschaft; *Int'l*, pg. 61
INTRACORP PEER REVIEW ORGANIZATION, INC.—Cigna Corp.; *U.S. Public*, pg. 362
JEFFERSON-PILOT PROPERTY INSURANCE COMPANY—Jefferson-Pilot Corporation; *U.S. Public*, pg. 926
JEWELERS MUTUAL INSURANCE COMPANY; *U.S. Private*, pg. 587
KMA INSURANCE AGENCY, INC.—Michigan Physicians Mutual Liability Inc.; *U.S. Private*, pg. 741
KANSAS CITY FIRE AND MARINE INSURANCE CO.—Loews Corporation; *U.S. Public*, pg. 1011
KANSAS FIRE & CASUALTY CO.—Berkshire Hathaway Inc.; *U.S. Public*, pg. 221
KEMPER INSURANCE COMPANIES; *U.S. Private*, pg. 614
KEMPER REINSURANCE CO.—Kemper Insurance Companies; *U.S. Private*, pg. 614
KENTUCKY INSURANCE CO.—The Seibels Bruce Group, Inc.; *U.S. Public*, pg. 1454
KIRBY CORPORATION; *U.S. Public*, pg. 961
KOHAP-NEW YORK LIFE INSURANCE LTD.—KOHAP Group; *Int'l*, pg. 742
KONINKLIJKE VAN OMMEREN NV; *Int'l*, pg. 758
KRAFT VERSICHERUNGS-AG—Allianz Aktiengesellschaft; *Int'l*, pg. 58
KVAERNER HILNOR A.S.—Kvaerner a.s.a.; *Int'l*, pg. 769
KYOEI FIRE & MARINE INSURANCE CO. (U.K.) LTD.—The Kyoei Mutual Fire & Marine Insurance Company; *Int'l*, pg. 777
THE KYOEI MUTUAL FIRE & MARINE INSURANCE COMPANY; *Int'l*, pg. 777
LA FONDIARIA ASSICURAZIONI S.P.A.; *Int'l*, pg. 784
LA PREVIDENTE S.P.A.—La Fondiaria Assicurazioni S.p.A.; *Int'l*, pg. 784
LAFAYETTE INSURANCE COMPANY—United Fire & Casualty Company; *U.S. Public*, pg. 1677
LAKE STATES INSURANCE CO.—Harleysville Group; *U.S. Public*, pg. 787
LAVORO & SICURTA—Allianz Aktiengesellschaft; *Int'l*, pg. 61
LEADER NATIONAL INSURANCE COMPANY—American Financial Group; *U.S. Public*, pg. 75
LEGAL & GENERAL AMERICA, INC.—Legal & General Group PLC; *Int'l*, pg. 805
LEGAL & GENERAL ASSURANCE HOLDINGS (AUSTRALIA) LIMITED—Legal & General Group PLC; *Int'l*, pg. 805
LEGAL & GENERAL GROUP PLC; *Int'l*, pg. 805
LEXINGTON INSURANCE CO.—American International Group, Inc.; *U.S. Public*, pg. 84
LIBERTY MUTUAL FIRE INSURANCE CO.—Liberty Mutual Insurance Co.; *U.S. Private*, pg. 666
LIBERTY MUTUAL INSURANCE CO.; *U.S. Private*, pg. 666
LIBERTY NATIONAL FIRE INSURANCE CO.—Torchmark Corporation; *U.S. Public*, pg. 1623
LIBERTY NATIONAL INSURANCE CORP.—Torchmark Corporation; *U.S. Public*, pg. 1623
LIBERTY NORTHWEST INSURANCE CORP.—Liberty Mutual Insurance Co.; *U.S. Private*, pg. 666

LINCOLN NATIONAL HEALTH & CASUALTY INSURANCE CO.—Lincoln National Corporation; *U.S. Public*, pg. 998
L'ITALICA—Allianz Aktiengesellschaft; *Int'l*, pg. 61
LOEWS CORPORATION; *U.S. Public*, pg. 1010
THE LONDON AGENCY, INC.—Xerox Corporation; *U.S. Public*, pg. 1784
LONDON-CANADA INSURANCE COMPANY—The Hartford Financial Services Group Inc.; *U.S. Public*, pg. 795
LONHRO EXPORTS LTD.—Lonrho plc; *Int'l*, pg. 817
LUMBERMEN'S MUTUAL CASUALTY COMPANY—Kemper Insurance Companies; *U.S. Private*, pg. 614
MMI COMPANIES, INC.; *U.S. Public*, pg. 1027
MSI INSURANCE COMPANIES; *U.S. Private*, pg. 688
MADISON ACCEPTANCE CORPORATION—Citation Insurance Group; *U.S. Public*, pg. 376
MAINE BONDING & CASUALTY COMPANY—Zurich Insurance Company; *Int'l*, pg. 1530
MAINLAND INSURANCE CO.—Harleysville Group; *U.S. Public*, pg. 787
MANULIFE (INTERNATIONAL) P & C LTD.—Manulife Financial (The Manufacturers Life Insurance Company); *Int'l*, pg. 841
THE MARINE CONTAINER INSURANCE CO. LTD.—Sea Containers Ltd.; *Int'l*, pg. 1213
MARITIME GENERAL INSURANCE COMPANY LIMITED—Cigna Corp.; *U.S. Public*, pg. 364
MARYLAND CASUALTY CO.—Zurich Insurance Company; *Int'l*, pg. 1530
MASSACHUSETTS BAY INSURANCE CO.—Allmerica Financial Corporation; *U.S. Public*, pg. 54
WM. H. MCGEE & CO., INC.—Orion Capital Corporation; *U.S. Public*, pg. 1231
MCWANE, INC.; *U.S. Private*, pg. 725
MEDICAL ASSURANCE, INC.; *U.S. Public*, pg. 1079
MEDICAL ASSURANCE OF WEST VIRGINIA—Medical Assurance, Inc.; *U.S. Public*, pg. 1080
THE MEDICAL PROTECTIVE COMPANY; *U.S. Private*, pg. 728
MERCANTILE INSURANCE SERVICES, INC.—Mercantile Bancorporation Inc.; *U.S. Public*, pg. 1088
MERCHANTS GROUP, INC.; *U.S. Public*, pg. 1090
MERCURY GENERAL CORPORATION; *U.S. Public*, pg. 1093
MERIDIAN INSURANCE GROUP, INC.; *U.S. Public*, pg. 1095
MERIDIAN SECURITY INSURANCE COMPANY—Meridian Insurance Group, Inc.; *U.S. Public*, pg. 1095
METROPOLITAN PROPERTY & CASUALTY INSURANCE CO. (MET P&C)—Metropolitan Life Insurance Co.; *U.S. Private*, pg. 737
MICO INSURANCE COMPANY—Motorists Mutual Insurance Co.; *U.S. Private*, pg. 764
MID-AMERICA INSURANCE CO.—Harleysville Group; *U.S. Public*, pg. 787
MIDDLESEX INSURANCE CO.—Sentry Insurance, A Mutual Company; *U.S. Private*, pg. 985
THE MIDLAND COMPANY; *U.S. Public*, pg. 1110
MIDWEST EMPLOYER'S CASUALTY COMPANY—W.R. Berkley Corporation; *U.S. Public*, pg. 215
MIDWEST MUTUAL INSURANCE CO.—Preferred Risk Mutual Insurance; *U.S. Private*, pg. 881
MILBANK INSURANCE CO.—Royal & Sun Alliance Insurance Group plc; *Int'l*, pg. 1131
MILLERS CLASSIFIED INSURANCE COMPANY—Millers Mutual Insurance Assn.; *U.S. Private*, pg. 748
MILLERS MUTUAL INSURANCE ASSN.; *U.S. Private*, pg. 748
MILWAUKEE GUARDIAN INSURANCE INC.—Unitrin, Inc.; *U.S. Public*, pg. 1694
MILWAUKEE INSURANCE GROUP—Unitrin, Inc.; *U.S. Public*, pg. 1694
MILWAUKEE SAFEGUARD INSURANCE CO.—Unitrin, Inc.; *U.S. Public*, pg. 1694
MINNESOTA FIRE & CASUALTY COMPANY—Harleysville Group; *U.S. Public*, pg. 787
MISSOURI MEDICAL INSURANCE COMPANY—Medical Assurance, Inc.; *U.S. Public*, pg. 1080
MITSUI MARINE & FIRE INSURANCE CO., LTD.—Mitsui & Co., Ltd.; *Int'l*, pg. 878
MONARCH INSURANCE COMPANY—Cigna Corp.; *U.S. Public*, pg. 363
MONUMENTAL GENERAL CASUALTY COMPANY—AEGON N.V.; *Int'l*, pg. 27
MOTORISTS MUTUAL INSURANCE CO.; *U.S. Private*, pg. 764
MT. HAWLEY INSURANCE COMPANY—RLI Corp.; *U.S. Public*, pg. 1356
MUNCHENER RUCKVERSICHERUNGS-GESELLSCHAFT; *Int'l*, pg. 897
MUTUA ASSICURATRICE COTONI—Allianz Aktiengesellschaft; *Int'l*, pg. 62
MUTUAL ASSURANCE, INC.—Medical Assurance, Inc.; *U.S. Public*, pg. 1080
MUTUAMAR - SOCIETA DI ASSICURAZIONI E RIASSICURAZIONI PER AZIONI—IRI Istituto Ricostruzione Industriale; *Int'l*, pg. 652
NAC RE CORP.; *U.S. Public*, pg. 1144
NAC REINSURANCE CORPORATION—NAC Re Corp.; *U.S. Public*, pg. 1144
NATIONAL GENERAL INSURANCE CO.—General Motors Corporation; *U.S. Public*, pg. 721
NATIONAL GENERAL INSURANCE COMPANY—General Motors Corporation; *U.S. Public*, pg. 720
NATIONAL INDEMNITY CO.—Berkshire Hathaway Inc.; *U.S. Public*, pg. 221
NATIONAL INDEMNITY COMPANY OF MID-AMERICA—Berkshire Hathaway Inc.; *U.S. Public*, pg. 221
NATIONAL INSURANCE GROUP; *U.S. Public*, pg. 1157
NATIONAL SURETY CORPORATION—Allianz Aktiengesellschaft; *Int'l*, pg. 59
NATIONAL UNION FIRE INS. CO. OF PITTSBURGH, PA.—American International Group, Inc.; *U.S. Public*, pg. 84
NATIONWIDE INSURANCE ENTERPRISE; *U.S. Private*, pg. 788
NAUTILUS INSURANCE COMPANY—W.R. Berkley Corporation; *U.S. Public*, pg. 216
NAVIGATOR AND GENERAL INSURANCE CO. LTD.—B.A.T Industries P.L.C.; *Int'l*, pg. 110
NEW HAMPSHIRE INSURANCE GROUP—American International Group, Inc.; *U.S. Public*, pg. 84
NEW PROVIDENCE CORP.—Allendale Mutual Insurance Co.; *U.S. Private*, pg. 37
NEW SOUTH INSURANCE COMPANY—General Motors Corporation; *U.S. Public*, pg. 720
NEW YORK CASUALTY INSURANCE CO.—Harleysville Group; *U.S. Public*, pg. 787
NEWARK INSURANCE CO.—Royal & Sun Alliance Insurance Group plc; *Int'l*, pg. 1131
NIAGARA FIRE INSURANCE CO.—Loews Corporation; *U.S. Public*, pg. 1011
NORDEUROPA FORSIKRINGSAKTIESELSKABET A/S—Allianz Aktiengesellschaft; *Int'l*, pg. 62
NORTH AMERICAN TRANSPORT INSURANCE CO.—Norfolk Southern Corporation; *U.S. Public*, pg. 1192
NORTH PACIFIC INSURANCE COMPANY—General Accident Fire and Life Assurance Corporation p.l.c.; *Int'l*, *pg. 543*
THE NORTH RIVER INSURANCE COMPANY—Xerox Corporation; *U.S. Public*, pg. 1784
OHIO CASUALTY CORPORATION; *U.S. Public*, pg. 1214
OHIO CASUALTY INSURANCE CO.—Ohio Casualty Corporation; *U.S. Public*, pg. 1214
THE OHIO CASUALTY INSURANCE GROUP—Ohio Casualty Corporation; *U.S. Public*, pg. 1214
OLD RELIABLE CASUALTY CO.—The Reliable Life Insurance Company; *U.S. Public*, pg. 1374
OLD REPUBLIC DEALER SERVICE CORPORATION—Old Republic International Corporation; *U.S. Public*, pg. 1218
OLD REPUBLIC INSURANCE CO.—Old Republic International Corporation; *U.S. Public*, pg. 1218
OLD REPUBLIC INTERNATIONAL CORPORATION; *U.S. Public*, pg. 1218
OMAHA PROPERTY AND CASUALTY INSURANCE CO.—Mutual of Omaha Insurance Company; *U.S. Private*, pg. 770
THE OPTIMUM FINANCIAL CORPORATION LTD.—EdperBrascan Corporation; *Int'l*, pg. 435
OREGON AUTOMOBILE INSURANCE COMPANY—General Accident Fire and Life Assurance Corporation p.l.c.; *Int'l*, pg. 543
ORION CAPITAL COMPANIES, INC.—Orion Capital Corporation; *U.S. Public*, pg. 1231
ORION CAPITAL CORPORATION; *U.S. Public*, pg. 1231
ORIX INSURANCE SERVICES CORPORATION—Orix Corporation; *Int'l*, pg. 1008
PAC RIM HOLDING CORPORATION; *U.S. Public*, pg. 1246
PACIFIC EMPLOYERS INSURANCE COMPANY—Cigna Corp.; *U.S. Public*, pg. 365
PACIFIC INDEMNITY CO.—The Chubb Corporation; *U.S. Public*, pg. 355
THE PACIFIC RIM ASSURANCE COMPANY—Pac Rim Holding Corporation; *U.S. Public*, pg. 1246
PAN ARABIAN INSURANCE COMPANY LIMITED—Cigna Corp.; *U.S. Public*, pg. 364
PARKLANE INSURANCE CO.—Ford Motor Company; *U.S. Public*, pg. 664
PARTHENON INSURANCE CO.—Columbia/HCA Healthcare Corporation; *U.S. Public*, pg. 405
PARTNERRE LTD.; *Int'l*, pg. 1024
PAULA FINANCIAL; *U.S. Public*, pg. 1266
PEERLESS INSURANCE COMPANY—ING Groep N.V.; *Int'l*, pg. 648
PENN NATIONAL INSURANCE; *U.S. Private*, pg. 850
PENNLAND INSURANCE CO.—Harleysville Group; *U.S. Public*, pg. 787
PENNSYLVANIA GENERAL INSURANCE COMPANY—General Accident Fire and Life Assurance Corporation p.l.c.; *Int'l*, pg. 543
PENNSYLVANIA MANUFACTURERS CORP.; *U.S. Public*, pg. 1272
PENTAL INSURANCE CO., LTD.—Tidewater Inc.; *U.S. Public*, pg. 1608
PEOPLE'S SECURITY LIFE INSURANCE—AEGON N.V.; *Int'l*, pg. 27
PHARMERICA, INC.; *U.S. Public*, pg. 1286
PHOENIX ASSURANCE OF NEW YORK, INC.—Royal & Sun Alliance Insurance Group plc; *Int'l*, pg. 1130
PHYSICIANS INSURANCE COMPANY OF INDIANA—Medical Assurance, Inc.; *U.S. Public*, pg. 1080
POE & BROWN, INC.; *U.S. Public*, pg. 1312
POTOMAC INSURANCE CO. OF ILLINOIS—General Accident Fire and Life Assurance Corporation p.l.c.; *Int'l*, *pg. 543*
PREFERRED AMERICA INSURANCE COMPANY—Preferred Risk Mutual Insurance; *U.S. Private*, pg. 880
PREFERRED RISK LLOYD'S INSURANCE COMPANY—Preferred Risk Mutual Insurance; *U.S. Private*, pg. 880
PREFERRED RISK MUTUAL INSURANCE; *U.S. Private*, pg. 880
PREMIER INSURANCE COMPANY—Fremont General Corporation; *U.S. Public*, pg. 681
PROGRESSIVE AMERICAN INSURANCE CO.—The Progressive Corporation; *U.S. Public*, pg. 1334
PROGRESSIVE CASUALTY INSURANCE CO.—The Progressive Corporation; *U.S. Public*, pg. 1334
THE PROGRESSIVE CORPORATION; *U.S. Public*, pg. 1334
PROGRESSIVE COUNTY MUTUAL INSURANCE CO.—The Progressive Corporation; *U.S. Public*, pg. 1335
PROGRESSIVE MAX INSURANCE CO.—The Progressive Corporation; *U.S. Public*, pg. 1335
PROGRESSIVE NORTHERN INSURANCE CO.—The Progressive Corporation; *U.S. Public*, pg. 1335
PROGRESSIVE PREFERRED INSURANCE CO.—The Progressive Corporation; *U.S. Public*, pg. 1335
PROGRESSIVE SOUTHEASTERN INSURANCE CO.—The Progressive Corporation; *U.S. Public*, pg. 1335
PROGRESSIVE SPECIALTY INSURANCE CO.—The Progressive Corporation; *U.S. Public*, pg. 1335
PROTECTION MUTUAL INSURANCE CO.; *U.S. Private*, pg. 891
PROTECTIVE INSURANCE COMPANY—Baldwin & Lyons, Inc.; *U.S. Public*, pg. 169
PROVIDIAN AUTO & HOME INSURANCE GROUP—AEGON N.V.; *Int'l*, pg. 27
PROVIDIAN PROPERTY & CASUALTY INSURANCE CO.—AEGON N.V.; *Int'l*, pg. 27
PRUDENTIAL CORPORATION PLC; *Int'l*, pg. 1073
THE PRUDENTIAL INSURANCE COMPANY OF AMERICA; *U.S. Private*, pg. 892
PRUDENTIAL OF AMERICA GENERAL INSURANCE CO. (CANADA)—The Prudential Insurance Company of America; *U.S. Private*, pg. 893
PRUDENTIAL PROPERTY & CASUALTY INSURANCE COMPANY—The Prudential Insurance Company of America; *U.S. Private*, pg. 892
PRUDENTIAL SERVICE CO.—The Prudential Insurance Company of America; *U.S. Private*, pg. 893
QUINCY MUTUAL FIRE INSURANCE COMPANY; *U.S. Private*, pg. 901
RLI BOSTON—RLI Corp.; *U.S. Public*, pg. 1356
RLI CLAIMS/P&C—RLI Corp.; *U.S. Public*, pg. 1356
RLI CORP.; *U.S. Public*, pg. 1356
RLI/HAWAII PRODUCT LINES—RLI Corp.; *U.S. Public*, pg. 1356
RLI PROGRAM UNDERWRITERS—RLI Corp.; *U.S. Public*, pg. 1356
RLI SPECIAL RISK—RLI Corp.; *U.S. Public*, pg. 1356
RECHTSSCHUTZ UNION VERSICHERUNGS-AG—Alte Leipziger Versicherung Aktiengesellschaft; *Int'l*, pg. 66
REGENT INTERNATIONAL INSURANCE COMPANY, LTD.—Reliance Group Holdings, Inc.; *U.S. Public*, pg. 1374
RELIANCE GROUP HOLDINGS, INC.; *U.S. Public*, pg. 1374
RELIANCE INSURANCE COMPANY—Reliance Group Holdings, Inc.; *U.S. Public*, pg. 1374
RELIANCE NATIONAL INSURANCE COMPANY—Reliance Group Holdings, Inc.; *U.S. Public*, pg. 1374
RELIANCE NATIONAL U.K. LIMITED—Reliance Group Holdings, Inc.; *U.S. Public*, pg. 1374
RENTOKIL INSURANCE LTD.—Sophus Berendsen A/S; *Int'l*, pg. 1285
REPUBLIC AMERICAN CORPORATION—American Financial Group; *U.S. Public*, pg. 75
REPUBLIC FIRE & CASUALTY INSURANCE COMPANY—Credit Suisse Group; *Int'l*, pg. 346
REPUBLIC INSURANCE CO.—Credit Suisse Group; *Int'l*, pg. 346
REPUBLIC LLOYDS—Credit Suisse Group; *Int'l*, pg. 346
REPUBLIC UNDERWRITERS INSURANCE CO.—Credit Suisse Group; *Int'l*, pg. 346
REPUBLIC-VANGUARD LIFE INSURANCE CO.—Credit Suisse Group; *Int'l*, pg. 346
REPUBLIC-VANGUARD REINSURANCE CO.—Credit Suisse Group; *Int'l*, pg. 346
RIUNIONE ADRIATICA DI SICURTA S.P.A.—Allianz Aktiengesellschaft; *Int'l*, pg. 61
RIYAD INSURANCE COMPANY LTD.—Cigna Corp.; *U.S. Public*, pg. 363
ROINS HOLDINGS LIMITED—Royal & Sun Alliance Insurance Group plc; *Int'l*, pg. 1131
ROYAL INDEMNITY CO.—Royal & Sun Alliance Insurance Group plc; *Int'l*, pg. 1131
ROYAL INSURANCE—Royal & Sun Alliance Insurance Group plc; *Int'l*, pg. 1130
ROYAL INSURANCE COMPANY OF AMERICA—Royal & Sun Alliance Insurance Group plc; *Int'l*, pg. 1131
ROYAL INSURANCE COMPANY OF CANADA—Royal & Sun Alliance Insurance Group plc; *Int'l*, pg. 1131
ROYAL INSURANCE ONTARIO REGIONAL CENTRE—Royal & Sun Alliance Insurance Group plc; *Int'l*, pg. 1131
S.A.S.A.-ASSICURAZIONI RIASSICURAZIONI SOCIETA PER AZIONI—IRI Istituto Ricostruzione Industriale; *Int'l*, pg. 652
SCOR UK GROUP—SCOR; *Int'l*, pg. 1153
SKF REINSURANCE CO. LTD.—AB SKF; *Int'l*, pg. 1157
SAFECO CORPORATION; *U.S. Public*, pg. 1423
SAFECO INSURANCE CO. OF AMERICA—SAFECO Corporation; *U.S. Public*, pg. 1423
SAFECO LLOYDS INSURANCE CO.—SAFECO Corporation; *U.S. Public*, pg. 1423
SAFECO NATIONAL INSURANCE CO.—SAFECO Corporation; *U.S. Public*, pg. 1423
SAFECO SURPLUS LINES INSURANCE CO.—SAFECO Corporation; *U.S. Public*, pg. 1423
SAFEGUARD INSURANCE CO.—Royal & Sun Alliance Insurance Group plc; *Int'l*, pg. 1131
SAGAMORE INSURANCE COMPANY—Baldwin & Lyons, Inc.; *U.S. Public*, pg. 169
THE ST. PAUL COMPANIES, INC.; *U.S. Public*, pg. 1429
ST. PAUL FIRE AND MARINE INSURANCE CO.—The St. Paul Companies, Inc.; *U.S. Public*, pg. 1429
SAN FRANCISCO INSURANCE COMPANY (U.K.) LTD.—Allianz Aktiengesellschaft; *Int'l*, pg. 59
SARK SIGORTA T.A.S. (RAS)—Allianz Aktiengesellschaft; *Int'l*, pg. 62
SASKATCHEWAN GOVERNMENT INSURANCE, SGI; *Int'l*, *pg. 1195*
SEA CONTAINERS LTD.; *Int'l*, pg. 1213
SEABOARD UNDERWRITERS AGENCY, INC.—Fremont General Corporation; *U.S. Public*, pg. 681
SEABOARD UNDERWRITERS, INC.—Fremont General Corporation; *U.S. Public*, pg. 681
SECURITY INDUSTRIAL INSURANCE CO., INC.—The Loewen Group, Inc.; *Int'l*, pg. 814
SECURITY INSURANCE CO. OF HARTFORD—Orion Capital Corporation; *U.S. Public*, pg. 1231
SEGUROS AZTECA, S.A.—Cigna Corp.; *U.S. Public*, pg. 363

SEGUROS CIGNA, S.A.—Cigna Corp.; *U.S. Public*, pg. 363
SEGUROS MONTERREY, S.A.—Aetna Inc.; *U.S. Public*, pg. 27
THE SEIBELS BRUCE GROUP, INC.; *U.S. Public*, pg. 1453
SELECTIVE INSURANCE GROUP, INC; *U.S. Public*, pg. 1455
SELF-INSURERS' MANAGEMENT CORPORATION—Cigna Corp.; *U.S. Public*, pg. 366
SENTRY INSURANCE, A MUTUAL COMPANY; *U.S. Private*, pg. 984
SHEFFIELD INSURANCE CO.—Torchmark Corporation; *U.S. Public*, pg. 1622
SHELTER MUTUAL INSURANCE COMPANY; *U.S. Private*, *pg. 992*
THE SIGNATURE GROUP—Montgomery Ward & Co., Inc.; *U.S. Private*, pg. 758
SILVEY CORPORATION—General Accident Fire and Life Assurance Corporation p.l.c.; *Int'l*, pg. 543
SIME DARBY BERHAD; *Int'l*, pg. 1249
SIME DARBY BERHAD INSURANCE SERVICES DIVISION—Sime Darby Berhad; *Int'l*, pg. 1250
THE SINCERE INSURANCE & INVESTMENT CO. LTD.—The Sincere Co. Ltd.; *Int'l*, pg. 1252
SKANDIA INSURANCE COMPANY LIMITED; *Int'l*, pg. 1256
SKANDIA UK INSURANCE PLC—Skandia Insurance Company Limited; *Int'l*, pg. 1258
SOUTH CAROLINA INSURANCE COMPANY—The Seibels Bruce Group, Inc.; *U.S. Public*, pg. 1453
SOUTHERN COUNTY MUTUAL INSURANCE COMPANY—Credit Suisse Group; *Int'l*, pg. 346
SOUTHERN FARM BUREAU CASUALTY INSURANCE COMPANY; *U.S. Private*, pg. 1016
SOUTHERN INSURANCE CO.—Credit Suisse Group; *Int'l*, pg. 346
SOUTHERN LIFE AND HEALTH INSURANCE COMPANY—Geneve Corporation; *U.S. Private*, pg. 447
SOUTHERN UNDERWRITERS INSURANCE COMPANY—Credit Suisse Group; *Int'l*, pg. 346
SOUTHWEST RISK SERVICES INC.—W.R. Berkley Corporation; *U.S. Public*, pg. 215
SPECIALTY UNDERWRITERS, INC.—American Financial Group; *U.S. Public*, pg. 75
SSANGYONG BUSINESS GROUP; *Int'l*, pg. 1291
STATE AUTOMOBILE MUTUAL INSURANCE CO.; *U.S. Private*, pg. 1036
STATE FARM COUNTY MUTUAL INSURANCE CO. OF TEXAS—State Farm Mutual Automobile Insurance Company; *U.S. Private*, pg. 1036
STATE FARM FIRE AND CASUALTY CO.—State Farm Mutual Automobile Insurance Company; *U.S. Private*, pg. 1036
STATE FARM GENERAL INSURANCE CO.—State Farm Mutual Automobile Insurance Company; *U.S. Private*, pg. 1036
STATE FARM LLOYDS, INC.—State Farm Mutual Automobile Insurance Company; *U.S. Private*, pg. 1036
STATE FARM MUTUAL AUTOMOBILE INSURANCE COMPANY; *U.S. Private*, pg. 1036
STATE VOLUNTEER MUTUAL INSURANCE CO.; *U.S. Private*, pg. 1037
STONEWALL INSURANCE CO.—American Financial Group; *U.S. Public*, pg. 75
SUMITOMO MARINE MGMT SERVICES—Sumitomo Heavy Industries, Ltd.; *Int'l*, pg. 1314
SUN ALLIANCE USA, INC.—Royal & Sun Alliance Insurance Group plc; *Int'l*, pg. 1131
SUN INSURANCE CO. OF NEW YORK—Royal & Sun Alliance Insurance Group plc; *Int'l*, pg. 1131
SUNTRUST INSURANCE COMPANY—SunTrust Banks, Inc.; *U.S. Public*, pg. 1538
SWISS REINSURANCE COMPANY; *Int'l*, pg. 1332
TIG HOLDINGS, INC.; *U.S. Public*, pg. 1555
TIG INSURANCE CO.—TIG Holdings, Inc.; *U.S. Public*, pg. 1556
TALEGEN CORPORATION—Xerox Corporation; *U.S. Public*, pg. 1784
TAPIOLA-YHTIOT; *Int'l*, pg. 1354
TEACHERS INSURANCE COMPANY—Horace Mann Educators Corporation; *U.S. Public*, pg. 836
TELA VERSICHERUNG AG—Allianz Aktiengesellschaft; *Int'l*, pg. 58
TEMPLE INSURANCE COMPANY LIMITED—Cigna Corp.; *U.S. Public*, pg. 360
TENNECO ASSET MANAGEMENT CO.—Tenneco Inc.; *U.S. Public*, pg. 1578
TENNECO INSURANCE VENTURES—Tenneco Inc.; *U.S. Public*, pg. 1578
TERRA NOVA INSURANCE COMPANY LTD.—Aetna Inc.; *U.S. Public*, pg. 27
TEXAS GENERAL INDEMNITY CO.—American Indemnity Financial Corp.; *U.S. Public*, pg. 83
THURINGIA VERSICHERUNG AG—AMB Aachener und Muenchener Beteiligungs-AG; *Int'l*, pg. 15
THE TOKIO MARINE & FIRE INSURANCE COMPANY, LTD.; *Int'l*, pg. 1391
TOKIO RE CORPORATION—The Tokio Marine & Fire Insurance Company, Ltd.; *Int'l*, pg. 1392
THE TOP FIVE CLUB, INC.—Berkshire Hathaway Inc.; *U.S. Public*, pg. 220
TRANS PACIFIC INSURANCE COMPANY—The Tokio Marine & Fire Insurance Company, Ltd.; *Int'l*, pg. 1392
TRANSATLANTIC REINSURANCE CO.—American International Group, Inc.; *U.S. Public*, pg. 84
TRANSPORT INSURANCE CO.—American Financial Group; *U.S. Public*, pg. 75
TRAVELERS PROPERTY CASUALTY CORP.—Travelers Group; *U.S. Public*, pg. 1633
TRI-STATE INSURANCE COMPANY OF MINNESOTA—W.R. Berkley Corporation; *U.S. Public*, pg. 215
TRILON FINANCIAL CORP.—EdperBrascan Corporation; *Int'l*, pg. 434
TRINITY UNIVERSAL INSURANCE CO.—Unitrin, Inc.; *U.S. Public*, pg. 1694
TRYGG-HANSA; *Int'l*, pg. 1425
TRYGG-HANSA INSURANCE CO. LTD.—Trygg-Hansa; *Int'l*, pg. 1425
URM INSURANCE AGENCY—URM Stores, Inc.; *U.S. Private*, pg. 1114
USAA (UNITED SERVICES AUTOMOBILE ASSOCIATION); *U.S. Private*, pg. 1114
USF&G CORPORATION; *U.S. Public*, pg. 1659
ULICO CASUALTY COMPANY—ULLICO Inc.; *U.S. Private*, pg. 1116
UNICARE INSURANCE COMPANY—Blue Cross of California; *U.S. Private*, pg. 152
UNIGARD INDEMNITY CO.—Credit Suisse Group; *Int'l*, pg. 345
UNIGARD INSURANCE CO.—Credit Suisse Group; *Int'l*, pg. 345
UNION INSURANCE COMPANY—W.R. Berkley Corporation; *U.S. Public*, pg. 216
UNION STANDARD INSURANCE COMPANY—W.R. Berkley Corporation; *U.S. Public*, pg. 216
UNIONE SUBALPINA DI ASSICURAZIONI—Allianz Aktiengesellschaft; *Int'l*, pg. 62
UNISUN INSURANCE CO.—Orion Capital Corporation; *U.S. Public*, pg. 1231
UNITED CAPITOL INSURANCE COMPANY—Capsure Holdings Corp.; *U.S. Public*, pg. 303
UNITED CAPITOL INSURANCE COMPANY—Frontier Insurance Group, Inc.; *U.S. Public*, pg. 685
UNITED FARM FAMILY LIFE INSURANCE CO.; *U.S. Private*, pg. 1122
UNITED FIRE & CASUALTY COMPANY; *U.S. Public*, pg. 1677
UNITED STATES FIDELITY & GUARANTY COMPANY—USF&G Corporation; *U.S. Public*, pg. 1659
UNITED STATES FIRE INSURANCE COMPANY—Xerox Corporation; *U.S. Public*, pg. 1784
USA CASUALTY COMPANY—ULLICO Inc.; *U.S. Private*, pg. 1116
UNIVERSAL INSURANCE CO.—Kirby Corporation; *U.S. Public*, pg. 962
UNIVERSAL INSURANCE CO.—The Seibels Bruce Group, Inc.; *U.S. Public*, pg. 1454
UNIVERSAL UNDERWRITERS INSURANCE CO.—Zurich Insurance Company; *Int'l*, pg. 1530
UTICA LLOYDS OF TEXAS—Utica Mutual Insurance Company; *U.S. Private*, pg. 1130
UTICA MUTUAL INSURANCE COMPANY; *U.S. Private*, pg. 1129
UTICA NATIONAL INSURANCE CO. OF TEXAS—Utica Mutual Insurance Company; *U.S. Private*, pg. 1130
VALMONT INDEMNITY CO. LTD.—Chancellor Corporation; *U.S. Public*, pg. 335
VASA BROUGHER, INC.—Eureko B.V.; *Int'l*, pg. 464
VIGILANT INSURANCE CO.—The Chubb Corporation; *U.S. Public*, pg. 355
VISTA INSURANCE SERVICES, INC.—The Walt Disney Company; *U.S. Public*, pg. 514
VOLKSFURSORGE DEUTSCHE SACHVERSICHERUNG—AMB Aachener und Muenchener Beteiligungs-AG; *Int'l*, pg. 16
WELLINGTON INSURANCE COMPANY—EdperBrascan Corporation; *Int'l*, pg. 435
WESTCHESTER FIRE INSURANCE COMPANY—Xerox Corporation; *U.S. Public*, pg. 1784
WESTERN ASSURANCE COMPANY—Royal & Sun Alliance Insurance Group plc; *Int'l*, pg. 1131
WESTERN SURETY COMPANY—Capsure Holdings Corp.; *U.S. Public*, pg. 303
WESTPAC FINANCIAL SERVICES GROUP LIMITED—Westpac Banking Corporation; *Int'l*, pg. 1496
WESTPAC INSURANCE SERVICES (BROKERS) LIMITED—Westpac Banking Corporation; *Int'l*, pg. 1496
WILLIS CORROON CORP.—Willis Corroon Group PLC; *Int'l*, pg. 1504
WINTERTHUR U.S. HOLDINGS INC.—Credit Suisse Group; *Int'l*, pg. 345
THE WORCESTER INSURANCE CO.—Harleysville Group; *U.S. Public*, pg. 787
THE YASUDA FIRE & MARINE INSURANCE COMPANY LIMITED; *Int'l*, pg. 1519
THE YASUDA FIRE & MARINE INSURANCE CO. OF AMERICA—The Yasuda Fire & Marine Insurance Company Limited; *Int'l*, pg. 1519
YOSEMITE INSURANCE CO.—American General Corporation; *U.S. Public*, pg. 77
ZENITH NATIONAL INSURANCE CORP.; *U.S. Public*, pg. 1790
ZENITH VERSICHERUNG AG—Alte Leipziger Versicherung Aktiengesellschaft; *Int'l*, pg. 66
ZURICH AMERICAN INSURANCE COMPANY OF ILLINOIS—Zurich Insurance Company; *Int'l*, pg. 1530
ZURICH INSURANCE COMPANY; *Int'l*, pg. 1529

6351 — SURETY INSURANCE

AXA-UAP; *Int'l*, pg. 18
ACCEL INTERNATIONAL CORPORATION; *U.S. Public*, pg. 14
ACCELERATION LIFE INSURANCE AGENCY, INC.—ACCEL International Corporation; *U.S. Public*, pg. 14
ACCELERATION NATIONAL INSURANCE COMPANY—ACCEL International Corporation; *U.S. Public*, pg. 14
ALASKA PACIFIC ASSURANCE COMPANY—Cigna Corp.; *U.S. Public*, pg. 366
ALLIANZ BETEILIGUNGSGESELLSCHAFT MBH—Allianz Aktiengesellschaft; *Int'l*, pg. 58
ALLIED DUNBAR ASSURANCE PLC—B.A.T Industries P.L.C.; *Int'l*, pg. 110
ALLIED INSURANCE COMPANY—Cigna Corp.; *U.S. Public*, *pg. 362*
AMERICAN FIDELITY CORP.; *U.S. Private*, pg. 54
AMERICAN HEALTH AND LIFE INSURANCE CO.—Travelers Group; *U.S. Public*, pg. 1633
ASSOCIATED INDEMNITY CORP.—Allianz Aktiengesellschaft; *Int'l*, pg. 59
ATLANTIC EMPLOYERS INSURANCE COMPANY—Cigna Corp.; *U.S. Public*, pg. 366
AUTO-OWNERS INSURANCE; *U.S. Private*, pg. 100
BANC ONE CORPORATION; *U.S. Public*, pg. 172
BANK OF BOSTON CONNECTICUT—BankBoston Corporation; *U.S. Public*, pg. 184
BANKERS STANDARD FIRE & MARINE COMPANY—Cigna Corp.; *U.S. Public*, pg. 365
BANKERS STANDARD INSURANCE COMPANY—Cigna Corp.; *U.S. Public*, pg. 365
BRADSTOCK GROUP PLC; *Int'l*, pg. 210
CMAC INVESTMENT CORPORATION; *U.S. Public*, pg. 278
CAPSURE HOLDINGS CORP.; *U.S. Public*, pg. 303
THE CENTRAL NATIONAL LIFE INSURANCE CO. OF OMAHA, INC.—Beneficial Corporation; *U.S. Public*, pg. 211
CENTURY INDEMNITY COMPANY—Cigna Corp.; *U.S. Public*, pg. 365
CIGNA CORP.; *U.S. Public*, pg. 356
CIGNA FIRE UNDERWRITERS INSURANCE COMPANY—Cigna Corp.; *U.S. Public*, pg. 365
CIGNA INSURANCE COMPANY—Cigna Corp.; *U.S. Public*, pg. 365
CIGNA INSURANCE COMPANY OF TEXAS—Cigna Corp.; *U.S. Public*, pg. 365
CIGNA INSURANCE NEW ZEALAND LIMITED—Cigna Corp.; *U.S. Public*, pg. 364
CIGNA PROPERTY & CASUALTY INSURANCE COMPANY—Cigna Corp.; *U.S. Public*, pg. 364
CIGNA REINSURANCE COMPANY (U.K.) LIMITED—Cigna Corp.; *U.S. Public*, pg. 363
CIGNA SPECIALTY INSURANCE COMPANY—Cigna Corp.; *U.S. Public*, pg. 366
COMMERCIAL UNION PLC; *Int'l*, pg. 308
COMPAGNIE D'ASSURANCE DU QUEBEC—Royal & Sun Alliance Insurance Group plc; *Int'l*, pg. 1131
CONFEDERATION MORTGAGE SERVICES LIMITED—Sun Life Assurance Company of Canada; *Int'l*, pg. 1319
COREGIS GROUP—General Electric Company; *U.S. Public*, *pg. 711*
CRABTREE PREMIUM FINANCE—United Fire & Casualty Company; *U.S. Public*, pg. 1677
CREDIT INSURANCE ASSOCIATION—Inchcape PLC; *Int'l*, pg. 671
CREDITOR RESOURCES, INC.—AEGON N.V.; *Int'l*, pg. 27
DELAWARE REINSURANCE COMPANY—Cigna Corp.; *U.S. Public*, pg. 363
DESJARDINS LAURENTIAN LIFE ASSURANCE—Desjardins-Laurentian Financial Corporation; *Int'l*, pg. 396
EFG TECHNOLOGIES INC.—United Insurance Companies, Inc.; *U.S. Public*, pg. 1679
ENVIRONMENTAL SERVICE INSURANCE CO.—Quexco Incorporated; *U.S. Private*, pg. 900
EQUIFAX INSURANCE SERVICES INC.—Equifax Inc.; *U.S. Public*, pg. 588
FBOH CREDIT LIFE INSURANCE CO.—FirstMerit Corporation; *U.S. Public*, pg. 647
FIDELITY & DEPOSIT COMPANY OF MARYLAND—Zurich Insurance Company; *Int'l*, pg. 1530
FIREMAN'S FUND INDEMNITY CORPORATION—Allianz Aktiengesellschaft; *Int'l*, pg. 59
FIREMAN'S FUND INSURANCE COMPANY—Allianz Aktiengesellschaft; *Int'l*, pg. 58
FORTWAY FINANCE LIMITED—HSBC Holdings plc; *Int'l*, pg. 581
GENERAL REINSURANCE CORP.—General Re Corporation; *U.S. Public*, pg. 725
GENERAL STAR MANAGEMENT COMPANY—General Re Corporation; *U.S. Public*, pg. 725
GLOBE LIFE AND ACCIDENT INSURANCE CO. OF OKLAHOMA, INC.—Torchmark Corporation; *U.S. Public*, pg. 1622
THE HANOVER INSURANCE COMPANY—Allmerica Financial Corporation; *U.S. Public*, pg. 54
ILLINOIS UNION INSURANCE COMPANY—Cigna Corp.; *U.S. Public*, pg. 365
THE IMPERIAL LIFE ASSURANCE CO.—Desjardins-Laurentian Financial Corporation; *Int'l*, pg. 396
INDEMNITY INSURANCE COMPANY OF NORTH AMERICA—Cigna Corp.; *U.S. Public*, pg. 366
INDEPENDENCE HOLDING COMPANY—Geneve Corporation; *U.S. Private*, pg. 446
INDUSTRIAL INDEMNITY COMPANY—Fremont General Corporation; *U.S. Public*, pg. 681
INDUSTRIAL INDEMNITY FINANCIAL CORPORATION—Fremont General Corporation; *U.S. Public*, pg. 681
THE INNOVATIVE COMPANY—The Seibels Bruce Group, Inc.; *U.S. Public*, pg. 1454
INSURANCE COMPANY OF NORTH AMERICA—Cigna Corp.; *U.S. Public*, pg. 366
INSURANCE COMPANY OF NORTH AMERICA (U.K.) LIMITED—Cigna Corp.; *U.S. Public*, pg. 363
INVESTORS NATIONAL LIFE INSURANCE CO.—The Seibels Bruce Group, Inc.; *U.S. Public*, pg. 1454
JARDINE CREDIT INSURANCE LTD.—Jardine Matheson Holdings Limited; *Int'l*, pg. 705
KMA INSURANCE AGENCY, INC.—Michigan Physicians Mutual Liability Inc.; *U.S. Private*, pg. 741
KENTUCKY MEDICAL INSURANCE COMPANY, HOSPITAL DIVISION—Michigan Physicians Mutual Liability Inc.; *U.S. Private*, pg. 741
KENTUCKY MEDICAL INSURANCE COMPANY (KMIC)—Michigan Physicians Mutual Liability Inc.; *U.S. Private*, pg. 741
KIMMINS CORP.; *U.S. Public*, pg. 960
LEND LEASE CORPORATION LIMITED; *Int'l*, pg. 806
L'ITALICA—Allianz Aktiengesellschaft; *Int'l*, pg. 61
MBIA ASSURANCE S.A.—MBIA Inc.; *U.S. Public*, pg. 1023
MBIA INC.; *U.S. Public*, pg. 1023
MBIA MUNICIPAL INVESTORS SERVICE CORPORATION—MBIA Inc.; *U.S. Public*, pg. 1023

MGIC INVESTMENT CORPORATION; *U.S. Public*, pg. 1026
MSI INSURANCE COMPANIES; *U.S. Private*, pg. 688
MADISON ACCEPTANCE CORPORATION—Citation Insurance Group; *U.S. Public*, pg. 376
MAPFRE HIPOTECARIA S.C.H., S.A.—Corporacion MAPFRE, Compania Internacional de Reaseguros, S.A.; *Int'l*, pg. 332
MARYLAND CASUALTY CO.—Zurich Insurance Company; *Int'l*, pg. 1530
THE MEDICAL PROTECTIVE COMPANY; *U.S. Private*, pg. 728
MERIT LIFE INSURANCE CO.—American General Corporation; *U.S. Public*, pg. 77
MICHIGAN PHYSICIANS MUTUAL LIABILITY INC.; *U.S. Private*, pg. 741
MISSISSIPPI VALLEY LIFE INSURANCE COMPANY—Mercantile Bancorporation Inc.; *U.S. Public*, pg. 1087
THE MORTGAGE INSURANCE COMPANY OF CANADA—CIGL Holdings Ltd.; *Int'l*, pg. 241
MUNICIPAL BOND INVESTORS ASSURANCE CORPORATION—MBIA Inc.; *U.S. Public*, pg. 1023
NBD CREDIT INSURANCE AGENCY, INC.—First Chicago NBD Corporation; *U.S. Public*, pg. 628
NATIONAL PROGRAMS DIVISION—Poe & Brown, Inc.; *U.S. Public*, pg. 1312
NATIONAL SURETY CORPORATION—Allianz Aktiengesellschaft; *Int'l*, pg. 59
NATIONSBANK INSURANCE INC.—NationsBank Corporation; *U.S. Public*, pg. 1162
OHIO INDEMNITY COMPANY—Bancinsurance Corp.; *U.S. Public*, pg. 175
OLD REPUBLIC INTERNATIONAL CORPORATION; *U.S. Public*, pg. 1218
PACIFIC EMPLOYERS INSURANCE COMPANY—Cigna Corp.; *U.S. Public*, pg. 365
POE & BROWN, INC.; *U.S. Public*, pg. 1312
PREFERRED SURETY CORPORATION—SunTrust Banks, Inc.; *U.S. Public*, pg. 1538
RLI CORP.; *U.S. Public*, pg. 1356
RELIANCE SURETY CORP.—Reliance Group Holdings, Inc.; *U.S. Public*, pg. 1374
RIUNIONE ADRIATICA DI SICURTA S.P.A.—Allianz Aktiengesellschaft; *Int'l*, pg. 61
ROYAL INSURANCE ATLANTIC REGIONAL CENTRE—Royal & Sun Alliance Insurance Group plc; *Int'l*, pg. 1131
ROYAL INSURANCE COMPANY OF CANADA—Royal & Sun Alliance Insurance Group plc; *Int'l*, pg. 1131
ROYAL INSURANCE HAMILTON REGIONAL CENTRE—Royal & Sun Alliance Insurance Group plc; *Int'l*, pg. 1131
ROYAL INSURANCE OTTAWA REGIONAL CENTRE—Royal & Sun Alliance Insurance Group plc; *Int'l*, pg. 1131
SCOR UK GROUP—SCOR; *Int'l*, pg. 1153
THE ST. PAUL COMPANIES, INC.; *U.S. Public*, pg. 1429
ST. PAUL FIRE AND MARINE INSURANCE CO.—The St. Paul Companies, Inc.; *U.S. Public*, pg. 1429
THE SEIBELS BRUCE GROUP, INC.; *U.S. Public*, pg. 1453
SELECTIVE INSURANCE GROUP, INC; *U.S. Public*, pg. 1455
THE SHELBY INSURANCE COMPANIES—Vesta Insurance Group, Inc.; *U.S. Public*, pg. 1718
SIRIUS REINSURANCE CORPORATION—ABB Asea Brown Boveri (Holding) Ltd.; *Int'l*, pg. 4
STATE VOLUNTEER MUTUAL INSURANCE CO.; *U.S. Private*, pg. 1037
TM CLAIMS SERVICE, INC.—The Tokio Marine & Fire Insurance Company, Ltd.; *Int'l*, pg. 1392
TEMPLE-INLAND FINANCIAL SERVICES, INC—Temple-Inland Inc.; *U.S. Public*, pg. 1575
TEMPLE-INLAND INC.; *U.S. Public*, pg. 1574
USF&G CORPORATION; *U.S. Public*, pg. 1659
UNIONE SUBALPINA DI ASSICURAZIONI—Allianz Aktiengesellschaft; *Int'l*, pg. 62
U.S. BANCORP INSURANCE AGENCY, INC.—U.S. Bancorp; *U.S. Public*, pg. 1681
UNITED STATES FIDELITY & GUARANTY COMPANY—USF&G Corporation; *U.S. Public*, pg. 1659
USLIFE AGENCY SERVICES, INC.—American General Corporation; *U.S. Public*, pg. 77
USLIFE INSURANCE SERVICES CORPORATION—American General Corporation; *U.S. Public*, pg. 77
UNIVERSAL INSURANCE CO.—The Seibels Bruce Group, Inc.; *U.S. Public*, pg. 1454
UNIVERSAL SURETY OF AMERICA—Capsure Holdings Corp.; *U.S. Public*, pg. 303
VOYAGER GROUP, INC.—American Bankers Insurance Group, Inc.; *U.S. Public*, pg. 68
WESTCHESTER SPECIALTY GROUP—Fremont General Corporation; *U.S. Public*, pg. 681
WESTERN SURETY COMPANY—Capsure Holdings Corp.; *U.S. Public*, pg. 303
WESTFIELD COMPANIES; *U.S. Private*, pg. 1169
WESTPAC INSURANCE SERVICES (BROKERS) LIMITED—Westpac Banking Corporation; *Int'l*, pg. 1496
WINTERTHUR REINSURANCE CORPORATION OF AMERICA—Credit Suisse Group; *Int'l*, pg. 346
ZURICH AMERICAN INSURANCE COMPANY OF ILLINOIS—Zurich Insurance Company; *Int'l*, pg. 1530

6361 — TITLE INSURANCE

AXA-UAP; *Int'l*, pg. 18
ALLIED CAPITAL CORPORATION; *U.S. Public*, pg. 47
ATTORNEYS' TITLE INSURANCE FUND; *U.S. Private*, pg. 98
THE CAMDEN FIRE INSURANCE ASSN.—General Accident Fire and Life Assurance Corporation p.l.c.; *Int'l*, *pg. 543*
CENTRAL REGISTRATION HONG KONG LTD.—HSBC Holdings plc; *Int'l*, pg. 581
CHARLESTON FINANCIAL SERVICES, INC.—First Financial Holdings, Inc.; *U.S. Public*, pg. 634
CHICAGO TITLE & TRUST CO.—Alleghany Corporation; *U.S. Public*, pg. 42
CHICAGO TITLE INSURANCE CO.—Alleghany Corporation; *U.S. Public*, pg. 42
COMMERCIAL UNION PLC; *Int'l*, pg. 308
COMMONWEALTH LAND TITLE INSURANCE COMPANY—Reliance Group Holdings, Inc.; *U.S. Public*, pg. 1374
COMPAGNIE D'ASSURANCE DU QUEBEC—Royal & Sun Alliance Insurance Group plc; *Int'l*, pg. 1131
DESJARDINS LAURENTIAN LIFE ASSURANCE—Desjardins-Laurentian Financial Corporation; *Int'l*, pg. 396
ELAN TITLE SERVICES, INC.—Firstar Corporation; *U.S. Public*, pg. 643
FIDELITY NATIONAL FINANCIAL, INC.; *U.S. Public*, pg. 620
FIDELITY NATIONAL TITLE INSURANCE COMPANY OF PENNSYLVANIA—Fidelity National Financial, Inc.; *U.S. Public*, pg. 621
FIRST AMERICAN CO. OF ALASKA—The First American Financial Corporation; *U.S. Public*, pg. 625
THE FIRST AMERICAN FINANCIAL CORPORATION; *U.S. Public*, pg. 624
FIRST SOUTHEAST INSURANCE AGENCY—First Financial Holdings, Inc.; *U.S. Public*, pg. 634
FLORIDA HOMES TITLE—Lennar Corporation; *U.S. Public*, *pg. 988*
FRANKFORD ABSTRACT CO.—Keystone Financial Inc.; *U.S. Public*, pg. 956
G.E. CAPITAL MORTGAGE SERVICES—General Electric Company; *U.S. Public*, pg. 712
GENERAL ACCIDENT FIRE AND LIFE ASSURANCE CORPORATION P.L.C.; *Int'l*, pg. 542
HOME-OWNERS INSURANCE CO.—Auto-Owners Insurance; *U.S. Private*, pg. 100
THE IMPERIAL LIFE ASSURANCE CO.—Desjardins-Laurentian Financial Corporation; *Int'l*, pg. 396
INDIANA TITLE INSURANCE COMPANY—Ameriana Bancorp; *U.S. Public*, pg. 66
THE INNOVATIVE COMPANY—The Seibels Bruce Group, Inc.; *U.S. Public*, pg. 1454
INTEGON CORPORATION—General Motors Corporation; *U.S. Public*, pg. 719
INTERCOUNTY TITLE CO. OF ILLINOIS; *U.S. Private*, pg. 567
JEFFERSON-PILOT TITLE INSURANCE CO.—Jefferson-Pilot Corporation; *U.S. Public*, pg. 926
KENTUCKY MEDICAL INSURANCE COMPANY (KMIC)—Michigan Physicians Mutual Liability Inc.; *U.S. Private*, pg. 741
LAWYERS TITLE INSURANCE CORPORATION; *U.S. Public*, pg. 981
MSI INSURANCE COMPANIES; *U.S. Private*, pg. 688
MORTGAGE GUARANTEE & TITLE CO.—The First American Financial Corporation; *U.S. Public*, pg. 626
PORT LAWRENCE TITLE & TRUST CO.—The First American Financial Corporation; *U.S. Public*, pg. 626
RELIANCE GROUP HOLDINGS, INC.; *U.S. Public*, pg. 1374
RESOURCE AMERICA, INC.; *U.S. Public*, pg. 1382
ROYAL INSURANCE COMPANY OF CANADA—Royal & Sun Alliance Insurance Group plc; *Int'l*, pg. 1131
THE SEIBELS BRUCE GROUP, INC.; *U.S. Public*, pg. 1453
STEWART INFORMATION SERVICES CORPORATION; *U.S. Public*, pg. 1518
TCF FINANCIAL CORP.; *U.S. Public*, pg. 1554
TITLE INSURANCE COMPANY OF MINNESOTA—Old Republic International Corporation; *U.S. Public*, pg. 1218
UNIVERSAL TITLE INSURORS, INC.—Lennar Corporation; *U.S. Public*, pg. 989

6371 — PENSION, HEALTH & WELFARE FUNDS

ABB INVESTMENT MANAGEMENT—ABB Asea Brown Boveri (Holding) Ltd.; *Int'l*, pg. 4
ADMINISTRADORA DE FONDOS DE PENSIONES QUALITAS S.A.—Skandia Insurance Company Limited; *Int'l*, pg. 1258
AETNA CANADA HOLDINGS LTD.—Aetna Inc.; *U.S. Public*, pg. 27
AETNA HEALTH (NEW ZEALAND) LIMITED—Aetna Inc.; *U.S. Public*, pg. 27
AETNA INTERNATIONAL CHILE S.A.—Aetna Inc.; *U.S. Public*, pg. 27
AETNA UNIVERSAL INSURANCE SDN. BHD.—Aetna Inc.; *U.S. Public*, pg. 27
ALEXANDER & ALEXANDER SERVICES INC.—AON Corporation; *U.S. Public*, pg. 117
AMERITAS LIFE INSURANCE CORP.; *U.S. Private*, pg. 65
ANTHEM, INC.; *U.S. Private*, pg. 76
BARCLAYS FINANCIAL SERVICES CO. LTD.—Barclays Bank PLC; *Int'l*, pg. 164
BARCLAYS LIFE ASSURANCE CO. LTD.—Barclays Bank PLC; *Int'l*, pg. 165
BEAR STEARNS FIDUCIARY SERVICES, INC.—The Bear Stearns Companies Inc.; *U.S. Public*, pg. 198
BERKSHIRE LIFE INSURANCE COMPANY; *U.S. Private*, pg. 136
SANFORD C. BERNSTEIN & CO., INC.; *U.S. Private*, pg. 137
CAJA MADRID DE PENSIONES, E.G.F.P., S.A.—Caja de Madrid Group; *Int'l*, pg. 251
CALFARM INSURANCE AGENCY—Zenith National Insurance Corp.; *U.S. Public*, pg. 1791
CALFARM INSURANCE COMPANY—Zenith National Insurance Corp.; *U.S. Public*, pg. 1791
THE CANADA LIFE ASSURANCE COMPANY; *Int'l*, pg. 254
CENTURY PENSIONS LIMITED—Invesco Group Asset Management Ltd.; *Int'l*, pg. 685
CONFEDERATION PENSION INVESTMENT MANAGEMENT LIMITED—Sun Life Assurance Company of Canada; *Int'l*, pg. 1319
CUSTODIAL TRUST COMPANY—The Bear Stearns Companies Inc.; *U.S. Public*, pg. 198
THE DEARBORN GROUP; *U.S. Private*, pg. 319
DONGBU AETNA LIFE INSURANCE CO., LTD.—Aetna Inc.; *U.S. Public*, pg. 27
EMPLOYEE BENEFITS DIV.—Anglo American Corporation of South Africa Limited; *Int'l*, pg. 77
FONDITEL ENTIDAD GESTORA DE FONDOS DE PENSIONES, S.A.—Telefonica de Espana, S.A.; *Int'l*, pg. 1371
GESCAT, ENTIDAD GESTORA DE FONDOS DE PENSIONES, S.A.—Caixa d'Estalvis de Catalunya; *Int'l*, pg. 250
HSBC ASSET MANAGEMENT AMERICAS, INC.—HSBC Holdings plc; *Int'l*, pg. 581
THE HOLDEN GROUP—EdperBrascan Corporation; *Int'l*, pg. 435
INSURANCE COMPANY OF NORTH AMERICA (U.K.) LIMITED—Cigna Corp.; *U.S. Public*, pg. 363
INVESCO INC.—Invesco Group Asset Management Ltd.; *Int'l*, pg. 685
JEFFERSON-PILOT CORPORATION; *U.S. Public*, pg. 925
KENTUCKY MEDICAL INSURANCE COMPANY (KMIC)—Michigan Physicians Mutual Liability Inc.; *U.S. Private*, pg. 741
KVAERNERKONSERNETS PENSJONSKASSE—Kvaerner a.s.a.; *Int'l*, pg. 770
LINCOLN NATIONAL CORPORATION; *U.S. Public*, pg. 997
MANULIFE FINANCIAL HOLDINGS LIMITED—Manulife Financial (The Manufacturers Life Insurance Company); *Int'l*, pg. 840
MANULIFE FINANCIAL SERVICES LIMITED—Manulife Financial (The Manufacturers Life Insurance Company); *Int'l*, pg. 840
MASSACHUSETTS MUTUAL LIFE INSURANCE CO.; *U.S. Private*, pg. 712
MERCURY ASSET MANAGEMENT GROUP PLC—Swiss Bank Corporation; *Int'l*, pg. 1331
MERCURY ASSET MANAGEMENT PLC—Swiss Bank Corporation; *Int'l*, pg. 1331
MERCURY FUND MANAGERS LTD.—Swiss Bank Corporation; *Int'l*, pg. 1331
METROPOLITAN LIFE INSURANCE CO.; *U.S. Private*, pg. 737
MIDLAND LIFE LIMITED—HSBC Holdings plc; *Int'l*, pg. 580
MONTREAL TRUSTCO-CORPORATE SERVICES DIV.—The Bank of Nova Scotia; *Int'l*, pg. 155
MONTREAL TRUSTCO INVESTMENT MANAGEMENT SERVICES—The Bank of Nova Scotia; *Int'l*, pg. 155
MONTREAL TRUSTCO-PERSONAL SERVICES DIVISION—The Bank of Nova Scotia; *Int'l*, pg. 155
MONTRUSCO ASSOCIATES, INC.; *Int'l*, pg. 888
MORGAN STANLEY ASSET MANAGEMENT, INC.—Morgan Stanley Dean Witter & Co.; *U.S. Public*, pg. 1132
NATIONAL EMPLOYEE BENEFITS CORPORATION—Cigna Corp.; *U.S. Public*, pg. 366
NEWPORT—Metropolitan Life Insurance Co.; *U.S. Private*, pg. 738
PACIFIC LIFE INSURANCE COMPANY; *U.S. Private*, pg. 831
THE PAUL REVERE CORPORATION—Provident Companies, Inc.; *U.S. Public*, pg. 1338
THE PAUL REVERE VARIABLE ANNUITY LIFE INSURANCE CO.—Provident Companies, Inc.; *U.S. Public*, pg. 1338
POTTER WARBURG ASSET MANAGEMENT—Swiss Bank Corporation; *Int'l*, pg. 1331
POTTER WARBURG ASSET MANAGEMENT LTD.—Swiss Bank Corporation; *Int'l*, pg. 1331
PRUDENTIAL DEFINED CONTRIBUTION SERVICES—The Prudential Insurance Company of America; *U.S. Private*, pg. 892
SBC WARBURG GROUP PLC—Swiss Bank Corporation; *Int'l*, pg. 1330
SCOTTISH WIDOWS' FUND & LIFE ASSURANCE SOCIETY; *Int'l*, pg. 1212
SEGUROS DE VIDA Y PENSIONES ANTARES, S.A.—Telefonica de Espana, S.A.; *Int'l*, pg. 1371
SEGUROS GENESIS, S.A.—Metropolitan Life Insurance Co.; *U.S. Private*, pg. 738
SELF-INSURERS' MANAGEMENT CORPORATION—Cigna Corp.; *U.S. Public*, pg. 366
STANDARD INSURANCE CO.; *U.S. Private*, pg. 1031
STANHOPE PENSION TRUST LTD.—The General Electric Company, p.l.c.; *Int'l*, pg. 545
STRUCTURED COMPENSATION LTD.—Inchcape PLC; *Int'l*, pg. 671
THE SWISS LIFE/RENTENANSTALT GROUP; *Int'l*, pg. 1332
TRILON FINANCIAL CORP.—EdperBrascan Corporation; *Int'l*, pg. 434
UNUM LIFE INSURANCE COMPANY OF AMERICA—UNUM Corporation; *U.S. Public*, pg. 1699
WADDELL & REED ASSET MNGMT. CO.—Torchmark Corporation; *U.S. Public*, pg. 1623
WARBURG ASSET MANAGEMENT ISLE OF MAN LTD.—Swiss Bank Corporation; *Int'l*, pg. 1331
WARBURG ASSET MANAGEMENT JAPAN LTD.—Swiss Bank Corporation; *Int'l*, pg. 1331
WARBURG ASSET MANAGEMENT JERSEY LTD.—Swiss Bank Corporation; *Int'l*, pg. 1331
ZENITH NATIONAL INSURANCE CORP.; *U.S. Public*, pg. 1790

6399 — INSURANCE CARRIERS, NEC

AFIA—Cigna Corp.; *U.S. Public*, pg. 366
AGA RE—AGA AB; *Int'l*, pg. 13
AXA ASSICURAZIONI—AXA-UAP; *Int'l*, pg. 19

AXA ASSURANCES—AXA-UAP; *Int'l*, pg. 18
AXA EQUITY & LAW LIFE ASSURANCE SOCIETY PLC—AXA-UAP; *Int'l*, pg. 19
AXA INSURANCE—AXA-UAP; *Int'l*, pg. 19
AXA LIFE OFFICE—AXA-UAP; *Int'l*, pg. 19
AXA MARINE & AVIATION INSURANCE UK LTD.—AXA-UAP; *Int'l*, pg. 19
AXA SEGUROS Y REASEGUROS—AXA-UAP; *Int'l*, pg. 19
AGRI-SERVICE AGENCIES, INC.—Dairylea Cooperative Inc.; *U.S. Private*, pg. 308
ALL NATION INSURANCE COMPANY; *U.S. Private*, pg. 35
ALPHA ASSURANCES—AXA-UAP; *Int'l*, pg. 18
AMERIANA INSURANCE AGENCY—Ameriana Bancorp; *U.S. Public*, pg. 66
AMERICAN BANKERS INSURANCE CO. OF FLORIDA—American Bankers Insurance Group, Inc.; *U.S. Public*, pg. 67
AMERICAN FAMILY MUTUAL INSURANCE CO.; *U.S. Private*, pg. 53
AMERICAN INSURANCE AGENCY, INC.—Servco Pacific Inc.; *U.S. Private*, pg. 986
AMERISURE COMPANIES; *U.S. Private*, pg. 65
ATICAM—AXA-UAP; *Int'l*, pg. 18
AURORA POLAR—AXA-UAP; *Int'l*, pg. 19
AUTARKA GMBH, VERMITTLUNG VON VERSICHERUNGEN ALLER ART—Dyckerhoff & Widmann AG; *Int'l*, pg. 423
AVEMCO CORPORATION; *U.S. Public*, pg. 151
AXIVA—AXA-UAP; *Int'l*, pg. 18
BERWIND CORPORATION; *U.S. Private*, pg. 138
BOLIVAR, COMPANIA DE SEGUROS DEL ECUADOR—The Chubb Corporation; *U.S. Public*, pg. 355
CG TRUST COMPANY—Cigna Corp.; *U.S. Public*, pg. 358
CALIFORNIA CAPITAL INSURANCE COMPANY—Kelly-Moore Paint Company, Inc.; *U.S. Private*, pg. 613
CERTIFIED GROCERS OF CALIFORNIA; *U.S. Private*, pg. 226
CIBA-GEIGY VERSICHERUNGSVERMITTLUNG GHBH—Novartis AG; *Int'l*, pg. 980
CIGNA INTERNATIONAL REINSURANCE COMPANY LTD.—Cigna Corp.; *U.S. Public*, pg. 364
CIGNA REINSURANCE COMPANY (U.K.) LIMITED—Cigna Corp.; *U.S. Public*, pg. 363
CIGNA SALUD ISAPRE S.A.—Cigna Corp.; *U.S. Public*, pg. 364
CIRCLE FREIGHT INTERNATIONAL (U.S.A.)—Circle International Group, Inc.; *U.S. Public*, pg. 370
CIRCLE INTERNATIONAL—Circle International Group, Inc.; *U.S. Public*, pg. 371
CIRCLE INTERNATIONAL GROUP, INC.; *U.S. Public*, pg. 370
COMMERCIAL AND POLITICAL RISK CONSULTANTS—Inchcape PLC; *Int'l*, pg. 671
DEFENSE CIVILE—AXA-UAP; *Int'l*, pg. 18
DIRECT ASSURANCE—AXA-UAP; *Int'l*, pg. 18
FARMERS UNION MARKETING & PROCESSING ASSOCIATION; *U.S. Private*, pg. 395
FIDELIDADE—Caixa Geral de Depositos; *Int'l*, pg. 250
FINAXA—AXA-UAP; *Int'l*, pg. 18
FIRST SECURITY LIFE INS. CO. OF ARIZONA—First Security Corporation; *U.S. Public*, pg. 638
GENEVE CAPITAL GROUP INC.—Geneve Corporation; *U.S. Private*, pg. 446
GRAND ISLAND CONTRACT CARRIERS & BROKERAGE, INC.—Chief Industries, Inc.; *U.S. Private*, pg. 236
GUARANTEE NATIONAL INSURANCE COMPANY—Orion Capital Corporation; *U.S. Public*, pg. 1231
HSBC INSURANCE HOLDINGS LIMITED—HSBC Holdings plc; *Int'l*, pg. 580
JC PENNEY FINANCIAL SERVICES, INC.—JC Penney Company, Inc.; *U.S. Public*, pg. 917
KEMPER INSURANCE COMPANIES; *U.S. Private*, pg. 614
KVAERNER INSURANCE A/S—Kvaerner a.s.a.; *Int'l*, pg. 769
LA FEDERACION COMPANIA DE SEGUROS, C.A.—The Chubb Corporation; *U.S. Public*, pg. 355
LA FEDERAL COMPANIA DE SEGUROS, S.A.—The Chubb Corporation; *U.S. Public*, pg. 355
LEGAL & GENERAL ASSURANCE SOCIETY LIMITED—Legal & General Group PLC; *Int'l*, pg. 805
MANUFACTURERS LIFE MORTGAGE SECURITIES CORPORATION—Manulife Financial (The Manufacturers Life Insurance Company); *Int'l*, pg. 840
MONUMENTAL GENERAL MASS MARKETING, INC.—AEGON N.V.; *Int'l*, pg. 27
MUTUEEL SAINT-CHRISTOPHE—AXA-UAP; *Int'l*, pg. 19
MUTUELLE DE L'EST—AXA-UAP; *Int'l*, pg. 19
MUTUELLE DE MARSEILLE—AXA-UAP; *Int'l*, pg. 19
MUTUELLE PHOCEENNE ASSURANCE—AXA-UAP; *Int'l*, pg. 19
NATIONAL AMERICAN INSURANCE COMPANY OF CALIFORNIA—Danielson Holding Corporation; *U.S. Public*, pg. 483
NATIONAL INSURANCE AGENCY, INC.—American Bankers Insurance Group, Inc.; *U.S. Public*, pg. 67
NIAGARA ASSET CORPORATION—Keycorp; *U.S. Public*, pg. 955
NIAGARA PORTFOLIO MANAGEMENT CORPORATION—Keycorp; *U.S. Public*, pg. 955
NITTSU SHOJI CO., LTD.—Nippon Express Co., Ltd.; *Int'l*, pg. 934
NOVARTIS—Novartis AG; *Int'l*, pg. 972
OLDE ENGLISH EQUINE INSURANCE AGENCY, INC.—International Thoroughbred Breeders, Inc.; *U.S. Public*, pg. 908
PRE-PAID LEGAL SERVICES, INC.; *U.S. Public*, pg. 1320
PRUDENTIAL ASSURANCE CO. LTD.—Prudential Corporation PLC; *Int'l*, pg. 1073
PRUDENTIAL COMMERCIAL INSURANCE CO.—The Prudential Insurance Company of America; *U.S. Private*, pg. 892
THE PRUDENTIAL INSURANCE COMPANY OF AMERICA; *U.S. Private*, pg. 892
SKANDIA INSURANCE COMPANY LIMITED; *Int'l*, pg. 1256
SOCIETE DE REASSURANCE DES RISQUES RELATIFS AUX APPLICATIONS SPATIALES (S3R)—Arianespace SA; *Int'l*, pg. 81
TELE-TRIP COMPANY—Mutual of Omaha Insurance Company; *U.S. Private*, pg. 770
TRANSMISSION EPARGNE VIE—AXA-UAP; *Int'l*, pg. 19
ULICO INDEMNITY—ULLICO Inc.; *U.S. Private*, pg. 1116
UNI EUROPE—AXA-UAP; *Int'l*, pg. 19
UNITED COASTAL INSURANCE COMPANY—ACMAT Corporation; *U.S. Public*, pg. 16
UNITED WORLD LIFE INSURANCE COMPANY—Mutual of Omaha Insurance Company; *U.S. Private*, pg. 770
UNUM SALES CORP.—UNUM Corporation; *U.S. Public*, pg. 1700
VANLINER GROUP, INC.—UniGroup, Inc.; *U.S. Private*, pg. 1117
VANLINER INSURANCE CO.—UniGroup, Inc.; *U.S. Private*, pg. 1117
VERSAR RISK MANAGEMENT, INC.—Versar Inc.; *U.S. Public*, pg. 1717
WESTFIELD COMPANIES; *U.S. Private*, pg. 1169
WUESTENROT HOLDING GMBH; *Int'l*, pg. 1514

6411 — INSURANCE AGENTS, BROKERS & SERVICE

ABI MANAGEMENT, INC.—American Financial Group; *U.S. Public*, pg. 74
ABN ASSURANTIE HOLDING B.V.—ABN-AMRO Holding N.V.; *Int'l*, pg. 9
ABN ASSURANTIEN B.V.—ABN-AMRO Holding N.V.; *Int'l*, pg. 9
AIG RISK MANAGEMENT, INC.—American International Group, Inc.; *U.S. Public*, pg. 85
AMB AACHENER UND MUENCHENER BETEILIGUNGS-AG; *Int'l*, pg. 15
AMEV V-A ARDANTA—Fortis; *Int'l*, pg. 499
AON, JAUCH & HUEBENER GRUPPE—AON Corporation; *U.S. Public*, pg. 118
AON SPECIALTY GROUP, INC.—AON Corporation; *U.S. Public*, pg. 117
AS. CO S.P.A.—Bastogi-S.p.A.; *Int'l*, pg. 170
ABRAHAM LINCOLN INSURANCE CO.—First Commonwealth Corporation; *U.S. Private*, pg. 406
ACONCAGUA SEGUROS DE RETIRO, S.A.—Corporacion MAPFRE, Compania Internacional de Reaseguros, S.A.; *Int'l*, pg. 333
ACORDIA NORTHEAST—Inchcape PLC; *Int'l*, pg. 671
ACSTAR INSURANCE COMPANY—ACMAT Corporation; *U.S. Public*, pg. 16
ADDISON INSURANCE AGENCY—United Fire & Casualty Company; *U.S. Public*, pg. 1677
ADMINISTRATIVE SERVICES, INC.—National Life Insurance Company; *U.S. Private*, pg. 785
AEGON FINANCIAL SERVICES GROUP (UK) LTD.—AEGON N.V.; *Int'l*, pg. 28
AEGON REINSURANCE COMPANY OF AMERICA—AEGON N.V.; *Int'l*, pg. 26
AEGON REINSURANCE N.V.—AEGON N.V.; *Int'l*, pg. 26
AEGON-UNION ASEGURADORA, S.A. DE SEGUROS Y REASEQUROS—AEGON N.V.; *Int'l*, pg. 28
AEGON USA, INC.—AEGON N.V.; *Int'l*, pg. 26
AETNA INC.; *U.S. Public*, pg. 26
AETNA INTERNATIONAL, INC.—Aetna Inc.; *U.S. Public*, pg. 26
AFLAC INCORPORATED; *U.S. Public*, pg. 28
AGENCY AUTO SALES, INC.—National Auto Credit Inc.; *U.S. Public*, pg. 1153
AGENCY SPECIALTY INC.—The Seibels Bruce Group, Inc.; *U.S. Public*, pg. 1454
AGRIPPINA RECHTSSCHUTZVERSICHERUNG AG—Zurich Insurance Company; *Int'l*, pg. 1531
AGRIPPINA VERSICHERUNG AKTIENGESELLSCHAFT—Zurich Insurance Company; *Int'l*, pg. 1531
AGWAY GENERAL AGENCY—Agway, Inc.; *U.S. Private*, pg. 27
ALEXANDER & ALEXANDER INC.—AON Corporation; *U.S. Public*, pg. 117
ALEXANDER & ALEXANDER SERVICES INC.—AON Corporation; *U.S. Public*, pg. 117
THE ALEXANDER CONSULTING GROUP INC.—AON Corporation; *U.S. Public*, pg. 117
ALGEMENE FRIESE ONDERLINGE SCHADEVERZEKERINGMAATSCHAPPIJ 'ZEVENWOUDEN' U.A.—AEGON N.V.; *Int'l*, pg. 26
ALL AMERICAN AGENCY FACILITIES, INC.—W.R. Berkley Corporation; *U.S. Public*, pg. 216
ALLIANZ COMPANIA DE SEGUROS S.A.—Allianz Aktiengesellschaft; *Int'l*, pg. 59
ALLIANZ CORNHILL INSURANCE (FAR EAST) LTD.—Allianz Aktiengesellschaft; *Int'l*, pg. 59
ALLIANZ INSURANCE (SINGAPORE) PTE. LTD.—Allianz Aktiengesellschaft; *Int'l*, pg. 59
ALLIANZ LIFE INSURANCE COMPANY OF NORTH AMERICA—Allianz Aktiengesellschaft; *Int'l*, pg. 58
ALLIANZ OF AMERICA, INC.—Allianz Aktiengesellschaft; *Int'l*, pg. 58
ALLIANZ UNDERWRITERS INSURANCE CO.—Allianz Aktiengesellschaft; *Int'l*, pg. 58
ALLIANZ VERSICHERUNGS-AG—Allianz Aktiengesellschaft; *Int'l*, pg. 58
ALLIED INSURANCE AGENCY—The Progressive Corporation; *U.S. Public*, pg. 1334
ALLINSURE—GIB Group; *Int'l*, pg. 532
ALPINA INSURANCE COMPANY—Zurich Insurance Company; *Int'l*, pg. 1529
ALSTADT INSURANCES—Zurich Insurance Company; *Int'l*, pg. 1529
AMERCO; *U.S. Private*, pg. 48
AMERICAN BANKERS INSURANCE GROUP, INC.; *U.S. Public*, pg. 67
AMERICAN BANKERS LIFE AGENTS SERVICES, INC.—American Bankers Insurance Group, Inc.; *U.S. Public*, pg. 67
AMERICAN BROKERAGE CORPORATION—Phoenix Home Life Mutual Insurance Company; *U.S. Private*, pg. 863
AMERICAN FAMILY LIFE ASSURANCE COMPANY OF NEW YORK—AFLAC Incorporated; *U.S. Public*, pg. 28
AMERICAN FINANCIAL GROUP—American Financial Group; *U.S. Public*, pg. 75
AMERICAN GENERAL CORPORATION; *U.S. Public*, pg. 76
AMERICAN GENERAL LIFE INSURANCE COMPANY OF NEW YORK—American General Corporation; *U.S. Public*, pg. 76
AMERICAN GENERAL PROPERTY INSURANCE COMPANY—American General Corporation; *U.S. Public*, pg. 76
AMERICAN GUARANTEE & LIABILITY INSURANCE COMPANY—Zurich Insurance Company; *Int'l*, pg. 1530
AMERICAN HOME ASSURANCE COMPANY NEW YORK, SWISS BRANCH—American International Group, Inc.; *U.S. Public*, pg. 85
AMERICAN INTERNATIONAL ADJUSTMENT COMPANY—American International Group, Inc.; *U.S. Public*, pg. 85
AMERICAN INTERNATIONAL CO. LTD.—American International Group, Inc.; *U.S. Public*, pg. 85
AMERICAN INTERNATIONAL GROUP, INC.; *U.S. Public*, pg. 83
AMERICAN INTERNATIONAL MANAGEMENT CO. (BARBADOS) LTD.—American International Group, Inc.; *U.S. Public*, pg. 85
AMERICAN INTERNATIONAL MANAGERS LTD.—American International Group, Inc.; *U.S. Public*, pg. 85
AMERICAN INTERNATIONAL UNDERWRITERS CORP.—American International Group, Inc.; *U.S. Public*, pg. 85
AMERICAN INTERNATIONAL UNDERWRITERS (UK) LTD.—American International Group, Inc.; *U.S. Public*, pg. 85
AMERICAN RENAISSANCE INSURANCE COMPANY—Ford Motor Company; *U.S. Public*, pg. 664
AMERICAN RISK ASSOCIATES, LTD.—Day & Zimmermann, Inc.; *U.S. Private*, pg. 317
AMERICAN ZURICH INSURANCE COMPANY—Zurich Insurance Company; *Int'l*, pg. 1530
AMERINSURANCE, INC.—Corporacion MAPFRE, Compania Internacional de Reaseguros, S.A.; *Int'l*, pg. 333
AMINS, INC.—ACMAT Corporation; *U.S. Public*, pg. 16
AMSTAR INSURANCE COMPANY—Corporacion MAPFRE, Compania Internacional de Reaseguros, S.A.; *Int'l*, pg. 333
ANDERSON HILL INSURANCE LIMITED—PepsiCo, Inc.; *U.S. Public*, pg. 1277
ANGLO-ELEMENTAR VERSICHERUNGS-AG—Allianz Aktiengesellschaft; *Int'l*, pg. 60
ANNUITY NETWORK INC.—St. Paul Bancorp, Inc.; *U.S. Public*, pg. 1428
ANTAH SEDGWICK CHARTERED INSURANCE BROKERS SDN BERHAD—Standard Chartered Bank PLC; *Int'l*, pg. 1297
ANTHEM, INC.; *U.S. Private*, pg. 76
AON RISK SERVICES INC. OF ILLINOIS—AON Corporation; *U.S. Public*, pg. 117
ASSECURANZ-COMPAGNIE MERCUR AG—Allianz Aktiengesellschaft; *Int'l*, pg. 58
ASSOCIATED AVIATION UNDERWRITERS—The Chubb Corporation; *U.S. Public*, pg. 355
ASSOCIATED WHOLESALE GROCERS, INC.; *U.S. Private*, pg. 93
ASSURANCE COMPANY OF AMERICA—Zurich Insurance Company; *Int'l*, pg. 1530
ASSURANCES DE LA POSTE—Groupe Bruxelles Lambert S.A.; *Int'l*, pg. 562
ATLANTIC MUTUAL COMPANIES; *U.S. Private*, pg. 95
AUTO INSURANCE SOLUTIONS INC.—The Progressive Corporation; *U.S. Public*, pg. 1334
AUTO-OWNERS LIFE INSURANCE CO.—Auto-Owners Insurance; *U.S. Private*, pg. 100
AVEMCO CORPORATION; *U.S. Public*, pg. 151
B & L INSURANCE, LTD.—Baldwin & Lyons, Inc.; *U.S. Public*, pg. 169
BA AGENCY, INC.—BankAmerica Corporation; *U.S. Public*, pg. 180
B.A.T INDUSTRIES P.L.C.; *Int'l*, pg. 110
BB&T OF SOUTH CAROLINA—BB&T Corporation; *U.S. Public*, pg. 160
BAIN HOGG GROUP PLC—Inchcape PLC; *Int'l*, pg. 671
BAIN HOGG INSURANCE BROKERS—Inchcape PLC; *Int'l*, pg. 671
BAIN HOGG INSURANCE MANAGEMENT GUERNSEY LTD.—Inchcape PLC; *Int'l*, pg. 671
BALFOUR, WILLIAMSON & CO. LTD.—Lonrho plc; *Int'l*, pg. 817
BANK OF AMERICA BUSINESS CREDIT—BankAmerica Corporation; *U.S. Public*, pg. 180
BANKAMERICA INSURANCE GROUP—BankAmerica Corporation; *U.S. Public*, pg. 181
BANKERS LIFE & CASUALTY COMPANY—Conseco Inc.; *U.S. Public*, pg. 433
BARCLAYS INSURANCE BROKERS INTERNATIONAL LTD.—Barclays Bank PLC; *Int'l*, pg. 164
BARCLAYS INSURANCE SERVICES CO. LTD.—Barclays Bank PLC; *Int'l*, pg. 165
BASTOGI-S.P.A.; *Int'l*, pg. 170
BAVARIA WIRTSCHAFTSAGENTUR GMBH—Bayerische Motoren Werke Aktiengesellschaft; *Int'l*, pg. 177
BAYSIDE UNDERWRITERS INSURANCE AGENCY, INC.—The Progressive Corporation; *U.S. Public*, pg. 1334
BENEFICIAL CORPORATION; *U.S. Public*, pg. 211
BENEFIT CONSULTANTS, INC. (CT)—Cendant Corporation; *U.S. Public*, pg. 320
BERKLEY ADMINISTRATORS—W.R. Berkley Corporation; *U.S. Public*, pg. 216

BERKLEY INFORMATION SERVICES—W.R. Berkley Corporation; U.S. Public, pg. 216
BERMEAD INSURANCE COMPANY LTD.—The Mead Corporation; U.S. Public, pg. 1076
BEST INSURORS, INC.—Walter Industries, Inc.; U.S. Public, pg. 1736
BETTER HOMES INSURANCE ASSOCIATES, INC.—AEGON N.V.; Int'l, pg. 27
BIPIEMME-GESTIONE POLIZZE DI ASSICURAZIONE S.P.A.—Banca Popolare di Milano; Int'l, pg. 137
BLUE CROSS OF CALIFORNIA; U.S. Private, pg. 152
BOATMEN'S NATIONAL MORTGAGE INC.—NationsBank Corporation; U.S. Public, pg. 1165
THE BOILER INSPECTION & INSURANCE CO. OF CANADA—The Hartford Steam Boiler Inspection & Insurance Co.; U.S. Public, pg. 795
BRADSTOCK BLUNT & THOMPSON—Bradstock Group plc; Int'l, pg. 210
BRADSTOCK BLUNT (PLASTICS) LTD.—Bradstock Group plc; Int'l, pg. 210
BRADSTOCK INSURANCE BROKERS LIMITED—Bradstock Group plc; Int'l, pg. 210
BRITTANY HOLDINGS LTD.—Petrofina S.A.; Int'l, pg. 1044
BROOKS-SHETTLE CO.—Avemco Corporation; U.S. Public, pg. 152
BROUGHER AGENCY, INC.—Eureko B.V.; Int'l, pg. 464
JOHN BURNHAM & CO.; U.S. Private, pg. 186
BURNS & WILCOX LTD.—H.W. Kaufman Financial Group, Inc.; U.S. Private, pg. 609
THE BURTON COMPANY—Hilb, Rogal and Hamilton Company; U.S. Public, pg. 826
BUSINESS MENS INSURANCE CORPORATION; U.S. Private, pg. 189
C.E.A.I.S.A.—Petrofina S.A.; Int'l, pg. 1043
CNA INSURANCE COMPANIES—Loews Corporation; U.S. Public, pg. 1010
CNP ASSURANCES; Int'l, pg. 241
CSE INSURANCE GROUP; U.S. Private, pg. 197
CUC INTERNATIONAL, INC.—Cendant Corporation; U.S. Public, pg. 320
CAIRNGORM INSURANCE LTD.—Burmah Castrol plc; Int'l, pg. 235
CAL-AG INSURANCE SERVICES, INC.—Zenith National Insurance Corp.; U.S. Public, pg. 1791
CANADA LIFE ASSURANCE COMPANY OF GREAT BRITAIN LIMITED—The Canada Life Assurance Company; Int'l, pg. 255
THE CANADA LIFE ASSURANCE COMPANY OF IRELAND LIMITED—The Canada Life Assurance Company; Int'l, pg. 255
CANADA LIFE INSURANCE COMPANY OF NEW YORK—The Canada Life Assurance Company; Int'l, pg. 255
CAPITAL NATIONAL INSURANCE COMPANY—OHM Corporation; U.S. Public, pg. 1207
CAPITAL RE CORPORATION—Minnesota Power; U.S. Public, pg. 1116
CAPSURE HOLDINGS CORP.; U.S. Public, pg. 303
CARDEM INSURANCE CO., LTD.—Walter Industries, Inc.; U.S. Public, pg. 1736
CARLINGFORD SWIRE ASSURANCE LTD.—HSBC Holdings plc; Int'l, pg. 581
CAROLINA CASUALTY INSURANCE COMPANY—W.R. Berkley Corporation; U.S. Public, pg. 216
GUY CARPENTER & CO., INC—Marsh & McLennan Companies, Inc.; U.S. Public, pg. 1048
CATERPILLAR INSURANCE CO., LTD.—Caterpillar Inc.; U.S. Public, pg. 316
CAUDAL S.A. DE SEGUROS Y REASEGUROS—Zurich Insurance Company; Int'l, pg. 1531
CENDANT CORPORATION; U.S. Public, pg. 320
CENTRAL INSURANCE CORP. OF TALLAHASSEE—Killearn Properties, Inc.; U.S. Public, pg. 956
CENTRE REINSURANCE (BERMUDA) LTD.—Zurich Insurance Company; Int'l, pg. 1531
CHIYODA MUTUAL LIFE INSURANCE COMPANY; Int'l, pg. 286
CHRYSLER INSURANCE CO.—Chrysler Corporation; U.S. Public, pg. 354
CHUBB & SON, INC.—The Chubb Corporation; U.S. Public, pg. 355
CHUBB CUSTOM MARKET, INC.—The Chubb Corporation; U.S. Public, pg. 355
CHUBB LLOYDS INSURANCE CO. OF TX—The Chubb Corporation; U.S. Public, pg. 355
CIGNA ASSOCIATES, INC.—Cigna Corp.; U.S. Public, pg. 358
CIGNA BOND SERVICES, INC.—Cigna Corp.; U.S. Public, pg. 362
CIGNA BRASIL EMPREENDIMENTOS LTDA.—Cigna Corp.; U.S. Public, pg. 363
CIGNA COMPANIA DE SEGUROS DE PANAMA S.A.—Cigna Corp.; U.S. Public, pg. 364
CIGNA DE VENEZUELA INTERMEDIARIOS DE REASEGUROS, S.A.—Cigna Corp.; U.S. Public, pg. 364
CIGNA EXCESS & SURPLUS INSURANCE SERVICES, INC. (GA)—Cigna Corp.; U.S. Public, pg. 362
CIGNA EXCESS & SURPLUS INSURANCE SERVICES, INC. (IL)—Cigna Corp.; U.S. Public, pg. 363
CIGNA INTERNATIONAL BROKERS, LTD.—Cigna Corp.; U.S. Public, pg. 364
CIGNA INTERNATIONAL INSURANCE MANAGERS, LTD.—Cigna Corp.; U.S. Public, pg. 364
CIGNA INTERNATIONAL REINSURANCE COMPANY LTD.—Cigna Corp.; U.S. Public, pg. 364
CIGNA OVERSEAS FINANCE N.V.—Cigna Corp.; U.S. Public, pg. 364
CIGNA REASEGUROS, S.A.—Cigna Corp.; U.S. Public, pg. 364
CIGNA SERVICES U.K. LIMITED—Cigna Corp.; U.S. Public, pg. 363
CIGNA THAI COMPANY LIMITED—Cigna Corp.; U.S. Public, pg. 363
CIGNA WORLDWIDE, INCORPORATED—Cigna Corp.; U.S. Public, pg. 363
CIVIL SERVICE EMPLOYEES INSURANCE CO.—CSE Insurance Group; U.S. Private, pg. 197
CLAIMS SERVICE INTERNATIONAL, INC.—UNUM Corporation; U.S. Public, pg. 1699
CLEARFIELD INSURANCE, LTD.—Boise Cascade Corporation; U.S. Public, pg. 243
HERBERT CLOUGH, INC.—General Re Corporation; U.S. Public, pg. 726
C.J. COLEMAN HOLDINGS LTD.; Int'l, pg. 306
ROBERT F. COLEMAN, INC.—Cigna Corp.; U.S. Public, pg. 366
COLORADO NATIONAL BANKSHARES, INC.—U.S. Bancorp; U.S. Public, pg. 1680
COLUMBIA SERVICES, INC.—Washington Mutual Inc.; U.S. Public, pg. 1742
COLUMBUS VERSICHERUNGS VERMITTLUNGS—Nationwide Insurance Enterprise; U.S. Private, pg. 789
COMBINED INSURANCE COMPANY OF AMERICA—AON Corporation; U.S. Public, pg. 118
COMBINED INSURANCE CO. OF AUSTRALIA, LTD.—AON Corporation; U.S. Public, pg. 118
COMBINED LIFE INSURANCE CO. OF NEW YORK—AON Corporation; U.S. Public, pg. 118
COMMERCE & INDUSTRY INSURANCE CO. OF CANADA—American International Group, Inc.; U.S. Public, pg. 85
COMMERCE PROPERTY & CASUALTY AGENCY, INC.—Commerce Bancshares, Inc.; U.S. Public, pg. 410
COMMERCIAL FEDERAL BANK—Commercial Federal Corporation; U.S. Public, pg. 411
COMMERCIAL GUARANTY INSURANCE COMPANY—Ford Motor Company; U.S. Public, pg. 663
COMMERCIAL UNION ASSURANCE COMPANY OF CANADA—Commercial Union plc; Int'l, pg. 308
COMMERCIAL UNION CORPORATION—Commercial Union plc; Int'l, pg. 308
COMPAGNIE INTERNATIONALE D'ASSURANCES ET REASSURANCES (CIAR)—Corporacion MAPFRE, Compania Internacional de Reaseguros, S.A.; Int'l, pg. 335
COMPANHIA DE SEGUROS METROPOLE S.A.—Zurich Insurance Company; Int'l, pg. 1531
COMPANIA DE SEGUROS DE VIDA EUROAMERICA, S.A.—Corporacion MAPFRE, Compania Internacional de Reaseguros, S.A.; Int'l, pg. 333
COMPANIA DE SEGUROS GENERALES EUROAMERICA S.A.—Corporacion MAPFRE, Compania Internacional de Reaseguros, S.A.; Int'l, pg. 333
COMPREHENSIVE BENEFITS SERVICE CO., INC.—First Health Group Corp.; U.S. Public, pg. 635
CONNECTICUT SPECIALTY INSURANCE COMPANY—Orion Capital Corporation; U.S. Public, pg. 1231
CONSTRUCTION COUNSELLORS, INC.; U.S. Private, pg. 266
CONSULTEC, INC.—General American Life Insurance Co.; U.S. Private, pg. 443
CONSULTORA ACTUARIAL Y DE PENSIONES MAPFRE VIDA, S.A.—Corporacion MAPFRE, Compania Internacional de Reaseguros, S.A.; Int'l, pg. 334
CONSUMER SUPPORT SERVICES, INC.—Torchmark Corporation; U.S. Public, pg. 1623
CONTINENTAL INSURANCE CO. (U.K.) LTD.—Loews Corporation; U.S. Public, pg. 1011
CONTINENTAL REINSURANCE CORP.—Loews Corporation; U.S. Public, pg. 1011
COOP LEBENSVERSICHERUNGS GENOSSENSCHAFT—Coop Switzerland; Int'l, pg. 330
COOP RECHTSSCHUTZ—Coop Switzerland; Int'l, pg. 330
COOP SWITZERLAND; Int'l, pg. 329
CORNHILL INSURANCE PLC—Allianz Aktiengesellschaft; Int'l, pg. 60
CORNWALL & STEVENS CO., INC.—MSI Insurance Companies; U.S. Private, pg. 688
COUNTRYWIDE AGENCY, INC.—Countrywide Home Loans Inc.; U.S. Public, pg. 452
COUNTRYWIDE HOME LOANS INC.; U.S. Public, pg. 452
CRAVENS, DARGAN & COMPANY, PACIFIC COAST—Cigna Corp.; U.S. Public, pg. 365
CRAVENS, DARGAN & COMPANY, PACIFIC COAST OF ILLINOIS, INC.—Cigna Corp.; U.S. Public, pg. 366
CRAWFORD & COMPANY; U.S. Public, pg. 458
CRAWFORD & COMPANY INSURANCE ADJUSTERS LTD.—Crawford & Company; U.S. Public, pg. 458
CRAWFORD & COMPANY INTERNATIONAL, INC.—Crawford & Company; U.S. Public, pg. 458
CRESTAR INSURANCE AGENCY INCORPORATED—Crestar Financial Corporation; U.S. Public, pg. 458
CRUM & FORSTER MANAGERS CORPORATION (NY)—Xerox Corporation; U.S. Public, pg. 1784
CURTIS BAY INSURANCE CO. LTD.—Hercules Incorporated; U.S. Public, pg. 810
DA DEUTSCHE ALLGEMEINE VERSICHERUNGS-AKTIENGELLSCHAFT—Zurich Insurance Company; Int'l, pg. 1531
DAIDO LIFE INSURANCE COMPANY; Int'l, pg. 363
DANUBIO COMPAGNIA DI ASSICURAZIONI E RIASSICURAZIONI GENERALI S.P.A.—Zurich Insurance Company; Int'l, pg. 1531
JOHN DEERE INSURANCE COMPANY—Deere & Company; U.S. Public, pg. 492
DEMPSEY & SIDERS INSURANCE AGENCY—American Financial Group; U.S. Public, pg. 75
A.N. DERINGER, INC.; U.S. Private, pg. 326
DESIGN PROFESSIONAL INSURANCE CO.—Orion Capital Corporation; U.S. Public, pg. 1231
DESJARDINS LAURENTIAN LIFE ASSURANCE—Desjardins-Laurentian Financial Corporation; Int'l, pg. 396
DIGITAL INSURANCE SERVICES—Digital Solutions, Inc.; U.S. Public, pg. 508
DISABILITY CLAIM SERVICES, INC.—Cigna Corp.; U.S. Public, pg. 362
DIVERSA-VERSICHERUNGSKONTOR GMBH—Viag AG; Int'l, pg. 1464
DIVERSIFIED INSURANCE AGENCY, INC.—Cigna Corp.; U.S. Public, pg. 366
DORINCO REINSURANCE CO.—The Dow Chemical Company; U.S. Public, pg. 522
ROBERT F. DRIVER CO., INC.; U.S. Private, pg. 343
DUN & BRADSTREET PENSION SERVICES, INC.—The Dun & Bradstreet Corporation; U.S. Public, pg. 536
DURCO AGENCY, INC.—AEGON N.V.; Int'l, pg. 27
E & D TAYLOR (INSURANCE BROKERS) LIMITED—Taylor Woodrow plc; Int'l, pg. 1358
EBI INDEMNITY COMPANY—Orion Capital Corporation; U.S. Public, pg. 1231
EBP LIFE INSURANCE CO.—First Health Group Corp.; U.S. Public, pg. 635
ELCO INSURANCE COMPANY LTD.—Eli Lilly and Company; U.S. Public, pg. 993
ERJ INSURANCE GROUP—American Heritage Life Investment Corp.; U.S. Public, pg. 79
ESIS INTERNATIONAL ASESORIAS LIMITADA—Cigna Corp.; U.S. Public, pg. 363
ESIS INTERNATIONAL, INC.—Cigna Corp.; U.S. Public, pg. 366
EAGLE GENERAL AGENCY—Credit Suisse Group; Int'l, pg. 346
EAGLE STAR INSURANCE CO.—B.A.T Industries P.L.C.; Int'l, pg. 110
EASTERN INSURANCE COMPANY LTD.—Tenneco Inc.; U.S. Public, pg. 1579
EERSTE SURINAAMS-NEDERLANDSE LEVENSVERZEKERING MAATSCHAPPIJ ENNA NV—AEGON N.V.; Int'l, pg. 28
ELAN INSURANCE SERVICES, INC.—Firstar Corporation; U.S. Public, pg. 643
EMPIRE INDEMNITY INSURANCE COMPANY—Zurich Insurance Company; Int'l, pg. 1530
EMPLOYERS LIFE INS. CO. OF WAUSAU—Nationwide Insurance Enterprise; U.S. Private, pg. 789
EQUIFAX INC.; U.S. Public, pg. 588
EQUIFAX INSURANCE SERVICES INC.—Equifax Inc.; U.S. Public, pg. 588
EQUIPMENT ASSURANCE LTD.—Bucyrus International; U.S. Private, pg. 177
THE EQUITABLE COMPANIES INCORPORATED; U.S. Public, pg. 588
ERIE INDEMNITY COMPANY—Erie Family Life Insurance Company; U.S. Public, pg. 591
ERIE INSURANCE EXCHANGE—Erie Family Life Insurance Company; U.S. Public, pg. 591
ERNEST LINSDELL LIMITED—Cigna Corp.; U.S. Public, pg. 363
EUROC REINSURANCE S.A.—Scancem AB; Int'l, pg. 1199
EXECUTIVE RISK, INC.; U.S. Public, pg. 599
EXXON CORPORATION; U.S. Public, pg. 601
F&G RE, INC.—USF&G Corporation; U.S. Public, pg. 1659
FBS LIFE INSURANCE COMPANY—U.S. Bancorp; U.S. Public, pg. 1681
FHI BENEFIT SYSTEMS, INC.—Robert F. Driver Co., Inc.; U.S. Private, pg. 343
FMC INSURANCE COMPANY LIMITED—FMC Corporation; U.S. Public, pg. 606
FARMERS INSURANCE GROUP—B.A.T Industries P.L.C.; Int'l, pg. 111
FARMERS MUTUAL HAIL INSURANCE CO. OF IOWA; U.S. Private, pg. 395
FASTRAC SYSTEMS, INC.—National Insurance Group; U.S. Public, pg. 1158
FAUGERE & JUTHEAU S.A.—Marsh & McLennan Companies, Inc.; U.S. Public, pg. 1049
FENCOURT REINSURANCE CO. LTD.—The Hartford Financial Services Group Inc.; U.S. Public, pg. 795
FINA INSURANCE S.A.—Petrofina S.A.; Int'l, pg. 1043
FINANCIAL ASSOCIATES; U.S. Private, pg. 404
FINANCIAL EXCHANGE, INC.—American Bankers Insurance Group, Inc.; U.S. Public, pg. 67
FINANCIAL INSURANCE MARKETING GROUP—Equifax Inc.; U.S. Public, pg. 588
FIRE UNDERWRITERS ASSOCIATION—B.A.T Industries P.L.C.; Int'l, pg. 110
FIREMEN'S INSURANCE COMPANY OF WASHINGTON, D.C.—W.R. Berkley Corporation; U.S. Public, pg. 215
FIRST AMERICAN INSURANCE AGENCIES, INC.—Bremer Financial Corporation; U.S. Private, pg. 167
FIRST AMERICAN TRUST CO.—The First American Financial Corporation; U.S. Public, pg. 626
FIRST COMMONWEALTH CORPORATION; U.S. Private, pg. 406
FIRST HEALTH SERVICES—First Health Group Corp.; U.S. Public, pg. 635
FIRST INSURANCE AGENCY, INC.—Washington Federal Savings; U.S. Public, pg. 1740
FIRST INTERNATIONAL REINSURANCE COMPANY—Geneve Corporation; U.S. Private, pg. 446
FIRST NATIONWIDE ASSURANCE CORPORATION—Zurich Insurance Company; Int'l, pg. 1532
FIRST SECURITY INSURANCE, INC.—First Security Corporation; U.S. Public, pg. 638
1ST SOURCE INSURANCE—1st Source Corporation; U.S. Public, pg. 638
FIRST TENNESSEE NATIONAL CORPORATION; U.S. Public, pg. 638
FIRSTATE SERVICES, INC.—FSF Financial Corp.; U.S. Public, pg. 608
FLAGSHIP CITY INSURANCE COMPANY—Erie Family Life Insurance Company; U.S. Public, pg. 591
FORD CREDIT AB—Ford Motor Company; U.S. Public, pg. 666
FORSAKRINGSAKTIEBOLAGET SIRIUS—ABB Asea Brown Boveri (Holding) Ltd.; Int'l, pg. 7
FORTIS; Int'l, pg. 498
FORTIS (U.K.) LIMITED—Fortis; Int'l, pg. 499
FORWARD INSURANCE BROKERS LIMITED—Britax International plc; Int'l, pg. 216

FREMONT INDEMNITY CO./MEDICAL PROFESSIONAL LIAB. DIV.—Fremont General Corporation; *U.S. Public*, pg. 681
FREMONT PREMIUM FINANCE CORP.—Fremont General Corporation; *U.S. Public*, pg. 681
FRONTIER INSURANCE GROUP, INC.; *U.S. Public*, pg. 684
GA INSURANCE SERVICES—H.W. Kaufman Financial Group, Inc.; *U.S. Private*, pg. 609
GB LEX—Groupe Bruxelles Lambert S.A.; *Int'l*, pg. 562
GTA AGENCY, INC.—Green Tree Financial Corporation; *U.S. Public*, pg. 762
GTE REINSURANCE COMPANY LIMITED—GTE Corporation; *U.S. Public*, pg. 697
J. GORDON GAINES INSURANCE SERVICES, INC.—Torchmark Corporation; *U.S. Public*, pg. 1622
J. GORDON GAINES OF TEXAS, INC.—Torchmark Corporation; *U.S. Public*, pg. 1623
GARANTIAS Y CREDITO DE CHILE S.A.—Corporacion MAPFRE, Compania Internacional de Reaseguros, S.A.; *Int'l*, pg. 335
GARDEN STATE LIFE INSURANCE COMPANY—American National Insurance Company; *U.S. Public*, pg. 88
GATES, MCDONALD & CO.—Nationwide Insurance Enterprise; *U.S. Private*, pg. 789
GENELCO, INC.—General American Life Insurance Co.; *U.S. Private*, pg. 443
GENEVA GENERAL INSURANCE COMPANY—Zurich Insurance Company; *Int'l*, pg. 1529
GERBER LIFE INSURANCE CO.—Novartis AG; *Int'l*, pg. 973
GESTORA DE SEGUROS DE MAPFRE DIVERSOS, SOCIEDAD DE AGENCIA, S.A.—Corporacion MAPFRE, Compania Internacional de Reaseguros, S.A.; *Int'l*, pg. 332
GIBBS GULF INSURANCE CONSULTANTS LIMITED—HSBC Holdings plc; *Int'l*, pg. 581
GLOBE INSURANCE AGENCY, INC.—Torchmark Corporation; *U.S. Public*, pg. 1622
GODWINS BOOKE & DICKENSON, INC.—AON Corporation; *U.S. Public*, pg. 118
GODWINS LIMITED—AON Corporation; *U.S. Public*, pg. 119
GOLD KEY INSURANCE AGENCY—The Progressive Corporation; *U.S. Public*, pg. 1334
GOLD MEDAL INSURANCE CO.—General Mills, Inc.; *U.S. Public*, pg. 718
GOLDEN ISLES ASSURANCE CO., LTD.—Magellan Health Services, Inc.; *U.S. Public*, pg. 1036
GOSCHEN HOPPEN - HOME MUTUAL INSURANCE CO.—Old Guard Insurance Group; *U.S. Public*, pg. 1216
GRADMANN & HOLLER & GMBH—Marsh & McLennan Companies, Inc.; *U.S. Public*, pg. 1049
GRAHAM MILLER GROUP LIMITED—Crawford & Company; *U.S. Public*, pg. 458
GRANCOL, ASESORAMIENTO Y SERVICIOS LTDA.—Cigna Corp.; *U.S. Public*, pg. 364
GRANITE STATE INSURANCE CO.—American International Group, Inc.; *U.S. Public*, pg. 84
THE GREAT EASTERN LIFE ASSURANCE COMPANY LIMITED; *Int'l*, pg. 557
GREEN TREE AGENCY, INC.—Green Tree Financial Corporation; *U.S. Public*, pg. 763
GREEN TREE AGENCY OF NEVADA, INC.—Green Tree Financial Corporation; *U.S. Public*, pg. 763
GREENBERG FINANCIAL INSURANCE SERVICES, INC.—The Progressive Corporation; *U.S. Public*, pg. 1334
GROCERS AND MERCHANTS INSURANCE, INC.—Certified Grocers of California; *U.S. Private*, pg. 227
GROVE INSURANCE COMPANY LTD.—Bristol-Myers Squibb Company; *U.S. Public*, pg. 256
HBA INSURANCE LTD.—Chattem, Inc.; *U.S. Public*, pg. 342
HRH INSURANCE SERVICES OF THE COACHELLA VALLEY, INC.—Hilb, Rogal and Hamilton Company; *U.S. Public*, pg. 826
HSB ENGINEERING INSURANCE LIMITED—The Hartford Steam Boiler Inspection & Insurance Co.; *U.S. Public*, pg. 795
HSBC GIBBS BENEFIT CONSULTANTS LIMITED—HSBC Holdings plc; *Int'l*, pg. 579
HSBC GIBBS HARNETT AND RICHARDSON LIMITED—HSBC Holdings plc; *Int'l*, pg. 582
HSBC GIBBS SINGAPORE PTE LTD—HSBC Holdings plc; *Int'l*, pg. 582
HALCYON INSURANCE CO.—The Progressive Corporation; *U.S. Public*, pg. 1335
HALLMAN & LORBER, INC.—Harcourt General, Inc.; *U.S. Public*, pg. 783
HAMILTON MUTUAL INSURANCE COMPANY OF CINCINNATI; *U.S. Private*, pg. 497
HANNA INSURANCE SERVICES DIVISION—M.A. Hanna Company; *U.S. Public*, pg. 781
HANSA INDUSTRIAL INSURANCE N.V.—Trygg-Hansa; *Int'l*, pg. 1425
HARBOR FINANCIAL/NEW AMERICA—FirstCity Financial Corporation; *U.S. Public*, pg. 644
HARCO INSURANCE SERVICES, INC.—Navistar International Corporation; *U.S. Public*, pg. 1167
HARTFORD INSURANCE GROUP OF CANADA—The Hartford Financial Services Group Inc.; *U.S. Public*, pg. 794
HAYHURST ELIAS DUDEK, INC.—Hilb, Rogal and Hamilton Company; *U.S. Public*, pg. 827
HEALTH EDUCATION CENTER INC.—Highmark Inc.; *U.S. Private*, pg. 529
HEALTHCARE SERVICES GROUP, INC.; *U.S. Public*, pg. 803
HELMSMAN MANAGEMENT SERVICES, INC.—Liberty Mutual Insurance Co.; *U.S. Private*, pg. 666
HENRIJEAN & CIE. S.A.—Marsh & McLennan Companies, Inc.; *U.S. Public*, pg. 1049
HIBARI KAIHATSU CO., LTD.—Skylark Co., Ltd.; *Int'l*, pg. 1262
HIGHMARK INC.; *U.S. Private*, pg. 528
HILB, ROGAL AND HAMILTON COMPANY; *U.S. Public*, pg. 826
HILB, ROGAL AND HAMILTON COMPANY OF FORT LAUDERDALE—Hilb, Rogal and Hamilton Company; *U.S. Public*, pg. 827
HILB, ROGAL AND HAMILTON COMPANY OF PORT HURON—Hilb, Rogal and Hamilton Company; *U.S. Public*, pg. 827
JOHN HOLT GROUP LTD.—Lonrho plc; *Int'l*, pg. 817
HORAN GOLDMAN COMPANIES INC.—Jardine Matheson Holdings Limited; *Int'l*, pg. 705
HORNOR, TOWNSEND & KENT—The Penn Mutual Life Insurance Company; *U.S. Private*, pg. 849
HOUSEHOLD FINANCE CORPORATION—Household International, Inc.; *U.S. Public*, pg. 842
HOUSEHOLD FINANCIAL CORPORATION LIMITED—Household International, Inc.; *U.S. Public*, pg. 842
HOUSEHOLD RETAIL SERVICES, INC.—Household International, Inc.; *U.S. Public*, pg. 842
HOUSTON GENERAL INSURANCE CO.—The Tokio Marine & Fire Insurance Company, Ltd.; *Int'l*, pg. 1392
HUDSON REINSURANCE COMPANY LIMITED—Skandia Insurance Company Limited; *Int'l*, pg. 1257
HUMANA INSURANCE COMPANY—Humana Inc.; *U.S. Public*, pg. 848
HYDE INSURANCE AGENCY, INC.—Fleming Companies, Inc.; *U.S. Public*, pg. 653
INA SPECIAL RISK FACILITIES, INC.—Cigna Corp.; *U.S. Public*, pg. 366
INAC CORP.—Cigna Corp.; *U.S. Public*, pg. 366
IGUAZU COMPANIA DE SEGUROS—Zurich Insurance Company; *Int'l*, pg. 1531
ILLINOIS NATIONAL INSURANCE CO.—American International Group, Inc.; *U.S. Public*, pg. 84
THE IMPERIAL LIFE ASSURANCE CO.—Desjardins-Laurentian Financial Corporation; *Int'l*, pg. 396
INDEPENDENCE HOLDING COMPANY—Geneve Corporation; *U.S. Private*, pg. 446
INDI SERVICIOS C. LTDA.—Cigna Corp.; *U.S. Public*, pg. 363
INDIANAPOLIS LIFE INSURANCE CO.; *U.S. Private*, pg. 560
INDUSTRIE-RING SACH-UND VERSICHERUNGS-VERMITTLUNGSGESELLSCHAFT MBH—Saarbergwerke Aktiengesellschaft; *Int'l*, pg. 1166
INGRAM INDUSTRIES INC.; *U.S. Private*, pg. 562
INLAND NATIONAL INS. CO.—American International Group, Inc.; *U.S. Public*, pg. 84
THE INNOVATIVE COMPANY—The Seibels Bruce Group, Inc.; *U.S. Public*, pg. 1454
INSURANCE ADMINISTRATION CENTER., INC.—Poe & Brown, Inc.; *U.S. Public*, pg. 1312
INSURANCE BROKERS & MANAGERS, INC.—United Fire & Casualty Company; *U.S. Public*, pg. 1677
INSURANCE CONFORMATION SERVICES—The Progressive Corporation; *U.S. Public*, pg. 1334
INSURANCE INTERMEDIARIES, INC.—Nationwide Insurance Enterprise; *U.S. Private*, pg. 789
INSURANCE MANAGEMENT ASSOCIATES; *U.S. Private*, pg. 565
INSURATEX, LTD.—Burlington Industries, Inc.; *U.S. Public*, pg. 268
INTER-GLOBAL INSURANCE AGENCY—Torchmark Corporation; *U.S. Public*, pg. 1622
INTERCONTINENTAL CORPORATION—Eureko B.V.; *Int'l*, pg. 464
INTERNATIONAL INSURANCE UNDERWRITERS, INC.—Berkshire Hathaway Inc.; *U.S. Public*, pg. 220
INTERNATIONAL SURPLUS ADJUSTING SERVICES—Cigna Corp.; *U.S. Public*, pg. 366
J&H MARSH & MCLENNAN, INC.—Marsh & McLennan Companies, Inc.; *U.S. Public*, pg. 1049
J&H MARSH & MCLENNAN LTD.—Marsh & McLennan Companies, Inc.; *U.S. Public*, pg. 1049
JC PENNEY COMPANY, INC.; *U.S. Public*, pg. 916
P.T. JARDINE INSURANCE BROKERS INDONESIA—Jardine Matheson Holdings Limited; *Int'l*, pg. 705
JARDINE INSURANCE BROKERS INTERNATIONAL LIMITED—Jardine Matheson Holdings Limited; *Int'l*, pg. 705
JARDINE INSURANCE BROKERS LTD.—Jardine Matheson Holdings Limited; *Int'l*, pg. 705
JARDINE (LLOYD'S UNDERWRITING AGENTS) LTD.—Jardine Matheson Holdings Limited; *Int'l*, pg. 705
JARDINE MATHESON HOLDINGS LIMITED; *Int'l*, pg. 703
JEWEL RECOVERY, LP—Zale Corporation; *U.S. Public*, pg. 1789
JOHN HANCOCK INSURANCE COMPANY OF BERMUDA LTD.—John Hancock Mutual Life Insurance Company; *U.S. Private*, pg. 590
JOHN HANCOCK MUTUAL LIFE INSURANCE COMPANY; *U.S. Private*, pg. 589
JOHN HANCOCK PROPERTY AND CASUALTY HOLDING CO.—John Hancock Mutual Life Insurance Company; *U.S. Private*, pg. 590
AXEL JOHNSON INSURANCE COMPANY LTD.—Axel Johnson AB; *Int'l*, pg. 711
KDJ-VMBH—FAG Group; *Int'l*, pg. 468
KIC, LTD.—Hanson PLC; *Int'l*, pg. 594
KMA INSURANCE AGENCY, INC.—Michigan Physicians Mutual Liability Inc.; *U.S. Private*, pg. 741
H.W. KAUFMAN FINANCIAL GROUP, INC.; *U.S. Private*, pg. 609
KEYSTONE HEALTH PLAN WEST, INC.—Highmark Inc.; *U.S. Private*, pg. 529
KILLEARN PROPERTIES, INC.; *U.S. Public*, pg. 956
J.I. KISLAK INC.; *U.S. Private*, pg. 624
KRAUS-ANDERSON INSURANCE—Kraus-Anderson Incorporated; *U.S. Private*, pg. 635
KRAUSS-MAFFEI VERSICHERUNGSDIENST GMBH—Mannesmann A.G.; *Int'l*, pg. 836
KVAERNER HILNOR A.S.—Kvaerner a.s.a.; *Int'l*, pg. 769
LA GARANTIE GENERALE MAROCAINE (G.G.M.)—Zurich Insurance Company; *Int'l*, pg. 1531
LA VENEZOLANA DE VIDA COMPANIA ANONIMA DE SEGUROS—Cigna Corp.; *U.S. Public*, pg. 363
LABOUCHERE N.V.—AEGON N.V.; *Int'l*, pg. 26
LACLEDE GAS FAMILY SERVICES, INC.—Laclede Gas Company; *U.S. Public*, pg. 974
LAKESIDE INSURANCE AGENCY, INC.—The Progressive Corporation; *U.S. Public*, pg. 1334
THE RICHARD LEAHY CORPORATION—Lincoln National Corporation; *U.S. Public*, pg. 997
LIBERTY MORTGAGE CO.—Banc One Corporation; *U.S. Public*, pg. 174
LINCOLN FINANCIAL GROUP, INC.—Lincoln National Corporation; *U.S. Public*, pg. 997
LLOYD 1885—Allianz Aktiengesellschaft; *Int'l*, pg. 61
LLOYDS BANK INSURANCE SERVICES LTD.—Lloyds TSB Group PLC; *Int'l*, pg. 813
LONDON LIFE INSURANCE GROUP—EdperBrascan Corporation; *Int'l*, pg. 435
LOSS MANAGEMENT SERVICES, INC.—Avemco Corporation; *U.S. Public*, pg. 152
LUTHERAN BROTHERHOOD; *U.S. Private*, pg. 681
LYKES INSURANCE INC.—Lykes Brothers Inc.; *U.S. Private*, pg. 682
M & C BROKERAGE SERVICES, INC.—Cigna Corp.; *U.S. Public*, pg. 366
MBC AGENCY, INC.—Mercantile Bankshares Corporation; *U.S. Public*, pg. 1089
MBL LIFE ASSURANCE CORPORATION; *U.S. Private*, pg. 685
MSI INSURANCE COMPANIES; *U.S. Private*, pg. 688
FRANK R. MACNEILL & SON, INC.—Jardine Matheson Holdings Limited; *Int'l*, pg. 705
MALAYAN INSURANCE COMPANY, INC.—Zurich Insurance Company; *Int'l*, pg. 1532
MALAYAN OVERSEAS INSURANCE CORPORATION—Zurich Insurance Company; *Int'l*, pg. 1532
MALAYAN ZURICH INSURANCE COMPANY, INC.—Zurich Insurance Company; *Int'l*, pg. 1532
MAPFRE ACONCAGUA CIA. DE SEGUROS, S.A.—Corporacion MAPFRE, Compania Internacional de Reaseguros, S.A.; *Int'l*, pg. 333
MAPFRE ASISTENCIA CIA. INTERNACIONAL DE SEGUROS Y REASEGUROS, S.A.—Corporacion MAPFRE, Compania Internacional de Reaseguros, S.A.; *Int'l*, pg. 334
MAPFRE BALEAR, CIA. DE SEGUROS GENERALES Y DE REASEGUROS—Corporacion MAPFRE, Compania Internacional de Reaseguros, S.A.; *Int'l*, pg. 333
MAPFRE CAUCION Y CREDITO CIA INTERNACIONAL DE SEGUROS Y REASEGUROS, S.A.—Corporacion MAPFRE, Compania Internacional de Reaseguros, S.A.; *Int'l*, pg. 335
MAPFRE GUANARTEME CIA. DE SEGUROS GENERALES Y REASEGUROS DE CANARIAS, S.A.—Corporacion MAPFRE, Compania Internacional de Reaseguros, S.A.; *Int'l*, pg. 333
MAPFRE INDUSTRIAL, S.A. DE SEGUROS—Corporacion MAPFRE, Compania Internacional de Reaseguros, S.A.; *Int'l*, pg. 333
MAPFRE INSURANCE COMPANY OF AMERICA, INC.—Corporacion MAPFRE, Compania Internacional de Reaseguros, S.A.; *Int'l*, pg. 333
MAPFRE SEGUROS GENERALES CIA. DE SEGUROS Y REASEGUROS, S.A.—Corporacion MAPFRE, Compania Internacional de Reaseguros, S.A.; *Int'l*, pg. 332
MAPFRE VIDA PENSIONES ENTIDAD GESTORA DE FONDOS DE PENSIONES S.A.—Corporacion MAPFRE, Compania Internacional de Reaseguros, S.A.; *Int'l*, pg. 334
MAPFRE VIDA, S.A. DE SEGUROS Y REASEGUROS SOBRE LA VIDA HUMANA—Corporacion MAPFRE, Compania Internacional de Reaseguros, S.A.; *Int'l*, pg. 334
MARKEL CORPORATION; *U.S. Public*, pg. 1046
MARQUETTE NATIONAL LIFE INSURANCE CO.—Southwestern Financial Corporation; *U.S. Private*, pg. 1018
MARSH & MCLENNAN COMPANIES, INC.; *U.S. Public*, pg. 1048
MARYLAND INSURANCE COMPANY—Zurich Insurance Company; *Int'l*, pg. 1530
MATTERHORN BANK PROGRAMS, INC.—Avemco Corporation; *U.S. Public*, pg. 152
MEAD REASSURANCE S.A.—The Mead Corporation; *U.S. Public*, pg. 1076
MEDIBARNA, S.L.—Caixa d'Estalvis de Catalunya; *Int'l*, pg. 250
MEIKA KOSAN CO., LTD.—Meiji Seika Kaisha, Ltd.; *Int'l*, pg. 855
METROPOLITAN LIFE INSURANCE CO.; *U.S. Private*, pg. 737
METROPOLITAN LIFE INSURANCE COMPANY OF CANADA—Metropolitan Life Insurance Co.; *U.S. Private*, pg. 738
METROPOLITAN LIFE INSURANCE COMPANY OF HONG KONG, LTD.—Metropolitan Life Insurance Co.; *U.S. Private*, pg. 738
METROPOLITAN LIFE SEGUROS DE VIDA, S.A.—Metropolitan Life Insurance Co.; *U.S. Private*, pg. 738
MID-AMERICA INSURANCE AGENCY, INC.—Banc One Corporation; *U.S. Public*, pg. 175
MIDDLESEX INSURANCE—Sentry Insurance, A Mutual Company; *U.S. Private*, pg. 985
MIDLAND WALWYN CAPITAL INC.—Midland Walwyn Inc.; *Int'l*, pg. 865
MIDLAND WALWYN INC.; *Int'l*, pg. 865
MINERVA ASSICURAZIONI S.P.A.—Zurich Insurance Company; *Int'l*, pg. 1531
MINET, INC.—AON Corporation; *U.S. Public*, pg. 118
MONTGOMERY & COLLINS, INC.—Cigna Corp.; *U.S. Public*, pg. 366

MONY LIFE INSURANCE CO. OF AMERICA—The Mutual Life Insurance Company of New York; *U.S. Private*, pg. 769
MORGAN KEEGAN INSURANCE AGENCY OF LOUISIANA, INC.—Morgan Keegan, Inc.; *U.S. Public*, pg. 1131
MUNICH AMERICAN REINSURANCE CO. (MARC)—Munchener Ruckversicherungs-Gesellschaft; *Int'l*, pg. 897
MUNICH AMERICAN REINSURANCE CO. (MARC LIFE)—Munchener Ruckversicherungs-Gesellschaft; *Int'l*, pg. 897
THE MUTUAL LIFE INSURANCE COMPANY OF NEW YORK; *U.S. Private*, pg. 769
MUTUAL SERVICE CORPORATION—Pacific Life Insurance Company; *U.S. Private*, pg. 831
NVG LEVENSVERZEKERINGMAATSCHAPPIJ NV—AEGON N.V.; *Int'l*, pg. 26
NVG SCHADEVERZEKERINGMAATSCHAPPIJ NV—AEGON N.V.; *Int'l*, pg. 26
NVG UITAARTVERZEKERINGMAATSCHAPPIJ NV—AEGON N.V.; *Int'l*, pg. 26
NANTO CORPORATION—The Nanto Bank, Ltd.; *Int'l*, pg. 905
NATIONAL CONTINENTAL INSURANCE CO.—The Progressive Corporation; *U.S. Public*, pg. 1335
NATIONAL GROUP MARKETING CORP.—Conseco Inc.; *U.S. Public*, pg. 433
NATIONAL STANDARD INSURANCE COMPANY—Zurich Insurance Company; *Int'l*, pg. 1530
NATIONAL WESTMINSTER INSURANCE SERVICES LIMITED—National Westminster Bank PLC; *Int'l*, pg. 910
NATIONSBANK INSURANCE AGENCY, INC.—NationsBank Corporation; *U.S. Public*, pg. 1163
NATIONWIDE COMMERCIAL CO.—Amerco; *U.S. Private*, pg. 49
NAVILLUS INSURANCE LTD.—Borden, Inc.; *U.S. Private*, pg. 159
NEDERLANDSE VERZEKERINGS GROEP NV—AEGON N.V.; *Int'l*, pg. 26
NEFFSVILLE MUTUAL FIRE INSURANCE CO.—Old Guard Insurance Group; *U.S. Public*, pg. 1216
THE NEW ENGLAND—Metropolitan Life Insurance Co.; *U.S. Private*, pg. 737
NEW ENGLAND INVESTMENT ASSOCIATES—Metropolitan Life Insurance Co.; *U.S. Private*, pg. 737
NEW YORK LIFE INSURANCE COMPANY; *U.S. Private*, pg. 794
NEWBURY INSURANCE CO.—Metropolitan Life Insurance Co.; *U.S. Private*, pg. 738
NICHOLSON LESLIE INTERNATIONAL LIMITED—AON Corporation; *U.S. Public*, pg. 119
NOBEL INSURANCE AGENCY—Nobel Insurance Limited; *Int'l*, pg. 951
NOBEL INSURANCE GROUP—Nobel Insurance Limited; *Int'l*, pg. 951
NOBEL INSURANCE LIMITED; *Int'l*, pg. 951
NORTHERN INSURANCE COMPANY OF NEW YORK—Zurich Insurance Company; *Int'l*, pg. 1530
NORTHWEST PACIFIC INDEMNITY CO.—The Chubb Corporation; *U.S. Public*, pg. 355
NORTON INSURANCE LIMITED—Saint-Gobain; *Int'l*, pg. 1175
NORWEST INSURANCE, INC.—Norwest Corporation; *U.S. Public*, pg. 1202
NUTMEG INSURANCE LIMITED—Olin Corporation; *U.S. Public*, pg. 1219
O.O.M. ONDERLINGE MOLESTVERZEKERING-MAATSCHAPPIJ U.A.—AEGON N.V.; *Int'l*, pg. 26
O.O.M. ONDERLINGE VERZEKERING-MAATSCHAPPIJ U.A—AEGON N.V.; *Int'l*, pg. 26
O.O.M. ONDERLINGE ZIEKTEKOSTENVERZEKERING-MAATSCHAPPIJ U.A.—AEGON N.V.; *Int'l*, pg. 26
OBAYASHI CORPORATION; *Int'l*, pg. 995
ODYSSEY REINSURANCE CORPORATION—Skandia Insurance Company Limited; *Int'l*, pg. 1258
OLD GUARD INSURANCE GROUP; *U.S. Public*, pg. 1216
OLD REPUBLIC INTERNATIONAL CORPORATION; *U.S. Public*, pg. 1218
ONE INVESTMENT AGENCY, INC.—The Somerset Group, Inc.; *U.S. Public*, pg. 1484
OWNERS INSURANCE CO.—Auto-Owners Insurance; *U.S. Private*, pg. 100
OXFORD HEALTH PLANS INC.; *U.S. Public*, pg. 1238
OXFORD LIFE INSURANCE CO.—Amerco; *U.S. Private*, pg. 49
PC INVESTMENT COMPANY—The Progressive Corporation; *U.S. Public*, pg. 1335
PCS HEALTH SYSTEMS, INC.—Eli Lilly and Company; *U.S. Public*, pg. 993
P.S.R. INVESTMENTS, INC.—New Century Energies, Inc.; *U.S. Public*, pg. 1170
PACIFIC INTERNATIONAL BROKERS, LTD.—Willis Corroon Group PLC; *Int'l*, pg. 1504
PAN AMERICAN INSURANCE COMPANY—Corporacion MAPFRE, Compania Internacional de Reaseguros, S.A.; *Int'l*, pg. 333
PAN KOREA INSURANCE CO.—LG Group; *Int'l*, pg. 779
PATRIA VERSICHERUNG AKTIENGESELLSCHAFT—Zurich Insurance Company; *Int'l*, pg. 1531
PATRIOT GENERAL INSURANCE CO.—Sentry Insurance, A Mutual Company; *U.S. Private*, pg. 985
PENN CMO CORPORATION—The Penn Mutual Life Insurance Company; *U.S. Private*, pg. 850
PERMANENT GENERAL COMPANIES—Ingram Industries Inc.; *U.S. Private*, pg. 563
PHILADELPHIA AMERICAN LIFE INSURANCE COMPANY—I.C.H. Corporation; *U.S. Public*, pg. 853
PINACO—PNC Bank Corp.; *U.S. Public*, pg. 1244
PINNACLE DATA CORPORATION—National Insurance Group; *U.S. Public*, pg. 1158
PIPER INDEMNITY LTD.—Occidental Petroleum Corporation; *U.S. Public*, pg. 1210
PLEYADE PENINSULAR CORREDURIA DE SEGUROS, S.A.—Telefonica de Espana, S.A.; *Int'l*, pg. 1371
PLYMOUTH INSURANCE COMPANY LTD.—Magellan Health Services, Inc.; *U.S. Public*, pg. 1036
POE & BROWN, INC.; *U.S. Public*, pg. 1312
PONDEROSA HOLDINGS INC.—Amerco; *U.S. Private*, pg. 49
PREFERRED RISK INSURANCE COMPANY—Corporacion MAPFRE, Compania Internacional de Reaseguros, S.A.; *Int'l*, pg. 333
PREUSSAG VERSICHERRUNGSDIENST GMBH—Preussag AG; *Int'l*, pg. 1070
PRIESTLY INSURANCE CO. LTD.—The BOC Group plc; *Int'l*, pg. 122
PRINCIPAL MARKETING SERVICES, INC.—The Principal Financial Group; *U.S. Private*, pg. 886
THE PROGRESSIVE CORPORATION; *U.S. Public*, pg. 1334
PROGRESSIVE CORP., AGENCY GROUP—The Progressive Corporation; *U.S. Public*, pg. 1334
PROGRESSIVE FARMER INSURANCE SERVICE, INC.—Time Warner Inc.; *U.S. Public*, pg. 1613
PROGRESSIVE INSURANCE AGENCY, INC.—The Progressive Corporation; *U.S. Public*, pg. 1335
PROPERTY-OWNERS INSURANCE CO.—Auto-Owners Insurance; *U.S. Private*, pg. 101
PROVIDENT COMPANIES, INC.; *U.S. Public*, pg. 1337
PROVIDENT NATIONAL ASSURANCE CO.—Provident Companies, Inc.; *U.S. Public*, pg. 1338
PROVIDENTIA; *Int'l*, pg. 1072
PRUDENTIAL DEFINED CONTRIBUTION SERVICES—The Prudential Insurance Company of America; *U.S. Private*, pg. 892
PRUDENTIAL GENERAL INSURANCE CO.—The Prudential Insurance Company of America; *U.S. Private*, pg. 892
THE PRUDENTIAL INSURANCE COMPANY OF AMERICA; *U.S. Private*, pg. 892
PT METLIFE SEJAHTERA—Metropolitan Life Insurance Co.; *U.S. Private*, pg. 738
PUBLIC EMPLOYEES BENEFIT SERVICES CORP.—Nationwide Insurance Enterprise; *U.S. Private*, pg. 789
PUERTO RICAN AMERICAN INSURANCE COMPANY—Corporacion MAPFRE, Compania Internacional de Reaseguros, S.A.; *Int'l*, pg. 333
PUERTO RICAN INSURANCE AGENCY INC.—Corporacion MAPFRE, Compania Internacional de Reaseguros, S.A.; *Int'l*, pg. 333
PUTNAM REINSURANCE CO.—American International Group, Inc.; *U.S. Public*, pg. 84
RAILROAD INSURANCE BROKERS, INC.—Cigna Corp.; *U.S. Public*, pg. 366
RATHBONE, KING & SEELEY INSURANCE SERVICES—H.W. Kaufman Financial Group, Inc.; *U.S. Private*, pg. 610
RATHBONE, KING & SEELEY INSURANCE SERVICES, INC.—H.W. Kaufman Financial Group, Inc.; *U.S. Private*, pg. 610
RECOVERY SERVICES INTERNATIONAL, INC.—Cigna Corp.; *U.S. Public*, pg. 366
REED STENHOUSE COMPANIES LTD.—AON Corporation; *U.S. Public*, pg. 118
REGENCE BLUECROSS BLUESHIELD OF OREGON; *U.S. Private*, pg. 917
RELIANCE REINSURANCE CORP.—Reliance Group Holdings, Inc.; *U.S. Public*, pg. 1374
REPUBLIC DIVERSIFIED SERVICES, INC.—Credit Suisse Group; *Int'l*, pg. 346
REPUBLIC GROUP NO. TWO—Credit Suisse Group; *Int'l*, pg. 346
REPUBLIC INSURANCE CO.—Credit Suisse Group; *Int'l*, pg. 346
REPUBLIC-VANGUARD REINSURANCE CO.—Credit Suisse Group; *Int'l*, pg. 346
REPUBLIC WESTERN INSURANCE CO.—Amerco; *U.S. Private*, pg. 49
RIDGEWAY INSURANCE CO. LTD.—Kimberly-Clark Corporation; *U.S. Public*, pg. 960
RISK PLANNERS, INC.—SuperValu, Inc.; *U.S. Public*, pg. 1541
RISK SCIENCE INTERNATIONAL INC.—AON Corporation; *U.S. Public*, pg. 117
RIUNIONE ADRIATICA DI SICURTA—Allianz Aktiengesellschaft; *Int'l*, pg. 61
ROLLINS BURDICK HUNTER CO. (BERMUDA) LTD.—AON Corporation; *U.S. Public*, pg. 119
ROLLINS BURDICK HUNTER INTL. INC.—AON Corporation; *U.S. Public*, pg. 119
ROYAL & SUN ALLIANCE INSURANCE GROUP—Royal & Sun Alliance Insurance Group plc; *Int'l*, pg. 1130
ROYAL & SUN ALLIANCE INSURANCE GROUP PLC; *Int'l*, pg. 1130
ROYAL FINANCIAL SERVICES INC.—Royal & Sun Alliance Insurance Group plc; *Int'l*, pg. 1130
ROYAL INSURANCE SERVICE CO. (GUERNSEY) LTD.—Royal & Sun Alliance Insurance Group plc; *Int'l*, pg. 1130
ROYAL INSURANCE SERVICE CO. (ISLE OF MAN) LTD.—Royal & Sun Alliance Insurance Group plc; *Int'l*, pg. 1130
ROYAL INSURANCE (UK) LTD.—Royal & Sun Alliance Insurance Group plc; *Int'l*, pg. 1130
ROYALE BELGE S.A.—Groupe Bruxelles Lambert S.A.; *Int'l*, pg. 562
ROYALE UAP IARD—Groupe Bruxelles Lambert S.A.; *Int'l*, pg. 562
ROYALE UAP VIE—Groupe Bruxelles Lambert S.A.; *Int'l*, pg. 562
SCEM REINSURANCE S.A.—Skanska AB; *Int'l*, pg. 1261
SCOR; *Int'l*, pg. 1152
SS SERVICE CORPORATION—Washington Mutual Inc.; *U.S. Public*, pg. 1742
ST. PAUL SERVICE, INC.—St. Paul Bancorp, Inc.; *U.S. Public*, pg. 1428
SAN FRANCISCO REINSURANCE CO.—Allianz Aktiengesellschaft; *Int'l*, pg. 59
SAUDI NATIONAL INSURANCE COMPANY EC (SNIC)—Zurich Insurance Company; *Int'l*, pg. 1532
VICTOR O. SCHINNERER & CO., LTD.—Marsh & McLennan Companies, Inc.; *U.S. Public*, pg. 1049
SEABURY & SMITH, INC.—Marsh & McLennan Companies, Inc.; *U.S. Public*, pg. 1049
SECURITY INSURANCE CO. (U.K.) LTD.—Orion Capital Corporation; *U.S. Public*, pg. 1231
SECURITY NATIONAL LIFE INSURANCE CO.—Corporacion MAPFRE, Compania Internacional de Reaseguros, S.A.; *Int'l*, pg. 334
SECURITY REINSURANCE CO.—Orion Capital Corporation; *U.S. Public*, pg. 1231
SEDGWICK CHARTERED LIMITED—Standard Chartered Bank PLC; *Int'l*, pg. 1297
SEDGWICK CHARTERED PRIVATE LIMITED—Standard Chartered Bank PLC; *Int'l*, pg. 1297
SEDGWICK GROUP PLC; *Int'l*, pg. 1217
SEDGWICK, INC.—Sedgwick Group plc; *Int'l*, pg. 1218
SEDGWICK INSURANCE BROKERS (PTY) LIMITED—Standard Chartered Bank PLC; *Int'l*, pg. 1297
SEDGWICK JAMES INSURANCE BROKERS (PRIVATE) LIMITED—Standard Chartered Bank PLC; *Int'l*, pg. 1297
SEDGWICK LIMITED—Sedgwick Group plc; *Int'l*, pg. 1218
SEGURADORA ROMA, S.A.—Corporacion MAPFRE, Compania Internacional de Reaseguros, S.A.; *Int'l*, pg. 334
SEGUROS GENESIS, S.A.—Metropolitan Life Insurance Co.; *U.S. Private*, pg. 738
SEGUROS TEPEYAC, S.A.—Corporacion MAPFRE, Compania Internacional de Reaseguros, S.A.; *Int'l*, pg. 334
SEIBELS, BRUCE & CO.—The Seibels Bruce Group, Inc.; *U.S. Public*, pg. 1454
THE SEIBELS BRUCE GROUP, INC.; *U.S. Public*, pg. 1453
SELF-INSURERS SERVICE, INC.—AON Corporation; *U.S. Public*, pg. 117
SELIGMAN & ASSOCIATES, INC.; *U.S. Private*, pg. 982
SERVICE GENERAL—H.W. Kaufman Financial Group, Inc.; *U.S. Private*, pg. 609
SHEFFIELD INSURANCE CORPORATION—Torchmark Corporation; *U.S. Public*, pg. 1623
SHERWOOD INSURANCE SERVICES, INC.—AON Corporation; *U.S. Public*, pg. 118
SICURTA 1879 ASSICURANZIONI S.P.A.—Zurich Insurance Company; *Int'l*, pg. 1531
SIERRA HEALTH SERVICES, INC.; *U.S. Public*, pg. 1469
SIERRA HEALTHCARE OPTIONS, INC.—Sierra Health Services, Inc.; *U.S. Public*, pg. 1469
SIGNET STAR REINSURANCE COMPANY—W.R. Berkley Corporation; *U.S. Public*, pg. 216
KARL SINGER COMPANIES, INC.—AON Corporation; *U.S. Public*, pg. 118
SKANDIA AMERICA REINSURANCE CORP., SAN FRANCISCO BRANCH OFFICE—Skandia Insurance Company Limited; *Int'l*, pg. 1257
SKANDIA INTERNATIONAL INSURANCE CORPORATION—Skandia Insurance Company Limited; *Int'l*, pg. 1256
SKANDIA S.A.—Skandia Insurance Company Limited; *Int'l*, pg. 1256
SKANDIA UK INSURANCE PLC—Skandia Insurance Company Limited; *Int'l*, pg. 1258
SOCIETA ITALIANA ASSICURAZIONI E REASSICURAZIONI S.P.A.—Zurich Insurance Company; *Int'l*, pg. 1531
SOUTHERN UNDERWRITERS, INC.—Skandia Insurance Company Limited; *Int'l*, pg. 1257
SOUTHWESTERN FINANCIAL CORPORATION; *U.S. Private*, pg. 1018
SOUTHWESTERN FINANCIAL SERVICES CORP.—Southwestern Financial Corporation; *U.S. Private*, pg. 1018
SOUTHWESTERN LIFE INSURANCE COMPANY—Southwestern Financial Corporation; *U.S. Private*, pg. 1018
D.R. SPARKS INSURANCE SERVICES, INC.—Millers Mutual Insurance Assn.; *U.S. Private*, pg. 748
SPECIALTY INSURANCE UNDERWRITERS, INC.—Avemco Corporation; *U.S. Public*, pg. 152
SPECIALTY UNDERWRITERS REINSURANCE FACILITY—Michigan Physicians Mutual Liability Inc.; *U.S. Private*, pg. 741
STEADFAST INSURANCE COMPANY—Zurich Insurance Company; *Int'l*, pg. 1530
STENHOUSE (S.E. ASIA) PTE. LTD.—AON Corporation; *U.S. Public*, pg. 118
SUMARE PROCESSAMENTO E SERVICOS S.A.—Cigna Corp.; *U.S. Public*, pg. 363
SUMBANK LIFE INSURANCE CO.—Synovus Financial Corp.; *U.S. Public*, pg. 1549
SUMMIT BANCORP; *U.S. Public*, pg. 1527
SUNAMERICA INC.; *U.S. Public*, pg. 1532
SUNTRUST—SunTrust Banks, Inc.; *U.S. Public*, pg. 1537
SUNTRUST BANKS, INC.; *U.S. Public*, pg. 1537
SUPERMARKET INSURANCE AGENCY, INC.—Associated Wholesale Grocers, Inc.; *U.S. Private*, pg. 93
SUPPLEMENTAL INSURANCE DIVISION, INC.—AEGON N.V.; *Int'l*, pg. 27
SURASSUR, S.A.—Corporacion MAPFRE, Compania Internacional de Reaseguros, S.A.; *Int'l*, pg. 333
SWISS REINSURANCE COMPANY; *Int'l*, pg. 1332
TIG INSURANCE CO.—TIG Holdings, Inc.; *U.S. Public*, pg. 1556
TAMPA RETAIL DIVISION—Poe & Brown, Inc.; *U.S. Public*, pg. 1312
TATE & LYLE REINSURANCE LTD.—Tate & Lyle PLC; *Int'l*, pg. 1357
TEMPLE-INLAND INC.; *U.S. Public*, pg. 1574
TEMPLE-INLAND MORTGAGE CORPORATION—Temple-Inland Inc.; *U.S. Public*, pg. 1575
TETHERCREST—Inchcape PLC; *Int'l*, pg. 671

TEXAS PACIFIC INDEMNITY CO.—The Chubb Corporation; *U.S. Public*, pg. 355
TEXTRON INC.; *U.S. Public*, pg. 1588
TILLINGHAST-TOWERS PENN—Towers Perrin; *U.S. Private*, pg. 1093
TOBACCO INSURANCE CO. LTD.—B.A.T Industries P.L.C.; *Int'l*, pg. 110
TOHEI CO., LTD.—Matsuya Company Ltd.; *Int'l*, pg. 848
THE TOKIO MARINE MANAGEMENT (AUSTRALIA) PTY. LTD.—The Tokio Marine & Fire Insurance Company, Ltd.; *Int'l*, pg. 1393
JAMES P. TONER COMPANY, INC.—Cigna Corp.; *U.S. Public*, pg. 358
TOPA INSURANCE COMPANY—Topa Equities Ltd. Inc.; *U.S. Private*, pg. 1091
TORCHMARK CORPORATION; *U.S. Public*, pg. 1622
TOSHIBA INSURANCE SERVICE CORPORATION—Toshiba Corporation; *Int'l*, pg. 1404
TOWERS PERRIN REINSURANCE—Towers Perrin; *U.S. Private*, pg. 1093
TRANS ASIAN INSURANCE SERVICES, INC.—Cigna Corp.; *U.S. Public*, pg. 366
TRANS-GENERAL LIFE & CASUALTY GROUP, INC.—Highmark Inc.; *U.S. Private*, pg. 529
TRANSAMERICA CORPORATION; *U.S. Public*, pg. 1629
TRANSATLANTIC HOLDINGS INC.—American International Group, Inc.; *U.S. Public*, pg. 84
TRANSCON INSURANCE LTD.—Ford Motor Company; *U.S. Public*, pg. 667
TRANSPORTATION RECOVERIES INC.—The Progressive Corporation; *U.S. Public*, pg. 1335
TRENWICK AMERICA REINSURANCE CORPORATION—Trenwick Group Inc.; *U.S. Public*, pg. 1634
TRENWICK GROUP INC.; *U.S. Public*, pg. 1634
TRI-STATE INSURANCE COMPANY OF MINNESOTA—W.R. Berkley Corporation; *U.S. Public*, pg. 215
TRIVEST INSURANCE NETWORK LTD.—EdperBrascan Corporation; *Int'l*, pg. 435
TRUCK UNDERWRITERS ASSOCIATION—B.A.T Industries P.L.C.; *Int'l*, pg. 110
TRYGG-HANSA; *Int'l*, pg. 1425
TUREGUM INSURANCE COMPANY—Zurich Insurance Company; *Int'l*, pg. 1530
UAB—Groupe Bruxelles Lambert S.A.; *Int'l*, pg. 562
UAP-NIEUWROTTERDAM LEVEN—Groupe Bruxelles Lambert S.A.; *Int'l*, pg. 562
UAP-NIEUWROTTERDAM SCHADE—Groupe Bruxelles Lambert S.A.; *Int'l*, pg. 562
UNAT RE, S.A.—American International Group, Inc.; *U.S. Public*, pg. 85
UNAT, S.A.—American International Group, Inc.; *U.S. Public*, pg. 85
ULSTER BANK INSURANCE SERVICES LIMITED—National Westminster Bank PLC; *Int'l*, pg. 911
UNION INSURANCE COMPANY—W.R. Berkley Corporation; *U.S. Public*, pg. 216
UNIRISC, INC.—AON Corporation; *U.S. Public*, pg. 117
UNITED CAPITOL INSURANCE COMPANY—Capsure Holdings Corp.; *U.S. Public*, pg. 303
UNITED FINANCIAL CASUALTY CO.—The Progressive Corporation; *U.S. Public*, pg. 1335
UNITED MISSOURI INSURANCE CO.—UMB Financial Corporation; *U.S. Public*, pg. 1655
U.S. BANK INSURANCE AGENCY—U.S. Bancorp; *U.S. Public*, pg. 1681
USLIFE CORPORATION—American General Corporation; *U.S. Public*, pg. 77
USLIFE FINANCIAL INSTITUTION MARKETING GROUP, INC.—American General Corporation; *U.S. Public*, pg. 77
UNITED STATES PROTECTION AND INDEMNITY AGENCY, INC.—Loews Corporation; *U.S. Public*, pg. 1011
U.S. SPECIALTY INSURANCE CO.—Avemco Corporation; *U.S. Public*, pg. 152
U.S. TRAILS; *U.S. Public*, pg. 1688
UNIVERSAL GUARANTEE LIFE INSURANCE—First Commonwealth Corporation; *U.S. Private*, pg. 406
UNIVERSAL INSURANCE CO.—The Seibels Bruce Group, Inc.; *U.S. Public*, pg. 1454
VALIANT INSURANCE COMPANY—Zurich Insurance Company; *Int'l*, pg. 1530
VALMONT FINANCIAL CORPORATION—Chancellor Corporation; *U.S. Public*, pg. 335
THE VARIABLE ANNUITY LIFE INSURANCE CO.—American General Corporation; *U.S. Public*, pg. 76
THE VARIABLE ANNUITY MARKETING CO.—American General Corporation; *U.S. Public*, pg. 76
VASA BROUGHER, INC.—Eureko B.V.; *Int'l*, pg. 464
VASA LIFE INSURANCE CO.—Eureko B.V.; *Int'l*, pg. 464
VASA NORTH ATLANTIC INSURANCE COMPANY—Eureko B.V.; *Int'l*, pg. 464
VENDOPOLIS—Vendex International N.V.; *Int'l*, pg. 1463
VERA CRUZ S.A. DE PREVIDENCIA PRIVADA—Corporacion MAPFRE, Compania Internacional de Reaseguros, S.A.; *Int'l*, pg. 334
VERA CRUZ SEGURADORA, S.A.—Corporacion MAPFRE, Compania Internacional de Reaseguros, S.A.; *Int'l*, pg. 334
VERILY ENTERPRISES, INC.—Harcourt General, Inc.; *U.S. Public*, pg. 783
VESSELFOREWARD LTD.—Inchcape PLC; *Int'l*, pg. 671
VIRGINIA SURETY CO., INC.—AON Corporation; *U.S. Public*, pg. 118
VISTA INSURANCE COMPANY—Ford Motor Company; *U.S. Public*, pg. 664
VOLKSFURSORGE HOLDING AG—AMB Aachener und Muenchener Beteiligungs-AG; *Int'l*, pg. 15
VOLVO GROUP INSURANCE FORSAKRINGS AB—AB Volvo; *Int'l*, pg. 1476
W & R INSURANCE AGENCY, INC. OF ALABAMA, INC.—Torchmark Corporation; *U.S. Public*, pg. 1623
WADDELL AND REED, INC.—Torchmark Corporation; *U.S. Public*, pg. 1623
WAUSAU GENERAL INSURANCE COMPANY—Nationwide Insurance Enterprise; *U.S. Private*, pg. 789
WAUSAU UNDERWRITERS INSURANCE CO.—Nationwide Insurance Enterprise; *U.S. Private*, pg. 789
WELLPOINT HEALTH NETWORKS, INC.—Blue Cross of California; *U.S. Private*, pg. 152
WESCO-FINANCIAL INSURANCE COMPANY—Berkshire Hathaway Inc.; *U.S. Public*, pg. 217
FLOYD WEST & COMPANY—H.W. Kaufman Financial Group, Inc.; *U.S. Private*, pg. 609
WEST JAPAN RAILWAY COMPANY; *Int'l*, pg. 1490
WESTCORP; *U.S. Public*, pg. 1756
WESTDEUTSCHES ASSEKURANZ-KONTOR GMBH—Fried. Krupp AG; *Int'l*, pg. 512
WESTERN PENNSYLVANIA CARING FOUNDATION, INC.—Highmark Inc.; *U.S. Private*, pg. 529
WESTERN REINSURANCE BROKERS, INC.; *U.S. Private*, pg. 1168
WESTERN RESERVE ADMINISTRATIVE SERVICES, INC.—Central Reserve Life Corporation; *U.S. Public*, pg. 326
WESTPLAN INSURANCE AGENCY, INC.—Westcorp; *U.S. Public*, pg. 1757
THE WHITESTONE CORPORATION—AEGON N.V.; *Int'l*, pg. 27
WIENER ALLIANZ VERSICHERUNGS-AG—Allianz Aktiengesellschaft; *Int'l*, pg. 62
WILLIS CORROON ADMINISTRATIVE SERVICES, INC.—Willis Corroon Group PLC; *Int'l*, pg. 1504
WILLIS CORROON CORP.—Willis Corroon Group PLC; *Int'l*, pg. 1504
WILLIS CORROON CORP. OF TEXAS—Willis Corroon Group PLC; *Int'l*, pg. 1507
WILLIS CORROON GROUP PLC; *Int'l*, pg. 1501
WILLIS FABER & DUMAS LIMITED—Willis Corroon Group PLC; *Int'l*, pg. 1503
RALPH C. WILSON ENTERPRISES; *U.S. Private*, pg. 1181
WISCONSIN INSURANCE MANAGEMENT, INC.—Associated Banc-Corp; *U.S. Public*, pg. 141
GARY WOOD ASSOCIATES, INC.—Harcourt General, Inc.; *U.S. Public*, pg. 783
F.E. WRIGHT GROUP—Lonrho plc; *Int'l*, pg. 818
YAMAICHI ECHO & CO., LTD.—Yamaichi Securities Co., Ltd.; *Int'l*, pg. 1516
THE YASUDA FIRE & MARINE INSURANCE COMPANY LIMITED; *Int'l*, pg. 1519
ZETA FINANZA S.P.A.—Zurich Insurance Company; *Int'l*, pg. 1531
ZIONS BANCORPORATION; *U.S. Public*, pg. 1792
ZIONS INSURANCE AGENCY, INC.—Zions Bancorporation; *U.S. Public*, pg. 1793
ZURICH AMERICAN INSURANCE COMPANY OF ILLINOIS—Zurich Insurance Company; *Int'l*, pg. 1530
ZURICH AMERICAN LLOYDS—Zurich Insurance Company; *Int'l*, pg. 1530
ZURICH-ANGLO SEGURADORA S.A.—Zurich Insurance Company; *Int'l*, pg. 1532
ZURICH AUSTRALIAN INSURANCE LIMITED—Zurich Insurance Company; *Int'l*, pg. 1531
ZURICH BIZTOSITO RT.—Zurich Insurance Company; *Int'l*, pg. 1532
ZURICH COMPAGNIE D'ASSURANCES—Zurich Insurance Company; *Int'l*, pg. 1530
ZURICH COMPANIA DE SEGUROS—Zurich Insurance Company; *Int'l*, pg. 1531
ZURICH EPARGNE—Zurich Insurance Company; *Int'l*, pg. 1531
ZURICH FORSAKRING—Zurich Insurance Company; *Int'l*, pg. 1531
ZURICH IGUAZU COMPANIA DE SEGUROS DE RETIRO S.A.—Zurich Insurance Company; *Int'l*, pg. 1532
ZURICH INDEMNITY COMPANY OF CANADA—Zurich Insurance Company; *Int'l*, pg. 1531
ZURICH INSURANCE COMPANY—Zurich Insurance Company; *Int'l*, pg. 1531
ZURICH INSURANCE COMPANY (ASIA) LIMITED—Zurich Insurance Company; *Int'l*, pg. 1532
ZURICH INSURANCE (GUAM), INC.—Zurich Insurance Company; *Int'l*, pg. 1532
P.T. ZURICH INSURANCE INDONESIA—Zurich Insurance Company; *Int'l*, pg. 1532
ZURICH INSURANCE (MALAYSIA) SDN. BHD.—Zurich Insurance Company; *Int'l*, pg. 1532
ZURICH INSURANCE SERVICES (MIDDLE EAST) E.C.—Zurich Insurance Company; *Int'l*, pg. 1532
ZURICH INSURANCE (SINGAPORE) PTE. LTD.—Zurich Insurance Company; *Int'l*, pg. 1532
ZURICH INTERNATIONAL DE VENEZUELA C.A. DE CORRETAJE DE REASEGUROS—Zurich Insurance Company; *Int'l*, pg. 1532
ZURICH KAUTIONS-UND KREDITVERSICHERUNGS AKTIENGESELLSCHAFT—Zurich Insurance Company; *Int'l*, pg. 1532
ZURICH KOSMOS VERSICHERUNGEN AG—Zurich Insurance Company; *Int'l*, pg. 1532
ZURICH LIFE ASSURANCE COMPANY LIMITED—Zurich Insurance Company; *Int'l*, pg. 1532
ZURICH PENSION FUND CONSULTANTS & INVESTMENTS MNGMT. LTD.—Zurich Insurance Company; *Int'l*, pg. 1530
ZURICH RE (UK) LIMITED—Zurich Insurance Company; *Int'l*, pg. 1532
ZURICH RECHTSSCHUTZVERISCHERUNGS-AKTIENGESELLSCHAFT—Zurich Insurance Company; *Int'l*, pg. 1532
ZURICH REINSURANCE CENTRE—Zurich Insurance Company; *Int'l*, pg. 1530
ZURICH UBEZPIECZENIE SERVICE SP. Z O.O.—Zurich Insurance Company; *Int'l*, pg. 1532
ZURICH VERSICHERUNGS-GESELLSCHAFT—Zurich Insurance Company; *Int'l*, pg. 1531
ZURICH VERZEKERINGEN—Zurich Insurance Company; *Int'l*, pg. 1531
ZURIGO COMPAGNIA DI ASSICURAZIONI—Zurich Insurance Company; *Int'l*, pg. 1531

6512 — OPERATORS OF NONRESIDENTIAL BUILDINGS

A & B DEVELOPMENT CO. (CALIFORNIA)—Alexander & Baldwin, Inc.; *U.S. Public*, pg. 39
A & B-HAWAII, INC.—Alexander & Baldwin, Inc.; *U.S. Public*, pg. 39
A & B PROPERTIES, INC.—Alexander & Baldwin, Inc.; *U.S. Public*, pg. 39
AM MANAGEMENT CORP.—The Rouse Company; *U.S. Public*, pg. 1409
AU MANAGEMENT CORP.—The Rouse Company; *U.S. Public*, pg. 1409
ADWIN REALTY CO.—PECO Energy Company; *U.S. Public*, pg. 1268
AETNA REALTY INVESTORS, INC.—Aetna Inc.; *U.S. Public*, pg. 26
AFFILIATED BANKS BUILDING CO.—Banc One Corporation; *U.S. Public*, pg. 173
AKER BRYGGE DRIFT A/S—Aker Raj Asa; *Int'l*, pg. 41
ALEXANDER & BALDWIN, INC.; *U.S. Public*, pg. 39
ALMEDA MALL, INC.—The Rouse Company; *U.S. Public*, pg. 1409
ALPHA AIRPORTS GROUP PLC—Alpha Airports Group Plc; *Int'l*, pg. 65
AMERCO REAL ESTATE COMPANY—Amerco; *U.S. Private*, pg. 49
THE AMERICAN CITY CORP.—The Rouse Company; *U.S. Public*, pg. 1407
AMERICAN TRADING AND PRODUCTION CORPORATION; *U.S. Private*, pg. 63
AMOCO DEVELOPMENT COMPANY—Amoco Corporation; *U.S. Public*, pg. 103
AMPROP FINANCE COMPANY—Amoco Corporation; *U.S. Public*, pg. 103
THE ARNDALE PROPERTY TRUST LTD.—The Peninsular and Oriental Steam Navigation Company; *Int'l*, pg. 1034
ARTUS, INC.—Forest City Enterprises, Inc.; *U.S. Public*, pg. 668
ATLANTIC SHOPPING CENTRES LIMITED—Empire Company Limited; *Int'l*, pg. 454
ATLANTIC SOUTHERN PROPERTIES, INC.—Conectiv; *U.S. Public*, pg. 430
AUGUSTA MALL, INC.—The Rouse Company; *U.S. Public*, pg. 1408
BMW INGENIEUR ZENTRUM GMBH & CO.—Bayerische Motoren Werke Aktiengesellschaft; *Int'l*, pg. 177
BT PROPERTY LTD.—British Telecommunications plc; *Int'l*, pg. 222
BALLSTON DEVELOPMENT CORPORATION—Forest City Enterprises, Inc.; *U.S. Public*, pg. 668
BANC ONE BUILDING MANAGEMENT CORPORATION—Banc One Corporation; *U.S. Public*, pg. 173
BANC ONE REALTY COLUMBUS CORP.—Banc One Corporation; *U.S. Public*, pg. 175
BANK ONE, COLORADO—Banc One Corporation; *U.S. Public*, pg. 173
BARCLAYS PROPERTY HOLDINGS—Barclays Bank PLC; *Int'l*, pg. 165
RAULF BAU GMBH—Hollandsche Beton Groep NV; *Int'l*, pg. 630
BAYERISCHE IMMOBILIEN-LEASING GMBH—Bayerische Vereinsbank Group; *Int'l*, pg. 179
BEACHWOOD PLACE, INC.—The Rouse Company; *U.S. Public*, pg. 1408
BEAR VALLEY, INC.—Forest City Enterprises, Inc.; *U.S. Public*, pg. 668
BENEFICIAL CORPORATION; *U.S. Public*, pg. 211
BIG A AUTO PARTS—APS Holding Corporation; *U.S. Public*, pg. 10
BIG Y FOODS INC.; *U.S. Private*, pg. 143
BINSWANGER MANAGEMENT CORP.—Binswanger; *U.S. Private*, pg. 144
BOEING REALTY CORPORATION—The Boeing Company; *U.S. Public*, pg. 241
BOSTON WHARF COMPANY—The Peninsular and Oriental Steam Navigation Company; *Int'l*, pg. 1035
BRADLEY SPECIALTY RETAILING—W.C. Bradley Co.; *U.S. Private*, pg. 164
BRASCAN BRAZIL—EdperBrascan Corporation; *Int'l*, pg. 435
BROOKFIELD HOMES—Brookfield Properties Corporation; *Int'l*, pg. 228
BROOKFIELD HOMES LTD.—Brookfield Properties Corporation; *Int'l*, pg. 228
BROOKFIELD HOMES PARTNERS—Brookfield Properties Corporation; *Int'l*, pg. 228
BROOKFIELD HOMES-WESTERN REGION—Brookfield Properties Corporation; *Int'l*, pg. 228
BRUNCOR, INC.; *Int'l*, pg. 230
BRUNSWICK SQUARE LTD.—Bruncor, Inc.; *Int'l*, pg. 230
BUILDERS INC.—Garvey Industries, Inc.; *U.S Private*, pg. 440
BUNDY PROPERTIES—Roll International Corporation; *U.S. Private*, pg. 941
CBL & ASSOCIATES PROPERTIES, INC.; *U.S. Public*, pg. 273
CCL LTD.—The Peninsular and Oriental Steam Navigation Company; *Int'l*, pg. 1034
C.I. PROPERTY & INVESTMENTS LIMITED—Christies International plc; *Int'l*, pg. 290
CNG REALTY CO.—CTG Resources, Inc.; *U.S. Public*, pg. 285
C.V. REALTY, INC.—Central Vermont Public Service Corporation; *U.S. Public*, pg. 328
CALIFORNIA MEC, INC.—Mitsubishi Estate Co., Ltd.; *Int'l*, pg. 873
CAMBRIDGE SHOPPING CENTRES LIMITED; *Int'l*, pg. 253

S.I.C. Index

CAMBRIDGE WESTERN LEASEHOLDS LIMITED—Cambridge Shopping Centres Limited; *Int'l*, pg. 253
CARAVAN BROKAY—Caravan Products Company, Inc.; *U.S. Private*, pg. 208
CARDINAL REDEVELOPMENT CORPORATION—Ford Motor Company; *U.S. Public*, pg. 663
CAROTHERS ROAD, INC.—Forest City Enterprises, Inc.; *U.S. Public*, pg. 668
CARREFOUR; *Int'l*, pg. 272
CATELLUS DEVELOPMENT CORPORATION; *U.S. Public*, pg. 314
CAVENHAM FOREST INDUSTRIES INC.—Hanson PLC; *Int'l*, pg. 593
THE CEDARWOOD CONSTRUCTION COMPANY; *U.S. Private*, pg. 221
CHAGRIN BEACHWOOD INC.—Forest City Enterprises, Inc.; *U.S. Public*, pg. 668
CHALLENGE PROPERTIES LIMITED—Fletcher Challenge Limited; *Int'l*, pg. 495
CHARAN INDUSTRIES, INC.; *U.S. Private*, pg. 229
CHARLOTTETOWN, INC.—The Rouse Company; *U.S. Public*, pg. 1407
CHARLOTTETOWN NORTH, INC.—The Rouse Company; *U.S. Public*, pg. 1407
CHARTWELL LAND PLC.—Kingfisher plc; *Int'l*, pg. 733
CHERRY HILL CENTER, INC.—The Rouse Company; *U.S. Public*, pg. 1408
CHESTERFIELD INDUSTRIAL PARK, INC.—Watlow Electric Manufacturing Company; *U.S. Private*, pg. 1153
CHRISTIANA COMPANIES, INC.; *U.S. Public*, pg. 352
CHRYSLER REALTY CORP.—Chrysler Corporation; *U.S. Public*, pg. 354
CIGNA CONFERENCE FACILITIES, INC.—Cigna Corp.; *U.S. Public*, pg. 358
CIVIC CENTER CORPORATION—Anheuser-Busch Companies, Inc.; *U.S. Public*, pg. 114
CLUB MED BOUTIQUE—Club Mediterranee SA; *Int'l*, pg. 298
COLFAX, INC.; *U.S. Private*, pg. 252
THE COLONIAL BANCGROUP BUILDING CORPORATION—The Colonial BancGroup, Inc.; *U.S. Public*, pg. 400
COLONIE VENTURES, INC.—Galesi Group; *U.S. Private*, pg. 438
COLUMBIA EXECUTIVE ASSOCIATES—Galesi Group; *U.S. Private*, pg. 438
COLUMBIA MALL, INC.—The Rouse Company; *U.S. Public*, *pg. 1407*
COMMONWEALTH ENERGY SYSTEM; *U.S. Public*, pg. 414
CONCOURSE DEVELOPMENT, INC.—Forest City Enterprises, Inc.; *U.S. Public*, pg. 668
CONSOLIDATED-TOMOKA LAND CO.; *U.S. Public*, pg. 437
CONSTELLATION REAL ESTATE GROUP INC.—Baltimore Gas and Electric Company; *U.S. Public*, pg. 172
COOP SWITZERLAND; *Int'l*, pg. 329
COREQ, INC.—The Chase Manhattan Corporation; *U.S. Public*, pg. 338
CORPOREX COMPANIES, INC.; *U.S. Private*, pg. 276
COSCAN WASHINGTON, INC.—Brookfield Properties Corporation; *Int'l*, pg. 228
COSCAN WATERWAYS, INC.—Brookfield Properties Corporation; *Int'l*, pg. 228
CRETE CARRIER CORP.; *U.S. Private*, pg. 289
CROWN AMERICAN REALTY TRUST; *U.S. Public*, pg. 461
CROWN POWER & REDEVELOPMENT CORP.—Hallmark Cards, Inc.; *U.S. Private*, pg. 496
CULBRO LAND RESOURCES, INC.—General Cigar Holdings Inc; *U.S. Public*, pg. 708
CUSHMAN & WAKEFIELD—Mitsubishi Estate Co., Ltd.; *Int'l*, pg. 873
CUSHMAN & WAKEFIELD, ATLANTA OFFICE—Mitsubishi Estate Co., Ltd.; *Int'l*, pg. 873
CUSHMAN & WAKEFIELD, INC.—Mitsubishi Estate Co., Ltd.; *Int'l*, pg. 873
DKM PROPERTIES CORPORATION—The Dyson-Kissner-Moran Corporation; *U.S. Private*, pg. 351
DST REALTY, INC.—Kansas City Southern Industries, Inc.; *U.S. Public*, pg. 943
DAHLEM COMPANY, INC.; *U.S. Private*, pg. 306
DAIN RAUSCHER CORPORATION; *U.S. Public*, pg. 476
THE DANIS COMPANIES; *U.S. Private*, pg. 310
DARIGOLD, INC.; *U.S. Private*, pg. 311
DEAD RIVER PROPERTIES—Dead River Company; *U.S. Private*, pg. 318
THE EDWARD J. DEBARTOLO CORPORATION; *U.S. Private*, pg. 319
DELMARVA SERVICES CO.—Conectiv; *U.S. Public*, pg. 431
DENVER TECHNOLOGICAL CENTER—The Peninsular and Oriental Steam Navigation Company; *Int'l*, pg. 1035
DIAMOND LEASE CO., LTD.; *Int'l*, pg. 413
DOMIBAIL—Credit Nationale; *Int'l*, pg. 344
DOMINION STORES, INC.—Tultex Corporation; *U.S. Public*, *pg. 1644*
EASTFIELD MALL, INC.—The Rouse Company; *U.S. Public*, pg. 1408
ECHELON MALL, INC.—The Rouse Company; *U.S. Public*, pg. 1408
ECHELON URBAN CENTER, INC.—The Rouse Company; *U.S. Public*, pg. 1408
EL PUERTO DE LIVERPOOL S.A.; *Int'l*, pg. 435
ENERGY REALTY, INC.—Indiana Energy, Inc.; *U.S. Public*, pg. 875
ERIKSBERGS FORVALTNINGS AB—Celsius AB; *Int'l*, pg. 277
EXTON SQUARE, INC.—The Rouse Company; *U.S. Public*, *pg. 1407*
F.C. LAUREL, INC.—Forest City Enterprises, Inc.; *U.S. Public*, pg. 668
F.C. PARKLABREA TOWERS, INC.—Forest City Enterprises, Inc.; *U.S. Public*, pg. 668
F.C. SOUTHRIDGE CORP.—Forest City Enterprises, Inc.; *U.S. Public*, pg. 668
F.C. TEANECK, INC.—Forest City Enterprises, Inc.; *U.S. Public*, pg. 668
FHB PROPERTIES, INC.—First Hawaiian, Inc.; *U.S. Public*, pg. 635
FAIRMONT MORTGAGE, INC.—Del Webb Corporation; *U.S. Public*, pg. 495
FANEUIL HALL MARKETPLACE, INC.—The Rouse Company; *U.S. Public*, pg. 1408
FARMERS INVESTMENT COMPANY, INC.—Bale Of Kentucky, Inc.; *U.S. Private*, pg. 112
5601 MEDICAL PLAZA—Genesis Health Ventures, Inc.; *U.S. Public*, pg. 729
THE FIRST REPUBLIC BUILDING CORP.—The First Republic Corporation of America; *U.S. Public*, pg. 637
THE FIRST REPUBLIC CORPORATION OF AMERICA; *U.S. Public*, pg. 637
FIRST UNION MANAGEMENT, INC.—First Union Real Estate Investments; *U.S. Public*, pg. 641
FISHER PROPERTIES, INC.—Giant Eagle, Inc.; *U.S. Private*, pg. 451
THE FLATLEY COMPANY; *U.S. Private*, pg. 410
FLORIDA PROGRESS CORPORATION; *U.S. Public*, pg. 655
FOLEY HOLDING COMPANY, INC.; *U.S. Private*, pg. 416
FOREST BAY, INC.—Forest City Enterprises, Inc.; *U.S. Public*, pg. 668
FOREST CITY BURBANK, INC.—Forest City Enterprises, Inc.; *U.S. Public*, pg. 668
FOREST CITY RENTAL PROPERTIES CORPORATION—Forest City Enterprises, Inc.; *U.S. Public*, pg. 668
FOREST CITY SAN VICENTE CORP.—Forest City Enterprises, Inc.; *U.S. Public*, pg. 669
1480 WELTON, INC.—New Century Energies, Inc.; *U.S. Public*, pg. 1170
FRANKLIN PARK MALL, INC.—The Rouse Company; *U.S. Public*, pg. 1408
FREDERICTON BUSINESS PARK LTD.—Bruncor, Inc.; *Int'l*, pg. 230
FRIENDLY CHEVROLET CO. INC.; *U.S. Private*, pg. 428
GF INDUSTRIES, INC.; *U.S. Private*, pg. 434
GABLE HOUSE ESTATES LTD.—Ladbroke Group Plc; *Int'l*, *pg. 787*
GALESI ENTERPRISES—Galesi Group; *U.S. Private*, pg. 437
GENERAL CIGAR HOLDINGS INC; *U.S. Public*, pg. 707
GETTY PETROLEUM MARKETING INC.; *U.S. Public*, pg. 740
GETTY TERMINALS, INC.—Getty Petroleum Marketing Inc.; *U.S. Public*, pg. 741
GOSNELL BUILDERS—Pointe Group Ltd.; *U.S. Private*, pg. 873
GOVERNOR'S SQUARE, INC.—The Rouse Company; *U.S. Public*, pg. 1408
GREENGATE MALL, INC.—The Rouse Company; *U.S. Public*, pg. 1407
CURTIS C. GUNN, INC.; *U.S. Private*, pg. 488
HAWA GRUNDSTUECKS GMBH U. CO. OHG HOTELVERWALTUNG—Bayerische Vereinsbank Group; *Int'l*, pg. 179
HARBORPLACE—The Rouse Company; *U.S. Public*, pg. 1407
HARRIS BUILDING SERVICES CORPORATION—Bank of Montreal; *Int'l*, pg. 154
HARTZ GROUP—The Hartz Mountain Corp.; *U.S. Private*, pg. 508
HARTZ MOUNTAIN INDUSTRIES—The Hartz Mountain Corp.; *U.S. Private*, pg. 508
HARUNDALE MALL—The Rouse Company; *U.S. Public*, pg. 1407
BILL HEARD ENTERPRISES, INC.; *U.S. Private*, pg. 515
THE HEARST CORPORATION; *U.S. Private*, pg. 515
HELMERICH & PAYNE PROPERTIES, INC.—Helmerich & Payne, Inc.; *U.S. Public*, pg. 808
HILCO, INC.—Bank of Ireland; *Int'l*, pg. 153
HOLDER CORPORATION; *U.S. Private*, pg. 533
HORIZON ENTERPRISES GROUP LLC; *U.S. Private*, pg. 539
HORIZON INVESTMENT GROUP—Horizon Enterprises Group LLC; *U.S. Private*, pg. 539
HOSPITAL INVESTORS, INC.—Magellan Health Services, Inc.; *U.S. Public*, pg. 1036
HOWER CORP.—Forest City Enterprises, Inc.; *U.S. Public*, pg. 669
HUDSON PRECAST PROPERTIES, INC.—Forest City Enterprises, Inc.; *U.S. Public*, pg. 669
IPCF PROPERTIES INC.—George Weston Limited; *Int'l*, pg. 1495
IKEA NORTH AMERICA, INC.—Ikea Holdings AB; *Int'l*, pg. 660
IMMOBILIARIA CONEK S.A.—Caterpillar Inc.; *U.S. Public*, pg. 316
IMMOBILIERE DE BEAUFAYS—GIB Group; *Int'l*, pg. 533
IN TOWN PARKING, INC.—Forest City Enterprises, Inc.; *U.S. Public*, pg. 669
IN TOWN SHOPPING CENTER, INC.—Forest City Enterprises, Inc.; *U.S. Public*, pg. 669
INDIGO DEVELOPMENT INC.—Consolidated-Tomoka Land Co.; *U.S. Public*, pg. 437
INDIGO GROUP LTD.—Consolidated-Tomoka Land Co.; *U.S. Public*, pg. 437
INGLES MARKETS, INCORPORATED; *U.S. Public*, pg. 878
JC PENNEY COMPANY, INC.; *U.S. Public*, pg. 916
JCP REALTY, INC.—JC Penney Company, Inc.; *U.S. Public*, *pg. 917*
JACOBSON STORES REALTY COMPANY—Jacobson Stores Inc.; *U.S. Public*, pg. 922
JONES PROPERTIES, INC.—Jones International, Ltd.; *U.S. Private*, pg. 597
KEMMONS WILSON, INC.; *U.S. Private*, pg. 613
KOGER EQUITY INC.; *U.S. Public*, pg. 965
LB INDUSTRIES INC.; *U.S. Private*, pg. 639
LADBROKE GROUP PROPERTIES LTD.—Ladbroke Group Plc; *Int'l*, pg. 787
LEEMILTS PETROLEUM, INC.—Getty Petroleum Marketing Inc.; *U.S. Public*, pg. 741
LEND LEASE CORPORATION LIMITED; *Int'l*, pg. 806
LIBERTY REAL ESTATE CO.—Banc One Corporation; *U.S. Public*, pg. 175
LIMITED REAL ESTATE—The Limited, Inc.; *U.S. Public*, pg. 995
LINCOLN PROPERTY COMPANY; *U.S. Private*, pg. 668
LINCOLN PROPERTY CO., NORTHERN CALIFORNIA—Lincoln Property Company; *U.S. Private*, pg. 668
LLOYDS BANK COMMERCIAL PROPERTIES LTD.—Lloyds TSB Group PLC; *Int'l*, pg. 813
LOEWS THEATRE MANAGEMENT CORP.—Sony Corporation; *Int'l*, pg. 1282
LONDON & LEEDS (USA) CORPORATION—Ladbroke Group Plc; *Int'l*, pg. 788
LONDON CITY & INTERNATIONAL LIMITED—Lonrho plc; *Int'l*, pg. 817
LOUISVILLE SHOPPING CENTER, INC.—The Rouse Company; *U.S. Public*, pg. 1407
MEC UK LIMITED—Mitsubishi Estate Co., Ltd.; *Int'l*, pg. 873
MRCO—ULLICO Inc.; *U.S. Private*, pg. 1116
MALL ST. MATTHEWS CORPORATION—The Rouse Company; *U.S. Public*, pg. 1408
K/S MARKEDET HAUGESUND—Aker Raj Asa; *Int'l*, pg. 41
MARKETING CORP. OF AMERICA; *U.S. Private*, pg. 704
THE MAY DEPARTMENT STORES COMPANY; *U.S. Public*, pg. 1063
MCKENZIE TANK LINES, INC.; *U.S. Private*, pg. 723
MEAD REALTY CORP.—Consolidated Papers, Inc.; *U.S. Public*, pg. 436
MENARDS, INC.; *U.S. Private*, pg. 731
METROPOLITAN LIFE INSURANCE CO.; *U.S. Private*, pg. 737
THE MIAMI MARGARINE CO.; *U.S. Private*, pg. 740
MID-AMERICA FINANCIAL CORP.—Commerce Bancshares, Inc.; *U.S. Public*, pg. 410
MISSION WEST PROPERTIES; *U.S. Public*, pg. 1117
MITCHELL ENERGY & DEVELOPMENT CORP.; *U.S. Public*, pg. 1117
MITSUBISHI ESTATE CO., LTD.; *Int'l*, pg. 873
MITSUBISHI ESTATE NEW YORK, INC.—Mitsubishi Estate Co., Ltd.; *Int'l*, pg. 873
MONDAWMIN CORPORATION—The Rouse Company; *U.S. Public*, pg. 1407
MONTANA SUN, INC.—Energy West Inc.; *U.S. Public*, pg. 581
MOVIE STAR FACTORY OUTLET STORES—Movie Star, Inc.; *U.S. Public*, pg. 1141
NZ PROPERTIES, INC.—New Mexico & Arizona Land Co.; *U.S. Public*, pg. 1172
NATIONAL LUMBER CO.; *U.S. Private*, pg. 785
NATIONSBANK PLAZA CHARLOTTE, INC.—NationsBank Corporation; *U.S. Public*, pg. 1165
NATIONSBANK PROPERTIES, INC.—NationsBank Corporation; *U.S. Public*, pg. 1165
K/S NEDRE ELVEHAVN TRONDHEIM—Aker Raj Asa; *Int'l*, *pg. 41*
NEW BUSINESS—The Rouse Company; *U.S. Public*, pg. 1407
NEW VALLEY REALTY CORP.—New Valley Corporation; *U.S. Public*, pg. 1173
NORTH STAR MALL, INC.—The Rouse Company; *U.S. Public*, pg. 1409
NORTHWEST MALL, INC.—The Rouse Company; *U.S. Public*, pg. 1409
NORWEST PROPERTIES, INC.—Norwest Corporation; *U.S. Public*, pg. 1202
O&Y PROPERTIES CORPORATION; *Int'l*, pg. 993
OCCOQUAN LAND CORPORATION—American Water Works Company, Inc.; *U.S. Public*, pg. 95
121 S.W. SALMON ST. CORP.—Enron Corp.; *U.S. Public*, pg. 585
ONEOK INC.; *U.S. Public*, pg. 1226
ONEOK LEASING CO.—ONEOK Inc.; *U.S. Public*, pg. 1226
ONLY DEALS, INC.—Universal International, Inc.; *U.S. Public*, pg. 1697
O'REILLY AUTOMOTIVE INC.; *U.S. Public*, pg. 1230
ORO GRANDE, INC.—Forest City Enterprises, Inc.; *U.S. Public*, pg. 669
OUTLET SQUARE OF ATLANTA, INC.—The Rouse Company; *U.S. Public*, pg. 1408
P&O PROPERTIES INTERNATIONAL—The Peninsular and Oriental Steam Navigation Company; *Int'l*, pg. 1034
P&O SHOPPING CENTRES LTD.—The Peninsular and Oriental Steam Navigation Company; *Int'l*, pg. 1034
PNC REALTY CO., OHIO—PNC Bank Corp.; *U.S. Public*, pg. 1243
PNC REALTY HOLDING CORPORATION—PNC Bank Corp.; *U.S. Public*, pg. 1244
PACWEST CENTER—Mitsubishi Estate Co., Ltd.; *Int'l*, pg. 873
PALACE THEATER LONDON LIMITED—Really Useful Holdings Limited; *Int'l*, pg. 1089
PARAMUS PARK, INC.—The Rouse Company; *U.S. Public*, *pg. 1408*
PECO ENERGY COMPANY; *U.S. Public*, pg. 1268
PENGUIN HUIS B.V.—Jotun A/S; *Int'l*, pg. 715
THE PEP BOYS-MANNY, MOE & JACK; *U.S. Public*, pg. 1276
THE PEP BOYS-MANNY, MOE & JACK OF CALIFORNIA—The Pep Boys-Manny, Moe & Jack; *U.S. Public*, pg. 1276
PERIMETER CENTER, INC.—The Rouse Company; *U.S. Public*, pg. 1408
PERIMETER MALL, INC.—The Rouse Company; *U.S. Public*, pg. 1408
PERIMETER MALL MANAGEMENT CORP.—The Rouse Company; *U.S. Public*, pg. 1408
P.T. PETRO CORP.—Getty Petroleum Marketing Inc.; *U.S. Public*, pg. 741

PLAIN STREET PROPERTIES, INC.—Hannaford Bros. Co.; *U.S. Public*, pg. 782
PLAYHOUSE SQUARE INVESTMENTS, INC.—Forest City Enterprises, Inc.; *U.S. Public*, pg. 669
PLYMOUTH MEETING MALL, INC.—The Rouse Company; *U.S. Public*, pg. 1407
POST OFFICE BUILDING CO.—Forest City Enterprises, Inc.; *U.S. Public*, pg. 669
PROPERTY DEVELOPMENT ASSOCIATES—Safeway Inc.; *U.S. Public*, pg. 1426
PROREMA AN-UND VERMIETUNGSGESELLSCHAFT MBH—Dyckerhoff & Widmann AG; *Int'l*, pg. 423
THE PRUDENTIAL REALTY GROUP—The Prudential Insurance Company of America; *U.S. Private*, pg. 892
QUEENS PROPERTIES—Philipp Holzmann AG; *Int'l*, pg. 633
QUEMETCO REALTY, INC.—Quexco Incorporated; *U.S. Private*, pg. 900
RALEIGH ENTERPRISES, INC.; *U.S. Private*, pg. 907
RECKSON ASSOCIATES REALTY CORP.; *U.S. Public*, pg. 1368
REICO, INC.; *U.S. Private*, pg. 919
RICE-CARDEN CORP.—Kansas City Southern Industries, Inc.; *U.S. Public*, pg. 944
RIDGEDALE CENTER—The Rouse Company; *U.S. Public*, pg. 1407
RIVERWALK—The Rouse Company; *U.S. Public*, pg. 1408
ROCKEFELLER GROUP, INC.—Mitsubishi Estate Co., Ltd.; *Int'l*, pg. 873
THE ROOST, INC.—The Rouse Company; *U.S. Public*, pg. 1409
ROUSE CENTRAL PARK SHOPPING CENTER, INC.—The Rouse Company; *U.S. Public*, pg. 1409
ROUSE COMMERCE, INC.—The Rouse Company; *U.S. Public*, pg. 1407
THE ROUSE COMPANY; *U.S. Public*, pg. 1407
THE ROUSE COMPANY OF CALIFORNIA, INC.—The Rouse Company; *U.S. Public*, pg. 1407
ROUSE-MILWAUKEE, INC.—The Rouse Company; *U.S. Public*, pg. 1409
ROUSE OPERATING PROPERTIES DIV.—The Rouse Company; *U.S. Public*, pg. 1407
ROUSE RETAIL LEASING DIV.—The Rouse Company; *U.S. Public*, pg. 1407
ROUSE SERVICE (CANADA) LIMITED—The Rouse Company; *U.S. Public*, pg. 1409
ROUSE SI SHOPPING MANAGEMENT, INC.—The Rouse Company; *U.S. Public*, pg. 1408
ROYAL LEPAGE LIMITED; *Int'l*, pg. 1143
RYAN CONSTRUCTION COMPANY OF MINNESOTA, INC.; *U.S. Private*, pg. 953
S&S ENERGY PRODUCTS—General Electric Company; *U.S. Public*, pg. 711
S-E-BANKEN FASTIGHETER AB—Skandinaviska Enskilda Banken; *Int'l*, pg. 1259
SABA FASTIGHETS AB—Carnegie Holding AB; *Int'l*, pg. 272
SAFEGUARD SCIENTIFICS, INC.; *U.S. Public*, pg. 1424
SALEM MALL, INC.—The Rouse Company; *U.S. Public*, pg. 1408
SALVATORPLATZ-GRUNDSTUECKSGESELLSCHAFT MBH—Bayerische Vereinsbank Group; *Int'l*, pg. 180
SANTA MONICA PLACE—The Rouse Company; *U.S. Public*, pg. 1408
SAUL CENTERS INC.; *U.S. Public*, pg. 1435
SCHWEGMANN GIANT SUPER MARKETS—Kohlberg & Company, LLC; *U.S. Private*, pg. 629
SCOTTS HOLDINGS LIMITED; *Int'l*, pg. 1212
SEALASKA CORPORATION; *U.S. Private*, pg. 978
SEAWAY SHOPPING CENTERS, INC.—Charan Industries, Inc.; *U.S. Private*, pg. 229
SETON COMPANY; *U.S. Private*, pg. 987
SHAPELL INDUSTRIES, INC.; *U.S. Private*, pg. 990
SHOPPING CENTRE GROUP—Cambridge Shopping Centres Limited; *Int'l*, pg. 253
SHORENSTEIN COMPANY; *U.S. Private*, pg. 996
SIEMENS AG; *Int'l*, pg. 1244
SIME DARBY HONG KONG LIMITED—Sime Darby Berhad; *Int'l*, pg. 1251
THE SINCERE COMPANY (P.M.) LTD.—The Sincere Co. Ltd.; *Int'l*, pg. 1252
SISTEMA ARGOS S.A.; *Int'l*, pg. 1256
SOBEY LEASED PROPERTIES LIMITED—Empire Company Limited; *Int'l*, pg. 454
SOCIETE CIVILE IMMOBILIERE—Castorama Dubois Investissements S.C.A.; *Int'l*, pg. 275
SONAT INC.; *U.S. Public*, pg. 1484
SOUTH BAY GALLERIA, INC.—Forest City Enterprises, Inc.; *U.S. Public*, pg. 669
SOUTH DEKALB—The Rouse Company; *U.S. Public*, pg. 1408
SOUTHEAST PROPERTIES HOLDING CORPORATION, INC.—Kogor Equity Inc.; *U.S. Public*, pg. 965
SOUTHERN LIFE PROPERTY HOLDINGS LIMITED—Anglo American Corporation of South Africa Limited; *Int'l*, pg. 77
SPARTAN OIL CORP.; *U.S. Private*, pg. 1021
STEWART & STEVENSON REALTY CORPORATION—Stewart & Stevenson Services, Inc.; *U.S. Public*, pg. 1518
KYLE STEWART LTD.—Hollandsche Beton Groep NV; *Int'l*, pg. 630
OY STOCKMANN AB; *Int'l*, pg. 1301
SUMMIT BANCORP; *U.S. Public*, pg. 1527
SUNRISE RESTAURANT INC.—Brierley Investments Limited; *Int'l*, pg. 216
SUZUKI REAL ESTATE CO., LTD.—Suzuki Motor Corporation; *Int'l*, pg. 1323
SVERDRUP CORPORATION; *U.S. Private*, pg. 1057
TCF FINANCIAL CORP.; *U.S. Public*, pg. 1554
TDW BUILDING CORPORATION—T.D. Williamson, Inc.; *U.S. Private*, pg. 1180
TAYLOR WOODROW PROPERTY COMPANY LTD.—Taylor Woodrow plc; *Int'l*, pg. 1359
TERMINAL MANAGEMENT, INC.—Forest City Enterprises, Inc.; *U.S. Public*, pg. 669
TOKYU CORPORATION; *Int'l*, pg. 1394
TOPS APPLIANCE CITY; *U.S. Public*, pg. 1622
TOWER CITY DEVELOPMENT, INC.—Forest City Enterprises, Inc.; *U.S. Public*, pg. 669
TOWER CITY LAND CORPORATION—Forest City Enterprises, Inc.; *U.S. Public*, pg. 669
TOWER CITY PROPERTIES—Forest City Enterprises, Inc.; *U.S. Public*, pg. 668
TOWER HOTELS, INC.—Forest City Enterprises, Inc.; *U.S. Public*, pg. 669
TOWN PUMP, INC.; *U.S. Private*, pg. 1093
TRAFALGAR HOUSE PLC—Kvaerner a.s.a.; *Int'l*, pg. 772
TRANSAMERICA CORPORATION; *U.S. Public*, pg. 1629
TRANSAMERICA REALTY SERVICES, INC.—Transamerica Corporation; *U.S. Public*, pg. 1630
TRANSTATES PROPERTIES, INC.—Union Camp Corporation; *U.S. Public*, pg. 1666
TRIZECHAHN CENTERS INC.—TrizecHahn Corporation; *Int'l*, pg. 1425
TRIZECHAHN CORPORATION; *Int'l*, pg. 1424
TRIZECHAHN PROPERTIES INC.—TrizecHahn Corporation; *Int'l*, pg. 1425
THE TRUMP GROUP; *U.S. Private*, pg. 1107
TRUMP ORGANIZATION; *U.S. Private*, pg. 1108
TRUMP TOWERS—Trump Organization; *U.S. Private*, pg. 1108
TURNER OMNI VENTURE, INC.—Time Warner Inc.; *U.S. Public*, pg. 1615
TUSAR, INC.—Forest City Enterprises, Inc.; *U.S. Public*, pg. 669
USX REALTY DEVELOPMENT—USX Corporation; *U.S. Public*, pg. 1661
UNIBAIL; *Int'l*, pg. 1431
UNITED STATES REALTY & INVESTMENT CO.; *U.S. Private*, pg. 1125
UNIVERSAL INTERNATIONAL, INC.; *U.S. Public*, pg. 1697
URBAN GROUP—Cambridge Shopping Centres Limited; *Int'l*, pg. 253
URSTADT BIDDLE PROPERTIES, INC.; *U.S. Public*, pg. 1700
UTICA SQUARE SHOPPING CENTER, INC.—Helmerich & Payne, Inc.; *U.S. Public*, pg. 808
VANTAGE COMPANIES; *U.S. Private*, pg. 1134
THE VILLAGE OF CROSS KEYS, INC.—The Rouse Company; *U.S. Public*, pg. 1409
WAL-MART REALTY COMPANY—Wal-Mart Stores, Inc.; *U.S. Public*, pg. 1733
WARM BROTHERS CONSTRUCTION COMPANY; *U.S. Private*, pg. 1150
WATKINS ASSOCIATED DEVELOPERS—Watkins Associated Industries Inc.; *U.S. Private*, pg. 1153
WEST MORRIS PROPERTIES, INC.—Quexco Incorporated; *U.S. Private*, pg. 901
WESTLAKE HARDWARE, INC.; *U.S. Private*, pg. 1169
WHITE MARSH MALL, INC.—The Rouse Company; *U.S. Public*, pg. 1409
WIMPEY PROPERTY HOLDINGS LTD.—George Wimpey PLC; *Int'l*, pg. 1510
WOODBRIDGE CENTER, INC.—The Rouse Company; *U.S. Public*, pg. 1408
WORLD TRADE CENTER NORTHWEST CORPORATION—Enron Corp.; *U.S. Public*, pg. 585
WORLD TRADE CENTRE IN LONDON LTD.—Taylor Woodrow plc; *Int'l*, pg. 1359
YELLOW REDEVELOPMENT CORP.—Yellow Corporation; *U.S. Public*, pg. 1788

6513 — OPERATORS OF APARTMENT BUILDINGS

A & B DEVELOPMENT CO. (CALIFORNIA)—Alexander & Baldwin, Inc.; *U.S. Public*, pg. 39
AETNA INC.; *U.S. Public*, pg. 26
AFFILIATED PUBLISHERS, INC.; *U.S. Private*, pg. 26
AKER BRYGGE DRIFT A/S—Aker Raj Asa; *Int'l*, pg. 41
ALADDIN HOTEL & CASINO; *U.S. Private*, pg. 30
ASSOCIATED BANC-CORP; *U.S. Public*, pg. 140
RAULF BAU GMBH—Hollandsche Beton Groep NV; *Int'l*, pg. 630
BLAIR TOWER LIMITED PARTNERSHIP—Cooper Communities, Inc.; *U.S. Private*, pg. 274
BOYKIN LODGING CO.; *U.S. Public*, pg. 249
BROOKFIELD HOMES LTD.—Brookfield Properties Corporation; *Int'l*, pg. 228
BRUTGER EQUITIES, INC.; *U.S. Private*, pg. 176
BUILDERS DEVELOPMENT INC.—Garvey Industries, Inc.; *U.S. Private*, pg. 440
BUILDERS INC.—Garvey Industries, Inc.; *U.S. Private*, pg. 440
CLASSIC RESIDENCE BY HYATT—Hyatt Corporation; *U.S. Private*, pg. 551
CLAYTON, WILLIAMS & SHERWOOD, INC.; *U.S. Private*, pg. 245
CONSTELLATION REAL ESTATE GROUP INC.—Baltimore Gas and Electric Company; *U.S. Public*, pg. 172
COSCAN FLORIDA, INC.—Brookfield Properties Corporation; *Int'l*, pg. 228
COSCAN STEWART LIMITED PARTNERSHIP—Brookfield Properties Corporation; *Int'l*, pg. 228
DAIMLER-BENZ INTERSERVICES (DEBIS) AG—Daimler-Benz Aktiengesellschaft; *Int'l*, pg. 367
THE ERIN COMPANY; *U.S. Private*, pg. 381
ESSEX HOUSE LIMITED PARTNERSHIP—Cooper Communities, Inc.; *U.S. Private*, pg. 274
FAIRMONT MORTGAGE, INC.—Del Webb Corporation; *U.S. Public*, pg. 495
FELDSCHLOSSCHEN HURLIMANN HOLDING; *Int'l*, pg. 479
THE FLATLEY COMPANY; *U.S. Private*, pg. 410
FOREST CITY SOUTHPARK CORP.—Forest City Enterprises, Inc.; *U.S. Public*, pg. 668
FOREST CITY SOUTHPARK TWO, INC.—Forest City Enterprises, Inc.; *U.S. Public*, pg. 669
FREDERICTON BUSINESS PARK LTD.—Bruncor, Inc.; *Int'l*, pg. 230
I.H. FRENCH & CO. INC.; *U.S. Private*, pg. 427
GARDENWOOD LIMITED PARTNERSHIP—Cooper Communities, Inc.; *U.S. Private*, pg. 274
GARVEY INDUSTRIES, INC.; *U.S. Private*, pg. 440
GENERAL SERVICES CORPORATION; *U.S. Private*, pg. 445
GOLF HOSTS, INC.—Starwood Capital Group LLC; *U.S. Private*, pg. 1036
GULF COAST RECYCLING; *U.S. Private*, pg. 487
HAI SUN HUP GROUP LTD.; *Int'l*, pg. 586
HIGHLANDS AT BRIARCLIFF LIMITED PARTNERSHIP—Cooper Communities, Inc.; *U.S. Private*, pg. 274
THE HILLS—Paragon Health Network, Inc.; *U.S. Public*, pg. 1257
HORIZON ENTERPRISES GROUP LLC; *U.S. Private*, pg. 539
HORIZON INVESTMENT GROUP—Horizon Enterprises Group LLC; *U.S. Private*, pg. 539
HORIZON PROPERTIES—Horizon Enterprises Group LLC; *U.S. Private*, pg. 539
HOTEL LOWEN SCHRUNS GMBH—Liebherr-International AG; *Int'l*, pg. 808
HOVNANIAN ENTERPRISES, INC.; *U.S. Public*, pg. 843
K. HOVNANIAN INVESTMENT PROPERTIES, INC.—Hovnanian Enterprises, Inc.; *U.S. Public*, pg. 843
THE INLAND GROUP, INC.; *U.S. Private*, pg. 564
INTERALPEN-HOTEL TYROL GMBH—Liebherr-International AG; *Int'l*, pg. 808
JEFFERSON ADAMS CORP.—Volt Information Sciences, Inc.; *U.S. Public*, pg. 1724
KAUFMAN AND BROAD OF TEXAS, LTD.—Kaufman and Broad Home Corporation; *U.S. Public*, pg. 945
KEMMONS WILSON, INC.; *U.S. Private*, pg. 613
KILLARNEY HOTELS LTD.—Liebherr-International AG; *Int'l*, pg. 809
KILLEARN APARTMENT MANAGEMENT, INC.—Killearn Properties, Inc.; *U.S. Public*, pg. 956
L.D. TOLEDO CORP.—Forest City Enterprises, Inc.; *U.S. Public*, pg. 669
LEXFORD RESIDENTIAL TRUST; *U.S. Public*, pg. 991
LIMA LIMITED DIVIDEND CORP.—Forest City Enterprises, Inc.; *U.S. Public*, pg. 669
LINCOLN PROPERTY CO., NORTHERN CALIFORNIA—Lincoln Property Company; *U.S. Private*, pg. 668
LITTLE AMERICA HOTELS—Sinclair Oil Corp.; *U.S. Private*, pg. 1003
LONDON CITY & INTERNATIONAL LIMITED—Lonrho plc; *Int'l*, pg. 817
LONDON CITY & WESTCLIFF PROPERTIES—Lonrho plc; *Int'l*, pg. 817
LYONNAISE DES EAUX S.A.; *Int'l*, pg. 822
THE MACERICH COMPANY; *U.S. Public*, pg. 1030
MARRIOTT SENIOR LIVING SERVICES—Marriott International, Inc.; *U.S. Public*, pg. 1048
THE MAY DEPARTMENT STORES COMPANY; *U.S. Public*, pg. 1063
MIDWEST MANAGEMENT CO.—Lennar Corporation; *U.S. Public*, pg. 988
MITSUI REAL ESTATE DEVELOPMENT CO., LTD.—Mitsui & Co., Ltd.; *Int'l*, pg. 878
NATIONAL LUMBER CO.; *U.S. Private*, pg. 785
K/S NEDRE ELVEHAVN TRONDHEIM—Aker Raj Asa; *Int'l*, pg. 41
OXFORD REALTY FINANCIAL GROUP; *U.S. Private*, pg. 825
PACIFIC GATEWAY PROPERTIES; *U.S. Public*, pg. 1250
PARDEE CONSTRUCTION COMPANY—Weyerhaeuser Company; *U.S. Public*, pg. 1764
PURCELL CO., INC.; *U.S. Private*, pg. 895
REALTY ONE; *U.S. Private*, pg. 914
RESIDENCE INN—Marriott International, Inc.; *U.S. Public*, pg. 1048
ROTTERDAM VENTURES INC.—Galesi Group; *U.S. Private*, pg. 437
ROYAL LEPAGE LIMITED; *Int'l*, pg. 1143
SEASONS CONGREGATE LIVING, INC.—The Western and Southern Life Insurance Company; *U.S. Private*, pg. 1164
SMITH MANAGEMENT CO., INC.; *U.S. Private*, pg. 1009
SOUTHERN LIFE PROPERTY HOLDINGS LIMITED—Anglo American Corporation of South Africa Limited; *Int'l*, pg. 77
SOUTHWEST DIVERSIFIED COSCAN PARTNERSHIPS—Brookfield Properties Corporation; *Int'l*, pg. 228
SOUTHWEST VILLAGES—Pacific Gateway Properties; *U.S. Public*, pg. 1250
THE SPANOS COMPANIES; *U.S. Private*, pg. 1020
SPRINGFIELD L.D. CORP.—Forest City Enterprises, Inc.; *U.S. Public*, pg. 669
KYLE STEWART LTD.—Hollandsche Beton Groep NV; *Int'l*, pg. 630
SURFSIDE TOWERS II, INC.—Forest City Enterprises, Inc.; *U.S. Public*, pg. 669
TAYLOR-MORLEY, INC.; *U.S. Private*, pg. 1071
TOKYU CORPORATION; *Int'l*, pg. 1394
TRANS MOUNTAIN HOUSING LTD.—BC Gas Inc.; *Int'l*, pg. 114
THE TRUMP GROUP; *U.S. Private*, pg. 1107
TRUMP PLAZA OF THE PALM BEACHES; *U.S. Private*, pg. 1108
TRUMP TOWERS—Trump Organization; *U.S. Private*, pg. 1108
VOLT INFORMATION SCIENCES, INC.; *U.S. Public*, pg. 1724
XENIA L.D. CORP.—Forest City Enterprises, Inc.; *U.S. Public*, pg. 670

6514 — OPERATORS OF DWELLINGS OTHER THAN APARTMENT BUILDINGS

A & B PROPERTIES, INC.—Alexander & Baldwin, Inc.; U.S. Public, pg. 39
CPB INC.; U.S. Public, pg. 282
CPB PROPERTIES, INC.—CPB Inc.; U.S. Public, pg. 283
CARLSON REAL ESTATE COMPANY—Carlson Companies, Inc.; U.S. Private, pg. 212
CHARLWOOD ALLIANCE HOLDINGS LTD.—The Peninsular and Oriental Steam Navigation Company; Int'l, pg. 1034
CHRISTIANA COMPANIES, INC.; U.S. Public, pg. 352
CLAYTON, WILLIAMS & SHERWOOD, INC.; U.S. Private, pg. 245
CONSTELLATION REAL ESTATE GROUP INC.—Baltimore Gas and Electric Company; U.S. Public, pg. 172
DAIMLER-BENZ AKTIENGESELLSCHAFT; Int'l, pg. 366
DAIMLER-BENZ INTERSERVICES (DEBIS) AG—Daimler-Benz Aktiengesellschaft; Int'l, pg. 367
DOMIBAIL—Credit Nationale; Int'l, pg. 344
EDENS INDUSTRIAL PARK, INC.—Continental Materials Corporation; U.S. Public, pg. 441
FOREST CITY RENTAL PROPERTIES CORPORATION—Forest City Enterprises, Inc.; U.S. Public, pg. 668
FOREST CITY SOUTHPARK TWO, INC.—Forest City Enterprises, Inc.; U.S. Public, pg. 669
FOREST CITY VINEYARD VILLAGE, INC.—Forest City Enterprises, Inc.; U.S. Public, pg. 669
GABLE HOUSE ESTATES LTD.—Ladbroke Group Plc; Int'l, pg. 787
HORIZON PROPERTIES—Horizon Enterprises Group LLC; U.S. Private, pg. 539
LADBROKE GROUP PROPERTIES LTD.—Ladbroke Group Plc; Int'l, pg. 787
LARIO ENTERPRISES, INC.—Lario Oil & Gas Company; U.S. Private, pg. 651
LONDON CITY & INTERNATIONAL LIMITED—Lonrho plc; Int'l, pg. 817
LONDON CITY & WESTCLIFF PROPERTIES—Lonrho plc; Int'l, pg. 817
MICHAEL J. MUNGO COMPANY, INC.; U.S. Private, pg. 767
NORTH TUCSON BUSINESS CENTER—Pacific Gateway Properties; U.S. Public, pg. 1250
PACIFIC GATEWAY PROPERTIES; U.S. Public, pg. 1250
RADISSON SUITE HOTEL—Pacific Gateway Properties; U.S. Public, pg. 1250
ROYAL LEPAGE LIMITED; Int'l, pg. 1143
SAFECARE COMPANY—SAFECO Corporation; U.S. Public, pg. 1423
SAFECO CORPORATION; U.S. Public, pg. 1423
SOUTHERN LIFE PROPERTY HOLDINGS LIMITED—Anglo American Corporation of South Africa Limited; Int'l, pg. 77
TOKYU CORPORATION; Int'l, pg. 1394
VILLAGE COMMON SHOPPING CENTER—Pacific Gateway Properties; U.S. Public, pg. 1250
WINMAR COMPANY—SAFECO Corporation; U.S. Public, pg. 1423

6515 — OPERATORS OF RESIDENTIAL MOBILE HOME SITES

CMH PARKS, INC.—Clayton Homes, Inc.; U.S. Public, pg. 383
CHATEAU COMMUNITIES, INC.; U.S. Public, pg. 341
CLAYTON HOMES, INC.; U.S. Public, pg. 382
CLAYTON, WILLIAMS & SHERWOOD, INC.; U.S. Private, pg. 245
COUNTRYWIDE PARTNERSHIP INVESTMENTS, INC.—Countrywide Home Loans Inc.; U.S. Public, pg. 453
PURCELL CO., INC.; U.S. Private, pg. 895
STANDING ROCK CAMPGROUND—Commerce Group Corp.; U.S. Public, pg. 410

6517 — LESSORS OF RAILROAD PROPERTY

CRC PROPERTIES, INC.—Conrail, Inc.; U.S. Public, pg. 432
THE LAKEFRONT DOCK & RAILROAD TERMINAL CO.—Conrail, Inc.; U.S. Public, pg. 432
NICHOLAS, FAYETTE & GREENBRIER RR CO.—Conrail, Inc.; U.S. Public, pg. 432
THE ST. LAWRENCE & ADIRONDACK RAILWAY CO.—Conrail, Inc.; U.S. Public, pg. 432
TOKYU CORPORATION; Int'l, pg. 1394
TRI-STATE LAND COMPANY—Canadian Pacific Limited; Int'l, pg. 259

6519 — LESSORS OF REAL PROPERTY, NEC

ALICO, INC.; U.S. Public, pg. 41
ALPAC CONSTRUCTION & SURVEYS LIMITED—BC Gas Inc.; Int'l, pg. 114
AMERICAN TRADING AND PRODUCTION CORPORATION; U.S. Private, pg. 63
AMFAC/JMB HAWAII, INC.—JMB Realty Corporation; U.S. Private, pg. 577
AQUARION COMPANY; U.S. Public, pg. 126
ARVIN FINANCE CORP.—Arvin Industries, Inc.; U.S. Public, pg. 137
ARVIN INDUSTRIES, INC.; U.S. Public, pg. 136
AYRSHIRE LAND COMPANY—Cyprus Amax Minerals Company; U.S. Public, pg. 471
BA LEASING & CAPITAL CORPORATION—BankAmerica Corporation; U.S. Public, pg. 181
BDW CORP.—PP&L Resources; U.S. Public, pg. 1244
BHF & IKB IMMOBILIEN-LEASING GMBH—BHF-BANK AG; Int'l, pg. 119
BNP BAIL—Banque Nationale de Paris; Int'l, pg. 163
BERWIND CORPORATION; U.S. Private, pg. 138
BOEING AGRI-INDUSTRIAL CO.—The Boeing Company; U.S. Public, pg. 242
BRECK OPERATING CORP.—States, Inc.; U.S. Private, pg. 1037
COM/ENERGY ACUSHNET REALTY—Commonwealth Energy System; U.S. Public, pg. 414
COM/ENERGY CAMBRIDGE REALTY—Commonwealth Energy System; U.S. Public, pg. 414
COM/ENERGY FREETOWN REALTY—Commonwealth Energy System; U.S. Public, pg. 414
COM/ENERGY RESEARCH PARK REALTY—Commonwealth Energy System; U.S. Public, pg. 414
CAMBRIDGE LEASEHOLDS LIMITED—Cambridge Shopping Centres Limited; Int'l, pg. 253
CHEMICAL PROPERTIES, INC.—Chemical Leaman Corporation; U.S. Private, pg. 233
CODY COMPANY; U.S. Private, pg. 249
CODY ENERGY, INC.—Cody Company; U.S. Private, pg. 249
COMMONWEALTH ENERGY SYSTEM; U.S. Public, pg. 414
D.P.&L. COMMUNITY URBAN REDEVELOPMENT CORP.—DPL Inc.; U.S. Public, pg. 473
D.Q.F., INC.—Berkshire Hathaway Inc.; U.S. Public, pg. 220
DARVEL REALTY TRUST—Commonwealth Energy System; U.S. Public, pg. 415
DOUGLAS MANAGEMENT COMPANY—Lynden Incorporated; U.S. Private, pg. 683
EDISON DEVELOPMENT CANADA, INC.—Unicom Corporation; U.S. Public, pg. 1664
FBC FINANCE CO.—Farmer Brothers Company; U.S. Public, pg. 613
FFP MARKETING COMPANY, INC.; U.S. Public, pg. 604
FIRST MARYLAND LEASECORP—Allied Irish Banks, p.l.c.; Int'l, pg. 64
1ST SOURCE LEASING—1st Source Corporation; U.S. Public, pg. 638
GENERAL ELECTRIC (USA) AVIATION SERVICE OPERATION PTE. LTD.—General Electric Company; U.S. Public, pg. 714
GRAN CENTRAL CORPORATION—St. Joe Corp.; U.S. Public, pg. 1427
GREAT NORTHERN IRON ORE—Great Northern Iron Ore Properties; U.S. Public, pg. 760
GREAT NORTHERN IRON ORE PROPERTIES; U.S. Public, pg. 760
GULFSTREAM LEASING CORPORATION—NationsBank Corporation; U.S. Public, pg. 1162
HAMER PROPERTIES, INC.—Walter Industries, Inc.; U.S. Public, pg. 1736
HARPEN AG; Int'l, pg. 597
HELMERICH & PAYNE, INC.; U.S. Public, pg. 808
HYATT CORPORATION; U.S. Private, pg. 551
INTERNATIONAL AIRCRAFT SERVICES—James Crean PLC; Int'l, pg. 340
GAY JOHNSON'S INC.; U.S. Private, pg. 595
JONES COMPANY, INC.; U.S. Private, pg. 596
KAROSSERIEWERK PORSCHE GMBH—Porsche AG; Int'l, pg. 1063
KENTUCKY BERWIND LAND COMPANY—Berwind Corporation; U.S. Private, pg. 138
KWICKIE/FLASH FOODS, INC.—Jones Company, Inc.; U.S. Private, pg. 596
LAKE BUENA VISTA COMMUNITIES, INC.—The Walt Disney Company; U.S. Public, pg. 513
LEISURE COLONY MANAGEMENT CORP.—Lennar Corporation; U.S. Public, pg. 988
LOCABEL S.A.—Bank Brussels Lambert; Int'l, pg. 147
MBC REALTY, INC.—Mercantile Bankshares Corporation; U.S. Public, pg. 1089
MASSACHUSETTS CAPITAL RESOURCES COMPANY—American Water Works Company, Inc.; U.S. Public, pg. 95
MCKENZIE TANK LINES, INC.; U.S. Private, pg. 723
MEADOWLARK, INC.—Cyprus Amax Minerals Company; U.S. Public, pg. 471
MEREDITH CORPORATION; U.S. Public, pg. 1094
METRO PARKING SYSTEMS—Metropolitan Properties Systems; U.S. Private, pg. 739
MIAMI VALLEY LEASING, INC.—DPL Inc.; U.S. Public, pg. 474
MINEMET AUSTRALIA PTY. LTD.—Imetal; Int'l, pg. 661
MINEMET HOLDING—Imetal; Int'l, pg. 661
MINEMET ITALIA—Imetal; Int'l, pg. 661
MINEMET S.A.—Imetal; Int'l, pg. 661
MISSION WEST PROPERTIES; U.S. Public, pg. 1117
MOLINE ACCESSORIES CORPORATION—Kone Corporation; Int'l, pg. 746
MONTANA SUN, INC.—Energy West Inc.; U.S. Public, pg. 581
NATIONSBANK LEASING CORP.—NationsBank Corporation; U.S. Public, pg. 1165
NEW MEXICO & ARIZONA LAND CO.; U.S. Public, pg. 1172
NISSEI LEASING CO., LTD.—Nippon Life Insurance Co.; Int'l, pg. 935
OCCOQUAN LAND CORPORATION—American Water Works Company, Inc.; U.S. Public, pg. 95
OFFICE LEASING—IRI Istituto Ricostruzione Industriale; Int'l, pg. 652
OMARK PROPERTIES, INC.—Blount International, Inc.; U.S. Public, pg. 239
ONEOK INC.; U.S. Public, pg. 1226
ONEOK LEASING CO.—ONEOK Inc.; U.S. Public, pg. 1226
ONEOK PARKING CO.—ONEOK Inc.; U.S. Public, pg. 1226
PNC COMMUNITY DEVELOPMENT CORP.—PNC Bank Corp.; U.S. Public, pg. 1243
PNC REALTY CORPORATION—PNC Bank Corp.; U.S. Public, pg. 1243
PENN VIRGINIA CORPORATION; U.S. Public, pg. 1271
PETROBRAS - PETROLEO BRASILEIRO S.A.; Int'l, pg. 1041
PETROLEOS DE VENEZUELA S.A.; Int'l, pg. 1045
THE PITTSTON COMPANY; U.S. Public, pg. 1305
PITTSTON MINERALS GROUP, INC.—The Pittston Company; U.S. Public, pg. 1305
PRESIDENTIAL REALTY CORPORATION; U.S. Public, pg. 1323
PRIMARK STORAGE LEASING CORPORATION—Primark Corporation; U.S. Public, pg. 1325
REALCONN, INC.—Cigna Corp.; U.S. Public, pg. 365
ROTTERDAM VENTURES INC.—Galesi Group; U.S. Private, pg. 437
SFIC PROPERTIES, INC.—Kuwait Petroleum Corporation; Int'l, pg. 765
SNET REAL ESTATE INC.—Southern New England Telecommunications Corporation; U.S. Public, pg. 1491
SEABREEZE PROPERTIES, INC.—Oriole Homes Corp.; U.S. Public, pg. 1231
SPACE CENTER, INC.—Helmerich & Payne, Inc.; U.S. Public, pg. 808
SUMITOMO CORPORATION OF AMERICA—Sumitomo Corporation; Int'l, pg. 1312
SUMMIT BANCORP; U.S. Public, pg. 1527
TIMCO, INC.—Aquarion Company; U.S. Public, pg. 126
TOKYU CORPORATION; Int'l, pg. 1394
TREDEGAR INDUSTRIES INC.; U.S. Public, pg. 1633
TREXLERTOWN PROPERTIES, INC.—Air Products and Chemicals, Inc.; U.S. Public, pg. 31
URSTADT BIDDLE PROPERTIES, INC.; U.S. Public, pg. 1700
J.W. WALTER, INC.—Walter Industries, Inc.; U.S. Public, pg. 1736
WILMORE COAL COMPANY—Berwind Corporation; U.S. Private, pg. 138
WINNEBAGO INDUSTRIES, INC.; U.S. Public, pg. 1772

6531 — REAL ESTATE AGENTS & MANAGERS

AEW CAPITAL MANAGEMENT, L.P.—Metropolitan Life Insurance Co.; U.S. Private, pg. 737
ANR REN-CEN, INC.—The Coastal Corporation; U.S. Public, pg. 389
ABRAMS INDUSTRIES, INC.; U.S. Public, pg. 14
ABRAMS PROPERTIES, INC.—Abrams Industries, Inc.; U.S. Public, pg. 14
ADASON PROPERTIES LIMITED—The Canada Life Assurance Company; Int'l, pg. 254
AHOLD VASTGOED B.V.—Koninklijke Ahold NV; Int'l, pg. 749
ROBERT B. AIKENS & ASSOCIATES LLC.; U.S. Private, pg. 28
AIRTOUCH PROPERTIES—AirTouch Communications, Inc.; U.S. Public, pg. 34
ALBRECHT INC.—The Fred W. Albrecht Grocery Co.; U.S. Private, pg. 32
ALCOA PROPERTIES, INC.—Aluminum Company of America; U.S. Public, pg. 61
ALITALIA LINEE AEREE ITALIANE S.P.A.—IRI Istituto Ricostruzione Industriale; Int'l, pg. 652
ALLIANCE MANAGEMENT, INC.; U.S. Private, pg. 38
ALLIANZ GRUNDSTUECKS-AG—Allianz Aktiengesellschaft; Int'l, pg. 58
ALLIANZ OF AMERICA, INC.—Allianz Aktiengesellschaft; Int'l, pg. 58
AMERIAN APPRAISAL PROPERTY TAX SERVICES, INC.—American Appraisal Associates, Inc.; U.S. Private, pg. 50
AMERICAN APPRAISAL ASSOCIATES, INC.; U.S. Private, pg. 49
AMERICAN APPRAISAL MEXICO—American Appraisal Associates, Inc.; U.S. Private, pg. 50
AMERICAN GENERAL CORPORATION; U.S. Public, pg. 76
AMERICAN TRADING REAL ESTATE PROPERTIES, INC.—American Trading and Production Corporation; U.S. Private, pg. 64
AMURCON CORPORATION; U.S. Private, pg. 69
AMWAY CORPORATION; U.S. Private, pg. 69
ANREM CO.—American National Insurance Company; U.S. Public, pg. 88
THE APOGEE COMPANIES, INC.; U.S. Private, pg. 77
ARAMARK CORP.; U.S. Private, pg. 78
THE ARLEN CORPORATION; U.S. Public, pg. 131
ARLEN MANAGEMENT CORP.—The Arlen Corporation; U.S. Public, pg. 131
ARLINGTON SECURITIES PLC—British Aerospace p.l.c.; Int'l, pg. 217
ARRENDADORA GORVAC S.A. DE C.V.—Tootsie Roll Industries, Inc.; U.S. Public, pg. 1621
ARROWOOD SOUTHERN EXECUTIVE PARK INC.—Norfolk Southern Corporation; U.S. Public, pg. 1190
ASAHI SOGO KANRI CO., LTD.—The Asahi Bank, Ltd.; Int'l, pg. 82
ASEMAP, ASESORAMIENTO E INVERSIONES, S.A.—Corporacion MAPFRE, Compania Internacional de Reaseguros, S.A.; Int'l, pg. 332
ASSOCIATED REALTY, INC.—Associated Banc-Corp; U.S. Public, pg. 140
ASSOCIATES RELOCATION MANAGEMENT COMPANY, INC.—Ford Motor Company; U.S. Public, pg. 663
ATLANTIC GULF COMMUNITIES CORPORATION; U.S. Public, pg. 144
THE ATRIUM DEVELOPMENT CO.—Time Warner Inc.; U.S. Public, pg. 1613
AUTRANET, INC.—The Equitable Companies Incorporated; U.S. Public, pg. 589
BHF IMMOBILIEN-GMBH—BHF-BANK AG; Int'l, pg. 119
BAIRD & WARNER INC.; U.S. Private, pg. 111
D.A. BARANSKI & CO.—Barancorp; U.S. Private, pg. 115
BASTOGI-S.P.A.; Int'l, pg. 170
BEAR STEARNS REAL ESTATE GROUP INC.—The Bear Stearns Companies Inc.; U.S. Public, pg. 198
BEAVER FREE CORP.—Pacifica Real Estate Group; U.S. Private, pg. 832
BEAZER GROUP PLC; Int'l, pg. 181

BEDFORD ASSOCIATES, INC.—BT Financial Corporation; *U.S. Public*, pg. 164
BELL ATLANTIC PROPERTIES, INC.—Bell Atlantic Corporation; *U.S. Public*, pg. 203
BENCHMARK APPRAISAL GROUP—Mercantile Bankshares Corporation; *U.S. Public*, pg. 1089
BENDERSON DEVELOPMENT CO., INC.; *U.S. Private*, pg. 132
BENETONE LAND & HOUSES CO., LTD.; *Int'l*, pg. 186
BERMUDEZ-BINSWANGER—Binswanger; *U.S. Private*, pg. 144
BERNHEIM-COMOFI—Groupe Bruxelles Lambert S.A.; *Int'l*, *pg. 562*
BERWIND CORPORATION; *U.S. Private*, pg. 138
BETTER HOMES AND GARDENS REAL ESTATE SERVICE—Meredith Corporation; *U.S. Public*, pg. 1094
BINSWANGER; *U.S. Private*, pg. 144
BIPIEMME FIDUCIARIA SPA—Banca Popolare di Milano; *Int'l*, pg. 137
BLACK HORSE AGENCIES LTD.—Lloyds TSB Group PLC; *Int'l*, pg. 813
BOMBARDIER REAL ESTATE LTD.—Bombardier Inc.; *Int'l*, *pg. 200*
BRANDYWINE SPORTS, INC.; *U.S. Private*, pg. 165
BROAD NATIONAL REALTY CORPORATION—Broad National Bancorporation; *U.S. Public*, pg. 258
BROWN BROTHERS HARRIMAN & CO.; *U.S. Private*, pg. 173
BROWN, HARRIS, STEVENS, INC.; *U.S. Private*, pg. 174
CB COMMERCIAL REAL ESTATE; *U.S. Public*, pg. 272
CB COMMERCIAL REAL ESTATE GROUP, INC.—CB Commercial Real Estate; *U.S. Public*, pg. 272
CG EQUITY VENTURES, INC.—Cigna Corp.; *U.S. Public*, pg. 365
CSX CORPORATION; *U.S. Public*, pg. 284
CSX LIS—CSX Corporation; *U.S. Public*, pg. 284
CTB, INC.—The Dickerson Group, Inc.; *U.S. Private*, pg. 331
THE CAFARO CO.; *U.S. Private*, pg. 198
CAIXA-IMOBILIARIO-SOCIEDADE DE GESTAO E INVESTIMENTO IMOBILIARIO S.A.—Caixa Geral de Depositos; *Int'l*, pg. 250
CALMAT PROPERTIES CO.—CalMat Co.; *U.S. Public*, pg. 295
CAMDEV PROPERTIES INC.—O&Y Properties Corporation; *Int'l*, pg. 993
CAMPUS POINT REALTY CORPORATION—Science Applications International Corp.; *U.S. Private*, pg. 976
CAPE CORAL REALTY, INC.—Avatar Holdings Inc.; *U.S. Public*, pg. 151
CAPITAL DEVELOPMENT CO.; *U.S. Private*, pg. 205
CARLSBERG FINANCIAL CORP.; *U.S. Private*, pg. 211
THE CARLYLE GROUP—Carlyle Holding Corporation; *U.S. Private*, pg. 213
CARLYLE HOLDING CORPORATION; *U.S. Private*, pg. 213
CARR REAL ESTATE SERVICES—CarrAmerica Realty; *U.S. Public*, pg. 309
CARRAMERICA REALTY; *U.S. Public*, pg. 308
CARTER & ASSOCIATES; *U.S. Private*, pg. 216
CATELLUS DEVELOPMENT CORPORATION; *U.S. Public*, pg. 314
CENTRAL VERMONT PUBLIC SERVICE CORPORATION; *U.S. Public*, pg. 327
CENTRO DE INFORMACION Y SERVICIOS DEL MERCADO INMOBILIARIO, S.A.—Caja de Madrid Group; *Int'l*, pg. 251
CENTURY 21 AGMONT REAL ESTATE, INC.; *U.S. Private*, pg. 226
CENTURY 21 REAL ESTATE CORP.—Cendant Corporation; *U.S. Public*, pg. 321
CHARAN REALTY GROUP—Charan Industries, Inc.; *U.S. Private*, pg. 229
CHARLES DUNN COMPANY, INC.; *U.S. Private*, pg. 229
CHESAPEAKE PACKAGING CO./SCOTIA—Chesapeake Corporation; *U.S. Public*, pg. 347
CHESTERTON BINSWANGER CAPITAL ADVISORS—Binswanger; *U.S. Private*, pg. 144
CHOCK FULL O' NUTS CORPORATION; *U.S. Public*, pg. 351
CIMENTA, ADMON. DE FONDOS DE INVERSION, S.A.—Corporacion MAPFRE, Compania Internacional de Reaseguros, S.A.; *Int'l*, pg. 335
CITADEL HOLDINGS CORP.—Craig Corporation; *U.S. Public*, pg. 456
CITADEL REALTY, INC.—Craig Corporation; *U.S. Public*, pg. 456
CITICO REALTY CO.—Norfolk Southern Corporation; *U.S. Public*, pg. 1191
CITY CLUB OF CHARLOTTE—Fairfield Communities, Inc.; *U.S. Public*, pg. 610
CLOVE DEVELOPMENT CORP.—Orange and Rockland Utilities, Inc.; *U.S. Public*, pg. 1229
COFHYLUX SA—Banque Generale du Luxembourg SA; *Int'l*, pg. 162
COLDWELL BANKER REAL ESTATE CORPORATION—Cendant Corporation; *U.S. Public*, pg. 321
COLE-LAYER-TRUMBLE COMPANY (CLT)—Day & Zimmermann, Inc.; *U.S. Private*, pg. 317
COLOMET, INC.—American Electric Power Company, Inc.; *U.S. Public*, pg. 72
COLONIAL DRILLING & EXPLORATION CORPORATION—Colonial Oil Industries; *U.S. Private*, pg. 254
COLORADO NATIONAL BANKSHARES, INC.—U.S. Bancorp; *U.S. Public*, pg. 1680
COMMERCIAL REALTY & RESOURCES CORP.—New Jersey Resources Corporation; *U.S. Public*, pg. 1172
COMPANIA NACIONAL DE RENTAS—Corporacion MAPFRE, Compania Internacional de Reaseguros, S.A.; *Int'l*, pg. 335
CONSOLIDATED-TOMOKA LAND CO.; *U.S. Public*, pg. 437
CONSTELLATION REAL ESTATE GROUP INC.—Baltimore Gas and Electric Company; *U.S. Public*, pg. 172
CORMORANT CORP.—Northern States Power Company; *U.S. Public*, pg. 1195
COUNTY REALTY CORP.—Commerce Bancshares, Inc.; *U.S. Public*, pg. 409
CRIIMI MAE; *U.S. Public*, pg. 459
CUSHMAN & WAKEFIELD—Mitsubishi Estate Co., Ltd.; *Int'l*, pg. 873
CUSHMAN & WAKEFIELD, INC.—Mitsubishi Estate Co., Ltd.; *Int'l*, pg. 873
CUSTOM SOURCE REALTY CORPORATION—St. Paul Bancorp, Inc.; *U.S. Public*, pg. 1429
DCA REALTY INC.—Lennar Corporation; *U.S. Public*, pg. 988
DAIN RAUSCHER CORPORATION; *U.S. Public*, pg. 476
THE DAIWA REAL ESTATE CO., LTD.—Daiwa Securities Co. Ltd.; *Int'l*, pg. 375
DANAHER CORPORATION; *U.S. Public*, pg. 480
DARIGOLD, INC.; *U.S. Private*, pg. 311
DART REALTY CO. LTD.—Brodart Company; *U.S. Private*, pg. 170
DAY & ZIMMERMANN, INC.; *U.S. Private*, pg. 316
DEAD RIVER COMPANY; *U.S. Private*, pg. 318
JOHN DEERE-LANZ VERWALTUNGS A.G.—Deere & Company; *U.S. Public*, pg. 493
DEL AMERICAN PROPERTIES, INC.; *U.S. Private*, pg. 321
DELMARVA PROPERTIES, INC.—Chesapeake Corporation; *U.S. Public*, pg. 347
DESARROLLOS MULTIPLES INSULARES, INC.—Puerto Rican Cement Co., Inc.; *U.S. Public*, pg. 1342
DEVCO LAND CORP.—Lennar Corporation; *U.S. Public*, pg. 988
DEVELOPERS DIVERSIFIED REALTY CORPORATION; *U.S. Public*, pg. 502
DEVELOPMENT CORPORATION OF AMERICA—Lennar Corporation; *U.S. Public*, pg. 987
THE DICKERSON GROUP, INC.; *U.S. Private*, pg. 331
DICKERSON REALTY CORP.—The Dickerson Group, Inc.; *U.S. Private*, pg. 331
WALTER DICKINSON INC.; *U.S. Private*, pg. 331
WALTER DICKINSON, INC.—Walter Dickinson Inc.; *U.S. Private*, pg. 331
DOBSON & JOHNSON, INC.; *U.S. Private*, pg. 337
DOMGROUP LTD.—Hollinger Inc.; *Int'l*, pg. 631
DOMINION LANDS, INC.—Dominion Resources, Inc.; *U.S. Public*, pg. 516
DOUGLAS ELLIMAN; *U.S. Private*, pg. 341
DUKE REALTY INVESTMENTS, INC.; *U.S. Public*, pg. 535
DUNN REALITY, INC.—Dunn Industries Inc.; *U.S. Private*, pg. 347
DUQUESNE ENTERPRISES—DQE Inc.; *U.S. Public*, pg. 474
E & A INDUSTRIES, INC.; *U.S. Private*, pg. 352
EFS SERVICE CORPORATION—St. Paul Bancorp, Inc.; *U.S. Public*, pg. 1428
ERA REAL ESTATE—Cendant Corporation; *U.S. Public*, pg. 321
EDISON HOMES-SOUTHEAST, INC.—Columbia/HCA Healthcare Corporation; *U.S. Public*, pg. 404
EDISON PARKING PROPERTIES, LLC; *U.S. Private*, pg. 364
ELLESMERE BRITANNIA LTD.—Agra Inc.; *Int'l*, pg. 31
ELLESMERE DEVELOPMENTS LTD.—Agra Inc.; *Int'l*, pg. 31
ERIKSBERGS FORVALTNINGS AB—Celsius AB; *Int'l*, pg. 277
ESSPA-EDILIZIA SICILIANA S.P.A.—Bastogi-S.p.A.; *Int'l*, pg. 170
EZON PRODUCTS, INC.; *U.S. Private*, pg. 388
FFG TRUST, INC.—Firstbank of Illinois Co.; *U.S. Public*, pg. 644
FH CENTER, INC.—First Hawaiian, Inc.; *U.S. Public*, pg. 635
FARNSWORTH DEVELOPMENT CO.—Farnsworth Companies; *U.S. Private*, pg. 397
FIGGIE PROPERTIES INC.—Figgie International Inc.; *U.S. Public*, pg. 622
FIRST CAPITAL FINANCIAL CORP.—Great American Management & Investment, Inc.; *U.S. Private*, pg. 473
FIRST COLUMBIA ESCROW, INC.—Washington Mutual Inc.; *U.S. Public*, pg. 1742
FIRST FLORIDA EQUITIES, INC.; *U.S. Private*, pg. 407
FIRST PACIFIC DAVIES LIMITED—First Pacific Company Limited; *Int'l*, pg. 487
THE FIRST REPUBLIC BUILDING CORP.—The First Republic Corporation of America; *U.S. Public*, pg. 637
THE FIRST REPUBLIC CORPORATION OF AMERICA; *U.S. Public*, pg. 637
FIRSTAR DEVELOPMENT CORPORATION—Firstar Corporation; *U.S. Public*, pg. 643
FIRSTAR REAL ESTATE SERVICES, INC.—Firstar Corporation; *U.S. Public*, pg. 643
FISCHBACH & DOUGHERTY, INC.; *U.S. Private*, pg. 408
FISHER COMPANIES INC.; *U.S. Public*, pg. 647
FISHER PROPERTIES INC.—Fisher Companies Inc.; *U.S. Public*, pg. 648
FLEMING COMPANY—Fleming Companies, Inc.; *U.S. Public*, pg. 653
FLETCHER HOMES LIMITED—Fletcher Challenge Limited; *Int'l*, pg. 495
FOMENTO DE OBRAS URBANAS EUROPEAS, S.A.—Caja de Madrid Group; *Int'l*, pg. 252
FORD MOTOR LAND DEVELOPMENT CORPORATION—Ford Motor Company; *U.S. Public*, pg. 663
FOSTER MORTGAGE CORPORATION—United Companies Financial Corporation; *U.S. Public*, pg. 1675
FOSTER WHEELER REAL ESTATE DEVELOPMENT CORP.—Foster Wheeler Corporation; *U.S. Public*, pg. 677
FOUNTAIN SQUARE MANAGEMENT CO.—Fifth Third Bancorp; *U.S. Public*, pg. 622
FRANKLIN PROPERTY CO.—Saul Centers Inc.; *U.S. Public*, pg. 1435
FRANKLIN REAL ESTATE CO.—American Electric Power Company, Inc.; *U.S. Public*, pg. 72
GFS REALTY, INC.—Giant Food Inc.; *U.S. Public*, pg. 741
GWC PROPERTIES, INC.—McCall Oil & Chemical Corp.; *U.S. Private*, pg. 719
GWL PROPERTIES INC.—The Great-West Life Assurance Company; *Int'l*, pg. 558
GWP, INC.; *U.S. Private*, pg. 437
GALEN ALASKA REALTY, INC.—Columbia/HCA Healthcare Corporation; *U.S. Public*, pg. 404
GARTEN UND HEIM GMBH—Philipp Holzmann AG; *Int'l*, pg. 632
THE GATES CORPORATION—Tomkins PLC; *Int'l*, pg. 1396
GEICO FACILITIES CORPORATION—Berkshire Hathaway Inc.; *U.S. Public*, pg. 219
GEICO PROPERTIES, INC.—Berkshire Hathaway Inc.; *U.S. Public*, pg. 220
GEICO WASHINGTON PROPERTIES, INC.—Berkshire Hathaway Inc.; *U.S. Public*, pg. 220
GENERAL GROWTH PROPERTIES INC.; *U.S. Public*, pg. 715
GENERAL SERVICES CORPORATION; *U.S. Private*, pg. 445
GENESEE CORPORATION; *U.S. Public*, pg. 728
GENESEE VENTURES, INC.—Genesee Corporation; *U.S. Public*, pg. 728
GEOREX INC.—CGG Group; *Int'l*, pg. 241
GIANT FOOD INC.; *U.S. Public*, pg. 741
GILBANE PROPERTIES, INC.—Gilbane Building Company; *U.S. Private*, pg. 453
GOLUB & CO.; *U.S. Private*, pg. 463
SHELDON GOOD & CO.; *U.S. Private*, pg. 463
GRAY REAL ESTATE & DEVELOPMENT CO.—Gray Communications Systems, Inc.; *U.S. Public*, pg. 759
GREAT ATLANTIC HOSPITALITY CO. INC.—The Great Atlantic Management Company; *U.S. Private*, pg. 473
GREAT ATLANTIC MANAGEMENT CO. INC.—The Great Atlantic Management Company; *U.S. Private*, pg. 473
THE GREAT ATLANTIC MANAGEMENT COMPANY; *U.S. Private*, pg. 473
GREAT-WEST REALTY INVESTMENTS, INC.—The Great-West Life Assurance Company; *Int'l*, pg. 558
GREENE COUNTY REALTY COMPANY—O'Reilly Automotive Inc.; *U.S. Public*, pg. 1230
ALBERT M. GREENFIELD & COMPANY; *U.S. Private*, pg. 477
GRENADIER REALTY CORP.—Starrett HRH; *U.S. Private*, pg. 1035
GROUPE GTM—Lyonnaise des Eaux S.A.; *Int'l*, pg. 823
GROVE DIVISION—Orange-Co., Inc.; *U.S. Public*, pg. 1229
GRUBB & ELLIS COMPANY; *U.S. Public*, pg. 767
GRUPO PROTEXA S.A. DE C.V.; *Int'l*, pg. 576
GRUPO SITUR SA DE CV—Grupo Sidek, S.A. de C.V.; *Int'l*, pg. 576
HCBECK; *U.S. Private*, pg. 490
HFS MOBILITY SERVICES—Cendant Corporation; *U.S. Public*, pg. 321
HALLWOOD COMMERCIAL REAL ESTATE, INC.—The Hallwood Group Incorporated; *U.S. Public*, pg. 778
HALLWOOD REALTY CORPORATION—The Hallwood Group Incorporated; *U.S. Public*, pg. 778
HALLWOOD REALTY PARTNERS, L.P.—The Hallwood Group Incorporated; *U.S. Public*, pg. 778
HANIEL REEDEREI HOLDING GMBH—Franz Haniel & Cie, GmbH; *Int'l*, pg. 592
HARPEN IMMOBILIEN VERW.U. BETEILIG GES.MBH—Harpen AG; *Int'l*, pg. 597
HASEKO LIVENET INC.—Haseko Corporation; *Int'l*, pg. 600
HASEKO REALTY (CALIFORNIA), INC.—Haseko Corporation; *Int'l*, pg. 600
HASEKO REALTY INC.—Haseko Corporation; *Int'l*, pg. 600
HASEKO URBAN CO., LTD.—Haseko Corporation; *Int'l*, pg. 600
HASEKO URBEST INC.—Haseko Corporation; *Int'l*, pg. 600
HEARST REAL ESTATE DIVISION—The Hearst Corporation; *U.S. Private*, pg. 518
HEARST REALTY DEVELOPMENT CO., INC.—The Hearst Corporation; *U.S. Private*, pg. 515
HELMSLEY ENTERPRISES, INC.; *U.S. Private*, pg. 521
HELMSLEY-NOYES CO., INC.—Helmsley Enterprises, Inc.; *U.S. Private*, pg. 521
HELMSLEY-SPEAR INC.—Helmsley Enterprises, Inc.; *U.S. Private*, pg. 521
HONDA SOGO TATEMONO CO., LTD.—Honda Motor Co., Ltd.; *Int'l*, pg. 634
THE HONG KONG LAND PROPERTY COMPANY LTD.—Jardine Matheson Holdings Limited; *Int'l*, pg. 704
HOSTMARK MANAGEMENT GROUP; *U.S. Private*, pg. 541
HOWARD HUGHES CORPORATION—The Rouse Company; *U.S. Public*, pg. 1407
IBM REAL ESTATE & CONSTRUCTION DIV.—International Business Machines Corporation; *U.S. Public*, pg. 896
ICA FASTIGHETS AB—ICA Handlarnas AB; *Int'l*, pg. 643
ISC REALTY CORPORATION—Interstate/Johnson Lane, Inc.; *U.S. Public*, pg. 910
IMOCASCAIS GESTAO MOBILIARIA E IMMOBILIARIA—Corporacion MAPFRE, Compania Internacional de Reaseguros, S.A.; *Int'l*, pg. 333
IMPERIAL BANK REALTY COMPANY—Imperial Bancorp; *U.S. Public*, pg. 872
INDIANA FRANKLIN REALTY, INC.—American Electric Power Company, Inc.; *U.S. Public*, pg. 72
INDIGO GROUP INC.—Consolidated-Tomoka Land Co.; *U.S. Public*, pg. 437
INDIGO GROUP LTD.—Consolidated-Tomoka Land Co.; *U.S. Public*, pg. 437
THE INLAND GROUP, INC.; *U.S. Private*, pg. 564
INMOBILIARIA CONDOMINIO PARQUE ZAPALLAR S.A.—Corporacion MAPFRE, Compania Internacional de Reaseguros, S.A.; *Int'l*, pg. 335
INPAU, S.A.—Caixa d'Estalvis de Catalunya; *Int'l*, pg. 250
INSIGNIA FINANCIAL GROUP, INC.; *U.S. Public*, pg. 881
INSIGNIA RESIDENTIAL GROUP—Insignia Financial Group, Inc.; *U.S. Public*, pg. 881

INTERAMERICAN-STAR GROUP—Zuercher Lagerhaus AG; Int'l, pg. 1529
INTERNATIONAL PAPER REALTY CORP.—International Paper Company; U.S. Public, pg. 904
INVERCARTERA, S.A.—Caixa d'Estalvis de Catalunya; Int'l, pg. 250
INVERSIONES IBERICAS S.A.—Corporacion MAPFRE, Compania Internacional de Reaseguros, S.A.; Int'l, pg. 335
INVEST WEST FINANCIAL CORPORATION—Pacifica Real Estate Group; U.S. Private, pg. 832
THE IRVINE COMPANY; U.S. Private, pg. 575
JC PENNEY PROPERTIES, INC.—JC Penney Company, Inc.; U.S. Public, pg. 917
JAMES BUILDING CORPORATION; U.S. Private, pg. 580
J.M. JAYSON & CO., INC.; U.S. Private, pg. 584
JENNINGS LAND COMPANY—Danaher Corporation; U.S. Public, pg. 481
GAY JOHNSON'S INC.; U.S. Private, pg. 595
KAUFMAN AND BROAD HOME CORPORATION; U.S. Public, pg. 944
KENNEDY-WILSON, INC.; U.S. Public, pg. 951
KETTLER BROTHERS, INC.; U.S. Private, pg. 617
KILLEARN REALTY, INC.—Killearn Properties, Inc.; U.S. Public, pg. 956
L. ROBERT KIMBALL & ASSOCIATES; U.S. Private, pg. 619
J.I. KISLAK INC.; U.S. Private, pg. 624
KOHLER COMPANY; U.S. Private, pg. 630
KORMAN SERVICES, L.P.; U.S. Private, pg. 632
KRAUS-ANDERSON, INCORPORATED—Kraus-Anderson Incorporated; U.S. Private, pg. 635
KRAUS-ANDERSON REALTY COMPANY—Kraus-Anderson Incorporated; U.S. Private, pg. 635
KRUPP HOESCH IMMOBILIEN GMBH—Fried. Krupp AG; Int'l, pg. 512
KRUSE INTERNATIONAL; U.S. Private, pg. 636
KYODO BUILDING CORPORATION—Toshiba Corporation; Int'l, pg. 1403
KYOEI DO BRASIL COMPANHIA DE SEGUROS—The Kyoei Life Insurance Co., Ltd.; Int'l, pg. 777
KYOEI DO BRASIL S/A-EMPREENDIMENTOS IMOBILIARIOS—The Kyoei Life Insurance Co., Ltd.; Int'l, pg. 777
LBS IMMOBILIEN GMBH—Landesbank Hessen-Thuringen Girozentrale; Int'l, pg. 799
LACLEDE DEVELOPMENT CO.—Laclede Gas Company; U.S. Public, pg. 974
LACLEDE INVESTMENT CORP.—Laclede Gas Company; U.S. Public, pg. 974
LAKE INVESTMENT CO.—Tech-Sym Corporation; U.S. Public, pg. 1563
LAKESIDE TRADING ESTATE LTD.—Pearson plc; Int'l, pg. 1025
LAMAR CORPORATION; U.S. Private, pg. 644
LAMBERT SMITH HAMPTON; Int'l, pg. 797
LANDSAFE TITLE AGENCY, INC.—Countrywide Home Loans Inc.; U.S. Public, pg. 453
LASALLE ADVISORS LIMITED—LaSalle Partners; U.S. Public, pg. 979
LASALLE PARTNERS; U.S. Public, pg. 978
LEE NATIONAL CORPORATION; U.S. Private, pg. 658
LEHMAN ASSOCIATES, INC.—United States Realty & Investment Co.; U.S. Private, pg. 1125
LENNAR MANAGEMENT CORP.—Lennar Corporation; U.S. Public, pg. 988
LENNAR REALTY, INC.—Lennar Corporation; U.S. Public, pg. 988
LEXFORD RESIDENTIAL TRUST; U.S. Public, pg. 991
LIBERTY PROPERTY MANAGEMENT CO.—Banc One Corporation; U.S. Public, pg. 174
LIEBHERR-GUTSVERWALTUNG GMBH—Liebherr-International AG; Int'l, pg. 808
LIEBHERR-WOHNUNGBAU GMBH—Liebherr-International AG; Int'l, pg. 808
LINCAM PROPERTIES, INC.—Lincoln National Corporation; U.S. Public, pg. 997
LINSCO REINSURANCE COMPANY—Lincoln National Corporation; U.S. Public, pg. 998
LLOYD PROPERTIES; U.S. Private, pg. 672
THE LOEWEN GROUP, INC.; Int'l, pg. 814
LOEWEN GROUP INTERNATIONAL, INC.—The Loewen Group, Inc.; Int'l, pg. 814
LONE STAR EQUITIES INC.; U.S. Private, pg. 674
THE LONG & FOSTER COMPANIES, INC.; U.S. Private, pg. 674
LOS ANGELES UNION TERMINAL, INC.—Union Pacific Corporation; U.S. Public, pg. 1668
THE LOUISIANA PURCHASE—AMREP Corporation; U.S. Public, pg. 105
MAR, INC.—NationsBank Corporation; U.S. Public, pg. 1163
MCO PROPERTIES INC.—Maxxam Inc.; U.S. Public, pg. 1062
M.D.C. HOLDINGS, INC.; U.S. Public, pg. 1025
MRM PROPERTIES, INC.—NationsBank Corporation; U.S. Public, pg. 1163
MACGREGOR PARK, INC.—DPL Inc.; U.S. Public, pg. 473
MACRISTY INDUSTRIES, INC.; U.S. Private, pg. 693
MAGAEL, INC.—Madison Gas and Electric Company; U.S. Public, pg. 1033
MAGUIRE GROUP INC.; U.S. Private, pg. 696
MAGUIRE PARTNERS; U.S. Private, pg. 696
MAIN STREET SOUTH CORP.—Aquarion Company; U.S. Public, pg. 126
MANULIFE HOLDINGS (HONG KONG) LIMITED—Manulife Financial (The Manufacturers Life Insurance Company); Int'l, pg. 841
MAPFRE ECUADOR, S.A.—Corporacion MAPFRE, Compania Internacional de Reaseguros, S.A.; Int'l, pg. 333
MARISO BULLE S.A.—Liebherr-International AG; Int'l, pg. 808
MARRIOTT OWNERSHIP RESORTS—Marriott International, Inc.; U.S. Public, pg. 1048
MARTINIQUE HOLDINGS—Christiana Companies, Inc.; U.S. Public, pg. 352
MARYLAND VENTURES, INC.—Berkshire Hathaway Inc.; U.S. Public, pg. 220
MAUI VARIETIES, LTD.; U.S. Private, pg. 715
MAURIN-OGDEN PROPERTIES; U.S. Private, pg. 715
MCCALL OIL REAL ESTATE CORPORATION—McCall Oil & Chemical Corp.; U.S. Private, pg. 719
MCRAE INDUSTRIES, INC.; U.S. Public, pg. 1073
MEIKA KOSAN CO., LTD.—Meiji Seika Kaisha, Ltd.; Int'l, pg. 855
MELITTA NORTH AMERICA, INC.—Melitta Unternehmensgruppe Bentz KG; Int'l, pg. 857
MENDIK MANAGEMENT CO., INC.; U.S. Private, pg. 731
MEREDITH CORPORATION; U.S. Public, pg. 1094
MERRILL LYNCH, PIERCE, FENNER & SMITH, INC.—Merrill Lynch & Co., Inc.; U.S. Public, pg. 1098
METRO ATLANTA PROPERTIES—Fischbach & Dougherty, Inc.; U.S. Private, pg. 408
METROPOLITAN LIFE INSURANCE CO.; U.S. Private, pg. 737
MICHAEL'S DEVELOPMENT COMPANY; U.S. Private, pg. 740
MID STATE PRODUCTS CO.—Osco Industries Inc.; U.S. Private, pg. 821
MIDWEST EMPLOYER'S CASUALTY COMPANY—W.R. Berkley Corporation; U.S. Public, pg. 215
MIDWESTERN HOLDINGS, INC.—Bank of Montreal; Int'l, pg. 155
MILL MAPLE PROPERTIES, INC.—Washington Mutual Inc.; U.S. Public, pg. 1742
MILL PLAIN FOUR, INC.—Washington Mutual Inc.; U.S. Public, pg. 1742
MILL PLAIN THREE, INC.—Washington Mutual Inc.; U.S. Public, pg. 1742
MILL PLAIN TWO, INC.—Washington Mutual Inc.; U.S. Public, pg. 1742
MINATO BUILDING CO., LTD.—Toshiba Corporation; Int'l, pg. 1403
MINYARD PROPERTIES, INC.—Minyard Food Stores, Inc.; U.S. Private, pg. 752
MIRACETI, S.A.—Corporacion MAPFRE, Compania Internacional de Reaseguros, S.A.; Int'l, pg. 334
MISCO INDUSTRIES; U.S. Private, pg. 752
MISSION LAND COMPANY—Edison International; U.S. Public, pg. 564
MITCHELL ENERGY & DEVELOPMENT CORP.; U.S. Public, pg. 1117
MITSUBISHI LOGISTICS CORP.; Int'l, pg. 874
MITSUI FUDOSAN (USA), INC.—Mitsui Fudosan Co., Ltd.; Int'l, pg. 882
MITSUI HOME CO., LTD.—Mitsui & Co., Ltd.; Int'l, pg. 877
MITSUI MATSUSHIMA CO., LTD.—Mitsui & Co., Ltd.; Int'l, pg. 877
MONTREAL TRUSTCO-PERSONAL SERVICES DIVISION—The Bank of Nova Scotia; Int'l, pg. 155
CHELSEA MOORE COMPANY—The Western and Southern Life Insurance Company; U.S. Private, pg. 1164
MORECO INC.—Modern Group Ltd.; U.S. Private, pg. 755
MURPHEY FAVRE HOUSING MANAGERS, INC.—Washington Mutual Inc.; U.S. Public, pg. 1742
MURPHEY FAVRE PROPERTIES, INC.—Washington Mutual Inc.; U.S. Public, pg. 1742
NCB PROPERTIES, INC.—Keycorp; U.S. Public, pg. 955
NS MANAGEMENT CORP.—The Rouse Company; U.S. Public, pg. 1409
NTS DEVELOPMENT COMPANY; U.S. Private, pg. 772
NW MANAGEMENT CORP.—The Rouse Company; U.S. Public, pg. 1409
NZ PROPERTIES, INC.—New Mexico & Arizona Land Co.; U.S. Public, pg. 1172
NANTO ESTATE CO., LTD.—The Nanto Bank, Ltd.; Int'l, pg. 905
NATIONAL DEVELOPMENT CO., INC.—Sunstates Corporation; U.S. Public, pg. 1536
NATIONAL REAL ESTATE SERVICES, INC.; Int'l, pg. 909
NATIONSBANK CORPORATION; U.S. Public, pg. 1162
NATIONSBANK OF TEXAS NATIONAL BANK PROPERTIES INC.—NationsBank Corporation; U.S. Public, pg. 1163
NETWORK REAL ESTATE INC.; U.S. Private, pg. 791
NEW JERSEY RESOURCES CORPORATION; U.S. Public, pg. 1172
NEW MEXICO & ARIZONA LAND CO.; U.S. Public, pg. 1172
NEWCARE HEALTH CORPORATION; U.S. Public, pg. 1176
THE NICKEL PLATE IMPROVEMENT CO., INC.—Norfolk Southern Corporation; U.S. Public, pg. 1190
NIPSCO DEVELOPMENT COMPANY, INC.—NIPSCO Industries, Inc.; U.S. Public, pg. 1185
NISSHO IWAI REAL ESTATE CORP.—Nissho Iwai Corporation; Int'l, pg. 947
NITTSU REAL ESTATE CO., LTD.—Nippon Express Co., Ltd.; Int'l, pg. 934
NOMURA LAND & BUILDING CO. LTD.—The Nomura Securities Co., Ltd.; Int'l, pg. 956
NOMURA REAL ESTATE DEVELOPMENT CO., LTD.—The Nomura Securities Co., Ltd.; Int'l, pg. 956
NOMURA REALTY ADVISORS INC.—The Nomura Securities Co., Ltd.; Int'l, pg. 956
NORCONN PROPERTIES, INC.—Yankee Energy System, Inc.; U.S. Public, pg. 1787
NORDISKA KOMPANIET (NK) AB—NCC AB; Int'l, pg. 899
NORMANDALE PROPERTIES—Opus South Corporation; U.S. Private, pg. 818
NORTH AMERICAN ACCEPTANCE CORPORATION—Washington Mutual Inc.; U.S. Public, pg. 1742
NORTHRIDGE INDUSTRIES, INC.—Hyatt Corporation; U.S. Private, pg. 551
NORTHWESTERN ENGINEERING CO.; U.S. Private, pg. 806
O&Y PROPERTIES CORPORATION; Int'l, pg. 993
OFB BAUVERMITTLUNGS UND GEWERBEBAU GESELLSCHAFT MBH—Landesbank Hessen-Thuringen Girozentrale; Int'l, pg. 799
OFB GRUNDSTUECKSVERWALTUNGS GMBH—Landesbank Hessen-Thuringen Girozentrale; Int'l, pg. 799
O.R.E. SUBSIDIARY CORP.—TrustCo Bank Corp., NY; U.S. Public, pg. 1643
OBAYASHI CORPORATION; Int'l, pg. 995
ORION PROPERTIES CORP.—Orion Capital Corporation; U.S. Public, pg. 1231
OXFORD REALTY FINANCIAL GROUP; U.S. Private, pg. 825
PHH CORPORATION—Cendant Corporation; U.S. Public, pg. 321
PM REALTY ADVISORS INC.—Pacific Life Insurance Company; U.S. Private, pg. 831
PACIFIC HOLDING CORPORATION; U.S. Private, pg. 831
PACIFICA REAL ESTATE GROUP; U.S. Private, pg. 832
PARAGON RESOURCES, INC.—Public Service Company of New Mexico; U.S. Public, pg. 1339
PARAMOUNT DEVELOPMENT ASSOCS., INC.—Perini Corporation; U.S. Public, pg. 1278
PEARSON PLC; Int'l, pg. 1025
PENN VIRGINIA COAL COMPANY—Penn Virginia Corporation; U.S. Public, pg. 1271
PERINI LAND AND DEVELOPMENT CO.—Perini Corporation; U.S. Public, pg. 1278
PERSIS CORPORATION; U.S. Private, pg. 855
PHELPS DODGE EXPLORATION CORPORATION—Phelps Dodge Corporation; U.S. Public, pg. 1287
POCAHONTAS LAND CORPORATION—Norfolk Southern Corporation; U.S. Public, pg. 1192
PRESTON PROPERTIES OF ARIZONA, INC.—Washington Mutual Inc.; U.S. Public, pg. 1742
PRESTON PROPERTIES OF CALIFORNIA, INC.—Washington Mutual Inc.; U.S. Public, pg. 1742
PRESTON PROPERTIES TEXAS, INC.—Washington Mutual Inc.; U.S. Public, pg. 1742
PRESTON PROPERTY MANAGEMENT COMPANY—Washington Mutual Inc.; U.S. Public, pg. 1742
PRETABAIL-SICOMI—Total S.A.; Int'l, pg. 1409
PRICE ENTERPRISES, INC.; U.S. Public, pg. 1324
PRINCEVILLE CORPORATION; U.S. Private, pg. 885
PRINCEVILLE MANAGEMENT CORPORATION—Princeville Corporation; U.S. Private, pg. 885
PRINCEVILLE REALTY CORPORATION—Princeville Corporation; U.S. Private, pg. 885
PROFESSIONAL APARTMENT MANAGEMENT, INC.; U.S. Private, pg. 889
PROGRESS WEST CORPORATION; U.S. Private, pg. 890
PROMOTORA CATALUNYA MEDITERRANEA, S.A.—Caixa d'Estalvis de Catalunya; Int'l, pg. 250
PROMOTORA MAPFRE CARIBE CARIMA, S.A.—Corporacion MAPFRE, Compania Internacional de Reaseguros, S.A.; Int'l, pg. 334
PROYECTOS Y CONSTRUCCIONES CATALUNYA, S.A.—Caixa d'Estalvis de Catalunya; Int'l, pg. 250
PRUDENTIAL REAL ESTATE AFFILIATES INC.—The Prudential Insurance Company of America; U.S. Private, pg. 892
THE PRUDENTIAL REALTY GROUP—The Prudential Insurance Company of America; U.S. Private, pg. 892
PUGET WESTERN, INC.—Puget Sound Energy, Inc.; U.S. Public, pg. 1342
PURCELL CO., INC.; U.S. Private, pg. 895
RIM - RHEINMETALL IMMOBILIEN MANAGEMENT GMBH—Rheinmetall Group; Int'l, pg. 1108
RE/MAX INTERNATIONAL, INC.; U.S. Private, pg. 912
REALTY CO. OF PENNSYLVANIA—PP&L Resources; U.S. Public, pg. 1244
REALTY ONE; U.S. Private, pg. 914
REDLAND PROPERTIES LTD.—Redland PLC; Int'l, pg. 1091
REGENCY GROUP INC.; U.S. Private, pg. 918
RELIANCE REALTY, INC.—The Chubb Corporation; U.S. Public, pg. 355
RICE FOOD MARKETS INC.; U.S. Private, pg. 927
RICOH DEVELOPMENT OF CALIFORNIA, INC.—Ricoh Company, Ltd.; Int'l, pg. 1114
RIO RANCHO—AMREP Corporation; U.S. Public, pg. 105
ROBSON COMMUNITIES; U.S. Private, pg. 937
ROCKEFELLER CENTER DEVELOPMENT CORPORATION—Mitsubishi Estate Co., Ltd.; Int'l, pg. 873
ROCKEFELLER CENTER MANAGEMENT CORPORATION—Mitsubishi Estate Co., Ltd.; Int'l, pg. 873
ROLEX INDUSTRIES, INC.—Rolex Watch Co. SA; Int'l, pg. 1126
ROSEN ASSOCIATES MANAGEMENT CORP.; U.S. Private, pg. 945
ROSEWOOD CORPORATION—Caroline Hunt Trust Estate; U.S. Private, pg. 548
ROSEWOOD PROPERTY COMPANY; U.S. Private, pg. 946
ROTHSCHILD NORTH AMERICA INC.; U.S. Private, pg. 947
ROTTERDAM VENTURES INC.—Galesi Group; U.S. Private, pg. 437
THE ROUSE COMPANY OF IOWA, INC.—The Rouse Company; U.S. Public, pg. 1408
THE ROUSE COMPANY OF LOUISIANA—The Rouse Company; U.S. Public, pg. 1408
ROUSE MANAGEMENT, INC.—The Rouse Company; U.S. Public, pg. 1409
ROYAL LEPAGE - BRITISH COLUMBIA OFFICE—Royal LePage Limited; Int'l, pg. 1143
ROYAL LEPAGE LIMITED; Int'l, pg. 1143
ROYAL LEPAGE - OTTAWA OFFICE—Royal LePage Limited; Int'l, pg. 1143

ROYAL LEPAGE - QUEBEC OFFICE—Royal LePage Limited; *Int'l*, pg. 1143
ROYAL LEPAGE REAL ESTATE SERVICES LTD.—Royal LePage Limited; *Int'l*, pg. 1143
SAFECO PROPERTIES, INC.—SAFECO Corporation; *U.S. Public*, pg. 1423
ST. KATHARINE BY THE TOWER LIMITED—Taylor Woodrow plc; *Int'l*, pg. 1358
SALS INVESTORS PARTNERSHIP—Colonial Commercial Corp.; *U.S. Public*, pg. 400
SAN FRANCISCO REALTIES—The Hearst Corporation; *U.S. Private*, pg. 518
SANDS INVESTMENTS, INC.; *U.S. Private*, pg. 964
SAPPORO BREWERIES LTD.; *Int'l*, pg. 1193
SAUNDERS REALTY CORPORATION—Trans-Lux Corporation; *U.S. Public*, pg. 1629
EARL SCHEIB REALTY CORP.—Earl Scheib, Inc.; *U.S. Public*, pg. 1437
ALLAN SCHNEIDER ASSOCIATES; *U.S. Private*, pg. 971
SEA ISLAND COMPANY; *U.S. Private*, pg. 977
SEA ISLAND PROPERTIES, INC.—Sea Island Company; *U.S. Private*, pg. 978
SEASIDE FINANCIAL CORPORATION—FirstFed Financial Corp.; *U.S. Public*, pg. 646
SELIGMAN & ASSOCIATES, INC.; *U.S. Private*, pg. 982
SHANNON PROPERTIES—Dana Corporation; *U.S. Public*, pg. 480
SHAPELL INDUSTRIES, INC.; *U.S. Private*, pg. 990
SHELDON GOOD & COMPANY AUCTIONS—Sheldon Good & Co.; *U.S. Private*, pg. 464
SHENANDOAH-VIRGINIA CORPORATION—Norfolk Southern Corporation; *U.S. Public*, pg. 1191
SHOLODGE, INC.; *U.S. Public*, pg. 1467
SHORE LINE SHOPS, INC.—NIPSCO Industries, Inc.; *U.S. Public*, pg. 1185
THE SIERRA CAPITAL COMPANIES; *U.S. Private*, pg. 998
SIMON DEBARTOLO GROUP, INC.; *U.S. Public*, pg. 1474
THE SINCERE CO. LTD.; *Int'l*, pg. 1252
SKIPJACK, INC.—Chesapeake Utilities Corporation; *U.S. Public*, pg. 347
SMITHGROUP, INC.; *U.S. Private*, pg. 1010
SNAM S.P.A.—ENI S.p.A.; *Int'l*, pg. 428
SOCIEDAD CONSTRUCTORA Y DE INVERSIONES MARTIN ZAMORA LTD.—Corporacion MAPFRE, Compania Internacional de Reaseguros, S.A.; *Int'l*, pg. 335
SOCIETA INIZIATIVE INDUSTRIALI S.R.L.—ENI S.p.A.; *Int'l*, pg. 428
SOCIETE IMMOBILIERE LA MANDRAGORE S.A.—Liebherr-International AG; *Int'l*, pg. 808
SOTHEBY'S HOLDINGS INC.; *U.S. Public*, pg. 1487
SOTHEBY'S INTERNATIONAL REALTY—Sotheby's Holdings Inc.; *U.S. Public*, pg. 1487
SOUTH PADRE LAND CO.—American General Corporation; *U.S. Public*, pg. 77
SOUTH SHORE HARBOUR DEVELOPMENT—American National Insurance Company; *U.S. Public*, pg. 88
SOUTHEASTERN REALTY GROUP INC.; *U.S. Private*, pg. 1015
SOUTHERN GUARANTY INSURANCE COMPANIES—Credit Suisse Group; *Int'l*, pg. 346
SOUTHERN LIVING REAL ESTATE, INC.—Time Warner Inc.; *U.S. Public*, pg. 1613
SOUTHERN REGION INDUSTRIAL REALTY, INC.—Norfolk Southern Corporation; *U.S. Public*, pg. 1190
SOUTHERN REGION MATERIALS SUPPLY, INC.—Norfolk Southern Corporation; *U.S. Public*, pg. 1191
SOUWESTCON PROPERTIES, INC.—United Illuminating Company; *U.S. Public*, pg. 1679
SPAULDING & SLYE; *U.S. Private*, pg. 1021
STAR STATES DEVELOPMENT CO.—WSFS Financial Corporation; *U.S. Public*, pg. 1729
STARRETT HRH; *U.S. Private*, pg. 1035
STILES CORPORATION; *U.S. Private*, pg. 1043
STIRLING PROPERTIES, INC.—Maurin-Ogden Properties; *U.S. Private*, pg. 715
STONEHOUSE, INC.—Chesapeake Corporation; *U.S. Public*, pg. 347
STORE EQUIPMENT, INC.—Fleming Companies, Inc.; *U.S. Public*, pg. 653
SUDDEUTSCHE GROSSBAUTEN GMBH—Philipp Holzmann AG; *Int'l*, pg. 633
SUDDEUTSCHE WOHNUNGSBAU GMBH—Hochtief AG; *Int'l*, pg. 623
SULCUS COMPUTER CORP.; *U.S. Public*, pg. 1527
SUMMIT BANCORP; *U.S. Public*, pg. 1527
SUNSTATES REALTY GROUP INC.—Sunstates Corporation; *U.S. Public*, pg. 1536
SYNDECO REALTY—DTE Energy Company; *U.S. Public*, pg. 476
SYSTEMS PARKING, INC.; *U.S. Private*, pg. 1061
TASACIONES MADRID, S.A.—Caja de Madrid Group; *Int'l*, pg. 252
TAYLOR - MORLEY MANAGEMENT COMPANY—Taylor-Morley, Inc.; *U.S. Private*, pg. 1071
TAYLOR WOODROW DEVELOPMENTS LTD.—Taylor Woodrow plc; *Int'l*, pg. 1358
TAYLOR WOODROW INTERNATIONAL NZ LIMITED—Taylor Woodrow plc; *Int'l*, pg. 1359
TAYLOR WOODROW OF CALIFORNIA INC.—Taylor Woodrow plc; *Int'l*, pg. 1359
TAYLOR WOODROW PROPERTY COMPANY (GEORGIA) INC.—Taylor Woodrow plc; *Int'l*, pg. 1359
TAYLOR WOODROW PROPERTY HOLDINGS PTY. LTD.—Taylor Woodrow plc; *Int'l*, pg. 1360
TAYLOR WOODROW (VICTORIA) PTY. LTD.—Taylor Woodrow plc; *Int'l*, pg. 1360
TECH-SYM CORPORATION; *U.S. Public*, pg. 1563
TEMPLE-INLAND INC.; *U.S. Public*, pg. 1574
TERRASSENHAUS-BAU GMBH—Philipp Holzmann AG; *Int'l*, pg. 633
TOKYU CORPORATION; *Int'l*, pg. 1394
TOSHIBA OSAKA BUILDING CO., LTD.—Toshiba Corporation; *Int'l*, pg. 1404
TOWER REALTY TRUST, INC.; *U.S. Public*, pg. 1625
TOWNE DEVELOPMENT OF HAWAII, INC.—Zilber, Ltd.; *U.S. Private*, pg. 1206
TOWNE PROPERTIES; *U.S. Private*, pg. 1093
TRAFALGAR HOUSE PROPERTY LTD.—Kvaerner a.s.a.; *Int'l*, pg. 773
TRAMMELL CROW COMPANY; *U.S. Public*, pg. 1628
TRAMMELL CROW RESIDENTIAL SERVICES; *U.S. Private*, pg. 1095
TRERICE TOSTO COLLIERS INTERNATIONAL; *U.S. Private*, pg. 1099
TRI-PALM ESTATE—GWP, Inc.; *U.S. Private*, pg. 437
TRIZECHAHN CORPORATION; *Int'l*, pg. 1424
TUCSON REALTY & TRUST CO.; *U.S. Private*, pg. 1109
TWINLOCK PLC—Fortune Brands, Inc.; *U.S. Public*, pg. 675
USAA (UNITED SERVICES AUTOMOBILE ASSOCIATION); *U.S. Private*, pg. 1114
UNICORP AMERICAN CORPORATION—Unicorp Canada Corporation; *Int'l*, pg. 1433
UNITED LAND CORP.—Walter Industries, Inc.; *U.S. Public*, pg. 1736
UNITED PARKING, INC.; *U.S. Private*, pg. 1123
UNITED POWER & LAND CO.—Northern States Power Company; *U.S. Public*, pg. 1195
USLIFE REAL ESTATE SERVICES CORP.—American General Corporation; *U.S. Public*, pg. 77
UNITED STATES REALTY & INVESTMENT CO.; *U.S. Private*, pg. 1125
UNITIL REALTY CORPORATION—Unitil Corporation; *U.S. Public*, pg. 1692
UNIVERSAL STUDIOS DEVELOPMENT CO.—The Seagram Company Ltd.; *Int'l*, pg. 1215
UNIVERSAL STUDIOS, INC.—The Seagram Company Ltd.; *Int'l*, pg. 1215
UTILITIES & INDUSTRIES MANAGEMENT CORP.—Shepaug Corporation; *U.S. Private*, pg. 993
VAIL ASSOCIATES, INC.—Vail Resorts, Inc.; *U.S. Public*, pg. 1704
VAIL RESORTS, INC.; *U.S. Public*, pg. 1704
THE VAN METRES COMPANIES; *U.S. Private*, pg. 1132
VANFED APPRAISAL COMPANY—Washington Mutual Inc.; *U.S. Public*, pg. 1742
VENGROFF WILLIAMS REALTY MANAGEMENT—Vengroff Williams & Associates, Inc.; *U.S. Private*, pg. 1135
VIAD REALTY CORP.—Viad Corp; *U.S. Public*, pg. 1718
THE VIERA COMPANY—A. Duda & Sons Inc.; *U.S. Private*, pg. 344
VORELCO, INC.—Volkswagen AG; *Int'l*, pg. 1474
VORELCO LTD.—Volkswagen AG; *Int'l*, pg. 1475
WNY GROUP; *U.S. Private*, pg. 1144
WALLINGFORD PROPERTY HOLDINGS CO.—The Unimax Corporation; *U.S. Private*, pg. 1118
WASHINGTON SERVICES, INC.—Washington Federal Savings; *U.S. Public*, pg. 1740
WEATHERALL GREEN & SMITH; *Int'l*, pg. 1488
WEICHERT COMPANY; *U.S. Private*, pg. 1159
WEICHERT REALTY, INC.—Weichert Company; *U.S. Private*, pg. 1159
WEST LYNN CREAMERY REALTY CORPORATION—Scangas Brothers Holdings, Inc.; *U.S. Private*, pg. 969
WESTCORP; *U.S. Public*, pg. 1756
WESTERN CONSUMER SERVICES, INC.—Westcorp; *U.S. Public*, pg. 1757
WHITE MARSH EQUITIES CORP.—The Rouse Company; *U.S. Public*, pg. 1409
WICKLAND PROPERTIES—Wickland Corporation; *U.S. Private*, pg. 1175
THE WILDER COMPANIES; *U.S. Private*, pg. 1176
THE WILLOWBROOK CORP.—The Rouse Company; *U.S. Public*, pg. 1408
WIRTZ CORPORATION; *U.S. Private*, pg. 1184
WISCONSIN CONSULTAR ENGENHARIA, LTD.—American Appraisal Associates, Inc.; *U.S. Private*, pg. 50
WOHN-UND GESCHAEFTSBAUTEN GMBH—Philipp Holzmann AG; *Int'l*, pg. 633
ZILBER, LTD.; *U.S. Private*, pg. 1206
ZION'S SECURITIES CORP.—Deseret Management Corporation; *U.S. Private*, pg. 327
ZUERCHER LAGERHAUS AG; *Int'l*, pg. 1529

6541 — TITLE ABSTRACT OFFICES

CALIFORNIA RECONVEYANCE CO.—Washington Mutual Inc.; *U.S. Public*, pg. 1741
THE FIRST AMERICAN FINANCIAL CORPORATION; *U.S. Public*, pg. 624
ILLINOIS BANC ONE TITLE CO.—Banc One Corporation; *U.S. Public*, pg. 174
LINCOLN INVESTMENT MANAGEMENT INC.—Lincoln National Corporation; *U.S. Public*, pg. 998
TCF FINANCIAL CORP.; *U.S. Public*, pg. 1554

6552 — LAND SUBDIVIDERS & DEVELOPERS, EXCEPT CEMETERIES

AMD PROPERTIES—Advanced Micro Devices, Inc.; *U.S. Public*, pg. 21
AMEV ONTWIKKELING MAATSCHAPPIJ N.V.—Fortis; *Int'l*, pg. 499
APL LIMITED—Neptune Orient Lines Ltd.; *Int'l*, pg. 912
A.W. REALTY CO.—Southwestern Energy Company; *U.S. Public*, pg. 1494
ABBELL ASSOCIATES; *U.S. Private*, pg. 9
ABRAMS INDUSTRIES, INC.; *U.S. Public*, pg. 14
ABRAMS PROPERTIES, INC.—Abrams Industries, Inc.; *U.S. Public*, pg. 14
AEGON USA, INC.—AEGON N.V.; *Int'l*, pg. 26
ROBERT B. AIKENS & ASSOCIATES LLC.; *U.S. Private*, pg. 28
AKER EIENDOM—Aker Raj Asa; *Int'l*, pg. 41
ALANDCO INC.—FPL Group, Inc.; *U.S. Public*, pg. 608
ALEXANDER & BALDWIN, INC.; *U.S. Public*, pg. 39
ALFA INVESTMENT CORP. & BUILDERS INC.—Alfa Corporation; *U.S. Public*, pg. 40
ALFA REALTY, INC.—Alfa Corporation; *U.S. Public*, pg. 40
ALFER CONSULTING IMMOBILIARIO, S.A.—Vallehermoso, S.A.; *Int'l*, pg. 1447
ALUMOB ALUSUISSE REAL ESTATE LTD.—Alusuisse-Lonza Holding Ltd.; *Int'l*, pg. 67
AMERICAN AGGREGATES CORP.—CSR Limited; *Int'l*, pg. 245
AMERICAN GENERAL CORPORATION; *U.S. Public*, pg. 76
AMERICAN GENERAL LIFE & ACCIDENT INSURANCE CO.—American General Corporation; *U.S. Public*, pg. 76
AMERICAN PACIFIC CORPORATION; *U.S. Public*, pg. 88
AMERICAN PRESIDENT REAL ESTATE CO., LTD.—Neptune Orient Lines Ltd.; *Int'l*, pg. 912
AMERICAN TRADING REAL ESTATE PROPERTIES, INC.—American Trading and Production Corporation; *U.S. Private*, pg. 64
AMFAC/JMB HAWAII, INC.—JMB Realty Corporation; *U.S. Private*, pg. 577
AMLI REALTY, INC.—Baldwin & Lyons, Inc.; *U.S. Public*, pg. 169
AMOCO REALTY COMPANY—Amoco Corporation; *U.S. Public*, pg. 103
AMPAC DEVELOPMENT COMPANY—American Pacific Corporation; *U.S. Public*, pg. 88
AMREP SOUTHWEST, INC.—AMREP Corporation; *U.S. Public*, pg. 104
AMURCON CORPORATION; *U.S. Private*, pg. 69
ARAPILES, S.A.—Vallehermoso, S.A.; *Int'l*, pg. 1447
THE ARLEN CORPORATION; *U.S. Public*, pg. 131
ARTESIAN RESOURCES CORPORATION; *U.S. Public*, pg. 135
ARVIDA—JMB Realty Corporation; *U.S. Private*, pg. 578
ATLANTIC GULF COMMUNITIES CORPORATION; *U.S. Public*, pg. 144
AVATAR DEVELOPMENT CORP.—Avatar Holdings Inc.; *U.S. Public*, pg. 151
AVATAR HOLDINGS INC.; *U.S. Public*, pg. 151
AVATAR PROPERTIES INC.—Avatar Holdings Inc.; *U.S. Public*, pg. 151
AVATAR REALTY, INC.—Avatar Holdings Inc.; *U.S. Public*, pg. 151
AVATAR UTILITIES, INC.—Avatar Holdings Inc.; *U.S. Public*, pg. 151
BB&T OF SOUTH CAROLINA—BB&T Corporation; *U.S. Public*, pg. 160
BE & K, INC.; *U.S. Private*, pg. 106
BICC DEVELOPMENTS LTD.—BICC plc; *Int'l*, pg. 120
BMC FORESTRY CORPORATION—Benguet Corporation; *Int'l*, pg. 186
BNE LAND & DEVELOPMENT CO.—Boddie-Noell Enterprises Inc.; *U.S. Private*, pg. 154
THE BALCOR COMPANY—American Express Company; *U.S. Public*, pg. 74
BANCA POPOLARE DI MILANO; *Int'l*, pg. 137
BARKERS LANDING 365
BARRATT AMERICAN INC.—Barratt Developments Plc; *Int'l*, pg. 168
BARRATT DEVELOPMENTS PLC; *Int'l*, pg. 167
BAZIMO—GIB Group; *Int'l*, pg. 533
BELLEMEAD DEVELOPMENT CORP.—The Chubb Corporation; *U.S. Public*, pg. 355
BELZ ENTERPRISES; *U.S. Private*, pg. 132
BENDERSON DEVELOPMENT CO., INC.; *U.S. Private*, pg. 132
BENEFICIAL CORPORATION; *U.S. Public*, pg. 211
BENGUET MANAGEMENT CORPORATION—Benguet Corporation; *Int'l*, pg. 186
BERKSHIRE REALTY COMPANY, INC.; *U.S. Public*, pg. 221
BINSWANGER; *U.S. Private*, pg. 144
BLOUNT DEVELOPMENT CORP.—Blount International, Inc.; *U.S. Public*, pg. 239
BOCA GREENS INC.—Lennar Corporation; *U.S. Public*, pg. 987
BODDIE-NOELL ENTERPRISES INC.; *U.S. Private*, pg. 154
BOMBARDIER INC.; *Int'l*, pg. 199
BRANDYWINE SPORTS, INC.; *U.S. Private*, pg. 165
BRANDYWOOD ESTATES, INC.—Washington Gas Light Co.; *U.S. Public*, pg. 1741
THE BRANIGAR ORGANIZATION, INC.—Union Camp Corporation; *U.S. Public*, pg. 1666
BRASCAN BRAZIL—EdperBrascan Corporation; *Int'l*, pg. 435
BRIM, INC.; *U.S. Private*, pg. 168
M.J. BROCK & SONS, INC.—The Ryland Group, Inc.; *U.S. Public*, pg. 1414
BROOKFIELD HOMES LTD.—Brookfield Properties Corporation; *Int'l*, pg. 228
BROOKHOLLOW CORP.—Texas Industries, Inc.; *U.S. Public*, pg. 1585
BROOKS RESOURCES CORPORATION; *U.S. Private*, pg. 172
OWEN BROWN B DEVELOPMENT CO.—The Rouse Company; *U.S. Public*, pg. 1409
BRUNCOR, INC.; *Int'l*, pg. 230
BRYANT FINANCIAL CORP.—Washington Mutual Inc.; *U.S. Public*, pg. 1741
BUDCO GROUP INC.; *U.S. Private*, pg. 178
BUILDERS DEVELOPMENT INC.—Garvey Industries, Inc.; *U.S. Private*, pg. 440
BUILDERS INC.—Garvey Industries, Inc.; *U.S. Private*, pg. 440
BUSCH PROPERTIES, INC.—Anheuser-Busch Companies, Inc.; *U.S. Public*, pg. 114
CBS CORPORATION; *U.S. Public*, pg. 273
CC INDUSTRIES, INC.; *U.S. Private*, pg. 192
CC PLAZA CO.—CalMat Co.; *U.S. Public*, pg. 295
CABOT PLACE LTD.—Manulife Financial (The Manufacturers Life Insurance Company); *Int'l*, pg. 840
THE CAFARO CO.; *U.S. Private*, pg. 198

A.B. CAIRNS LIMITED—Taylor Woodrow plc; Int'l, pg. 1359
CALIFORNIA MEC, INC.—Mitsubishi Estate Co., Ltd.; Int'l, pg. 873
CALMAT LAND CO.—CalMat Co.; U.S. Public, pg. 295
CALMAT PROPERTIES CO.—CalMat Co.; U.S. Public, pg. 295
CAMBRIDGE SHOPPING CENTRES LIMITED; Int'l, pg. 253
CAPITAL PACIFIC HOLDINGS; U.S. Public, pg. 302
CARDINAL REDEVELOPMENT CORPORATION—Ford Motor Company; U.S. Public, pg. 663
CARRAMERICA REALTY; U.S. Public, pg. 308
CARREFOUR ARGENTINE S.A.—Carrefour; Int'l, pg. 272
CARTER & ASSOCIATES; U.S. Private, pg. 216
CASTLE & COOKE INC.; U.S. Public, pg. 313
CATELLUS DEVELOPMENT CORPORATION; U.S. Public, pg. 314
CEDAR CREEK PROPERTIES INC.—Ash Grove Cement Company; U.S. Private, pg. 88
CEDAR CREEK REALTY CO., INC.—Ash Grove Cement Company; U.S. Private, pg. 88
THE CEDARWOOD CONSTRUCTION COMPANY; U.S. Private, pg. 221
CELSIUS AB; Int'l, pg. 276
CENTENNIAL HOMES INC.—Weyerhaeuser Company; U.S. Public, pg. 1764
CENTEX CORPORATION; U.S. Public, pg. 322
CENTRO INMOBILIARIO CAJA DE MADRID, S.A.—Caja de Madrid Group; Int'l, pg. 251
CHARAN INDUSTRIES, INC.; U.S. Private, pg. 229
CHARLES DUNN COMPANY, INC.; U.S. Private, pg. 229
CHELSEA HARBOUR LTD.—The Peninsular and Oriental Steam Navigation Company; Int'l, pg. 1034
CHEVRON LAND & DEVELOPMENT COMPANY—Chevron Corporation; U.S. Public, pg. 348
CIGNA CORP.; U.S. Public, pg. 356
CIMINELLI DEVELOPMENT COMPANY, INC.; U.S. Private, pg. 239
CINERGY CORP.—Cinergy Corp.; U.S. Public, pg. 369
CITICORP COMMUNITY DEVELOPMENT, INC.—Citicorp; U.S. Public, pg. 377
CLOVER FINANCIAL CORPORATION; U.S. Private, pg. 247
CODY COMPANY; U.S. Private, pg. 249
COLONIAL OIL INDUSTRIES; U.S. Private, pg. 253
COLUMBIA WILLAMETTE DEVELOPMENT CO.—Enron Corp.; U.S. Public, pg. 585
COMFORTABLE MORTGAGES, INC.—NationsBank Corporation; U.S. Public, pg. 1163
COMMERCE GROUP CORP.; U.S. Public, pg. 410
COMMUNITY PSYCHIATRIC CENTERS PROPERTIES, INC.—Vencor, Inc.; U.S. Public, pg. 1712
COMMUNITY RESEARCH & DEVELOPMENT, INC.—The Rouse Company; U.S. Public, pg. 1407
CONCORD ASSETS GROUP; U.S. Private, pg. 261
CONSTELLATION HOLDINGS, INC.—Baltimore Gas and Electric Company; U.S. Public, pg. 172
CONSTRUCTION COUNSELLORS, INC.; U.S. Private, pg. 266
COOPER COMMUNITIES, INC.; U.S. Private, pg. 273
COOPER VENTURES, INC.—Cooper Communities, Inc.; U.S. Private, pg. 274
CORPOREX COMPANIES, INC.; U.S. Private, pg. 276
COSCAN ADLER LIMITED PARTNERSHIP—Brookfield Properties Corporation; Int'l, pg. 228
COSCAN FLORIDA, INC.—Brookfield Properties Corporation; Int'l, pg. 228
COSCAN STEWART LIMITED PARTNERSHIP—Brookfield Properties Corporation; Int'l, pg. 228
COSCAN WATERWAYS, INC.—Brookfield Properties Corporation; Int'l, pg. 228
COURTAULDS U.S. DEVELOPMENTS INC.—Courtaulds plc; Int'l, pg. 339
CROSSMANN COMMUNITIES, INC.; U.S. Public, pg. 461
CROWN AMERICAN REALTY TRUST; U.S. Public, pg. 461
CULBRO LAND RESOURCES, INC.—General Cigar Holdings Inc; U.S. Public, pg. 708
CULLUM DEVELOPMENT CO.—Randalls Food Markets, Inc.; U.S. Private, pg. 909
DCA OF CALIFORNIA, INC.—Lennar Corporation; U.S. Public, pg. 988
DKM PROPERTIES CORPORATION—The Dyson-Kissner-Moran Corporation; U.S. Private, pg. 351
DSL SERVICE CO.—Downey Financial Corp.; U.S. Public, pg. 527
DAHLBUSCH AG—Pilkington Plc; Int'l, pg. 1056
THE DANIS COMPANIES; U.S. Private, pg. 310
DEAN OPERATIONS INC.; U.S. Private, pg. 318
THE EDWARD J. DEBARTOLO CORPORATION; U.S. Private, pg. 319
DEERFIELD HOMES, INC.—The Rouse Company; U.S. Public, pg. 1409
DEL AMERICAN PROPERTIES, INC.; U.S. Private, pg. 321
DEL WEBB CORPORATION; U.S. Public, pg. 494
DELTIC TIMBER CORPORATION; U.S. Public, pg. 498
DESC, S.A. DE C.V.; Int'l, pg. 395
DETROIT DOWNTOWN DEVELOPMENT CORPORATION—Ford Motor Company; U.S. Public, pg. 664
DEVCON INTERNATIONAL CORP.; U.S. Public, pg. 502
DEVELOPERS DIVERSIFIED REALTY CORPORATION; U.S. Public, pg. 502
DEVELOPMENT CORPORATION OF AMERICA—Lennar Corporation; U.S. Public, pg. 987
DIAGONAL SARRIA, S.A.—Caja de Madrid Group; Int'l, pg. 251
DIXON TICONDEROGA COMPANY; U.S. Public, pg. 514
DOMBUR INVESTMENTS LIMITED—Manulife Financial (The Manufacturers Life Insurance Company); Int'l, pg. 840
THE DOMINION REALTY COMPANY LIMITED—Canadian Imperial Bank of Commerce; Int'l, pg. 256
DONAHUE SCHRIBER—Cambridge Shopping Centres Limited; Int'l, pg. 253
THE DONOHOE COMPANIES, INC.; U.S. Private, pg. 340
E'TOWN PROPERTIES INC.—E'Town Corporation; U.S. Public, pg. 540
EFC PROPERTY MANAGEMENT, INC.—Orion Capital Corporation; U.S. Public, pg. 1231
ERI REALTY, INC.—Equitable Resources, Inc.; U.S. Public, pg. 589
ESI MORTGAGE DEVELOPMENT CORPORATION—Promus Hotel Corporation; U.S. Public, pg. 1335
ECHO FARMS GOLF & COUNTRY CLUB, INC.—The Rouse Company; U.S. Public, pg. 1409
EDIFICACIONES EN MADRID Y PROVINCIA, S.A.—Vallehermoso, S.A.; Int'l, pg. 1447
EDIFICIOS AURORA—Allianz Aktiengesellschaft; Int'l, pg. 61
EL PUERTO DE LIVERPOOL S.A.; Int'l, pg. 435
EMBASSY SYRACUSE DEVELOPMENT CORPORATION—Promus Hotel Corporation; U.S. Public, pg. 1335
ENPRO, INC.—Delta Natural Gas Company, Inc.; U.S. Public, pg. 497
EQUITY FUND ADVISORS INC.; U.S. Private, pg. 380
ERIKSBERGS FORVALTNINGS AB—Celsius AB; Int'l, pg. 277
EUROTUNNEL DEVELOPMENTS S.A.—The Eurotunnel Group; Int'l, pg. 466
EXCAVATOR ENTERPRISES, INC.—Tenneco Inc.; U.S. Public, pg. 1578
FPA CORPORATION; U.S. Public, pg. 608
FAIRFIELD COMMUNITIES, INC.; U.S. Public, pg. 610
FAIRFIELD MYRTLE BEACH, INC.—Fairfield Communities, Inc.; U.S. Public, pg. 611
FAIRMONT MORTGAGE, INC.—Del Webb Corporation; U.S. Public, pg. 495
FARNSWORTH DEVELOPMENT CO.—Farnsworth Companies; U.S. Private, pg. 397
FASTIGHETSAKTIEBOLAGET HUFVUDSTADEN; Int'l, pg. 478
FIRST FINANCIAL GROUP, INC.; U.S. Private, pg. 407
FIRST FLORIDA EQUITIES, INC.; U.S. Private, pg. 407
FIRST WORTHING COMPANY; U.S. Private, pg. 408
FLETCHER HOMES LIMITED—Fletcher Challenge Limited; Int'l, pg. 495
FLINT RIVER—Galesi Group; U.S. Private, pg. 437
FLORIDA PROGRESS CORPORATION; U.S. Public, pg. 655
FOLMAR & ASSOCIATES; U.S. Private, pg. 417
FOMENTO DE OBRAS URBANAS EUROPEAS, S.A.—Caja de Madrid Group; Int'l, pg. 252
FORD COLORADO PROPERTIES, INC.—Ford Motor Company; U.S. Public, pg. 663
FORD MOTOR DEALERSHIP FACILITIES CO.—Ford Motor Company; U.S. Public, pg. 664
FORD MOTOR LAND DEVELOPMENT CORPORATION—Ford Motor Company; U.S. Public, pg. 663
FORECAST GROUP; U.S. Private, pg. 418
FOREST CITY ENTERPRISES, INC.; U.S. Public, pg. 667
FRANKLIN PROPERTIES, INC.—Franklin Resources, Inc.; U.S. Public, pg. 680
CARL M. FREEMAN ASSOCIATES, INC.; U.S. Private, pg. 426
FRIENDSWOOD DEVELOPMENT COMPANY—Lennar Corporation; U.S. Public, pg. 988
THE FUSCO CORPORATION; U.S. Private, pg. 432
GSG SIEDLUNGSGESELLSCHAFT FUER WOHNUNGS-UND STAEDTEBAU MBH—Landesbank Hessen-Thuringen Girozentrale; Int'l, pg. 799
GAGGIANO S.R.L.—Allianz Aktiengesellschaft; Int'l, pg. 61
GARNEY HOLDING COMPANY, INC.; U.S. Private, pg. 440
GARVEY INDUSTRIES, INC.; U.S. Private, pg. 440
GATES LAND CO.—Cody Company; U.S. Private, pg. 249
GENERAL CIGAR HOLDINGS INC; U.S. Public, pg. 707
GENERAL GROWTH PROPERTIES INC.; U.S. Public, pg. 715
GENE B. GLICK COMPANY, INC.; U.S. Private, pg. 457
GOLUB & CO.; U.S. Private, pg. 463
GOSNELL BUILDERS—Pointe Group Ltd.; U.S. Private, pg. 873
W.M. GRACE DEVELOPMENT; U.S. Private, pg. 468
GRAHAM GROUP, INC.; U.S. Private, pg. 468
GRAY REAL ESTATE & DEVELOPMENT CO.—Gray Communications Systems, Inc.; U.S. Public, pg. 759
THE GREAT ATLANTIC MANAGEMENT COMPANY; U.S. Private, pg. 473
GREEN MEADOWS, LTD.—Pioneer Hi-Bred International, Inc.; U.S. Public, pg. 1299
GREENFIELD PROPERTIES, INC.—Ford Motor Company; U.S. Public, pg. 663
GRIMMER REALTY CO. INC.; U.S. Private, pg. 482
GUARDIAN ROYAL EXCHANGE PLC; Int'l, pg. 577
HALL FINANCIAL GROUP, INC.; U.S. Private, pg. 495
HAMBURGISCHE GRUNDSTUECKS GESELLSCHAFT MBH—Commerzbank AG; Int'l, pg. 310
HANSON PROPERTIES LIMITED—Hanson PLC; Int'l, pg. 593
HARBERT CORPORATION; U.S. Private, pg. 500
HARBOR FINANCIAL/NEW AMERICA—FirstCity Financial Corporation; U.S. Public, pg. 644
HARBOUR ISLAND, INC.—Beneficial Corporation; U.S. Public, pg. 211
HARROWSTON DEVELOPMENTS CORPORATION—Harrowston Corporation; Int'l, pg. 599
HASEKO CORPORATION; Int'l, pg. 599
HASEKO DEVELOPMENT INC.—Haseko Corporation; Int'l, pg. 600
HASEKO (NEW YORK) INC.—Haseko Corporation; Int'l, pg. 600
HASEKO REAL ESTATE INC.—Haseko Corporation; Int'l, pg. 600
THE HASSINGER COMPANIES HOFFMAN HOMES; U.S. Private, pg. 510
HAUS CRAMER GMBH & CO. IMMOBILIEN MANAGEMENT K.G.—Warsteiner Brauerei Haus Cramer GmbH & Co.; Int'l, pg. 1486
HAWTHORNE PROPERTIES, INC.—Hawthorne Corp.; U.S. Private, pg. 512
THE HEARST CORPORATION; U.S. Private, pg. 515
HELMSLEY ENTERPRISES, INC.; U.S. Private, pg. 521
HIGH INDUSTRIES, INC.; U.S. Private, pg. 528
HISPALAND, S.A.—Vallehermoso, S.A.; Int'l, pg. 1447
HOMESPAN REALTY CO., INC.—Commerce Group Corp.; U.S. Public, pg. 410
HONG FOK CORPORATION LTD.; Int'l, pg. 635
HOVNANIAN ENTERPRISES, INC.; U.S. Public, pg. 843
K. HOVNANIAN COMPANIES NORTHEAST, INC.—Hovnanian Enterprises, Inc.; U.S. Public, pg. 843
HOWARD HUGHES CORPORATION—The Rouse Company; U.S. Public, pg. 1407
HOYT DEVELOPMENT; U.S. Private, pg. 543
HOYT HOME IMPROVEMENT; U.S. Private, pg. 543
HUDSON KOHALA INC.—Hudson General Corporation; U.S. Public, pg. 845
HUNT BUILDING CORPORATION; U.S. Private, pg. 548
CAROLINE HUNT TRUST ESTATE; U.S. Private, pg. 548
HUNTINGTON BEACH CO.—Chevron Corporation; U.S. Public, pg. 348
IES INVESTMENTS INC.—IES Industries Inc.; U.S. Public, pg. 855
IDEAL HOMES HOLDINGS PLC—Kvaerner a.s.a.; Int'l, pg. 773
IHOP REALTY CORP.—IHOP Corp.; U.S. Public, pg. 862
IMMOBILIERE SAINT DOMINIQUE—Credit Nationale; Int'l, pg. 344
INDUMOB, S.A.—Vallehermoso, S.A.; Int'l, pg. 1447
INIBERICA, S.A.—Vallehermoso, S.A.; Int'l, pg. 1447
INSTALACIONES Y PROYECTOS DE TELECOMUNICACIONES, S.A.—Vallehermoso, S.A.; Int'l, pg. 1447
INTERSTATE LAND CORP.—Questar Corporation; U.S. Public, pg. 1352
THE IRVINE COMPANY; U.S. Private, pg. 575
JCP REALTY, INC.—JC Penney Company, Inc.; U.S. Public, pg. 917
JMB REALTY CORPORATION; U.S. Private, pg. 577
THE RICHARD E. JACOBS GROUP; U.S. Private, pg. 580
JAMES BUILDING CORPORATION; U.S. Private, pg. 580
KG (HAWAII) CORPORATION—Kumagai Gumi Co., Ltd.; Int'l, pg. 764
KG LAND CALIFORNIA CORPORATION—Kumagai Gumi Co., Ltd.; Int'l, pg. 764
KABUTO DECOM INC.; Int'l, pg. 721
KABUTO INTERNATIONAL PHOENIX INC.—Kabuto Decom Inc.; Int'l, pg. 721
THE KAEMPFER COMPANY, INVESTMENT BUILDERS; U.S. Private, pg. 604
KAISER PACIFIC PROPERTIES CORP.—Hanson PLC; Int'l, pg. 593
KAISER STEEL LAND DEVELOPMENT, INC.—Kaiser Ventures, Inc.; U.S. Public, pg. 941
KAJIMA DEVELOPMENT CORP.—Kajima Corporation; Int'l, pg. 722
KAPALUA LAND CO., LTD.—Maui Land & Pineapple Co., Inc.; U.S. Public, pg. 1060
KAUFMAN AND BROAD HOME CORPORATION; U.S. Public, pg. 944
KAUFMAN AND BROAD OF TEXAS, LTD.—Kaufman and Broad Home Corporation; U.S. Public, pg. 945
KEMMONS WILSON, INC.; U.S. Private, pg. 613
KERN COUNTY LAND CO.—Tenneco Inc.; U.S. Public, pg. 1578
KEVALAND CORP.—Holderbank Financiere Glaris Ltd.; Int'l, pg. 628
KEVALAND TEXAS CORP.—Holderbank Financiere Glaris Ltd.; Int'l, pg. 628
THE KEYES COMPANY REALTORS; U.S. Private, pg. 618
KILLEARN PROPERTIES, INC.; U.S. Public, pg. 956
KIMCO REALTY CORPORATION; U.S. Public, pg. 960
KINGFISHER PLC; Int'l, pg. 733
KITCHELL CORPORATION; U.S. Private, pg. 624
KLEINWORT BENSON LIMITED—Dresdner Bank AG; Int'l, pg. 420
KOLL CO.; U.S. Private, pg. 631
KOLL-TUSTIN BUSINESS CENTER—Cigna Corp.; U.S. Public, pg. 361
KORMAN SERVICES, L.P.; U.S. Private, pg. 632
KUMAGAI GUMI CO., LTD.; Int'l, pg. 763
KUMAGAI GUMI CO., LTD. HAWAII BRANCH—Kumagai Gumi Co., Ltd.; Int'l, pg. 764
KUMAGAI PROPERTIES INC.—Kumagai Gumi Co., Ltd.; Int'l, pg. 764
KVAERNER EIENDOM A.S—Kvaerner a.s.a.; Int'l, pg. 766
KVAERNER EIENDOM A.S, OSTFOLD FREDRIKSTAD DIVISION—Kvaerner a.s.a.; Int'l, pg. 766
KVAERNER EIENDOM A.S, OSTFOLD MOSS DIVISION—Kvaerner a.s.a.; Int'l, pg. 766
LB INDUSTRIES INC.; U.S. Private, pg. 639
LGS CONCORD CORP.—Citizens Utilities Company; U.S. Public, pg. 380
LL&E PROPERTIES, INC.—Burlington Resources Inc.; U.S. Public, pg. 269
LAING CONSTRUCTION SERVICES—John Laing PLC; Int'l, pg. 797
JOHN LAING DEVELOPMENTS, LTD.—John Laing PLC; Int'l, pg. 796
JOHN LAING PLC; Int'l, pg. 796
LAKE TAMARISK DEVELOPMENT CORPORATION—Kaiser Ventures, Inc.; U.S. Public, pg. 941
LANAI CO., LTD.—Castle & Cooke Inc.; U.S. Public, pg. 313
LANDAU & HEYMAN INC.; U.S. Private, pg. 646
LANDS OF SIERRA—Sierra Pacific Resources; U.S. Public, pg. 1470
LAVACA REALTY CO.—Southern Union Company; U.S. Public, pg. 1491

LEE VALLEY DEVELOPMENTS—British Aerospace p.l.c.; *Int'l*, pg. 218
LEFRAK ORGANIZATION INC.; *U.S. Private*, pg. 658
LENNAR CORPORATION; *U.S. Public*, pg. 987
THE LEVY ORGANIZATION; *U.S. Private*, pg. 664
LEVY REAL ESTATE PARTNERS—The Levy Organization; *U.S. Private*, pg. 664
LINCOLN PROPERTY COMPANY; *U.S. Private*, pg. 668
LLOYD PROPERTIES; *U.S. Private*, pg. 672
LONDON & LEEDS (USA) CORPORATION—Ladbroke Group Plc; *Int'l*, pg. 788
THE LOUISIANA PURCHASE—AMREP Corporation; *U.S. Public*, pg. 105
LUMAS REALTY, INC.; *U.S. Private*, pg. 680
LUSK; *U.S. Private*, pg. 681
M & T PARTNERS; *U.S. Private*, pg. 684
MCO PROPERTIES INC.—Maxxam Inc.; *U.S. Public*, pg. 1062
M.D.C. HOLDINGS, INC.; *U.S. Public*, pg. 1025
MDS INC.; *Int'l*, pg. 826
MEPC AMERICAN PROPERTIES; *U.S. Private*, pg. 686
THE MACERICH COMPANY; *U.S. Public*, pg. 1030
MAGUIRE PARTNERS; *U.S. Private*, pg. 696
MAJOR GROUP INC.—Acceptance Insurance Co., Inc.; *U.S. Public*, pg. 15
MALAMA PACIFIC CORP.—Hawaiian Electric Industries, Inc.; *U.S. Public*, pg. 800
MANUCAB LTD.—Manulife Financial (The Manufacturers Life Insurance Company); *Int'l*, pg. 840
MANUFACTURERS LIFE PROPERTY CORPORATION—Manulife Financial (The Manufacturers Life Insurance Company); *Int'l*, pg. 840
MANULIFE FINANCIAL—Manulife Financial (The Manufacturers Life Insurance Company); *Int'l*, pg. 840
MARKS & SPENCER PROPERTY HOLDINGS LIMITED—Marks & Spencer PLC; *Int'l*, pg. 842
AC MARTIN PARTNERS; *U.S. Private*, pg. 708
MATTEL REALTY CORPORATION—Mattel, Inc.; *U.S. Public*, pg. 1058
MAUI LAND & PINEAPPLE CO., INC.; *U.S. Public*, pg. 1060
MAURIN-OGDEN PROPERTIES; *U.S. Private*, pg. 715
MAXXAM INC.; *U.S. Public*, pg. 1062
MAXXAM PROPERTY COMPANY—Maxxam Inc.; *U.S. Public*, pg. 1062
MCKELLAR COMPANIES; *U.S. Private*, pg. 723
MENALVARO, S.A.—Vallehermoso, S.A.; *Int'l*, pg. 1447
METRO PARKING SYSTEMS—Metropolitan Properties Systems; *U.S. Private*, pg. 739
METROPOLITAN PROPERTIES SYSTEMS; *U.S. Private*, pg. 739
MICHAEL'S DEVELOPMENT COMPANY; *U.S. Private*, pg. 740
MILLER & SMITH, INC.; *U.S. Private*, pg. 746
THE MILLS CORPORATION; *U.S. Public*, pg. 1113
MILLSTEIN INDUSTRIES; *U.S. Private*, pg. 749
MISSION LAND COMPANY—Edison International; *U.S. Public*, pg. 564
MISSION VALLEY DEVELOPMENT CO.—CalMat Co.; *U.S. Public*, pg. 295
MISSION VIEJO COMPANY—Philip Morris Companies Inc.; *U.S. Public*, pg. 1289
MISSION WEST PROPERTIES; *U.S. Public*, pg. 1117
MITCHELL ENERGY & DEVELOPMENT CORP.; *U.S. Public*, pg. 1117
MITSUBISHI ESTATE CO., LTD.; *Int'l*, pg. 873
MITSUBISHI ESTATE NEW YORK, INC.—Mitsubishi Estate Co., Ltd.; *Int'l*, pg. 873
MITSUI FUDOSAN CO., LTD.; *Int'l*, pg. 882
MITSUI HARBOUR & URBAN CONSTRUCTION CO., LTD.—Mitsui & Co., Ltd.; *Int'l*, pg. 877
MITSUI REAL ESTATE DEVELOPMENT CO., LTD.—Mitsui & Co., Ltd.; *Int'l*, pg. 878
MOBIM—Allianz Aktiengesellschaft; *Int'l*, pg. 61
MOCENPLAZA DEVELOPMENT CORPORATION—Blount International, Inc.; *U.S. Public*, pg. 239
MONACHIA GRUNDSTUCKS-AKTIENGESELLSCHAFT—Hochtief AG; *Int'l*, pg. 623
MONARCH CONSTRUCTION LTD.—Taylor Woodrow plc; *Int'l*, pg. 1359
THE MONARCH GROUP—Taylor Woodrow plc; *Int'l*, pg. 1359
MONY VENTURES, INC.—The Mutual Life Insurance Company of New York; *U.S. Private*, pg. 769
MORGAN GRENFELL LAURIE LTD.—Deutsche Bank AG; *Int'l*, pg. 405
MOUNT BACHELOR VILLAGE CORP.—Brooks Resources Corporation; *U.S. Private*, pg. 172
JOHN MOWLEM & COMPANY PLC; *Int'l*, pg. 896
THE MUTUAL LIFE INSURANCE COMPANY OF NEW YORK; *U.S. Private*, pg. 769
NKK CORPORATION; *Int'l*, pg. 902
NLI PROPERTIES—Nippon Life Insurance Co.; *Int'l*, pg. 935
NTS DEVELOPMENT COMPANY; *U.S. Private*, pg. 772
NZ DEVELOPMENT CORPORATION—New Mexico & Arizona Land Co.; *U.S. Public*, pg. 1172
NATIONAL AMERICAN CORPORATION—U.S. Trails; *U.S. Public*, pg. 1688
NATIONAL BULK CARRIERS, INC.; *U.S. Private*, pg. 780
NATIONAL CITY COMMUNITY DEVELOPMENT CORP.—National City Corporation; *U.S. Public*, pg. 1154
NATIONAL DEVELOPMENT CO., INC.—Sunstates Corporation; *U.S. Public*, pg. 1536
NAVAJO WESTERN LAND CO.—Watkins Associated Industries Inc.; *U.S. Private*, pg. 1153
NAVINCA, S.A.—Vallehermoso, S.A.; *Int'l*, pg. 1447
THE NEWHALL LAND AND FARMING COMPANY; *U.S. Public*, pg. 1178
AL NEYER, INC.; *U.S. Private*, pg. 797
NORTH AMERICAN COMPANY; *U.S. Private*, pg. 803
NORTH WHITFORDS ESTATES PTY. LTD.—Taylor Woodrow plc; *Int'l*, pg. 1359
NORTHWESTERN ENGINEERING CO.; *U.S. Private*, pg. 806
OCEAN PROPERTIES, LTD.; *U.S. Private*, pg. 811
OERLIKON BUHRLE IMMOBILIEN AG—Oerlikon-Buhrle Holding AG; *Int'l*, pg. 998
OMAN INTERNATIONAL DEVELOPMENT CO. (LLC)—Taylor Woodrow plc; *Int'l*, pg. 1359
OPUS CORP.; *U.S. Private*, pg. 818
ORIENT-EXPRESS HOTELS INC.—Sea Containers Ltd.; *Int'l*, pg. 1213
ORIOLE HOMES CORP.; *U.S. Public*, pg. 1230
ORIX REAL ESTATE EQUITIES, INC.—Orix Corporation; *Int'l*, pg. 1009
OXFORD REALTY FINANCIAL GROUP; *U.S. Private*, pg. 825
P&O PROPERTY DEVELOPMENTS LTD.—The Peninsular and Oriental Steam Navigation Company; *Int'l*, pg. 1034
PIC REALTY CANADA LTD.—The Prudential Insurance Company of America; *U.S. Private*, pg. 893
PACIFIC HOLDING CORPORATION; *U.S. Private*, pg. 831
PACIFIC LIBRARY TOWER—Pacific Enterprises; *U.S. Public*, pg. 1249
PACIFIC LIGHTING REAL ESTATE GROUP—Pacific Enterprises; *U.S. Public*, pg. 1249
PACIFIC SQUARE CORPORATION—Northwest Natural Gas Company; *U.S. Public*, pg. 1200
PARAMOUNT DEVELOPMENT ASSOCS., INC.—Perini Corporation; *U.S. Public*, pg. 1278
PECO ENERGY COMPANY; *U.S. Public*, pg. 1268
PENN CENTRAL REAL ESTATE GROUP—American Financial Group; *U.S. Public*, pg. 75
PERCHERON PROPERTIES—Vaux Group Plc; *Int'l*, pg. 1454
PERFORMA ENTERTAINMENT REAL ESTATE, INC.; *U.S. Private*, pg. 853
PERINI LAND AND DEVELOPMENT CO.—Perini Corporation; *U.S. Public*, pg. 1278
J.M. PETERS CO.—Capital Pacific Holdings; *U.S. Public*, pg. 302
PETERSBURG LONG DISTANCE INC.; *Int'l*, pg. 1040
PETRON, INC.; *U.S. Private*, pg. 859
PHILIP MORRIS COMPANIES INC.; *U.S. Public*, pg. 1287
PIONEER HI-BRED INTERNATIONAL, INC.; *U.S. Public*, pg. 1298
PITTWAY CORPORATION; *U.S. Public*, pg. 1305
PITTWAY REAL ESTATE—Pittway Corporation; *U.S. Public*, pg. 1306
PORTA HOLDINGS INC.—Melitta Unternehmensgruppe Bentz KG; *Int'l*, pg. 857
PORTAGE DEVELOPMENT, INC.—Forest City Enterprises, Inc.; *U.S. Public*, pg. 669
PORTUMBRIA, S.A.—Vallehermoso, S.A.; *Int'l*, pg. 1447
POTO PI, S.A.—Vallehermoso, S.A.; *Int'l*, pg. 1447
PROCOTER, S.A.—Vallehermoso, S.A.; *Int'l*, pg. 1447
PROFESSIONAL APARTMENT MANAGEMENT, INC.; *U.S. Private*, pg. 889
PROGRESS WEST CORPORATION; *U.S. Private*, pg. 890
PROPERTIES DIVISION—Reynolds Metals Company; *U.S. Public*, pg. 1386
THE PRUDENTIAL - JON DOUGLAS COMPANY—The Prudential Insurance Company of America; *U.S. Private*, pg. 892
THE PRUDENTIAL REALTY GROUP—The Prudential Insurance Company of America; *U.S. Private*, pg. 892
PUGET WESTERN, INC.—Puget Sound Energy, Inc.; *U.S. Public*, pg. 1342
PURCELL CO., INC.; *U.S. Private*, pg. 895
LAT PURSER & ASSOCIATES; *U.S. Private*, pg. 896
THE PYRAMID COMPANIES; *U.S. Private*, pg. 896
QUADRANGLE DEVELOPMENT CORPORATION; *U.S. Private*, pg. 898
THE QUADRANT CORPORATION—Weyerhaeuser Company; *U.S. Public*, pg. 1764
R & R HOMES, INC.—Forest City Enterprises, Inc.; *U.S. Public*, pg. 669
REDGO PROPERTIES, INC.—Relm Wireless Corp.; *U.S. Public*, pg. 1376
REGENCY ASSOCIATES LIMITED PARTNERSHIP; *U.S. Private*, pg. 918
REGENCY GROUP INC.; *U.S. Private*, pg. 918
REGIONAL DEVELOPMENT CORP.—Family Inns of America, Inc.; *U.S. Private*, pg. 393
RELIANCE DEVELOPMENT GROUP INC.—Reliance Group Holdings, Inc.; *U.S. Public*, pg. 1374
RELIANCE LAND CO.—CalMat Co.; *U.S. Public*, pg. 296
RENAISSANCE HOTEL GROUP N.V.—Marriott International, Inc.; *U.S. Public*, pg. 1048
RENDFIELD LAND COMPANY, INC.—Minnesota Power; *U.S. Public*, pg. 1116
REUBEN ORGANIZATION; *U.S. Private*, pg. 925
REYNEN, BARDIS & WINN; *U.S. Private*, pg. 926
RIDGEWOOD PROPERTIES, INC.; *U.S. Public*, pg. 1389
RIO GRANDE LAND CO.—Union Pacific Corporation; *U.S. Public*, pg. 1668
RIO NORTE ESTE CO.—CalMat Co.; *U.S. Public*, pg. 296
RIO RANCHO—AMREP Corporation; *U.S. Public*, pg. 105
RIUNIONE ADRIATICA DI SICURTA S.P.A.—Allianz Aktiengesellschaft; *Int'l*, pg. 61
RIVER VISTA DEVELOPMENT CO.—CalMat Co.; *U.S. Public*, pg. 296
RIVIERA LAND CORP.—Lennar Corporation; *U.S. Public*, pg. 989
ROBSON COMMUNITIES; *U.S. Private*, pg. 937
ROCKY RIVER REALTY COMPANY—Northeast Utilities; *U.S. Public*, pg. 1195
ROSEN ASSOCIATES MANAGEMENT CORP.; *U.S. Private*, pg. 945
ROSENSHEIN ASSOCIATES; *U.S. Private*, pg. 945
ROSEWOOD PROPERTY COMPANY; *U.S. Private*, pg. 946
JACK ROSS MOTORS INC.; *U.S. Private*, pg. 946
ROTHCHILD REALTY INC.—Rothschild North America Inc.; *U.S. Private*, pg. 947
ROTTERDAM VENTURES INC.—Galesi Group; *U.S. Private*, pg. 437
ROUSE COMMERCIAL DEVELOPMENT DIV.—The Rouse Company; *U.S. Public*, pg. 1407
THE ROUSE COMPANY; *U.S. Public*, pg. 1407
ROUSE OFFICE & COMMUNITY DEVELOPMENT DIV.—The Rouse Company; *U.S. Public*, pg. 1407
H.J. RUSSELL & CO.; *U.S. Private*, pg. 952
SFIC PROPERTIES, INC.—Kuwait Petroleum Corporation; *Int'l*, pg. 765
SJW CORP.; *U.S. Public*, pg. 1418
SJW LAND COMPANY—SJW Corp.; *U.S. Public*, pg. 1418
SRDC, INC.—Forest City Enterprises, Inc.; *U.S. Public*, pg. 670
SACHS HOLDING COMPANY; *U.S. Private*, pg. 959
SADDLEBAG LAKE RESORTS, INC.—Alico, Inc.; *U.S. Public*, pg. 41
ST. PAUL FINANCIAL DEVELOPMENT CORP.—St. Paul Bancorp, Inc.; *U.S. Public*, pg. 1429
SAN JUVA, S.A.—Vallehermoso, S.A.; *Int'l*, pg. 1447
SAN LUIS ESTATES, INC.—Commerce Group Corp.; *U.S. Public*, pg. 410
L.M. SANDLER & SONS; *U.S. Private*, pg. 964
SCANA—SCANA Corporation; *U.S. Public*, pg. 1436
SEACO TEXAS PROPERTIES INC.—Sea Containers Ltd.; *Int'l*, pg. 1213
KENNETH M. SEATON ENTERPRISES—Family Inns of America, Inc.; *U.S. Private*, pg. 393
SHAPCO, INC.; *U.S. Private*, pg. 989
SHAPELL INDUSTRIES, INC.; *U.S. Private*, pg. 990
SHERWAY CENTER LIMITED—The Canada Life Assurance Company; *Int'l*, pg. 255
SHIMIZU CORPORATION; *Int'l*, pg. 1233
SHOLODGE, INC.; *U.S. Public*, pg. 1467
SHOPPING CENTRE GROUP—Cambridge Shopping Centres Limited; *Int'l*, pg. 253
SHUWA CORPORATION; *Int'l*, pg. 1237
SHUWA CORP. OF NEW YORK—Shuwa Corporation; *Int'l*, pg. 1237
SHUWA INVESTMENTS CORP.—Shuwa Corporation; *Int'l*, pg. 1237
SHUWA TRUST OF BOSTON—Shuwa Corporation; *Int'l*, pg. 1237
SIERRA PACIFIC RESOURCES; *U.S. Public*, pg. 1470
SILVER BROOK REAL ESTATE DEVELOPMENT COMPANY—Cigna Corp.; *U.S. Public*, pg. 358
SIME DARBY BERHAD; *Int'l*, pg. 1249
SINOCHEM INTERNATIONAL PETROLEUM CO. LTD.; *Int'l*, pg. 1254
SKANSKA AB; *Int'l*, pg. 1260
SKANSKA (U.S.A.) INC.—Skanska AB; *Int'l*, pg. 1261
SMITHGROUP, INC.; *U.S. Private*, pg. 1010
THE SOLENDER GROUP, INC.; *U.S. Private*, pg. 1012
SOUTHEASTERN DEVELOPMENT COMPANY—Southeastern Michigan Gas Enterprises, Inc.; *U.S. Public*, pg. 1489
SOUTHEASTERN REALTY GROUP INC.; *U.S. Private*, pg. 1015
SOUTHERN CALIFORNIA GAS TOWER—Pacific Enterprises; *U.S. Public*, pg. 1249
SOUTHERN DEVELOPMENT CO.—Kansas City Southern Industries, Inc.; *U.S. Public*, pg. 944
SOUTHERN LIFE PROPERTY HOLDINGS LIMITED—Anglo American Corporation of South Africa Limited; *Int'l*, pg. 77
SOUTHWESTERN ENERGY COMPANY; *U.S. Public*, pg. 1494
SPATZ CENTERS INC.; *U.S. Private*, pg. 1021
SPEEDWAY DEVELOPMENT CORP.—Kaiser Ventures, Inc.; *U.S. Public*, pg. 941
SSANGYONG ENGINEERING & CONSTRUCTION (AMERICA), INC.—Ssangyong Business Group; *Int'l*, pg. 1292
SSANGYONG INTERNATIONAL INC.—Ssangyong Business Group; *Int'l*, pg. 1292
SSANGYONG SACRAMENTO LTD.—Ssangyong Business Group; *Int'l*, pg. 1292
STEARNS ENTERPRISES, INC.; *U.S. Private*, pg. 1037
STEINBERG INC.—Socanav Inc.; *Int'l*, pg. 1272
STILES CORPORATION; *U.S. Private*, pg. 1043
STONE & WEBSTER, INCORPORATED; *U.S. Public*, pg. 1519
SUMIKIN BUSSAN CORPORATION; *Int'l*, pg. 1308
SUN COMPANY, INC.; *U.S. Public*, pg. 1530
SUNCOR DEVELOPMENT COMPANY—Pinnacle West Capital Corporation; *U.S. Public*, pg. 1298
SUNRISE DEVELOPMENT CO.—Forest City Enterprises, Inc.; *U.S. Public*, pg. 669
SUNRISE LAND CO.—Forest City Enterprises, Inc.; *U.S. Public*, pg. 670
SUNSTATES CORPORATION; *U.S. Public*, pg. 1536
SUNSTATES REALTY GROUP INC.—Sunstates Corporation; *U.S. Public*, pg. 1536
SVERDRUP CORPORATION; *U.S. Private*, pg. 1057
SYNDESIS DEVELOPMENT CORP.—Wisconsin Energy Corporation; *U.S. Public*, pg. 1773
TRI REALTY, INC.—Case Corporation; *U.S. Public*, pg. 312
TAISEI CORPORATION; *Int'l*, pg. 1347
TALLEY INDUSTRIES, INC.—Carpenter Technology Corporation; *U.S. Public*, pg. 307
TALLEY REALTY GROUP—Carpenter Technology Corporation; *U.S. Public*, pg. 308
TALLEY REALTY INVESTMENT GROUP, INC.—Carpenter Technology Corporation; *U.S. Public*, pg. 308
TAYLOR-MORLEY, INC.; *U.S. Private*, pg. 1071
TAYLOR WOODROW (AUSTRALIA) PTY. LIMITED—Taylor Woodrow plc; *Int'l*, pg. 1359
TAYLOR WOODROW CORSER PTY. LIMITED—Taylor Woodrow plc; *Int'l*, pg. 1359
TAYLOR WOODROW INTERNATIONAL NZ LIMITED—Taylor Woodrow plc; *Int'l*, pg. 1359
TAYLOR WOODROW OF GIBRALTAR LIMITED—Taylor Woodrow plc; *Int'l*, pg. 1360
TAYLOR WOODROW OF NIGERIA LIMITED—Taylor Woodrow plc; *Int'l*, pg. 1360

TAYLOR WOODROW PROPERTY HOLDINGS PTY. LTD.—Taylor Woodrow plc; Int'l, pg. 1360
TAYLOR WOODROW-TOWELL CO. (LLC)—Taylor Woodrow plc; Int'l, pg. 1360
TAYLOR WOODROW (VICTORIA) PTY. LTD.—Taylor Woodrow plc; Int'l, pg. 1360
TAYSEC PROPERTIES LTD.—Taylor Woodrow plc; Int'l, pg. 1360
TEAMWORK SAUDI ARABIA LIMITED—Taylor Woodrow plc; Int'l, pg. 1360
TECH-SYM CORPORATION; U.S. Public, pg. 1563
TECLA, S.A.—Caja de Madrid Group; Int'l, pg. 252
TEJON RANCH COMPANY; U.S. Public, pg. 1566
TEMPLE-INLAND FINANCIAL SERVICES, INC—Temple-Inland Inc.; U.S. Public, pg. 1575
TEMPLE-INLAND INC.; U.S. Public, pg. 1574
TEMPLE-INLAND MORTGAGE CORPORATION—Temple-Inland Inc.; U.S. Public, pg. 1575
TENNECO REALTY, INC.—Tenneco Inc.; U.S. Public, pg. 1578
TEXAS INDUSTRIES, INC.; U.S. Public, pg. 1585
TEXAS PACIFIC LAND TRUST; U.S. Public, pg. 1586
THETA LAND CORPORATION—Pennsylvania Enterprises Inc.; U.S. Public, pg. 1272
TISHMAN REALTY & CONSTRUCTION CO., INC.; U.S. Private, pg. 1089
TOSHIBA BUILDING CORPORATION—Toshiba Corporation; Int'l, pg. 1403
TOWNE PROPERTIES; U.S. Private, pg. 1093
TOWNE REALTY, INC.—Zilber, Ltd.; U.S. Private, pg. 1206
TRAFALGAR HOUSE PLC—Kvaerner a.s.a.; Int'l, pg. 772
TRAFALGAR HOUSE PROPERTY, INC.—Kvaerner a.s.a.; Int'l, pg. 774
TRAMMELL CROW COMPANY; U.S. Public, pg. 1628
TRAMMELL CROW RESIDENTIAL SERVICES; U.S. Private, pg. 1095
TRANSAMERICA REALTY SERVICES, INC.—Transamerica Corporation; U.S. Public, pg. 1630
TRI-STATE IMPROVEMENT CO.—Cinergy Corp.; U.S. Public, pg. 369
TRIDEL ENTERPRISES INC.; Int'l, pg. 1423
THE TRUMP GROUP; U.S. Private, pg. 1107
TRUMP ORGANIZATION; U.S. Private, pg. 1108
THE TURNER CORPORATION; U.S. Public, pg. 1645
TURNER DEVELOPMENT CORPORATION—The Turner Corporation; U.S. Public, pg. 1646
TUROVALLES, S.A.—Vallehermoso, S.A.; Int'l, pg. 1447
UMB PROPERTIES, INC.—UMB Financial Corporation; U.S. Public, pg. 1655
USX REALTY DEVELOPMENT—USX Corporation; U.S. Public, pg. 1661
UNION PACIFIC CORPORATION; U.S. Public, pg. 1667
UNITED OVERSEAS LAND LIMITED; Int'l, pg. 1443
UNITED PROPERTIES GROUP—United Water Resources; U.S. Public, pg. 1692
U S WEST INC.; U.S. Public, pg. 1688
UNITIKA LTD.; Int'l, pg. 1444
UNIVERSAL AMERICAN REALTY CORP.—Lennar Corporation; U.S. Public, pg. 989
UNIVERSAL DEVELOPERS, INC.—Commerce Group Corp.; U.S. Public, pg. 410
UNIVERSAL WILTON INC.—Universal Corporation; U.S. Public, pg. 1695
UNIVESCO INC.; U.S. Private, pg. 1128
UNUM DEVELOPMENT CORP.—UNUM Corporation; U.S. Public, pg. 1699
URBAN GROUP—Cambridge Shopping Centres Limited; Int'l, pg. 253
URLOCER, S.A.—Vallehermoso, S.A.; Int'l, pg. 1447
UTO ALBIS AG—Oerlikon-Buhrle Holding AG; Int'l, pg. 998
UTRAS—Allianz Aktiengesellschaft; Int'l, pg. 62
VALLE AGORA S.A.—Vallehermoso, S.A.; Int'l, pg. 1447
VALLEHERMOSO, S.A.; Int'l, pg. 1447
THE VAN METRES COMPANIES; U.S. Private, pg. 1132
VAUX GROUP PLC; Int'l, pg. 1453
VERISOL, S.A.—Vallehermoso, S.A.; Int'l, pg. 1447
W.B. HOMES, INC.—Lennar Corporation; U.S. Public, pg. 989
WCI COMMUNITIES, INC.; U.S. Private, pg. 1144
J.W. WALTER, INC.—Walter Industries, Inc.; U.S. Public, pg. 1736
WALTER LAND CO.—Walter Industries, Inc.; U.S. Public, pg. 1737
WASHINGTON SERVICES, INC.—Washington Federal Savings; U.S. Public, pg. 1740
WATERWAY HOLDINGS, INC.—NIPSCO Industries, Inc.; U.S. Public, pg. 1185
WEST JAPAN RAILWAY COMPANY; Int'l, pg. 1490
WESTINGHOUSE INDUSTRIES & TECHNOLOGIES GROUP—CBS Corporation; U.S. Public, pg. 273
WESTVACO DEVELOPMENT CORP.—Westvaco Corporation; U.S. Public, pg. 1762
WEYERHAEUSER COMPANY; U.S. Public, pg. 1764
THE WILDER COMPANIES; U.S. Private, pg. 1176
WILMINGTON HOMES, INC.—The Rouse Company; U.S. Public, pg. 1409
WILMORITE, INC.; U.S. Private, pg. 1180
WILSEY BENNETT CO.; U.S. Private, pg. 1180
WILSEY BENNETT REAL ESTATE DIVISION—Wilsey Bennett Co.; U.S. Private, pg. 1180
JIM WILSON & ASSOCIATES, INC.; U.S. Private, pg. 1181
WILSON MILLS LAND COMPANY—The Progressive Corporation; U.S. Public, pg. 1335
WINMAR COMPANY—SAFECO Corporation; U.S. Public, pg. 1423
WINROCK ENTERPRISES, INC.; U.S. Private, pg. 1183
WISCONSIN ENERGY CORPORATION; U.S. Public, pg. 1773
WISPARK CORPORATION—Wisconsin Energy Corporation; U.S. Public, pg. 1773
WOHN-UND GESCHAEFTSBAUTEN GMBH—Philipp Holzmann AG; Int'l, pg. 633
WUESTENROT HOLDING GMBH; Int'l, pg. 1514
XEROX REALTY CORPORATION—Xerox Corporation; U.S. Public, pg. 1785
ZAREMBA GROUP, INC.; U.S. Private, pg. 1204

6553 — CEMETERY SUBDIVIDERS & DEVELOPERS

CHRISTIAN MEMORIAL CULTURAL CENTER; U.S. Private, pg. 238
DESC, S.A. DE C.V.; Int'l, pg. 395
D.W. NEWCOMER'S SONS, INC.; U.S. Private, pg. 796
SECURITY INDUSTRIAL INSURANCE CO., INC.—The Loewen Group, Inc.; Int'l, pg. 814
SERVICE CORPORATION INTERNATIONAL; U.S. Public, pg. 1460
STEWART ENTERPRISES, INC.; U.S. Public, pg. 1518
ASHLEY F. WARD, INC.; U.S. Private, pg. 1149

6712 — OFFICES OF BANK HOLDING COMPANIES

ABN-AMRO HOLDING N.V.; Int'l, pg. 8
ABN-AMRO NORTH AMERICA INC., CHICAGO—ABN-AMRO Holding N.V.; Int'l, pg. 10
ABN/LASALLE NORTH AMERICA INC.—ABN-AMRO Holding N.V.; Int'l, pg. 11
API GROUP INC.; U.S. Private, pg. 7
ADVANTA CORP.; U.S. Public, pg. 22
ALBANK FINANCIAL CORPORATION; U.S. Public, pg. 36
ALGEMENE BANK NEDERLAND N.V.—ABN-AMRO Holding N.V.; Int'l, pg. 9
ALLIED IRISH BANKS, P.L.C.; Int'l, pg. 64
ALMANIJ N.V.; Int'l, pg. 65
AMERIANA BANCORP; U.S. Public, pg. 66
AMSOUTH BANCORPORATION; U.S. Public, pg. 105
AMSTERDAM-ROTTERDAM BANK N.V.—ABN-AMRO Holding N.V.; Int'l, pg. 9
ANCHOR FINANCIAL CORPORATION; U.S. Public, pg. 111
ANDOVER BANCORP, INC.; U.S. Public, pg. 111
ARROW FINANCIAL CORPORATION; U.S. Public, pg. 135
ASIAN CAPITAL PARTNERS HOLDINGS LIMITED—Dresdner Bank AG; Int'l, pg. 420
ASSOCIATED BANC-CORP; U.S. Public, pg. 140
AUSTIN JET LTD.; U.S. Private, pg. 100
BB&T CORPORATION; U.S. Public, pg. 159
BB&T OF SOUTH CAROLINA—BB&T Corporation; U.S. Public, pg. 160
BB&T REGIONAL HEADQUARTERS—BB&T Corporation; U.S. Public, pg. 160
B.M.J. FINANCIAL CORP.—Summit Bancorp; U.S. Public, pg. 1528
BNP UK HOLDINGS LTD.—Banque Nationale de Paris; Int'l, pg. 164
BOK FINANCIAL CORP.; U.S. Public, pg. 163
BT FINANCIAL CORPORATION; U.S. Public, pg. 163
BANC ONE CAPITAL CORPORATION—Banc One Corporation; U.S. Public, pg. 175
BANC ONE CORPORATION; U.S. Public, pg. 172
BANC ONE INDIANA CORPORATION—Banc One Corporation; U.S. Public, pg. 173
BANC ONE KENTUCKY CORPORATION—Banc One Corporation; U.S. Public, pg. 173
BANC ONE OHIO CORPORATION—Banc One Corporation; U.S. Public, pg. 173
BANCA DI ROMA; Int'l, pg. 135
BANCA MARCH S.A.; Int'l, pg. 136
BANCO POPULAR DE PUERTO RICO; U.S. Public, pg. 175
BANCO SANTANDER; Int'l, pg. 143
BANCORP SOUTH INC.; U.S. Public, pg. 176
BANK OF AMERICA—BankAmerica Corporation; U.S. Public, pg. 180
BANK OF BOSTON CONNECTICUT—BankBoston Corporation; U.S. Public, pg. 184
THE BANK OF NEW YORK COMPANY, INC.; U.S. Public, pg. 178
THE BANK OF TOKYO-MITSUBISHI, LTD.; Int'l, pg. 157
BANK ONE, COLORADO—Banc One Corporation; U.S. Public, pg. 173
BANK ONE, LOUISIANA—Banc One Corporation; U.S. Public, pg. 173
BANK ONE, ROCKFORD, NA—Banc One Corporation; U.S. Public, pg. 173
BANK ONE, WISCONSIN—Banc One Corporation; U.S. Public, pg. 174
BANKAMERICA CORPORATION; U.S. Public, pg. 179
BANKATLANTIC BANCORP, INC.; U.S. Public, pg. 183
BANKBOSTON CORPORATION; U.S. Public, pg. 183
BANKERS TRUST NEW YORK CORPORATION; U.S. Public, pg. 185
BANKMONT FINANCIAL CORP.—Bank of Montreal; Int'l, pg. 154
BANKNORTH GROUP INC.; U.S. Public, pg. 186
BANPONCE CORPORATION—Banco Popular de Puerto Rico; U.S. Public, pg. 176
BANQUE DE FRANCE; Int'l, pg. 160
BANQUE IPPA & ASSOCIATES—Groupe Bruxelles Lambert S.A.; Int'l, pg. 562
BARCLAYS BANK PLC; Int'l, pg. 164
BARCLAYS EUROPEAN INVESTMENT HOLDINGS SA—Barclays Bank PLC; Int'l, pg. 166
BARCLAYS MERCANTILE BUSINESS FINANCE LIMITED—Barclays Bank PLC; Int'l, pg. 165
BARNETT BANKS, INC.—NationsBank Corporation; U.S. Public, pg. 1162
BARTLETT & CO.—Legg Mason, Inc.; U.S. Public, pg. 985
BAY AREA BANCSHARES; U.S. Private, pg. 124
BAY VIEW CAPITAL CORPORATION; U.S. Public, pg. 197
BAYBANKS, INC.—BankBoston Corporation; U.S. Public, pg. 184
BOULEVARD BANCORP, INC.—U.S. Bancorp; U.S. Public, pg. 1680
BRENTON BANKS, INC.; U.S. Public, pg. 251
BROAD NATIONAL BANCORPORATION; U.S. Public, pg. 257
CB BETEILIGUNGS UND VERWALTUNGSGESELLSCHAFT MBH—The Chase Manhattan Corporation; U.S. Public, pg. 339
CCB CO-OP BANK LIMITED—Coop Switzerland; Int'l, pg. 329
CFX BANK; U.S. Public, pg. 277
CIBC HOLDINGS (CAYMAN) LIMITED—Canadian Imperial Bank of Commerce; Int'l, pg. 257
CIBC NEW ZEALAND HOLDINGS LIMITED—Canadian Imperial Bank of Commerce; Int'l, pg. 258
CNB BANCSHARES, INC.; U.S. Public, pg. 280
CPB INC.; U.S. Public, pg. 282
CALIFORNIA STATE BANK-LA HABRA—California State Bank; U.S. Public, pg. 294
CANADIAN IMPERIAL HOLDINGS, INC.—Canadian Imperial Bank of Commerce; Int'l, pg. 257
CANADIAN WESTERN BANK; Int'l, pg. 259
CASCO-NORTHERN CORPORATION—BankBoston Corporation; U.S. Public, pg. 184
CATHAY FINANCE INTERNATIONAL (HOLDINGS) LIMITED—The International Commercial Bank of China; Int'l, pg. 684
CENTURA BANKS, INC.; U.S. Public, pg. 328
CHARTER ONE FINANCIAL, INC.; U.S. Public, pg. 336
THE CHASE MANHATTAN CORPORATION; U.S. Public, pg. 337
CHEMICAL FINANCIAL CORPORATION; U.S. Public, pg. 345
CHITTENDEN CORPORATION; U.S. Public, pg. 350
CHRISTIANIA BANK-LONDON BRANCH—Christiania Bank og Kreditkasse ASA; Int'l, pg. 289
CITICORP; U.S. Public, pg. 376
CITIZENS BANK OF CENTRAL INDIANA—CNB Bancshares, Inc.; U.S. Public, pg. 280
CITIZENS FINANCIAL GROUP, INC.—The Royal Bank of Scotland plc; Int'l, pg. 1132
CITY NATIONAL CORPORATION; U.S. Public, pg. 380
COAST SAVINGS FINANCIAL, INC.; U.S. Public, pg. 388
THE COLONIAL BANCGROUP, INC.; U.S. Public, pg. 400
COLORADO BUSINESS BANKSHARES, INC.; U.S. Private, pg. 255
COLORADO NATIONAL BANKSHARES, INC.—U.S. Bancorp; U.S. Public, pg. 1680
COMERICA INCORPORATED; U.S. Public, pg. 408
COMMERCE BANCSHARES, INC.; U.S. Public, pg. 409
COMMERCIAL FEDERAL CORPORATION; U.S. Public, pg. 411
COMMUNITY BANCORP; U.S. Public, pg. 416
COMPASS BANCSHARES, INC.; U.S. Public, pg. 418
CORESTATES FINANCIAL CORP.; U.S. Public, pg. 446
CORPORACION FINANCIERA CAJA DE MADRID, S.A.—Caja de Madrid Group; Int'l, pg. 251
COUNTRYWIDE HOME LOANS INC.; U.S. Public, pg. 452
CREDIT SUISSE GROUP; Int'l, pg. 345
CRESTAR FINANCIAL CORPORATION; U.S. Public, pg. 458
CULLEN/FROST BANKERS, INC.; U.S. Public, pg. 467
CUMMINS-ALLISON CORP.; U.S. Private, pg. 295
D & N FINANCIAL CORPORATION; U.S. Public, pg. 472
DBS CAPITAL INVESTMENTS LTD.—DBS Bank Ltd.; Int'l, pg. 350
DE NEUFLIZE, SCHLUMBERGER, MALLET S.A.—ABN-AMRO Holding N.V.; Int'l, pg. 12
DEPOSIT GUARANTY CORP.; U.S. Public, pg. 500
DORLING KINDERSLEY HOLDINGS PLC; Int'l, pg. 416
EUROPEAN AMERICAN BANK—ABN-AMRO Holding N.V.; Int'l, pg. 9
EXCHANGE BANK; U.S. Public, pg. 599
FHI INTERNATIONAL, INC.—First Hawaiian, Inc.; U.S. Public, pg. 634
F.N.B. CORPORATION; U.S. Public, pg. 607
F.W.S.F. CORPORATION—Firstar Corporation; U.S. Public, pg. 643
FAIRFAX FINANCIAL HOLDINGS LIMITED; Int'l, pg. 476
FEDERATED DEPARTMENT STORES, INC.; U.S. Public, pg. 617
FIFTH THIRD BANCORP; U.S. Public, pg. 621
FINANCIAL TRUST CORP—Keystone Financial Inc.; U.S. Public, pg. 956
FIRST AMERICAN CORPORATION; U.S. Public, pg. 624
THE FIRST AMERICAN FINANCIAL CORPORATION; U.S. Public, pg. 624
FIRST BANKS AMERICA, INC.; U.S. Public, pg. 626
FIRST BANKS, INC.—First Banks America, Inc.; U.S. Public, pg. 626
FIRST CHARTER CORPORATION; U.S. Public, pg. 627
FIRST CHICAGO FINANCIAL CORP.—First Chicago NBD Corporation; U.S. Public, pg. 628
FIRST CHICAGO NBD CORPORATION; U.S. Public, pg. 627
FIRST CITIZENS BANC SHARES, INC.; U.S. Public, pg. 628
FIRST COMMERCE CORPORATION; U.S. Public, pg. 629
FIRST COMMERCIAL CORPORATION; U.S. Public, pg. 630
FIRST EMPIRE STATE CORPORATION; U.S. Public, pg. 631
FIRST FARMERS & MERCHANTS NATIONAL BANK; U.S. Private, pg. 407
FIRST FINANCIAL BANCORP; U.S. Public, pg. 632
FIRST FINANCIAL BANKSHARES, INC.; U.S. Public, pg. 633
FIRST FINANCIAL CORPORATION; U.S. Public, pg. 633
FIRST FINANCIAL CORPORATION—Associated Banc-Corp; U.S. Public, pg. 140
FIRST FINANCIAL HOLDINGS, INC.; U.S. Public, pg. 634
FIRST HAWAIIAN, INC.; U.S. Public, pg. 634
FIRST INDIANA CORPORATION—The Somerset Group, Inc.; U.S. Public, pg. 1484

FIRST INTERNATIONAL BANCORP, INC.; *U.S. Public*, pg. 635
FIRST MARYLAND BANCORP—Allied Irish Banks, p.l.c.; *Int'l*, pg. 64
FIRST MIDWEST BANCORP, INC.; *U.S. Public*, pg. 636
FIRST NATIONAL BANK HOLDINGS LIMITED; *Int'l*, pg. 487
FIRST OF AMERICA BANK CORPORATION; *U.S. Public*, pg. 636
FIRST PACIFIC COMPANY LIMITED; *Int'l*, pg. 487
FIRST SECURITY CORPORATION; *U.S. Public*, pg. 637
1ST SOURCE CORPORATION; *U.S. Public*, pg. 638
FIRST TENNESSEE NATIONAL CORPORATION; *U.S. Public*, pg. 638
FIRST UNION CORPORATION; *U.S. Public*, pg. 639
FIRST UNION NATIONAL BANK OF FLORIDA—First Union Corporation; *U.S. Public*, pg. 640
FIRST UNION NATIONAL BANK OF GEORGIA—First Union Corporation; *U.S. Public*, pg. 640
FIRST UNITED BANCSHARES, INC.; *U.S. Public*, pg. 641
FIRST VALLEY CORPORATION—Summit Bancorp; *U.S. Public*, pg. 1528
FIRST VIRGINIA BANKS, INC.; *U.S. Public*, pg. 641
FIRST WESTERN BANCORP, INC.; *U.S. Public*, pg. 642
FIRSTAR CORPORATION; *U.S. Public*, pg. 642
FIRSTAR CORPORATION-IOWA—Firstar Corporation; *U.S. Public*, pg. 643
FIRSTFED FINANCIAL CORP.; *U.S. Public*, pg. 645
FIRSTMERIT CORPORATION; *U.S. Public*, pg. 646
FLEET BANK, N.A.—Fleet Financial Group, Inc.; *U.S. Public*, pg. 649
FLEET BANK NH—Fleet Financial Group, Inc.; *U.S. Public*, pg. 649
FLEET BANK OF MAINE—Fleet Financial Group, Inc.; *U.S.* Public, pg. 649
FLEET BANK OF MASSACHUSETTS, N.A.—Fleet Financial Group, Inc.; *U.S. Public*, pg. 649
FLEET FINANCIAL GROUP, INC.; *U.S. Public*, pg. 648
FRONT ROYAL, INC.; *U.S. Private*, pg. 430
THE FUJI BANK, LIMITED; *Int'l*, pg. 519
GSC ENTERPRISES, INC.; *U.S. Private*, pg. 436
GESMADRID S.G.I.I.C., S.A.—Caja de Madrid Group; *Int'l*, pg. 251
GOLDEN WEST FINANCIAL CORPORATION; *U.S. Public*, pg. 750
GREAT LAKES FINANCIAL RESOURCES, INC.; *U.S. Private*, pg. 474
GREAT WESTERN FINANCIAL CORPORATION—Washington Mutual Inc.; *U.S. Public*, pg. 1741
GREATBANC, INC.; *U.S. Public*, pg. 760
GROUPE BRUXELLES LAMBERT S.A.; *Int'l*, pg. 561
GUARANTEE TITLE & TRUST CO.; *U.S. Private*, pg. 485
HSBC AMERICAS—HSBC Holdings plc; *Int'l*, pg. 580
HSBC HOLDINGS INC.—HSBC Holdings plc; *Int'l*, pg. 581
HSBC HOLDINGS PLC; *Int'l*, pg. 579
HARRIS BANKCORP, INC.—Bank of Montreal; *Int'l*, pg. 154
HELLER INTERNATIONAL CORPORATION—The Fuji Bank, Limited; *Int'l*, pg. 519
HIBERNIA CORPORATION; *U.S. Public*, pg. 825
HIGH POINT FINANCIAL CORP.; *U.S. Public*, pg. 826
HOME BENEFICIAL CORPORATION—American General Corporation; *U.S. Public*, pg. 76
THE HONGKONG AND SHANGHAI BANKING CORPORATION LIMITED (HONGKONGBANK)—HSBC Holdings plc; *Int'l*, pg. 583
HORIZON BANCORP; *U.S. Private*, pg. 538
HORIZON BANCORP, INC.; *U.S. Public*, pg. 836
HUBCO, INC.; *U.S. Public*, pg. 845
HUNTINGTON BANCSHARES INC.; *U.S. Public*, pg. 849
ILLINOIS BANC ONE CORPORATION—Banc One Corporation; *U.S. Public*, pg. 174
IMPERIAL BANCORP; *U.S. Public*, pg. 871
INDEPENDENT BANK CORPORATION; *U.S. Public*, pg. 874
INDEPENDENT BANKSHARES, INC.; *U.S. Public*, pg. 874
INDUSTRIE-BETEILIGUNGS GESELLSCHAFTMBH—BHF-BANK AG; *Int'l*, pg. 119
INTERNATIONAL BANCSHARES CORP; *U.S. Private*, pg. 568
JARDINE FLEMING HOLDINGS LTD.—Robert Fleming Holdings Ltd.; *Int'l*, pg. 494
KEY BANK OF COLORADO—Keycorp; *U.S. Public*, pg. 954
KEYCORP; *U.S. Public*, pg. 954
KEYSTONE BANK—Keystone Financial Inc.; *U.S. Public*, pg. 956
KEYSTONE HERITAGE GROUP, INC.—Fulton Financial Corp.; *U.S. Public*, pg. 687
J.I. KISLAK MORTGAGE CORPORATION—J.I. Kislak Inc.; *U.S. Private*, pg. 624
LAKELAND FINANCIAL CORPORATION; *U.S. Public*, pg. 975
LEGG MASON, INC.; *U.S. Public*, pg. 984
LIBERTY BANCORP, INC.—Banc One Corporation; *U.S. Public*, pg. 174
LIECHTENSTEIN GLOBAL TRUST LIMITED; *Int'l*, pg. 809
MNC FINANCIAL, INC.—First Tennessee National Corporation; *U.S. Public*, pg. 639
MAGNA GROUP, INC.; *U.S. Public*, pg. 1037
MAINSTREET BANKGROUP INCORPORATED; *U.S. Public*, pg. 1038
MELLON BANK CORPORATION; *U.S. Public*, pg. 1084
MERCANTILE BANCORPORATION INC.; *U.S. Public*, pg. 1087
MERCANTILE BANK OF IOWA—Mercantile Bancorporation Inc.; *U.S. Public*, pg. 1087
MERCANTILE BANKSHARES CORPORATION; *U.S. Public*, pg. 1088
MICHIGAN NATIONAL CORPORATION—National Australia Bank Limited; *Int'l*, pg. 906
NBD BANK—First Chicago NBD Corporation; *U.S. Public*, pg. 628
NBD BANK (INDIANA)—First Chicago NBD Corporation; *U.S. Public*, pg. 628
N.B.M. CORP.; *U.S. Private*, pg. 771
NBSC CORPORATION—Synovus Financial Corp.; *U.S. Public*, pg. 1549
NBT BANCORP INC.; *U.S. Public*, pg. 1144
NATIONAL BANCORP OF ALASKA, INC.; *U.S. Public*, pg. 1153
NATIONAL CITY BANCORP; *U.S. Public*, pg. 1153
NATIONAL CITY CORPORATION; *U.S. Public*, pg. 1154
NATIONAL COMMERCE BANCORPORATION; *U.S. Public*, pg. 1154
NATIONAL PENN BANCSHARES, INC.; *U.S. Public*, pg. 1158
NATIONSBANK CORPORATION; *U.S. Public*, pg. 1162
NATIONSBANK PLAZA CHARLOTTE, INC.—NationsBank Corporation; *U.S. Public*, pg. 1165
NATIONSBANK SUNWEST, INC.—NationsBank Corporation; *U.S. Public*, pg. 1165
NATIONSBANK WEST—NationsBank Corporation; *U.S. Public*, pg. 1164
NEVADA NATIONAL BANCORPORATION—BankAmerica Corporation; *U.S. Public*, pg. 181
NORTH FORK BANCORPORATION, INC.; *U.S. Public*, pg. 1194
NORTHERN TRUST CORPORATION; *U.S. Public*, pg. 1195
NORWEST CORPORATION; *U.S. Public*, pg. 1201
NORWICH FINANCIAL CORP.; *U.S. Public*, pg. 1203
OLD KENT FINANCIAL CORPORATION; *U.S. Public*, pg. 1216
OLD NATIONAL BANCORP; *U.S. Public*, pg. 1217
OMEGA FINANCIAL CORPORATION; *U.S. Public*, pg. 1222
ONBANCORP, INC.—First Empire State Corporation; *U.S. Public*, pg. 631
PNC BANCORP INC.—PNC Bank Corp.; *U.S. Public*, pg. 1243
PNC BANK—PNC Bank Corp.; *U.S. Public*, pg. 1242
PNC BANK CORP.; *U.S. Public*, pg. 1242
PNC BANK, DELAWARE—PNC Bank Corp.; *U.S. Public*, pg. 1243
PACIFIC CAPITAL BANCORP; *U.S. Public*, pg. 1247
PACIFIC CENTURY FINANCIAL CORPORATION; *U.S. Public*, pg. 1248
PARFINANCE S.A.—Groupe Bruxelles Lambert S.A.; *Int'l*, pg. 562
PEOPLES HERITAGE FINANCIAL GROUP, INC.; *U.S. Public*, pg. 1275
PINNACLE FINANCIAL SERVICES INC.; *U.S. Public*, pg. 1297
PIONEER AMERICAN HOLDING COMPANY; *U.S. Public*, pg. 1298
PONCEBANK, F.S.B.; *U.S. Public*, pg. 1316
PONTIAC BANCORP, INC.; *U.S. Public*, pg. 1316
PRIME BANCSHARES INC.; *U.S. Public*, pg. 1326
PROGRESSIVE BANK, INC.; *U.S. Public*, pg. 1334
PROVIDENT BANKSHARES CORPORATION; *U.S. Public*, pg. 1337
PROVIDENT FINANCIAL GROUP, INC.; *U.S. Public*, pg. 1338
PULSE BANCORP, INC.; *U.S. Public*, pg. 1344
RIHT FINANCIAL CORPORATION—BankBoston Corporation; *U.S. Public*, pg. 184
RAMAPO FINANCIAL CORPORATION; *U.S. Public*, pg. 1360
RARITAN BANCORP INC.; *U.S. Public*, pg. 1361
REGIONS BANK—Regions Financial Corporation; *U.S. Public*, pg. 1371
REGIONS FINANCIAL CORPORATION; *U.S. Public*, pg. 1371
REPUBLIC NATIONAL BANK OF MIAMI; *U.S. Private*, pg. 924
REPUBLIC NEW YORK CORPORATION; *U.S. Public*, pg. 1380
RIGGS NATIONAL CORPORATION; *U.S. Public*, pg. 1389
RIVER OAKS BANCORPORATION—Compass Bancshares, Inc.; *U.S. Public*, pg. 419
SJNB FINANCIAL CORP.; *U.S. Public*, pg. 1418
SPF INSURANCE AGENCY—St. Paul Bancorp, Inc.; *U.S. Public*, pg. 1428
ST. PAUL BANCORP, INC.; *U.S. Public*, pg. 1428
THE SAN FRANCISCO CO.; *U.S. Public*, pg. 1430
THE SANWA BANK LIMITED; *Int'l*, pg. 1189
SEAFIRST CORPORATION—BankAmerica Corporation; *U.S. Public*, pg. 181
SECURITY PACIFIC OREGON BANCORP—BankAmerica Corporation; *U.S. Public*, pg. 182
SHIZUOKA BANK, LTD.; *Int'l*, pg. 1236
SIEMENS CORPORATION—Siemens AG; *Int'l*, pg. 1245
SIERRA WEST BANCORP; *U.S. Public*, pg. 1470
SKANDINAVISKA ENSKILDA BANKEN; *Int'l*, pg. 1258
SOCIETE FINANCERE DE GENEVE—CERUS - Compagnies Europeennes Reunies; *Int'l*, pg. 240
SOUTH CAROLINA NATIONAL CORPORATION—Wachovia Corporation; *U.S. Public*, pg. 1730
SOUTH TRUST BANK OF GEORGIA—SouthTrust Corporation; *U.S. Public*, pg. 1492
SOUTHTRUST CORPORATION; *U.S. Public*, pg. 1491
SOUTHWEST NATIONAL CORPORATION; *U.S. Public*, pg. 1493
SOVEREIGN BANCORP, INC.; *U.S. Public*, pg. 1494
STATE STREET CORPORATION; *U.S. Public*, pg. 1513
SUMMIT BANCORP; *U.S. Public*, pg. 1527
SUN BANCORP, INC.; *U.S. Public*, pg. 1529
SUNTRUST—SunTrust Banks, Inc.; *U.S. Public*, pg. 1537
SUNTRUST BANKS, INC.; *U.S. Public*, pg. 1537
SUNTRUST BANKS OF GEORGIA, INC.—SunTrust Banks, Inc.; *U.S. Public*, pg. 1538
SUSQUEHANNA BANCSHARES, INC.; *U.S. Public*, pg. 1542
SVENSKA HANDELSBANKEN; *Int'l*, pg. 1327
SYNOVUS FINANCIAL CORP.; *U.S. Public*, pg. 1548
TAYLOR CAPITAL GROUP; *U.S. Private*, pg. 1070
TEPPCO PARTNERS L.P.—Duke Energy Corporation; *U.S. Public*, pg. 534
TEXAS COMMERCE BANK—The Chase Manhattan Corporation; *U.S. Public*, pg. 339
TOMPKINS COUNTY TRUST COMPANY; *U.S. Public*, pg. 1621
THE TRUSTCOMPANY BANCORPORATION; *U.S. Public*, pg. 1643
TRUSTMARK CORPORATION; *U.S. Public*, pg. 1643
UMB FINANCIAL CORPORATION; *U.S. Public*, pg. 1653
UNION BANK OF CALIFORNIA—The Bank of Tokyo-Mitsubishi, Ltd.; *Int'l*, pg. 157
UNION PLANTERS BANK OF MISSISSIPPI—Union Planters Corporation; *U.S. Public*, pg. 1669
UNION PLANTERS CORPORATION; *U.S. Public*, pg. 1668
U.S. BANCORP; *U.S. Public*, pg. 1680
U.S. TRUST CORPORATION; *U.S. Public*, pg. 1688
VALLEY NATIONAL BANCORP; *U.S. Public*, pg. 1705
WSFS FINANCIAL CORPORATION; *U.S. Public*, pg. 1728
WACHOVIA CORPORATION; *U.S. Public*, pg. 1730
WASHINGTON TRUST BANCORP, INC.; *U.S. Public*, pg. 1744
WAYCROSSE INC.; *U.S. Private*, pg. 1155
WELLS FARGO & COMPANY—Wells Fargo & Company; *U.S. Public*, pg. 1753
WEST COAST BANCORP; *U.S. Public*, pg. 1755
WESTAMERICA BANCORPORATION; *U.S. Public*, pg. 1756
WESTDEUTSCHE LANDESBANK GIROZENTRALE; *Int'l*, pg. 1492
WESTMINSTER CAPITAL INC.; *U.S. Public*, pg. 1761
WHITNEY HOLDING CORPORATION; *U.S. Public*, pg. 1766
WILMINGTON TRUST CORPORATION; *U.S. Public*, pg. 1770
ZIONS BANCORPORATION; *U.S. Public*, pg. 1792

6719 — OFFICES OF HOLDING COMPANIES, NEC

A-OK DELAWARE INC.—GIB Group; *Int'l*, pg. 533
AAF INDUSTRIES PLC; *Int'l*, pg. 1
AAH PLC—Franz Haniel & Cie, GmbH; *Int'l*, pg. 591
ABB INDUSTRI A/S—ABB Asea Brown Boveri (Holding) Ltd.; *Int'l*, pg. 2
ABB TECNOMASIO S.P.A.—ABB Asea Brown Boveri (Holding) Ltd.; *Int'l*, pg. 2
ABCO, INC.—Fortune Brands, Inc.; *U.S. Public*, pg. 674
ABN AMRO CHICAGO CORPORATION—ABN-AMRO Holding N.V.; *Int'l*, pg. 10
ACI AMERICA HOLDINGS INC.—BTR plc; *Int'l*, pg. 129
ACI EUROPE LTD.—BTR plc; *Int'l*, pg. 129
ACI HOLDING INC.—EULER; *Int'l*, pg. 464
ACI HOLDING INC.—Swiss Reinsurance Company; *Int'l*, pg. 1332
ACI INTERNATIONAL LTD.—BTR plc; *Int'l*, pg. 128
ACI NEW ZEALAND LTD.—BTR plc; *Int'l*, pg. 129
AEA INVESTORS INC.; *U.S. Private*, pg. 4
AEI HOLDING CO., INC.; *U.S. Private*, pg. 4
AEW PARTNERS, L.P.; *U.S. Private*, pg. 5
AFIA (CIGNA) CORPORATION, LIMITED—Cigna Corp.; *U.S. Public*, pg. 364
AFIA FINANCE CORPORATION—Cigna Corp.; *U.S. Public*, pg. 363
AFIA (INA) CORPORATION, LIMITED—Cigna Corp.; *U.S. Public*, pg. 366
AGIV GROUP; *Int'l*, pg. 14
AGP INDUSTRIAL CORPORATION; *Int'l*, pg. 14
AIC HOLDINGS, INC.—Cigna Corp.; *U.S. Public*, pg. 362
AMB AACHENER UND MUENCHENER BETEILIGUNGS-AG; *Int'l*, pg. 15
AMEV NEDERLAND N.V.—Fortis; *Int'l*, pg. 498
AMR CORPORATION; *U.S. Public*, pg. 9
ANI AMERICA, INC.—Australian National Industries Limited; *Int'l*, pg. 101
ANR GASIFICATION PROPERTIES CO.—The Coastal Corporation; *U.S. Public*, pg. 389
ANR WESTERN STORAGE CO.—The Coastal Corporation; *U.S. Public*, pg. 389
API GROUP INC.; *U.S. Private*, pg. 7
APT COIN MACHINES, INC.—Alliance Gaming Corporation; *U.S. Public*, pg. 47
APV U.K. PLC—Siebe plc; *Int'l*, pg. 1240
ARC INTERNATIONAL CORPORATION; *Int'l*, pg. 17
ASC INCORPORATED; *U.S. Private*, pg. 8
ASI INVESTMENTS HOLDING CO.—A. Schulman, Inc.; *U.S. Public*, pg. 1441
AUSA HOLDING COMPANY—AEGON N.V.; *Int'l*, pg. 27
AUSA LIFE INSURANCE CO.—AEGON N.V.; *Int'l*, pg. 27
THE AARQUE COMPANIES; *U.S. Private*, pg. 9
ABRAMS INDUSTRIES, INC.; *U.S. Public*, pg. 14
ACADEMY INSURANCE GROUP, INC.—AEGON N.V.; *Int'l*, pg. 27
ACCEL INTERNATIONAL CORPORATION; *U.S. Public*, pg. 14
ACCO UK LIMITED—Fortune Brands, Inc.; *U.S. Public*, pg. 675
ACCOR NORTH AMERICA—Accor S.A.; *Int'l*, pg. 21
ACCOR UK—Accor S.A.; *Int'l*, pg. 21
ACROMETAL COMPANIES, INC.; *U.S. Private*, pg. 14
ACTIVE BIOTECH AB; *Int'l*, pg. 23
ACUSHNET INTERNATIONAL INC.—Fortune Brands, Inc.; *U.S. Public*, pg. 675
ADMINISTRACION Y MANDATOS LA TRANSADINA—Corporacion MAPFRE, Compania Internacional de Reaseguros, S.A.; *Int'l*, pg. 333
ADVANCED ELECTRONIC SYSTEMS—Litton Industries, Inc.; *U.S. Public*, pg. 1002
ADVANCED LIGHTING TECHNOLOGIES, INC.; *U.S. Public*, pg. 20
ADVANCED MACHINE VISION CORP.; *U.S. Public*, pg. 20
ADVANTICA RESTAURANT GROUP, INC.; *U.S. Public*, pg. 22
AEGON INTERNATIONAL B.V.—AEGON N.V.; *Int'l*, pg. 25
AEGON N.V.; *Int'l*, pg. 25

S.I.C. Index

AEGON U.S. HOLDING CORP.—AEGON N.V.; *Int'l*, pg. 26
AEGON USA, INC.—AEGON N.V.; *Int'l*, pg. 26
AETNA INC.; *U.S. Public*, pg. 26
AGIE U.S.A. LTD.—Georg Fischer Ltd.; *Int'l*, pg. 490
H.F. AHMANSON & CO.; *U.S. Public*, pg. 29
AHOLD FINANCE COMPANY (NEDERLANDSE ANTILLEN) NV—Koninklijke Ahold NV; *Int'l*, pg. 750
AIR & WATER TECHNOLOGIES CORPORATION; *U.S. Public*, pg. 29
AIR LIQUIDE AMERICA CORPORATION—Air Liquide S.A.; *Int'l*, pg. 37
AIR PRODUCTS INTERNATIONAL CORP.—Air Products and Chemicals, Inc.; *U.S. Public*, pg. 31
AIR PRODUCTS REF-FUEL HOLDING CORP.—Air Products and Chemicals, Inc.; *U.S. Public*, pg. 31
AISIN WORLD CORP. OF AMERICA—Aisin Seiki Co. Ltd.; *Int'l*, pg. 39
AKER BUILDING AND CEMENT MATERIALS—Aker Raj Asa; *Int'l*, pg. 42
AKRON AB—Proventus AB; *Int'l*, pg. 1072
AKZO COATINGS B.V.—Akzo Nobel N.V.; *Int'l*, pg. 42
AKZO NOBEL N.V.; *Int'l*, pg. 42
ALADDIN HOLDING COMPANY—Aladdin Industries, Incorporated; *U.S. Private*, pg. 31
ALARMGUARD HOLDINGS, INC.; *U.S. Public*, pg. 35
ALASKA AIR GROUP, INC.; *U.S. Public*, pg. 35
ALCAN EMPREENDIMENTOS LTDA.—Alcan Aluminium Limited; *Int'l*, pg. 50
ALCAN FINANCES (BERMUDA) LTD.—Alcan Aluminium Limited; *Int'l*, pg. 51
ALCAN IRELAND LTD.—Alcan Aluminium Limited; *Int'l*, pg. 51
ALCAN SOUTH PACIFIC LTD.—Alcan Aluminium Limited; *Int'l*, pg. 51
ALCATEL FRANCE—Alcatel Alsthom Compagnie Generale D'Electricite; *Int'l*, pg. 55
ALCATEL USA CORP.—Alcatel Alsthom Compagnie Generale D'Electricite; *Int'l*, pg. 55
JOHN ALDEN FINANCIAL CORPORATION; *U.S. Public*, pg. 39
ALENCO, INC.—Alberta Energy Company, Ltd.; *Int'l*, pg. 48
ALFA CORPORATION; *U.S. Public*, pg. 40
ALFA LAVAL INC.—Tetra Laval Group; *Int'l*, pg. 1378
ALGERNON BLAIR INTERNATIONAL; *U.S. Private*, pg. 33
ALLBRITTON GROUP, INC.—Perpetual Corporation; *U.S. Private*, pg. 854
ALLEGHENY POWER SYSTEM, INC.; *U.S. Public*, pg. 42
ALLFINCO, INC.—Perpetual Corporation; *U.S. Private*, pg. 854
ALLIANZ OF AMERICA, INC.—Allianz Aktiengesellschaft; *Int'l*, pg. 58
ALLIED HOLDINGS, INC.; *U.S. Public*, pg. 48
ALLIED INDUSTRIAL GROUP, INC.; *U.S. Private*, pg. 39
ALLMERICA FINANCIAL CORPORATION; *U.S. Public*, pg. 54
ALLTEL CORPORATION; *U.S. Public*, pg. 55
ALOHA AIRGROUP, INC.; *U.S. Private*, pg. 44
THE ALPINE GROUP, INC.; *U.S. Public*, pg. 58
ALTENBERG ZINK AG—Union Miniere; *Int'l*, pg. 1442
ALTERNATIVE RESOURCES CORPORATION; *U.S. Public*, pg. 59
ALUMAX INC.; *U.S. Public*, pg. 59
ALUSUISSE-LONZA AMERICA INC.—Alusuisse-Lonza Holding Ltd.; *Int'l*, pg. 67
ALUSUISSE OF AUSTRALIA LTD—Alusuisse-Lonza Holding Ltd.; *Int'l*, pg. 68
ALVIS INDUSTRIES LIMITED—Alvis plc; *Int'l*, pg. 69
AMALGAMATED AUTOMOTIVE INDUSTRIES, INC.; *U.S. Private*, pg. 48
AMALGAMET, INC.—Preussag AG; *Int'l*, pg. 1071
AMAX ENERGY, INC.—Cyprus Amax Minerals Company; *U.S. Public*, pg. 470
AMBAC FINANCIAL GROUP, INC.; *U.S. Public*, pg. 62
AMER GROUP LTD.; *Int'l*, pg. 72
AMEREN CORPORATION; *U.S. Public*, pg. 65
AMERICA WEST HOLDINGS CORPORATION; *U.S. Public*, *pg. 66*
AMERICAN BANKERS INSURANCE GROUP, INC.; *U.S. Public*, pg. 67
AMERICAN BIO CORPORATION—Groupe Limagrain; *Int'l*, pg. 566
AMERICAN BUSINESS PRODUCTS, INC.; *U.S. Public*, pg. 70
AMERICAN COMMONWEALTH COMPANY—American Water Works Company, Inc.; *U.S. Public*, pg. 95
AMERICAN ECOLOGY CORPORATION; *U.S. Public*, pg. 71
AMERICAN ELECTRIC POWER COMPANY, INC.; *U.S. Public*, pg. 71
AMERICAN FINANCIAL ENTERPRISES, INC.—American Financial Group; *U.S. Public*, pg. 74
AMERICAN FINANCIAL GROUP; *U.S. Public*, pg. 74
AMERICAN GENERAL CORPORATION; *U.S. Public*, pg. 76
AMERICAN HERITAGE LIFE INVESTMENT CORP.; *U.S. Public*, pg. 78
AMERICAN INCOME HOLDING, INC.—Torchmark Corporation; *U.S. Public*, pg. 1622
AMERICAN INDEMNITY FINANCIAL CORP.; *U.S. Public*, pg. 83
AMERICAN INDUSTRIAL PARTNERS; *U.S. Private*, pg. 56
AMERICAN INTERNATIONAL GROUP, INC.; *U.S. Public*, pg. 83
AMERICAN MARINE HOLDINGS INC.; *U.S. Private*, pg. 58
AMERICAN MARKETING INDUSTRIES, INC.; *U.S. Private*, *pg. 58*
AMERICAN MEDIA, INC.; *U.S. Public*, pg. 87
AMERICAN MODERN HOME INSURANCE GROUP—The Midland Company; *U.S. Public*, pg. 1110
AMERICAN NATURAL OFFSHORE CO.—The Coastal Corporation; *U.S. Public*, pg. 389
AMERICAN PETROFINA HOLDING CO.—Petrofina S.A.; *Int'l*, pg. 1044
AMERICAN RE CORPORATION—Munchener Ruckversicherungs-Gesellschaft; *Int'l*, pg. 897
AMERICAN SKIING COMPANY; *U.S. Private*, pg. 61
AMERICAN STORES COMPANY; *U.S. Public*, pg. 92
AMERICAN TRACTEBEL CORPORATION—Tractebel; *Int'l*, pg. 1415
AMERIFOODS INC.; *U.S. Private*, pg. 65
AMGEN HOLDING, INC.—Amgen Inc.; *U.S. Public*, pg. 101
AMIC INDUSTRIES LIMITED—Anglo American Corporation of South Africa Limited; *Int'l*, pg. 76
AMOCO CHEMICAL HOLDING CO.—Amoco Corporation; *U.S. Public*, pg. 102
AMOCO COMPANY—Amoco Corporation; *U.S. Public*, pg. 102
AMOCO CORPORATION; *U.S. Public*, pg. 101
AMOCO TECHNOLOGY COMPANY—Amoco Corporation; *U.S. Public*, pg. 103
AMTRAN, INC.; *U.S. Public*, pg. 106
AMVESTORS FINANCIAL CORPORATION—American Mutual Life Holding Co.; *U.S. Private*, pg. 59
ANALOG DEVICES MARKETING LTD.—Analog Devices, Inc.; *U.S. Public*, pg. 108
ANALYTIC TSA GLOBAL ASSET MANAGEMENT INC.—United Asset Management Corporation; *U.S. Public*, pg. 1672
ANDERSEN GROUP, INC.; *U.S. Public*, pg. 111
ANDERSON INDUSTRIES, INC.—Excel Industries, Inc.; *U.S. Public*, pg. 599
ANDREWS GROUP, INCORPORATED—MacAndrews & Forbes Holdings Inc.; *U.S. Private*, pg. 689
ANGLESEY ALUMINIUM LTD. (ANGLESEY)—Maxxam Inc.; *U.S. Public*, pg. 1062
ANGLO AMERICAN CORPORATION OF SOUTH AFRICA LIMITED; *Int'l*, pg. 76
ANJOU INTERNATIONAL COMPANY—Compagnie Generale Des Eaux; *Int'l*, pg. 321
ANNTAYLOR STORES CORPORATION; *U.S. Public*, pg. 116
ANSALDO SIGNAL N.V.; *Int'l*, pg. 77
ANSCHUTZ CORPORATION; *U.S. Private*, pg. 75
AON CORPORATION; *U.S. Public*, pg. 117
APEX SPECIALTY MATERIALS, INC.; *U.S. Private*, pg. 77
APOINT S.A.—Corporacion MAPFRE, Compania Internacional de Reaseguros, S.A.; *Int'l*, pg. 333
APOLLO GROUP, INC.; *U.S. Public*, pg. 120
AQUA CARE SYSTEMS INC.; *U.S. Public*, pg. 126
ARAMARK CORP.; *U.S. Private*, pg. 78
ARBOR ACRES FARM, INC.—Booker PLC; *Int'l*, pg. 202
ARDEE MUSIC PUBLISHING, INC.—The Reader's Digest Association, Inc.; *U.S. Public*, pg. 1367
ARGONAUT GROUP, INC.; *U.S. Public*, pg. 129
ARINC INC. (CONSOLIDATED); *U.S. Private*, pg. 81
ARITMOS AB—Proventus AB; *Int'l*, pg. 1072
ARJAY HOLDINGS, INC.—RJR Nabisco Holdings Corp.; *U.S. Public*, pg. 1355
ARKANSAS BEST CORPORATION; *U.S. Public*, pg. 130
THE ARLEN CORPORATION; *U.S. Public*, pg. 131
ARMADA CORPORATION; *U.S. Private*, pg. 82
ARMSTRONG CORK FINANCE CORP.—Armstrong World Industries, Inc.; *U.S. Public*, pg. 132
ARMSTRONG INTERNATIONAL, INC.; *U.S. Private*, pg. 83
BEN ARNOLD CO., INC.; *U.S. Private*, pg. 83
ARNOLD INDUSTRIES, INC.; *U.S. Public*, pg. 132
ARNOLD TRANSPORTATION SERVICES—Arnold Industries, Inc.; *U.S. Public*, pg. 132
ASAHI GLASS AMERICA, INC.—Asahi Glass Co., Ltd.; *Int'l*, *pg. 84*
ASBURY CARBONS, INC.; *U.S. Private*, pg. 87
ASCOM HOLDING AG; *Int'l*, pg. 86
ASEA BROWN BOVERI AG—ABB Asea Brown Boveri (Holding) Ltd.; *Int'l*, pg. 1
ASEA BROWN BOVERI DANMARK A/S—ABB Asea Brown Boveri (Holding) Ltd.; *Int'l*, pg. 8
ASEA BROWN BOVERI S.A.—ABB Asea Brown Boveri (Holding) Ltd.; *Int'l*, pg. 3
ASHLAND PARTCIPACOES LTD.—Ashland, Inc.; *U.S. Public*, pg. 140
ASSICURAZIONI GENERALI S.P.A.; *Int'l*, pg. 89
ASSOCIATED BUILDING SYSTEMS—Jannock Limited; *Int'l*, pg. 699
ASSOCIATED HOSTS, INC.—Brierley Investments Limited; *Int'l*, pg. 215
ASSURANCE VIE DESJARDINS-LAURENTIENNE—Desjardins-Laurentian Financial Corporation; *Int'l*, pg. 396
ASTEC INTERNATIONAL LIMITED; *Int'l*, pg. 92
ASTON MARTIN LAGONDA GROUP LIMITED—Ford Motor Company; *U.S. Public*, pg. 665
ASTORIA FINANCIAL CORPORATION; *U.S. Public*, pg. 141
ATLANTIC AMERICAN CORPORATION; *U.S. Public*, pg. 143
ATLAS COPCO NORTH AMERICA INC.—Atlas Copco AB; *Int'l*, pg. 96
ATLAS EDITIONS; *Int'l*, pg. 96
ATRION CORPORATION; *U.S. Public*, pg. 146
AU BON MARCHE; *Int'l*, pg. 97
AUDIOFINA S.A.—Groupe Bruxelles Lambert S.A.; *Int'l*, pg. 561
AUSTRALIAN CHAR HOLDING PTY., LTD.—Nissho Iwai Corporation; *Int'l*, pg. 947
AUSTRALIAN CHEMICAL HOLDINGS LTD.—Hercules Incorporated; *U.S. Public*, pg. 810
AVATAR HOLDINGS INC.; *U.S. Public*, pg. 151
AVEMCO CORPORATION; *U.S. Public*, pg. 151
AVONDALE INCORPORATED; *U.S. Private*, pg. 102
B & K STEEL & SUPPLY, INC.; *U.S. Private*, pg. 105
BASF AKTIENGESELLSCHAFT—BASF AG; *Int'l*, pg. 104
B.A.T CIGARETTENFABRIKEN B.A.T.—B.A.T Industries P.L.C.; *Int'l*, pg. 111
B.A.T INDUSTRIES P.L.C.; *Int'l*, pg. 110
B.A.T NETHERLANDS B.V.—B.A.T Industries P.L.C.; *Int'l*, pg. 111
BBS HOLDINGS, INC.—BellSouth Corporation; *U.S. Public*, pg. 209
BBS ONTARIO INCORPORATED—Baton Broadcasting Incorporated; *Int'l*, pg. 171
BBS SASKATCHEWAN INCORPORATED—Baton Broadcasting Incorporated; *Int'l*, pg. 171
BCI HOLDING CORPORATION; *U.S. Private*, pg. 106
BEC INC.; *U.S. Private*, pg. 106
BHP HAWAII, INC.—The Broken Hill Proprietary Company Limited; *Int'l*, pg. 225
BI HOLDINGS CORP.—Blount International, Inc.; *U.S. Public*, pg. 238
BIL (FAR EAST HOLDINGS) LTD.—Brierley Investments Limited; *Int'l*, pg. 215
BM MANNHEIM BETEILIGUNGEN GMBH—Corange Limited; *Int'l*, pg. 331
BMW HOLDING AG—Bayerische Motoren Werke Aktiengesellschaft; *Int'l*, pg. 178
BMW HOLDING B.V.—Bayerische Motoren Werke Aktiengesellschaft; *Int'l*, pg. 178
BMW (US) HOLDING CORPORATION—Bayerische Motoren Werke Aktiengesellschaft; *Int'l*, pg. 177
BNP BAIL—Banque Nationale de Paris; *Int'l*, pg. 163
THE BOC GROUP PLC; *Int'l*, pg. 121
BP AMERICA INC.—The British Petroleum Company P.L.C.; *Int'l*, pg. 220
BPB INDUSTRIES PLC; *Int'l*, pg. 122
BT PROPERTY LTD.—British Telecommunications plc; *Int'l*, *pg. 222*
BT-U.S.A., INC.—N.V. Koninklijke KNP BT; *Int'l*, pg. 756
BTR, INC.—BTR plc; *Int'l*, pg. 127
BTR PLC; *Int'l*, pg. 124
BTU INTERNATIONAL, INC.; *U.S. Public*, pg. 164
B.U.S. ENVIRONMENTAL SERVICES, INC.—Metallgesellschaft AG; *Int'l*, pg. 860
BABCOCK AUSTRALIA HOLDINGS LTD.—FKI Plc; *Int'l*, pg. 474
BACARDI LIMITED; *Int'l*, pg. 131
BACOU U.S.A., INC.—Bacou S.A.; *Int'l*, pg. 132
BAIRNCO CORPORATION; *U.S. Public*, pg. 165
BAKER HUGHES INCORPORATED; *U.S. Public*, pg. 165
MICHAEL BAKER CORPORATION; *U.S. Public*, pg. 168
BALLY TOTAL FITNESS HOLDINGS CORPORATION; *U.S. Public*, pg. 171
BAMBURI TANKERS HOLDING (NAURU) CORP.—Lafarge S.A.; *Int'l*, pg. 789
BANCINSURANCE CORP.; *U.S. Public*, pg. 175
THE BANK FUNDS COMPANY LLC; *U.S. Private*, pg. 113
BANK OF BOSTON—BankBoston Corporation; *U.S. Public*, *pg. 184*
BANKERS LEASING CORP.—Citicorp; *U.S. Public*, pg. 377
BANKERS LIFE HOLDING CORP.—Conseco Inc.; *U.S. Public*, pg. 433
BANKGESELLSCHAFT BERLIN; *Int'l*, pg. 159
BANKMANAGERS CORP.; *U.S. Private*, pg. 114
W.O. BANKSTON ENTERPRISES INC.—Republic Industries, Inc.; *U.S. Public*, pg. 1379
BANNER AEROSPACE, INC.; *U.S. Public*, pg. 187
BANPONCE FINANCIAL CORP.—Banco Popular de Puerto Rico; *U.S. Public*, pg. 176
BARDON USA INC.—Bardon Group PLC; *Int'l*, pg. 166
BARLOW LTD.; *Int'l*, pg. 167
BARRY CONTROLS CORP.—Applied Power Inc.; *U.S. Public*, pg. 124
BARTLETT & CO.—Legg Mason, Inc.; *U.S. Public*, pg. 985
BASKIN-ROBBINS INTERNATIONAL CO.—Allied Domecq PLC; *Int'l*, pg. 63
BASS ENTERPRISES PRODUCTION COMPANY; *U.S. Private*, pg. 122
BASTOGI-S.P.A.; *Int'l*, pg. 170
BAWDEN CORPORATION; *U.S. Private*, pg. 124
BAYER AG; *Int'l*, pg. 171
BAYER FOREIGN INVESTMENTS LTD. (BAYFORIN)—Bayer AG; *Int'l*, pg. 175
BEACON GROUP; *U.S. Private*, pg. 126
THE BEACON GROUP; *U.S. Private*, pg. 125
BEAR CREEK CORPORATION—Yamanouchi Pharmaceutical Co. Ltd.; *Int'l*, pg. 1518
THE BEAR STEARNS COMPANIES INC.; *U.S. Public*, pg. 197
BEAZER GROUP PLC; *Int'l*, pg. 181
BEERS CONSTRUCTION COMPANY—Skanska AB; *Int'l*, pg. 1261
BEGEMANN BELGIUM N.V.—Royal Begemann Group; *Int'l*, *pg. 1134*
BELL ATLANTIC CAPITAL CORPORATION—Bell Atlantic Corporation; *U.S. Public*, pg. 202
BELL ATLANTIC CORPORATION; *U.S. Public*, pg. 201
BELLSOUTH CORPORATION; *U.S. Public*, pg. 207
BELLSOUTH ENTERPRISES, INC.—BellSouth Corporation; *U.S. Public*, pg. 208
BELMONT INDUSTRIES, INC.—RGP Holding, Inc.; *U.S. Private*, pg. 903
BENEFICIAL CORPORATION; *U.S. Public*, pg. 211
BENETTON U.S.A. CORPORATION—Benetton Group S.p.A.; *Int'l*, pg. 186
BERISFORD PLC; *Int'l*, pg. 188
W.R. BERKLEY CORPORATION; *U.S. Public*, pg. 215
THE BERKLINE CORPORATION—Furnishings International, Inc.; *U.S. Private*, pg. 432
ARNOLD BERNHARD & CO.; *U.S. Private*, pg. 137
BERRIEL VITTEL FRANCE—Nestle S.A.; *Int'l*, pg. 918
BERTELSMANN INC.—Bertelsmann AG; *Int'l*, pg. 191
BESSEMER GROUP, INC.; *U.S. Private*, pg. 139
BESSIN CORPORATION—Sara Lee Corporation; *U.S. Public*, pg. 1433
BEXLEY COMERCIO E PARTICIPACAO LTDA., BRAZIL DIV.—Borden, Inc.; *U.S. Private*, pg. 159
BIDWELL INDUSTRIAL GROUP, INC.; *U.S. Private*, pg. 142
BIG Y FOODS INC.; *U.S. Private*, pg. 143
BIOZIM B.V.—Novartis AG; *Int'l*, pg. 975
BISCAYNE APPAREL INC.; *U.S. Public*, pg. 232
BITREK CORPORATION; *U.S. Private*, pg. 145

BLACK & DECKER (OVERSEAS) A.G.—The Black & Decker Corporation; *U.S. Public*, pg. 234
BLACKHAWK HOLDING COMPANY—Torchmark Corporation; *U.S. Public*, pg. 1623
THE BLACKSTONE GROUP; *U.S. Private*, pg. 147
B.H. BLACKWELL LTD.; *Int'l*, pg. 197
BLOUNT HOLDINGS LTD.—Blount International, Inc.; *U.S. Public*, pg. 239
BLUE CIRCLE AMERICA INC.—Blue Circle Industries PLC; *Int'l*, pg. 197
BLUE SEAL FEEDS, INC.—Varied Investments, Inc.; *U.S. Private*, pg. 1134
BOHLER UDDEHOLM AG—Voest-Alpine Stahl AG; *Int'l*, pg. 1471
BOLSWESSANEN AG—Koninklijke BolsWessanen nv; *Int'l*, pg. 752
BOLSWESSANEN BETEILIGUNG GMBH—Koninklijke BolsWessanen nv; *Int'l*, pg. 752
BOLSWESSANEN INTERNATIONAL BV—Koninklijke BolsWessanen nv; *Int'l*, pg. 751
BOLSWESSANEN NEDERLAND BV—Koninklijke BolsWessanen nv; *Int'l*, pg. 751
BOLSWESSANEN TRANSATLANTIC HOLDINGS BV—Koninklijke BolsWessanen nv; *Int'l*, pg. 751
BOLSWESSANEN USA, INC.—Koninklijke BolsWessanen nv; *Int'l*, pg. 752
BOMAINE CORPORATION; *U.S. Private*, pg. 155
BORAL INDUSTRIES INC.—Boral Limited; *Int'l*, pg. 203
BORDEN, S.A.—Borden, Inc.; *U.S. Private*, pg. 159
BORDERS GROUP, INC.; *U.S. Public*, pg. 245
BOSTON OVERSEAS HOLDING CORP.—BankBoston Corporation; *U.S. Public*, pg. 184
BOSTON SCIENTIFIC CORP.; *U.S. Public*, pg. 247
BOURY ENTERPRISES; *U.S. Private*, pg. 162
BOVIS INC.—The Peninsular and Oriental Steam Navigation Company; *Int'l*, pg. 1033
BOWL AMERICA, INCORPORATED; *U.S. Public*, pg. 248
BRAMBLES HOLDINGS LIMITED—Brambles Industries Limited; *Int'l*, pg. 211
BRAMMER PLC; *Int'l*, pg. 212
BRASCADE RESOURCES INC.—EdperBrascan Corporation; *Int'l*, pg. 433
BRASCAN BRAZIL—EdperBrascan Corporation; *Int'l*, pg. 435
BREMER FINANCIAL CORPORATION; *U.S. Private*, pg. 167
BRIDGEWATER RESOURCES CORPORATION; *U.S. Private*, pg. 168
BRIDON PLC; *Int'l*, pg. 215
BRIDPORT-GUNDRY LTD. (U.K.)—Bridport-Gundry p.l.c.; *Int'l*, pg. 215
BRIERLEY INVESTMENTS LIMITED; *Int'l*, pg. 215
BRIGHTON COMMUNICATION CORP.—Lynch Corporation; *U.S. Public*, pg. 1021
BRINKMANN INSTRUMENTS, INC.; *U.S. Private*, pg. 169
BRITAX INTERNATIONAL PLC; *Int'l*, pg. 216
BRITISH AEROSPACE (LIVERPOOL AIRPORT) LIMITED—British Aerospace p.l.c.; *Int'l*, pg. 217
BRITISH ALCAN ALUMINIUM PLC—Alcan Aluminium Limited; *Int'l*, pg. 51
BRITISH-AMERICAN TOBACCO CO. LTD.—B.A.T Industries P.L.C.; *Int'l*, pg. 111
BRITISH BAKERIES LIMITED—Tomkins PLC; *Int'l*, pg. 1396
BRITISH CAR AUCTION GROUP—Tyco International Ltd.; *U.S. Public*, pg. 1649
BRITISH MOHAIR HOLDINGS PLC; *Int'l*, pg. 219
BRITISH STEEL, INC.—British Steel Plc; *Int'l*, pg. 221
BRITISH TELECOMMUNICATIONS PLC; *Int'l*, pg. 222
BROCKMORE LIMITED—Avonmore Waterford Group plc; *Int'l*, pg. 102
BROE COMPANIES; *U.S. Private*, pg. 171
BROOKE GROUP LTD.; *U.S. Public*, pg. 259
BROOKE INDUSTRIAL HOLDINGS PLC; *Int'l*, pg. 228
BRUNCOR, INC.; *Int'l*, pg. 230
BRUNEL HOLDINGS PLC; *Int'l*, pg. 230
BRUNTEL HOLDINGS LTD.—Bruncor, Inc.; *Int'l*, pg. 230
BUCKHORN INC.—Myers Industries, Inc.; *U.S. Public*, pg. 1143
BUDERUS AG—Metallgesellschaft AG; *Int'l*, pg. 861
BULL ELECTRONICS—Compagnie des Machines Bull; *Int'l*, pg. 316
BULL HOLDING—Compagnie des Machines Bull; *Int'l*, pg. 318
BUNZL PLC; *Int'l*, pg. 232
BURLINGTON NORTHERN SANTA FE CORPORATION; *U.S. Public*, pg. 268
BURMAH CASTROL FRANCE HOLDINGS SA—Burmah Castrol plc; *Int'l*, pg. 235
BURMAH CASTROL USA INC.—Burmah Castrol plc; *Int'l*, pg. 235
BURMAH OIL INVESTMENTS HOLDINGS LTD.—Burmah Castrol plc; *Int'l*, pg. 234
BUSINESSHIP INTERNATIONAL INC.; *U.S. Private*, pg. 189
BUSS HOLDING GMBH—Georg Fischer Ltd.; *Int'l*, pg. 490
BUTCHER & CO., INC.; *U.S. Private*, pg. 189
BUTLER INTERNATIONAL, INC.; *U.S. Public*, pg. 270
BUYCO, INC.; *U.S. Private*, pg. 190
C & J CLARK AMERICA, INC.—Clarks International; *Int'l*, pg. 297
CAF HOLDING COMPANY; *U.S. Private*, pg. 192
CAM INTERNATIONAL HOLDINGS LTD.; *Int'l*, pg. 238
CBP RESOURCES, INC.; *U.S. Private*, pg. 192
CC INDUSTRIES, INC.; *U.S. Private*, pg. 192
CCB FINANCIAL CORPORATION; *U.S. Public*, pg. 276
CCT HOLDINGS CORP.—Charter Communications, Inc.; *U.S. Private*, pg. 230
CDI CORP.; *U.S. Public*, pg. 276
C.E.P. COMMUNICATION GROUP; *Int'l*, pg. 239
CERUS - COMPAGNIES EUROPEENNES REUNIES; *Int'l*, pg. 240
CF GROUP; *U.S. Private*, pg. 193
CFI PTY., LTD.—Sizzler International, Inc.; *U.S. Public*, pg. 1475
CG TRUST COMPANY—Cigna Corp.; *U.S. Public*, pg. 358
CHB CORP.; *U.S. Private*, pg. 194
CHF INDUSTRIES, INC.—Trace International Holdings, Inc.; *U.S. Private*, pg. 1094
CIBC (U.K.) HOLDINGS LIMITED—Canadian Imperial Bank of Commerce; *Int'l*, pg. 257
CIFRA, S.A. DE C.V.; *Int'l*, pg. 241
CIGL HOLDINGS LTD.; *Int'l*, pg. 241
CLR CORPORATION—Empire of Carolina, Inc.; *U.S. Public*, pg. 579
CMC STEEL HOLDING CO.—Commercial Metals Company; *U.S. Public*, pg. 412
CMI HOLDING CO.—Torchmark Corporation; *U.S. Public*, pg. 1623
CMI HOLDING CORP.; *U.S. Private*, pg. 195
CMI INTERNATIONAL INC.; *U.S. Private*, pg. 195
CMS ENERGY CORPORATION; *U.S. Public*, pg. 279
CMS ENTERPRISES, INC.—CMS Energy Corporation; *U.S. Public*, pg. 279
CNF INDUSTRIES INC.—Kenetech Corp.; *U.S. Public*, pg. 950
CNF TRANSPORTATION INC.; *U.S. Public*, pg. 281
CNL FINANCIAL CORP.; *U.S. Public*, pg. 281
COFINEC (COMPAGNIE FINANCIERE POUR L'EUROPE CENTRALE)—CERUS - Compagnies Europeennes Reunies; *Int'l*, pg. 240
COFIR (CORPORACION FINANCIERA REUNIDA)—CERUS - Compagnies Europeennes Reunies; *Int'l*, pg. 240
COGECOM—France Telecom; *Int'l*, pg. 503
COP COMMUNICATIONS; *U.S. Private*, pg. 196
CRR INDUSTRIES, INC.—Conrail, Inc.; *U.S. Public*, pg. 432
CSA HOLDINGS LTD.; *Int'l*, pg. 242
CSA MANAGEMENT INC.; *Int'l*, pg. 243
CSE INSURANCE GROUP; *U.S. Private*, pg. 197
CSG SYSTEMS INTERNATIONAL, INC.; *U.S. Public*, pg. 283
CSR AMERICA INC.—CSR Limited; *Int'l*, pg. 245
CSS INDUSTRIES, INC.; *U.S. Public*, pg. 283
CSX CORPORATION; *U.S. Public*, pg. 284
CTD DE MEXICO, S.A.—Kennametal Inc.; *U.S. Public*, pg. 950
CTG RESOURCES, INC.; *U.S. Public*, pg. 285
CTT SCETA—SNCF; *Int'l*, pg. 1163
CVB FINANCIAL CORP.; *U.S. Public*, pg. 286
C.W.A. HOLDINGS LTD.—Unilever Plc; *Int'l*, pg. 1434
CABLE & WIRELESS OF NORTH AMERICA, INC.—Cable and Wireless plc; *Int'l*, pg. 247
CABLE MICHIGAN, INC.; *U.S. Public*, pg. 287
CABRE CORP.; *U.S. Public*, pg. 289
CADMUS COMMUNICATIONS CORPORATION; *U.S. Public*, pg. 290
CALIBER SYSTEM, INC.—FDX Corporation; *U.S. Public*, pg. 604
CALSONIC INTERNATIONAL, INC.—Nissan Motor Co., Ltd.; *Int'l*, pg. 944
CANADIAN NATIONAL RAILWAY COMPANY; *Int'l*, pg. 258
CANADIAN PACIFIC RAILWAY—Canadian Pacific Limited; *Int'l*, pg. 259
CANLYTE INCORPORATED—The Genlyte Group Incorporated; *U.S. Public*, pg. 730
CAP GEMINI S.A.; *Int'l*, pg. 263
CAPARO GROUP LTD.; *Int'l*, pg. 264
CAPARO INDUSTRIES PLC—Caparo Group Ltd.; *Int'l*, pg. 264
CAPARO INDUSTRIES PLC.—Caparo Group Ltd.; *Int'l*, pg. 265
CAPITAL GRAPHICS INC.; *U.S. Private*, pg. 206
CAPITAL MARKETS ASSURANCE CORPORATION—MBIA Inc.; *U.S. Public*, pg. 1023
CAPITOL INDEMNITY CORPORATION; *U.S. Public*, pg. 302
CAPITOL OUTDOOR ACQUISITION CO., INC.—Cigna Corp.; *U.S. Public*, pg. 361
CAPSURE HOLDINGS CORP.; *U.S. Public*, pg. 303
CARADON (USA) INC.—Caradon Plc; *Int'l*, pg. 267
CARCLO ENGINEERING GROUP PLC; *Int'l*, pg. 268
CARDO AB; *Int'l*, pg. 268
CARLSON COMPANIES, INC.; *U.S. Private*, pg. 211
CARLYLE HOLDING CORPORATION; *U.S. Private*, pg. 213
CARNEGIE HOLDING AB; *Int'l*, pg. 272
CAROLINA FIRST CORPORATION; *U.S. Public*, pg. 306
CARRIS FINANCIAL GROUP; *U.S. Private*, pg. 215
CARTER HOLT HARVEY BUILDING PRODUCTS GROUP LIMITED—International Paper Company; *U.S. Public*, pg. 904
CARTER HOLT HARVEY PLASTIC PRODUCTS GROUP LIMITED—International Paper Company; *U.S. Public*, pg. 904
CARTER HOLT HARVEY WOOD PRODUCTS LIMITED—International Paper Company; *U.S. Public*, pg. 904
CASABLANCA FAN COMPANY—Hunter Fan Company; *U.S. Private*, pg. 549
THE CASCADES GROUP; *Int'l*, pg. 273
CASINO-GUICHARD PERRACHON & CIE—Groupe Casino; *Int'l*, pg. 562
CASINO U.S.A., INC.—Groupe Casino; *Int'l*, pg. 563
CASTORAMA DUBOIS INVESTISSEMENTS S.C.A.; *Int'l*, pg. 275
CATAMOUNT PETROLEUM; *U.S. Private*, pg. 220
CATHERINES STORES CORPORATION; *U.S. Public*, pg. 317
CEDARTONE SPECIALTIES—E.R. Probyn Ltd.; *Int'l*, pg. 1071
CELSIUS INVEST AB—Celsius AB; *Int'l*, pg. 276
CEMENTIA HOLDING AG—Lafarge S.A.; *Int'l*, pg. 790
CENTENNIAL ENERGY HOLDINGS, INC.—MDU Resources Group, Inc.; *U.S. Public*, pg. 1025
CENTEX CONSTRUCTION PRODUCTS, INC.—Centex Corporation; *U.S. Public*, pg. 322
CENTRAL AND SOUTH WEST CORPORATION; *U.S. Public*, pg. 324
CENTRAL RESERVE LIFE CORPORATION; *U.S. Public*, pg. 326
CENTRAL WISCONSIN DEVELOPMENT CORPORATION—Madison Gas and Electric Company; *U.S. Public*, pg. 1033
CENTRIS GROUP INC.; *U.S. Public*, pg. 328
CENTURY TELEPHONE ENTERPRISES, INC.; *U.S. Public*, pg. 329
CERBCO, INC.; *U.S. Public*, pg. 330
CERTAINTEED WEAVING CORP.—Saint-Gobain; *Int'l*, pg. 1171
CHAMBERLAIN JOHN DEERE PTY. LTD.—Deere & Company; *U.S. Public*, pg. 492
CHAMPION ENTERPRISES, INC.; *U.S. Public*, pg. 332
CHANCELLOR MEDIA CORPORATION; *U.S. Public*, pg. 335
CHANNEL TECHNOLOGIES, INC.; *U.S. Private*, pg. 228
CHARTER PLC; *Int'l*, pg. 280
CHARTERHOUSE GROUP INTERNATIONAL, INC.; *U.S. Private*, pg. 230
CHARTWELL RE CORPORATION; *U.S. Public*, pg. 336
THE CHASE MANHATTAN CORPORATION; *U.S. Public*, pg. 337
CHEMICAL LEAMAN CORPORATION; *U.S. Private*, pg. 233
CHESAPEAKE SERVICES COMPANY—Chesapeake Utilities Corporation; *U.S. Public*, pg. 347
CHESTERFIELD INDUSTRIAL PARK, INC.—Watlow Electric Manufacturing Company; *U.S. Private*, pg. 1153
CHEVRON OVERSEAS PETROLEUM LIMITED—Chevron Corporation; *U.S. Public*, pg. 348
CHIC—Conseco Inc.; *U.S. Public*, pg. 433
CHICAGO HOLDINGS, INC.; *U.S. Private*, pg. 234
CHICAGO WEST PULLMAN CORPORATION; *U.S. Private*, pg. 235
J.W. CHILDS ASSOCIATES, L.P.; *U.S. Private*, pg. 237
CHILTEM GROUP SAM—Alpha Omikron Limited; *Int'l*, pg. 65
CHOCOAMERICAN INC.—Midial S.A.; *Int'l*, pg. 865
CHRISTIES INTERNATIONAL PLC; *Int'l*, pg. 289
CHRYSLER CORPORATION; *U.S. Public*, pg. 352
THE CHUBB CORPORATION; *U.S. Public*, pg. 354
THE CHURCHILL COMPANIES; *U.S. Private*, pg. 239
CIGNA CORP.; *U.S. Public*, pg. 356
CIGNA DENTAL HEALTH, INC.—Cigna Corp.; *U.S. Public*, pg. 358
CIGNA FINANCIAL PARTNERS, INC.—Cigna Corp.; *U.S. Public*, pg. 358
CIGNA G.B. HOLDINGS, LTD.—Cigna Corp.; *U.S. Public*, pg. 363
CIGNA GUARANTY HOLDINGS, INC.—Cigna Corp.; *U.S. Public*, pg. 357
CIGNA HEALTH CORPORATION—Cigna Corp.; *U.S. Public*, pg. 359
CIGNA HEALTHCARE, INC.—Cigna Corp.; *U.S. Public*, pg. 359
CIGNA HOLDINGS, INC.—Cigna Corp.; *U.S. Public*, pg. 357
CIGNA INTERNATIONAL FINANCE INC.—Cigna Corp.; *U.S. Public*, pg. 357
CIGNA INVESTMENT GROUP, INC.—Cigna Corp.; *U.S. Public*, pg. 357
CIGNA PROPERTIES, INC.—Cigna Corp.; *U.S. Public*, pg. 358
CIGNA REAL ESTATE, INC.—Cigna Corp.; *U.S. Public*, pg. 365
CIGNA SERVICES U.K. LIMITED—Cigna Corp.; *U.S. Public*, pg. 363
CILCORP INC.; *U.S. Public*, pg. 367
CIMENTS FRANCAIS; *Int'l*, pg. 292
CINCINNATI BELL TELEPHONE; *U.S. Public*, pg. 367
CINCINNATI FINANCIAL CORP.; *U.S. Public*, pg. 368
CINCINNATI MILACRON HOLDING GESELLSCHAFT MBH—Cincinnati Milacron Inc.; *U.S. Public*, pg. 368
CIRCLE INTERNATIONAL GROUP, INC.; *U.S. Public*, pg. 370
CIRCUS CIRCUS HOTEL CASINOS, INC.—Circus Circus - Las Vegas; *U.S. Public*, pg. 374
CIRCUS CIRCUS - LAS VEGAS; *U.S. Public*, pg. 374
CITATION PLASTICS, CO.—The West Company, Incorporated; *U.S. Public*, pg. 1755
CITFED BANCORP, INC.; *U.S. Public*, pg. 376
CITICORP DEL-LEASE, INC.—Citicorp; *U.S. Public*, pg. 377
CITIZENS BANKING CORPORATION; *U.S. Public*, pg. 379
CITIZENS SECURITY MUTUAL INSURANCE—Meridian Insurance Group, Inc.; *U.S. Public*, pg. 1095
CLAVIS MARIS FINLANDIAE OY—Kvaerner a.s.a.; *Int'l*, pg. 771
CLESTRA HOLDING AG—Groupe Strafor Facom; *Int'l*, pg. 570
CLEVELAND CAPITAL HOLDINGS; *U.S. Private*, pg. 246
CLUB CORPORATION OF AMERICA—Club Corporation International; *U.S. Private*, pg. 247
THE COASTAL CORPORATION; *U.S. Public*, pg. 389
COASTAL STATES ENERGY CO.—The Coastal Corporation; *U.S. Public*, pg. 390
COATS PATONS (NORTH AMERICA) INC.—Coats Viyella plc; *Int'l*, pg. 300
COATS PATONS PLC—Coats Viyella plc; *Int'l*, pg. 299
COLE NATIONAL CORPORATION; *U.S. Public*, pg. 396
C.J. COLEMAN HOLDINGS LTD.; *Int'l*, pg. 306
COLONIAL COMMERCIAL CORP.; *U.S. Public*, pg. 400
COLONIAL COMPANIES, INC.—UNUM Corporation; *U.S. Public*, pg. 1699
COLONIAL PENN GROUP, INC.—Leucadia National Corporation; *U.S. Public*, pg. 990
COLORADO INTERSTATE GAS CO.—The Coastal Corporation; *U.S. Public*, pg. 390
COLORADO MEDTECH, INC.; *U.S. Public*, pg. 401
COLTEC HOLDINGS INC; *U.S. Public*, pg. 401
COLTEC INDUSTRIES INC.—Coltec Holdings Inc; *U.S. Public*, pg. 401
COLUMBIA ENERGY GROUP; *U.S. Public*, pg. 402

COMAIR HOLDINGS, INC.; U.S. Public, pg. 406
COMAU FINANZIARIA S.P.A.—Fiat Auto SpA; Int'l, pg. 480
COMMERCE GROUP CORP.; U.S. Public, pg. 410
COMMERCIAL UNION CORPORATION—Commercial Union plc; Int'l, pg. 308
COMMERCIAL UNION OF CANADA HOLDINGS LTD—Commercial Union plc; Int'l, pg. 308
COMMONWEALTH ENERGY SYSTEM; U.S. Public, pg. 414
COMMONWEALTH TELEPHONE ENTERPRISES, INC.; U.S. Public, pg. 415
COMMUNITY NEWSPAPER HOLDINGS INC.; U.S. Private, pg. 259
COMPAGNIE CII-HB INTERNATIONALE N.V.—Compagnie des Machines Bull; Int'l, pg. 319
COMPAGNIE GENERALE DES ETABLISSEMENTS MICHELIN; Int'l, pg. 322
COMPAGNIE GENERALE MARITIME ET FINANCIERE; Int'l, pg. 322
COMPART SPA; Int'l, pg. 324
CONCORP, INC.; U.S. Private, pg. 262
CONECTIV; U.S. Public, pg. 430
CONESTOGA CORPORATION; U.S. Private, pg. 262
CONFED ADMIN. SERVICES, INC.—Confederation Life Insurance Company; Int'l, pg. 326
CONNECTICUT ENERGY CORPORATION; U.S. Public, pg. 431
CONNECTICUT GENERAL CORPORATION—Cigna Corp.; U.S. Public, pg. 358
CONSECO CAPITAL PARTNERS II, L.P.—Conseco Inc.; U.S. Public, pg. 432
CONSECO INC.; U.S. Public, pg. 432
CONSOLIDATED FURNITURE CORPORATION; U.S. Private, pg. 265
CONSOLIDATED NATURAL GAS COMPANY; U.S. Public, pg. 435
CONSOLIDATED PRODUCTS, INC.; U.S. Public, pg. 436
CONSOLIDATED STORES CORP.; U.S. Public, pg. 437
CONSTELLATION HOLDINGS, INC.—Baltimore Gas and Electric Company; U.S. Public, pg. 172
CONSTITUTION HOLDING INC.—Exor Group; Int'l, pg. 467
CONSTITUTION RE CORP.—Exor Group; Int'l, pg. 467
CONSUMERS FINANCIAL CORPORATION; U.S. Public, pg. 437
CONSUMERS WATER COMPANY; U.S. Public, pg. 438
CONTINENTAL AIRLINE HOLDINGS, INC.—Scandinavian Airlines System (SAS); Int'l, pg. 1202
CONTINENTAL GRAPHICS HOLDINGS, INC.; U.S. Private, pg. 268
CONTINENTAL WATER COMPANY; U.S. Private, pg. 269
CONTRAN CORPORATION; U.S. Private, pg. 270
CONTROL LASER CORPORATION—Excel Technology, Inc.; U.S. Public, pg. 599
CONTROLADORA COMERCIAL MEXICANA, S.A. DE C.V.; Int'l, pg. 328
COOKSON AMERICA INC.—Cookson Group plc; Int'l, pg. 328
COPAMEX INDUSTRIAS S.A. DE C.V.; Int'l, pg. 330
CORDIS, A JOHNSON & JOHNSON COMPANY—Johnson & Johnson; U.S. Public, pg. 928
COREPRO B.V.—Forbo Holding SA; Int'l, pg. 497
CORPORACION INTERNACIONAL DE AVIACION (CINTRA); Int'l, pg. 332
CORT BUSINESS SERVICES CORPORATION; U.S. Public, pg. 451
CORTEC GROUP; U.S. Private, pg. 277
COSBEL PETROLEUM CORP.—The Coastal Corporation; U.S. Public, pg. 390
COSCOL PETROLEUM CORP.—The Coastal Corporation; U.S. Public, pg. 390
COSTAIN GROUP PLC; Int'l, pg. 336
COSTAIN HOLDINGS, INC.—Costain Group PLC; Int'l, pg. 337
COUNTRY LIFE INSURANCE COMPANY; U.S. Private, pg. 278
COX COMMUNICATIONS, INC.—Cox Enterprises, Inc.; U.S. Private, pg. 282
COYOTE NETWORK SYSTEMS, INC.; U.S. Public, pg. 455
CRACKEN, HARKEY, STREET & CO., LLC; U.S. Private, pg. 283
CRAIG CORPORATION; U.S. Public, pg. 456
CRAVEY, GREEN & WAHLEN, INCORPORATED; U.S. Private, pg. 287
THE CRAWFORD GROUP; U.S. Private, pg. 287
JAMES CREAN HOLDINGS (UK) LTD.—James Crean PLC; Int'l, pg. 341
CREATIVE PUBLICATIONS; U.S. Private, pg. 288
CREDIT SUISSE FIRST BOSTON, INC.—Credit Suisse Group; Int'l, pg. 345
CROSSMANN COMMUNITIES, INC.; U.S. Public, pg. 461
CROWN ANDERSEN INC.; U.S. Public, pg. 462
CROWN CENTRAL HOLDING CORP.—Crown Central Petroleum Corporation; U.S. Public, pg. 462
CROWN FINANCIAL MANAGEMENT LIMITED—Extendicare Inc.; Int'l, pg. 468
CROWN HOLDINGS, INC.; U.S. Private, pg. 293
CROWN LANCE, INC.—Bolliger, Inc.; U.S. Private, pg. 155
CRUISE HOLDINGS LTD.; U.S. Private, pg. 293
CRUSH U.S.A.—Cadbury Schweppes p.l.c.; Int'l, pg. 248
CUBAN ELECTRIC CO.—Boise Cascade Corporation; U.S. Public, pg. 243
CULLMAN VENTURES, INC.; U.S. Private, pg. 294
CULVERDALE INVESTMENTS LIMITED—Jardine Matheson Holdings Limited; Int'l, pg. 703
CUNA MUTUAL INSURANCE SOCIETY; U.S. Private, pg. 296
CUNNINGHAM-LIMP DEVELOPMENT CO.; U.S. Private, pg. 297
CURRAN GROUP, INC.; U.S. Private, pg. 297
THE CYPRESS COMPANIES; U.S. Private, pg. 299
THE CYPRESS GROUP LLC; U.S. Private, pg. 300
CYPRUS CLIMAX METALS COMPANY—Cyprus Amax Minerals Company; U.S. Public, pg. 471
D & W CAPITAL CORP.—Dyckerhoff & Widmann AG; Int'l, pg. 424
DBS PTE. LTD.—DBS Bank Ltd.; Int'l, pg. 351
DBS SECURITIES HOLDING PTE. LTD.—DBS Bank Ltd.; Int'l, pg. 351
DBSF INVESTMENTS PTE. LTD.—DBS Bank Ltd.; Int'l, pg. 351
DEC INTERNATIONAL, INC.; U.S. Private, pg. 301
DG FOODS, LLC; U.S. Private, pg. 301
DHL WORLDWIDE EXPRESS; U.S. Private, pg. 301
DIC TRADING (USA) INC.—Dainippon Ink & Chemicals, Inc.; Int'l, pg. 369
DNAP HOLDING CORP.—Empressa La Moderna SA de CV; Int'l, pg. 454
DPL INC.; U.S. Public, pg. 473
DQE INC.; U.S. Public, pg. 474
DAIMLER-BENZ AKTIENGESELLSCHAFT; Int'l, pg. 366
DAIMLER-BENZ INTERSERVICES (DEBIS) AG—Daimler-Benz Aktiengesellschaft; Int'l, pg. 367
DAIMLER-BENZ NORTH AMERICA CORPORATION—Daimler-Benz Aktiengesellschaft; Int'l, pg. 368
DAINIPPON INK & CHEMICALS, INC.; Int'l, pg. 369
DAIRY FARM MANAGEMENT LIMITED—Jardine Matheson Holdings Limited; Int'l, pg. 703
DAIRY MART CONVENIENCE STORES, INC.; U.S. Public, pg. 476
DALTON HOLDINGS LTD.—Bristol-Myers Squibb Company; U.S. Public, pg. 256
DAMART S.A.; Int'l, pg. 376
DAMSMITH CORP.; U.S. Private, pg. 309
DANA COMMERCIAL CREDIT CORPORATION—Dana Corporation; U.S. Public, pg. 479
DANAHER CORPORATION; U.S. Public, pg. 480
DARIGOLD, INC.; U.S. Private, pg. 311
DARTFORD PARTNERSHIP; U.S. Private, pg. 312
DATA DOCUMENTS HOLDINGS, INC.—Corporate Express, Inc.; U.S. Public, pg. 449
DATASCOPE HOLDING CORP.—Datascope Corp.; U.S. Public, pg. 487
DATRON INCORPORATED; U.S. Private, pg. 313
DAUBERT INDUSTRIES, INC.; U.S. Private, pg. 313
THEO. H. DAVIES & CO., LTD—Jardine Matheson Holdings Limited; Int'l, pg. 704
DAVIS COMPANIES; U.S. Private, pg. 315
THE DAVIS SERVICE GROUP PLC.; Int'l, pg. 385
DAWSON INTERNATIONAL INVESTMENTS (KINROSS) INC—Dawson International PLC; Int'l, pg. 386
DAWSON INTERNATIONAL PLC; Int'l, pg. 385
DEAN OPERATIONS INC.; U.S. Private, pg. 318
JOHN DEERE CREDIT COMPANY—Deere & Company; U.S. Public, pg. 492
DEL TACO, INC.; U.S. Private, pg. 321
DEL WEBB'S COVENTRY HOMES—Del Webb Corporation; U.S. Public, pg. 495
DELAWARE MANAGEMENT HOLDINGS, INC.—Lincoln National Corporation; U.S. Public, pg. 997
DELAWARE NORTH COMPANIES, INC.; U.S. Private, pg. 321
DELCO REMY INTERNATIONAL, INC.; U.S. Public, pg. 495
DELHAIZE THE LION AMERICA, INC.—Etablissements Delhaize Freres Et Cie "Le Lion" S.A.; Int'l, pg. 463
DELIMMO S.A.—Etablissements Delhaize Freres Et Cie "Le Lion" S.A.; Int'l, pg. 463
DELPANAMA S.A.—Cigna Corp.; U.S. Public, pg. 364
DELTA CABLES HOLDINGS LTD.—Delta plc; Int'l, pg. 390
DELTA CROMPTON HOLDINGS LTD.—Delta plc; Int'l, pg. 390
DELTA ENFIELD CABLES (HOLDINGS) LTD.—Delta plc; Int'l, pg. 390
DELTA ENGINEERING HOLDING LTD.—Delta plc; Int'l, pg. 390
DELTA GROUP AUSTRALIA PTY. LTD.—Delta plc; Int'l, pg. 391
DELTA LIFE CORPORATION—American Mutual Life Holding Co.; U.S. Private, pg. 59
DELTA PLC; Int'l, pg. 389
DENSTREE CORPORATION LTD.—Jardine Matheson Holdings Limited; Int'l, pg. 703
DENTSPLY INTERNATIONAL INC.; U.S. Public, pg. 498
DERBY CYCLE CORPORATION—Derby International Corporation S.A.; Int'l, pg. 394
DERWENT INSURANCE LIMITED—Severn Trent Plc; Int'l, pg. 1226
DESERET MANAGEMENT CORPORATION; U.S. Private, pg. 327
DEUTSCHE BABCOCK AG; Int'l, pg. 398
DEUTSCHE BABCOCK-BETEILIGUNG GMBH—Deutsche Babcock AG; Int'l, pg. 401
DEUTSCHE BABCOCK TECHNOLOGIES, INC.—Deutsche Babcock AG; Int'l, pg. 401
DEUTSCHE UNILEVER GMBH—Unilever Plc; Int'l, pg. 1436
DIAGEO PLC; Int'l, pg. 408
DIAMOND FINANCIAL HOLDINGS, INC.—Dana Corporation; U.S. Public, pg. 480
DIEBOLD MEXICO HOLDING COMPANY, INC.—Diebold, Incorporated; U.S. Public, pg. 506
DIVERSIFIED DYNAMICS CORPORATION; U.S. Private, pg. 336
DIVERSIFIED GROUP, INC.; U.S. Private, pg. 336
DIXONS GROUP PLC; Int'l, pg. 413
DOBSON PARK INDUSTRIES PLC—Harnischfeger Industries, Inc.; U.S. Public, pg. 789
DOMGROUP LTD.—Hollinger Inc.; Int'l, pg. 631
DOMINGUEZ SERVICES CORPORATION; U.S. Public, pg. 516
DOMINION RESOURCES, INC.; U.S. Public, pg. 516
DOMINION TEXTILE INTERNATIONAL B.V.—Dominion Textile Inc.; Int'l, pg. 415
DOWNEY FINANCIAL CORP.; U.S. Public, pg. 525
DREISON INTERNATIONAL, INC.; U.S. Private, pg. 342
DUBIN-CLARK & COMPANY; U.S. Private, pg. 344
DUGAN & MEYERS CONSTRUCTION CO.—Dugan & Meyers Interests, Inc.; U.S. Private, pg. 345
DUGAN & MEYERS INTERESTS, INC.; U.S. Private, pg. 345
DUKE ENERGY INTERNATIONAL, L.L.C.—Duke Energy Corporation; U.S. Public, pg. 534
DUNLOP AEROSPACE GROUP—BTR plc; Int'l, pg. 125
DUNLOP HOLDINGS PLC—BTR plc; Int'l, pg. 124
DUNN INDUSTRIES INC.; U.S. Private, pg. 347
J.E. DUNN EQUITIES, INC.—Dunn Industries Inc.; U.S. Private, pg. 347
DURACELL HOLDINGS B.V.—The Gillette Company; U.S. Public, pg. 744
DURO-LITE INTERNATIONAL; U.S. Private, pg. 349
DUSSELDORF-MUENCHENER BETEILIGUNGS-GESELLSCHAFT MBH—Bayerische Vereinsbank Group; Int'l, pg. 179
DYNA TECHNOLOGY INCORPORATED; U.S. Private, pg. 350
E'TOWN CORPORATION; U.S. Public, pg. 540
E-Z SERVE CORP.; U.S. Public, pg. 540
ECC OVERSEAS INVESTMENTS LIMITED—English China Clays Plc; Int'l, pg. 455
EIP GROUP PLC; Int'l, pg. 426
EIS GROUP PLC; Int'l, pg. 426
EMI GROUP PLC; Int'l, pg. 426
ERO, INC.—Hicks, Muse, Tate & Furst Inc.; U.S. Private, pg. 526
ESJ HOTEL CORPORATION—Patriot American Hospitality, Inc.; U.S. Public, pg. 1265
EAGLE STAR—B.A.T Industries P.L.C.; Int'l, pg. 110
EASTERN ENTERPRISES; U.S. Public, pg. 548
EASTERN PENNSYLVANIA DEVELOPMENT CO.—PECO Energy Company; U.S. Public, pg. 1268
EASTERN UTILITIES ASSOCIATES; U.S. Public, pg. 549
EASTEX ENERGY INC.—El Paso Natural Gas Co.; U.S. Public, pg. 567
EASTMAN TECHNOLOGY INC.—Eastman Kodak Company; U.S. Public, pg. 551
EATELCORP INC.; U.S. Private, pg. 358
EATON LIMITED—Eaton Corporation; U.S. Public, pg. 558
EBASCO AUSTRALIA PTY. LIMITED—Texas Utilities Company; U.S. Public, pg. 1587
EBASCO CAYMAN LIMITED—Texas Utilities Company; U.S. Public, pg. 1587
EBY CORPORATION; U.S. Private, pg. 359
THE EDISON ILLUMINATING CO. OF DETROIT—DTE Energy Company; U.S. Public, pg. 476
EDISON INTERNATIONAL; U.S. Public, pg. 564
A.G. EDWARDS, INC.; U.S. Public, pg. 565
EDWARDSTONE & COMPANY, INC.; U.S. Private, pg. 365
EKCO GROUP, INC.; U.S. Public, pg. 566
ELECTRAFINA—Groupe Bruxelles Lambert S.A.; Int'l, pg. 562
ELECTROWATT LTD.—Siemens AG; Int'l, pg. 1246
ELF SANOFI INC.—Elf Aquitane; Int'l, pg. 445
B. ELLIOTT PLC.; Int'l, pg. 448
ELLIS COMMUNICATIONS—Raycom Media, Inc.; U.S. Private, pg. 912
ELOMETA CORPORATION—Treadwell Corporation; U.S. Private, pg. 1098
ELSEVIER SA—Reed Elsevier plc; Int'l, pg. 1093
ELYO CORP.—Lyonnaise des Eaux S.A.; Int'l, pg. 823
EMCEE CELLULAR, INC.—Emcee Broadcast Products, Inc.; U.S. Public, pg. 571
EMERSON ELECTRIC (ASIA)—Emerson Electric Co.; U.S. Public, pg. 576
EMERSON ELECTRIC NEDERLAND B.V.—Emerson Electric Co.; U.S. Public, pg. 576
EMERSON ELECTRIC U.K. LTD.—Emerson Electric Co.; U.S. Public, pg. 576
EMESS PLC; Int'l, pg. 453
EMHART INTERNATIONAL LTD.—The Black & Decker Corporation; U.S. Public, pg. 233
EMONS RAILROAD GROUP, INC.—Emons Transportation Group, Inc.; U.S. Public, pg. 578
EMPIRE COMPANY LIMITED; Int'l, pg. 453
EMPIRE INSURANCE GROUP—Leucadia National Corporation; U.S. Public, pg. 990
EMPLOYEE BENEFITS INSURANCE COMPANY—Orion Capital Corporation; U.S. Public, pg. 1231
EMPRESSA LA MODERNA SA DE CV; Int'l, pg. 454
ENERGEN CORPORATION; U.S. Public, pg. 581
ENERGY & MINERALS, INC.—South Jersey Industries, Inc.; U.S. Public, pg. 1488
ENERGYNORTH, INC.; U.S. Public, pg. 581
ENERMARK INCOME FUND; Int'l, pg. 454
ENGLISH CHINA CLAYS PLC; Int'l, pg. 455
ENKA INTERNATIONAL BV—Akzo Nobel N.V.; Int'l, pg. 45
ENSERCH FAR EAST LTD.—Texas Utilities Company; U.S. Public, pg. 1587
ENSIS CORPORATION INC.; Int'l, pg. 455
ENSTAR, INC.; U.S. Public, pg. 585
ENTECH, INC.—Montana Power Company; U.S. Public, pg. 1127
ENTERGY CORPORATION; U.S. Public, pg. 585
ENTERPRISE DIVERSIFIED HOLDINGS INCORPORATED—Public Service Enterprise Group Incorporated; U.S. Public, pg. 1340
ENTERPRISES INTERNATIONAL INC.; U.S. Private, pg. 377
ENVIROSOURCE, INC.; U.S. Public, pg. 587
EQUICOR-CIGNA CORPORATION—Cigna Corp.; U.S. Public, pg. 362
EQUICOR HOLDINGS, INC.—Cigna Corp.; U.S. Public, pg. 362
EQUITABLE HOLDING CORPORATION—The Equitable Companies Incorporated; U.S. Public, pg. 589
EQUITABLE INVESTMENT CORPORATION—The Equitable Companies Incorporated; U.S. Public, pg. 589
EQUITY GROUP INVESTMENTS; U.S. Private, pg. 380
ERICSSON GE MOBILE COMMUNICATIONS HOLDING INC.—Telefonaktiebolaget LM Ericsson; Int'l, pg. 1365

ERICSSON HOLDING INTERNATIONAL B.V.—Telefonaktiebolaget LM Ericsson; *Int'l*, pg. 1367
ERICSSON HOLDING NEDERLAND B.V.—Telefonaktiebolaget LM Ericsson; *Int'l*, pg. 1367
ERICSSON NORTH AMERICA, INC.—Telefonaktiebolaget LM Ericsson; *Int'l*, pg. 1364
ERVEN LUCAS BOLS ITALIA S.P.A.—Koninklijke BolsWessanen nv; *Int'l*, pg. 751
ESELCO, INC.; *U.S. Public*, pg. 591
ESSILOR OF AMERICA—Essilor International Compagnie Generale d'Optique; *Int'l*, pg. 462
ESSROC MATERIALS INC.—Ciments Francais; *Int'l*, pg. 292
ETHAN ALLEN INTERIORS INC.; *U.S. Public*, pg. 595
ETHIKA CORPORATION; *U.S. Public*, pg. 595
ETMOFINA S.A.—Petrofina S.A.; *Int'l*, pg. 1043
EUFIDIS—GIB Group; *Int'l*, pg. 534
EUREKO B.V.; *Int'l*, pg. 464
EUROCAMP PLC; *Int'l*, pg. 464
EURODIS ELECTRON PLC—Siemens AG; *Int'l*, pg. 1247
B.V. EUROPESE TABAK MAATSCHAPPIJ—Universal Corporation; *U.S. Public*, pg. 1695
EVEREST REINSURANCE HOLDINGS; *U.S. Public*, pg. 597
EXOR GROUP; *Int'l*, pg. 467
EXPLOITATIEMAATSCHAPPIJ LELIEGRACHT B.V.—Koninklijke BolsWessanen nv; *Int'l*, pg. 751
EXPLOITATIEMAATSCHAPPIJ ROZENGRACHT B.V.—Koninklijke BolsWessanen nv; *Int'l*, pg. 751
EXTENDICARE INC.; *Int'l*, pg. 468
EXXON CORPORATION; *U.S. Public*, pg. 601
EXXON INSURANCE HOLDINGS, INC.—Exxon Corporation; *U.S. Public*, pg. 602
FIL (U.S.) INC.—Russel Metals Inc.; *Int'l*, pg. 1151
FKI INDUSTRIES, INC.—FKI Plc; *Int'l*, pg. 472
FLS INDUSTRIES A/S; *Int'l*, pg. 474
FMR CORP.—Fidelity Investments (FMR Corp.); *U.S. Private*, pg. 403
FPL GROUP, INC.; *U.S. Public*, pg. 608
FZ CORPORATION—Crown Central Petroleum Corporation; *U.S. Public*, pg. 462
FAMILIAN PIPE INC.—Wolseley Plc.; *Int'l*, pg. 1512
FARNSWORTH COMPANIES; *U.S. Private*, pg. 397
FASCO SENSORS & CONTROLS DIVISION—BTR plc; *Int'l*, pg. 127
FEDERAL INDUSTRIES CONSUMER GROUP, INC.—Russel Metals Inc.; *Int'l*, pg. 1150
FEDERAL INDUSTRIES INDUSTRIAL GROUP, INC.—Russel Metals Inc.; *Int'l*, pg. 1150
FEINTOOL INTERNATIONAL HOLDING AG; *Int'l*, pg. 479
FENWAY PARTNERS INC.; *U.S. Private*, pg. 401
FERMENTA AB; *Int'l*, pg. 480
FIAT AUTO (UK) LTD.—Fiat Auto SpA; *Int'l*, pg. 483
FIAT AUTOMISVEIS S.A.—Fiat Auto SpA; *Int'l*, pg. 483
FIAT CONCORD S.A.—Fiat Auto SpA; *Int'l*, pg. 483
FIAT DEUTSCHLAND—Fiat Auto SpA; *Int'l*, pg. 483
FIAT FRANCE—Fiat Auto SpA; *Int'l*, pg. 483
FIAT IBERICA S.A.—Fiat Auto SpA; *Int'l*, pg. 483
FIAT USA INC.—Fiat Auto SpA; *Int'l*, pg. 483
FIATIMPRESIT S.P.A.—Fiat Auto SpA; *Int'l*, pg. 481
FIDELITY CAPITAL—Fidelity Investments (FMR Corp.); *U.S. Private*, pg. 403
FIDIS S.P.A.—Fiat Auto SpA; *Int'l*, pg. 482
5300 RICHMOND ROAD CORPORATION—Giant Eagle, Inc.; *U.S. Private*, pg. 451
FIMA METAL BOX HOLDINGS SENDIRIAN BERHAD—Caradon Plc; *Int'l*, pg. 267
FINA HOLDING DEUTSCHLAND GMBH—Petrofina S.A.; *Int'l*, pg. 1043
FINA INTERNATIONAL N.V.—Petrofina S.A.; *Int'l*, pg. 1044
FINANCIAL INDUSTRIES CORP.; *U.S. Public*, pg. 622
FINANCIAL LIFE COMPANIES, INC.; *U.S. Private*, pg. 404
FINANCIAL SECURITY ASSURANCE HOLDINGS LTD.; *U.S. Public*, pg. 622
FINANCIERA BAMERICAL S.A.—BankAmerica Corporation; *U.S. Public*, pg. 183
FINLAY ENTERPRISES, INC.; *U.S. Public*, pg. 623
FINMECCANICA S.P.A.—IRI Istituto Ricostruzione Industriale; *Int'l*, pg. 653
FINNIGAN MAT—Thermo Electron Corporation; *U.S. Public*, pg. 1591
THE FINOVA GROUP INC.; *U.S. Public*, pg. 624
FIREFIN SRL—Williams Holdings Plc; *Int'l*, pg. 1500
FIRST CENTRAL FINANCIAL CORPORATION; *U.S. Private*, pg. 406
FIRST COMMONWEALTH CORPORATION; *U.S. Private*, pg. 406
FIRST COMMONWEALTH CORPORATION—First Commonwealth Corporation; *U.S. Private*, pg. 406
FIRST FEDERAL CAPITAL CORP.; *U.S. Public*, pg. 632
FIRST MARATHON INC.; *Int'l*, pg. 486
FIRSTBANK OF ILLINOIS CO.; *U.S. Public*, pg. 643
FIRSTENERGY CORP.; *U.S. Public*, pg. 644
FIRTH-RIXSON PLC; *Int'l*, pg. 487
FISCHBACH CORPORATION—American International Group, Inc.; *U.S. Public*, pg. 84
ALBERT FISHER NORTH AMERICA—The Albert Fisher Group PLC; *Int'l*, pg. 491
FISHER COMPANIES INC.; *U.S. Public*, pg. 647
FLAMBEAU CORPORATION; *U.S. Private*, pg. 409
FLEETWOOD CANADA LTD.—Fleetwood Enterprises, Inc.; *U.S. Public*, pg. 651
FLETCHER CHALLENGE CANADA LIMITED—Fletcher Challenge Limited; *Int'l*, pg. 495
FLETCHER CHALLENGE LIMITED; *Int'l*, pg. 494
FLORIDA EAST COAST INDUSTRIES INC.—St. Joe Corp.; *U.S. Public*, pg. 1427
FLORIDA PROGRESS CORPORATION; *U.S. Public*, pg. 655
FOAMEX INTERNATIONAL INC.—Trace International Holdings, Inc.; *U.S. Private*, pg. 1094
FOODCORP LIMITED; *Int'l*, pg. 496
FORBO AMERICA INC.—Forbo Holding SA; *Int'l*, pg. 497
FORBO BETEILIGUNGEN GMBH—Forbo Holding SA; *Int'l*, pg. 497
FORBO FINANZ SA—Forbo Holding SA; *Int'l*, pg. 497
FORBO IMMOB SA—Forbo Holding SA; *Int'l*, pg. 497
FORBO INTERNATIONAL SA—Forbo Holding SA; *Int'l*, pg. 497
FORBO INVEST LTD.—Forbo Holding SA; *Int'l*, pg. 497
FORBO NL HOLDING B.V.—Forbo Holding SA; *Int'l*, pg. 497
FORBO PARTICIPATIONS SA—Forbo Holding SA; *Int'l*, pg. 498
FORBO UK LTD.—Forbo Holding SA; *Int'l*, pg. 498
FORD HOLDINGS INC.—Ford Motor Company; *U.S. Public*, pg. 663
FORDSON COAL COMPANY—Ford Motor Company; *U.S. Public*, pg. 664
FOREMOST CORPORATION OF AMERICA; *U.S. Public*, pg. 667
FORSTMANN LITTLE & CO.; *U.S. Private*, pg. 419
FORTE FINANCE N.V.—Granada Group PLC; *Int'l*, pg. 556
FORTIS, INC.—Fortis; *Int'l*, pg. 499
FORTIS INTERNATIONAL N.V.—Fortis; *Int'l*, pg. 499
FORTUNE BRANDS INTERNATIONAL CORPORATION—Fortune Brands, Inc.; *U.S. Public*, pg. 675
FORVALTNINGS AB RATOS; *Int'l*, pg. 500
FOSECO HOLDING INC.—Burmah Castrol plc; *Int'l*, pg. 234
FOSECO PLC—Burmah Castrol plc; *Int'l*, pg. 234
FOSTER MANAGEMENT CO.; *U.S. Private*, pg. 421
FOSTER WHEELER INTERNATIONAL CORPORATION—Foster Wheeler Corporation; *U.S. Public*, pg. 677
FOUR WINDS INVESTMENT CORP.; *U.S. Private*, pg. 422
FOX, INC.—The News Corporation Limited; *Int'l*, pg. 926
FOX VALLEY CORPORATION; *U.S. Private*, pg. 422
FRANCHISE SERVICES, INC.; *U.S. Private*, pg. 423
FRANCOSTEEL CORPORATION—Groupe Usinor; *Int'l*, pg. 572
FRANKLIN RESOURCES, INC.; *U.S. Public*, pg. 679
FRANKLINS HOLDINGS LTD.—Jardine Matheson Holdings Limited; *Int'l*, pg. 703
FREEDOM FORGE CORPORATION; *U.S. Private*, pg. 425
FREMONT GENERAL CORPORATION; *U.S. Public*, pg. 681
FRIGO CHEESE CORP.—Stella Foods, Inc.; *U.S. Private*, pg. 1040
FRONTIER HOLDINGS INC.—Wainoco Oil Corporation; *U.S. Public*, pg. 1732
FRONTIER INSURANCE GROUP, INC.; *U.S. Public*, pg. 684
FUJITSU NETWORKS INDUSTRIES—Fujitsu Limited; *Int'l*, pg. 529
FULLER OFFSHORE FINANCE CORP., B.V.—FLS Industries A/S; *Int'l*, pg. 475
FUND AMERICAN ENTERPRISES HOLDINGS, INC.; *U.S. Public*, pg. 688
FUNDAMENTAL MANAGEMENT, INC.—Industrial Wire Products Corporation; *U.S. Private*, pg. 561
FURNESS BV; *Int'l*, pg. 530
FURNISHINGS INTERNATIONAL, INC.; *U.S. Private*, pg. 431
LOU FUSZ AUTOMOTIVE NETWORK; *U.S. Private*, pg. 432
G B STORES—Schottenstein Stores Corporation; *U.S. Private*, pg. 972
G-I HOLDINGS INC.—GAF Corporation; *U.S. Private*, pg. 433
G INDUSTRIES CORPORATION—GAF Corporation; *U.S. Private*, pg. 433
GACC HOLDING COMPANY—American Financial Group; *U.S. Public*, pg. 75
GAF CORPORATION; *U.S. Private*, pg. 433
GAF MATERIALS CORPORATION—GAF Corporation; *U.S. Private*, pg. 433
GC COMPANIES, INC.; *U.S. Public*, pg. 693
GCI HOLDINGS CORPORATION; *U.S. Private*, pg. 434
G.E. LIGHTING LTD.—General Electric Company; *U.S. Public*, pg. 713
GEC PRECISION CORP.—The General Electric Company, p.l.c.; *Int'l*, pg. 545
GF INDUSTRIES, INC.; *U.S. Private*, pg. 434
GGRI, INC.—Griffin Group, Inc.; *U.S. Private*, pg. 480
GIB GROUP; *Int'l*, pg. 532
GKN AUTOMOTIVE INTERNATIONAL GMBH—GKN plc; *Int'l*, pg. 535
GKN AUTOMOTIVE LTD.—GKN plc; *Int'l*, pg. 534
GKN COMERCIAL LIMITADA—GKN plc; *Int'l*, pg. 536
GKN SANKEY LTD.—GKN plc; *Int'l*, pg. 534
GPT HOLDINGS LTD.—Siemens AG; *Int'l*, pg. 1248
GPU, INC.; *U.S. Public*, pg. 695
GTE MOBILE COMMUNICATIONS INCORPORATED—GTE Corporation; *U.S. Public*, pg. 696
GWC HEALTH, INC.; *U.S. Private*, pg. 436
J. GORDON GAINES, INC.—Torchmark Corporation; *U.S. Public*, pg. 1622
GALEN INTERNATIONAL HOLDINGS, INC.—Columbia/HCA Healthcare Corporation; *U.S. Public*, pg. 404
GALLAHER INVESTMENTS LIMITED—Gallaher Limited; *Int'l*, pg. 539
GAMMA INAC, INC.—Cigna Corp.; *U.S. Public*, pg. 365
GAN NORTH AMERICA INC.—Groupe GAN; *Int'l*, pg. 564
GAN SA—Groupe GAN; *Int'l*, pg. 565
GANNETT COMPANY, INC.; *U.S. Public*, pg. 698
GARTELL LIMITED—Avonmore Waterford Group plc; *Int'l*, pg. 102
THE GATES CORPORATION—Tomkins PLC; *Int'l*, pg. 1396
GEBRUDER SULZER HOLDING GMBH—Sulzer Ltd.; *Int'l*, pg. 1308
GEFINOR S.A. LUXEMBOURG; *Int'l*, pg. 542
GEFINOR U.S.A., INC.—Gefinor S.A. Luxembourg; *Int'l*, pg. 542
GEICO CORPORATION—Berkshire Hathaway Inc.; *U.S. Public*, pg. 219
GEM INDUSTRIES FINANCE CORPORATION; *U.S. Private*, pg. 442
GENDIS INC.; *Int'l*, pg. 542
GENERAL DATACOMM INDUSTRIES, INC.; *U.S. Public*, pg. 708
GENERAL DYNAMICS SERVICES CO.—General Dynamics Corporation; *U.S. Public*, pg. 709
GENERAL GRAPHICS, INC.—Cigna Corp.; *U.S. Public*, pg. 362
GENERAL PORTFOLIOS CORP.—GPU, Inc.; *U.S. Public*, pg. 695
GENERAL RE CORPORATION; *U.S. Public*, pg. 725
GENERALE FINANCE LUXEMBOURG SA—Banque Generale du Luxembourg SA; *Int'l*, pg. 162
GENEVE CORPORATION; *U.S. Private*, pg. 446
GERBER AUSTRALIA, LTD.—Novartis AG; *Int'l*, pg. 973
GHIA, INC.—Ford Motor Company; *U.S. Public*, pg. 664
GILMAN INVESTMENT COMPANY, INC.; *U.S. Private*, pg. 454
GIST-BROCADES, INC.—Royal Gist-Brocades N.V.; *Int'l*, pg. 1143
GLEASON CORPORATION; *U.S. Public*, pg. 746
GLOBAL ENVIRONMENTAL CORP.; *U.S. Public*, pg. 747
GLOBAL MARINE INC.; *U.S. Public*, pg. 748
GLYNWED INTERNATIONAL PLC; *Int'l*, pg. 554
GOLD PEAK INDUSTRIES (HOLDINGS) LIMITED—GP Batteries International Ltd.; *Int'l*, pg. 537
GOLDEN BOOKS FAMILY ENTERTAINMENT INC.; *U.S. Public*, pg. 749
GOLDEN ENTERPRISES INC.; *U.S. Public*, pg. 749
THE GOLDFIELD CONSOLIDATED MINES CO.—The Goldfield Corporation; *U.S. Public*, pg. 750
GOLDNER HAWN JOHNSONS & MORRISON INCORPORATED; *U.S. Private*, pg. 462
GRABOWSKY & POORT BV—Heidemij N.V.; *Int'l*, pg. 606
GRADCO SYSTEMS, INC.; *U.S. Public*, pg. 757
GRAHAM VACUUM & HEAT TRANSFER LTD.—Graham Corporation; *U.S. Public*, pg. 757
GRAMERCY ASSETS CORPORATION—Consolidated Edison Company of New York, Inc.; *U.S. Public*, pg. 435
GRAND TRUNK CORPORATION (GTC)—Canadian National Railway Company; *Int'l*, pg. 258
GRANT, INC.—Northwestern Public Service; *U.S. Public*, pg. 1201
GRAYCOR OPERATING COMPANIES; *U.S. Private*, pg. 472
GRAYSTONE PLC; *Int'l*, pg. 557
GREAT AMERICAN HOLDING CORPORATION—American Financial Group; *U.S. Public*, pg. 74
GREAT AMERICAN INDUSTRIES, INC.; *U.S. Private*, pg. 473
GREAT AMERICAN MANAGEMENT & INVESTMENT, INC.; *U.S. Private*, pg. 473
GREEN EQUITY INVESTORS L.P.—Leonard Green & Partners; *U.S. Private*, pg. 477
GREENWAY PARTNERS, L.P.; *U.S. Private*, pg. 478
GREENWICH STREET CAPITAL PARTNERS, INC.; *U.S. Private*, pg. 479
GREENWICH WATER SYSTEM, INC.—American Water Works Company, Inc.; *U.S. Public*, pg. 95
GREMAC INC.—Macromedia Incorporated; *U.S. Private*, pg. 693
GREYHOUND LINES, INC.; *U.S. Public*, pg. 765
GROUPE STRAFOR FACOM; *Int'l*, pg. 569
GROUPE ZODIAC; *Int'l*, pg. 572
GRUPO CARSO S.A. DE C.V.; *Int'l*, pg. 572
GRUPO COMERCIAL CHEDRAUI S.A. DE C.V.; *Int'l*, pg. 573
GRUPO MEXICANO DE DESARROLLO; *Int'l*, pg. 575
GRUPO TABAQUERO CANARIO, S.A.—Tabacalera, S.A.; *Int'l*, pg. 1346
GUILFORD TRANSPORTATION INDUSTRIES INC.; *U.S. Private*, pg. 487
GUINNESS PLC—Diageo Plc; *Int'l*, pg. 412
GUTHRIE CANADIAN INVESTMENTS LIMITED—BBA Group plc; *Int'l*, pg. 113
THE GUTHRIE CORPORATION, PLC—BBA Group plc; *Int'l*, pg. 113
GUTHRIE NORTH AMERICA, INC.—BBA Group plc; *Int'l*, pg. 113
H&K HOLDINGS, INC.—Klockner-Werke AG; *Int'l*, pg. 737
HC HOLDINGS; *U.S. Private*, pg. 489
HIG CAPITAL MANAGEMENT; *U.S. Private*, pg. 490
HM INTERNATIONAL; *U.S. Private*, pg. 491
HND CORPORATION—Hitachi Koki Co., Ltd.; *Int'l*, pg. 620
THE HOH ORGANIZATIONS; *U.S. Private*, pg. 492
HPI HOLDING S.A.; *Int'l*, pg. 579
HAAS, WHEAT & PARTNERS; *U.S. Private*, pg. 492
THE H.T. HACKNEY CO.; *U.S. Private*, pg. 493
HADEN DRYSYS INTERNATIONAL LTD.—Haden Maclellan Holdings plc; *Int'l*, pg. 585
HADEN, INC.—Haden Maclellan Holdings plc; *Int'l*, pg. 586
HADEN MACLELLAN HOLDINGS PLC; *Int'l*, pg. 585
HAI SUN HUP GROUP LTD.; *Int'l*, pg. 586
HAKING INTERNATIONAL—Haking Enterprises; *Int'l*, pg. 587
HALL FINANCIAL GROUP, INC.; *U.S. Private*, pg. 495
MATTHEW HALL & CO.—AMEC Plc; *Int'l*, pg. 16
HALLIBURTON COMPANY; *U.S. Public*, pg. 775
HALMA HOLDINGS INC.—Halma p.l.c.; *Int'l*, pg. 590
HALMA P.L.C.; *Int'l*, pg. 589
HAMPSHIRE GROUP, LTD.; *U.S. Public*, pg. 778
HANDELMAATSCHAPPIJ NOORDA B.V.—Unilever Plc; *Int'l*, pg. 1437
HANES COMPANIES, INC.—Leggett & Platt, Incorporated; *U.S. Public*, pg. 986
HANJIN SHIPPING COMPANY LTD.; *Int'l*, pg. 592
HANSON NORTH AMERICA—Hanson PLC; *Int'l*, pg. 593
HAPAG-LLOYD (AMERICA), INC.—Hapag-Lloyd AG; *Int'l*, pg. 596
HARBERT CORPORATION; *U.S. Private*, pg. 500
HARBOUR GROUP LTD.; *U.S. Private*, pg. 500
HARCOURT BRACE & COMPANY - ELEMENTARY DIV.—Harcourt General, Inc.; *U.S. Public*, pg. 783

HARCOURT BRACE & COMPANY REAL PROPERTIES CORPORATION—Harcourt General, Inc.; *U.S. Public*, pg. 783
HARD ROCK CAFE INTERNATIONAL INC.—The Rank Group PLC; *Int'l*, pg. 1087
HARNISCHFEGER INDUSTRIES, INC.; *U.S. Public*, pg. 788
HARRAH'S RENO HOLDING COMPANY—Harrah's Entertainment, Inc.; *U.S. Public*, pg. 791
HARRIS CHEMICAL GROUP, INC.; *U.S. Private*, pg. 505
HARRIS ENTERPRISES INC.; *U.S. Private*, pg. 505
HARRISONS & CROSFIELD (AUSTRALIA) LTD.—Harrisons & Crosfield plc; *Int'l*, pg. 599
HARROW INDUSTRIES; *U.S. Private*, pg. 506
HARROWSTON CORPORATION; *Int'l*, pg. 599
HART HOLDING COMPANY, INC.; *U.S. Private*, pg. 507
HARVEST PARTNERS INC.; *U.S. Private*, pg. 508
HARVEY ELECTRONICS, INC.; *U.S. Public*, pg. 796
HAWAIIAN AIRLINES, INC.; *U.S. Public*, pg. 799
HAWAIIAN ELECTRIC INDUSTRIES, INC.; *U.S. Public*, pg. 799
HAWKEYE HOLDING, INC.—AEGON N.V.; *Int'l*, pg. 27
HAYSELTON ENTERPRISES LIMITED—Jardine Matheson Holdings Limited; *Int'l*, pg. 703
HEALDS AG—Avonmore Waterford Group plc; *Int'l*, pg. 102
HEARTLAND DEVELOPMENT CORPORATION—WPL Holdings, Inc.; *U.S. Public*, pg. 1728
HEARTLAND EXPRESS, INC.; *U.S. Public*, pg. 803
HEDSTROM HOLDING CO.—Hicks, Muse, Tate & Furst Inc.; *U.S. Private*, pg. 526
HEIDELBERG CEMENT INC.—Heidelberger Zement A.G.; *Int'l*, pg. 605
HEIN DE WINDT B.V.—Fuchs Petrolub AG Oel + Chemie; *Int'l*, pg. 517
HEINRICH INDUSTRIE-UND HANDELS-AKTIENGESELLSCHAFT—Harpen AG; *Int'l*, pg. 597
H.J. HEINZ CENTRAL EUROPE S.A.—H.J. Heinz Company; *U.S. Public*, pg. 806
HEINZ U.S.A. DIV.—H.J. Heinz Company; *U.S. Public*, pg. 805
HELIAN ASC OF NORTHRIDGE, INC.—Vencor, Inc.; *U.S. Public*, pg. 1715
HELIAN HEALTH GROUP OF FRESNO, INC.—Vencor, Inc.; *U.S. Public*, pg. 1715
HELIAN RECOVERY CORP.—Vencor, Inc.; *U.S. Public*, pg. 1715
HELM RESOURCES INC.; *U.S. Public*, pg. 808
HENDRICK AUTOMOTIVE GROUP; *U.S. Private*, pg. 522
JA. HENNESSY & CO.—LVMH Moet Hennessy Louis Vuitton; *Int'l*, pg. 780
HEPWORTH PLC; *Int'l*, pg. 614
HERAEUS HOLDING GMBH; *Int'l*, pg. 615
HERAEUS INSTRUMENTS INC.—Heraeus Holding GmbH; *Int'l*, pg. 616
HERLITZ PBS AKTIENGESELLSCHAFT; *Int'l*, pg. 616
HESTA TEX AG; *Int'l*, pg. 617
HICKS OIL-HICKS GAS, INC.; *U.S. Private*, pg. 526
HICKSON INTERNATIONAL PLC; *Int'l*, pg. 618
HIGH INDUSTRIES, INC.; *U.S. Private*, pg. 528
HIGH VOLTAGE ENGINEERING CORPORATION; *U.S. Private*, pg. 528
HILLENBRAND INDUSTRIES, INC.; *U.S. Public*, pg. 828
HILLSDOWN HOLDINGS PLC; *Int'l*, pg. 619
HIPPOCRENE HOLDINGS—Pegasus Gold Corporation; *U.S. Public*, pg. 1269
HOAK CAPITAL; *U.S. Private*, pg. 531
HOCHE FRIEDLAND—C.E.P. Communication Group; *Int'l*, pg. 239
HOECHST AKTIENGESELLSCHAFT; *Int'l*, pg. 624
HOLBERG INDUSTRIES, INC.; *U.S. Private*, pg. 533
HOLDERBANK FINANCIERE GLARIS LTD.; *Int'l*, pg. 628
HOLLINGER INC.; *Int'l*, pg. 630
HOLNAM INC.—Holderbank Financiere Glaris Ltd.; *Int'l*, pg. 628
PHILIPP HOLZMANN USA, LTD.—Philipp Holzmann AG; *Int'l*, pg. 633
HOMELAND HOLDING CORP.; *U.S. Public*, pg. 832
HOMETOWN COMMUNICATIONS NETWORK, INC.; *U.S. Private*, pg. 537
HONEYWELL BULL AG—Compagnie des Machines Bull; *Int'l*, pg. 318
HONG FOK CORPORATION LTD.; *Int'l*, pg. 635
HONGKONG LAND HOLDINGS LIMITED—Jardine Matheson Holdings Limited; *Int'l*, pg. 704
HOOGOVENS GROEP B.V.—Koninklijke Hoogovens N.V.; *Int'l*, pg. 753
HOOGOVENS STAALVERWERKING EN HANDEL BV—Koninklijke Hoogovens N.V.; *Int'l*, pg. 754
HOOGOVENS TECHNISCHE DIENSTVERLENING BV—Koninklijke Hoogovens N.V.; *Int'l*, pg. 754
HORACE MANN EDUCATORS CORPORATION; *U.S. Public*, pg. 835
HORIZON ENTERPRISES GROUP LLC; *U.S. Private*, pg. 539
HORSEHEAD INDUSTRIES, INC.; *U.S. Private*, pg. 540
HOTELTOUR—Club Mediterranee SA; *Int'l*, pg. 298
HOUSEWARES HOLDING COMPANY—NACCO Industries, Inc.; *U.S. Public*, pg. 1149
HOUSTON INDUSTRIES INCORPORATED; *U.S. Public*, pg. 842
HOWDEN GROUP CANADA LIMITED—Howden Group Plc; *Int'l*, pg. 636
HOWDEN GROUP PLC; *Int'l*, pg. 636
HOXAN AMERICA INCORPORATED—Daido Hoxan Inc.; *Int'l*, pg. 363
HUBBARD EUROPA B.V.—Merck & Co., Inc.; *U.S. Public*, pg. 1091
CAROLINE HUNT TRUST ESTATE; *U.S. Private*, pg. 548
HUNT FOREIGN INVESTMENT CORP.—Olin Corporation; *U.S. Public*, pg. 1219
HUNTCO NEVADA, INC.—Huntco Inc.; *U.S. Public*, pg. 849
HUNTER DOUGLAS HOLDINGS LTD.—Hunter Douglas N.V.; *Int'l*, pg. 640
HUNTER DOUGLAS N.V.; *Int'l*, pg. 639
HYDRO-QUEBEC; *Int'l*, pg. 640
HYDROCORP, INC.—Aquarion Company; *U.S. Public*, pg. 126
HYUNDAI MOTOR COMPANY; *Int'l*, pg. 641
ICF INCORPORATED—ICF Kaiser International Inc.; *U.S. Public*, pg. 853
I.C.H. CORPORATION; *U.S. Public*, pg. 853
ICI AMERICAN HOLDINGS INC.—Imperial Chemical Industries PLC; *Int'l*, pg. 663
ICN PHARMACEUTICALS, INC.; *U.S. Public*, pg. 853
ICS INTANGIBLES HOLDING COMPANY—Harcourt General, Inc.; *U.S. Public*, pg. 783
IDB DEVELOPMENT CORPORATION LIMITED—IDB Holding Corporation; *Int'l*, pg. 644
IEI INVESTMENTS, INC.—Indiana Energy, Inc.; *U.S. Public*, pg. 875
IES INDUSTRIES INC.; *U.S. Public*, pg. 855
I.H.F. S.A.—Fiat Auto SpA; *Int'l*, pg. 483
IL INTERNATIONAL INC.; *U.S. Public*, pg. 855
IL (STRATFORD), INC.—IL International Inc.; *U.S. Public*, pg. 856
ILA FINANCIAL SERVICES, INC.—Franklin Resources, Inc.; *U.S. Public*, pg. 680
INA CORPORATION—Cigna Corp.; *U.S. Public*, pg. 362
INA FINANCIAL CORPORATION—Cigna Corp.; *U.S. Public*, pg. 362
INA OVERSEAS PROPERTIES, LTD.—Cigna Corp.; *U.S. Public*, pg. 363
INX CORPORATION—Sumitomo Chemical Company, Ltd.; *Int'l*, pg. 1311
IRI ISTITUTO RICOSTRUZIONE INDUSTRIALE; *Int'l*, pg. 652
ISO HOLDING, AG—Armstrong World Industries, Inc.; *U.S. Public*, pg. 132
ISP HOLDINGS, INC.; *U.S. Public*, pg. 858
ISS HOLDING S.A.—ISS-International Service System A/S; *Int'l*, pg. 657
ISS SCANDINAVIA A/S—ISS-International Service System A/S; *Int'l*, pg. 656
ISS SERVISYSTEM COM. E. IND. LTDA.—ISS-International Service System A/S; *Int'l*, pg. 657
ISS U.K. LTD.—ISS-International Service System A/S; *Int'l*, pg. 657
IWC RESOURCES CORPORATION—NIPSCO Industries, Inc.; *U.S. Public*, pg. 1185
IBSTOCK PLC; *Int'l*, pg. 658
ICELAND GROUP PLC; *Int'l*, pg. 658
IDEON GROUP, INC.—Cendant Corporation; *U.S. Public*, pg. 320
IHOP CORP.; *U.S. Public*, pg. 862
IKEA HOLDINGS AB; *Int'l*, pg. 659
ILLINOIS CENTRAL CORPORATION; *U.S. Public*, pg. 864
ILLINOVA INC.; *U.S. Public*, pg. 869
ILSCO; *U.S. Private*, pg. 558
IMETAL; *Int'l*, pg. 661
IMODIS—GIB Group; *Int'l*, pg. 533
IMPERIAL CREDIT INDUSTRIES, INC.; *U.S. Public*, pg. 872
INACAN HOLDINGS LTD.—Cigna Corp.; *U.S. Public*, pg. 366
INCA INVESTIMENTI SPA ALFA ROMEO ALFASUD—Fiat Auto SpA; *Int'l*, pg. 481
INCHCAPE PLC; *Int'l*, pg. 671
INCO UNITED STATES INC.—Inco Limited; *Int'l*, pg. 672
INDEPENDENT BANKSHARES, INC.; *U.S. Public*, pg. 874
INDIANA ENERGY, INC.; *U.S. Public*, pg. 874
INDIVERS B.V.; *Int'l*, pg. 673
INDUCTOTHERM INDUSTRIES, INC.; *U.S. Private*, pg. 560
INDUSTRIAL EQUITY LIMITED; *Int'l*, pg. 676
INDUSTRIAS BACHOCO S.A. DE C.V.; *Int'l*, pg. 677
INFOVEST, INC.; *U.S. Private*, pg. 562
INGERSOLL INTERNATIONAL INC.; *U.S. Private*, pg. 562
INISHTECH PLC—James Crean PLC; *Int'l*, pg. 341
INLAND STEEL INDUSTRIES, INC.; *U.S. Public*, pg. 879
INSILCO CORPORATION; *U.S. Public*, pg. 881
INTERLAKEN CAPITAL, INC.; *U.S. Private*, pg. 567
INTERLOCK INDUSTRIES, INC.; *U.S. Private*, pg. 567
INTERMAGNETICS GENERAL (EUROPE) LIMITED—Intermagnetics General Corporation; *U.S. Public*, pg. 894
INTERMEDIATE HOLDINGS, INC.—Conseco Inc.; *U.S. Public*, pg. 433
INTERMOUNTAIN INDUSTRIES, INC.; *U.S. Private*, pg. 568
INTERNATIONAL ALUMINUM CORPORATION; *U.S. Public*, pg. 894
INTERNATIONAL COMMUNICATIONS HOLDINGS, INC.—PacifiCorp; *U.S. Public*, pg. 1252
INTERNATIONAL FIBERCOM; *U.S. Public*, pg. 898
INTERNATIONAL INVESTMENT & UNDERWRITING LTD.; *Int'l*, pg. 684
INTERNATIONAL SAINT-GOBAIN—Saint-Gobain; *Int'l*, pg. 1177
INTERNATIONAL SYSTEMS & CONTROLS CORP.; *U.S. Private*, pg. 572
INTERNAZIONALE HOLDING FIAT SA—Fiat Auto SpA; *Int'l*, pg. 483
INTERPHARM GROEP B.V.—Internatio-Muller N.V.; *Int'l*, pg. 682
THE INTERPUBLIC GROUP OF COMPANIES, INC.; *U.S. Public*, pg. 908
THE INTERTECH GROUP INC.—BBA Group plc; *Int'l*, pg. 113
INTRENET, INC.; *U.S. Public*, pg. 910
INVERSIONES CONTINENTAL, S.A. DE C.V.—Cigna Corp.; *U.S. Public*, pg. 363
INVERSIONES INA LIMITADA—Cigna Corp.; *U.S. Public*, pg. 364
INVERSIONES ISICA, C.A.—Jefferson Smurfit Group p.l.c.; *Int'l*, pg. 1271
INVESCO GROUP ASSET MANAGEMENT LTD.; *Int'l*, pg. 685
INVESTCORP INTERNATIONAL; *Int'l*, pg. 686
INVESTOR AB; *Int'l*, pg. 686
INVESTORS INSURANCE GROUP, INC.; *U.S. Public*, pg. 911
INVESTORS MANAGEMENT CORP.; *U.S. Private*, pg. 574
IPALCO ENTERPRISES, INC.; *U.S. Public*, pg. 912
IRON AGE HOLDINGS CORPORATION—Fenway Partners Inc.; *U.S. Private*, pg. 401
IRON ROAD RAILWAYS INC.; *U.S. Private*, pg. 575
THE ISRAEL LAND DEVELOPMENT CO., LTD.; *Int'l*, pg. 691
ITALIMPIANTI OF AMERICA, INCORPORATED—IRI Istituto Ricostruzione Industriale; *Int'l*, pg. 655
ITOCHU INTERNATIONAL INC.—Itochu Corporation; *Int'l*, pg. 694
IVEX PACKAGING CORPORATION; *U.S. Public*, pg. 915
J. & P. COATS LIMITED—Coats Viyella plc; *Int'l*, pg. 299
JAH ENTERPRISES, INC.; *U.S. Private*, pg. 577
JC PENNEY COMPANY, INC.; *U.S. Public*, pg. 916
JC PENNEY EUROPE, INC.—JC Penney Company, Inc.; *U.S. Public*, pg. 917
JFC INC.; *U.S. Private*, pg. 577
JIB GROUP PLC—Jardine Matheson Holdings Limited; *Int'l*, pg. 705
JL PROPERTY HOLDINGS LTD.—John Laing PLC; *Int'l*, pg. 796
JPE, INC.; *U.S. Public*, pg. 919
JSB FINANCIAL; *U.S. Public*, pg. 919
JACKS INTERNATIONAL LIMITED; *Int'l*, pg. 697
JACOBS BELGIQUE S.A.—Philip Morris Companies Inc.; *U.S. Public*, pg. 1288
JACOBS SUCHARD SERVICE AG—Philip Morris Companies Inc.; *U.S. Public*, pg. 1288
JARDINE DAVIES INC.—Jardine Matheson Holdings Limited; *Int'l*, pg. 705
JARDINE INSURANCE SERVICES LIMITED—Jardine Matheson Holdings Limited; *Int'l*, pg. 705
JARDINE INTERNATIONAL MOTOR HOLDINGS LTD.—Jardine Matheson Holdings Limited; *Int'l*, pg. 705
JARDINE, MATHESON & CO., LTD.—Jardine Matheson Holdings Limited; *Int'l*, pg. 704
JARDINE MATHESON HOLDINGS LIMITED; *Int'l*, pg. 703
JARDINE MATHESON (MALAYSIA) SDN BHD—Jardine Matheson Holdings Limited; *Int'l*, pg. 705
JARDINE MATHESON (SINGAPORE) LTD—Jardine Matheson Holdings Limited; *Int'l*, pg. 705
JARDINE STRATEGIC HOLDINGS LTD.—Jardine Matheson Holdings Limited; *Int'l*, pg. 703
JARVIS PLC; *Int'l*, pg. 705
JEFFERIES GROUP, INC.; *U.S. Public*, pg. 924
JEFFERSON-PILOT CORPORATION; *U.S. Public*, pg. 925
JILLIAN'S ENTERTAINMENT CORPORATION; *U.S. Private*, pg. 587
JOHN HANCOCK SUBSIDIARIES, INC.—John Hancock Mutual Life Insurance Company; *U.S. Private*, pg. 589
AXEL JOHNSON AB; *Int'l*, pg. 707
JOHNSON FRY HOLDINGS PLC; *Int'l*, pg. 713
JOHNSTOWN AMERICA INDUSTRIES; *U.S. Public*, pg. 933
JONES INTERNATIONAL, LTD.; *U.S. Private*, pg. 597
J.A. JONES, INC.—Philipp Holzmann AG; *Int'l*, pg. 633
JOURNAL COMMUNICATIONS INC.; *U.S. Private*, pg. 601
JUPITER INDUSTRIES, INC.; *U.S. Private*, pg. 602
K.C.S.A. HOLDINGS (PTY.) LTD.—Kimberly-Clark Corporation; *U.S. Public*, pg. 959
KHD DEUTZ OF AMERICA CORPORATION—Deutz AG; *Int'l*, pg. 408
KOA HOLDINGS; *U.S. Private*, pg. 603
KTM HOLDINGS CORP.; *U.S. Private*, pg. 604
KU ENERGY; *U.S. Public*, pg. 940
KAISER ALUMINUM CORPORATION—Maxxam Inc.; *U.S. Public*, pg. 1062
KALAMAZOO HOLDINGS, INC.; *U.S. Private*, pg. 606
KALMAR INDUSTRIES AB—Trelleborg AB; *Int'l*, pg. 1420
KAMELEON BEHEER IV—Royal Begemann Group; *Int'l*, pg. 1133
KAMYR HOLDING AG—Kvaerner a.s.a.; *Int'l*, pg. 770
KANEB SERVICES, INC.; *U.S. Public*, pg. 942
KANSAS CITY SOUTHERN INDUSTRIES, INC.; *U.S. Public*, pg. 943
KAPLAN ELECTRONICS; *U.S. Private*, pg. 607
KAPPLER SAFETY GROUP, INC.; *U.S. Private*, pg. 607
KATHARINE GIBBS SCHOOL, INC.—Career Education Corporation; *U.S. Private*, pg. 209
KAUFEL AMERICA INC.—Kaufel Group Ltd.; *Int'l*, pg. 725
KAWASAKI HEAVY INDUSTRIES, LTD.; *Int'l*, pg. 725
KEARNEY-NATIONAL CANADA LTD.—The Dyson-Kissner-Moran Corporation; *U.S. Private*, pg. 351
KELLWOOD ASIA LIMITED—Kellwood Company; *U.S. Public*, pg. 948
KELTATIM PUBLISHING COMPANY; *U.S. Private*, pg. 613
KEMIRA AGRO U.K. LTD.—Kemira Oy; *Int'l*, pg. 728
KEMIRA HOLDINGS INC.—Kemira Oy; *Int'l*, pg. 729
KEMIRA OY; *Int'l*, pg. 727
KENTUCKY INVESTORS, INC.; *U.S. Public*, pg. 951
KEY BANK OF MAINE—Keycorp; *U.S. Public*, pg. 954
KEYSTONE BREWERS, INC.; *U.S. Private*, pg. 618
KEYSTONE FINANCIAL INC.; *U.S. Public*, pg. 956
KEYSTONE INDUSTRIES, INC.—Varlen Corporation; *U.S. Public*, pg. 1711
KEYSTONE INTERNATIONAL HOLDINGS CORP.—Tyco International Ltd.; *U.S. Public*, pg. 1650
KEYWELL CORPORATION; *U.S. Private*, pg. 619
KEYWELL CORPORATION—Keywell Corporation; *U.S. Private*, pg. 619
KIDDE FIRE PROTECTION LTD.—Williams Holdings Plc; *Int'l*, pg. 1499
PETER KIEWIT SONS INC.; *U.S. Private*, pg. 619
KIM ENG HOLDINGS LIMITED; *Int'l*, pg. 733
KINGFISHER PLC; *Int'l*, pg. 733
J.I. KISLAK INC.; *U.S. Private*, pg. 624
KITCHELL CORPORATION; *U.S. Private*, pg. 624
KITCHEN INVESTMENT GROUP; *U.S. Private*, pg. 624
KLEER-VU PLASTICS, INC.; *U.S. Public*, pg. 962
KLEINWORT BENSON (U.S.A.) INC.—Dresdner Bank AG; *Int'l*, pg. 420

KNIGHT-RIDDER, INC.; *U.S. Public*, pg. 963
KNURR USA EAST—Knurr AG; *Int'l*, pg. 739
KOBE STEEL U.S.A. INC. (NEW YORK)—Kobe Steel, Ltd.; *Int'l*, pg. 740
KOHLBERG & COMPANY, LLC; *U.S. Private*, pg. 629
KONICA CORPORATION; *Int'l*, pg. 748
KONICA HEADQUARTERS NORTH AMERICA, INC.—Konica Corporation; *Int'l*, pg. 748
KONINKLIJKE AHOLD NV; *Int'l*, pg. 749
KONINKLIJKE BOLSWESSANEN NV; *Int'l*, pg. 750
KRAUS-ANDERSON INCORPORATED; *U.S. Private*, pg. 635
KROFAM INC.; *U.S. Private*, pg. 636
KRONOS INTERNATIONAL, INC.—Contran Corporation; *U.S. Private*, pg. 271
KUBOTA AMERICA CORP.—Kubota Corp.; *Int'l*, pg. 762
KUBOTA CORP.; *Int'l*, pg. 762
KUEHNE & NAGEL INTERNATIONAL AG; *Int'l*, pg. 763
KVAERNER A.S. FAST FERRIES—Kvaerner a.s.a.; *Int'l*, pg. 766
KVAERNER DAVY—Kvaerner a.s.a.; *Int'l*, pg. 774
KVAERNER ENGINEERING (UK) LTD.—Kvaerner a.s.a.; *Int'l*, pg. 772
KVAERNER HOLDING UK LTD.—Kvaerner a.s.a.; *Int'l*, pg. 771
KYOCERA INTERNATIONAL, INC.—Kyocera Corporation; *Int'l*, pg. 775
KYOTARU USA—Kyotaru Co., Ltd.; *Int'l*, pg. 778
L & D GROUP; *U.S. Private*, pg. 638
L3 COMMUNICATIONS; *U.S. Private*, pg. 638
LB INDUSTRIES INC.; *U.S. Private*, pg. 639
LCC HOLDING COMPANY—The Mead Corporation; *U.S. Public*, pg. 1076
LEP PROFIT INTERNATIONAL, INC.—International Logistics Limited; *U.S. Private*, pg. 571
LG & E ENERGY CORP.; *U.S. Public*, pg. 970
LG GROUP; *Int'l*, pg. 778
LM ERICSSON HOLDINGS LTD.—Telefonaktiebolaget LM Ericsson; *Int'l*, pg. 1368
LSB INDUSTRIES, INC.; *U.S. Public*, pg. 970
LVMH MOET HENNESSY LOUIS VUITTON; *Int'l*, pg. 779
LABATT BREWING COMPANY LIMITED—Interbrew S.A.; *Int'l*, pg. 679
LABINAL SA; *Int'l*, pg. 785
LACLEDE VENTURE CO.—Laclede Gas Company; *U.S. Public*, pg. 974
LAFARGE CONSTRUCTION MATERIALS—Lafarge S.A.; *Int'l*, pg. 788
LAFARGE CORPORATION—Lafarge S.A.; *Int'l*, pg. 788
LAFARGE PLATRE—Lafarge S.A.; *Int'l*, pg. 789
STEPHEN LAFRANCE HOLDINGS, INC.; *U.S. Private*, pg. 642
LAIDLAW INC.—Canadian Pacific Limited; *Int'l*, pg. 259
LANCASTER PLC—Jardine Matheson Holdings Limited; *Int'l*, pg. 705
LAND INSTRUMENTS INTERNATIONAL LTD.; *Int'l*, pg. 798
LANE INDUSTRIES, INC.; *U.S. Private*, pg. 649
LAPORTE AMERICA INC.—Laporte plc; *Int'l*, pg. 802
LAPORTE INC.—Laporte plc; *Int'l*, pg. 802
LAPORTE PLC; *Int'l*, pg. 801
LATINA HOLDINGS, LTD.—Cigna Corp.; *U.S. Public*, pg. 363
LAURA ASHLEY HOLDINGS PLC; *Int'l*, pg. 804
THE LAURENTIAN GROUP CORPORATION—Desjardins-Laurentian Financial Corporation; *Int'l*, pg. 396
LAWSON MARDON PACKAGING INC.—Alusuisse-Lonza Holding Ltd.; *Int'l*, pg. 68
LEAF RIVER CORP.—Georgia-Pacific Corporation; *U.S. Public*, pg. 736
LEAR SIEGLER DIVERSIFIED HOLDINGS CORP.; *U.S. Private*, pg. 655
ALEX LEE, INC.; *U.S. Private*, pg. 657
THOMAS H. LEE CO.; *U.S. Private*, pg. 658
LEGACY MARKETING GROUP; *U.S. Private*, pg. 658
LEGAL & GENERAL AMERICA, INC.—Legal & General Group PLC; *Int'l*, pg. 805
LEGAL & GENERAL ASSURANCE HOLDINGS (AUSTRALIA) LIMITED—Legal & General Group PLC; *Int'l*, pg. 805
LEGAL & GENERAL GROUP PLC; *Int'l*, pg. 805
LEGAL & GENERAL HOLDINGS (FRANCE) S.A.—Legal & General Group PLC; *Int'l*, pg. 805
LEGG MASON, INC.; *U.S. Public*, pg. 984
LEGWEAR HOLDINGS, INC.—Grupo Synkro, S.A. de C.V.; *Int'l*, pg. 576
LEHMAN BROTHERS HOLDINGS INC.; *U.S. Public*, pg. 987
LENNAR CORPORATION; *U.S. Public*, pg. 987
LENNOX INTERNATIONAL INC.; *U.S. Private*, pg. 659
LEUCADIA NATIONAL CORPORATION; *U.S. Public*, pg. 989
LEVER BROTHERS (NEW ZEALAND) LTD.—Unilever Plc; *Int'l*, pg. 1437
LEVITZ FURNITURE INCORPORATED; *U.S. Public*, pg. 990
LIBERTY CABLE, INC.—TCI Communications, Inc.; *U.S. Public*, pg. 1555
LIBERTY CORPORATION; *U.S. Public*, pg. 991
LIBERTY HOLDINGS, INC.—TCI Communications, Inc.; *U.S. Public*, pg. 1555
LIBERTY INVESTMENT GROUP, INC.—Liberty Corporation; *U.S. Public*, pg. 992
LIBERTY MANAGEMENT SERVICES, INC.—Torchmark Corporation; *U.S. Public*, pg. 1622
LIBERTY PROGRAM INVESTMENTS, INC.—TCI Communications, Inc.; *U.S. Public*, pg. 1555
LIBERTY PROGRAMMING CORPORATION—TCI Communications, Inc.; *U.S. Public*, pg. 1555
LIBERTY SPORTS, INC.—TCI Communications, Inc.; *U.S. Public*, pg. 1555
LIEBHERR-AMERICA INC.—Liebherr-International AG; *Int'l*, pg. 808
LIEBHERR-AUSTRIA-HOLDING GMBH—Liebherr-International AG; *Int'l*, pg. 808
LIEBHERR-HOLDING GMBH—Liebherr-International AG; *Int'l*, pg. 808
LIEBHERR (IRELAND) HOLDING LTD.—Liebherr-International AG; *Int'l*, pg. 808
LIEBHERR-SWISSHOLDING AG—Liebherr-International AG; *Int'l*, pg. 808
LIFE SCIENCES INTERNATIONAL PLC—Thermo Electron Corporation; *U.S. Public*, pg. 1594
LIFE TECHNOLOGIES INVESTMENT HOLDINGS, INC.—The Dexter Corporation; *U.S. Public*, pg. 505
ELI LILLY GROUP LIMITED—Eli Lilly and Company; *U.S. Public*, pg. 994
LINCOLN NATIONAL CORPORATION; *U.S. Public*, pg. 997
LIPHA CHEMICALS S.A.; *Int'l*, pg. 812
LIPHA PHARMACEUTICALS, INC.—Lipha Chemicals S.A.; *Int'l*, pg. 812
LIPOMA B.V.—Unilever Plc; *Int'l*, pg. 1438
LITTON INTERNATIONAL S.A.—Litton Industries, Inc.; *U.S. Public*, pg. 1004
LIVINGSTON U.K. LIMITED—Brammer plc; *Int'l*, pg. 212
LOEWS CORPORATION; *U.S. Public*, pg. 1010
LOGISTIC SERVICES DIVISION—Royal Nedlloyd Group N.V.; *Int'l*, pg. 1144
LOMBARDI HOLDINGS INC.; *U.S. Private*, pg. 673
LONDON FOG INDUSTRIES, INC.; *U.S. Private*, pg. 673
LONDON INTERNATIONAL GROUP PLC; *Int'l*, pg. 815
LONDON INTERNATIONAL, U.S. HOLDINGS INC.—London International Group plc; *Int'l*, pg. 815
LONE STAR TECHNOLOGIES, INC.; *U.S. Public*, pg. 1012
LONG ISLAND BANCORP, INC.; *U.S. Public*, pg. 1013
LONG REACH HOLDINGS INC.; *U.S. Private*, pg. 675
LONGMAN GROUP (OVERSEAS HOLDING) LIMITED—Pearson plc; *Int'l*, pg. 1025
LONGS DRUG STORES CORPORATION; *U.S. Public*, pg. 1013
LONRHO PLC; *Int'l*, pg. 817
LOOK-O-LOOK BV—Van Melle N.V.; *Int'l*, pg. 1451
LUFTHANSA COMMERCIAL HOLDING GMBH—Deutsche Lufthansa AG; *Int'l*, pg. 407
LUND FOOD HOLDINGS, INC.; *U.S. Private*, pg. 680
LUND INTERNATIONAL HOLDINGS, INC.; *U.S. Public*, pg. 1020
LUSK; *U.S. Private*, pg. 681
LYNCH CORPORATION; *U.S. Public*, pg. 1021
LYNCH MANUFACTURING CORPORATION—Lynch Corporation; *U.S. Public*, pg. 1022
LYNCH MULTIMEDIA CORPORATION—Lynch Corporation; *U.S. Public*, pg. 1022
LYNCH TELEPHONE CORPORATION IV—Lynch Corporation; *U.S. Public*, pg. 1021
LYNCH TELEPHONE CORPORATION VII—Lynch Corporation; *U.S. Public*, pg. 1021
LYNCH TELEPHONE CORPORATION VI—Lynch Corporation; *U.S. Public*, pg. 1021
LYNCH TELEPHONE CORPORATION III—Lynch Corporation; *U.S. Public*, pg. 1022
LYNCH TELEPHONE CORPORATION II—Lynch Corporation; *U.S. Public*, pg. 1022
LYNDEN INCORPORATED; *U.S. Private*, pg. 683
LYONNAISE DES EAUX S.A.; *Int'l*, pg. 822
MAN AKTIENGESELLSCHAFT; *Int'l*, pg. 824
MB AMERICA, INC.—Caradon Plc; *Int'l*, pg. 267
MBI INC.; *U.S. Private*, pg. 685
MBIA INC.; *U.S. Public*, pg. 1023
MBS HOLDING, INC.; *U.S. Private*, pg. 685
MBT HOLDING, LTD.—Viag AG; *Int'l*, pg. 1465
MCM PRODUCTS, INC.—Fortune Brands, Inc.; *U.S. Public*, pg. 675
MCN ENERGY GROUP, INC.; *U.S. Public*, pg. 1024
MDU RESOURCES GROUP, INC.; *U.S. Public*, pg. 1025
MIMLIC CORP.—The Minnesota Mutual Life Insurance Company; *U.S. Private*, pg. 750
MMC CORP.; *U.S. Private*, pg. 687
MPI INTERNATIONAL, INC.—Klockner-Werke AG; *Int'l*, pg. 737
MRS. FIELDS' ORIGINAL COOKIES, INC.; *U.S. Private*, pg. 688
MTL INC.; *U.S. Public*, pg. 1028
MAC FRUGAL'S BARGAINS CLOSE-OUTS INC.—Consolidated Stores Corp.; *U.S. Public*, pg. 437
MACANDREWS & FORBES GROUP, INC.—MacAndrews & Forbes Holdings Inc.; *U.S. Private*, pg. 689
MACMILLAN LTD.—Georg von Holtzbrinck GmbH; *Int'l*, pg. 1479
MAGNETI MARELLI S.P.A.—Fiat Auto SpA; *Int'l*, pg. 482
MAGNETICS DATA INC.; *U.S. Private*, pg. 695
MAIL BOXES ETC.—U.S. Office Products Company; *U.S. Public*, pg. 1687
MAIL-WELL INC.; *U.S. Public*, pg. 1037
MAKINO USA INC.—Makino Milling Machine Co. Ltd.; *Int'l*, pg. 831
MANDARIN ORIENTAL INTERNATIONAL LIMITED—Jardine Matheson Holdings Limited; *Int'l*, pg. 704
MANNESMANN A.G.; *Int'l*, pg. 834
MANOR CARE, INC.; *U.S. Public*, pg. 1041
MANULIFE INVESTMENT HOLDINGS LIMITED—Manulife Financial (The Manufacturers Life Insurance Company); *Int'l*, pg. 840
MAP HOLDING—Corporacion MAPFRE, Compania Internacional de Reaseguros, S.A.; *Int'l*, pg. 333
MAPFRE ARGENTINA S.A.—Corporacion MAPFRE, Compania Internacional de Reaseguros, S.A.; *Int'l*, pg. 333
MAPFRE CHILE REASEGUROS, S.A.—Corporacion MAPFRE, Compania Internacional de Reaseguros, S.A.; *Int'l*, pg. 334
MAPFRE CHILE SEGUROS, S.A.—Corporacion MAPFRE, Compania Internacional de Reaseguros, S.A.; *Int'l*, pg. 333
MAPFRE CORPORATION OF FLORIDA—Corporacion MAPFRE, Compania Internacional de Reaseguros, S.A.; *Int'l*, pg. 333
MAPFRE INTERNATIONAL S.A.—Corporacion MAPFRE, Compania Internacional de Reaseguros, S.A.; *Int'l*, pg. 333
MAPFRE LONDON LTD.—Corporacion MAPFRE, Compania Internacional de Reaseguros, S.A.; *Int'l*, pg. 335
THE MARCUS CORPORATION; *U.S. Public*, pg. 1044
MARGA B.V.—Unilever Plc; *Int'l*, pg. 1438
MARITIME LEISURE CORPORATION—Accor S.A.; *Int'l*, pg. 21
MARK VII, INC.; *U.S. Public*, pg. 1046
MARKS & SPENCER HOLDINGS CANADA INC.—Marks & Spencer PLC; *Int'l*, pg. 843
MARKS & SPENCER PROPERTY HOLDINGS LIMITED—Marks & Spencer PLC; *Int'l*, pg. 842
MARKS & SPENCER RETAIL FINANCIAL SERVICES HOLDINGS LIMITED—Marks & Spencer PLC; *Int'l*, pg. 842
MARKS & SPENCER US HOLDINGS INC.—Marks & Spencer PLC; *Int'l*, pg. 843
MARLEY PLASTICS HOLDINGS (USA) INC.—Marley PLC; *Int'l*, pg. 843
MARLEY (U.S.A.) HOLDING CORPORATION—Marley PLC; *Int'l*, pg. 843
THE MARMON GROUP, INC.; *U.S. Private*, pg. 706
MARQUETTE BANCSHARES INC.; *U.S. Private*, pg. 706
MARSH & MCLENNAN COMPANIES, INC.; *U.S. Public*, pg. 1048
MARSHALL & ILSLEY CORPORATION; *U.S. Public*, pg. 1049
MARUBENI AMERICA CORPORATION—Marubeni Corporation; *Int'l*, pg. 844
MARY KAY CORPORATION; *U.S. Private*, pg. 710
MASON & HANGER CORPORATION, INC.; *U.S. Private*, pg. 711
MASTEC, INC.; *U.S. Public*, pg. 1055
MASTERBRAND INDUSTRIES, INC.—Fortune Brands, Inc.; *U.S. Public*, pg. 675
MATSUSHITA ELECTRIC WORKS, LTD.; *Int'l*, pg. 847
MATTEL G, INC.—Mattel, Inc.; *U.S. Public*, pg. 1058
MATTEL HOLDING, INC.—Mattel, Inc.; *U.S. Public*, pg. 1058
MATTEL I., INC.—Mattel, Inc.; *U.S. Public*, pg. 1058
MATTEL OVERSEAS, INC.—Mattel, Inc.; *U.S. Public*, pg. 1058
MAUI DIVERS OF HAWAII; *U.S. Private*, pg. 715
MAUI VARIETIES, LTD.; *U.S. Private*, pg. 715
MAUNA LOA RESOURCES INC.—Buyco, Inc.; *U.S. Private*, pg. 191
MAVIBEL (MAATSCHAPPIJ VOOR INTERNATIONALE BELEGGINGEN) B.V.—Unilever Plc; *Int'l*, pg. 1438
MAXCO, INC.; *U.S. Public*, pg. 1061
MCCARTHY BUILDING COMPANIES; *U.S. Private*, pg. 719
MCCRORY CORPORATION; *U.S. Private*, pg. 720
MCPHERSON'S AMERICA, INC.—McPherson's Limited; *Int'l*, pg. 852
MEAD HOLDINGS S.A.—The Mead Corporation; *U.S. Public*, pg. 1076
MECO USA INC.—L. Possehl & Co. mbH; *Int'l*, pg. 1064
MEGGITT HOLDINGS PLC.—BTR plc; *Int'l*, pg. 124
MEINA HOLDING AG—Unilever Plc; *Int'l*, pg. 1438
MELITTA NORTH AMERICA, INC.—Melitta Unternehmensgruppe Bentz KG; *Int'l*, pg. 857
MELLOY BROS. ENTERPRISES; *U.S. Private*, pg. 730
MERCK HOLDINGS, INC.—Merck & Co., Inc.; *U.S. Public*, pg. 1091
MERIDIAN INSURANCE GROUP, INC.; *U.S. Public*, pg. 1095
MERRILL LYNCH & CO., INC.; *U.S. Public*, pg. 1097
MERRILL LYNCH GROUP, INC.—Merrill Lynch & Co., Inc.; *U.S. Public*, pg. 1097
MERRILL LYNCH INTERNATIONAL, INC.—Merrill Lynch & Co., Inc.; *U.S. Public*, pg. 1098
MESABA HOLDINGS, INC.; *U.S. Public*, pg. 1099
MET-COIL SYSTEMS CORP.; *U.S. Public*, pg. 1099
METALLGESELLSCHAFT CAPITAL CORP.—Metallgesellschaft AG; *Int'l*, pg. 861
METALLGESELLSCHAFT CORP.—Metallgesellschaft AG; *Int'l*, pg. 861
METALLGESELLSCHAFT INDUSTRIE AG—Metallgesellschaft AG; *Int'l*, pg. 861
METALLGESELLSCHAFT TRADE SERVICES CO.—Metallgesellschaft AG; *Int'l*, pg. 862
METAPOINT PARTNERS; *U.S. Private*, pg. 735
METROMEDIA COMPANY; *U.S. Private*, pg. 736
METROPOLITAN LIFE HOLDINGS, LTD.—Metropolitan Life Insurance Co.; *U.S. Private*, pg. 737
FRED MEYER INCORPORATED; *U.S. Public*, pg. 1103
MEYER INTERNATIONAL PLC; *Int'l*, pg. 864
MICHELIN CORPORATION—Compagnie Generale des Etablissements Michelin; *Int'l*, pg. 322
MICROTEL INTERNATIONAL INC.; *U.S. Public*, pg. 1108
MID-AMERICA CAPITAL RESOURCES, INC.—Ipalco Enterprises, Inc.; *U.S. Public*, pg. 913
MID STATE PRODUCTS CO.—Osco Industries Inc.; *U.S. Private*, pg. 821
MIDAMERICAN ENERGY HOLDINGS; *U.S. Public*, pg. 1109
MIDCON CORP.—Occidental Petroleum Corporation; *U.S. Public*, pg. 1210
THE MIDLAND COMPANY; *U.S. Public*, pg. 1110
MIDLAND WALWYN INC.; *Int'l*, pg. 865
MIDWEST EXPRESS HOLDINGS, INC.; *U.S. Public*, pg. 1111
MIKI HOLDING COMPANY—Miki Pulley Co., Ltd.; *Int'l*, pg. 866
MIKRON HOLDING AG; *Int'l*, pg. 866
MILLER INDUSTRIES, INC.; *U.S. Public*, pg. 1112
MILLS & PARTNERS—Hicks, Muse, Tate & Furst Inc.; *U.S. Private*, pg. 526

S.I.C. Index

MILLSTEIN INDUSTRIES; *U.S. Private*, pg. 749
MINEMET HOLDING—Imetal; *Int'l*, pg. 661
MINNESOTA-DAKOTA GENERATING CO.—Otter Tail Power Company; *U.S. Public*, pg. 1235
MIRCAL—Imetal; *Int'l*, pg. 662
MIROITERIES DE L'OUEST—Saint-Gobain; *Int'l*, pg. 1172
MISCO INDUSTRIES; *U.S. Private*, pg. 752
THE MISSION GROUP—Edison International; *U.S. Public*, pg. 564
MISSISSIPPI VALLEY GAS CO.; *U.S. Private*, pg. 753
MITSUBISHI ELECTRIC AMERICA, INC.—Mitsubishi Electric Corporation; *Int'l*, pg. 872
MITSUBISHI ELECTRIC (UK) LTD.—Mitsubishi Electric Corporation; *Int'l*, pg. 873
MIZUNO CORPORATION OF AMERICA—Mizuno Corporation; *Int'l*, pg. 885
MOBIL OIL CORPORATION; *U.S. Public*, pg. 1118
MOBILECOMM; *U.S. Public*, pg. 1120
MONTEDISON S.P.A.—Compart SpA; *Int'l*, pg. 324
THE MONTICELLO COMPANIES, INC.; *U.S. Private*, pg. 759
MONUMENTAL GENERAL INSURANCE GROUP, INC.—AEGON N.V.; *Int'l*, pg. 27
MOORE COMPANY; *U.S. Private*, pg. 759
MORGAN CHEMICAL PRODUCTS INC.—Morgan Crucible Co. Plc; *Int'l*, pg. 892
MORGAN CRUCIBLE CO. PLC; *Int'l*, pg. 890
THE MORGAN GROUP, INC.—Lynch Corporation; *U.S. Public*, pg. 1022
MORGAN HOLDINGS CORP.—J.P. Morgan Co. Incorporated; *U.S. Public*, pg. 1129
J.P. MORGAN CO. INCORPORATED; *U.S. Public*, pg. 1129
MORGAN KEEGAN, INC.; *U.S. Public*, pg. 1131
MORGAN STANLEY DEAN WITTER & CO.; *U.S. Public*, pg. 1132
MUGLER TRIUMVIRAT—Clarins; *Int'l*, pg. 295
MUNCHENER RUCKVERSICHERUNGS-GESELLSCHAFT; *Int'l*, pg. 897
MURATA MANUFACTURING CO., LTD.; *Int'l*, pg. 897
THE MUTUAL LIFE INSURANCE COMPANY OF NEW YORK; *U.S. Private*, pg. 769
MYCOGEN CORPORATION; *U.S. Public*, pg. 1142
MYRESJO AB—Skanska AB; *Int'l*, pg. 1260
NAC RE CORP.; *U.S. Public*, pg. 1144
NBSC CORPORATION—Synovus Financial Corp.; *U.S. Public*, pg. 1549
NBSC HOLDINGS INC.—High Point Financial Corp.; *U.S. Public*, pg. 826
NBSC PROPERTIES INC.—High Point Financial Corp.; *U.S. Public*, pg. 826
NBSC REAL ESTATE COMPANY INC.—High Point Financial Corp.; *U.S. Public*, pg. 826
NETG HOLDING, INC.—Harcourt General, Inc.; *U.S. Public*, pg. 784
NFC INTERNATIONAL HOLDINGS (U.S.A.) INC.—NFC plc; *Int'l*, pg. 901
NFC PLC; *Int'l*, pg. 901
NGE ENTERPRISES, INC.—New York State Electric & Gas Corporation; *U.S. Public*, pg. 1173
NGL HOLDINGS INC.—National Guardian Life Insurance Company; *U.S. Private*, pg. 784
NL INDUSTRIES DEUTSCHLAND, GMBH—Contran Corporation; *U.S. Private*, pg. 271
NMB (USA) INC.—Minebea Co., Ltd.; *Int'l*, pg. 868
NS FINANCE, INC.—Nippon Steel Corporation; *Int'l*, pg. 940
NS FINANCE III, INC.—Nippon Steel Corporation; *Int'l*, pg. 940
NS GROUP, INC.; *U.S. Public*, pg. 1147
NS KOTE, INC.—Nippon Steel Corporation; *Int'l*, pg. 940
NS TEK—Nippon Steel Corporation; *Int'l*, pg. 940
NWNL BENEFITS CORP.—ReliaStar Financial Corp.; *U.S. Public*, pg. 1375
NABISCO INTERNATIONAL INCORPORATED—RJR Nabisco Holdings Corp.; *U.S. Public*, pg. 1355
NABORS INDUSTRIES, INC.; *U.S. Public*, pg. 1148
NACCO INDUSTRIES, INC.; *U.S. Public*, pg. 1149
NACOLAH HOLDING CORP. INC.—Sammons Enterprises, Inc.; *U.S. Private*, pg. 963
NATIONAL AMUSEMENTS, INC.; *U.S. Private*, pg. 775
NATIONAL BEVERAGE CORP.; *U.S. Public*, pg. 1153
NATIONAL FUEL GAS COMPANY; *U.S. Public*, pg. 1156
NATIONAL GAS & OIL COMPANY; *U.S. Public*, pg. 1156
NATIONAL HOLDING INVESTMENT CO.—National Presto Industries, Inc.; *U.S. Public*, pg. 1159
NATIONAL INFORMATION CORPORATION; *U.S. Private*, pg. 784
NATIONAL INSURANCE GROUP; *U.S. Public*, pg. 1157
NATIONAL LIFE INVESTMENT MANAGEMENT CO., INC.—National Life Insurance Company; *U.S. Private*, pg. 785
NATIONAL-OILWELL/DRECO HOLDINGS, INC.—National-Oilwell Inc.; *U.S. Public*, pg. 1158
NATIONAL-OILWELL/DRECO HOLDINGS LTD.—National-Oilwell Inc.; *U.S. Public*, pg. 1158
NATIONAL SERVICE INDUSTRIES, INC.; *U.S. Public*, pg. 1160
NATIONAL TRUSTCO INC.; *Int'l*, pg. 909
NATIONSBANK FLORIDA—NationsBank Corporation; *U.S. Public*, pg. 1162
NATIONWIDE INSURANCE ENTERPRISE; *U.S. Private*, pg. 788
NEBCO EVANS HOLDING CO.—Holberg Industries, Inc.; *U.S. Private*, pg. 533
NEDERLANDSE UNILEVER BEDRIJVEN B.V.—Unilever Plc; *Int'l*, pg. 1438
NEDLLOYD HOLDINGS (U.S.A.) INC.—Royal Nedlloyd Group N.V.; *Int'l*, pg. 1145
NEDLLOYD ROAD CARGO DIVISION—Royal Nedlloyd Group N.V.; *Int'l*, pg. 1145
NESCO, INC.; *U.S. Private*, pg. 791
NESTE OY; *Int'l*, pg. 912
NESTLE HOLDINGS, INC.—Nestle S.A.; *Int'l*, pg. 916
NEW CENTURY ENERGIES, INC.; *U.S. Public*, pg. 1170
NEW ENGLAND ELECTRIC SYSTEM; *U.S. Public*, pg. 1171
NEW ENGLAND INVESTMENT COMPANIES, INC.—Metropolitan Life Insurance Co.; *U.S. Private*, pg. 737
NYLIFE INC.—New York Life Insurance Company; *U.S. Private*, pg. 795
NEW YORK LIFE INTERNATIONAL INVESTMENT—New York Life Insurance Company; *U.S. Private*, pg. 795
NEW YORK LIFE WORLDWIDE HOLDING, INC.—New York Life Insurance Company; *U.S. Private*, pg. 795
NEWAGE INDUSTRIES INC.; *U.S. Private*, pg. 796
NEWELL INDUSTRIES CANADA, INC.—Newell Co.; *U.S. Public*, pg. 1178
NEWPORT AMERICA CORPORATION—Providence Energy Corporation; *U.S. Public*, pg. 1337
NEWS AMERICA HOLDINGS INC.—The News Corporation Limited; *Int'l*, pg. 925
THE NEWS CORPORATION LIMITED; *Int'l*, pg. 925
NEWS HOLDINGS CORP.; *U.S. Private*, pg. 797
NEWTEL ENTERPRISES LIMITED—BCE Inc.; *Int'l*, pg. 115
NICOR INC.; *U.S. Public*, pg. 1182
NIKE, INC.; *U.S. Public*, pg. 1184
NIPSCO INDUSTRIES, INC.; *U.S. Public*, pg. 1185
NISSAN DATSUN HOLDINGS LTD.—Nissan Motor Co., Ltd.; *Int'l*, pg. 945
NISSAN MOTOR CO., LTD.; *Int'l*, pg. 943
NOEL GROUP, INC.; *U.S. Public*, pg. 1187
NOKIA INC.—Oy Nokia Ab/Nokia Group; *Int'l*, pg. 952
NOKIA SOURCING, INC.—Oy Nokia Ab/Nokia Group; *Int'l*, pg. 953
NOMURA HOLDING AMERICA, INC.—The Nomura Securities Co., Ltd.; *Int'l*, pg. 956
NORFOLK SOUTHERN CORPORATION; *U.S. Public*, pg. 1190
NORFOODS, INC.; *U.S. Private*, pg. 802
NORSTAN, INC.; *U.S. Public*, pg. 1192
NORTH COAST INVESTMENT CORPORATION—Cigna Corp.; *U.S. Public*, pg. 361
NORTHEAST UTILITIES; *U.S. Public*, pg. 1194
NORTHWEST AIRLINES CORP.; *U.S. Public*, pg. 1199
NORTHWEST PARS, INC.—Northwest Airlines Corp.; *U.S. Public*, pg. 1200
NORTHWESTERN ENGINEERING CO.; *U.S. Private*, pg. 806
NORTHWESTERN NETWORKS, INC.—Northwestern Public Service; *U.S. Public*, pg. 1201
NORWESCO, INC.; *U.S. Private*, pg. 808
NOVARTIS AG; *Int'l*, pg. 971
NOVO NORDISK OF NORTH AMERICA, INC.—Novo Nordisk A/S; *Int'l*, pg. 987
NUBURN CAPITAL; *Int'l*, pg. 990
OCE HOLDING USA—Oce-van der Grinten N.V.; *Int'l*, pg. 994
OCE (U.K.) LIMITED—Oce-van der Grinten N.V.; *Int'l*, pg. 995
OCE-VAN DER GRINTEN N.V.; *Int'l*, pg. 993
OCG HOLDINGS, INC.—Olin Corporation; *U.S. Public*, pg. 1219
OHM ENVIRONMENTAL RESOURCES MANAGEMENT CORP.—OHM Corporation; *U.S. Public*, pg. 1208
OM GROUP; *U.S. Public*, pg. 1208
OPIC (OVERSEAS PETROLEUM INVESTMENT GROUP)—Chinese Petroleum Corporation; *Int'l*, pg. 286
OAKWOOD HOMES CORPORATION; *U.S. Public*, pg. 1209
OERLIKON BUHRLE USA, INC.—Oerlikon-Buhrle Holding AG; *Int'l*, pg. 998
OHIO CASUALTY CORPORATION; *U.S. Public*, pg. 1214
OLD GUARD GROUP, INC.—Old Guard Insurance Group; *U.S. Public*, pg. 1216
OLD REPUBLIC INTERNATIONAL CORPORATION; *U.S. Public*, pg. 1218
OLDCASTLE, INC.—CRH, plc; *Int'l*, pg. 242
THE OLDENBURG GROUP COMPANIES; *U.S. Private*, pg. 814
OMNICOM GROUP INC.; *U.S. Public*, pg. 1223
OMNIFLIGHT, INC.; *U.S. Private*, pg. 816
OMNIUM GESTION FINANCIERE (OGF)—Lyonnaise des Eaux S.A.; *Int'l*, pg. 824
ONCE—Corporacion MAPFRE, Compania Internacional de Reaseguros, S.A.; *Int'l*, pg. 334
ONEX CORPORATION; *Int'l*, pg. 1006
OPPENHEIMERFUNDS DISTRIBUTOR, INC.; *U.S. Private*, pg. 818
OREO CORPORATION—Keycorp; *U.S. Public*, pg. 955
ORION CAPITAL COMPANIES, INC.—Orion Capital Corporation; *U.S. Public*, pg. 1231
ORMET CORPORATION; *U.S. Private*, pg. 820
OSHMAN'S SPORTING GOODS, INC.; *U.S. Public*, pg. 1233
OSTERREICHISCHE INDUSTRIEHOLDING AG; *Int'l*, pg. 1012
OUTDOOR COMMUNICATIONS, INC.; *U.S. Private*, pg. 822
OVERSEAS ASSETS HOLDINGS INC.—BankAmerica Corporation; *U.S. Public*, pg. 181
OVERSEAS SHIPHOLDING GROUP, INC.; *U.S. Public*, pg. 1236
OWOSSO CORPORATION; *U.S. Public*, pg. 1238
OXFORD REALTY FINANCIAL GROUP; *U.S. Private*, pg. 825
OYO CORPORATION U.S.A.—OYO Corporation; *Int'l*, pg. 1019
P & F INDUSTRIES, INC.; *U.S. Public*, pg. 1239
P&O AUSTRALIA LTD.—The Peninsular and Oriental Steam Navigation Company; *Int'l*, pg. 1035
P&O BULK SHIPPING LTD.—The Peninsular and Oriental Steam Navigation Company; *Int'l*, pg. 1033
PCC TECHNICAL INDUSTRIES, INC.—American Financial Group; *U.S. Public*, pg. 75
PG&E CORPORATION; *U.S. Public*, pg. 1240
PHC HOLDINGS, INC.—Pacific Holding Corporation; *U.S. Private*, pg. 831
PM HOLDINGS, INC.—Phoenix Home Life Mutual Insurance Company; *U.S. Private*, pg. 863
PMC EASTERN EUROPE LTD—Corporacion MAPFRE, Compania Internacional de Reaseguros, S.A.; *Int'l*, pg. 334
PS GROUP HOLDINGS; *U.S. Public*, pg. 1245
PAC PAPER INC.; *U.S. Private*, pg. 828
PACIFIC HOLDING CORPORATION; *U.S. Private*, pg. 831
PACIFIC TELESIS GROUP—SBC Communications Inc.; *U.S. Public*, pg. 1415
PACIFICA REAL ESTATE GROUP; *U.S. Private*, pg. 832
PACIFICORP GROUP HOLDINGS COMPANY—PacifiCorp; *U.S. Public*, pg. 1251
PACKAGING RESOURCES, INCORPORATED; *U.S. Private*, pg. 833
PACKWOOD LIMITED—Avonmore Waterford Group plc; *Int'l*, pg. 102
PAGE HOLDINGS, INC.; *U.S. Private*, pg. 834
PAINEWEBBER GROUP INCORPORATED; *U.S. Public*, pg. 1252
PAKHOED USA INC.—Royal Pakhoed NV; *Int'l*, pg. 1147
PALUPE-COMERCIO, PARTICIPACAO E SERVICOS LTDA.—The Chase Manhattan Corporation; *U.S. Public*, pg. 341
R.B. PAMPLIN CORP.; *U.S. Private*, pg. 835
PAN AMERICAN CORPORATION—Corporacion MAPFRE, Compania Internacional de Reaseguros, S.A.; *Int'l*, pg. 333
THE PARK CIRCLE MOTOR CO.; *U.S. Private*, pg. 839
PARKWAY HOLDINGS LIMITED; *Int'l*, pg. 1023
PARSONS & WHITTEMORE, INC.; *U.S. Private*, pg. 840
PARSONS BRINCKERHOFF INC.; *U.S. Private*, pg. 841
PATERSON ZOCHONIS PLC; *Int'l*, pg. 1024
PATRIOT AMERICAN HOSPITALITY OPERATING COMPANY—Patriot American Hospitality, Inc.; *U.S. Public*, pg. 1265
PATTON MANAGEMENT, INC.; *U.S. Private*, pg. 843
PAULA FINANCIAL; *U.S. Public*, pg. 1266
PAX WORLD FUND FAMILY; *U.S. Public*, pg. 1266
PEABODY HOLDING COMPANY, INC.—Hanson PLC; *Int'l*, pg. 594
PEARSON, INC.—Pearson plc; *Int'l*, pg. 1026
PEARSON LONGMAN INC.—Pearson plc; *Int'l*, pg. 1026
PECO ENERGY COMPANY; *U.S. Public*, pg. 1268
PEERLESS CARPET CORPORATION; *Int'l*, pg. 1032
PENHALL INTERNATIONAL; *U.S. Private*, pg. 849
PENNCORP FINANCIAL GROUP, INC.; *U.S. Public*, pg. 1271
PENNSYLVANIA ENTERPRISES INC.; *U.S. Public*, pg. 1271
PENNSYLVANIA REAL ESTATE INVESTMENT TRUST; *U.S. Public*, pg. 1272
PENTASTAR TRANSPORTATION CORP.—Chrysler Corporation; *U.S. Public*, pg. 354
PENTLAND GROUP PLC; *Int'l*, pg. 1035
PENTZER CORPORATION—The Washington Water Power Company; *U.S. Public*, pg. 1744
PEOPLES ENERGY CORPORATION; *U.S. Public*, pg. 1274
PEPSI-GEMEX SA DE CV; *Int'l*, pg. 1036
PERPETUAL CORPORATION; *U.S. Private*, pg. 854
PERRY GRAPHIC COMMUNICATIONS, INC.; *U.S. Private*, pg. 855
PERSTORP NEDERLAND B.V.—Perstorp AB; *Int'l*, pg. 1038
PETROLEUM INC.; *U.S. Private*, pg. 858
PEUGEOT S.A.—PSA Peugeot Citroen; *Int'l*, pg. 1020
PHARMACIA & UPJOHN HOLDING NEDERLAND BV—Pharmacia & Upjohn, Inc.; *Int'l*, pg. 1050
PHARMACIA & UPJOHN INTERNATIONAL NV—Pharmacia & Upjohn, Inc.; *Int'l*, pg. 1050
PHARMACIA & UPJOHN U.S. INC.—Pharmacia & Upjohn, Inc.; *Int'l*, pg. 1049
THE PHILADELPHIA BOURSE, INC.; *U.S. Private*, pg. 861
PHILADELPHIA INVESTMENT CORPORATION OF DELAWARE—Cigna Corp.; *U.S. Public*, pg. 357
PHILADELPHIA JEFFERSON CORPORATION—Cigna Corp.; *U.S. Public*, pg. 365
PHILADELPHIA SUBURBAN CORPORATION; *U.S. Public*, pg. 1287
PHILIPP HOLZMANN USA, INC.—Philipp Holzmann AG; *Int'l*, pg. 633
PHILIPS CANADA LTD.—Philips Electronics N.V.; *Int'l*, pg. 1055
PHILIPS ELECTRONICS N.V.; *Int'l*, pg. 1051
PHILIPS INTERNATIONAL B.V.—Philips Electronics N.V.; *Int'l*, pg. 1051
PHILLIPS INVESTMENT COMPANY—Phillips Petroleum Company; *U.S. Public*, pg. 1291
PILKINGTON AUSTRALASIA LIMITED—Pilkington Plc; *Int'l*, pg. 1057
PILLSBURY CANADA LTD.—Diageo Plc; *Int'l*, pg. 411
THE PILLSBURY COMPANY—Diageo Plc; *Int'l*, pg. 411
PINAULT PRINTEMPS; *Int'l*, pg. 1057
PINNACLE AUTOMATION INC.; *U.S. Private*, pg. 866
PINNACLE WEST CAPITAL CORPORATION; *U.S. Public*, pg. 1297
PIONEER INTERNATIONAL LTD.; *Int'l*, pg. 1058
PIPER JAFFRAY COMPANIES, INC.; *U.S. Public*, pg. 1300
PIRELLI UK PLC—Pirelli S.p.A.; *Int'l*, pg. 1059
PITTSBURGH ASSOCIATES; *U.S. Private*, pg. 867
PLAID CLOTHING COMPANY—Hartmarx Corporation; *U.S. Public*, pg. 796
PLATINUM EQUITY HOLDINGS, LLC; *U.S. Private*, pg. 872
PLAYMATES HOLDINGS LTD.; *Int'l*, pg. 1060
PLAYTEX INVESTMENT CORP.—Playtex Products Inc.; *U.S. Public*, pg. 1311
PLAYTEX PRODUCTS INC.; *U.S. Public*, pg. 1310
PLEASANTVILLE MUSIC PUBLISHING, INC.—The Reader's Digest Association, Inc.; *U.S. Public*, pg. 1367
POLYGRAM HOLDING, INC.—Philips Electronics N.V.; *Int'l*, pg. 1052
POLYPHASE CORPORATION; *U.S. Public*, pg. 1315

PORSCHE ENTERPRISES INC.—Porsche AG; *Int'l*, pg. 1063
PORTLAND GENERAL HOLDINGS, INC.—Enron Corp.; *U.S. Public*, pg. 585
POST-NEWSWEEK STATIONS, INC.—The Washington Post Company; *U.S. Public*, pg. 1743
POTAMKIN COMPANY; *U.S. Private*, pg. 876
POUGHKEEPSIE FINANCIAL CORP.; *U.S. Public*, pg. 1319
POWELL DUFFRYN PLC; *Int'l*, pg. 1065
PREFERRED RISK MUTUAL INSURANCE; *U.S. Private*, pg. 880
PREMIER INDUSTRIAL (U.K.) LTD.—Premier Farnell plc; *Int'l*, pg. 1068
PREMIER METAL PRODUCTS CO.; *U.S. Private*, pg. 881
PREUSSAG AG; *Int'l*, pg. 1069
PREUSSAG NORTH AMERICA—Preussag AG; *Int'l*, pg. 1070
PRIMAC CORP.; *U.S. Private*, pg. 883
PRIMEDIA INC.; *U.S. Public*, pg. 1327
PRIMERICA FINANCIAL SERVICES—Travelers Group; *U.S. Public*, pg. 1633
PRODAIR CORPORATION—Air Products and Chemicals, Inc.; *U.S. Public*, pg. 31
PRODUCTION PAYMENTS, INC.—IDC Services, Inc.; *U.S. Private*, pg. 554
PRODUITS SANDOZ S.A.—Novartis AG; *Int'l*, pg. 983
PROGRESS CAPITAL HOLDINGS, INC.—Florida Progress Corporation; *U.S. Public*, pg. 655
THE PROGRESSIVE CORPORATION; *U.S. Public*, pg. 1334
PROGRESSIVE INVESTMENT COMPANY, INC.—The Progressive Corporation; *U.S. Public*, pg. 1335
PROPERTY ASSET MANAGEMENT; *U.S. Private*, pg. 891
PROTECTIVE LIFE CORPORATION; *U.S. Public*, pg. 1336
PROTON; *Int'l*, pg. 1071
PROVENTUS AB; *Int'l*, pg. 1072
PROVIDENT INVESTMENT COUNSEL, INC.—United Asset Management Corporation; *U.S. Public*, pg. 1674
PRUDENTIAL ASIA INVESTMENTS LIMITED—The Prudential Insurance Company of America; *U.S. Private*, pg. 893
PRUDENTIAL CAPITAL & INVESTMENT SERVICES, INC.—The Prudential Insurance Company of America; *U.S. Private*, pg. 892
THE PRUDENTIAL INSURANCE COMPANY OF AMERICA; *U.S. Private*, pg. 892
PRUDENTIAL SECURITIES GROUP INC.—The Prudential Insurance Company of America; *U.S. Private*, pg. 893
PRUSERVICOS PARTICIPACOES, S.A., C/O PRUDENTIAL ATLANTIC COMPANHIA BRASILEIRA DE SEGUROS—The Prudential Insurance Company of America; *U.S. Private*, pg. 893
PUBLIC SERVICE COMPANY OF COLORADO—New Century Energies, Inc.; *U.S. Public*, pg. 1170
PUBLIC STORAGE, INC.; *U.S. Public*, pg. 1340
PUGH OIL COMPANY; *U.S. Private*, pg. 894
PUTNAM INVESTMENTS, INC.—Marsh & McLennan Companies, Inc.; *U.S. Public*, pg. 1049
QUAKER STATE CORPORATION; *U.S. Public*, pg. 1348
QUEBEC STREET INVESTMENTS, INC.—Cigna Corp.; *U.S. Public*, pg. 361
QUESTAR CORPORATION; *U.S. Public*, pg. 1352
QUEXCO INCORPORATED; *U.S. Private*, pg. 900
RCG INTERNATIONAL INC.—Reliance Group Holdings, Inc.; *U.S. Public*, pg. 1374
RCM INDUSTRIES; *U.S. Private*, pg. 902
R D I S CORPORATION; *U.S. Private*, pg. 903
RGP HOLDING, INC.; *U.S. Private*, pg. 903
RI HOLDINGS; *U.S. Private*, pg. 904
RJR NABISCO HOLDINGS CORP.; *U.S. Public*, pg. 1354
RLI CORP.; *U.S. Public*, pg. 1356
RNL FACILITIES CORPORATION; *U.S. Private*, pg. 905
RPM, INC.; *U.S. Public*, pg. 1356
RSI HOLDINGS INC.; *U.S. Public*, pg. 1358
RSI INTERNATIONAL, LTD.—COMSAT Corporation; *U.S. Public*, pg. 424
RTZ PILLAR LTD.—Caradon Plc; *Int'l*, pg. 267
RWE AG; *Int'l*, pg. 1081
THE RACAL CORPORATION—Racal Electronics Plc; *Int'l*, pg. 1082
RADIOMETER GMBH—Radiometer A/S; *Int'l*, pg. 1084
RADIOMETER (UK) LTD.—Radiometer A/S; *Int'l*, pg. 1084
THE RADOS COMPANIES; *U.S. Private*, pg. 907
RAILCO, INC.—Broe Companies; *U.S. Private*, pg. 171
RALCORP HOLDINGS INC.; *U.S. Public*, pg. 1359
RANK AMERICA, INC.—The Rank Group PLC; *Int'l*, pg. 1087
RANK INVESTMENTS LIMITED—The Rank Group PLC; *Int'l*, pg. 1087
RANK LEISURE HOLDINGS PLC—The Rank Group PLC; *Int'l*, pg. 1087
RANK OVERSEAS HOLDING LIMITED—The Rank Group PLC; *Int'l*, pg. 1087
RANK RX HOLDINGS LIMITED—The Rank Group PLC; *Int'l*, pg. 1087
RANKS HOVIS MCDOUGALL LIMITED—Tomkins PLC; *Int'l*, pg. 1395
RAYCOM MEDIA, INC.; *U.S. Private*, pg. 911
RAYTHEON OVERSEAS LTD.—Raytheon Company; *U.S. Public*, pg. 1366
RECKITT & COLMAN INC.—Reckitt & Colman plc; *Int'l*, pg. 1090
RED APPLE COMPANIES; *U.S. Private*, pg. 914
RED WINGS INC.—Tomkins PLC; *Int'l*, pg. 1398
REDLAND HOLDING BV—Redland PLC; *Int'l*, pg. 1093
REDLAND, INC.—Redland PLC; *Int'l*, pg. 1091
REEVES INTERNATIONAL—Hart Holding Company, Inc.; *U.S. Private*, pg. 507
REGENCY GROUP INC.; *U.S. Private*, pg. 918
REHABILITATIVE BACK CENTER OF ATLANTA, INC.—Vencor, Inc.; *U.S. Public*, pg. 1715
RELIABILITY INCORPORATED; *U.S. Public*, pg. 1373
RELIANCE GROUP HOLDINGS, INC.; *U.S. Public*, pg. 1374
RELIASTAR FINANCIAL CORP.; *U.S. Public*, pg. 1375
RELM WIRELESS CORP.; *U.S. Public*, pg. 1376
RENAISSANCE COSMETICS, INC.; *U.S. Private*, pg. 922
REPAP ENTERPRISES INC.; *Int'l*, pg. 1104
REPUBLIC FINANCIAL SERVICES, INC.—Credit Suisse Group; *Int'l*, pg. 346
THE RESERVE GROUP; *U.S. Private*, pg. 924
RESORTS INTERNATIONAL HOTEL FINANCING, INC.—Griffin Group, Inc.; *U.S. Private*, pg. 480
THE RESTAURANT COMPANY; *U.S. Private*, pg. 925
REUTERS HOLDINGS PLC; *Int'l*, pg. 1105
REVLON, INC.—MacAndrews & Forbes Holdings Inc.; *U.S. Private*, pg. 689
R.J. REYNOLDS, INC.—RJR Nabisco Holdings Corp.; *U.S. Public*, pg. 1355
RHEINISCHE ZINKGESELLSCHAFT GMBH—Metallgesellschaft AG; *Int'l*, pg. 861
RHEINMETALL GROUP; *Int'l*, pg. 1108
RICE, SANGALIS, TOOLE & WILSON; *U.S. Private*, pg. 928
RICHFOOD HOLDINGS, INC.; *U.S. Public*, pg. 1388
JOHN RICKSON PROPERTIES—I.C. System, Inc.; *U.S. Private*, pg. 553
RIETER HOLDINGS; *Int'l*, pg. 1116
RIO TINTO PLC; *Int'l*, pg. 1118
RIO TINTO SOUTH AFRICA LTD.—Rio Tinto PLC; *Int'l*, pg. 1119
RIPPLEWOOD HOLDINGS L.L.C.; *U.S. Private*, pg. 931
RITE AID CORPORATION; *U.S. Public*, pg. 1390
RIVERSIDE GROUP, INC.; *U.S. Public*, pg. 1391
RIVIANA INTERNATIONAL INC.—Riviana Foods Inc.; *U.S. Public*, pg. 1392
ROBBE RADIATOREN B.V.—Caradon Plc; *Int'l*, pg. 267
J.H. ROBERTS INDUSTRIES INC.; *U.S. Private*, pg. 935
ROBINSON LUMBER & EXPORT COMPANY; *U.S. Private*, pg. 936
ROCKEFELLER GROUP, INC.—Mitsubishi Estate Co., Ltd.; *Int'l*, pg. 873
ROCOR TRANSPORTATION COMPANIES INC.; *U.S. Private*, pg. 938
ROHM U.S.A., INC.—Rohm Co., Ltd.; *Int'l*, pg. 1125
ROINS HOLDINGS LIMITED—Royal & Sun Alliance Insurance Group plc; *Int'l*, pg. 1131
ROLL INTERNATIONAL CORPORATION; *U.S. Private*, pg. 941
ROLLINS, INC.; *U.S. Public*, pg. 1404
ROLLS-ROYCE INC.—Rolls-Royce plc; *Int'l*, pg. 1127
RONSON CORPORATION; *U.S. Public*, pg. 1405
ROSS LOOS HOSPITAL, INC.—Cigna Corp.; *U.S. Public*, pg. 360
ROTHENBERGER GROUP GMBH; *Int'l*, pg. 1127
ROTHENBERGER HOLDING GES.M.B.H.—Rothenberger Group GmbH; *Int'l*, pg. 1129
ROTHMANS INC.—Rothmans UK Holdings Limited; *Int'l*, pg. 1129
ROTHMANS UK HOLDINGS LIMITED; *Int'l*, pg. 1129
THE ROUSE COMPANY; *U.S. Public*, pg. 1407
ROUTE 206 DEVELOPMENT CORP.—High Point Financial Corp.; *U.S. Public*, pg. 826
THE ROWE CORPORATION; *U.S. Private*, pg. 948
ROYAL BEGEMANN GROUP; *Int'l*, pg. 1133
ROYAL INSURANCE—Royal & Sun Alliance Insurance Group plc; *Int'l*, pg. 1130
RUDDICK CORPORATION; *U.S. Public*, pg. 1412
RUSSEL METALS INC.; *Int'l*, pg. 1149
RYAN INSURANCE GROUP, INC.—AON Corporation; *U.S. Public*, pg. 118
RYOBI NORTH AMERICA, INC.—Ryobi Ltd.; *Int'l*, pg. 1151
S & P COMPANY; *U.S. Private*, pg. 954
S&S DOMESTIC INTERNATIONAL SALES CORP.—Stewart & Stevenson Services, Inc.; *U.S. Public*, pg. 1517
SAMC ACIERES—Groupe Usinor; *Int'l*, pg. 572
SBC COMMUNICATIONS INC.; *U.S. Public*, pg. 1415
SBS ENTERPRISES INC.; *U.S. Private*, pg. 955
SBS HOLDINGS, INC.; *U.S. Private*, pg. 955
SCOR; *Int'l*, pg. 1152
SEB INTERNATIONALE—Groupe SEB; *Int'l*, pg. 568
SEI HOLDING CORP.; *U.S. Private*, pg. 956
SGS NORTH AMERICA INC.—SGS Societe Generale de Surveillance Holding S.A.; *Int'l*, pg. 1153
SGS SOCIETE GENERALE DE SURVEILLANCE HOLDING S.A.; *Int'l*, pg. 1153
SHV HOLDINGS N.V.; *Int'l*, pg. 1154
SJW CORP.; *U.S. Public*, pg. 1418
SLD HOLDINGS LTD.; *Int'l*, pg. 1160
SLM HOLDING CORP.; *U.S. Public*, pg. 1419
SNAM INTERNATIONAL LTD.—ENI S.p.A.; *Int'l*, pg. 429
SNC-LAVALIN INC.—SNC-Lavalin Group Inc.; *Int'l*, pg. 1162
SPAFI—Saint-Gobain; *Int'l*, pg. 1177
SSB LEEWAY CORP.—Somerset Savings Bank; *U.S. Public*, pg. 1484
STS CONSULTANTS, INC.; *U.S. Private*, pg. 959
SABOMA—GIB Group; *Int'l*, pg. 533
SAFECO CORPORATION; *U.S. Public*, pg. 1423
SAFECO PROPERTIES, INC.—SAFECO Corporation; *U.S. Public*, pg. 1423
SAFEGUARD FINANCIAL CORP.—Safeguard Business Systems, Inc.; *U.S. Private*, pg. 960
SAFEWAY U.S. HOLDINGS, INC.—Safeway Inc.; *U.S. Public*, pg. 1426
SAFIAL B.V.—Unilever Plc; *Int'l*, pg. 1438
SAHARA ENTERPRISES INC.; *U.S. Private*, pg. 960
SAHARA ILLINOIS CORP.—Santa Fe Gaming Corporation; *U.S. Public*, pg. 1432
SAHARA NEVADA CORP.—Santa Fe Gaming Corporation; *U.S. Public*, pg. 1432
SAHARA RESORTS—Santa Fe Gaming Corporation; *U.S. Public*, pg. 1432
ST. JAMES'S PLACE CAPITAL PLC.; *Int'l*, pg. 1177
ST. JOE INDUSTRIES, INC.—St. Joe Corp.; *U.S. Public*, pg. 1427
THE ST. PAUL COMPANIES, INC.; *U.S. Public*, pg. 1429
SALEM GROUP, INC.; *U.S. Private*, pg. 961
SALZGITTER GMBH—Preussag AG; *Int'l*, pg. 1070
SAMSUNG GROUP; *Int'l*, pg. 1181
SANDOZ CORPORATION—Novartis AG; *Int'l*, pg. 974
SANDOZ HOLDING LTD.—Novartis AG; *Int'l*, pg. 972
SANDOZ HOLDING NETHERLANDS B.V.—Novartis AG; *Int'l*, pg. 984
SANDOZ HOLDINGS GREAT BRITAIN LTD.—Novartis AG; *Int'l*, pg. 984
SANDOZ INTERNATIONAL LTD.—Novartis AG; *Int'l*, pg. 972
SANDOZ VENEZUELA S.A.—Novartis AG; *Int'l*, pg. 985
SANDVIK, INC.—Sandvik AB; *Int'l*, pg. 1185
SANFORD BEROC CORP.—Newell Co.; *U.S. Public*, pg. 1178
THE SANTA ANITA COMPANIES—Meditrust Corporation; *U.S. Public*, pg. 1081
SANTA FE COFFEE COMPANY—Santa Fe Gaming Corporation; *U.S. Public*, pg. 1432
SANTA FE GAMING CORPORATION; *U.S. Public*, pg. 1432
SANTA FE SPRINGS HOLDING COMPANY—Hicks, Muse, Tate & Furst Inc.; *U.S. Private*, pg. 526
SAO LOURENCO—Saint-Gobain; *Int'l*, pg. 1177
SAPONIA B.V.—Unilever Plc; *Int'l*, pg. 1438
SARGENTO FOODS INC.; *U.S. Private*, pg. 966
SARMA-NOPRI GROUP—GIB Group; *Int'l*, pg. 533
SAUDI ARABIAN PARSONS LTD.—Parsons Corporation; *U.S. Private*, pg. 842
SAWGRASS ELECTRONICS GROUP INC.; *U.S. Private*, pg. 968
SCANGAS BROTHERS HOLDINGS, INC.; *U.S. Private*, pg. 969
R.P. SCHERER CORPORATION; *U.S. Public*, pg. 1437
SCHERING BERLIN INC.—Schering AG; *Int'l*, pg. 1204
SCHERING-PLOUGH HOLDINGS LTD.—Schering-Plough Corporation; *U.S. Public*, pg. 1439
SCHINDLER HOLDING AG; *Int'l*, pg. 1204
SCHLUMBERGER LIMITED; *U.S. Public*, pg. 1439
SCHNEIDER S.A.; *Int'l*, pg. 1207
SCHOLASTIC CORPORATION; *U.S. Public*, pg. 1440
SCHURZ COMMUNICATIONS, INC.; *U.S. Private*, pg. 973
THE CHARLES SCHWAB CORPORATION; *U.S. Public*, pg. 1442
SCHWAB HOLDINGS, INC.—The Charles Schwab Corporation; *U.S. Public*, pg. 1443
SCHWINN CYCLING & FITNESS INC.—Schwinn Holdings; *U.S. Private*, pg. 975
SCHWINN HOLDINGS; *U.S. Private*, pg. 975
SCOTSMAN HOLDING INC.; *U.S. Private*, pg. 976
SCOTSMAN INDUSTRIES, INC.; *U.S. Public*, pg. 1444
SCOTT & STRINGFELLOW FINANCIAL, INC.; *U.S. Public*, pg. 1445
SCOTTISH & NEWCASTLE PLC; *Int'l*, pg. 1211
SEABOARD FLOUR CORPORATION—Seaboard Corporation; *U.S. Public*, pg. 1449
SEAFIELD CAPITAL CORPORATION; *U.S. Public*, pg. 1449
SEAGATE TECHNOLOGY HOLDINGS—Seagate Technology Inc.; *U.S. Public*, pg. 1449
SEAGATE TECHNOLOGY SINGAPORE, LTD.—Seagate Technology Inc.; *U.S. Public*, pg. 1450
SEALASKA CORPORATION; *U.S. Private*, pg. 978
SECURITY CAPITAL GROUP INCORPORATED; *U.S. Private*, pg. 980
SELECTIVE INSURANCE GROUP, INC; *U.S. Public*, pg. 1455
SEMCO INDUSTRIES INC.; *U.S. Private*, pg. 983
SENECA FOODS CORPORATION; *U.S. Public*, pg. 1456
SENIOR ENGINEERING GROUP, PLC.; *Int'l*, pg. 1220
SEPI; *Int'l*, pg. 1223
SERVICES GROUP OF AMERICA; *U.S. Private*, pg. 987
SERVICO, INC.; *U.S. Public*, pg. 1462
SETEMER, S.P.A.—Telefonaktiebolaget LM Ericsson; *Int'l*, pg. 1369
SEVERN TRENT OVERSEAS HOLDINGS LIMITED—Severn Trent Plc; *Int'l*, pg. 1226
SHAMROCK HOLDINGS, INC.; *U.S. Private*, pg. 989
SHAMROCK HOLDINGS OF CALIFORNIA, INC.—Shamrock Holdings, Inc.; *U.S. Private*, pg. 989
SHANDWICK AMERICAS—Shandwick International Plc; *Int'l*, pg. 1226
SHANDWICK EUROPE HOLDING CO. GMBH—Shandwick International Plc; *Int'l*, pg. 1227
SHANDWICK INTERNATIONAL PLC; *Int'l*, pg. 1226
THE SHANE GROUP INC.; *U.S. Private*, pg. 989
SHATO HOLDINGS LTD.; *Int'l*, pg. 1230
SHEFCO, INC.—Torchmark Corporation; *U.S. Public*, pg. 1622
SHELL AUSTRALIA LTD.—Royal Dutch/Shell Group of Companies; *Int'l*, pg. 1137
SHELL NEW ZEALAND HOLDING COMPANY LTD—Royal Dutch/Shell Group of Companies; *Int'l*, pg. 1137
SHELL OIL COMPANY—Royal Dutch/Shell Group of Companies; *Int'l*, pg. 1136
SHEPAUG CORPORATION; *U.S. Private*, pg. 993
SHOOK NATIONAL CORPORATION; *U.S. Private*, pg. 996
SHORELINE FINANCIAL CORP.; *U.S. Public*, pg. 1467
SHOWPLA INTERNATIONAL PTE. LTD.—Showpla Asia Limited; *Int'l*, pg. 1237
SHURE, GMBH—Shure Brothers Incorporated; *U.S. Private*, pg. 997
SIEBE NORTH INC.—Siebe plc; *Int'l*, pg. 1242
SIEMENS FINANZIERUNGSGESELLSCHAFT FUR INFORMATIONSTECHNIK GMBH—Siemens AG; *Int'l*, pg. 1245
SIERRA PACIFIC RESOURCES; *U.S. Public*, pg. 1470
SIERRA TECHNOLOGIES INC.; *U.S. Private*, pg. 999
SIGA, INC.; *U.S. Private*, pg. 999
SIGNET STAR HOLDINGS, INC.—W.R. Berkley Corporation; *U.S. Public*, pg. 216

SIKA FINANZ AG; *Int'l*, pg. 1248
SILGAN CORPORATION; *U.S. Public*, pg. 1473
SILVEY CORPORATION—General Accident Fire and Life Assurance Corporation p.l.c.; *Int'l*, pg. 543
SIME DARBY BERHAD; *Int'l*, pg. 1249
SIMMONS JUVENILE PRODUCTS; *U.S. Private*, pg. 1001
SIMON UNITED STATES HOLDINGS INC.—Simon Engineering plc; *Int'l*, pg. 1252
SIMPSON INVESTMENT CO.; *U.S. Private*, pg. 1003
SINGAPORE LAND LIMITED; *Int'l*, pg. 1252
SINGAPORE TECHNOLOGIES PTE. LTD.; *Int'l*, pg. 1253
SKANDIA HOLDING AB—Skandia Insurance Company Limited; *Int'l*, pg. 1256
SKYWEST INC.; *U.S. Public*, pg. 1476
SLATER STEELS CORPORATION—Slater Industries Inc.; *Int'l*, pg. 1263
SMITH & NEPHEW PLC; *Int'l*, pg. 1263
SMITH ENVIRONMENTAL TECHNOLOGIES CORP.—Smith Environmental Technologies Corp.; *U.S. Public*, pg. 1478
EVERETT SMITH GROUP, LTD.; *U.S. Private*, pg. 1007
SMITH INVESTMENT COMPANY; *U.S. Private*, pg. 1008
SMITHS INDUSTRIES AEROSPACE & DEFENSE SYSTEMS INC.-WASHINGTON D.C.—Smiths Industries plc; *Int'l*, pg. 1268
SMITHS INDUSTRIES INDUSTRIAL GROUP—Smiths Industries plc; *Int'l*, pg. 1267
SMURFIT INTERNATIONAL FRANCE S.A.—Jefferson Smurfit Group p.l.c.; *Int'l*, pg. 1271
SMURFIT INVESTMENTS U.K. LIMITED—Jefferson Smurfit Group p.l.c.; *Int'l*, pg. 1271
JEFFERSON SMURFIT CORPORATION—Jefferson Smurfit Group p.l.c.; *Int'l*, pg. 1271
JEFFERSON SMURFIT CORPORATION (U.S.)—Jefferson Smurfit Group p.l.c.; *Int'l*, pg. 1271
JEFFERSON SMURFIT GROUP P.L.C.; *Int'l*, pg. 1269
SOCANAV INC.; *Int'l*, pg. 1272
SOCIETE DE GESTION D'INTERETS PETROLIERS (SOGEDIP)—Compagnie Financiere de Paribas; *Int'l*, pg. 319
SOCIETE DES SPECIALITES SURGELEES A LANDEVANT—Grands Moulins de Paris S.A.; *Int'l*, pg. 556
SOCIETE FINANCIERE ET DE DEVELOPPEMENT ALIMENTAIRE—Grands Moulins de Paris S.A.; *Int'l*, pg. 557
SOCIETY NATIONAL BANK—Keycorp; *U.S. Public*, pg. 954
SOCO INTERNATIONAL, INC.—Snyder Oil Corporation; *U.S. Public*, pg. 1482
SODAL CORPORATION—GIB Group; *Int'l*, pg. 533
SOFCO-MEAD, INC.; *U.S. Private*, pg. 1012
SOFIAS—Allianz Aktiengesellschaft; *Int'l*, pg. 62
SOFINPAR—Fiat Auto SpA; *Int'l*, pg. 482
SOFTBANK HOLDINGS INC.—Softbank Corporation; *Int'l*, pg. 1276
SOGESVAL: SOCIETE EN COURS DE LIQUIDATION—Club Mediterranee SA; *Int'l*, pg. 298
SOIGESTI—GIB Group; *Int'l*, pg. 533
SOLO CUP COMPANY; *U.S. Private*, pg. 1013
SOLVAY AMERICA INC.—Solvay S.A.; *Int'l*, pg. 1278
SOMERFIELD PLC; *Int'l*, pg. 1280
THE SOMERSET GROUP, INC.; *U.S. Public*, pg. 1484
SOPHUS BERENDSEN A/S; *Int'l*, pg. 1284
SOTHEBY'S HOLDINGS INC.; *U.S. Public*, pg. 1487
SOUTH AFRICAN BREWERIES, LTD.; *Int'l*, pg. 1286
SOUTH JERSEY INDUSTRIES, INC.; *U.S. Public*, pg. 1488
SOUTHEASTERN MICHIGAN GAS ENTERPRISES, INC.; *U.S. Public*, pg. 1489
SOUTHERN COMPANY; *U.S. Public*, pg. 1489
SOUTHERN NEW ENGLAND TELECOMMUNICATIONS CORPORATION; *U.S. Public*, pg. 1490
SOUTHLAND CORPORATION - CANADA NATIONAL OFFICE—Ito-Yokado Co., Ltd.; *Int'l*, pg. 694
SOUTHWESTERN FINANCIAL CORPORATION; *U.S. Private*, pg. 1018
SOUTHWESTERN FINANCIAL SERVICES CORP.—Southwestern Financial Corporation; *U.S. Private*, pg. 1018
SOUTHWESTERN/GREAT AMERICAN INC.; *U.S. Private*, pg. 1018
SOUZA CRUZ, S.A.—B.A.T Industries P.L.C.; *Int'l*, pg. 112
SPARTAN MILLS; *U.S. Private*, pg. 1020
SPECTRA-PHYSICS USA, INC.—Spectra-Physics AB; *Int'l*, pg. 1289
SPEEDFAN INTERNATIONAL, INC.; *U.S. Public*, pg. 1497
SPELLING ENTERTAINMENT GROUP, INC.—National Amusements, Inc.; *U.S. Private*, pg. 776
SPORTO CORP.; *U.S. Private*, pg. 1026
SQUARE D COMPANY EUROPE—Schneider S.A.; *Int'l*, pg. 1209
SSANGYONG BUSINESS GROUP; *Int'l*, pg. 1291
STAGE STORES, INC.; *U.S. Private*, pg. 1028
STAMFORD CAPITAL; *U.S. Private*, pg. 1029
STANDARD BANK INVESTMENT CORPORATION LIMITED; *Int'l*, pg. 1293
STANDARD COMMERCIAL CORPORATION; *U.S. Public*, pg. 1501
STANDARD MANAGEMENT CORPORATION; *U.S. Public*, pg. 1502
STANDARD PACIFIC CORP.; *U.S. Public*, pg. 1503
STAR BUFFET, INC.—CKE Restaurants Inc.; *U.S. Public*, pg. 278
STARBANC CORPORATION; *U.S. Public*, pg. 1510
STARCAN CORPORATION; *Int'l*, pg. 1297
STATER BROTHERS HOLDINGS—Craig Corporation; *U.S. Public*, pg. 456
STEEGO CORPORATION—Brierley Investments Limited; *Int'l*, pg. 216
STEWART & STEVENSON OVERSEAS, INC.—Stewart & Stevenson Services, Inc.; *U.S. Public*, pg. 1517
STOREHOUSE PLC; *Int'l*, pg. 1304
STORK N.V.; *Int'l*, pg. 1304
STRAUBE REGIONAL CENTER LLC; *U.S. Private*, pg. 1046
SUFFOLK CAPITAL MANAGEMENT—United Asset Management Corporation; *U.S. Public*, pg. 1674
SULZER (UK) HOLDINGS LIMITED—Sulzer Ltd.; *Int'l*, pg. 1307
SUMITOMO CORPORATION OF AMERICA—Sumitomo Corporation; *Int'l*, pg. 1312
SUMMIT BANCORP; *U.S. Public*, pg. 1527
SUN CITY INDUSTRIES, INC.; *U.S. Public*, pg. 1529
SUN LIFE ASSURANCE COMPANY OF CANADA; *Int'l*, pg. 1318
SUN LIFE FINANCIAL HOLDINGS INC.—Sun Life Assurance Company of Canada; *Int'l*, pg. 1319
SUNTORY INTERNATIONAL CORP.—Suntory Ltd.; *Int'l*, pg. 1321
SUPER D DRUGS ACQUISITION CO.—Stephen LaFrance Holdings, Inc.; *U.S. Private*, pg. 642
SUPER SKY PRODUCTS, INC.; *U.S. Private*, pg. 1054
SUPERIOR CONSULTANT HOLDINGS CORP.; *U.S. Public*, pg. 1538
SUSPA COMPART AG; *Int'l*, pg. 1322
SVENSKA UNILEVER FORVALTNINGS AB—Unilever Plc; *Int'l*, pg. 1438
SWEDISH ERICSSON COMPANY LTD.—Telefonaktiebolaget LM Ericsson; *Int'l*, pg. 1370
SWIFT TRANSPORTATION CO.; *U.S. Public*, pg. 1543
SYBRON INTERNATIONAL CORPORATION; *U.S. Public*, pg. 1544
SYNERGISM, INC.; *U.S. Private*, pg. 1060
SYNERGISTICS CHEMICALS, INC.—The Geon Company; *U.S. Public*, pg. 734
SYNETIC, INC.; *U.S. Public*, pg. 1548
SYRATECH CORPORATION; *U.S. Private*, pg. 1060
T & N PLC; *Int'l*, pg. 1334
TAL FINANCIAL CORPORATION—TCA Cable TV, Inc.; *U.S. Public*, pg. 1553
TCI INTERNATIONAL INC.; *U.S. Public*, pg. 1555
TDK CORPORATION OF AMERICA—TDK Corporation; *Int'l*, pg. 1336
TDK ELECTRONICS CORPORATION—TDK Corporation; *Int'l*, pg. 1336
THD, INC.—Conseco Inc.; *U.S. Public*, pg. 433
THP UNITED ENTERPRISES—Thyssen AG; *Int'l*, pg. 1389
TNP ENTERPRISES, INC.; *U.S. Public*, pg. 1557
TRC HOLDING CO. OF WASHINGTON, D.C.—The Rouse Company; *U.S. Public*, pg. 1409
TVESCO, INC.; *U.S. Private*, pg. 1066
TABLEX, S.A. DE C.V.; *Int'l*, pg. 1346
TACT HOLDING; *U.S. Private*, pg. 1067
TAETEL, S.L.—Telefonica de Espana, S.A.; *Int'l*, pg. 1371
TANG INDUSTRIES INC.; *U.S. Private*, pg. 1068
TARMAC AMERICA, INC.—Tarmac plc; *Int'l*, pg. 1355
THE TATA IRON AND STEEL CO. LTD.; *Int'l*, pg. 1356
TATE & LYLE INDUSTRIES LIMITED—Tate & Lyle PLC; *Int'l*, pg. 1356
TATE & LYLE INVESTMENTS LIMITED—Tate & Lyle PLC; *Int'l*, pg. 1356
TAYLOR WOODROW OF GIBRALTAR LIMITED—Taylor Woodrow plc; *Int'l*, pg. 1360
TAYLOR WOODROW PLC; *Int'l*, pg. 1358
TECFOR INC.—Electrolux, AB; *Int'l*, pg. 440
THE TECH GROUP; *U.S. Private*, pg. 1071
TECH-SYM CORPORATION; *U.S. Public*, pg. 1563
TECHNOCORP HOLDING S.A.—SMH Swiss Corporation for Micro Electronics & Watchmaking Indus. Ltd.; *Int'l*, pg. 1161
TECMAR TECHNOLOGIES, INC.—Tecmar Technologies International, Inc.; *Int'l*, pg. 1361
TECNOVER—Saint-Gobain; *Int'l*, pg. 1172
TECO DIVERSIFIED, INC.—TECO Energy, Inc.; *U.S. Public*, *pg. 1565*
TECO ENERGY, INC.; *U.S. Public*, pg. 1565
TELCO CAPITAL CORPORATION; *U.S. Private*, pg. 1073
TELECARTERA, S.A.—Telefonica de Espana, S.A.; *Int'l*, pg. 1371
TELEPHONE AND DATA SYSTEMS, INC.; *U.S. Public*, pg. 1570
TELERIC PTY. LTD.—Telefonaktiebolaget LM Ericsson; *Int'l*, pg. 1371
TELUS CORPORATION; *Int'l*, pg. 1374
TEMASEK HOLDINGS PTE. LTD.; *Int'l*, pg. 1374
TEMPLE-INLAND INC.; *U.S. Public*, pg. 1574
TENNECO HOLDINGS B.V.—Tenneco Inc.; *U.S. Public*, pg. 1580
TENNECO UNITED KINGDOM HOLDINGS LIMITED—Tenneco Inc.; *U.S. Public*, pg. 1580
TERRA NOVA (BERMUDA) HOLDINGS LTD.—Cigna Corp.; *U.S. Public*, pg. 365
TERUYA BROS., LIMITED; *U.S. Private*, pg. 1077
TEXAS PACIFIC GROUP; *U.S. Private*, pg. 1078
TEXAS UTILITIES COMPANY; *U.S. Public*, pg. 1586
TEXTRON CANADA LTD.—Textron Inc.; *U.S. Public*, pg. 1590
THACKERAY CORPORATION; *U.S. Public*, pg. 1590
THOMAS TILLING LIMITED—BTR plc; *Int'l*, pg. 124
THOMSON CANADA LIMITED—The Thomson Corporation; *U.S. Public*, pg. 1602
THOMSON CORPORATION OF AMERICA—Thomson S.A.; *Int'l*, pg. 1383
THE THOMSON CORPORATION; *U.S. Public*, pg. 1599
THOMSON S.A.; *Int'l*, pg. 1381
THOMSON U.S. INC.—The Thomson Corporation; *U.S. Public*, pg. 1601
THORN EMI INC.—EMI Group plc; *Int'l*, pg. 427
THORN-EUROPE—Thorn plc; *Int'l*, pg. 1386
THORN GROUP—Thorn plc; *Int'l*, pg. 1385
THORN LIGHTING GROUP PLC; *Int'l*, pg. 1385
THORN PLC; *Int'l*, pg. 1385
THRIGE AGRO A/S—Thrige-Titan Group; *Int'l*, pg. 1386
TIMPTE INDUSTRIES, INC.; *U.S. Private*, pg. 1088
TINTAS ROBBIALAC S.A.—Williams Holdings Plc; *Int'l*, pg. 1501
TIOXIDE GROUP LIMITED—Imperial Chemical Industries PLC; *Int'l*, pg. 663
TITLEIST & FOOT-JOY WORLDWIDE—Fortune Brands, Inc.; *U.S. Public*, pg. 675
TOKHEIM INVESTMENT CORP.—Tokheim Corporation; *U.S. Public*, pg. 1620
TOMKINS CORPORATION—Tomkins PLC; *Int'l*, pg. 1397
THE TONGAT-HULETT GROUP LIMITED—Anglo American Corporation of South Africa Limited; *Int'l*, pg. 76
TOOTAL CLOTHING LTD.—Coats Viyella plc; *Int'l*, pg. 300
TOOTAL TEXTILES HOLDINGS LTD.—Coats Viyella plc; *Int'l*, pg. 300
TOOTAL THREAD LTD.—Coats Viyella plc; *Int'l*, pg. 299
TOOTSIE ROLLS-LATIN AMERICA, INC.—Tootsie Roll Industries, Inc.; *U.S. Public*, pg. 1621
TOPEKA GROUP, INCORPORATED—Minnesota Power; *U.S. Public*, pg. 1116
TOPS MARKETS, INC.—Koninklijke Ahold NV; *Int'l*, pg. 750
TORCH ENERGY ADVISORS, INCORPORATED—Torchmark Corporation; *U.S. Public*, pg. 1623
TORCH ENERGY CORP.—Torchmark Corporation; *U.S. Public*, pg. 1623
TORCHMARK CORPORATION; *U.S. Public*, pg. 1622
TORSTAR CORPORATION; *Int'l*, pg. 1402
TOSHIBA AMERICA INC.—Toshiba Corporation; *Int'l*, pg. 1405
TOSHIBA CORPORATION; *Int'l*, pg. 1402
TOTAL RENAL CARE HOLDINGS, INC.; *U.S. Public*, pg. 1625
TOTEM RESOURCES CORPORATION; *U.S. Private*, pg. 1092
TOUCHE REMNANT HOLDINGS, LTD.—Henderson Administration Group PLC; *Int'l*, pg. 609
TRACE INTERNATIONAL HOLDINGS, INC.; *U.S. Private*, pg. 1094
TRACINDA CORPORATION; *U.S. Private*, pg. 1095
TRACOR AEROSPACE ELECTRONICS SYSTEMS, INC.—Tracor, Inc.; *U.S. Public*, pg. 1627
TRAFALGAR HOUSE ENGINEERING—Kvaerner a.s.a.; *Int'l*, pg. 773
TRAFALGAR HOUSE HOLDINGS INC.—Kvaerner a.s.a.; *Int'l*, pg. 774
TRAFALGAR HOUSE PLC—Kvaerner a.s.a.; *Int'l*, pg. 772
TRANS MOUNTAIN HOLDINGS LTD.—BC Gas Inc.; *Int'l*, pg. 114
TRANSACTION SYSTEMS ARCHITECTS, INC.; *U.S. Public*, pg. 1629
TRANSALTA ENERGY CORPORATION—Transalta Corporation; *Int'l*, pg. 1416
TRANSATLANTIC HOLDINGS INC.—American International Group, Inc.; *U.S. Public*, pg. 84
TRANSMARCO LIMITED; *Int'l*, pg. 1417
TRANSPORT DEVELOPMENT GROUP PLC; *Int'l*, pg. 1418
TRANSPORT HOLDINGS INC.—Conseco Inc.; *U.S. Public*, pg. 433
TRANSWORLD INTERWEAVING AG (TIAG); *Int'l*, pg. 1418
TRAVELERS GROUP; *U.S. Public*, pg. 1632
TREK CORPORATION; *U.S. Private*, pg. 1099
TREMONT CORPORATION—Contran Corporation; *U.S. Private*, pg. 270
TRIARC COMPANIES, INC.; *U.S. Public*, pg. 1634
TRIDENT SEAFOOD CORPORATION—ConAgra, Inc.; *U.S. Public*, pg. 429
TRIMAC CORPORATION; *Int'l*, pg. 1423
TRIPLE F, INC.; *U.S. Private*, pg. 1104
TRIUMPH GROUP, INC.; *U.S. Public*, pg. 1640
TRIZECHAHN CORPORATION; *Int'l*, pg. 1424
TROPHY HOLDINGS INC.; *U.S. Private*, pg. 1105
THE TRUMP GROUP; *U.S. Private*, pg. 1107
TRYGG-HANSA; *Int'l*, pg. 1425
TSUMURA INTERNATIONAL—Tsumura & Co.; *Int'l*, pg. 1426
THE TULSA CORPORATION—Cigna Corp.; *U.S. Public*, pg. 359
THE TURNER GROUP—American Eco Corporation; *Int'l*, pg. 74
2110 DAVIE CORPORATION—American Vanguard Corporation; *U.S. Public*, pg. 94
TYCO HOLDINGS CORPORATION—Mattel, Inc.; *U.S. Public*, pg. 1058
TYCO INTERNATIONAL LTD.—Tyco International Ltd.; *U.S.* Public, pg. 1648
TYCO INVESTMENTS (AUSTRALIA) LIMITED—Tyco International Ltd.; *U.S. Public*, pg. 1651
TYCO VALVES LIMITED—Tyco International Ltd.; *U.S. Public*, pg. 1651
TYLER CORPORATION; *U.S. Public*, pg. 1651
U.A.C. HOLDINGS LTD.—Unilever Plc; *Int'l*, pg. 1434
UAC INTERNATIONAL LTD.—Unilever Plc; *Int'l*, pg. 1434
UB FOODS U.S., INC.—United Biscuits (Holdings) Plc; *Int'l*, *pg. 1442*
UN (OVERSEAS) LTD.—United News & Media plc; *Int'l*, pg. 1443
USG CORPORATION; *U.S. Public*, pg. 1660
USTC KANSAS, INC.—Lynch Corporation; *U.S. Public*, pg. 1021
UFIMA S.A.—Fiat Auto SpA; *Int'l*, pg. 482
ULLICO INC.; *U.S. Private*, pg. 1115
UNICAN SECURITY SYSTEMS LTD.; *Int'l*, pg. 1432
UNICARE FINANCIAL CORP.—Blue Cross of California; *U.S. Private*, pg. 152
UNICOM CORPORATION; *U.S. Public*, pg. 1664
UNICORP AMERICAN CORPORATION—Unicorp Canada Corporation; *Int'l*, pg. 1433
UNICORP CANADA CORPORATION; *Int'l*, pg. 1433
UNIGATE PLC; *Int'l*, pg. 1433
UNIGROUP, INC.; *U.S. Private*, pg. 1117
UNILEVER CANADA LIMITED—Unilever Plc; *Int'l*, pg. 1439
UNILEVER (COMMONWEALTH HOLDINGS) LTD.—Unilever Plc; *Int'l*, pg. 1434
UNILEVER ESPANA S.A.—Unilever Plc; *Int'l*, pg. 1439
UNILEVER SOUTH AFRICA (PTY.) LTD.—Unilever Plc; *Int'l*, pg. 1439
UNILEVER U.K. HOLDINGS LTD.—Unilever Plc; *Int'l*, pg. 1434

UNILEVER UNITED STATES INC.—Unilever Plc; Int'l, pg. 1435
UNION CARBIDE CORPORATION; U.S. Public, pg. 1666
UNION ELECTRIC DEVELOPMENT CORPORATION—Ameren Corporation; U.S. Public, pg. 66
UNION PACIFIC CORPORATION; U.S. Public, pg. 1667
UNIQUE CASUAL RESTAURANTS, INC.—Compass Group plc; Int'l, pg. 324
UNIROYAL CHEMICAL CORPORATION—Crompton & Knowles Corporation; U.S. Public, pg. 459
UNISOURCE ENERGY CORPORATION; U.S. Public, pg. 1670
UNITED ACQUISITION CORPORATION—Red Apple Companies; U.S. Private, pg. 915
UNITED ASSET MANAGEMENT CORPORATION; U.S. Public, pg. 1672
UNITED ASSET MANAGEMENT (JAPAN), INC.—United Asset Management Corporation; U.S. Public, pg. 1674
UNITED COMPANIES FINANCIAL CORPORATION; U.S. Public, pg. 1675
UNITED GUARANTY CORP.—American International Group, Inc.; U.S. Public, pg. 84
UNITED INDUSTRIAL CORPORATION; U.S. Public, pg. 1679
UNITED INVESTORS MANAGEMENT COMPANY—Torchmark Corporation; U.S. Public, pg. 1623
UNITED PROPERTIES GROUP—United Water Resources; U.S. Public, pg. 1692
UNITED PROVINCIAL NEWSPAPERS LTD.—United News & Media plc; Int'l, pg. 1443
UNITED RESOURCES, INC.—United Illuminating Company; U.S. Public, pg. 1678
UNITED STANDARD ASSET GROWTH CORP.—AEGON N.V.; Int'l, pg. 26
US AIRWAYS GROUP, INC.; U.S. Public, pg. 1680
U.S. HEALTHCARE PROPERTIES, INC.—Aetna Inc.; U.S. Public, pg. 27
U.S. INDUSTRIES, INC.; U.S. Public, pg. 1683
USLIFE CORPORATION—American General Corporation; U.S. Public, pg. 77
USA NETWORKS, INC.; U.S. Public, pg. 1685
U S WEST INC.; U.S. Public, pg. 1688
UNITED UTILITIES PLC; Int'l, pg. 1444
UNITED WATER RESOURCES; U.S. Public, pg. 1691
UNITED WATER WORKS—United Water Resources; U.S. Public, pg. 1692
UNITIL CORPORATION; U.S. Public, pg. 1692
UNIVERSAL CORPORATION; U.S. Public, pg. 1694
UNIVERSAL STUDIOS ARTISTS (ENGLAND) LTD.—The Seagram Company Ltd.; Int'l, pg. 1216
UNIVERSAL STUDIOS CANADA LTD.—The Seagram Company Ltd.; Int'l, pg. 1216
UNIVERSAL TELEPHONE, INC.—Century Telephone Enterprises, Inc.; U.S. Public, pg. 330
UNUM CORPORATION; U.S. Public, pg. 1699
UNUM HOLDING COMPANY—UNUM Corporation; U.S. Public, pg. 1699
VDM HOLDING CO.—Diebold, Incorporated; U.S. Public, pg. 506
V.T. INC.; U.S. Private, pg. 1131
VAIL RESORTS, INC.; U.S. Public, pg. 1704
VALHI, INC.—Contran Corporation; U.S. Private, pg. 270
VALLEY RESOURCES, INC.; U.S. Public, pg. 1706
VALMET SVENSKA AB—Valmet Corporation; Int'l, pg. 1449
VALOR LTD.—Newmond PLC; Int'l, pg. 925
VAN MELLE DEUTSCHLAND GMBH—Van Melle N.V.; Int'l, pg. 1451
VAN MELLE HOLDING GMBH—Van Melle N.V.; Int'l, pg. 1451
VAN MELLE INTERNATIONAL HOLDING B.V.—Van Melle N.V.; Int'l, pg. 1451
VAN MELLE INTERNATIONAL TRUST B.V.—Van Melle N.V.; Int'l, pg. 1451
VAN MELLE NEDERLAND HOLDING B.V.—Van Melle N.V.; Int'l, pg. 1451
VAN OMMEREN USA INC.—Koninklijke Van Ommeren NV; Int'l, pg. 758
VARIED INVESTMENTS, INC.; U.S. Private, pg. 1134
VEBA AG; Int'l, pg. 1454
VECTOR INDUSTRIES, LTD.; Int'l, pg. 1461
VEDA INTERNATIONAL, INC.—Veridian; U.S. Private, pg. 1136
VEDIOR INTERNATIONAL—Vendex International N.V.; Int'l, pg. 1463
VEGLA VEREINIGTE GLASHANDELS-GESELLSCHAFT MBH (VGG)—Saint-Gobain; Int'l, pg. 1173
VENDEX FASHION GROUP—Vendex International N.V.; Int'l, pg. 1462
VENDEX FOOD GROEP—Vendex International N.V.; Int'l, pg. 1463
VENDEX INTERNATIONAL N.V.; Int'l, pg. 1462
VERITAS DGC INC—Veritas DGC Inc.; U.S. Private, pg. 1136
VERTEC—Saint-Gobain; Int'l, pg. 1171
VESPER CORPORATION—Arrowhead Holding Corporation; U.S. Private, pg. 86
VESTA INSURANCE GROUP, INC.; U.S. Public, pg. 1718
VESTER CORPORATION—Arrowhead Holding Corporation; U.S. Private, pg. 86
VIACOM INC.—National Amusements, Inc.; U.S. Private, pg. 775
VIAD CORP; U.S. Public, pg. 1718
VIAG AG; Int'l, pg. 1464
VICTORIA HALL COMPANY LIMITED—Cigna Corp.; U.S. Public, pg. 363
VICTORY FINANCIAL GROUP, INC.; U.S. Private, pg. 1139
VIRGIN HOTEL; Int'l, pg. 1468
VIRGINIA FIRST FINANCIAL CORP.; U.S. Public, pg. 1721
VIRGINIA HOLDING CORPORATION—Norfolk Southern Corporation; U.S. Public, pg. 1190
VOEST-ALPINE INTERNATIONAL CORPORATION—Voest-Alpine Stahl AG; Int'l, pg. 1470
VOLKSFURSORGE HOLDING AG—AMB Aachener und Muenchener Beteiligungs-AG; Int'l, pg. 15
AB VOLVO; Int'l, pg. 1476
VOLVO CANADIAN HOLDINGS LTD.—AB Volvo; Int'l, pg. 1477
VULKAN VERWALTUNGS-UND BETEILIGUNGSGESELLSCHAFT MBH—Heidelberger Zement A.G.; Int'l, pg. 606
W.A. PUBLICATIONS, INC.—The Reader's Digest Association, Inc.; U.S. Public, pg. 1368
WEA INTL., INC.—Time Warner Inc.; U.S. Public, pg. 1612
WHG RESORTS & CASINOS—Patriot American Hospitality, Inc.; U.S. Public, pg. 1265
WMS INDUSTRIES INC.; U.S. Public, pg. 1727
WPL HOLDINGS, INC.; U.S. Public, pg. 1727
WPS RESOURCES CORP.; U.S. Public, pg. 1728
WPT, INC.; U.S. Private, pg. 1144
WRH WALTER REIST HOLDING AG; Int'l, pg. 1484
WRM, INCOPORATED; U.S. Private, pg. 1144
WAJAX LIMITED; Int'l, pg. 1484
WALSH GROUP; U.S. Private, pg. 1148
WALTER INDUSTRIES, INC.; U.S. Public, pg. 1736
WANTAGE AVENUE HOLDING COMPANY, INC.—Selective Insurance Group, Inc; U.S. Public, pg. 1456
WARNACO INC.; U.S. Public, pg. 1738
WATERFORD FOODS INVESTMENTS LIMITED—Avonmore Waterford Group plc; Int'l, pg. 102
WATERFORD FOODS USA, INC.—Avonmore Waterford Group plc; Int'l, pg. 102
WATERFORD WEDGWOOD PLC; Int'l, pg. 1487
WATKINS ASSOCIATED INDUSTRIES INC.; U.S. Private, pg. 1153
WATSON PHARMACEUTICALS, INC.; U.S. Public, pg. 1746
WAUSAU METALS, NANIK DIVISION—Springs Industries, Inc.; U.S. Public, pg. 1500
WAUSAU SERVICE CORP.—Nationwide Insurance Enterprise; U.S. Private, pg. 789
WAYCROSSE INC.; U.S. Private, pg. 1155
WEATHERLY PRIVATE CAPITAL, INC.; U.S. Private, pg. 1156
THE WEATHERVANE RETAIL CORP.; U.S. Private, pg. 1156
WEBSTER FINANCIAL CORPORATION; U.S. Public, pg. 1751
WECHCO, INC.; U.S. Private, pg. 1158
WEDGE ENERGY GROUP INC.; U.S. Private, pg. 1158
WEGENER CORPORATION; U.S. Public, pg. 1751
WEHCO MEDIA, INC.; U.S. Private, pg. 1159
WEINERS STORES, INC.; U.S. Private, pg. 1160
MICHAEL WEINIG AG; Int'l, pg. 1488
WEIR GROUP PLC; Int'l, pg. 1488
WEL-COM FINANCIAL SERVICES, INC.—Colonial Commercial Corp.; U.S. Public, pg. 400
WELLA BETEILIGUNGEN AG—Wella Group; Int'l, pg. 1490
WELLS FARGO & COMPANY; U.S. Public, pg. 1753
WELSH CARSON ANDERSON & STOWE; U.S. Private, pg. 1162
WEMADO B.V.—Unilever Plc; Int'l, pg. 1439
WESCO FINANCIAL CORPORATION—Berkshire Hathaway Inc.; U.S. Public, pg. 217
WESSANEN AG—Koninklijke BolsWessanen nv; Int'l, pg. 753
WEST COAST BANCORP; U.S. Public, pg. 1755
THE WEST COMPANY GROUP LIMITED—The West Company, Incorporated; U.S. Public, pg. 1756
THE WEST COMPANY OF DELAWARE, INC.—The West Company, Incorporated; U.S. Public, pg. 1755
THE WESTERN GROUP; U.S. Private, pg. 1165
WESTERN NATIONAL CORPORATION—American General Corporation; U.S. Public, pg. 76
WESTERN TRUST & SAVINGS HOLDINGS LTD.—Manulife Financial (The Manufacturers Life Insurance Company); Int'l, pg. 841
WESTIN, INC.; U.S. Private, pg. 1169
WESTPAC BANKING CORPORATION; Int'l, pg. 1495
WEYERHAEUSER CANADA LTD.—Weyerhaeuser Company; U.S. Public, pg. 1764
WEYERHAEUSER (FAR EAST) LTD.—Weyerhaeuser Company; U.S. Public, pg. 1764
WHALING INDUSTRIES, INC.; U.S. Private, pg. 1170
WHEELABRATOR TECHNOLOGIES INC.—Waste Management, Inc.; U.S. Public, pg. 1745
WHIRLPOOL DO BRAZIL S.A.—Whirlpool Corporation; U.S. Public, pg. 1765
WHITE RIVER CORPORATION; U.S. Public, pg. 1765
WHITE ROCK DISTILLERIES INC.; U.S. Private, pg. 1173
WICKLAND CORPORATION; U.S. Private, pg. 1174
WICOR, INC.; U.S. Public, pg. 1767
WIGGINS ARJO ITALIANA SRL—Groupe Saint Louis; Int'l, pg. 567
WILCO REPROGRAPHIC, INC.; U.S. Private, pg. 1176
WILLIAMS HOLDINGS PLC; Int'l, pg. 1499
WILLIAMS INDUSTRIES, INC.; U.S. Public, pg. 1769
WILLIAMS INTERNATIONAL INDUSTRIES, INC.; U.S. Private, pg. 1178
WILSEY BENNETT CO.; U.S. Private, pg. 1180
WILSON CONNOLLY; Int'l, pg. 1510
JIM WILSON & ASSOCIATES, INC.; U.S. Private, pg. 1181
WINDPOINT PARTNERS; U.S. Private, pg. 1182
WINTERTHUR U.S. HOLDINGS INC.—Credit Suisse Group; Int'l, pg. 345
WISCONSIN ENERGY CORPORATION; U.S. Public, pg. 1773
WOLSELEY PLC.; Int'l, pg. 1511
THE WOODFIN SUITE HOTELS; U.S. Private, pg. 1187
WOODSIDE PETROLEUM LTD.—Royal Dutch/Shell Group of Companies; Int'l, pg. 1137
WOOLWORTH CORPORATION; U.S. Public, pg. 1777
WORLD FINANCIAL PROPERTIES, INC.—Olympia & York Developments Ltd.; Int'l, pg. 1004
WORLD MINERALS INC.—Alleghany Corporation; U.S. Public, pg. 42
WORLD PUBLISHING COMPANY; U.S. Private, pg. 1190
WORLDWIDE SPORTS & RECREATION, INC.; U.S. Private, pg. 1191
BARRY WRIGHT INTL. CORP.—Applied Power Inc.; U.S. Public, pg. 124
WYNN'S INTERNATIONAL, INC.; U.S. Public, pg. 1782
A.P. WYOTT; U.S. Private, pg. 1193
X-L-CO, INC.—Xtra Corporation; U.S. Public, pg. 1787
XTRA CORPORATION; U.S. Public, pg. 1786
YKK CORPORATION OF AMERICA—YKK Corporation; Int'l, pg. 1515
YRJ CORPORATION—Wilco Reprographic, Inc.; U.S. Private, pg. 1176
YALE ELECTRONICS ASIA - PACIFIC LIMITED—Williams Holdings Plc; Int'l, pg. 1499
YAMAHA CORPORATION; Int'l, pg. 1515
YANKEE ENERGY SYSTEM, INC.; U.S. Public, pg. 1787
YEO HIAP SENG LIMITED—Orchard Parade Holdings Limited; Int'l, pg. 1008
YOKOHAMA CORPORATION OF NORTH AMERICA—The Yokohama Rubber Co., Ltd.; Int'l, pg. 1521
YORK INTERNATIONAL CORPORATION; U.S. Public, pg. 1788
YOUNG'S HOLDINGS INC.; U.S. Private, pg. 1202
H.B. ZACHRY; U.S. Private, pg. 1203
THE ZIEGLER COMPANIES, INC.; U.S. Public, pg. 1791
ZIFF-DAVIS CONSUMER MEDIA GROUP—Softbank Corporation; Int'l, pg. 1276
ZIFF-DAVIS INTERNATIONAL MEDIA GROUP—Softbank Corporation; Int'l, pg. 1276
ZIMMERMAN HOLDINGS, INC.; U.S. Private, pg. 1206
ZURICH AMERICAN INSURANCE COMPANY OF ILLINOIS—Zurich Insurance Company; Int'l, pg. 1530

6722 — MANAGEMENT INVESTMENT COMPANIES, OPEN-END

AIB INTERNATIONAL FINANCIAL SERVICES LTD—Allied Irish Banks, p.l.c.; Int'l, pg. 64
AMEV BELEGGINGSCONSORTIUM N.V.—Fortis; Int'l, pg. 499
ANZ MANAGED INVESTMENTS LIMITED—Australia & New Zealand Banking Group Limited; Int'l, pg. 98
AELTUS INVESTMENT MANAGEMENT, INC.—Aetna Inc.; U.S. Public, pg. 27
AETNA INVESTMENT MANAGEMENT (JAPAN), K.K.—Aetna Inc.; U.S. Public, pg. 27
AETNA INVESTMENT MANAGEMENT LIMITED—Aetna Inc.; U.S. Public, pg. 27
ALLIED CAPITAL CORPORATION II—Allied Capital Corporation; U.S. Public, pg. 47
AMERICAN EXPRESS FINANCIAL ADVISOR—American Express Company; U.S. Public, pg. 73
BHF INVESTMENT MANAGEMENT AG—BHF-BANK AG; Int'l, pg. 120
BT SECURITIES CORP.—Bankers Trust New York Corporation; U.S. Public, pg. 185
BANQUE DUMENIL-LEBLE—CERUS - Compagnies Europeennes Reunies; Int'l, pg. 240
BANQUE MORGAN GRENFELL EN SUISSE S. A. (SWITZERLAND)—Deutsche Bank AG; Int'l, pg. 406
BEAR STEARNS REAL ESTATE GROUP INC.—The Bear Stearns Companies Inc.; U.S. Public, pg. 198
BONNET RESOURCES CORP.—Banc One Corporation; U.S. Public, pg. 175
CAIXAGEST—Caixa Geral de Depositos; Int'l, pg. 250
CAPITAL HOUSE INVESTMENT MANAGEMENT LIMITED—The Royal Bank of Scotland plc; Int'l, pg. 1132
CIGNA INTERNATIONAL ASSET FUND LTD.—Cigna Corp.; U.S. Public, pg. 357
CIGNA INTERNATIONAL FUND MANAGERS (CI) LTD.—Cigna Corp.; U.S. Public, pg. 364
CILCORP INVESTMENT MANAGEMENT INC.—CILCORP Inc.; U.S. Public, pg. 367
COFINA—Allianz Aktiengesellschaft; Int'l, pg. 61
COST CARE, INC.—John Hancock Mutual Life Insurance Company; U.S. Private, pg. 589
CROWN LIFE INVESTMENT MANAGEMENT COMPANY (CLIMCO)—Extendicare Inc.; Int'l, pg. 468
DBS ASSET MANAGEMENT LTD.—DBS Bank Ltd.; Int'l, pg. 350
DAIWA ASSET MANAGEMENT CO. LTD.—Daiwa Securities Co. Ltd.; Int'l, pg. 374
DART GROUP FINANCIAL CORP.—Dart Group Corporation; U.S. Public, pg. 484
DAVIS SELECTED ADVISORS, L.P.; U.S. Private, pg. 315
THE DEARBORN GROUP; U.S. Private, pg. 319
DEUTSCHE BANK FINANCE N.V.—Deutsche Bank AG; Int'l, pg. 405
DIVAL—Allianz Aktiengesellschaft; Int'l, pg. 61
DRUMM & ASSOCIATES, INC.; U.S. Private, pg. 343
ENSKILDA S.A.—Skandinaviska Enskilda Banken; Int'l, pg. 1259
FMR CORP.—Fidelity Investments (FMR Corp.); U.S. Private, pg. 403
FIDELITY INVESTMENTS (FMR CORP.); U.S. Private, pg. 402
FIDRAS—Allianz Aktiengesellschaft; Int'l, pg. 61
FINANCIAL ASSET MANAGEMENT CORPORATION—M.D.C. Holdings, Inc.; U.S. Public, pg. 1025
FINANCIERE ATLAS S.A.—BHF-BANK AG; Int'l, pg. 120
FIRST WISCONSIN ASSET MANAGEMENT, INC.—Firstar Corporation; U.S. Public, pg. 643
FIRSTAR COMMUNITY INVESTMENT CORP.—Firstar Corporation; U.S. Public, pg. 643
FLEET EQUITY PARTNERS—Fleet Financial Group, Inc.; U.S. Public, pg. 650
FLEET INVESTMENT ADVISORS, INC.—Fleet Financial Group, Inc.; U.S. Public, pg. 650
FRANKFURT-TRUST INVESTMENT GMBH—BHF-BANK AG; Int'l, pg. 119
GESBANSANDER—Banco Santander; Int'l, pg. 143

GESMADRID PATRIMONIOS, S.G.C., S.A.—Caja de Madrid Group; *Int'l*, pg. 251
GESTIRAS—Allianz Aktiengesellschaft; *Int'l*, pg. 61
GREAT LAKES POWER INC.—EdperBrascan Corporation; *Int'l*, pg. 433
HSBC CAPITAL (THAILAND) LIMITED—HSBC Holdings plc; *Int'l*, pg. 582
HANDELSBANKEN FONDER AB—Svenska Handelsbanken; *Int'l*, pg. 1327
HENCO, INC.; *U.S. Private*, pg. 521
THE HILLMAN COMPANY; *U.S. Private*, pg. 530
THE HONGKONG AND SHANGHAI BANKING CORPORATION LIMITED (HONGKONGBANK)—HSBC Holdings plc; *Int'l*, pg. 583
IPD MARKETING SERVICES, INC.—Protective Life Corporation; *U.S. Public*, pg. 1336
INCHCAPE MANAGEMENT SERVICES LTD.—Inchcape PLC; *Int'l*, pg. 671
INVESCO CAPITAL MANAGEMENT—Invesco Group Asset Management Ltd.; *Int'l*, pg. 685
INVESCO FUNDS GROUP—Invesco Group Asset Management Ltd.; *Int'l*, pg. 685
INVESCO GROUP ASSET MANAGEMENT LTD.; *Int'l*, pg. 685
JOHN HANCOCK ADVISERS INTERNATIONAL, LTD.—John Hancock Mutual Life Insurance Company; *U.S. Private*, pg. 590
S.C. JOHNSON & SON, INC.; *U.S. Private*, pg. 592
KEYES ASSET MANAGEMET—The Keyes Company Realtors; *U.S. Private*, pg. 618
LEGAL & GENERAL INVESTMENT MANAGEMENT (HOLDINGS) LIMITED—Legal & General Group PLC; *Int'l*, pg. 805
LEHMAN COMMERCIAL PAPER INC.—Lehman Brothers Holdings Inc.; *U.S. Public*, pg. 987
LOCUST STREET SECURITIES, INC.—ING Groep N.V.; *Int'l*, pg. 647
LOWRY HILL INVESTMENT ADVISORS, INC.—Norwest Corporation; *U.S. Public*, pg. 1201
MANULIFE INVESTMENT MANAGEMENT CORPORATION—Manulife Financial (The Manufacturers Life Insurance Company); *Int'l*, pg. 840
MAPFRE INVERSION 2, SOC. GESTORA DE INSTITUCIONES DE INVERSION COLECTIVA—Corporacion MAPFRE, Compania Internacional de Reaseguros, S.A.; *Int'l*, pg. 334
MIDDLE EAST FINANCE CO. LTD.—HSBC Holdings plc; *Int'l*, pg. 583
MORGAN GRENFELL ASSET MANAGEMENT LIMITED—Deutsche Bank AG; *Int'l*, pg. 405
MORGAN GRENFELL CAPITAL MANAGEMENT INCORPORATED—Deutsche Bank AG; *Int'l*, pg. 405
MORGAN GRENFELL INTERNATIONAL ASSET MANAGEMENT CO. LTD. (TOKYO)—Deutsche Bank AG; *Int'l*, pg. 406
MUTUAL OF OMAHA INVESTOR SERVICES, INC.—Mutual of Omaha Insurance Company; *U.S. Private*, pg. 770
NATIONAL CITY CAPITAL CORP.—National City Corporation; *U.S. Public*, pg. 1154
NATIONSBANK OF TEXAS NATIONAL INTERNATIONAL CO.—NationsBank Corporation; *U.S. Public*, pg. 1163
THE JOHN NUVEEN COMPANY—The St. Paul Companies, Inc.; *U.S. Public*, pg. 1429
ORIX CAPITAL CORPORATION—Orix Corporation; *Int'l*, pg. 1008
PAINEWEBBER GROUP INCORPORATED; *U.S. Public*, pg. 1252
PAUL REVERE INVESTMENT MANAGEMENT COMPANY INC. (PRIMCO)—Provident Companies, Inc.; *U.S. Public*, pg. 1338
PEREGRINE CAPITAL MANAGEMENT, INC.—Norwest Corporation; *U.S. Public*, pg. 1202
PREVICOMMERICO—Allianz Aktiengesellschaft; *Int'l*, pg. 62
PRUDENTIAL FUND MANAGEMENT CANADA LTD.—The Prudential Insurance Company of America; *U.S. Private*, pg. 893
RASFID—Allianz Aktiengesellschaft; *Int'l*, pg. 62
RESOURCES TRUST COMPANY—SunAmerica Inc.; *U.S. Public*, pg. 1533
SEI FINANCIAL SERVICES COMPANY—SEI Investments; *U.S. Public*, pg. 1417
S.L. DE GESTION MOBILIARIA—Caja de Madrid Group; *Int'l*, pg. 252
SANTANDER DE PATRIMONIOS—Banco Santander; *Int'l*, pg. 143
SCOTT & STRINGFELLOW FINANCIAL, INC.; *U.S. Public*, *pg. 1445*
SCOTT & STRINGFELLOW, INC.—Scott & Stringfellow Financial, Inc.; *U.S. Public*, pg. 1445
SCUDDER KEMPER INVESTMENTS, INC.—Zurich Insurance Company; *Int'l*, pg. 1530
THE SOUTHERN LIFE ASSOCIATION LIMITED—Anglo American Corporation of South Africa Limited; *Int'l*, pg. 77
STATE STREET RESEARCH INVESTMENT SERVICES, INC.—Metropolitan Life Insurance Co.; *U.S. Private*, pg. 738
STRATTON MANAGEMENT COMPANY; *U.S. Private*, pg. 1046
TSB HILL SAMUEL BANK HOLDING CO PLC—Lloyds TSB Group PLC; *Int'l*, pg. 813
TRAVELERS GROUP; *U.S. Public*, pg. 1632
TRILON FINANCIAL CORP.—EdperBrascan Corporation; *Int'l*, pg. 434
TRUST CORPORATION OF CANADA—Royal Bank of Canada; *Int'l*, pg. 1131
TRUST FUND ADVISORS, INC.—ULLICO Inc.; *U.S. Private*, *pg. 1116*
WAYFOONG CREDIT LTD.—HSBC Holdings plc; *Int'l*, pg. 584
WAYFOONG FINANCE LTD.—HSBC Holdings plc; *Int'l*, pg. 584
WESTIM RESOURCES LTD.—EdperBrascan Corporation; *Int'l*, pg. 435
WESTPAC FINANCIAL SERVICES GROUP LIMITED—Westpac Banking Corporation; *Int'l*, pg. 1496

6726 — UNIT INVESTMENT TRUSTS, FACE-AMOUNT CERTIFICATE OFFICES, CLOSED-END MANAGEMENT INVESTMENT OFFICES

ADAMS EXPRESS CO.—Petroleum & Resources Corp.; *U.S. Public*, pg. 1280
ADRIATICA GESTIONI—Allianz Aktiengesellschaft; *Int'l*, pg. 61
AETNA CAPITAL MANAGEMENT INVESTMENT LIMITED—Aetna Inc.; *U.S. Public*, pg. 27
AETNA INTERNATIONAL (AUSTRALIA) PTY. LTD.—Aetna Inc.; *U.S. Public*, pg. 27
AETNA INVESTMENT MANAGEMENT LIMITED—Aetna Inc.; *U.S. Public*, pg. 27
ALLMERICA SECURITIES TRUST; *U.S. Public*, pg. 54
BAI GEST S.P.A.—Deutsche Bank AG; *Int'l*, pg. 403
BHF TRUST MANAGEMENT GESELLSCHAFT FUR VERMOEGENSVERWALTUNG MBH—BHF-BANK AG; *Int'l*, pg. 119
BANQUE MORGAN GRENFELL EN SUISSE S. A. (SWITZERLAND)—Deutsche Bank AG; *Int'l*, pg. 406
BARCLAYS FINANCIAL SERVICES CO. LTD.—Barclays Bank PLC; *Int'l*, pg. 164
BOLS ROYAL DISTILLERIES—Koninklijke BolsWessanen nv; *Int'l*, pg. 751
CAIXA CATALUNYA GESTIO—Caixa d'Estalvis de Catalunya; *Int'l*, pg. 250
CAIXAGEST—Caixa Geral de Depositos; *Int'l*, pg. 250
CAPITAL HOUSE INVESTMENT MANAGEMENT LIMITED—The Royal Bank of Scotland plc; *Int'l*, pg. 1132
CASTLE CONVERTIBLE FUND, INC.; *U.S. Public*, pg. 313
CENTRAL SECURITIES CORPORATION; *U.S. Public*, pg. 326
CHARTERHOUSE BANK LTD.—Credit Commercial de France; *Int'l*, pg. 342
CIGNA CORP.; *U.S. Public*, pg. 356
COFINA—Allianz Aktiengesellschaft; *Int'l*, pg. 61
COST CARE, INC.—John Hancock Mutual Life Insurance Company; *U.S. Private*, pg. 589
COUNTRY LIFE INSURANCE COMPANY; *U.S. Private*, pg. 278
DAIWA ASSET MANAGEMENT CO. LTD.—Daiwa Securities Co. Ltd.; *Int'l*, pg. 374
DIVAL—Allianz Aktiengesellschaft; *Int'l*, pg. 61
DRUMM & ASSOCIATES, INC.; *U.S. Private*, pg. 343
1838 BOND-DEBENTURE TRADING FUND; *U.S. Public*, pg. 566
FIDRAS—Allianz Aktiengesellschaft; *Int'l*, pg. 61
FINANCIAL ASSET MANAGEMENT CORPORATION—M.D.C. Holdings, Inc.; *U.S. Public*, pg. 1025
FORTIS FINANCIAL GROUP—Fortis; *Int'l*, pg. 499
GENERAL AMERICAN INVESTORS COMPANY, INC.; *U.S. Public*, pg. 706
GESTIRAS—Allianz Aktiengesellschaft; *Int'l*, pg. 61
HEI INVESTMENT CORP.—Hawaiian Electric Industries, Inc.; *U.S. Public*, pg. 800
HANDELSBANKEN FONDER AB—Svenska Handelsbanken; *Int'l*, pg. 1327
HENCO, INC.; *U.S. Private*, pg. 521
IDS TRUST CO.—American Express Company; *U.S. Public*, *pg. 73*
IMPERIAL FUND MANAGERS—Canadian Imperial Bank of Commerce; *Int'l*, pg. 257
INVESCO EUROPE LTD.—Invesco Group Asset Management Ltd.; *Int'l*, pg. 685
INVESCO GROUP ASSET MANAGEMENT LTD.; *Int'l*, pg. 685
JOHNSTON, LEMON & CO. INC.; *U.S. Private*, pg. 595
LEGAL & GENERAL INVESTMENT MANAGEMENT (HOLDINGS) LIMITED—Legal & General Group PLC; *Int'l*, pg. 805
LEHMAN BROTHERS, INC.—Lehman Brothers Holdings Inc.; *U.S. Public*, pg. 987
LINCOLN NATIONAL INCOME FUND, INC.—Lincoln National Corporation; *U.S. Public*, pg. 998
LLOYDS ABBEY LIFE PLC—Lloyds TSB Group PLC; *Int'l*, pg. 813
LLOYDS BANK TRUST COMPANY (CHANNEL ISLANDS) LIMITED—Lloyds TSB Group PLC; *Int'l*, pg. 813
MASSMUTUAL CORPORATE INVESTORS; *U.S. Public*, pg. 1055
MONTGOMERY ST. INCOME SECURITIES, INC.; *U.S. Public*, pg. 1127
MORGAN GRENFELL ASSET MANAGEMENT LIMITED—Deutsche Bank AG; *Int'l*, pg. 405
MORGAN GRENFELL CAPITAL MANAGEMENT INCORPORATED—Deutsche Bank AG; *Int'l*, pg. 405
MORGAN GRENFELL INTERNATIONAL ASSET MANAGEMENT CO. LTD. (TOKYO)—Deutsche Bank AG; *Int'l*, pg. 406
NIPPON STEEL U.S.A., INC.—Nippon Steel Corporation; *Int'l*, pg. 939
THE JOHN NUVEEN COMPANY—The St. Paul Companies, Inc.; *U.S. Public*, pg. 1429
PACIFIC AMERICAN INCOME SHARES, INC.; *U.S. Public*, *pg. 1247*
PAINEWEBBER GROUP INCORPORATED; *U.S. Public*, pg. 1252
PETROLEUM & RESOURCES CORP.; *U.S. Public*, pg. 1280
PHOENIX FOUNDERS, INC—Phoenix Home Life Mutual Insurance Company; *U.S. Private*, pg. 863
PIPER, JAFFRAY & HOPWOOD INCORPORATED, LONDON—Piper Jaffray Companies, Inc.; *U.S. Public*, pg. 1303
PIPER JAFFRAY COMPANIES, INC.; *U.S. Public*, pg. 1300
PREVICOMMERICO—Allianz Aktiengesellschaft; *Int'l*, pg. 62
RASFID—Allianz Aktiengesellschaft; *Int'l*, pg. 62
REAFIN—SCOR; *Int'l*, pg. 1152
SANTANDER DE PATRIMONIOS—Banco Santander; *Int'l*, pg. 143
SOCIETE FINANCIERE D'AUTEUIL (SFA)—Total S.A.; *Int'l*, *pg. 1409*
SOURCE CAPITAL, INC.; *U.S. Public*, pg. 1488
THE SOUTHERN LIFE ASSOCIATION LIMITED—Anglo American Corporation of South Africa Limited; *Int'l*, pg. 77
TRI-CONTINENTAL CORPORATION—J. & W. Seligman & Co.; *U.S. Private*, pg. 982
UNITED PRESIDENTIAL LIFE INSURANCE CO.—Conseco Inc.; *U.S. Public*, pg. 434
UNIVERSAL SECURITIES CO., LTD.; *Int'l*, pg. 1444
VAN KAMPEN/AMERICAN CAPITAL INC.—Morgan Stanley Dean Witter & Co.; *U.S. Public*, pg. 1132
THE VANGUARD GROUP, INC.; *U.S. Private*, pg. 1133
WESTPAC FINANCIAL SERVICES GROUP LIMITED—Westpac Banking Corporation; *Int'l*, pg. 1496
YAMAICHI ASSET MANAGEMENT (HONG KONG) LTD.—Yamaichi Securities Co., Ltd.; *Int'l*, pg. 1517
YAMAICHI ASSET MANAGEMENT (SINGAPORE) PTE LTD.—Yamaichi Securities Co., Ltd.; *Int'l*, pg. 1517
ZUIDERHOUT B.V.—Koninklijke BolsWessanen nv; *Int'l*, pg. 751

6732 — EDUCATIONAL, RELIGIOUS & CHARITABLE TRUSTS

CHRISTIAN CHILDREN'S FUND, INC.; *U.S. Private*, pg. 238
THE DUN & BRADSTREET CORPORATE FOUNDATION—The Dun & Bradstreet Corporation; *U.S. Public*, pg. 535
INVESTORS FIDUCIARY TRUST COMPANY—State Street Corporation; *U.S. Public*, pg. 1513
THE JOSTENS FOUNDATION, INC.—Jostens; *U.S. Public*, pg. 934
PACIFIC TELESIS FOUNDATION—SBC Communications Inc.; *U.S. Public*, pg. 1416
POLAROID FOUNDATION—Polaroid Corporation; *U.S. Public*, pg. 1314
THE XEROX FOUNDATION INC.—Xerox Corporation; *U.S. Public*, pg. 1785

6733 — TRUSTS, EXCEPT EDUCATIONAL, RELIGIOUS & CHARITABLE

ABN-AMRO TRUST COMPANY (VIRGIN ISLANDS)—ABN-AMRO Holding N.V.; *Int'l*, pg. 11
ABN TRUSTCOMPANY (LUXEMBOURG) S.A.—ABN-AMRO Holding N.V.; *Int'l*, pg. 11
ABN TRUSTCOMPANY (SUISSE) S.A.—ABN-AMRO Holding N.V.; *Int'l*, pg. 12
ABN TRUSTCOMPANY (NEDERLAND) B.V.—ABN-AMRO Holding N.V.; *Int'l*, pg. 9
AMCORE TRUST COMPANY—Amcore Financial, Inc.; *U.S. Public*, pg. 65
B OF B (EUROPE) LIMITED—The Bank of Bermuda Limited; *Int'l*, pg. 151
BBME TRUSTEE (JERSEY) LIMITED—HSBC Holdings plc; *Int'l*, pg. 580
BHF TRUST MANAGEMENT GESELLSCHAFT FUR VERMOEGENSVERWALTUNG MBH—BHF-BANK AG; *Int'l*, pg. 119
BANK OF BERMUDA (GUERNSEY) LIMITED—The Bank of Bermuda Limited; *Int'l*, pg. 151
THE BANK OF BERMUDA LIMITED-HONG KONG BRANCH—The Bank of Bermuda Limited; *Int'l*, pg. 151
BANK OF BERMUDA (NEW YORK) LIMITED—The Bank of Bermuda Limited; *Int'l*, pg. 151
BARCLAYS UNICORN LTD.—Barclays Bank PLC; *Int'l*, pg. 165
CBS PENSION TRUSTEES U.K. LIMITED—CBS Corporation; *U.S. Public*, pg. 275
CANTAY HOLDINGS INC.—Manulife Financial (The Manufacturers Life Insurance Company); *Int'l*, pg. 840
CHASE MANHATTAN TRUST CAYMAN LTD.—The Chase Manhattan Corporation; *U.S. Public*, pg. 340
DAIWA SECURITIES TRUST COMPANY—Daiwa Securities Co. Ltd.; *Int'l*, pg. 375
ERICSSON TREASURY SERVICES AB—Telefonaktiebolaget LM Ericsson; *Int'l*, pg. 1364
FAR EAST BANK AND TRUST COMPANY—The Sakura Bank, Limited; *Int'l*, pg. 1180
FIDUCIARY TRUST COMPANY INTERNATIONAL; *U.S. Public*, pg. 621
FIDUCIARY TRUST INTERNATIONAL OF CALIFORNIA—Fiduciary Trust Company International; *U.S. Public*, pg. 621
FIDUCIARY TRUST INTERNATIONAL OF THE SOUTH—Fiduciary Trust Company International; *U.S. Public*, pg. 621
FIRST STATE COMPUTING PTY LTD—British Telecommunications plc; *Int'l*, pg. 222
FIRST TRUST CORPORATION—Fiserv, Inc.; *U.S. Public*, pg. 647
GENERAL ELECTRIC INVESTMENT CORP.—General Electric Company; *U.S. Public*, pg. 712
HSBC FUTURES, INC.—HSBC Holdings plc; *Int'l*, pg. 581
HSBC FUTURES (SINGAPORE) PTE LIMITED—HSBC Holdings plc; *Int'l*, pg. 582
HSBC INTERNATIONAL TRUSTEE LIMITED—HSBC Holdings plc; *Int'l*, pg. 580
HSBC INTERNATIONAL TRUSTEE (SINGAPORE) LIMITED—HSBC Holdings plc; *Int'l*, pg. 582
HSBC (MALAYSIA) TRUSTEE BERHAD—HSBC Holdings plc; *Int'l*, pg. 582
HSBC TRUSTEE (JERSEY) LIMITED—HSBC Holdings plc; *Int'l*, pg. 580

HELABA TRUST BERATUNGS-UND MANAGEMENT GESELLSCHAFT MBH—Landesbank Hessen-Thuringen Girozentrale; *Int'l*, pg. 799
HUNTINGTON BANCSHARES INC.; *U.S. Public*, pg. 849
THE HUNTINGTON TRUST COMPANY OF FLORIDA, N.A.—Huntington Bancshares Inc.; *U.S. Public*, pg. 850
INSTRON REALTY TRUST—Instron Corporation; *U.S. Public*, pg. 883
KMIC INVESTMENT COMPANY—Michigan Physicians Mutual Liability Inc.; *U.S. Private*, pg. 741
LAURENTIAN TRUST OF CANADA—Desjardins-Laurentian Financial Corporation; *Int'l*, pg. 396
LIBERTY NATIONAL GROUPCARE, INC.—Torchmark Corporation; *U.S. Public*, pg. 1623
LINCOLN HOLDINGS, INC.—Fiserv, Inc.; *U.S. Public*, pg. 647
LION INTERNATIONAL MANAGEMENT LIMITED—HSBC Holdings plc; *Int'l*, pg. 580
LLOYDS BANK UNIT TRUST MANAGERS LTD.—Lloyds TSB Group PLC; *Int'l*, pg. 813
MANULIFE MANAGEMENT LTD.—Manulife Financial (The Manufacturers Life Insurance Company); *Int'l*, pg. 841
MERRILL LYNCH FIDUCIARY SERVICES, INC.—Merrill Lynch & Co., Inc.; *U.S. Public*, pg. 1098
MIDLAND BANK TRUST COMPANY LIMITED—HSBC Holdings plc; *Int'l*, pg. 580
MIDLAND BANK TRUST CORPORATION (CAYMAN) LIMITED—HSBC Holdings plc; *Int'l*, pg. 583
MIDLAND BANK TRUSTEE (GUERNSEY) LIMITED—HSBC Holdings plc; *Int'l*, pg. 580
MONTREAL TRUSTCO-CORPORATE SERVICES DIV.—The Bank of Nova Scotia; *Int'l*, pg. 155
MONTREAL TRUSTCO INVESTMENT MANAGEMENT SERVICES—The Bank of Nova Scotia; *Int'l*, pg. 155
MONTREAL TRUSTCO-PERSONAL SERVICES DIVISION—The Bank of Nova Scotia; *Int'l*, pg. 155
J.P. MORGAN DELAWARE—J.P. Morgan Co. Incorporated; *U.S. Public*, pg. 1129
PROPERTY CAPITAL TRUST; *U.S. Public*, pg. 1335
SAKURA FINANCE INTERNATIONAL LIMITED—The Sakura Bank, Limited; *Int'l*, pg. 1180
SAKURA TRUST COMPANY—The Sakura Bank, Limited; *Int'l*, pg. 1179
STANDARD CHARTERED EQUITOR TRUSTEE SINGAPORE LIMITED—Standard Chartered Bank PLC; *Int'l*, pg. 1296
STANDARD CHARTERED FUTURES (SINGAPORE) PTE LIMITED—Standard Chartered Bank PLC; *Int'l*, pg. 1295
SUN LIFE ASSURANCE COMPANY OF CANADA; *Int'l*, pg. 1318
SUN LIFE TRUST COMPANY—Sun Life Assurance Company of Canada; *Int'l*, pg. 1319
SUNTRUST BANK, EAST CENTRAL FLORIDA—SunTrust Banks, Inc.; *U.S. Public*, pg. 1537
SUNTRUST BANK, MIAMI, N.A.—SunTrust Banks, Inc.; *U.S. Public*, pg. 1537
ULSTER BANK DUBLIN TRUST COMPANY—National Westminster Bank PLC; *Int'l*, pg. 912
UNITED MISSOURI TRUST COMPANY OF NEW YORK—UMB Financial Corporation; *U.S. Public*, pg. 1655
VALUE PROPERTY TRUST; *U.S. Public*, pg. 1707
VALUE PROPERTY TRUST—Value Property Trust; *U.S. Public*, pg. 1707

6792 — OIL ROYALTY TRADERS

BLACKHAWK HOLDING COMPANY—Torchmark Corporation; *U.S. Public*, pg. 1623
CRYSTAL PROGRAM LTD., INC.—Crystal Oil Company; *U.S. Public*, pg. 466
DYAS B.V.—SHV Holdings N.V.; *Int'l*, pg. 1155
FINA ANTWERP OLEFINS N.V.—Petrofina S.A.; *Int'l*, pg. 1043
PETROBRAS - PETROLEO BRASILEIRO S.A.; *Int'l*, pg. 1041
PETROLEOS DE VENEZUELA S.A.; *Int'l*, pg. 1045
SOCO CALIFORNIA PROPERTIES, INC.—Snyder Oil Corporation; *U.S. Public*, pg. 1482
SOCO THOMASVILLE, INC.—Snyder Oil Corporation; *U.S. Public*, pg. 1482
TORCH ENERGY ADVISORS, INCORPORATED—Torchmark Corporation; *U.S. Public*, pg. 1623
TORCH OPERATING CO.—Torchmark Corporation; *U.S. Public*, pg. 1623
TRANSCOR S.A.—Groupe Bruxelles Lambert S.A.; *Int'l*, pg. 562

6794 — PATENT OWNERS & LESSORS

AVC/NU-VISION, INC.; *U.S. Private*, pg. 9
J. ALEXANDERS CORPORATION; *U.S. Public*, pg. 40
AMERICAN DAIRY QUEEN CORPORATION—Berkshire Hathaway Inc.; *U.S. Public*, pg. 220
TRUMAN ARNOLD COMPANIES; *U.S. Private*, pg. 84
ATHLETIC ATTIC RETAIL COMPANY—Just For Feet, Inc.; *U.S. Public*, pg. 936
AU BON PAIN CO., INC.; *U.S. Public*, pg. 146
BANDAG, INCORPORATED; *U.S. Public*, pg. 177
BANDAG LICENSING CORPORATION—Bandag, Incorporated; *U.S. Public*, pg. 177
THE BARBERS, HAIRSTYLING FOR MEN & WOMEN, INC.; *U.S. Private*, pg. 115
BASKIN-ROBBINS USA CO.—Allied Domecq PLC; *Int'l*, pg. 63
BEN & JERRY'S HOMEMADE INC.; *U.S. Public*, pg. 210
BIG O TIRES INCORPORATED—TBC Corporation; *U.S. Public*, pg. 1553
BLIMPIE INTERNATIONAL, INC.; *U.S. Public*, pg. 236
BLIMPIE INTERNATIONAL, INC.—Blimpie International, Inc.; *U.S. Public*, pg. 236
BLIMPIE SUBS & SALADS—Blimpie International, Inc.; *U.S. Public*, pg. 236
BRESLER'S INDUSTRIES, INC.—Yogen Fruz Worldwide Inc.; *Int'l*, pg. 1520
BUDGET GROUP, INC.; *U.S. Private*, pg. 178
BUDGET RENT A CAR CORPORATION—Budget Group, Inc.; *U.S. Private*, pg. 178
CARDINAL HEALTH INC.; *U.S. Public*, pg. 304
CAREER BLAZERS SERVICE COMPANY, INC.—Career Blazers Inc.; *U.S. Private*, pg. 209
THE CATO CORPORATION; *U.S. Public*, pg. 318
CENTURY DATA SERVICES, INC.—Century Business Credit Corporation; *U.S. Private*, pg. 226
CENTURY 21 REAL ESTATE CORP.—Cendant Corporation; *U.S. Public*, pg. 321
CHEMED CORPORATION; *U.S. Public*, pg. 343
CHEROKEE INC.; *U.S. Public*, pg. 345
CLUPAK, INC.—Westvaco Corporation; *U.S. Public*, pg. 1762
COLORTYME, INC.; *U.S. Private*, pg. 255
COMPREHENSIVE BUSINESS SERVICES INC.—Franchise Services, Inc.; *U.S. Private*, pg. 423
THE JEAN COUTU GROUP (PJC) INC.; *Int'l*, pg. 340
CUTCO INDUSTRIES, INC.; *U.S. Public*, pg. 470
DBT ONLINE, INC.; *U.S. Public*, pg. 472
DAIRY QUEEN CORPORATE STORE—Berkshire Hathaway Inc.; *U.S. Public*, pg. 220
DOLLAR RENT A CAR—Chrysler Corporation; *U.S. Public*, pg. 354
DOMINO'S PIZZA INTERNATIONAL, INC.—Domino's Pizza Inc.; *U.S. Private*, pg. 339
DUNHILL PERSONNEL SYSTEM, INC.—Watsco, Inc.; *U.S. Public*, pg. 1746
THE DWYER GROUP, INC.; *U.S. Public*, pg. 537
ESKIMO PIE CORPORATION; *U.S. Public*, pg. 592
GENERAL NUTRITION FRANCHISING, INC.—General Nutrition, Inc.; *U.S. Public*, pg. 725
GILES & RANSOME, INC.; *U.S. Private*, pg. 453
GOLDEN CORRAL CORPORATION—Investors Management Corp.; *U.S. Private*, pg. 575
GREAT CLIPS, INC.; *U.S. Private*, pg. 473
GROW BIZ INTERNATIONAL, INC.; *U.S. Public*, pg. 767
THE HAAGEN-DAZS COMPANY INC.—Diageo Plc; *Int'l*, pg. 411
HARCOURT-BRACE—Harcourt General, Inc.; *U.S. Public*, pg. 783
HARCOURT BRACE & COMPANY - ELEMENTARY DIV.—Harcourt General, Inc.; *U.S. Public*, pg. 783
HARCOURT BRACE & COMPANY INTL. CORP.—Harcourt General, Inc.; *U.S. Public*, pg. 783
HICKORY FARMS, INC.; *U.S. Private*, pg. 525
HILTON HOTELS CORPORATION; *U.S. Public*, pg. 828
HILTON INNS, INC.—Hilton Hotels Corporation; *U.S. Public*, pg. 829
J.G. HOOK, INC.; *U.S. Private*, pg. 538
IHOP CORP.; *U.S. Public*, pg. 862
INSITUFORM TECHNOLOGIES, INC.; *U.S. Public*, pg. 881
INTERNATIONAL DAIRY QUEEN, INC.—Berkshire Hathaway Inc.; *U.S. Public*, pg. 220
INTERNATIONAL HOUSE OF PANCAKES, INC.—IHOP Corp.; *U.S. Public*, pg. 862
JACMAR COMPANIES, INC.; *U.S. Private*, pg. 580
JUICE WORKS DEVELOPMENT, INC.—TCBY Enterprises Inc.; *U.S. Public*, pg. 1554
KOA HOLDINGS; *U.S. Private*, pg. 603
KV PHARMACEUTICAL COMPANY; *U.S. Public*, pg. 941
KARMELKORN SHOPPES—Berkshire Hathaway Inc.; *U.S. Public*, pg. 220
LA ROSA'S, INC.; *U.S. Private*, pg. 640
LEE MYLES ASSOCIATES CORPORATION; *U.S. Private*, pg. 657
LIFESTYLE BRANDS, LTD.—Playboy Enterprises, Inc.; *U.S. Public*, pg. 1310
LONG JOHN SILVER'S, INC.; *U.S. Private*, pg. 674
MARKGRAAF—Vendex International N.V.; *Int'l*, pg. 1463
MASTER INTERNATIONAL CORP.; *U.S. Private*, pg. 713
MEDICINE SHOPPE INTERNATIONAL, INC.—Cardinal Health Inc.; *U.S. Public*, pg. 304
MERCHANDISING CORP. OF AMERICA, INC.—The Seagram Company Ltd.; *Int'l*, pg. 1216
MICROAGE, INC.; *U.S. Public*, pg. 1104
MORAN INDUSTRIES, INC.; *U.S. Private*, pg. 760
NATIONAL AMUSEMENTS, INC.; *U.S. Private*, pg. 775
NESTLE DAIRY SYSTEMS, LICENSING DIVISION—Nestle S.A.; *Int'l*, pg. 918
OEL, LTD.—Elcor Corporation; *U.S. Public*, pg. 568
OCEAN CHEVROLET, INC.; *U.S. Private*, pg. 810
THE OHIO MATTRESS COMPANY LICENSING & COMPONENTS GROUP—Sealy Corporation; *U.S. Private*, pg. 979
PAYLESS CAR RENTAL SYSTEM, INC.; *U.S. Private*, pg. 844
PHYSICIANS WEIGHT LOSS CENTERS, INC.; *U.S. Private*, pg. 864
PLAYBOY CLUBS INTERNATIONAL, INC.—Playboy Enterprises, Inc.; *U.S. Public*, pg. 1310
PLAYBOY ENTERPRISES, INC.; *U.S. Public*, pg. 1309
PLAYBOY FRANCHISINGS INC.—Playboy Enterprises, Inc.; *U.S. Public*, pg. 1310
PLAYBOY PRODUCTS & SERVICES INTERNATIONAL, B.V.—Playboy Enterprises, Inc.; *U.S. Public*, pg. 1310
POLO/RALPH LAUREN CORPORATION; *U.S. Private*, pg. 874
PONDEROSA STEAKHOUSE—Metromedia Company; *U.S. Private*, pg. 736
PONY INTERNATIONAL INC.—Pentland Group PLC; *Int'l*, pg. 1036
PRECISION TUNE AUTOCARE INC.; *U.S. Public*, pg. 1321
PRESIDENT BAKING COMPANY—President Enterprises Corp.; *Int'l*, pg. 1069
PRONTO, INC.—The Chase Manhattan Corporation; *U.S. Public*, pg. 338
THE PSYCHOLOGICAL CORP.—Harcourt General, Inc.; *U.S. Public*, pg. 784
REALLY USEFUL HOLDINGS LIMITED; *Int'l*, pg. 1089
RENT-A-CENTER, INC.—Thorn plc; *Int'l*, pg. 1385
RESTAURANT DEVELOPERS CORP.; *U.S. Private*, pg. 925
ROTO-ROOTER—Chemed Corporation; *U.S. Public*, pg. 344
M. RUBIN & SONS INC.; *U.S. Private*, pg. 949
SANDOZ TECHNOLOGY LTD.—Novartis AG; *Int'l*, pg. 972
W.B. SAUNDERS COMPANY—Harcourt General, Inc.; *U.S. Public*, pg. 784
SIZZLER USA, INC.—Sizzler International, Inc.; *U.S. Public*, pg. 1475
SONIC CORPORATION; *U.S. Public*, pg. 1485
SONIC RESTAURANTS, INC.—Sonic Corporation; *U.S. Public*, pg. 1485
SOUTHWESTERN BELL MEDIA VENTURES—SBC Communications Inc.; *U.S. Public*, pg. 1415
STRAW HAT COOPERATIVE CORP.; *U.S. Private*, pg. 1046
SUBWAY FRANCHISE ADVERTISING FUND TRUST; *U.S. Private*, pg. 1048
TCBY ENTERPRISES INC.; *U.S. Public*, pg. 1553
TCBY SYSTEMS, INC.—TCBY Enterprises Inc.; *U.S. Public*, pg. 1554
TEXACO DEVELOPMENT CORP.—Texaco Inc.; *U.S. Public*, pg. 1583
THE TOPPS COMPANY, INC.; *U.S. Public*, pg. 1621
TOPSY'S INTERNATIONAL INC.; *U.S. Private*, pg. 1092
TRIARC COMPANIES, INC.; *U.S. Public*, pg. 1634
TRIARC RESTAURANT GROUP—Triarc Companies, Inc.; *U.S. Public*, pg. 1635
UNI-MARTS, INC.; *U.S. Public*, pg. 1664
UNITED BISCUITS (HOLDINGS) PLC; *Int'l*, pg. 1442
UNIVERSAL STUDIOS MUSIC AUSTRALIA—The Seagram Company Ltd.; *Int'l*, pg. 1216
VANSTAR CORPORATION; *U.S. Public*, pg. 1708
VERTEL; *U.S. Public*, pg. 1717
VIACOM INTERNATIONAL INC.—National Amusements, Inc.; *U.S. Private*, pg. 778
VICORP RESTAURANTS, INC.; *U.S. Public*, pg. 1719
WENDY'S INTERNATIONAL INC.; *U.S. Public*, pg. 1754
WHITBREAD PUB PARTNERSHIPS—Whitbread PLC; *Int'l*, pg. 1498
WHITBREAD RESTAURANTS & LEISURE—Whitbread PLC; *Int'l*, pg. 1498
WICKS 'N STICKS, LTD; *U.S. Private*, pg. 1175
ZIEBART INTERNATIONAL CORPORATION; *U.S. Private*, pg. 1205

6798 — REAL ESTATE INVESTMENT TRUSTS

ANF PARTNERS 361
AXA-UAP; *Int'l*, pg. 18
AETNA INTERNATIONAL CHILE S.A.—Aetna Inc.; *U.S. Public*, pg. 27
ALLIANCE MANAGEMENT, INC.; *U.S. Private*, pg. 38
ALLIED CAPITAL COMMERCIAL CORPORATION—Allied Capital Corporation; *U.S. Public*, pg. 47
ANGELES HOUSING CONCEPTS; *U.S. Private*, pg. 74
BHF IMMOBILIEN-GMBH—BHF-BANK AG; *Int'l*, pg. 119
BIP SUB1, INC.—Nationwide Health Properties Inc.; *U.S. Public*, pg. 1166
BENJAMIN CENTER ASSOCIATES—Cigna Corp.; *U.S. Public*, pg. 361
BERDEL, INC.—Pennsylvania Real Estate Investment Trust; *U.S. Public*, pg. 1272
BERFLA, INC.—Pennsylvania Real Estate Investment Trust; *U.S. Public*, pg. 1272
BERKSHIRE REALTY COMPANY, INC.; *U.S. Public*, pg. 221
BRADLEY REAL ESTATE, INC.; *U.S. Public*, pg. 250
CB PARTNERS—Cigna Corp.; *U.S. Public*, pg. 357
CRI LIQUIDATING REIT, INC.—CRIIMI MAE; *U.S. Public*, pg. 459
CV REIT, INC.; *U.S. Public*, pg. 286
CALISAR ASSOCIATES—Cigna Corp.; *U.S. Public*, pg. 361
CAMDEN PROPERTY TRUST; *U.S. Public*, pg. 298
CAPSTEAD MORTGAGE CORPORATION; *U.S. Public*, pg. 303
CENTRUM SOUTH PARTNERS—Cigna Corp.; *U.S. Public*, pg. 361
CHANTILLY PARTNERS—Cigna Corp.; *U.S. Public*, pg. 361
CHAPPARAL PARTNERS—Cigna Corp.; *U.S. Public*, pg. 365
CHARTER OAK VENTURES—Cigna Corp.; *U.S. Public*, pg. 361
CIGNA CORP.; *U.S. Public*, pg. 356
CLAYTON, WILLIAMS & SHERWOOD, INC.; *U.S. Private*, pg. 245
CLOVER FINANCIAL CORPORATION; *U.S. Private*, pg. 247
COLUMBUS SQUARE SHOPPING CENTER COMPANY—Cigna Corp.; *U.S. Public*, pg. 361
CONNECTICUT GENERAL REALTY RESOURCES, INC. - FOURTH—Cigna Corp.; *U.S. Public*, pg. 359
CONNECTICUT GENERAL REALTY RESOURCES, INC. - SECOND—Cigna Corp.; *U.S. Public*, pg. 359
CONNECTICUT GENERAL REALTY RESOURCES, INC. - THIRD—Cigna Corp.; *U.S. Public*, pg. 359
BENJAMIN COOKE ASSOCIATES—Cigna Corp.; *U.S. Public*, pg. 361
CORNERSTONE REAL ESTATE—Massachusetts Mutual Life Insurance Co.; *U.S. Private*, pg. 712
COUSINS PROPERTIES INCORPORATED; *U.S. Public*, pg. 453
CRIIMI MAE; *U.S. Public*, pg. 459
THE CROSSINGS ASSOCIATES—Cigna Corp.; *U.S. Public*, pg. 361
CROW WOOD GLEN ASSOCIATES—Cigna Corp.; *U.S. Public*, pg. 361
THE DAIWA BUILDING CO., LTD.—Daiwa Securities Co. Ltd.; *Int'l*, pg. 374
THE DEARBORN GROUP; *U.S. Private*, pg. 319
DEVELOPERS INVESTORS, INC.—W.C. Bradley Co.; *U.S. Private*, pg. 164

DUTTON PARTNERS—Cigna Corp.; U.S. Public, pg. 361
EAGLE PROPERTIES, INC.—The Western and Southern Life Insurance Company; U.S. Private, pg. 1164
ELLIOT GROVE ASSOCIATES—Cigna Corp.; U.S. Public, pg. 361
ENTERPRISE GROUP DEVELOPMENT CORPORATION—Public Service Enterprise Group Incorporated; U.S. Public, pg. 1340
EQUITY RESIDENTIAL PROPERTIES TRUST; U.S. Public, pg. 590
EXECUTIVE CAPITAL CORP.; U.S. Private, pg. 388
FALKLAND PARTNERS—Cigna Corp.; U.S. Public, pg. 361
FEDERAL REALTY INVESTMENT TRUST; U.S. Public, pg. 616
FIRST UNION REAL ESTATE INVESTMENTS; U.S. Public, pg. 640
FORBES, INC.; U.S. Private, pg. 417
FOREST PLACE ASSOCIATES—Cigna Corp.; U.S. Public, pg. 361
FUNDIMO—Caixa Geral de Depositos; Int'l, pg. 250
GMP REAL ESTATE CORP.—Green Mountain Power Corporation; U.S. Public, pg. 761
GLENBOROUGH REALTY TRUST INCORPORATED; U.S. Public, pg. 747
GLENDALE ASSOCIATES—Cigna Corp.; U.S. Public, pg. 361
GLENDALE LIMITED PARTNERSHIP ASSOCIATES - II—Cigna Corp.; U.S. Public, pg. 361
THE GREAT ATLANTIC MANAGEMENT COMPANY; U.S. Private, pg. 473
GREYLAND BUSINESS PARK, PHASE I—Cigna Corp.; U.S. Public, pg. 361
GREYLANDS BUSINESS PARK, PHASE 2—Cigna Corp.; U.S. Public, pg. 361
GWYNEDD PARTNERS—Cigna Corp.; U.S. Public, pg. 361
HAMPTON LAKES ASSOCIATES—Cigna Corp.; U.S. Public, pg. 361
HAMPTON TRUST PLC; Int'l, pg. 591
HEALTH AND RETIREMENT PROPERTIES TRUST; U.S. Public, pg. 801
HEALTH CARE PROPERTY INVESTORS, INC.; U.S. Public, pg. 801
THE HEARST CORPORATION; U.S. Private, pg. 515
HORIZON PLACE ASSOCIATES—Cigna Corp.; U.S. Public, pg. 361
IRT MANAGEMENT COMPANY—IRT Property Company; U.S. Public, pg. 858
IRT PROPERTY COMPANY; U.S. Public, pg. 858
INDIANA FINANCIAL INVESTORS, INC.—R D I S Corporation; U.S. Private, pg. 903
JMB REALTY CORPORATION; U.S. Private, pg. 577
JAMES BUILDING CORPORATION; U.S. Private, pg. 580
THE KAEMPFER COMPANY, INVESTMENT BUILDERS; U.S. Private, pg. 604
THE KEYES COMPANY REALTORS; U.S. Private, pg. 618
KOLL CENTER IRVINE NO. 2 PARTNERSHIP—Cigna Corp.; U.S. Public, pg. 361
LP ASSOCIATES—Cigna Corp.; U.S. Public, pg. 365
LARMES, INC.—Pennsylvania Real Estate Investment Trust; U.S. Public, pg. 1272
MALL OF NEW HAMPSHIRE—Cigna Corp.; U.S. Public, pg. 361
MANAGED PROPERTIES, INC.—St. Paul Bancorp, Inc.; U.S. Public, pg. 1428
MANCHESTER MALL JOINT VENTURE—Cigna Corp.; U.S. Public, pg. 361
MCCALL PROPERTIES, INC.—McCall Oil & Chemical Corp.; U.S. Private, pg. 719
MCCANDLESS SAN TOMAS NO. 2—Cigna Corp.; U.S. Public, pg. 361
MCCANDLESS TOWERS, PHASE II—Cigna Corp.; U.S. Public, pg. 365
MEDITRUST CORPORATION; U.S. Public, pg. 1081
MERRILL LYNCH TRUST COMPANY (NEW JERSEY)—Merrill Lynch & Co., Inc.; U.S. Public, pg. 1098
MERRY LAND & INVESTMENT COMPANY, INC.; U.S. Public, pg. 1098
MESIROW FINANCIAL; U.S. Private, pg. 733
MIAMI VALLEY LEASING, INC.—DPL Inc.; U.S. Public, pg. 474
MISSION VIEJO ASSOCIATES—Cigna Corp.; U.S. Public, pg. 361
MORGAN STANLEY REALTY, INC.—Morgan Stanley Dean Witter & Co.; U.S. Public, pg. 1132
NWL 806 MAIN, INC.—National Western Life Insurance Company; U.S. Public, pg. 1161
NWL INVESTMENTS, INC.—National Western Life Insurance Company; U.S. Public, pg. 1161
NATIONAL INCOME REALTY TRUST; U.S. Public, pg. 1157
NATIONWIDE HEALTH PROPERTIES FINANCE CORP.—Nationwide Health Properties Inc.; U.S. Public, pg. 1166
NATIONWIDE HEALTH PROPERTIES INC.; U.S. Public, pg. 1166
NEW ORLEANS RIVERWALK ASSOCIATES—Cigna Corp.; U.S. Public, pg. 361
NEW PLAN REALTY TRUST; U.S. Public, pg. 1172
NYLIFE DEPOSITARY CORPORATION—New York Life Insurance Company; U.S. Private, pg. 795
NOMURA SECURITIES INTERNATIONAL, INC.—The Nomura Securities Co., Ltd.; Int'l, pg. 956
OAKS AT BAYMEADOW ASSOCIATES—Cigna Corp.; U.S. Public, pg. 361
OAKS AT REGENCY ASSOCIATES—Cigna Corp.; U.S. Public, pg. 361
ORCHARD GLEN VENTURE—Cigna Corp.; U.S. Public, pg. 361
PALMER PLAZA, LIMITED—Cigna Corp.; U.S. Public, pg. 361
PARAMUS PARK SHOPPING CENTER LIMITED PARTNERSHIP—Cigna Corp.; U.S. Public, pg. 365
PARCWOOD-SACRAMENTO JOINT VENTURE—Cigna Corp.; U.S. Public, pg. 362
PATRIOT AMERICAN HOSPITALITY, INC.; U.S. Public, pg. 1265
PATRIOT AMERICAN HOSPITALITY OPERATING COMPANY—Patriot American Hospitality, Inc.; U.S. Public, pg. 1265
THE PAVILION VENTURE—Cigna Corp.; U.S. Public, pg. 365
PEACHTREE WYNFREY ASSOCIATES—Cigna Corp.; U.S. Public, pg. 362
PENNSYLVANIA REAL ESTATE INVESTMENT TRUST; U.S. Public, pg. 1272
PILKINGTON PROPERTIES LIMITED—Pilkington Plc; Int'l, pg. 1056
PRESIDENTIAL REALTY CORPORATION; U.S. Public, pg. 1323
PRIME GROUP REALTY TRUST; U.S. Public, pg. 1326
PROGRESS WEST CORPORATION; U.S. Private, pg. 890
RA, INC.—Pennsylvania Real Estate Investment Trust; U.S. Public, pg. 1272
RBC REALTY INC.—Daniel Industries, Inc.; U.S. Public, pg. 483
REINALT-THOMAS CORP.; U.S. Private, pg. 919
RESOURCE AMERICA, INC.; U.S. Public, pg. 1382
RESOURCE MORTGAGE CAPITAL, INC.; U.S. Public, pg. 1382
ROSEN ASSOCIATES MANAGEMENT CORP.; U.S. Private, pg. 945
SADDLEBACK II ASSOCIATES—Cigna Corp.; U.S. Public, pg. 362
SAN RAMON PARTNERS—Cigna Corp.; U.S. Public, pg. 362
SAN TOMAS NO. 1 LIMITED PARTNERSHIP—Cigna Corp.; U.S. Public, pg. 362
SAN TOMAS NO. 2 LIMITED PARTNERSHIP—Cigna Corp.; U.S. Public, pg. 362
THE SANTA ANITA COMPANIES—Meditrust Corporation; U.S. Public, pg. 1081
SANTA ANITA ENTERPRISES, INC.—Meditrust Corporation; U.S. Public, pg. 1081
THE SCOTTSDALE EXECUTIVE CENTRE CORPORATION—Cigna Corp.; U.S. Public, pg. 365
SECON PROPERTIES—Cigna Corp.; U.S. Public, pg. 362
SHERWAY CENTER LIMITED—The Canada Life Assurance Company; Int'l, pg. 255
THE SHIDLER GROUP; U.S. Private, pg. 994
6100 FAIRVIEW ASSOCIATES—Cigna Corp.; U.S. Public, pg. 362
STARWOOD CAPITAL GROUP LLC; U.S. Private, pg. 1036
STEARNS COMPANY LIMITED—Stearns Enterprises, Inc.; U.S. Private, pg. 1037
STEARNS ENTERPRISES, INC.; U.S. Private, pg. 1037
STEARNS PHOENIX BROADWAY—Stearns Enterprises, Inc.; U.S. Private, pg. 1037
SUN HUNG KAI PROPERTIES LTD.; Int'l, pg. 1318
TARRAGON REALTY INVESTORS; U.S. Public, pg. 1561
TOKIO MARINE PROPERTY LIMITED—The Tokio Marine & Fire Insurance Company, Ltd.; Int'l, pg. 1393
TOKIO MARINE REALTY CO., LTD.—The Tokio Marine & Fire Insurance Company, Ltd.; Int'l, pg. 1392
TOWN BROOKE ASSOCIATES—Cigna Corp.; U.S. Public, pg. 365
TOWN COLONY ASSOCIATES—Cigna Corp.; U.S. Public, pg. 362
TOWN COLONY II ASSOCIATES—Cigna Corp.; U.S. Public, pg. 362
TRAMMELL CROW COMPANY; U.S. Public, pg. 1628
TRANSCONTINENTAL REALTY INVESTORS, INC.; U.S. Public, pg. 1630
TYLER MALL ASSOCIATES—Cigna Corp.; U.S. Public, pg. 362
TYSON'S CORNER HOTEL ASSOCIATES—Cigna Corp.; U.S. Public, pg. 362
UNITED DOMINION REALTY TRUST, INC.; U.S. Public, pg. 1677
UNIVESCO INC.; U.S. Private, pg. 1128
VW MALL, INC.—IRT Property Company; U.S. Public, pg. 858
VENGROFF WILLIAMS REALTY MANAGEMENT—Vengroff Williams & Associates, Inc.; U.S. Private, pg. 1135
VORNADO REALTY TRUST; U.S. Public, pg. 1725
WARNER NEWHOPE ASSOCIATES—Cigna Corp.; U.S. Public, pg. 362
WASHINGTON REAL ESTATE INVESTMENT TRUST; U.S. Public, pg. 1743
WEINGARTEN REALTY INVESTORS; U.S. Public, pg. 1751
WESTCORP; U.S. Public, pg. 1756
WESTERN RECONVEYANCE COMPANY, INC.—Westcorp; U.S. Public, pg. 1757
WINDGATE PARTNERS—Cigna Corp.; U.S. Public, pg. 362
WOOD FOREST ASSOCIATES—Cigna Corp.; U.S. Public, pg. 362
WOOD HILLS ASSOCIATES—Cigna Corp.; U.S. Public, pg. 362
WORCESTER CENTER—Cigna Corp.; U.S. Public, pg. 362

6799 — INVESTORS, NEC

AB-SMALL BUSINESS INVESTMENT COMPANY, INC.—Bozzuto's Inc.; U.S. Public, pg. 249
ABM INVESTMENT LTD.—Viag AG; Int'l, pg. 1465
AARON INVESTMENT COMPANY—Aaron Rents, Inc.; U.S. Public, pg. 12
ADVENT INTERNATIONAL; U.S. Private, pg. 22
ADVISERS CAPITAL MANAGEMENT INC.; U.S. Private, pg. 23
ALCOA PROPERTIES, INC.—Aluminum Company of America; U.S. Public, pg. 61
ALLIED CAPITAL CORPORATION; U.S. Public, pg. 47
AMERICAN NATIONAL GROWTH FUND, INC.—American National Insurance Company; U.S. Public, pg. 87
AMERICAN NATIONAL INCOME FUND, INC.—American National Insurance Company; U.S. Public, pg. 87
AMERICAN NATIONAL INVESTMENT ACCOUNTS—American National Insurance Company; U.S. Public, pg. 87
AMERICAN NATIONAL TRIFLEX FUND, INC.—American National Insurance Company; U.S. Public, pg. 87
AMERISTAR CAPITAL MARKETS, INC.—First American Corporation; U.S. Public, pg. 624
AMERITECH DEVELOPMENT CORPORATION—Ameritech Corporation; U.S. Public, pg. 98
AMFAC PROPERTY INVESTMENT CORP.—JMB Realty Corporation; U.S. Private, pg. 577
ANDERSEN GROUP, INC.; U.S. Public, pg. 111
ANDERSON INDUSTRIES, INC.—Excel Industries, Inc.; U.S. Public, pg. 599
ANHEUSER-BUSCH INVESTMENT CAPITAL CORPORATION—Anheuser-Busch Companies, Inc.; U.S. Public, pg. 114
ATHENA VENTURE PARTNERS L.P.—IDB Holding Corporation; Int'l, pg. 644
ATLANTIC INVESTMENT COMPANY—Norfolk Southern Corporation; U.S. Public, pg. 1190
AZTEC TRADING COMPANY, S.A.—Georgia-Pacific Corporation; U.S. Public, pg. 739
BA VENTURES, INC.—BankAmerica Corporation; U.S. Public, pg. 180
BIL PARTICIPATION S.A.—Banque Internationale a Luxembourg S.A.; Int'l, pg. 162
BT INTERNATIONAL TRADING CORP.—Bankers Trust New York Corporation; U.S. Public, pg. 185
BANCBOSTON VENTURES INC.—BankBoston Corporation; U.S. Public, pg. 184
BANK OF AMERICA—BankAmerica Corporation; U.S. Public, pg. 180
BANK OF AMERICA CAPITAL—BankAmerica Corporation; U.S. Public, pg. 180
BANK ONE VENTURE CORPORATION—Banc One Corporation; U.S. Public, pg. 174
BANKAMERICA CAPITAL INVESTMENTS, INC.—BankAmerica Corporation; U.S. Public, pg. 181
BELL ATLANTIC INVESTMENT DEVELOPMENT CORPORATION—Bell Atlantic Corporation; U.S. Public, pg. 202
BERGSTROM CAPITAL CORPORATION; U.S. Public, pg. 215
BIRMINGHAM VENTURES INC.—Birmingham Steel Corporation; U.S. Public, pg. 232
BOHLER—Voest-Alpine Stahl AG; Int'l, pg. 1471
BROWN & SHARPE INTL. CAPITAL CORP.—Brown & Sharpe Manufacturing Company; U.S. Public, pg. 260
CEP GROUP, INC.—PP&L Resources; U.S. Public, pg. 1244
CERUS - COMPAGNIES EUROPEENNES REUNIES; Int'l, pg. 240
CGAS, INC.—Enron Corp.; U.S. Public, pg. 585
CIBC VENTURES, INC.—Canadian Imperial Bank of Commerce; Int'l, pg. 256
CSW CREDIT, INC.—Central and South West Corporation; U.S. Public, pg. 324
CSW ENERGY, INC.—Central and South West Corporation; U.S. Public, pg. 324
CSW FINANCIAL INC.—Central and South West Corporation; U.S. Public, pg. 324
CSW LEASING, INC.—Central and South West Corporation; U.S. Public, pg. 324
CU CAPITALCORP—Citizens Utilities Company; U.S. Public, pg. 380
CAPITAL FOR BUSINESS, INC.—Commerce Bancshares, Inc.; U.S. Public, pg. 410
CAPITAL RESOURCES, INC.—Alex Lee, Inc.; U.S. Private, pg. 657
CAREAL HOLDING AG; Int'l, pg. 271
CARIBBEAN FOREIGN TRADE CORPORATION—Ceteco N.V.; Int'l, pg. 279
CARLSON ACQUISITION GROUP—Carlson Companies, Inc.; U.S. Private, pg. 212
THE CARLYLE GROUP—Carlyle Holding Corporation; U.S. Private, pg. 213
CARLYLE HOLDING CORPORATION; U.S. Private, pg. 213
CASA MADRID DEVELOPPEMENT—Caja de Madrid Group; Int'l, pg. 252
CAVEXSA—Magellan International Trading; U.S. Private, pg. 694
CHARTER OAK ENERGY, INC.—Northeast Utilities; U.S. Public, pg. 1194
CHASE EQUITY INCORPORATED—The Chase Manhattan Corporation; U.S. Public, pg. 338
CHATHAM VENTURES, INC.—The Chase Manhattan Corporation; U.S. Public, pg. 338
CHORI CO., LTD.; Int'l, pg. 268
CHRISTIANA COMPANIES, INC.; U.S. Public, pg. 352
CIGNA ENERGY RESOURCES, INC.—Cigna Corp.; U.S. Public, pg. 358
CIGNA INTERNATIONAL SPECIAL INVESTMENTS INC.—Cigna Corp.; U.S. Public, pg. 357
CIGNA INVESTMENTS & PLACEMENTS COMPANY—Cigna Corp.; U.S. Public, pg. 357
CIGNA MEZZANINE CAPITAL, INC.—Cigna Corp.; U.S. Public, pg. 357
CIGNA MEZZANINE HOLDINGS, INC.—Cigna Corp.; U.S. Public, pg. 357
CIGNA MEZZANINE PARTNERS III, INC.—Cigna Corp.; U.S. Public, pg. 357
CIGNA MEZZANINE PARTNERS II, L.P.—Cigna Corp.; U.S. Public, pg. 357
CIGNA MORTGAGE SECURITIES, INC.—Cigna Corp.; U.S. Public, pg. 361
CIGNA SICAV I—Cigna Corp.; U.S. Public, pg. 364
CIPSCO INVESTMENT COMPANY—Ameren Corporation; U.S. Public, pg. 66
CITICORP CAPITAL INVESTORS LTD.—Citicorp; U.S. Public, pg. 378

CITICORP VENTURE CAPITAL LTD.—Citicorp; U.S. Public, pg. 379
COMAIR INVESTMENT COMPANY—Comair Holdings, Inc.; U.S. Public, pg. 406
COMERICA INCORPORATED; U.S. Public, pg. 408
COMMERCE BROKERAGE SERVICES, INC.—Commerce Bancshares, Inc.; U.S. Public, pg. 410
COMMUNITY FINANCE CORPORATION—St. Paul Bancorp, Inc.; U.S. Public, pg. 1428
COMPAGNIE AUXILIARE DE TELECOMMUNICATIONS—France Telecom; Int'l, pg. 503
COMPAGNIE FRANCAISE D'INVESTISSEMENT—Compagnie des Machines Bull; Int'l, pg. 316
CONAGRA TRADING COMPANIES (CTC)—ConAgra, Inc.; U.S. Public, pg. 428
CONGEN PROPERTIES, INC.—Cigna Corp.; U.S. Public, pg. 365
CONNECTICUT GENERAL REALTY RESOURCES, INC.—Cigna Corp.; U.S. Public, pg. 359
CONSECO CAPITAL MANAGEMENT, INC.—Conseco Inc.; U.S. Public, pg. 433
CONSTELLATION INVESTMENTS, INC.—Baltimore Gas and Electric Company; U.S. Public, pg. 172
CONSTELLATION POWER, INC.—Baltimore Gas and Electric Company; U.S. Public, pg. 172
CONSTELLATION REAL ESTATE GROUP INC.—Baltimore Gas and Electric Company; U.S. Public, pg. 172
CONTINENTAL ILLINOIS VENTURE CORP.—BankAmerica Corporation; U.S. Public, pg. 181
COUNTRYWIDE ASSET MANAGEMENT CORPORATION—Countrywide Home Loans Inc.; U.S. Public, pg. 452
CREDIT NATIONALE; Int'l, pg. 344
CUMBERLAND SECURITIES CORP.—Central Maine Power Company; U.S. Public, pg. 325
CURACAO TRADING COMPANY (DOMINICANA) C. POR A.—Ceteco N.V.; Int'l, pg. 280
D & B ENTERPRISES INC—The Dun & Bradstreet Corporation; U.S. Public, pg. 535
DB CAPITAL MARKETS (ASIA) LTD. (TOKYO)—Deutsche Bank AG; Int'l, pg. 404
DAHLBUSCH AG—Pilkington Plc; Int'l, pg. 1056
DALGETY PLC; Int'l, pg. 376
DEARBORN CAPITAL CORPORATION—Ford Motor Company; U.S. Public, pg. 663
THE DEARBORN GROUP; U.S. Private, pg. 319
DELMARVA CAPITAL INVESTMENTS, INC.—Conectiv; U.S. Public, pg. 431
DELTAIR U.K. INVESTMENTS LTD.—Delta Air Lines, Inc.; U.S. Public, pg. 497
DESCO DE SCHULTHESS LTD.; Int'l, pg. 396
DISCOUNT INVESTMENT CORPORATION LTD.—IDB Holding Corporation; Int'l, pg. 644
E & A INVESTORS, L.P.—E & A Industries, Inc.; U.S. Private, pg. 352
EUA ENERGY INVESTMENT CORPORATION—Eastern Utilities Associates; U.S. Public, pg. 549
EDISON CAPITAL—Edison International; U.S. Public, pg. 564
EL DORADO INVESTMENT COMPANY—Pinnacle West Capital Corporation; U.S. Public, pg. 1298
ELECTROLUX JORDAN TRADING COMPANY LTD.—Electrolux, AB; Int'l, pg. 443
ELRON TECHNOLOGIES INC.—IDB Holding Corporation; Int'l, pg. 644
EMBASSY PACIFIC EQUITY CORPORATION—Promus Hotel Corporation; U.S. Public, pg. 1335
ENVIRONMENTAL FINANCIAL SERVICES CORP.—OHM Corporation; U.S. Public, pg. 1208
FINANCIAL LIFE COMPANIES, INC.; U.S. Private, pg. 404
FIOTEC, INC.—Itochu Corporation; Int'l, pg. 694
FIRST CAPITAL CORP. OF CHICAGO—First Chicago NBD Corporation; U.S. Public, pg. 628
FIRST CHICAGO TRADING CO.—First Chicago NBD Corporation; U.S. Public, pg. 628
FIRST NATIONAL CINCINNATI CORPORATION—Starbanc Corporation; U.S. Public, pg. 1510
FLORIDA PROGRESS CORPORATION; U.S. Public, pg. 655
FORD BANK AKTIENGESELLSCHAFT (AUSTRIA)—Ford Motor Company; U.S. Public, pg. 665
FORD CREDIT OVERSEAS FINANCE N.V.—Ford Motor Company; U.S. Public, pg. 665
FORECAST GROUP; U.S. Private, pg. 418
FOREST CITY ENTERPRISES, INC.; U.S. Public, pg. 667
ABDULLA FOUAD CO. LTD.; Int'l, pg. 501
I.H. FRENCH & CO. INC.; U.S. Private, pg. 427
FURMANITE WORLDWIDE, INC.—Kaneb Services, Inc.; U.S. Public, pg. 942
GIB COORDINATION CENTER—GIB Group; Int'l, pg. 533
GENERAL AMERICAN INVESTORS COMPANY, INC.; U.S. Public, pg. 706
GLEACHER MORGAN GRENFELL INC.—Deutsche Bank AG; Int'l, pg. 405
GREAT UNIVERSAL CAPITAL CORP.—Lee National Corporation; U.S. Private, pg. 658
GREATER WASHINGTON INVESTMENTS, INC.—Johnston Industries, Inc.; U.S. Public, pg. 933
GRIFFIN FINANCIAL SERVICES—H.F. Ahmanson & Co.; U.S. Public, pg. 29
HBS MARKETING (ASIA) LIMITED—GP Batteries International Ltd.; Int'l, pg. 537
HBS MARKETING (ASIA) LIMITED TAIPEI BRANCH OFFICE—GP Batteries International Ltd.; Int'l, pg. 537
HARBERT CORPORATION; U.S. Private, pg. 500
HARRIS SCARFE HOLDINGS LIMITED; Int'l, pg. 597
HARRISCORP CAPITAL CORPORATION—Bank of Montreal; Int'l, pg. 155
HARROWSTON CORPORATION; Int'l, pg. 599
HEINRICH INDUSTRIE-UND HANDELS-AKTIENGESELLSCHAFT—Harpen AG; Int'l, pg. 597
HELABA INVEST KAPITALANLAGEGESELLSCHAFT MBH—Landesbank Hessen-Thuringen Girozentrale; Int'l, pg. 799
HERCULES CREDIT, INC.—Hercules Incorporated; U.S. Public, pg. 810
HERCULES INTERNATIONAL TRADE CORP., LTD. (HINTCO)—Hercules Incorporated; U.S. Public, pg. 811
HILL SAMUEL INC.—Lloyds TSB Group PLC; Int'l, pg. 813
HOLDERBANK FINANCIERE GLARIS LTD.; Int'l, pg. 628
HOMES OF MERIT INC.; U.S. Private, pg. 537
HYUNDAI MOTOR COMPANY; Int'l, pg. 641
ICC INDUSTRIES, INC.; U.S. Private, pg. 553
ICO, INC.—Cigna Corp.; U.S. Public, pg. 361
IFD PROPERTIES, INC.-FIRST—Cigna Corp.; U.S. Public, pg. 359
IMCO INVESTMENT COMPANY—IMCO Recycling Inc.; U.S. Public, pg. 871
IDACORP, INC.—Idaho Power Company; U.S. Public, pg. 862
IDEX INVESTOR SERVICES, INC.—AEGON N.V.; Int'l, pg. 27
IMPERIAL INTERNATIONAL BANK—Imperial Bancorp; U.S. Public, pg. 872
IMPERIAL REAL ESTATE VENTURES—Imperial Bancorp; U.S. Public, pg. 872
IMPERIAL VENTURES, INC.—Imperial Bancorp; U.S. Public, pg. 872
INCHCAPE PLC; Int'l, pg. 671
S.A. INDUSTRIAL CURACAO COSTA RICA—Ceteco N.V.; Int'l, pg. 280
INTELLIGENT SYSTEMS CORP.; U.S. Public, pg. 888
INTERNATIONAL THOROUGHBRED BREEDERS, INC.; U.S. Public, pg. 908
INVESTMENT FUND BREDA B.V.—Royal Begemann Group; Int'l, pg. 1133
INVESTMENT LEASING SERVICES, INC.—Telco Capital Corporation; U.S. Private, pg. 1073
ISOMEDIX INVESTMENTS, INC.—Steris Corporation; U.S. Public, pg. 1515
J & J SNACK FOODS INVESTMENT CORP.—J & J Snack Foods Corporation; U.S. Public, pg. 916
JACOBSON CREDIT CORPORATION—Jacobson Stores Inc.; U.S. Public, pg. 922
JOHNSON FRY HOLDINGS PLC; Int'l, pg. 713
JOHNSON FRY PLC—Johnson Fry Holdings PLC; Int'l, pg. 713
JOHNSON MATTHEY AB—Johnson Matthey Public Limited Company; Int'l, pg. 714
JOHNSON MATTHEY & CO. GMBH.—Johnson Matthey Public Limited Company; Int'l, pg. 714
JOHNSON MATTHEY SA—Johnson Matthey Public Limited Company; Int'l, pg. 714
JOHNSON VENTURE CAPITAL, INC.—S.C. Johnson & Son, Inc.; U.S. Private, pg. 592
THE JORDAN COMPANY; U.S. Private, pg. 597
KANEMATSU CORPORATION; Int'l, pg. 722
KAWASHO CORPORATION; Int'l, pg. 726
KEITHLEY INTERNATIONAL INVESTMENT CORP.—Keithley Instruments, Inc.; U.S. Public, pg. 947
KESKOMETALLI OY—Kesko Ltd.; Int'l, pg. 732
KIRKPATRICK PETTIS SMITH POLIAN, INC.—Mutual of Omaha Insurance Company; U.S. Private, pg. 770
KVAERNER VENTURE A.S—Kvaerner a.s.a.; Int'l, pg. 770
LG & E ENERGY SYSTEMS INC.—LG & E Energy Corp.; U.S. Public, pg. 970
LGS FINANCIAL SERVICES, INC.—Citizens Utilities Company; U.S. Public, pg. 380
LANGE INTERNATIONAL S.A.—Rossignol S.A.; Int'l, pg. 1127
LAURA ASHLEY INVESTMENTS BV—Laura Ashley Holdings Plc; Int'l, pg. 804
LAUREL COMMUNITY DEVELOPMENT CORPORATION—BT Financial Corporation; U.S. Public, pg. 164
LEGG MASON CAPITAL MANAGEMENT INC.—Legg Mason, Inc.; U.S. Public, pg. 985
LEHMAN BROTHERS HOLDINGS INC.; U.S. Public, pg. 987
LEHMAN BROTHERS, INC.—Lehman Brothers Holdings Inc.; U.S. Public, pg. 987
LIEBHERR-AUSTRALIA PTY. LTD.—Liebherr-International AG; Int'l, pg. 808
LIEBHERR-INTERTRADING AG—Liebherr-International AG; Int'l, pg. 808
LLOYDS DEVELOPMENT CAPITAL LTD.—Lloyds TSB Group PLC; Int'l, pg. 813
LONRHO PLC; Int'l, pg. 817
M & I CAPITAL MARKETS GROUP, INC.—Marshall & Ilsley Corporation; U.S. Public, pg. 1051
M&T CAPITAL CORPORATION—First Empire State Corporation; U.S. Public, pg. 631
M.I.M. TECHNOLOGY MARKETING LIMITED—M.I.M. Holdings Ltd.; Int'l, pg. 827
MWR TELECOM INC.—McLeodUSA Incorporated; U.S. Public, pg. 1073
MAGINVEST—GIB Group; Int'l, pg. 533
MALROSIAN, INC.—Cigna Corp.; U.S. Public, pg. 357
MARKETDYNE INTERNATIONAL, INC.—Cigna Corp.; U.S. Public, pg. 366
MARUBENI AUSTRALIA LTD.—Marubeni Corporation; Int'l, pg. 845
MARUBENI CANADA LTD.—Marubeni Corporation; Int'l, pg. 845
MARUBENI DEUTSCHLAND GMBH—Marubeni Corporation; Int'l, pg. 845
MARUBENI MEXICO S.A. DE C.V.—Marubeni Corporation; Int'l, pg. 845
MARUBENI NEW ZEALAND LTD.—Marubeni Corporation; Int'l, pg. 845
MARUBENI SCANDINAVIA AB—Marubeni Corporation; Int'l, pg. 845
MARUBENI U.K. PLC.—Marubeni Corporation; Int'l, pg. 845
MAISON MATHIEU, S.A.; Int'l, pg. 846
MECHANISCHE WEBEREI UND ZWIRNEREI ROSENHAMMER GMBH—The Procter & Gamble Company; U.S. Public, pg. 1333
MERRILL LYNCH SPECIALISTS INC.—Merrill Lynch & Co., Inc.; U.S. Public, pg. 1098
MESIROW FINANCIAL; U.S. Private, pg. 733
METROPOLITAN MORTGAGE & SECURITIES CO., INC.; U.S. Private, pg. 738
METROPOLITAN PROPERTIES SYSTEMS; U.S. Private, pg. 739
MITSUBISHI CORPORATION; Int'l, pg. 871
SAMUEL MONTAGU & CO. LIMITED—HSBC Holdings plc; Int'l, pg. 580
MORGAN STANLEY DEAN WITTER & CO.; U.S. Public, pg. 1132
MORGAN STANLEY GROUP INC.—Morgan Stanley Dean Witter & Co.; U.S. Public, pg. 1132
MOTOROLA INTERNATIONAL CAPITAL CORP.—Motorola, Inc.; U.S. Public, pg. 1138
NNG FINANCIAL CORPORATION—Northwest Natural Gas Company; U.S. Public, pg. 1200
NRG ENERGY MINING COMPANY—Telco Capital Corporation; U.S. Private, pg. 1073
NRG TECHNOLOGY, INC.—Telco Capital Corporation; U.S. Private, pg. 1073
NS INVEST, INC.—Nippon Steel Corporation; Int'l, pg. 940
NS INVEST II, INC.—Nippon Steel Corporation; Int'l, pg. 940
NARRAGANSETT CAPITAL INC.; U.S. Private, pg. 774
NATIONAL CITY VENTURE CORP.—National City Corporation; U.S. Public, pg. 1154
NATIONSBANK LEASE INVESTMENTS, INC.—NationsBank Corporation; U.S. Public, pg. 1165
NEW PIER OPERATING COMPANY, INC.—Griffin Group, Inc.; U.S. Private, pg. 480
NYLIFE EQUITY INC.—New York Life Insurance Company; U.S. Private, pg. 795
NYLIFE REALTY INC.—New York Life Insurance Company; U.S. Private, pg. 795
NICHIMEN CORPORATION; Int'l, pg. 927
NIPPON INVESTMENT & FINANCE CO. LTD.—Daiwa Securities Co. Ltd.; Int'l, pg. 375
NOMURA ASSET MANAGEMENT CO., LTD.—The Nomura Securities Co., Ltd.; Int'l, pg. 955
NOMURA CHINA INVESTMENT CO., LTD.—The Nomura Securities Co., Ltd.; Int'l, pg. 955
NOMURA INVESTMENT MANAGEMENT CO., LTD. (NIMCO)—The Nomura Securities Co., Ltd.; Int'l, pg. 955
NOMURA INVESTOR RELATIONS CO., LTD.—The Nomura Securities Co., Ltd.; Int'l, pg. 956
NOMURA WASSERSTEIN PERELLA CO., LTD.—The Nomura Securities Co., Ltd.; Int'l, pg. 956
NORDDEUTSCHE LANDESBANK (NORD/LB); Int'l, pg. 957
NORTH AMERICAN COMPANY; U.S. Private, pg. 803
NORWEST VENTURE CAPITAL MANAGEMENT, INC.—Norwest Corporation; U.S. Public, pg. 1202
NOZAL S.A.—Groupe Usinor; Int'l, pg. 570
O & R DEVELOPMENT, INC.—Orange and Rockland Utilities, Inc.; U.S. Public, pg. 1229
OES CAPITAL, INC.—FirstEnergy Corp.; U.S. Public, pg. 645
ONEOK INC.; U.S. Public, pg. 1226
ORIX INVESTMENT AND MANAGEMENT PRIVATE LIMITED—Orix Corporation; Int'l, pg. 1009
OXBOW CORPORATION; U.S. Private, pg. 825
PG ENERGY SERVICES—Pennsylvania Enterprises Inc.; U.S. Public, pg. 1272
PNC CAPITAL CORP.—PNC Bank Corp.; U.S. Public, pg. 1243
PNC ESOP FUNDING CORPORATION—PNC Bank Corp.; U.S. Public, pg. 1243
PNC VENTURE CORPORATION—PNC Bank Corp.; U.S. Public, pg. 1244
PSEG CAPITAL CORPORATION—Public Service Enterprise Group Incorporated; U.S. Public, pg. 1340
PACIFIC DIVERSIFIED CAPITAL COMPANY—Enova Corp; U.S. Public, pg. 584
PACIFIC LIFE INSURANCE COMPANY; U.S. Private, pg. 831
PACIFIC MINERALS, INC.—PacifiCorp; U.S. Public, pg. 1252
PAINEWEBBER GROUP INCORPORATED; U.S. Public, pg. 1252
PENNSYLVANIA COAL RESOURCES CORP.—PP&L Resources; U.S. Public, pg. 1244
PERNOVO—Perstorp AB; Int'l, pg. 1036
PHOENIX AMERICAN INCORPORATED; U.S. Private, pg. 862
PIONEER CAPITAL CORPORATION—The Pioneer Group, Inc.; U.S. Public, pg. 1298
PIONEER FUNDS MARKETING GMBH—The Pioneer Group, Inc.; U.S. Public, pg. 1298
THE PIONEER GROUP, INC.; U.S. Public, pg. 1298
PIONEER PLANS CORPORATION—The Pioneer Group, Inc.; U.S. Public, pg. 1298
PIONEER SBIC CORP.—The Pioneer Group, Inc.; U.S. Public, pg. 1298
PIONEERING MANAGEMENT CORPORATION—The Pioneer Group, Inc.; U.S. Public, pg. 1298
PIONEERING SERVICES CORPORATION—The Pioneer Group, Inc.; U.S. Public, pg. 1298
POWER MARKETS DEVELOPMENT COMPANY—PP&L Resources; U.S. Public, pg. 1244
THE PRINCIPAL FINANCIAL GROUP; U.S. Private, pg. 885
PROVIDENT LIFE CAPITAL CO.—Provident Companies, Inc.; U.S. Public, pg. 1338
PUBLIC SERVICE ENTERPRISE GROUP INCORPORATED; U.S. Public, pg. 1340
PUBLIC SERVICE RESOURCES CORPORATION—Public Service Enterprise Group Incorporated; U.S. Public, pg. 1340
QUIXX CORPORATION—New Century Energies, Inc.; U.S. Public, pg. 1170
RBS/PNCF INC.—PNC Bank Corp.; U.S. Public, pg. 1244
RESEARCH CENTER, INC.—United Illuminating Company; U.S. Public, pg. 1678

REVUE AUSTRALIA PTY. LTD.—The Seagram Company Ltd.; Int'l, pg. 1216
ROANOKE VALLEY PLANT—LG & E Energy Corp.; U.S. Public, pg. 970
ROTHSCHILD NORTH AMERICA INC.; U.S. Private, pg. 947
SCE CAPITAL COMPANY—Edison International; U.S. Public, pg. 564
SLM HOLDING CORP.; U.S. Public, pg. 1419
SM&R CAPITAL FUNDS INC.—American National Insurance Company; U.S. Public, pg. 88
SALOMON SMITH BARNEY HOLDINGS, INC.—Travelers Group; U.S. Public, pg. 1633
SANDOZ INVESTMENT N.V.—Novartis AG; Int'l, pg. 984
SANTRADE LTD.—Sandvik AB; Int'l, pg. 1187
SAUDI LIEBHERR COMPANY LTD.—Liebherr-International AG; Int'l, pg. 809
SAUL CENTERS INC.; U.S. Public, pg. 1435
SCIENTIFIC ADVANCES INC.—Battelle Memorial Institute; U.S. Private, pg. 123
SCOTT & STRINGFELLOW FINANCIAL, INC.; U.S. Public, pg. 1445
SCOTT & STRINGFELLOW, INC.—Scott & Stringfellow Financial, Inc.; U.S. Public, pg. 1445
SECURITIES MANAGEMENT & RESEARCH—American National Insurance Company; U.S. Public, pg. 88
SECURITY CAPITAL PACIFIC TRUST—Security Capital Group Incorporated; U.S. Private, pg. 981
SERVCO INVESTMENT CORP.—Servco Pacific Inc.; U.S. Private, pg. 986
SHAYKIN & COMPANY; U.S. Private, pg. 990
SOCIEDAD DE PARTICIPACION Y PROMOCION EMPRESARIAL CAJA DE MADRID—Caja de Madrid Group; Int'l, pg. 252
SOGEM—Union Miniere; Int'l, pg. 1442
SOUTHWESTERN CAPITAL CORPORATION—Citizens Utilities Company; U.S. Public, pg. 380
SOUTHWESTERN INVESTMENTS, INC.—Citizens Utilities Company; U.S. Public, pg. 380
STARWOOD HOTELS & RESORTS; U.S. Public, pg. 1512
STONINGTON PARTNERS INC.; U.S. Private, pg. 1045
SUMMIT BANCORP; U.S. Public, pg. 1527
SUN CITY SEWER COMPANY—Citizens Utilities Company; U.S. Public, pg. 380
SYSTEMS CAPITAL CORPORATION—Telco Capital Corporation; U.S. Private, pg. 1073
TCI DEVELOPMENT CORP.—TCI Communications, Inc.; U.S. Public, pg. 1555
TIC INVESTMENT CORP.—TIC United Corporation; U.S. Private, pg. 1064
T.K.K. CO., LTD.—Tekken Corporation; Int'l, pg. 1362
TECO INVESTMENTS, INC.—TECO Energy, Inc.; U.S. Public, pg. 1565
TECO PROPERTIES, INC.—TECO Energy, Inc.; U.S. Public, pg. 1565
TELCO CAPITAL CORPORATION; U.S. Private, pg. 1073
TENNECO VENTURES,INC.—Tenneco Inc.; U.S. Public, pg. 1578
TERMINAL INVESTMENTS, INC.—Forest City Enterprises, Inc.; U.S. Public, pg. 669
3I GROUP PLC; Int'l, pg. 1386
THYSSEN AG; Int'l, pg. 1387
TIME WARNER ENTERPRISES—Time Warner Inc.; U.S. Public, pg. 1611
TOHOKU ELECTRIC POWER CO., INC.—Tohoku Electric Power Co., Ltd.; Int'l, pg. 1391
TOMEN AMERICA INC.—Tomen Corporation; Int'l, pg. 1395
TOMEN CORPORATION; Int'l, pg. 1395
TRADCOR INTERNATIONAL LIMITED—International Paper Company; U.S. Public, pg. 904
TRANSAMERICA REAL ESTATE INFORMATION COMPANIES—Transamerica Corporation; U.S. Public, pg. 1630
TYCO ACQUISITIONS—Mattel, Inc.; U.S. Public, pg. 1058
TYCO INVESTMENT CORP.—Mattel, Inc.; U.S. Public, pg. 1058
UNICORP AMERICAN CORPORATION—Unicorp Canada Corporation; Int'l, pg. 1433
UNION CARBIDE AUSTRIA GMBH—Union Carbide Corporation; U.S. Public, pg. 1667
UNION CARBIDE INTER-AMERICA, INC.—Union Carbide Corporation; U.S. Public, pg. 1667
UNITED ASSET MANAGEMENT CORPORATION; U.S. Public, pg. 1672
UNITED MISSOURI CAPITAL CORPORATION—UMB Financial Corporation; U.S. Public, pg. 1655
UNITED STATES REALTY & INVESTMENT CO.; U.S. Private, pg. 1125
VEBA AG; Int'l, pg. 1454
VIDEO KING GAMING SYSTEMS, INC.—Stuart Entertainment Inc.; U.S. Public, pg. 1526
VOEST-ALPINE TRADING U.S.A. CORP.—Voest-Alpine Stahl AG; Int'l, pg. 1471
WAGNER STOTT CLEARING CORP.—Merrill Lynch & Co., Inc.; U.S. Public, pg. 1097
WEATHERLY PRIVATE CAPITAL, INC.; U.S. Private, pg. 1156
WESTDEUTSCHE LANDESBANK (EUROPA) AG—Westdeutsche Landesbank Girozentrale; Int'l, pg. 1493
WHITEHALL PROPERTIES LIMITED—GP Batteries International Ltd.; Int'l, pg. 537
WISCONSIN MICHIGAN INVESTMENT CORP.—Wisconsin Energy Corporation; U.S. Public, pg. 1773
WISVEST CORPORATION—Wisconsin Energy Corporation; U.S. Public, pg. 1773
WITECH CORPORATION—Wisconsin Energy Corporation; U.S. Public, pg. 1773
WOODWARD & DICKERSON; U.S. Private, pg. 1188

7011 — HOTELS & MOTELS

AFI HOTELS LIMITED—Granada Group PLC; Int'l, pg. 556
ANA HOTEL—All Nippon Airways Co. Ltd.; Int'l, pg. 57
THE ACCOR GROUP, INC.—Accor S.A.; Int'l, pg. 21
ACCOR NORTH AMERICA—Accor S.A.; Int'l, pg. 21
ACCOR S.A.; Int'l, pg. 20
ADOLPHUS HOTEL—Noble House Hotels and Resorts; U.S. Private, pg. 800
ADVENTURE LANDS OF AMERICA, INC.; U.S. Private, pg. 22
ALADDIN HOTEL & CASINO; U.S. Private, pg. 30
ALBERGHIERA FIESOLANA S.R.L.—Sea Containers Ltd.; Int'l, pg. 1213
ALL NIPPON AIRWAYS CO. LTD.; Int'l, pg. 57
AMANA-NORDSTROM MOTEL CO.—Amana Society, Inc.; U.S. Private, pg. 48
AMWAY HOTEL CORPORATION—Amway Corporation; U.S. Private, pg. 69
AOKI CORPORATION; Int'l, pg. 78
APOLLO HOTEL B.V.—Granada Group PLC; Int'l, pg. 556
ARAMARK CORP.; U.S. Private, pg. 78
ARITMOS AB—Proventus AB; Int'l, pg. 1072
ATLANTIC CITY HILTON—Hilton Hotels Corporation; U.S. Public, pg. 829
ATLAS HOTELS, INC.; U.S. Private, pg. 96
ATTITASH BEAR PEAK—American Skiing Company; U.S. Private, pg. 61
AZTAR CORPORATION; U.S. Public, pg. 158
BALLY'S GRAND INC. (LAS VEGAS)—Hilton Hotels Corporation; U.S. Public, pg. 829
BALLY'S PARK PLACE, INC.—Hilton Hotels Corporation; U.S. Public, pg. 829
BASS TAVERNS LTD.—Bass PLC; Int'l, pg. 170
BELA VISTA LIMITADA—Jardine Matheson Holdings Limited; Int'l, pg. 704
BENSON'S, INC.; U.S. Private, pg. 134
BEST WESTERN INTERNATIONAL, INC.; U.S. Private, pg. 140
BEST WESTERN OGDEN PARK HOTEL—Sunstone Hotel Investors, Inc.; U.S. Public, pg. 1537
THE BEVERLY HILLS HOTEL; U.S. Private, pg. 142
BLUEWAVE INN CORPORATION—Orix Corporation; Int'l, pg. 1008
BOARDWALK REGENCY CORPORATION—Starwood Hotels & Resorts; U.S. Public, pg. 1512
BOYD GAMING CORPORATION; U.S. Public, pg. 249
BRIGHTON CORPORATION—Haseko Corporation; Int'l, pg. 600
BRISTOL HOTELS & RESORTS; U.S. Public, pg. 253
BROADMOOR HOTEL, INC.; U.S. Private, pg. 170
BROOKDALE RESORTS, INC.—Starwood Hotels & Resorts; U.S. Public, pg. 1512
BRUTGER EQUITIES, INC.; U.S. Private, pg. 176
BUDAPEST MARRIOTT HOTEL; Int'l, pg. 232
BUTLIN'S LIMITED—The Rank Group PLC; Int'l, pg. 1086
CSX CORPORATION; U.S. Public, pg. 284
CAESARS WORLD, INC.—Starwood Hotels & Resorts; U.S. Public, pg. 1512
CANADIAN PACIFIC HOTELS & RESORTS INC.—Canadian Pacific Limited; Int'l, pg. 258
CANTERBURY HOTEL—Taj International Hotels; U.S. Private, pg. 1067
CARLSON COMPANIES, INC.; U.S. Private, pg. 211
CARNIVAL HOTELS & CASINOS—Patriot American Hospitality, Inc.; U.S. Public, pg. 1265
CARRIER PIDGIN—United Technologies Corporation; U.S. Public, pg. 1689
CASINO AZTAR—Aztar Corporation; U.S. Public, pg. 158
CAVALIER HOTEL CORP.—Kyanite Mining Corporation; U.S. Private, pg. 638
CENDANT CORPORATION; U.S. Public, pg. 320
CENTER PARCS N.V.—Scottish & Newcastle plc; Int'l, pg. 1212
CHARTWELL LEISURE—Goldman, Sachs & Co.; U.S. Private, pg. 462
CHATTANOOGA CHOO-CHOO HOLIDAY INN; U.S. Private, pg. 231
CHOICE HOTELS INTERNATIONAL, INC.; U.S. Public, pg. 351
CIRCUS CIRCUS - LAS VEGAS; U.S. Public, pg. 374
CLUB MED, INC.—Club Mediterranee SA; Int'l, pg. 298
CLUB MEDITERRANEE SA; Int'l, pg. 298
CLUB RESORTS HOLDING, INC.—Club Corporation International; U.S. Private, pg. 247
COLONNADE ENTERPRISE CORPORATION—Bacardi Limited; Int'l, pg. 132
COLORADO BELLE—Circus Circus - Las Vegas; U.S. Public, pg. 375
COMPANHIA HOTELS PALACE—Sea Containers Ltd.; Int'l, pg. 1214
CONDADO PLAZA HOTEL & CASINO—Patriot American Hospitality, Inc.; U.S. Public, pg. 1265
CONSOLIDATED-TOMOKA LAND CO.; U.S. Public, pg. 437
COOP SWITZERLAND; Int'l, pg. 329
COUNTRY KITCHEN INTERNATIONAL, INC.—Kitchen Investment Group; U.S. Private, pg. 624
COURTYARD BY MARRIOTT—Marriott International, Inc.; U.S. Public, pg. 1048
COVE HAVEN, INC.—Starwood Hotels & Resorts; U.S. Public, pg. 1512
CRESTED BUTTE MARRIOTT RESORT—Crested Butte Mountain Resort, Inc.; U.S. Private, pg. 289
CRESTED BUTTE MOUNTAIN RESORT, INC.; U.S. Private, pg. 289
DAYS INNS OF AMERICA, INC.—Cendant Corporation; U.S. Public, pg. 321
DESERT PALACE, INC.—Starwood Hotels & Resorts; U.S. Public, pg. 1512
WALT DISNEY ATTRACTIONS-WALT DISNEY WORLD—The Walt Disney Company; U.S. Public, pg. 513
DISNEYLAND HOTEL—The Walt Disney Company; U.S. Public, pg. 513
DIVI HOTELS, INC.; U.S. Private, pg. 336
DORAL HOTEL & RESORTS MANAGEMENT CO.; U.S. Private, pg. 340
DOUBLETREE CORPORATION—Promus Hotel Corporation; U.S. Public, pg. 1335
DU PONT PROTEIN TECHNOLOGIES INTERNATIONAL—Du Pont (E.I. Du Pont De Nemours & Co.); U.S. Public, pg. 531
EJP CORPORATION—Promus Hotel Corporation; U.S. Public, pg. 1335
EPAM CORPORATION—Promus Hotel Corporation; U.S. Public, pg. 1335
ESI-AIR, INC.—Harrah's Entertainment, Inc.; U.S. Public, pg. 790
ESJ HOTEL CORPORATION—Patriot American Hospitality, Inc.; U.S. Public, pg. 1265
EDGEWATER HOTEL CORP.—Circus Circus - Las Vegas; U.S. Public, pg. 375
EL SAN JUAN HOTEL & CASINO—Patriot American Hospitality, Inc.; U.S. Public, pg. 1265
ELSINORE CORPORATION; U.S. Public, pg. 570
ELSINORE SHORE ASSOCIATES—Elsinore Corporation; U.S. Public, pg. 570
EURO-SUITES—Sunstone Hotel Investors, Inc.; U.S. Public, pg. 1537
EVER-SKI PROPERTIES, INC.—Santa Fe Gaming Corporation; U.S. Public, pg. 1432
EXCELSIOR HOTEIS E INVESTIMENTOS LIMITADA—Jardine Matheson Holdings Limited; Int'l, pg. 704
EXCELSIOR HOTEL GALLIA S.P.A.—Granada Group PLC; Int'l, pg. 556
THE EXCELSIOR HOTEL, HONG KONG—Jardine Matheson Holdings Limited; Int'l, pg. 704
FAIRFIELD INN—Marriott International, Inc.; U.S. Public, pg. 1048
THE FAIRMONT HOTELS; U.S. Private, pg. 391
FAMILY INNS OF AMERICA, INC.; U.S. Private, pg. 392
FAMILY INNS OF NEW ORLEANS, INC.—Family Inns of America, Inc.; U.S. Private, pg. 392
FARMERS INVESTMENT COMPANY, INC.—Bale Of Kentucky, Inc.; U.S. Private, pg. 112
THE FIRST REPUBLIC CORPORATION OF AMERICA; U.S. Public, pg. 637
THE FLATLEY COMPANY; U.S. Private, pg. 410
FORD MOTOR COMPANY; U.S. Public, pg. 661
FORTE (BERMUDA) LIMITED—Granada Group PLC; Int'l, pg. 556
FORTE FRANCE S.A.—Granada Group PLC; Int'l, pg. 556
FORTE HOLDINGS IRELAND LIMITED—Granada Group PLC; Int'l, pg. 556
FORTE HOTELS (DEUTSCHLAND) GMBH—Granada Group PLC; Int'l, pg. 556
FORTE HOTELS (UK) LIMITED—Granada Group PLC; Int'l, pg. 556
FORTE ITALIA SPA—Granada Group PLC; Int'l, pg. 556
FOUR QUEENS INC.—Elsinore Corporation; U.S. Public, pg. 570
FOUR SEASONS CLIFT HOTEL—Four Seasons Hotels Inc.; Int'l, pg. 502
FOUR SEASONS HOTELS & RESORTS—Four Seasons Hotels Inc.; Int'l, pg. 502
FOUR SEASONS HOTELS INC.; Int'l, pg. 502
FOUR SEASONS OLYMPIC HOTEL—Four Seasons Hotels Inc.; Int'l, pg. 502
FOUR SEASONS RESORTS—Four Seasons Hotels Inc.; Int'l, pg. 502
FOUR SEASONS WASHINGTON—Four Seasons Hotels Inc.; Int'l, pg. 502
FRISCH'S RESTAURANTS, INC.; U.S. Public, pg. 682
GNL, CORP.—Mirage Resorts Incorporated; U.S. Public, pg. 1116
GNLV, CORP.—Mirage Resorts Incorporated; U.S. Public, pg. 1117
GAYLORD ENTERTAINMENT CO.; U.S. Public, pg. 704
GLACIER PARK, INC.—Viad Corp; U.S. Public, pg. 1718
GOLDSTRIKE HOTEL—Circus Circus - Las Vegas; U.S. Public, pg. 375
GOLF HOSTS, INC.—Starwood Capital Group LLC; U.S. Private, pg. 1036
GOSNELL BUILDERS—Pointe Group Ltd.; U.S. Private, pg. 873
GREAT ATLANTIC HOSPITALITY CO. INC.—The Great Atlantic Management Company; U.S. Private, pg. 473
THE GREAT ATLANTIC MANAGEMENT COMPANY; U.S. Private, pg. 473
GREATE BAY CASINO CORPORATION; U.S. Public, pg. 760
GREEN OAKS PARK HOTEL—Sunstone Hotel Investors, Inc.; U.S. Public, pg. 1537
THE GREENBRIER—CSX Corporation; U.S. Public, pg. 284
GRIFFIN GROUP, INC.; U.S. Private, pg. 480
GROSVENOR CASINOS LTD.—The Rank Group PLC; Int'l, pg. 1086
GROUPE ACCOR OF CANADA INC.—Accor S.A.; Int'l, pg. 21
GROWTH MANAGEMENT CORP.—Family Inns of America, Inc.; U.S. Private, pg. 392
GRUPO POSADAS S.A. DE C.V.; Int'l, pg. 576
GRUPO SIDEK, S.A. DE C.V.; Int'l, pg. 576
GRUPO SITUR SA DE CV—Grupo Sidek, S.A. de C.V.; Int'l, pg. 576
GUEST SERVICES, INC.; U.S. Private, pg. 486
GUINNESS ENTERPRISES LTD.—Diageo Plc; Int'l, pg. 412
HBE CORPORATION/DESIGN BUILD DIVISIONS; U.S. Private, pg. 489
HFS, INCORPORATED—Cendant Corporation; U.S. Public, pg. 321
HACIENDA HAWAIIAN PROPERTIES, INC.—Santa Fe Gaming Corporation; U.S. Public, pg. 1432
HACIENDA HOTEL INC.—Santa Fe Gaming Corporation; U.S. Public, pg. 1432
HALLWOOD HOTELS INC.—The Hallwood Group Incorporated; U.S. Public, pg. 778
HAMPSHIRE HOTEL—Taj International Hotels; U.S. Private, pg. 1067
HAMPTON INNS, INC.—Promus Hotel Corporation; U.S. Public, pg. 1335

HANJIN SHIPPING COMPANY LTD.; *Int'l*, pg. 592
HARRAH'S ENTERTAINMENT, INC.; *U.S. Public*, pg. 790
HARRAH'S HOLIDAY INNS OF NEW JERSEY INC.—Harrah's Entertainment, Inc.; *U.S. Public*, pg. 790
HARRAH'S MANAGEMENT CO.—Harrah's Entertainment, Inc.; *U.S. Public*, pg. 790
HARRIS FARMS, INC.; *U.S. Private*, pg. 505
HASEKO (HAWAII) INC.—Haseko Corporation; *Int'l*, pg. 600
HAYSTACK SKI RESORT AT MOUNT SNOW—American Skiing Company; *U.S. Private*, pg. 61
HELMSLEY ENTERPRISES, INC.; *U.S. Private*, pg. 521
HELMSLEY-SPEAR INC.—Helmsley Enterprises, Inc.; *U.S. Private*, pg. 521
HIDDEN VALLEY RESORT—Kettler Brothers, Inc.; *U.S. Private*, pg. 617
HIGH INDUSTRIES, INC.; *U.S. Private*, pg. 528
HILTON CANADA INC.—Ladbroke Group Plc; *Int'l*, pg. 788
HILTON HOTELS CORPORATION; *U.S. Public*, pg. 828
HILTON INTERNATIONAL CO.—Ladbroke Group Plc; *Int'l*, pg. 787
HILTON INTERNATIONAL HOTELS (U.K.) LTD.—Ladbroke Group Plc; *Int'l*, pg. 787
HILTON INTERNATIONAL (SWITZERLAND) AG—Ladbroke Group Plc; *Int'l*, pg. 788
HOLIDAY INN—Benson's, Inc.; *U.S. Private*, pg. 134
HOLIDAY INN DOWNTOWN—Sunstone Hotel Investors, Inc.; *U.S. Public*, pg. 1537
THE HOLIDAY INN LANCASTER HOST HOTEL & CONFERENCE CENTER; *U.S. Private*, pg. 534
HOLIDAY INN WORLDWIDE—Bass PLC; *Int'l*, pg. 170
HOLLY'S INC.; *U.S. Private*, pg. 535
HOLLYWOOD CASINO CORP; *U.S. Public*, pg. 830
THE HOMESTEAD L.C.—Club Corporation International; *U.S. Private*, pg. 247
HOST MARRIOTT CORPORATION; *U.S. Public*, pg. 841
HOSTMARK MANAGEMENT GROUP; *U.S. Private*, pg. 541
HOTEL CIPRIANI S.P.A.—Sea Containers Ltd.; *Int'l*, pg. 1213
HOTEL CORPORATION OF AMERICA; *U.S. Private*, pg. 541
HOTEL INTER-CONTINENTAL—The Saison Group; *Int'l*, pg. 1178
HOTEL MEAD CORP.—Consolidated Papers, Inc.; *U.S. Public*, pg. 436
HOTEL RITZ MADRID S.A.—Granada Group PLC; *Int'l*, pg. 556
HOTEL SHILLA CO. LTD.—Nissho Iwai Corporation; *Int'l*, pg. 947
HOTEL ZURICH AG—Oerlikon-Buhrle Holding AG; *Int'l*, pg. 996
HOWARD JOHNSON—Taj International Hotels; *U.S. Private*, pg. 1067
HYATT HOTELS CORPORATION—Hyatt Corporation; *U.S. Private*, pg. 551
ITT CORPORATION—Starwood Hotels & Resorts; *U.S. Public*, pg. 1512
ITT SHERATON CORPORATION—Starwood Hotels & Resorts; *U.S. Public*, pg. 1512
IMPERIAL HOTELS; *U.S. Private*, pg. 558
IN TOWN HOTELS, INC.—Forest City Enterprises, Inc.; *U.S. Public*, pg. 669
INDUSTRIAL EQUITY LIMITED; *Int'l*, pg. 676
INN AT HARRIS RANCH—Harris Farms, Inc.; *U.S. Private*, pg. 506
INNCO MANAGEMENT CORP.—Family Inns of America, Inc.; *U.S. Private*, pg. 392
INNISBROOK/HILTON RESORT—Starwood Capital Group LLC; *U.S. Private*, pg. 1036
INTER-CONTINENTAL AND FORUM HOTELS—The Saison Group; *Int'l*, pg. 1178
INTER-CONTINENTAL HOTELS—The Saison Group; *Int'l*, pg. 1178
INTER-CONTINENTAL HOTELS CORPORATION—The Saison Group; *Int'l*, pg. 1178
INTERVAL INTERNATIONAL INC.—Cendant Corporation; *U.S. Public*, pg. 320
JOTSA, S.A. EMPRESSA CONSTRUCTOR—Philipp Holzmann AG; *Int'l*, pg. 634
JRN, INC.; *U.S. Private*, pg. 578
JACKPOT CASINO, INC.—Jackpot Enterprises, Inc.; *U.S. Public*, pg. 920
JACKSON HOLE SKI RESORT; *U.S. Private*, pg. 579
JARDINE MATHESON HOLDINGS LIMITED; *Int'l*, pg. 703
P.T. JAYA MANDARIN AGUNG—Jardine Matheson Holdings Limited; *Int'l*, pg. 704
W.B. JOHNSON PROPERTIES, LLC; *U.S. Private*, pg. 594
JUPITER BEACH RESORT—Noble House Hotels and Resorts; *U.S. Private*, pg. 800
KABUTO DECOM INC.; *Int'l*, pg. 721
THE KAHLER HOTEL—Sunstone Hotel Investors, Inc.; *U.S. Public*, pg. 1537
KAHLER INN & SUITES—Sunstone Hotel Investors, Inc.; *U.S. Public*, pg. 1537
KAHLER PARK HOTEL—Sunstone Hotel Investors, Inc.; *U.S. Public*, pg. 1537
KAHLER PLAZA HOTEL—Sunstone Hotel Investors, Inc.; *U.S. Public*, pg. 1537
KEUM KANG DEVELOPMENT INDUSTRIAL CO., LTD.—Hyundai Motor Company; *Int'l*, pg. 642
KILLINGTON LIMITED—American Skiing Company; *U.S. Private*, pg. 61
KNIGHTS FRANCHISE SYSTEMS, INC.—Cendant Corporation; *U.S. Public*, pg. 321
KOHLER COMPANY; *U.S. Private*, pg. 630
LA QUINTA INNS, INC.; *U.S. Public*, pg. 972
LADBROKE GROUP PLC; *Int'l*, pg. 787
LAKEVIEW RESORT & CONFERENCE CENTER—Sunstone Hotel Investors, Inc.; *U.S. Public*, pg. 1537
LANE INDUSTRIES, INC.; *U.S. Private*, pg. 649
LARKEN INC.; *U.S. Private*, pg. 651
LAS COLINAS INN & CONFERENCE CENTER—Four Seasons Hotels Inc.; *Int'l*, pg. 502
LE CONCORDE—Loews Corporation; *U.S. Public*, pg. 1011
LEASED HOTELS LIMITED—Granada Group PLC; *Int'l*, pg. 556
LEISURE RESORTS MANAGEMENT—Barratt Developments Plc; *Int'l*, pg. 168
LES GRANDS HOTELS ASSOCIES S.A.—Granada Group PLC; *Int'l*, pg. 556
LEXFORD RESIDENTIAL TRUST; *U.S. Public*, pg. 991
LODGE PROPERTIES, INC. (LODGE AT VAIL)—Sea Containers Ltd.; *Int'l*, pg. 1213
LOEWS CORPORATION; *U.S. Public*, pg. 1010
LOEWS HOTELS—Loews Corporation; *U.S. Public*, pg. 1011
LOEWS MONTE CARLO—Loews Corporation; *U.S. Public*, pg. 1011
LOEWS NEW YORK—Loews Corporation; *U.S. Public*, pg. 1011
LONRHO PLC; *Int'l*, pg. 817
LOTTE SHOPPING CO. LTD.—Lotte Company Ltd.; *Int'l*, pg. 819
LUCKY INNS OF AMERICA, INC.—Family Inns of America, Inc.; *U.S. Private*, pg. 393
LUSOTEL INDUSTRIA HOTELEIRA LTDA.—Granada Group Plc; *Int'l*, pg. 556
LUXOR HOTEL—Circus Circus - Las Vegas; *U.S. Public*, pg. 375
MGM GRAND HOTEL, INC.—MGM Grand, Inc.; *U.S. Public*, pg. 1027
MGM GRAND, INC.; *U.S. Public*, pg. 1026
MANDARIN ORIENTAL, HONG KONG LIMITED—Jardine Matheson Holdings Limited; *Int'l*, pg. 704
MANDARIN ORIENTAL HOTEL GROUP LIMITED—Jardine Matheson Holdings Limited; *Int'l*, pg. 704
MANILA MANDARIN HOTEL INCORPORATED—Jardine Matheson Holdings Limited; *Int'l*, pg. 704
MANOR CARE, INC.; *U.S. Public*, pg. 1041
MARCOR DEVELOPMENT CO.—Rio Hotel & Casino Inc.; *U.S. Public*, pg. 1390
MARCOR RESORT PROPERTIES, INC.—Rio Hotel & Casino Inc.; *U.S. Public*, pg. 1390
THE MARCUS CORPORATION; *U.S. Public*, pg. 1044
MARCUS HOTEL CORP.—The Marcus Corporation; *U.S. Public*, pg. 1044
MARINA BAY HOTEL PRIVATE LIMITED—Jardine Matheson Holdings Limited; *Int'l*, pg. 704
MARRIOTT INTERNATIONAL, INC.; *U.S. Public*, pg. 1047
MCRAE INDUSTRIES, INC.; *U.S. Public*, pg. 1073
MEDITERRANEA INIZIATIVE TURISTICHE ALBERGHIERE SPA—Granada Group PLC; *Int'l*, pg. 556
MERIDIAN HOTELS, INC.—Granada Group PLC; *Int'l*, pg. 556
MERIDIEN S.A.—Granada Group PLC; *Int'l*, pg. 556
METROPOLE HOTELS (HOLDINGS) LTD.—Lonrho plc; *Int'l*, pg. 817
THE MIRAGE CASINO/HOTEL—Mirage Resorts Incorporated; *U.S. Public*, pg. 1117
MIRAGE RESORTS INCORPORATED; *U.S. Public*, pg. 1116
MITSUI KANKO DEVELOPMENT CO., LTD.—Mitsui & Co., Ltd.; *Int'l*, pg. 878
MOTEL 6 OPERATING L.P.—Accor S.A.; *Int'l*, pg. 21
MOUNT NELSON HOTEL LTD.—Sea Containers Ltd.; *Int'l*, pg. 1214
MOUNT SNOW RESORT—American Skiing Company; *U.S. Private*, pg. 61
NANA DEVELOPMENT CORPORATION—Nana Regional Corporation, Inc.; *U.S. Private*, pg. 774
NANA REGIONAL CORPORATION, INC.; *U.S. Private*, pg. 774
NATIONAL HOTEL CORP.—Carlson Companies, Inc.; *U.S. Private*, pg. 212
NEVADA LANDING—Circus Circus - Las Vegas; *U.S. Public*, pg. 375
NEW CASTLE CORP.—Circus Circus - Las Vegas; *U.S. Public*, pg. 375
NEW WORLD HOTELS (HOLDINGS) LTD.—Marriott International, Inc.; *U.S. Public*, pg. 1048
NEWFOUNDLAND CAPITAL CORPORATION LIMITED; *Int'l*, pg. 924
NISSHO IWAI CORPORATION; *Int'l*, pg. 946
NOBLE HOUSE HOTELS AND RESORTS; *U.S. Private*, pg. 800
NOVOTEL UK LTD.—Accor S.A.; *Int'l*, pg. 21
OBAYASHI CORPORATION; *Int'l*, pg. 995
OCEAN PROPERTIES, LTD.; *U.S. Private*, pg. 811
OCEAN SHOWBOAT, INC.—Showboat, Incorporated; *U.S. Public*, pg. 1469
OLYMPIA PARK HOTEL—Sunstone Hotel Investors, Inc.; *U.S. Public*, pg. 1537
OMNI HOTELS—TRT Holdings Inc.; *U.S. Private*, pg. 1065
ORIENT-EXPRESS HOTELS INC.—Sea Containers Ltd.; *Int'l*, pg. 1213
THE ORIENTAL HOTEL (THAILAND) PCL—Jardine Matheson Holdings Limited; *Int'l*, pg. 704
PARADISE STREAM, INC.—Starwood Hotels & Resorts; *U.S. Public*, pg. 1512
PARKWORLD HOLIDAYS LTD.—The Rank Group PLC; *Int'l*, pg. 1086
THE PIERRE—Four Seasons Hotels Inc.; *Int'l*, pg. 502
PIONEER HOTEL INC.—Santa Fe Gaming Corporation; *U.S. Public*, pg. 1432
PLAYA DE MADRID, S.A.—Telefonica de Espana, S.A.; *Int'l*, pg. 1371
PLAYERS INTERNATIONAL, INC.; *U.S. Public*, pg. 1310
POCONO PALACE, INC.—Starwood Hotels & Resorts; *U.S. Public*, pg. 1512
PONTIN'S LIMITED—Scottish & Newcastle plc; *Int'l*, pg. 1211
PREFERRED/KAHLER ASSOCIATES—Sunstone Hotel Investors, Inc.; *U.S. Public*, pg. 1537
PRIME HOSPITALITY CORP.; *U.S. Public*, pg. 1326
PRINCESS CASINOS INC.—Lonrho plc; *Int'l*, pg. 818
PRINCESS HOTELS INTERNATIONAL INC.—Lonrho plc; *Int'l*, pg. 818
PRINCEVILLE CORPORATION; *U.S. Private*, pg. 885
PROFIT MANAGEMENT CORP.—Family Inns of America, Inc.; *U.S. Private*, pg. 393
PROMUS HOTEL CORPORATION; *U.S. Public*, pg. 1335
PULLMAN INTERNATIONAL HOTEL—Accor S.A.; *Int'l*, pg. 20
QUALITY HOTEL CENTRAL—Frisch's Restaurants, Inc.; *U.S. Public*, pg. 682
QUALITY HOTEL DOWNTOWN—Taj International Hotels; *U.S. Private*, pg. 1067
QUALITY HOTEL RIVERVIEW—Frisch's Restaurants, Inc.; *U.S. Public*, pg. 682
RIU INTERNATIONAL PAN AMERICAN OCEAN RESORT HOTEL; *U.S. Private*, pg. 904
RADISSON HOTEL CORPORATION—Carlson Companies, Inc.; *U.S. Private*, pg. 212
RADISSON HOTELS INTERNATIONAL INC.—Carlson Companies, Inc.; *U.S. Private*, pg. 212
RAILROAD PASS CASINO—Circus Circus - Las Vegas; *U.S. Public*, pg. 375
RALEIGH ENTERPRISES, INC.; *U.S. Private*, pg. 907
RALSTON PURINA COMPANY; *U.S. Public*, pg. 1359
RAMADA EXPRESS—Aztar Corporation; *U.S. Public*, pg. 158
RANK ENTERTAINMENT LIMITED—The Rank Group PLC; *Int'l*, pg. 1087
RANK HOLIDAYS & HOTELS LIMITED—The Rank Group PLC; *Int'l*, pg. 1087
RED ROOF INNS, INC.; *U.S. Public*, pg. 1369
REGENCY HOTEL—Loews Corporation; *U.S. Public*, pg. 1011
RENAISSANCE HOTEL GROUP N.V.—Marriott International, Inc.; *U.S. Public*, pg. 1048
RENAISSANCE INTERNATIONAL HOTELS—Marriott International, Inc.; *U.S. Public*, pg. 1048
RESORTS CASINO HOTEL—Sun International Hotels Limited; *U.S. Public*, pg. 1531
RESORTS USA INC.—The Rank Group PLC; *Int'l*, pg. 1087
RICHFIELD HOSPITALITY SERVICES; *U.S. Private*, pg. 929
RIO HOTEL & CASINO INC.; *U.S. Public*, pg. 1390
RIO PROPERTIES, INC.—Rio Hotel & Casino Inc.; *U.S. Public*, pg. 1390
THE RITZ-CARLTON—Four Seasons Hotels Inc.; *Int'l*, pg. 502
THE RITZ-CARLTON HOTEL COMPANY LLC—W.B. Johnson Properties, LLC; *U.S. Private*, pg. 594
ROSEWOOD PROPERTY COMPANY; *U.S. Private*, pg. 946
SAS INTERNATIONAL HOTELS A/S—Scandinavian Airlines System (SAS); *Int'l*, pg. 1202
SAS PARK ROYAL HOTEL—Scandinavian Airlines System (SAS); *Int'l*, pg. 1202
SHSO—Accor S.A.; *Int'l*, pg. 20
SMP II, L.P.—Sunstone Hotel Investors, Inc.; *U.S. Public*, pg. 1537
THE SAISON GROUP; *Int'l*, pg. 1178
SAMSUNG GROUP; *Int'l*, pg. 1181
SANDESTIN RESORT INC.—Sime Darby Berhad; *Int'l*, pg. 1250
THE SANDS REGENT; *U.S. Public*, pg. 1431
SANDY BAY HOTEL LIMITED—International Investment & Underwriting Ltd.; *Int'l*, pg. 684
SANTA FE GAMING CORPORATION; *U.S. Public*, pg. 1432
SANTA FE HOTEL INC.—Santa Fe Gaming Corporation; *U.S. Public*, pg. 1432
SANTA FE VALLEY, INC.—Santa Fe Gaming Corporation; *U.S. Public*, pg. 1432
P.T. SARINITOKYU HOTEL CORP.—Nissho Iwai Corporation; *Int'l*, pg. 949
SCANDINAVIAN AIRLINES SYSTEM (SAS); *Int'l*, pg. 1201
SCANDINAVIAN LEISURE GROUP A.B.—Airtours Plc; *Int'l*, pg. 39
SCOTTISH & NEW CASTLE RETAIL—Scottish & Newcastle plc; *Int'l*, pg. 1212
SCOTTISH & NEWCASTLE PLC; *Int'l*, pg. 1211
SCOTT'S HOTELS LIMITED—Scott's Restaurants Inc.; *Int'l*, pg. 1213
SEA ISLAND COMPANY; *U.S. Private*, pg. 977
SEA ISLAND SERVICES, INC.—Sea Island Company; *U.S. Private*, pg. 978
S.E.A.T.—Danone Group; *Int'l*, pg. 381
SEPHI—Accor S.A.; *Int'l*, pg. 20
SERVICO, INC.; *U.S. Public*, pg. 1462
SHARONVILLE HOTEL CORPORATION—Saul Centers Inc.; *U.S. Public*, pg. 1435
SHEARINGS LIMITED—The Rank Group PLC; *Int'l*, pg. 1087
SHOLODGE, INC.; *U.S. Public*, pg. 1467
SHOWBOAT, INCORPORATED; *U.S. Public*, pg. 1469
SIGNATURE INNS, INC.; *U.S. Public*, pg. 1473
SOCIEDADE TURISTICA DA PENINA SARL—Granada Group PLC; *Int'l*, pg. 556
SOCIETE DE GESTION DE RESTAURANTS-BARS SUR LES AUTEOROUTES SA—Granada Group PLC; *Int'l*, pg. 556
SOCIETE HOTELIERE PARIS VANVES—Accor S.A.; *Int'l*, pg. 20
SOCIETE INTERNATIONALE DES HOTELS NOVOTEL—Accor S.A.; *Int'l*, pg. 21
SOL MELIA; *Int'l*, pg. 1277
SONESTA INTERNATIONAL HOTELS CORPORATION; *U.S. Public*, pg. 1485
SONOMA MISSION INN & SPA; *U.S. Private*, pg. 1014
SOUTH AFRICAN BREWERIES, LTD.; *Int'l*, pg. 1286
SPHERE SA—Accor S.A.; *Int'l*, pg. 21
SSANGYONG BUSINESS GROUP; *Int'l*, pg. 1291
STRATTON CORPORATION—Intrawest Corporation; *Int'l*, pg. 685
SUGARBUSH—American Skiing Company; *U.S. Private*, pg. 62
SULCUS COMPUTER CORP.; *U.S. Public*, pg. 1527
SUNCOR DEVELOPMENT COMPANY—Pinnacle West Capital Corporation; *U.S. Public*, pg. 1298

SUNRIDGE HOTEL & CONFERENCE CENTER—Lombardi Holdings Inc.; *U.S. Private*, pg. 673
SUNSTONE HOTEL INVESTORS, INC.; *U.S. Public*, pg. 1536
SUPER 8 MOTELS, INC.—Cendant Corporation; *U.S. Public*, pg. 322
SWALLOW HOTELS LIMITED—Vaux Group Plc; *Int'l*, pg. 1454
THE SWISSAIR GROUP; *Int'l*, pg. 1333
T A HOLDINGS LIMITED; *Int'l*, pg. 1334
TAJ INTERNATIONAL HOTELS; *U.S. Private*, pg. 1067
TAMARRON DIVISION—Starwood Capital Group LLC; *U.S. Private*, pg. 1036
TOKYU CORPORATION; *Int'l*, pg. 1394
TOLLMAN/HUNDLEY HOTELS; *U.S. Private*, pg. 1090
TOP OF THE WORLD HOTEL—Arctic Slope Regional Corporation; *U.S. Private*, pg. 80
TOWN PUMP, INC.; *U.S. Private*, pg. 1093
TRAPP FAMILY LODGE, INC.; *U.S. Private*, pg. 1098
TRAVEL PORTS OF AMERICA INC.; *U.S. Public*, pg. 1632
TRAVELODGE—Cendant Corporation; *U.S. Public*, pg. 322
TREASURE ISLAND, CORP.—Mirage Resorts Incorporated; *U.S. Public*, pg. 1117
TRIDENT ENTERPRISE LTD.—Club Mediterranee SA; *Int'l*, pg. 298
TROPICANA CASINO & RESORT—Aztar Corporation; *U.S. Public*, pg. 159
TROPICANA RESORT & CASINO—Aztar Corporation; *U.S. Public*, pg. 159
TRUMP ORGANIZATION; *U.S. Private*, pg. 1108
TRUSTHOASE FORTE PLC—Bass PLC; *Int'l*, pg. 170
TURTLE BAY HILTON GOLF & TENNIS RESORT—Hilton Hotels Corporation; *U.S. Public*, pg. 829
UNIVERSITY INN ASSOCIATES—Sunstone Hotel Investors, Inc.; *U.S. Public*, pg. 1537
VAIL ASSOCIATES, INC.—Vail Resorts, Inc.; *U.S. Public*, pg. 1704
VAUX GROUP PLC; *Int'l*, pg. 1453
VENICE SIMPLON-ORIENT-EXPRESS LTD.—Sea Containers Ltd.; *Int'l*, pg. 1213
VILLA SOUTH INC.—Thiele Kaolin Co.; *U.S. Private*, pg. 1081
WCO PORT PROPERTIES, INC.—The Walt Disney Company; *U.S. Public*, pg. 514
WHG RESORTS & CASINOS—Patriot American Hospitality, Inc.; *U.S. Public*, pg. 1265
WARNER HOLIDAYS LIMITED—The Rank Group PLC; *Int'l*, pg. 1087
WARREN PROPERTIES; *U.S. Private*, pg. 1151
WELCOME BREAK GROUP LIMITED—Investcorp International; *Int'l*, pg. 686
WEST JAPAN RAILWAY COMPANY; *Int'l*, pg. 1490
WESTIN HOTELS & RESORTS—Starwood Hotels & Resorts; *U.S. Public*, pg. 1512
WHARF HOTEL INVESTMENTS LTD.; *Int'l*, pg. 1497
WIGWAM RESORT—Kabuto Decom Inc.; *Int'l*, pg. 721
WILLIAMS HOSPITALITY GROUP INC.—Patriot American Hospitality, Inc.; *U.S. Public*, pg. 1265
THE WINDHAM COMPANY; *U.S. Private*, pg. 1182
WINDSOR COURT HOTEL L.P.—Sea Containers Ltd.; *Int'l*, pg. 1214
THE WOODFIN SUITE HOTELS; *U.S. Private*, pg. 1187
YAMAHA RECREATION CO., LTD.—Yamaha Corporation; *Int'l*, pg. 1516
YOSEMITE CONCESSION SERVICES CO.—The Seagram Company Ltd.; *Int'l*, pg. 1216
ZANTE, INC.—The Sands Regent; *U.S. Public*, pg. 1431

7033 — RECREATIONAL VEHICLE PARKS & CAMPSITES

ADVENTURE LANDS OF AMERICA, INC.; *U.S. Private*, pg. 22
THE CEDAR POINT BRIDGE CO.—Cedar Fair, L.P.; *U.S. Public*, pg. 319
COMMERCE GROUP CORP.; *U.S. Public*, pg. 410
DADE COUNTY LAND HOLDING CO.—St. Joe Corp.; *U.S. Public*, pg. 1427
WALT DISNEY ATTRACTIONS-WALT DISNEY WORLD—The Walt Disney Company; *U.S. Public*, pg. 513
KOA HOLDINGS; *U.S. Private*, pg. 603
KAMPGROUNDS OF AMERICA (CANADA) LTD.—KOA Holdings; *U.S. Private*, pg. 603
SILVER DOLLAR CITY, INC.; *U.S. Private*, pg. 1000
STANDING ROCK CAMPGROUND—Commerce Group Corp.; *U.S. Public*, pg. 410

7041 — ORGANIZATION HOTELS & LODGING HOUSES ON MEMBERSHIP BASIS

INTERVAL INTERNATIONAL INC.—Cendant Corporation; *U.S. Public*, pg. 320
SOL MELIA; *Int'l*, pg. 1277

7211 — POWER LAUNDRIES, FAMILY & COMMERCIAL

DOMESTIC UNIFORM RENTAL CO.; *U.S. Private*, pg. 338
THE TIMES LEADER—Knight-Ridder, Inc.; *U.S. Public*, pg. 964

7212 — GARMENT PRESSING & AGENTS FOR LAUNDRIES & DRY CLEANERS

LAWLER'S, INC.—Sunstone Hotel Investors, Inc.; *U.S. Public*, pg. 1537
TEXTILE CARE SERVICES, INC.—Sunstone Hotel Investors, Inc.; *U.S. Public*, pg. 1537

7213 — LINEN SUPPLY SERVICES

A & P COAT, APRON & LINEN SUPPLY; *U.S. Private*, pg. 1
AMERIPRIDE SERVICE COMPANY; *U.S. Private*, pg. 65
ANGELICA CORPORATION; *U.S. Public*, pg. 113
ANGELICA TEXTILE SERVICES, INC.—Angelica Corporation; *U.S. Public*, pg. 113
ARAMARK CORP.; *U.S. Private*, pg. 78
BERENDSEN TEXTIL SERVICE A/S—Sophus Berendsen A/S; *Int'l*, pg. 1284
BEST MANUFACTURING, INC.; *U.S. Private*, pg. 139
BRAMBLES TEXTILE RENTAL & LAUNDRY SERVICES—Brambles Industries Limited; *Int'l*, pg. 211
THE DAVIS SERVICE GROUP PLC.; *Int'l*, pg. 385
DOMESTIC UNIFORM RENTAL CO.; *U.S. Private*, pg. 338
INITIAL TEXTILE SERVICE—Sophus Berendsen A/S; *Int'l*, pg. 1285
MISSION INDUSTRIES; *U.S. Private*, pg. 752
NATIONAL LINEN & UNIFORM SERVICE—National Service Industries, Inc.; *U.S. Public*, pg. 1160
NATIONAL SERVICE INDUSTRIES, INC.; *U.S. Public*, pg. 1160
NATIONAL UNIFORM SERVICE—G&K Services, Inc.; *U.S. Public*, pg. 690
PERTH LINEN SERVICE—Brambles Industries Limited; *Int'l*, pg. 211
RENTOKIL INITIAL USA—Sophus Berendsen A/S; *Int'l*, pg. 1286
THE SERVICEMASTER COMPANY; *U.S. Public*, pg. 1461
SERVITEX, INC.—National Distributing Co., Inc.; *U.S. Private*, pg. 781
SKETCHLEY PLC; *Int'l*, pg. 1261
STEINER CORPORATION; *U.S. Private*, pg. 1039
THE SUNLIGHT SERVICE GROUP LTD.—The Davis Service Group Plc.; *Int'l*, pg. 385
UNITOG COMPANY; *U.S. Public*, pg. 1693
VERSA SERVICES LTD.—Aramark Corp.; *U.S. Private*, pg. 79

7215 — COIN-OPERATED LAUNDRIES & DRY CLEANING

MAC-GRAY CORPORATION; *U.S. Public*, pg. 1029

7216 — DRY CLEANING PLANTS, EXCEPT RUG CLEANING

ARAMARK CORP.; *U.S. Private*, pg. 78
RITE AID CORPORATION; *U.S. Public*, pg. 1390
SKETCHLEY PLC; *Int'l*, pg. 1261

7217 — CARPET & UPHOLSTERY CLEANING

ASAB SERVICEFORETAGET AB—Electrolux, AB; *Int'l*, pg. 438
CASTEX INCORPORATED—Tennant Company; *U.S. Public*, pg. 1577
THE SERVICEMASTER COMPANY; *U.S. Public*, pg. 1461
STANLEY STEEMER INTERNATIONAL, INC.; *U.S. Private*, pg. 1033

7218 — INDUSTRIAL LAUNDERERS

AMERIPRIDE SERVICE COMPANY; *U.S. Private*, pg. 65
ARAMARK CORP.; *U.S. Private*, pg. 78
ARAMARK UNIFORM SERVICES—Aramark Corp.; *U.S. Private*, pg. 79
BERENDSEN TEXTIL SERVICE A/S—Sophus Berendsen A/S; *Int'l*, pg. 1284
BRAMBLES TEXTILE RENTAL & LAUNDRY SERVICES—Brambles Industries Limited; *Int'l*, pg. 211
CINTAS CORPORATION; *U.S. Public*, pg. 370
THE DAVIS SERVICE GROUP PLC.; *Int'l*, pg. 385
DOMESTIC UNIFORM RENTAL CO.; *U.S. Private*, pg. 338
G&K SERVICES, INC.; *U.S. Public*, pg. 690
INDUSTRIAL TOWEL & UNIFORM; *U.S. Private*, pg. 561
MISSION INDUSTRIES; *U.S. Private*, pg. 752
NATIONAL UNIFORM SERVICE—G&K Services, Inc.; *U.S. Public*, pg. 690
THE SUNLIGHT SERVICE GROUP LTD.—The Davis Service Group Plc.; *Int'l*, pg. 385
TEXAS INDUSTRIAL SERVICES, INC.—UniFirst Corporation; *U.S. Public*, pg. 1665
TEXTILEASE CORPORATION; *U.S. Private*, pg. 1079
UNIFIRST CORPORATION; *U.S. Public*, pg. 1665
UNITOG COMPANY; *U.S. Public*, pg. 1693
VAN DYNE-CROTTY, INC.; *U.S. Private*, pg. 1132
VERSA SERVICES LTD.—Aramark Corp.; *U.S. Private*, pg. 79
WORK WEAR CANADA—G&K Services, Inc.; *U.S. Public*, pg. 690

7219 — LAUNDRY & GARMENT SERVICES, NEC

CHANGE-O-MATIC/WESCO—Steiner Corporation; *U.S. Private*, pg. 1039
MATSUYA FASHION SERVICE CO., LTD.—Matsuya Company Ltd.; *Int'l*, pg. 848
UNIFIRST CORPORATION; *U.S. Public*, pg. 1665

7221 — PHOTOGRAPHIC STUDIOS, PORTRAIT

AMFAC, INC.—JMB Realty Corporation; *U.S. Private*, pg. 577
BELL & HOWELL LTD., (UK) MAILHANDLING DIV.—Bell & Howell Holdings; *U.S. Public*, pg. 201
CPI CORP.; *U.S. Public*, pg. 283
CINE MAGNETICS, INC.; *U.S. Private*, pg. 240
KODAK PRINTER PRODUCTS DIV.—Eastman Kodak Company; *U.S. Public*, pg. 555
LIFETOUCH, PORTRAIT STUDIOS, *U.S. Private*, pg. 667
OLAN MILLS, INC.; *U.S. Private*, pg. 749
PCA INTERNATIONAL, INC.; *U.S. Public*, pg. 1240

7231 — BEAUTY SHOPS

AHF SALONS, INC.—Opal Concepts, Inc.; *U.S. Private*, pg. 818
THE BARBERS, HAIRSTYLING FOR MEN & WOMEN, INC.; *U.S. Private*, pg. 115
CITY LOOKS SALONS—The Barbers, Hairstyling for Men & Women, Inc.; *U.S. Private*, pg. 115
COST CUTTERS—The Barbers, Hairstyling for Men & Women, Inc.; *U.S. Private*, pg. 115
CREATIVE HAIRDRESSERS; *U.S. Private*, pg. 287
FS CANADA, INC.—Opal Concepts, Inc.; *U.S. Private*, pg. 818
FS CONCEPTS, INC.—Opal Concepts, Inc.; *U.S. Private*, pg. 818
GREAT CLIPS, INC.; *U.S. Private*, pg. 473
THE HAIR CUTTERY—Creative Hairdressers; *U.S. Private*, pg. 287
HAIRCUTS PLUS, INC.—Opal Concepts, Inc.; *U.S. Private*, pg. 818
JC PENNEY COMPANY, INC.; *U.S. Public*, pg. 916
MIDWEST BEAUTY L.P.—Opal Concepts, Inc.; *U.S. Private*, pg. 818
OPAL CONCEPTS, INC.; *U.S. Private*, pg. 817
ORLANE INSTITUT DE BEAUTE—Orlane; *Int'l*, pg. 1011
PREMIER SALONS INTERNATIONAL; *U.S. Private*, pg. 881
PRO-CUTS, INC.—Opal Concepts, Inc.; *U.S. Private*, pg. 818
REGIS CORPORATION; *U.S. Public*, pg. 1373
SCOPE INDUSTRIES; *U.S. Public*, pg. 1444
SUPERCUTS, INC.—Regis Corporation; *U.S. Public*, pg. 1373
VISIBLE CHANGES; *U.S. Private*, pg. 1141

7241 — BARBER SHOPS

FS CONCEPTS, INC.—Opal Concepts, Inc.; *U.S. Private*, pg. 818
JC PENNEY COMPANY, INC.; *U.S. Public*, pg. 916
OPAL CONCEPTS, INC.; *U.S. Private*, pg. 817

7261 — FUNERAL SERVICE & CREMATORIES

FUNERAL SECURITY PLANS, INC.—D.W. Newcomer's Sons, Inc.; *U.S. Private*, pg. 796
THE LOEWEN GROUP, INC.; *Int'l*, pg. 814
LOEWEN GROUP INTERNATIONAL, INC.—The Loewen Group, Inc.; *Int'l*, pg. 814
D.W. NEWCOMER'S SONS, INC.; *U.S. Private*, pg. 796
SECURITY INDUSTRIAL INSURANCE CO., INC.—The Loewen Group, Inc.; *Int'l*, pg. 814
SERVICE CORPORATION INTERNATIONAL; *U.S. Public*, pg. 1460
STEWART ENTERPRISES, INC.; *U.S. Public*, pg. 1518

7291 — TAX RETURN PREPARATION SERVICES

CG INDIVIDUAL TAX BENEFITS PAYMENTS, INC.—Cigna Corp.; *U.S. Public*, pg. 358
CG LIFE PENSION BENEFITS PAYMENTS, INC.—Cigna Corp.; *U.S. Public*, pg. 358
CG LINA PENSION BENEFITS PAYMENTS, INC.—Cigna Corp.; *U.S. Public*, pg. 358
CERIDIAN EMPLOYER SERVICES—Ceridian Corporation; *U.S. Public*, pg. 331
H & R BLOCK, INC.; *U.S. Public*, pg. 770
ULSTER BANK DUBLIN TRUST COMPANY—National Westminster Bank PLC; *Int'l*, pg. 912
WESTTAX, INC.—The Western and Southern Life Insurance Company; *U.S. Private*, pg. 1165

7299 — MISCELLANEOUS PERSONAL SERVICES, NEC

ADVANCE ROSS CORPORATION—Cendant Corporation; *U.S. Public*, pg. 320
ALIANT COMMUNICATIONS INC.; *U.S. Public*, pg. 40
ARAMARK CORP.; *U.S. Private*, pg. 78
DAY & ZIMMERMANN LLC—Day & Zimmermann, Inc.; *U.S. Private*, pg. 317
DOMESTIC UNIFORM RENTAL CO.; *U.S. Private*, pg. 338
EUROPE TAX-FREE SHOPPING LTD.—Cendant Corporation; *U.S. Public*, pg. 320
FORM-YOU-3 INTERNATIONAL, INC.; *U.S. Private*, pg. 418
GINGISS INTERNATIONAL; *U.S. Private*, pg. 455
GROUPE MORROW INC.; *Int'l*, pg. 566
JENNY CRAIG, INC.; *U.S. Public*, pg. 926
MISSION INDUSTRIES; *U.S. Private*, pg. 752
NORCOSTCO, INC.; *U.S. Private*, pg. 801
REPUBLIC STORAGE SYSTEMS COMPANY INC.; *U.S. Private*, pg. 924
SGD INTERNATIONAL CORP.; *U.S. Private*, pg. 957
THE SERVICEMASTER COMPANY; *U.S. Public*, pg. 1461
TOWER CITY PROPERTIES—Forest City Enterprises, Inc.; *U.S. Public*, pg. 669
TOWER CITY VALET PARKING—Forest City Enterprises, Inc.; *U.S. Public*, pg. 669
WEIGHT WATCHERS FOODS CENTRAL EUROPE B.V.—H.J. Heinz Company; *U.S. Public*, pg. 807
WILLIAMSON-DICKIE MFG. CO.; *U.S. Private*, pg. 1179

7311 — ADVERTISING AGENCIES

AGA CATALOG MARKETING & DESIGN; U.S. Private, pg. 5
ALS TONIC—BDDP Group; Int'l, pg. 116
AMA LEO BURNETT—Leo Burnett Company, Inc.; U.S. Private, pg. 184
ARA/BDDP—BDDP Group; Int'l, pg. 117
ARC ADVERTISING; Int'l, pg. 17
ARS/DMB&B—DMB&B Communications; U.S. Private, pg. 303
ABELSON-TAYLOR, INC.; U.S. Private, pg. 10
ACKERMAN MCQUEEN, INC.; U.S. Private, pg. 12
THE AD TEAM OF FLORIDA INC.; U.S. Private, pg. 16
ADLER BOSCHETTO PEEBLES & PARTNERS, INC.; U.S. Private, pg. 17
ADPLUS—The Lowe Group; U.S. Private, pg. 678
ADVANSWERS MEDIA/PROGRAMMING—BDDP Group; Int'l, pg. 117
ADVERTISING PROMOTIONS, INC.—Scott's Liquid Gold-Inc.; U.S. Public, pg. 1447
ADVICO YOUNG & RUBICAM AG—Young & Rubicam Inc.; U.S. Private, pg. 1198
ADWORKS, INC.; U.S. Private, pg. 23
AFFICHAGE CENTRE VILLE (A.C.V.)—Lagardere Groupe; Int'l, pg. 791
AGENCY MEDIA SERVICES, INC.—Norfolk Southern Corporation; U.S. Public, pg. 1190
AGRI-GRAPHICS, INC.—Altair Corporation; U.S. Private, pg. 46
ALICE—The Lowe Group; U.S. Private, pg. 678
ALLIED ADVERTISING AGENCY, PUBLIC RELATIONS; U.S. Private, pg. 38
ALPHA WAVE HEALTHCARE COMMUNICATIONS—Ketchum Communications Inc.; U.S. Private, pg. 617
ALS CONSEIL—BDDP Group; Int'l, pg. 116
AMERCO; U.S. Private, pg. 48
AMERICAN BUSINESS ADVERTISING; U.S. Private, pg. 51
AMMIRATI, PURIS & LINTAS, INC.; U.S. Private, pg. 66
AMMIRATI PURIS LINTAS WORLDWIDE—The Interpublic Group of Companies, Inc.; U.S. Public, pg. 908
ANDERSON & LEMBKE INC.; U.S. Private, pg. 72
ANDREN & WERNE LEO BURNETT AB—Leo Burnett Company, Inc.; U.S. Private, pg. 184
ANSPACH GROSSMAN ENTERPRISE—WPP Group plc; Int'l, pg. 1483
AOMORI HAKUHODO INC.—Hakuhodo Incorporated; Int'l, pg. 587
JAN ARBMAN EURO RSCG—Havas Advertising; Int'l, pg. 602
ARNOLD COMMUNICATIONS, INC.; U.S. Private, pg. 83
ASAHI ADVERTISING INC.; Int'l, pg. 81
ASATSU AMERICA INC.—Asatsu Inc.; Int'l, pg. 86
ASATSU (DEUTSCHLAND) GMBH—Asatsu Inc.; Int'l, pg. 86
ASATSU HONG KONG LTD.—Asatsu Inc.; Int'l, pg. 86
ASATSU INC.; Int'l, pg. 85
ASATSU INTERNATIONAL INC.—Asatsu Inc.; Int'l, pg. 86
ASHER/GOULD ADVERTISING, INC.; U.S. Private, pg. 88
ATA TONIC—Havas Advertising; Int'l, pg. 602
AUDITOIRE—BDDP Group; Int'l, pg. 116
AUSTIN KELLEY ADVERTISING, INC.; U.S. Private, pg. 100
AUSTRALIE—Havas Advertising; Int'l, pg. 600
AVRETT, FREE & GINSBERG, INC.; U.S. Private, pg. 103
AYER INTERNATIONAL—N.W. Ayer & Partners; U.S. Private, pg. 104
N.W. AYER & PARTNERS; U.S. Private, pg. 103
N.W. AYER & PARTNERS CHICAGO—N.W. Ayer & Partners; U.S. Private, pg. 104
AYTON YOUNG & RUBICAM LTD.—Young & Rubicam Inc.; U.S. Private, pg. 1198
B COMMUNICATIONS/GGK—TBWA GGK Zurick; Int'l, pg. 1335
BBDO CANADA—N.W. Ayer & Partners; U.S. Private, pg. 104
BBDO OSLO—Omnicom Group Inc.; U.S. Public, pg. 1224
BBDO WORLDWIDE INC.—Omnicom Group Inc.; U.S. Public, pg. 1223
BCP GROUP LTD.; Int'l, pg. 116
BDDP—BDDP Group; Int'l, pg. 116
BDDP CORPORATE—BDDP Group; Int'l, pg. 116
BDDP GROUP; Int'l, pg. 116
BDDP HOLDINGS (UK) LTD.—BDDP Group; Int'l, pg. 117
BDDP MILAN—BDDP Group; Int'l, pg. 117
BDDP NORTH AMERICA, INC.—BDDP Group; Int'l, pg. 117
BDG/MCCOLL—WPP Group plc; Int'l, pg. 1482
BDH ADVERTISING LIMITED; Int'l, pg. 118
BGM HEALTH COMMUNICATIONS, INC.—Omnicom Group Inc.; U.S. Public, pg. 1223
BLD EUROPE S.A.—Dentsu Inc.; Int'l, pg. 394
BSA ADVERTISING, INC.; U.S. Private, pg. 107
BSMG WORLDWIDE—True North Diversified Companies; U.S. Public, pg. 1642
BVK/MCDONALD; U.S. Private, pg. 108
B/W WERBEAGENTUR GWA; Int'l, pg. 130
BADER RUTTER & ASSOC., INC.; U.S. Private, pg. 110
BALDI, BLOOM & WHELAN ADVERTISING; U.S. Private, pg. 112
BARKLEY & EVERGREEN ADVERTISING, INC.; U.S. Private, pg. 116
BARTLE BOGLE HEGARTY LIMITED; Int'l, pg. 169
BATEY ADS SINGAPORE; Int'l, pg. 170
BATEY ADS TAIWAN—BDDP Group; Int'l, pg. 117
BATEY COULDREY JONES ADVERTISING—BDDP Group; Int'l, pg. 117
BEBER & SILVERSTEIN & PARTNERS, INC.; U.S. Private, pg. 128
ROBERT A. BECKER—Havas Advertising; Int'l, pg. 601
BELLSOUTH CORPORATION; U.S. Public, pg. 207
BENJAMENS, VAN DOORN EURO RSCG—Havas Advertising; Int'l, pg. 602
BERCUM BOENDER CARDOZO & WERKENDAM B.V.—Young & Rubicam Inc.; U.S. Private, pg. 1198
BERENTER GREENHOUSE & WEBSTER, INC.; U.S. Private, pg. 135
BERNSTEIN-REIN ADVERTISING, INC.; U.S. Private, pg. 137
BERRY NETWORK, INC.; U.S. Private, pg. 137
BIEDERMAN, KELLY & SHAFFER, INC.; U.S. Private, pg. 142
BIGGS GILMORE COMMUNICATIONS; U.S. Private, pg. 143
BLACK ROGERS SULLIVAN GOODNIGHT, INC.; U.S. Private, pg. 147
BORDELAIS, LEMEUNIER-LEO BURNETT PARIS—Leo Burnett Company, Inc.; U.S. Private, pg. 184
BORSCH, STENGEL & PARTNER GMBH; Int'l, pg. 203
BOZELL RETAIL; Int'l, pg. 209
BRIERLEY & PARTNERS; U.S. Private, pg. 168
BRIERLEY & PARTNERS—Brierley & Partners; U.S. Private, pg. 168
BROWN MARKETING COMMUNICATIONS; U.S. Private, pg. 174
THE BUNTIN GROUP; U.S. Private, pg. 181
LEO BURNETT ADVERTISING SDN.BHD.—Leo Burnett Company, Inc.; U.S. Private, pg. 184
LEO BURNETT BRUSSELS—Leo Burnett Company, Inc.; U.S. Private, pg. 185
LEO BURNETT COMPANY, INC.; U.S. Private, pg. 183
LEO BURNETT-COSTA RICA—Leo Burnett Company, Inc.; U.S. Private, pg. 185
LEO BURNETT INC.—Leo Burnett Company, Inc.; U.S. Private, pg. 185
BURRELL COMMUNICATIONS GROUP INC.; U.S. Private, pg. 188
BURSON-MARSTELLER—Young & Rubicam Inc.; U.S. Private, pg. 1197
BUTLER LUTOS SUTTON WILKINSON; Int'l, pg. 237
BUTTERFIELD DAY DEVITO HOCKNEY LTD.; Int'l, pg. 237
CARL BYOIR & ASSOCIATES, INC.—WPP Group plc; Int'l, pg. 1483
CCCE NELSON/BABYLONE—BDDP Group; Int'l, pg. 116
CDP; Int'l, pg. 239
CF2GS; U.S. Private, pg. 194
CGR COMMUNICATIONS—Saatchi & Saatchi Advertising Worldwide; U.S. Public, pg. 1422
CKS GROUP; U.S. Private, pg. 195
CME KHBB; Int'l, pg. 241
CSI INTERNATIONAL CORPORATION; U.S. Private, pg. 197
CALDWELL VANRIPER, INC.; U.S. Private, pg. 200
CAMELOT COMMUNICATIONS, INC.; U.S. Private, pg. 203
CAMPBELL-EWALD ADVERTISING—The Interpublic Group of Companies, Inc.; U.S. Public, pg. 908
CAMPBELL MITHUN ESTY; U.S. Private, pg. 204
CARAT ICG; U.S. Private, pg. 207
CARLSON & PARTNERS, INC.; U.S. Private, pg. 211
CARLSON PROMOTION DIVISION—Carlson Companies, Inc.; U.S. Private, pg. 212
CARMICHAEL LYNCH, INC.; U.S. Private, pg. 213
CARRAFIELLO, DIEHL & ASSOCIATES, INC.; U.S. Private, pg. 215
CASE ADVERTISING, INC.—Coca-Cola Bottling Co. Consolidated; U.S. Public, pg. 391
CAUSA PUBLICIDAD—Leo Burnett Company, Inc.; U.S. Private, pg. 184
CHAITRA LEO BURNETT PRIVATE LTD.—Leo Burnett Company, Inc.; U.S. Private, pg. 184
CHAPMAN WARWICK INC.—Warwick Baker O'Neill; U.S. Private, pg. 1152
THE CHISHOLM-MINGO GROUP; U.S. Private, pg. 237
CHUO SENKO ADVERTISING CO., LTD.; Int'l, pg. 291
CINEPONTO/LEO BURNETT PUBLICIDADE LDA.—Leo Burnett Company, Inc.; U.S. Private, pg. 184
CITRON HALIGMAN BEDECARRE; U.S. Private, pg. 241
CLARITY COVERDALE FURY ADVERTISING; U.S. Private, pg. 242
CLINE, DAVIS & MANN, INC.; U.S. Private, pg. 246
THE COAKLEY HEAGERTY ADVERTISING & PUBLIC RELATIONS CO.; U.S. Private, pg. 248
COHIBA—BDDP Group; Int'l, pg. 117
COHN & WELLS—Havas Advertising; Int'l, pg. 601
COLEY PORTER BELL—WPP Group plc; Int'l, pg. 1482
COLLE & MCVOY, INC.; U.S. Private, pg. 252
COLONIAL WILLIAMSBURG FOUNDATION; U.S. Private, pg. 254
COLORADO—Havas Advertising; Int'l, pg. 601
COLUMBIAN ADVERTISING INC.; U.S. Private, pg. 256
COMMUNICATIE & DESIGN—TBWA GGK Zurick; Int'l, pg. 1335
COMMUNICATIONS INTERNATIONAL (NY); U.S. Private, pg. 259
CONQUEST EUROPE S.A.—WPP Group plc; Int'l, pg. 1484
CONQUEST EUROPE S.A.R.L.—WPP Group plc; Int'l, pg. 1484
CONQUEST S.P.A.—WPP Group plc; Int'l, pg. 1484
MICHAEL CONRAD & LEO BURNETT GMBH—Leo Burnett Company, Inc.; U.S. Private, pg. 184
CONTINENTAL PROMOTION GROUP; U.S. Private, pg. 269
THE WILLIAM COOK AGENCY, INC.; U.S. Private, pg. 273
CORBETT HEALTHCONNECT, A FRANK J. CORBETT, INC., COMPANY—Omnicom Group Inc.; U.S. Public, pg. 1223
CORIS-MOBIUM CREATIVE GROUP—R.R. Donnelley & Sons Company; U.S. Public, pg. 518
THE CORPORATE COMMUNICATIONS GROUP; U.S. Private, pg. 276
COSSETTE COMMUNICATION MARKETING; Int'l, pg. 335
CRAMER-KRASSELT; U.S. Private, pg. 285
CRANFORD JOHNSON ROBINSON WOODS; U.S. Private, pg. 286
DAVID CRAVIT & ASSOCIATES ADVERTISING; U.S. Private, pg. 287
CREATIVE ALLIANCE, INC.; U.S. Private, pg. 287
CREATIVE MARKETING INTERNATIONAL CORP.; U.S. Private, pg. 287
CREHALET POUGET POUSSIELGUES—Warwick Baker O'Neill; U.S. Private, pg. 1152
CRESWELL, MUNSELL, FULTZ & ZIRBEL, L.P.—Young & Rubicam Inc.; U.S. Private, pg. 1197
CRISPIN PORTER & BOGUSKY; U.S. Private, pg. 290
CUSTOMER DEVELOPMENT CORPORATION; U.S. Private, pg. 298
D & S MARKETING—Bel-Art Products; U.S. Private, pg. 130
DCA ADVERTISING, INC.—Dentsu Inc.; Int'l, pg. 393
DDB NEEDHAM WORLDWIDE INC.—Daehong Advertising Inc.; Int'l, pg. 357
DDB NEEDHAM WORLDWIDE INC.—Omnicom Group Inc.; U.S. Public, pg. 1223
DKB & PARTNERS, INC.; U.S. Private, pg. 302
DMB&B/BUDAPEST—DMB&B Communications; U.S. Private, pg. 303
DMB&B COMMUNICATIONS; U.S. Private, pg. 302
DMB&B DUSSELDORF—DMB&B Communications; U.S. Private, pg. 303
DMB&B LISBON—DMB&B Communications; U.S. Private, pg. 304
DMB&B S.A. DE C.V.—DMB&B Communications; U.S. Private, pg. 304
DMB&B/WEEKES MORRIS OSBORN—DMB&B Communications; U.S. Private, pg. 304
DPZ-DUAILIBI, PETIT, ZARAGOZA, PROPAGANDA S.A.; Int'l, pg. 352
DAEHONG ADVERTISING INC.; Int'l, pg. 357
OY DAGMAR AB; Int'l, pg. 359
DAI-ICHI KIKAKU CO. LTD.—Daehong Advertising Inc.; Int'l, pg. 357
DAIKO ADVERTISING, INC.; Int'l, pg. 365
DAIKO HWG ADVERTISING CORP.—Daiko Advertising, Inc.; Int'l, pg. 366
DAILEY & ASSOCIATES—The Interpublic Group of Companies, Inc.; U.S. Public, pg. 909
D'ARCY MASIUS BENTON & BOWLES, S.A.—DMB&B Communications; U.S. Private, pg. 304
DASSAS COMMUNICATION; Int'l, pg. 383
DAVISELEN ADVERTISING, INC.; U.S. Private, pg. 316
MICHAEL DE KRETSER CONSULTANTS—BDDP Group; Int'l, pg. 117
DE LA CRUZ & ASSOCIATES; U.S. Private, pg. 318
DEL RIVERO MESSIANU ADVERTISING, LTD.; U.S. Private, pg. 321
DEMNER, MERLICEK & BERGMANN WERBEGESELLSCHAFT MBH; Int'l, pg. 392
DENTSU EUROPE-AMSTERDAM—Dentsu Inc.; Int'l, pg. 393
DENTSU EUROPE-DUSSELDORF—Dentsu Inc.; Int'l, pg. 393
DENTSU EUROPE LTD.-LONDON—Dentsu Inc.; Int'l, pg. 393
DENTSU INC.; Int'l, pg. 392
DENTSU INC. TAIPEI—Dentsu Inc.; Int'l, pg. 393
DENTSU, SUDLER & HENNESSEY INC.—Dentsu Young & Rubicam Partnerships; U.S. Private, pg. 325
DENTSU USA-ATLANTA OFFICE—Dentsu Inc.; Int'l, pg. 393
DENTSU YOUNG & RUBICAM PARTNERSHIPS; U.S. Private, pg. 325
DESCO ADVERTISING & MARKETING—Desco Corporation; U.S. Private, pg. 327
DEUTSCH, INC.; U.S. Private, pg. 328
DEVON DIRECT MARKETING & ADVERTISING, INC.; U.S. Private, pg. 329
DIAMOND ADVERTISING LTD.—Saatchi & Saatchi Advertising Worldwide; U.S. Public, pg. 1422
DIE HAGER—The Lowe Group; U.S. Private, pg. 678
DOMINO; Int'l, pg. 415
DOREMUS & COMPANY—Omnicom Group Inc.; U.S. Public, pg. 1223
DUGAN VALVA CONTESS INC.; U.S. Private, pg. 345
DUNN REBER GLENN MARZ; U.S. Private, pg. 347
EPG/TBWA—TBWA Chiat/Day; U.S. Private, pg. 1062
EWA LTD.—WPP Group plc; Int'l, pg. 1482
ECOM ET PARTENAIRE; Int'l, pg. 433
EILER & RIEMEL - TESTA—Testa International; Int'l, pg. 1377
EINSON FREEMAN INC.—WPP Group plc; Int'l, pg. 1483
HENRY EISEN ADV. AGENCY, INC.—Tootsie Roll Industries, Inc.; U.S. Public, pg. 1621
EISNER & ASSOCIATES, INC.; U.S. Private, pg. 366
EMMERLING POST, INC.; U.S. Private, pg. 374
ENTERPRISES MEDIA GROUP—Coca-Cola Enterprises Inc.; U.S. Public, pg. 393
EQUATOR—Havas Advertising; Int'l, pg. 602
EQUIPE—Havas Advertising; Int'l, pg. 602
ERVACO GRUPPEN AB; Int'l, pg. 459
EURAD RSCG—Havas Advertising; Int'l, pg. 602
EURO RSCG—Havas Advertising; Int'l, pg. 602
EURO RSCG BARCELONA—Havas Advertising; Int'l, pg. 603
EURO RSCG, COPENHAGEN—Havas Advertising; Int'l, pg. 602
EURO RSCG DAHLIN SMITH WHITE, LLC; U.S. Private, pg. 384
EURO RSCG FRANCE—Havas Advertising; Int'l, pg. 601
EURO RSCG HEALTHCARE—Havas Advertising; Int'l, pg. 603
EURO RSCG MEZZANO COSTANTINI MIGNANI—Havas Advertising; Int'l, pg. 603
EURO RSCG PARTNERSHIP—Havas Advertising; Int'l, pg. 602
EURO RSCG TATHAM—Havas Advertising; Int'l, pg. 601
EURO RSCG WNEK GOSPER—Havas Advertising; Int'l, pg. 603

EUROCOM CONCATO DI PACE SRL—Havas Advertising; *Int'l*, pg. 603
EVANS, HARDY & YOUNG, INC.; *U.S. Private*, pg. 384
EVANSGROUP; *U.S. Private*, pg. 385
FCA!BMZ; *Int'l*, pg. 469
FCA!BMZ CID; *Int'l*, pg. 469
NEIL FABER MEDIA INC.; *U.S. Private*, pg. 390
FAHLGREN; *U.S. Private*, pg. 391
FERRELLCALVILLO COMMUNICATIONS, INC.; *U.S. Private*, pg. 401
FINANCIAL DYNAMICS LTD.—BDDP Group; *Int'l*, pg. 117
FISHER GRAPHIC INDUSTRIES—Container Graphics Corporation; *U.S. Private*, pg. 267
FITZGERALD & CO.; *U.S. Private*, pg. 409
FLEISHMAN-HILLARD INC.; *U.S. Private*, pg. 411
FOCUS MEDIA; *U.S. Private*, pg. 415
FOCUS2020, INC.; *U.S. Private*, pg. 415
FOGARTY KLEIN & PARTNERS; *U.S. Private*, pg. 415
FOGARTY KLEIN & PARTNERS YELLOW PAGES, INC.—Fogarty Klein & Partners; *U.S. Private*, pg. 416
FORD COMMUNICATIONS, INC.—Ford Motor Company; *U.S. Public*, pg. 664
FORTUNE COMMUNICATION HOLDINGS LTD.; *Int'l*, pg. 500
FOVA, INC.—Grey Advertising Inc.; *U.S. Public*, pg. 764
FRANKEL & COMPANY; *U.S. Private*, pg. 424
FRANKFURT BALKIND PARTNERS; *U.S. Private*, pg. 424
LYNNE FRANKS LTD.—BDDP Group; *Int'l*, pg. 117
FREEMAN ASSOCIATES, INC.; *U.S. Private*, pg. 425
CLIFF FREEMAN & PARTNERS—Saatchi & Saatchi Advertising Worldwide; *U.S. Public*, pg. 1422
FUKUSHIMA HAKUHODO INC.—Hakuhodo Incorporated; *Int'l*, pg. 587
GGK ATHENS—TBWA GGK Zurick; *Int'l*, pg. 1335
GGK BARCELONA—TBWA GGK Zurick; *Int'l*, pg. 1335
GGK BASEL—TBWA GGK Zurick; *Int'l*, pg. 1335
GGK BRUSSELS—TBWA GGK Zurick; *Int'l*, pg. 1335
GGK BUDAPEST—TBWA GGK Zurick; *Int'l*, pg. 1335
GGK COMMUNICATIONS—TBWA GGK Zurick; *Int'l*, pg. 1335
GGK COPENHAGEN—TBWA GGK Zurick; *Int'l*, pg. 1335
GGK DUBLIN—TBWA GGK Zurick; *Int'l*, pg. 1335
GGK DUSSELDORF—TBWA GGK Zurick; *Int'l*, pg. 1335
GGK LONDON LTD.—TBWA GGK Zurick; *Int'l*, pg. 1335
GGK MADRID—TBWA GGK Zurick; *Int'l*, pg. 1335
GGK OSLO—TBWA GGK Zurick; *Int'l*, pg. 1335
GGK PARIS—TBWA GGK Zurick; *Int'l*, pg. 1335
GGK SALZBURG—TBWA GGK Zurick; *Int'l*, pg. 1335
GGK SAO PAULO—TBWA GGK Zurick; *Int'l*, pg. 1335
GGK TEL AVIV—TBWA GGK Zurick; *Int'l*, pg. 1336
GGK VIENNA—TBWA GGK Zurick; *Int'l*, pg. 1336
GGK ZURICH—TBWA GGK Zurick; *Int'l*, pg. 1335
GGT ADVERTISING LTD.; *Int'l*, pg. 532
GGT DIRECT ADVERTISING; *Int'l*, pg. 532
GSD&M; *U.S. Private*, pg. 436
GAGE MARKETING GROUP; *U.S. Private*, pg. 437
GARBARSKI EURO RSCG—Havas Advertising; *Int'l*, pg. 603
GARIBOLDI PARISI VERGA/INTERAD—The Lowe Group; *U.S. Private*, pg. 678
GEE, JEFFERY & PARTNERS ADVERTISING INC.; *Int'l*, pg. 542
GEERS GROSS ADVERTISING LIMITED; *Int'l*, pg. 542
GENERAL MILLS, MARKETING SERVICES DIV.—General Mills, Inc.; *U.S. Public*, pg. 718
GEO-YOUNG & RUBICAM—Young & Rubicam Inc.; *U.S. Private*, pg. 1199
GETINGE/CASTLE, INC.; *U.S. Private*, pg. 449
GIANETTINO & MEREDITH ADVERTISING; *U.S. Private*, pg. 450
GILLESPIE; *U.S. Private*, pg. 453
GILLESPIE PUBLIC RELATIONS—Gillespie; *U.S. Private*, pg. 454
GIRGENTI, HUGHES, BUTLER & MCDOWELL; *U.S. Private*, pg. 455
GITAM/BBDO; *Int'l*, pg. 552
GLOBAL MARKETING RESOURCES (GMR); *U.S. Private*, pg. 457
GOLDBERG MOSER O'NEILL; *U.S. Private*, pg. 459
GOLDSMITH/JEFFREY INC.; *U.S. Private*, pg. 462
LEON SHAFFER GOLNICK ADVERTISING, INC.; *U.S. Private*, pg. 463
GRACE & ROTHSCHILD; *U.S. Private*, pg. 468
GRAFFITI/DMB&B—DMB&B Communications; *U.S. Private*, *pg. 304*
GRANT/JACOBY, INC.; *U.S. Private*, pg. 470
GRANT MARKETING COMMUNICATIONS; *U.S. Private*, pg. 470
GRASS ROOTS GROUP PLC—WPP Group plc; *Int'l*, pg. 1482
GREENSTONE ROBERTS ADVERTISING; *U.S. Public*, pg. 763
GREY ADVERTISING INC.; *U.S. Public*, pg. 764
GREY ASIA PACIFIC—Grey Advertising Inc.; *U.S. Public*, pg. 765
GREY DAIKO ADVERTISING, INC.—Daiko Advertising, Inc.; *Int'l*, pg. 366
GREY EUROPE/BRUSSELS—Grey Advertising Inc.; *U.S. Public*, pg. 765
GRIFFIN BACAL INC.; *U.S. Private*, pg. 480
GRIZZARD; *U.S. Private*, pg. 482
GRUNER + JAHR INTERNATIONAL MARKETING- AND MEDIA SERVICES, INC.—Bertelsmann AG; *Int'l*, pg. 190
GUTHY-RENKER CORP.; *U.S. Private*, pg. 488
H&C, LEO BURNETT—Leo Burnett Company, Inc.; *U.S. Private*, pg. 184
HLPB—Testa International; *Int'l*, pg. 1377
HLS CORP.—WPP Group plc; *Int'l*, pg. 1483
HMS PARTNERS; *U.S. Private*, pg. 491
HAKUHODO ADVERTISING AMERICA INC.—Hakuhodo Incorporated; *Int'l*, pg. 588
HAKUHODO DEUTSCHLAND GMBH—Hakuhodo Incorporated; *Int'l*, pg. 588
HAKUHODO FRANCE S.A.—Hakuhodo Incorporated; *Int'l*, pg. 588
HAKUHODO HONG KONG LTD.—Hakuhodo Incorporated; *Int'l*, pg. 588
HAKUHODO INCORPORATED; *Int'l*, pg. 587
HAKUHODO LINTAS—Hakuhodo Incorporated; *Int'l*, pg. 587
HAKUHODO MALAYSIA SDN. BHD.—Hakuhodo Incorporated; *Int'l*, pg. 588
HAKUHODO PRO'S, INC.—Hakuhodo Incorporated; *Int'l*, pg. 588
HAKUHODO SINGAPORE PTE. LTD.—Hakuhodo Incorporated; *Int'l*, pg. 588
HAKUHODO U.K. LTD.—Hakuhodo Incorporated; *Int'l*, pg. 588
HAMILTON COMMUNICATIONS GROUP, INC.; *U.S. Private*, pg. 497
HAMPEL/STEFANIDES; *U.S. Private*, pg. 498
HANFT BYRNE RABOY ABRAMS & PARTNERS, INC.; *U.S. Private*, pg. 499
HARRIS DRURY COHEN; *U.S. Private*, pg. 505
HARRISON & STAR, INC.; *U.S. Private*, pg. 506
HAVAS ADVERTISING; *Int'l*, pg. 600
HAWAIIAN ADVERTISING & PUBLIC RELATIONS, INC.—Servco Pacific Inc.; *U.S. Private*, pg. 986
HAWORTH GROUP INC.; *U.S. Private*, pg. 511
HAWTHORNE COMMUNICATIONS, INC.; *U.S. Private*, pg. 512
HEALTH EDUCATION TECHNOLOGIES (HET) DIV.—Omnicom Group Inc.; *U.S. Public*, pg. 1224
HEIL-BRICE RETAIL ADVERTISING; *U.S. Private*, pg. 519
HEMISPHERE-LEO BURNETT, INC.—Leo Burnett Company, Inc.; *U.S. Private*, pg. 184
HERRING NEWMAN; *U.S. Private*, pg. 524
HILL, HOLLIDAY, CONNORS, COSMOPULOS, INC.; *U.S. Private*, pg. 529
BERNARD HODES GROUP—Omnicom Group Inc.; *U.S. Public*, pg. 1224
MICHAEL HOGG-YOUNG & RUBICAM (PVT.) LTD.—Young & Rubicam Inc.; *U.S. Private*, pg. 1198
HOLLAND MARK MARTIN; *U.S. Private*, pg. 534
HOLLISTER ADVERTISING; *U.S. Public*, pg. 830
HOUSTON HERSTEK FAVAT; *U.S. Private*, pg. 542
HOWARD, MERRELL & PARTNERS, INC.; *U.S. Private*, pg. 542
HOWELL HENRY CHALDECOTT LURY & PARTNERS; *Int'l*, pg. 637
I&S CORP.; *Int'l*, pg. 642
ICON INTERNATIONAL; *U.S. Private*, pg. 556
IMPACT COMMUNICATIONS GROUP—True North Communications Inc.; *U.S. Public*, pg. 1641
IMPULS ADVERTISING AG; *Int'l*, pg. 666
INDUSTRIE-RING SACH-UND VERSICHERUNGS-VERMITTLUNGSGESELLSCHAFT MBH—Saarbergwerke Aktiengesellschaft; *Int'l*, pg. 1166
INGALLS; *U.S. Private*, pg. 562
INTEGRATED MARKETING GROUP; *U.S. Private*, pg. 566
INTERBRAND SCHECHTER—Omnicom Group Inc.; *U.S. Public*, pg. 1224
INTERMARKETS ADVERTISING; *Int'l*, pg. 680
THE INTERPUBLIC GROUP OF COMPANIES, INC.; *U.S. Public*, pg. 908
ITALIA/GAL ADVERTISING; *U.S. Private*, pg. 576
J&M COMPANY—My Own Meals, Inc.; *U.S. Private*, pg. 770
JL MEDIA, INC.; *U.S. Private*, pg. 577
JLH ADVERTISING, INC.—BeautiControl Cosmetics, Inc.; *U.S. Public*, pg. 198
JWG ASSOCIATES, INC.; *U.S. Private*, pg. 579
JANIK & ASSOCIATES, INC.; *U.S. Private*, pg. 582
JAVELIN/YOUNG & RUBICAM—Young & Rubicam Inc.; *U.S. Private*, pg. 1199
JAY ADVERTISING, INC.; *U.S. Private*, pg. 583
JIMENEZ/DMB&B—DMB&B Communications; *U.S. Private*, *pg. 304*
JORDAN, MCGRATH, CASE & TAYLOR INC.; *U.S. Private*, pg. 598
JORDAN TAMRAZ CARUSO ADVERTISING, INC.; *U.S. Private*, pg. 599
JUMP—BDDP Group; *Int'l*, pg. 116
K-C ADVERTISING, INC.—Kimberly-Clark Corporation; *U.S.* Public, pg. 959
KKBR/CONQUEST—WPP Group plc; *Int'l*, pg. 1484
KPR—Omnicom Group Inc.; *U.S. Public*, pg. 1224
KABUTO INTERNATIONAL PHOENIX INC.—Kabuto Decom Inc.; *Int'l*, pg. 721
KARAKAS, VANSICKLE, OUELLETTE ADVERTISING & PUBLIC RELATIONS; *U.S. Private*, pg. 607
KEILER & COMPANY; *U.S. Private*, pg. 611
KELLER CRESCENT CO.; *U.S. Private*, pg. 612
KELLY, SCOTT AND MADISON, INC.; *U.S. Private*, pg. 613
KELLY WEEDON SHUTE PARTNERSHIP; *Int'l*, pg. 727
KENDO—Havas Advertising; *Int'l*, pg. 601
KETCHUM COMMUNICATIONS INC.; *U.S. Private*, pg. 616
KEYES MARTIN; *U.S. Private*, pg. 618
KIRSHENBAUM, BOND & PARTNERS; *U.S. Private*, pg. 624
KLEMTNER ADVERTISING INC.—Saatchi & Saatchi Advertising Worldwide; *U.S. Public*, pg. 1422
KOREY, KAY & PARTNERS; *U.S. Private*, pg. 632
KOVEL KRESSER & PARTNERS; *U.S. Private*, pg. 634
KRAGIE/NEWELL; *U.S. Private*, pg. 634
KUPPER PARKER COMMUNICATIONS INC.; *U.S. Private*, *pg. 637*
KYODO ADVERTISING CO., LTD.; *Int'l*, pg. 776
LVL ADVERTISING; *U.S. Private*, pg. 640
LAGON—Havas Advertising; *Int'l*, pg. 601
LALLY, MCFARLAND & PANTELLO INC.—Havas Advertising; *Int'l*, pg. 601
LANSDOWN CONQUEST—WPP Group plc; *Int'l*, pg. 1482
LARKIN MEEDER & SCHWEIDEL; *U.S. Private*, pg. 651
LAUGHLIN/CONSTABLE, INC.; *U.S. Private*, pg. 653
LE NOUVEL ELDORADO—Havas Advertising; *Int'l*, pg. 600
THE LEAP PARTNERSHIP; *U.S. Private*, pg. 655
AL PAUL LEFTON CO., INC.; *U.S. Private*, pg. 658
LEVENSON & HILL, INC.; *U.S. Private*, pg. 662
JACK LEVY ASSOCIATES; *U.S. Private*, pg. 664
LIGGETT-STASHOWER, INC.; *U.S. Private*, pg. 667
LOIS/EJL CHICAGO—Lois/USA Inc.; *U.S. Public*, pg. 1011
LOIS/EJL NEW YORK—Lois/USA Inc.; *U.S. Public*, pg. 1011
LOIS/USA INC.; *U.S. Public*, pg. 1011
LOIS/EJL LOS ANGELES; *U.S. Private*, pg. 673
LOUIS LONDON ADVERTISING & SALES PROMOTION; *U.S. Private*, pg. 674
THE LORD GROUP—Dentsu Young & Rubicam Partnerships; *U.S. Private*, pg. 325
LORD, SULLIVAN & YODER INC. MARKETING COMMUNICATIONS; *U.S. Private*, pg. 676
LOTAS MINARD PATTON MCGIVER; *U.S. Private*, pg. 677
LOWE & PARTNERS—The Lowe Group; *U.S. Private*, pg. 678
THE LOWE GROUP; *U.S. Private*, pg. 677
LOWE HOWARD-SPINK—The Lowe Group; *U.S. Private*, pg. 678
LOWE KUIPER & SCHOUTEN—The Lowe Group; *U.S. Private*, pg. 678
LOWE MBAC—The Lowe Group; *U.S. Private*, pg. 678
LOWE MCADAMS HEALTHCARE; *U.S. Private*, pg. 678
LOWE TROOST—The Lowe Group; *U.S. Private*, pg. 678
LYONS LAVEY NICKEL SWIFT, INC.—Omnicom Group Inc.; *U.S. Public*, pg. 1224
MCL—Saatchi & Saatchi Advertising Worldwide; *U.S. Public*, pg. 1422
MHI PARTNERS WERBEAGENTUR GMBH—Saatchi & Saatchi Advertising Worldwide; *U.S. Public*, pg. 1422
MK-MAINOS OY—Kesko Ltd.; *Int'l*, pg. 732
M.L.&S. WERBEAGENTUR GMBH; *Int'l*, pg. 827
MRA, AN INTEGRATED MARKETING COMMUNICATIONS AGENCY; *U.S. Private*, pg. 687
MACNAMARA, STEWART & SAPERSTEIN; *U.S. Private*, pg. 692
MAGNA MEDIA INC.—Macromedia Incorporated; *U.S. Private*, pg. 693
MAN NEN SHA INC.; *Int'l*, pg. 834
MAPFRE VIDEO Y COMUNICAION, S.A.—Corporacion MAPFRE, Compania Internacional de Reaseguros, S.A.; *Int'l*, pg. 334
MARC; *U.S. Private*, pg. 701
MARGEOTES/FERTITTA & PARTNERS INC.; *U.S. Private*, *pg. 702*
MARKETFORCE ADVERTISING PHILIPPINES INC.—Dentsu Young & Rubicam Partnerships; *U.S. Private*, pg. 325
MARKETING CORP. OF AMERICA; *U.S. Private*, pg. 704
MARKETING SUPPORT, INCORPORATED; *U.S. Private*, pg. 705
MARKOM/LEO BURNETT A.S.—Leo Burnett Company, Inc.; *U.S. Private*, pg. 186
MARS ADVERTISING CO.; *U.S. Private*, pg. 706
MARSHALL JACCOMA MITCHELL ADVERTISING; *U.S. Private*, pg. 708
MARTIN/WILLIAMS ADVERTISING INC.; *U.S. Private*, pg. 710
MCCABE & COMPANY; *U.S. Private*, pg. 719
MCCANN-ERICKSON WORLDWIDE—The Interpublic Group of Companies, Inc.; *U.S. Public*, pg. 909
THE MCCLURE GROUP; *U.S. Private*, pg. 719
MCCONNAUGHY STEIN SCHMIDT BROWN; *U.S. Private*, pg. 720
MCKINNEY & MCKINNEY ADVERTISING; *U.S. Private*, pg. 723
MCKINNEY & SILVER; *U.S. Private*, pg. 723
MEDIA FIRST INTERNATIONAL, INC.; *U.S. Private*, pg. 726
THE MEDIA INVESTMENT GROUP; *U.S. Private*, pg. 726
MEDIA PA—BDDP Group; *Int'l*, pg. 116
MEDIA RESOURCES INTERNATIONAL; *U.S. Private*, pg. 727
MEDIA THAT WORKS; *U.S. Private*, pg. 727
MEGA ADVERTISING, INC.—Media General, Inc.; *U.S. Public*, pg. 1078
MEITSU INC.; *Int'l*, pg. 856
MELDRUM & FEWSMITH COMMUNICATIONS INC.; *U.S. Private*, pg. 730
MELVILLE ADVERTISING INC.—Sbarro, Inc.; *U.S. Public*, pg. 1436
MENDELSOHN/ZIEN ADVERTISING, INC.; *U.S. Private*, pg. 731
MENDOZA, DILLON & ASOCIADOS, INC.—WPP Group plc; *Int'l*, pg. 1483
MESSAGES & TEQUILA—BDDP Group; *Int'l*, pg. 116
J.W. MESSNER, INC.; *U.S. Private*, pg. 734
MESSNER VETERE BERGER MCNAMEE SCHMETTERER/EURO RSCG—Havas Advertising; *Int'l*, *pg. 602*
MEZZINA/BROWN INC.; *U.S. Private*, pg. 739
MICKELBERRY COMMUNICATIONS, INC.; *U.S. Private*, pg. 741
MILLER ADVERTISING AGENCY INC.; *U.S. Private*, pg. 746
MILLER/KADANOFF/HUBER DIRECT & INTERACTIVE; *U.S. Private*, pg. 747
MILLER MEESTER ADVERTISING INC.; *U.S. Private*, pg. 747
MILLWARD BROWN INTERNATIONAL—WPP Group plc; *Int'l*, pg. 1482
MINTZ & HOKE INC.; *U.S. Private*, pg. 751
MORIOKA HAKUHODO INC.—Hakuhodo Incorporated; *Int'l*, pg. 588
MOROCH & ASSOC., INC.; *U.S. Private*, pg. 762
ERIC MOWER AND ASSOCIATES/BUFFALO, INC.—Eric Mower and Associates, Inc.; *U.S. Private*, pg. 765
ERIC MOWER AND ASSOCIATES, INC.; *U.S. Private*, pg. 765
MULLEN ADVERTISING, INC.; *U.S. Private*, pg. 766
NAMBOKUSHA INC.; *Int'l*, pg. 904

NAVAR BDDP—BDDP Group; *Int'l*, pg. 117
NEWS AMERICA MARKETING—The News Corporation Limited; *Int'l*, pg. 925
NICKEL—BDDP Group; *Int'l*, pg. 116
NIHON KEIZAI SHIMBUN AMERICA, INC.—Nihon Keizai Shimbun, Inc.; *Int'l*, pg. 929
NIHON KEIZAI SHIMBUN EUROPE LTD.-FRANKFURT—Nihon Keizai Shimbun, Inc.; *Int'l*, pg. 930
NIHON KEIZAI SHIMBUN EUROPE LTD.-PARIS—Nihon Keizai Shimbun, Inc.; *Int'l*, pg. 930
NIKKEI ADVERTISING CO.; *Int'l*, pg. 930
NIPPO CORPORATION; *Int'l*, pg. 932
NITTSU REAL ESTATE CO., LTD.—Nippon Express Co., Ltd.; *Int'l*, pg. 934
NOBLE & ASSOCIATES; *U.S. Private*, pg. 800
NOORDERVLIET & WINNINGHOFF/LEO BURNETT B.V.—Leo Burnett Company, Inc.; *U.S. Private*, pg. 186
NORTH CASTLE PARTNERS ADVERTISING, INC.; *U.S. Private*, pg. 804
NORTH CENTRAL LIFE INSURANCE COMPANY—Financial Life Companies, Inc.; *U.S. Private*, pg. 404
NORTHLICH STOLLEY LAWARRE; *U.S. Private*, pg. 806
NOUVELLE VAGUE—BDDP Group; *Int'l*, pg. 116
OAKLEY YOUNG/4TH DIMENSION—WPP Group plc; *Int'l*, pg. 1482
OGILVY & MATHER WORLDWIDE, INC.—WPP Group plc; *Int'l*, pg. 1483
OMNICOM GROUP INC.; *U.S. Public*, pg. 1223
154-TESTA—Testa International; *Int'l*, pg. 1377
ORICOM INC.; *Int'l*, pg. 1008
OSPREY PARK LTD.; *Int'l*, pg. 1012
OUTDOOR SYSTEMS, INC.—Outdoor Systems, Inc.; *U.S. Public*, pg. 1235
PDS AGENCY, INC.—Proffitt's, Inc.; *U.S. Public*, pg. 1334
PMSVW/YOUNG & RUBICAM B.V.—Young & Rubicam Inc.; *U.S. Private*, pg. 1199
PACE ADVERTISING—WPP Group plc; *Int'l*, pg. 1483
PALISADES MEDIA GROUP, INC.; *U.S. Private*, pg. 834
PALMER JARVIS COMMUNICATIONS; *Int'l*, pg. 1022
PARADIGM COMMUNICATIONS; *U.S. Private*, pg. 838
PARTNERS & SHEVACK, INC.; *U.S. Private*, pg. 842
PEDONE & PARTNERS ADV., INC.; *U.S. Private*, pg. 846
RICARDO PEREZ ASOCIADOS; *Int'l*, pg. 1036
PERISCOPE MARKETING COMMUNICATIONS; *U.S. Private*, pg. 853
PERWANAL/D'ARCY MASIUS BENTON & BOWLES—DMB&B Communications; *U.S. Private*, pg. 305
PICCADILLY ADVERTISING AGENCY, INC.—Commerce Group Corp.; *U.S. Public*, pg. 410
PIRELLA GOTTSCHE LOWE—The Lowe Group; *U.S. Private*, pg. 678
PLUSPOINT—N.V. Koninklijke Bijenkorf Beheer KBB; *Int'l*, pg. 750
POPPE TYSON—True North Diversified Companies; *U.S. Public*, pg. 1642
POSNICK & KOLKER, INC.; *U.S. Private*, pg. 876
POULTER COMMUNICATIONS PLC; *Int'l*, pg. 1065
PRICE/MCNABB, INC.; *U.S. Private*, pg. 883
PRODUCTA-TBWA—TBWA Chiat/Day; *U.S. Private*, pg. 1062
PROLAM/YOUNG & RUBICAM S.A.—Young & Rubicam Inc.; *U.S. Private*, pg. 1200
PUBLICIS/BLOOM—FCA!BMZ; *Int'l*, pg. 469
PUBLICIS/BLOOM INC.—FCA!BMZ; *Int'l*, pg. 470
PUBLICITARIA CUMBRE—Saatchi & Saatchi Advertising Worldwide; *U.S. Public*, pg. 1422
PUBLICITAS C.A.—Saatchi & Saatchi Advertising Worldwide; *U.S. Public*, pg. 1422
QUANTA ADVERTISING CORPORATION—Carrols Corporation; *U.S. Private*, pg. 216
QUANTUM MEDIA INTERNATIONAL, INC.; *U.S. Private*, pg. 899
RBT/STRUM; *U.S. Private*, pg. 902
RET CORP.—Time Warner Inc.; *U.S. Public*, pg. 1615
RT REKLAMEBUREAU A/S; *Int'l*, pg. 1081
RTCDIRECT—WPP Group plc; *Int'l*, pg. 1483
RADIO DIRECT RESPONSE; *U.S. Private*, pg. 906
REDIFFUSION-DY&R PVT. LTD.—Dentsu Young & Rubicam Partnerships; *U.S. Private*, pg. 326
RESOURCE MARKETING, INC.; *U.S. Private*, pg. 924
RHEA & KAISER MARKETING COMMUNICATIONS; *U.S. Private*, pg. 927
THE RICHARDS GROUP, INC.; *U.S. Private*, pg. 929
RILEY ADVERTISING LIMITED; *Int'l*, pg. 1117
HAL RINEY & PARTNERS HEARTLAND—Hal Riney & Partners, Inc.; *U.S. Private*, pg. 931
HAL RINEY & PARTNERS, INC.; *U.S. Private*, pg. 931
RIVES CARLBERG; *U.S. Private*, pg. 934
ROBERTSON LEO BURNETT PTY. LTD.—Leo Burnett Company, Inc.; *U.S. Private*, pg. 186
ROCKETT, BURKHEAD, LEWIS & WINSLOW; *U.S. Private*, pg. 938
ROMANN & TANNENHOLZ ADVERTISING, INC.; *U.S. Private*, pg. 942
ROSS ROY COMMUNICATIONS, INC.; *U.S. Private*, pg. 946
RUBIN EHRENTHAL & ASSOCIATES; *U.S. Private*, pg. 949
RUBIN POSTAER & ASSOCIATES; *U.S. Private*, pg. 949
RUIZ NICOLI GROUP—Havas Advertising; *Int'l*, pg. 603
RUPPMAN MARKETING TECHNOLOGIES, INC.; *U.S. Private*, pg. 951
RYAN DROSSMAN & PARTNERS; *U.S. Private*, pg. 953
SBC ADVERTISING; *U.S. Private*, pg. 955
SFM MEDIA CORPORATION; *U.S. Private*, pg. 956
SAATCHI & SAATCHI ADVERTISING WORLDWIDE; *U.S. Public*, pg. 1422
THE ST. GEORGE GROUP, INC.; *U.S. Private*, pg. 960
SANCHO S.A.—Saatchi & Saatchi Advertising Worldwide; *U.S. Public*, pg. 1422
SANGAM COMMUNICATIONS CO., LTD.—Grey Advertising Inc.; *U.S. Public*, pg. 765
SANKOSHA ADVERTISING AGENCY, LTD.; *Int'l*, pg. 1189
THE SAWTOOTH GROUP; *U.S. Private*, pg. 969
SAWYER RILEY COMPTON INC.; *U.S. Private*, pg. 969
SCAN-AD GRUPPEN A/S; *Int'l*, pg. 1198
SCHOLZ & FRIENDS GMBH; *Int'l*, pg. 1210
PAUL SCHULMAN CO.—BDDP Group; *Int'l*, pg. 117
SCHUSTER & PARTNER; *Int'l*, pg. 1210
SCOTT STERN ASSOCIATES LIMITED—WPP Group plc; *Int'l*, pg. 1482
SELECT COMMUNICATIONS, L.P.; *U.S. Private*, pg. 982
SEOUL DMB&B, INC.; *Int'l*, pg. 1223
SERINO COYNE INC.; *U.S. Private*, pg. 985
SERVICEPLAN GMBH; *Int'l*, pg. 1225
SHAKER ADVERTISING AGENCY; *U.S. Private*, pg. 988
SHANDWICK INTERNATIONAL PLC; *Int'l*, pg. 1226
SHANGHAI INDUSTRIAL CONSULTANTS; *Int'l*, pg. 1228
SHERWOOD & JAMES ADVERTISING, INC.—Union Camp Corporation; *U.S. Public*, pg. 1666
SICOLAMARTIN INC.; *U.S. Private*, pg. 998
SIMMONS, DURHAM & ASSOCIATES; *U.S. Private*, pg. 1000
SIMON & ASSOCIATES; *U.S. Private*, pg. 1001
SIMONS PALMER DENTON CLEMMOW & JOHNSON LTD.; *Int'l*, pg. 1252
SIVE/YOUNG & RUBICAM L.P.—Young & Rubicam Inc.; *U.S. Private*, pg. 1197
THE SLOAN-MAJOR AGENCY, INC.—Golden Enterprises Inc.; *U.S. Public*, pg. 750
SOGEI INC.; *Int'l*, pg. 1277
SOJE/LONSDALE ADVERTISING INC—Saatchi & Saatchi Advertising Worldwide; *U.S. Public*, pg. 1422
SONNENBERG MURPHY LEO BURNETT—Leo Burnett Company, Inc.; *U.S. Private*, pg. 186
STACKIG ADVERTISING AND PUBLIC RELATIONS; *U.S. Private*, pg. 1028
STATE ADVERTISING AGENCY, INC.—Evans, Inc.; *U.S. Public*, pg. 597
THE STEPHENZ GROUP, INC.; *U.S. Private*, pg. 1040
SUISSA MILLER ADVERTISING, INC.; *U.S. Private*, pg. 1049
THE SUNFLOWER GROUP; *U.S. Private*, pg. 1052
SYNERGIE—Havas Advertising; *Int'l*, pg. 601
SYNERGIE TOKYU DMB&B LTD.—DMB&B Communications; *U.S. Private*, pg. 305
TBWA CHIAT/DAY; *U.S. Private*, pg. 1062
TBWA CHIAT/DAY ST. LOUIS—TBWA Chiat/Day; *U.S. Private*, pg. 1062
TBWA DUSSELDORF GMBH—TBWA Chiat/Day; *U.S. Private*, pg. 1063
TBWA GERMANY—TBWA Chiat/Day; *U.S. Private*, pg. 1063
TBWA GGK ZURICK; *Int'l*, pg. 1335
TLPARTNERSHIP—Omnicom Group Inc.; *U.S. Public*, pg. 1224
TMD CARAT ADVERTISING LIMITED; *Int'l*, pg. 1342
TMP WORLDWIDE, INC.; *U.S. Private*, pg. 1064
TMP WORLDWIDE PTY LIMITED; *Int'l*, pg. 1342
TN ENTERTAINMENT—True North Communications Inc.; *U.S. Public*, pg. 1641
TTA/NEWPORT, INC.—Ted Thomas Associates Inc. Advertising; *U.S. Private*, pg. 1083
TARGET ADVERTISING AGENCY LIMITED; *Int'l*, pg. 1355
TARGET EURO RSCG—Havas Advertising; *Int'l*, pg. 603
TARGETCOM, INC.; *U.S. Private*, pg. 1069
TARGETS-LEO BURNETT ADVERTISING—Leo Burnett Company, Inc.; *U.S. Private*, pg. 186
TAUBE/VIOLANTE, INC.; *U.S. Private*, pg. 1069
TAUSCHE MARTIN LONSDORF; *U.S. Private*, pg. 1069
TELEPHONE DIRECTORY ADVERTISING; *U.S. Private*, pg. 1073
TEMKIN & TEMKIN; *U.S. Private*, pg. 1074
TESTA INTERNATIONAL; *Int'l*, pg. 1376
TEXTUEL—BDDP Group; *Int'l*, pg. 116
THAI HAKUHODO CO., LTD.—Hakuhodo Incorporated; *Int'l*, pg. 589
THE MEDIA EDGE; *U.S. Private*, pg. 1079
TED THOMAS ASSOCIATES INC. ADVERTISING; *U.S. Private*, pg. 1083
J. WALTER THOMPSON COMPANY—WPP Group plc; *Int'l*, pg. 1483
TIERNEY & PARTNERS—True North Communications Inc.; *U.S. Public*, pg. 1641
TIMMONS & COMPANY INC.—WPP Group plc; *Int'l*, pg. 1483
TINSLEY ADVERTISING; *U.S. Private*, pg. 1088
TODD ADVERTISING AGENCY, INC.—J.L. Todd Auction Co.; *U.S. Private*, pg. 1090
TOKYO SENKO INTERNATIONAL INC.; *Int'l*, pg. 1394
TOKYU AGENCY INTERNATIONAL/DMB&B JAPAN—DMB&B Communications; *U.S. Private*, pg. 305
TOSTMANN & DOMANN—TBWA GGK Zurick; *Int'l*, pg. 1336
TOTH DESIGN; *U.S. Private*, pg. 1093
TOWNE, SILVERSTEIN, ROTTER INC.; *U.S. Private*, pg. 1093
TRAHAN, BURDEN & CHARLES, INC.; *U.S. Private*, pg. 1095
TRONE ADVERTISING, INC.; *U.S. Private*, pg. 1104
TRUE NORTH COMMUNICATIONS INC.; *U.S. Public*, pg. 1641
TRUE NORTH DIVERSIFIED COMPANIES; *U.S. Public*, pg. 1642
U-HAUL INTERNATIONAL, INC.—Amerco; *U.S. Private*, pg. 49
URM STORES, INC.; *U.S. Private*, pg. 1114
UNITED-ASATSU INTERNATIONAL LTD.—Asatsu Inc.; *Int'l*, pg. 86
UNITROS—Havas Advertising; *Int'l*, pg. 603
UNIWORLD GROUP, INC.; *U.S. Private*, pg. 1128
V UND B—Havas Advertising; *Int'l*, pg. 603
VPV EURO RSCG—Havas Advertising; *Int'l*, pg. 603
VALENTINE RADFORD, INC.; *U.S. Private*, pg. 1131
VAN ZANDBEEK/THE CORPORATE COMPANY—BDDP Group; *Int'l*, pg. 118
VEDA DESIGN GROUP—Veridian; *U.S. Private*, pg. 1136
VILLADCO INC.—Banfi Vintners; *U.S. Private*, pg. 113
VINIZIUS/YOUNG & RUBICAM, S.A.—Young & Rubicam Inc.; *U.S. Private*, pg. 1199
VITRUVIO-LEO BURNETT—Leo Burnett Company, Inc.; *U.S. Private*, pg. 186
VITRUVIO/LEO BURNETT—Leo Burnett Company, Inc.; *U.S. Private*, pg. 186
WCRS—Havas Advertising; *Int'l*, pg. 603
WOB MARKETINGKOMMUNIKATION AG; *Int'l*, pg. 1482
WPP GROUP PLC; *Int'l*, pg. 1482
WPP GROUP USA INC.—WPP Group plc; *Int'l*, pg. 1483
WARING & LAROSA, INC.; *U.S. Private*, pg. 1150
WARWICK BAKER O'NEILL; *U.S. Private*, pg. 1152
THE WEIGHTMAN GROUP; *U.S. Private*, pg. 1159
WEISS, WHITTEN, STAGLIANO INC.; *U.S. Private*, pg. 1160
WELLS BDDP, INC.—BDDP Group; *Int'l*, pg. 117
WEST ADVERTISING/PUBLIC RELATIONS, INC.—KOA Holdings; *U.S. Private*, pg. 603
WESTAG WERBEAGENTUR; *Int'l*, pg. 1491
THE WESTERFELDS, INC.; *U.S. Private*, pg. 1164
WESTERN INTERNATIONAL MEDIA CORPORATION; *U.S. Private*, pg. 1165
WESTWAYNE, INC.; *U.S. Private*, pg. 1170
WIEDEN & KENNEDY, INC.; *U.S. Private*, pg. 1175
WILLIAMS WORLDWIDE; *U.S. Private*, pg. 1179
WINKLER ADVERTISING; *U.S. Private*, pg. 1183
WINNER COMMUNICATIONS, INC.; *U.S. Private*, pg. 1183
WUNDERMAN CATO JOHNSON—Young & Rubicam Inc.; *U.S. Private*, pg. 1197
WUNDERMAN WORLDWIDE LIMITED—Young & Rubicam Inc.; *U.S. Private*, pg. 1199
WYSE ADVERTISING; *U.S. Private*, pg. 1193
Y&R MATTINGLY—Dentsu Young & Rubicam Partnerships; *U.S. Private*, pg. 325
YAFFE & COMPANY; *U.S. Private*, pg. 1195
YAR COMMUNICATIONS; *U.S. Private*, pg. 1195
YESAWICH, PEPPERDINE & BROWN; *U.S. Private*, pg. 1195
YOMIKO ADVERTISING INC.; *Int'l*, pg. 1522
YOUNG & RUBICAM FINLAND—Young & Rubicam Inc.; *U.S. Private*, pg. 1199
YOUNG & RUBICAM INC.; *U.S. Private*, pg. 1196
ZICCARDI & PARTNERS, INC.; *U.S. Private*, pg. 1205
ZIMMERMAN & PARTNERS ADVERTISING, INC.; *U.S. Private*, pg. 1206

7312 — OUTDOOR ADVERTISING SERVICES

ACKERLEY COMMUNICATIONS OF FLORIDA, INC.—The Ackerley Group; *U.S. Public*, pg. 16
ACKERLEY COMMUNICATIONS OF THE NORTHWEST-PORTLAND—The Ackerley Group; *U.S. Public*, pg. 15
ACKERLEY COMMUNICATIONS OF THE NORTHWEST-SEATTLE—The Ackerley Group; *U.S. Public*, pg. 15
THE ACKERLEY GROUP; *U.S. Public*, pg. 15
CAPITOL OUTDOOR ADVERTISING, INC.—Cigna Corp.; *U.S. Public*, pg. 361
DUALITE INC.; *U.S. Private*, pg. 344
ELLER MEDIA COMPANY—Clear Channel Communications, Inc.; *U.S. Public*, pg. 383
HAVAS ADVERTISING; *Int'l*, pg. 600
MORRIS COMMUNICATIONS CORPORATION—Shivers Trading & Operating Co.; *U.S. Private*, pg. 995
OUTDOOR COMMUNICATIONS, INC.; *U.S. Private*, pg. 822
SHIVERS TRADING & OPERATING CO.; *U.S. Private*, pg. 994
SIGNBOARD HILL PRODUCTIONS—Hallmark Cards, Inc.; *U.S. Private*, pg. 496

7313 — RADIO, TELEVISION & PUBLISHERS' ADVERTISING REPRESENTATIVES

ABC, INC—The Walt Disney Company; *U.S. Public*, pg. 511
ALL AMERICAN COMMUNICATIONS, INC.; *U.S. Public*, pg. 41
ALL AMERICAN TELEVISION, INC.—All American Communications, Inc.; *U.S. Public*, pg. 41
BLAIR TELEVISION; *U.S. Private*, pg. 148
CABLEREP, INC.—Cox Communications, Inc.; *U.S. Public*, pg. 455
CANADIAN BROADCAST SALES—WIC Western International Communications Ltd.; *Int'l*, pg. 1482
CAPITAL CITIES/ABC BROADCAST GROUP—The Walt Disney Company; *U.S. Public*, pg. 511
CAPITAL CITIES/ABC NATIONAL TELEVISION SALES, INC.—The Walt Disney Company; *U.S. Public*, pg. 511
CHRISTAL RADIO—Chancellor Media Corporation; *U.S. Public*, pg. 335
EASTMAN RADIO, INC.—Chancellor Media Corporation; *U.S. Public*, pg. 335
KATZ AMERICAN TELEVISION—Chancellor Media Corporation; *U.S. Public*, pg. 335
KATZ CONTINENTAL TELEVISION—Chancellor Media Corporation; *U.S. Public*, pg. 335
KATZ HISPANIC MEDIA—Chancellor Media Corporation; *U.S. Public*, pg. 335
KATZ MEDIA GROUP, INC.—Chancellor Media Corporation; *U.S. Public*, pg. 335
KATZ NATIONAL TELEVISION—Chancellor Media Corporation; *U.S. Public*, pg. 335
KATZ RADIO—Chancellor Media Corporation; *U.S. Public*, pg. 335
KNIGHT-RIDDER, INC.; *U.S. Public*, pg. 963
MEDIASPOT, INC.; *U.S. Private*, pg. 727
THE NETWORK OF CITY BUSINESS JOURNALS, INC.—Advance Publications Inc.; *U.S. Private*, pg. 19
NEWHOUSE NEWSPAPERS METRO-SUBURBIA, INC.—Advance Publications Inc.; *U.S. Private*, pg. 20
NEWSPAPERS FIRST—Knight-Ridder, Inc.; *U.S. Public*, pg. 964
NIKKEI INTERNATIONAL LTD.—Nihon Keizai Shimbun, Inc.; *Int'l*, pg. 929

R.J. PALMER, INC.; *U.S. Private*, pg. 835
RAINBOW ADVERTISING SALES CORPORATION (RASCO)—Cablevision Systems Corporation; *U.S. Public*, *pg. 288*
RIZZOLI INTERNATIONAL PUBLICATIONS, INC.—R.C.S. Editori S.p.A.; *Int'l*, pg. 1078
SAN FRANCISCO NEWSPAPER AGENCY—Chronicle Publishing Co. Inc.; *U.S. Private*, pg. 239
SIMON & ASSOCIATES; *U.S. Private*, pg. 1001
TELEMUNDO GROUP, INC.; *U.S. Public*, pg. 1570
TELEREP, INCORPORATED—Cox Enterprises, Inc.; *U.S. Private*, pg. 282
TURNER BROADCASTING SALES, INC.—Time Warner Inc.; *U.S. Public*, pg. 1615
TURNER RECIPROCAL ADVERTISING CORPORATION—Time Warner Inc.; *U.S. Public*, pg. 1615
WESTERN BROADCAST SALES LTD.—WIC Western International Communications Ltd.; *Int'l*, pg. 1482

7319 — ADVERTISING, NEC

AIS MEDIA; *Int'l*, pg. 15
THE ACKERLEY GROUP; *U.S. Public*, pg. 15
AMERICAN MANUFACTURING COMPANY; *U.S. Private*, pg. 58
AMERICAN PASSAGE MEDIA CORPORATION; *U.S. Private*, pg. 60
JOHN AYLING AND ASSOCIATES LIMITED; *Int'l*, pg. 103
BUSCH CREATIVE SERVICES CORPORATION—Anheuser-Busch Companies, Inc.; *U.S. Public*, pg. 114
CCS—Blade Communications, Inc.; *U.S. Private*, pg. 147
CPM, INC.; *U.S. Private*, pg. 196
CRN INTERNATIONAL, INC.; *U.S. Private*, pg. 197
CARAT MBS; *U.S. Private*, pg. 208
CHICAGO SHOW PRINTING CO.; *U.S. Private*, pg. 235
COMPETITIVE MEDIA REPORTING—VNU Verenigde Nederlandse Uitgeversbedrijven B.V.; *Int'l*, pg. 1447
CORINTHIAN MEDIA, INC.; *U.S. Private*, pg. 275
DEWITT MEDIA, INC.; *U.S. Private*, pg. 329
THE ERICSSON CORPORATION—Telefonaktiebolaget LM Ericsson; *Int'l*, pg. 1364
NEIL FABER MEDIA INC.; *U.S. Private*, pg. 390
FORD DIRECT MARKETS, INCORPORATED—Ford Motor Company; *U.S. Public*, pg. 664
GOLDEN BOOKS FAMILY ENTERTAINMENT INC.; *U.S. Public*, pg. 749
HBS MARKETING (ASIA) LIMITED TAIPEI BRANCH OFFICE—GP Batteries International Ltd.; *Int'l*, pg. 537
HARRISON, YOUNG, PESONEN & NEWELL INC.; *Int'l*, pg. 598
HAVAS ADVERTISING; *Int'l*, pg. 600
HOUSTON HERSTEK FAVAT; *U.S. Private*, pg. 542
JII/SALES PROMOTION ASSOCIATES, INC.—Jordan Industries, Inc.; *U.S. Private*, pg. 598
THE MEDIA CENTRE; *Int'l*, pg. 852
MEDIA INCORPORATED; *U.S. Private*, pg. 726
THE MEDIA SHOP LIMITED; *Int'l*, pg. 853
MEDIAPOLIS; *Int'l*, pg. 853
MILLER FREEMAN INC.—United News & Media plc; *Int'l*, pg. 1443
MILLER FREEMAN PLC—United News & Media plc; *Int'l*, pg. 1443
MUZAK LIMITED PARTNERSHIP—Center Partners Management LLC; *U.S. Private*, pg. 222
NEWS AMERICA MARKETING—The News Corporation Limited; *Int'l*, pg. 925
PERQ RESEARCH CORPORATION—VNU Verenigde Nederlandse Uitgeversbedrijven B.V.; *Int'l*, pg. 1447
PHARMACISTS PUBLIC RELATIONS BUREAU—Cullman Ventures, Inc.; *U.S. Private*, pg. 295
QUAD/GRAPHICS, INC.; *U.S. Private*, pg. 897
RNF MEDIA CORPORATION INC.; *U.S. Private*, pg. 905
RAINBOW ADVERTISING SALES CORPORATION (RASCO)—Cablevision Systems Corporation; *U.S. Public*, *pg. 288*
RAMA GROUP OF COMPANIES; *U.S. Private*, pg. 908
R.J. REYNOLDS TOBACCO FRANCE, S.A.—RJR Nabisco Holdings Corp.; *U.S. Public*, pg. 1356
SOUTHWESTERN BELL YELLOW PAGES INC.—SBC Communications Inc.; *U.S. Public*, pg. 1415
SPIRE CORPORATION; *U.S. Public*, pg. 1499
SQUIRES ROBERTSON GILL; *Int'l*, pg. 1291
THE STOP & SHOP COMPANIES, INC.—Koninklijke Ahold NV; *Int'l*, pg. 750
THE SUMMIT MEDIA GROUP; *U.S. Private*, pg. 1050
VSM, INC.; *U.S. Private*, pg. 1130
VITT MEDIA INTERNATIONAL, INC.; *U.S. Private*, pg. 1142
WEST JAPAN RAILWAY COMPANY; *Int'l*, pg. 1490
ZENITH MEDIA SERVICES, INC.; *U.S. Private*, pg. 1204

7322 — ADJUSTMENT & COLLECTION SERVICES

AMERICAN ADJUSTMENT COMPANY, INC.—Cigna Corp.; *U.S. Public*, pg. 365
AMERICAN LENDERS FACILITIES, INC.—Cigna Corp.; *U.S. Public*, pg. 366
AUSECO, S.A.—Caja de Madrid Group; *Int'l*, pg. 252
BARNETT RECOVERY CORPORATION—NationsBank Corporation; *U.S. Public*, pg. 1162
CAPITAL CREDIT CORPORATION—The Union Corporation; *U.S. Public*, pg. 1667
CITICORP INSURANCE SERVICES, INC.—Citicorp; *U.S. Public*, pg. 377
THE CREDIT BUREAU, INC. OF GEORGIA—Equifax Inc.; *U.S. Public*, pg. 588
EQUIFAX INC.; *U.S. Public*, pg. 588
FCA HOLDINGS, INC.—FCA International Ltd.; *Int'l*, pg. 471
FCA INTERNATIONAL LTD.; *Int'l*, pg. 470
FINANCIAL COLLECTION AGENCIES (INTERNATIONAL) INC.—FCA International Ltd.; *Int'l*, pg. 470
FINANCIAL COLLECTION AGENCIES (1990) INC.—FCA International Ltd.; *Int'l*, pg. 471
FINANCIAL COLLECTION AGENCIES OF PENNSYLVANIA INC—FCA International Ltd.; *Int'l*, pg. 471
FINANCIAL COLLECTION AGENCIES (UK) LIMITED—FCA International Ltd.; *Int'l*, pg. 471
FORD CONSUMER DISCOUNT COMPANY—Ford Motor Company; *U.S. Public*, pg. 664
FORD CONSUMER FINANCE COMPANY, INC.—Ford Motor Company; *U.S. Public*, pg. 664
I.C. SYSTEM, INC.; *U.S. Private*, pg. 553
JC PENNEY BUSINESS SERVICES—JC Penney Company, Inc.; *U.S. Public*, pg. 917
JONES FINANCIAL SERVICES—Jones & Jones, Inc.; *U.S. Private*, pg. 596
NATIONWIDE CREDIT—First Data Corporation; *U.S. Public*, *pg. 631*
NATIONWIDE CREDIT INC.; *U.S. Private*, pg. 788
PAYCO AMERICAN CORPORATION; *U.S. Public*, pg. 1267
PRIORITY FULFILLMENT SERVICES, INC.—Daisytek International Corporation; *U.S. Public*, pg. 477
REEDS FINANCIAL SERVICES, INC.—Reeds Jewelers, Inc.; *U.S. Public*, pg. 1370
TELECREDIT COLLECTION SERVICE—Equifax Inc.; *U.S. Public*, pg. 588
TRANSWORLD SYSTEMS, INC.—The Union Corporation; *U.S. Public*, pg. 1667
TREEGROVE MANAGEMENT CORP.—Reunion Industries, Inc.; *U.S. Public*, pg. 1383
UNIVERSITY ACCOUNTING SERVICE, INC.—Payco American Corporation; *U.S. Public*, pg. 1267
VENGROFF WILLIAMS & ASSOCIATES, INC.; *U.S. Private*, pg. 1135

7323 — CREDIT REPORTING SERVICES

ALLIANCE DATA SYSTEMS—The Limited, Inc.; *U.S. Public*, pg. 995
BURNHAM GENERAL PARTNER, INC.—Investcorp International; *Int'l*, pg. 686
CSC CREDIT SERVICES, INC.—Computer Sciences Corporation; *U.S. Public*, pg. 423
THE CREDIT BUREAU, INC. OF GEORGIA—Equifax Inc.; *U.S. Public*, pg. 588
THE DUN & BRADSTREET CORPORATION; *U.S. Public*, pg. 535
DUN & BRADSTREET FRANCE SA—The Dun & Bradstreet Corporation; *U.S. Public*, pg. 536
DUN & BRADSTREET HUNGARIA KFT.—The Dun & Bradstreet Corporation; *U.S. Public*, pg. 536
DUN & BRADSTREET (INDIA) PVT. LTD.—The Dun & Bradstreet Corporation; *U.S. Public*, pg. 536
DUN & BRADSTREET JAPAN LTD.—The Dun & Bradstreet Corporation; *U.S. Public*, pg. 536
DUN & BRADSTREET POLAND SP. Z.O.O.—The Dun & Bradstreet Corporation; *U.S. Public*, pg. 536
DUN & BRADSTREET SCHIMMELPFENG GMBH—The Dun & Bradstreet Corporation; *U.S. Public*, pg. 537
EQUIFAX CANADA—Equifax Inc.; *U.S. Public*, pg. 588
EQUIFAX INC.; *U.S. Public*, pg. 588
FIMASER—GIB Group; *Int'l*, pg. 533
NATIONAL ACCOUNT SYSTEMS, INC.—Payco American Corporation; *U.S. Public*, pg. 1267
PAYCO-GENERAL AMERICAN CREDITS, INC.—Payco American Corporation; *U.S. Public*, pg. 1267
REEDS FINANCIAL SERVICES, INC.—Reeds Jewelers, Inc.; *U.S. Public*, pg. 1370
SEOUL FINANCE CORPORATION—KOHAP Group; *Int'l*, pg. 743
SHANGHAI YIN TONG TRUST CO., LTD.—Orix Corporation; *Int'l*, pg. 1010
SYNDICATED OFFICE SYSTEMS, INC.—Tenet Healthcare Corporation; *U.S. Public*, pg. 1577
THE UNION CORPORATION; *U.S. Public*, pg. 1667

7331 — DIRECT MAIL ADVERTISING SERVICES

ACXIOM CORPORATION; *U.S. Public*, pg. 18
ACXIOM CORPORATION - PUBLICITY CENTRE—Acxiom Corporation; *U.S. Public*, pg. 18
ADVO, INC.; *U.S. Public*, pg. 23
AMERICAN BUSINESS INFORMATION, INC.; *U.S. Public*, pg. 69
AMERICAN LIST CORPORATION—Snyder Communications, Inc.; *U.S. Public*, pg. 1481
ASBURY PARK PRESS, INC.—Gannett Company, Inc.; *U.S. Public*, pg. 699
ATLAS PEN & PENCIL CORPORATION; *U.S. Private*, pg. 96
CHANNING L. BETE CO., INC.; *U.S. Private*, pg. 140
BLADE COMMUNICATIONS, INC.; *U.S. Private*, pg. 147
BRADFORD EXCHANGE LTD.; *U.S. Private*, pg. 163
BRIAN UNLIMITED DISTRIBUTION COMPANY, INC.; *U.S. Private*, pg. 167
BRONNER SLOSBERG HUMPHREY/STRATEGIC INTERACTIVE GROUP; *U.S. Private*, pg. 171
CGF INDUSTRIES; *U.S. Private*, pg. 194
CADMUS COMMUNICATIONS CORPORATION; *U.S. Public*, pg. 290
CHICAGO TRIBUNE DIRECT—Tribune Company; *U.S. Public*, pg. 1635
CONTINENTAL WEB PRESS, INC.; *U.S. Private*, pg. 269
CURTIN & PEASE/PENECO, INC—Pittway Corporation; *U.S. Public*, pg. 1306
DATABASE AMERICA COMPANIES; *U.S. Private*, pg. 312
EPSILON—American Express Company; *U.S. Public*, pg. 74
EQUIFAX CREDIT MARKETING SERVICES, INC.—Equifax Inc.; *U.S. Public*, pg. 588
EQUIFAX INC.; *U.S. Public*, pg. 588
EVA-TONE INC.; *U.S. Private*, pg. 384
FLEMING PACKAGING CORP.; *U.S. Private*, pg. 411
GL DIRECT—Great Lakes Lithograph Co.; *U.S. Private*, pg. 475
GSP MARKETING SERVICES, INC.; *U.S. Private*, pg. 436
GANNETT DIRECT MARKETING SERVICES—Gannett Company, Inc.; *U.S. Public*, pg. 699
GREY ADVERTISING INC.; *U.S. Public*, pg. 764
HM1, HEUSER, MAYER & PARTNER DIRECT MARKETING GMBH; *Int'l*, pg. 579
HAINES & CO., INC.; *U.S. Private*, pg. 494
HAKUHODO INCENTIVE PROMOTIONS INC.—Hakuhodo Incorporated; *Int'l*, pg. 588
HARTE-HANKS COMMUNICATIONS, INC.; *U.S. Public*, pg. 793
HAWTHORNE ADV., INC.; *U.S. Private*, pg. 512
HEATH COMPANY—Compagnie des Machines Bull; *Int'l*, pg. 317
THE HIBBERT COMPANY; *U.S. Private*, pg. 525
HOUSTON HERSTEK FAVAT; *U.S. Private*, pg. 542
I.C. SYSTEM, INC.; *U.S. Private*, pg. 553
IPD PRINTING & DISTRIBUTING, INC.—Wallace Computer Services, Inc.; *U.S. Public*, pg. 1735
IMPERIAL LITHO & DRYOGRAPHY, INC.; *U.S. Private*, pg. 558
INITIO, INC.; *U.S. Public*, pg. 879
INKTEL MARKETING—Avanti Press Inc.; *U.S. Private*, pg. 101
THE INSTANT WEB COMPANIES; *U.S. Private*, pg. 565
JOHNSON & QUIN, INC.; *U.S. Private*, pg. 590
LCS INDUSTRIES, INC.; *U.S. Public*, pg. 970
LINCOLN MARKETING, INC.—Synovus Financial Corp.; *U.S. Public*, pg. 1550
MACLEAN HUNTER MAILING SERVICES—Rogers Communications, Inc.; *Int'l*, pg. 1124
MAIL BOXES ETC.—U.S. Office Products Company; *U.S. Public*, pg. 1687
MAIL WELL SERVICES INC.—Primedia Inc.; *U.S. Public*, pg. 1328
MAILTEK, INC.—Synovus Financial Corp.; *U.S. Public*, pg. 1550
MARKET DATA RETRIEVAL—The Dun & Bradstreet Corporation; *U.S. Public*, pg. 536
MARKETING COMMUNICATIONS—Harte-Hanks Communications, Inc.; *U.S. Public*, pg. 794
MATRIXX MARKETING INC.—Cincinnati Bell Telephone; *U.S. Public*, pg. 368
MAY & SPEH, INC.; *U.S. Public*, pg. 1063
MEREDITH LIST MARKETING—Meredith Corporation; *U.S. Public*, pg. 1094
METROMAIL CORPORATION; *U.S. Public*, pg. 1102
MILLER FREEMAN PLC—United News & Media plc; *Int'l*, pg. 1443
JACK NADEL, INC.; *U.S. Private*, pg. 773
NESCO AMEICAN HARVEST INC.—The Metal Ware Corp.; *U.S. Private*, pg. 735
OUTLOOK GROUP CORPORATION; *U.S. Public*, pg. 1235
PITTWAY CORPORATION; *U.S. Public*, pg. 1305
R.L. POLK & CO.; *U.S. Private*, pg. 874
RAPP COLLINS WORLDWIDE—Omnicom Group Inc.; *U.S. Public*, pg. 1224
SEC (SOFT, EVENT & PROMOTION) PLANNING, INC.—Hakuhodo Incorporated; *Int'l*, pg. 588
SCICOM DATA SERVICES, LTD.; *U.S. Private*, pg. 975
THE SEGERDAHL CORP.; *U.S. Private*, pg. 981
THE SIGNATURE GROUP—Montgomery Ward & Co., Inc.; *U.S. Private*, pg. 758
SUNGARD COMPUTER SERVICES GROUP—SunGard Data Systems Inc.; *U.S. Public*, pg. 1534
SUNGARD MAILING SERVICES—SunGard Data Systems Inc.; *U.S. Public*, pg. 1534
TBWA PAYNE STRACEY; *Int'l*, pg. 1336
TEAM ONE ADVERTISING—Saatchi & Saatchi Advertising Worldwide; *U.S. Public*, pg. 1422
TELEMUNDO GROUP, INC.; *U.S. Public*, pg. 1570
3 SCORE, INC.—Cadmus Communications Corporation; *U.S. Public*, pg. 291
TURNER MARKETING, INC.—Time Warner Inc.; *U.S. Public*, pg. 1615
U S WEST INC.; *U.S. Public*, pg. 1688
WASHBURN DIRECT MARKETING, INC.—Cadmus Communications Corporation; *U.S. Public*, pg. 291
WEBCRAFT TECHNOLOGIES, INC.—Big Flower Press Holdings, Inc.; *U.S. Public*, pg. 228

7334 — PHOTOCOPY & DUPLICATING SERVICES

ARCO BLUEPRINTERS—Wallace Computer Services, Inc.; *U.S. Public*, pg. 1735
DANKA BUSINESS SYSTEMS—Danka Business Systems PLC; *Int'l*, pg. 379
DANKA BUSINESS SYSTEMS PLC; *Int'l*, pg. 379
IMAGING TECHNOLOGIES—Wallace Computer Services, Inc.; *U.S. Public*, pg. 1735
IMAGING TECHNOLOGIES SERVICES—Wallace Computer Services, Inc.; *U.S. Public*, pg. 1735
KINKO'S CORPORATION; *U.S. Private*, pg. 622
MACON BLUE PRINT COMPANY—Wallace Computer Services, Inc.; *U.S. Public*, pg. 1735
MAIL BOXES ETC.—U.S. Office Products Company; *U.S. Public*, pg. 1687
MERRILL CORPORATION; *U.S. Public*, pg. 1097
MULTICOPY INTERNATIONAL B.V.—Moore Corporation Limited; *Int'l*, pg. 890
NORTHSIDE BLUEPRINT & SUPPLY COMPANY—Wallace Computer Services, Inc.; *U.S. Public*, pg. 1735
PHOTO-ME INTERNATIONAL PLC; *Int'l*, pg. 1055
SIR SPEEDY, INC.—Franchise Services, Inc.; *U.S. Private*, pg. 423
STEIN FACILITIES MANAGEMENT—Wallace Computer Services, Inc.; *U.S. Public*, pg. 1736
TRM COPY CENTERS CORPORATION; *U.S. Public*, pg. 1558

TOWER PRINTING COMPANY—Wallace Computer Services, Inc.; U.S. Public, pg. 1736
WILCO REPROGRAPHIC, INC.; U.S. Private, pg. 1176
XEROX BUSINESS SERVICES—Xerox Corporation; U.S. Public, pg. 1784
YRJ CORPORATION—Wilco Reprographic, Inc.; U.S. Private, pg. 1176

7335 — COMMERCIAL PHOTOGRAPHY

ABD GROUP INC.—Devon Group, Inc.; U.S. Public, pg. 503
AERO SERVICE CORP.—Litton Industries, Inc.; U.S. Public, pg. 1003
AMBROSI & ASSOCIATES, INC.—Devon Group, Inc.; U.S. Public, pg. 503
APPLIED GRAPHICS TECHNOLOGIES—U.S. News & World Report; U.S. Private, pg. 1125
BLACK DOT GRAPHICS, INC.—Devon Group, Inc.; U.S. Public, pg. 503
EARLE PALMER BROWN; U.S. Private, pg. 173
CONTINENTAL CAN CO.; U.S. Public, pg. 439
DELMAR STUDIOS—Continental Graphics Holdings, Inc.; U.S. Private, pg. 268
DEVON GROUP, INC.; U.S. Public, pg. 503
R.R. DONNELLEY BARBADOS—R.R. Donnelley & Sons Company; U.S. Public, pg. 519
FRANKLIN PRESS—Continental Graphics Holdings, Inc.; U.S. Private, pg. 268
GOLDEN BOOKS FAMILY ENTERTAINMENT INC.; U.S. Public, pg. 749
HAKUHODO PHOTO CREATIVE INC.—Hakuhodo Incorporated; Int'l, pg. 588
KODAK MEXICANA SA DE C.V.—Eastman Kodak Company; U.S. Public, pg. 554
MANDO MARKETING LIMITED—WPP Group plc; Int'l, pg. 1482
PCA INTERNATIONAL, INC.; U.S. Public, pg. 1240
PHOTO-ME INTERNATIONAL PLC; Int'l, pg. 1055
SHANDWICK INTERNATIONAL PLC; Int'l, pg. 1226
WALKER-PIONEER GRAPHICS; U.S. Private, pg. 1147
WEST COAST CREATIVE—Devon Group, Inc.; U.S. Public, pg. 503

7336 — COMMERCIAL ART & GRAPHIC DESIGN

ABD GROUP INC.—Devon Group, Inc.; U.S. Public, pg. 503
AMBROSI & ASSOCIATES, INC.—Devon Group, Inc.; U.S. Public, pg. 503
W.E. ANDREWS CO., INC.—Wallace Computer Services, Inc.; U.S. Public, pg. 1735
APPLIED GRAPHICS TECHNOLOGIES—U.S. News & World Report; U.S. Private, pg. 1125
BTGRAPHIC SA DE CV—N.V. Koninklijke KNP BT; Int'l, pg. 757
BLACK DOT GRAPHICS, INC.—Devon Group, Inc.; U.S. Public, pg. 503
EARLE PALMER BROWN; U.S. Private, pg. 173
COBB REPROGRAPHICS & OFFICE SUPPLY—Wallace Computer Services, Inc.; U.S. Public, pg. 1735
DEVON GROUP, INC.; U.S. Public, pg. 503
DROYHURST LIMITED—James Crean PLC; Int'l, pg. 341
DYNAMIC GRAPHICS INC.—Bertelsmann AG; Int'l, pg. 191
EDWARDS & BROUGHTON COMPANY—Wallace Computer Services, Inc.; U.S. Public, pg. 1735
FAG-VRG SA—N.V. Koninklijke KNP BT; Int'l, pg. 757
GOLDEN BOOKS FAMILY ENTERTAINMENT INC.; U.S. Public, pg. 749
GRAPHIC INDUSTRIES, INC.—Wallace Computer Services, Inc.; U.S. Public, pg. 1735
HITEK PRODUCT FINISHING, INC.—Cowden Metal Specialties, Inc.; U.S. Private, pg. 280
HOPKINS & BAILEY LTD.—Shandwick International Plc; Int'l, pg. 1226
IN FOCUS SERVICES, INC.—In Focus Systems, Inc.; U.S. Public, pg. 873
LSI INDUSTRIES, INC.; U.S. Public, pg. 971
LINCOLN GRAPHICS INC.—Devon Group, Inc.; U.S. Public, pg. 503
LINOTYPE FRANCE SA—N.V. Koninklijke KNP BT; Int'l, pg. 757
MSG SA DIVISIE PLANTIN—N.V. Koninklijke KNP BT; Int'l, pg. 757
MACCHINE E ACCESSORI PER L'INDUSTRIA GRAFICA MACCHINGRAF SPA—N.V. Koninklijke KNP BT; Int'l, pg. 757
MADISON GRAHAM COLORGRAPHICS, INC.; U.S. Private, pg. 694
MAQUINARIA ARTES GRAFICAS HARTMANN SA—N.V. Koninklijke KNP BT; Int'l, pg. 757
MARS GRAPHICS, INC.—Harte-Hanks Communications, Inc.; U.S. Public, pg. 793
MARTIN UNIVERSAL DESIGN, INC.; U.S. Private, pg. 709
MERIDIAN RETAIL, INC.—Devon Group, Inc.; U.S. Public, pg. 503
NOBART, INC.—Devon Group, Inc.; U.S. Public, pg. 503
NOBART, INC.; U.S. Private, pg. 800
OFMI-GARAMONT SA—N.V. Koninklijke KNP BT; Int'l, pg. 757
ORENT GRAPHICARTS, INC.—Devon Group, Inc.; U.S. Public, pg. 503
PASCO CORPORATION; Int'l, pg. 1024
HAROLD M. PITMAN CO., INC.; U.S. Private, pg. 867
PRIZMA PHOTOGRAPHICS—Wallace Computer Services, Inc.; U.S. Public, pg. 1735
PROOF POSITIVE/FARROWLYNE ASSOCIATES, INC.—Devon Group, Inc.; U.S. Public, pg. 503
RALEIGH ENTERPRISES, INC.; U.S. Private, pg. 907
RAM GRAPHICS, INC.; U.S. Private, pg. 908
SBG ENTERPRISE—WPP Group plc; Int'l, pg. 1483
SGI INTEGRATED GRAPHIC SYSTEMS—LSI Industries, Inc.; U.S. Public, pg. 971
SAMPSON TYRRELL ENTERPRISE—WPP Group plc; Int'l, pg. 1482
SHANDWICK INTERACTIVE LTD.—Shandwick International Plc; Int'l, pg. 1227
STUDIO 70—SuperValu, Inc.; U.S. Public, pg. 1541
TAPROOT INTERACTIVE, INC.—Devon Group, Inc.; U.S. Public, pg. 503
TETTERODE-NEDERLAND BV—N.V. Koninklijke KNP BT; Int'l, pg. 757
TYPO-GRAPHICS, INC.—Devon Group, Inc.; U.S. Public, pg. 503
VELLUS SA—N.V. Koninklijke KNP BT; Int'l, pg. 757
VOTRA-HYMSUN LTD—N.V. Koninklijke KNP BT; Int'l, pg. 757
VOTRA (MALAYSIA) SDN BHD—N.V. Koninklijke KNP BT; Int'l, pg. 757
VOTRA (PHILIPPINES) INC—N.V. Koninklijke KNP BT; Int'l, pg. 757
VOTRA SA—N.V. Koninklijke KNP BT; Int'l, pg. 757
VOTRA (SINGAPORE) PTE LTD—N.V. Koninklijke KNP BT; Int'l, pg. 757
VOTRA (TAIWAN) LTD—N.V. Koninklijke KNP BT; Int'l, pg. 757
VOTRA (THAILAND) CO LTD—N.V. Koninklijke KNP BT; Int'l, pg. 757
VOYUNGSA LTD—N.V. Koninklijke KNP BT; Int'l, pg. 757
WALKER-PIONEER GRAPHICS; U.S. Private, pg. 1147
WEST COAST CREATIVE—Devon Group, Inc.; U.S. Public, pg. 503
WETMORE & COMPANY—Wallace Computer Services, Inc.; U.S. Public, pg. 1736
WILLIAMS PRINTING COMPANY—Wallace Computer Services, Inc.; U.S. Public, pg. 1736

7342 — DISINFECTING & PEST CONTROL SERVICES

ABM INDUSTRIES; U.S. Public, pg. 2
CWS INTERNATIONAL A.G.—Franz Haniel & Cie, GmbH; Int'l, pg. 592
W.A. FLICK & CO. PTY. LIMITED; Int'l, pg. 495
FRANZ HANIEL & CIE, GMBH; Int'l, pg. 591
INDISCO GMBH—Sophus Berendsen A/S; Int'l, pg. 1286
INDISCO NEDERLAND BV—Sophus Berendsen A/S; Int'l, pg. 1286
LUWA BAHNSON, INC.; U.S. Private, pg. 682
ORKIN EXTERMINATING CO., INC.—Rollins, Inc.; U.S. Public, pg. 1404
PERMA-FIX ENVIRONMENTAL SERVICES, INC.—Perma-Fix Environmental Services, Inc.; U.S. Public, pg. 1279
PEST ELIMINATION—Ecolab Inc.; U.S. Public, pg. 562
POWELL'S PEST CONTROL PTY. LTD.—Sophus Berendsen A/S; Int'l, pg. 1286
PRISM INTEGRATED SANITATION MANAGEMENT, INC.—S.C. Johnson & Son, Inc.; U.S. Private, pg. 592
RENTOKIL BAHAMAS LTD.—Sophus Berendsen A/S; Int'l, pg. 1286
RENTOKIL GMBH—Sophus Berendsen A/S; Int'l, pg. 1286
RENTOKIL INITIAL PLC—Sophus Berendsen A/S; Int'l, pg. 1285
RENTOKIL LTD.—Sophus Berendsen A/S; Int'l, pg. 1285
RENTOKIL PEST CONTROL LTD.—Sophus Berendsen A/S; Int'l, pg. 1286
RENTOKIL (PTY.) LTD.—Sophus Berendsen A/S; Int'l, pg. 1286
N.V. RENTOKIL SA—Sophus Berendsen A/S; Int'l, pg. 1286
ROLLINS, INC.; U.S. Public, pg. 1404
THE SERVICEMASTER COMPANY; U.S. Public, pg. 1461
TERMINIX SERVICE, INC.; U.S. Private, pg. 1077
TRIANGLE SERVICES, INC.; U.S. Private, pg. 1102

7349 — BUILDING CLEANING & MAINTENANCE SERVICES, NEC

ABM INDUSTRIES; U.S. Public, pg. 2
ADMIRAL MAINTENANCE SERVICE L.P.; U.S. Private, pg. 17
AIR CRAFTERS INC.—Aero Data Metal Crafters; U.S. Private, pg. 24
AMERICAN BLDG. MAINTENANCE CO.—ABM Industries; U.S. Public, pg. 2
ANTARES GROUP INC.; U.S. Private, pg. 76
ARAMARK CORP.; U.S. Private, pg. 78
ARAMARK SERVICES, PLC—Aramark Corp.; U.S. Private, pg. 79
ASAHI BANK BUILDING CO., LTD.—The Asahi Bank, Ltd.; Int'l, pg. 82
ASAHI BANK BUILDING MAINTENANCE CO., LTD.—The Asahi Bank, Ltd.; Int'l, pg. 82
ASAHI BANK SOGO SERVICE CO., LTD.—The Asahi Bank, Ltd.; Int'l, pg. 82
ASAHI BANK SUPPLY CO., LTD.—The Asahi Bank, Ltd.; Int'l, pg. 82
BUILDING MAINTENANCE PRODUCTS, INC.—Temco Service Industries; U.S. Public, pg. 1574
CMI GROUP, INC.—The ServiceMaster Company; U.S. Public, pg. 1462
CUC INTERNATIONAL, INC.—Cendant Corporation; U.S. Public, pg. 320
CABINAS TELEFONICAS, S.A. (CABITEL)—Telefonica de Espana, S.A.; Int'l, pg. 1371
CENDANT CORPORATION; U.S. Public, pg. 320
COLIN SERVICE SYSTEMS, INC.; U.S. Private, pg. 252
THE DAVIS SERVICE GROUP PLC.; Int'l, pg. 385
DEFENDER SERVICES, INC.; U.S. Private, pg. 320
DIVERSCO, INC.; U.S. Private, pg. 336
ECOLAB INC.; U.S. Public, pg. 562
G.E. POWER SYSTEMS—General Electric Company; U.S. Public, pg. 711
GVA INDUSTRISERVICE AB—Celsius AB; Int'l, pg. 276
HYGIENIC SERVICE GEBAUDEREINIGUNG BETRIEBS-KG.—Vorwerk & Co.; Int'l, pg. 1480
HYGIENIC SERVICE GEBAUDEREINIGUNG UND GEBAUDEDIENSTE KG—Vorwerk & Co.; Int'l, pg. 1480
ISS CLEANING SERVICES GROUP, INC.—ISS-International Service System A/S; Int'l, pg. 656
ISS ENERGY SERVICES, INC.—ISS-International Service System A/S; Int'l, pg. 656
ISS HOLDING GMBH—ISS-International Service System A/S; Int'l, pg. 657
ISS INTERNATIONAL SERVICE SYSTEM, INC.—ISS-International Service System A/S; Int'l, pg. 656
ISS LANDSCAPE MANAGEMENT SERVICES, INC.—ISS-International Service System A/S; Int'l, pg. 656
ISS LONDON LTD.—ISS-International Service System A/S; Int'l, pg. 657
ISS MALL SERVICES, INC.—ISS-International Service System A/S; Int'l, pg. 656
ISS SERVISYSTEM—ISS-International Service System A/S; Int'l, pg. 657
ISS SERVISYSTEM B.V.—ISS-International Service System A/S; Int'l, pg. 657
ISS SERVISYSTEM D.O.O.—ISS-International Service System A/S; Int'l, pg. 657
ISS SERVISYSTEM GESMBH—ISS-International Service System A/S; Int'l, pg. 657
ISS SERVISYSTEM KFT.—ISS-International Service System A/S; Int'l, pg. 657
ISS SERVISYSTEM LTD.—ISS-International Service System A/S; Int'l, pg. 657
ISS SERVISYSTEM S.A.—ISS-International Service System A/S; Int'l, pg. 657
ISS SERVISYSTEM S.A.-N.V.—ISS-International Service System A/S; Int'l, pg. 657
ISS SULAMERICANA COMERCIAL LTDA.—ISS-International Service System A/S; Int'l, pg. 657
ISS SUOMI OY—ISS-International Service System A/S; Int'l, pg. 656
ISS SVERIGE AB—ISS-International Service System A/S; Int'l, pg. 656
INTEGROL—Staveley Industries PLC; Int'l, pg. 1298
JANI KING INTERNATIONAL, INC.; U.S. Private, pg. 581
JARDINE MATHESON HOLDINGS LIMITED; Int'l, pg. 703
JOFFKO INTERNATIONAL; U.S. Private, pg. 589
KAISER WHOLESALE, INC.; U.S. Private, pg. 605
LI SERVICE COMPANY—Lukens Inc.; U.S. Public, pg. 1020
MFRI INC.; U.S. Public, pg. 1026
MAINTENANCE BUILDING & SIGNAGE—Vaux Group Plc; Int'l, pg. 1454
MATSUYA ENGINEERING SERVICE CO., LTD.—Matsuya Company Ltd.; Int'l, pg. 848
MODERN BUILDING CLEANING INC.—Aramark Corp.; U.S. Private, pg. 79
NSC CORPORATION—OHM Corporation; U.S. Public, pg. 1208
NATIONAL CHEMSEARCH (SWITZERLAND) AG—NCH Corporation; U.S. Public, pg. 1145
PALL MALL SUPPORT SERVICES LIMITED—The Davis Service Group Plc.; Int'l, pg. 385
PHARMACIA & UPJOHN DATA AB—Pharmacia & Upjohn, Inc.; Int'l, pg. 1048
RENTOKIL INITIAL PLANT SERVICES (USA) INC.—Sophus Berendsen A/S; Int'l, pg. 1285
RENTOKIL INITIAL PLC—Sophus Berendsen A/S; Int'l, pg. 1285
RENTOKIL LTD.—Sophus Berendsen A/S; Int'l, pg. 1285
RISCOMP INDUSTRIES, INC.; U.S. Private, pg. 932
ROUSE-MILWAUKEE GARAGE MAINTENANCE, INC.—The Rouse Company; U.S. Public, pg. 1409
S & C MAINTENANCE CORP.—Spatz Centers Inc.; U.S. Private, pg. 1021
SAEL—ISS-International Service System A/S; Int'l, pg. 657
SADCO LTD.—Joffko International; U.S. Private, pg. 589
THE SERVICEMASTER COMPANY; U.S. Public, pg. 1461
SERVICEMASTER INTERNATIONAL—The ServiceMaster Company; U.S. Public, pg. 1462
SOUTHERN SERVICES INC.—Sophus Berendsen A/S; Int'l, pg. 1286
TEMCO BUILDING MAINTENANCE, INC.—Temco Service Industries; U.S. Public, pg. 1574
TEMCO SERVICE INDUSTRIES; U.S. Public, pg. 1574
TRIANGLE SERVICES, INC.; U.S. Private, pg. 1102
VENDEX INTERNATIONAL N.V.; Int'l, pg. 1462
VERSA SERVICES LTD.—Aramark Corp.; U.S. Private, pg. 79
VORWERK & CO.; Int'l, pg. 1480

7352 — MEDICAL EQUIPMENT RENTAL & LEASING

AMERICAN SHARED HOSPITAL SERVICES; U.S. Public, pg. 91
BERWIND PHARMACEUTICAL SERVICES, INC.—Berwind Corporation; U.S. Private, pg. 139
BESPAK PLC; Int'l, pg. 193
CAIRE, INC.—Minnesota Valley Engineering/Cryogenic Association; U.S. Private, pg. 751
CLINICARE SYSTEMS, INC.—Gaymar Industries, Inc.; U.S. Private, pg. 442
DVI, INC.; U.S. Public, pg. 476
ESC MEDICAL SYSTEMS LTD.; Int'l, pg. 429
HILLENBRAND INDUSTRIES, INC.; U.S. Public, pg. 828
KENTUCKY MEDICAL INSURANCE COMPANY (KMIC)—Michigan Physicians Mutual Liability Inc.; U.S. Private, pg. 741
KEY PLASTICS, INC.; U.S. Private, pg. 618
KINETIC CONCEPTS, INC.; U.S. Private, pg. 620
LINC ANTHEM INC.—LINC Capital Group; U.S. Public, pg. 996
LINC EQUIPMENT SERVICES—LINC Capital Group; U.S. Public, pg. 996
LINC MANAGEMENT SERVICES—LINC Capital Group; U.S. Public, pg. 996

LINC MEDICAL IMAGING—LINC Capital Group; U.S. Public, pg. 996
LINC QUANTUM ANALYTICS—LINC Capital Group; U.S. Public, pg. 996
LASER INDUSTRIES LTD.—ESC Medical Systems Ltd.; Int'l, pg. 429
MEDICAL RESOURCES INC.—Medical Resources Inc.; U.S. Public, pg. 1080
MEDIQ/PRN LIFE SUPPORT SERVICES, INC.—MEDIQ Incorporated; U.S. Public, pg. 1081
MINNESOTA VALLEY ENGINEERING/CRYOGENIC ASSOCIATION; U.S. Private, pg. 751
MOBILE TECHNOLOGY INC.; U.S. Private, pg. 754
NARCO MEDICAL SERVICES INC.—Vickers PLC; Int'l, pg. 1468
NYCOMED IMAGING AS—Nycomed Amersham plc; Int'l, pg. 993
NYCOMED PHARMA AS—Nycomed Amersham plc; Int'l, pg. 993
M.E. OTSUKA CO., LTD.—Otsuka Pharmaceutical Co., Ltd.; Int'l, pg. 1014
SELLES MEDICAL LIMITED—Alliance UniChem PLC; Int'l, pg. 58
SHARPLAN LASERS (EUROPE) LTD.—ESC Medical Systems Ltd.; Int'l, pg. 429
SHARPLAN LASERS GMBH—ESC Medical Systems Ltd.; Int'l, pg. 429
SHERWOOD MEDICAL INDUSTRIES LTD.—American Home Products Corporation; U.S. Public, pg. 82
SYRACUSE SUPPLY COMPANY; U.S. Private, pg. 1060
TAYLOR HOME HEALTH INC.—Integrated Health Services, Inc.; U.S. Public, pg. 885
TRANS LEASING INTERNATIONAL INC.; U.S. Public, pg. 1628
UNITED LEASING COMPANY—Michigan Physicians Mutual Liability Inc.; U.S. Private, pg. 741
VARIAN-TEM LTD.—Varian Associates, Inc.; U.S. Public, pg. 1710

7353 — HEAVY CONSTRUCTION EQUIPMENT RENTAL & LEASING

ABERDEEN SCAFFOLDING COMPANY LTD.—Sophus Berendsen A/S; Int'l, pg. 1285
ACTION EQUIPMENT; U.S. Private, pg. 14
AMERICAN AGGREGATES CORP.—CSR Limited; Int'l, pg. 245
AUSTRALIAN NATIONAL INDUSTRIES LIMITED; Int'l, pg. 100
BELLAMY BROTHERS CONTRACTING COMPANY—Bellamy Brothers, Inc.; U.S. Private, pg. 132
BRAMBLES DIV. OF BRAMBLES EQUIPMENT SERVICES INC.—Brambles Industries Limited; Int'l, pg. 211
BRAMBLES EQUIPMENT SERVICES INC.—Brambles Industries Limited; Int'l, pg. 211
BRAMBLES USA INC.—Brambles Industries Limited; Int'l, pg. 211
EMPIRE MACHINERY—Empire Southwest Co.; U.S. Private, pg. 374
EMPIRE SOUTHWEST CO.; U.S. Private, pg. 374
FIRSTAR LEASING CORPORATION—Firstar Corporation; U.S. Public, pg. 643
FOLEY HOLDING COMPANY, INC.; U.S. Private, pg. 416
GRAYSTON, WHITE & SPARROW LTD.—Sophus Berendsen A/S; Int'l, pg. 1285
HERTZ EQUIPMENT RENTAL CORP.—Ford Motor Company; U.S. Public, pg. 664
AB JAN RALLING—Skanska AB; Int'l, pg. 1261
MANESS INDUSTRIES, INC.; U.S. Private, pg. 699
MI-JACK PRODUCTS, INC.; U.S. Private, pg. 740
MUSTANG TRACTOR & EQUIP. CO.; U.S. Private, pg. 768
OBAYASHI CORPORATION; Int'l, pg. 995
P&O (NEW ZEALAND) LTD.—The Peninsular and Oriental Steam Navigation Company; Int'l, pg. 1035
PATTERSON SERVICES, INC.—RPC Incorporated; U.S. Public, pg. 1356
SKANSKA MASKIN AB—Skanska AB; Int'l, pg. 1261
SPARROWS OFFSHORE SERVICES LTD.—Sophus Berendsen A/S; Int'l, pg. 1285
STEPHENSON EQUIPMENT, INC.; U.S. Private, pg. 1040
SYRACUSE SUPPLY COMPANY; U.S. Private, pg. 1060
TEREX CORPORATION; U.S. Public, pg. 1581
TEREX TRUCKS—Terex Corporation; U.S. Public, pg. 1581
UP-RIGHT, INC.; U.S. Private, pg. 1128
WILLIAMS INTERNATIONAL INDUSTRIES, INC.; U.S. Private, pg. 1178
WYSEPLANT LTD.—The Peninsular and Oriental Steam Navigation Company; Int'l, pg. 1035

7359 — EQUIPMENT RENTAL & LEASING, NEC

A & N LEASING—Service Motor Company; U.S. Private, pg. 986
ABN LEASING ESPANA, S.A.—ABN-AMRO Holding N.V.; Int'l, pg. 11
ABN LEASING ITALIA S.P.A.—ABN-AMRO Holding N.V.; Int'l, pg. 11
AEL LEASING CO., INC.—ABN-AMRO Holding N.V.; Int'l, pg. 9
AKF KREDITBANK GMBH. & CO.—Vorwerk & Co.; Int'l, pg. 1481
AKF LEASING BETEILIGUNGSGESELLSCHAFT M.B.H.—Vorwerk & Co.; Int'l, pg. 1481
AKF LEASING GMBH & CO. KG—Vorwerk & Co.; Int'l, pg. 1481
AT&T CORPORATION; U.S. Public, pg. 10
AARON RENTS CONVENTION FURNISHINGS—Aaron Rents, Inc.; U.S. Public, pg. 12
AARON RENTS, INC.; U.S. Public, pg. 12
ADREMA LEASING CORPORATION—Pitney Bowes Inc.; U.S. Public, pg. 1304
ADVANTAGE COMPANIES, INC.; U.S. Private, pg. 22
ADWIN EQUIPMENT CO.—PECO Energy Company; U.S. Public, pg. 1268
AGUSTA S.P.A.; Int'l, pg. 32
ALDEN ELECTRONICS, INC.—Platinum Equity Holdings, LLC; U.S. Private, pg. 872
ALGEMENE LEASE MAATSCHAPPIJ B.V.—ABN-AMRO Holding N.V.; Int'l, pg. 9
ALLBRITTON NEWS BUREAU, INC.—Perpetual Corporation; U.S. Private, pg. 854
AMEDA AG—Hollister Incorporated; U.S. Private, pg. 535
AMERICAN COMMERCIAL CREDIT CORP.—ABN-AMRO Holding N.V.; Int'l, pg. 9
AMERICAN EQUIPMENT COMPANY, INC.—Fluor Corporation; U.S. Public, pg. 660
AMERICAN FINANCE GROUP, INC.—PLM International, Inc.; U.S. Public, pg. 1241
AMES TAPING TOOL SYSTEMS CO.—AXIA Incorporated; U.S. Private, pg. 103
AMSTEL LEASE N.V.—ABN-AMRO Holding N.V.; Int'l, pg. 9
ASCOM TELEMATIC AG—Ascom Holding AG; Int'l, pg. 86
ASHLAND SERVICES COMPANY—Ashland, Inc.; U.S. Public, pg. 139
ASSOCIATED BANC-CORP; U.S. Public, pg. 140
ASSOCIATED LEASING, INC.—Associated Banc-Corp; U.S. Public, pg. 140
ASSOCIATES COMMERCIAL CORPORATION—Ford Motor Company; U.S. Public, pg. 663
ASSOCIATES INTERNATIONAL MANAGEMENT COMPANY—Ford Motor Company; U.S. Public, pg. 663
ATLANTIC NATIONAL CORPORATION—Hawthorne Corp.; U.S. Private, pg. 512
ATLAS COPCO RENTAL INC.—Atlas Copco AB; Int'l, pg. 96
AUSTRALIAN NATIONAL INDUSTRIES LIMITED; Int'l, pg. 100
BAI LEASING S.P.A.—Deutsche Bank AG; Int'l, pg. 403
BB&T OF SOUTH CAROLINA—BB&T Corporation; U.S. Public, pg. 160
BLC CORP.—Citicorp; U.S. Public, pg. 377
BPO FINANCE CORPORATION—Baldwin Piano & Organ Company; U.S. Public, pg. 169
BT EQUIPMENT LEASING, INC.—Bankers Trust New York Corporation; U.S. Public, pg. 185
BABCOCK & BROWN, INC.—The Nomura Securities Co., Ltd.; Int'l, pg. 956
BANC ONE LEASING CORPORATION—Banc One Corporation; U.S. Public, pg. 175
BANCBOSTON LEASING INC.—BankBoston Corporation; U.S. Public, pg. 184
BANCIRELAND/FIRST FINANCIAL INC.—Bank of Ireland; Int'l, pg. 152
BANDAG, INCORPORATED; U.S. Public, pg. 177
BANKERS LEASING CORP.—Citicorp; U.S. Public, pg. 377
BLUMBERG COMMUNICATIONS INC.—Caribiner International, Inc.; U.S. Public, pg. 305
BOWHEAD EQUIPMENT COMPANY—Lynden Incorporated; U.S. Private, pg. 683
BRAMBLES DIV. OF BRAMBLES EQUIPMENT SERVICES INC.—Brambles Industries Limited; Int'l, pg. 211
BRAMBLES EQUIPMENT & FORKLIFTS—Brambles Industries Limited; Int'l, pg. 211
BRAMBLES EQUIPMENT SERVICES INC.—Brambles Industries Limited; Int'l, pg. 211
BRAMBLES INDUSTRIES LIMITED; Int'l, pg. 210
BRAMBLES MANFORD—Brambles Industries Limited; Int'l, pg. 211
BRAMBLES MARINE SERVICES PTY. LTD.—Brambles Industries Limited; Int'l, pg. 211
BRAMBLES USA INC.—Brambles Industries Limited; Int'l, pg. 211
BUDCO GROUP INC.; U.S. Private, pg. 178
BUXTON & SKINNER PRINTING COMPANY—Pubco Corporation; U.S. Public, pg. 1339
CAC LEASING A.S., PRAGUE—Creditanstalt-Bankverein; Int'l, pg. 348
CFC INVESTMENT CORP.—Cincinnati Financial Corp.; U.S. Public, pg. 368
CAPITAL ASSOCIATES, INC.; U.S. Public, pg. 302
CARLAND, INC.—Kansas City Southern Industries, Inc.; U.S. Public, pg. 944
CARLSON LEASING, INC.—Carlson Companies, Inc.; U.S. Private, pg. 212
CHANCELLOR ASSET CORPORATION—Chancellor Corporation; U.S. Public, pg. 335
CHANCELLOR CORPORATION; U.S. Public, pg. 335
P.T. CHASE LEASING INDONESIA—The Chase Manhattan Corporation; U.S. Public, pg. 339
CHASE LEASING (S.A.E.)—The Chase Manhattan Corporation; U.S. Public, pg. 339
THE CHASE MANHATTAN CORPORATION; U.S. Public, pg. 337
CHASE MANHATTAN LEASING—The Chase Manhattan Corporation; U.S. Public, pg. 338
CHASE MANHATTAN LEASING GMBH—The Chase Manhattan Corporation; U.S. Public, pg. 339
CHEMCO EQUIPMENT FINANCE LIMITED—The Chase Manhattan Corporation; U.S. Public, pg. 341
CHEP CANADA INC.—Brambles Industries Limited; Int'l, pg. 212
CHEP EUROP S.A.—Brambles Industries Limited; Int'l, pg. 212
CHEP FRANCE SA—Brambles Industries Limited; Int'l, pg. 212
CHEP IN EUROPE—Brambles Industries Limited; Int'l, pg. 212
CHEP UK LIMITED—Brambles Industries Limited; Int'l, pg. 212
CHICAGO HOLDINGS, INC.; U.S. Private, pg. 234
CHINA KANG FU INTERNATIONAL LEASING CO., LTD.—The Fuji Bank, Limited; Int'l, pg. 521
CINCINNATI FINANCIAL CORP.; U.S. Public, pg. 368
CITICORP; U.S. Public, pg. 376
CITICORP DEL-LEASE, INC.—Citicorp; U.S. Public, pg. 377
CITILEASE INTERNACIONAL, S.A.—Citicorp; U.S. Public, pg. 379
CITIZENS RESOURCES COMPANY—Citizens Utilities Company; U.S. Public, pg. 380
CLARKLIFT OF MINNESOTA, INC.; U.S. Private, pg. 243
CLOVERDALE EQUIPMENT CO.; U.S. Private, pg. 247
COLONIAL PACIFIC LEASING CORP.—Pitney Bowes Inc.; U.S. Public, pg. 1303
COLORADO NATIONAL BANKSHARES, INC.—U.S. Bancorp; U.S. Public, pg. 1680
COLUMBIA FARMS DISTRIBUTION—Columbia Farms Inc.; U.S. Private, pg. 255
COLUMBIA TRI-STAR INTERNATIONAL RELEASING CORP.—Sony Corporation; Int'l, pg. 1281
COMMCORP FINANCIAL SERVICES INC.—Canadian Imperial Bank of Commerce; Int'l, pg. 256
COMMETRO LEASING, INC.—Citicorp; U.S. Public, pg. 377
COMMONWEALTH CONTROL, INC.—Citicorp; U.S. Public, pg. 377
THE COMMONWEALTH PLAN, INC.—Citicorp; U.S. Public, pg. 377
THE COMMONWEALTH SYSTEM, INC.—Citicorp; U.S. Public, pg. 377
COMPLAN, INC.—Citicorp; U.S. Public, pg. 377
CONNELL CO.; U.S. Private, pg. 264
COPELCO FINANCIAL SERVICES GROUP INC.—Itochu Corporation; Int'l, pg. 694
CORT BUSINESS SERVICES CORPORATION; U.S. Public, pg. 451
CUDD PRESSURE CONTROL, INC.—RPC Incorporated; U.S. Public, pg. 1356
THE CURRY CORPORATION; U.S. Private, pg. 297
DB EXPORT LEASING G.M.B.H.—Deutsche Bank AG; Int'l, pg. 402
D.Q.F., INC.—Berkshire Hathaway Inc.; U.S. Public, pg. 220
DANA COMMERCIAL CREDIT SMALL TKT—Dana Corporation; U.S. Public, pg. 480
DATA RENTAL/SALES, DIVISION—Electro Rent Corporation; U.S. Public, pg. 568
DATACOMM LEASING CORP.—General Datacomm Industries, Inc.; U.S. Public, pg. 708
DEBORAH SERVICES—Sophus Berendsen A/S; Int'l, pg. 1285
DIAMOND LEASE CO., LTD.; Int'l, pg. 413
DRAVO LEASING CO.—Dravo Corporation; U.S. Public, pg. 527
DUMEZ-GTM—Lyonnaise des Eaux S.A.; Int'l, pg. 823
EPL PLANT & ACCESS—John Laing PLC; Int'l, pg. 796
EATON LEASING CORP.—Eaton Corporation; U.S. Public, pg. 558
ECONOCOM-USA INC.; U.S. Private, pg. 361
ELECTRO RENT CORPORATION; U.S. Public, pg. 568
ELECTRO RENT CORPORATION-ESD, INC.—Electro Rent Corporation; U.S. Public, pg. 568
ENERGY LAND, INCORPORATED—Minnesota Power; U.S. Public, pg. 1116
ENERGY NETWORKS, INC. (ENI)—CTG Resources, Inc.; U.S. Public, pg. 285
EQUIS FINANCIAL GROUP; U.S. Private, pg. 379
ERSKINE HOUSE GROUP PLC—Ikon Office Solutions, Inc.; U.S. Public, pg. 864
FHL LEASE HOLDING COMPANY, INC.—First Hawaiian, Inc.; U.S. Public, pg. 634
FALL RIVER GAS APPLIANCE CO., INC.—Fall River Gas Company; U.S. Public, pg. 612
FINANCIAL LEASING CORP.—Citicorp; U.S. Public, pg. 377
FIRELANDS TOOL RENTAL—Jennings & Churella Construction Company; U.S. Private, pg. 586
FIRST CHICAGO LEASING CORP.—First Chicago NBD Corporation; U.S. Public, pg. 628
FIRST HAWAIIAN LEASING, INC.—First Hawaiian, Inc.; U.S. Public, pg. 635
FIRST LEASING & RENTAL CORPORATION—Firstbank Puerto Rico; U.S. Public, pg. 644
FIRST SECURITY LEASING CO.—First Security Corporation; U.S. Public, pg. 638
FIRSTAR LEASING CORPORATION—Firstar Corporation; U.S. Public, pg. 643
FIRSTCORP—Firstcorp; U.S. Private, pg. 408
FLEET CREDIT CORPORATION—Fleet Financial Group, Inc.; U.S. Public, pg. 650
THE FLIGHT INTERNATIONAL GROUP, INC.; U.S. Public, pg. 654
FLORIDA PROGRESS CORPORATION; U.S. Public, pg. 655
THE FOOTHILL GROUP, INC.—Norwest Corporation; U.S. Public, pg. 1201
FREMONT GENERAL CORPORATION; U.S. Public, pg. 681
FUJI LEASING (DEUTSCHLAND) GMBH—The Fuji Bank, Limited; Int'l, pg. 521
FUJI LEASING (UK) LIMITED—The Fuji Bank, Limited; Int'l, pg. 521
FURNIVAL/STATE MACHINERY CO.—Komatsu Ltd.; Int'l, pg. 744
FUYO GENERAL LEASE CO. LTD.—Citicorp; U.S. Public, pg. 379
G.E. CAPITAL FLEET SERVICES—General Electric Company; U.S. Public, pg. 710
GES EXPOSITION SERVICES, INC.—Viad Corp; U.S. Public, pg. 1718
GPA GROUP PLC—Air Canada; Int'l, pg. 37
GENERAL ELECTRIC CAPITAL SERVICES, INC.—General Electric Company; U.S. Public, pg. 711
GESTETNER A/S—Ricoh Company, Ltd.; Int'l, pg. 1115
GESTETNER CHILE S.A.—Ricoh Company, Ltd.; Int'l, pg. 1115
GESTETNER DO BRASIL, S.A. SISTEMAS REPROGRAPHICOS—Ricoh Company, Ltd.; Int'l, pg. 1115
GESTETNER S.A.—Ricoh Company, Ltd.; Int'l, pg. 1115
GESTETNER SECURITIES B.V.—Ricoh Company, Ltd.; Int'l, pg. 1115

GLOBE FURNITURE RENTALS; *U.S. Private*, pg. 458
GLOBE FURNITURE RENTALS—Globe Furniture Rentals; *U.S. Private*, pg. 458
GOODMANS, INC.; *U.S. Private*, pg. 464
GRAPHLINE INC.; *U.S. Private*, pg. 471
GREAT AMERICAN MANAGEMENT SERVICES, INC.—American Financial Group; *U.S. Public*, pg. 75
GREENWAY CORPORATION—Williams Industries, Inc.; *U.S. Public*, pg. 1770
GRIFFIN TECHNOLOGY INCORPORATED—Diebold, Incorporated; *U.S. Public*, pg. 506
GROCERS EQUIPMENT CO.—Certified Grocers of California; *U.S. Private*, pg. 227
HSBC AMERICAS—HSBC Holdings plc; *Int'l*, pg. 580
HSS HIRE SERVICE GROUP PLC—The Davis Service Group Plc.; *Int'l*, pg. 385
HARCO LEASING CO., INC.—Navistar International Corporation; *U.S. Public*, pg. 1167
HARRISCORP LEASING, INC.—Bank of Montreal; *Int'l*, pg. 155
LEX HARVEY LTD.; *Int'l*, pg. 599
HASPER EQUIPMENT CO.—Cloverdale Equipment Co.; *U.S. Private*, pg. 247
HAWKEYE LEASING CORPORATION—Mercantile Bancorporation Inc.; *U.S. Public*, pg. 1087
HERTZ EQUIPMENT RENTAL CORP.—Ford Motor Company; *U.S. Public*, pg. 664
HIGHLINE FINANCIAL SERVICES, INC.—Xerox Corporation; *U.S. Public*, pg. 1785
HOECHST MARION ROUSSEL, INC.—Hoechst Aktiengesellschaft; *Int'l*, pg. 624
HOLLISTER MEDICAL SYSTEMS DIVISION—Hollister Incorporated; *U.S. Private*, pg. 535
HOLMAN BOILER WORKS, INC.—Copes-Vulcan Inc.; *U.S. Private*, pg. 274
HOUSTON MARINE CONTAINERS INC.—Sea Containers Ltd.; *Int'l*, pg. 1214
IKON OFFICE SYSTEMS—Ikon Office Solutions, Inc.; *U.S. Public*, pg. 864
ILLINOIS BANC ONE LEASING CORP.—Banc One Corporation; *U.S. Public*, pg. 174
INDECK POWER EQUIPMENT COMPANY; *U.S. Private*, pg. 559
INDUSTRIAL CHEMICAL & EQUIPMENT—Hawkins Chemical, Inc.; *U.S. Public*, pg. 800
INSTITUTIONAL EQUIPMENT & INTERIORS, INC.—Piccadilly Cafeterias, Inc.; *U.S. Public*, pg. 1294
INTER LEASING MOROCCO—Banque Nationale de Paris; *Int'l*, pg. 163
INTER-TEL LEASING, INC.—Inter-Tel, Incorporated; *U.S. Public*, pg. 888
INTERLEASE TRADING CORP.—American International Group, Inc.; *U.S. Public*, pg. 85
INTERNATIONAL AIRLINE SUPPORT GROUP, INC.; *U.S. Public*, pg. 894
INTERNATIONAL LEASE FINANCE CORPORATION—American International Group, Inc.; *U.S. Public*, pg. 85
J & J SNACK FOODS CORPORATION; *U.S. Public*, pg. 916
P.T. JAYA FUJI LEASING PRATAMA—The Fuji Bank, Limited; *Int'l*, pg. 521
THE DAVID J. JOSEPH COMPANY—SHV Holdings N.V.; *Int'l*, pg. 1155
KENTUCKY MEDICAL INSURANCE COMPANY (KMIC)—Michigan Physicians Mutual Liability Inc.; *U.S. Private*, pg. 741
KEYCORP LEASING LTD.—Keycorp; *U.S. Public*, pg. 954
KOREA DEVELOPMENT LEASING CORPORATION—Orix Corporation; *Int'l*, pg. 1010
KOREA DEVELOPMENT LEASING CORPORATION—The Sanwa Bank Limited; *Int'l*, pg. 1190
LEASE-ELEC, INC.—Green Mountain Power Corporation; *U.S. Public*, pg. 761
LEASING SOLUTIONS, INC.; *U.S. Public*, pg. 982
LEASING SOLUTIONS INTERNATIONAL, LTD.—Leasing Solutions, Inc.; *U.S. Public*, pg. 983
LIBMAR FOUR, INC.—The Chase Manhattan Corporation; *U.S. Public*, pg. 341
LINC CAPITAL GROUP; *U.S. Public*, pg. 996
LLOYDS ASSOCIATED AIR LEASING LTD.—Lloyds TSB Group PLC; *Int'l*, pg. 813
LLOYDS EQUIPMENT LEASING LTD.—Lloyds TSB Group PLC; *Int'l*, pg. 813
LLOYDS INDUSTRIAL LEASING LTD.—Lloyds TSB Group PLC; *Int'l*, pg. 813
LOCABEL S.A.—Bank Brussels Lambert; *Int'l*, pg. 147
LOCATEL—Alcatel Alsthom Compagnie Generale D'Electricite; *Int'l*, pg. 54
M & I FIRST NATIONAL LEASING CORP.—Marshall & Ilsley Corporation; *U.S. Public*, pg. 1051
M&T FINANCIAL CORPORATION—First Empire State Corporation; *U.S. Public*, pg. 631
MAN NUTZFAHRZEUGE LEASING GMBH—MAN Aktiengesellschaft; *Int'l*, pg. 824
MH LEASING INTERNATIONAL—The Chase Manhattan Corporation; *U.S. Public*, pg. 338
MSA NEDERLAND B.V.—Mine Safety Appliances Co.; *U.S. Public*, pg. 1115
THE MARMON GROUP, INC.; *U.S. Private*, pg. 706
MARSHALL & ILSLEY CORPORATION; *U.S. Public*, pg. 1049
MCGRATH RENTCORP; *U.S. Public*, pg. 1069
MCJUNKIN - APPALACHAIN—McJunkin Corporation; *U.S. Private*, pg. 722
MCRAE INDUSTRIES, INC.; *U.S. Public*, pg. 1073
MILWAUKEE ELECTRIC TOOL (CANADA) LTD.—Assa Abloy AB; *Int'l*, pg. 18
MITSUI LEASING & DEVELOPMENT LTD.—Mitsui & Co., Ltd.; *Int'l*, pg. 878
THE MITSUI WAREHOUSE CO., LTD.—Mitsui & Co., Ltd.; *Int'l*, pg. 878
MODERN EQUIPMENT RENTALS INC.—Modern Group Ltd.; *U.S. Private*, pg. 754
MODERN GROUP LTD.; *U.S. Private*, pg. 754
JOHN MOWLEM & COMPANY PLC; *Int'l*, pg. 896
NBD EQUIPMENT FINANCE, INC.—First Chicago NBD Corporation; *U.S. Public*, pg. 628
NRG BENELUX B.V.—Ricoh Company, Ltd.; *Int'l*, pg. 1116
NRG COMUNICACIONES S.A.—Ricoh Company, Ltd.; *Int'l*, pg. 1116
NRG FRANCE S.A.—Ricoh Company, Ltd.; *Int'l*, pg. 1116
NRG GROUP LIMITED—Ricoh Company, Ltd.; *Int'l*, pg. 1114
NRG INCORPORATED—Telco Capital Corporation; *U.S. Private*, pg. 1073
NRG INTERNATIONAL LTD. (BERMUDA)—Ricoh Company, Ltd.; *Int'l*, pg. 1116
NRG ITALIA S.P.A.—Ricoh Company, Ltd.; *Int'l*, pg. 1116
NANTO LEASE CO., LTD.—The Nanto Bank, Ltd.; *Int'l*, pg. 906
NATIONSBANK LEASING CORPORATION—NationsBank Corporation; *U.S. Public*, pg. 1163
NATIONSBANK OF TEXAS NATIONAL LEASING CORP.—NationsBank Corporation; *U.S. Public*, pg. 1163
NATIONSCREDIT COMMERCIAL CORPORATION—NationsBank Corporation; *U.S. Public*, pg. 1165
NIPPON UNIVAC KAISHA, LTD.—Mitsui & Co., Ltd.; *Int'l*, pg. 879
NORLEASE, INC.—Northern Trust Corporation; *U.S. Public*, pg. 1196
NORTH AMERICAN FINANCIAL CORP.—Carlson Companies, Inc.; *U.S. Private*, pg. 212
NORWEST CORPORATION; *U.S. Public*, pg. 1201
O/B LEASING COMPANY—Budco Group Inc.; *U.S. Private*, pg. 178
OBAYASHI CORPORATION; *Int'l*, pg. 995
P&O VENDING—The Peninsular and Oriental Steam Navigation Company; *Int'l*, pg. 1034
PHH CORPORATION—Cendant Corporation; *U.S. Public*, pg. 321
PLM INTERNATIONAL, INC.; *U.S. Public*, pg. 1241
PS GROUP HOLDINGS; *U.S. Public*, pg. 1245
PTP AERIAL PLATFORMS LTD.—Sophus Berendsen A/S; *Int'l*, pg. 1285
PABTEX, INC.—Kansas City Southern Industries, Inc.; *U.S. Public*, pg. 944
PACIFIC ENTERPRISES LEASING CO.—Pacific Enterprises; *U.S. Public*, pg. 1249
THE PACIFIC PLAN, INC.—Citicorp; *U.S. Public*, pg. 377
PHOENIX FIBER LINK INC.—Phoenix American Incorporated; *U.S. Private*, pg. 863
PHOENIX SYSTEMS EXCHANGE, INC.—Phoenix American Incorporated; *U.S. Private*, pg. 863
PITNEY BOWES CREDIT CORPORATION—Pitney Bowes Inc.; *U.S. Public*, pg. 1303
PITNEY BOWES INC.; *U.S. Public*, pg. 1303
PITNEY BOWES OF CANADA LTD.-LEASING DIV.—Pitney Bowes Inc.; *U.S. Public*, pg. 1304
PLUNT ACROW LTD.—Ashtead Group PLC; *Int'l*, pg. 88
PROPAK SYSTEMS LTD.; *Int'l*, pg. 1071
R D I S CORPORATION; *U.S. Private*, pg. 903
RPC INCORPORATED; *U.S. Public*, pg. 1356
RAINBOW RENTALS, INC.; *U.S. Private*, pg. 907
RAY SATELLITE NETWORK—Ray Communications, Inc.; *U.S. Private*, pg. 911
REMCO AMERICA, INC.—Thorn plc; *Int'l*, pg. 1385
RENT-A-CENTER, INC.—Thorn plc; *Int'l*, pg. 1385
RENT-WAY, INC.; *U.S. Public*, pg. 1377
RENTOKIL INITIAL PLANT SERVICES (USA) INC.—Sophus Berendsen A/S; *Int'l*, pg. 1285
RENTOKIL INITIAL PLC—Sophus Berendsen A/S; *Int'l*, pg. 1285
RENTOKIL LTD.—Sophus Berendsen A/S; *Int'l*, pg. 1285
RENTWAY INC.—Trimac Corporation; *Int'l*, pg. 1424
RENTWAY TRUCK LEASING—Trimac Corporation; *Int'l*, pg. 1424
REX-ROTARY UK LIMITED—Ricoh Company, Ltd.; *Int'l*, pg. 1114
ROLLINS, INC.; *U.S. Public*, pg. 1404
SGB CONSTRUCTION SERVICES, INC.—John Mowlem & Company plc; *Int'l*, pg. 896
SAFETY-KLEEN CORP.; *U.S. Public*, pg. 1425
SALTON/MAXIM HOUSEWARES, INC.; *U.S. Public*, pg. 1430
P.T. SANWA-BRI FINANCE—The Sanwa Bank Limited; *Int'l*, pg. 1190
SANYO ELECTRIC CREDIT CO. LTD.—Sanyo Electric Co., Ltd.; *Int'l*, pg. 1191
THE SARATOGA EQUIP. CORP.—The Rouse Company; *U.S. Public*, pg. 1409
SAVA LEASING S.P.A.—Fiat Auto SpA; *Int'l*, pg. 482
SAVIN CORPORATION—Ricoh Company, Ltd.; *Int'l*, pg. 1114
SEA CONTAINERS AGENCIES INC.—Sea Containers Ltd.; *Int'l*, pg. 1214
SEA CONTAINERS AMERICA INC.—Sea Containers Ltd.; *Int'l*, pg. 1213
SEA CONTAINERS ASIA LTD.—Sea Containers Ltd.; *Int'l*, pg. 1214
SEA CONTAINERS AUSTRALIA LTD.—Sea Containers Ltd.; *Int'l*, pg. 1214
SEA CONTAINERS BRITISH ISLES LTD.—Sea Containers Ltd.; *Int'l*, pg. 1214
SEA CONTAINERS CARIBBEAN INC.—Sea Containers Ltd.; *Int'l*, pg. 1214
SEA CONTAINERS FRANCE S.A.—Sea Containers Ltd.; *Int'l*, pg. 1214
SEA CONTAINERS GMBH—Sea Containers Ltd.; *Int'l*, pg. 1214
SEA CONTAINERS HONG KONG LTD.—Sea Containers Ltd.; *Int'l*, pg. 1214
SEA CONTAINERS ITALIA SRL—Sea Containers Ltd.; *Int'l*, pg. 1214
SEA CONTAINERS NORTH AMERICAN OPERATIONS & ACCOUNTING GROUP—Sea Containers Ltd.; *Int'l*, pg. 1214
SEA CONTAINERS SERVICES LTD.—Sea Containers Ltd.; *Int'l*, pg. 1214
SEA CONTAINERS U.S. GULF INC.—Sea Containers Ltd.; *Int'l*, pg. 1214
SEA CONTAINERS WEST INC.—Sea Containers Ltd.; *Int'l*, pg. 1214
SECURITY PACIFIC LEASING CORPORATION—BankAmerica Corporation; *U.S. Public*, pg. 182
SELMABIPIEMME LEASING SPA—Banca Popolare di Milano; *Int'l*, pg. 137
SERVICE MOTOR CO.—Service Motor Company; *U.S. Private*, pg. 986
SERVICE MOTOR COMPANY; *U.S. Private*, pg. 986
SIMCO, INC.—American Electric Power Company, Inc.; *U.S. Public*, pg. 72
SODEXHO S.A.; *Int'l*, pg. 1274
SOUTH ATLANTIC EQUIPMENT, INC.—The Dickerson Group, Inc.; *U.S. Private*, pg. 331
SOUTHERN GROUP, INC.—Kansas City Southern Industries, Inc.; *U.S. Public*, pg. 944
SOUTHERN LEASING OF KANSAS CITY, INC.—Kansas City Southern Industries, Inc.; *U.S. Public*, pg. 944
STANDARD CHARTERED LEASING COMPANY LTD.—Standard Chartered Bank PLC; *Int'l*, pg. 1296
STANDARD CHARTERED LEASING GMBH—Standard Chartered Bank PLC; *Int'l*, pg. 1297
P.T. STANDARD CHARTERED LEASING—Standard Chartered Bank PLC; *Int'l*, pg. 1297
STEINER CORPORATION; *U.S. Private*, pg. 1039
SUN FINANCIAL GROUP, INC.—GATX Corporation; *U.S. Public*, pg. 691
SUNWEST LEASING CORP. (SLC)—West Coast Bancorp; *U.S. Public*, pg. 1755
SYRACUSE SUPPLY COMPANY; *U.S. Private*, pg. 1060
TSE LEASING CO.—I. Spiewak & Sons, Inc.; *U.S. Private*, pg. 1025
TELCO CAPITAL CORP.—R D I S Corporation; *U.S. Private*, pg. 903
THORN AMERICAS—Thorn plc; *Int'l*, pg. 1385
TOLMAK, INC.—Kansas City Southern Industries, Inc.; *U.S. Public*, pg. 944
TRANS LEASING INTERNATIONAL INC.; *U.S. Public*, pg. 1628
TRANS-LUX CORPORATION; *U.S. Public*, pg. 1628
TRANSAMERICA CORPORATION; *U.S. Public*, pg. 1629
TRANSAMERICA LEASING INC.—Transamerica Corporation; *U.S. Public*, pg. 1630
TRANSPORTATION EQUIPMENT CORPORATION—PLM International, Inc.; *U.S. Public*, pg. 1241
UNITED LEASING COMPANY—Michigan Physicians Mutual Liability Inc.; *U.S. Private*, pg. 741
UNITED MISSOURI LEASING CORPORATION—UMB Financial Corporation; *U.S. Public*, pg. 1655
UNITED STATES AIRLEASE, INCORPORATED—Ford Motor Company; *U.S. Public*, pg. 664
US AIRWAYS LEASING & SERVICES, INC.—US Airways Group, Inc.; *U.S. Public*, pg. 1680
UP-RIGHT, INC.; *U.S. Private*, pg. 1128
VAMCO—Valley Resources, Inc.; *U.S. Public*, pg. 1706
VANGUARD FINANCIAL SERVICES—Old Kent Financial Corporation; *U.S. Public*, pg. 1216
VENDOR FUNDING CO., INC.—Bank of Ireland; *Int'l*, pg. 153
VICTAULIC TOOL COMPANY—Victaulic Company of America; *U.S. Private*, pg. 1138
WACHOVIA LEASING CORPORATION—Wachovia Corporation; *U.S. Public*, pg. 1731
WEATHERFORD US INC.—Weatherford Enterra Incorporated; *U.S. Public*, pg. 1749
WILLIAMS EQUIPMENT CORPORATION—Williams Industries, Inc.; *U.S. Public*, pg. 1770
WILLIAMS SCOTSMAN, INC.—Scotsman Holding Inc.; *U.S. Private*, pg. 976
WILSON INDUSTRIES INC.; *U.S. Private*, pg. 1181
THE WORCESTER PLAN, INC.—Citicorp; *U.S. Public*, pg. 377
WORLDWIDE LEASING—Illinois Tool Works Inc.; *U.S. Public*, pg. 866
XTRA CORPORATION; *U.S. Public*, pg. 1786
YALE/CHASE MATERIALS HANDLING, INC.; *U.S. Private*, pg. 1195
YOUNG ELECTRIC SIGN COMPANY; *U.S. Private*, pg. 1201
ZIEGLER LEASING CORP.—The Ziegler Companies, Inc.; *U.S. Public*, pg. 1792

7361 — EMPLOYMENT AGENCIES

ATC HEALTHCARE SERVICES INC.; *U.S. Private*, pg. 8
ACCOUNTEMPS—Robert Half International Inc.; *U.S. Public*, pg. 775
ADECCO S.A.; *Int'l*, pg. 23
THE AFFILIATES—Robert Half International Inc.; *U.S. Public*, pg. 775
ASAHI BANK CAREER SERVICE CO., LTD.—The Asahi Bank, Ltd.; *Int'l*, pg. 82
CDI CORP.; *U.S. Public*, pg. 276
CAPITOL INDUSTRIES-EMI INC.—EMI Group plc; *Int'l*, pg. 427
CAREER BLAZERS AGENCY, INC.—Career Blazers Inc.; *U.S. Private*, pg. 209
CAREER BLAZERS INC.; *U.S. Private*, pg. 209
EUROTUNNEL SERVICES LIMITED—The Eurotunnel Group; *Int'l*, pg. 466
FIRSTAFF, INC.—AccuStaff Incorporated; *U.S. Public*, pg. 15
FUTURES PERSONNEL SERVICES; *U.S. Private*, pg. 433
GENERAL EMPLOYMENT ENTERPRISES—General Employment Enterprises, Inc.; *U.S. Public*, pg. 714
GENERAL EMPLOYMENT ENTERPRISES, INC.; *U.S. Public*, pg. 714
GENERAL EMPLOYMENT ENTERPRISES, INC.—General Employment Enterprises, Inc.; *U.S. Public*, pg. 714
GOODWILL INDUSTRIES INTERNATIONAL; *U.S. Private*, pg. 464

GROCERS DEVELOPMENT CO.—Certified Grocers of California; U.S. Private, pg. 227
GULF ASIA INTERNATIONAL CORPORATION—EEI Corporation; Int'l, pg. 426
ROBERT HALF—Robert Half International Inc.; U.S. Public, pg. 775
ROBERT HALF INTERNATIONAL INC.; U.S. Public, pg. 774
C.H. HEIST CORP.; U.S. Public, pg. 807
KORN/FERRY INTERNATIONAL; U.S. Private, pg. 632
MILLER PERSONNEL, INC.—Miller Resources International, Inc.; U.S. Private, pg. 748
MILLER RESOURCES INTERNATIONAL, INC.; U.S. Private, pg. 748
MILLER SCIENTIFIC, INC.—Miller Resources International, Inc.; U.S. Private, pg. 748
MILLER TEMPORARIES, INC.—Miller Resources International, Inc.; U.S. Private, pg. 748
NES HOLDINGS, INC.; U.S. Private, pg. 771
NANTO STAFF SERVICE CO., LTD.—The Nanto Bank, Ltd.; Int'l, pg. 906
NURSES INC.—Sophus Berendsen A/S; Int'l, pg. 1285
OFFICETEAM—Robert Half International Inc.; U.S. Public, pg. 775
PSICOR, INC.—Baxter International Inc.; U.S. Public, pg. 196
POLESTAR LABS, INC.; U.S. Private, pg. 874
PROGRESSIVE DRIVER SERVICES, INC.; U.S. Private, pg. 890
RHI CONSULTING—Robert Half International Inc.; U.S. Public, pg. 775
RHI MANAGEMENT RESOURCES—Robert Half International Inc.; U.S. Public, pg. 775
RJR TOBACCO COMPANY, INC.—RJR Nabisco Holdings Corp.; U.S. Public, pg. 1355
SMITH'S PERSONNEL SERVICE, INC.; U.S. Private, pg. 1010
SNELLING PERSONNEL SERVICES; U.S. Private, pg. 1010
SOURCE SERVICES CORPORATION; U.S. Public, pg. 1488
STAFFING SOLUTIONS; U.S. Private, pg. 1028
STAR MULTI CARE SERVICES INC.; U.S. Public, pg. 1510
TALENT TREE PERSONNEL SERVICES INC.—Sophus Berendsen A/S; Int'l, pg. 1286
TOP BILLING INC.; U.S. Private, pg. 1091
WATSCO, INC.; U.S. Public, pg. 1745
WEATHERBY HEALTH CARE; U.S. Private, pg. 1155
WESTERN STAFF SERVICES; U.S. Public, pg. 1760
WINSTON RESOURCES, INC.; U.S. Public, pg. 1772

7363 — HELP SUPPLY SERVICES

ADHOC—Vendex International N.V.; Int'l, pg. 1463
ASB—Vendex International N.V.; Int'l, pg. 1463
ASB INTERIM—Vendex International N.V.; Int'l, pg. 1463
ACCUSTAFF INCORPORATED; U.S. Public, pg. 15
ADECCO EMPLOYMENT SERVICES—Adecco S.A.; Int'l, pg. 24
ADECCO S.A.; Int'l, pg. 23
ALTERNATIVE RESOURCES CORPORATION; U.S. Public, pg. 59
ASAHI BANK CAREER SERVICE CO., LTD.—The Asahi Bank, Ltd.; Int'l, pg. 82
BERGALL CORPORATION—Staff Builders Inc.; U.S. Public, pg. 1501
BUTLER INTERNATIONAL, INC.; U.S. Public, pg. 270
CDI CORP.; U.S. Public, pg. 276
CORS; U.S. Private, pg. 196
CARECO, INC.—Staff Builders Inc.; U.S. Public, pg. 1501
CAREER BLAZERS INC.; U.S. Private, pg. 209
CAREER BLAZERS LEARNING CENTER—Career Blazers Inc.; U.S. Private, pg. 209
CAREER BLAZERS TEMPORARY PERSONNEL—Career Blazers Inc.; U.S. Private, pg. 209
CAREERS USA INC.; U.S. Private, pg. 209
COMFORCE/UNIFORCE STAFFING SERVICES—Comforce Corporation; U.S. Public, pg. 409
COMPDATA SERVICES CORP.—CDI Corp.; U.S. Public, pg. 277
COMPUTER ENTERPRISES, INC.—Technical Aid Corporation; U.S. Private, pg. 1072
DACTYLO—Vendex International N.V.; Int'l, pg. 1463
THE DAISHI STAFF SERVICE CO. LTD.—The Daishi Bank, Ltd.; Int'l, pg. 372
DAY & ZIMMERMANN, INC.; U.S. Private, pg. 316
DIGITAL SOLUTIONS, INC.; U.S. Public, pg. 508
DIVERSCO, INC.; U.S. Private, pg. 336
DURATEK CORPORATION—GP Strategies Corporation; U.S. Public, pg. 694
EDP/TEMPS INC.—Technical Aid Corporation; U.S. Private, pg. 1072
EG & G MANAGEMENT SYSTEMS—EG & G, Inc.; U.S. Public, pg. 543
GENERAL EMPLOYMENT ENTERPRISES—General Employment Enterprises, Inc.; U.S. Public, pg. 714
GENERAL EMPLOYMENT ENTERPRISES, INC.; U.S. Public, pg. 714
GENERAL EMPLOYMENT ENTERPRISES, INC.—General Employment Enterprises, Inc.; U.S. Public, pg. 714
GREGG INTERIM—Vendex International N.V.; Int'l, pg. 1463
GREGG KNOWHOW—Vendex International N.V.; Int'l, pg. 1463
HEALTH MANAGEMENT, INC.—Counsel Corporation; Int'l, pg. 338
HOME CARE P.R.N., INC.—Technical Aid Corporation; U.S. Private, pg. 1072
HOSPITAL STAFFING SERVICES, INC.; U.S. Public, pg. 840
INTERIM SERVICES (CANADA) LTD.—Interim Services Inc.; U.S. Public, pg. 892
KELLY SERVICES, INC.; U.S. Public, pg. 949
MANAGEMENT RECRUITERS INTERNATIONAL, INC.—CDI Corp.; U.S. Public, pg. 277
MANPOWER INC.; U.S. Public, pg. 1042
MICROTEMPS SYSTEMS & PROGRAMMING—Technical Aid Corporation; U.S. Private, pg. 1072
NATIONAL TECHNICAL SYSTEMS, INC.; U.S. Public, pg. 1161
NORRELL CORPORATION; U.S. Public, pg. 1192
NOVACARE EMPLOYEE SERVICES, INC.—NovaCare Inc.; U.S. Public, pg. 1203
OFFICE ANGELS LIMITED—Olsten Corporation; U.S. Public, pg. 1221
OLSTEN CORPORATION; U.S. Public, pg. 1220
OUTSOURCE INTERNATIONAL; U.S. Public, pg. 1236
PGL INDUSTRIES, INC.—Staff Builders Inc.; U.S. Public, pg. 1501
PENSKE LOGISTICS—Penske Corporation; U.S. Private, pg. 851
PEOPLEMARK, INC.—Guardsmark, Inc.; U.S. Private, pg. 486
PLANT MAINTENANCE, INC.—Snelling Personnel Services; U.S. Private, pg. 1011
PROFESSIONAL DETAIL SERVICES, INC.—Staff Builders Inc.; U.S. Public, pg. 1501
REMEDYTEMP, INC.; U.S. Public, pg. 1376
SMITH'S PERSONNEL SERVICE, INC.; U.S. Private, pg. 1010
SNELLING PERSONNEL SERVICES; U.S. Private, pg. 1010
SOURCE SERVICES CORPORATION; U.S. Public, pg. 1488
STAFFING SOLUTIONS; U.S. Private, pg. 1028
STERLING OFFICE SERVICES—Olsten Corporation; U.S. Public, pg. 1221
STRATUS SERVICES GROUP, INC.; U.S. Private, pg. 1046
SYSTEMS MANAGEMENT & DEVELOPMENT—Technical Aid Corporation; U.S. Private, pg. 1072
TAC/MEDICAL SERVICES INC.—Technical Aid Corporation; U.S. Private, pg. 1072
TAC/TEMPS INC.—Technical Aid Corporation; U.S. Private, pg. 1072
TECH/AID—Technical Aid Corporation; U.S. Private, pg. 1072
TECHNICAL AID CORPORATION; U.S. Private, pg. 1072
TEMPS & COMPANY; U.S. Private, pg. 1075
TENDER LOVING CARE HOME CARE SERVICES, INC.—Staff Builders Inc.; U.S. Public, pg. 1501
TODAYS TEMPORARY, INC.—CDI Corp.; U.S. Public, pg. 277
TODAYS TEMPORARY, LTD.—CDI Corp.; U.S. Public, pg. 277
TRIAD PERSONNEL SERVICES—General Employment Enterprises, Inc.; U.S. Public, pg. 715
VEDIOR—Vendex International N.V.; Int'l, pg. 1463
VEDIOR COMPUHELP—Vendex International N.V.; Int'l, pg. 1463
VEDIOR FRANCE—Vendex International N.V.; Int'l, pg. 1463
VICTOR TEMPORARY SERVICES, LTD.—Interim Services Inc.; U.S. Public, pg. 892
VOLT INFORMATION SCIENCES, INC.; U.S. Public, pg. 1724
VOLT MANAGEMENT CORP.—Volt Information Sciences, Inc.; U.S. Public, pg. 1724
WATKINS SYSTEM INC.; U.S. Private, pg. 1153
WESTERN MEDICAL SERVICES INC.—Western Staff Services; U.S. Public, pg. 1760
WESTERN STAFF SERVICES; U.S. Public, pg. 1760
WESTERN STAFF SERVICES PTY. LTD.—Western Staff Services; U.S. Public, pg. 1760
WESTERN STAFF SERVICES (USA), INC.—Western Staff Services; U.S. Public, pg. 1760
WESTERN TEMPORARY SERVICES DIV.—Western Staff Services; U.S. Public, pg. 1760
WISE & ASSOCIATES/S&W TECHNICAL SERVICES—National Technical Systems, Inc.; U.S. Public, pg. 1161
H.L. YOH GROUP LLC—Day & Zimmermann, Inc.; U.S. Private, pg. 317
YOH STAFFING SERVICES—Day & Zimmermann, Inc.; U.S. Private, pg. 317
YOUR STAFF, INC.—Kelly Services, Inc.; U.S. Public, pg. 949

7371 — COMPUTER PROGRAMMING SERVICES

ABC, INC—The Walt Disney Company; U.S. Public, pg. 511
AMS OPERATIONS CORPORATION, INC.—American Management Systems, Inc.; U.S. Public, pg. 86
APPX SOFTWARE INC.—Tredegar Industries Inc.; U.S. Public, pg. 1634
ASI PROPERTIES, INC.—American Software, Inc.; U.S. Public, pg. 91
AT&T STRATEGY & NEW SERVICE INNOVATIONS—AT&T Corporation; U.S. Public, pg. 11
ADRA SYSTEMS, INC.; U.S. Private, pg. 18
AMERICAN MANAGEMENT SYSTEMS, INC.; U.S. Public, pg. 86
AMERIDATA TECHNOLOGIES, INC.—General Electric Company; U.S. Public, pg. 711
ANALYSTS INTERNATIONAL CORPORATION; U.S. Public, pg. 110
ANASAZI INC.—Reed Elsevier plc; Int'l, pg. 1098
ARTISOFT, INC.; U.S. Public, pg. 136
AVANTI; U.S. Public, pg. 151
AXENT TECHNOLOGIES; U.S. Public, pg. 157
BGS SYSTEMS, INC.; U.S. Public, pg. 161
BANKVISION SOFTWARE, LTD.—Jack Henry & Associates, Inc.; U.S. Public, pg. 809
BARRA, INC.; U.S. Public, pg. 191
BEDFORD ASSOCIATES, INC.—British Airways PLC; Int'l, pg. 219
BELL MOBILITY RADIO INC.—BCE Inc.; Int'l, pg. 115
BELLCORE—Science Applications International Corp.; U.S. Private, pg. 976
BENTLEY SYSTEMS, INC.; U.S. Private, pg. 134
BOCA RESEARCH INC.; U.S. Public, pg. 239
THE BOEING COMPANY; U.S. Public, pg. 239
BOEING COMPUTER SERVICES - EUROPE—The Boeing Company; U.S. Public, pg. 242
BORLAND INTERNATIONAL, INC.; U.S. Public, pg. 246
BRIGHTWARE, INC.; U.S. Private, pg. 168
CACI INTERNATIONAL INC; U.S. Public, pg. 272
CAP GEMINI AMERICA (MANAGEMENT CONSULTING BRANCH)—CAP Gemini S.A.; Int'l, pg. 264
CCI/TRIAD CORPORATION; U.S. Private, pg. 193
CAPITAL DATA SYSTEMS, INC.—Chesapeake Utilities Corporation; U.S. Public, pg. 347
CARA CORPORATION—William Blair & Company L.L.C.; U.S. Private, pg. 148
CARNEGIE HOLDING AB; Int'l, pg. 272
CHARLESTON FINANCIAL SERVICES, INC.—First Financial Holdings, Inc.; U.S. Public, pg. 634
CINCOM SYSTEMS, INC.; U.S. Private, pg. 240
CIRRUS LOGIC, INC.; U.S. Public, pg. 375
COMCOTEC, INC.—Dynatech Corporation; U.S. Public, pg. 539
COMMLINK—Jack Henry & Associates, Inc.; U.S. Public, pg. 809
COMMONWEALTH ENERGY SYSTEM; U.S. Public, pg. 414
COMPASS DESIGN AUTOMATION INC.—VLSI Technology, Inc.; U.S. Public, pg. 1703
COMPTEK FEDERAL SYSTEMS, INC.—Comptek Research, Inc.; U.S. Public, pg. 419
COMPTEK RESEARCH, INC.; U.S. Public, pg. 419
COMPUTER CORPORATION OF AMERICA; U.S. Private, pg. 260
COMPUTER HORIZONS CORP.; U.S. Public, pg. 421
COMPUTER METHODS CORPORATION; U.S. Private, pg. 260
COMPUTER POWER GROUP LIMITED; Int'l, pg. 325
COMPUTER SCIENCES CORPORATION; U.S. Public, pg. 422
COMPUTER TASK GROUP, INC. (CTG); U.S. Public, pg. 423
COMSHARE LTD.—Comshare, Incorporated; U.S. Public, pg. 425
CONSILIUM, INC.; U.S. Public, pg. 434
COREL CORPORATION—Corel Corporation; Int'l, pg. 331
D&Z UTILITY SERVICES—Day & Zimmermann, Inc.; U.S. Private, pg. 317
DMR CONSULTING GROUP, INC.—Fujitsu Limited; Int'l, pg. 527
DMR GROUP, INC.—Fujitsu Limited; Int'l, pg. 527
DAIWA SOFTWARE RESEARCH CO., LTD.—Daiwa Securities Co. Ltd.; Int'l, pg. 375
DASSAULT SYSTEMES—Dassault Aviation Group; Int'l, pg. 383
DATA GENERAL CORPORATION; U.S. Public, pg. 485
DATA GENERAL CUSTOMER SERVICE DIVISION—Data General Corporation; U.S. Public, pg. 485
DATAPOINT DEVELOPMENT CENTER, INC.—Datapoint Corporation; Int'l, pg. 384
DENTSPLY NEW IMAGE—Dentsply International Inc.; U.S. Public, pg. 499
DIGITAL LINK CORPORATION; U.S. Public, pg. 508
DYNAMICS RESEARCH CORPORATION; U.S. Public, pg. 539
DYNATECH CORPORATION; U.S. Public, pg. 539
EQUITRAC CORPORATION; U.S. Public, pg. 590
ERICSSON BUSINESS COMMUNICATIONS, INC.—Telefonaktiebolaget LM Ericsson; Int'l, pg. 1364
ERICSSON PROGRAMATIC SWEDEN AB—Telefonaktiebolaget LM Ericsson; Int'l, pg. 1363
EXCALIBUR TECHNOLOGIES CORPORATION; U.S. Public, pg. 598
FLUKE CORPORATION; U.S. Public, pg. 659
GKN COMPUTER SERVICES LTD.—GKN plc; Int'l, pg. 534
GKN INFORMATIK GMBH—GKN plc; Int'l, pg. 536
GENERAL AUTOMATION, INC.; U.S. Public, pg. 706
GENRAD ELECTRONIC MANUFACTURING TESTS SYSTEMS—GenRad, Inc.; U.S. Public, pg. 731
GENRAD, INC.; U.S. Public, pg. 731
GEONEX—Geonex Corporation; U.S. Private, pg. 448
GEONEX CORPORATION; U.S. Private, pg. 447
GLOBAL TURNKEY SYSTEMS INC.; U.S. Private, pg. 457
GLOBAL VILLAGE COMMUNICATION; U.S. Public, pg. 748
GLOBELLE CORPORATION; Int'l, pg. 554
GTECH CORPORATION; U.S. Public, pg. 767
HBO & COMPANY/CYCARE BUSINESS GROUP—HBOC; U.S. Public, pg. 770
HARRIS PROTOCALL, INC.—Harris Corporation; U.S. Public, pg. 792
HARRIS SPACE SYSTEMS CORP.—Harris Corporation; U.S. Public, pg. 791
JACK HENRY & ASSOCIATES, INC.; U.S. Public, pg. 808
HYPERION SOFTWARE; U.S. Public, pg. 851
IPC CORPORATION LTD.; Int'l, pg. 651
ICONOVEX CORPORATION—Innovex, Inc.; U.S. Public, pg. 880
INFORMATION TECHNOLOGY, INC.—Fiserv, Inc.; U.S. Public, pg. 647
INFOSEEK CORPORATON; U.S. Public, pg. 876
INTEGRAL SYSTEMS, INC.; U.S. Public, pg. 883
INTEGRATED TECHNOLOGIES—Litton Industries, Inc.; U.S. Public, pg. 1004
INTERFACE SYSTEMS, INC.; U.S. Public, pg. 889
INTERMETRICS, INC.; U.S. Private, pg. 567
INTERMETRICS SECURITIES, INC.—Intermetrics, Inc.; U.S. Private, pg. 568
INTERNATIONAL BUSINESS MACHINES CORPORATION; U.S. Public, pg. 895
INTERSYS, INC.—Integral Systems, Inc.; U.S. Public, pg. 883
KEANE, INC.; U.S. Public, pg. 946

KRUPP ENTWICKLUNGSZENTRUM GMBH—Fried. Krupp AG; *Int'l*, pg. 512
KRUPP HOESCH INFORMATIONSVERARBEITUNG GMBH—Fried. Krupp AG; *Int'l*, pg. 512
KYOEI FACOM S/A-CENTRO DE COMPUTACAO—The Kyoei Life Insurance Co., Ltd.; *Int'l*, pg. 777
L.C.G. MALMBERG BV—VNU Verenigde Nederlandse Uitgeversbedrijven B.V.; *Int'l*, pg. 1445
LANDMARK GRAPHICS CORPORATION—Halliburton Company; *U.S. Public*, pg. 776
LANDMARK SYSTEMS CORPORATION; *U.S. Private*, pg. 649
LEGACY STORAGE SYSTEMS CORP.; *Int'l*, pg. 805
LEGATO SYSTEMS, INC.; *U.S. Public*, pg. 984
LEVEL FIVE RESEARCH INC.—Information Builders; *U.S. Private*, pg. 561
LODGISTIX, INC.—Sulcus Computer Corp.; *U.S. Public*, pg. 1527
LOGICA INC.—Logica Plc; *Int'l*, pg. 814
LOGICA, INC.—Logica Plc; *Int'l*, pg. 814
LOGICA INC.—Logica Plc; *Int'l*, pg. 814
LOGICA PLC; *Int'l*, pg. 814
LOGICON GEODYNAMIC—Northrop Grumman Corporation; *U.S. Public*, pg. 1199
LOGICON, INC.—Northrop Grumman Corporation; *U.S. Public*, pg. 1198
M-INFORMATICS AG—Migros; *Int'l*, pg. 865
MIS—Geotek Communications; *U.S. Public*, pg. 740
MRV COMMUNICATIONS, INC.; *U.S. Public*, pg. 1027
MAGNUS SOFTWARE CORPORATION—New York Life Insurance Company; *U.S. Private*, pg. 795
MAMAN DIVISION—Israel Aircraft Industries Ltd.; *Int'l*, pg. 690
MANATRON, INC.; *U.S. Public*, pg. 1040
MANUGISTICS GROUP, INC.; *U.S. Public*, pg. 1042
MANUGISTICS INC.—Manugistics Group, Inc.; *U.S. Public*, pg. 1042
MARCAM SOLUTIONS, INC.; *U.S. Public*, pg. 1042
MARKETPULSE—Computer Corporation of America; *U.S. Private*, pg. 260
MESTEK, INC.; *U.S. Public*, pg. 1099
MONEY MANAGEMENT SYSTEMS, INC.—SunGard Data Systems Inc.; *U.S. Public*, pg. 1535
NCR CORPORATION; *U.S. Public*, pg. 1146
NRG MANAGEMENT—Sulcus Computer Corp.; *U.S. Public*, pg. 1527
NANTO COMPUTER SERVICE CO., LTD.—The Nanto Bank, Ltd.; *Int'l*, pg. 905
NELLCOR PURITAN BENNETT—Mallinckrodt Inc.; *U.S. Public*, pg. 1040
NETWORK SYSTEMS CORPORATION—Storage Technology Corporation; *U.S. Public*, pg. 1522
NORAND MOBILE SYSTEMS DIV.—UNOVA, Inc.; *U.S. Public*, pg. 1699
NOTIFIER ENGINEERED SYSTEMS COMPANY, INC. (NESCO)—Pittway Corporation; *U.S. Public*, pg. 1306
NUANCE COMMUNICATIONS—SRI International; *U.S. Private*, pg. 958
OACIS HEALTHCARE SYSTEMS, INC.; *U.S. Public*, pg. 1208
OCTEL COMMUNICATIONS LTD.—Lucent Technologies Inc.; *U.S. Public*, pg. 1018
OLIVETTI SPA; *Int'l*, pg. 1002
OMNI INDUSTRY—Global Turnkey Systems Inc.; *U.S. Private*, pg. 458
OPTIMAGE INTERACTIVE SERVICES CO.—Philips Electronics N.V.; *Int'l*, pg. 1054
ORBOTECH LTD.; *Int'l*, pg. 1007
ORIX COMPUTER SYSTEMS CORPORATION—Orix Corporation; *Int'l*, pg. 1008
PSC BAR CODE LTD.—PSC Inc.; *U.S. Public*, pg. 1246
PSDI; *U.S. Private*, pg. 828
PEOPLESOFT, INC.; *U.S. Public*, pg. 1276
PICTURETEL; *U.S. Public*, pg. 1294
PLATINUM TECHNOLOGY - SANTA BARBARA LABORATORY—Platinum Technology, Inc.; *U.S. Public*, pg. 1309
POMEROY COMPUTER RESOURCES; *U.S. Public*, pg. 1315
PRIMARK CORPORATION; *U.S. Public*, pg. 1325
PUBCO CORPORATION; *U.S. Public*, pg. 1339
QAD.AB—QAD Inc; *U.S. Public*, pg. 1345
QAD.AUSTRALIA PTY LTD—QAD Inc; *U.S. Public*, pg. 1345
QAD.EUROPE B.V.—QAD Inc; *U.S. Public*, pg. 1345
QAD.FRANCE EURL—QAD Inc; *U.S. Public*, pg. 1345
QAD.GERMANY GMBH—QAD Inc; *U.S. Public*, pg. 1345
QAD INC; *U.S. Public*, pg. 1345
QAD.JAPAN K.K.—QAD Inc; *U.S. Public*, pg. 1345
QAD.UNITED KINGDOM LTD.—QAD Inc; *U.S. Public*, pg. 1345
RMS TECHS, INC.; *U.S. Private*, pg. 905
REAL DECISIONS CORP.—Cognizant Corporation; *U.S. Public*, pg. 395
SAIC—Science Applications International Corp.; *U.S. Private*, pg. 976
SCT—Systems & Computer Technology Corporation; *U.S. Public*, pg. 1552
SCT GOVERNMENT SYSTEMS—Systems & Computer Technology Corporation; *U.S. Public*, pg. 1552
SANDERSON TECHNOLOGY LTD.; *Int'l*, pg. 1184
SCITEX AMERICA CORP.—IDB Holding Corporation; *Int'l*, pg. 644
SEER TECHNOLOGIES, INC.; *U.S. Public*, pg. 1453
SENSORS & ELECTRONIC SYSTEMS—Raytheon Company; *U.S. Public*, pg. 1365
SIEMENS S.A.—Siemens AG; *Int'l*, pg. 1248
SILICON GRAPHICS, INC.; *U.S. Public*, pg. 1473
SOFTECH, INC.; *U.S. Public*, pg. 1482
SOFTWARE AG; *Int'l*, pg. 1276
SOFTWARE AG AMERICAS, INC.; *U.S. Public*, pg. 1482
SORD COMPUTER CORPORATION—Toshiba Corporation; *Int'l*, pg. 1403
SSANGYONG BUSINESS GROUP; *Int'l*, pg. 1291
STARSIGHT TELECAST, INC.—Gemstar International Group Limited; *U.S. Public*, pg. 705
STERLING SOFTWARE APPLICATION DEVELOPMENT DIVISION—Sterling Software, Inc.; *U.S. Public*, pg. 1516
STRATEGIC SYSTEMS INTERNATIONAL LIMITED—Powell Duffryn PLC; *Int'l*, pg. 1065
SULCUS COMPUTER CORP.; *U.S. Public*, pg. 1527
SULCUS LAW MANAGEMENT SERVICES, INC.—Sulcus Computer Corp.; *U.S. Public*, pg. 1527
SUN MICROSYSTEMS, INC.; *U.S. Public*, pg. 1531
SUNTEL CORP.—Logica Plc; *Int'l*, pg. 814
SVERDRUP CORPORATION; *U.S. Private*, pg. 1057
SVERDRUP TECHNOLOGY, INC.—Sverdrup Corporation; *U.S. Private*, pg. 1057
SYBASE, INC.; *U.S. Public*, pg. 1544
SYMIX SYSTEMS, INC.; *U.S. Public*, pg. 1546
SYMIX SYSTEMS, INC.—Symix Systems, Inc.; *U.S. Public*, pg. 1547
SYNTAX PROCESSING—Olivetti SpA; *Int'l*, pg. 1002
SYSTEMS & COMPUTER TECHNOLOGY CORPORATION; *U.S. Public*, pg. 1552
SYSTEMS ENGINEERING DIV.—Computer Sciences Corporation; *U.S. Public*, pg. 423
TSR CONSULTING SERVICES, INC.—TSR Inc.; *U.S. Public*, pg. 1559
TSR INC.; *U.S. Public*, pg. 1559
TANGRAM ENTERPRISE SOLUTIONS, INC.—Safeguard Scientifics, Inc.; *U.S. Public*, pg. 1424
TECHNOLOGY MARKETING (SECOMT)—Petrobras - Petroleo Brasileiro S.A.; *Int'l*, pg. 1042
TITAN INFORMATION SYSTEMS—The Titan Corporation; *U.S. Public*, pg. 1618
TOSHIBA CHUBU SERVICE & ENGINEERING CO. LTD.—Toshiba Corporation; *Int'l*, pg. 1403
TOSHIBA ENGINEERING CO., LTD.—Toshiba Corporation; *Int'l*, pg. 1404
TOSHIBA HOKKAIDO SERVICE & ENGINEERING CO., LTD.—Toshiba Corporation; *Int'l*, pg. 1404
TOSHIBA INFORMATION SYSTEMS (JAPAN) CORPORATION—Toshiba Corporation; *Int'l*, pg. 1404
TOSHIBA KYUSHU SERVICES & ENGINEERING CO,. LTD.—Toshiba Corporation; *Int'l*, pg. 1404
TOSHIBA NISHI NIHON SERVICE & ENGINEERING CO., LTD.—Toshiba Corporation; *Int'l*, pg. 1404
TOSHIBA SHUTOKEN SERVICE & ENGINEERING CO., LTD.—Toshiba Corporation; *Int'l*, pg. 1404
TOSHIBA TOHOKU SERVICE & ENGINEERING CO., LTD.—Toshiba Corporation; *Int'l*, pg. 1405
TRICORD SYSTEMS, INC.; *U.S. Public*, pg. 1637
UNIFY CORPORATION; *U.S. Public*, pg. 1665
UNION PACIFIC TECHNOLOGIES—Union Pacific Corporation; *U.S. Public*, pg. 1668
U S WEST DEX—U S West Inc.; *U.S. Public*, pg. 1689
U S WEST INC.; *U.S. Public*, pg. 1688
VG LABORATORY SYSTEMS LTD.—Thermo Electron Corporation; *U.S. Public*, pg. 1595
VEDA INCORPORATED—Veridian; *U.S. Private*, pg. 1136
VISIONEER, INC.; *U.S. Public*, pg. 1722
W.I.N. SYSTEMS, INC.—Automobile Protection Corporation-APCO; *U.S. Public*, pg. 150
WALL DATA INCORPORATED; *U.S. Public*, pg. 1734
WESTERN DATA SYSTEMS; *U.S. Private*, pg. 1165
WONDERWARE CORPORATION; *U.S. Public*, pg. 1775
XETA CORPORATION; *U.S. Public*, pg. 1783
YAHOO!, INC.; *U.S. Public*, pg. 1787

7372 — PREPACKAGED SOFTWARE

ABB SIMCON, INC.—ABB Asea Brown Boveri (Holding) Ltd.; *Int'l*, pg. 5
ABC CABLE & INTERNATIONAL BROADCAST, INC.—The Walt Disney Company; *U.S. Public*, pg. 512
ACI COMPUTER SERVICES—BTR plc; *Int'l*, pg. 128
ACI INTERNATIONAL LTD.—BTR plc; *Int'l*, pg. 128
APPX SOFTWARE INC.—Tredegar Industries Inc.; *U.S. Public*, pg. 1634
ASDC (APPLIED SOFTWARE DEVELOPMENT CENTER)—The Macneal-Schwendler Corp.; *U.S. Public*, pg. 1031
AT&T ISTEL LIMITED—AT&T Corporation; *U.S. Public*, pg. 11
AT&T STRATEGY & NEW SERVICE INNOVATIONS—AT&T Corporation; *U.S. Public*, pg. 11
ACCESS CORPORATION—Oce-van der Grinten N.V.; *Int'l*, pg. 994
ACCOR S.A.; *Int'l*, pg. 20
ACER/ALTOS COMPUTER SYSTEMS—Acer Incorporated; *Int'l*, pg. 22
ACTIVISION; *U.S. Public*, pg. 17
ACTIVISION UK—Activision; *U.S. Public*, pg. 17
ADOBE SYSTEMS CO. LIMITED—Adobe Systems Incorporated; *U.S. Public*, pg. 20
ADOBE SYSTEMS INCORPORATED; *U.S. Public*, pg. 20
ADVANCED DIGITAL SYSTEMS INC.—The Titan Corporation; *U.S. Public*, pg. 1618
ADVANTAGE LEARNING SYSTEMS, INC.; *U.S. Public*, pg. 22
AFORA LTD.—ABB Asea Brown Boveri (Holding) Ltd.; *Int'l*, pg. 5
AGUSTA S.P.A.; *Int'l*, pg. 32
AKER STORD A.S.—Aker Raj Asa; *Int'l*, pg. 42
ALCATEL ISR—Alcatel Alsthom Compagnie Generale D'Electricite; *Int'l*, pg. 56
ALIAS WAVEFRONT—Silicon Graphics, Inc.; *U.S. Public*, pg. 1474
ALLIEDSIGNAL AEROSPACE—AlliedSignal Inc.; *U.S. Public*, pg. 50
ALLTEL INFORMATION SERVICES, INC.—ALLTEL Corporation; *U.S. Public*, pg. 56
ALPHA MICROSYSTEMS; *U.S. Public*, pg. 57
ALTANA AG; *Int'l*, pg. 65
AMDAHL CORPORATION—Fujitsu Limited; *Int'l*, pg. 527
AMERICAN SOFTWARE, INC.; *U.S. Public*, pg. 91
ANALYSTS INTERNATIONAL CORPORATION; *U.S. Public*, pg. 110
APPLICON INC.—Gores Technology Group; *U.S. Private*, pg. 465
APPLIED COMMUNICATIONS, INC.—Transaction Systems Architects, Inc.; *U.S. Public*, pg. 1629
APPLIED MICROSYSTEMS CORPORATION; *U.S. Public*, pg. 123
ARBOR SOFTWARE CORPORATION; *U.S. Public*, pg. 127
ARTISOFT, INC.; *U.S. Public*, pg. 136
ASPEC TECHNOLOGY, INC.; *U.S. Private*, pg. 89
ASTEC INTERNATIONAL LIMITED; *Int'l*, pg. 92
ATTACHMATE; *U.S. Private*, pg. 98
AURA SYSTEMS, INC.; *U.S. Public*, pg. 147
AUSTRALASIAN ONLINE SYSTEMS PTY. LTD.—COMPAQ Computer Corporation; *U.S. Public*, pg. 417
AUTODESK, INC.; *U.S. Public*, pg. 148
AUTOMATED PRODUCTS, INC. (LEADER SYSTEMS, INC.)—USF&G Corporation; *U.S. Public*, pg. 1659
AXENT TECHNOLOGIES; *U.S. Public*, pg. 157
AXENT TECHNOLOGIES—Axent Technologies; *U.S. Public*, pg. 157
BDM INTERNATIONAL, INC.—TRW Inc.; *U.S. Public*, pg. 1558
BMC SOFTWARE B.V.—BMC Software, Inc.; *U.S. Public*, pg. 162
BMC SOFTWARE BELGIUM N.V.-S.A.—BMC Software, Inc.; *U.S. Public*, pg. 162
BMC SOFTWARE GMBH—BMC Software, Inc.; *U.S. Public*, pg. 162
BMC SOFTWARE, INC.; *U.S. Public*, pg. 162
BMC SOFTWARE KOREA LTD.—BMC Software, Inc.; *U.S. Public*, pg. 163
BNA SOFTWARE—The Bureau of National Affairs, Inc.; *U.S. Private*, pg. 182
BANCTEC PAYMENT SYSTEMS—BancTec, Inc.; *U.S. Public*, pg. 177
BANYAN SYSTEMS INC.; *U.S. Public*, pg. 189
BARNETT TECHNOLOGIES, INC.—NationsBank Corporation; *U.S. Public*, pg. 1162
BARRISTER INFORMATION SYSTEMS CORPORATION; *U.S. Public*, pg. 192
BELLWETHER TECHNOLOGY CORPORATION; *U.S. Private*, pg. 132
BEST SOFTWARE, INC.; *U.S. Public*, pg. 223
BETAC CORPORATION—Betac International Corporation; *U.S. Private*, pg. 140
BOEING COMPUTER SERVICES—The Boeing Company; *U.S. Public*, pg. 240
BOOLE & BABBAGE, INC.; *U.S. Public*, pg. 244
BORLAND FRANCE—Borland International, Inc.; *U.S. Public*, pg. 246
BORLAND UK—Borland International, Inc.; *U.S. Public*, pg. 246
BRIDGESTONE MULTI-MEDIA GROUP; *U.S. Private*, pg. 168
BROADWAY & SEYMOUR, INC.; *U.S. Public*, pg. 258
BRODERBUND SOFTWARE, INC.; *U.S. Public*, pg. 258
BROOKTREE ROCKWELL SEMICONDUCTOR SYSTEMS DIV.—Rockwell International Corporation; *U.S. Public*, pg. 1398
BULL HN INFORMATION SYSTEMS INC.—Compagnie des Machines Bull; *Int'l*, pg. 316
BULL S.A.—Compagnie des Machines Bull; *Int'l*, pg. 315
CCI/TRIAD AUTOMOTIVE—CCI/Triad Corporation; *U.S. Private*, pg. 193
CSC FINANCIAL SERVICES GROUP—Computer Sciences Corporation; *U.S. Public*, pg. 422
CSC HEALTHCARE SYSTEMS—Computer Sciences Corporation; *U.S. Public*, pg. 423
CTB/MCGRAW HILL—The McGraw-Hill Companies; *U.S. Public*, pg. 1070
CAD SERVER LTD.—The Macneal-Schwendler Corp.; *U.S. Public*, pg. 1031
CADENCE DESIGN SYSTEMS, INC.; *U.S. Public*, pg. 290
CAERE CORPORATION; *U.S. Public*, pg. 291
CAERE FSC CORPORATION—Caere Corporation; *U.S. Public*, pg. 291
CAERE GMBH—Caere Corporation; *U.S. Public*, pg. 291
CANDLE CORPORATION; *U.S. Private*, pg. 204
CAP GEMINI S.A.; *Int'l*, pg. 263
CARA CORPORATION—William Blair & Company L.L.C.; *U.S. Private*, pg. 148
CERNER CORPORATION; *U.S. Public*, pg. 331
CHASE GLOBAL FUNDS SERVICE COMPANY—The Chase Manhattan Corporation; *U.S. Public*, pg. 338
CHECK POINT SOFTWARE TECHNOLOGIES LTD.—Check Point Software Technologies Ltd.; *U.S. Public*, pg. 342
CHEYENNE—Computer Associates International, Inc.; *U.S. Public*, pg. 420
CHIPS AND TECHNOLOGIES, INC.; *U.S. Public*, pg. 349
CINCINNATI BELL INFORMATION SYSTEMS INC.—Cincinnati Bell Telephone; *U.S. Public*, pg. 367
CINCOM SYSTEMS, INC.; *U.S. Private*, pg. 240
CLARIFY INC.; *U.S. Public*, pg. 382
CLARIS CORPORATION—Apple Computer, Inc.; *U.S. Public*, pg. 121
COGITIEL—Alcatel Alsthom Compagnie Generale D'Electricite; *Int'l*, pg. 53
COGNIZANT CORPORATION; *U.S. Public*, pg. 395
COGNIZANT TECHNOLOGY SOLUTIONS CORP.—Cognizant Corporation; *U.S. Public*, pg. 395
COGNOS BARBADOS LTD.—Cognos Inc.; *Int'l*, pg. 306
COGNOS FAR EAST PTE. LIMITED—Cognos Inc.; *Int'l*, pg. 306
COGNOS INC.; *Int'l*, pg. 305
COGNOS JAPAN KK—Cognos Inc.; *Int'l*, pg. 306
COLORBUS INC.; *U.S. Private*, pg. 255
COMARCO, INC.; *U.S. Public*, pg. 406
COMMUNICATIONS DATA SERVICES, INC.—The Hearst Corporation; *U.S. Private*, pg. 517

COMPAGNIE D'ETUDES ET DE TRAITMENT DE L'INFORMATION S.A.—Halliburton Company; *U.S. Public*, pg. 776
COMPAGNIE DES MACHINES BULL; *Int'l*, pg. 315
COMPUMOD PTY. LTD.—The Macneal-Schwendler Corp.; *U.S. Public*, pg. 1031
COMPUSERVE INTERACTIVE SERVICES, INC.—America Online Incorporated; *U.S. Public*, pg. 66
COMPUTER ASSOCIATES INTERNATIONAL, INC.; *U.S. Public*, pg. 420
COMPUTER CORPORATION OF AMERICA; *U.S. Private*, pg. 260
COMPUTER CURRICULUM CORPORATION—National Amusements, Inc.; *U.S. Private*, pg. 778
COMPUTER DATA SYSTEMS, INC.—Affiliated Computer Services, Inc.; *U.S. Public*, pg. 28
COMPUTER LANGUAGE RESEARCH, INC.; *U.S. Public*, pg. 421
COMPUTER METHODS CORPORATION; *U.S. Private*, pg. 260
COMPUTER POWER GROUP LIMITED; *Int'l*, pg. 325
COMPUTER SYSTEMS RESEARCH, INC.—The McGraw-Hill Companies; *U.S. Public*, pg. 1070
COMPUWARE CORPORATION; *U.S. Public*, pg. 423
COMSHARE, INCORPORATED; *U.S. Public*, pg. 425
COMSHARE LTD.—Comshare, Incorporated; *U.S. Public*, pg. 425
CONCORD COMMUNICATIONS, INC.; *U.S. Public*, pg. 429
CONCURRENT COMPUTER CORPORATION; *U.S. Public*, pg. 430
CONNECTIX CORPORATION; *U.S. Private*, pg. 264
CONTROL DYNAMICS DIVISION—bd Systems, Inc; *U.S. Private*, pg. 106
CONVEX TECHNOLOGY CENTER - HEWLETT-PACKARD—Hewlett-Packard Company; *U.S. Public*, pg. 815
COREL CORPORATION; *Int'l*, pg. 331
COREL CORPORATION—Corel Corporation; *Int'l*, pg. 331
CORPORATE SOFTWARE LTD., KK—R.R. Donnelley & Sons Company; *U.S. Public*, pg. 519
CYBERGUARD CORPORATION; *U.S. Public*, pg. 470
CYBORG SYSTEMS ASIA, LTD.—Cyborg Systems, Inc.; *U.S. Private*, pg. 299
CYBORG SYSTEMS, INC.; *U.S. Private*, pg. 299
CYBORG SYSTEMS SOUTH AFRICA, LTD.—Cyborg Systems, Inc.; *U.S. Private*, pg. 299
D & B SOFTWARE LTD.—Geac Computer Corporation Limited; *Int'l*, pg. 532
DAIMLER-BENZ INTERSERVICES (DEBIS) AG—Daimler-Benz Aktiengesellschaft; *Int'l*, pg. 367
DAIN RAUSCHER CORPORATION; *U.S. Public*, pg. 476
DAKCO DISTRIBUTORS, INC.; *U.S. Private*, pg. 308
DATA DIMENSIONS, INC.; *U.S. Public*, pg. 485
DATA GENERAL CORPORATION; *U.S. Public*, pg. 485
DATA I/O CANADA CORPORATION—Data I/O Corporation; *U.S. Public*, pg. 486
DATA I/O CORPORATION; *U.S. Public*, pg. 486
DATA MEDIA CORPORATION—Axent Technologies; *U.S. Public*, pg. 157
DATAPOINT CORPORATION; *Int'l*, pg. 384
DATAPOINT DEVELOPMENT CENTER, INC.—Datapoint Corporation; *Int'l*, pg. 384
DATASTREAM INTERNATIONAL LTD.—Primark Corporation; *U.S. Public*, pg. 1325
DATASTREAM INTERNATIONAL LIMITED—Primark Corporation; *U.S. Public*, pg. 1326
DATEL TECHNOLOGIES LTD.; *Int'l*, pg. 384
DEBIS SYSTEMHAUS GMBH—Daimler-Benz Aktiengesellschaft; *Int'l*, pg. 368
DECISIONS & DESIGN, INC.—Comarco, Inc.; *U.S. Public*, pg. 406
DELTA PLC; *Int'l*, pg. 389
DEVELOPMENT AND MANUFACTURING—Xerox Corporation; *U.S. Public*, pg. 1784
DIGITAL EQUIPMENT CORPORATION; *U.S. Public*, pg. 507
DISCUS ELECTRONIC TRAINING—Eastman Kodak Company; *U.S. Public*, pg. 551
DISEL (DISENO E INGENIERIA DE SISTEMAS ELECTRONICOS S.A.)—The Macneal-Schwendler Corp.; *U.S. Public*, pg. 1032
DISTRIBUTOR CONCEPTS—King Group, Inc.; *U.S. Private*, pg. 620
DORON PRECISION SYSTEMS, INC.; *U.S. Private*, pg. 341
DREAMWORKS INTERACTIVE—DreamWorks SKG; *U.S. Private*, pg. 342
DREAMWORKS SKG; *U.S. Private*, pg. 342
THE DUN & BRADSTREET CORPORATION; *U.S. Public*, pg. 535
K.K. DUN & BRADSTREET SOFTWARE—Geac Computer Corporation Limited; *Int'l*, pg. 532
DYNAMICS RESEARCH CORPORATION; *U.S. Public*, pg. 539
DYNAMIX, INC.—Cendant Corporation; *U.S. Public*, pg. 321
EDS FIDES—Electronic Data Systems Corporation; *U.S. Public*, pg. 570
EMC CORPORATION; *U.S. Public*, pg. 545
EMS-MICHIGAN—Effective Management Systems; *U.S. Public*, pg. 565
J.D. EDWARDS & COMPANY; *U.S. Private*, pg. 365
EFFECTIVE MANAGEMENT SYSTEMS; *U.S. Public*, pg. 565
ELECTRONIC ARTS; *U.S. Public*, pg. 569
ELECTRONIC FORM SYSTEMS—The Reynolds and Reynolds Company; *U.S. Public*, pg. 1385
ELECTRONIC TAX SYSTEMS, INC.—Computer Language Research, Inc.; *U.S. Public*, pg. 421
ELSTREE COMPUTING LTD.—John Laing PLC; *Int'l*, pg. 796
ENTERTAINMENT UK LTD.—Kingfisher plc; *Int'l*, pg. 733
EPSILON/WEST—American Express Company; *U.S. Public*, pg. 74
ERISCO, INC.—Cognizant Corporation; *U.S. Public*, pg. 395
EXCALIBUR TECHNOLOGIES CORPORATION; *U.S. Public*, pg. 598
EXPERIENCE IN SOFTWARE, INC.; *U.S. Private*, pg. 388
FDP CORP.; *U.S. Public*, pg. 603
FTP SOFTWARE INC.; *U.S. Public*, pg. 609
FARO TECHNOLOGIES, INC.; *U.S. Public*, pg. 613
FAST-TAX—Computer Language Research, Inc.; *U.S. Public*, pg. 421
FILENET CORPORATION; *U.S. Public*, pg. 622
FLIGHTSAFETY INTERNATIONAL INC.—Berkshire Hathaway Inc.; *U.S. Public*, pg. 218
FRANKLIN ELECTRONIC PUBLISHERS, INC.; *U.S. Public*, pg. 679
FUNCO, INC.; *U.S. Public*, pg. 688
GE CAPITAL/IT SOLUTIONS—General Electric Company; *U.S. Public*, pg. 711
GEAC COMPUTER CORPORATION LIMITED; *Int'l*, pg. 532
GECI (GROUPE D'ETUDES ET CONSEILS EN INGENIERIE)—The Macneal-Schwendler Corp.; *U.S. Public*, pg. 1032
GT INTERACTIVE SOFTWARE CORP.; *U.S. Public*, pg. 696
GTE INTERNETWORKING—GTE Corporation; *U.S. Public*, pg. 696
GATEFIELD CORPORATION; *U.S. Public*, pg. 703
GENSYM CORPORATION; *U.S. Public*, pg. 731
GEONEX CORPORATION; *U.S. Private*, pg. 447
GERBER GARMENT TECHNOLOGY, INC.—Gerber Scientific, Inc.; *U.S. Public*, pg. 740
GLOBAL SOFTWARE, INC.; *U.S. Private*, pg. 457
GORES TECHNOLOGY GROUP; *U.S. Private*, pg. 465
GOVERNMENT AEROSPACE SYSTEMS DIVISION-ORLANDO OPERATIONS—Harris Corporation; *U.S. Public*, pg. 792
GRIFFIN TECHNOLOGY INCORPORATED—Diebold, Incorporated; *U.S. Public*, pg. 506
GROLIER EDUCATIONAL CORPORATION—Lagardere Groupe; *Int'l*, pg. 794
GROUP 1 SOFTWARE, INC.—COMNET Corporation; *U.S. Public*, pg. 417
HBO & COMPANY/CYCARE BUSINESS GROUP—HBOC; *U.S. Public*, pg. 770
HBOC; *U.S. Public*, pg. 770
HADRON, INC.; *U.S. Public*, pg. 773
HANDLEMAN COMPANY; *U.S. Public*, pg. 779
HARTLEY COURSEWARE—Jostens Learning Corporation; *U.S. Private*, pg. 601
HATHAWAY CORPORATION; *U.S. Public*, pg. 798
HEIMSOETH—Borland International, Inc.; *U.S. Public*, pg. 246
JACK HENRY & ASSOCIATES, INC.; *U.S. Public*, pg. 808
JACK HENRY INTERNATIONAL—Jack Henry & Associates, Inc.; *U.S. Public*, pg. 809
HOGAN SYSTEMS, INC.—Computer Sciences Corporation; *U.S. Public*, pg. 422
HONEYWELL-MEASUREX CORPORATION—Honeywell Inc.; *U.S. Public*, pg. 833
HOSKYNS GROUP PLC—CAP Gemini S.A.; *Int'l*, pg. 264
HOUGHTON MIFFLIN COLLEGE DIV.—Houghton Mifflin Company; *U.S. Public*, pg. 841
HOUGHTON MIFFLIN COMPANY; *U.S. Public*, pg. 841
IBM PROGRAMMING SYSTEMS—International Business Machines Corporation; *U.S. Public*, pg. 895
ICL PLC—Fujitsu Limited; *Int'l*, pg. 528
ICSA (INGENIERIA Y COMPUTACION, S.A.)—The Macneal-Schwendler Corp.; *U.S. Public*, pg. 1032
IFS SYSTEMS, INC.—The Western and Southern Life Insurance Company; *U.S. Private*, pg. 1165
ING REAL ESTATE—ING Groep N.V.; *Int'l*, pg. 648
IQ SOFTWARE CORPORATION; *U.S. Public*, pg. 858
IRAD DEVELOPMENT LTD.—Scientific Software-Intercomp, Inc.; *U.S. Public*, pg. 1444
IRI SOFTWARE—Information Resources, Inc.; *U.S. Public*, pg. 876
ISI SYSTEMS INC.—Teleglobe, Inc.; *Int'l*, pg. 1373
ISYS CORP.—International Business Machines Corporation; *U.S. Public*, pg. 896
ICON INTERNATIONAL, INC.—Sanyo Electric Co., Ltd.; *Int'l*, pg. 1191
IN-SITU RESEARCH AND ENGINEERING LTD.—Scientific Software-Intercomp, Inc.; *U.S. Public*, pg. 1444
INACOM CORP.; *U.S. Public*, pg. 873
INFORMATION & ENGINEERING TECHNOLOGY—DynCorp; *U.S. Private*, pg. 351
INFORMATION BUILDERS; *U.S. Private*, pg. 561
INFORMATION RESOURCES, INC.; *U.S. Public*, pg. 875
INFORMATION SYSTEMS & NETWORK CORPORATION; *U.S. Private*, pg. 561
INPOWER INC.—CSA Holdings Ltd.; *Int'l*, pg. 242
INSO CORPORATION; *U.S. Public*, pg. 882
INSTRUCTIONAL SYSTEMS DIVISION—Berkshire Hathaway Inc.; *U.S. Public*, pg. 218
INTEGRAL SYSTEMS, INC.—CSA Holdings Ltd.; *Int'l*, pg. 242
INTEGRATED SYSTEMS, INC.; *U.S. Public*, pg. 885
INTELLICORP INC.; *U.S. Public*, pg. 887
INTELLIGENT SYSTEMS CORP.; *U.S. Public*, pg. 888
INTERACTIVE DATA CORPORATION—Pearson plc; *Int'l*, pg. 1025
INTERCOMP RESOURCE DEVELOPMENT & ENGINEERING (CANADA) LTD.—Scientific Software-Intercomp, Inc.; *U.S. Public*, pg. 1444
INTERCONNECTIONS, INC.—Emulex Corporation; *U.S. Public*, pg. 579
INTERET CORPORATION; *U.S. Private*, pg. 567
INTERLEAF, INC.; *U.S. Public*, pg. 893
INTERMETRICS, INC.; *U.S. Private*, pg. 567
INTERMETRICS SECURITIES, INC.—Intermetrics, Inc.; *U.S. Private*, pg. 568
INTERNATIONAL BUSINESS MACHINES CORPORATION; *U.S. Public*, pg. 895
INTERNATIONAL BUSINESS SERVICES, INC.—Comarco, Inc.; *U.S. Public*, pg. 406
INTERPLAY OEM, INC.—Interplay Productions, Inc.; *U.S. Private*, pg. 573
INTERPLAY PRODUCTIONS, INC.; *U.S. Private*, pg. 572
INTUIT, INC.; *U.S. Public*, pg. 911
INVESTMENT TECHNOLOGY GROUP, INC.—Jefferies Group, Inc.; *U.S. Public*, pg. 924
ISRAEL AIRCRAFT INDUSTRIES LTD.; *Int'l*, pg. 689
JEFFERSON-PILOT CORPORATION; *U.S. Public*, pg. 925
JOSTENS HOME LEARNING—Jostens Learning Corporation; *U.S. Private*, pg. 601
JOSTENS LEARNING CORPORATION; *U.S. Private*, pg. 601
KEITHLEY INSTRUMENTS, INC.; *U.S. Public*, pg. 946
KLOCKNER-MOELLER GMBH; *Int'l*, pg. 736
KONAMI CO. LTD.; *Int'l*, pg. 745
LNW NETWORKS—CD Products, Inc.; *U.S. Public*, pg. 276
JOHN LAING PLC; *Int'l*, pg. 796
LANIER WORLDWIDE INC.—Harris Corporation; *U.S. Public*, pg. 791
LASERMASTER TECHNOLOGIES, INC.; *U.S. Public*, pg. 979
LAWSON SOFTWARE; *U.S. Private*, pg. 654
LOGIC ASSOCIATES, INC.; *U.S. Private*, pg. 673
LOGICA, INC.—Logica Plc; *Int'l*, pg. 814
LOGICON GEODYNAMIC—Northrop Grumman Corporation; *U.S. Public*, pg. 1199
LOGICON, INC.—Northrop Grumman Corporation; *U.S. Public*, pg. 1198
LOGICON SYSCON CORPORATION—Northrop Grumman Corporation; *U.S. Public*, pg. 1199
LOGISTIX; *U.S. Private*, pg. 673
LOTUS DEVELOPMENT CORPORATION—International Business Machines Corporation; *U.S. Public*, pg. 896
M & I DATA SERVICES, INC.—Marshall & Ilsley Corporation; *U.S. Public*, pg. 1050
MIPS TECHNOLOGIES, INC.—Silicon Graphics, Inc.; *U.S. Public*, pg. 1473
MPSI SYSTEMS INC.; *U.S. Public*, pg. 1027
MPSI SYSTEMS LTD.—MPSI Systems Inc.; *U.S. Public*, pg. 1027
MSC EASTERN ENGINEERING SERVICES OFFICE—The Macneal-Schwendler Corp.; *U.S. Public*, pg. 1031
MSC EASTERN REGIONAL OFFICE—The Macneal-Schwendler Corp.; *U.S. Public*, pg. 1031
MSC ENGINEERING/ELECTROMAGNETICS APPLICATIONS DEPARTMENT—The Macneal-Schwendler Corp.; *U.S. Public*, pg. 1031
MSC (ITALIA) S.R.L.—The Macneal-Schwendler Corp.; *U.S. Public*, pg. 1032
MSC JAPAN LTD.—The Macneal-Schwendler Corp.; *U.S. Public*, pg. 1032
MSC MIDWEST REGIONAL OFFICE—The Macneal-Schwendler Corp.; *U.S. Public*, pg. 1031
MSC NORTHEAST OFFICE—The Macneal-Schwendler Corp.; *U.S. Public*, pg. 1031
MSC SOUTHEAST OFFICE—The Macneal-Schwendler Corp.; *U.S. Public*, pg. 1031
MSC SOUTHWEST REGIONAL OFFICE—The Macneal-Schwendler Corp.; *U.S. Public*, pg. 1031
MSC WESTERN REGIONAL OFFICE—The Macneal-Schwendler Corp.; *U.S. Public*, pg. 1031
MSI ENGINEERING SOFTWARE LTD.—The Macneal-Schwendler Corp.; *U.S. Public*, pg. 1032
MACDONALD DETTWILER & ASSOCIATES LTD.—Orbital Sciences Corporation; *U.S. Public*, pg. 1229
MACMILLAN PUBLISHING USA—National Amusements, Inc.; *U.S. Private*, pg. 777
THE MACNEAL-SCHWENDLER CORP.; *U.S. Public*, pg. 1030
MACNEAL-SCHWENDLER CORP.—The Macneal-Schwendler Corp.; *U.S. Public*, pg. 1031
MACNEAL-SCHWENDLER GMBH—The Macneal-Schwendler Corp.; *U.S. Public*, pg. 1032
MACRO COMPUTER PRODUCTS INC.; *U.S. Private*, pg. 693
MACRO SOFT—Macro Computer Products Inc.; *U.S. Private*, pg. 693
MANATRON, INC.; *U.S. Public*, pg. 1040
MANUFACTURERS TECHNOLOGIES, INC.; *U.S. Private*, pg. 701
MANULIFE COMPUTER CORP. LTD.—Manulife Financial (The Manufacturers Life Insurance Company); *Int'l*, pg. 840
MAPINFO CORP.; *U.S. Public*, pg. 1042
MARCAM SOLUTIONS, INC.; *U.S. Public*, pg. 1042
MARTIN MARIETTA CANADA LTD.—Lockheed Martin Corporation; *U.S. Public*, pg. 1009
THE MCGRAW-HILL COMPANIES; *U.S. Public*, pg. 1069
MCGRAW-HILL HEALTHCARE PUBLICATIONS GROUP—The McGraw-Hill Companies; *U.S. Public*, pg. 1071
METIER MANAGEMENT SYSTEMS—Lockheed Martin Corporation; *U.S. Public*, pg. 1010
MICROCOM—COMPAQ Computer Corporation; *U.S. Public*, pg. 417
MICROCOMP MANAGEMENT LTD.—Scientific Software-Intercomp, Inc.; *U.S. Public*, pg. 1444
MICROSOFT AG—Microsoft Corporation; *U.S. Public*, pg. 1108
MICROSOFT CORPORATION; *U.S. Public*, pg. 1107
MICROSOFT GMBH—Microsoft Corporation; *U.S. Public*, pg. 1108
MICROTEC DIVISION—Mentor Graphics Corporation; *U.S. Public*, pg. 1086
MIGHTY EXIM CORPORATION—The Macneal-Schwendler Corp.; *U.S. Public*, pg. 1032
MINDSCAPE, INC.—Pearson plc; *Int'l*, pg. 1026
MISYS PLC; *Int'l*, pg. 870
MONEY MANAGEMENT SYSTEMS, INC.—SunGard Data Systems Inc.; *U.S. Public*, pg. 1535
MOORE CORPORATION LIMITED; *Int'l*, pg. 888
NDC TOKYO REPRESENTATIVE OFFICE—National Data Corporation; *U.S. Public*, pg. 1156
NETG APPLIED LEARNING GMBH—Harcourt General, Inc.; *U.S. Public*, pg. 784

NETG LIMITED—Harcourt General, Inc.; *U.S. Public*, pg. 784
NSI (NUSANTARA SYSTEMS INTERNATIONAL INC.)—The Macneal-Schwendler Corp.; *U.S. Public*, pg. 1032
NATIONAL COMPUTER SYSTEMS; *U.S. Public*, pg. 1155
NATIONAL EDUCATION TRAINING GROUP—Harcourt General, Inc.; *U.S. Public*, pg. 784
NATIONSBANK OF TEXAS NATIONAL BANK SERVICES CORPORATION—NationsBank Corporation; *U.S. Public*, pg. 1163
NETOPIA, INC.; *U.S. Public*, pg. 1168
NETWORK COMPUTING DEVICES, INC.; *U.S. Public*, pg. 1168
NETWORK SYSTEMS CORPORATION—Storage Technology Corporation; *U.S. Public*, pg. 1522
A.C. NIELSEN; *U.S. Public*, pg. 1183
A.C. NIELSEN COMPANY—A.C. Nielsen; *U.S. Public*, pg. 1183
NISSAY COMPUTER CO., LTD.—Nippon Life Insurance Co.; *Int'l*, pg. 935
J.S. NOLEN & ASSOCIATES—Litton Industries, Inc.; *U.S. Public*, pg. 1004
NORDIC SYSTEMS, LTD.—Flambeau Corporation; *U.S. Private*, pg. 410
NORTH CENTRAL LIFE INSURANCE COMPANY—Financial Life Companies, Inc.; *U.S. Private*, pg. 404
NOVELL, INC.; *U.S. Public*, pg. 1203
NUMETRIX LTD.; *Int'l*, pg. 990
NUMETRIX S.A.—Numetrix Ltd.; *Int'l*, pg. 990
NXTREND TECHNOLOGY, INC.; *U.S. Private*, pg. 809
OTD&C A/S (OFFSHORE TECHNOLOGY DEVELOPMENT & CONSULTING)—The Macneal-Schwendler Corp.; *U.S. Public*, pg. 1032
OBAYASHI CORPORATION; *Int'l*, pg. 995
OLICOM A/S; *Int'l*, pg. 1001
OLICOM, INC.—Olicom A/S; *Int'l*, pg. 1001
OLSY NORTH AMERICA INC.—Olivetti SpA; *Int'l*, pg. 1002
OMEGA RESEARCH INC.; *U.S. Public*, pg. 1222
ORACLE CORPORATION; *U.S. Public*, pg. 1227
ORACLE CORPORATION CANADA—Oracle Corporation; *U.S. Public*, pg. 1228
ORCAD INC.; *U.S. Public*, pg. 1230
PDA INTERNATIONAL FRANCE—The Macneal-Schwendler Corp.; *U.S. Public*, pg. 1031
PRC, INC.—Litton Industries, Inc.; *U.S. Public*, pg. 1003
PACE RESOURCES, INC.; *U.S. Private*, pg. 829
PARAMETRIC TECHNOLOGY CORPORATION; *U.S. Public*, pg. 1257
PERSOFT, INC.; *U.S. Private*, pg. 856
PERVASIVE SOFTWARE INC.; *U.S. Public*, pg. 1280
PETROLEUM AND FACILITIES ENGINEERING LTD.—Scientific Software-Intercomp, Inc.; *U.S. Public*, pg. 1444
PHARMACIA & UPJOHN, INC.; *Int'l*, pg. 1047
PHOENIX TECHNOLOGIES LTD.; *U.S. Public*, pg. 1292
PHOENIX TECHNOLOGIES LTD.—Phoenix Technologies Ltd.; *U.S. Public*, pg. 1292
PICTURETEL; *U.S. Public*, pg. 1294
PILOT SOFTWARE—Platinum Equity Holdings, LLC; *U.S. Private*, pg. 872
PITNEY BOWES SOFTWARE SYSTEMS—Pitney Bowes Inc.; *U.S. Public*, pg. 1304
PLATINUM SOLUTIONS—Platinum Technology, Inc.; *U.S. Public*, pg. 1309
PLATINUM TECHNOLOGY, INC.; *U.S. Public*, pg. 1309
PLATINUM TECHNOLOGY - SANTA BARBARA LABORATORY—Platinum Technology, Inc.; *U.S. Public*, pg. 1309
POLICY MANAGEMENT SYSTEMS CORPORATION; *U.S. Public*, pg. 1314
PRIMAVERA SYSTEMS, INC.; *U.S. Private*, pg. 884
PROGRAMART CORPORATION; *U.S. Private*, pg. 890
PROGRAMART FRANCE INCORPORATED—Programart Corporation; *U.S. Private*, pg. 890
PROLOGUE S.A.—Compagnie des Machines Bull; *Int'l*, pg. 316
QAD.AB—QAD Inc; *U.S. Public*, pg. 1345
QAD.AUSTRALIA PTY LTD—QAD Inc; *U.S. Public*, pg. 1345
QAD.EUROPE B.V.—QAD Inc; *U.S. Public*, pg. 1345
QAD.FRANCE EURL—QAD Inc; *U.S. Public*, pg. 1345
QAD.GERMANY GMBH—QAD Inc; *U.S. Public*, pg. 1345
QAD INC; *U.S. Public*, pg. 1345
QAD.JAPAN K.K.—QAD Inc; *U.S. Public*, pg. 1345
QAD.UNITED KINGDOM LTD.—QAD Inc; *U.S. Public*, pg. 1345
QUAKER CHEMICAL CORPORATION; *U.S. Public*, pg. 1346
QUALITY SYSTEMS INC.—Tracor, Inc.; *U.S. Public*, pg. 1627
QUARK INC.; *U.S. Private*, pg. 900
QUARTERDECK CORP.; *U.S. Public*, pg. 1350
QUINTUS CORPORATION; *U.S. Private*, pg. 901
RADIX CORPORATION; *U.S. Private*, pg. 906
RADIX MICRO DEVICES, PLC—Radix Corporation; *U.S. Private*, pg. 907
RAINBOW TECHNOLOGIES, INC.; *U.S. Public*, pg. 1359
RATIONAL SOFTWARE CORPORATION; *U.S. Public*, pg. 1361
RENT ROLL, INC—Computer Language Research, Inc.; *U.S. Public*, pg. 421
ROSS SYSTEMS, INC.; *U.S. Public*, pg. 1406
SAS CONSULTING SERVICES, INC.—SAS Institute Inc.; *U.S. Private*, pg. 966
SAS SOFTWARE, LTD.—SAS Institute Inc.; *U.S. Private*, pg. 967
SCSG (SCS-GRUMMAN SYSTEMS PTE LTD.)—The Macneal-Schwendler Corp.; *U.S. Public*, pg. 1032
SCSM (SCS COMPUTER SYSTEMS SDN.BHD.)—The Macneal-Schwendler Corp.; *U.S. Public*, pg. 1032
SCT GOVERNMENT SYSTEMS—Systems & Computer Technology Corporation; *U.S. Public*, pg. 1552
SCT UTILITIES SYSTEMS, INC.—Systems & Computer Technology Corporation; *U.S. Public*, pg. 1552
SDS (SAMSUNG DATA SYSTEMS CO. LTD.)—The Macneal-Schwendler Corp.; *U.S. Public*, pg. 1032
SEI INVESTMENTS; *U.S. Public*, pg. 1417
SPR, INC.; *U.S. Public*, pg. 1419
SPSS INC.; *U.S. Public*, pg. 1420
SQA, INC.—Rational Software Corporation; *U.S. Public*, pg. 1361
SRS TECHNOLOGIES; *U.S. Private*, pg. 958
SWUMC (SOUTH WEST UNITED MACHINERY CORPORATION)—The Macneal-Schwendler Corp.; *U.S. Public*, pg. 1032
SAFEGUARD BUSINESS SYSTEMS, INC.; *U.S. Private*, pg. 960
SAFEGUARD SCIENTIFICS, INC.; *U.S. Public*, pg. 1424
SALES TECHNOLOGIES—Cognizant Corporation; *U.S. Public*, pg. 395
SANDERSON COMPUTER SERVICES—Sanderson Technology Ltd.; *Int'l*, pg. 1184
SANDERSON COMPUTERS LIMITED—Sanderson Technology Ltd.; *Int'l*, pg. 1184
SANDWELL INC.; *Int'l*, pg. 1188
SAS INSTITUTE INC.; *U.S. Private*, pg. 966
SCHLUMBERGER LIMITED; *U.S. Public*, pg. 1439
SCHOLASTIC CORPORATION; *U.S. Public*, pg. 1440
SCIENTIFIC CALCULATIONS, INC.—Harris Corporation; *U.S. Public*, pg. 792
SCIENTIFIC SOFTWARE-INTERCOMP, INC.; *U.S. Public*, pg. 1443
SETPOINT INC.—Alcatel Alsthom Compagnie Generale D'Electricite; *Int'l*, pg. 53
SHEPARD'S—Reed Elsevier plc; *Int'l*, pg. 1095
SHEPARD'S—The Times Mirror Company; *U.S. Public*, pg. 1616
SHIP ANALYTICS, INC.; *U.S. Private*, pg. 994
SIERRA ON-LINE, INC.—Cendant Corporation; *U.S. Public*, pg. 321
SILICON GRAPHICS CANADA INC.—Silicon Graphics, Inc.; *U.S. Public*, pg. 1474
SOFTECHNICS INC.; *U.S. Private*, pg. 1012
SOFTWARE PLUS INC.; *U.S. Private*, pg. 1012
SOFTWARE PLUS INC.—Software Plus Inc.; *U.S. Private*, pg. 1012
SOFTWARE PUBLISHING CORPORATION; *U.S. Public*, pg. 1483
SSANGYONG BUSINESS GROUP; *Int'l*, pg. 1291
SSANGYONG INFORMATION & COMMUNICATION CORPORATION—Ssangyong Business Group; *Int'l*, pg. 1292
STARBOARD DATA SERVICES, INC.—Arrowhead Holding Corporation; *U.S. Private*, pg. 86
STAUFFER MEDIA SYSTEMS, INC.—Shivers Trading & Operating Co.; *U.S. Private*, pg. 995
STERLING COMMERCE, INC.; *U.S. Public*, pg. 1515
STERLING SOFTWARE, INC.; *U.S. Public*, pg. 1516
STRATEGIC SYSTEMS INTERNATIONAL LIMITED—Powell Duffryn PLC; *Int'l*, pg. 1065
STRUCTURAL DYNAMICS RESEARCH CORP.; *U.S. Public*, pg. 1525
SUN MICROSYSTEMS, INC.; *U.S. Public*, pg. 1531
SUNGARD ASSET MANAGEMENT SYSTEMS—SunGard Data Systems Inc.; *U.S. Public*, pg. 1535
SUNGARD COMPUTER SERVICES GROUP—SunGard Data Systems Inc.; *U.S. Public*, pg. 1534
SUNGARD DATA SYSTEMS INC.; *U.S. Public*, pg. 1534
SUNGARD EMPLOYEE BENEFITS SYSTEMS—SunGard Data Systems Inc.; *U.S. Public*, pg. 1534
SUNGARD FINANCIAL SYSTEMS, INC.—SunGard Data Systems Inc.; *U.S. Public*, pg. 1534
SUNGARD PLANNING SOLUTIONS INC.—SunGard Data Systems Inc.; *U.S. Public*, pg. 1535
SUNGARD TRUST & SHAREHOLDER SYSTEMS GROUP—SunGard Data Systems Inc.; *U.S. Public*, pg. 1535
SUNTRUST—SunTrust Banks, Inc.; *U.S. Public*, pg. 1537
SUNTRUST BANKS, INC.; *U.S. Public*, pg. 1537
SUPPORT SYSTEMS ASSOCIATES, INC.; *U.S. Private*, pg. 1056
SVERDRUP CORPORATION; *U.S. Private*, pg. 1057
SVERDRUP TECHNOLOGY, INC.—Sverdrup Corporation; *U.S. Private*, pg. 1057
SYBASE, INC.; *U.S. Public*, pg. 1544
SYMANTEC CORPORATION; *U.S. Public*, pg. 1545
SYMANTEC CORPORATION - BEAVERTON SITE—Symantec Corporation; *U.S. Public*, pg. 1545
SYNON CORPORATION; *U.S. Private*, pg. 1060
SYSTEM SOFTWARE ASSOCIATES, INC.; *U.S. Public*, pg. 1552
SYSTEMS & COMPUTER TECHNOLOGY CORPORATION; *U.S. Public*, pg. 1552
SYSTEMS ENGINEERING DIV.—Computer Sciences Corporation; *U.S. Public*, pg. 423
TDS COMPUTING SERVICES, INC.—Telephone and Data Systems, Inc.; *U.S. Public*, pg. 1572
TSR INC.; *U.S. Public*, pg. 1559
TANO AUTOMATION, INC.—Westwood Corporation; *U.S. Public*, pg. 1763
TELEGLOBE, INC.; *Int'l*, pg. 1373
TELXON CORPORATION; *U.S. Public*, pg. 1573
TERADYNE ASSEMBLY TEST/WEST DIVISION—Teradyne, Inc.; *U.S. Public*, pg. 1581
THOMSON SOFTWARE PRODUCTS—Thomson S.A.; *Int'l*, pg. 1384
TIMBERLINE SOFTWARE CORPORATION; *U.S. Public*, pg. 1609
TRANSACTION TECHNOLOGY INC.—Citicorp; *U.S. Public*, pg. 377
TRAVELING SOFTWARE INC.; *U.S. Private*, pg. 1098
TRIAD SYSTEMS CANADA LTD.—CCI/Triad Corporation; *U.S. Private*, pg. 193
TRIDEX SYSTEMS LTD.—CCI/Triad Corporation; *U.S. Private*, pg. 193
USCS INTERNATIONAL, INC.; *U.S. Public*, pg. 1659
UNISYS CORPORATION; *U.S. Public*, pg. 1671
U.S. QUALITY ALGORITHMS, INC.—Aetna Inc.; *U.S. Public*, pg. 27
USSI—Transaction Systems Architects, Inc.; *U.S. Public*, pg. 1629
U S WEST DEX—U S West Inc.; *U.S. Public*, pg. 1689
U S WEST INC.; *U.S. Public*, pg. 1688
UTILITY & MUNICIPAL SERVICES, INC.—Philadelphia Suburban Corporation; *U.S. Public*, pg. 1287
VERTEL; *U.S. Public*, pg. 1717
VOLT DELTA RESOURCES, INC.—Volt Information Sciences, Inc.; *U.S. Public*, pg. 1724
VOLT INFORMATION SCIENCES, INC.; *U.S. Public*, pg. 1724
WRQ, INC.; *U.S. Private*, pg. 1145
WADSWORTH PUBLISHING CO.—The Thomson Corporation; *U.S. Public*, pg. 1600
WALL DATA INCORPORATED; *U.S. Public*, pg. 1734
WANG LABORATORIES, INC.; *U.S. Public*, pg. 1737
WENGER CORPORATION; *U.S. Private*, pg. 1162
WESTERN DATA SYSTEMS; *U.S. Private*, pg. 1165
WESTERN DIGITAL CORPORATION; *U.S. Public*, pg. 1758
WHESSOE COMPUTING SYSTEMS LTD.—Whessoe Plc; *Int'l*, pg. 1498
WHESSOE PLC; *Int'l*, pg. 1498
WIND RIVER SYSTEMS, INC.; *U.S. Public*, pg. 1770
WIPRO INFORMATION TECHNOLOGY LIMITED—The Macneal-Schwendler Corp.; *U.S. Public*, pg. 1032
WYLE DATA SERVICES—Veba AG; *Int'l*, pg. 1457
XEROX COMPUTER SERVICES—Xerox Corporation; *U.S. Public*, pg. 1784
XILINX, INC.; *U.S. Public*, pg. 1786

7373 — COMPUTER INTEGRATED SYSTEMS DESIGN

ASDC (APPLIED SOFTWARE DEVELOPMENT CENTER)—The Macneal-Schwendler Corp.; *U.S. Public*, pg. 1031
AT&T ISTEL LIMITED—AT&T Corporation; *U.S. Public*, pg. 11
ATS AUTOMATION TOOLING SYSTEMS, INC.; *Int'l*, pg. 18
ALIAS WAVEFRONT—Silicon Graphics, Inc.; *U.S. Public*, pg. 1474
ALLIEDSIGNAL COMPUTER-AIDED ENGINEERING CENTER—AlliedSignal Inc.; *U.S. Public*, pg. 50
AMERICAN MANAGEMENT SYSTEMS, INC.; *U.S. Public*, pg. 86
ARTECON, INC.—Flambeau Corporation; *U.S. Private*, pg. 409
AUTO-TROL TECHNOLOGY CORPORATION; *U.S. Public*, pg. 148
BTG, INC.; *U.S. Public*, pg. 164
BABCOCK TURNKEY OPERATIONS LTD.—FKI Plc; *Int'l*, pg. 472
BANYAN SYSTEMS INC.; *U.S. Public*, pg. 189
BARRISTER INFORMATION SYSTEMS CORPORATION; *U.S. Public*, pg. 192
BELL ATLANTIC SYSTEMS INTEGRATION CORP.—Bell Atlantic Corporation; *U.S. Public*, pg. 203
BETAC CORPORATION—Betac International Corporation; *U.S. Private*, pg. 140
BROOKTREE ROCKWELL SEMICONDUCTOR SYSTEMS DIV.—Rockwell International Corporation; *U.S. Public*, pg. 1398
BULL CORPORATION OF JAPAN—Compagnie des Machines Bull; *Int'l*, pg. 318
BULL INGENIERIE S.A.—Compagnie des Machines Bull; *Int'l*, pg. 316
CETT (COMPAGNIE EUROPEENE DE TELETRANSMISSION)—Alcatel Alsthom Compagnie Generale D'Electricite; *Int'l*, pg. 53
CSC CONSULTING GROUP—Computer Sciences Corporation; *U.S. Public*, pg. 422
CAD SERVER LTD.—The Macneal-Schwendler Corp.; *U.S. Public*, pg. 1031
CADENCE DESIGN SYSTEMS, INC.; *U.S. Public*, pg. 290
CAMBRIDGE TECHNOLOGY PARTNERS—Safeguard Scientifics, Inc.; *U.S. Public*, pg. 1424
CARDINAL HEALTH INC.; *U.S. Public*, pg. 304
CEATRON TECHNOLOGY LTD.—Auto-trol Technology Corporation; *U.S. Public*, pg. 148
CELSIUS AB; *Int'l*, pg. 276
CHIPS AND TECHNOLOGIES, INC.; *U.S. Public*, pg. 349
CIMLINC INCORPORATED; *U.S. Private*, pg. 239
CISCO SYSTEMS, INC.; *U.S. Public*, pg. 375
COGNEX CORPORATION; *U.S. Public*, pg. 394
COMPAGNIE DES MACHINES BULL; *Int'l*, pg. 315
COMPUMOD PTY. LTD.—The Macneal-Schwendler Corp.; *U.S. Public*, pg. 1031
COMPUTER CORPORATION OF AMERICA; *U.S. Private*, pg. 260
COMPUTER DATA SYSTEMS, INC.—Affiliated Computer Services, Inc.; *U.S. Public*, pg. 28
COMPUTER HORIZONS CORP.; *U.S. Public*, pg. 421
COMPUTER POWER GROUP LIMITED; *Int'l*, pg. 325
COMPUTER SCIENCES CORPORATION; *U.S. Public*, pg. 422
COMPUTER TASK GROUP, INC. (CTG); *U.S. Public*, pg. 423
COMPUTERLAND CANADA—SHL Systemhouse; *Int'l*, pg. 1154
CONGRESSIONAL INFORMATION SERVICE (CIS)—Reed Elsevier plc; *Int'l*, pg. 1096
CONTROL DATA SYSTEMS, INC.; *U.S. Public*, pg. 441
CRANKSHAFT MACHINE GROUP—Avis Industrial Corporation; *U.S. Private*, pg. 102
DSI GROUP—Alcatel Alsthom Compagnie Generale D'Electricite; *Int'l*, pg. 52
DVM GMBH—Compagnie des Machines Bull; *Int'l*, pg. 318
DEERE & COMPANY; *U.S. Public*, pg. 491
DENTSPLY NEW IMAGE—Dentsply International Inc.; *U.S. Public*, pg. 499

DIGITAL EQUIPMENT CORPORATION; *U.S. Public*, pg. 507
DISEL (DISENO E INGENIERIA DE SISTEMAS ELECTRONICOS S.A.)—The Macneal-Schwendler Corp.; *U.S. Public*, pg. 1032
DORON PRECISION SYSTEMS, INC.; *U.S. Private*, pg. 341
DUCOST ENGINEERING LTD.—Haden Maclellan Holdings plc; *Int'l*, pg. 585
DYNAMICS RESEARCH CORPORATION; *U.S. Public*, pg. 539
ECI TELECOM GMBH—IDB Holding Corporation; *Int'l*, pg. 643
ECI TELECOM (THAILAND)—IDB Holding Corporation; *Int'l*, *pg. 643*
ECI TELEMATICS SARL—IDB Holding Corporation; *Int'l*, pg. 644
EDO COMBAT SYSTEMS—EDO Corporation; *U.S. Public*, pg. 542
EDS OF CANADA LTD.—Electronic Data Systems Corporation; *U.S. Public*, pg. 570
EG & G STRUCTURAL KINEMATICS—EG & G, Inc.; *U.S. Public*, pg. 544
ENS GROUP—Alcatel Alsthom Compagnie Generale D'Electricite; *Int'l*, pg. 52
EDUCATION & ENTERTAINMENT—Evans & Sutherland Computer Corporation; *U.S. Public*, pg. 596
ENTEX INFORMATION SERVICES; *U.S. Private*, pg. 378
ERICSSON NETWORKS, INC.—Telefonaktiebolaget LM Ericsson; *Int'l*, pg. 1367
ERICSSON THAI NETWORKS COMPANY LTD.—Telefonaktiebolaget LM Ericsson; *Int'l*, pg. 1368
ESCA CORPORATION—Alcatel Alsthom Compagnie Generale D'Electricite; *Int'l*, pg. 53
EUROPEAN GROUP—Computer Sciences Corporation; *U.S. Public*, pg. 423
EVANS & SUTHERLAND COMPUTER CORPORATION; *U.S. Public*, pg. 595
EXXON COMPUTING SERVICES COMPANY—Exxon Corporation; *U.S. Public*, pg. 601
EXXON UPSTREAM TECHNICAL COMPUTING COMPANY—Exxon Corporation; *U.S. Public*, pg. 601
FLAMBEAU CORPORATION; *U.S. Private*, pg. 409
FOSTER-MILLER, INC.; *U.S. Private*, pg. 421
GECI (GROUPE D'ETUDES ET CONSEILS EN INGENIERIE)—The Macneal-Schwendler Corp.; *U.S. Public*, pg. 1032
GHAFARI ASSOCIATES, INC.; *U.S. Private*, pg. 450
HBOC; *U.S. Public*, pg. 770
HK SYSTEMS—HK Systems, Inc.; *U.S. Private*, pg. 491
H.M.G. WORLDWIDE CORP.; *U.S. Public*, pg. 771
JACK HENRY & ASSOCIATES, INC.; *U.S. Public*, pg. 808
HEURIKON CORPORATION—Computer Products, Inc.; *U.S. Public*, pg. 422
HONEYWELL BULL AG—Compagnie des Machines Bull; *Int'l*, pg. 318
HONEYWELL INC.; *U.S. Public*, pg. 833
IA CORPORATION; *U.S. Private*, pg. 553
IBM APPLICATION SOLUTIONS—International Business Machines Corporation; *U.S. Public*, pg. 895
ICSA (INGENIERIA Y COMPUTACION, S.A.)—The Macneal-Schwendler Corp.; *U.S. Public*, pg. 1032
IKOS SYSTEMS, INC.—IKOS Systems, Inc.; *U.S. Public*, pg. 864
ITK INTERNATIONAL, INC.; *U.S. Private*, pg. 556
ITK TELECOMMUNICATIONS, INC.—ITK International, Inc.; *U.S. Private*, pg. 556
IKOS SYSTEMS, INC.; *U.S. Public*, pg. 864
IKOS SYSTEMS INC.—IKOS Systems, Inc.; *U.S. Public*, pg. 864
INFORMATION SYSTEMS & NETWORK CORPORATION; *U.S. Private*, pg. 561
INTEGRAL SYSTEMS, INC.; *U.S. Public*, pg. 883
INTERGRAPH CORPORATION; *U.S. Public*, pg. 890
INTERMARK CORP.—H.M.G. Worldwide Corp.; *U.S. Public*, *pg. 771*
INTERMETRICS, INC.; *U.S. Private*, pg. 567
INTERMETRICS SECURITIES, INC.—Intermetrics, Inc.; *U.S.* Private, pg. 568
INTERNATIONAL BUSINESS MACHINES CORPORATION; *U.S. Public*, pg. 895
INTERSYS, INC.—Integral Systems, Inc.; *U.S. Public*, pg. 883
KOCKUMS COMPUTER SYSTEMS AB—Celsius AB; *Int'l*, pg. 277
KOCKUMS COMPUTER SYSTEMS A/S—Celsius AB; *Int'l*, pg. 277
KRUG INTERNATIONAL TECHNOLOGY/SCIENTIFIC SERVICES, INC.—Krug International Corp.; *U.S. Public*, pg. 968
LAMB TECHNICON—Litton Industries, Inc.; *U.S. Public*, pg. 1004
LAMB TECHNICON UK—Litton Industries, Inc.; *U.S. Public*, *pg. 1004*
MFS TELECOM COMPANIES—WorldCom, Inc.; *U.S. Public*, pg. 1779
MMC NETWORKS, INC.; *U.S. Public*, pg. 1027
MSC EASTERN ENGINEERING SERVICES OFFICE—The Macneal-Schwendler Corp.; *U.S. Public*, pg. 1031
MSC EASTERN REGIONAL OFFICE—The Macneal-Schwendler Corp.; *U.S. Public*, pg. 1031
MSC ENGINEERING/ELECTROMAGNETICS APPLICATIONS DEPARTMENT—The Macneal-Schwendler Corp.; *U.S. Public*, pg. 1031
MSC (ITALIA) S.R.L.—The Macneal-Schwendler Corp.; *U.S.* Public, pg. 1032
MSC JAPAN LTD.—The Macneal-Schwendler Corp.; *U.S. Public*, pg. 1032
MSC MIDWEST REGIONAL OFFICE—The Macneal-Schwendler Corp.; *U.S. Public*, pg. 1031
MSC NORTHEAST OFFICE—The Macneal-Schwendler Corp.; *U.S. Public*, pg. 1031
MSC SOUTHEAST OFFICE—The Macneal-Schwendler Corp.; *U.S. Public*, pg. 1031
MSC SOUTHWEST REGIONAL OFFICE—The Macneal-Schwendler Corp.; *U.S. Public*, pg. 1031
MSC WESTERN REGIONAL OFFICE—The Macneal-Schwendler Corp.; *U.S. Public*, pg. 1031
MSI ENGINEERING SOFTWARE LTD.—The Macneal-Schwendler Corp.; *U.S. Public*, pg. 1032
THE MACNEAL-SCHWENDLER CORP.; *U.S. Public*, pg. 1030
MACNEAL-SCHWENDLER GMBH—The Macneal-Schwendler Corp.; *U.S. Public*, pg. 1032
MARCAM SOLUTIONS, INC.; *U.S. Public*, pg. 1042
MATRA DATAVISION S.A.—Lagardere Groupe; *Int'l*, pg. 793
MEDICAL MANAGER CORPORATION; *U.S. Public*, pg. 1080
MEDICUS SYSTEMS CORPORATION; *U.S. Public*, pg. 1080
MESTEK, INC.; *U.S. Public*, pg. 1099
MICROBILT CORPORATION—First Data Corporation; *U.S. Public*, pg. 631
MICROLOG CORPORATION; *U.S. Public*, pg. 1105
MIGHTY EXIM CORPORATION—The Macneal-Schwendler Corp.; *U.S. Public*, pg. 1032
NCR CORPORATION; *U.S. Public*, pg. 1146
N.E.T. FEDERAL—Network Equipment Technologies, Inc.; *U.S. Public*, pg. 1169
NSI (NUSANTARA SYSTEMS INTERNATIONAL INC.)—The Macneal-Schwendler Corp.; *U.S. Public*, pg. 1032
NELLCOR PURITAN BENNETT—Mallinckrodt Inc.; *U.S. Public*, pg. 1040
NETWORK EQUIPMENT TECHNOLOGIES, INC.; *U.S. Public*, pg. 1168
NETWORK SYSTEMS INTEGRATION—General Electric Company; *U.S. Public*, pg. 711
NORDIC BULL NET—Compagnie des Machines Bull; *Int'l*, pg. 318
NORTHROP GRUMMAN CORPORATION; *U.S. Public*, pg. 1197
ODS NETWORKS, INC.; *U.S. Public*, pg. 1206
O/E AUTOMATION, INC.; *U.S. Private*, pg. 809
OTD&C A/S (OFFSHORE TECHNOLOGY DEVELOPMENT & CONSULTING)—The Macneal-Schwendler Corp.; *U.S.* Public, pg. 1032
OPEN MARKET, INC.; *U.S. Public*, pg. 1226
PDA INTERNATIONAL FRANCE—The Macneal-Schwendler Corp.; *U.S. Public*, pg. 1031
PITTWAY CORPORATION; *U.S. Public*, pg. 1305
RADIUS INC.; *U.S. Public*, pg. 1358
THE REYNOLDS AND REYNOLDS COMPANY; *U.S. Public*, pg. 1384
ROSS TECHNOLOGY, INC.—Fujitsu Limited; *Int'l*, pg. 526
SCSG (SCS-GRUMMAN SYSTEMS PTE LTD.)—The Macneal-Schwendler Corp.; *U.S. Public*, pg. 1032
SCSM (SCS COMPUTER SYSTEMS SDN.BHD.)—The Macneal-Schwendler Corp.; *U.S. Public*, pg. 1032
SCT GOVERNMENT SYSTEMS—Systems & Computer Technology Corporation; *U.S. Public*, pg. 1552
SDS (SAMSUNG DATA SYSTEMS CO. LTD.)—The Macneal-Schwendler Corp.; *U.S. Public*, pg. 1032
SHL SYSTEMHOUSE; *Int'l*, pg. 1154
SIELTE DATA NET S.P.A.—Telefonaktiebolaget LM Ericsson; *Int'l*, pg. 1370
SWUMC (SOUTH WEST UNITED MACHINERY CORPORATION)—The Macneal-Schwendler Corp.; *U.S. Public*, pg. 1032
SAFEGUARD SCIENTIFICS, INC.; *U.S. Public*, pg. 1424
SANCHEZ COMPUTER ASSOCIATES—Safeguard Scientifics, Inc.; *U.S. Public*, pg. 1425
SEIKO INSTRUMENTS INC.; *Int'l*, pg. 1219
SEQUENT COMPUTER SYSTEMS, INC.; *U.S. Public*, pg. 1459
SEQUENT GMBH—Sequent Computer Systems, Inc.; *U.S. Public*, pg. 1460
SETPOINT INC.—Alcatel Alsthom Compagnie Generale D'Electricite; *Int'l*, pg. 53
SOCIETE INDUSTRIELLE D'AUTOMATISATION BANCAIRE-SIAB S.A.—Compagnie des Machines Bull; *Int'l*, pg. 316
SSANGYONG BUSINESS GROUP; *Int'l*, pg. 1291
SSANGYONG INFORMATION & COMMUNICATION CORPORATION—Ssangyong Business Group; *Int'l*, pg. 1292
STERLING SOFTWARE APPLICATION DEVELOPMENT DIVISION—Sterling Software, Inc.; *U.S. Public*, pg. 1516
SULCUS LAW MANAGEMENT SERVICES, INC.—Sulcus Computer Corp.; *U.S. Public*, pg. 1527
SUN DATA INC.; *U.S. Private*, pg. 1050
SUNGARD DATA SYSTEMS INC.; *U.S. Public*, pg. 1534
SVERDRUP CORPORATION; *U.S. Private*, pg. 1057
SVERDRUP TECHNOLOGY, INC.—Sverdrup Corporation; *U.S. Private*, pg. 1057
SYMPLEX COMMUNICATIONS CORP.; *U.S. Private*, pg. 1060
SYSTEMS & COMPUTER TECHNOLOGY CORPORATION; *U.S. Public*, pg. 1552
SYSTEMS ENGINEERING DIV.—Computer Sciences Corporation; *U.S. Public*, pg. 423
TANDEM COMPUTERS-NOWAY—COMPAQ Computer Corporation; *U.S. Public*, pg. 418
TANDEM TELECOMMUNICATIONS SYSTEMS, INC.—COMPAQ Computer Corporation; *U.S. Public*, pg. 417
TECHNOLOGY MANAGEMENT GROUP—Computer Sciences Corporation; *U.S. Public*, pg. 423
TELEMATICS INC.—IDB Holding Corporation; *Int'l*, pg. 643
TRUEVISION, INC.; *U.S. Public*, pg. 1642
TRUEVISION, INC.—Truevision, Inc.; *U.S. Public*, pg. 1643
VEDA INCORPORATED—Veridian; *U.S. Private*, pg. 1136
VIEWLOGIC SYSTEMS GROUP—Synopsys, Inc.; *U.S. Public*, pg. 1548
WANG FED INC.—Wang Laboratories, Inc.; *U.S. Public*, pg. 1737
WHITTAKER COMMUNICATIONS, INC.—Whittaker Corporation; *U.S. Public*, pg. 1767
WIPRO INFORMATION TECHNOLOGY LIMITED—The Macneal-Schwendler Corp.; *U.S. Public*, pg. 1032
XATA CORPORATION; *U.S. Public*, pg. 1783
XETRON—Pittway Corporation; *U.S. Public*, pg. 1306
ZELLWEGER USTER AG—Hesta Tex AG; *Int'l*, pg. 618

7374 — COMPUTER PROCESSING & DATA PREPARATION & PROCESSING SERVICES

ACXIOM CORPORATION; *U.S. Public*, pg. 18
ACXIOM CORPORATION—Acxiom Corporation; *U.S. Public*, pg. 18
ADVANCED AUTOMATION ASSOCIATES, INC.—Saztec International, Inc.; *U.S. Public*, pg. 1435
AFFILIATED BANKS SERVICE CO.—Banc One Corporation; *U.S. Public*, pg. 173
AFFILIATED COMPUTER SERVICES, INC.; *U.S. Public*, pg. 27
ALLTEL INFORMATION SERVICES, INC.—ALLTEL Corporation; *U.S. Public*, pg. 56
ALPHA ONE EXCHANGE; *U.S. Private*, pg. 45
AMERITECH APPLIED TECHNOLOGIES, INC.—Ameritech Corporation; *U.S. Public*, pg. 98
ANACOMP, INC.; *U.S. Public*, pg. 106
APPLICON INC.—Gores Technology Group; *U.S. Private*, pg. 465
ASHLAND SERVICES COMPANY—Ashland, Inc.; *U.S. Public*, pg. 139
ASPEN SYSTEMS CORP.—Wolters Kluwer N.V.; *Int'l*, pg. 1513
AUTOMATIC DATA PROCESSING, INC.; *U.S. Public*, pg. 150
AUTOMATISERINGCENTRUM IDETA B.V.—N.V. Koninklijke Bijenkorf Beheer KBB; *Int'l*, pg. 750
BCS RICHLAND INC.—The Boeing Company; *U.S. Public*, pg. 241
BMS ON-LINE SERVICES, INC.—Fiserv, Inc.; *U.S. Public*, pg. 647
BANC ONE CORPORATION; *U.S. Public*, pg. 172
BANC ONE SERVICES CORPORATION—Banc One Corporation; *U.S. Public*, pg. 175
BANK ONE, COLORADO—Banc One Corporation; *U.S. Public*, pg. 173
BASINFORM-BASTOGI SERVIZI INFORMATIVI S.P.A.—Bastogi-S.p.A.; *Int'l*, pg. 170
BELL ATLANTIC SERVICES—Bell Atlantic Corporation; *U.S. Public*, pg. 203
BENEFICIAL TECHNOLOGY CORPORATION—Beneficial Corporation; *U.S. Public*, pg. 211
BERKLEY INFORMATION SERVICES—W.R. Berkley Corporation; *U.S. Public*, pg. 216
THE BOEING COMPANY; *U.S. Public*, pg. 239
BOEING COMPUTER SUPPORT SERVICES, INC.—The Boeing Company; *U.S. Public*, pg. 240
BRAMBLES SECURITIES SERVICES LIMITED—Brambles Industries Limited; *Int'l*, pg. 211
BRIAN UNLIMITED DISTRIBUTION COMPANY, INC.; *U.S.* Private, pg. 167
BUSINESS INFORMATION GROUP—Conseco Inc.; *U.S. Public*, pg. 433
CAP PROGRAMMATOR—CAP Gemini S.A.; *Int'l*, pg. 264
CAP SESA FINANCE—CAP Gemini S.A.; *Int'l*, pg. 263
CAP SESA HOSKYNS—CAP Gemini S.A.; *Int'l*, pg. 263
CAP SESA INDUSTRIE—CAP Gemini S.A.; *Int'l*, pg. 263
CAP SESA INFORMATIQUE HOSPITALIERE—CAP Gemini S.A.; *Int'l*, pg. 263
CAP SESA MAINTENENCE TOUR ANJOU—CAP Gemini S.A.; *Int'l*, pg. 263
CAP SESA TERTIAIRE—CAP Gemini S.A.; *Int'l*, pg. 263
CAP VOLMAC—CAP Gemini S.A.; *Int'l*, pg. 264
CCH COMPUTAX INC.—Wolters Kluwer N.V.; *Int'l*, pg. 1513
CCH INCORPORATED—Wolters Kluwer N.V.; *Int'l*, pg. 1513
CD PRODUCTS, INC.; *U.S. Public*, pg. 276
CFC DATA CORP.—Chemical Financial Corporation; *U.S. Public*, pg. 345
CGG AMERICAN SERVICES INC.—CGG Group; *Int'l*, pg. 241
COM/ENERGY SERVICES CO.—Commonwealth Energy System; *U.S. Public*, pg. 414
CSB BUREAUTIQUE—CAP Gemini S.A.; *Int'l*, pg. 263
CSR—Raytheon Company; *U.S. Public*, pg. 1365
CSX TECHNOLOGY, INC.—CSX Corporation; *U.S. Public*, pg. 284
CAP GEMINI S.A.; *Int'l*, pg. 263
CAPITAL DATA SYSTEMS, INC.—Chesapeake Utilities Corporation; *U.S. Public*, pg. 347
CARA CORPORATION—William Blair & Company L.L.C.; *U.S. Private*, pg. 148
CAREAL HOLDING AG; *Int'l*, pg. 271
CATALINA MARKETING CORPORATION; *U.S. Public*, pg. 314
CATERPILLAR INC.; *U.S. Public*, pg. 315
CERNER CORPORATION; *U.S. Public*, pg. 331
CHASE GLOBAL FUNDS SERVICE COMPANY—The Chase Manhattan Corporation; *U.S. Public*, pg. 338
CHESAPEAKE UTILITIES CORPORATION; *U.S. Public*, pg. 347
CIGNA INFORMATION SERVICES, INC.—Cigna Corp.; *U.S.* Public, pg. 357
CIGNA SERVICES U.K. LIMITED—Cigna Corp.; *U.S. Public*, *pg. 363*
CIMENTS FRANCAIS DATA PROCESSING CENTER—Ciments Francais; *Int'l*, pg. 292
CITICORP INFO SYSTEMS RESEARCH—Citicorp; *U.S. Public*, pg. 378
CITIZENS INFORMATION SYSTEMS, INC.—CNB Bancshares, Inc.; *U.S. Public*, pg. 281
COMARCO, INC.; *U.S. Public*, pg. 406
COMDATA CORPORATION—Ceridian Corporation; *U.S. Public*, pg. 331

COMMERCE GENERAL CORPORATION—National Commerce Bancorporation; *U.S. Public*, pg. 1155
COMMUNICATIONS EQUIPMENT CO.—CD Products, Inc.; *U.S. Public*, pg. 276
COMNET CORPORATION; *U.S. Public*, pg. 416
COMPAGNIE DES MACHINES BULL; *Int'l*, pg. 315
COMPTEK RESEARCH, INC.; *U.S. Public*, pg. 419
COMPUTASIA LIMITED—Cable and Wireless plc; *Int'l*, pg. 247
COMPUTER DATA SYSTEMS, INC.—Affiliated Computer Services, Inc.; *U.S. Public*, pg. 28
COMPUTER SCIENCES CORPORATION; *U.S. Public*, pg. 422
COMPUTER SYSTEMS RESEARCH, INC.—The McGraw-Hill Companies; *U.S. Public*, pg. 1070
COMPUWARE CORPORATION; *U.S. Public*, pg. 423
CONTABILIDAD MECANIZADA, SOCIEDAD ANONIMA—Cigna Corp.; *U.S. Public*, pg. 364
THE CONTINENTAL CORPORATION—Loews Corporation; *U.S. Public*, pg. 1011
CRAWFORD & COMPANY; *U.S. Public*, pg. 458
DMR CONSULTING GROUP, INC.—Fujitsu Limited; *Int'l*, pg. 527
DMR GROEP B.V.—Fujitsu Limited; *Int'l*, pg. 528
DMR GROUP (BELGIUM) S.A.-N.V.—Fujitsu Limited; *Int'l*, pg. 528
DMR GROUP, INC.—Fujitsu Limited; *Int'l*, pg. 527
DMR GROUP LIMITED—Fujitsu Limited; *Int'l*, pg. 528
DMR GRUPPE AG—Fujitsu Limited; *Int'l*, pg. 528
DMR GRUPPE GMBH—Fujitsu Limited; *Int'l*, pg. 528
DST SYSTEMS, INC.—Kansas City Southern Industries, Inc.; *U.S. Public*, pg. 943
DAIMLER-BENZ INTERSERVICES (DEBIS) AG—Daimler-Benz Aktiengesellschaft; *Int'l*, pg. 367
DAIN RAUSCHER CORPORATION; *U.S. Public*, pg. 476
DAKCO DISTRIBUTORS, INC.; *U.S. Private*, pg. 308
DASSAULT SYSTEMES—Dassault Aviation Group; *Int'l*, pg. 383
DATA-TRONICS CORP.—Arkansas Best Corporation; *U.S. Public*, pg. 130
DATABASE AMERICA COMPANIES; *U.S. Private*, pg. 312
DATACARD EUROPE LTD.—DataCard Corporation; *U.S. Private*, pg. 312
DATACARD JAPAN LTD—DataCard Corporation; *U.S. Private*, pg. 313
DATACOR/ISM (INFORMATION SYSTEMS MANAGEMENT ATLANTIC CORP.)—Bruncor, Inc.; *Int'l*, pg. 230
DATALINK SYSTEMS, LLC—Fiserv, Inc.; *U.S. Public*, pg. 647
DATAPRO SERVICES—The McGraw-Hill Companies; *U.S. Public*, pg. 1072
DATAQUEST INCORPORATED—The Dun & Bradstreet Corporation; *U.S. Public*, pg. 535
DATASCAN SERVICES CO.—Alpha One Exchange; *U.S. Private*, pg. 45
DATASCAN TECHNOLOGY—Alpha One Exchange; *U.S. Private*, pg. 45
DATASTREAM INTERNATIONAL LTD.—Primark Corporation; *U.S. Public*, pg. 1325
DEBIS SYSTEMHAUS GMBH—Daimler-Benz Aktiengesellschaft; *Int'l*, pg. 368
DECISIONS & DESIGN, INC.—Comarco, Inc.; *U.S. Public*, pg. 406
DESIGN CONCEPTS INTEGRATION, INC.—International Research & Evaluation; *U.S. Private*, pg. 572
DET NORSKE VERITAS; *Int'l*, pg. 396
DIGITALE KARTSYSTEMER—Kvaerner a.s.a.; *Int'l*, pg. 766
DISTRIBUTED SYSTEMS DIVISION—Storage Technology Corporation; *U.S. Public*, pg. 1522
DYNAMICS RESEARCH CORPORATION; *U.S. Public*, pg. 539
DYNCORP; *U.S. Private*, pg. 351
E-P CONSULTING GROUP AB—Telefonaktiebolaget LM Ericsson; *Int'l*, pg. 1363
EDS, BUSINESS OPERATIONS GROUP—Electronic Data Systems Corporation; *U.S. Public*, pg. 570
EDS, FINANCIAL AND INSURANCE GROUP—Electronic Data Systems Corporation; *U.S. Public*, pg. 570
EDS, GOVERNMENT SYSTEMS GROUP—Electronic Data Systems Corporation; *U.S. Public*, pg. 570
EDS, INTERNATIONAL, COMMERCIAL AND COMMUNICATIONS GROUPS—Electronic Data Systems Corporation; *U.S. Public*, pg. 570
EDS OF CANADA LTD.—Electronic Data Systems Corporation; *U.S. Public*, pg. 570
EFG TECHNOLOGIES INC.—United Insurance Companies, Inc.; *U.S. Public*, pg. 1679
ELECTRONIC DATA SYSTEMS CORPORATION; *U.S. Public*, pg. 569
ELSEVIER EDITORIAL SERVICES—Reed Elsevier plc; *Int'l*, pg. 1100
ELSEVIER ELECTRONIC PUBLISHING SERVICES—Reed Elsevier plc; *Int'l*, pg. 1100
EPSILON—American Express Company; *U.S. Public*, pg. 74
EQUIFAX CHECK SERVICE—Equifax Inc.; *U.S. Public*, pg. 588
FBS INFORMATION SERVICES CORPORATION—U.S. Bancorp; *U.S. Public*, pg. 1681
FEDERAL DATA CORPORATION; *U.S. Private*, pg. 398
FEDERATED SYSTEMS GROUP—Federated Department Stores, Inc.; *U.S. Public*, pg. 618
FIRST DATA CORPORATION; *U.S. Public*, pg. 630
FIRST DATA RESOURCES—First Data Corporation; *U.S. Public*, pg. 631
FIRST HEALTH SERVICES—First Health Group Corp.; *U.S. Public*, pg. 635
FIRST SECURITY INFORMATION TECHNOLOGY, INC.—First Security Corporation; *U.S. Public*, pg. 637
FISERV, INC.; *U.S. Public*, pg. 647
FLEET SERVICES CORP.—Fleet Financial Group, Inc.; *U.S. Public*, pg. 650
FLORIDA ASSOCIATED SERVICES, INC.—American Heritage Life Investment Corp.; *U.S. Public*, pg. 79
GEC COMPUTER SERVICES LTD.—The General Electric Company, p.l.c.; *Int'l*, pg. 544
GTE DATA SERVICES INCORPORATED—GTE Corporation; *U.S. Public*, pg. 696
GTE LEASING CORPORATION—GTE Corporation; *U.S. Public*, pg. 696
GTM CONSTRUCTION—Lyonnaise des Eaux S.A.; *Int'l*, pg. 823
GANDALF CANADA LTD.—Gandalf Technologies Inc.; *Int'l*, pg. 540
GANDALF DIGITAL COMMUNICATIONS LTD.—Gandalf Technologies Inc.; *Int'l*, pg. 540
GANDALF INTERNATIONAL LTD.—Gandalf Technologies Inc.; *Int'l*, pg. 540
GANDALF NEDERLAND B.V.—Gandalf Technologies Inc.; *Int'l*, pg. 540
GANDALF S.A.—Gandalf Technologies Inc.; *Int'l*, pg. 541
GANDALF SYSTEMS CORPORATION—Gandalf Technologies Inc.; *Int'l*, pg. 540
GANDALF TECHNOLOGIES INC.; *Int'l*, pg. 540
GENERAL NUTRITION SERVICES, INC.—General Nutrition, Inc.; *U.S. Public*, pg. 725
GEONEX CORPORATION; *U.S. Private*, pg. 447
GEOREX INC.—CGG Group; *Int'l*, pg. 241
GORES TECHNOLOGY GROUP; *U.S. Private*, pg. 465
GRAND METROPOLITAN INFORMATION SERVICES LTD.—Diageo Plc; *Int'l*, pg. 408
GROCERS EQUIPMENT CO.—Certified Grocers of California; *U.S. Private*, pg. 227
HBO & COMPANY/CYCARE BUSINESS GROUP—HBOC; *U.S. Public*, pg. 770
HADRON, INC.; *U.S. Public*, pg. 773
HARTE-HANKS DATA TECHNOLOGIES—Harte-Hanks Communications, Inc.; *U.S. Public*, pg. 794
HEALTH CARE INSTITUTIONAL SERVICES—National Data Corporation; *U.S. Public*, pg. 1156
HEALTH MANAGEMENT SYSTEMS, INC.; *U.S. Public*, pg. 802
HELM, INC.; *U.S. Private*, pg. 520
HOOPER HOLMES CORPORATION; *U.S. Public*, pg. 835
IBM INFORMATION SERVICES LIMITED—International Business Machines Corporation; *U.S. Public*, pg. 897
ISI SYSTEMS INC.—Teleglobe, Inc.; *Int'l*, pg. 1373
ISS-INTERNATIONAL SERVICE SYSTEM A/S; *Int'l*, pg. 656
ITMI—CAP Gemini S.A.; *Int'l*, pg. 263
INFORMATION & ENGINEERING TECHNOLOGY—DynCorp; *U.S. Private*, pg. 351
INFORMATION HANDLING SERVICES—TBG Management S.A.M.; *Int'l*, pg. 1335
INSTINET CORPORATION—Reuters Holdings PLC; *Int'l*, pg. 1106
INTEREALTY CORPORATION—News Holdings Corp.; *U.S. Private*, pg. 797
INTERNATIONAL BENEFIT SERVICE CORPORATION—Cigna Corp.; *U.S. Public*, pg. 362
INTERNATIONAL BUSINESS MACHINES CORPORATION; *U.S. Public*, pg. 895
INTERNATIONAL BUSINESS SERVICES, INC.—Comarco, Inc.; *U.S. Public*, pg. 406
INTERNATIONAL COMPUTER SERVICES, INC.—American International Group, Inc.; *U.S. Public*, pg. 84
INTERNATIONAL RESEARCH & EVALUATION; *U.S. Private*, pg. 571
JCI DATA PROCESSING, INC.; *U.S. Private*, pg. 577
JONES INTERACTIVE, INC.—Jones International, Ltd.; *U.S. Private*, pg. 597
KEY SERVICES CORPORATION—Keycorp; *U.S. Public*, pg. 954
KEYSTONE FINANCIAL SERVICE GROUP, INC.—Keystone Financial Inc.; *U.S. Public*, pg. 956
KRUPP HOESCH INFORMATIONSVERARBEITUNG GMBH—Fried. Krupp AG; *Int'l*, pg. 512
LKS DATEN-SERVICE A.G.—Compagnie des Machines Bull; *Int'l*, pg. 318
LM ERICSSON DATA SERVICES AB—Telefonaktiebolaget LM Ericsson; *Int'l*, pg. 1364
LITTON COMPUTER SERVICES DIV.—Litton Industries, Inc.; *U.S. Public*, pg. 1002
LITTON COMPUTER SERVICES-EASTERN REGIONAL DATA CENTER—Litton Industries, Inc.; *U.S. Public*, pg. 1002
LITTON COMPUTER SERVICES-WESTERN REGIONAL DATA CENTER—Litton Industries, Inc.; *U.S. Public*, pg. 1002
LOCKHEED MARTIN CORPORATION; *U.S. Public*, pg. 1006
LOGICON SYSCON CORPORATION—Northrop Grumman Corporation; *U.S. Public*, pg. 1199
M & I DATA SERVICES, INC.—Marshall & Ilsley Corporation; *U.S. Public*, pg. 1050
MSI AUSTRALIA PTY. LTD.—Symbol Technologies, Inc.; *U.S. Public*, pg. 1546
MSI DATA AUSTRIA—Symbol Technologies, Inc.; *U.S. Public*, pg. 1546
MSI DATA GMBH—Symbol Technologies, Inc.; *U.S. Public*, pg. 1546
MSI DATA INTERNATIONAL, EUROPEAN HDQTRS.—Symbol Technologies, Inc.; *U.S. Public*, pg. 1546
MSI DATA ITALIA S.R.L.—Symbol Technologies, Inc.; *U.S. Public*, pg. 1546
MSI DATA LIMITED, UNITED KINGDOM—Symbol Technologies, Inc.; *U.S. Public*, pg. 1546
MSI FRANCE S.A.R.L.—Symbol Technologies, Inc.; *U.S. Public*, pg. 1546
MAGELLAN MEDICAL INFORMATION SERVICES, INC.—Magellan Health Services, Inc.; *U.S. Public*, pg. 1036
MANAGISTICS INCORPORATED—BankAmerica Corporation; *U.S. Public*, pg. 181
MANATRON, INC.; *U.S. Public*, pg. 1040
MARTIN MARIETTA INFORMATION SYSTEMS—Lockheed Martin Corporation; *U.S. Public*, pg. 1007
MATRA CAP SYSTEMS—Lagardere Groupe; *Int'l*, pg. 792
MATRA DATAVISION S.A.—Lagardere Groupe; *Int'l*, pg. 793
MAY & SPEH, INC.; *U.S. Public*, pg. 1063
MCKESSON HEALTH SYSTEMS—McKesson Corporation; *U.S. Public*, pg. 1073
MEDIA GENERAL, INC.; *U.S. Public*, pg. 1077
MEDIC COMPUTER SYSTEMS, INC.—Misys PLC; *Int'l*, pg. 870
METIER MANAGEMENT SYSTEMS—Lockheed Martin Corporation; *U.S. Public*, pg. 1010
MOORE CORPORATION LIMITED; *Int'l*, pg. 888
NCR CORPORATION; *U.S. Public*, pg. 1146
NDC TOKYO REPRESENTATIVE OFFICE—National Data Corporation; *U.S. Public*, pg. 1156
NABANCO—First Data Corporation; *U.S. Public*, pg. 631
NANTO COMPUTER SERVICE CO., LTD.—The Nanto Bank, Ltd.; *Int'l*, pg. 905
NATIONAL COMPUTER SYSTEMS; *U.S. Public*, pg. 1155
NATIONAL DATA CORPORATION; *U.S. Public*, pg. 1155
NATIONAL DATA CORPORATION OF CANADA LTD.—National Data Corporation; *U.S. Public*, pg. 1156
NEW YORK SWITCH CORPORATION—The Chase Manhattan Corporation; *U.S. Public*, pg. 339
THE NEW YORK TIMES INDEX—The New York Times Company; *U.S. Public*, pg. 1174
NEWSEDGE CORPORATION; *U.S. Public*, pg. 1180
A.C. NIELSEN COMPANY—A.C. Nielsen; *U.S. Public*, pg. 1183
NISSAY COMPUTER CO., LTD.—Nippon Life Insurance Co.; *Int'l*, pg. 935
NISSHO ELECTRONICS CORP.—Nissho Iwai Corporation; *Int'l*, pg. 946
NORWEST SERVICES, INC.—Norwest Corporation; *U.S. Public*, pg. 1202
OLSY NORTH AMERICA INC.—Olivetti SpA; *Int'l*, pg. 1002
O'NEIL DATA SYSTEMS, INC.—William O'Neil & Co., Inc.; *U.S. Private*, pg. 817
WILLIAM O'NEIL & CO., INC.; *U.S. Private*, pg. 817
PRC, INC.—Litton Industries, Inc.; *U.S. Public*, pg. 1003
PAYCHEX, INC.; *U.S. Public*, pg. 1267
PHILADELPHIA SUBURBAN CORPORATION; *U.S. Public*, pg. 1287
POLICY MANAGEMENT SYSTEMS CORPORATION; *U.S. Public*, pg. 1314
PROBUSINESS SERVICES, INC.; *U.S. Public*, pg. 1330
PUBCO CORPORATION; *U.S. Public*, pg. 1339
QUALITY MEDICAL ADJUDICATION, INC.—Health Management Systems, Inc.; *U.S. Public*, pg. 802
QUESTAR INFOCOMM—Questar Corporation; *U.S. Public*, pg. 1352
RX INFORMATION CENTRE LTD.—The Jean Coutu Group (PJC) Inc.; *Int'l*, pg. 340
RALEIGH ENTERPRISES, INC.; *U.S. Private*, pg. 907
RESOURCE AMERICA FIELD & ACCOUNTING OPERATIONS HEADQUARTERS—Resource America, Inc.; *U.S. Public*, pg. 1382
REYNA CAPITAL CORP.—The Reynolds and Reynolds Company; *U.S. Public*, pg. 1385
REYNOLDS AND REYNOLDS (CANADA) LTD.—The Reynolds and Reynolds Company; *U.S. Public*, pg. 1385
RISK SCIENCES GROUP, INC.—Crawford & Company; *U.S. Public*, pg. 458
RURBANC DATA SERVICES, INC.—Rurban Financial Corp.; *U.S. Public*, pg. 1413
SAIC COMSYSTEMS—Science Applications International Corp.; *U.S. Private*, pg. 976
SBC WARBURG GROUP MANAGEMENT LTD.—Swiss Bank Corporation; *Int'l*, pg. 1331
SEI BENEFIT SERVICES CORPORATION—SEI Investments; *U.S. Public*, pg. 1417
SEI FINANCIAL SERVICES COMPANY—SEI Investments; *U.S. Public*, pg. 1417
SEI INVESTMENTS; *U.S. Public*, pg. 1417
SKF DATASERVICE AB—AB SKF; *Int'l*, pg. 1157
SMS CORP Y CIA S.R.C.—Shared Medical Systems Corporation; *U.S. Public*, pg. 1463
SMS INTERNATIONAL DIVISION—Shared Medical Systems Corporation; *U.S. Public*, pg. 1463
SMS SERVICES CORP.—Shared Medical Systems Corporation; *U.S. Public*, pg. 1463
SMS SYSTEMS MAINTENANCE INC.—Shared Medical Systems Corporation; *U.S. Public*, pg. 1463
SAZTEC EUROPE LTD.—Saztec International, Inc.; *U.S. Public*, pg. 1435
SAZTEC INTERNATIONAL, INC.; *U.S. Public*, pg. 1435
SCAN-OPTICS, INC.; *U.S. Public*, pg. 1436
SCICOM DATA SERVICES, LTD.; *U.S. Private*, pg. 975
SCIENCE MANAGEMENT CORPORATION—Versar Inc.; *U.S. Public*, pg. 1717
SECURITY PACIFIC INFORMATION SERVICES CORPORATION—BankAmerica Corporation; *U.S. Public*, pg. 182
SHARED MEDICAL SYSTEMS CORPORATION; *U.S. Public*, pg. 1463
SIEMENS-NIXDORF INFORMATIONSSYSTEME AG—Siemens AG; *Int'l*, pg. 1245
J.M. SMITH CORP.; *U.S. Private*, pg. 1008
SORBUS EUROPE, LTD.—Bell Atlantic Corporation; *U.S. Public*, pg. 204
SOUTHTRUST DATA SERVICES, INC.—SouthTrust Corporation; *U.S. Public*, pg. 1492
STANDARD CHARTERED BANK PLC; *Int'l*, pg. 1294
SUNGARD DATA SYSTEMS INC.; *U.S. Public*, pg. 1534
SUNGARD EMPLOYEE BENEFITS SYSTEMS—SunGard Data Systems Inc.; *U.S. Public*, pg. 1534
SUNGARD TRUST & SHAREHOLDER SYSTEMS GROUP—SunGard Data Systems Inc.; *U.S. Public*, pg. 1535
SUNTRUST—SunTrust Banks, Inc.; *U.S. Public*, pg. 1537
SUNTRUST BANKS, INC.; *U.S. Public*, pg. 1537
SVERDRUP CORPORATION; *U.S. Public*, pg. 1057
SVERDRUP TECHNOLOGY, INC.—Sverdrup Corporation; *U.S. Private*, pg. 1057
THE SWISS COLONY, INC; *U.S. Private*, pg. 1059

S.I.C. Index

SYCOM SERVICES INC.—Hadron, Inc.; U.S. Public, pg. 773
SYNERGY COMPUTER GRAPHICS CORPORATION—Nippon Steel Corporation; Int'l, pg. 940
SYSTEMS DEVELOPMENT LTD.—International Business Machines Corporation; U.S. Public, pg. 897
SYSTEMS ENGINEERING DIV.—Computer Sciences Corporation; U.S. Public, pg. 423
TCF FINANCIAL CORP.; U.S. Public, pg. 1554
TSR INC.; U.S. Public, pg. 1559
TECHNODES S.A.—Ciments Francais; Int'l, pg. 292
TELECHECK SERVICES, INC.—First Data Corporation; U.S. Public, pg. 631
TELEGLOBE, INC.; Int'l, pg. 1373
TELEGLOBE INSURANCE SYSTEMS—Teleglobe, Inc.; Int'l, pg. 1373
TELEPHONE AND DATA SYSTEMS, INC.; U.S. Public, pg. 1570
THOMSON INFORMATION SERVICES LTD.—The Thomson Corporation; U.S. Public, pg. 1601
TOPPAN MOORE DATA PRODUCTS LTD.—DataCard Corporation; U.S. Private, pg. 313
TOTAL SYSTEM SERVICES, INC.—Synovus Financial Corp.; U.S. Public, pg. 1550
TRILOG, INC.—Cigna Corp.; U.S. Public, pg. 362
TRIMIN ENTERPRISES, INC.; Int'l, pg. 1424
U-HAUL INTERNATIONAL, INC.—Amerco; U.S. Private, pg. 49
USLIFE CORPORATION—American General Corporation; U.S. Public, pg. 77
USLIFE SYSTEMS CORPORATION—American General Corporation; U.S. Public, pg. 77
UTILITY & MUNICIPAL SERVICES, INC.—Philadelphia Suburban Corporation; U.S. Public, pg. 1287
UTILITY DATA CORPORATION—NIPSCO Industries, Inc.; U.S. Public, pg. 1185
VAC DATA MANAGEMENT, INC.—Emerson Electric Co.; U.S. Public, pg. 575
VW GEDAS CONSULT GMBH—Volkswagen AG; Int'l, pg. 1474
VW-GESELLSCHAFT FUR TECHNISCHE DATANVERARBEITUNGSSYSTEME MBH—Volkswagen AG; Int'l, pg. 1474
VALUE LINE—Arnold Bernhard & Co.; U.S. Private, pg. 137
VERITAS DGC INC—Veritas DGC Inc.; U.S. Private, pg. 1136
VIKING COMPUTER SERVICES—D & K Healthcare Resources, Inc.; U.S. Public, pg. 472
VORWERK & CO.; Int'l, pg. 1480
WALLACE COMPUTER SERVICES, INC.; U.S. Public, pg. 1735
JIM WALTER COMPUTER SERVICES, INC.—Walter Industries, Inc.; U.S. Public, pg. 1737
WARDLEY DATA SERVICES LTD.—HSBC Holdings plc; Int'l, pg. 584
WASHBURN DIRECT MARKETING, INC.—Cadmus Communications Corporation; U.S. Public, pg. 291
WESTCORP; U.S. Public, pg. 1756
WYLE DATA SERVICES—Veba AG; Int'l, pg. 1457
XEROX REAL ESTATE & GENERAL SERVICES DIVISION—Xerox Corporation; U.S. Public, pg. 1785
ZEDA GESELLSCHAFT FUR DATENVERARBEITUNG UND EDV-BERATUNG MBH. & CO.—Vorwerk & Co.; Int'l, pg. 1481
ZIFF TECHNOLOGIES—Softbank Corporation; Int'l, pg. 1276
ZIONS DATA SERVICE CO.—Zions Bancorporation; U.S. Public, pg. 1793

7375 — INFORMATION RETRIEVAL SERVICES

AAH MEDITEL LIMITED—Franz Haniel & Cie, GmbH; Int'l, pg. 591
ABB SIMCON, INC.—ABB Asea Brown Boveri (Holding) Ltd.; Int'l, pg. 5
AT&T ISTEL GLOBAL MESSAGING SERVICES LTD.—AT&T Corporation; U.S. Public, pg. 11
AMERICA ONLINE INCORPORATED; U.S. Public, pg. 66
AMERICAN BUSINESS INFORMATION, INC.; U.S. Public, pg. 69
ANACOMP, INC.; U.S. Public, pg. 106
ASPEN SYSTEMS CORP.—Wolters Kluwer N.V.; Int'l, pg. 1513
AUTOMATIC DATA PROCESSING, INC.; U.S. Public, pg. 150
BNA PLUS—The Bureau of National Affairs, Inc.; U.S. Private, pg. 182
BATTELLE MEMORIAL INSTITUTE; U.S. Private, pg. 123
BELL ATLANTIC ENTERPRISES CORPORATION—Bell Atlantic Corporation; U.S. Public, pg. 202
BELL CANADA—BCE Inc.; Int'l, pg. 115
BOSTON INTERNATIONAL DATA SERVICES, INC.—BankBoston Corporation; U.S. Public, pg. 184
R.R. BOWKER—Reed Elsevier plc; Int'l, pg. 1096
BOWNE BUSINESS COMMUNICATIONS, INC.—Bowne & Co., Inc.; U.S. Public, pg. 248
BROOKTREE ROCKWELL SEMICONDUCTOR SYSTEMS DIV.—Rockwell International Corporation; U.S. Public, pg. 1398
THE BUREAU OF NATIONAL AFFAIRS, INC.; U.S. Private, pg. 181
BUTTERWORTH & CO. PUBLISHERS LTD.—Reed Elsevier plc; Int'l, pg. 1095
BUTTERWORTHS BRITISH AND IRISH LEGAL—Reed Elsevier plc; Int'l, pg. 1095
CESI CENTRO ELABORAZIONI E STUDI INFORMATICI S.P.A.—Telefonaktiebolaget LM Ericsson; Int'l, pg. 1365
CUC INTERNATIONAL, INC.—Cendant Corporation; U.S. Public, pg. 320
CADMUS COMMUNICATIONS CORPORATION; U.S. Public, pg. 290
CENDANT CORPORATION; U.S. Public, pg. 320
CERNER CORPORATION; U.S. Public, pg. 331
CIMENTS FRANCAIS DATA PROCESSING CENTER—Ciments Francais; Int'l, pg. 292
CITICORP INFORMATION RESOURCES, INC.—Citicorp; U.S. Public, pg. 377
COMMODITY INFORMATION SERVICES GROUP—The McGraw-Hill Companies; U.S. Public, pg. 1071
COMP-U-CARD DIVISION—Cendant Corporation; U.S. Public, pg. 320
COMPTEK RESEARCH, INC.; U.S. Public, pg. 419
COMPUSERVE INTERACTIVE SERVICES, INC.—America Online Incorporated; U.S. Public, pg. 66
COMPUTASIA LIMITED—Cable and Wireless plc; Int'l, pg. 247
COMPUTER CORPORATION OF AMERICA; U.S. Private, pg. 260
COMPUTER SCIENCES CORPORATION; U.S. Public, pg. 422
CONGRESSIONAL INFORMATION SERVICE (CIS)—Reed Elsevier plc; Int'l, pg. 1096
CONGRESSIONAL QUARTERLY—The Times Publishing Co.; U.S. Private, pg. 1088
DBT ONLINE, INC.; U.S. Public, pg. 472
DRI EUROPE, INC.—The McGraw-Hill Companies; U.S. Public, pg. 1072
DRI EUROPE (U.K.) LTD.—The McGraw-Hill Companies; U.S. Public, pg. 1072
DRI/MCGRAW-HILL—The McGraw-Hill Companies; U.S. Public, pg. 1071
DATA TRANSMISSION NETWORK CORPORATION; U.S. Public, pg. 486
DATAPRO SERVICES—The McGraw-Hill Companies; U.S. Public, pg. 1072
DATAQUEST INCORPORATED—The Dun & Bradstreet Corporation; U.S. Public, pg. 535
DATASTREAM INTERNATIONAL LTD.—Primark Corporation; U.S. Public, pg. 1325
DATASTREAM INTERNATIONAL LIMITED—Primark Corporation; U.S. Public, pg. 1326
THE DIALOG CORPORATION—The Dialog Corporation plc; Int'l, pg. 412
THE DIALOG CORPORATION PLC; Int'l, pg. 412
DISTRIBUTED SYSTEMS DIVISION—Storage Technology Corporation; U.S. Public, pg. 1522
F.W. DODGE GROUP—The McGraw-Hill Companies; U.S. Public, pg. 1070
R.R. DONNELLEY & SONS COMPANY; U.S. Public, pg. 517
DOW JONES & COMPANY, INC.; U.S. Public, pg. 524
DUN & BRADSTREET FRANCE SA—The Dun & Bradstreet Corporation; U.S. Public, pg. 536
DUN & BRADSTREET POLAND SP. Z.O.O.—The Dun & Bradstreet Corporation; U.S. Public, pg. 536
DUN & BRADSTREET SCHIMMELPFENG GMBH—The Dun & Bradstreet Corporation; U.S. Public, pg. 537
DUNSGATE—The Dun & Bradstreet Corporation; U.S. Public, pg. 535
EBSCO INDUSTRIES, INC.; U.S. Private, pg. 358
ELSEVIER NV—Reed Elsevier plc; Int'l, pg. 1093
ELSEVIER SCIENCE (INTERNATIONAL)—Reed Elsevier plc; Int'l, pg. 1099
EPSILON—American Express Company; U.S. Public, pg. 74
THE FAXON COMPANY, INC.—Dawson Holdings PLC; Int'l, pg. 385
FIRST DATA CORPORATION; U.S. Public, pg. 630
FIRSTAR INFORMATION SERVICES CORPORATION—Firstar Corporation; U.S. Public, pg. 643
GALE RESEARCH INC.—The Thomson Corporation; U.S. Public, pg. 1600
GANNETT SATELLITE INFORMATION NETWORK, INC.—Gannett Company, Inc.; U.S. Public, pg. 700
GROLIER ELECTRONIC PUBLISHING, INC.—Lagardere Groupe; Int'l, pg. 794
HILTON RESERVATIONS WORLDWIDE—Hilton Hotels Corporation; U.S. Public, pg. 829
HOME SHOPPING NETWORK, INC.—USA Networks, Inc.; U.S. Public, pg. 1685
HOOPER HOLMES CORPORATION; U.S. Public, pg. 835
IDX SYSTEMS CORPORATION; U.S. Public, pg. 854
IFI/PLENUM DATA CORPORATION—Plenum Publishing Corporation; U.S. Public, pg. 1311
ISI SYSTEMS INC.—Teleglobe, Inc.; Int'l, pg. 1373
THE IMAGINATION NETWORK—America Online Incorporated; U.S. Public, pg. 66
INFORMATION ACCESS CO.—The Thomson Corporation; U.S. Public, pg. 1600
INFORMATION HANDLING SERVICES—TBG Management S.A.M.; Int'l, pg. 1335
INSTINET CORPORATION—Reuters Holdings PLC; Int'l, pg. 1106
INTEGRATED MARKETING SERVICES—First Data Corporation; U.S. Public, pg. 631
INTELLICALL, INC.; U.S. Public, pg. 887
INTERA INFORMATION TECHNOLOGIES CORP.—Trimac Corporation; Int'l, pg. 1424
INTERACTIVE DATA CORPORATION—Pearson plc; Int'l, pg. 1025
INTERNATIONAL BUSINESS MACHINES CORPORATION; U.S. Public, pg. 895
JEPPESEN SANDERSON—The Times Mirror Company; U.S. Public, pg. 1616
KYOBO INFORMATION & COMMUNICATION CO., LTD.—The Kyoei Life Insurance Co., Ltd.; Int'l, pg. 777
LEGI-SLATE INC.—The Washington Post Company; U.S. Public, pg. 1743
LEGI-TECH—McClatchy Newspapers Inc.; U.S. Public, pg. 1066
LEXIS LAW PUBLISHING—Reed Elsevier plc; Int'l, pg. 1096
LEXIS-NEXIS—Reed Elsevier plc; Int'l, pg. 1096
THE M/A/R/C GROUP; U.S. Public, pg. 1022
M/A/R/C MARKETING AND RESEARCH COUNSELORS, INC.—The M/A/R/C Group; U.S. Public, pg. 1023
MDL INFORMATION SYSTEMS, INC.—Reed Elsevier plc; Int'l, pg. 1100
MPSI SYSTEMS INC.; U.S. Public, pg. 1027
MPSI SYSTEMS LTD.—MPSI Systems Inc.; U.S. Public, pg. 1027
MACMILLAN PUBLISHING USA—National Amusements, Inc.; U.S. Private, pg. 777
MASTER DATA CENTER—National Amusements, Inc.; U.S. Private, pg. 778
MATRIXX MARKETING INC.—Cincinnati Bell Telephone; U.S. Public, pg. 368
MAXWELL MACMILLAN PROFESSIONAL & BUSINESS REFERENCE PUBLISHING—The Thomson Corporation; U.S. Public, pg. 1602
MCCLATCHY NEWSPAPERS INC.; U.S. Public, pg. 1065
MCGRAW-HILL HEALTHCARE PUBLICATIONS GROUP—The McGraw-Hill Companies; U.S. Public, pg. 1071
MCGRAW-HILL INFORMATION SYSTEMS CO. OF CANADA LTD.—The McGraw-Hill Companies; U.S. Public, pg. 1072
MCGRAW-HILL INTERNATIONAL PUBLICATIONS CO. LTD.—The McGraw-Hill Companies; U.S. Public, pg. 1072
MICROMEDEX, INC.—The Thomson Corporation; U.S. Public, pg. 1601
MONEY MARKET DIRECTORIES—The McGraw-Hill Companies; U.S. Public, pg. 1071
ND COMMUNICATIONS CO. LTD.—Daiwa Securities Co. Ltd.; Int'l, pg. 375
NATIONAL REGISTER PUBLISHING—Reed Elsevier plc; Int'l, pg. 1096
NEWSEDGE CORPORATION; U.S. Public, pg. 1180
A.C. NIELSEN COMPANY—A.C. Nielsen; U.S. Public, pg. 1183
NIHON KEIZAI SHIMBUN AMERICA, INC.—Nihon Keizai Shimbun, Inc.; Int'l, pg. 929
NIHON KEIZAI SHIMBUN EUROPE LTD.—Nihon Keizai Shimbun, Inc.; Int'l, pg. 929
NIHON KEIZAI SHIMBUN, INC.; Int'l, pg. 929
NIHON KEIZAI SHIMBUN SINGAPORE PTE. LTD.—Nihon Keizai Shimbun, Inc.; Int'l, pg. 930
THE NIKKAN KOGYO SHIMBUN, LTD.; Int'l, pg. 930
OAG—Reed Elsevier plc; Int'l, pg. 1097
ON COMMAND VIDEO—Ascent Entertainment Group, Inc.; U.S. Public, pg. 138
P.R. NEWSWIRE ASSOCIATION INC.—United News & Media plc; Int'l, pg. 1443
PANEL PUBLISHERS, INC.—Wolters Kluwer N.V.; Int'l, pg. 1513
PIERS—Pearson plc; Int'l, pg. 1026
POLICY MANAGEMENT SYSTEMS LIFE, INC.—Policy Management Systems Corporation; U.S. Public, pg. 1314
PREDICASTS—The Thomson Corporation; U.S. Public, pg. 1600
PRIMARK CORPORATION; U.S. Public, pg. 1325
QUICK CORP.—Nihon Keizai Shimbun, Inc.; Int'l, pg. 929
REED ELSEVIER PLC; Int'l, pg. 1093
REED INTERNATIONAL P.L.C.—Reed Elsevier plc; Int'l, pg. 1093
REED TECHNOLOGY AND INFORMATION SERVICES INC.—Reed Elsevier plc; Int'l, pg. 1096
REED TRAVEL GROUP—Reed Elsevier plc; Int'l, pg. 1097
REUTERS AMERICA INC.—Reuters Holdings PLC; Int'l, pg. 1106
REUTERS HOLDINGS PLC; Int'l, pg. 1105
REUTERS HONG KONG LIMITED—Reuters Holdings PLC; Int'l, pg. 1105
REUTERS JAPAN KABUSHIKI KAISHA—Reuters Holdings PLC; Int'l, pg. 1105
REUTERS LIMITED—Reuters Holdings PLC; Int'l, pg. 1105
REUTERS SERVICES SARL—Reuters Holdings PLC; Int'l, pg. 1105
REUTERS SINGAPORE PTE LIMITED—Reuters Holdings PLC; Int'l, pg. 1106
REUTERS TELEVISION LIMITED—Reuters Holdings PLC; Int'l, pg. 1105
REYNA CAPITAL CORP.—The Reynolds and Reynolds Company; U.S. Public, pg. 1385
S & P COMSTOCK—The McGraw-Hill Companies; U.S. Public, pg. 1071
SBC WARBURG GROUP MANAGEMENT LTD.—Swiss Bank Corporation; Int'l, pg. 1331
SANDOZ TECHNOLOGY LTD.—Novartis AG; Int'l, pg. 972
SCAN-OPTICS, INC.; U.S. Public, pg. 1436
SECURITIES DATA COMPANY, INC.—The Thomson Corporation; U.S. Public, pg. 1600
SEITEL, INC.; U.S. Public, pg. 1454
SEITEL OFFSHORE CORP.—Seitel, Inc.; U.S. Public, pg. 1454
SEMCO INDUSTRIES INC.; U.S. Private, pg. 983
SHEPARD'S—Reed Elsevier plc; Int'l, pg. 1095
SHEPARD'S—The Times Mirror Company; U.S. Public, pg. 1616
SKANSKA DATA AB—Skanska AB; Int'l, pg. 1260
SPAULDING COMPANY, INC.—Semco Industries Inc.; U.S. Private, pg. 983
STANDARD & POOR'S COMPUSTAT SERVICES, INC.—The McGraw-Hill Companies; U.S. Public, pg. 1071
STANDARD & POOR'S INTERNATIONAL S.A.—The McGraw-Hill Companies; U.S. Public, pg. 1072
STANDARD & POOR'S RATINGS SERVICES—The McGraw-Hill Companies; U.S. Public, pg. 1071
SWEET'S DIV.—The McGraw-Hill Companies; U.S. Public, pg. 1070
SYSTEMS ENGINEERING DIV.—Computer Sciences Corporation; U.S. Public, pg. 423
TACTECH, INC.—Zing Technologies, Inc.; U.S. Public, pg. 1792
TARGETBASE MARKETING—The M/A/R/C Group; U.S. Public, pg. 1023
TATA MCGRAW-HILL PUBLISHING CO., PRIVATE LIMITED—The McGraw-Hill Companies; U.S. Public, pg. 1072
TECHNODES S.A.—Ciments Francais; Int'l, pg. 292
TELEGLOBE, INC.; Int'l, pg. 1373

TELEGLOBE INSURANCE SYSTEMS—Teleglobe, Inc.; *Int'l*, pg. 1373
THOMSON & THOMSON—The Thomson Corporation; *U.S. Public*, pg. 1601
THOMSON FINANCIAL SERVICES, INC.—The Thomson Corporation; *U.S. Public*, pg. 1600
THOMSON HOLDINGS INC.—The Thomson Corporation; *U.S. Public*, pg. 1601
TIMES ON-LINE SERVICES, INC.—The New York Times Company; *U.S. Public*, pg. 1174
TRANSAX DATA—Pearson plc; *Int'l*, pg. 1026
UMI DATA COURIER—Bell & Howell Holdings; *U.S. Public*, pg. 201
U S WEST INC.; *U.S. Public*, pg. 1688
VNU USA, INC.—VNU Verenigde Nederlandse Uitgeversbedrijven B.V.; *Int'l*, pg. 1447
VNU VERENIGDE NEDERLANDSE UITGEVERSBEDRIJVEN B.V.; *Int'l*, pg. 1445
VIKING COMPUTER SERVICES—D & K Healthcare Resources, Inc.; *U.S. Public*, pg. 472
WORD, INCORPORATED—Gaylord Entertainment Co.; *U.S. Public*, pg. 704
YAMAICHI INFORMATION SYSTEMS CO., LTD.—Yamaichi Securities Co., Ltd.; *Int'l*, pg. 1516
ZIFF TECHNOLOGIES—Softbank Corporation; *Int'l*, pg. 1276

7376 — COMPUTER FACILITIES MANAGEMENT SERVICES

CETT (COMPAGNIE EUROPEENE DE TELETRANSMISSION)—Alcatel Alsthom Compagnie Generale D'Electricite; *Int'l*, pg. 53
CIS TECHNOLOGIES, INC.—National Data Corporation; *U.S. Public*, pg. 1155
CAPITAL DATA SYSTEMS, INC.—Chesapeake Utilities Corporation; *U.S. Public*, pg. 347
CARNEGIE HOLDING AB; *Int'l*, pg. 272
CIMENTS FRANCAIS DATA PROCESSING CENTER—Ciments Francais; *Int'l*, pg. 292
COMPUTER HORIZONS CORP.; *U.S. Public*, pg. 421
COMPUTER SCIENCES CORPORATION; *U.S. Public*, pg. 422
COMSOURCE, INC.—SIGCORP, Inc.; *U.S. Public*, pg. 1471
DBS COMPUTER SERVICES PTE. LTD.—DBS Bank Ltd.; *Int'l*, pg. 350
DSM N.V.; *Int'l*, pg. 352
DATAFLEX CORPORATION; *U.S. Private*, pg. 313
DYNCORP; *U.S. Private*, pg. 351
ESCA CORPORATION—Alcatel Alsthom Compagnie Generale D'Electricite; *Int'l*, pg. 53
EUROPEAN GROUP—Computer Sciences Corporation; *U.S. Public*, pg. 423
ISI SYSTEMS INC.—Teleglobe, Inc.; *Int'l*, pg. 1373
INTEGRATED MARKETING SERVICES—First Data Corporation; *U.S. Public*, pg. 631
INTERNATIONAL BUSINESS MACHINES CORPORATION; *U.S. Public*, pg. 895
KODAK SOFTWARE SYSTEMS DIVISION—Eastman Kodak Company; *U.S. Public*, pg. 555
LOGICON, INC.—Northrop Grumman Corporation; *U.S. Public*, pg. 1198
MCS, INC.—Mestek, Inc.; *U.S. Public*, pg. 1099
MFS TELECOM COMPANIES—WorldCom, Inc.; *U.S. Public*, pg. 1779
MASON & HANGER CORPORATION, INC.; *U.S. Private*, pg. 711
THE MAXIMA CORPORATION; *U.S. Private*, pg. 716
MESTEK, INC.; *U.S. Public*, pg. 1099
SBC WARBURG GROUP MANAGEMENT LTD.—Swiss Bank Corporation; *Int'l*, pg. 1331
SEI INVESTMENTS; *U.S. Public*, pg. 1417
SCOTTISH & COURAGE BREWERIES (SERVICES) LIMITED—Scottish & Newcastle plc; *Int'l*, pg. 1212
SKANSKA DATA AB—Skanska AB; *Int'l*, pg. 1260
SVERDRUP CORPORATION; *U.S. Private*, pg. 1057
SVERDRUP TECHNOLOGY, INC.—Sverdrup Corporation; *U.S. Private*, pg. 1057
SYSTEMS & COMPUTER TECHNOLOGY CORPORATION; *U.S. Public*, pg. 1552
TECHNODES S.A.—Ciments Francais; *Int'l*, pg. 292
TECHNOLOGY MANAGEMENT GROUP—Computer Sciences Corporation; *U.S. Public*, pg. 423
TECNOST-MAEL—Olivetti SpA; *Int'l*, pg. 1002
TELUB TEKNIK AB—Celsius AB; *Int'l*, pg. 278

7377 — COMPUTER RENTAL & LEASING

COMMERCIAL UNION CAPITAL CORPORATION—Commercial Union plc; *Int'l*, pg. 308
COMPUTER SALES INTERNATIONAL INC.; *U.S. Private*, pg. 260
DISTRIBUTED SYSTEMS DIVISION—Storage Technology Corporation; *U.S. Public*, pg. 1522
ECONOCOM-USA INC.; *U.S. Private*, pg. 361
EL CAMINO RESOURCES, LTD.; *U.S. Private*, pg. 366
GREYVEST CAPITOL INC.; *Int'l*, pg. 559
HBOC; *U.S. Public*, pg. 770
IDEA COURIER, INC.—IDEA Corporation; *U.S. Private*, pg. 557
INTERNATIONAL BUSINESS MACHINES CORPORATION; *U.S. Public*, pg. 895
KEYCORP LEASING LTD.—Keycorp; *U.S. Public*, pg. 954
MCS, INC.—Mestek, Inc.; *U.S. Public*, pg. 1099
MACRO COMPUTER PRODUCTS INC.; *U.S. Private*, pg. 693
MARUZEN SYSTEM SERVICE CO., LTD.—Maruzen Company Limited; *Int'l*, pg. 846
MERIDIAN TECHNOLOGY LEASING SERVICES; *U.S. Private*, pg. 732
NCR CORPORATION; *U.S. Public*, pg. 1146
NATIONSCREDIT COMMERCIAL CORPORATION—NationsBank Corporation; *U.S. Public*, pg. 1165
NEW YORK SYSTEMS EXCHANGE CORP.—Syracuse Supply Company; *U.S. Private*, pg. 1060
NOMURA BABCOCK & BROWN CO., LTD.—The Nomura Securities Co., Ltd.; *Int'l*, pg. 955
NUMBER NINE VISUAL TECHNOLOGY; *U.S. Public*, pg. 1206
O/E AUTOMATION, INC.; *U.S. Private*, pg. 809
OBAYASHI CORPORATION; *Int'l*, pg. 995
OMAN ORIX LEASING SAOG—Orix Corporation; *Int'l*, pg. 1009
ORLEANS LEASING CORPORATION—CCI/Triad Corporation; *U.S. Private*, pg. 193
POMEROY COMPUTER RESOURCES; *U.S. Public*, pg. 1315
RANDOLPH COMPUTER CORPORATION—BankBoston Corporation; *U.S. Public*, pg. 184
REYNA CAPITAL CORP.—The Reynolds and Reynolds Company; *U.S. Public*, pg. 1385
SANDERSON TECHNOLOGY LTD.; *Int'l*, pg. 1184
SECURITY DYNAMICS TECHNOLOGIES; *U.S. Public*, pg. 1453
STANDARD CHARTERED BANK PLC; *Int'l*, pg. 1294
SUN DATA INC.; *U.S. Private*, pg. 1050
SYQUEST TECHNOLOGY, INC.; *U.S. Public*, pg. 1550
TOSHIBA LEASING CORPORATION—Toshiba Corporation; *Int'l*, pg. 1404
TRIAD SYSTEMS FINANCIAL CORP.—CCI/Triad Corporation; *U.S. Private*, pg. 193
TROPIC COMMUNICATIONS INC.; *U.S. Public*, pg. 1641
VERNON COMPUTER LEASING INC.—Greyvest Capitol Inc.; *Int'l*, pg. 559
VERNON RENTALS & LEASING INC.—Greyvest Capitol Inc.; *Int'l*, pg. 559

7378 — COMPUTER MAINTENANCE & REPAIR

AT&T ISTEL LIMITED—AT&T Corporation; *U.S. Public*, pg. 11
ANACOMP, LTD.—Anacomp, Inc.; *U.S. Public*, pg. 107
ANACOMP S.A. (FRANCE)—Anacomp, Inc.; *U.S. Public*, pg. 107
AURORA ELECTRONICS—Aurora Electronics, Inc.; *U.S. Public*, pg. 147
AUTOMATED WAGERING—Power House Technologies, Inc.; *U.S. Public*, pg. 1319
CARDINAL HEALTH INC.; *U.S. Public*, pg. 304
DATA GENERAL CORPORATION; *U.S. Public*, pg. 485
DATA GENERAL CUSTOMER SERVICE DIVISION—Data General Corporation; *U.S. Public*, pg. 485
DATA GENERAL HONG KONG SALES & SERVICE, LTD.—Data General Corporation; *U.S. Public*, pg. 486
ECONOCOM-USA INC.; *U.S. Private*, pg. 361
FUJITSU NEW ZEALAND LTD.—Fujitsu Limited; *Int'l*, pg. 528
GE CAPITAL/IT SOLUTIONS—General Electric Company; *U.S. Public*, pg. 711
GECOTEC—GIB Group; *Int'l*, pg. 533
GENICOM CORPORATION; *U.S. Public*, pg. 729
HAYES MICROCOMPUTER PRODUCTS (CANADA) LTD.—Hayes Corporation; *U.S. Public*, pg. 801
HONEYWELL INC.; *U.S. Public*, pg. 833
HONEYWELL-MEASUREX (IRELAND) SERVICE LTD.—Honeywell Inc.; *U.S. Public*, pg. 833
IKON OFFICE SOLUTIONS—Ikon Office Solutions, Inc.; *U.S. Public*, pg. 863
INTERNATIONAL BUSINESS MACHINES CORPORATION; *U.S. Public*, pg. 895
MAGNETICS DATA, INC.—Magnetics Data Inc.; *U.S. Private*, pg. 696
NCR CORPORATION; *U.S. Public*, pg. 1146
NATIONSCREDIT COMMERCIAL CORPORATION—NationsBank Corporation; *U.S. Public*, pg. 1165
NETWORK SYSTEMS LIMITED—Storage Technology Corporation; *U.S. Public*, pg. 1522
NUMBER NINE VISUAL TECHNOLOGY; *U.S. Public*, pg. 1206
PERIPHONICS CORP.; *U.S. Public*, pg. 1278
RECON SERVICES, INC.—Computer Sales International Inc.; *U.S. Private*, pg. 260
SPR, INC.; *U.S. Public*, pg. 1419
SAND TECHNOLOGY SYSTEMS; *Int'l*, pg. 1183
SANDERSON TECHNOLOGY LTD.; *Int'l*, pg. 1184
SENTINEL TECHNOLOGIES INC.; *U.S. Private*, pg. 984
SIEMENS S.A.—Siemens AG; *Int'l*, pg. 1248
STRATUS COMPUTER, INC.; *U.S. Public*, pg. 1524
STRATUS COMPUTER, LTD.—Stratus Computer, Inc.; *U.S. Public*, pg. 1524
STRATUS COMPUTER PTY, LTD.—Stratus Computer, Inc.; *U.S. Public*, pg. 1524
STRATUS COMPUTER S.A.—Stratus Computer, Inc.; *U.S. Public*, pg. 1524
STRATUS JAPAN CO. LTD.—Stratus Computer, Inc.; *U.S. Public*, pg. 1524
T AND S SERVICOS INDUSTRIAS S/C LTDA.—Toshiba Corporation; *Int'l*, pg. 1406
THOMAINFOR—Thomson S.A.; *Int'l*, pg. 1383
UNISYS CORPORATION; *U.S. Public*, pg. 1671
THE VIRTUAL GROUP; *U.S. Private*, pg. 1141

7379 — COMPUTER RELATED SERVICES, NEC

ACEC-OSI—Tractebel; *Int'l*, pg. 1415
AFSA DATA CORP.—Fleet Financial Group, Inc.; *U.S. Public*, pg. 649
ASI LANDMARK, INC.—Analytical Surveys, Inc.; *U.S. Public*, pg. 110
AT&T ISTEL LIMITED—AT&T Corporation; *U.S. Public*, pg. 11
AERO SYSTEMS AVIATION CORP.; *U.S. Private*, pg. 24
AERO SYSTEMS ENGINEERING INC.—Celsius AB; *Int'l*, pg. 276
ALTERNATIVE RESOURCES CORPORATION; *U.S. Public*, pg. 59
AMDAHL CORPORATION—Fujitsu Limited; *Int'l*, pg. 527
AMERICAN MANAGEMENT SYSTEMS, INC.; *U.S. Public*, pg. 86
ANACOMP, INC.; *U.S. Public*, pg. 106
ANALYTICAL SURVEYS, INC.; *U.S. Public*, pg. 110
ANDOVER CONTROLS; *U.S. Private*, pg. 73
APERTUS TECHNOLOGIES INCORPORATED; *U.S. Public*, pg. 119
APPLICON INC.—Gores Technology Group; *U.S. Private*, pg. 465
ARKANSAS BEST CORPORATION; *U.S. Public*, pg. 130
AUTOMATED WAGERING—Power House Technologies, Inc.; *U.S. Public*, pg. 1319
AUTOMATIC DATA PROCESSING, INC.; *U.S. Public*, pg. 150
BDM INTERNATIONAL, INC.—TRW Inc.; *U.S. Public*, pg. 1558
BGS SYSTEMS, INC.; *U.S. Public*, pg. 161
BRC HOLDINGS; *U.S. Public*, pg. 163
BARNETT TECHNOLOGIES, INC.—NationsBank Corporation; *U.S. Public*, pg. 1162
BAYBANKS, INC.—BankBoston Corporation; *U.S. Public*, pg. 184
BELLSOUTH NETWORK SOLUTIONS, INC.—BellSouth Corporation; *U.S. Public*, pg. 209
BOOLE & BABBAGE, INC.; *U.S. Public*, pg. 244
BRODART COMPANY; *U.S. Private*, pg. 170
BUSINESS INFORMATION TECHNOLOGY—Ciber, Inc.; *U.S. Public*, pg. 356
CAE ELEKTRONIK GMBH—CAE Inc.; *Int'l*, pg. 238
CB COMPUTER SERVICES GMBH—The Chase Manhattan Corporation; *U.S. Public*, pg. 339
C.E. SERVICES—Fujitsu Limited; *Int'l*, pg. 527
CEM COMPUTERS LIMITED—Siemens AG; *Int'l*, pg. 1247
CSC FINANCIAL SERVICES GROUP—Computer Sciences Corporation; *U.S. Public*, pg. 422
CUC INTERNATIONAL, INC.—Cendant Corporation; *U.S. Public*, pg. 320
CXR SA—Microtel International Inc.; *U.S. Public*, pg. 1108
CAP GEMINI S.A.; *Int'l*, pg. 263
CELSIUS INVEST AB—Celsius AB; *Int'l*, pg. 276
CENDANT CORPORATION; *U.S. Public*, pg. 320
CHIPS AND TECHNOLOGIES, INC.; *U.S. Public*, pg. 349
THE CHUBB INSTITUTE—The Chubb Corporation; *U.S. Public*, pg. 355
CIBER, INC.; *U.S. Public*, pg. 356
CINCINNATI BELL INFORMATION SYSTEMS INC.—Cincinnati Bell Telephone; *U.S. Public*, pg. 367
COLUMBINE JDS SYSTEMS, INC.—Big Flower Press Holdings, Inc.; *U.S. Public*, pg. 228
COMDISCO, INC.; *U.S. Public*, pg. 407
COMPUSERVE INTERACTIVE SERVICES, INC.—America Online Incorporated; *U.S. Public*, pg. 66
COMPUTER CORPORATION OF AMERICA; *U.S. Private*, pg. 260
COMPUTER METHODS CORPORATION; *U.S. Private*, pg. 260
COMPUTER SCIENCES CORPORATION; *U.S. Public*, pg. 422
COMPUTING DEVICES CO. LTD.—Ceridian Corporation; *U.S. Public*, pg. 331
COMPUWARE CORPORATION; *U.S. Public*, pg. 423
COMSHARE, INCORPORATED; *U.S. Public*, pg. 425
CONCORD EFS, INC.; *U.S. Public*, pg. 429
CONCURRENT COMPUTER CORPORATION; *U.S. Public*, pg. 430
DMR CONSULTING GROUP, INC.—Fujitsu Limited; *Int'l*, pg. 527
DMR GROUP, INC.—Fujitsu Limited; *Int'l*, pg. 527
DSM N.V.; *Int'l*, pg. 352
DATA COMMUNICATIONS & NETWORKS—Northern Telecom Limited; *Int'l*, pg. 969
DATA GENERAL CUSTOMER SERVICE DIVISION—Data General Corporation; *U.S. Public*, pg. 485
DATABASE AMERICA COMPANIES; *U.S. Private*, pg. 312
DATAGEN, INC.—Data General Corporation; *U.S. Public*, pg. 485
DATAPRODUCTS INTERNATIONAL LTD.—Hitachi Koki Co., Ltd.; *Int'l*, pg. 621
DATAPRODUCTS S.A.R.L.—Hitachi Koki Co., Ltd.; *Int'l*, pg. 621
DATASPHERE, INC.—Construction Specialties, Inc.; *U.S. Private*, pg. 266
DATATEAM DANMARK A/S—Axel Johnson AB; *Int'l*, pg. 710
DECISION SYSTEMS INTERNATIONAL SPA—Olivetti SpA; *Int'l*, pg. 1002
DESIGN DATA, INC.—Data General Corporation; *U.S. Public*, pg. 485
DETECTOR ELECTRONICS CORPORATION—Williams Holdings Plc; *Int'l*, pg. 1500
DIGITAL EQUIPMENT CORPORATION; *U.S. Public*, pg. 507
DIGITAL TYPEFACE CORPORATION—LaserMaster Technologies, Inc.; *U.S. Public*, pg. 979
DISTRIBUTED SYSTEMS DIVISION—Storage Technology Corporation; *U.S. Public*, pg. 1522
DOW JONES MARKETS—Dow Jones & Company, Inc.; *U.S. Public*, pg. 525
DOW JONES TELERATE HOLDINGS, INC.—Dow Jones & Company, Inc.; *U.S. Public*, pg. 525
DURATEK CORPORATION—GP Strategies Corporation; *U.S. Public*, pg. 694
DYNAMICS RESEARCH CORPORATION; *U.S. Public*, pg. 539
EG & G STRUCTURAL KINEMATICS—EG & G, Inc.; *U.S. Public*, pg. 544
EMC CORPORATION; *U.S. Public*, pg. 545
EMS-MICHIGAN—Effective Management Systems; *U.S. Public*, pg. 565
EARTH TECHNOLOGY CORP.—Tyco International Ltd.; *U.S. Public*, pg. 1648
ECONOCOM-USA INC.; *U.S. Private*, pg. 361

EFFECTIVE MANAGEMENT SYSTEMS; U.S. Public, pg. 565
ENTERPRISE SERVICE SOLUTIONS—Genicom Corporation; U.S. Public, pg. 729
EQUIFAX CHECK SERVICE—Equifax Inc.; U.S. Public, pg. 588
EUROPEAN GROUP—Computer Sciences Corporation; U.S. Public, pg. 423
FDP CORP.; U.S. Public, pg. 603
FINANCIAL DATA PLANNING CORP.—FDP Corp.; U.S. Public, pg. 603
FIRST DATA CORPORATION; U.S. Public, pg. 630
FORE SYSTEMS, INC.; U.S. Public, pg. 667
GDE SYSTEMS, INC.—Tracor, Inc.; U.S. Public, pg. 1627
GE CAPITAL/IT SOLUTIONS—General Electric Company; U.S. Public, pg. 711
GEONEX—Geonex Corporation; U.S. Private, pg. 448
GOLDEN BOOKS FAMILY ENTERTAINMENT INC.; U.S. Public, pg. 749
GORES TECHNOLOGY GROUP; U.S. Private, pg. 465
GREAT AMERICAN MANAGEMENT SERVICES, INC.—American Financial Group; U.S. Public, pg. 75
HBO & COMPANY/CYCARE BUSINESS GROUP—HBOC; U.S. Public, pg. 770
HADRON, INC.; U.S. Public, pg. 773
JACK HENRY & ASSOCIATES, INC.; U.S. Public, pg. 808
HEWLETT-PACKARD COMPANY; U.S. Public, pg. 813
HOGAN SYSTEMS, INC.—Computer Sciences Corporation; U.S. Public, pg. 422
HOSPITAL DATA PROCESSING—Columbia/HCA Healthcare Corporation; U.S. Public, pg. 405
IBM APPLICATION SOLUTIONS—International Business Machines Corporation; U.S. Public, pg. 895
IBM SYSTEMS INTEGRATION DIV.—International Business Machines Corporation; U.S. Public, pg. 896
IFI/PLENUM DATA CORPORATION—Plenum Publishing Corporation; U.S. Public, pg. 1311
INACOM CORP.; U.S. Public, pg. 873
INBAR COMPUTER TRAINING LTD.—Onyx Technologies Ltd.; Int'l, pg. 1007
INFORMIX SOFTWARE; U.S. Public, pg. 876
INTEGRAL SYSTEMS, INC.—CSA Holdings Ltd.; Int'l, pg. 242
INTERET CORPORATION; U.S. Private, pg. 567
INTERNATIONAL BUSINESS MACHINES CORPORATION; U.S. Public, pg. 895
INTERNATIONAL COMPUTER SERVICES, INC.—American International Group, Inc.; U.S. Public, pg. 84
JEUMONT-SCHNEIDER TRENFORMETEURS; Int'l, pg. 706
KING GROUP, INC.; U.S. Private, pg. 620
KLEINSCHMIDT INC.; U.S. Private, pg. 625
LAKE BUSINESS PRODUCTS, INC.; U.S. Private, pg. 643
LANDISC SYSTEMS—Day & Zimmermann, Inc.; U.S. Private, pg. 317
LEXIS LAW PUBLISHING—Reed Elsevier plc; Int'l, pg. 1096
LEXIS-NEXIS—Reed Elsevier plc; Int'l, pg. 1096
LOGICA SA/NV—Logica Plc; Int'l, pg. 815
LOGICA UK LTD.—Logica Plc; Int'l, pg. 814
LOGICON, INC.—Northrop Grumman Corporation; U.S. Public, pg. 1198
MCI INTERNATIONAL INC.—MCI Communications Corp.; U.S. Public, pg. 1024
MCRB SERVICE BUREAU, INC.; U.S. Private, pg. 686
MAPFRE SERVICIOS INFORMATICA, S.A.—Corporacion MAPFRE, Compania Internacional de Reaseguros, S.A.; Int'l, pg. 333
MAPTEL, S.A.—Telefonica de Espana, S.A.; Int'l, pg. 1372
AC MARTIN PARTNERS; U.S. Private, pg. 708
MATSUSHITA SERVICES CO. DIV.—Matsushita Electric Industrial Co., Ltd.; Int'l, pg. 847
THE MAXIMA CORPORATION; U.S. Private, pg. 716
MAY & SPEH, INC.; U.S. Public, pg. 1063
MERRILL CORPORATION; U.S. Public, pg. 1097
METLIFE CAPITAL HOLDINGS, INC.—Metropolitan Life Insurance Co.; U.S. Private, pg. 737
MICROSOFT CONSULTING SERVICES—Microsoft Corporation; U.S. Public, pg. 1108
MITCHELL INTERNATIONAL—The Thomson Corporation; U.S. Public, pg. 1601
MOBIL DATA SERVICES, LTD.—Mobil Oil Corporation; U.S. Public, pg. 1119
MONEY MANAGEMENT SYSTEMS, INC.—SunGard Data Systems Inc.; U.S. Public, pg. 1535
NCR CORPORATION; U.S. Public, pg. 1146
NATIONSCREDIT COMMERCIAL CORPORATION—NationsBank Corporation; U.S. Public, pg. 1165
A.C. NIELSEN; U.S. Public, pg. 1183
A.C. NIELSEN COMPANY—A.C. Nielsen; U.S. Public, pg. 1183
NISSHO ELECTRONICS CORP.—Nissho Iwai Corporation; Int'l, pg. 946
NORDIC SYSTEMS, LTD.—Flambeau Corporation; U.S. Private, pg. 410
NORTHERN TELECOM CANADA LIMITED, TELECOM SERVICES DIV.—Northern Telecom Limited; Int'l, pg. 969
NORTHWESTERN SYSTEMS, INC.—Northwestern Public Service; U.S. Public, pg. 1201
O/E AUTOMATION, INC.; U.S. Private, pg. 809
OLIVETTI SPA; Int'l, pg. 1002
ONYX INTERACTIVE MULTIMEDIA LTD.—Onyx Technologies Ltd.; Int'l, pg. 1007
ONYX TECHNOLOGIES LTD.; Int'l, pg. 1007
PHH CORPORATION—Cendant Corporation; U.S. Public, pg. 321
PRC, INC.—Litton Industries, Inc.; U.S. Public, pg. 1003
PACKARD BELL NEC; U.S. Private, pg. 833
PAR GOVERNMENT SYSTEMS CORPORATION—PAR Technology Corporation; U.S. Public, pg. 1256
PAR MICROSYSTEMS CORPORATION—PAR Technology Corporation; U.S. Public, pg. 1256
PAR TECHNOLOGY CORPORATION; U.S. Public, pg. 1256
PHASE3 SYSTEMS INC.—SunGard Data Systems Inc.; U.S. Public, pg. 1535
PRIMARK CORPORATION; U.S. Public, pg. 1325
PRODIGY INC.; U.S. Private, pg. 888
PROFESSIONAL INFORMATION MANAGMENT—Seligman & Associates, Inc.; U.S. Private, pg. 982
QUALITY SYSTEMS INC.—Tracor, Inc.; U.S. Public, pg. 1627
QUICK CORP.—Nihon Keizai Shimbun, Inc.; Int'l, pg. 929
QUIXX CORPORATION—New Century Energies, Inc.; U.S. Public, pg. 1170
RACAL ELECTRONICS PLC; Int'l, pg. 1082
RESEARCH DATA CORP—U.M. Holding Limited; U.S. Private, pg. 1114
SBE, INC.; U.S. Public, pg. 1416
SPR, INC.; U.S. Public, pg. 1419
SRS TECHNOLOGIES; U.S. Private, pg. 958
SAFIRE PRIVATE LIMITED—Cigna Corp.; U.S. Public, pg. 363
SANDERSON COMPUTERS HONG KONG LTD.—Sanderson Technology Ltd.; Int'l, pg. 1185
SANDERSON COMPUTERS PTE. LTD.—Sanderson Technology Ltd.; Int'l, pg. 1185
SANDERSON TECHNOLOGY LTD.; Int'l, pg. 1184
SCHLUMBERGER SATELLITE—Schlumberger Limited; U.S. Public, pg. 1439
SCIENCE MANAGEMENT CORPORATION—Versar Inc.; U.S. Public, pg. 1717
SHAW DATA SERVICES—SunGard Data Systems Inc.; U.S. Public, pg. 1534
SIEMENS-NIXDORF INFORMATIONSSYSTEME AG—Siemens AG; Int'l, pg. 1245
SIMON-DIASOL—Simon Engineering plc; Int'l, pg. 1251
SIMON PETROLEUM TECHNOLOGY LTD.—Simon Engineering plc; Int'l, pg. 1251
SPECTRAL—Jeumont-Schneider Trenformeteurs; Int'l, pg. 706
STRATEGIC SYSTEMS INTERNATIONAL LIMITED—Powell Duffryn PLC; Int'l, pg. 1065
SUN DATA INC.; U.S. Private, pg. 1050
SUNGARD DATA SYSTEMS INC.; U.S. Public, pg. 1534
SUNGARD FINANCIAL SYSTEMS, INC.—SunGard Data Systems Inc.; U.S. Public, pg. 1534
SUNGARD INVESTMENT SYSTEMS INC.—SunGard Data Systems Inc.; U.S. Public, pg. 1535
SUNGARD RECOVERY SERVICES GROUP—SunGard Data Systems Inc.; U.S. Public, pg. 1535
SUNGARD SHAREHOLDER SYSTEMS INC.—SunGard Data Systems Inc.; U.S. Public, pg. 1535
SUNGARD TRADING SYSTEMS GROUP—SunGard Data Systems Inc.; U.S. Public, pg. 1535
SUNGARD TRUST & SHAREHOLDER SYSTEMS GROUP—SunGard Data Systems Inc.; U.S. Public, pg. 1535
SUNGARD TRUST SYSTEMS INC.—SunGard Data Systems Inc.; U.S. Public, pg. 1535
SUNRISE LEASING CORPORATION; U.S. Public, pg. 1535
SUPPORT SYSTEMS ASSOCIATES, INC.; U.S. Private, pg. 1056
SYNDICATED OFFICE SYSTEMS, INC.—Tenet Healthcare Corporation; U.S. Public, pg. 1577
SYSTEM SOFTWARE ASSOCIATES, INC.; U.S. Public, pg. 1552
SYSTEMS STRATEGIES, INC.—Apertus Technologies Incorporated; U.S. Public, pg. 120
TANDY CORPORATION; U.S. Public, pg. 1560
TANO AUTOMATION, INC.—Westwood Corporation; U.S. Public, pg. 1763
TECHNOLOGY MANAGEMENT GROUP—Computer Sciences Corporation; U.S. Public, pg. 423
TECHNOLOGY TRANSFER INSTITUTE; U.S. Private, pg. 1072
TELECREDIT SERVICE CORP.—Equifax Inc.; U.S. Public, pg. 588
TELUB AB—Celsius AB; Int'l, pg. 277
TELUB TEKNIK AB—Celsius AB; Int'l, pg. 278
TEXTRON SYSTEMS—Textron Inc.; U.S. Public, pg. 1589
TOSHIBA OA CONSULTANTS LTD.—Toshiba Corporation; Int'l, pg. 1404
TRACE MOUNTAIN PRODUCTS; U.S. Private, pg. 1095
TRACOR, INC.; U.S. Public, pg. 1627
TRANSNET CORPORATION; U.S. Public, pg. 1631
U.M. HOLDING LIMITED; U.S. Private, pg. 1113
UNISYS CORPORATION; U.S. Public, pg. 1671
VEDA INCORPORATED—Veridian; U.S. Private, pg. 1136
WSA SYSTEMS & SERVICES, INC.—Data General Corporation; U.S. Public, pg. 485
WANG LABORATORIES, INC.; U.S. Public, pg. 1737
WANG (UK) LIMITED—Wang Laboratories, Inc.; U.S. Public, pg. 1738
WARRINGTON FINANCIAL SYSTEMS INC.—SunGard Data Systems Inc.; U.S. Public, pg. 1535
WESTWOOD CORPORATION; U.S. Public, pg. 1763
THE WHEATLEY GROUP, INC.—Avemco Corporation; U.S. Public, pg. 152
XEROX ENGINEERING SYSTEMS DIVISION—Xerox Corporation; U.S. Public, pg. 1784
ZIFF TECHNOLOGIES—Softbank Corporation; Int'l, pg. 1276

7381 — DETECTIVE, GUARD & ARMORED CAR SERVICES

APG SECURITY, INC.; U.S. Private, pg. 7
ADVANCE SECURITY—U.S. Security Associates, Inc.; U.S. Private, pg. 1126
ALLIED SECURITY, INC.; U.S. Private, pg. 40
ALVIS VEHICLES LIMITED—Alvis plc; Int'l, pg. 70
AMERICAN COMMERCIAL SECURITY & INVESTIGATIVE SERVICES—ABM Industries; U.S. Public, pg. 2
BRAMBLES SECURITIES SERVICES LIMITED—Brambles Industries Limited; Int'l, pg. 211
BRAMBLES SECURITY SERVICES INC.—Brambles Industries Limited; Int'l, pg. 211
BRAMBLES USA INC.—Brambles Industries Limited; Int'l, pg. 211
BRINKS-ALLIED—Arnotts plc; Int'l, pg. 81
BRINK'S, INC.—The Pittston Company; U.S. Public, pg. 1305
CENTRAL SECURITY GUARDS, INC.—Tyco International Ltd.; U.S. Public, pg. 1649
CHAMBERS USA WASTE, INC.—USA Waste Services, Inc.; U.S. Public, pg. 1686
COLIN SERVICE SYSTEMS, INC.; U.S. Private, pg. 252
DEFENDER SERVICES, INC.; U.S. Private, pg. 320
DIVERSCO, INC.; U.S. Private, pg. 336
GKN DEFENCE LTD.—GKN plc; Int'l, pg. 534
GLOVER WEBB LTD.—GKN plc; Int'l, pg. 535
GUARDIAN ALARM CO.; U.S. Private, pg. 485
GUARDSMARK, INC.; U.S. Private, pg. 486
HONG KONG SECURITY LTD.—Jardine Matheson Holdings Limited; Int'l, pg. 704
ISS SECURISYSTEM GESMBH—Veba AG; Int'l, pg. 1458
INMOBILIARIA WACKENHUT, S.A. DE C.V.—The Wackenhut Corporation; U.S. Public, pg. 1731
INTERCON SECURITY LIMITED—Jannock Limited; Int'l, pg. 699
JARDINE MATHESON HOLDINGS LIMITED; Int'l, pg. 703
JARDINE SECURICOR LTD.—Jardine Matheson Holdings Limited; Int'l, pg. 705
KINDERGARD—Mace Security International, Inc.; U.S. Public, pg. 1030
MARK LIPMAN DIV.—Guardsmark, Inc.; U.S. Private, pg. 486
LOOMIS-FARGO & CO.—Borg-Warner Security Corporation; U.S. Public, pg. 245
OBAYASHI CORPORATION; Int'l, pg. 995
PINKERTON'S INC.; U.S. Public, pg. 1296
THE PITTSTON COMPANY; U.S. Public, pg. 1305
RICE FOOD MARKETS INC.; U.S. Private, pg. 927
SEARCH ORGANIZATION DE SEGURIDAD, S.A.—The Wackenhut Corporation; U.S. Public, pg. 1731
SECURAIR LTD.—Jardine Matheson Holdings Limited; Int'l, pg. 705
SEGURIDAD MOVIL DEL ECUADOR, S.A.—The Wackenhut Corporation; U.S. Public, pg. 1731
SEQURIDAD TECNICA, S.A.—The Wackenhut Corporation; U.S. Public, pg. 1731
SERVICES SECURIVOL INC.—The Jean Coutu Group (PJC) Inc.; Int'l, pg. 340
SHIELD SECURITY, INC.; U.S. Private, pg. 994
STANLEY SMITH SECURITY, INC.—Sophus Berendsen A/S; Int'l, pg. 1286
SPARTAN SECURITY SERVICES—Temco Service Industries; U.S. Public, pg. 1574
U.S. SECURITY ASSOCIATES, INC.; U.S. Private, pg. 1126
VSK GROUP—Allied Research Corporation; U.S. Public, pg. 49
THE WACKENHUT CORPORATION; U.S. Public, pg. 1731

7382 — SECURITY SYSTEMS SERVICES

ADT DIVERSIFIED SERVICES, INC.—Tyco International Ltd.; U.S. Public, pg. 1649
ADT GREECE, S.A.—Tyco International Ltd.; U.S. Public, pg. 1649
ADT ITALIANA, S.P.A.—Tyco International Ltd.; U.S. Public, pg. 1649
ADT/PROEGUR, S.A.—Tyco International Ltd.; U.S. Public, pg. 1649
ADT SECURITY SERVICES, INC.—Tyco International Ltd.; U.S. Public, pg. 1649
ADT SECURITY SYSTEMS—Tyco International Ltd.; U.S. Public, pg. 1649
AFA PROTECTIVE SYSTEMS, INC.; U.S. Public, pg. 5
ARI GROUP EUROPE—Tyco International Ltd.; U.S. Public, pg. 1650
ADVANCE SECURITY—U.S. Security Associates, Inc.; U.S. Private, pg. 1126
ALARMGUARD HOLDINGS, INC.; U.S. Public, pg. 35
ALLIED RESEARCH CORPORATION; U.S. Public, pg. 48
AMERICAN COMMERCIAL SECURITY & INVESTIGATIVE SERVICES—ABM Industries; U.S. Public, pg. 2
AMERITECH—Ameritech Corporation; U.S. Public, pg. 97
ANTARES GROUP INC.; U.S. Private, pg. 76
ASAHI BANK BUILDING MAINTENANCE CO., LTD.—The Asahi Bank, Ltd.; Int'l, pg. 82
ATLANTIC WORKS—Lucent Technologies Inc.; U.S. Public, pg. 1017
BEL-AIR PATROL—Borg-Warner Security Corporation; U.S. Public, pg. 245
BENDIX SECURITY SYSTEMS—AlliedSignal Inc.; U.S. Public, pg. 51
BORG-WARNER PROTECTIVE SERVICES CORPORATION—Borg-Warner Security Corporation; U.S. Public, pg. 245
BORG-WARNER SECURITY CORPORATION; U.S. Public, pg. 245
BRINK'S HOME SECURITY, INC.—The Pittston Company; U.S. Public, pg. 1305
CHUBB HONG KONG LTD.—Jardine Matheson Holdings Limited; Int'l, pg. 705
CODE-ALARM, INC.; U.S. Public, pg. 393
CONSTRUCTIVE COMMUNICATIONS, INC.—Tyco International Ltd.; U.S. Public, pg. 1649
DESIGN SECURITY INC.—Detex Corporation; U.S. Private, pg. 328
EPEX GROUP—Alcatel Alsthom Compagnie Generale D'Electricite; Int'l, pg. 52
ELECTRIC PROTECTION SERVICES (EPS)—Tyco International Ltd.; U.S. Public, pg. 1650
ELECTRO PROTECTION SERVICES/CEPS—Tyco International Ltd.; U.S. Public, pg. 1650

EUROPE AUTO EQUIPMENT—Code-Alarm, Inc.; *U.S. Public*, pg. 394
FOLGER ADAM SECURITY INC.; *U.S. Private*, pg. 416
FORE LINE SECURITY—Reeves Southeastern Corporation; *U.S. Private*, pg. 917
FORTRESS SECURITY PTY LIMITED—Halma p.l.c.; *Int'l*, pg. 590
FUJITSU TEN CORP. OF AMERICA—Fujitsu Limited; *Int'l*, pg. 526
GUARDIAN ALARM CO.; *U.S. Private*, pg. 485
GUARDSMARK, INC.; *U.S. Private*, pg. 486
GYYR, INC.—Odetics Inc.; *U.S. Public*, pg. 1212
H F SECURITE S.A.—Halma p.l.c.; *Int'l*, pg. 590
HALMA P.L.C.; *Int'l*, pg. 589
HOLMES PROTECTION GROUP, INC.—Tyco International Ltd.; *U.S. Public*, pg. 1649
HONEYWELL INC.; *U.S. Public*, pg. 833
ISS ENERGY SERVICES, INC.—ISS-International Service System A/S; *Int'l*, pg. 656
ISS MALL SERVICES, INC.—ISS-International Service System A/S; *Int'l*, pg. 656
ISS SECURISYSTEM GESMBH—Veba AG; *Int'l*, pg. 1458
ILCO UNICAN (U.K.) LTD.—Unican Security Systems Ltd.; *Int'l*, pg. 1432
INTER-GLOBE SECURITY SERVICES LTD.—Hanson PLC; *Int'l*, pg. 593
JARDINE MATHESON HOLDINGS LIMITED; *Int'l*, pg. 703
KASTLE SYSTEMS LLC; *U.S. Private*, pg. 608
LEASING SERVICES CORP.—Novar Electronics; *U.S. Private*, pg. 808
LEVY SECURITY CORP.; *U.S. Private*, pg. 664
MOSLER INC.; *U.S. Private*, pg. 763
MUL-T-LOCK GROUP—IDB Holding Corporation; *Int'l*, pg. 644
ODETICS INC.; *U.S. Public*, pg. 1212
PEDUS BUILDING SERVICES—Pedus Services, Inc.; *U.S. Private*, pg. 846
PEDUS SECURITY SERVICES—Pedus Services, Inc.; *U.S. Private*, pg. 846
PEDUS SERVICES, INC.; *U.S. Private*, pg. 846
PERUANA DE SEGURIDAD Y VIGILANCIA, S.A. (PESEVISA)—The Wackenhut Corporation; *U.S. Public*, pg. 1731
PHARMACIA & UPJOHN DATA AB—Pharmacia & Upjohn, Inc.; *Int'l*, pg. 1048
THE PITTSTON COMPANY; *U.S. Public*, pg. 1305
PLETTAC AG; *Int'l*, pg. 1061
PROTECTION TECHNOLOGY—Day & Zimmermann, Inc.; *U.S. Private*, pg. 317
RMS TECHS, INC.; *U.S. Private*, pg. 905
ROLLINS, INC.; *U.S. Public*, pg. 1404
SLC TECHNOLOGIES—Berwind Corporation; *U.S. Private*, pg. 138
SAFE ALARM, INC.; *U.S. Private*, pg. 960
SAFETY 1ST, INC.; *U.S. Public*, pg. 1425
SECOM CO., LTD.; *Int'l*, pg. 1217
SECOMERICA, INC.—Secom Co., Ltd.; *Int'l*, pg. 1217
SECURITYLINK FROM AMERITECH—Ameritech Corporation; *U.S. Public*, pg. 98
SHORROCK MILITARY SYSTEMS INC.—Sophus Berendsen A/S; *Int'l*, pg. 1286
SIMPLEX TIME RECORDER CO.; *U.S. Private*, pg. 1002
TOTAL SECURITY SOLUTIONS—Borg-Warner Security Corporation; *U.S. Public*, pg. 245
TYCO INTERNATIONAL LTD.—Tyco International Ltd.; *U.S. Public*, pg. 1648
UNIVERSAL SECURITY INSTRUMENTS INC.; *U.S. Public*, *pg. 1697*
VOLUMATIC LIMITED—Halma p.l.c.; *Int'l*, pg. 590
WACKENHUT AIRLINE SERVICES, INC.—The Wackenhut Corporation; *U.S. Public*, pg. 1731
THE WACKENHUT CORPORATION; *U.S. Public*, pg. 1731
WACKENHUT SECURITY (HELLAS), LTD.—The Wackenhut Corporation; *U.S. Public*, pg. 1732
WELLS FARGO ALARM SERVICES, INC.—Borg-Warner Security Corporation; *U.S. Public*, pg. 246
WESTEC SECURITY INC.—Secom Co., Ltd.; *Int'l*, pg. 1217

7383 — NEWS SYNDICATES

ABC NEWS & SPORTS—The Walt Disney Company; *U.S. Public*, pg. 511
ABC NEWS, INC.—The Walt Disney Company; *U.S. Public*, pg. 511
ADVERTISING CHECKING BUREAU INCORPORATED; *U.S. Private*, pg. 23
AGENCIA EFE, S.A.—Telefonica de Espana, S.A.; *Int'l*, pg. 1372
THE ASSOCIATED PRESS; *U.S. Private*, pg. 92
ASSOCIATED PRESS—The Associated Press; *U.S. Private*, *pg. 92*
DOW JONES & COMPANY, INC.; *U.S. Public*, pg. 524
DOW JONES CANADA, INC.—Dow Jones & Company, Inc.; *U.S. Public*, pg. 525
INDEPENDENT RADIO FEATURES LIMITED—Dow Jones & Company, Inc.; *U.S. Public*, pg. 525
KRT NEWS & INFORMATION SERVICES—Knight-Ridder, Inc.; *U.S. Public*, pg. 965
KNIGHT-RIDDER, INC.; *U.S. Public*, pg. 963
LEBHAR-FRIEDMAN, INC.; *U.S. Private*, pg. 656
LONDON BUREAU LTD.—The New York Times Company; *U.S. Public*, pg. 1176
LOS ANGELES TIMES SYNDICATE—The Times Mirror Company; *U.S. Public*, pg. 1616
LOS ANGELES TIMES-WASHINGTON POST NEWS SERVICE, INC.—The Washington Post Company; *U.S. Public*, pg. 1743
THE MCGRAW-HILL COMPANIES; *U.S. Public*, pg. 1069
THE NEW YORK TIMES SYNDICATION SALES CORPORATION—The New York Times Company; *U.S. Public*, pg. 1174
NORTH AMERICA SYNDICATE, INC.—The Hearst Corporation; *U.S. Private*, pg. 515
P.R. NEWSWIRE ASSOCIATION INC.—United News & Media plc; *Int'l*, pg. 1443
RADIOCOR TELERATE S.P.A.—Dow Jones & Company, Inc.; *U.S. Public*, pg. 525
REUTERS AG—Reuters Holdings PLC; *Int'l*, pg. 1105
REUTERS AMERICA INC.—Reuters Holdings PLC; *Int'l*, pg. 1106
REUTERS AUSTRALIA PTY. LTD.—Reuters Holdings PLC; *Int'l*, pg. 1105
REUTERS HOLDINGS PLC; *Int'l*, pg. 1105
REUTERS HONG KONG LIMITED—Reuters Holdings PLC; *Int'l*, pg. 1105
REUTERS ITALIA SPA—Reuters Holdings PLC; *Int'l*, pg. 1105
REUTERS JAPAN KABUSHIKI KAISHA—Reuters Holdings PLC; *Int'l*, pg. 1105
REUTERS LIMITED—Reuters Holdings PLC; *Int'l*, pg. 1105
REUTERS SA—Reuters Holdings PLC; *Int'l*, pg. 1105
REUTERS SERVICES SARL—Reuters Holdings PLC; *Int'l*, pg. 1105
REUTERS SINGAPORE PTE LIMITED—Reuters Holdings PLC; *Int'l*, pg. 1106
REUTERS TELEVISION LIMITED—Reuters Holdings PLC; *Int'l*, pg. 1105
SATELLITE DATA BROADCAST NETWORKS, INC. (SATNET)—The Associated Press; *U.S. Private*, pg. 92
THE E.W. SCRIPPS COMPANY; *U.S. Public*, pg. 1447
TRIBUNE COMPANY; *U.S. Public*, pg. 1635
TRIBUNE MEDIA SERVICES, INC.—Tribune Company; *U.S. Public*, pg. 1636
UNITED MEDIA CANADA—The E.W. Scripps Company; *U.S. Public*, pg. 1448
UNITED MEDIA EUROPE/SCRIPPS—The E.W. Scripps Company; *U.S. Public*, pg. 1448
UNITED MEDIA JAPAN—The E.W. Scripps Company; *U.S. Public*, pg. 1448
VNU BUSINESS INFORMATION EUROPE—VNU Verenigde Nederlandse Uitgeversbedrijven B.V.; *Int'l*, pg. 1445
WIDE WORLD PHOTOS, INC.—The Associated Press; *U.S. Private*, pg. 92

7384 — PHOTOFINISHING LABORATORIES

AMERICAN PHOTO GROUP—Eastman Kodak Company; *U.S. Public*, pg. 551
ANDREWS GROUP, INCORPORATED—MacAndrews & Forbes Holdings Inc.; *U.S. Private*, pg. 689
AVID TECHNOLOGY, INC.; *U.S. Public*, pg. 154
CPI CORP.; *U.S. Public*, pg. 283
CINE MAGNETICS, INC.; *U.S. Private*, pg. 240
DEAN'S GRAND CANYON PHOTOS—Dean's Photo Service; *U.S. Private*, pg. 319
DEAN'S PHOTO SERVICE; *U.S. Private*, pg. 319
DIXONS STORES GROUP LTD.—Dixons Group plc; *Int'l*, pg. 414
FOTOLABO CLUB (FRANCE) S.A.—Fotolabo S.A.; *Int'l*, pg. 501
FOTOLABO CLUB S.A.—Fotolabo S.A.; *Int'l*, pg. 501
FOTOLABO S.A.; *Int'l*, pg. 501
FOUR MEDIA COMPANIES; *U.S. Private*, pg. 422
FOX PHOTO, INC.—CPI Corp.; *U.S. Public*, pg. 283
FOX PHOTO, INC.—Eastman Kodak Company; *U.S. Public*, *pg. 551*
GENOVESE DRUG STORES, INC.; *U.S. Public*, pg. 730
GREAT LAKES TECHNOLOGIES CORP.; *U.S. Private*, pg. 475
GUARDIAN INDUSTRIES CORP.; *U.S. Private*, pg. 485
JOSTENS; *U.S. Public*, pg. 934
KODAK & H-COLOR A/S—Eastman Kodak Company; *U.S. Public*, pg. 552
KODAK A/S—Eastman Kodak Company; *U.S. Public*, pg. 552
KODAK IMAGICA K.K. (KI)—Eastman Kodak Company; *U.S. Public*, pg. 555
KODAK KOREA LTD.—Eastman Kodak Company; *U.S. Public*, pg. 555
KODAK PROCESSING LABORATORIES—Eastman Kodak Company; *U.S. Public*, pg. 551
KODAK S.A.—Eastman Kodak Company; *U.S. Public*, pg. 554
KODAK (THAILAND) LTD.—Eastman Kodak Company; *U.S. Public*, pg. 555
KONICA PHOTO SERVICE U.S.A., INC.—Konica Corporation; *Int'l*, pg. 748
LIVING COLOR DIV.—Genovese Drug Stores, Inc.; *U.S. Public*, pg. 730
MACANDREWS & FORBES HOLDINGS INC.; *U.S. Private*, *pg. 689*
MOTO PHOTO, INC.; *U.S. Public*, pg. 1136
MYSTIC COLOR LAB, INC.—Fotolabo S.A.; *Int'l*, pg. 501
NASHUA CORPORATION; *U.S. Public*, pg. 1152
NASHUA PHOTO DELMONT LTD.—Nashua Corporation; *U.S. Public*, pg. 1152
NASHUA PHOTO LIMITED—Nashua Corporation; *U.S. Public*, pg. 1152
PCA INTERNATIONAL, INC.; *U.S. Public*, pg. 1240
PACIFIC FILM LABORATORIES—Eastman Kodak Company; *U.S. Public*, pg. 552
QUALEX INC.—Eastman Kodak Company; *U.S. Public*, pg. 551
RADIO TV STEINER AG—Coop Switzerland; *Int'l*, pg. 330
SCHOOL PRODUCTS GROUP—Jostens; *U.S. Public*, pg. 934
THE STOP & SHOP COMPANIES, INC.—Koninklijke Ahold NV; *Int'l*, pg. 750

7389 — BUSINESS SERVICES, NEC

A&M RECORDS—Philips Electronics N.V.; *Int'l*, pg. 1052
ABC, INC—The Walt Disney Company; *U.S. Public*, pg. 511
ACI TELECENTRICS, INC.; *U.S. Public*, pg. 3
ACI TELECENTRICS INC.—ACI Telecentrics, Inc.; *U.S. Public*, pg. 3
AT&T LANGUAGE LINE SERVICES—AT&T Corporation; *U.S. Public*, pg. 11
ATC COMMUNICATIONS GROUP, INC.; *U.S. Public*, pg. 11
AVO MULTI-AMP SERVICES CORP.—TBG Management S.A.M.; *Int'l*, pg. 1335
AVW AUDIOVISUAL, INC.—Freeman Decorating Co.; *U.S. Private*, pg. 426
ABLE TRANSLATIONS LIMITED—Berlitz International, Inc.; *U.S. Public*, pg. 221
ADVANCED SEPARATION TECHNOLOGIES INCORPORATED—Florida Progress Corporation; *U.S. Public*, pg. 655
AFFILIATED BUILDING SERVICES, INC.—Compagnie Generale Des Eaux; *Int'l*, pg. 322
AIR CALL COMMUNICATIONS LTD.—Vodafone Group PLC; *Int'l*, pg. 1470
ALLEGHENY GEAR CORPORATION—Astronics Corporation; *U.S. Public*, pg. 142
ALLIEDSIGNAL TECHNICAL SERVICE—AlliedSignal Inc.; *U.S. Public*, pg. 50
ALPNET INC.; *U.S. Public*, pg. 58
AMERICAN APPRAISAL PROPERTY TAX SERVICES, INC.—American Appraisal Associates, Inc.; *U.S. Private*, pg. 50
AMERICAN APPRAISAL ASSOCIATES, INC.; *U.S. Private*, *pg. 49*
AMERICAN APPRAISAL MEXICO—American Appraisal Associates, Inc.; *U.S. Private*, pg. 50
AMERICAN ARBITRATION ASSOCIATION; *U.S. Private*, pg. 50
AMERICAN BIBLE SOCIETY; *U.S. Private*, pg. 51
AMERICAN EXPRESS COMPANY; *U.S. Public*, pg. 73
AMERICAN PAYMENT SYSTEMS, INC.—United Illuminating Company; *U.S. Public*, pg. 1678
AMERITECH AUDIOTEX SERVICES INC.—Ameritech Corporation; *U.S. Public*, pg. 98
AMERITECH CORPORATION; *U.S. Public*, pg. 97
ANALYSTS INTERNATIONAL CORPORATION; *U.S. Public*, pg. 110
ANALYTICAL SURVEYS, INC. - NORTHEAST DIVISION—Analytical Surveys, Inc.; *U.S. Public*, pg. 110
ANDERSON INDUSTRIES, INC.—Excel Industries, Inc.; *U.S. Public*, pg. 599
APPLIED INDUSTRIAL TECHNOLOGIES—Applied Industrial Technologies; *U.S. Public*, pg. 122
APPRAISAL SERVICES, INC.—Associated Banc-Corp; *U.S. Public*, pg. 141
ARDENT SOFTWARE, INC.; *U.S. Public*, pg. 129
ARMSTRONG LABS.—Medeva PLC; *Int'l*, pg. 852
ARTESIAN RESOURCES CORPORATION; *U.S. Public*, pg. 135
ASAHI BANK BUILDING CO., LTD.—The Asahi Bank, Ltd.; *Int'l*, pg. 82
ASAHI BANK KOSEI SERVICE CO., LTD.—The Asahi Bank, Ltd.; *Int'l*, pg. 82
ASAHI CARD CO., LTD.—The Asahi Bank, Ltd.; *Int'l*, pg. 82
ASGARD FINANCIAL SERVICES LTD—Arnotts plc; *Int'l*, pg. 81
ASGROW GMBH—Pharmacia & Upjohn, Inc.; *Int'l*, pg. 1049
ASSOCIATED HOSTS, INC.—Brierley Investments Limited; *Int'l*, pg. 215
ASSOCIATES RELOCATION MANAGEMENT COMPANY, INC.—Ford Motor Company; *U.S. Public*, pg. 663
ATELIERS SUCRE LIQUIDE ET CONDITIONNEMENT DE LYON—Generale Sucriere SNC; *Int'l*, pg. 549
ATELIERS SUCRE LIQUIDE ET CONDITIONNEMENT-LABORATOIRE DE RECHERCHE DE NASSANDRES—Generale Sucriere SNC; *Int'l*, pg. 549
ATELIERS SUCRE LIQUIDE ET DEPOT DE TOULOUSE/COLOMIERS—Generale Sucriere SNC; *Int'l*, pg. 549
AUSTRIAN POSTAL & TELEGRAPH ADMINISTRATION; *Int'l*, pg. 101
AUTO DRIVEAWAY CO.; *U.S. Private*, pg. 100
AUTOMATIC LIQUID PACKAGING, INC.; *U.S. Private*, pg. 101
AUTOTROL CORPORATION—Osmonics, Inc.; *U.S. Public*, pg. 1234
AUTOTROL FRANCE, S.A.—Osmonics, Inc.; *U.S. Public*, pg. 1234
BDM INTERNATIONAL, INC.—TRW Inc.; *U.S. Public*, pg. 1558
BALTIMORE STATIONERY CO./TOTAL OFFICE; *U.S. Private*, pg. 113
M.F. BANK & COMPANY, INC.; *U.S. Private*, pg. 113
BARANCORP; *U.S. Private*, pg. 115
JOSEPH A. BARANSKI LITERARY AGENCY—Barancorp; *U.S. Private*, pg. 115
BASEL TRADING COMPANY LTD.; *Int'l*, pg. 169
BEL AIR MARKETS—Raley's & Bel Air; *U.S. Private*, pg. 908
BELL MOBILITY PAGING INC.—BCE Inc.; *Int'l*, pg. 115
BERKSHIRE HATHAWAY INC.; *U.S. Public*, pg. 217
BERLITZ TRANSLATION SERVICES, INC.—Berlitz International, Inc.; *U.S. Public*, pg. 221
BERNARD KRIEF MOTIVATION, S.A., CARLSON MARKETING GROUP—Carlson Companies, Inc.; *U.S. Private*, pg. 212
J. BIBBY & SONS PLC—Barlow Ltd.; *Int'l*, pg. 167
BIOIMAGE PRODUCTS—Millipore Corporation; *U.S. Public*, *pg. 1112*
BIOSPHERICS INCORPORATED; *U.S. Public*, pg. 232
BLACK HORSE RELOCATION SERVICES LIMITED—Lloyds TSB Group PLC; *Int'l*, pg. 813
BLIMPIE INTERNATIONAL, INC.; *U.S. Public*, pg. 236
BLUE CHIP STAMPS—Berkshire Hathaway Inc.; *U.S. Public*, pg. 217
BORON LEPORE GROUP; *U.S. Public*, pg. 246
ROBERT BOSCH CORPORATION—Robert Bosch GmbH; *Int'l*, pg. 204

BOWNE BUSINESS COMMUNICATIONS, INC.—Bowne & Co., Inc.; *U.S. Public*, pg. 248
BRENTWOOD BENSON PUBLISHING GROUP—Zomba Recording Corp.; *Int'l*, pg. 1529
BRINK'S, INC.—The Pittston Company; *U.S. Public*, pg. 1305
BROCK INTERNATIONAL INC.; *U.S. Public*, pg. 258
BUCKA, SPIERO COMERCIO INDUSTRIA E IMPORTACAO LTDA./WALTER KIDDE S.A. INDUSTRIA E COMERCIO—Hanson PLC; *Int'l*, pg. 594
BUDCO GROUP INC.; *U.S. Private*, pg. 178
BUDGET MARKETING, INC.; *U.S. Private*, pg. 178
BURNHAM WORLD FORWARDING INC.—Investcorp International; *Int'l*, pg. 686
CACI INTERNATIONAL INC; *U.S. Public*, pg. 272
CCH INCORPORATED—Wolters Kluwer N.V.; *Int'l*, pg. 1513
CCH LEGAL INFORMATION SERVICES, INC.—Wolters Kluwer N.V.; *Int'l*, pg. 1513
CCL CUSTOM MANUFACTURING—CCL Industries, Inc.; *Int'l*, pg. 238
CDI CORP.; *U.S. Public*, pg. 276
C.E.P. COMMUNICATION GROUP; *Int'l*, pg. 239
CH & A CORPORATION—SGS Societe Generale de Surveillance Holding S.A.; *Int'l*, pg. 1153
CT CORPORATION SYSTEM—Wolters Kluwer N.V.; *Int'l*, pg. 1513
CAESARS WORLD, INC.—Starwood Hotels & Resorts; *U.S. Public*, pg. 1512
CAESARS WORLD MERCHANDISING, INC.—Starwood Hotels & Resorts; *U.S. Public*, pg. 1512
CALL INTERACTIVE—First Data Corporation; *U.S. Public*, pg. 631
CARD TECHNOLOGY CORP.—NBS Technologies, Inc.; *Int'l*, pg. 898
CARDINAL HEALTH INC.; *U.S. Public*, pg. 304
CARIBINER INTERNATIONAL, INC.; *U.S. Public*, pg. 305
CARLSON COMPANIES, INC.; *U.S. Private*, pg. 211
CARLSON INTERNATIONAL DIVISION—Carlson Companies, Inc.; *U.S. Private*, pg. 212
CARLSON MARKETING GROUP, INC.—Carlson Companies, Inc.; *U.S. Private*, pg. 212
CARLSON RETAIL MARKETING—Carlson Companies, Inc.; *U.S. Private*, pg. 212
CAROLINA MAILING SERVICE—Wallace Computer Services, Inc.; *U.S. Public*, pg. 1735
CATERPILLAR OF DELAWARE, INC.—Caterpillar Inc.; *U.S. Public*, pg. 316
CATHODIC PROTECTION SERVICES COMPANY—Michael Curran & Associates; *U.S. Private*, pg. 297
CATHODIC PROTECTION SERVICES COMPANY—Offshore Logistics, Inc.; *U.S. Public*, pg. 1213
CENTRO DE TRATAMEINTO DE LA DOCUMENTACION, S.A.—Caja de Madrid Group; *Int'l*, pg. 252
CHARLESTON INDUSTRIES—Petersen Aluminum Corporation; *U.S. Private*, pg. 856
CHASE ACCESS SERVICES CORP.—The Chase Manhattan Corporation; *U.S. Public*, pg. 337
CHEXSYSTEMS, INC.—Deluxe Corporation; *U.S. Public*, pg. 498
CHRISTIE, MANSON & WOODS LIMITED—Christies International plc; *Int'l*, pg. 290
CHRISTIE'S AMSTERDAM B.V.—Christies International plc; *Int'l*, pg. 290
CHRISTIE'S INC.—Christies International plc; *Int'l*, pg. 290
CHRISTIES INTERNATIONAL PLC; *Int'l*, pg. 289
CHRISTIE'S (INTERNATIONAL) S.A.—Christies International plc; *Int'l*, pg. 290
CHRISTIE'S SOUTH KENSINGTON LIMITED—Christies International plc; *Int'l*, pg. 290
CIGNA DIRECT MARKETING COMPANY, INC.—Cigna Corp.; *U.S. Public*, pg. 362
CITIBANK CREDIT CARD MARKETING—Citicorp; *U.S. Public*, pg. 377
DICK CLARK CORPORATE PRODUCTIONS, INC.—Dick Clark Productions, Inc.; *U.S. Public*, pg. 382
CLASSIC MARKETS CORP.; *U.S. Private*, pg. 244
CLINTON MACHINERY AND SUPPLY—Willcox & Gibbs, Inc.; *U.S. Private*, pg. 1177
CLOUD CORPORATION; *U.S. Private*, pg. 247
CLUETT INTERNATIONAL GROUP—Bidermann International S.A.; *Int'l*, pg. 194
COE & CLERICI, INC.—Coeclerici Group; *Int'l*, pg. 304
COECLERICI GROUP; *Int'l*, pg. 303
COMCAST CORPORATION; *U.S. Public*, pg. 406
COMMERCIAL MARKETING SYSTEMS—Royal & Sun Alliance Insurance Group plc; *Int'l*, pg. 1131
COMMERCIAL TESTING & ENGINEERING CO.—SGS Societe Generale de Surveillance Holding S.A.; *Int'l*, pg. 1153
COMMONWEALTH RELOCATION SERVICES, INC.—Reliance Group Holdings, Inc.; *U.S. Public*, pg. 1374
COMSKILL LEARNING CENTERS, INC.—ITC Learning Corp.; *U.S. Public*, pg. 859
CONNECTICUT GENERAL BENEFIT PAYMENTS, INC.—Cigna Corp.; *U.S. Public*, pg. 360
CONSOLIDATED NATURAL GAS SERVICE CO., INC.—Consolidated Natural Gas Company; *U.S. Public*, pg. 435
CONTINENTAL CAN CO.; *U.S. Public*, pg. 439
CONTINENTAL PARTNERS GROUP, INC.—BankAmerica Corporation; *U.S. Public*, pg. 181
CONTRACT INTERIORS INC.; *U.S. Private*, pg. 270
CORT BUSINESS SERVICES CORPORATION; *U.S. Public*, pg. 451
CRANE INSPECTION & CERTIFICATION BUREAU—SGS Societe Generale de Surveillance Holding S.A.; *Int'l*, pg. 1153
CREATIVE PRODUCTIONS; *U.S. Private*, pg. 288
DBS CARD CENTRE PTE. LTD.—DBS Bank Ltd.; *Int'l*, pg. 350
DG FOODS, LLC; *U.S. Private*, pg. 301
DRI/MCGRAW-HILL—The McGraw-Hill Companies; *U.S. Public*, pg. 1071
DST SECURITIES, INC.—Kansas City Southern Industries, Inc.; *U.S. Public*, pg. 943
DAIWA SECURITIES BUSINESS CENTER CO. LTD.—Daiwa Securities Co. Ltd.; *Int'l*, pg. 375
DALE FOODS—DG Foods, LLC; *U.S. Private*, pg. 301
DAW TECHNOLOGIES, INC.; *U.S. Public*, pg. 489
DEBIS MARKETING SERVICES GMBH—Daimler-Benz Aktiengesellschaft; *Int'l*, pg. 368
DECOFLEX LIMITED—Moore Corporation Limited; *Int'l*, pg. 889
DEMERT & DOUGHERTY, INC.; *U.S. Private*, pg. 323
DERWENT PUBLICATIONS LTD.—The Thomson Corporation; *U.S. Public*, pg. 1601
DESCO DE SCHULTHESS LTD.; *Int'l*, pg. 396
DESIGN-BUILD WEST—RNL Facilities Corporation; *U.S. Private*, pg. 905
DET NORSKE VERITAS; *Int'l*, pg. 396
W.A. DEUTSHER PTY. LTD.—Illinois Tool Works Inc.; *U.S. Public*, pg. 867
DIAL BANK—Norwest Corporation; *U.S. Public*, pg. 1202
DIMENSIONAL MERCHANDISING, INC.; *U.S. Private*, pg. 333
DIRECTORY DISTRIBUTING ASSOCIATES, INC.; *U.S. Private*, pg. 334
DISTRIBUTION SERVICES, INC.—American Media, Inc.; *U.S. Public*, pg. 87
DOW JONES INTERNATIONAL MARKETING SERVICES GMBH—Dow Jones & Company, Inc.; *U.S. Public*, pg. 525
DOW JONES INTERNATIONAL MARKETING SERVICES (U.K.) LTD.—Dow Jones & Company, Inc.; *U.S. Public*, pg. 525
DUN & BRADSTREET—The Dun & Bradstreet Corporation; *U.S. Public*, pg. 535
DUN & BRADSTREET BUSINESS EDUCATION SERVICES—The Dun & Bradstreet Corporation; *U.S. Public*, pg. 536
THE DUN & BRADSTREET CORPORATION; *U.S. Public*, pg. 535
EG & G, INC.; *U.S. Public*, pg. 542
EARL'S COURT & OLYMPIA LTD.—The Peninsular and Oriental Steam Navigation Company; *Int'l*, pg. 1033
EBSCO INDUSTRIES, INC.; *U.S. Private*, pg. 358
EDISON PARKING PROPERTIES, LLC; *U.S. Private*, pg. 364
ELSEVIER NV—Reed Elsevier plc; *Int'l*, pg. 1093
EMERALD WAREHOUSE & DISTRIBUTION SERVICES—Mail-Well Inc.; *U.S. Public*, pg. 1038
EMERSON RADIO HONG KONG LTD.—Emerson Radio Corp.; *U.S. Public*, pg. 578
ENROUTE CARD INC.—Air Canada; *Int'l*, pg. 36
ENVIROSOURCE-INTERNATIONAL MILL SERVICE, INC.—EnviroSource, Inc.; *U.S. Public*, pg. 587
EQUIFAX CHECK SERVICE—Equifax Inc.; *U.S. Public*, pg. 588
EQUIFAX INC.; *U.S. Public*, pg. 588
EQUIFAX INSURANCE SERVICES INC.—Equifax Inc.; *U.S. Public*, pg. 588
ERNST & YOUNG, LLP; *U.S. Private*, pg. 381
EXHIBITGROUP/GILTSPUR—Viad Corp; *U.S. Public*, pg. 1718
EXSIL, INC.—Laporte plc; *Int'l*, pg. 802
FTD, INC./FLORISTS TRANSWORLD DELIVERY, INC.; *U.S. Private*, pg. 389
FAIR, ISAAC AND COMPANY, INC.; *U.S. Public*, pg. 609
FAMILY PHARMACY GENERAL OFFICE—AmeriSource Health Corp.; *U.S. Public*, pg. 97
THE FAXON COMPANY, INC.—Dawson Holdings PLC; *Int'l*, pg. 385
FIND/SVP, INC.; *U.S. Public*, pg. 623
FINORA COMPANY, INC.—Norfoods, Inc.; *U.S. Private*, pg. 802
SUE FIRESTONE & ASSOC.; *U.S. Private*, pg. 406
FIRST DATA CORPORATION; *U.S. Public*, pg. 630
FIRST FINANCIAL BUILDING CORPORATION; *U.S. Private*, pg. 407
FIRST IMAGE MANAGEMENT CO.—First Data Corporation; *U.S. Public*, pg. 631
FIRST SECURITY PROCESSING SERVICES, INC.—First Security Corporation; *U.S. Public*, pg. 638
FIRST SOURCE FINANCIAL, INC—Household International, Inc.; *U.S. Public*, pg. 842
FORD GRAPHICS; *U.S. Private*, pg. 418
ABDULLA FOUAD AUCTIONEERS—Abdulla Fouad Co. Ltd.; *Int'l*, pg. 502
FRANCHISE FINANCE CORP. OF AMERICA; *U.S. Public*, pg. 679
FREEMAN DECORATING CO.; *U.S. Private*, pg. 426
FUKADA-KIDDE CO., LTD.—Hanson PLC; *Int'l*, pg. 594
GAB ROBINS NORTH AMERICA, INC.—SGS Societe Generale de Surveillance Holding S.A.; *Int'l*, pg. 1153
GEC ESTATES DEPARTMENT—The General Electric Company, p.l.c.; *Int'l*, pg. 544
GES EXPOSITION SERVICES, INC.—Viad Corp; *U.S. Public*, pg. 1718
GKN TECHNOLOGY LTD.—GKN plc; *Int'l*, pg. 535
GKN TECHNOLOGY US—GKN plc; *Int'l*, pg. 535
GL DIRECT—Great Lakes Lithograph Co.; *U.S. Private*, pg. 475
GP TAURIO, INC.—GP Strategies Corporation; *U.S. Public*, pg. 694
GPU SERVICE CORP.—GPU, Inc.; *U.S. Public*, pg. 695
GANNETT NEWS SERVICE, INC.—Gannett Company, Inc.; *U.S. Public*, pg. 700
GANNETT OFFSET-SPRINGFIELD PLANT—Gannett Company, Inc.; *U.S. Public*, pg. 700
GANNETT TELEMARKETING INC.—Gannett Company, Inc.; *U.S. Public*, pg. 699
GELCO INFORMATION NETWORK, INC.; *U.S. Private*, pg. 442
GENERAL BINDING CORPORATION; *U.S. Public*, pg. 707
GENERAL PHYSICS FINANCE INC.—GP Strategies Corporation; *U.S. Public*, pg. 694
GENERAL PHYSICS MOHAWK CORPORATION—GP Strategies Corporation; *U.S. Public*, pg. 694
GENERAL PHYSICS NIAGARA CORPORATION—GP Strategies Corporation; *U.S. Public*, pg. 694
GENERAL PHYSICS OHIO CORPORATION—GP Strategies Corporation; *U.S. Public*, pg. 694
GENERAL PHYSICS PHILADELPHIA CORPORATION—GP Strategies Corporation; *U.S. Public*, pg. 694
GENERAL TECHNICAL SERVICES, INC.—GP Strategies Corporation; *U.S. Public*, pg. 695
GEONEX—Geonex Corporation; *U.S. Private*, pg. 448
GEONEX CORPORATION; *U.S. Private*, pg. 447
SHELDON GOOD & CO.; *U.S. Private*, pg. 463
GOODKIND & O'DEA, INC.—Dewberry & Davis; *U.S. Private*, pg. 329
GRAFIBA SOCIEDAD ANONIMA—Reynolds Metals Company; *U.S. Public*, pg. 1387
GRAHAM-FIELD HEALTH PRODUCTS, INC.; *U.S. Public*, pg. 757
THE GREAT ATLANTIC MANAGEMENT COMPANY; *U.S. Private*, pg. 473
JACK GRIGGS INC.; *U.S. Private*, pg. 482
GRUBB & ELLIS COMPANY; *U.S. Public*, pg. 767
GRUMMAN OHIO CORP.—Northrop Grumman Corporation; *U.S. Public*, pg. 1198
GRUPO IBERPHONE INVERSIONES, S.A.—Caja de Madrid Group; *Int'l*, pg. 252
GULFMARK OFFSHORE INC.; *U.S. Public*, pg. 769
HADRON, INC.; *U.S. Public*, pg. 773
HAMAMATSU KOHAN KAKO CO., LTD.—Nissho Iwai Corporation; *Int'l*, pg. 946
HARLEY VALVE & INSTRUMENT—Innovative Valve Technology, Inc.; *U.S. Public*, pg. 880
HARPEN AG; *Int'l*, pg. 597
HARRISONS & CROSFIELD (HONG KONG) LTD.—Harrisons & Crosfield plc; *Int'l*, pg. 599
HARTE-HANKS MARKETING SERVICES—Harte-Hanks Communications, Inc.; *U.S. Public*, pg. 794
HEATH CONSULTANTS INCORPORATED; *U.S. Private*, pg. 518
HELM, INC.; *U.S. Private*, pg. 520
HELM RESOURCES INC.; *U.S. Public*, pg. 808
HENDERSON AUCTIONS—JAH Enterprises, Inc.; *U.S. Private*, pg. 577
HILL-LOMA, INC.—Goldman Financial Group; *U.S. Private*, pg. 461
HOLLOWAY WHITE ALLOM LTD.—John Laing PLC; *Int'l*, pg. 796
HOMEOWNERS GROUP, INC.; *U.S. Public*, pg. 832
HORIZON ENTERPRISES GROUP LLC; *U.S. Private*, pg. 539
HORIZON INVESTMENT GROUP—Horizon Enterprises Group LLC; *U.S. Private*, pg. 539
HOSPITALITY PROCUREMENT DIVISION—Carlson Companies, Inc.; *U.S. Private*, pg. 212
HOUSEHOLD RETAIL SERVICES, INC.—Household International, Inc.; *U.S. Public*, pg. 842
HUFFY SERVICE FIRST, INC.—Huffy Corporation; *U.S. Public*, pg. 846
HYOSUNG AMERICA, INC.—Hyosung Group; *Int'l*, pg. 641
HYTEK FINISHES CO.—Esterline Technologies Corporation; *U.S. Public*, pg. 594
I.C.E. INTERNATIONAL CAPITAL EQUIPMENT, INC.—International Capital Equipment Limited; *Int'l*, pg. 683
ICO, INC.; *U.S. Public*, pg. 853
IDC SERVICES, INC.; *U.S. Private*, pg. 554
INS INVESTIGATIONS BUREAU, INC.—SGS Societe Generale de Surveillance Holding S.A.; *Int'l*, pg. 1153
ITC LEARNING CORP.; *U.S. Public*, pg. 859
ITI MARKETING SERVICES, INC.; *U.S. Private*, pg. 555
ITT CORPORATION—Starwood Hotels & Resorts; *U.S. Public*, pg. 1512
IBERPHONE ANDALUCIA, S.A.—Caja de Madrid Group; *Int'l*, pg. 252
IBERPHONE CATALUNA, S.A.—Caja de Madrid Group; *Int'l*, pg. 252
IBERPHONE PORTUGAL TELEMARKETING—Caja de Madrid Group; *Int'l*, pg. 252
IBERPHONE, S.A.—Caja de Madrid Group; *Int'l*, pg. 252
ILLINOIS BANC ONE SERVICES, INC.—Banc One Corporation; *U.S. Public*, pg. 174
INDEPENDENT PUBLICATIONS, INC.; *U.S. Private*, pg. 559
INKTEL MARKETING—Avanti Press Inc.; *U.S. Private*, pg. 101
INSIGNIA SYSTEMS, INC.; *U.S. Public*, pg. 881
INSTITUTIONAL FINANCING SERVICES—Tyler Corporation; *U.S. Public*, pg. 1652
INSTRUMENT MARKETING SERVICES, INC.—SGS Societe Generale de Surveillance Holding S.A.; *Int'l*, pg. 1153
INTERACTIVE MARKET SYSTEMS, INC.—VNU Verenigde Nederlandse Uitgeversbedrijven B.V.; *Int'l*, pg. 1447
INTERMODAL TRANSPORTATION SERVICES, INC.—SGS Societe Generale de Surveillance Holding S.A.; *Int'l*, pg. 1153
INTERNATIONAL DATA GROUP; *U.S. Private*, pg. 569
INTERNATIONAL TOTAL SERVICES; *U.S. Public*, pg. 908
INTEROP, INC.—The Thomson Corporation; *U.S. Public*, pg. 1600
INTRACORP, INC.—Cigna Corp.; *U.S. Public*, pg. 362
INVENTORY MANAGEMENT CORP.—GP Strategies Corporation; *U.S. Public*, pg. 694
IRVING CONVENTION & VISITORS BUREAU; *U.S. Private*, pg. 575
ISOTECH G.M.B.H.—Novartis AG; *Int'l*, pg. 983
JB OXFORD HOLDINGS INC.; *U.S. Public*, pg. 916
JC PENNEY PURCHASING CORP.—JC Penney Company, Inc.; *U.S. Public*, pg. 917
JCB INTERNATIONAL CREDIT CARD CO., LTD.-USA—JCB International Co., Ltd.; *Int'l*, pg. 696
JAPS-OLSON COMPANY; *U.S. Private*, pg. 582

JOHNSON & JOHNSON DEVELOPMENT CORPORATION—Johnson & Johnson; U.S. Public, pg. 928
JOHNSON CONTROLS WORLD SERVICES INC.—Johnson Controls, Inc.; U.S. Public, pg. 932
JOSTENS; U.S. Public, pg. 934
K-YHTIOT OY—Kesko Ltd.; Int'l, pg. 732
KEMPER INSURANCE COMPANIES; U.S. Private, pg. 614
KETCHUM, INC.; U.S. Private, pg. 617
KLOECKNER-PENTAPACK GMBH—Klockner-Werke AG; Int'l, pg. 737
KOLLMORGEN CORPORATION; U.S. Public, pg. 965
KRUSE INTERNATIONAL; U.S. Private, pg. 636
KVAERNER COMPUTING & CONSULTANCY LTD.—Kvaerner a.s.a.; Int'l, pg. 771
KVAERNER PROCESS SYSTEMS A/S—Kvaerner a.s.a.; Int'l, pg. 766
LAING TECHNOLOGY GROUP LTD.—John Laing PLC; Int'l, pg. 796
NORMAN LEVY ASSOCIATES, INC.; U.S. Private, pg. 664
LINA BENEFIT PAYMENTS, INC.—Cigna Corp.; U.S. Public, pg. 362
THE LINC CORP.—Compagnie Generale Des Eaux; Int'l, pg. 322
LINCOLN NATIONAL CORPORATION; U.S. Public, pg. 997
LITTON BUSINESS SYSTEMS HOLLAND B.V.—Litton Industries, Inc.; U.S. Public, pg. 1004
LUNCHEON VOUCHERS LTD.—Accor S.A.; Int'l, pg. 21
MCRB SERVICE BUREAU, INC.; U.S. Private, pg. 686
M.F. BANK RESTORATION CO.—M.F. Bank & Company, Inc.; U.S. Private, pg. 114
MHM SERVICES INC.; U.S. Public, pg. 1027
MHT DIVISION—Israel Aircraft Industries Ltd.; Int'l, pg. 690
MNC FINANCIAL, INC.—First Tennessee National Corporation; U.S. Public, pg. 639
MTPB - EAST COAST REGION—Malaysia Tourism Promotion Board (MTPB); Int'l, pg. 833
MTPB - NORTHERN REGION—Malaysia Tourism Promotion Board (MTPB); Int'l, pg. 833
MTPB - SABAH REGION—Malaysia Tourism Promotion Board (MTPB); Int'l, pg. 833
MTPB - SARAWAK REGION—Malaysia Tourism Promotion Board (MTPB); Int'l, pg. 833
MTPB - SOUTHERN REGION—Malaysia Tourism Promotion Board (MTPB); Int'l, pg. 833
E.F. MACDONALD MOTIVATION DIV.—Carlson Companies, Inc.; U.S. Private, pg. 212
THE E.F. MACDONALD VERKAUFSFORDERUNG GMBH—Carlson Companies, Inc.; U.S. Private, pg. 212
MACE PRODUCTS—Osmonics, Inc.; U.S. Public, pg. 1234
MACMILLAN PUBLISHING USA—National Amusements, Inc.; U.S. Private, pg. 777
MAIL BOXES ETC.—U.S. Office Products Company; U.S. Public, pg. 1687
MALAYSIA TOURISM PROMOTION BOARD (MTPB); Int'l, pg. 832
MARINE MIDLAND BUSINESS LOANS, INC.—HSBC Holdings plc; Int'l, pg. 581
MARITZ PERFORMANCE IMPROVEMENT COMPANY—Maritz Inc.; U.S. Private, pg. 704
AC MARTIN PARTNERS; U.S. Private, pg. 708
MARTIN MARIETTA ENERGY GROUP—Lockheed Martin Corporation; U.S. Public, pg. 1007
MASON & HANGER CORPORATION, INC.—Mason & Hanger Corporation, Inc.; U.S. Private, pg. 711
MATRIXX MARKETING INC.—Cincinnati Bell Telephone; U.S. Public, pg. 368
MATRIXX PHONE MARKETING SERVICES, S.A.—Cincinnati Bell Telephone; U.S. Public, pg. 368
MCCORMICK & COMPANY, INCORPORATED; U.S. Public, pg. 1066
THE MCGRAW-HILL COMPANIES; U.S. Public, pg. 1069
MEADOWS RESOURCES, INC.—Public Service Company of New Mexico; U.S. Public, pg. 1339
MEDEX ASSISTANCE CORPORATION—Avemco Corporation; U.S. Public, pg. 152
MEDIA RECOVERY, INC.; U.S. Private, pg. 726
MEDIQ DIAGNOSTIC CENTERS—MEDIQ Incorporated; U.S. Public, pg. 1081
MEDIQ INCORPORATED; U.S. Public, pg. 1081
METRO INFORMATION SERVICES; U.S. Public, pg. 1102
MIKOHN GAMING CORPORATION; U.S. Public, pg. 1111
MISTAL, INC.—Tenneco Inc.; U.S. Public, pg. 1579
MITCHELL INTERNATIONAL—The Thomson Corporation; U.S. Public, pg. 1601
MOBILE COMMUNICATIONS CORPORATION OF AMERICA—MobileComm; U.S. Public, pg. 1120
MOLEX SERVICES GMBH—Molex Incorporated; U.S. Public, pg. 1122
MORTON SALT—Morton International Inc.; U.S. Public, pg. 1135
MOTORS TRADING CORPORATION—General Motors Corporation; U.S. Public, pg. 721
MUSEUM BOUTIQUE INTERCONTINENTAL, LTD.; U.S. Private, pg. 768
MUZAK LIMITED PARTNERSHIP—Center Partners Management LLC; U.S. Private, pg. 222
NBBJ; U.S. Private, pg. 771
NBS TECHNOLOGIES, INC.; Int'l, pg. 898
NFO RESEARCH, INC.; U.S. Public, pg. 1146
NTS—First Data Corporation; U.S. Public, pg. 631
NABISCO MUSIC PUBLISHERS, INC.—RJR Nabisco Holdings Corp.; U.S. Public, pg. 1355
NABISCO MUSIC VENTURES, INC.—RJR Nabisco Holdings Corp.; U.S. Public, pg. 1355
NANTO BUSINESS SERVICE CO., LTD.—The Nanto Bank, Ltd.; Int'l, pg. 905
NATIONAL ASSOCIATED DESIGN CO.—Brierley Investments Limited; Int'l, pg. 215
NATIONAL CARD CONTROL, INC.—Cendant Corporation; U.S. Public, pg. 321
NATIONAL LOSS CONTROL SERVICE CORP.—Kemper Insurance Companies; U.S. Private, pg. 614
NATIONAL YELLOW PAGES MONITOR (NYPM)—NFO Research, Inc.; U.S. Public, pg. 1146
NELSON WESTERBERG INTERNATIONAL INC.—Nelson Westerberg, Inc.; U.S. Private, pg. 1164
NEW JERSEY SIGN COMPANY INC.—Edison Parking Properties, LLC; U.S. Private, pg. 364
THE NEW YORK TIMES NEWS SERVICE—The New York Times Company; U.S. Public, pg. 1174
NIPSCO ENERGY TRADING CORPORATION, INC.—NIPSCO Industries, Inc.; U.S. Public, pg. 1185
NISCO STEEL SERVICES, INC.—Nissho Iwai Corporation; Int'l, pg. 947
NISSAY CARD SERVICES CO., LTD.—Nippon Life Insurance Co.; Int'l, pg. 935
NOMURA BUSINESS SERVICES CO., LTD.—The Nomura Securities Co., Ltd.; Int'l, pg. 956
NOMURA TOURIST BUREAU, INC.—The Nomura Securities Co., Ltd.; Int'l, pg. 956
NORFOODS, INC.; U.S. Private, pg. 802
NORTHERN CROSS, LTD.—Barancorp; U.S. Private, pg. 115
NOVUS SERVICES, INC.—Morgan Stanley Dean Witter & Co.; U.S. Public, pg. 1132
OCEANEERING A/S—Oceaneering International, Inc.; U.S. Public, pg. 1211
OCEANEERING AUSTRALIA PTY. LTD.—Brambles Industries Limited; Int'l, pg. 211
OCEANEERING AUSTRALIA PTY. LTD.—Oceaneering International, Inc.; U.S. Public, pg. 1211
OCEANEERING INTERNATIONAL, INC.; U.S. Public, pg. 1211
OCEANEERING INTERVENTION ENGINEERING—Oceaneering International, Inc.; U.S. Public, pg. 1211
OCEANEERING MULTIFLEX—Oceaneering International, Inc.; U.S. Public, pg. 1211
OCEANEERING TECHNOLOGIES—Oceaneering International, Inc.; U.S. Public, pg. 1211
OGLEBAY NORTON COMPANY; U.S. Public, pg. 1213
OLD KENT FINANCIAL CORPORATION; U.S. Public, pg. 1216
OPPENHEIMERFUNDS DISTRIBUTOR, INC.; U.S. Private, pg. 818
OSMONICS ASIA/PACIFIC, LTD.—Osmonics, Inc.; U.S. Public, pg. 1234
OSMONICS ASIA/PACIFIC LTD.—Osmonics, Inc.; U.S. Public, pg. 1234
OSMONICS, INC.; U.S. Public, pg. 1233
OUTDOOR SYSTEMS, INC.-NEW YORK—Outdoor Systems, Inc.; U.S. Public, pg. 1235
OZONE RESEARCH & EQUIPMENT CORP.—Osmonics, Inc.; U.S. Public, pg. 1234
PHB TOOL & DIE—PHB Die Casting; U.S. Private, pg. 826
PHH CORPORATION—Cendant Corporation; U.S. Public, pg. 321
PRC, INC.—Litton Industries, Inc.; U.S. Public, pg. 1003
PARTEL RESEARCH CORP.—AEGON N.V.; Int'l, pg. 27
PASCO-CERTEZA COMPUTER MAPPING CORPORATION—Pasco Corporation; Int'l, pg. 1024
PER PAK (BROOK)—Jefferson Smurfit Group p.l.c.; Int'l, pg. 1270
PETROLEOS DE VENEZUELA UK, S.A.—Petroleos de Venezuela S.A.; Int'l, pg. 1046
PIONEER DIRECT CORPORATION—Conseco Inc.; U.S. Public, pg. 433
PIONEER FINANCE CORP.—Santa Fe Gaming Corporation; U.S. Public, pg. 1432
PIPETRONIX LTD.—Preussag AG; Int'l, pg. 1071
PITNEY BOWES INC.; U.S. Public, pg. 1303
PLAYBOY MODELS, INC.—Playboy Enterprises, Inc.; U.S. Public, pg. 1310
POLICY MANAGEMENT SYSTEMS CORPORATION; U.S. Public, pg. 1314
POLK AUTOMOTIVE DATA SERVICES DIV.—R.L. Polk & Co.; U.S. Private, pg. 874
R.L. POLK & CO.; U.S. Private, pg. 874
MAYER POLLACK STEEL CORPORATION—The Pollock Corp.; U.S. Private, pg. 874
THE POLLOCK CORP.; U.S. Private, pg. 874
POLYGRAM N.V.—Philips Electronics N.V.; Int'l, pg. 1051
THE POWER LINE—Publishers Clearing House; U.S. Private, pg. 893
POWER MANAGEMENT ASSOCIATES, INC.—GP Strategies Corporation; U.S. Public, pg. 695
PREMIUMS INTL. LTD.—Carlson Companies, Inc.; U.S. Private, pg. 212
PRICE WATERHOUSE L.L.P. - U.S.; U.S. Private, pg. 883
THE PRINCIPAL FINANCIAL GROUP; U.S. Private, pg. 885
PRINCIPAL HEALTH CARE, INC.—The Principal Financial Group; U.S. Private, pg. 885
PRINCOR FINANCIAL SERVICES CORPORATION—The Principal Financial Group; U.S. Private, pg. 886
PRINCOR MANAGEMENT CORPORATION—The Principal Financial Group; U.S. Private, pg. 886
PROLER INTERNATIONAL CORP.—Schnitzer Steel Industries, Inc.; U.S. Public, pg. 1440
PROTO-POWER CORPORATION—Kollmorgen Corporation; U.S. Public, pg. 965
THE PSYCHOLOGICAL CORP.—Harcourt General, Inc.; U.S. Public, pg. 784
PUBLISHERS CLEARING HOUSE; U.S. Private, pg. 893
PUERTO RICO TOURISM COMPANY; U.S. Private, pg. 894
PURE SOLUTIONS—Ionics, Incorporated; U.S. Public, pg. 912
QSP, INC.—The Reader's Digest Association, Inc.; U.S. Public, pg. 1367
QUALITY EDUCATION DATA (QED)—Peterson's Guides, Inc.; U.S. Private, pg. 858
QUALITY FOOD OILS, INC.—Associated British Foods plc; Int'l, pg. 92
RNL/INTERPLAN—RNL Facilities Corporation; U.S. Private, pg. 905
RANK HOLIDAYS & HOTELS LIMITED—The Rank Group PLC; Int'l, pg. 1087
RE/MAX INTERNATIONAL, INC.; U.S. Private, pg. 912
THE REALLY USEFUL RECORD COMPANY LIMITED—Really Useful Holdings Limited; Int'l, pg. 1089
RECOGNITION DIVISION—Jostens; U.S. Public, pg. 934
REED ELSEVIER PLC; Int'l, pg. 1093
REED EXHIBITION COMPANIES—Reed Elsevier plc; Int'l, pg. 1096
REED EXHIBITION COMPANIES-NORTH AMERICA—Reed Elsevier plc; Int'l, pg. 1096
REED EXHIBITION COMPANIES-SOUTH ASIA/PACIFIC—Reed Elsevier plc; Int'l, pg. 1097
REED INTERNATIONAL P.L.C.—Reed Elsevier plc; Int'l, pg. 1093
REED MIDEM ORGANISATION INC.—Reed Elsevier plc; Int'l, pg. 1096
RENTOKIL INITIAL PLC—Sophus Berendsen A/S; Int'l, pg. 1285
RESEARCH PUBLICATIONS, INC.—The Thomson Corporation; U.S. Public, pg. 1600
RESORT CONDOMINIUMS INTERNATIONAL—Cendant Corporation; U.S. Public, pg. 322
RESORT MARKETING INTERNATIONAL—Santa Fe Gaming Corporation; U.S. Public, pg. 1432
REXAM PLC; Int'l, pg. 1106
R.J. REYNOLDS TOBACCO INTERNATIONAL (MEXICO) INC.—RJR Nabisco Holdings Corp.; U.S. Public, pg. 1355
ROLL INTERNATIONAL CORPORATION; U.S. Private, pg. 941
ROLLINS, INC.; U.S. Public, pg. 1404
RURAL METRO CORPORATION; U.S. Public, pg. 1412
RYKA INCORPORATED; U.S. Public, pg. 1414
S&H CITADEL, INC.—Leucadia National Corporation; U.S. Public, pg. 990
SBC WARBURG GROUP MANAGEMENT LTD.—Swiss Bank Corporation; Int'l, pg. 1331
SGD INTERNATIONAL CORP.; U.S. Private, pg. 957
SGS CONTROL SERVICES INC.—SGS Societe Generale de Surveillance Holding S.A.; Int'l, pg. 1153
SGS GOVERNMENT PROGRAMS INC.—SGS Societe Generale de Surveillance Holding S.A.; Int'l, pg. 1153
SGS INDUSTRIAL SERVICES—SGS Societe Generale de Surveillance Holding S.A.; Int'l, pg. 1153
SGS INTERNATIONAL CERTIFICATION SERVICES, INC.—SGS Societe Generale de Surveillance Holding S.A.; Int'l, pg. 1153
SGS U.S. TESTING COMPANY, INC.—SGS Societe Generale de Surveillance Holding S.A.; Int'l, pg. 1153
SKF INTERTRADE S.A.—AB SKF; Int'l, pg. 1158
SRA INTERNATIONAL INC.; U.S. Private, pg. 957
SAFETY-KLEEN CORP.; U.S. Public, pg. 1425
SAHARA LAS VEGAS CORP.—Santa Fe Gaming Corporation; U.S. Public, pg. 1432
SAHARA MISSISSIPPI MANAGEMENT COMPANY, INC.—Santa Fe Gaming Corporation; U.S. Public, pg. 1432
SAHARA PARKVILLE, INC.—Santa Fe Gaming Corporation; U.S. Public, pg. 1432
SAMSUNG GROUP; Int'l, pg. 1181
SANTA FE GAMING CORPORATION; U.S. Public, pg. 1432
SAPROMA S.A.—Carlson Companies, Inc.; U.S. Private, pg. 212
SAX ARTS & CRAFTS—U.S. Office Products Company; U.S. Public, pg. 1687
SAX ARTS & CRAFTS, INC.—U.S. Office Products Company; U.S. Public, pg. 1687
SCHLUMBERGER MALCO INC.—N. Schlumberger & Cie; Int'l, pg. 1206
SCIENTIFIC SOFTWARE-INTERCOMP, INC.; U.S. Public, pg. 1443
SEMCO INDUSTRIES INC.; U.S. Private, pg. 983
SEPIC—C.E.P. Communication Group; Int'l, pg. 239
THE SERVICEMASTER COMPANY; U.S. Public, pg. 1461
SHADOW BROADCAST SERVICES—Westwood One, Inc.; U.S. Public, pg. 1763
SHAKLEE CANADA INC.—Yamanouchi Pharmaceutical Co. Ltd.; Int'l, pg. 1518
SHAKLEE JAPAN K.K.—Yamanouchi Pharmaceutical Co. Ltd.; Int'l, pg. 1518
SHREDDED PRODUCTS CORP.—Roanoke Electric Steel Corporation; U.S. Public, pg. 1392
THE SIGNATURE GROUP—Montgomery Ward & Co., Inc.; U.S. Private, pg. 758
SOFTRANS INTERNATIONAL, LTD.—Berlitz International, Inc.; U.S. Public, pg. 222
SOLUS OCEANEERING (MALAYSIA) SDN. BHD.—Oceaneering International, Inc.; U.S. Public, pg. 1211
SONY U.S.A.—Sony Corporation; Int'l, pg. 1281
SOTHEBY'S HOLDINGS INC.; U.S. Public, pg. 1487
SOUTHEASTERN FINANCIAL SERVICES, INC.—Southeastern Michigan Gas Enterprises, Inc.; U.S. Public, pg. 1489
SOUTHWESTERN BELL MESSAGING SERVICES—SBC Communications Inc.; U.S. Public, pg. 1416
SPAULDING COMPANY, INC.—Semco Industries Inc.; U.S. Private, pg. 983
THE SPERRY & HUTCHINSON COMPANY, INC.—Leucadia National Corporation; U.S. Public, pg. 990
I. SPIEWAK & SONS, INC.; U.S. Private, pg. 1025
SPIRE CORPORATION; U.S. Public, pg. 1499
STET SOCIETA FINANZIARIA TELEFONICA—IRI Istituto Ricostruzione Industriale; Int'l, pg. 655
SUMMIT TELEMARKETING—SBC Communications Inc.; U.S. Public, pg. 1415
SUNGARD DATA SYSTEMS INC.; U.S. Public, pg. 1534
SUPERIOR AUCTIONEERS & MARKETING, INC.; U.S. Private, pg. 1054
SUPERIOR REPROGRAPHICS—Ford Graphics; U.S. Private, pg. 418
SURPLUS WAREHOUSE-ALEXANDRIA—E.C. Barton & Company; U.S. Private, pg. 119

SUZUKI TRANSPORTATION AND PACKAGING CO., LTD.—Suzuki Motor Corporation; *Int'l*, pg. 1323
THE SWISSAIR GROUP; *Int'l*, pg. 1333
TDW DELAWARE, INC.—T.D. Williamson, Inc.; *U.S. Private*, *pg. 1180*
TDW FOREIGN SALES CORP.—T.D. Williamson, Inc.; *U.S. Private*, pg. 1180
TDW TRADING, INC.—T.D. Williamson, Inc.; *U.S. Private*, pg. 1180
TECHNOLOGY SOLUTIONS COMPANY (TSC); *U.S. Public*, pg. 1564
TELE-QUOTE CORPORATION—AEGON N.V.; *Int'l*, pg. 28
TELE-QUOTE, INC.—AEGON N.V.; *Int'l*, pg. 28
TELECREDIT SERVICE CORP.—Equifax Inc.; *U.S. Public*, pg. 588
TELEFLORA, LLC—Roll International Corporation; *U.S. Private*, pg. 941
TEMPO ADVERTISING, INC.—Santa Fe Gaming Corporation; *U.S. Public*, pg. 1432
TENNECO ASSET PLANNING CO.—Tenneco Inc.; *U.S. Public*, pg. 1578
TENNECO DOMESTIC INTERNATIONAL SALES CORP.—Tenneco Inc.; *U.S. Public*, pg. 1578
TENNECO NORGE, INC.—Tenneco Inc.; *U.S. Public*, pg. 1578
TESCO—Vendex International N.V.; *Int'l*, pg. 1463
TESTCOM, INC.—SGS Societe Generale de Surveillance Holding S.A.; *Int'l*, pg. 1154
TETRA TECH NUS, INC.—Tetra Tech, Inc.; *U.S. Public*, pg. 1582
THOSE CHARACTERS FROM CLEVELAND, INC.—American Greetings Corporation; *U.S. Public*, pg. 78
J.L. TODD AUCTION CO.; *U.S. Private*, pg. 1090
TOURISM MALAYSIA - L.A. OFFICE—Malaysia Tourism Promotion Board (MTPB); *Int'l*, pg. 833
TOWERS PERRIN; *U.S. Private*, pg. 1093
TRADE SHOW ENTERPRISES—I. Spiewak & Sons, Inc.; *U.S. Private*, pg. 1025
TRADEMARK RESEARCH CORPORATION—Wolters Kluwer N.V.; *Int'l*, pg. 1513
TRANSAMERICA CORPORATION; *U.S. Public*, pg. 1629
TRANSMEDIA NETWORK INC.; *U.S. Public*, pg. 1631
TUBE CITY INC.; *U.S. Private*, pg. 1108
TYLER CORPORATION; *U.S. Public*, pg. 1651
UAL CORPORATION; *U.S. Public*, pg. 1652
URS GREINER ENGINEERING, INC.—URS Corporation; *U.S. Public*, pg. 1658
ULLO INTERNATIONAL, INC.; *U.S. Private*, pg. 1116
UNITED LEASING, INC.—UniGroup, Inc.; *U.S. Private*, pg. 1117
UNITED NEWS & MEDIA PLC; *Int'l*, pg. 1443
U.S. FILTER/POLYMETRICS—United States Filter Corporation; *U.S. Public*, pg. 1682
UNIVERSAL STUDIOS MUSIC ENTERTAINMENT GROUP—The Seagram Company Ltd.; *Int'l*, pg. 1215
UNIVERSAL STUDIOS PUBLISHING GROUP—The Seagram Company Ltd.; *Int'l*, pg. 1215
URBANA IBERICA, S.A.—Telefonica de Espana, S.A.; *Int'l*, pg. 1372
UTELL INTERNATIONAL—Reed Elsevier plc; *Int'l*, pg. 1098
UTELL INTERNATIONAL-CANADA—Reed Elsevier plc; *Int'l*, pg. 1098
UTELL INTERNATIONAL-GERMANY—Reed Elsevier plc; *Int'l*, pg. 1098
UTELL INTERNATIONAL-UNITED KINGDOM—Reed Elsevier plc; *Int'l*, pg. 1098
UTLAS INTERNATIONAL—The Thomson Corporation; *U.S. Public*, pg. 1600
VNU USA, INC.—VNU Verenigde Nederlandse Uitgeversbedrijven B.V.; *Int'l*, pg. 1447
VALMET CORPORATION SERVICE DEVELOPMENT—Valmet Corporation; *Int'l*, pg. 1449
VALUE LINE SECURITIES, INC.—Arnold Bernhard & Co.; *U.S. Private*, pg. 137
VANCE PUBLISHING CORPORATION; *U.S. Private*, pg. 1133
VAPONICS INC.—Osmonics, Inc.; *U.S. Public*, pg. 1234
VENCHURS PACKAGING, INC.; *U.S. Private*, pg. 1135
THE VERNON COMPANY; *U.S. Private*, pg. 1137
VIAD CORP; *U.S. Public*, pg. 1718
VIRGINIA TOURISM CORP.; *U.S. Private*, pg. 1141
VMARK ASIA-PACIFIC PTY. LTD.—Ardent Software, Inc.; *U.S. Public*, pg. 129
VMARK SOFTWARE, LTD.—Ardent Software, Inc.; *U.S. Public*, pg. 129
WFS CLEARING SERVICES—First Union Corporation; *U.S. Public*, pg. 640
THE WACKENHUT CORPORATION; *U.S. Public*, pg. 1731
WACKENHUT CORRECTIONS CORPORATION—The Wackenhut Corporation; *U.S. Public*, pg. 1731
WARMINGTON HOMES; *U.S. Private*, pg. 1150
WARRANTECH CORPORATION; *U.S. Public*, pg. 1740
WASHINGTON INVENTORY SERVICE—Huffy Corporation; *U.S. Public*, pg. 846
WEATHERALL GREEN & SMITH; *Int'l*, pg. 1488
WERSHOW-ASH-LEWIS; *U.S. Private*, pg. 1162
WESTERN FILTER—Osmonics, Inc.; *U.S. Public*, pg. 1234
WESTWOOD ONE ENTERTAINMENT—Westwood One, Inc.; *U.S. Public*, pg. 1763
WESTWOOD ONE, INC.; *U.S. Public*, pg. 1763
WESTWOOD ONE RADIO NETWORKS—Westwood One, Inc.; *U.S. Public*, pg. 1763
WHITBREAD PROPERTY—Whitbread PLC; *Int'l*, pg. 1498
WIELAND FINANCIAL SERVICES, INC.—John Wieland Homes Inc.; *U.S. Private*, pg. 1175
WIMPEY GROUP SERVICES LTD.—George Wimpey PLC; *Int'l*, pg. 1510
WISCONSIN CONSULTAR ENGENHARIA, LTD.—American Appraisal Associates, Inc.; *U.S. Private*, pg. 50
WOOLWORTH OVERSEAS CORP.—Woolworth Corporation; *U.S. Public*, pg. 1778
WOOLWORTH WORLD TRADE CORP.—Woolworth Corporation; *U.S. Public*, pg. 1778
WORLD EXPO CORPORATION—International Data Group; *U.S. Private*, pg. 571
XEROX REAL ESTATE & GENERAL SERVICES DIVISION—Xerox Corporation; *U.S. Public*, pg. 1785
YAMAICHI FINANCE CO., LTD.—Yamaichi Securities Co., Ltd.; *Int'l*, pg. 1516
YELLOW PAGES SALES LIMITED—British Telecommunications plc; *Int'l*, pg. 222
ZETEC, INC.; *U.S. Private*, pg. 1205

7513 — TRUCK RENTAL & LEASING, WITHOUT DRIVERS

AVA; *U.S. Private*, pg. 8
AVA LEASING SERVICE COMPANY—AVA; *U.S. Private*, pg. 8
AMERCO; *U.S. Private*, pg. 48
BEAUDRY FORD, INC.; *U.S. Private*, pg. 127
THE CURRY CORPORATION; *U.S. Private*, pg. 297
DAF TRUCKS N.V.—Paccar Inc.; *U.S. Public*, pg. 1247
DSU LEASING, INC.—D.S.U.-Peterbilt & GMC, Inc.; *U.S. Private*, pg. 306
DONLEN CORP.; *U.S. Private*, pg. 340
EQUIS FINANCIAL GROUP; *U.S. Private*, pg. 379
EXECUTIVE CAR LEASING, INC.; *U.S. Private*, pg. 388
FRANK CONSOLIDATED ENTERPRISES INC.; *U.S. Private*, pg. 423
FREMONT GENERAL CORPORATION; *U.S. Public*, pg. 681
G.E. CAPITAL FLEET SERVICES—General Electric Company; *U.S. Public*, pg. 710
LEX HARVEY LTD.; *Int'l*, pg. 599
BILL HEARD ENTERPRISES, INC.; *U.S. Private*, pg. 515
THE HERTZ CORPORATION—Ford Motor Company; *U.S. Public*, pg. 664
HOLMAN ENTERPRISES; *U.S. Private*, pg. 535
JEROME-DUNCAN FORD; *U.S. Private*, pg. 586
K & R EXPRESS SYSTEMS INC.; *U.S. Private*, pg. 602
KENWORTH OF INDIANAPOLIS INC.; *U.S. Private*, pg. 615
KORPIVAARA MOOTTORIALAN LUOTTO OY—Amer Group Ltd.; *Int'l*, pg. 72
KORPIVAARA OY - FORKLIFTS—Amer Group Ltd.; *Int'l*, pg. 72
LEX HARVEY—Lex Service PLC; *Int'l*, pg. 807
LEX KOMATSU FORKLIFT (UK)—Lex Service PLC; *Int'l*, pg. 807
LEX SERVICE PLC; *Int'l*, pg. 806
LEX TRANSFLEET—Lex Service PLC; *Int'l*, pg. 807
MCKENZIE TANK LINES, INC.; *U.S. Private*, pg. 723
MODERN GROUP LTD.; *U.S. Private*, pg. 754
NATIONAL TRUCK LEASING SYSTEM; *U.S. Private*, pg. 787
PHH CORPORATION—Cendant Corporation; *U.S. Public*, pg. 321
PLM INTERNATIONAL, INC.; *U.S. Public*, pg. 1241
PST VANS, INC.; *U.S. Public*, pg. 1246
PACCAR LEASING CORPORATION—Paccar Inc.; *U.S. Public*, pg. 1247
PENSKE CORPORATION; *U.S. Private*, pg. 850
PENSKE TRUCK LEASING COMPANY LP—Penske Corporation; *U.S. Private*, pg. 850
RAYMOND LEASING CORPORATION—BT Industries AB; *Int'l*, pg. 123
RED BALL LEASING, INC.—Atlas World Group, Inc.; *U.S. Private*, pg. 97
ROLLINS TRUCK LEASING CORP.; *U.S. Public*, pg. 1405
RYDER SYSTEM, INC.; *U.S. Public*, pg. 1413
SALEM CARRIERS. INC.—Salem National Corporation; *U.S. Private*, pg. 962
SALEM LEASING CORP.—Salem National Corporation; *U.S. Private*, pg. 962
SALEM NATIONAL CORPORATION; *U.S. Private*, pg. 962
SELTRA—Lex Service PLC; *Int'l*, pg. 807
SIME DIAMOND LEASING (SINGAPORE) PTE. LTD.—Sime Darby Berhad; *Int'l*, pg. 1251
SOUTHSIDE FORD TRUCK SALES INC.; *U.S. Private*, pg. 1018
STRICK LEASE, INC.—Xtra Corporation; *U.S. Public*, pg. 1787
SYRACUSE SUPPLY COMPANY; *U.S. Private*, pg. 1060
SYRACUSE SUPPLY LEASING CO., INC.—Syracuse Supply Company; *U.S. Private*, pg. 1060
DAVE SYVERSON LINCOLN MERCURY; *U.S. Private*, pg. 1061
TRANSPORT INTERNATIONAL POOL OF CANADA LIMITED—General Electric Company; *U.S. Public*, pg. 713
TRINITY INDUSTRIES INC.; *U.S. Public*, pg. 1638
UNITED LEASING, INC.—UniGroup, Inc.; *U.S. Private*, pg. 1117
UNITED STATES FLEET LEASING, INC.—Ford Motor Company; *U.S. Public*, pg. 664
VILLAGE CAR COMPANY; *U.S. Private*, pg. 1140
WALSER AUTOMOTIVE GROUP; *U.S. Private*, pg. 1148
WATKINS SYSTEM INC.; *U.S. Private*, pg. 1153
C. WEAVER CHEVROLET, INC.; *U.S. Private*, pg. 1156
WESTLIE MOTOR COMPANY; *U.S. Private*, pg. 1169
WOOD TERMINAL COMPANY—Fortune Brands, Inc.; *U.S. Public*, pg. 675
XON LEASING—Maxon Industries, Inc.; *U.S. Private*, pg. 717

7514 — PASSENGER CAR RENTAL

ALAMO RENT-A-CAR INC.—Republic Industries, Inc.; *U.S. Public*, pg. 1379
AVIS AUTOVERMIETUNG AG—Cendant Corporation; *U.S. Public*, pg. 321
AVIS CAR LEASING—Cendant Corporation; *U.S. Public*, pg. 321
AVIS RENT A CAR SYSTEM, INC.—Cendant Corporation; *U.S. Public*, pg. 321
BMW BANK GMBH—Bayerische Motoren Werke Aktiengesellschaft; *Int'l*, pg. 177
BEAUDRY FORD, INC.; *U.S. Private*, pg. 127
BRITAX AUTOLEASE B.V.—Britax International plc; *Int'l*, pg. 216
BUDGET GROUP, INC.; *U.S. Private*, pg. 178
BUDGET RENT A CAR CORPORATION—Budget Group, Inc.; *U.S. Private*, pg. 178
BUERKLE BUICK-HONDA CO.; *U.S. Private*, pg. 178
CFC INVESTMENT CORP.—Cincinnati Financial Corp.; *U.S. Public*, pg. 368
CAM CARS—Chrysler Corporation; *U.S. Public*, pg. 354
CHASE MANHATTAN SERVICE CORPORATION—The Chase Manhattan Corporation; *U.S. Public*, pg. 338
CINCINNATI FINANCIAL CORP.; *U.S. Public*, pg. 368
DANA COMMERCIAL CREDIT CORP. (OHIO)—Dana Corporation; *U.S. Public*, pg. 479
DOLLAR RENT A CAR—Chrysler Corporation; *U.S. Public*, pg. 354
EAGLE LINCOLN MERCURY INC.; *U.S. Private*, pg. 355
ENTERPRISE RENT-A-CAR COMPANY; *U.S. Private*, pg. 377
FHL LEASE HOLDING COMPANY, INC.—First Hawaiian, Inc.; *U.S. Public*, pg. 634
FIRST GRAY LINE CORPORATION; *U.S. Private*, pg. 407
FIRST HAWAIIAN LEASING, INC.—First Hawaiian, Inc.; *U.S. Public*, pg. 635
STEVE FOLEY CADILLAC; *U.S. Private*, pg. 416
FRANK CONSOLIDATED ENTERPRISES INC.; *U.S. Private*, pg. 423
THE HERTZ CORPORATION—Ford Motor Company; *U.S. Public*, pg. 664
HOLMAN ENTERPRISES; *U.S. Private*, pg. 535
KINGS TOYOTA SUZUKI; *U.S. Private*, pg. 621
LB INDUSTRIES INC.; *U.S. Private*, pg. 639
LEX VEHICLE LEASING—Lex Service PLC; *Int'l*, pg. 807
LIBERTYVILLE LINCOLN-MERCURY SALES, INC.; *U.S. Private*, pg. 666
MERCEDES-BENZ LEASING GMBH—Daimler-Benz Aktiengesellschaft; *Int'l*, pg. 368
MERCHANTS RENT A CAR, INC.; *U.S. Private*, pg. 732
NATIONAL AUTO CREDIT INC.; *U.S. Public*, pg. 1152
NATIONAL CAR RENTAL SYSTEM, INC.—Republic Industries, Inc.; *U.S. Public*, pg. 1379
NATIONAL FLEET & LEASE—Chrysler Corporation; *U.S. Public*, pg. 354
NATIONAL MANAGEMENT, INC.—Georgia-Pacific Corporation; *U.S. Public*, pg. 736
NATIONAL PARKS TRANSPORTATION, INC.—SkyWest Inc.; *U.S. Public*, pg. 1476
NISSAN CAR LEASING CO., LTD.—Nissan Motor Co., Ltd.; *Int'l*, pg. 944
ORIX CAR RENTALS PTE LTD.—Orix Corporation; *Int'l*, pg. 1009
ORIX CAR RENTALS SDN. BHD.—Orix Corporation; *Int'l*, pg. 1009
ORIX RENT-A-CAR—Orix Corporation; *Int'l*, pg. 1009
POPULAR LEASING & RENTAL, INC.—Banco Popular de Puerto Rico; *U.S. Public*, pg. 176
REPLACEMENT RENT-A-CAR—National Auto Credit Inc.; *U.S. Public*, pg. 1153
SCAMP AUTO—Chrysler Corporation; *U.S. Public*, pg. 354
SERVICE ASSETS CORP.—Bromar Inc.; *U.S. Private*, pg. 171
SIME DIAMOND LEASING (SINGAPORE) PTE. LTD.—Sime Darby Berhad; *Int'l*, pg. 1251
SNAPPY CAR RENTAL, INC.; *U.S. Private*, pg. 1010
TAMAROFF LEASING CO.—Tamaroff Buick Inc.; *U.S. Private*, pg. 1067
TARTAN, INC.—Chrysler Corporation; *U.S. Public*, pg. 354
UGLY DUCKLING CORP.; *U.S. Public*, pg. 1662
UNITED STATES FLEET LEASING, INC.—Ford Motor Company; *U.S. Public*, pg. 664
VANDERGRIFF CHEVROLET GEO; *U.S. Private*, pg. 1133
VELCO—Banco Popular de Puerto Rico; *U.S. Public*, pg. 176
WALSER AUTOMOTIVE GROUP; *U.S. Private*, pg. 1148
WALSER LEASING INC.—Walser Automotive Group; *U.S. Private*, pg. 1148
WESTLIE MOTOR COMPANY; *U.S. Private*, pg. 1169

7515 — PASSENGER CAR LEASING

ABN AUTO LEASE B.V.—ABN-AMRO Holding N.V.; *Int'l*, pg. 9
MIKE ALBERT LEASING, INC.; *U.S. Private*, pg. 32
AMLECO LEASING LIMITED—Empire Company Limited; *Int'l*, pg. 454
AUTO LEASE HOLLAND B.V.—ABN-AMRO Holding N.V.; *Int'l*, pg. 9
AUTOLEASE FLEETS LIMITED—Britax International plc; *Int'l*, pg. 216
AUTOLEASE LIMITED—Britax International plc; *Int'l*, pg. 216
AUTOMOTIVE RENTALS, INC. (ARI)—Holman Enterprises; *U.S. Private*, pg. 535
BANKERS LEASING CORP.—Citicorp; *U.S. Public*, pg. 377
BRITAX INTERNATIONAL PLC; *Int'l*, pg. 216
BYERLY FORD-NISSAN INC.; *U.S. Private*, pg. 191
CAMDEN MOTORS LTD.—Barclays Bank PLC; *Int'l*, pg. 165
CAPITOL CHEVROLET CADILLAC GEO SUBARU INC.; *U.S. Private*, pg. 206
CITICORP DEL-LEASE, INC.—Citicorp; *U.S. Public*, pg. 377
THE CURRY CORPORATION; *U.S. Private*, pg. 297
DAF TRUCKS N.V.—Paccar Inc.; *U.S. Public*, pg. 1247
EAGLE LINCOLN MERCURY INC.; *U.S. Private*, pg. 355
EMKAY, INC.; *U.S. Private*, pg. 374
EMPIRE COMPANY LIMITED; *Int'l*, pg. 453
ENTERPRISE RENT-A-CAR COMPANY; *U.S. Private*, pg. 377
EUROPCAR AUTOVERMIETUNG GMBH—Volkswagen AG; *Int'l*, pg. 1473

EXECUTIVE CAR LEASING, INC.; *U.S. Private*, pg. 388
FORD LEASING DEVELOPMENT CO.—Ford Motor Company; *U.S. Public*, pg. 664
FORD LEASING SPA—Ford Motor Company; *U.S. Public*, pg. 666
G.E. CAPITAL FLEET SERVICES—General Electric Company; *U.S. Public*, pg. 710
GILLOGLY CHEVROLET & GEO, INC.; *U.S. Private*, pg. 454
JEROME-DUNCAN FORD; *U.S. Private*, pg. 586
KENTUCKY MEDICAL INSURANCE COMPANY (KMIC)—Michigan Physicians Mutual Liability Inc.; *U.S. Private*, pg. 741
KINGS TOYOTA SUZUKI; *U.S. Private*, pg. 621
LB INDUSTRIES INC.; *U.S. Private*, pg. 639
LEX SERVICE PLC; *Int'l*, pg. 806
MACROMEDIA LEASING—Macromedia Incorporated; *U.S. Private*, pg. 693
MERCHANTS RENT A CAR, INC.; *U.S. Private*, pg. 732
THE MOTORLEASE CORP.; *U.S. Private*, pg. 764
NISSAN MOTORIST SERVICE CO., LTD.—Nissan Motor Co., Ltd.; *Int'l*, pg. 944
PHH CORPORATION—Cendant Corporation; *U.S. Public*, pg. 321
PROSPECT MOTORS, INC.; *U.S. Private*, pg. 891
RENAULT USA—Renault; *Int'l*, pg. 1102
SENATOR FORD; *U.S. Private*, pg. 983
I. SPIEWAK & SONS, INC.; *U.S. Private*, pg. 1025
TSE LEASING CO.—I. Spiewak & Sons, Inc.; *U.S. Private*, pg. 1025
TAMAROFF LEASING CO.—Tamaroff Buick Inc.; *U.S. Private*, pg. 1067
THOMSON MACCONNELL CADILLAC, INC.; *U.S. Private*, pg. 1084
TRADE SHOW ENTERPRISES—I. Spiewak & Sons, Inc.; *U.S. Private*, pg. 1025
UNITED LEASING COMPANY—Michigan Physicians Mutual Liability Inc.; *U.S. Private*, pg. 741
VANDERGRIFF CHEVROLET GEO; *U.S. Private*, pg. 1133
VOLKSWAGEN LEASING ANLAGEN GMBH—Volkswagen AG; *Int'l*, pg. 1474
VOLKSWAGEN LEASING S.A. DE C.V.—Volkswagen AG; *Int'l*, pg. 1475
WSFS CREDIT CORP.—WSFS Financial Corporation; *U.S. Public*, pg. 1729
WALSER LEASING INC.—Walser Automotive Group; *U.S. Private*, pg. 1148
C. WEAVER CHEVROLET, INC.; *U.S. Private*, pg. 1156
BUFF WHELAN CHEVROLET & GEO, INC.; *U.S. Private*, pg. 1171

7519 — UTILITY TRAILER & RECREATIONAL VEHICLE RENTAL

AMERCO; *U.S. Private*, pg. 48
AMERICAN LAND CRUISERS—Budget Group, Inc.; *U.S. Private*, pg. 178
CRUISE AMERICA, INC.—Budget Group, Inc.; *U.S. Private*, pg. 178
CRUISE CANADA, INC.—Budget Group, Inc.; *U.S. Private*, pg. 178
FLEXI-VAN LEASING, INC.—Flexi-Van Leasing, Inc.; *U.S. Private*, pg. 413
FLEXI-VAN UNITED KINGDOM—Flexi-Van Leasing, Inc.; *U.S. Private*, pg. 413
FLEXI-VAN LEASING, INC.; *U.S. Private*, pg. 413
G.E. CAPITAL FLEET SERVICES—General Electric Company; *U.S. Public*, pg. 710
HOLIDAY RV RENTAL/LEASING, INC.—Holiday RV Superstores, Inc.; *U.S. Public*, pg. 829
HOLIDAY RV SUPERSTORES, INC.; *U.S. Public*, pg. 829
NATIONAL TRUCK LEASING SYSTEM; *U.S. Private*, pg. 787
PLM INTERNATIONAL, INC.; *U.S. Public*, pg. 1241
PLM TRAILER LEASING—PLM International, Inc.; *U.S. Public*, pg. 1241
RENTCO TRAILER CORPORATION—Xtra Corporation; *U.S. Public*, pg. 1787
STILLMAN & HOAG, INC.; *U.S. Private*, pg. 1043
TRANSAMERICA LEASING INC.—Transamerica Corporation; *U.S. Public*, pg. 1630
U-HAUL LEASING & SALES COMPANY—Amerco; *U.S. Private*, pg. 49
XTRA CORPORATION; *U.S. Public*, pg. 1786

7521 — AUTOMOBILE PARKING

ALLRIGHT CORPORATION; *U.S. Private*, pg. 42
ALLRIGHT PARKING CORPORATION—Allright Corporation; *U.S. Private*, pg. 43
AMPCO AUTO SYSTEM PARKING—ABM Industries; *U.S. Public*, pg. 2
APCOA, INC.—Holberg Industries, Inc.; *U.S. Private*, pg. 533
ATLANTIC EAST COAST TERMINAL—St. Joe Corp.; *U.S. Public*, pg. 1427
BAY PARK, INC.—Allright Corporation; *U.S. Private*, pg. 43
DUTCH PARKING INC.—Allright Corporation; *U.S. Private*, pg. 43
EDISON PARKING PROPERTIES, LLC; *U.S. Private*, pg. 364
IDEAL PARKING, INC.—Allright Corporation; *U.S. Private*, pg. 44
KINNEY SYSTEM, INC.; *U.S. Private*, pg. 622
KNOX ALLRIGHT, INC.—Allright Corporation; *U.S. Private*, pg. 43
KRUPP STAHLBAU BERLIN GMBH & CO. KG—Fried. Krupp AG; *Int'l*, pg. 508
METROPOLITAN PROPERTIES SYSTEMS; *U.S. Private*, pg. 739
MULTIPLE PARKING SERVICES, INC.—Allright Corporation; *U.S. Private*, pg. 43
NORTHWEST PARKING SERVICES INC.—Allright Corporation; *U.S. Private*, pg. 43
ONEOK PARKING CO.—ONEOK Inc.; *U.S. Public*, pg. 1226
PENNSYLVANIA PARKING, INC.—Allright Corporation; *U.S. Private*, pg. 43
PREEM PETROLEUM AB; *Int'l*, pg. 1066
SQUARE INDUSTRIES, INC.—Central Parking Corp.; *U.S. Public*, pg. 326
SQUARE PLUS GARAGE INC.—Central Parking Corp.; *U.S. Public*, pg. 326
SQUARE PLUS OPERATING CORPORATION—Central Parking Corp.; *U.S. Public*, pg. 326
SYSTEMS PARKING, INC.; *U.S. Private*, pg. 1061
UNITED PARKING, INC.; *U.S. Private*, pg. 1123
UNITED PARKING SERVICES, INC.—Central Parking Corp.; *U.S. Public*, pg. 326

7532 — TOP, BODY, UPHOLSTERY REPAIR SHOPS & PAINT SHOPS

BAUGHER CHEVROLET-BUICK INC.; *U.S. Private*, pg. 123
BEACH CITY CHEVROLET CO.; *U.S. Private*, pg. 125
DALLAS PETERBILT, INC.; *U.S. Private*, pg. 309
EAGLE LINCOLN MERCURY INC.; *U.S. Private*, pg. 355
MAACO ENTERPRISES INC.; *U.S. Private*, pg. 689
MEL FARR AUTOMOTIVE GROUP, INC.; *U.S. Private*, pg. 729
MULTIPLE ALLIED SERVICES, INC.; *U.S. Private*, pg. 767
ROBERTSONS AUTO BODY—Robertson's Auto Salvage; *U.S. Private*, pg. 936
ROYALE PAINT & BODY—Regency Lincoln Mercury, Inc.; *U.S. Private*, pg. 918
EARL SCHEIB, INC.; *U.S. Public*, pg. 1437
STARCRAFT CORPORATION; *U.S. Public*, pg. 1510

7533 — AUTOMOTIVE EXHAUST SYSTEM REPAIR SHOPS

METPELA OY—Kemira Oy; *Int'l*, pg. 729
MIDWEST TIRE & MUFFLER, INC.; *U.S. Private*, pg. 745
SPEEDY CAR-X, INC.—Tenneco Inc.; *U.S. Public*, pg. 1578
TUFFY ASSOCIATES CORP.; *U.S. Private*, pg. 1109

7534 — TIRE RETREADING & REPAIR SHOPS

ARKANSAS BEST CORPORATION; *U.S. Public*, pg. 130
BURRIS FOODS, INC.; *U.S. Private*, pg. 188
CONDERE CORPORATION; *U.S. Private*, pg. 262
MONRO MUFFLER/BRAKE, INC.; *U.S. Public*, pg. 1124
PARRISH TIRE COMPANY, INC.; *U.S. Private*, pg. 840
REDBURN TIRE COMPANY; *U.S. Private*, pg. 915
TREADCO, INC.—Arkansas Best Corporation; *U.S. Public*, pg. 131

7536 — AUTOMOTIVE GLASS REPLACEMENT SHOPS

AUTO GLASS SPECIALISTS; *U.S. Private*, pg. 100
SMITH & SMITH GLASS LTD.—International Paper Company; *U.S. Public*, pg. 904

7537 — AUTOMOTIVE TRANSMISSION REPAIR SHOPS

COTTMAN TRANSMISSION SYSTEMS, INC.; *U.S. Private*, pg. 278
LEE MYLES ASSOCIATES CORPORATION; *U.S. Private*, pg. 657
U.S. TRANSPARTS—Moran Industries, Inc.; *U.S. Private*, pg. 760
C. WEAVER CHEVROLET, INC.; *U.S. Private*, pg. 1156

7538 — GENERAL AUTOMOTIVE REPAIR SHOPS

A A CATER TRUCK MANUFACTURING COMPANY, INC.; *U.S. Private*, pg. 1
A S H, INC.; *U.S. Private*, pg. 2
ASSOCIATED POWER, INC.; *U.S. Private*, pg. 92
BAST CHEVROLET INC.; *U.S. Private*, pg. 122
BEACH CITY CHEVROLET CO.; *U.S. Private*, pg. 125
BRIDGESTONE/FIRESTONE, INC.—Bridgestone Corporation; *Int'l*, pg. 213
BROADWAY CHEVROLET; *U.S. Private*, pg. 170
BYERLY FORD-NISSAN INC.; *U.S. Private*, pg. 191
CAMPBELL OIL CO.; *U.S. Private*, pg. 204
CAPITOL CHEVROLET CADILLAC GEO SUBARU INC.; *U.S. Private*, pg. 206
CHICAGO AUTOWERKS, INC.—Stamford Capital; *U.S. Private*, pg. 1030
CLARK DETROIT-DIESEL ALLISON; *U.S. Private*, pg. 242
CUMMINS CUMBERLAND INC.; *U.S. Private*, pg. 295
CUMMINS MID-SOUTH, INC.; *U.S. Private*, pg. 295
D.S.U.-PETERBILT & GMC, INC.; *U.S. Private*, pg. 306
DAVIS-MOORE OLDSMOBILE, INC.; *U.S. Private*, pg. 315
JACK DEMMER FORD, INC.; *U.S. Private*, pg. 323
DRIVE TRAIN INDUSTRIES; *U.S. Private*, pg. 343
EAGLE LINCOLN MERCURY INC.; *U.S. Private*, pg. 355
EARNHARDT'S MOTOR COMPANIES; *U.S. Private*, pg. 356
ELVINS EQUIPMENT SALES LIMITED—Wajax Limited; *Int'l*, pg. 1485
ENSABLADORA CENTROAMERICANA DE COSTA RICA S.A.—Toyota Motor Corporation; *Int'l*, pg. 1413
FREE SERVICE TIRE COMPANY, INC.; *U.S. Private*, pg. 425
FRIENDLY CHEVROLET CO. INC.; *U.S. Private*, pg. 428
GETTY PETROLEUM MARKETING INC.; *U.S. Public*, pg. 740
GETTY TERMINALS, INC.—Getty Petroleum Marketing Inc.; *U.S. Public*, pg. 741
GREAT LAKES PETERBILT, GMC; *U.S. Private*, pg. 475
HONDA MOTOR PARTS SERVICE CO., LTD.—Honda Motor Co., Ltd.; *Int'l*, pg. 634
HYUNDAI MOTOR SERVICE CO., LTD.—Hyundai Motor Company; *Int'l*, pg. 641
ILLINOIS AUTO CENTRAL DIV.—Illinois Auto Electric Co.; *U.S. Private*, pg. 558
KENWORTH OF INDIANAPOLIS INC.; *U.S. Private*, pg. 615
JIM KOONS MANAGEMENT; *U.S. Private*, pg. 632
LA MESA R V CENTER, INC.; *U.S. Private*, pg. 640
LEEMILTS PETROLEUM, INC.—Getty Petroleum Marketing Inc.; *U.S. Public*, pg. 741
LEX HARVEY—Lex Service PLC; *Int'l*, pg. 807
LISTER-PETTER INC.—BTR plc; *Int'l*, pg. 127
MCQUICK'S OILUBE, INC.—Quaker State Corporation; *U.S. Public*, pg. 1348
MID AMERICA INTERNATIONAL TRUCKS, INC.; *U.S. Private*, pg. 743
MULTIPLE ALLIED SERVICES, INC.; *U.S. Private*, pg. 767
OCEAN CHEVROLET, INC.; *U.S. Private*, pg. 810
PGA MOTORS—Lex Service PLC; *Int'l*, pg. 807
PATSY'S, INC.; *U.S. Private*, pg. 843
P.T. PETRO CORP.—Getty Petroleum Marketing Inc.; *U.S. Public*, pg. 741
PREDELIVERY SERVICE CORPORATION—Ford Motor Company; *U.S. Public*, pg. 664
PREEM PETROLEUM AB; *Int'l*, pg. 1066
QUICK 10—Investors Management Corp.; *U.S. Private*, pg. 575
RIHM MOTOR COMPANY; *U.S. Private*, pg. 931
SAAB AUTOMOBILE AB—Investor AB; *Int'l*, pg. 687
SAAB AUTOMOBILE AB—General Motors Corporation; *U.S. Public*, pg. 725
DAVE SYVERSON LINCOLN MERCURY; *U.S. Private*, pg. 1061
TRACTION DIV.—UAP, Inc.; *Int'l*, pg. 1426
UAP, INC.; *Int'l*, pg. 1426
VON HOUSEN MOTORS; *U.S. Private*, pg. 1143
WAJAX LIMITED; *Int'l*, pg. 1484
WATEROUS DETROIT DIESEL-ALLISON INC.—Wajax Limited; *Int'l*, pg. 1485
C. WEAVER CHEVROLET, INC.; *U.S. Private*, pg. 1156
BUFF WHELAN CHEVROLET & GEO, INC.; *U.S. Private*, pg. 1171

7539 — AUTOMOBILE REPAIR SHOPS, NEC

A K H COMPANY, INC.; *U.S. Private*, pg. 2
APOGEE ENTERPRISES, INC.; *U.S. Public*, pg. 120
AUTO GLASS SPECIALISTS; *U.S. Private*, pg. 100
BAKER SUPPORT SERVICES, INC.—Michael Baker Corporation; *U.S. Public*, pg. 168
BALCRANK PRODUCTS—The General Chemical Group, Inc.; *U.S. Public*, pg. 707
CAMDEN MOTORS LTD.—Barclays Bank PLC; *Int'l*, pg. 165
CHICAGO AUTOWERKS, INC.—Stamford Capital; *U.S. Private*, pg. 1030
D.S.U.-PETERBILT & GMC, INC.; *U.S. Private*, pg. 306
GLOBE-AMERADA GLASS COMPANY; *U.S. Private*, pg. 458
HARMON GLASS COMPANY—Apogee Enterprises, Inc.; *U.S. Public*, pg. 120
HARMON GLASS OF FLORIDA, INC.—Apogee Enterprises, Inc.; *U.S. Public*, pg. 120
INTERSTATE GLASS CO. INC.—Apogee Enterprises, Inc.; *U.S. Public*, pg. 120
KASSBOHRER NORTH AMERICA—Daimler-Benz Aktiengesellschaft; *Int'l*, pg. 368
MONRO MUFFLER/BRAKE, INC.; *U.S. Public*, pg. 1124
MOTORCAR PARTS & ACCESSORIES; *U.S. Public*, pg. 1136
NITTSU KIKO UNYU CO., LTD.—Nippon Express Co., Ltd.; *Int'l*, pg. 934
PACIFIC DISTRIBUTION—Pacific Dunlop Limited; *Int'l*, pg. 1021
PREMIER FARNELL PLC; *Int'l*, pg. 1068
TRACTION DIV.—UAP, Inc.; *Int'l*, pg. 1426
UAP, INC.; *Int'l*, pg. 1426
W.W. WALLWORK, INC.; *U.S. Private*, pg. 1148
WATEROUS DETROIT DIESEL-ALLISON INC.—Wajax Limited; *Int'l*, pg. 1485
C. WEAVER CHEVROLET, INC.; *U.S. Private*, pg. 1156
WESTERN AUTOMOTIVE REBUILDERS—Acklands Limited; *Int'l*, pg. 23
WESTLIE MOTOR COMPANY; *U.S. Private*, pg. 1169

7542 — CAR WASHES

REN-VASK A/S—Electrolux, AB; *Int'l*, pg. 441
F.L. ROBERTS & CO. INC.; *U.S. Private*, pg. 935

7549 — AUTOMOBILE SERVICES, EXCEPT REPAIR & CAR WASHES

ALLIEDSIGNAL AUTOMOTIVE PROVING GROUNDS—AlliedSignal Inc.; *U.S. Public*, pg. 51
JACK BYRNE MINUTEMAN LUBE—Jack Byrne Ford & Mercury, Inc.; *U.S. Private*, pg. 191
CITYWIDE TOWING—Stamford Capital; *U.S. Private*, pg. 1030
COLONIAL OIL INDUSTRIES; *U.S. Private*, pg. 253
CONDERE CORPORATION; *U.S. Private*, pg. 262
FLORIDA EAST COAST INSPECTIONS, INC.—St. Joe Corp.; *U.S. Public*, pg. 1427
FORD AUTO CLUB, INC.—Ford Motor Company; *U.S. Public*, pg. 663

S.I.C. Index

FORD MOTOR COMPANY; *U.S. Public*, pg. 661
GREASE MONKEY INTERNATIONAL INC.; *U.S. Public*, pg. 759
MARTA TECHNOLOGIES, INC.—Allen Telecom, Inc.; *U.S. Public*, pg. 46
PAC MANUFACTURING & DISTRIBUTING CO.—Precision Tune Autocare Inc.; *U.S. Public*, pg. 1321
PENNZOIL COMPANY; *U.S. Public*, pg. 1272
PRECISION TUNE AUTOCARE INC.; *U.S. Public*, pg. 1321
PREDELIVERY SERVICE CORPORATION—Ford Motor Company; *U.S. Public*, pg. 664
QUAKER STATE CORPORATION; *U.S. Public*, pg. 1348
10 MINUTE OIL CHANGE—Pennzoil Company; *U.S. Public*, *pg. 1272*
TIDY CAR INTERNATIONAL, INC.—Ziebart International Corporation; *U.S. Private*, pg. 1205
ZIEBART INTERNATIONAL CORPORATION; *U.S. Private*, *pg. 1205*

7622 — RADIO & TELEVISION REPAIR SHOPS

AAR CORP.; *U.S. Public*, pg. 1
AERO SYSTEMS AVIATION CORP.; *U.S. Private*, pg. 24
CUTTER AVIATION ALBUQUERQUE, INC; *U.S. Private*, pg. 298
EROL'S INTERNET; *U.S. Private*, pg. 382
MARS AIRCRAFT SERVICES CO. OF NEW JERSEY—AAR Corp.; *U.S. Public*, pg. 1
MASTERCARE LIMITED—Dixons Group plc; *Int'l*, pg. 414
PTS ELECTRONICS CORPORATION; *U.S. Private*, pg. 828
RADIO HOLLAND ELECTRONICS—SAIT-RadioHolland Group S.A.; *Int'l*, pg. 1151
RADIO HOLLAND GROUP-FISHERY EQUIP.—SAIT-RadioHolland Group S.A.; *Int'l*, pg. 1151
RADIO HOLLAND GROUP-SURVEY EQUIP.—SAIT-RadioHolland Group S.A.; *Int'l*, pg. 1151
RAULAND-BORG (CANADA) INC.—Rauland-Borg Corporation; *U.S. Private*, pg. 911
SAILTRON B.V.—SAIT-RadioHolland Group S.A.; *Int'l*, pg. 1151
SINGAPORE ENGINE OVERHAUL CENTRE (PTE.) LTD.—Temasek Holdings Pte. Ltd.; *Int'l*, pg. 1374
ZENITH VIDEO TECH CORPORATION—Zenith Electronics Corp.; *U.S. Public*, pg. 1790

7623 — REFRIGERATION & AIR CONDITIONING SERVICE & REPAIR SHOPS

AMERICAN HOME SHIELD CORPORATION—The ServiceMaster Company; *U.S. Public*, pg. 1461
ARIZONA REFRIGERATION SUPPLIES, INC.—Kitchell Corporation; *U.S. Private*, pg. 624
CAL-AIR INC.; *U.S. Private*, pg. 199
CUMMINS SOUTHWEST INC.; *U.S. Private*, pg. 296
FROZEN FOOD EXPRESS INDUSTRIES, INC.; *U.S. Public*, *pg. 685*
HADEN ENGINEERING PTY—Haden Maclellan Holdings plc; *Int'l*, pg. 586
HONEYWELL INC.; *U.S. Public*, pg. 833
ILLINOIS AUTO CENTRAL DIV.—Illinois Auto Electric Co.; *U.S. Private*, pg. 558
INDUSTRIAL COMPONENTS GROUP—BTR plc; *Int'l*, pg. 127
KVAERNER EUREKA INC.—Kvaerner a.s.a.; *Int'l*, pg. 770
KVAERNER EUREKA, TROMSO DIVISION—Kvaerner a.s.a.; *Int'l*, pg. 767
LEC REFRIGERATION PLC—Sime Darby Berhad; *Int'l*, pg. 1251
MFRI INC.; *U.S. Public*, pg. 1026
MAYTAG CUSTOMER SERVICE—Maytag Corporation; *U.S. Public*, pg. 1064
THE SERVICEMASTER COMPANY; *U.S. Public*, pg. 1461
TD INDUSTRIES INC.; *U.S. Private*, pg. 1063
TOSHIBA AIR CONDITIONING CO., LTD.—Toshiba Corporation; *Int'l*, pg. 1403
W & B REFRIGERATION SERVICE CO.—Frozen Food Express Industries, Inc.; *U.S. Public*, pg. 685
WESTINGHOUSE DE VENEZUELA S.A.—CBS Corporation; *U.S. Public*, pg. 275

7629 — ELECTRICAL & ELECTRONIC REPAIR SHOPS, NEC

AAR CORP.; *U.S. Public*, pg. 1
AERO ELECTRONICS INCORPORATED—Memphis Group, Inc.; *U.S. Private*, pg. 731
AERO SYSTEMS AVIATION CORP.; *U.S. Private*, pg. 24
AISIN WORLD CORP.-DETROIT—Aisin Seiki Co. Ltd.; *Int'l*, pg. 39
AMERICAN HOME SHIELD CORPORATION—The ServiceMaster Company; *U.S. Public*, pg. 1461
AMERICAN TECHNICAL SERVICES GROUP, INC.—Strategic Distribution Inc.; *U.S. Public*, pg. 1523
AUTOTROL CORPORATION—Osmonics, Inc.; *U.S. Public*, pg. 1234
AUTOTROL FRANCE, S.A.—Osmonics, Inc.; *U.S. Public*, pg. 1234
BECKER—Harman International Industries, Inc.; *U.S. Public*, pg. 787
BLUMBERG COMMUNICATIONS INC.—Caribiner International, Inc.; *U.S. Public*, pg. 305
BRUMKO MAGNETICS—Magnetics Data Inc.; *U.S. Private*, pg. 696
BYTEX DATACOM LTD.—Storage Technology Corporation; *U.S. Public*, pg. 1522
CAE ELECTRONICS, LTD.—CAE Inc.; *Int'l*, pg. 237
CHROMA VIDEO, INC.—Video Display Corporation; *U.S. Public*, pg. 1720
CHRONOS RICHARDSON—Staveley Industries PLC; *Int'l*, pg. 1299
ER-ELECTRIC A/S—ABB Asea Brown Boveri (Holding) Ltd.; *Int'l*, pg. 3
ELECTRICAL EQUIPMENT COMPANY; *U.S. Private*, pg. 368
ELECTRICAL EQUIPMENT COMPANY—Electrical Equipment Company; *U.S. Private*, pg. 368
ELECTRONIC DRIVES AND CONTROLS; *U.S. Private*, pg. 370
ELECTRONIC SYSTEMS DIVISION—The Boeing Company; *U.S. Public*, pg. 241
ELSCINT DE MEXICO S. DE R.L. DE C.V.—Elscint Ltd.; *Int'l*, pg. 450
ELSCINT ITALIA S.R.L.—Elscint Ltd.; *Int'l*, pg. 450
ELSCINT NV/SA—Elscint Ltd.; *Int'l*, pg. 450
EPSON DEUTSCHLAND GMBH (E.D.G.)—Seiko Epson Corporation; *Int'l*, pg. 1219
ERICSSON GE TELECOMMUNICATION INC.—Telefonaktiebolaget LM Ericsson; *Int'l*, pg. 1366
FERGUSON ELECTRIC EQUIPMENT CORPORATION—Ferguson Electric Construction Co., Inc.; *U.S. Private*, pg. 401
FLUKE CORPORATION; *U.S. Public*, pg. 659
HONEYWELL INC.; *U.S. Public*, pg. 833
INNOSERV TECHNOLOGIES, INC.; *U.S. Public*, pg. 879
INNOSERV TECHNOLOGIES, INC.—InnoServ Technologies, Inc.; *U.S. Public*, pg. 880
MACE PRODUCTS—Osmonics, Inc.; *U.S. Public*, pg. 1234
MAGNETEK, INC.; *U.S. Public*, pg. 1037
MAYTAG CUSTOMER SERVICE—Maytag Corporation; *U.S. Public*, pg. 1064
MED-LAB SUPPLY COMPANY, INC.; *U.S. Private*, pg. 726
MEDELEC ESPANA S.A.—Vickers PLC; *Int'l*, pg. 1467
MEDELEC NORTHERN EUROPE—Vickers PLC; *Int'l*, pg. 1467
MEMPHIS GROUP, INC.; *U.S. Private*, pg. 730
MILWAUKEE ELECTRIC TOOL (CANADA) LTD.—Assa Abloy AB; *Int'l*, pg. 18
MOLEX SERVICES GMBH—Molex Incorporated; *U.S. Public*, pg. 1122
MOTOR GROUP—Rockwell International Corporation; *U.S. Public*, pg. 1398
NATIONAL AIRMOTIVE CORPORATION; *U.S. Private*, pg. 775
NATIONAL TECHNICAL SERVICES—Strategic Distribution Inc.; *U.S. Public*, pg. 1523
NIPPON DIONEX K.K.—Dionex Corporation; *U.S. Public*, pg. 510
OSMONICS ASIA/PACIFIC, LTD.—Osmonics, Inc.; *U.S. Public*, pg. 1234
OSMONICS ASIA/PACIFIC LTD.—Osmonics, Inc.; *U.S. Public*, pg. 1234
OSMONICS, INC.; *U.S. Public*, pg. 1233
OXFORD INSTRUMENTS-MEDICAL SYSTEMS DIV.—Oxford Instruments plc; *Int'l*, pg. 1018
OZONE RESEARCH & EQUIPMENT CORP.—Osmonics, Inc.; *U.S. Public*, pg. 1234
PACIFICA SERVICES, INC.; *U.S. Private*, pg. 832
PIONEER-STANDARD ELECTRONICS, INC.; *U.S. Public*, pg. 1300
PITNEY BOWES INC.; *U.S. Public*, pg. 1303
REX-ROTARY UK LIMITED—Ricoh Company, Ltd.; *Int'l*, pg. 1114
S & W ELEKTROMEDIZIN GMBH—Vickers PLC; *Int'l*, pg. 1467
SPX CORPORATION; *U.S. Public*, pg. 1420
SARELEM—Jeumont-Schneider Trenformeteurs; *Int'l*, pg. 706
SERVICE SOLUTION—SPX Corporation; *U.S. Public*, pg. 1421
THE SERVICEMASTER COMPANY; *U.S. Public*, pg. 1461
SHARE TECHNOLOGIES - FAIRCHILD—Tel-Save Holdings, Inc.; *U.S. Public*, pg. 1568
SINGAPORE ENGINE OVERHAUL CENTRE (PTE.) LTD.—Temasek Holdings Pte. Ltd.; *Int'l*, pg. 1374
SONOTRON HOLDING AG—IDB Holding Corporation; *Int'l*, *pg. 644*
STANDARD MEDICAL IMAGING, INC.; *U.S. Private*, pg. 1032
SUNBEAM CORPORATION (CANADA) LIMITED—Sunbeam Corporation; *U.S. Public*, pg. 1533
SYSECA INC.—Thomson S.A.; *Int'l*, pg. 1384
TIE/COMMUNICATIONS, INC.; *U.S. Private*, pg. 1085
TOSHIBA AKITA DENKI CO., LTD.—Toshiba Corporation; *Int'l*, pg. 1403
TOSHIBA ELEMEC CORPORATION—Toshiba Corporation; *Int'l*, pg. 1404
TOSHIBA ELETEC CHUBU CORPORATION—Toshiba Corporation; *Int'l*, pg. 1404
TOSHIBA ELETEC HIGASHI NIHON CORPORATION—Toshiba Corporation; *Int'l*, pg. 1404
TOSHIBA ELETEC NISHINIHON CORPORATION—Toshiba Corporation; *Int'l*, pg. 1404
TOSHIBA IWATE DENKI CO., LTD.—Toshiba Corporation; *Int'l*, pg. 1404
TOSHIBA KYUSHU DENKI CO., LTD.—Toshiba Corporation; *Int'l*, pg. 1404
TOSHIBA OU DENKI CO., LTD.—Toshiba Corporation; *Int'l*, *pg. 1404*
TOSHIBA SHIKOKU ELECTRIC CO., LTD.—Toshiba Corporation; *Int'l*, pg. 1404
TOSHIBA TECHNICAL SERVICES INTERNATIONAL CORPORATION—Toshiba Corporation; *Int'l*, pg. 1405
TOSHIBA TOHOKU DENKI CO., LTD.—Toshiba Corporation; *Int'l*, pg. 1405
VAPONICS INC.—Osmonics, Inc.; *U.S. Public*, pg. 1234
VICKER MEDICAL NEDERLANDS—Vickers PLC; *Int'l*, pg. 1467
VITAL NETWORK SERVICE, INC.—General Datacomm Industries, Inc.; *U.S. Public*, pg. 708
WESTERN FILTER—Osmonics, Inc.; *U.S. Public*, pg. 1234

7631 — WATCH, CLOCK & JEWELRY REPAIR

FINLAY ENTERPRISES, INC.; *U.S. Public*, pg. 623
ROLEX INDUSTRIES, INC.—Rolex Watch Co. SA; *Int'l*, pg. 1126

7692 — WELDING REPAIR

ANCHOR TOOL & DIE COMPANY; *U.S. Private*, pg. 71
CHARLESTON CONTAINERS SHOPS INC.—Sea Containers Ltd.; *Int'l*, pg. 1214
FOSBEL, INC.—Burmah Castrol plc; *Int'l*, pg. 234
MUNROE, INC.; *U.S. Private*, pg. 767
OXARC INC.; *U.S. Private*, pg. 825
L.B. SMITH, INC.; *U.S. Private*, pg. 1009
TRACTOR MACHINING CO.—Empire Southwest Co.; *U.S. Private*, pg. 375

7694 — ARMATURE REWINDING SHOPS

CLEVELAND ELECTRIC CO.—Cleveland Group, Inc.; *U.S. Private*, pg. 246
CLEVELAND GROUP, INC.; *U.S. Private*, pg. 246
ELECTRICAL EQUIPMENT COMPANY; *U.S. Private*, pg. 368
ELECTRICAL EQUIPMENT COMPANY—Electrical Equipment Company; *U.S. Private*, pg. 368
HMI ELECTRIC—Heavy Machines, Inc.; *U.S. Private*, pg. 518
HEAVY MACHINES, INC.; *U.S. Private*, pg. 518
STEINER ELECTRIC COMPANY—Steiner Electric Company; *U.S. Private*, pg. 1039
TRI-STATE ARMATURE & ELECTRIC WORKS; *U.S. Private*, pg. 1100

7699 — REPAIR SHOPS & RELATED SERVICES, NEC

AAR CORP.; *U.S. Public*, pg. 1
ACCESSORY SERVICES-TEXAS—General Electric Company; *U.S. Public*, pg. 710
AERO SYSTEMS AVIATION CORP.; *U.S. Private*, pg. 24
ALASKA TOOL & EQUIPMENT SERVICE—Alaska Industrial Hardware Inc.; *U.S. Private*, pg. 31
ALBAN TRACTOR CO. INC.; *U.S. Private*, pg. 32
ALDEN ELECTRONICS, INC.—Platinum Equity Holdings, LLC; *U.S. Private*, pg. 872
ALLIED SECURITY, INTERNATIONAL; *U.S. Private*, pg. 41
AMERICAN EQUIPMENT COMPANY, INC.—Fluor Corporation; *U.S. Public*, pg. 660
ASEA BROWN BOVERI MACHINERY SERVICE DIV.—ABB Asea Brown Boveri (Holding) Ltd.; *Int'l*, pg. 2
BROWN & SHARPE MANUFACTURING COMPANY; *U.S. Public*, pg. 260
CARTER CHAMBERS SUPPLY, INC.; *U.S. Private*, pg. 216
CHEMED CORPORATION; *U.S. Public*, pg. 343
CHROMALLOY GAS TURBINE CORP.—Sequa Corporation; *U.S. Public*, pg. 1458
CHROME CRANKSHAFT OF ILLINOIS—Varlen Corporation; *U.S. Public*, pg. 1710
CLAYTON MANUFACTURING DIV., DYNAMIC EQUIPMENT—Clayton Industries Co.; *U.S. Private*, pg. 245
COLE GIFT CENTERS, INC.—Cole National Corporation; *U.S. Public*, pg. 396
COLE NATIONAL CORPORATION; *U.S. Public*, pg. 396
CONTAINER PORT GROUP—World Shipping, Inc.; *U.S. Private*, pg. 1191
CROWLEY MARITIME CORPORATION; *U.S. Private*, pg. 292
CUMMINS SOUTHWEST INC.; *U.S. Private*, pg. 296
DANIELLI & C. FAR EAST—Danielli & C. Officine Meccaniche S.p.A.; *Int'l*, pg. 378
DANIELLI OF AMERICA—Danielli & C. Officine Meccaniche S.p.A.; *Int'l*, pg. 378
DAYTON PROCESS B.V.—Indivers B.V.; *Int'l*, pg. 673
ELDIM B.V.—Indivers B.V.; *Int'l*, pg. 673
AB ELEKTROSERVICE—Electrolux, AB; *Int'l*, pg. 439
ELLIOTT TURBOMACHINERY LTD.—Elliott Company; *U.S. Private*, pg. 373
EQUIPAMENTOS CIENTIFICOS INSTRON LTD.—Instron Corporation; *U.S. Public*, pg. 883
EUROKASCO—Bairnco Corporation; *U.S. Public*, pg. 165
FAG GROUP; *Int'l*, pg. 468
FSA REBUILDING OF VIRGINIA, INC.—Varlen Corporation; *U.S. Public*, pg. 1711
JOHN FABICK TRACTOR COMPANY; *U.S. Private*, pg. 390
THE GREAT FRAME UP SYSTEMS, INC.; *U.S. Private*, pg. 473
HISSI-ALA OY—Kone Corporation; *Int'l*, pg. 746
HOLEC MACHINES & APPARATEN B.V.—Royal Begemann Group; *Int'l*, pg. 1133
HOLMAN BOILER WORKS, INC.—Copes-Vulcan Inc.; *U.S. Private*, pg. 274
HUFFY CORPORATION; *U.S. Public*, pg. 846
ILLINOIS AUTO ELECTRIC CO.; *U.S. Private*, pg. 557
INSTRON JAPAN CO., LTD.—Instron Corporation; *U.S. Public*, pg. 882
INTERTURBINE DALLAS AIRFOIL—United Technologies Corporation; *U.S. Public*, pg. 1690
INTERTURBINE DALLAS CASINGS—United Technologies Corporation; *U.S. Public*, pg. 1690
INTERTURBINE HOLLAND B.V.—Indivers B.V.; *Int'l*, pg. 673
INTERTURBINE SINGAPORE PTE. LTD.—United Technologies Corporation; *U.S. Public*, pg. 1690
KANEB SERVICES, INC.; *U.S. Public*, pg. 942
KENNEDY EQUIPMENT CO., INC.—Kennedy Tank & Manufacturing Co., Inc.; *U.S. Private*, pg. 614
KENNEDY TANK & MANUFACTURING CO., INC.; *U.S. Private*, pg. 614
KING FUELS INC.; *U.S. Private*, pg. 620

KINGSBURY SERVICE CORP.—Kingsbury Corporation; *U.S. Private*, pg. 622
KONE AUFZUG GMBH—Kone Corporation; *Int'l*, pg. 747
KONE BELGIUM S.A.—Kone Corporation; *Int'l*, pg. 747
KONE ELEVADORES LTDA.—Kone Corporation; *Int'l*, pg. 747
KONE LIFTS LTD.—Kone Corporation; *Int'l*, pg. 747
KONE SOWITSCH AG—Kone Corporation; *Int'l*, pg. 748
KVAERNER EUREKA ISLANDI—Kvaerner a.s.a.; *Int'l*, pg. 767
L & L MAINTENANCE & REPAIR—L & L Oil Company, Inc.; *U.S. Private*, pg. 638
LIPS PROPELLER INC.—Lips United B.V.; *Int'l*, pg. 812
LIVORNO MARINE CONTAINERS S.R.L.—Sea Containers Ltd.; *Int'l*, pg. 1214
MACGREGOR (AUS) PTY. LTD.—Incentive AB; *Int'l*, pg. 670
MACGREGOR GROUP—Incentive AB; *Int'l*, pg. 670
MACGREGOR (SGP) PTE. LTD.—Incentive AB; *Int'l*, pg. 671
MACGREGOR (USA) INC.—Incentive AB; *Int'l*, pg. 670
MIRRLEES BLACKSTONE (CANADA) LTD.—BTR plc; *Int'l*, pg. 125
MOTOR GROUP—Rockwell International Corporation; *U.S. Public*, pg. 1398
MOULINEX CANADA LTD.—Moulinex S.A.; *Int'l*, pg. 896
MUNROE, INC.; *U.S. Private*, pg. 767
THE NATKIN SERVICE CO.—American International Group, Inc.; *U.S. Public*, pg. 84
NAVCOM DEFENSE ELECTRONICS, INC.—NavCom Defense Electronics, Inc.; *U.S. Private*, pg. 789
THE NEWTRON GROUP INC.; *U.S. Private*, pg. 797
NICOLET INSTRUMENT GMBH—Thermo Electron Corporation; *U.S. Public*, pg. 1594
NICOLET INSTRUMENT S.A.R.L.—Thermo Electron Corporation; *U.S. Public*, pg. 1594
NICOLET JAPAN CORP.-OSAKA—Thermo Electron Corporation; *U.S. Public*, pg. 1594
NICOLET LIMITED—Thermo Electron Corporation; *U.S. Public*, pg. 1594
OEC MEDICAL SYSTEMS, INC.; *U.S. Public*, pg. 1207
OMEGA ENVIRONMENTAL INC.—Omega Environmental Inc.; *U.S. Public*, pg. 1222
PHILIPS CONSUMER ELECTRONICS—Philips Electronics N.V.; *Int'l*, pg. 1055
PLANT MAINTENANCE SERVICE CORPORATION; *U.S. Private*, pg. 869
PRATT & WHITNEY—United Technologies Corporation; *U.S. Public*, pg. 1690
RADIO HOLLAND ELECTRONICS—SAIT-RadioHolland Group S.A.; *Int'l*, pg. 1151
RELIANCE ELEVATOR COMPANY; *U.S. Private*, pg. 921
RENISHAW INC.—Renishaw plc; *Int'l*, pg. 1103
ROAD MACHINERY COMPANY; *U.S. Private*, pg. 934
ROEHLEN INDUSTRIES PTY. LTD. PROCON PUMP DIV.—Standex International Corporation; *U.S. Public*, pg. 1507
ROTO-ROOTER—Chemed Corporation; *U.S. Public*, pg. 344
SNK AMERICA, INC.—Shin Nippon Koki Co. Ltd.; *Int'l*, pg. 1234
SANYO FISHER SERVICE CORP.—Sanyo Electric Co., Ltd.; *Int'l*, pg. 1191
SCHIESS-AMERICA CORP.—Metallgesellschaft AG; *Int'l*, pg. 860
SCHIESS (UK) LTD.—Metallgesellschaft AG; *Int'l*, pg. 860
SECURITY GROUP INC.; *U.S. Private*, pg. 981
SHIPLEY COMPANIES; *U.S. Private*, pg. 994
SOUTHERN PETROLEUM EQUIPMENT CO., INC.—Kennedy Tank & Manufacturing Co., Inc.; *U.S. Private*, pg. 614
SOUTHERN TANK & MANUFACTURING, INC.—Kennedy Tank & Manufacturing Co., Inc.; *U.S. Private*, pg. 614
STANDEX INTERNATIONAL GMBH—Standex International Corporation; *U.S. Public*, pg. 1507
STANDEX INTERNATIONAL S.R.L. (PROCON DIVISION)—Standex International Corporation; *U.S. Public*, pg. 1508
STARKEY LABORATORIES, INC.; *U.S. Private*, pg. 1035
STEPHENSON EQUIPMENT, INC.; *U.S. Private*, pg. 1040
SUNDSTRAND SERVICE CORP.—Sundstrand Corporation; *U.S. Public*, pg. 1534
TECNOST-MAEL—Olivetti SpA; *Int'l*, pg. 1002
TRACTOR MACHINING CO.—Empire Southwest Co.; *U.S. Private*, pg. 375
TRIANGLE SERVICES, INC.; *U.S. Private*, pg. 1102
VALMET CORPORATION SERVICE DEVELOPMENT—Valmet Corporation; *Int'l*, pg. 1449
VARLEN CORPORATION; *U.S. Public*, pg. 1710
VARLEN INSTRUMENTS, INC.—Varlen Corporation; *U.S. Public*, pg. 1711
VARTA BATTERIES INC.—VARTA AG; *Int'l*, pg. 1452
VULCAN MATERIALS COMPANY; *U.S. Public*, pg. 1725
WALKER NATIONAL, INC.—Walker Magnetics Group, Inc.; *U.S. Private*, pg. 1147
WASHINGTON GAS LIGHT CO.; *U.S. Public*, pg. 1740
WESTINGHOUSE ELECTRIC AUSTRALASIA LTD.-VICTORIA DIV.—CBS Corporation; *U.S. Public*, pg. 275
WESTINGHOUSE INDUSTRY SERVICES ASIA PTE. LTD.—CBS Corporation; *U.S. Public*, pg. 275
WINTERBURN LTD.—Thermo Electron Corporation; *U.S. Public*, pg. 1596
YALE/CHASE MATERIALS HANDLING, INC.; *U.S. Private*, pg. 1195

7812 — MOTION PICTURE & VIDEO TAPE PRODUCTION

A&M RECORDS—Philips Electronics N.V.; *Int'l*, pg. 1052
ABC INC.—The Walt Disney Company; *U.S. Public*, pg. 511
ABC PRODUCTIONS—The Walt Disney Company; *U.S. Public*, pg. 511
ABC SPORTS, INC.—The Walt Disney Company; *U.S. Public*, pg. 511
ABINGDON PRESS—The United Methodist Publishing House; *U.S. Private*, pg. 1123
ALL AMERICAN COMMUNICATIONS, INC.; *U.S. Public*, pg. 41
ALL AMERICAN TELEVISION, INC.—All American Communications, Inc.; *U.S. Public*, pg. 41
ALLIANCE COMMUNICATIONS CORPORATION; *Int'l*, pg. 57
ALTA LOMA PRODUCTIONS, INC.—Playboy Enterprises, Inc.; *U.S. Public*, pg. 1310
AMERICAN EDUCATIONAL PRODUCTS; *U.S. Public*, pg. 71
AMERICAN INTERACTIVE MEDIA, INC.—Philips Electronics N.V.; *Int'l*, pg. 1052
ARTS & ENTERTAINMENT NETWORK/ABC/NBC—The Walt Disney Company; *U.S. Public*, pg. 512
ARTS & ENTERTAINMENT NETWORK/ABC/NBC—The Hearst Corporation; *U.S. Private*, pg. 516
BNA COMMUNICATIONS, INC.—The Bureau of National Affairs, Inc.; *U.S. Private*, pg. 182
THE BAYWATCH PRODUCTION COMPANY—All American Communications, Inc.; *U.S. Public*, pg. 41
BERTELSMANN AG; *Int'l*, pg. 189
BFA EDUCATIONAL MEDIA—The Phoenix Learning Group, Inc.; *U.S. Private*, pg. 863
BLOCKBUSTER ENTERTAINMENT GROUP—National Amusements, Inc.; *U.S. Private*, pg. 775
BRENTWOOD BENSON PUBLISHING GROUP—Zomba Recording Corp.; *Int'l*, pg. 1529
THE BUREAU OF NATIONAL AFFAIRS, INC.; *U.S. Private*, pg. 181
CBS—CBS Corporation; *U.S. Public*, pg. 273
CBS BROADCAST GROUP—CBS Corporation; *U.S. Public*, pg. 274
CBS ENTERTAINMENT—CBS Corporation; *U.S. Public*, pg. 274
CBS/MTM COMPANY—CBS Corporation; *U.S. Public*, pg. 275
CFCN COMMUNICATIONS LIMITED—Rogers Communications, Inc.; *Int'l*, pg. 1123
CLT-UFA—Groupe Bruxelles Lambert S.A.; *Int'l*, pg. 561
CARSEY-WERNER COMPANY, LLC; *U.S. Private*, pg. 216
CINEPLEX ODEON CORPORATION; *Int'l*, pg. 292
DICK CLARK PRODUCTIONS, INC.; *U.S. Public*, pg. 382
COLUMBIA PICTURES—Sony Corporation; *Int'l*, pg. 1281
COLUMBIA PICTURES EASTERN DIVISION—Sony Corporation; *Int'l*, pg. 1281
COLUMBIA PICTURES INTERNATIONAL TELEVISION—Sony Corporation; *Int'l*, pg. 1282
COLUMBIA PICTURES OF ARGENTINA, INC.—Sony Corporation; *Int'l*, pg. 1282
COLUMBIA PICTURES SOUTHERN DIVISION—Sony Corporation; *Int'l*, pg. 1281
COLUMBIA PICTURES TELEVISION—Sony Corporation; *Int'l*, pg. 1282
COLUMBIA PICTURES TELEVISION PTY. LTD.—Sony Corporation; *Int'l*, pg. 1282
COLUMBIA PICTURES WESTERN DIVISION—Sony Corporation; *Int'l*, pg. 1281
COLUMBIA TRI-STAR FILMS OF BRAZIL, INC.—Sony Corporation; *Int'l*, pg. 1282
COLUMBIA TRI-STAR FILMS (UK)—Sony Corporation; *Int'l*, pg. 1281
COLUMBIA TRI-STAR HOME VIDEO—Sony Corporation; *Int'l*, pg. 1282
COLUMBIA TRI-STAR INTERNATIONAL TELEVISION—Sony Corporation; *Int'l*, pg. 1281
COLUMBIA TRISTAR TELEVISION—Sony Corporation; *Int'l*, pg. 1282
CORONET/MTI—The Phoenix Learning Group, Inc.; *U.S. Private*, pg. 863
COSCIENT GROUP INC.; *Int'l*, pg. 335
THE CREATIVE SERVICES INC.—Proudfoot plc; *Int'l*, pg. 1072
CULVER STUDIOS—Sony Corporation; *Int'l*, pg. 1283
DIC ENTERTAINMENT—The Walt Disney Company; *U.S. Public*, pg. 513
THE DARTNELL CORPORATION; *U.S. Private*, pg. 312
THE DISNEY CHANNEL—The Walt Disney Company; *U.S. Public*, pg. 513
THE WALT DISNEY COMPANY; *U.S. Public*, pg. 511
WALT DISNEY ENTERPRISES OF JAPAN LTD.—The Walt Disney Company; *U.S. Public*, pg. 514
WALT DISNEY NETWORK TELEVISION—The Walt Disney Company; *U.S. Public*, pg. 511
WALT DISNEY PICTURES AND TELEVISION—The Walt Disney Company; *U.S. Public*, pg. 513
DREAMWORKS SKG; *U.S. Private*, pg. 342
EMC CORPORATION; *U.S. Public*, pg. 545
EPS/ENTERTAINMENT PROGRAMMING SERVICES LTD.—Sony Corporation; *Int'l*, pg. 1282
ESPN, INC.—The Walt Disney Company; *U.S. Public*, pg. 512
ENTERTAINMENT UK LTD.—Kingfisher plc; *Int'l*, pg. 733
EUROPE 1 COMMUNICATION—Lagardere Groupe; *Int'l*, pg. 792
FILMS FOR THE HUMANITIES & SCIENCES, INC.—Primedia Inc.; *U.S. Public*, pg. 1327
FILMS PARAMOUNT S.A.—National Amusements, Inc.; *U.S. Private*, pg. 777
FOUR STAR HOLDINGS CORP.—MacAndrews & Forbes Holdings Inc.; *U.S. Private*, pg. 689
GROUP W SATELLITE COMMUNICATIONS—CBS Corporation; *U.S. Public*, pg. 275
THE GUBER PETERS ENTERTAINMENT COMPANY—Sony Corporation; *Int'l*, pg. 1283
HB ENTERTAINMENT CO.—Time Warner Inc.; *U.S. Public*, pg. 1615
HSN TELECOMMUNICATIONS, INC.—USA Networks, Inc.; *U.S. Public*, pg. 1685
HANNA-BARBERA PRODUCTIONS, INC.—Time Warner Inc.; *U.S. Public*, pg. 1614
HARPO ENTERTAINMENT GROUP; *U.S. Private*, pg. 504
HASBRO, INC.; *U.S. Public*, pg. 797
HEARST ENTERTAINMENT PRODUCTIONS, INC.—The Hearst Corporation; *U.S. Private*, pg. 516
ICM HOLDINGS INC.; *U.S. Private*, pg. 554
ITC LEARNING CORP.; *U.S. Public*, pg. 859
IMAGINE ENTERTAINMENT; *U.S. Private*, pg. 558
INNERVISION STUDIOS INC.—Anheuser-Busch Companies, Inc.; *U.S. Public*, pg. 114
INTERACTIVE INSTRUCTIONAL SYSTEMS INC.—Really Useful Holdings Limited; *Int'l*, pg. 1089
INTERACTIVE VIDEO SYSTEMS LIMITED—Really Useful Holdings Limited; *Int'l*, pg. 1089
ISLAND ENTERTAINMENT GROUP, INC.—Philips Electronics N.V.; *Int'l*, pg. 1052
IWERKS ENTERTAINMENT; *U.S. Public*, pg. 915
IWERKS ENTERTAINMENT—Iwerks Entertainment; *U.S. Public*, pg. 915
JAPAN INTERNATIONAL ENTERPRISES, INC.—Sony Corporation; *Int'l*, pg. 1282
JEFFERSON-PILOT CORPORATION; *U.S. Public*, pg. 925
JEFFERSON-PILOT TELEPRODUCTIONS—Jefferson-Pilot Corporation; *U.S. Public*, pg. 926
QUINCY JONES ENTERTAINMENT—Time Warner Inc.; *U.S. Public*, pg. 1611
KAJIMA INTERNATIONAL, INC.—Kajima Corporation; *Int'l*, pg. 722
ROBERT KEESHAN ASSOCIATES, INC.—ICM Holdings Inc.; *U.S. Private*, pg. 554
KING FEATURES SYNDICATE DIVISION—The Hearst Corporation; *U.S. Private*, pg. 518
KING WORLD PRODUCTIONS—King World Productions, Inc.; *U.S. Public*, pg. 961
KING WORLD PRODUCTIONS, INC.; *U.S. Public*, pg. 961
KODANSHA LTD.; *Int'l*, pg. 742
LIBERTY MEDIA CORPORATION—TCI Communications, Inc.; *U.S. Public*, pg. 1555
LIVE FILM & MEDIAWORKS—LIVE Entertainment Inc.; *U.S. Private*, pg. 671
LUCASFILM LTD.; *U.S. Private*, pg. 679
MGM ENTERTAINMENT COMPANY—Time Warner Inc.; *U.S. Public*, pg. 1614
MTI/THE IMAGE GROUP, INC.; *U.S. Private*, pg. 688
MTM ENTERPRISES, INC.—The News Corporation Limited; *Int'l*, pg. 927
THE MAGNETIC NORTH CORPORATION—Rogers Communications, Inc.; *Int'l*, pg. 1124
THE MAGNETIC SOUTH CORPORATION—Rogers Communications, Inc.; *Int'l*, pg. 1124
MAPFRE VIDEO Y COMUNICAION, S.A.—Corporacion MAPFRE, Compania Internacional de Reaseguros, S.A.; *Int'l*, pg. 334
THE MASTER'S WORKSHOP CORPORATION—Rogers Communications, Inc.; *Int'l*, pg. 1124
METRO-GOLDWYN-MAYER INC.; *U.S. Public*, pg. 1101
METRO-GOLDWYN-MAYER PICTURES, INC.—Metro-Goldwyn-Mayer Inc.; *U.S. Public*, pg. 1102
METRO GROUP—WPP Group plc; *Int'l*, pg. 1482
METROMEDIA INTERNATIONAL GROUP, INC.; *U.S. Public*, pg. 1102
NATIONAL AMUSEMENTS, INC.; *U.S. Private*, pg. 775
NATIONAL BROADCASTING CO., INC.—General Electric Company; *U.S. Public*, pg. 712
NATIONAL FIRE PROTECTION ASSOCIATION; *U.S. Private*, pg. 782
NEW LINE CINEMA CORPORATION—Time Warner Inc.; *U.S. Public*, pg. 1614
NEW WORLD ENTERTAINMENT, INC.—The News Corporation Limited; *Int'l*, pg. 926
NEWS AMERICA PUBLISHING INC.—The News Corporation Limited; *Int'l*, pg. 925
THE NEWS CORPORATION LIMITED; *Int'l*, pg. 925
ONC COMPANY—Sony Corporation; *Int'l*, pg. 1283
PARAMOUNT BRITISH PICTURES LTD.—National Amusements, Inc.; *U.S. Private*, pg. 777
PARAMOUNT PICTURES (AUSTRALIA) PTY. LTD.—National Amusements, Inc.; *U.S. Private*, pg. 777
PARAMOUNT PICTURES CORPORATION—National Amusements, Inc.; *U.S. Private*, pg. 776
PARAMOUNT PICTURES INTERNATIONAL—National Amusements, Inc.; *U.S. Private*, pg. 777
PARAMOUNT PRODUCTIONS, INC.—National Amusements, Inc.; *U.S. Private*, pg. 777
PARAMOUNT TELEVISION LTD.—National Amusements, Inc.; *U.S. Private*, pg. 777
PASSPORT BOOKS—Tribune Company; *U.S. Public*, pg. 1636
PATHE; *Int'l*, pg. 1024
PHOENIX FILMS & VIDEO—The Phoenix Learning Group, Inc.; *U.S. Private*, pg. 863
THE PHOENIX LEARNING GROUP, INC.; *U.S. Private*, pg. 863
PINEWOOD STUDIOS LIMITED—The Rank Group PLC; *Int'l*, pg. 1086
PIXAR ANIMATION STUDIOS; *U.S. Public*, pg. 1307
PLAYBOY ENTERPRISES, INC.; *U.S. Public*, pg. 1309
PLAYBOY ENTERTAINMENT GROUP, INC.—Playboy Enterprises, Inc.; *U.S. Public*, pg. 1310
PLAYBOY VIDEO ENTERPRISES, INC.—Playboy Enterprises, Inc.; *U.S. Public*, pg. 1310
POLYGRAM INTERNATIONAL LTD.—Philips Electronics N.V.; *Int'l*, pg. 1053
POLYGRAM N.V.—Philips Electronics N.V.; *Int'l*, pg. 1051
PRIMEDIA INC.; *U.S. Public*, pg. 1327
PRODUCT INFORMATION NETWORK—Jones International, Ltd.; *U.S. Private*, pg. 597
RADIO-HOLLAND AV SYSTEMS GROUP—SAIT-RadioHolland Group S.A.; *Int'l*, pg. 1151
THE RANK GROUP PLC; *Int'l*, pg. 1086
RANK VIDEO SERVICES AMERICA INC.—The Rank Group PLC; *Int'l*, pg. 1087
RANK VIDEO SERVICES LTD.—The Rank Group PLC; *Int'l*, pg. 1087
THE REALLY USEFUL PICTURE COMPANY—Really Useful Holdings Limited; *Int'l*, pg. 1089

REPUBLIC ENTERTAINMENT, INC.—National Amusements, Inc.; *U.S. Private*, pg. 776
RESOURCE, INC.—International Business Machines Corporation; *U.S. Public*, pg. 896
ROMPER ROOM ENTERPRISES, INC.—Hasbro, Inc.; *U.S. Public*, pg. 797
SAS MEDIAPARTNER AB—Scandinavian Airlines System (SAS); *Int'l*, pg. 1202
SAS TRADING—Scandinavian Airlines System (SAS); *Int'l*, pg. 1202
SCANDINAVIAN AIRLINES SYSTEM (SAS); *Int'l*, pg. 1201
SCHOLASTIC CORPORATION; *U.S. Public*, pg. 1440
SCOTTI BROTHERS ENTERTAINMENT INDUSTRIES—All American Communications, Inc.; *U.S. Public*, pg. 41
SCRIPPS HOWARD PRODUCTIONS—The E.W. Scripps Company; *U.S. Public*, pg. 1448
SHANDWICK INTERNATIONAL PLC; *Int'l*, pg. 1226
SHANNOCK QUEBEC AUDIO AND VIDEO INC.—TSC Shannock Corporation; *Int'l*, pg. 1343
SHEPARD'S—Reed Elsevier plc; *Int'l*, pg. 1095
SHEPARD'S—The Times Mirror Company; *U.S. Public*, pg. 1616
SONY PICTURES ENTERTAINMENT—Sony Corporation; *Int'l*, pg. 1281
SONY PICTURES ENTERTAINMENT TELEVISION GROUP—Sony Corporation; *Int'l*, pg. 1282
SPELLING TELEVISION—National Amusements, Inc.; *U.S. Private*, pg. 776
TBS PRODUCTIONS, INC.—Time Warner Inc.; *U.S. Public*, pg. 1615
T.V. OVERSEAS, S.R.L.—Sony Corporation; *Int'l*, pg. 1282
TEL-AD JERUSALEM STUDIO LTD.—IDB Holding Corporation; *Int'l*, pg. 644
TELE-MUNCHEN FERNSEH GMBH & CO.; *Int'l*, pg. 1362
TELEMUNDO GROUP, INC.; *U.S. Public*, pg. 1570
TIME WARNER INC.; *U.S. Public*, pg. 1610
THE TODD-AO CORPORATION; *U.S. Public*, pg. 1619
TODD-AO STUDIOS/EAST—The Todd-AO Corporation; *U.S. Public*, pg. 1619
TRIBUNE ENTERTAINMENT COMPANY—Tribune Company; *U.S. Public*, pg. 1636
TRISTAR PICTURES—Sony Corporation; *Int'l*, pg. 1283
TRISTAR PICTURES CENTRAL DIVISION—Sony Corporation; *Int'l*, pg. 1283
TRISTAR PICTURES EASTERN DIVISION—Sony Corporation; *Int'l*, pg. 1283
TRISTAR PICTURES SOUTHERN DIVISION—Sony Corporation; *Int'l*, pg. 1283
TRISTAR PICTURES WESTERN DIVISION—Sony Corporation; *Int'l*, pg. 1283
TWENTIETH CENTURY FOX FILM CORP.—The News Corporation Limited; *Int'l*, pg. 926
TYNDALE HOUSE PUBLISHERS, INC.; *U.S. Private*, pg. 1112
UFA FILM UND FERNSEH GMBH—Bertelsmann AG; *Int'l*, pg. 190
UNITED MEDIA—The E.W. Scripps Company; *U.S. Public*, pg. 1448
THE UNITED METHODIST PUBLISHING HOUSE; *U.S. Private*, pg. 1122
UNITEL VIDEO, INC.; *U.S. Public*, pg. 1692
UNIVERSAL STUDIOS HOLLYWOOD—The Seagram Company Ltd.; *Int'l*, pg. 1216
UNIVERSAL STUDIOS, INC.—The Seagram Company Ltd.; *Int'l*, pg. 1215
UNIVERSAL STUDIOS JAPAN, LTD.—The Seagram Company Ltd.; *Int'l*, pg. 1216
UNIVERSAL TELEVISION DIV.—The Seagram Company Ltd.; *Int'l*, pg. 1216
USA BROADCASTING—USA Networks, Inc.; *U.S. Public*, pg. 1686
VIACOM INTERNATIONAL INC.—National Amusements, Inc.; *U.S. Private*, pg. 778
VIACOM PRODUCTIONS INC.—National Amusements, Inc.; *U.S. Private*, pg. 779
VITT CORPORATION—Toshiba Corporation; *Int'l*, pg. 1405
WIC ENTERTAINMENT LTD.—WIC Western International Communications Ltd.; *Int'l*, pg. 1482
WIC TELEVISION LTD.—WIC Western International Communications Ltd.; *Int'l*, pg. 1482
WARNER BROS. STUDIOS, INC.—Time Warner Inc.; *U.S. Public*, pg. 1611
WARNER BROS. TELEVISION, INC.—Time Warner Inc.; *U.S. Public*, pg. 1611
WARNER COMMUNICATIONS INC.—Time Warner Inc.; *U.S. Public*, pg. 1611
WARNER HOME VIDEO—Time Warner Inc.; *U.S. Public*, pg. 1611
WARNER MUSIC GROUP, INC.—Time Warner Inc.; *U.S. Public*, pg. 1612

7819 — SERVICES ALLIED TO MOTION PICTURE PRODUCTION

ABC, INC—The Walt Disney Company; *U.S. Public*, pg. 511
ALLIED DIGITAL TECHNOLOGIES; *U.S. Public*, pg. 48
ALLIED DIGITAL TECHNOLOGIES CORPORATION—Allied Digital Technologies; *U.S. Public*, pg. 48
AMERICAN MULTI-CINEMA, INC.—AMC Entertainment, Inc.; *U.S. Private*, pg. 6
ANDREWS GROUP, INCORPORATED—MacAndrews & Forbes Holdings Inc.; *U.S. Private*, pg. 689
C & L MARKETING INC.—EMI Group plc; *Int'l*, pg. 428
CFCN COMMUNICATIONS LIMITED—Rogers Communications, Inc.; *Int'l*, pg. 1123
CARLTON COMMUNICATIONS PLC; *Int'l*, pg. 272
CINE MAGNETICS, INC.; *U.S. Private*, pg. 240
CINEPLEX ODEON CORPORATION; *Int'l*, pg. 292
DICK CLARK MEDIA ARCHIVES—Dick Clark Productions, Inc.; *U.S. Public*, pg. 382
DELUXE LABORATORIES, INC.—The Rank Group PLC; *Int'l*, pg. 1087
DELUXE TORONTO LIMITED—The Rank Group PLC; *Int'l*, pg. 1087
EMC CORPORATION; *U.S. Public*, pg. 545
FOUR MEDIA COMPANIES; *U.S. Private*, pg. 422
GRUPO VIDEO VISA S.A. DE C.V.; *Int'l*, pg. 577
HB ENTERTAINMENT CO.—Time Warner Inc.; *U.S. Public*, pg. 1615
IDC SERVICES, INC.; *U.S. Private*, pg. 554
MGM ENTERTAINMENT COMPANY—Time Warner Inc.; *U.S. Public*, pg. 1614
MTI/THE IMAGE GROUP, INC.; *U.S. Private*, pg. 688
THE MASTER'S WORKSHOP CORPORATION—Rogers Communications, Inc.; *Int'l*, pg. 1124
POLYGRAM INTERNATIONAL LTD.—Philips Electronics N.V.; *Int'l*, pg. 1053
RADIO-HOLLAND AV SYSTEMS GROUP—SAIT-RadioHolland Group S.A.; *Int'l*, pg. 1151
RALEIGH ENTERPRISES, INC.; *U.S. Private*, pg. 907
RANK FILM LABORATORIES LIMITED—The Rank Group PLC; *Int'l*, pg. 1087
REPUBLIC ENTERTAINMENT, INC.—National Amusements, Inc.; *U.S. Private*, pg. 776
TECHNICOLOR, INC.—Carlton Communications Plc; *Int'l*, pg. 272
TELEMATION PRODUCTIONS INC.—USA Networks, Inc.; *U.S. Public*, pg. 1685
TWENTIETH CENTURY FOX FILM CORP.—The News Corporation Limited; *Int'l*, pg. 926
20TH CENTURY FOX HOME ENTERTAINMENT—CBS Corporation; *U.S. Public*, pg. 275
UNITEL VIDEO, INC.; *U.S. Public*, pg. 1692
WIC ENTERTAINMENT LTD.—WIC Western International Communications Ltd.; *Int'l*, pg. 1482
WIC TELEVISION LTD.—WIC Western International Communications Ltd.; *Int'l*, pg. 1482

7822 — MOTION PICTURE & VIDEO TAPE DISTRIBUTION

ASCO MUSIC—Cox Enterprises, Inc.; *U.S. Private*, pg. 282
BEEPEE MUSIC—Cox Enterprises, Inc.; *U.S. Private*, pg. 282
BRITISH FILM INSTITUTE; *Int'l*, pg. 219
CARLTON COMMUNICATIONS PLC; *Int'l*, pg. 272
CARLTON FILM DISTRIBUTORS—Carlton Communications Plc; *Int'l*, pg. 272
CINEMA INTERNATIONAL CORP., N.V.—The Seagram Company Ltd.; *Int'l*, pg. 1216
DICK CLARK PRODUCTIONS, INC.; *U.S. Public*, pg. 382
CLASTER TELEVISION—Hasbro, Inc.; *U.S. Public*, pg. 797
COLUMBIA PICTURES MERCHANDISING—Sony Corporation; *Int'l*, pg. 1281
COLUMBIA TRI-STAR FILM DISTRIBUTORS INTERNATIONAL—Sony Corporation; *Int'l*, pg. 1281
COLUMBIA TRI-STAR TELEVISION DISTRIBUTION—Sony Corporation; *Int'l*, pg. 1282
COSCIENT-ASTRAL DISTRIBUTION—Coscient Group Inc.; *Int'l*, pg. 335
BING CROSBY PRODUCTIONS, INC.—Cox Enterprises, Inc.; *U.S. Private*, pg. 282
DISNEY EDUCATIONAL PRODUCTIONS—The Walt Disney Company; *U.S. Public*, pg. 513
THE WALT DISNEY COMPANY; *U.S. Public*, pg. 511
THE WALT DISNEY COMPANY (ITALIA)—The Walt Disney Company; *U.S. Public*, pg. 514
WALT DISNEY ENTERPRISES OF JAPAN LTD.—The Walt Disney Company; *U.S. Public*, pg. 514
FAMOUS PLAYERS INC.—National Amusements, Inc.; *U.S. Private*, pg. 779
FOUR STAR HOLDINGS CORP.—MacAndrews & Forbes Holdings Inc.; *U.S. Private*, pg. 689
FOXVIDEO (ESPANOLA) S.A.—The News Corporation Limited; *Int'l*, pg. 926
FOXVIDEO (FAR EAST) K.K.—The News Corporation Limited; *Int'l*, pg. 926
FOXVIDEO (FRANCE) S.A.—The News Corporation Limited; *Int'l*, pg. 926
FOXVIDEO (GERMANY) G.M.B.H.—The News Corporation Limited; *Int'l*, pg. 926
FOXVIDEO LIMITED—The News Corporation Limited; *Int'l*, pg. 926
FOXVIDEO (NEW ZEALAND) LIMITED—The News Corporation Limited; *Int'l*, pg. 926
FOXVIDEO (SOUTH PACIFIC) PTY., LTD.—The News Corporation Limited; *Int'l*, pg. 926
THE SAMUEL GOLDWYN COMPANY; *U.S. Private*, pg. 463
GRAMERCY PICTURES; *U.S. Private*, pg. 468
MERV GRIFFIN ENTERPRISES—Sony Corporation; *Int'l*, pg. 1282
GRUPO VIDEO VISA S.A. DE C.V.; *Int'l*, pg. 577
HBO PICTURES, INC.—Time Warner Inc.; *U.S. Public*, pg. 1612
HBO VIDEO, INC.—Time Warner Inc.; *U.S. Public*, pg. 1612
HEARST ENTERTAINMENT—The Hearst Corporation; *U.S. Private*, pg. 516
INGRAM DISTRIBUTION GROUP INC.—Ingram Industries Inc.; *U.S. Private*, pg. 563
IWERKS ENTERTAINMENT—Iwerks Entertainment; *U.S. Public*, pg. 915
KING WORLD PRODUCTIONS, INC.; *U.S. Public*, pg. 961
LIVE ENTERTAINMENT INC.; *U.S. Private*, pg. 671
LIVE FILM & MEDIAWORKS—LIVE Entertainment Inc.; *U.S. Private*, pg. 671
MGM/UA DISTRIBUTION CO.—Metro-Goldwyn-Mayer Inc.; *U.S. Public*, pg. 1102
MGM/UA HOME ENTERTAINMENT, INC.—Metro-Goldwyn-Mayer Inc.; *U.S. Public*, pg. 1102
MIRAMAX FILMS, INC.—The Walt Disney Company; *U.S. Public*, pg. 514
NETG APPLIED LEARNING GMBH—Harcourt General, Inc.; *U.S. Public*, pg. 784
NETG LIMITED—Harcourt General, Inc.; *U.S. Public*, pg. 784
NATIONAL AMUSEMENTS, INC.; *U.S. Private*, pg. 775
NATIONAL BROADCASTING CO., INC.—General Electric Company; *U.S. Public*, pg. 712
NEW LINE CINEMA CORPORATION—Time Warner Inc.; *U.S. Public*, pg. 1614
THE NEWS CORPORATION LIMITED; *Int'l*, pg. 925
PLAYBOY ENTERPRISES, INC.; *U.S. Public*, pg. 1309
PLAYBOY ENTERTAINMENT GROUP, INC.—Playboy Enterprises, Inc.; *U.S. Public*, pg. 1310
PLAYBOY VIDEO ENTERPRISES, INC.—Playboy Enterprises, Inc.; *U.S. Public*, pg. 1310
PROCTER & GAMBLE PRODUCTIONS, INC.—The Procter & Gamble Company; *U.S. Public*, pg. 1331
THE PROGRAM EXCHANGE—Saatchi & Saatchi Advertising Worldwide; *U.S. Public*, pg. 1422
RADIO-HOLLAND AV SYSTEMS GROUP—SAIT-RadioHolland Group S.A.; *Int'l*, pg. 1151
RANK VIDEO SERVICES AMERICA INC.—The Rank Group PLC; *Int'l*, pg. 1087
REPUBLIC ENTERTAINMENT, INC.—National Amusements, Inc.; *U.S. Private*, pg. 776
SKALA HOME ELECTRONICS—Thorn plc; *Int'l*, pg. 1386
SONY PICTURES ENTERTAINMENT—Sony Corporation; *Int'l*, pg. 1281
SONY PICTURES STUDIOS—Sony Corporation; *Int'l*, pg. 1283
SPELLING ENTERTAINMENT GROUP, INC.—National Amusements, Inc.; *U.S. Private*, pg. 776
TSC SHANNOCK CORPORATION; *Int'l*, pg. 1343
TELEMUNDO GROUP, INC.; *U.S. Public*, pg. 1570
THORN—Thorn plc; *Int'l*, pg. 1386
TIME WARNER INC.; *U.S. Public*, pg. 1610
TITANUS DISTRIBUZIONE S.P.A.—Bastogi-S.p.A.; *Int'l*, pg. 170
TRIBUNE COMPANY; *U.S. Public*, pg. 1635
TRIMARK HOLDINGS, INC.; *U.S. Public*, pg. 1638
TRIUMPH RELEASING CORPORATION—Sony Corporation; *Int'l*, pg. 1282
TURNER PROGRAM SERVICES, INC.—Time Warner Inc.; *U.S. Public*, pg. 1615
UNOCO—The Walt Disney Company; *U.S. Public*, pg. 514
UNITED WORLD FILMS DIV.—The Seagram Company Ltd.; *Int'l*, pg. 1216
UNIVERSAL CITY STUDIOS (DISC), INC.—The Seagram Company Ltd.; *Int'l*, pg. 1216
UNIVERSAL FILM EXCHANGES, INC.—The Seagram Company Ltd.; *Int'l*, pg. 1216
UNIVERSAL STUDIOS ARTISTS (ENGLAND) LTD.—The Seagram Company Ltd.; *Int'l*, pg. 1216
UNIVERSAL STUDIOS AUSTRALIA PTY. LTD.—The Seagram Company Ltd.; *Int'l*, pg. 1216
UNIVERSAL STUDIOS FILMES DO BRAZIL LTDA—The Seagram Company Ltd.; *Int'l*, pg. 1216
UNIVERSAL STUDIOS INTERNATIONAL B.V.—The Seagram Company Ltd.; *Int'l*, pg. 1216
UNIVERSAL STUDIOS JAPAN, LTD.—The Seagram Company Ltd.; *Int'l*, pg. 1216
UNIVERSAL STUDIOS TELEVISION LTD.—The Seagram Company Ltd.; *Int'l*, pg. 1216
UNIVERSAL STUDIOS TV—The Seagram Company Ltd.; *Int'l*, pg. 1215
UNIVERSAL STUDIOS TV (TELEVISION) G.M.B.H.—The Seagram Company Ltd.; *Int'l*, pg. 1217
UNIVERSAL STUDIOS VIDEODISC, INC.—The Seagram Company Ltd.; *Int'l*, pg. 1216
VIACOM ENTERPRISES—National Amusements, Inc.; *U.S. Private*, pg. 779
VIACOM INTERNATIONAL INC.—National Amusements, Inc.; *U.S. Private*, pg. 778
VIDEO PRODUCTS DISTRIBUTORS, INC.; *U.S. Private*, pg. 1139
WARNER COMMUNICATIONS INC.—Time Warner Inc.; *U.S. Public*, pg. 1611
WORLDVISION ENTERPRISES—National Amusements, Inc.; *U.S. Private*, pg. 776
WORLDVISION ENTERPRISES, INC.—National Amusements, Inc.; *U.S. Private*, pg. 776

7829 — SERVICES ALLIED TO MOTION PICTURE DISTRIBUTION

ABC, INC—The Walt Disney Company; *U.S. Public*, pg. 511
DICK CLARK MEDIA ARCHIVES—Dick Clark Productions, Inc.; *U.S. Public*, pg. 382
MGM ENTERTAINMENT COMPANY—Time Warner Inc.; *U.S. Public*, pg. 1614
OCTOBER FILMS, INC.—The Seagram Company Ltd.; *Int'l*, pg. 1216
REPUBLIC ENTERTAINMENT, INC.—National Amusements, Inc.; *U.S. Private*, pg. 776
UNIVERSAL STUDIOS FLORIDA—The Rank Group PLC; *Int'l*, pg. 1087
UNIVERSAL STUDIOS HOLLYWOOD—The Seagram Company Ltd.; *Int'l*, pg. 1216

7832 — MOTION PICTURE THEATERS, EXCEPT DRIVE-IN

AMC ENTERTAINMENT, INC.; *U.S. Private*, pg. 6
AMERICAN MULTI-CINEMA, INC.—AMC Entertainment, Inc.; *U.S. Private*, pg. 6
BASTOGI-S.P.A.; *Int'l*, pg. 170
CARMIKE CINEMAS, INC.; *U.S. Public*, pg. 305
CINAMERICA THEATRES, L.P.; *U.S. Private*, pg. 239
CINEMARK USA, INC.; *U.S. Private*, pg. 240
CINEPLEX ODEON CORPORATION; *Int'l*, pg. 292
CINESTELLA S.P.A.—Bastogi-S.p.A.; *Int'l*, pg. 170
EMPIRE COMPANY LIMITED; *Int'l*, pg. 453
EMPIRE THEATERS LIMITED—Empire Company Limited; *Int'l*, pg. 454

FLOYD THEATRES, INC.—MasTec, Inc.; *U.S. Public*, pg. 1056
GENERAL CINEMA THEATRES, INC.—GC Companies, Inc.; *U.S. Public*, pg. 693
IMAX CORPORATION; *Int'l*, pg. 661
THE MARCUS CORPORATION; *U.S. Public*, pg. 1044
MARCUS THEATRES CORP.—The Marcus Corporation; *U.S. Public*, pg. 1044
MASTEC, INC.; *U.S. Public*, pg. 1055
METRO-GOLDWYN-MAYER INC.; *U.S. Public*, pg. 1101
MONDIALCINE S.P.A.—Bastogi-S.p.A.; *Int'l*, pg. 170
ODEON CINEMAS LTD.—The Rank Group PLC; *Int'l*, pg. 1086
REGAL CINEMAS INC.; *U.S. Public*, pg. 1371
TELE-MUNCHEN FERNSEH GMBH & CO.; *Int'l*, pg. 1362
TRANS-LUX CORPORATION; *U.S. Public*, pg. 1628
UNITED ARTISTS THEATRE CIRCUITS INCORPORATED; *U.S. Private*, pg. 1120
UNIVERSAL AMPHITHEATRE—The Seagram Company Ltd.; *Int'l*, pg. 1216
UNIVERSAL PICTURES—The Seagram Company Ltd.; *Int'l*, pg. 1216
WOMETCO ENTERPRISES, INC.; *U.S. Private*, pg. 1186

7833 — DRIVE-IN MOTION PICTURE THEATERS

CINEPLEX ODEON CORPORATION; *Int'l*, pg. 292
EMPIRE THEATERS LIMITED—Empire Company Limited; *Int'l*, pg. 454
METRO-GOLDWYN-MAYER INC.; *U.S. Public*, pg. 1101
NATIONAL AMUSEMENTS, INC.; *U.S. Private*, pg. 775

7841 — VIDEO TAPE RENTAL

BLOCKBUSTER ENTERTAINMENT GROUP—National Amusements, Inc.; *U.S. Private*, pg. 775
BLOCKBUSTER VIDEO LIMITED PARTNERSHIP—National Amusements, Inc.; *U.S. Private*, pg. 776
H.E. BUTT GROCERY CO.; *U.S. Private*, pg. 190
GRUPO VIDEO VISA S.A. DE C.V.; *Int'l*, pg. 577
HOLLYWOOD ENTERTAINMENT CORP.; *U.S. Private*, pg. 535
THE MUSIC AND VIDEO CLUB LIMITED—Kingfisher plc; *Int'l*, pg. 733
NATIONAL VIDEO, INC.—West Coast Entertainment Inc.; *U.S. Public*, pg. 1755
THE PENN TRAFFIC COMPANY; *U.S. Public*, pg. 1270
PUEBLO XTRA INTERNATIONAL, INC.; *U.S. Private*, pg. 894
RENTRAK CORPORATION; *U.S. Public*, pg. 1377
ROGERS ENTERTAINMENT INC.—Rogers Communications, Inc.; *Int'l*, pg. 1123
WEST COAST ENTERTAINMENT INC.; *U.S. Public*, pg. 1755

7922 — THEATRICAL PRODUCERS, (EXCEPT MOTION PICTURE) & MISCELLANEOUS THEATRICAL SERVICES

ALLBRITTON TELEVISION PRODUCTIONS, INC.—Perpetual Corporation; *U.S. Private*, pg. 854
AUTOMATED STUDIO LIGHTING, INC.—Sony Corporation; *Int'l*, pg. 1283
BARRIS MUSIC, INC.—Sony Corporation; *Int'l*, pg. 1283
BARRIS PRODUCTIONS, INC.—Sony Corporation; *Int'l*, pg. 1283
CFCN-TV (CALGARY & LETHBRIDGE)—Rogers Communications, Inc.; *Int'l*, pg. 1123
CHCH-TV—Rogers Communications, Inc.; *Int'l*, pg. 1124
COSCIENT GROUP INC.; *Int'l*, pg. 335
DESERT PRODUCTION CENTER—MAC America Communications, Inc.; *U.S. Private*, pg. 685
EUROPE 1 COMMUNICATION—Lagardere Groupe; *Int'l*, pg. 792
GAYLORD ENTERTAINMENT/OPRYLAND USA—Gaylord Entertainment Co.; *U.S. Public*, pg. 704
GREY ADVERTISING INC.; *U.S. Public*, pg. 764
THE GUBER PETERS ENTERTAINMENT COMPANY—Sony Corporation; *Int'l*, pg. 1283
HARPO ENTERTAINMENT GROUP; *U.S. Private*, pg. 504
ICM ARTISTS, LTD.—ICM Holdings Inc.; *U.S. Private*, pg. 554
ICM HOLDINGS INC.; *U.S. Private*, pg. 554
LORIMAR TELEVISION—Time Warner Inc.; *U.S. Public*, pg. 1611
MADISON SQUARE GARDEN NETWORK—Cablevision Systems Corporation; *U.S. Public*, pg. 288
MISS UNIVERSE, L.P.—Trump Organization; *U.S. Private*, pg. 1108
NATIONAL MEDIA CORPORATION; *U.S. Public*, pg. 1158
THE NEWS CORPORATION LIMITED; *Int'l*, pg. 925
NISSAY CULTURE FOUNDATION—Nippon Life Insurance Co.; *Int'l*, pg. 935
RADIO CITY PRODUCTIONS—Mitsubishi Estate Co., Ltd.; *Int'l*, pg. 873
RAINBOW PROGRAMMING HOLDINGS, INC.—Cablevision Systems Corporation; *U.S. Public*, pg. 288
THE REALLY USEFUL COMPANY, INC.—Really Useful Holdings Limited; *Int'l*, pg. 1089
THE REALLY USEFUL THEATER COMPANY LIMITED—Really Useful Holdings Limited; *Int'l*, pg. 1089
SABAN ENTERTAINMENT; *U.S. Private*, pg. 959
TICKETMASTER CORPORATION; *U.S. Private*, pg. 1084
TIME WARNER INC.; *U.S. Public*, pg. 1610

7929 — BANDS, ORCHESTRAS, ACTORS, & OTHER ENTERTAINERS & ENTERTAINMENT GROUPS

GAYLORD ENTERTAINMENT CO.; *U.S. Public*, pg. 704
GOODTIMES ENTERTAINMENT CO.; *U.S. Private*, pg. 464
GROSVENOR THEATRICAL PRODUCTIONS LTD.—Granada Group PLC; *Int'l*, pg. 556
PLAYBOY SHOWS, INC.—Playboy Enterprises, Inc.; *U.S. Public*, pg. 1310
YAMAHA HALL CO., LTD.—Yamaha Corporation; *Int'l*, pg. 1515

7933 — BOWLING ALLEYS

AMF AZALEA BOWL—AMF Bowling Worldwide; *U.S. Private*, pg. 7
AMF BOWLING CENTERS INC.—AMF Bowling Worldwide; *U.S. Private*, pg. 7
AMF LANG'S BOWLARAMA INC.—AMF Bowling Worldwide; *U.S. Private*, pg. 7
AMERICAN RECREATION CENTERS, INC.; *U.S. Public*, pg. 90
BOWL AMERICA, INCORPORATED; *U.S. Public*, pg. 248
BOWLERAMA LANES, INC.—Great Lakes Realty Corp.; *U.S. Private*, pg. 475
BRUNSWICK INDOOR RECREATION GROUP—Brunswick Corporation; *U.S. Public*, pg. 265
CHARAN INDUSTRIES, INC.; *U.S. Private*, pg. 229
CLOVERLANES, INC.—Great Lakes Realty Corp.; *U.S. Private*, pg. 475
FAIRLANES BOWL, INC.—Great Lakes Realty Corp.; *U.S. Private*, pg. 475
GREAT LAKES REALTY CORP.; *U.S. Private*, pg. 475
SHOWBOAT, INCORPORATED; *U.S. Public*, pg. 1469
YPSI-ARBOR LANES—Great Lakes Realty Corp.; *U.S. Private*, pg. 475

7941 — PROFESSIONAL SPORTS CLUBS & PROMOTERS

THE ACKERLEY GROUP; *U.S. Public*, pg. 15
ARIZONA CARDINALS; *U.S. Private*, pg. 81
ATLANTA BRAVES, INC.—Time Warner Inc.; *U.S. Public*, pg. 1614
ATLANTA HAWKS, INC.—Time Warner Inc.; *U.S. Public*, pg. 1614
ATLANTA NATIONAL LEAGUE BASEBALL CLUB, INC.—Time Warner Inc.; *U.S. Public*, pg. 1614
BIRMINGHAM BASEBALL CLUB, INC.—Suntory Ltd.; *Int'l*, pg. 1321
BOSTON CELTICS LIMITED PARTNERSHIP; *U.S. Public*, pg. 246
CHICAGO NATIONAL LEAGUE BALL CLUB, INC. (CHICAGO CUBS)—Tribune Company; *U.S. Public*, pg. 1635
CLEARWATER PHILLIES—The Phillies-A Limited Partnership; *U.S. Private*, pg. 861
JACK KENT COOKE, INC.; *U.S. Private*, pg. 273
THE EDWARD J. DEBARTOLO CORPORATION; *U.S. Private*, pg. 319
ELIZABETHTON TWINS BASEBALL CLUB—Minnesota Twins Baseball Club; *U.S. Private*, pg. 751
FORT MYERS MIRACLE—Minnesota Twins Baseball Club; *U.S. Private*, pg. 751
FORT WAYNE WIZARDS—Minnesota Twins Baseball Club; *U.S. Private*, pg. 751
FULL HOUSE SPORTS & ENTERTAINMENT—The Ackerley Group; *U.S. Public*, pg. 16
GOLDEN WEST BASEBALL CLUB—Golden West Broadcasters; *U.S. Private*, pg. 461
GOLDEN WEST BROADCASTERS; *U.S. Private*, pg. 461
HARDWARE CITY ROCK CATS—Minnesota Twins Baseball Club; *U.S. Private*, pg. 751
LABATT BREWING COMPANY LIMITED—Interbrew S.A.; *Int'l*, pg. 679
MADISON SQUARE GARDEN CENTER INC.—Cablevision Systems Corporation; *U.S. Public*, pg. 288
MADISON SQUARE GARDEN CORPORATION—Cablevision Systems Corporation; *U.S. Public*, pg. 288
MILWAUKEE BUCKS, INC.; *U.S. Private*, pg. 749
MINNESOTA TWINS BASEBALL CLUB; *U.S. Private*, pg. 750
NATIONAL BASKETBALL ASSOCIATION; *U.S. Private*, pg. 780
NATIONAL FOOTBALL LEAGUE PROPERTIES, INC.; *U.S. Private*, pg. 783
NEW YORK KNICKERBOCKERS—Cablevision Systems Corporation; *U.S. Public*, pg. 288
NEW YORK RANGERS HOCKEY CLUB—Cablevision Systems Corporation; *U.S. Public*, pg. 288
ORIX BASEBALL CLUB—Orix Corporation; *Int'l*, pg. 1008
THE PHILLIES-A LIMITED PARTNERSHIP; *U.S. Private*, pg. 861
PITTSBURGH PIRATES—Pittsburgh Associates; *U.S. Private*, pg. 867
RICH PRODUCTS CORP.; *U.S. Private*, pg. 928
SACRAMENTO KINGS; *U.S. Private*, pg. 959
ST. LOUIS NATIONAL BASEBALL CLUB L.P.; *U.S. Private*, pg. 961
SAN DIEGO CHARGERS; *U.S. Private*, pg. 964
SAN FRANCISCO GIANTS BASEBALL CLUB; *U.S. Private*, pg. 964
SPEEDWAY MOTORSPORTS, INC.; *U.S. Public*, pg. 1498
TORONTO BLUE JAYS BASEBALL CLUB, INC.—Interbrew S.A.; *Int'l*, pg. 680
TRIBUNE COMPANY; *U.S. Public*, pg. 1635

7948 — RACING, INCLUDING TRACK OPERATION

BAY MEADOWS RACE TRACK—Patriot American Hospitality, Inc.; *U.S. Public*, pg. 1265
BRANDYWINE SPORTS, INC.; *U.S. Private*, pg. 165
CHARLES TOWN RACES—Penn National Gaming, Inc.; *U.S. Public*, pg. 1270
CHURCHILL DOWNS, INC.; *U.S. Public*, pg. 356
DAIRYLAND GREYHOUND PARK, INC.; *U.S. Private*, pg. 307
THE EDWARD J. DEBARTOLO CORPORATION; *U.S. Private*, pg. 319
DELAWARE NORTH COMPANIES, INC.; *U.S. Private*, pg. 321
FAIR GROUNDS CORPORATION; *U.S. Public*, pg. 609
GARDEN STATE RACE TRACK, INC.—International Thoroughbred Breeders, Inc.; *U.S. Public*, pg. 908
HENDRICK MOTORSPORTS—Hendrick Automotive Group; *U.S. Private*, pg. 522
HOLLYWOOD PARK OPERATING COMPANY—Hollywood Park, Inc.; *U.S. Public*, pg. 831
KEENELAND ASSOC., INC.; *U.S. Private*, pg. 611
LOUISIANA DOWNS—The Edward J. DeBartolo Corporation; *U.S. Private*, pg. 319
MALIBU ENTERTAINMENT WORLDWIDE; *U.S. Public*, pg. 1039
NEW YORK RACING ASSOCIATION; *U.S. Private*, pg. 795
PATRIOT AMERICAN HOSPITALITY OPERATING COMPANY—Patriot American Hospitality, Inc.; *U.S. Public*, pg. 1265
PENN NATIONAL GAMING, INC.; *U.S. Public*, pg. 1270
THE SANTA ANITA COMPANIES—Meditrust Corporation; *U.S. Public*, pg. 1081
SARATOGA EQUINE SPORTS CENTER; *U.S. Private*, pg. 965
SUNFLOWER RACING INC.—Hollywood Park, Inc.; *U.S. Public*, pg. 831
TURF PARADISE, INC.—Hollywood Park, Inc.; *U.S. Public*, pg. 831

7991 — PHYSICAL FITNESS FACILITIES

AQUA CHEM DIVISION—Imperial Chemical Industries PLC; *Int'l*, pg. 663
JAZZERCISE, INC.; *U.S. Private*, pg. 584
GEORGETTE KLINGER, INC.; *U.S. Private*, pg. 626
NUTRI/SYSTEM INC.—Pettibone Corporation; *U.S. Private*, pg. 859
WEIGHT WATCHERS INTERNATIONAL, INC.—H.J. Heinz Company; *U.S. Public*, pg. 806

7992 — PUBLIC GOLF COURSES

AMERICAN GOLF CORPORATION; *U.S. Private*, pg. 55
JOYAMA KAIHATSU LTD.—Makita Corporation; *Int'l*, pg. 831
KOHLER COMPANY; *U.S. Private*, pg. 630
ORIOLE GOLF & TENNIS CLUB, INC.—Oriole Homes Corp.; *U.S. Public*, pg. 1231
SHADOWOOD GOLF INC.—Kocolene Oil Corp.; *U.S. Private*, pg. 629
SHOWBOAT, INCORPORATED; *U.S. Public*, pg. 1469
SQUARE TWO GOLF INCORPORATED; *U.S. Public*, pg. 1501
SUNLAND CO., LTD.—Mitsui & Co., Ltd.; *Int'l*, pg. 878
YAMAHA RECREATION CO., LTD.—Yamaha Corporation; *Int'l*, pg. 1516

7993 — COIN-OPERATED AMUSEMENT DEVICES

AUTOMATIC MUSIC SERVICE OF BILLINGS, INC.—Power House Technologies, Inc.; *U.S. Public*, pg. 1319
AZTAR CORPORATION; *U.S. Public*, pg. 158
BALLY GAMING INC.—Alliance Gaming Corporation; *U.S. Public*, pg. 47
CARDIVAN CO.—Jackpot Enterprises, Inc.; *U.S. Public*, pg. 920
CORRAL COIN, INC.—Jackpot Enterprises, Inc.; *U.S. Public*, pg. 920
CORRAL UNITED, INC.—Jackpot Enterprises, Inc.; *U.S. Public*, pg. 920
GRAND CASINOS, INC.; *U.S. Public*, pg. 758
GREATE BAY CASINO CORPORATION; *U.S. Public*, pg. 760
GRIFFIN GROUP, INC.; *U.S. Private*, pg. 480
HACIENDA HOTEL INC.—Santa Fe Gaming Corporation; *U.S. Public*, pg. 1432
HARRAH'S ENTERTAINMENT, INC.; *U.S. Public*, pg. 790
HOLLYWOOD CASINO CORP; *U.S. Public*, pg. 830
IGT NORTH AMERICA—International Game Technology; *U.S. Public*, pg. 900
INTERNATIONAL GAME TECHNOLOGY; *U.S. Public*, pg. 900
JACKPOT CITY, INC.—Jackpot Enterprises, Inc.; *U.S. Public*, pg. 920
JACKPOT ENTERPRISES, INC.; *U.S. Public*, pg. 920
JACKPOT GAMING, INC.—Jackpot Enterprises, Inc.; *U.S. Public*, pg. 920
MIDWAY HOME ENTERTAINMENT INC.—WMS Industries Inc.; *U.S. Public*, pg. 1727
PRESIDENT CASINOS, INC.; *U.S. Public*, pg. 1323
RESORTS CASINO HOTEL—Sun International Hotels Limited; *U.S. Public*, pg. 1531
SILVER CITY CASINO—Circus Circus - Las Vegas; *U.S. Public*, pg. 375
SLOTS-A-FUN, INC.—Circus Circus - Las Vegas; *U.S. Public*, pg. 375
WMS INDUSTRIES INC.; *U.S. Public*, pg. 1727

7996 — AMUSEMENT PARKS

ADVENTURE ISLAND—Anheuser-Busch Companies, Inc.; *U.S. Public*, pg. 114
ADVENTURE LANDS OF AMERICA, INC.; *U.S. Private*, pg. 22
ANHEUSER-BUSCH COMPANIES, INC.; *U.S. Public*, pg. 113

S.I.C. Index

BUSCH GARDENS TAMPA—Anheuser-Busch Companies, Inc.; *U.S. Public*, pg. 114
BUSCH GARDENS WILLIAMSBURG—Anheuser-Busch Companies, Inc.; *U.S. Public*, pg. 114
CEDAR FAIR, L.P.; *U.S. Public*, pg. 319
CEDAR POINT—Cedar Fair, L.P.; *U.S. Public*, pg. 319
WALT DISNEY ATTRACTIONS DIVISION—The Walt Disney Company; *U.S. Public*, pg. 511
WALT DISNEY ATTRACTIONS-WALT DISNEY WORLD—The Walt Disney Company; *U.S. Public*, pg. 513
DISNEYLAND—The Walt Disney Company; *U.S. Public*, pg. 511
DORNEY PARK & WILDWATER KINGDOM—Cedar Fair, L.P.; *U.S. Public*, pg. 319
KNOTT'S BERRY FARM; *U.S. Private*, pg. 627
MALIBU ENTERTAINMENT WORLDWIDE; *U.S. Public*, pg. 1039
MANTECH CO., LTD.—Abdulla Fouad Co. Ltd.; *Int'l*, pg. 502
MARINE WORLD AFRICA USA; *U.S. Private*, pg. 703
PARAMOUNT CAROWINDS—National Amusements, Inc.; *U.S. Private*, pg. 776
PARAMOUNT PARKS—National Amusements, Inc.; *U.S. Private*, pg. 776
PEARSON PLC; *Int'l*, pg. 1025
PREMIER PARKS INC.; *U.S. Public*, pg. 1323
RANK AMUSEMENTS LIMITED—The Rank Group PLC; *Int'l*, pg. 1087
SEA WORLD OF CALIFORNIA—Anheuser-Busch Companies, Inc.; *U.S. Public*, pg. 114
SEA WORLD OF FLORIDA—Anheuser-Busch Companies, Inc.; *U.S. Public*, pg. 114
SEA WORLD OF OHIO—Anheuser-Busch Companies, Inc.; *U.S. Public*, pg. 114
SESAME PLACE—Anheuser-Busch Companies, Inc.; *U.S. Public*, pg. 114
SIX FLAGS ASTROWORLD/SIX FLAGS WATERWORLD/SIX FLAGS HOUSTON—Time Warner Inc.; *U.S. Public*, pg. 1611
SIX FLAGS THEME PARKS INC.—Time Warner Inc.; *U.S. Public*, pg. 1611
SUZUKA CIRCUITLAND CO., LTD.—Honda Motor Co., Ltd.; *Int'l*, pg. 634
UNIVERSAL STUDIOS FLORIDA—The Rank Group PLC; *Int'l*, pg. 1087
UNIVERSAL STUDIOS HOLLYWOOD—The Seagram Company Ltd.; *Int'l*, pg. 1216
VALLEYFAIR—Cedar Fair, L.P.; *U.S. Public*, pg. 319
WORLDS OF FUN & OCEANS OF FUN—Cedar Fair, L.P.; *U.S. Public*, pg. 319

7997 — MEMBERSHIP SPORTS & RECREATION CLUBS

ANDREW SPORTS CLUB INC.; *U.S. Private*, pg. 73
ATLANTA MOTOR SPEEDWAY—Speedway Motorsports, Inc.; *U.S. Public*, pg. 1498
BALLY TOTAL FITNESS CORPORATION—Bally Total Fitness Holdings Corporation; *U.S. Public*, pg. 171
CLUB CORPORATION INTERNATIONAL; *U.S. Private*, pg. 247
FOUR-TEN CORP.—Wm. Wrigley Jr. Company; *U.S. Public*, pg. 1781
GALA LEISURE LTD.—Bass PLC; *Int'l*, pg. 170
GREATE BAY CASINO CORPORATION; *U.S. Public*, pg. 760
INNISBROOK/HILTON RESORT—Starwood Capital Group LLC; *U.S. Private*, pg. 1036
KANSAS CITY CHIEFS FOOTBALL CLUB, INC.; *U.S. Private*, pg. 607
KAWAGUCHIKO COUNTRY CLUB CO., LTD.—Matsuya Company Ltd.; *Int'l*, pg. 848
KOHLER COMPANY; *U.S. Private*, pg. 630
LAKE KEOWEE COUNTRY CLUB, INC.—Saint-Gobain; *Int'l*, pg. 1171
LYONNAISE DES EAUX S.A.; *Int'l*, pg. 822
MEIJI KAIHATSU CO., LTD.—Meiji Seika Kaisha, Ltd.; *Int'l*, pg. 855
NISSAY ATHLETICS CO., LTD.—Nippon Life Insurance Co.; *Int'l*, pg. 935
OCEANS RACQUET CLUB, INC.—The Chubb Corporation; *U.S. Public*, pg. 355
OKAZAKI GOLF CLUB KK—Tekken Corporation; *Int'l*, pg. 1362
SHOWBOAT, INCORPORATED; *U.S. Public*, pg. 1469
TAMARRON DIVISION—Starwood Capital Group LLC; *U.S. Private*, pg. 1036
TOP RANK LIMITED—The Rank Group PLC; *Int'l*, pg. 1087

7999 — AMUSEMENT AND RECREATION SERVICES, NEC

ALASKA BOAT CO.—Wards Cove Packing Company; *U.S. Private*, pg. 1150
AMANA SOCIETY, INC.; *U.S. Private*, pg. 48
ANHEUSER-BUSCH COMPANIES, INC.; *U.S. Public*, pg. 113
AUTOMATED WAGERING—Power House Technologies, Inc.; *U.S. Public*, pg. 1319
AUTOMATED WAGERING INTERNATIONAL, INC.—Power House Technologies, Inc.; *U.S. Public*, pg. 1319
AUTOTOTE CORPORATION; *U.S. Public*, pg. 150
AZTAR CORPORATION; *U.S. Public*, pg. 158
BALLY'S PARK PLACE, INC.—Hilton Hotels Corporation; *U.S. Public*, pg. 829
BASS LEISURE—Bass PLC; *Int'l*, pg. 170
BICYCLE CLUB CASINO; *U.S. Private*, pg. 142
BILLCOM EXPOSITION & CONFERENCE—VNU Verenigde Nederlandse Uitgeversbedrijven B.V.; *Int'l*, pg. 1446
BOARDWALK REGENCY CORPORATION—Starwood Hotels & Resorts; *U.S. Public*, pg. 1512
BUSCH ENTERTAINMENT CORP.—Anheuser-Busch Companies, Inc.; *U.S. Public*, pg. 114
CAESARS WORLD, INC.—Starwood Hotels & Resorts; *U.S. Public*, pg. 1512
CALGARY FLAMES HOCKEY CLUB; *Int'l*, pg. 252
CIRCUS CIRCUS - LAS VEGAS; *U.S. Public*, pg. 374
COLORADO BELLE—Circus Circus - Las Vegas; *U.S. Public*, pg. 375
CORAL RACING LTD.—Bass PLC; *Int'l*, pg. 170
DALLAS STARS; *U.S. Private*, pg. 309
DAVE & BUSTER'S; *U.S. Public*, pg. 488
DENVER NUGGETS LIMITED PARTNERSHIP—Ascent Entertainment Group, Inc.; *U.S. Public*, pg. 138
DESERT PALACE, INC.—Starwood Hotels & Resorts; *U.S. Public*, pg. 1512
WALT DISNEY IMAGINEERING—The Walt Disney Company; *U.S. Public*, pg. 513
DIVERSIFIED COMMUNICATIONS; *U.S. Private*, pg. 336
EARL'S COURT & OLYMPIA LTD.—The Peninsular and Oriental Steam Navigation Company; *Int'l*, pg. 1033
EDGEWATER HOTEL CORP.—Circus Circus - Las Vegas; *U.S. Public*, pg. 375
EL SAN JUAN HOTEL & CASINO—Patriot American Hospitality, Inc.; *U.S. Public*, pg. 1265
FAIR GROUNDS CORPORATION; *U.S. Public*, pg. 609
FELD PRODUCTIONS; *U.S. Private*, pg. 399
FLORIDA PANTHERS HOLDINGS, INC.; *U.S. Public*, pg. 654
GRAND CASINOS, INC.; *U.S. Public*, pg. 758
GUEST SERVICES, INC.; *U.S. Private*, pg. 486
HACIENDA HOTEL INC.—Santa Fe Gaming Corporation; *U.S. Public*, pg. 1432
HARRAH'S ATLANTIC CITY, INC.—Harrah's Entertainment, Inc.; *U.S. Public*, pg. 790
HARRAH'S ILLINOIS CORPORATION—Harrah's Entertainment, Inc.; *U.S. Public*, pg. 790
HARRAH'S LAS VEGAS—Harrah's Entertainment, Inc.; *U.S. Public*, pg. 790
HARRAH'S NEW JERSEY, INC.—Harrah's Entertainment, Inc.; *U.S. Public*, pg. 790
HARRAH'S SOUTH SHORE CORP.—Harrah's Entertainment, Inc.; *U.S. Public*, pg. 791
HOLLYWOOD PARK, INC.; *U.S. Public*, pg. 830
THE HOMESTEAD L.C.—Club Corporation International; *U.S. Private*, pg. 247
ITS AUSTRALIA PTY., LTD.—International Lottery & Totalizator Systems, Inc.; *U.S. Public*, pg. 900
ITT CORPORATION—Starwood Hotels & Resorts; *U.S. Public*, pg. 1512
INTERNATIONAL DATA GROUP; *U.S. Private*, pg. 569
INTERNATIONAL LOTTERY & TOTALIZATOR SYSTEMS, INC.; *U.S. Public*, pg. 900
JILLIAN'S ENTERTAINMENT CORPORATION; *U.S. Private*, pg. 587
KEUM KANG DEVELOPMENT INDUSTRIAL CO., LTD.—Hyundai Motor Company; *Int'l*, pg. 642
KILLINGTON LIMITED—American Skiing Company; *U.S. Private*, pg. 61
LDI, LTD.; *U.S. Private*, pg. 639
LADBROKE GROUP PLC; *Int'l*, pg. 787
LADBROKE RACECOURSE MANAGEMENT LTD.—Ladbroke Group Plc; *Int'l*, pg. 787
LADBROKE RACING LTD.—Ladbroke Group Plc; *Int'l*, pg. 787
MAJOR VIDEO CONCEPTS, INC.—LDI, Ltd.; *U.S. Private*, pg. 639
MALIBU ENTERTAINMENT WORLDWIDE; *U.S. Public*, pg. 1039
THE MIGHTY DUCKS OF ANAHEIM—The Walt Disney Company; *U.S. Public*, pg. 513
MOUNT SNOW RESORT—American Skiing Company; *U.S. Private*, pg. 61
NYT EVENT/SPORTS MARKETING—The New York Times Company; *U.S. Public*, pg. 1174
NEW CASTLE CORP.—Circus Circus - Las Vegas; *U.S. Public*, pg. 375
NEW YORK ISLANDERS HOCKEY CLUB; *U.S. Private*, pg. 794
NIAGARA FRONTIER HOCKEY, L.P.; *U.S. Private*, pg. 798
OAKLAND RAIDERS; *U.S. Private*, pg. 809
OGDEN CORPORATION; *U.S. Public*, pg. 1213
OGDEN ENTERTAINMENT, INC.—Ogden Corporation; *U.S. Public*, pg. 1213
PARI MUTUEL URBAIN; *Int'l*, pg. 1023
PEARSON PLC; *Int'l*, pg. 1025
PHILLIPS FINE ART AUCTIONEERS; *U.S. Private*, pg. 861
PICK'S COVE MARINA—Pickering Inc.; *U.S. Private*, pg. 865
POWER HOUSE TECHNOLOGIES, INC.; *U.S. Public*, pg. 1319
PUTT PUTT GOLF COURSES OF AMERICA, INC.; *U.S. Private*, pg. 896
RAMADA EXPRESS—Aztar Corporation; *U.S. Public*, pg. 158
RANK LEISURE MACHINE SERVICES LTD.—The Rank Group PLC; *Int'l*, pg. 1087
RINGLING BROS., BARNUM & BAILEY COMBINED SHOWS, INC.—Feld Productions; *U.S. Private*, pg. 400
SEA WORLD OF TEXAS—Anheuser-Busch Companies, Inc.; *U.S. Public*, pg. 114
SHOWBIZ PIZZA TIME, INC.; *U.S. Public*, pg. 1468
SHOWBOAT, INCORPORATED; *U.S. Public*, pg. 1469
SILVER DOLLAR CITY, INC.; *U.S. Private*, pg. 1000
SILVERTON MARINE CORPORATION; *U.S. Private*, pg. 1000
SISTEMAS TECNICOS LOTERIAS DEL ESTADO (S.T.L.)—Telefonica de Espana, S.A.; *Int'l*, pg. 1372
SODAK GAMING, INC.; *U.S. Public*, pg. 1482
TATTERSALLS; *Int'l*, pg. 1357
TOP RANK LIMITED—The Rank Group PLC; *Int'l*, pg. 1087
TOTALIZATOR SYSTEMS (UK) LIMITED—International Lottery & Totalizator Systems, Inc.; *U.S. Public*, pg. 900
TROPICANA RESORT & CASINO—Aztar Corporation; *U.S. Public*, pg. 159
TRUMP'S MARINA CASINO RESORT—Trump Organization; *U.S. Private*, pg. 1108
THE TUSSAUDS GROUP LIMITED—Pearson plc; *Int'l*, pg. 1026
VERNONS POOLS LIMITED—Ladbroke Group Plc; *Int'l*, pg. 787
WMS INDUSTRIES INC.; *U.S. Public*, pg. 1727
WATER COUNTRY USA—Anheuser-Busch Companies, Inc.; *U.S. Public*, pg. 114
WESTERN REGIONAL OFF TRACK BETTING; *U.S. Private*, pg. 1168
WILLIAMS HOSPITALITY GROUP INC.—Patriot American Hospitality, Inc.; *U.S. Public*, pg. 1265

8011 — OFFICES & CLINICS OF DOCTORS OF MEDICINE

ALLEGIANT PHYSICIAN SERVICES; *U.S. Public*, pg. 45
BEHAVIORAL HEALTHCARE OPTIONS, INC.—Sierra Health Services, Inc.; *U.S. Public*, pg. 1469
COLUMBIA/H.C.A.—Columbia/HCA Healthcare Corporation; *U.S. Public*, pg. 404
ELAN CLINICAL SERVICES LTD.—Elan Corporation Plc; *Int'l*, pg. 436
GALEN OF VIRGINIA, INC.—Columbia/HCA Healthcare Corporation; *U.S. Public*, pg. 404
HEALTHSOUTH CORPORATION—Healthsouth Corporation; *U.S. Public*, pg. 803
HUMANA INC.; *U.S. Public*, pg. 847
LA METAIRE CLINIC—Magellan Health Services, Inc.; *U.S. Public*, pg. 1036
MAGELLAN IMAGING, INC.—Magellan Health Services, Inc.; *U.S. Public*, pg. 1036
MERITCARE HEALTH SYSTEM; *U.S. Private*, pg. 733
PHP HEALTHCARE CORPORATION; *U.S. Public*, pg. 1241
QUEST DIAGNOSTIC-VINELAND—Quest Diagnostics, Inc.; *U.S. Public*, pg. 1352
QUEST DIAGNOSTIC-WAYNE—Quest Diagnostics, Inc.; *U.S. Public*, pg. 1352
QUEST DIAGNOSTIC-WILLIAMSPORT—Quest Diagnostics, Inc.; *U.S. Public*, pg. 1352
QUEST STAFFING—Allegiant Physician Services; *U.S. Public*, pg. 45
SALICK HEALTH CARE, INC.—Zeneca Group Plc; *Int'l*, pg. 1524
SIERRA HEALTH SERVICES, INC.; *U.S. Public*, pg. 1469
SOUTHWEST MEDICAL ASSOCIATES, INC.—Sierra Health Services, Inc.; *U.S. Public*, pg. 1470
UHP HEALTHCARE; *U.S. Private*, pg. 1113

8021 — OFFICES & CLINICS OF DENTISTS

SHARPE DRY GOODS CO., INC.; *U.S. Private*, pg. 990

8042 — OFFICES & CLINICS OF OPTOMETRISTS

DOLLAND & AITCHISON SERVICES LTD.—Dolland & Aitchison Ltd.; *Int'l*, pg. 414
FOR EYES PLC—Dolland & Aitchison Ltd.; *Int'l*, pg. 414
HAMBLIN OPTICAL SERVICES LTD.—Dolland & Aitchison Ltd.; *Int'l*, pg. 414
MIDWEST VISION CENTERS; *U.S. Private*, pg. 745
PEARLE INC.—Cole National Corporation; *U.S. Public*, pg. 396
PEARLE VISION, INC.—Cole National Corporation; *U.S. Public*, pg. 397

8049 — OFFICES & CLINICS OF HEALTH PRACTITIONERS, NEC

CONTINENTAL HEALTH AFFILIATES, INC.; *U.S. Public*, pg. 440
HEALTH CARE & RETIREMENT CORPORATION; *U.S. Public*, pg. 801
HEALTHSOUTH CORPORATION—Healthsouth Corporation; *U.S. Public*, pg. 803
LIFE EXTENSION INSTITUTE—U.M. Holding Limited; *U.S. Private*, pg. 1114
PRO-THERAPY OF AMERICA—Horizon/CMS Healthcare Corporation; *U.S. Public*, pg. 839
QUEST DIAGNOSTIC-BINGHAMTON—Quest Diagnostics, Inc.; *U.S. Public*, pg. 1351
QUEST DIAGNOSTIC-SYRACUSE—Quest Diagnostics, Inc.; *U.S. Public*, pg. 1352
REHABCARE OUTPATIENT SERVICES, INC.—RehabCare Group, Inc.; *U.S. Public*, pg. 1373
REHABWORKS INC.—Horizon/CMS Healthcare Corporation; *U.S. Public*, pg. 839
VTA MANAGEMENT SERVICES, INC.—Horizon/CMS Healthcare Corporation; *U.S. Public*, pg. 839

8051 — SKILLED NURSING CARE FACILITIES

ADAMS HOUSE HEALTHCARE—Vencor, Inc.; *U.S. Public*, pg. 1711
ALPINE TERRACE—Paragon Health Network, Inc.; *U.S. Public*, pg. 1256
ALTA VISTA HEALTHCARE—Vencor, Inc.; *U.S. Public*, pg. 1711
ALVARADO CONVALESCENT & REHABILITATION HOSPITAL SAN DIEGO—Vencor, Inc.; *U.S. Public*, pg. 1711
ANDREW HOUSE HEALTHCARE—Vencor, Inc.; *U.S. Public*, pg. 1711
AUBURN MANOR—Horizon/CMS Healthcare Corporation; *U.S. Public*, pg. 838
BALTIC COUNTRY MANOR—Horizon/CMS Healthcare Corporation; *U.S. Public*, pg. 838

BANCROFT HOUSE HEALTHCARE—Vencor, Inc.; *U.S. Public*, pg. 1711
BAY BREEZE CENTER—Horizon/CMS Healthcare Corporation; *U.S. Public*, pg. 836
BEVERLY ENTERPRISES, INC.; *U.S. Public*, pg. 227
BIRCHWOOD CARE CENTER—Horizon/CMS Healthcare Corporation; *U.S. Public*, pg. 837
BIRCHWOOD TERRACE HEALTHCARE—Vencor, Inc.; *U.S. Public*, pg. 1712
BLUEBERRY HILL HEALTHCARE—Vencor, Inc.; *U.S. Public*, pg. 1712
BOARDMAN COMMUNITY CARE CENTER—Horizon/CMS Healthcare Corporation; *U.S. Public*, pg. 838
BOCA RATON CONVALESCENT CENTER—Vencor, Inc.; *U.S. Public*, pg. 1712
BOULDER CITY CARE CENTER—Horizon/CMS Healthcare Corporation; *U.S. Public*, pg. 837
BOULEVARD MANOR NURSING CENTER—Paragon Health Network, Inc.; *U.S. Public*, pg. 1256
BOWLING GREEN HEALTH CARE CENTER—Vencor, Inc.; *U.S. Public*, pg. 1712
BOZEMAN CARE CENTER—Vencor, Inc.; *U.S. Public*, pg. 1712
BRYANT NURSING CENTER—Horizon/CMS Healthcare Corporation; *U.S. Public*, pg. 839
BUTTE CONVALESCENT CENTER—Horizon/CMS Healthcare Corporation; *U.S. Public*, pg. 837
BUTTE PARK ROYAL—Horizon/CMS Healthcare Corporation; *U.S. Public*, pg. 837
CANTERBURY VILLA OF ALLIANCE—Horizon/CMS Healthcare Corporation; *U.S. Public*, pg. 838
CARSON CONVALESCENT CENTER—Horizon/CMS Healthcare Corporation; *U.S. Public*, pg. 837
CASA ARENA BLANCA—Horizon/CMS Healthcare Corporation; *U.S. Public*, pg. 838
CASA MARIA HEALTH CARE CENTER—Horizon/CMS Healthcare Corporation; *U.S. Public*, pg. 838
CASA REAL HEALTH CARE CENTER—Horizon/CMS Healthcare Corporation; *U.S. Public*, pg. 838
CEDAR CREST—Paragon Health Network, Inc.; *U.S. Public*, pg. 1256
THE CEDARS—Paragon Health Network, Inc.; *U.S. Public*, pg. 1256
CHAMPION HEALTHCARE CORPORATION; *U.S. Public*, pg. 333
CHELTENHAM-YORK ROAD NURSING & REHABILITATION CENTER—Genesis Health Ventures, Inc.; *U.S. Public*, pg. 729
CHERRY CREEK VILLAGE NURSING CENTER—Horizon/CMS Healthcare Corporation; *U.S. Public*, pg. 837
CLAYTON HOUSE HEALTHCARE—Vencor, Inc.; *U.S. Public*, pg. 1712
CLIFTON HOUSE REHABILITATION CENTER—Horizon/CMS Healthcare Corporation; *U.S. Public*, pg. 836
CLOVERLEAF HEALTHCARE—Vencor, Inc.; *U.S. Public*, pg. 1712
COBBS CREEK NURSING CENTER—Genesis Health Ventures, Inc.; *U.S. Public*, pg. 729
COLONIAL MANOR—Horizon/CMS Healthcare Corporation; *U.S. Public*, pg. 838
COLONIAL MANOR NURSING & CONVALESCENT HOSPITAL—Vencor, Inc.; *U.S. Public*, pg. 1712
COLONIAL MANOR OF DEER LODGE—Horizon/CMS Healthcare Corporation; *U.S. Public*, pg. 837
COLONIAL MANOR OF WHITEFISH—Horizon/CMS Healthcare Corporation; *U.S. Public*, pg. 837
COLONY HOUSE HEALTHCARE—Vencor, Inc.; *U.S. Public*, pg. 1712
COLUMBIA CORPORATION; *U.S. Private*, pg. 255
COLUMBIA HOUSE HEALTHCARE—Vencor, Inc.; *U.S. Public*, pg. 1712
COMPREMEDX, INC.—Continental Health Affiliates, Inc.; *U.S. Public*, pg. 440
CONTINENTAL HEALTH AFFILIATES, INC.; *U.S. Public*, pg. 440
CONVALESCENT CENTER OF THE PALM BEACHES—Vencor, Inc.; *U.S. Public*, pg. 1712
CRESTWOOD CARE CENTER—Horizon/CMS Healthcare Corporation; *U.S. Public*, pg. 838
DAVIDSON NURSING CENTER, INC.—Vencor, Inc.; *U.S. Public*, pg. 1712
DESERT HAVEN NURSING CENTER—Paragon Health Network, Inc.; *U.S. Public*, pg. 1256
DESERT LANE CARE CENTER—Horizon/CMS Healthcare Corporation; *U.S. Public*, pg. 837
DESERT TERRACE NURSING CENTER—Paragon Health Network, Inc.; *U.S. Public*, pg. 1256
DIRKSEN HOUSE HEALTHCARE—Vencor, Inc.; *U.S. Public*, pg. 1712
DOVER HOUSE HEALTHCARE—Vencor, Inc.; *U.S. Public*, pg. 1712
DUNN NURSING HOME—Paragon Health Network, Inc.; *U.S. Public*, pg. 1256
EAST MANOR MEDICAL CARE CENTER—Vencor, Inc.; *U.S. Public*, pg. 1712
EAST MOORE NURSING CENTER—Horizon/CMS Healthcare Corporation; *U.S. Public*, pg. 839
EDGEWATER CARE CENTER—Paragon Health Network, Inc.; *U.S. Public*, pg. 1256
ELMS HAVEN CARE CENTER—Horizon/CMS Healthcare Corporation; *U.S. Public*, pg. 836
EMBASSY HOUSE HEALTHCARE—Vencor, Inc.; *U.S. Public*, pg. 1712
EXTENDICARE (CANADA) INC.—Extendicare Inc.; *Int'l*, pg. 468
EXTENDICARE INC.; *Int'l*, pg. 468
FAIRVIEW CARE CENTER OF BETHLEHEM PIKE—Genesis Health Ventures, Inc.; *U.S. Public*, pg. 729
FAIRVIEW CARE CENTER OF PAPERMILL RD.—Genesis Health Ventures, Inc.; *U.S. Public*, pg. 729
FAIRVIEW NURSING HOME—Paragon Health Network, Inc.; *U.S. Public*, pg. 1256
FALLON CONVALESCENT CENTER—Horizon/CMS Healthcare Corporation; *U.S. Public*, pg. 837
FIFTH AVENUE CONVALESCENT HOUSE—Vencor, Inc.; *U.S. Public*, pg. 1712
THE FOUNTAINS—Paragon Health Network, Inc.; *U.S. Public*, pg. 1256
FRANKLIN HOUSE HEALTHCARE—Vencor, Inc.; *U.S. Public*, pg. 1712
FREMONT MANNOR NURSING & CONVALESCENT HOME—Vencor, Inc.; *U.S. Public*, pg. 1712
GENESIS ELDERCARE—Genesis Health Ventures, Inc.; *U.S. Public*, pg. 728
GOLDEN PLAINS CARE CENTER—Horizon/CMS Healthcare Corporation; *U.S. Public*, pg. 837
GREAT BARRINGTON HEALTHCARE—Vencor, Inc.; *U.S. Public*, pg. 1712
GREENBRIAR TERRACE HEALTHCARE—Vencor, Inc.; *U.S. Public*, pg. 1712
GREENERY EXTENDED CARE CENTER OF BEVERLY—Horizon/CMS Healthcare Corporation; *U.S. Public*, pg. 836
GREENERY HEALTH CARE CENTER—Horizon/CMS Healthcare Corporation; *U.S. Public*, pg. 837
GREENERY HEALTH CARE CENTER AT CLARKSTON—Horizon/CMS Healthcare Corporation; *U.S. Public*, pg. 837
GREENERY NEUROLOGICAL REHABILITATION—Horizon/CMS Healthcare Corporation; *U.S. Public*, pg. 837
GREENERY REHAB - WATERBURY—Horizon/CMS Healthcare Corporation; *U.S. Public*, pg. 836
GREENERY REHABILITATION & SKILLED NURSING CENTER—Horizon/CMS Healthcare Corporation; *U.S. Public*, pg. 837
GREENERY REHABILITATION CENTER—Horizon/CMS Healthcare Corporation; *U.S. Public*, pg. 837
GULFPORT CONVALESCENT CENTER MANOR—Vencor, Inc.; *U.S. Public*, pg. 1713
HACIENDA DE SALUD - BLOOMFIELD—Horizon/CMS Healthcare Corporation; *U.S. Public*, pg. 838
HACIENDA DE SALUD - ESPANOLA—Horizon/CMS Healthcare Corporation; *U.S. Public*, pg. 838
HAMILTON PAVILION HEALTHCARE—Vencor, Inc.; *U.S. Public*, pg. 1713
HANOVER TERRACE HEALTHCARE—Vencor, Inc.; *U.S. Public*, pg. 1713
HARBOR VIEW CARE CENTER—Horizon/CMS Healthcare Corporation; *U.S. Public*, pg. 839
HARRODSBURG HEALTH CARE—Vencor, Inc.; *U.S. Public*, pg. 1713
HARTFORD CARE CENTER—Horizon/CMS Healthcare Corporation; *U.S. Public*, pg. 840
HEARTHSTONE OF NORTHERN NEVADA—Horizon/CMS Healthcare Corporation; *U.S. Public*, pg. 837
HENDERSON CONVALESCENT HOSPITAL—Horizon/CMS Healthcare Corporation; *U.S. Public*, pg. 837
HERITAGE CARE CENTER—Horizon/CMS Healthcare Corporation; *U.S. Public*, pg. 838
HERITAGE GARDENS—Horizon/CMS Healthcare Corporation; *U.S. Public*, pg. 839
HERITAGE HILLHAVEN NURSING HOME—Vencor, Inc.; *U.S. Public*, pg. 1713
HIGHLAND MANOR NURSING HOME—Paragon Health Network, Inc.; *U.S. Public*, pg. 1257
HILLCREST HEALTH CARE, INC.—Vencor, Inc.; *U.S. Public*, pg. 1713
HILLSIDE MANOR CONVALESCENT HOSPITAL—Vencor, Inc.; *U.S. Public*, pg. 1714
HILLTOP VILLAGE—Paragon Health Network, Inc.; *U.S. Public*, pg. 1257
HOBBS HEALTHCARE CENTER—Horizon/CMS Healthcare Corporation; *U.S. Public*, pg. 838
HORIZON/CMS HEALTHCARE CORPORATION; *U.S. Public*, pg. 836
HORIZON HEALTHCARE NURSING CENTER—Horizon/CMS Healthcare Corporation; *U.S. Public*, pg. 838
HORIZON HEALTHCARE & SPECIALTY CENTER—Horizon/CMS Healthcare Corporation; *U.S. Public*, pg. 836
HORIZON MEADOWS—Horizon/CMS Healthcare Corporation; *U.S. Public*, pg. 838
HORIZON SPECIALTY CENTER OF PENSACOLA—Horizon/CMS Healthcare Corporation; *U.S. Public*, pg. 836
HORIZON SPECIALTY & REHABILITATION CENTER OF KISSIMMEE—Horizon/CMS Healthcare Corporation; *U.S. Public*, pg. 836
HORIZON VILLAGE NURSING & REHABILITATION—Horizon/CMS Healthcare Corporation; *U.S. Public*, pg. 838
HORIZON'S BAYSIDE MANOR—Horizon/CMS Healthcare Corporation; *U.S. Public*, pg. 836
HUDSON ELMS NURSING HOME—Horizon/CMS Healthcare Corporation; *U.S. Public*, pg. 838
IMPERIAL SKILLED CARE CENTER—Horizon/CMS Healthcare Corporation; *U.S. Public*, pg. 838
INDIAN CREEK NURSING CENTER—Horizon/CMS Healthcare Corporation; *U.S. Public*, pg. 837
INDIAN MEADOWS NURSING CENTER—Horizon/CMS Healthcare Corporation; *U.S. Public*, pg. 837
INTEGRATED HEALTH SERVICES, INC.; *U.S. Public*, pg. 884
KANNAPOLIS REST HOME, INC.—Vencor, Inc.; *U.S. Public*, pg. 1714
KIMBERLY MANOR NURSING AND CONVALESCENT HOME—Vencor, Inc.; *U.S. Public*, pg. 1714
KNOLLWOOD HALL—Vencor, Inc.; *U.S. Public*, pg. 1714
LAKE EUSTIS CARE CENTER—Horizon/CMS Healthcare Corporation; *U.S. Public*, pg. 837
LAKE HAVEN HEALTH CARE CENTER—Vencor, Inc.; *U.S. Public*, pg. 1714
LAKEVIEW MANOR—Vencor, Inc.; *U.S. Public*, pg. 1714
LAS CRUCES NURSING CENTER—Horizon/CMS Healthcare Corporation; *U.S. Public*, pg. 838
LAS FLORES NURSING CENTER—Paragon Health Network, Inc.; *U.S. Public*, pg. 1257
LAS PALMA NURSING CENTER—Vencor, Inc.; *U.S. Public*, pg. 1714
LAS VEGAS CONVALESCENT CENTER—Vencor, Inc.; *U.S. Public*, pg. 1714
LESLIE PLACE—Paragon Health Network, Inc.; *U.S. Public*, pg. 1257
LINCOLN NURSING CENTER, INC.—Vencor, Inc.; *U.S. Public*, pg. 1714
LIVINGSTON CONVALESCENT CENTER NO. 434—Vencor, Inc.; *U.S. Public*, pg. 1714
LYNWOOD MANOR—Horizon/CMS Healthcare Corporation; *U.S. Public*, pg. 837
MANOR CARE, INC.; *U.S. Public*, pg. 1041
MANOR HEALTHCARE CORP.—Manor Care, Inc.; *U.S. Public*, pg. 1041
MAYO CENTER—Genesis Health Ventures, Inc.; *U.S. Public*, pg. 729
MAYWOOD ACRES HEALTHCARE—Vencor, Inc.; *U.S. Public*, pg. 1714
MCKINLEY MANOR—Horizon/CMS Healthcare Corporation; *U.S. Public*, pg. 838
MEADOWVIEW CARE CENTER—Horizon/CMS Healthcare Corporation; *U.S. Public*, pg. 838
MEDICAL CENTER NURSING FACILITY—Horizon/CMS Healthcare Corporation; *U.S. Public*, pg. 839
MEDICALODGES, INC.; *U.S. Private*, pg. 728
MEDICANA NURSING CENTER—Paragon Health Network, Inc.; *U.S. Public*, pg. 1257
MERITCARE, INC.; *U.S. Private*, pg. 733
MISSOURI RIVER MANOR—Horizon/CMS Healthcare Corporation; *U.S. Public*, pg. 837
MONTEREY NURSING CENTER—Paragon Health Network, Inc.; *U.S. Public*, pg. 1257
MONTROSE BAY HEALTH CARE CENTER—Paragon Health Network, Inc.; *U.S. Public*, pg. 1257
MOUNTAIN TOWERS HEALTHCARE—Vencor, Inc.; *U.S. Public*, pg. 1714
MOUNTAIN VIEW HEALTHCARE—Vencor, Inc.; *U.S. Public*, pg. 1714
MOUNTAIN VIEW PLACE—Horizon/CMS Healthcare Corporation; *U.S. Public*, pg. 839
NWNL BENEFITS CORP.—ReliaStar Financial Corp.; *U.S. Public*, pg. 1375
NATIONAL HEALTH CARE AFFILIATES, INC.; *U.S. Private*, pg. 784
NORTH LAS VEGAS CARE CENTER—Horizon/CMS Healthcare Corporation; *U.S. Public*, pg. 837
NUTMEG PAVILION HEALTHCARE—Vencor, Inc.; *U.S. Public*, pg. 1714
OJAI MANOR—Vencor, Inc.; *U.S. Public*, pg. 1714
PALMER HOUSE HEALTHCARE—Vencor, Inc.; *U.S. Public*, pg. 1714
PARAGON HEALTH NETWORK, INC.; *U.S. Public*, pg. 1256
PARK MANOR NURSING & CONVALESCENT HOME—Vencor, Inc.; *U.S. Public*, pg. 1714
PARKVIEW ACRES—Vencor, Inc.; *U.S. Public*, pg. 1714
PARKWAY PAVILION HEALTHCARE—Vencor, Inc.; *U.S. Public*, pg. 1714
PARKWOOD PLACE—Horizon/CMS Healthcare Corporation; *U.S. Public*, pg. 839
PHENIX CITY NURSING HOME—Paragon Health Network, Inc.; *U.S. Public*, pg. 1257
PHYSICIANS HOSPITAL FOR EXTENDED CARE—Horizon/CMS Healthcare Corporation; *U.S. Public*, pg. 837
PIEDMONT NURSING CENTER, INC.—Vencor, Inc.; *U.S. Public*, pg. 1714
PINE TOWERS CONVALESCENT HOSPITAL—Vencor, Inc.; *U.S. Public*, pg. 1714
PINEVILLE HEALTH CARE CENTER, INC.—Vencor, Inc.; *U.S. Public*, pg. 1714
POST ACUTE DIVISION—Paragon Health Network, Inc.; *U.S. Public*, pg. 1256
QUAIL CREEK NURSING & RETIREMENT CENTER—Horizon/CMS Healthcare Corporation; *U.S. Public*, pg. 839
RED ROCKS CARE CENTER—Horizon/CMS Healthcare Corporation; *U.S. Public*, pg. 838
REHABILITATION INSTITUTE OF OKLAHOMA—Vencor, Inc.; *U.S. Public*, pg. 1714
RENAISSANCE—Paragon Health Network, Inc.; *U.S. Public*, pg. 1257
RENO CONVALESCENT CENTER—Vencor, Inc.; *U.S. Public*, pg. 1714
RIDGECREST CARE CENTER—Horizon/CMS Healthcare Corporation; *U.S. Public*, pg. 838
RIVER TERRACE HEALTHCARE—Vencor, Inc.; *U.S. Public*, pg. 1714
ROCKINGHAM NURSING CENTER—Vencor, Inc.; *U.S. Public*, pg. 1714
ROSEWOOD MANOR—Horizon/CMS Healthcare Corporation; *U.S. Public*, pg. 838
ROSWELL NURSING CENTER—Horizon/CMS Healthcare Corporation; *U.S. Public*, pg. 838
RUIDOSO CARE CENTER—Horizon/CMS Healthcare Corporation; *U.S. Public*, pg. 838
SABLE CARE CENTER—Horizon/CMS Healthcare Corporation; *U.S. Public*, pg. 836
ST. ANDREWS HOMES—Vaux Group Plc; *Int'l*, pg. 1454
SALEMHAVEN—Vencor, Inc.; *U.S. Public*, pg. 1714
SAN FRANCISCO CONVALESCENT CENTER—Vencor, Inc.; *U.S. Public*, pg. 1714
SAN JACINTO MANOR—Horizon/CMS Healthcare Corporation; *U.S. Public*, pg. 839
SAN JUAN MANOR—Horizon/CMS Healthcare Corporation; *U.S. Public*, pg. 838
SANTA PAULA HEALTHCARE—Vencor, Inc.; *U.S. Public*, pg. 1714
SAVANNAH CONVALESCENT CENTER—Vencor, Inc.; *U.S. Public*, pg. 1714
SAYLOR LANE CONVALESCENT HOSPITAL—Vencor, Inc.; *U.S. Public*, pg. 1714

SEVEN OAKS CARE CENTER—Horizon/CMS Healthcare Corporation; *U.S. Public*, pg. 839
SHERWOOD CONVALESCENT HOSPITAL—Vencor, Inc.; *U.S. Public*, pg. 1714
SIERRA CONVALESCENT CENTER—Horizon/CMS Healthcare Corporation; *U.S. Public*, pg. 837
SILAS CREEK MANOR—Vencor, Inc.; *U.S. Public*, pg. 1714
SILVER CREEK MANOR NURSING CENTER—Paragon Health Network, Inc.; *U.S. Public*, pg. 1257
SILVER SPRINGS NURSING & REHABILITATION CENTER—Horizon/CMS Healthcare Corporation; *U.S. Public*, pg. 839
SILVERADO CONVALESCENT HOSPITAL—Vencor, Inc.; *U.S. Public*, pg. 1714
SILVERBROOK MANOR—Horizon/CMS Healthcare Corporation; *U.S. Public*, pg. 837
SILVERCREST MANOR—Horizon/CMS Healthcare Corporation; *U.S. Public*, pg. 837
SILVERSTREAM CENTER—Genesis Health Ventures, Inc.; *U.S. Public*, pg. 729
SOUTH HAVEN MANOR NURSING HOME—Paragon Health Network, Inc.; *U.S. Public*, pg. 1257
SOUTHERN OAKS HEALTH CARE CENTER—Horizon/CMS Healthcare Corporation; *U.S. Public*, pg. 837
SOUTHLAND NURSING HOME—Paragon Health Network, Inc.; *U.S. Public*, pg. 1257
SOUTHWEST SENIOR CARE CENTER—Horizon/CMS Healthcare Corporation; *U.S. Public*, pg. 838
SPANISH MEADOW NURSING CENTER—Horizon/CMS Healthcare Corporation; *U.S. Public*, pg. 839
SUN VALLEY HEALTH CARE CENTER—Horizon/CMS Healthcare Corporation; *U.S. Public*, pg. 839
SUNRISE HEALTHCARE CORPORATION—Sun Healthcare Group Inc.; *U.S. Public*, pg. 1531
SUNSET VILLA NURSING HOME—Horizon/CMS Healthcare Corporation; *U.S. Public*, pg. 838
SUNSHINE HAVEN—Horizon/CMS Healthcare Corporation; *U.S. Public*, pg. 838
TERRACE VILLA CONVALESCENT CENTER—Vencor, Inc.; *U.S. Public*, pg. 1715
TORREY PINES CARE CENTER—Vencor, Inc.; *U.S. Public*, pg. 1715
TWIN PINES HEALTHCARE—Vencor, Inc.; *U.S. Public*, pg. 1715
UNITED HEALTH, INC.—Extendicare Inc.; *Int'l*, pg. 468
UNIVERSITY NURSING CENTER—Vencor, Inc.; *U.S. Public*, pg. 1715
VALLE NORTE CARING CENTER—Horizon/CMS Healthcare Corporation; *U.S. Public*, pg. 838
VALLEY GRANDE MANOR—Horizon/CMS Healthcare Corporation; *U.S. Public*, pg. 839
VALLEY HOUSE HEALTHCARE—Vencor, Inc.; *U.S. Public*, pg. 1715
VALLEY MANOR APARTMENTS—Vencor, Inc.; *U.S. Public*, pg. 1715
VAN ARK CARE CENTER—Horizon/CMS Healthcare Corporation; *U.S. Public*, pg. 838
VAUX GROUP PLC; *Int'l*, pg. 1453
VEGAS VALLEY CONVALESCENT CENTER—Horizon/CMS Healthcare Corporation; *U.S. Public*, pg. 837
VICTORIAN CONVALESCENT HOSPITAL—Vencor, Inc.; *U.S. Public*, pg. 1715
THE VILLA—Genesis Health Ventures, Inc.; *U.S. Public*, pg. 729
VILLAGE CARE CENTER—Horizon/CMS Healthcare Corporation; *U.S. Public*, pg. 838
VILLAGE SQUARE NURSING CENTER—Horizon/CMS Healthcare Corporation; *U.S. Public*, pg. 838
WALDEN HOUSE HEALTHCARE—Vencor, Inc.; *U.S. Public*, pg. 1715
WARREN MANOR NURSING HOME—Paragon Health Network, Inc.; *U.S. Public*, pg. 1257
WASATCH VILLA CONVALESCENT NURSING HOME—Vencor, Inc.; *U.S. Public*, pg. 1715
WASHINGTON SQUARE NURSING CENTER—Horizon/CMS Healthcare Corporation; *U.S. Public*, pg. 838
WASHOE CARE CENTER—Horizon/CMS Healthcare Corporation; *U.S. Public*, pg. 838
WESLEYAN NURSING HOME, INC.—Vencor, Inc.; *U.S. Public*, pg. 1715
WESTERN CARE NURSING HOME NO. 439—Vencor, Inc.; *U.S. Public*, pg. 1715
WILLOWBROOK CARE CENTER, INC.—Vencor, Inc.; *U.S. Public*, pg. 1715
WILLOWBROOK MANOR—Horizon/CMS Healthcare Corporation; *U.S. Public*, pg. 837
WILSON CONVALESCENT CENTER—Vencor, Inc.; *U.S. Public*, pg. 1715
WINDSOR HEALTH CARE CENTER—Vencor, Inc.; *U.S. Public*, pg. 1715
WINDSOR MANOR—Horizon/CMS Healthcare Corporation; *U.S. Public*, pg. 837
WINSTON-SALEM CONVALESCENT CENTER—Vencor, Inc.; *U.S. Public*, pg. 1715
WINTER HAVEN—Horizon/CMS Healthcare Corporation; *U.S. Public*, pg. 839
WOODLEY MANOR NURSING HOME—Paragon Health Network, Inc.; *U.S. Public*, pg. 1257

8052 — INTERMEDIATE CARE FACILITIES

ALPINE TERRACE—Paragon Health Network, Inc.; *U.S. Public*, pg. 1256
BOULEVARD MANOR NURSING CENTER—Paragon Health Network, Inc.; *U.S. Public*, pg. 1256
CAPITAL SENIOR LIVING, INC.; *U.S. Public*, pg. 302
CASA DEL SOL—Horizon/CMS Healthcare Corporation; *U.S. Public*, pg. 838
CEDAR CREST—Paragon Health Network, Inc.; *U.S. Public*, pg. 1256
THE CEDARS—Paragon Health Network, Inc.; *U.S. Public*, pg. 1256
CHELTENHAM-YORK ROAD NURSING & REHABILITATION CENTER—Genesis Health Ventures, Inc.; *U.S. Public*, pg. 729
COBBS CREEK NURSING CENTER—Genesis Health Ventures, Inc.; *U.S. Public*, pg. 729
COMPREMEDX, INC.—Continental Health Affiliates, Inc.; *U.S. Public*, pg. 440
CONSTELLATION REAL ESTATE GROUP INC.—Baltimore Gas and Electric Company; *U.S. Public*, pg. 172
DESERT HAVEN NURSING CENTER—Paragon Health Network, Inc.; *U.S. Public*, pg. 1256
DESERT TERRACE NURSING CENTER—Paragon Health Network, Inc.; *U.S. Public*, pg. 1256
DUNN NURSING HOME—Paragon Health Network, Inc.; *U.S. Public*, pg. 1256
EDGEWATER CARE CENTER—Paragon Health Network, Inc.; *U.S. Public*, pg. 1256
FAIRVIEW CARE CENTER OF BETHLEHEM PIKE—Genesis Health Ventures, Inc.; *U.S. Public*, pg. 729
FAIRVIEW CARE CENTER OF PAPERMILL RD.—Genesis Health Ventures, Inc.; *U.S. Public*, pg. 729
FAIRVIEW NURSING HOME—Paragon Health Network, Inc.; *U.S. Public*, pg. 1256
THE FOUNTAINS—Paragon Health Network, Inc.; *U.S. Public*, pg. 1256
GENESIS ELDERCARE—Genesis Health Ventures, Inc.; *U.S. Public*, pg. 728
HIGHLAND MANOR NURSING HOME—Paragon Health Network, Inc.; *U.S. Public*, pg. 1257
HILLTOP VILLAGE—Paragon Health Network, Inc.; *U.S. Public*, pg. 1257
LAS FLORES NURSING CENTER—Paragon Health Network, Inc.; *U.S. Public*, pg. 1257
LESLIE PLACE—Paragon Health Network, Inc.; *U.S. Public*, pg. 1257
MAYO CENTER—Genesis Health Ventures, Inc.; *U.S. Public*, pg. 729
MEDICANA NURSING CENTER—Paragon Health Network, Inc.; *U.S. Public*, pg. 1257
MONTEREY NURSING CENTER—Paragon Health Network, Inc.; *U.S. Public*, pg. 1257
MONTROSE BAY HEALTH CARE CENTER—Paragon Health Network, Inc.; *U.S. Public*, pg. 1257
NWNL BENEFITS CORP.—ReliaStar Financial Corp.; *U.S. Public*, pg. 1375
PARAGON HEALTH NETWORK, INC.; *U.S. Public*, pg. 1256
PHENIX CITY NURSING HOME—Paragon Health Network, Inc.; *U.S. Public*, pg. 1257
POST ACUTE DIVISION—Paragon Health Network, Inc.; *U.S. Public*, pg. 1256
RENAISSANCE—Paragon Health Network, Inc.; *U.S. Public*, pg. 1257
RES-CARE INCORPORATED; *U.S. Public*, pg. 1382
SILVER CREEK MANOR NURSING CENTER—Paragon Health Network, Inc.; *U.S. Public*, pg. 1257
SILVERSTREAM CENTER—Genesis Health Ventures, Inc.; *U.S. Public*, pg. 729
SOUTH HAVEN MANOR NURSING HOME—Paragon Health Network, Inc.; *U.S. Public*, pg. 1257
SUNRISE HEALTHCARE CORPORATION—Sun Healthcare Group Inc.; *U.S. Public*, pg. 1531
THE VILLA—Genesis Health Ventures, Inc.; *U.S. Public*, pg. 729
WARREN MANOR NURSING HOME—Paragon Health Network, Inc.; *U.S. Public*, pg. 1257
WOODLEY MANOR NURSING HOME—Paragon Health Network, Inc.; *U.S. Public*, pg. 1257

8059 — NURSING & PERSONAL CARE FACILITIES, NEC

BEVERLY ENTERPRISES, INC.; *U.S. Public*, pg. 227
BRANDYWINE HALL CARE CENTER—Genesis Health Ventures, Inc.; *U.S. Public*, pg. 728
BURLINGTON WOODS CONVALESCENT HOME—Genesis Health Ventures, Inc.; *U.S. Public*, pg. 728
CARE CENTER OF LOPATCONG—Genesis Health Ventures, Inc.; *U.S. Public*, pg. 729
CARE CENTER OF PHILLIPSBURG—Genesis Health Ventures, Inc.; *U.S. Public*, pg. 729
THE CARE PAVILION OF WALNUT PARK PLAZA—Genesis Health Ventures, Inc.; *U.S. Public*, pg. 729
CHELTENHAM NURSING & REHABILITATION CENTER—Genesis Health Ventures, Inc.; *U.S. Public*, pg. 729
CHELTENHAM-YORK ROAD NURSING & REHABILITATION CENTER—Genesis Health Ventures, Inc.; *U.S. Public*, pg. 729
CHERRY CREEK VILLAGE RETIREMENT CENTER—Horizon/CMS Healthcare Corporation; *U.S. Public*, pg. 837
COBBS CREEK NURSING CENTER—Genesis Health Ventures, Inc.; *U.S. Public*, pg. 729
COMPREMEDX, INC.—Continental Health Affiliates, Inc.; *U.S. Public*, pg. 440
COOPER RIVER CONVALESCENT CENTER—Genesis Health Ventures, Inc.; *U.S. Public*, pg. 729
CRESTVIEW—Genesis Health Ventures, Inc.; *U.S. Public*, pg. 729
GENESIS ELDERCARE—Genesis Health Ventures, Inc.; *U.S. Public*, pg. 728
HAMILTON ARMS NURSING & REHABILITATION CENTER—Genesis Health Ventures, Inc.; *U.S. Public*, pg. 729
HILLCREST CENTER—Genesis Health Ventures, Inc.; *U.S. Public*, pg. 729
HORIZON/CMS HEALTHCARE CORPORATION; *U.S. Public*, pg. 836
INTEGRATED HEALTH SERVICES, INC.; *U.S. Public*, pg. 884
KRESSON VIEW CENTER—Genesis Health Ventures, Inc.; *U.S. Public*, pg. 729
MAJESTIC PINES CARE CENTER—Meritcare, Inc.; *U.S. Private*, pg. 733
MANOR CARE, INC.; *U.S. Public*, pg. 1041
MAYO CENTER—Genesis Health Ventures, Inc.; *U.S. Public*, pg. 729
MERITCARE, INC.; *U.S. Private*, pg. 733
NEXTHEALTH INC.; *U.S. Public*, pg. 1181
PARK AVENUE VILLA—Horizon/CMS Healthcare Corporation; *U.S. Public*, pg. 838
REHABILITATION & NURSING CARE CENTER—Meritcare, Inc.; *U.S. Private*, pg. 733
RITTENHOUSE CARE CENTER—Genesis Health Ventures, Inc.; *U.S. Public*, pg. 729
SILVERSTREAM CENTER—Genesis Health Ventures, Inc.; *U.S. Public*, pg. 729
TWIN PALMS CARE CENTER—Meritcare, Inc.; *U.S. Private*, pg. 733
VALLEY MANOR CARE CENTER—Meritcare, Inc.; *U.S. Private*, pg. 733
THE VILLA—Genesis Health Ventures, Inc.; *U.S. Public*, pg. 729

8062 — GENERAL MEDICAL & SURGICAL HOSPITALS

A.C. MEDICAL, INC.—Columbia/HCA Healthcare Corporation; *U.S. Public*, pg. 403
ACH, INC.—Columbia/HCA Healthcare Corporation; *U.S. Public*, pg. 403
AUBURN GENERAL HOSPITAL—Universal Health Services, Inc.; *U.S. Public*, pg. 1696
CENTRAL DUPAGE HEALTH SYSTEM; *U.S. Private*, pg. 223
CENTRAL DUPAGE HOSPITAL ASSOCIATION—Central DuPage Health System; *U.S. Private*, pg. 223
CHALMETTE MEDICAL CENTER—Universal Health Services, Inc.; *U.S. Public*, pg. 1697
CHAMPION HEALTHCARE CORPORATION; *U.S. Public*, pg. 333
CHARTER CLINIC NIGHTINGALE—Magellan Health Services, Inc.; *U.S. Public*, pg. 1036
CHARTER MEDICAL (CAYMAN ISLANDS) LTD.—Magellan Health Services, Inc.; *U.S. Public*, pg. 1036
CHARTER MEDICAL OF ENGLAND LTD.—Magellan Health Services, Inc.; *U.S. Public*, pg. 1036
CHICAGO MEDICAL SCHOOL HOSPITAL, INC.—Columbia/HCA Healthcare Corporation; *U.S. Public*, pg. 404
COLUMBIA MEDICAL CENTER DALLAS SOUTHWEST—Columbia/HCA Healthcare Corporation; *U.S. Public*, pg. 404
COMMUNITY HEALTH SYSTEMS, INC.—Forstmann Little & Co.; *U.S. Private*, pg. 419
DOCTORS HOSPITAL OF SHREVEPORT—Universal Health Services, Inc.; *U.S. Public*, pg. 1697
EXTENDICARE PROPERTIES, INC.—Columbia/HCA Healthcare Corporation; *U.S. Public*, pg. 404
FLORIDA MEDICAL CENTER SOUTH—Tenet Healthcare Corporation; *U.S. Public*, pg. 1577
GALEN BH, INC.—Columbia/HCA Healthcare Corporation; *U.S. Public*, pg. 404
GALEN HOSPITAL-ALASKA—Columbia/HCA Healthcare Corporation; *U.S. Public*, pg. 404
HCS, INC.—Magellan Health Services, Inc.; *U.S. Public*, pg. 1036
H.H.U.K., INC.—Columbia/HCA Healthcare Corporation; *U.S. Public*, pg. 405
HEALTH MANAGEMENT ASSOCIATES, INC.; *U.S. Public*, pg. 802
HEALTH MANAGEMENT SYSTEMS, INC.; *U.S. Public*, pg. 802
HUMANA INC.; *U.S. Public*, pg. 847
INLAND VALLEY REGIONAL MEDICAL CENTER—Universal Health Services, Inc.; *U.S. Public*, pg. 1697
MHM SERVICES INC.; *U.S. Public*, pg. 1027
MAGELLAN HEALTH SERVICES, INC.; *U.S. Public*, pg. 1033
MAGELLAN MEDICAL INTERNATIONAL, INC.—Magellan Health Services, Inc.; *U.S. Public*, pg. 1036
MANOR CARE, INC.; *U.S. Public*, pg. 1041
MANOR HEALTHCARE CORP.—Manor Care, Inc.; *U.S. Public*, pg. 1041
MCALLEN MEDICAL CENTER—Universal Health Services, Inc.; *U.S. Public*, pg. 1697
MEDICAL CENTER OF BATON ROUGE—Columbia/HCA Healthcare Corporation; *U.S. Public*, pg. 405
OWEN HEALTH CARE, INC.—Cardinal Health Inc.; *U.S. Public*, pg. 304
RIVER OAKS HOSPITAL—Universal Health Services, Inc.; *U.S. Public*, pg. 1697
RIVER PARISHES HOSPITAL—Universal Health Services, Inc.; *U.S. Public*, pg. 1697
SOCIEDE ANONYME DE L'EXPLOITATION DE L'HOPITAL DE LA TOUR—Columbia/HCA Healthcare Corporation; *U.S. Public*, pg. 405
SPARKS FAMILY HOSPITAL—Universal Health Services, Inc.; *U.S. Public*, pg. 1697
STUART CIRCLE HOSPITAL CORPORATION—Magellan Health Services, Inc.; *U.S. Public*, pg. 1036
SUBANG JAYA MEDICAL CENTRE SDN. BHD.—Sime Darby Berhad; *Int'l*, pg. 1250
SUTTER AUBURN FAITH COMMUNITY HOSPITAL—Sutter Health; *U.S. Private*, pg. 1057
TENET HEALTHCARE CORPORATION; *U.S. Public*, pg. 1576
TENET HEALTHSYSTEM HEALTHCORP—Tenet Healthcare Corporation; *U.S. Public*, pg. 1577
TENET HEALTHSYSTEM HOSPITALS, INC.—Tenet Healthcare Corporation; *U.S. Public*, pg. 1577
TENET HEALTHSYSTEM MEDICAL, INC.—Tenet Healthcare Corporation; *U.S. Public*, pg. 1577
UNIVERSAL HEALTH SERVICES, INC.; *U.S. Public*, pg. 1696

VALLEY HOSPITAL MEDICAL CENTER—Universal Health Services, Inc.; *U.S. Public*, pg. 1697
VENCOR, INC.; *U.S. Public*, pg. 1711
VICTORIA REGIONAL MEDICAL CENTER—Universal Health Services, Inc.; *U.S. Public*, pg. 1697
WELLINGTON REGIONAL MEDICAL CENTER—Universal Health Services, Inc.; *U.S. Public*, pg. 1697
WEST JAPAN RAILWAY COMPANY; *Int'l*, pg. 1490
WESTLAKE MEDICAL CENTER—Universal Health Services, Inc.; *U.S. Public*, pg. 1697

8063 — PSYCHIATRIC HOSPITALS

THE ARBOUR HOSPITAL—Universal Health Services, Inc.; *U.S. Public*, pg. 1696
BRIDGEWAY HOSPITAL—Universal Health Services, Inc.; *U.S. Public*, pg. 1696
CPC OF LOUISIANA, INC.—Vencor, Inc.; *U.S. Public*, pg. 1712
CPC OF TEXAS, INC.—Vencor, Inc.; *U.S. Public*, pg. 1712
CHARTER HOSPITAL OF MOBILE, INC.—Magellan Health Services, Inc.; *U.S. Public*, pg. 1034
CHARTER-PROVO SCHOOL, INC.—Magellan Health Services, Inc.; *U.S. Public*, pg. 1035
COLUMBIA/HCA HEALTHCARE CORPORATION; *U.S. Public*, pg. 403
COMPREHENSIVE CARE CORPORATION; *U.S. Public*, pg. 419
COMPREHENSIVE CARE INTEGRATION—Comprehensive Care Corporation; *U.S. Public*, pg. 419
DEL AMO HOSPITAL—Universal Health Services, Inc.; *U.S. Public*, pg. 1697
FLORIDA HEALTH FACILITIES, INC.—Magellan Health Services, Inc.; *U.S. Public*, pg. 1035
FLORIDA RESIDENTIAL TREATMENT CENTERS, INC.—Magellan Health Services, Inc.; *U.S. Public*, pg. 1035
FOREST VIEW PSYCHIATRIC HOSPITAL—Universal Health Services, Inc.; *U.S. Public*, pg. 1697
GLEN OAKS HOSPITAL—Universal Health Services, Inc.; *U.S. Public*, pg. 1697
HCA PSYCHIATRIC CO.—Columbia/HCA Healthcare Corporation; *U.S. Public*, pg. 405
HRI HOSPITAL—Universal Health Services, Inc.; *U.S. Public*, pg. 1697
LA AMISTAD RESIDENTIAL TREATMENT CENTER—Universal Health Services, Inc.; *U.S. Public*, pg. 1697
MCC BEHAVIORAL CARE, INC.—Cigna Corp.; *U.S. Public*, pg. 362
MCC INDEPENDENT PRACTICE ASSOCIATION OF GREATER NEW YORK—Cigna Corp.; *U.S. Public*, pg. 362
MAGELLAN HEALTH SERVICES, INC.; *U.S. Public*, pg. 1033
OLD ORCHARD HOSPITAL, INC.—Vencor, Inc.; *U.S. Public*, pg. 1714
RAMSAY-HAVENWYCK, INC.—Ramsay Health Care, Inc.; *U.S. Public*, pg. 1361
RAMSAY HEALTH CARE, INC.; *U.S. Public*, pg. 1360
RIVER CREST HOSPITAL—Universal Health Services, Inc.; *U.S. Public*, pg. 1697
SIERRA TUCSON, INC.—NextHealth Inc.; *U.S. Public*, pg. 1181
SUNRISE HEALTHCARE CORPORATION—Sun Healthcare Group Inc.; *U.S. Public*, pg. 1531
TWO RIVERS PSYCHIATRIC HOSPITAL—Universal Health Services, Inc.; *U.S. Public*, pg. 1697
UNIVERSAL HEALTH SERVICES, INC.; *U.S. Public*, pg. 1696

8069 — SPECIALTY HOSPITALS, EXCEPT PSYCHIATRIC

CMS THERAPIES, INC.—Horizon/CMS Healthcare Corporation; *U.S. Public*, pg. 839
COLUMBIA/HCA HEALTHCARE CORPORATION; *U.S. Public*, pg. 403
COMPREHENSIVE CARE CORPORATION; *U.S. Public*, pg. 419
COMPREHENSIVE CARE INTEGRATION—Comprehensive Care Corporation; *U.S. Public*, pg. 419
CONTINENTAL HEALTH AFFILIATES, INC.; *U.S. Public*, pg. 440
CONTINENTAL MEDICAL SYSTEMS, INC.—Horizon/CMS Healthcare Corporation; *U.S. Public*, pg. 839
ENGLEWOOD COMMUNITY HOSPITAL, INC.—Columbia/HCA Healthcare Corporation; *U.S. Public*, pg. 404
FAWCETT MEMORIAL HOSPITAL, INC.—Columbia/HCA Healthcare Corporation; *U.S. Public*, pg. 404
HORIZON SPECIALTY HOSPITAL—Horizon/CMS Healthcare Corporation; *U.S. Public*, pg. 839
HORIZON SPECIALTY HOSPITAL - ALBUQUERQUE—Horizon/CMS Healthcare Corporation; *U.S. Public*, pg. 838
INNOVATIVE HEALTH ALLIANCES—Horizon/CMS Healthcare Corporation; *U.S. Public*, pg. 839
KEYSTONE CENTER—Universal Health Services, Inc.; *U.S. Public*, pg. 1697
MEDICAL SUPPLIES DIVISION—Abdulla Fouad Co. Ltd.; *Int'l*, pg. 502
MERIDELL ACHIEVEMENT CENTER—Universal Health Services, Inc.; *U.S. Public*, pg. 1697
MERIDIAN NEURO CARE—Horizon/CMS Healthcare Corporation; *U.S. Public*, pg. 839
RESPONSE ONCOLOGY, INC.—Seafield Capital Corporation; *U.S. Public*, pg. 1449
SELECTREHAB—Horizon/CMS Healthcare Corporation; *U.S. Public*, pg. 839
SIERRA TUCSON, INC.—NextHealth Inc.; *U.S. Public*, pg. 1181
SUNRISE HEALTHCARE CORPORATION—Sun Healthcare Group Inc.; *U.S. Public*, pg. 1531
SUTTER HEALTH; *U.S. Private*, pg. 1057
TURNING POINT CARE CENTER—Universal Health Services, Inc.; *U.S. Public*, pg. 1697
UNIVERSAL HEALTH SERVICES, INC.; *U.S. Public*, pg. 1696

8071 — MEDICAL LABORATORIES

ALLIED CLINICAL LABORATORIES, INC.—Laboratory Corp. of America Holdings; *U.S. Public*, pg. 973
BRISTOL-MYERS PHARMACEUTICAL RESEARCH & DEVELOPMENT DIVISION—Bristol-Myers Squibb Company; *U.S. Public*, pg. 254
COVANCE, INC.; *U.S. Public*, pg. 453
COVANCE INC.—Covance, Inc.; *U.S. Public*, pg. 454
DIANON SYSTEMS, INC.; *U.S. Public*, pg. 506
DYNACARE-ALBERTA—Dynacare, Inc.; *Int'l*, pg. 425
DYNACARE-ONTARIO—Dynacare, Inc.; *Int'l*, pg. 425
DYNACARE-WASHINGTON—Dynacare, Inc.; *Int'l*, pg. 425
DYNACARE-WYOMING—Dynacare, Inc.; *Int'l*, pg. 425
ELDON LABORATORIES LIMITED—Alliance UniChem PLC; *Int'l*, pg. 58
FORTRESS SCIENTIFIC LIMITED—MDS Inc.; *Int'l*, pg. 826
GENZYME CORPORATION; *U.S. Public*, pg. 733
GENZYME GENETICS DIV.—Genzyme Corporation; *U.S. Public*, pg. 733
HEAD OFFICE REFERENCE LABORATORY, LTD.—Seafield Capital Corporation; *U.S. Public*, pg. 1449
HEICO CORPORATION; *U.S. Public*, pg. 804
IG LABORATORIES, INC.—Genzyme Corporation; *U.S. Public*, pg. 733
INGRAM & BELL INC.—MDS Inc.; *Int'l*, pg. 826
INSIGHT HEALTH SERVICES CORP.; *U.S. Public*, pg. 880
LABORATORIOS JULIAN DE MEXICO, S.A.—SmithKline Beecham plc; *Int'l*, pg. 1265
LABORATORY CORP. OF AMERICA HOLDINGS; *U.S. Public*, pg. 973
LOUISIANA REFERENCE LABORATORY—SmithKline Beecham plc; *Int'l*, pg. 1265
MDS INC.; *Int'l*, pg. 826
MAGELLAN HEALTH SERVICES, INC.—Magellan Health Services, Inc.; *U.S. Public*, pg. 1036
MEDSCREEN LIMITED—PharmChem Laboratories, Inc.; *U.S. Public*, pg. 1286
NABI; *U.S. Public*, pg. 1148
PANLABS INTERNATIONAL OPERATIONS—MDS Inc.; *Int'l*, pg. 827
PHARMCHEM LABORATORIES, INC.; *U.S. Public*, pg. 1285
THE PRUDENTIAL INSURANCE COMPANY OF AMERICA; *U.S. Private*, pg. 892
QUEST DIAGNOSTIC—Quest Diagnostics, Inc.; *U.S. Public*, *pg. 1351*
QUEST DIAGNOSTICS, INC.; *U.S. Public*, pg. 1351
SCIEX—MDS Inc.; *Int'l*, pg. 827
SKYLAND SCIENTIFIC SERVICES, INC.—Steris Corporation; *U.S. Public*, pg. 1515
SMITHKLINE BEECHAM CLINICAL LABORATORIES, INC.—SmithKline Beecham plc; *Int'l*, pg. 1264
SMITHKLINE BEECHAM CLINICAL LABORATORIES—SmithKline Beecham plc; *Int'l*, pg. 1265
SMITHKLINE BEECHAM CORPORATION—SmithKline Beecham plc; *Int'l*, pg. 1264
THE SQUIBB INSTITUTE FOR MEDICAL RESEARCH—Bristol-Myers Squibb Company; *U.S. Public*, pg. 254
UHP HEALTHCARE; *U.S. Private*, pg. 1113
UNIVERSAL STANDARD HEALTHCARE, INC.; *U.S. Public*, pg. 1697

8082 — HOME HEALTH CARE SERVICES

ATC HEALTHCARE SERVICES INC.; *U.S. Private*, pg. 8
AMBULATORY RESOURCES, INC.—Magellan Health Services, Inc.; *U.S. Public*, pg. 1033
APRIA HEALTHCARE GROUP INC.; *U.S. Public*, pg. 125
ARBOR HEALTH CARE COMPANY—Extendicare Inc.; *Int'l*, *pg. 468*
CAPITAL SENIOR LIVING, INC.; *U.S. Public*, pg. 302
THE CARE GROUP, INC.; *U.S. Public*, pg. 305
THE CARE GROUP OF NEW YORK, INC.—The Care Group, Inc.; *U.S. Public*, pg. 305
THE CARE GROUP OF TEXAS, INC.—The Care Group, Inc.; *U.S. Public*, pg. 305
CARE LINE, INC.—The Care Group, Inc.; *U.S. Public*, pg. 305
CARECO, INC.—Staff Builders Inc.; *U.S. Public*, pg. 1501
CAREMARK INTERNATIONAL INC—Medpartners Inc.; *U.S.* Public, pg. 1082
CHEMED CORPORATION; *U.S. Public*, pg. 343
CHILDREN'S NURSING SERVICES, LTD.—The Care Group, Inc.; *U.S. Public*, pg. 305
CONTINENTAL HEALTH AFFILIATES, INC.; *U.S. Public*, pg. 440
EXTENDICARE (CANADA) INC.—Extendicare Inc.; *Int'l*, pg. 468
EXTENDICARE INC.; *Int'l*, pg. 468
FAMILY HEALTHCARE SERVICES, INC.—Sierra Health Services, Inc.; *U.S. Public*, pg. 1469
FAMILY HOME HOSPICE, INC.—Sierra Health Services, Inc.; *U.S. Public*, pg. 1469
HEALTH ACQUISITION CORP.—National Home Health Care Corp.; *U.S. Public*, pg. 1157
HEALTH MANAGEMENT, INC.—Counsel Corporation; *Int'l*, pg. 338
HOME CARE P.R.N., INC.—Technical Aid Corporation; *U.S.* Private, pg. 1072
KELLY ASSISTED LIVING SERVICES, INC.—Kelly Services, Inc.; *U.S. Public*, pg. 949
KELLY SERVICES, INC.; *U.S. Public*, pg. 949
MEDPARTNERS INC.; *U.S. Public*, pg. 1082
MID-SOUTH COMPREHENSIVE HOME HEALTH—Hospital Staffing Services, Inc.; *U.S. Public*, pg. 841
NATIONAL HOME HEALTH CARE CORP.; *U.S. Public*, pg. 1157
OLSTEN HEALTH SERVICES—Olsten Corporation; *U.S. Public*, pg. 1221
PATIENT CARE, INC.—Chemed Corporation; *U.S. Public*, pg. 344
ROTECH MEDICAL CORPORATION—Integrated Health Services, Inc.; *U.S. Public*, pg. 884
SALICK HEALTH CARE, INC.—Zeneca Group Plc; *Int'l*, pg. 1524
SECOMERICA, INC.—Secom Co., Ltd.; *Int'l*, pg. 1217
THE SERVICEMASTER COMPANY; *U.S. Public*, pg. 1461
STADTLANDER HMI—Counsel Corporation; *Int'l*, pg. 338
STAFF BUILDERS INC.; *U.S. Public*, pg. 1501
TAC/MEDICAL SERVICES INC.—Technical Aid Corporation; *U.S. Private*, pg. 1072
TENDER LOVING CARE HOME CARE SERVICES, INC.—Staff Builders Inc.; *U.S. Public*, pg. 1501
WESTERN MEDICAL SERVICES INC.—Western Staff Services; *U.S. Public*, pg. 1760

8092 — KIDNEY DIALYSIS CENTERS

CENTURY DIALYSIS CORPORATION—Zeneca Group Plc; *Int'l*, pg. 1525
DIALYSIS CORPORATION OF AMERICA—Medicore Inc.; *U.S. Public*, pg. 1080
DIALYSIS CORPORATION OF HARRISBURG—Medicore Inc.; *U.S. Public*, pg. 1080
DIALYSIS SERVICE OF FLORIDA—Medicore Inc.; *U.S. Public*, pg. 1080
FRESENIUS MEDICAL CARE, INC.—Fresenius AG; *Int'l*, pg. 505
MEDICORE INC.; *U.S. Public*, pg. 1080
RENEX CORP.; *U.S. Public*, pg. 1377
SALICK HEALTH CARE, INC.—Zeneca Group Plc; *Int'l*, pg. 1524
TOTAL RENAL CARE—Total Renal Care Holdings, Inc.; *U.S. Public*, pg. 1625
TOTAL RENAL CARE HOLDINGS, INC.; *U.S. Public*, pg. 1625
USHAWL, INC.—Zeneca Group Plc; *Int'l*, pg. 1525
VIVRA INCORPORATED; *U.S. Public*, pg. 1723

8093 — SPECIALTY OUTPATIENT FACILITIES, NEC

BEHAVIORAL HEALTH SERVICES—Central DuPage Health System; *U.S. Private*, pg. 223
CARDIO DATA SERVICES—U.M. Holding Limited; *U.S. Private*, pg. 1114
CENTRAL DUPAGE HEALTH SYSTEM; *U.S. Private*, pg. 223
CENTRAL MARYLAND SURGERY CENTER—Healthsouth Corporation; *U.S. Public*, pg. 803
COMPREHENSIVE CANCER CENTERS—Zeneca Group Plc; *Int'l*, pg. 1525
CONTINENTAL HEALTH AFFILIATES, INC.; *U.S. Public*, pg. 440
DIALYSIS CORPORATION OF HARRISBURG—Medicore Inc.; *U.S. Public*, pg. 1080
DIALYSIS SERVICE OF FLORIDA—Medicore Inc.; *U.S. Public*, pg. 1080
GRANDVIEW SURGERY CENTER—Healthsouth Corporation; *U.S. Public*, pg. 803
HEALTHSOUTH CORPORATION; *U.S. Public*, pg. 803
HELIAN HEALTH GROUP, INC.—Vencor, Inc.; *U.S. Public*, pg. 1715
INLAND SURGERY CENTER—Healthsouth Corporation; *U.S. Public*, pg. 803
INTERMOUNTAIN HEALTH CARE INC.; *U.S. Private*, pg. 568
INTERNATIONAL REHABILITATION ASSOCIATES, INC.—Cigna Corp.; *U.S. Public*, pg. 362
MCC BEHAVIORAL CARE, INC.—Cigna Corp.; *U.S. Public*, pg. 362
MCC INDEPENDENT PRACTICE ASSOCIATION OF GREATER NEW YORK—Cigna Corp.; *U.S. Public*, pg. 362
MONTGOMERY SURGERY CENTER—Healthsouth Corporation; *U.S. Public*, pg. 803
NATIONAL SURGERY CENTERS, INC.; *U.S. Public*, pg. 1161
NORTHRIDGE SURGERY CENTER—Vencor, Inc.; *U.S. Public*, pg. 1715
PHP HEALTHCARE CORPORATION; *U.S. Public*, pg. 1241
PRIME CARDIAC REHABILITATION SERVICES, INC.—Prime Medical Services, Inc.; *U.S. Public*, pg. 1327
PRIME DIAGNOSTIC SERVICES, INC.—Prime Medical Services, Inc.; *U.S. Public*, pg. 1327
RECOVERY INN OF MENLO PARK—Vencor, Inc.; *U.S. Public*, pg. 1715
REHAB LEASING CORP.—Prime Medical Services, Inc.; *U.S. Public*, pg. 1327
REHABCARE GROUP, INC.; *U.S. Public*, pg. 1373
RESEARCH DATA CORP—U.M. Holding Limited; *U.S. Private*, pg. 1114
SURGECENTER OF PALO ALTO—Vencor, Inc.; *U.S. Public*, pg. 1716
TRANSWORLD HOME HEALTHCARE, INC.; *U.S. Public*, pg. 1632
U.M. HOLDING LIMITED; *U.S. Private*, pg. 1113
VENCARE, INCORPORATED—Vencor, Inc.; *U.S. Public*, pg. 1715
VENTURI INC.; *U.S. Private*, pg. 1136

8099 — HEALTH & ALLIED SERVICES, NEC

ATC HEALTHCARE SERVICES INC.; *U.S. Private*, pg. 8
ALABAMA RENAL STONE INSTITUTE, INC.—Prime Medical Services, Inc.; *U.S. Public*, pg. 1327
AMERICAN HEALTHCORP INC.; *U.S. Public*, pg. 78
AMERICAN SHARED HOSPITAL SERVICES; *U.S. Public*, pg. 91

S.I.C. Index

CARDIO DATA SERVICES—U.M. Holding Limited; *U.S. Private*, pg. 1114
CAVCO INDUSTRIES, INC.—Centex Corporation; *U.S. Public*, pg. 323
CENTER FOR COMPREHENSIVE EXAMINATIONS—Vencor, Inc.; *U.S. Public*, pg. 1715
CHARLOTTE COMMUNITY HOSPITAL—Columbia/HCA Healthcare Corporation; *U.S. Public*, pg. 404
CIGNA CORP.; *U.S. Public*, pg. 356
COMMUNITY BIO-RESOURCES—Baxter International Inc.; *U.S. Public*, pg. 196
CONFED MANAGED HEALTHCARE, INC.—Confederation Life Insurance Company; *Int'l*, pg. 326
CONTINENTAL HEALTH AFFILIATES, INC.; *U.S. Public*, pg. 440
CORAM HEALTHCARE CORPORATION; *U.S. Public*, pg. 446
CURACARE, INC.—American Shared Hospital Services; *U.S. Public*, pg. 91
DIAGNOSTIC IMAGING OF ATLANTA, L.P.—Vencor, Inc.; *U.S. Public*, pg. 1715
DIET CENTER WORLDWIDE, INC.—Physicians Weight Loss Centers, Inc.; *U.S. Private*, pg. 864
EXPERT SYSTEMS, INC.—National Health Enhancement Systems, Inc.; *U.S. Public*, pg. 1157
EXTENDICARE (CANADA) INC.—Extendicare Inc.; *Int'l*, pg. 468
EXTENDICARE INC.; *Int'l*, pg. 468
FIRST HEALTH GROUP CORP.; *U.S. Public*, pg. 635
FIRST STRATEGIC GROUP—National Health Enhancement Systems, Inc.; *U.S. Public*, pg. 1157
FRESENIUS MEDICAL CARE, INC.—Fresenius AG; *Int'l*, pg. 505
GK FINANCING, LLC—American Shared Hospital Services; *U.S. Public*, pg. 91
GALEN MEDICAL CORPORATION—Columbia/HCA Healthcare Corporation; *U.S. Public*, pg. 404
HEALTH CARE MANAGEMENT CORP., INC.—Columbia/HCA Healthcare Corporation; *U.S. Public*, pg. 405
HEALTH PROFESSIONALS, INC.; *U.S. Public*, pg. 802
HEALTHCARE AMERICA, INC.; *U.S. Private*, pg. 515
HEALTHCARE PRESCRIPTION SERVICES, INC.—Columbia/HCA Healthcare Corporation; *U.S. Public*, pg. 405
HELIAN OCCUPATIONAL-SOUTH—Vencor, Inc.; *U.S. Public*, pg. 1715
HOWELL INDUSTRIAL CLINIC—Vencor, Inc.; *U.S. Public*, pg. 1715
HOWELL MEDICAL CENTER—Vencor, Inc.; *U.S. Public*, pg. 1715
IMMTECH INTERNATIONAL, INC.—Criticare Systems, Inc.; *U.S. Public*, pg. 459
INDUSTRIAL CLINIC—Vencor, Inc.; *U.S. Public*, pg. 1715
INFU-TECH—Continental Health Affiliates, Inc.; *U.S. Public*, pg. 440
ISOMEDIX MANAGEMENT INC.—Steris Corporation; *U.S. Public*, pg. 1515
ISOMEDIX OPERATIONS INC.—Steris Corporation; *U.S. Public*, pg. 1515
LITHOTRIPTERS, INC.—Prime Medical Services, Inc.; *U.S. Public*, pg. 1327
MDS INC.; *Int'l*, pg. 826
MGH MEDICAL, INC.—Columbia/HCA Healthcare Corporation; *U.S. Public*, pg. 405
MMRI INC.—American Shared Hospital Services; *U.S. Public*, pg. 91
MAXUM HEALTH CORP.—Insight Health Services Corp.; *U.S. Public*, pg. 881
MEDICAL RESOURCES INC.—Medical Resources Inc.; *U.S. Public*, pg. 1080
MEDICAL SUPPLIES DIVISION—Abdulla Fouad Co. Ltd.; *Int'l*, pg. 502
MEDIQ INCORPORATED; *U.S. Public*, pg. 1081
MEDTRONIC, INC.; *U.S. Public*, pg. 1082
MERIT BEHAVIORAL CARE CORP.—Magellan Health Services, Inc.; *U.S. Public*, pg. 1036
MOBILE TECHNOLOGY INC.; *U.S. Private*, pg. 754
NABI; *U.S. Public*, pg. 1148
NATIONAL HEALTH CARE AFFILIATES, INC.; *U.S. Private*, pg. 784
NATIONAL HEALTH ENHANCEMENT SYSTEMS, INC.; *U.S. Public*, pg. 1157
NOVACARE INC.; *U.S. Public*, pg. 1203
OCCUPATIONAL-URGENT CARE HEALTH SYSTEMS (OUCH)—First Health Group Corp.; *U.S. Public*, pg. 635
OHIO LITHO INC.—Prime Medical Services, Inc.; *U.S. Public*, pg. 1327
PHP HEALTHCARE CORPORATION; *U.S. Public*, pg. 1241
PRIME DIAGNOSTIC CORP. OF FLORIDA—Prime Medical Services, Inc.; *U.S. Public*, pg. 1327
PRIME KIDNEY STONE TREATMENT, INC.—Prime Medical Services, Inc.; *U.S. Public*, pg. 1327
PRIME LITHOTRIPTER OPERATIONS, INC.—Prime Medical Services, Inc.; *U.S. Public*, pg. 1327
PRIME MEDICAL SERVICES, INC.; *U.S. Public*, pg. 1327
R.R. LITHO, INC.—Prime Medical Services, Inc.; *U.S. Public*, pg. 1327
RESEARCH DATA CORP—U.M. Holding Limited; *U.S. Private*, pg. 1114
RITE AID CORPORATION; *U.S. Public*, pg. 1390
SISTEMAS DE TERAPIA RESPIRATORIA S.A., INC.—Magellan Health Services, Inc.; *U.S. Public*, pg. 1036
SOUTHERN BACK & ORTHOPAEDIC CENTER-DUNWOODY—Vencor, Inc.; *U.S. Public*, pg. 1716
STAFF BUILDERS INC.; *U.S. Public*, pg. 1501
STAR MULTI CARE SERVICES INC.; *U.S. Public*, pg. 1510
SUN MEDICAL TECHNOLOGIES, INC.—Prime Medical Services, Inc.; *U.S. Public*, pg. 1327
TEXAS LITHO, INC.—Prime Medical Services, Inc.; *U.S. Public*, pg. 1327
U.M. HOLDING LIMITED; *U.S. Private*, pg. 1113
UNIHEALTH; *U.S. Private*, pg. 1117
UNITED HEALTH, INC.—Extendicare Inc.; *Int'l*, pg. 468
VIVRA INCORPORATED; *U.S. Public*, pg. 1723

8111 — LEGAL SERVICES

AMWAY CORPORATION; *U.S. Private*, pg. 69
BARANSKI & ASSOCIATES—Barancorp; *U.S. Private*, pg. 115
CALTEX SERVICES CORP.—Chevron Corporation; *U.S. Public*, pg. 348
THE CONTINENTAL CORPORATION—Loews Corporation; *U.S. Public*, pg. 1011
DU PONT INTERNATIONAL SALES CORP.—Du Pont (E.I. Du Pont De Nemours & Co.); *U.S. Public*, pg. 531
JONES, DAY, REAVIS & POGUE; *U.S. Private*, pg. 596
PEPPER, HAMILTON & SCHEETZ—Pepper, Hamilton & Scheetz; *U.S. Private*, pg. 851
PEPPER, HAMILTON & SCHEETZ; *U.S. Private*, pg. 851
ROUSE LEGAL DIV.—The Rouse Company; *U.S. Public*, pg. 1407
SHARED SERVICES DIVISION—Black & Veatch; *U.S. Private*, pg. 146
SKADDEN, ARPS, SLATE, MEAGHER & FLOM LLP; *U.S. Private*, pg. 1004
SKADDEN, ARPS, SLATE, MEAGHER & FLOM LLP—Skadden, Arps, Slate, Meagher & Flom LLP; *U.S. Private*, pg. 1004
U-HAUL INTERNATIONAL, INC.—Amerco; *U.S. Private*, pg. 49
WOLF, BLOCK, SCHORR & SOLIS-COHEN; *U.S. Private*, pg. 1185

8211 — ELEMENTARY & SECONDARY SCHOOLS

JOTSA, S.A. EMPRESSA CONSTRUCTOR—Philipp Holzmann AG; *Int'l*, pg. 634
SSANGYONG BUSINESS GROUP; *Int'l*, pg. 1291

8221 — COLLEGES, UNIVERSITIES & PROFESSIONAL SCHOOLS

APOLLO GROUP, INC.; *U.S. Public*, pg. 120
DEVRY INSTITUTES; *U.S. Public*, pg. 503
HEALD COLLEGES; *U.S. Private*, pg. 514
ARTHUR D. LITTLE SCHOOL OF MANAGEMENT—Arthur D. Little, Inc.; *U.S. Private*, pg. 670

8222 — JUNIOR COLLEGES & TECHNICAL INSTITUTES

CAREER EDUCATION CORPORATION; *U.S. Private*, pg. 209
DEVRY INSTITUTES; *U.S. Public*, pg. 503
KATHARINE GIBBS SCHOOL, INC.—Career Education Corporation; *U.S. Private*, pg. 209
SAAB TECHTRADE AB—Investor AB; *Int'l*, pg. 687

8231 — LIBRARIES & INFORMATION CENTERS

GESTION DE CENTROS CULTURALES, S.A.—Caja de Madrid Group; *Int'l*, pg. 251
STONE & WEBSTER, INCORPORATED; *U.S. Public*, pg. 1519
TEXTRON INC.; *U.S. Public*, pg. 1588
TEXTRON SYSTEMS—Textron Inc.; *U.S. Public*, pg. 1589

8243 — DATA PROCESSING SCHOOLS

CARA CORPORATION—William Blair & Company L.L.C.; *U.S. Private*, pg. 148
COMPUTER SYSTEMS RESEARCH, INC.—The McGraw-Hill Companies; *U.S. Public*, pg. 1070
DATA GENERAL CORPORATION; *U.S. Public*, pg. 485
DATA GENERAL CUSTOMER SERVICE DIVISION—Data General Corporation; *U.S. Public*, pg. 485
KODAK SOFTWARE SYSTEMS DIVISION—Eastman Kodak Company; *U.S. Public*, pg. 555
LOGICAL OPERATIONS—Softbank Corporation; *Int'l*, pg. 1276
NATIONAL EDUCATION TRAINING GROUP—Harcourt General, Inc.; *U.S. Public*, pg. 784
TECHNOLOGY TRANSFER INSTITUTE; *U.S. Private*, pg. 1072

8244 — BUSINESS & SECRETARIAL SCHOOLS

KELLER GRADUATE SCHOOL OF MANAGEMENT—DeVry Institutes; *U.S. Public*, pg. 504

8249 — VOCATIONAL SCHOOLS, NEC

BUREAU OF ENGRAVING; *U.S. Private*, pg. 181
CHARLES ATLAS, LTD.; *U.S. Private*, pg. 229
CONCORDE CAREER COLLEGES, INC.; *U.S. Public*, pg. 430
DALE CARNEGIE TRAINING; *U.S. Private*, pg. 308
FLIGHTSAFETY ACADEMY—Berkshire Hathaway Inc.; *U.S. Public*, pg. 218
FLIGHTSAFETY INTERNATIONAL INC.—Berkshire Hathaway Inc.; *U.S. Public*, pg. 218
ITT EDUCATIONAL SERVICES, INC.—Starwood Hotels & Resorts; *U.S. Public*, pg. 1512
INTERNATIONAL CORRESPONDENCE SCHOOLS, INC.—Harcourt General, Inc.; *U.S. Public*, pg. 783
INTERTEXT GROUP, LTD.—Harcourt General, Inc.; *U.S. Public*, pg. 784
ISVOR S.P.A.—Fiat Auto SpA; *Int'l*, pg. 482
KONINKLIJKE PBNA BV—Reed Elsevier plc; *Int'l*, pg. 1100
LEX COMMERCIALS—Lex Service PLC; *Int'l*, pg. 807
MARINELLO SCHOOLS OF BEAUTY—Scope Industries; *U.S. Public*, pg. 1444
MARINESAFETY INTERNATIONAL—Berkshire Hathaway Inc.; *U.S. Public*, pg. 218
THE MCGRAW-HILL COMPANIES; *U.S. Public*, pg. 1069
MCGRAW-HILL CONTINUING EDUCATION CENTER—The McGraw-Hill Companies; *U.S. Public*, pg. 1070
NRI SCHOOLS—The McGraw-Hill Companies; *U.S. Public*, pg. 1071
RAILWAY EDUCATIONAL BUREAU—Simmons-Boardman Publishing Corp.; *U.S. Private*, pg. 1000
THE SCHOOL OF ACCOUNTANCY—Harcourt General, Inc.; *U.S. Public*, pg. 784
TOKYO FASHION INSTITUTE—Matsuya Company Ltd.; *Int'l*, pg. 848
WEICHERT REALTY CAREER DEVELOPMENT—Weichert Company; *U.S. Private*, pg. 1159
YAMAHA KYOHAN CO., LTD.—Yamaha Corporation; *Int'l*, pg. 1516

8299 — SCHOOLS AND EDUCATIONAL SERVICES, NEC

ALPINE CENTER, S.R.L. (BERLITZ)—Berlitz International, Inc.; *U.S. Public*, pg. 221
ALPS INSTITUTE S.R.L. (BERLITZ)—Berlitz International, Inc.; *U.S. Public*, pg. 221
AMERICAN COUNCIL FOR INTERNATIONAL STUDIES—American Institute for Foreign Study; *U.S. Private*, pg. 57
AMERICAN INSTITUTE FOR FOREIGN STUDY; *U.S. Private*, pg. 56
ASIA-PACIFIC TRAINING & SIMULATION LIMITED—British Aerospace p.l.c.; *Int'l*, pg. 218
ATLANTA LEARNING CENTER—Berkshire Hathaway Inc.; *U.S. Public*, pg. 218
AU PAIR IN AMERICA—American Institute for Foreign Study; *U.S. Private*, pg. 56
AUGSBURG FORTRESS, PUBLISHERS; *U.S. Private*, pg. 98
OY BERLITZ AB—Berlitz International, Inc.; *U.S. Public*, pg. 221
BERLITZ INTERNATIONAL, INC.; *U.S. Public*, pg. 221
BETHANY LEARNING CENTER—Berkshire Hathaway Inc.; *U.S. Public*, pg. 218
BRITISH AEROSPACE FLYING COLLEGE LTD.—British Aerospace p.l.c.; *Int'l*, pg. 217
BUREAU OF ENGRAVING; *U.S. Private*, pg. 181
CAMP AMERICA—American Institute for Foreign Study; *U.S. Private*, pg. 57
CENTRO DE IDIOMAS BERLITZ DE VENEZUELA—Berlitz International, Inc.; *U.S. Public*, pg. 222
COMAIR AVIATION ACADEMY, INC.—Comair Holdings, Inc.; *U.S. Public*, pg. 406
DALE CARNEGIE & ASSOCIATES—Dale Carnegie Training; *U.S. Private*, pg. 308
DALEVILLE LEARNING CENTER—Berkshire Hathaway Inc.; *U.S. Public*, pg. 218
DOTHAN LEARNING CENTER—Berkshire Hathaway Inc.; *U.S. Public*, pg. 218
ESCUELAS DE IDIOMAS BERLITZ DE ESPANA, S.A.—Berlitz International, Inc.; *U.S. Public*, pg. 222
EUROPE LANGUAGE CENTER SRL—Berlitz International, Inc.; *U.S. Public*, pg. 222
FLIGHTSAFETY INTERNATIONAL INC.—Berkshire Hathaway Inc.; *U.S. Public*, pg. 218
FLIGHTSAFETY SERVICES CORPORATION—Berkshire Hathaway Inc.; *U.S. Public*, pg. 218
GENERAL PHYSICS CORPORATION—GP Strategies Corporation; *U.S. Public*, pg. 694
GREATER PHILADELPHIA/WILMINGTON—Berkshire Hathaway Inc.; *U.S. Public*, pg. 218
HAKUHODO INSTITUTE OF LIFE AND LIVING—Hakuhodo Incorporated; *Int'l*, pg. 588
HARCOURT BRACE & COMPANY LEGAL AND PROFESSIONAL PUBLICATIONS, INC.—Harcourt General, Inc.; *U.S. Public*, pg. 783
HOUSTON LEARNING CENTER—Berkshire Hathaway Inc.; *U.S. Public*, pg. 218
ISS-INTERNATIONAL SERVICE SYSTEM A/S; *Int'l*, pg. 656
INNER CITY, INC.—Polaroid Corporation; *U.S. Public*, pg. 1313
INSTITUTO DE IDIOMAS COLOMBIA, S.A.—Berlitz International, Inc.; *U.S. Public*, pg. 222
JOSTENS LEARNING CORPORATION; *U.S. Private*, pg. 601
KAPLAN EDUCATIONAL CENTERS LTD.—The Washington Post Company; *U.S. Public*, pg. 1743
KASET INTERNATIONAL—The Times Mirror Company; *U.S. Public*, pg. 1617
KINDERCARE LEARNING CENTERS, INC.; *U.S. Public*, pg. 961
LAGUARDIA LEARNING CENTER—Berkshire Hathaway Inc.; *U.S. Public*, pg. 218
LAKELAND FLIGHT ACADEMY—Berkshire Hathaway Inc.; *U.S. Public*, pg. 218
LANGUAGE INSTITUTE FOR ENGLISH (L.I.F.E.)—Berlitz International, Inc.; *U.S. Public*, pg. 221
LONG BEACH LEARNING CENTER—Berkshire Hathaway Inc.; *U.S. Public*, pg. 218
MARINESAFETY INTERNATIONAL—Berkshire Hathaway Inc.; *U.S. Public*, pg. 218
MIAMI LEARNING CENTER—Berkshire Hathaway Inc.; *U.S. Public*, pg. 219
MILLER COMPREHENSIVE CPA REVIEW, INC.—Harcourt General, Inc.; *U.S. Public*, pg. 783
MONTREAL LEARNING CENTER—Berkshire Hathaway Inc.; *U.S. Public*, pg. 219
MULTI LANGUAGE CENTER SRL—Berlitz International, Inc.; *U.S. Public*, pg. 222
NEW YORK LANGUAGE CENTER—Berlitz International, Inc.; *U.S. Public*, pg. 222
PARIS LEARNING CENTER—Berkshire Hathaway Inc.; *U.S. Public*, pg. 219

PRINCETON LANGUAGE CENTER—Berlitz International, Inc.; *U.S. Public*, pg. 222
THE PSYCHOLOGICAL CORP.—Harcourt General, Inc.; *U.S. Public*, pg. 784
REFLECTONE TRAINING SYSTEMS, INC.—British Aerospace p.l.c.; *Int'l*, pg. 218
ST. LOUIS AIRLINE LEARNING CENTER—Berkshire Hathaway Inc.; *U.S. Public*, pg. 219
ST. LOUIS SABRELINER LEARNING CENTER—Berkshire Hathaway Inc.; *U.S. Public*, pg. 219
SALT LAKE CITY AIRLINE LEARNING CENTER—Berkshire Hathaway Inc.; *U.S. Public*, pg. 219
SAN ANTONIO LEARNING CENTER—Berkshire Hathaway Inc.; *U.S. Public*, pg. 219
SAVANNAH LEARNING CENTER—Berkshire Hathaway Inc.; *U.S. Public*, pg. 219
SEATTLE AIRLINE LEARNING CENTER—Berkshire Hathaway Inc.; *U.S. Public*, pg. 219
SYLVAN LEARNING SYSTEMS INC.; *U.S. Public*, pg. 1545
TECHNICOMP, INC.—Brown & Sharpe Manufacturing Company; *U.S. Public*, pg. 260
TETERBORO LEARNING CENTER—Berkshire Hathaway Inc.; *U.S. Public*, pg. 219
TETRA TECH NUS, INC.—Tetra Tech, Inc.; *U.S. Public*, pg. 1582
TOLEDO LEARNING CENTER—Berkshire Hathaway Inc.; *U.S. Public*, pg. 219
TORONTO LEARNING CENTER—Berkshire Hathaway Inc.; *U.S. Public*, pg. 219
TUCSON LEARNING CENTER—Berkshire Hathaway Inc.; *U.S. Public*, pg. 219
VISTA MULTI METHOD—Berlitz International, Inc.; *U.S. Public*, pg. 222
VISTA MULTI NATIONAL—Berlitz International, Inc.; *U.S. Public*, pg. 222
WASHINGTON LANGUAGE CENTER—Berlitz International, Inc.; *U.S. Public*, pg. 222
THE WASHINGTON POST COMPANY; *U.S. Public*, pg. 1742
WEST PALM BEACH TRAINING CENTER—Berkshire Hathaway Inc.; *U.S. Public*, pg. 219
WICHITA CESSNA LEARNING CENTER—Berkshire Hathaway Inc.; *U.S. Public*, pg. 219
WICHITA CESSNA MAINTENANCE LEARNING CENTER—Berkshire Hathaway Inc.; *U.S. Public*, pg. 219
WICHITA LEARJET LEARNING CENTER—Berkshire Hathaway Inc.; *U.S. Public*, pg. 219
WICHITA RAYTHEON MAINTENANCE LEARNING CENTER—Berkshire Hathaway Inc.; *U.S. Public*, pg. 219
WORLD LANGUAGES SRL—Berlitz International, Inc.; *U.S. Public*, pg. 222

8322 — INDIVIDUAL & FAMILY SOCIAL SERVICES

CATHOLIC RELIEF SERVICES; *U.S. Private*, pg. 220
WORK/FAMILY DIRECTIONS; *U.S. Private*, pg. 1188

8331 — JOB TRAINING & VOCATIONAL REHABILITATION SERVICES

RES-CARE INCORPORATED; *U.S. Public*, pg. 1382
WOLTERS KLUWER N.V.; *Int'l*, pg. 1512

8351 — CHILD DAY CARE SERVICES

ARAMARK EDUCATIONAL RESOURCES INC. INC.—Aramark Corp.; *U.S. Private*, pg. 79
KINDERCARE LEARNING CENTERS, INC.; *U.S. Public*, pg. 961
LA PETITE ACADEMY INC.; *U.S. Private*, pg. 640
MERRYHILL COUNTRY SCHOOLS, INC.—Nobel Education Dynamics, Inc.; *U.S. Public*, pg. 1186
NOBEL EDUCATION DYNAMICS, INC.; *U.S. Public*, pg. 1185
ROCKING HORSE ONE—Nobel Education Dynamics, Inc.; *U.S. Public*, pg. 1186

8361 — RESIDENTIAL CARE

BEVERLY ENTERPRISES, INC.; *U.S. Public*, pg. 227
CAREER BLAZERS LEARNING CENTER OF MELVILLE—Career Blazers Inc.; *U.S. Private*, pg. 209
CAREER BLAZERS LEARNING CENTER OF STAMFORD—Career Blazers Inc.; *U.S. Private*, pg. 209
CONSTELLATION HOLDINGS, INC.—Baltimore Gas and Electric Company; *U.S. Public*, pg. 172
CORRECTIONS CORPORATION OF AMERICA; *U.S. Public*, pg. 450
MANOR CARE, INC.; *U.S. Public*, pg. 1041
MANOR HEALTHCARE CORP.—Manor Care, Inc.; *U.S. Public*, pg. 1041
NISSAY SEIREI HEALTH & WELFARE FOUNDATION—Nippon Life Insurance Co.; *Int'l*, pg. 935
PLAN INTERNATIONAL USA, INC.; *U.S. Private*, pg. 869
THE PRUDENTIAL INSURANCE COMPANY OF AMERICA; *U.S. Private*, pg. 892

8399 — SOCIAL SERVICES, NEC

ADVOCATE HEALTH CARE; *U.S. Private*, pg. 23
COMPREHENSIVE BEHAVIORAL CARE, INC.—Comprehensive Care Corporation; *U.S. Public*, pg. 419
THE DETROIT MEDICAL CENTER; *U.S. Private*, pg. 328
DYNACARE, INC.; *Int'l*, pg. 425
HEALTHWISE OF AMERICA—United HealthCare Corporation; *U.S. Public*, pg. 1678
HUMANA HEALTH PLAN OF GEORGIA, INC.—Humana Inc.; *U.S. Public*, pg. 848
MED+CARE HEALTH SERVICES—Dynacare, Inc.; *Int'l*, pg. 425
MEDNET, MPC CORPORATION; *U.S. Public*, pg. 1082
NATIONSBANK COMMUNITY DEVELOPMENT CORP.—NationsBank Corporation; *U.S. Public*, pg. 1165

8412 — MUSEUMS & ART GALLERIES

ANDREAS GALLERIES, INC.—Lantzsch-Andreas Enterprises, Inc.; *U.S. Private*, pg. 650
THE FRANKLIN INSTITUTE; *U.S. Private*, pg. 424
WCO PORT PROPERTIES, INC.—The Walt Disney Company; *U.S. Public*, pg. 514

8422 — ARBORETA & BOTANICAL OR ZOOLOGICAL GARDENS

MARINE EXHIBITION CORPORATION—Wometco Enterprises, Inc.; *U.S. Private*, pg. 1186
SAN DIEGO WILD ANIMAL PARK—Zoological Society of San Diego; *U.S. Private*, pg. 1207
JOHN G. SHEDD AQUARIUM; *U.S. Private*, pg. 991
WOMETCO ENTERPRISES, INC.; *U.S. Private*, pg. 1186
ZOOLOGICAL SOCIETY OF SAN DIEGO; *U.S. Private*, pg. 1207

8611 — BUSINESS ASSOCIATIONS

ANIE-ASSOCIAZIONE NAZIONALE INDUSTRIE ELETTROTECNICHE ED ELETTRONICHE; *Int'l*, pg. 16
THE AMERICAN BANKERS ASSOCIATION; *U.S. Private*, pg. 51
AMERICAN BUREAU OF SHIPPING; *U.S. Private*, pg. 51
ASSOCIATION OF CREDIT UNION LEAGUE EXECUTIVES—Credit Union National Association; *U.S. Private*, pg. 288
BASF EAST AFRICA LTD.—BASF AG; *Int'l*, pg. 106
BASF KOREA LTD.—BASF AG; *Int'l*, pg. 106
BANK MARKETING ASSOCIATION—The American Bankers Association; *U.S. Private*, pg. 51
THE BIONETICS CORPORATION; *U.S. Private*, pg. 145
BRADY MARKETING COMPANY; *U.S. Private*, pg. 165
CALIFORNIA STRAWBERRY COMMISSION; *U.S. Private*, pg. 201
CREDIT UNION BENEFITS SERVICES, INC.—Credit Union National Association; *U.S. Private*, pg. 288
CREDIT UNION NATIONAL ASSOCIATION; *U.S. Private*, pg. 288
CUNA MORTGAGE CORPORATION—CUNA Mutual Insurance Society; *U.S. Private*, pg. 296
CUNA SERVICE GROUP, INC.—Credit Union National Association; *U.S. Private*, pg. 288
DEFENSE CREDIT UNION COUNCIL—Credit Union National Association; *U.S. Private*, pg. 288
EDMONSON WHEAT GROWERS, INC.; *U.S. Private*, pg. 364
FILENE RESEARCH INSTITUTE—Credit Union National Association; *U.S. Private*, pg. 288
THE FLORISTS ASSN. OF GREATER CLEVELAND, INC.; *U.S. Private*, pg. 415
GETKO GROUP INC.—Cendant Corporation; *U.S. Public*, pg. 320
HAI SUN HUP GROUP LTD.; *Int'l*, pg. 586
FRANZ HANIEL & CIE, GMBH; *Int'l*, pg. 591
INTERSTATE PRODUCERS LIVESTOCK ASSOCIATION; *U.S. Private*, pg. 573
JARDINE MATHESON HOLDINGS LIMITED; *Int'l*, pg. 703
LEHNKERING MONTAN TRANSPORT AG—Metallgesellschaft AG; *Int'l*, pg. 862
LEHNKERING MONTAN TRANSPORT AG—Preussag AG; *Int'l*, pg. 1070
MEMPHIS LIGHT, GAS & WATER; *U.S. Private*, pg. 731
NATIONAL ELECTRICAL MANUFACTURERS ASSOCIATION; *U.S. Private*, pg. 782
NATIONAL FEDERATION OF COMMUNITY DEVELOPMENT CREDIT UNIONS—Credit Union National Association; *U.S. Private*, pg. 288
NATIONAL FIRE PROTECTION ASSOCIATION; *U.S. Private*, pg. 782
PROFESSIONAL PUTTERS ASSOCIATION—Putt Putt Golf Courses of America, Inc.; *U.S. Private*, pg. 896
QUALITY CHEKD DAIRIES, INC.; *U.S. Private*, pg. 898
RUMS OF PUERTO RICO; *U.S. Private*, pg. 951
SWITZERLAND CHEESE ASSOCIATION, INC.—Schweizerische Kaseunion AG; *Int'l*, pg. 1211
UHP HEALTHCARE; *U.S. Private*, pg. 1113
USAA (UNITED SERVICES AUTOMOBILE ASSOCIATION); *U.S. Private*, pg. 1114
U.S. CENTRAL CREDIT UNION—Credit Union National Association; *U.S. Private*, pg. 288
WELCOME WAGON-INTL., INC.—Cendant Corporation; *U.S. Public*, pg. 321
WORLD COUNCIL OF CREDIT UNIONS—Credit Union National Association; *U.S. Private*, pg. 288
WORLD TRADE CENTER NORTHWEST CORPORATION—Enron Corp.; *U.S. Public*, pg. 585

8621 — PROFESSIONAL MEMBERSHIP ORGANIZATIONS

AMERICAN INSTITUTE OF C.P.A.'S INC.; *U.S. Private*, pg. 57
AMWAY CORPORATION; *U.S. Private*, pg. 69
ENCORE MARKETING INTERNATIONAL, INC.; *U.S. Public*, pg. 580
HEIDEMIJ N.V.; *Int'l*, pg. 606
KLOCKNER STADLER HURTER, LTD.—RWE AG; *Int'l*, pg. 1081
THE NATIONAL ASSOCIATION FOR FEMALE EXECUTIVES, INC.—MacDonald Communications; *U.S. Private*, pg. 691
U-HAUL INTERNATIONAL, INC.—Amerco; *U.S. Private*, pg. 49

8631 — LABOR UNIONS & SIMILAR LABOR ORGANIZATIONS

CERIDIAN EMPLOYER SERVICES—Ceridian Corporation; *U.S. Public*, pg. 331

8641 — CIVIC, SOCIAL & FRATERNAL ASSOCIATIONS

B.A.S.S., INC.; *U.S. Private*, pg. 105
BASSMASTER MAGAZINE—B.A.S.S., Inc.; *U.S. Private*, pg. 105

8651 — POLITICAL ORGANIZATIONS

DEMOCRATIC NATIONAL COMMITTEE; *U.S. Private*, pg. 324

8699 — MEMBERSHIP ORGANIZATIONS, NEC

AMERICAN WATER WORKS ASSOCIATION; *U.S. Public*, pg. 94
CUC INTERNATIONAL, INC.—Cendant Corporation; *U.S. Public*, pg. 320
CENDANT CORPORATION; *U.S. Public*, pg. 320
CIGNA ROAD & TRAVEL CLUB, INC.—Cigna Corp.; *U.S. Public*, pg. 362
LIBERTY NATIONAL AUTO CLUB, INC.—Torchmark Corporation; *U.S. Public*, pg. 1623
NODAK MUTUAL INSURANCE COMPANY; *U.S. Private*, pg. 800
THE SIGNATURE GROUP—Montgomery Ward & Co., Inc.; *U.S. Private*, pg. 758
UNITED STATES AUTO CLUB, MOTORING DIVISION, INC.—Ford Motor Company; *U.S. Public*, pg. 663

8711 — ENGINEERING SERVICES

A-L SERVICES FRANCE S.N.C.—Alusuisse-Lonza Holding Ltd.; *Int'l*, pg. 68
ABB ENVIRONMENTAL SERVICES INC.—ABB Asea Brown Boveri (Holding) Ltd.; *Int'l*, pg. 4
ABB INC.—ABB Asea Brown Boveri (Holding) Ltd.; *Int'l*, pg. 3
ABB LUMMUS GLOBAL INC.—ABB Asea Brown Boveri (Holding) Ltd.; *Int'l*, pg. 4
ABS INTEGRATED SERVICES—American Bureau of Shipping; *U.S. Private*, pg. 51
ACEC-OSI—Tractebel; *Int'l*, pg. 1415
ACI OPERATIONS PTY. LTD.—BTR plc; *Int'l*, pg. 128
ACT MANUFACTURING; *U.S. Public*, pg. 3
AEP RESOURCES SERVICE COMPANY—American Electric Power Company, Inc.; *U.S. Public*, pg. 72
AGA INDUSTRIAL GAS ENGINEERING AB—AGA AB; *Int'l*, pg. 12
AM GENERAL CORPORATION—Renco Group; *U.S. Private*, pg. 922
AMB DEVELOPMENT GROUP LLC; *U.S. Private*, pg. 6
AMEC CIVIL ENGINEERING LTD.—AMEC Plc; *Int'l*, pg. 16
AMEC CONSTRUCTION SCOTLAND LTD.—AMEC Plc; *Int'l*, pg. 16
AMEC ENGINEERING LTD.-C.V. BUCHAN (CONCRETE) LTD.—AMEC Plc; *Int'l*, pg. 16
AMEC PLC; *Int'l*, pg. 16
AMEC PROCESS & ENERGY—AMEC Plc; *Int'l*, pg. 16
ANI ENGINEERING—Australian National Industries Limited; *Int'l*, pg. 100
ANR VENTURE MANAGEMENT CO.—The Coastal Corporation; *U.S. Public*, pg. 389
APV ROSISTA LTD.—Siebe plc; *Int'l*, pg. 1241
APX INTERNATIONAL; *U.S. Private*, pg. 7
ASC INCORPORATED; *U.S. Private*, pg. 8
ASCG, INC.—Arctic Slope Regional Corporation; *U.S. Private*, pg. 80
ASRC CONTACTING COMPANY, INC. (ACCI)—Arctic Slope Regional Corporation; *U.S. Private*, pg. 80
AT&T ISTEL LIMITED—AT&T Corporation; *U.S. Public*, pg. 11
ABETONG TEKNIK AB—Scancem AB; *Int'l*, pg. 1199
ACCORD CONTRACT SERVICES—Veba AG; *Int'l*, pg. 1458
ACOS VILLARES MECHANICAL ENGINEERING UNIT—Acos Villares S.A.; *Int'l*, pg. 23
ACTON ENVIRONMENTAL TESTING—National Technical Systems, Inc.; *U.S. Public*, pg. 1161
ADVANCED MARINE ENTERPRISES, INC.—Nichols Research Corporation; *U.S. Public*, pg. 1182
ADVANCO CONSTRUCTORS, INC.—Zurn Industries, Inc.; *U.S. Public*, pg. 1795
AERO SYSTEMS ENGINEERING INC.—Celsius AB; *Int'l*, pg. 276
AEROSPACE CORPORATION; *U.S. Private*, pg. 24
AEROSPATIALE; *Int'l*, pg. 28
AGRA CAMBRIAN INC.—Agra Inc.; *Int'l*, pg. 30
AGRA EARTH & ENVIRONMENTAL, INC.—Agra Inc.; *Int'l*, pg. 31
AGRA EARTH & ENVIRONMENTAL LIMITED—Agra Inc.; *Int'l*, pg. 30
AGRA FOUNDATIONS (PACIFIC) LIMITED—Agra Inc.; *Int'l*, pg. 30
AGRA INC.; *Int'l*, pg. 30
AGROTECHNIP S.A.—Technip; *Int'l*, pg. 1360
AHLSTROM MACHINERY PAIVARINNE WORKS—A. Ahlstrom Corporation; *Int'l*, pg. 33
AHLSTROM MACHINERY RECOVERY BOILERS & HEAT ENGINEERING—A. Ahlstrom Corporation; *Int'l*, pg. 33

AHLSTROM MACHINERY SAVONLINNA ENGINEERING WORKS—A. Ahlstrom Corporation; Int'l, pg. 34
AIR & WATER TECHNOLOGIES CORPORATION; U.S. Public, pg. 29
AIR LIQUIDE S.A.; Int'l, pg. 37
AIRCO COMMERCIAL SERVICES, INC.—Airco Mechanical Inc.; U.S. Private, pg. 29
AKER RAJ ASA; Int'l, pg. 41
AL-NABOODAH LAING (PRIVATE) LTD.—John Laing PLC; Int'l, pg. 797
AL OTAIBA-COSTAIN COMPANY—Costain Group PLC; Int'l, pg. 337
ALASKA PETROLEUM CONTRACTORS—Arctic Slope Regional Corporation; U.S. Private, pg. 80
ALBACORA FIELD DEVELOPMENT—Petrobras - Petroleo Brasileiro S.A.; Int'l, pg. 1041
ALCAN ALUMINUM CORPORATION—Alcan Aluminium Limited; Int'l, pg. 50
ALESA ALUSUISSE ENGINEERING CANADA LTD.—Alusuisse-Lonza Holding Ltd.; Int'l, pg. 68
ALESA ALUSUISSE ENGINEERING LTD.-(ALESA)—Alusuisse-Lonza Holding Ltd.; Int'l, pg. 67
ALFA-LAVAL ENGINEERING K.K.—Tetra Laval Group; Int'l, pg. 1380
ALFA LAVAL INC.—Tetra Laval Group; Int'l, pg. 1378
ALFA-LAVAL NIREX ENGINEERING A/S—Tetra Laval Group; Int'l, pg. 1379
ALLEN & HOSHALL, INC.; U.S. Private, pg. 36
ALLIEDSIGNAL COMPUTER-AIDED ENGINEERING CENTER—AlliedSignal Inc.; U.S. Public, pg. 50
ALUSUISSE HOLDINGS LTD.—Alusuisse-Lonza Holding Ltd.; Int'l, pg. 67
ALUSUISSE-LONZA A.G. FUR KREISLAUFWIRTSCHAFT—Alusuisse-Lonza Holding Ltd.; Int'l, pg. 67
ALUSUISSE-LONZA CAPITAL LTD—Alusuisse-Lonza Holding Ltd.; Int'l, pg. 68
ALUSUISSE-LONZA ENERGIE AG—Alusuisse-Lonza Holding Ltd.; Int'l, pg. 67
ALUSUISSE-LONZA FRANCE S.A.—Alusuisse-Lonza Holding Ltd.; Int'l, pg. 68
ALUSUISSE-LONZA GMBH—Alusuisse-Lonza Holding Ltd.; Int'l, pg. 68
ALUSUISSE-LONZA HOLDING LTD.; Int'l, pg. 66
ALUSUISSE-LONZA NEDERLAND B.V.—Alusuisse-Lonza Holding Ltd.; Int'l, pg. 68
ALUSUISSE-LONZA SERVICES LTD.—Alusuisse-Lonza Holding Ltd.; Int'l, pg. 67
ALUSUISSE-LONZA UK LTD.—Alusuisse-Lonza Holding Ltd.; Int'l, pg. 68
ALUSUISSE ROAD & RAIL LTD.—Alusuisse-Lonza Holding Ltd.; Int'l, pg. 67
AMCLYDE ENGINEERED PRODUCTS CO., INC.—Halter Marine Group, Inc.; U.S. Public, pg. 778
AMERICAN ECOLOGY CORPORATION; U.S. Public, pg. 71
AMERICAN ENVIRONMENTAL NETWORK, INC.—Texas Utilities Company; U.S. Public, pg. 1587
AMERICAN FINANCIAL GROUP—American Financial Group; U.S. Public, pg. 75
AMERICAN FINANCIAL GROUP; U.S. Public, pg. 74
AMERICAN SYSTEMS CORPORATION; U.S. Private, pg. 63
AMERICAN SYSTEMS ENGINEERING CORPORATION—Science Applications International Corp.; U.S. Private, pg. 976
ANALYSIS & TECHNOLOGY, INC.; U.S. Public, pg. 109
ANDREWS & CLARK, INC.—Thermo Electron Corporation; U.S. Public, pg. 1593
ANSALDO ARGENTINA S.A.—IRI Istituto Ricostruzione Industriale; Int'l, pg. 654
ANSALDO DE COLOMBIA S.A.—IRI Istituto Ricostruzione Industriale; Int'l, pg. 654
ANSALDO DE MEXICO—IRI Istituto Ricostruzione Industriale; Int'l, pg. 654
ANSALDO DEUTSCHLAND—IRI Istituto Ricostruzione Industriale; Int'l, pg. 654
ANSALDO DO BRASIL EQUIP ELECTROMECANICOS S.A.—IRI Istituto Ricostruzione Industriale; Int'l, pg. 654
ANSALDO INTERNATIONAL SERVICES—IRI Istituto Ricostruzione Industriale; Int'l, pg. 654
ANSALDO SAUDIA LTD.—IRI Istituto Ricostruzione Industriale; Int'l, pg. 654
ANSEVEN—IRI Istituto Ricostruzione Industriale; Int'l, pg. 654
APPLIED INTELLIGENCE SYSTEMS, INC.—Electro Scientific Industries, Inc.; U.S. Public, pg. 569
ARABIAN ENVIRONMENTAL SERVICES COMPANY LIMITED—Halliburton Company; U.S. Public, pg. 777
ARCTIC SLOPE REGIONAL CORPORATION; U.S. Private, pg. 80
ARIANESPACE, INC.—Arianespace SA; Int'l, pg. 81
ARIANESPACE KOUROU—Arianespace SA; Int'l, pg. 81
ARIANESPACE SA; Int'l, pg. 81
ARVIN INDUSTRIES, INC.; U.S. Public, pg. 136
ASEA BROWN BOVERI LTDA.—ABB Asea Brown Boveri (Holding) Ltd.; Int'l, pg. 8
ASSOCIATED ENGINEERS & CONSULTANTS, INC.—Stone & Webster, Incorporated; U.S. Public, pg. 1519
ASTON MARTIN LAGONDA DESIGN LIMITED—Ford Motor Company; U.S. Public, pg. 665
ATCO GROUP CO.; Int'l, pg. 95
ATLAS COPCO ELECTRIC TOOLS—Atlas Copco AB; Int'l, pg. 96
ATLAS COPCO INDUSTRIAL TOOLS & EQUIPMENT—Atlas Copco AB; Int'l, pg. 96
AUST-AMEC PTY.—AMEC Plc; Int'l, pg. 16
THE AUSTIN COMPANY; U.S. Private, pg. 99
BCE INC.; Int'l, pg. 114
BCP TECHNICAL SERVICE, INC.; U.S. Private, pg. 106
BD SYSTEMS, INC; U.S. Private, pg. 106
BE & C ENGINEERS INC.—The Boeing Company; U.S. Public, pg. 241
BE & K, INC.; U.S. Private, pg. 106
BLD PRODUCTS, LTD.—MascoTech, Inc.; U.S. Public, pg. 1055
BMW INGENIEUR ZENTRUM VERWALTUNGS GMBH—Bayerische Motoren Werke Aktiengesellschaft; Int'l, pg. 177
BRW, INC.; U.S. Private, pg. 107
BS & B PROCESS SYSTEMS, INC.—International Systems & Controls Corp.; U.S. Private, pg. 572
BTG, INC.; U.S. Public, pg. 164
BTU EUROPE—BTU International, Inc.; U.S. Public, pg. 164
BABCOCK AFRICA (PTY) LTD.—Babcock International Group PLC; Int'l, pg. 131
BABCOCK CONSTRUCTION LIMITED—Babcock International Group PLC; Int'l, pg. 130
BABCOCK ENERGY LIMITED—Babcock International Group PLC; Int'l, pg. 130
BABCOCK ENGINEERING CONTRACTORS (PTY) LTD—Babcock International Group PLC; Int'l, pg. 131
BABCOCK ENGINEERING CONTRACTORS (PTY) LTD.—FKI Plc; Int'l, pg. 474
BABCOCK ENGINEERING LTD.—FKI Plc; Int'l, pg. 474
BABCOCK INTERNATIONAL GROUP PLC; Int'l, pg. 130
BABCOCK KING - WILKINSON LIMITED—Babcock International Group PLC; Int'l, pg. 131
BABCOCK MINERALS ENGINEERING LTD.—FKI Plc; Int'l, pg. 472
BABCOCK POWER LIMITED-RESEARCH DIV.—FKI Plc; Int'l, pg. 472
BAKER ENGINEERING, INC.—Michael Baker Corporation; U.S. Public, pg. 168
BAKER ENGINEERING, NY, INC.—Michael Baker Corporation; U.S. Public, pg. 168
BAKER ENVIRONMENTAL, INC.—Michael Baker Corporation; U.S. Public, pg. 168
MICHAEL BAKER CORPORATION; U.S. Public, pg. 168
MICHAEL BAKER, JR., INC.—Michael Baker Corporation; U.S. Public, pg. 168
BALFOUR BEATTY LIMITED—BICC plc; Int'l, pg. 120
BALLAST NEDAM NV; Int'l, pg. 133
BANNER ASSOCIATES INC.; U.S. Private, pg. 114
BANTREL INC.—BFC Construction Corporation; Int'l, pg. 118
BARNES & REINECKE, INC.—Allied Research Corporation; U.S. Public, pg. 49
BARRACUDA FIELD DEVELOPMENT—Petrobras - Petroleo Brasileiro S.A.; Int'l, pg. 1041
BARTON-ASCHMAN ASSOCIATES, INC.—Parsons Corporation; U.S. Private, pg. 841
BASTOGI-S.P.A.; Int'l, pg. 170
BECHTEL CIVIL, INC.—Bechtel Group, Inc.; U.S. Private, pg. 128
BECHTEL GROUP, INC.; U.S. Private, pg. 128
BECHTEL LTD.—Bechtel Group, Inc.; U.S. Private, pg. 128
BECHTEL MINING & METALS—Bechtel Group, Inc.; U.S. Private, pg. 128
BECHTEL PETROLEUM & CHEMICAL—Bechtel Group, Inc.; U.S. Private, pg. 128
BECHTEL POWER CORPORATION—Bechtel Group, Inc.; U.S. Private, pg. 128
R.W. BECK, INC.; U.S. Private, pg. 128
BELL MOBILITY RADIO INC.—BCE Inc.; Int'l, pg. 115
BELLISS & MORCOM—Powell Duffryn PLC; Int'l, pg. 1065
BELLISS & MORCOM INDIA—Powell Duffryn PLC; Int'l, pg. 1065
LOUIS BERGER INTERNATIONAL INC.; U.S. Private, pg. 135
BERNARD JOHNSON YOUNG INC.; U.S. Private, pg. 136
BETTIGOLE, ANDREWS & CLARK, INC.—Thermo Electron Corporation; U.S. Public, pg. 1593
BIOFIN HOLDING INTERNATIONAL BV—Fiat Auto SpA; Int'l, pg. 483
BISSEUIL—Bouygues; Int'l, pg. 206
BLACK & VEATCH; U.S. Private, pg. 146
BLACK & VEATCH PRITCHARD, INC.—Black & Veatch; U.S. Private, pg. 146
BOEING AEROSPACE OPERATIONS—The Boeing Company; U.S. Public, pg. 241
BOEING NORTH AMERICA, SPACE SYSTEMS DIVISION—The Boeing Company; U.S. Public, pg. 241
BOEING PETROLEUM SERVICES, INC.—The Boeing Company; U.S. Public, pg. 242
BOOZ, ALLEN & HAMILTON INC.; U.S. Private, pg. 157
BORAL ACROW LTD. (NEW ZEALAND)—Boral Limited; Int'l, pg. 203
BORAL LIMITED; Int'l, pg. 203
BOSCH BRAKING SYSTEMS-NORTH AMERICA—Robert Bosch GmbH; Int'l, pg. 204
BOUYGUES; Int'l, pg. 206
BOUYGUES NIGERIA LIMITED (B.N.L.)—Bouygues; Int'l, pg. 207
BOUYGUES OFFSHORE—Bouygues; Int'l, pg. 206
BOYLE ENGINEERING CORP.; U.S. Private, pg. 163
THE BRAAS GROUP—Redland PLC; Int'l, pg. 1091
BRAUN TRANSWORLD CORP.—Kuwait Petroleum Corporation; Int'l, pg. 765
BRITISH AEROSPACE (CONSULTANCY SERVICES) LIMITED—British Aerospace p.l.c.; Int'l, pg. 217
BRITISH AEROSPACE P.L.C.; Int'l, pg. 217
BRITISH STEEL ENGINEERING—British Steel Plc; Int'l, pg. 220
BROWN AND CALDWELL; U.S. Private, pg. 173
JOHN BROWN E & C CORPORATE OFFICES (U.S.)—Kvaerner a.s.a.; Int'l, pg. 774
JOHN BROWN - ENGINEERING & CONSTRUCTION SECTOR—Kvaerner a.s.a.; Int'l, pg. 772
R.J. BROWN AMERICA, INC.—Kvaerner a.s.a.; Int'l, pg. 766
R.J. BROWN AND ASSOCIATES CORPORATION AG—Kvaerner a.s.a.; Int'l, pg. 766
R.J. BROWN & ASSOCIATES (UK) LIMITED—Kvaerner a.s.a.; Int'l, pg. 772
BUCHART HORN INC.—Pace Resources, Inc.; U.S. Private, pg. 830
BUFETE INDUSTRIAL S.A. DE C.V.; Int'l, pg. 232
BUILDINGS DIVISION—Black & Veatch; U.S. Private, pg. 146
BURGESS & NIPLE, LIMITED; U.S. Private, pg. 182
BURNS & MCDONNELL ENGINEERS-ARCHITECTS-CONSULTANTS; U.S. Private, pg. 187
BURNS & MCDONNELL WASTE CONSULTANTS, INC.—Burns & McDonnell Engineers-Architects-Consultants; U.S. Private, pg. 187
BURNS & ROE ENTERPRISES, INC.; U.S. Private, pg. 187
BUTLER DESIGN SERVICES, INC.—Butler International, Inc.; U.S. Public, pg. 271
BUTLER SERVICE GROUP, INC.—Butler International, Inc.; U.S. Public, pg. 271
C-E INTERNATIONAL (TECHNOLOGICAL BRANCH)—ABB Asea Brown Boveri (Holding) Ltd.; Int'l, pg. 5
CACI INTERNATIONAL INC; U.S. Public, pg. 272
CBS OPERATIONS & ADMINISTRATION DIV.—CBS Corporation; U.S. Public, pg. 274
CDI CORP.; U.S. Public, pg. 276
CDI ENGINEERING GROUP, INC.—CDI Corp.; U.S. Public, pg. 277
CDI MARINE COMPANY—CDI Corp.; U.S. Public, pg. 277
CDI TELECOMMUNICATIONS, INC.—CDI Corp.; U.S. Public, pg. 277
CDM FEDERAL PROGRAMS CORPORATION—Camp Dresser & McKee Inc.; U.S. Private, pg. 204
CESL ENGINEERING LIMITED—Cominco, Ltd.; Int'l, pg. 307
CFEM—Groupe Usinor; Int'l, pg. 571
CGG GEOPHYSICS CANADA LTD.—CGG Group; Int'l, pg. 241
CGG NORGE A/S—CGG Group; Int'l, pg. 241
CGG PAN INDIA LTD.—CGG Group; Int'l, pg. 241
CH2M HILL COMPANIES, LTD.; U.S. Private, pg. 195
CH2M HILL, INC.—CH2M Hill Companies, Ltd.; U.S. Private, pg. 195
CH2M HILL INDUSTRIAL DESIGN CORP.—CH2M Hill Companies, Ltd.; U.S. Private, pg. 195
CMS ENGINEERING CO.—CMS Energy Corporation; U.S. Public, pg. 280
CMS MIDLAND, INC.—CMS Energy Corporation; U.S. Public, pg. 280
CRSS CONSTRUCTORS, INC.—Jacobs Engineering Group Inc.; U.S. Public, pg. 922
CRSS INC.—Tractebel; Int'l, pg. 1415
CRSS INTERNATIONAL, INC.—Jacobs Engineering Group Inc.; U.S. Public, pg. 922
CSR—Raytheon Company; U.S. Public, pg. 1365
CTIP S.P.A.—Bastogi-S.p.A.; Int'l, pg. 170
CABOT INTERNATIONAL SERVICES CORP.—Cabot Corporation; U.S. Public, pg. 289
CALTY DESIGN RESEARCH, INC.—Toyota Motor Corporation; Int'l, pg. 1412
CAMBY—Bouygues; Int'l, pg. 207
CAMP DRESSER & MCKEE INC.; U.S. Private, pg. 203
CAMPENON BERNARD—Compagnie Generale Des Eaux; Int'l, pg. 321
CANNON; U.S. Private, pg. 205
CANUCK ENGINEERING INC.—Agra Inc.; Int'l, pg. 31
CAPITOL ENGINEERING—Dewberry & Davis; U.S. Private, pg. 329
CAR PROGRAMS MANAGEMENT—Ford Motor Company; U.S. Public, pg. 662
CARCLO ENGINEERING GROUP PLC; Int'l, pg. 268
CASCADE PACIFIC ENGINEERING, INC.—Republic Industries, Inc.; U.S. Public, pg. 1379
CASTAGNETTI—Fiat Auto SpA; Int'l, pg. 481
CEGELEC—Alcatel Alsthom Compagnie Generale D'Electricite; Int'l, pg. 52
CEGELEC DE MEXICO—Alcatel Alsthom Compagnie Generale D'Electricite; Int'l, pg. 53
CEGELEC ENTREPRISES, INC.—Alcatel Alsthom Compagnie Generale D'Electricite; Int'l, pg. 53
CEGELEC GMBH—Alcatel Alsthom Compagnie Generale D'Electricite; Int'l, pg. 53
CEGELEC (M) SDN BHD—Alcatel Alsthom Compagnie Generale D'Electricite; Int'l, pg. 53
CELSIUS INVEST AB—Celsius AB; Int'l, pg. 276
CEMENTATION MINING LIMITED—Kvaerner a.s.a.; Int'l, pg. 772
CEMINDIA COMPANY LIMITED—Kvaerner a.s.a.; Int'l, pg. 774
CHARTER PLC; Int'l, pg. 280
CHEMTEX ENGINEERING—Mitsubishi Corporation; Int'l, pg. 872
CHEMTEX FIBERS EXPORT, INC.—Mitsubishi Corporation; Int'l, pg. 872
CHEMTEX FIBERS INC.—Mitsubishi Corporation; Int'l, pg. 872
CHEMTEX INTERNATIONAL, INC.—Mitsubishi Corporation; Int'l, pg. 872
CHEMTEX OVERSEAS, INC.—Mitsubishi Corporation; Int'l, pg. 872
CHILTEM GROUP SAM—Alpha Omikron Limited; Int'l, pg. 65
CILCORP INC.; U.S. Public, pg. 367
CITY COM B.V.—Internatio-Muller N.V.; Int'l, pg. 681
COBHAM PLC; Int'l, pg. 301
COKEN COMPANY, INC.; U.S. Private, pg. 250
COLE, SHERMAN & ASSOCIATES LTD.—URS Corporation; U.S. Public, pg. 1657
COMARCO, INC.; U.S. Public, pg. 406
COMMONWEALTH COMMUNICATIONS—RCN Corporation; U.S. Public, pg. 1354
COMMONWEALTH TELEPHONE ENTERPRISES, INC.; U.S. Public, pg. 415
COMPAGNIE AFRICAINE DE GEOPHYSIQUE—CGG Group; Int'l, pg. 241
COMPAGNIE GENERALE DE GEOPHYSIQUE (FAR EAST)—CGG Group; Int'l, pg. 241
COMPANIA GENERAL DE GEOFISICA S.A.—CGG Group; Int'l, pg. 241
COMPANIA MEXICANA DE GEOFISICA—CGG Group; Int'l, pg. 241

COMPUDYNE CORPORATION; *U.S. Public*, pg. 419
COMSAT CORPORATION; *U.S. Public*, pg. 424
COMSEARCH, INC.—Allen Telecom, Inc.; *U.S. Public*, pg. 46
COMSTOCK CANADA LTD.—EMCOR Group, Inc.; *U.S. Public*, pg. 572
CONGAREE CONSTRUCTION CO., INC.; *U.S. Private*, pg. 263
CONSTRUCTIONS ENTREPRISES GENERALES, IMPREFER S.A.—Fiat Auto SpA; *Int'l*, pg. 482
CONTINENTAL CAN CO.; *U.S. Public*, pg. 439
THE CONVERSE PROFESSIONAL GROUP, INC.; *U.S. Private*, pg. 271
CONVERSION SYSTEMS, INC.—EnviroSource, Inc.; *U.S. Public*, pg. 587
COOPER COMMUNITIES, INC.; *U.S. Private*, pg. 273
CORE LABORATORIES (NETHERLANDS)—Litton Industries, Inc.; *U.S. Public*, pg. 1004
CORE LABORATORIES (SINGAPORE)—Litton Industries, Inc.; *U.S. Public*, pg. 1004
CORE LABORATORIES (UK)—Litton Industries, Inc.; *U.S. Public*, pg. 1004
COSTAIN (AFRICA) LIMITED—Costain Group PLC; *Int'l*, pg. 337
COSTAIN CIVIL ENGINEERING LTD.—Costain Group PLC; *Int'l*, pg. 336
COSTAIN GROUP PLC; *Int'l*, pg. 336
COSTAIN INTERNATIONAL LIMITED—Costain Group PLC; *Int'l*, pg. 336
COSTAIN (WEST AFRICA) LTD.—Costain Group PLC; *Int'l*, pg. 337
COURTAULDS ENGINEERING LTD.—Courtaulds plc; *Int'l*, pg. 339
COURTAULDS PLC; *Int'l*, pg. 338
CUBIC DEFENSE SYSTEMS—Cubic Corporation; *U.S. Public*, pg. 466
CUNNINGHAM-LIMP DEVELOPMENT CO.; *U.S. Private*, pg. 297
D&Z MICROELECTRONICS—Day & Zimmermann, Inc.; *U.S. Private*, pg. 317
D&Z UTILITY SERVICES—Day & Zimmermann, Inc.; *U.S. Private*, pg. 317
DBA SYSTEMS, INC.; *U.S. Public*, pg. 472
DEI DIVISION—Alcatel Alsthom Compagnie Generale D'Electricite; *Int'l*, pg. 52
DMR GROUP, INC.—Fujitsu Limited; *Int'l*, pg. 527
DSI GROUP—Alcatel Alsthom Compagnie Generale D'Electricite; *Int'l*, pg. 52
DSS ENGINEERS, INC.—Stone & Webster, Incorporated; *U.S. Public*, pg. 1519
DALLA VERA—Bouygues; *Int'l*, pg. 206
LEO A. DALY COMPANY; *U.S. Private*, pg. 309
DAMES & MOORE INC.—Hochtief AG; *Int'l*, pg. 624
DATA COMMAND SYSTEMS—Litton Industries, Inc.; *U.S. Public*, pg. 1002
DATEL TECHNOLOGIES LTD.; *Int'l*, pg. 384
DAVY DRAVO DIVISION—Kvaerner a.s.a.; *Int'l*, pg. 774
DAVY INTERNATIONAL—Kvaerner a.s.a.; *Int'l*, pg. 773
DAVY INTERNATIONAL, CANADA—Kvaerner a.s.a.; *Int'l*, pg. 775
DAVY JOHN BROWN PTY LIMITED—Kvaerner a.s.a.; *Int'l*, pg. 775
DAVY MCKEE CHILE LTDA.—Kvaerner a.s.a.; *Int'l*, pg. 775
DAVY MCKEE ENGENHARIA S/A—Kvaerner a.s.a.; *Int'l*, pg. 775
DAVY PITTSBURGH—Kvaerner a.s.a.; *Int'l*, pg. 774
THE DAVY ROLL CO. LTD.—Kvaerner a.s.a.; *Int'l*, pg. 773
DAY & ZIMMERMANN, INC.; *U.S. Private*, pg. 316
DAY & ZIMMERMANN INTERNATIONAL, INC.—Day & Zimmermann, Inc.; *U.S. Private*, pg. 317
DEDERT CORPORATION; *U.S. Private*, pg. 320
JOHN DEERE TECHNOLOGIES INTERNATIONAL, INC.—Deere & Company; *U.S. Public*, pg. 492
DEFIANCE, INC.; *U.S. Public*, pg. 493
DEFIANCE TESTING & ENGINEERING SERVICES—Defiance, Inc.; *U.S. Public*, pg. 493
DEIND—Petrobras - Petroleo Brasileiro S.A.; *Int'l*, pg. 1041
DEKKO TECHNICAL CENTER—Group Dekko; *U.S. Private*, pg. 484
DELEUW, CATHER & COMPANY—Parsons Corporation; *U.S. Private*, pg. 841
DELEUW, CATHER INTERNATIONAL LTD.—Parsons Corporation; *U.S. Private*, pg. 842
DERLAN INDUSTRIES LIMITED; *Int'l*, pg. 395
DET NORSKE VERITAS; *Int'l*, pg. 396
DETELINE DEUTSCHE TELEKOM KOMMUNIKATIONSNETZE GMBH—Deutsche Telekom AG; *Int'l*, pg. 407
DEUTSCHE ASPHALT GMBH—Philipp Holzmann AG; *Int'l*, pg. 632
DEUTSCHE BABCOCK AG; *Int'l*, pg. 398
DEUTSCHE BABCOCK TECHNOLOGIES, INC.—Deutsche Babcock AG; *Int'l*, pg. 401
DEUTSCHE VAN RIETSCHOTEN & HOUWENS GMBH—Internatio-Muller N.V.; *Int'l*, pg. 682
DEWBERRY & DAVIS; *U.S. Private*, pg. 329
DEWBERRY DESIGN GROUP—Dewberry & Davis; *U.S. Private*, pg. 329
DIPLAC—Petrobras - Petroleo Brasileiro S.A.; *Int'l*, pg. 1041
DIVANE BROS. ELECTRIC CO.; *U.S. Private*, pg. 336
DIVISIONE AMBIENTE—IRI Istituto Ricostruzione Industriale; *Int'l*, pg. 653
DOW PLASTICS DEVELOPMENT AG—The Dow Chemical Company; *U.S. Public*, pg. 524
DRAKE & SCULL ENGINEERING LTD.—EMCOR Group, Inc.; *U.S. Public*, pg. 572
DRESSER INDUSTRIES, INC.; *U.S. Public*, pg. 528
DREW INDUSTRIAL—Ashland, Inc.; *U.S. Public*, pg. 139
DU PONT CANADA-KINGSTON WORKS—Du Pont (E.I. Du Pont De Nemours & Co.); *U.S. Public*, pg. 532
DUKE ENGINEERING & SERVICES, INC.—Duke Energy Corporation; *U.S. Public*, pg. 534
DUKE/FLUOR DANIEL—Duke Energy Corporation; *U.S. Public*, pg. 535
DUKE/FLUOR DANIEL—Fluor Corporation; *U.S. Public*, pg. 660
DUMEZ-GTM—Lyonnaise des Eaux S.A.; *Int'l*, pg. 823
THOMAS K. DYER, INC.—HNTB Corporation; *U.S. Private*, pg. 492
DYNACAST DEUTSCHLAND GMBH—Coats Viyella plc; *Int'l*, pg. 300
DYNACAST DO BRAZIL LTDA.—Coats Viyella plc; *Int'l*, pg. 301
DYNAMICS RESEARCH CORPORATION; *U.S. Public*, pg. 539
E & L ENGINEERING—Texas Utilities Company; *U.S. Public*, pg. 1587
EA ENGINEERING, SCIENCE & TECHNOLOGY, INC.; *U.S. Public*, pg. 540
EG & G ENVIRONMENTAL, INC.—EG & G, Inc.; *U.S. Public*, pg. 543
EG & G, INC.; *U.S. Public*, pg. 542
EG & G SERVICES INFORMATION TECHNOLOGIES—EG & G, Inc.; *U.S. Public*, pg. 544
ENI S.P.A.; *Int'l*, pg. 428
EPEX GROUP—Alcatel Alsthom Compagnie Generale D'Electricite; *Int'l*, pg. 52
EQE INTERNATIONAL; *U.S. Private*, pg. 354
ERM-ENVIROCLEAN—Environmental Resources Management; *U.S. Private*, pg. 379
EARTH TECHNOLOGY CORP.—Tyco International Ltd.; *U.S. Public*, pg. 1648
EBARA INDUSTRIAS MECANICAS E COMERCIO LTDA.—Ebara Corporation; *Int'l*, pg. 432
EBARA ITALIA S.P.A.—Ebara Corporation; *Int'l*, pg. 432
EBASCO ARABIA LIMITED—Texas Utilities Company; *U.S. Public*, pg. 1587
EBASCO B.V.—Texas Utilities Company; *U.S. Public*, pg. 1587
EBASCO CORPORATION—Texas Utilities Company; *U.S. Public*, pg. 1587
EBASCO-CTCI CORPORATION—Texas Utilities Company; *U.S. Public*, pg. 1587
EBASCO ESPANA, S.A.—Texas Utilities Company; *U.S. Public*, pg. 1587
EBASCO ITALIA S.R.L.—Texas Utilities Company; *U.S. Public*, pg. 1587
EBASCO SERVICES SINGAPORE PTE. LTD.—Texas Utilities Company; *U.S. Public*, pg. 1587
ECOLOGY AND ENVIRONMENT, INC.; *U.S. Public*, pg. 562
EDWARDS & KELCEY CONSTRUCTION, INC.—Edwards and Kelcey, Inc.; *U.S. Private*, pg. 364
EDWARDS & KELCEY ENGINEERS, INC.—Edwards and Kelcey, Inc.; *U.S. Private*, pg. 364
EDWARDS AND KELCEY, INC.; *U.S. Private*, pg. 364
EDWARDS & KELCEY WIRELESS—Edwards and Kelcey, Inc.; *U.S. Private*, pg. 364
EFFICIENT ENGINEERING CO.; *U.S. Private*, pg. 365
EKOTECH—Technip; *Int'l*, pg. 1360
ELASTOMERIC TECHNOLOGIES, INC.—Thomas & Betts Corporation; *U.S. Public*, pg. 1598
ELECTRIFICATION CHARPENTE LEVAGE (E.C.L.)—Pechiney S.A.; *Int'l*, pg. 1028
ELECTROSCON NETWORK ENGINEERING SDN. BHD.—Telefonaktiebolaget LM Ericsson; *Int'l*, pg. 1366
ELECTROSPACE SYSTEMS, INC.—Raytheon Company; *U.S. Public*, pg. 1365
ELGIN NATIONAL INDUSTRIES, INC.; *U.S. Private*, pg. 370
EMCON; *U.S. Public*, pg. 571
ENAVAL—Petrobras - Petroleo Brasileiro S.A.; *Int'l*, pg. 1041
ENCAP SYSTEMS, INC.—Hayes, Seay, Mattern & Mattern, Inc.; *U.S. Private*, pg. 513
ENERGY & ENVIRONMENTAL RESEARCH CORP.; *U.S. Private*, pg. 376
ENERGY SYSTEMS INDUSTRIES, INC.; *U.S. Private*, pg. 376
ENGINEERING & TECHNICAL SERVICES, INC.—American Financial Group; *U.S. Public*, pg. 75
ENGINEERING SERVICE, INC.; *U.S. Private*, pg. 376
ENGINEERING SERVICES (SEGEN)—Petrobras - Petroleo Brasileiro S.A.; *Int'l*, pg. 1041
ENGINEERING TECHNOLOGY LTD. (E.T.); *U.S. Private*, pg. 377
ENPROTECH CORP.—Itochu Corporation; *Int'l*, pg. 694
ENSERCH CORPORATION—Texas Utilities Company; *U.S. Public*, pg. 1587
ENVIRONMENTAL RESOURCES MANAGEMENT; *U.S. Private*, pg. 378
A. EPSTEIN AND SONS, INTL., INC.; *U.S. Private*, pg. 379
A. EPSTEIN & SONS (NEW YORK)—A. Epstein and Sons, Intl., Inc.; *U.S. Private*, pg. 379
EPSTEIN CIVIL ENGINEERING, INC.—A. Epstein and Sons, Intl., Inc.; *U.S. Private*, pg. 379
ERICSSON NETWORK CONSTRUCTIONS AB—Telefonaktiebolaget LM Ericsson; *Int'l*, pg. 1363
ERICSSON NETWORK ENGINEERING LTD.—Telefonaktiebolaget LM Ericsson; *Int'l*, pg. 1367
ERICSSON NETWORK ENGINEERING PTE. LTD.—Telefonaktiebolaget LM Ericsson; *Int'l*, pg. 1367
ERVINS GROUP—Acme Mills Co. Inc.; *U.S. Private*, pg. 13
ESSEX CORPORATION; *U.S. Public*, pg. 593
ESTECH CORPORATION—Structural Dynamics Research Corp.; *U.S. Public*, pg. 1525
EUROPEAN TECHNICAL CENTER—General Motors Corporation; *U.S. Public*, pg. 721
EUROTEC SYSTEMTEILE GMBH—Klockner-Werke AG; *Int'l*, pg. 737
FAG GROUP; *Int'l*, pg. 468
FSEC, INC.—Arctic Slope Regional Corporation; *U.S. Private*, pg. 80
THE FAILURE GROUP, INC.; *U.S. Public*, pg. 609
FATA-NEW HUNTER ENGINEERING S.P.A.—FKI Plc; *Int'l*, pg. 474
FAY, SPOFFORD & THORNDIKE, INC.; *U.S. Private*, pg. 397
FIAT AUTO SPA; *Int'l*, pg. 480
FISH INTERNATIONAL CO.—KTI Fish; *U.S. Private*, pg. 604
THE FLETCHER CONSTRUCTION COMPANY LIMITED—Fletcher Challenge Limited; *Int'l*, pg. 495
FLETCHER SMITH LTD.—Booker PLC; *Int'l*, pg. 202
FLUOR CORPORATION; *U.S. Public*, pg. 659
FLUOR DANIEL GTI, INC.—Fluor Corporation; *U.S. Public*, pg. 660
FLUOR DANIEL INC.—Fluor Corporation; *U.S. Public*, pg. 660
FORD, BACON & DAVIS COMPANIES INC.—Deutsche Babcock AG; *Int'l*, pg. 401
FORD BODY ENGINEERING—Ford Motor Company; *U.S. Public*, pg. 662
FORD DESIGN STAFF—Ford Motor Company; *U.S. Public*, pg. 663
FORD ENVIRONMENTAL & SAFETY ENGINEERING STAFF—Ford Motor Company; *U.S. Public*, pg. 663
FORD NORTH AMERICAN DESIGN—Ford Motor Company; *U.S. Public*, pg. 662
FORD RESEARCH STAFF—Ford Motor Company; *U.S. Public*, pg. 664
FOSTER WHEELER ANDINA, S.A.—Foster Wheeler Corporation; *U.S. Public*, pg. 677
FOSTER WHEELER BIMAS—Foster Wheeler Corporation; *U.S. Public*, pg. 677
FOSTER WHEELER CORPORATION; *U.S. Public*, pg. 676
FOSTER WHEELER ENERGIA OY—Foster Wheeler Corporation; *U.S. Public*, pg. 677
FRAMATOME SA; *Int'l*, pg. 502
FUGRO GROUP COMPANIES; *U.S. Private*, pg. 430
FUJITSU LABORATORIES LTD.—Fujitsu Limited; *Int'l*, pg. 526
GAI CONSULTANTS, INC.; *U.S. Private*, pg. 433
GAI CONSULTANTS, INC.—GAI Consultants, Inc.; *U.S. Private*, pg. 434
GAI CONSULTANTS-NC, INC.—GAI Consultants, Inc.; *U.S. Private*, pg. 434
G.C.A.—Bouygues; *Int'l*, pg. 206
GDE SYSTEMS, INC.—Tracor, Inc.; *U.S. Public*, pg. 1627
G.E. NUCLEAR ENERGY—General Electric Company; *U.S. Public*, pg. 711
G.E. POWER SYSTEMS—General Electric Company; *U.S. Public*, pg. 711
G.F.C.—Bouygues; *Int'l*, pg. 206
GFG CORPORATION—Derlan Industries Limited; *Int'l*, pg. 395
GMS CORPORATION; *U.S. Private*, pg. 435
GSI ENGINEERING, INC.—Worthington Industries, Inc.; *U.S. Public*, pg. 1780
G.T.F.C.—Bouygues; *Int'l*, pg. 206
GVT GESELLSCHAFT FUER VERSORGUNGSTECHNIK MBH—Saarbergwerke Aktiengesellschaft; *Int'l*, pg. 1167
GZA GEOENVIRONMENTAL TECHNOLOGIES, INC.; *U.S. Public*, pg. 697
GANNETT FLEMING AFFILIATES, INC.; *U.S. Private*, pg. 439
GEINP—Petrobras - Petroleo Brasileiro S.A.; *Int'l*, pg. 1041
GENERAL CABLE CO.—Wassall Plc; *Int'l*, pg. 1487
GEO- AMBIENTAL CONSULTORES CIA LTDA.—GAI Consultants, Inc.; *U.S. Private*, pg. 434
GHAFARI ASSOCIATES, INC.; *U.S. Private*, pg. 450
GIFFELS ASSOCIATES, INC.; *U.S. Private*, pg. 452
GIFFELS ASSOCIATES INC.—Giffels Associates, Inc.; *U.S. Private*, pg. 452
GIFFELS HOYEM BASSO, INC.—Giffels Associates, Inc.; *U.S. Private*, pg. 452
GILBERT/COMMONWEALTH INTERNATIONAL, INC.—Parsons Corporation; *U.S. Private*, pg. 841
GOODKIND & O'DEA, INC.—Dewberry & Davis; *U.S. Private*, pg. 329
GOTAVERKEN ENERGY DO BRASIL—Kvaerner a.s.a.; *Int'l*, pg. 771
JAMES N. GRAY CONSTRUCTION CO., INC.; *U.S. Private*, pg. 472
GRAYSTONE CORPORATION—Northern States Power Company; *U.S. Public*, pg. 1195
GREENHORNE & O'MARA, INC.; *U.S. Private*, pg. 477
GROUND WATER ASSOCIATES, INC.—Hydro Group, Inc.; *U.S. Private*, pg. 552
GROUP LOTUS LTD.—Proton; *Int'l*, pg. 1071
HBW, HOLLANDSCHE BETON EN WATERBOUW B.V.—Hollandsche Beton Groep NV; *Int'l*, pg. 630
HDR ARCHITECTURE—Bouygues; *Int'l*, pg. 206
HDR ENGINEERING, INC.—Bouygues; *Int'l*, pg. 207
HDR INC.—Bouygues; *Int'l*, pg. 206
HLW INTERNATIONAL LLP; *U.S. Private*, pg. 491
HNTB CORPORATION; *U.S. Private*, pg. 492
HNTB DESIGN & BUILD—HNTB Corporation; *U.S. Private*, pg. 492
HOH ENGINEERS, INC.—The HOH Organizations; *U.S. Private*, pg. 492
THE HOH ORGANIZATIONS; *U.S. Private*, pg. 492
HSMM FACILITIES, INC.—Hayes, Seay, Mattern & Mattern, Inc.; *U.S. Private*, pg. 513
HADEN RESEARCH & DEVELOPMENT CORPORATION—Haden Maclellan Holdings plc; *Int'l*, pg. 586
HADEN SCHWEITZER CORPORATION—Haden Maclellan Holdings plc; *Int'l*, pg. 586
HADEN TECHNICAL SERVICES CORPORATION—Haden Maclellan Holdings plc; *Int'l*, pg. 586
HALLIBURTON COMPANY; *U.S. Public*, pg. 775
HALLIBURTON ENERGY SERVICES, INC.—Halliburton Company; *U.S. Public*, pg. 776
HAMMEL, GREEN & ABRAHAMSON, INC.; *U.S. Private*, pg. 497
HAMWORTHY ENGINEERING LIMITED—Powell Duffryn PLC; *Int'l*, pg. 1065
HAMWORTHY INDUSTRAMAR LIMITED—Powell Duffryn PLC; *Int'l*, pg. 1065
HANSON AMALGAMATED INDUSTRIES—Hanson PLC; *Int'l*, pg. 592
HANSON ENGINEERS INC.; *U.S. Private*, pg. 500

HARDING LAWSON ASSOCIATES—Harding Lawson Associates Group, Inc.; *U.S. Public*, pg. 785
HARDING LAWSON ASSOCIATES GROUP, INC.; *U.S. Public*, pg. 785
HARDING LAWSON ASSOCIATES, INFRASTRUCTURE, INC.—Harding Lawson Associates Group, Inc.; *U.S. Public*, pg. 785
HARLAND BARTHOLOMEW & ASSOCIATES INC.—Parsons Corporation; *U.S. Private*, pg. 841
HARLEY ELLINGTON DESIGN; *U.S. Private*, pg. 503
HARNISCHFEGER INDUSTRIES, INC.; *U.S. Public*, pg. 788
HARRIS SPACE SYSTEMS CORP.—Harris Corporation; *U.S. Public*, pg. 791
HART CROWSER, INC.; *U.S. Private*, pg. 507
HART, FENTON & CO. LTD.—Sea Containers Ltd.; *Int'l*, pg. 1214
HARTUNG, KUHN, & CO., MASCHINENFABRIK GMBH—Fried. Krupp AG; *Int'l*, pg. 511
HARZA ENGINEERING CO.; *U.S. Private*, pg. 509
HARZA ENGINEERING COMPANY OF CALIFORNIA—Harza Engineering Co.; *U.S. Private*, pg. 509
HARZA ENVIRONMENTAL SERVICES, INC.—Harza Engineering Co.; *U.S. Private*, pg. 509
HARZA-HIDROBRASILEIRA ENGENHARIA E PROJETOS LTDA—Harza Engineering Co.; *U.S. Private*, pg. 509
HARZA NORTHEAST, INC.—Harza Engineering Co.; *U.S. Private*, pg. 509
HARZA NORTHWEST, INC.—Harza Engineering Co.; *U.S. Private*, pg. 509
HASEKO CORPORATION; *Int'l*, pg. 599
HAYES, SEAY, MATTERN & MATTERN, INC.; *U.S. Private*, pg. 513
HAZEN & SAWYER; *U.S. Private*, pg. 514
S.A. HEALY COMPANY—Fiat Auto SpA; *Int'l*, pg. 483
HEERY INTERNATIONAL, INC.; *U.S. Private*, pg. 519
HARRY O. HEFTER-ASSOCIATES, INC.—The HOH Organizations; *U.S. Private*, pg. 492
HEIN, LEHMANN AG—Arbed S.A.; *Int'l*, pg. 80
HENKELS & MCCOY, INC.; *U.S. Private*, pg. 522
HENNINGSON, DURHAM & RICHARDSON INC.—Bouygues; *Int'l*, pg. 207
HERITAGE AIR SYSTEMS, INC.—EMCOR Group, Inc.; *U.S. Public*, pg. 572
J.C. HIGGINS CORP.—EMCOR Group, Inc.; *U.S. Public*, pg. 572
HOCHTIEF AG; *Int'l*, pg. 623
HOCHTIEF LIMITED—Hochtief AG; *Int'l*, pg. 624
HOECHST MARION ROUSSEL AG—Hoechst Aktiengesellschaft; *Int'l*, pg. 624
HOFFMAN-MILLER ENGINEERS, INC.—Parsons Corporation; *U.S. Private*, pg. 842
JOHN HOLLAND ENGINEERING PTY LTD.—John Holland Group Pty. Ltd.; *Int'l*, pg. 630
JOHN HOLLAND GROUP PTY. LTD.; *Int'l*, pg. 630
HOLLANDSCHE BETON GROEP NV; *Int'l*, pg. 630
HOLSTEIN AND KAPPERT GMBH—Klockner-Werke AG; *Int'l*, pg. 737
HOOGOVENS TECHNICAL SERVICES BV—Koninklijke Hoogovens N.V.; *Int'l*, pg. 754
HOUSTON CONTRACTING COMPANY-ALASKA, LTD.—Arctic Slope Regional Corporation; *U.S. Private*, pg. 80
HOW GROUP LIMITED; *Int'l*, pg. 636
HOWE AGRA LIMITED—Agra Inc.; *Int'l*, pg. 31
HOWE (INDIA) PRIVATE LTD.—Agra Inc.; *Int'l*, pg. 31
HUDSON ENGINEERING & PROJECT MANAGEMENT SERVICES—McDermott International, Inc.; *U.S. Public*, pg. 1068
HUDSON ENGINEERING CORP.—McDermott International, Inc.; *U.S. Public*, pg. 1068
HUITT-ZOLLARS, INC.; *U.S. Private*, pg. 547
HUMPHREYS & GLASGOW EUROPE LTD.—Texas Utilities Company; *U.S. Public*, pg. 1587
HUMPHREYS MINERAL INDUSTRIES, INC.—Reunion Industries, Inc.; *U.S. Public*, pg. 1383
HYOSUNG-EBARA COMPANY LTD.—Ebara Corporation; *Int'l*, pg. 432
HYUNDAI ENGINEERING & CONSTRUCTION CO., LTD.—Hyundai Motor Company; *Int'l*, pg. 641
HYUNDAI ENGINEERING CO., LTD.—Hyundai Motor Company; *Int'l*, pg. 641
ICF KAISER ENGINEERS—ICF Kaiser International Inc.; *U.S. Public*, pg. 853
ICF KAISER ENGINEERS, INC.—ICF Kaiser International Inc.; *U.S. Public*, pg. 853
ICF KAISER INTERNATIONAL INC.; *U.S. Public*, pg. 852
IMS INGENIEURGESELLSCHAFT MBH—Philipp Holzmann AG; *Int'l*, pg. 633
ITS GROUP—Alcatel Alsthom Compagnie Generale D'Electricite; *Int'l*, pg. 53
IDEMITSU KOSAN CO., LTD.; *Int'l*, pg. 659
IFFLAND KAVANAGH WATERBURY, PLLC—Edwards and Kelcey, Inc.; *U.S. Private*, pg. 364
IMPELL CORPORATION U.K. LTD.—ABB Asea Brown Boveri (Holding) Ltd.; *Int'l*, pg. 6
IMPRESIT S.P.A.—Fiat Auto SpA; *Int'l*, pg. 481
IMTECH PROJECTS ZUIT B.V.—Internatio-Muller N.V.; *Int'l*, pg. 681
INCO LIMITED; *Int'l*, pg. 672
INDECK ENERGY SERVICES, INC.—Indeck Power Equipment Company; *U.S. Private*, pg. 559
INDUSTRA INC.—American Eco Corporation; *Int'l*, pg. 74
INDUSTRIAL COMPONENTS GROUP—BTR plc; *Int'l*, pg. 127
INDUSTRIAL CONTRACTING OF FAIRMONT, INC.—Salem Group, Inc.; *U.S. Private*, pg. 961
INDUSTRIAL RESOURCES, INC.—Salem Group, Inc.; *U.S. Private*, pg. 961
INGERSOLL MASCHINEN UND WERKZEUGE GMBH—Ingersoll International Inc.; *U.S. Private*, pg. 562
INTEGRATED SYSTEMS ANALYSTS, INC.; *U.S. Private*, pg. 566
INTEGRATED TECHNOLOGIES—Litton Industries, Inc.; *U.S. Public*, pg. 1004
INTERBETON B.V.—Hollandsche Beton Groep NV; *Int'l*, pg. 630
INTERNATIO-MULLER N.V.; *Int'l*, pg. 680
INTERNATIONAL GAS APPARATUS LIMITED—Ruhrgas Aktiengesellschaft; *Int'l*, pg. 1149
INTERNATIONAL INFRASTRUCTURE DIVISION—Morrison Knudsen Corporation; *U.S. Public*, pg. 1134
INTERNATIONAL TECHNOLOGY CORPORATION; *U.S. Public*, pg. 907
INTERSERVICIOS Y TECNOLOGIA S.A., BARCELONA—Internatio-Muller N.V.; *Int'l*, pg. 681
INTESYS TECHNOLOGIES; *U.S. Private*, pg. 574
G.I.E. IPEDEX INTERNATIONAL—Technip; *Int'l*, pg. 1361
ITOCHU INTERNATIONAL INC.—Itochu Corporation; *Int'l*, pg. 694
JGC CORPORATION; *Int'l*, pg. 697
JTC ENVIRONMENTAL CONSULTANTS, INC.—GP Strategies Corporation; *U.S. Public*, pg. 694
JACOBS APPLIED TECHNOLOGY, INC.—Jacobs Engineering Group Inc.; *U.S. Public*, pg. 921
JACOBS ENGINEERING GROUP INC.; *U.S. Public*, pg. 921
JACOBS INTERNATIONAL LIMITED, INC.—Jacobs Engineering Group Inc.; *U.S. Public*, pg. 922
JACOBS SIRRINE ENGINEERS, INC.—Jacobs Engineering Group Inc.; *U.S. Public*, pg. 921
JALAL-COSTAIN W.L.L.—Costain Group PLC; *Int'l*, pg. 337
JARDINE MATHESON HOLDINGS LIMITED; *Int'l*, pg. 703
J. JARVIS & SONS P.L.C.—Jarvis Plc; *Int'l*, pg. 705
JARVIS PLC; *Int'l*, pg. 705
C.G. JENSEN A/S—Skanska AB; *Int'l*, pg. 1261
JEUMONT-SCHNEIDER TRENFORMETEURS; *Int'l*, pg. 706
JOFFKO INTERNATIONAL; *U.S. Private*, pg. 589
JOFFKO PHILIPPINES, INC.—Joffko International; *U.S. Private*, pg. 589
JOHNSON-LOFT ENGINEERING, INC.—Tetra Laval Group; *Int'l*, pg. 1378
JONES MANAGEMENT SERVICES, INC.—Philipp Holzmann AG; *Int'l*, pg. 633
JUPITER INDUSTRIES, INC.; *U.S. Private*, pg. 602
KTI FISH; *U.S. Private*, pg. 604
KTI GAS PROCESSORS LTD.—Mannesmann A.G.; *Int'l*, pg. 837
KTI GROUP B.V.—Mannesmann A.G.; *Int'l*, pg. 837
ALBERT KAHN ASSOCIATES, INC.; *U.S. Private*, pg. 604
KAJIMA CORPORATION; *Int'l*, pg. 721
KAJIMA ENGINEERING AND CONSTRUCTION INC.—Kajima Corporation; *Int'l*, pg. 722
KAJIMA U.S.A., INC.—Kajima Corporation; *Int'l*, pg. 722
KAMYR ENGINEERING AB—Kvaerner a.s.a.; *Int'l*, pg. 771
THE M.W. KELLOGG COMPANY—Dresser Industries, Inc.; *U.S. Public*, pg. 528
KESSER—Bouygues; *Int'l*, pg. 206
L. ROBERT KIMBALL & ASSOCIATES; *U.S. Private*, pg. 619
KINETICS TECHNOLOGY INTERNATIONAL BV—Mannesmann A.G.; *Int'l*, pg. 837
KLOCKNER-WERKE AG; *Int'l*, pg. 736
KLOECKNER & CO. AG; *Int'l*, pg. 737
LESTER B. KNIGHT & ASSOCIATES, INC.; *U.S. Private*, pg. 626
KNOWSLEY SK LTD.—Internatio-Muller N.V.; *Int'l*, pg. 681
KOCKUMS ENGINEERING AB—Celsius AB; *Int'l*, pg. 277
KONICA TECHNOLOGY, INC.—Konica Corporation; *Int'l*, pg. 748
KRONA MARIN AB—Celsius AB; *Int'l*, pg. 277
KRUG INTERNATIONAL CORP.; *U.S. Public*, pg. 967
KRUPP ENTWICKLUNGSZENTRUM GMBH—Fried. Krupp AG; *Int'l*, pg. 512
KRUPP HOESCH INFORMATIONSVERARBEITUNG GMBH—Fried. Krupp AG; *Int'l*, pg. 512
KRUPP KOPPERS GMBH—Fried. Krupp AG; *Int'l*, pg. 511
KRUPP WILPUTTE CORP.—Fried. Krupp AG; *Int'l*, pg. 512
KUMAGAI GUMI CO., LTD.; *Int'l*, pg. 763
KVAERNER ARCTIC OFFSHORE A/S—Kvaerner a.s.a.; *Int'l*, pg. 769
KVAERNER A.S.A.; *Int'l*, pg. 766
KVAERNER DAVY—Kvaerner a.s.a.; *Int'l*, pg. 774
KVAERNER EARL AND WRIGHT, INC.—Kvaerner a.s.a.; *Int'l*, pg. 771
KVAERNER ENGINEERING A/S—Kvaerner a.s.a.; *Int'l*, pg. 766
KVAERNER ENGINEERING, BERGEN—Kvaerner a.s.a.; *Int'l*, pg. 766
KVAERNER ENGINEERING, MILJO—Kvaerner a.s.a.; *Int'l*, pg. 766
KVAERNER ENGINEERING SDN BHD—Kvaerner a.s.a.; *Int'l*, pg. 766
KVAERNER ENGINEERING, STAVANGER DIVISION—Kvaerner a.s.a.; *Int'l*, pg. 766
KVAERNER ENGINEERING (UK) LTD.—Kvaerner a.s.a.; *Int'l*, pg. 772
KVAERNER EUREKA A/S, TRANBY—Kvaerner a.s.a.; *Int'l*, pg. 766
KVAERNER FLORO CONSULT A.S.—Kvaerner a.s.a.; *Int'l*, pg. 769
KVAERNER H&G OFFSHORE LTD—Kvaerner a.s.a.; *Int'l*, pg. 771
KVAERNER-JOHN BROWN LTD.—Kvaerner a.s.a.; *Int'l*, pg. 773
KVAERNER KIMEK A.S.—Kvaerner a.s.a.; *Int'l*, pg. 770
KVAERNER MASA MARINE INC.—Kvaerner a.s.a.; *Int'l*, pg. 771
KVAERNER PROFESSIONAL SERVICES LIMITED—Kvaerner a.s.a.; *Int'l*, pg. 768
KVAERNER R J BROWN PTE. LTD.—Kvaerner a.s.a.; *Int'l*, pg. 767
KVAERNER R J BROWN PTY LTD—Kvaerner a.s.a.; *Int'l*, pg. 767
KVAERNER TAMTURBINE OY—Kvaerner a.s.a.; *Int'l*, pg. 772
LG & E POWER SYSTEMS INC.—LG & E Energy Corp.; *U.S. Public*, pg. 970
LAING ABU DHABI—John Laing PLC; *Int'l*, pg. 797
LAING EMIRATES—John Laing PLC; *Int'l*, pg. 797
JOHN LAING CONSTRUCTION LTD.—John Laing PLC; *Int'l*, pg. 796
JOHN LAING PLC; *Int'l*, pg. 796
LAING OMAN LLC—John Laing PLC; *Int'l*, pg. 797
LAING PROJECTS BV—John Laing PLC; *Int'l*, pg. 797
LAKE ERIE ELECTRIC, INC.; *U.S. Private*, pg. 643
ROBERT E. LAMB, INC.; *U.S. Private*, pg. 644
LATTICE SEMICONDUCTOR CORPORATION; *U.S. Public*, pg. 979
LAW ENGINEERING, INC.; *U.S. Private*, pg. 653
LIEBHERR-VERZAHNTECHNIK GMBH—Liebherr-International AG; *Int'l*, pg. 808
LIFE SCIENCES INTERNATIONAL—Day & Zimmermann, Inc.; *U.S. Private*, pg. 317
LIN & ROE COMPANY—Burns & Roe Enterprises, Inc.; *U.S. Private*, pg. 187
LINDE AG WERKSGRUPPE TVT—Linde AG; *Int'l*, pg. 811
LIVERNOIS ENGINEERING COMPANY; *U.S. Private*, pg. 672
LIVERNOIS VEHICLE CO.—Livernois Engineering Company; *U.S. Private*, pg. 672
LOCKHEED ENGINEERING & SCIENCES CO., INC.—Lockheed Martin Corporation; *U.S. Public*, pg. 1009
LOCKHEED MARTIN SPACE INFORMATION SYSTEMS—Lockheed Martin Corporation; *U.S. Public*, pg. 1009
LOCKHEED MARTIN TRAINING & TECHNICAL SERVICES—Lockheed Martin Corporation; *U.S. Public*, pg. 1009
LOCKWOOD GREENE ENGINEERS, INC.—Philipp Holzmann AG; *Int'l*, pg. 633
LOCKWOOD KESSLER & BARTLETT, INC.—Continental Can Co.; *U.S. Public*, pg. 440
LOCUS, INC.—Kaman Corporation; *U.S. Public*, pg. 942
LOGICON, INC.—Northrop Grumman Corporation; *U.S. Public*, pg. 1198
LONZA EUROPE BV—Alusuisse-Lonza Holding Ltd.; *Int'l*, pg. 69
LOS ALAMOS TECHNICAL ASSOCIATES, INC.; *U.S. Private*, pg. 676
LOTEPRO CORPORATION—Linde AG; *Int'l*, pg. 811
LOTUS CARS LTD.—Proton; *Int'l*, pg. 1071
LUCAS AEROSPACE—LucasVarity plc; *Int'l*, pg. 819
LUCASVARITY PLC—LucasVarity plc; *Int'l*, pg. 819
LUMMUS ALIREZA LTD. CO.—ABB Asea Brown Boveri (Holding) Ltd.; *Int'l*, pg. 6
THE LUMMUS CO. LTD.—ABB Asea Brown Boveri (Holding) Ltd.; *Int'l*, pg. 6
LUMMUS CO. VENEZUELA C.A.—ABB Asea Brown Boveri (Holding) Ltd.; *Int'l*, pg. 6
LUMMUS-JAPAN CO. LTD.—ABB Asea Brown Boveri (Holding) Ltd.; *Int'l*, pg. 6
LUMMUS NEDERLAND B.V.—ABB Asea Brown Boveri (Holding) Ltd.; *Int'l*, pg. 6
LUMMUS OVERSEAS CORP.—ABB Asea Brown Boveri (Holding) Ltd.; *Int'l*, pg. 6
LURGI AG—Metallgesellschaft AG; *Int'l*, pg. 861
LURGI CORPORATION—Metallgesellschaft AG; *Int'l*, pg. 861
LURGI ESPANOLA S.A.—Metallgesellschaft AG; *Int'l*, pg. 861
LUSOTECNA—Technip; *Int'l*, pg. 1361
LYSAKER REISEBYRA A.S.—Kvaerner a.s.a.; *Int'l*, pg. 769
THE M&T COMPANY—CDI Corp.; *U.S. Public*, pg. 277
MAN GHH (GREAT BRITAIN) LTD.—MAN Aktiengesellschaft; *Int'l*, pg. 824
MAN URANIT GRONAU GMBH—MAN Aktiengesellschaft; *Int'l*, pg. 825
MBT (AUSTRALIA) PTY. LTD.—Viag AG; *Int'l*, pg. 1465
MBT ENVIRONMENTAL ENGINEERING LTD.—Viag AG; *Int'l*, pg. 1465
MHIA HOUSTON TECHNICAL SERVICE BRANCH—Mitsubishi Heavy Industries Ltd.; *Int'l*, pg. 874
MK CENTENNIAL—Morrison Knudsen Corporation; *U.S. Public*, pg. 1134
MTE—Jeumont-Schneider Trenformeteurs; *Int'l*, pg. 706
MACROMERIC DIVISION—Furon Company; *U.S. Public*, pg. 689
MAERZ OFENBAU AG—RGP Holding, Inc.; *U.S. Private*, pg. 904
MAGNETIC TECHNOLOGIES CORPORATION—SPS Technologies, Inc.; *U.S. Public*, pg. 1420
MAKO CONSTRUCTION CO.—Henkels & McCoy, Inc.; *U.S. Private*, pg. 522
MANNESMANN A.G.; *Int'l*, pg. 834
MARLIM FIELD DEVELOPMENT—Petrobras - Petroleo Brasileiro S.A.; *Int'l*, pg. 1041
AC MARTIN PARTNERS; *U.S. Private*, pg. 708
MASCHINENFABRIK LORENZ GMBH—Liebherr-International AG; *Int'l*, pg. 808
MASON & HANGER CORPORATION, INC.; *U.S. Private*, pg. 711
MASON & HANGER CORPORATION, INC.—Mason & Hanger Corporation, Inc.; *U.S. Private*, pg. 711
MASON & HANGER ENGINEERING INC.—Mason & Hanger Corporation, Inc.; *U.S. Private*, pg. 711
MASTER BUILDERS N.V.—Viag AG; *Int'l*, pg. 1465
MASTER BUILDERS TECHNOLOGIES LTD.—Viag AG; *Int'l*, pg. 1465
THE MAXIMA CORPORATION; *U.S. Private*, pg. 716
MAXUM ENGINEERING ENTERPRISES LTD.—Agra Inc.; *Int'l*, pg. 31
MCDERMOTT INTERNATIONAL, INC.; *U.S. Public*, pg. 1067
MCHAL CORPORATION—Salem Group, Inc.; *U.S. Private*, pg. 961
MCLAREN/HART ENVIRONMENTAL ENGINEERING COMPANY—Viag AG; *Int'l*, pg. 1465
JOHN J. MCMULLEN ASSOCIATES—Carpenter Technology Corporation; *U.S. Public*, pg. 308
MECANARBED DOMMELDANGE S.A.R.L.—Arbed S.A.; *Int'l*, pg. 80
MEDLINE INDUSTRIES, INC.; *U.S. Private*, pg. 728

MEIJI ENGINEERING LTD—Meiji Seika Kaisha, Ltd.; *Int'l*, pg. 855
MERIDIONALE DE TRAVAUX—Bouygues; *Int'l*, pg. 206
METCALF & EDDY COMPANIES INC.—Air & Water Technologies Corporation; *U.S. Public*, pg. 29
MI-JACK PRODUCTS, INC.; *U.S. Private*, pg. 740
MILLIPORE INTERTECH—Millipore Corporation; *U.S. Public*, pg. 1113
MINCO INTERNATIONAL AB—Trelleborg AB; *Int'l*, pg. 1423
MINITEL USA—France Telecom; *Int'l*, pg. 504
MISTRAL TRAVAUX—Bouygues; *Int'l*, pg. 206
MITSUBISHI CORPORATION; *Int'l*, pg. 871
MITSUI CONSTRUCTION CO., LTD.—Mitsui & Co., Ltd.; *Int'l*, pg. 877
MITSUI CONSULTANTS CO., LTD.—Mitsui & Co., Ltd.; *Int'l*, pg. 877
MITSUI OCEAN DEVELOPMENT & ENGINEERING CO., LTD.—Mitsui & Co., Ltd.; *Int'l*, pg. 878
MODERN ENGINEERING, INC.—CDI Corp.; *U.S. Public*, pg. 277
MODERN PROTOTYPE COMPANY—CDI Corp.; *U.S. Public*, pg. 277
MONA INDUSTRIES, INC.; *U.S. Private*, pg. 756
MONTGOMERY WATSON; *U.S. Private*, pg. 759
MONTGOMERY WATSON—Montgomery Watson; *U.S. Private*, pg. 759
MORRISON KNUDSEN CORPORATION; *U.S. Public*, pg. 1133
MOUNTAINEER RESOURCES, INC.—Salem Group, Inc.; *U.S. Private*, pg. 961
MUNITIONS TECHNOLOGY DIVISION—Day & Zimmermann, Inc.; *U.S. Private*, pg. 317
MYTTON'S LIMITED—Bristile Clay Tiles, Ltd.; *Int'l*, pg. 216
NCC AB; *Int'l*, pg. 898
NCC CIVIL ENGINEERING—NCC AB; *Int'l*, pg. 899
NCC ESKILSTUNA—NCC AB; *Int'l*, pg. 899
NKK AMERICA INC.—NKK Corporation; *Int'l*, pg. 902
NKK EUROPE LTD.-DUSSELDORF OFFICE—NKK Corporation; *Int'l*, pg. 903
NKK EUROPE LTD.-LONDON OFFICE—NKK Corporation; *Int'l*, pg. 903
NKK NETHERLANDS B.V.-ROTTERDAM OFFICE—NKK Corporation; *Int'l*, pg. 903
NRG ENERGY, INC.—Northern States Power Company; *U.S. Public*, pg. 1195
NTH CONSULTANTS, LTD.; *U.S. Private*, pg. 772
NTS DETROIT—National Technical Systems, Inc.; *U.S. Public*, pg. 1161
NTS ENGINEERING—National Technical Systems, Inc.; *U.S. Public*, pg. 1161
NACCO INDUSTRIES, INC.; *U.S. Public*, pg. 1149
NAMKWANG ENGINEERING & CONSTRUCTION CO., LTD.—Ssangyong Business Group; *Int'l*, pg. 1291
NATIONAL ENERGY PRODUCTION CORPORATION—Zurn Industries, Inc.; *U.S. Public*, pg. 1795
NATIONAL TECHNICAL SYSTEMS, INC.; *U.S. Public*, pg. 1161
NESCO, INC.; *U.S. Private*, pg. 791
NESMA-COSTAIN PROCESS CO. LIMITED—Costain Group PLC; *Int'l*, pg. 337
NETTENBOUW B.V., AMERSFOORT—Internatio-Muller N.V.; *Int'l*, pg. 681
NEW HUNTER ENGINEERING—FKI Plc; *Int'l*, pg. 474
NEYRPIC FRAMATOME MECANIQUE (NFM)—Framatome SA; *Int'l*, pg. 503
NICHOLS RESEARCH CORPORATION; *U.S. Public*, pg. 1182
NISSAN DESIGN INTERNATIONAL, INC.—Nissan Motor Co., Ltd.; *Int'l*, pg. 944
NOELL GMBH—Preussag AG; *Int'l*, pg. 1069
NOFSINGER, INC.—Burns & McDonnell Engineers-Architects-Consultants; *U.S. Private*, pg. 187
NORMANDEAU ASSOCIATES, INC.—Thermo Electron Corporation; *U.S. Public*, pg. 1594
NORMANDEAU ENGINEERS INC.—Thermo Electron Corporation; *U.S. Public*, pg. 1593
NORPAC—Bouygues; *Int'l*, pg. 206
THE NORTH AMERICAN MANUFACTURING CO.; *U.S. Private*, pg. 803
NUCLEAR ENERGY SERVICES, INC.—American Financial Group; *U.S. Public*, pg. 75
NUEVO CAMINO CONSTRUCTORS CO.—Zurn Industries, Inc.; *U.S. Public*, pg. 1795
EDMUND NUTTALL LTD.—Hollandsche Beton Groep NV; *Int'l*, pg. 630
OEL, LTD.—Elcor Corporation; *U.S. Public*, pg. 568
OHM CORPORATION; *U.S. Public*, pg. 1207
OCEANEERING A/S—Oceaneering International, Inc.; *U.S. Public*, pg. 1211
OCEANEERING AUSTRALIA PTY. LTD.—Brambles Industries Limited; *Int'l*, pg. 211
OCEANEERING AUSTRALIA PTY. LTD.—Oceaneering International, Inc.; *U.S. Public*, pg. 1211
OCEANEERING INTERNATIONAL, INC.; *U.S. Public*, pg. 1211
OCEANEERING INTERVENTION ENGINEERING—Oceaneering International, Inc.; *U.S. Public*, pg. 1211
OCEANEERING MULTIFLEX—Oceaneering International, Inc.; *U.S. Public*, pg. 1211
OCEANEERING PRODUCTION SYSTEMS—Oceaneering International, Inc.; *U.S. Public*, pg. 1211
OCEANEERING SPACE SYSTEMS—Oceaneering International, Inc.; *U.S. Public*, pg. 1211
OCEANEERING TECHNOLOGIES—Oceaneering International, Inc.; *U.S. Public*, pg. 1211
OLD DOMINION SYSTEMS OF MARYLAND—Micrologic Corporation; *U.S. Public*, pg. 1105
OMEGA ENVIRONMENTAL SERVICES—Omega Environmental Inc.; *U.S. Public*, pg. 1222
OPUS CORP.; *U.S. Private*, pg. 818
ORENDA (CANADA)—Hawker Siddeley Canada Inc.; *Int'l*, pg. 604
ORR-SCHELEN-MAYERON & ASSOC., INC.—Publicker Industries Inc.; *U.S. Public*, pg. 1341
OUTER DRIVE MANUFACTURING TECHNICAL CENTER—Chrysler Corporation; *U.S. Public*, pg. 353
OUTOKUMPU ENGINEERING CONTRACTORS OY—Outokumpu Oyj; *Int'l*, pg. 1017
OUTOKUMPU ENGINEERING SERVICES OY—Outokumpu Oyj; *Int'l*, pg. 1017
OYO CORPORATION; *Int'l*, pg. 1019
P AND G SPECIALTY INSURANCE SERVICES—EQE International; *U.S. Private*, pg. 354
P&O (NEW ZEALAND) LTD.—The Peninsular and Oriental Steam Navigation Company; *Int'l*, pg. 1035
PCL-BRAUN-SIMONS LTD.—Kuwait Petroleum Corporation; *Int'l*, pg. 765
PRC ENVIRONMENTAL MANAGEMENT, INC.—Tetra Tech, Inc.; *U.S. Public*, pg. 1582
THE PACE CONSULTANTS, INC.—Jacobs Engineering Group Inc.; *U.S. Public*, pg. 921
PACIFICA SERVICES, INC.; *U.S. Private*, pg. 832
PARSONS BRINCKERHOFF INC.; *U.S. Private*, pg. 841
PARSONS BRINCKERHOFF LTD.—Parsons Brinckerhoff Inc.; *U.S. Private*, pg. 841
PARSONS ENGINEERING SCIENCE, INC.—Parsons Corporation; *U.S. Private*, pg. 842
PARSONS GROUP INTERNATIONAL LIMITED—Parsons Corporation; *U.S. Private*, pg. 842
PARSONS INFRASTRUCTURE & TECHNOLOGY GROUP INC.—Parsons Corporation; *U.S. Private*, pg. 842
PARSONS INTERNATIONAL LTD.—Parsons Corporation; *U.S. Private*, pg. 842
PARSONS OVERSEAS CO. CHILE LIMITADA—Parsons Corporation; *U.S. Private*, pg. 842
PARSONS PROCESS GROUP INC.—Parsons Corporation; *U.S. Private*, pg. 842
PASCO U.S.A., INC.—Pasco Corporation; *Int'l*, pg. 1024
PEABODY ENGINEERING CORP.—Powell Duffryn PLC; *Int'l*, pg. 1065
PEGASUS ENGINEERING LTD.—Jacobs Engineering Group Inc.; *U.S. Public*, pg. 922
PERPETUAL MACHINE—Textile Rubber & Chemical Company; *U.S. Private*, pg. 1079
PERTUY—Bouygues; *Int'l*, pg. 206
PETRO STAR INC.—Arctic Slope Regional Corporation; *U.S. Private*, pg. 80
PHELPS DODGE INTL. CORP.—Phelps Dodge Corporation; *U.S. Public*, pg. 1286
PHILIPS DISPLAY COMPONENTS—Philips Electronics N.V.; *Int'l*, pg. 1055
PICO DESIGN, INC.—Motorola, Inc.; *U.S. Public*, pg. 1138
PIEBURG AG—Rheinmetall Group; *Int'l*, pg. 1108
PILLAR ENGINEERING LTD.—Caradon Plc; *Int'l*, pg. 267
MALCOLM PIRNIE, INC.; *U.S. Private*, pg. 867
POLAROID CORP.- CAMERA DIVISION—Polaroid Corporation; *U.S. Public*, pg. 1313
POST BUCKLEY SCHUH & JERNIGAN—The PBS&J Corporation; *U.S. Private*, pg. 826
POWELL DUFFRYN PLC; *Int'l*, pg. 1065
POWELL DUFFRYN STANDARD LIMITED—Powell Duffryn PLC; *Int'l*, pg. 1065
POWER BUSINESS—Black & Veatch; *U.S. Private*, pg. 146
PRECISION CONTROLS DIVISION—COMSAT Corporation; *U.S. Public*, pg. 424
PRECISION POWER, INC.—United Illuminating Company; *U.S. Public*, pg. 1678
WILLIAM PRESS ENGINEERING SERVICES (NZ) LTD.—AMEC Plc; *Int'l*, pg. 16
PREUSSAG ANLAGENBAU GMBH—Preussag AG; *Int'l*, pg. 1069
PRIMARK CORPORATION; *U.S. Public*, pg. 1325
PROCESS & INDUSTRIAL DIVISION—Day & Zimmermann, Inc.; *U.S. Private*, pg. 317
PROCESS SYSTEMS INC.; *U.S. Private*, pg. 888
PRODUCTION MANAGEMENT COMPANIES, INC.; *U.S. Private*, pg. 888
PROMETHEE—Jeumont-Schneider Trenformeteurs; *Int'l*, pg. 706
PROPAK SYSTEMS LTD.; *Int'l*, pg. 1071
PROYEPARSONS, C.A.—Parsons Corporation; *U.S. Private*, pg. 842
PSOMAS & ASSOCIATES; *U.S. Private*, pg. 893
PTI ENVIRONMENTAL—The Failure Group, Inc.; *U.S. Public*, pg. 609
PUBLIC SERVICE ENTERPRISE GROUP INCORPORATED; *U.S. Public*, pg. 1340
QST ENVIRONMENTAL INC.—CILCORP Inc.; *U.S. Public*, pg. 367
QUALITY SYSTEMS INC.—Tracor, Inc.; *U.S. Public*, pg. 1627
QUANTA SYSTEMS CORPORATION—CompuDyne Corporation; *U.S. Public*, pg. 420
QUEMENEUR—Bouygues; *Int'l*, pg. 206
R&B FALCON CORPORATION; *U.S. Public*, pg. 1354
R&H AUSTRALIA PTY. LTD.—Internatio-Muller N.V.; *Int'l*, pg. 681
RJO ENTERPRISES, INC.; *U.S. Private*, pg. 904
RMT, INC.—WPL Holdings, Inc.; *U.S. Public*, pg. 1728
RTKL ASSOCIATES INC.; *U.S. Private*, pg. 906
THE RTZ CORPORATION PLC—Rio Tinto PLC; *Int'l*, pg. 1118
RADIAN INTERNATIONAL LLC—The Dow Chemical Company; *U.S. Public*, pg. 522
RAYTECH CORPORATION; *U.S. Public*, pg. 1363
RAYTHEON ENGINEERS & CONSTRUCTORS INTERNATIONAL, INC.—Raytheon Company; *U.S. Public*, pg. 1366
RAYTHEON ENGINEERS & CONSTRUCTORS INTERNATIONAL—Raytheon Company; *U.S. Public*, pg. 1366
RAYTHEON ENVIRONMENTAL SERVICES COMPANY—Raytheon Company; *U.S. Public*, pg. 1366
RAYTHEON INFRASTRUCTURE INCORPORATED—Raytheon Company; *U.S. Public*, pg. 1366
READING & BATES CORPORATION—R&B Falcon Corporation; *U.S. Public*, pg. 1354
READING & BATES DEVELOPMENT CO.—R&B Falcon Corporation; *U.S. Public*, pg. 1354
REFRACTORIES CONSULTING & ENGINEERING GMBH—RGP Holding, Inc.; *U.S. Private*, pg. 904
RENCO GROUP; *U.S. Private*, pg. 922
RENTENBACH ENGINEERING COMPANY; *U.S. Private*, pg. 923
RESEARCH-COTTRELL—Air & Water Technologies Corporation; *U.S. Public*, pg. 29
REUTER MANUFACTURING INC.; *U.S. Public*, pg. 1383
REXAM MEDICAL PACKAGING—Rexam PLC; *Int'l*, pg. 1106
REXEL ENGINEERING LTD.—Fortune Brands, Inc.; *U.S. Public*, pg. 675
ROBERTS & SCHAEFER CO.—Elgin National Industries, Inc.; *U.S. Private*, pg. 371
ROBERTS & SCHAEFER COMPANY-SALT LAKE CITY—Elgin National Industries, Inc.; *U.S. Private*, pg. 371
ROCKTON ASSOCIATES, INCORPORATED—Stone & Webster, Incorporated; *U.S. Public*, pg. 1519
ROCKTON TECHNICAL SERVICES CORPORATION—Stone & Webster, Incorporated; *U.S. Public*, pg. 1519
ROSSER INTERNATIONAL, INC.; *U.S. Private*, pg. 946
ROXON OY—Tamrock Corp.; *Int'l*, pg. 1353
RUST ENVIRONMENT & INFRASTRUCTURE—CBS Corporation; *U.S. Public*, pg. 273
RUST ENVIRONMENT & INFRASTRUCTURE, INC.—Waste Management, Inc.; *U.S. Public*, pg. 1745
RUST INTERNATIONAL INC.—Raytheon Company; *U.S. Public*, pg. 1366
S & C ELECTRIC COMPANY; *U.S. Private*, pg. 954
SAIC CANADA—Science Applications International Corp.; *U.S. Private*, pg. 976
SAIC COMMERCIAL ENTERPRISES, INC.—Science Applications International Corp.; *U.S. Private*, pg. 976
SAIC ENGINEERING, INC.—Science Applications International Corp.; *U.S. Private*, pg. 976
SAIC UK LIMITED—Science Applications International Corp.; *U.S. Private*, pg. 976
SCS ENGINEERS; *U.S. Private*, pg. 955
SDRC AG—Structural Dynamics Research Corp.; *U.S. Public*, pg. 1525
SDRC BELGIUM N.V./S.A.—Structural Dynamics Research Corp.; *U.S. Public*, pg. 1525
SDRC ENGINEERING SERVICES DIVISION, INC.—Structural Dynamics Research Corp.; *U.S. Public*, pg. 1525
SDRC ENGINEERING SERVICES INC.—Structural Dynamics Research Corp.; *U.S. Public*, pg. 1525
SDRC ESPANA, S.A.—Structural Dynamics Research Corp.; *U.S. Public*, pg. 1525
SDRC FRANCE S.A.—Structural Dynamics Research Corp.; *U.S. Public*, pg. 1525
SDRC ITALIA, SRL.—Structural Dynamics Research Corp.; *U.S. Public*, pg. 1525
SDRC JAPAN K.K.—Structural Dynamics Research Corp.; *U.S. Public*, pg. 1525
SDRC KOREA LIMITED—Structural Dynamics Research Corp.; *U.S. Public*, pg. 1525
SDRC NEDERLAND B.V.—Structural Dynamics Research Corp.; *U.S. Public*, pg. 1525
SDRC SINGAPORE PTE. LTD.—Structural Dynamics Research Corp.; *U.S. Public*, pg. 1525
SDRC SVENSKA AB—Structural Dynamics Research Corp.; *U.S. Public*, pg. 1525
SDRC U.K. LIMITED—Structural Dynamics Research Corp.; *U.S. Public*, pg. 1525
SFA, INC.; *U.S. Private*, pg. 956
SIELTE ENGINEERING S.P.A.—Telefonaktiebolaget LM Ericsson; *Int'l*, pg. 1370
SKF ENGINEERING PRODUCTS LIMITED—AB SKF; *Int'l*, pg. 1158
SKF NOVA AB—AB SKF; *Int'l*, pg. 1157
SMC ENVIRONMENTAL SERVICES GROUP INC.—Versar Inc.; *U.S. Public*, pg. 1717
SMC MCEVER INC.—Versar Inc.; *U.S. Public*, pg. 1717
SNC-LAVALIN GROUP INC.; *Int'l*, pg. 1161
STER—SNC-Lavalin Group Inc.; *Int'l*, pg. 1163
STS SERVICES INC.—CDI Corp.; *U.S. Public*, pg. 277
STV CONSTRUCTION SERVICES—STV Group, Inc.; *U.S. Public*, pg. 1421
STV ENVIRONMENTAL—STV Group, Inc.; *U.S. Public*, pg. 1421
STV GROUP, INC.; *U.S. Public*, pg. 1421
STV INCORPORATED—STV Group, Inc.; *U.S. Public*, pg. 1421
SAARBERG-INTERPLAN GESELLSCHAFT FUER ROHSTOFF-, ENERGIE-UND INGENIEURTECHNIK MBH—Saarbergwerke Aktiengesellschaft; *Int'l*, pg. 1167
SADCO LTD.—Joffko International; *U.S. Private*, pg. 589
SAIPEM S.P.A.—ENI S.p.A.; *Int'l*, pg. 428
SALEM CORPORATION—Salem Group, Inc.; *U.S. Private*, pg. 961
SALEM ELECTRIC COMPANY—Salem Group, Inc.; *U.S. Private*, pg. 961
SALEM ERECTORS—Salem Group, Inc.; *U.S. Private*, pg. 961
SALEM FURNACE CO.—Salem Group, Inc.; *U.S. Private*, pg. 961
SALZGITTER-LUMMUS G.M.B.H.—ABB Asea Brown Boveri (Holding) Ltd.; *Int'l*, pg. 6
SANDWELL INC.; *Int'l*, pg. 1188
SANTOS BASIN DEVELOPMENT—Petrobras - Petroleo Brasileiro S.A.; *Int'l*, pg. 1041
SARGENT & LUNDY; *U.S. Private*, pg. 965
SCHEU & WIRTH AG—Philipp Holzmann AG; *Int'l*, pg. 633
SCHLUMBERGER LIMITED; *U.S. Public*, pg. 1439
SCHNURPFEIL BOHR-GMBH—Dyckerhoff & Widmann AG; *Int'l*, pg. 423
SCIENCE & ENGINEERING ASSOCIATES; *U.S. Private*, pg. 975

SCIENCE MANAGEMENT CORPORATION—Versar Inc.; U.S. Public, pg. 1717
SCIENTIFIC DESIGN CO., INC.—Linde AG; Int'l, pg. 811
SCORIA INCORPORATED—Northern States Power Company; U.S. Public, pg. 1195
SEACORE LIMITED—Agra Inc.; Int'l, pg. 31
SELAS FLUID PROCESSING CORP.—Linde AG; Int'l, pg. 811
SEPROB—Bouygues; Int'l, pg. 207
SETAO—Bouygues; Int'l, pg. 207
SEVENSON ENVIRONMENTAL SERVICES, INC.; U.S. Public, pg. 1462
SHANNON & WILSON, INC.; U.S. Private, pg. 989
SHARP MICROELECTRONICS TECHNOLOGY, INC.—Sharp Corporation; Int'l, pg. 1229
SHIMIZU CORPORATION; Int'l, pg. 1233
SHIN NIPPON AIR CONDITIONING ENGINEERING CO., LTD.—Mitsui & Co., Ltd.; Int'l, pg. 877
SHIP ANALYTICS, INC.; U.S. Private, pg. 994
SHOBISHA CO., LTD.—Matsuya Company Ltd.; Int'l, pg. 848
SIEBE PLC; Int'l, pg. 1240
SIME DARBY BERHAD MALAYSIA REGION—Sime Darby Berhad; Int'l, pg. 1250
SIMON ENGINEERING PLC; Int'l, pg. 1251
SIMON UNITED STATES HOLDINGS INC.—Simon Engineering plc; Int'l, pg. 1252
SIMPSON GUMPERTZ & HEGER INC.; U.S. Private, pg. 1002
SISSING ELEKTROTECHNIEK B.V.—Royal Begemann Group; Int'l, pg. 1133
SITA—Lyonnaise des Eaux S.A.; Int'l, pg. 824
SKANSKA OY—Skanska AB; Int'l, pg. 1261
SKANSKA TEKNIK AB—Skanska AB; Int'l, pg. 1261
SMITH ENVIRONMENTAL TECHNOLOGIES CORP.—Smith Environmental Technologies Corp.; U.S. Public, pg. 1478
SMITH HINCHMAN GRYLLS ASSOCIATES, INC.—SmithGroup, Inc.; U.S. Private, pg. 1010
SMITHGROUP, INC.; U.S. Private, pg. 1010
SOCIETE GENERALE POUR LES TECHNIQUES NOUVELLES S.A. (SGN)—Technip; Int'l, pg. 1361
SOCIETE INTERNATIONALE D'INGENIERIE ET DE MAINTENANCE S.A. (2IM)—Technip; Int'l, pg. 1361
SOGELERG—Alcatel Alsthom Compagnie Generale D'Electricite; Int'l, pg. 54
SOGREAH—Alcatel Alsthom Compagnie Generale D'Electricite; Int'l, pg. 54
SOLECTRON CORPORATION; U.S. Public, pg. 1483
SOLUS OCEANEERING (MALAYSIA) SDN. BHD.—Oceaneering International, Inc.; U.S. Public, pg. 1211
SORDONI SKANSKA CONSTRUCTION CO.—Skanska AB; Int'l, pg. 1261
SOUTHERN COMPANY SERVICES, INC.—Southern Company; U.S. Public, pg. 1490
SOUTHERN INSTRUMENTS, INC.—Jacobs Engineering Group Inc.; U.S. Public, pg. 921
SPARROWS INDUSTRIAL SERVICES, LTD.—Sophus Berendsen A/S; Int'l, pg. 1285
SPEC HOLDINGS INC.; U.S. Private, pg. 1022
SPECTRUM CONTROL, INC.; U.S. Public, pg. 1497
SPERRY RAIL SERVICES—American Financial Group; U.S. Public, pg. 75
SPIE BATIGNOLLES—AMEC Plc; Int'l, pg. 16
SPRINGBORN TESTING & RESEARCH, INC.; U.S. Private, pg. 1027
SSANGYONG BUSINESS GROUP; Int'l, pg. 1291
SSANGYONG ENGINEERING CO., LTD.—Ssangyong Business Group; Int'l, pg. 1292
THE STANLEY CONSULTANTS GROUP; U.S. Private, pg. 1032
STEINMAN, BOYNTON, GRONQUIST & BIRDSALL INC.—Parsons Corporation; U.S. Private, pg. 842
L. & C. STEINMUELLER GMBH—Philipp Holzmann AG; Int'l, pg. 633
STONE & WEBSTER, INCORPORATED; U.S. Public, pg. 1519
STORA PROJECT—NCC AB; Int'l, pg. 899
STRUCTURAL DYNAMICS RESEARCH CORP.; U.S. Public, pg. 1525
SUDDEUTSCHE BRENNSTOFFHANDELSGESELLSCHAFT MBH—Saarbergwerke Aktiengesellschaft; Int'l, pg. 1167
SUMITOMO CHEMICAL ENGINEERING CO., LTD.—Sumitomo Chemical Company, Ltd.; Int'l, pg. 1311
SUMITOMO METAL INDUSTRIES, LTD.; Int'l, pg. 1315
SUMITOMO METAL MINING CO., LTD.; Int'l, pg. 1316
SVERDRUP CORPORATION; U.S. Private, pg. 1057
SVERDRUP ENVIRONMENTAL INC.—Sverdrup Corporation; U.S. Private, pg. 1057
SVERDRUP TECHNOLOGY, INC.—Sverdrup Corporation; U.S. Private, pg. 1057
THE SWISSAIR GROUP; Int'l, pg. 1333
SYSTRA-SOFRETU-SOFRERAIL—SNCF; Int'l, pg. 1165
TAD RESOURCES INTERNATIONAL, INC.; U.S. Private, pg. 1062
TD ELECTRONICS, INC.—Twin Disc, Incorporated; U.S. Public, pg. 1646
TECI—Technip; Int'l, pg. 1361
TI GROUP PLC; Int'l, pg. 1337
TRC COMPANIES, INC.; U.S. Public, pg. 1557
TRC ENVIRONMENTAL SOLUTIONS, INC.—TRC Companies, Inc.; U.S. Public, pg. 1558
TRC MARIAH ASSOCIATES, INC.—TRC Companies, Inc.; U.S. Public, pg. 1558
TAISEI AMERICA CORP.—Taisei Corporation; Int'l, pg. 1347
TAISEI CORPORATION; Int'l, pg. 1347
TALTRON B.V., OMMEN—Maxxim Medical, Inc.; U.S. Public, pg. 1063
TARMAC CANADA INC.—Tarmac plc; Int'l, pg. 1355
TARMAC CONSTRUCTION INTL.—Tarmac plc; Int'l, pg. 1355
TAUGBOL & OVERLAND A/S—Aker Raj Asa; Int'l, pg. 42
TAYLOR WOODROW CONSTRUCTION LIMITED—Taylor Woodrow plc; Int'l, pg. 1358
TAYLOR WOODROW MANAGEMENT & ENGINEERING LIMITED—Taylor Woodrow plc; Int'l, pg. 1358
TAYLOR WOODROW OF GHANA LIMITED—Taylor Woodrow plc; Int'l, pg. 1360
TAYLOR WOODROW OF NIGERIA LIMITED—Taylor Woodrow plc; Int'l, pg. 1360
TAYLOR WOODROW PLC; Int'l, pg. 1358
TAYLOR WOODROW SERVICES LTD.—Taylor Woodrow plc; Int'l, pg. 1359
TAYMECH LIMITED—Taylor Woodrow plc; Int'l, pg. 1359
TAYMECH (U.S.A) INC.—Taylor Woodrow plc; Int'l, pg. 1359
TAYSEC CONSTRUCTION LTD.—Taylor Woodrow plc; Int'l, pg. 1360
TAYWOOD ENERGY SERVICES INC.—Taylor Woodrow plc; Int'l, pg. 1359
TAYWOOD ENGINEERING LTD.—Taylor Woodrow plc; Int'l, pg. 1359
TEAM, INC.; U.S. Public, pg. 1562
TEAM INDUSTRIAL SERVICES, INC.—Team, Inc.; U.S. Public, pg. 1562
TEAMWORK DEVELOPMENTS LIMITED—Taylor Woodrow plc; Int'l, pg. 1360
TEBODIN BV CONSULTANTS & ENGINEERS—Hollandsche Beton Groep NV; Int'l, pg. 630
TECH-ATLAN—Technip; Int'l, pg. 1360
TECHNICAL SERVICES GROUP—Namanco LLC; U.S. Private, pg. 773
TECHNIP; Int'l, pg. 1360
TECHNIP ANLAGENBAU GMBH—Technip; Int'l, pg. 1361
TECHNIP CLE—Technip; Int'l, pg. 1360
TECHNIP CLEPLAN—Technip; Int'l, pg. 1361
TECHNIP INTERNATIONAL AG—Technip; Int'l, pg. 1361
TECHNIP UK LTD.—Technip; Int'l, pg. 1361
TECMINEMET—Imetal; Int'l, pg. 662
TECNOLOGIE PROGETTI LAVORI SPA—Technip; Int'l, pg. 1361
TECPLANT INGEST—Technip; Int'l, pg. 1361
TEKKEN CORPORATION; Int'l, pg. 1362
TELEGLOBE INTERNATIONAL INC.—Teleglobe, Inc.; Int'l, pg. 1373
TELEGLOBE MARINE INC.—Teleglobe, Inc.; Int'l, pg. 1373
TELESYSTEMES—France Telecom; Int'l, pg. 503
TETRA-PAK PROCESSING SYSTEMS—Tetra Laval Group; Int'l, pg. 1379
TETRA TECH NUS, INC.—Tetra Tech, Inc.; U.S. Public, pg. 1582
TETRA TECHNOLOGIES; U.S. Public, pg. 1582
TEXAS ELECTRIC COOPERATIVES, INC.; U.S. Private, pg. 1078
THERMATOME—Jeumont-Schneider Trenformeteurs; Int'l, pg. 706
THERMO CONSULTING ENGINEERS INC.—Thermo Electron Corporation; U.S. Public, pg. 1594
THERMO ELECTRON CORPORATION; U.S. Public, pg. 1591
I.C. THOMASSON ASSOCIATES, INC.; U.S. Private, pg. 1083
THOMPSON-STARRETT CONSTRUCTION COMPANY, INC.—Elgin National Industries, Inc.; U.S. Private, pg. 371
THREE QUAYS MARINE SERVICES LTD.—The Peninsular and Oriental Steam Navigation Company; Int'l, pg. 1035
TIPIEL COLOMBIA—Technip; Int'l, pg. 1361
THE TITAN CORPORATION; U.S. Public, pg. 1618
TITAN SYSTEMS, INC.—The Titan Corporation; U.S. Public, pg. 1618
TODD PACIFIC SHIPYARDS CORP.; U.S. Public, pg. 1619
TOLK, INC.—Dewberry & Davis; U.S. Private, pg. 329
TOPLIS PAINTERS LIMITED—Costain Group PLC; Int'l, pg. 337
TORCHINSKY ENGINEERING LTD—Agra Inc.; Int'l, pg. 31
TOYO ENGINEERING CORP.—Mitsui & Co., Ltd.; Int'l, pg. 878
TOYOTA CENTRAL RESEARCH & DEVELOPMENT LABORATORIES, INC.—Toyota Motor Corporation; Int'l, pg. 1412
TOYOTA TECHNICAL CENTER, U.S.A., INC.—Toyota Motor Corporation; Int'l, pg. 1413
TRACOR AEROSPACE ELECTRONICS SYSTEMS, INC.—Tracor, Inc.; U.S. Public, pg. 1627
TRACOR AEROSPACE, INC.—Tracor, Inc.; U.S. Public, pg. 1627
TRACOR, INC.; U.S. Public, pg. 1627
TRACTEBEL; Int'l, pg. 1414
TRAFALGAR HOUSE INC.—Kvaerner a.s.a.; Int'l, pg. 774
TRAFALGAR HOUSE PLC—Kvaerner a.s.a.; Int'l, pg. 772
TRANSDYN CONTROLS, INC.—Powell Industries, Inc.; U.S. Public, pg. 1319
TRAUTMAN & SHREVE, INC.—EMCOR Group, Inc.; U.S. Public, pg. 572
UIP ENGINEERED PRODUCTS, INC.—Pettibone Corporation; U.S. Private, pg. 860
UM ENGINEERING—Union Miniere; Int'l, pg. 1442
UOP—AlliedSignal Inc.; U.S. Public, pg. 52
URS CORPORATION; U.S. Public, pg. 1655
URS GREINER ENGINEERING, INC.—URS Corporation; U.S. Public, pg. 1658
URS GREINER, INC.—URS Corporation; U.S. Public, pg. 1658
URS GREINER, INC. MID-ATLANTIC—URS Corporation; U.S. Public, pg. 1659
URS GREINER, INC. SOUTHWEST—URS Corporation; U.S. Public, pg. 1659
URS GREINER INTERNATIONAL LTD.—URS Corporation; U.S. Public, pg. 1659
USX ENGINEERS & CONSULTANTS, INC.—USX Corporation; U.S. Public, pg. 1662
ULTRASYSTEMS DEFENSE—Northrop Grumman Corporation; U.S. Public, pg. 1199
UNDERGROUND TECHNOLOGIES—Thomas & Betts Corporation; U.S. Public, pg. 1598
UNITED AUSTRALIAN AUTOMOTIVE INDUSTRIES LTD.—General Motors Corporation; U.S. Public, pg. 725
UTILITY ENGINEERING CORPORATION—New Century Energies, Inc.; U.S. Public, pg. 1170
VALTEK/AUSTRALIA—Flowserve Corporation; U.S. Public, pg. 659
VALUE ENGINEERING & MANAGEMENT, INC.—Edwards and Kelcey, Inc.; U.S. Private, pg. 365
VAN BUUREN-VAN SWAAY MARINE AIRCONDITIONING, ZOETERMEER—Internatio-Muller N.V.; Int'l, pg. 681
VAN SWAAY INTERNATIONAL CONTRACTING B.V.—Internatio-Muller N.V.; Int'l, pg. 681
VARA INTERNATONAL—Calgon Carbon Corporation; U.S. Public, pg. 293
VEDA INCORPORATED—Veridian; U.S. Private, pg. 1136
VENTILEX MILIEUTECHNIEK B.V., HEERDE—Internatio-Muller N.V.; Int'l, pg. 681
VENTURE ENGINEERING INC.—Gradco Systems, Inc.; U.S. Public, pg. 757
VEREBUS ENGINEERING B.V., THE HAGUE—Internatio-Muller N.V.; Int'l, pg. 680
VERIDIAN; U.S. Private, pg. 1136
VERSATECH ENGINEERING—Mason & Hanger Corporation, Inc.; U.S. Private, pg. 712
VICKERS PLC; Int'l, pg. 1466
VICKERS PROPERTIES LIMITED—Vickers PLC; Int'l, pg. 1467
VIEW ENGINEERING—General Motors Corporation; U.S. Public, pg. 721
VINLAND INDUSTRIES LTD.—Kvaerner a.s.a.; Int'l, pg. 770
VITRO SERVICES CORPORATION—Tracor, Inc.; U.S. Public, pg. 1627
VOEST-ALPINE SERVICES AND TECHNOLOGIES CORP.-MATERIAL HANDLING EQUIPMENT—Voest-Alpine Stahl AG; Int'l, pg. 1471
J.M. VOITH AG—J.M. Voith, GmbH; Int'l, pg. 1473
J.M. VOITH, GMBH; Int'l, pg. 1472
VOITH S.A. MAQUINAS E EQUIPAMENTOS—J.M. Voith, GmbH; Int'l, pg. 1473
VOITH TURBO GMBH & CO. KG—J.M. Voith, GmbH; Int'l, pg. 1473
VON ROLL AG DEPARTEMENT UMWELTTECHNIK—Von Roll AG; Int'l, pg. 1480
VON ROLL, INC.—Von Roll AG; Int'l, pg. 1480
VON ROLL MACHINERY & HANDLING SYSTEMS—Von Roll AG; Int'l, pg. 1480
WCI UMWELTTECHNIK GMBH FRANKFURT—URS Corporation; U.S. Public, pg. 1657
WALK, HAYDEL & ASSOCIATES, INC.—Hochtief AG; Int'l, pg. 624
WALKER GROUP/CNI INC.—WPP Group plc; Int'l, pg. 1483
WASTE STREAM TECHNOLOGY, INC.—Sevenson Environmental Services, Inc.; U.S. Public, pg. 1463
WATKINS ENGINEERS & CONSTRUCTORS, INC.—Dillingham Construction Corporation; U.S. Private, pg. 333
WATSON STEEL & CO. (CONSTRUCTIONAL ENGINEERS) LTD.—AMEC Plc; Int'l, pg. 16
WEBB, MURRAY & ASSOCIATES; U.S. Private, pg. 1157
WELLMAN, INC.; U.S. Public, pg. 1752
WEST VIRGINIA ELECTRIC CORP.—Salem Group, Inc.; U.S. Private, pg. 962
WESTERN ATLAS INC.; U.S. Public, pg. 1757
WESTINGHOUSE ELECTRIC AUSTRALASIA LTD.-VICTORIA DIV.—CBS Corporation; U.S. Public, pg. 275
WESTINGHOUSE ENERGY SYSTEMS INTERNATIONAL, INC.—CBS Corporation; U.S. Public, pg. 275
WESTON INTERNATIONAL, INC.—Roy F. Weston, Inc.; U.S. Public, pg. 1761
ROY F. WESTON, INC.; U.S. Public, pg. 1761
WHEELABRATOR TECHNOLOGIES INC.—Waste Management, Inc.; U.S. Public, pg. 1745
WHITING CORPORATION; U.S. Private, pg. 1173
WILLIAMS FAIREY ENGINEERING LTD.—Williams Holdings Plc; Int'l, pg. 1500
GEORGE WIMPEY INTERNATIONAL LTD.—George Wimpey PLC; Int'l, pg. 1510
WOODWARD-CLYDE—URS Corporation; U.S. Public, pg. 1656
WOODWARD-CLYDE GROUP, INC.—URS Corporation; U.S. Public, pg. 1655
WOODWARD-CLYDE INTERNATIONAL—URS Corporation; U.S. Public, pg. 1658
WOOLPERT; U.S. Private, pg. 1188
WORTHINGTON INDUSTRIES, INC.; U.S. Public, pg. 1780
PAUL WURTH S.A.—Arbed S.A.; Int'l, pg. 80
WYLE ELECTRONICS—Veba AG; Int'l, pg. 1457
WYLE LABORATORIES, INC.; U.S. Private, pg. 1193
XEROX CORPORATE RESEARCH GROUP—Xerox Corporation; U.S. Public, pg. 1784
YAHYA COSTAIN LLC—Costain Group PLC; Int'l, pg. 337
BERNARD JOHNSON YOUNG INC.—Bernard Johnson Young Inc.; U.S. Private, pg. 136
ZALK JOSEPH FABRICATIONS, INC.—Pettibone Corporation; U.S. Private, pg. 860
ZURN CONSTRUCTORS, INC.—Zurn Industries, Inc.; U.S. Public, pg. 1795

8712 — ARCHITECTURAL SERVICES

AMB DEVELOPMENT GROUP LLC; U.S. Private, pg. 6
ARROW BUILDING CENTERS—Consolidated Lumber Co.; U.S. Private, pg. 265
THE AUSTIN COMPANY; U.S. Private, pg. 99
BCP TECHNICAL SERVICE, INC.; U.S. Private, pg. 106
BE & C ENGINEERS INC.—The Boeing Company; U.S. Public, pg. 241
BANNER ASSOCIATES INC.; U.S. Private, pg. 114
BAXTER HODELL DONNELLY PRESTON INC.; U.S. Private, pg. 124
BAXTER/PEAS—Baxter Hodell Donnelly Preston Inc.; U.S. Private, pg. 124
BERNARD JOHNSON YOUNG INC.; U.S. Private, pg. 136
BIRDAIR, INC.—Taiyo Kogyo Corporation; Int'l, pg. 1348

BLACK & VEATCH; *U.S. Private*, pg. 146
BOVIS CONSTRUCTION LTD.—The Peninsular and Oriental Steam Navigation Company; *Int'l*, pg. 1032
BOYLE ENGINEERING CORP.; *U.S. Private*, pg. 163
BUCHART HORN INC.—Pace Resources, Inc.; *U.S. Private*, pg. 830
BURGESS & NIPLE, LIMITED; *U.S. Private*, pg. 182
BURNS & MCDONNELL ENGINEERS-ARCHITECTS-CONSULTANTS; *U.S. Private*, pg. 187
CRSS ARABIA LTD.—Tractebel; *Int'l*, pg. 1415
CRSS INC.—Tractebel; *Int'l*, pg. 1415
CRSS INTERNATIONAL, INC.—Jacobs Engineering Group Inc.; *U.S. Public*, pg. 922
CANNON; *U.S. Private*, pg. 205
CONSOLIDATED LUMBER CO.; *U.S. Private*, pg. 265
COSTAIN ENGINEERING & CONSTRUCTION LIMITED—Costain Group PLC; *Int'l*, pg. 336
CREST ARABIA LTD.—ABB Asea Brown Boveri (Holding) Ltd.; *Int'l*, pg. 5
CREST ENGINEERING (MALAYSIA) SBN. BHD.—ABB Asea Brown Boveri (Holding) Ltd.; *Int'l*, pg. 5
CREST ENGINEERING OVERSEAS, INC.—ABB Asea Brown Boveri (Holding) Ltd.; *Int'l*, pg. 5
CREST NETHERLANDS INC.—ABB Asea Brown Boveri (Holding) Ltd.; *Int'l*, pg. 5
CREST VENEZUELA INC.—ABB Asea Brown Boveri (Holding) Ltd.; *Int'l*, pg. 5
D&Z MICROELECTRONICS—Day & Zimmermann, Inc.; *U.S. Private*, pg. 317
LEO A. DALY COMPANY; *U.S. Private*, pg. 309
DAVY INTERNATIONAL—Kvaerner a.s.a.; *Int'l*, pg. 773
DAVY MCKEE CHILE LTDA.—Kvaerner a.s.a.; *Int'l*, pg. 775
DAVY MCKEE ENGENHARIA S/A—Kvaerner a.s.a.; *Int'l*, pg. 775
THE DAVY ROLL CO. LTD.—Kvaerner a.s.a.; *Int'l*, pg. 773
DAY & ZIMMERMANN, INC.; *U.S. Private*, pg. 316
DAY & ZIMMERMANN INTERNATIONAL, INC.—Day & Zimmermann, Inc.; *U.S. Private*, pg. 317
DESIGN-BUILD WEST—RNL Facilities Corporation; *U.S. Private*, pg. 905
DEWBERRY & DAVIS; *U.S. Private*, pg. 329
DEWBERRY DESIGN GROUP—Dewberry & Davis; *U.S. Private*, pg. 329
EG & G ENVIRONMENTAL, INC.—EG & G, Inc.; *U.S. Public*, pg. 543
EASTMAN KODAK CO.—Eastman Kodak Company; *U.S. Public*, pg. 555
A. EPSTEIN AND SONS, INTL., INC.; *U.S. Private*, pg. 379
A. EPSTEIN & SONS (NEW YORK)—A. Epstein and Sons, Intl., Inc.; *U.S. Private*, pg. 379
FARMERS INSURANCE GROUP—B.A.T Industries P.L.C.; *Int'l*, pg. 111
FLUOR CORPORATION; *U.S. Public*, pg. 659
FOSTER WHEELER CORPORATION; *U.S. Public*, pg. 676
GHAFARI ASSOCIATES, INC.; *U.S. Private*, pg. 450
GIFFELS ASSOCIATES, INC.; *U.S. Private*, pg. 452
GIFFELS ASSOCIATES INC.—Giffels Associates, Inc.; *U.S. Private*, pg. 452
GIFFELS HOYEM BASSO, INC.—Giffels Associates, Inc.; *U.S. Private*, pg. 452
GIFFELS STRATEGIC CONSULTANTS, L.L.C.—Giffels Associates, Inc.; *U.S. Private*, pg. 452
GROUPE GTM—Lyonnaise des Eaux S.A.; *Int'l*, pg. 823
HDR INC.—Bouygues; *Int'l*, pg. 206
HLW INTERNATIONAL LLP; *U.S. Private*, pg. 491
HNTB CORPORATION; *U.S. Private*, pg. 492
HOH ARCHITECTS, INC.—The HOH Organizations; *U.S. Private*, pg. 492
THE HOH ORGANIZATIONS; *U.S. Private*, pg. 492
HSMM FACILITIES, INC.—Hayes, Seay, Mattern & Mattern, Inc.; *U.S. Private*, pg. 513
HAMMEL, GREEN & ABRAHAMSON, INC.; *U.S. Private*, pg. 497
HARLEY ELLINGTON DESIGN; *U.S. Private*, pg. 503
HARZA ENGINEERING CO.; *U.S. Private*, pg. 509
HARZA NORTHEAST, INC.—Harza Engineering Co.; *U.S. Private*, pg. 509
HARZA NORTHWEST, INC.—Harza Engineering Co.; *U.S. Private*, pg. 509
HAYES, SEAY, MATTERN & MATTERN, INC.; *U.S. Private*, pg. 513
HEERY INTERNATIONAL, INC.; *U.S. Private*, pg. 519
HELLMUTH, OBATA & KASSABAUM, INC.; *U.S. Private*, pg. 520
HENNINGSON, DURHAM & RICHARDSON INC.—Bouygues; *Int'l*, pg. 207
HUITT-ZOLLARS, INC.; *U.S. Private*, pg. 547
INDECO, INC.—Johnson Bros. Corporation; *U.S. Private*, pg. 591
INTERIOR SPACE INTERNATIONAL—A. Epstein and Sons, Intl., Inc.; *U.S. Private*, pg. 379
INTERPLAN—RNL Facilities Corporation; *U.S. Private*, pg. 905
JOFFKO INTERNATIONAL; *U.S. Private*, pg. 589
JOFFKO PHILIPPINES, INC.—Joffko International; *U.S. Private*, pg. 589
ALBERT KAHN ASSOCIATES, INC.; *U.S. Private*, pg. 604
KAJIMA CORPORATION; *Int'l*, pg. 721
KAJIMA U.S.A., INC.—Kajima Corporation; *Int'l*, pg. 722
KELLER & GANNON—Lester B. Knight & Associates, Inc.; *U.S. Private*, pg. 626
L. ROBERT KIMBALL & ASSOCIATES; *U.S. Private*, pg. 619
KNIGHT ARCHITECTS ENGINEERS PLANNERS, INC.—Lester B. Knight & Associates, Inc.; *U.S. Private*, pg. 626
LESTER B. KNIGHT & ASSOCIATES, INC.; *U.S. Private*, pg. 626
LESTER B. KNIGHT FACILITIES MANAGEMENT, INC.—Lester B. Knight & Associates, Inc.; *U.S. Private*, pg. 627
KVAERNER DAVY—Kvaerner a.s.a.; *Int'l*, pg. 774
KVAERNER MOSS TECHNOLOGY A.S., MOSS DIVISION—Kvaerner a.s.a.; *Int'l*, pg. 769
ROBERT E. LAMB, INC.; *U.S. Private*, pg. 644
LIMITED STORE PLANNING—The Limited, Inc.; *U.S. Public*, pg. 995
LIVERNOIS ENGINEERING COMPANY; *U.S. Private*, pg. 672
LOCKWOOD GREENE TECHNOLOGIES—Philipp Holzmann AG; *Int'l*, pg. 633
MBT ARCHITECTURE; *U.S. Private*, pg. 686
MPS CORPORATION; *U.S. Private*, pg. 687
MAGUIRE GROUP ARCHITECTS, INC.—Maguire Group Inc.; *U.S. Private*, pg. 696
MAGUIRE GROUP INC.; *U.S. Private*, pg. 696
AC MARTIN PARTNERS; *U.S. Private*, pg. 708
MASON & HANGER ENGINEERING INC.—Mason & Hanger Corporation, Inc.; *U.S. Private*, pg. 711
JOHN J. MCMULLEN ASSOCIATES—Carpenter Technology Corporation; *U.S. Public*, pg. 308
METALLGESELLSCHAFT AG; *Int'l*, pg. 860
METCALF & EDDY COMPANIES INC.—Air & Water Technologies Corporation; *U.S. Public*, pg. 29
MI-JACK PRODUCTS, INC.; *U.S. Private*, pg. 740
MIZUNO CORPORATION; *Int'l*, pg. 884
NBBJ; *U.S. Private*, pg. 771
NADEL ARCHITECTS, INC.; *U.S. Private*, pg. 773
NADEL ARCHITECTS INC. & MARVIN FITCH—Nadel Architects, Inc.; *U.S. Private*, pg. 773
NUTTER ENGINEERING—Harsco Corporation; *U.S. Public*, pg. 793
OPUS CORP.; *U.S. Private*, pg. 818
OPUS SOUTH CORPORATION; *U.S. Private*, pg. 818
THE PBS&J CORPORATION; *U.S. Private*, pg. 825
PASCO ENGINEERING LIMITED—Tarmac plc; *Int'l*, pg. 1355
RNL DESIGN—RNL Facilities Corporation; *U.S. Private*, pg. 905
RNL FACILITIES CORPORATION; *U.S. Private*, pg. 905
RNL/INTERPLAN—RNL Facilities Corporation; *U.S. Private*, pg. 905
RTKL ASSOCIATES INC.; *U.S. Private*, pg. 906
ROSSER INTERNATIONAL, INC.; *U.S. Private*, pg. 946
STV ARCHITECTS—STV Group, Inc.; *U.S. Public*, pg. 1421
STV GROUP, INC.; *U.S. Public*, pg. 1421
STV/SILVER & ZISKIND—STV Group, Inc.; *U.S. Public*, pg. 1421
SADCO LTD.—Joffko International; *U.S. Private*, pg. 589
SMITH HINCHMAN GRYLLS ASSOCIATES, INC.—SmithGroup, Inc.; *U.S. Private*, pg. 1010
SMITHGROUP, INC.; *U.S. Private*, pg. 1010
THE STANLEY CONSULTANTS GROUP; *U.S. Private*, pg. 1032
SVERDRUP CORPORATION; *U.S. Private*, pg. 1057
SVERDRUP ENVIRONMENTAL INC.—Sverdrup Corporation; *U.S. Private*, pg. 1057
TAD RESOURCES INTERNATIONAL, INC.; *U.S. Private*, pg. 1062
TPS PEYRARD—Technip; *Int'l*, pg. 1360
LEE KIM TAH HOLDINGS LTD.; *Int'l*, pg. 1346
TAKENAKA CORPORATION; *Int'l*, pg. 1351
TAUGBOL & OVERLAND A/S—Aker Raj Asa; *Int'l*, pg. 42
TETRA TECH NUS, INC.—Tetra Tech, Inc.; *U.S. Public*, pg. 1582
URS CORPORATION; *U.S. Public*, pg. 1655
WOOLPERT; *U.S. Private*, pg. 1188
BERNARD JOHNSON YOUNG INC.—Bernard Johnson Young Inc.; *U.S. Private*, pg. 136

8713 — SURVEYING SERVICES

ASI LANDMARK, INC.—Analytical Surveys, Inc.; *U.S. Public*, pg. 110
AERO SERVICE (GREAT BRITAIN) C/O WESTERN GEOPHYSICAL CO.—Litton Industries, Inc.; *U.S. Public*, pg. 1004
ANALYTICAL SURVEYS, INC.; *U.S. Public*, pg. 110
ANALYTICAL SURVEYS, INC. - NORTHEAST DIVISION—Analytical Surveys, Inc.; *U.S. Public*, pg. 110
AQUACONSULT S.A. DE C.V.—FKI Plc; *Int'l*, pg. 474
BECHTEL GROUP, INC.; *U.S. Private*, pg. 128
BLACK HORSE AGENCIES LTD.—Lloyds TSB Group PLC; *Int'l*, pg. 813
CREST ARABIA LTD.—ABB Asea Brown Boveri (Holding) Ltd.; *Int'l*, pg. 5
CREST ENGINEERING (MALAYSIA) SBN. BHD.—ABB Asea Brown Boveri (Holding) Ltd.; *Int'l*, pg. 5
CREST ENGINEERING OVERSEAS, INC.—ABB Asea Brown Boveri (Holding) Ltd.; *Int'l*, pg. 5
CREST NETHERLANDS INC.—ABB Asea Brown Boveri (Holding) Ltd.; *Int'l*, pg. 5
CREST VENEZUELA INC.—ABB Asea Brown Boveri (Holding) Ltd.; *Int'l*, pg. 5
DET NORSKE VERITAS; *Int'l*, pg. 396
DET NORSKE VERITAS INDUSTRY—Det Norske Veritas; *Int'l*, pg. 396
DEWBERRY & DAVIS; *U.S. Private*, pg. 329
EPSTEIN CIVIL ENGINEERING, INC.—A. Epstein and Sons, Intl., Inc.; *U.S. Private*, pg. 379
GEONEX—Geonex Corporation; *U.S. Private*, pg. 448
GIFFELS ASSOCIATES, INC.; *U.S. Private*, pg. 452
GOODKIND & O'DEA, INC.—Dewberry & Davis; *U.S. Private*, pg. 329
HUITT-ZOLLARS, INC.; *U.S. Private*, pg. 547
L. ROBERT KIMBALL & ASSOCIATES; *U.S. Private*, pg. 619
MAPFRE SERVICIOS MARITIMOS, COMISARIADO Y LIQUIDACION DE AVERIAS—Corporacion MAPFRE, Compania Internacional de Reaseguros, S.A.; *Int'l*, pg. 333
AC MARTIN PARTNERS; *U.S. Private*, pg. 708
OCEANEERING A/S—Oceaneering International, Inc.; *U.S. Public*, pg. 1211
OCEANEERING AUSTRALIA PTY. LTD.—Brambles Industries Limited; *Int'l*, pg. 211
OCEANEERING AUSTRALIA PTY. LTD.—Oceaneering International, Inc.; *U.S. Public*, pg. 1211
OCEANEERING INTERNATIONAL, INC.; *U.S. Public*, pg. 1211
PSOMAS & ASSOCIATES; *U.S. Private*, pg. 893
SCHLUMBERGER LIMITED; *U.S. Public*, pg. 1439
SEITEL, INC.; *U.S. Public*, pg. 1454
SEITEL OFFSHORE CORP.—Seitel, Inc.; *U.S. Public*, pg. 1454
SOLUS OCEANEERING (MALAYSIA) SDN. BHD.—Oceaneering International, Inc.; *U.S. Public*, pg. 1211
SVERDRUP CORPORATION; *U.S. Private*, pg. 1057
TAD RESOURCES INTERNATIONAL, INC.; *U.S. Private*, pg. 1062
WATER ENGINEERING DIVISION—FKI Plc; *Int'l*, pg. 472
WOOLPERT; *U.S. Private*, pg. 1188

8721 — ACCOUNTING, AUDITING & BOOKKEEPING SERVICES

ADECCO S.A.; *Int'l*, pg. 23
ALCOA EUROPE LIMITED—Aluminum Company of America; *U.S. Public*, pg. 62
AMERCO; *U.S. Private*, pg. 48
ANDERSEN WORLDWIDE; *U.S. Private*, pg. 72
ARTHUR ANDERSEN—Andersen Worldwide; *U.S. Private*, pg. 72
BDO SEIDMAN, LLP; *U.S. Private*, pg. 106
BP AUSTRALIA LTD.—The British Petroleum Company P.L.C.; *Int'l*, pg. 220
BP JAPAN KK—The British Petroleum Company P.L.C.; *Int'l*, pg. 220
COM/ENERGY SERVICES CO.—Commonwealth Energy System; *U.S. Public*, pg. 414
CARLSBERG FINANCIAL CORP.; *U.S. Private*, pg. 211
CERIDIAN CORPORATION; *U.S. Public*, pg. 330
CERIDIAN EMPLOYER SERVICES—Ceridian Corporation; *U.S. Public*, pg. 331
COMMONWEALTH ENERGY SYSTEM; *U.S. Public*, pg. 414
COMPREHENSIVE BUSINESS SERVICES INC.—Franchise Services, Inc.; *U.S. Private*, pg. 423
COOPERATIVE SERVICE CO.—Nationwide Insurance Enterprise; *U.S. Private*, pg. 789
COOPERS & LYBRAND; *U.S. Private*, pg. 274
DATA TRACK ACCOUNT SERVICES, INC.—National Fuel Gas Company; *U.S. Public*, pg. 1156
DELOITTE & TOUCHE LLP; *U.S. Private*, pg. 322
DIGITAL SOLUTIONS, INC.; *U.S. Public*, pg. 508
ENTERTAINMENT PARTNERS—IDC Services, Inc.; *U.S. Private*, pg. 554
ERNST & YOUNG, LLP; *U.S. Private*, pg. 381
FRIEDMAN, EISENSTEIN, RAEMER AND SCHWARTZ, LLP; *U.S. Private*, pg. 428
FROST COMPANY; *U.S. Private*, pg. 430
GLOBAL TRAVEL COMPUTER HOLDINGS LTD.—Air Canada; *Int'l*, pg. 36
GRANT THORNTON LLP; *U.S. Private*, pg. 470
HAWKEYE QUALITY SERVICE CORPORATION—Mercantile Bancorporation Inc.; *U.S. Public*, pg. 1087
IDC SERVICES, INC.; *U.S. Private*, pg. 554
INTEGRATEC—Equifax Inc.; *U.S. Public*, pg. 588
KPMG LLP; *U.S. Private*, pg. 603
LIVING CENTERS OF AMERICA—Paragon Health Network, Inc.; *U.S. Public*, pg. 1257
MEES & HOPE CORPORATE FINANCE LTD.—ABN-AMRO Holding N.V.; *Int'l*, pg. 12
MINIDATA SERVICES, INC.—Ceridian Corporation; *U.S. Public*, pg. 331
NAC INC.—Bandag, Incorporated; *U.S. Public*, pg. 177
NTS—First Data Corporation; *U.S. Public*, pg. 631
NORWEST AUDIT SERVICES, INC.—Norwest Corporation; *U.S. Public*, pg. 1201
PAYCHEX, INC.; *U.S. Public*, pg. 1267
PRICE WATERHOUSE L.L.P. - U.S.; *U.S. Private*, pg. 883
RESUMIX—Ceridian Corporation; *U.S. Public*, pg. 331
TALENT PARTNERS—IDC Services, Inc.; *U.S. Private*, pg. 554
U-HAUL INTERNATIONAL, INC.—Amerco; *U.S. Private*, pg. 49
USLD COMMUNICATIONS CORP.—LCI International, Inc.; *U.S. Public*, pg. 969
XEROX REAL ESTATE & GENERAL SERVICES DIVISION—Xerox Corporation; *U.S. Public*, pg. 1785

8731 — COMMERCIAL PHYSICAL & BIOLOGICAL RESEARCH

AAI CORPORATION—United Industrial Corporation; *U.S. Public*, pg. 1679
APX INTERNATIONAL; *U.S. Private*, pg. 7
AVX ISRAEL LTD.—Kyocera Corporation; *Int'l*, pg. 776
ACCORD CONTRACT SERVICES—Veba AG; *Int'l*, pg. 1458
ADVANCED SEPARATION TECHNOLOGIES INCORPORATED—Florida Progress Corporation; *U.S. Public*, pg. 655
AEROSPACE SYSTEMS & EQUIPMENT—Moog Incorporated; *U.S. Public*, pg. 1127
AEROTEST OPERATIONS, INC.—OEA, Inc.; *U.S. Public*, pg. 1207
AEROVIRONMENT, INC.; *U.S. Private*, pg. 25
AGMET LTD.—Electro-Science Laboratories, Inc.; *U.S. Private*, pg. 369
AKZO NOBEL FIBERS, INC.—Akzo Nobel N.V.; *Int'l*, pg. 48
ALBANY INTERNATIONAL RESEARCH CO.—Albany International Corp.; *U.S. Public*, pg. 36
ALCELL TECHNOLOGIES INC.—Repap Enterprises Inc.; *Int'l*, pg. 1104
ALLIEDSIGNAL CONTROLS & ACCESSORIES—AlliedSignal Inc.; *U.S. Public*, pg. 50
ALLIEDSIGNAL MICROELECTRONICS & TECHNOLOGY CENTER—AlliedSignal Inc.; *U.S. Public*, pg. 50

ALZA DEVELOPMENT CORPORATION—Alza Corporation; *U.S. Public*, pg. 62
AMERICAN SCIENCE & ENGINEERING, INC.; *U.S. Public*, *pg. 90*
ANSALDO RICERCHE SRL—IRI Istituto Ricostruzione Industriale; *Int'l*, pg. 653
APPLIED BIOSYSTEMS—The Perkin-Elmer Corporation; *U.S. Public*, pg. 1279
ARES-SERONO S.A.; *Int'l*, pg. 80
ARJO WIGGINS RESEARCH AND DEVEL. LTD.—Groupe Saint Louis; *Int'l*, pg. 567
ARTESIAN RESOURCES CORPORATION; *U.S. Public*, pg. 135
ARVIN INDUSTRIES, INC.; *U.S. Public*, pg. 136
ASAHI CHEMICAL INDUSTRY AMERICA, INC.—Asahi Chemical Industry Co., Ltd.; *Int'l*, pg. 84
ASSOCIATED TESTING LABORATORIES, INC.—Publicker Industries Inc.; *U.S. Public*, pg. 1341
ASTRA ARCUS AB—Astra AB; *Int'l*, pg. 93
ASTRA DRACO AB—Astra AB; *Int'l*, pg. 93
ASTRA HASSLE AB—Astra AB; *Int'l*, pg. 93
ASTRA PAIN CONTROL AB—Astra AB; *Int'l*, pg. 93
ASTRE CORPORATE GROUP; *U.S. Private*, pg. 93
AURA SYSTEMS, INC.; *U.S. Public*, pg. 147
BCE INC.; *Int'l*, pg. 114
BDM INTERNATIONAL, INC.—TRW Inc.; *U.S. Public*, pg. 1558
BNR, INC.—Northern Telecom Limited; *Int'l*, pg. 969
BP AMERICA INC.—The British Petroleum Company P.L.C.; *Int'l*, pg. 220
BARRINGER INSTRUMENTS, INC.—Barringer Technologies Inc.; *U.S. Public*, pg. 192
BATTELLE MEMORIAL INSTITUTE; *U.S. Private*, pg. 123
BAYER AG—Bayer AG; *Int'l*, pg. 172
BECKMAN INSTRUMENTS, INC.; *U.S. Public*, pg. 199
BECTON DICKINSON RESEARCH CENTER—Becton Dickinson & Company; *U.S. Public*, pg. 199
BEHRINGWERKE AG—Hoechst Aktiengesellschaft; *Int'l*, pg. 624
BELL-NORTHERN RESEARCH LTD.—BCE Inc.; *Int'l*, pg. 116
BELL-NORTHERN RESEARCH LTD.—Northern Telecom Limited; *Int'l*, pg. 969
BERLEX LABORATORIES INC.—Schering AG; *Int'l*, pg. 1204
BETAC CORPORATION—Betac International Corporation; *U.S. Private*, pg. 140
BETAC INTERNATIONAL CORPORATION; *U.S. Private*, pg. 140
BINKS RESEARCH & DEVELOPMENT CORP.—Binks Sames Corporation; *U.S. Public*, pg. 229
BIO-TEK INSTRUMENTS, INC.; *U.S. Private*, pg. 144
BIO-CYPHER LABORATORIES; *U.S. Private*, pg. 145
BIOTECHNICA INTERNATIONAL—Groupe Limagrain; *Int'l*, pg. 566
BOEHRINGER MANNHEIM PHARMACEUTICALS CORP.—Corange Limited; *Int'l*, pg. 331
BOSCH BRAKING SYSTEMS-NORTH AMERICA, ENGINEERING CENTER—Robert Bosch GmbH; *Int'l*, pg. 205
BRACCO RESEARCH, INC.—Bracco S.p.A.; *Int'l*, pg. 210
C. BREWER & COMPANY, LIMITED—Buyco, Inc.; *U.S. Private*, pg. 190
BRISTOL-MYERS HEALTH CARE GROUP—Bristol-Myers Squibb Company; *U.S. Public*, pg. 253
BROWN AND CALDWELL; *U.S. Private*, pg. 173
DR. CHRISTIAN BRUNNENGRABER CHEMISCHE FABRIK GMBH—Novartis AG; *Int'l*, pg. 975
CLS LASER SYSTEMS—Litton Industries, Inc.; *U.S. Public*, pg. 1002
CALGENE LLC—Monsanto Company; *U.S. Public*, pg. 1124
CAMBRIDGE CONSULTANTS LIMITED—Arthur D. Little, Inc.; *U.S. Private*, pg. 671
CARDIO-FITNESS CORPORATION—H.J. Heinz Company; *U.S. Public*, pg. 806
CELLPRO, INCORPORATED; *U.S. Public*, pg. 320
CENTOCOR PARTNERS III, L.P.—Centocor, Inc.; *U.S. Public*, pg. 323
CENTRAL RESEARCH LABORATORIES—Dover Corporation; *U.S. Public*, pg. 521
CENTRO RICERCHE S.P.A.—Fiat Auto SpA; *Int'l*, pg. 480
CERAMATEC—Elkem ASA; *Int'l*, pg. 448
CHARLES RIVER BIOTECHNICAL SERVICES, INC.—Bausch & Lomb Incorporated; *U.S. Public*, pg. 194
CHEVRON RESEARCH AND TECHNOLOGY COMPANY—Chevron Corporation; *U.S. Public*, pg. 348
CIBA CORNING DIAGNOSTICS CORP.—Novartis AG; *Int'l*, *pg. 973*
CIBA SPECIALTY CHEMICALS—Ciba Specialty Chemicals Holding Inc.; *Int'l*, pg. 291
CIMLINC INCORPORATED; *U.S. Private*, pg. 239
THE CLOROX COMPANY; *U.S. Public*, pg. 386
COHERENT, INC.; *U.S. Public*, pg. 395
COHERENT TUCSON RESEARCH CENTER—Coherent, Inc.; *U.S. Public*, pg. 395
COLUMBIA ANALYTICAL SERVICES, INC.—EMCON; *U.S. Public*, pg. 571
COMMONWEALTH RESEARCH CORP.—Unicom Corporation; *U.S. Public*, pg. 1664
COMSAT CORPORATION; *U.S. Public*, pg. 424
COMSAT LABORATORIES—COMSAT Corporation; *U.S. Public*, pg. 424
CONDEA CHEMIE GMBH; *Int'l*, pg. 325
CONNAUGHT LABORATORIES LIMITED—Rhone-Poulenc S.A.; *Int'l*, pg. 1109
CONSOLIDATION COAL RESEARCH & DEVELOPMENT—Du Pont (E.I. Du Pont De Nemours & Co.); *U.S. Public*, pg. 531
COR SAM GLASS TEC RESEARCH & DEVELOPMENT CENTER—Corning Incorporated; *U.S. Public*, pg. 449
CORNING FRANCE, S.A.—Corning Incorporated; *U.S. Public*, pg. 449
COVANCE LABORATORIES—Covance, Inc.; *U.S. Public*, pg. 454
CYTOGEN CORPORATION; *U.S. Public*, pg. 471
DNA PLANT TECHNOLOGY CORP.—Empressa La Moderna SA de CV; *Int'l*, pg. 454
DNAP HOLDING CORP.—Empressa La Moderna SA de CV; *Int'l*, pg. 454
DAEWOO INTERNATIONAL AMERICA CORP. - SANTA CLARA—Daewoo Corporation; *Int'l*, pg. 357
DAIHATSU MOTOR CO., LTD.—Daihatsu Motor Corporation, Ltd.; *Int'l*, pg. 365
DATA GENERAL SYSTEMS DEVELOPMENT DIVISION—Data General Corporation; *U.S. Public*, pg. 485
DATARANGE COMMUNICATIONS PLC—SFA, Inc.; *U.S. Private*, pg. 956
DET NORSKE VERITAS; *Int'l*, pg. 396
DOTY LABORATORIES, INC.—Inchcape PLC; *Int'l*, pg. 671
DU PONT CANADA-KINGSTON RESEARCH—Du Pont (E.I. Du Pont De Nemours & Co.); *U.S. Public*, pg. 532
DYNACARE-ALBERTA—Dynacare, Inc.; *Int'l*, pg. 425
DYNACARE-ONTARIO—Dynacare, Inc.; *Int'l*, pg. 425
DYNACARE-WASHINGTON—Dynacare, Inc.; *Int'l*, pg. 425
DYNACARE-WYOMING—Dynacare, Inc.; *Int'l*, pg. 425
EG & G, INC.; *U.S. Public*, pg. 542
ESL S.N.C.—Electro-Science Laboratories, Inc.; *U.S. Private*, pg. 369
EARTH TECHNOLOGY CORP.—Tyco International Ltd.; *U.S. Public*, pg. 1648
ECOS GROUP, INC.; *U.S. Public*, pg. 563
ELAN/PRI LTD.—Elan Corporation Plc; *Int'l*, pg. 436
ELAN TRANSDERMAL LTD.—Elan Corporation Plc; *Int'l*, pg. 436
ELECTRO-BIOLOGY, INC.—Biomet, Inc.; *U.S. Public*, pg. 231
ELECTRO-SCIENCE DEUTSCHLAND—Electro-Science Laboratories, Inc.; *U.S. Private*, pg. 369
ELECTRO-SCIENCE LABORATORIES, INC.; *U.S. Private*, pg. 369
ELECTRONIC PRINTING SYSTEMS—Eastman Kodak Company; *U.S. Public*, pg. 551
ELKEM TECHNOLOGY SERVICES—Elkem ASA; *Int'l*, pg. 448
ENVIRON CORPORATION—Pharmaceutical Product Development, Inc.; *U.S. Public*, pg. 1285
ENZON, INC.; *U.S. Public*, pg. 587
ENZON, INC.—Enzon, Inc.; *U.S. Public*, pg. 588
ERICSSON BUSINESS COMMUNICATIONS, INC.—Telefonaktiebolaget LM Ericsson; *Int'l*, pg. 1364
ERIEZ MAGNETICS; *U.S. Private*, pg. 381
EXPLORATION & PRODUCTION RESEARCH CENTER—Chinese Petroleum Corporation; *Int'l*, pg. 286
FIDCO (FOOD INGREDIENT DEVELOPMENT COMPANY)—Nestle S.A.; *Int'l*, pg. 917
THE FLIGHT INTERNATIONAL GROUP, INC.; *U.S. Public*, *pg. 654*
FLORIDA PROGRESS CORPORATION; *U.S. Public*, pg. 655
FLORIGENE BV—Novartis AG; *Int'l*, pg. 982
FONAR CORPORATION; *U.S. Public*, pg. 661
GAI CONSULTANTS, INC.; *U.S. Private*, pg. 433
GCO MINERALS CO.—International Paper Company; *U.S. Public*, pg. 902
GN DANAVOX A/S—GN Great Nordic Ltd.; *Int'l*, pg. 537
GTE INTERNETWORKING—GTE Corporation; *U.S. Public*, pg. 696
GTE LABORATORIES INCORPORATED—GTE Corporation; *U.S. Public*, pg. 697
GENERAL MILLS OPERATIONS, INC.—General Mills, Inc.; *U.S. Public*, pg. 718
GENERAL SCIENCES CORP.—Science Applications International Corp.; *U.S. Private*, pg. 976
GENETIC SYSTEMS CORPORATION—Elf Aquitane; *Int'l*, pg. 445
GENETICS INSTITUTE, INC.—American Home Products Corporation; *U.S. Public*, pg. 79
GENZYME TRANSGENICS—Genzyme Corporation; *U.S. Public*, pg. 733
GEO-CENTERS, INC.; *U.S. Private*, pg. 447
GEOSAFE CORPORATION—Battelle Memorial Institute; *U.S. Private*, pg. 123
GIVAUDAN-ROURE RESEARCH LTD.—Roche Holding Ltd.; *Int'l*, pg. 1119
GLAXO WELLCOME INC.—Glaxo Wellcome plc; *Int'l*, pg. 552
HART CROWSER, INC.; *U.S. Private*, pg. 507
HEATH CONSULTANTS INCORPORATED; *U.S. Private*, pg. 518
HILLESHOG AB—Novartis AG; *Int'l*, pg. 982
HILLESHOG MONO-HY INC.—Novartis AG; *Int'l*, pg. 973
HILLESHOG RESEARCH AB—Novartis AG; *Int'l*, pg. 982
HOECHST MARION ROUSSEL NORTH AMERICA—Hoechst Aktiengesellschaft; *Int'l*, pg. 625
HOFFMANN-LA ROCHE INC.—Roche Holding Ltd.; *Int'l*, pg. 1120
HONDA R&D NORTH AMERICA, INC.—Honda Motor Co., Ltd.; *Int'l*, pg. 634
HOXAN AMERICA INCORPORATED—Daido Hoxan Inc.; *Int'l*, pg. 363
HUGHES RESEARCH LABORATORIES—General Motors Corporation; *U.S. Public*, pg. 721
HYCLONE EUROPE LTD.—Perstorp AB; *Int'l*, pg. 1037
IBM RESEARCH DIV.—International Business Machines Corporation; *U.S. Public*, pg. 896
IWC SERVICES, INC.—NIPSCO Industries, Inc.; *U.S. Public*, *pg. 1185*
IMMUNEX RESEARCH AND DEVELOPMENT CORPORATION—Immunex Corporation; *U.S. Public*, pg. 871
INEDECA S.A.—Nestle S.A.; *Int'l*, pg. 920
THE INSTITUTE OF BIOPHARMACEUTICS LTD.—Elan Corporation Plc; *Int'l*, pg. 436
INTERGEN COMPANY; *U.S. Private*, pg. 567
INTERVET LABORATORIES LTD.—Akzo Nobel N.V.; *Int'l*, pg. 45
INTERX RESEARCH CORP.—Merck & Co., Inc.; *U.S. Public*, pg. 1091
ITSEMAP IBERICA, S.A.—Corporacion MAPFRE, Compania Internacional de Reaseguros, S.A.; *Int'l*, pg. 332
JTC ENVIRONMENTAL CONSULTANTS, INC.—GP Strategies Corporation; *U.S. Public*, pg. 694
JOHNSON & JOHNSON/MERCK CONSUMER PHARMACEUTICALS CO.—Johnson & Johnson; *U.S. Public*, pg. 929
JOHNSON & JOHNSON/MERCK CONSUMER PHARMACEUTICALS CO.—Merck & Co., Inc.; *U.S. Public*, pg. 1091
JOHNSON MATTHEY PHARMACEUTICALS MATERIALS—Johnson Matthey Public Limited Company; *Int'l*, pg. 713
KAMAN AEROSPACE CORP.—Kaman Corporation; *U.S. Public*, pg. 942
KILAUEA AGRONOMICS, INC.—Buyco, Inc.; *U.S. Private*, pg. 190
KOBE-MIDREX RESEARCH—Kobe Steel, Ltd.; *Int'l*, pg. 740
KOBE STEEL USA INC. (LOS ANGELES)—Kobe Steel, Ltd.; *Int'l*, pg. 740
KODAK BIO-PRODUCTS DIVISION—Eastman Kodak Company; *U.S. Public*, pg. 551
KRUG LIFE SCIENCES INC.—Krug International Corp.; *U.S. Public*, pg. 968
LABORA MANNHEIM GMBH FUR LABORTECHNIK—Corange Limited; *Int'l*, pg. 331
LABORATOIRES SANDOZ S.A.R.L.—Novartis AG; *Int'l*, pg. 983
LAMBDA PHYSIK—Coherent, Inc.; *U.S. Public*, pg. 395
LAQUE CENTER FOR CORROSION TECHNOLOGY, INC.—Inco Limited; *Int'l*, pg. 672
LILLY RESEARCH LABORATORIES—Eli Lilly and Company; *U.S. Public*, pg. 993
LIMAGRAIN GENETICS CORP.—Groupe Limagrain; *Int'l*, pg. 566
LIPHA PHARMACEUTICALS, INC.—Lipha Chemicals S.A.; *Int'l*, pg. 812
LIPHATECH, INC.—Lipha Chemicals S.A.; *Int'l*, pg. 812
ARTHUR D. LITTLE, INC.; *U.S. Private*, pg. 670
LOCKHEED MARTIN TRAINING & TECHNICAL SERVICES—Lockheed Martin Corporation; *U.S. Public*, pg. 1009
LOGICON GEODYNAMIC—Northrop Grumman Corporation; *U.S. Public*, pg. 1199
LOGICON, INC.—Northrop Grumman Corporation; *U.S. Public*, pg. 1198
LOGICON R & D ASSOCIATES—Northrop Grumman Corporation; *U.S. Public*, pg. 1199
MATSUSHITA ELECTRIC WORKS RESEARCH & DEVELOPMENT LABORATORY INC.—Matsushita Electric Works, Ltd.; *Int'l*, pg. 848
THE MAXIMA CORPORATION; *U.S. Private*, pg. 716
MAXWELL TECHNOLOGIES, INC.; *U.S. Public*, pg. 1061
MECHANICAL TECHNOLOGY INC.; *U.S. Public*, pg. 1077
MEDIMMUNE, INC.; *U.S. Public*, pg. 1081
MEDTRONIC, INC.; *U.S. Public*, pg. 1082
MEDTRONIC MILACA, INC.—Medtronic, Inc.; *U.S. Public*, pg. 1083
MERCK & CO., INC.; *U.S. Public*, pg. 1090
MERCK RESEARCH LABORATORIES—Merck & Co., Inc.; *U.S. Public*, pg. 1091
MERCK SHARP & DOHME SCIENTIFIC & MANAGEMENT CORP.—Merck & Co., Inc.; *U.S. Public*, pg. 1091
MERIDIAN MEDICAL TECHNOLOGY, INC.; *U.S. Public*, pg. 1095
METAL BOX PLC., RESEARCH & DEVELOPMENT DIV.—Caradon Plc; *Int'l*, pg. 267
METEOR-EXPERIMENTAL FACILITY—IRI Istituto Ricostruzione Industriale; *Int'l*, pg. 653
MIAMI VALLEY DEVELOPMENT CO.—DPL Inc.; *U.S. Public*, pg. 474
MIDREX CORP.—Kobe Steel, Ltd.; *Int'l*, pg. 740
MINEMET RECHERCHE—Imetal; *Int'l*, pg. 661
MOBIL RESEARCH AND DEVELOPMENT CORPORATION—Mobil Oil Corporation; *U.S. Public*, pg. 1118
MYCOGEN CORPORATION; *U.S. Public*, pg. 1142
NCH CORPORATION; *U.S. Public*, pg. 1145
NEC RESEARCH INSTITUTE, INC.—NEC Corporation; *Int'l*, *pg. 900*
NATIONAL SYSTEMS & RESEARCH CO.; *U.S. Private*, pg. 787
NEUROGEN CORPORATION; *U.S. Public*, pg. 1169
NICHOLAS TURKEY BREEDING FARMS—Booker PLC; *Int'l*, pg. 202
NICHOLS RESEARCH CORPORATION; *U.S. Public*, pg. 1182
NOBEL BIOCARE; *Int'l*, pg. 951
NOKIA MOBILE PHONES R & D—Oy Nokia Ab/Nokia Group; *Int'l*, pg. 952
NORTHERN RESEARCH & ENGINEERING CORP.—Ingersoll-Rand Company; *U.S. Public*, pg. 877
NORTHRUP KING CO.—Novartis AG; *Int'l*, pg. 974
NOVO NORDISK BIOINDUSTRIALS, INC.—Novo Nordisk A/S; *Int'l*, pg. 987
OCE-NEDERLAND B.V.—Oce-van der Grinten N.V.; *Int'l*, pg. 994
OLIVETTI ADVANCED TECHNOLOGY CENTER, INC.—Olivetti SpA; *Int'l*, pg. 1002
OLIVETTI RICERCA—Olivetti SpA; *Int'l*, pg. 1002
OLIVETTI SPA; *Int'l*, pg. 1002
ORGANON TEKNIKA MEDIZINSCHE PRODUKTE GMBH—Akzo Nobel N.V.; *Int'l*, pg. 45
PPD PHARMACO, INC.—Pharmaceutical Product Development, Inc.; *U.S. Public*, pg. 1285
PACER INFOTEC INC.; *U.S. Private*, pg. 830
PALO ALTO RESEARCH CENTER—Xerox Corporation; *U.S. Public*, pg. 1784
PARAVANT COMPUTER SYSTEMS, INC.; *U.S. Public*, pg. 1257
PAREXEL INTERNATIONAL CORPORATION; *U.S. Public*, *pg. 1257*
PERSTORP ANALYTICAL AB-DISTRIBUTION HQ—Perstorp AB; *Int'l*, pg. 1039

PERSTORP ANALYTICAL B.V—Perstorp AB; Int'l, pg. 1039
PERSTORP ANALYTICAL GMBH—Perstorp AB; Int'l, pg. 1039
PERSTORP ANALYTICAL INC. DIVISION NIRSYSTEMS—Perstorp AB; Int'l, pg. 1039
PERSTORP ANALYTICAL S.A.—Perstorp AB; Int'l, pg. 1040
PERSTORP ANALYTICAL TECATOR AB—Perstorp AB; Int'l, pg. 1040
PERSTORP PHARMA AB—Perstorp AB; Int'l, pg. 1036
PHARMACEUTICAL PRODUCT DEVELOPMENT, INC.; U.S. Public, pg. 1285
PHYSICS INTERNATIONAL CO.—Olin Corporation; U.S. Public, pg. 1219
PILOT RESEARCH CORP.—Alba-Waldensian, Inc.; U.S. Public, pg. 36
PIONEER HI-BRED INTERNATIONAL, INC.; U.S. Public, pg. 1298
PLANNING SYSTEMS INC.; U.S. Private, pg. 869
POLY-CRAFT SYSTEMS—Binks Sames Corporation; U.S. Public, pg. 229
PRIMEDICA—Genzyme Corporation; U.S. Public, pg. 733
PRODUCTS RESEARCH & CHEMICAL CORP. RESEARCH LABORATORIES—Courtaulds plc; Int'l, pg. 339
PROSESS-STYRING A/S—Perstorp AB; Int'l, pg. 1040
QUESTAR CORPORATION; U.S. Public, pg. 1352
QUESTAR DEVELOPMENT CORPORATION—Questar Corporation; U.S. Public, pg. 1352
QUINTRON SYSTEMS, INC.; U.S. Private, pg. 901
RHM TECHNOLOGY LTD.—Tomkins PLC; Int'l, pg. 1396
RADIAN INTERNATIONAL LLC—The Dow Chemical Company; U.S. Public, pg. 522
RAND; U.S. Private, pg. 908
RANGEN AQUACULTURE RESEARCH—Rangen, Inc.; U.S. Private, pg. 909
RECORDATI INDUSTRIA CHIMICA E FARMACEUTICA S.P.A.; Int'l, pg. 1090
REFINING & MANUFACTURING RESEARCH CENTER—Chinese Petroleum Corporation; Int'l, pg. 286
REICHHOLD CHEMICALS DIV.—Dainippon Ink & Chemicals, Inc.; Int'l, pg. 370
RELECMAP, S.A.—Corporacion MAPFRE, Compania Internacional de Reaseguros, S.A.; Int'l, pg. 333
REPLIGEN SANDOZ RESEARCH CORP.—Novartis AG; Int'l, pg. 974
RESEARCH & DEVELOPMENT DEPT.—Mobil Oil Corporation; U.S. Public, pg. 1118
RESEARCH TRIANGLE INSTITUTE; U.S. Private, pg. 924
RETI SA—Akzo Nobel N.V.; Int'l, pg. 45
REVLON RESEARCH CENTER, INC.—MacAndrews & Forbes Holdings Inc.; U.S. Private, pg. 690
RHONE-POULENC RORER LTD.—Rhone-Poulenc S.A.; Int'l, pg. 1110
RICERA INC.—Ishihara Sangyo Kaisha, Ltd.; Int'l, pg. 689
RING AROUND PRODUCTS, INC.—Occidental Petroleum Corporation; U.S. Public, pg. 1210
ROHM LSI SYSTEMS INC.—Rohm Co., Ltd.; Int'l, pg. 1125
ROTHENBERGER ROHRSANIERUNG GMBH—Rothenberger Group GmbH; Int'l, pg. 1128
SBC WARBURG GROUP MANAGEMENT LTD.—Swiss Bank Corporation; Int'l, pg. 1331
SDS BIOTECH K.K.—Novartis AG; Int'l, pg. 984
SEB DEVELOPPEMENT S.A.—Groupe SEB; Int'l, pg. 568
SFA, INC.; U.S. Private, pg. 956
SRS TECHNOLOGIES; U.S. Private, pg. 958
S.T. RESEARCH; U.S. Private, pg. 958
STI OPTRONICS—Spectra-Physics AB; Int'l, pg. 1289
SACOM, INC.—SFA, Inc.; U.S. Private, pg. 956
SANDOZ AGRO, INC.—Novartis AG; Int'l, pg. 974
SANDOZ AGRO LTD.—Novartis AG; Int'l, pg. 972
SANDOZ AGRO S.A.—Novartis AG; Int'l, pg. 984
SANDOZ AGRO S.A.E.—Novartis AG; Int'l, pg. 984
SANDOZ AGRO S.P.A.—Novartis AG; Int'l, pg. 984
SANDOZ CORPORATION—Novartis AG; Int'l, pg. 974
SANDOZ FORSCHUNGSINSTITUT GESELLSCHAFT M.B.H.—Novartis AG; Int'l, pg. 984
SANDOZ PHARMA LTD.—Novartis AG; Int'l, pg. 972
SANDOZ RESEARCH INSTITUTE BERNE LTD.—Novartis AG; Int'l, pg. 972
SANDOZ SEEDS LTD.—Novartis AG; Int'l, pg. 972
SANDOZ TECHNOLOGY LTD.—Novartis AG; Int'l, pg. 972
SANOFI RESEARCH CO. INC.—Elf Aquitaine; Int'l, pg. 445
SANOFI RESEARCH DIVISION—Elf Aquitaine; Int'l, pg. 445
SANTA BARBARA RESEARCH CENTER—Raytheon Company; U.S. Public, pg. 1365
SARNOFF CORPORATION—SRI International; U.S. Private, pg. 958
SCIENCE APPLICATIONS INTERNATIONAL CORP.; U.S. Private, pg. 975
SCIENTIFIC PROTEIN LABORATORIES, INC.—American Home Products Corporation; U.S. Public, pg. 80
SCIOS INC.; U.S. Public, pg. 1444
SERVIPHARM LTD.—Novartis AG; Int'l, pg. 972
SHELL DEVELOPMENT CO.—Royal Dutch/Shell Group of Companies; Int'l, pg. 1136
SHELL RESEARCH LTD.—Royal Dutch/Shell Group of Companies; Int'l, pg. 1139
SHIP ANALYTICS, INC.; U.S. Private, pg. 994
J.E. SIEBEL & SONS COMPANY INC.—Rhone-Poulenc S.A.; Int'l, pg. 1110
SIEMENS MICROELECTRONICS CENTER GMBH & CO.—Siemens AG; Int'l, pg. 1245
SIMON LABORATORIES—Simon Engineering plc; Int'l, pg. 1251
SMITH & NEPHEW RESEARCH LTD.—Smith & Nephew PLC; Int'l, pg. 1263
SMITH ENVIRONMENTAL TECHNOLOGIES CORP.—Smith Environmental Technologies Corp.; U.S. Public, pg. 1478
SMITHKLINE BEECHAM PHARMACEUTICALS, RESEARCH DIVISION—SmithKline Beecham plc; Int'l, pg. 1264
SMITHKLINE DIAGNOSTICS—Beckman Instruments, Inc.; U.S. Public, pg. 199
SOCIETE DES PRODUITS NESTLE S.A.—Nestle S.A.; Int'l, pg. 916
SOUTHEASTERN WISCONSIN PRODUCTS CO., INC.—Campbell Soup Company; U.S. Public, pg. 299
SOUTHWESTERN BELL TECHNOLOGY RESOURCES—SBC Communications Inc.; U.S. Public, pg. 1416
SOWERBY RESEARCH CENTRE—British Aerospace p.l.c.; Int'l, pg. 218
SPRINGBORN TESTING & RESEARCH, INC.; U.S. Private, pg. 1027
SURFACE SCIENCE LABORATORIES—Rhone-Poulenc S.A.; Int'l, pg. 1111
SURVEY RESEARCH ASSOCIATES—Battelle Memorial Institute; U.S. Private, pg. 123
SVERDRUP CORPORATION; U.S. Private, pg. 1057
SYNTEX—Roche Holding Ltd.; Int'l, pg. 1120
SYSTEM PLANNING CORP.; U.S. Private, pg. 1061
TSI ARGUS RESEARCH LABORATORIES & CENTER FOR PHOTOBIOLOGY—Genzyme Corporation; U.S. Public, pg. 733
TSI CORPORATION—Genzyme Corporation; U.S. Public, pg. 733
TSI MASON LABORATORIES—Genzyme Corporation; U.S. Public, pg. 733
TECSTAR INC.; U.S. Private, pg. 1072
TECUMSEH PRODUCTS RESEARCH LAB.—Tecumseh Products Company; U.S. Public, pg. 1566
TETRA TECH NUS, INC.—Tetra Tech, Inc.; U.S. Public, pg. 1582
THERMO ELECTRON CORPORATION; U.S. Public, pg. 1591
THERMOTREX—Thermo Electron Corporation; U.S. Public, pg. 1595
UES, INC.; U.S. Private, pg. 1112
U.M. HOLDING LIMITED; U.S. Private, pg. 1113
UNILEVER RESEARCH & DEVELOPMENT CO.—Unilever Plc; Int'l, pg. 1436
UNILEVER U.K. CENTRAL RESOURCES LTD.—Unilever Plc; Int'l, pg. 1434
U.S. BIOSCIENCE, INC.; U.S. Public, pg. 1681
VG INSTRUMENTS PLC—Thermo Electron Corporation; U.S. Public, pg. 1595
VILJAVUUSPALVELU OY—Kemira Oy; Int'l, pg. 728
AB VOLVO, TECHNOLOGICAL DEVELOPMENT—AB Volvo; Int'l, pg. 1476
WAMPOLE LABORATORIES—Carter-Wallace, Inc.; U.S. Public, pg. 310
WATERFORD GLASS RESEARCH & DEVELOPMENT LTD.—Waterford Wedgwood Plc; Int'l, pg. 1487
WYLE LABORATORIES, INC.; U.S. Private, pg. 1193
XEROX CORPORATE RESEARCH GROUP—Xerox Corporation; U.S. Public, pg. 1784
ZEXEL USA CORPORATION—Zexel Corporation; Int'l, pg. 1528
ZYGO CORPORATION; U.S. Public, pg. 1795
ZYMA SA—Novartis AG; Int'l, pg. 972
ZYMOGENETICS, INC.—Novo Nordisk A/S; Int'l, pg. 987

8732 — COMMERCIAL ECONOMIC, SOCIOLOGICAL & EDUCATIONAL RESEARCH

ASI MARKET RESEARCH, INC.—IDC Services, Inc.; U.S. Private, pg. 554
ARIANESPACE SA; Int'l, pg. 81
THE BIS GROUP LIMITED—Bell Atlantic Corporation; U.S. Public, pg. 204
BNR EUROPE LIMITED—Northern Telecom Limited; Int'l, pg. 969
BASES WORLDWIDE; U.S. Private, pg. 120
BELDEN ASSOCIATES—VNU Verenigde Nederlandse Uitgeversbedrijven B.V.; Int'l, pg. 1447
BOOZ, ALLEN & HAMILTON INC.; U.S. Private, pg. 157
CSELT—Telecom Italia S.p.A.; Int'l, pg. 1362
CANNONGATE TECHNOLOGY LIMITED—Scottish & Newcastle plc; Int'l, pg. 1211
CERIDIAN CORPORATION; U.S. Public, pg. 330
CHILTON RESEARCH SERVICES—Reed Elsevier plc; Int'l, pg. 1096
CLARITAS, INC.—VNU Verenigde Nederlandse Uitgeversbedrijven B.V.; Int'l, pg. 1447
COGNIZANT CORPORATION; U.S. Public, pg. 395
COMPUTER INTELLIGENCE—Softbank Corporation; Int'l, pg. 1276
COMPUTER INTELLIGENCE INFOCORP—Softbank Corporation; Int'l, pg. 1276
DATAQUEST INCORPORATED—The Dun & Bradstreet Corporation; U.S. Public, pg. 535
THE DUN & BRADSTREET CORPORATION; U.S. Public, pg. 535
EIDESIGN TECHNOLOGIES, INC.—Nippon Steel Corporation; Int'l, pg. 940
ELRICK & LAVIDGE, INC.—Equifax Inc.; U.S. Public, pg. 588
EQUIFAX INC.; U.S. Public, pg. 588
ESTRATEGIAS TELEFONICAS, S.A. (ESTRATEL)—Telefonica de Espana, S.A.; Int'l, pg. 1371
GOLDMAN FINANCIAL GROUP; U.S. Private, pg. 461
THE HENLEY CENTRE—WPP Group plc; Int'l, pg. 1482
IN-STAT INCORPORATED—Reed Elsevier plc; Int'l, pg. 1096
INFOCORP—Softbank Corporation; Int'l, pg. 1276
INFORMATION RESOURCES, INC.; U.S. Public, pg. 875
INTERNATIONAL DATA GROUP; U.S. Private, pg. 569
K-LUOTTO OY—Kesko Ltd.; Int'l, pg. 732
MARITZ MARKETING RESEARCH, INC.—Maritz Inc.; U.S. Private, pg. 704
MARKET FACTS, INC.; U.S. Public, pg. 1046
MARKET FACTS, INC.—Market Facts, Inc.; U.S. Public, pg. 1047
MARKET FACTS OF CANADA, LTD.—Market Facts, Inc.; U.S. Public, pg. 1047
MEDICAL MARKETING GROUP, INC.—Merck & Co., Inc.; U.S. Public, pg. 1091
MITSUBISHI HEAVY INDUSTRIES AMERICA, INC. (MHIA)—Mitsubishi Heavy Industries Ltd.; Int'l, pg. 874
NATIONAL RESEARCH CORPORATION; U.S. Public, pg. 1159
A.C. NIELSEN COMPANY AB—A.C. Nielsen; U.S. Public, pg. 1183
A.C. NIELSEN CO.—A.C. Nielsen; U.S. Public, pg. 1183
NIELSEN MARKETING RESEARCH A/S—A.C. Nielsen; U.S. Public, pg. 1184
NIELSEN NORGE—A.C. Nielsen; U.S. Public, pg. 1184
NIPPON STEEL U.S.A., INC.—Nippon Steel Corporation; Int'l, pg. 939
ORGANON LABORATORIES LTD.—Akzo Nobel N.V.; Int'l, pg. 45
PHILIPS LABORATORIES—Philips Electronics N.V.; Int'l, pg. 1054
PRIMARK CORPORATION; U.S. Public, pg. 1325
RMS TECHS, INC.; U.S. Private, pg. 905
ROPER STARCH WORLDWIDE; U.S. Private, pg. 944
RYOBI AMERICA CORP.—Ryobi Ltd.; Int'l, pg. 1151
SCARBOROUGH RESEARCH CORPORATION—VNU Verenigde Nederlandse Uitgeversbedrijven B.V.; Int'l, pg. 1447
SHANDWICK DETROIT—Shandwick International Plc; Int'l, pg. 1227
SOFRES AM, S.A.—Telefonica de Espana, S.A.; Int'l, pg. 1372
SOLVAY TECHNOLOGIES INC—Solvay S.A.; Int'l, pg. 1277
STRATEGIC MARKETING SERVICES LONDON—Total Research Corporation; U.S. Public, pg. 1625
SURVEY SAMPLING, INC.; U.S. Private, pg. 1056
TOSOH USA, INC.-NEW JERSEY OFFICE—Tosoh Corporation; Int'l, pg. 1407
TOTAL RESEARCH CORPORATION; U.S. Public, pg. 1625
TOTAL RESEARCH CORPORATION—Total Research Corporation; U.S. Public, pg. 1625
TOYO SEIKAN KAISHA, LTD. (U.S.A.)—Toyo Seikan Kaisha, Ltd.; Int'l, pg. 1411
TRAFALGAR HOUSE CORPORATE DEVELOPMENT LTD.—Kvaerner a.s.a.; Int'l, pg. 773
WESTAT INC.; U.S. Private, pg. 1163

8733 — NONCOMMERCIAL RESEARCH ORGANIZATIONS

ACME PRINTING INK CO., INC.—Sumitomo Chemical Company, Ltd.; Int'l, pg. 1311
AMERICAN ENTERPRISE INSTITUTE FOR PUBLIC POLICY RESEARCH; U.S. Private, pg. 53
AMERICAN HEALTH ASSISTANCE FOUNDATION; U.S. Private, pg. 56
ANSER (ANALYTIC SERVICES INC.); U.S. Private, pg. 75
ANTARCTIC SUPPORT ASSOCIATES—EG & G, Inc.; U.S. Public, pg. 544
BIO-RAD LABORATORIES, INC.; U.S. Public, pg. 230
DNA PLANT TECHNOLOGY CORP.—Empressa La Moderna SA de CV; Int'l, pg. 454
DNAP HOLDING CORP.—Empressa La Moderna SA de CV; Int'l, pg. 454
ELDON LABORATORIES LIMITED—Alliance UniChem PLC; Int'l, pg. 58
ELSEVIER SCIENCE (INTERNATIONAL)—Reed Elsevier plc; Int'l, pg. 1099
GTE INTERNETWORKING—GTE Corporation; U.S. Public, pg. 696
GENOME THERAPEUTICS CORPORATION; U.S. Public, pg. 730
HARCOURT BRACE & COMPANY - ELEMENTARY DIV.—Harcourt General, Inc.; U.S. Public, pg. 783
IIT RESEARCH INSTITUTE; U.S. Private, pg. 555
KVAERNER EUREKA A/S, TRANBY—Kvaerner a.s.a.; Int'l, pg. 766
LILLY RESEARCH CENTRE LIMITED—Eli Lilly and Company; U.S. Public, pg. 994
MRB GROUP, INC.—WPP Group plc; Int'l, pg. 1483
MARSHFIELD CLINIC; U.S. Private, pg. 708
MITRE CORPORATION; U.S. Private, pg. 753
NLI RESEARCH INSTITUTE—Nippon Life Insurance Co.; Int'l, pg. 935
NIPPON LIFE INSURANCE FOUNDATION—Nippon Life Insurance Co.; Int'l, pg. 935
NISSAY SEIREI HEALTH & WELFARE FOUNDATION—Nippon Life Insurance Co.; Int'l, pg. 935
ORBITAL SCIENCES CORPORATION; U.S. Public, pg. 1229
THE RESEARCH INSTITUTE OF LIFE INSURANCE WELFARE—Nippon Life Insurance Co.; Int'l, pg. 935
SADTLER RESEARCH LABORATORIES—Bio-Rad Laboratories, Inc.; U.S. Public, pg. 230
SVERDRUP CORPORATION; U.S. Private, pg. 1057
SVERDRUP TECHNOLOGY, INC.—Sverdrup Corporation; U.S. Private, pg. 1057
THERMO CARDIOSYSTEMS INC.—Thermo Electron Corporation; U.S. Public, pg. 1592

8734 — TESTING LABORATORIES

ABB STEAM POWER GENERATION COMPANY—ABB Asea Brown Boveri (Holding) Ltd.; Int'l, pg. 4
ACCORD CONTRACT SERVICES—Veba AG; Int'l, pg. 1458
ACTON ENVIRONMENTAL TESTING—National Technical Systems, Inc.; U.S. Public, pg. 1161
AGRA EARTH & ENVIRONMENTAL, INC.—Agra Inc.; Int'l, pg. 31
AGRA EARTH & ENVIRONMENTAL LIMITED—Agra Inc.; Int'l, pg. 30
AMERICAN WASTE SERVICES, INC.; U.S. Public, pg. 94
ANALYTICAL SERVICES CORPORATION—OHM Corporation; U.S. Public, pg. 1207
ANALYTICAL TECHNOLOGIES, INC.—Bacardi Limited; Int'l, pg. 131

S.I.C. Index

ARCTIC ALASKA TESTING LABORATORIES—Shannon & Wilson, Inc.; *U.S. Private*, pg. 989
ARIANESPACE SA; *Int'l*, pg. 81
ASSOCIATED TESTING LABORATORIES, INC.—Publicker Industries Inc.; *U.S. Public*, pg. 1341
ATLAS ELECTRIC DEVICES CO.; *U.S. Private*, pg. 96
BACARDI CORPORATION—Bacardi Limited; *Int'l*, pg. 131
CR QUALITY SERVICES, INC.—Conrail, Inc.; *U.S. Public*, pg. 432
COMSEARCH APPLIED TECHNOLOGY, INC.—Allen Telecom, Inc.; *U.S. Public*, pg. 46
COMSEARCH, INC.—Allen Telecom, Inc.; *U.S. Public*, pg. 46
CONSOLIDATED X-RAY SERVICE CORPORATION—Costain Group PLC; *Int'l*, pg. 337
CROSBY & OVERTON, INC.; *U.S. Private*, pg. 290
DEERE & COMPANY; *U.S. Public*, pg. 491
DYNAMICS RESEARCH CORPORATION; *U.S. Public*, pg. 539
EG & G AUTOMOTIVE RESEARCH—EG & G, Inc.; *U.S. Public*, pg. 544
EG & G STRUCTURAL KINEMATICS—EG & G, Inc.; *U.S. Public*, pg. 544
ECOLOGY AND ENVIRONMENT, INC.; *U.S. Public*, pg. 562
EIDESIGN TECHNOLOGIES, INC.—Nippon Steel Corporation; *Int'l*, pg. 940
ENGINEERING TEST SERVICES—Cummins Engine Company, Inc.; *U.S. Public*, pg. 468
ENVIRON, INC.—Ford Motor Company; *U.S. Public*, pg. 664
ERIEZ MAGNETICS; *U.S. Private*, pg. 381
FOSTER WHEELER CORPORATION; *U.S. Public*, pg. 676
GKN TECHNOLOGY LTD.—GKN plc; *Int'l*, pg. 535
GKN TECHNOLOGY US—GKN plc; *Int'l*, pg. 535
GP INSTRUMENT SERVICES—GP Strategies Corporation; *U.S. Public*, pg. 694
GZA GEOENVIRONMENTAL TECHNOLOGIES, INC.; *U.S. Public*, pg. 697
GEONEX—Geonex Corporation; *U.S. Private*, pg. 448
GEONEX CORPORATION; *U.S. Private*, pg. 447
GREAT LAKES CHEMICAL CORPORATION; *U.S. Public*, pg. 760
GRIFFITH MICRO SCIENCE INTERNATIONAL INC.—Griffith Laboratories Worldwide, Inc.; *U.S. Private*, pg. 481
HADEN ENVIRONMENTAL CORPORATION—Haden Maclellan Holdings plc; *Int'l*, pg. 586
HART CROWSER, INC.; *U.S. Private*, pg. 507
HONDA RACING CORPORATION—Honda Motor Co., Ltd.; *Int'l*, pg. 634
HUDSON, RCI; *U.S. Private*, pg. 546
IEA, INC.-MASSACHUSETTS—Aquarion Company; *U.S. Public*, pg. 126
INDUSTRIAS METALURGICAS LIEBAU S.A.—FKI Plc; *Int'l*, *pg. 473*
LAB ONE—Seafield Capital Corporation; *U.S. Public*, pg. 1449
LANDAUER, INC.; *U.S. Public*, pg. 977
LAW ENGINEERING, INC.; *U.S. Private*, pg. 653
LORD RESEARCH & DEVELOPMENT—Lord Corporation; *U.S. Private*, pg. 676
MAXWELL TECHNOLOGIES, INC.; *U.S. Public*, pg. 1061
NTH CONSULTANTS, LTD.; *U.S. Private*, pg. 772
NTS DETROIT—National Technical Systems, Inc.; *U.S. Public*, pg. 1161
NAGASE-LANDAUER, LTD.—Landauer, Inc.; *U.S. Public*, pg. 977
NATIONAL TECHNICAL SYSTEMS, INC.; *U.S. Public*, pg. 1161
NEWPARK ENVIRONMENTAL SERVICES, INC.—Newpark Resources, Inc.; *U.S. Public*, pg. 1179
A.C. NIELSEN CO. (BELGIUM) S.A.—A.C. Nielsen; *U.S. Public*, pg. 1183
NISSAN RESEARCH & DEVELOPMENT CORP.—Nissan Motor Co., Ltd.; *Int'l*, pg. 945
NOKIA MOBILE PHONES, INC.—Oy Nokia Ab/Nokia Group; *Int'l*, pg. 952
NOKIA MOBILE PHONES MANUFACTURING (USA) LTD.—Oy Nokia Ab/Nokia Group; *Int'l*, pg. 952
NOKIA MOBILE PHONES R & D—Oy Nokia Ab/Nokia Group; *Int'l*, pg. 952
NOKIA MOBILE PHONES R & D CENTER—Oy Nokia Ab/Nokia Group; *Int'l*, pg. 952
NORTHRUP KING SEMILLAS S.A.—Novartis AG; *Int'l*, pg. 983
PACCAR TECHNICAL CENTER—Paccar Inc.; *U.S. Public*, pg. 1246
PACE ANALYTICAL SERVICES; *U.S. Private*, pg. 829
PHARMACIA & UPJOHN, INC.; *Int'l*, pg. 1047
PHARMAKINETICS LABORATORIES, INC.; *U.S. Public*, pg. 1285
QC, INC.—Land O'Lakes, Inc.; *U.S. Private*, pg. 646
RTI LABORATORIES DIVISION—Detrex Corporation; *U.S. Public*, pg. 502
RELIABILITY INCORPORATED; *U.S. Public*, pg. 1373
STR SHANGHAI OFFICE—Springborn Testing & Research, Inc.; *U.S. Private*, pg. 1027
SIMON LABORATORIES—Simon Engineering plc; *Int'l*, pg. 1251
SITA—Lyonnaise des Eaux S.A.; *Int'l*, pg. 824
SMITH-EMERY COMPANY; *U.S. Private*, pg. 1007
SMITHKLINE BEECHAM LABS—SmithKline Beecham plc; *Int'l*, pg. 1265
THE SOMERSET GROUP, INC.; *U.S. Public*, pg. 1484
SOUTH FLORIDA TEST SERVICE—Atlas Electric Devices Co.; *U.S. Private*, pg. 96
SPRINGBORN TESTING & RESEARCH, INC.; *U.S. Private*, *pg. 1027*
SVERDRUP CORPORATION; *U.S. Private*, pg. 1057
SVERDRUP TECHNOLOGY, INC.—Sverdrup Corporation; *U.S. Private*, pg. 1057
TSI CORPORATION—Genzyme Corporation; *U.S. Public*, pg. 733
TECHNODES S.A.—Ciments Francais; *Int'l*, pg. 292
TERRA TECH LABS, INC.—Thermo Electron Corporation; *U.S. Public*, pg. 1594
THERMO ELECTRON CORPORATION; *U.S. Public*, pg. 1591
THE TITAN CORPORATION; *U.S. Public*, pg. 1618
TITAN SYSTEMS, INC.—The Titan Corporation; *U.S. Public*, pg. 1618
TURNER/CAS LABORATORIES, INC.—EMCON; *U.S. Public*, pg. 571
U.M. HOLDING LIMITED; *U.S. Private*, pg. 1113
UNIKIS JAPAN CO. LTD.—Unican Security Systems Ltd.; *Int'l*, pg. 1432
VRG INTERNATIONAL, INC.—Roberts Pharmaceutical Corporation; *U.S. Public*, pg. 1393
VARLEN CORPORATION; *U.S. Public*, pg. 1710
VARLEN INSTRUMENTS, INC.—Varlen Corporation; *U.S. Public*, pg. 1711
WIL RESEARCH LABORATORIES, INC.—Great Lakes Chemical Corporation; *U.S. Public*, pg. 760
WYLE LABORATORIES, INC.; *U.S. Private*, pg. 1193

8741 — MANAGEMENT SERVICES

ABB SERVICE AB—ABB Asea Brown Boveri (Holding) Ltd.; *Int'l*, pg. 7
ABN MANAGEMENT SERVICES A.G.—ABN-AMRO Holding N.V.; *Int'l*, pg. 11
ALIC, INCORPORATED—Cigna Corp.; *U.S. Public*, pg. 364
ADMINISTRATIVE SERVICES, INC.—National Life Insurance Company; *U.S. Private*, pg. 785
ADVANCED MARINE ENTERPRISES, INC.—Nichols Research Corporation; *U.S. Public*, pg. 1182
ADVENT INTERNATIONAL; *U.S. Private*, pg. 22
THE AEGIS GROUP, INC.—Automobile Protection Corporation-APCO; *U.S. Public*, pg. 150
AEROFLEX SYSTEMS CORP.—Aeroflex Incorporated; *U.S. Public*, pg. 24
ALLIANCE CONSTRUCTION SOLUTIONS, INC.; *U.S. Private*, pg. 38
AMACO B.V., AMSTELVEEN—Internatio-Muller N.V.; *Int'l*, pg. 682
AMAX ENERGY, INC.—Cyprus Amax Minerals Company; *U.S. Public*, pg. 470
AMERICAN COMMONWEALTH MANAGEMENT SERVICES COMPANY, INC.—American Water Works Company, Inc.; *U.S. Public*, pg. 95
AMERICAN INTERNATIONAL WATER SERVICES COMPANY—American Water Works Company, Inc.; *U.S. Public*, pg. 95
AMERICAN ROCHE INTL. INC.—Roche Holding Ltd.; *Int'l*, pg. 1120
AMERICAN TRADING & PRODUCTION CORPORATION, OIL & GAS DIV.—American Trading and Production Corporation; *U.S. Private*, pg. 64
AMERICAN WATER WORKS COMPANY, INC.; *U.S. Public*, pg. 95
AMERICAN WATER WORKS SERVICE COMPANY, INC.—American Water Works Company, Inc.; *U.S. Public*, pg. 95
AMERICANANGLIAN ENVIRONMENTAL TECHNOLOGIES, INC.—American Water Works Company, Inc.; *U.S. Public*, pg. 95
AMOCO SERVICES, INC.—Amoco Corporation; *U.S. Public*, *pg. 103*
THE ARBITRON COMPANY—Ceridian Corporation; *U.S. Public*, pg. 331
ARCTIC SLOPE REGIONAL CORPORATION; *U.S. Private*, *pg. 80*
ARRINGTON-HILLGATE INTERNATIONAL—Arrington Travel Center Inc.; *U.S. Private*, pg. 85
ASAHI BANK JIMU SERVICE CO., LTD.—The Asahi Bank, Ltd.; *Int'l*, pg. 82
ASPEN SYSTEMS CORP.—Wolters Kluwer N.V.; *Int'l*, pg. 1513
ASSOCIATED MERCHANDISING CORP. (AMC); *U.S. Private*, pg. 91
ASSOCIATION MANAGEMENT CORP.—Conseco Inc.; *U.S. Public*, pg. 433
ATCO GAS SERVICES LTD.—ATCO Group Co.; *Int'l*, pg. 95
ATHENA AB—Incentive AB; *Int'l*, pg. 666
GEORGE W. AUCH CO.; *U.S. Private*, pg. 98
BA INVESTMENT MANAGERS—BankAmerica Corporation; *U.S. Public*, pg. 180
BP AUSTRALIA LTD.—The British Petroleum Company P.L.C.; *Int'l*, pg. 220
BP JAPAN KK—The British Petroleum Company P.L.C.; *Int'l*, pg. 220
BRE GROUP—Alcatel Alsthom Compagnie Generale D'Electricite; *Int'l*, pg. 52
BRI GROUP—Alcatel Alsthom Compagnie Generale D'Electricite; *Int'l*, pg. 52
BS-SERVICE B.V., ZOETERMEER—Internatio-Muller N.V.; *Int'l*, pg. 682
BARTON MALOW CO.—Barton Malow Enterprises, Inc.; *U.S. Private*, pg. 120
BASES INTERNATIONAL—BASES Worldwide; *U.S. Private*, *pg. 120*
BASES WORLDWIDE—BASES Worldwide; *U.S. Private*, pg. 120
BAY COUNTY JAIL—Corrections Corporation of America; *U.S. Public*, pg. 450
BECHTEL GROUP, INC.; *U.S. Private*, pg. 128
BELL ATLANTIC NETWORK SERVICES, INC.—Bell Atlantic Corporation; *U.S. Public*, pg. 202
BELLSOUTH TELECOMMUNICATIONS, INC.—BellSouth Corporation; *U.S. Public*, pg. 209
BENEFICIAL INSURANCE GROUP, INC.—Beneficial Corporation; *U.S. Public*, pg. 211
BENEFICIAL MANAGEMENT CORPORATION—Beneficial Corporation; *U.S. Public*, pg. 211
BENSON MOTORS CORPORATION; *U.S. Private*, pg. 134
BILLCOM EXPOSITION & CONFERENCE—VNU Verenigde Nederlandse Uitgeversbedrijven B.V.; *Int'l*, pg. 1446
BOBST GMBH—Bobst S.A.; *Int'l*, pg. 199
BORG WARNER AUTOMOTIVE, INC.; *U.S. Public*, pg. 245
BOUYGUES OFFSHORE USA—Bouygues; *Int'l*, pg. 206
BOVIS INTERNATIONAL CALIFORNIA—The Peninsular and Oriental Steam Navigation Company; *Int'l*, pg. 1035
BRICE BUILDING CO., INC.; *U.S. Private*, pg. 167
BRIM, INC.; *U.S. Private*, pg. 168
BRITISH AEROSPACE (CONSULTANCY SERVICES) LIMITED—British Aerospace p.l.c.; *Int'l*, pg. 217
BRITISH AEROSPACE P.L.C.; *Int'l*, pg. 217
THE BURKE INSTITUTE—BASES Worldwide; *U.S. Private*, pg. 120
LEO BURNETT/CONNAGHAN & MAY PTY. LTD.—Leo Burnett Company, Inc.; *U.S. Private*, pg. 185
LEO BURNETT WORLDWIDE ASIA/PACIFIC HDQTRS.—Leo Burnett Company, Inc.; *U.S. Private*, pg. 186
LEO BURNETT WORLDWIDE, LATIN AMERICAN HDQTRS.—Leo Burnett Company, Inc.; *U.S. Private*, pg. 184
BURNS & ROE CONSTRUCTION GROUP INC.—Burns & Roe Enterprises, Inc.; *U.S. Private*, pg. 187
CCA INTERNATIONAL, INC.—Corrections Corporation of America; *U.S. Public*, pg. 451
CGA-HBS (COMPAGNIE GENERALE D'AUTOMATISME)—Alcatel Alsthom Compagnie Generale D'Electricite; *Int'l*, pg. 53
CIS TECHNOLOGIES, INC.—National Data Corporation; *U.S. Public*, pg. 1155
CMS GENERATION CO.—CMS Energy Corporation; *U.S. Public*, pg. 280
C.P. REHAB CORP. OF DELAWARE—Prime Medical Services, Inc.; *U.S. Public*, pg. 1327
CABLE SERVICES GROUP—CSG Systems International, Inc.; *U.S. Public*, pg. 283
CALUMET CONSTRUCTION CORPORATION; *U.S. Private*, pg. 201
CANNON; *U.S. Private*, pg. 205
CANUCK ENGINEERING INC.—Agra Inc.; *Int'l*, pg. 31
CARDINAL HEALTH INC.; *U.S. Public*, pg. 304
W.P. CAREY & CO., INC.; *U.S. Private*, pg. 209
THE P.J. CARLIN CONSTRUCTION COMPANY; *U.S. Private*, pg. 211
CARLSON LEARNING COMPANY—Carlson Companies, Inc.; *U.S. Private*, pg. 212
J.I. CASE INTERNATIONAL SALES—Case Corporation; *U.S. Public*, pg. 312
CEBCOR (CONSOLIDATED EMPLOYMENT BENEFITS CORP.); *U.S. Private*, pg. 220
CENTRAL AND SOUTH WEST CORPORATION; *U.S. Public*, pg. 324
CENTRAL AND SOUTH WEST SERVICES, INC.—Central and South West Corporation; *U.S. Public*, pg. 324
CENTRAL ARIZONA DETENTION CENTER—Corrections Corporation of America; *U.S. Public*, pg. 450
CERTAINTEED FOREIGN SALES CORP.—Saint-Gobain; *Int'l*, pg. 1171
CHAMPION HEALTHCARE CORPORATION; *U.S. Public*, pg. 333
CHASE FINANCIAL MANAGEMENT CORP.—The Chase Manhattan Corporation; *U.S. Public*, pg. 338
CHASE FINANCIAL SERVICES CORP.—The Chase Manhattan Corporation; *U.S. Public*, pg. 338
CHICAGO WEST PULLMAN CORPORATION; *U.S. Private*, *pg. 235*
CIGNA RUN-OFF SERVICES, INC.—Cigna Corp.; *U.S. Public*, pg. 365
CITY BLDG. KANRI CO., LTD.—Matsuya Company Ltd.; *Int'l*, pg. 848
CLEVELAND GROUP, INC.; *U.S. Private*, pg. 246
CLEVELAND PRE-RELEASE CENTER—Corrections Corporation of America; *U.S. Public*, pg. 450
CLUNE CONSTRUCTION LIMITED; *U.S. Private*, pg. 247
COASTAL STATES MANAGEMENT CORP.—The Coastal Corporation; *U.S. Public*, pg. 390
COLORADO PLAINS MEDICAL CENTER—Brim, Inc.; *U.S. Private*, pg. 169
COMMUNITY HOSPITALS OF GALEN, INC.—Columbia/HCA Healthcare Corporation; *U.S. Public*, pg. 404
CONAGRA SEAFOOD COMPANIES—ConAgra, Inc.; *U.S. Public*, pg. 427
CONSTRUCTION MANAGEMENT SERVICE; *U.S. Private*, pg. 266
COOPER COMMUNITIES, INC.; *U.S. Private*, pg. 273
CORNING ENTERPRISES INC.—Corning Incorporated; *U.S. Public*, pg. 448
CORRECTIONS CORPORATION OF AMERICA; *U.S. Public*, pg. 450
CRIIMI MAE; *U.S. Public*, pg. 459
DEI DIVISION—Alcatel Alsthom Compagnie Generale D'Electricite; *Int'l*, pg. 52
DPR CONSTRUCTION, INC.; *U.S. Private*, pg. 305
DAIHATSU MOTOR CO., LTD.—Daihatsu Motor Corporation, Ltd.; *Int'l*, pg. 365
DANA COMMERCIAL CREDIT CORPORATION—Dana Corporation; *U.S. Public*, pg. 479
DAVCO SERVICE, INC.—Lombardi Holdings Inc.; *U.S. Private*, pg. 673
DAY & ZIMMERMANN INTERNATIONAL, INC.—Day & Zimmermann, Inc.; *U.S. Private*, pg. 317
DENNISON INTERNATIONAL CO.—Avery Dennison Corporation; *U.S. Public*, pg. 153
DESCO ADVERTISING & MARKETING—Desco Corporation; *U.S. Private*, pg. 327
DU PONT PROTEIN TECHNOLOGIES INTERNATIONAL—Du Pont (E.I. Du Pont De Nemours & Co.); *U.S. Public*, pg. 531
DUGAN & MEYERS CONSTRUCTION CO.—Dugan & Meyers Interests, Inc.; *U.S. Private*, pg. 345
DUGAN & MEYERS INTERESTS, INC.; *U.S. Private*, pg. 345
E & A INDUSTRIES, INC.; *U.S. Private*, pg. 352
EC III—EG & G, Inc.; *U.S. Public*, pg. 543

EG & G DYNATREND—EG & G, Inc.; *U.S. Public*, pg. 544
ELCO MANAGEMENT CORPORATION—Eli Lilly and Company; *U.S. Public*, pg. 993
ERM-ENVIROCLEAN—Environmental Resources Management; *U.S. Private*, pg. 379
EARTH TECHNOLOGY CORP.—Tyco International Ltd.; *U.S. Public*, pg. 1648
EBASCO ENERGY A.G.—Texas Utilities Company; *U.S. Public*, pg. 1587
ELAN INTERNATIONAL FINANCE LTD.—Elan Corporation Plc; *Int'l*, pg. 436
ELEY AMERICAS INC.—IMI Plc; *Int'l*, pg. 646
EMBASSY SUITES (PUERTO RICO), INC.—Promus Hotel Corporation; *U.S. Public*, pg. 1335
EMCO CUSTOM PRODUCTS GROUP—Emco Limited; *Int'l*, *pg. 453*
ENGELHARD METALS LTD.—Engelhard Corporation; *U.S. Public*, pg. 582
ENRON AMERICAS, INC.—Enron Corp.; *U.S. Public*, pg. 584
THE ERICSSON CORPORATION—Telefonaktiebolaget LM Ericsson; *Int'l*, pg. 1364
A.J. ETKIN CONSTRUCTION CO.—Alex J. Etkin, Inc.; *U.S. Private*, pg. 384
ALEX J. ETKIN, INC.; *U.S. Private*, pg. 384
EXECUTIVE MANAGEMENT AND CONSULTANT SERVICES, INC.—AEGON N.V.; *Int'l*, pg. 27
FISI MADISON FINANCIAL CORPORATION—Cendant Corporation; *U.S. Public*, pg. 320
FAIRFIELD MAXWELL LTD.; *U.S. Private*, pg. 391
FINANCIAL RESEARCH ASSOCIATES—First Financial Building Corporation; *U.S. Private*, pg. 407
FIRST SECURITY SERVICE COMPANY—First Security Corporation; *U.S. Public*, pg. 638
FLUOR CORPORATION; *U.S. Public*, pg. 659
FOLLETT COLLEGE STORES CORP.—Follett Corporation; *U.S. Private*, pg. 417
FORD ASIA-PACIFIC, INC.—Ford Motor Company; *U.S. Public*, pg. 664
FORD MARKETING STAFF—Ford Motor Company; *U.S. Public*, pg. 663
FORD OF EUROPE, INCORPORATED—Ford Motor Company; *U.S. Public*, pg. 664
FORD PRODUCT ASSURANCE—Ford Motor Company; *U.S. Public*, pg. 662
FORD PURCHASING & SUPPLY STAFF—Ford Motor Company; *U.S. Public*, pg. 664
FORD TECHNICAL AFFAIRS & OPERATING STAFFS—Ford Motor Company; *U.S. Public*, pg. 662
FOSTER WHEELER CORPORATION; *U.S. Public*, pg. 676
FOSTER WHEELER ENVIRONMENTAL CORPORATION—Foster Wheeler Corporation; *U.S. Public*, pg. 677
FOUNDATION HEALTH PREFERRED ADMINISTRATORS—Foundation Health Systems, Inc.; *U.S. Public*, pg. 678
FUNDAMENTAL MANAGEMENT, INC.—Industrial Wire Products Corporation; *U.S. Private*, pg. 561
GECC GROUP—Alcatel Alsthom Compagnie Generale D'Electricite; *Int'l*, pg. 53
GKN NORTH AMERICA SERVICES INC.—GKN plc; *Int'l*, pg. 535
GMOC JAPAN—General Motors Corporation; *U.S. Public*, pg. 723
GPI INTERNATIONAL LIMITED—GP Batteries International Ltd.; *Int'l*, pg. 537
GPI (JAPAN) LIMITED—GP Batteries International Ltd.; *Int'l*, pg. 537
GSL SOLAR CONSULTANTS & ADVISORS, INC.—Harris Chemical Group, Inc.; *U.S. Private*, pg. 505
GALEN HOSPITAL CORPORATION, INC.—Columbia/HCA Healthcare Corporation; *U.S. Public*, pg. 404
GENCON SERVICES, INC.—George W. Auch Co.; *U.S. Private*, pg. 98
GENERAL ELECTRIC INTERNATIONAL OPERATIONS—General Electric Company; *U.S. Public*, pg. 713
GENERAL HOSPITAL—Brim, Inc.; *U.S. Private*, pg. 169
GENERAL HOSPITALS OF GALEN, INC.—Columbia/HCA Healthcare Corporation; *U.S. Public*, pg. 404
GEO-CON, INC.—URS Corporation; *U.S. Public*, pg. 1657
GEUPEL DEMARS, INC.; *U.S. Private*, pg. 449
GLENROY CONSTRUCTION CO. INC.; *U.S. Private*, pg. 456
HAB MERCATOR—Axel Johnson AB; *Int'l*, pg. 708
HBO FILM MANAGEMENT, INC.—Time Warner Inc.; *U.S. Public*, pg. 1612
HCA-CLUSTER—Columbia/HCA Healthcare Corporation; *U.S. Public*, pg. 403
HCA-FLORIDA GROUP—Columbia/HCA Healthcare Corporation; *U.S. Public*, pg. 403
HCA INTERNATIONAL CO.—Columbia/HCA Healthcare Corporation; *U.S. Public*, pg. 405
HRH/ATLAS CONSTRUCTION INC.—Starrett HRH; *U.S. Private*, pg. 1035
HADRON, INC.; *U.S. Public*, pg. 773
HEALTHCARE AMERICA, INC.; *U.S. Private*, pg. 515
HEERY INTERNATIONAL, INC.; *U.S. Private*, pg. 519
HELABA INTERNATIONAL FINANCE PLC—Landesbank Hessen-Thuringen Girozentrale; *Int'l*, pg. 799
HERNANDO COUNTY JAIL—Corrections Corporation of America; *U.S. Public*, pg. 450
HIGH INDUSTRIES, INC.; *U.S. Private*, pg. 528
HOOGOVENS ALUMINIUM BV—Koninklijke Hoogovens N.V.; *Int'l*, pg. 753
HOSPITAL DEVELOPMENT CO.—Columbia/HCA Healthcare Corporation; *U.S. Public*, pg. 405
HOUSTON PROCESSING CENTER—Corrections Corporation of America; *U.S. Public*, pg. 450
THE HUNT CORPORATION; *U.S. Private*, pg. 548
HUNT-WESSON CONSUMER ADVERTISING DIV.—ConAgra, Inc.; *U.S. Public*, pg. 428
HUNT-WESSON MARKETING SERVICES DIVISION—ConAgra, Inc.; *U.S. Public*, pg. 428
IDC SERVICES, INC.; *U.S. Private*, pg. 554
IMCO MANAGEMENT PARTNERSHIP L.P.—IMCO Recycling Inc.; *U.S. Public*, pg. 871
IMG; *U.S. Private*, pg. 555
IMI CORNELIUS INC. (MN)—IMI Plc; *Int'l*, pg. 646
IDEX MANAGEMENT, INC.—AEGON N.V.; *Int'l*, pg. 27
INTERACTIVE MARKET SYSTEMS, INC.—VNU Verenigde Nederlandse Uitgeversbedrijven B.V.; *Int'l*, pg. 1447
INTERLEASE MANAGEMENT CORPORATION—American International Group, Inc.; *U.S. Public*, pg. 85
INTERNATIONAL BENEFIT SERVICE CORPORATION—Cigna Corp.; *U.S. Public*, pg. 362
INVESTORS SERVICES GROUP—First Data Corporation; *U.S. Public*, pg. 631
JLW FINANCIAL MANAGEMENT SYSTEMS, INC.—AEGON N.V.; *Int'l*, pg. 28
JAPAN ENERGY (U.S.A.), INC.—Japan Energy Corporation; *Int'l*, pg. 702
JARDINE MATHESON HOLDINGS LIMITED; *Int'l*, pg. 703
JOFFKO INTERNATIONAL; *U.S. Private*, pg. 589
JOFFKO PHILIPPINES, INC.—Joffko International; *U.S. Private*, pg. 589
M.B. KAHN CONSTRUCTION CO., INC.; *U.S. Private*, pg. 604
DANIEL J. KEATING CO.; *U.S. Private*, pg. 610
KELSEY CONSTRUCTION, INC.; *U.S. Private*, pg. 613
KILLEARN ADVISERS, INC.—Killearn Properties, Inc.; *U.S. Public*, pg. 956
KITCHELL CORPORATION; *U.S. Private*, pg. 624
KNIGHT WENDLING AG—Lester B. Knight & Associates, Inc.; *U.S. Private*, pg. 627
KNIGHT WENDLING LTD.—Lester B. Knight & Associates, Inc.; *U.S. Private*, pg. 627
KOHAP ENG. & CONST. CO., LTD.—KOHAP Group; *Int'l*, pg. 742
KRONOS WORLDWIDE SERVICES SA/NV—Contran Corporation; *U.S. Private*, pg. 271
KVAERNER BOVING—Kvaerner a.s.a.; *Int'l*, pg. 772
KVAERNER ENGINEERING A/S—Kvaerner a.s.a.; *Int'l*, pg. 766
LAREDO PROCESSING CENTER—Corrections Corporation of America; *U.S. Public*, pg. 450
LEHMAN BROTHERS INTERNATIONAL LIMITED—Lehman Brothers Holdings Inc.; *U.S. Public*, pg. 987
ELI LILLY ASIA, INC.—Eli Lilly and Company; *U.S. Public*, pg. 993
LINCOLN NATIONAL ADMINISTRATIVE SERVICES CORP.—Lincoln National Corporation; *U.S. Public*, pg. 998
LIPHA PHARMACEUTICALS, INC.—Lipha Chemicals S.A.; *Int'l*, pg. 812
ARTHUR D. LITTLE ENTERPRISES, INC.—Arthur D. Little, Inc.; *U.S. Private*, pg. 670
LOBLAW INTERNATIONAL MERCHANTS—George Weston Limited; *Int'l*, pg. 1495
LOCKHEED INFORMATION MANAGEMENT SERVICES CO.—Lockheed Martin Corporation; *U.S. Public*, pg. 1009
LOCKHEED MARTIN SKUNK WORKS—Lockheed Martin Corporation; *U.S. Public*, pg. 1007
LUNDY CONSTRUCTION CO., INC.; *U.S. Private*, pg. 681
LYNDEN LOGISTICS, INC.—Lynden Incorporated; *U.S. Private*, pg. 684
MAN VERWALTUNGS-GESELLSCHAFT MIT BESCHRAENKTER HAFTUNG—MAN Aktiengesellschaft; *Int'l*, pg. 825
MEC USA, INC.—Mitsubishi Estate Co., Ltd.; *Int'l*, pg. 873
MFS INTELENET COMPANIES—WorldCom, Inc.; *U.S. Public*, pg. 1779
MFS WORLDCOM, INC.—WorldCom, Inc.; *U.S. Public*, pg. 1779
MANAGEMENT DATA SERVICE—US SerVis; *U.S. Public*, pg. 1687
MANAGEMENT DYNAMICS; *U.S. Public*, pg. 1040
MARITZ INC.; *U.S. Private*, pg. 703
MARKS & SPENCER EXPORT CORPORATION LIMITED—Marks & Spencer PLC; *Int'l*, pg. 842
MARKS & SPENCER SERVICES INC.—Marks & Spencer PLC; *Int'l*, pg. 843
MARSH & MCLENNAN COMPANIES, INC.; *U.S. Public*, pg. 1048
MATRIXONE, INC.—Adra Systems, Inc.; *U.S. Private*, pg. 18
MCCARTHY BUILDING COMPANIES; *U.S. Private*, pg. 719
MEAD PACKAGING EUROPE S.A.R.L.—The Mead Corporation; *U.S. Public*, pg. 1076
MEDIQ MANAGEMENT SERVICES, INC.—MEDIQ Incorporated; *U.S. Public*, pg. 1081
MENTOR INVESTMENT GROUP—First Union Corporation; *U.S. Public*, pg. 640
METRO DAVIDSON CO. DF—Corrections Corporation of America, *U.S. Public*, pg. 450
MINYARD PROPERTIES, INC.—Minyard Food Stores, Inc.; *U.S. Private*, pg. 752
MODO PAPER PSM—Mo och Domsjo AB; *Int'l*, pg. 887
MODO SKOG AB—Mo och Domsjo AB; *Int'l*, pg. 887
MOLINAS DE PUERTO RICO—ConAgra, Inc.; *U.S. Public*, pg. 427
THE MONAHAN COMPANY; *U.S. Private*, pg. 756
MONUMENTAL GENERAL ADMINISTRATORS, INC.—AEGON N.V.; *Int'l*, pg. 27
MOORE BUSINESS PRODUCTS & SERVICES DIVISIONS—Moore Corporation Limited; *Int'l*, pg. 890
MORSE DIESEL INTERNATIONAL, INC.; *U.S. Private*, pg. 762
ED MORSE AUTOMOTIVE GROUP; *U.S. Private*, pg. 763
MORTON CHEMICAL DIV.—Morton International Inc.; *U.S. Public*, pg. 1135
MOTOROLA G.M.B.H.—Motorola, Inc.; *U.S. Public*, pg. 1139
MOTOROLA SUISSE S.A.—Motorola, Inc.; *U.S. Public*, pg. 1140
MUSCATINE HOLDINGS, INC.—Bandag, Incorporated; *U.S.* Public, pg. 177
NAAO PRODUCTION PURCHASING—Ford Motor Company; *U.S. Public*, pg. 662
NEC SYSTEMS LABORATORY, INC.—NEC Corporation; *Int'l*, pg. 900
NUS DEUTSCHLAND GMBH—National Utility Service, Inc.; *U.S. Private*, pg. 787
NUS INTERNATIONAL PTY. LTD.—National Utility Service, Inc.; *U.S. Private*, pg. 787
NUS ITALIA, S.R.L.—National Utility Service, Inc.; *U.S. Private*, pg. 787
NANA DEVELOPMENT CORPORATION—Nana Regional Corporation, Inc.; *U.S. Private*, pg. 774
NASON AND CULLEN GROUP INCORPORATED; *U.S. Private*, pg. 775
NATIONAL ECONOMIC RESEARCH ASSOCIATES (NERA)—Marsh & McLennan Companies, Inc.; *U.S. Public*, pg. 1049
NATIONAL HOME HEALTH CARE CORP.; *U.S. Public*, pg. 1157
NATIONAL UTILITY SERVICE (CANADA) LTD.—National Utility Service, Inc.; *U.S. Private*, pg. 787
NATIONAL UTILITY SERVICE, S.A.—National Utility Service, Inc.; *U.S. Private*, pg. 787
NICOR ENERGY SERVICES COMPANY—NICOR Inc.; *U.S.* Public, pg. 1182
NICOR INC.; *U.S. Public*, pg. 1182
A.C. NIELSEN CO. OF CANADA, LTD.—A.C. Nielsen; *U.S. Public*, pg. 1183
NOMURA AUTOMATION MANAGEMENT INC.—The Nomura Securities Co., Ltd.; *Int'l*, pg. 956
NOMURA CORPORATE RESEARCH & ASSET MANAGEMENT INC.—The Nomura Securities Co., Ltd.; *Int'l*, pg. 956
NOMURA MORTGAGE FUND MANAGEMENT CORPORATION—The Nomura Securities Co., Ltd.; *Int'l*, pg. 956
NORD PACIFIC LIMITED—Nord Resources Corporation; *U.S. Public*, pg. 1188
NORDDEUTSCHE GESELLSCHAFT ZUR BERATUNG UND DURCHFUEHRUNG VON ENTSORGUNGSAUFGABEN BEI KERNKRAFTWERKEN MBH—Veba AG; *Int'l*, pg. 1456
NORTHWESTERN ENGINEERING CO.; *U.S. Private*, pg. 806
OKI AMERICA INC.—Oki Electric Industry Company, Ltd.; *Int'l*, pg. 1000
OUTOKUMPU ENGINEERING SERVICES OY—Outokumpu Oyj; *Int'l*, pg. 1017
OUTOKUMPU TECHNOLOGY OY—Outokumpu Oyj; *Int'l*, pg. 1017
OUTSOURCE INTERNATIONAL; *U.S. Public*, pg. 1236
OWEN HEALTH CARE, INC.—Cardinal Health Inc.; *U.S. Public*, pg. 304
OXFORD HEALTH PLANS INC.; *U.S. Public*, pg. 1238
PHH CORPORATION—Cendant Corporation; *U.S. Public*, pg. 321
PMM, INC.—Columbia/HCA Healthcare Corporation; *U.S. Public*, pg. 405
PACCAR WINCH DIVISION—Paccar Inc.; *U.S. Public*, pg. 1246
PACIFICORP TRANS, INC.—PacifiCorp; *U.S. Public*, pg. 1252
PACKARD ELECTRIC EUROPA GES.M.B.H.—General Motors Corporation; *U.S. Public*, pg. 723
PARDEE CONSTRUCTION COMPANY—Weyerhaeuser Company; *U.S. Public*, pg. 1764
PARLIAMENT COMPANY; *U.S. Private*, pg. 840
PARSONS BRINCKERHOFF CONSTRUCTION SERVICES, INC.—Parsons Brinckerhoff Inc.; *U.S. Private*, pg. 841
PEDUS OFFICE SERVICES—Pedus Services, Inc.; *U.S. Private*, pg. 846
PHARMACIA & UPJOHN COORDINATION CENTER N.V.—Pharmacia & Upjohn, Inc.; *Int'l*, pg. 1049
PHELPS DODGE INTL. CORP.—Phelps Dodge Corporation; *U.S. Public*, pg. 1286
PIER 1 IMPORTS CANADA—Pier 1 Imports, Inc.; *U.S. Public*, pg. 1295
PRECISION POWER, INC.—United Illuminating Company; *U.S. Public*, pg. 1678
PRIMARY MEDICAL MANAGEMENT, INC.—Columbia/HCA Healthcare Corporation; *U.S. Public*, pg. 405
PRIME MANAGEMENT, INC.—Prime Medical Services, Inc.; *U.S. Public*, pg. 1327
PRIME MEDICAL OPERATING, INC.—Prime Medical Services, Inc.; *U.S. Public*, pg. 1327
PROCESS SYSTEMS INC.; *U.S. Private*, pg. 888
PROMATEL—Jeumont-Schneider Trenformeteurs; *Int'l*, pg. 706
PUBLIC SERVICE ENTERPRISE GROUP INCORPORATED; *U.S. Public*, pg. 1340
QUORUM HEALTH GROUP, INC.; *U.S. Public*, pg. 1353
RHM FOODS LIMITED—Tomkins PLC; *Int'l*, pg. 1396
RPR & ASSOCIATES, INC.; *U.S. Private*, pg. 905
THE RACAL CORPORATION—Racal Electronics Plc; *Int'l*, pg. 1083
RALSTON PURINA INTERNATIONAL—Ralston Purina Company; *U.S. Public*, pg. 1360
WILLIAM A. RANDOLPH, INC.; *U.S. Private*, pg. 909
RANK HOVIS LIMITED—Tomkins PLC; *Int'l*, pg. 1396
RAYTHEON OVERSEAS LTD.—Raytheon Company; *U.S. Public*, pg. 1366
REDLAND PROPERTIES LTD.—Redland PLC; *Int'l*, pg. 1091
REECE-CAMPBELL, INC.; *U.S. Private*, pg. 916
THE RIVET GROUP L.L.C.; *U.S. Private*, pg. 934
ROTHSCHILD NORTH AMERICA INC.; *U.S. Private*, pg. 947
ROUSE PERSONNEL & ADMINISTRATIVE SERVICES DIV.—The Rouse Company; *U.S. Public*, pg. 1407
ROUSE RESEARCH & SITE STRATEGY DIV.—The Rouse Company; *U.S. Public*, pg. 1407
ROXON COMPANIES OY—Tamrock Corp.; *Int'l*, pg. 1353
THE RUHLIN COMPANY; *U.S. Private*, pg. 951

SEI BENEFIT SERVICES CORPORATION—SEI Investments; *U.S. Public*, pg. 1417
SKW/ESKIMOS INC.—Arctic Slope Regional Corporation; *U.S. Private*, pg. 80
SADCO LTD.—Joffko International; *U.S. Private*, pg. 589
SAFECARE COMPANY—SAFECO Corporation; *U.S. Public*, *pg. 1423*
SAFIRE PRIVATE LIMITED—Cigna Corp.; *U.S. Public*, pg. 363
SALEM ASSET MANAGEMENT CORP.—Salem Group, Inc.; *U.S. Private*, pg. 961
SANDWELL INC.; *Int'l*, pg. 1188
SANTA FE DETENTION CENTER—Corrections Corporation of America; *U.S. Public*, pg. 451
SCHAL BOVIS INC.—The Peninsular and Oriental Steam Navigation Company; *Int'l*, pg. 1033
SCIENCE MANAGEMENT CORPORATION—Versar Inc.; *U.S. Public*, pg. 1717
THE SERVICEMASTER COMPANY; *U.S. Public*, pg. 1461
SHELBY COUNTY TRAINING CENTER—Corrections Corporation of America; *U.S. Public*, pg. 451
SILVERDALE FACILITIES—Corrections Corporation of America; *U.S. Public*, pg. 451
SKANSKA (U.S.A.) INC.—Skanska AB; *Int'l*, pg. 1261
SMITH ENVIRONMENTAL TECHNOLOGIES CORP.—Smith Environmental Technologies Corp.; *U.S. Public*, pg. 1478
SMITHGROUP, INC.; *U.S. Private*, pg. 1010
SODEXHO USA—Sodexho S.A.; *Int'l*, pg. 1274
SONESTA INTERNATIONAL HOTELS CORPORATION; *U.S. Public*, pg. 1485
SORDONI SKANSKA CONSTRUCTION CO.—Skanska AB; *Int'l*, pg. 1261
SOUTH CENTRAL CORRECTIONAL CENTER—Corrections Corporation of America; *U.S. Public*, pg. 451
STONE & WEBSTER MANAGEMENT CONSULTANTS, INC.—Stone & Webster, Incorporated; *U.S. Public*, pg. 1519
STONE & WEBSTER OVERSEAS CONSULTANTS, INC.—Stone & Webster, Incorporated; *U.S. Public*, pg. 1519
STONE & WEBSTER OVERSEAS GROUP, INC.—Stone & Webster, Incorporated; *U.S. Public*, pg. 1519
SVERDRUP CORPORATION; *U.S. Private*, pg. 1057
SVERDRUP ENVIRONMENTAL INC.—Sverdrup Corporation; *U.S. Private*, pg. 1057
SVERDRUP TECHNOLOGY, INC.—Sverdrup Corporation; *U.S. Private*, pg. 1057
TCI INTERNATIONAL SALES CORP.—Tenneco Inc.; *U.S. Public*, pg. 1578
TM MANAGEMENT SERVICES LIMITED—The Tokio Marine & Fire Insurance Company, Ltd.; *Int'l*, pg. 1392
TU SERVICES—Texas Utilities Company; *U.S. Public*, pg. 1588
TALL TREES—Corrections Corporation of America; *U.S. Public*, pg. 451
TELEPHONE AND DATA SYSTEMS, INC.; *U.S. Public*, pg. 1570
TENNECO INTERNATIONAL INC.—Tenneco Inc.; *U.S. Public*, pg. 1578
TENNECO INTERNATIONAL N.V.—Tenneco Inc.; *U.S. Public*, pg. 1578
TENNECO NEDERLAND B.V.—Tenneco Inc.; *U.S. Public*, pg. 1580
TERMINAL MANAGEMENT, INC.—Forest City Enterprises, Inc.; *U.S. Public*, pg. 669
TEXACO INTERNATIONAL TRADER INC.—Texaco Inc.; *U.S. Public*, pg. 1583
TIME SYSTEMS, INC.; *U.S. Private*, pg. 1086
TISHMAN REALTY & CONSTRUCTION CO., INC.; *U.S. Private*, pg. 1089
TOMKINS PLC; *Int'l*, pg. 1395
TORRANCE COUNTY DETENTION FACILITY—Corrections Corporation of America; *U.S. Public*, pg. 451
TRAFALGAR HOUSE GROUP SERVICES LTD.—Kvaerner a.s.a.; *Int'l*, pg. 773
TUNDRA MESA CONSTRUCTORS—Arctic Slope Regional Corporation; *U.S. Private*, pg. 80
U-HAUL INTERNATIONAL, INC.—Amerco; *U.S. Private*, pg. 49
U.M. HOLDING LIMITED; *U.S. Private*, pg. 1113
USG INTERNATIONAL—USG Corporation; *U.S. Public*, pg. 1660
US SERVIS; *U.S. Public*, pg. 1687
VASCOR—Neptune Orient Lines Ltd.; *Int'l*, pg. 912
VASCOR, LTD.—Neptune Orient Lines Ltd.; *Int'l*, pg. 912
VAUBEL & PARTNERS LTD.—Deutsche Bank AG; *Int'l*, pg. 405
VENUS PRE-RELEASE CENTER—Corrections Corporation of America; *U.S. Public*, pg. 451
THE VOUCHER CORPORATION—Accor S.A.; *Int'l*, pg. 21
WACHOVIA CORPORATE SERVICES, INC.—Wachovia Corporation; *U.S. Public*, pg. 1730
WACHOVIA INVESTMENTS, INC.—Wachovia Corporation; *U.S. Public*, pg. 1730
WALK, HAYDEL & ASSOCIATES, INC.—Hochtief AG; *Int'l*, pg. 624
WASHINGTON SERVICE BUREAU, INC.—Wolters Kluwer N.V.; *Int'l*, pg. 1513
WEBSTER RESEARCH CENTER—Xerox Corporation; *U.S. Public*, pg. 1784
WEST TENNESSEE DETENTION FACILITY—Corrections Corporation of America; *U.S. Public*, pg. 451
WESTINGHOUSE ENERGY SYSTEMS INTERNATIONAL, INC.—CBS Corporation; *U.S. Public*, pg. 275
F.A. WILHELM CONSTRUCTION CO., INC.; *U.S. Private*, pg. 1176
WINN CORRECTIONAL CENTER—Corrections Corporation of America; *U.S. Public*, pg. 451
THE WOODFIN SUITE HOTELS; *U.S. Private*, pg. 1187
WOODLANDS LICENSE MANAGEMENT/FIBRE PROCUREMENT—Fort James Corporation; *U.S. Public*, pg. 672
X-L-CO, INC.—Xtra Corporation; *U.S. Public*, pg. 1787
XEROX BUSINESS SERVICES—Xerox Corporation; *U.S. Public*, pg. 1784
XEROX FINANCIAL SERVICES INC.—Xerox Corporation; *U.S. Public*, pg. 1784
XEROX REAL ESTATE & GENERAL SERVICES DIVISION—Xerox Corporation; *U.S. Public*, pg. 1785
YAMAICHI REAL ESTATE INC.—Yamaichi Securities Co., Ltd.; *Int'l*, pg. 1517
YOUNG PECAN COMPANY WEST, INC.—Young Pecan Company (A Partnership); *U.S. Private*, pg. 1201
ZENITH ADMINISTRATORS, INC.—ULLICO Inc.; *U.S. Private*, pg. 1116

8742 — MANAGEMENT CONSULTING SERVICES

AAF CONSULTANTS LTD.—AAF Industries Plc; *Int'l*, pg. 1
AMC—Associated Merchandising Corp. (AMC); *U.S. Private*, *pg. 92*
AT&T ISTEL LIMITED—AT&T Corporation; *U.S. Public*, pg. 11
ADECCO S.A.; *Int'l*, pg. 23
ADVANCED MARKETING CONCEPTS, INC.—Washington Gas Light Co.; *U.S. Public*, pg. 1741
ADVERTISING CHECKING BUREAU INCORPORATED; *U.S. Private*, pg. 23
ALEXANDER & ALEXANDER SERVICES INC.—AON Corporation; *U.S. Public*, pg. 117
THE ALEXANDER CONSULTING GROUP INC.—AON Corporation; *U.S. Public*, pg. 117
ALLEN & OHARA, INC.; *U.S. Private*, pg. 36
ALLIED RESEARCH CORPORATION LIMITED—Allied Research Corporation; *U.S. Public*, pg. 49
ANALYSIS & APPLIED RESEARCH DIV.—Tracor, Inc.; *U.S. Public*, pg. 1627
ANDERSEN WORLDWIDE; *U.S. Private*, pg. 72
ARMSTRONG EUROPE SERVICES—Armstrong World Industries, Inc.; *U.S. Public*, pg. 132
ARTHUR ANDERSEN—Andersen Worldwide; *U.S. Private*, pg. 72
ASGROW CANADA, LTD.—Pharmacia & Upjohn, Inc.; *Int'l*, pg. 1049
ASGROW DO BRASIL SEMENTES LTDA.—Pharmacia & Upjohn, Inc.; *Int'l*, pg. 1049
ASGROW FRANCE S.A.—Pharmacia & Upjohn, Inc.; *Int'l*, pg. 1049
ASGROW MEXICANA S.A. DE C.V.—Pharmacia & Upjohn, Inc.; *Int'l*, pg. 1049
ASSOCIATED COMPANY MANAGEMENT OF EBASCO LIMITED—Texas Utilities Company; *U.S. Public*, pg. 1587
ASSOCIATED MERCHANDISING-SINGAPORE—Associated Merchandising Corp. (AMC); *U.S. Private*, pg. 92
ATHENA AB—Incentive AB; *Int'l*, pg. 666
THEODORE BARRY & ASSOCIATES; *U.S. Private*, pg. 118
BECHTEL CIVIL, INC.—Bechtel Group, Inc.; *U.S. Private*, pg. 128
BECHTEL GROUP, INC.; *U.S. Private*, pg. 128
BECHTEL LTD.—Bechtel Group, Inc.; *U.S. Private*, pg. 128
BECHTEL MINING & METALS—Bechtel Group, Inc.; *U.S. Private*, pg. 128
BECHTEL PETROLEUM & CHEMICAL—Bechtel Group, Inc.; *U.S. Private*, pg. 128
BECHTEL POWER CORPORATION—Bechtel Group, Inc.; *U.S. Private*, pg. 128
R.W. BECK, INC.; *U.S. Private*, pg. 128
BECON CONSTRUCTION COMPANY, INC.—Bechtel Group, Inc.; *U.S. Private*, pg. 128
BOOZ, ALLEN & HAMILTON INC.; *U.S. Private*, pg. 157
BOURTON GROUP; *U.S. Private*, pg. 162
BOURTON GROUP—Bourton Group; *U.S. Private*, pg. 162
BOVIS INTERNATIONAL CALIFORNIA—The Peninsular and Oriental Steam Navigation Company; *Int'l*, pg. 1035
BUGAMOR PHARMA SRL MILAN—Pharmaceutical Marketing Services Inc.; *U.S. Public*, pg. 1284
CCC INFORMATION SERVICES—InfoVest, Inc.; *U.S. Private*, pg. 562
CRN INTERNATIONAL, INC.; *U.S. Private*, pg. 197
CSC INDEX, INC.—Computer Sciences Corporation; *U.S. Public*, pg. 422
CEBCOR (CONSOLIDATED EMPLOYMENT BENEFITS CORP.); *U.S. Private*, pg. 220
CENTRAL DUPAGE HEALTH SYSTEM; *U.S. Private*, pg. 223
CERIDIAN EMPLOYER SERVICES—Ceridian Corporation; *U.S. Public*, pg. 331
CHASE NATIONAL CORPORATE SERVICES, INC.—The Chase Manhattan Corporation; *U.S. Public*, pg. 338
CHESAPEAKE UTILITIES CORPORATION; *U.S. Public*, pg. 347
CHORE-TIME/BROCK INTERNATIONAL—CTB International Corp.; *U.S. Public*, pg. 285
CLUNE CONSTRUCTION LIMITED; *U.S. Private*, pg. 247
COLORADO PLAINS MEDICAL CENTER—Brim, Inc.; *U.S. Private*, pg. 169
COMBUSTION ENGINEERING-EUROPE—ABB Asea Brown Boveri (Holding) Ltd.; *Int'l*, pg. 5
COMBUSTION ENGINEERING EUROPE S.A.R.L.—ABB Asea Brown Boveri (Holding) Ltd.; *Int'l*, pg. 5
COMPUTER SCIENCES CORPORATION; *U.S. Public*, pg. 422
PHILIP CROSBY ASSOCIATES, INC.—Proudfoot plc; *Int'l*, pg. 1072
CURRIN & ASSOCIATES, INC.—Chesapeake Utilities Corporation; *U.S. Public*, pg. 347
DAY & ZIMMERMANN HAWTHORNE CORPORATION—Day & Zimmermann, Inc.; *U.S. Private*, pg. 317
DELAWARE MANAGEMENT HOLDINGS, INC.—Lincoln National Corporation; *U.S. Public*, pg. 997
DET NORSKE VERITAS; *Int'l*, pg. 396
DET NORSKE VERITAS INDUSTRY—Det Norske Veritas; *Int'l*, pg. 396
DETALJINVEST/VIVO-FAVOR—Carnegie Holding AB; *Int'l*, pg. 272
DOBBS BROTHERS MANAGEMENT; *U.S. Private*, pg. 337
DORSCH CONSULT GMBH—Texas Utilities Company; *U.S. Public*, pg. 1587
DYNCORP; *U.S. Private*, pg. 351
EDI INTERNATIONAL, INC.; *U.S. Private*, pg. 353
EG & G DYNATREND—EG & G, Inc.; *U.S. Public*, pg. 544
EBASCO-CTCI CORPORATION—Texas Utilities Company; *U.S. Public*, pg. 1587
EBASCO V.I. INC.—Texas Utilities Company; *U.S. Public*, pg. 1587
EGGLAND'S BEST, INC.; *U.S. Private*, pg. 366
ELCO DOMINICANA, S.A.—Eli Lilly and Company; *U.S. Public*, pg. 993
ENVIRONMENTAL RESOURCES MANAGEMENT; *U.S. Private*, pg. 378
EPSILON—American Express Company; *U.S. Public*, pg. 74
A. EPSTEIN AND SONS, INTL., INC.; *U.S. Private*, pg. 379
ERNST & YOUNG, LLP; *U.S. Private*, pg. 381
EUROPEAN GROUP—Computer Sciences Corporation; *U.S. Public*, pg. 423
FAMILY PHARMACY GENERAL OFFICE—AmeriSource Health Corp.; *U.S. Public*, pg. 97
FINA EUROPE S.A.—Petrofina S.A.; *Int'l*, pg. 1043
FINA NEDERLAND B.V.—Petrofina S.A.; *Int'l*, pg. 1043
FINA PLC—Petrofina S.A.; *Int'l*, pg. 1043
FINNISH RICH COFFEE LTD.—Kesko Ltd.; *Int'l*, pg. 732
FOREMOST INGREDIENT GROUP—Foremost Farms USA Cooperative; *U.S. Private*, pg. 418
FORUM ASIA LTD.—The Forum Corporation; *U.S. Private*, pg. 420
THE FORUM CORPORATION; *U.S. Private*, pg. 420
FORUM CORPORATION OF CANADA, LTD.—The Forum Corporation; *U.S. Private*, pg. 420
FORUM EUROPE LTD.—The Forum Corporation; *U.S. Private*, pg. 420
FROST & SULLIVAN; *U.S. Private*, pg. 430
ARTHUR J. GALLAGHER & CO.; *U.S. Public*, pg. 698
GEMINI CONSULTING—CAP Gemini S.A.; *Int'l*, pg. 264
GENERAL BUSINESS SERVICES, INC.—The Dwyer Group, Inc.; *U.S. Public*, pg. 538
GENERAL HOSPITAL—Brim, Inc.; *U.S. Private*, pg. 169
GENERAL MANAGEMENT CO.—Management Dynamics; *U.S. Public*, pg. 1040
GENERAL PHYSICS CORPORATION—GP Strategies Corporation; *U.S. Public*, pg. 694
GEO-CENTERS, INC.; *U.S. Private*, pg. 447
GIFFELS STRATEGIC CONSULTANTS, L.L.C.—Giffels Associates, Inc.; *U.S. Private*, pg. 452
GODWINS, BOOKE & DICKENSON, INC.—AON Corporation; *U.S. Public*, pg. 117
GOLDMAN FINANCIAL GROUP; *U.S. Private*, pg. 461
GOODWILL INDUSTRIES INTERNATIONAL; *U.S. Private*, pg. 464
HADEN MANAGEMENT CORPORATION—Haden Maclellan Holdings plc; *Int'l*, pg. 586
HAWAIIAN DREDGING & CONSTRUCTION COMPANY—Dillingham Construction Corporation; *U.S. Private*, pg. 333
HEWITT ASSOCIATES LLC; *U.S. Private*, pg. 524
HILL INTERNATIONAL INC.; *U.S. Private*, pg. 529
HONEYWELL-MEASUREX CREDIT CORPORATION—Honeywell Inc.; *U.S. Public*, pg. 833
HOUSTON HERSTEK FAVAT; *U.S. Private*, pg. 542
HUB GROUP, INC.; *U.S. Public*, pg. 844
HUBER, HUNT & NICHOLS, INC.—The Hunt Corporation; *U.S. Private*, pg. 548
HYATT INTERNATIONAL CORPORATION—Hyatt Corporation; *U.S. Private*, pg. 551
IE MANAGEMENT CONSULTANT PTY. LTD.—Bourton Group; *U.S. Private*, pg. 162
IMS/INTERNATIONAL—International Data Group; *U.S. Private*, pg. 569
ITA GROUP INC.; *U.S. Private*, pg. 555
INSTITUTE FOR HUMAN RESOURCES—United HealthCare Corporation; *U.S. Public*, pg. 1678
INTERIOR SPACE INTERNATIONAL—A. Epstein and Sons, Intl., Inc.; *U.S. Private*, pg. 379
INTERNATIONAL BUSINESS ANALYSIS PROPRIETARY LIMITED—Westpac Banking Corporation; *Int'l*, pg. 1496
INTERNATIONAL DATA GROUP; *U.S. Private*, pg. 569
INTERPLAN—RNL Facilities Corporation; *U.S. Private*, pg. 905
INTERWOOD MARKETING GROUP; *Int'l*, pg. 685
INVESTORS MARKETING GROUP, INC.—Investors Insurance Group, Inc.; *U.S. Public*, pg. 912
JACOBS SUCHARD MANAGEMENT & CONSULTING AG—Philip Morris Companies Inc.; *U.S. Public*, pg. 1288
JARDINE MATHESON HOLDINGS LIMITED; *Int'l*, pg. 703
JOHN HANCOCK INTL. SERVICES S.A.—John Hancock Mutual Life Insurance Company; *U.S. Private*, pg. 590
JOHN HANCOCK SERVICOS INTERNACIONAIS S/C., LTDA.—John Hancock Mutual Life Insurance Company; *U.S. Private*, pg. 590
JOHNSTON, LEMON & CO. INC.; *U.S. Private*, pg. 595
KAISER JAMAICA BAUXITE CO.—Maxxam Inc.; *U.S. Public*, pg. 1062
KANSAI PAINT (AMERICA), INC.—Kansai Paint Co., Ltd.; *Int'l*, pg. 723
KEPNER-TREGOE, INC.—USF&G Corporation; *U.S. Public*, *pg. 1659*
KING WILKINSON LTD.—Babcock International Group PLC; *Int'l*, pg. 131
KITCHELL CORPORATION; *U.S. Private*, pg. 624
KLOECKNER INDUSTRIE-ANLAGEN GMBH—RWE AG; *Int'l*, pg. 1081
LESTER B. KNIGHT & ASSOCIATES, INC.; *U.S. Private*, pg. 626
KODAK SOFTWARE SYSTEMS DIVISION—Eastman Kodak Company; *U.S. Public*, pg. 555
KRUG INTERNATIONAL TECHNOLOGY/SCIENTIFIC SERVICES, INC.—Krug International Corp.; *U.S. Public*, pg. 968

JOHN LAING SERVICES LTD.—John Laing PLC; *Int'l*, pg. 796
ROBERT E. LAMB, INC.; *U.S. Private*, pg. 644
LASON, INC.; *U.S. Public*, pg. 979
LEARNING INTERNATIONAL—The Times Mirror Company; *U.S. Public*, pg. 1617
LEHNKERING MONTAN TRANSPORT AG—Metallgesellschaft AG; *Int'l*, pg. 862
LEHNKERING MONTAN TRANSPORT AG—Preussag AG; *Int'l*, pg. 1069
ARTHUR D. LITTLE, INC.; *U.S. Private*, pg. 670
LOWRANCE CANADA—Lowrance Electronics, Inc.; *U.S. Public*, pg. 1016
LURGI AG—Metallgesellschaft AG; *Int'l*, pg. 861
LURGI ESPANOLA S.A.—Metallgesellschaft AG; *Int'l*, pg. 861
MBT ENVIRONMENTAL ENGINEERING LTD.—Viag AG; *Int'l*, pg. 1465
MALONE ADVERTISING, INC.; *U.S. Private*, pg. 698
MANAGEMENT DYNAMICS; *U.S. Public*, pg. 1040
MANAGEMENT ENGINEERS GMBH—Bourton Group; *U.S. Private*, pg. 162
MANUFACTURERS' SERVICES LTD.; *U.S. Private*, pg. 701
MARITZ EUROPA LIMITED—Maritz Inc.; *U.S. Private*, pg. 704
MARITZ INC.; *U.S. Private*, pg. 703
MARKET FACTS, INC.; *U.S. Public*, pg. 1046
MARKET FACTS, INC.—Market Facts, Inc.; *U.S. Public*, pg. 1047
MARKET FACTS OF CANADA, LTD.—Market Facts, Inc.; *U.S. Public*, pg. 1047
MARKET STATISTICS—VNU Verenigde Nederlandse Uitgeversbedrijven B.V.; *Int'l*, pg. 1446
MARKETFORCE (UK) LIMITED—IPC Magazines Limited; *Int'l*, pg. 651
MARKETING CORP. OF AMERICA; *U.S. Private*, pg. 704
MARKETSOURCE CORPORATION; *U.S. Private*, pg. 705
MARTIN MARIETTA INTERNATIONAL, INC.—Lockheed Martin Corporation; *U.S. Public*, pg. 1010
GEORGE S. MAY CANADA, LTD.—George S. May International Company; *U.S. Private*, pg. 717
GEORGE S. MAY INTERNATIONAL COMPANY; *U.S. Private*, pg. 717
MCCARTHY BROTHERS CO.—McCarthy Building Companies; *U.S. Private*, pg. 719
MCKINSEY & COMPANY, INC.; *U.S. Private*, pg. 723
MEDIQ INCORPORATED; *U.S. Public*, pg. 1081
MEDIQ MANAGEMENT SERVICES, INC.—MEDIQ Incorporated; *U.S. Public*, pg. 1081
MERCER MANAGEMENT CONSULTING, INC.—Marsh & McLennan Companies, Inc.; *U.S. Public*, pg. 1049
MINIDATA SERVICES, INC.—Ceridian Corporation; *U.S. Public*, pg. 331
MOBIL EUROPE, INC.—Mobil Oil Corporation; *U.S. Public*, pg. 1119
MODERN MEDICAL MODALITIES CORP.; *U.S. Public*, pg. 1121
NBBJ; *U.S. Private*, pg. 771
NPS ENERGY SERVICES, INC.—Day & Zimmermann, Inc.; *U.S. Private*, pg. 317
NATIONAL CATTLEMEN'S BEEF ASSOCIATION—National Cattlemen's Beef Association; *U.S. Private*, pg. 780
NATIONAL HEALTH SERVICES, INC.—Conseco Inc.; *U.S. Public*, pg. 433
NATIONAL UTILITY SERVICE LTD.—National Utility Service, Inc.; *U.S. Private*, pg. 787
A.C. NIELSEN; *U.S. Public*, pg. 1183
A.C. NIELSEN COMPANY—A.C. Nielsen; *U.S. Public*, pg. 1183
A.C. NIELSEN PTY., LTD.—A.C. Nielsen; *U.S. Public*, pg. 1184
A.C. NIELSEN CO., GMBH—A.C. Nielsen; *U.S. Public*, pg. 1183
NOMURA HUMAN RESOURCES DEVELOPMENT CO., LTD.—The Nomura Securities Co., Ltd.; *Int'l*, pg. 955
NORDFOR TRAINING & CONSULTATION AB—Electrolux, AB; *Int'l*, pg. 439
OMEGA PERFORMANCE GROUP; *U.S. Private*, pg. 816
ORGANIZATIONAL DYNAMICS INC.; *U.S. Private*, pg. 819
OVERSEAS SERVICE CORPORATION; *U.S. Private*, pg. 823
PB LEASING LTD.—Pitney Bowes Inc.; *U.S. Public*, pg. 1304
PMSI, AUSTRIA—Pharmaceutical Marketing Services Inc.; *U.S. Public*, pg. 1284
PS PROMOTIONS, INC.; *U.S. Private*, pg. 828
PACIFICA SERVICES, INC.; *U.S. Private*, pg. 832
PENSKE PERFORMANCE, INC.—Penske Corporation; *U.S. Private*, pg. 850
PETERSON'S GUIDES, INC.; *U.S. Private*, pg. 858
PHARMACEUTICAL MARKETING SERVICES INC.; *U.S. Public*, pg. 1284
PHARMACIA & UPJOHN RISK MANAGEMENT SERVICE AB—Pharmacia & Upjohn, Inc.; *Int'l*, pg. 1048
PHILIPS DISPLAY COMPONENTS—Philips Electronics N.V.; *Int'l*, pg. 1055
PHILLIPS PETROLEUM CO. EUROPE-AFRICA—Phillips Petroleum Company; *U.S. Public*, pg. 1291
J.D. POWER AND ASSOCIATES; *U.S. Private*, pg. 878
PRACTICE DEVELOPMENT INSTITUTE—Friedman, Eisenstein, Raemer and Schwartz, LLP; *U.S. Private*, pg. 428
PRIMUS INC.; *U.S. Private*, pg. 884
PROCESS & ENERGY CONSULTANTS LTD.—Texas Utilities Company; *U.S. Public*, pg. 1588
PROFESCO CORPORATION—John Hancock Mutual Life Insurance Company; *U.S. Private*, pg. 590
PROUDFOOT PLC; *Int'l*, pg. 1071
PROUDFOOT USA COMPANY—Proudfoot plc; *Int'l*, pg. 1072
PRUDENTIAL OVERSEAS FUNDING CORP. N.V.—The Prudential Insurance Company of America; *U.S. Private*, pg. 893
PYRAMID SERVICES, INC.—AON Corporation; *U.S. Public*, pg. 118
QUALITY SPECIAL PRODUCTS; *Int'l*, pg. 1075
RCG INTERNATIONAL INC.—Reliance Group Holdings, Inc.; *U.S. Public*, pg. 1374
RJ ASSOCIATES—RisComp Industries, Inc.; *U.S. Private*, pg. 932
RELIANCE GROUP HOLDINGS, INC.; *U.S. Public*, pg. 1374
RESUMIX—Ceridian Corporation; *U.S. Public*, pg. 331
R.J. REYNOLDS FINANCE S.A.—RJR Nabisco Holdings Corp.; *U.S. Public*, pg. 1355
RIGHT MANAGEMENT CONSULTANTS, INC.; *U.S. Public*, pg. 1390
RISCOMP INDUSTRIES, INC.; *U.S. Private*, pg. 932
RUSS REID COMPANY, INC.; *U.S. Private*, pg. 952
RYDER SYSTEM, INC.; *U.S. Public*, pg. 1413
SEI FINANCIAL MANAGEMENT CORPORATION—SEI Investments; *U.S. Public*, pg. 1417
SEI INVESTMENTS; *U.S. Public*, pg. 1417
SABENA INTERSERVICE CENTER LIMITED—Sabena; *Int'l*, pg. 1168
SABRE TRAVEL INFORMATION NETWORK—AMR Corporation; *U.S. Public*, pg. 10
SANDOZ TECHNOLOGY LTD.—Novartis AG; *Int'l*, pg. 972
SHANDWICK INTERNATIONAL PLC; *Int'l*, pg. 1226
SHARED SERVICES DIVISION—Black & Veatch; *U.S. Private*, pg. 146
SIMON MARKETING, INC.; *U.S. Private*, pg. 1001
SNYDER COMMUNICATIONS, INC.; *U.S. Public*, pg. 1481
SPEEDWING CONSULTING—British Airways PLC; *Int'l*, pg. 219
STANDEX HOLDINGS LIMITED—Standex International Corporation; *U.S. Public*, pg. 1507
SUPERIOR CONSULTANT COMPANY, INC.—Superior Consultant Holdings Corp.; *U.S. Public*, pg. 1539
SUPERIOR CONSULTANT HOLDINGS CORP.; *U.S. Public*, pg. 1538
SVERDRUP CORPORATION; *U.S. Private*, pg. 1057
SYSTRA-SOFRETU-SOFRERAIL—SNCF; *Int'l*, pg. 1165
TMC—WPP Group plc; *Int'l*, pg. 1482
TELLUS, INC.—Puget Sound Energy, Inc.; *U.S. Public*, pg. 1342
TENERA ENERGY, LLC—Tenera, Inc.; *U.S. Public*, pg. 1576
TENERA, INC.; *U.S. Public*, pg. 1576
I.C. THOMASSON ASSOCIATES, INC.; *U.S. Private*, pg. 1083
TOKIO MANAGEMENT SERVICES (ASIA) PTE. LTD.—The Tokio Marine & Fire Insurance Company, Ltd.; *Int'l*, pg. 1392
TORAY INDUSTRIES, INC.; *Int'l*, pg. 1399
TORCON, INC.; *U.S. Private*, pg. 1092
TOWERS PERRIN; *U.S. Private*, pg. 1093
USAA (UNITED SERVICES AUTOMOBILE ASSOCIATION); *U.S. Private*, pg. 1114
VEDA INCORPORATED—Veridian; *U.S. Private*, pg. 1136
VISUAL SERVICES INC.—VSI Holdings, Inc.; *U.S. Public*, pg. 1703
WABCO STANDARD INC.—American Standard Inc.; *U.S. Public*, pg. 92
WASSERSTEIN PERELLA GROUP, INC.—The Nomura Securities Co., Ltd.; *Int'l*, pg. 956
WATSON WYATT WORLDWIDE; *U.S. Private*, pg. 1154
WATT, ROOP & CO.; *U.S. Private*, pg. 1154
WELLSPRING RESOURCES, LLC—Watson Wyatt Worldwide; *U.S. Private*, pg. 1154
WELLSPRING RESOURCES, LLC—State Street Corporation; *U.S. Public*, pg. 1513
WERNER INTERNATIONAL—Reliance Group Holdings, Inc.; *U.S. Public*, pg. 1374
WILLIAMSON INTERNATIONAL CORP.—T.D. Williamson, Inc.; *U.S. Private*, pg. 1180
WOLF MANSFIELD BOLLING ADVERTISING INC.; *U.S. Private*, pg. 1185
THE W.B. WOOD COMPANY; *U.S. Private*, pg. 1186
WORK/FAMILY DIRECTIONS; *U.S. Private*, pg. 1188

8743 — PUBLIC RELATIONS SERVICES

AT&T WIRELESS SERVICES—AT&T Corporation; *U.S. Public*, pg. 11
BADER RUTTER & ASSOC., INC.; *U.S. Private*, pg. 110
BRAIN FORUM CO., LTD.—Skylark Co., Ltd.; *Int'l*, pg. 1262
EARLE PALMER BROWN; *U.S. Private*, pg. 173
COMMONWEALTH TOY & NOVELTY COMPANY; *U.S. Private*, pg. 258
CONTINENTAL PIR COMMUNICATIONS, INC.—Shandwick International Plc; *Int'l*, pg. 1226
DENTSU BURSON MARSTELLER, INC.—Dentsu Inc.; *Int'l*, pg. 393
DEWE ROGERSON LIMITED; *Int'l*, pg. 408
DIX & EATON INCORPORATED; *U.S. Private*, pg. 336
EDELMAN PUBLIC RELATIONS WORLDWIDE; *U.S. Private*, pg. 362
EVANSGROUP; *U.S. Private*, pg. 385
FOGARTY KLEIN & PARTNERS PUBLIC RELATIONS—Fogarty Klein & Partners; *U.S. Private*, pg. 416
GOLIN/HARRIS COMMUNICATIONS, INC.—Shandwick International Plc; *Int'l*, pg. 1226
GOLIN/HARRIS TECHNOLOGIES—Shandwick International Plc; *Int'l*, pg. 1227
GREY ADVERTISING INC.; *U.S. Public*, pg. 764
HLB COMMUNICATIONS, INC.; *U.S. Private*, pg. 491
HILL AND KNOWLTON, INC.—WPP Group plc; *Int'l*, pg. 1483
HOUSTON HERSTEK FAVAT; *U.S. Private*, pg. 542
IDC SERVICES, INC.; *U.S. Private*, pg. 554
IMPULS ADVERTISING AG; *Int'l*, pg. 666
INTEGRATED MARKETING GROUP; *U.S. Private*, pg. 566
INTERNATIONAL PUBLIC RELATIONS CO. LTD.—Shandwick International Plc; *Int'l*, pg. 1227
INTERNATIONAL PUBLIC RELATIONS (NZ) LTD.—Shandwick International Plc; *Int'l*, pg. 1227
INTERNATIONAL PUBLIC RELATIONS, PTY. LTD.—Shandwick International Plc; *Int'l*, pg. 1227
INTERNATIONAL RESEARCH & EVALUATION; *U.S. Private*, pg. 571
JAL INTERNATIONAL SERVICES—Japan Airlines Company, Ltd.; *Int'l*, pg. 700
KIRSHENBAUM, BOND & PARTNERS; *U.S. Private*, pg. 624
LEVENSON & HILL, INC.; *U.S. Private*, pg. 662
LIGGETT-STASHOWER, INC.; *U.S. Private*, pg. 667
LIPPINCOTT & MARGULIES, INC.—Marsh & McLennan Companies, Inc.; *U.S. Public*, pg. 1048
MCDONALD'S INTL.—McDonald's Corporation; *U.S. Public*, pg. 1069
MCDONALD'S U.S.A.—McDonald's Corporation; *U.S. Public*, pg. 1069
MILLER SHANDWICK TECHNOLOGIES—Shandwick International Plc; *Int'l*, pg. 1227
NEW ZEALAND DAIRY BOARD; *Int'l*, pg. 923
NITTO CO., LTD.—Meiji Seika Kaisha, Ltd.; *Int'l*, pg. 855
NOBLE & ASSOCIATES; *U.S. Private*, pg. 800
NORTH CASTLE PARTNERS ADVERTISING, INC.; *U.S. Private*, pg. 804
PADILLA SPEER BEARDSLEY INC.; *U.S. Private*, pg. 833
ROGERS & COWAN, INC.—Shandwick International Plc; *Int'l*, pg. 1227
SANDS INVESTMENTS, INC.; *U.S. Private*, pg. 964
SHANDWICK AMERICAS—Shandwick International Plc; *Int'l*, pg. 1226
SHANDWICK CONSULTANTS LTD.—Shandwick International Plc; *Int'l*, pg. 1227
SHANDWICK DETROIT—Shandwick International Plc; *Int'l*, pg. 1227
SHANDWICK DEUTSCHLAND GMBH—Shandwick International Plc; *Int'l*, pg. 1227
SHANDWICK FRANCE—Shandwick International Plc; *Int'l*, pg. 1227
SHANDWICK INTERNATIONAL PLC; *Int'l*, pg. 1226
SHANDWICK LUTZ BOHME PUBLIC RELATIONS GMBH—Shandwick International Plc; *Int'l*, pg. 1227
SHANDWICK MARKETING COMMUNICATION SRL—Shandwick International Plc; *Int'l*, pg. 1227
SHANDWICK MINNEAPOLIS—Shandwick International Plc; *Int'l*, pg. 1227
SHANDWICK NORTH LTD.—Shandwick International Plc; *Int'l*, pg. 1227
SHANDWICK/PRESKO LTD.—Shandwick International Plc; *Int'l*, pg. 1227
SHANDWICK PTE LTD.—Shandwick International Plc; *Int'l*, pg. 1227
SHANDWICK S.A. INFOPUBLIC N.V.—Shandwick International Plc; *Int'l*, pg. 1228
SHANDWICK SCOTLAND LTD.—Shandwick International Plc; *Int'l*, pg. 1226
SHANDWICK USA—Shandwick International Plc; *Int'l*, pg. 1227
SHANDWICK VAN DE MEEBERG PR—Shandwick International Plc; *Int'l*, pg. 1227
TEXTRON FINANCIAL CORPORATION—Textron Inc.; *U.S. Public*, pg. 1590
THIOKOL GOVERNMENT RELATIONS—Thiokol Corporation; *U.S. Public*, pg. 1597
U.I.C.A. S.P.A.—Fiat Auto SpA; *Int'l*, pg. 481
UNIVERSAL PUBLIC RELATIONS INC.—Shandwick International Plc; *Int'l*, pg. 1228
V.A.G. MARKETING MANAGEMENT INSTITUT GMBH—Volkswagen AG; *Int'l*, pg. 1473
VINUM INC.—Banfi Vintners; *U.S. Private*, pg. 113
WELBECK GOLIN/HARRIS COMMUNICATIONS LTD.—Shandwick International Plc; *Int'l*, pg. 1226
WESTWAYNE, INC.; *U.S. Private*, pg. 1170

8744 — FACILITIES SUPPORT MANAGEMENT SERVICES

ACCORD CONTRACT SERVICES—Veba AG; *Int'l*, pg. 1458
AMERICAN COMMONWEALTH MANAGEMENT SERVICES COMPANY, INC.—American Water Works Company, Inc.; *U.S. Public*, pg. 95
AMERICAN INTERNATIONAL WATER SERVICES COMPANY—American Water Works Company, Inc.; *U.S. Public*, pg. 95
AMERICAN WATER WORKS COMPANY, INC.; *U.S. Public*, pg. 95
AMERICANANGLIAN ENVIRONMENTAL TECHNOLOGIES, INC.—American Water Works Company, Inc.; *U.S. Public*, pg. 95
ANTARCTIC SUPPORT ASSOCIATES—EG & G, Inc.; *U.S. Public*, pg. 544
THE ARGOS GROUP—Barton Malow Enterprises, Inc.; *U.S. Private*, pg. 120
ATLANTIC SHOPPING CENTRES LIMITED—Empire Company Limited; *Int'l*, pg. 454
BARTON MALOW ENTERPRISES, INC.; *U.S. Private*, pg. 120
BOEING NORTH AMERICA, SPACE SYSTEMS DIVISION—The Boeing Company; *U.S. Public*, pg. 241
BRIM, INC.; *U.S. Private*, pg. 168
COMMONWEALTH COMMUNICATIONS—RCN Corporation; *U.S. Public*, pg. 1354
COMMONWEALTH TELEPHONE ENTERPRISES, INC.; *U.S. Public*, pg. 415
CORRECTIONAL SERVICES CORPORATION; *U.S. Public*, pg. 450
CORRECTIONS CORPORATION OF AMERICA; *U.S. Public*, pg. 450
DAY & ZIMMERMAN INFRASTRUCTURE, INC.—Day & Zimmermann, Inc.; *U.S. Private*, pg. 317
DUQUESNE ENTERPRISES—DQE Inc.; *U.S. Public*, pg. 474

DYNCORP; *U.S. Private*, pg. 351
EC III—EG & G, Inc.; *U.S. Public*, pg. 543
EG & G DEFENSE MATERIALS DIVISION—EG & G, Inc.; *U.S. Public*, pg. 543
EG & G FLORIDA—EG & G, Inc.; *U.S. Public*, pg. 544
EG & G MANAGEMENT SYSTEMS—EG & G, Inc.; *U.S. Public*, pg. 543
ENECO TECH GROUP; *U.S. Private*, pg. 376
ENTERPRISE MANAGEMENT—DynCorp; *U.S. Private*, pg. 351
HEATH CONSULTANTS INCORPORATED; *U.S. Private*, pg. 518
INTEGROL—Staveley Industries PLC; *Int'l*, pg. 1298
INTERIM SERVICES INC.; *U.S. Public*, pg. 892
INTERIOR SPACE INTERNATIONAL—A. Epstein and Sons, Intl., Inc.; *U.S. Private*, pg. 379
INTERNATIONAL RESEARCH & EVALUATION; *U.S. Private*, pg. 571
MAY & SPEH, INC.; *U.S. Public*, pg. 1063
NEW JERSEY-AMERICAN RESOURCES COMPANY—American Water Works Company, Inc.; *U.S. Public*, pg. 95
NEW MEXICO WOMENS CORRECTIONAL FACILITY—Corrections Corporation of America; *U.S. Public*, pg. 450
NORTHROP GRUMMAN CORPORATION; *U.S. Public*, pg. 1197
OGDEN CORPORATION; *U.S. Public*, pg. 1213
OGDEN ENTERTAINMENT, INC.—Ogden Corporation; *U.S. Public*, pg. 1213
RENTOKIL INITIAL PLC—Sophus Berendsen A/S; *Int'l*, pg. 1285
RENTOKIL LTD.—Sophus Berendsen A/S; *Int'l*, pg. 1285
THE SERVICEMASTER COMPANY; *U.S. Public*, pg. 1461
SVERDRUP CORPORATION; *U.S. Private*, pg. 1057
SVERDRUP TECHNOLOGY, INC.—Sverdrup Corporation; *U.S. Private*, pg. 1057
TENERA, INC.; *U.S. Public*, pg. 1576
TENERA ROCKY FLATS, LLC—Tenera, Inc.; *U.S. Public*, pg. 1576
TRACOR FLIGHT SYSTEMS, INC.—Tracor, Inc.; *U.S. Public*, pg. 1627
TRACOR, INC.; *U.S. Public*, pg. 1627
TRIANGLE SERVICES, INC.; *U.S. Private*, pg. 1102
THE WACKENHUT CORPORATION; *U.S. Public*, pg. 1731
WACKENHUT CORRECTIONS CORPORATION—The Wackenhut Corporation; *U.S. Public*, pg. 1731
WESTINGHOUSE ENERGY SYSTEMS INTERNATIONAL, INC.—CBS Corporation; *U.S. Public*, pg. 275
WYLE ELECTRONICS—Veba AG; *Int'l*, pg. 1457

8748 — BUSINESS CONSULTING SERVICES, NEC

ABB ENVIRONMENTAL SERVICES INC.—ABB Asea Brown Boveri (Holding) Ltd.; *Int'l*, pg. 4
AIB INTERNATIONAL CONSULTANTS LTD.—Allied Irish Banks, p.l.c.; *Int'l*, pg. 64
AGRA EARTH & ENVIRONMENTAL, INC.—Agra Inc.; *Int'l*, pg. 31
AGRA EARTH & ENVIRONMENTAL LIMITED—Agra Inc.; *Int'l*, pg. 30
ALLEN & OHARA, INC.; *U.S. Private*, pg. 36
AMCOR CAPITAL CORPORATION; *U.S. Public*, pg. 64
AMERICAN WASTE SERVICES, INC.; *U.S. Public*, pg. 94
ASAHIGIN SOFTWARE CO., LTD.—The Asahi Bank, Ltd.; *Int'l*, pg. 82
BKNT, INC.—VSI Holdings, Inc.; *U.S. Public*, pg. 1703
BEAR STEARNS REAL ESTATE GROUP INC.—The Bear Stearns Companies Inc.; *U.S. Public*, pg. 198
BELL CANADA INTERNATIONAL, INC.—BCE Inc.; *Int'l*, pg. 115
BOLT GEOPHYSICAL CORPORATION—Bolt Technology Corporation; *U.S. Public*, pg. 244
BOOZ, ALLEN & HAMILTON INC.; *U.S. Private*, pg. 157
CCA INTERNATIONAL, INC.—Corrections Corporation of America; *U.S. Public*, pg. 451
CTB/MCGRAW HILL—The McGraw-Hill Companies; *U.S. Public*, pg. 1070
CANTERBURY CORPORATE SERVICES, INC.; *U.S. Public*, pg. 301
CASCADE PACIFIC ENGINEERING, INC.—Republic Industries, Inc.; *U.S. Public*, pg. 1379
CELSIUS AB; *Int'l*, pg. 276
CHEMICAL ADMINISTRACAO E CONSULTORIA ECONOMICO FINANCEIRA LTDA.—The Chase Manhattan Corporation; *U.S. Public*, pg. 341
CIGNA EMPLOYEE BENEFITS SERVICES, INC.—Cigna Corp.; *U.S. Public*, pg. 358
CLARIANT CORPORATION—Hoechst Aktiengesellschaft; *Int'l*, pg. 624
COASTAL POWER PRODUCTION COMPANY—The Coastal Corporation; *U.S. Public*, pg. 390
COGNIZANT CORPORATION; *U.S. Public*, pg. 395
COMMERCIAL AND POLITICAL RISK CONSULTANTS—Inchcape PLC; *Int'l*, pg. 671
DRI EUROPE, INC.—The McGraw-Hill Companies; *U.S. Public*, pg. 1072
DRI EUROPE (U.K.) LTD.—The McGraw-Hill Companies; *U.S. Public*, pg. 1072
THE DARTNELL CORPORATION; *U.S. Private*, pg. 312
DATA GENERAL CUSTOMER SERVICE DIVISION—Data General Corporation; *U.S. Public*, pg. 485
DET NORSKE VERITAS; *Int'l*, pg. 396
DET NORSKE VERITAS INDUSTRY—Det Norske Veritas; *Int'l*, pg. 396
DILLINGHAM CONSTRUCTION N.A., INC.—Dillingham Construction Corporation; *U.S. Private*, pg. 333
DIVERSIFIED PHARMACEUTICAL SERVICES, INC.—SmithKline Beecham plc; *Int'l*, pg. 1265
DRAKE BEAM MORIN, INC.—Harcourt General, Inc.; *U.S. Public*, pg. 783
DYNAMICS RESEARCH CORPORATION; *U.S. Public*, pg. 539
EG & G DYNATREND—EG & G, Inc.; *U.S. Public*, pg. 544
ECOLOGY AND ENVIRONMENT, INC.; *U.S. Public*, pg. 562
EMCON; *U.S. Public*, pg. 571
ENVIRON CORPORATION—Pharmaceutical Product Development, Inc.; *U.S. Public*, pg. 1285
ENVIRON INTERNATIONAL—Pharmaceutical Product Development, Inc.; *U.S. Public*, pg. 1285
ENVIRON INTERNATIONAL CORPORATION-EMERYVILLE—Pharmaceutical Product Development, Inc.; *U.S. Public*, pg. 1285
EPSILON—American Express Company; *U.S. Public*, pg. 74
ERLY INDUSTRIES, INC.; *U.S. Public*, pg. 591
FAMEX, INC.—Allianz Aktiengesellschaft; *Int'l*, pg. 59
FIREMAN'S FUND RISK MANAGEMENT SERVICES, INC.—Allianz Aktiengesellschaft; *Int'l*, pg. 59
FLOURO-PRECISION COATINGS—TI Group plc; *Int'l*, pg. 1338
FRIEDMAN, EISENSTEIN, RAEMER AND SCHWARTZ, LLP; *U.S. Private*, pg. 428
GVA CONSULTANTS AB—Celsius AB; *Int'l*, pg. 277
GENERAL BUSINESS SERVICES, INC.—The Dwyer Group, Inc.; *U.S. Public*, pg. 538
GLEACHER MORGAN GRENFELL INC.—Deutsche Bank AG; *Int'l*, pg. 405
GUARDSMARK, INC.; *U.S. Private*, pg. 486
HLW INTERNATIONAL LLP; *U.S. Private*, pg. 491
HLW INTERNATIONAL SERVICES CORPORATION—HLW International LLP; *U.S. Private*, pg. 491
HLW SERVICES CORPORATION—HLW International LLP; *U.S. Private*, pg. 491
HARROD DEVITT SOCIEDAD ANONIMA—The Prudential Insurance Company of America; *U.S. Private*, pg. 893
HORIZON ENTERPRISES GROUP LLC; *U.S. Private*, pg. 539
INSPECTORATE PLC; *Int'l*, pg. 679
INSPECTORATE (SUISSE) S.A.—Inspectorate Plc; *Int'l*, pg. 679
INTERNATIONAL BUSINESS MACHINES CORPORATION; *U.S. Public*, pg. 895
JACOR, INC.—Jaymark, Inc.; *U.S. Private*, pg. 584
JAYMARK, INC.; *U.S. Private*, pg. 584
KCS ENERGY RISK MANAGEMENT—KCS Energy Inc.; *U.S. Public*, pg. 939
KOCKUMS AB—Celsius AB; *Int'l*, pg. 277
KVAERNER ENGINEERING A/S—Kvaerner a.s.a.; *Int'l*, pg. 766
LAW ENGINEERING, INC.; *U.S. Private*, pg. 653
LEARNING INTERNATIONAL—The Times Mirror Company; *U.S. Public*, pg. 1617
LIBERTY INVESTMENT GROUP, INC.—Liberty Corporation; *U.S. Public*, pg. 992
LIVING EARTH TECHNOLOGY CO.—Republic Industries, Inc.; *U.S. Public*, pg. 1379
LLOYDS BANK UK MANAGEMENT LTD.-CORP. BANKING & TREASURY—Lloyds TSB Group PLC; *Int'l*, pg. 813
THE M/A/R/C GROUP; *U.S. Public*, pg. 1022
M/A/R/C MARKETING AND RESEARCH COUNSELORS, INC.—The M/A/R/C Group; *U.S. Public*, pg. 1023
MBT (AUSTRALIA) PTY. LTD.—Viag AG; *Int'l*, pg. 1465
MANAGEMENT DYNAMICS; *U.S. Public*, pg. 1040
MARKET FACTS, INC.; *U.S. Public*, pg. 1046
MARKET FACTS, INC.—Market Facts, Inc.; *U.S. Public*, pg. 1047
MARKET FACTS OF CANADA, LTD.—Market Facts, Inc.; *U.S. Public*, pg. 1047
AC MARTIN PARTNERS; *U.S. Private*, pg. 708
MASTER BUILDERS TECHNOLOGIES LTD.—Viag AG; *Int'l*, pg. 1465
MATSUYA SHOJI CO., LTD.—Matsuya Company Ltd.; *Int'l*, pg. 848
MITRE CORPORATION; *U.S. Private*, pg. 753
MOLEX SINGAPORE PTE. LTD.—Molex Incorporated; *U.S. Public*, pg. 1122
NATIONAL CATTLEMEN'S BEEF ASSOCIATION—National Cattlemen's Beef Association; *U.S. Private*, pg. 780
NATIONAL UTILITY SERVICE, INC.; *U.S. Private*, pg. 787
NIELSEN MEDIA RESEARCH—Cognizant Corporation; *U.S. Public*, pg. 395
NIPSCO ENERGY SERVICES, INC.—NIPSCO Industries, Inc.; *U.S. Public*, pg. 1185
NOROESTE CHEMICAL S.A. ARRENDAMENTO MERCANTIL NORCHEM—The Chase Manhattan Corporation; *U.S. Public*, pg. 341
OHM CORPORATION; *U.S. Public*, pg. 1207
OLIVETTI MANAGEMENT OF AMERICA, INC.—Olivetti SpA; *Int'l*, pg. 1002
OPERATIONS MANAGEMENT INTERNATIONAL, INC.—CH2M Hill Companies, Ltd.; *U.S. Private*, pg. 195
PHI MARKETING SERVICES—Pioneer Hi-Bred International, Inc.; *U.S. Public*, pg. 1299
PESAG AKTIENGESELLSCHAFT—Veba AG; *Int'l*, pg. 1456
PROFESSIONAL ECONOMIC SERVICES, INC.—John Hancock Mutual Life Insurance Company; *U.S. Private*, pg. 590
QST ENVIRONMENTAL INC.—CILCORP Inc.; *U.S. Public*, pg. 367
RED BAND SERVICES N.V.—CSM N.V.; *Int'l*, pg. 245
ROCKTON TECHNICAL SERVICES CORPORATION—Stone & Webster, Incorporated; *U.S. Public*, pg. 1519
SPC INTERNATIONAL CORP.—System Planning Corp.; *U.S. Private*, pg. 1061
SCIENCE MANAGEMENT CORPORATION—Versar Inc.; *U.S. Public*, pg. 1717
SCOTTISH ENTERPRISE; *Int'l*, pg. 1212
WILBUR SMITH ASSOCIATES; *U.S. Private*, pg. 1009
SPRINGBORN TESTING & RESEARCH, INC.; *U.S. Private*, pg. 1027
TARGETBASE MARKETING—The M/A/R/C Group; *U.S. Public*, pg. 1023
TECHNICAL SERVICES GROUP—Namanco LLC; *U.S. Private*, pg. 773
21ST VISION—Horizon Enterprises Group LLC; *U.S. Private*, pg. 539
XEROX INTERNATIONAL CENTER FOR TRAINING & MANAGEMENT DEVELOPMENT—Xerox Corporation; *U.S. Public*, pg. 1785

8999 — SERVICES, NEC

ABS INTEGRATED SERVICES—American Bureau of Shipping; *U.S. Private*, pg. 51
AGRI-FINANCIAL SERVICES—Dairylea Cooperative Inc.; *U.S. Private*, pg. 308
ALMEGA CORPORATION—ERD Waste Corp.; *U.S. Public*, pg. 546
ALMEGA CORPORATION-CA—ERD Waste Corp.; *U.S. Public*, pg. 546
BARNETT INTERNATIONAL/PAREXEL—PAREXEL International Corporation; *U.S. Public*, pg. 1258
BECHTEL CIVIL, INC.—Bechtel Group, Inc.; *U.S. Private*, pg. 128
BECHTEL LTD.—Bechtel Group, Inc.; *U.S. Private*, pg. 128
BECHTEL MINING & METALS—Bechtel Group, Inc.; *U.S. Private*, pg. 128
BECHTEL PETROLEUM & CHEMICAL—Bechtel Group, Inc.; *U.S. Private*, pg. 128
BECHTEL POWER CORPORATION—Bechtel Group, Inc.; *U.S. Private*, pg. 128
BETZDEARBORN INC.—BetzDearborn Inc.; *U.S. Public*, pg. 227
BROCKHOUSE C & F MACHINING LIMITED—EIP Group plc; *Int'l*, pg. 426
CANISCO RESOURCES, INC.; *U.S. Public*, pg. 301
COAST TO COAST CORPORATION—Cigna Corp.; *U.S. Public*, pg. 366
COLLOID ENVIRONMENTAL TECHNOLOGIES COMPANY (CETCO)—AMCOL International Corp.; *U.S. Public*, pg. 64
CROSBY & OVERTON, INC.; *U.S. Private*, pg. 290
CROWN CENTRAL PETROLEUM FOUNDATION—Crown Central Petroleum Corporation; *U.S. Public*, pg. 462
DEUTSCHE FINANCIAL SERVICES CORPORATION—Deutsche Bank AG; *Int'l*, pg. 403
EXECUTIVE MANAGEMENT AND CONSULTANT SERVICES, INC.—AEGON N.V.; *Int'l*, pg. 27
FINANCIAL MANAGEMENT—BankAmerica Corporation; *U.S. Public*, pg. 181
FIRST USA PAYMENTECH, INC.—Banc One Corporation; *U.S. Public*, pg. 174
GENERAL DYNAMICS CORPORATION; *U.S. Public*, pg. 708
GEOMET TECHNOLOGIES, INC.—Versar Inc.; *U.S. Public*, pg. 1717
JWK INTERNATIONAL CORP.; *U.S. Private*, pg. 579
JACOBS SUCHARD SERVICE GMBH & CO. KG—Philip Morris Companies Inc.; *U.S. Public*, pg. 1289
KAISER STEEL CORPORATION—Kaiser Ventures, Inc.; *U.S. Public*, pg. 941
KINETICS TECHNOLOGY INTERNATIONAL GMBH—Mannesmann A.G.; *Int'l*, pg. 836
LAING CONSTRUCTION SERVICES—John Laing PLC; *Int'l*, pg. 797
LIBERTY INVESTMENT GROUP, INC.—Liberty Corporation; *U.S. Public*, pg. 992
LIGHT SIGNATURES, INC.—Equifax Inc.; *U.S. Public*, pg. 588
LINCOLN NATIONAL ADMINISTRATIVE SERVICES CORP.—Lincoln National Corporation; *U.S. Public*, pg. 998
MACSAVEER FINANCIAL SERVICES—Heilig-Meyers Company; *U.S. Public*, pg. 805
MARITZ EUROPA LIMITED—Maritz Inc.; *U.S. Private*, pg. 704
MARITZ INC.; *U.S. Private*, pg. 703
MARVIN LUMBER & CEDAR COMPANY; *U.S. Private*, pg. 710
MERCER CONSULTING GROUP, INC.—Marsh & McLennan Companies, Inc.; *U.S. Public*, pg. 1049
WILLIAM M. MERCER LIMITED—Marsh & McLennan Companies, Inc.; *U.S. Public*, pg. 1049
MURPHY EASTERN OIL CO.—Murphy Oil Corporation; *U.S. Public*, pg. 1142
NAMANCO LLC; *U.S. Private*, pg. 773
NATIONAL ELECTRONICS WARRANTY CORPORATION; *U.S. Private*, pg. 782
NATIONAL EMPLOYEE BENEFITS CORPORATION—Cigna Corp.; *U.S. Public*, pg. 366
NOMURA RESEARCH INSTITUTE, LTD.—The Nomura Securities Co., Ltd.; *Int'l*, pg. 956
NORLIGHT TELECOMMUNICATIONS INC.—Journal Communications Inc.; *U.S. Private*, pg. 601
OHM CORPORATION; *U.S. Public*, pg. 1207
ORKLA FINANS A.S—Orkla A.S.A.; *Int'l*, pg. 1011
PEABODY DEVELOPMENT COMPANY—Hanson PLC; *Int'l*, pg. 594
QUINTANA PETROLEUM CORP.; *U.S. Private*, pg. 901
QUINTANA PETROLEUM SERVICES—Quintana Petroleum Corp.; *U.S. Private*, pg. 901
REPUBLIC SECURITY BANK—Republic Security Financial Corporation; *U.S. Public*, pg. 1382
REPUBLIC SECURITY FINANCIAL CORPORATION; *U.S. Public*, pg. 1381
SAFECARD SERVICES, INC.—Cendant Corporation; *U.S. Public*, pg. 320
SCOTT ENVIRONMENTAL TECHNOLOGY—ERD Waste Corp.; *U.S. Public*, pg. 546
SELF-INSURERS' MANAGEMENT CORPORATION—Cigna Corp.; *U.S. Public*, pg. 366
SERV-TECH, INC.; *U.S. Public*, pg. 1460
SUN LIFE ASSURANCE COMPANY OF CANADA; *Int'l*, pg. 1318
SUN LIFE OF CANADA BENEFIT MANAGEMENT LIMITED—Sun Life Assurance Company of Canada; *Int'l*, pg. 1319
TECHNICAL SERVICES GROUP—Namanco LLC; *U.S. Private*, pg. 773

TRI-S ENVIRONMENTAL CONSULTING—ERD Waste Corp.; *U.S. Public*, pg. 546
TRI-S INCORPORATED—ERD Waste Corp.; *U.S. Public*, pg. 546
VERSAR INC.; *U.S. Public*, pg. 1717
WARNER BROS. CONSUMER PRODUCTS—Time Warner Inc.; *U.S. Public*, pg. 1610
R.O. WHITESELL & ASSOCIATES, INC; *U.S. Private*, pg. 1173
WILLIS CORROON RISK MANAGEMENT LIMITED—Willis Corroon Group PLC; *Int'l*, pg. 1503
WOOLWICH PLC; *Int'l*, pg. 1514
YORKSHIRE BUILDING SOCIETY; *Int'l*, pg. 1522

9223 — CORRECTIONAL INSTITUTIONS

CORRECTIONAL FOODSERVICES MANAGEMENT—The Wackenhut Corporation; *U.S. Public*, pg. 1731
THE WACKENHUT CORPORATION; *U.S. Public*, pg. 1731
WACKENHUT CORRECTIONS CORPORATION—The Wackenhut Corporation; *U.S. Public*, pg. 1731

9224 — FIRE PROTECTION

RURAL METRO CORPORATION; *U.S. Public*, pg. 1412
TRIDATA INC.—System Planning Corp.; *U.S. Private*, pg. 1061

9311 — PUBLIC FINANCE, TAXATION & MONETARY POLICY

BARCLAYS FINANCIAL SERVICES CO. LTD.—Barclays Bank PLC; *Int'l*, pg. 164

9431 — ADMINISTRATION OF PUBLIC HEALTH PROGRAMS

COASTAL PHYSICIAN GROUP, INC.; *U.S. Public*, pg. 391
COUNSEL CORPORATION; *Int'l*, pg. 338
DAARBERG-OEKOTECHNIK GMBH—Saarbergwerke Aktiengesellschaft; *Int'l*, pg. 1167
HANIEL ENVIRSERVICE GMBH—Franz Haniel & Cie, GmbH; *Int'l*, pg. 592
KEMRON ENVIRONMENTAL SERVICES, INC.; *U.S. Private*, pg. 614
NIPPON LIFE HEALTH CONSULTANT—Nippon Life Insurance Co.; *Int'l*, pg. 935
NIPPON LIFE LIFESAVING SOCIETY (SAISEI-KAI)—Nippon Life Insurance Co.; *Int'l*, pg. 935

9511 — AIR & WATER RESOURCE & SOLID WASTE MANAGEMENT

ACUREX ENVIRONMENTAL CORP.—Heidemij N.V.; *Int'l*, pg. 607
ADDINGTON RESOURCES, INC.—Republic Industries, Inc.; *U.S. Public*, pg. 1379
AMERICA NORTH INC.—EMCON; *U.S. Public*, pg. 571
BENTHOS, INC.; *U.S. Public*, pg. 212
E & A ENVIRONMENTAL CONSULTANTS, INC.—EMCON; *U.S. Public*, pg. 571
ENVIRONMENTAL/GOVERNMENT GROUP—Morrison Knudsen Corporation; *U.S. Public*, pg. 1134
GENERAL SCIENCES CORP.—Science Applications International Corp.; *U.S. Private*, pg. 976
GREENWAYS LANDFILL—Hanson PLC; *Int'l*, pg. 592
FRANZ HANIEL & CIE, GMBH; *Int'l*, pg. 591
KAISER VENTURES, INC.; *U.S. Public*, pg. 941
L & L ENVIRONMENTAL SERVICES—L & L Oil Company, Inc.; *U.S. Private*, pg. 638
MED/WASTE, INC.; *U.S. Public*, pg. 1077
PERMA-FIX ENVIRONMENTAL SERVICES, INC.; *U.S. Public*, pg. 1279
SAFETY DISPOSAL SYSTEM, INC.—Med/Waste, Inc.; *U.S. Public*, pg. 1077
TETRA TECHNOLOGIES; *U.S. Public*, pg. 1582
TURNER LABORATORIES—EMCON; *U.S. Public*, pg. 571
UNITED WASTE SYSTEMS, INC.; *U.S. Public*, pg. 1691
UNITED WATER MID-ATLANTIC—United Water Resources; *U.S. Public*, pg. 1692

9512 — LAND, MINERAL, WILDLIFE & FOREST CONSERVATION

GERAGHTY & MILLER, INC.—Heidemij N.V.; *Int'l*, pg. 607
ONE PROPERTY CORPORATION—The Somerset Group, Inc.; *U.S. Public*, pg. 1484

9532 — ADMINISTRATION OF URBAN PLANNING & COMMUNITY & RURAL DEVELOPMENT

NBD COMMUNITY DEVELOPMENT CORPORATION—First Chicago NBD Corporation; *U.S. Public*, pg. 628
NBD NEIGHBORHOOD REVITALIZATION CORP.—First Chicago NBD Corporation; *U.S. Public*, pg. 628
RNL FACILITIES CORPORATION; *U.S. Private*, pg. 905

9611 — ADMINISTRATION OF GENERAL ECONOMIC PROGRAMS

BANCO MUNDIAL—The World Bank; *U.S. Private*, pg. 1189
BANQUE MONDIALE—The World Bank; *U.S. Private*, pg. 1189
BLACK & VEATCH INTERNATIONAL-ENERGY—Black & Veatch; *U.S. Private*, pg. 146
GENERAL ATOMICS; *U.S. Private*, pg. 443
TRC COMPANIES, INC.; *U.S. Public*, pg. 1557
TRC ENVIRONMENTAL SOLUTIONS, INC.—TRC Companies, Inc.; *U.S. Public*, pg. 1558
TRC MARIAH ASSOCIATES, INC.—TRC Companies, Inc.; *U.S. Public*, pg. 1558
THE WORLD BANK; *U.S. Private*, pg. 1188

9621 — REGULATION & ADMINISTRATION OF TRANSPORTATION PROGRAMS

EAGLE TECH INC.—Northrop Grumman Corporation; *U.S. Public*, pg. 1199
INTERNATIO HOUT B.V.—Internatio-Muller N.V.; *Int'l*, pg. 682
NEWELL BRIDGE & RAILWAY COMPANY—The Homer Laughlin China Company; *U.S. Private*, pg. 653
PORT OF HOUSTON AUTHORITY; *U.S. Private*, pg. 876
PORT OF PORTLAND; *U.S. Private*, pg. 876
SOUTHEASTERN PENNSYLVANIA TRANSPORTATION AUTHORITY; *U.S. Private*, pg. 1015
TEESSIDE HOLDINGS LIMITED—Powell Duffryn PLC; *Int'l*, *pg. 1065*

9631 — REGULATION & ADMINISTRATION OF COMMUNICATION, ELECTRIC, GAS & OTHER UTILITIES

STAMICARBON BV—DSM N.V.; *Int'l*, pg. 354
TELIA AB; *Int'l*, pg. 1373

9641 — REGULATION OF AGRICULTURAL MARKETING & COMMODITIES

AMFAC AGRIBUSINESS, INC.—JMB Realty Corporation; *U.S. Private*, pg. 578
BLACKWELL LAND CO.—Pearson plc; *Int'l*, pg. 1027
GENERAL INSTRUMENT CORPORATION—General Instrument Corporation; *U.S. Public*, pg. 716
SSD&W INTEGRATED MARKETING COMMUNICATIONS; *U.S. Private*, pg. 958
STAMICARBON BV—DSM N.V.; *Int'l*, pg. 354
TOSOH EUROPE B.V.—Tosoh Corporation; *Int'l*, pg. 1408
U-HAUL INTERNATIONAL, INC.—Amerco; *U.S. Private*, pg. 49

9651 — REGULATION, LICENSING & INSPECTION OF MISCELLANEOUS COMMERCIAL SECTORS

DISCOVISION ASSOCIATES—Pioneer Electronic Corporation; *Int'l*, pg. 1057
MONSANTO OVERSEAS, S.A.—Monsanto Company; *U.S. Public*, pg. 1126
THE PROMOTION IN MOTION COMPANIES; *U.S. Private*, pg. 890

9661 — SPACE RESEARCH & TECHNOLOGY

BALL AEROSPACE & TECHNOLOGIES CORP.—Ball Corporation; *U.S. Public*, pg. 171
LOCKHEED AUSTIN DIVISION—Lockheed Martin Corporation; *U.S. Public*, pg. 1008
OCEANEERING SPACE SYSTEMS—Oceaneering International, Inc.; *U.S. Public*, pg. 1211

9711 — NATIONAL SECURITY

S.A. USA—Ship Analytics, Inc.; *U.S. Private*, pg. 994

9999 — NONCLASSIFIABLE ESTABLISHMENTS

ALLENERGY MARKETING COMPANY, L.L.C.—Eastern Enterprises; *U.S. Public*, pg. 549
ALLENERGY MARKETING COMPANY, L.L.C.—New England Electric System; *U.S. Public*, pg. 1172
AMERICAN ONCOLOGY RESOURCES, INC.; *U.S. Public*, pg. 88
AMERIPATH, INC.; *U.S. Public*, pg. 96
ATMEL CORPORATION; *U.S. Public*, pg. 145
AUTODESK, INC.—Autodesk, Inc.; *U.S. Public*, pg. 149
BRASS EAGLE INC.; *U.S. Public*, pg. 250
BROADVISION, INC.; *U.S. Public*, pg. 258
CNG INTERNATIONAL CORP.—Consolidated Natural Gas Company; *U.S. Public*, pg. 435
CNG POWER SERVICES CORPORATION—Consolidated Natural Gas Company; *U.S. Public*, pg. 435
CELERITEK, INC.; *U.S. Public*, pg. 319
CERTIFIED APPAREL SERVICES OF HONDURAS, S.A.—Kleinert's, Inc.; *U.S. Private*, pg. 625
COMMAND SECURITY CORPORATION—Command Security Corporation; *U.S. Public*, pg. 409
CONSTRUCTION LENDING CORPORATION OF AMERICA-BUILDER DIVISION—INMC Mortgage Holdings, Inc.; *U.S. Public*, pg. 857
CYBEROPTICS CORPORATION; *U.S. Public*, pg. 470
CYPRUS EXPLORATION & DEVELOPMENT CORPORATION—Cyprus Amax Minerals Company; *U.S.* Public, pg. 471
CYPRUS ROD CHICAGO CORPORATION—Cyprus Amax Minerals Company; *U.S. Public*, pg. 471
DESTEC ENERGY, INC.—NGC Corporation; *U.S. Public*, pg. 1146
EA INDUSTRIES; *U.S. Public*, pg. 541
ECHELON INTERNATIONAL CORPORATION; *U.S. Public*, *pg. 560*
ELCOTEL, INC.; *U.S. Public*, pg. 568
EMPLOYEE SOLUTIONS, INC.; *U.S. Public*, pg. 579
GEOTEK COMMUNICATIONS; *U.S. Public*, pg. 739
HIGHWOOD RESOURCES LTD.—Royal Oak Mines Inc.; *U.S. Public*, pg. 1411
HOWELL CORPORATION; *U.S. Public*, pg. 843
INDIMAC MORTGAGE OBLIGATIONS, II, INC.—INMC Mortgage Holdings, Inc.; *U.S. Public*, pg. 858
INDIMAC MORTGAGE OBLIGATIONS, INC.—INMC Mortgage Holdings, Inc.; *U.S. Public*, pg. 858
INTERNATIONAL FLAVORS & FRAGRANCES I.F.F. (NEDERLAND) B.V.—International Flavors & Fragrances, Inc.; *U.S. Public*, pg. 899
KLEINERT'S INC. OF FLORIDA—Kleinert's, Inc.; *U.S. Private*, pg. 625
KRONOS INCORPORATED; *U.S. Public*, pg. 967
MAYER & SCHWEITZER, INC.—The Charles Schwab Corporation; *U.S. Public*, pg. 1443
MCKENZIE TOWABLES BY MONACO—Monaco Coach Corporation; *U.S. Public*, pg. 1123
MOLTEN METAL TECHNOLOGY, INC.; *U.S. Public*, pg. 1123
MOODY'S INVESTORS SERVICE, INC.—The Dun & Bradstreet Corporation; *U.S. Public*, pg. 536
MORRISON HEALTH CARE INC.; *U.S. Public*, pg. 1133
MORROW WEST BEACH; *U.S. Public*, pg. 1134
NDSI, INC.—American Media, Inc.; *U.S. Public*, pg. 87
THE NET MARKET COMPANY—Cendant Corporation; *U.S.* Public, pg. 321
NETWORK LONG DISTANCE, INC.; *U.S. Public*, pg. 1169
NETWORK PERIPHERALS INC.; *U.S. Public*, pg. 1169
NEXTLINK COMMUNICATIONS INC.; *U.S. Public*, pg. 1181
NIPSCO CAPITAL MARKETS, INC.—NIPSCO Industries, Inc.; *U.S. Public*, pg. 1185
OSI SYSTEMS, INC.; *U.S. Public*, pg. 1208
PMR CORPORATION; *U.S. Public*, pg. 1242
PFLEIDERER AG; *Int'l*, pg. 1046
PHYCOR, INC.; *U.S. Public*, pg. 1293
PUMP REPAIR CENTERS—Ingersoll-Rand Company; *U.S. Public*, pg. 877
ROYALE COACH—Monaco Coach Corporation; *U.S. Public*, *pg. 1123*
S3 INCORPORATED; *U.S. Public*, pg. 1415
SANMINA CORPORATION; *U.S. Public*, pg. 1431
SIMULA, INC.; *U.S. Public*, pg. 1475
SWING-N-SLIDE CORP.; *U.S. Public*, pg. 1543
T-NETIX, INC.; *U.S. Public*, pg. 1553
UUNET TECHNOLOGIES, INC.—WorldCom, Inc.; *U.S. Public*, pg. 1779
VACATION BREAK USA—Fairfield Communities, Inc.; *U.S. Public*, pg. 611
WAREHOUSE LENDING CORPORATION OF AMERICA—INMC Mortgage Holdings, Inc.; *U.S. Public*, pg. 857
WIRELESS TELECOM GROUP, INC.; *U.S. Public*, pg. 1772
YALE INDUSTRIAL PRODUCTS—Columbus McKinnon Corp.; *U.S. Public*, pg. 406

MASTER PERSONNEL INDEX

ADVERTISING

A'Hearn, Barbara, Mgr.-Adv.--Essex International, Inc., Fort Wayne, IN; *U.S. Public*, pg. 593

Aaberg, Erick, Grp. V.P.-Mktg.--Jotun A/S, Sandefjord, Norway; *Int'l*, pg. 714

Aaronson, Morton C., Chief Mktg. Officer & V.P.--K N Energy, Inc., Lakewood, CO; *U.S. Public*, pg. 937

Abbate, Eileen, V.P.-Adv. & Mktg.--PharmHouse, Inc., New York, NY; *U.S. Public*, pg. 1286

Abbott, Michael E., Chm. Bd. & Chief Exec. Officer--American Republic Insurance Co., Des Moines, IA; *U.S. Private*, pg. 61

Abdalla, Donna, Dir.-Adv.--Pennsylvania Enterprises Inc., Wilkes-Barre, PA; *U.S. Public*, pg. 1271

Abdallah, Davina, Mgr.-Adv. & Mktg.--Henry Birks & Sons (1993) Inc., Montreal, Canada; *Int'l*, pg. 196

Abels, Terry, Sr. V.P.-Sls. & Mktg.--CFA Holding Company, Charlotte, MI; *U.S. Private*, pg. 194

Abnee, Conn, Mgr.-Mktg. & Adv.--East Kentucky Power Co-op, Winchester, KY; *U.S. Private*, pg. 356

Abrahamson, David A., Pres. & Chief Exec. Officer--Medicine Shoppe International, Inc., Saint Louis, MO; *U.S. Public*, pg. 304

Abramouitz, Ellen, Dir.-Adv.--Seventeen Magazine, New York, NY; *U.S. Public*, pg. 1328

Abramowitz, Harvey, Dir.-Adv.--Stern's, Paramus, NJ; *U.S. Public*, pg. 618

Abramson, Daniel, Pres.-Professional Search Div.--Dunhill Personnel System, Inc., Hauppauge, NY; *U.S. Public*, pg. 1746

Abramson, Larry, Pres.--Camerican International, Paramus, NJ; *U.S. Public*, pg. 426

Abramson, Mark, Dir.-Mktg.--Cadaco, Chicago, IL; *U.S. Private*, pg. 910

Accola, Richard M., V.P.-Sls. & Mktg.--Gravymaster Inc., Branford, CT; *U.S. Private*, pg. 471

Achee, Vickie, Dir.-Adv.--Lost Arrow Corporation, Ventura, CA; *U.S. Private*, pg. 676

Achepohl, Al, Dir.-Creative Services--John O. Butler Co., Chicago, IL; *Int'l*, pg. 1320

Acker, Rolf-Dieter, Dr., Head-Adv. & Pub. Rels.--BASF AG, Ludwigshafen, Germany; *Int'l*, pg. 103

Ackroyd, Jack, V.P.-Adv.--Hughes Family Markets, Inc., Irwindale, CA; *U.S. Public*, pg. 1349

Acton, Vaughan, V.P.-Brand Mngmt.--Kaiser Permanente, Oakland, CA; *U.S. Private*, pg. 605

Acusti, Pere, Dir.-Mktg. & Adv.--Mattel Espana, S.A., Barcelona, Spain; *U.S. Public*, pg. 1059

Adamovich, Kelly, Mgr.-Adv.--OfficeMax, Shaker Heights, OH; *U.S. Public*, pg. 1212

Adams, Bob, Dir.-Adv.--Monro Muffler/Brake, Inc., Rochester, NY; *U.S. Public*, pg. 1124

Adams, Douglass H., Exec. V.P.--United Bankshares, Inc., Parkersburg, WV; *U.S. Public*, pg. 1674

Adams, John T., Mgr.-Adv.--Merillat Industries Inc., Adrian, MI; *U.S. Public*, pg. 1053

Adams, Margaret, V.P.-Adv.--IBJ Schroder Bank & Trust Company, New York, NY; *Int'l*, pg. 674

Adams, Raymond T., V.P.-Corp. Commun.--DSC Communications Corporation, Plano, TX; *U.S. Public*, pg. 475

Adams, Ricardo, Dir.-Mktg.--Philips do Brasil-Walita Div., Sao Paulo, Brazil; *Int'l*, pg. 1055

Adams, Tim, Dir.-Sls. & Mktg.--Ipsen International, Inc., Cherry Valley, IL; *Int'l*, pg. 1149

Adkins, Brooke, V.P.-Catalogue, Mktg. & Pub. Rels.--F.A.O. Schwarz, New York, NY; *Int'l*, pg. 750

Adler, Paul, Mgr.-Adv.--Wolohan Lumber Co., Saginaw, MI; *U.S. Public*, pg. 1774

Affledt, Dawn, Acct. Mgr.-Adv.--Burlington Motor Holdings Inc., Daleville, IN; *U.S. Private*, pg. 183

Agnese, Carlos E., Exec. V.P.-Bus. Devel., Mktg., Estimating & Contract Admin.--Norfolk Shipbuilding & Drydock Corporation, Norfolk, VA; *U.S. Private*, pg. 802

Aguillard, John, Dir.-Mktg. & Adv.--Superior Auctioneers & Marketing, Inc., San Antonio, TX; *U.S. Private*, pg. 1054

Ahle, Diane, V.P.-Recruitment Adv.--Keyes Martin, East Hanover, NJ; *U.S. Private*, pg. 618

Ahlstrom, Craig, Dir.-Adv., Mktg., Opers. & Sls.--Farnsworth Development Co., Mesa, AZ; *U.S. Private*, pg. 397

Ahmer, Al, V.P.-Sls. & Mktg.--Calavo Growers of California, Santa Ana, CA; *U.S. Private*, pg. 199

Aho, Colleen, Mgr.-Sls. Specialist--Howden Fluid Systems, Santa Barbara, CA; *U.S. Public*, pg. 1045

Ai, Lee Kuo, Mgr.-Corp. Affairs & Devel.--Orchard Parade Holdings Limited, Singapore, Singapore; *Int'l*, pg. 1007

Aiken, Janet, Dir.-Adv.--Xerox Canada Ltd., North York, Canada; *U.S. Public*, pg. 1785

Aizawa, T., Dir.-Gen. Mktg., Sls. & Adv.--Otto Sumisho Inc., Tokyo, Japan; *Int'l*, pg. 1015

Akers, Barry J., Mgr.-Corp. Commun.--Fletcher Challenge Limited, Auckland, New Zealand; *Int'l*, pg. 494

Al-Zaid, F., Sr. Reg. Dir.--Kuwait Airways Corp., New York, NY; *Int'l*, pg. 764

Albaugh, Robert, Mgr.-Mktg.--Hurco Companies, Inc., Indianapolis, IN; *U.S. Public*, pg. 850

Albert, Allan, V.P.-Adv.--The Harodite Finishing Company Inc., North Dighton, MA; *U.S. Private*, pg. 503

Albert, Larry, Pres.--R.L. Albert & Son, Inc., Greenwich, CT; *U.S. Private*, pg. 32

Albert, Lawrence S., Gen. Mgr.--Ventura Foods, Omaha, NE; *U.S. Private*, pg. 508

Albrecht, William, Pres.--Barry Controls, Brighton, MA; *U.S. Public*, pg. 124

Albright, Judy, Dir.-Pub. Rels.--The Genie Company, Alliance, OH; *U.S. Private*, pg. 823

Alderson, Ken, Dir.-Adv.--Kentucky Indiana Lumber Co. Inc., Louisville, KY; *U.S. Private*, pg. 615

Alen, Rob, Mgr.-Acura Adv.--American Honda Motor Co., Inc., Torrance, CA; *Int'l*, pg. 634

Alessandro, Jim, Dir.-Adv.--Walt Disney Attractions-Walt Disney World, Lake Buena Vista, FL; *U.S. Public*, pg. 513

Alexander, Bill, Mgr.-Mktg. & Prod. Devel.--Mine Safety Appliances Co., Pittsburgh, PA; *U.S. Public*, pg. 1114

Alexander, Lori, Mgr.-Adv.--B.C. Hydro, Vancouver, Canada; *Int'l*, pg. 114

Alexander, Phillip, V.P.-Mktg. & Adv.--Pearle Vision, Inc., Dallas, TX; *U.S. Public*, pg. 397

Alfaro, Carlos, Mgr.-Adv.--Taca International Airlines, S. A., San Salvador, El Salvador; *Int'l*, pg. 1346

Alfirevic, Karen, Mgr.-Midwest Adv.--Conde Nast Traveler, New York, NY; *U.S. Private*, pg. 20

Alfonso, Al, Dir.-Corp. Adv.--Physician Corporation of America, Miami, FL; *U.S. Public*, pg. 1293

Alicandu, Jose Rafael, Mgr.-Adv.--Banco Provincial S.A. Banco Universal, Caracas, Venezuela; *Int'l*, pg. 142

Allebrand, John, V.P. & Dir.-Adv. & Mktg.--Glendale Federal Bank, F.S.B., Glendale, CA; *U.S. Public*, pg. 747

Allen, Bob, V.P.-Mktg.--Vigortone AG Products, Inc., Cedar Rapids, IA; *Int'l*, pg. 1357

Allen, Danita, Editor--Country America Magazine, Des Moines, IA; *U.S. Public*, pg. 1094

Allen, James R., V.P.-Pub. Rels. & Adv.--CNF Transportation Inc., Palo Alto, CA; *U.S. Public*, pg. 281

Allen, Joe, Asst. Mgr.-Adv. & Promo.--Berkley Publishing Corp., New York, NY; *Int'l*, pg. 1027

Allen, Joel, V.P.-Lasco Foods--Allen Foods, Inc., Saint Louis, MO; *U.S. Private*, pg. 37

Allen, Joseph, V.P.-Commun.--Cognizant Corporation, Westport, CT; *U.S. Public*, pg. 395

Allen, Mitchell K., V.P.-Adv.--The Beacon Journal Publishing Company, Akron, OH; *U.S. Public*, pg. 963

Allen, Sally, V.P.-Admin. & Govt. Affairs--Gary-Williams Energy Corporation, Denver, CO; *U.S. Private*, pg. 440

Allen, Thomas L., Corp. V.P.-Mktg.--Skyline Chili, Inc., Fairfield, OH; *U.S. Public*, pg. 1475

Allens, Cliff, Mgr.-Corp. Adv.--Matsushita Electric Corporation of America, Secaucus, NJ; *Int'l*, pg. 847

Alles, Don, Mgr.-Mktg. Communications--Eaton Corporation, Truck Components Operations-North America, Galesburg, MI; *U.S. Public*, pg. 557

Allison, Garran, Mgr.-Adv.--The Topeka Capital-Journal, Topeka, KS; *U.S. Private*, pg. 995

Allo, Leo, V.P.-Commun.--Valmet Corporation, Helsinki, Finland; *Int'l*, pg. 1447

Allsbury, Fran, Exec. Sec.--Tamaqua Cable Products Corp., Schuylkill Haven, PA; *Int'l*, pg. 417

Allwin, Chuck, Dir.-Mktg. Services--Baldwin Filters, Kearney, NE; *U.S. Public*, pg. 381

Almeida, Rodrigo de, Mgr.-Corp. Communications--Monsanto do Brasil Ltda. (Mobra S.A.), Sao Paulo, Brazil; *U.S. Public*, pg. 1125

Almond, Jeff, Dir.-Mktg.--Heatcraft, Inc.-Refrigeration Products Division, Stone Mountain, GA; *U.S. Private*, pg. 659

Alperson, Steven, Exec. V.P.--Rolled Steel Products Corporation, Los Angeles, CA; *U.S. Private*, pg. 941

Alsing, Rolf, Editor--Aftonbladet AB, Stockholm, Sweden; *Int'l*, pg. 29

Alstrup, Andrea, V.P.-Adv.--Johnson & Johnson, New Brunswick, NJ; *U.S. Public*, pg. 927

Alten, Lawrence, Sr. V.P.-Creative Svcs. & Adv.--U.S. Healthcare, Inc., Blue Bell, PA; *U.S. Public*, pg. 26

Alvarez-Recio, Emilio, V.P.-Global Adv.--Colgate-Palmolive Company, New York, NY; *U.S. Public*, pg. 397

Alvarez, Patricia, Dir.-Adv.--William Morrow & Co., Inc., New York, NY; *U.S. Private*, pg. 515

Amberger, Tom, Dir.-Mktg.--Galardi Group, Inc., Newport Beach, CA; *U.S. Private*, pg. 437

Amdursky, Jon, Dir.-Worldwide Adv. & Communications--International Specialty Products, Inc., Wayne, NJ; *U.S. Public*, pg. 858

Ammons, Dennis, V.P.-Mktg.--American Drew, Greensboro, NC; *U.S. Public*, pg. 974

Amos, Rick, Mgr.-Adv. & Promo.--Toronto Blue Jays Baseball Club, Inc., Toronto, Canada; *Int'l*, pg. 680

Amsden, Deborah C., Mgr.-Bus. Devel.--Alliance Construction Solutions, Inc., Fort Collins, CO; *U.S. Private*, pg. 38

Anagnostos, Olga, Coord.-Adv. & Media Buyer--Lifetime Television/ABC, New York, NY; *U.S. Public*, pg. 512

Anagnostos, Olga, Coord.-Adv. & Media Buyer--Lifetime Television/ABC, New York, NY; *U.S. Private*, pg. 516

Anastaskis, Tiffany, Dir.-Adv.--St. John Knits, Irvine, CA; *U.S. Private*, pg. 960

Ancona, John, V.P.-Adv.--The New York Post, New York, NY; *Int'l*, pg. 927

Anctil, Paula, Dir.-Mktg. & Adv.--United Grocers Inc., Portland, OR; *U.S. Private*, pg. 1122

Anders, Mary, Dir.-Sls. & Mktg.--Levlad, Inc., Chatsworth, CA; *U.S. Private*, pg. 663

Andersen, Beth, Mgr.-Adv. & Pub. Rels.--Recoton Auto Corporation, Lincolnshire, IL; *U.S. Public*, pg. 1369

Andersen, Linda, V.P.-Music Club Adv.--Columbia House Music Club, New York, NY; *Int'l*, pg. 1281

Anderson, Angi, Dir.-Mktg.--Affiliated Computer Services, Inc., Dallas, TX; *U.S. Public*, pg. 27

Anderson, Bruce, Pres. & Chief Exec. Officer--IWI Holding Limited, Westmont, IL; *U.S. Public*, pg. 861

Anderson, Catherine, Mgr.-Mktg. & Communications--O.I. Corporation, College Station, TX; *U.S. Public*, pg. 1208

Anderson, Cheryl, Mgr.-Adv. & Communications--General Semiconductor, Inc., Melville, NY; *U.S. Public*, pg. 726

Anderson, D.J., Pres.--International Nickel, Inc., Saddle Brook, NJ; *Int'l*, pg. 672

Anderson, Jan, Coord.-Sls. & Co-op Adv.--Berryman Products, Inc., Arlington, TX; *U.S. Private*, pg. 138

Anderson, Jeff, Dir.-Adv.--The Rottlund Company, Inc., Roseville, MN; *U.S. Public*, pg. 1400

Anderson, Jon, V.P.-Mktg.-Europe--Columbia Tri-Star Films (UK), London, United Kingdom; *Int'l*, pg. 1281

Anderson, Kent T., Chm. Bd., Pres. & Chief Exec. Officer--B.B. Walker Company, Asheboro, NC; *U.S. Public*, pg. 1734

Anderson, Nina, Dir.-Adv.--The Hotsy Corporation, Englewood, CO; *U.S. Private*, pg. 500

Anderson, Patricia, Mgr.-Pub. Rels.--Sargent & Lundy, Chicago, IL; *U.S. Private*, pg. 965

Anderson, Sally, Dir.-Adv.--Duchossois Industries, Inc., Elmhurst, IL; *U.S. Private*, pg. 344

Anderson, Sarah S., Dir.-Adv.--The Chamberlain Group, Inc., Elmhurst, IL; *U.S. Private*, pg. 344

Anderson, Suzanne, Fund Asst.--Center Partners Management LLC, New York, NY; *U.S. Private*, pg. 222

Anderson, Tim, Mgr.-Classified Adv.--Dayton Newspapers, Inc., Dayton, OH; *U.S. Private*, pg. 281

Andreas, Martin L., Sr. V.P.-Sls. & Mktg.--Archer Daniels Midland Company (ADM), Decatur, IL; *U.S. Public*, pg. 127

Andresen, Trond, Sr. V.P.-Corp. Communications--Kvaerner a.s.a., Lysaker, Norway; *Int'l*, pg. 766

Andress, Brad, V.P.-Mktg.--Lund International Holdings, Inc., Anoka, MN; *U.S. Public*, pg. 1020
Andrews, Beth, Dir.-Mktg. Communications--Cincinnati Bell Telephone Company, Cincinnati, OH; *U.S. Public*, pg. 367
Andrews, Mark, Mgr.-Adv. & Public Relations--Century Telephone Enterprises, Inc., Monroe, LA; *U.S. Public*, pg. 329
Andrews, Sandy, Dir.-Adv.--Adray Appliance & Photo Center, Inc., Dearborn, MI; *U.S. Private*, pg. 18
Andrews, Theron, Dir.-Adv.--Famous Footwear, Madison, WI; *U.S. Public*, pg. 262
Andrews, Tom, Pres.--Lubriquip, Inc., Cleveland, OH; *U.S. Public*, pg. 862
Andrews, William H., Jr., Sr. V.P.-Mktg.--Union Planters Corporation, Cordova, TN; *U.S. Public*, pg. 1668
Anello, Patrick, Dir.-Mktg.--Wahl Clipper Corp., Sterling, IL; *U.S. Private*, pg. 1146
Angus, Jan, Dir.-Mktg. Communications--AlliedSignal Aerospace, Torrance, CA; *U.S. Public*, pg. 50
Anneberg, Karen, Mgr.-Mktg.--NTH Consultants, Ltd., Farmington, MI; *U.S. Private*, pg. 772
Anschutz, Philip, Pres.--Anschutz Corporation, Denver, CO; *U.S. Private*, pg. 75
Antes, Ernie, Pres.--Casting Materials Division, Chattanooga, TN; *U.S. Private*, pg. 525
Antle, Joe, Dir.-Adv.--The Virginian-Pilot, Norfolk, VA; *U.S. Private*, pg. 649
Anzaldo, Marianne W., Chief Info. Officer, Sec. & Mgr.-Adv.--E.P. Henry Corporation, Woodbury, NJ; *U.S. Private*, pg. 522
Apatoff, Robert S., Sr. V.P.-Adv.--U.S. Healthcare, Inc., Blue Bell, PA; *U.S. Public*, pg. 26
Apollo, Denise, Mgr.--Merry Land & Investment Company, Inc., Augusta, GA; *U.S. Public*, pg. 1098
Appel, Marcia, Sr. V.P.-Adv., Natl. Promo. & Corp. Communications--Musicland Group Inc., Minnetonka, MN; *U.S. Public*, pg. 1142
Appleman, Kurt, Mgr.-Adv. & Mktg.--The Davey Tree Expert Company, Kent, OH; *U.S. Private*, pg. 314
Aquila, G., Mgr.-Adv.--Nuovo Pignone S.p.a., Florence, Italy; *Int'l*, pg. 990
Aras, P.S., Adv.--BASF India Ltd., Mumbai, India; *Int'l*, pg. 106
Arbetman, Meg, Mgr.-Adv.-Wayne Feed Div.--Continental Grain Company, New York, NY; *U.S. Private*, pg. 268
Archer, Dave, Prod. Mgr.--Macrotech Plyseal, Inc., Salt Lake City, UT; *U.S. Private*, pg. 693
Archer, Pat, Mgr.-Adv.--T. Rowe Price Associates, Inc., Baltimore, MD; *U.S. Public*, pg. 1324
Archibald, David R., Sr. V.P.-Corp. Mktg.--Huntington National Bank, Columbus, OH; *U.S. Public*, pg. 850
Arevalo, Hector, Mgr.-Adv. & Promo.--Juan Minetti S.A., Cordoba, Argentina; *Int'l*, pg. 869
Argiro, Elaine, Dir.-Adv.--Paul Stuart, Inc., New York, NY; *U.S. Private*, pg. 844
Arkulari, Cathie, Mgr.-Mktg. Admin.--Standard & Poor's Compustat Services, Inc., Englewood, CO; *U.S. Public*, pg. 1071
Armstrong, Terry, Mgr.-Mktg. Communications--Biomet, Inc., Warsaw, IN; *U.S. Public*, pg. 231
Arnav, Javier, Dir.-Communications--Bancomer, S.A., Mexico, Mexico; *Int'l*, pg. 145
Arndt, Kathleen, Mgr.-Adv.--Louisiana Pacific Corporation, Portland, OR; *U.S. Public*, pg. 1015
Arnholt, Christine, Dir.-Mktg. Svcs.--Carnival Corporation, Miami, FL; *U.S. Public*, pg. 306
Arnold, Allen, Dir.-Adv.--Word, Incorporated, Dallas, TX; *U.S. Public*, pg. 704
Arnold, Allen, V.P.-Adv. & Promo.--Thomas Nelson Inc., Nashville, TN; *U.S. Public*, pg. 1167
Arnold, Cassie, Asst. Dir.-Adv. & Pub. Rels.--Ernst & Young, LLP, New York, NY; *U.S. Private*, pg. 381
Arnold, Gary, Adv. Asst.--Acxiom Corporation, Conway, AR; *U.S. Public*, pg. 18
Arnold, Jim, Mgr.-Adv. & Pub. Affairs--Helena Chemical Company, Memphis, TN; *Int'l*, pg. 845
Arnold, Martin, Dir.-Corp. Communications--Rayonier Inc., Stamford, CT; *U.S. Public*, pg. 1363
Arons, Pam, Adv. Assoc.--New England Electric System, Westborough, MA; *U.S. Public*, pg. 1171
Aronson, Sid, Dir.-Commun.--Russ Berrie and Company, Inc., Oakland, NJ; *U.S. Public*, pg. 222
Arsenault, Karen, Asst. V.P.-Branding & Mktg. Commun.--The Dun & Bradstreet Corporation, Murray Hill, NJ; *U.S. Public*, pg. 535
Artandi, George, Pres. & Chief Oper. Officer--Book of the Month Club, New York, NY; *U.S. Public*, pg. 1612
Arthur, R.B., Mgr.-Mfg. & Sls.--North State Pyrophyllite, Greensboro, NC; *U.S. Private*, pg. 924
Artin, Cynthia, Dir.-Creative Svcs.--The American Stock Exchange, New York, NY; *U.S. Private*, pg. 62
Artman, Pam, Mgr.-Mktg. Svcs.--Leggett & Platt, Incorporated, Carthage, MO; *U.S. Public*, pg. 985
Asawa, Yosuke, Mgr.-Adv.--Canon U.S.A., Inc., Lake Success, NY; *Int'l*, pg. 262
Asboth, Kara, Mgr.-Adv.--Fournier Furniture, Saint Paul, VA; *U.S. Private*, pg. 422
Asher, Russell, Pres.--Master Craft Corp., Kalamazoo, MI; *Int'l*, pg. 267
Ashner, Iva K., Dir.-Adv.--W.W. Norton & Company, Inc., New York, NY; *U.S. Private*, pg. 807
Ashooh, Nicholas J., V.P.-Pub. Affairs & Corp. Communications--Niagara Mohawk Power Corporation, Syracuse, NY; *U.S. Public*, pg. 1181
Askew, L. Rudolph, V.P.-Sls. & Mktg.--Jouan, Inc., Winchester, VA; *U.S. Private*, pg. 601
Askinas, Milton, Pres. & Chief Exec. Officer--Glen Oaks Industries, Inc., New York, NY; *U.S. Private*, pg. 456
Assad, Dennis, V.P.-Sls. & Mktg.--UniFirst Corporation, Wilmington, MA; *U.S. Public*, pg. 1665
Assimon, Bill, V.P.-Mktg.--Sentry Group, Rochester, NY; *U.S. Private*, pg. 984
Ast, Eileen, V.P.-Corp. Communications--The Mutual Life Insurance Company of New York, New York, NY; *U.S. Private*, pg. 769
Atha, Allen, III, V.P. & Chief Mktg. Officer--Amvestors Financial Corporation, Topeka, KS; *U.S. Private*, pg. 59
Atkins, Rod, Adv. Mgr.--Trucks GMC--Pontiac-GMC Truck Division, Pontiac, MI; *U.S. Public*, pg. 720
Atkins, Sharon, Dir.-Pub. Affairs & Promo.--WAXY (FM), Fort Lauderdale, FL; *U.S. Public*, pg. 925
Atkinson, Paul, V.P.-Adv.--Dow Jones & Company, Inc., New York, NY; *U.S. Public*, pg. 524
Atols, Robert M., Pres.--Atols Tool and Mold Corp., Schiller Park, IL; *U.S. Private*, pg. 97
Attarian, Leon, Mgr.-Mktg. Commun. & Info.--Penn Engineering & Manufacturing Corp., Danboro, PA; *U.S. Public*, pg. 1269
Aubuchon, William E., III, Chief Exec. Officer & V.P.-Mktg. & Adv.--W.E. Aubuchon Co., Inc., Westminster, MA; *U.S. Private*, pg. 98
Aucoin, Doug, Dir.-Adv.--Aladdin Mills, Dalton, GA; *U.S. Public*, pg. 1121
Austin, Bill, Mgr.-Adv.--Makita U.S.A., Inc., La Mirada, CA; *Int'l*, pg. 831
Austin, Diane, V.P.-Mktg. Devel. Grp.--Rich Products Corp., Buffalo, NY; *U.S. Private*, pg. 928
Austin, John T., Jr., V.P.-Regional Sls.--James Austin Co., Mars, PA; *U.S. Private*, pg. 99
Austin, Michael C., V.P.-Corp. Commun.--Utica Mutual Insurance Company, New Hartford, NY; *U.S. Private*, pg. 1129
Austin, Terry, Dir.-Mktg.-London Region--Shoppers Drug Mart, Ltd., London, Canada; *Int'l*, pg. 112
Avery, Nathan M., Chm. Bd., Pres. & Chief Exec. Officer--Galveston-Houston Company, Houston, TX; *U.S. Private*, pg. 438
Avril, John G., Pres.--Sakrete, Inc., Cincinnati, OH; *U.S. Private*, pg. 961
Ayers, Dean, Dir.-Pub. Rels.--Warren Petroleum Company, Houston, TX; *U.S. Public*, pg. 1146
Babicz, Gregory, Dir.-Commun.--Union Switch & Signal Inc., Pittsburgh, PA; *Int'l*, pg. 77
Baccarella, Pat, V.P.--Plastic Reel Corp. of America, Lyndhurst, NJ; *U.S. Private*, pg. 871
Bachleda, Lauren, Mgr.-Pub. Rels. & Adv.--Arrow Pneumatics Co. Inc., Lake Zurich, IL; *U.S. Private*, pg. 85
Bachman, Vernon E., V.P.--Vulcan International Corporation, Wilmington, DE; *U.S. Public*, pg. 1725
Bachus, Richard, V.P.--Southern Missouri Containers Inc., Springfield, MO; *U.S. Private*, pg. 1017
Bacon, Peter, Mgr.-Mktg. Services--Unison Industries, Jacksonville, FL; *U.S. Private*, pg. 1120
Badger, Timothy C., V.P.-Mktg.--Arrow Financial Corporation, Glens Falls, NY; *U.S. Public*, pg. 135
Badgley, Jeff, Pres.--Miller Industries, Inc., Ooltewah, TN; *U.S. Public*, pg. 1112
Badrick, John, Pres.--Turnkey Technologies, Inc., Edison, NJ; *U.S. Private*, pg. 1110
Baenisch, John, V.P.-Adv.--Foley-Belsaw Company, Minneapolis, MN; *U.S. Private*, pg. 416
Baer, Linda A., V.P.-Adv.--The Spring Air Company, Des Plaines, IL; *U.S. Private*, pg. 1027
Baez, Ivan, Dir.-Pub. Rels.--Puerto Rican Cement Co., Inc., Guaynabo, PR; *U.S. Public*, pg. 1341
Bagger, Guy, Mgr.-Mktg. & Adv.--Raynor Garage Doors, Dixon, IL; *U.S. Private*, pg. 912
Baggett, Louise, Mgr.-Adv.--Sport Supply Group, Inc., Dallas, TX; *U.S. Public*, pg. 1499
Bagley, Rachel, Dir.-Corp. Commun.--Public Service Company of North Carolina, Inc., Gastonia, NC; *U.S. Public*, pg. 1340
Bagnall, George, Pres.--Industrial Components Group, Shelton, CT; *Int'l*, pg. 127
Bailey, Doug, Mgr.-Mktg.--Action Instruments, Inc., San Diego, CA; *U.S. Private*, pg. 15
Bailey, Robert, II, Chm. Bd. & Chief Fin. Officer--Mid American Elevator Co., Inc., Chicago, IL; *U.S. Private*, pg. 743
Baillie, Doug, Dir.-Mktg. Communications--MagneTek Lighting Products Group, Nashville, TN; *U.S. Public*, pg. 1037
Bain, Sean, Mgr.-Adv.--DIC Entertainment, Burbank, CA; *U.S. Public*, pg. 513
Bainton, Steven, Dir.-Corp. Communications--Continental Can Co., Norwalk, CT; *U.S. Public*, pg. 439
Baits, Mary, Mgr.-Adv.--Aristech Chemical Corporation, Pittsburgh, PA; *Int'l*, pg. 872
Baker-Smith, Linda, Dir.-Adv.--Caldor, Inc., Norwalk, CT; *U.S. Public*, pg. 292
Baker, Bill, Mgr.-Gen. Sls.--Regency Lincoln Mercury, Inc., Dallas, TX; *U.S. Private*, pg. 918
Baker, Brent, Dir.-Adv.--Zions Co-operative Mercantile Institution, Salt Lake City, UT; *U.S. Public*, pg. 1793
Baker, Frederick W., Asst. V.P.-Communications--Harleysville Group, Harleysville, PA; *U.S. Public*, pg. 786
Baker, Gary, Mgr.-Mktg.--Dialight Corporation, Manasquan, NJ; *Int'l*, pg. 1130
Baker, H. Forrest, V.P. & Oper. Mgr.-Filtration Div.--Perry Equipment Corporation, Mineral Wells, TX; *U.S. Private*, pg. 855
Baker, Jayme, Dir.-Art & Creative/Great Plains--Great Plains Manufacturing, Inc., Salina, KS; *U.S. Private*, pg. 475
Baker, Kelli, Mgr.-Mktg. & Adv.--Park Distributors, Inc., Bridgeport, CT; *U.S. Private*, pg. 839
Baker, Kelli, Mgr.-Mktg. & Adv.--Universal Relay, Bridgeport, CT; *U.S. Private*, pg. 839
Baker, Kerry, Dir.-Adv.--Unisys Corporation, Blue Bell, PA; *U.S. Public*, pg. 1671
Baker, Liz, Mgr.-Mktg.--Gatorade Worldwide Division, Chicago, IL; *U.S. Public*, pg. 1347
Baker, Marybeth, Mgr.-Adv. & Pub. Rels.--Galpin Motors, North Hills, CA; *U.S. Private*, pg. 438
Baker, Rick, V.P.-Mktg. & Sls.--Silver Dollar City, Inc., Branson, MO; *U.S. Private*, pg. 1000
Baker, Robert, Dir.-Mktg.--Wagner Lighting Products, Chesterfield, MO; *U.S. Public*, pg. 442
Baker, Robert L., Pres.--Plant Maintenance Service Corporation, Memphis, TN; *U.S. Private*, pg. 869
Baker, Roger W., Dir.-Commun.--Fortune Brands, Inc., Old Greenwich, CT; *U.S. Public*, pg. 674
Baker, Sandra, Dir.-Adv.--United Artists Theatre Circuits Incorporated, Englewood, CO; *U.S. Private*, pg. 1120
Baker, William, V.P. & Gen. Mgr.--Hearst Business Publishing, Inc./UTP Division, Garden City, NY; *U.S. Private*, pg. 515
Balbi, Mary Thomas, Dir.-Adv.--Governing Magazine, Washington, DC; *U.S. Private*, pg. 1088
Balch, Kenna, Dir.-Mktg.--Sholodge, Inc., Hendersonville, TN; *U.S. Public*, pg. 1467
Baldi, Laurel, Asst. to Pres.--Speedling Incorporated, Sun City, FL; *U.S. Private*, pg. 1024
Baldridge, Doris, Coord.-Sls. & Adv.--Trinity Difco, Findlay, OH; *U.S. Public*, pg. 1639
Baldwin, Ann T., V.P.-Corp. Communications--AAR Corp., Wood Dale, IL; *U.S. Public*, pg. 1
Baldwin, Roger M., Dir.-Mktg. & Bus. Devel.--Dugan & Meyers Interests, Inc., Cincinnati, OH; *U.S. Private*, pg. 345
Baldwin, Tom R., Mgr.-Adv.--Flexsteel Industries, Inc., Dubuque, IA; *U.S. Public*, pg. 653
Ballinger, Tim, Mgr.-Mktg. Communications--Sloan Technology, Santa Barbara, CA; *U.S. Public*, pg. 1711
Balsano, Gina, Mgr.-Adv. Promo/Bantam--Bantam Doubleday Dell Publishing Group, Inc., New York, NY; *Int'l*, pg. 191
Baltrusaitis, Irene, Adv. Mgr.--The Independence Examiner, Independence, MO; *U.S. Private*, pg. 995
Baner, Mike, V.P.-Mktg.--Ragu Foods, Inc., Trumbull, CT; *Int'l*, pg. 1436
Banicki, Paul, Dir.-Adv.--Hughes Family Markets, Inc., Irwindale, CA; *U.S. Public*, pg. 1349
Bankers, Eugene E., Sr. V.P.-Mktg.--Ames Department Stores, Inc., Rocky Hill, CT; *U.S. Public*, pg. 99
Banks, Charles, Pres. & V.P.-Adv.--Energy & Process Corp., Tucker, GA; *Int'l*, pg. 1512
Bannell, Scott, V.P.-Mktg. & Adv.--The Stanley Works, New Britain, CT; *U.S. Public*, pg. 1508
Bannister, J. Michael, Mgr.-Adv.--Bank One, Louisiana, Baton Rouge, LA; *U.S. Public*, pg. 173
Banno, Mieko, Adv.--BASF Japan Ltd., Tokyo, Japan; *Int'l*, pg. 106
Bannon, Theresa, Sr. Dir.-Mktg.--Spirit Cruises, Inc., Norfolk, VA; *Int'l*, pg. 1274
Bannwolf, Donna, Mgr.-Corp. Commun.--Greate Bay Casino Corporation, Atlantic City, NJ; *U.S. Public*, pg. 760
Baphiste, Jean-Jacques, Mgr.-Adv.--Case France S.A., Paris, France; *U.S. Public*, pg. 1579
Baracz, Robert, Mgr.-Mktg.--Zoological Society of San Diego, San Diego, CA; *U.S. Private*, pg. 1207
Baradari, Fotus, Mgr.-Mktg.--Microlog Corporation, Germantown, MD; *U.S. Public*, pg. 1105
Baratta, Christine, Adv. Assoc.--New England Electric System, Westborough, MA; *U.S. Public*, pg. 1171
Barattini, John, Mgr.-Adv.--Partlow Corporation, New Hartford, NY; *U.S. Public*, pg. 482
Barbera, William, Mgr.-Mktg.--Wire-Pro Inc., Salem, NJ; *U.S. Private*, pg. 1184
Barcalow, Nancy, Mgr.-Adv.-Life Co.--Nationwide Insurance Enterprise, Columbus, OH; *U.S. Private*, pg. 788
Barcenan, Miquel Angel, Dir.-Adv.--Pepsico de Mexico, S.A. de C.V., Mexico, Mexico; *U.S. Public*, pg. 1277
Barganti, Bill, Dir.-Adv.--Zurich Kemper Investments, Inc., Chicago, IL; *Int'l*, pg. 1530
Barhite, James T., V.P.-Sls. & Mktg.--Interface Electronics Corporation, Hopkinton, MA; *U.S. Private*, pg. 567
Barker, Jerry, Sr. V.P.-Mktg.--Tom's Foods, Inc., Columbus, GA; *U.S. Private*, pg. 1090
Barker, Kea, Coord.-Corp. Commun.--Cominco, Ltd., Vancouver, Canada; *Int'l*, pg. 307
Barkley, D.L., Adv. Coord.--Interim Services Inc., Fort Lauderdale, FL; *U.S. Public*, pg. 892
Barley, Gilbert R., Dir.-Communication--Thiokol Corporation, Ogden, UT; *U.S. Public*, pg. 1596
Barma, Ron, Mgr.-Sls. Admin. & Adv.--Simpson Electric Co., Elgin, IL; *U.S. Private*, pg. 1002
Barmash, Arthur, Dir.-Grp. Adv.--Prime Option Services, Sandy, UT; *U.S. Public*, pg. 1132
Barmash, Arthur E., Dir.-Adv./Novus Brands--Dean Witter, Discover & Co., New York, NY; *U.S. Public*, pg. 1132
Barnes, Don, Sr. V.P.-Sls. & Mktg.--Presidential Life Corporation, Nyack, NY; *U.S. Public*, pg. 1323
Barnett, Cecil C., Chm. Bd., Pres. & Chief Exec. Officer--Algood Food Company, Louisville, KY; *U.S. Private*, pg. 34
Barnett, Doug, Dir.-Adv.--Gazette Telegraph, Colorado Springs, CO; *U.S. Private*, pg. 425
Barnett, Mark, Dir.-Adv. & Promo.--Richey Electronics, Inc., Garden Grove, CA; *U.S. Public*, pg. 1388
Barnhart, Dale A., Sr. V.P.-Mktg. & Sls.--Wolverine Tube Inc., Huntsville, AL; *U.S. Public*, pg. 1774
Barnhart, Mike, V.P.-Mktg. & Mdsg.--Quality Food Centers, Inc., Bellevue, WA; *U.S. Public*, pg. 1349
Barnhill, John W., Jr., Exec. V.P. & Gen. Mgr.-Sls.--Blue Bell Creameries, L.P., Brenham, TX; *U.S. Private*, pg. 150
Barone, Vivian, Sr. Adv. Mgr.-Lady Foot Locker--Foot Locker, New York, NY; *U.S. Public*, pg. 1777
Barr, Michael, V.P.-Mktg. & Adv.--American Century Investments, Kansas City, MO; *U.S. Private*, pg. 52
Barr, R.G., Dir.-Sls. & Mktg.--Bespak plc, Norfolk, United Kingdom; *Int'l*, pg. 193
Barr, Thomas, Mgr.-Mktg. & Commun.--Sellstrom Manufacturing Co., Palatine, IL; *U.S. Private*, pg. 983
Barraza, Liz, Mgr.-Communications & Adv.--Courtaulds Aerospace, Glendale, CA; *Int'l*, pg. 339
Barrett, M. Patricia, V.P.-Corp. Commun.--AmerenUE, Saint Louis, MO; *U.S. Public*, pg. 66
Barrett, Stella, Mgr.-Media Svcs.--Ace Hardware Corporation, Oak Brook, IL; *U.S. Private*, pg. 12

Barrett, William R., Dir.-Pub. Rels. & Adv.--Service Corporation International, Houston, TX; *U.S. Public*, pg. 1460
Barro, Dan, V.P. & Corp. Sec.--Lamp Post Franchise Corporation, Tustin, CA; *U.S. Private*, pg. 644
Barron, Bill, Gen. Mgr.-Creative Services--National Football League Properties, Inc., New York, NY; *U.S. Private*, pg. 783
Barrows, James E., Dir.-Mktg.--GF Office Furniture Ltd., Gallatin, TN; *U.S. Private*, pg. 434
Barry, James P., V.P.-Sls. & Mktg.--Remcor Products Co., Glendale Heights, IL; *Int'l*, pg. 646
Barry, Ken, Dir.-Adv. & Plng.--Pharmacia & Upjohn, Kalamazoo, MI; *Int'l*, pg. 1048
Barser, Joy, Rep.-Sls. Promo.--Dillard, A ResourceNet International Company, Knoxville, TN; *U.S. Public*, pg. 902
Barsky, Richard, V.P.-Mktg. & Adv.--Field Packing Company, Owensboro, KY; *U.S. Private*, pg. 403
Bartlett, Brad, Dir.-Mktg. & Adv.--North American Recreation Products Company, Wichita, KS; *U.S. Private*, pg. 691
Bartlett, Nancy, Mgr.-Adv. & Promo.--Bruncor, Inc., Saint John, Canada; *Int'l*, pg. 230
Bartley, Edward A., Mgr.-Adv. Detroit--Scientific American, Inc., New York, NY; *Int'l*, pg. 1479
Bartley, Lester G., Mgr.-Adv.--J.L. Hammett Company, Braintree, MA; *U.S. Private*, pg. 498
Bartley, Roland, Mgr.-Adv. & Sls.--Danuser Machine Co., Fulton, MO; *U.S. Private*, pg. 310
Bartman, Erica, Dir.-Adv.--Vogue Magazine, New York, NY; *U.S. Private*, pg. 20
Barton, Trisha, Dir.-Adv.--Adventure Lands of America, Inc., Des Moines, IA; *U.S. Private*, pg. 22
Bass, Amy, Dir.-Corp. Communications--The Empire District Electric Company, Joplin, MO; *U.S. Public*, pg. 579
Bastian, Doug, Dir.-Sls.--L.L. Olds Seed Company, Madison, WI; *U.S. Private*, pg. 814
Bastian, Kimberly S., Mgr.-Adv. & Corp. Info.--Public Service Company of North Carolina, Inc., Gastonia, NC; *U.S. Public*, pg. 1340
Bastian, Michael, Mgr.-Adv. & Pub. Rels.--Sotheby's International Realty, New York, NY; *U.S. Public*, pg. 1487
Batchelar, Peter, V.P.-Sls.--Jason Industrial, Inc., Fairfield, NJ; *U.S. Private*, pg. 583
Bateman, Lesley, Dir.-Mktg. Commun. & Pub. Rels.--Paradyne, Largo, FL; *U.S. Private*, pg. 838
Bates, Kevin, Mgr.-Regional Adv.--Precision Tune Autocare Inc., Leesburg, VA; *U.S. Public*, pg. 1321
Batson, Deborah, Dir.-Adv.--American Freightways Corporation, Harrison, AR; *U.S. Public*, pg. 75
Battaglia, Carol, Mgr.-Mktg. & Commun.--Dataram Corporation, Princeton, NJ; *U.S. Public*, pg. 487
Battaglia, Emi, V.P.-Publicity--Warner Books, Inc., New York, NY; *U.S. Public*, pg. 1614
Battalini, Richard, V.P.-Sls.--Victor Technology, Addison, IL; *U.S. Private*, pg. 1139
Baublitz, Linda, Dir.-Adv.--Acco Chain & Lifting Products, York, PA; *Int'l*, pg. 473
Bauer, Liz, Mgr.-Adv. Comm.--Keystone Financial Inc., Harrisburg, PA; *U.S. Public*, pg. 956
Baughman, James H., Dir.-Sls. & Mktg.--Planes Moving And Storage, Inc., Cincinnati, OH; *U.S. Private*, pg. 869
Bauman, Kent, Mgr.-Adv.--Hawk Corp., Cleveland, OH; *U.S. Private*, pg. 511
Baumann, David, Dir.-Adv. & Promo.--KSTP-TV, Saint Paul, MN; *U.S. Private*, pg. 544
Bawden, Mark, Pres.--Bawden Corporation, Eldridge, IA; *U.S. Private*, pg. 124
Baxter, Harry, Vice Chm.--Bancorp South Inc., Tupelo, MS; *U.S. Public*, pg. 176
Baxter, James G., Chief Fin. Officer & Pres.-Consumer Prods. Grp.--CSS Industries, Inc., Philadelphia, PA; *U.S. Public*, pg. 283
Baynes, Ron, V.P.-Sls.--Curtis-Toledo, Inc., Saint Louis, MO; *U.S. Private*, pg. 298
Beal, Steve, V.P.-Mktg. & Sls.--Applied Magnetics Corporation, Goleta, CA; *U.S. Public*, pg. 123
Bean, Barbara, Dir.-Communications--Kitchell Corporation, Phoenix, AZ; *U.S. Private*, pg. 624
Beardon, Blanche, Mgr.-Adv.--Long's Electronics, Inc., Birmingham, AL; *U.S. Private*, pg. 675
Beasley, Marvin, Sr. V.P.-Mdsg.--Helzberg's Diamond Shops, Inc., Kansas City, MO; *U.S. Public*, pg. 220
Beason, John, Sr. V.P.-Sls. & Mktg.--Guilford of Maine, Inc., Guilford, ME; *U.S. Public*, pg. 889
Beaulieu, Diane, Mgr.-Adv. & Sls. Promo.--Davis Standard Corporation, Pawcatuck, CT; *U.S. Public*, pg. 459
Beausejour, Denis F., V.P.-Adv.--The Procter & Gamble Company, Cincinnati, OH; *U.S. Public*, pg. 1330
Beavor, John, Mgr.-Adv.--Rogers Tool Works, Inc., Rogers, AR; *U.S. Public*, pg. 950
Beca, John, Dir.-Adv.--ITT A-C Pump/ITT Marlow, Cincinnati, OH; *U.S. Public*, pg. 860
Beck, Charles A., Jr., Dir.-Mktg. Programs--Atlas Van Lines, Inc., Evansville, IN; *U.S. Private*, pg. 97
Beck, Douglas A., V.P.-Sls. & Mktg.--Clark Grave Vault Co., Columbus, OH; *U.S. Private*, pg. 243
Becker, Amy, Div. Mgr.--AT&T Corporation, Basking Ridge, NJ; *U.S. Public*, pg. 10
Becker, Hugh E., Dir.-Corp. Communications--Robbins & Myers, Inc., Dayton, OH; *U.S. Public*, pg. 1393
Becker, Jamie, Coord.-Mktg. Commun. Projects--Trendway Corporation, Holland, MI; *U.S. Private*, pg. 1099
Becker, Jim, Pres. & Dir.-Adv. & Sls.--Speedrack Products Group, Ltd., Sparta, MI; *U.S. Private*, pg. 1024
Becker, Patricia, Dir.-Mktg. Commun.--Gelco Information Network, Inc., Eden Prairie, MN; *U.S. Private*, pg. 442
Bede, Jessica I., Sr. V.P.-Medical Products--Capintec Inc., Ramsey, NJ; *U.S. Private*, pg. 205
Bee, Jerry, V.P.-Adv.--Stater Bros. Inc., Colton, CA; *U.S. Public*, pg. 456
Bee, Kathleen, Mgr.-Adv. & Pub. Rels.--Micro Motion Inc., Boulder, CO; *U.S. Public*, pg. 574
Beebe, Whit, Dir.-Adv. (Mistic & Snapple)--Triarc Companies, Inc., New York, NY; *U.S. Public*, pg. 1634
Beebe, Whit, Dir.-Adv.--Snapple Beverage Company, White Plains, NY; *U.S. Public*, pg. 1635
Beehler, Barry, V.P.-Mktg.-Watercraft Marine Prods.--Kawasaki Motors Corp., U.S.A., Irvine, CA; *Int'l*, pg. 725
Beelar, Melanie, V.P.-Adv.--Bank One, Kentucky, NA, Louisville, KY; *U.S. Public*, pg. 173
Beene, Brant, Dir.-Adv.--Liberty National Life Insurance Co., Birmingham, AL; *U.S. Public*, pg. 1622
Beers, Bob, Sr. V.P.-Mktg. & Bus. Devel.--KTI, Orange, CA; *U.S. Public*, pg. 939
Beffa, Carlene, V.P.-Mktg.--Physicians Mutual Insurance Co., Omaha, NE; *U.S. Private*, pg. 864
Behan, Simon, Mgr.-Adv. & Sls. Promo.--Texaco (Ireland) Ltd., Dublin, Ireland; *U.S. Public*, pg. 1584
Behar, Steven, Mgr.-Adv.--Thermometrics, Inc., Edison, NJ; *Int'l*, pg. 208
Behm, Lon, V.P.-Adv.--Roundy's, Inc., Pewaukee, WI; *U.S. Private*, pg. 948
Behnke, William, Sr. V.P.-Sls. & Mktg.--General Communication, Inc., Anchorage, AK; *U.S. Public*, pg. 708
Behounek, Bruce, Mgr.-Corp. Sponsorships & Adv.--ReliaStar Financial Corp., Minneapolis, MN; *U.S. Public*, pg. 1375
Beinecke, Gunther, Intl. Adv. Coord.--Miele & Cie, GmbH, Gutersloh, Germany; *Int'l*, pg. 865
Beiser, John W., Pres.--Atlantic Southeast Airlines Inc., Atlanta, GA; *U.S. Public*, pg. 144
Belak, Cynthia, V.P.-Adv.--People's Bank, Bridgeport, CT; *U.S. Public*, pg. 1274
Belanger, Jim, Dir.-Communications & Adv.--Rockbestos-Suprenant Cable Corp., Clinton, MA; *U.S. Private*, pg. 938
Belchick, George, Dir.-Adv. & Sls. Promo.--Westinghouse Air Brake Company, Wilmerding, PA; *U.S. Public*, pg. 1760
Beld, Ron, Mgr.-Adv.--The Holland Hitch Company, Holland, MI; *U.S. Private*, pg. 534
Belin, Marie-Anne, Mgr.-Commun.--Compagnie Generale Maritime et Financiere, Suresnes, France; *Int'l*, pg. 322
Belisto, Jacqueline, Mgr.-Adv.--Cognos Corp., Burlington, MA; *Int'l*, pg. 306
Bell-Warner, Susan, Specialist-Adv.--Fireman's Fund Insurance Company, Novato, CA; *Int'l*, pg. 58
Bell, Bradford D., V.P.-Mktg. & Intl.--Ballard Medical Products, Draper, UT; *U.S. Public*, pg. 171
Bell, Charles C., Dir.-Mktg. & Adv.--Baker Knapp & Tubbs Inc., Grand Rapids, MI; *U.S. Private*, pg. 630
Bell, Keith, Mgr.-Adv.--Bell Gas, Inc., Roswell, NM; *U.S. Private*, pg. 131
Bell, Pam, Adv.--Mrs. Smith's Bakery of Pennsylvania, Pottstown, PA; *U.S. Public*, pg. 658
Bell, Pamela A., Mgr.-Adv.--Texas Refinery Corp., Fort Worth, TX; *U.S. Private*, pg. 1078
Bell, Robert C., Dir.-Internal Art, Meetings Plng., Video & Mgr.-Communications--Battenfeld Gloucester Engineering Co. Inc., Gloucester, MA; *U.S. Private*, pg. 123
Bellamy, Debbie, C.B.C., Dir.-Mktg. Services--American Software, Inc., Atlanta, GA; *U.S. Public*, pg. 91
Bellessa, David, V.P.-Mktg.--Romacorp, Inc., Dallas, TX; *U.S. Public*, pg. 1147
Bellingham, Fran, Adv. Specialist--The History Channel, New York, NY; *U.S. Public*, pg. 512
Bellrose, David, V.P.--Telechron of North Carolina, Inc., Leland, NC; *U.S. Private*, pg. 1073
Belmont, Dennis, Mgr.-Mktg.--A.L. Hansen Manufacturing Co., Waukegan, IL; *U.S. Private*, pg. 500
Belotti, David, Supvr.-Adv.--Fiatallis North America, Inc., Carol Stream, IL; *Int'l*, pg. 483
Belzer, John D., Pres. & Chief Oper. Officer--TCI Aluminum, Gardena, CA; *U.S. Private*, pg. 1063
Bemis, Adrienne, Coord.-Adv.--The Upper Deck Company, LLC, Carlsbad, CA; *U.S. Private*, pg. 1129
Bemoras, David, V.P.-Adv.--GNWC Wire, Cable & Network Products, Downers Grove, IL; *U.S. Private*, pg. 259
Benafatti, Thomas, Dir.-Adv.--Big V Supermarkets, Inc., Florida, NY; *U.S. Private*, pg. 143
Benard, Seymour, Dir.-Adv.--Stocko Corp., Carlstadt, NJ; *Int'l*, pg. 1301
Benben, Nancy, Dir.-Adv.--The Hartford Financial Services Group Inc., Hartford, CT; *U.S. Public*, pg. 794
Bender, Jane, Mgr.-Adv.--Henredon Furniture Industries, Inc., Morganton, NC; *U.S. Private*, pg. 432
Benedict, Stu, V.P.-Adv.--Prestone Products Corporation, Danbury, CT; *U.S. Public*, pg. 51
Benenson, Sarah, Dir.-Adv. Western--Discover, New York, NY; *U.S. Public*, pg. 513
Benevento, Kelli, Specialist-Mktg. Communications--Maxtor Corporation, Milpitas, CA; *Int'l*, pg. 641
Benham, Chris, Strategic Mktg. Dir.--Symantec Corporation - Beaverton Site, Beaverton, OR; *U.S. Public*, pg. 1545
Benik, Jamye C., Dir.-Adv.--Spencer's Inc., Mount Airy, NC; *U.S. Private*, pg. 1025
Benn, Elizabeth, Mgr.-Mkt. Communications--Pease Industries, Inc., Fairfield, OH; *U.S. Private*, pg. 845
Bennett, Farren E., Dir.-Mktg. Communications--Hilti Inc., Tulsa, OK; *Int'l*, pg. 620
Bennett, Gwen, Dir.-Adv.--Beall's, Inc., Bradenton, FL; *U.S. Private*, pg. 126
Bennett, Mike, Sr. Mgr.-Adv.--Converse Inc., North Reading, MA; *U.S. Public*, pg. 441
Bennett, Stanley T., Pres.--Oakhurst Dairy, Portland, ME; *U.S. Private*, pg. 809
Bennett, Thomas, Dir.-Adv.--Steiger Tractor, Fargo, ND; *U.S. Public*, pg. 311
Bennewitz, Dallas, Mgr.-Adv.--Bashas, Chandler, AZ; *U.S. Private*, pg. 120
Benson, Ben, Dir.-Adv.--SAFECO Corporation, Seattle, WA; *U.S. Public*, pg. 1423
Benson, Larry R., Pres.--Benson's, Inc., Bogart, GA; *U.S. Private*, pg. 134
Bentelspacher, Fred, V.P.-Sls. Promo. & Adv.--Gottschalks Inc., Fresno, CA; *U.S. Public*, pg. 754
Bentley, Janet, Dir.-Tech. Publications--Teledyne Brown Engineering, Huntsville, AL; *U.S. Public*, pg. 43
Berberian, Paula, Dir.-Adv.--California Products Corp., Cambridge, MA; *U.S. Private*, pg. 201
Berdine, Jamie, Mgr.-Mktg. Commun.--CENTRIA, Moon Township, PA; *U.S. Private*, pg. 225
Berg, David, Chief Oper. Officer & Exec. V.P.-Sls.--PremiumWear, Inc., Minneapolis, MN; *U.S. Public*, pg. 1323
Berg, Harris, V.P. & Gen. Mgr.--Wick Bldg. Systems Inc. Manufactured Homes Div., Marshfield, WI; *U.S. Private*, pg. 1174
Berg, Tanya, V.P.-Communications--Old Kent Bank, Grand Rapids, MI; *U.S. Public*, pg. 1216
Berger, David A., Exec. V.P.-Mktg. & Adv.--The Coast Distribution System, San Jose, CA; *U.S. Public*, pg. 388
Berges, Emil H. Jr., V.P.-Sls. & Adv.--Abbott Ball Company, West Hartford, CT; *U.S. Private*, pg. 9
Bergh, Gloria, Mgr.-Pub. Rels.--Modern Woodmen of America, Rock Island, IL; *U.S. Private*, pg. 755
Berghoef, Julie, Mgr.-Mktg. Commun.--Trendway Corporation, Holland, MI; *U.S. Private*, pg. 1099
Bergold, Roy, V.P.-Adv.--McDonald's Corporation, Oak Brook, IL; *U.S. Public*, pg. 1068
Berkun, Judy, Mgr.-Copr. Mktg.--Malcolm Pirnie, Inc., White Plains, NY; *U.S. Private*, pg. 867
Berkus, David, Mgr.-Sls. Promo., Mdsg., Pub. Rels. & Adv.--Sanyo Office Automation, Chatsworth, CA; *Int'l*, pg. 1191
Berkwitt, Glenn, Mgr.-Mktg. Commun.--Applied Microsystems Corporation, Redmond, WA; *U.S. Public*, pg. 123
Berlow, Myer, Sr. V.P.-Interactive Mktg.--America Online Incorporated, Dulles, VA; *U.S. Public*, pg. 66
Berman, Bernard, Gen. Mgr.--Butler Ventamatic Corp., Mineral Wells, TX; *U.S. Private*, pg. 190
Berman, Bob, Mgr.-Adv. & Pub. Rels.--Market Facts, Inc., Arlington Heights, IL; *U.S. Public*, pg. 1046
Berman, Robert, Treas. & Sec.--Metpar Corp., Westbury, NY; *U.S. Private*, pg. 735
Bernacchi, Karmen, Sr. Media Analyst--Best Power, Necedah, WI; *U.S. Private*, pg. 140
Bernal, Alex, Dir.-Adv.--GSC Enterprises, Inc., Sulphur Springs, TX; *U.S. Private*, pg. 436
Bernereggi, Mr., Dir.-Adv.--Snam S.P.A., Milan, Italy; *Int'l*, pg. 428
Berntson, B., V.P.-Mktg. & Engrng.--Emerson Motor Company, Sturgeon Bay, WI; *U.S. Public*, pg. 573
Berolzheimer, Philip, Pres.--California Cedar Products, Inc., Stockton, CA; *U.S. Private*, pg. 200
Berris, Brian, Partner-Private Client--Brown Brothers Harriman & Co., New York, NY; *U.S. Private*, pg. 173
Berry-Gallegos, Ann, Dir.-Adv.--National Semiconductor Corporation, Santa Clara, CA; *U.S. Public*, pg. 1159
Berry, Dan, Mgr.-Adv.--The Georgia Marble Company, Kennesaw, GA; *U.S. Private*, pg. 448
Berry, Phyllis, V.P.-Corp. Communications--Sun Healthcare Group Inc., Albuquerque, NM; *U.S. Public*, pg. 1530
Bertini, Chuck, Dir.-Adv.--Moto Photo, Inc., Dayton, OH; *U.S. Public*, pg. 1136
Bertrand, J. C., Asst.-Mktg. & Adv.--Ferraz Corporation, Parsippany, NJ; *Int'l*, pg. 1028
Bertrim, Paul, Dir.-Adv.--Brown Shoe Co. of Canada Ltd., Perth, Canada; *U.S. Public*, pg. 262
Berube, Ned, Mgr.-Adv.--Watts Industries, Inc., North Andover, MA; *U.S. Public*, pg. 1746
Besch, Andrew, Sr. V.P.-Mktg.--USA Networks, New York, NY; *U.S. Public*, pg. 1686
Bessant, Hugh, Mgr.-Adv.--Redland Roof Tiles Ltd., Reigate, United Kingdom; *Int'l*, pg. 1091
Beu, Robert, V.P. & Adv. Div. Mgr.--Hutchins/Young & Rubicam, Rochester, NY; *U.S. Private*, pg. 1197
Beumler, Melissa, V.P.-Sls. Promo. & Adv.--Commercial Federal Corporation, Omaha, NE; *U.S. Public*, pg. 411
Bevan, Michael A., Mgr.-Natl. Adv.--Toyota Motor Sales, U.S.A., Inc., Torrance, CA; *Int'l*, pg. 1412
Beverly, Lisa, Mgr.-Adv.--Adobe Systems Incorporated, San Jose, CA; *U.S. Public*, pg. 20
Bevilaqua, Victor H., V.P.-Mktg.--The B. Manischewitz Company, Jersey City, NJ; *U.S. Private*, pg. 699
Bevridge, Beryl, Dir.-Adv.--Clydesdale Bank PLC, Glasgow, United Kingdom; *Int'l*, pg. 906
Beynon, Don, Coord.-Motorcycles Mktg. & Adv.--Honda Canada Inc., Scarborough, Canada; *Int'l*, pg. 635
Bhanoo, Milind, Prod. Mgr.--Cyberex, Inc., Mentor, OH; *U.S. Public*, pg. 481
Bibee, Sam, Mgr.-Adv.--Craddock-Terry Inc., Lynchburg, VA; *U.S. Private*, pg. 284
Bibler, Laurie, Chief Fin. Officer, Treas. & Sec.--Bibler Brothers, Inc., Russellville, AR; *U.S. Private*, pg. 142
Bickrest, Edward J., Mgr.-Mktg. Commun.--Ferro Corporation, Cleveland, OH; *U.S. Public*, pg. 618
Biddle, Jim, Dir.-Adv.--Marsh Supermarkets, Inc., Indianapolis, IN; *U.S. Public*, pg. 1049
Bidwell, Donald, Jr., V.P.-Mktg.--Magnagrip, Middletown, CT; *U.S. Private*, pg. 142
Bieker, Don, V.P.-Sls. & Mktg. & Adv.--Columbia Manufacturing Inc., Westfield, MA; *U.S. Private*, pg. 255
Bielawski, Dave, Mgr.-Adv.--Curtis Lumber Company, Ballston Spa, NY; *U.S. Private*, pg. 297
Bielli, Greg, Reg. V.P.-M.C.O. Properties--MCO Properties Inc., Fountain Hills, AZ; *U.S. Public*, pg. 1062
Bier, Larry, V.P.-Adv.--RadioShack, Fort Worth, TX; *U.S. Public*, pg. 1560
Bierley, Robert, V.P.-Adv.--Heilig Meyers Furniture Co., Richmond, VA; *U.S. Public*, pg. 804
Biermann, Linda, Mgr.-Adv.--Trimfoot Company, Farmington, MO; *U.S. Public*, pg. 1684
Biespiel, Mathew, Dir.-Adv.--Visa U.S.A. Inc., San Francisco, CA; *U.S. Private*, pg. 1141

Biever, Barton R., Jr., Pres.--Alpha Mills Corp., Schuylkill Haven, PA; *U.S. Private*, pg. 45

Biever, Richard D., V.P.-Adv.--Alpha Mills Corp., Schuylkill Haven, PA; *U.S. Private*, pg. 45

Bigelow, Elizabeth, Mgr.-Adv.--Edward Hines Lumber Co., Itasca, IL; *U.S. Private*, pg. 530

Bigey, Michel, Dir.-Adv.--Bazar de L'Hotel de Ville, Paris, France; *Int'l*, pg. 181

Bigos, Irene, V.P.-Mktg.--Ogden Corporation, New York, NY; *U.S. Public*, pg. 1213

Bill, John, Dir.-Adv.--Sixth Avenue Electronics City, Springfield, NJ; *U.S. Private*, pg. 1004

Billingsley, Kay, V.P.-Adv., Mktg. Commun. & Special Projects--Trigon Blue Cross & Blue Shield, Richmond, VA; *U.S. Public*, pg. 1637

Billmyer, Denis, Dir.-Adv., Art & Creative--Hypro Corporation, New Brighton, MN; *U.S. Public*, pg. 1767

Binkley, Rick, Mgr.-Mktg. Commun.--Yellow Corporation, Overland Park, KS; *U.S. Public*, pg. 1788

Binzer, Corrina, Mgr.-Pub. Rels.--Knurr AG, Munich, Germany; *Int'l*, pg. 739

Bird, Robert H., Pres.--Blue Chip Stamps, Los Angeles, CA; *U.S. Public*, pg. 217

Birdsong, Lee, Mgr.-Adv.--Southern Company, Atlanta, GA; *U.S. Public*, pg. 1489

Birg, Hermann, Dir.-Adv.--Robert Bosch Lda, Lisbon, Portugal; *Int'l*, pg. 205

Birrittella, Buffy, Sr. V.P.-Adv. & Women's Design--Polo/Ralph Lauren Corporation, New York, NY; *U.S. Private*, pg. 874

Birschbach, Jim, V.P.-Adv. & Sls.--TCI Communications, Inc., Englewood, CO; *U.S. Public*, pg. 1554

Bishop, Brad, Dir.-Communications--Zimmer, Inc., Warsaw, IN; *U.S. Public*, pg. 254

Bishop, Eileen, Dir.-Retail Mktg.--Levitz Furniture Incorporated, Boca Raton, FL; *U.S. Public*, pg. 990

Bissell, Ronald, Dir.-Commun.--Furon Company, Laguna Niguel, CA; *U.S. Public*, pg. 688

Bitter, Adriana Scalamandre, Pres.--Scalamandre, Inc., Long Island City, NY; *U.S. Private*, pg. 969

Bittle, Kevin L., Mgr.-Creative Services--Met-Pro Corporation, Harleysville, PA; *U.S. Public*, pg. 1100

Bitz, Ginger, Mktg. Asst.--Schlumberger Malco Inc., Owings Mills, MD; *Int'l*, pg. 1206

Bjorndal, Signe, Dir.-Adv.--Norwegian Cruise Line, Miami, FL; *U.S. Private*, pg. 808

Bjorneboe, Jan, Dir.-Mktg. & Adv. & Sls. Mgr.--ISS Norge a.s., Oslo, Norway; *Int'l*, pg. 656

Black, David, Pres.-MacIntosh Div.--Clarion Corporation of America, Gardena, CA; *Int'l*, pg. 296

Black, David, V.P. & Gen. Mgr.--Admiral Heintz, Inc., Wadsworth, OH; *U.S. Public*, pg. 1143

Black, Frank C., Chm. Bd. & Pres.--Vogler Motor Company, Inc., Carbondale, IL; *U.S. Private*, pg. 1143

Black, John, Dir.-Mktg. Services--White-Rodgers Div., Emerson Electric Co., Saint Louis, MO; *U.S. Public*, pg. 573

Black, Rita A., Mgr.-Mktg. & Adv.--Deloitte & Touche LLP, Wilton, CT; *U.S. Private*, pg. 322

Black, William J., Dir.-Adv. & Mktg.--Sun TV & Appliances, Inc., Groveport, OH; *U.S. Public*, pg. 1532

Blackford, Scott, Dir.-Mktg.--Todco, Marion, OH; *U.S. Private*, pg. 823

Blackmon, Rod, Mgr.-Adv. & Pub. Rels.--The M.W. Kellogg Company, Houston, TX; *U.S. Public*, pg. 528

Blackmore, Lisa, Coord.-Adv.--Heatcraft, Inc.-Refrigeration Products Division, Stone Mountain, GA; *U.S. Private*, pg. 659

Blackwelder, Debbie, Dir.-Adv. & Promo.--Southern Progress Corporation, Birmingham, AL; *U.S. Public*, pg. 1612

Blackwell, Lorraine, Sr. Dir.-Adv.--Hawaiian Airlines, Inc., Honolulu, HI; *U.S. Public*, pg. 799

Blaine, Thomas, Mgr.-Adv. & Sls.--Gentex Optics, Inc., Simpson, PA; *Int'l*, pg. 462

Blair, Gary, Dir.-Adv.--Haarmann & Reimer Corp., Springfield, NJ; *Int'l*, pg. 173

Blair, Gary, Dir.-Adv.--Florasynth Inc., Teterboro, NJ; *Int'l*, pg. 173

Blais, Russell A., V.P.-Mktg.--Naylor Pipe Company, Chicago, IL; *U.S. Private*, pg. 789

Blaisdell-Snowdon, Deborah, Exec. V.P. & Corp. Sec.--The U.S. Baird Corporation, Stratford, CT; *U.S. Private*, pg. 1124

Blake, David, Dir.-Adv.--Crain's Chicago Business, Chicago, IL; *U.S. Private*, pg. 285

Blake, Robert, V.P.-Adv. Service--General Mills, Inc., Minneapolis, MN; *U.S. Public*, pg. 717

Blakemore, John, Dir.-Adv. Svcs.--SmithKline Beecham plc, Brentford, United Kingdom; *Int'l*, pg. 1264

Blalock, Adam, V.P.-Sls. & Mktg.--Daisy Manufacturing Company, Inc., Rogers, AR; *U.S. Private*, pg. 308

Blank, Susan K., Dir.-Adv.--Glamour, New York, NY; *U.S. Private*, pg. 20

Blankenship, Truman, Pres., Chief Exec. Officer & Chief Oper. Officer--Berryman Products, Inc., Arlington, TX; *U.S. Private*, pg. 138

Blanton, David, V.P.-Adv. & Creative Serv.--Maybelline, Inc., New York, NY; *Int'l*, pg. 819

Blanvillain, Anne, Mgr.-Adv.--Editions Scientifiques et Medicales Elsevier, Paris, France; *Int'l*, pg. 1099

Blashill, G.L., Dir.-Sls. & Mktg.--Imperial Tobacco Group, Ltd., Bristol, United Kingdom; *Int'l*, pg. 666

Blatt, Sara, Dir.-Adv. & Promo.--IHOP Corp., Glendale, CA; *U.S. Public*, pg. 862

Blauer, Stephen, V.P.-Sls.--Blauer Manufacturing Co., Inc., Boston, MA; *U.S. Private*, pg. 149

Blazye, A.R., Mgr.-Brand Positioning & Adv.--Shell Oil Company, Houston, TX; *Int'l*, pg. 1136

Blend, Jackie, Mgr.-Adv.--Carstens Inc., Chicago, IL; *U.S. Private*, pg. 216

Bliesath, Nick, Market Anayst--Plastic Suppliers, Inc., Columbus, OH; *U.S. Private*, pg. 871

Blizman, Wayne, V.P.-Corp. Plng. & Devel.--Durakon Industries, Inc., Lapeer, MI; *U.S. Public*, pg. 537

Bloch, Michael, Pres.--Bloch/New England, Inc., Worcester, MA; *U.S. Private*, pg. 149

Block, Randolf E., V.P.-Sls. & Promo.--Screw Conveyor Corp., Hammond, IN; *U.S. Private*, pg. 977

Block, Richard, V.P.-Adv.--Nobody Beats the Wiz, Carteret, NJ; *U.S. Private*, pg. 800

Blomstrom, Don, Mgr.-Natl. Sls.-Medical--Instrumentarium Imaging, Inc., Milwaukee, WI; *U.S. Private*, pg. 565

Blount, Karen, Supvr.-Adv.--Ilco Unican Corp., Rocky Mount, NC; *Int'l*, pg. 1432

Blue, Larry, Adv. Auditor--Cain & Bultman, Jacksonville, FL; *U.S. Private*, pg. 199

Blum, Bill, Mgr.-Mktg. Communications--Chevron Chemical Co., San Ramon, CA; *U.S. Public*, pg. 348

Blum, Bill, Dir.-Mktg.--Sonoma Mission Inn & Spa, Sonoma, CA; *U.S. Private*, pg. 1014

Blum, Richard J., Pres.--The Kirk & Blum Mfg. Co., Cincinnati, OH; *U.S. Private*, pg. 623

Blumenstock, Mike, V.P.-Mktg. & Sls.--EGA, Seymour, CT; *Int'l*, pg. 436

Blythe, Ron, Dir.-Mktg.--Stanley Fastening Systems, East Greenwich, RI; *U.S. Public*, pg. 1509

Bobich, Tom, Dir.-Adv. & Mktg.--AirTouch Communications, Inc., San Francisco, CA; *U.S. Public*, pg. 34

Bobinchuck, Michael, Pres.--Par Industries, Inc., Medina, OH; *U.S. Private*, pg. 838

Bock, Gayle, V.P.-Adv. & Consumer Mktg.--Delta Air Lines, Inc., Atlanta, GA; *U.S. Public*, pg. 497

Bockstanz, David, Pres.--Frank Industries, Inc., Brown City, MI; *U.S. Private*, pg. 423

Bode, Ron, Mgr.-Retail--The Gazette Company, Cedar Rapids, IA; *U.S. Private*, pg. 442

Boehlke, Jim, Adv. Specialist--Cannon Equipment, Chattanooga, TN; *Int'l*, pg. 646

Boehm, Ingrid, Dir.-Adv.--Irwin Toy Ltd., Toronto, Canada; *Int'l*, pg. 688

Boesch, Katy, Dir.-Adv. & Pub. Rels.--Williams-Sonoma, Inc., San Francisco, CA; *U.S. Public*, pg. 1770

Boese, Mary Ann, Mgr.-Adv.--The Renovator's Supply, Inc., Conway, NH; *U.S. Private*, pg. 923

Boesing, Danny, Mgr.-Mktg.--Samtec Inc., New Albany, IN; *U.S. Private*, pg. 963

Bogacz, Bob, Mgr.-Adv.--Amway Corporation, Ada, MI; *U.S. Private*, pg. 69

Boggess, W.T., V.P.-Strategic Plng.--Emerson Power Transmission Corporation, Ithaca, NY; *U.S. Public*, pg. 573

Boghigian, Harry, V.P. & Dir.-Mkt. Plng.--Hoffmann-La Roche Inc., Nutley, NJ; *Int'l*, pg. 1120

Bogs, George J., Mgr.-Sls. Promo.--United States Pipe & Foundry Company, Inc., Birmingham, AL; *U.S. Public*, pg. 1736

Bohach, John P., V.P.-Mktg. Services & Adv.--Tyco Toys, Inc., Mount Laurel, NJ; *U.S. Public*, pg. 1058

Bohannon, David, Gen. Mgr.--Acme Canvas Co., Inc., Malden, MA; *U.S. Private*, pg. 13

Bohannon, Nancy C., Sr. V.P. & Dir.-Mktg.--First Farmers & Merchants National Bank, Columbia, TN; *U.S. Private*, pg. 407

Bohlman, Victor, Dir.-Mktg.--RHC/Spacemaster Corporation, Melrose Park, IL; *U.S. Private*, pg. 904

Bohn, Mary Lou, Dir.-Adv.--Titleist & Foot-Joy Worldwide, Fairhaven, MA; *U.S. Public*, pg. 675

Bohn, Mary Lou, Dir.-Adv.--Acushnet Company, Fairhaven, MA; *U.S. Public*, pg. 675

Boland, John P., Mgr.-Trade Adv.--The Goodyear Tire & Rubber Company, Akron, OH; *U.S. Public*, pg. 752

Bolanowski, Patii, Mgr.-Mktg.--Jimlar Corporation, Great Neck, NY; *U.S. Private*, pg. 587

Boldig, Kathleen, Mgr.-Adv. & Mktg.--Ajay Leisure Products, Inc., Delavan, WI; *U.S. Public*, pg. 34

Boldrini, Ezo, Mgr.-Corp. Mktg.--3M Chile S.A., Santiago, Chile; *U.S. Public*, pg. 1606

Bolen, Dennis, Mgr.-Adv. NAO--General Motors Corporation, Detroit, MI; *U.S. Public*, pg. 718

Bolen, Mike, Dir.-Sls. & Mktg.--The Zippertubing Co., Los Angeles, CA; *U.S. Private*, pg. 1207

Boling, Bart, V.P.-Opers. Support--Cash America International, Inc., Fort Worth, TX; *U.S. Public*, pg. 312

Bollinger, Ron, Pres. & Chief Exec. Officer--N.B.F. Bollinger Industries, Americus, GA; *U.S. Public*, pg. 243

Bolton, Bonnie, V.P.-Adv.--ShopKo Stores, Inc., Green Bay, WI; *U.S. Public*, pg. 1467

Bolton, Jan E., V.P.-Corp. Sls. & Promo.--Dillard's, Inc., Little Rock, AR; *U.S. Public*, pg. 509

Bonde, Agneda, Dir.-Adv.--Telefonaktiebolaget LM Ericsson, Stockholm, Sweden; *Int'l*, pg. 1363

Bondioli, Carlo, Mgr.-Prod. & Mktg.--Bondioli & Pavesi S.p.A., Suzzara, Italy; *Int'l*, pg. 201

Bonnet, M., Dir.-Adv.--Rowenta France S.A., Vernon, France; *Int'l*, pg. 569

Bono, Giacomo, Mgr.-Adv.--Estee Lauder S.R.L., Milan, Italy; *U.S. Public*, pg. 594

Bonsall, Rob, V.P.-Adv.--CoreStates Financial Corp., Philadelphia, PA; *U.S. Public*, pg. 446

Bonsing, J., Mgr.-Adv.--Amici, Houten, Netherlands; *Int'l*, pg. 750

Bontrager, Larry, Asst. V.P.-Adv.--Coachmen Industries, Inc., Elkhart, IN; *U.S. Public*, pg. 387

Bonwill, Mary Ellen, Dir.-Adv.--Cerdec Corporation, Washington, PA; *Int'l*, pg. 292

Bonyun, David, Coord.-Adv. & Mktg.--McGuffey's Restaurants, Inc., Asheville, NC; *U.S. Private*, pg. 721

Bookstaver, Chuck, V.P.-Mktg.--Flexible Flyer Toys, West Point, MS; *U.S. Private*, pg. 412

Boone, Pamela, Mgr.-Office Support--Overholtzer Church Furniture, Inc., Modesto, CA; *U.S. Private*, pg. 823

Boone, Rhonda, V.P.-Adv.--Western Atlas International, Inc., Houston, TX; *U.S. Public*, pg. 1757

Boone, Rhonda G., Mgr.-Corp. Communications--Western Geophysical, Houston, TX; *U.S. Public*, pg. 1757

Boone, Rhonda G., Mgr.-Corp. Communications--Western Atlas International, Inc., Houston, TX; *U.S. Public*, pg. 1757

Booth, Mark, Dir.-Grp. Mktg.--Royal & Sun Alliance Insurance Group plc, London, United Kingdom; *Int'l*, pg. 1130

Booth, Rich, Mgr.-Adv.--Canon U.S.A., Inc., Lake Success, NY; *Int'l*, pg. 262

Bootz, Heidi, Mgr.-Adv.--Firstar Corporation, Milwaukee, WI; *U.S. Public*, pg. 642

Borde, Emmanuelle, Mgr.-Creative Adv.--Twentieth Century Fox Film Corp., Los Angeles, CA; *Int'l*, pg. 926

Bordelon, Clarence J., V.P.-Sls. & Admin.--Tyler Elevator Products, Inc., Valley View, OH; *U.S. Private*, pg. 1112

Boren, Leland E., Chm. Bd., Pres. & Chief Exec. Officer--Avis Industrial Corporation, Upland, IN; *U.S. Private*, pg. 102

Borgen, David, Dir.-Adv.--Jennifer Convertibles Inc., Woodbury, NY; *U.S. Public*, pg. 926

Borgensen, Ray, Mgr.-Mktg.--Tecknit Incorporated, Cranford, NJ; *U.S. Private*, pg. 1072

Borger, Karen, Mgr.-Mktg. Communications--AlliedSignal, Automotive Aftermarket, Rumford, RI; *U.S. Public*, pg. 51

Borgmann, Carolyn, Exec. Asst.--Beacon Container Corporation, Birdsboro, PA; *U.S. Private*, pg. 125

Borja, Susan, Dir.-Mktg. & Adv.--I. Spiewak & Sons, Inc., New York, NY; *U.S. Private*, pg. 1025

Borja, Susan, Dir.-Mktg. & Adv.--Golden Fleece Outerwear Co., New York, NY; *U.S. Private*, pg. 1025

Borok, Leslie, Dir.-Adv. (Phonad)--Motown Record Company, J.P., New York, NY; *Int'l*, pg. 1052

Borowiec, John, V.P.-Sls.--GS Electric, Carlisle, PA; *U.S. Public*, pg. 726

Borowsky, Ned S., Pres. & Chief Oper. Officer--North American Publishing Company, Philadelphia, PA; *U.S. Private*, pg. 803

Borrok, Leslie, Dir.-Adv.--Polygram Records, Inc., New York, NY; *Int'l*, pg. 1052

Bortoluzzi, Sergio, Mgr.-Grp. Adv.--AB SKF, Goteborg, Sweden; *Int'l*, pg. 1156

Bosca, D'Orsi, Mgr.-Adv.--Hugo Bosca Co., Inc., Springfield, OH; *U.S. Private*, pg. 160

Bose, Henry, V.P.-Strategic Svcs.--The Fairmont Hotels, San Francisco, CA; *U.S. Private*, pg. 391

Bosler, G.A., Mgr.-Adv. & Promo.--PQ Corporation, Berwyn, PA; *U.S. Private*, pg. 827

Boster, Kari, Dir.-Mktg.--Bluewater, Mora, MN; *U.S. Private*, pg. 153

Boston, Dennis H., V.P. & Midwest Adv. Dir.--Johnson Publishing Company, Inc., Chicago, IL; *U.S. Private*, pg. 591

Boter, Marina, Product Mgr.-Mktg. & Adv.--Telefonica de Espana, S.A., Madrid, Spain; *Int'l*, pg. 1371

Bother, David, Mgr.-Adv.--CNF Transportation Inc., Palo Alto, CA; *U.S. Public*, pg. 281

Botticher, Pam, Mgr.-Mktg. Coord.--Manatron, Inc., Kalamazoo, MI; *U.S. Public*, pg. 1040

Botvin, George B., Chm. Bd., Chief Exec. Officer & Treas.--ACS Industries, Inc., Woonsocket, RI; *U.S. Private*, pg. 3

Boucher, Bruce, V.P.-Adv.--The Coast Distribution System, San Jose, CA; *U.S. Public*, pg. 388

Boucher, Lorna, V.P.-Corp. Adv.--Bankers Trust New York Corporation, New York, NY; *U.S. Public*, pg. 185

Boulais, Dee, Mgr.-Sls. & Service--Lan-O-Sheen, Inc., Saint Paul, MN; *U.S. Private*, pg. 645

Boundy, Edward, V.P.-Sls. & Mktg.--The Weetabix Company, Inc., Clinton, MA; *Int'l*, pg. 1488

Bourdelot, Jacqueline, Mgr.-Adv.--Aerospatiale, Paris, France; *Int'l*, pg. 28

Bourjot, Frank J., Dir.-Adv.--Toronto Star Newspapers Ltd., Toronto, Canada; *Int'l*, pg. 1402

Bourne, Nina, V.P.-Adv.--Alfred A. Knopf, Inc., New York, NY; *U.S. Private*, pg. 21

Boutcher, Ann, V.P.-Mktg. Svcs.--Audiovox Corporation, Hauppauge, NY; *U.S. Public*, pg. 147

Boutin, Michel A., Dir.-Intl. Adv.--National Geographic Magazine, Paris, France; *U.S. Private*, pg. 784

Bouwmeester, Erick, V.P.-Pub Rels. & Corp. Communications--DSM N.V., Heerlen, Netherlands; *Int'l*, pg. 352

Boville, Ramon Sanjuan, Dir.-Mktg., Pub. Rels., Sls. & Adv.--Cabinas Telefonicas, S.A. (Cabitel), Madrid, Spain; *Int'l*, pg. 1371

Bowen, Jack, Gen. Dir.-Adv.--Buick Motor Div. General Motors Corp., Flint, MI; *U.S. Public*, pg. 720

Bowen, Maurice, Dir.-Mktg.--Hyundai Motor America, Fountain Valley, CA; *Int'l*, pg. 641

Bower, Greg, Dir.-Adv.--Advertising Age, New York, NY; *U.S. Private*, pg. 284

Boyce, Hugh, Mng. Dir.--Flexfab Horizons International, Inc., Hastings, MI; *U.S. Private*, pg. 412

Boyles, Brad, Mgr.-Adv., Sls. & Mktg.--Gunver Manufacturing Co., Manchester, CT; *U.S. Private*, pg. 488

Boynton, Laura-Jo, Mktg. & Adv.--Swiss Prestige, Inc., Winchester, VA; *Int'l*, pg. 697

Boyo, Mel, Dir.-Mktg.--Beutler Heating & Air Conditioning Inc., Sacramento, CA; *U.S. Private*, pg. 141

Brachocki, Edward, V.P.-Corp. Devel.--Go-Video, Inc., Scottsdale, AZ; *U.S. Public*, pg. 748

Bracken, Thomas, V.P.-Adv. & Creative Services--DirecTV Inc., El Segundo, CA; *U.S. Public*, pg. 720

Bradley, Jeriann, Art Dir. & Mgr.-Adv.--Austin Productions, Inc., Holbrook, NY; *U.S. Private*, pg. 100

Bradner, Rebecca, Dir.-Adv.--Hawaii Newspaper Agency, Inc., Honolulu, HI; *U.S. Public*, pg. 701

Bradshaw, Sara, Dir.-Adv.-Southwest Reg.--Smith's Food & Drug Centers, Inc., Salt Lake City, UT; *U.S. Public*, pg. 1103

Brady, Julie, V.P.-Mktg.--Croscill, Inc., New York, NY; *U.S. Private*, pg. 290

Brah, John, Mgr.-Adv.--M.W. Kasch Company, Mequon, WI; *U.S. Private*, pg. 608

Braman, Marvin L., Dir.-Communications--Sanders, A Lockheed Martin Company, Nashua, NH; *U.S. Public*, pg. 1008

Bramen, Bruce, V.P.-Mktg.--William B. Reily & Co., Inc., New Orleans, LA; *U.S. Private*, pg. 919

Bramy, Brad S., V.P.-Adv.--The Good Guys, Inc., Brisbane, CA; *U.S. Public*, pg. 750

Branca, Sal, Dir.-Corp. Communications--New Hampshire Insurance Group, New York, NY; *U.S. Public*, pg. 84

Brandt, Debbie, Mgr.-Eastern Adv.--Redbook, New York, NY; *U.S. Private*, pg. 517

Brandt, James E., Mgr.-Mktg. Services--Simpson Door Company, McCleary, WA; *U.S. Private*, pg. 1003

Brangier, Natalie, Mgr.-Fin., Commun.& Adv.--Compagnie Financiere de Paribas, Paris, France; *Int'l*, pg. 319

Brannon, Roy, V.P.-Adv.--Pro-Line Corporation, Dallas, TX; *U.S. Private*, pg. 887

Branstetter, Tim, Mgr.-Sls.--Bethel Mills, Inc., Bethel, VT; *U.S. Private*, pg. 141

Branston, Robert F., Dir.-Creative Services--Regal Ware, Inc., Kewaskum, WI; *U.S. Private*, pg. 917

Bras, Robert W., Pres.--Menu Foods, Inc., Pennsauken, NJ; *U.S. Private*, pg. 731

Bratz, Keith, Dir.-Communications--Provident Mutual Life Insurance Co., Berwyn, PA; *U.S. Private*, pg. 891

Brauer, Jennifer, Dir.-Adv.--Hollywood Entertainment Corp., Wilsonville, OR; *U.S. Private*, pg. 535

Braun, Jerry, Dir.-Mktg.--Newly Weds Foods Inc., Chicago, IL; *U.S. Private*, pg. 796

Braun, Mitch T., Mgr.-Adv.--Carboline Co., Saint Louis, MO; *U.S. Public*, pg. 1357

Braunstein, Judy, Mgr.-Adv.--Woman's Day, New York, NY; *Int'l*, pg. 795

Bravieri, Richard, Mgr.-Mktg. Svcs.--Safety-Kleen Corp., Elgin, IL; *U.S. Public*, pg. 1425

Bray, Hugh, Dir.-Worldwide Adv. & Communications--BMCA Insulation Products, Inc., Ontario, CA; *U.S. Private*, pg. 433

Bray, Maggie, Mgr.-Mktg.--Tippins Incorporated, Pittsburgh, PA; *U.S. Private*, pg. 1088

Brayer, Rich, V.P.-Adv.--TruServ Corporation, Chicago, IL; *U.S. Private*, pg. 1108

Brazell, Amelia, Dir.-Mktg.--Zoological Society of San Diego, San Diego, CA; *U.S. Private*, pg. 1207

Bready, Richard L., Chm. Bd. & Chief Exec. Officer--Nortek, Inc., Providence, RI; *U.S. Public*, pg. 1192

Brechbiel, Steve, Mgr.-Communications--Reichhold Chemicals, Inc., Durham, NC; *Int'l*, pg. 370

Breese, Carolyn, Coord.-Adv.--Young-Phillips Sales Co., Clemmons, NC; *U.S. Private*, pg. 1201

Brelsford, Robin, Mgr.-Adv.--Telematics Inc., Fort Lauderdale, FL; *Int'l*, pg. 643

Brennan, Michael J., Pres.--Micromatic Textron, Holland, MI; *U.S. Public*, pg. 1589

Brennen, Fran, Mgr.-Mktg. & Commun.--Veeco Instruments, Inc., Plainview, NY; *U.S. Public*, pg. 1711

Breth, Robin, Dir.-Mktg. & Adv.--Gold Medal Products Co., Cincinnati, OH; *U.S. Private*, pg. 459

Breuggeman, Pam, Mgr.-Adv.--Auburndale Star, Auburndale, FL; *U.S. Private*, pg. 995

Brevik, John, Exec. V.P.-Sls., Adv. & Mktg.--Exotic Rubber & Plastics Corp., Farmington Hills, MI; *U.S. Private*, pg. 388

Brewer, Ned, Gen. Mgr.-Sls.--McDowell Mfg. Co. Inc., Du Bois, PA; *U.S. Private*, pg. 300

Brewer, Reagan, V.P.-Mktg.--Grolsch Importers Inc., Atlanta, GA; *Int'l*, pg. 559

Brewer, Yvonne, Dir.-Adv.--Big Valley Marketing Corp., Fremont, CA; *U.S. Private*, pg. 1186

Brewis, Cathy, Dir.-Adv.--The News Tribune, Tacoma, WA; *U.S. Public*, pg. 1066

Brickell, Rob, Mgr.-Mktg. Commun.--Trion, Inc., Sanford, NC; *U.S. Public*, pg. 1639

Bricken, Sandra, Mgr.-Adv.--Shirmax Leasing Ltd., Montreal, Canada; *Int'l*, pg. 1235

Bridge, Jude, Dir.-Mktg./Snacks Div.--United Biscuits (UK) Limited, West Drayton, United Kingdom; *Int'l*, pg. 1442

Briese, Dietrich, Dir.-Adv.--Resart GmbH, Mainz, Germany; *Int'l*, pg. 104

Brigham, Sharon A., Asst. Mgr.-Sls.--Rodman Industries, Marinette, WI; *U.S. Private*, pg. 402

Bright, David E., V.P. & Dir.-Communications--Trace International Holdings, Inc., New York, NY; *U.S. Private*, pg. 1094

Brightbill, Darlene, Rep.-Adv. & Sls.--Credit Union National Association, Madison, WI; *U.S. Private*, pg. 288

Brightbill, Darlene, Adv. Mgr.--CUNA Service Group, Inc., Madison, WI; *U.S. Private*, pg. 288

Brill-Geffner, Stephanie, Mgr.-Adv.--Longevity International, Ltd., New York, NY; *U.S. Private*, pg. 444

Bringgold, Terese, Mgr.-Mktg. Communications--Food & Beverage, Saint Paul, MN; *U.S. Public*, pg. 562

Briozzo, Laura, Mgr. Communication & Image--SASIB SpA, Bologna, Italy; *Int'l*, pg. 1194

Briscoe, Ken, Dir.-Adv.--Canadian National Railway Company, Montreal, Canada; *Int'l*, pg. 258

Britton, Barbara, Dir.-Adv.--Essence Communications Inc., New York, NY; *U.S. Private*, pg. 383

Brock, Jerry, Pres.--Jacobs Applied Technology, Inc., Orangeburg, SC; *U.S. Public*, pg. 921

Brock, Tony, Exec. V.P. & Treas.--Beadles Lumber Company, Inc., Moultrie, GA; *U.S. Private*, pg. 126

Brockbank, Michael, Mgr.-Adv.--Unilever Plc, London, United Kingdom; *Int'l*, pg. 1433

Brockmann, Sue, V.P.-Mktg.--Recreational Equipment, Inc., Kent, WA; *U.S. Private*, pg. 914

Brod, Jack, Dir.-Adv.--Empire Diamond Corporation, New York, NY; *U.S. Private*, pg. 374

Broda, Cynsie, Mgr.-Adv.--Stratton Corporation, Stratton Mountain, VT; *Int'l*, pg. 685

Brodey, Larry, Pres.--Jaclo Inc., Mountainside, NJ; *U.S. Private*, pg. 349

Brodsky, Barbara, Dir.-Adv.--BTG, Inc., Fairfax, VA; *U.S. Public*, pg. 164

Brody, Carolyn, Dir.-Pub. Rels.--Harry Winston, Inc., New York, NY; *U.S. Private*, pg. 1183

Brolick, Emil J., Sr. V.P.-Strategic Plng. & Res.--Wendy's International Inc., Dublin, OH; *U.S. Public*, pg. 1754

Brooklier, John L., V.P.-Corp. Communications--Heller Financial, Inc., Chicago, IL; *Int'l*, pg. 519

Brooks, Henry A., Dir.-Sls.--Lawter International, Inc., Kenosha, WI; *U.S. Public*, pg. 980

Brooks, Kenneth, Mgr.-Mktg.--Preferred Utilities Manufacturing Corp., Danbury, CT; *U.S. Private*, pg. 881

Brooks, Michele, Dir.-Adv.--Rent-Way, Inc., Erie, PA; *U.S. Public*, pg. 1377

Brooks, TaJuana, Mgr.-Mktg. Svcs.--Carlisle Food Service Products, Oklahoma City, OK; *U.S. Public*, pg. 305

Broomfield, William, Mgr.-Adv.--L.D. Caulk Division, Milford, DE; *U.S. Public*, pg. 499

Brous, David, V.P.-Mktg.--JM Company, Hasbrouck Heights, NJ; *U.S. Private*, pg. 577

Brout, Ellen, Mgr.-Corp. Adv.--PeopleSoft, Inc., Pleasanton, CA; *U.S. Public*, pg. 1276

Brower, Daryl, Mgr.-Adv. Promo.--Butterick Company, Inc., New York, NY; *U.S. Private*, pg. 190

Brown, Ada, Mktg. Mgr.--Clarion Cosmetics, Hunt Valley, MD; *U.S. Public*, pg. 1330

Brown, Ann, Admin. Specialist--Carolina Steel Corporation, Greensboro, NC; *U.S. Private*, pg. 214

Brown, Dwight, V.P.-Adv.--Houston Chronicle, Houston, TX; *U.S. Private*, pg. 517

Brown, Frank, Dir.-Adv. Sls.--MTV Europe, London, United Kingdom; *U.S. Private*, pg. 779

Brown, James, Mgr.-Adv.--Bulgari Corporation of America, New York, NY; *Int'l*, pg. 232

Brown, Jan, Mgr.-Adv.--Bedroom Superstores, Phoenix, AZ; *U.S. Private*, pg. 129

Brown, Jody A., Dir.-Bus. Commun.--CACI International Inc, Arlington, VA; *U.S. Public*, pg. 272

Brown, Karyn H., Coord.-Adv.--Georgia/Durango Boot Company, Franklin, TN; *U.S. Public*, pg. 1684

Brown, Kathy, Dir.-Adv. & Mktg.--Williams Controls, Inc., Portland, OR; *U.S. Public*, pg. 1769

Brown, Kenneth, Mgr.-Sls.--Trimtex Co. Inc., Williamsport, PA; *U.S. Private*, pg. 1103

Brown, Linda, Sr. Mgr.-Adv. Sls.--Discovery Networks, Inc., Bethesda, MD; *U.S. Private*, pg. 334

Brown, Loretta, Coord.-Mktg.--Boyer Candy Company Inc., Altoona, PA; *U.S. Private*, pg. 162

Brown, Marion, Dir.-Publicity & Adv.--Pantheon Books, Inc., New York, NY; *U.S. Private*, pg. 21

Brown, Mary Anne, Dir.-Adv.--Kaufmann's, Pittsburgh, PA; *U.S. Public*, pg. 1063

Brown, Mary Rose, Mgr.-Adv.--Valero Energy Corporation, San Antonio, TX; *U.S. Public*, pg. 1704

Brown, Merv, V.P.-Adv.--Koret of California, Inc., San Francisco, CA; *U.S. Private*, pg. 632

Brown, Michael C., Mgr.-Adv.--Bowen Tools, Houston, TX; *U.S. Public*, pg. 858

Brown, Michele, Dir.-Adv. Sls.--Butterick Company, Inc., New York, NY; *U.S. Private*, pg. 190

Brown, Michele, Sr. Supvr.-Adv.--International Specialty Products, Inc., Wayne, NJ; *U.S. Public*, pg. 858

Brown, Michelle, Sr. Adv. Specialist--Building Materials Corporation of America, Wayne, NJ; *U.S. Private*, pg. 433

Brown, P.J., Dir.-Commun.--Cooper Tire & Rubber Company, Findlay, OH; *U.S. Public*, pg. 445

Brown, Randi, Sr. V.P.-Creative Adv.--Metro-Goldwyn-Mayer Inc., Santa Monica, CA; *U.S. Public*, pg. 1101

Brown, Renee C., Sr. V.P.-Adv., Sls. & Mktg.--Pro-Line Corporation, Dallas, TX; *U.S. Private*, pg. 887

Brown, Steve, Dir.-Corp. Communications--Chattanooga Group, Inc., Hixson, TN; *U.S. Private*, pg. 231

Brown, Steve, Supvr.-Adv. Production--Beaver Lumber Company Limited, Markham, Canada; *Int'l*, pg. 887

Brown, Tom, Mgr.-Mktg.--Frick Company, Waynesboro, PA; *U.S. Public*, pg. 1788

Brown, Tommy, Coord.-Adv.--Continental Eagle Corporation, Prattville, AL; *U.S. Private*, pg. 267

Brown, Virginia, Dir.-Adv.--Bruce Foods Corp., Cade, LA; *U.S. Private*, pg. 175

Browner, Michael A., Exec. Dir.-Media Opers.--General Motors Corporation, Detroit, MI; *U.S. Public*, pg. 718

Browning, Lewis, Dir.-Mktg.--Ambac International Corp., Columbia, SC; *U.S. Private*, pg. 48

Brownrout, Todd, V.P.-Adv.--Philadelphia Daily News, Philadelphia, PA; *U.S. Public*, pg. 964

Brownrout, Todd, V.P.-Adv.--The Philadelphia Inquirer, Philadelphia, PA; *U.S. Public*, pg. 964

Brownstein, Hy, V.P.-Mktg.--Uniflex, Inc., Hicksville, NY; *U.S. Public*, pg. 1665

Broyles, Katherine, V.P.-Print Adv.--CBS Television Network, New York, NY; *U.S. Public*, pg. 274

Brubeck, Daniel J., Dir.-Communications Adv. & Corp. Identity--Eaton Corporation, Cleveland, OH; *U.S. Public*, pg. 555

Bruce, Rick, Mktg. Devel.--Puritan/Churchill Chemical Company, Atlanta, GA; *U.S. Private*, pg. 895

Brunette, Meg, Project Mgr.-Adv.--Central Maine Power Company, Augusta, ME; *U.S. Public*, pg. 325

Brunnberg, Franz, Dir.-Adv.--Adidas AG, Herzogenaurach, Germany; *Int'l*, pg. 24

Bruno, John, Sr. V.P.-Sls. & Mktg.--Cagle's Inc., Atlanta, GA; *U.S. Public*, pg. 291

Bruno, Kendra Elliott, Pres.--Dixie Brewing Co., Inc., New Orleans, LA; *U.S. Private*, pg. 336

Brush, Sue, V.P.-Adv. & Pub. Rels.--Westin Hotels & Resorts, Seattle, WA; *U.S. Public*, pg. 1512

Brusher, Nancy C., Dir.-Mktg. Communications & Adv.--Stiles Corporation, Fort Lauderdale, FL; *U.S. Private*, pg. 1043

Bryans, Phil, Mgr.-Sls. Promo.--Dayton Rogers Mfg. Co., Blaine, MN; *U.S. Private*, pg. 318

Bryant, Carlton, V.P.-Bus. Devel.--American Passage Media Corporation, Seattle, WA; *U.S. Private*, pg. 60

Brylewski, Jim, Mgr.-Adv. & Promotions--The Orioles, Inc., Baltimore, MD; *U.S. Private*, pg. 819

Buck, David, Dir.-Adv. Sls.--The Phillies-A Limited Partnership, Philadelphia, PA; *U.S. Private*, pg. 861

Buckland, Ross, Chief Exec. Officer--Unigate PLC, London, United Kingdom; *Int'l*, pg. 1433

Buckley, Sheila, Dir.-Adv.--Money, New York, NY; *U.S. Public*, pg. 1613

Buckly, Lanoi, Mgr.-Mktg. Svcs.--A. Duda & Sons Inc., Oviedo, FL; *U.S. Private*, pg. 344

Buddig, Thomas R., V.P.-Sls. & Mktg.--Carl Buddig & Company, Homewood, IL; *U.S. Private*, pg. 178

Bugajski, R.S., Dir.-Adv.--State Farm Mutual Automobile Insurance Company, Bloomington, IL; *U.S. Private*, pg. 1036

Bull, Sheryl, Dir.-Adv.--Modern Healthcare, Chicago, IL; *U.S. Private*, pg. 285

Bullock, Gayle, Mgr.-Mktg. & Communications--California Micro Devices, Milpitas, CA; *U.S. Public*, pg. 293

Bulls, Ken, Adv. & Promo. Specialist--Exxon Company, U.S.A., Houston, TX; *U.S. Public*, pg. 601

Bultz, P.M., Mgr.-Adv. & Pub. Rels.--Crane Limited U.K., Ipswich, United Kingdom; *U.S. Public*, pg. 458

Bunnell, Alan, Dir.-Corp. Commun.--Tucson Electric Power Company, Tucson, AZ; *U.S. Public*, pg. 1670

Burbage, C.T., V.P.-Bus. Devel. & Product Support--Lockheed Aeronautical Systems Company, Marietta, GA; *U.S. Public*, pg. 1007

Burch, Howe, Sr. V.P.-Adv. & Communications--Fila USA, Sparks, MD; *Int'l*, pg. 484

Burchfield, Randy, V.P.-Adv.--Deposit Guaranty Corp., Jackson, MS; *U.S. Public*, pg. 500

Burchman, Suzanne, Asst. V.P.-Adv. & Mktg. Support--Sanwa Bank California, Los Angeles, CA; *Int'l*, pg. 1189

Burgay, Stephen P., Second V.P.-Adv. & Pub. Affairs--John Hancock Mutual Life Insurance Company, Boston, MA; *U.S. Private*, pg. 589

Burk, Bob, Mgr.-Adv. Promo.--King Industries, Inc., Norwalk, CT; *U.S. Private*, pg. 620

Burke, Laurie, V.P.-Adv. & Mdsg.--Warner Bros. Records, Inc., Burbank, CA; *U.S. Public*, pg. 1611

Burke, Louise, V.P.-Adv., Promo. & Pub.--Berkley Publishing Corp., New York, NY; *Int'l*, pg. 1027

Burke, Michael, Mktg. Coord.--Flambeau Products Corp., Middlefield, OH; *U.S. Private*, pg. 409

Burke, R., Dir.-Communications--Cochrane, Inc., King of Prussia, PA; *U.S. Public*, pg. 456

Burke, Robert P., Sr. V.P.-Mktg.--Luby's Cafeterias, Inc., San Antonio, TX; *U.S. Public*, pg. 1017

Burkett, Bud, Dir.-Adv. & Mktg. Commun.--Cosco, Inc., Columbus, IN; *U.S. Private*, pg. 277

Burkett, Cynthia, Mktg. Strategist--GS Electric, Carlisle, PA; *U.S. Public*, pg. 726

Burkhalter, Charles, Dir.-Mktg.--Salant Corporation, New York, NY; *U.S. Public*, pg. 1429

Burkhalter, Charles, Dir.-Adv.--The Manhattan Shirt Co., New York, NY; *U.S. Public*, pg. 1429

Burkhardt, William C., Pres. & Chief Exec. Officer--Austin Quality Foods, Cary, NC; *U.S. Private*, pg. 100

Burkhart, Susie, Mgr.-Adv.--J.M. Smucker Company, Orrville, OH; *U.S. Public*, pg. 1480

Burkle, Ronald, Mng. Partner--The Yucaipa Companies, Los Angeles, CA; *U.S. Private*, pg. 1202

Burleson, Kelly, Coord.-Adv.--Henredon Furniture Industries, Inc., Morganton, NC; *U.S. Private*, pg. 432

Burlingame, Keith, Mgr.-Sls. Admin. & Mktg.--Easco Inc., Girard, OH; *U.S. Public*, pg. 548

Burnett, Bruce, Dir.-Mktg.--Trebor Bassett Ltd., Maple Cross, United Kingdom; *Int'l*, pg. 248

Burnett, R. Curtis, V.P.-Pub. Affairs--Questar Corporation, Salt Lake City, UT; *U.S. Public*, pg. 1352

Burney, Michael J., V.P.-Corp. Affairs--Jefferson-Pilot Corporation, Greensboro, NC; *U.S. Public*, pg. 925

Burningham, Dirk, Dir.-Adv.-Intermountain Reg.--Smith's Food & Drug Centers, Inc., Salt Lake City, UT; *U.S. Public*, pg. 1103

Burns, Barbara, Natl. Dir.-Adv.--WEA Corp., Burbank, CA; *U.S. Public*, pg. 1612

Burns, Charles, Sr. V.P.-Adv.--Minyard Food Stores, Inc., Coppell, TX; *U.S. Private*, pg. 752

Burns, Gretchen, Art Dir.--GH Hensley Industries, Inc., Dallas, TX; *U.S. Private*, pg. 439

Burr, David T., Mgr.-Mktg.--Interlake Material Handling Div., Naperville, IL; *U.S. Public*, pg. 893

Burtom, Chuck, Dir.-Adv. & Mktg.--Tandy Corporation, Fort Worth, TX; *U.S. Public*, pg. 1560

Burton, Bonnie, V.P.-Mktg. & Adv.--Kay-Bee Toy & Hobby Shops, Inc., Pittsfield, MA; *U.S. Public*, pg. 437

Burton, R., Mgr.-Mktg.--Servo Corporation of America, Westbury, NY; *U.S. Private*, pg. 987

Bushkin, Nancy, V.P. Corp. Commun.--Spelling Entertainment Group, Inc., Los Angeles, CA; *U.S. Private*, pg. 776

Bushor, Ed, Dir.-Mktg.--McConnell Cabinets, Inc., El Monte, CA; *U.S. Private*, pg. 720

Butcher, Leanne, Dir.-Adv.--Arkwright, Inc, Fiskeville, RI; *Int'l*, pg. 994

Butkovich, John, Sr. V.P.-Media Adv.--Columbia Pictures, Culver City, CA; *Int'l*, pg. 1281

Butler, Skip, Dir.-Communications--Carriage Industries, Inc., Calhoun, GA; *U.S. Public*, pg. 514

Buxton, Sarah, Mgr.-Adv.--Air New Zealand Ltd. (U.S.A.), El Segundo, CA; *Int'l*, pg. 38

Byanski, Cindy, Mgr.-Adv.--House of White Birches, Inc., Berne, IN; *U.S. Private*, pg. 542

Bye, Conrad, Dir.-Fin.--Dynamic Homes, Inc., Detroit Lakes, MN; *U.S. Public*, pg. 538

Byer, David, Mgr.-Adv.--Yamaha Motor Corp., U.S.A., Cypress, CA; *Int'l*, pg. 1516

Byer, Marion, Dir.-Adv. & Sls.--CNN (Cable News Network), Atlanta, GA; *U.S. Public*, pg. 1614

Byerly, Ron, V.P.-Training, Mktg. & Adv.--O'Reilly Automotive Inc., Springfield, MO; *U.S. Public*, pg. 1230

Bykerk, Larry, V.P.-Sls.--Apollo Colors Inc., Northbrook, IL; *U.S. Private*, pg. 77
Byrne, Bob, Dir.-Adv.--Wells Fargo & Company, San Francisco, CA; *U.S. Public*, pg. 1753
Byrne, Paul, V.P.-Sls. & Mktg.--Precor, Inc., Bothell, WA; *U.S. Public*, pg. 1322
Byrne, Timothy W., Chief Fin. Officer, Sr. V.P. & Sec.--United States Lime & Minerals, Dallas, TX; *U.S. Public*, pg. 1684
Byrnes, Ed, V.P. & Gen. Mgr.-Sls. & Adv.--The Weather Channel, Atlanta, GA; *U.S. Private*, pg. 647
Byrnes, Ralph R., Sr. V.P.-Automotive Resource Dir.--Consumers Financial Corporation, Camp Hill, PA; *U.S. Public*, pg. 437
Byron, Jill C., Principal Area Leader-Corp. Branding & Customer--DTE Energy Company, Detroit, MI; *U.S. Public*, pg. 475
Caddock, Richard E. Jr., V.P.-Engrng. & Mktg.--Caddock Electronics, Inc., Riverside, CA; *U.S. Private*, pg. 198
Cadovius, Jo-Ann, Mgr.-Adv. & Promo.--InterLake Papers, Inc., Stamford, CT; *U.S. Public*, pg. 436
Cagar, Virginia F., V.P.-Bus. Devel.--Federal Home Loan Bank of New York, New York, NY; *U.S. Private*, pg. 399
Cahill, Michael, Dir.-Adv.--Mox-Med, Inc., Portage, WI; *U.S. Public*, pg. 124
Calabrese, F.P., Mgr.-Natl. Sls.--The Grieve Corporation, Round Lake, IL; *U.S. Private*, pg. 480
Calabro, Joseph, Dir.-Adv.--Mathews & Boucher, Rochester, NY; *U.S. Private*, pg. 714
Calahan, Katie, Dir.-Mktg.--Country Home Bakery, Inc., Bridgeport, CT; *U.S. Private*, pg. 278
Calandra, T.M., Pres.--Starcrest Products of California, Perris, CA; *U.S. Private*, pg. 1035
Caldarone, Bob, Dir.-Mktg.--Cruise America, Inc., Mesa, AZ; *U.S. Private*, pg. 178
Caldwell, Henry, V.P.-Mktg. & Communications--Anixter Inc., Skokie, IL; *U.S. Public*, pg. 115
Caldwell, Judy, Coord. Adv. Services--Westwood-Squibb Pharmaceuticals Inc., Buffalo, NY; *U.S. Public*, pg. 255
Caldwell, Michelle, Mgr.-Adv./Carrier--Carrier Corp., Indianapolis, IN; *U.S. Public*, pg. 1690
Caliendo, Valerie, Adv. & Pub. Rels. Assoc.--Benetton U.S.A. Corporation, New York, NY; *Int'l*, pg. 186
Callander, Sally, Sr. Mgr.-Communications--Sandoz Agro, Inc., Des Plaines, IL; *Int'l*, pg. 974
Calleja, Carmen Lopez, Dir.-Mktg.--Iberia Air Lines of Spain, Miami, FL; *Int'l*, pg. 575
Calthorpe, William A., V.P.-Sls., Adv. & Mktg.--Weeks Dairy Foods, Inc., Concord, NH; *Int'l*, pg. 752
Caluori, Peter, V.P.-Mktg. & Advertising--Liechtenstein Global Trust Limited, Vaduz, Liechtenstein; *Int'l*, pg. 809
Calvert, Mona, Mgr.-Mktg.--CIS Technologiès, Inc., Tulsa, OK; *U.S. Public*, pg. 1155
Calway, Jamie, V.P.-Kenwood Adv.--Oneida Ltd., Oneida, NY; *U.S. Public*, pg. 1225
Camera, Tony, Mgr.-Adv.--GH Hensley Industries, Inc., Dallas, TX; *U.S. Private*, pg. 439
Cameron, Donald, Grp. Head-Pub. Rels.--Schroders PLC, London, United Kingdom; *Int'l*, pg. 1210
Campagna, Curt, Dir.-Mktg.--Lawson Products, Inc., Des Plaines, IL; *U.S. Public*, pg. 980
Campanella, Thomas, Exec. V.P.-Adv. & Promo.--Paramount Pictures Corporation, Los Angeles, CA; *U.S. Private*, pg. 776
Campbell, Bob, Mgr.-Pub. Rels. & Adv.--Inter-Continental Hotels & Resorts Corporation, New York, NY; *Int'l*, pg. 1178
Campbell, Darrell, Pres.-VPI Comml., Inc.--TCA Cable TV, Inc., Tyler, TX; *U.S. Public*, pg. 1553
Campbell, Deborah A., Mgr.-Adv.--Plan International USA, Inc., Warwick, RI; *U.S. Private*, pg. 869
Campbell, Earl, Mgr.-Market Rep.--American Honda Motor Co., Inc. Automobile Sales Division, Torrance, CA; *Int'l*, pg. 634
Campbell, Jack, Pres.--Minigrip Zip-Pak, Orangeburg, NY; *U.S. Public*, pg. 867
Campbell, Joe, Mgr.-Mktg.--Sunny Fresh Foods, Monticello, MN; *U.S. Private*, pg. 210
Campbell, Kenilee, Communications Specialist--Interpoint, Redmond, WA; *U.S. Public*, pg. 457
Campbell, Rhys, Mgr.-Worldwide Adv.--Blount, Inc. Oregon Cutting Systems Division, Portland, OR; *U.S. Public*, pg. 238
Campbell, Robin W., Mgr.-Mktg. Svcs. & Adv.--Stanley Furniture Co. Inc., Stanleytown, VA; *U.S. Public*, pg. 1508
Campbell, Susan J., V.P.-Commun. & Investor Rels.--NovaCare Inc., King of Prussia, PA; *U.S. Public*, pg. 1203
Campobasso, Richard, V.P.-Standard Prods.--Binks Sames Corporation, Franklin Park, IL; *U.S. Public*, pg. 229
Canac, Claude, Mktg. & Adv.--C.M.C. SA, Saint Quentin-en-Yvelines, France; *Int'l*, pg. 792
Canada, Dra. Paula, Head-Client Services--Transportes Aereos Portugueses, Lisbon, Portugal; *Int'l*, pg. 1418
Candray, Jean, Coord.-Mktg.--SGS U.S. Testing Company, Inc., Fairfield, NJ; *Int'l*, pg. 1153
Cangtihean, Virginia, Mgr.-Adv.--Honda Motor do Brasil Ltda., Sao Paulo, Brazil; *Int'l*, pg. 635
Canino, Jill, Dir.-Adv. Bus.--MCI Communications Corp., Atlanta, GA; *U.S. Public*, pg. 1023
Canning, Tim, V.P.-Mktg. & Adv.--Premier, Inc., Greenwich, CT; *U.S. Private*, pg. 647
Cannon, Bruce A., Chief Fin. Officer, Sr. V.P., Treas. & Sec.--SpecTran Corporation, Sturbridge, MA; *U.S. Public*, pg. 1497
Cannon, John, Mgr.-Mktg. Communications--InterVoice, Inc., Dallas, TX; *U.S. Public*, pg. 910
Cantin, Robert L., Dir.-Communications & Adv.--Karsten Manufacturing Corporation, Phoenix, AZ; *U.S. Private*, pg. 608
Cantler, Mary, Dir.-Adv.--The Weathervane Retail Corp., New Britain, CT; *U.S. Private*, pg. 1156
Cantrell, Bruce, Mgr.-Adv.--Rotary Lift, Madison, IN; *U.S. Public*, pg. 521
Cantrell, Kevin, Mgr.-Mktg.--American Tank & Fabricating Co., Cleveland, OH; *U.S. Private*, pg. 63
Capassela, Richard, V.P.-Video Club Adv.--Columbia House Music Club, New York, NY; *Int'l*, pg. 1281
Capobianco, Florence, Mgr.-Ad Production--Electrical World, New York, NY; *U.S. Public*, pg. 1071
Caponi, Colleen, Dir.-Mktg. & Adv.--Apple Vacations West Inc., Elk Grove Village, IL; *U.S. Private*, pg. 78
Cappa, Sylvia, Asst. V.P.-Mktg. & Publications--The Wheatley Group, Inc., Stamford, CT; *U.S. Public*, pg. 152
Cappellino, Mary H., Mgr.-Prod. Training--Garlock Sealing Technologies, Palmyra, NY; *U.S. Public*, pg. 402
Cappeloni, Carolina, Adv.--BASF Argentina S.A., Buenos Aires, Argentina; *Int'l*, pg. 105
Cappiello, Dan, Mgr.-Adv.--Atlantic Recording Corporation, New York, NY; *U.S. Public*, pg. 1611
Cappo, Joe, Sr. V.P.-Intl.--Advertising Age, Chicago, IL; *U.S. Private*, pg. 284
Carano, Vickie, Supvr.-Print Adv.--Longs Drug Stores Corporation, Walnut Creek, CA; *U.S. Public*, pg. 1013
Carballo, Ramon A., Grp. Prod. Mgr.--La Tondena Distillers, Inc., Manila, Philippines; *Int'l*, pg. 785
Carbee, Patty, 2nd V.P.-Mktg.--National Life Insurance Company, Montpelier, VT; *U.S. Private*, pg. 785
Carbone, Gerald, Dir.-Adv.--The Sports Authority Inc., Fort Lauderdale, FL; *U.S. Public*, pg. 1499
Card, Keith, Dir.-Mktg. & Pub. Rels.--Benihana, Inc., Miami, FL; *U.S. Public*, pg. 211
Carden, Lisa K., Mgr.-Adv.-West Coast--Scientific American, Inc., New York, NY; *Int'l*, pg. 1479
Cardwell, Colleen, Mgr.-Mktg.--GF Office Furniture Ltd., Gallatin, TN; *U.S. Private*, pg. 434
Carey, Carolyn, V.P.-Mktg.--Knott's Berry Farm, Buena Park, CA; *U.S. Private*, pg. 627
Carlin, Lisa, Dir.-Mktg. Communications--General Signal Networks, Shelton, CT; *U.S. Public*, pg. 727
Carlo, Judith, V.P.-Mktg. & Creative--Zotos International, Darien, CT; *Int'l*, pg. 1236
Carlson, George W., Dir.-Publicity--Saratoga Equine Sports Center, Saratoga Springs, NY; *U.S. Private*, pg. 965
Carlson, Kathleen, V.P.-Mktg. & Commun.--Grubb & Ellis Company, Northbrook, IL; *U.S. Public*, pg. 767
Carlson, Nancy, Global Brand Mgr.--Mobil Oil Corporation, Fairfax, VA; *U.S. Public*, pg. 1118
Carlson, Peggy, Specialist-Mktg.--Menasha Corp., Printed Systems Div., Neenah, WI; *U.S. Private*, pg. 731
Carlson, Ray, Mgr.-Mktg.--Hedwin Corporation, Baltimore, MD; *Int'l*, pg. 1278
Carlson, Ruth, V.P.-Mktg.--Scholl U.S.A., Memphis, TN; *U.S. Public*, pg. 1438
Carlton, Ron, Ph.D., Dir.-Mktg.--AmeriPath, Inc., Riviera Beach, FL; *U.S. Public*, pg. 96
Carman, Ernest, Mgr.-Adv.--Sethco Division, Hauppauge, NY; *U.S. Public*, pg. 1100
Carmody, Francine, Mgr.-Trade Mdsg.--Goody Products, Inc., Peachtree City, GA; *U.S. Public*, pg. 1177
Carney, Mike, Dir.-Mktg. Commun.--Lowrance Electronics, Inc., Tulsa, OK; *U.S. Public*, pg. 1015
Carol, Jean, Dir.-Adv.--H.W. Kaufman Financial Group, Inc., Farmington, MI; *U.S. Private*, pg. 609
Caron, Patty, Adv. Admin.--The Great-West Life Assurance Company, Winnipeg, Canada; *Int'l*, pg. 557
Carozza, Francesca, Mgr.-Adv.--Portland General Electric Co., Portland, OR; *U.S. Public*, pg. 584
Carpenter, Craig, Dir.-Adv. & Sls. Promo.--Eckerd Corporation, Largo, FL; *U.S. Public*, pg. 917
Carpenter, Marian J., Dir.-Corp. Communications--Republic Engineered Steels, Inc., Massillon, OH; *U.S. Public*, pg. 1378
Carpenter, Patrick, Mgr.-Pub. Rels.--Alcan Aluminum Corporation, Cleveland, OH; *Int'l*, pg. 50
Carpenter, Richard A., Mgr.-Adv. & Sales Promo.--Hauck Mfg. Co., Cleona, PA; *U.S. Private*, pg. 510
Carpenter, Robert, V.P.-Sls. & Adv.--Sequa Can Machinery, East Rutherford, NJ; *U.S. Public*, pg. 1458
Carr, Kevin, Mgr.-Adv.--Nestle Chocolate & Confection, Glendale, CA; *Int'l*, pg. 917
Carr, Kirk, Dir.-Adv. Services--The Wall Street Journal, New York, NY; *U.S. Public*, pg. 524
Carr, Logan, Dir.-Pub. Rels.--Dick Clark Productions, Inc., Burbank, CA; *U.S. Public*, pg. 382
Carrasco, Patricia A., Mgr.-Pub. Rels., Adv. & Mktg.--Casio, Inc., Dover, NJ; *Int'l*, pg. 274
Carroll, Amy, Mgr.-Mktg. Services--GoodMark Foods, Inc., Raleigh, NC; *U.S. Public*, pg. 751
Carroll, Ed, Exec. V.P.-Adv.--Carson Pirie Scott & Company, Chicago, IL; *U.S. Public*, pg. 309
Carroll, Michael, Mgr.-Adv.--Air France, New York, NY; *Int'l*, pg. 560
Carroll, Pat, Mgr.-Adv. & Pub. Rels--Kubota Tractor Corp., Torrance, CA; *Int'l*, pg. 762
Carroll, Tom, Adv.--Anemostat Products, Scranton, PA; *U.S. Public*, pg. 286
Carrona, Sally, Adv. & Media Specialist--Samuel Cabot, Inc., Newburyport, MA; *U.S. Private*, pg. 198
Carson, David, Mgr.-Adv.--Panduit Corp., Tinley Park, IL; *U.S. Private*, pg. 836
Carson, Pati, Mgr.-Mktg.--Franklin Electronic Publishers, Inc., Burlington, NJ; *U.S. Public*, pg. 679
Carson, R. Jean, Mgr.-Adv.--Osborn Manufacturing, Cleveland, OH; *U.S. Public*, pg. 924
Carstens, Matthew, Pres.--United Steel & Wire Co., Battle Creek, MI; *U.S. Private*, pg. 1126
Carter, Anne, Dir.-Adv. P & A--Ames Department Stores, Inc., Rocky Hill, CT; *U.S. Public*, pg. 99
Carter, Dennis, V.P. -Corp. Mktg. Grp.--Intel Corporation, Santa Clara, CA; *U.S. Public*, pg. 886
Carter, Joel, V.P.-Mktg. & Adv.--Computer City, Fort Worth, TX; *U.S. Public*, pg. 1560
Carter, Kirk T., Mgr.-Bus. Devel.--Potter-Shackelford Construction Co., Greenville, SC; *U.S. Private*, pg. 877
Carter, Mary Randolph, V.P.-Adv.--Polo/Ralph Lauren Corporation, New York, NY; *U.S. Private*, pg. 874
Carver, Diane, Mgr.-Adv. Production--Automotive News, Detroit, MI; *U.S. Private*, pg. 284
Casady, Ken, Mgr.-Adv. & Sls. Promo.--Raytheon E-Systems, Greenville, TX; *U.S. Public*, pg. 1365
Casarella, R. G., Adv. & Communications Mgr.--Permacel Tape, North Brunswick, NJ; *U.S. Public*, pg. 153
Casarella, Ronald G., Mgr.-Adv.--Permacel, New Brunswick, NJ; *Int'l*, pg. 950
Casazza, Elisabeth, Mgr.-Adv.--Evans, Inc., Chicago, IL; *U.S. Public*, pg. 596
Cascade, Susan, Dir.-Adv. & Sls.--Crain's Detroit Business, Detroit, MI; *U.S. Private*, pg. 285
Cascarelli, Patricia A., Mgr.-Adv. & Promo.--Dairy Mart Convenience Stores, Inc., Cuyahoga Falls, OH; *U.S. Public*, pg. 476
Case, Becky, V.P.-Adv.--Hecht's, Arlington, VA; *U.S. Public*, pg. 1063
Case, Peter, V.P.-Adv. & Dir.-Mktg.--Royal Bank of Canada, Toronto, Canada; *Int'l*, pg. 1131
Casey, Faye M., Mgr.-Mktg. Communications--Getinge/Castle Inc., Rochester, NY; *Int'l*, pg. 551
Cashion, Herschell A., Jr., Sr. V.P.-Bus. Devel.--The North American Coal Corporation, Dallas, TX; *U.S. Public*, pg. 1149
Cashman, Sandra, Communications Coord.--Fiskars Inc., Wausau, WI; *Int'l*, pg. 492
Cason, Kenny, Dir.-Adv. & Pub. Affairs--Chief Auto Parts, Dallas, TX; *U.S. Private*, pg. 236
Caspari, John, Dir.-Adv.--Northwestern Mutual Life Insurance Co., Milwaukee, WI; *U.S. Private*, pg. 807
Casper, Bert, V.P.-Mktg.--Remmele Engineering, Inc., New Brighton, MN; *U.S. Private*, pg. 921
Cassayre, Michelle, Dir.-Adv.--Oracle Corporation, Redwood City, CA; *U.S. Public*, pg. 1227
Cassin, Mr., Coord.-Adv.--Laboratoire LaChartre S.A., Blois, France; *U.S. Public*, pg. 1331
Cassin, Thomas C., V.P.-Mktg.--Pitco Frialator Inc., Bow, NH; *U.S. Public*, pg. 1065
Castaldi, Tony, V.P.-Mktg.--Cutco Industries, Inc., Syosset, NY; *U.S. Public*, pg. 470
Castellini, Kathy, V.P.-Sls.--Consolidated Metal Products, Inc., Cincinnati, OH; *U.S. Private*, pg. 265
Castiglione, Frank, Dir.-Adv.--Mervyn's California, Hayward, CA; *U.S. Public*, pg. 489
Castillo, Nancy M., Sr. Mgr.-Adv. & Sls.--Quintus Corporation, Fremont, CA; *U.S. Private*, pg. 901
Castro Almeida, Luis Torres, Gen. Mgr.-Sls Promo, Adv. & Pub. Rels.--Banco Totta & Acores, Lisbon, Portugal; *Int'l, pg. 144*
Caswell, Daniel M., Mgr.-Adv.--Lockport Union Sun & Journal, Lockport, NY; *U.S. Public*, pg. 1078
Catalano, Sam, Dir.-Adv.--Radiator Specialty Company, Charlotte, NC; *U.S. Private*, pg. 906
Cattell, Elizabeth, Coord.-Adv.--RenoAir Inc., Reno, NV; *U.S. Private*, pg. 922
Cattlin, David, Mgr.-Adv.--Courtaulds Aerospace, Littleborough, United Kingdom; *Int'l*, pg. 338
Cattlin, Sara, Coord.-Mktg. & Adv.--Chico's Fas Inc, Fort Myers, FL; *U.S. Public*, pg. 349
Caudell, Karen, V.P.-Adv.--Peoples National Bank, Lawrenceville, IL; *U.S. Public*, pg. 1217
Caulkins, William, V.P.-Adv. & Prod. Devel.--Sherman & Reilly, Inc., Chattanooga, TN; *U.S. Private*, pg. 993
Causey, Mary, Coord.-Mktg.--BGF Industries Inc., Greensboro, NC; *U.S. Private*, pg. 106
Cavello, Butch, Mgr.-Mktg.--American Louver Co., Skokie, IL; *U.S. Private*, pg. 58
Cavuto, Anthony, V.P.-Sls.--Cornell Dubilier Electronics, Wayne, NJ; *U.S. Private*, pg. 607
Cawley, Kraig, Dir.-Adv. & Sls.--Tribune Review Publishing Co., Greensburg, PA; *U.S. Private*, pg. 1102
Cayne, Janis, Mgr.-Mktg. Svcs.--The Spencer Turbine Co., Windsor, CT; *U.S. Private*, pg. 1025
Cazel, David, Graphics Coordinator--Time Systems, Inc., Phoenix, AZ; *U.S. Private*, pg. 1086
Cebula, Eileen, Mgr.-Adv.--Farmers Group, Inc., Los Angeles, CA; *Int'l*, pg. 110
Cekirge, Arzu, Mgr.-Adv. & Pub. Rels.--Sabanci Holding A.S., Istanbul, Turkey; *Int'l*, pg. 1167
Celata, Sheila, V.P.-Mktg.--UST Corporation, Boston, MA; *U.S. Public*, pg. 1660
Celentano, Domenick, Chm. Bd. & Pres.--Celentano Bros. Inc., Verona, NJ; *U.S. Private*, pg. 221
Cellentani, Tom, Mgr.-Adv.--Cadillac Motor Car Division, Warren, MI; *U.S. Public*, pg. 720
Cersosimo, Bonita, Mgr.-Corp. Communication Services--Aluminum Company of America, Pittsburgh, PA; *U.S. Public*, pg. 60
Chabot, Lee, Dir.-Adv. & Creative Dir.--CVS Corp., Woonsocket, RI; *U.S. Public*, pg. 287
Chaffetz, Alex, Dir.-Adv. Sls.--Product Information Network, Englewood, CO; *U.S. Private*, pg. 597
Chaine, Nicolas, Head-Corp. Commun.--Credit Lyonnais S.A., Paris, France; *Int'l*, pg. 343
Chainey, Hughette, Dir.-Promo.--Domtar Inc., Montreal, Canada; *Int'l*, pg. 416
Chaisuroj, Suang, Mgr.-Adv.--Benetone Land & Houses Co., Ltd., Bangkok, Thailand; *Int'l*, pg. 186
Challerton, Ed, Sr. Exec. Dir.-Adv.--SBC Communications Inc., San Antonio, TX; *U.S. Public*, pg. 1415
Chambers, Matthew, Mgr.-Adv.--Marks & Spencer PLC, London, United Kingdom; *Int'l*, pg. 842
Chambers, Tim, Mgr.-Adv.-Agri.--Case Corporation, Racine, WI; *U.S. Public*, pg. 311
Chandler, J. Harold, Sr. Exec. V.P.-Mktg.--NationsBank South, Atlanta, GA; *U.S. Public*, pg. 1163
Chandler, Ron, V.P.-Sls.--Antenna Products Corp., Mineral Wells, TX; *U.S. Public*, pg. 289
Chandr-Ruang-Phen, P., Dir.-Communications--Avon Cosmetics (Thailand) Ltd., Bangkok, Thailand; *U.S. Public*, pg. 156

Chaney, Barbara, Coord.-Adv.--Parlux Fragrances Inc., Fort Lauderdale, FL; *U.S. Public*, pg. 1264
Chaney, Barbara, Coord.-Pub. Rels. & Adv.--Parlux, Ltd., Fort Lauderdale, FL; *U.S. Public*, pg. 1264
Chang, Primalia, V.P.-Adv. & Bus. Mgr.--Conde Nast Publications, Los Angeles, CA; *U.S. Private*, pg. 20
Chaplin, GeneAnn, Adv. Coord.--ITT Jabsco, Costa Mesa, CA; *U.S. Public*, pg. 860
Chapman, Burt, V.P.-Mktg. & Adv.--Today's Man, Inc., Moorestown, NJ; *U.S. Public*, pg. 1619
Chapman, Charles, Mgr.-Adv.--Ford Meter Box Company, Wabash, IN; *U.S. Private*, pg. 418
Chappelle, Carol, Mgr.-Adv.--Arbor Drugs, Inc., Troy, MI; *U.S. Public*, pg. 126
Charbanic, Diane, Sr. V.P.-Coop Adv.--New Line Cinema Corporation, New York, NY; *U.S. Public*, pg. 1614
Chareste, Michael, Mgr.-Adv.--Beauty Enterprises Inc., Hartford, CT; *U.S. Private*, pg. 128
Charkiewicz, Nancy, Mgr.-Adv.--Manufacturers Technologies, Inc., West Springfield, MA; *U.S. Private*, pg. 701
Charles, Nick, Mgr.-Adv.--CXR Telcom Corporation, Fremont, CA; *U.S. Public*, pg. 1108
Charlton, Richard G., V.P.-Corp. Commun.--Parker Hannifin Corporation, Cleveland, OH; *U.S. Public*, pg. 1259
Charness, Wayne, V.P.-Corp. Communications--Hasbro, Inc., Pawtucket, RI; *U.S. Public*, pg. 797
Charney, M. Jeffrey, V.P.-Mktg. & Commun.--Kaufman and Broad Home Corporation, Los Angeles, CA; *U.S. Public*, pg. 944
Chartier, Keith A., Dir.-Adv.--Ogden Publishing, Topeka, KS; *U.S. Private*, pg. 812
Chase, Helen, Dir.-Pub. Rels.--Hannaford Bros. Co., Scarborough, ME; *U.S. Public*, pg. 781
Chastain, Roger W., Pres. & Chief Oper. Officer--Mount Vernon Mills, Inc., Greenville, SC; *U.S. Private*, pg. 835
Chastain, Stephanie, Dir.-Mktg.--California Strawberry Commission, Watsonville, CA; *U.S. Private*, pg. 201
Chattin, Juanita, Admin. Asst.--The Karges Furniture Company Inc., Evansville, IN; *U.S. Private*, pg. 607
Chaves, D. Doc, Asst. V.P.-Corp. Communications--Ameritas Life Insurance Corp., Lincoln, NE; *U.S. Private*, pg. 65
Chavez, Cassandra, Art Dir.--Heald Colleges, San Francisco, CA; *U.S. Private*, pg. 514
Chavez, Susan J., Dir.-Adv. & Special Projects--John Hancock Mutual Life Insurance Company, Boston, MA; *U.S. Private*, pg. 589
Cheatham, Edward W., V.P.-Corp. Communications--The Racal Corporation, Sunrise, FL; *Int'l*, pg. 1082
Chen, Jane, Special Asst.-Pub. Rels.--Acer Incorporated, Taipei, Taiwan; *Int'l*, pg. 22
Cheney, Luanne, Dir.-Mktg. Commun.--Candle Corporation, Santa Monica, CA; *U.S. Private*, pg. 204
Cheng, Eng Hwee, Sr. V.P.-Corp. Affairs--Superior Metal Printing Limited, Singapore, Singapore; *Int'l*, pg. 1322
Chenin, Bert, Mgr.-Bus. Devel.--Western Atlas Logging Services, Houston, TX; *U.S. Public*, pg. 1757
Chernowetz, Laura, Mgr.-Adv. & Promotions & Communications--Wallace Laboratories, Cranbury, NJ; *U.S. Public*, pg. 310
Cherry, Cindy, Mgr.-Adv.--Alamo Group, Inc., La Grange, IL; *U.S. Public*, pg. 35
Chester, Reed, Pres.-Adv. Promo. Inc.--Scott's Liquid Gold-Inc., Denver, CO; *U.S. Public*, pg. 1447
Chestnov, Robert, Pres. & Chief Exec. Officer--Jaclyn, Inc., West New York, NJ; *U.S. Public*, pg. 920
Cheung, Barbara Booth, Mgr.-Adv.--Altera Corporation, San Jose, CA; *U.S. Public*, pg. 59
Chevalier, Dominque, Mng. Dir.-Mktg.--Industrias Lever Portuguesa, Lda., Lisbon, Portugal; *Int'l*, pg. 1437
Chia Wee Chang, Joseph, Controller--Showpla Asia Limited, Singapore, Singapore; *Int'l*, pg. 1237
Chiba, Masanobu, Dir. & Gen. Mgr.-Adv. Bureau--Nihon Keizai Shimbun, Inc., Tokyo, Japan; *Int'l*, pg. 929
Chiericozzi, Pete, V.P.-Mktg. & Sls.--Wisconsin Tissue Mills, Inc., Menasha, WI; *U.S. Public*, pg. 347
Chihaya, Mari, V.P.-Adv. & Pub. Rels.--Shiseido Cosmetics (America) Ltd., New York, NY; *Int'l*, pg. 1235
Chihocky, Janet, Mgr.-Corp. Commun.--Orbital Sciences Corporation, Dulles, VA; *U.S. Public*, pg. 1229
Chilabato, Oscar, Dir.-Adv. & Public Rels.--The Richman Brothers Co., Fall River, MA; *U.S. Public*, pg. 1777
Childs, Sam, Dir.-Adv.--Northwest Florida Daily News, Fort Walton Beach, FL; *U.S. Private*, pg. 425
Ching, Meredith J., V.P.-Govt. & Community Rels.--Alexander & Baldwin, Inc., Honolulu, HI; *U.S. Public*, pg. 39
Chokwatana, Boonkiet, Dep. Chm. & Pres.--International Cosmetics Co., Ltd., Bangkok, Thailand; *Int'l*, pg. 684
Chole, Raquel, Mktg. Specialist--Dudek & Bock Spring Manufacturing Company, Chicago, IL; *U.S. Private*, pg. 344
Chomeau, John, Mgr.-Adv.--The Pillsbury Company, Minneapolis, MN; *Int'l*, pg. 411
Chomeau, John, Mgr.-Adv.--The Haagen-Dazs Company Inc., Minneapolis, MN; *Int'l*, pg. 411
Chrietzberg, Gloria, Dir.-Mktg.--One Price Clothing Stores, Inc., Duncan, SC; *U.S. Public*, pg. 1225
Christensen, Jennifer, Asst. Pub. Rels. & Adv.--OshKosh B'Gosh, Inc., Oshkosh, WI; *U.S. Public*, pg. 1232
Christensen, Ken, Mgr.-Adv.--Norrell Corporation, Atlanta, GA; *U.S. Public*, pg. 1192
Christensen, Ken, Mgr.-Adv.--Norrell Services Inc., Atlanta, GA; *U.S. Public*, pg. 1192
Christensen, Margo, Mgr.-Adv.--Martin/F. Weber Company, Philadelphia, PA; *U.S. Private*, pg. 710
Christensen, Pam, Sr. Mgr.-Mktg.--Lifetouch, Portrait Studios, Eden Prairie, MN; *U.S. Private*, pg. 667
Christians, Glenn, Mgr.-Adv./Massey Ferguson--AGCO Corporation, Duluth, GA; *U.S. Public*, pg. 28
Christiansen, Danielle, Coord.-Retail Adv.--Hammacher, Schlemmer & Co., Inc., Chicago, IL; *U.S. Private*, pg. 497
Christiansen, E.M., V.P.-Sls.--SmithKline Beecham Laboratories, Bristol, TN; *Int'l*, pg. 1264
Christiansen, P., Mgr.-Mktg.--Toyota Norge A/S, Drammen, Norway; *Int'l*, pg. 1414
Christmas, Bob, Dir.-Adv.--Keystone Steel & Wire Co., Peoria, IL; *U.S. Public*, pg. 955
Christmas, Donna, Adv. Asst.--Harden Furniture Company, McConnellsville, NY; *U.S. Private*, pg. 501
Christoff, Greg, V.P.-Mktg.--Paterno Imports Limited, Lake Bluff, IL; *U.S. Private*, pg. 843
Chubb, Sarah, Dir.-Adv.--Allure, New York, NY; *U.S. Private*, pg. 20
Chung, Ki Nam, Gen. Mgr.--Cho Hung Bank, Seoul, Korea; *Int'l*, pg. 287
Chwalek, Joe, V.P.-Sls. & Mktg.--IKG Industries, Clark, NJ; *U.S. Public*, pg. 793
Chye, Tan Peng, Sr. Mgr.-Mktg.--The Great Eastern Life Assurance Company Limited, Singapore, Singapore; *Int'l*, pg. 557
Cianciaruso, C. J., Mgr.-Sls.--Dunn Industries Inc., Kansas City, MO; *U.S. Private*, pg. 347
Ciavola, Rex, Dir.-Print/Production--Viking Office Products, Torrance, CA; *U.S. Public*, pg. 1720
Cihock, Steve, Mgr.-Adv. & Pub. Rels.--Komatsu America International Company, Vernon Hills, IL; *Int'l*, pg. 744
Cilento, Mr., Adv.--R.C.S. Editori S.p.A., Milan, Italy; *Int'l*, pg. 1078
Cimalore, Patti, Mgr.-Sls. & Mktg.--Jan-Co., Inc., Cranston, RI; *U.S. Private*, pg. 581
Cira, Laura, Mgr.-Adv.--Monaco Coach Corporation, Coburg, OR; *U.S. Public*, pg. 1123
Cira, Laura, Mgr.-Adv.--Holiday Rambler, Wakarusa, IN; *U.S. Public*, pg. 1123
Ciriello, Frank, Dir.-Adv.--Hoechst Marion Roussel, Inc., Bridgewater, NJ; *Int'l*, pg. 624
Ciriello, Frank, Dir.-Adv.--Hoechst Marion Roussel North America, Kansas City, MO; *Int'l*, pg. 625
Claes, Marry Anne, Mgr.-Mktg.--Lee Europe N.V., Brussels, Belgium; *U.S. Public*, pg. 1702
Clancy, Kevin, Mgr.-Sls.--Homes of Merit Inc., Bartow, FL; *U.S. Private*, pg. 537
Clapes, Jorge, Chief Fin. Officer--Johnson & Johnson de Argentina, S.A., Buenos Aires, Argentina; *U.S. Public*, pg. 930
Clapp, Amy, Mgr.-Mktg. Commun.--TelCom Semiconductor, Inc., Mountain View, CA; *U.S. Public*, pg. 1569
Clark, Debra, V.P.-Mktg.--First Union National Bank of Florida, Jacksonville, FL; *U.S. Public*, pg. 640
Clark, Don, Mgr.-Adv.--Sequentia Inc., Strongsville, OH; *U.S. Private*, pg. 985
Clark, Duncan, Sr. V.P.-Intl. Adv. & Publicity--Columbia Tri-Star Film Distributors International, Culver City, CA; *Int'l*, pg. 1281
Clark, James, Dir.-Adv.--Jake Sweeney Automotive Inc., Cincinnati, OH; *U.S. Private*, pg. 1058
Clark, Joseph, Sr. Mgr.-Adv.--Wakefern Food Corporation, Elizabeth, NJ; *U.S. Private*, pg. 1146
Clark, Lamar, V.P.-Adv., Mktg. & Sls.--Binning's Building Products, Inc., Lexington, NC; *U.S. Public*, pg. 67
Clark, Leslie, Mgr.-Mktg. Communications--Butler Manufacturing Company, Kansas City, MO; *U.S. Public*, pg. 271
Clark, Robert, Asst. V.P.-Corp. Adv.--Continental Assurance Company, Chicago, IL; *U.S. Private*, pg. 267
Clarke, Celine, Mgr.-Adv. & Sls. Promo.--Cushman & Wakefield, Inc., New York, NY; *Int'l*, pg. 873
Clarke, Duane, Dir.-Adv.--Koch Engineering Company, Inc., Akron, OH; *U.S. Private*, pg. 628
Clarkson, Colin, Chief Exec. Officer & V.P.-Mktg.--Lotus Cars USA, Inc., Lawrenceville, GA; *Int'l*, pg. 1071
Clarvit, Jill, Coord.-Adv.--The New Home Sewing Machine Co., Mahwah, NJ; *Int'l*, pg. 699
Claxton, Robert, V.P.-Adv.--Montgomery Ward & Co., Inc., Chicago, IL; *U.S. Private*, pg. 758
Claypoole, Joanne, Mgr.-Commun.--A. Schulman, Inc., Akron, OH; *U.S. Public*, pg. 1441
Cleare, Penny, V.P.-Mdsg. Adv.--Heublein, Inc., Hartford, CT; *Int'l*, pg. 410
Cleary-Salisbury, Janet, Mgr.-Adv.--The Brulin Corporation, Indianapolis, IN; *U.S. Private*, pg. 176
Clem, Patricia, Mgr.-Mktg. Communications--UTILX Corporation, Kent, WA; *U.S. Public*, pg. 1701
Clemens, Richard E., Pres. & Chief Exec. Officer--The Monarch Machine Tool Company, Sidney, OH; *U.S. Public*, pg. 1123
Clements, Colleen P., Dir.-Corp. Commun.--LaBarge, Inc., Saint Louis, MO; *U.S. Public*, pg. 973
Cleveland, Arthur E., Dir.-Prod. Devel. & Mktg.--Spartech Plastics, Portage, WI; *U.S. Public*, pg. 1496
Clevenger, Mark, Mgr.-Mktg. Communications--Inland Container Corporation, Indianapolis, IN; *U.S. Public*, pg. 1575
Cliff, Gerry, Mgr.-Adv.--Blount, Inc. Sporting Equipment Group, Lewiston, ID; *U.S. Public*, pg. 238
Clifford, Lee, Dir.-Adv.--Didde Corporation, Overland Park, KS; *U.S. Private*, pg. 331
Clifford, Lee, Dir.-Adv.--Didde Web Press, Emporia, KS; *U.S. Private*, pg. 331
Clifton, Dianne, Mgr.-Mktg. & Communications--Centex Corporation, Dallas, TX; *U.S. Public*, pg. 322
Cline, Amy, Dir.-Mktg.--ATCOM, Inc., Research Triangle Park, NC; *U.S. Private*, pg. 94
Clipez, Patrice, Mgr.-Adv.--Renault, Boulogne-Billancourt, France; *Int'l*, pg. 1102
Clonan, Jeanette, V.P.-Corp. Communications & Adv.--Loral Space & Communications, New York, NY; *U.S. Public*, pg. 1014
Close, Allyn D., Pres., Chief Exec. Officer & Mgr.-Sls. & Mktg.--Interpacific Investors Services, Seattle, WA; *U.S. Private*, pg. 572
Cluelow, Sue, Dir.-Mktg.--Paul Harris Stores, Inc., Indianapolis, IN; *U.S. Public*, pg. 792
Cobbs, Julia, Dir.-Adv.--Carlson Wagonlit Travel, Minneapolis, MN; *U.S. Private*, pg. 212
Cobuzzi, Peter, V.P.-Mktg.--Tourneau Inc., New York, NY; *U.S. Private*, pg. 1093
Cochran, Thomas, Dir.-Adv.--Austin Powder Co., Cleveland, OH; *U.S. Private*, pg. 100
Cockrill, Al, V.P.-Sls. & Mktg.--York Barbell Co., Inc., York, PA; *U.S. Private*, pg. 1196
Cody, Cris, Mgr.-Adv.--A&M Records, Hollywood, CA; *Int'l*, pg. 1052
Coffarello, Linda, Mgr.-Media Svcs.--The Quaker Oats Company, Chicago, IL; *U.S. Public*, pg. 1347
Coffey, Cathey B., V.P.-Adv.--Cox Newspapers, Inc., Atlanta, GA; *U.S. Private*, pg. 281
Cogen, Jeff, V.P.-Mktg. & Adv.--Dallas Stars, Irving, TX; *U.S. Private*, pg. 309
Cognetta, Gary, Mgr.-Display Adv.--Advance Publications Inc., Staten Island, NY; *U.S. Private*, pg. 18
Cohan, Ed, Dir.-Adv.--Wacoal America Inc., New York, NY; *Int'l*, pg. 1484
Cohen, Arnold, Dir.-Adv. & Promotions--Dean Witter, Discover & Co., New York, NY; *U.S. Public*, pg. 1132
Cohen, Arnold, Dir.-Grp. Adv.--NOVUS Financial Corporation, Riverwoods, IL; *U.S. Public*, pg. 1132
Cohen, Barbara, Office Mgr.--Summit Specialty Chemicals Corporation, Fort Lee, NJ; *Int'l*, pg. 1312
Cohen, Daniel, Sr. V.P.-Adv.--The New York Times Company, New York, NY; *U.S. Public*, pg. 1173
Cohen, Daniel, Sr. V.P.-Adv.--The New York Times, New York, NY; *U.S. Public*, pg. 1174
Cohen, Debbie, Mgr.-Adv.--Wheelock Inc., Long Branch, NJ; *U.S. Private*, pg. 1171
Cohen, Gary, Art-Dir.--Martin Lawrence Limited Editions, Inc., North Hollywood, CA; *U.S. Private*, pg. 709
Cohen, Gerald A., V.P.-Adv.--Olga Div., Bridgeport, CT; *U.S. Public*, pg. 1738
Cohen, Marci, Mgr.-Creative Svcs.--Dakotah, Inc., Webster, SD; *U.S. Public*, pg. 477
Cohen, Milton L., Chm. Bd. & Pres.--Lifetime Hoan Corp., Westbury, NY; *U.S. Public*, pg. 992
Cohen, Tracy, Mgr.-Adv.--Tropicana Casino & Resort, Atlantic City, NJ; *U.S. Public*, pg. 159
Cohen, William L., Chm. Bd., Pres. & Chief Exec. Officer--Andover Togs, Inc., New York, NY; *U.S. Public*, pg. 112
Cohodes, Mary D., Admin.--Independent Metals, Germantown, WI; *U.S. Private*, pg. 559
Coladarci, Paul H., V.P.-Mktg.--Broad National Bancorporation, Newark, NJ; *U.S. Public*, pg. 257
Colasacco, D.G., Mgr.-Exhibits--A.O. Smith Corporation, Milwaukee, WI; *U.S. Public*, pg. 1476
Cole, Charles, Dir.-Sls. & Mktg.--Protective Closures Co., Inc., Buffalo, NY; *U.S. Public*, pg. 1045
Cole, Chuck, Dir.-Mktg.--Utility Trailer Manufacturing Co., City of Industry, CA; *U.S. Private*, pg. 1130
Cole, Hunter, Mgr.-Adv.--Bassmaster Magazine, Montgomery, AL; *U.S. Private*, pg. 105
Cole, Joe C., V.P.-Corp. Commun.--Aztar Corporation, Phoenix, AZ; *U.S. Public*, pg. 158
Cole, Judy, V.P.-Adv.--Sally Beauty Company, Inc., Denton, TX; *U.S. Public*, pg. 38
Cole, Julie, Mgr.-Mktg.--Barnhardt Manufacturing Co., Charlotte, NC; *U.S. Private*, pg. 116
Coleman, Heather, Mgr.-Adv.--Merck Frosst Canada Inc., Kirkland, Canada; *U.S. Public*, pg. 1092
Coleman, Paul, V.P.- Adv. & Mktg.--Farmer Jack Supermarkets, Detroit, MI; *Int'l*, pg. 1375
Coleman, Roxanne, Supvr.-Mktg., Adv. & Sls.--Shakespeare Fishing Tackle, Columbia, SC; *U.S. Public*, pg. 940
Coles, Carl R., Mgr.-Mktg.--MD Pneumatics, Springfield, MO; *U.S. Private*, pg. 1111
Colford, Matt, Mgr.-Mktg.--Old Dutch Foods, Inc., Roseville, MN; *U.S. Private*, pg. 814
Collette, Rod, V.P.-Adv.--Pawling Corporation, Pawling, NY; *U.S. Private*, pg. 844
Collier, Deanie, V.P.-Adv.--Stein Mart, Inc., Jacksonville, FL; *U.S. Public*, pg. 1514
Collier, Kevin, Dir.-Distributor Mktg.--Performance Food Group Company, Richmond, VA; *U.S. Public*, pg. 1278
Collins, Anne Marie, Dir.-Classified--VV Publishing Corp., New York, NY; *U.S. Private*, pg. 1131
Collins, Bill, Mgr.-Sls.--Don Massey Cadillac Inc., Plymouth, MI; *U.S. Private*, pg. 712
Collins, C.G., Adv. Mgr.--Fairmont Tamper, West Columbia, SC; *U.S. Public*, pg. 793
Collins, Carol A., Leader-Services Delivery--Bay State Gas Company, Westborough, MA; *U.S. Public*, pg. 196
Collins, Janet, Dir.-Communications--Philips Medical Systems North America Company, Shelton, CT; *Int'l*, pg. 1055
Collins, Judy, Mgr.-Adv.--George W. Park Seed Co., Inc., Greenwood, SC; *U.S. Private*, pg. 839
Collins, Paula, Mgr.-Reg. Adv.--Delta Air Lines, Inc., Atlanta, GA; *U.S. Public*, pg. 497
Collord, Margaret, Dir.-Adv.--Lechters, Inc., Harrison, NJ; *U.S. Public*, pg. 983
Colonna, Mark, Chief Oper. Officer-Mktg & Exec. V.P.--Colonna Bros., Inc., North Bergen, NJ; *U.S. Private*, pg. 254
Colvert, Sylvia, V.P.-Admin. & Adv.--SunPure Ltd., Avon Park, FL; *U.S. Private*, pg. 1053
Colwell, Howard O., V.P.-Adv.--Combe Incorporated, White Plains, NY; *U.S. Private*, pg. 257
Colwell, Tim, Dir.-Pub. Rels.--Parker Drilling Company, Tulsa, OK; *U.S. Public*, pg. 1259
Combs, Tom, Gen. Sls. Mgr.--WLFI-TV, West Lafayette, IN; *U.S. Private*, pg. 148
Compton, Sherre, Mgr.-Mktg. & Adv.--Wells/Bloomfield, Verdi, NV; *U.S. Public*, pg. 1497
Cone, Tim, Dir.-Sls. & Mktg.--Hahn Automotive Warehouse, Inc., Rochester, NY; *U.S. Public*, pg. 774
Conkel, Debra K., Publications Editor--State Automobile Mutual Insurance Co., Columbus, OH; *U.S. Private*, pg. 1036
Conklin, Dean C., Mgr.-Corp. Communications--Montana Power Company, Butte, MT; *U.S. Public*, pg. 1126

Conley, Ted, Brand Mgr.--Durex Consumer Products, Norcross, GA; *Int'l*, pg. 815
Conn, Eric, Sr. Mgr.-Adv.--American Honda Motor Co., Inc., Torrance, CA; *Int'l*, pg. 634
Connelly, Timothy, V.P.-Media Rels.--Fleet Bank, N.A., Jersey City, NJ; *U.S. Public*, pg. 649
Conner, Stephen D., V.P.-Corp. Commun.--Piedmont Natural Gas Co., Inc., Charlotte, NC; *U.S. Public*, pg. 1295
Connolly, John, V.P.-Adv. Sls.--The Edmonton Journal, Edmonton, Canada; *Int'l*, pg. 631
Connors, Lynne, Dir.-Mktg. Communications--Encore Computer Corporation, Fort Lauderdale, FL; *U.S. Public*, pg. 580
Conover, Clay, V.P.-Adv. Specialty--The At-A-Glance Group, Sidney, NY; *U.S. Private*, pg. 295
Conover, Scott, Dir.-Adv.--Lakeland Industries, Inc., Ronkonkoma, NY; *U.S. Public*, pg. 975
Conrad, Rita A., Dir.-Corp. Commun.--Flint Ink Corp., Detroit, MI; *U.S. Private*, pg. 413
Conte, Leo, Pres. & Chief Exec. Officer--Montebello Brands Inc., Baltimore, MD; *U.S. Private*, pg. 758
Contos, Dixie, V.P.-Adv. & Dir.-Pub. Rels.--Pay Less Super Markets, Inc., Anderson, IN; *U.S. Private*, pg. 844
Conway, Charles T., Asst. V.P. & Dir.-Corp. Commun. & Adv.--Policy Management Systems Corporation, Blythewood, SC; *U.S. Public*, pg. 1314
Conway, Kelly, V.P.-Mktg. & Adv.--The Sports Authority Inc., Fort Lauderdale, FL; *U.S. Public*, pg. 1499
Coogan, Michael, Dir.-Mktg./Adv.--Hang Ten, Montreal, Canada; *Int'l*, pg. 549
Cook, Bob, Sr. V.P.-Mktg. & Adv.--The Guber Peters Entertainment Company, Los Angeles, CA; *Int'l*, pg. 1283
Cook, J.W., V.P.-Sls.--Ajax Magnethermic Corp., Warren, OH; *Int'l*, pg. 113
Cook, Lynne, Dir.-Adv.--Houston Chronicle, Houston, TX; *U.S. Private*, pg. 517
Cook, Robert E., Pres.--Frigidaire Home Products, Augusta, GA; *Int'l*, pg. 439
Cooley, Laura, Graphic Designer--Quest Technologies, Inc., Oconomowoc, WI; *U.S. Private*, pg. 900
Coombs, John, Dir.-Adv.--British Aerospace p.l.c., Farnborough, United Kingdom; *Int'l*, pg. 217
Coombs, Whitney, V.P.-Mktg.--Hanover Foods Corporation, Hanover, PA; *U.S. Private*, pg. 499
Cooner, Alice, Dir.-Adv.--Fairfield Communities, Inc., Little Rock, AR; *U.S. Public*, pg. 610
Cooney, Susan, Mgr.-Adv.--American Heritage Magazine, New York, NY; *U.S. Private*, pg. 417
Coonrod, Linda, Mgr.-Adv.--Duke Manufacturing Co., Inc., Saint Louis, MO; *U.S. Private*, pg. 346
Coons, David, Dir.-Adv.-Consumer & Specialty Services--Blue Cross of California, Woodland Hills, CA; *U.S. Private*, pg. 152
Cooper, Brian, V.P.-Adv. & Mktg.--First American Corporation, Nashville, TN; *U.S. Public*, pg. 624
Cooper, Cathy, V.P.-Mktg. & Investor Rels.--Washington Federal Savings, Seattle, WA; *U.S. Public*, pg. 1740
Cooper, Chuck, Mgr.-Adv. Dept.--W.S. Badcock Corporation, Mulberry, FL; *U.S. Private*, pg. 109
Cooper, Freny, Mgr.-Adv.--Claris Corporation, Santa Clara, CA; *U.S. Public*, pg. 121
Cooper, Kenneth, Dir.-Adv. & Creative Services--Doubleday Book Club, Garden City, NY; *Int'l*, pg. 191
Cooper, Norton J., Pres. & Chief Exec. Officer--Charles Jacquin et Cie, Inc., Philadelphia, PA; *U.S. Private*, pg. 580
Cooper, Phil, V.P.-Publicity & Adv.--Caesars World, Inc., Las Vegas, NV; *U.S. Public*, pg. 1512
Cooper, Phil, V.P.-Pub. Rels. & Adv.--Caesars Palace, Las Vegas, NV; *U.S. Public*, pg. 1512
Coopmans, Marc, Mgr.-Adv.- Lancia--Fiat Auto Belgio SA, Brussels, Belgium; *Int'l*, pg. 481
Copeland, R. Bruce Jr., V.P.-Mktg. & Pub. Rels.--First Financial Holdings, Inc., Charleston, SC; *U.S. Public*, pg. 634
Coppinger, Donna, V.P.-Mktg. Services--Duke Realty Investments, Inc., Indianapolis, IN; *U.S. Public*, pg. 535
Coppinger, Gary, Mgr.-Corp. Retail & Niche Adv.--TruServ Corporation, Chicago, IL; *U.S. Private*, pg. 1108
Corbett, Gerard F., Dir.-Corp. Communications--Hitachi America, Ltd., Tarrytown, NY; *Int'l*, pg. 622
Corbett, Martin, Mgr.-Sls. & Adv.--Harold Leonard & Company, Inc., Union, NJ; *U.S. Private*, pg. 660
Corcoran, Kevin, Mgr.-Design--Platinum Technology, Inc., Oak Brook Terrace, IL; *U.S. Public*, pg. 1309
Cordery, Pamela, Mgr.-Adv.--Dynagear Oil Pumps, Inc., Maquoketa, IA; *U.S. Private*, pg. 350
Corkery, Padriad, Mgr.-Adv.--Telecom Eireann, Dublin, Ireland; *Int'l*, pg. 1362
Cornell, Robert, Dir.-Adv.--Johnson Newspaper Corporation, Watertown, NY; *U.S. Private*, pg. 591
Cornell, Steve, Adv. Asst.--Standard Register-Barrington, Barrington, IL; *U.S. Public*, pg. 1505
Cornish, George A., Mgr.-Adv. & Prod.--BNA Communications, Inc., Rockville, MD; *U.S. Private*, pg. 182
Cornog, R., Pres.--Broderick & Bascom Rope Co., Sedalia, MO; *U.S. Private*, pg. 68
Cornwall, Dave, Dir.-Adv.--Press Enterprise Company, Riverside, CA; *U.S. Public*, pg. 209
Cornwell, John, Mgr.-Corp. Mktg. & Pub. Affairs--3M, Saint Paul, MN; *U.S. Public*, pg. 1604
Corr, Van, Mgr.-Adv.--Midwest Industries, Inc., Ida Grove, IA; *U.S. Private*, pg. 744
Corradini, Vicky, Dir.-Adv.--Perugina Brands of America, Saddle Brook, NJ; *Int'l*, pg. 917
Corrigan, Eileen P., Dir.-Adv. & Sls. Promo.--Symbol Technologies, Inc., Holtsville, NY; *U.S. Public*, pg. 1546
Corsten, Josefine, Dir.-Corp. Commun.--KSB Aktiengesellschaft, Frankenthal, Germany; *Int'l*, pg. 721
Coryell, Debbie, Mgr.-Adv.--Jantzen, Portland, OR; *U.S. Public*, pg. 1702
Cosaert, John P., Chief Fin. Officer, Exec. V.P.-Intl. Fin., Treas. & Controller--Heartland Express, Inc., Coralville, IA; *U.S. Public*, pg. 803
Cosby, Mark, V.P.-Adv.--Edwards Super Food Stores, Carlisle, PA; *Int'l*, pg. 749
Cosby, Mark, V.P.-Adv. & Pub. Rels.--Giant Food Stores Inc., Carlisle, PA; *Int'l*, pg. 750
Cosby, Paige, Dir.-Corp. Communications--Coram Healthcare Corporation, Denver, CO; *U.S. Public*, pg. 446
Cosman, Gary, Mgr.-Adv.--Harris Semiconductor, Melbourne, FL; *U.S. Public*, pg. 792
Costanzo, Donald J., Dir.-Mktg. & Product Devel.--The Vernon Company, Newton, IA; *U.S. Private*, pg. 1137
Costanzo, Robert, Dir.-Adv.-Travel & Entertainment--Providence Journal-Bulletin, Providence, RI; *U.S. Public*, pg. 209
Costello, Christine, Dir.-Adv.--Express Newspapers plc, London, United Kingdom; *Int'l*, pg. 1443
Costello, Edward W., Dir.-Mktg. & Sls.--Polhemus Inc., Colchester, VT; *U.S. Private*, pg. 605
Costello, Wade, Mgr.-Mktg.--Bodine Assembly and Test Systems, Bridgeport, CT; *U.S. Private*, pg. 154
Couch, Huey, Mgr.-Adv.--Harp's Food Stores, Inc., Springdale, AR; *U.S. Private*, pg. 504
Coughlan, Anthony, Sr. Assoc.-Adv.--Bayer Corporation/Pharmaceutical Division, West Haven, CT; *Int'l*, pg. 173
Coughlin, Neil P., V.P.-Sls. & Mktg.--Kingsbury Corporation, Keene, NH; *U.S. Private*, pg. 621
Coulombe, Roland L., V.P.-Adv. & Opers.--Lawrence & Company, Lewiston, ME; *U.S. Private*, pg. 1173
Coulombe, Roland L., V.P.-Adv. & Opers.--Maine Bottlers, Lewiston, ME; *U.S. Private*, pg. 1173
Courtney, Bob, Asst. Dir.-Adv.--Sun TV & Appliances, Inc., Groveport, OH; *U.S. Public*, pg. 1532
Courtney, James D., Dir.-Mktg. Communications--Bethlehem Steel Corporation, Bethlehem, PA; *U.S. Public*, pg. 226
Covey, Stephen M.R., Exec. V.P.-Mktg. & Innovation--Franklin Covey, Salt Lake City, UT; *U.S. Public*, pg. 679
Cowen, Nancy, Dir.-Mktg. Svcs.--Borden, Inc., Columbus, OH; *U.S. Private*, pg. 157
Cowman, Chad, Dir.-Adv. & Mktg.--Drug Emporium, Inc., Powell, OH; *U.S. Public*, pg. 530
Cox, Carol, Dir.-Corp. Communications--Union Texas Petroleum Holdings, Houston, TX; *U.S. Public*, pg. 1669
Cox, Gary L., Mgr.-Mktg. & Sls.--Mitchel & Scott Machine Co., Inc., Indianapolis, IN; *U.S. Private*, pg. 753
Cox, Jerry, V.P.-Sls. & Mktg.--Union City Body Company, L.P., Union City, IN; *U.S. Private*, pg. 1118
Cox, Jim, Mgr.-Adv.--Ansul Incorporated, Marinette, WI; *U.S. Public*, pg. 1648
Cox, Patti, V.P.-Adv.--Pergament Home Centers, Inc., Melville, NY; *U.S. Private*, pg. 853
Coy, Bill, Mgr.-Support Communications--Royal Insurance, Charlotte, NC; *Int'l*, pg. 1130
Coyle, Christine, Mgr.-Bus./The American Enterprise--American Enterprise Institute for Public Policy Research, Washington, DC; *U.S. Private*, pg. 53
Crabb, Greg, Mgr.-Adv.--SouthTrust Corporation, Birmingham, AL; *U.S. Public*, pg. 1491
Crabtree, Susan, Dir.-Adv.--Lincoln National Corporation, Fort Wayne, IN; *U.S. Public*, pg. 997
Craghead, Greg, Mgr.-Adv.--Essex International, Inc., Fort Wayne, IN; *U.S. Public*, pg. 593
Cravath, L.M., Mgr.-Adv.--Ohmite Manufacturing Company, Skokie, IL; *U.S. Private*, pg. 813
Craven, James, Dir.-Adv./South East & Caribbean--Reed Travel Publishing-Miami, Hollywood, FL; *Int'l*, pg. 1097
Crawley, Bill, Brand Mgr.--Central and South West Corporation, Dallas, TX; *U.S. Public*, pg. 324
Creed, Pat, Exec. Sec.-Adv. Sls.--Playboy Enterprises, Inc., Chicago, IL; *U.S. Public*, pg. 1309
Cregar, Holly, Mgr.-Mktg.--TNT Vacations, Boston, MA; *U.S. Private*, pg. 1065
Crespo, Javier, Dir.-Commun.--Sol Melia, Palma de Mallorca, Spain; *Int'l*, pg. 1277
Crick, Robert, Mgr.-Mktg.--Benmar Marine Electronics, Inc., Santa Ana, CA; *U.S. Private*, pg. 133
Criner, Donald, Mgr.-Adv.--Elliott Company, Jeannette, PA; *U.S. Private*, pg. 373
Crisman, Richard, V.P.-Pub. Rels. & Adv.--The Gap, Inc., San Francisco, CA; *U.S. Public*, pg. 672
Crocker, Suzanne, Mgr.-Adv. & Promo.--The Toronto Dominion Bank, Toronto, Canada; *Int'l*, pg. 1401
Croft, Jerry L., Sr. V.P.-Adv. & Publr.--Century Publishing Company, Evanston, IL; *U.S. Private*, pg. 226
Croglio, Betty, Mgr.-Adv.--Dunlop Tire Corporation, Buffalo, NY; *Int'l*, pg. 1317
Cronkright, Roger, V.P.-Sls.--Interkal, Inc., Kalamazoo, MI; *Int'l*, pg. 759
Cronn, Mary, Coord.-Adv. & Admin. Asst.--Harcros Chemicals Inc., Kansas City, KS; *Int'l*, pg. 598
Crosby, Diane A., Mgr.-Adv.--Gussco Manufacturing, Inc., Brooklyn, NY; *U.S. Private*, pg. 488
Crosby, Julia, Mgr.-Adv.--Amoco Fabrics & Fibers Company, Atlanta, GA; *U.S. Public*, pg. 102
Crosland, Jo, Mgr.-Adv. & Corp. Communications-London Office--Investcorp International, New York, NY; *Int'l*, pg. 686
Cross, Bill, Grp. V.P.-Adv--Service Merchandise Company, Inc., Brentwood, TN; *U.S. Public*, pg. 1461
Crossen, Michael, Mgr.-Adv.--Sargent Manufacturing Company, New Haven, CT; *Int'l*, pg. 18
Crossen, Mike, Mgr.-Adv.--Essex Industries, New Haven, CT; *Int'l*, pg. 18
Crothers, Chicky, Mgr.-Adv.--Northrop Grumman Corporation, Los Angeles, CA; *U.S. Public*, pg. 1197
Crotty, Carole, Mgr.-Adv.--Landmark Systems Corporation, Vienna, VA; *U.S. Private*, pg. 649
Crotty, Robert S., V.P. & Dir.-Mktg.--Van Dyne-Crotty, Inc., Dayton, OH; *U.S. Private*, pg. 1132
Crouse, Nancy, V.P.-Sls. Admin.--Superba, Inc., Los Angeles, CA; *U.S. Private*, pg. 1054
Crowley, Mark M., V.P. & Mgr.-Corp. Adv.--National City Corporation, Cleveland, OH; *U.S. Public*, pg. 1154
Crowley, Stephen, V.P.-Mktg. & Sls.--Rome Cable Corporation, Rome, NY; *U.S. Private*, pg. 942
Crum, Brad, V.P.-Affiliate Adv. & Promo--CBS Broadcast Group, New York, NY; *U.S. Public*, pg. 274
Crum, Brad, V.P.-Affiliate Adv., Promo. & Network Projects--CBS Television Network, New York, NY; *U.S. Public*, pg. 274
Crum, John, Mgr.-Adv. Svcs., Elec.--The Lamson & Sessions Co., Cleveland, OH; *U.S. Public*, pg. 976
Crum, Niles D., Publr.--ID Magazine, New York, NY; *Int'l*, pg. 1446
Crumbaugh, Susan, Mgr.-Agency Devel.--State Farm Mutual Automobile Insurance Company, Bloomington, IL; *U.S. Private*, pg. 1036
Cruz, Carol, Coord.-Adv.--Caravan Brokay, Totowa, NJ; *U.S. Private*, pg. 208
Crye, Bob, Contract Administrator--ABB Environmental Systems (ABBES), Knoxville, TN; *Int'l*, pg. 4
Crylen, Paul, Mgr.-Adv.--Blue Cross & Blue Shield of Illinois, Chicago, IL; *U.S. Private*, pg. 151
Crystal, J. Scott, V.P. & Dir.-Adv.--National Geographic Magazine, Paris, France; *U.S. Private*, pg. 784
Crystal, Scott, V.P. & Dir.-Adv.--National Geographic Society, Washington, DC; *U.S. Private*, pg. 783
Csehill, John, Dir.-Mktg.--Admiral Maintenance Service L.P., Lincolnwood, IL; *U.S. Private*, pg. 17
Csepregi, Roger, Mgr.-Adv.--Gast Mfg. Corp., Benton Harbor, MI; *U.S. Private*, pg. 440
Cubell, Lee, Dir.-Mktg., Adv. & Pub. Rels.--Kingsdown, Inc., Mebane, NC; *U.S. Private*, pg. 622
Cudahy, Mike, Dir.-Mktg. Commun.--Farmers and Traders Life Insurance Co., Syracuse, NY; *U.S. Private*, pg. 394
Cueto, Debbie, Mgr.-Adv.--Aydin Displays (East), Horsham, PA; *U.S. Public*, pg. 158
Cullen, Cyril C., Mgr.-Opers.--Stebbins Engineering & Mfg. Co., Watertown, NY; *U.S. Private*, pg. 1037
Cullers-Delp, Carolyn, Dir.-Field Mktg., Promo. & Adv.--Max & Erma's Restaurants, Columbus, OH; *U.S. Public*, pg. 1060
Culley, P.L., Mgr.-Mktg. Communications--ABB Kent Plc, Luton, United Kingdom; *Int'l*, pg. 2
Culver, Robert, Dir.-Adv. Svcs.--The Okonite Company, Ramsey, NJ; *U.S. Private*, pg. 813
Cummings, Donald P., V.P.-Professional Hand Tools--Hyde Manufacturing Co., Southbridge, MA; *U.S. Private*, pg. 551
Cummins, Mike, Mgr.-Corp. Commun.--Clariant Corporation, Charlotte, NC; *Int'l*, pg. 624
Cunningham, Ina C., Mgr.-Adv.--CH2M Hill Companies, Ltd., Greenwood Village, CO; *U.S. Private*, pg. 195
Cunnold, F., Mgr.-Adv.--Weiser Inc., Burnaby, Canada; *U.S. Public*, pg. 1055
Curran, Kitty, Admin. Asst.-Adv. & Mktg.--Dahlberg, Inc., Golden Valley, MN; *U.S. Public*, pg. 194
Curran, Thomas P., V.P.-Adv.--Haverty Furniture Companies, Inc., Atlanta, GA; *U.S. Public*, pg. 799
Curtis, Alvin L., V.P.-Mktg.--Serigraph, Inc., West Bend, WI; *U.S. Private*, pg. 985
Curtis, Cheryl, Special Projects/Adv.--Cookie Tree Inc., Salt Lake City, UT; *U.S. Private*, pg. 273
Curtis, Kim, Mgr.-Creative & Design Svcs.--The Lincoln National Life Insurance Co., Fort Wayne, IN; *U.S. Public*, pg. 998
Curtis, Trumbull, Dir.-Adv. & Mktg. Services--BankBoston Corporation, Boston, MA; *U.S. Public*, pg. 183
Curto, D., Coord.-Mktg.--Echelon International Corporation, Saint Petersburg, FL; *U.S. Public*, pg. 560
Cusano, Donna, Dir.-Intl. Mktg. & Adv.--Avis Rent A Car System, Inc., Garden City, NY; *U.S. Public*, pg. 321
Cussman, Nancy, Corp. Mgr.-Communications--The West Company, Incorporated, Lionville, PA; *U.S. Public*, pg. 1755
Czapko, Ray, Mgr.-Adv.--Surco Products, Inc., Pittsburgh, PA; *U.S. Private*, pg. 1056
D'Aurora, Jackie, Dir.-Adv.--SuperValu, Inc.-Food Marketing Div., Fort Wayne, IN; *U.S. Public*, pg. 1540
Da Rola, Sonia, Mgr.-Pub. Rels.--Opticos S.r.l., Brembate di Sopra, Italy; *Int'l*, pg. 1007
Daboshi, Yoshikuni, Exec. Mng. Dir.--Kubota Corp., Osaka, Japan; *Int'l*, pg. 762
Dadiego, Sharon, Admin.-Sls. & Mktg.--Connors Brunswick, Inc., South Portland, ME; *U.S. Private*, pg. 264
Daffey, Lisa, Mgr.-Mktg. & Transportation--Freeman Energy Corporation, Springfield, IL; *U.S. Public*, pg. 709
Dahl, Cheri, Dir.-Devel.--Christian Children's Fund, Inc., Richmond, VA; *U.S. Private*, pg. 238
Dailey, Kenneth E., Gen. Mgr.--Seaman Timber Company, Inc., Montevallo, AL; *U.S. Private*, pg. 979
Daley, Kip, V.P.-Adv.--Regal Cinemas Inc., Knoxville, TN; *U.S. Public*, pg. 1371
Dallaire, Lucien, Mgr.-Sls. & Mktg.--NAPCO, Inc., Terryville, CT; *U.S. Public*, pg. 1592
Dallavo, C.J., Dir.-Adv.--Roberds, Inc., Carrollton, OH; *U.S. Public*, pg. 1393
Dalpe, Liz, Natl. Sls. Mgr.--Steven Manufacturing Co., Hermann, MO; *U.S. Private*, pg. 1042
Dalton, James S., V.P.-Sls.--Bardons & Oliver, Inc., Solon, OH; *U.S. Private*, pg. 116
Dalton, Linda, Adv.--The Lane Company, Inc., Altavista, VA; *U.S. Public*, pg. 688
Daly, George, Dir.-Adv.--Whessoe Varec, Cypress, CA; *Int'l*, pg. 1498
Daman, Tim, Dir.-Adv. & Mktg.--Spartan International Inc., Holt, MI; *U.S. Private*, pg. 1020
Damask, Donald, Sr. V.P.-Mktg.--Brown Group, Inc., Saint Louis, MO; *U.S. Public*, pg. 262
Dambrosio, Daniello, Dir.-Adv.--Procter & Gamble Health & Beauty Care So. Europe, Rome, Italy; *U.S. Public*, pg. 1332
Daneliuc, Rafael, Dir.-Adv.--Nestle Del Uruguay S.A., Montevideo, Uruguay; *Int'l*, pg. 921

Danenberg, Alan M., Mgr.-Mdsg. & Mktg. Commun.--Elkay Manufacturing Company, Oak Brook, IL; *U.S. Private,* pg. 372
Danford, Erica, Mgr.-Adv.--Killington Limited, Killington, VT; *U.S. Private,* pg. 61
Daniels, Jeremy, V.P.-Adv.--Dutton-Lainson Co., Hastings, NE; *U.S. Private,* pg. 350
Daniels, John, Mgr.-Bus. Devel.--Banner Aerospace, Inc., Washington, DC; *U.S. Public,* pg. 187
Danko, Dan, Mgr.-Mkt. Adv. & Special Projects--Mack Trucks, Inc., Allentown, PA; *Int'l,* pg. 1102
Darby, Fred W., Pres.--Niagara Transformer Corp., Buffalo, NY; *U.S. Private,* pg. 798
Darosa, Mario, V.P.-Mktg.--Sandvik/Milford Corporation, Branford, CT; *Int'l,* pg. 1185
Darr, Lauren, Mgr.-Mktg.--Harris Broadcast Division, Richmond, IN; *U.S. Public,* pg. 791
Darwin, Gary R., Exec. V.P.--Cardinal Inc., Rahway, NJ; *U.S. Private,* pg. 208
Daugherty, Paul J., Mgr.-Adv. & Mkt. Analyst--Sandusky International Inc., Sandusky, OH; *U.S. Private,* pg. 964
Davey, Beth, V.P. & Dir.-Publicity--Little, Brown & Co., New York, NY; *U.S. Public,* pg. 1612
Davidowitz, Suzie, V.P.-Corp. Pub. Rels.--Cosmair, Inc., New York, NY; *Int'l,* pg. 818
Davidson, Christopher, Dir.-Pub. Rel. & Corp. Communications--Guinness Plc, London, United Kingdom; *Int'l,* pg. 412
Davidson, Ronald, V.P.-Adv.--The Wichita Eagle and Beacon Publishing Co., Inc., Wichita, KS; *U.S. Public,* pg. 964
Davies, Richard E., Sr., Mgr.-Adv.--Bell Helicopter Textron, Hurst, TX; *U.S. Public,* pg. 1588
Davis-Fritsch, Doris, Mgr.-Mktg. Communications--Danka Office Imaging, Rochester, NY; *U.S. Public,* pg. 551
Davis, Aaron L., V.P.-Mktg.--American Power Conversion Corporation, West Kingston, RI; *U.S. Public,* pg. 89
Davis, Bob, Mgr.-Mktg. Commu.--Sunnen Products Company, Saint Louis, MO; *U.S. Private,* pg. 1053
Davis, Cathy, V.P.-Adv.--Phoenix Newspapers, Inc., Phoenix, AZ; *U.S. Public,* pg. 326
Davis, Darren, Mgr.-Adv.--Trimark Holdings, Inc., Santa Monica, CA; *U.S. Public,* pg. 1638
Davis, Deborah, Mgr.-Adv.--Exact Equipment Corporation, Langhorne, PA; *U.S. Private,* pg. 387
Davis, DeForest P., Jr., Chm. Bd. & Chief Exec. Officer--Lester B. Knight & Associates, Inc., Chicago, IL; *U.S. Private,* pg. 626
Davis, Dennis, V.P.-Adv., Sls. & Mktg.--Davis Wood Products, Inc., Hudson, NC; *U.S. Private,* pg. 315
Davis, Doug, V.P.-Mktg.--B&B Corporate Holdings, Inc., Tampa, FL; *U.S. Private,* pg. 104
Davis, J. Dan, V.P.-Sls. & Mktg.--Prym-Dritz Corporation, Spartanburg, SC; *Int'l,* pg. 1499
Davis, James M., Sr. V.P.-Mktg. & Adv.--Quality Stores Inc., Muskegon, MI; *U.S. Private,* pg. 899
Davis, Jeffrey, Dir.-Mktg. & Adv.--Tuffy Associates Corp., Toledo, OH; *U.S. Private,* pg. 1109
Davis, Julie, Mgr.-Adv.--Callaway Golf Company, Carlsbad, CA; *U.S. Public,* pg. 294
Davis, Larry C., V.P.-Adv.--Kmart Corporation, Troy, MI; *U.S.* Public, pg. 963
Davis, Michelle, Mktg. & Adv.--Howell Instruments Inc., Fort Worth, TX; *U.S. Private,* pg. 543
Davis, Mickey, Sr. V.P.-Mktg.--Plasti-Line, Inc., Knoxville, TN; *U.S. Public,* pg. 1308
Davis, Mike, Mgr.-Mktg. & Adv.--Flavor House Products, Inc., Dothan, AL; *U.S. Private,* pg. 410
Davis, Mike, V.P.-Entertainment Div.--Disneyland, Anaheim, CA; *U.S. Public,* pg. 511
Davis, Nancy, Mgr.-Adv.--Linotype-Hell Company, Hauppauge, NY; *Int'l,* pg. 604
Davis, Neil, Dir.-Adv.--Lowe's Food Stores, Inc., Winston Salem, NC; *U.S. Private,* pg. 657
Davis, Penny, Mgr.-Adv. & Promo. Tourbook--St. Martins Press, Inc., New York, NY; *Int'l,* pg. 1479
Davis, Ray, Pres.--SunGard Employee Benefits Systems, Birmingham, AL; *U.S. Public,* pg. 1534
Davis, Sally, Mgr.-Adv.--Gaston County Dyeing Machine Co., Mount Holly, NC; *U.S. Private,* pg. 441
Davis, Shea, Asst. V.P. & Dir.-Corp. Commun.--Quorum Health Group, Inc., Brentwood, TN; *U.S. Public,* pg. 1353
Dawahare, Michael, Dir.-Adv. & Media--Dawahares, Inc., Lexington, KY; *U.S. Private,* pg. 316
Dawson, Bill, Dir.-Corp. Communications--Gelman Sciences, Inc., Ann Arbor, MI; *U.S. Public,* pg. 1253
Dawson, William R., Dir.-Adv.--Redding Record Searchlight, Redding, CA; *U.S. Public,* pg. 1448
Day, Leslie, Dir.-Mktg.--Bar-S Foods Co., Phoenix, AZ; *U.S. Private,* pg. 114
Day, R., Mgr.-Adv.--Festo Corporation, Hauppauge, NY; *Int'l,* pg. 480
Day, Stephanie M., V.P.-Corp. Commun.--California Microwave, Inc., Sunnyvale, CA; *U.S. Public,* pg. 293
Dayan, Allison, Dir.-Adv.--The Atlantic Monthly Magazine, Boston, MA; *U.S. Private,* pg. 95
De Angelo, Joe, V.P.-Adv.--Penn-Daniels, Inc., Quincy, IL; *U.S. Public,* pg. 1467
de Brsissia, Patrice, Mgr.-Adv.--Credit Commercial de France, Paris, France; *Int'l,* pg. 341
De Keersmaecker, L., Mgr.-Adv., Sls. Promo. & Direct Mktg.--Sabena, Zaventem, Belgium; *Int'l,* pg. 1168
De Lisser, Delia, Sr. Dir.-Adv.--Avon Products, Inc., New York, NY; *U.S. Public,* pg. 155
de Marzi, Fedora, Dir.-Mktg.--Industrias Pacocha S.A. (Unilever), Lima, Peru; *Int'l,* pg. 1437
de Monnink, Peter, Deputy Dir.-Adv.--Bonaventura, Amsterdam, Netherlands; *Int'l,* pg. 1099
de Mouline, Jacqueline, Dir.-Adv.--Nestle Italiana S.P.A., Milan, Italy; *Int'l,* pg. 921
De Paolis, L. Andrew, V.P.-Adv. & Mktg.--The Grand Union Company, Wayne, NJ; *U.S. Public,* pg. 758
De Quesada, Raul, V.P.-Adv. & Sls.--Travel Channel-Latin America, Miami, FL; *U.S. Private,* pg. 647
De Roy Vanzunewijn, Rudolph F., Mgr.-Adv.--OPEL Nederland B.V., Sliedrecht, Netherlands; *U.S. Public,* pg. 723
de Vasconcelos, Walter Nunes, Jr., Mgr.-Promo. & Adv.--Banco do Brasil, Brasilia, Brazil; *Int'l,* pg. 141
De Waal, John, Dir.-Adv.--New Era Cap. Co., Derby, NY; *U.S. Private,* pg. 793
de Zuniga, Rose, Mgr.-Adv.--Aviateca, Guatemala, Guatemala; *Int'l,* pg. 102
Deakins, Nancy, Mgr.-Adv.--Hardwick Clothes Inc., Cleveland, TN; *U.S. Private,* pg. 502
Dean, Henry, Pres.--Monticello Drug Co., Jacksonville, FL; *U.S. Private,* pg. 759
Deary, Grant, Co.-Chm. Bd. & Pres.--Nor-Cal Beverage Co., Inc., West Sacramento, CA; *U.S. Private,* pg. 801
DeBerry, James, Mgr.-Adv.--AGL Resources, Atlanta, GA; *U.S. Public,* pg. 6
Debiase, Mark, Mgr.-Adv. & Mktg. Svcs.--Grinnell Corporation, Exeter, NH; *U.S. Public,* pg. 1651
Debrodt, Donna, Dir.-Mktg.--Compuware Corporation, Farmington Hills, MI; *U.S. Public,* pg. 423
Dechow, Anne J., Mgr.-Adv./Msdg.--Delco Electronics Corporation, Kokomo, IN; *U.S. Public,* pg. 720
Decker, Dave, Coord.-Mktg.--Dwyer Instruments Inc., Michigan City, IN; *U.S. Private,* pg. 350
Decker, Lisa, Assoc. V.P.--Cache, Inc., New York, NY; *U.S. Public,* pg. 289
Decker, Lois, Mgr.-Adv.--Crowley, Milner & Company, Detroit, MI; *U.S. Public,* pg. 461
Decker, Lois, Mgr.-Adv.--Steinbach Stores, Inc., Detroit, MI; *U.S. Public,* pg. 461
Dedmond, Dennis, Dir.-Mktg.--Nakano Foods Inc., Arlington Heights, IL; *Int'l,* pg. 883
Deegan, Mary, Sec.--H.J. Baker & Bro., Inc., Stamford, CT; *U.S. Private,* pg. 112
Deets, John, Mgr.-Technical Publications--Howell Instruments Inc., Fort Worth, TX; *U.S. Private,* pg. 543
Degelman, Jack, Mgr.-Mktg.--Degelman Industries Ltd., Regina, Canada; *Int'l,* pg. 388
DeGood, Paul W., Mgr.-Mktg. Services--M.C. Gill Corporation, El Monte, CA; *U.S. Private,* pg. 453
Degraff, John, Mgr.-Mktg.--Jones Dairy Farm, Fort Atkinson, WI; *U.S. Private,* pg. 596
Deines, Shelly, Dir.-Corp. Adv.--MacMillan Bloedel Limited, Vancouver, Canada; *Int'l,* pg. 828
Del Beccaro, Lisa, Dir.-Adv. & Pub. Rels.--International Flavors & Fragrances, Inc., New York, NY; *U.S. Public,* pg. 898
Del Belso, Richard, Sr. V.P.-Worldwide Adv. & Mktg. Res.--Warner Bros. Studios, Inc., Burbank, CA; *U.S. Public,* pg. 1611
Del Cueto, Francisco, Dir.-Adv.--Industrias CH, S.A. de C.V., Tlalnepantla, Mexico; *Int'l,* pg. 677
Del Valle, Egnacio, Mgr.-Mktg. & Adv.--Bacardi Centroamerica, S.A., Panama, Panama; *Int'l,* pg. 132
Delacroix, Alain, Dir.-Adv.--Robert Bosch (France) SA, Saint Ouen, France; *Int'l,* pg. 205
Delaney, Marnie, Sr. V.P. & Dir.-Adv. & Mktg. Communcaitons--BankAmerica Corporation, San Francisco, CA; *U.S. Public,* pg. 179
Delany, George, Pres.--Powermatic, McMinnville, TN; *U.S. Public,* pg. 502
Delea, Lois, Mgr.-Corp. Communications--Selective Insurance Group, Inc, Branchville, NJ; *U.S. Public,* pg. 1455
Deleski, Joe, Dir.-Adv.--Kawai America Corporation, Compton, CA; *Int'l,* pg. 725
DelGandio, Christine, Mgr.-Natl. Adv.--Marriott International, Inc., Washington, DC; *U.S. Public,* pg. 1047
Delia, Patricia M., Mgr.-Adv.--Associated Testing Laboratories, Inc., Burlington, MA; *U.S. Public,* pg. 1341
Dellacqueila, Rick, V.P.-Adv. & Production Svcs.--Mattel, Inc., El Segundo, CA; *U.S. Public,* pg. 1057
DeLonghi, Charles S., Mgr.-Bus. Unit--ITW Woodworth, Ferndale, MI; *U.S. Public,* pg. 867
DeLozier, D. Barrett, Mgr.-Adv.--Energen Corporation, Birmingham, AL; *U.S. Public,* pg. 581
DeLuca, John, Dir.-Adv.--The Cosmetic Center Inc., Columbia, MD; *U.S. Private,* pg. 689
Deluca, Peter, V.P.-Adv.--Charles Schwab & Co. Inc., San Francisco, CA; *U.S. Public,* pg. 1443
Demaio, Joseph, Mgr.-Adv.--Magnetic Analysis Corp., Mount Vernon, NY; *U.S. Private,* pg. 695
DeMartini, David P., Pres.-Chief Oper. Officer & Merger/ Acquisitions Contact--Mitsui Foods, Inc., Norwood, NJ; *Int'l,* pg. 879
Demers, Richard P., V.P.-Mktg., Sls. & Adv.--EnergyNorth, Inc., Manchester, NH; *U.S. Public,* pg. 581
Demmerle, Stephanie, Coord.-Adv.--KLM Royal Dutch Airlines, Elmsford, NY; *Int'l,* pg. 719
Demos, Mark, Mgr.-Adv.--Weyco Group, Inc., Milwaukee, WI; *U.S. Public,* pg. 1763
DeNardin, Tom, V.P.-Mktg. & Adv.--Thrifty Rent-a-Car System, Inc., Tulsa, OK; *U.S. Public,* pg. 354
Denig, Kaaryn, V.P. & Dir.-Mktg. & Adv.--Jordache Enterprises, Inc., New York, NY; *U.S. Private,* pg. 597
Denise, Robert, Chm. Bd., Pres., Chief Exec. Officer & Chief Fin. Officer--Bucilla Corporation, Hazleton, PA; *U.S.* Private, pg. 352
Densmore, Tom, Dir.-Sls. & Mktg.--Whitfield Foods, Inc., Montgomery, AL; *U.S. Private,* pg. 1173
DePaola, Grace, Dir.-Adv.--Bell Atlantic Mobile, Bedminster, NJ; *U.S. Public,* pg. 202
DePaola, Kenneth, V.P.-Adv.--Chicago Sun Times, Chicago, IL; *Int'l,* pg. 632
DePeau, Norman, Dir.-Sls. & Mktg.--Lewis Engineering Company, Naugatuck, CT; *U.S. Public,* pg. 402
Depuy, Shelley, Dir.-Mktg.--Tokheim Corporation, Fort Wayne, IN; *U.S. Public,* pg. 1620
Derby, Michael, Dir.-Mktg. & Adv.--Seed Corporation of America, Baltimore, MD; *U.S. Private,* pg. 981
Derby, Michael P., Dir.-Adv.--Green Seed Co., Baltimore, MD; *U.S. Private,* pg. 477
DeRose, Camille, Dir.-Mktg.--The Gibson-Homans Company, Twinsburg, OH; *U.S. Private,* pg. 451
DeRousse, Edwina, Mgr.-Corp. Commun.--Coherent, Inc., Santa Clara, CA; *U.S. Public,* pg. 395
Derusha, Alfert, Dir.-Adv.--Great Lakes Media, Inc., Pontiac, MI; *U.S. Public,* pg. 513
DeSalme, Carla, Adv. & Promo. Asst.--Six Flags St. Louis, Eureka, MO; *U.S. Public,* pg. 1612
DeSantis, Pat, Mgr.-Adv. & Publicity--Boye Needle, Chicago, IL; *U.S. Private,* pg. 1192
Desantis, Patricia, V.P.-Sls. Promo.--Wm. E. Wright Limited Partnership, West Warren, MA; *U.S. Private,* pg. 1192
DeSantos, Minda, Mgr.-Mktg.--Philippine Airlines, Inc., San Francisco, CA; *Int'l,* pg. 1051
Desatvich, Rob, V.P.-Global Adv. Svcs.--Campbell Soup Company, Camden, NJ; *U.S. Public,* pg. 298
Desbien, Robert, Mgr.-Adv.--Southern States Cooperative, Inc., Richmond, VA; *U.S. Private,* pg. 1017
Desfosses, Anyk, Coord.-Adv. & Mdsg.--Peerless Carpet Corporation, Acton Vale, Canada; *Int'l,* pg. 1032
DeShano, Don, V.P.-Mktg. & Adv.--LaSalle Bristol Corp., Elkhart, IN; *Int'l,* pg. 618
Despres, Germain L., Exec. V.P.--Danisco Ingredients USA, Inc., New Century, KS; *Int'l,* pg. 378
DeStefano, James L., Pres. & Chief Exec. Officer--Emcee Broadcast Products, Inc., White Haven, PA; *U.S. Public,* pg. 570
DeStefano, Michael, V.P.-Mktg./Adv.--Mercantile Stores Company, Inc., Fairfield, OH; *U.S. Public,* pg. 1089
Deterding, Mark, V.P. & Gen. Mgr.--Banta Publications Group, Long Prairie, MN; *U.S. Public,* pg. 188
Detling, Bill, Dir.-Adv.--Delta Foremost Chemical Corp., Memphis, TN; *U.S. Private,* pg. 322
DeTomaso, Steve, Mgr.-Adv. & Sls.--Sachs Boge of America, Westlake, OH; *Int'l,* pg. 835
DeTour, Walter, V.P.-Mktg. & Sls.--Universal Photonics, Inc., Hicksville, NY; *U.S. Private,* pg. 1127
Deutsch, Ellen, V.P.-Mktg.--The Hain Food Group Inc., Uniondale, NY; *U.S. Public,* pg. 774
Devenzio, Huck, Mgr.-Adv. & Pub. Rels.--Hickson Corporation, Smyrna, GA; *Int'l,* pg. 619
Devine, Beth, Dir.-Mktg.--Plasticrete Block & Supply Corp., North Haven, CT; *U.S. Private,* pg. 871
Devinney, Debbie, Dir.-Graphics--Continental Plastic Card Co., Coral Springs, FL; *U.S. Private,* pg. 269
Devlin, Allison, Dir.-Adv.--DK Publishing, New York, NY; *Int'l,* pg. 417
Devlin, Joseph V., Dir.-Adv.--Iveco Trucks Of North America Inc., Bensalem, PA; *Int'l,* pg. 484
Dewar, Brent, Mgr.-Adv.--General Motors do Brasil Ltda., Sao Caetano do Sul, Brazil; *U.S. Public,* pg. 722
Dewar, Susan, V.P.-Mktg. & Adv.--Markel Corporation, Glen Allen, VA; *U.S. Public,* pg. 1046
Dey, Rebecca, Mgr.-Adv. & Pub. Rels.--Whitney Holding Corporation, New Orleans, LA; *U.S. Public,* pg. 1766
Di Bartolomeo, Diana, Adv. Asst.--FAG Bearings Corporation, Danbury, CT; *Int'l,* pg. 469
Di Muro, Marinella, Mgr.-Adv.--Dateo Import S.P.A., Milan, Italy; *Int'l,* pg. 385
Di Zazzo, James G., Pres.--Oomphies, Inc., Lawrence, MA; *U.S. Private,* pg. 817
Diage, Mickey, Dir.-Adv.--Capitol Records, Inc., Hollywood, CA; *Int'l,* pg. 428
Dias, Georgio, Mgr.-Sls.--Overholtzer Church Furniture, Inc., Modesto, CA; *U.S. Private,* pg. 823
Dicken, Cindy, Mgr.-Communications & Adv.--Providian Agency Group, Louisville, KY; *Int'l,* pg. 27
Dickhoff, Bill, Dir.-Sls., Mktg. & Adv.--Roofing Wholesale Co., Inc., Phoenix, AZ; *U.S. Private,* pg. 943
Dickie, D. Kent, Dir.-Mktg.--McGean-Rohco, Inc., Cleveland, OH; *U.S. Private,* pg. 721
Dickinson, Carol, Dir.-Customer Rels.--Seattle City Light, Seattle, WA; *U.S. Private,* pg. 979
Dickinson, Doug, Mgr.-Adv.--Linear Technology Corp., Milpitas, CA; *U.S. Public,* pg. 1000
Dickman, Sheila, Mgr.-Adv.--Provident Financial Group, Inc., Cincinnati, OH; *U.S. Public,* pg. 1338
Dickman, Sheila, Mgr.-Adv.--The Provident Bank, Cincinnati, OH; *U.S. Public,* pg. 1338
Dickson, James G., Jr., Sr. V.P.--Prime Bancshares Inc., Houston, TX; *U.S. Public,* pg. 1326
Didlick, Andrew, Mgr.-Adv.--Peugeot Motor Co. Plc, Coventry, United Kingdom; *Int'l,* pg. 1021
Diebel, Craig, V.P. & Dir.-Adv.--Star-Telegram Newspaper, Inc., Fort Worth, TX; *U.S. Public,* pg. 964
Dieckman, Christine, Dir.-Mktg.--New Plan Realty Trust, New York, NY; *U.S. Public,* pg. 1172
Diedrick, Arthur Hill, Chm. Bd.--Communications International (NY), New York, NY; *U.S. Private,* pg. 259
Diehl, Don, Art Dir.--Harleysville Group, Harleysville, PA; *U.S. Public,* pg. 786
DiEleonora, Mary Beth, Mgr.-Adv.--Brooks Instrument, Hatfield, PA; *U.S. Public,* pg. 574
Dielske, Krista, Asst. Mgr.-Adv.--Multi-Clean Inc., Shoreview, MN; *Int'l,* pg. 587
Diemer, Susan, Mgr.-Product Devel.--Candle-Lite, A Lancaster Colony Co., Cincinnati, OH; *U.S. Public,* pg. 976
Dietheln, Zack, Dir.-Adv.--Deutsche Bahn, Frankfurt/Main, Germany; *Int'l,* pg. 401
Dietrich, Lovonne, V.P.-Sls. & Mktg.--Stella Foods, Inc., Green Bay, WI; *U.S. Private,* pg. 1040
Dietrich, Wendell, Chm. Bd. & Chief Exec. Officer--Vidar, Inc., New London, MN; *U.S. Private,* pg. 1139
Dietrick, Steve, Dir.-Promo. & Adv.--Sea World of Texas, San Antonio, TX; *U.S. Public,* pg. 114
Dilcher, Richard, Mgr.-Sls.--Patterson Laboratories, Inc., Detroit, MI; *U.S. Private,* pg. 843
Dill, Sheri, V.P.-Mktg.--The Wichita Eagle and Beacon Publishing Co., Inc., Wichita, KS; *U.S. Public,* pg. 964
DiMasi, Steve, Dir.-Adv.--PRO Group, Inc., Englewood, CO; *U.S. Private,* pg. 887
DiMatteo, Carmen, Sr. V.P.-Services & Sls.--Semco Industries Inc., Stoughton, MA; *U.S. Private,* pg. 983

DiMingo, Ed, Dir.-Corp. Commun.--Kulicke & Soffa Industries, Inc., Willow Grove, PA; *U.S. Public*, pg. 968
Dimmick, Rhonda, Dir.-Mktg.--Security Lawn & Garden Co., Phoenix, AZ; *U.S. Private*, pg. 397
Dinkel, Linda, V.P.--Andover Bancorp, Inc., Andover, MA; *U.S. Public*, pg. 111
Dinsdale, Chris, Pres.-Tillamook Food Sls.--Tillamook County Creamery Assn., Tillamook, OR; *U.S. Private*, pg. 1086
DiPaolo, Tony, Pres.--Jos. M. Herman Shoe Co., Armonk, NY; *U.S. Private*, pg. 524
Dippel, Clem, Dir.-Sls. & Adv.--Fishing Tackle Retailer, Montgomery, AL; *U.S. Private*, pg. 105
DiPrimio, Anne, Mgr.-Commun.--Cole Hersee Company, Boston, MA; *U.S. Private*, pg. 251
Dirat, Henri, Mgr.-Communications--Compaq Computer S.A.R.L., Les Ulis, France; *U.S. Public*, pg. 418
Disantis, Dee, Dir.-Adv.--Phar-Mor, Inc., Youngstown, OH; *U.S. Public*, pg. 1284
Disbrow, Daphne, Dir.-Adv.--Resorts Casino Hotel, Atlantic City, NJ; *U.S. Public*, pg. 1531
DiTrolio, Lisa, Sls. Promo. Admin.--Ronson Corporation, Somerset, NJ; *U.S. Public*, pg. 1405
Ditto, Laura, Mgr.-Adv. & Mktg.--Central Mutual Insurance Co., Van Wert, OH; *U.S. Private*, pg. 223
Diver, Deb, Dir.-Adv. & Retail Sls.--360 Degrees Communications Company, Chicago, IL; *U.S. Public*, pg. 1607
Dix, Bill, Chief Commercial Officer--The Eurotunnel Group, London, United Kingdom; *Int'l*, pg. 466
Dixon, Diane B., V.P.-Worldwide Communications & Adv.--Avery Dennison Corporation, Pasadena, CA; *U.S. Public*, pg. 152
Dobel, Betsy, Dir.-Adv.--Norwest Corporation, Minneapolis, MN; *U.S. Public*, pg. 1201
Dobrowski, Norm, Dir.-Adv. & Sls. Promo.--Maremont Exhaust Systems Product Division, Loudon, TN; *U.S. Public*, pg. 137
Dobson, Kate, Assoc. Publr. & Dir.-Adv.--Scientific American, Inc., New York, NY; *Int'l*, pg. 1479
Dobson, Rich, Sr. V.P.-Adv.--Milwaukee Journal Sentinel, Milwaukee, WI; *U.S. Private*, pg. 601
Dodea, Renee, Admin.-Mktg. Communications--Thomas & Betts Electronics Division, Memphis, TN; *U.S. Public*, pg. 1597
Dodge, Ally, Sr. Mgr.-Media & Sls. Promo.--Pier 1 Imports, Inc., Fort Worth, TX; *U.S. Public*, pg. 1295
Dodge, Larry, Dir.-Sls. & Mktg.--Booth Newspapers, Inc., Grand Rapids, MI; *U.S. Private*, pg. 157
Dodge, Laura F., Dir.-Mktg. & Adv.--Dodge Regupol, Inc., Lancaster, PA; *U.S. Private*, pg. 337
Dodson, Larry, Mgr.-Sls.--North American Royalties, Inc., Chattanooga, TN; *U.S. Private*, pg. 803
Doeckel, Bill, Dir.-Adv.--Ball Horticultural Company, West Chicago, IL; *U.S. Private*, pg. 112
Doench, Debra, Mgr.-Corp. Communications--Hobart Brothers Co., Troy, OH; *U.S. Public*, pg. 866
Doenik, Ulihe, Mgr.-Adv. & Mktg.--Bayerische Vereinsbank Group, Munich, Germany; *Int'l*, pg. 178
Doer, Jayne, Mgr.-Adv. Promo.--Clipper Belt Lacer Company, Grand Rapids, MI; *U.S. Private*, pg. 413
Dombrowski, Wendy, Dir.-Adv.--Mirage Resorts Incorporated, Las Vegas, NV; *U.S. Public*, pg. 1116
Domenge, Muriel, Dir.-Pub. Rels.--Bongrain S.A., Viroflay, France; *Int'l*, pg. 201
Dominguez, Laura, Mgr.-Adv.--Telefonica Publicidad e Informac., Madrid, Spain; *Int'l*, pg. 1372
Donabauer, Mike, Dir.-Wolverine Footwear Grp.--Wolverine World Wide, Inc., Rockford, MI; *U.S. Public*, pg. 1775
Donaghue, Mary Jane, Mgr.-Adv.--SPS Technologies, Inc., Jenkintown, PA; *U.S. Public*, pg. 1419
Donahue, Robert, V.P. & Adv. Mgr.--Bank of Boston Connecticut, Hartford, CT; *U.S. Public*, pg. 184
Donaldson, David, Mgr.-Adv.--Sony Music Entertainment (UK) Limited, London, United Kingdom; *Int'l*, pg. 1284
Donaldson, P. Kit, V.P.-Mktg. & Adv.--Man-Gill Chemical Company, Cleveland, OH; *U.S. Private*, pg. 699
Donnan, Kirk, Mgr.-Adv.--Mindscape, Inc., Novato, CA; *Int'l*, pg. 1026
Donnell, Thomas, Pres.--Cain's Coffee Co., Oklahoma City, OK; *U.S. Public*, pg. 351
Donnelly, Bob, Dir.-Adv.--Winston Tire Company, Burbank, CA; *U.S. Private*, pg. 514
Donohue, Stephen B., Dir.-Specialized Adv.--Engineering News-Record Magazine, New York, NY; *U.S. Public*, pg. 1070
Donovan, Mary, Sr. V.P.-Publicity--New Line Cinema Corporation, New York, NY; *U.S. Public*, pg. 1614
Doodson, N., Adv. Mgr.--Deminex UK Oil and Gas Ltd., London, United Kingdom; *Int'l*, pg. 1461
Doolittle, James H., Pres. & Chief Oper. Officer--Time Warner Cable, Stamford, CT; *U.S. Public*, pg. 1610
Dooner, Mary Anne, Mgr.-Admin.--Weldotron Corporation, Piscataway, NJ; *U.S. Public*, pg. 1752
Doornenbal, Fritz, Mgr.-Adv.--Polygram N.V., Baarn, Netherlands; *Int'l*, pg. 1051
Doran, Cork, Mgr.-Adv. & Office Mgr.--Ace Doran Hauling & Rigging Company, Cincinnati, OH; *U.S. Private*, pg. 340
Doran, Cork, Mgr.-Adv.--Ace Doran Brokerage, Cincinnati, OH; *U.S. Private*, pg. 340
Dorfman, Robert, Pres.--King Wire Inc., North Chicago, IL; *U.S. Private*, pg. 621
Doria, Robert, Chief Fin. Officer & V.P.--Chipwich Inc., Ridgewood, NJ; *U.S. Private*, pg. 237
Dorman, Larry, V.P.-Adv.--Callaway Golf Company, Carlsbad, CA; *U.S. Public*, pg. 294
Dorme, Patrick J., Chief Fin. Officer & V.P.-Fin.--Dynamics Corporation of America, Greenwich, CT; *U.S. Public*, pg. 286
Dorris, William C., V.P.-Corp. Devel. & Tech.--Lilly Industries, Inc., Indianapolis, IN; *U.S. Public*, pg. 994
Doss, Kent, V.P.-Sls.-U.S.--Tambrands Inc., Cincinnati, OH; *U.S. Public*, pg. 1331
Doty, Tim, Mgr.-Adv. Display--The Dispatch Printing Company, Columbus, OH; *U.S. Private*, pg. 334
Dougherty, Gavin, Mgr.-Adv.--AST Research Inc., Irvine, CA; *Int'l*, pg. 1181
Dow, Jerry, Mgr.-Mktg. Commun.--Pella Corporation, Pella, IA; *U.S. Private*, pg. 848
Dow, Rick, V.P.-Mktg. Programs & Worldwide Adv.--Northwest Airlines, Inc., Saint Paul, MN; *U.S. Public*, pg. 1200
Dow, Sarah, Mgr.-Mktg. Commun.--Vermeer Manufacturing Company, Pella, IA; *U.S. Private*, pg. 1137
Dowd, Tom, Mgr.-Adv.--Hardings, Inc., Elmira, NY; *U.S. Private*, pg. 502
Dowis, Randy, Dir.-Mktg.--NHT, Benicia, CA; *U.S. Public*, pg. 1369
Dowling, G.A., Mgr.-Adv.--Kaufman Footwear, Kitchener, Canada; *Int'l*, pg. 725
Downes, John F., V.P.-Mktg. & Branch Admin.--Prime Bancorp, Inc., Fort Washington, PA; *U.S. Public*, pg. 1326
Downing, Dolores K., Mngmt. Asst.-Outside Sls.--Linde Hydraulics Corporation, Canfield, OH; *Int'l*, pg. 810
Doyle, David, First V.P.-Consumer Mktg.--Countrywide Home Loans Inc., Pasadena, CA; *U.S. Public*, pg. 452
Doyle, Jim, V.P.-Mktg. & Sls.--A. Finkl & Sons Co., Chicago, IL; *U.S. Private*, pg. 405
Doyle, John F., Sr. V.P.-Mktg. & Field Admin.--General Accident Insurance, Philadelphia, PA; *Int'l*, pg. 543
Doyle, Katie, V.P.-Adv. & Mktg.--McKesson Corporation, San Francisco, CA; *U.S. Public*, pg. 1072
Doyle, Tara, Adv. Coord.--Mastercard International, Inc., Purchase, NY; *U.S. Private*, pg. 714
Doyle, Willie, Mgr.-Adv.--Lands' End, Inc., Dodgeville, WI; *U.S. Public*, pg. 977
Drake, Kerlin, Dir.-Adv.--Anthony Forest Products Co., Inc., El Dorado, AR; *U.S. Private*, pg. 76
Drasher, Glenn D., Exec. V.P.-Mktg.--Buffets, Inc., Eden Prairie, MN; *U.S. Public*, pg. 267
Dreier, Kathy, Adv. Coord.--Abbey Etna Machine Company, Perrysburg, OH; *U.S. Private*, pg. 9
Drescher, David, V.P.-Adv.--Jockey International, Inc., Kenosha, WI; *U.S. Private*, pg. 588
Dresner, Mark, Dir.-Corp. Communications--Engelhard Corporation, Iselin, NJ; *U.S. Public*, pg. 582
Drever, K., Mgr.-Pub. Affairs--ATCO Group Co., Calgary, Canada; *Int'l*, pg. 95
Drexinger, Jim, V.P.-Mktg. & Sls.--NIBCO, Inc., Elkhart, IN; *U.S. Private*, pg. 798
Driscoll, John P., Exec. V.P.--Murata Electronics North America, Inc., Smyrna, GA; *Int'l*, pg. 897
Driver, Jody, Mgr.-Adv. & Pub. Rels.--Kraft Food Ingredients Corp., Memphis, TN; *U.S. Public*, pg. 1288
Drumm, Hughes D., V.P.-Adv. & Pub. Rels.--Stewart Enterprises, Inc., Metairie, LA; *U.S. Public*, pg. 1518
Drury, Lisa, Adv. Asst.--Bargain Supply Company, Louisville, KY; *U.S. Private*, pg. 116
Dubas, Leonard, V.P.-Mktg. & Adv.--Angelo Brothers Co., Philadelphia, PA; *U.S. Private*, pg. 74
Dube, Michel, V.P. & Bus. Mgr.-Flex Compounds--Synergistics Industries Limited, Mississauga, Canada; *U.S. Public*, pg. 734
Dubin, Howard S., Chm. Bd. & Chief Exec. Officer--Manufacturers' News, Inc., Evanston, IL; *U.S. Private*, pg. 700
Duckworth, Amanda, Dir.-Corp. Commun.--NationsBank Montgomery Securities LLC, San Francisco, CA; *U.S. Public*, pg. 1162
Dudgeon, Kathy, Mgr.-Consumer Promo. & Adv.--Oscar Mayer Foods Corp., Madison, WI; *U.S. Public*, pg. 1288
Dudowicz, Frank, Mgr.-Adv.--Quaker State Corporation, Irving, TX; *U.S. Public*, pg. 1348
Duer, Doug, Coord.-Adv.--Manitowoc Ice, Inc., Manitowoc, WI; *U.S. Public*, pg. 1041
DuFault, Paulette, Sr. V.P.-Adv. & Creative Services--Elizabeth Arden Company, New York, NY; *Int'l*, pg. 1435
Duff, Kim, Mgr.-Adv.--Blue Shield of California, San Francisco, CA; *U.S. Private*, pg. 153
Duffus, Cheryl, Asst. V.P. & Mgr.-Mktg.--Pacific Capital Bancorp, Salinas, CA; *U.S. Public*, pg. 1247
Duffy, Peter A., V.P.-Sls. & Mktg.--Haskel International, Inc., Burbank, CA; *U.S. Public*, pg. 798
Duffy, Teresa, Mgr.-Commun.--I.C. System, Inc., Vadnais Heights, MN; *U.S. Private*, pg. 553
Dugan, Sherman E., Chief Info. Officer & V.P.-Pub. Rels.--Dugan Production Corp., Farmington, NM; *U.S. Private*, pg. 345
Dugan, Sherman E., Mgr.-Adv.--Dugan Production Corp., Farmington, NM; *U.S. Private*, pg. 345
Duggan, Michael, Pres.--Melard Manufacturing Corporation, Passaic, NJ; *U.S. Private*, pg. 729
Dugo, Barbara, Mgr.-Adv.--Butera Finer Foods Inc., Elgin, IL; *U.S. Private*, pg. 189
Duguid, Mike, Dir.-Adv., Pub. Rels. & Mktg.--York International Corporation, York, PA; *U.S. Public*, pg. 1789
Dumars, Kelly, Dir.-Adv.--Mobile Telecommunications Technologies Corp., Jackson, MS; *U.S. Public*, pg. 1120
Dumas, Kelly, Dir.-Adv.--SkyTel Corp., Washington, DC; *U.S. Public*, pg. 1120
Dumortier, Dominique, Mgr.-Adv. & Pub. Rels.--Michelin North America (Canada) Inc., Laval, Canada; *Int'l*, pg. 322
Dunbar-Johnson, Stephen, Mgr.-Display Ads--The Financial Times Ltd., London, United Kingdom; *Int'l*, pg. 1025
Duncan, Helena, Mgr.--The Colonial BancGroup, Inc., Montgomery, AL; *U.S. Public*, pg. 400
Duncan, Mark, Mktg. & Adv.--Ferguson Limited, Enfield, United Kingdom; *Int'l*, pg. 1384
Duncan, Michael F., Mgr.-Pub. Rels.--Monaco Coach Corporation, Coburg, OR; *U.S. Public*, pg. 1123
Duncan, Susan, Mgr.-Mktg.--Courier Corporation, North Chelmsford, MA; *U.S. Public*, pg. 453
Dunn, Dan, Dir.-Print Adv.--Giant Eagle, Inc., Pittsburgh, PA; *U.S. Private*, pg. 450
Dunn, Donald G., Chm. Bd.--Plaskolite Inc., Columbus, OH; *U.S. Private*, pg. 870
Dunn, Michelle, Mgr.-Adv.--Mattel, Inc., El Segundo, CA; *U.S. Public*, pg. 1057
Dunn, Norma F., V.P.-Investor & Pub. Rels.--El Paso Natural Gas Co., Houston, TX; *U.S. Public*, pg. 567
Dunnigan, Jim, Dir.-Adv. & Pub. Rels.--City National Corporation, Beverly Hills, CA; *U.S. Public*, pg. 380
Dunst, Frank, Mgr.-Natl. Truck Adv.--Toyota Motor Sales, U.S.A., Inc., Torrance, CA; *Int'l*, pg. 1412
Duplissie, Gary, Dir.-Adv.--Vision Financial Corporation, Keene, NH; *U.S. Private*, pg. 1141
Dupuy, William L., V.P.-Corp. Communications--Charter One Financial, Inc., Cleveland, OH; *U.S. Public*, pg. 336
Duran, Lucille, Dir.-Adv.--Gourmet, New York, NY; *U.S. Private*, pg. 20
Durand, Mary K., Sec.--American Republic Insurance Co., Des Moines, IA; *U.S. Private*, pg. 61
Durinsky, Stephen A., Dir.-Adv. & Pub. Rels.--Myers Industries, Inc., Akron, OH; *U.S. Public*, pg. 1143
Durlam, Joyce, Dir.-Mktg.--Anderson Erickson Dairy Company, Des Moines, IA; *U.S. Private*, pg. 72
Durnil, Glenda, Mgr.-Adv.--Carrier Vibrating Equipment, Inc., Louisville, KY; *U.S. Private*, pg. 215
Durrani, M., Mgr.-Adv. Sls.--Pakistan International Airlines Corporation, New York, NY; *Int'l*, pg. 1022
Dusek, Glen, Dir.-Mktg. & Adv.--Contractors Steel Company, Livonia, MI; *U.S. Private*, pg. 270
Dutra, Luiz Carlos, Jr., Mgr.-Adv.--Johnson & Johnson Ltda., Sao Paulo, Brazil; *U.S. Public*, pg. 931
Duvall, Martine, Mgr.-Adv. & Pub. Rels.--Perdue Farms, Inc., Showell, MD; *U.S. Private*, pg. 852
Dwight, Rodger, Mgr.-Adv.--Electro Scientific Industries, Inc., Portland, OR; *U.S. Public*, pg. 568
Dworznik, Art, Mgr.-Mktg. & Adv.--Freeway Corporation, Cleveland, OH; *U.S. Private*, pg. 426
Dwyer, Walter, Dir.-Adv. & Mktg.--Airtron, Morris Plains, NJ; *U.S. Public*, pg. 1003
Dye, Janet, Mgr.-Adv. & Promo.--Rubbermaid Incorporated, Wooster, OH; *U.S. Public*, pg. 1411
Dyer, Jerry, Dir.-Adv.--Topflight Corp., York, PA; *U.S. Private*, pg. 1091
Dyke, Kim, Dir.-Adv.--Anaheim Manufacturing Company, Anaheim, CA; *U.S. Private*, pg. 70
Eadie, Wayne, Dir.-Adv. Sls. & Adv. Res. & Devel.--The Reader's Digest Association, Inc., Pleasantville, NY; *U.S.* Public, pg. 1367
Eadie, Wayne, Dir.-Res.-Adv. Res. Svcs.--Reader's Digest Publications-US Sales Div., New York, NY; *U.S. Public*, pg. 1367
Eady, Darla, Mgr.-Coop Adv.--New Line Cinema Corporation, New York, NY; *U.S. Public*, pg. 1614
Earl, Bryan R., Dir.-Mktg. Communications & Adv.--American Woodmark Corporation, Winchester, VA; *U.S. Public*, pg. 96
Earle, Randolph A., Pres. & Gen. Mgr.--Mrs. Giles Country Kitchens, Inc., Lynchburg, VA; *U.S. Public*, pg. 596
Early, Brian, Mgr.-Adv.--Gulf Oil Limited Partnership, Chelsea, MA; *U.S. Private*, pg. 487
Eastman, Tracey, Mgr.-Corp. Commun.--Computer Task Group, Inc. (CTG), Buffalo, NY; *U.S. Public*, pg. 423
Eaton, Esther, Coord.-Adv. & Media--Seaman Furniture Company, Inc., Woodbury, NY; *U.S. Public*, pg. 1452
Ebaugh, Susan, V.P.-Adv.--Serta, Inc., Itasca, IL; *U.S. Private*, pg. 985
Ebeling, Dick, Mgr.-Adv.--Curries Company, Mason City, IA; *Int'l*, pg. 18
Eberhardt, John, V.P.-Mktg. & Sls.--Delta Faucet Corporation, Indianapolis, IN; *U.S. Public*, pg. 1053
Ebert, Carol, Dir.-Mktg. Communications--Iomega Corporation, Roy, UT; *U.S. Public*, pg. 912
Eckart, Cathy, V.P.-Adv. Svcs.--Del Laboratories, Inc., Farmingdale, NY; *U.S. Public*, pg. 494
Ecker, Jackie, Coord.-Mktg. & Adv.--Interstate Van Lines, Inc., Springfield, VA; *U.S. Private*, pg. 573
Eckerling, Heather, Dir.-Sls. & Adv.--Universal Overall Company, Chicago, IL; *U.S. Private*, pg. 1127
Eckerling, Sara, Dir.-Sls., Pur. & Adv.--Universal Overall Company, Chicago, IL; *U.S. Private*, pg. 1127
Eckles, Mike, Dir.-Adv.--The Vons Companies, Inc., Arcadia, CA; *U.S. Public*, pg. 1426
Ecleberry, Ronald, V.P.-Sls. & Mktg.--Modern Welding Co., Inc., Owensboro, KY; *U.S. Private*, pg. 755
Eddy, Brenda, Sr. V.P.-Adv.--Choice Hotels International, Inc., Silver Spring, MD; *U.S. Public*, pg. 351
Edelbrock, Camee, Dir.-Adv.--Edelbrock Corp., Torrance, CA; *U.S. Public*, pg. 563
Edinger, Carol, Mgr.-Retail Adv.-Coast to Coast--TruServ Corporation, Chicago, IL; *U.S. Private*, pg. 1108
Edmondson, Dave, Sr. V.P.-Adv. & Mktg.--RadioShack, Fort Worth, TX; *U.S. Public*, pg. 1560
Edmund, Nicole, Dir.-Adv.--Edmund Scientific Company, Barrington, NJ; *U.S. Private*, pg. 364
Edmundson, Edwin, Product Mgr.--Eatelcorp Inc., Gonzales, LA; *U.S. Private*, pg. 358
Edwards, Barrie, Pres.--Music Sales Corporation, New York, NY; *U.S. Private*, pg. 768
Edwards, Florine, V.P. & Mgr.-Adv. & Corp. Rels.--Allendale Mutual Insurance Co., Johnston, RI; *U.S. Private*, pg. 37
Edwards, Roy, Mgr.-Adv. Intl.--Scientific American, Inc., New York, NY; *Int'l*, pg. 1479
Egan, Neil, Sr. Dir.-Mktg. & Adv.--Snapper Power Equipment, Mc Donough, GA; *U.S. Public*, pg. 1103
Egeler, D., Mgr.-Mktg.-Holland--Grolsch N.V., Enschede, Netherlands; *Int'l*, pg. 559
Egen, Bob, Exec. V.P. & Gen. Mgr.--Sherwood-Davis & Geck, Saint Louis, MO; *U.S. Public*, pg. 80
Egger, Ernst, Mgr.-Adv.--DG Bank, Frankfurt/Main, Germany; *Int'l*, pg. 351
Ehrlich, Jay, V.P.-Sls. & Mktg.-Printing Equip.--Wisconsin Automated Machinery Corp., Oshkosh, WI; *U.S. Private*, pg. 1184
Ehrlich, Robert W., Dir.-Adv. & Sls. Promo.--Reed & Barton Corporation, Taunton, MA; *U.S. Private*, pg. 916

Eichenseer, Mike, V.P. & Gen. Mgr.--Koken Mfg. Co. Inc., Saint Louis, MO; *Int'l*, pg. 1349
Eichler, Larry, V.P.-Sls. & Mktg.--Prentiss Incorporated, Floral Park, NY; *U.S. Private*, pg. 882
Eigner, Carole, Coord.-Pub. Rels. & Adv.--Cubic Corporation, San Diego, CA; *U.S. Public*, pg. 466
Einwalter, Pat, Mgr.-Fast/Lock Sls.--Deco Products Co., Decorah, IA; *U.S. Private*, pg. 320
Eisenberg, Alan I., V.P.-Sls. & Mktg.--Plymouth Rubber Company, Inc., Canton, MA; *U.S. Public*, pg. 1311
Eitzenberger, Kevin, Mgr.-Adv.--Allen Organ Company, Macungie, PA; *U.S. Public*, pg. 45
Eklow, Peo, Dir.-Adv.--Trygg-Hansa, Stockholm, Sweden; *Int'l*, pg. 1425
Elbert, Miles, Mgr.-Adv.--Autodesk, Inc., San Rafael, CA; *U.S. Public*, pg. 148
Elder, Susan, Mgr.-Corp. Commun.--Invacare Corporation, Elyria, OH; *U.S. Public*, pg. 911
Eldridge, John, Mgr.-Adv.--Marquette Coppersmithing Co., Inc., Philadelphia, PA; *U.S. Private*, pg. 706
Elefson, Matt, Mgr.-Sls.--L.G. Everist Inc., Sioux Falls, SD; *U.S. Private*, pg. 386
Elkhatib, Hasan M., Pres. & Chief Exec. Officer--Dena Corporation, Elk Grove Village, IL; *U.S. Private*, pg. 324
Eller, Betty Lynn, Dir.-Adv. & Consumer Mktg.--Drexel Heritage Furnishings Inc., Drexel, NC; *U.S. Private*, pg. 432
Eller, S. Heidi, Dir.-Mktg.--The Great Lakes Cheese Co., Newbury, OH; *U.S. Private*, pg. 473
Ellickson, Nancy, V.P.-Bus. Mktg.--Genus Inc., Sunnyvale, CA; *U.S. Public*, pg. 732
Elliot, Sarah, Mgr.-Adv. & Promotion--Simon & Schuster Children's Publishing, New York, NY; *U.S. Private*, pg. 777
Elliott, Dee, Mktg. Asst.--Trumbull Corporation/P.J. Dick, Inc., West Mifflin, PA; *U.S. Private*, pg. 1107
Ellis, Bruce, Mgr.-Adv.--Siemens Medical Systems, Inc., Iselin, NJ; *Int'l*, pg. 1246
Ellis, David, Dir.-Adv.--Kohl's Food Stores, Wauwatosa, WI; *Int'l*, pg. 1375
Ellis, Kevin, V.P.-Adv.--Karakas, Vansickle, Ouellette Advertising & Public Relations, Mountain View, CA; *U.S. Private*, pg. 607
Ellis, Mark, Pres.--STAR Anchors & Fasteners, Mountainville, NY; *U.S. Private*, pg. 1033
Ellis, Robert, V.P.-Mktg.--Watson Wyatt Worldwide, Bethesda, MD; *U.S. Private*, pg. 1154
Ellixson, Marita, Mktg. Editor--Game Time, Inc., Fort Payne, AL; *U.S. Public*, pg. 1543
Ellsworth, Heidi, Coord.-Mktg.--Herbert Malarkey Roofing Company, Portland, OR; *U.S. Private*, pg. 698
Elowitz, David, V.P.--Honey Fashions Ltd., New York, NY; *U.S. Private*, pg. 537
Elwell, Bill, V.P.-Adv.--Comerica Incorporated, Detroit, MI; *U.S. Public*, pg. 408
Elwwod, Kevin, Mgr.-Adv.--Manning & Lewis Engineering Co., Union, NJ; *U.S. Private*, pg. 700
Emerson, Mary Ann, Coord.-Mktg. & Adv.--C.I. Hayes, Inc., Cranston, RI; *U.S. Private*, pg. 513
Emerson, Nedwin, Pres.-Family Adv. Agency--The Troy Savings Bank, Troy, NY; *U.S. Private*, pg. 1106
Emerson, Ron, Dir.-Adv.--B&B Corporate Holdings, Inc., Tampa, FL; *U.S. Private*, pg. 104
Emmerling, Paul E., V.P.-Sls., Mktg. & Gen. Mgr.--American Welding & Manufacturing Co., Warren, OH; *U.S. Private*, pg. 425
Enck, Jeffrey J., Asst. Sls. Mgr.--Lancaster Malleable Castings Company, Lancaster, PA; *U.S. Private*, pg. 645
Endieveri, Tony, V.P.-Mktg.--ICO, Inc., Houston, TX; *U.S. Public*, pg. 853
Endres, Roy M., Exec. V.P.--Multi-Ad Services, Incorporated, Peoria, IL; *U.S. Private*, pg. 766
Engel, Bruce L., Pres.--WTD Industries, Inc., Portland, OR; *U.S. Public*, pg. 1729
Engel, Julie M., Sr. V.P.-Adv.--Best Buy Co., Inc., Eden Prairie, MN; *U.S. Public*, pg. 223
Engel, Robert A., Jr., Sr. V.P.-Film & Adv.--Regal Cinemas Inc., Knoxville, TN; *U.S. Public*, pg. 1371
Engelage, Dean, Asst. Dir.-Adv. & Mgr.-Matls.--Woodard Inc., Owosso, MI; *U.S. Private*, pg. 192
England, Stephen, V.P.-Adv.--Micro Warehouse, Inc., Norwalk, CT; *U.S. Public*, pg. 1104
Engles, Carla, Coord.-Adv.--Schwan's Sales Enterprises, Marshall, MN; *U.S. Private*, pg. 974
English, Claudia, Mgr.-Mktg.--MapInfo Corp., Troy, NY; *U.S. Public*, pg. 1042
Eno, Julius Ralph, Pres.--Hamamatsu Corp., Bridgewater, NJ; *U.S. Private*, pg. 497
Enstad, David, Dir.-Adv.--Memphis Publishing Co., Memphis, TN; *U.S. Public*, pg. 1448
Enyart, Jeanie, V.P.-Adv.--The Miami Herald, Miami, FL; *U.S. Public*, pg. 964
Eorgoff, Monica, Dir.-Adv. & Mktg. Svcs. National Cattlemen's Beef Association, Chicago, IL; *U.S. Private*, pg. 780
Ephron, Michael, Dir.-Mktg.--Vanity Fair, New York, NY; *U.S. Private*, pg. 20
Epstein, Ed, Mgr.-Adv.--Success Development International, Jacksonville, FL; *U.S. Private*, pg. 1048
Epstein, Scott, Dir.-Adv. & Pub. Rels.--Excite, Inc., Redwood City, CA; *U.S. Public*, pg. 599
Epstein, Willa, Mgr.-Adv.--Milgray Electronics, Inc., Farmingdale, NY; *U.S. Public*, pg. 205
Erickson, Bob, Mgr.-Adv. & Pub. Rels.--Hennessy Industries, Inc., La Vergne, TN; *U.S. Public*, pg. 481
Erickson, D., Mgr.-Sls. & Retail Adv.--JC Penney Company, Inc., Plano, TX; *U.S. Public*, pg. 916
Erickson, Debbie, Mgr.-Adv.--Six Flags Magic Mountain & Six Flags Hurricane Harbor, Valencia, CA; *U.S. Public*, pg. 1611
Erickson, R., Mgr.-Adv.--Power Distribution Division, Milwaukee, WI; *U.S. Public*, pg. 557
Eriusen, Frode, Mgr.-Mktg.--A/S Ivaran Rederi, Lysaker, Norway; *Int'l*, pg. 696
Erlandsen, Linda, Adv. Asst.--Motown Record Company, J.P., New York, NY; *Int'l*, pg. 1052
Erneast, Don, Gen. Mgr.-Adv.--Calumet Photographic, Inc., Bensenville, IL; *U.S. Private*, pg. 202
Ernest, Bob, V.P.-Customer Support--Integrated Metal Technologies, Inc., Spring Lake, MI; *U.S. Public*, pg. 1112
Ernst, Matthew, Mktg. Specialist--Carter Day International, Minneapolis, MN; *U.S. Private*, pg. 216
Ervin, Mike, V.P.-Sls. & Distr.--Hercules Engine Company, Canton, OH; *U.S. Private*, pg. 523
Escowitz, Sidney, V.P.-Creative Services--Butterick Company, Inc., New York, NY; *U.S. Private*, pg. 190
Eshlaman, Dennis N., V.P.-Mktg.--Hershey Pasta and Grocery Group, Hershey, PA; *U.S. Public*, pg. 812
Espinoza, Matt, Dir.-Adv.--Clayton Industries Co., El Monte, CA; *U.S. Private*, pg. 245
Esposito, Linda, V.P.-Consumer Insight--DowBrands, L.P., Indianapolis, IN; *U.S. Public*, pg. 523
Essen, Arthur, Mgr.-Mktg. & Adv.--American Express Service Europe Ltd., Amsterdam, Netherlands; *U.S. Public*, pg. 74
Esser, Patrick J., V.P.-Adv. Sls.--Cox Communications, Inc., Atlanta, GA; *U.S. Public*, pg. 454
Esterly, Cheryl, Assoc.-Adv.--The American Stock Exchange, New York, NY; *U.S. Private*, pg. 62
Estes, Donald, V.P.--Ray Bell Construction Co. Inc., Brentwood, TN; *U.S. Private*, pg. 131
Estony, Robert J., Dir.-Communications--Ikegami Electronics (U.S.A.), Inc., Maywood, NJ; *Int'l*, pg. 660
Etherington, Martyn, Sr. Dir.-Corp. Communications--Sequent Computer Systems, Inc., Beaverton, OR; *U.S. Public*, pg. 1459
Etter, Christoph, Exec. V.P.--Sulzer Ltd., Winterthur, Switzerland; *Int'l*, pg. 1305
Ettridge, Steven, Pres.--Temps & Company, Washington, DC; *U.S. Private*, pg. 1075
Etzkorn, Rick, Mgr.-Adv.--Lake Wales Daily Highlander, Lake Wales, FL; *U.S. Private*, pg. 995
Etzkorn, Rick, Adv. Mgr.--Winter Haven News Chief, Winter Haven, FL; *U.S. Private*, pg. 995
Eulich, John, Pres.--Mark Andy, Inc., Chesterfield, MO; *U.S. Public*, pg. 521
Evans, Heather, Mgr.-Adv.- Pratt & Lambert & Martin Senour--The Sherwin-Williams Company, Cleveland, OH; *U.S. Public*, pg. 1465
Evans, Heather, Mgr.-Adv.- Dutch Boy--Sherwin-Williams Consumer Brands Division, Cleveland, OH; *U.S. Public*, pg. 1466
Evans, Megan, Adv. & Promo. Asst.--Nintendo of America, Redmond, WA; *Int'l*, pg. 932
Evans, Paul, Mgr.-Media--Crosfield Electronics Limited, Hemel Hempstead, United Kingdom; *U.S. Public*, pg. 532
Evans, Robert S., Chm. Bd. & Chief Exec. Officer--Crane Co., Stamford, CT; *U.S. Public*, pg. 456
Evans, Tony, V.P.-Communications--White Consolidated Industries, Inc., Cleveland, OH; *Int'l*, pg. 439
Evdoe, Brian, Dir.-Mktg. & Sls.--ACF Industries, Inc., Saint Charles, MO; *U.S. Private*, pg. 556
Evenson, Douglas, Dir.-Adv.--Americo Manufacturing Co., Inc., Acworth, GA; *U.S. Private*, pg. 64
Everett, Samuel, Dir.-Corp. Communications--JPS Elastomerics Corp., Holyoke, MA; *U.S. Private*, pg. 578
Everling, Lawrence J., V.P.-Mktg. & Adv.--The CIT Group/ Equipment Financing, Livingston, NJ; *Int'l*, pg. 360
Evers, W., Mgr.-Adv.--Wavin Bv, Zwolle, Netherlands; *Int'l*, pg. 1135
Ewald, Jessica, Mgr.-Mktg.--Plastag Corporation, Elk Grove Village, IL; *U.S. Private*, pg. 870
Fabel, Gary, Dir.-Mktg.--Bongards Creameries Inc., Norwood, MN; *U.S. Private*, pg. 156
Facchin, Rina, Mgr.-Adv.- Alfa Romeo--Fiat Auto Belgio SA, Brussels, Belgium; *Int'l*, pg. 481
Fagan, Doyle, Mgr.-Natl. Adv.--Memphis Publishing Co., Memphis, TN; *U.S. Public*, pg. 1448
Fagan, Elizabeth, Dir.-Grp. Adv.--Dixons Group plc, Hemel Hempstead, United Kingdom,; *Int'l*, pg. 413
Fahey, Jack, V.P.-Sls. & Mktg.--Temco Fireplace Products, Inc., Nashville, TN; *U.S. Public*, pg. 1576
Fahey, John, Asst. V.P.-Mktg.--Huntington National Bank, Morgantown, WV; *U.S. Public*, pg. 850
Fales, Marsha, Dir.-Media & Mktg.--Norman Levy Associates, Inc., Southfield, MI; *U.S. Private*, pg. 664
Falk, Lloyd, Pres., Chief Exec. Officer & Chief Oper. Officer--Fort Lock Corporation, River Grove, IL; *U.S. Private*, pg. 419
Falzer, L., V.P.-Mktg. & Adv.--Raypak, Inc., Westlake Village, CA; *Int'l*, pg. 1022
Fama, Maureen C., Mgr.-Communications--Uniroyal Chemical Company, Inc., Middlebury, CT; *U.S. Public*, pg. 460
Fancher, Charles, V.P.-Communications & Pub. Affairs--Philadelphia Daily News, Philadelphia, PA; *U.S. Public*, pg. 964
Farkash, Martha, Mgr.-Adv.--Laser Industries Ltd., Tel Aviv, Israel; *Int'l*, pg. 429
Farley, Kevin, Sr. Mgr.-Sls.--Comair Holdings, Inc., Erlanger, KY; *U.S. Public*, pg. 406
Farley, William F., Chm. Bd., Pres. & Chief Exec. Officer--Farley, Inc., Chicago, IL; *U.S. Private*, pg. 394
Farlow, Kim, Dir.-Adv.--Virginia Electric and Power Company, Richmond, VA; *U.S. Public*, pg. 516
Farmer, Ann, Mgr.-Corp. Communications--DPL Inc., Dayton, OH; *U.S. Public*, pg. 473
Farmer, H. Randolph, Sr. V.P.-Corp. Commun. & Investor Rels.--Lawyers Title Insurance Corporation, Richmond, VA; *U.S. Public*, pg. 981
Farmer, Jeri, Mgr.-Adv. & Promo.--Six Flags Over Georgia, Austell, GA; *U.S. Public*, pg. 1612
Fashjian, Maura, Sr. Assoc.-Adv.--Bayer Corporation/ Pharmaceutical Division, West Haven, CT; *Int'l*, pg. 173
Fasola, Kenneth J., V.P. & Mgr.-Natl. Sls.--Humana Inc., Louisville, KY; *U.S. Public*, pg. 847
Faust, Laura, Admin Asst.-Adv. & Promo.--Visa U.S.A. Inc., San Francisco, CA; *U.S. Private*, pg. 1141
Faust, Tammy, Dir.-Adv.--Dairy Queen Corporate Store, Louisville, KY; *U.S. Public*, pg. 220
Faves, Mark, Mgr.-Adv.--World Color-Chicago Div., Elk Grove Village, IL; *U.S. Public*, pg. 1778
Feagan, Dawn, Adv. Coord.--A.I. Root Company, Medina, OH; *U.S. Private*, pg. 944
Federle, Mike, Dir.-Adv. & Sls.--Fortune, New York, NY; *U.S. Public*, pg. 1613
Feeney, Anne, Mgr.-Special Events--Marshall Field, Chicago, IL; *U.S. Public*, pg. 489
Feeney, Chris T., Dir.-Adv.--Indianapolis Power & Light Company, Indianapolis, IN; *U.S. Public*, pg. 913
Feenstra, Jim, V.P.-Mktg.--Penske Logistics, Reading, PA; *U.S. Private*, pg. 851
Fehlandt, Ricardo, Exec. Pres.--Bayer de Chile S.A., Santiago, Chile; *Int'l*, pg. 175
Fehring, Thomas H., Sec.--Wisconsin Energy Corporation, Milwaukee, WI; *U.S. Public*, pg. 1773
Feichtner, Jack P., V.P.-Adv. & Mktg.--Central Tractor Farm & Country, Inc., Des Moines, IA; *U.S. Private*, pg. 237
Feil, Kim, Sr. V.P.-Mktg--Cadbury Beverages, Stamford, CT; *Int'l*, pg. 248
Feinseth, Miriam, Dir.-Adv. & Communication--Hunter Douglas, Inc., Upper Saddle River, NJ; *Int'l*, pg. 639
Fela, Leonard J., Mgr.-Mktg.--Lightnin Mixers, Rochester, NY; *U.S. Public*, pg. 726
Feld, Patrick, V.P.-Adv.--Pay Less Super Markets, Inc., Anderson, IN; *U.S. Private*, pg. 844
Fellows, Bill, Dir.-Mktg. & Adv.--Kepner-Tregoe, Inc., Skillman, NJ; *U.S. Public*, pg. 1659
Felman, Mark, Dir.-Adv.--Allou Health & Beauty Care, Inc., Brentwood, NY; *U.S. Public*, pg. 55
Ferguson, Dennis, V.P.-Buying & Adv.--Bel Air Markets, West Sacramento, CA; *U.S. Private*, pg. 908
Ferguson, F.C., Mgr.-Adv.--Mine Safety Appliances Co., Pittsburgh, PA; *U.S. Public*, pg. 1114
Ferguson, Larry J., V.P.-Sls. & Mktg.--Master Molded Products Corporation, Elgin, IL; *U.S. Private*, pg. 714
Ferguson, Peter, Mgr.-Mktg. Communications--Universal Instruments Corporation, Binghamton, NY; *U.S. Public*, pg. 522
Ferguson, Robert, Mgr.-Adv. & Sls. Promo.--Dualite Inc., Williamsburg, OH; *U.S. Private*, pg. 344
Ferlet, Sandrine, Mgr.-Adv.--American Power Conversion Corp., Lognes, France; *U.S. Public*, pg. 89
Fermino, Alex, Mktg & Adv. Coord.--DX Communications, Inc., Deerfield Beach, FL; *Int'l*, pg. 694
Fernandez, Julio Cesar, Mgr.-Adv.--Bagley S.A., Buenos Aires, Argentina; *Int'l*, pg. 379
Fernandez, Lorenzo, Mgr.-Adv. & Pub. Rels.--Degussa Corporation, Ridgefield Park, NJ; *Int'l*, pg. 388
Ferraiole, Tom, Mgr.-Communications--Long Island Lighting Company, Hicksville, NY; *U.S. Public*, pg. 1013
Ferrarin, Kim, Dir.-Adv.--Sunbelt Nursery Group Inc., Fort Worth, TX; *U.S. Public*, pg. 715
Ferraro, Karen L., Dir.-Mktg.--Periphonics Corp., Bohemia, NY; *U.S. Public*, pg. 1278
Ferrer, Sr., Mgr.-Adv.--CIBA-GEIGY S.A., Barcelona, Spain; *Int'l*, pg. 979
Ferris, Russel, Mgr.-Adv./Graphics--Behlen Mfg. Co., Columbus, NE; *U.S. Private*, pg. 130
Ferrucci, Anne, Asst. V.P.-Mktg.--The F.A. Bartlett Tree Expert Co., Stamford, CT; *U.S. Private*, pg. 119
Feske, Tom, Natl. Mgr.-Etonic Athletic--Etonic Tretorn, Brockton, MA; *U.S. Private*, pg. 629
Fette, Jim, Sr. Mgr.-Mktg. Commun. & Adv.--LCI International, Inc., Dublin, OH; *U.S. Public*, pg. 969
Fickbolm, Joan, Mgr.-Adv.--Lewis Drug, Inc., Sioux Falls, SD; *U.S. Private*, pg. 665
Fidler, Karen L., V.P.-Mktg.--Bachman Company, Reading, PA; *U.S. Private*, pg. 109
Fiery, D.E., Pres.--Miller Chemical & Fertilizer Corp., Hanover, PA; *U.S. Private*, pg. 33
Figg, Marjorie, Mgr.-Mktg.--Georg Fischer Disa, Inc., Holly, MI; *Int'l*, pg. 490
Figi, Stefian M., Adv. Coord.--Quad/Graphics, Inc., Pewaukee, WI; *U.S. Private*, pg. 897
Filho, Jose Ermirio de Moraes, Pres. & Dir.-Adv.--S.A. Industrias Votorantim, Sao Paulo, Brazil; *Int'l*, pg. 677
Filion, Hugues, Sr. Advisor-Institutional Promotion--Assurance vie Desjardins-Laurentienne, Levis, Canada; *Int'l*, pg. 396
Finch, David, Dir.-Adv. & Visual--Aaron Brothers, Inc., City of Commerce, CA; *U.S. Public*, pg. 1104
Finch, Jeff, V.P.-Sls. & Mktg., Aeroquip--Aeroquip-Vickers, Inc., Maumee, OH; *U.S. Public*, pg. 24
Fine, Christopher, Mgr.-Mktg. Commun.--Alvey Systems, Inc, Saint Louis, MO; *U.S. Private*, pg. 47
Fineran, James V., Mgr.-Adv.--Dresser Industries Wayne Division, Austin, TX; *U.S. Public*, pg. 528
Finger, Larry E., Chief Fin. Officer & Sr. V.P.--Washington Real Estate Investment Trust, Kensington, MD; *U.S. Public*, pg. 1743
Fingerhut, Augie, Dir.-Sls. & Pur., Mgr.-Adv.--Manhattan Industries Intl. Div., New York, NY; *U.S. Public*, pg. 1429
Finley, Gene, Mgr.-Natl. Mktg.--A.M. Castle & Co., Franklin Park, IL; *U.S. Public*, pg. 312
Finley, Jon, Dir.-Sls. & Mktg.--Rundel Products, Inc., Portland, OR; *U.S. Private*, pg. 951
Finley, Richard L., Sr. V.P.-Sls. & Mktg.--Allied Security, Inc., Pittsburgh, PA; *U.S. Private*, pg. 40
Finn, Anne, Commun. Analyst--Electronic Tele-Communications, Inc., Waukesha, WI; *U.S. Public*, pg. 570
Finn, Tom, Mgr-Adv.--Capitol Group, Springfield, IL; *U.S. Private*, pg. 206
Finnen, Paula, Mgr.-Category--United Dairy Farmers, Inc., Cincinnati, OH; *U.S. Private*, pg. 1121
Finneran, Ben, Dir.-Mktg.--Dairy Mart Southeast, Louisville, KY; *U.S. Public*, pg. 476
Finney, Deryl, Dir.-Corp. Commun.--General Automation, Inc., Irvine, CA; *U.S. Public*, pg. 706

Fioravanti, Paul, Adv. Mgr.--Valley Resources, Inc., Cumberland, RI; *U.S. Public,* pg. 1706
Fiore, Pete, V.P.-Mktg.--Ardent Software, Inc., Westborough, MA; *U.S. Public,* pg. 129
Fischer, Del, Mgr.-Adv. & Promotion--Millennium Petrochemicals, Inc., Cincinnati, OH; *Int'l,* pg. 594
Fischer, Mark, Dir.-Adv. & Creative Services--Johnsonville Foods, Inc., Kohler, WI; *U.S. Private,* pg. 595
Fischerbacher, Robert, Dir.-Pub. Rels.--Knurr AG, Munich, Germany; *Int'l,* pg. 739
Fish, Jean, Mgr.-Media--Lever Brothers Co., New York, NY; *Int'l,* pg. 1435
Fish, Julia C., Dir.-Corp. Commun.--Sedgwick Group plc, London, United Kingdom; *Int'l,* pg. 1217
Fish, Lauren, Recruitment Adv. Specialist--Keane, Inc., Boston, MA; *U.S. Public,* pg. 946
Fisher, Barbara, Adv. & Sls. Dept.--Universal Studios TV, Universal City, CA; *Int'l,* pg. 1215
Fisher, Brett, V.P.-Art--Christian Dior Perfumes Inc., New York, NY; *Int'l,* pg. 781
Fisher, Debbie, Dir.-Corp. Communications--Mettler-Toledo, Inc., Hightstown, NJ; *U.S. Private,* pg. 4
Fisher, George, Mgr.-Adv.--Be-Lo Markets Inc., Norfolk, VA; *U.S. Private,* pg. 203
Fisher, Marcy, Mgr.-Adv.--Barrister Information Systems Corporation, Buffalo, NY; *U.S. Public,* pg. 192
Fisher, Randy, V.P.-Adv.--Krause's Sofa Factory, Brea, CA; *U.S. Public,* pg. 967
Fisher, Robert B., Mktg. Specialist--Metra Commuter Rail, Chicago, IL; *U.S. Private,* pg. 919
Fisher, Susan, Mgr.-Adv. Corp. Info. & Public Affairs--B.A.T Industries P.L.C., London, United Kingdom; *Int'l,* pg. 110
Fisher, Susan, Mgr.-Jenn-Air Adv.--Jenn-Air, Newton, IA; *U.S. Public,* pg. 1064
Fisher, Warren F., V.P.-Sls. & Mktg.--Moeller Products Co., Inc., Greenville, MS; *U.S. Private,* pg. 755
Fitzgerald, Brian, Dir.-Adv. & External Rels.--Ameritech Corporation, Chicago, IL; *U.S. Public,* pg. 97
Fitzgibbons, Debbie, Mgr.-Mktg. Communications & Adv.--Thermo Jarrell Ash Corporation, Franklin, MA; *U.S. Public,* pg. 1594
Fitzmaurice, Robert, Sr. V.P.-Mktg.--UST Inc., Greenwich, CT; *U.S. Public,* pg. 1660
Fixa, Charles W., Dir.-Sls. & Mktg. & Mgr.-Adv. & Pub. Rels.--Spectrol Electronics Corporation, Ontario, CA; *U.S. Private,* pg. 351
Flaemig, Horst, Dir.-Mktg.--Girmes GmbH, Grefrath, Germany; *Int'l,* pg. 552
Flaherty, James P., V.P.-Adv. & Mktg.--Nature's Bounty Inc., Bohemia, NY; *U.S. Public,* pg. 1166
Flaherty, Lauren, Dir.-WW Adv.--International Business Machines Corporation, Armonk, NY; *U.S. Public,* pg. 895
Flaherty, W., Dir.-Sls.-Rubber--Farrel Corporation, Ansonia, CT; *U.S. Public,* pg. 614
Flanagan, Larry, V.P.-Adv.--Mastercard International, Inc., Purchase, NY; *U.S. Private,* pg. 714
Flechtner, Gretchen, Adv. & Mktg. Asst.--Webster Industries Inc., Tiffin, OH; *U.S. Private,* pg. 1157
Fleckney, Kathleen, Mgr.-Mktg. Communications--Crompton & Knowles Ingredient Technology Corp., Mahwah, NJ; *U.S. Public,* pg. 459
Fleenor, Roger H., Pres.--Red Apple, Inc., Ontario, OR; *U.S.* Private, pg. 915
Fleischmann, F., Dir.-Adv.--Riedel-de Haen AG, Seelze, Germany; *Int'l,* pg. 625
Fleming, Jack, Bentree Real Estate Grp.--Calprop Corporation, Marina Del Rey, CA; *U.S. Public,* pg. 296
Fleshel, Marcia, Dir.-Adv.--Blue Cross and Blue Shield of Massachusetts, Boston, MA; *U.S. Private,* pg. 151
Fletcher, Linda, Mgr.-Adv.--J.L. Todd Auction Co., Rome, GA; *U.S. Private,* pg. 1090
Flint, Bill, Jr., V.P.-Mktg.--Flambeau Corporation, Baraboo, WI; *U.S. Private,* pg. 409
Flint, Richard, Mgr.-Adv. & Mktg.--Mautz Paint Co., Madison, WI; *U.S. Private,* pg. 715
Floccuzio, Luana, Dir.-Adv. NAO--General Motors Corporation, Detroit, MI; *U.S. Public,* pg. 718
Flood, Diane, Mgr.-Adv.--Cytec Industries Inc., West Paterson, NJ; *U.S. Public,* pg. 471
Florin, Jack L., Dir.-Adv. & Promo.--The Kelly-Springfield Tire Company, Cumberland, MD; *U.S. Public,* pg. 753
Flory, Don, Mgr.-Mktg. Services--R.A. Jones & Co. Inc., Covington, KY; *U.S. Private,* pg. 597
Flosdorff, Gerhard, Dir.-Mktg.--Hugo Boss AG, Metzingen, Germany; *Int'l,* pg. 637
Floyd, Liz, Dir.-Adv.--Concurrent Industries Group, Inc., New York, NY; *U.S. Private,* pg. 262
Foden, Jennifer, Mgr.-Mktg.--Advanced Circuit Technology, Nashua, NH; *U.S. Private,* pg. 21
Foertsch, James, Mgr.-Adv.--Scania USA Inc., Orange, CT; *Int'l,* pg. 687
Fogg, David, Mgr.-Adv.--Spar (UK) Ltd., Harrow, United Kingdom; *Int'l,* pg. 1288
Foley, Janice, Mgr.-Corp. Communications & Adv.--Keyport Life Insurance Company, Boston, MA; *U.S. Private,* pg. 666
Foley, Ron, Mgr.-Adv.--LSI Industries, Inc., Cincinnati, OH; *U.S. Public,* pg. 971
Fonville, Ken, Pres.--Pennsylvania House Casegoods, Lewisburg, PA; *U.S. Public,* pg. 975
Foo, Ginger, Mgr.-Adv.-Screen Printing--Tetko, Inc., Briarcliff Manor, NY; *U.S. Private,* pg. 1078
Footer, Eli, V.P.-Sls. & Mktg.--Schwartz & Benjamin, Inc., New York, NY; *U.S. Private,* pg. 974
Forcelle, Joyce, Mgr.-Intl. Sls.--WINCO, Le Center, MN; *U.S. Private,* pg. 350
Ford, Barbara, Dir.-Adv.--Kraft Foods, Inc., Northfield, IL; *U.S. Public,* pg. 1287
Ford, Lance, Dir.-Adv.--Bon Appetit Magazine, New York, NY; *U.S. Private,* pg. 20
Forhan, Phillip, Dir.-Bus. Devel.--Active Tool & Manufacturing Co., Inc., Roseville, MI; *U.S. Private,* pg. 16
Forrer, Dan J., Dir.-Adv.--FirstEnergy Corp., Akron, OH; *U.S.* Public, pg. 644
Forslund, Scott, Mgr.-Adv.--Puget Sound Energy, Inc., Bellevue, WA; *U.S. Public,* pg. 1342
Forti, Patty, V.P.-Adv. & Mktg.--Huffman Koos, River Edge, NJ; *U.S. Private,* pg. 546
Forystek, Dallas N., Coord.-Adv.--Component Operations, Warren, MI; *U.S. Public,* pg. 353
Foss, Adam, Corp. Commun. Officer--GN Great Nordic Ltd., Copenhagen, Denmark; *Int'l,* pg. 536
Foss, Andrew, Mgr.-Adv.--Yuasa-Exide, Inc., Reading, PA; *Int'l,* pg. 1522
Foss, Gary, Sr. V.P.--Office Depot Inc., Delray Beach, FL; *U.S. Public,* pg. 1212
Foss, K. Michael, Mgr.-Western Adv.--Automotive News, Detroit, MI; *U.S. Private,* pg. 284
Fossum, Jennifer, Creative Dir.--Northland Cranberries, Inc., Wisconsin Rapids, WI; *U.S. Public,* pg. 1197
Foster, Allan, V.P.-Sls. & Mktg.--J.W. Allen & Company, Wheeling, IL; *U.S. Private,* pg. 37
Foster, F.S., Mgr.-Mktg. & Adv.--Electroid Co., Springfield, NJ; *U.S. Private,* pg. 369
Foster, Feather, Mgr.-Adv.--Electroid Corp., Springfield, NJ; *U.S. Private,* pg. 1131
Foster, Herb, V.P.-Communications--Entex Information Services, Rye Brook, NY; *U.S. Private,* pg. 378
Foster, Scott, Dir.-Adv.--Bel-Art Products, Pequannock, NJ; *U.S. Private,* pg. 130
Foster, Scott, Mgr.-Mktg. Commun.--Bel-Art Products, Pequannock, NJ; *U.S. Private,* pg. 130
Foster, Scott, Mgr.-Adv.--D & S Marketing, Pequannock, NJ; *U.S. Private,* pg. 130
Foulds, Peter J., V.P.-Adv.--Kentucky Fried Chicken Corporation (KFC), Louisville, KY; *U.S. Public,* pg. 1636
Fourrier, Dawn, Mgr.-Adv.--Quartet Manufacturing Co., Skokie, IL; *U.S. Public,* pg. 707
Fowler, C. Thomas, Sr. V.P.-Mktg.--Motion Industries, Inc., Irondale, AL; *U.S. Public,* pg. 732
Fowler, Frank, V.P.--D.C. Taylor Co., Cedar Rapids, IA; *U.S.* Private, pg. 1070
Fox, Anne W., V.P.-Adv. & Media--Nestle USA, Glendale, CA; *Int'l,* pg. 916
Fox, David, Mgr.-Adv.-Sports--Unisys Limited, Uxbridge, United Kingdom; *U.S. Public,* pg. 1671
Fox, Herbert A., Jr., V.P.--Murphy Oil Corporation, El Dorado, AR; *U.S. Public,* pg. 1141
Fox, Lisa, Dir.-Adv.--Ingram Micro Inc., Santa Ana, CA; *U.S.* Public, pg. 878
Fox, Mitchell, Publisher & V.P.--The Conde Nast Publications Inc., New York, NY; *U.S. Private,* pg. 20
Frailly, Ronald, Dir.-Adv.--The Advocate, Newark, OH; *U.S. Private,* pg. 23
Framke, Donna, V.P.-Adv. & Mktg.--Beverly Bancorporation Inc., Chicago, IL; *U.S. Public,* pg. 227
Francis, J.M., Mgr.-Adv.--Trico Products Corporation, Buffalo, NY; *Int'l,* pg. 1397
Francis, Janis, Mgr.-Adv.--Heery International, Inc., Atlanta, GA; *U.S. Private,* pg. 519
Francis, Nancy, Dir.-Adv.--Eveready Battery Co., Saint Louis, MO; *U.S. Public,* pg. 1360
Franey, Scott, V.P.-Adv.--Princess Cruise Lines, Los Angeles, CA; *Int'l,* pg. 1035
Frank, Jessica, Dir.-Promo., Publicity & Adv.--Golden Books Family Entertainment Inc., New York, NY; *U.S. Public,* pg. 749
Frank, Jessica, Dir.-Promo., Publicity & Adv.--Golden Books Publishing, New York, NY; *U.S. Public,* pg. 749
Frank, Jim, V.P.-Mdsg.--Wickes Inc., Vernon Hills, IL; *U.S. Public,* pg. 1391
Frank, Karl, Gen. Mgr.--Tucker Rocky Distributing, Portland, OR; *U.S. Private,* pg. 639
Frank, Rudy, Mgr.-Adv. & Pub. Rels.--Kennametal Inc., Latrobe, PA; *U.S. Public,* pg. 950
Frankel, Marc, Dir.-Corp. Communications--Polychrome Corp. Div., Fort Lee, NJ; *Int'l,* pg. 370
Frankel, Richard, V.P.-Sls. & Mktg.--Universal Industrial Products Co., Pioneer, OH; *U.S. Public,* pg. 1677
Frankiewicz, Anita, Dir.-Mktg.--Restonic Mattress Corporation, Rosemont, IL; *U.S. Private,* pg. 925
Franklin, E. Thomas, Chm., Pres. & Treas.--Franklin Baking Co., Inc., Goldsboro, NC; *U.S. Private,* pg. 424
Franklin, John R., Mgr.-Mktg. & Adv.--Baltimore Stationery Co./Total Office, Baltimore, MD; *U.S. Private,* pg. 113
Frasch, Richard, Mgr.-Mktg.--Cargill Animal Nutrition Div., Minneapolis, MN; *U.S. Private,* pg. 210
Fraser, Mike, Mgr.-Adv.--Makita Canada Inc., Whitby, Canada; *Int'l,* pg. 832
Fratzke, Beth, Mgr.-Adv.--Lutheran Brotherhood, Minneapolis, MN; *U.S. Private,* pg. 681
Frazier, Kim, Mgr.-Adv.--Bill's Dollar Stores, Inc., Ridgeland, MS; *U.S. Private,* pg. 144
Frazier, Walter, V.P.-Sls. & Mktg.--Roller Derby Skate Corp., Litchfield, IL; *U.S. Private,* pg. 941
Frederick, Sherry, Mgr.-Adv. & Direct Mktg.--Tech Data Corporation, Clearwater, FL; *U.S. Public,* pg. 1562
Frederiksen, Walter, Dir.-Adv. & Promo.--Ziebart International Corporation, Troy, MI; *U.S. Private,* pg. 1205
Fredriksen, Ronald I., V.P.-Adv.--Auto Driveaway Co., Chicago, IL; *U.S. Private,* pg. 100
Freeberg, Madonna, Adv. Asst.--Hypro Corporation, New Brighton, MN; *U.S. Public,* pg. 1767
Freeborough, Helen, Mgr.-Adv.--Legal & General Group PLC, London, United Kingdom; *Int'l,* pg. 805
Freel, Marilyn, Mgr.-Adv.--National Fire Protection Association, Quincy, MA; *U.S. Private,* pg. 782
Freeland, Bethany, Mgr.-Mktg.--Renosol Corp., Saline, MI; *U.S. Private,* pg. 922
Freeman-Cardone, Marian, Mgr.-Mktg. Communications--Anorad Corporation, Hauppauge, NY; *U.S. Private,* pg. 75
Freeman, James W., V.P.-Corp. Communications--American United Life Insurance Company, Indianapolis, IN; *U.S. Private,* pg. 64
Freeman, Paula, V.P.-Adv.--Disneyland, Anaheim, CA; *U.S. Public,* pg. 511
Freeze, Cynthia J., Mgr.-Mktg. Services--Kewaunee Scientific Corporation, Statesville, NC; *U.S. Public,* pg. 953
Freibert, David, Mgr.-Adv.--Kentucky Utilities Company, Lexington, KY; *U.S. Public,* pg. 941
Freitas, Ken, V.P.-Mktg. & Adv.--The Timberland Company, Stratham, NH; *U.S. Public,* pg. 1609
Freitas, Stephen, V.P.-Mktg.--Eller Media Company, Phoenix, AZ; *U.S. Public,* pg. 383
Freiwald, Ray, Mgr.-Adv. Support--Warner Electric Industrial Products Division, South Beloit, IL; *U.S. Public,* pg. 480
French, Rachel, Dir.-Adv.--IBM United Kingdom Holdings Limited, Portsmouth, United Kingdom; *U.S. Public,* pg. 897
Frese, Patti, Mktg. Coordinator--FDP Corp., Miami, FL; *U.S. Public,* pg. 603
Fresne, Thierry, Adv. & Communications--Elf Aquitane, Paris, France; *Int'l,* pg. 444
Freuler, Susan, Mgr.-Mktg. Services--The Vendo Company, Fresno, CA; *Int'l,* pg. 1184
Frey, James E., V.P.-Bus. Devel.--J.S. Alberici Construction Co., Inc., Saint Louis, MO; *U.S. Private,* pg. 32
Friberg, Peter A., Sr. V.P.-Memorial Sls. & Dir.-Sls. & Mktg.--Rock of Ages Corporation, Graniteville, VT; *U.S. Public,* pg. 1396
Friday, Sally, Dir.-Mktg.--Amurcon Corporation, Southfield, MI; *U.S. Private,* pg. 69
Friedman, A., V.P. & Dir.-Creative Services--Shieffelin Somerset Co., New York, NY; *Int'l,* pg. 412
Friedman, Irwin, Pres.--International Components Corporation, Melville, NY; *U.S. Private,* pg. 569
Friedman, J. Roger, Pres. & Chief Exec. Officer--Lebhar-Friedman, Inc., New York, NY; *U.S. Private,* pg. 656
Friel, John P., Sr. V.P. & Gen. Mgr.--Medrad, Inc., Indianola, PA; *Int'l,* pg. 1204
Friend, Howard, Pres.--On-Cor Frozen Foods Inc., Northbrook, IL; *U.S. Private,* pg. 817
Fries, Donald B., Dir.-Adv. Sls.--Life Magazine, New York, NY; *U.S. Public,* pg. 1613
Fries, Kathy, Internal Art Dir.--Carme' Cosmeceutical Sciences, Inc., Napa, CA; *U.S. Private,* pg. 213
Frith, Marlene, Dir.-Integrated Commun. & Investor Rels.--Brite Voice Systems, Inc., Heathrow, FL; *U.S. Public,* pg. 257
Fritz, Susan C., Dir.-Commun.--Jewelers Mutual Insurance Company, Neenah, WI; *U.S. Private,* pg. 587
Fritzke, Tom L., Pres.--Heresite Protective Coatings Inc., Manitowoc, WI; *U.S. Private,* pg. 523
Frost, Jeffrey, Dir.-Global Adv.--Nike, Inc., Beaverton, OR; *U.S. Public,* pg. 1184
Frye, Susan, Dir.-Admin. Svcs.--Dorsey Trailers, Inc., Atlanta, GA; *U.S. Public,* pg. 520
Fuerbach, W.F., Jr., Chm. Bd., Pres. & Treas.--S.M. Frank & Co., Inc., Peekskill, NY; *U.S. Private,* pg. 423
Fujimori, Kunio, Mgr.-Adv.--Matsuya Company Ltd., Tokyo, Japan; *Int'l,* pg. 848
Fujiwara, Setsuraku, Dir.-Mkt. Devel.--Sankyo Company Limited, Tokyo, Japan; *Int'l,* pg. 1189
Fujlmori, Danny, Asst. Mgr.-Motorcycle Adv.--American Honda Motor Co., Inc. Motorcycle Division, Torrance, CA; *Int'l,* pg. 634
Fuldner, John E., Mgr.-Mktg. & Adv.--Efco Corporation, Monett, MO; *U.S. Private,* pg. 353
Fulks, Robert, Dir.-Mktg.--Weatherford Enterra Incorporated, Houston, TX; *U.S. Public,* pg. 1749
Fuller, Jill Tingley, Dir.-Adv.--Fortunoff, Uniondale, NY; *U.S. Private,* pg. 420
Fuller, Leslie, Mgr.-Mktg.--Research, Incorporated, Eden Prairie, MN; *U.S. Public,* pg. 1382
Fuller, Scott, Sr. V.P.-Commercial Adv.--Texas Commerce Bank, Houston, TX; *U.S. Public,* pg. 339
Fulton, James, Pres. & Chief Exec. Officer--FKI Industries. Inc., Fairfield, CT; *Int'l,* pg. 472
Fulton, Louisa, Mgr.-Communications--Bayer Corporation/ Diagnostics Division, Tarrytown, NY; *Int'l,* pg. 173
Funk, Edmund, Dr., Dir.-Mktg.--Sun Chemical General Printing Inc., Northlake, IL; *Int'l,* pg. 370
Fuortes, Beverly, Dir.-Corp. Devel.--Amtech Corporation, Dallas, TX; *U.S. Public,* pg. 105
Furca, Lenae, Mgr.-Adv.--Active Electrical Supply Company, Chicago, IL; *U.S. Private,* pg. 15
Furlong, Bill, Dir.-Adv.--Business Marketing, Chicago, IL; *U.S. Private,* pg. 285
Furman, Diana, Mgr.-Dir. Mktg.--Caswell-Massey Co. Ltd., Edison, NJ; *U.S. Private,* pg. 219
Furstenberg, Tricia, Dir.-Adv.--Southwest Airlines Co., Dallas, TX; *U.S. Public,* pg. 1493
Furth, Daniel R., Dir.-Corp. Rels.--MTL Inc., Plant City, FL; *U.S. Public,* pg. 1028
Gabe, Jon, V.P.-Sls. & Mktg.--Fred Usinger, Inc., Milwaukee, WI; *U.S. Private,* pg. 1129
Gabelier, Philippe, V.P.-Pub. Affairs--Caisse de depot et placement du Quebec, Montreal, Canada; *Int'l,* pg. 249
Gabor, Dick, Mgr.-Adv.--Sommer & Maca Industries, Inc., Cicero, IL; *U.S. Private,* pg. 1013
Gabriel, Pam, Coord.-Mktg.--True Temper Hardware Company, Camp Hill, PA; *U.S. Public,* pg. 846
Gabriele, Judy, Mgr.-Adv.--Hillsdale Daily News, Hillsdale, MI; *U.S. Private,* pg. 995
Gagliardi, T., Mgr.-Mktg. Svcs.--RFL Electronics, Inc., Boonton, NJ; *U.S. Private,* pg. 903
Gagnon, Michel, Adv. Dir.--UAP, Inc., Montreal, Canada; *Int'l,* pg. 1426
Gaige, Chris, Dir.-Mktg. & Sls.--MascoTech Tubular Products, Inc., Canton, MI; *U.S. Public,* pg. 1055
Gaines, Lynne, Mgr.-Adv.--Amano Cincinnati, Inc., Roseland, NJ; *Int'l,* pg. 70
Gallager, Leslie, Dir.-Adv. & Promo.--The Putnam & Grosset Group, New York, NY; *Int'l,* pg. 1027
Gallagher, J., Dir.-Sls. & Mktg. Services--Menley & James Laboratories, Inc., Horsham, PA; *U.S. Public,* pg. 1086

Gallagher, John, Dir.-Adv.--People, New York, NY; *U.S. Public*, pg. 1613
Gallaher, Jacqueline, Asst. Sec.--Phoenix Medical Technology, Inc., Andrews, SC; *U.S. Public*, pg. 1292
Gallaher, Stephanie, Mgr.-Mktg.--Squire-Cogswell Company, Gurnee, IL; *U.S. Private*, pg. 1027
Gallemore, William II, Chief Oper. Officer--National Banner Company, Inc., Dallas, TX; *U.S. Private*, pg. 780
Gallgher, John, Dir.-Adv.-People--Time Inc., New York, NY; *U.S. Public*, pg. 1612
Gallo, Jennifer, Assoc. Publr.-Adv.--Cosmopolitan, New York, NY; *U.S. Private*, pg. 517
Gallo, Peter B., Mgr.-Adv.--Maxell Corp. Of America, Fair Lawn, NJ; *Int'l*, pg. 621
Galloway, Michael, Dir.-Adv.--Star Furniture Company, Houston, TX; *U.S. Public*, pg. 221
Galpin, Donna, Dir.-Adv.--Fashion Bug, Bensalem, PA; *U.S. Public*, pg. 336
Galvin, James, Dir.-Adv. & Mktg. & Mgr.-Sls.--MAC America Communications, Inc., Phoenix, AZ; *U.S. Private*, pg. 685
Galvin, Kathleen, Dir.-Mktg.--Parlux Fragrances Inc., Fort Lauderdale, FL; *U.S. Public*, pg. 1264
Gandy, Jim, Mgr.-Sls.--Morgantown Machine & Hydraulics, Inc., Morgantown, WV; *Int'l*, pg. 280
Ganek, Carol, Dir.-Mktg.--Rowe International, Inc., Grand Rapids, MI; *U.S. Private*, pg. 904
Gangone, Joe, Sr. V.P.-Adv.--Madison Square Garden Network, New York, NY; *U.S. Public*, pg. 288
Ganot, Harvey, Pres.-Adv. & Promo. Sls.--MTV Networks, New York, NY; *U.S. Private*, pg. 779
Gans, Mary Anne, Dir.-Mktg.--Globelle Corporation, Mississauga, Canada; *Int'l*, pg. 554
Gans, Terry A., V.P.-Adv. & Sls. Promo.--Giant Food Inc., Landover, MD; *U.S. Public*, pg. 741
Ganz, Susan, Pres.--Lion Brothers Company, Inc., Owings Mills, MD; *U.S. Private*, pg. 669
Garavelli, John, Mgr.-Sls. & Adv.--Thomas & Betts Corporation, Memphis, TN; *U.S. Public*, pg. 1597
Garavelli, John, Mgr.-Adv. & Sls.--Thomas & Betts Reznor Division, Memphis, TN; *U.S. Public*, pg. 1598
Garber, David, Dir.-Mktg.--Kemps Foods, Inc., Lancaster, PA; *Int'l*, pg. 752
Garber, Sue, Mgr.-Adv.--Ludwig Industries, Monroe, NC; *U.S. Public*, pg. 1514
Garbizo, Kay, V.P.-Adv.--Ralphs Grocery Company, Compton, CA; *U.S. Private*, pg. 1202
Garbutt, George A., Exec. V.P.-Gen. Mgr. & Dir.-Adv.--Maserati Automobiles, Incorporated, Baltimore, MD; *Int'l*, *pg. 482*
Garbuzinski, Kathy, Coord. & Mgr.-Corp. Communications--Morgan Keegan, Inc., Memphis, TN; *U.S. Public*, pg. 1131
Garcia, Anna Maria, Dir.-Adv.--Banco Exterior, S.A., Montevideo, Uruguay; *Int'l*, pg. 81
Garcia, Jose, Dir.-Adv.--Townsend Engineering Co., Des Moines, IA; *U.S. Private*, pg. 1094
Garcia, Joseph T., Dir.-Field Mktg.--International House of Pancakes, Inc., Glendale, CA; *U.S. Public*, pg. 862
Gardiner, Kevin, V.P.-Adv. (Creative)--The Bon Marche, Inc., Seattle, WA; *U.S. Public*, pg. 617
Gardner, Julie, V.P.-Adv. & Mktg.--Eckerd Corporation, Largo, FL; *U.S. Public*, pg. 917
Gardner, Julie, V.P.-Adv. & Mktg.--Eckerd Drug Co., Clearwater, FL; *U.S. Public*, pg. 917
Garfinkle, Shirley, Mgr.-Adv. & Corp. Communications--Mitchel-Lincoln Packaging, Saint-Laurent, Canada; *Int'l*, pg. 870
Gargone, Sal, Mgr.-Adv.--Lee Myles Associates Corporation, Paramus, NJ; *U.S. Private*, pg. 657
Garicano, Jose, Dir.-Pub. Rels.--Opel Espana, Zaragoza, Spain; *U.S. Public*, pg. 724
Garland, Dwight, V.P.-Retail Adv.--Staples, Inc., Westborough, MA; *U.S. Public*, pg. 1509
Garland, Frank, V.P.-Adv. Sls.--The Weather Channel, Atlanta, GA; *U.S. Private*, pg. 647
Garman, M. Lawrence, Pres. & Chief Exec. Officer--Daubert Industries, Inc., Westchester, IL; *U.S. Private*, pg. 313
Garner, Laurie, V.P.-Adv.--Belk Stores Services Inc., Charlotte, NC; *U.S. Private*, pg. 131
Garretty, Rod, Mgr.-Adv.--Distillers Corporation S.A., Stellenbosch, South Africa; *Int'l*, pg. 1129
Garrison, Dennis, Adv. Mgr.--The Newton Kansan, Newton, KS; *U.S. Private*, pg. 995
Garrity, Jim, Sr. V.P. & Dir.-Adv. & Mktg.--First Union Corporation, Charlotte, NC; *U.S. Public*, pg. 639
Garro, Robert, Dir.-Mktg.--RMT Technology, Bellwood, IL; *U.S. Private*, pg. 927
Garrow, Jeff, Dir.-Adv.--ABC Supply Company, Inc., Beloit, WI; *U.S. Private*, pg. 3
Garry, Jeff, Mgr.-Adv., Sls. & Mktg.-Sportswear--Raven Industries, Inc., Sioux Falls, SD; *U.S. Public*, pg. 1361
Garvens, Kent, Pres.--Electro-Coatings, Inc., Berkeley, CA; *U.S. Private*, pg. 368
Garvey, Tom J., Mgr.-Mktg.--Sioux Tools, Inc., Sioux City, IA; *U.S. Public*, pg. 1480
Garvick, Debra, Mgr.-Mktg.--Buck Knives, Inc., El Cajon, CA; *U.S. Private*, pg. 177
Gasmovic, David J., Exec. V.P.--McLaughlin Manufacturing Company, Greenville, SC; *U.S. Private*, pg. 724
Gasparro, Anthony, V.P.-Adv.--The Great Atlantic & Pacific Tea Company, Inc., Montvale, NJ; *Int'l*, pg. 1375
Gasperson, Bill, Pres.--Flowers Baking Co. of West Virginia, Bluefield, WV; *U.S. Public*, pg. 657
Gasson, Anthony, Pres. & Dir.-Adv.--Swirl, II LTD, New York, NY; *U.S. Private*, pg. 1059
Gates, Greg, V.P.-Direct Mktg. & Adv.--Nationwide Insurance Enterprise, Columbus, OH; *U.S. Private*, pg. 788
Gaucher, Gerard, Dir.-Adv.--Banque Nationale de Paris, Paris, France; *Int'l*, pg. 163
Gaul, David, V.P.--Denver Wholesale Florists Company, Denver, CO; *U.S. Private*, pg. 326
Gault, Graham, Mgr.-Adv.--First Interstate Bank of Arizona, N.A., Phoenix, AZ; *U.S. Public*, pg. 1753
Gavelek, Mike, Dir.-Mktg. Svcs.--Budget Rent A Car Corporation, Lisle, IL; *U.S. Private*, pg. 178
Gazda, Dolores, Mgr.-Adv.--Rose Packing Company, Barrington, IL; *U.S. Private*, pg. 945
Gebhard, Klaus-Dieter, Dir.-Adv.--Wintershall Gas GmbH, Kassel, Germany; *Int'l*, pg. 105
Gehrett, Gretchan, Dir.-Adv.--MCI Telecommunications Corp., Washington, DC; *U.S. Public*, pg. 1024
Geiselman, R.D., Mgr.-Mktg. Communications--Houghton International Inc., Valley Forge, PA; *U.S. Private*, pg. 541
Geiser, Jim, Mgr.-Adv. & Promo.--Six Flags Astroworld/Six Flags Waterworld/Six Flags Houston, Houston, TX; *U.S. Public*, pg. 1611
Geisler, Jim, Mgr.-Mktg. Communications--Killark Electric Manufacturing Co., Saint Louis, MO; *U.S. Public*, pg. 844
Geissler, Christine, Dir.-Adv.--Rohm GmbH, Darmstadt, Germany; *Int'l*, pg. 1454
Gekler, Brooks, Sr. V.P.-Mktg.--General Mills Canada Inc., Etobicoke, Canada; *U.S. Public*, pg. 718
Gelfer, I., Mgr.-Adv.--Elbit Computers Ltd., Haifa, Israel; *Int'l*, *pg. 644*
Gell, Mark, Dir.-Adv.--Boral Limited, Sydney, Australia; *Int'l*, pg. 203
Gellert, George G., Chm. Bd. & Pres.--Atalanta Corporation, Elizabeth, NJ; *U.S. Private*, pg. 93
Gemmel, Kari, Dir.-Mktg.--Jackson Hole Ski Resort, Teton Village, WY; *U.S. Private*, pg. 579
Genrett, Gretchen, Exec. Dir.-Adv. Communications--MCI Communications Corp., Atlanta, GA; *U.S. Public*, pg. 1023
Genther, Bruce, Mgr.-Adv.--First American Metro Corp., Mc Lean, VA; *U.S. Public*, pg. 640
George, Marcella, Mgr.-Mktg.--Swiss Army Brands, Inc., Shelton, CT; *U.S. Public*, pg. 1544
Georgoulis, Stratton, Chm. Bd., Pres. & Chief Exec. Officer--TIC United Corporation, Dallas, TX; *U.S. Private*, pg. 1063
Geovanello, Frank, Asst. Mgr.-Media Marlboro--Philip Morris U.S.A., New York, NY; *U.S. Public*, pg. 1289
Gerardi, Charles, Dir.-Adv.--The Dallas Morning News, Inc., Dallas, TX; *U.S. Public*, pg. 209
Geraty, Colleen, Principal-Adv.--Edward Jones, Saint Louis, MO; *U.S. Private*, pg. 597
Gerber, Allen, Mgr.-Adv.--Brooklyn Union, Brooklyn, NY; *U.S. Public*, pg. 259
Gerber, Dylan, Sr. V.P.-Adv. & Mktg.--UPN-United Paramount Network, Los Angeles, CA; *U.S. Public*, pg. 352
Gerber, Dylan, Sr. V.P.-Adv. & Mktg.--UPN-United Paramount Network, Los Angeles, CA; *U.S. Private*, pg. 777
Gerber, Kimberly, Mgr.-Adv.--Fleetwood Enterprises, Inc., Riverside, CA; *U.S. Public*, pg. 650
Gerdeman, Brad, Mgr.-Natl. Adv.--Delta Air Lines, Inc., Atlanta, GA; *U.S. Public*, pg. 497
Gerdy, Harvey, Chm. Bd., Pres. & Chief Exec. Officer--International Seaway Trading Corporation, Boca Raton, FL; *U.S. Private*, pg. 572
Gerigery, Kelly, Dir.-Corp. Mktg.--Donnelly Corporation, Holland, MI; *U.S. Public*, pg. 519
Germain, Linda, Mgr.-Adv.--Air Alliance, Sainte-Foy, Canada; *Int'l*, pg. 36
Gersback, Tony, Dir.-Adv.--Email Limited-Major Appliance Group, Riverwood, Australia; *Int'l*, pg. 450
Gershberg, Jay, Sr. V.P. & Pres.-Travel Nurse Grp.--Hospital Staffing Services, Inc., Fort Lauderdale, FL; *U.S. Public*, pg. 840
Gerstein, Mel, Treas. & Dir.-Mktg., Adv. & Pub. Rels.--Thermwell Products Co., Inc., Paterson, NJ; *U.S. Private*, *pg. 1081*
Getson, Lisa M., Sr. V.P-Mktg.--Apria Healthcare Group Inc., Costa Mesa, CA; *U.S. Public*, pg. 125
Gettlefinger, Dennis, V.P.-Adv.--The Apparel Group, Ltd., Louisville, KY; *U.S. Private*, pg. 78
Gewehr, Chris, V.P. & Dir.-Adv.--McSwain Carpets Inc., Cincinnati, OH; *U.S. Private*, pg. 725
Gezon, Bruce, V.P.-Mktg.--Helmick Corporation, Fairmont, WV; *U.S. Private*, pg. 520
Gezundhajt, B., Sr. V.P.-Mktg. & Sls.--Zim-American Israeli Shipping Co., New York, NY; *U.S. Private*, pg. 1206
Giacchetti, Richard, V.P.-Mktg.--Fox River Paper Company, Appleton, WI; *U.S. Private*, pg. 422
Giaguinto, John, Dir.-Adv.--Syratech Corporation, East Boston, MA; *U.S. Private*, pg. 1060
Giampaglia, Mario, Mgr.-Adv., Audio Prods.--Sony Electronics, Park Ridge, NJ; *Int'l*, pg. 1281
Giangiulio, Mary Ellen, Mgr.-Mktg.--Streamlight Inc., Norristown, PA; *U.S. Private*, pg. 1047
Giaquinto, John, Dir.-Adv.--Wallace International Silversmiths, Inc., East Boston, MA; *U.S. Private*, pg. 1061
Gibbons, Duane, Dir.-Adv. & Mktg. Photo Control Corporation, Minneapolis, MN; *U.S. Public*, pg. 1292
Gibbons, Jim, Exec. V.P.-Creative Services--Paramount Pictures Corporation, Los Angeles, CA; *U.S. Private*, pg. 776
Gibbs, David G., Mgr.-Bus. Devel.--Electro Kinetics Div., Santa Barbara, CA; *U.S. Public*, pg. 1250
Gibson, Grant S., Dir.-Corp. Commun.--Protocol Systems, Inc., Beaverton, OR; *U.S. Public*, pg. 1336
Gibson, Pam, Mgr.-Category--United Dairy Farmers, Inc., Cincinnati, OH; *U.S. Private*, pg. 1121
Gibson, Roberta J., V.P.-Adv. & Pub. Rels.--Hill-Behan Lumber Company, Saint Louis, MO; *U.S. Private*, pg. 529
Giezenaar, R.W.M., Mgr.-Adv.--Bayer B.V., Mijdrecht, Netherlands; *Int'l*, pg. 175
Gilbert, Duane, Dir.-Adv.--Cone Drive Textron, Traverse City, MI; *U.S. Public*, pg. 1589
Gilbert, Glen, V.P.-Adv. & Social Responsibility--GTE Corporation, Stamford, CT; *U.S. Public*, pg. 696
Gilbert, Robert, V.P.-Sls.--Benchmark Electronics Inc., Angleton, TX; *U.S. Public*, pg. 210
Gilbert, Trisha, Mgr.-Adv.--Builder Marts of America, Inc., Greenville, SC; *U.S. Private*, pg. 179
Gilbertson, Cydney, Mgr.-Mktg. Communications--Chemical Leaman Corporation, Exton, PA; *U.S. Private*, pg. 233
Giles, Jessica, Mgr.-Adv.--Mount Snow Resort, Mount Snow, VT; *U.S. Private*, pg. 61
Gill, Janet E., Dir.-Exec. Services--Chicago Tube & Iron Co., Chicago, IL; *U.S. Private*, pg. 235
Gillespie, Jerry, Sr. V.P.-Opers.--Hutch Sports USA, Inc., Hebron, KY; *U.S. Public*, pg. 1354
Gillespie, Robert C., Second V.P.-Adv. & Corp. Communications--The Guardian Life Insurance Company of America, New York, NY; *U.S. Private*, pg. 486
Gilligan, Peter, Mgr.-Mktg.--New Zealand Lamb Co., Inc., White Plains, NY; *U.S. Private*, pg. 796
Gilmore, Daniel E., Dir.-Communications--The Foxboro Company, Foxboro, MA; *Int'l*, pg. 1243
Gilmore, Howard N., Jr., Chief Exec. Officer--Gilmore Envelope Corp., Los Angeles, CA; *U.S. Private*, pg. 454
Gilmore, Janet, Mgr.-Adv.--Transalta Corporation, Calgary, Canada; *Int'l*, pg. 1416
Gilmore, Kathleen, Mgr.-Sls..--Gilmore Envelope Corp., Los Angeles, CA; *U.S. Private*, pg. 454
Gilmore, Ronald J., Exec. V.P.-Adv. & Mktg.--CompUSA, Dallas, TX; *U.S. Public*, pg. 420
Ginsberg, Terry, Dir.-Adv.--Singleton Seafood Co., Tampa, FL; *U.S. Public*, pg. 427
Ginsburg, Allan, Chm. Bd.--Jaclyn, Inc., West New York, NJ; *U.S. Public*, pg. 920
Gioia, Philip, Mgr.-Mktg.--Barr Laboratories Inc., Pomona, NY; *U.S. Public*, pg. 191
Giordano, Jennifer, Coord.-Mktg. Services--Sika Corporation, Lyndhurst, NJ; *Int'l*, pg. 1249
Giordano, Joan, Supvr.-Customer Svcs.--H. Freeman & Son, Inc., Philadelphia, PA; *U.S. Private*, pg. 426
Gipson, Jim L., Jr., V.P.-Corp. Communications--The Williams Companies, Inc., Tulsa, OK; *U.S. Public*, pg. 1769
Girardi, Frank, Dir.-Inv. Rels.--IGI, Inc., Buena, NJ; *U.S. Public*, pg. 855
Githens, Suzanne, Mgr.-Communications--Cyro Industries, Rockaway, NJ; *Int'l*, pg. 1454
Giuffrida, Caroline, Mgr.-Mktg.-Retail--Cains Foods, L.P., Ayer, MA; *U.S. Private*, pg. 199
Gjestvang, Rosie, Mgr.-Adv. & Commun.--MLT Vacations, Inc., Minnetonka, MN; *U.S. Public*, pg. 1200
Gladieux, Gerry M., V.P.-Adv.--Camelot Music, Inc., Canton, OH; *U.S. Private*, pg. 203
Glaser, Janice, V.P.-Adv.--Columbia Tri-Star Home Video, Burbank, CA; *Int'l*, pg. 1282
Glasheen, Jennifer, Dir.-Adv.--VARTA Batteries Inc., Elmsford, NY; *Int'l*, pg. 1452
Glass, Alex G., Asst. Mgr.-Adv.--Berkley Publishing Corp., New York, NY; *Int'l*, pg. 1027
Glasser, Barbara, First V.P., Dir.-Adv.--Prudential Securities Inc., New York, NY; *U.S. Private*, pg. 892
Glassey, Susan, Mgr.-Adv.--Micron Technology Inc., Boise, ID; *U.S. Public*, pg. 1105
Glavin, Pat, Dir.-XL Connect--Intelligent Electronics, Inc., Exton, PA; *U.S. Public*, pg. 887
Glazer, Libby, V.P.-Adv., Pub. Rels. & Corp. Commun.--Credit Lyonnais Americas, New York, NY; *Int'l*, pg. 344
Glenn, Alison, V.P.-Mktg.--Taco Cabana, San Antonio, TX; *U.S. Public*, pg. 1559
Glenn, Tom, Dir.-Adv.--Genuardi Family Markets Inc., Norristown, PA; *U.S. Private*, pg. 447
Glennon, Debrah, Sr. Mgr.-Adv. & Brand--Nortel, Nashville, TN; *Int'l*, pg. 970
Glivar, Debbie, Adv. Admin.--Sea World of California, San Diego, CA; *U.S. Public*, pg. 114
Glow, Krista, Mgr.-Adv.--The Rockport Company, Marlborough, MA; *U.S. Public*, pg. 1370
Gloyd, Lawrence E., Chm. Bd. & Chief Exec. Officer--CLARCOR, Inc., Rockford, IL; *U.S. Public*, pg. 381
Gmunder, Thomas, Dir.-Adv. & Sls.--Schweizer Verband der Raiffeisenbanken, Saint Gallen, Switzerland; *Int'l*, pg. 1211
Gobble, Harry, Mgr.-Mktg.--Glen Raven Mills, Inc., Glen Raven, NC; *U.S. Private*, pg. 456
Goddard, Bill, Mgr.-Classified Adv.--The Dispatch Printing Company, Columbus, OH; *U.S. Private*, pg. 334
Godfredson, Dave, Dir.-Adv. & Promo.--Food Lion, Inc., Salisbury, NC; *Int'l*, pg. 463
Godhwani, Neeta, Sr. Mgr.-Mktg. Services--Genzyme Diagnostics, Medix Biotech, San Carlos, CA; *U.S. Public*, pg. 733
Goding, Keith L, Chief Devel. Officer & Exec. V.P.--RehabCare Group, Inc., Saint Louis, MO; *U.S. Public*, pg. 1373
Goeb, Carl, Mgr.-Mktg.--Neway Anchorlok International Inc., Muskegon, MI; *U.S. Private*, pg. 796
Goede, Caroline, Mgr.-Adv.--Trippe Mfg. Co., Chicago, IL; *U.S. Private*, pg. 1104
Goehrke, Robert, V.P.-Mktg.--Matrix Essentials, Inc., Solon, OH; *U.S. Public*, pg. 254
Goetschi, Pierre, Mng. Dir. & Adv.--Schweizerische Kaseunion AG, Bern, Switzerland; *Int'l*, pg. 1211
Goetz, Bill, V.P.-Mktg. & Mdsg.--Cintas Corporation, Mason, OH; *U.S. Public*, pg. 370
Goetz, Tim, Chief Fin. Officer, Treas. & Dir.-Mktg.--Robinson Helicopter Company, Torrance, CA; *U.S. Private*, pg. 936
Goff, Steven E., Dir.-Mktg. & Adv.--Mrs. Giles Country Kitchens, Inc., Lynchburg, VA; *U.S. Public*, pg. 596
Goh, Clara, Mgr.-Mktg. Svcs.--F.J. Benjamin Fashions (M) Sdn. Bhd., Kuala Lumpur, Malaysia; *Int'l*, pg. 187
Gold, Michael, Sr. V.P.-Corp. Commun. & Adv.--Packard Bell NEC, Sacramento, CA; *U.S. Private*, pg. 833
Goldberg, David, V.P.--Hooper Holmes Corporation, Basking Ridge, NJ; *U.S. Public*, pg. 835
Goldberg, David, V.P.-Adv. & Promo.--Time Warner Cable of New York City, New York, NY; *U.S. Public*, pg. 1611
Goldberg, Ellen, Dir.-Adv.--Maidenform Worldwide, New York, NY; *U.S. Private*, pg. 697
Goldberg, Ellen, Dir.-Adv.--True Form Intimate Apparel, New York, NY; *U.S. Private*, pg. 697

Goldberg, Marshall, Mgr.-Mktg. Prod.--Sigma Designs, Inc., Fremont, CA; *U.S. Public*, pg. 1472
Golde, Mark, Rep.-Sls. Promo.--Dillard, A ResourceNet International Company, Charlotte, NC; *U.S. Public*, pg. 902
Goldenberg, Sandy, Coord.-Mktg. Communications--Datasouth Computer Corporation, Charlotte, NC; *U.S. Public*, pg. 267
Goldfarb, David, Dir.-Mktg.--Consolidated Cigar Corporation, Fort Lauderdale, FL; *U.S. Private*, pg. 690
Goldie, Dorothy, Mgr.-Adv.--U.S. Bancorp, Minneapolis, MN; *U.S. Public*, pg. 1680
Goldin, Susan, Dir.-Adv.--Getty Petroleum Marketing Inc., Jericho, NY; *U.S. Public*, pg. 740
Goldklank, Mitchell, Sr. V.P.-Sls. & Mktg.--LCS Industries, Inc., Clifton, NJ; *U.S. Public*, pg. 970
Goldman, David, V.P.-Mktg.--Ross Stores, Inc., Newark, CA; *U.S. Public*, pg. 1405
Goldman, Ed, Mktg. & Adv.--Avia, Irvine, CA; *U.S. Private*, pg. 62
Goldman, Kenneth, Corp. Dir.-Adv.--Tecumseh Products Company, Tecumseh, MI; *U.S. Public*, pg. 1565
Goldman, Marc, Pres. & Chief Exec. Officer--Farmland Dairies, Wallington, NJ; *U.S. Private*, pg. 395
Goldman, Thomas, Pres.--Iowa Paint Mfg. Company, Inc., Des Moines, IA; *U.S. Private*, pg. 575
Goldschmidt, Mark E., Sr. V.P.-Adv. & Mktg.--Hearst Magazines Division, New York, NY; *U.S. Private*, pg. 516
Goldsmith, Gini, Coord.-Adv.--Omaha Public Power District, Omaha, NE; *U.S. Private*, pg. 815
Goldstine, Josh, Sr. V.P.-Creative Adv.--Columbia Pictures, Culver City, CA; *Int'l*, pg. 1281
Goldstone, Caren, V.P.-Adv.--Handleman Company, Troy, MI; *U.S. Public*, pg. 779
Golemo, Stanley M., Jr., Chm. Bd. & Pres.--Hood & Company, Hamburg, PA; *Int'l*, pg. 572
Gomar, R. Ian, V.P.-Mktg.--Starter Corp., New Haven, CT; *U.S. Public*, pg. 1511
Gomatos, John, Dir.-Mktg.--Kirin USA, Inc., Los Angeles, CA; *Int'l*, pg. 736
Goncalves, Heitor Laso, Mgr.-Mktg. Services--Brastemp S.A., Sao Bernardo do Campo, Brazil; *U.S. Public*, pg. 1765
Gonda, Michael S., Mgr.-Adv.--Acustar, Inc., Troy, MI; *U.S. Public*, pg. 353
Gonner, Renae, Dir.-Adv.--Payless Cashways, Inc., Kansas City, MO; *U.S. Public*, pg. 1267
Gonos, G., Dir.-Mktg.--Leader Instruments Corporation, Hauppauge, NY; *U.S. Private*, pg. 655
Gonzalez, David, Mgr.-Adv.--BASF Espanola S.A., Barcelona, Spain; *Int'l*, pg. 106
Gonzalez, Rafel Vega, Dir.-Adv.--Grupo Banco Exterior, Madrid, Spain; *Int'l*, pg. 80
Gonzalez, Rita, Dir.-Mktg.--Lennar Homes Inc., Miami, FL; *U.S. Public*, pg. 988
Gonzalez, Steve, Mgr.-Adv.--Houston Lighting & Power Company, Houston, TX; *U.S. Public*, pg. 843
Goodall, J.M., Mgr.-Adv.--Weil-McLain, Michigan City, IN; *U.S. Public*, pg. 1676
Goodell, Brenda, V.P.-Mktg. Communications--Reebok International Ltd., Stoughton, MA; *U.S. Public*, pg. 1369
Goodman, John, V.P.-Mktg.--Helzberg's Diamond Shops, Inc., Kansas City, MO; *U.S. Public*, pg. 220
Goodman, Milda C., Dir.-Adv. & Pub. Rels.--Pacific Life Insurance Company, Newport Beach, CA; *U.S. Private*, pg. 831
Goodrich, Todd, Dir.-Promo. & Adv.--Six Flags St. Louis, Eureka, MO; *U.S. Public*, pg. 1616
Goodsell, Jeanne, Supvr.-Adv.--Smith & Wesson Corp., Springfield, MA; *Int'l*, pg. 1397
Goon, Julie, Dir.-Adv.--Columbian Mutual Life Insurance Co., Binghamton, NY; *U.S. Private*, pg. 256
Gorby, Jane, V.P.-Mktg. Dir.--Downey Savings & Loan Association, F.A., Newport Beach, CA; *U.S. Public*, pg. 526
Gordon, Don, V.P.-Adv.--CDW Computer Centers, Inc., Vernon Hills, IL; *U.S. Public*, pg. 277
Gordon, J.R., Mgr.-Retail Adv. & Sls. Promo.--Chevron Corporation, San Francisco, CA; *U.S. Public*, pg. 347
Gordon, Kenneth, Dir.-Adv. & Card Brand Strategy--Citibank Credit Card Marketing, Long Island City, NY; *U.S. Public*, pg. 377
Gordon, Lucy, V.P.-Adv.--The Vanguard Group, Inc., Valley Forge, PA; *U.S. Private*, pg. 1133
Gorell, Frank, Pres.--Jamison Bedding, Inc., Franklin, TN; *U.S. Private*, pg. 581
Goren, Bruce, Mgr.-Natl. Adv.--Hyundai Motor America, Fountain Valley, CA; *Int'l*, pg. 641
Gorman, D., Exec. V.P.-Sls.--R.T. Vanderbilt Company, Inc., Norwalk, CT; *U.S. Private*, pg. 1133
Gorney, Emily A., Asst. V.P. & Mgr.-Adv.--CitFed Bancorp, Inc., Dayton, OH; *U.S. Public*, pg. 376
Gorol, Michelle, Dir.-Adv.--MicroAge, Inc., Tempe, AZ; *U.S. Public*, pg. 1104
Goss, Mary, Mgr.-Mktg. Services--Danaher Tool Group, Lancaster, PA; *U.S. Public*, pg. 480
Gotlin, Amy, Dir.-Promotions--Flowers USA, Uniondale, NY; *U.S. Private*, pg. 415
Goto, Milton K., Dir.-Mktg. Svcs. & Adv.--Aloha Airgroup, Inc., Honolulu, HI; *U.S. Private*, pg. 44
Gott, Leigh, Dir.-Mktg.--Wisconsin Machine and Tool Corporation, Milwaukee, WI; *U.S. Private*, pg. 1185
Gould, Brenda, Dir.-Corp. Commun.--Olympic Steel Inc., Cleveland, OH; *U.S. Public*, pg. 1221
Gould, Doyle, V.P. & Gen. Mgr.-Flow Measure Div.--Perry Equipment Corporation, Mineral Wells, TX; *U.S. Private*, pg. 855
Gould, William, Mgr.-Sls. & Mktg.--Brady Enterprises, Inc., East Weymouth, MA; *U.S. Private*, pg. 165
Gould, William, Mgr.-Sls. & Mktg.--The William G. Bell Company, East Weymouth, MA; *U.S. Private*, pg. 165
Govern, Dan, Dir.-Adv.--Golf Shop Operations, Trumbull, CT; *U.S. Public*, pg. 1174
Grabowski, Jerry, Dir.-Adv.--Toledo Blade Co., Toledo, OH; *U.S. Private*, pg. 147
Graham-Peterson, Lisa, Dir.-Corp. Commun.--MSI Insurance Companies, Arden Hills, MN; *U.S. Private*, pg. 688
Graham, Jack, Mgr.-Corp. Communications--Ethyl Corporation, Richmond, VA; *U.S. Public*, pg. 595
Graham, Nancy, Dir.-Adv.--Classic Nissan, Orlando, FL; *U.S. Private*, pg. 8
Graham, Page, Adv. Coord.--Hubbard Farms, Inc., Walpole, NH; *U.S. Public*, pg. 1092
Graham, Page, Adv. Coord.--Hubbard Farms, Inc., Walpole, NH; *Int'l*, pg. 1114
Graham, Rich, Dir.-Art--Sherwood-Davis & Geck, Saint Louis, MO; *U.S. Public*, pg. 80
Graham, William, Mgr.-Adv. Prod.--Chemical Engineering, New York, NY; *U.S. Public*, pg. 1071
Granacki, Evelyn, Sr. Mgr.-Mktg. Communications--Computer Sciences Corporation, El Segundo, CA; *U.S. Public*, pg. 422
Grandle, Pat, Sec. & Mgr.-Mktg. & Adv.--Tricon Industries, Inc., Lisle, IL; *U.S. Private*, pg. 1102
Grandsen, R.A., Dir.-Adv.--Viking Pump, Inc., Cedar Falls, IA; *U.S. Public*, pg. 862
Grandy, J. Patrick, Mgr.-Adv.--Zippo Manufacturing Company, Bradford, PA; *U.S. Private*, pg. 1207
Granger, Lee F., Mng. Dir.-Mktg.--American Automobile Association, Heathrow, FL; *U.S. Private*, pg. 50
Grant, Kathryn, Adv. Dir.--Kennedy-Wilson, Inc., Santa Monica, CA; *U.S. Public*, pg. 951
Grant, Marilyn B., V.P.-Adv.--Carmike Cinemas, Inc., Columbus, GA; *U.S. Public*, pg. 305
Grant, Michele, Mgr.-Adv.--The Toro Company, Bloomington, MN; *U.S. Public*, pg. 1623
Grant, Thomas W., Pres.--Pax World Fund Family, Portsmouth, NH; *U.S. Public*, pg. 1266
Grass, Martin L., Chm. Bd. & Chief Exec. Officer--Rite Aid Corporation, Camp Hill, PA; *U.S. Public*, pg. 1390
Grasso, Amanda, Mgr.-Adv. & Mktg.--Giles & Ransome, Inc., Bensalem, PA; *U.S. Private*, pg. 453
Graton, Jean Loup, Mgr.-Adv.--Radio France, Paris, France; *Int'l*, pg. 1083
Gray, James, V.P.-Sls.--Capintec Inc., Ramsey, NJ; *U.S. Private*, pg. 205
Gray, Jim, Dir.-Mktg. Svcs.--Aearo Company, Boston, MA; *U.S. Private*, pg. 23
Gray, Richard, V.P.-Sls. & Mktg.--Rochester-Midland ICL, Omaha, NE; *U.S. Private*, pg. 937
Gray, Roland, V.P.-Mktg.--Blue Bird Corporation, Macon, GA; *U.S. Private*, pg. 151
Grazier, George, Pres.--Farmland Foods, Inc., Kansas City, MO; *U.S. Private*, pg. 396
Grebey, Nancy V., Sr. V.P.-Mktg. & Adv.--Crestar Financial Corporation, Richmond, VA; *U.S. Public*, pg. 458
Green, Bartley C., Dir.-Adv.--San Francisco Newspaper Agency, San Francisco, CA; *U.S. Private*, pg. 239
Green, Clifford, V.P.-Sls., Mktg. & Adv.--Highfield Manufacturing Co., Bridgeport, CT; *Int'l*, pg. 127
Green, Dan, Dir.-Adv.--Capitol Chevrolet Cadillac GEO Subaru Inc., Salem, OR; *U.S. Private*, pg. 206
Green, Kevin, V.P.-Mktg.--Lillian Vernon Corporation, New Rochelle, NY; *U.S. Public*, pg. 1716
Green, Mary Ann, V.P.-Pub. Rels.--MBL Life Assurance Corporation, Newark, NJ; *U.S. Private*, pg. 685
Green, Michael, V.P. & Dir.-Adv. & Special Events--Carson Pirie Scott & Company-Dept. Stores Div., Chicago, IL; *U.S. Public*, pg. 309
Greenberg, Jayne, V.P.-Adv. Media--The Gap, Inc., San Francisco, CA; *U.S. Public*, pg. 702
Greenberg, Mark E., V.P.-Pub. Rels. & External Communications--AlliedSignal Inc., Morristown, NJ; *U.S. Public*, pg. 49
Greenberg, Robert, V.P. & Gen. Mgr.-Communications--Panasonic Consumer Electric Co., Secaucus, NJ; *Int'l*, pg. 847
Greene, Gilbert K., Mgr.-Mktg. Svcs.--Victaulic Company of America, Easton, PA; *U.S. Private*, pg. 1138
Greene, James D., Dir.-Creative Media--Midway Games, Inc., Chicago, IL; *U.S. Public*, pg. 1727
Greene, Lewis, Dir.-Adv.--Gerald Group Inc., Rego Park, NY; *U.S. Private*, pg. 448
Greene, Wendy, Mgr.-Pub. Rels.--Hughes Communications, Inc., Long Beach, CA; *U.S. Public*, pg. 721
Greenip, John, Mgr.-Technical Svcs.-Tubular Prods.--Hydril Company, Houston, TX; *U.S. Private*, pg. 551
Greenisen, G.J., Dir.-Adv.--Electric Furnace Co., Salem, OH; *U.S. Private*, pg. 367
Greenleaf, Maylene, Mgr.-Adv.--Legacy Marketing Group, Petaluma, CA; *U.S. Private*, pg. 658
Greenlee, Algernon F., Mgr.-Retail Bus.--Blue Diamond Growers, Sacramento, CA; *U.S. Private*, pg. 152
Greenstein, Davina, Publ. Rels. Specialist--Dataproducts Corporation, Simi Valley, CA; *Int'l*, pg. 620
Greenwald, Mark, Dir.-Mktg. & Adv.--D&H Distributing Company, Harrisburg, PA; *U.S. Private*, pg. 300
Greenwood, Bob, Dir.-Adv.--The Penn Traffic Company, Syracuse, NY; *U.S. Public*, pg. 1270
Greer, John, Dir.-Adv. & Pub. Rels.--Arkansas Best Corporation, Fort Smith, AR; *U.S. Public*, pg. 130
Greer, Kate, Editor-In-Chief--Weight Watchers Magazine, Birmingham, AL; *U.S. Public*, pg. 1612
Greer, Krista, Mgr.-Adv.--O'Reilly Automotive Inc., Springfield, MO; *U.S. Public*, pg. 1230
Greer, Lou, V.P.-Partners Mktg.--Network Computing Devices, Inc., Mountain View, CA; *U.S. Public*, pg. 1168
Greer, Rita, V.P.-Adv. & Design--Reliable Knitting Works, Milwaukee, WI; *U.S. Private*, pg. 920
Greer, Rita, V.P.-Design--Halper Bros., Milwaukee, WI; *U.S. Private*, pg. 920
Gregorecs, Andor, Mgr.-Adv.--AGA Progas A/S, Oslo, Norway; *Int'l*, pg. 13
Gregorio, Margaret D., V.P.-Contract & Commercial Adv.--Staples, Inc., Westborough, MA; *U.S. Public*, pg. 1509
Gregory, Bob, Mgr.-Adv.--Viking Range Corp., Greenwood, MS; *U.S. Private*, pg. 1140
Gregory, Dave, Dir.-Mktg. & Mdsg.--Star Lumber & Supply Company, Inc., Wichita, KS; *U.S. Private*, pg. 1034
Greitzer, Ron, Mgr.-Adv., Video Prods.--Sony Electronics, Park Ridge, NJ; *Int'l*, pg. 1281
Gremaud, Laurent, Chief Information Officer & Sr. V.P.-Mktg.--UMS Swiss Metalworks Holding Ltd, Dornach, Switzerland; *Int'l*, pg. 1427
Gresle-Farthing, Rachel, Dir.-Adv.--Elsevier Science Limited, Kidlington, United Kingdom; *Int'l*, pg. 1100
Gretzinger, Laura, Mgr.-Print Adv.--The Andersons Incorporated, Maumee, OH; *U.S. Public*, pg. 111
Gretzinger, Ruth, Mgr.-Adv.--UMI, Ann Arbor, MI; *U.S. Public*, pg. 201
Gribbin, Stephen, Mgr.-Adv.--Slant/Fin Corporation, Greenvale, NY; *U.S. Private*, pg. 1005
Grider, Ann, Adv. Mgr.--Circle Seal Controls, Inc., Corona, CA; *U.S. Public*, pg. 1746
Griffin, Claire, V.P. & Dir.-Adv. & Promo--HarperCollins Publishers, New York, NY; *Int'l*, pg. 926
Griffin, Howard L., Dir.-Corp. Adv.--Journal Register Company, Trenton, NJ; *U.S. Public*, pg. 934
Griffin, John, Mgr.-Adv.--Skokie Valley Beverage Co., Wheeling, IL; *U.S. Private*, pg. 1005
Griffin, Ria, Mgr.-Commun.--Port of Houston Authority, Houston, TX; *U.S. Private*, pg. 876
Griffin, Toni L., V.P.-Corp. Commun.--American Arbitration Association, New York, NY; *U.S. Private*, pg. 50
Griffiths, Claudia, V.P.-Adv. & Graphic Design--American Rug Craftsmen, Sugar Valley, GA; *U.S. Public*, pg. 1121
Grimes, Gary, V.P.-Sls. & Mktg.--Directory Distributing Associates, Inc., Saint Louis, MO; *U.S. Private*, pg. 334
Grindstaff, Evelyn S., V.P.-Sls.--Chi Systems Division, Ann Arbor, MI; *U.S. Public*, pg. 1539
Grinnell, Suzanne, Mktg. Specialist--Frank Consolidated Enterprises Inc., Des Plaines, IL; *U.S. Private*, pg. 423
Grisanti, Michael J., Pres. & Chief Exec. Officer--Grisanti, Inc., Louisville, KY; *U.S. Private*, pg. 482
Grissom, Chip, V.P.-Mktg.--Norrell Services Inc., Atlanta, GA; *U.S. Public*, pg. 1192
Grob, J. Murray, Pres.--Caravan Brokay, Totowa, NJ; *U.S. Private*, pg. 208
Grobet, Arnaud, Acting Dir.-Adv. & Pub. Rels.--Banque Edouard Constant, Geneva, Switzerland; *U.S. Public*, pg. 1197
Grobman, Richard, V.P. & Buyer-Non-Foods--Dan's Supreme Super Markets Inc., Hempstead, NY; *U.S. Private*, pg. 310
Groh, K.L., Mgr.-Corp. & Mktg. Communications--The Timken Company, Canton, OH; *U.S. Public*, pg. 1617
Groome, John, Mgr.-Pub. Rels.--Northern Foods plc, Hull, United Kingdom; *Int'l*, pg. 967
Gross, Holly, Mgr.-Adv.--Chefs International, Inc., Point Pleasant Beach, NJ; *U.S. Public*, pg. 343
Gross, William, Dir.-Adv.--Unity Manufacturing Co., Chicago, IL; *U.S. Private*, pg. 1126
Grossenburg, Gene C., Exec. V.P.--Grossenburg Implements, Incorporated, Winner, SD; *U.S. Private*, pg. 483
Grossman, Janice, Exec. V.P.-Mktg. & Adv.--New York Magazine, New York, NY; *U.S. Public*, pg. 1328
Grosso, Glen, Mgr.-Adv.--Potamkin Toyota, Inc., Miami, FL; *U.S. Private*, pg. 877
Grosz, Deborah, Mgr.-Adv. & Promotions--Tellabs Operations, Inc., Lisle, IL; *U.S. Public*, pg. 1572
Grove, Trish, Mgr.-Communications--Whitmire Micro-gen Research Laboratories Inc., Saint Louis, MO; *U.S. Private*, pg. 592
Grow, Robert B., Dir.-Adv.--Raytheon Systems Co., Kirkwood, NY; *U.S. Public*, pg. 1364
Grueneberg, Jeffrey, Mgr.-Mktg.--Rockford Products Corp., Rockford, IL; *U.S. Private*, pg. 938
Grupp, Andreas, Dir.-Adv. & Mktg.--Spindelfabrik Suessen, Suessen, Germany; *Int'l*, pg. 1290
Grymes, John, Pres.-Williamhouse Div.--American Pad and Paper Company, Dallas, TX; *U.S. Public*, pg. 88
Grytz, K., Mgr.-Adv.--Semikron International, GmbH & Co. KG, Nuremberg, Germany; *Int'l*, pg. 1220
Grzan, Ann Marie, Category Dir.-Pharmaceutical Adv.--Good Housekeeping, New York, NY; *U.S. Private*, pg. 517
Gualtieri, Pat, Sr. Dir.-Mktg. & Adv.--Medicine Shoppe International, Inc., Saint Louis, MO; *U.S. Public*, pg. 304
Guarascio, Philip, V.P. & Gen. Mgr-Mktg. & Adv.-NAO--General Motors Corporation, Detroit, MI; *U.S. Public*, pg. 718
Guenther, John S., Sr. V.P.--Ball Horticultural Company, West Chicago, IL; *U.S. Private*, pg. 112
Guenther, Nancy, Dir.-Adv. & Pub. Rels.--ITT Fluid Handling, Morton Grove, IL; *U.S. Public*, pg. 860
Guillet, Benoit, Dir.-Adv. & Pub. Rels.--Riber, Rueil-Malmaison, France; *Int'l*, pg. 1114
Guillo, Emanuel, Dir.-Adv.--Chloride Industrial Batteries Ltd., Manchester, United Kingdom; *Int'l*, pg. 125
Guise, Tom, Dir.-Adv. & Mktg.--PRO Group, Inc., Englewood, CO; *U.S. Private*, pg. 887
Guliano, Neil, V.P.-Adv.--CVS Corp., Woonsocket, RI; *U.S. Public*, pg. 287
Gulino, Dennis, Mgr.-Adv.--Kester Solder, Des Plaines, IL; *U.S. Public*, pg. 1003
Gulley, James L., Mgr.-Mktg. Promo.--Moscom Corporation, Pittsford, NY; *U.S. Public*, pg. 1136
Gulliksen, J.E., Dir.-Mktg.--Koehler Manufacturing Company, Marlborough, MA; *U.S. Private*, pg. 706
Gump, Andrea M., Coord.-Adv.--Telsmith, Inc., Mequon, WI; *U.S. Public*, pg. 141
Gundelfinger, Dina, V.P.-Adv.--CompUSA, Dallas, TX; *U.S. Public*, pg. 420
Gunderson, Carl, Dir.-Mktg.--Hougen Manufacturing Inc., Swartz Creek, MI; *U.S. Private*, pg. 541
Gunduz, Zeynep, Dir.-Adv. & Promo.--Midas-International Corp., Chicago, IL; *U.S. Public*, pg. 1766
Gunn, Charlene, Dir.-Mktg. & Industry Sls.--Payless Car Rental System, Inc., Saint Petersburg, FL; *U.S. Private*, pg. 844

Gunn, Norman L., Dir.-Mktg.--Interstate/Johnson Lane, Inc., Charlotte, NC; *U.S. Public*, pg. 909
Gura, Jerry, Dir.-Pub. Affairs--Amsted Industries Incorporated, Chicago, IL; *U.S. Private*, pg. 68
Gurda, Richard J., Sr. V.P.-Corp. Communications--Telxon Corporation, Akron, OH; *U.S. Public*, pg. 1573
Gurwell, Kathy, Mgr.-Adv.--Rice Food Markets Inc., Houston, TX; *U.S. Private*, pg. 927
Gustafson, Amy, Coord.-Adv.--Hobbs Corporation, Springfield, IL; *Int'l*, pg. 127
Gustavson, Susann, Mgr.-Mktg.--Laura Ashley (USA) Inc., Boston, MA; *Int'l*, pg. 804
Guth, Frank Suessen, Mgr.-Adv.--Deutsche Bank AG, Frankfurt/Main, Germany; *Int'l*, pg. 401
Guthrie, A. D., Dir.-Adv. & Mgr.- Sls. & Mktg.--Sterling Davis Standard, South Plainfield, NJ; *Int'l*, pg. 1240
Gutierrez, Jeannette, Dir.-Art--Crain Communications, Inc., Chicago, IL; *U.S. Private*, pg. 284
Gutterman, Arthur, Chm. Bd., Pres., Chief Exec. & Chief Oper. Officer--Jelmar Company, Lincolnwood, IL; *U.S. Private*, pg. 585
Guze, Jack, Chief Mktg. Officer--Reebok International Ltd., Stoughton, MA; *U.S. Public*, pg. 1369
Guzman, Carolina, Mgr.-Adv.--BASF Quimica Colombiana S.A., Bogota, Colombia; *Int'l*, pg. 107
Gwinn, Victor L., Mgr.-Sls.--Mrs. Cubbison's Foods, Inc., Montebello, CA; *U.S. Public*, pg. 909
Ha, Shita, Dir.-Import & Export Adv.--Lotte Shopping Co. Ltd., Seoul, Korea; *Int'l*, pg. 819
Haag, Carolyn, Coord.-Adv. & Promos.--Heath Consultants Incorporated, Houston, TX; *U.S. Private*, pg. 518
Haag, Mel, Mgr.-Corp. Communications--Franklin Electric Co., Inc., Bluffton, IN; *U.S. Public*, pg. 679
Haas, Eric, V.P.-Adv.--National Band & Tag Co., Newport, KY; *U.S. Private*, pg. 780
Haas, Steve, Mgr.-Adv.--E & A Industries, Inc., Indianapolis, IN; *U.S. Private*, pg. 352
Haas, Thomas, Mgr.-Mktg. Communications--Siemens Corporation, New York, NY; *Int'l*, pg. 1245
Haber, Charles, Dir.-Art--Leviton Mfg. Co., Inc., Little Neck, NY; *U.S. Private*, pg. 663
Haberland, B.W., Mgr.-Mktg. Services--Schering Nederland B.V., Weesp, Netherlands; *Int'l*, pg. 1204
Habetler, Chuck, Mgr.-Sls. & Mktg.--Atlas Cylinder, Eugene, OR; *U.S. Public*, pg. 1261
Hadley, Jacqueline H., Dir.-Govt. & Pub. Rels.--The Union Central Life Insurance Co., Cincinnati, OH; *U.S. Private*, pg. 1118
Hagberg, Nancy, Mgr.-Communications--EMPI, Inc., Saint Paul, MN; *U.S. Public*, pg. 545
Hagen, Wendy, Dir.-Creative Resources--Lockheed Martin Corporation, Bethesda, MD; *U.S. Public*, pg. 1006
Haggai, Allan, Mgr.-Adv.--Thomas Built Buses, Inc., High Point, NC; *U.S. Private*, pg. 1082
Hagler, Steve, Mgr.-Adv.--Hussmann Corp., Bridgeton, MO; *U.S. Public*, pg. 1766
Haglich, Jeanette, Mgr.-Adv.--Plenum Publishing Corporation, New York, NY; *U.S. Public*, pg. 1311
Hahn, Alan C., Sr. V.P.-Deal Direct Mktg.--Jackson National Life Insurance Company, Lansing, MI; *Int'l*, pg. 1073
Hahn, Horst, Pres., Chief Exec. Officer & Gen. Mgr.--Multimatic Corporation, Northvale, NJ; *U.S. Private*, pg. 767
Hahnenstein, Geri, V.P.-Mktg. Commun.--Allegiance Healthcare Corp., McGaw Park, IL; *U.S. Public*, pg. 44
Haines, Lee, Mgr.-Pub. Rels. & Advertising--AAR Corp., Wood Dale, IL; *U.S. Public*, pg. 1
Haines, Rebecca, Dir.-Prod. Adv.--John Hancock Mutual Life Insurance Company, Boston, MA; *U.S. Private*, pg. 589
Hale, Joseph, Gen. Mgr.-Corp. Communications & Investor Rels.--Cinergy Corp., Cincinnati, OH; *U.S. Public*, pg. 369
Hale, Roger, Creative Svcs. Dir.--Reed Business Information, Sutton, United Kingdom; *Int'l*, pg. 1094
Hale, Roger W., Chm. Bd., Pres. & Chief Exec. Officer--LG & E Energy Corp., Louisville, KY; *U.S. Public*, pg. 970
Haley, Jerry, Dir.-Adv.--Chicago Pneumatic Tool Company, Rock Hill, SC; *Int'l*, pg. 96
Hall, Alison, Mgr.-Adv. & Plng.--Guardian & Observer, London, United Kingdom; *Int'l*, pg. 577
Hall, Deanna L., V.P.-Strategic Plng. & Sec.--Acme Design Technology, Co., Crozet, VA; *U.S. Private*, pg. 13
Hall, John, Adv. Specialist--Bushnell Corporation, Overland Park, KS; *U.S. Private*, pg. 1191
Hall, Laura, Mgr.-Mktg. Res.--Southern Progress Corporation, Birmingham, AL; *U.S. Public*, pg. 1612
Hall, Mark, Exec. V.P. & Dir.-Adv. & Sls.--Monarch Avalon, Inc., Baltimore, MD; *U.S. Public*, pg. 1123
Hall, Melanie, Dir.-Commun.--Heavy Machines, Inc., Memphis, TN; *U.S. Private*, pg. 518
Hall, Roger, Mgr.-Adv.--Blockbuster Entertainment Corporation Limited (U.K.), Uxbridge, United Kingdom; *U.S. Private*, pg. 776
Hall, Sarah, Mgr.-Mktg.--Brauns Fashions Corporation, Plymouth, MN; *U.S. Public*, pg. 251
Hall, Suzanne, Dir.-Adv.--Intel Corporation, Santa Clara, CA; *U.S. Public*, pg. 886
Halliburton, Roberta, Mgr.-Mktg. Communications--Astec America Inc., Carlsbad, CA; *Int'l*, pg. 93
Halliday, Laurie, Sr. Dir.-Adv. Media--Old Navy Stores, San Francisco, CA; *U.S. Public*, pg. 703
Halligan, Patrick D., Adv. Officer--James Walker & Co. Limited, Woking, United Kingdom; *Int'l*, pg. 1485
Hallquist, Harlan, V.P.--Adolfson & Peterson, Inc., Minneapolis, MN; *U.S. Private*, pg. 17
Halls, Pat, Dir.-Adv.--Calgary Flames Hockey Club, Calgary, Canada; *Int'l*, pg. 252
Halsey, Bob, Mgr.-Adv.--Shasta Beverages, Inc., Hayward, CA; *U.S. Public*, pg. 1153
Ham, Marianne, Sr. Mgr.-Global Adv. Svcs.--Campbell Soup Company, Camden, NJ; *U.S. Public*, pg. 298
Ham, Marianne, Adv. Svcs.--Swanson, Camden, NJ; *U.S. Public*, pg. 299
Hamblin, Connie, Sec. & Dir.-Corp. Commun.--Gentex Corporation, Zeeland, MI; *U.S. Public*, pg. 731
Hamburger, Diane L., Div. V.P.-Mktg. Communications--Nalco Chemical Company, Naperville, IL; *U.S. Public*, pg. 1150
Hamill, Jeff, Assoc. Publr. & Dir.-Adv.--Good Housekeeping, New York, NY; *U.S. Private*, pg. 517
Hamilton, Dean C., Mgr.-Mktg. Communications--ATMI, Inc., Danbury, CT; *U.S. Public*, pg. 12
Hamilton, Fred, Dir.-Mktg. & Communications--The Franklin Institute, Philadelphia, PA; *U.S. Private*, pg. 424
Hamilton, Fred, Dir.-Adv. Sls.--Kalmbach Publishing Co., Waukesha, WI; *U.S. Private*, pg. 606
Hamlin, Craig, Pres. & Chief Exec. Officer--ADM Milling Co., Overland Park, KS; *U.S. Public*, pg. 128
Hamlin, John, Mgr.-Intl. Sls.--Beutlich, L.P., Waukegan, IL; *U.S. Private*, pg. 141
Hamm, Jerry T., Pres.--Jerry Hamm Chevrolet Inc., Jacksonville, FL; *U.S. Private*, pg. 497
Hammalrath, Mark, V.P.-Mktg. & Adv.--Riverwood International Corporation, Atlanta, GA; *U.S. Public*, pg. 1391
Hammerberg, David L., V.P.-Opers.--Reames Foods Inc., Clive, IA; *U.S. Public*, pg. 977
Hammersland, Margareta, Asst. Corp. Communications--NCC AB, Solna, Sweden; *Int'l*, pg. 898
Hammill, Dick, Sr. V.P.-Adv. & Mktg.--The Home Depot, Inc., Atlanta, GA; *U.S. Public*, pg. 831
Hammill, Richard S., V.P.-Adv.--The Pep Boys-Manny, Moe & Jack, Philadelphia, PA; *U.S. Public*, pg. 1276
Hammond, Peter S., Mgr.-Adv.--Whiting Corporation, Harvey, IL; *U.S. Private*, pg. 1173
Hammons, Lora Cassano, Coord.-Pub. Rels. Mktg.--Cassano's Inc., Dayton, OH; *U.S. Private*, pg. 218
Hamner, Nathan, Pres.--Seward Inc., Petersburg, VA; *U.S. Private*, pg. 988
Hampel, Jeff, Dir.-Consumer Adv.--LCI International, Inc., Dublin, OH; *U.S. Public*, pg. 969
Hampson, Jim, Sr. V.P.-Mktg.--Great Western Consumer Finance Group, Tampa, FL; *U.S. Public*, pg. 1741
Hampton, Kay, Dir.-Adv. & Mktg./Corp.--Computer Language Research, Inc., Carrollton, TX; *U.S. Public*, pg. 421
Hampton, Wade, V.P.-Mktg.--Koger Equity Inc., Jacksonville, FL; *U.S. Public*, pg. 965
Hamrick, Lynn, Mgr.-Adv. & Promos.--Donlee Technologies Inc., York, PA; *U.S. Private*, pg. 339
Hanes, Doug, V.P.-Adv.--The Orange County Register, Santa Ana, CA; *U.S. Private*, pg. 425
Hanger, David J., Publisher--The Economist Group Limited., London, United Kingdom; *Int'l*, pg. 1026
Hanke, Dean, Mgr.-Sls. Devel. & Adv.--J-Star Industries, Inc., Fort Atkinson, WI; *U.S. Private*, pg. 576
Hankins, Bill, Team Leader-Managed Care--Boehringer Ingelheim Pharmaceuticals, Inc., Ridgefield, CT; *Int'l*, pg. 199
Hanly, Mike, Dir.-Corp. Adv. & Brand Identity--Bellcore, Morristown, NJ; *U.S. Private*, pg. 976
Hanna, David E., Mgr.-Sls. & Mktg.--Owatonna Canning Company, Owatonna, MN; *U.S. Public*, pg. 349
Hannah, Michele, Mgr.-Adv.--MidAmerican Energy Holdings, Des Moines, IA; *U.S. Public*, pg. 1109
Hannedt, Ray, V.P.-Adv.--Grossenburg Implements, Incorporated, Winner, SD; *U.S. Private*, pg. 483
Hannon, John, Dir.-Adv.--Nexstar Pharmaceuticals, Inc., Boulder, CO; *U.S. Public*, pg. 1180
Hano, Greg, Dir.-Adv.--Popular Mechanics, New York, NY; *U.S. Private*, pg. 517
Hansen, D.K., Pres.--Crystal Cream & Butter Company, Sacramento, CA; *U.S. Private*, pg. 294
Hansen, Joan, Mgr.-Communications--Interstate Electronics Corp., Anaheim, CA; *U.S. Public*, pg. 622
Hansen, Kent, V.P.-Mktg. Sales & Adv.--Nobel Insurance Limited, Hamilton, Bermuda; *Int'l*, pg. 951
Hansen, Mike, Mgr.-Adv.--Data Transmission Network Corporation, Omaha, NE; *U.S. Public*, pg. 486
Hansen, Neil, Mgr.-Adv.--EnviroTech PumpSystems, Salt Lake City, UT; *Int'l*, pg. 1489
Hansen, Preben, Mgr.-Adv.-Philips Light--Philips Danmark A/S, Copenhagen, Denmark; *Int'l*, pg. 1055
Hansen, Roy, Chief Info. Officer--Eagle Iron Works, Des Moines, IA; *U.S. Private*, pg. 354
Hanson, Al, Mgr.-Adv. & Production--CUNA Mutual Insurance Society, Madison, WI; *U.S. Private*, pg. 296
Hanson, Barbara, Dir.-Mktg.--Thomas Publishing Company, New York, NY; *U.S. Private*, pg. 1082
Hanson, Jody, Mgr.-Adv.--Raytheon Appliances, Ripon, WI; *U.S. Public*, pg. 1366
Hanson, John N., Chm. & Chief Exec. Officer--Beloit Corporation, Beloit, WI; *U.S. Public*, pg. 789
Hanson, Larry, V.P.-Mktg. & Sls.--Twin City Foods, Inc., Stanwood, WA; *U.S. Private*, pg. 1111
Hanz, Melanie G., Mgr.-Adv. & Sls. Promo.--Wide-Lite, San Marcos, TX; *U.S. Public*, pg. 730
Happ, Suzanne, Adv. Coord.--Republic Entertainment, Inc., Los Angeles, CA; *U.S. Private*, pg. 776
Happel, Marvin H., V.P.-Organization & Admin.--Crompton & Knowles Corporation, Stamford, CT; *U.S. Public*, pg. 459
Harakal, Joe, Mgr.-Mktg. & Commun.--Digital Link Corporation, Sunnyvale, CA; *U.S. Public*, pg. 508
Haraldson, William, Chief Oper. Officer & Exec. V.P.-Mktg.--Rosauers Supermarkets, Inc., Spokane, WA; *U.S. Private*, pg. 944
Harbaugh, John C., Mgr.-Mktg. & Adv.--Landis, Waynesboro, PA; *U.S. Public*, pg. 1699
Harbin, John P., Chm. Bd. & Chief Exec. Officer--Lone Star Technologies, Inc., Dallas, TX; *U.S. Public*, pg. 1012
Harbula, Gene, V.P.-Govt. Mktg. & Corp. Communications--Sabreliner Corporation, Saint Louis, MO; *U.S. Private*, pg. 959
Harcourt, Patricia A., Dir.-Corp. Commun.--Belden & Blake Corporation, Canton, OH; *U.S. Private*, pg. 1078
Hargraves, Richard N., Dir.-Corp. Communications--Laclede Gas Company, Saint Louis, MO; *U.S. Public*, pg. 973
Harkness, Susan P., Coord.-Adv.--OGE Energy Corp., Oklahoma City, OK; *U.S. Public*, pg. 1207
Harlan, Beverly C., Dir.-Adv.--Riceland Foods, Inc., Stuttgart, AR; *U.S. Private*, pg. 928
Harlan, Richard K., V.P.-Sls. & Mktg.--E.W. Knauss & Son, Inc., Quakertown, PA; *U.S. Private*, pg. 626
Harman, James, Mgr.-Prod.--Bock Industries Inc., Elkhart, IN; *Int'l*, pg. 265
Harman, James, Mgr.-Corp. Adv.--General Electric Company, Fairfield, CT; *U.S. Public*, pg. 709
Harmon, Brad, Dir.-Retail Adv.--The Cincinnati Enquirer, Inc., Cincinnati, OH; *U.S. Public*, pg. 700
Harmon, Jenifer, Dir.-Natl. Adv.--Denny's, Inc., Spartanburg, SC; *U.S. Public*, pg. 23
Harms, Barbara J., V.P. & Dir.-Corp. Communications & Adv.--Chicago Title & Trust Co., Chicago, IL; *U.S. Public*, pg. 42
Harper, Ed, Mgr.-Adv./ Sales Promo.--Dayton Tire Company, Oklahoma City, OK; *Int'l*, pg. 213
Harper, Greg, V.P.-Mktg.--Johnny Appleseed's, Inc., Beverly, MA; *U.S. Private*, pg. 590
Harper, Janyce, Mgr.-Adv.--Siemens Business Communication Systems, Inc., Santa Clara, CA; *Int'l*, pg. 1245
Harper, Karen, Mgr.-Adv.--Great Financial Bank FSB, Louisville, KY; *U.S. Private*, pg. 473
Harpster, Jane, Dir.-Adv.--Fort James Corporation, Richmond, VA; *U.S. Public*, pg. 670
Harrigan, Gayle, Mgr.-Adv.--Satellite Data Networks, San Diego, CA; *U.S. Public*, pg. 716
Harrington, Kathleen, Dir.-Adv.--COMPAQ Computer Corporation, Houston, TX; *U.S. Public*, pg. 417
Harris, Bob, Dir.-Sls.--Wright Brand Foods, Inc., Vernon, TX; *U.S. Private*, pg. 1192
Harris, Carl, Dir.-Pub. Affairs & Adv.--Bell Helicopter Textron, Hurst, TX; *U.S. Public*, pg. 1588
Harris, Chris, Dir.-Adv.--Tire Business, Akron, OH; *U.S. Private*, pg. 285
Harris, Jennifer, Coord.-Adv.--Berkley Publishing Corp., New York, NY; *Int'l*, pg. 1027
Harris, R. Macy, III, V.P., Sec. & Mgr.-Adv.--The Ailing & Cory Company, Rochester, NY; *U.S. Public*, pg. 1666
Harris, Suzanne, Media/Adv. Coord.--Synchro-Start Products, Inc., Niles, IL; *U.S. Private*, pg. 627
Harrison, David, Corp. Communications--ITOCHU International Inc., New York, NY; *Int'l*, pg. 694
Harrison, Monroe, Coord.-Co-op Adv.--Hughes Supply, Inc., Orlando, FL; *U.S. Public*, pg. 846
Harrison, Tom, Dir.-Mktg. Services--Samsonite Corporation, Denver, CO; *U.S. Public*, pg. 1430
Harrison, Walter, Mgr.-Mktg.--Delta Pride Catfish, Inc., Indianola, MS; *U.S. Private*, pg. 322
Hart, Jennifer, Dir.-Adv.--HarperCollins Publishers, New York, NY; *Int'l*, pg. 926
Hart, Jennifer, Dir.-Adv.--HarperCollins Adult Trade Division, New York, NY; *Int'l*, pg. 926
Hart, Jennifer, Dir.-Adv.-Harper Collins Publr.--Harper Audio, New York, NY; *Int'l*, pg. 926
Hart, Jennifer, Dir.-Adv.--Basic Books, Inc., New York, NY; *Int'l*, pg. 927
Hart, Kay, V.P.-Mktg.--Informix Software, Menlo Park, CA; *U.S. Public*, pg. 876
Hart, Kris, Dir.-Mktg.--Arch Communications Group, Inc., Westborough, MA; *U.S. Public*, pg. 127
Hart, Linda, V.P.-Mktg.--The Cook Bates Division, Venice, FL; *Int'l*, pg. 815
Hart, Patricia, Mgr.-Adv.--Central Maine Power Company, Augusta, ME; *U.S. Public*, pg. 325
Harting, Tom, V.P.-Sls. & Mktg.--Mrs. Alison's Cookie Company, Saint Louis, MO; *U.S. Private*, pg. 765
Hartranft, Debbie, Mgr.-Mktg.--Reading Body Works, Inc., Reading, PA; *U.S. Private*, pg. 913
Hartwell, Woody, Mgr.-Mktg.--Kathryn Beich, Inc., Bloomington, IL; *Int'l*, pg. 917
Hartzel, Fred, Plant Mgr.--A. Goodman & Sons, Inc., Deer Park, NY; *U.S. Private*, pg. 158
Harvey, Dan, Dir.-Adv.--Coward-McCann, Inc., New York, NY; *Int'l*, pg. 1027
Harvey, Daniel G., V.P. & Deputy Publr.-Putnam Publishing Grp.--The Putnam Berkley Group, Inc., New York, NY; *Int'l*, pg. 1027
Harvey, Peter R., Pres.--Artra Group Incorporated, Northfield, IL; *U.S. Public*, pg. 136
Harwood, Carol, Team Leader-Adv. & Mktg.--CFX Bank, Keene, NH; *U.S. Public*, pg. 277
Harwood, Michael, Dir.-Adv.-Local--Providence Journal-Bulletin, Providence, RI; *U.S. Public*, pg. 209
Hasek, Ronald W., Mgr.-Mktg. Services & Pub. Rels.--Ampco-Pittsburgh Corporation, Pittsburgh, PA; *U.S. Public*, pg. 103
Hashiba, Nobuhiro, Gen. Mng. Dir.-Adv. & Mdsg.--Sapporo Breweries Ltd., Tokyo, Japan; *Int'l*, pg. 1193
Hashimoto, Clark, Pres.--Glory USA, Inc., West Caldwell, NJ; *Int'l*, pg. 554
Haskins, Louise, Mgr.-Adv.--BNFL, Warrington, United Kingdom; *Int'l*, pg. 120
Hasluck, Lynn, Mgr.-Adv. Promo.--PC Magazine, New York, NY; *Int'l*, pg. 1276
Hastings, Lyndell, Dir.-Mktg. Commun.--Atomic Energy of Canada Ltd., Mississauga, Canada; *Int'l*, pg. 97
Hattangadi, Manohar, Dir.-Mktg.--Bachmann Industries, Inc., Philadelphia, PA; *U.S. Private*, pg. 109
Haumersen, Brian, Dir.-Adv.--AT&T Strategy & New Service Innovations, Parsippany, NJ; *U.S. Public*, pg. 11
Hauser, Cindy, Sr. V.P.-Print Adv.--Fox Broadcasting Company (FBC), Beverly Hills, CA; *Int'l*, pg. 926
Hausler, Robert J., V.P.-Sls. & Mktg.--Mark Lighting Fixture Co., Inc., Edison, NJ; *U.S. Private*, pg. 704
Hausman, Thomas, Dir.-Editorial Services--Harris Corporation, Melbourne, FL; *U.S. Public*, pg. 791
Hauter, John, Mgr.-Adv.--G. Leblanc Corporation, Kenosha, WI; *U.S. Private*, pg. 656
Havay, Robin, Coord.-Adv. & Trade Show--Milton Roy Company, Ivyland, PA; *U.S. Public*, pg. 1534

Haviland, Susan, V.P.-Adv.--Dexter Shoe Company, Dexter, ME; *U.S. Public*, pg. 217
Hawes, Aubrey, Sr. V.P.-Corp. Mktg. Resources--The Chase Manhattan Bank, New York, NY; *U.S. Public*, pg. 338
Haworth, Missy, V.P.-Sls. & Mktg.--Broder Bros. Co., Plymouth, MI; *U.S. Private*, pg. 170
Hawrysz, Joe, Mgr.-Mktg. Services--Evans Tempcon Inc., Grand Rapids, MI; *U.S. Private*, pg. 7
Hayden, Bonnie, Mgr.-Adv.--John Deere Ltd., Grimsby, Canada; *U.S. Public*, pg. 493
Hayes, C.A., Dir.-Pur., Adv. & Mktg.--Blevins Inc., Nashville, TN; *U.S. Private*, pg. 149
Hayes, Denise, Mgr.-Adv.--BC Gas Inc., Vancouver, Canada; *Int'l*, pg. 114
Hayes, Joel, Dir.-Adv.--Amlings Flowerland, Hinsdale, IL; *U.S. Private*, pg. 66
Hayes, John D., Exec. V.P.-Global Adv.--American Express Company, New York, NY; *U.S. Public*, pg. 73
Hayes, Katie, Dir.-Adv.--Supercuts, Inc., San Francisco, CA; *U.S. Public*, pg. 1373
Hayes, Kelsey, Dir.-Mktg.--Lincoln Property Company, Dallas, TX; *U.S. Private*, pg. 668
Hayes, Mary, Dir.-Adv.--Ostrow Textile Co., Inc., Rock Hill, SC; *U.S. Private*, pg. 821
Hayes, Sally, Media Buyer--NCH Corporation, Irving, TX; *U.S. Public*, pg. 1145
Hayman, Derick, Mgr.-Mktg. Services--The Valspar Corp. Protective Coatings Div., Baltimore, MD; *U.S. Public*, pg. 1707
Haynes, Tom, Dir.-Adv.--Hughes Christensen, Houston, TX; *U.S. Public*, pg. 166
Hayward, Peter, Dir.-Adv.--Ridge Tool Co., Elyria, OH; *U.S. Public*, pg. 574
Head, George V., V.P.-Sls.--Southland Mower Corp., Selma, AL; *U.S. Private*, pg. 1144
Headbloom, Gust, Jr., Pres.--Apex Broach & Machine Co., Detroit, MI; *U.S. Private*, pg. 77
Headley, Douglas, Dir.-Adv.--Deere & Company, Moline, IL; *U.S. Public*, pg. 491
Headley, T., V.P. & Dir.-Sls. & Adv.--Midwesco Filter Resources Inc., Winchester, VA; *U.S. Public*, pg. 1026
Healey, Tom, Partner & Dir.-Media & Adv.--J.D. Power and Associates, Agoura Hills, CA; *U.S. Private*, pg. 878
Heaphy, Janis, Sr. V.P.-Adv.--Los Angeles Times, Los Angeles, CA; *U.S. Public*, pg. 1616
Hearn, Kathleen, Mgr.-Community & Government Rels.--Boston Gas Company, Boston, MA; *U.S. Public*, pg. 549
Heaslip, Harold C., Dir.-Adv. & Promo.--Northrop Grumman Corporation, Los Angeles, CA; *U.S. Public*, pg. 1197
Heath, Kristen, Mgr.-Adv.--PSDI, Bedford, MA; *U.S. Private*, pg. 828
Heazlitt, Michael, V.P.-Sls. & Mktg.--Paoli, Inc., Orleans, IN; *U.S. Private*, pg. 837
Hebert, Wally, Dir.-Adv. & Sls. & Mktg.--JRN, Inc., Columbia, TN; *U.S. Private*, pg. 578
Heckel, Paula, Admin. Asst.--Redland Ohio Inc., Woodville, OH; *Int'l*, pg. 1091
Hedges, Helen, Dir.-Mktg.--Jack Schwartz Shoes, Inc., New York, NY; *U.S. Private*, pg. 974
Heffron, Howard, Sr. Mgr.-Communications--Sandoz Agro, Inc., Des Plaines, IL; *Int'l*, pg. 974
Hegyi, Terry M., Mgr.-Pub. Rels.--Firmenich Incorporated, Plainsboro, NJ; *Int'l*, pg. 486
Heide, David, Mgr.-Adv.--Snap-On Tools Corporation, Kenosha, WI; *U.S. Public*, pg. 1480
Heidenreich, G.E., IV, Dir.-Adv. & Sls. Promo.--Consolidated Papers, Inc., Wisconsin Rapids, WI; *U.S. Public*, pg. 436
Heidenreich, Vincent J., Mgr.-Adv. & Sls. Promotion--Bayer Corporation/Pharmaceutical Division, West Haven, CT; *Int'l*, pg. 173
Heider, Ed, Mgr.-Natl. Sls.--Akzo Nobel Coatings Inc., Columbus, OH; *Int'l*, pg. 48
Heidl, Deb, Admin. Asst.--Integrated Material Handling Company, Oshkosh, WI; *Int'l*, pg. 1397
Heigl, F. Thomas, Sr. Assoc.-Adv.--Bayer Corporation/Pharmaceutical Division, West Haven, CT; *Int'l*, pg. 173
Heim, Millie, Dir.-Sls. & Adv.--Jumping Jacks, Monett, MO; *U.S. Private*, pg. 767
Heime, Fred, V.P.--N.B.F. Bollinger Industries, Americus, GA; *U.S. Public*, pg. 243
Heinrichs, Joan, Dir.-Adv. Space--The Haband Co., Prospect Park, NJ; *U.S. Private*, pg. 492
Heinz, Christian, Dir.-Mktg., Adv. & Pub. Rels.--Credit Suisse, Zurich, Switzerland; *Int'l*, pg. 345
Held, Peter, Mgr.-Adv.--Alusuisse-Lonza Holding Ltd., Zurich, Switzerland; *Int'l*, pg. 66
Hellen, Rob, V.P.--Future Foam, Inc., Council Bluffs, IA; *U.S. Private*, pg. 433
Heller, John, Dir.-Opers. & Asst. to the Pres.--The IDI Group Companies, Arlington, VA; *U.S. Private*, pg. 554
Helstab, Susan, V.P.-Corp. Communications--Four Seasons Hotels & Resorts, Don Mills, Canada; *Int'l*, pg. 502
Helstein, Richard, V.P.-Adv. & Mktg. Services/Kraft--Kraft Foods Inc., Rye Brook, NY; *U.S. Public*, pg. 1288
Hembree, LaDonna, Mgr.-Classified Adv.--Knoxville News-Sentinel Company, Knoxville, TN; *U.S. Public*, pg. 1448
Henderson-King, Robin, Coord.-Adv.--RE/MAX International, Inc., Englewood, CO; *U.S. Private*, pg. 912
Henderson, Beth, Mgr.-Mktg. Services--Double-Cola Co.-USA, Chattanooga, TN; *U.S. Private*, pg. 341
Henderson, D.W., Mgr.-Adv.--Northern Rock PLC, Newcastle upon Tyne, United Kingdom; *Int'l*, pg. 968
Henderson, David, V.P. & Gen. Mgr.--American Locker Group, Inc., Jamestown, NY; *U.S. Public*, pg. 85
Henderson, Scott, Mgr.-Retail Adv.-Specialties--TruServ Corporation, Chicago, IL; *U.S. Private*, pg. 1108
Henderson, Theresa, Dir.-Corp. Comm.--Current Technology, Inc., Irving, TX; *U.S. Public*, pg. 480
Hendin, Marty, V.P.-Community Rels.--St. Louis National Baseball Club L.P., Saint Louis, MO; *U.S. Private*, pg. 961
Hendricks, Adele, Pres. & Retail Dir.--Dean's Photo Service, San Diego, CA; *U.S. Private*, pg. 319
Hendrix, Terry, Mgr.-Adv.--The Tog Shop, Americus, GA; *U.S. Private*, pg. 1090
Henington, Caroline, Mgr.-Adv.--Calor Group plc, Warwick, United Kingdom; *Int'l*, pg. 1155
Henning, Beth, Mgr.-Natl. Car Adv.--Toyota Motor Sales, U.S.A., Inc., Torrance, CA; *Int'l*, pg. 1412
Henningsen, Ronald J., Dir.-Adv.--Fleming Company, Waukesha, WI; *U.S. Public*, pg. 653
Henry, Charles, Dir.-Adv.--Great Dane Trailers, Inc., Savannah, GA; *U.S. Private*, pg. 1030
Henry, David, V.P.--Golub Corporation, Schenectady, NY; *U.S. Private*, pg. 463
Hensel, Nancy, V.P.-Mktg. & Mdsg.--The Popcorn Factory, Lake Forest, IL; *U.S. Private*, pg. 421
Henshaw, John, Dir.-Adv.--Northern Telecom Limited, Brampton, Canada; *Int'l*, pg. 968
Hepker, Joanna, Adv. Coord.--HON Industries Inc., Muscatine, IA; *U.S. Public*, pg. 772
Herasimchuk, David A., V.P.-Mktg. Devel.--Global Marine Inc., Houston, TX; *U.S. Public*, pg. 748
Hering, Jennifer, Mgr.-Mktg. Communications--Port of Portland, Portland, OR; *U.S. Private*, pg. 876
Herman, Cheri, V.P.-Adv.--Universal Studios Hollywood, Universal City, CA; *Int'l*, pg. 1216
Herman, Cindy, Dir.-Corp. Consumer Adv. & Pub. Rels.--OshKosh B'Gosh, Inc., Oshkosh, WI; *U.S. Public*, pg. 1232
Herman, June, Dir.-Adv.--Jabel, Inc., Irvington, NJ; *U.S. Private*, pg. 579
Herman, R., Liaison Communications--KDI Precision Products, Inc., Cincinnati, OH; *U.S. Private*, pg. 603
Hermance, Earl, Mgr.-Adv.--Westvaco Corporation-Envelope Div., Springfield, MA; *U.S. Public*, pg. 1762
Hermanson, Terry, Pres.--Mr. Christmas Inc., New York, NY; *U.S. Private*, pg. 765
Hermas, Fran, Mgr.-Adv.--Payson Casters, Inc., Gurnee, IL; *U.S. Private*, pg. 844
Hermes, Steve, V.P.-Sls. Promo. & Adv.--Waddell & Reed, Inc., Shawnee Mission, KS; *U.S. Public*, pg. 1623
Hermsen, Shelley, Adv. Coord.--Drug Emporium of Arizona, Scottsdale, AZ; *U.S. Private*, pg. 343
Hernandez, Ron, Mgr.-Adv.--Simon & Schuster, New York, NY; *U.S. Private*, pg. 777
Herr, W., Mgr.-Pub. Rels. & Adv.--Deminex-Deutsche GmbH, Essen, Germany; *Int'l*, pg. 1460
Herron, Michael, Dir.-Communications--Environmental Resources Management, Exton, PA; *U.S. Private*, pg. 378
Herschman, Linda D., V.P.-External Affairs--Southern New England Telecommunications Corporation, New Haven, CT; *U.S. Public*, pg. 1490
Herskowitz, Sam, Dir.- Mktg. & Adv.--Sterling Vision, Inc., East Meadow, NY; *U.S. Public*, pg. 1516
Herzog, Jim, Mgr.-Corp. Communications, Sls., Mktg. & Adv.--Armco Inc., Pittsburgh, PA; *U.S. Public*, pg. 131
Herzog, Michael, Mgr.-Office--Lincoln Steel, Lincoln, NE; *U.S. Private*, pg. 824
Hess, Kathie, Dir.-Adv.--Pizza Inn, Inc., Dallas, TX; *U.S. Public*, pg. 1307
Hewgley, William M., Jr., Exec. V.P.-Sls. & Mktg.--American Manufacturing Company, Chattanooga, TN; *U.S. Private*, pg. 58
Hickling, Donna, Mgr.-Mktg. Communications--Schlegel Corporation, Rochester, NY; *Int'l*, pg. 128
Hickox, Jennifer, Sls. & Mktg. Asst.--Sunroc Corporation, Dover, DE; *U.S. Private*, pg. 1053
Hickox, Jennifer, Sls. & Mktg. Asst.--Telkee, Dover, DE; *U.S. Private*, pg. 1053
Hicks, Lisa, Mgr.-Packaging Design & Trade Communications--Perdue Farms Incorporated, Salisbury, MD; *U.S. Private*, pg. 852
Hidinger, Jim, Mgr.-Corp. & Mktg. Communications--LeFebure Corp., Cedar Rapids, IA; *Int'l*, pg. 387
Hinrich, Andreas J., Prod. Mgr.--Inka Paletten GmbH, Hoehenkirchen, Germany; *Int'l*, pg. 678
Hier, Mark, Dir.-Pub. Rels. & Adv.--The Minnesota Mutual Life Insurance Company, Saint Paul, MN; *U.S. Private*, pg. 750
Higginbotham, Colleen, Coord.-Media--Distillers Corporation S.A., Stellenbosch, South Africa; *Int'l*, pg. 1129
Higgins, Jeanie, Mgr.-Adv.--Genovese Drug Stores, Inc., Melville, NY; *U.S. Public*, pg. 730
Higgins, Kathy, Mgr.-Mktg. Communications--Smith & Nephew Endoscopy, Andover, MA; *Int'l*, pg. 1263
Higgins, Sandra, Mgr.-Commun.--Physio-Control Corporation, Redmond, WA; *U.S. Public*, pg. 1294
Higgly, David, Dir.-Adv.--Icon Health & Fitness, Inc., Logan, UT; *U.S. Private*, pg. 556
Highly, Ann Marie, Mgr.-Adv. Pub. Rels.--Reuters Holdings PLC, London, United Kingdom; *Int'l*, pg. 1105
Hightower, George H., Jr., Exec. V.P.-Sls. & Adv.--Thomaston Mills, Inc., Thomaston, GA; *U.S. Public*, pg. 1599
Hilbert, Steve, V.P.-Fin. & Admin.--Telonic Berkeley, Inc., Laguna Beach, CA; *U.S. Private*, pg. 1074
Hildenbiddle, John, V.P.-Creative--Champion International Corp., Stamford, CT; *U.S. Public*, pg. 333
Hile, James, Mgr.-Prod. Brand Recognition--Gemini Consulting, Morristown, NJ; *Int'l*, pg. 264
Hilger-Johans, J., Dir.-Adv.--Zimmermann & Jansen GmbH, Duren, Germany; *Int'l*, pg. 1528
Hill-Engler, Judy, Mgr.-Corp. Adv. & Media Rels.--Hughes Electronics Corporation, Westchester, CA; *U.S. Public*, pg. 720
Hill, Bill, Dir.-Communications--Diversey Water Technologies, Inc., Chagrin Falls, OH; *U.S. Public*, pg. 1150
Hill, Linda, Dir.-Adv.--Hampshire Chemical Corp., Lexington, MA; *U.S. Private*, pg. 498
Hillebrecht, Alexandra, Mgr.-Adv. & Promo.--Stevens International, Inc., Fort Worth, TX; *U.S. Public*, pg. 1517
Hillenbrand, W August, Pres. & Chief Exec. Officer--Hillenbrand Industries, Inc., Batesville, IN; *U.S. Public*, pg. 828
Hiller, Yvonne, Dir.-Mktg. & Adv.--Elsinore Corporation, Las Vegas, NV; *U.S. Public*, pg. 570
Hillman, Jem, Dir.-Pub. Promo.--Executive Software, Glendale, CA; *U.S. Private*, pg. 388
Hillock, John, Exec. Dir.-Adv.--Conde Nast Traveler, New York, NY; *U.S. Private*, pg. 20
Hills, Steve, V.P.-Adv.--The Washington Post, Washington, DC; *U.S. Public*, pg. 1743
Hilmarsson, Thorsteinn, Mgr.-Info.--Landsvirkjun - The National Power Co., Reykjavik, Iceland; *Int'l*, pg. 801
Hilton, Michael R., Pub. Rels. Dir.--SmithKline Beecham Laboratories, Bristol, TN; *Int'l*, pg. 1264
Hilton, Mike, Mgr.-Sls. & Adv.--Dexion Group plc, Hemel Hempstead, United Kingdom; *U.S. Public*, pg. 893
Hines, Michael, V.P.-Adv.--The Prudential Insurance Company of America, Newark, NJ; *U.S. Private*, pg. 892
Hines, Steve, Mgr.-Gen. Sls. & Mktg.--Belliss & Morcom, Birmingham, United Kingdom; *Int'l*, pg. 1065
Hingst, Marie, Mgr.-Classified Adv.--Automotive News, Detroit, MI; *U.S. Private*, pg. 284
Hinke, Dave, Coord.-Adv.--Weinbrenner Shoe Company, Inc., Merrill, WI; *U.S. Private*, pg. 1160
Hinkle, Jane K., V.P.-Sls. & Mktg.--Octagon Process Inc., Edgewater, NJ; *U.S. Private*, pg. 811
Hinte, Michael, Mgr.-Adv. & Pub. Rels.--GESTRA GmbH, Bremen, Germany; *Int'l*, pg. 549
Hinton, Bruce, Sr. Dir.-Pub. Rels.--Long John Silver's, Inc., Lexington, KY; *U.S. Private*, pg. 674
Hinton, Kaki, Dir.-Adv.--Warner-Lambert Company, Morris Plains, NJ; *U.S. Public*, pg. 1738
Hinton, Kaki, Dir.-Adv. Services--Parke-Davis Group, Morris Plains, NJ; *U.S. Public*, pg. 1739
Hipple, Therese, Coord.-Mktg. Services--CiMatrix L.L.C., Canton, MA; *U.S. Public*, pg. 1395
Hirakawa, Hiroyuki, Asst. Mgr.-Adv.--Toyota Motor Corporation, Tokyo, Japan; *Int'l*, pg. 1411
Hirata, Ken, Mgr.-Adv.--Teac America, Inc., Montebello, CA; *Int'l*, pg. 1360
Hisbrook, David, V.P.-Mktg. & Adv.--Barnes & Noble Inc., New York, NY; *U.S. Public*, pg. 189
Hitch, Arthur, Pur. Agent--Allied Old English, Inc., Port Reading, NJ; *U.S. Private*, pg. 39
Hitch, John L., Mgr.-Mktg. Communications--Belden Inc., Saint Louis, MO; *U.S. Public*, pg. 200
Hiznay, Paul A., Sr. V.P.-Sls. & Adv.--Mona Industries, Inc., Paterson, NJ; *U.S. Private*, pg. 756
Hladun, Carol, Mgr.-Display Adv.--VV Publishing Corp., New York, NY; *U.S. Private*, pg. 1131
Hmelar, Anni, Mgr.-Marcom--Elo TouchSystems, Inc., Fremont, CA; *U.S. Public*, pg. 1362
Hoag, Kim, Dir.-Adv.--MMI Products, Inc., Houston, TX; *U.S. Private*, pg. 687
Hoagland, James P., Corp. Dir.-Mktg. & Product Devel.--Rocco Inc., Harrisonburg, VA; *U.S. Private*, pg. 937
Hobor, Nancy A., V.P.-Commun. & Investor Rels.--Morton International Inc., Chicago, IL; *U.S. Public*, pg. 1134
Hochhalter, Gordon R., Dir.-Adv.--R.R. Donnelley & Sons Company, Chicago, IL; *U.S. Public*, pg. 517
Hockstad, Doug, Dir.-Corp. Communications--Comshare, Incorporated, Ann Arbor, MI; *U.S. Public*, pg. 425
Hodges, Gene, Dir.-Adv.--The Home Depot, Inc., Atlanta, GA; *U.S. Public*, pg. 831
Hodges, W. Randolph, Dir.-Adv.--Shelby Williams Industries, Inc., Morristown, TN; *U.S. Public*, pg. 1464
Hodgson, Linda, V.P. & Mng. Dir.-Ghurka--Trafalgar Ghurka Ltd., Norwalk, CT; *U.S. Private*, pg. 1095
Hoehn, Hugo, Dir.-Adv.--Hilti AG, Schaan, Liechtenstein; *Int'l*, pg. 619
Hoerner, Jody, Mgr.-Adv.--Interstate Payco Seed Company, West Fargo, ND; *U.S. Private*, pg. 573
Hoerner, John Lee, Grp. Chief Exec.--The Burton Group PLC, London, United Kingdom; *Int'l*, pg. 237
Hofer, Nick, Mgr.-Adv.--Gateway 2000, North Sioux City, SD; *U.S. Public*, pg. 703
Hofer, Thomas W., Pres.--Spring-Green Lawn Care Corporation, Plainfield, IL; *U.S. Private*, pg. 1027
Hoff, Bernie, Dir.-Adv.--Capital-Gazette Communications, Inc., Annapolis, MD; *U.S. Private*, pg. 649
Hoff, Doan, Mgr.-Adv. & Pub. Rels.--Yamaha Electronics Corp. USA, Buena Park, CA; *Int'l*, pg. 1516
Hoffins, Steve, Mgr.-Adv.--Mercury Marine, Fond Du Lac, WI; *U.S. Public*, pg. 265
Hoffman, Charles, Pres.--Litton Applied Technology, San Jose, CA; *U.S. Public*, pg. 1003
Hoffman, John, Mgr.-Sls.--Waters Instruments, Inc., Rochester, MN; *U.S. Public*, pg. 1745
Hoffman, Leo, Sr. Mgr.-Adv.--Bristol-Myers Squibb Company, New York, NY; *U.S. Public*, pg. 253
Hoffman, Marv, V.P.-Mktg. Communications & Franchise Sls.--National Real Estate Services, Inc., Vancouver, Canada; *Int'l*, pg. 909
Hoffman, Nancye, Mgr.-Mktg. & Adv. Coord.--Nationwide Homes, Inc., Martinsville, VA; *U.S. Private*, pg. 788
Hoffman, Patty, Coord.-Promo. & Adv.--Gilbert Paper, Menasha, WI; *U.S. Public*, pg. 1074
Hoffman, Susan, Mgr.-Mktg. Svcs.--Hein-Werner Corporation, Waukesha, WI; *U.S. Public*, pg. 805
Hofmann, Don, V.P.-Adv.--Simmons Company, Atlanta, GA; *Int'l*, pg. 686
Hofmann, Rob, Sr. V.P.-Adv. & Mktg.--Chittenden Corporation, Burlington, VT; *U.S. Public*, pg. 350
Hogan, Debra, Mgr.-Adv.--Lee Pharmaceuticals, South El Monte, CA; *U.S. Public*, pg. 984
Holas, Frank W., Pres. & Chief Exec. Officer--Rich SeaPak Corp., Saint Simons Island, GA; *U.S. Private*, pg. 928
Holben, Elizabeth L., Mgr.-West Coast Adv.--Victoria, New York, NY; *U.S. Private*, pg. 517
Holbrook, Michele, Sr. Mgr.-Corp. Commun.--National Fuel Gas Company, Buffalo, NY; *U.S. Public*, pg. 1156
Holbrook, Michele, Sr. Mgr.-Corp. Commun.--National Fuel Gas Distribution Corp., Buffalo, NY; *U.S. Public*, pg. 1156
Holden, Fred, V.P.-Mktg.--World Finer Foods, Inc., Bloomfield, NJ; *U.S. Private*, pg. 1190

Holden, John, Mgr.-Pur. & Adv.--Victory Packaging, Plymouth, MI; *U.S. Private*, pg. 1139
Holdren, Mark, V.P.-Mktg. Svcs.--Genesee Corporation, Rochester, NY; *U.S. Public*, pg. 728
Holdsworth, Nick, Adv. Dir.--Dewe Rogerson Limited, London, United Kingdom; *Int'l*, pg. 408
Holland, Neysa, Mgr.-Adv.--Intergraph Corporation, Huntsville, AL; *U.S. Public*, pg. 890
Holley, Chuck, Mgr.-Mktg. Svcs.--Delta Consolidated Industries, Inc., Raleigh, NC; *U.S. Public*, pg. 481
Hollinger, Carl, Dir.-Sls. & Mktg.--John Copes Food Products, Inc., Rheems, PA; *U.S. Private*, pg. 274
Hollingsworth, Tom, Pres.--Sun Bulb Company, Inc., Arcadia, FL; *U.S. Private*, pg. 1050
Hollmann, Fran, Dir.-Adv.--King Kullen Grocery Co., Inc., Westbury, NY; *U.S. Private*, pg. 621
Holloway, J. David, V.P.-Mktg.--American Technical Publishers, Inc., Homewood, IL; *U.S. Private*, pg. 63
Hollywood, Steve, Dir.-Adv.--Thousand Oaks News-Chronicle, Thousand Oaks, CA; *U.S. Public*, pg. 1448
Holman, Denise, V.P.-Adv.--The Courier-Journal Louisville Times Co., Louisville, KY; *U.S. Public*, pg. 700
Holmblad, David, Mgr.-Adv.--L.L. Bean, Inc., Freeport, ME; *U.S. Private*, pg. 639
Holmes, Irvin R., Jr., V.P.-Mktg.--Del Monte Foods, San Francisco, CA; *U.S. Private*, pg. 321
Holmes, Michael H., V.P. & Gen. Mgr.-Chocolate--Hershey Chocolate U.S.A., Hershey, PA; *U.S. Public*, pg. 812
Holowaty, Howard, Dir.-Adv. & Mdsg.--The Midland Grocery Company, Westville, IN; *U.S. Private*, pg. 948
Holowell, Brent, Dir.-Mktg. Services--Adidas International, Portland, OR; *Int'l*, pg. 24
Holtkamp, Deb, Dir.-Adv. & Sls. Promo.--Royal Appliance Mfg. Co., Cleveland, OH; *U.S. Public*, pg. 1410
Holtzman, Jeff, V.P.--Goldberger Doll Mfg. Company, Inc., Brooklyn, NY; *U.S. Private*, pg. 459
Holzman, Jyll F., V.P.-Adv. Sls.--The New York Times, New York, NY; *U.S. Public*, pg. 1174
Holzwasser, Joel D., V.P.-Adv. & Pub. Rels.--Arrow Automotive Industries, Inc., Framingham, MA; *U.S. Public*, pg. 133
Homestead, Peter, V.P.-Design--Tropitone Furniture Co. Inc., Irvine, CA; *U.S. Private*, pg. 1105
Hone, W.K.L., Gen. Mgr.-Mktg. Strategy--Iscor, Pretoria, South Africa; *Int'l*, pg. 688
Honeycutt, Dave, Sr. Mgr.-Mktg. Communications--The Geon Company, Avon Lake, OH; *U.S. Public*, pg. 733
Hongosh, Edward J., Mgr.-Gen. Sls.--Eberhard Manufacturing, Strongsville, OH; *U.S. Public*, pg. 548
Hood, Melinda B., Mgr.-Commun.--Mississippi Chemical Corporation, Yazoo City, MS; *U.S. Public*, pg. 1117
Hoogewind, William H., Sec. & Dir.-Mktg.--Clipper Belt Lacer Company, Grand Rapids, MI; *U.S. Private*, pg. 413
Hoover, Brian, Dir.-Commun.--Triple F, Inc., Des Moines, IA; *U.S. Private*, pg. 1104
Hoover, Clark, Supvr.-Mktg. Svcs.--TB Wood's Corporation, Chambersburg, PA; *U.S. Public*, pg. 1562
Hopkins, John, Mgr.-Adv.--Prudential Corporation PLC, London, United Kingdom; *Int'l*, pg. 1073
Hopkins, Steve, Mgr.-Corp. Commun.--Standard Insurance Co., Portland, OR; *U.S. Private*, pg. 1031
Hopkinson, Ken, Dir.-Corp. Mktg. Communications--Beloit Corporation, Beloit, WI; *U.S. Public*, pg. 789
Hopley, Angela, Mgr.-Adv.--Air UK Ltd., Stansted, United Kingdom; *Int'l*, pg. 38
Hopson, Chris, V.P.-Adv.--Tower Records, West Sacramento, CA; *U.S. Private*, pg. 688
Hoque, Jeffery C., Pres. & Mgr.-Sls. & Adv.--Charles Atlas, Ltd., New York, NY; *U.S. Private*, pg. 229
Horan, Peter, Pres.-IMS--International Data Group, Boston, MA; *U.S. Private*, pg. 569
Horn, Christina, Dir.-Adv.--Mulberry Metal Products, Inc., Union, NJ; *U.S. Private*, pg. 766
Horn, Rick, V.P.-Sls. & Mktg.--Supreme Industries, Inc., Goshen, IN; *U.S. Public*, pg. 1541
Hornaday, David T., Mgr.-Mktg.--Wire Rope Corporation of America, Inc., Saint Joseph, MO; *U.S. Private*, pg. 1184
Horne, John, V.P. & Dir.-Adv.--Banknorth Group Inc., Burlington, VT; *U.S. Public*, pg. 186
Horstman, John, Mgr.-Specialty Mkts. Sls.--Horsehead Resource Development Company, Inc., Palmerton, PA; *U.S. Private*, pg. 540
Horton, Catherine, Mgr.-Adv. & Commun.--Safety 1st, Inc., Chestnut Hill, MA; *U.S. Public*, pg. 1425
Horton, Jeff, Mgr.-Adv.--Yamaha Motor Corp., U.S.A., Cypress, CA; *Int'l*, pg. 1516
Hoskins, William, V.P.-Sls. & Adv.--Penobscot Shoe Company, Old Town, ME; *U.S. Public*, pg. 1273
Hosstatter, Barbara, Coord.-Adv--Guerlain S.A., Paris, France; *Int'l*, pg. 780
Hotchkiss, M., Dir.-Sls.-Plastics--Farrel Corporation, Ansonia, CT; *U.S. Public*, pg. 614
Hotinger, Lizette, Dir.-Pub. Rels.--Paisano Publications, Inc., Agoura, CA; *U.S. Private*, pg. 834
Houde, Monic, Dir.-Adv.--Bell Canada, Montreal, Canada; *Int'l*, pg. 115
House, John H., Dir.-Communications--Dassault Falcon Jet Corp., South Hackensack, NJ; *Int'l*, pg. 383
Houseman, James E., Pres.--Harrop Industries, Inc., Columbus, OH; *U.S. Private*, pg. 506
Houston, Stephen, Mgr.-Adv. Bus.--Oshman's Sporting Goods, Inc., Houston, TX; *U.S. Public*, pg. 1233
Hovorka, Jeffrey, Mgr.-ID Solutions, Div.--Intelligent Controls Inc., Lynnwood, WA; *U.S. Private*, pg. 566
Howard, Rhonda S., Mgr.-Adv. & Promo.--Norfolk Southern Corporation, Norfolk, VA; *U.S. Public*, pg. 1190
Howard, Stephen, Dir.-Mktg. Services--Columbus Mills, Inc., Columbus, GA; *U.S. Private*, pg. 256
Howard, William, Mgr.-Adv.--Atotech U.S.A. Inc., Rock Hill, SC; *U.S. Private*, pg. 97
Howe, Michael, Dir.-Mktg. Communications--UAL Corporation, Elk Grove Village, IL; *U.S. Public*, pg. 1652
Howe, Robert, Dir.-Adv. & Field Mktg.--Miami Subs Corporation, Fort Lauderdale, FL; *U.S. Public*, pg. 1103
Howell, Josh, Sr. V.P.-Corp. Mktg.--MFS WorldCom, Inc., Omaha, NE; *U.S. Public*, pg. 1779
Howie, David, Mgr.-Corp. Communications--Rolls-Royce plc, London, United Kingdom; *Int'l*, pg. 1126
Howson, Debra, Dir.-Inside Sls. & Adv.--North American Capacitor Co., Indianapolis, IN; *U.S. Private*, pg. 803
Hrynewzcz, Alex, Dir.-Adv.--Zenith Electronics Corp., Glenview, IL; *U.S. Public*, pg. 1790
Hu, Alyson, Mgr.-Midwest Adv.--Redbook, New York, NY; *U.S. Private*, pg. 517
Hubbard, Charles G., Mgr.-Corp. Commun.--Baldor Electric Company, Fort Smith, AR; *U.S. Public*, pg. 168
Hubbard, Mike, Sr. V.P.-Sls.--Allen Canning Company, Siloam Springs, AR; *U.S. Private*, pg. 36
Hubner, C.E., Jr., Pres. & Chief Oper. Officer--Central/Shippee, Inc., Bloomingdale, NJ; *U.S. Private*, pg. 224
Huck, Bill, Dir.-Adv./Eastern--Metropolitan Sunday Newspapers, Inc., New York, NY; *U.S. Private*, pg. 739
Huck, Bill, Dir.-Eastern Adv.--Sunday Magazine Network, New York, NY; *U.S. Private*, pg. 739
Huddleston, C., Mgr.-Mktg Communications--Square D Company, Smyrna, TN; *Int'l*, pg. 1208
Hudec, Michele, Dir.-Mktg.--The Chicago Faucet Co., Des Plaines, IL; *U.S. Private*, pg. 234
Hudgins, A. Mark, Dir.-New Prod. Devel.--Automatic Signal/Eagle Signal, Austin, TX; *Int'l*, pg. 1245
Hudson, Charlie, Mgr.-Corp. Adv.--Chrysler Corporation, Auburn Hills, MI; *U.S. Public*, pg. 352
Hudson, Linda, Sr. Sec.--Del Webb's Coventry Homes, Phoenix, AZ; *U.S. Public*, pg. 495
Huebner, Keith, Mgr.-Mktg. & Communications--Cherry Electrical Products Corporation, Waukegan, IL; *U.S. Public*, pg. 346
Huether, Richard D., Pres. & Chief Exec. Officer--Independent Can Company, Belcamp, MD; *U.S. Private*, pg. 559
Huff, Dale, V.P.-Corp. Commun.--Amica Mutual Insurance Co., Lincoln, RI; *U.S. Private*, pg. 66
Huff, Dennis, Store Mgr.--Red Apple, Inc., Ontario, OR; *U.S. Private*, pg. 915
Hughes, Ben, Reg. Dir.--The Financial Times Ltd., London, United Kingdom; *Int'l*, pg. 1025
Hughes, Elaine, Dir.-Bus. Devel.--MYR Group Inc., Rolling Meadows, IL; *U.S. Public*, pg. 1029
Hughes, John J., Dir.-Adv.--GEICO Corporation, Washington, DC; *U.S. Public*, pg. 219
Hughes, Katherine, Mgr.-Adv.--Ultramar Diamond Shamrock Corporation, San Antonio, TX; *U.S. Public*, pg. 1663
Hughes, Kim, Mgr.-Mktg. & Adv.--Clothestime Stores, Inc., Anaheim, CA; *U.S. Public*, pg. 387
Hughes, Laura, V.P.-Strategic Mktg.--TeleCheck Services, Inc., Houston, TX; *U.S. Public*, pg. 631
Hughes, Maria, Mgr.-Natl. Adv.--Marriott International, Inc., Washington, DC; *U.S. Public*, pg. 1047
Hughes, Sharon, Dir.-Mktg.--American Consumer Products, Solon, OH; *U.S. Private*, pg. 1142
Hughes, Tim, Mktg. Analyst--Manufacturers Consolidation Service, Inc., Memphis, TN; *U.S. Private*, pg. 700
Hugo, James, Mgr.-Adv.--Perfection Corporation, Madison, OH; *Int'l*, pg. 1149
Hull, Jeff, Mgr.-Pub. Rels.--Matson Navigation Company, Inc., San Francisco, CA; *U.S. Public*, pg. 39
Hull, John L., Vice Chm. & Sec.--Hull Corporation, Hatboro, PA; *U.S. Private*, pg. 547
Hulsey, Slona, Dir.-Mktg. & Pub. Rels.--Pancho's Mexican Buffet, Inc., Fort Worth, TX; *U.S. Public*, pg. 1255
Humbertson, Don, Dir.-Adv.--Chicago Reader, Inc., Chicago, IL; *U.S. Private*, pg. 235
Hunsinger, Harold, Mgr.-Communications--Nordyne Inc., Saint Louis, MO; *U.S. Public*, pg. 1193
Hunt, Connie, Dir.-Human Resources--Empire of Carolina, Inc., Delray Beach, FL; *U.S. Public*, pg. 579
Hunt, Jeffrey S., V.P.--BT Financial Corporation, Johnstown, PA; *U.S. Public*, pg. 163
Hunt, Mary, Mgr.-Adv.--Kruger Inc., Montreal, Canada; *Int'l*, pg. 761
Hunter, Kate, Dir.-Mktg.--Kal Grafx, Kentwood, MI; *U.S. Private*, pg. 387
Huntsberry, Judy, Coord.-Adv. Services--Rheem Water Heater, Montgomery, AL; *Int'l*, pg. 1022
Hurdman, Charles, Mgr.-Adv.--UNUM Corporation, Portland, ME; *U.S. Public*, pg. 1699
Hurdman, Charles, Dir.-Corp. Adv.--UNUM Life Insurance Company of America, Portland, ME; *U.S. Public*, pg. 1699
Hurley, Jackie, Dir.-Natl. Adv./Residence Inn--Marriott International, Inc., Washington, DC; *U.S. Public*, pg. 1047
Hurley, Nancy, Adv. Dir.--Universal Underwriters Insurance Co., Overland Park, KS; *Int'l*, pg. 1530
Hushka, Alina, V.P.-Mktg.--Robson Communities, Sun Lakes, AZ; *U.S. Private*, pg. 937
Huso, Nathan, Mgr.-Comm & Mktg.--Dakota Electric Association, Farmington, MN; *U.S. Private*, pg. 308
Huston, Richard T., Exec. V.P.-Mktg.--ShowBiz Pizza Time, Inc., Irving, TX; *U.S. Public*, pg. 1468
Hutchings, Doug, Mgr.-Mktg.--ODL Incorporated, Zeeland, MI; *U.S. Private*, pg. 809
Hutchins, Bob, V.P.-Mktg.--Supershuttle Inc., Phoenix, AZ; *U.S. Private*, pg. 1056
Hutchins, Sid, Sr. Exec. V.P.-Communications--Maritz Inc., Fenton, MO; *U.S. Private*, pg. 703
Hutchison, D. Bruce, V.P.-Adv. & Mkt. Res.--Thomson Consumer Electronics Inc., Indianapolis, IN; *Int'l*, pg. 1383
Hutsell, Jeffrey A., Exec. V.P.-Creative--Enesco Corporation, Itasca, IL; *U.S. Public*, pg. 1508
Hutt, Libby, Mgr.-Category & Adv.--Contadina Dalla Casa Buitoni, Glendale, CA; *Int'l*, pg. 916
Hutton, Nancy, Controller, Treas. & Sec.--Crustbuster, Inc., Dodge City, KS; *U.S. Private*, pg. 293
Hyba, Karen, Mgr.-Adv.--Rauland-Borg Corporation, Skokie, IL; *U.S. Private*, pg. 911
Hyde, Leslie, Mgr.-Mktg.--Westbrae Natural, Inc., Carson, CA; *U.S. Public*, pg. 774
Hyde, Tom, Mgr.-Adv. & Customer Rels.--Colorado Interstate Gas Co., Colorado Springs, CO; *U.S. Public*, pg. 390
Hynes, Peter, V.P.-Corp. Pub. Rels.--Unisys Corporation, Blue Bell, PA; *U.S. Public*, pg. 1671
Hynes, Richard, Mgr.-Paper Technology Adv.--Hercules Incorporated, Wilmington, DE; *U.S. Public*, pg. 809
Hynes, Thomas, Dir. Mktg. & Dir. Response--Moxness Products, Inc., Racine, WI; *U.S. Public*, pg. 124
Iamele, Pat, Dir.- Adv.--The Genlyte Group Incorporated, Union, NJ; *U.S. Public*, pg. 729
Iamele, Pat, Dir.-Adv.--Lightolier Division, Fall River, MA; *U.S. Public*, pg. 730
Ibbotson, Gerry, Mgr.-Adv.--Halifax plc, Halifax, United Kingdom; *Int'l*, pg. 589
Ide, Masanori, Gen. Mgr.--Chiyoda Mutual Life Insurance Company, Tokyo, Japan; *Int'l*, pg. 286
Ifshin, Barbara, V.P.-Adv. & Creative Svcs.--Walt Disney Attractions-Walt Disney World, Lake Buena Vista, FL; *U.S. Public*, pg. 513
Ilaria, Peter E., Dir.-Mktg. & Sls.--Tropar Mfg. Co., Inc., Florham Park, NJ; *U.S. Private*, pg. 1105
Ildau, Peter M., V.P.-Corp. Commun.--Recoton Corporation, Lake Mary, FL; *U.S. Public*, pg. 1369
Illig, Lynn, Mgr.-Mktg. Commun.--Matthews International Corp., Pittsburgh, PA; *U.S. Public*, pg. 1059
Imler, Dan, Dir.-Adv. & Communications--Tension Envelope Corp., Kansas City, MO; *U.S. Private*, pg. 1077
Indyk, William, V.P.-Mktg. & Sls.--White Rock Products Corp., Whitestone, NY; *U.S. Private*, pg. 1173
Infanti, Daniel, V.P.-Corp. Communications & Mktg.--Sharp Electronics Corporation, Mahwah, NJ; *Int'l*, pg. 1228
Inferrera, Marie, Supvr.-Adv. & Publications--Atlantic Electric Co., Pleasantville, NJ; *U.S. Public*, pg. 430
Ingeno, Samuel D., Mgr.-Adv. Production--Koh-I-Noor, Inc., Bloomsbury, NJ; *U.S. Private*, pg. 629
Ingrassia, Patrice, Dir.-Adv. & Pub. Rels.--Ernst & Young, LLP, New York, NY; *U.S. Private*, pg. 381
Inkel, H. Albert, Sr. V.P.-Assoc. Rels. & Communication--Horace Mann Educators Corporation, Springfield, IL; *U.S. Public*, pg. 835
Innes, John, V.P.-Sls.--Cable Spinning Equipment Inc., New London, MN; *U.S. Private*, pg. 197
Innocent, Jean, Mgr.-Mktg. Communications--TRC Companies, Inc., Windsor, CT; *U.S. Public*, pg. 1557
Insel, Jackie, Dir.-Mktg., Pub. Rels. & Adv.--Phillips Fine Art Auctioneers, New York, NY; *U.S. Private*, pg. 861
Iott Rourke, Cathie, Dir.-Adv.--NBD Bank (Michigan), Troy, MI; *U.S. Public*, pg. 628
Irby, Mark, V.P.-Mktg. & Adv.--Publix Supermarkets Inc., Lakeland, FL; *U.S. Private*, pg. 893
Irelan, E. Glenn, Exec. V.P.-Mktg., Stores & Real Estate--Catherines Stores Corporation, Memphis, TN; *U.S. Public*, pg. 317
Irish, Dennis, Dir.-Adv.--G.I. Joe's Inc., Wilsonville, OR; *U.S. Private*, pg. 435
Ironside, Mike, Dir.-Adv.--Daily Mail & General Trust PLC, London, United Kingdom; *Int'l*, pg. 366
Ironside, Mike, Dir.-Adv.--Associated Newspaper Holdings Ltd., London, United Kingdom; *Int'l*, pg. 366
Irvin, John W., Pres.-Catalog Div.--Spiegel, Inc., Downers Grove, IL; *U.S. Public*, pg. 1498
Irwin, Marie, Dir.-Mktg.--Carrols Corporation, Syracuse, NY; *U.S. Private*, pg. 216
Irwin, Mike, Dir.-Mktg.--WD-40 Company, San Diego, CA; *U.S. Public*, pg. 1726
Irwin, Scott, Mgr.-Adv.--Irwin Sports, Inc., Toronto, Canada; *Int'l*, pg. 688
Isham, Carol A., Dir.-Adv.--SLJ Retail LLC, Smyrna, GA; *U.S. Private*, pg. 957
Isherwood, Tonya, Dir.-Adv. & Promo.--Niagara Frontier Hockey, L.P., Buffalo, NY; *U.S. Private*, pg. 798
Ishigaki, Akiro, Dir.-Adv.--Kirin Brewery Co., Ltd., Tokyo, Japan; *Int'l*, pg. 735
Ishihara, Ken, V.P.-Adv.--Toshiba America Inc., New York, NY; *Int'l*, pg. 1405
Israel, Rich, Dir.-Mktg.--San Diego Chargers, San Diego, CA; *U.S. Private*, pg. 964
Iunghuhn, Kathy, Dir.-Corp. Mktg.--Simon DeBartolo Group, Inc., Indianapolis, IN; *U.S. Public*, pg. 1474
Iverson, F. Kenneth, Chm. Bd.--Nucor Corporation, Charlotte, NC; *U.S. Public*, pg. 1205
Iverson, Mark, Dir.-Adv. & Pub. Rels.--DataCard Corporation, Minnetonka, MN; *U.S. Private*, pg. 312
Ivey, John Mark, Mgr.-Adv.--Channel Master, Smithfield, NC; *U.S. Private*, pg. 228
Ivie, Jill, Adv.--APL Limited, Oakland, CA; *Int'l*, pg. 912
Izawa, Hirotoshi, Gen. Mgr.--The Tokio Marine & Fire Insurance Company, Ltd., Tokyo, Japan; *Int'l*, pg. 1391
Izdepski, Michael, Mgr.-Adv.--Milton Bradley Company, East Longmeadow, MA; *U.S. Public*, pg. 797
Izquierdo, Alfredo, Sr. V.P.-Opers.--PonceBank, F.S.B., Ponce, PR; *U.S. Public*, pg. 1316
Jack, A.G., Sr. Mgr.-Adv.--Standard Bank Investment Corporation Limited, Johannesburg, South Africa; *Int'l*, pg. 1293
Jackson, Bonnie, Dir.-Adv. Programs/Chicago--Ameritech Corporation, Chicago, IL; *U.S. Public*, pg. 97
Jackson, Bonnie, Dir.-Adv.--Ameritech, Chicago, IL; *U.S. Public*, pg. 97
Jackson, Bonnie, Dir.-Adv. Programs--Ameritech, Detroit, MI; *U.S. Public*, pg. 97
Jackson, Bonnie, Dir.-Adv. Programs--Ameritech, Milwaukee, WI; *U.S. Public*, pg. 97
Jackson, Bonnie, Dir.-Adv. Programs--Ameritech Phone Company, Cleveland, OH; *U.S. Public*, pg. 98
Jackson, Gary, Mgr.-Adv. & Promo.--Porta Systems Corp., Syosset, NY; *U.S. Public*, pg. 1317
Jackson, Mary Ann, Sr. Mgr.-Corp. Pub. Rels. & Adv.--InterBold, Canton, OH; *U.S. Public*, pg. 506
Jackson, Nina, Coord.-Publications--Alimed, Inc., Dedham, MA; *U.S. Private*, pg. 34

Jackson, Peter, Grp. Mgr.-Communications--Royal & Sun Alliance Insurance Group plc, London, United Kingdom; *Int'l*, pg. 1130
Jackson, Riley, V.P.-Mktg., Pur. & Adv.--Federal Savings Bank, Fort Smith, AR; *U.S. Private*, pg. 614
Jackson, Stephen K., V.P.-Distr. Div., Mktg. & Adv.--Georgia-Pacific Distribution Div., Atlanta, GA; *U.S. Public*, pg. 735
Jacobazzi, Ralph, Mgr.-Utility Div. Sls.--W.H. Salisbury & Company, Skokie, IL; *Int'l*, pg. 1244
Jacobs, Bill, Coord.-Adv.--Lindsay Manufacturing Company, Lindsay, NE; *U.S. Public*, pg. 999
Jacobs, James, Coord.-Adv.--Jersey Central Power & Light Co., Morristown, NJ; *U.S. Public*, pg. 695
Jacobs, Jim, Bus. Devel. Mgr.--Advanced Marine Enterprises, Inc., Arlington, VA; *U.S. Public*, pg. 1182
Jacobs, Lisa, V.P.-Adv. & Consumer Promo.--Tyco Toys, Inc., Mount Laurel, NJ; *U.S. Public*, pg. 1058
Jacobs, Sherry, Coord.-Adv.--Sonoma Mission Inn & Spa, Sonoma, CA; *U.S. Private*, pg. 1014
Jacobsen, Keith, Dir.-Adv.--Fiesta Mart Inc., Houston, TX; *U.S. Private*, pg. 403
Jacobson, Allyn H., V.P.-Adv.--Advanta Corp., Spring House, PA; *U.S. Public*, pg. 22
Jacobson, Arnold E., Pres.--Goddess Bra Company, East Boston, MA; *U.S. Private*, pg. 458
Jacobson, Ellen, V.P.-Design & Mdsg.--Goddess Bra Company, East Boston, MA; *U.S. Private*, pg. 458
Jacobson, Paul E., Dir.-Communications--Ascent Entertainment Group, Inc., Denver, CO; *U.S. Public*, pg. 138
Jacoby, Judy, Dir.-Adv.--Doubleday Publishing Company, New York, NY; *Int'l*, pg. 191
Jaffe, Sandra, Dir.-Beauty Adv.--Mademoiselle, New York, NY; *U.S. Private*, pg. 20
Jaffke, Fred, Mgr.-Adv.--Federal Home Loan Mortgage Corporation, Mc Lean, VA; *U.S. Public*, pg. 615
James, Betty M., Pres. & Dir.-Mktg. & Pub. Rels.--James Industries Inc., Hollidaysburg, PA; *U.S. Private*, pg. 580
James, Randy, Mgr.-Adv.-Chicago--Scientific American, Inc., New York, NY; *Int'l*, pg. 1479
James, Sarah, Mgr.-Adv.--Kenneth Cole Productions, New York, NY; *U.S. Public*, pg. 951
Jamison, Martin, Dir.-Mktg. & Adv.--Dale Farm Dairies Ltd., Ballymena, United Kingdom; *Int'l*, pg. 968
Jandasek, Jim, Mgr.-Passenger Car Adv.--Chevrolet Motor Div. General Motors Corp., Warren, MI; *U.S. Public*, pg. 720
Janeway, Don, Dir.-Adv.--Ralphs Grocery Company, Compton, CA; *U.S. Private*, pg. 1202
Janks, Arlene A., Adv. Coord.--Acustar, Inc., Engineered Products Group, Troy, MI; *U.S. Public*, pg. 353
Jans, Karin, Mgr.-Adv. & Mktg. Services--C.P. Clare Corporation, Beverly, MA; *U.S. Public*, pg. 382
Janseu, Kay, Dir.-Adv.--Ecolab Inc., Saint Paul, MN; *U.S. Public*, pg. 562
Jaouen, Sandy, Mgr.-Mktg.--Alpha Wire Company, Elizabeth, NJ; *U.S. Public*, pg. 201
Jardine, Ian, Dir.-Mktg.--Finnigan Corporation, San Jose, CA; *U.S. Public*, pg. 1591
Jarnot, John, Dir.-Mktg. Services & Sls. Promo.--AON Corporation, Chicago, IL; *U.S. Public*, pg. 117
Jaros, Carol, Dir.-Adv.--Distribution America, Des Plaines, IL; *U.S. Private*, pg. 335
Jarrels, Ralph, Dir.-Adv.--Radiator Specialty Company, Charlotte, NC; *U.S. Private*, pg. 906
Jarrett, Toni, Mgr.-Adv.--Showboat, Incorporated, Las Vegas, NV; *U.S. Public*, pg. 1469
Jarvis, David, Mgr.-Media & Adv.--Nestle-Rowntree Ltd., York, United Kingdom; *Int'l*, pg. 921
Jarvis, Ken, Mgr.-Adv.--Ingles Markets, Incorporated, Black Mountain, NC; *U.S. Public*, pg. 878
Jaszewski, Ruth, Mktg. Asst.--Lucas Body Systems - North America, Winona, MN; *Int'l*, pg. 820
Javier, Rey M., V.P.-Corp. Dev.--EEI Corporation, Manila, Philippines; *Int'l*, pg. 425
Jaworski, Rick, Mgr.-Adv.--Wavetek Corporation, San Diego, CA; *U.S. Private*, pg. 1154
Jay, John, Assoc. Publisher/Dir.-Mktg.--Sports Illustrated, New York, NY; *U.S. Public*, pg. 1613
Jean, James, V.P.-Mktg.--United Service Equipment Company, Murfreesboro, TN; *U.S. Public*, pg. 1507
Jeanquenin, Adrian, Mgr.-Sls.--Tempil Inc., South Plainfield, NJ; *U.S. Private*, pg. 90
Jeffers, Mary, Dir.-Adv.--Meyer Jewelers, Taylor, MI; *U.S. Private*, pg. 739
Jefferson, Robert F., V.P.-Mktg.--Arinc Inc. (Consolidated), Annapolis, MD; *U.S. Private*, pg. 81
Jeffries, April, V.P.-Bakery Bus. Mktg.--Pepperidge Farm, Incorporated, Norwalk, CT; *U.S. Public*, pg. 299
Jelitko, M., Dir.-Adv.--ABG Allgemeine Baumaschinen-Gesellschaft mbH, Hameln, Germany; *U.S. Public*, pg. 877
Jellett, Hugo, Mgr.-Mktg.--Harper Audio, New York, NY; *Int'l*, pg. 926
Jembelis, Thomas, Sr. V.P.--Nozaki America, Inc., New York, NY; *Int'l*, pg. 990
Jenkins, Don, V.P.-Mktg.--Nocona Boot Co., Nocona, TX; *U.S. Public*, pg. 937
Jenkins, Rob, Mgr.-Mktg. Svcs.--Rev-A-Shelf, Louisville, KY; *U.S. Private*, pg. 925
Jenner, Peter, Dir.-Adv.--Coates Brothers (South Africa) Ltd., Cape Town, South Africa; *Int'l*, pg. 1409
Jennings, Katty, Mgr.-Adv.--Lazard Brothers & Co. Ltd., London, United Kingdom; *Int'l*, pg. 1026
Jensen, Alan, Dir.-Adv.--Anderson Brothers Construction Brainerd, Brainerd, MN; *U.S. Private*, pg. 72
Jensen, Darrel, Mgr.-Adv.--Harmon City, Inc., Salt Lake City, UT; *U.S. Private*, pg. 503
Jensen, Marcia, Mgr.-Mktg. Communications--U.S. Bancorp, Minneapolis, MN; *U.S. Public*, pg. 1680
Jensen, Mary, Dir.-Adv.--Reactor Experiments, Inc., Sunnyvale, CA; *U.S. Public*, pg. 1594
Jensen, Niels Christian, Mgr.-Adv.--Lego System A/S, Billund, Denmark; *Int'l*, pg. 805
Jensen, Rick, Mgr.-Adv.--U.S. Bank of Idaho, Boise, ID; *U.S. Public*, pg. 1681
Jensen, V. E., Mgr.-Adv. & Pub. Rels.--Square D Automation Products, Milwaukee, WI; *Int'l*, pg. 1208
Jermasek, Doug, Assoc. Dir.-VIRACEPT Prod. Sls.--Agouron Pharmaceuticals, Inc., La Jolla, CA; *U.S. Public*, pg. 28
Jernigan, Paul, V.P.-Sls. & Mktg.--Gibson Musical Instruments, Inc., Nashville, TN; *U.S. Private*, pg. 451
Jerome, Jerry K., Pres. & Chief Exec. Officer--Jerome Foods Inc., Barron, WI; *U.S. Private*, pg. 586
Jessie, Janelle M., Asst. V.P. & Dir.-Adv. & Pub. Rels.--Chemed Corporation, Cincinnati, OH; *U.S. Public*, pg. 343
Jessopp, Charles E.B., V.P.-Adv.--Northern Trust Corporation, Chicago, IL; *U.S. Public*, pg. 1195
Jewell, John, IV, V.P.-Opers.--The Parman Corporation, Nashville, TN; *U.S. Private*, pg. 840
Jimenez, Joe, Pres.-Wesson/Peter Pan Foods Co.--Hunt-Wesson, Inc., Fullerton, CA; *U.S. Public*, pg. 428
Jipp, Peter, Dir.-Adv.--Deutz AG, Cologne, Germany; *Int'l*, pg. 407
Jiran, J.J., Assoc. Mgr.-Adv.--Union Camp Corporation, Wayne, NJ; *U.S. Public*, pg. 1665
Jodar, Joey, Dir.-Mktg.--Wadsworth Publishing co., Belmont, CA; *U.S. Public*, pg. 1600
Joel, Stephanie, Assoc. Dir.-Adv.--John Wiley & Sons, Inc., New York, NY; *U.S. Public*, pg. 1768
Johansen, Benjamin C., V.P.-Mdsg.--EZ Paintr Corp., Saint Francis, WI; *U.S. Public*, pg. 1177
Johanson, Caroline, Dir.-Adv.--B & W Stormarknader AB, Malmo, Sweden; *Int'l*, pg. 708
Johnson, Alberto K., Mgr.-Pub. Rels. & Adv.--Neumaticos Goodyear SA, Buenos Aires, Argentina; *U.S. Public*, pg. 753
Johnson, D. David, Dir.-Worldwide Special Sections--Business Week, New York, NY; *U.S. Public*, pg. 1069
Johnson, Darrell, V.P. & Mgr.-Mktg.--Felton Brush Inc., Manchester, NH; *U.S. Private*, pg. 400
Johnson, David H., Mgr.-Mktg. Communications--Twin Disc, Incorporated, Racine, WI; *U.S. Public*, pg. 1646
Johnson, Diane, Mgr.-Adv.--TruGreen-ChemLawn, Memphis, TN; *U.S. Public*, pg. 1461
Johnson, Don, Dir.-Adv. & Mktg.--Detecto Scale Company, Webb City, MO; *U.S. Private*, pg. 209
Johnson, Don, V.P.-Sls. & Publ.--Krause Publications, Inc., Iola, WI; *U.S. Private*, pg. 635
Johnson, Dwayne, Mgr.-Mktg. Communications & Adv.--Republic Automotive-AEA Division, Charlotte, NC; *U.S. Public*, pg. 1377
Johnson, Eric, V.P.-Sls. & Mktg.--John Boos & Company, Effingham, IL; *U.S. Private*, pg. 156
Johnson, J. Dennis, V.P.-Mktg.--Kentucky Medical Insurance Company (KMIC), Louisville, KY; *U.S. Private*, pg. 741
Johnson, James R., Exec. V.P. & Sec.--Johnson Storage Moving Co, Denver, CO; *U.S. Private*, pg. 594
Johnson, Janilee, V.P.-Pub. Affairs, Promo. & Adv.--Bellcore, Morristown, NJ; *U.S. Private*, pg. 976
Johnson, Jim, Pres.--Lusk, Irvine, CA; *U.S. Private*, pg. 681
Johnson, Keith A., V.P.-Natl. Sls.--Clear Shield National, Inc., Wheeling, IL; *U.S. Public*, pg. 586
Johnson, Linda, Mgr.-Adv., Sls. Promo. & Pub. Rels.--Chloride Industrial Batteries Ltd., Manchester, United Kingdom; *Int'l*, pg. 125
Johnson, Mark, Adv. Coord.--Firestone Industrial Products Co., Carmel, IN; *Int'l*, pg. 214
Johnson, Mark R.S., Co-Chief Exec. Officer & Pres.-Mktg.--Hastings Manufacturing Company, Hastings, MI; *U.S. Public*, pg. 798
Johnson, Michelle, Coord.-Mktg. & Adv.--Heraeus Amersil Inc., Duluth, GA; *Int'l*, pg. 616
Johnson, P.J., Dir-Pub. Rels. & Adv.--Nomura Securities International, Inc., New York, NY; *Int'l*, pg. 956
Johnson, Randy, Dir.-Mktg. & Adv.--Barrel O'Fun Snack Foods Co., Perham, MN; *U.S. Private*, pg. 118
Johnson, Roger, Exec. V.P.--Aid Association for Lutherans, Appleton, WI; *U.S. Private*, pg. 27
Johnson, Suzanne C., Dir.-Adv. Production--Postgraduate Medicine, Minneapolis, MN; *U.S. Public*, pg. 1071
Johnston, J. Tyler, V.P.-Mktg.--Dreyer's Grand Ice Cream, Inc., Oakland, CA; *U.S. Public*, pg. 529
Johnston, Steve, V.P.-Adv.--Nationwide Mutual Insurance Co., Columbus, OH; *U.S. Private*, pg. 789
Jolin, Norman, Dir.-Adv.--Weis Markets, Inc., Sunbury, PA; *U.S. Public*, pg. 1751
Jolley, Don, Mgr.-Adv. & Mktg. Communications--Thermal Ceramics Inc., Augusta, GA; *Int'l*, pg. 894
Joly, John, Dir.-Pub. Affairs--Seattle Post-Intelligencer, Seattle, WA; *U.S. Private*, pg. 517
Jones, Biege, Mgr.-Adv. & Internal Art Dir.--Sport Obermeyer Ltd., USA, Aspen, CO; *U.S. Private*, pg. 1026
Jones, Clarke C., Exec. V.P.-Adv.--Saunders Oil Company, Inc., Richmond, VA; *U.S. Private*, pg. 968
Jones, Diane S., Mgr.-Corp. Rels. & Bus. Devel.--Westmoreland Coal Co., Colorado Springs, CO; *U.S. Public*, pg. 1761
Jones, Gwen, Mgr.-Adv.--Day-Timers, Inc., East Texas, PA; *U.S. Public*, pg. 674
Jones, J. Kevin, Pres.--Rev-A-Shelf, Louisville, KY; *U.S. Private*, pg. 925
Jones, James L., Sr., Chm. Bd. & Chief Exec. Officer--Jones & Jones, Inc., McAllen, TX; *U.S. Private*, pg. 596
Jones, Jayne, Mgr.-Adv.--American Express Financial Advisor, Minneapolis, MN; *U.S. Public*, pg. 73
Jones, Kasey, Dir.-Adv.--Kearney Company, Tucker, GA; *U.S. Public*, pg. 444
Jones, Kathryn H., Mgr.-Commun.--Roy F. Weston, Inc., West Chester, PA; *U.S. Public*, pg. 1761
Jones, Keith, Mgr.-Mktg. Services--Northern Telecom Inc., Rochester, NY; *Int'l*, pg. 970
Jones, Keith A., Dir.-Corp. Mktg.--Fermec Holdings, Ltd., Manchester, United Kingdom; *U.S. Public*, pg. 312
Jones, Keith W., Mgr.-Mktg. Commun.--Eriez Magnetics, Erie, PA; *U.S. Private*, pg. 381
Jones, Lloyd, Exec. V.P.--A.G. Simpson Co. Limited, Scarborough, Canada; *Int'l*, pg. 1252
Jones, Louise, Mgr.-Adv. & Mktg. Specialist--Schneider Group, Mississauga, Canada; *Int'l*, pg. 1208
Jones, M. Cheryl, Mgr.-Adv.--First Citizens Banc Shares, Inc., Raleigh, NC; *U.S. Public*, pg. 628
Jones, Maura, Mgr.-Adv.--T.J. Maxx, Framingham, MA; *U.S. Public*, pg. 1557
Jones, Ron, Mgr.-Adv.--Free Service Tire Company, Inc., Johnson City, TN; *U.S. Private*, pg. 425
Jones, Steve, Mgr.-Mktg--Rowenta (USA), Inc., Medford, MA; *Int'l*, pg. 569
Jones, Susan S., Mgr.-Mktg. Communications--BNA Software, Washington, DC; *U.S. Private*, pg. 182
Jones, Wiley, V.P. & Mgr.-Mktg & Adv.--Green Spot Packaging Inc., Claremont, CA; *U.S. Private*, pg. 477
Jones, Yolande, Sr. Admin. Asst.--Thompson Nutritional Products, Boca Raton, FL; *U.S. Public*, pg. 1384
Jonson, Bjorn, Dir.-Grp. Info.--Sandvik AB, Sandviken, Sweden; *Int'l*, pg. 1185
Jordan, James, Dir.-Mktg. & Adv.--Multiple Allied Services, Inc., Hayward, CA; *U.S. Private*, pg. 767
Jorgensen, Marty, Sr. V.P.-Pur. & Adv.--Video Products Distributors, Inc., Sacramento, CA; *U.S. Private*, pg. 1139
Jorgensen, Virgil, Mgr.-Adv. & Pub. Rels.--Hydro-Aire, Burbank, CA; *U.S. Public*, pg. 457
Joseph, Debbie, Mgr.-Adv.- Cuprinol & Thompson's Water Seal--The Sherwin-Williams Company, Cleveland, OH; *U.S. Public*, pg. 1465
Joseph, Thad, Asst. V.P.-Adv. & Pub. Rels.--Miracle Recreation Equipment Company, Monett, MO; *U.S. Private*, pg. 752
Jue, Herman, Dir.-Adv.--Chase & Sanborn Coffee, Inc., San Francisco, CA; *Int'l*, pg. 917
Julian, Ken, Dir.-Corp. Communications--Harsco Corporation, Camp Hill, PA; *U.S. Public*, pg. 792
Julian, Malcolm, Exec. V.P.-Sls. & Mktg.--Winstar Global Products, Inc., Fairfield, NJ; *U.S. Public*, pg. 1772
Junk, Robert L., Mgr.-Sls./Private Label--Doane Products Co., Branded Sales Div., Joplin, MO; *U.S. Private*, pg. 337
Juran, Linda, Mgr.-Adv.--Whiteswan/Meta, Libertyville, IL; *U.S. Private*, pg. 342
Jurek, Noreen, Sr. Mgr.-Mktg. Commun.--Tekelec, Calabasas, CA; *U.S. Public*, pg. 1566
Justice, Michael, Dir.-Sls. & Mktg.--RB&W Corporation, Cleveland, OH; *U.S. Public*, pg. 1259
Kabat, Randy, Mgr.-Adv.--Swatch Watch U.S.A., New York, NY; *Int'l*, pg. 1161
Kack, Steve, Mktg. Coord.--Davie Industries Inc., Levis, Canada; *Int'l*, pg. 385
Kadell, Sharon, V.P.-Adv. & Pur.--Waremart Inc., Boise, ID; *U.S. Private*, pg. 1150
Kadens, Greg, Dir.-Adv--Quill Corp., Lincolnshire, IL; *U.S. Private*, pg. 901
Kafarakis, Phil, V.P.-Sls. & Mktg.--Jones Dairy Farm, Fort Atkinson, WI; *U.S. Private*, pg. 596
Kagan, Dave, Dir.-Communications--Bissell Inc., Grand Rapids, MI; *U.S. Private*, pg. 145
Kagelmann-Holtz, Kris, Dir.-Adv.--Manpower Inc., Milwaukee, WI; *U.S. Public*, pg. 1042
Kahn, Judith, Mgr.-Pub. Rels.--Ark Restaurants Corp., New York, NY; *U.S. Public*, pg. 129
Kaiser, Mark P., Sr. V.P.-Sls., Mktg. & Procurement--JP Foodservice, Inc., Columbia, MD; *U.S. Public*, pg. 918
Kal, Alison, V.P.-Mktg. Commun.--Hilton Hotels Corporation, Beverly Hills, CA; *U.S. Public*, pg. 828
Kaldich, Gunter, Mgr.-Prod.--Intertractor Zweigniederlassung der Wirtgen GmbH, Gevelsberg, Germany; *Int'l*, pg. 1511
Kaletta, Jim, V.P.-Aviation--Scott Aviation, Lancaster, NY; *U.S. Public*, pg. 622
Kalish, Harry, Dir.-Adv.--Cottman Transmission Systems, Inc., Fort Washington, PA; *U.S. Private*, pg. 278
Kalishman, John F., Dir.-Mktg.--Insituform Technologies, Inc., Chesterfield, MO; *U.S. Public*, pg. 881
Kall, Janice, Mgr.-Trade Shows--Proxima Corporation, San Diego, CA; *U.S. Public*, pg. 1339
Kallman, Ralph, V.P.-Adv. Promo.--Eby-Brown Co., Naperville, IL; *U.S. Private*, pg. 359
Kalmus, Bob, Dir.-Adv.--Pensions & Investments, Chicago, IL; *U.S. Private*, pg. 285
Kalousek, Mary, Mgr.-Adv. & Corp. Communications--Rogers N.K. Seed Co., Boise, ID; *Int'l*, pg. 974
Kaluza, Johannes, Dir.-Mktg. & Adv.--Eckes AG, Nieder-Olm, Germany; *Int'l*, pg. 432
Kammer, Greg, Mgr.-Mktg.--Magline, Inc., Pinconning, MI; *U.S. Private*, pg. 695
Kammerer, Mark, Dir.-Mktg. Services--Royal Caribbean Cruises Ltd., Miami, FL; *U.S. Public*, pg. 1410
Kanas, Jackie, V.P.-Adv.--European American Bank & Trust Co., Uniondale, NY; *Int'l*, pg. 9
Kandel, Charlotte, Sr. V.P.-Worldwide Publicity & Promotion--Warner Bros. Studios, Inc., Burbank, CA; *U.S. Public*, pg. 1611
Kandel, Dave, V.P.-Mktg.--Herff Jones Inc., Indianapolis, IN; *U.S. Private*, pg. 523
Kane, Kelley, Mgr.-Prod./Mktg.--Azon Corporation, Johnson City, NY; *U.S. Private*, pg. 104
Kane, Kevin, Mgr.-Adv. & Mdsg.--Courtaulds Coatings Inc., Louisville, KY; *Int'l*, pg. 338
Kane, Kevin, Mgr.-Adv.--The Oak Ridger, Oak Ridge, TN; *U.S. Private*, pg. 995
Kane, Terry, Mgr.-Adv. & Pub. Rels.--G.E. Superabrasives, Worthington, OH; *U.S. Public*, pg. 711
Kannehan, Kathleen, V.P.-Adv. Svcs. Div.--Spiegel, Inc., Downers Grove, IL; *U.S. Public*, pg. 1498
Kano, Shigehiko, Gen. Mgr.-Mktg. Dept.--Maruha Corporation, Tokyo, Japan; *Int'l*, pg. 845
Kantor, Susan, Sr. V.P.-Adv. & Promo.-Worldwide TV Distrb.--Universal Studios TV, Universal City, CA; *Int'l*, pg. 1215

Kao, Deborah, Dir.-Pur.--Liuski International, Inc., Norcross, GA; *U.S. Public*, pg. 1005

Kaplan, Barbara, Mgr.-Mktg. Communications--Air Techniques, Inc., Hicksville, NY; *U.S. Private*, pg. 28

Kaplan, Israel, Mgr.-Adv.--Bank Leumi le-Israel B.M., Tel Aviv, Israel; *Int'l*, pg. 150

Kaplan, Janie, Asst. V.P.-Adv. & Mktg.--United States Fidelity & Guaranty Company, Baltimore, MD; *U.S. Public*, pg. 1659

Kaplan, Samuel, Pres., Chief Exec. Officer, Sec. & Dir.-Sls. & Pur.--Admiration Hosiery Mills, Inc., Charlotte, NC; *U.S. Private*, pg. 528

Kaplan, Stacy, Travel Trade/Partner Adv.--Avis Rent A Car System, Inc., Garden City, NY; *U.S. Public*, pg. 321

Kapnek, Robert, V.P.-Creative Services--Del Laboratories, Inc., Farmingdale, NY; *U.S. Public*, pg. 494

Kaputa, Catherine, Sr. V.P. & Dir.-Adv. & Community Affairs--Salomon Smith Barney Holdings, Inc., New York, NY; *U.S. Public*, pg. 1633

Kara, Alan, Sr. V.P.-Adv.--Calvin Klein, Inc., New York, NY; *U.S. Private*, pg. 202

Karakas, Steve, Principal & Adv.--Karakas, VanSickle, Ouellette Advertising & Public Relations, Portland, OR; *U.S. Private*, pg. 607

Karass, Audrey, V.P.-Mktg. & Dir.-Corp. Video Systems & Telecommunications--Caristrap International Inc., Laval, Canada; *Int'l*, pg. 271

Karl, Doug, Mgr.-Opers.--Feed Service Corp., Ohiowa, NE; *U.S. Private*, pg. 399

Karlyn, William M., Pres.--Autoroll Machine Co., LLC, Middleton, MA; *U.S. Private*, pg. 101

Karoll, Peter, Dir.-Adv-Intl.--Hanover Direct, Inc., Weehawken, NJ; *U.S. Public*, pg. 782

Karter, Norma, V.P.-Mktg.--Eateries, Inc., Oklahoma City, OK; *U.S. Public*, pg. 555

Kase, Dale L., Dir.-Mktg.--Schult Homes Corporation, Middlebury, IN; *U.S. Public*, pg. 1442

Kaspar, Josh, Mgr.-Adv.--Bassick by Kaspar, Shiner, TX; *U.S. Private*, pg. 122

Katayama, Michnori, Dir.-Mktg.--TDK Corporation, Tokyo, Japan; *Int'l*, pg. 1336

Katchur, Lark Wittens, Mgr.-Adv.--Globus & Cosmos, Littleton, CO; *U.S. Private*, pg. 458

Kato, Norio, Gen. Mgr.-Investor Rels.--Cosmo Oil Co., Ltd., Tokyo, Japan; *Int'l*, pg. 335

Katz, Barry, V.P.-Sls.--Unitel Video, Inc., New York, NY; *U.S. Public*, pg. 1692

Katz, Dina, Dir.-Adv.--Deb Shops, Inc., Philadelphia, PA; *U.S. Public*, pg. 491

Katz, Francine, Dir.-Worldwide Adv.--Zenith Data Systems, Deerfield, IL; *Int'l*, pg. 317

Katz, Mark, Dir.-Adv. & Res.--Lettuce Entertain You Enterprises, Inc., Chicago, IL; *U.S. Private*, pg. 661

Katzman, Michael, Pres.--Mastercraft Furniture Corp., Omaha, NE; *U.S. Private*, pg. 714

Kauffman, Ken, V.P.-Creative Adv. Svcs.--Mattel, Inc., El Segundo, CA; *U.S. Public*, pg. 1057

Kaufman, Carol, Dir.-Adv.--Fred V. Fowler Company, Inc., Newton, MA; *U.S. Private*, pg. 422

Kaufman, Lawrence H., Mng. Dir.-Corp. Communications--Southern Pacific Rail Corporation, San Francisco, CA; *U.S. Public*, pg. 1668

Kaufman, Lori, Admin.-Adv. Services--Carver Corporation, Lynnwood, WA; *U.S. Public*, pg. 310

Kaufmann, H.A., Mgr.-Adv.--Hermal Kurt Herrmann & Co., Reinbek, Germany; *Int'l*, pg. 616

Kaukas, Bruce, V.P.-Commun.--ABB Asea Brown Boveri (Holding) Ltd., Zurich, Switzerland; *Int'l*, pg. 1

Kaukol, Karen, Mgr.-Adv.--Federal Cartridge Co., Anoka, MN; *U.S. Public*, pg. 239

Kautzman, Steven, Admin.-Mktg.--Meridian Insurance Group, Inc., Indianapolis, IN; *U.S. Public*, pg. 1095

Kavanaugh, Megan, V.P.-Adv. & Promo.--Fingerhut Corp., Minnetonka, MN; *U.S. Public*, pg. 623

Kawa, C.J., Mgr.-Commercial Devel.--Alco Chemical, Chattanooga, TN; *Int'l*, pg. 1435

Kawashima, William, Grp. V.P.-Mktg. & Adv.--Servco Pacific Inc., Honolulu, HI; *U.S. Private*, pg. 986

Kay, Carroll, V.P.-Sls. & Traffic--Kyanite Mining Corporation, Dillwyn, VA; *U.S. Private*, pg. 638

Kay, Mike, V.P.-Sls.--The Kay Company, Inc., Frankfort, IN; *U.S. Private*, pg. 610

Kayastha, Nomita, Mgr.-Adv.--Ranjit Corporation, Cedar Knolls, NJ; *U.S. Private*, pg. 909

Kaye, Larry, Dir.-Adv.--Associated Testing Laboratories, Inc., Wayne, NJ; *U.S. Public*, pg. 1341

Kearns, Connie, Exec. Sec.--Airmaster Fan Co., Michigan Center, MI; *U.S. Private*, pg. 29

Keating, Richard P., V.P.-Corp. Communications & Adv.--USLIFE Corporation, New York, NY; *U.S. Public*, pg. 77

Keck, Paula, Commun. Coord.--Woodcraft Industries, Inc., Saint Cloud, MN; *U.S. Private*, pg. 1187

Keegan, Beth, Dir.-Adv.--Ames Department Stores, Inc., Rocky Hill, CT; *U.S. Public*, pg. 99

Keegan, Hugh, Adv. & Mkt. Res.--Ventre Packing Company, Inc., Syracuse, NY; *U.S. Private*, pg. 1135

Keel, Michael, V.P.-Adv. & Mdsg.--Philips Consumer Electronics, Knoxville, TN; *Int'l*, pg. 1054

Keen, Willard, V.P.-Sls. & Mktg.--Keen Compressed Gas Co., Wilmington, DE; *U.S. Private*, pg. 611

Keenan, Heather, Mktg. Commun. Specialist--IEC Electronics Corp., Newark, NY; *U.S. Public*, pg. 854

Keenan, Joe, Mgr.-Sls. & Mktg.--Hughes-Peters, Inc., Cincinnati, OH; *U.S. Private*, pg. 546

Keenan, Robert, Dir.-Adv.-Major Local--Providence Journal-Bulletin, Providence, RI; *U.S. Public*, pg. 209

Keenan, W. Michael, Mgr.-Corp. Adv.--Texaco Inc., White Plains, NY; *U.S. Public*, pg. 1582

Keene, Linda B., V.P.-Market Devel.--American Express Financial Advisor, Minneapolis, MN; *U.S. Public*, pg. 73

Kegami, I., Mgr.-Adv.--Isuzu Motors Limited, Tokyo, Japan; *Int'l*, pg. 692

Keightley, Greg, V.P.-Mktg. Commun.--Hibernia Corporation, New Orleans, LA; *U.S. Public*, pg. 825

Keister, Jim, Mgr.-Adv.--Flo-Pac Corporation, Minneapolis, MN; *U.S. Private*, pg. 414

Kell, Tom, Dir.-Mktg.--Plymouth Rubber Company, Inc., Canton, MA; *U.S. Public*, pg. 1311

Kellam, Douglas, V.P.-Mktg.--First Alert, Inc., Aurora, IL; *U.S. Private*, pg. 406

Keller, Candace, Dir.-Mktg. Commun.--Jami, Inc., Shawnee Mission, KS; *U.S. Private*, pg. 581

Keller, Michael, Exec. V.P.-Mktg.--Koo Koo Roo, Inc., Los Angeles, CA; *U.S. Public*, pg. 966

Keller, Tina, Mgr.-Adv.--Sutherland Lumber Co., Kansas City, MO; *U.S. Private*, pg. 1057

Kelley-Smith, Kathryn, Dir.-Adv.--House Beautiful, New York, NY; *U.S. Private*, pg. 517

Kelley, Bruce, Mgr.-Adv.--Maritime Telegraph & Telephone Company, Ltd., Halifax, Canada; *Int'l*, pg. 116

Kelley, Dale, Adv. Coord.--Bergen Brunswig Medical Corporation, Montgomery, AL; *U.S. Public*, pg. 214

Kelley, Lynette, Mgr.-Promos.--Michigan Blueberry Growers Assn., Grand Junction, MI; *U.S. Private*, pg. 740

Kelley, Marian Herbst, Dir.-Pub. Rels.--Tracor, Inc., Austin, TX; *U.S. Public*, pg. 1627

Kelley, Vera E., Mgr.-Adv.--Gale Research Inc., Detroit, MI; *U.S. Public*, pg. 1600

Kelley, W.T., V.P.-Public Affairs & Adv.--Canadian National Railway Company, Montreal, Canada; *Int'l*, pg. 258

Kelley, William E., Sr. V.P.-Sls., Adv. & Mktg.--Mohawk Paper Mills, Inc., Cohoes, NY; *U.S. Private*, pg. 755

Kellman, Cheri, V.P.-Architectural Glass Div.--Globe-Amerada Glass Company, Elk Grove Village, IL; *U.S. Private*, pg. 458

Kellogg, Jeanette, V.P.-Sls. & Mktg.--Genova Products, Inc., Davison, MI; *U.S. Private*, pg. 447

Kellogg, Lora, Dir.-Adv.--Scotty's, Inc., Winter Haven, FL; *Int'l*, pg. 533

Kelly-Bartley, Kim, Dir.-Mktg. & Pub. Rels.--White Castle System, Inc., Columbus, OH; *U.S. Private*, pg. 1171

Kelly, M.B., Mgr.-Adv. & Sls. Promo.--Union Camp Corporation, Wayne, NJ; *U.S. Public*, pg. 1665

Kelly, Mary Clair, Mgr.-Adv.--Canon (U.K.) Ltd., Wallington, United Kingdom; *Int'l*, pg. 263

Kelly, Patrick T., V.P.-Sls. & Mktg.--Haws Drinking Faucet Co., Berkeley, CA; *U.S. Private*, pg. 512

Kelly, Peggy, V.P.-Adv.--Bristol-Myers Squibb Company, New York, NY; *U.S. Public*, pg. 253

Kelly, Sharon, V.P.-Adv.--Pulaski Furniture Corporation, Pulaski, VA; *U.S. Public*, pg. 1342

Kelly, W., Mgr.-Adv., Sls. Promo. & Pub. Rels.--Arnotts plc, Dublin, Ireland; *Int'l*, pg. 81

Kelsay, Kris, V.P.-Mktg. Commun.--Wall Data Incorporated, Kirkland, WA; *U.S. Public*, pg. 1734

Kemper, Thomas, Dir.-Mktg.--Harpen AG, Dortmund, Germany; *Int'l*, pg. 597

Kempert, Don, Mgr.-Adv.--Trico Industries, Inc., San Marcos, TX; *U.S. Public*, pg. 1247

Kennedy, Bob, Mgr.-Corp. Adv.--Advanced Micro Devices, Inc., Sunnyvale, CA; *U.S. Public*, pg. 21

Kennedy, L., Dir.-Adv.--Allyn & Bacon, Needham, MA; *U.S. Private*, pg. 778

Kennedy, Maureen, V.P.& Dir.-Mktg., Illinois--Citibank, Federal Savings Bank (Illinois), Chicago, IL; *U.S. Public*, pg. 378

Kennedy, Susan, Dir.-Adv.--Paddock Pool Construction Co., Inc., Scottsdale, AZ; *U.S. Private*, pg. 833

Kennedy, Tom, Sr. V.P.-Creative Adv.--Metro-Goldwyn-Mayer Inc., Santa Monica, CA; *U.S. Public*, pg. 1101

Kenney, Susan M., Dir.-Mktg.--The Seibels Bruce Group, Inc., Columbia, SC; *U.S. Public*, pg. 1453

Kenny, Colleen, Dir.-Commun.--Security Mutual Life Insurance Co. of New York, Binghamton, NY; *U.S. Private*, pg. 981

Kenshol, David R., Sr. V.P.-Mktg. & Adv.--HomeBase, Inc., Irvine, CA; *U.S. Public*, pg. 832

Kent, Mike, V.P.-Adv. & Promo.--Six Flags Theme Parks Inc., Parsippany, NJ; *U.S. Public*, pg. 1611

Kentner, Pat, Gen. Mgr. & Dir.--Railway Educational Bureau, Omaha, NE; *U.S. Private*, pg. 1000

Kenton, James A., Pres.--Beiersdorf, Inc., Norwalk, CT; *Int'l, pg. 182*

Kenyon, Jeff, Dir.-Mktg. Communications--Keithley Instruments, Inc., Cleveland, OH; *U.S. Public*, pg. 946

Kepler, Gary, Dir.- Mktg. Svcs.--Sargent & Greenleaf, Inc., Nicholasville, KY; *U.S. Private*, pg. 965

Keprta, Nancy, V.P.-Adv.--Lucky Stores Northern California Division, San Leandro, CA; *U.S. Public*, pg. 93

Kern, Richard C., Mgr.-Sls. & Mktg.--Kern Industries, City of Industry, CA; *U.S. Private*, pg. 616

Kerper, Mike, Mgr.-Adv. Admin.--Sherwood-Davis & Geck, Saint Louis, MO; *U.S. Public*, pg. 80

Kerr, Carolyn, Mgr.-Mktg. Communications--Philips Lighting, Somerset, NJ; *Int'l*, pg. 1055

Kerr, Mary Ann, Dir.-Mktg.--US ScrVis, West Orange, NJ; *U.S. Public*, pg. 1687

Kershaw, Doug, Mgr.-Mktg. Services--Dayco Products Inc., Miamisburg, OH; *U.S. Public*, pg. 1045

Kershaw, Roger, Gen. Mgr.--Scotch Premium Meat, Gorgie, United Kingdom; *U.S. Public*, pg. 607

Kerstiens, Tom, Mgr.-Adv.--Delchamps, Inc., Mobile, AL; *U.S. Private*, pg. 588

Kestenbaum, Nancy, Dir.-Adv.--Omni Publications International Ltd., New York, NY; *U.S. Private*, pg. 444

Kestenbaum, Nancy, Dir.-Adv.--Longevity International, Ltd., New York, NY; *U.S. Private*, pg. 444

Keuhne, Richard W., Dir.-Adv. & Sls. Promo.--Nash Finch Company, Edina, MN; *U.S. Public*, pg. 1151

Kevorkian, Christopher, Dir.-Adv. Sls.--Sunset Publishing Corporation, Menlo Park, CA; *U.S. Public*, pg. 1613

Keyes, L. Shawn, Dir.-Mktg. & Adv.--Mohawk Commercial Carpet, Atlanta, GA; *U.S. Public*, pg. 1121

Kidd, Douglas, Sr. Mng. Dir.-Corp. Affairs--Bankers Trust New York Corporation, New York, NY; *U.S. Public*, pg. 185

Kidder, Brian, Dir.-Pub. Rels.--Allright Corporation, Houston, TX; *U.S. Private*, pg. 42

Kieckhefer, Robert, V.P.-Pub. Affairs & Adv.--Blue Cross & Blue Shield of Illinois, Chicago, IL; *U.S. Private*, pg. 151

Kiefer, William C., Chm. Bd. & Pres.--Bel-Ray Company, Inc., Farmingdale, NJ; *U.S. Private*, pg. 130

Kiefus, Jerry, Pres.--Big Joe Manufacturing Co., Lincolnwood, IL; *U.S. Private*, pg. 143

Kiehl, J. L., V.P.-Mktg. & Sls.--Carlisle Tire & Wheel Company, Aiken, SC; *U.S. Public*, pg. 305

Kiernan, Paul E., Dir.-Corp. Mktg.--Thermo Fibertek, Inc., Waltham, MA; *U.S. Public*, pg. 1593

Kiey, Maura, V.P.-Strategic Plng. & Devel.--Warren Gorham Lamont, New York, NY; *U.S. Public*, pg. 1602

Kiger, Estin, V.P.-Bear Creek Direct Adv.--Harry and David, Medford, OR; *Int'l*, pg. 1518

Kilbane, Paul, V.P.-Mktg.--E.T. Browne Drug Co., Inc., Englewood Cliffs, NJ; *U.S. Private*, pg. 175

Kildow, Steve, V.P.-Adv.--Dexter Axle Div., Elkhart, IN; *Int'l*, pg. 1396

Kilgore, J. Thomas, Jr., Gen. Mgr.-Mktg.--Gulf Power Company, Pensacola, FL; *U.S. Public*, pg. 1490

Killoren, Jack K., Sr. V.P.-Mktg.--Sterling Electronics Corporation, Houston, TX; *U.S. Public*, pg. 1051

Killus, Linell, V.P.-Mktg. Services--Jenny Craig, Inc., La Jolla, CA; *U.S. Public*, pg. 926

Kimball, Douglas, V.P.-Oil Equip. & Related Services--Eaton Metal Products Company, Denver, CO; *U.S. Private*, pg. 358

Kimber, Iris A., Corp. Communications Specialist--Millipore Corporation, Bedford, MA; *U.S. Public*, pg. 1112

Kimerbeek, Manerose, Mgr.-Adv.--Elsevier Science (International), Amsterdam, Netherlands; *Int'l*, pg. 1099

Kimmey, Jim, Dir.-Adv.--Adecco Employment Services, Redwood City, CA; *Int'l*, pg. 24

Kincade, John, Dir.-Mktg.--Circus Circus - Las Vegas, Las Vegas, NV; *U.S. Public*, pg. 374

Kincaid, Mary, V.P.-Adv. & Res.--Buena Vista Home Video, Burbank, CA; *U.S. Public*, pg. 513

Kinderdick, Don, V.P.-Mktg. & Prod. Devel.--Sterner Lighting Systems Incorporated, Eden Prairie, MN; *U.S. Private*, pg. 1042

Kiner, Tracee, Sr. V.P. & Dir.-Global Adv.--Hachette Filipacchi Magazines Inc., New York, NY; *Int'l*, pg. 794

King, Geoffrey, Dir.-Commun.--Cambior Inc., Montreal, Canada; *Int'l*, pg. 253

King, George, Mgr.-Sls. & Mktg.--Automatic Machine Products Company, Attleboro, MA; *U.S. Private*, pg. 101

King, Jane S., Dir.-Adv.--Southern California Gas Co., Los Angeles, CA; *U.S. Public*, pg. 1249

Kingsbry, Liz, Grp. Mgr.- Commun.--AMEC Plc, Northwich, United Kingdom; *Int'l*, pg. 16

Kinkler, Linda, V.P.-Adv. & Mktg. Services--WestPoint Stevens Inc., West Point, GA; *U.S. Public*, pg. 1762

Kinloch, Leon, Dir.-Adv.--Continental Express, Houston, TX; *U.S. Public*, pg. 439

Kinoshita, Mr., Gen. Mgr.-Adv.--Mitsubishi Motors Corporation, Tokyo, Japan; *Int'l*, pg. 875

Kirby, Jim, Dir.-Adv. & Mktg.--NHD Hardware, Stoughton, MA; *U.S. Private*, pg. 3

Kirchner, Beverly, Mgr.-Sls. Promo. & Adv.--Amecom Div., College Park, MD; *U.S. Public*, pg. 1002

Kirchner, William E., Sr. V.P.-Prod. Devel. & Adv.--Department 56 Inc., Eden Prairie, MN; *U.S. Public*, pg. 500

Kirk, Jerry, Mgr.-Adv.--Tennessee Farmers Co-op, La Vergne, TN; *U.S. Private*, pg. 1076

Kirk, Lise, Dir.-Adv. & Promo.--Midland Life Insurance Co., Columbus, OH; *U.S. Private*, pg. 744

Kirk, Tom, Dir.-H.R. & Adv.--Crestbrook Forest Industries Ltd., Cranbrook, Canada; *Int'l*, pg. 348

Kirkland, Joanna, Coord.-Adv.--Alliance Communications Corporation, Toronto, Canada; *Int'l*, pg. 57

Kirkley, Lenora, V.P.-Adv. & Corp. Communications--Ethan Allen, Inc., Danbury, CT; *U.S. Public*, pg. 595

Kirkman, Paul, Exec. V.P.-Mktg. & Sls.--Beverage Canners International Corp., Miami, FL; *U.S. Private*, pg. 106

Kirkwood, Nelson, Mgr.-Sls.--Airtex Products, Fairfield, IL; *U.S. Private*, pg. 1113

Kirpalani, John, V.P.-Mktg. & Sls.--Andrew Sports Club Inc., Secaucus, NJ; *U.S. Private*, pg. 73

Kirsch, Jan, Mgr.-Adv.--SunTrust Banks of Georgia, Inc., Atlanta, GA; *U.S. Public*, pg. 1538

Kirtley, Shan, Mgr.-Adv.--Charles Machine Works, Inc., Perry, OK; *U.S. Private*, pg. 230

Kirwin, Richard, Mgr.-Point of Purchase--AR Accessories Group, Inc., Milwaukee, WI; *U.S. Private*, pg. 7

Kissling, Mark, Plant Mgr.--A.C. Kissling, Inc., Philadelphia, PA; *U.S. Private*, pg. 624

Kittleson, John G., Sec.--Bituminous Roadways, Inc., Inver Grove Heights, MN; *U.S. Private*, pg. 146

Kizer, C., Mgr.-Prod. Sls.--Gemtron Corporation, Sweetwater, TN; *Int'l*, pg. 1523

Kjarsgaard, Steven, Mgr.-Adv.--National Presto Industries, Inc., Eau Claire, WI; *U.S. Public*, pg. 1159

Klass, Joe, Mgr.-Adv., Sls. & Mktg.-Plastics & Industrial--Raven Industries, Inc., Sioux Falls, SD; *U.S. Public*, pg. 1361

Klaubert, Annette, Adv.--BASF Australia Ltd., Melbourne, Australia; *Int'l*, pg. 105

Klausing, Trisha, Dir.-Mktg. & Sls.--The Commercial Bank, Delphos, OH; *U.S. Public*, pg. 410

Kleeman, Linda, Mgr.-Natl. Adv.--Houston Chronicle, Houston, TX; *U.S. Private*, pg. 517

Klein, Laura, Dir.-Assoc. Adv.--Woman's Day, New York, NY; *Int'l*, pg. 795

Klein, Lew, Mgr.-Mktg. Communications--Paslode, Vernon Hills, IL; *U.S. Public*, pg. 867

Klein, Robert, Mgr.-Natl. Sls.--Monarch Ware, Inc., Algoma, WI; *U.S. Private*, pg. 735

Kleinhenz, Allen, Dir.-Mktg.--Cramer Inc., Kansas City, KS; *U.S. Private*, pg. 285

Klemencic, Joy, V.P.-Corp. Mktg.--Hill's Pet Nutrition, Topeka, KS; *U.S. Public*, pg. 397

Kline, Lawrence M., Dir.-Adv.--Los Angeles Times, Los Angeles, CA; *U.S. Public*, pg. 1616

Klingele, Michael, Pres.--Hollytex Carpet Mills, Inc., Ontario, CA; *U.S. Private*, pg. 535
Klinger, Daniel, Dir.-Mktg.--Ceras Johnson Ltda., Rio de Janeiro, Brazil; *U.S. Private*, pg. 593
Klobuchar, Mike, Mgr.-Retail Adv.--The News Tribune, Tacoma, WA; *U.S. Public*, pg. 1066
Kloster, Dennis, V.P.-Mktg.--Unitary Products Group, York, PA; *U.S. Public*, pg. 1788
Kluge, John W., Chm. & Pres.--Metromedia Company, East Rutherford, NJ; *U.S. Private*, pg. 736
Knapp, Lori, Mgr.-Mktg. Services--Eaton Corporation, Engineered Fasteners Division, Brunswick, OH; *U.S. Public*, pg. 556
Knapstein, Annette S., Dir.-Integrated Mktg.--American Family Mutual Insurance Co., Madison, WI; *U.S. Private*, pg. 53
Kneese, Cathy, V.P.-Adv.--Management Dynamics, New Providence, NJ; *U.S. Public*, pg. 1040
Knierman, John, V.P.-Sls. & Mktg.--International Container Systems, Tampa, FL; *Int'l*, pg. 685
Knight, Anne, Mktg. Commun. Admin.--TCI International Inc., Sunnyvale, CA; *U.S. Public*, pg. 1555
Knight, Connie, Dir.-Corp. Commun.--Clariant Corporation, Charlotte, NC; *Int'l*, pg. 624
Knight, Linda, Sr. V.P.-Mktg.--Foley's, Houston, TX; *U.S. Public*, pg. 1063
Knight, Matt, Coord. Adv.--Ryobi America Corp., Anderson, SC; *Int'l*, pg. 1151
Knipp, Lillian H., Dir.-Corp. Commun.--Baltimore Gas and Electric Company, Baltimore, MD; *U.S. Public*, pg. 172
Knook, Cor N., Mgr.-Sls.--NAO, Inc., Philadelphia, PA; *U.S. Private*, pg. 771
Knopke, Don, Dir.-Mktg. & Adv.--Contractors Supply Company, Inc., Kansas City, MO; *U.S. Private*, pg. 270
Knoppa, Noreen, Mgr.-Adv.--David White, L.L.C., Germantown, WI; *U.S. Public*, pg. 1765
Knoppa, Noreen, Mgr.-Adv.--David White, L.L.C., Germantown, WI; *U.S. Private*, pg. 1765
Knudsen, Kenneth, V.P.-Mktg.--Bruning Paint Company, Baltimore, MD; *U.S. Private*, pg. 176
Knudsen, Larry, V.P.-Sls. & Mktg.--Camp Healthcare, Jackson, MI; *Int'l*, pg. 1425
Knutson, Marlys, Mgr.-Mktg. Communications--Polaris Industries, Inc., Minneapolis, MN; *U.S. Public*, pg. 1313
Koch, Bud, Mgr.-Mktg.--Radius Inc., Sunnyvale, CA; *U.S. Public*, pg. 1358
Kocon, Richard, V.P.-Mktg. & Adv.--Iams Company, Dayton, OH; *U.S. Private*, pg. 556
Kocsis, Maria, Dir.-Mktg.--Budapest Marriott Hotel, Budapest, Hungary; *Int'l*, pg. 232
Koehler, Ken, Mgr.-Adv. & Corp. Rels.--Arnold Machinery Company, Salt Lake City, UT; *U.S. Private*, pg. 84
Koenitzer, Jay G., V.P.-Mktg.--Helwig Carbon Products, Inc., Milwaukee, WI; *U.S. Private*, pg. 521
Koerner, Jurgen, Mgr.-Adv.--Wyeth-Pharma GmbH, Munster, Germany; *U.S. Public*, pg. 82
Kohls, Kris, Exec. V.P.-Strategic Devel.--Dart Transit Company, Eagan, MN; *U.S. Private*, pg. 311
Kojo, Krru, Dir.-Adv.--Koltek Oy, Vantaa, Finland; *Int'l*, pg. 1379
Kolb, James D., V.P.-Mktg.--EMCOR Group, Inc., Norwalk, CT; *U.S. Public*, pg. 571
Kolivosky, E.M., Dir.-Corp. Commu.--Auto-Owners Insurance, Lansing, MI; *U.S. Private*, pg. 100
Kollenborn, Don, V.P.-Sls. & Adv.--Hickory Printing Group, Inc., Conover, NC; *U.S. Private*, pg. 525
Koller, Marsha, Dir.-Adv.--Valvoline Company, Lexington, KY; *U.S. Public*, pg. 139
Komar, Michael J., Mgr.-Mktg. Serv.--Thermo King Corporation, Minneapolis, MN; *U.S. Public*, pg. 877
Komschlies, Andrea, Dir.-Mktg.--Witcher Construction Co., Minneapolis, MN; *U.S. Private*, pg. 1185
Konczakowski, Peter, Sr. V.P.-Mktg.--National City Bank, Pennsylvania, Pittsburgh, PA; *U.S. Public*, pg. 1154
Kondo, Junichiro, Deputy Gen. Mgr.-Pub. Rels.--Nissho Iwai Corporation, Tokyo, Japan; *Int'l*, pg. 946
Konecny, Karen, Mgr.-Adv.--Peterbilt Motors Co., Denton, TX; *U.S. Public*, pg. 1247
Konecny, Pavel, Dir.-Adv.--Renault V.I., Suresnes, France; *Int'l*, pg. 1102
Kong, Seok Y., Mgr.-Adv.--NURI Enterprise, Seoul, Korea; *Int'l*, pg. 348
Koning, Annemiek, Mgr.-Pub. Rels., Sls. & Promo.--Lips United B.V., Drunen, Netherlands; *Int'l*, pg. 812
Konrad, Don, Dir.-Adv. & Pub. Rels.--Fleischer Manufacturing, Inc., Columbus, NE; *U.S. Private*, pg. 410
Kontney, J., Mgr.-Artist Rels.--Shure Brothers Incorporated, Evanston, IL; *U.S. Private*, pg. 997
Kopel, Lisa, Mgr.-Adv.--Farrar, Straus & Giroux, Inc., New York, NY; *Int'l*, pg. 1479
Kopko, Edward M., Chm. Bd., Pres., Chief Exec. & Chief Oper. Officer--Butler International, Inc., Montvale, NJ; *U.S. Public*, pg. 270
Kornfeld, Nat, V.P.-Adv.--Army Times Publishing Co., Springfield, VA; *U.S. Public*, pg. 699
Kornhause, Henry, V.P.-Creative Svcs.--Church & Dwight Co., Inc., Princeton, NJ; *U.S. Public*, pg. 355
Korolis, Louis A., Mgr.-Indus. Affairs, USA--Olympic Airways, New York, NY; *Int'l*, pg. 1004
Kort, Raja, V.P.-Mktg. & Sls., Spirits--Austin Nichols & Co. Inc., New York, NY; *Int'l*, pg. 566
Korta, Amy, Mgr.-Adv. & Promo.--Paradyne, Largo, FL; *U.S. Private*, pg. 838
Kosewski, M., Coord.-Adv.--TBV, Inc., Westborough, MA; *U.S. Private*, pg. 1138
Koshiyania, June, Coord.-Adv.--Farr Company, El Segundo, CA; *U.S. Public*, pg. 613
Kosich, C.M., Gen. Mgr.-Worldwide Adv. & Sls. Promo.--Texaco Inc., White Plains, NY; *U.S. Public*, pg. 1582
Koss, David, Dir.-Mktg. Communications--Liberty Life Insurance Company, Greenville, SC; *U.S. Public*, pg. 992
Kost, Ed, Dir.-Adv.--The Courier-Journal Louisville Times Co., Louisville, KY; *U.S. Public*, pg. 700
Kota, Brenda, Mktg. Coord.--LubeCon Systems, Inc., White Cloud, MI; *U.S. Private*, pg. 679
Kotcher, Michele, Dir.-Sls. & Mktg.--F.X. Coughlin Co., Taylor, MI; *U.S. Private*, pg. 278
Kotkins, Henry L., Jr., Pres.--Skyway Luggage Co., Seattle, WA; *U.S. Private*, pg. 1005
Koukol, Hank, Dir.-Adv.--Bankers Life & Casualty Company, Chicago, IL; *U.S. Public*, pg. 433
Kovacevich, Dee Dee, V.P.-Mktg.--Jazzercise, Inc., Carlsbad, CA; *U.S. Private*, pg. 584
Kowalski, Jay, Mgr.-Natl. Adv.--Toledo Blade Co., Toledo, OH; *U.S. Private*, pg. 147
Kowynia, Bob, Mgr.-Adv. & Commun.--Lennox International Inc., Richardson, TX; *U.S. Private*, pg. 659
Koyanagi, Hirona, Adv. Dept.--The Japan Times, Ltd., Tokyo, Japan; *Int'l*, pg. 928
Kozak, Dennis, Dir.-Adv.--News Herald, Panama City, FL; *U.S. Private*, pg. 425
Kozub, John F., V.P.-Sls.--Janlynn Corporation, Indian Orchard, MA; *U.S. Private*, pg. 582
Kozuta, Kathy, Mktg. Services Specialist--Grace Cocoa/ Ambrosia Chocolate, Milwaukee, WI; *U.S. Public*, pg. 128
Kraemer, Larry, Dir.-Mktg.--Harkins Builders, Inc., Silver Spring, MD; *U.S. Private*, pg. 502
Kraines, Brad, Dir.-Mktg. & Adv.--Kraco Enterprises, Inc., Compton, CA; *U.S. Private*, pg. 634
Kramer, Jack, Sr. V.P.-Adv. & Corp. Communications--CVS Corp., Woonsocket, RI; *U.S. Public*, pg. 287
Kramer, Jay, Dir.-Adv.--Jewel-Osco, Melrose Park, IL; *U.S. Public*, pg. 93
Krandell, Frank, Dir.-Adv.--Boscov's Department Store, Inc., Reading, PA; *U.S. Private*, pg. 160
Krantz, Andy, Dir.-Adv.--Rheem Water Heater, Montgomery, AL; *Int'l*, pg. 1022
Krasnitz, Ron, Dir.-Mktg. & Adv.--Hirsch International Corp., Hauppauge, NY; *U.S. Public*, pg. 829
Kratochwill, Adam, V.P.-Creative Services--Block Drug Company, Inc., Jersey City, NJ; *U.S. Public*, pg. 236
Krause, Gary W., V.P. & Dir.-Sls. & Mktg.--Laird & Company, Eatontown, NJ; *U.S. Private*, pg. 642
Krause, Joan Mascio, Mgr.-Pub. Rels. & Adv.--The Austin Company, Cleveland, OH; *U.S. Private*, pg. 99
Krauss, Julie, V.P.-Mktg.--The Hartz Mountain Corp., Secaucus, NJ; *U.S. Private*, pg. 508
Kraut, Robert, Adv. Dir.-GMC Pontiac--Pontiac-GMC Truck Division, Pontiac, MI; *U.S. Public*, pg. 720
Kravzyk, Henry, Dir.-Adv.--Fred V. Fowler Company, Inc., Newton, MA; *U.S. Private*, pg. 422
Krebs, Pam, Mgr.-Adv.--Robert Bosch Corporation, Broadview, IL; *Int'l*, pg. 204
Kreeft, Jan, Dir.-Sls., Mktg. & Adv.--ISS Servisystem B.V., Amersfoort, Netherlands; *Int'l*, pg. 657
Kreger, Kate, Mgr.-Mktg. Commun. & Corp. Plng.--CPAC, Inc., Leicester, NY; *U.S. Public*, pg. 282
Kreiner, Jeff, V.P. & Creative Dir.-Adv. & Promo.--CBS Television Network, New York, NY; *U.S. Public*, pg. 274
Kreis, Eric, Mgr.-Adv.--Kenwood USA, Long Beach, CA; *Int'l*, pg. 730
Kreiter, Harry, Chm. Bd. & Pres.--Castcraft Industries, Inc., Skokie, IL; *U.S. Private*, pg. 219
Kremer, Manfred, Dir.-Adv. & Pub. Rels.--3M Deutschland GmbH, Neuss, Germany; *U.S. Public*, pg. 1606
Kremins, Carolyn, Mgr.-Adv.--Bon Appetit Magazine, New York, NY; *U.S. Private*, pg. 20
Kreusch, Leonard P., III, Pres.--Leonard Kreusch, Inc., Northvale, NJ; *U.S. Private*, pg. 635
Krieger, Joyce, Dir.-Adv. & Promo./Prof., Ref. & Trade Grp.--John Wiley & Sons, Inc., New York, NY; *U.S. Public*, pg. 1768
Krinsky, Peggy, Dir.-Adv. & Mktg. Svcs.--Sea World of Ohio, Aurora, OH; *U.S. Public*, pg. 114
Kritzer, Andrew, Mgr.-Adv. & Pub. Rels.--Samsung Electronics North America Inc., Ridgefield Park, NJ; *Int'l, pg. 1183*
Kroeber, Rita, Dir.-Adv.--Dow Jones Telerate Holdings, Inc., Jersey City, NJ; *U.S. Public*, pg. 525
Krogh, Lee, Dir.-Corp. Commun.--Otter Tail Power Company, Fergus Falls, MN; *U.S. Public*, pg. 1234
Krol, Bruce, Mgr.-Mktg. & Sls.--Vacudyne Inc., Chicago Heights, IL; *U.S. Private*, pg. 46
Kroll, Richard C., Dir.-Adv. & Pub. Rels.--Foster Wheeler Corporation, Clinton, NJ; *U.S. Public*, pg. 676
Kromer, Mary Lou, V.P.-Corp. Communications--W.R. Grace & Co., Boca Raton, FL; *U.S. Public*, pg. 754
Kromer, Pam, Mgr.-Adv. & Mktg.--Rapid Power Technologies, Inc., Brookfield, CT; *U.S. Private*, pg. 910
Krone, Philip S., V.P.-Mktg.--Krone Casting Corp., North Chicago, IL; *U.S. Private*, pg. 636
Kroot, Brian, Pres.--Northeastern Graphic Supply, Inc., Portland, ME; *U.S. Private*, pg. 805
Krost, Maggie, V.P.-Adv.--The Knight Publishing Co., Charlotte, NC; *U.S. Public*, pg. 964
Krueger, Richard G., V.P.-Sls. & Mgr.--The F.D. Lawrence Electric Co., Cincinnati, OH; *U.S. Private*, pg. 654
Krueger, Ted, Mgr.-Mktg. & Adv.--Rockford Acromatic Product Co., Rockford, IL; *U.S. Private*, pg. 938
Krugler, Philip, Mgr.-Mktg. Svcs.--Penco Products, Oaks, PA; *U.S. Private*, pg. 848
Kruize, Midde, Mgr.-Mktg. & Adv.--N.V. Van Melle S.A., Berchem, Belgium; *Int'l*, pg. 1451
Krulik, Richard, Chm. Bd. & Chief Oper. Officer--United States Luggage Company, Hauppauge, NY; *U.S. Private, pg. 1125*
Kryjak, Jeff, Mgr.-Adv. & Sls. Promo.--Avis Rent A Car System, Inc., Garden City, NY; *U.S. Public*, pg. 321
Kuah, Chia Boon, Mgr.-Adv. & Promo.--Singapore Airlines, Los Angeles, CA; *Int'l*, pg. 1374
Kubena, Charles L., Mgr.-Adv.--Stewart & Stevenson Services, Inc., Houston, TX; *U.S. Public*, pg. 1517
Kuecker, Tobey, Mgr.-Sls. & Svc.--Mosinee Converted Products, Columbus, WI; *U.S. Public*, pg. 1747
Kunz, Don, Dir.-Adv.--DMI Furniture Inc., Louisville, KY; *U.S.* Public, pg. 473
Kunze, Joerg, Dir.-Adv.--Robert Bosch GmbH, Gerlingen, Germany; *Int'l*, pg. 203
Kupec, Evelyn, Mgr.-Adv. & Communications--Joseph T. Ryerson & Son, Inc., Chicago, IL; *U.S. Public*, pg. 879
Kupferman, Spencer, Mgr.-Mktg.--Global Software, Inc., Raleigh, NC; *U.S. Private*, pg. 457
Kuroski, Elizabeth, Mktg. & Adv. Specialist--Delphi Harrison Thermal Systems, Lockport, NY; *U.S. Public*, pg. 719
Kurtze, Jack, Mgr.-Sls. & Mktg.--Maxcor Manufacturing, Inc., Colorado Springs, CO; *U.S. Private*, pg. 716
Kushch, George, Mgr.-Adv.--Sun Electric, Lincolnshire, IL; *U.S. Public*, pg. 1480
Kushner, Caron, Dir.-Mktg.--The Chas. H. Lilly Co., Portland, OR; *U.S. Private*, pg. 667
Kushner, E., Dir.-Mktg.--Frequency Electronics, Inc., Uniondale, NY; *U.S. Public*, pg. 681
Kushner, T.A., V.P.-Mktg. Communications--FINAST, Maple Heights, OH; *Int'l*, pg. 750
Kushner, Terry, Dir.-Adv.--Riser Foods, Inc., Bedford, OH; *U.S. Private*, pg. 450
Kuss, Brian, Coord.-Adv.--H. Wilson Company, South Holland, IL; *U.S. Private*, pg. 359
Kuttner, Ludwig, Chm. Bd., Pres. & Chief Exec. Officer--Hampshire Group, Ltd., Anderson, SC; *U.S. Public*, pg. 778
Kuwahira, Karen, V.P.-Mktg. & Adv.--Ralston Purina Canada Inc., Mississauga, Canada; *U.S. Public*, pg. 1360
Kuzemczak, Barbara, Asst. Mgr.-Adv.--Carquest Corporation, Lakewood, CO; *U.S. Private*, pg. 215
Kvicala, Michael, Mgr.-Adv.--Federal APD, Inc., Farmington, MI; *U.S. Public*, pg. 616
Kwasizur, John, V.P.-Whitehall Adv.--Charles Jacquin et Cie, Inc., Philadelphia, PA; *U.S. Private*, pg. 580
Kwock, Danny, V.P.-Adv. & Promo.--Quiksilver, Inc., Costa Mesa, CA; *U.S. Public*, pg. 1353
La Madrid, Carlos, Mgr.-Adv.--Town & Country, New York, NY; *U.S. Private*, pg. 517
La Magna, Mary, Mgr.-Adv. Sls.--National Business Employment Weekly, Princeton, NJ; *U.S. Public*, pg. 524
La Russo, Rosa, Mgr.-Adv.--Rubbermaid Canada Inc. Consumer Products, Mississauga, Canada; *U.S. Public*, pg. 1411
LaBatut, Marlene, Dir.-Media--Colgate-Palmolive France, Courbevoie, France; *U.S. Public*, pg. 398
Lackowitz, Ann, Office Mgr.--Argo International Corp., New York, NY; *U.S. Private*, pg. 322
Lade, Carol, Coord.-Adv.--Eddie Bauer, Inc., Redmond, WA; *U.S. Public*, pg. 1499
Ladhoff, Don, V.P.-Mktg. & Sls.--The Lion Brewery, Inc., Wilkes-Barre, PA; *U.S. Public*, pg. 1000
Ladue, David, Gen. Mgr.-Sls.--Yale/Chase Materials Handling, Inc., City of Industry, CA; *U.S. Private*, pg. 1195
LaFaro, Elizabeth, Mgr.-Adv.--Del Pharmaceuticals, Inc., Farmingdale, NY; *U.S. Public*, pg. 494
LaFlamme, Mindy, Mgr.-Mktg.--Pace, Arlington Heights, IL; *U.S. Private*, pg. 919
Lagerquist, Carl R., Mgr.-Natl. Adv. & Sls. Promo.--Graybar Electric Company, Inc., Clayton, MO; *U.S. Private*, pg. 472
Lagny, Claude, Dir.-Corp. Communications--Elida Faberge, Paris, France; *Int'l*, pg. 1437
Lagosz, Christine, Mgr.-Mktg.--Trumpf Inc., Farmington, CT; *U.S. Private*, pg. 1108
Lahey, Kevin, V.P.-Mktg.--Buffalo Rock Company, Birmingham, AL; *U.S. Private*, pg. 179
Lai, Cal, Adv. Chief Exec. Officer--LVL Interactive, Palo Alto, CA; *U.S. Private*, pg. 640
Laisne, Veronique, Dir.-Adv.--A.T. Cross Ltd., Ballina, Ireland; *U.S. Public*, pg. 461
Lake, Charlie, Mgr.-Mktg.--Jomac, Inc., Warrington, PA; *U.S.* Private, pg. 595
Lalanne, Jeff, Dir.-Adv.--Tanning Research Labs., Inc., Ormond Beach, FL; *U.S. Private*, pg. 1068
LaLonde, Kaye, V.P.-Adv.--The Orvis Company, Inc., Manchester, VT; *U.S. Private*, pg. 820
LaMarca, John, Mgr.-Eastern Adv.--Woman's Day, New York, NY; *Int'l*, pg. 795
Lambert, Bob, Supvr.-Mktg. Svcs.--Methode Electronics Inc., Chicago, IL; *U.S. Public*, pg. 1101
Lambert, Jania, Dir.-Adv.--Rio Hotel & Casino Inc., Las Vegas, NV; *U.S. Public*, pg. 1390
Lambert, Rob, Mgr.-Adv.--Belshaw Brothers, Inc., Seattle, WA; *Int'l*, pg. 188
Lambert, Suzanne, Dir.-Adv.--Caere Corporation, Los Gatos, CA; *U.S. Public*, pg. 291
Lambeth, Kathy, Dir.-Adv.--News & Record, Greensboro, NC; *U.S. Private*, pg. 649
Lamer, Allan, V.P.-Mktg. & Adv. Mgr.--Kewaunee Engineering Corp., Kewaunee, WI; *U.S. Private*, pg. 703
Lamer, Allan J., Exec. V.P.-Sls. & Mktg.--Marine Travelift, Inc., Sturgeon Bay, WI; *U.S. Private*, pg. 703
Lamm, Henri, Mng. Dir.-Adv.--Julius Meinl AG, Vienna, Austria; *Int'l*, pg. 856
Lammerhold, M., Mgr.-Adv.--Lufthansa Cargo AG, Frankfurt, Germany; *Int'l*, pg. 407
Lammers, Henry P., V.P.-Mktg.--Marketing Communications, Lenexa, KS; *U.S. Public*, pg. 794
Lamone, Gene, V.P.-Sls. & Mktg. & Adv.--Capitol Manufacturing Co., Westerville, OH; *U.S. Public*, pg. 793
Lamont, Gary, Asst. Dir.-Adv.--McKesson Water Products Company, Pasadena, CA; *U.S. Public*, pg. 1073
Lampert, Albert, Pres.--Aspen Systems Corp., Rockville, MD; *Int'l*, pg. 1513
Lampner, Claudia, V.P.-Adv.--Union Bank of California, San Francisco, CA; *Int'l*, pg. 157
Lampros, T., Mgr.-Adv.-Prod. Support--Case Corporation, Racine, WI; *U.S. Public*, pg. 311
Lancaster, Agnes, V.P. & Dir.-Natl. Adv.--Weider Publications, Inc., Woodland Hills, CA; *U.S. Private*, pg. 1159
Lancelot, Pascal, Dir.-Mktg.--Kone Corporation, Helsinki, Finland; *Int'l*, pg. 746

Land, Esther M., Mktg. Specialist--Rapistan Demag Corp., Grand Rapids, MI; *Int'l*, pg. 837
Land, Frank, Assoc. V.P.-Adv. & Pub. Rels.--First Colony Life Insurance Co., Lynchburg, VA; *U.S. Public*, pg. 711
Landaeta, Ruth K., Coord.-Commun.--Harza Engineering Co., Chicago, IL; *U.S. Private*, pg. 509
Landes, Gary, Pres. & Chief Exec. Officer--Meco Corporation, Greeneville, TN; *U.S. Private*, pg. 726
Landi, Paolo, Mgr.-Adv.--Benetton Group S.p.A., Ponzano Veneto, Italy; *Int'l*, pg. 186
Landis, Dean, Treas. & Sec.--United Credit Corp. & Patroit Funding, New York, NY; *U.S. Private*, pg. 1121
Lang, Amy, Admin. Asst.-Adv.--Reynolds Metals Co., Consumer Products Div., Richmond, VA; *U.S. Public*, pg. 1386
Lang, Richard A., Jr., V.P.-Adv., Sls. & Mktg.--Dad's Products Co., Inc., Meadville, PA; *U.S. Private*, pg. 306
Langbein, John, Mgr.-Mktg.--BHC Securities, Inc., Philadelphia, PA; *U.S. Public*, pg. 647
Lange, Cindy D., Mgr.-Promotions--Flowers USA, Uniondale, NY; *U.S. Private*, pg. 415
Lange, Debra S., Coord.-Adv.--Oldsmobile Div. General Motors Corp., Lansing, MI; *U.S. Public*, pg. 720
Lange, Joan, Dir.-Adv.--AEP Industries, Inc., South Hackensack, NJ; *U.S. Public*, pg. 4
Lange, Ronald F., Dir.-Mktg.--QT Optoelectronics, Sunnyvale, CA; *U.S. Private*, pg. 897
Lange, Sharon, Dir.-Adv. & Creative Svcs.--ACCO Brands, Inc., Wheeling, IL; *U.S. Public*, pg. 674
Lange, Sharon, Dir.-Adv. & Creative Svcs.--ACCO World Corporation, Lincolnshire, IL; *U.S. Public*, pg. 674
Lange, Wolf, Dir.-Adv.--Deutsche Unilever Gmbh, Hamburg, Germany; *Int'l*, pg. 1436
Langley, Edward, Gen. Mgr.--The Weetabix Company, Inc., Clinton, MA; *Int'l*, pg. 1488
Langston, Robert E., Pres.--Langston Companies, Memphis, TN; *U.S. Private*, pg. 650
Lankford, Beverly, Mgr.-Adv.--Glaxo Wellcome Inc., Research Triangle Park, NC; *Int'l*, pg. 552
Lanktree, Charles T., Pres., Chief Exec. Officer & Chief Oper. Officer--Eggland's Best, Inc., King of Prussia, PA; *U.S. Private*, pg. 366
Lanni, Steve, Dir.-Adv.--Pamida Holdings Corporation, Omaha, NE; *U.S. Public*, pg. 1255
Lanni, Steve, Dir.-Adv.--Seaway Importing Company, Omaha, NE; *U.S. Public*, pg. 1255
Lansdale, Darryl L., Analyst-Adv. & Fin.--Scotty's, Inc., Winter Haven, FL; *Int'l*, pg. 533
Lantow, Mike, Mgr.-Adv.--Emulex Corporation, Costa Mesa, CA; *U.S. Public*, pg. 579
Lanza, Jennifer, Div. V.P.-Adv.--PaineWebber Group Incorporated, New York, NY; *U.S. Public*, pg. 1252
Lanza, Jennifer, Div. V.P.-Adv.--PaineWebber Incorporated, New York, NY; *U.S. Public*, pg. 1252
Lapeyre, Jay, Jr., Chm. & Pres.--The Laitram Corporation, Harahan, LA; *U.S. Private*, pg. 643
Lapham, Edward, Exec. Editor--Automotive News, Detroit, MI; *U.S. Private*, pg. 284
LaPierre, Dexter, Dir.-Classified & Natl. Adv.--San Diego Union Tribune, San Diego, CA; *U.S. Private*, pg. 275
LaPlaca, Barbara, Dir.-Creative Svcs. & U.S. Adv. Sls.--The Reader's Digest Association, Inc., Pleasantville, NY; *U.S.* Public, pg. 1367
LaPoff, Gary, V.P.-Sls.--The Manhattan Shirt Co., New York, NY; *U.S. Public*, pg. 1429
LaPoff, Gary, Mgr.-Adv.--Salant Childrens Apparel Group, New York, NY; *U.S. Public*, pg. 1429
Laracy, Mark A., Pres.--Parfums De Coeur Ltd., Darien, CT; *U.S. Private*, pg. 839
Largay, George, Dir.-Grp. Adv.--ADT Automotive, Inc., Nashville, TN; *U.S. Public*, pg. 1648
Larkin, Neil, Dir.-Promotions--Snapple Beverage Company, White Plains, NY; *U.S. Public*, pg. 1635
Larock, Duane, Pres.--R.A. Mueller, Inc., Cincinnati, OH; *U.S. Private*, pg. 766
Larsen, David, Mgr.-Corp. Communications--Weyerhaeuser Canada Ltd., Vancouver, Canada; *U.S. Public*, pg. 1764
Larsen, Judy A., Mgr.-Adv. & Sls. Promo.--Svedala Industries Inc., Appleton, WI; *Int'l*, pg. 1325
Larsen, Mark, Mgr.-Communications--Eveready Battery Co., Saint Louis, MO; *U.S. Public*, pg. 1360
Larsen, Shirley, Mgr.-Adv.--TSC Shannock Corporation, Burnaby, Canada; *Int'l*, pg. 1343
Larson, Kenneth, Exec. V.P.--Monico Alloys, Inc., Los Angeles, CA; *U.S. Private*, pg. 757
Larson, Larry, Dir.-Media Services--U S West Communications Group, Inc., Englewood, CO; *U.S. Public*, pg. 1689
Laser, Joel, Dir.-Outdoor Adv. Programs--Red Roof Inns, Inc., Hilliard, OH; *U.S. Public*, pg. 1369
Laser, Leigh, Mgr.-Adv. & Mktg.--Books-A-Million, Inc., Birmingham, AL; *U.S. Public*, pg. 244
Lasher, John A., V.P.-Adv.--Blair Corporation, Warren, PA; *U.S. Public*, pg. 236
Laske, Michael, Dir.-Adv. & Pub. Rels.--Pittler Maschinenfabrik AG, Langen, Germany; *Int'l*, pg. 1128
Latella, George J., Mgr.-Adv. & Mktg.--Tasty Baking Company, Philadelphia, PA; *U.S. Public*, pg. 1561
Lathouras, Stephanie, Mgr.-Bus. Adv.--CompUSA, Dallas, TX; *U.S. Public*, pg. 420
Latimer, Becky, Mgr.-Sls.--Driv-Lok, Inc., Sycamore, IL; *U.S.* Private, pg. 343
Latourette, Everett, Reg. Mgr.-Sls. & Adv.--Cramer Company, Old Saybrook, CT; *U.S. Public*, pg. 1238
Lau, May, Mgr.-Pub. Rels. & Corp. Communications--Sun Hung Kai Properties Ltd., Wan Chai, Hong Kong; *Int'l*, pg. 1318
Laub, Mark, V.P.-Mktg. & Pub. Affairs--United Power Association, Elk River, MN; *U.S. Private*, pg. 1123
Lauderdale, Jim, V.P.-Mktg.-Dairy Foods Group--Mid-America Dairymen, Inc., Springfield, MO; *U.S. Private*, pg. 743
Laudisio, Glenda, Mgr.-Adv. & Pub. Rels.--Checkpoint Systems Inc., Thorofare, NJ; *U.S. Public*, pg. 343
Lauletta, John, V.P.-Mktg. & Adv.--Gould Instrument Systems, Inc., Valley View, OH; *U.S. Public*, pg. 1592
Laura, Henry, V.P.-Sls., Mktg. & Adv./Agency Svcs.--The Arbitron Company, New York, NY; *U.S. Public*, pg. 331
Laurencell, Gordie, Mgr.-Adv.--Trippe Mfg. Co., Chicago, IL; *U.S. Private*, pg. 1104
Lauri, Alicia, Mgr.-Adv.--Gillette Argentina S.A., Buenos Aires, Argentina; *U.S. Public*, pg. 744
Laveist, Douglas, Mgr.-Adv.--Michael Anthony Jewelers, Inc., Mount Vernon, NY; *U.S. Public*, pg. 1103
Lavin, Joseph, V.P.-External Affairs--Sandoz Corporation, New York, NY; *Int'l*, pg. 974
Lavin, Katherine, Dir.-Mktg. & Adv.--Dunmore Corporation, Newtown, PA; *U.S. Private*, pg. 346
Lavner, William, V.P.-Adv.--Traffic World, New York, NY; *Int'l*, pg. 1026
Lavorgna, Anthony N., Mgr.-Mktg. & Sales--Airflex Div. Eaton Corp., Cleveland, OH; *U.S. Public*, pg. 556
Lawrence, Beth, V.P. & Dir.-Adv.--USA Weekend, New York, NY; *U.S. Public*, pg. 701
Lawson, Chris, Dir.-Mktg. Communications--Grace Construction Products, Cambridge, MA; *U.S. Public*, pg. 755
Lawson, Gini, V.P. & Mgr.-Corp. Adv.--Washington Mutual Inc., Seattle, WA; *U.S. Public*, pg. 1741
Lawson, Gini, V.P.-Corp. Adv.--Great Western Financial Corporation, Chatsworth, CA; *U.S. Public*, pg. 1741
Lawton, Kristen, Coord.-Adv. & Mktg.--Hobie Cat Company, Oceanside, CA; *U.S. Private*, pg. 531
Lax, David, V.P.-Sls. & Adv.--John Hassall, Inc., Westbury, NY; *U.S. Private*, pg. 509
Lay, Alan, Technical Writer--Signtech USA, Ltd., San Antonio, TX; *U.S. Private*, pg. 999
Laychak, Bryan, Coord.-Adv.--Florsheim Group Inc., Chicago, IL; *U.S. Public*, pg. 656
Layman, Cynthia, Brand Mgr., Direct Response & Mkt. Res.--Barnes & Noble Inc., New York, NY; *U.S. Public*, pg. 189
Layton, Mitzi, Mgr.-Mktg. Communications--Coburn Optical Industries Inc., Tulsa, OK; *U.S. Private*, pg. 248
Layton, Walter, Dir.-Adv.-Whirlpool Brand--Whirlpool Corporation, Benton Harbor, MI; *U.S. Public*, pg. 1764
Lazar, Elizabeth C., Dir.-Media Opers.--General Motors Corporation, Detroit, MI; *U.S. Public*, pg. 718
Lazarus, Denise, Mktg. Devel.--Farm Stores, Miami, FL; *U.S. Private*, pg. 394
Lazarus, Robert J., Dir.-Mktg.--L&R Manufacturing Co., Kearny, NJ; *U.S. Private*, pg. 638
Leach, Antoinette, Mgr.-Bus. Devel.--Saft Nife Ltd., Hampton, United Kingdom; *Int'l*, pg. 55
Leader, M.L., Mgr.-Adv.--IDenticard Systems, Inc., Lancaster, PA; *U.S. Private*, pg. 557
Leaman, Donald H., Jr., Dir.-Adv. & Mktg.--Rystan Company, Inc., Little Falls, NJ; *U.S. Private*, pg. 436
Leary, John, Pres.--The Motorlease Corp., Farmington, CT; *U.S. Private*, pg. 764
Leblanc, Christiane, Adv. Coord.--Renault V.I., Suresnes, France; *Int'l*, pg. 1102
Lee, Bob, Dir.-Adv. Eastern--Discover, New York, NY; *U.S. Public*, pg. 513
Lee, Carole, Dir.-Mktg.--Conbraco Industries Inc., Matthews, NC; *U.S. Private*, pg. 261
Lee, Dani, Sls. & Mktg. Coord.--Gilliam Candy Brands, Edwardsville, KS; *U.S. Private*, pg. 454
Lee, Henry, V.P.-Mktg.--Noodle Kidoodle Inc., Syosset, NY; *U.S. Public*, pg. 1188
Lee, Robert E., Pres. & Chief Exec. Officer--Millennium Inorganic Chemicals, Hunt Valley, MD; *Int'l*, pg. 593
Lee, Robert S., V.P.--American Indemnity Financial Corp., Galveston, TX; *U.S. Public*, pg. 83
Lee, Ronald G., Chm. Bd. & Pres.--Lee Pharmaceuticals, South El Monte, CA; *U.S. Public*, pg. 984
Lee, Terry, Sr. V.P. & Mgr.-Corp. Commun.--First Tennessee National Corporation, Memphis, TN; *U.S. Public*, pg. 638
Lee, Thomas, Mgr.-Adv.--Lee Company, Westbrook, CT; *U.S. Private*, pg. 657
Lee, Won Young, Sr. V.P.-Cargo & Adv.--Korean Airlines Co., Ltd., Seoul, Korea; *Int'l*, pg. 758
Lee, Y.H., Dir.-Adv.--Hyundai Motor Company, Seoul, Korea; *Int'l*, pg. 641
Leech, Joann, Dir.-Adv. & Mkt. Res.--Rodney D. Young Insurance, Dallas, TX; *U.S. Private*, pg. 1202
Leenerman, Sue, Dir.-Mktg.--Ciprico, Inc., Plymouth, MN; *U.S. Public*, pg. 370
Legare, Sylvy, Mgr.-Adv.--Abbott Laboratories Ltd., Saint-Laurent, Canada; *U.S. Public*, pg. 13
LeGault, Sharon, Mgr.-Mktg.--Cooper Instrument Corp., Middlefield, CT; *U.S. Private*, pg. 274
Legge, Jeanne, Corp. Admin.-Adv.--CNA Insurance Companies, Chicago, IL; *U.S. Public*, pg. 1010
Legros, Dick, V.P.-Religious Sls. & Mktg.--Standard Publishing, Cincinnati, OH; *U.S. Public*, pg. 1506
Lehmbeck, Barney L., Sr. V.P.-Bus. Devel., Mktg. & Adv.--Liberty Bancorp, Inc., Oklahoma City, OK; *U.S. Public*, pg. 174
Lehning, Larry, Mgr.-Sls. & Mktg.--Liberty Precision Industries, Rochester, NY; *U.S. Private*, pg. 666
Leibowitz, Jennifer, Mktg., Commun., & Adv.--Medical Laboratory Automation, Inc., Pleasantville, NY; *U.S. Private*, pg. 727
Leider, Bruce, V.P.-Adv. & Sls. Promo.--Winkelman Stores, Inc., Plymouth, MI; *U.S. Private*, pg. 858
Leifker, Linda, Adv. Specialist--Springs Window Fashions Division, Middleton, WI; *U.S. Public*, pg. 1500
Leinauer, Marlise, Mgr.-Adv.--The Swissair Group, Zurich, Switzerland; *Int'l*, pg. 1333
Leinfuss, Ellen, V.P.-Mktg. & Commun.--EA Engineering, Science & Technology, Inc., Hunt Valley, MD; *U.S. Public*, pg. 540
Leipold, Erika M., Coord.-Adv. & Pub. Rels.-Commercial Div.--Continental General Tire, Inc., Charlotte, NC; *Int'l*, pg. 327
Leistritz, John P., V.P.-Mktg.--Paul Arpin Vanlines, Inc., West Warwick, RI; *U.S. Private*, pg. 85
Lemand, Terry, Mgr.-Adv.-Chemicals--Rhone-Poulenc S.A., Courbevoie, France; *Int'l*, pg. 1108
Lemke, Mike, V.P.-Adv.--Seattle Times Company, Seattle, WA; *U.S. Private*, pg. 980
Lemm, Dick, V.P.-Mktg. & Adv.--Mini Mart, Inc., Casper, WY; *U.S. Public*, pg. 967
Lenox, Dave A., Mgr.-Adv.--Consumer Tires-North America Tires--The Goodyear Tire & Rubber Company, Akron, OH; *U.S. Public*, pg. 752
Lenzo, Joe, Mgr.-Mktg.--Groschopp, Inc., Sioux Center, IA; *Int'l*, pg. 559
Leonard, Cindy, Mgr.-Adv. Production--Grandy's, Inc., Lewisville, TX; *U.S. Private*, pg. 61
Leone, Gina, Dir.-Adv. & Publicity--Aladdin Hotel & Casino, Las Vegas, NV; *U.S. Private*, pg. 30
Lerman, Jeanette, V.P.-Communications--Time Warner Inc., New York, NY; *U.S. Public*, pg. 1610
Lersch, David, Dir.-Promotional Support--Roman, Inc., Roselle, IL; *U.S. Private*, pg. 942
Lester, Clayton F., V.P.-Adv.--Associated Grocers, Inc., Baton Rouge, LA; *U.S. Private*, pg. 90
Lester, Tricia, V.P.-Mktg.--Syntellect, Inc., Phoenix, AZ; *U.S.* Public, pg. 1550
Leuchtmann, Lisa, Mgr.-Communications & Adv.--InteCom, Dallas, TX; *Int'l*, pg. 794
Leung, Rod, Dir.-Adv. & Media--Seattle Pacific Industries, Inc., Seattle, WA; *U.S. Private*, pg. 980
Leuthe, Paul, Mgr.-Corp. Mktg.--Sub-Zero Freezer Co., Inc., Madison, WI; *U.S. Private*, pg. 1048
Levan, Cynthia, Dir.-Adv.--Dominick's Finer Foods, Northlake, IL; *U.S. Private*, pg. 1202
Levenstein, Earle, V.P.-Adv.--Henredon Furniture Industries, Inc., Morganton, NC; *U.S. Private*, pg. 432
Lever, Edith, Dir.-Adv.--Craftmatic Organization, Inc., Trevose, PA; *U.S. Private*, pg. 284
LeVere, Bill, Dir.-Adv.--Earl May Seed & Nursery L.c., Shenandoah, IA; *U.S. Private*, pg. 356
Levi-Garza, Jalaane, Sr. V.P. & Dir.-Adv.--Mediatex Communications Corporation, Austin, TX; *U.S. Private*, pg. 727
Levin, Shirley, Mgr.-Adv.--Economy Folding Box Corp., Chicago, IL; *U.S. Private*, pg. 362
Levine, David, V.P.-Sls.--Human Affairs International Inc., Sandy, UT; *U.S. Public*, pg. 1036
Levine, Greg, Mgr.-Adv.--BP Chemicals, Inc., Cleveland, OH; *Int'l*, pg. 220
Levine, Gregg, Mgr.-Adv.--BP North America Petroleum Inc., Cleveland, OH; *Int'l*, pg. 220
Levine, Hy, Dir.-Print Mktg. (Motion Pictures)--The Walt Disney Company, Burbank, CA; *U.S. Public*, pg. 511
Levine, Jane, Publr.--Chicago Reader, Inc., Chicago, IL; *U.S. Private*, pg. 235
Levine, Kate, Mgr.-Adv. Design--American Technical Ceramics Corp., Huntington Station, NY; *U.S. Public*, pg. 93
Levine, Todd, V.P.-Mktg. & Sls.--Don Alleson, Inc., Rochester, NY; *U.S. Private*, pg. 339
Levine, Wendy, Oper. V.P.-Media Adv.--Bloomingdale's, New York, NY; *U.S. Public*, pg. 617
Levison, Michael, Dir.-Adv.--Shonac Corporation, Columbus, OH; *U.S. Private*, pg. 996
Levy, Lawrence J., V.P.-Corp. Adv.--The Chase Manhattan Bank, New York, NY; *U.S. Public*, pg. 338
Levy, Leslie W., Pres. & Chief Oper. Officer--Heritage Sportswear, Marion, SC; *U.S. Public*, pg. 1472
Lewin, Joseph, Chm. Bd., Pres. & Chief Exec. Officer--Health Products Corporation, Yonkers, NY; *U.S. Private*, pg. 514
Lewin, Sandra, Dir.-Corp. Communications & Pub. Rels.--George Wimpey PLC, London, United Kingdom; *Int'l*, pg. 1510
Lewis, Barbara, V.P.-Adv. & Sls. Promo.--Wherehouse Entertainment, Inc., Torrance, CA; *U.S. Private*, pg. 1171
Lewis, Barry L., Dir.-Pub. Rels. & Adv.--Huls America Inc., Somerset, NJ; *Int'l*, pg. 1455
Lewis, Brad, V.P.-Mktg. Devel.--Joy Mining Machinery, Warrendale, PA; *U.S. Public*, pg. 789
Lewis, David, Adv. Dir.--Dewe Rogerson Limited, London, United Kingdom; *Int'l*, pg. 408
Lewis, Kurt W., V.P.-Mktg. & Sls.--Fujisawa U.S.A. Inc., Deerfield, IL; *Int'l*, pg. 525
Lewis, Linda, Mktg. Asst.--Bender Shipbuilding & Repair Company, Inc., Mobile, AL; *U.S. Private*, pg. 132
Lewis, Paul, Mgr.-Adv. & Sls.--Prodigy Inc., White Plains, NY; *U.S. Private*, pg. 888
Lewis, Ray, V.P.-Adv. (Ameritech)--Indiana Bell Telephone Company, Inc., Indianapolis, IN; *U.S. Public*, pg. 98
Lewis, Robert B., V.P. & Gen. Mgr.--Asahi/America, Inc., Malden, MA; *U.S. Public*, pg. 137
Lewis, Tommy, Dir.-Mktg.--The United Methodist Publishing House, Nashville, TN; *U.S. Private*, pg. 1122
Lewis, Vern, Dir.-Mktg. & Mktg. Services--Medical Economics Company Inc., Montvale, NJ; *U.S. Public*, pg. 1601
Lewnes, Anne, Dir.-Worldwide Adv.--Intel Corporation, Santa Clara, CA; *U.S. Public*, pg. 886
Lichtendahl, Kenneth, Pres.--Hudepohl-Schoenling Brewing Company, Cincinnati, OH; *U.S. Private*, pg. 545
Lichtenfels, Brenda, Coord.-Adv.--Landmark Community Newspapers, Inc., Shelbyville, KY; *U.S. Private*, pg. 648
Lichter, Leslie, Dir.-Adv.--Scholastic Inc., New York, NY; *U.S. Public*, pg. 1440
Licoys, Gaelle, Dir.-Adv.--Compagnie Generale Des Eaux, Paris, France; *Int'l*, pg. 321
Liddic, Janice, Mgr.-Adv.--Gertrude Hawk Chocolates, Inc., Dunmore, PA; *U.S. Private*, pg. 449
Lieberman, Daniel, Pres.--A&W Restaurants, Inc.-Carousel Div., Minneapolis, MN; *U.S. Private*, pg. 2
Lieberman, Rita, Mgr.-Promos.--Thomas Register, New York, NY; *U.S. Private*, pg. 1082
Liebler, Arthur C., V.P.-Communications--Chrysler Corporation, Auburn Hills, MI; *U.S. Public*, pg. 352

Liebscher, Klaus, Dr., Dir.-Gen. Mngmt.--Raiffeisen Zentralbank Osterreich, Vienna, Austria; *Int'l*, pg. 1084
Lien, Grant, V.P.-Sls. & Mktg.--Tyler Industries, Benson, MN; *U.S. Private*, pg. 1112
Lieske, Laura, Mgr.-Mktg. Communications--Sennheiser Electronic Corp., Old Lyme, CT; *U.S. Private*, pg. 984
Light, Ted, V.P.-Sls. & Mktg.--DuBois Chemicals, Cincinnati, OH; *Int'l*, pg. 1437
Liinsoski, Kari, Mgr.-Adv.--Postipankki Ltd., Helsinki, Finland; *Int'l*, pg. 1064
Lilienthal, J.G., Mgr.-Adv.--Flowserve Corporation, Dayton, OH; *U.S. Public*, pg. 658
Lilly, Ed, Pres. & Chief Exec. Officer--Serta, Inc., Itasca, IL; *U.S. Private*, pg. 985
Lilly, Grant R., Gen. Mgr.-Australia & New Zealand--Air New Zealand Ltd., Auckland, New Zealand; *Int'l*, pg. 38
Lim, Cindy, Dir.-Intl Mktg-Div. II--Malaysia Tourism Promotion Board (MTPB), Kuala Lumpur, Malaysia; *Int'l*, pg. 832
Limay, Luis A., Dir.-Mktg., Pur. & Sls.--San Sebastian Gold Mines, Inc., Milwaukee, WI; *U.S. Public*, pg. 410
Limback, Cindy, Asst. Mgr.-Adv.--Besser Company, Alpena, MI; *U.S. Private*, pg. 139
Limbeck, Betsy, Dir.-Adv. Services--Kraft Foods Inc., Rye Brook, NY; *U.S. Public*, pg. 1288
Linaman, Mary Ann, V.P.-Adv. & Mktg. Svcs.--King Koil Licensing Company Inc., Saint Paul, MN; *U.S. Private*, pg. 621
Linbeck, Leo, III, Dir.-Sls. & Mktg.--Linbeck Construction Corp, Houston, TX; *U.S. Private*, pg. 667
Lincoln, Greg, Dir.-Brand Communications--The Haagen-Dazs Company Inc., Minneapolis, MN; *Int'l*, pg. 411
Lind, Roberta, Dir.-Adv.--Star Tribune, Minneapolis-St. Paul, Minneapolis, MN; *U.S. Private*, pg. 281
Lindberg, Peter, Mgr.-Adv.--Fujitsu Computer Products of America, Inc., San Jose, CA; *Int'l*, pg. 526
Linden, Joann, V.P.-Ad Specialties--Dri Mark Products, Inc., Port Washington, NY; *U.S. Private*, pg. 342
Lindsey, Marianne, Mgr.-Adv. & Promo.--Alaska Air Group, Inc., Seattle, WA; *U.S. Public*, pg. 35
Lindsey, Ralph, V.P.-Mktg. & Sls.--Barber Dairies, Inc., Birmingham, AL; *U.S. Private*, pg. 115
Lindstrom, Annette, Dir.-Adv. & Mktg. Svcs.--Home & Garden Television, Knoxville, TN; *U.S. Public*, pg. 1447
Lindstrom, Riitta-Leena, Dir.-Mktg. & Adv.--Masterfoods Oy, Helsinki, Finland; *U.S. Private*, pg. 707
Liner, Andrea, V.P.-Adv.--Corpak Inc., Wheeling, IL; *U.S. Public*, pg. 1592
Link, James, Mgr.-Mktg.--Meadville Forging Co., Meadville, PA; *U.S. Private*, pg. 726
Linkowski, Bobbi, Dir.-Adv. & Mktg.--BioChem ImmunoSystems, Inc., Allentown, PA; *Int'l*, pg. 196
Linscott, Ann, Dir.-Corp. Communications--Royal Doulton Plc., Stoke on Trent, United Kingdom; *Int'l*, pg. 1135
Linscott, Darlene, Dir.-Mktg.--Gitano Fashions Ltd., Bowling Green, KY; *U.S. Public*, pg. 686
Linton, Bill, Mgr.-Brand Mktg.--Bush Brothers & Company, Knoxville, TN; *U.S. Private*, pg. 189
Lipe, Randy, Mgr.-Adv. Opers.--Fleming Companies, Inc., Oklahoma City, OK; *U.S. Public*, pg. 652
Lipez, E., V.P.-Mktg.--Princess Hotels International Inc., New York, NY; *Int'l*, pg. 818
Lipka, Carole, Dir.-Mktg.--Keeney Manufacturing Co., Newington, CT; *U.S. Private*, pg. 611
Lippin, Howard, Mgr.-Adv.--New Hermes Incorporated, Duluth, GA; *U.S. Private*, pg. 793
Lipscomb, Anne, Grp. V.P.-Mktg.--The Mills Corporation, Arlington, VA; *U.S. Public*, pg. 1113
Lipscomb, William, V.P.-Sls. & Mktg.--Plastic Packaging, Inc., Hickory, NC; *U.S. Private*, pg. 871
Liscik, Raymond, V.P.-Adv., Mktg., Sls. & Pub. Rels.--JCI Data Processing, Inc., Cinnaminson, NJ; *U.S. Private*, pg. 577
Lishak, John, Jr., Pres.--Commercial Realty & Resources Corp., Wall, NJ; *U.S. Public*, pg. 1172
Listwa, Les, V.P.-Mktg.--Computer Power Incorporated, High Bridge, NJ; *U.S. Public*, pg. 421
Little, Freda, Dir.-Mdsg.--Fairfax Lumber & Millwork Company Inc., Springfield, VA; *U.S. Private*, pg. 391
Little, Terrance L., V.P.-Intl. Communications & Adv.--The Equitable Companies Incorporated, New York, NY; *U.S. Public*, pg. 588
Litwak, Jim, Exec. V.P.-Mdsg. & Mktg.--Trans World Entertainment Corporation, Albany, NY; *U.S. Public*, pg. 1629
Livermore, Russell, III, Mgr.-Mktg. Communications--ABT Building Products Corporation, Neenah, WI; *Int'l*, pg. 20
Livingston, Bev, Asst. Mgr.-Adv. & Promo.--General Motors of Canada Ltd., Oshawa, Canada; *U.S. Public*, pg. 722
Livingston, Ingrid, Mgr.-Mktg. Commun.--Highway Equipment Company, Cedar Rapids, IA; *U.S. Private*, pg. 529
Livingston, Linda, Mgr.-Circulation & Adv.--Dodge City Daily Globe, Dodge City, KS; *U.S. Private*, pg. 995
Livon, Irwin, V.P.-Mdse. & Adv.--Genovese Drug Stores, Inc., Melville, NY; *U.S. Public*, pg. 730
Lloyd, Sharon, Mgr.-Mktg.--Raley's & Bel Air, West Sacramento, CA; *U.S. Private*, pg. 907
Locke, Ralph, V.P.-Mktg.--Syar Industries, Inc., Napa, CA; *U.S. Private*, pg. 1059
Locker, John, Bus. Mgr.- Adv.--Linens 'n Things, Inc., Clifton, NJ; *U.S. Private*, pg. 668
Lockhart, Frank L., Dir.-Mktg./North America--Ranco North America, Plain City, OH; *Int'l*, pg. 1243
Lockman-Brooks, Linda, Mgr.-Mktg., Adv. & Sls.--Duke Energy Corporation, Charlotte, NC; *U.S. Public*, pg. 534
Lodding, C., Mgr.-Intl. Adv.--Bang & Olufsen A/S, Struer, Denmark; *Int'l*, pg. 145
Lodge, Thomas R., Sr., Pres.--Delaware Ribbon Manufacturers, Inc., Philadelphia, PA; *U.S. Private*, pg. 322
Loebig, Gary L., Sr. V.P.-Market & Prod. Devel.--Stuart Entertainment Inc., Council Bluffs, IA; *U.S. Public*, pg. 1526
Loechner, Barbara, Mgr.-Adv. & Communications--Nikon Inc., Melville, NY; *Int'l*, pg. 931
Loeffler, Bob, Mgr.-Mktg.--Miele Appliances, Inc., Somerset, NJ; *Int'l*, pg. 865
Loftus, Gary, Adv. Mgr.--The Grand Island Daily Independent, Grand Island, NE; *U.S. Private*, pg. 995
Logan, Janet, Mgr.-Adv.-Film--Fuji Photo Film (U.K.), Ltd., London, United Kingdom; *Int'l*, pg. 524
Logan, Judy, Dir.-Mktg. & Adv.--Netscape Communications Corp., Mountain View, CA; *U.S. Public*, pg. 1168
Lohmann, Ed, V.P.-Mktg.--Alexander Doll Company, Inc., New York, NY; *U.S. Private*, pg. 33
Lohrer, William F., Mgr.-Adv.--Hobart Corporation, Troy, OH; *U.S. Public*, pg. 1322
Lombardelli, Angelo, Adv. Dir.--Mandelli Industrie S.p.A., Piacenza, Italy; *Int'l*, pg. 834
Lonbaken, Clint, Mgr.-Adv.--Melroe Company, Fargo, ND; *U.S. Public*, pg. 877
Long, Cheri, Mgr.-Mktg. Services--The Kerite Company, Seymour, CT; *U.S. Public*, pg. 844
Long, Cheri, Mgr.-Adv.--The Ohio Brass Co., Wadsworth, OH; *U.S. Public*, pg. 845
Long, Jerry, Mgr.-Mass Commun.--Southwire Company, Carrollton, GA; *U.S. Private*, pg. 1019
Long, Nancy, Mgr.-Pub. Rels. & Adv.--Brother International Corporation, Somerset, NJ; *Int'l*, pg. 229
Longacre, Robert, Mgr.-Adv.--Hehr International Inc., Los Angeles, CA; *U.S. Private*, pg. 519
Longden, Marianne, Mgr.-Adv.--Purity Products Inc., Miami, FL; *U.S. Private*, pg. 896
Longenbach, M., Coord.-Adv.--Victaulic Tool Company, Easton, PA; *U.S. Private*, pg. 1138
Longtin, Joel C., Pres.--Mr. Gatti's, Inc., Kerrville, TX; *U.S. Private*, pg. 639
Looney, Jerry, Mgr.-Adv. & Sls. Promo.--Vulcan-Hart Corp., Louisville, KY; *U.S. Public*, pg. 1322
Loontiens, Charlotte, Adv. Asst.--Mazda Motor of America, Inc., Irvine, CA; *Int'l*, pg. 849
Loos, Sara, Dir.-Adv.--Ikea North America, Inc., Plymouth Meeting, PA; *Int'l*, pg. 660
Loosli, Heinz, Dir.-Adv.--Feintool International Holding AG, Lyss, Switzerland; *Int'l*, pg. 479
Loper, William, Sr. V.P.-Creative Adv.--TriStar Pictures, Culver City, CA; *Int'l*, pg. 1283
Lopez, Carmen, V.P. & Mng. Dir.-Sls.--The New Yorker Magazine, New York, NY; *U.S. Private*, pg. 795
Lopez, Filemon, Sr. V.P.-Adv. Sls.--Comcast Cable Communications, Inc., Philadelphia, PA; *U.S. Public*, pg. 407
Lorenzo, Gilbert, V.P.-Adv.--Burdines, Miami, FL; *U.S. Public*, pg. 618
Lorimor, Randall, Dir.-Corp. Adv. & Sls. Promo.--Country Life Insurance Company, Bloomington, IL; *U.S. Private*, pg. 278
Lorimor, Randy, Dir.-Corp. Adv. & Sls. Promo.--Country Mutual Insurance Company, Bloomington, IL; *U.S. Private*, pg. 279
Lorimor, Randy, Dir.-Corp. Adv. & Sls. Promo.--CC Services, Bloomington, IL; *U.S. Private*, pg. 279
Lorusso, Ester, Mgr.-Adv.--Alitalia Airlines, New York, NY; *Int'l*, pg. 652
Losie, Paul M., V.P.-Mktg. & Adv.--Amwest Insurance Group, Inc., Calabasas, CA; *U.S. Public*, pg. 106
Lot, Thierry, Dir.-Mktg.--Polive/Tricosteril, Courbevoie, France; *U.S. Public*, pg. 673
Loughlin, Pat, Plant Mgr.--Air Products, Langley, SC; *U.S. Public*, pg. 30
Louvar, David, Dir.-Sls. & Mktg.-Saws--Wisconsin Automated Machinery Corp., Oshkosh, WI; *U.S. Private*, pg. 1184
Love, Kelly, V.P.-Mktg.--Ohio Machinery Co., Cleveland, OH; *U.S. Private*, pg. 812
Loveland, Roelif M., Gen. Mgr. & Mgr.-Adv.--Maze Nails, Peru, IL; *U.S. Private*, pg. 718
Lovell, Robert B., V.P.-Mktg. & Adv.--Coca-Cola Bottling Co. United, Inc., Birmingham, AL; *U.S. Private*, pg. 248
Lovoy, Cynthia, Mgr.-Publicity--American Cast Iron Pipe Co., Birmingham, AL; *U.S. Private*, pg. 51
Lowe Eddowes, Sally, Mgr.-Adv. & Sls. Promo.--Fraser Papers, Inc., Stamford, CT; *Int'l*, pg. 434
Lowe, Dominic, V.P.-Mktg. & Adv.--Schweppes Europe Limited, Watford, United Kingdom; *Int'l*, pg. 248
Lowenthal, Meryle, Mgr.-Adv.-New York--Scientific American, Inc., New York, NY; *Int'l*, pg. 1479
Lowman, Blenda, Dir.-Retail Adv.--Drexel Heritage Furnishings Inc., Drexel, NC; *U.S. Private*, pg. 432
Lu Donnelley, Petra, Dir.-Adv.--Dionex Corporation, Sunnyvale, CA; *U.S. Public*, pg. 510
Luboja, Ed, Mgr.-Mktg. Communications--V-Band Corporation, Elmsford, NY; *U.S. Public*, pg. 1701
Lucas, Carl D., Dir.-Adv.--SCI Systems, Inc., Huntsville, AL; *U.S. Public*, pg. 1416
Lucas, Dave, Mgr.-Sls.--Roney Otman, Aurora, IL; *U.S. Private*, pg. 943
Lucas, Kristen, Coord.-Adv.--The TJX Companies, Inc., Framingham, MA; *U.S. Public*, pg. 1556
Lucas, Lauren, Exec. Sec.-Adv.--Nordstrom, Inc., Seattle, WA; *U.S. Public*, pg. 1190
Lucas, Stefanie, Adv. & Promo. Specialist--C-COR Electronics, Inc., State College, PA; *U.S. Public*, pg. 272
Luchetta, Rodolfo, Div. Mgr.-Mktg.--Y.P.F., S.A., Buenos Aires, Argentina; *Int'l*, pg. 1515
Luchs, Kenneth, Sr. V.P.-Mktg., Sls. & Adv.--Reliable Stores, Inc., Columbia, MD; *U.S. Private*, pg. 920
Luciani, Jeanine, Dir.-Adv.--Steelcase Wood Div., Kentwood, MI; *U.S. Private*, pg. 1038
Lucy, Tom, Mgr.-Adv.--G.E. Canada, Peterborough, Peterborough, Canada; *U.S. Public*, pg. 713
Ludgate, John, V.P.-Mktg.--International Paint Co., Inc., Union, NJ; *Int'l*, pg. 338
Ludlow, Susan, Dir.-Adv.--Bride's, New York, NY; *U.S. Private*, pg. 20
Ludlow, Ted, V.P.-Sls. & Mktg.--Bedford Industries, Inc., Worthington, MN; *U.S. Private*, pg. 129
Lueck, Guada, Mgr.-Adv. & Pub. Rels.--The PBS&J Corporation, Miami, FL; *U.S. Private*, pg. 825
Lugar, Todd, V.P.-Opers., Treas. & Sec.--Thomas L. Green & Co., Inc., Indianapolis, IN; *U.S. Private*, pg. 477
Luginbuhl, Dan R., V.P.-Commun.--Penske Corporation, Detroit, MI; *U.S. Private*, pg. 850
Lui, Susan, Mgr.-Corp. & Intl. Rels.--International Factors (Singapore) Ltd., Singapore, Singapore; *Int'l*, pg. 684
Lull, Mary, Dir.-U.S. Adv.--Toys "R" Us, Inc., Paramus, NJ; *U.S. Public*, pg. 1626
Lund, Terri, Admin.-Sls.--Rosco Manufacturing Co., Madison, SD; *U.S. Private*, pg. 944
Lundquist, E., Dir.-Mktg.--Flexible Products Company, Marietta, GA; *U.S. Private*, pg. 412
Lundy, Dee, Dir.-Sls. & Mktg.--Family Inns of America, Inc., Pigeon Forge, TN; *U.S. Private*, pg. 392
Lunt, Colby, V.P.-Mktg.--Rogers, Lunt & Bowlen Co., Greenfield, MA; *U.S. Private*, pg. 939
Lurati, Bruno, Dir.-Adv.--Robert Bosch AG, Otelfingen, Switzerland; *Int'l*, pg. 205
Lurndal, Art, V.P.-Adv., Promo. & Pub. Rels.--Kent Feeds Inc., Muscatine, IA; *U.S. Private*, pg. 1134
Lustig, Jane, V.P.-Mktg.--Vienna Sausage Mfg. Co., Chicago, IL; *U.S. Private*, pg. 1139
Lute, Graham, Dir.-Communications--Nestle S.A., Vevey, Switzerland; *Int'l*, pg. 915
Luter, Joseph W., IV, Sr. V.P.-Mktg. & Sls./Fresh Pork--The Smithfield Packing Co., Inc., Smithfield, VA; *U.S. Public*, pg. 1479
Luth, Klaus, Dir.-Sls.--Richardson G.m.b.H., Schwalbach, Germany; *U.S. Public*, pg. 1333
Lutz, Rekke, Sec.-Adv. Dept.--Castrol Austria GmbH, Wiener Neustadt, Austria; *Int'l*, pg. 235
Luvera, Janice, Dir.-Natl. Adv.--Domino's Pizza Inc., Ann Arbor, MI; *U.S. Private*, pg. 339
Lux, William, V.P.-Adv. & Mktg.--Rheem Manufacturing Co., New York, NY; *Int'l*, pg. 1022
Luzardo, Bill, Mgr.-Adv.--Amprobe Instrument, Lynbrook, NY; *U.S. Public*, pg. 1676
Lyall, Ken, Mgr.-Corp. Publications--Beckman Instruments, Inc., Fullerton, CA; *U.S. Public*, pg. 199
Lydic, John, Dir.-Mktg.--National Mine Service, Inc., Indiana, PA; *Int'l*, pg. 280
Lymum, Harald, Dir.-Adv.--Fokus Bank A/S, Trondheim, Norway; *Int'l*, pg. 496
Lynch, Eileen, V.P. & Dir.-Adv. & Promo.--Merrill Lynch & Co., Inc., New York, NY; *U.S. Public*, pg. 1097
Lynch, Eileen, V.P. & Dir.-Adv. & Promotion--Merrill Lynch, Pierce, Fenner & Smith, Inc., New York, NY; *U.S. Public*, *pg. 1098*
Lynch, Larry, Dir.-Mktg.--International Wine Accessories, Inc., Dallas, TX; *U.S. Private*, pg. 572
Lyndon, J., Mgr.-Adv., Pub. Rels. & Mktg. Communications--Aer Lingus, Melville, NY; *Int'l*, pg. 28
Lynn, Vicki, Mgr.-Adv.--Mohawk Commercial Carpet, Atlanta, GA; *U.S. Public*, pg. 1121
Lyon, Robert D., Dir.-Adv.--Ventura County Star-Free Press, Ventura, CA; *U.S. Public*, pg. 1448
Lyons, Arthur, Mgr.-Corp. Communications--Beckman Coulter, Miami, FL; *U.S. Public*, pg. 199
Lyons, Robert E., III, Sr. V.P.--Drug Emporium, Inc., Powell, OH; *U.S. Public*, pg. 530
Macatavish, F.A., V.P.-Transmission & Distr.--Manitoba Hydro, Winnipeg, Canada; *Int'l*, pg. 834
MacBeth, Margaret, Mgr.-Mktg. Svcs.--Atlas Electric Devices Co., Chicago, IL; *U.S. Private*, pg. 96
MacDonald, Bruce, Dir.-Mktg.--Darigold, Inc., Seattle, WA; *U.S. Private*, pg. 311
MacDonald, Mike, Mgr.-Corp. Adv.--IBM Canada Limited, Markham, Canada; *U.S. Public*, pg. 897
MacDonnell, Amy, Mktg. Communications Specialist--Metrologic Instruments, Inc., Blackwood, NJ; *U.S. Public*, *pg. 1102*
MacDougall, Bruce, V.P.-Mktg.--The Canadian Coleman Co., Ltd., Toronto, Canada; *U.S. Private*, pg. 691
Machles, Cindy, Exec. V.P. & Co-Dir.-Adv.--Grey Healthcare Group, New York, NY; *U.S. Public*, pg. 765
Machulak, Edward A., Exec. V.P., Sec. & Mktg., Sls. Promo, Adv. Dir.--Commerce Group Corp., Milwaukee, WI; *U.S. Public*, pg. 410
Machulak, Walter A., Sec. & Mgr.-Pur.--Homespan Realty Co., Inc., Milwaukee, WI; *U.S. Public*, pg. 410
Macius, Mindaugas A., Dir.-Adv. & Pub. Rels.--Houston Foods Company, Franklin Park, IL; *U.S. Private*, pg. 542
Mack, Gary, Dir.-Adv.--Couristan Inc., Fort Lee, NJ; *U.S. Private*, pg. 279
Mack, Lisbeth, V.P.-Adv. & Mktg. Programs--Trans World Airlines, Inc., Saint Louis, MO; *U.S. Public*, pg. 1629
Mack, Ruth, Exec. V.P.-Sls. & Mktg.--Wampler Foods, Timberville, VA; *U.S. Public*, pg. 1727
MacLaverty, Nina, V.P.-Retail Adv.--Sears Canada, Inc., Toronto, Canada; *U.S. Public*, pg. 1452
Macleod, Bruce, Pres.--Nance's Food Products, Inc., Macedon, NY; *U.S. Public*, pg. 1347
MacLeod, Roxanne, Dir.-Mktg. & Sls.--Nova Scotia Power Inc., Halifax, Canada; *Int'l*, pg. 971
MacNutt, James W., Mgr.-Publicity & Adv.--Cincinnati Milacron Industrial Systems Division, Cincinnati, OH; *U.S.* Public, pg. 368
Macomber, Laurie, Dir.-Mktg. Communications & Adv.--International Paper Company, Purchase, NY; *U.S. Public*, *pg. 901*
Macros, Marcos Enrique, Supvr.-Mktg.--Acos Villares S.A., Sao Paulo, Brazil; *Int'l*, pg. 23
Madigan, Susan, Dir.-Adv. & Sls. Promo.--National Car Rental System, Inc., Minneapolis, MN; *U.S. Public*, pg. 1379
Maggipinto, Donata, Mgr.-Adv. & Pub. Rels.--Williams-Sonoma, Inc., San Francisco, CA; *U.S. Public*, pg. 1770
Magnett, Edward, Dir.-Adv.--Kleinsleep, Port Washington, NY; *U.S. Private*, pg. 1006
Magnon, Ann, Dir.-Adv.--Nematron Corp., Ann Arbor, MI; *U.S. Private*, pg. 791

Magnussson, Monicka, Mgr.-Adv. Graphics--The News Tribune, Tacoma, WA; *U.S. Public*, pg. 1066
Mahenbroo, Vinod, Mgr. & Dir.-Global Mktg.--Applied Materials, Inc., Santa Clara, CA; *U.S. Public*, pg. 123
Maher, Larry, Mgr.-Sls. & Mkg.--Zappa Plastics, Phillipsburg, NJ; *U.S. Private*, pg. 172
Mahlanza, Sam, Mgr.-Pub. Rels.--Zimbabwe Electricity Supply Authority, Harare, Zimbabwe; *Int'l*, pg. 1528
Mahler, Darrell, Pres., Gen. Mgr. & Mgr.-Adv./Sls. Promo.--Blue Cross Laboratories, Saugus, CA; *U.S. Private*, pg. 152
Mahoney, Anne, Mgr.-Retail Adv.-True Value--TruServ Corporation, Chicago, IL; *U.S. Private*, pg. 1108
Mahoney, Gerald F., Pres.--Pavey Envelope & Tag Corp., Jersey City, NJ; *U.S. Public*, pg. 1038
Mahoney, Neil J., Mgr.-Mktg. & Adv.--Evans Rule Co., Inc., Charleston, SC; *U.S. Public*, pg. 1511
Maier, Karen F., V.P.-Mktg.--Frisch's Restaurants, Inc., Cincinnati, OH; *U.S. Public*, pg. 682
Mainolfi, Sylvio, Dir.-Mktg.--Branson Ultrasonics Corp.-Plastics Joining Div., Danbury, CT; *U.S. Public*, pg. 574
Maki, Kash, Mgr.-Mktg.--Dayton Tire Company, Oklahoma City, OK; *Int'l*, pg. 213
Makowski, Dieter, Dir.-Adv.--Prisma-Verlag GmbH & Co. KG, Dusseldorf, Germany; *Int'l*, pg. 190
Maladra, Keith, Dir.-Mktg. & Adv.--PetCare Plus, Inc., Aurora, IL; *U.S. Private*, pg. 856
Malehorn, Rodger A., V.P.-Comml. Opers.--Bayou Steel Corporation, La Place, LA; *U.S. Public*, pg. 197
Mallin, Ed, Pres.--Compilers Plus Inc., Montvale, NJ; *U.S. Public*, pg. 70
Malloy, Kevin C., Asst. V.P.-Adv.--Aetna Inc., Hartford, CT; *U.S. Public*, pg. 26
Maloof, Richard C., Pres. & Chief Oper. Officer--Bird Incorporated, Norwood, MA; *Int'l*, pg. 1170
Maloude, Paige, Mgr.-Mktg. Svcs.--Progress Lighting, Spartanburg, SC; *U.S. Public*, pg. 1684
Malta, Evonne, Mgr.-Consumer Adv.--Banco Chase Manhattan S.A., Rio de Janeiro, Brazil; *U.S. Public*, pg. 339
Manak, George, Sr. Dir.-Mktg.--Griffith Laboratories Worldwide, Inc., Alsip, IL; *U.S. Private*, pg. 481
Mancini, Skip, V.P.--B.T. Mancini Co., Inc., Milpitas, CA; *U.S. Private*, pg. 699
Mancuso, Kirt, Mgr.-Adv. & Mktg. Svcs.--Florsheim Group Inc., Chicago, IL; *U.S. Public*, pg. 656
Mandel, Sam, V.P.-Adv.--B & B Motor & Control Corporation, Long Island City, NY; *U.S. Private*, pg. 105
Mandeville, Mary, Mgr.-Communications--Aerovox Inc., New Bedford, MA; *U.S. Public*, pg. 25
Mandiola, Maria Ester, Mgr.-Adv.--General Motors Chile S.A., Industria Automotriz, Santiago, Chile; *U.S. Public*, pg. 721
Maney, Bruna, Dir.-Mktg.--Fownes Brothers & Co., Inc., New York, NY; *U.S. Private*, pg. 422
Mangold, Bob, V.P. & Gen. Mgr.-Auto Warehouse Div.--STRAFCO, Inc., San Antonio, TX; *U.S. Private*, pg. 1046
Manion, Martin, V.P.-Mktg.--McIlhenny Company, Avery Island, LA; *U.S. Private*, pg. 722
Manley, Jennifer, Mgr.-Adv.--Tanning Research Labs., Inc., Ormond Beach, FL; *U.S. Private*, pg. 1068
Manning, Jim T., Mgr.-Adv.-North America Tires--The Goodyear Tire & Rubber Company, Akron, OH; *U.S. Public*, pg. 752
Manning, John, V.P.-Sls. & Mktg.--Crane Plastics Company, Columbus, OH; *U.S. Private*, pg. 286
Manning, Laura, Mgr.-Bus. Adv.--The Bombay Company, Inc., Fort Worth, TX; *U.S. Public*, pg. 244
Mansell, Frank, Dir.-Pub. Info. & Adv.--Cascade Natural Gas Corporation, Seattle, WA; *U.S. Public*, pg. 311
Manuel, Tom, Pres.--ConAgra Trading & Processing Companies, Omaha, NE; *U.S. Public*, pg. 428
Mapes, Timothy W., Dir.-Worldwide Mktg. Communications--Delta Air Lines, Inc., Atlanta, GA; *U.S. Public*, pg. 497
Mar, Emni, Mgr.-Global Corp. Banking Adv.--Citicorp, New York, NY; *U.S. Public*, pg. 376
Marabuto, Marie, Mgr.-Corp. Mktg. Services--Troy Corporation, Florham Park, NJ; *U.S. Private*, pg. 1105
Marcadet, T., Mgr.-Adv. & Mktg.--Agfa-Gevaert S.A., Rueil-Malmaison, France; *Int'l*, pg. 174
Marcellus, Richard, Dir.-N. American Sls.--Simplicity Manufacturing, Inc., Port Washington, WI; *U.S. Private*, pg. 1002
Marconi, Frank, Mgr.-Adv. & Mktg.--Svedala Pumps & Process, Colorado Springs, CO; *Int'l*, pg. 1325
Marcucci, Tom, Dir.-Mktg.--Gonnella Baking Co., Chicago, IL; *U.S. Private*, pg. 463
Marcus, Guy T., V.P.-Investor Rels.--Halliburton Company, Dallas, TX; *U.S. Public*, pg. 775
Marty, Esther, Mgr.-Public Relations--Munck Automation Technology, Newport News, VA; *U.S. Private*, pg. 767
Margin, Rick, V.P.-Mktg.--Prince Sports Group Inc., Bordentown, NJ; *U.S. Private*, pg. 884
Marino, Luis, Dir.-Adv.--La Nacion S.A., Buenos Aires, Argentina; *Int'l*, pg. 785
Mark, Bill, Mgr.-Adv.--Mechanics Tool Div., Dallas, TX; *U.S. Public*, pg. 1509
Mark, Stacey, Dir.-Natl. Adv.--Denny's, Inc., Spartanburg, SC; *U.S. Public*, pg. 23
Marks, Amy, Adv. Coord.--Discover, New York, NY; *U.S. Public*, pg. 513
Marks, David, Mgr.-Natl. Adv.--Hyatt Hotels Corporation, Chicago, IL; *U.S. Private*, pg. 551
Marks, John, Dir.-Corp. Commun.--Medline Industries, Inc., Mundelein, IL; *U.S. Private*, pg. 728
Marlantes, Lorian L., Pres. & Chief Exec. Officer--Rockefeller Group, Inc., New York, NY; *Int'l*, pg. 873
Marlett, Wendy, Dir.-Adv.--Kaufman and Broad Home Corporation, Los Angeles, CA; *U.S. Public*, pg. 944
Marlo, Mike, Mgr.-Mktg.--Reilly Industries, Inc., Indianapolis, IN; *U.S. Private*, pg. 919
Marquardt, Robert J., Chm. Bd.--Gudebrod, Inc., Pottstown, PA; *U.S. Private*, pg. 486
Marques, Fatima de Jesus, Dir.-Mktg.--LPC Industrias Alimenticias S.A., Vila Jaguara, Brazil; *Int'l*, pg. 380
Marquis, Doug, Pres. & Chief Exec. Officer--Handgards Inc., Northbrook, IL; *U.S. Private*, pg. 499
Marriott, J.W., Jr., Chm. Bd. & Chief Exec. Officer--Marriott International, Inc., Washington, DC; *U.S. Public*, pg. 1047
Marrouchi, C.H., Mgr.-Communications & Adv.--CGC Inc., Mississauga, Canada; *U.S. Public*, pg. 1660
Marrus, Allan J., Pres.--The Arlen Corporation, New York, NY; *U.S. Public*, pg. 131
Marsh, Elizabeth, Dir.-Adv.--Borland International, Inc., Scotts Valley, CA; *U.S. Public*, pg. 246
Marsh, Jeffrey, Mgr.-Adv.--Littleton Coin Co., Inc., Littleton, NH; *U.S. Private*, pg. 671
Marshall, Barbara, V.P. & Dir.-Mktg.--Anchor Financial Corporation, Myrtle Beach, SC; *U.S. Public*, pg. 111
Marshall, Duff, Mgr.-Sls., Mktg. & Adv.--Marvin Lumber & Cedar Company, Warroad, MN; *U.S. Private*, pg. 710
Marshall, Vicky, Mgr.-Commun.--Nationwide Building Society, Swindon, United Kingdom; *Int'l*, pg. 912
Martensen, Buddy, Dir.-Adv. Retail Svcs.--Fleming Companies, Inc., Oklahoma City, OK; *U.S. Public*, pg. 652
Marti, Wayne, Pres.--Ott Food Products, Carthage, MO; *U.S. Private*, pg. 821
Martin, Andrew, Dir.-Publicity, Adv. & Promo.--Crown Publishers, Inc., New York, NY; *U.S. Private*, pg. 21
Martin, Andy, Mgr.-Mktg.--Lord Corporation, Cary, NC; *U.S. Private*, pg. 675
Martin, Angela, Dir.-Employee Communications & Adv.--Dollar General Corporation, Nashville, TN; *U.S. Public*, pg. 515
Martin, Bill, Dir.-Admin.--Clayton-Marcus Company, Inc., Hickory, NC; *U.S. Public*, pg. 975
Martin, Carol, Mgr.-Adv.--Pubco Corporation, Cleveland, OH; *U.S. Public*, pg. 1339
Martin, Cindy, Mgr.-Adv.--F.E. Myers, Ashland, OH; *U.S. Public*, pg. 1273
Martin, Dale, Dir.-Mktg.--Mylan Laboratories, Inc., Pittsburgh, PA; *U.S. Public*, pg. 1143
Martin, David, Mgr.-Mktg. Services--Iveco-Ford Truck Ltd., Watford, United Kingdom; *Int'l*, pg. 484
Martin, Debbie, Mgr.-Adv.--Pathmark Stores Incorporated, Woodbridge, NJ; *U.S. Private*, pg. 843
Martin, E. J., Pres. & Gen. Mgr.--GKN Walterscheid Inc., Burr Ridge, IL; *Int'l*, pg. 536
Martin, Fred, Mgr.-Adv.--Glenwood Post, Glenwood Springs, CO; *U.S. Private*, pg. 995
Martin, James, Mgr.-Adv. & Sales Promo.--Wilson/Shore Instruments, Canton, MA; *U.S. Public*, pg. 883
Martin, Jim, Gen. Mgr.-Lubes--J.D. Streett & Co., Inc., Maryland Heights, MO; *U.S. Private*, pg. 1047
Martin, Joe, Dir.-Adv.--Delphi Energy & Engine Management Systems, Flint, MI; *U.S. Public*, pg. 719
Martin, John H., Mgr.-Adv.--Uniroyal Chemical Company, Inc., Middlebury, CT; *U.S. Public*, pg. 460
Martin, John R., Jr., V.P.-Corp. Rels. & Mktg.--CBL & Associates Properties, Inc., Chattanooga, TN; *U.S. Public*, pg. 273
Martin, Karen, Dir.-Adv.--Rich's/Lazarus/Goldsmith's, Atlanta, GA; *U.S. Public*, pg. 618
Martin, Keith, Dir.-Adv. & Admin.--Treadco, Inc., Fort Smith, AR; *U.S. Public*, pg. 131
Martin, Michael, Dir.-Mktg. & Adv.--Martin Door Mfg., Inc., Salt Lake City, UT; *U.S. Private*, pg. 708
Martin, Robert A., Exec. V.P.-Mktg.--Applebee's International, Inc., Overland Park, KS; *U.S. Public*, pg. 122
Martin, Robert P., III, Mgr.-Creative Services--Snap-Tite, Inc., Erie, PA; *U.S. Private*, pg. 1010
Martin, Roger, Dir.-Mktg. Svcs.--Winnebago Industries, Inc., Forest City, IA; *U.S. Public*, pg. 1772
Martin, Vincent L., Chm. Bd. & Chief Exec. Officer--Jason Incorporated, Milwaukee, WI; *U.S. Public*, pg. 923
Martinez, Jerome, V.P.-Mktg.--American Furniture Company, Albuquerque, NM; *U.S. Private*, pg. 55
Martinez, Maritza, Sr. Assoc.-Adv. Communications--Howmedica, Inc., Rutherford, NJ; *U.S. Public*, pg. 1282
Martino, Wayne, Adv.--Stanley Door Systems, Troy, MI; *U.S. Public*, pg. 1509
Martynski, John, Dir.-Adv.--Raley's & Bel Air, West Sacramento, CA; *U.S. Private*, pg. 907
Martynski, John, Dir.-Adv.--Bel Air Markets, West Sacramento, CA; *U.S. Private*, pg. 908
Marzotto, Stefano Festa, Mgr.-Adv.--Belfe S.p.A., Marostica, Italy; *Int'l*, pg. 185
Mas, Assumpta, Head-Adv.--Caixa d'Estalvis de Catalunya, Barcelona, Spain; *Int'l*, pg. 249
Maschio, Joseph, Sr. V.P.-Mktg.--Newspapers First, New York, NY; *U.S. Public*, pg. 964
Mashburn, Walter, V.P.-Sls.--Sterling Electric, Inc., Irvine, CA; *U.S. Private*, pg. 1041
Maslan, Brad, Mgr.-Mktg.--Ferrero U.S.A., Inc., Somerset, NJ; *Int'l*, pg. 480
Maslow, Lester, Chm. Bd. & Pres.--Best Manufacturing, Inc., New York, NY; *U.S. Private*, pg. 139
Mason, Frederick L., Mgr.-Corp. Communications--Providence Energy Corporation, Providence, RI; *U.S. Public*, pg. 1337
Mason, Julie, Sls. & Mktg. Coordinator--Belcan Corporation, Cincinnati, OH; *U.S. Private*, pg. 131
Mason, Linda, Dir.-Adv.--Gentlemen's Quarterly, New York, NY; *U.S. Private*, pg. 20
Mason, Tim, V.P.-Mktg. & Sls.--Bridon Cordage Inc., Albert Lea, MN; *Int'l*, pg. 215
Massaro, Teresa, Mgr.-Corp. Commun.--Western Gas Resources, Inc., Denver, CO; *U.S. Public*, pg. 1758
Massey, Kristin, Dir.-Mktg.--Jackson MSC, Nashville, TN; *U.S. Private*, pg. 579
Mastricge, Janet, Admin. Asst.-Communications--Rhone-Poulenc Inc., Princeton, NJ; *Int'l*, pg. 1112
Mathes, Diane, Mgr.-Mktg. Communications--Vactor Mfg. Inc., Streator, IL; *U.S. Public*, pg. 617
Mathes, Johm, Dir.-Adv. & Mktg.--New York Carpet World, Dalton, GA; *U.S. Public*, pg. 1464
Mathews, Colin, Mgr.-Adv.--Abbey National Plc, London, United Kingdom; *Int'l*, pg. 19
Matis, Julie, V.P. & Dir.-Adv.--Summit Bancorp, Princeton, NJ; *U.S. Public*, pg. 1527
Matles, Hal, V.P.-Mktg.--M.H. Rhodes, Inc., Avon, CT; *U.S. Private*, pg. 927
Matousek, Mark, Mgr.-Adv.--Aliant Communications Co., Lincoln, NE; *U.S. Public*, pg. 40
Matsch, Terri, Corp. Commun. & Pub. Rels.--Columbia Paint & Coatings, Spokane, WA; *U.S. Private*, pg. 256
Matson, Bill, Mgr.-Adv.--Younkers, Inc., Des Moines, IA; *U.S. Public*, pg. 1334
Matsumoto, Noboru, Pres.--Kobelco Stewart Bolling, Inc., Hudson, OH; *Int'l*, pg. 740
Matteo, Maxine, Exec. V.P.-Adv., Mktg. & Bus. Devel.--INMC Mortgage Holdings, Inc., Pasadena, CA; *U.S. Public*, pg. 857
Matter, John, V.P.-Sls. & Mktg.--Equitable Savings & Loan Association, Wauwatosa, WI; *U.S. Private*, pg. 380
Matteson, Raymond W., V.P.-New Bus. Devel.--USCS International, Inc., Rancho Cordova, CA; *U.S. Public*, pg. 1659
Matteson, Richard A., Dir.-Corp. Communications--Consumers Energy, Jackson, MI; *U.S. Public*, pg. 280
Matthews, Gerard, Dir.-Mktg.--Lander Co., Inc., Englewood, NJ; *U.S. Private*, pg. 647
Matthews, Mary, Supvr.-Mktg.--Market Data Retrieval, Shelton, CT; *U.S. Public*, pg. 536
Mattke, John, Dir.-Adv. & Mktg.--Cold Spring Granite Company, Cold Spring, MN; *U.S. Private*, pg. 250
Mattos, William J., Mgr.-Promo. Svcs.--Spirol International Corp., Danielson, CT; *U.S. Private*, pg. 1026
Matusik, Valerie, V.P.-Pub. Rels.--Kokosing Construction Company, Inc., Fredericktown, OH; *U.S. Private*, pg. 631
Maupin, Patrick, Sr. V.P.-Sls. & Mktg.--Jaydon Incorporated, Rock Island, IL; *U.S. Private*, pg. 584
Maury, Nicole F., Dir.-Corp. Communications--Fremont General Corporation, Santa Monica, CA; *U.S. Public*, pg. 681
Maus, Michael, Dir.-Commun.--American Bible Society, New York, NY; *U.S. Private*, pg. 51
Maxon, Jean, Dir.-Adv. & Mktg.--Technic Incorporated, Cranston, RI; *U.S. Private*, pg. 1071
Maxwell, Jayne, Dir.-Adv.--Value Priced Clothing Inc., Culver City, CA; *U.S. Public*, pg. 1086
Maxwell, Nancy, Adv. Dir.--Crown Books Corporation, Landover, MD; *U.S. Public*, pg. 484
May, Hilary, Mgr.-Mktg. Svcs., Adv. & Pub. Rels.--Atalanta Corporation, Elizabeth, NJ; *U.S. Private*, pg. 93
May, Karen, Mgr.-Mktg., Automotive Aftermarket--Robertshaw Tennessee, Knoxville, TN; *Int'l*, pg. 1243
Mayer, Len, Pres.--Mayer & Schweitzer, Inc., Jersey City, NJ; *U.S. Public*, pg. 1443
Mays, Linda S., Mgr.-Customer Services--Copes-Vulcan Inc., Lake City, PA; *U.S. Private*, pg. 274
Mays, Stan, Dir.-Corp. Adv.--The Coastal Corporation, Houston, TX; *U.S. Public*, pg. 389
Mays, Stan, Dir.-Corp. Adv.--Coastal Refining & Marketing, Wichita, KS; *U.S. Public*, pg. 390
Mazin, Rafael, Dir.-Mktg. Services & External Rels.--Procter & Gamble Espana S.A., Madrid, Spain; *U.S. Public*, pg. 1332
Mazur, Jack, V.P.-Sls. & Mktg.--Johnstown Corporation, Johnstown, PA; *U.S. Private*, pg. 595
McAffee, Russ, Dir.-Adv.--Team, Inc., Alvin, TX; *U.S. Public*, pg. 1562
McAlear, Ronald J., V.P.-Adv. Programs & Mktg.--Avondale Industries, Inc., Avondale, LA; *U.S. Public*, pg. 156
McAlister, Linda, Dir.-Marcom--Western Staff Services, Walnut Creek, CA; *U.S. Public*, pg. 1760
McAndrew, Thomas J., Mgr.-Mktg.--Rodney Hunt Company, Orange, MA; *U.S. Private*, pg. 549
McArthur, Lynne, Mgr.-Corp. Devel.--BFC Construction Corporation, Scarborough, Canada; *Int'l*, pg. 118
McAvoy, Dale, Mgr.-Adv., Sls. & Mktg.-Flow Controls--Raven Industries, Inc., Sioux Falls, SD; *U.S. Public*, pg. 1361
McCabe, Brian, Mgr.-Market Devel.--Northwest Natural Gas Company, Portland, OR; *U.S. Public*, pg. 1200
McCabe, Nancy, Adv. Admin.--The TJX Companies, Inc., Framingham, MA; *U.S. Public*, pg. 1556
McCabe, R.T., Dir.-Mktg.--Interplastic Corp., Saint Paul, MN; *U.S. Private*, pg. 572
McCain, Kate, Mgr.-Adv. & Pub. Rels.--Doron Precision Systems, Inc., Binghamton, NY; *U.S. Private*, pg. 341
McCall, Carolyn, Dir.-Adv.--Guardian & Observer, London, United Kingdom; *Int'l*, pg. 577
McCall, Carolyn, Dir.-Bus. Communications--Olin Microelectronic Materials, Inc., Norwalk, CT; *U.S. Public*, pg. 1219
McCall, Claire, Dir.-Corp. Rels.--Genesco Inc., Nashville, TN; *U.S. Public*, pg. 728
McCarrick, Edward, Dir.-Adv. Sls.--Time, New York, NY; *U.S. Public*, pg. 1613
McCarthy, Bill, Exec. V.P.-Sls.--Risdon Corporation, Naugatuck, CT; *U.S. Public*, pg. 463
McCarthy, C. James, Pres.--Reily Foods Company, New Orleans, LA; *U.S. Private*, pg. 919
McCarty, Geoff, V.P.-Adv.--Hechinger Company Investors II, L.P., Largo, MD; *U.S. Private*, pg. 477
McCleary-La France, Kim, Dir.-Adv. & Customer Service--Los Angeles Times, Los Angeles, CA; *U.S. Public*, pg. 1616
McClelland, John, Corp. V.P.-Consumer Sls.--Scott Paper Limited, Mississauga, Canada; *Int'l*, pg. 762
McClelland, W. Allen, Mgr.-Mktg. Services & Adv.--Dayton Superior Corporation, Miamisburg, OH; *U.S. Private*, pg. 931
McClinton, Raymond, V.P.-Mktg.--Communications Instruments Inc., Fairview, NC; *U.S. Private*, pg. 259
McCluney, Nancy, Adv. Dir. Communications--The Check Store, Lakewood, CO; *U.S. Public*, pg. 785

McClure, Christine, Dir.-Brand Adv.-Consumer Bus. Office--Motorola, Inc., Schaumburg, IL; *U.S. Public*, pg. 1136
McCluskey, Richard T., Chm. Bd., Pres. & Chief Exec. Officer--Fiske Brothers Refining Company, Newark, NJ; *U.S. Private*, pg. 408
McCollum, Bruce, Exec. V.P.-Adv., Mktg. & Sls.--Tingley Rubber Corporation, South Plainfield, NJ; *U.S. Private*, pg. 1088
McConnell, Jim, Mgr.-Natl. Sls.--Rogers N.K. Seed Co., Boise, ID; *Int'l*, pg. 974
McCook-Wilson, Ferrell, Mgr.-Adv.--Martin Industries, Inc. (AL), Florence, AL; *U.S. Private*, pg. 709
McCord, R.L., Mgr.-Sls.--American Welding & Manufacturing Co., Warren, OH; *U.S. Private*, pg. 425
McCormick, Al, Mgr.-Adv.--Ford Motor Co. of Canada Ltd, Oakville, Canada; *U.S. Public*, pg. 666
McCormick, Greg, V.P.-Mktg.--Storck U.S.A., L.P., Chicago, IL; *Int'l*, pg. 1304
McCormick, Marcia E., Mktg. & Office Admin.--Williams, White & Co., Moline, IL; *U.S. Private*, pg. 1179
McCormick, Tom, Sec.--Kimray, Inc., Oklahoma City, OK; *U.S. Private*, pg. 620
McCoubrey, A.J., Mgr.-Adv.--Gorman-Rupp of Canada Ltd., Saint Thomas, Canada; *U.S. Public*, pg. 754
McCourt, Robert D., Sr. Dir.-Mktg. & Creative Services--American International Group, Inc., New York, NY; *U.S. Public*, pg. 83
McCray, Robert, Dir.-Adv.--PG Publishing Co., Pittsburgh, PA; *U.S. Private*, pg. 147
McCreary, Robert, Dir.-Adv.--Tighe Industries, Inc., York, PA; *U.S. Private*, pg. 1086
McCue, Michael, Mgr.-Adv.--The L.S. Starrett Company, Athol, MA; *U.S. Public*, pg. 1511
McCully, Duncan J., V.P.-Special Risks--Commercial Travelers Mutual Insurance Company, Utica, NY; *U.S. Private*, pg. 258
McCurdy, Jill, V.P.-Prod. Devel. & Mktg.--Koss Corporation, Milwaukee, WI; *U.S. Public*, pg. 966
McCutchen, Pete, Dir.-Adv.--Nation's Business, Washington, DC; *U.S. Private*, pg. 788
McDermott, Christine, Mgr.-Adv.--Xerox Corporation, Stamford, CT; *U.S. Public*, pg. 1783
McDevitt, Michelle, Coord.-Adv.--Aamco Transmissions, Inc., Bala Cynwyd, PA; *U.S. Private*, pg. 9
McDonagh, Jim, V.P.-Sls. & Mktg.--Riker Products, Inc., Toledo, OH; *U.S. Private*, pg. 300
McDonald, Dan, Sr. Dir.-Adv.--Michaels Stores, Inc., Irving, TX; *U.S. Public*, pg. 1104
McDonald, L. Terry, Sr. V.P.-Mktg.--ShopKo Stores, Inc., Green Bay, WI; *U.S. Public*, pg. 1467
McDonald, Rene, V.P.--Pharmacists Public Relations Bureau, Wichita, KS; *U.S. Private*, pg. 295
McDonough, H.R., Dir.-Adv.--E.C. Barton & Company, Jonesboro, AR; *U.S. Private*, pg. 119
McDonough, John, V.P.-Mktg. & Broadcasting--Chicago National League Ball Club, Inc. (Chicago Cubs), Chicago, IL; *U.S. Public*, pg. 1635
McDonough, Riley, Publr.--The Goldhirsh Group, Boston, MA; *U.S. Private*, pg. 461
McDougall, Sandy, Mgr.-Mktg. Sls. & Adv.--Air BC, Richmond, Canada; *Int'l*, pg. 36
McDowell, Jerry, Mgr.-Pub. Rels.--Objective Systems Integrators, Inc., Folsom, CA; *U.S. Public*, pg. 1209
McEnaney, Dennis H., Mgr.-Adv. & Sls. Promo.--Muro Pharmaceutical, Inc., Tewksbury, MA; *U.S. Private*, pg. 767
McFadden, Jean Marie, Mgr.-Adv.--Morgan Stanley & Co. Incorporated, New York, NY; *U.S. Public*, pg. 1132
McFadden, P.D., V.P.-Adv. Tech. & Engrng.--The Gates Rubber Company, Denver, CO; *Int'l*, pg. 1396
McFall, Michael, Asst. Dir.-Mdsg., Adv. & Communications--General Motors Acceptance Corporation (GMAC), Detroit, MI; *U.S. Public*, pg. 719
McFee, Susanne, Mgr.-Adv.--Lettuce Entertain You Enterprises, Inc., Chicago, IL; *U.S. Private*, pg. 661
McGee, Charlotte, Dir.-Adv.--Kinko's Corporation, Ventura, CA; *U.S. Private*, pg. 622
McGee, J. Brad, V.P.-Tyco Specialty Prods.--Ludlow Corporation, Exeter, NH; *U.S. Public*, pg. 1651
McGinley, Jennifer, Mgr.-Adv. Production--Angelo Brothers Co., Philadelphia, PA; *U.S. Private*, pg. 74
McGivern, Daniel M., Dir.-Mktg.--DOALL Company, Des Plaines, IL; *U.S. Private*, pg. 337
McGovern, Tom, Mgr.-Adv.--Hornady Manufacturing Company, Grand Island, NE; *U.S. Private*, pg. 539
McGowan, Bret, Dir.-Mktg. & Adv.--Vicon Industries, Inc., Hauppauge, NY; *U.S. Public*, pg. 1719
McGowan, Michael, Mgr.-Corp. Adv.--Benjamin Moore & Co., Montvale, NJ; *U.S. Private*, pg. 133
McGowen-Carnes, Kathy, Dir.-Mktg.--Advertising Display Co., Englewood Cliffs, NJ; *U.S. Private*, pg. 23
McGowen, Jordan, Mgr.-Adv. & Dealer Support--Reinke Manufacturing Co., Inc., Deshler, NE; *U.S. Private*, pg. 920
McGrady, Steve, Dir.-Intl. Mktg.--SpeedFan International, Inc., Chandler, AZ; *U.S. Public*, pg. 1497
McGrath, Patti, Mgr.-Adv., Men's Wear--Pendleton Woolen Mills, Inc., Portland, OR; *U.S. Private*, pg. 848
McGraw, Gregory P., V.P.-Sls. & Mktg.--TIE/Communications, Inc., Overland Park, KS; *U.S. Private*, pg. 1085
McGuigan, James A., Mgr.-Communications--Acheson Colloids Company, Port Huron, MI; *U.S. Private*, pg. 12
McHie, Stewart, Coord.-Adv. & Promo.--Exxon Company, U.S.A., Houston, TX; *U.S. Public*, pg. 601
McIlguham, David, V.P.-Mktg.--Sealy Mattress Company of Memphis, Memphis, TN; *U.S. Private*, pg. 979
McIlquham, David J., V.P.-Mktg.--Sealy Corporation, Cleveland, OH; *U.S. Private*, pg. 978
McIngvale, Jim, Dir.-Pub. Affairs & Adv.--Ingalls Shipbuilding, Pascagoula, MS; *U.S. Public*, pg. 1003
McIntire, Donald, Dir.-Adv.--American Tissue Mills of Greenwich, Middle Falls, NY; *U.S. Private*, pg. 63
McIntosh, Dorothy, Dir.-Adv.--Juki Union Special, Inc., Wayne, NJ; *Int'l*, pg. 716
McIntosh, Larry, V.P.-Adv.--Smartfoods, Inc., Plano, TX; *U.S. Public*, pg. 1277
McIntosh, Lawrence T., V.P.-Adv.--Frito-Lay Company, Plano, TX; *U.S. Public*, pg. 1277
McIntosh, Richard S., V.P.-Mktg.--Univex Corporation, Salem, NH; *U.S. Private*, pg. 1128
McIntosh, Ron, Dir.-Adv.--Petro-Canada, Calgary, Canada; *Int'l*, pg. 1041
McIntyre, Ann, Dir.-Adv.--Foster & Gallagher, Inc., Peoria, IL; *U.S. Private*, pg. 420
McIntyre, Ann, Dir.-Adv.--Spring Hill Nurseries Co., Peoria, IL; *U.S. Private*, pg. 420
McKeague, Marsha A., Mgr.-Woodlands--Great Northern Paper, Inc., Millinocket, ME; *U.S. Public*, pg. 248
McKeague, Meg, Art Dir.--Juno Lighting, Inc., Des Plaines, IL; *U.S. Public*, pg. 935
McKellar, Jann, Mgr.-Adv.--Spartan Stores Inc., Grand Rapids, MI; *U.S. Private*, pg. 1021
McKelvie, John, Dir.-Mktg.--Inductotherm Corp., Rancocas, NJ; *U.S. Private*, pg. 560
McKenna, Christine, Exec. V.P.-Mktg. & Adv.--Plasti-Kote Company Inc., Medina, OH; *U.S. Private*, pg. 870
McKenna, Kathy, Adv. Consultant--New Century Energies, Inc., Denver, CO; *U.S. Public*, pg. 1170
McKenna, Lore, Mgr.-Natl. Adv. & Pub. Rels.--American Suzuki Motor Corporation, Brea, CA; *Int'l*, pg. 1323
McKenna, Thomas G., V.P. & Dir.-Adv. & Brand Mngmt.--Mellon Bank Corporation, Pittsburgh, PA; *U.S. Public*, pg. 1084
McKenney, J.K., Pres.--The Figaro Company, Inc., Mesquite, TX; *U.S. Private*, pg. 404
McKenzie, C., V.P.-Adv.--SEIKO Corporation of America, Mahwah, NJ; *Int'l*, pg. 1218
McKenzie, Jay, Dir.-Adv.--AutoWeek, Detroit, MI; *U.S. Private*, pg. 284
McKenzie, Mary Alice, Pres.--McKenzies of Vermont, Inc., Burlington, VT; *U.S. Private*, pg. 723
McKeown, Patrick, V.P.-Mktg.--Christy's Markets, Inc., Brockton, MA; *U.S. Private*, pg. 238
McKinney, Dennis, Dir.-Adv.--Hy-Vee Food Stores Incorporated, West Des Moines, IA; *U.S. Private*, pg. 550
McKinniss, Sherman L., Chm. Bd., Pres. & Chief Exec. Officer--Rotonics Manufacturing Inc., Gardena, CA; *U.S. Public*, pg. 1406
McKinnon, A., Mgr.-Adv.--Ford Parts and Service Div., Dearborn, MI; *U.S. Public*, pg. 662
McKinnon, Tony, Gen. Mgr.-Sls.--The Howden Fan Co., Buffalo, NY; *U.S. Private*, pg. 543
McKnight, Ron, Exec. V.P.-Adv.--Franz Bakery, Portland, OR; *U.S. Private*, pg. 1124
McLachlan, Angela D., Corp. Dir.-Communications & Pub. Affairs--LaRoche Industries Inc., Atlanta, GA; *U.S. Private*, pg. 651
McLean, Jim, Project Leader--Parks LLC, Baltimore, MD; *U.S. Private*, pg. 840
McLeish, Charles H., Dir.-Mktg. Services--LEGO Systems, Inc., Enfield, CT; *Int'l*, pg. 805
McMahon, Sheldon, Grp. Mgr.-Mktg. Commun.--Nordson Corporation, Westlake, OH; *U.S. Public*, pg. 1188
McManimon, Thomas, Mng. Partner & Creative Dir.--Gillespie, Lawrenceville, NJ; *U.S. Private*, pg. 453
McManus, James A., Dir.-Grp. Adv.--Toronto Star Newspapers Ltd., Toronto, Canada; *Int'l*, pg. 1402
McManus, Joni, Mgr.-Adv.--Paychex, Inc., Rochester, NY; *U.S. Public*, pg. 1267
McMillan, Kevin, Dir.-Adv.--Sonic Corporation, Oklahoma City, OK; *U.S. Public*, pg. 1485
McMillan, Richard L., Mgr.-Adv.--Knoxville News-Sentinel Company, Knoxville, TN; *U.S. Public*, pg. 1448
McMillan, Robert, Brand Process Leader--The Progressive Corporation, Cleveland, OH; *U.S. Public*, pg. 1334
McMurray, Margot, Dir.-Adv.--Silver-Weibull, Aurora, CO; *U.S. Public*, pg. 705
McNabb, Cynthia, Mgr.-Product Adv.--Advanced Micro Devices, Inc., Sunnyvale, CA; *U.S. Public*, pg. 21
McNeil, John, Mgr.-Retail Adv.--Trend-Lines Inc., Revere, MA; *U.S. Private*, pg. 1099
McNeill, Michael, Pres. & Chief Exec. Officer--Gifford-Hill Company, Dallas, TX; *Int'l*, pg. 593
McNett, Laurence W., Mgr.-Adv.--Gardner Denver Machinery Inc., Quincy, IL; *U.S. Public*, pg. 703
McNett, Mike, Mgr.-Adv. Food Service--Tyson Foods, Inc., Springdale, AR; *U.S. Public*, pg. 1652
McNulty, Tom, V.P.-Mktg. & Adv.--Super 8 Motels, Inc., Aberdeen, SD; *U.S. Public*, pg. 322
McNutt, David, Mng. Dir.-Communications--Electro-Voice, Inc., Buchanan, MI; *U.S. Private*, pg. 479
McNutt, James, Mgr.-Adv.--Bryant Grinder Corp., Springfield, VT; *U.S. Private*, pg. 461
McOllough, Jeff, Mgr.-Adv., Sls., & Mktg.--Hagie Manufacturing Co., Clarion, IA; *U.S. Private*, pg. 493
McPhedrain, Larry L., Exec. V.P.-Opers.--Mary Maxim, Inc., Port Huron, MI; *U.S. Private*, pg. 716
McQueen, Edwin D., V.P.-Sls. & Mktg.--Steelox Systems Inc., Mason, OH; *U.S. Private*, pg. 1038
McSpadden, Dan, Dir.-Mktg.--Citrus World Inc., Lake Wales, FL; *U.S. Private*, pg. 241
McStay, William J., Sr. V.P.-Mktg. Communication--Jiffy Lube International, Inc., Houston, TX; *U.S. Public*, pg. 1272
McVeigh, Rick, Mgr.-Adv.--Shelter Mutual Insurance Company, Columbia, MO; *U.S. Private*, pg. 992
Mead, Larry, Dir.-Adv.--Esco Elevator Corp., Fort Worth, TX; *U.S. Private*, pg. 383
Mead, Suzanne, V.P.-Corp. Communications--Rite Aid Corporation, Camp Hill, PA; *U.S. Public*, pg. 1390
Mead, Thom, V.P.-Mktg.--Affiliated Computer Services, Inc., Dallas, TX; *U.S. Public*, pg. 27
Meade, David C., Chief Exec. Officer & Mgr.-Adv.--The Journal, Williamston, SC; *U.S. Private*, pg. 601
Means, Elizabeth, V.P.-Credit Card Adv.--Citibank N.A., Long Island City, NY; *U.S. Public*, pg. 377
Means, Jeannie, Mgr.-Adv.--Beckett Papers, East Granby, CT; *U.S. Public*, pg. 903
Mear, Christine, Coord.-Sls. Promo. & Sls. Admin.--Eversharp Pen Co., Franklin Park, IL; *U.S. Private*, pg. 386
Meddock, Larry, V.P.-Mktg.--Correct Craft, Inc., Orlando, FL; *U.S. Private*, pg. 276
Medund, Peter, Mgr.-Adv. New York--Cosmopolitan, New York, NY; *U.S. Private*, pg. 517
Meehan, Terry, V.P.-Mktg.--Periphonics Corp., Bohemia, NY; *U.S. Public*, pg. 1278
Meeker, Deborah, Mgr.-Adv.--Fechheimer Bros. Co., Cincinnati, OH; *U.S. Public*, pg. 217
Megling, Rita, Dir.-Mktg.--Marshall Industries, El Monte, CA; *U.S. Public*, pg. 1051
Mehrhof, Ken, Adv. & Pub. Rels. Consultant--Kathabar Incorporated, Somerset, NJ; *U.S. Private*, pg. 609
Meier, Norman M., Pres. & Chief Exec. Officer--Columbia Laboratories, Inc., Miami, FL; *U.S. Public*, pg. 405
Meier, Torsten, Dir.-Corp. Controlling--Continental AG, Hannover, Germany; *Int'l*, pg. 327
Meiers, Michele, Dir.-Adv.--The Pep Boys-Manny, Moe & Jack, Philadelphia, PA; *U.S. Public*, pg. 1276
Meijer-Jentink, N.L.H., Mgr.-Adv. & Sls. Promo.--Delft Instruments N.V., Delft, Netherlands; *Int'l*, pg. 388
Meilinger, Joe, V.P.-Mktg.--Monfort, Inc., Greeley, CO; *U.S. Public*, pg. 427
Meinel, William, V.P.-Adv.--Aramark Corp., Philadelphia, PA; *U.S. Private*, pg. 78
Meister, Eileen, Mgr.-Adv.--Patch Communications, Titusville, FL; *U.S. Private*, pg. 842
Melbourne, Dave, Dir.-Mktg.--Castleberry/Snow's Brands Inc., Augusta, GA; *U.S. Private*, pg. 219
Melcuit, Melanie, Graphic Artist--Pullman/Holt Corp., Tampa, FL; *U.S. Private*, pg. 1173
Melillo, John, Mgr.-Adv. & Media Services--Jersey Central Power & Light Co., Morristown, NJ; *U.S. Public*, pg. 695
Melillo, John, Mgr.-Adv. & Media/Reading--GPU Energy, Johnstown, PA; *U.S. Public*, pg. 695
Mell, Roberta, V.P.-Adv.--Home Box Office, Inc., New York, NY; *U.S. Public*, pg. 1612
Mellinger, Sandy, Mgr.-Retail Adv.-ServiStar--TruServ Corporation, Chicago, IL; *U.S. Private*, pg. 1108
Melnick, Dana, Dir.-Creative--Pentech International, Inc., Edison, NJ; *U.S. Public*, pg. 1274
Melum, Susan, Dir.-Mktg. Communications--Lanier Worldwide Inc., Atlanta, GA; *U.S. Public*, pg. 791
Melvin, Susan, Dir.-Corp. Adv.--ITT Sheraton Corporation, Boston, MA; *U.S. Public*, pg. 1512
Melwid, David, Dir.-Sls. & Mktg.--PTS Electronics Corporation, Bloomington, IN; *U.S. Private*, pg. 828
Menard, Guy, Mgr.-Mktg.--Alcan Aluminium Limited, Montreal, Canada; *Int'l*, pg. 50
Mendoza, Judy, Sr. V.P.-Mktg. & Sls. Promo.--Bergdorf Goodman, New York, NY; *U.S. Public*, pg. 785
Menozzi, Alberto, Mgr.-Adv. & Exhibition--Agusta S.P.A., Varese, Italy; *Int'l*, pg. 32
Meola, Peter, V.P.-Mktg. & Sls.--Castrol North America, Wayne, NJ; *Int'l*, pg. 235
Meranda, Tim, Mgr.-Mktg., Sls. & Adv.--HCC Inc., Mendota, IL; *U.S. Private*, pg. 490
Merandi, Jane, Sec.--Alamco, Inc., Charleston, WV; *U.S. Public*, pg. 403
Mercer, Howard R., Dir.-Pub. Rels. & Adv.--Griffon Corp., Jericho, NY; *U.S. Public*, pg. 766
Mercier, Maureen, Mgr.- Adv. & Sls. Promo.--LFE Instruments, Chesterland, OH; *U.S. Public*, pg. 482
Meredith, Edie L., Exec. Asst.--Steel Technologies Inc., Louisville, KY; *U.S. Public*, pg. 1513
Merrell, F.Max, Pres.--Mobil Mining & Minerals Company, Ashland, VA; *U.S. Public*, pg. 1118
Merrell, Gary D., V.P.-Adv.--The Dispatch Printing Company, Columbus, OH; *U.S. Private*, pg. 334
Merry, Carol, Dir.-Corp. & Shareholder Commun.--Lexford Residential Trust, Columbus, OH; *U.S. Public*, pg. 991
Meschkow, Alan, Dir.- Adv.--P.C. Richard & Son, Farmingdale, NY; *U.S. Private*, pg. 928
Meskell, Kevin M., V.P. & Sec.--Quincy Mutual Fire Insurance Company, Quincy, MA; *U.S. Private*, pg. 901
Messmer, Peter J., Dir.-Mktg. & Adv.--Liqui-Box Corporation, Worthington, OH; *U.S. Public*, pg. 1000
Metcalfe, Jeremy W., Pres. & Chief Exec. Officer--Millicom International Cellular SA, Bertrange, Luxembourg; *Int'l*, pg. 867
Metzner, Richard, V.P.-Mktg. Programs--Continental Airlines, Houston, TX; *U.S. Public*, pg. 439
Meyer, Craig, Mgr.-Adv.--Cooper Automotive Division, Chesterfield, MO; *U.S. Public*, pg. 443
Meyer, Doug, V.P.-Mktg. & Adv.--Syms Corporation, Secaucus, NJ; *U.S. Public*, pg. 1547
Meyer, Douglas, V.P.-Mktg.--Miles Kimball Company, Oshkosh, WI; *U.S. Private*, pg. 745
Meyer, Geoffrey E., Dir.-Adv. Sls.--Barron's The Dow Jones Business & Financial Weekly, New York, NY; *U.S. Public*, pg. 524
Meyer, Madame, Dir.-Communications--JS Telecommunications S.A., Louveciennes, France; *Int'l*, pg. 706
Meyer, Tom, Mgr.-Adv.--Warner Electric Industrial Products Division, South Beloit, IL; *U.S. Public*, pg. 480
Meyer, Virginia, V.P.-Adv. & Sls. Promo.--The Cato Corporation, Charlotte, NC; *U.S. Public*, pg. 318
Meyerriecks, Laurie, Coord.-Adv.--Rockbottom Stores, Inc., Lake Success, NY; *U.S. Private*, pg. 938
Meyers, Mike, Mgr.-Adv. & Sls. Promo.--Elgin Sweeper Company, Elgin, IL; *U.S. Public*, pg. 617
Meyers, Mindy, Mgr.-Adv. & Media--DePuy, Inc., Warsaw, IN; *Int'l*, pg. 331
Meyers, Robert S., V.P.-Corp. Communications & Investor Rels.--Scientific-Atlanta, Inc., Norcross, GA; *U.S. Public*, pg. 1443
Meyers, Vicki, Dir.-Adv.--Best Western International, Inc., Phoenix, AZ; *U.S. Private*, pg. 140

Miano, Denise, Mgr.-Adv.--Medicine Shoppe International, Inc., Saint Louis, MO; *U.S. Public*, pg. 304
Micha, Emil, V.P.-Design--Sotheby's Inc., New York, NY; *U.S. Public*, pg. 1487
Michaels, Becky, Mgr.-Adv.--Little, Brown & Co., New York, NY; *U.S. Public*, pg. 1612
Michalak, Elaine, Mgr.-Adv.--American Electric Power Company, Inc., Columbus, OH; *U.S. Public*, pg. 71
Michalowski, Paul, V.P.-Mdse. & Adv.--Distribution America, Des Plaines, IL; *U.S. Private*, pg. 335
Michel, Charles, Mgr.-H.R.--Southern Ohio Fabricators, Inc., Batavia, OH; *U.S. Private*, pg. 1017
Michele, Cherie, Mgr.-Adv.--Paramount Fitness Corp., Los Angeles, CA; *U.S. Private*, pg. 838
Mickels, Diane, Mgr.-Adv. & Sls. Promo--Ideal Industries, Inc., Sycamore, IL; *U.S. Private*, pg. 557
Mickle, J. Douglas, Dir.-Adv. & Mktg. Services--Reynolds Metals Co., Consumer Products Div., Richmond, VA; *U.S. Public*, pg. 1386
Middleton, Susan A., V.P.-Mktg.--Brothers Gourmet Coffees, Inc., Boca Raton, FL; *U.S. Public*, pg. 259
Miellen, Richard, Dir.-Mktg. & Adv.--MFG Union City Operations, Union City, PA; *U.S. Private*, pg. 756
Mignini, Kathy, Sr. Product Mgr.-Life-Like--Life-Like Products, Inc., Baltimore, MD; *U.S. Private*, pg. 666
Mika, John J., V.P.-Corp. Affairs--Santa Fe International Corporation, Dallas, TX; *Int'l*, pg. 765
Mikkelsen, Alice, Mgr.-Adv. & Mktg.--Schumacher Electric Corporation, Mount Prospect, IL; *U.S. Private*, pg. 973
Milanello, Angelo, Mgr.-Fin. & Mktg.--Belfe S.p.A., Marostica, Italy; *Int'l*, pg. 185
Miles, Ana, Asst. V.P.-Mktg.--BankAtlantic Bancorp, Inc., Fort Lauderdale, FL; *U.S. Public*, pg. 183
Milford, John, Dir.-Adv.--Georgia-Bonded Fibers, Inc., Newark, NJ; *U.S. Public*, pg. 734
Milhem, Janice, Mgr.-Mktg.--American Speedy Printing Centers, Inc., Troy, MI; *U.S. Private*, pg. 62
Millard, James J., Sr. Assoc.-Adv.--Bayer Corporation/ Pharmaceutical Division, West Haven, CT; *Int'l*, pg. 173
Millard, Peter, V.P.-Adv.--Psychology Today, New York, NY; *U.S. Private*, pg. 1056
Miller, Bill, Mgr.-Category--United Dairy Farmers, Inc., Cincinnati, OH; *U.S. Private*, pg. 1121
Miller, Bruce, V.P.-Mktg. & Sls.--E.A. Miller Company, Hyrum, UT; *U.S. Public*, pg. 428
Miller, David, Exec. V.P.--Hask Toiletries, Great Neck, NY; *U.S. Private*, pg. 509
Miller, David, Corp. Communications & Pub. Rels.--Etec Systems, Inc., Hayward, CA; *U.S. Public*, pg. 594
Miller, David, V.P.-Adv. & Mktg.--Multi-Local Media Corporation, Rockville Centre, NY; *U.S. Private*, pg. 767
Miller, David, Dir.-Adv.--Universal Studios Hollywood, Universal City, CA; *Int'l*, pg. 1216
Miller, Elaine, Mgr.-Adv.--United States Bakery, Portland, OR; *U.S. Private*, pg. 1124
Miller, Hank, Mgr.-Graphic arts--Intermatic Inc., Spring Grove, IL; *U.S. Private*, pg. 567
Miller, Jeff, V.P.-Sls. & Mktg.--Gilbert Paper, Menasha, WI; *U.S. Public*, pg. 1074
Miller, Ken, Pres.--Young Stuff Apparel Group, Inc., New York, NY; *U.S. Private*, pg. 1202
Miller, Kent, Dir.-Commun.--Farmway Co-Op Inc., Beloit, KS; *U.S. Private*, pg. 396
Miller, Larry, Dir.-Opers.--Ranch-Way Feed Inc., Fort Collins, CO; *U.S. Private*, pg. 908
Miller, Larry, Dir.-Adv.--Glencoe/Mc-Graw Hill, Westerville, OH; *U.S. Public*, pg. 1070
Miller, Larry, Div. Controller-Adv.--Toronto Star Newspapers Ltd., Toronto, Canada; *Int'l*, pg. 1402
Miller, Lloyd, Pres.--American Laubscher Corp., Farmingdale, NY; *U.S. Private*, pg. 58
Miller, Mark, Mgr.-Adv.--Matson Navigation Company, Inc., San Francisco, CA; *U.S. Public*, pg. 39
Miller, Mark, Mgr.-Adv.--Hiniker Company, Mankato, MN; *U.S. Private*, pg. 530
Miller, Mark, V.P.-Adv. Sls.--CNBC, Fort Lee, NJ; *U.S. Public*, pg. 712
Miller, Mary Ellen, Mgr.-Natl. Adv.--The Saturn Corporation, Troy, MI; *U.S. Public*, pg. 721
Miller, Michelle, Coord.-Adv. Svcs.--Appleton Electric Co., Chicago, IL; *U.S. Public*, pg. 572
Miller, Nadine, Mgr.-Pub. Rels.--Land O'Lakes, Inc., Kiel, WI; *U.S. Private*, pg. 646
Miller, Peter, Sr. V.P.-Adv.--Weider Publications, Inc., Woodland Hills, CA; *U.S. Private*, pg. 1159
Miller, R.S., Mgr.-Mktg.--Osmonics, Inc., Minnetonka, MN; *U.S. Public*, pg. 1233
Miller, Rudy, Mgr.-Corp. Adv.--Southwest Gas Corporation, Las Vegas, NV; *U.S. Public*, pg. 1493
Miller, San, V.P. & Classified Supvr.--Miller Advertising Agency Inc., New York, NY; *U.S. Private*, pg. 746
Miller, Sharon, Coord.-Adv.--Eddie Bauer, Inc., Redmond, WA; *U.S. Public*, pg. 1499
Miller, Tim, Natl. Sls. Mgr.-Fertilizer--Dempster Industries Inc., Beatrice, NE; *U.S. Private*, pg. 324
Miller, Wayne, V.P.-Mktg. & Sls.--Micron Separations, Inc., Westborough, MA; *U.S. Private*, pg. 742
Miller, William, Mgr.-Adv.--Reed Tool Company, Houston, TX; *U.S. Public*, pg. 298
Mills, Angela, Mgr.-Communications--American Rehability Services, Inc., Brentwood, TN; *U.S. Public*, pg. 1257
Mills, David W., V.P.-Sls. & Adv.--PETsMART, Inc., Phoenix, AZ; *U.S. Public*, pg. 1281
Mills, Howard, Mgr.-Adv.--Thermon Manufacturing Company, San Marcos, TX; *U.S. Private*, pg. 1080
Mills, Lisa, Sr. Asst.-Adv.--Zale Corporation, Irving, TX; *U.S. Public*, pg. 1789
Mills, Valerie, Asst. Dir.-Mktg.--Eateries, Inc., Oklahoma City, OK; *U.S. Public*, pg. 555
Minasi, Michael, V.P.-Adv.--Safeway Inc., Pleasanton, CA; *U.S. Public*, pg. 1426
Minor, Bill, V.P.-Mktg.--Ohio Casualty Corporation, Hamilton, OH; *U.S. Public*, pg. 1214
Minor, Bill, V.P.-Mktg.--The Ohio Casualty Insurance Group, Hamilton, OH; *U.S. Public*, pg. 1214
Mintzer, Elliot, Mgr.-Mktg. Svcs.--Tork, Inc., Mount Vernon, NY; *U.S. Private*, pg. 1092
Miraglio, Laura, Mgr.-Mktg. Communications--Aetrium Inc., Saint Paul, MN; *U.S. Public*, pg. 27
Mireles, Karen, Mgr.-Creative Adv.--Builders Square, Inc., San Antonio, TX; *U.S. Private*, pg. 477
Mirkiti, Gary, Dir.-Adv.--The Goldhirsh Group, Boston, MA; *U.S. Private*, pg. 461
Mitch, Warren, Mgr.-Inside Sls.--Bel Fuse Inc., Jersey City, NJ; *U.S. Public*, pg. 200
Mitchell-King, Peggy, V.P.-U.S. Adv.--American Express Company, New York, NY; *U.S. Public*, pg. 73
Mitchell, Dawn, Mgr.-Corp. Commun.--Canadian Pacific Limited, Calgary, Canada; *Int'l*, pg. 258
Mitchell, Holly, Mgr.-Media & Adv. Bus.--MCI Communications Corp., Atlanta, GA; *U.S. Public*, pg. 1023
Mitchell, Jim, Dir.-Mktg.--The NutraSweet Company, Deerfield, IL; *U.S. Public*, pg. 1125
Mitchell, John, Mgr.-Adv.--Nichols-Homeshield, Davenport, IA; *U.S. Public*, pg. 1350
Mitchell, Judy, Dir.-Adv. & Mktg.--Right Start, Inc., Westlake Village, CA; *U.S. Private*, pg. 930
Mitchell, William, Mgr.-Sls. & Services--Suntec Industries Inc., Rockford, IL; *U.S. Private*, pg. 1054
Mitchusson, Bob, Dir.-Adv.--Affiliated Foods, Inc., Amarillo, TX; *U.S. Private*, pg. 25
Mittleman, Ileene, V.P.-Adv. & Creative Services--CBS Television Network, New York, NY; *U.S. Public*, pg. 274
Mizrahi, Jill, Mgr.-Adv--Arrow Electronics, Inc., Melville, NY; *U.S. Public*, pg. 133
Mochiziuki, M., Mgr.-Adv.--Mitsubishi Electric Corporation, Tokyo, Japan; *Int'l*, pg. 872
Moffat, John, V.P.-OEM Devel. & Mktg.--Code Alarm Security Systems, Madison Heights, MI; *U.S. Public*, pg. 394
Moffat, Sheree, Dir.-Sls.--Turtle Bay Hilton Golf & Tennis Resort, Kahuku, HI; *U.S. Public*, pg. 829
Mogan, W.M., V.P.-Mktg.--Talley Defense Systems, Inc., Mesa, AZ; *U.S. Public*, pg. 308
Mohamed, Simon, Mgr.-Adv.--Toyota (Great Britain) Limited, Redhill, United Kingdom; *Int'l*, pg. 1414
Moidel, Harland E., V.P.-Adv. Sls.--Comcast Cable Communications, Inc., Philadelphia, PA; *U.S. Public*, pg. 407
Moilanen, Karl E., Mgr.-Crane Rental & Sls. Coord.--Cloverdale Equipment Co., Oak Park, MI; *U.S. Private*, pg. 247
Moley, Miriam, Exec. V.P.-Mktg.--Carson Products Company, Savannah, GA; *U.S. Public*, pg. 309
Molina, Jackie, Mgr. Asst.-Adv. Promo.--Coca-Cola Bottling Co. of Chicago, Niles, IL; *U.S. Private*, pg. 248
Monaco, Carmen, Sr. V.P.-Mktg. & Adv.--Goody's Family Clothing, Inc., Knoxville, TN; *U.S. Public*, pg. 753
Monahan, James, Dir.-Adv. & Publications--General American Life Insurance Co., Saint Louis, MO; *U.S. Private*, pg. 443
Monahan, Mona, V.P.-Mktg.--The Princess Marcella Borghese, Inc., New York, NY; *U.S. Private*, pg. 690
Monette, Jerry, Mgr.-Sls., Promo. & Adv.--Allison Transmission, Indianapolis, IN; *U.S. Public*, pg. 719
Monihan, Robin, V.P.-Adv. & Sls.--SAE Engineering, Inc., Santa Clara, CA; *U.S. Private*, pg. 955
Monique, Mark, Mgr.-Adv.--The Savogran Company, Norwood, MA; *U.S. Private*, pg. 968
Monreal, Rick, Mgr.-Adv.--Swagelok Company, Solon, OH; *U.S. Private*, pg. 1057
Monroe, Pat, Dir.-Art--Boss Manufacturing Company, Kewanee, IL; *U.S. Private*, pg. 1142
Monroe, William, Pres. & Chief Exec. Officer--Bertolli USA, Inc., Secaucus, NJ; *Int'l*, pg. 655
Monsport, John, Dir.-Adv.--Loews Theatre Management Corp., New York, NY; *Int'l*, pg. 1282
Montecallo, Susan, Dir.-Adv./Babies R Us--Toys "R" Us, Inc., Paramus, NJ; *U.S. Public*, pg. 1626
Monteith, Maggy, Dir.-Adv. & Mktg.--Columbia Tri-Star Films (UK), London, United Kingdom; *Int'l*, pg. 1281
Montgomery, Gina, Mgr.-Adv. & Sls. Promo.--Siemens Business Communication Systems, Inc., Santa Clara, CA; *Int'l*, pg. 1245
Montgomery, J.M., Dir.-Adv.-North America--The Goodyear Tire & Rubber Company, Akron, OH; *U.S. Public*, pg. 752
Montgomery, Mark, Mgr.-Mktg. & Plng. Devel.--AFG Industries, Inc., Kingsport, TN; *Int'l*, pg. 84
Montgomery, Tom, Dir.-Adv.--MFA Incorporated, Columbia, MO; *U.S. Private*, pg. 686
Montgomery, William, Mgr.-Mktg. Communications--Prairie Farms Dairy, Inc., Carlinville, IL; *U.S. Private*, pg. 878
Moody, Mary, Dir.-Casino Mktg.--Silver City Casino, Las Vegas, NV; *U.S. Public*, pg. 375
Moody, Robert, V.P.-Adv.--First Empire State Corporation, Buffalo, NY; *U.S. Public*, pg. 631
Moomjy, Walter, Treas. & Sec.--Einstein Moomjy Inc., Pine Brook, NJ; *U.S. Private*, pg. 366
Mooney, Dianne, V.P.-Custom Publ. & Promo.--Southern Progress Corporation, Birmingham, AL; *U.S. Public*, pg. 1612
Mooney, Joan, Mgr.-Mktg. Services--Meto, USA, Morris Plains, NJ; *Int'l*, pg. 460
Mooney, Joan, Mgr.-Mktg. Svcs.--Esselte Meto Kimball Systems, Morris Plains, NJ; *Int'l*, pg. 460
Mooney, Judy, Category Dir.-Beauty & Fashion Adv.--Good Housekeeping, New York, NY; *U.S. Private*, pg. 517
Mooney, Mike, Dir.-Publicity--Hollywood Park, Inc., Inglewood, CA; *U.S. Public*, pg. 830
Moore, Bob, V.P.-Sls.--Bush Hog Division, Selma, AL; *U.S. Public*, pg. 48
Moore, Brad R., V.P.-Div., Adv. & Television Programming--Hallmark Cards, Inc., Kansas City, MO; *U.S. Private*, pg. 495
Moore, Dan, V.P.-Sls. & Mktg.--Target Stamped Products Corp., Kinsman, OH; *U.S. Private*, pg. 1069
Moore, Deborah, Sr. Mgr.-Adv.--Rose's Stores, Inc., Henderson, NC; *U.S. Public*, pg. 1405
Moore, Gary M., Dir.-Adv.--San Diego Union Tribune, San Diego, CA; *U.S. Private*, pg. 275
Moore, Jack R., Pres. & Chief Exec. Officer--Stahl Specialty Company, Kingsville, MO; *U.S. Private*, pg. 1029
Moore, Joy, Dir.-Adv.--Park Newspapers of Sapulpa, Inc., Sapulpa, OK; *U.S. Public*, pg. 1079
Moore, Marilyn M., Dir.-Adv.--Statesville Record and Landmark, Statesville, NC; *U.S. Public*, pg. 1078
Moore, Sally, Dir.-Worldwide Adv.--Corel Corporation, Ottawa, Canada; *Int'l*, pg. 331
Moore, Silvia, Dir.-Adv.--Xerox Argentina I.C.S.A., Buenos Aires, Argentina; *U.S. Public*, pg. 1785
Mor, Li, Dir.-Adv.--Willoughby's, New York, NY; *U.S. Private*, pg. 1180
Morales Filho, Jose, Dir.-Adv.--Cement Div., Sao Paulo, Brazil; *Int'l*, pg. 677
Moran, Carolyn, Mgr.-Adv.--Bank of Ireland, Dublin, Ireland; *Int'l*, pg. 152
Moran, Edmund J., Jr., Pres.-Mid-Atlantic Grp.--Moran Towing of Maryland, Baltimore, MD; *U.S. Private*, pg. 761
Moran, Eileen, V.P.-Adv.--Maaco Enterprises Inc., King of Prussia, PA; *U.S. Private*, pg. 689
Moran, Jack, Dir.-Mktg. Communications--Sulcus Computer Corp., Greensburg, PA; *U.S. Public*, pg. 1527
Moran, Mark, Dir.-Adv.--Jones Chemicals, Inc., Le Roy, NY; *U.S. Private*, pg. 596
Moran, Steve, Dir.-Adv.--Invesco Funds Group, Denver, CO; *Int'l*, pg. 685
Mordaunt, Cam, Mgr.-Adv.- Dutch Boy--The Sherwin-Williams Company, Cleveland, OH; *U.S. Public*, pg. 1465
Moreno, Joan W., Mgr.-Adv.--Alabama Metal Industries Corporation, Birmingham, AL; *U.S. Private*, pg. 30
Moreno, Odivaldo, Mgr.-Adv.--3M Do Brasil Ltda., Sao Paulo, Brazil; *U.S. Public*, pg. 1606
Morgan, Bill, V.P.-Brand Mngmnt. & Adv.--SBC Communications Inc., San Antonio, TX; *U.S. Public*, pg. 1415
Morgan, Bill, V.P.-Brand Mngmnt. & Adv.--Pacific Telesis Group, San Francisco, CA; *U.S. Public*, pg. 1415
Morgan, Bill, V.P.-Adv. & Brand Mngmt.--Pacific Bell, San Ramon, CA; *U.S. Public*, pg. 1416
Morgan, Diane, V.P.-Natl. Adv.--Salomon Smith Barney Holdings, Inc., New York, NY; *U.S. Public*, pg. 1633
Morgan, Doug, Dir.-Mktg. Communications--Mosler Inc., Hamilton, OH; *U.S. Private*, pg. 763
Morgan, Mac, V.P.-Adv.--Coldwater Creek, Sandpoint, ID; *U.S. Public*, pg. 396
Morgan, Mary, Dir.-Adv.--Ladies' Home Journal, New York, NY; *U.S. Public*, pg. 1094
Morgan, Rob, Sr. V.P.-Mktg., Sls. & Engrng.--Buck Knives, Inc., El Cajon, CA; *U.S. Private*, pg. 177
Morigerato, Paul L., Asst. V.P.-Creative Svcs.--Beneficial Management Corporation, Peapack, NJ; *U.S. Public*, pg. 211
Morin, Jim, V.P.-Adv.--J. Baker, Inc., Canton, MA; *U.S. Public*, pg. 167
Moritz, Paul, V.P.-Adv.--Pavey Envelope & Tag Corp., Jersey City, NJ; *U.S. Public*, pg. 1038
Morkovsky, Susan, Mgr.-Direct Adv.--Fugro Group Companies, Houston, TX; *U.S. Private*, pg. 430
Morris, Anthony, Sr. V.P.--Long Island Bancorp, Inc., Melville, NY; *U.S. Public*, pg. 1013
Morris, George C., Pres.--Niagara Blower Company, Buffalo, NY; *U.S. Private*, pg. 798
Morris, Ken, Mgr.-Adv.--MacNeal-Schwendler Corp., Costa Mesa, CA; *U.S. Public*, pg. 1031
Morris, Sara, Sr. Dir.-Mktg. & Adv.--Polo/Ralph Lauren Corporation, New York, NY; *U.S. Private*, pg. 874
Morris, Sharon, Admin. Asst.--Staffing Solutions, Boulder, CO; *U.S. Private*, pg. 1028
Morris, Tom, Mng. Dir.-Adv.--AMR Corporation, Fort Worth, TX; *U.S. Public*, pg. 9
Morrison, Anne, Mgr.-Adv.--Allyn & Bacon, Needham, MA; *U.S. Private*, pg. 778
Morrison, John D., Mgr.-Adv. & Promotions--Northwest Paper Div., Cloquet, MN; *U.S. Public*, pg. 1318
Morrison, Peter, Dir.-Adv.--Bassett Furniture Industries, Incorporated, Bassett, VA; *U.S. Public*, pg. 193
Morrison, Robert, Dir.-Adv.--Everex Systems Inc., Fremont, CA; *Int'l*, pg. 498
Morrissey, Christopher, Mgr.-Mktg. Commun.--Rogers Corporation, Rogers, CT; *U.S. Public*, pg. 1402
Morrocchi, Lorenzo, V.P.-Communications & Adv.--New Holland Ltd., Brentford, United Kingdom; *Int'l*, pg. 484
Morrow, David, V.P.-Sls. & Mktg.--Sanderson Plumbing Products Inc., Columbus, MS; *U.S. Private*, pg. 964
Morrow, Melinda R., Coord.-Mktg. & Adv.--Lectrodryer Div., Ajax Magnethermic Corp., Richmond, KY; *Int'l*, pg. 113
Morrow, Michael, V.P.-Mktg.--Kelly Services, Inc., Troy, MI; *U.S. Public*, pg. 949
Morvay, Ronnie, Mgr.-Adv.--Racal-Datacom, Sunrise, FL; *Int'l*, pg. 1083
Mosca, Ken, V.P.-Sls.--DX Communications, Inc., Deerfield Beach, FL; *Int'l*, pg. 694
Moseley, Mark, V.P.-Mktg.--Rowe Furniture Corp., Mc Lean, VA; *U.S. Public*, pg. 1410
Moser, Steve, Mgr.-Western Adv.--Architectural Digest, Los Angeles, CA; *U.S. Private*, pg. 20
Mosey, Bill, V.P.-Sls. & Mktg.--K-D Lamp Company, Cincinnati, OH; *U.S. Private*, pg. 603
Mossberg, Margarite, Mgr.-Adv.--Avesta Sandvik Tube AB, Fagersta, Sweden; *Int'l*, pg. 221
Mott-Wall, Carl, Asst. V.P.-Adv.--MTS, Inc., West Sacramento, CA; *U.S. Private*, pg. 688
Mow, Genevieve, Sr. V.P.-Mktg.--Bugle Boy Industries, Inc., Simi Valley, CA; *U.S. Private*, pg. 179
Mowrey, Ronald W., Mgr.-Adv.-Promo. & Communications Div.-Office Prods.--Ricoh Corporation, West Caldwell, NJ; *Int'l*, pg. 1114

Moyer, Sandy, Dir.-Mktg.--International Envelope Company, Exton, PA; *U.S. Public*, pg. 70
Mrazek, George, Acct. Exec.--Chicago White Metal Casting, Inc., Bensenville, IL; *U.S. Private*, pg. 236
Muckerman, John, Dir.-Mktg. & Adv.--Dierbergs Markets Inc., Chesterfield, MO; *U.S. Private*, pg. 332
Mudebele, Lindiwe, Mgr.--Transnet Ltd., Parkview, South Africa; *Int'l*, pg. 1417
Mudge, William A., V.P.-Global Mktg. Communications--McQuay International, Minneapolis, MN; *U.S. Private*, pg. 3
Muelboeck, Erwin, Mgr.-Adv. & Public Rels.--Agrolinz Melamin GmbH, Lienz, Austria; *Int'l*, pg. 356
Muelenberg, Gary, Mgr.-Mktg. Communications--TSI Incorporated, Shoreview, MN; *U.S. Public*, pg. 1559
Mueller, Michael G., Dir.-Adv.--Kohler Company, Kohler, WI; *U.S. Private*, pg. 630
Mueller, Richard G., Mng. Dir.--Toro-Wheel Horse, South Bend, IN; *U.S. Public*, pg. 1624
Mueller, Terri F., V.P.-Adv.--ERA Real Estate, Parsippany, NJ; *U.S. Public*, pg. 321
Mueller, Therese, Mgr.-Corp. Adv.--Regal-Beloit Corporation, Beloit, WI; *U.S. Public*, pg. 1370
Muellner, T.M., Dir.-Adv.--Pyle Inc., Elmhurst, IL; *U.S. Private*, pg. 629
Mugica, Laura, Mgr.-Adv.--Peugeot Talbot Espana, Madrid, Spain; *Int'l*, pg. 1021
Muhlenbruch, Ron, Dir.-Adv.--Star Lumber & Supply Company, Inc., Wichita, KS; *U.S. Private*, pg. 1034
Muir, Chris, V.P.-Mktg.--C.H. Heist Corp., Clearwater, FL; *U.S. Public*, pg. 807
Muknerjee, D., Mgr.-Adv.--Kinetics Technology India Ltd., New Delhi, India; *Int'l*, pg. 837
Muldoon, Doreen, Dir.-Advertiser Sls. Mgmt.--Worldvision Enterprises, New York, NY; *U.S. Private*, pg. 776
Mullen, Jack, Sr. V.P.-Adv. & Sls. Promo.--The Elder-Beerman Stores Corp., Dayton, OH; *U.S. Private*, pg. 367
Mullen, Jack, V.P.-Adv.--Elder-Beerman Stores Div., Dayton, OH; *U.S. Private*, pg. 367
Mullen, Larry J., Mgr.-Mktg., Treas. & Sec.--Terral Seed Co., Inc., Lake Providence, LA; *U.S. Private*, pg. 1077
Muller, Jasmine, Asst. V.P.--Banque Cantonale Vaudoise, Lausanne, Switzerland; *Int'l*, pg. 160
Muller, Wilfried, Mgr.-Adv.--Alno AG, Pfullendorf, Germany; *Int'l*, pg. 65
Mullins, Kevin, V.P.-Sls. & Mktg.--LoJack Corporation, Dedham, MA; *U.S. Public*, pg. 1012
Mumo, N., Dir.-Mktg.--Pentel of America, Ltd., Torrance, CA; *Int'l*, pg. 1035
Mumper-Dickerson, Melanie, V.P.-Mktg. Services & Pub. Rels.--NFO Research, Inc., Greenwich, CT; *U.S. Public*, pg. 1146
Munchen, Paul, Dir.-Gen. Mktg., Sls. & Adv.--CLT-UFA, Luxembourg, Luxembourg; *Int'l*, pg. 561
Mundschau, John, Mgr.-Mktg.--Matec Corporation, Hopkinton, MA; *U.S. Public*, pg. 1056
Mundt, Thomas P., V.P.-Strategic Plng., Investor Rels. & Communications--Wolverine World Wide, Inc., Rockford, MI; *U.S. Public*, pg. 1775
Mundy, Al, Dir.-Adv.--International Research & Evaluation, Eagan, MN; *U.S. Private*, pg. 571
Munn, Linda, Acting Dir.-Adv.--The Bear Stearns Companies Inc., New York, NY; *U.S. Public*, pg. 197
Munoz, Brenda, Mgr.-Adv.--CIBA-GEIGY Uruguaya S.A., Montevideo, Uruguay; *Int'l*, pg. 980
Munoz, Selix, Dir.-Adv.--Compania Espanola de Petroleos, S.A. (CEPSA), Madrid, Spain; *Int'l*, pg. 323
Munson, Andrea, Coord.-Mktg.--Gould Packaging, Inc., Vancouver, WA; *U.S. Private*, pg. 466
Munson, Dorothy, Dir.-Communications--Ciba Specialty Chemicals, Tarrytown, NY; *Int'l*, pg. 291
Murphy-Scott, Kathleen, Asst. V.P.--General Re Corporation, Stamford, CT; *U.S. Public*, pg. 725
Murphy, Barb, Dir.-Sls. & Adv.--Buttrey Food & Drug Company, Great Falls, MT; *U.S. Public*, pg. 271
Murphy, George, Mgr.-Adv.--Reily Foods & Co., Knoxville, TN; *U.S. Private*, pg. 919
Murphy, Karen, Coord.-Mktg. Promo.--Syracuse Supply Company, Syracuse, NY; *U.S. Private*, pg. 1060
Murphy, Katherine, Mgr.-Adv.--Adams Extract Co., Inc., Austin, TX; *U.S. Private*, pg. 16
Murphy, L.D., V.P.-Mktg. & Sls.--Marlite, Dover, OH; *U.S. Private*, pg. 705
Murphy, Michael, Dir.-Adv. & MKtg. (UK)--The Financial Times Ltd., London, United Kingdom; *Int'l*, pg. 1025
Murphy, Sharon, Mgr.-Adv. & Mktg.--ITC Learning Corp., Herndon, VA; *U.S. Public*, pg. 859
Murphy, Tricia, Adv. Admin.--Cosmair, Inc., Ralph Lauren Fragrance Division, New York, NY; *Int'l*, pg. 818
Murphy, Wayne, Coord.-Adv.--The Harry Alter Company, Lansing, IL; *U.S. Private*, pg. 1075
Murphy, William, V.P. & Dir.-Customers Mktg.--Meredith Corporation, Des Moines, IA; *U.S. Public*, pg. 1094
Murphy, William K., V.P.-Corp. Communications, Adv. & Pub. Rels.--Atlantic Mutual Companies, New York, NY; *U.S. Private*, pg. 95
Murray, Adrienne, Mgr.-Adv. & Sponsorship--Allied Irish Banks, p.l.c., Dublin, Ireland; *Int'l*, pg. 64
Murray, Cheryl, Mgr.-Adv.--Mustang Tractor & Equip. Co., Houston, TX; *U.S. Private*, pg. 768
Murray, Douglas L., Sr. V.P.-Mktg. & Security Officer--First American Federal Savings Bank, Bristol, VA; *U.S. Public*, *pg. 624*
Murray, George, V.P.-Adv.--J.B. Robinson Jewelers, Inc., Akron, OH; *Int'l*, pg. 1248
Murray, Jamie, Dir.-Corp. Brands--Du Pont (E.I. Du Pont De Nemours & Co.), Wilmington, DE; *U.S. Public*, pg. 530
Murray, Joe, Sr. V.P.-Sls. & Mktg.--Frank Industries, Inc., Brown City, MI; *U.S. Private*, pg. 423
Murray, Marion, Dir.-Adv.--Altec Lansing Technologies, Inc., Milford, PA; *U.S. Private*, pg. 479
Murray, Mike, Mgr.-Mkt. Devel.--Seal Group, Irvine, CA; *U.S.* Public, pg. 1262
Murray, Richard, Dir.-Adv.-Automotive--Providence Journal-Bulletin, Providence, RI; *U.S. Public*, pg. 209
Murray, Robert W., V.P.-Communications--MagneTek, Inc., Nashville, TN; *U.S. Public*, pg. 1037
Murry, Alain A., Mgr.-Adv. & Office Equipment--Central Steel & Wire Company, Chicago, IL; *U.S. Public*, pg. 327
Mushill, Ed, Mgr.-Mktg. Communications--G.E. Harris Energy Control Systems, LLC, Melbourne, FL; *U.S. Public*, pg. 712
Mushkin, Albert S., Pres. & Chief Oper. Officer--Master Industries Corp., New York, NY; *U.S. Private*, pg. 713
Musil, Jerome A., Mgr.-Corp. Commun. & Pub. Affairs--St. Joseph Light & Power Co., Saint Joseph, MO; *U.S. Public*, pg. 1427
Musselman, Joe, Dir.-Adv.--Giant Food Stores Inc., Carlisle, PA; *Int'l*, pg. 750
Muth, Marilee, Mgr.-Mktg. Communications--Dorner Manufacturing Corp., Hartland, WI; *U.S. Private*, pg. 340
Myatt, Paul, Dir.-Inside Sls. & Mktg.--Magnetrol International, Downers Grove, IL; *U.S. Private*, pg. 696
Myers, Raymond F., V.P. & Mgr.-Adv.--Southwest National Corporation, Greensburg, PA; *U.S. Public*, pg. 1493
Myers, Robert W., V.P.-Sls. & Mktg.--Morris Coupling Co., Erie, PA; *U.S. Private*, pg. 762
Myers, Scott, Mgr.-Adv.--M K Diamond Products, Inc., Torrance, CA; *U.S. Private*, pg. 684
Myers, Steve, V.P.-Adv.--Fab Industries, Inc., New York, NY; *U.S. Public*, pg. 603
Myhr, Norman O., Sr. V.P.-Adv. & Sls. Promo.--Fred Meyer Stores, Portland, OR; *U.S. Public*, pg. 1103
Myland, Larry, Mgr.-Mktg.--Humphrey Products Company, Kalamazoo, MI; *U.S. Private*, pg. 547
Myrick, Timothy, Mgr.-Corp. Design--Hickok Incorporated, Cleveland, OH; *U.S. Public*, pg. 825
Na Ayudhya, Penpun Visuddhi, Chief Info. Officer & V.P.--Finance One Public Company Limited, Bangkok, Thailand; *Int'l*, pg. 484
Nader, Bill, Dir.-Broadcast Communications & Promo.--New York Racing Association, Jamaica, NY; *U.S. Private*, pg. 795
Nadolny, Gary, Dir.-Mktg.--Ansul Incorporated, Marinette, WI; *U.S. Public*, pg. 1648
Nadon, John, Dir.-Adv.--Prescolite Moldcast Lighting Company, San Leandro, CA; *U.S. Public*, pg. 1684
Naftel, Reese, Mgr.-Adv.--Koch Supplies Inc., Kansas City, MO; *U.S. Private*, pg. 628
Nagle, James, Dir.-Adv.--American Journal of Nursing Company, New York, NY; *Int'l*, pg. 1513
Nagle, Terry, Dir.-Communications--Land O'Lakes, Inc., Arden Hills, MN; *U.S. Private*, pg. 645
Nahmad, Albert H., Chm. Bd., Pres. & Chief Exec. Officer--Watsco, Inc., Coconut Grove, FL; *U.S. Public*, pg. 1745
Nakajima, Takao, Dir.-Adv.--JGC Corporation, Tokyo, Japan; *Int'l*, pg. 697
Nakamura, Waichi, Gen. Mgr.--Hitachi Zosen Corporation, Osaka, Japan; *Int'l*, pg. 622
Nakao, Tsuyoshi, Mgr.-Adv.--Tekken Corporation, Tokyo, Japan; *Int'l*, pg. 1362
Namiot, Milton, Pres. & Chief Exec. Officer--Deering Ice Cream, Inc., Portland, ME; *U.S. Private*, pg. 403
Nance, Larry, Mgr.-Corp. Commun.--Global Industrial Technologies, Dallas, TX; *U.S. Public*, pg. 747
Nanus, Wendy, Dir.-Adv.--Self, New York, NY; *U.S. Private*, pg. 20
Napoli, Paul, Dir.-Adv.--Bridgestone/Firestone, Inc., Nashville, TN; *Int'l*, pg. 213
Napoli, Rand, Dir.-Mktg.--Leather Center, Inc., Carrollton, TX; *U.S. Private*, pg. 656
Nardone, Louise, Adv. Specialist-Bus. & Professional Prods.--Sony Electronics, Park Ridge, NJ; *Int'l*, pg. 1281
Narita, Shigeyuki, Mng. Dir.-Corp. Communications--Omron Corporation, Kyoto, Japan; *Int'l*, pg. 1005
Nascimbene, Mario, Dir.-Mktg.--Davide Campari, Milan, Italy; *Int'l*, pg. 385
Nash, A.J., Dir.-Commercial--Taunton Cider Company P.L.C., Taunton, United Kingdom; *Int'l*, pg. 849
Nask, Aleene, Dir.-Mktg.--Olin Corporation, Norwalk, CT; *U.S. Public*, pg. 1218
Nass, James W., V.P.--Graham Paint and Varnish Company, Chicago, IL; *U.S. Private*, pg. 468
Nass, Richard, Dir.-Adv.--Aid Auto Stores, Inc., Westbury, NY; *U.S. Public*, pg. 29
Nastro, Ken, Dir.-Adv.--Key Food Stores Co-operative, Inc., Brooklyn, NY; *U.S. Private*, pg. 617
Natale, Lisa, Mgr.-Strategic Plng.--The Kendall-Betham Division, Piscataway, NJ; *U.S. Public*, pg. 1647
Nauffts, Bud, Dir.-Adv.--Crain's Cleveland Business, Cleveland, OH; *U.S. Private*, pg. 285
Naymark, Rick, Asst. V.P.-Adv. & Brand Devel.--ReliaStar Financial Corp., Minneapolis, MN; *U.S. Public*, pg. 1375
Nazziola, Thomas E., V.P.-Mktg.--Ilco Unican Corp., Simplex Access Controls Division, Winston Salem, NC; *Int'l*, pg. 1432
Neal, Andy, Dir.-Mktg.--United Distillers PLC, Edinburgh, United Kingdom; *Int'l*, pg. 412
Nebel, Laurie J., Mgr.-Adv.--Salsbury Laboratories, Inc., Charles City, IA; *Int'l*, pg. 1277
Needleman, Barbara, V.P.-Database & Adv. Prods.--Tribune Media Services, Inc., Chicago, IL; *U.S. Public*, pg. 1636
Neely, Jetta, Dir.-Adv.--Nurses Inc., Houston, TX; *Int'l*, pg. 1285
Neighbors, Sue, Mgr.-Communications--Baker Hughes Incorporated, Houston, TX; *U.S. Public*, pg. 165
Neill, Catherine, V.P.-Adv.--Jitney-Jungle Stores of America, Inc., Jackson, MS; *U.S. Private*, pg. 588
Neill, Linda K., Mgr.-Mdsg. & Adv.--Seymour Smith & Son, Oakville, CT; *U.S. Public*, pg. 575
Nelson, Gregg, Dir.-Adv. & Pub. Rels.--Wenger Corporation, Owatonna, MN; *U.S. Private*, pg. 1162
Nelson, James E., Dir.-Sls. & Mktg.--Ederer Inc., Seattle, WA; *U.S. Private*, pg. 363
Nelson, John, Mgr.-Natl. Adv.--Yamaha Corporation of America, Buena Park, CA; *Int'l*, pg. 1516
Nelson, Margaret, Dir.-Communications--Ponderosa Steakhouse, Dallas, TX; *U.S. Private*, pg. 736
Nelson, Richard, Mgr.-Pub. Rels.--Thorn Security Group, Ltd., Sunbury, United Kingdom; *Int'l*, pg. 1386
Nelson, Stephanie, Prod. Mgr.--Diadora America, Inc., Kent, WA; *U.S. Private*, pg. 330
Nelson, Thomas R., Asst. V.P.-Adv.--State Farm Mutual Automobile Insurance Company, Bloomington, IL; *U.S. Private*, pg. 1036
Nemecek, Jay, Adv. Rep.--Peoples Energy Corporation, Chicago, IL; *U.S. Public*, pg. 1274
Nemetz, Allen P., V.P.-Mktg. & Adv.--PIC Design, Middlebury, CT; *U.S. Private*, pg. 864
Nemetz, Mike, Dir.-Adv.--Talbots, Inc., Hingham, MA; *Int'l*, pg. 28
Nenninger, John, Sr. V.P. & Dir.-Mktg.--Starbanc Corporation, Cincinnati, OH; *U.S. Public*, pg. 1510
Neri, Enrique Gasca, Dir.-Mktg. & Qualtiy--Altos Hornos de Mexico, S.A., Monclova, Mexico; *Int'l*, pg. 66
Neri, Marion, Mgr.-Adv.- Fiat--Fiat Auto Suisse SA, Geneva, Switzerland; *Int'l*, pg. 481
Neubauer, Allyn, Dir.-Mktg. & Adv.--Amana Society, Inc., Amana, IA; *U.S. Private*, pg. 48
Neustadt, James C., V.P.-Adv.--Lowe's Companies, Inc., North Wilkesboro, NC; *U.S. Public*, pg. 1015
Neustel, Larry A., Mgr.-Adv. Design Services--Kohler Company, Kohler, WI; *U.S. Private*, pg. 630
Newberry, Dee, Coord.-Adv. & Mktg.--Chris-Craft Boats, Sarasota, FL; *U.S. Private*, pg. 478
Newcomb, Anne, Coord.-Adv.--American Mathematical Society, Inc., Providence, RI; *U.S. Private*, pg. 59
Newell, Michael, V.P.-Mktg.--Crystal Cream & Butter Company, Sacramento, CA; *U.S. Private*, pg. 294
Newell, Robert A., V.P.-Mktg.--NewTel Communications, Saint Johns, Canada; *Int'l*, pg. 115
Newhouse, Steve, Dir.-Mktg., Sls. & Adv.--Atlantic Builders Group Inc., Baltimore, MD; *U.S. Private*, pg. 95
Newman, Steve, Sr. V.P.-Adv. Sls.--Home & Garden Television, Knoxville, TN; *U.S. Public*, pg. 1447
Newmeister, John, V.P.-Mktg.--Matrix Service Company, Tulsa, OK; *U.S. Public*, pg. 1057
Newton, Shelly, Mgr.-Adv.--Dell Computer Corporation Ltd., Bracknell, United Kingdom; *U.S. Public*, pg. 496
Ng, Danny, Mgr.-Adv.--Bulova Watch Company Limited, Toronto, Canada; *U.S. Public*, pg. 1011
Nicandros, Constantine S., Pres. & Chief Exec. Officer--Conoco Inc., Houston, TX; *U.S. Public*, pg. 531
Nichol, Jeanne, Sr. Adv. Assoc.-Mktg. & Sls.--The Principal Financial Group, Des Moines, IA; *U.S. Private*, pg. 885
Nicholson, Debra, Dir.-Pub. Affairs--Freightliner Corp., Portland, OR; *Int'l*, pg. 368
Nicholson, Peter, V.P.-Adv. & Mktg. Services--Citizen Watch Co. of America, Inc., Lyndhurst, NJ; *Int'l*, pg. 294
Nicholson, Wendy, V.P. & Exec. Dir.-Public Relations--Simon & Schuster Trade Division, New York, NY; *U.S. Private*, pg. 777
Nickel, Scott, Sr. Tech. Writer--VASA Brougher, Inc., Indianapolis, IN; *Int'l*, pg. 464
Nickle, Dwayne, V.P.-Mktg.--Fabwel Inc., Elkhart, IN; *U.S. Private*, pg. 390
Nicol, F., Mgr.-Adv.--MLC Limited, Sydney, Australia; *Int'l*, pg. 806
Niderberg, Dave, Dir.-Mktg.--Therma-Tru Corp., Maumee, OH; *U.S. Private*, pg. 1079
Nielsen, Kathy, Mgr.-Mktg. Support Services--Harcourt Brace & Company - Elementary Div., Orlando, FL; *U.S. Public*, pg. 783
Nihei, S., Pres.-USA Leader--Leader Instruments Corporation, Hauppauge, NY; *U.S. Private*, pg. 655
Niles, Gary J., Exec. V.P.-Mktg. & Product Acquisition--Galoob Toys, Inc., South San Francisco, CA; *U.S. Public*, *pg. 698*
Ninnis, Mary Ann, Dir.-Adv.--Universal Health Services, Inc., King of Prussia, PA; *U.S. Public*, pg. 1696
Nishijima, Takao, Mgr.-Adv. & Pub. Rels.--Hitachi Zosen Corporation, Osaka, Japan; *Int'l*, pg. 622
Nixon, Bob, Dir.-Adv.--Robesonian, Lumberton, NC; *U.S. Public*, pg. 1078
Nixon, Brent, Dir.-Mktg.--Laserscope Surgical Systems, San Jose, CA; *U.S. Public*, pg. 979
Nobilitti, Paula, Mgr.-Adv.--Motor Boating & Sailing, New York, NY; *U.S. Private*, pg. 517
Nonnemacher, Marie, Mgr.-Adv. & Sls. Promotion--Linear Dynamics Inc., Parsippany, NJ; *U.S. Private*, pg. 668
Nordell, Peter, V.P.-Mktg. & Sls.--Edlund Company, Inc., Burlington, VT; *U.S. Private*, pg. 364
Norden, Roger C., Pres.--Standard Medical Imaging, Inc., Columbia, MD; *U.S. Private*, pg. 1032
Nordquist, Ake, Mgr.-Adv.--Skandia Insurance Company Limited, Stockholm, Sweden; *Int'l*, pg. 1256
Nordstrom, Jeff, Dir.-Mktg.--Whataburger, Inc., Corpus Christi, TX; *U.S. Private*, pg. 1170
Nordvi, Jan Erik, Sls. & Adv. Mgr.--ISS Catering a.s., Oslo, Norway; *Int'l*, pg. 656
Norman, Bruce E., V.P.-Mktg.--Mercury General Corporation, Los Angeles, CA; *U.S. Public*, pg. 1093
Norman, Ken, V.P.-Mktg.--National Spinning Co., Inc., New York, NY; *U.S. Private*, pg. 786
Norton, Nancy, Mgr.-Retail Adv.--Memphis Publishing Co., Memphis, TN; *U.S. Public*, pg. 1448
Nosal, Bob, Dir.-Mktg., Adv. & Pub. Rels.--Unichema U.S.A., Chicago, IL; *Int'l*, pg. 1436
Noskin, Steven, Exec. V.P.--Polymer Plastics Corporation, Hauppauge, NY; *U.S. Private*, pg. 875
Novachek, Bob, Mgr.-Adv.--Kerr Group, Inc., Lancaster, PA; *U.S. Public*, pg. 952
Novak, C.A., Mgr.-Adv.-Saturn/Saab/Isuzu--General Motors of Canada Ltd., Oshawa, Canada; *U.S. Public*, pg. 722
Novak, Maria, Mgr.-Mktg. Communications--Bailey, Fischer & Porter Company, Warminster, PA; *Int'l*, pg. 449
Nowicki, Margaret, Mgr.-Adv. & Mktg.--Dale Electronics, Inc., Columbus, NE; *U.S. Public*, pg. 1722
Noyes, Donald, Mgr.-Adv. & Pub. Rels.--Asarco Incorporated, New York, NY; *U.S. Public*, pg. 137

Nuckles, Gretchen, Mgr.-Adv.--Employers Insurance of Wausau, Wausau, WI; *U.S. Private*, pg. 788
Nunnally, Sandra B., V.P.-Adv. Admin.--Heilig-Meyers Company, Richmond, VA; *U.S. Public*, pg. 804
Nuss, Kevin Marie, V.P.-Mktg.--Churchill Downs, Inc., Louisville, KY; *U.S. Public*, pg. 356
Nustad, Deborah, Mgr.-Adv.-CE--Case Corporation, Racine, WI; *U.S. Public*, pg. 311
Nutt, Orval J., Chief Mktg. Officer & V.P.-Mktg.--Amdahl Corporation, Sunnyvale, CA; *Int'l*, pg. 527
Nyberg, Riitta, Mgr.-Adv. & Communications--Oy Algol AB, Espoo, Finland; *Int'l*, pg. 15
Nybo, Howard J., Pres.--Will & Baumer Incorporated, Liverpool, NY; *U.S. Private*, pg. 1176
O'Brian, Mike, Publisher--The Daily Tidings, Ashland, OR; *U.S. Public*, pg. 983
O'Brien, Bill, V.P.-Adv.--The Franklin Mint, Franklin Center, PA; *U.S. Private*, pg. 941
O'Brien, Candice, Exec. Dir.-Corp. Communications--Tenneco Inc., Greenwich, CT; *U.S. Public*, pg. 1577
O'Brien, Jack, Dir.-Mktg. Commun.--Eclipse Inc., Rockford, IL; *U.S. Private*, pg. 360
O'Brien, Laraine, Mgr.-Customer Communications--Wisconsin Gas Company, Milwaukee, WI; *U.S. Public*, pg. 1767
O'Callaghan, Craig, V.P.--Universal Builders Supply, Inc., Mount Vernon, NY; *U.S. Private*, pg. 1126
O'Connor, David, Pres.--Merle Norman Cosmetics, Inc., Los Angeles, CA; *U.S. Private*, pg. 733
O'Connor, Kathy, Mgr.-Adv.--Patent Construction Systems, Paramus, NJ; *U.S. Public*, pg. 793
O'Connor, Neal, Pres.--George T. Schmidt, Niles, IL; *U.S. Private*, pg. 970
O'Dell, Pat, Natl. Mktg. Mgr.-Special Prods./White Cement--Lehigh Portland Cement Company, Allentown, PA; *Int'l*, pg. 605
O'Donnell, Christine, Dir.-Corp. Commun.--GAI Consultants, Inc., Monroeville, PA; *U.S. Private*, pg. 433
O'Donnell, Tom, Mgr.-Adv.--Donnkenny, Inc., New York, NY; *U.S. Public*, pg. 519
O'Grady, Laura S., V.P.-Adv. & Mktg.--S & K Famous Brands, Inc., Glen Allen, VA; *U.S. Public*, pg. 1414
O'Halloran, Anna, Corp. Sec.--Royer Industries, Inc., Kingston, PA; *Int'l*, pg. 1066
O'Hanlon, Rosemary, Coord.-Sls.--Amphenol Corporation, Wallingford, CT; *U.S. Private*, pg. 629
O'Hanlon, Rosemary, Coord.-Sls.--Times Fiber Communications, Inc., Wallingford, CT; *U.S. Private*, pg. 629
O'Hara, Jan, Mgr.-Adv. & Sls. Promo.--Buster Brown Apparel, Inc., Chattanooga, TN; *U.S. Private*, pg. 189
O'Hare, Michael, Mgr.-Adv.--Andes Candies Inc., Delavan, WI; *U.S. Private*, pg. 163
O'Leary, Robert W., V.P.-Mktg., Sls. & Adv.--Scanforms, Inc., Bristol, PA; *U.S. Public*, pg. 228
O'Malia, Daniel J., Pres. & Chief Exec. Officer--O'Malia Food Markets Inc., Carmel, IN; *U.S. Private*, pg. 816
O'Mara, Thomas K., Mgr.-Sls. & Mktg.--Autocam Corporation, Grand Rapids, MI; *U.S. Public*, pg. 148
O'Meara, John, Pres.--Telegenix Inc., Cherry Hill, NJ; *U.S. Private*, pg. 1073
O'Neal, Peg, Mgr.-Mktg. Commun.--Avo International, Blue Bell, PA; *U.S. Private*, pg. 9
O'Neil, Deb, Mgr.-Mktg.--Labelon Corporation, Canandaigua, NY; *U.S. Private*, pg. 641
O'Neil, Frank B., Sr. V.P.-Corp. Commun.--Medical Assurance, Inc., Birmingham, AL; *U.S. Public*, pg. 1079
O'Neill, Jacque, Dir.-Adv.--Tuesday Morning Corporation, Dallas, TX; *U.S. Public*, pg. 1644
O'Neill, Joyce, V.P.-Human Resources--Data Dimensions, Inc., Culver City, CA; *U.S. Public*, pg. 485
O'Neill, Kevin, V.P.-Mktg. & Sls.--Wilbur Chocolate Co., Inc., Lititz, PA; *U.S. Private*, pg. 210
O'Neill, Kevin M., Sr. V.P.-Bus. Devel. & Strategy--Anacomp, Inc., Indianapolis, IN; *U.S. Public*, pg. 106
O'Neill, Robert G., V.P. & Dir.-Adv.--The Times-Picayune Publishing Corp., New Orleans, LA; *U.S. Private*, pg. 1087
O'Neill, Stacy, Adv.--Astra USA, Inc., Westborough, MA; *Int'l*, pg. 93
O'Reilly, Kelley, Pres.-Impact Adv. Inc. & V.P.-Mktg.--Big O Tires Incorporated, Englewood, CO; *U.S. Public*, pg. 1553
O'Rourke, Betsy, Sr. V.P.-Adv.--Choice Hotels International, Inc., Silver Spring, MD; *U.S. Public*, pg. 351
O'Rourke, Bill, Gen. Mgr.--Sani-Mist, Inc., Bala Cynwyd, PA; *U.S. Private*, pg. 965
O'Rourke, Thomas J., Sr. V.P.-Mktg.--The CIT Group Holdings, Inc., New York, NY; *Int'l*, pg. 360
O'Shea, Tim, V.P.-Mktg.--Fresh Choice, Inc., Santa Clara, CA; *U.S. Public*, pg. 682
Oakes, Karin, Mgr.-Mktg. Communications--ESA, Inc., Chelmsford, MA; *U.S. Private*, pg. 354
Obana, Mary, V.P.-Mktg.--The Keds Corporation, Lexington, MA; *U.S. Public*, pg. 1525
Obana, Yuji, Mng. Dir.-Admin., Personnel, Safety, Sls., Adv. & Customer Serv.--Nikon Corporation, Tokyo, Japan; *Int'l*, pg. 931
Oberritter, Claudia, Mgr.-Adv. & Corp. Sec.--Deutsche Bahn, Frankfurt/Main, Germany; *Int'l*, pg. 401
Oddi, Michael, V.P. & Integrated Adv. Dir.--Kovel Kresser & Partners, Santa Monica, CA; *U.S. Private*, pg. 634
Odillard, Martine, V.P.-Corp. Commun. & H.R.--Chargeurs, Paris, France; *Int'l*, pg. 280
Odza, Bruce, Dir.-Adv.--Electronic Data Systems Corporation, Plano, TX; *U.S. Public*, pg. 569
Oerehagen, Perge, Reg. Mgr.-Mktg. Europe--Luxo A/S, Oslo, Norway; *Int'l*, pg. 821
Oesterle, Carl, Dir.-Adv.--View-Master, Inc., Mount Laurel, NJ; *U.S. Public*, pg. 1058
Ogawa, Kohoichi, Mgr.-Adv.--Eisai Co., Ltd., Tokyo, Japan; *Int'l*, pg. 435
Ogden, Brad, Jr., Pres.--Bargain Supply Company, Louisville, KY; *U.S. Private*, pg. 116
Ohanian, Bob, Mgr.-Category--E-Z Serve Corp., Houston, TX; *U.S. Public*, pg. 540
Oikarinen, M., Dir.-Adv.--Valmet Automation Kajaani Ltd., Kajaani, Finland; *Int'l*, pg. 1449
Okawara, Kathy, Mgr.-Media--Kraft Canada Inc., Don Mills, Canada; *U.S. Public*, pg. 1288
Okle, Debbie L., Dir.-Pub. Rels.--Commercial Metals Company, Dallas, TX; *U.S. Public*, pg. 411
Okon, Joseph, V.P.-Adv. & Mktg. Communications--Marriott International, Inc., Washington, DC; *U.S. Public*, pg. 1047
Okon, Joseph, Sr. V.P.-Natl. Adv.--Fairfield Inn, Washington, DC; *U.S. Public*, pg. 1048
Oktavec, Thomas, V.P.-Mktg.--Kocolene Oil Corp., Seymour, IN; *U.S. Private*, pg. 629
Olinger, Jack, Exec. V.P.-Adv.--The Hammerblow Corp., Wausau, WI; *U.S. Private*, pg. 498
Oliver, Steve, Mgr.-Corp. Adv.--Lexmark International Group, Inc., Lexington, KY; *U.S. Public*, pg. 991
Oliver, Steve, Mgr.-Corp. Adv.--Lexmark International, Inc., Lexington, KY; *U.S. Public*, pg. 991
Oller, Otto, Dir.-Adv.--ITW Plastiglide, Rancho Dominguez, CA; *U.S. Public*, pg. 867
Olsen, Al, Sr. V.P.-Adv.--Reinalt-Thomas Corp., Ann Arbor, MI; *U.S. Private*, pg. 919
Olson, Howard, V.P.-Adv. & Sls. Promo.--Unisource, Doraville, GA; *U.S. Public*, pg. 1671
Olson, Susan, Dir.-Adv. & Communications--Shenandoah Mfg. Co. Inc., Harrisonburg, VA; *U.S. Private*, pg. 992
Omohundro, Barbara, Dir.-Adv.--American Frozen Foods, Inc., Stratford, CT; *U.S. Private*, pg. 55
Ong, C.T., Gen. Mgr.-Pub. Affairs--China Steel Corporation, Kao-hsiung, Taiwan; *Int'l*, pg. 285
Onodera, Yasuo, Gen. Mgr.-Corp. Commun.--Toyo Tire & Rubber Co., Ltd., Osaka, Japan; *Int'l*, pg. 1411
Ontoso, Isabel, Dir.-Corp. Mktg. & Adv.--Telefonica de Espana, S.A., Madrid, Spain; *Int'l*, pg. 1371
Orban, David, Dir.-Bus. Devel.--Adams Rite Manufacturing Co., City of Industry, CA; *U.S. Private*, pg. 17
Orban, Rus, V.P.-Mktg.--Rutt Custom Cabinetry, Goodville, PA; *U.S. Private*, pg. 507
Orem, Glen, Dir.-Mktg.--SouthCo. Inc., Concordville, PA; *U.S. Private*, pg. 1014
Orenstein, Bonnie, Sr. V.P. & Mgr.-Adv.--PaineWebber Group Incorporated, New York, NY; *U.S. Public*, pg. 1252
Orenstein, Bonnie, Sr. V.P. & Mgr.-Adv.--PaineWebber Incorporated, New York, NY; *U.S. Public*, pg. 1252
Orenstein, Robert S., Pres.--International Wine Accessories, Inc., Dallas, TX; *U.S. Private*, pg. 572
Orfinik, Michael H., Pres.--Melnor Inc., Winchester, VA; *U.S. Public*, pg. 1234
Origer, Terry, Mgr.-Mkt. Research--Sheldahl, Inc., Northfield, MN; *U.S. Public*, pg. 1465
Orr, Bob, Gen. Mgr.--Vollrath-Kewaunee Plant, Kewaunee, WI; *U.S. Private*, pg. 1143
Orr, Tommy, Sr. V.P.--Harbor Financial Mortgage Corp., Houston, TX; *U.S. Public*, pg. 644
Ortegon, Genny, V.P.-Mktg.--Advanced Logic Research, Inc., Irvine, CA; *U.S. Public*, pg. 703
Orth, Mark, Gen. Mgr.-Telecomm. & Mgr.-Sls.--Times Printing Company, Inc., Random Lake, WI; *U.S. Private*, pg. 1087
Orth, Mary, Mgr.-Classified--The Gazette Company, Cedar Rapids, IA; *U.S. Private*, pg. 442
Ortiz, Ana Maria, Mgr.-Adv. & Pub. Rels.--Sony Corporation of Panama, Panama, Panama; *Int'l*, pg. 1284
Osburn, Dave, Dir.-Mktg.--Royal Rubber & Manufacturing Co., South Gate, CA; *U.S. Private*, pg. 949
Osten, Gail, V.P.-Adv.--Chicago Mercantile Exchange, Chicago, IL; *U.S. Private*, pg. 235
Ostrom, Denis, Adv. Dept.--Pharmaceuticals Division, Saint Paul, MN; *U.S. Public*, pg. 1605
Ostrow, Eric, V.P.-Mktg.--Ce De Candy, Inc., Union, NJ; *U.S. Private*, pg. 220
Ostrowski, Cyndi, V.P.-Adv.--CoreStates Bank of Delaware NA, Wilmington, DE; *U.S. Public*, pg. 447
Otani, C., Coord.-Mktg.--Pentax Canada Inc., Mississauga, Canada; *Int'l*, pg. 85
Otis, Martha S., V.P.-Adv. & Promotion--Warner Books, Inc., New York, NY; *U.S. Public*, pg. 1614
Ottervik, Barbara, Mgr.-Adv. & Promo.--The H.W. Wilson Co., Bronx, NY; *U.S. Private*, pg. 1180
Ottey, Jean, Mgr.-Communications--Millennium Inorganic Chemicals, Hunt Valley, MD; *Int'l*, pg. 593
Ottie, Timothy W., Pres. & Gen. Mgr.--Thermal Transfer Corp., Monroeville, PA; *U.S. Public*, pg. 29
Ousley, Karen, Coord.-Adv.--House of White Birches, Inc., Berne, IN; *U.S. Private*, pg. 542
Overby, Ray, Plant Mgr.--Dry Manufacturing Co., Winters, TX; *U.S. Public*, pg. 1795
Overstreet, David, Dir.-Sls. & Adv.--Duckwall Alco Stores, Inc., Abilene, KS; *U.S. Public*, pg. 533
Overton, Jackie, Dir.-Adv.--Loehmann's, Inc., Bronx, NY; *U.S. Public*, pg. 1010
Oviedo, Rodolfo, Dir.-Corp. Communications--Embraer-Empresa Brasileira de Aeronautica S.A., Sao Jose dos Campos, Brazil; *Int'l*, pg. 452
Owaki, Akinori, V.P.-Adv.--Sapporo U.S.A., Inc., New York, New York, NY; *Int'l*, pg. 1193
Owen, Barbara, Dir.-Promo. & Pub. Rels.--Sport Obermeyer Ltd., USA, Aspen, CO; *U.S. Private*, pg. 1026
Owen, Dick, V.P.-Adv.--The Kroger Co., Cincinnati, OH; *U.S. Public*, pg. 967
Owen, Joseph, Mgr.-Natl. Accts.--The Hall China Company, East Liverpool, OH; *U.S. Private*, pg. 494
Owen, Steve, Dir.-Adv. & Communications--Brodart Company, Williamsport, PA; *U.S. Private*, pg. 170
Owens, Caroline, Dir.-Adv.--Blue Seal Feeds, Inc., Londonderry, NH; *U.S. Private*, pg. 1134
Owens, K.R., Mgr.-Sls. Promo. & Adv.--Inco Alloys International, Inc., Huntington, WV; *Int'l*, pg. 672
Owens, Karin, V.P.-Adv. & Admin.--National Video, Inc., Langhorne, PA; *U.S. Public*, pg. 1755
Owens, R. Harold, Pres. & Chief Oper. Officer--World Acceptance Corporation, Greenville, SC; *U.S. Public*, pg. 1778
Owens, Sherrill, Adv. Specialist--Parker Hannifin Corporation, Cleveland, OH; *U.S. Public*, pg. 1259
Owens, Stephen, V.P.-Sls. & Mktg.--Hofmann Industries, Inc., Sinking Spring, PA; *U.S. Private*, pg. 533
Owens, Thomas P., Sr. V.P.-Creative--Publishers Clearing House, Port Washington, NY; *U.S. Private*, pg. 893
Owings, Charlene, Dir.-Creative--Russell Stover Candies, Inc., Kansas City, MO; *U.S. Private*, pg. 953
Oyster, William, Pres., Chief Oper. Officer & Mgr.-Adv., Sls. & Mktg.--Dallas Gold & Silver Exchange, Inc., Dallas, TX; *U.S. Public*, pg. 478
Paakkanen, Eija Sdiina, Dir.-Adv.--Bronto Skylift Oy AB, Tampere, Finland; *U.S. Public*, pg. 617
Paauwe, Jim, V.P.-Adv.--Michigan Bulb Company, Grand Rapids, MI; *U.S. Private*, pg. 421
Pacheco, Diosilda, Dir.-Adv.--Goya Foods, Inc., Secaucus, NJ; *U.S. Private*, pg. 468
Pacheco, Enrico, Dir.-Adv. & Sls.--Zivi S.A. Cutelaria, Porto Alegre, Brazil; *Int'l*, pg. 1529
Pacheco, Steve, Mgr.-Adv. & Mktg.--Hammermill Papers, Memphis, TN; *U.S. Public*, pg. 902
Packard, Debra, Acct. Exec.-Adv.--Harrington's of Vermont, Inc., Richmond, VT; *U.S. Private*, pg. 504
Packer, Kathy, Sr. V.P.-Adv.--CUC International, Inc., Stamford, CT; *U.S. Public*, pg. 320
Packer, Kathy, Sr. V.P.-Adv.--Entertainment Publications, Inc., Troy, MI; *U.S. Public*, pg. 320
Packer, Kathy, Sr. V.P.-Adv.--Welcome Wagon-Intl., Inc., Trumbull, CT; *U.S. Public*, pg. 321
Padua, Ricardo, Mgr.-Publishing--Controladora Comercial Mexicana, S.A. de C.V., Mexico, Mexico; *Int'l*, pg. 328
Paglierani, Joan, Mgr.-Mktg. Communications--Unitrode Corporation, Merrimack, NH; *U.S. Public*, pg. 1694
Pahidis, Peter, Pres. & Chief Exec. Officer--Cedar Farms Company, Inc., Philadelphia, PA; *U.S. Private*, pg. 221
Pain, Madame, Dir.-Adv.--Degremont Inc., Rueil-Malmaison, France; *Int'l*, pg. 822
Palmer, Becky, Dir.-Adv.--MCI Systemhouse, Atlanta, GA; *U.S. Public*, pg. 1024
Palmer, Charlotte, Mgr.-Adv. & Mkt. Planning--WHX Corporation, New York, NY; *U.S. Public*, pg. 1726
Palmer, Charlotte, Mgr.-Adv.--Wheeling Corrugating Co., Wheeling, WV; *U.S. Public*, pg. 1727
Palmer, Paula, Adv. Assoc.--Bayer Corporation/ Pharmaceutical Division, West Haven, CT; *Int'l*, pg. 173
Palmisano, Steve, Asst. V.P.-Adv.--American Home Products Corporation, Madison, NJ; *U.S. Public*, pg. 79
Palmisano, Steve, Asst. V.P.-Adv.--Whitehall-Robins Healthcare, Madison, NJ; *U.S. Public*, pg. 80
Paluzzi, Gina, Coord.-Mktg.--Stocker & Yale, Inc., Salem, NH; *U.S. Public*, pg. 1518
Pando, Marina Villa, Mgr.-Adv.--Symantec Corporation, Cupertino, CA; *U.S. Public*, pg. 1545
Panebianco, James, Dir.-Mktg.--Conap Inc., Olean, NY; *U.S. Private*, pg. 261
Panessidi, Joseph, Dir.-Adv. & Promo.--Kinney Shoe Corporation, New York, NY; *U.S. Public*, pg. 1777
Panicola, Laura, Dir.-Adv.--Belliss & Morcom (USA) Inc., West Chicago, IL; *Int'l*, pg. 1065
Panzer, Mark C., V.P.-Adv. & Sls.--American Drug Stores Inc., Oak Brook, IL; *U.S. Public*, pg. 93
Pape, Janet, Mktg. Analyst--Schwab Corp., Lafayette, IN; *U.S. Private*, pg. 974
Pappas, Diane, Dir.-Adv.--Showboat, Incorporated, Las Vegas, NV; *U.S. Public*, pg. 1469
Parashis, Pete, Adv. Admin.--Koret of California, Inc., San Francisco, CA; *U.S. Private*, pg. 632
Parent, Huguette, Mgr.-Adv. & Promo-U.S.A.--Air Canada, New York, NY; *Int'l*, pg. 36
Parikh, Anand, V.P.-Mkt. Devel. & Bus. Plng.--Telco Systems, Inc., Norwood, MA; *U.S. Public*, pg. 1568
Parker, Bruce, Sr. Exec. V.P. & Chief Merchant--Callaway Golf Company, Carlsbad, CA; *U.S. Public*, pg. 294
Parker, Jackie, Sr. Mktg. Analyst--Columbine JDS Systems, Inc., Denver, CO; *U.S. Public*, pg. 228
Parker, Linda, Mgr.-Adv., Women's Wear--Pendleton Woolen Mills, Inc., Portland, OR; *U.S. Private*, pg. 848
Parker, Susan, Mgr.-Co-op Adv.--Metropolitan Life Insurance Co., New York, NY; *U.S. Private*, pg. 737
Parkhill, Joanne, Dir.-Adv.--Nutri/System Inc., Horsham, PA; *U.S. Private*, pg. 859
Parks, Kent R., Dir.-Adv.--Nasco, Fort Atkinson, WI; *U.S. Private*, pg. 446
Parks, Kent R., Dir.-Adv.--Nasco International, Inc., Fort Atkinson, WI; *U.S. Private*, pg. 446
Parlak, Pamela, Mgr.-Mktg. & Adv.-Lenox Retail--Lenox Brands, Lawrenceville, NJ; *U.S. Public*, pg. 261
Parlato, Roberto, Mgr.-Pub. Rels.--Nestle Industrial e Commercial Ltda., Sao Paulo, Brazil; *Int'l*, pg. 921
Parmeter, Jack, V.P.-On-Air Promo.--CBS Broadcast Group, New York, NY; *U.S. Public*, pg. 274
Parmley, Dave, V.P.-Adv.--Karakas, VanSickle, Ouellette Advertising & Public Relations, Portland, OR; *U.S. Private*, pg. 607
Parque, Ronald D., Pres.--Mrs. Cubbison's Foods, Inc., Montebello, CA; *U.S. Public*, pg. 909
Parrick, Gail, Mgr.-Consumer Adv.--Blount, Inc. Oregon Cutting Systems Division, Portland, OR; *U.S. Public*, pg. 238
Parrish, Diana, Mgr.-Adv. & Mktg.--Thomasville Upholstery, Inc., Hickory, NC; *U.S. Public*, pg. 688
Parrotta, Linda, V.P.-Mktg.--Costa Cruise Lines, N.V., Miami, FL; *U.S. Private*, pg. 278
Parson, Helen, Dir.-Adv.--Bike Athletic Co., Knoxville, TN; *U.S. Private*, pg. 143
Parsons, John, V.P.-Sls.--Knoll Pharmaceutical Company, Whippany, NJ; *Int'l*, pg. 105
Pascocello, Rick, Dir.-Adv.--Berkley Publishing Corp., New York, NY; *Int'l*, pg. 1027
Pascucci, Marc, V.P.-Adv.--Loews Theatre Management Corp., New York, NY; *Int'l*, pg. 1282

Pastor, Bernard, Mgr.-Adv.--Arianespace SA, Evry, France; *Int'l*, pg. 81
Paszamant, David, Vice Chm., Exec. V.P. & Dir.-Mktg.--Adams Wine Co., Atlanta, GA; *U.S. Private*, pg. 17
Patch, Ed, Pres.--Benchmark Industries, Brookville, OH; *U.S. Private*, pg. 132
Pate, Sharman, Dir.-Adv.--Whatman Inc., Clifton, NJ; *Int'l*, pg. 1498
Pate, William, V.P.-Adv. & Pub. Rels.--BellSouth Corporation, Atlanta, GA; *U.S. Public*, pg. 207
Patel, Neepa, Coord.-Adv.--Wherehouse Entertainment, Inc., Torrance, CA; *U.S. Private*, pg. 1171
Paterson, Amanda, Dir.-Adv.--Bally Management, New Rochelle, NY; *Int'l*, pg. 998
Patmor, Roxanne, Mgr.-Mktg. Communications--Edison International, Rosemead, CA; *U.S. Public*, pg. 564
Patrick, Allan, Exec. V.P.- Mdsg., Adv. & Distr.--Genovese Drug Stores, Inc., Melville, NY; *U.S. Public*, pg. 730
Patrick, Barbara A., Mgr.-Adv. & Communications--Tax Management, Inc., Washington, DC; *U.S. Private*, pg. 182
Patten, Michael, Mgr.-Corp. Affairs--Avonmore Waterford Group plc, Killkenny, Ireland; *Int'l*, pg. 102
Patten, Michael, Mgr.-Corp. Affairs--Avenmore Waterford Foods plc, Waterford, Ireland; *Int'l*, pg. 102
Patterson, Sue, Dir.-Brdcst. Adv.--Giant Eagle, Inc., Pittsburgh, PA; *U.S. Private*, pg. 450
Patton, Robert, Media Buyer--Cosmetique, Inc., Vernon Hills, IL; *U.S. Private*, pg. 277
Pauker, Johann, Mgr.-Adv.--Feodor Burgmann Dichtungswerke GmbH, Wolfratshausen, Germany; *Int'l*, pg. 233
Paul, Susan, Dir.-Adv.--Rockwell International Corporation, Costa Mesa, CA; *U.S. Public*, pg. 1397
Pauler, Ingo, V.P.-Auto Lubricants Mktg./Americas/Southern Europe--Fuchs Petrolub AG Oel + Chemie, Mannheim, Germany; *Int'l*, pg. 517
Paulin, Nancy, Mgr.-Mktg. Commun.--Thomas Lighting-C&I Indoor Divison, Tupelo, MS; *U.S. Public*, pg. 1599
Paulk, Wayne, Plant Mgr.--Cooper Tools, Statesboro, GA; *U.S. Public*, pg. 444
Paulson, David, Mgr.-Adv.--The Oilgear Company, Milwaukee, WI; *U.S. Public*, pg. 1215
Pavenstedt, T., Mgr.-Adv.--American Barmag Co., Charlotte, NC; *U.S. Private*, pg. 51
Paxton, Edgar L., V.P.-Adv. & Sls. Promo.--Family Dollar Stores, Inc., Matthews, NC; *U.S. Public*, pg. 612
Payne, James P., V.P. & Sec.--National Western Life Insurance Company, Austin, TX; *U.S. Public*, pg. 1161
Payne, Patrick, Mgr.-Corp. Image--Duke Energy Corporation, Charlotte, NC; *U.S. Public*, pg. 534
Peacock, Gary, Gen. Mgr.--Covington Foods, Inc., Covington, IN; *U.S. Private*, pg. 280
Pearsall, Barbara K., Dir.-Adv.--Quoizel Inc., Goose Creek, SC; *U.S. Private*, pg. 901
Pease, Doug, Mgr.-Customer & Vendor Rels.--Bose Corporation, Framingham, MA; *U.S. Private*, pg. 160
Peavler, Shannon, Asst. Mgr.-Adv.--Ogden Publishing, Topeka, KS; *U.S. Private*, pg. 812
Peccolo, Pam, Mgr.-Adv.--J.D. Edwards & Company, Denver, CO; *U.S. Private*, pg. 365
Pechauer, Greg, Mgr.-Adv.--A.O. Smith Water Products Company, Irving, TX; *U.S. Public*, pg. 1477
Peck, Chuck, Sr. V.P.-Mktg., Prods., Organization & Devel.--American Institute of C.P.A.'s Inc., New York, NY; *U.S. Private*, pg. 57
Peck, Faye, Dir.-Adv--Associated Grocers, Inc., Seattle, WA; *U.S. Private*, pg. 90
Peck, Lori J., Mgr.-Communications--Netzsch Incorporated, Exton, PA; *U.S. Private*, pg. 792
Peck, Lucille, Mgr.-Adv.--Adrien Arpel, New York, NY; *U.S. Public*, pg. 40
Peckham, Terry, Mgr.-Marcom-Mktg.--Brown and Caldwell, Pleasant Hill, CA; *U.S. Private*, pg. 173
Pecson, Reuben N., Asst. V.P.-Mktg. & Adv.--Philippine Airlines, Inc., Manila, Philippines; *Int'l*, pg. 1050
Pederon, Jim, Mgr.-Mktg. & Adv.--Lee Grocery Company, Everett, WA; *U.S. Private*, pg. 657
Pederson, Eric, Dir.-Pub. Rels. & Adv.--Allison Engine Company Inc., Indianapolis, IN; *Int'l*, pg. 1127
Pedone, Michael, Dir.-Adv.--Cumberland Packing Corp., Brooklyn, NY; *U.S. Private*, pg. 295
Peek, Vangie, Dir.-Adv.--McDowell News, Marion, NC; *U.S. Public*, pg. 1078
Peiker, Butch, Mgr.-Classified Inside Sls.--St. Petersburg Times, Saint Petersburg, FL; *U.S. Private*, pg. 1088
Pellegrini, Mary Ann, Mgr.-Mktg. & Adv.--Cablewave Systems, North Haven, CT; *U.S. Private*, pg. 197
Peltier, William H., V.P.-Pub. Rels. & Adv.--Viad Corp, Phoenix, AZ; *U.S. Public*, pg. 1718
Pence, Tony, Mgr.-Sls. Promo.--Bridgestone/Firestone Inc. Retail Operations, Rolling Meadows, IL; *Int'l*, pg. 213
Pendergast, Ellen, V.P.-Adv. & Pub. Rels.--Trans-Lux Corporation, Norwalk, CT; *U.S. Public*, pg. 1628
Pendrill, Richard, Mgr.-Honda Adv.--Honda Canada Inc., Scarborough, Canada; *Int'l*, pg. 635
Penn, Brad, V.P.-Mdsg.--Gem-Dandy, Inc., Madison, NC; *U.S. Private*, pg. 442
Pennanen, Tarja, Mgr.-Adv.--Oy Electrolux Ab-ELEKTRO HELIOS, Helsinki, Finland; *Int'l*, pg. 441
Pennell, Gary B., V.P.-Mktg., Sls. & Adv.--Diamond Chain Company, Indianapolis, IN; *U.S. Private*, pg. 68
Penoncello-King, Tracey, Buyer-Adv.--Windsor Fashions, Los Angeles, CA; *U.S. Private*, pg. 1182
Peppas, John, Mgr.-Internet Adv.--Bellcore, Morristown, NJ; *U.S. Private*, pg. 976
Peres, Edward J., Div. Mgr.--Fuchs Lubricants, Midlantic Div., Baltimore, MD; *Int'l*, pg. 518
Pereyra, Cil, Dir.-Media & Adv. Services--Wherehouse Entertainment, Inc., Torrance, CA; *U.S. Private*, pg. 1171
Perfater, Judith O., V.P. & Dir.-Adv--The Roanoke Times, Roanoke, VA; *U.S. Private*, pg. 649
Pergantis, D., Dir.-Adv.--Air France, Athens, Greece; *Int'l*, pg. 561
Pericron, Pierre, Dir.-Mktg.--SmithKline Beecham Products France S.A., Nanterre, France; *Int'l*, pg. 1266
Perkins, Glenn, Mgr.-Adv.--Powell Equipment Ltd., Winnipeg, Canada; *Int'l*, pg. 1066
Perkins, Sherry, Dir.-Mktg. & Adv.--J.E. Higgins Lumber Co., Concord, CA; *U.S. Private*, pg. 527
Perlmuter, Michael, Pres.--Perlmuter Printing Company, Cleveland, OH; *Int'l*, pg. 1177
Perozzi, Donald J., Grp. Pres.-Adv. & Publ.--BellSouth Enterprises, Inc., Atlanta, GA; *U.S. Public*, pg. 208
Perry, Chris, Mgr.-Natl. Adv.--American Isuzu Motors Inc., Whittier, CA; *Int'l*, pg. 692
Perry, Elisabeth L., Mgr.-Bus. Commun.--Consumers Water Company, Portland, ME; *U.S. Public*, pg. 438
Perry, Gregg, Dir.-Adv. & Pub. Rels.--Mackie Designs, Inc., Woodinville, WA; *U.S. Public*, pg. 1030
Perry, Michele, Dir.-Communications--Molten Metal Technology, Inc., Fall River, MA; *U.S. Public*, pg. 1123
Perry, Ralph, V.P.-Consumer Mktg.--Rydelle Laboratories, Racine, WI; *U.S. Private*, pg. 592
Perry, Thomas E., Mgr.-Mktg. Communications--Philips Components-Discrete Products Division, Slatersville, RI; *Int'l*, pg. 1054
Perry, William, Mgr.-Mktg.--National Machinery, Tiffin, OH; *U.S. Private*, pg. 785
Peruccelli, Silvia, Mgr.-Mktg.--Caffaro S.p.A., Milan, Italy; *Int'l*, pg. 248
Peschio, Judy, V.P.-Adv.--Applied Communications, Inc., Omaha, NE; *U.S. Public*, pg. 1629
Pestovic, Edward J., V.P.-Adv.--Crowley, Milner & Company, Detroit, MI; *U.S. Public*, pg. 461
Pestovic, Edward J., V.P.-Adv.--Steinbach Stores, Inc., Detroit, MI; *U.S. Public*, pg. 461
Peterka, Curt D., Mgr.-Mktg. Svcs.--Portec, Inc.-Construction Equipment Div., Yankton, SD; *U.S. Public*, pg. 1318
Peters, Joe, Dir.-Adv. & Pur.--McKee Door, Inc., Aurora, IL; *U.S. Public*, pg. 69
Peters, Kay, V.P.-Sls.-Wallcovering Div.--Evans Adhesive Corp., Columbus, OH; *U.S. Private*, pg. 384
Peters, Laura, Dir.-Mktg.--Burnham, Atlanta, GA; *Int'l*, pg. 686
Peters, Rich, 2nd V.P.-Mktg. Svcs. & Pub. Rels.--Woodmen Accident & Life Co., Lincoln, NE; *U.S. Private*, pg. 1187
Petersen, Wayne, Mgr.-Adv. & Brdcst.--Minnesota Twins Baseball Club, Minneapolis, MN; *U.S. Private*, pg. 750
Peterson, Craig, Dir.-Adv.--Albertson's, Inc., Boise, ID; *U.S. Public*, pg. 38
Peterson, Phyllis, Rep.-Adv. & Sls.--Credit Union National Association, Madison, WI; *U.S. Private*, pg. 288
Peterson, Raymond J., Exec. V.P.-Adv.--Hearst Magazines Division, New York, NY; *U.S. Private*, pg. 516
Peterson, Susan, Dir.-Adv.--Schwegmann Giant Super Markets, New Orleans, LA; *U.S. Private*, pg. 629
Peterzell, Lori, Dir.-Adv.--The History Channel, New York, NY; *U.S. Public*, pg. 512
Petigrew, Walter, Adv. Mgr.--LK Tool USA, Inc., Brighton, MI; *Int'l*, pg. 1418
Petit, Jean-Jacques, Mgr.-Adv.--L'Oreal S.A., Clichy, France; *Int'l*, pg. 818
Petite, Joe, V.P.-Mktg.--Hyponex Corporation, Marysville, OH; *U.S. Public*, pg. 1447
Petrak, Michael R., Exec. V.P. & Gen. Mgr.--The Kansas City Star Company, Kansas City, MO; *U.S. Public*, pg. 964
Petrosemolo, Lynn M., Adv. Traffic Coord.--Bayer Corporation/Pharmaceutical Division, West Haven, CT; *Int'l*, pg. 173
Pettigrove, Sharon, Coord.-Adv.--O'Malia Food Markets Inc., Carmel, IN; *U.S. Private*, pg. 816
Petz, Deede, Adv. Coord.--Gerber Products Company, Fremont, MI; *Int'l*, pg. 973
Peyrat, Gloria, Mgr.-Communications--Circon Corporation, Santa Barbara, CA; *U.S. Public*, pg. 373
Peyser, Michael J., Mgr.-Mktg. Services & Adv.--AEC, Inc., Wood Dale, IL; *U.S. Private*, pg. 500
Phair, Georgia, Sr. Mgr.-Adv.--Northern Telecom Limited, Brampton, Canada; *Int'l*, pg. 968
Pheil, D.L., V.P.-Sls.--Landis, Waynesboro, PA; *U.S. Public*, pg. 1699
Phelan, Kevin, V.P.-Telecommunications--B-Line Systems, Inc., Highland, IL; *U.S. Public*, pg. 1471
Phelps, Patricia, Dir.-Print Production--DM Management Company, Hingham, MA; *U.S. Public*, pg. 473
Phelps, Wendy, Mgr.-Adv.--Guilford Mills, Inc., Greensboro, NC; *U.S. Public*, pg. 768
Phieffer, Kevin, Dir.-Adv.--Westlake Hardware, Inc., Lenexa, KS; *U.S. Private*, pg. 1169
Philbin, J.W., Dir.-Mktg. & Adv.--Harvest Brands, Inc., Pittsburg, KS; *U.S. Private*, pg. 46
Philbin, John W., Dir.-Mktg. & Sls.--Altair Corporation, Lincolnshire, IL; *U.S. Private*, pg. 46
Philips, Lisa, Dir.-Adv.--Johanson Manufacturing Corporation, Boonton, NJ; *U.S. Private*, pg. 589
Phillips, AJ, Coord.-Adv. & Promo.--Westronics, Inc., Kingwood, TX; *U.S. Public*, pg. 1593
Phillips, Annika, Creative Dir. & Mgr.-Adv. & Promo.--Omaha Steaks, Omaha, NE; *U.S. Private*, pg. 815
Phillips, Chery, Mgr.-Adv.--BayBanks, Inc., Boston, MA; *U.S. Public*, pg. 184
Phillips, Connie Ann, Mgr.-Adv.--Vogue Magazine, New York, NY; *U.S. Private*, pg. 20
Phillips, Craig, Dir.-Adv.--Donaldson Company, Inc., Minneapolis, MN; *U.S. Public*, pg. 517
Phillips, Glenn, Mgr.-Export--Varel Manufacturing Co., Dallas, TX; *U.S. Private*, pg. 1134
Phillips, Helen E., V.P.-Bus. Commun. & Adv.--Rockwell International Corporation, Costa Mesa, CA; *U.S. Public*, pg. 1397
Phillips, Henry, Mgr.-Mktg. Svcs.--United McGill Corp., Groveport, OH; *U.S. Private*, pg. 1122
Phillips, John, Jr., V.P.-Mktg. & Sls.--McKee Foods Corporation, Collegedale, TN; *U.S. Private*, pg. 723
Phillips, Kathleen, Dir.-Adv.--Homeside Lending Company, Jacksonville, FL; *Int'l*, pg. 906
Phillips, Kim, Asst. V.P.-Adv.--Nationsbank/Tennessee, Nashville, TN; *U.S. Public*, pg. 1163
Phillips, Wayne, Dir.-Retail Mktg.--Perdue Farms Incorporated, Salisbury, MD; *U.S. Private*, pg. 852
Phones, Hugh, Adv. Specialist--Gulf Power Company, Pensacola, FL; *U.S. Public*, pg. 1490
Phy, Ann, Coord.-Mktg.--NewAge Industries Inc., Willow Grove, PA; *U.S. Private*, pg. 796
Piantanida, Nancy, Mgr.-Adv.--Lindal Cedar Homes, Inc., Seattle, WA; *U.S. Public*, pg. 998
Piastrelli, Denise, Dir.-Pub. Rels.--ICF Kaiser International Inc., Fairfax, VA; *U.S. Public*, pg. 852
Pickett, Jane, Dir.-Adv.--Corange U.S. Holdings, Inc, Indianapolis, IN; *Int'l*, pg. 331
Pickett, Michael H., Pres. & Publisher--Harcourt Brace & Company Farm Publications Inc., Orlando, FL; *U.S. Public*, pg. 783
Pickle, Jeff, Corp. Planner--NuTone, Inc., Cincinnati, OH; *Int'l*, pg. 1499
Pieklo, David A., Dir.-Adv. & Promotions--McDougal/Littell, Evanston, IL; *U.S. Public*, pg. 841
Pierce, Ed, Dir.-Mktg. Communications & Mgr.-Adv.--Automotive Rentals, Inc. (ARI), Mount Laurel, NJ; *U.S. Private*, pg. 535
Pierce, Rosemary, Natl. Adv. Coord.--WEA Corp., Burbank, CA; *U.S. Public*, pg. 1612
Pierle, Michael A., V.P.-Environ. Safety & Health--Monsanto Company, Saint Louis, MO; *U.S. Public*, pg. 1124
Pierpont, Valerie, Adv. Traffic Coord.--Bayer Corporation/Pharmaceutical Division, West Haven, CT; *Int'l*, pg. 173
Pigford, Nancy M., Mgr.-Mktg. Communications--Raytheon Engineers & Constructors International, Inc., Lexington, MA; *U.S. Public*, pg. 1366
Pike, Debbie, Sr. V.P.-Mktg.--Mrs. Winner's Chicken & Biscuit Restaurants, Atlanta, GA; *U.S. Private*, pg. 766
Pilcicki, Mary, Coord.-Communications--Teleflex Incorporated, Plymouth Meeting, PA; *U.S. Public*, pg. 1569
Pile, Tim, Adv. Dir.--Dewe Rogerson Limited, London, United Kingdom; *Int'l*, pg. 408
Pilsner, James, Dir.-Adv.--Rite Aid Corporation, Camp Hill, PA; *U.S. Public*, pg. 1390
Pilz, Allen, V.P.-Adv.--The Lathrop Company, Toledo, OH; *U.S. Public*, pg. 1645
Pilz, Laura, Dir.-Adv.--BankAmerica Corporation, San Francisco, CA; *U.S. Public*, pg. 179
Pinkard, Lee S., Natl. Dir.-Mktg. & Commun.--Coopers & Lybrand, New York, NY; *U.S. Private*, pg. 274
Pinna, John, V.P.-Sls. & Mktg.--Roussel Corporation, Montvale, NJ; *Int'l*, pg. 625
Pintozzi, Mike, Mgr.-Adv.--Schutte & Koerting Division, Bensalem, PA; *U.S. Private*, pg. 604
Pinzino, Thomas F., Pres. & Chief Exec. Officer--Sunnyland Refining Co., Inc., Birmingham, AL; *U.S. Private*, pg. 607
Pirnik, Lou, Jr., Dir.-Adv.--TV Host Inc., Harrisburg, PA; *U.S. Private*, pg. 1066
Piro, David, Dir.-Adv.--Winona Knits, Winona, MN; *U.S. Private*, pg. 1183
Pirrone, Tom, Dir.-Adv.--Dial A Mattress USA, Long Island City, NY; *U.S. Private*, pg. 330
Pitcher, Sarah, V.P.-Corp. Commun.--Mesa Air Group, Las Vegas, NV; *U.S. Public*, pg. 1098
Pitrone, Scott, V.P.--Leader National Insurance Company, Dallas, TX; *U.S. Public*, pg. 75
Pittman, Robert, Exec. V.P.--Trend Offset Printing Services, Los Alamitos, CA; *U.S. Private*, pg. 1099
Pittman, Rod, V.P.-Mktg. & Sls.--Lufkin Industries, Inc., Lufkin, TX; *U.S. Public*, pg. 1019
Pizzo, Thomas V., Exec. V.P.--Century Business Credit Corporation, New York, NY; *U.S. Private*, pg. 225
Pizzuti, Everett V., Pres. & Chief Oper. Officer--Astro-Med, Inc., West Warwick, RI; *U.S. Public*, pg. 141
Pla, Sebastian, Dir.-Mktg. & Adv.--Noblex Argentina S.A.C. e I., Buenos Aires, Argentina; *Int'l*, pg. 951
Platt, Deborah, Mgr.-Adv. Art.--Van Son Holland Ink Corp. of America, Mineola, NY; *U.S. Private*, pg. 1133
Platt, Stuart, Pres.--DRS Precision Echo, Inc., Santa Clara, CA; *U.S. Public*, pg. 474
Pleszko, E.J., V.P.-Mktg.--Preformed Line Products, Cleveland, OH; *U.S. Public*, pg. 1321
Plummer, Terry, V.P.-Sls. & Mktg.--Boise Cascade Paper Div., Boise, ID; *U.S. Public*, pg. 243
Poe, Lisa, Mgr.-Mktg. Services--Jacuzzi Bros., Jacuzzi, Inc., Little Rock, AR; *U.S. Public*, pg. 1684
Poe, Sam R., Mgr.-Pub. Rels.--AmerenCIPS, Springfield, IL; *U.S. Public*, pg. 65
Poehler, Patricia A., Sr. V.P.-Admin.--United Farm Family Life Insurance Co., Indianapolis, IN; *U.S. Private*, pg. 1122
Poehling, Jim, V.P.-Mktg. & Adv.--Greenfield Industries, Cleveland, OH; *U.S. Public*, pg. 950
Pofcher, Paul, Gen. Mgr.--Rowenta (USA), Inc., Medford, MA; *Int'l*, pg. 569
Pogue, Ryan, Mgr.-Adv. & Project Specialist--Eager Beaver, Lake Wales, FL; *U.S. Private*, pg. 354
Pohl, John, V.P.-Mktg.--Cobra Electronics Corporation, Chicago, IL; *U.S. Public*, pg. 391
Pointer, Danny, Mgr.-Adv.--Amtran, Inc., Indianapolis, IN; *U.S. Public*, pg. 106
Poissant, Michael, Exec. V.P. & Gen. Mgr.--A&Z Hayward, Inc., East Providence, RI; *U.S. Private*, pg. 2
Pokorny, J.J., Mgr.-Mktg.--Raytheon Engineers & Constructors, Inc., Englewood, CO; *U.S. Public*, pg. 1366
Polakob, Corey, Dir.-Adv.--Hollywood Park, Inc., Inglewood, CA; *U.S. Public*, pg. 830
Pollack, Marvin, Dir.-Adv.--Hyatt Hotels Corporation, Chicago, IL; *U.S. Private*, pg. 551
Pollack, Peggy, Dir.-Adv.--Mademoiselle, New York, NY; *U.S. Private*, pg. 20
Pollinger, Richard, Pres.--Stapo Hollander Industries, Lakewood, NJ; *U.S. Private*, pg. 1033
Pollock, Dennis, Mgr.-Adv.--Wawa, Inc., Media, PA; *U.S. Private*, pg. 1155

Pollock, Mayer, II, Pres., Chief Exec. Officer & Chief Oper. Officer--The Pollock Corp., Pottstown, PA; *U.S. Private*, pg. 874
Polowyk, George, Mgr.-Mktg. Services--Greenfield Industries, Cleveland, OH; *U.S. Public*, pg. 950
Pomerantz, Greg, Dir.-Adv. & Promo.--Dahlberg, Inc., Golden Valley, MN; *U.S. Public*, pg. 194
Pomeranz, Edward, Pres.--Stanley Roberts, Inc., Lodi, NJ; *U.S. Private*, pg. 936
Pondo, Marina Villa, Mgr.-Adv.--Symantec Corporation - Beaverton Site, Beaverton, OR; *U.S. Public*, pg. 1545
Poor, Dean, Dir.-Promo. & Adv.--Fisher Broadcasting Inc., Seattle, WA; *U.S. Public*, pg. 648
Poore, Michael, V.P.-Adv. & Sls. Promo.--Shaw's Supermarkets, Inc., East Bridgewater, MA; *Int'l*, pg. 1170
Pope, Julie, Coord.-Mktg.--Joern's Sunrise Medical, Stevens Point, WI; *U.S. Public*, pg. 1536
Popkowski, John, Exec. V.P.-Adv. Sls.-MTV Networks--MTV Networks, New York, NY; *U.S. Private*, pg. 779
Popp, John B., V.P.-Mktg.--Perfection Bakeries Inc., Fort Wayne, IN; *U.S. Private*, pg. 852
Popplewell, Bill, Mgr.-Adv. & Coord.-Mktg.--Husky Oil Ltd., Calgary, Canada; *Int'l*, pg. 640
Poppy, Christine, Mgr.-Adv.--Dansk International Designs Ltd., White Plains, NY; *U.S. Public*, pg. 261
Porpora, John, Dir.-Adv.--Metropolitan Life Insurance Co., New York, NY; *U.S. Private*, pg. 737
Portada, Joseph, Mgr.-Intl. Sls.--Dynamics Research Corporation, Andover, MA; *U.S. Public*, pg. 539
Porter, Ed, Dir.-Adv.--The Stop & Shop Companies, Inc., Quincy, MA; *Int'l*, pg. 750
Porterfield, Scott, Mgr.-Retail Adv.--Goldbergs Marine Distributors, Edison, NJ; *U.S. Public*, pg. 1756
Portnoy, Alice, Mgr.-Mktg. & Adv.--Neff (UK) Limited, Milton Keynes, United Kingdom; *Int'l*, pg. 912
Porto, Rui, Mgr.-Media & Communications--Sao Paulo Alpargatas S.A., Sao Paulo, Brazil; *Int'l*, pg. 1193
Posey, Bob, Dir.-Sls. & Mktg.--Aeroglide Corporation, Cary, NC; *U.S. Private*, pg. 24
Posner, Eberhard, Dir.-Corp. Commun.--Siemens AG, Munich, Germany; *Int'l*, pg. 1244
Possenreid, Bob, V.P.-Adv.--Henry Schein, Inc., Melville, NY; *U.S. Public*, pg. 1437
Post, Jeffrey, V.P.-Design & Mktg.--ATHOL Corporation, Butner, NC; *U.S. Private*, pg. 94
Postrel, Pamela, V.P.-Creative Adv.--Universal Pictures, Universal City, CA; *Int'l*, pg. 1216
Potter, Ray, Mgr.-Adv.--Princeton University Press, Princeton, NJ; *U.S. Private*, pg. 885
Potts, Richard W., Pres.--Peerless Tube Company, Bloomfield, NJ; *U.S. Public*, pg. 1269
Potts, Shirley, Dir.-Adv.--Hollingsworth Saco Lowell Corporation, Inc., Easley, SC; *U.S. Private*, pg. 535
Powell, James R., Sr. V.P.-Sls. & Mktg.--Daisytek International Corporation, Plano, TX; *U.S. Public*, pg. 477
Powell, Jenny, Mgr.-Retail Mktg.--Starbanc Corporation, Cincinnati, OH; *U.S. Public*, pg. 1510
Powell, Jim, V.P. & Dir.-Adv.--Brookshire Grocery, Tyler, TX; *U.S. Private*, pg. 172
Powell, Michelle, Dir.-Adv. & Mktg.--Mity-Lite, Inc., Orem, UT; *U.S. Public*, pg. 1118
Powell, Walter, Dir.-Adv--Glaxo Wellcome Inc., Research Triangle Park, NC; *Int'l*, pg. 552
Powell, Walter, Dir.-Adv.--Glaxo Wellcome PLC, Research Triangle Park, NC; *Int'l*, pg. 553
Powers, Juanita, Coord.-Adv.--Warner-Jenkinson Co., Saint Louis, MO; *U.S. Public*, pg. 1696
Powers, Kevin, Dir.-Adv. & Design--Lotus Development Corporation, Cambridge, MA; *U.S. Public*, pg. 896
Powers, William J., Mgr.-Adv.--Appleton Papers Inc., Appleton, WI; *Int'l*, pg. 567
Poynter, Dennis, Mgr.-Adv.--American Trans Air, Inc., Indianapolis, IN; *U.S. Public*, pg. 106
Poythress, H.C., Sr. V.P.-Adv.--Heilig-Meyers Company, Richmond, VA; *U.S. Public*, pg. 804
Poythress, H.C., Sr. V.P.-Special Mkt. Research--Heilig Meyers Furniture Co., Richmond, VA; *U.S. Public*, pg. 804
Pratt, Keith, Dir.-Sls. & Mktg.--JSB Electrical PLC, Crewe, United Kingdom; *Int'l*, pg. 453
Precious, Dana, V.P.-Creative Adv.--Sony Pictures Studios, Culver City, CA; *Int'l*, pg. 1283
Preen, Kevin, Dir.-Adv.--Philips International B.V., Eindhoven, Netherlands; *Int'l*, pg. 1051
Preisel, Thomas G., V.P.-Opers., Sls. & Mktg.--Baltek Corporation, Northvale, NJ; *U.S. Public*, pg. 171
Prendergast, Kevin, Natl. Dir.-Consumer Mktg. & Adv.--Better Homes and Gardens Real Estate Service, Des Moines, IA; *U.S. Public*, pg. 1094
Prentice, Mike, Dir.-Sls. & Mktg.--API Harowe, West Chester, PA; *U.S. Public*, pg. 90
Presley, Rick, V.P.-Sls.--Cook Manufacturing Corporation, Duncan, OK; *U.S. Private*, pg. 272
Pressley, Adrian W., Asst. to Pres.--Transus Intermodal L.L.C., Atlanta, GA; *U.S. Private*, pg. 1097
Preston, Charlie, V.P.-Mktg.--First Security Bank of Idaho, N.A., Boise, ID; *U.S. Public*, pg. 637
Preston, Charlie, V.P.-Mktg.--First Security Bank of Utah, N.A., Salt Lake City, UT; *U.S. Public*, pg. 637
Prettyman, Glenn, V.P.-Advertising--American Business Advertising, Omaha, NE; *U.S. Private*, pg. 51
Prettyman, Glenn, V.P.-Adv.--American Business Information, Inc., Omaha, NE; *U.S. Public*, pg. 69
Price, Chad, Mgr.-Mktg.--Woodward Governor Company, Rockford, IL; *U.S. Public*, pg. 1776
Price, David A., V.P.-Adv. & Sls.--ACMAT Corporation, New Britain, CT; *U.S. Public*, pg. 16
Price, Lisa, Mgr.-Mktg.--American Recreation Products, Inc., Saint Louis, MO; *U.S. Public*, pg. 948
Price, Rick, V.P.-Mktg.--Krazy Glue Inc., New York, NY; *U.S. Private*, pg. 158
Price, William, Pres. & Mgr.-Adv. & Mktg.--Your Man Tours, Inc., Inglewood, CA; *U.S. Private*, pg. 1202
Priceu, Claire, Mgr.-Adv. & Communications--Clarins, Neuilly-sur-Seine, France; *Int'l*, pg. 295
Pridemore, Stephen, Pres.--Bright of America, Inc., Summersville, WV; *U.S. Public*, pg. 223
Priem, Ted, Chm., Pres. & Chief Exec. Officer--Nobles Mfg. Inc., Saint Croix Falls, WI; *U.S. Private*, pg. 800
Prijatel, Donald, Sr. V.P.-Adv. & Promo.--King World Productions, Inc., New York, NY; *U.S. Public*, pg. 961
Prijatel, Donald, Sr. V.P.-Adv. & Promo.--King World Productions, Los Angeles, CA; *U.S. Public*, pg. 961
Prince, D.R., Dir.-Mktg.--J. Hungerford Smith Company, Fullerton, CA; *U.S. Public*, pg. 428
Prince, Phil, V.P.- Sls. Promo. & Mktg. Services--Fieldcrest Cannon, Inc., Kannapolis, NC; *U.S. Public*, pg. 1296
Prince, Phil, V.P.-Sls. Promo. & Mktg. Services--Fieldcrest/ Cannon Bed Fashions Division, New York, NY; *U.S. Public*, pg. 1296
Prior, Heidi, Mgr.-Mktg. Opers.--Marketing Displays International, Farmington Hills, MI; *U.S. Private*, pg. 705
Prisco, Edward, V.P.-Mktg. & Adv.--San Antonio Express News, San Antonio, TX; *U.S. Private*, pg. 517
Pritchard, Randy L., V.P.-Mktg.--Boddie-Noell Enterprises Inc., Rocky Mount, NC; *U.S. Private*, pg. 154
Pritchard, Rod, Dir.-Communications, Pub. Rels. & Adv.--Vigortone AG Products, Inc., Cedar Rapids, IA; *Int'l*, pg. 1357
Pritchett, Mark, Mgr.-Adv.--Mirror Group plc, London, United Kingdom; *Int'l*, pg. 869
Pritt, Roger, V.P. & Gen. Mgr.-Auto Store Div.--STRAFCO, Inc., San Antonio, TX; *U.S. Private*, pg. 1046
Privette, Dean, Mgr.-Adv.--The Paty Company, Piney Flats, TN; *U.S. Private*, pg. 844
Privitera, Lorri, Mgr.-Media Rels.--The Pfaltzgraff Co., York, PA; *U.S. Private*, pg. 860
Proctor, Frank, Dir.-Adv.--Merle Norman Cosmetics, Inc., Los Angeles, CA; *U.S. Private*, pg. 733
Proffitt, Steven, Copy Chief--Mervyn's California, Hayward, CA; *U.S. Public*, pg. 489
Profumo, Frank, Dir.-Adv.--The Laitram Corporation, Harahan, LA; *U.S. Private*, pg. 643
Profuno, Frank, Dir.-Adv.--Intralox, Inc., Harahan, LA; *U.S. Private*, pg. 643
Proider, Linda, Admin. Asst.--Kamax-G.B. DuPont L.P., Troy, MI; *U.S. Private*, pg. 606
Prokopp, Terry, Sec. & Adv. Mgr.--Pontiac-GMC Division, Detroit, MI; *U.S. Public*, pg. 720
Prosperi, Janice, Mgr.-Adv.--Invista Capital Management Inc., Des Moines, IA; *U.S. Private*, pg. 885
Prosperi, Janice, Mgr.-Adv.--Principal Mutual Life Insurance Co., Des Moines, IA; *U.S. Private*, pg. 886
Protzman, Robert, V.P.-Sls. & Mktg.--Schneider National, Inc., Green Bay, WI; *U.S. Private*, pg. 971
Proudfit, Donna, Dir.-Mktg.--Pickering Inc., Tacoma, WA; *U.S. Private*, pg. 864
Pruett, Greg, V.P.-Corp. Comm.--PG&E Corporation, San Francisco, CA; *U.S. Public*, pg. 1240
Prushansky, Gary, Mgr.-Adv. & New Bus. Devel.--BIC Corporation, Milford, CT; *Int'l*, pg. 1273
Pszenny, Lawrence J., V.P.-Fin.--Bickford's Family Restaurants, Brighton, MA; *U.S. Public*, pg. 545
Ptacek, Anna M., Mgr.-Communications--Calgon Vestal Laboratories, Saint Louis, MO; *U.S. Public*, pg. 1515
Puccia, Vincent, V.P.-Sls. & Mktg.--American International Airways, Ypsilanti, MI; *U.S. Private*, pg. 57
Puckett, Todd, Dir.-Mktg. & Adv.--Halter Marine Group, Inc., Gulfport, MS; *U.S. Public*, pg. 778
Puk, John J., Dir.-Mktg.--Monsey-Bakor, Kimberton, PA; *U.S. Private*, pg. 757
Pully, Henry, Dir.-Mktg.--Lance, Inc., Charlotte, NC; *U.S. Public*, pg. 977
Pulver, Kenneth, V.P.-Corp. Commun.--Albany International Corp., Albany, NY; *U.S. Public*, pg. 36
Pulver, Kenneth, V.P.-Corp. Communications--Albany Mount Vernon Dryers, Greenville, SC; *U.S. Public*, pg. 36
Puoti, Maria, Dir.-Gloval Adv. Svcs.--Campbell Soup Company, Camden, NJ; *U.S. Public*, pg. 298
Purcell, Bob, Mgr.-Adv.--American Copper & Nickel Company, Inc., Wheat Ridge, CO; *Int'l*, pg. 672
Purdell, Michael, Mktg. Asst.--Cooper Instrument Corp., Middlefield, CT; *U.S. Private*, pg. 274
Purdy, Cathie, Mgr.-Adv.--Brush Wellman Inc., Cleveland, OH; *U.S. Public*, pg. 266
Puricelli, Enrique, Exec. Pres.--Sudamtex de Uruguay, S.A., Montevideo, Uruguay; *Int'l*, pg. 1304
Purles, Marc, Dir.-Adv.--Associated Food Stores Inc., Salt Lake City, UT; *U.S. Private*, pg. 90
Purnell, Elaine, Dir.-Midwest Adv.--Woman's Day, New York, NY; *Int'l*, pg. 795
Pursel, Harry, V.P.-Bus. Devel.--Litton Applied Technology, San Jose, CA; *U.S. Public*, pg. 1003
Purtill, Tom, V.P.-Sls. & Mktg.--Baylor Company, Sugar Land, TX; *Int'l*, pg. 1134
Putnicki, Patti, V.P.-Adv. & Mktg.--Dry Manufacturing Co., Winters, TX; *U.S. Public*, pg. 1795
Putz, Katherine, Sr. Dir.-Mktg. Commun.--Jones Medical Industries Inc., Saint Louis, MO; *U.S. Public*, pg. 933
Qamar, Robert K., Mgr.-Adv.--Dictaphone Corp., Stratford, CT; *U.S. Private*, pg. 1045
Qualls, Sherry, Gen. Mgr.-Adv.--Armstrong World Industries, Inc., Lancaster, PA; *U.S. Public*, pg. 131
Qualman, Jeff, Dir.-Adv.--Hirsh Company, Skokie, IL; *U.S. Public*, pg. 963
Quarles, Susan, Mgr.-Mktg.--Smith International, Inc., Houston, TX; *U.S. Public*, pg. 1478
Quenneville, Joan, Mgr.-Adv. & Sls. Promo.--Talbots, Inc., Hingham, MA; *Int'l*, pg. 28
Quertinmont, Tom, Mgr.-Mktg. Communications--Mettler-Toledo Inc., Worthington, OH; *U.S. Private*, pg. 4
Quesada, Juan, Exec. V.P.-Sls., Mktg. & Adv.--Cox Lumber Co., Saint Petersburg, FL; *U.S. Private*, pg. 283
Quesada, Vicki, Adv. Specialist--Halliburton Energy Services, Carrollton, TX; *U.S. Public*, pg. 776
Quesnel, Norman, Mgr.-Mktg. Communications--Chomerics Inc., Woburn, MA; *U.S. Public*, pg. 1262
Quey, K., Dir.-Mktg.-USA--China Airlines Ltd., Los Angeles, CA; *Int'l*, pg. 284
Quick, Michelle, Mgr.-Adv. & Promo.--Ferro Corporation, Cleveland, OH; *U.S. Public*, pg. 618
Quick, Michelle, Mgr.-Adv. & Promo.--Diamonite Plant, Shreve, OH; *U.S. Public*, pg. 618
Quinlivan, Helen, Mgr.-Classified Ads.--The Financial Times Ltd., London, United Kingdom; *Int'l*, pg. 1025
Quinn, Mike, Dir.-Regional Mktg.--Doubletree Corporation, Memphis, TN; *U.S. Public*, pg. 1335
Quint, Marcia, Mgr.-Adv.--Quality Food Centers, Inc., Bellevue, WA; *U.S. Public*, pg. 1349
Quon, Yin, Coord.-Adv. & Media--Nestle USA, Glendale, CA; *Int'l*, pg. 916
Quon, Yin, Coord.-Adv. & Media--Food Division, Solon, OH; *Int'l*, pg. 916
Quon, Yin, Coord.-Adv. & Media--Food Services Division, Glendale, CA; *Int'l*, pg. 917
Quon, Yin, Coord.-Adv. & Media--Foreign Trade Division, Glendale, CA; *Int'l*, pg. 917
Quon, Yin, Adv. & Media Coord.--Nestle Frozen, Refrigerated, and Ice Cream Companies, Solon, OH; *Int'l*, pg. 918
Rabadan, William, V.P.-Mktg.--Spinnerin Inc., South Hackensack, NJ; *U.S. Private*, pg. 1025
Rabbidge, Charles, Mgr.-Sls. & Mktg.--Scania USA Inc., Orange, CT; *Int'l*, pg. 687
Rabelo, Joao Pinto, Mgr.-Promo. & Adv.--Banco do Brasil, Brasilia, Brazil; *Int'l*, pg. 141
Rabeno, Lou, Mgr.-Mktg.--Lawrence Metal Products, Inc., Bay Shore, NY; *U.S. Private*, pg. 654
Rabin, Hal, V.P.-Mktg.--Sonic Couriers of Arizona, Inc., Scottsdale, AZ; *U.S. Private*, pg. 1123
Rabinovitch, Donald, Pres.--AFP Imaging Corporation, Elmsford, NY; *U.S. Public*, pg. 6
Rabinowitz, Beth, Mgr.-Adv.--Alarm Device Manufacturing Company, Syosset, NY; *U.S. Public*, pg. 1306
Racek, Todd, Mgr.-Adv.--United HealthCare Corporation, Minnetonka, MN; *U.S. Public*, pg. 1677
Rachmann, K., Dir.-Communications--Dumez-GTM, Nanterre, France; *Int'l*, pg. 823
Radde, Eric, Mgr.-Adv.--Williamson-Dickie Mfg. Co., Fort Worth, TX; *U.S. Private*, pg. 1179
Rademacher, R.W., Mgr.-Mktg. Services--Beaird Industries, Inc., Shreveport, LA; *U.S. Public*, pg. 1639
Radler, Toni, Dir.-Mktg. & Adv.--Hohner/HSS Inc., Ashland, VA; *U.S. Private*, pg. 533
Radsord, David, Dir.-Adv.--Barclays Bank PLC, London, United Kingdom; *Int'l*, pg. 164
Radtke, H. Helmut, Pres. & Chief Exec. Officer--Melitta U.S.A., Inc., Clearwater, FL; *Int'l*, pg. 857
Radwill, Scott, Pres., Chief Exec., Oper. & Fin. Officer--Master Appliance Corp., Racine, WI; *U.S. Private*, pg. 713
Raffa, Louise M., V.P.-Corp. Communications & Adv.--Molded Fiber Glass Co., Union City, PA; *U.S. Private*, pg. 756
Raffaelli, Richard, V.P.-Sls. & Mktg.--Muskin Leisure Products, Inc., Wilkes-Barre, PA; *U.S. Private*, pg. 768
Ragland, Christine, Mgr.-Bus. Promo.--Sealright Company, Inc., De Soto, KS; *U.S. Public*, pg. 1451
Rainer, Mel, Mgr.-Adv.--Kent Electronics Corp., Houston, TX; *U.S. Public*, pg. 951
Rainwater, Nancy, Mgr.-Adv.--The Testor Corporation, Rockford, IL; *U.S. Public*, pg. 1358
Ralston, Ronald, Exec. V.P.-Mktg. & Sls.--Parfums International Ltd., New York, NY; *Int'l*, pg. 1435
Ramalho, Americo, Dr., Mgr.-Pub. Rels.--Portuguese Railways (CP), Lisbon, Portugal; *Int'l*, pg. 1063
Rambo, Virgil A., V.P.-Sls. & Mktg.--CorryHiebert Corporation, Corry, PA; *U.S. Public*, pg. 772
Ramer, Tim, Mgr.-Mktg. Commun.--Dana Corporation, Toledo, OH; *U.S. Public*, pg. 479
Ramos, Wendy, Mgr.-Mktg. & Adv.--Corcom, Inc., Libertyville, IL; *U.S. Public*, pg. 446
Ramsay, C. Steve, Gen. Mgr.--Fiskars Inc., Wausau, WI; *Int'l*, pg. 492
Ramsay, Dan, Mgr.-Mktg. Communications--Kenworth Truck Company, Kirkland, WA; *U.S. Public*, pg. 1246
Ramsby, Bob, Supvr.-Mktg. Communications--CTS Corporation-Connector Division, New Hope, MN; *U.S. Public*, pg. 285
Ramsby, Robert, Supvr.-Mktg. Communications--CTS Corporation, Elkhart, IN; *U.S. Public*, pg. 285
Ramsey, Chuck, Mgr.-Mktg. Services--Magnetek Motors & Generators, Saint Louis, MO; *U.S. Public*, pg. 1037
Ramsey, Duane, Mgr.-Adv.--Citizens Insurance Company of America, Howell, MI; *U.S. Public*, pg. 54
Ramyarupa, Apichart, Sr. V.P. & Gen. Mgr.--Bangkok Bank Public Company Limited, Bangkok, Thailand; *Int'l*, pg. 146
Ranaldi, Ken, Dir.-Promo. & Adv.--Careers USA Inc., Philadelphia, PA; *U.S. Private*, pg. 209
Ranbaud, Pierre, Dir.-Adv. & Promo.--Procter & Gamble France, Neuilly-sur-Seine, France; *U.S. Public*, pg. 1332
Randazzo, Cindy, V.P.-Mktg.--May & Speh, Inc., Downers Grove, IL; *U.S. Public*, pg. 1063
Randl, Ron, Mgr.-Adv. Svcs.--RAM Golf Corporation, Melrose Park, IL; *U.S. Private*, pg. 908
Raney, Alan, Mgr.-Adv.--YSI Incorporated, Yellow Springs, OH; *U.S. Private*, pg. 1195
Raney, Ken, Dir.-Adv.--Excel Industries, Inc., Hesston, KS; *U.S. Private*, pg. 387
Rankin, Alfred M. Jr., Chm. Bd., Pres. & Chief Exec. Officer--NACCO Industries, Inc., Cleveland, OH; *U.S. Public*, pg. 1149
Rapaport, Michael, Dir.-Mktg.--Bresler's Industries, Inc., Des Plaines, IL; *Int'l*, pg. 1520
Rapp, Steven, Mktg. Commun. Writer--Best Power, Necedah, WI; *U.S. Private*, pg. 140
Rappaport, Fran, Dir.-Mktg.--Restaurant Associates Corporation, New York, NY; *U.S. Private*, pg. 924
Raptes, Jim, Mgr.-Custom Sls.--Deco Products Co., Decorah, IA; *U.S. Private*, pg. 320

Raser, Holly, Mgr.-Adv.--Peirce-Phelps, Inc., Philadelphia, PA; *U.S. Private*, pg. 847
Rash, Edward, Dir.-Adv. & Pub. Rels.--Hannay Reels, Westerlo, NY; *U.S. Private*, pg. 499
Rashti, Dana, Mgr.-Adv.-Fleet Fin.--Fleet National Bank, Providence, RI; *U.S. Public*, pg. 649
Rashti, Dana, Mgr.-Adv.-Fleet Fin. Grp.--Fleet Bank-NH, Nashua, NH; *U.S. Public*, pg. 649
Rask, Sharon, Dir.-Adv. & Mktg.--United HealthCare Corporation, Minnetonka, MN; *U.S. Public*, pg. 1677
Rasnick, Steve, Dir.-Adv.(In-House Agency)--Sonesta International Hotels Corporation, Boston, MA; *U.S. Public*, pg. 1485
Ratcliffe, Mary, Dir.-Adv.--Takeda America Inc., New York, NY; *Int'l*, pg. 1350
Ratcliffe, Mary, Adv. Consultant--Takeda USA Inc., Orangeburg, NY; *Int'l*, pg. 1350
Rath, Mark, Dir.-Adv.--Hydro Agri North America, Tampa, FL; *Int'l*, pg. 961
Rathmachers, Petra, Mgr.-Adv.--Wandel & Goltermann GmbH & Co., Elektronische Messtechnik, Eningen, Germany; *Int'l*, pg. 1485
Rau, Lisa, Dir.-Publicity--Silver Dollar City, Inc., Branson, MO; *U.S. Private*, pg. 1000
Raufeisen, R.R., Mgr.-Adv.--Sloan Valve Company, Franklin Park, IL; *U.S. Private*, pg. 1006
Rauscher, Craig D., Mgr.-Mktg.--Stewart-Warner South Wind Corp., Indianapolis, IN; *Int'l*, pg. 127
Rauss, William G., V.P.-Sls. & Mktg.--Edwin B. Stimpson Company, Inc., Bayport, NY; *U.S. Private*, pg. 1043
Rava, Victorio, Dir.-Adv.--Fiat Auto S.p.A., Milan, Italy; *Int'l*, pg. 481
Rava, Victorio, Dr., Dir.-Adv.--Fiat Auto SpA, Turin, Italy; *Int'l*, pg. 480
Rawlinson, John T., V.P.-Sls. & Mktg.--Renold, Inc., Westfield, NY; *Int'l*, pg. 1104
Ray, Mike, Mgr.-Reg. Adv.--Mazda Motor of America, Inc., Irvine, CA; *Int'l*, pg. 849
Ray, Monica, Dir.-Pub. Affairs--Kennecott Holdings Corporation, Magna, UT; *Int'l*, pg. 1119
Raz, Mike, Mgr.-Adv.--Guard Publishing Company, Eugene, OR; *U.S. Private*, pg. 485
Reader, Marty, V.P.-Mktg.--G&K Services, Inc., Minnetonka, MN; *U.S. Public*, pg. 690
Reagor, Craig, Exec. V.P.--QST Industries, Inc., Chicago, IL; *U.S. Private*, pg. 897
Ream, Marcy, Mgr.-Mktg. Commun. & Adv.--Republic Storage Systems Company Inc., Canton, OH; *U.S. Private*, pg. 924
Recalcati, L., Mgr.-Sls.--Solplant, Milan, Italy; *Int'l*, pg. 1524
Redfern, Ron, Sr. V.P. & Adviser-Mktg.--The Orange County Register, Santa Ana, CA; *U.S. Private*, pg. 425
Redmond, John, Mgr.-Sls.--Hopkinsville Milling Co., Hopkinsville, KY; *U.S. Private*, pg. 538
Redmond, John, Pres. & Chief Exec. Officer--Hoover Group, Inc., Alpharetta, GA; *U.S. Private*, pg. 538
Reed, Bruce N., Sr. Consultant--Belmont Metals, Inc., Brooklyn, NY; *U.S. Private*, pg. 132
Reed, Jennifer, V.P.-Adv. & Mktg.--Filene's Basement, Inc., Wellesley, MA; *U.S. Public*, pg. 622
Reed, John E., Chm. Bd., Pres. & Chief Exec. Officer--Mestek, Inc., Westfield, MA; *U.S. Public*, pg. 1099
Reed, Kathleen, Dir.-Adv.--International Rectifier Corporation, El Segundo, CA; *U.S. Public*, pg. 906
Reed, Kenneth, V.P.-Sls. & Mktg.--TriEnda Corporation, Portage, WI; *U.S. Private*, pg. 1103
Reed, Paul, Dir.-Mktg.--Norbest, Inc., Midvale, UT; *U.S. Private*, pg. 801
Rees, P.K., Grp. Dir.-Mktg.--John Laing PLC, London, United Kingdom; *Int'l*, pg. 796
Rees, Thomas L., V.P. & Dir.-Adv.--Pulitzer Publishing Company, Saint Louis, MO; *U.S. Public*, pg. 1343
Reese, Judy, Dir.-Adv.--Hoffman Seeds, Inc., Landisville, PA; *U.S. Private*, pg. 532
Reese, Michele, V.P.-Adv. & Mktg.--Disneyland, Anaheim, CA; *U.S. Public*, pg. 511
Reeves, Dale, Dir.-Communications, Mktg. & Adv.--John Brown Plastics Machinery, Attleboro, MA; *Int'l*, pg. 773
Reeves, Ralph, Dir.-Mktg.--Kwal-Howells, Inc.(Denver), Denver, CO; *Int'l*, pg. 1501
Reeves, Richard, Dir.-Adv.--The Times Publishing Co., Saint Petersburg, FL; *U.S. Private*, pg. 1087
Regan, Kathy, Mgr.-Adv.--Barnstead/Thermolyne Corporation, Dubuque, IA; *U.S. Public*, pg. 1545
Regiec, Donna, Mgr.-Adv.--Hinkley Lighting Inc., Cleveland, OH; *U.S. Private*, pg. 530
Regnier, Tom, Coord.-Adv.--Crenlo, Inc., Rochester, MN; *U.S. Private*, pg. 288
Rego, Maryanne, Mgr.-Adv.--Foodarama Supermarkets, Inc., Freehold, NJ; *U.S. Public*, pg. 661
Rehome, Donna, Coord.-Adv.--Mico Inc., North Mankato, MN; *U.S. Private*, pg. 741
Reich, T.O., Mgr.-Adv.--Crucible Materials Corp., Solvay, NY; *U.S. Private*, pg. 293
Reichart, James J., Mgr.-Adv.--Midwest Express Airlines, Inc., Oak Creek, WI; *U.S. Public*, pg. 1111
Reichart, Lee, V.P.-Adv.--Scott's Miracle-Gro Products, Inc., Port Washington, NY; *U.S. Public*, pg. 1447
Reichert, James, Mgr.-Adv.--Midwest Express Holdings, Inc., Oak Creek, WI; *U.S. Public*, pg. 1111
Reicherter, Derek, V.P.-Member Acquisition & Print Adv.--Book of the Month Club, New York, NY; *U.S. Public*, pg. 1612
Reid, Andrew W., V.P.-Sls.--Moore-Handley, Inc., Pelham, AL; *U.S. Public*, pg. 1128
Reid, John W., Exec. V.P. & Chief Fin. Officer--Ranco North America, Plain City, OH; *Int'l*, pg. 1243
Reider, Thomas D., V.P.-Domestic Sls. & Mktg.--Ruslander & Sons, Inc., Buffalo, NY; *U.S. Private*, pg. 952
Reif-Snyder, Jody, Mgr.-Corp. Communications--GMAC Mortgage Corporation, Horsham, PA; *U.S. Public*, pg. 720
Reilly, Paul, Mgr.-Adv.--Teleport Communications Group, Staten Island, NY; *U.S. Public*, pg. 1572
Reilly, Terry, Mgr.-Adv. Sls.--Iowa Farmer Today, Cedar Rapids, IA; *U.S. Private*, pg. 442
Reiman, Beverly J., Dir.-Corp. Communication--The Standard Register Company, Dayton, OH; *U.S. Public*, pg. 1505
Reimenn, Kurt, Dir.-Mktg. & Adv.--Fonar Corporation, Melville, NY; *U.S. Public*, pg. 661
Rein, Bernstein, Mgr.-Corp. Adv.--Farmland Industries, Inc., Kansas City, MO; *U.S. Private*, pg. 395
Reinhardt, Ron, Mgr.-Adv.--Research Products Corporation, Madison, WI; *U.S. Private*, pg. 924
Reisner, M., Dir.-Mktg.--Alva/Amco Pharmacal Companies, Inc., Chicago, IL; *U.S. Private*, pg. 47
Reitmeier, Debbie, Asst. V.P.-Mktg. & Sls.--Key Pharmaceuticals, Kenilworth, NJ; *U.S. Public*, pg. 1438
Remington, John, Dir.-Creative Services--The Department Store Division of Dayton Hudson Corporation, Minneapolis, MN; *U.S. Public*, pg. 489
Remmert, Joe, Mgr.-Adv.--Springs Window Fashions Division, Middleton, WI; *U.S. Public*, pg. 1500
Remus, Ken, Mgr.-Mktg., Adv. & Brandname--Symons Corporation, Centralia, IL; *U.S. Private*, pg. 932
Rennels, Jack, V.P.-Mktg.--Emkay, Inc., Itasca, IL; *U.S. Private*, pg. 374
Reno, David, Mgr.-Mktg.--Kern's Bakeries, Incorporated, Knoxville, TN; *U.S. Public*, pg. 547
Reno, Larry, V.P.-Adv.--Credit Suisse First Boston, Inc., New York, NY; *Int'l*, pg. 345
Rentneester, Dianne, Dir.-Print & Brdcst. Adv.--ShopKo Stores, Inc., Green Bay, WI; *U.S. Public*, pg. 1467
Renzulli, Ernest, Dir.-Adv.--Playboy Enterprises, Inc., Chicago, IL; *U.S. Public*, pg. 1309
Repholz, Kathy, Mgr.-Graphics--American Library Association, Chicago, IL; *U.S. Private*, pg. 58
Resnick, Michael, Dir.-Adv.--Masters, Inc., Westbury, NY; *U.S. Private*, pg. 714
Restmeyer, William, Mgr.-Mktg. Communications--Tool & Hoist Division, Liberty Corner, NJ; *U.S. Public*, pg. 877
Retteu, Megan, Mgr.-Collateral--Open Market, Inc., Burlington, MA; *U.S. Public*, pg. 1226
Reynolds, Alasdair, Mgr.-Adv. & Pub.--Airbus Industrie, Blagnac, France; *Int'l*, pg. 39
Reynolds, Curt, V.P.-Mktg. & Sls.--Comlinear Corporation, Fort Collins, CO; *U.S. Public*, pg. 1160
Reynolds, Martin, Mgr.-Corp. Commun.--EG & G, Inc., Wellesley, MA; *U.S. Public*, pg. 542
Rhees, Herb, V.P.-Sls.--Champion Pneumatic Machinery Co., Inc., Princeton, IL; *U.S. Private*, pg. 228
Rhoads, John, Mgr.-Adv. & Pub. Rels.--Heat Controller, Inc., Jackson, MI; *U.S. Private*, pg. 518
Rhodaberger, W.R., V.P.-Sales--Ervin Industries, Inc., Ann Arbor, MI; *U.S. Private*, pg. 382
Rhodes, Camilla, Deputy Gen. Mgr.-Adv. & Dir.--News International plc, London, United Kingdom; *Int'l*, pg. 927
Rhodes, Sabeaua, Mgr.-Adv.--The Crispin Company, Houston, TX; *U.S. Private*, pg. 290
Rhodes, Susan, Mgr.-Adv.--Jaguar Cars, Mahwah, NJ; *U.S. Public*, pg. 664
Rhyne, Dot, Dir.-Adv. & Sls. Promo.--A.H. Belo Corporation, Dallas, TX; *U.S. Public*, pg. 209
Riccioli, Fred, Mgr.-Adv.--Neles-Jamesbury Corp., Worcester, MA; *Int'l*, pg. 1428
Rice, Tim, Mgr.-Adv. & Mdsg.--Federated Mutual Insurance Company, Owatonna, MN; *U.S. Private*, pg. 399
Riceman, Ron, Dir.-Pub. Rels. & Adv.--Elizabethtown Gas Co., Union, NJ; *U.S. Public*, pg. 1147
Richards, Bryan, V.P.-Adv.--Meijer, Inc., Grand Rapids, MI; *U.S. Private*, pg. 729
Richards, Doug, V.P.-Mktg. & Sls.--Weibel Winery, Lodi, CA; *U.S. Private*, pg. 1159
Richards, Paul J., Mgr.-Corp. Communications & Mktg. Svcs.--Motorists Mutual Insurance Co., Columbus, OH; *U.S. Private*, pg. 764
Richardson, Ann, V.P.-Adv.--Neiman Marcus Co., Dallas, TX; *U.S. Public*, pg. 785
Richardson, Lee, V.P.-U.S. Adv.--Toys "R" Us, Inc., Paramus, NJ; *U.S. Public*, pg. 1626
Richardson, Lee, V.P.-Adv.--Toys "R" Us United States, Paramus, NJ; *U.S. Public*, pg. 1626
Richardson, Rachelle, Mgr.-Adv.--Lundia Div. of MII, Inc., Jacksonville, IL; *U.S. Private*, pg. 680
Richfield, Mark, Mgr.-Mktg. Svcs.--Vilter Manufacturing Corporation, Cudahy, WI; *U.S. Private*, pg. 1140
Richmond, Robert, Mgr.-Mktg.--Warn Industries, Inc., Clackamas, OR; *U.S. Private*, pg. 1150
Richter, Amy, Dir.-Adv.--Atlanta National League Baseball Club, Inc., Atlanta, GA; *U.S. Public*, pg. 1614
Richter, Hans Joachim, Dir.-Mktg.--Philip Morris Gmbh, Munich, Germany; *U.S. Public*, pg. 1290
Richter, Richard A., Mgr.-Prod. Communications--Graco Inc., Golden Valley, MN; *U.S. Public*, pg. 756
Rickborn, Chris, V.P.-Mktg. & Prod. Plng.--Equitrac Corporation, Coral Gables, FL; *U.S. Public*, pg. 590
Ricksecker, Robert, Mgr.-Adv.--The Wooster Brush Company, Wooster, OH; *U.S. Private*, pg. 1188
Riedel, Judith K., Art. & Adv. Dir.--Stuart Hall Co., Inc., Kansas City, MO; *U.S. Public*, pg. 1178
Rief, Jeff, Mgr.-Adv.--Larson Manufacturing Company, Brookings, SD; *U.S. Private*, pg. 652
Riefler, Elizabeth, Mgr.-Adv.--T.L. Smith Machine, Springville, NY; *U.S. Private*, pg. 1009
Riemann, Mark, Mgr.-Adv. & Mktg.--Cook Composites & Polymers Inc., Kansas City, MO; *Int'l*, pg. 1409
Riera, Lisette, Dir.-Pub. Rels.--Telemundo Group, Inc., Hialeah, FL; *U.S. Public*, pg. 1570
Ries, Mary, Mgr.-Adv.--The Vons Companies, Inc., Arcadia, CA; *U.S. Public*, pg. 1426
Rieson, Dean A., Pres. & Chief Exec. Officer--Carlson Real Estate Company, Minnetonka, MN; *U.S. Private*, pg. 212
Riess, Frank, V.P.-Mktg. Communications--The Stolle Corporation, Sidney, OH; *U.S. Public*, pg. 61
Rigdon, Pamela, Mgr.-Corp. Communication--Odetics Inc., Anaheim, CA; *U.S. Public*, pg. 1212
Rigg, Andrew, Grp. Head-Adv. & Sls. Promo.--Puma AG Rudolf Dassler Sport, Herzogenaurach, Germany; *Int'l*, pg. 1072
Rigsby, Tom, Dir.-Mktg.--Matthew Bender & Company, Incorporated, New York, NY; *U.S. Public*, pg. 1616
Rihek, John, Dir.-Adv.--Nissan Motor Corporation in U.S.A., Gardena, CA; *Int'l*, pg. 945
Riklis, Meshulam, Chm. Bd. & Chief Exec. Officer--McCrory Corporation, New York, NY; *U.S. Private*, pg. 720
Riley, Barbara, Dir.-Media--Four Seasons Solar Products Corp., Holbrook, NY; *U.S. Private*, pg. 422
Riley, John, Mgr.-Adv.--Malden Mills Industries, Inc., Lawrence, MA; *U.S. Private*, pg. 698
Riley, Michael T., Sr. V.P.-Mktg., Infosvcs. & Opers.--First Financial Bancorp, Hamilton, OH; *U.S. Public*, pg. 632
Rinaldi, Richard A., Pres. & Chief Exec. Officer--CCX, Inc., Charlotte, NC; *U.S. Private*, pg. 193
Rinaldis, Phylis, Mgr.-Adv.--Farinon Div. Harris Corp., Redwood City, CA; *U.S. Public*, pg. 791
Riner, Carla, Mgr.-Mktg. Publicity--American Packaging Corporation, Philadelphia, PA; *U.S. Private*, pg. 60
Riskin, Gregg, Mgr.-Mktg.--Samuel Cabot, Inc., Newburyport, MA; *U.S. Private*, pg. 198
Rissmeyer, Henry, Chief Adv.--Metropolitan Transportation Authority, New York, NY; *U.S. Private*, pg. 739
Ritchie, Roger, Dir.-Communications--FlightSafety International Inc., Flushing, NY; *U.S. Public*, pg. 218
Ritter, Byron, Mgr.-Adv.--Ag-Chem Equipment Co., Inc., Minnetonka, MN; *U.S. Public*, pg. 6
Ritter, Tony, V.P.-Adv.--The Eureka Company, Bloomington, IL; *Int'l*, pg. 440
Rivard, Jill, V.P.-Adv. & Mktg.--Paul A. Schmitt Music Company, Minneapolis, MN; *U.S. Private*, pg. 971
Rivera, Angela, Mgr.-Corp. Communications--FPA Medical Management, Inc., San Diego, CA; *U.S. Public*, pg. 608
Rivera, Claudia, Adv. Asst.--Kodak America, Ltda., Lima, Peru; *U.S. Public*, pg. 554
Rivet, David, Dir.-Adv.--Genovese Drug Stores, Inc., Melville, NY; *U.S. Public*, pg. 730
Rizvi, Qasim, Sr. Mgr.-Comml.--National Refinery Limited, Karachi, Pakistan; *Int'l*, pg. 909
Rizzi, Rich, Dir.-Adv.--Imprint Newpapers, Bristol, CT; *U.S. Public*, pg. 935
Rizzuto, Joseph W., Dir.-Bus. Comm.--Rohm and Haas Company, Philadelphia, PA; *U.S. Public*, pg. 1403
Roach, James, V.P.-Mktg., Sls. & Adv.--TII Industries, Inc., Copiague, NY; *U.S. Public*, pg. 1556
Roadruck, David K., Mgr.-Adv.--Flex-O-Glass, Inc., Chicago, IL; *U.S. Private*, pg. 412
Roadruck, David K., Mgr.-Adv.--Warp Brothers, Chicago, IL; *U.S. Private*, pg. 412
Roan, Larry A., Dir.-Mktg. & Adv.--F.A. Wilhelm Construction Co., Inc., Indianapolis, IN; *U.S. Private*, pg. 1176
Robbins, Bob, Dir.-Mktg. Services & Corp. Communications--Mentor Corporation, Santa Barbara, CA; *U.S. Public*, pg. 1086
Robbins, Susan, Mgr.-Mktg. & Commun.--Digital Sound Corporation, Carpinteria, CA; *U.S. Public*, pg. 508
Robellard, Jim, Dir.-Mktg. & Adv.--The Valspar Corporation, Minneapolis, MN; *U.S. Public*, pg. 1707
Roberts, Bruce L., V.P.-Adv.--Morgan Guaranty Trust Company of New York, New York, NY; *U.S. Public*, pg. 1129
Roberts, Graham, Dir.-Mktg. & Adv.--Unisys Limited, Uxbridge, United Kingdom; *U.S. Public*, pg. 1671
Roberts, H. Wayne, V.P.-Adv. Premium Markets--Continental American Corp., Wichita, KS; *U.S. Private*, pg. 267
Roberts, John, Mgr.-Adv. & Customer Service--Parks Products, Inc., Hollywood, CA; *U.S. Private*, pg. 840
Roberts, John, Dir.-Adv.-Magnetic Prods.--Sony Electronics, Park Ridge, NJ; *Int'l*, pg. 1281
Roberts, John F., Dir.-Corp. Admin.--Morrison Knudsen Corporation, Boise, ID; *U.S. Public*, pg. 1133
Roberts, Kathleen, Mktg. Communications Specialist--Engineering News-Record Magazine, New York, NY; *U.S. Public*, pg. 1070
Roberts, Lynn T., V.P.-Adv.--The Echo Design Group, Inc., New York, NY; *U.S. Private*, pg. 359
Roberts, Paul, Dir.-Corp. Commun.--Analogic Corporation, Peabody, MA; *U.S. Public*, pg. 109
Roberts, Suzie, Mgr.-Residential Upholstery Fabrics--Dickson Elberton Mills Inc., Elberton, GA; *U.S. Private*, pg. 331
Roberts, Wendy, Dir.-Adv.--Blue Cross and Blue Shield of Massachusetts, Boston, MA; *U.S. Private*, pg. 151
Roberts, William, Mgr.-Communications--Senco Products, Inc., Cincinnati, OH; *U.S. Private*, pg. 984
Robertson, C. Frank, V.P.-Mktg.--Osmose Wood Preserving, Inc., Buffalo, NY; *U.S. Private*, pg. 821
Robertson, Walter, Sr. V.P.-Commercial--GS Industries, Inc., Charlotte, NC; *U.S. Private*, pg. 435
Robillard, Jean-Pierre, Dir.-Commun.--Dassault Aviation Group, Vaucresson, France; *Int'l*, pg. 383
Robinius, Vern, V.P.-Mktg.--Q & B Foods, Inc., Irwindale, CA; *Int'l*, pg. 1074
Robins, Peter, Mgr.-Adv. & Prod.--Cincinnati Milacron Inc., Cincinnati, OH; *U.S. Public*, pg. 368
Robins, Peter, Mgr.-Adv. & Product Mktg.--Cincinnati Milacron U.K. Limited, Birmingham, United Kingdom; *U.S. Public*, pg. 368
Robinson, Irene, Dir.-Adv.--Fyrnetics, Inc., Roselle, IL; *Int'l*, pg. 1499
Robinson, John H., Grp. Chief Exec. Officer--Smith & Nephew PLC, London, United Kingdom; *Int'l*, pg. 1263
Robison, Pete, V.P.-Adv.--Watt, Roop & Co., Cleveland, OH; *U.S. Private*, pg. 1154
Robitaille, Carole, Advertising--Rolland Inc., Fine Papers Division, Saint-Jerome, Canada; *Int'l*, pg. 274
Roblard, Jim, Dir.-Adv. & Mktg.--Colony Paints, Kansas City, MO; *U.S. Public*, pg. 1707
Rocafort, Irene C., Coord.-Mktg. Svcs.--Royal Olympic Cruises, New York, NY; *U.S. Public*, pg. 1411

Rocco, Giancarlo, Dir.-Adv. & Pub. Rels.--Pirelli S.p.A., Milan, Italy; *Int'l*, pg. 1058
Rochowansky, Thomas, Mgr.-Adv. & Pub. Rels.--AGA Ges.m.b.H., Vienna, Austria; *Int'l*, pg. 13
Rockafellow, Allen, V.P. & Dir.-Mktg.--Aluma Shield Industries, Inc., Daytona Beach, FL; *U.S. Private*, pg. 47
Rockman, Elena, Dir.-Adv. & Sls.--Childrens Press Inc., Danbury, CT; *Int'l*, pg. 794
Rockwell, Rick, Mgr.-Pub. Rels.--Denison Hydraulics, Inc., Marysville, OH; *U.S. Private*, pg. 324
Rodak, Ron, Mgr.-Adv.--Graphic Enterprises of Ohio, Inc., Canton, OH; *U.S. Private*, pg. 471
Roddy, David, V.P.-Mktg. Svcs.--Deluxe Corporation, Shoreview, MN; *U.S. Public*, pg. 498
Rodefeld, James A., Sr. V.P.-Mktg.--Jacobson Stores Inc., Jackson, MI; *U.S. Public*, pg. 922
Rodehorst, Rachael, Adv. Asst.--Fleischer Manufacturing, Inc., Columbus, NE; *U.S. Private*, pg. 410
Rodemer, Steve T., Dir.-Adv.--Fedders North America, Inc., Whitehouse, NJ; *U.S. Public*, pg. 614
Rodenberg, Clinton F., Sr. V.P.-Mktg.--Schieffelin & Somerset Co., New York, NY; *Int'l*, pg. 412
Rodgers, Lisa, Mgr.-Natl. Sls.--Irma Shorell, Inc., Lynchburg, VA; *U.S. Private*, pg. 1101
Rodgers, Marc, Mgr.-Mkt. Plng. & Devel.--Amerada Hess Corporation, New York, NY; *U.S. Public*, pg. 65
Rodigues, Ronald, Dir.-Mktg.--Industrias Gessy Lever Ltda., Sao Paulo, Brazil; *Int'l*, pg. 1437
Rodriguez, Bob, Dir.-Adv.--W.L. Gore & Associates, Inc., Newark, DE; *U.S. Private*, pg. 465
Rodriguez, Jim, Dir.-Corp. Communications--CMI Corporation, Oklahoma City, OK; *U.S. Public*, pg. 278
Rodriguez, Joe, Dir.-Worldwide Adv.--Novell, Inc., Orem, UT; *U.S. Public*, pg. 1203
Rodriguez, Larissa, Mgr.-Pub. Rels.--Hammel, Green & Abrahamson, Inc., Minneapolis, MN; *U.S. Private*, pg. 497
Rodriguez, Tim, Dir.-Adv.--Madison Newspapers, Inc., Madison, WI; *U.S. Public*, pg. 984
Roedig, Cynthia, Mgr.-Mktg. Commun.--Burr-Brown Corporation, Tucson, AZ; *U.S. Public*, pg. 270
Roessle, Erwin H., V.P.-Mktg.--Dreis & Krump Manufacturing Company, Chicago, IL; *U.S. Private*, pg. 342
Roessner, John K., III, Chm. Bd. & Pres.--E.J. Brooks Company, Newark, NJ; *U.S. Private*, pg. 172
Roger, Ian, Mgr.-Adv. & Pub. Intl.--Reuters Holdings PLC, London, United Kingdom; *Int'l*, pg. 1105
Rogers, Caitlin, Mgr.-Adv.--Minuteman International, Inc., Addison, IL; *Int'l*, pg. 587
Rogers, Caitlin, Mgr.-Adv.--Multi-Clean Inc., Shoreview, MN; *Int'l*, pg. 587
Rogers, Fred, Dir.-Appliance Div.--Rangaire Inc., Cleburne, TX; *U.S. Public*, pg. 1193
Rogers, P.G., Pres. & Chief Exec. Officer--Cashco, Inc., Ellsworth, KS; *U.S. Private*, pg. 218
Rogers, Susan, Mgr.-Pub. Rels.--Horizon Enterprises Group LLC, Taylor, MI; *U.S. Private*, pg. 539
Rogerson, William D., Pres.--De-Sta-Co, A Dover Resources Co., Troy, MI; *U.S. Public*, pg. 521
Rogge, Joyce, V.P.-Adv. & Promo.--Southwest Airlines Co., Dallas, TX; *U.S. Public*, pg. 1493
Rohan, Mary, Dir.-Adv.--George Kovacs Lighting, Inc., Glendale, NY; *U.S. Private*, pg. 634
Rohe, Ronn, Specialist-Mktg. Communications--Cohu, Inc., San Diego, CA; *U.S. Public*, pg. 396
Rohrer, Doug, Sr. V.P.-Adv. Sls.-MTV & VH1--MTV Networks, New York, NY; *U.S. Private*, pg. 779
Rohrer, Maria, Mgr.-Pontiac Adv.--Pontiac-GMC Division, Detroit, MI; *U.S. Public*, pg. 720
Roistacher, Sandy, Dir.-Art & Adv.--Metropolitan Mortgage & Securities Co., Inc., Spokane, WA; *U.S. Private*, pg. 738
Rollins, Donna, V.P.-Adv. & Creative--Marchon Eyewear, Melville, NY; *U.S. Private*, pg. 702
Roman, David, V.P.-Corp. Adv. & Brand Mktg.--Apple Computer, Inc., Cupertino, CA; *U.S. Public*, pg. 121
Roman, Sofia, Coord.-Adv.--Heald Colleges, San Francisco, CA; *U.S. Private*, pg. 514
Rombouts, A., Dir.-Sls. & Mktg.--Holmatro Industrial & Rescue Equipment, Raamsdonksveer, Netherlands; *Int'l*, pg. 632
Romeo, Teri, Communications Services Specialist--Sea-Land Service, Inc., Charlotte, NC; *U.S. Public*, pg. 284
Romero, Alvaro, V.P.-Mfg.--Conway Import Co. Inc., Elmsford, NY; *U.S. Private*, pg. 272
Romero, Armando, Dir.-Adv.--Justin Boot Company, Fort Worth, TX; *U.S. Public*, pg. 937
Ronco, G., Dir.-Adv.--Electrolux San Jose, Pordenone, Italy; *Int'l*, pg. 442
Rondeau, Terri, Mgr.-Adv.--Besser Company, Alpena, MI; *U.S. Private*, pg. 139
Rondinelli, Karen, Dir.-Adv. & Mktg.--Allen-Edmonds Shoe Corp., Port Washington, WI; *U.S. Private*, pg. 36
Rongo, Stephen, Dir.-Adv.-Food & Drug--Providence Journal-Bulletin, Providence, RI; *U.S. Public*, pg. 209
Roodt, Brian, Pub. Rels. Officer--De Beers Consolidated Mines Limited, Kimberley, South Africa; *Int'l*, pg. 76
Root, Debra, Adv. & Sls. Promo. Admin.--Dresser-Rand Co. (Wellsville), Wellsville, NY; *U.S. Public*, pg. 529
Rooyakkers, Mark, Dir.-Mktg. & Adv.--Klipsch, Inc., Hope, AR; *U.S. Private*, pg. 626
Ropson, Ardin, Sr. V.P.-Impulse Sls.--Good Humor/Breyers Ice Cream, Green Bay, WI; *Int'l*, pg. 1435
Rosas, Luis, Dir.-Adv.--Banco Santander, Madrid, Spain; *Int'l*, pg. 143
Rose, Anthony D., Jr., Sr. V.P.-Adv.--AutoZone, Inc., Memphis, TN; *U.S. Public*, pg. 150
Rose, Harry, Asst. V.P.-Mktg. & Corp. Communications--Atlantic Gulf Communities Corporation, Miami, FL; *U.S. Public*, pg. 144
Rose, J. Kenneth, Mgr.-Adv.--The Gorman-Rupp Company, Mansfield, OH; *U.S. Public*, pg. 754
Rose, Keith, Dir.-Mktg. & Adv.--Dain Rauscher Incorporated, Minneapolis, MN; *U.S. Public*, pg. 476
Rose, Scott, Dir.-Adv. & Sls. Promo.--Sea World of California, San Diego, CA; *U.S. Public*, pg. 114
Roselli, Eleni, V.P.-Mktg. & Adv.--Bon Jour International Ltd., New York, NY; *U.S. Private*, pg. 156
Rosen, David, Pres. & Chief Exec. Officer--CB North America, Inc., Saratoga Springs, NY; *U.S. Private*, pg. 192
Rosen, David, V.P.-Leasing, Mktg. & Adv.--Rosen Associates Management Corp., Jericho, NY; *U.S. Private*, pg. 945
Rosen, Dick, V.P.-Adv. Svcs. Div.--Spiegel, Inc., Downers Grove, IL; *U.S. Public*, pg. 1498
Rosenberg, Andrew, Sr. V.P.-Mktg.--General Textiles, San Diego, CA; *U.S. Private*, pg. 445
Rosenberg, Andrew, V.P.-Adv.--Family Bargain Corporation, San Diego, CA; *U.S. Public*, pg. 612
Rosenberg, Katie, Coord.-Adv.--Little Switzerland, Inc., Charlotte Amalie, VI; *U.S. Public*, pg. 1001
Rosenberg, Michael, First V.P.-Mktg.--LaSalle National Bank, Chicago, IL; *Int'l*, pg. 10
Rosenberg, Ron, Coord.-Adv.--Beutlich, L.P., Waukegan, IL; *U.S. Private*, pg. 141
Rosenberger, Linda, Coord.-Adv.--Coats North America, Charlotte, NC; *Int'l*, pg. 300
Rosenblum, Steven E., V.P., Specialty Adv. Mgr. & Mngmt. Supvr.--Doremus & Company, New York, NY; *U.S. Public*, pg. 1223
Rosenblum, Steven G., Dir.-Adv.--Cadillac Motor Car Division, Warren, MI; *U.S. Public*, pg. 720
Rosenkoetter, Vicki, V.P.-Adv.--Famous-Barr, Saint Louis, MO; *U.S. Public*, pg. 1063
Rosenman, Kelly, Adv. Asst.--Universal Studios Hollywood, Universal City, CA; *Int'l*, pg. 1216
Rosenstein, Earl, Chief Fin. Officer--Ronco, Inventions. LLC, Chatsworth, CA; *U.S. Private*, pg. 943
Rosentreter, Paula, Dir.-Adv. & Sls. Promo.--Follett College Stores Corp., Elmhurst, IL; *U.S. Private*, pg. 417
Roskvist, Christer, Dir.-Pub. Rels.--Cardo AB, Malmo, Sweden; *Int'l*, pg. 268
Ross-Sirola, Heather, Mgr.-Mktg. & Corp Adv.--Partek Corporation, Helsinki, Finland; *Int'l*, pg. 1024
Ross, Georgette, V.P.-Customer Svcs.--CMP Media, Inc., Manhasset, NY; *U.S. Public*, pg. 279
Ross, Janine, Mgr.-Adv.--Dielectric Polymers, Inc., Holyoke, MA; *U.S. Public*, pg. 1258
Ross, Laura, Dir.-Adv. & Promo.--Simon & Schuster, New York, NY; *U.S. Private*, pg. 777
Ross, Lezlea, Mgr.-Mktg.--Hygeia Dairy Co., Inc., Harlingen, TX; *U.S. Private*, pg. 552
Ross, Liz, Dir.-Home Office Opers.--Putt Putt Golf Courses of America, Inc., Fayetteville, NC; *U.S. Private*, pg. 896
Ross, Marty, Dir.-Adv.--Business Insurance, Chicago, IL; *U.S. Private*, pg. 285
Ross, Mike, Mgr.-Adv.--Network Long Distance, Inc., Baton Rouge, LA; *U.S. Public*, pg. 1169
Ross, Richard, Dir.-Adv.--Pfaff American Sales Corp., Paramus, NJ; *Int'l*, pg. 1046
Ross, Thomas, Sr. V.P.-Adv. & Creative Services--Oneida Ltd., Oneida, NY; *U.S. Public*, pg. 1225
Rossi, Francesca, Dir.-Mktg. & Mgr.-Adv.--I.B.I.S.-S.p.A., Busseto, Italy; *Int'l*, pg. 642
Rossi, John, V.P.-Adv. & Mktg.--American Trouser, Inc., Columbus, MS; *U.S. Private*, pg. 64
Rotchford, Robert, V.P.- Sls. & Mktg.--Massachusetts Envelope Co., Somerville, MA; *U.S. Private*, pg. 712
Roth, Chuck, V.P.-Adv.--Farm Progress Publications, Carol Stream, IL; *U.S. Public*, pg. 513
Rotherham, Jack, Dir.-Adv.--Rolling Stone Magazine, New York, NY; *U.S. Private*, pg. 1162
Rothschild, Martin, V.P.-Mktg.-Healthcare--Aladdin Synergetics, Inc., Nashville, TN; *U.S. Private*, pg. 31
Rothschild, Ralph, V.P.-Bus. Affairs--Volt Delta Resources, Inc., New York, NY; *U.S. Public*, pg. 1724
Rotta, Patti, V.P.-Adv.--ACO Inc., Farmington Hills, MI; *U.S. Private*, pg. 3
Rotunno, Dave, Dir.-Mktg. & Adv.--Dean Foods Company, Franklin Park, IL; *U.S. Public*, pg. 489
Roush, Rita, Mgr.-Sls. Promo. & Adv.--Autry Greer & Sons, Inc., Prichard, AL; *U.S. Private*, pg. 479
Rovai, Ellie, Dir.-Mktg. Commun.--Berg Electronics, Saint Louis, MO; *U.S. Public*, pg. 212
Rowan, Marcie M., Mgr.-Adv.--Baldwin Piano & Organ Company, Loveland, OH; *U.S. Public*, pg. 169
Rowden, Ian, Dir.-Adv.--The Coca-Cola Company, Atlanta, GA; *U.S. Public*, pg. 392
Rowe, Sharon H., Dir.-Adv. & Pub. Rels.--The Greenbrier, White Sulphur Springs, WV; *U.S. Public*, pg. 284
Rowland, Jay, Mgr.-Adv.--Fossil Inc., Richardson, TX; *U.S. Private*, pg. 420
Rowland, Linda, Mgr.- Conventions & Shows Cooper Hand Tools, Raleigh, NC; *U.S. Public*, pg. 444
Rowley, Ellen, Mgr.-Mktg. & Communications--Modcomp, Fort Lauderdale, FL; *U.S. Public*, pg. 283
Roy, Michel L., Dir.-Mktg.--Gaz Metropolitain & Company, Montreal, Canada; *Int'l*, pg. 541
Roy, Terri, Mgr.-Sls. & Adv.--Installation Products Div., Lancaster, PA; *U.S. Public*, pg. 132
Royder, Una, Mgr.-Adv.--Aer Lingus, Dublin, Ireland; *Int'l*, pg. 28
Rozelle, Daniel, Sr. V.P. & Corp. Mktg. Dir.--Fort Wayne National Corporation, Fort Wayne, IN; *U.S. Public*, pg. 673
Rozier, Cheryl, Mgr.-Adv.--Warner Books, Inc., New York, NY; *U.S. Public*, pg. 1614
Rubin, Eric, V.P.-Adv. & Pur.--M. Rubin & Sons Inc., Long Island City, NY; *U.S. Private*, pg. 949
Rubis, Linda, Mgr.-Adv. Svcs.--Outdoor Technologies Group, Spirit Lake, IA; *U.S. Private*, pg. 822
Ruby-Mako, Alyssa, Dir.-Adv.--Tropicana Casino & Resort, Atlantic City, NJ; *U.S. Public*, pg. 159
Rucidlo, Martin, Dir.-Mktg.--Superior Label Systems, Inc., Mason, OH; *U.S. Private*, pg. 1055
Rucker, Warren, Dir.-Adv.--America West Airlines, Inc., Phoenix, AZ; *U.S. Public*, pg. 67
Rucks, Don, Mgr.-Adv.--Citgo Petroleum Corporation, Tulsa, OK; *Int'l*, pg. 1045
Ruda, Steve, Mgr.-Adv. & Sls.--Travel U.K., London, United Kingdom,; *U.S. Private*, pg. 647
Rudd, Barbara E., V.P. & Western Adv. Dir.--Johnson Publishing Company, Inc., Chicago, IL; *U.S. Private*, pg. 591
Ruddick, I.W., Dir.-Commercial Adv.--Ranks Hovis McDougall Limited, Marlow, United Kingdom; *Int'l*, pg. 1395
Ruddock, Jennifer, Mgr.-Investor Rels.--Catellus Development Corporation, San Francisco, CA; *U.S. Public*, pg. 314
Ruddy, Kevin, Dir.-Adv. & Mktg.--The Food Emporium, Bronx, NY; *Int'l*, pg. 1375
Rudnick, Forrest, Dir.-Adv.--Rheometric Scientific, Piscataway, NJ; *U.S. Public*, pg. 1387
Rudolf, Christoph, Mgr.-Adv.--Brauerei AG, Zurich, Switzerland; *Int'l*, pg. 479
Rudolph, Dana, Dir.-Sls., Mktg. & Adv.--Rough Brothers, Inc., Cincinnati, OH; *U.S. Private*, pg. 947
Rudolph, Randy, Dir.-Adv.--Damark International, Inc., Minneapolis, MN; *U.S. Public*, pg. 478
Rudolph, Richard M., Exec. V.P.-Sls. & Mktg.--Rudolph Foods Company, Lima, OH; *U.S. Private*, pg. 950
Ruediger, Bernt E., V.P.-Mktg.--Troy Mills, Inc., Troy, NH; *U.S. Private*, pg. 1106
Rufo, Dina, Dir.-Mktg.--Europa Cruises Corporation, Saint Petersburg, FL; *U.S. Public*, pg. 595
Ruhter, Don, Mktg. & Commun. Officer--Kemper Insurance Companies, Long Grove, IL; *U.S. Private*, pg. 614
Rumac, Barry, Dir.-Corp. Comm.--VTEL Corporation, Austin, TX; *U.S. Public*, pg. 1703
Ruman, Nicole, Mgr.-Devel. Coord.--American Enterprise Institute for Public Policy Research, Washington, DC; *U.S. Private*, pg. 53
Runquist, Al, Dr., Mgr.-Publications & Promo.--Aldrich Chemical Co., Inc., Milwaukee, WI; *U.S. Public*, pg. 1471
Runstedler, Ronald L., V.P. & Dir.-Sls. & Mktg.--Union City Chair Co., Union City, PA; *U.S. Private*, pg. 170
Rupprecht, C., Mgr.-Natl. Sls. & Mktg.--Marsh Bellofram Corp., Newell, WV; *U.S. Private*, pg. 707
Rus, William, Sr. V.P.-Creative Adv.--Paramount Pictures Corporation, Los Angeles, CA; *U.S. Private*, pg. 776
Rushworth, Ken, Dir.-Adv.--Strouds, Inc., City of Industry, CA; *U.S. Public*, pg. 1525
Russack, Richard A., V.P.-Corp. Rels.--Burlington Northern Santa Fe Corporation, Fort Worth, TX; *U.S. Public*, pg. 268
Russell, Duane, Dir.-Adv.--REDA, Bartlesville, OK; *U.S. Public*, pg. 298
Russell, John A., Dir.-Corp. Commun.--Banc One Corporation, Columbus, OH; *U.S. Public*, pg. 172
Russell, Rebecca, Coord.-Adv.--National Welders Supply Co. Inc., Charlotte, NC; *U.S. Private*, pg. 788
Russell, Richard R., Pres., Chief Exec. Officer & Mng. Dir.--The General Chemical Group, Inc., Hampton, NH; *U.S. Public*, pg. 707
Russell, Roncy, Mgr.-Adv.--Darling's, Bangor, ME; *U.S. Private*, pg. 311
Russell, Susan, V.P.-Coop Adv.--New Line Cinema Corporation, New York, NY; *U.S. Public*, pg. 1614
Russo, Daniel, Dir.-Mktg.--Horizon Air Industries, Seattle, WA; *U.S. Public*, pg. 35
Russo, Karen L., Dir.-Intl. Sls. & Mgr.-Promo.--Eastern Air Devices, Inc., Dover, NH; *U.S. Private*, pg. 357
Russo, Patricia, Mgr.-Adv.--Coldwater Seafood Corporation, Rowayton, CT; *U.S. Private*, pg. 251
Russo, Patty, Mgr.-Adv.--Ryobi Outdoor Products, Chandler, AZ; *Int'l*, pg. 1151
Ruth, Jon, Exec. V.P.--North Star Steel Co., Wayzata, MN; *U.S. Private*, pg. 210
Rutherford, Joan, Dir.-Adv. & Mktg. Services--Fuji Photo Film U.S.A., Inc., Elmsford, NY; *Int'l*, pg. 524
Ruthman, T.R., Pres., Gen. Mgr. & Adv. Dir.--Gusher Pumps, Inc., Dry Ridge, KY; *U.S. Private*, pg. 488
Ruyak, Kathy, V.P.-Media--Honickman Affiliates, Pennsauken, NJ; *U.S. Private*, pg. 537
Ruzic, Ed, Mgr.-Natl. Acct. Sls./St. Charles--Masonite Corporation, Chicago, IL; *U.S. Public*, pg. 904
Ryan, Becky, Dir.-Mktg.-Bel Brands--Bel/Kaukauna USA, Little Chute, WI; *U.S. Private*, pg. 130
Ryan, James R., Dir.-Promo.--Bumble Bee Seafoods Inc., San Diego, CA; *U.S. Private*, pg. 526
Ryan, Jim, Adv.-Retail Display--The Orange County Register, Santa Ana, CA; *U.S. Private*, pg. 425
Ryan, Nancy E., Dir.-Communications & Media--Klockner Pentaplast of America, Inc., Gordonsville, VA; *Int'l*, pg. 737
Ryan, Robert E., Jr., V.P.-Sls. & Mktg.--Mike Albert Leasing, Inc., Cincinnati, OH; *U.S. Private*, pg. 32
Ryan, Robert M., V.P. & Dir.-Mktg.--Gooch Foods, Inc., Lincoln, NE; *U.S. Public*, pg. 128
Ryan, Sally Mason, Creative Dir./Writer--W. Braun Company, Chicago, IL; *U.S. Private*, pg. 166
Ryden, Cindy-Lee, Dir.-Adv.--Vistakon Johnson & Johnson Vision Products, Inc., Jacksonville, FL; *U.S. Public*, pg. 929
Rydin, Craig, Pres.--Godiva Chocolatier, Inc., New York, NY; *U.S. Public*, pg. 299
Rymeski, Robert, V.P.-Mktg. & Adv.--The Hilsinger Co. L.P., Plainville, MA; *U.S. Private*, pg. 530
Rynberg, Thomas, Mgr.-Mktg.--La-Co Industries Markal Company, Elk Grove Village, IL; *U.S. Private*, pg. 640
Sabin, Kevin, Dir.-Mktg.--First Commercial Bank, N.A., Little Rock, AR; *U.S. Public*, pg. 630
Sabin, Pam, Dir.-Adv.--Pocket Books, New York, NY; *U.S. Private*, pg. 777
Sachs, Christopher, Dir.-Adv.--Men's Journal, New York, NY; *U.S. Private*, pg. 1162
Sachs, Ruth, Mgr.-Adv.--Yale University Press, New Haven, CT; *U.S. Private*, pg. 1195

Sadauskas, Michele, Mgr.-Adv. & Mktg.--Guess ?, Inc., Los Angeles, CA; U.S. Public, pg. 768
Saeger, Bob, Exec. V.P.-Mktg. & Adv. Services--Visa U.S.A. Inc., San Francisco, CA; U.S. Private, pg. 1141
Saegesser, Paul, Dir.-Mktg.--Nordson Schweiz AG, Munchenstein, Switzerland; U.S. Public, pg. 1189
Safier, Robert S., V.P.-Mktg.--Patent Construction Systems, Paramus, NJ; U.S. Public, pg. 793
Sagalski, Laura, Dir.-Commun.--Omni Hotels, Irving, TX; U.S. Private, pg. 1065
Sahertian, Pat, Dir.-Mktg. & Adv.--Austin Productions, Inc., Holbrook, NY; U.S. Private, pg. 100
Sajkowski, Debra, Mgr.-Adv.--Milwaukee Electric Tool Corp., Brookfield, WI; Int'l, pg. 96
Sakoutis, Steve, V.P.-Sls. & Mktg.--P & F Industries, Inc., Farmingdale, NY; U.S. Public, pg. 1239
Sakuma, Toshiharu, Mng. Dir.-Adv.--Nihon Keizai Shimbun, Inc., Tokyo, Japan; Int'l, pg. 929
Salahab, Tom, Dir.-Adv.--Information & Engineering Technology, Fairfax, VA; U.S. Private, pg. 351
Salazar, Chris, V.P.-Sls. & Mktg.--Karnak Corporation, Clark, NJ; U.S. Private, pg. 607
Salber, Daniel, Dr., Mgr.-Adv. & Pub. Rels.--Rheinische Olefinwerke GmbH, Wesseling, Germany; Int'l, pg. 105
Salcedo, Eduardo A., Dir.-Mktg.--Procter & Gamble Venezuela, C.A., Caracas, Venezuela; U.S. Public, pg. 1332
Salcido, Lorene, Dir.-Adv. & Pub. Rels.--Bridgford Foods Corporation, Anaheim, CA; U.S. Public, pg. 252
Salinas, Sergio, V.P.-Adv.--A.H. Belo Corporation, Dallas, TX; U.S. Public, pg. 209
Salinas, Sergio, V.P.-Adv.--The Dallas Morning News, Inc., Dallas, TX; U.S. Public, pg. 209
Saliture, Santo, Assoc. Dir.-Adv.--Northwestern Mutual Life Insurance Co., Milwaukee, WI; U.S. Private, pg. 807
Salkind, Susan, Mgr.-Corp. Commun.--CSE Insurance Group, San Francisco, CA; U.S. Private, pg. 197
Sallee, Fern, Coord.-Mktg.--Griffin Manufacturing Co., Muskogee, OK; U.S. Private, pg. 481
Salmon, Jeff, Mgr.-Adv.--Fike Corporation, Blue Springs, MO; U.S. Private, pg. 404
Salter, J., Mgr.-Adv.--GEC Plessey Semiconductors, Swindon, United Kingdom; Int'l, pg. 544
Saltoun, M., Pres. & Dir.-Opers.--A.S. Management Corporation, Stamford, CT; U.S. Private, pg. 7
Samet, Andy, Dir.-Adv.--Worldvision Enterprises, New York, NY; U.S. Private, pg. 776
Sameth, David, Head of Adv.--DreamWorks SKG, Universal City, CA; U.S. Private, pg. 342
Samide, Karen, Mgr.-Adv.--Northeast Utilities, Berlin, CT; U.S. Public, pg. 1194
Sammon, Karen E., Dir.-Mktg.--PAR Technology Corporation, New Hartford, NY; U.S. Public, pg. 1256
Sammons, Bill, Dir.-Adv. & Promotion--Homeland Stores, Inc., Oklahoma City, OK; U.S. Public, pg. 832
Sammons, Megan, Dir.-Adv.--Up-Right, Inc., Selma, CA; U.S. Private, pg. 1128
Sampogna, Frank, Mng. Partner-Adv. Services--Gillespie, Lawrenceville, NJ; U.S. Private, pg. 453
Samuels, Pete, Mgr.-Adv.--Karsten Manufacturing Corporation, Phoenix, AZ; U.S. Private, pg. 608
Sandelli-Gerlach, Allegra, Dir.-Adv.--Midlantic Bank, N.A., Edison, NJ; U.S. Public, pg. 1242
Sanderlin, Joe, Supvr.-Adv. & Promo.--Simon & Schuster Children's Publishing, New York, NY; U.S. Private, pg. 777
Sanders, Gina, Dir.-Adv.--Details Magazine, New York, NY; U.S. Private, pg. 20
Sanders, Holly, Dir.-Creative Services--Home Shopping Network, Inc., Saint Petersburg, FL; U.S. Public, pg. 1685
Sanders, Mike, Mgr.-MarCom--Micropolis Corporation, Chatsworth, CA; U.S. Private, pg. 742
Sanderson, Amy, Dir.-Adv.--Farmer Jack Supermarkets, Detroit, MI; Int'l, pg. 1375
Sanderson, Bill, Dir.-Mktg.--Sanderson Farms, Inc., Laurel, MS; U.S. Public, pg. 1430
Sanderson, George, Sls. Mgr.-Mktg.-Wirth Howden--Howden Group Plc, Renfrew, United Kingdom; Int'l, pg. 636
Sandin, Terry, Mgr.-Corp. Adv.--Longs Drug Stores Corporation, Walnut Creek, CA; U.S. Public, pg. 1013
Sands, John F., Jr., Dir.-Pub. Affairs--Barnes Group Inc., Bristol, CT; U.S. Public, pg. 189
Sands, Mike, Dir.-Adv.--Oldsmobile Div. General Motors Corp., Lansing, MI; U.S. Public, pg. 720
Sani, Sunil, V.P.-Opers. & Adv.--CGS Industries, Inc., Long Island City, NY; U.S. Private, pg. 194
Sanson, Ampelio, Gen. Dir. & Dir.-Adv.--Bonomelli S.R.L., Lecco, Italy; Int'l, pg. 201
Santoleri, Mark, V.P.-Adv.--InterDigital Communications Corp., King of Prussia, PA; U.S. Public, pg. 889
Santori, M., Mgr.-Mktg.--Tuthill Pump, Alsip, IL; U.S. Private, pg. 1111
Santos, Debbie, Asst. Mgr.-Adv.--Bestform Foundations, Inc., Long Island City, NY; U.S. Private, pg. 140
Santos, Debbie, Asst. Mgr.-Adv.--Lily of France, Inc., New York, NY; U.S. Private, pg. 140
Santos, Richard, Dir.-Mktg.--A-P-A Transport Corp., North Bergen, NJ; U.S. Private, pg. 2
Saras, Amy, Mgr.-Mktg. Communications--The Kendall Company, Mansfield, MA; U.S. Public, pg. 1647
Sartain, Cindy, Mgr.-Adv.--Daniel Industries, Inc., Houston, TX; U.S. Public, pg. 482
Sass, George, Mgr.-Adv.--GB Holdings, Jurong, Singapore; Int'l, pg. 531
Sass, Harvey, V.P.-Mktg.--Minwax Company Div., Upper Saddle River, NJ; U.S. Public, pg. 1466
Satchell, Leslie, Mgr.-Adv.--Gateway Apparel, Inc., Saint Louis, MO; U.S. Private, pg. 441
Satchell, Maria, Creative Dir.--Sound Advice, Inc., Dania, FL; U.S. Public, pg. 1488
Sato, Toru, Mgr.-Adv.--Toto Ltd., Kitakyushu, Japan; Int'l, pg. 1410
Saturn, Lionel, Dir.-Adv. Opers.--The New York Post, New York, NY; Int'l, pg. 927
Saul, Jerry, Mgr.-Adv. & Sls. Promo.--Arrow Group Industries, Inc., Wayne, NJ; U.S. Private, pg. 477
Saunders, Corbett, Dir.-Adv.--S.D. Warren Co., Boston, MA; Int'l, pg. 1193
Saunders, Lenore, Dir.-Adv.--Nady Systems, Inc., Emeryville, CA; U.S. Private, pg. 773
Savage, David, Dir.-Prod. Mngmt.--Dow Jones Financial News Services, Princeton, NJ; U.S. Public, pg. 524
Savaria, Yvon, Mgr.-Adv.--Sico Inc., Longueuil, Canada; Int'l, pg. 1239
Savary, Marie-Francoise, Dir.-Adv.--Yves Saint Laurent Parfums S.A., Neuilly-sur-Seine, France; Int'l, pg. 445
Sawamura, Fumio, Sr. Mng. Dir.--Hosokawa Micron Corporation, Osaka, Japan; Int'l, pg. 635
Sawyer-Lueck, Jessica, Media Supvr.--Viskase Corporation, Chicago, IL; U.S. Public, pg. 586
Sayer, David C., Exec. Dir.-Adv. & Pub. Rels.--Publishers Clearing House, Port Washington, NY; U.S. Private, pg. 893
Sayers, Jo-Anne, Fin. Controller--Inmet Mining Corporation, Toronto, Canada; Int'l, pg. 678
Scaglione, Ralph, Mgr.-Retail Adv.--St. Petersburg Times, Saint Petersburg, FL; U.S. Private, pg. 1088
Scalera, Ron, Sr. V.P. & Creative Dir.-Adv. & Promo.--CBS Television Network, New York, NY; U.S. Public, pg. 274
Scarangella, Frank, Sr. V.P.--The Bank of New York Company, Inc., New York, NY; U.S. Public, pg. 178
Schadler, John, V.P.-Adv.--Mirage Resorts Incorporated, Las Vegas, NV; U.S. Public, pg. 1116
Schaebel, N.J., Mgr.-Acctg. & Adv.--F.L. Smidth & Co. A/S, Copenhagen, Denmark; Int'l, pg. 475
Schaefer, Jeffrey N., V.P.-Sls.--Diebel Manufacturing Co., Morton Grove, IL; U.S. Private, pg. 331
Schaefer, Roy, Mgr.-Classified Adv.--Seattle Times Company, Seattle, WA; U.S. Private, pg. 980
Schaefer, Susie, Mgr.-Mktg. & Adv.--Midwest Grain Products, Inc., Atchison, KS; U.S. Public, pg. 1111
Schaeffer, David G., V.P.-Sls.--American Crane & Equipment Corp., Douglassville, PA; U.S. Private, pg. 52
Schaffhauser, John O., V.P.-Sls. & Adv.--Anderson-Tully Co., Memphis, TN; U.S. Private, pg. 73
Schaller, Scott, V.P.-New Bus. Devel.--Vision-Ease Lens Inc., Brooklyn Park, MN; U.S. Public, pg. 162
Schambach, Linda, Exec. Dir.-Adv.--Christianity Today, Inc., Carol Stream, IL; U.S. Private, pg. 238
Schapdick, Chris, Product Mgr.--Rosenthal U.S.A. Limited, Carlstadt, NJ; Int'l, pg. 1127
Scharf, Edward W., Dir. & Coord.-Sls.--Southern States Cooperative, Inc., Richmond, VA; U.S. Private, pg. 1017
Scharfberg, Vicki, Dir.-Adv.--Six Flags Great Adventure Theme Park & Wild Safari Animal Park, Jackson, NJ; U.S. Public, pg. 1611
Schaumann, Robert, Dir.-Fin. Reporting--The Marmon Group, Inc., Chicago, IL; U.S. Private, pg. 706
Schawacker, William H., Mgr.-Corp. Commun.--Nooter Corporation, Saint Louis, MO; U.S. Private, pg. 801
Schenck, Jane, Mgr.-Mktg. Communications--Freudenberg Nonwovens, Durham, NC; Int'l, pg. 505
Schenk, Ad, Dir.-Mktg.--British-American Tobacco (Germany) GmbH, Hamburg, Germany; Int'l, pg. 111
Schenk, Mike, Dir.-Mktg.--Hutch Sports USA, Inc., Hebron, KY; U.S. Public, pg. 1354
Scher, David, Dir.-Adv.--Autoroll Machine Co., LLC, Middleton, MA; U.S. Private, pg. 101
Scherb, M.P., Dir.-Corp. Advertising & Mktg. Communications--Union Camp Corporation, Wayne, NJ; U.S. Public, pg. 1665
Schere, Jay, Mgr.-Category--United Dairy Farmers, Inc., Cincinnati, OH; U.S. Private, pg. 1121
Scheske, Jan, Mgr.-Adv. & Mktg. Devel.--Johnson Outboards Marine Corp., Waukegan, IL; U.S. Private, pg. 478
Schiciano, Jason C., Pres.--The Coon-De Visser Co., Royal Oak, MI; U.S. Private, pg. 273
Schiering, Dave, Mgr.-Mktg.--Spectra-Tech, Shelton, CT; U.S. Public, pg. 1593
Schiffbauer, Sharon, Mgr.-Adv.--Hardware Wholesalers, Inc., Fort Wayne, IN; U.S. Private, pg. 502
Schimelman, Joan K., Sr. V.P.-H.R. & Mktg./Adv.--Republic Security Financial Corporation, West Palm Beach, FL; U.S. Public, pg. 1381
Schimpf, Glenn P., Vice Chm.--The Danis Companies, Dayton, OH; U.S. Private, pg. 310
Schindel, Bernard, Mgr.-Adv.--Reltec, Inc., Warrenville, IL; U.S. Private, pg. 921
Schindler, Robert A., Mgr.-Adv.--Great Lakes Window, Inc., Toledo, OH; U.S. Public, pg. 1193
Schloss, James D., V.P.-Adv. & Mktg.--Smithfield Foods, Inc., Norfolk, VA; U.S. Public, pg. 1479
Schlumpg, Stephan W., V.P.-Adv.--Goldbergs Marine Distributors, Edison, NJ; U.S. Public, pg. 1756
Schmale, Manfred, Mgr.-Adv.--BASF Coatings AG, Munster, Germany; Int'l, pg. 104
Schmid, Josef A., Dir.-Adv. & Mktg.--Mazda Austria GmbH, Klagenfurt, Austria; Int'l, pg. 849
Schmidt, Hans, Dir.-Adv.--VLSI Technology, Inc., San Jose, CA; U.S. Public, pg. 1703
Schmidt, Jeff, Dir.-Adv.--The HON Co., Muscatine, IA; U.S. Public, pg. 772
Schmidt, Klaus, Dir.-Mktg.--Koenig & Bauer-Albert AG, Wurzburg, Germany; Int'l, pg. 742
Schmitz, M., Dir.-Adv.--Thyssen AG, Dusseldorf, Germany; Int'l, pg. 1387
Schmitz, Peg, Mgr.-Ad Opers.--The Gazette Company, Cedar Rapids, IA; U.S. Private, pg. 442
Schneider, Gretel, Mgr.-Adv.--The New Yorker Magazine, New York, NY; U.S. Private, pg. 795
Schneider, Peter, Dir.-Adv.--Avon Books, New York, NY; U.S. Private, pg. 515
Schneider, Ron, V.P.-Adv. Sls.--A&E Television Networks, New York, NY; U.S. Private, pg. 515
Schneider, Tom, Gen. Mgr.--Royal Waterbeds, Maryland Heights, MO; Int'l, pg. 949
Schnepp, John, Dir.-Adv.--Big Y Foods Inc., Springfield, MA; U.S. Private, pg. 143
Schnure, Dorothy, Mgr.-Corp. Communications--Green Mountain Power Corporation, South Burlington, VT; U.S. Public, pg. 761
Schoenauer, Thomas E., V.P.-Sls. & Mgr.-Adv.--A&A Manufacturing Co., New Berlin, WI; U.S. Private, pg. 1
Schoenberger, Diana L., V.P.-Mktg. Commun. & Investor Rels.--CitFed Bancorp, Inc., Dayton, OH; U.S. Public, pg. 376
Schoener, H., V.P.--Detecto Scale Company, Webb City, MO; U.S. Private, pg. 209
Schoenfeld, Helene, Dir.-Creative Services--Inverness Corp., Fair Lawn, NJ; U.S. Private, pg. 574
Schoenholzer, Andrea, Coord.-Mktg. Communications--Jelmoli AG, Zurich, Switzerland; Int'l, pg. 705
Schofield, Colin, V.P.-Mktg.--Avedis Zildjian Company, Norwell, MA; U.S. Private, pg. 1206
Schofner, Nan, Mgr.-Adv.--Masco Corporation, Taylor, MI; U.S. Public, pg. 1052
Scholl, Tom, V.P.-Sls.--Philway Products, Inc., Ashland, OH; U.S. Private, pg. 862
Schollhammer, Stefan, Mng. Dir.--Klafs Saunabau GmbH & Co. KG Medizinische Technik, Schwabisch Hall, Germany; Int'l, pg. 736
School, Dave, Freelance Adv.--ABN AMRO Chicago Corp., Chicago, IL; Int'l, pg. 10
Schoonbordt, Michelle, Adv.--Millicom International Cellular SA, Bertrange, Luxembourg; Int'l, pg. 867
Schoonyoung, Frank, Pres. & Gen. Mgr.-Industrial Yeast North America--Fleischmann's Yeast, Fenton, MO; Int'l, pg. 237
Schouten, Peter, V.P.-Adv. & Mktg.--Vision-Ease Lens Inc., Brooklyn Park, MN; U.S. Public, pg. 162
Schownir, Peter, Mgr.-Adv.--Our Sunday Visitor, Inc., Huntington, IN; U.S. Private, pg. 821
Schrage, Lori, Mgr.-Coop. Adv.--Artistic Greetings, Inc., Elmira, NY; U.S. Public, pg. 136
Schreiber, Hans, Dir.-Adv. & Sls.--J. Dieffenbacher GmbH & Co., Eppingen, Germany; Int'l, pg. 413
Schreitmueller, Robert, Dir.-Mktg.--Electrovert, Grand Prairie, TX; Int'l, pg. 328
Schrijver, Robert, Dir.-Adv.--PepsiCo Wines & Spirits International, Purchase, NY; U.S. Public, pg. 1277
Schrine, Ron, V.P.-Sls. & Adv.--Ingersoll-Rand Company, Woodcliff Lake, NJ; U.S. Public, pg. 876
Schroat, Becky, Dir.-Adv.--Goodheart-Willcox Publisher, Tinley Park, IL; U.S. Private, pg. 464
Schrodt, Daniel, Exec. V.P.--Jiffy Products of America, Inc., Batavia, IL; Int'l, pg. 706
Schroeder, Richard, Pres.--Cresline Plastic Pipe Co. Inc., Evansville, IN; U.S. Private, pg. 289
Schropp, Mary Lou, Dir.-Corp. Communications--PHP Healthcare Corporation, Reston, VA; U.S. Public, pg. 1241
Schrumm, Roger, Dir.-Public Affairs--SCANA Corporation, Columbia, SC; U.S. Public, pg. 1436
Schub, Craig, Sr. V.P.--PacifiCare Health Systems, Inc., Cypress, CA; U.S. Public, pg. 1250
Schubert, J.R., Pres.--The Springwall Mattress Co., Akron, OH; U.S. Private, pg. 973
Schuetz, Gary A., V.P.-Mktg.--Amurol Confections Co., Yorkville, IL; U.S. Public, pg. 1781
Schuetz, Michael, Dir.-Adv.--The Texwipe Co., Inc., Upper Saddle River, NJ; U.S. Private, pg. 1079
Schuh, Don, Specialist-Mktg.--Neenah Foundry Company, Neenah, WI; U.S. Private, pg. 790
Schuler, Susan, Mktg. Asst.-Adv.--David Manufacturing Company (DMC), Mason City, IA; U.S. Private, pg. 436
Schulist, Stacy, Dir.-Mktg.--Lyon's Restaurants, Inc., Foster City, CA; U.S. Private, pg. 684
Schulte, Lynne M., Mgr.-Sls. Service--Dixon Ticonderoga Company, Heathrow, FL; U.S. Public, pg. 514
Schultz, Harry, Controller--Trimfit, Inc., Bristol, PA; U.S. Private, pg. 1103
Schultz, Jane, Adv. Asst.--Scott Forseman/Addison Wesley, Glenview, IL; Int'l, pg. 927
Schultz, Lisa, Dir.-Mktg.--The Keyes Company Realtors, Miami, FL; U.S. Private, pg. 618
Schulz, Jim, Area V.P.--Borden Italian Foods, Northbrook, IL; U.S. Private, pg. 158
Schulze, Laura, Mgr.-Adv. & Pub. Rels.--Furman Lumber Company, Inc., Billerica, MA; U.S. Private, pg. 431
Schumacher, Bill, Dir.-Adv.--Kraft Foods, Inc., Northfield, IL; U.S. Public, pg. 1287
Schumacher, Lori, Dir.-Adv.--Vail Associates, Inc., Vail, CO; U.S. Public, pg. 1704
Schumacher, William, Dir.-KGF Adv.--Kraft Foods Inc., Glenview, IL; U.S. Public, pg. 1288
Schumaker, Mandy, Dir.-Adv.--The Portland Newspapers, Portland, ME; U.S. Private, pg. 439
Schuster, Kurt, Mgr.-Mktg.--Intervet America, Inc., Millsboro, DE; Int'l, pg. 48
Schwab, John, V.P.-Adv. & Quality--Tenneco Packaging, Consumer Products Group, Deerfield, IL; U.S. Public, pg. 1579
Schwartz, Diane, V.P.-Adv. & Pub. Rels.--Christian Dior Perfumes Inc., New York, NY; Int'l, pg. 781
Schwartz, Michael, Mgr.-Adv.-Electronics--Raven Industries, Inc., Sioux Falls, SD; U.S. Public, pg. 1361
Schwarz, Robin, Supvr. Admin. Svcs.--The CIT Group/Capital Finance Inc., New York, NY; Int'l, pg. 360
Schweber, Dennis, V.P.-Mktg.--Jaco Electronics, Inc., Hauppauge, NY; U.S. Public, pg. 920
Schwietzer, Jeff, Mgr.-Pub. Rels.--American Crystal Sugar Company, Moorhead, MN; U.S. Private, pg. 52
Schwindeman, Gail, Mgr.-Product & Svcs.--Duke Energy Corporation, Charlotte, NC; U.S. Public, pg. 534
Schwinke, Del, Mgr.-Adv. Display--Pulitzer Publishing Company, Saint Louis, MO; U.S. Public, pg. 1343
Schwinke, Del, Mgr.-Display Adv.--St. Louis Post-Dispatch, Saint Louis, MO; U.S. Public, pg. 1343

Schwoerer, John, V.P.-Sls.--NAO, Inc., Philadelphia, PA; *U.S. Private*, pg. 771

Scibetta, Lisa, Mgr.-Mktg. & Adv.--Ultimate Technology Corporation, Victor, NY; *U.S. Public*, pg. 1637

Sciera, Tamara D., Dir.-Strategic Plng.--Marietta Corporation, Cortland, NY; *U.S. Private*, pg. 702

Scoby, Richard, V.P.-Adv.--RTG Furniture Corp., Seffner, FL; *U.S. Private*, pg. 905

Scolnick, Edward M., M.D., Exec. V.P. & Pres.-Merck Res. Laboratories--Merck & Co., Inc., Whitehouse Station, NJ; *U.S. Public*, pg. 1090

Scott, Ann, Mgr.-Adv.--Orbit Semiconductor, Inc., Sunnyvale, CA; *U.S. Private*, pg. 819

Scott, Carl E., Sr. V.P.-Prod. Mngmt. & Natl. Adv.--Mutual of Omaha Insurance Company, Omaha, NE; *U.S. Private*, pg. 769

Scott, Cynthia, Dir.-Adv.--Baltimore Gas and Electric Company, Baltimore, MD; *U.S. Public*, pg. 172

Scott, Debbie, Mgr.-Pub. Rels. & Media-North America--IcelandAir, Columbia, MD; *Int'l*, pg. 658

Scott, Elaine, Dir.-Mktg. & Adv.--Henry I. Siegel Company, Inc., New York, NY; *U.S. Private*, pg. 998

Scott, Eric, Mgr.-Adv.--Atlas Pen & Pencil Corporation, Hollywood, FL; *U.S. Private*, pg. 96

Scott, James A., Mgr.-Mktg.--Alkota Cleaning Systems, Inc., Alcester, SD; *U.S. Private*, pg. 34

Scott, Lynette, Dir.-Adv.--World Publishing Company, Tulsa, OK; *U.S. Private*, pg. 1190

Scott, Norman A., V.P. & Dir.-New Bus. Devel.--ARGOSystems, Inc., Sunnyvale, CA; *U.S. Public*, pg. 240

Scott, Robert L., V.P.-Sls. & Mktg.--Cosmo Communications Corporation, Miami, FL; *U.S. Public*, pg. 451

Scottman, Andrea, Mgr.-Adv.--Avis Autovermietung AG, Glattbrugg, Switzerland; *U.S. Public*, pg. 321

Scully, David, Dir.-Retail Oper.--Camellia Food Stores, Inc., Norfolk, VA; *U.S. Private*, pg. 203

Scully, Keith, V.P.--Progress Paint Mfg. Co., Louisville, KY; *U.S. Private*, pg. 890

Sczcepaniak, Joe, V.P.-Sls. & Mktg./North America--Software Publishing Corporation, Fairfield, NJ; *U.S. Public*, pg. 1483

Seagell, Linda, Dir.-Adv.--Native Textiles, New York, NY; *U.S. Public*, pg. 1684

Seale, T.S., Mgr.-Adv.--Alcatel Telecom, Richardson, TX; *Int'l*, pg. 55

Seamon, Sue, Mgr.-Adv.--Printronix, Inc., Irvine, CA; *U.S. Public*, pg. 1329

Searcy, Diane L., Dir.-Commun.--MFA Oil Company, Columbia, MO; *U.S. Private*, pg. 687

Searight, Bruce, Mgr.-Mktg., Sls. & Adv.--Energy Systems Industries, Inc., Boston, MA; *U.S. Private*, pg. 376

Searl, Craig A., Dir.-Mktg. & Adv.--Bee Line Company, Bettendorf, IA; *U.S. Private*, pg. 129

Searle, Heather, V.P.-Mktg.--Michael Foods, Inc., Minneapolis, MN; *U.S. Public*, pg. 1103

Searle, James A., Jr., V.P.-Admin.--CSX Corporation, Richmond, VA; *U.S. Public*, pg. 284

Sechkinger, Bill, Dir.-Adv.--Stuart Anderson's Black Angus/Cattle Company Restaurants, Los Altos, CA; *U.S. Private*, pg. 61

Sechrist, Mary, Dir.-Mktg. & Adv.--Alba-Waldensian, Inc., Valdese, NC; *U.S. Public*, pg. 35

Secoy, Owen W., Mgr.-Adv.--Richmond Screw Anchor Company, Fort Worth, TX; *U.S. Private*, pg. 932

Secrist, Rich, Jr., Exec. V.P.--The George E. Failing Company, Enid, OK; *U.S. Private*, pg. 153

Secrist, Richard, Chm. Bd., Pres. & Chief Exec. Officer--Blue Tee Corporation, New York, NY; *U.S. Private*, pg. 153

See, Gary H., Grp. V.P.-Mktg.--International Dairy Queen, Inc., Minneapolis, MN; *U.S. Public*, pg. 220

Seeburger, Stacy, Dir.-Mktg.--Jacmar Companies, Inc., Alhambra, CA; *U.S. Private*, pg. 580

Seeliger, Michael, V.P.-Investor Rels. & Corp. Rels.--Horizon/CMS Healthcare Corporation, Albuquerque, NM; *U.S. Public*, pg. 836

Seely, Blaine, V.P.-Mktg. Svcs.--North American Van Lines, Inc., Fort Wayne, IN; *U.S. Public*, pg. 1191

Seffren, Randy, V.P.-Mktg.--D.P. Fitness, Opelika, AL; *U.S. Public*, pg. 1354

Segal, Linda, Mgr.-Co-op Adv.--Del Laboratories, Inc., Farmingdale, NY; *U.S. Public*, pg. 494

Segal, William, V.P. & Dir.-Adv.--Republic New York Corporation, New York, NY; *U.S. Public*, pg. 1380

Seibert, Dane, Sr. V.P.-Sls. & Mktg.--Glacier Water Services Inc., Carlsbad, CA; *U.S. Public*, pg. 745

Seibert, Ron, Gen. Sls. Mgr.--PACCAR Winch Division, Broken Arrow, OK; *U.S. Public*, pg. 1246

Seidel, Bill, Dir.-Mktg.--Justin Industries, Inc., Fort Worth, TX; *U.S. Public*, pg. 936

Seitz, Mark, Mgr.-Sls., Mktg., Adv. & Pub. Rels.--Service Supply Co. Inc. of Indiana, Indianapolis, IN; *U.S. Private*, pg. 987

Seitz, Stephanie, Mgr.-Adv.--Berkley Publishing Corp., New York, NY; *Int'l*, pg. 1027

Seldin, James, Pres.--Miss Elaine Inc., Saint Louis, MO; *U.S. Private*, pg. 752

Seligmann, Philippe, Dir.-Adv.--Leclerc, Issy-les-Moulineaux, France; *Int'l*, pg. 805

Selke, Gus, Brand Mgr.-Strategy & Adv.--AirTouch Cellular - Western Region, Bellevue, WA; *U.S. Public*, pg. 34

Sell, Madeline, V.P.-Adv. & Mktg. Support--Sanwa Bank California, Los Angeles, CA; *Int'l*, pg. 1189

Sella, Tony, Sr. V.P.-Creative Adv.--Twentieth Century Fox Film Corp., Los Angeles, CA; *Int'l*, pg. 926

Sellers, Gerald, V.P.-Mktg.--Shapell Industries, Inc., Beverly Hills, CA; *U.S. Private*, pg. 990

Sellers, Paul, Mgr.-Honda Automobile Adv.--American Honda Motor Co., Inc., Torrance, CA; *Int'l*, pg. 634

Sellers, Tracy, Mgr.-Adv.--ASICS Tiger Corporation, Fountain Valley, CA; *U.S. Private*, pg. 89

Seltzer, Sherwin, V.P., Gen. Sls. Mgr. & Mgr.-Sls. Promo., Pub. Rels. & Adv.--Villazon Company Inc., Upper Saddle River, NJ; *U.S. Private*, pg. 1140

Selvaggio, Leonard, Mgr.-Corp. Communication--Olsy North America Inc., Liberty Lake, WA; *Int'l*, pg. 1002

Semelsberger, Kenneth J., Pres. & Chief Oper. Officer--The Scott Fetzer Company, Westlake, OH; *U.S. Public*, pg. 217

Semen, Barbara, V.P.-Mktg.--Fabri-Centers of America, Inc., Hudson, OH; *U.S. Public*, pg. 609

Sementilli, Don, Mgr.-Mktg. Communications--O-Z/Gedney Co., Farmington, CT; *U.S. Public*, pg. 727

Senador da Silva, Andre Luiz, Mgr.-Adv.--BASF S.A., Sao Bernardo do Campo, Brazil; *Int'l*, pg. 107

Seoane, Charlene, Mgr.-Adv. Services--OAG, Oak Brook, IL; *Int'l*, pg. 1097

Serafin, Kristine, Dir.-Adv. & Pub. Rels.--Omni Hotels, Irving, TX; *U.S. Private*, pg. 1065

Serrichio, Jose Roberto Frolov, Mgr.-Adv.--EAC-Embraer Aircraft Corporation, Fort Lauderdale, FL; *Int'l*, pg. 452

Serulneck, Lester, Chm. Bd.--Allmetal Screw Products Corp., Deer Park, NY; *U.S. Private*, pg. 41

Setford, Alida, Dir.-Adv. & Promo./Educational Publ. Grp.--John Wiley & Sons, Inc., New York, NY; *U.S. Public*, pg. 1768

Sewak, Carrie, Mgr.-Media--United Air Specialists, Inc., Cincinnati, OH; *U.S. Public*, pg. 382

Sewell, Carol, Second V.P.-Adv.--Conseco Inc., Carmel, IN; *U.S. Public*, pg. 432

Sexton, Linda, Mgr.-Transportation Svcs.--Exxon Company, U.S.A., Houston, TX; *U.S. Public*, pg. 601

Seybert, David C., Mgr.-Adv. & Corp. Commun.--L.B. Foster Company, Pittsburgh, PA; *U.S. Public*, pg. 675

Shabazz, Zalmai, Dir.-Adv.--General Railway Signal Corp., Rochester, NY; *Int'l*, pg. 1194

Shade, Robert, Jr., Pres.--Sierra Coating Technologies, De Pere, WI; *U.S. Private*, pg. 998

Shaffer, Gill, Mgr.-Pub. Rels.--Fuller, Smith & Turner Plc, London, United Kingdom; *Int'l*, pg. 529

Shaffer, Michael, V.P.-Sls.--Breuer/Tornado, Chicago, IL; *U.S. Private*, pg. 167

Shafir, Sheri, Mgr.-Adv.--McBee Systems, Inc., Parsippany, NJ; *U.S. Private*, pg. 718

Shah, Satish, Pres. & Chief Exec. Officer--Accra Pac Group, Elkhart, IN; *U.S. Private*, pg. 11

Shakespear, George, V.P.-Corp. Mktg. Communications & Adv.--J.P. Morgan Co. Incorporated, New York, NY; *U.S. Public*, pg. 1129

Shalley, Jo, Dir.-Adv.--The Toro Company, Bloomington, MN; *U.S. Public*, pg. 1623

Shalley, Jo, Dir.-Adv.--The Toro Company Irrigation Products, Riverside, CA; *U.S. Public*, pg. 1624

Shane, Ken, Dir.-Hospitality--Brutger Equities, Inc., Saint Cloud, MN; *U.S. Private*, pg. 176

Shannon, Christy, Natl. Adv. Mgr.-Marriott Hotels, Resorts & Suites--Marriott Hotels, Resorts, and Suites, Washington, DC; *U.S. Public*, pg. 1048

Shannon, Jim, Dir.-Adv.--Cleveland Chair Company, Cleveland, TN; *U.S. Private*, pg. 579

Shapiro, Albert, Pres.--Commander Oil Corporation, Oyster Bay, NY; *U.S. Private*, pg. 257

Shapiro, David, V.P.-Mktg.--Pressman Toy Corp., New York, NY; *U.S. Private*, pg. 882

Shapiro, Marc, V.P.-Mktg.--The Wackenhut Corporation, Palm Beach Gardens, FL; *U.S. Public*, pg. 1731

Sharga, Rick, V.P. & Grp. Supvr.-Adv. & Pub. Rels.--Shafer, Irvine, CA; *U.S. Private*, pg. 988

Sharp, Tim, Dir.-Corp. Communications--BICC plc, London, United Kingdom; *Int'l*, pg. 120

Sharpe, Luke, Dir.-Adv.--Sharpe Dry Goods Co., Inc., Checotah, OK; *U.S. Private*, pg. 990

Shaughnessy, Greg, Mgr.-Sls.-Major Accts.--San Diego Union Tribune, San Diego, CA; *U.S. Private*, pg. 275

Shaughnessy, Tom, Chief Exec. Officer & Adv. Dir.--Unidigital/Cardinal Corp., New York, NY; *U.S. Public*, pg. 1664

Shaull, Wendy, Mgr.-Adv.--First National Bank of Commerce, New Orleans, LA; *U.S. Public*, pg. 629

Shaver, Dave, V.P.-Adv. & Brand Mngmt.--Lucent Technologies Inc., Murray Hill, NJ; *U.S. Public*, pg. 1017

Shaw, Bob, V.P.-Sls./Window Div.--Cameo Window Furnishings, New York, NY; *U.S. Private*, pg. 1094

Shaw, George, Mgr.-Adv.--Selas Corporation of America, Dresher, PA; *U.S. Public*, pg. 1454

Shaw, Nat, Mgr.-Mktg.--Pioneer/Eclipse Corp., Sparta, NC; *Int'l*, pg. 71

Shaw, Richard C., V.P.-Commun., Organizational Learning & Quality Standards--Applied Industrial Technologies, Cleveland, OH; *U.S. Public*, pg. 122

Shaw, Ronald K., Dir.-Adv. & Mktg.--Pinnacle Bank, Jasper, AL; *U.S. Public*, pg. 1297

Shaw, Russ, V.P.-Adv. & Brand Mngmt.--American Express Europe Limited, London, United Kingdom; *U.S. Public*, pg. 74

Shawe, Larry, V.P.-Sls. & Mktg.--Engle Homes, Inc., Boca Raton, FL; *U.S. Public*, pg. 583

Shaykin, Leonard, Mng. Partner--Shaykin & Company, New York, NY; *U.S. Private*, pg. 990

Shea, Chip, Corp. Dir.-Adv.--Hunter Marine Corporation, Alachua, FL; *U.S. Private*, pg. 549

Shea, Chip, Dir.-Mktg.--Luhrs Corporation, Saint Augustine, FL; *U.S. Private*, pg. 680

Shea, Chip, Dir.-Mktg.--Mainship Corporation, Saint Augustine, FL; *U.S. Private*, pg. 697

Sheard, Kelly, Dir.-Corp. Communications--The Canada Life Assurance Company, Toronto, Canada; *Int'l*, pg. 254

Shechtman, Allen L., Mgr.-Adv. & Pub. Rels.--W.W. Grainger, Inc., Lincolnshire, IL; *U.S. Public*, pg. 758

Shecter, Amy, V.P. & Gen. Mgr.-Mdsg. Kids Foot Locker--Foot Locker, New York, NY; *U.S. Public*, pg. 1777

Shedaker, Budd A., Asst. V.P.-Equity Communications--Equity Services, Inc., Montpelier, VT; *U.S. Private*, pg. 785

Shelby, Blake, Mgr.-Adv. & Promo--Remington Arms Company, Inc., Madison, NC; *U.S. Private*, pg. 921

Shelley, Donna, Mgr.-Adv.--Graphic Enterprises of Ohio, Inc., Canton, OH; *U.S. Private*, pg. 471

Shelton, Mark, Dir.-Corp. Commun.--Roadway Express, Inc., Akron, OH; *U.S. Public*, pg. 1392

Shelton, Paul, Dir.-Adv. & Promo.--Astec Industries, Inc., Chattanooga, TN; *U.S. Public*, pg. 141

Shemesh, Jacob, Exec. V.P.-Sls.--IIS Intelligent Information Systems Ltd., Yokneam, Israel; *Int'l*, pg. 645

Shepard, Terri J., Adv.--Stepan Company, Northfield, IL; *U.S. Public*, pg. 1514

Shepherd, Nick, Gen. Mgr.-Coffee & Food--Kraft Jacobs Suchard, Cheltenham, United Kingdom; *U.S. Public*, pg. 1290

Shepherdson, Don, Sr. Master Counselor-Adv.--Ace Novelty Company, Inc., Woodinville, WA; *U.S. Public*, pg. 1309

Sherburn, Roger, Mgr.-Corp. Services--Sanden International (U.S.A.), Inc., Wylie, TX; *Int'l*, pg. 1184

Sheridan, Rick, Mgr.-Adv.--Credit Union National Association, Madison, WI; *U.S. Private*, pg. 288

Sherliker, Lorraine, Mgr.-Mktg. & Adv.--Camden Motors Ltd., Leighton Buzzard, United Kingdom; *Int'l*, pg. 165

Sherlock, Joseph M., Mgr.-Sls. & Adv.--Tinius Olsen Testing Machine Co., Inc., Willow Grove, PA; *U.S. Private*, pg. 1088

Sherlock, Mike, Sr. V.P. & Gen. Mgr.--Gitano Fashions Ltd., Bowling Green, KY; *U.S. Public*, pg. 686

Sherry, Joyce, Creative Dir. & Mgr.-Adv.--Beltone Electronics Corporation, Chicago, IL; *U.S. Private*, pg. 132

Sheske, Jan, Mgr.-Adv. & Mktg. Devel.--Outboard Marine Corporation, Waukegan, IL; *U.S. Public*, pg. 478

Shevchik, Joan, Dir.-Publications--Cincinnati Financial Corp., Fairfield, OH; *U.S. Public*, pg. 368

Shidler, Jay, Pres. & Mng. Partner--The Shidler Group, Honolulu, HI; *U.S. Private*, pg. 994

Shields, Ann, Mgr.-Adv.--Scottish Widows' Fund & Life Assurance Society, Edinburgh, United Kingdom; *Int'l*, pg. 1212

Shields, J.J., Dir.-Adv.--Snap-On Tools Corporation, Kenosha, WI; *U.S. Public*, pg. 1480

Shikama, Yoji, V.P.-Mktg.--Mita Copystar America Inc., Fairfield, NJ; *Int'l*, pg. 870

Shiller, Linda, V.P.-Adv., Mktg. & Sls.--The Vagabond Inns, San Diego, CA; *U.S. Private*, pg. 558

Shimaoka, Tadafumi, Mng. Dir.--Haseko Corporation, Tokyo, Japan; *Int'l*, pg. 599

Shimizu, Tsuyoshi, Mng. Dir.-Pub. Rels & Adv.--Ajinomoto Company Inc., Tokyo, Japan; *Int'l*, pg. 40

Shinnick, Cindy, Mgr.-Adv.--Sierra Health Services, Inc., Las Vegas, NV; *U.S. Public*, pg. 1469

Shireman, John, Mgr.-Adv. & Creative Services--Kansas City Power & Light Company, Kansas City, MO; *U.S. Public*, pg. 943

Shiwanov, Ernest, Mgr.-Mktg. & Adv.--Turntec, Irvine, CA; *U.S. Private*, pg. 62

Shoffner, Harry, Dir.-Adv.--Carolina Biological Supply Co., Burlington, NC; *U.S. Private*, pg. 213

Shomake, Beth, Mgr.-Corp. Communication--Reeves Southeastern Corporation, Tampa, FL; *U.S. Private*, pg. 916

Shook, Gregory R., Sr. V.P.-Admin. & Sec.--Branford Savings Bank, Branford, CT; *U.S. Public*, pg. 250

Short, Len, Sr. V.P.-Adv.--Charles Schwab & Co. Inc., San Francisco, CA; *U.S. Public*, pg. 1443

Short, Leonard, Sr. V.P.-Adv. & Brand Mngmt.--The Charles Schwab Corporation, San Francisco, CA; *U.S. Public*, pg. 1442

Shortal, T. Michael, V.P.-Mktg.--Kastle Systems LLC, Arlington, VA; *U.S. Private*, pg. 608

Showers, Jacqui, Mgr.-Mktg. & Pub. Rels.--National Electrical Manufacturers Association, Arlington, VA; *U.S. Private*, pg. 782

Shuckhart, Robert, Mgr.-Natl. Adv.--The News Tribune, Tacoma, WA; *U.S. Public*, pg. 1066

Shuffield, Randy, V.P.-Adv.--Minyard Food Stores, Inc., Coppell, TX; *U.S. Private*, pg. 752

Shumway, Howard E., Mgr.-Mktg. Services--Shepard Niles, Inc., Montour Falls, NY; *U.S. Private*, pg. 992

Shure, Daniel B., Pres. & Chief Exec. Officer--Strombecker Corporation, Chicago, IL; *U.S. Private*, pg. 1047

Shusterman, Dan, Dir.-Mktg. & Adv.--Superior Industries International, Inc., Van Nuys, CA; *U.S. Public*, pg. 1539

Sibbick, Bill, Sr. V.P.-Sls.--Stanley Furniture Co. Inc., Stanleytown, VA; *U.S. Public*, pg. 1508

Sicard, Mary, Mgr.-Mktg. Communications--GIW Industries, Inc., Grovetown, GA; *Int'l*, pg. 721

Sichert, P., Chief Information Officer & V.P.-Pub. Affairs--The Budd Company, Troy, MI; *Int'l*, pg. 1388

Sickles, Paul, Mgr.-Mktg.--Nashua Corporation, Nashua, NH; *U.S. Public*, pg. 1152

Siddall, Warren C., Dir.-Adv. Svcs.--SmithKline Beecham Consumer Healthcare, U.S., Pittsburgh, PA; *Int'l*, pg. 1264

Sides, Bryce A., Dir.-Adv. & Sls. Promo.--Country Mutual Insurance Company, Bloomington, IL; *U.S. Private*, pg. 279

Siegel, Fred, Sr. V.P.-Mktg.--QVC, Inc., West Chester, PA; *U.S. Private*, pg. 897

Siegel, Todd, V.P.-MTV Adv. Sls.--MTV Networks, New York, NY; *U.S. Private*, pg. 779

Siegle, Rich, Dir.-Adv.--Fender Musical Instruments, Scottsdale, AZ; *U.S. Private*, pg. 400

Siembab, Kevin J., Mgr.-Sls.--Mele Manufacturing Co., Inc., Utica, NY; *U.S. Private*, pg. 730

Siewert, Monica, Mgr.-Media & Mktg. Svcs.--Sacramento Municipal Utility District, Sacramento, CA; *U.S. Private*, pg. 959

Sigal, Mary Charles, Dir.-Adv.--KPMG LLP, New York, NY; *U.S. Private*, pg. 603

Sikes, Roderick, Mgr.-Adv.--Markem Corporation, Keene, NH; *U.S. Private*, pg. 704

Silberman, Gerald, Mgr.-Adv.--Serfilco, Ltd., Northbrook, IL; *U.S. Private*, pg. 985

Silberstein, Bruce Jay, Pres.--Columbus Pipe & Equipment Company, Columbus, OH; *U.S. Private*, pg. 257

Sills, Liz, Dir.-Adv.--The Albany Herald Publishing Co., Inc., Albany, GA; *U.S. Public*, pg. 759

Silva, Helen, Adv. Asst.--Wells Fargo & Company, San Francisco, CA; *U.S. Public*, pg. 1753

Silva, Joe, Dir.-Adv.--Circuit City Stores, Inc., Richmond, VA; *U.S. Public*, pg. 374

Silvani, Marco, Dir.-Mktg.--Banca Commerciale Italiana, Milan, Italy; *Int'l*, pg. 135

Silver, Bertram R., Pres.--Jenkins Spirits Corp. Ltd., Londonderry, NH; *U.S. Private*, pg. 585

Silver, Carln, V.P.-Adv.--International Cutlery, LTD, New York, NY; *U.S. Private*, pg. 569

Silver, Cliff, Dir.-Adv.--Silicon Systems, Inc., Tustin, CA; *U.S. Public*, pg. 1585

Silver, Debra, Mgr.-Adv.-San Francisco--Scientific American, Inc., New York, NY; *Int'l*, pg. 1479

Silver, Lawrence A., Sr. V.P.-Investor Rels.--Raymond James Financial, Inc., Saint Petersburg, FL; *U.S. Public*, pg. 923

Silver, Liz, V.P.-Adv.--Visa U.S.A. Inc., San Francisco, CA; *U.S. Private*, pg. 1141

Silverman, Paul, Sr. Mgr.-Global Adv. Svcs.--Campbell Soup Company, Camden, NJ; *U.S. Public*, pg. 298

Silverstein, Marc, Mgr.-Mktg.--Friendship Dairies, Inc., Jericho, NY; *U.S. Private*, pg. 429

Silvestri, John, Exec. V.P.-Adv. Sls.--USA Networks, New York, NY; *U.S. Public*, pg. 1686

Simariut, Wichian, Mgr.-Bus.--Bangkok Athletic Co., Ltd., Bangkok, Thailand; *Int'l*, pg. 146

Simmon, Rena, Dir.-Mktg.--Yogen Fruz Worldwide Inc., Markham, Canada; *Int'l*, pg. 1520

Simmons, Jim, Mgr.-Adv.--General Motors of Canada Ltd., Oshawa, Canada; *U.S. Public*, pg. 722

Simmons, Victoria L., Mktg. Administrator--NavCom Defense Electronics, Inc., El Monte, CA; *U.S. Private*, pg. 789

Simms-Brown, Judy, Dir.-Sls. & Mktg.--Watlow Gordon, Richmond, IL; *U.S. Private*, pg. 1153

Simolin, Botho, Dir.-Communications--Kemira Oy, Helsinki, Finland; *Int'l*, pg. 727

Simon, Cheri, V.P.-Mktg. & Adv. (Indianapolis)--The Edward J. DeBartolo Corporation, Youngstown, OH; *U.S. Private*, *pg. 319*

Simon, Jeremy, V.P.-Sls. & Mktg.--Del Global Technologies, Valhalla, NY; *U.S. Public*, pg. 493

Simon, Martin, Pres.--Triangle Brass Manufacturing, Los Angeles, CA; *U.S. Private*, pg. 1101

Simonetti, Randall, V.P.-Adv. & Mktg. Communications--Frontier Communications Services, Bingham Farms, MI; *U.S. Public*, pg. 684

Simonetti, Randall A., V.P.-Adv. & Mktg. Communications--Frontier Corporation, Rochester, NY; *U.S. Public*, pg. 683

Simpkins, Juliet, Adv. Mgr.--The Tussauds Group Limited, London, United Kingdom; *Int'l*, pg. 1026

Simpson, Dick, V.P.-Pub. Rels.--Crowley Maritime Corporation, Oakland, CA; *U.S. Private*, pg. 292

Simrod, Cathy, Admin. Asst.--Duncan Equipment Company, Oklahoma City, OK; *U.S. Private*, pg. 346

Sims, Mark, Dir.-Mktg. & Adv.--Kellogg Company of Great Britain Ltd., Manchester, United Kingdom; *U.S. Public*, pg. 947

Sinclair, Graig M., Div. V.P.-Adv.--Walgreen Co., Deerfield, IL; *U.S. Public*, pg. 1733

Siner, Judy, Dir.-Adv.--Detroit Monthly, Detroit, MI; *U.S. Private*, pg. 285

Sinett, Lee, Creative Dir.--Outsource International, Deerfield Beach, FL; *U.S. Public*, pg. 1236

Singer, David, Mgr.-Adv. & Mktg.--Westwood Computer Corporation, Springfield, NJ; *U.S. Private*, pg. 1170

Singh, Anil, V.P.-Adv. Sls.--Yahoo!, Inc., Santa Clara, CA; *U.S. Public*, pg. 1787

Sipe, Alan W., V.P.-Sls. & Mktg.--Klein Tools Inc., Skokie, IL; *U.S. Private*, pg. 625

Sisson, Warren, Dir.-Mktg.--U.S. Intec, Inc., Port Arthur, TX; *U.S. Private*, pg. 433

Six, Chris, Mgr.-Publications--Dettra Flag Company, Oaks, PA; *U.S. Private*, pg. 328

Sjuts, David, Adv. Mgr.--The York News-Times, York, NE; *U.S. Private*, pg. 995

Skala, Tom, Mgr.-Adv.--Unger Company, Cleveland, OH; *U.S. Private*, pg. 1117

Skeabeck, Scott, Mgr.-Adv.--Equitable Life Insurance Company of Iowa, Des Moines, IA; *Int'l*, pg. 647

Skelton, Brenda, Sr. V.P.-Mktg. & Customer Svc.--Midwest Express Airlines, Inc., Oak Creek, WI; *U.S. Public*, pg. 1111

Skidmore, James A., Jr., Chm. Bd., Pres. & Chief Exec. Officer--Science Management Corporation, Bridgewater, NJ; *U.S. Public*, pg. 1717

Skindzelewski, Kelly, V.P. & Dir.-Communications & Pub. Rels.--Bank One, Wisconsin, Milwaukee, WI; *U.S. Public*, *pg. 174*

Skipper, Sheila A., Mgr.-Corp. Commun.--ChemFirst Inc., Jackson, MS; *U.S. Public*, pg. 344

Skochdopole, Angela, Mgr.-Commun. & Adv./AGCO Brands--AGCO Corporation, Duluth, GA; *U.S. Public*, pg. 28

Skyberg, Diane, Mgr.-Adv.--Talk-A-Phone Co., Chicago, IL; *U.S. Private*, pg. 1067

Slack, Michael, Mgr.-Adv. Leupold--Leupold & Stevens, Inc., Beaverton, OR; *U.S. Private*, pg. 662

Slagle, Paula, Dir.-Mktg.--Alloy Technology International Inc., West Nyack, NY; *U.S. Private*, pg. 42

Slater, Kelly, Dir.-Mktg. Communications--Apertus Technologies Incorporated, Eden Prairie, MN; *U.S. Public*, pg. 119

Slater, Roger, Mgr.-Mktg. Services--Young Radiator Company, Racine, WI; *U.S. Private*, pg. 1201

Slater, Scott, V.P.-Mktg.--Intercraft Company, Taylor, TX; *U.S. Public*, pg. 1177

Slaton, Lori, Mgr.-Adv.--Hayes Microcomputer Products, Inc., Norcross, GA; *U.S. Public*, pg. 801

Slaughter, Susan, Mgr.-Mktg. Communications--Wavetek Corporation, San Diego, CA; *U.S. Private*, pg. 1154

Slavin, E.A., V.P.-Sls. & Mktg.--NVF Company, Yorklyn, DE; *U.S. Private*, pg. 772

Slavin, Rachel, Adv. Program Asst.--Canon U.S.A., Inc., Lake Success, NY; *Int'l*, pg. 262

Sledd, Robert C., Chm. Bd. & Chief Exec. Officer--Performance Food Group Company, Richmond, VA; *U.S. Public*, pg. 1278

Slezak, Eric, V.P.-Mktg.--Kester Solder, Des Plaines, IL; *U.S. Public*, pg. 1003

Sloan, Jim, Mgr.-Adv.--Aamco Transmissions, Inc., Bala Cynwyd, PA; *U.S. Private*, pg. 9

Smalley, Richard, Mgr.-Communications & Sls. Promo.--Balderson Inc., Wamego, KS; *U.S. Public*, pg. 315

Smallwood, Kim, Mgr.-Adv.--Cato Oil & Grease Co., Oklahoma City, OK; *Int'l*, pg. 1045

Smart, Joe, Mgr.-Adv.--Brainerd Daily Dispatch, Brainerd, MN; *U.S. Private*, pg. 995

Smelser, Cessi, Dir.-Adv.--Academy Corporation, Katy, TX; *U.S. Private*, pg. 11

Smetana, Bob, Dir.-Adv.--United Stationers Inc., Des Plaines, IL; *U.S. Public*, pg. 1689

Smiddy, Deborah G., Dir.-Adv.--Knoxville News-Sentinel Company, Knoxville, TN; *U.S. Public*, pg. 1448

Smikle, Deborah A., Dir.-Mktg. Communications--F.W. Dodge Group, New York, NY; *U.S. Public*, pg. 1070

Smith-Sanderson, Dianne, V.P.-Adv. & Corp. Communications--CT Financial Services, Inc., Toronto, Canada; *Int'l*, pg. 112

Smith, Andrea, Mgr.-Corp. & Mktg. Communications--Concurrent Computer Corporation, Fort Lauderdale, FL; *U.S. Public*, pg. 430

Smith, Anne, Mgr.-Mktg. Communications--LORAD Corporation, Danbury, CT; *U.S. Public*, pg. 1595

Smith, Ashley, Mgr.-Promo. & Mdsg.-Southern Accents--Southern Progress Corporation, Birmingham, AL; *U.S. Public*, pg. 1612

Smith, Barbara, Mgr.-Sls.--Minerallac Co., Addison, IL; *U.S. Private*, pg. 750

Smith, Bill, Gen. Mgr.--Metz Baking Co., Chicago, IL; *U.S. Private*, pg. 1022

Smith, C.E., V.P.-Sls. & Mktg.--The American Group, Ferndale, WA; *U.S. Private*, pg. 56

Smith, Chet, Mgr.-Mktg. Comm.--Spectronics Corporation, Westbury, NY; *U.S. Private*, pg. 1024

Smith, Craig, V.P. & Dir.-Mktg.--FirstFed Financial Corp., Santa Monica, CA; *U.S. Public*, pg. 645

Smith, David, V.P.-Mktg.--Metabo Corporation, West Chester, PA; *U.S. Private*, pg. 734

Smith, Debbie, Mktg. Communications Specialist--Power-One, Inc., Camarillo, CA; *U.S. Private*, pg. 878

Smith, Debbie, Dir.-Adv.--Earl Scheib, Inc., Beverly Hills, CA; *U.S. Public*, pg. 1437

Smith, Dennis, Mng. Dir.-Adv.-Motors--Toyota Motor Distributors (Ireland) Ltd., Dublin, Ireland; *Int'l*, pg. 1413

Smith, Dick, Dir.-Adv.--The Lincoln Electric Company, Cleveland, OH; *U.S. Public*, pg. 996

Smith, Donald, Adv. Mgr.--The Hannibal Courier-Post, Hannibal, MO; *U.S. Private*, pg. 995

Smith, Eileen, Dir.-Adv.--GTCO Corporation, Columbia, MD; *U.S. Private*, pg. 436

Smith, Fred, Dir.-Adv.--Hale-Halsell Company, Tulsa, OK; *U.S. Private*, pg. 494

Smith, G.E., Mgr.-Adv.--Hartwell Corporation, Placentia, CA; *U.S. Private*, pg. 1168

Smith, Gail L., Adv. & Mktg. Specialist--Harrington Hoists, Inc., Manheim, PA; *U.S. Private*, pg. 504

Smith, Gene, Dir.-Adv.--Billboard Magazine, New York, NY; *Int'l*, pg. 1446

Smith, George E., Pres. & Chief Exec. Officer--Alco Industries, Inc., Valley Forge, PA; *U.S. Private*, pg. 32

Smith, Jenny, Mgr.-Adv.--Daily Racing Form, Inc., Phoenix, AZ; *U.S. Public*, pg. 1327

Smith, Joanie, Dir.-Adv.--The Monarch Company, Inc., Atlanta, GA; *U.S. Private*, pg. 756

Smith, Joseph H., Pres.--40 Fort Eye Associates, Forty Fort, PA; *U.S. Private*, pg. 420

Smith, Kathy, Dir.-Mktg. Communications--Browning-Ferris Industries, Inc., Houston, TX; *U.S. Public*, pg. 262

Smith, Larry, V.P.-Mdsg.--Boye Needle, Chicago, IL; *U.S. Private*, pg. 1192

Smith, Laura, Dir.-Pub. Rels. & Adv.--Cross Creek Apparel, Inc., Mount Airy, NC; *U.S. Public*, pg. 1413

Smith, Laurel, Mgr.-Adv.--The Hertz Corporation, Park Ridge, NJ; *U.S. Public*, pg. 664

Smith, Linda, Asst. Mgr.-Adv.--Bell Atlantic-Washington, D.C., Inc., Washington, DC; *U.S. Public*, pg. 203

Smith, Lisa, Asst. V.P.-Mktg. Communications--Old Kent Bank, Grand Rapids, MI; *U.S. Public*, pg. 1216

Smith, Mark, V.P.-Mktg. & Adv.--Mott's Inc., Stamford, CT; *Int'l*, pg. 248

Smith, Mark, Dir.-Natl. Sls.--Shivers Trading & Operating Co., Augusta, GA; *U.S. Private*, pg. 994

Smith, Matthew C., Mgr.- Mktg.--United States Ceramic Tile Co., East Sparta, OH; *U.S. Private*, pg. 1124

Smith, Michael, Mgr.-Mktg. Communications--Parker Hannifin Corp., Quick Coupling Div., Minneapolis, MN; *U.S. Public*, pg. 1260

Smith, Paul, Adv.--HPM Corporation, Mount Gilead, OH; *U.S. Private*, pg. 492

Smith, Randy, V.P.-Mktg.--Virco Mfg. Corporation, Torrance, CA; *U.S. Public*, pg. 1721

Smith, Rebecca J., V.P.-Mktg.--The Disston Co., Greensboro, NC; *U.S. Public*, pg. 950

Smith, Richard L., Pres.--The Fremont Co., Fremont, OH; *U.S. Private*, pg. 426

Smith, Rick, Adv. Mgr.--Gentlemen's Quarterly, New York, NY; *U.S. Private*, pg. 20

Smith, Rick, Mgr.-Adv.--Delta Resins & Refractories, Inc., Milwaukee, WI; *U.S. Private*, pg. 323

Smith, Rick, Reg. Dir.--Ireland Coffee Tea, Inc., Pleasantville, NJ; *U.S. Public*, pg. 351

Smith, Rick, Reg. Dir.--The Lenson Coffee Co., Pleasantville, NJ; *U.S. Public*, pg. 351

Smith, Robert, V.P. & Gen. Mgr.--Avery Dennison Corporation Label Group, Ontario, CA; *U.S. Public*, pg. 153

Smith, Roger S., Mgr.-Corp. Adv. & Pub. Affairs--A.O. Smith Corporation, Milwaukee, WI; *U.S. Public*, pg. 1476

Smith, Sandy, Dir.-Mktg. Devel. & Promo.--The Psychological Corp., San Antonio, TX; *U.S. Public*, pg. 784

Smith, Tiffani, Coord.-Adv. Programs--Knouse Foods Inc., Peach Glen, PA; *U.S. Private*, pg. 627

Smith, Tim, Mgr.-Mktg.--Taco Incorporated, Cranston, RI; *U.S. Private*, pg. 1066

Smith, Virginia R., V.P.-Corp. Adv.--Inductotherm Industries, Inc., Rancocas, NJ; *U.S. Private*, pg. 560

Smith, W.T., Pres. & Gen. Mgr.--Tidelands Oil Production Co., Long Beach, CA; *U.S. Private*, pg. 1084

Smolen, Leslie, Dir.-Mktg.--Tastee Freez International Inc., Utica, MI; *U.S. Private*, pg. 1069

Smollar, Marvin, Pres. & Chief Oper. Officer--CLR Corporation, Tarboro, NC; *U.S. Public*, pg. 579

Smultski, Debbie, Dir-Adv.--Drug Guild Div., Secaucus, NJ; *U.S. Public*, pg. 1169

Smusz, Robert, V.P.-Mktg. & Mdsg.--Arvey Paper & Office Products, Chicago, IL; *U.S. Public*, pg. 903

Snediker, James M., Pres., Chief Exec. Officer & Chief Oper. Officer--Chicago Show Printing Co., Morton Grove, IL; *U.S. Private*, pg. 235

Sneed, Amy, Dir.-New Mkt. Devel.--J. Crew Group, Inc., New York, NY; *U.S. Private*, pg. 1078

Snelling, Mark H., Pres.--The Shelburne Corporation, Shelburne, VT; *U.S. Private*, pg. 991

Snelling, William, Sr. V.P.-Adv.--Cineplex Odeon Corporation, Toronto, Canada; *Int'l*, pg. 292

Snider, Larry D., Dir.-Mktg. Commun.--Eastman Chemical Company, Kingsport, TN; *U.S. Public*, pg. 550

Snow, James, Mgr.-Mktg. Communications--International Lottery & Totalizator Systems, Inc., Carlsbad, CA; *U.S. Public*, pg. 900

Snow, Richard F., Editor--American Heritage Magazine, New York, NY; *U.S. Private*, pg. 417

Snyder, Kathy M., Dir.-Communications & Shareholder Rels.--The First American Financial Corporation, Santa Ana, CA; *U.S. Public*, pg. 624

Sobel, Susan, Assoc. V.P.-Mktg.--ECI Telecom Ltd., Petah Tiqwa, Israel; *Int'l*, pg. 643

Sober, Sheryl-Sue, Coord.-Adv. Production--Psychology Today, New York, NY; *U.S. Private*, pg. 1056

Socci, Melissa, Mgr.-Adv.--Prudential Securities Inc., New York, NY; *U.S. Private*, pg. 892

Soderberg, Olle, Sr. V.P.-Adv.--Skandinaviska Enskilda Banken, Stockholm, Sweden; *Int'l*, pg. 1258

Soell, Alan, Mgr.-Media Svcs.--Maclean-Fogg Co., Mundelein, IL; *U.S. Private*, pg. 692

Soell, Alan, Mgr.-Media Svcs.--MacLean Molded Products, Inc., Wheeling, IL; *U.S. Private*, pg. 692

Soetaert, Wyatt, Mgr.-Adv.--The Rival Company, Kansas City, MO; *U.S. Public*, pg. 1391

Soininen, Kari, V.P.-Adv.--Kesko Ltd., Helsinki, Finland; *Int'l*, *pg. 732*

Sokolowski, George, Sr. V.P.-Corp. Mktg.--The TJX Companies, Inc., Framingham, MA; *U.S. Public*, pg. 1556

Sokup, B.J., Dir.-Adv.--Spectrum Industries, Inc., Chippewa Falls, WI; *U.S. Private*, pg. 1024

Solan, Veronica, Mktg. Specialist--VG Laboratory Systems Ltd., Altrincham, United Kingdom; *U.S. Public*, pg. 1595

Soliman, Anwar, Chm. Bd. & Chief Exec. Officer--American Restaurant Group, Inc., Newport Beach, CA; *U.S. Private*, pg. 61

Solis, Becky, Mgr.-Adv.--The Monitor, McAllen, TX; *U.S. Private*, pg. 425

Solley, Anne, Sr. Mktg. Mgr.--Sea World of Florida, Orlando, FL; *U.S. Public*, pg. 114

Solomon, Bonnie, V.P.-Adv. & Mktg.--Barneys Inc., New York, NY; *U.S. Private*, pg. 116

Solomon, Steve, Dir.-Adv.--ComEd, Chicago, IL; *U.S. Public*, *pg. 1664*

Soltero, Sharon, Mgr.-Corp. Commun.--Nebraska Public Power District, Columbus, NE; *U.S. Private*, pg. 789

Sommer, Ronald, V.P.-Indus. Rels. & Communications--Dravo Lime Company, Pittsburgh, PA; *U.S. Public*, pg. 527

Sommers, Nick, Mgr.-Communications--Akzo Nobel Inc., Chicago, IL; *Int'l*, pg. 47

Somoza, Kelly Fawcett, V.P.-Investor Rels.--U.S. Home Corporation, Houston, TX; *U.S. Public*, pg. 1682

Sonntag, Willi, Sr. V.P.-Adv. & Pub. Rels.--Commerzbank AG, Frankfurt, Germany; *Int'l*, pg. 308

Sorensen, Gordon, V.P.-Adv.--Karakas, VanSickle, Ouellette Advertising & Public Relations, Portland, OR; *U.S. Private*, pg. 607

Sorensen, Richard T., Mgr.-Adv. & Pub. Rel.--International Game Technology, Reno, NV; *U.S. Public*, pg. 900

Soriano, Antonio, Mgr.-Mktg.--McNally Manufacturing, Pittsburg, KS; *Int'l*, pg. 1326

Sorrentino, Art, Mgr.-Adv. & Product Promo.--General Datacomm Industries, Inc., Middlebury, CT; *U.S. Public*, pg. 708

Soteropolus, Coord.-Productions Facility--Boston Store, Milwaukee, WI; *U.S. Public*, pg. 309

Soucy, Mark, Mgr.-Mktg.--Schrader Bellows Division, Cuyahoga Falls, OH; *U.S. Public*, pg. 1261

Sowa, Collin, Dir.-Adv. & Mdsg.--A&M Records, Hollywood, CA; *Int'l*, pg. 1052

Sowa, Monica, Mgr.-Adv. & Mktg.--Cruises Only Inc., Orlando, FL; *U.S. Private*, pg. 293

Sowerby, Desmond, Dir.-Intl. Adv.--Daily Mail & General Trust PLC, London, United Kingdom; *Int'l*, pg. 366

Soya, Aoi, V.P.-Worldwide Adv.--Tiffany & Co., New York, NY; *U.S. Public*, pg. 1608

Spadone, John C., Pres. & Treas.--Spadone Inc., Norwalk, CT; *U.S. Private*, pg. 1019

Spamer, Tanja, Mgr.-Adv.--Honda Deutschland GmbH, Offenbach/Main, Germany; *Int'l*, pg. 635
Spanbauer, Sue, Dir.-Adv.--Anchor Inc., Orange Park, FL; *U.S. Public*, pg. 903
Spangler, David B., Pres. & Chief Exec. Officer--Jefferson Mills, Inc., Pulaski, VA; *U.S. Private*, pg. 584
Spangler, Larry, Gen. Mgr. & Adv. & Mktg. Services--Thomasville Furniture Industries, Inc., Thomasville, NC; *U.S. Public*, pg. 688
Spear, Kathleen, Coord.-Adv.--Andiamo, Inc., Fountain Valley, CA; *U.S. Private*, pg. 73
Spears, Gil, Dir.-Adv.--Successful Farming Magazine, Des Moines, IA; *U.S. Public*, pg. 1094
Spears, James, V.P.-Mktg. & Adv.--AT&T Business Communications Services, Bridgewater, NJ; *U.S. Public*, pg. 10
Speer, Mark, Mgr.-Adv.--Villard Books, New York, NY; *U.S. Private*, pg. 21
Speer, Mark, Mgr.-Adv.--Times Books, New York, NY; *U.S. Private*, pg. 21
Spellman, Leo, Dir.-Adv. & Pub. Rels.--Steinway Musical Instruments, Inc., Waltham, MA; *U.S. Public*, pg. 1514
Spelts, Bob, Dir.-Adv. & Sls. Promotion--SuperValu, Inc., Eden Prairie, MN; *U.S. Public*, pg. 1540
Spencer, Les, Mgr.-Adv.--Intermountain Farmers Association, Salt Lake City, UT; *U.S. Private*, pg. 568
Spencer, Mark, Sr. Grp. Dir.-Adv.--Toronto Star Newspapers Ltd., Toronto, Canada; *Int'l*, pg. 1402
Spencer, Mary, Mgr.-Adv. & Sls.--Little Giant Pump Company, Oklahoma City, OK; *U.S. Public*, pg. 1566
Spencer, P.L., Mgr.-Adv.--Capital Controls Company Inc., Colmar, PA; *Int'l*, pg. 1226
Spencer, Todd, Mgr.-Adv.--Del Webb Corporation, Phoenix, AZ; *U.S. Public*, pg. 494
Speranza, Ernest V., Sr. V.P.-Adv. & Mktg. Worldwide--Toys "R" Us, Inc., Paramus, NJ; *U.S. Public*, pg. 1626
Speranza, Ernest V., Sr. V.P.-Adv./Mktg.--Toys "R" Us United States, Paramus, NJ; *U.S. Public*, pg. 1626
Sperling, Elisabeth, Mgr.-Adv.--Henkel KGaA, Dusseldorf, Germany; *Int'l*, pg. 609
Spessard, Robert W., V.P.-Sls.--Ragu Foods, Inc., Trumbull, CT; *Int'l*, pg. 1436
Spiesshoefer, Peter, Dr., Exec. V.P.-Adv. & Intl. Sls.--Burda Holding GmbH & Co., KG, Munich, Germany; *Int'l*, pg. 233
Spina, Peter, V.P. & Grp. Publr.--SRDS, Des Plaines, IL; *U.S. Private*, pg. 958
Spoelstra, Kit, Dir.-Adv.--Jacobson Stores Inc., Jackson, MI; *U.S. Public*, pg. 922
Spolin, Tom, Dir.-Adv.--Compuware Corporation, Farmington Hills, MI; *U.S. Public*, pg. 423
Sponsler, Linda, V.P.-Adv. & Pub. Commun.--Blue Cross and Blue Shield of Oklahoma, Tulsa, OK; *U.S. Private*, pg. 151
Spooler, John, Sr. V.P. & Dir. of Agencies--Academy Insurance Group, Inc., Alpharetta, GA; *Int'l*, pg. 27
Spooner, Elizabeth, Dir.-Adv.--Montana Power Company, Butte, MT; *U.S. Public*, pg. 1126
Spragg, Edwin L., V.P.-Adv. & Special Mkts.--Acme Markets, Malvern, PA; *U.S. Public*, pg. 93
Spring, Marsha, Mgr.-Corp. Adv.--Lincoln Property Company, Dallas, TX; *U.S. Private*, pg. 668
Springer, Heiner, Dir.-Corp. Commun.--Bayer AG, Leverkusen, Germany; *Int'l*, pg. 171
Springer, Richard N., Mgr.-Mktg. Commun.--Wyle Electronics, Irvine, CA; *Int'l*, pg. 1457
Sproule, Andrew, Mgr.-Adv.--Utell International, Brentford, United Kingdom; *Int'l*, pg. 1098
Squires, Troy, V.P.--Southwest Recreational Industries Inc., Leander, TX; *U.S. Private*, pg. 1018
Srivastava, Dewesh, Mgr.-Adv.--LG Group Inc., Englewood Cliffs, NJ; *Int'l*, pg. 779
St. Clair, Eleanor, Mgr.-Adv.--The Camden Fire Insurance Assn., Philadelphia, PA; *Int'l*, pg. 543
St. Clair, William, Mgr.-Adv.--Foster Wheeler Corporation, Clinton, NJ; *U.S. Public*, pg. 676
St. Gean, Debra D., Mgr.-Adv.--Maxon Industries, Inc., Huntington Park, CA; *U.S. Private*, pg. 717
Stabile, Jeffrey, Pres. & Chief Exec. Officer--Aero Systems Aviation Corp., Miami, FL; *U.S. Private*, pg. 24
Stacey, Colleen, Mktg. Assoc.--Circle Business Credit, Inc., Indianapolis, IN; *U.S. Public*, pg. 1785
Stager, Robert, Mgr.-Sls.--Sheffield Steel Corporation-Joliet, Joliet, IL; *U.S. Private*, pg. 991
Stahl, Kirk, Chief Oper. Officer, Exec. V.P. & Acct. Exec.--Caldwell VanRiper, Inc., Indianapolis, IN; *U.S. Private*, pg. 200
Stai, Harlan C., Exec. V.P.-Opers.--Owen Health Care, Inc., Houston, TX; *U.S. Public*, pg. 304
Stake, Randy J., Mgr.-Mktg. Commun.--Weber Marking Systems, Inc., Arlington Heights, IL; *U.S. Private*, pg. 1157
Staller, Chris, Dir.-Indus. Sls., Mktg. & Adv.--Vibro-Meter Corp., Long Beach, CA; *U.S. Private*, pg. 1138
Stanek, Bill, Mgr.-Mktg.-Filtration--Tetko, Inc., Briarcliff Manor, NY; *U.S. Private*, pg. 1078
Stange, Markicia T., V.P.-Adv.--Dayton Newspapers, Inc., Dayton, OH; *U.S. Private*, pg. 281
Stanhope, Phillip, Dir.-Corp. Commun.--Titan International, Inc., Quincy, IL; *U.S. Public*, pg. 1618
Staniar, Linda B., Sr. V.P.-Corp. Communications, Adv. & Video Systems--New York Life Insurance Company, New York, NY; *U.S. Private*, pg. 794
Stanley, Mike, Mgr.-Classified Adv.--Memphis Publishing Co., Memphis, TN; *U.S. Public*, pg. 1448
Stanley, R.J., Dir.-Corp. Adv. & Video Commun.--Phillips Petroleum Company, Bartlesville, OK; *U.S. Public*, pg. 1290
Stanyon, Jack, V.P.-Adv. & Pub. Rels.--Fortis, Inc., New York, NY; *Int'l*, pg. 499
Stark, Cheryl, Coord.-Adv.--Adams U.S.A., Morris Plains, NJ; *U.S. Public*, pg. 1739
Starkenberg, Robin, Adv. & Promo. Specialist--Holstein Association USA, Inc., Brattleboro, VT; *U.S. Private*, pg. 536
Starnes, Wayne, Exec. V.P.-Sls. & Mktg.--Stainless Ice-Tainer Co. (SITCO), Roswell, GA; *Int'l*, pg. 646
Starr, Bob, Mgr.-Natl. Communications--Yamaha Motor Corp., U.S.A., Cypress, CA; *Int'l*, pg. 1516
Startek, G.E., Asst. Mgr.-Adv. & Promo.--General Motors of Canada Ltd., Oshawa, Canada; *U.S. Public*, pg. 722
Stashkiw, Walter, V.P.-Mktg., Sls. & Adv.--The Will-Burt Company, Orrville, OH; *U.S. Private*, pg. 1177
Stasolla, Patrick, Dir.-Adv.--International Home Foods Inc., Parsippany, NJ; *U.S. Private*, pg. 526
States, Judy, Dir.-Corp. Communications--APS, Phoenix, AZ; *U.S. Public*, pg. 1297
Staudt, John, Pres. & Chief Exec. Officer--Frontier Foundry, Inc., Titusville, PA; *U.S. Private*, pg. 430
Stauffacher, Debbie, Mgr.-Adv.--Strouds, Inc., City of Industry, CA; *U.S. Public*, pg. 1525
Stauffer, Michael G., Dir.-Sls. & Mktg.--Keystone Powdered Metal Company, Saint Marys, PA; *U.S. Private*, pg. 619
Stautzenbach, Edward G., V.P.-Mktg.--Mercury Finance Co., Lake Forest, IL; *U.S. Public*, pg. 1093
Stavropulos, Dir.-Communications--Bull HN Information Systems Inc., Billerica, MA; *Int'l*, pg. 316
Stavropulos, Peter, Dir.-Commun.--Bull Electronics, Lowell, MA; *Int'l*, pg. 316
Stavros, Nick, V.P.-Sls.--John Sterling Corporation, Richmond, IL; *U.S. Private*, pg. 1041
Stay, Christine, Mgr.-Mktg. Communications--Philips Components, Jupiter, FL; *Int'l*, pg. 1054
Stayer, Alice, Dir.-Creative Svcs.--Johnsonville Foods, Inc., Kohler, WI; *U.S. Private*, pg. 595
Stearns, Doug, Dir.-Sls. & Mktg.--Seneca Wire & Manufacturing Co., Fostoria, OH; *U.S. Private*, pg. 984
Stearns, Richard E., Pres. & Chief Exec. Officer--Lenox, Incorporated, Lawrenceville, NJ; *U.S. Public*, pg. 261
Stebbins, Liz, Dir.-Mktg.--Sterling Financial Corporation, Spokane, WA; *U.S. Public*, pg. 1516
Steeves, Michael A., Dir.-Investor Rels.--Homestake Mining Company, San Francisco, CA; *U.S. Public*, pg. 832
Steffen, Katherine, Mgr.-Adv.--Arvey Paper & Office Products, Chicago, IL; *U.S. Public*, pg. 903
Steffen, Rob, V.P.-Adv.--Evans, Inc., Chicago, IL; *U.S. Public*, pg. 596
Steffensen, Dwight A., Chm. Bd. & Chief Exec. Officer--Merisel, Inc., El Segundo, CA; *U.S. Public*, pg. 1095
Steffes, Edward J., V.P.-Mktg.--DeVry Institutes, Oak Brook Terrace, IL; *U.S. Public*, pg. 503
Stein, Jean, Dir.-Adv.--MMC Electronics America Inc., Rolling Meadows, IL; *Int'l*, pg. 875
Stein, Sheryl, Mgr.-Pub. Rels. & Adv.--El Al Israel Airlines, Ltd., New York, NY; *Int'l*, pg. 435
Steinberg, Selwyn, Sr. V.P.-Adv.--Slant/Fin Corporation, Greenvale, NY; *U.S. Private*, pg. 1005
Steinberg, Stephen, Dir.-Mktg.--Spaulding & Slye, Boston, MA; *U.S. Private*, pg. 1021
Steinbrecker, John E., V.P.-Retail Deposits & Brokerage Services--First Northern Capital Corp., Green Bay, WI; *U.S. Public*, pg. 636
Steiner, Alan, Mgr.-Sls., Mktg., Adv. & Distr.--ITW Switches, Chicago, IL; *U.S. Public*, pg. 867
Steiner, Beate, Mgr.-Adv.--Asea Brown Boveri AG, Vienna, Austria; *Int'l*, pg. 2
Steiner, Irene, Dir.-Mktg. & Sls.--The Vermont Teddy Bear Company, Inc., Shelburne, VT; *U.S. Public*, pg. 1716
Steinhart, Conrad, Controller, Treas. & Sec.--Happy Holiday Tree Farms, Sheridan, MI; *U.S. Private*, pg. 254
Steinkamp, Mark, Coord.-Pub. Rels & Adv.--Daktronics, Inc., Brookings, SD; *U.S. Public*, pg. 478
Steinmetz, Herb, Dir.-Adv.--B.A. Mason, Chippewa Falls, WI; *U.S. Private*, pg. 712
Steinmiller, John, V.P.-Bus. Opers. & Mktg.--Milwaukee Bucks, Inc., Milwaukee, WI; *U.S. Private*, pg. 749
Stemmler, Robert M., Pres. & Chief Exec. Officer--AirSensors, Inc., Seattle, WA; *U.S. Public*, pg. 33
Stemmler, Robert M., Pres. & Chief Exec. Officer--IMPCO AirSensors Technologies, Cerritos, CA; *U.S. Public*, pg. 34
Stenbeck, Roger, Dir.-Adv.--Aftonbladet AB, Stockholm, Sweden; *Int'l*, pg. 29
Stencel, Mark, Dir.-Adv.--Frigid Coil West, Santa Fe Springs, CA; *U.S. Public*, pg. 1789
Stephan, Ursula, Adv. Coord.--Buhler Inc., Minneapolis, MN; *U.S. Private*, pg. 179
Stephens, Bonnie, Mgr.-Mktg. Commun.--Branson Ultrasonics Corp.-Plastics Joining Div., Danbury, CT; *U.S. Public*, pg. 574
Stephens, Brenda, Coord.-Adv.--Intergraph Corporation, Huntsville, AL; *U.S. Public*, pg. 890
Stephens, Buddy, V.P. & Dir.-Mktg.--Hale-Halcoll Company, Tulsa, OK; *U.S. Private*, pg. 494
Stephens, Terry, Dir.-Natl. Adv.--Interstate Bakeries Corporation, Kansas City, MO; *U.S. Public*, pg. 909
Stephenson, Sandy, V.P.--Stephenson, Inc., Alexandria, VA; *U.S. Private*, pg. 1040
Stern, Andrew, Sr. V.P.-Strategic Plng. & Corp. Mktg.--United States Fidelity & Guaranty Company, Baltimore, MD; *U.S. Public*, pg. 1659
Stern, Kenneth, V.P.-Adv. & Corp. Devel.--Axsys Technologies, Inc., New York, NY; *U.S. Public*, pg. 157
Sternfeld, Ilana, Corp. Adv. & Foreign Press--Israel Aircraft Industries Ltd., Israel; *Int'l*, pg. 689
Sterns, Julian, Mgr.-Adv.--Construction Specialties, Inc., Cranford, NJ; *U.S. Private*, pg. 266
Stevens, C.G., Dir.-Pub. Rels.--The Ziegler Companies, Inc., West Bend, WI; *U.S. Public*, pg. 1791
Stevens, Mel, Dir.-Adv.--Arrow Fastener Co., Inc., Saddle Brook, NJ; *U.S. Private*, pg. 85
Stevens, Michael K., Dir.-Adv.--Bremerton Sun, Bremerton, WA; *U.S. Public*, pg. 1447
Stevenson, Bruce, Dir.-Mktg.--Hill Phoenix, Colonial Heights, VA; *U.S. Public*, pg. 521
Stevenson, Greg, Dir.-Adv.--Hilland Dairy Company, Wichita, KS; *U.S. Private*, pg. 879
Stevenson, Philip, V.P.-Adv.--Super D Drug Stores, Memphis, TN; *U.S. Private*, pg. 642
Stevenson, R.H., Sr. V.P.-Sls. & Mktg.--North State Pyrophyllite, Greensboro, NC; *U.S. Private*, pg. 924
Stevenson, Richard, Dir.-Mktg.--Control Laser Corporation, Orlando, FL; *U.S. Public*, pg. 599
Stevenson, Robert, V.P.-Sls. & Mktg.--Pioneer Plastics Corporation, Auburn, ME; *U.S. Private*, pg. 867
Stewart, C. Jim III, V.P.-Mktg.--Stewart & Stevenson Services, Inc., Houston, TX; *U.S. Public*, pg. 1517
Stewart, Joe, V.P.-Mktg.--Bar-S Foods Co., Phoenix, AZ; *U.S. Private*, pg. 114
Stewart, Lynda J., Dir.-Communications--Cox Enterprises, Inc., Atlanta, GA; *U.S. Private*, pg. 281
Stewart, Rob, Dir.-Sls.--Stadelman Fruit L.L.C., Yakima, WA; *U.S. Private*, pg. 1028
Stiffler, Carolyn S., Pres. & Chief Exec. Officer--Classic Markets Corp., Norcross, GA; *U.S. Private*, pg. 244
Stigi, Peter, Sr. V.P.-Sls. & Mktg.--Tuscan/Lehigh Dairies LP, Union, NJ; *U.S. Private*, pg. 1110
Stimac, Tom, Prod. Mgr.--De-Sta-Co, A Dover Resources Co., Troy, MI; *U.S. Public*, pg. 521
Stine, Don, Dir.-Adv.--Weiners Stores, Inc., Houston, TX; *U.S. Private*, pg. 1160
Stirr, T.G., Mgr.-Adv. Promotion--Canadian Kawasaki Motors Inc., Don Mills, Canada; *Int'l*, pg. 726
Stix, Louise A., Mgr.-Corp. Communications--Savin Corporation, Stamford, CT; *Int'l*, pg. 1114
Stock, Mike, Visual Design Specialist--Cadillac Plastic & Chemical Co., Troy, MI; *U.S. Public*, pg. 781
Stockett, Peter, V.P.-Adv., Sls. & Mktg.--Sun Bancorp, Inc., Selinsgrove, PA; *U.S. Public*, pg. 1529
Stoebner, Tom, Mgr.-Adv., Sls. & Mktg.-Films--Raven Industries, Inc., Sioux Falls, SD; *U.S. Public*, pg. 1361
Stoeckel, Howard, Sr. V.P.-Mktg.--Wawa, Inc., Media, PA; *U.S. Private*, pg. 1155
Stoepel, F. Christopher, V.P.-Adv.--American National Bank & Trust Co. of Chicago, Chicago, IL; *U.S. Public*, pg. 628
Stokely, Gregg, V.P.-Commercial Mktg.--BEI Sensors and Systems Company, Sylmar, CA; *U.S. Public*, pg. 160
Stokes, Paul, Mgr.-Mktg.--Staveley Sensors Division, East Hartford, CT; *Int'l*, pg. 1299
Stollberg, Scott, Dir.-Adv. Sls.--Kalmbach Publishing Co., Waukesha, WI; *U.S. Private*, pg. 606
Stone, Ann, Mgr.-Exhibits & Adv.--AAI Corporation, Hunt Valley, MD; *U.S. Public*, pg. 1679
Stone, Daniel B., V.P.-Corp. Commun.--Alberto-Culver Company, Melrose Park, IL; *U.S. Public*, pg. 37
Stone, David, Second V.P. & Dir.-Adv. & Video--Transamerica Life Companies, Los Angeles, CA; *U.S. Public*, pg. 1630
Stone, Harold, Dir.-Mktg.--Radica USA Limited, Dallas, TX; *U.S. Private*, pg. 906
Stone, Laurie, Mgr.-Corp. Commun.--American Management Systems, Inc., Fairfax, VA; *U.S. Public*, pg. 86
Stone, Richard, Mgr.-Adv.--Engineer Control Intl., Elon College, NC; *U.S. Private*, pg. 376
Stone, W. Arthur, Grp. Dir.-Pub. Rels. & Adv.--Ryder System, Inc., Miami, FL; *U.S. Public*, pg. 1413
Stonehouse, Kate, Mgr.-Adv., Mktg. & Communications--SLM Holding Corp., Washington, DC; *U.S. Public*, pg. 1419
Storey, David, Dir.-Adv. & Mktg.--The Gazette Company, Cedar Rapids, IA; *U.S. Private*, pg. 442
Storey, Tom, Exec. V.P.-Sales & Mktg.--Doubletree Corporation, Memphis, TN; *U.S. Public*, pg. 1335
Storti, Paula, Mgr.-Adv.--Red Wing Shoe Co., Inc., Red Wing, MN; *U.S. Private*, pg. 915
Stoudt, Craig, Pres.-Ampad Div.--American Pad and Paper Company, Dallas, TX; *U.S. Public*, pg. 88
Stout, Carl A., V.P.-Sls. & Dir.-Mktg.--Morgan Foods, Inc., Austin, IN; *U.S. Private*, pg. 761
Stout, R.M., V.P.-Land & Mktg.--Rio Algom Mining Corp., Oklahoma City, OK; *Int'l*, pg. 1118
Stovall, Juli, Mgr.-Mktg. & Commun.--Paul Mueller Company, Springfield, MO; *U.S. Public*, pg. 1141
Stracner, S.D., V.P.-Commun. & Pub. Affairs--Ameron International Corporation, Pasadena, CA; *U.S. Public*, pg. 98
Strafalace, Dan, V.P.-Gas Detection--Bacharach Inc., Pittsburgh, PA; *U.S. Private*, pg. 109
Strahan, Vicki, Dir.-Mktg.--Blumberg Communications Inc., Minneapolis, MN; *U.S. Public*, pg. 305
Strain, Laura, Sr. V.P.-Mktg. & Communications--First Bank N.A., Milwaukee, WI; *U.S. Public*, pg. 1680
Stranathan, Lee, V.P.-Mktg.--Igloo Products Corporation, Houston, TX; *U.S. Public*, pg. 265
Strand, Steven A., Mgr.-Adv.--S & C Electric Company, Chicago, IL; *U.S. Private*, pg. 954
Strange, Jeanne, Dir.-Mktg. & Adv.--First Southwest Company, Dallas, TX; *U.S. Private*, pg. 407
Stratford, Ray, V.P.-Mktg.--Travel Ports of America Inc., Rochester, NY; *U.S. Public*, pg. 1632
Strauss-Locke, Barbara, Dir.-Adv. & Promo.--Hyatt Hotels Corporation, Chicago, IL; *U.S. Private*, pg. 551
Strauss, Julie, Dir.-Mktg.--Golden Flake Snack Foods, Inc., Birmingham, AL; *U.S. Public*, pg. 750
Strauss, Karen L., Dir.-Mktg. Commun.--Owens Corning, Toledo, OH; *U.S. Public*, pg. 1236
Strauss, Michele, Supvr.-Adv.--Anderson, Greenwood & Co., Stafford, TX; *U.S. Public*, pg. 1650
Strauss, Ricky, V.P.-Creative Adv.--TriStar Pictures, Culver City, CA; *Int'l*, pg. 1283
Strazella, Francis, Dir.-Adv.--Stroehmann Bakeries, Harrisburg, PA; *Int'l*, pg. 1495
Street, C. Murphy, Dir.-Adv.--The Free Lance-Star Publishing Co., Fredericksburg, VA; *U.S. Private*, pg. 424
Streeter, Laura, Mgr.-Corp. Communications--Memorex Telex Corp., Irving, TX; *Int'l*, pg. 857
Streff, Bill, Dir.-Mktg.--H.C. Miller Company, Milwaukee, WI; *U.S. Private*, pg. 747

Streng, Kathy, Dir.-Adv.--Yenkin-Majestic Paint Corporation, Columbus, OH; *U.S. Private*, pg. 1195
Strickland, D. Gordon, Pres. & Chief Exec. Officer--Kerr Group, Inc., Lancaster, PA; *U.S. Public*, pg. 952
Strickland, Eleanor, V.P. & Mgr.-Adv.--Compass Bancshares, Inc., Birmingham, AL; *U.S. Public*, pg. 418
Striebel, Patrick, Dir.-Adv.--The Marcus Corporation, Milwaukee, WI; *U.S. Public*, pg. 1044
Stroman, Randy, Dir.-Mktg. Communications--Stainless Incorporated, Deerfield Beach, FL; *U.S. Private*, pg. 1029
Stromberg, Gordon, Sr. V.P.-Adv.--Shoppers Drug Mart, Ltd., Toronto, Canada; *Int'l*, pg. 112
Stromberg, Greg, V.P.-Mktg.--Sakata Inx USA Corp., Elk Grove Village, IL; *Int'l*, pg. 1311
Strong, Brian, Mgr.-Adv. & Mktg.--F.W. Woolworth Co. Limited, Canada, Weston, Canada; *U.S. Public*, pg. 1778
Stroud, Mickey, V.P.-Mktg. & Adv.--Old America Stores, Howe, TX; *U.S. Public*, pg. 1215
Stroupe, Rick, Sr. V.P.-Worldwide Sls.--Telecom Solutions, San Jose, CA; *U.S. Public*, pg. 1547
Strumolo, Albert, Dir.-Adv.-Natl. Chain--Providence Journal-Bulletin, Providence, RI; *U.S. Public*, pg. 209
Strumpf, Jeff, Dir.-Adv. & mgr.-Corp. Rels.--Alpha Metals, Inc., Jersey City, NJ; *Int'l*, pg. 328
Stuber, Paul, Dir.-Adv. & Mktg.--Rolex Watch Co. SA, Geneva, Switzerland; *Int'l*, pg. 1126
Stucki, Connie, Mgr.-Mktg. & Export--U.S. Safety, Lenexa, KS; *U.S. Private*, pg. 1125
Studin, Jan, V.P.-Adv.--Woman's Day, New York, NY; *Int'l*, pg. 795
Stukenberg, Susan, Dir.-Corp. Communications--QST Environmental Inc., Peoria, IL; *U.S. Public*, pg. 367
Stull, Walt, Mgr.-Corp. Mktg Commun.--ADC Telecommunications, Inc., Minnetonka, MN; *U.S. Public*, pg. 4
Stump, Kirk V., Dir.-Mktg. & Adv.--Quick & Reilly, Inc., New York, NY; *U.S. Public*, pg. 650
Sturm, H., V.P.-Mktg. Services--Midwesco Filter Resources Inc., Winchester, VA; *U.S. Public*, pg. 1026
Sturtevant, Nancy B., Mgr.-Mktg.--Bradley Corporation, Menomonee Falls, WI; *U.S. Private*, pg. 164
Succoso, Marian, V.P.-Adv. & Mktg. Programs--Loews Corporation, New York, NY; *U.S. Public*, pg. 1010
Suever, Ted, Mgr.-Adv.--Triplett Corporation, Bluffton, OH; *U.S. Private*, pg. 1104
Sugar, David C., V.P., Sec. & Dir.-Mktg.--National Guardian Life Insurance Company, Madison, WI; *U.S. Private*, pg. 784
Sukie, Linda, Acct. Exec.--Royal Caribbean Cruises Ltd., Miami, FL; *U.S. Public*, pg. 1410
Sullivan, Anne-Marie, Dir.-Adv.--Frederick's of Hollywood, Inc., Hollywood, CA; *U.S. Private*, pg. 424
Sullivan, Colleen, Mgr.-Adv.--Atlas/Soundolier, Fenton, MO; *U.S. Private*, pg. 64
Sullivan, Floyd, Mgr.-Adv.--Noritake Co., Inc., Secaucus, NJ; *Int'l*, pg. 959
Sullivan, Jerry, Gen. Mgr.-Adv.--Martin Gas Corporation, Kilgore, TX; *U.S. Private*, pg. 709
Sullivan, John, Dir.-Adv. Admin.--Chicago Sun Times, Chicago, IL; *Int'l*, pg. 632
Sullivan, John J., V.P.-Sls.--SmarTrunk Systems, Inc., Hayward, CA; *U.S. Private*, pg. 1006
Sullivan, Lawrence, V.P.-Adv.--Huntington Bancshares Inc., Columbus, OH; *U.S. Public*, pg. 849
Sullivan, Mike, V.P.-Sls. & Mgr.-Adv.--Lawrence Paper Company, Lawrence, KS; *U.S. Private*, pg. 654
Sullivan, Richard, Sr. V.P.-Adv.--The Home Depot, Inc., Atlanta, GA; *U.S. Public*, pg. 831
Sullivan, Stephen G., Sr. V.P. & Mgr.-Commun. Svcs.--Liberty Mutual Insurance Co., Boston, MA; *U.S. Private*, pg. 666
Sullivan, Terrence P., V.P.-Mdsg., Adv. & Communications--General Motors Acceptance Corporation (GMAC), Detroit, MI; *U.S. Public*, pg. 719
Sullivan, Will, Chief Mktg. Officer--Imation Corporation, Oakdale, MN; *U.S. Public*, pg. 870
Sullivan, William, Sr. V.P.-Adv.--Rolex Watch U.S.A., Inc., New York, NY; *Int'l*, pg. 1126
Sumas, James, Chm. Bd., Chief Oper. Officer, Treas., & Dir.-Adv.--Village Super Market Inc., Springfield, NJ; *U.S. Public*, pg. 1721
Sundblad, Ola, Adv. Mgr.--Aftonbladet AB, Stockholm, Sweden; *Int'l*, pg. 29
Sundermeyer, Ron, Exec. V.P.--S.A.S.I. Corporation, Collinsville, IL; *U.S. Private*, pg. 955
Sundquist, J.W., V.P.-Underwriting & Mgr.-Adv.--Bituminous Casualty Corp., Rock Island, IL; *U.S. Public*, pg. 1218
Sung, N.J., Mgr.-Mktg. Communications--Kodak Korea Ltd., Seoul, Korea; *U.S. Public*, pg. 555
Suptic, Dave, Dir.-Adv. & Mktg.--The Marley Cooling Tower Co., Overland Park, KS; *U.S. Public*, pg. 1676
Susco, Vincent F., Jr., V.P.-Admin. & Sec.--Connecticut Water Service, Inc., Clinton, CT; *U.S. Public*, pg. 431
Sussex, Thomas M., Jr., Dir.-Corp. Communications--Sparton Corporation, Jackson, MI; *U.S. Public*, pg. 1496
Sutton, Don, Dir.-Mktg. & Adv.--Benjamin Franklin Literary & Medical Society, Inc., Indianapolis, IN; *U.S. Private*, pg. 133
Sutton, Ginger, Mgr.-Adv.--New York Magazine, New York, NY; *U.S. Public*, pg. 1328
Swails, Richard, Mgr.-Adv.--Cedarapids, Inc., Cedar Rapids, IA; *U.S. Public*, pg. 1365
Swain, Mike, Dir.-Adv.--Southern Outdoors Magazine, Montgomery, AL; *U.S. Private*, pg. 106
Swan, Alex, Gen. Mgr.--ITOCHU Building Products Co., Inc., Miami, FL; *Int'l*, pg. 694
Swan, Tom, Dir.-New Prod. Devel.--R.J. Corr Naturals, Inc., Posen, IL; *U.S. Private*, pg. 276
Swanson, Dee, Mgr.-Adv.--Chief Agri/Industrial Division, Kearney, NE; *U.S. Private*, pg. 236
Swanson, Lori, Dir.-Adv.--Cub Foods Stores, Stillwater, MN; *U.S. Public*, pg. 1541
Swant, Jacky, Mgr.-Classified Adv.--The News Tribune, Tacoma, WA; *U.S. Public*, pg. 1066
Swaynie, Karen, Adv. Administrator--Benjamin Franklin Literary & Medical Society, Inc., Indianapolis, IN; *U.S. Private*, pg. 133
Swearingen, Tom, Dir.-Adv.--Washington State Apple Commission, Wenatchee, WA; *U.S. Private*, pg. 1152
Sweda, G.J., Dir.-Pub. & Investor Rels.--Modine Manufacturing Company, Racine, WI; *U.S. Public*, pg. 1121
Sweeney, Kerry E., Mgr.-N. American Pub. Rels.--Brown & Sharpe Manufacturing Company, North Kingstown, RI; *U.S. Public*, pg. 260
Sweeney, Mary S., Pres. & Dir.-Adv.--Jake Sweeney Auto Leasing, Inc., Cincinnati, OH; *U.S. Private*, pg. 1058
Sweeney, Terrence, Mgr.-Adv.--British Airways, Flushing, NY; *Int'l*, pg. 219
Sweet, Jane, Specialist-Communications--Milk Marketing Inc., Strongsville, OH; *U.S. Private*, pg. 745
Swenson, Steve, Dir.-Sls.--Vail Associates, Inc., Vail, CO; *U.S. Public*, pg. 1704
Swift, Dave, Mgr.-Adv.--Tektronix-Video & Networking Div., Grass Valley Products, Nevada City, CA; *U.S. Public*, pg. 1567
Swift, Humphrey H., Pres., Chief Exec. Officer & Mgr.-Adv. & Sls. Promo.--Swift Instruments, Inc., Dorchester, MA; *U.S. Private*, pg. 1058
Swinden, Jean, Mgr.-Credit--Imperial Schrade Corp., Ellenville, NY; *U.S. Private*, pg. 559
Switalla, Robert, Mgr.-Adv.--Bennett Brothers, Inc., Chicago, IL; *U.S. Private*, pg. 133
Sylvia, Kenneth A., Sr. V.P., Grp. Publr. & Publr. Consultant--Cliggott Publishing, Greenwich, CT; *U.S. Private*, pg. 246
Szczepanik, David, Sr. Mgr.-Mktg. Communications--J.J. Keller & Associates, Inc., Neenah, WI; *U.S. Private*, pg. 612
Szerlag, Traci, Mgr.-Communications & Adv.--Sciaky, Inc., Chicago, IL; *U.S. Private*, pg. 862
Tabaksblat, Israel, V.P.-Mktg. & Sls.--Allomatic Products Company, Sullivan, IN; *U.S. Public*, pg. 1363
Tabora, Cristina, Dir.-Mktg. & Corp. Communications--Hyatt International Corporation, Chicago, IL; *U.S. Private*, pg. 551
Tacy, Karen, Mgr.-Mktg. Services & Direct Response--Rainbow Technologies, Inc., Irvine, CA; *U.S. Public*, pg. 1359
Tada, Ryokichi, Dir.-Pub. Rels. & Adv.--Japan Airlines American Region, New York, NY; *Int'l*, pg. 700
Taguchi, Kiyoteru, Dir.-Adv. Bureau--The Nikkan Kogyo Shimbun, Ltd., Tokyo, Japan; *Int'l*, pg. 930
Tahinos, Pete, Mgr.-Regional Mktg.--Precision Tune Autocare Inc., Leesburg, VA; *U.S. Public*, pg. 1321
Talley, Lucy, Dir.-Adv.--Evening Post Publishing Co., Charleston, SC; *U.S. Private*, pg. 385
Tang, Oscar L., Chm. Bd. & Pres.--KOA Holdings, New York, NY; *U.S. Private*, pg. 603
Tanklage, Robert C., Chm. Bd., Chief Exec. & Chief Oper. Officer--La Victoria Foods, Inc., City of Industry, CA; *U.S. Private*, pg. 641
Taormina, Frank, Mgr.-Adv.--General Tools Mfg., Co. Inc., New York, NY; *U.S. Private*, pg. 445
Tardanico, Susan M., Dir.-Corp. Commun.--Textron Inc., Providence, RI; *U.S. Public*, pg. 1588
Tarnat, Jacky, Dir.-Commercial Mkt.--Lati Industria Termoplastici S.p.A., Vedano Olona, Italy; *Int'l*, pg. 804
Tassin, Ed, Pres. & Chief Exec. Officer--Capital Imaging, Summerville, SC; *U.S. Private*, pg. 206
Taton, Sher, Mgr.-Corp. Adv.--Texas Instruments Incorporated, Dallas, TX; *U.S. Public*, pg. 1585
Tatsuma, Toshiro, Mgr.-Adv.--The Japan Times, Ltd., Tokyo, Japan; *Int'l*, pg. 928
Tay, Shirley, Adv. & Promotions Executive--Hong Fok Corporation Ltd., Singapore, Singapore; *Int'l*, pg. 635
Taylor, John, V.P.-Pub. Rels. & Adv.--Intermountain Health Care Inc., Salt Lake City, UT; *U.S. Private*, pg. 568
Taylor, Karla, Mgr.-Mktg. & Adv.--Pearlstine Distributors Inc., Charleston, SC; *U.S. Private*, pg. 845
Taylor, Lee Ann, Dir.-Adv.--Architectural Digest, Los Angeles, CA; *U.S. Private*, pg. 20
Taylor, Madeline, Mgr.-Adv.--Allen Telecom Inc., Solon, OH; *U.S. Public*, pg. 45
Taylor, Melissa, Coord.-Adv.--Six Flags Magic Mountain & Six Flags Hurricane Harbor, Valencia, CA; *U.S. Public*, pg. 1611
Taylor, Milt, Mgr.-Adv.--United Grocers Inc., Portland, OR; *U.S. Private*, pg. 1122
Taylor, Sandy, Mgr.-Mktg. Services--Citizens Gas & Coke Utility, Indianapolis, IN; *U.S. Private*, pg. 241
Taylor, William, V.P.-Sls.--The Butcher Company, Marlborough, MA; *U.S. Private*, pg. 189
Tcheu, Arnie, Mgr.-Adv. & Mdse.--Autolatina Brasil S.A., Sao Paulo, Brazil; *U.S. Public*, pg. 665
Teenor, Kelly, Mgr.-Corp. Communications--Yokohama Tire Corporation, Fullerton, CA; *Int'l*, pg. 1521
Teer, Diane, V.P.-Mktg.--Campbell Soup Company Ltd., Toronto, Canada; *U.S. Public*, pg. 299
Tegt, Robert, V.P.-Mktg.--Jennie-O Foods, Inc., Willmar, MN; *U.S. Public*, pg. 840
Teh, Laurie, Mgr.-Corp. Adv.--The British Petroleum Company P.L.C., London, United Kingdom; *Int'l*, pg. 219
Teichert, Niccona, Dir.-Adv. & Promotion--Penguin Putnam Inc., New York, NY; *Int'l*, pg. 1027
Telford, George, V.P.-Adv. & Brand Mngmt.--Lorillard Tobacco Company, Greensboro, NC; *U.S. Public*, pg. 1011
Temley, L., Mgr.-Adv.--Stimson Lane Ltd., Woodinville, WA; *U.S. Public*, pg. 1661
Terrell, Marilyn, Mgr.-Adv.--Ruska Instrument Corporation, Houston, TX; *U.S. Private*, pg. 952
Terry, Howard, Dir.-Mktg.--Metromedia Steakhouses, Inc., Vandalia, OH; *U.S. Private*, pg. 736
Terry, James, Team Leader-Mktg. Commun.--New York State Electric & Gas Corporation, Binghamton, NY; *U.S. Public*, pg. 1173
Tesoro, Paul, Dir.-Adv.--Central Hudson Gas & Electric Corporation, Poughkeepsie, NY; *U.S. Public*, pg. 324
Teufel, Robert J., Pres. & Chief Oper. Officer--Rodale Press, Inc., Emmaus, PA; *U.S. Private*, pg. 939
Thacker, Bob, V.P.-Adv.--Dayton Hudson Corporation, Minneapolis, MN; *U.S. Public*, pg. 489
Thacker, Louise, Mgr.-Mktg.--Hart Graphics Inc., Austin, TX; *U.S. Private*, pg. 507
Thanepohn, Susan, Office Mgr.--Georg Fischer Disa Inc., Oswego, IL; *Int'l*, pg. 382
Thede, Merv, Pres.--Alcoa Steamship Co., Inc., Pittsburgh, PA; *U.S. Public*, pg. 61
Theodores, James, V.P.-Sls.--Kaiser Cement Corporation, Pleasanton, CA; *Int'l*, pg. 593
Therpe, Susan, Dir.-Adv.--Swiss Bank Corporation, Basel, Switzerland; *Int'l*, pg. 1329
Thesing, Wilhelm, Div. Mgr.--Durkopp Adler AG, Bielefeld, Germany; *Int'l*, pg. 468
Thibodeau, Kevin, Pres.-Waverly, N.A.--Waverly, Inc., Baltimore, MD; *U.S. Public*, pg. 1748
Thie, Mark A., Dir.-Adv.--Carpeteria, Inc., Valencia, CA; *U.S. Private*, pg. 215
Thiel, Stephen, Chm. Bd., Pres. & Chief Exec. Officer--Thiel Cheese Co., Hilbert, WI; *U.S. Private*, pg. 1081
Thigpen, Kathy, Dir.-Bus. Devel. & Sls.--Westgate Inc., Port Allen, LA; *U.S. Private*, pg. 1169
Thill, Tracy, Mgr.-Creative Service Production--Storz Instrument Co., Saint Louis, MO; *U.S. Public*, pg. 79
Thobie, Jean-George, Dir.-Adv.--Alcatel Alsthom Compagnie Generale D'Electricite, Paris, France; *Int'l*, pg. 52
Thokey, Jim, Dir.-Adv.--Russ Darrow Group, West Bend, WI; *U.S. Private*, pg. 311
Tholen, Sarah, Mgr.-Adv., Roofing Div.--Johns Manville Corporation, Denver, CO; *U.S. Public*, pg. 927
Thomas, Bob, Dir.-Resouce Devel.--Frozen Food Express Industries, Inc., Dallas, TX; *U.S. Public*, pg. 685
Thomas, Brad, Dir.-Adv.--American Radio Relay League, Newington, CT; *U.S. Private*, pg. 60
Thomas, Gerald, Adv. Asst.--Astec Industries, Inc., Chattanooga, TN; *U.S. Public*, pg. 141
Thomas, Gerald, Mgr.-Ntl. Sls.--O-Z/Gedney, Nelson Firestop Products, Tulsa, OK; *U.S. Public*, pg. 726
Thomas, John, Dir.-Adv.--Maytag Corporation, Newton, IA; *U.S. Public*, pg. 1064
Thomas, John, Dir.-Adv.--Maytag Cleveland Cooking Products, Cleveland, TN; *U.S. Public*, pg. 1064
Thomas, John, Dir.-Adv.--Jenn-Air, Newton, IA; *U.S. Public*, pg. 1064
Thomas, John, Dir.-Adv.--Maytag Galesburg Refrigeration Products, Galesburg, IL; *U.S. Public*, pg. 1064
Thomas, Linda, Dir.-Investor Rels.--Unit Corporation, Tulsa, OK; *U.S. Public*, pg. 1672
Thomas, Mary, Dir.-External Commun.--Baxter International Inc., Deerfield, IL; *U.S. Public*, pg. 196
Thomas, Owen, Dir.-Pub. Rels. & Adv.--Integrated Marketing Services, Omaha, NE; *U.S. Public*, pg. 631
Thomas, Patty, Vendor Rep.--NationsBank of Texas, N.A., Dallas, TX; *U.S. Public*, pg. 1163
Thomas, Ray, Dir.-Corp. Communications--Data General Corporation, Westborough, MA; *U.S. Public*, pg. 485
Thomas, Steve, Mgr.-Promo.--Subway Franchise Advertising Fund Trust, Milford, CT; *U.S. Private*, pg. 1048
Thomason, Scott L., Pres. & Chief Exec. Officer--Thomason Auto Group, Gladstone, OR; *U.S. Private*, pg. 1083
Thompson, Anthony, Grp. V.P.-Mktg.--Proudfoot USA Company, West Palm Beach, FL; *Int'l*, pg. 1072
Thompson, Brad, Mgr.-Mktg.--Laboratory Supply Company, Inc., Louisville, KY; *U.S. Private*, pg. 641
Thompson, Daniel J., V.P. & Gen. Counsel-Adv. & Publ.--BellSouth Enterprises, Inc., Atlanta, GA; *U.S. Public*, pg. 208
Thompson, David, Dir.-Adv.--Oklahoma Publishing Company, Oklahoma City, OK; *U.S. Private*, pg. 813
Thompson, David L., Dir.-Adv.--The Daily & Sunday Oklahoman, Oklahoma City, OK; *U.S. Private*, pg. 813
Thompson, Eve, Dir.-Adv.--Fireman's Fund Insurance Company, Novato, CA; *Int'l*, pg. 58
Thompson, Janelle E., V.P.-Mktg. & Adv.--Wine World Estates Company, Saint Helena, CA; *Int'l*, pg. 917
Thompson, John P., Mgr.-Mktg. Communications--Packaging and Material Handling Equipment Div., Homer City, PA; *U.S. Public*, pg. 606
Thompson, L.M., Mgr.-Trade Shows--MTS Systems Corporation, Eden Prairie, MN; *U.S. Public*, pg. 1028
Thompson, Leo G., Pres. & Chief Exec. Officer--Lindberg Corporation, Rosemont, IL; *U.S. Public*, pg. 999
Thompson, Lisa, Coor.-Adv.--United Supermarkets Inc., Lubbock, TX; *U.S. Private*, pg. 1126
Thompson, Olivia, Exec. V.P.-Publishing--Fairchild Publications, New York, NY; *U.S. Public*, pg. 513
Thompson, Sarah J., Asst. V.P.-Adv. & Pub. Rels.--Avemco Corporation, Frederick, MD; *U.S. Public*, pg. 151
Thompson, Sheri C., Commun. Specialist--EBSCO Industries, Inc., Birmingham, AL; *U.S. Private*, pg. 358
Thompson, Terrie J., Sr. V.P.--AmClyde Engineered Products Co., Inc., Saint Paul, MN; *U.S. Public*, pg. 778
Thompson, Walt, Natl. Program Mgr.-Special Events--Xerox Business Services, Rochester, NY; *U.S. Public*, pg. 1784
Thomsen, Buo, V.P. & Gen. Mgr.--Lincoln Steel, Lincoln, NE; *U.S. Private*, pg. 824
Thonen, Greg, Mgr.-Adv. & Promo.--Marley Pump, Overland Park, KS; *U.S. Public*, pg. 1676
Thorne, Dan, Mgr.-Mktg.--Gilster Mary Lee Corp., Chester, IL; *U.S. Private*, pg. 455
Thorne, E.C., Dir.-Adv., Sls. Promo. & New Product Devel.--Morton Salt, Chicago, IL; *U.S. Public*, pg. 1135
Thornhill, Christine, V.P. & Asst. Sec.--Thornhill Oil Company, Inc., Fort Wayne, IN; *U.S. Private*, pg. 1084
Thorpe, Susan, Dir.-Adv.--Swiss Bank Corporation, New York, NY; *Int'l*, pg. 1329
Thurman, Jimmy, V.P.-Sls. & Mktg.--Harrington & King, Chicago, IL; *U.S. Private*, pg. 504
Ticco, John A., Mgr.-Mktg.--Louis P. Ciminelli Construction Co. Inc., Buffalo, NY; *U.S. Private*, pg. 239

Ticktin, Karen, V.P.-Adv.--Showtime Networks Inc., New York, NY; *U.S. Private*, pg. 779

Tidwell, Wayne, Dir.-Creative Media Svcs.--Scientific-Atlanta, Inc., Norcross, GA; *U.S. Public*, pg. 1443

Tieger, Jeff, V.P.-Adv., Pub. Rels. & Sls. Promo.--Starbrite Corp., Fort Lauderdale, FL; *U.S. Public*, pg. 1510

Tieger, Jeffrey, V.P. & Sec.--Ocean Bio-Chem Inc., Fort Lauderdale, FL; *U.S. Public*, pg. 1211

Tilis, Jerome S., V.P.-Mktg.--Knight-Ridder, Inc., Miami, FL; *U.S. Public*, pg. 963

Timp, Gary, Mgr.-Window/Door Sls.--Deco Products Co., Decorah, IA; *U.S. Private*, pg. 320

Tipton, Jim, Mgr.-Adv. & Mktg.--Beer Nuts, Inc., Bloomington, IL; *U.S. Private*, pg. 130

Tissu, Christian, Mgr.-Adv.--Lafarge Aluminates, Paris, France; *Int'l*, pg. 789

Toback, Harvey, Dir.-Adv.--Bestform Foundations, Inc., Long Island City, NY; *U.S. Private*, pg. 140

Toback, Harvey, Dir.-Adv.--Lily of France, Inc., New York, NY; *U.S. Private*, pg. 140

Tobak, Steve, V.P.-Corp. Mktg.--Cyrix Corporation, Richardson, TX; *U.S. Public*, pg. 1160

Tobey, Bill, Mgr.-Mktg. Communicaitons--Eimco Process Equipment Co., Salt Lake City, UT; *U.S. Public*, pg. 166

Tobias, Sally, Sec. & Adv. Sls.--Warner Cable Communications, Inc., Columbus, OH; *U.S. Public*, pg. 1611

Todd, Jerry, Mgr.-Adv.--Lantech Inc., Louisville, KY; *U.S. Private*, pg. 650

Todd, John, Mgr.-Customer Support & Engrng.--Yarway Corporation, Blue Bell, PA; *U.S. Public*, pg. 1650

Togher, Renee, Dir.-Mktg. & Sls.--Azteca Foods, Incorporated, Chicago, IL; *U.S. Private*, pg. 104

Tolbert, Robert, Dir.-Mktg.--Moore-Handley, Inc., Pelham, AL; *U.S. Public*, pg. 1128

Toledo, Deborah, Mgr.-Communications--Essex Specialty Products, Auburn Hills, MI; *U.S. Public*, pg. 523

Toliver, Harold, Dir.-Mktg.--Golden State Mutual Life Insurance Company, Los Angeles, CA; *U.S. Private*, pg. 461

Tolman, Larry, V.P.-Mktg.--Merit Medical Systems, Inc., South Jordan, UT; *U.S. Public*, pg. 1096

Tomas, Antonio Condal, Dir.-Legal, Pur. & Personnel--Agropecuaria de Guissona, S. Coop. Ltda., Guisona, Spain; *Int'l*, pg. 31

Toms, Paul, Sr. V.P.-Mktg.--Hooker Furniture Corporation, Martinsville, VA; *U.S. Private*, pg. 538

Tonkin, Cheryl, Mgr.-Adv. & Mktg.--Utah Power & Light, Salt Lake City, UT; *U.S. Public*, pg. 1251

Toole, Steven, Mgr.-Mktg. Programs--Axent Technologies, Rockville, MD; *U.S. Public*, pg. 157

Toomey, Rodger, Sr. V.P.-Mktg. & Bus. Devel.--Food Services of America, Seattle, WA; *U.S. Private*, pg. 987

Toplin, Irving, Mgr.-Mktg. Services--Carl Zeiss, Inc., Thornwood, NY; *Int'l*, pg. 1523

Topolniski, Jim, Mgr.-Adv.-Intl.--Ilco Unican Corp., Rocky Mount, NC; *Int'l*, pg. 1432

Torjussen, Karl T., Mgr.-Adv.--Westvaco Corporation, New York, NY; *U.S. Public*, pg. 1762

Torrell, Kathleen, Dir.-Adv.--McKesson Water Products Company, Pasadena, CA; *U.S. Public*, pg. 1073

Torres, Judi, Mgr.-Adv.--Raymour and Flanigan Furniture Co., Liverpool, NY; *U.S. Private*, pg. 912

Toscuti, Linda, Mgr.-Co-op Adv.--Williams-Sonoma, Inc., San Francisco, CA; *U.S. Public*, pg. 1770

Tosi, Mark, Pres.--The Pastene Companies Ltd., Canton, MA; *U.S. Private*, pg. 842

Totaro, David J., Chief Mktg. Officer & Exec. V.P.--The Dime Savings Bank of New York, New York, NY; *U.S. Public*, pg. 509

Tourville, Glenn, Mgr.-Adv.--Resort Condominiums International, Indianapolis, IN; *U.S. Public*, pg. 322

Touw, P., Mgr.-Adv.--Fokker Aircraft Services B.V., Hoogerheyde, Netherlands; *Int'l*, pg. 1304

Townes, Eric, Mgr.-Adv.--Laminaire Corporation, Rahway, NJ; *U.S. Public*, pg. 1596

Toyota, Wayne, Sr. Mgr.-Promos.--American Honda Motor Co., Inc. Motorcycle Division, Torrance, CA; *Int'l*, pg. 634

Trace, Debra B., Mgr.-Corp. Commun.--STV Group, Inc., Douglassville, PA; *U.S. Public*, pg. 1421

Trahan, Gary W., Mgr.-Adv.--The Bartell Drug Company, Seattle, WA; *U.S. Private*, pg. 118

Trainor, Barbara H., Dir.-Pub. Rels. & Adv.--Providence Gas Co., Providence, RI; *U.S. Public*, pg. 1337

Trainor, Michael, V.P.-Mktg. & Adv.--Century 21 Real Estate Corp., Parsippany, NJ; *U.S. Public*, pg. 321

Trapolino, Kay, Mktg. Coord.--The Accor Group, Inc., Corona Del Mar, CA; *Int'l*, pg. 21

Trastek, Victor F., Sr. V.P.--The Metal Ware Corp., Two Rivers, WI; *U.S. Private*, pg. 734

Travis, Sandy, Adv. Coord.--Texas Micro, Inc., Houston, TX; *U.S. Public*, pg. 1586

Trawinski, Eileen, First V.P.-Mktg.--Emigrant Savings Bank, New York, NY; *U.S. Private*, pg. 373

Tredinnick, David, Mgr.-Natl. Sls.--Miether Bearing Products, Inc., Odessa, TX; *U.S. Private*, pg. 33

Treiber, David, Dir.-Adv.--United Dairymen of Arizona, Tempe, AZ; *U.S. Private*, pg. 1121

Trelease, Julia, Admin.-Adv. Services--Kraft Foods, Inc., Northfield, IL; *U.S. Public*, pg. 1287

Trelut, Lynda, V.P.-Adv. & Pub. Rels.--Nob Hill General Store, Inc., Gilroy, CA; *U.S. Private*, pg. 799

Triantafellou, Michael, V.P.-Retail Opers.--FFP Marketing Company, Inc., Fort Worth, TX; *U.S. Public*, pg. 604

Trick, Chris, Dir.-Natl. Mktg.--La Quinta Inns, Inc., San Antonio, TX; *U.S. Public*, pg. 972

Trifunovich, Lea, Mgr.-Corp. Adv.--TruServ Corporation, Chicago, IL; *U.S. Private*, pg. 1108

Trimble, Neill, V.P.-Adv.--Banfi Vintners, Old Brookville, NY; *U.S. Private*, pg. 113

Tripoli, Diane, Prod. Mgr.--Wallace International Silversmiths, Inc., East Boston, MA; *U.S. Private*, pg. 1061

Trocher, John A., V.P.-Mktg. & Sls.--American Credit Indemnity, Baltimore, MD; *Int'l*, pg. 464

Trodden, Jody, Admin. Asst.--Creative Hairdressers, Falls Church, VA; *U.S. Private*, pg. 287

Tron, Dionn, V.P.-Corp. Communications--AGFA Division of Bayer Corporation, Ridgefield Park, NJ; *Int'l*, pg. 172

Troy, Bill, Dir.-Brand Adv.--Digital Equipment Corporation, Maynard, MA; *U.S. Public*, pg. 507

Troyer, Darrel, V.P.-Sls. & Adv.--Troyer Potato Products, Inc., Waterford, PA; *U.S. Private*, pg. 1106

Troyer, Paul E., V.P.-Sls., Mktg. & Adv.--Hanover Wire Cloth, Hanover, PA; *U.S. Private*, pg. 193

Truman, Gregg, Dir.-Adv.--Air Jamaica Ltd., Miami, FL; *U.S. Private*, pg. 28

Trybus, Tom, Sr. V.P.-Mktg. & Sls.--Belvedere Company, Belvidere, IL; *U.S. Private*, pg. 1008

Tsuchida, Masahiro, Dir.-Grp. Gen. Mgr.--Duskin Co., Ltd., Osaka, Japan; *Int'l*, pg. 422

Tsuda, Katunari, Dir.-Adv.--Rohto Pharmaceutical Co., Osaka, Japan; *Int'l*, pg. 1126

Tsunokawa, Mister, Dir.-Adv.--Sanyo Electric Co., Ltd., Osaka, Japan; *Int'l*, pg. 1190

Tsuruda, Ron, V.P.-Adv.--Gramercy Pictures, Beverly Hills, CA; *U.S. Private*, pg. 468

Tuchman, Nanci, Mgr.-Adv. & Promo.--Paramount Canada's Wonderland, Vaughan, Canada; *U.S. Private*, pg. 776

Tucker, Alison, Mgr.-Adv.--Buckman Laboratories Inc., Memphis, TN; *U.S. Private*, pg. 180

Tucker, James E., V.P.-Sls. & Mktg.--R.M. Palmer Company, Reading, PA; *U.S. Private*, pg. 835

Tuggle, Donna, Mgr.-Natl. Adv.--Seattle Times Company, Seattle, WA; *U.S. Private*, pg. 980

Tuley, Rolland, Dir.-Adv. & Creative Svcs.--Mead Johnson Nutritional Group, Evansville, IN; *U.S. Public*, pg. 254

Tunchumrus, Boonsom, Exec. V.P.--Siam City Bank Public Company Limited, Bangkok, Thailand; *Int'l*, pg. 1239

Tuner, Susanne, Coord.-Corp. Commun. Project--Berkshire Life Insurance Company, Pittsfield, MA; *U.S. Private*, pg. 136

Tung, Stephen, Mgr.-Sls.--Sun Hung Kai Properties Ltd., Wan Chai, Hong Kong; *Int'l*, pg. 1318

Turin, George, Dir.-Indus. Sls.--Frigid Products, Inc., Elizabeth, NJ; *U.S. Private*, pg. 883

Turk, Penny, Mgr.-Mktg. Commun.--Multigraphics Inc., Mount Prospect, IL; *U.S. Public*, pg. 1141

Turner, JamesA., V.P.--Knight Architects Engineers Planners, Inc., Chicago, IL; *U.S. Private*, pg. 626

Turner, Janet M., V.P.-Investor Rels.--PLM International, Inc., San Francisco, CA; *U.S. Public*, pg. 1241

Turner, John A., V.P.-Sls. & Mktg.--Hatfield Quality Meats, Hatfield, PA; *U.S. Private*, pg. 510

Turner, Steve, Mgr.-Sls.--Fleischli Oil Company, Inc., Cheyenne, WY; *U.S. Private*, pg. 410

Turner, Steve, Mgr.-Mktg. & Adv.--Turner Holding LLC, Covington, TN; *U.S. Private*, pg. 1109

Turrin, Phyllis, Dir.-Mktg.--Georgette Klinger, Inc., New York, NY; *U.S. Private*, pg. 626

Turrisi, Jeff, Dir.-Mktg.--Greater New York Mutual Insurance Company, New York, NY; *U.S. Private*, pg. 476

Turse, Bill, V.P.-Mktg. & Sls., Dir.-Adv.--Ferraz Corporation, Parsippany, NJ; *Int'l*, pg. 1028

Tury, Wendy, Dir.-Publicity--Transworld Publishers Ltd., London, United Kingdom; *Int'l*, pg. 191

Tuthill, James G., Jr., Pres. & Chief Exec. Officer--Tuthill Corporation, Hinsdale, IL; *U.S. Private*, pg. 1110

Tutor, Dean, Dir.-Adv., Media & Pub. Rels.--L.A. Gear, Inc., Santa Monica, CA; *U.S. Public*, pg. 969

Tuttle, Terri, Dir.-Adv.--Tyton Corporation, Milwaukee, WI; *Int'l*, pg. 208

Tuttle, Terri, Mgr.-Adv.--Humphrey, Inc., San Diego, CA; *U.S. Public*, pg. 1376

Twardowski, Jerry, V.P.-Mktg.--Atwood & Morrill Co., Inc., Salem, MA; *Int'l*, pg. 1489

Twyman, Bruce A., Dir.-Adv.--Virginia Tourism Corp., Richmond, VA; *U.S. Private*, pg. 1141

Tyburski, Steve, Mgr.-Adv. & Promo.--HFS, Incorporated, Parsippany, NJ; *U.S. Public*, pg. 321

Tynan, Carol W., V.P., Dir.-Adv. & Publ.--Channing L. Bete Co., Inc., South Deerfield, MA; *U.S. Private*, pg. 140

Uhrenbacher, Michael, Dir.-Mktg. & Adv.--Bierbrauerei Fohrenburg, Bludenz, Austria; *Int'l*, pg. 194

Uhrich, Melissa, Dir.-Adv.--Egghead, Inc., Liberty Lake, WA; *U.S. Public*, pg. 566

Uillaro, Maria Antonia, Coord.-Adv.--Ford Espana S.A., Madrid, Spain; *U.S. Public*, pg. 665

Ullenberg, Ronald T., Pres.--World Pacific Ullenberg Corp., Chattanooga, TN; *U.S. Public*, pg. 861

Ullman, Diana, Dir.-Adv. & Mktg.--Tops Appliance City, Edison, NJ; *U.S. Public*, pg. 1622

Ulrich, Larry, Dir.-Adv.--New England Business Service, Inc., Groton, MA; *U.S. Public*, pg. 1170

Ulrich, Melissa A., Mgr.-Adv. & Promo.--Swartwout Industries, Grandview, MO; *Int'l*, pg. 1398

Umans, Don, Dir.-Mktg.--Value Line, Inc., New York, NY; *U.S. Private*, pg. 137

Ungar, Lawrence, Mgr.-Adv.--Heinen's Inc., Cleveland, OH; *U.S. Private*, pg. 519

Unger, David, Pres.--MFRI Inc., Niles, IL; *U.S. Public*, pg. 1026

Unger, John, Gen. Mgr. & Dir.-Mktg.--United Aircraft Products, Forest, OH; *U.S. Public*, pg. 1262

Untiedt, Dan, Dir.-Mktg.--McLaughlin Gormley King Company, Minneapolis, MN; *U.S. Private*, pg. 723

Updike, Steven, V.P.-Food & Beverage Opers.--Ocean Properties, Ltd., Delray Beach, FL; *U.S. Private*, pg. 811

Updyke, Jerry, V.P.-Sls. & Mktg.--Lance Industries, Sylmar, CA; *U.S. Private*, pg. 645

Urban, Eugene M., Dir.-Adv.--Akrochem Corporation, Akron, OH; *U.S. Private*, pg. 30

Urban, Mike, V.P.--MAGVS, Inc., Cleveland, OH; *U.S. Private*, pg. 696

Urbas, Eytan, Dir.-Mktg. Commun.--Guthy-Renker Corp., Palm Desert, CA; *U.S. Private*, pg. 488

Urch, James, Mgr.-Adv. & Mktg.--Telescope Casual Furniture, Inc., Granville, NY; *U.S. Private*, pg. 1074

Urquhart, Margaret, Pres.--Lowe's Food Stores, Inc., Winston Salem, NC; *U.S. Private*, pg. 657

Uttermohlen, Dee, Mgr.-Mktg., Adv. & Pub. Rels.--Safelite AutoGlass, Columbus, OH; *U.S. Private*, pg. 960

Utzman-O'Neill, Diane, Mgr.-Brand Adv.--Andersen Corporation, Bayport, MN; *U.S. Private*, pg. 71

Uynski, M. Rycs, Mgr.-Adv. & Media--Philips Electronics N.V., Eindhoven, Netherlands; *Int'l*, pg. 1051

Vacco, Michelle, Sr. Sec.-Adv.--Bayer Corporation/ Pharmaceutical Division, West Haven, CT; *Int'l*, pg. 173

Vack, Eric, Mgr.-Adv. & Sls.--Abell-Howe Company, Forest Park, IL; *U.S. Private*, pg. 10

Vagnini, K.L., V.P., Sec. & Treas.--The Gerstenslager Company, Wooster, OH; *U.S. Public*, pg. 1780

Valaitis, Robert J., 1st V.P. & Dir.-Mktg.--St. Paul Bancorp, Inc., Chicago, IL; *U.S. Public*, pg. 1428

Valan, Sherry B., Sr. V.P.-Adv. Standards & Bus. Affairs--DMB&B New York, New York, NY; *U.S. Private*, pg. 302

Valeiras, Luis, V.P.-Sls., Mktg. & Adv.--Gator Industries Inc., Hialeah, FL; *U.S. Private*, pg. 441

Valencia, Phaedra, Dir.-Mktg.--Tucson Realty & Trust Co., Tucson, AZ; *U.S. Private*, pg. 1109

Valenti, Lewis, Pres.-Ladies Div.--Swank, Inc., Attleboro, MA; *U.S. Public*, pg. 1543

Valis, Charlie, Mgr.-Adv. & Sls. Promo.--Crown Central Petroleum Corporation, Baltimore, MD; *U.S. Public*, pg. 462

Valkenaar, Lisa, Mgr.-Mktg. Commun.--Creative Publications, Mountain View, CA; *U.S. Private*, pg. 288

Valles, Adrea, Dir.-Adv. & Mktg.--CPC Spain, S.A., Barcelona, Spain; *U.S. Public*, pg. 225

Valtin, Don, Dir.-Adv.--Seaway Food Town, Inc., Maumee, OH; *U.S. Public*, pg. 1452

Valvo, Gary, V.P.-Sls. & Mktg.--Quincy Compressor Division Coltec Industries, Quincy, IL; *U.S. Public*, pg. 402

Van Allen, Barbara, Mng. Dir.-Corp. Communications--Cushman & Wakefield, Inc., New York, NY; *Int'l*, pg. 873

Van Brandmeyer, Rick, V.P.-Adv. & Mdsg.--JTS Corporation, San Jose, CA; *U.S. Public*, pg. 919

Van Buuren, Dick, Mgr.-Adv. & Sls. Promo.--Oce-van der Grinten N.V., Venlo, Netherlands; *Int'l*, pg. 993

Van Cauter, S., Dir.-Mktg.--Packard Instrument Co., Inc., Meriden, CT; *U.S. Private*, pg. 833

Van Doren, Richard, V.P.-Mktg.--See's Candy Shops, Inc., South San Francisco, CA; *U.S. Public*, pg. 221

Van Dussen, Bett, Coord.-Adv.--Howard Miller, Zeeland, MI; *U.S. Private*, pg. 747

Van Dyke, Jan, Asst. V.P.-Corp. Communications--Regence BlueCross BlueShield of Oregon, Portland, OR; *U.S. Private*, pg. 917

Van Dyne, Denese D., V.P.-Corp. Communications--Landmark Graphics Corporation, Houston, TX; *U.S. Public*, pg. 776

Van Gendt, G., Dir.-Mktg.--Bac Color Franseweg, Steenbergen, Netherlands; *Int'l*, pg. 131

Van Horn, Lucy, Dir.-Mktg.--American Recreation Centers, Inc., Sacramento, CA; *U.S. Public*, pg. 90

Van Name, Christopher K., Dir.-Mktg. & Adv.--Goodway Technologies Corporation, Stamford, CT; *U.S. Private*, pg. 464

van Nek, Cor, Mgr.-Adv.--Elsevier Bedrijfinformatie B.V., Doetinchem, Netherlands; *Int'l*, pg. 1099

Van Norman, Jim, V.P.-Mktg. Svcs.--Jamison Door Company, Hagerstown, MD; *U.S. Private*, pg. 581

Van Remortel, Steve, Mgr.-Natl. Sls. & Mktg.--Enzopac, Inc., Sheboygan, WI; *U.S. Private*, pg. 379

Van Sant, Margaret, Adv. Mgr.--The Holland Sentinel, Holland, MI; *U.S. Private*, pg. 995

Van Sickle, Deb, Adv. Specialist--Exabyte Corporation, Boulder, CO; *U.S. Public*, pg. 597

Van Waart, Caron, Mgr.-Adv. & Public Rels.--Relm Communications, Inc., Indianapolis, IN; *U.S. Public*, pg. 1376

Van Winkle, Linda, Mgr.-Adv.--Seafirst Corporation, Seattle, WA; *U.S. Public*, pg. 181

Van-Deemer, Harry, Dir.-Mktg. & Adv.--NORDX/CDT, Rolling Meadows, IL; *U.S. Public*, pg. 287

Vanacker, Greg, Dir.-Adv. & Mktg. Communications--Okidata Group, Mount Laurel, NJ; *Int'l*, pg. 1000

Vanasse, Tanya, V.P.-Mktg.--Bank of the Hudson, Poughkeepsie, NY; *U.S. Public*, pg. 1319

Vance, Phyllis, Mgr.-Pub. Affairs--BASF Corporation Fiber Products Division, Charlotte, NC; *Int'l*, pg. 105

Vandenburg, Jill, Mgr.-Adv.--Frutarom Meer Corporation, North Bergen, NJ; *U.S. Private*, pg. 554

Vanderzee, J.B., Mgr.-Adv.--Ford Division, Detroit, MI; *U.S. Public*, pg. 662

VanLeeuwen, Karen, Adv. Mgr.--Pittsburg Morning Sun, Pittsburg, KS; *U.S. Private*, pg. 995

Vanitosky, Kurt, Dir.-Adv.--Central Maine Newspapers, Augusta, ME; *U.S. Private*, pg. 439

Vanzura, Liz, Dir.-Adv.--Volkswagen of America, Inc., Auburn Hills, MI; *Int'l*, pg. 1474

Varpahle, Larry, Dir.-Mktg./Grocery Prods.--Hormel Foods Corp., Austin, MN; *U.S. Public*, pg. 840

Varrone, Joyce, Dir.-Adv.--Conair Corporation, Stamford, CT; *U.S. Private*, pg. 261

Vasilenko, Janet, Dir.-Public Rels.--Tootsie Roll Industries, Inc., Chicago, IL; *U.S. Public*, pg. 1621

Vasques, Gary, Exec. V.P.-Mktg.--Kohl's Corporation, Menomonee Falls, WI; *U.S. Public*, pg. 965

Vastano, Julie, Mgr.-Intl. Bus.--Iomega Corporation, Roy, UT; *U.S. Public*, pg. 912

Vaughan, Tim, Dir.-Adv. & Sls. Promo.--American Greetings Corporation, Cleveland, OH; *U.S. Public*, pg. 77

Vaughn, Mary Ann, Coord.-Adv. & Mktg.--Anchor Industries Inc., Evansville, IN; *U.S. Private*, pg. 71

Vaughn, William M., III, Exec. V.P.-Human Resources & Support Services--The Stop & Shop Companies, Inc., Quincy, MA; *Int'l*, pg. 750

Veach-Lytle, Tracy, Coord.-Adv.--Star Bronze Company, Alliance, OH; *U.S. Private*, pg. 1034

Veale, Ernest, V.P.-Sls., Mktg., Mdse. & Adv.--The Stellar Group Inc., Jacksonville, FL; *U.S. Private*, pg. 1040
Vedejs, Melita, Mgr.-Adv.--Mueller Sports Medicine, Inc., Prairie Du Sac, WI; *U.S. Private*, pg. 766
Velasco, Miguel Aleman, V.P.-Promotion & Advert.--Grupo Televisa, S.A. de C.V., Mexico, Mexico; *Int'l*, pg. 576
VeltKamp, Vicki J., Mgr.-Corp. Commun.--Hecla Mining Company, Coeur D'Alene, ID; *U.S. Public*, pg. 803
Venarchick, Walter, V.P.-Sls.--Bon Ton Foods, Inc., York, PA; *U.S. Private*, pg. 65
Venturi, Guiseppi, Exec. V.P.-US Opers.--G.D. Packaging Machinery Inc., Richmond, VA; *Int'l*, pg. 531
Verboort, Tracy, Coord.-Adv.--ShopKo Stores, Inc., Green Bay, WI; *U.S. Public*, pg. 1467
Vereen, Barbara B., V.P.-Adv. & Travel--Riverside Manufacturing Co., Moultrie, GA; *U.S. Private*, pg. 934
Vermette, Lynn, V.P.-Adv.--The Jean Coutu Group (PJC) Inc., Longueuil, Canada; *Int'l*, pg. 340
VerSteegh, Jerry, Dir.-Adv. & Commun. Production--Growmark, Inc., Bloomington, IL; *U.S. Private*, pg. 484
Vestuto, Vicki, Admin.-Adv.--Olympus America Inc., Melville, NY; *Int'l*, pg. 1005
Vetterli, Michael O., V.P.-Sls. & Mktg.--The Flecto Co., Inc., Oakland, CA; *U.S. Private*, pg. 410
Viana, Mariano Garcia, Mgr.-Corp. Mktg. & Adv.--Telefonica de Espana, S.A., Madrid, Spain; *Int'l*, pg. 1371
Vice, Matthew T., Coord.-Adv.--SLJ Retail LLC, Smyrna, GA; *U.S. Private*, pg. 957
Vicini, Donna M., Asst. V.P.-Adv.--Blair Corporation, Warren, PA; *U.S. Public*, pg. 236
Villarreal, Benet, Coord.-Adv.--Academy Corporation, Katy, TX; *U.S. Private*, pg. 11
Villicana, Lic Rogelio, Adv.--BASF Mexicana S.A. de C.V., Mexico, Mexico; *Int'l*, pg. 106
Vincent, Jami, Mgr.-Mktg.--Sunstone Hotel Investors, Inc., San Clemente, CA; *U.S. Public*, pg. 1536
Vincent, Scott, Dir.-Mktg. & Adv.--Flying J. Inc., Brigham City, UT; *U.S. Private*, pg. 415
Viner, Lucinda, Sec.-Adv. Dept.--Elsevier Science Limited, Kidlington, United Kingdom; *Int'l*, pg. 1100
Vinet, Daniel, V.P.-Mktg.--EnRoute Card Inc., Montreal, Canada; *Int'l*, pg. 36
Viney, Allan G., Brand Mgr.-Farm Equipment Div.--DMI, Inc., Goodfield, IL; *U.S. Private*, pg. 305
Virgo, Paul, Dir.-Mktg. & Adv.--Pro-Log Corporation, Monterey, CA; *U.S. Private*, pg. 887
Vitale, Terri, Dir.-Adv.--Oh Boy Corporation, San Fernando, CA; *U.S. Private*, pg. 812
Vitali, Carlo, Dir.-Mktg.--Olivetti SpA, Turin, Italy; *Int'l*, pg. 1002
Vitelli, Tom, Dir.-Pub. Rels. & Adv.--Intermountain Health Care Inc., Salt Lake City, UT; *U.S. Private*, pg. 568
Vitrio, Rolla, Admin. Asst.--Kraft Foods Inc., Rye Brook, NY; *U.S. Public*, pg. 1288
Vittorio, David, Mktg. Specialist--New England Coffee Company, Malden, MA; *U.S. Private*, pg. 792
Vizzini, Paul, V.P.-Mktg. & Sls.--Lifeline Systems, Inc., Cambridge, MA; *U.S. Public*, pg. 992
Vlahos, Lou, Asst. V.P. & Dir.-Adv.--The Western and Southern Life Insurance Company, Cincinnati, OH; *U.S. Private*, pg. 1164
Vlk, Leroy F., Exec. Sec.--The Florists Assn. of Greater Cleveland, Inc., Cleveland, OH; *U.S. Private*, pg. 415
Voellinger, Korinn, Dir.-Commun.--BGW Systems, Inc., Hawthorne, CA; *U.S. Private*, pg. 107
Vogel, Diane, Dir.-Adv.--Parisian, Inc., Birmingham, AL; *U.S. Public*, pg. 1333
Vogel, Diane, Mgr.-Adv.--Parisian, Inc., Birmingham, AL; *U.S. Public*, pg. 1333
Vogel, Scott T., Mgr.-Adv.--Thermo Black Clawson, Inc., Middletown, OH; *U.S. Public*, pg. 1593
Vogt, Erika, Head-Adv. Dept.--LGT Bank in Liechtenstein Aktiengesellschaft, Vaduz, Liechtenstein; *Int'l*, pg. 809
Volanowski, Patty, Dir.-Adv.--The Frye Company, Great Neck, NY; *U.S. Private*, pg. 430
Volstad, Stephen A., Mgr.-Customer Commun.--Carolina Power & Light Company, Raleigh, NC; *U.S. Public*, pg. 306
von Alten, Gottfried, Dir.-Pub. Rels. & Adv.--O&K Orenstein & Koppel Aktiengesellschaft, Dortmund, Germany; *Int'l*, pg. 516
Von Der Bruegge, Karen, V.P.-Strategic Mktg.--Harrah's Entertainment, Inc., Memphis, TN; *U.S. Public*, pg. 790
von Gillen, J. Creig, Dir.-Adv.--Monex Deposit Co., Newport Beach, CA; *U.S. Private*, pg. 757
Von Gruben, Brian G., Exec. V.P. & Dir.-Admin. Svcs.--Piccadilly Cafeterias, Inc., Baton Rouge, LA; *U.S. Public*, pg. 1294
Von Gunten, Karen, Mgr.-Adv.--Electro Rent Corporation, Van Nuys, CA; *U.S. Public*, pg. 568
Von Yeast, Lisa, Art Dir. & Mgr.-Adv.--H.B. Fuller Company, Saint Paul, MN; *U.S. Public*, pg. 686
vonder Porten, Bob, Pres.--Speedy Car-X, Inc., Chicago, IL; *U.S. Public*, pg. 1578
Vorsheim, George A., Jr., Dir.-Commun.--Environment/One Corporation, Niskayuna, NY; *U.S. Public*, pg. 586
Vota, Gail, Mgr.-Adv. & External Communications--Sabena Belgian World Airlines, Manhasset, NY; *Int'l*, pg. 1168
Votzmeyer, Ray, Mgr.-Adv.--Crafty Beaver Home Center, Skokie, IL; *U.S. Private*, pg. 284
Wachtel, Kenneth, Sr. V.P.-Adv.--Excite, Inc., Redwood City, CA; *U.S. Public*, pg. 599
Wachter, Mark, Prod. Mgr.--Diadora America, Inc., Kent, WA; *U.S. Private*, pg. 330
Wade, Birgitta, Dir.-Adv.--Empire Kosher Poultry, Inc., Mifflintown, PA; *U.S. Private*, pg. 374
Wade, Jim, V.P.-Sls. & Mktg.--Crane Carrier Company, Tulsa, OK; *U.S. Private*, pg. 286
Wade, Stewart H., V.P.-Mktg. & Adv.--American Bureau of Shipping, New York, NY; *U.S. Private*, pg. 51
Wadensten, Ted S., Pres. & Adv. Mgr.--Vibco Inc., Wyoming, RI; *U.S. Private*, pg. 1138
Wadsworth, Martha, Dir.-Adv. & Mktg.--Thonet, Statesville, NC; *U.S. Public*, pg. 1465
Wager, Dawn, Sr. Mgr.-Consumer Adv.--MCI Communications Corp., Atlanta, GA; *U.S. Public*, pg. 1023
Wagner, Angela, Dir.-Adv.--Sylvan Learning Systems Inc., Baltimore, MD; *U.S. Public*, pg. 1545
Wagner, Erica, Adv. Asst.--Microsoft Corporation, Redmond, WA; *U.S. Public*, pg. 1107
Wagner, Jim, Sr. V.P.-Adv. & Mdsg.--Warner Bros. Records, Inc., Burbank, CA; *U.S. Public*, pg. 1611
Wagner, K., V.P.-Mktg. & Sls. Foundry--Brillion Iron Works, Inc., Brillion, WI; *U.S. Public*, pg. 933
Wagner, Karyn, V.P.-Mktg. & Adv.--Family Restaurants, Inc., Irvine, CA; *U.S. Private*, pg. 393
Wagner, Lynda, Mgr.-Adv.--Ain Plastics, Inc., Mount Vernon, NY; *Int'l*, pg. 1388
Wagner, Rodger, V.P.-Sls. & Mktg.--KYB Corporation of America, Lombard, IL; *Int'l*, pg. 727
Wagner, Ron, Supvr.-Retail Adv. & Mktg.--GMAC Mortgage Corporation, Horsham, PA; *U.S. Public*, pg. 720
Wagner, Sharon, Mgr.-Adv.--Richardson Electronics, Ltd., Lafox, IL; *U.S. Public*, pg. 1387
Wagner, Steve, V.P.-Mktg., Carrier Sls. & Bus. Devel.--USLD Communications Corp., San Antonio, TX; *U.S. Public*, pg. 969
Wagovich, Joseph M., Mgr.-Pub. Rels. & Adv.--Sanders, A Lockheed Martin Company, Nashua, NH; *U.S. Public*, pg. 1008
Wahl, Rich, V.P.-Adv. & Sec.--Vibra Screw Inc., Totowa, NJ; *U.S. Private*, pg. 1138
Wahlin, Helena, Mgr.-Mktg. & Sls.--Foga Systems, Oxnard, CA; *Int'l*, pg. 496
Waite, Rick, Mgr.-Sls. & Mktg.--Burke Engineering Company, South El Monte, CA; *U.S. Private*, pg. 183
Waite, Robert E., V.P.-Corp. Rels. & Mktg.--CAE Inc., Toronto, Canada; *Int'l*, pg. 237
Walborn, Robert L., V.P.-Sls. & Mktg.--Farmer's Pride, Inc., Fredericksburg, PA; *U.S. Private*, pg. 395
Walding, Cindy, Asst. To Pres.--Wing Industries, Inc., Greenville, TX; *U.S. Private*, pg. 1183
Waldorf, Jennifer, Asst.-Sls. & Adv.--Parents Magazine, New York, NY; *Int'l*, pg. 191
Waldridge, Bob, Mgr.-Adv.--Despatch Industries, Minneapolis, MN; *U.S. Private*, pg. 327
Walker, Bob, Mgr.-Sls. & Mktg.--Ipsen International, Inc., Cherry Valley, IL; *Int'l*, pg. 1149
Walker, Chuck, V.P.-Mktg. & Adv.--Spaghetti Warehouse, Inc., Garland, TX; *U.S. Public*, pg. 1495
Walker, David, V.P.-Adv.--Kids "R" Us, Paramus, NJ; *U.S. Public*, pg. 1626
Walker, G.M.A., Dir.-Mktg. & Controller--Cussons (U.K.) LTD., Cheadle, United Kingdom; *Int'l*, pg. 1024
Walker, Sylvia, Dir.-Adv. & Corp. Rels.--Blue Cross and Blue Shield Association, Chicago, IL; *U.S. Private*, pg. 151
Wall, Brad, Mgr.-Mktg.--ANESCO, Kingston, PA; *U.S. Private*, pg. 74
Wall, Jack, Pres.--Al Larson Boat Shop, Inc., Terminal Island, CA; *U.S. Private*, pg. 652
Wall, Robert, Gen. Mgr.--Creative Card Co., Chicago, IL; *U.S. Public*, pg. 89
Wallace, Rose, Mgr.-Mktg.--Transitions Optical, Inc., Pinellas Park, FL; *U.S. Public*, pg. 1245
Wallace, Thomas T., Pres.--Johnston, Lemon & Co. Inc., Washington, DC; *U.S. Private*, pg. 595
Walser, Val, Div. V.P.-Adv. Opers.--The Bon Marche, Inc., Seattle, WA; *U.S. Public*, pg. 617
Walsh, Dan, Dir.-Adv.--Automobile Protection Corporation-APCO, Atlanta, GA; *U.S. Public*, pg. 150
Walsh, David, Deputy Dir. & Mgr.-Adv.--Times Newspapers Ltd., London, United Kingdom; *Int'l*, pg. 927
Walsh, Ellie, Dir.-Admin. Services--ABM Industries, San Francisco, CA; *U.S. Public*, pg. 2
Walsh, James F., V.P.-Adv.--Paddock Publications, Inc., Arlington Heights, IL; *U.S. Private*, pg. 833
Walsh, Janet, Mktg. Support--Altron Incorporated, Wilmington, MA; *U.S. Public*, pg. 59
Walsh, Mick, Dir.-Adv.--Current, Inc., Colorado Springs, CO; *U.S. Public*, pg. 498
Walsh, Patrick J., Dir.-Field Svcs.--Ferrellgas Partners, L.P., Liberty, MO; *U.S. Public*, pg. 618
Walsh, William G., Dir.-Adv./Discover--Dean Witter, Discover & Co., New York, NY; *U.S. Public*, pg. 1132
Walter, John, Mgr.-Corp. Commun.--Burns & McDonnell Engineers-Architects-Consultants, Kansas City, MO; *U.S. Private*, pg. 187
Walters, Kate, Mgr.-Adv.-Magnetic--Fuji Photo Film (U.K.), Ltd., London, United Kingdom; *Int'l*, pg. 524
Waltz, Tom, Dir.-Adv.--Proffitt's, Inc., Alcoa, TN; *U.S. Public*, pg. 1333
Wan, Kathy, Dir.-Mktg.--Casa Bonita, Inc., Carrollton, TX; *U.S. Public*, pg. 278
Wandell, Andrew, V.P.-Mktg. & Adv.--Knapp Shoes Inc., Penn Yan, NY; *U.S. Private*, pg. 401
Wang, Jin-Koung, V.P. & Gen. Mgr.--Wei-Chuan Foods Corporation, Taipei, Taiwan; *Int'l*, pg. 1488
Wangmann, Brett, Mgr.-Adv.--Andrew Corporation, Orland Park, IL; *U.S. Public*, pg. 112
Ward, Brian, V.P.-Sls. & Mktg.--Spectrum Control, Inc., Erie, PA; *U.S. Public*, pg. 1497
Ward, Jeff, Publisher & Exec. V.P.--Weight Watchers Magazine, Birmingham, AL; *U.S. Public*, pg. 1612
Ward, Neil, Mgr.-Adv.-Professional--Fuji Photo Film (U.K.), Ltd., London, United Kingdom; *Int'l*, pg. 524
Ward, Peter A., Mgr.-Mktg.--Ward Trucking Corp., Altoona, PA; *U.S. Private*, pg. 1149
Ward, Simon, Mgr.-Investor Relations--Transamerican Natural Gas Corporation, Houston, TX; *U.S. Private*, pg. 1096
Warner, Abbey, Dir.-Adv.--Federal National Mortgage Association (Fannie Mae), Washington, DC; *U.S. Public*, pg. 615
Warner, Barton, Dir.-Adv. & Mktg.--Johnson & Johnson Limited, Maidenhead, United Kingdom; *U.S. Public*, pg. 930
Warner, Fred, Pres.--Laubeck Corporation/Cross, Carbondale, PA; *U.S. Private*, pg. 652
Warner, Glen, Mgr.-Regional Sls.--Molded Fiber Glass Companies, Ashtabula, OH; *U.S. Private*, pg. 755
Warner, Harold, Dir.-Adv.--Mokon, Buffalo, NY; *U.S. Public*, pg. 1045
Warner, James J., Pres.--Warner Vineyards, Paw Paw, MI; *U.S. Private*, pg. 1151
Warren, David, Dir.-H.R.--Windmere-Durable Holdings, Hialeah, FL; *U.S. Public*, pg. 1771
Warren, Gregg S., Dir.-Corp. Commun. & Govt. Rels.--Weirton Steel Corporation, Weirton, WV; *U.S. Public*, pg. 1751
Warren, Janice, Mgr.-Corp. Commun.--FiberMark Inc., Brattleboro, VT; *U.S. Public*, pg. 620
Warren, Jenell, Coord.-Adv.--Acustar, Inc., Electronics Group, Troy, MI; *U.S. Public*, pg. 353
Warren, Ken, Dir.-Adv.--Consolidated Publishing Company, Anniston, AL; *U.S. Private*, pg. 266
Warren, Robert E., V.P.-Intl. Mktg.--Pride International, Inc., Houston, TX; *U.S. Public*, pg. 1324
Washington, George, Mgr.-Mktg. Commun.--The Flood Company, Hudson, OH; *U.S. Private*, pg. 414
Wasserman, Phyllis, Sr. V.P.-Adv. & Commun.--Staples, Inc., Westborough, MA; *U.S. Public*, pg. 1509
Watanabe, Hiroshi, Dir.--Skylark Co., Ltd., Tokyo, Japan; *Int'l*, pg. 1262
Waterman, Lisa, Dir.-Adv.--Lambda Electronics Inc., Melville, NY; *Int'l*, pg. 1241
Waterman, Win, V.P.-Mktg. & Sls.--Spotnails, Rolling Meadows, IL; *U.S. Private*, pg. 845
Watkins, Henry, Natl. Adv. Dir.--DC Comics, Inc., New York, NY; *U.S. Public*, pg. 1614
Watkins, Peg, Grp. Mgr.-Mktg. Commun.--Nordson Corporation, Westlake, OH; *U.S. Public*, pg. 1188
Watson, Bob, V.P. & Dir.-Corp. Adv.--Fleet Bank, N.A., Hartford, CT; *U.S. Public*, pg. 649
Watson, Donald B., Plant Mgr.--Luden's Inc., Reading, PA; *U.S. Public*, pg. 812
Watson, Marsha, Mgr.-Adv.--The Dometic Corporation, Elkhart, IN; *Int'l*, pg. 440
Watson, N.A., Admin.-Adv.--MacMillan Bloedel Limited, Vancouver, Canada; *Int'l*, pg. 828
Watson, Nancy, Dir.-U.S. Corp. Communications--Willis Corroon Corp., Nashville, TN; *Int'l*, pg. 1504
Watson, Russell A., Dir.-Mktg.--The Pepper Companies, Inc., Chicago, IL; *U.S. Private*, pg. 851
Watson, Susie E., Dir.-Adv. & Pub. Rels.--Timex Corporation, Middlebury, CT; *U.S. Private*, pg. 1088
Watson, Thomas, Mgr.-Adv.--Harley-Davidson, Inc., Milwaukee, WI; *U.S. Public*, pg. 786
Watt, William F., Exec. V.P. & Dir.-Mktg./Retail Banking--FirstFed Financial Corp., Santa Monica, CA; *U.S. Public*, pg. 645
Wattman, Kenneth E., Pres.--Kao Corporation of America (DE), Wilmington, DE; *Int'l*, pg. 717
Wayne, Joel, Exec. V.P.-Worldwide Creative Adv. Projects--Warner Bros. Studios, Inc., Burbank, CA; *U.S. Public*, pg. 1611
Weatherhead, John, V.P.-Construction Equip. Adv.--Engineering News-Record Magazine, New York, NY; *U.S. Public*, pg. 1070
Weaver, Craig, Product Mgr.--ODL Incorporated, Zeeland, MI; *U.S. Private*, pg. 809
Weaver, Donna B., Mgr.-Corp. Communications--Kellwood Company, Chesterfield, MO; *U.S. Public*, pg. 948
Weaver, Kristen, Mktg. & Communications--Medtronics Inc., Parker, CO; *U.S. Public*, pg. 1083
Weaver, P. Jill, V.P.-Adv.--The Allstate Corporation, Northbrook, IL; *U.S. Public*, pg. 55
Weaver, Steve, Dir.-Adv.--San Jose Mercury News, San Jose, CA; *U.S. Public*, pg. 964
Webb, James R., Pres.--Uncle Ben's, Inc., Houston, TX; *U.S. Private*, pg. 707
Webb, Karen, Dir.-Adv.--Aberdeen Citizen News-Record, Aberdeen, NC; *U.S. Public*, pg. 1079
Webb, Perry, Sr. V.P.--Ketchum, Inc., Pittsburgh, PA; *U.S. Private*, pg. 617
Webb, Rollie, Pres. & Chief Oper. Officer--Todd Pacific Shipyards Corp., Seattle, WA; *U.S. Public*, pg. 1619
Webber, Sandy, V.P.-Sls. & Mktg.--Watsco, Inc., Coconut Grove, FL; *U.S. Public*, pg. 1745
Weber, Barbara, Supvr.-Mktg. Svcs.--Pierce Manufacturing, Inc., Appleton, WI; *U.S. Public*, pg. 1233
Weber, Douglas, Sr. V.P.-Adv.--Journal of Commerce, Inc., New York, NY; *Int'l*, pg. 1026
Weber, Holly, Mktg. Coord.--Camosy, Inc., Russell, IL; *U.S. Private*, pg. 203
Weddle, Timothy, Dir.-Adv.--News-Press & Gazette Company, Saint Joseph, MO; *U.S. Private*, pg. 797
Weg, Kenneth E., Pres.--Bristol-Myers Squibb International, Princeton, NJ; *U.S. Public*, pg. 254
Wehberg, Joyce, Pres.--Shillcraft, Inc., Baltimore, MD; *U.S. Private*, pg. 994
Wehberg, Keith, Chief Oper. Officer & V.P.-Mktg.--Shillcraft, Inc., Baltimore, MD; *U.S. Private*, pg. 994
Wehling, Robert L., Sr. V.P.-Adv., Market Res. & Govt. Rels.--The Procter & Gamble Company, Cincinnati, OH; *U.S. Public*, pg. 1330
Weiden, Michael, Pres.-Adv. Sls.--All American Television, Inc., New York, NY; *U.S. Public*, pg. 41
Weidman, Sheila, Corp. Dir.-External Communication--Georgia-Pacific Corporation, Atlanta, GA; *U.S. Public*, pg. 735
Weigandt, Dave, Mgr.-Natl. Adv.--Madison Newspapers, Inc., Madison, WI; *U.S. Public*, pg. 984
Weil, Peter, Mgr.-Adv.--Bayerische Motoren Werke Aktiengesellschaft, Munich, Germany; *Int'l*, pg. 177
Weiland, Byron, Mgr.-Adv.--BMW Japan Corp., Mihana, Japan; *Int'l*, pg. 178
Weiland, William, V.P.--Carter Chambers Supply, Inc., Baton Rouge, LA; *U.S. Private*, pg. 216
Weimer, Lynnette, Mgr.-Mktg. & Sls.--Group Dekko, Kendallville, IN; *U.S. Private*, pg. 484

Weinberg, Arlene, Mgr.-Adv.--Hachette Filipacchi Magazines Inc., New York, NY; *Int'l*, pg. 794
Weiner, Eugene L., Exec. V.P., Sec. & Treas.--Paradise, Inc., Plant City, FL; *U.S. Public*, pg. 1256
Weiner, Tina C., Dir.-Mktg.--Yale University Press, New Haven, CT; *U.S. Private*, pg. 1195
Weinstein, Michael, Pres. & Chief Exec. Officer--Ark Restaurants Corp., New York, NY; *U.S. Public*, pg. 129
Weis, Bob, Dir.-New Product Devel.--Master Lock Company, Milwaukee, WI; *U.S. Public*, pg. 675
Weischer, Carsten, Mgr.-Pub. Rels.--Knurr AG, Munich, Germany; *Int'l*, pg. 739
Weiser, John, Sr. V.P.-West Coast Adv. & Sls.--The Guber Peters Entertainment Company, Los Angeles, CA; *Int'l*, pg. 1283
Weisman, Ezra, Pres. & Chief Exec. Officer--New Brunswick Scientific Co., Inc., Edison, NJ; *U.S. Public*, pg. 1169
Weiss, Ellen R., Sr. V.P.-Mktg. & Communications--Binswanger, Philadelphia, PA; *U.S. Private*, pg. 144
Weiss, Rachelle, Coord.-Pub.--Trifari Jewelers, New York, NY; *U.S. Private*, pg. 757
Weitz, Eric, Pres. & Chief Oper. Officer--Apparal America, Inc., New York, NY; *U.S. Public*, pg. 120
Weitzell, Roy, Mgr.-Mktg.--ComSonics, Inc., Harrisonburg, VA; *U.S. Private*, pg. 260
Welch, Kimberly A., V.P.-Corp. Commun.--Federal-Mogul Corporation, Southfield, MI; *U.S. Public*, pg. 615
Weldon, Jerrie, Adv.--Wicks 'n Sticks, Ltd, Houston, TX; *U.S. Private*, pg. 1175
Welle, Tom, Sr. Commun. Rep.--Potomac Electric Power Company, Washington, DC; *U.S. Public*, pg. 1318
Wellek, Richard L., Chm. Bd. & Chief Exec. Officer--Varlen Corporation, Naperville, IL; *U.S. Public*, pg. 1710
Weller, Staci, Mgr.-Adv.--Columbia Gas Distribution Companies, Columbus, OH; *U.S. Public*, pg. 402
Wells, Betty, Mgr.-Prod. Sls.--S.T. Research, Newington, VA; *U.S. Private*, pg. 958
Wells, Gay Lynn, Dir.-Adv.--Cadence Design Systems, Inc., San Jose, CA; *U.S. Public*, pg. 290
Wells, Heather, Adv.--Carlson Wagonlit Travel, Minneapolis, MN; *U.S. Private*, pg. 212
Wells, Jim, Mgr.-Adv.--Thriftway, Inc., Louisville, KY; *U.S. Public*, pg. 1771
Wellzahn, Nancy, Mgr.-Mktg.--Niagara Frontier Transit & Metro System, Buffalo, NY; *U.S. Private*, pg. 798
Welty, John, Chm. Bd., Pres. & Dir.-Mktg. & Adv.--Swensen's Ice Cream Co., Ronkonkoma, NY; *U.S. Public*, pg. 883
Wender, Sam, Dir.-Adv.--Crain's New York Business, New York, NY; *U.S. Private*, pg. 285
Wenmoth, Maureen, Dir.-Mktg. Services--Moen Incorporated, North Olmsted, OH; *U.S. Public*, pg. 675
Wenzel, Gary, Dir.-Mktg.--U.S. Electrical Motor Division, Saint Louis, MO; *U.S. Public*, pg. 573
Wermlinger, Bruce, Dir.-Adv.--84 Lumber Company, Eighty Four, PA; *U.S. Private*, pg. 366
Wesley, Charles, V.P.-Sls. & Mktg.--Hyer Industries Inc./Thayer Scale, Pembroke, MA; *U.S. Private*, pg. 552
Wessel, Stefan, Prod. Mgr.--FAG Bearings Corporation, Danbury, CT; *Int'l*, pg. 469
West, Cecily, Dir.-Mktg.--800-FLOWERS, Inc., Westbury, NY; *U.S. Private*, pg. 366
West, Elena F., Mgr.-Mktg. Svcs.--The Ohio Art Company, Inc., Bryan, OH; *U.S. Public*, pg. 1214
West, Krista, Mgr.-Pub. Rels.--Advanced Input Devices, Inc., Coeur D'Alene, ID; *U.S. Private*, pg. 21
West, Ross D., Dir.-Mktg.--American Felt & Filter, Newburgh, NY; *U.S. Private*, pg. 54
Westall, Rich, Dir.-Mktg. Services & Adv.--Mayfran International, Inc., Cleveland, OH; *Int'l*, pg. 1397
Westergaard, Jackie, Adv. Mgr.--Delavan Gas Turbine Products Division, West Des Moines, IA; *U.S. Public*, pg. 401
Westhoff, Stacy, Dir.-Mktg. & Adv.--O'Keeffe's, Inc., San Francisco, CA; *U.S. Private*, pg. 813
Westin, C.W., V.P.-Adv.--Westin, Inc., Omaha, NE; *U.S. Private*, pg. 1169
Westphal, Kenneth, V.P.-Bldg. Sys. Svcs. Grp.--Air Conditioning Co., Inc., Glendale, CA; *U.S. Private*, pg. 28
Wetterauer, Michael, Sr. V.P.-Sls. & Mktg.--Case-Swayne Co. Inc., Corona, CA; *U.S. Private*, pg. 218
Whalen, Andrea, V.P.-Adv.--Datawatch Corporation, Wilmington, MA; *U.S. Public*, pg. 488
Wheeler, Ian, Mgr.-Adv. & Sls. Promo.--Mark IV Automotive Canada Inc., Weston, Canada; *U.S. Public*, pg. 1045
Wheeler, Kimberly, Mgr.-Mktg. Services--The New Piper Aircraft, Inc., Vero Beach, FL; *U.S. Private*, pg. 794
Wheeler, Patrick J., Dir.-Corp. Communications--Consolidated Edison Company of New York, Inc., New York, NY; *U.S. Public*, pg. 434
Wheeless, Charlene, Dir.-Corp. Commun.--DynCorp, Reston, VA; *U.S. Private*, pg. 351
Whelan, Gerard, Mgr.-Corp. Communications--IMI Plc, Witton, United Kingdom; *Int'l*, pg. 646
Whisenhunt, Randy, Adv. Coord.--Collingwood Grain, Inc., Hutchinson, KS; *U.S. Public*, pg. 128
Whisner, R.M., Mgr.-Truck Adv.--Chevrolet Motor Div. General Motors Corp., Warren, MI; *U.S. Public*, pg. 720
White, Bob, Mgr.-Advertising & Promotion--Paramount Carowinds, Charlotte, NC; *U.S. Private*, pg. 776
White, Dale, Mgr.-Natl. Sls.--Capsonic Group, Inc., Elgin, IL; *U.S. Private*, pg. 207
White, Don, Mgr.-Adv.--Suitt Construction Company, Inc., Greenville, SC; *U.S. Private*, pg. 106
White, Dori, Asst. V.P.-Adv./Mktg.--Computer Associates International, Inc., Islandia, NY; *U.S. Public*, pg. 420
White, Douglas, V.P.-Mktg.--Broan Mfg. Co., Inc., Hartford, WI; *U.S. Public*, pg. 1193
White, James C., Mgr.-Plng. & Communications--Danfoss Fluid Power, Racine, WI; *Int'l*, pg. 377
White, James D., Mgr.-Adv. & Pub. Rels.--ITT Jabsco, Costa Mesa, CA; *U.S. Public*, pg. 860
White, Liz, Mktg. & Adv. Coord.--Ortel Corporation, Alhambra, CA; *U.S. Public*, pg. 1232
White, Marc, Dir.-Adv.--Electronic Media, Chicago, IL; *U.S. Private*, pg. 285
White, Mike, V.P.-Sls. & Mktg.--Hutchens Industries Inc., Springfield, MO; *U.S. Private*, pg. 550
Whiteford, Russell E., Pres. & Chief Exec. Officer--DHP Limited Partnership, Chicopee, MA; *U.S. Private*, pg. 302
Whitfield, Ross, Dir.-Mktg.--Dow Hickam Pharmaceuticals Inc., Sugar Land, TX; *U.S. Public*, pg. 1143
Whitley, Steve A., Sr. V.P.-Retail Banking--Virginia First Savings Bank, F.S.B., Petersburg, VA; *U.S. Public*, pg. 1721
Whitley, Tom, V.P.-Adv. & Promo.--Popeye's Chicken & Biscuits, Atlanta, GA; *U.S. Private*, pg. 5
Whitlow, Don, Pres. & Chief Oper. Officer--Barbour Thread, Inc., Blue Mountain, AL; *Int'l*, pg. 618
Whitmer, Becky, Engr.-Sls.--Baum USA, Sidney, OH; *Int'l*, pg. 1293
Whitmore, Rob, Dir.-Mktg. & Adv.--Alaska Industrial Hardware Inc., Anchorage, AK; *U.S. Private*, pg. 31
Whitney, Jim, V.P.-Sls. & Mktg.--Educational Insights, Inc., Carson, CA; *U.S. Public*, pg. 565
Whitsett, Michele, V.P.-Adv.--Bristol Hotels & Resorts, Dallas, TX; *U.S. Public*, pg. 253
Whittaker, Diane, Dir.-Adv.--Hit or Miss, Inc., Stoughton, MA; *U.S. Private*, pg. 531
Whittaker, Enez, Mgr.-Adv. & Pub. Rels.--Jamaica Flour Mills, Ltd., Kingston, Jamaica; *Int'l*, pg. 411
Whittemore, Erica, Coord.-Adv.--Southwest Airlines Co., Dallas, TX; *U.S. Public*, pg. 1493
Whittle, Ronnie, Dir.-Communications--Huntsman Corporation, Salt Lake City, UT; *U.S. Private*, pg. 549
Wholley, Gina, V.P.-Mktg. & Human Resources--Lat Purser & Associates, Charlotte, NC; *U.S. Private*, pg. 896
Wiater, Dennis, Mgr.-Adv.--Zenger-Miller, San Jose, CA; *U.S. Public*, pg. 1617
Wick, Tom, Mgr.-Adv.--Wick Building Systems, Mazomanie, WI; *U.S. Private*, pg. 1174
Wicken, Michael J., Pres. & Chief Exec. Officer--Motch Corporation, Cleveland, OH; *Int'l*, pg. 1128
Wickersham, John, Pres. & Chief Exec. Officer--Bill Communications, Inc., New York, NY; *Int'l*, pg. 1446
Widdis, Jonathan, Mgr.-Mktg.--ASCG, Inc., Anchorage, AK; *U.S. Private*, pg. 80
Widmayer, Karen, V.P.-Commun.--CarrAmerica Realty, Washington, DC; *U.S. Public*, pg. 308
Wiedeman, Wayne, Gen. Mgr.--Sherms Thunderbird Market, Medford, OR; *U.S. Private*, pg. 993
Wiedenfeld, Steve, Mgr.-Mktg.--Nordco, Inc., Milwaukee, WI; *U.S. Public*, pg. 1209
Wiehe, Bill, Sr. V.P.-Adv. Sls.--The Weather Channel, Atlanta, GA; *U.S. Private*, pg. 647
Wiehe, Gail, Adv. Specialist--Buick Motor Div. General Motors Corp., Flint, MI; *U.S. Public*, pg. 720
Wiel, Carol, V.P.-Adv.--Ingram Entertainment Inc., La Vergne, TN; *U.S. Private*, pg. 563
Wien, Larry, Dir.-Mktg. & Adv.--Al & Ed's Auto Sound Center, Monterey Park, CA; *U.S. Private*, pg. 30
Wienholz, Ken, V.P.-Sls & Mktg.--Bell-Carter Foods, Inc., Lafayette, CA; *U.S. Private*, pg. 131
Wiese, Arienne, Dir.-Investor Relations--Ultrak Inc., Lewisville, TX; *U.S. Public*, pg. 1663
Wiest, Doug, Coord.-Adv.--Idaho Power Company, Boise, ID; *U.S. Public*, pg. 861
Wiggerman, Dawn, Mgr.-Natl. Sls.--Sampler Publications Inc., Saint Charles, IL; *U.S. Private*, pg. 963
Wiggins, K.C., Mgr.-Domestic Sls.--Carver, Inc., Savannah, GA; *U.S. Private*, pg. 217
Wigginton, Stephanie, Mgr.-Adv. & Promo.--Royal Appliance Mfg. Co., Cleveland, OH; *U.S. Public*, pg. 1410
Wilcox, Marna, Mgr.-Corp. Adv.--PacifiCorp, Portland, OR; *U.S. Public*, pg. 1251
Wilcox, Marna, Mgr.-Corp. Adv. & Communications--Utah Power & Light, Salt Lake City, UT; *U.S. Public*, pg. 1251
Wiley, Harry T., Dir.-Adv. & Commun.--Ashland, Inc., Russell, KY; *U.S. Public*, pg. 138
Wilk, Steven J., Pres.--TransNet Corporation, Somerville, NJ; *U.S. Public*, pg. 1631
Wilkes, David, Exec. V.P. & Dir.-Adv.--Meadow Steel Products, Tampa, FL; *Int'l*, pg. 593
Wilkeson, Dale, Mgr.-Media & Adv.--QuikTrip Corporation, Tulsa, OK; *U.S. Private*, pg. 901
Wilkins, Leigh, Mgr.-Adv.--Camping World, Inc., Bowling Green, KY; *U.S. Private*, pg. 204
Wilkins, Sherry, Adv. Mgr.--Shawnee News-Star, Shawnee, OK; *U.S. Private*, pg. 995
Wilkins, Stazy, Mgr.-Adv.--Dell Computer Corporation, Round Rock, TX; *U.S. Public*, pg. 495
Wilkinson, Dennis, Adv. Mgr.--Haines City Herald & Ridge Shopper, Haines City, FL; *U.S. Private*, pg. 995
Wilkinson, Georgia, Mgr.-Mktg. Services--Cab-o-Sil Div. Cabot Corp., Tuscola, IL; *U.S. Public*, pg. 289
Willardson, Kris, Dir.-Communications--Wagner Spray Tech Corp., Plymouth, MN; *U.S. Private*, pg. 1146
Willersdorf, Bill, V.P. & Gen. Mgr.--U.S. Filter/Permutit, Warren, NJ; *U.S. Public*, pg. 1682
Willey, Glenn, V.P.-Sls.--Allfast Fastening Systems, Inc., City of Industry, CA; *U.S. Private*, pg. 37
Williams-Kirby, Lori, Mgr.-Adv.--Genova Products, Inc., Davison, MI; *U.S. Private*, pg. 447
Williams-Owen, Cathy, Controller--Dri Mark Products, Inc., Port Washington, NY; *U.S. Private*, pg. 342
Williams, Andrew, Brand Mgr.-Commun.--Prudential Corporation PLC, London, United Kingdom; *Int'l*, pg. 1073
Williams, Ann, Mgr.-Mktg.--G.S. Blodgett Corporation, Burlington, VT; *U.S. Public*, pg. 1064
Williams, Ann E., Mgr.-Mktg., Adv. & Pub. Rels.--The Blodgett Oven Co., Inc., Burlington, VT; *U.S. Public*, pg. 1064
Williams, Beth, Mgr.-Mktg.--Telos Corporation, Ashburn, VA; *U.S. Public*, pg. 1573
Williams, Deb, Adv. & Mktg. Asst.--Webster Industries Inc., Tiffin, OH; *U.S. Private*, pg. 1157
Williams, Debbie, Mgr.-Adv.--M&W, Gibson City, IL; *U.S. Public*, pg. 35
Williams, Doug, Mgr.-Natl. Sls.--Universal Fasteners Inc., Lawrenceburg, KY; *Int'l*, pg. 1515
Williams, Francis M., Chm. Bd., Pres. & Chief Exec. Officer--Kimmins Corp., Tampa, FL; *U.S. Public*, pg. 960
Williams, Glenn, Sr. V.P.-Mktg.--Globe Life And Accident Insurance Co., Oklahoma City, OK; *U.S. Public*, pg. 1622
Williams, Holly, Mgr.-Communications--Bio-Logic Systems Corp., Mundelein, IL; *U.S. Public*, pg. 230
Williams, James, Pres.--BC-USA, New Holland, PA; *Int'l*, pg. 201
Williams, John, V.P.-Mktg.--King & Prince Seafood Corporation, Brunswick, GA; *U.S. Private*, pg. 620
Williams, Jonas, Dir.-Mktg.--Adams Rite Sabre International, Glendale, CA; *U.S. Private*, pg. 1203
Williams, Lori, Admin.-Sls. & Mktg.--Eaton Corporation, Pressure Sensors Division, Bethel, CT; *U.S. Public*, pg. 557
Williams, Pat, Coord.-Events--McAlpin's, Cincinnati, OH; *U.S. Public*, pg. 1090
Williams, Perry, Mgr.-Adv. Trng.--The Dallas Morning News, Inc., Dallas, TX; *U.S. Public*, pg. 209
Williams, R.L., Pres. & Chief Oper. Officer--Dan River Inc., Danville, VA; *U.S. Public*, pg. 478
Williams, Roger D., Exec. V.P.-Mktg.-Food Products--Bob Evans Farms, Inc. Sausage Division, Columbus, OH; *U.S. Public*, pg. 596
Williams, Scott, Mktg. Analyst--Baxter-Hyland, Glendale, CA; *U.S. Public*, pg. 196
Williamson, Charles, Mgr.-Communications--Toastmaster, Inc., Columbia, MO; *U.S. Public*, pg. 1619
Williamson, Charles P., Mgr.-Adv.--Sico Incorporated, Edina, MN; *U.S. Private*, pg. 997
Williamson, Patricia, Asst. V.P.--DRS Technologies, Inc., Parsippany, NJ; *U.S. Public*, pg. 474
Willis, Barbara, Asst. V.P.-Adv.--Metropolitan Life Insurance Co., New York, NY; *U.S. Private*, pg. 737
Willis, Carolyn, Dir.-Adv. & Promo./Bantam--Bantam Doubleday Dell Publishing Group, Inc., New York, NY; *Int'l*, pg. 191
Willman, Todd, Mgr.-Adv. & Promo.--JLG Industries, Inc., McConnellsburg, PA; *U.S. Public*, pg. 918
Willox, Bruce A., Mgr.-Mktg. Communications--A.T. Cross Co., Lincoln, RI; *U.S. Public*, pg. 460
Willson, Barry, Gen. Mgr. & Dir.-Mktg., Adv. & Sls.--Eberline Instrument Corporation, Santa Fe, NM; *U.S. Public*, pg. 1593
Wilmsen, Tammie, Mgr.-Corp. Communications--Tecmar Technologies, Inc., Longmont, CO; *Int'l*, pg. 1361
Wilson, Allison, Dir.-Adv.--Le Peep's Grill Inc., Littleton, CO; *U.S. Private*, pg. 655
Wilson, Bob, Dir.-Natl. Adv.--Hoover Company, Canton, OH; *U.S. Public*, pg. 1065
Wilson, Holly, Mgr.-Adv.--Michael Business Machines Corporation, Charleston, SC; *U.S. Private*, pg. 740
Wilson, Janet, Mgr.-Mktg.--McBride and Associates, Inc., Albuquerque, NM; *U.S. Private*, pg. 719
Wilson, Laura, Mgr.-Media & Exhibits--SAS Institute Inc., Cary, NC; *U.S. Private*, pg. 966
Wilson, Linette, Adv. Sls. Asst.--Pfaudler, Inc., Rochester, NY; *U.S. Public*, pg. 1393
Wilson, Lon, Mgr.-Tech. Mktg.--Roquette America Inc., Keokuk, IA; *U.S. Private*, pg. 944
Wilson, Mary Ann, Mgr.-Adv.--Audi of America, Auburn Hills, MI; *Int'l*, pg. 1474
Wilson, Paula, Mgr.-Adv.--Aetna Inc., Hartford, CT; *U.S. Public*, pg. 26
Wilson, Steven A., Dir.-Sls, Mktg. & Adv.--Music Sales Corporation, New York, NY; *U.S. Private*, pg. 768
Wilson, Webster, Mgr.-Adv.--Scott Lumber Company, Bridgeport, OH; *U.S. Private*, pg. 977
Windham, Lisa, Dir.-Adv.--Monterey's Acquisition Corp., Houston, TX; *U.S. Private*, pg. 758
Windrum, Tom, V.P.-Adv.--Wajax Limited, Delta, Canada; *Int'l*, pg. 1484
Windsor, Hugh, Mgr.-Sls. & Adv.--Thomas & Betts Corporation, Memphis, TN; *U.S. Public*, pg. 1597
Windsor, Hugh, Mgr.-Sls. & Adv.--Thomas & Betts Reznor Division, Memphis, TN; *U.S. Public*, pg. 1598
Winer, Linda, Mgr.-Adv. & Sls. Promo.--Duro-Test Corporation, Fairfield, NJ; *U.S. Private*, pg. 349
Winer, Linda, Mgr.-Adv. Promo.--Duro-Test Intl. Corp., Fairfield, NJ; *U.S. Private*, pg. 349
Winfrey, Jane, Dir.-Mktg./Bed & Bath Div.--Jakson-A CHF Company, New York, NY; *U.S. Private*, pg. 1094
Wingert, Mary, Mgr.-Adv.--Horsehead Resource Development Company, Inc., Palmerton, PA; *U.S. Private*, pg. 540
Winking, Kim, Mgr.-Mktg. Svcs.--Broadcast Electronics, Inc., Quincy, IL, *U.S. Private*, pg. 531
Winkler, Allyson, Dir.-Adv. & Mdsg.--MCA Records, Inc., Universal City, CA; *Int'l*, pg. 1215
Winkler, Ann, Dir.-Adv--Apple Computer, Inc., Cupertino, CA; *U.S. Public*, pg. 121
Winkler, Barbara, Adv. Mgr.--The Ardmore Daily Ardmoreite, Ardmore, OK; *U.S. Private*, pg. 995
Winkler, Patricia, Dir.-Mktg. Commun.--The Fairmont Hotels, San Francisco, CA; *U.S. Private*, pg. 391
Winn, Patrick, Dir.-Mktg. Devel.--Lamb-Weston, Inc., Kennewick, WA; *U.S. Public*, pg. 427
Winston, Rick, Corp. Communications & Adv.--Sun Life Assurance Company of Canada, Toronto, Canada; *Int'l*, pg. 1318
Winters, Ted, Dir.-Adv.--Jewelcor Companies, Wilkes-Barre, PA; *U.S. Private*, pg. 587
Wischnia, Abe, Dir.-Corp. Commun.--Cubic Corporation, San Diego, CA; *U.S. Public*, pg. 466
Wise, Tom, Coord.-Mktg.--Heath Company, Benton Harbor, MI; *Int'l*, pg. 317
Wissler, Robert C., Pres. & Chief Oper. Officer--Comprehensive Business Services Inc., Mission Viejo, CA; *U.S. Private*, pg. 423

Witbrod, Marla, Mgr.-Adv.--Amoco Performance Products, Inc., Alpharetta, GA; *U.S. Public*, pg. 102

Witcher, Jimmy, Mgr.-Mktg.--Tech Spray, Inc., Amarillo, TX; *U.S. Private*, pg. 1071

Witmer, Stephen B., Mgr.-Corp. Communications--Watkins-Johnson Company, Palo Alto, CA; *U.S. Public*, pg. 1745

Witt, O., Dir.-Mktg. & Adv.--Battenfeld GmbH, Meinerzhagen, Germany; *Int'l*, pg. 825

Witzgall, Annemarie, Gen. Mgr.-Sls. & Mktg.--Essex County Gas Company, Amesbury, MA; *U.S. Public*, pg. 593

Wixted, Kevin, Dir.-Adv. & Pub. Rels.--La-Z-Boy Incorporated, Monroe, MI; *U.S. Public*, pg. 972

Wodzinski, Dale M., V.P.-Mktg. & Adv.--ESAB Welding & Cutting Products, Hanover, PA; *Int'l*, pg. 281

Wohlschlaeger, Rick, Dir.-Mktg.--Doane Products Co., Joplin, MO; *U.S. Private*, pg. 337

Wolfe, Karen, Coord.-Mktg. Media--Airflex Div. Eaton Corp., Cleveland, OH; *U.S. Public*, pg. 556

Wolka, Wendell, Dir.-Mktg.--Ranco North America, Plain City, OH; *Int'l*, pg. 1243

Woll, Alan, Mgr.-Mktg., Automotive Aftermarket--Robertshaw Tennessee, Knoxville, TN; *Int'l*, pg. 1243

Wollert, Randy, Grp. Mgr.--Worthington Foods Inc., Worthington, OH; *U.S. Public*, pg. 1780

Woltering, Mark, V.P.-Sls. & Mktg.--Amot Controls Corporation, Richmond, CA; *U.S. Public*, pg. 1405

Wong, Audrey, Sr. Mgr.-Mktg. Commun.--F. J. Benjamin Holdings Ltd., Singapore, Singapore; *Int'l*, pg. 187

Wong, James, Pres.--AIC International, Inc., New York, NY; *U.S. Private*, pg. 6

Wong, Katherine, Mgr.-Mktg. Svcs.--F.J. Benjamin Fashions (HK) Ltd., Causeway Bay, Hong Kong; *Int'l*, pg. 187

Woo-Nelson, Yeanna, Sr. V.P.-Mktg./Men's--Jay Jacobs, Inc., Seattle, WA; *U.S. Public*, pg. 922

Wood, Mary, Dir.-Adv.--Kaiser Permanente, Central East Division, Rockville, MD; *U.S. Private*, pg. 605

Wood, Sandra, Dir.-Pub. Rels. & Adv.--ITT Cannon, Santa Ana, CA; *U.S. Public*, pg. 859

Woodall, James, Mgr.-Opers.--Beechmont Investments Inc., Cincinnati, OH; *U.S. Private*, pg. 129

Woodard, Ken, Dir.-Group Adv.--B.A.S.S., Inc., Montgomery, AL; *U.S. Private*, pg. 105

Woodard, Robert, Mgr.-Mktg.--Tupperware U.S., Inc., Orlando, FL; *U.S. Public*, pg. 1644

Woodhull, John R., Pres. & Chief Exec. Officer--Logicon, Inc., Torrance, CA; *U.S. Public*, pg. 1198

Woodley, Janice, Sr. Dir.-Adv. & Mktg.--Loblaw Companies Limited, North York, Canada; *Int'l*, pg. 1495

Woodley, Janice, Sr. Dir.-Adv. & Mktg.--Loblaw Supermarkets Inc., North York, Canada; *Int'l*, pg. 1495

Woods, Curt, Mgr.-Natl. & Coop. Adv.--The Gazette Company, Cedar Rapids, IA; *U.S. Private*, pg. 442

Woods, Mark, V.P.-Marlon--Avnet, Inc., Great Neck, NY; *U.S. Public*, pg. 155

Woodson, Melinda, Pres.--Wholesale Electronic Supply, Dallas, TX; *U.S. Private*, pg. 1174

Woodward, Craig, Dir.-Commun. & Adv.--Kappler Safety Group, Inc., Guntersville, AL; *U.S. Private*, pg. 607

Woodward, Scott, Dir.-Adv.--Bausch & Lomb Incorporated, Rochester, NY; *U.S. Public*, pg. 194

Woody, Patricia A., V.P.-Commercial Lines Opers.--Amerisure Companies, Farmington Hills, MI; *U.S. Private, pg. 65*

Wooldridge, Lori, Exec. Admin. Asst.--Jerome Foods Inc., Barron, WI; *U.S. Private*, pg. 586

Wooten, Sidney C., Jr., V.P.-Mktg. & Sls.--Lane Limited, Tucker, GA; *Int'l*, pg. 1129

Workman, Eric, V.P.-Natl. Accts.--Consolidated Cigar Corp., Fort Lauderdale, FL; *U.S. Private*, pg. 690

Worley, Charley, Asst. V.P.-Adv.--Woolworth Corporation, New York, NY; *U.S. Public*, pg. 1777

Worrall, Sandra E., Mgr.-Mktg.--N.G. Bailey & Co. Ltd., Ilkley, United Kingdom; *Int'l*, pg. 132

Wortell, Brent, Pres.--Triton Industries, Inc., Chicago, IL; *U.S. Private*, pg. 1104

Worthington, Kristen, Asst. V.P.-Sls Promo & Consumer Mktg.--Associates Financial Services Corporation, Dallas, TX; *U.S. Public*, pg. 663

Worthington, Rosemary, Asst. to Pres.--LeaRonal, Inc., Freeport, NY; *U.S. Public*, pg. 982

Wortmann, Tom, Mgr.-Mktg. Svcs.--Littelfuse, Inc., Des Plaines, IL; *U.S. Public*, pg. 1001

Wright, Brian, Dir.-Adv.--Sharp Electronics (U.K.) Ltd., Manchester, United Kingdom; *Int'l*, pg. 1230

Wright, David J., Coord.-Adv.--Brown & Sharpe Manufacturing Company, North Kingstown, RI; *U.S. Public*, pg. 260

Wright, Gary, Mgr.-Corp. Commun.--RLI Corp., Peoria, IL; *U.S. Public*, pg. 1356

Wright, Jerome, Sr. Admin. Asst.-Adv.--Nortel, Nashville, TN; *Int'l*, pg. 970

Wright, Karen B., Dir.-Adv.--Ariel Corporation, Mount Vernon, OH; *U.S. Private*, pg. 81

Wright, Laurie, Dir.-Mktg.--Advance Business Graphics, Mira Loma, CA; *U.S. Private*, pg. 18

Wright, Marge, Dir.-Adv.--Blonder-Tongue Laboratories, Inc., Old Bridge, NJ; *U.S. Public*, pg. 237

Wright, Mary, Dir.-Adv. & Mktg.--Mac Frugal's Bargains Close-Outs Inc., Rancho Dominguez, CA; *U.S. Public*, pg. 437

Wright, Mary Beth, Dir.-Adv.--Us Magazine, New York, NY; *U.S. Private*, pg. 1162

Wright, Paula, Mgr.-Adv.--Computerworld, Inc., Framingham, MA; *U.S. Private*, pg. 569

Wright, Rick, Dir.-Adv.--Farmers Group, Inc., Los Angeles, CA; *Int'l*, pg. 110

Wright, Sheila, Mgr.-Mktg. Communications--Citizens Insurance Company of America, Howell, MI; *U.S. Public*, pg. 54

Wright, Tim, Pres.--Mr. Wright's Amazing Coffee Factory, San Jose, CA; *U.S. Private*, pg. 765

Wuertz, Frank, Dir.-Adv. & Communications--Lonza Inc., Fair Lawn, NJ; *Int'l*, pg. 67

Wulffson, Laurie, Mgr.-Publications--Silicon Systems, Inc., Tustin, CA; *U.S. Public*, pg. 1585

Wurster, Hans C., Exec. V.P.-Mktg. & Sls.--Bel/Kaukauna USA, Little Chute, WI; *U.S. Private*, pg. 130

Wyard, M. Corinne, Asst. V.P.--State Street Bank & Trust Co., Boston, MA; *U.S. Public*, pg. 1513

Wyble, Ronnie, Adv. Consultant--Prime Hospitality Corp., Fairfield, NJ; *U.S. Public*, pg. 1326

Wylock, Monique, Mgr.-Pub. Rels.--Digital Equipment N.V./S.A., Brussels, Belgium; *U.S. Public*, pg. 508

Wyman, K., Mgr.-Sls. & Adv.--Trippe Mfg. Co., Chicago, IL; *U.S. Private*, pg. 1104

Wynes, Bryant, Mgr.-Adv. & Sls. Promo., Springfield Div.--Associated Wholesale Grocers, Inc., Kansas City, KS; *U.S. Private*, pg. 93

Wysocki, Verna, Mgr.-Adv. & Mktg.--Beaver Lumber Company Limited, Markham, Canada; *Int'l*, pg. 887

Yacker, Jeffrey B., Mgr.-Communications--BPA International, New York, NY; *U.S. Private*, pg. 107

Yahn, Chuck, Pres. & Chief Exec. Officer--Ajay Leisure Products, Inc., Delavan, WI; *U.S. Public*, pg. 34

Yakamara, Mr., Dir.-Adv.--Bridgestone Corporation, Tokyo, Japan; *Int'l*, pg. 213

Yang, S.W., Chief Information Officer & Mgr.-Adv.--Tainan Spinning Co., Ltd., Tai-nan, Taiwan; *Int'l*, pg. 1347

Yarborough, W. Glen, V.P.--Allied Research Corporation, Vienna, VA; *U.S. Public*, pg. 48

Yarnbrough, Ernie, Dir.-Adv.--The Rockdale Citizen Publishing Company, Conyers, GA; *U.S. Public*, pg. 759

Yasger, Sheryl, Dir.-Adv.--SPS Payment Systems, Inc., Riverwoods, IL; *U.S. Public*, pg. 1132

Yasuba, Shoichi, Gen. Mgr.-Sls. & Mktg--Okuma Corporation, Niwa, Japan; *Int'l*, pg. 1000

Yasutaka, Sanga, Mgr.-Adv.--Mitsubishi Corporation, Tokyo, Japan; *Int'l*, pg. 871

Yaw, William R., Jr., Sr. V.P.--Standard Federal Bank, Troy, MI; *Int'l*, pg. 10

Yeakley, Ron, Dir.-Adv.--Medieval Times Dinner & Tournament, Inc., Buena Park, CA; *U.S. Private*, pg. 728

Yeandel, Victor F., V.P.--Consolidated Products, Inc., Indianapolis, IN; *U.S. Public*, pg. 436

Yeldin, Mary, V.P.-Mktg.--Warner Bros. Consumer Products, Burbank, CA; *U.S. Public*, pg. 1610

Yelen, Dennis, V.P.-Mktg. & Adv.--Coats & Clark Inc., Greenville, SC; *Int'l*, pg. 300

Yepsen, Robert E., Mgr.-Sls.--Damascus Bishop Tube Co., Greenville, PA; *Int'l*, pg. 842

Yoder, Del, Dir.-Mktg.--Supreme Corporation, Goshen, IN; *U.S. Public*, pg. 1542

Yokiel, Leo, Mgr.-Adv. Commercial & Canadian--Maytag Corporation, Newton, IA; *U.S. Public*, pg. 1064

Yokiel, Leo, Mgr.-Adv.-Commercial & Canada--Maytag Cleveland Cooking Products, Cleveland, TN; *U.S. Public, pg. 1064*

Yonker, Pat, Dir.-Mktg. Svcs.--GraphLine Inc., Tamarac, FL; *U.S. Private*, pg. 471

York, Andrew, Dir.-Mktg.--Nicklaus Golf Company, L.C., West Palm Beach, FL; *U.S. Private*, pg. 799

Yoshida, Katsumi, Pres.--Ricoh Electronics, Inc., Tustin, CA; *Int'l*, pg. 1114

Yoshimura, Hisao, Exec. V.P.-Circulation & Advertising, Personnel--Nikkei Business Publications Inc., Tokyo, Japan; *Int'l*, pg. 929

Yost, Gary, Dir.-Mktg.--Valassis Communications, Inc., Livonia, MI; *U.S. Public*, pg. 1704

Yost, Roger W., V.P.-Adv. & Event Mktg.--Jantzen, Portland, OR; *U.S. Public*, pg. 1702

Youmans, Bruce, Mgr.-Mktg. Communications & Adv.--TDK Electronics Corporation, Port Washington, NY; *Int'l*, pg. 1336

Younanpour, Ailen, Asst. Corp. Sec.--Pacific Scientific Company, Newport Beach, CA; *U.S. Public*, pg. 1250

Young, Christine, Mgr.-Adv.--Allens Of Hastings, Inc., Hastings, NE; *U.S. Private*, pg. 37

Young, Edward S., Chm. Bd.--Ken-Mac Metals, Inc., Cleveland, OH; *Int'l*, pg. 1388

Young, Gayle, Mgr.-Adv. & Promo.--Lapp Insulator Company, Le Roy, NY; *U.S. Private*, pg. 473

Young, Kathy, Adv. & Pub. Rels. Coord.--Pearle Inc., Dallas, TX; *U.S. Public*, pg. 396

Young, Linette, Dir.-Corp. Communications--Honeywell-Measurex Corporation, Cupertino, CA; *U.S. Public*, pg. 833

Young, Michael T., Pres.--Young Electric Sign Company, Salt Lake City, UT; *U.S. Private*, pg. 1201

Young, Ryan, Dir.-Mktg.--Daw Technologies, Inc., Salt Lake City, UT; *U.S. Public*, pg. 489

Young, Thomas R., Dir.-Adv. & Corp. Communications--McDonnell Aircraft & Missile Systems Div., Berkeley, MO; *U.S. Public*, pg. 241

Yount, Charles, Mgr.-Adv. & Publications--Detroit Diesel Corp., Detroit, MI; *U.S. Private*, pg. 850

Yung, Steve, V.P.-Mktg./McCain Foods (Canada)--McCain Foods Limited, Florenceville, Canada; *Int'l*, pg. 850

Yurechko, Olga, V.P.-Mktg.--Hampshire Designers Inc., Anderson, SC; *U.S. Public*, pg. 778

Yvan, Jo, V.P.-Sls. & Mktg.--Pride Products, Inc., Elizabeth, NJ; *U.S. Private*, pg. 883

Zabetakis, David B., Asst. V.P.-Market Devel.--Unitil Corporation, Hampton, NH; *U.S. Public*, pg. 1692

Zacek, Diane, Mgr.-Adv.--Solvay Animal Health, Inc., Mendota Heights, MN; *Int'l*, pg. 1277

Zakzeski, Jim, V.P.-Mktg.--Cubix Corporation, Carson City, NV; *U.S. Private*, pg. 294

Zambelli, Janet, Dir.-Adv.--Greer Steel Co., Dover, OH; *U.S. Private*, pg. 479

Zander, Timon D., Dir.-Adv.--Zander's Creamery Inc., Cross Plains, WI; *U.S. Private*, pg. 1203

Zapciz, David, Dir.-Mktg. Commun.--The First Years Inc., Avon, MA; *U.S. Public*, pg. 642

Zaran, Greg, Dir.-Adv.--Drug Emporium of Arizona, Scottsdale, AZ; *U.S. Private*, pg. 343

Zarrella, Ronald L., V.P. & Grp. Exec.-North American Sls., Svc. & Mktg.--General Motors Corporation, Detroit, MI; *U.S. Public*, pg. 718

Zarzecki, Suzanne, Dir.-Adv.--Arizona Instrument Corporation, Phoenix, AZ; *U.S. Public*, pg. 129

Zarzynski, Ken, Dir.-Adv.--The Allstate Corporation, Northbrook, IL; *U.S. Public*, pg. 55

Zazzarino, Terri, Coord.-Adv.--Farrell Lines Incorporated, New York, NY; *U.S. Private*, pg. 397

Zbella, Emil, V.P.-Adv.--LaSalle-Talman Bank, Chicago, IL; *Int'l*, pg. 11

Zeichick, Robert, V.P.-Adv. & Sls. Promo.--Signature Eyewear, Inc., Inglewood, CA; *U.S. Public*, pg. 1473

Zeigler, Steve, Dir.-Adv.--Universal Coach Parts, Inc., Des Plaines, IL; *Int'l*, pg. 326

Zeilinger, Scott, V.P.--Magic American Corporation, Cleveland, OH; *U.S. Private*, pg. 695

Zellers, Jean I., Dir.-Adv.--Highmark Inc., Pittsburgh, PA; *U.S. Private*, pg. 528

Zentz, Peter, Mgr.-Commun.--Benthos, Inc., North Falmouth, MA; *U.S. Public*, pg. 212

Zidek, Charles, Dir.-Corp. Commun.--U.S.S. Seko Worldwide, Elk Grove Village, IL; *U.S. Private*, pg. 1115

Zieger, Henning, Dir.-Mktg. & Adv.--Interbath, Inc., City of Industry, CA; *U.S. Private*, pg. 566

Zielinski, Bella P., Dir.-Mktg. Communications--The Inland Group, Inc., Oak Brook, IL; *U.S. Private*, pg. 564

Zielinski, Pat, Dir.-Mktg.--CompuDyne Corporation, Willimantic, CT; *U.S. Public*, pg. 419

Zietz, Bill, Dir.-Adv.-Intl.--Nike, Inc., Beaverton, OR; *U.S. Public*, pg. 1184

Zillman, Sue, Dir.-Adv. & Mgr.-Corp. Communications--UOP, Des Plaines, IL; *U.S. Public*, pg. 52

Zimmerman, Terri, Mgr.-Adv. & Pub. Rels.--Oak Grigsby, Sugar Grove, IL; *U.S. Public*, pg. 1209

Zimmermann, Don, V.P.-Opers.--Ferguson Manufacturing & Equipment Company, Inc., Dallas, TX; *U.S. Private*, pg. 401

Zipin, Larry, V.P.-Adv. & Sls.--Time Warner Cable, Stamford, CT; *U.S. Public*, pg. 1610

Zirkle, Steven, Gen. Mgr.-Sales--Eaton Corporation, Engine Components Division, Marshall, MI; *U.S. Public*, pg. 556

Zitel, Michelle, Mgr.-Mktg. Communications--CEM Corporation, Matthews, NC; *U.S. Public*, pg. 277

Zobel, Mike, Dir.-Sls. & Mktg.--Vacu-Dry Company, Sebastopol, CA; *U.S. Public*, pg. 1704

Zoehfeld, Robert, Dir.-Corp. Mktg.--Howe Furniture Corporation, Trumbull, CT; *U.S. Private*, pg. 543

Zoerb, Douglas G., Mgr.-Adv.--Grove WorldWide, Shady Grove, PA; *Int'l*, pg. 593

Zubler, R., Dir.-Sls.--Cruspi S.A., Dallikon, Switzerland; *Int'l*, pg. 348

Zucker, Lloyd, V.P.-Sls.--Shillcraft, Inc., Baltimore, MD; *U.S. Private*, pg. 994

Zukowski, Paul, V.P.-Sls. & Adv.--The Hibbert Company, Trenton, NJ; *U.S. Private*, pg. 525

Zunic, Joseph P., V.P.-Adv. & Promo.--Richfood Pennsylvania, Harrisburg, PA; *U.S. Public*, pg. 1389

Zurlo, Brandon, Dir.-Intl. Adv.--Northwest Airlines, Inc., Saint Paul, MN; *U.S. Public*, pg. 1200

Zwingler, Robert L., Dir.-Mktg. Services-North America Tires--The Goodyear Tire & Rubber Company, Akron, OH; *U.S. Public*, pg. 752

CHAIRMAN OF THE BOARD

Aakvaag, Torvild, Chm. Bd.--Norsk Hydro a.s, Oslo, Norway; *Int'l*, pg. 959

Abaticll, Anthony, Chm. Bd.--Vermont Financial Services Corp., Brattleboro, VT; *U.S. Public*, pg. 1716

Abbell, Joseph J., Chm. Bd. & Pres.--Abbell Associates, Chicago, IL; *U.S. Private*, pg. 9

Abbey, Nelson Dan, Jr., Chm. Bd.--Abbey Etna Machine Company, Perrysburg, OH; *U.S. Private*, pg. 9

Abbott, Helen, Chm. Bd.--Cine Magnetics, Inc., Armonk, NY; *U.S. Private*, pg. 240

Abbott, Michael E., Chm. Bd. & Chief Exec. Officer--American Republic Insurance Co., Des Moines, IA; *U.S. Private*, pg. 61

Abdallah, M.H., Chm. Bd.--Banque du Caire Barclays Intl. Bank SAE, Cairo, Egypt; *Int'l*, pg. 165

Abdoo, Richard A., Chm. Bd., Pres. & Chief Exec. Officer--Wisconsin Energy Corporation, Milwaukee, WI; *U.S. Public*, pg. 1773

Abe, Kohei, Chm. Bd.--Chubu Electric Power Company, Inc., Nagoya, Japan; *Int'l*, pg. 290

Aberg, Richard S., Chm. Bd.--Rigel Energy Corporation, Calgary, Canada; *Int'l*, pg. 1117

Ablon, R. Richard, Chm. Bd., Pres. & Chief Exec. Officer--Ogden Corporation, New York, NY; *U.S. Public*, pg. 1213

Ablon, R. Richard, Chm. Bd. & Chief Exec. Officer--Ogden Energy Group, Inc., Fairfield, NJ; *U.S. Public*, pg. 1213

Aboumrad, Alejandro, Chm. Bd.--Porcelanite, Inc., Lexington, NC; *Int'l*, pg. 573

Abplanalp, Robert H., Chm. Bd., Pres. & Chief Exec. Officer--Precision Valve Corporation, Yonkers, NY; *U.S. Private*, pg. 880

Abraham, Otto W., Chm. Bd. & Pres.--Engineered Products, Inc., Pittsburgh, PA; *U.S. Private*, pg. 376

Abraham, S. Daniel, Chm. Bd.--Slim-Fast Foods Company, West Palm Beach, FL; *U.S. Private*, pg. 1006

Abrahams, B., Chm. Bd. & Chief Exec. Officer--Greenham Trading Limited, Isleworth, United Kingdom; *Int'l*, pg. 1358

Abrams, Allan, Chm. Bd., Pres., Chief Exec. Officer & Chief Oper. Officer--Arrow Fastener Co., Inc., Saddle Brook, NJ; *U.S. Private*, pg. 85

Abrams, Bernard, Chm. Bd. & Chief Exec. Officer--Three D Departments, Inc., Costa Mesa, CA; *U.S. Public*, pg. 1604

Abrams, Bernard W., Chm. Emeritus--Abrams Industries, Inc., Atlanta, GA; *U.S. Public*, pg. 14

Abrams, Edward M., Chm. Bd.--Abrams Industries, Inc., Atlanta, GA; *U.S. Public*, pg. 14

Abrams, Gerald W., Chm. Bd.--Hearst Entertainment Productions, Inc., Los Angeles, CA; *U.S. Private*, pg. 516
Abramson, Earl, Chm. Bd. & Pres.--Rapid Mounting & Finishing Co., Chicago, IL; *U.S. Private*, pg. 910
Abramson, Morrie K., Chm. Bd., Pres. & Chief Exec. Officer--Kent Electronics Corp., Houston, TX; *U.S. Public*, pg. 951
Absalonsen, Mogens, Chm. Bd.--Scan-Ad Gruppen A/S, Arhus, Denmark; *Int'l*, pg. 1198
Ach, Roger W., II, Chm. Bd., Pres. & Chief Exec. Officer--Chicago West Pullman Corporation, Cincinnati, OH; *U.S. Private*, pg. 235
Ackerley, Barry A., Co-Chm. Bd. & Chief Exec. Officer--The Ackerley Group, Seattle, WA; *U.S. Public*, pg. 15
Ackerley, Ginger, Co.-Chm. Bd.--The Ackerley Group, Seattle, WA; *U.S. Public*, pg. 15
Ackerman, Don E., Chm. Bd.--Genicom Corporation, Chantilly, VA; *U.S. Public*, pg. 729
Ackerman, Roger G., Chm. Bd. & Chief Exec. Officer--Corning Incorporated, Corning, NY; *U.S. Public*, pg. 448
Ackert, Robert C., Chm. Bd. & Chief Exec. Officer--SouthTrust Bank, Southwest Florida, Fort Myers, FL; *U.S. Public*, pg. 1492
Acklie, Duane W., Chm. Bd.--Crete Carrier Corp., Lincoln, NE; *U.S. Private*, pg. 289
Ackroyd, Keith, Chm. Bd.-Non-Exec.--Silentnight Holdings Plc, Colne, United Kingdom; *Int'l*, pg. 1249
Acridge, James E., Chm. Bd., Pres. & Chief Exec. Officer--Giant Industries Inc., Scottsdale, AZ; *U.S. Public*, pg. 741
Adam, P.J., Chm. Bd. & Chief Exec. Officer--Black & Veatch, Kansas City, MO; *U.S. Private*, pg. 146
Adamek, Marek, Chm.--Ekokonrem Spolka z o.o., Wroclaw, Poland; *Int'l*, pg. 608
Adams, Charles R., Chm. Bd. & Chief Exec. Officer--Chad Therapeutics, Chatsworth, CA; *U.S. Public*, pg. 332
Adams, Jacob, Chm. Bd., Pres. & Chief Exec. Officer--Arctic Slope Regional Corporation, Barrow, AK; *U.S. Private*, pg. 80
Adams, James R., Chm. Bd.--Texas Instruments Incorporated, Dallas, TX; *U.S. Public*, pg. 1585
Adams, John, Chm. & Chief Exec. Officer--The Martin Agency, Richmond, VA; *U.S. Private*, pg. 678
Adams, John B., Jr., Chm. & Chief Exec. Officer--The Martin Agency, Richmond, VA; *U.S. Private*, pg. 678
Adams, John B., Jr., Chm. & Chief Exec. Officer--The Martin Agency, Richmond, VA; *U.S. Public*, pg. 909
Adams, John C., Chm. Bd., Pres. & Chief Exec. Officer--Russell Corporation, Alexander City, AL; *U.S. Public*, pg. 1413
Adams, John W., Chm. Bd. & Chief Exec. Officer--Harvard Industries, Inc., Tampa, FL; *U.S. Public*, pg. 796
Adams, John W., Chm. Bd.--Servico, Inc., West Palm Beach, FL; *U.S. Public*, pg. 1462
Adams, Johnston C., Chm. Bd. & Chief Exec. Officer--AutoZone, Inc., Memphis, TN; *U.S. Public*, pg. 150
Adams, K.S., Jr., Chm. Bd., Pres. & Chief Exec. Officer--Adams Resources & Energy, Inc., Houston, TX; *U.S. Public*, pg. 18
Adams, Peter D., Chm. Bd. & Chief Exec. Officer--Adams Rite Manufacturing Co., City of Industry, CA; *U.S. Private*, pg. 17
Adams, Richard M., Chm. Bd. & Chief Exec. Officer--United Bankshares, Inc., Parkersburg, WV; *U.S. Public*, pg. 1674
Adams, Robert J., Chm. Bd.--R.P. Adams Company, Inc., Tonawanda, NY; *U.S. Public*, pg. 19
Adams, W. Randolph, Chm. Bd. & Chief Exec. Officer--Mercantile Bank of St. Louis N.A., Saint Louis, MO; *U.S. Public*, pg. 1087
Adamson, James B., Chm. Bd., Pres. & Chief Exec. Officer--Advantica Restaurant Group, Inc., Spartanburg, SC; *U.S. Public*, pg. 22
Adareth, Jonathan, Chm. Bd.--Elscint Inc., Hackensack, NJ; *Int'l*, pg. 450
Addison, E. Christopher, Chm. Bd.--Addison Steel Inc., Albany, GA; *U.S. Private*, pg. 17
Addison, Edward L., Chm. Exec. Committee--Southern Company Services, Inc., Atlanta, GA; *U.S. Public*, pg. 1490
Aden, Mohamed, Chm.--BCI Mer Rouge, Djibouti, Djibouti; *Int'l*, pg. 163
Ades, Alan, Chm. Bd., Pres. & Chief Exec. Officer--A&E Stores, Inc., Teterboro, NJ; *U.S. Private*, pg. 1
Adikes, Park T., Chm. Bd. & Chief Exec. Officer--JSB Financial, Lynbrook, NY; *U.S. Public*, pg. 919
Adkins, Ralph J., Chm. Bd. & Chief Exec. Officer--Chesapeake Utilities Corporation, Dover, DE; *U.S. Public*, pg. 347
Adler, Frederick R., Chm. Exec. Committee--Data General Corporation, Westborough, MA; *U.S. Public*, pg. 485
Adler, Lionello, Chm. Bd.--Banca Commerciale Italiana, Milan, Italy; *Int'l*, pg. 135
Adler, Michael F., Chm. Bd. & Chief Exec. Officer--Moto Photo, Inc., Dayton, OH; *U.S. Public*, pg. 1136
Adolfson, David G., Chm. Bd.--Adolfson & Peterson, Inc., Minneapolis, MN; *U.S. Private*, pg. 17
Adorjan, J. Joe, Chm. Bd., Pres. & Chief Exec. Officer--Borg-Warner Security Corporation, Chicago, IL; *U.S. Public*, pg. 245
Afeyan, Noubar B., Chm. Bd. & Chief Exec. Officer--PerSeptive Biosystems, Inc., Framingham, MA; *U.S. Public*, pg. 1279
Agan, R.E., Chm. Bd., & Chief Exec. Officer--Hardings, Inc., Elmira, NY; *U.S. Private*, pg. 502
Agathos, Louis, Chm. Bd., Pres. & Chief Exec. Officer--Belshaw Brothers, Inc., Seattle, WA; *Int'l*, pg. 188
Aginsky, Phillip C., Chm. Bd. & Chief Exec. Officer--Tekgraf, Inc., Norcross, GA; *U.S. Private*, pg. 1073
Aglialoro, John, Chm. Bd. & Chief Exec. Officer--U.M. Holding Limited, Haddonfield, NJ; *U.S. Private*, pg. 1113
Aglialoro, John, Chm. Bd.--Cybex International, Inc., Medway, MA; *U.S. Private*, pg. 1114
Agnew, R.I.J., Chm. Bd.--LASMO plc, London, United Kingdom; *Int'l*, pg. 803
Agnew, R.I.J., Chm. Bd.--Redland PLC, Reigate, United Kingdom; *Int'l*, pg. 1090
Agresta, Michael, Chm. Bd.--Michael Stevens Ltd., Sayreville, NJ; *U.S. Private*, pg. 1042
Agrup, Sven, Chm. Bd.--AGA AB, Lidingo, Sweden; *Int'l*, pg. 12
Aguirre, Carlos E., Chm. Bd., Pres. & Chief Exec. Officer--Oregon Metallurgical Corporation, Albany, OR; *U.S. Public*, pg. 43
Aharu, Pato Mohd, Chm. Bd.--Malaysian Tobacco Co./B.A.T. Indust., Kuala Lumpur, Malaysia; *Int'l*, pg. 111
Ahearn, Lance W., Chm. Bd. & Chief Exec. Officer--RMT, Inc., Madison, WI; *U.S. Public*, pg. 1728
Ahern, John E., Chm. Bd. & Chief Exec. Officer--J.F. Ahern Co., Fond Du Lac, WI; *U.S. Private*, pg. 27
Ahlmann, Kaj, Chm., Pres. & Chief Exec. Officer--Employers Reinsurance Corp., Overland Park, KS; *U.S. Public*, pg. 711
Ahmed, Firozuddin, Chm. Bd.--National Refinery Limited, Karachi, Pakistan; *Int'l*, pg. 909
Ahn, Sangwoo, Chm. Bd.--Quaker Fabric Corporation, Fall River, MA; *U.S. Public*, pg. 1347
Ahnger, Donald C., Chm. Bd.--Midway Ford Truck Center Inc., Kansas City, MO; *U.S. Private*, pg. 744
Ahonen, Seppo, Chm. Bd.--Korpivaara Oy - Toyota Group, Korso, Finland; *Int'l*, pg. 72
Ahrens, Jay, Chm. Bd., Pres. & Chief Exec. Officer--Holly's Inc., Grand Rapids, MI; *U.S. Private*, pg. 535
Aibel, Howard J., Esq., Chm. Bd.--American Arbitration Association, New York, NY; *U.S. Private*, pg. 50
Aikawa, Kentaro, Chm. Bd.--Mitsubishi Heavy Industries Ltd., Tokyo, Japan; *Int'l*, pg. 873
Aiken, Hugh, Chm. Bd. & Chief Exec. Officer--Prospect Foundry, Inc., Minneapolis, MN; *U.S. Public*, pg. 142
Aiken, Hugh H., Chm. Bd., Pres. & Chief Exec. Officer--Atchison Casting Corporation, Atchison, KS; *U.S. Public*, pg. 142
Aiken, William, Chm. Bd. & Chief Exec. Officer--ACO Inc., Farmington Hills, MI; *U.S. Private*, pg. 3
Aikens, Robert B., Chm. Bd.--Robert B. Aikens & Associates LLC., Troy, MI; *U.S. Private*, pg. 28
Aiki, Shigeo, Chm. Bd.--Aisin Seiki Co. Ltd., Kariya, Japan; *Int'l*, pg. 39
Ain, Mark S., Chm. Bd. & Chief Exec. Officer--Kronos Incorporated, Waltham, MA; *U.S. Public*, pg. 967
Aitken, Timothy M., Chm. Bd. & Chief Exec. Officer--Transworld Home Healthcare, Inc., New York, NY; *U.S. Public*, pg. 1632
Akema, Teruyuki, Chm. Bd.--Tohoku Electric Power Co., Ltd., Sendai, Japan; *Int'l*, pg. 1390
Akers, James F., Chm. Bd.--The Crystal Tissue Co., Middletown, OH; *U.S. Private*, pg. 294
Akers, William C., Chm. Bd.--Akers Packaging Service Inc., Middletown, OH; *U.S. Private*, pg. 29
Akerson, Daniel F., Chm. Bd. & Chief Exec. Officer--Nextel Communications, Mc Lean, VA; *U.S. Public*, pg. 1180
Akins, Carl, Chm.--Catellus Residential Group, Irvine, CA; *U.S. Public*, pg. 315
Aksoy, Atilla, Chm.--Young & Rubicam Turkey, Istanbul, Turkey; *U.S. Private*, pg. 1200
Akutsu, Tetsuzo, Chm. Bd.--Terumo Corporation, Tokyo, Japan; *Int'l*, pg. 1375
Al Touq, Ibrahim, Chm.--Al Bank Al Saudi Al Franki, Riyadh, Saudi Arabia; *Int'l*, pg. 315
Al-Medej, Abdulmohsen Medej, Dr., Chm. Bd.--Kuwait Petroleum Corporation, Safat, Kuwait; *Int'l*, pg. 764
Alagen, Beny, Chm. Bd., Pres. & Chief Exec. Officer--Packard Bell NEC, Sacramento, CA; *U.S. Private*, pg. 833
Albarelli, Michael, Jr., Chm. Bd. & Pres.--Amloid Corporation, Saddle Brook, NJ; *U.S. Private*, pg. 66
Albareto, Enrico, Chm.--ELSAG Bailey Process Automation N.V., Schiphol, Netherlands; *Int'l*, pg. 449
Alberici, Gabriel J., Chm. Bd. & Treas.--J.S. Alberici Construction Co., Inc., Saint Louis, MO; *U.S. Private*, pg. 32
Albert, Andrew B., Co-Chm. Bd. & Co-Chief Exec. Officer--Rittenhouse Inc., Park Ridge, IL; *U.S. Private*, pg. 933
Albert, Carl, Chm. Bd. & Chief Exec. Officer--Fairchild Aerospace Corporation, San Antonio, TX; *U.S. Private*, pg. 391
Albert, Carl A., Chm. Bd. & Chief Exec. Officer--Fairchild Dornier USA, San Antonio, TX; *U.S. Private*, pg. 391
Albert, Harvey B., Chm. Bd.--First National Bank of Clifton Forge, Clifton Forge, VA; *U.S. Public*, pg. 1039
Albert, Michael P., Chm. Bd. & Pres.--The Harodite Finishing Company Inc., North Dighton, MA; *U.S. Private*, pg. 503
Alberthal, Lester M., Jr., Chm. Bd. & Chief Exec. Officer--Electronic Data Systems Corporation, Plano, TX; *U.S. Public*, pg. 569
Albertini, William O., Chm. Bd.--Bell Atlantic Investment Development Corporation, Philadelphia, PA; *U.S. Public*, pg. 202
Albrecht, Fred, Chm. Bd.--Albrecht Inc., Akron, OH; *U.S. Private*, pg. 32
Albrecht, Randal A., Chm. Bd.--DEC International, Inc., Madison, WI; *U.S. Private*, pg. 301
Albrecht, Steven, Chm. Bd., Pres. & Chief Exec. Officer--The Fred W. Albrecht Grocery Co., Akron, OH; *U.S. Private*, pg. 32
Albrechtsen, Gerhard, Chm. Bd.--Nilfisk A/S, Brondby, Denmark; *Int'l*, pg. 932
Albright, David, Chm. Bd.--Pepperidge Farm, Incorporated, Norwalk, CT; *U.S. Public*, pg. 299
Alcone, Matt, Chm. Bd. & Chief Exec. Officer--Alcone Marketing Group, Irvine, CA; *U.S. Public*, pg. 1223
Alcorn, David S., Chm. Bd. & Chief Exec. Officer--Donlee Technologies Inc., York, PA; *U.S. Private*, pg. 339
Aldinger, William F., Chm. Bd. & Chief Exec. Officer--Household International, Inc., Prospect Heights, IL; *U.S. Public*, pg. 842
Alessi, Alessandro, Chm. Bd.--La Centrale Fondi S.p.A., Milan, Italy; *Int'l*, pg. 138
Alexander, Anthony G.L., Chm. Bd.--Marley PLC, Sevenoaks, United Kingdom; *Int'l*, pg. 843
Alexander, Kobi, Chm. Bd., Pres. & Chief Exec. Officer--Comverse Technology, Inc., Woodbury, NY; *U.S. Public*, pg. 425
Alexander, Lord, Chm. Bd.--National Westminster Bank PLC, London, United Kingdom; *Int'l*, pg. 910
Alexander, Michael, Chm. Bd. & Chief Exec. Officer--Intermetrics, Inc., Burlington, MA; *U.S. Private*, pg. 567
Alexander, Norman, Chm. Bd.--Chock Full O' Nuts Corporation, New York, NY; *U.S. Public*, pg. 351
Alexander, Norman E., Chm. Bd.--Ampacet Corporation, Tarrytown, NY; *U.S. Private*, pg. 67
Alexander, Norman E., Chm. Bd. & Chief Exec. Officer--Sequa Corporation, New York, NY; *U.S. Public*, pg. 1458
Alexander, Patrick D., Chm. Bd. & Chief Exec. Officer--Cold Spring Granite Company, Cold Spring, MN; *U.S. Private*, pg. 250
Alexander, Stanford, Chm. Bd. & Chief Exec. Officer--Weingarten Realty Investors, Houston, TX; *U.S. Public*, pg. 1751
Alexander, William B., Chm. Bd. & Chief Exec. Officer--Turnbull Enterprises, Inc., Baltimore, MD; *U.S. Private*, pg. 1109
Alfi, Moataz Al, Chm. & Chief Exec. Officer--Cairo Foods Industries SAE, Cairo, Egypt; *U.S. Public*, pg. 806
Alfiero, Sal H., Chm. Bd. & Chief Exec. Officer--Mark IV Industries Inc., Amherst, NY; *U.S. Public*, pg. 1044
Alfond, Harold, Chm. Bd.--Dexter Shoe Company, Dexter, ME; *U.S. Public*, pg. 217
Alger, Fred M., Chm. Bd.--Castle Convertible Fund, Inc., New York, NY; *U.S. Public*, pg. 313
Alibrandi, Joseph F., Chm. Bd.--BioWhittaker, Inc., Walkersville, MD; *U.S. Public*, pg. 297
Alibrandi, Joseph F., Chm. Bd., Pres. & Chief Exec. Officer--Whittaker Corporation, Simi Valley, CA; *U.S. Public*, pg. 1766
Allaire, J.J., Chm. Bd. & Chief Tech. Officer--Allaire Corporation, Cambridge, MA; *U.S. Private*, pg. 36
Allaire, Paul A., Chm. Bd., Chief Exec. Officer & Chm.-Exec. Committee--Xerox Corporation, Stamford, CT; *U.S. Public*, pg. 1783
Allan, Thomas, Chm. Bd.--Flanders Corp., Washington, NC; *U.S. Public*, pg. 648
Allanbrook, Wye Jamison, Chm. Bd.--Jamison Door Company, Hagerstown, MD; *U.S. Private*, pg. 581
Allard, Gerald R., Chm. Bd.--Allard Industries, Manchester, NH; *U.S. Private*, pg. 36
Allard, Gerald R., Chm. Bd.--The Jewell Electrical Instruments Co., Manchester, NH; *U.S. Private*, pg. 36
Allard, Jean Marc, Chm. Bd., Pres. & Chief Exec. Officer--Hubbard Construction Co., Winter Park, FL; *U.S. Private*, pg. 544
Allbritton, J.L., Chm. Bd. & Chief Exec. Officer--Riggs National Corporation, Washington, DC; *U.S. Public*, pg. 1389
Allbritton, J.L., Chm. Bd.--Riggs Bank N.A., Washington, DC; *U.S. Public*, pg. 1390
Allbritton, Joe L., Chm. Bd. & Chief Exec. Officer--Perpetual Corporation, Washington, DC; *U.S. Private*, pg. 854
Allbritton, Joe L., Chm. Bd.--Allbritton Group, Inc., Washington, DC; *U.S. Private*, pg. 854
Allbritton, Joe L., Chm. Bd.--Allfinco, Inc., Wilmington, DE; *U.S. Private*, pg. 854
Allemand, Jacques, Chm. Bd. & Chief Exec. Officer--GTM Construction, Nanterre, France; *Int'l*, pg. 823
Allen, Benjamin F., Chm. Bd.--Allen Foods, Inc., Saint Louis, MO; *U.S. Private*, pg. 37
Allen, Brent, Chm. Bd. & Chief Exec. Officer--Lifetime Products Inc., Clearfield, UT; *U.S. Private*, pg. 667
Allen, Darryl F., Chm. Bd., Pres. & Chief Exec. Officer--Aeroquip-Vickers, Inc., Maumee, OH; *U.S. Public*, pg. 24
Allen, David, Chm. Bd., Pres., Chief Exec. Officer & Chief Fin. Officer--AMD Industries Inc., Cicero, IL; *U.S. Private*, pg. 6
Allen, Joan, Chm. Bd.--Aztex Enterprises, Knoxville, TN; *U.S. Private*, pg. 104
Allen, John W., Chm. Bd.--J.W. Allen & Company, Wheeling, IL; *U.S. Private*, pg. 37
Allen, Joseph P., Chm. Bd.--Veridian, Alexandria, VA; *U.S. Private*, pg. 1136
Allen, Joseph P., Chm. Bd.--Calspan SRL Corporation, Washington, DC; *U.S. Private*, pg. 1136
Allen, Leo, Chm. Bd.--M.S. Walker, Inc., Somerville, MA; *U.S. Private*, pg. 1147
Allen, Leon, Chm. Bd. & Chief Exec. Officer--The Tetley Group Limited, Greenford, United Kingdom; *Int'l*, pg. 1377
Allen, M.J., Chm.--Trafalgar House Technology Limited (Kenfig Industrial Estate), Port Talbot, United Kingdom; *Int'l*, pg. 773
Allen, M.J., Chm.--Trafalgar House Technology Limtied (Mitcham House), Croydon, United Kingdom; *Int'l*, pg. 774
Allen, M.J., Chm.--Trafalgar House Technology Limited (Maple Cross House), Rickmansworth, United Kingdom; *Int'l*, pg. 774
Allen, Richard R., Chm. Bd.--Ladd Furniture, Inc., Greensboro, NC; *U.S. Public*, pg. 974
Allen, Robert, Chm. Bd.--Tuscan/Lehigh Dairies LP, Union, NJ; *U.S. Private*, pg. 1110
Allen, Roderick L., Chm. Bd. & Chief Exec. Officer--Allen Canning Company, Siloam Springs, AR; *U.S. Private*, pg. 36
Allen, Roger William, Chm. Bd.--Computer Power Group Limited, Melbourne, Australia; *Int'l*, pg. 325
Allen, Ronald, Chm. Bd., Pres. & Chief Exec. Officer--American Foodservice Corp., King of Prussia, PA; *U.S. Private*, pg. 54
Allen, Roy K., Chm. Bd.--Buckeye Corrugated Inc., Wooster, OH; *U.S. Private*, pg. 177
Allen, Terrence J., Chm. Bd. & Pres.--Pemco Die Casting Corporation, Bridgman, MI; *U.S. Private*, pg. 848

Allen, Theodore M., Chm. & Pres.--United Grain Growers Ltd., Winnipeg, Canada; *Int'l*, pg. 1442
Allen, Thomas W., Chm. Bd. & Chief Exec. Officer--First Midwest Trust Company, N.A., Joliet, IL; *U.S. Public*, pg. 636
Allen, W.W., Chm. Bd. & Chief Exec. Officer--Phillips Petroleum Company, Bartlesville, OK; *U.S. Public*, pg. 1290
Allen, W.W., Chm. Bd.--Phillips Gas Company, Bartlesville, OK; *U.S. Public*, pg. 1291
Allender, Richard C., Chm. Bd., Pres. & Chief Exec. Officer--Farah Incorporated, El Paso, TX; *U.S. Public*, pg. 612
Alliance, David, Chm. Bd.--Coats Viyella plc, Manchester, United Kingdom; *Int'l*, pg. 299
Allington, Robert W., Chm. Bd. & Chief Exec. Officer--Isco, Inc., Lincoln, NE; *U.S. Public*, pg. 913
Allison, John A., Chm. Bd. & Chief Exec. Officer--BB&T Corporation, Winston Salem, NC; *U.S. Public*, pg. 159
Allison, Robert J., Jr., Chm. Bd., Pres. & Chief Exec. Officer--Anadarko Petroleum Corporation, Houston, TX; *U.S. Public*, pg. 107
Allsop, M.V.F., Chm. Bd.--NatWest Corporate Investments Limited, London, United Kingdom; *Int'l*, pg. 910
Allsup, Lonnie D., Chm. Bd. & Pres.--Allsups Convenience Stores Inc., Clovis, NM; *U.S. Private*, pg. 44
Almeida Chabre, Oscar, Chm. Bd.--Internacional de Ceramica S.A. de C.V., Chihuahua, Mexico; *Int'l*, pg. 680
Almeida, Richard J., Chm. Bd., Pres. & Chief Exec. Officer--Heller International Corporation, Chicago, IL; *Int'l*, pg. 519
Almeida, Richard J., Chm. & Chief Exec. Officer--Heller International Group, Inc., Chicago, IL; *Int'l*, pg. 519
Almeida, Richard J., Chm. Bd., Pres. & Chief Exec. Officer--Heller International, Chicago, IL; *U.S. Private*, pg. 520
Almog, Yuval, Chm. Bd.--Tricord Systems, Inc., Plymouth, MN; *U.S. Public*, pg. 1637
Alperson, Robert, Chm. Bd. & Pres.--Rolled Steel Products Corporation, Los Angeles, CA; *U.S. Private*, pg. 941
Alperson, Robert, Chm. Bd. & Pres.--E & E Steel, Inc., Los Angeles, CA; *U.S. Private*, pg. 941
Alpert, Norman R., Chm. Bd., Pres. & Chief Exec. Officer--Bio-Tek Instruments, Inc., Winooski, VT; *U.S. Private*, pg. 144
Alpert, Warren, Chm. Bd.--Warren Equities Inc., Providence, RI; *U.S. Private*, pg. 1151
Alphandery, Edmond, Chm. Bd.--Electricite de France, Paris, France; *Int'l*, pg. 437
Alred, Michael W., Chm. Bd. & Chief Exec. Officer--SouthTrust Bank of Marshall County, Boaz, AL; *U.S. Public*, pg. 1492
Alstadt, Donald M., Chm. Bd.--Lord Corporation, Cary, NC; *U.S. Private*, pg. 675
Alter, Dennis, Chm. Bd. & Chief Exec. Officer--Advanta Corp., Spring House, PA; *U.S. Public*, pg. 22
Alter, Robert A., Chm. Bd., Pres. & Sec.--Sunstone Hotel Investors, Inc., San Clemente, CA; *U.S. Public*, pg. 1536
Althaver, Lambert E., Chm. Bd. & Chief Exec. Officer--Walbro Corporation, Cass City, MI; *U.S. Public*, pg. 1733
Altick, James A., Chm. Bd.--Central Bank of Monroe, Monroe, LA; *U.S. Public*, pg. 629
Altman, Jeffery, Chm. Bd.--Value Property Trust, New Brunswick, NJ; *U.S. Public*, pg. 1707
Altman, Lyle D., Chm. Bd.--Network Systems Corporation, Minneapolis, MN; *U.S. Public*, pg. 1522
Altschiller, David, Chm. & Chief Creative Officer--Hill, Holliday/Altschiller, New York, NY; *U.S. Private*, pg. 529
Altschuler, Samuel, Chm. Bd. & Pres.--Altron Incorporated, Wilmington, MA; *U.S. Public*, pg. 59
Alvarez, Antonio C., Chm. Bd. & Pres.--Long MFG. NC, Inc., Tarboro, NC; *U.S. Private*, pg. 674
Alvarez, Tony, Chm. Bd., Pres. & Chief Exec. Officer--Wherehouse Entertainment, Inc., Torrance, CA; *U.S. Private*, pg. 1171
Amann, James J., Chm. Bd.--The FACS Group, Mason, OH; *U.S. Public*, pg. 618
Amann, James J., Chm.--Federated Systems Group, Norcross, GA; *U.S. Public*, pg. 618
Amant, Charles, Chm. Bd.--Alkota Cleaning Systems, Inc., Alcester, SD; *U.S. Private*, pg. 34
Amaral, Donald J., Chm. Bd. & Chief Exec. Officer--Coram Healthcare Corporation, Denver, CO; *U.S. Public*, pg. 446
Ambros, Dieter, Dr., Chm. Bd.--Chemische Fabrik Grunau GmbH, Illertissen, Germany; *Int'l*, pg. 609
Amemiya, M., Chm. Bd. & Chief Exec. Officer--Interkal, Inc., Kalamazoo, MI; *Int'l*, pg. 759
Amen, Lou, Chm. Bd.--Certified Grocers of California, Los Angeles, CA; *U.S. Private*, pg. 226
Ames, B. Charles, Chm. Bd.--WESCO Distribution, Inc., Pittsburgh, PA; *U.S. Private*, pg. 244
Ames, Donald S., Chm. Bd.--Cortland Line Co., Inc., Cortland, NY; *U.S. Private*, pg. 277
Ames, Richard S., Chm. Bd., Pres. & Chief Exec. Officer--Command Plastic Corporation, Akron, OH; *U.S. Private*, pg. 257
Ames, Roger, Chm. Bd. & Chief Exec. Officer--PolyGram International Ltd., London, United Kingdom; *Int'l*, pg. 1053
Amin, Mark S., Chm. Bd. & Chief Exec. Officer--Trimark Holdings, Inc., Santa Monica, CA; *U.S. Public*, pg. 1638
Amman, Robert J., Chm., Pres. & Chief Exec. Officer--John H. Harland Company, Decatur, GA; *U.S. Public*, pg. 785
Ammirati, Ralph, Chm.--Ammirati, Puris & Lintas, Inc., New York, NY; *U.S. Private*, pg. 66
Ammon, R. Theodore, Chm. Bd.--Treasure Chest Advertising Co., Inc., Glendora, CA; *U.S. Public*, pg. 228
Ammon, Theodore, Chm. Bd.--Big Flower Press Holdings, Inc., New York, NY; *U.S. Public*, pg. 228
Amos, George H., III, Chm. Bd. & Pres.--Tucson Realty & Trust Co., Tucson, AZ; *U.S. Private*, pg. 1109
Amos, Paul S., Chm. Bd.--AFLAC Incorporated, Columbus, GA; *U.S. Public*, pg. 28
Amsterdam, J., Chm. Bd.--Leviton Mfg. Co., Inc., Little Neck, NY; *U.S. Private*, pg. 663
Amstutz, Max D., Chm. Bd. & Pres.--Von Roll AG, Gerlafingen, Switzerland; *Int'l*, pg. 1480
Anchel, Edward, Chm. Bd. & Pres.--Altec Lansing Technologies, Inc., Milford, PA; *U.S. Private*, pg. 479
Anderegg, John S., Jr., Chm. Bd.--Dynamics Research Corporation, Andover, MA; *U.S. Public*, pg. 539
Andersen, Anthony L., Chm. Bd.--H.B. Fuller Company, Saint Paul, MN; *U.S. Public*, pg. 686
Andersen, Jens Munk, Chm. Bd.--Thrige-Titan Group, Odense, Denmark; *Int'l*, pg. 1386
Andersen, Sarah, Chm. Bd.--Andersen Corporation, Bayport, MN; *U.S. Private*, pg. 71
Andersen, Vagn, Chm. Bd.--Novo Nordisk A/S, Bagsvaerd, Denmark; *Int'l*, pg. 987
Anderson, Charles, Chm. Bd.--Books-A-Million, Inc., Birmingham, AL; *U.S. Public*, pg. 244
Anderson, Clifford I., Chm. Bd. & Pres.--Crown Holdings, Inc., Roseville, MN; *U.S. Private*, pg. 293
Anderson, Curtis, Chm. & Chief Exec. Officer--Arrow Tru-Line, Inc., Archbold, OH; *U.S. Private*, pg. 85
Anderson, Edward, R., Chm. Bd., Pres. & Chief Exec. Officer--Rose's Stores, Inc., Henderson, NC; *U.S. Public*, *pg. 1405*
Anderson, G. A., Chm. Bd.--TSB Bank Scotland Plc, Edinburgh, United Kingdom; *Int'l*, pg. 813
Anderson, Gavin, Chm. Bd. & Chief Exec. Officer--Gavin Anderson & Company, New York, NY; *U.S. Public*, pg. 1223
Anderson, Gordon B., Chm. Bd.--Gordy's, Inc., Worthington, MN; *U.S. Private*, pg. 465
Anderson, Gordon M., Chm. Bd. & Chief Exec. Officer--Santa Fe International Corporation, Dallas, TX; *Int'l*, pg. 765
Anderson, Jack, Chm. Bd.--Pacificare Health Systems, Santa Ana, CA; *U.S. Public*, pg. 1251
Anderson, James, Chm. Bd., Chief Exec. Officer & Pres.--Anderson Brothers Construction Brainerd, Brainerd, MN; *U.S. Private*, pg. 72
Anderson, James T., Chm. Bd.--Anderson Wholesale Company, Muskogee, OK; *U.S. Private*, pg. 73
Anderson, John H., Chm. Bd. & Chief Exec. Officer--BT Financial Corporation, Johnstown, PA; *U.S. Public*, pg. 163
Anderson, Joseph, Chm. Bd.--Chivas Products Ltd., Sterling Heights, MI; *U.S. Private*, pg. 238
Anderson, Karry, Chm. Bd.--Lexington Co-Op Oil Co., Lexington, NE; *U.S. Private*, pg. 666
Anderson, Kent T., Chm. Bd., Pres. & Chief Exec. Officer--B.B. Walker Company, Asheboro, NC; *U.S. Public*, pg. 1734
Anderson, Kurt, Chm. Bd.--Dansk Industri Syndikat A/S, Herlev, Denmark; *Int'l*, pg. 381
Anderson, Lee R., Sr., Chm. Bd. & Chief Exec. Officer--API Group Inc., Saint Paul, MN; *U.S. Private*, pg. 7
Anderson, Lowell C., Chm. Bd., Pres. & Chief Exec. Officer--Allianz Life Insurance Company of North America, Minneapolis, MN; *Int'l*, pg. 58
Anderson, Lynn A., Chm. Bd.--Willis Corroon Corp. of Utah, Salt Lake City, UT; *Int'l*, pg. 1507
Anderson, Michael, Chm.-Asia/Pacific--Bozell Worldwide, Inc., New York, NY; *U.S. Public*, pg. 1642
Anderson, Michael H., Chm. Bd., Pres. & Chief Exec. Officer--Hogan Systems, Inc., Dallas, TX; *U.S. Public*, pg. 422
Anderson, Neal, Chm. Bd.--The May Apparel Group, Inc., Mebane, NC; *U.S. Private*, pg. 717
Anderson, R. Quintus, Chm. Bd.--The Aarque Companies, Jamestown, NY; *U.S. Private*, pg. 9
Anderson, Ralph, Chm Bd., Pres., & Chief Exec. Officer--Belcan Corporation, Cincinnati, OH; *U.S. Private*, pg. 131
Anderson, Ray C., Chm. Bd. & Chief Exec. Officer--Interface Inc., Atlanta, GA; *U.S. Public*, pg. 889
Anderson, Richard, Chm.--Compton Partners, New York, NY; *U.S. Public*, pg. 1422
Anderson, Richard A., Chm.--BellSouth Communication Systems, Inc., Roanoke, VA; *U.S. Public*, pg. 209
Anderson, Richard A., Chm.--BellSouth Financial Services Corporation, Atlanta, GA; *U.S. Public*, pg. 209
Anderson, Richard E., Chm. Bd. & Chief Exec. Officer--Cadet Manufacturing Company, Vancouver, WA; *U.S. Private*, pg. 198
Anderson, Richard P., Chm. Bd. & Chief Exec. Officer--The Andersons Incorporated, Maumee, OH; *U.S. Public*, pg. 111
Anderson, Roy, Jr., Chm. Bd.--Roy Anderson Corp., Gulfport, MS; *U.S. Private*, pg. 72
Anderson, Thomas H., Chm. Emeritus--The Andersons Incorporated, Maumee, OH; *U.S. Public*, pg. 111
Anderson, William, Chm. Bd.--Dylex Limited, Toronto, Canada; *Int'l*, pg. 425
Anderson, William, Chm. Bd.--Repap Enterprises Inc., Montreal, Canada; *Int'l*, pg. 1104
Anderson, William, Chm. Bd.--Repap New Brunswick Inc., Montreal, Canada; *Int'l*, pg. 1104
Andersson, Erland, Chm. Bd.--Jonkopings Lantman Ek. For., Jonkoping, Sweden; *Int'l*, pg. 714
Andersson, Rune, Chm.--Esselte AB, Solna, Sweden; *Int'l*, pg. 459
Andersson, Rune, Chm. Bd.--Getinge Industrier AB, Getinge, Sweden; *Int'l*, pg. 551
Andersson, Rune, Chm. Bd.--Svedala Industri AB, Malmo, Sweden; *Int'l*, pg. 1323
Andis, M. L., Chm. Bd. & Pres.--Andis Company, Sturtevant, WI; *U.S. Private*, pg. 73
Ando, Momofuku, Chm. Bd.--Nissin Food Products Co., Ltd., Osaka, Japan; *Int'l*, pg. 949
Andonian, Andy K., Co-Chm.--A K H Company, Inc., City of Commerce, CA; *U.S. Private*, pg. 2
Andonian, Hratch K., Co-Chm., Exec. V.P., Treas. & Sec.--A K H Company, Inc., City of Commerce, CA; *U.S. Private*, *pg. 2*
Andrade, Jose E., Chm. Bd.--Thomas Publishing Company, New York, NY; *U.S. Private*, pg. 1082
Andrade, T.E., Chm. Bd.--Industrial Equipment News, New York, NY; *U.S. Private*, pg. 1082
Andrasick, James S., Chm. Bd.--Ka'u Agribusiness Co., Inc., Pahala, HI; *U.S. Private*, pg. 190
Andrasick, James S., Chm. Bd.--Kilauea Agronomics, Inc., Kilauea, HI; *U.S. Private*, pg. 190
Andrasick, James S., Chm. Bd.--Superior Coffee & Foods/Hawaii, Aiea, HI; *U.S. Private*, pg. 191
Andrea, Frank A.D., Jr., Chm. Bd. & Chief Exec. Officer--Andrea Electronics Corporation, Long Island City, NY; *U.S. Public*, pg. 112
Andreae, Hans-Georg, Dr., Chm. Bd.--Sudzucker AG Mannheim/Ochsenfurt, Mannheim, Germany; *Int'l*, pg. 1305
Andreas, David L., Chm. Bd. & Chief Exec. Officer--National City Bancorp, Minneapolis, MN; *U.S. Public*, pg. 1153
Andreas, Dwayne O., Chm. Bd.--Archer Daniels Midland Company (ADM), Decatur, IL; *U.S. Public*, pg. 127
Andreoli, Robert M., Chm. Bd.--Victoria Creations, Inc., Warwick, RI; *U.S. Private*, pg. 1139
Andreoni, Frank G., Chm. Bd.--Southeastern Michigan Gas Enterprises, Inc., Port Huron, MI; *U.S. Public*, pg. 1489
Andresen, Johan H., Chm. Bd.--Tiedemanns - Joh.H.Andresen ANS, Oslo, Norway; *Int'l*, pg. 1389
Andrews, Coleman, Chm. Bd.--World Airways, Inc., Herndon, VA; *U.S. Public*, pg. 1780
Andrews, George W., Chm. Bd. & Pres.--Keco Industry, Inc., Florence, KY; *U.S. Private*, pg. 611
Andrews, Mark, Jr., Chm. Bd.--Mark Andy, Inc., Chesterfield, MO; *U.S. Public*, pg. 521
Andrews, T. Coleman, Chm. Bd.--WorldCorp, Inc., Herndon, VA; *U.S. Public*, pg. 1779
Angel, David L., Chm. Bd. & Chief Exec. Officer--Information Storage Devices, San Jose, CA; *U.S. Public*, pg. 876
Angelich, Samuel M., Chm. Bd. & Pres.--Amelco Corporation, Gardena, CA; *U.S. Public*, pg. 65
Angelos, Peter, Chm. Bd. & Chief Oper. Officer--The Orioles, Inc., Baltimore, MD; *U.S. Private*, pg. 819
Angus, Michael, Sir, Chm. Bd.--The Boots Company PLC, Nottingham, United Kingdom; *Int'l*, pg. 202
Angus, Sir Michael, Chm. Bd.--Whitbread PLC, London, United Kingdom; *Int'l*, pg. 1498
Angus, Stuart, Chm. Bd.--B C Sugar Refinery, Ltd., Vancouver, Canada; *Int'l*, pg. 103
Anixter, Alan B., Chm. Bd.--Anicom, Inc., Rosemont, IL; *U.S. Public*, pg. 115
Anixter, Scott C., Chm. Bd. & Chief Exec. Officer--Anicom, Inc., Rosemont, IL; *U.S. Public*, pg. 115
Anker, Robert A., Chm. Bd.--American States Insurance Companies, Indianapolis, IN; *U.S. Public*, pg. 997
Ankers, Neal, Chm. Bd. & Mng. Dir.--Hampton Trust Plc, London, United Kingdom; *Int'l*, pg. 591
Annexstad, Stein H., Chm. Bd.--Luxo A/S, Oslo, Norway; *Int'l*, pg. 821
Annexstad, Stein Holst, Chm. Bd.--Fokus Bank A/S, Trondheim, Norway; *Int'l*, pg. 496
Ansary, Hushang, Chm. Bd. & Chief Exec. Officer--IRI International Corporation, Houston, TX; *U.S. Public*, pg. 858
Anthony, Beryl, Sr., Chm. Bd.--Anthony Forest Products Co., Inc., El Dorado, AR; *U.S. Private*, pg. 76
Anthony, Harry S., Chm. Bd.--J.E. Higgins Lumber Co., Concord, CA; *U.S. Private*, pg. 527
Anthony, John E., Chm. Bd., Pres. & Chief Exec. Officer--Bearden Lumber Company, Inc., Bearden, AR; *U.S. Private*, pg. 127
Anton, Frederick W., III, Chm. Bd.--Pennsylvania Manufacturers Corp., Blue Bell, PA; *U.S. Public*, pg. 1272
Antonini, Richard L., Chm. Bd., Pres. & Chief Exec. Officer--Foremost Corporation of America, Caledonia, MI; *U.S. Public*, pg. 667
Aoki, Hatsuo, Chm. Bd.--Fujisawa U.S.A., Deerfield, IL; *Int'l*, *pg. 525*
Aoki, Hiroshi, Chm. Bd. & Chief Exec. Officer--Daido Hoxan Inc., Tokyo, Japan; *Int'l*, pg. 363
Aoki, Hiroyoshi, Chm.--Aoki Corporation, Tokyo, Japan; *Int'l*, *pg. 78*
Aoki, Rocky H., Chm. Bd.--Benihana, Inc., Miami, FL; *U.S. Public*, pg. 211
Aoki, Rocky H., Chm. Bd.--Benihana Schaumburg Corp., Schaumburg, IL; *U.S. Public*, pg. 212
Aoki, Rocky H., Chm. Bd.--Big Splash Kendall Corp., Miami, FL; *U.S. Public*, pg. 212
Aoki, Rocky H., Chm. Bd.--Teppan Restaurants, Beaverton, OR; *U.S. Public*, pg. 212
Aoki, Rocky H., Chm. Bd.--Benihana Sunrise Corp., Citrus Heights, CA; *U.S. Public*, pg. 212
Aoki, Rocky H., Chm. Bd.--Benihana National Corp., Miami, FL; *U.S. Public*, pg. 212
Aposporos, Thomas C., Chm. Bd.--Progressive Bank, Inc., Fishkill, NY; *U.S. Public*, pg. 1334
Appell, L.J., Jr., Chm. Bd.--The Pfaltzgraff Co., York, PA; *U.S. Private*, pg. 860
Appell, Louis J., Jr., Chm. Bd.--The Pfaltzgraff Co., York, PA; *U.S. Private*, pg. 860
Appelle, Harvey, Chm. Bd.--Donnkenny, Inc., New York, NY; *U.S. Public*, pg. 519
Apperson, R.P., Chm. Bd. & Pres.--Apperson Business Forms, Inc., Los Angeles, CA; *U.S. Private*, pg. 78
Applebaum, Arnold N., Chm. Bd., Pres. & Chief Exec. Officer--Solid State Devices, Inc., La Mirada, CA; *U.S. Private*, pg. 1012
Applebaum, Eugene, Chm. Bd., Pres. & Chief Exec. Officer--Arbor Drugs, Inc., Troy, MI; *U.S. Public*, pg. 126
Appleby, Robert S., Chm. Bd.--George & Lynch, Inc., New Castle, DE; *U.S. Private*, pg. 448
Applegate, Leslie T., Chm. Bd. & Chief Exec. Officer--Surgical Appliance Industries, Inc., Cincinnati, OH; *U.S. Private*, pg. 1056
Appleton, Steve, Chm. Bd., Pres & Chief Exec. Officer--Micron Technology Inc., Boise, ID; *U.S. Public*, pg. 1105

Appold, James, Chm. Bd., Pres. & Chief Exec. Officer--Consolidated Biscuit Co., Mc Comb, OH; *U.S. Private*, pg. 265

Apthorp, James W., Chm. Bd.--Atlantic Gulf Communities Corporation, Miami, FL; *U.S. Public*, pg. 144

Aquilina, Joseph, Chm. Bd.--Victoria Packing Corporation, Brooklyn, NY; *U.S. Private*, pg. 1139

Arabia, James R., Chm. Bd., Pres. & Chief Exec. Officer--I.C.H. Corporation, La Jolla, CA; *U.S. Public*, pg. 853

Arai, Akira, Chm. Bd.--Nihon Keizai Shimbun, Inc., Tokyo, Japan; *Int'l*, pg. 929

Arant, Willaims E., Jr., Chm. Bd.--First Vantage-Tennessee, Knoxville, TN; *U.S. Public*, pg. 641

Araskog, Rand V., Chm.-Supv. Bd.--Alcatel N.V., Amsterdam, Netherlands; *Int'l*, pg. 55

Araskog, Rand V., Chm. Bd. & Chief Exec. Officer--ITT Corporation, New York, NY; *U.S. Public*, pg. 1512

Arata, Toshio, Chm. Bd.--NSK Ltd., Tokyo, Japan; *Int'l*, pg. 903

Araujo, Edgar, Chm. Bd.--Varig Brazilian Airlines S.A., Rio de Janeiro, Brazil; *Int'l*, pg. 1451

Arazi, Efraim, Chm. Bd.--Electronics For Imaging, Inc., San Mateo, CA; *U.S. Public*, pg. 570

Arborio, Joseph A., Chm. Bd.--Dutchess Quarry & Supply Co. Inc., Pleasant Valley, NY; *U.S. Private*, pg. 350

Arcati, Thomas, Chm. Bd.--Champion Aluminum Window Corporation, Syosset, NY; *U.S. Private*, pg. 227

Arceneaux, William, Chm. Bd.--SLM Holding Corp., Washington, DC; *U.S. Public*, pg. 1419

Arch, D.C., Chm. Bd. & Chief Exec. Officer--Blistex, Inc., Oak Brook, IL; *U.S. Private*, pg. 149

Archer, James P., Chm. Bd. & Chief Exec. Officer--Jackson Paper Company, Jackson, MS; *U.S. Private*, pg. 579

Archer, Robert A., Chm. Bd.--SJNB Financial Corp., San Jose, CA; *U.S. Public*, pg. 1418

Archibald, Nolan D., Chm. Bd., Pres. & Chief Exec. Officer--The Black & Decker Corporation, Towson, MD; *U.S. Public*, pg. 233

Archuleta, George, Chm., Pres. & Chief Exec. Officer--Alantec Corp., San Jose, CA; *U.S. Public*, pg. 667

Arcuti, Luigi, Chm. Bd.--Istituto Mobiliare Italiano, Rome, Italy; *Int'l*, pg. 692

Ardia, Stephen V., Chm. Bd., Pres. & Chief Exec. Officer--Environment/One Corporation, Niskayuna, NY; *U.S. Public*, pg. 586

Ardizzone, Ramon D., Chm. Bd.--Glenayre Technologies, Inc., Charlotte, NC; *U.S. Public*, pg. 746

Arduini, Giovanni, Chm. Bd., Pres., Chief Exec. & Oper. Officer--I.B.I.S.-S.p.A., Busseto, Italy; *Int'l*, pg. 642

Arend, John R., Chm. Bd. & Chief Exec. Officer--International Chemical Company, Tulsa, OK; *U.S. Private*, pg. 568

Arends, H.J., Chm. Bd. & Chief Exec. Officer--Auto-Owners Insurance, Lansing, MI; *U.S. Private*, pg. 100

Argov, Gideon, Chm. Bd., Pres. & Chief Exec. Officer--Kollmorgen Corporation, Waltham, MA; *U.S. Public*, pg. 965

Arguetty, Isaac, Chm. Bd., Pres. & Chief Exec. Officer--Jan Bell Marketing Inc., Sunrise, FL; *U.S. Public*, pg. 207

Arias, Jeronimo Arango, Chm. Bd.--CIFRA, S.A. de C.V., Mexico, Mexico; *Int'l*, pg. 241

Ariely, Uri, Chm.--Ariely Advertising, Tel Aviv, Israel; *U.S. Private*, pg. 678

Arimoto, Masahiko, Pres.--Yamaha Corp. of America, Sporting Goods Div., Buena Park, CA; *Int'l*, pg. 1516

Arison, Micky, Chm. Bd. & Chief Exec. Officer/Carnival Corp.--Carnival Corporation, Miami, FL; *U.S. Public*, pg. 306

Aristimuno, Oscar, Chm. Bd.--Sudamtex de Uruguay, S.A., Montevideo, Uruguay; *Int'l*, pg. 1304

Arkin, Moshe, Chm. Bd., Pres. & Chief Exec. Officer--Agis Industries Ltd., Bnei-Brak, Israel; *Int'l*, pg. 30

Arledge, David A., Chm. Bd, Pres. & Chief Exec. Officer--The Coastal Corporation, Houston, TX; *U.S. Public*, pg. 389

Armbrecht, Edward C., Jr., Chm. Bd.--Stone & Thomas, Wheeling, WV; *U.S. Private*, pg. 1044

Armstrong, C. Michael, Chm. & Chief Exec. Officer--AT&T Corporation, Basking Ridge, NJ; *U.S. Public*, pg. 10

Armstrong, Frank A., Chm. Bd.--The Monarch Company, Inc., Atlanta, GA; *U.S. Private*, pg. 756

Armstrong, Frank, III, Chm. Bd. & Pres.--National Fruit Product Company, Winchester, VA; *U.S. Private*, pg. 783

Armstrong, J. Hord, III, Chm. Bd. & Chief Exec. Officer--D & K Healthcare Resources, Inc., Saint Louis, MO; *U.S. Public*, pg. 471

Armstrong, Lord of Ilminster, Chm. Bd.--Bristol & West Building Society, Bristol, United Kingdom; *Int'l*, pg. 216

Armstrong, M.H., Chm., Pres. & Chief Exec. Officer--Armstrong International, Inc., Three Rivers, MI; *U.S. Private*, pg. 83

Armstrong, Neil A., Chm. Bd.--AIL Systems Inc., Deer Park, NY; *U.S. Public*, pg. 556

Armstrong, Richard M., Jr., Chm. Bd.--The Children's Hospital of Philadelphia, Philadelphia, PA; *U.S. Private*, pg. 236

Armstrong, W. Charles, Chm. & Pres.--Bank of America Oregon, Portland, OR; *U.S. Public*, pg. 180

Arnault, Bernard, Chm. Bd. & Chief Exec. Officer--LVMH Moet Hennessy Louis Vuitton, Paris, France; *Int'l*, pg. 779

Arnault, Bernard, Chm. Bd. & ChiefExec. Officer--Guerlain S.A., Paris, France; *Int'l*, pg. 780

Arnberg, Henry, Chm. Bd., Pres. & Chief Exec. Officer--Hirsch International Corp., Hauppauge, NY; *U.S. Public*, pg. 829

Arnell, Gordon E., Chm. Bd. & Chief Exec. Officer--Brookfield Properties Corporation, Toronto, Canada; *Int'l*, pg. 228

Arnetz-Hansen, Lars, Chm. Bd.--Pronova A/S, Lysaker, Norway; *Int'l*, pg. 961

Arnhold, Henry H., Co-Chm. Bd.--Arnhold and S. Bleichroeder, Inc., New York, NY; *U.S. Private*, pg. 83

Arnkvaern, Harald, Chm. Bd.--Christiania Bank og Kreditkasse ASA, Oslo, Norway; *Int'l*, pg. 289

Arnold, David, Chm. Bd.--L.M. Scofield Company, Los Angeles, CA; *U.S. Private*, pg. 976

Arnold, E.H., Chm. Bd., Pres. & Chief Exec. Officer--Arnold Industries, Inc., Lebanon, PA; *U.S. Public*, pg. 132

Arnold, H.G., Chm. Bd. & Chief Fin. Officer--Convenience Plus Partners Ltd., Denver, CO; *U.S. Private*, pg. 271

Arnold, Isaac, Jr., Chm. Bd.--Quintana Petroleum Corp., Houston, TX; *U.S. Private*, pg. 901

Arnold, John M., Chm. Bd.--Petroleum Products Corp., Middletown, PA; *U.S. Private*, pg. 859

Arnold, N.D., Chm.--Lucas France SA, Paris, France; *Int'l*, pg. 820

Arnold, Robert H., Chm. Bd.--Ames Safety Envelope Company, Inc., Somerville, MA; *U.S. Private*, pg. 66

Arnold, Truman, Chm. Bd. & Chief Exec. Officer--Truman Arnold Companies, Texarkana, TX; *U.S. Private*, pg. 84

Aron, Adam, Chm. Bd. & Chief Exec. Officer--Vail Resorts, Inc., Vail, CO; *U.S. Public*, pg. 1704

Aronoff, Morton, Chm. Bd.--Gate City Beverage Distributors, San Bernardino, CA; *U.S. Private*, pg. 441

Arp, Fredrik, Chm. Bd.--Munksjo AB, Jonkoping, Sweden; *Int'l*, pg. 1423

Arpin, Paul G., Chm. Bd. & Chief Exec. Officer--Paul Arpin Vanlines, Inc., West Warwick, RI; *U.S. Private*, pg. 85

Arquilla, George, Jr., Chm. Bd.--Burnside Construction Co., Downers Grove, IL; *U.S. Private*, pg. 187

Arrambide, Jesse, III, Chm. Bd. & Chief Oper. Officer--Pancho's Mexican Buffet, Inc., Fort Worth, TX; *U.S. Public*, pg. 1255

Arriola, Joe, Chm. Bd. & Chief Exec. Officer--Avanti Press Inc., Miami, FL; *U.S. Private*, pg. 101

Arth, Lawrence J., Chm. Bd. & Chief Exec. Officer--Ameritas Life Insurance Corp., Lincoln, NE; *U.S. Private*, pg. 65

Arwas, Michael, Chm. Bd.--CMC Trading AG, Zug, Switzerland; *U.S. Public*, pg. 414

Asch, Arthur L., Chm. Bd. & Chief Exec. Officer--Rexx Environmental Corp., New York, NY; *U.S. Public*, pg. 1384

Asch, Robert, Chm. Bd.--Twincraft, Inc., Winooski, VT; *U.S. Private*, pg. 1111

Aschinger, Carl J., Jr., Chm. Bd., Pres. & Chief Exec. Officer--Columbus Show Case Company, Columbus, OH; *U.S. Private*, pg. 257

Aschinger, Carl J., Jr., Chm. Bd. & Pres.--Columbus Showcase, Ashland Division, Ashland, KY; *U.S. Private*, pg. 257

Ash, Jerome W., Chm. Bd.--Sam Ash Music Corp., Hicksville, NY; *U.S. Private*, pg. 88

Ashemimry, Nasir M., Chm. Bd.--Businesship International Inc., Coral Gables, FL; *U.S. Private*, pg. 189

Asher, Harold, Chm.--Asher/Gould Advertising, Inc., Los Angeles, CA; *U.S. Private*, pg. 88

Ashkenazi, Ely, Chm. Bd. & Chief Exec. Officer--SDI Technologies Inc., Rahway, NJ; *U.S. Private*, pg. 956

Ashton, Harris J., Chm. Bd., Pres. & Chief Exec. Officer--General Host Corporation, Stamford, CT; *U.S. Public*, pg. 715

Asplundh, Carl, Jr., Chm. Bd.--Asplundh Tree Expert Co., Willow Grove, PA; *U.S. Private*, pg. 89

Asscher, Jean-Claude, Chm. Bd.--Tekelec, Calabasas, CA; *U.S. Public*, pg. 1566

Assumma, Frank, Vice Chm.-BDDP Worldwide, Chm. & CEO-Wells BDDP-NY--BDDP Group, Paris, France; *Int'l*, pg. 116

Astrom, Lars-Eric, Chm. Bd.--Sodra Cell AB, Vaxjo, Sweden; *Int'l*, pg. 1275

Atanasoff, John V., II, Chm. Bd., Pres. & Chief Exec. Officer--Colorado MEDtech, Inc., Boulder, CO; *U.S. Public*, pg. 401

Athanasopoulos, Takis, Chm.--Inchcape Greece S.A., Athens, Greece; *Int'l*, pg. 672

Atkin, Jerry C., Chm. Bd., Pres. & Chief Exec. Officer--SkyWest Inc., Saint George, UT; *U.S. Public*, pg. 1476

Atkinson, R.J., Chm. & Pres.--Ferrum Inc., Brampton, Canada; *Int'l*, pg. 414

Atols, John M., Chm. Bd. & Chief Exec. Officer--Atols Tool and Mold Corp., Schiller Park, IL; *U.S. Private*, pg. 97

Atterton, David, Chm. Bd.--Guinness Mahon Holdings Plc, London, United Kingdom; *Int'l*, pg. 159

Attuissimo, Andrew M., Chm. Bd. & Chief Exec. Officer--First Central Financial Corporation, Lynbrook, NY; *U.S. Private*, pg. 406

Auberry, Horace, Chm. Bd.--Wellco Enterprises, Inc., Waynesville, NC; *U.S. Public*, pg. 1752

Auch, Fred J., Jr., Chm. Bd. & Chief Exec. Officer--George W. Auch Co., Pontiac, MI; *U.S. Private*, pg. 98

Audie, Joseph, Chm. Bd.--McKenzie Tank Lines, Inc., Tallahassee, FL; *U.S. Private*, pg. 723

Audour, Jean-Pierre, Chm.--Audour, Soum, Larue/SMS, Paris, France; *U.S. Private*, pg. 678

Augustine, Norman R., Chm. Bd.--Lockheed Martin Corporation, Bethesda, MD; *U.S. Public*, pg. 1006

Auhll, Richard, Chm. & Chief Exec. Officer--Circon ACMI, Stamford, CT; *U.S. Public*, pg. 373

Auhll, Richard A., Chm. Bd., Pres. & Chief Exec. Officer--Circon Corporation, Santa Barbara, CA; *U.S. Public*, pg. 373

Ausburn, Ross B., Chm. Bd. & Chief Exec. Officer--Southern Missouri Containers Inc., Springfield, MO; *U.S. Private*, pg. 1017

Ausherman, Ernest W., Chm. Bd.--Ausherman Construction Company, Frederick, MD; *U.S. Private*, pg. 99

Auslander, Norman L., Chm. Bd. & Chief Exec. Officer--Lander Co., Inc., Englewood, NJ; *U.S. Private*, pg. 647

Austad, Dave, Chm. Bd. & Chief Exec. Officer--The Austad Company, San Diego, CA; *U.S. Public*, pg. 782

Austin, Aubrey L., Chm. Bd., Pres. & Chief Exec. Officer--Santa Monica Bank, Santa Monica, CA; *U.S. Public*, pg. 1757

Austin, Harry G., Jr., Chm. Bd.--James Austin Co., Mars, PA; *U.S. Private*, pg. 99

Austin, John H., M.D., Chm. Bd.--Coventry Corporation, Nashville, TN; *U.S. Public*, pg. 454

Austin, Robert, Chm. Bd.--Meco Corporation, Greeneville, TN; *U.S. Private*, pg. 726

Austin, William F., Chm. Bd. & Chief Exec. Officer--Starkey Laboratories, Inc., Eden Prairie, MN; *U.S. Private*, pg. 1035

Autrey Maza, Adolfo I., Chm. Bd.--Grupo Casa Autrey, Mexico, Mexico; *Int'l*, pg. 573

Autrey Maza, Xavier, Chm. Bd.--Grupo Acerero del Norte S.A. de C.V. (GAN), Mexico, Mexico; *Int'l*, pg. 572

Autry, Gene, Chm. Bd., Pres. & Chief Exec. Officer--Golden West Broadcasters, Los Angeles, CA; *U.S. Private*, pg. 461

Auvil, Tom, Chm. Bd.--Tree Top, Inc., Selah, WA; *U.S. Private*, pg. 1098

Avchen, Malvin, Chm. Bd. & Chief Exec. Officer--Sun City Industries, Inc., Fort Lauderdale, FL; *U.S. Public*, pg. 1529

Aveni, Joseph T., Chm. Bd. & Chief Exec. Officer--Realty One, Cleveland, OH; *U.S. Private*, pg. 914

Aveni, Vincent T., Chm. Emeritus--Realty One, Cleveland, OH; *U.S. Private*, pg. 914

Averett, J.N., Jr., Chm. Bd. & Chief Exec. Officer--Crystal Eurasia Oil Co., Shreveport, LA; *U.S. Public*, pg. 466

Avery, Nathan M., Chm. Bd., Pres. & Chief Exec. Officer--Galveston-Houston Company, Houston, TX; *U.S. Private*, pg. 438

Avery, William J., Chm. Bd. & Chief Exec. Officer--Crown Cork & Seal Company, Inc., Philadelphia, PA; *U.S. Public*, pg. 462

Avrett, John G., Co-Chm. & New Bus. Contact--Avrett, Free & Ginsberg, Inc., New York, NY; *U.S. Private*, pg. 103

Awrey, Robert C., Chm. Bd. & Chief Exec. Officer--Awrey Bakeries, Inc., Livonia, MI; *U.S. Private*, pg. 103

Axell, Goran, Chm. Bd.--KF/Konsum Coop Group, Stockholm, Sweden; *Int'l*, pg. 718

Axelrod, Norman, Chm. Bd., Pres. & Chief Exec. Officer--Linens 'n Things, Inc., Clifton, NJ; *U.S. Private*, pg. 668

Axtell, Maynard, Chm. Bd.--National Travelers Life Co., West Des Moines, IA; *U.S. Private*, pg. 787

Ayed, Adbessalem Ben, Chm.--UBCI (Tunisia), Tunis, Tunisia; *Int'l*, pg. 163

Ayres, John R., Chm. Bd.--Petron, Inc., Alexandria, LA; *U.S. Private*, pg. 859

Ayton, Vernon, Chm. Bd.--Ayton Young & Rubicam Ltd., Nairobi, Kenya; *U.S. Private*, pg. 1198

Azcarraga Andrade, Gaston, Chm. Bd.--Grupo Posadas S.A. de C.V., Mexico, Mexico; *Int'l*, pg. 576

Azrielant, Ofer, Chm. Bd. & Chief Exec. Officer--Andin International Inc., New York, NY; *U.S. Private*, pg. 73

Azubel, Amos, Chm. Bd.--Elscint NV/SA, Zaventem, Belgium; *Int'l*, pg. 450

Azzar, James D., Chm. Bd.--Hollymatic Corporation, Countryside, IL; *U.S. Private*, pg. 535

Azzoli, Val, Co-Chm. & Co-Chief Exec. Officer--Atlantic Recording Corporation, New York, NY; *U.S. Public*, pg. 1611

Babbio, Lawrence T., Jr., Chm. Bd.--Bell Atlanticom Systems, Inc., Princeton, NJ; *U.S. Public*, pg. 203

Babbitt, Elton, Chm. Bd.--MTL Inc., Plant City, FL; *U.S. Public*, pg. 1028

Babcock, Barry, Chm. Bd.--Charter Communications, Inc., Saint Louis, MO; *U.S. Private*, pg. 230

Babcock, Barry, Chm. Bd.--CCT Holdings Corp., Saint Louis, MO; *U.S. Private*, pg. 230

Babcock, Gregory, Chm. Bd.--Snokist Growers, Yakima, WA; *U.S. Private*, pg. 1011

Babcock, James F., Chm. Bd. & Chief Exec. Officer--First Virginia Bank of Tidewater, Norfolk, VA; *U.S. Public*, pg. 642

Bacal, Joe, Co-Chm. & Crèative Services Dir.--Griffin Bacal Inc., New York, NY; *U.S. Private*, pg. 480

Bach, Kenneth W., Chm. Bd., Pres. & Chief Exec. Officer--Electro Metrics, Inc., Johnstown, NY; *U.S. Private*, pg. 369

Bachar, Tobi, Chm. Bd.--Elscint MR Inc., Fort Collins, CO; *Int'l*, pg. 450

Bachar, Tobi, Chm. Bd.--Elscint Cryomagnetics Ltd., Wallington, United Kingdom; *Int'l*, pg. 450

Bachhuber, Carl, Chm. Bd., Pres. & Chief Exec. Officer--Mayville Engineering Co., Inc., Mayville, WI; *U.S. Private*, pg. 718

Bachman, Todd L., Chm. Bd. & Chief Exec. Officer--Bachman's, Inc., Minneapolis, MN; *U.S. Private*, pg. 109

Bachmann, Gerhard, Dr., Chm. Bd.--Deutsche Spezialglas AG, Glunanplan, Germany; *Int'l*, pg. 1523

Backe, John E., Chm. Bd.--Grant Marketing Communications, Ardmore, PA; *U.S. Private*, pg. 470

Backe, John E., Chm. Bd.--Kingswood Advertising, Inc., Ardmore, PA; *U.S. Private*, pg. 622

Backhouse, David, Chm. Bd.--Johnson Fry Holdings PLC, London, United Kingdom; *Int'l*, pg. 713

Bacon, Donald G., Chm. Bd., Pres. & Chief Exec. Officer--West Kootenay Power, Trail, Canada; *U.S. Public*, pg. 1701

Bacon, James C., Chm. Bd.--NBS Technologies, Inc., Mississauga, Canada; *Int'l*, pg. 898

Bacot, J. Carter, Chm. Bd. & Chief Exec. Officer--The Bank of New York Company, Inc., New York, NY; *U.S. Public*, pg. 178

Bacou, Henry, Chm.--Bacou S.A., Roissy Charles de Gaulle, France; *Int'l*, pg. 132

Bacou, Henry, Chm. Bd.--Bacou U.S.A., Inc., Smithfield, RI; *Int'l*, pg. 132

Badawi, Samir T., Chm. Bd.--Gundle/SLT Environmental, Inc., Houston, TX; *U.S. Public*, pg. 769

Badcock, Ben M., Chm. Bd., Pres. & Chief Exec. Officer--W.S. Badcock Corporation, Mulberry, FL; *U.S. Private*, pg. 109

Baden, John, Chm. Bd.--Girobank, London, United Kingdom; *Int'l*, pg. 57

Badran, Ibrahim, Chm. Bd.--Egypt Otsuka Pharmaceutical Co., S.A.E., Cairo, Egypt; *Int'l*, pg. 1014

Badtke, Donald J., Chm. Bd. & Pres.--Stanley Knight Corporation, New Troy, MI; *U.S. Private*, pg. 1033

Baer, Albert, Chm. Bd. & Chief Exec. Officer--Imperial Schrade Corp., Ellenville, NY; *U.S. Private*, pg. 559

Baer, Richard, Chm. Bd. & Pres.--Nuevo Federal S.A., Buenos Aires, Argentina; *Int'l*, pg. 990

Baer, William, Chm. Bd.--The Crown Group, Inc., Warren, MI; *U.S. Private*, pg. 292

Baggett, Larry, Chm. Bd.--Arkansas Electric Cooperatives Inc., Little Rock, AR; *U.S. Private*, pg. 82

Baggott, George E., Chm. Bd.--Cres-Cor, Cleveland, OH; *U.S. Private*, pg. 288

Bagley, Edward Neff, Chm. Bd.--Mining Services International, Inc., Sandy, UT; *U.S. Public*, pg. 1115

Bailey, Coley L., Chm. Bd.--Mississippi Chemical Corporation, Yazoo City, MS; *U.S. Public*, pg. 1117

Bailey, J.H., Chm. Bd. & Chief Exec. Officer--The Cretex Companies, Elk River, MN; *U.S. Private*, pg. 289

Bailey, John, Chm. Bd., Pres., Chief Exec. & Fin. Officer & Treas.--Cal Emblem Labels, Inc., Fresno, CA; *U.S. Private*, pg. 199

Bailey, John, Chm. Bd.--Cal Emblem, Inc., Denver, CO; *U.S. Private*, pg. 199

Bailey, John H., Chm. Bd., Pres., Chief Exec. & Chief Oper. Officer--The Climatic Corp., Columbia, SC; *U.S. Private*, pg. 246

Bailey, Keith E., Chm. Bd., Pres. & Chief Exec. Officer--The Williams Companies, Inc., Tulsa, OK; *U.S. Public*, pg. 1769

Bailey, Robert L., Chm. Bd. & Chief Exec. Officer--State Automobile Mutual Insurance Co., Columbus, OH; *U.S. Private*, pg. 1036

Bailey, Robert, II, Chm. Bd. & Chief Fin. Officer--Mid American Elevator Co., Inc., Chicago, IL; *U.S. Private*, pg. 743

Baileys, Steven J., D.D.S., Chm. Bd., Pres. & Chief Exec. Officer--Safeguard Health Enterprises, Inc., Anaheim, CA; *U.S. Public*, pg. 1424

Bailleres Gonzalez, Alberto, Chm. Bd.--Industrias Penoles S.A. de C.V., Cuauhtemoc, Mexico; *Int'l*, pg. 677

Bailleros Gonzalez, Alberto, Chm. Bd.--Grupo Palacio de Hierro S.A. de C.V., Mexico, Mexico; *Int'l*, pg. 576

Bain, John H., Chm. Bd. & Pres.--Homewood Corporation, Columbus, OH; *U.S. Private*, pg. 537

Bain, Lorne D., Chm. Bd. & Chief Exec. Officer--Sanifill, Inc., Houston, TX; *U.S. Public*, pg. 1686

Bainsfair, Paul, Joint Chm., Joint Chief Exec. Officer & Pres.--BST-BDDP, London, United Kingdom; *Int'l*, pg. 117

Bainton, Donald J., Chm. Bd. & Chief Exec. Officer--Continental Can Co., Norwalk, CT; *U.S. Public*, pg. 439

Bainum, Stewart, Jr., Chm. Bd.--Choice Hotels International, Inc., Silver Spring, MD; *U.S. Public*, pg. 351

Baird, Byron, Chm. Bd.--Mrs. Baird's Bakeries, Inc., Fort Worth, TX; *U.S. Private*, pg. 765

Baird, Charles F., Chm. Bd.--Leiner Health Products, Inc., Carson, CA; *U.S. Private*, pg. 659

Baird, Euan, Chm. Bd., Pres. & Chief Exec. Officer--Schlumberger Limited, New York, NY; *U.S. Public*, pg. 1439

Baird, John W., Chm. Bd.--Baird & Warner Inc., Chicago, IL; *U.S. Private*, pg. 111

Baird, William D., Jr., Chm.--Princeton Bank & Trust Company National Association, East Brunswick, NJ; *U.S. Public*, pg. 338

Baker, Andrew H., Chm. Bd., Pres. & Chief Exec. Officer--Unilab Corporation, Tarzana, CA; *U.S. Public*, pg. 1352

Baker, C.E., Jr., Chm. Bd. & Chief Exec. Officer--Arch Communications Group, Inc., Westborough, MA; *U.S. Public*, pg. 127

Baker, Charles A., Chm. Bd. & Chief Exec. Officer--The Liposome Company, Inc., Princeton, NJ; *U.S. Public*, pg. 1000

Baker, Daniel, Chm. Bd., Pres. & Chief Exec. Officer--Tate Access Floors, Inc., Jessup, MD; *U.S. Private*, pg. 1069

Baker, Daniel L., Chm. Bd. & Pres.--Baker Concrete Construction, Inc., Monroe, OH; *U.S. Private*, pg. 111

Baker, Edward L., Chm. Bd.--Florida Rock Industries, Inc., Jacksonville, FL; *U.S. Public*, pg. 655

Baker, Edwin M., Chm. Bd.--Guard Publishing Company, Eugene, OR; *U.S. Private*, pg. 485

Baker, George F., Chm. Bd. & Chief Exec. Officer--Whitehall Corporation, Dallas, TX; *U.S. Public*, pg. 1765

Baker, Jack, Chm. & Chief Exec. Officer--Baker's Supermarkets, Inc., Omaha, NE; *U.S. Public*, pg. 652

Baker, John, Chm. Bd.--Medeva PLC, London, United Kingdom; *Int'l*, pg. 852

Baker, L.M. Jr., Chm. Bd.--Wachovia Bank of North Carolina, N.A., Winston Salem, NC; *U.S. Public*, pg. 1730

Baker, Newell A., Chm. Bd--J.D. Streett & Co., Inc., Maryland Heights, MO; *U.S. Private*, pg. 1047

Baker, R.A., Chm.--Senior Bigwood Limited, West Bromwich, United Kingdom; *Int'l*, pg. 1220

Baker, R.E., Chm. Bd.--Newage Industries Inc., Testing Instruments Group, Willow Grove, PA; *U.S. Private*, pg. 796

Baker, Raymond E., Chm. Bd.--NewAge Industries Inc., Willow Grove, PA; *U.S. Private*, pg. 796

Baker, Raymond E., Chm. Bd.--Newage Industries Inc., Plastics Technology Group, Willow Grove, PA; *U.S. Private*, pg. 796

Baker, Robert L., Pres.--Plant Maintenance Service Corporation, Memphis, TN; *U.S. Private*, pg. 869

Baker, Sherman N., Chm. Bd.--J. Baker, Inc., Canton, MA; *U.S. Public*, pg. 167

Baker, Sherman N., Chm. Bd.--Morse Shoe, Inc., Canton, MA; *U.S. Public*, pg. 168

Baker, Sherman N., Chm. Bd.--Casual Male, Inc., Hyde Park, MA; *U.S. Public*, pg. 168

Baker, Wilder D., Chm. Bd. & Chief Exec. Officer--Warwick Baker O'Neill, New York, NY; *U.S. Private*, pg. 1152

Baker, William C., Chm. Bd., Pres. & Chief Exec. Officer--The Santa Anita Companies, Arcadia, CA; *U.S. Public*, pg. 1081

Baker, William C., Chm. Bd. & Chief Exec. Officer--Santa Anita Enterprises, Inc., Arcadia, CA; *U.S. Public*, pg. 1081

Bakhshi, B.K., Chm. Bd.--Indian Oil Corporation Limited, New Delhi, India; *Int'l*, pg. 673

Balaguer, James J., Chm. Bd.--Willis Corroon Corp. of Northern Ohio, Cleveland, OH; *Int'l*, pg. 1506

Balch, Alan, Chm. Bd. & Chief Exec. Officer--Lane Limited, Tucker, GA; *Int'l*, pg. 1129

Baldwin, Cyril C., Jr., Chm. Bd.--Cambrex Corporation, East Rutherford, NJ; *U.S. Public*, pg. 297

Baldwin, Doug, Chm. Bd.--Schneider Group, Mississauga, Canada; *Int'l*, pg. 1208

Baldwin, H. Furlong, Chm. Bd., Pres. & Chief Exec. Officer--Mercantile Bankshares Corporation, Baltimore, MD; *U.S. Public*, pg. 1088

Baldwin, J.W., Chm. Bd.--Caterpillar Logistics Services, Inc., Peoria, IL; *U.S. Public*, pg. 316

Baldwin, Sandra Kaye, Pres. & Treas.--H & H Distributing Company, Inc., West Union, IA; *U.S. Private*, pg. 489

Balfo, Bruno, Chm. Bd.--Duferco Steel Inc., Laurence Harbor, NJ; *U.S. Private*, pg. 345

Balkind, Aubrey, Chm. & Chief Exec. Officer--Frankfurt Balkind Partners, New York, NY; *U.S. Private*, pg. 424

Ball, Anna C., Chm. Bd., Pres. & Chief Exec. Officer--Ball Horticultural Company, West Chicago, IL; *U.S. Private*, pg. 112

Ball, Fred, Chm. Bd.--Associated Wholesale Grocers, Inc., Kansas City, KS; *U.S. Private*, pg. 93

Ball, John H., Chm. Bd. & Chief Exec. Officer--R.M. Shoemaker Co., West Conshohocken, PA; *U.S. Private*, pg. 996

Ballard, Dale H., Chm. Bd., Pres. & Chief Exec. Officer--Ballard Medical Products, Draper, UT; *U.S. Public*, pg. 171

Ballard, Larry C., Chm. Bd.--Sentry Insurance, A Mutual Company, Stevens Point, WI; *U.S. Private*, pg. 984

Ballas, Jacob, Chm. Bd.--F. J. Benjamin Holdings Ltd., Singapore, Singapore; *Int'l*, pg. 187

Ballenger, Thomas C., Chm. Bd.--Plastic Packaging, Inc., Hickory, NC; *U.S. Private*, pg. 871

Ballesteros, Jorge, Chm. Bd.--Grupo Mexicano de Desarrollo, Mexico, Mexico; *Int'l*, pg. 575

Balloun, James S., Chm. Bd., Pres. & Chief Exec. Officer--National Service Industries, Inc., Atlanta, GA; *U.S. Public*, pg. 1160

Balm, Walter, Chm. Bd.--International Microwave Corporation, Norwalk, CT; *U.S. Private*, pg. 571

Balmuth, Marc, Chm. Bd. & Chief Exec. Officer--Bob's Stores, Inc., Meriden, CT; *U.S. Public*, pg. 287

Balogh, Alex G., Chm. Bd. & Chief Exec. Officer--Falconbridge Limited, Toronto, Canada; *Int'l*, pg. 433

Balouris, C., Chm. Bd.--Energizer Eveready Ltd., London, United Kingdom; *U.S. Public*, pg. 1360

Balsamo, Salvatore, Chm. Bd. & Chief Exec. Officer--Technical Aid Corporation, Newton, MA; *U.S. Private*, pg. 1072

Banatao, Diosdado P., Chm. Bd.--S3 Incorporated, Santa Clara, CA; *U.S. Public*, pg. 1415

Banducci, Barry R., Chm. Bd.--TransPro, Inc., New Haven, CT; *U.S. Public*, pg. 1631

Baney, John E., Chm. Bd.--Cigna Worldwide, Incorporated, Philadelphia, PA; *U.S. Public*, pg. 363

Bangert, Steven, Chm. Bd.--Colorado Business Bankshares, Inc., Denver, CO; *U.S. Private*, pg. 255

Banham, John, Sir, Chm. Bd.--Kingfisher plc, London, United Kingdom; *Int'l*, pg. 733

Banham, John, Sir, Chm.--Tarmac plc, Wolverhampton, United Kingdom; *Int'l*, pg. 1355

Bank, Morton B., Chm. Bd.--M.F. Bank & Company, Inc., Minneapolis, MN; *U.S. Private*, pg. 113

Banks, David, Chm. Bd.--AT&T Capital Corporation, Morristown, NJ; *Int'l*, pg. 924

Banks, David R., Chm. Bd. & Chief Exec. Officer--Beverly Enterprises, Inc., Fort Smith, AR; *U.S. Public*, pg. 227

Banks, Jacob W., Chm. Bd.--Bearing Service Company, Pittsburgh, PA; *U.S. Private*, pg. 127

Bankston, James G., Chm. Bd., Pres. & Chief Exec. Officer--W.O. Bankston Enterprises Inc., Dallas, TX; *U.S. Public*, pg. 1379

Bankuty, Geza E., Chm. Bd., Pres. & Chief Exec. Officer--New England Machinery, Inc., Bradenton, FL; *U.S. Private*, pg. 793

Bannister, Dan R., Chm. Bd.--DynCorp, Reston, VA; *U.S. Private*, pg. 351

Bannister, Larry, Chm. Bd.--The Spring Air Company, Des Plaines, IL; *U.S. Private*, pg. 1027

Banucci, Gene G., Ph.D., Chm. Bd., Pres. & Chief Exec. Officer--ATMI, Inc., Danbury, CT; *U.S. Public*, pg. 12

Barad, Jill Elikann, Chm. Bd. & Chief Exec. Officer--Mattel, Inc., El Segundo, CA; *U.S. Public*, pg. 1057

Baranski, Dennis, Chm. Bd.--Baranski & Associates, Lecompton, KS; *U.S. Private*, pg. 115

Baranski, Dennis, Chm. Bd.--Baranski Publishing Company, Lecompton, KS; *U.S. Private*, pg. 115

Baranski, Dennis, Chm. Bd.--D.A. Baranski & Co., Lecompton, KS; *U.S. Private*, pg. 115

Baranski, Dennis, Chm. Bd.--Joseph A. Baranski Literary Agency, Lecompton, KS; *U.S. Private*, pg. 115

Baranski, Dennis A., Chm. Bd., Pres. & Chief Exec. Officer--Barancorp, Lecompton, KS; *U.S. Private*, pg. 115

Barba, J. Brendan, Chm. Bd., Pres. & Chief Exec. Officer--AEP Industries, Inc., South Hackensack, NJ; *U.S. Public*, pg. 4

Barbakow, Jeffrey C., Chm. Bd. & Chief Exec. Officer--Tenet Healthcare Corporation, Santa Barbara, CA; *U.S. Public*, pg. 1576

Barbanell, Robert L., Chm. Bd.--Marine Drilling Companies, Inc., Sugar Land, TX; *U.S. Public*, pg. 1044

Barbarye, Rene, Chm.-Bd. of Mngmt.--Groupe des Caises d'Epargne, Paris, France; *Int'l*, pg. 563

Barbato, Gianfranco, Chm. Bd.--C.S.O. Centrale Supporti Operativi S.p.A., Torri di Quartesolo, Italy; *Int'l*, pg. 138

Barbato, Gianfranco, Chm. Bd.--Itaservice S.p.A., Milan, Italy; *Int'l*, pg. 138

Barbee, Robert P., Chm. Bd. & Chief Exec. Officer--Pneumafil Corporation, Charlotte, NC; *U.S. Private*, pg. 873

Barber, Albert F., Chm. Bd. & Chief Exec. Officer--Stuart Entertainment Inc., Council Bluffs, IA; *U.S. Public*, pg. 1526

Barber, David S., Chm. Bd.--Halma p.l.c., Amersham, United Kingdom; *Int'l*, pg. 589

Barber, George W., Jr., Chm. Bd.--Barber Dairies, Inc., Birmingham, AL; *U.S. Private*, pg. 115

Barber, Irving K., Chm. Bd., Pres. & Chief Exec. Officer--Slocan Forest Products Ltd., Richmond, Canada; *Int'l*, pg. 1263

Barbera, Robert N., Chm. Bd.--Wire-Pro Inc., Salem, NJ; *U.S. Private*, pg. 1184

Barbour, W. Robert, Chm. Bd.--Northwest Pipe Fittings, Inc., Billings, MT; *U.S. Private*, pg. 806

Barclay, H. Douglas, Chm. Bd.--Syracuse Supply Company, Syracuse, NY; *U.S. Private*, pg. 1060

Barclay, John P., Jr., Chm. Bd. & Chief Exec. Officer--Wire Rope Corporation of America, Inc., Saint Joseph, MO; *U.S. Private*, pg. 1184

Barclay, Joseph J., Chm. Bd.--Cascade Corporation, Troutdale, OR; *U.S. Public*, pg. 310

Bard, I. Gary, Chm. Bd. & Chief Exec. Officer--Aydin Corporation, Horsham, PA; *U.S. Public*, pg. 158

Bard, Richard O., Chm. Bd.--Bard Mfg. Co., Bryan, OH; *U.S. Private*, pg. 116

Barden, G. Richard, Chm. Bd.--Barden & Robeson Corporation, Middleport, NY; *U.S. Private*, pg. 116

Bardes, Merrilyn, Co-Chm. Bd.--Ilsco, Cincinnati, OH; *U.S. Private*, pg. 558

Barensfeld, Robert, Chm. Bd.--Ellwood Group, Inc., Ellwood City, PA; *U.S. Private*, pg. 373

Bares, W.G., Chm. Bd., Pres. & Chief Exec. Officer--The Lubrizol Corporation, Wickliffe, OH; *U.S. Public*, pg. 1016

Barford, R.M., Chm. Bd.--GSW Inc., Guelph, Canada; *Int'l*, pg. 538

Baring, N.H., Chm. Bd.--Commercial Union plc, London, United Kingdom; *Int'l*, pg. 308

Barkeley, Norman A., Chm. Bd. & Chief Exec. Officer--Ducommun Incorporated, Carson, CA; *U.S. Public*, pg. 533

Barker, G. Carlton, Chm. Bd., Pres. & Chief Exec. Officer--Regions Bank/Montgomery/Alexander City, Montgomery, AL; *U.S. Public*, pg. 1372

Barker, James R., Chm. Bd.--The Pittston Company, Glen Allen, VA; *U.S. Public*, pg. 1305

Barker, Norman, Jr., Chm. Bd.--Pacific American Income Shares, Inc., Pasadena, CA; *U.S. Public*, pg. 1247

Barker, Paul, Chm. Bd.--McLaughlin Manufacturing Company, Greenville, SC; *U.S. Private*, pg. 724

Barkley, Rufus C., Jr., Chm. Bd.--Cameron & Barkley Company, Charleston, SC; *U.S. Private*, pg. 203

Barlow, Frank, Chm. Bd.--Logica Plc, London, United Kingdom; *Int'l*, pg. 814

Barnes, Andrew, Chm. Bd., Chief Exec. Officer & Editor--The Times Publishing Co., Saint Petersburg, FL; *U.S. Private*, pg. 1087

Barnes, Bradford, Chm. Bd. & Chief Exec. Officer--Crouch Supply Company, Inc., Fort Worth, TX; *U.S. Private*, pg. 291

Barnes, J. Mark, Chm.--Outdoor Services, San Francisco, CA; *U.S. Private*, pg. 1166

Barnes, James E., Chm. Bd., Pres. & Chief Exec. Officer--Mapco Inc., Tulsa, OK; *U.S. Public*, pg. 1042

Barnes, Mair, Chm. Bd.--Dolland & Aitchison Ltd., Birmingham, United Kingdom; *Int'l*, pg. 414

Barnes, Thomas O., Chm. Bd. & Sr. V.P.-Admin.--Barnes Group Inc., Bristol, CT; *U.S. Public*, pg. 189

Barnes, Wallace, Chm. Bd.--Rohr, Inc., Chula Vista, CA; *U.S. Public*, pg. 751

Barnes, William, Chm. Bd.--Spectrulite Consortium, Inc., Madison, IL; *U.S. Private*, pg. 1024

Barnett, Cecil C., Chm. Bd., Pres. & Chief Exec. Officer--Algood Food Company, Louisville, KY; *U.S. Private*, pg. 34

Barnett, Charles E., Chm. Bd.--Barnett Millworks, Inc., Theodore, AL; *U.S. Private*, pg. 116

Barnett, Dana G., Chm. Bd. & Chief Exec. Officer--Somerset Pharmaceuticals Inc., Tampa, FL; *U.S. Public*, pg. 1143

Barnett, Richard M., Chm. Bd., Pres. & Chief Exec. Officer--Reliable Stores, Inc., Columbia, MD; *U.S. Private*, pg. 920

Barnett, T., Chm. Bd. & Chief Exec. Officer--CIBA-GEIGY (Pty.) Ltd., Isando, South Africa; *Int'l*, pg. 978

Barnett, Victor, Chm. Bd.--Arcade Inc., Chattanooga, TN; *U.S. Private*, pg. 79

Barnettte, Curtis H., Chm. Bd. & Chief Exec. Officer--Bethlehem Steel Corporation, Bethlehem, PA; *U.S. Public*, pg. 226

Barnevik, Percy, Chm. Bd.--ABB Asea Brown Boveri (Holding) Ltd., Zurich, Switzerland; *Int'l*, pg. 1

Barnevik, Percy, Chm. Bd.--Sandvik AB, Sandviken, Sweden; *Int'l*, pg. 1185

Barnhardt, T.M., III, Chm. Bd.--Barnhardt Manufacturing Co., Charlotte, NC; *U.S. Private*, pg. 116

Barnhill, R.E., Chm. Bd.--Barnhill Contracting Company, Tarboro, NC; *U.S. Private*, pg. 117

Barnhill, Robert B., Jr., Chm. Bd., Pres. & Chief Exec. Officer--Tessco Technologies, Inc., Sparks, MD; *U.S. Public*, pg. 1582

Barnum, T.B., Chm. Bd., Pres. & Chief Exec. Officer--Max & Erma's Restaurants, Columbus, OH; *U.S. Public*, pg. 1060

Barr, Edward, Chm. Bd. & Chief Exec. Officer--Sun Chemical Corp., Fort Lee, NJ; *Int'l*, pg. 370

Barr, Thomas A., Chm. Bd.--Barr & Barr, Inc., New York, NY; *U.S. Private*, pg. 117

Barre, Stephen A., Chm. Bd., Pres., Chief Exec. Officer & Sec.--Servo Corporation of America, Westbury, NY; *U.S. Private*, pg. 987
Barrett, Matthew W., Chm. Bd. & Chief Exec. Officer--Bank of Montreal, Toronto, Canada; *Int'l*, pg. 153
Barrett, Robert, Pres. & Chm. Bd.--Banc One Services Corporation, Columbus, OH; *U.S. Public*, pg. 175
Barrett, Tom, Chm. Bd.--RBX Corporation, Roanoke, VA; *U.S. Private*, pg. 56
Barrett, Tom, Chm. Bd.--Rubatex Corporation, Roanoke, VA; *U.S. Private*, pg. 56
Barrett, William, Chm. Bd.--Shelter Components Corporation, Elkhart, IN; *U.S. Public*, pg. 952
Barrett, William J., Chm. Bd.--Barrett Resources Corporation, Denver, CO; *U.S. Public*, pg. 191
Barringer, Paul B., II, Chm. Bd. & Chief Exec. Officer--Coastal Lumber Company, Weldon, NC; *U.S. Private*, pg. 248
Barrow, Martin G., Chm.--Jardine Matheson (China) Ltd., Beijing, China; *Int'l*, pg. 705
Barry, A.D., Chm. Bd.--CRH, plc, Dublin, Ireland; *Int'l*, pg. 242
Barry, Herbert, Chm. Bd. & Chief Exec. Officer--Uniflex, Inc., Hicksville, NY; *U.S. Public*, pg. 1665
Barry, James V., Chm. Bd.--United Missouri Bank Northwest, Saint Joseph, MO; *U.S. Public*, pg. 1654
Barry, John S., Chm. Bd.--WD-40 Company, San Diego, CA; *U.S. Public*, pg. 1726
Barry, Tom, Chm. Bd., Pres. & Chief Oper. Officer--Mighty Distributing System, Norcross, GA; *U.S. Private*, pg. 745
Barry, W. Russell, Chm. Bd.--Turner Program Services, Inc., Atlanta, GA; *U.S. Public*, pg. 1615
Barsalou, Yves, Chm. Bd.--Credit Agricole, Bonvin, France; *Int'l*, pg. 341
Bartel, Robert J., Chm. Bd.--First American Federal Savings Bank, Bristol, VA; *U.S. Public*, pg. 624
Bartelds, J.L.M., Chm. Exec. Bd.--Fortis, Utrecht, Netherlands; *Int'l*, pg. 498
Bartell, George, Jr., Chm. Bd.--The Bartell Drug Company, Seattle, WA; *U.S. Private*, pg. 118
Bartelli, James, Chm. Bd., Pres. & Chief Exec. Officer--Mercury Computer Systems, Inc., Chelmsford, MA; *U.S. Private*, pg. 732
Bartels, Juergen, Chm. Bd. & Chief Exec. Officer--Westin Hotels & Resorts, Seattle, WA; *U.S. Public*, pg. 1512
Bartholomay, Bill, Chm. Bd.--Atlanta National League Baseball Club, Inc., Atlanta, GA; *U.S. Public*, pg. 1614
Bartlett, Paul D., Jr., Chm. Bd.--Bartlett and Company, Kansas City, MO; *U.S. Private*, pg. 118
Bartlett, Robert A., Chm. Bd. & Chief Exec. Officer--The F.A. Bartlett Tree Expert Co., Stamford, CT; *U.S. Private*, *pg. 119*
Barto, Jerrel C., Chm. Bd.--Paramount Petroleum Corp., Paramount, CA; *U.S. Private*, pg. 838
Bartoli, Henry E., Chm. & Chief Exec. Officer--Foster Wheeler Energy International, Inc., Clinton, NJ; *U.S. Public*, pg. 676
Barton, A.P., Jr., Chm. Bd., Pres. & Chief Exec. Officer--Mutual Manufacturing & Supply Co., Cincinnati, OH; *U.S.* Private, pg. 769
Barton, Francis J., Chm. & Chief Exec. Officer--Wahlstrom & Company, Stamford, CT; *U.S. Public*, pg. 1641
Barton, Glen A., Chm. Bd.--Caterpillar Paving Products Inc., Minneapolis, MN; *U.S. Public*, pg. 316
Bartscht, Karl G., Chm. Bd. & Chief Exec. Officer--Chi Systems Division, Ann Arbor, MI; *U.S. Public*, pg. 1539
Bartz, Carol, Chm. Bd. & Chief Exec. Officer--Autodesk, Inc., San Rafael, CA; *U.S. Public*, pg. 148
Basha, Edward N., II, Chm. Bd.--Bashas, Chandler, AZ; *U.S.* Private, pg. 120
Bashaw, Gerald B., Chm. Bd.--Modtech, Inc., Perris, CA; *U.S. Public*, pg. 1121
Baskin, Shale, Chm. Bd.--Mark Shale, Burr Ridge, IL; *U.S. Private*, pg. 989
Basler, William L., Chm. Bd., Chief Exec. Officer & Treas.--Basler Electric Company, Highland, IL; *U.S. Private*, pg. 121
Bass, Herbert, Chm. Bd.--Unitel Video, Inc., New York, NY; *U.S. Public*, pg. 1692
Bass, Hyman, Chm. Bd.--American Mathematical Society, Inc., Providence, RI; *U.S. Private*, pg. 59
Bass, Lee M., Chm. Bd.--National Farms Inc., Kansas City, MO; *U.S. Private*, pg. 782
Bass, Paul M., Chm. Bd.--First Southwest Company, Dallas, TX; *U.S. Private*, pg. 407
Bass, Sid R., Chm. Bd.--Bass Enterprises Production Company, Fort Worth, TX; *U.S. Private*, pg. 122
Bassat, Luis, Chm. & Chief Creative Dir.-Barcelona--Ogilvy & Mather Worldwide, Inc., New York, NY; *Int'l*, pg. 1483
Basserman, Michael, Chm. Bd. & Chief Exec. Officer--Mercedes-Benz of North America, Inc., Montvale, NJ; *Int'l*, pg. 368
Bassett, James E., III, Chm. Bd.--Keeneland Assoc., Inc., Lexington, KY; *U.S. Private*, pg. 611
Bassett, William A., Chm. Bd., Pres. & Chief Exec. Officer--Decorator Industries, Inc., Pembroke Pines, FL; *U.S. Public*, pg. 491
Bassetti, Aldo, Chm.--Publifactoring S.p.A., Milan, Italy; *Int'l*, *pg. 138*
Bassetti, Aldo, Chm. Bd.--Publicfactoring S.p.A., Milan, Italy; *Int'l*, pg. 138
Baszucki, Paul, Chm. Bd. & Chief Exec. Officer--Norstan, Inc., Plymouth, MN; *U.S. Public*, pg. 1192
Bata, T.G., Chm. Bd.--CHB Corp., Belcamp, MD; *U.S. Private*, pg. 194
Batchelder, David H., Chm. Bd.--Mac Frugal's Bargains Close-Outs Inc., Rancho Dominguez, CA; *U.S. Public*, pg. 437
Bateman, Edward D., Chm. Bd.--Bateman Brothers Lumber Co., Inc., New Britain, PA; *U.S. Private*, pg. 122
Bateman, Giles H., Chm. Bd.--CompUSA, Dallas, TX; *U.S. Public*, pg. 420
Bateman, Walter R., Chm. Bd. & Chief Exec. Officer--Great Oaks Insurance Company, Dublin, OH; *U.S. Public*, pg. 786
Bateman, Walter R., Chm. Bd. & Pres.--Harleysville Services Inc, Harleysville, PA; *U.S. Public*, pg. 787
Bateman, Walter R., Chm., Pres. & Chief Oper. Officer--Mainland Insurance Co., Harleysville, PA; *U.S. Public*, pg. 787
Bates, Ernest A., M.D., Chm. Bd., Pres., Chief Exec. & Oper. Officer--American Shared Hospital Services, San Francisco, CA; *U.S. Public*, pg. 91
Bates, John C., Chm. of Bd., Pres. & Chief Exec. Officer--Heidtman Steel Products, Inc., Toledo, OH; *U.S. Private*, pg. 519
Bates, Malcolm, Chm. Bd.--Picker International, Inc., Cleveland, OH; *Int'l*, pg. 545
Bates, Malcolm R., Chm. Bd.--Premier Farnell plc, Wetherby, United Kingdom; *Int'l*, pg. 1068
Bates, Robert D., Chm. Bd., Pres. & Chief Exec. Officer--Guarantee Life Insurance Co., Omaha, NE; *U.S. Public*, pg. 768
Bates, Wesley, Chm. Bd. & Pres.--Stanley Steemer International, Inc., Dublin, OH; *U.S. Private*, pg. 1033
Batey, Ian, Grp. Chm.--Batey Ads Singapore, Singapore, Singapore; *Int'l*, pg. 170
Batinovich, Robert, Chm. Bd. & Chief Exec. Officer--Glenborough Realty Trust Incorporated, San Mateo, CA; *U.S. Public*, pg. 747
Batista, Eike F., Chm. Bd.--TVX Gold Inc., Toronto, Canada; *Int'l*, pg. 1345
Batkin, Sanford L., Chm. Bd, Chief Exec. Officer & Treas.--Universal Folding Box Company, Inc., Hoboken, NJ; *U.S.* Private, pg. 1127
Batteast, Robert V., Chm. Bd., Pres. & Treas.--Batteast Construction Company, Inc., South Bend, IN; *U.S. Private*, pg. 123
Batten, Frank, Sr., Chm. Bd.--Landmark Communications, Inc., Norfolk, VA; *U.S. Private*, pg. 647
Batten, Howard, Chm. Bd.--Jannock Imaging Companies Limited, Toronto, Canada; *Int'l*, pg. 698
Batten, Michael E., Chm. Bd. & Chief Exec. Officer--Twin Disc, Incorporated, Racine, WI; *U.S. Public*, pg. 1646
Battle, Edward G., Chm. Bd.--Norcen Energy Resources Limited, Calgary, Canada; *Int'l*, pg. 434
Baudron, Michel, Chm. Bd.--Riber, Rueil-Malmaison, France; *Int'l*, pg. 1114
Bauer, Chris M., Chm. Bd. & Chief Exec. Officer--Firstar Milwaukee Bank, N.A., Milwaukee, WI; *U.S. Public*, pg. 643
Bauer, Fred T., Chm. Bd. & Chief Exec. Officer--Gentex Corporation, Zeeland, MI; *U.S. Public*, pg. 731
Baugh, John F., Sr. Chm. Bd.--Sysco Corporation, Houston, TX; *U.S. Public*, pg. 1550
Baughman, Walter, Chm. Bd.--Plastomer Corp., Livonia, MI; *U.S. Private*, pg. 872
Baum, Charles C., Chm. & Chief Exec. Officer--The Morgan Group, Inc., Elkhart, IN; *U.S. Public*, pg. 1022
Baum, David, Chm. Bd., Pres. & Chief Exec. Officer--Arcon Construction Co., Inc., Harris, MN; *U.S. Private*, pg. 80
Baum, Herbert M., Chm. Bd. & Chief Exec. Officer--Quaker State Corporation, Irving, TX; *U.S. Public*, pg. 1348
Baum, Stephen L., Chm. Bd. & Chief Exec. Officer--Enova Corp, San Diego, CA; *U.S. Public*, pg. 583
Baum, W.A., Jr., Chm. Bd.--W.A. Baum Company, Inc., Copiague, NY; *U.S. Private*, pg. 124
Bauman, Robert, Chm. Bd.--British Aerospace p.l.c., Farnborough, United Kingdom; *Int'l*, pg. 217
Bauman, Robert L., Chm. Bd., Pres. & Chief Exec. Officer--Hickok Incorporated, Cleveland, OH; *U.S. Public*, pg. 825
Baumann, Per, Chm. Bd.--Toyota Norge A/S, Drammen, Norway; *Int'l*, pg. 1414
Baumberger, Hans Ulrich, Dr., Chm. Bd.--SIG Schweizerische Industrie-Gesellschaft Holding AG, Neuhausen, Switzerland; *Int'l*, pg. 1156
Baumgardner, J. Dwane, Ph.D., Chm. Bd., Pres. & Chief Exec. Officer--Donnelly Corporation, Holland, MI; *U.S. Public*, pg. 519
Baumgartner, Vito H., Chm. Bd.--Caterpillar Overseas S.A., Geneva, Switzerland; *U.S. Public*, pg. 316
Baumhauer, William H., Chm. Bd. & Chief Exec. Officer--Unique Casual Restaurants, Inc., Danvers, MA; *Int'l*, pg. 324
Baur, Elmar F., Prof., Chm. Bd.--Feodor Burgmann Dichtungswerke GmbH, Wolfratshausen, Germany; *Int'l*, pg. 233
Baur, Philip J., Jr., Chm. Bd.--Tasty Baking Company, Philadelphia, PA; *U.S. Public*, pg. 1561
Baur, Philip J., Jr., Chm. Bd.--TBC Financial Services, Philadelphia, PA; *U.S. Public*, pg. 1561
Baxter, Frank E., Chm. Bd., Pres. & Chief Exec. Officer--Jefferies Group, Inc., Los Angeles, CA; *U.S. Public*, pg. 924
Baxter, Harold J., Chm. Bd. & Chief Exec. Officer--Newbold's Asset Management Inc., Bryn Mawr, PA; *U.S.* Public, pg. 1673
Baxter, Harold J., Chm. Bd. & Chief Exec. Officer--Pilgram Baxter & Associates, Wayne, PA; *U.S. Public*, pg. 1673
Bay, Mogens C., Chm. Bd. & Chief Exec. Officer--Valmont Industries, Inc., Valley, NE; *U.S. Public*, pg. 1706
Bayer, Richard, Chm. Bd.--Target Stamped Products Corp., Kinsman, OH; *U.S. Private*, pg. 1069
Bayer, Robert, Chm. Bd., Pres. & Chief Exec. Officer--Bayer Clothing Group, New York, NY; *U.S. Private*, pg. 124
Bayless, Charles E., Chm. Bd., Pres. & Chief Exec. Officer--UniSource Energy Corporation, Tucson, AZ; *U.S. Public*, pg. 1670
Bayless, Charles E., Chm. Bd., Pres. & Chief Exec. Officer--Tucson Electric Power Company, Tucson, AZ; *U.S. Public*, pg. 1670
Bayley, Robert E., Chm. Bd. & Chief Exec. Officer--Robert E. Bayley Construction, Seattle, WA; *U.S. Private*, pg. 125
Bayman, James L., Chm. Bd. & Chief Exec. Officer--Pioneer-Standard Electronics, Inc., Cleveland, OH; *U.S. Public*, pg. 1300
Bays, John, Asst. Chm. Bd.--Cheltenham & Gloucester plc, Gloucester, United Kingdom; *Int'l*, pg. 283
Bazoli, Giovanni, Chm. Bd.--Banco Ambrosiano Veneto S.p.A., Milan, Italy; *Int'l*, pg. 138
Beach, Roger C., Chm. Bd. & Chief Exec. Officer--Unocal Corporation, El Segundo, CA; *U.S. Public*, pg. 1698
Beach, William H., Chm. Bd., Pres., Chief Exec. & Oper. Officer--Beach Mold & Tool Inc., New Albany, IN; *U.S. Private*, pg. 125
Beal, Maureen, Chm. Bd.--National Van Lines, Inc., Broadview, IL; *U.S. Private*, pg. 788
Bean, Jerome B., Jr., Chm. Bd.--R.O. Whitesell & Associates, Inc, Indianapolis, IN; *U.S. Private*, pg. 1173
Bean, Vernon J., Chm. Bd.--D.D. Bean & Sons Co., Jaffrey, NH; *U.S. Private*, pg. 126
Beard, A.D., Chm. Bd. & Pres.--Formation, Inc., Moorestown, NJ; *U.S. Private*, pg. 419
Beard, Frederick K., Exec. V.P. & Chm. Bd., Pres. & Chief Exec. Officer-Mellon Bank--Mellon Bank Corporation, Pittsburgh, PA; *U.S. Public*, pg. 1084
Beard, Frederick K., Chm. Bd., Pres. & Chief Exec. Officer--Mellon Bank (MD), Rockville, MD; *U.S. Public*, pg. 1085
Beard, James S., Chm. Bd.--Caterpillar Finance France S.A., Saint Denis, France; *U.S. Public*, pg. 315
Beard, Thomas G., Chm. Bd., Pres. & Chief Exec. Officer--Palmer Electric Co., Winter Park, FL; *U.S. Private*, pg. 834
Beardall, James C., Chm. Bd., Pres. & Chief Exec. Officer--Anderson Lumber Company, Ogden, UT; *U.S. Private*, pg. 72
Beardsley, John R., Chm. Bd. & Chief Exec. Officer--Padilla Speer Beardsley Inc., Minneapolis, MN; *U.S. Private*, pg. 833
Beaton, Bradford, Chm. Bd., Pres. & Chief Exec. Officer--New England Newspaper Supply Company, Inc., Millbury, MA; *U.S. Private*, pg. 793
Beattie, Allan L., Chm. Bd.--Baton Broadcasting Incorporated, Scarborough, Canada; *Int'l*, pg. 170
Beaubien, Philippe de Gaspe, Chm. Bd.--Telemedia Inc., Montreal, Canada; *Int'l*, pg. 1373
Beauchamp, Patrick L., Chm. Bd., Pres. & Treas.--Beauchamp Distributing Company, Compton, CA; *U.S. Private*, pg. 127
Beaudoin, Laurent, Chm. Bd. & Chief Exec. Officer--Bombardier Inc., Montreal, Canada; *Int'l*, pg. 199
Beaver, Jeffrey T., Chm. Bd.--Aquila Biopharmaceuticals, Inc., Worcester, MA; *U.S. Public*, pg. 126
Bebb, R.D., Chm. Bd.--Senior Engineering, Lyman, SC; *Int'l*, *pg. 1222*
Bebear, Claude, Chm. Bd. & Pres.--AXA-UAP, Paris, France; *Int'l*, pg. 18
Beber, Joyce, Co-Chm. Bd.--Beber & Silverstein & Partners, Inc., Miami, FL; *U.S. Private*, pg. 128
Bech, Jan, Chm. Bd.--Olicom A/S, Lyngby, Denmark; *Int'l*, pg. 1001
Bechat, Jean-Paul, Chm. & Chief Exec. Officer--SNECMA - Societe Nationale d'Etude et de Construction de Moteurs d'Aviation, Paris, France; *Int'l*, pg. 1165
Becher, F. James, Jr., Chm. Bd., Pres. & Chief Exec. Officer--Geneva Corporation, Greensboro, NC; *U.S. Private*, pg. 446
Becherer, Hans W., Chm. Bd. & Chief Exec. Officer--Deere & Company, Moline, IL; *U.S. Public*, pg. 491
Becherer, Hans W., Chm. Bd.--John Deere Credit Company, Moline, IL; *U.S. Public*, pg. 492
Bechtel, Riley, Chm. Bd. & Chief Exec. Officer--Bechtel Group, Inc., San Francisco, CA; *U.S. Private*, pg. 128
Bechtler, Thomas W., Chm.--Zellweger Uster AG, Uster, Switzerland; *Int'l*, pg. 618
Beck, David A., Chm. Bd. & Pres.--Clark Grave Vault Co., Columbus, OH; *U.S. Private*, pg. 243
Beck, H. Thomas, Chm. Bd. & Chief Exec. Officer--Noma Industries Limited, North York, Canada; *Int'l*, pg. 954
Beck, James A., Chm. Bd., Pres. & Chief Exec. Officer--SouthTrust Bank of North Carolina, Raleigh, NC; *U.S. Public*, pg. 1492
Beck, Jeffrey L., Co-Chm. Bd. & Chief Exec. Officer--Capital Senior Living, Inc., Dallas, TX; *U.S. Public*, pg. 302
Beck, Martin, Chm.--Young & Rubicam Prague, Prague, Czech Republic; *U.S. Private*, pg. 1199
Beck, Scott, Co-Chm. & Pres.--Boston Chicken, Inc., Golden, CO; *U.S. Public*, pg. 247
Beck, Scott, Chm.--Einstein/Noah Bagel Corp., Golden, CO; *U.S. Public*, pg. 247
Beck, W.F. De La Harpe, Chm. Bd.--Coates Brothers (South Africa) Ltd., Cape Town, South Africa; *Int'l*, pg. 1409
Becker, B. Frederick, Chm. Bd. & Chief Exec. Officer--MMI Companies, Inc., Deerfield, IL; *U.S. Public*, pg. 1027
Becker, Don C., Chm. Bd.--Traffic World, New York, NY; *Int'l*, pg. 1026
Becker, Eugene E., Chm. Bd.--Bankers American Life Assurance Company, Pearl River, NY; *U.S. Public*, pg. 68
Becker, John A., Chm. Bd.--Firstar Information Services Corporation, Milwaukee, WI; *U.S. Public*, pg. 643
Becker, W. Marston, Chm. Bd. & Chief Exec. Officer--Orion Capital Corporation, New York, NY; *U.S. Public*, pg. 1231
Beckerman, David, Chm. Bd. & Chief Exec. Officer--Starter Corp., New Haven, CT; *U.S. Public*, pg. 1511
Beckett, M.E., Chm. Bd.--Watts Blake Bearne & Co. Plc, Newton Abbot, United Kingdom; *Int'l*, pg. 1487
Beckwith, F.W., Chm. Bd. & Chief Exec. Officer--Fareway Stores, Inc., Boone, IA; *U.S. Private*, pg. 393
Beckwith, James S. III, Chm. Bd.--Beckwith Machinery Company, Murrysville, PA; *U.S. Private*, pg. 129
Beddor, William N., Chm. Bd.--Japs-Olson Company, Minneapolis, MN; *U.S. Private*, pg. 582
Bedecarre, Tom, Chm.--Citron Haligman Bedecarre, San Francisco, CA; *U.S. Private*, pg. 241

Bedell, Thomas, Chm. Bd. & Pres.--Outdoor Technologies Group, Spirit Lake, IA; *U.S. Private*, pg. 822

Bedford, Steve, Chm. Bd.--Blazer Plc, London, United Kingdom; *Int'l*, pg. 896

Bednarowski, Keith P., Chm. Bd.--Opus South Corporation, Tampa, FL; *U.S. Private*, pg. 818

Beech, Wally, Chm. Bd.--Garland Commercial Ranges, Ltd., Mississauga, Canada; *Int'l*, pg. 189

Beeler, Donald, Chm. Bd.--Snyder's Drug Stores, Inc., Minnetonka, MN; *U.S. Private*, pg. 1011

Beffa, Jean-Louis, Chm. Bd. & Chief Exec. Officer--Saint-Gobain, Courbevoie, France; *Int'l*, pg. 1170

Begel, Thomas M., Chm. Bd., Pres. & Chief Exec. Officer--Johnstown America Industries, Chicago, IL; *U.S. Public*, pg. 933

Begnone, Piero, Deputy Chm. & Chief Exec. Officer--Hunter Engineering Co., Inc., Riverside, CA; *Int'l*, pg. 474

Behan, William L., Jr., Chm. Bd.--Hill-Behan Lumber Company, Saint Louis, MO; *U.S. Private*, pg. 529

Beharrell, B., Chm. Bd.--Amercard, Moscow, Russia; *Int'l*, pg. 993

Behler, A. Donald, Chm. Bd & Pres.--Blue Ridge Pressure Castings, Inc., Lehighton, PA; *U.S. Private*, pg. 153

Behrendt, Peter D., Chm. Bd., Pres. & Chief Exec. Officer--Exabyte Corporation, Boulder, CO; *U.S. Public*, pg. 597

Behrens, Fred H., Chm. Bd., Chief Exec. Officer & Chief Fin. Officer--Amcor Capital Corporation, Coachella, CA; *U.S. Public*, pg. 64

Beissinger, Frederick W., Chm. Bd., Pres. & Chief Exec. Officer--American General Finance, Inc., Evansville, IN; *U.S. Public*, pg. 76

Beitzel, George, Chm. Bd. & Chief Exec. Officer--Blue Anchor, Inc., Dinuba, CA; *U.S. Private*, pg. 150

Beitzel, George, Chm. Bd.--Colonial Williamsburg Foundation, Williamsburg, VA; *U.S. Private*, pg. 254

Belatti, Frank J., Chm. Bd. & Chief Exec. Officer--AFC Enterprises, Atlanta, GA; *U.S. Private*, pg. 5

Belber, Henry, Chm. Bd.--Army Times Publishing Co., Springfield, VA; *U.S. Public*, pg. 699

Belcher, Donald D., Chm. Bd., Pres. & Chief Exec. Officer--Banta Corporation, Menasha, WI; *U.S. Public*, pg. 187

Belemthal, Dan, Chm. Bd.--Villazon Company Inc., Upper Saddle River, NJ; *U.S. Private*, pg. 1140

Belenguier, B., Chm. Bd.--Gan UK plc, London, United Kingdom; *Int'l*, pg. 565

Belgrad, D.A., Chm. Bd., Pres. & Chief Exec. Officer--Schnadig Corporation, Des Plaines, IL; *U.S. Private*, pg. 971

Belinguier, B., Chm. Bd.--Gan North America Inc., New York, NY; *Int'l*, pg. 564

Belk, John M., Chm. Bd. & Chief Exec. Officer--Belk Stores Services Inc., Charlotte, NC; *U.S. Private*, pg. 131

Belkin, Steve, Chm. Bd.-Trans National Group--TNT Vacations, Boston, MA; *U.S. Private*, pg. 1065

Bell, A.J., Chm. & Chief Exec.--Senior Control Engineering Limited, Derby, United Kingdom; *Int'l*, pg. 1220

Bell, G. C., Chm.--Stanbic Bank Botswana Limited, Gaborone, Botswana; *Int'l*, pg. 1293

Bell, Graham S., Chm. & Mng. Dir.--The Crown Company (Singapore) Ltd., Jurong, Singapore; *U.S. Public*, pg. 464

Bellamy, Otis, Chm. Bd.--Bellamy Brothers, Inc., Ellenwood, GA; *U.S. Private*, pg. 132

Bellati, Craig, Chm. Bd.--Straw Hat Cooperative Corp., Dublin, CA; *U.S. Private*, pg. 1046

Bellina, Gerald, Chm. Bd., V.P.-Engrng. & Treas.--DAQ Electronics Inc., Piscataway, NJ; *U.S. Private*, pg. 300

Bellis, Gerald, Chm. Bd.--Unitech Industries, Inc., Tempe, AZ; *U.S. Public*, pg. 1672

Bello, Regis, Chm. & Chief Exec. Officer--De Dietrich & Co., Niederbronn-les-Bains, France; *Int'l*, pg. 386

Bello, Regis, Chm. & Chief Exec. Officer--Cogifer SA, Croissy-sur-Seine, France; *Int'l*, pg. 386

Bellon, Pierre, Chm. Bd. & Chief Exec. Officer--Sodexho S.A., Montigny-le-Bretonneux, France; *Int'l*, pg. 1274

Bells, Gerald, Chm. Bd.--Solidex, Scottsdale, AZ; *U.S. Public*, pg. 1672

Bellwood, Wesley E., Chm. Emeritus--Wynn's International, Inc., Orange, CA; *U.S. Public*, pg. 1782

Belmonte, Dennis R., Chm. & Pres.--Benguet Management Corporation, Manila, Philippines; *Int'l*, pg. 186

Beltz, William A., Chm. Bd.--The Bureau of National Affairs, Inc., Washington, DC; *U.S. Private*, pg. 181

Belz, Jack A., Chm. Bd.--Belz Enterprises, Memphis, TN; *U.S. Private*, pg. 132

Belz, Philip, Chm. Bd. Emeritus--Belz Enterprises, Memphis, TN; *U.S. Private*, pg. 132

Belzberg, William, Chm. Bd.--Westminster Capital Inc., Beverly Hills, CA; *U.S. Public*, pg. 1761

Belzer, Burton E., Chm. Bd., Chief Exec. Officer, Chief Fin. Officer & Treas.--TCI Aluminum, Gardena, CA; *U.S. Private*, pg. 1063

Belzer, Burton E., Chm. Bd., Chief Exec. Officer, Cheif Fin. Officer & Treas.--E-Z Lok, Gardena, CA; *U.S. Private*, pg. 1063

Ben-Gal, A.Y., Chm. Bd.--Israel Aircraft Industries Ltd., Israel; *Int'l*, pg. 689

Benaroya, Raphael, Chm. Bd., Pres. & Chief Exec. Officer--United Retail Group, Inc., Rochelle Park, NJ; *U.S. Public*, *pg. 1679*

Benavides Pompa, Jaime M., Chm. Bd.--Far-Ben S.A. de C.V., Monterrey, Mexico; *Int'l*, pg. 478

Bender, Robert L., Chm., Pres., Chief Exec. Officer & Chief Oper. Officer--Lord, Sullivan & Yoder Inc. Marketing Communications, Columbus, OH; *U.S. Private*, pg. 676

Bender, Thomas B., Jr., Chm. Bd., Pres. & Chief Exec. Officer--Bender Shipbuilding & Repair Company, Inc., Mobile, AL; *U.S. Private*, pg. 132

Bendheim, C.H., Chm. Bd.--Philipp Brothers Chemicals, Inc., Fort Lee, NJ; *U.S. Private*, pg. 861

Benenson, James, Jr., Chm. Bd. & Pres.--Arrowhead Holding Corporation, Brecksville, OH; *U.S. Private*, pg. 86

Benenson, James, Jr., Chm. Bd.--Vester Corporation, Newtown Square, PA; *U.S. Private*, pg. 86

Benenson, James, Jr., Chm. Bd. & Pres.--Vesper Corporation, Brecksville, OH; *U.S. Private*, pg. 86

Benesch, Valli, Chm. Bd. & Chief Exec. Officer--Fritzi of California Manufacturing Corp., San Francisco, CA; *U.S. Private*, pg. 429

Benetton, Luciano, Chm. Bd. & Pres.--Benetton Group S.p.A., Ponzano Veneto, Italy; *Int'l*, pg. 186

Benfield, Ron, Chm. Bd. & Pres.--Central Lincoln People's Utility District, Newport, OR; *U.S. Private*, pg. 223

Bengtson, Jon, Chm. Bd.--Radica USA Limited, Dallas, TX; *U.S. Private*, pg. 906

Benhamou, Eric A., Chm. Bd., Pres. & Chief Exec. Officer--3Com Corporation, Santa Clara, CA; *U.S. Public*, pg. 1603

Benhamou, Guy, Chm. Bd., Pres. & Chief Exec. Officer--Oroamerica, Inc., Burbank, CA; *U.S. Public*, pg. 1232

Beningson, Robert M., Chm. Bd., Pres. & Chief Exec. Officer--York Research Corporation, New York, NY; *U.S.* Public, pg. 1789

Benjamens, Rob, Chm.--Benjamens, Van Doorn EURO RSCG, Amstelveen, Netherlands; *Int'l*, pg. 602

Benjamin, Colin, Chm. Bd.--Asoma Corporation, White Plains, NY; *U.S. Private*, pg. 89

Benjamin, Morley, Chm. Bd.--Morley Builders, Santa Monica, CA; *U.S. Private*, pg. 761

Benjamin, V.W., Chm. Bd.--Beazer Group Plc, Bath, United Kingdom; *Int'l*, pg. 181

Bennett, D.A., Chm.--Texaco Britain Limited, London, United Kingdom; *U.S. Public*, pg. 1584

Bennett, D.A., Chm. Bd.--Texaco Limited, London, United Kingdom; *U.S. Public*, pg. 1584

Bennett, D.A., Chm. Bd.--Texaco North Sea U.K. Co., Aberdeen, United Kingdom; *U.S. Public*, pg. 1584

Bennett, David, Chm. Bd.--Omega Performance Group, Sausalito, CA; *U.S. Private*, pg. 816

Bennett, Donald D., Chm. Bd.--Richfood Holdings, Inc., Glen Allen, VA; *U.S. Public*, pg. 1388

Bennett, Donald H., Chm. Bd.--Oakhurst Dairy, Portland, ME; *U.S. Private*, pg. 809

Bennett, Gary P., Chm. Bd., Pres. & Chief Exec. Officer--Analysis & Technology, Inc., North Stonington, CT; *U.S. Public*, pg. 109

Bennett, Gary P., Chm.--Prism-Dae, Inc., Mc Lean, VA; *U.S.* Public, pg. 110

Bennett, Paul F., Chm. Bd. & Chief Exec. Officer--Utility Trailer Manufacturing Co., City of Industry, CA; *U.S. Private*, pg. 1130

Bennett, Robert J., Chm. Bd., Pres. & Chief Exec. Officer--ONBANCorp, Inc., Syracuse, NY; *U.S. Public*, pg. 631

Bennett, Robert R., Chm. Bd.--America's Store, Saint Petersburg, FL; *U.S. Public*, pg. 1685

Bennett, Roy F., Chm. Bd.--Midland Walwyn Inc., Toronto, Canada; *Int'l*, pg. 865

Benson, Christopher, Chm. Bd.--Costain Group PLC, London, United Kingdom; *Int'l*, pg. 336

Benson, Christopher, Sir, Chm. Bd.--Albright & Wilson plc, Oldbury, United Kingdom; *Int'l*, pg. 49

Benson, Craig R., Chm. Bd. & Treas.--Cabletron Systems, Inc., Rochester, NH; *U.S. Public*, pg. 288

Benson, H.E., Chm. Bd.--Benson's Inc., Bogart, GA; *U.S. Private*, pg. 134

Benson, James, Chm. Bd.--PHB Die Casting, Fairview, PA; *U.S. Private*, pg. 826

Benson, N. W., Chm. Bd.--Moss Bros Group PLC, London, United Kingdom; *Int'l*, pg. 895

Benson, N.W., Chm. Bd.--The Davis Service Group Plc., London, United Kingdom; *Int'l*, pg. 385

Benson, Tom, Chm. Bd. & Chief Exec. Officer--Benson Motors Corporation, Metairie, LA; *U.S. Private*, pg. 134

Benson, Tom, Jr., Chm. Bd.--Benson Automotive World, San Antonio, TX; *U.S. Private*, pg. 133

Benstock, Gerald M., Chm. Bd. & Chief Exec. Officer--Superior Surgical Mfg. Co., Inc., Seminole, FL; *U.S. Public*, pg. 1539

Bentall, L. Edward, Chm. Bd.--Bentalls plc, Kingston upon Thames, United Kingdom; *Int'l*, pg. 187

Bentas, Lilly, Chm. Bd. & Pres.--Cumberland Farms, Inc., Canton, MA; *U.S. Private*, pg. 295

Bentley, Greg, Chm. Bd. & Pres.--Bentley Systems, Inc., Exton, PA; *U.S. Private*, pg. 134

Bentley, Peter J.G., Chm. Bd. & Chief Exec. Officer--Canfor Corporation, Vancouver, Canada; *Int'l*, pg. 260

Bently, Donald E., Chm. Bd. & Chief Exec. Officer--Bently Nevada Corporation, Minden, NV; *U.S. Private*, pg. 134

Benton, Virgil, II., Chm. Bd. & Chief Exec. Officer--Keystone Automotive Industries, Inc., Pomona, CA; *U.S. Public*, pg. 955

Benton, William B., Chm. Bd., Chief Exec. Officer & Chief Fin. Officer--Mid South Sales, Helena, AR; *U.S. Private*, pg. 744

Beracha, Barry H., Chm. Bd.--Metal Container Corporation, Saint Louis, MO; *U.S. Public*, pg. 114

Berard, Andre, Chm. Bd. & Chief Exec. Officer--National Bank of Canada, Montreal, Canada; *Int'l*, pg. 907

Berard, Dailey J., Chm. Bd., Pres. & Chief Exec. Officer--Unifab International Inc., New Iberia, LA; *U.S. Public*, pg. 1665

Berberian, Ronald, Chm. Bd. & Pres.--Bank of Agriculture & Commerce, Stockton, CA; *U.S. Private*, pg. 114

Berdass, Fred P., Chm. Bd.--Bermo, Inc., Circle Pines, MN; *U.S. Private*, pg. 136

Berdin, Jerry, Chm. Bd. & Chief Exec. Officer--Allied Office Supplies, Hasbrouck Heights, NJ; *U.S. Private*, pg. 39

Beren, S.O., Chm. Bd., Pres. & Chief Exec. Officer--Misco Industries, Wichita, KS; *U.S. Private*, pg. 752

Beren, S.O., Chm. Bd.--Mountain Iron & Supply Company, Wichita, KS; *U.S. Private*, pg. 764

Berenter, Bill, Chm. Bd. & Co-Creative Dir.--Berenter Greenhouse & Webster, Inc., New York, NY; *U.S. Private*, pg. 135

Berenzweig, Stanley, Chm. Bd. & Chief Exec. Officer--Rag Shops, Inc., Hawthorne, NJ; *U.S. Public*, pg. 1358

Berer, Stanley H., Co.-Chm. & Co.-Chief Exec. Officer--Totem Resources Corporation, Seattle, WA; *U.S. Private*, *pg. 1092*

Beres, Donald R., Chm. Bd.--Crafty Beaver Home Center, Skokie, IL; *U.S. Private*, pg. 284

Berg, Kenneth, Chm. Bd. & Chief Exec. Officer--Koo Koo Roo, Inc., Los Angeles, CA; *U.S. Public*, pg. 966

Berg, R.W., Chm. Bd.--ITA Group Inc., West Des Moines, IA; *U.S. Private*, pg. 555

Berge, Paul M., Chm. & Chief Exec. Officer--M & I Madison Bank, Madison, WI; *U.S. Public*, pg. 1050

Berge, Pierre, Chm. Bd.--Yves Saint Laurent Parfums S.A., Neuilly-sur-Seine, France; *Int'l*, pg. 445

Bergen, Lee D., Chm. Bd. & Sec.--Peter Lumber Company, Pleasantville, NJ; *U.S. Private*, pg. 856

Berger, Charles M., Chm. Bd., Pres. & Chief Exec. Officer--The Scotts Company, Marysville, OH; *U.S. Public*, pg. 1446

Berger, Ron, Chm. Bd., Pres., Chief Exec. Officer--Rentrak Corporation, Portland, OR; *U.S. Public*, pg. 1377

Berger, S.J., Exec. Chm.--Amalgamated Retail Ltd., Braamfontein, South Africa; *Int'l*, pg. 1286

Berger, Stanley I., Chm. Bd.--Designs, Inc., Needham, MA; *U.S. Public*, pg. 501

Berger, Ted, Chm. Bd.--Dreison International, Inc., Cleveland, OH; *U.S. Private*, pg. 342

Berggren, Bo, Chm. Bd.--Astra AB, Sodertalje, Sweden; *Int'l*, pg. 93

Berglass, Robert, Chm. Bd. & Pres.--Dep Corporation, Rancho Dominguez, CA; *U.S. Public*, pg. 500

Berglund, Thomas R., M.D., Chm. Bd. & Pres.--Michigan Physicians Mutual Liability Inc., East Lansing, MI; *U.S. Private*, pg. 741

Bergman, Klaus, Chm. Bd.--Allegheny Power System, Inc., Hagerstown, MD; *U.S. Public*, pg. 42

Bergman, Stanley M., Chm. Bd., Pres. & Chief Exec. Officer--Henry Schein, Inc., Melville, NY; *U.S. Public*, pg. 1437

Bergmann, Horst A., Chm. Bd., Pres. & Chief Exec. Officer--Jeppesen Sanderson, Englewood, CO; *U.S. Public*, pg. 1616

Bergmann, Horst A., Chm. Bd., Pres. & Chief Exec. Officer--Jeppesen and Co. GmbH, Frankfurt/Main, Germany; *U.S. Public*, pg. 1617

Bergmann, Horst A., Chm., Pres. & Chief Exec. Officer--Achieve Global, Tampa, FL; *U.S. Public*, pg. 1617

Bergougnoux, Jean, Chm. Bd.--SNCF, Paris, France; *Int'l*, pg. 1163

Bergquist, Carl R., Jr., Chm. Bd., Pres. & Chief Exec. Officer--The Bergquist Company, Minneapolis, MN; *U.S. Private*, pg. 135

Bergren, Bo, Chm. Bd.--Scandinavian Airlines System (SAS), Solna, Sweden; *Int'l*, pg. 1201

Bergson, Arnold, Chm. Bd.--Acordia Northeast, Boston, MA; *Int'l*, pg. 671

Bergstein, Melvyn E., Chm. Bd. & Chief Exec. Officer--Diamond Technology Partners, Chicago, IL; *U.S. Public*, pg. 1424

Bergstrom, Erik E., Chm. Bd.--Bergstrom Capital Corporation, Seattle, WA; *U.S. Public*, pg. 215

Berkeley, D.J., Chm. Bd. & Mng. Dir.--Standard Bank (Jersey) Limited, Saint Helier, United Kingdom; *Int'l*, pg. 1294

Berkeley, Frederick D., Chm. Bd. & Chief Exec. Officer--Graham Corporation, Batavia, NY; *U.S. Public*, pg. 757

Berkley, E. Bertram, Chm. Bd.--Tension Envelope Corp., Kansas City, MO; *U.S. Private*, pg. 1077

Berkley, Stephen M., Chm. Bd.--Quantum Corporation, Milpitas, CA; *U.S. Public*, pg. 1350

Berkley, William, Chm. Bd. & Chief Exec. Officer--Interlaken Capital, Inc., Greenwich, CT; *U.S. Private*, pg. 567

Berkley, William R., Chm. Bd. & Chief Exec. Officer--W.R. Berkley Corporation, Greenwich, CT; *U.S. Public*, pg. 215

Berkley, William R., Chm. Bd.--Midwest Employer's Casualty Company, Maryland Heights, MO; *U.S. Public*, pg. 215

Berkman, A. William, Jr., Chm. Bd.--Embedded Performance, Inc., Milpitas, CA; *U.S. Private*, pg. 373

Berkman, Louis, Chm. Bd.--Ampco-Pittsburgh Corporation, Pittsburgh, PA; *U.S. Public*, pg. 103

Berkowitz, David H., Chm. Bd. & Chief Exec. Officer--Central Lewmar, Newark, NJ; *U.S. Private*, pg. 223

Berkowitz, Edwin J., Chm. Bd.--J.E. Berkowitz, LP, Westville, NJ; *U.S. Private*, pg. 135

Berlin, David N., Chm. Bd. & Pres.--Metalloy Corporation, Hudson, MI; *U.S. Private*, pg. 735

Berman, Barry H., Chm. Bd. & Pres.--CRN International, Inc., Hamden, CT; *U.S. Private*, pg. 197

Berman, Ira W., Chm. Bd. & Chief Fin. Officer--CCA Industries, Inc., East Rutherford, NJ; *U.S. Public*, pg. 276

Berman, Larry S., Chm. Bd. & Pres.--MNP Corp., Utica, MI; *U.S. Private*, pg. 687

Berman, Lyle, Chm. Bd. & Chief Exec. Officer--Grand Casinos, Inc., Minnetonka, MN; *U.S. Public*, pg. 758

Berman, Milton I., Chm. Bd., Pres. & Treas.--Avibank Mfg., Inc., Burbank, CA; *U.S. Private*, pg. 101

Berman, Richard N., Chm. Bd., Pres. & Chief Exec. Officer--R&B, Inc., Colmar, PA; *U.S. Public*, pg. 1354

Berman, Walter S., Chm. Bd.--American Express Credit Corporation, Wilmington, DE; *U.S. Public*, pg. 74

Bern, Dorrit J., Chm. Bd., Pres. & Chief Exec. Officer--Charming Shoppes, Inc., Bensalem, PA; *U.S. Public*, pg. 335

Bernard, Daniel, Chm. Bd.--Carrefour, Paris, France; *Int'l*, pg. 272

Bernard, Norman, Chm. Bd. & Chief Exec. Officer--Master Industries Corp., New York, NY; *U.S. Private*, pg. 713

Bernard, Stephen, Chm. Bd.--Cape Cod Potato Chip Company, Hyannis, MA; *U.S. Private*, pg. 205

Bernards, Douglas, Chm. Bd., Pres. & Chief Exec. Officer--Bernards Brothers, Inc., San Fernando, CA; *U.S. Private*, *pg. 136*

Bernaver, Willi, Chm. Bd.--Mactavish Machine Manufacturing Company, Richmond, VA; *U.S. Private*, pg. 693

Berndsen, L.J.M., Chm. Bd.--Royal Nedlloyd Group N.V., Rotterdam, Netherlands; *Int'l*, pg. 1143

Berner, Edgar R., Chm. Bd.--Republic Automotive Parts, Inc., Brentwood, TN; *U.S. Public*, pg. 1377

Berner, Harry B., Chm. Bd.--Berner Ltd., Helsinki, Finland; *Int'l*, pg. 189

Berners, Franz-Josef, Dr., Chm. Bd.--Bayer A/S, Skytta, Norway; *Int'l*, pg. 174

Bernheim, Antoine, Chm. Bd. & Mng. Dir.--Assicurazioni Generali S.p.A., Trieste, Italy; *Int'l*, pg. 89

Bernstein, Allen J., Chm. Bd., Pres. & Chief Exec. Officer--Morton's Restaurant Group, Inc., New Hyde Park, NY; *U.S. Public*, pg. 1136

Bernstein, Allen J., Chm. Bd.--Morton's of Chicago, Inc., Chicago, IL; *U.S. Public*, pg. 1136

Bernstein, Armyan, Chm. Bd.--Beacon Communications, Los Angeles, CA; *U.S. Public*, pg. 138

Bernstein, David, Chm. Bd.--Samuel Meisel & Company, Inc., Glen Burnie, MD; *Int'l*, pg. 103

Bernstein, Elliot, Chm. Bd. & Chief Exec. Officer--Bel Fuse Inc., Jersey City, NJ; *U.S. Public*, pg. 200

Bernstein, Howard, Chm. Bd.--Atlas Lift Truck Rentals & Sales, Inc., Schiller Park, IL; *U.S. Private*, pg. 96

Bernstein, Jay, Chm. Bd.--Northville Industries Corp., Melville, NY; *U.S. Private*, pg. 806

Bernstein, Philip, Chm. Bd.--Crown Crafts, Inc., Atlanta, GA; *U.S. Public*, pg. 465

Bernstein, Robert, Chm. Bd., Pres. & Chief Exec. Officer--Bernstein-Rein Advertising, Inc., Kansas City, MO; *U.S. Private*, pg. 137

Bernstein, S.J., Chm. Bd. & Chief Exec. Officer--The Biltrite Corporation, Waltham, MA; *U.S. Private*, pg. 144

Berra, Phillip, Chm. Bd.--The Hercules Tire & Rubber Company, Findlay, OH; *U.S. Private*, pg. 523

Berrie, Russell, Chm. Bd. & Chief Exec. Officer--Russ Berrie and Company, Inc., Oakland, NJ; *U.S. Public*, pg. 222

Berry, Claude A., Jr., Chm. Bd. & Pres.--Wehr Constructors Inc., Louisville, KY; *U.S. Private*, pg. 1159

Berry, Dan W., Chm. Bd., Pres. & Chief Exec. Officer--American Trouser, Inc., Columbus, MS; *U.S. Private*, pg. 64

Berry, Fred F., Jr., Chm. Bd.--Berry Companies, Inc., Wichita, KS; *U.S. Private*, pg. 137

Berry, Robert E., Chm. Bd. & Chief Exec. Officer--Berry-Brown Advertising, Inc., Dallas, TX; *U.S. Private*, pg. 137

Bershad, Stephen W., Chm. Bd. & Chief Exec. Officer--Axsys Technologies, Inc., New York, NY; *U.S. Public*, pg. 157

Bershad, Stephen W., Chm. Bd.--Vernitron Sensor Systems, Saint Petersburg, FL; *U.S. Public*, pg. 157

Bersoff, Edward H., Dr., Chm. Bd., Pres. & Chief Exec. Officer--BTG, Inc., Fairfax, VA; *U.S. Public*, pg. 164

Bersticker, Albert C., Chm. Bd. & Chief Exec. Officer--Ferro Corporation, Cleveland, OH; *U.S. Public*, pg. 618

Bertacchi, Larry, Chm. Bd.--Casa Di Bertacchi, Vineland, NJ; *U.S. Private*, pg. 928

Berthelot, Michael J., Chm. Bd. & Chief Exec. Officer--TransTechnology Corporation, Liberty Corner, NJ; *U.S. Public*, pg. 1632

Berthiaume, Douglas A., Chm. Bd., Pres. & Chief Exec. Officer--Waters Corporation, Milford, MA; *U.S. Public*, pg. 1745

Berthold, James K., Chm. Bd. & Pres.--Sunnen Products Company, Saint Louis, MO; *U.S. Private*, pg. 1053

Bertran, Joaquin, Chm. Bd.--Asland S.A., Madrid, Spain; *Int'l*, pg. 790

Berwind, C. Graham, Chm. Bd.--Berwind Pharmaceutical Services, Inc., West Point, PA; *U.S. Private*, pg. 139

Berwind, C. Graham, Jr., Chm. Bd.--Berwind Corporation, Philadelphia, PA; *U.S. Private*, pg. 138

Beshouri, Peter, Chm. Bd., Pres. & Chief Exec. Officer--Sound Advice, Inc., Dania, FL; *U.S. Public*, pg. 1488

Besley, M.A., Chm. Bd.--Commonwealth Bank Group, Sydney, Australia; *Int'l*, pg. 312

Bethune, Gordon, Chm. Bd. & Chief Exec. Officer--Continental Airlines, Houston, TX; *U.S. Public*, pg. 439

Bethurum, George M., Chm. Bd., Pres. & Chief Exec. Officer--Bethurum Research & Development, Inc., Texas City, TX; *U.S. Private*, pg. 141

Beumer, R.E., Chm. Bd. & Chief Exec. Officer--Sverdrup Corporation, Maryland Heights, MO; *U.S. Private*, pg. 1057

Beutler, Gary, Chm. Bd.--Beutler Heating & Air Conditioning Inc., Sacramento, CA; *U.S. Private*, pg. 141

Beutlich, Fred W., Limited Partner--Beutlich, L.P., Waukegan, IL; *U.S. Private*, pg. 141

Bever, Jay, Chm. Bd.--B&B Corporate Holdings, Inc., Tampa, FL; *U.S. Private*, pg. 104

Beverly, Joe E., Chm. Bd.--Commercial Bank, Thomasville, GA; *U.S. Public*, pg. 1549

Bevier, Deborah L., Chm. Bd. & Chief Exec. Officer--Key Bank of Washington, Tacoma, WA; *U.S. Public*, pg. 954

Bevington, John F., Chm.--The National Super Service Co., Toledo, OH; *U.S. Private*, pg. 787

Bewkes, Jeffrey L, Chm. Bd., Pres. & Chief Exec. Officer--Home Box Office, Inc., New York, NY; *U.S. Public*, pg. 1612

Beyer, Sonya Z., Chm. Bd. & Chief Exec. Officer--Midco International Inc., Chicago, IL; *U.S. Private*, pg. 744

Beyster, J.R., Chm. Bd. & Chief Exec. Officer--Science Applications International Corp., San Diego, CA; *U.S. Private*, pg. 975

Bezos, Jeffrey P., Chm. Bd., Pres. & Chief Exec. Officer--Amazon.com, Inc., Seattle, WA; *U.S. Public*, pg. 62

Bhargava, Rai P.K., Chm. Bd.--Citizens Gas Fuel Company, Adrian, MI; *U.S. Public*, pg. 1025

Biagi, Ronald G., Chm.--Bank of America Texas, Dallas, TX; *U.S. Public*, pg. 180

Bianco, James S., Sr., Chm. Bd. & Pres.--Control Module, Inc., Enfield, CT; *U.S. Private*, pg. 271

Bible, Geoffrey C., Chm. Bd. & Chief Exec. Officer--Philip Morris Companies Inc., New York, NY; *U.S. Public*, pg. 1287

Bibler, James, Chm. Bd. & Chief Exec. Officer--Bibler Brothers, Inc., Russellville, AR; *U.S. Private*, pg. 142

Biblio, Davidi, Chm. Bd.--DSP Communications Inc., Cupertino, CA; *U.S. Public*, pg. 475

Bich, Bruno, Chm. Bd. & Chief Exec. Officer--Societe BIC S.A., Clichy, France; *Int'l*, pg. 1272

Bich, Bruno, Chm. Bd. & Chief Exec. Officer--BIC Corporation, Milford, CT; *Int'l*, pg. 1273

Bicknell, O. Gene, Chm. Bd. & Chief Exec. Officer--NPC International, Inc., Pittsburg, KS; *U.S. Public*, pg. 1146

Bickner, Bruce P., Chm. Bd. & Chief Exec. Officer--Dekalb Genetics Corporation, De Kalb, IL; *U.S. Public*, pg. 493

Biddinger, John W., Chm. Bd.--ADT Security Systems, Inc., Carmel, IN; *U.S. Public*, pg. 1649

Biddulph, Kemp, Chm. Bd.--Biddulph Automotive Group, Glendale, AZ; *U.S. Private*, pg. 142

Bidermann, Maurice, Chm.--Bidermann International S.A., Paris, France; *Int'l*, pg. 194

Bieber, William F., Chm. Bd.--Acrometal Companies, Inc., Plymouth, MN; *U.S. Private*, pg. 14

Biederman, Barry, Chm. Bd. & Creative Dir.--Biederman, Kelly & Shaffer, Inc., New York, NY; *U.S. Private*, pg. 142

Biegler, David W., Chm. Bd. & Chief Exec. Officer--Lone Star Gas Co., Dallas, TX; *U.S. Public*, pg. 1587

Biehl, Hans-Reiner, Mng. Bd. Chm.--Saarbergwerke Aktiengesellschaft, Saarbruecken, Germany; *Int'l*, pg. 1166

Bierer, William, Chm. Bd. & Chief Exec. Officer--Essex Grain Products, Inc., Frazer, PA; *U.S. Private*, pg. 383

Bierich, Marcus, Chm.-Supervisory Council--Robert Bosch GmbH, Gerlingen, Germany; *Int'l*, pg. 203

Bierwirth, Rolf, Dr., Chm.-Mngmt. Bd.--Harpen AG, Dortmund, Germany; *Int'l*, pg. 597

Bigger, Daniele, Chm.--Coop Graubunden-Sarganserland, Chur, Switzerland; *Int'l*, pg. 329

Bigger, Danielle, Chm.--Coop Ticino, Saint Antonino, Switzerland; *Int'l*, pg. 329

Biggerstaff, Bobby G., Chm. Bd.--Key Risk Management Services, Inc., Greensboro, NC; *U.S. Public*, pg. 216

Biggs, Barton, Chm. Bd.--Morgan Stanley Asset Management, Inc., New York, NY; *U.S. Public*, pg. 1132

Bigio, Gilbert, Chm. Bd.--BCI Holding Corporation, Miami, FL; *U.S. Private*, pg. 106

Bigio, Gilbert, Chm. Bd.--Beverage Canners International Corp., Miami, FL; *U.S. Private*, pg. 106

Bigony, Frederick, Co.-Chm. Bd.--Harvey Industries, Inc., Waltham, MA; *U.S. Private*, pg. 508

Bigot, Charles, Chm.--Arianespace SA, Evry, France; *Int'l*, pg. 81

Bijur, Peter I., Chm. Bd. & Chief Exec. Officer--Texaco Inc., White Plains, NY; *U.S. Public*, pg. 1582

Billett, James F., Jr., Chm. Bd., Pres. & Chief Exec. Officer--Trenwick Group Inc., Stamford, CT; *U.S. Public*, pg. 1634

Billig, Erwin H., Chm. Bd.--Titan International, Inc., Quincy, IL; *U.S. Public*, pg. 1618

Billups, Charles E., Chm. Bd.--Essex County Gas Company, Amesbury, MA; *U.S. Public*, pg. 593

bin Marican, Dato' Mohd Hassan, Chm. Bd.--Petroliam Nasional Berhad (Petronas), Kuala Lumpur, Malaysia; *Int'l*, pg. 1046

Binch, D., Chm. Bd.--Champlain Cable Corp., Colchester, VT; *Int'l*, pg. 637

Binder, Gorden, Chm. Bd.--Amgen Boulder, Inc., Boulder, CO; *U.S. Public*, pg. 101

Binder, Gordon M., Chm. Bd. & Chief Exec. Officer--Amgen Inc., Thousand Oaks, CA; *U.S. Public*, pg. 100

Binder, Heinrich, Dr., Chm. Bd.--Pieburg AG, Neckarsulm, Germany; *Int'l*, pg. 1108

Binder, Stanley S., Chm. Bd., Pres & Chief Exec. Officer--Barringer Technologies Inc., New Providence, NJ; *U.S. Public*, pg. 191

Bindley, William E., Chm. Bd. & Chief Exec. Officer--Bindley Western Industries, Inc., Indianapolis, IN; *U.S. Public*, pg. 228

Bing, Dave, Chm. Bd. & Owner--Bing Steel Inc., Detroit, MI; *U.S. Private*, pg. 144

Binswanger, Frank G., Jr., Chm. Bd.--Binswanger, Philadelphia, PA; *U.S. Private*, pg. 144

Biondi, Frank J., Jr., Chm. Bd. & Chief Exec. Officer--Universal Studios, Inc., Universal City, CA; *Int'l*, pg. 1215

Birchall, Adrian, Chm. Bd. & Chief Exec. Officer--The Media Centre, London, United Kingdom; *Int'l*, pg. 852

Birdsong, T.H., III, Chm. Bd.--Birdsong Corporation, Suffolk, VA; *U.S. Private*, pg. 145

Birge, Clifford A., Chm. Bd.--Seymour Manufacturing Company, Seymour, IN; *U.S. Private*, pg. 988

Birkenruth, Harry H., Chm. Bd.--Rogers Corporation, Rogers, CT; *U.S. Public*, pg. 1402

Birkhauser, Robert R., III, Chm. Bd. & Pres.--Auto Glass Specialists, Madison, WI; *U.S. Private*, pg. 100

Birkin, Derek, Sir, Chm. Bd.--The RTZ Corporation PLC, London, United Kingdom; *Int'l*, pg. 1118

Birks, H. Jonathan, Chm. Bd.--Henry Birks & Sons (1993) Inc., Montreal, Canada; *Int'l*, pg. 196

Birnbach, Gerald, Chm. Bd., Pres. & Chief Exec. Officer--Rowe Furniture Corp., Mc Lean, VA; *U.S. Public*, pg. 1410

Birney, Arthur A., Chm. Bd.--Washington Real Estate Investment Trust, Kensington, MD; *U.S. Public*, pg. 1743

Bischoff, Manfred, Dr., Chm. Bd.--Daimler-Benz Aerospace AG, Munich, Germany; *Int'l*, pg. 367

Bischoff, Win, Chm. Bd.--Schroders PLC, London, United Kingdom; *Int'l*, pg. 1210

Bishko, Roy Collin, Chm. Bd.--Tie Rack plc, Brentford, United Kingdom; *Int'l*, pg. 1389

Bishop, Benjamin M., Chm. Bd. & Chief Exec. Officer--The Western Group, Saint Louis, MO; *U.S. Private*, pg. 1165

Bishop, Robert R., Chm. Bd.-Silicon Graphics World Trade--Silicon Graphics, Inc., Mountain View, CA; *U.S. Public*, pg. 1473

Bishop, Thomas A., Chm. Bd. & Chief Exec. Officer--California State Bank, West Covina, CA; *U.S. Public*, pg. 294

Bishop, Vernon, Chm. Bd. & Chief Exec. Officer--Lebanon Seaboard Corporation, Lebanon, PA; *U.S. Private*, pg. 656

Bissell, John M., Chm. Bd.--Bissell Inc., Grand Rapids, MI; *U.S. Private*, pg. 145

Bither, Richard A., PE, Chm. Bd., Pres. & Chief Exec. Officer--Giffels Associates, Inc., Southfield, MI; *U.S. Private*, pg. 452

Bitter, Edwin W., Chm. Bd.--Scalamandre, Inc., Long Island City, NY; *U.S. Private*, pg. 969

Bixby, B.C., Chm. Bd.--Bixby International Corp., Newburyport, MA; *U.S. Private*, pg. 146

Bixby, Joseph R., Chm. Bd.--Kansas City Life Insurance Co., Kansas City, MO; *U.S. Public*, pg. 942

Bixby, Walter E., Chm. Bd.--Sunset Life Insurance Co. of America, Olympia, WA; *U.S. Public*, pg. 943

Bixby, Walter E., Chm. Bd. & Chief Exec. Officer--Old American Insurance Co., Kansas City, MO; *U.S. Public*, pg. 943

Bjernfalk, Bengt, Chm.--ITT Flygt Corporation, Trumbull, CT; *U.S. Public*, pg. 860

Bjorny, Trond, Chm. Bd.--Norsk Vekst ASA, Oslo, Norway; *Int'l*, pg. 965

Bjorny, Trond, Chm. Bd.--Kaldnes Heavy Lift Trucks, Tonsberg, Norway; *Int'l*, pg. 965

Blaauw, A.C.W., Chm. Bd. & Pres.--Meco Development Limited, Hong Kong, Hong Kong; *Int'l*, pg. 852

Black, C. Robert, Chm. & Pres.--Texaco Overseas Holdings Inc., White Plains, NY; *U.S. Public*, pg. 1583

Black, Conrad M., Chm. Bd. & Chief Exec. Officer--Hollinger Inc., Vancouver, Canada; *Int'l*, pg. 630

Black, Conrad M., Chm. Bd. & Chief Exec. Officer--Southam Inc., Don Mills, Canada; *Int'l*, pg. 631

Black, Frank C., Chm. Bd. & Pres.--Vogler Motor Company, Inc., Carbondale, IL; *U.S. Private*, pg. 1143

Black, James, Chm. Bd. & Pres.--Johnson County Farm Bureau Co-op, Franklin, IN; *U.S. Private*, pg. 591

Black, James T., Chm. Bd.--Petro-Canada, Calgary, Canada; *Int'l*, pg. 1041

Black, L. David, Chm. Bd., Pres., & Chief Exec. Officer--JLG Industries, Inc., McConnellsburg, PA; *U.S. Public*, pg. 918

Black, L.K., Chm. Bd.--Teleflex Incorporated, Plymouth Meeting, PA; *U.S. Public*, pg. 1569

Black, Lennox K., Chm. Bd.--Penn Virginia Corporation, Radnor, PA; *U.S. Public*, pg. 1271

Black, Leon, Chm. Bd.--Telemundo Group, Inc., Hialeah, FL; *U.S. Public*, pg. 1570

Black, Scott, Chm. & Chief Exec. Officer--Black Rogers Sullivan Goodnight, Inc., Houston, TX; *U.S. Private*, pg. 147

Black, Stuart M., Chm. Bd.--Black & Co., Decatur, IL; *U.S. Private*, pg. 146

Black, William H., II, Chm. Bd.--Black Cadillac Olds, Inc., Greensboro, NC; *U.S. Private*, pg. 146

Blackhall, Rick Scott, Deputy Grp. Chm.--Batey Ads Singapore, Singapore, Singapore; *Int'l*, pg. 170

Blackwell, Richard M., Chm. Bd.--B.H. Blackwell Ltd., Oxford, United Kingdom; *Int'l*, pg. 197

Blair, Michael D., Chm. Bd. & Chief Exec. Officer--Cyborg Systems, Inc., Chicago, IL; *U.S. Private*, pg. 299

Blair, R. Cary, Chm. Bd., Pres. & Chief Exec. Officer--Westfield Companies, Westfield Center, OH; *U.S. Private*, pg. 1169

Blake, Norman P., Jr., Chm. Bd., Pres. & Chief Exec. Officer--USF&G Corporation, Baltimore, MD; *U.S. Public*, pg. 1659

Blakeman, Raymond H., Chm. Bd.--Met-Coil Systems Corp., Cedar Rapids, IA; *U.S. Public*, pg. 1099

Blampied, P.G., Chm. Bd.--Barclays Bank Finance Co. (Jersey) Ltd., Saint Helier, United Kingdom; *Int'l*, pg. 165

Blanch, E.W., Jr., Chm. Bd. & Chief Exec. Officer--E.W. Blanch Wholesale Insurance Services Inc., Minneapolis, MN; *U.S. Public*, pg. 236

Blanch, Edgar W., Jr., Chm. Bd., Chief Exec. Officer--E.W. Blanch Holdings, Inc., Minneapolis, MN; *U.S. Public*, pg. 236

Blanchard, J.A.(Gus), III, Chm. Bd., Pres. & Chief Exec. Officer--Deluxe Corporation, Shoreview, MN; *U.S. Public*, *pg. 498*

Blanchard, James H., Chm. Bd. & Chief Exec. Officer--Synovus Financial Corp., Columbus, GA; *U.S. Public*, pg. 1548

Blanchard, Kenneth E., Chm. Bd., Pres. & Chief Exec. Officer--Phonetics, Inc., Aston, PA; *U.S. Private*, pg. 863

Blanchard, Roger, Chm. Bd.--ACR Industries Inc., Macomb Township, MI; *U.S. Private*, pg. 3

Bland, Christopher, Sir, Chm. Bd.--NFC plc, London, United Kingdom; *Int'l*, pg. 901

Bland, Christopher, Sir, Chm. Bd.--Life Sciences International Plc, London, United Kingdom; *U.S. Public*, pg. 1594

Bland, Peter G., Chm. Bd.--Fleet Capital Corporation, Glastonbury, CT; *U.S. Public*, pg. 649

Blank, Martin J., Chm. Bd., Chief Oper. Officer & Sec.--Automobile Protection Corporation-APCO, Atlanta, GA; *U.S. Public*, pg. 150

Blank, Matthew C., Chm. Bd.--Showtime Networks Inc., New York, NY; *U.S. Private*, pg. 779

Blankenship, C. Ronald, Chm. Bd.--Security Capital Pacific Trust, El Paso, TX; *U.S. Private*, pg. 981

Blankenship, Don L., Chm. Bd., Pres. & Chief Exec. Officer--A.T. Massey Coal Company, Inc., Richmond, VA; *U.S. Public*, pg. 660

Blankley, Walter E., Chm. Bd. & Chief Exec. Officer--AMETEK, Inc., Paoli, PA; *U.S. Public*, pg. 99

Blatt, Lee N., Chm. Bd.--Herley Industries, Inc., Lancaster, PA; *U.S. Public*, pg. 811

Blattner, Simon J., Jr., Co-Chm. Bd. & Co-Chief Exec. Officer--Rittenhouse Inc., Park Ridge, IL; *U.S. Private*, pg. 933

Blau, Barry, Chm. Bd. & Chief Exec. Officer--Blau Marketing Technologies, Inc., Wilton, CT; *U.S. Private*, pg. 148

Blau, Harvey R., Chm. Bd. & Chief Exec. Officer--Aeroflex Incorporated, Plainview, NY; *U.S. Public*, pg. 23

Blau, Harvey R., Chm. Bd.--Griffon Corp., Jericho, NY; *U.S. Public*, pg. 766

Blauer, Charles, Chm. Bd., Pres.,Chief Exec. Officer & Treas.--Blauer Manufacturing Co., Inc., Boston, MA; *U.S. Private*, pg. 149

Blennow, Rutger, Chm. Bd.--Skandinaviska Enskilda Banken South East Asia Limited, Singapore, Singapore; *Int'l*, pg. 1260

Blessing, Floyd K., Chm. Bd.--Southern States Cooperative, Inc., Richmond, VA; *U.S. Private*, pg. 1017

Blessios, Nicholaos, Chm.--Olympic Airways, New York, NY; *Int'l*, pg. 1004

Blessios, Nicolas, Chm. Bd.--Olympic Airways, S.A., Athens, Greece; *Int'l*, pg. 1004

Blethen, Frank A., Chm. Bd., Chief Exec. Officer & Publr.--Seattle Times Company, Seattle, WA; *U.S. Private*, pg. 980

Bliss, David C., Chm. Bd., Pres. & Chief Exec. Oficer--Quality Stores Inc., Muskegon, MI; *U.S. Private*, pg. 899

Bloch, Henry W., Chm. Bd.--H & R Block, Inc., Kansas City, MO; *U.S. Public*, pg. 770

Block, Alvin V., Chm. Bd.--ESA, Inc., Chelmsford, MA; *U.S. Private*, pg. 354

Block, Annabelle, Chm. Bd.--Annabelle Candy Company, Inc., Hayward, CA; *U.S. Private*, pg. 75

Block, James A., Chm. Bd.--Block Drug Company, Inc., Jersey City, NJ; *U.S. Public*, pg. 236

Block, Leonard, Sr. Chm. Bd.--Block Drug Company, Inc., Jersey City, NJ; *U.S. Public*, pg. 236

Block, William, Chm. Bd.--Blade Communications, Inc., Toledo, OH; *U.S. Private*, pg. 147

Blodgett, Mark, Chm. Bd. & Chief Exec. Officer--Stocker & Yale, Inc., Salem, NH; *U.S. Public*, pg. 1518

Bloem, H.J., Chm.--Atlas Tag & Label Inc., Neenah, WI; *U.S. Private*, pg. 145

Blommer, Henry, Jr., Chm. Bd.--Blommer Chocolate Co., Chicago, IL; *U.S. Private*, pg. 150

Blomquist, Robert O., Chm. Bd.--Lutheran Brotherhood, Minneapolis, MN; *U.S. Private*, pg. 681

Blondeau, Gilles, Chm. Bd. & Chief Exec. Officer--Domtar Inc., Montreal, Canada; *Int'l*, pg. 416

Blondeau, Jacques, Chm. Bd. & Chief Exec. Officer--SCOR, Paris, France; *Int'l*, pg. 1152

Blondeau, Jacques, Chm.--SCOR U.S. Corporation, New York, NY; *Int'l*, pg. 1152

Blondeau, Jean, Chm. Bd.--Banque PSA Finance Holding, Paris, France; *Int'l*, pg. 1021

Bloom, Geoffrey B., Chm. Bd. & Chief Exec. Officer--Wolverine World Wide, Inc., Rockford, MI; *U.S. Public*, pg. 1775

Bloom, Martin J., Co-Chm. Bd.--Valley Forge Corporation, San Rafael, CA; *U.S. Public*, pg. 1705

Bloom, Robert H., Chm. Bd. & Chief Exec. Officer--Publicis/Bloom Inc., New York, NY; *Int'l*, pg. 470

Bloomberg, Stuart J., Chm.--ABC Inc., Los Angeles, CA; *U.S. Public*, pg. 511

Blount, S. Robert, Chm. Bd.--Meadowcraft, Inc., Birmingham, AL; *U.S. Private*, pg. 725

Blount, W. "Red", Chm. Bd.--Blount, Inc. Sporting Equipment Group, Lewiston, ID; *U.S. Public*, pg. 238

Blount, Winton M., Chm. Bd.--Blount International, Inc., Montgomery, AL; *U.S. Public*, pg. 237

Blount, Winton M., Chm. Bd.--Blount, Inc., Montgomery, AL; *U.S. Public*, pg. 238

Bloxham, J.L., Chm. & Mng. Dir.--Cincinnati Milacron U.K. Limited, Birmingham, United Kingdom; *U.S. Public*, pg. 368

Blue, J. Neal, Chm. Bd., Pres. & Chief Exec. Officer--General Atomics, San Diego, CA; *U.S. Private*, pg. 443

Bluestone, Stanton, Chm. Bd. & Pres.--Boston Store, Milwaukee, WI; *U.S. Public*, pg. 309

Bluestone, Stanton J., Chm. Bd. & Chief Exec. Officer--Carson Pirie Scott & Co., Milwaukee, WI; *U.S. Public*, pg. 309

Blum, Georges, Chm. Bd.--Swiss Bank Corporation, Basel, Switzerland; *Int'l*, pg. 1329

Blumberg, Donald D., Chm. Bd. & Treas.--Blumberg Communications Inc., Minneapolis, MN; *U.S. Public*, pg. 305

Blumenthahl, Adam, Chm. Bd.--Four-S Baking Company, Los Angeles, CA; *U.S. Private*, pg. 422

Blumenthal, Bernard, Chm. Bd.--Lion Brand Yarn Co., New York, NY; *U.S. Private*, pg. 669

Blumenthal, Herman, Chm. Bd. & Chief Exec. Officer--Radiator Specialty Company, Charlotte, NC; *U.S. Private*, pg. 906

Blumenthal, Robert, Chm. Bd.--The Penn Companies, Philadelphia, PA; *U.S. Private*, pg. 849

Blumenthal, Robert S., Chm. Bd.--Advance Mechanical Systems, Inc., Mount Prospect, IL; *U.S. Private*, pg. 18

Blumenthal, Thomas A., Chm. Bd, Pres. & Chief Exec. Officer--Norwalk Powdered Metals, Inc., Norwalk, CT; *U.S. Private*, pg. 808

Blundell, William, Chm. Bd.--Lawson Mardon Packaging Inc., Mississauga, Canada; *Int'l*, pg. 68

Blundell, William R.C., Chm. Bd.--Manulife Financial (The Manufacturers Life Insurance Company), Toronto, Canada; *Int'l*, pg. 840

Blystone, John B., Chm. Bd., Pres. & Chief Exec. Officer--SPX Corporation, Muskegon, MI; *U.S. Public*, pg. 1420

Bo, Hans, Chm. Bd.--Union Bank of Norway, Oslo, Norway; *Int'l*, pg. 1439

Bobins, Norman, Vice Chm. & Chief Lending Officer--ABN/LaSalle North America Inc., Chicago, IL; *Int'l*, pg. 11

Bobit, Edward J., Chm. Bd. & Chief Exec. Officer--Bobit Publishing Company, Torrance, CA; *U.S. Private*, pg. 154

Boch, Ernest J., Chm. Bd.--Subaru of New England, Inc., Norwood, MA; *Int'l*, pg. 523

Bocock, Frederic Scott, Chm. Bd.--Scott & Stringfellow Capital Management, Inc., Richmond, VA; *U.S. Public*, pg. 1445

Boddie, Ben Mayo, Chm. Bd.--Boddie-Noell Enterprises Inc., Rocky Mount, NC; *U.S. Private*, pg. 154

Bodeen, George H., Chm. Bd.--Lindberg Corporation, Rosemont, IL; *U.S. Public*, pg. 999

Bodin, Manfred, Dr., Chm.-Bd. of Mngmt.--Norddeutsche Landesbank (NORD/LB), Hannover, Germany; *Int'l*, pg. 957

Bodine, Paul J., Chm. Bd.--Bodine Electric Company, Chicago, IL; *U.S. Private*, pg. 154

Bodman, James W., Co-Chm. & Chief Exec. Officer--Vienna Sausage Mfg. Co., Chicago, IL; *U.S. Private*, pg. 1139

Bodman, Samuel W., Chm. Bd. & Chief Exec. Officer--Cabot Corporation, Boston, MA; *U.S. Public*, pg. 288

Bodson, Baron, Chm. Bd.--Electrabel S.A., Brussels, Belgium; *Int'l*, pg. 436

Boehm, William J., Chm. Bd., Pres. & Chief Exec. Officer--Connector Manufacturing Company, Hamilton, OH; *U.S. Private*, pg. 264

Boermons, Huib, Chm. of the Mng. Bd.--RTL4, Luxembourg, Luxembourg; *Int'l*, pg. 561

Boesch, Fritz F., Chm. Bd.--Feintool AG Lyss, Lyss, Switzerland; *Int'l*, pg. 479

Boetius, Jan, Dr., Chm.-Bd. of Mgmnt.--Deutsche Krankenversicherung AG, Cologne, Germany; *Int'l*, pg. 58

Boetticher, Jeffrey M., Chm. Bd. & Chief Exec. Officer--Black Box Corporation of PA, Lawrence, PA; *U.S. Public*, pg. 235

Bogen, Ernest, Chm. Bd.--Ark Restaurants Corp., New York, NY; *U.S. Public*, pg. 129

Bogle, John C., Sr. Chm.--The Vanguard Group, Inc., Valley Forge, PA; *U.S. Private*, pg. 1133

Boh, Robert H., Chm. Bd.--Boh Bros. Construction Co., LLC, New Orleans, LA; *U.S. Private*, pg. 154

Boh, Robert H., Chm. Bd.--Hibernia Corporation, New Orleans, LA; *U.S. Public*, pg. 825

Bohannon, Robert H., Chm. Bd., Pres. & Chief Exec. Officer--Viad Corp, Phoenix, AZ; *U.S. Public*, pg. 1718

Bohannon, Robert H., Chm. Bd.--Dobbs International Services, Inc., Memphis, TN; *U.S. Public*, pg. 1718

Bohbot, Allen J., Chm. & Chief Exec. Officer--Quantum Media International, Inc., New York, NY; *U.S. Private*, pg. 899

Bohla, Ulf, Chm. Bd.--o.tel.o Communications GmbH Co., Dusseldorf, Germany; *Int'l*, pg. 1082

Bohm, Friedrich K.M., Chm. Bd.--NBBJ, Columbus, OH; *U.S. Private*, pg. 771

Bohn, Robert G., Chm. Bd. & Chief Exec. Officer--Preferred Utilities Manufacturing Corp., Danbury, CT; *U.S. Private*, pg. 881

Bohn, Robert G., Chm. Bd. & Chief Exec. Officer--Preferred Instruments, Danbury, CT; *U.S. Private*, pg. 881

Boisrond, Etienne, Chm.--Young & Rubicam France, Paris, France; *U.S. Private*, pg. 1199

Boisset, Alain, Chm.--JANIN, Montreal, Canada; *Int'l*, pg. 823

Boisson, P., Chm. Bd.--Eramet-SLN, Paris, France; *Int'l*, pg. 661

Boix-Vives, Laurent, Chm. Bd.--Rossignol S.A., Voiron, France; *Int'l*, pg. 1127

Bok, Joan T., Chm. Bd.--New England Electric System, Westborough, MA; *U.S. Public*, pg. 1171

Boker, Karl, Chm. Bd.--Wiemer und Trachte, Dortmund, Germany; *Int'l*, pg. 824

Boklund, Thomas B., Chm. Bd. & Chief Exec. Officer--Oregon Steel Mills Inc., Portland, OR; *U.S. Public*, pg. 1230

Boland, David, Chm. Bd., Pres. & Chief Exec. Officer--David Boland, Inc., Titusville, FL; *U.S. Private*, pg. 154

Bolch, Carl, Jr., Chm. Bd. & Chief Exec. Officer--Racetrac Petroleum, Inc., Smyrna, GA; *U.S. Private*, pg. 906

Bolduc, J.P., Chm. Bd.--Crowe Rope Industries L.L.C., Waterville, ME; *U.S. Private*, pg. 291

Bolduc, John, Chm. Bd.--Johnstown Corporation, Johnstown, PA; *U.S. Private*, pg. 595

Bolender, David F., Chm. Bd.--Electro Scientific Industries, Inc., Portland, OR; *U.S. Public*, pg. 568

Boler, John, Chm. Bd. & Pres.--Boler Company, Itasca, IL; *U.S. Private*, pg. 155

Bolger, Ronald J., Chm. Bd.--Telecom Eireann, Dublin, Ireland; *Int'l*, pg. 1362

Bolinger, Robert S., Chm. Bd. & Chief Exec. Officer--Farmers First Bank, Lititz, PA; *U.S. Public*, pg. 1542

Boll, John, Chm. Bd.--Chateau Communities, Inc., Englewood, CO; *U.S. Public*, pg. 341

Bolle, M.B., Chm. Bd. & Gen. Mgr.--Westland/Utrecht Hypotheekbank, Amsterdam, Netherlands; *Int'l*, pg. 647

Bollerer, Fred L., Chm. Bd. & Chief Exec. Officer--First American Metro Corp., Mc Lean, VA; *U.S. Public*, pg. 640

Bolliger, Richard, Chm. Bd.--Bolliger, Inc., Stamford, CT; *U.S. Private*, pg. 155

Bollinger, Don M., Chm. Bd. & Chief Exec. Officer--The John C. Groub Company Inc., Seymour, IN; *U.S. Private*, pg. 484

Bollinger, Glenn D., Chm. Bd. & Chief Exec. Officer--Bollinger Industries Inc., Grand Prairie, TX; *U.S. Public*, pg. 243

Bologna, William J., Chm. Bd.--Columbia Laboratories, Inc., Miami, FL; *U.S. Public*, pg. 405

Bolsover, J.D., Chm.--Baring Asset Management, London, United Kingdom; *Int'l*, pg. 648

Bolton, Brian J., Chm. Bd. & Chief Exec. Officer--Overhead Door Corporation, Dallas, TX; *U.S. Private*, pg. 822

Bolton, Charles P., Chm. Bd.--Brittany Corporation, Cleveland, OH; *U.S. Private*, pg. 169

Bolton, William J., Chm.--Graham Miller Group Limited, London, United Kingdom; *U.S. Public*, pg. 458

Boman, Charles F., Chm. Bd.--SouthTrust Bank, Gadsden, Gadsden, AL; *U.S. Public*, pg. 1491

Bon, Michel, Chm. Bd.--France Telecom, Paris, France; *Int'l*, pg. 503

Bonafe, Pierre, Chm.-Systems Sector--Alcatel Alsthom Compagnie Generale D'Electricite, Paris, France; *Int'l*, pg. 52

Bond, John, Chm. Bd.--HSBC Holdings plc, London, United Kingdom; *Int'l*, pg. 579

Bond, John, Chm. Bd.--Midland Bank PLC, London, United Kingdom; *Int'l*, pg. 580

Bond, John R.H., Chm. Bd.--HongKong Bank of Canada, Vancouver, Canada; *Int'l*, pg. 583

Bond, Jonathan, Co-Chm.--Kirshenbaum, Bond & Partners, New York, NY; *U.S. Private*, pg. 624

Bond, Richard J., Chm. Bd.--Security Bank & Trust Co., Vincennes, IN; *U.S. Public*, pg. 1217

Bondi, Enrico, Dep. Chm.--Fondiaria S.P.A., Florence, Italy; *Int'l*, pg. 496

Bonds, Patrick J., Chm.--Hilb, Rogal and Hamilton Company of Dallas, Dallas, TX; *U.S. Public*, pg. 827

Bongrain, Jean Noel, Chm. Bd.--BC-USA, New Holland, PA; *Int'l*, pg. 201

Bonham, Derek, Chm. Bd.--Imperial Tobacco Group, Ltd., Bristol, United Kingdom; *Int'l*, pg. 666

Bonham, Donald L., Chm. Bd.--Fiesta Mart Inc., Houston, TX; *U.S. Private*, pg. 403

Boniols, Charles, Chm. Bd.--Model Glass Company, Anaheim, CA; *U.S. Private*, pg. 754

Bonnet, Denis, Chm. & Chief Exec. Officer-OgilvyOne worldwide Paris--Ogilvy & Mather Worldwide, Inc., New York, NY; *Int'l*, pg. 1483

Bonney, Weston, Chm. Bd.--PG Vinyl Windows/PG Proglass Construction, Westbrook, ME; *U.S. Private*, pg. 826

Bonsignore, Michael R., Chm. Bd. & Chief Exec. Officer--Honeywell Inc., Minneapolis, MN; *U.S. Public*, pg. 833

Bontrager, John, Chm. Bd. & Pres.--Signature Inns, Inc., Indianapolis, IN; *U.S. Public*, pg. 1473

Bontrager, Wilbur, Chm. Bd.--Jayco Inc., Middlebury, IN; *U.S. Private*, pg. 583

Boon, John, Chm.--Mills & Boon Ltd., Richmond, United Kingdom; *Int'l*, pg. 1402

Boon, Sim Kee, Exec. Chm.--Keppel Corporation Limited, Singapore, Singapore; *Int'l*, pg. 731

Boon, Y.C., Chm. Bd.--Jardine Matheson (Singapore) Ltd, Singapore, Singapore; *Int'l*, pg. 705

Boone, Thomas H., Chm. Bd. & Chief Exec. Officer--Countrywide Agency, Inc., Pasadena, CA; *U.S. Public*, pg. 452

Boone, Thomas H., Chm. Bd. & Chief Oper. Officer--Countrywide Title Corporation, Pasadena, CA; *U.S. Public*, pg. 453

Boonstra, C., Chm. Bd. & Pres.--Philips Electronics N.V., Eindhoven, Netherlands; *Int'l*, pg. 1051

Boonyaratevej, Dolchai, Chm. Bd.--Dentsu Young & Rubicam Ltd. (Bangkok), Bangkok, Thailand; *U.S. Private*, pg. 325

Booth, John J., Acting Chm. Bd., Pres. & Chief Exec. Officer--INCSTAR Corporation, Stillwater, MN; *Int'l*, pg. 483

Booth, Ralph H., II, Chm. Bd. & Chief Fin. Officer--Booth American, Detroit, MI; *U.S. Private*, pg. 156

Borba, George, Chm. Bd.--CVB Financial Corp., Ontario, CA; *U.S. Public*, pg. 286

Borchardt, Herbert H., Co-Chm. Bd.--Recoton Corporation, Lake Mary, FL; *U.S. Public*, pg. 1369

Borchardt, Robert L., Co-Chm. Bd, Pres. & Chief Exec. Officer--Recoton Corporation, Lake Mary, FL; *U.S. Public*, pg. 1369

Borchardt, Robert L., Chm. Bd. & Chief Exec. Officer--Interact Accessories, Inc., Hunt Valley, MD; *U.S. Public*, pg. 1369

Borchardt, Robert L., Chm. Bd. & Chief Exec. Officer--Christie Design, Chatsworth, CA; *U.S. Public*, pg. 1369

Borck, Chester E., Chm. Bd.--Country Home Bakery, Inc., Bridgeport, CT; *U.S. Private*, pg. 278

Bordas, G., Chm. & Gen. Mgr.--Nationale-Nederlanden, Budapest, Hungary; *Int'l*, pg. 650

Borden, Lorraine, Chm. Bd., Chief Exec. Officer, Chief Fin. Officer, Pres.--Great Scott Advertising Co. Inc., New York, NY; *U.S. Private*, pg. 475

Bordon, M. Scott, Chm. Bd.--Chicago Mercantile Exchange, Chicago, IL; *U.S. Private*, pg. 235

Boreham, Roland S., Jr., Chm. Bd.--Baldor Electric Company, Fort Smith, AR; *U.S. Public*, pg. 168

Borel, Daniel, Chm. Bd.--Logitech International SA, Morges, Switzerland; *Int'l*, pg. 815

Boren, L.E., Chm. Bd. & Chief Exec. Officer--Badger Equipment Co., Winona, MN; *U.S. Private*, pg. 102

Boren, Leland E., Chm. Bd., Pres. & Chief Exec. Officer--Avis Industrial Corporation, Upland, IN; *U.S. Private*, pg. 102

Borer, Edward T., Chm. Bd.--EnergyNorth, Inc., Manchester, NH; *U.S. Public*, pg. 581

Borg, Malcolm A., Chm. Bd., Pres. & Chief Exec. Officer--Macromedia Incorporated, Hackensack, NJ; *U.S. Private*, pg. 693

Borgeaud, Pierre, Chm. Bd.--Sulzer Ltd., Winterthur, Switzerland; *Int'l*, pg. 1305

Borghese, Francesco, Chm. Bd. & Pres.--Orlane, Inc., New York, NY; *Int'l*, pg. 1011

Borick, Louis L., Chm. Bd. & Pres.--Superior Industries International, Inc., Van Nuys, CA; *U.S. Public*, pg. 1539

Boris, James R., Chm. & Chief Exec. Officer--EVEREN Securities, Inc., Chicago, IL; *U.S. Public*, pg. 597

Borislow, Daniel, Chm. Bd. & Chief Exec. Officer--Tel-Save Holdings, Inc., New Hope, PA; *U.S. Public*, pg. 1568

Borland, Clifford R., Chm. Bd. & Chief Exec. Officer--NS Group, Inc., Newport, KY; *U.S. Public*, pg. 1147

Borman, Frank, Chm. Bd.--DBT Online, Inc., Las Vegas, NV; *U.S. Public*, pg. 472

Born, Allen, Chm. Bd. & Chief Exec. Officer--Alumax Inc., Atlanta, GA; *U.S. Public*, pg. 59

Bornheim, Hans Georg, Chm. Bd.--Black & Decker G.m.b.H., Idstein, Germany; *U.S. Public*, pg. 234

Bornhuetter, Ronald L., Chm. Bd. & Chief Exec. Officer--NAC Re Corp., Greenwich, CT; *U.S. Public*, pg. 1144
Bornhuetter, Ronald L., Chm. Bd.--Greenwich Insurance Company, Greenwich, CT; *U.S. Public*, pg. 1144
Bornhuetter, Ronald L., Chm. Bd.--Indian Harbor Insurance Company, Greenwich, CT; *U.S. Public*, pg. 1144
Borowsky, I.J., Chm. Bd.--North American Publishing Company, Philadelphia, PA; *U.S. Private*, pg. 803
Borrell, Mark, Non-Exec. Chm. Bd.--Royal Doulton Plc., Stoke on Trent, United Kingdom; *Int'l*, pg. 1135
Bosch, Fritz F., Chm. Bd.--Feintool Engineering Co. Ltd., Atsugi, Japan; *Int'l*, pg. 479
Boschell, Greg, Chm. Bd. & Pres.--Wattyl, Canada Bay, Australia; *Int'l*, pg. 1488
Boschetti, G., Chm. Bd.--Iveco-Ford Truck Ltd., Watford, United Kingdom; *Int'l*, pg. 484
Boscov, Albert, Chm. Bd. & Chief Exec. Officer--Boscov's Department Store, Inc., Reading, PA; *U.S. Private*, pg. 160
Bose, Amar G., Dr., Chm. Bd. & Tech. Dir.--Bose Corporation, Framingham, MA; *U.S. Private*, pg. 160
Boshart, James S., III, Vice Chm.--Salomon Smith Barney Holdings, Inc., New York, NY; *U.S. Public*, pg. 1633
Boss, Bradford R., Chm. Bd.--A.T. Cross Co., Lincoln, RI; *U.S. Public*, pg. 460
Bossett, Barry P., Chm. Bd. & Chief Exec. Officer--Scotsman Holding Inc., Baltimore, MD; *U.S. Private*, pg. 976
Bossidy, Lawrence A., Chm. Bd. & Chief Exec. Officer--AlliedSignal Inc., Morristown, NJ; *U.S. Public*, pg. 49
Bossier, Albert L., Jr., Chm. Bd., Pres. & Chief Exec. Officer--Avondale Industries, Inc., Avondale, LA; *U.S. Public*, pg. 156
Bostock, Roy J., Chm. & Chief Exec. Officer--The MacManus Group, Inc., New York, NY; *U.S. Private*, pg. 692
Bosworth, Michael F., Chm. Bd., Pres. & Chief Exec. Officer--OrCAD Inc., Beaverton, OR; *U.S. Public*, pg. 1230
Botin, Emilio, Chm. Bd. & Chief Exec. Officer--Banco Santander, Madrid, Spain; *Int'l*, pg. 143
Botta, Andrea, Chm. Bd.--Western Industries, Inc., Milwaukee, WI; *U.S. Private*, pg. 1165
Botta, G. Andrea, Chm. Bd.--Constitution Holding Inc., New York, NY; *Int'l*, pg. 467
Botta, G. Andrea, Chm. Bd.--Constitution Re Corp., New York, NY; *Int'l*, pg. 467
Bottcher, Eric, Chm.--Suez Nederland Securities N.V., Amsterdam, Netherlands; *Int'l*, pg. 314
Bottorff, Dennis C., Chm. Bd., Pres. & Chief Exec. Officer--First American Corporation, Nashville, TN; *U.S. Public*, pg. 624
Botts, William W., Chm. Bd., Pres. & Chief Exec. Officer--O.I. Corporation, College Station, TX; *U.S. Public*, pg. 1208
Botvin, George B., Chm. Bd., Chief Exec. Officer & Treas.--ACS Industries, Inc., Woonsocket, RI; *U.S. Private*, pg. 3
Bouchard, John E., III, Chm. Bd. & Pres.--John Bouchard & Sons Company, Nashville, TN; *U.S. Private*, pg. 161
Boucher, Allen C., Chm. Bd.--Caldwell Manufacturing Company, Rochester, NY; *U.S. Private*, pg. 200
Bouckaert, G.P., Chm. Bd. & Chief Exec. Officer--Nooter Corporation, Saint Louis, MO; *U.S. Private*, pg. 801
Boudieau, Edward J., Jr., Chm. & Chief Exec. Officer--Berkeley Financial Group, Boston, MA; *U.S. Private*, pg. 589
Bougard, Jean, Chm. Bd.--Systra-Sofretu-Sofrerail, Paris, France; *Int'l*, pg. 1165
Bougie, Jacques, Chm. Bd.--Alcan Aluminum Corporation, Cleveland, OH; *Int'l*, pg. 50
Bouhelier, Jacques, Chm. Bd. & Chief Exec. Officer--Messier-Dowty SAS, Velizy-Villacoublay, France; *Int'l*, pg. 1340
Bouley, Bruno, Chm. Bd. & Chief Exec. Officer--Dumez Construction, Malakoff, France; *Int'l*, pg. 823
Boulis, Gus, Chm. Bd., Pres. & Chief Exec. Officer--Miami Subs Corporation, Fort Lauderdale, FL; *U.S. Public*, pg. 1103
Bourguignon, Phillippe, Chm. Bd.--Club Mediterranee SA, Paris, France; *Int'l*, pg. 298
Bourland, Curtis F., Chm. Bd., Pres. & Chief Exec. Officer--Continental Graphics Holdings, Inc., Los Angeles, CA; *U.S. Private*, pg. 268
Bourlet, Jean Francois, Chm.--CAP Sesa Informatique Hospitaliere, Paris, France; *Int'l*, pg. 263
Bourne, Peter A.C., Chm.--Delta Electrical & Engineering Services Ltd., Kwai Chung, Hong Kong; *Int'l*, pg. 390
Bourns, Gordon L., Chm. Bd. & Pres.--Bourns, Inc., Riverside, CA; *U.S. Private*, pg. 161
Bourns, Gordon L., Chm. Bd.--Recon/Optical, Inc., Barrington, IL; *U.S. Private*, pg. 914
Bourven, Monique J., Chm. Bd. & Chief Exec. Officer--State Street Banque S.A., Paris, France; *U.S. Public*, pg. 1513
Boury, George, Chm. Bd.--Boury Enterprises, Wheeling, WV; *U.S. Private*, pg. 162
Boutonnat, Pierr-Louis, Chm. Bd.--EMC-Belgique, Brussels, Belgium; *Int'l*, pg. 459
Boutonnet, Edward, Chm. Bd. & Pres.--Ocean Mist Farms Corp., Castroville, CA; *U.S. Private*, pg. 811
Bouts, Larry, Chm. & Chief Exec. Officer--Six Flags Theme Parks Inc., Parsippany, NJ; *U.S. Public*, pg. 1611
Bouts, Larry D., Chm. Bd. & Chief Exec. Officer--Six Flags Great Adventure Theme Park & Wild Safari Animal Park, Jackson, NJ; *U.S. Public*, pg. 1611
Bouwman, T.G.G., Chm. Bd.--VNU Tijdschriftengroep Nederland Bv, Amstelveen, Netherlands; *Int'l*, pg. 1445
Bouygues, Martin, Chm. Bd. & Chief Exec. Officer--Bouygues, Saint Quentin-en-Yvelines, France; *Int'l*, pg. 206
Bovaird, W.J., Chm. Bd., Pres. & Chief Exec. Officer--Bovaird Supply Co., Tulsa, OK; *U.S. Private*, pg. 162
Bovie, F., Chm. Bd.--ESAB Consumables, Hanover, PA; *Int'l*, pg. 281
Bowe, Richard E., Chm. Bd.--Ellicott Machine Corporation International, Baltimore, MD; *U.S. Private*, pg. 372
Bowen, Robert, Chm. Bd. & Chief Exec. Officer--Group 1 Software, Inc., Lanham, MD; *U.S. Public*, pg. 417
Bowkett, Alan, Chm. Bd.--Magnet Ltd., Keighley, United Kingdom; *Int'l*, pg. 188
Bowlin, Mike R., Chm. Bd. & Chief Exec. Officer--Atlantic Richfield Company, Los Angeles, CA; *U.S. Public*, pg. 144
Bowman, Brian, Chm. Bd. & Chief Fin. Officer--Ryan Herco Products Corp., Burbank, CA; *U.S. Private*, pg. 953
Bowman, C.H., Chm. Bd.--BP Oil Co., Cleveland, OH; *Int'l*, pg. 220
Bowman, Harry W., Chm. Bd., Pres. & Chief Exec. Officer--Outboard Marine Corporation, Waukegan, IL; *U.S. Private*, pg. 478
Box, Sam W., Chm. Bd., Pres. & Chief Exec. Officer--Foster Wheeler Environmental Corporation, Livingston, NJ; *U.S.* Public, pg. 677
Boxall, Gerald, Chm. & Chief Exec. Officer--Vickers Defence Systems, Armstrong Works, Newcastle upon Tyne, United Kingdom; *Int'l*, pg. 1467
Boyce, Donald N., Chm. Bd., Pres. & Chief Exec. Officer--IDEX Corporation, Northbrook, IL; *U.S. Public*, pg. 862
Boyce, Frank L., Chm. Bd.--Sioux Falls Construction Company, Sioux Falls, SD; *U.S. Private*, pg. 1003
Boyd, Bill, Chm. Bd.--Muzak Limited Partnership, Seattle, WA; *U.S. Private*, pg. 222
Boyd, L., Chm.--Amic Industries Limited, Johanesburg, South Africa; *Int'l*, pg. 76
Boyd, William S., Chm. Bd. & Chief Exec. Officer--Boyd Gaming Corporation, Las Vegas, NV; *U.S. Public*, pg. 249
Boyd, William W., Chm. Bd.--Sterling Plumbing Group, Inc., Rolling Meadows, IL; *U.S. Private*, pg. 630
Boyle, Patrick G., Chm. Bd.--Monitor Capital Advisors Inc., Princeton, NJ; *U.S. Private*, pg. 795
Boyle, R.E., Chm. Bd., Pres. & Chief Exec. Officer--Ormet Corporation, Wheeling, WV; *U.S. Private*, pg. 820
Boyle, Richard, Chm. Bd. & Chief Exec. Officer--Spinnaker Industries, Inc., Dallas, TX; *U.S. Public*, pg. 1022
Boze, Jimmy R., Chm. Bd., Pres. & Chief Exec. Officer--The Security Bank, Harrison, Harrison, AR; *U.S. Public*, pg. 630
Bozic, Michael, Chm. Bd. & Chief Exec. Officer--Levitz Furniture Incorporated, Boca Raton, FL; *U.S. Public*, pg. 990
Bozic, Michael, Chm. Bd. & Chief Exec. Officer--John M. Smyth Co., Downers Grove, IL; *U.S. Public*, pg. 990
Bozzuto, Adam J., Chm. Bd.--Bozzuto's Inc., Cheshire, CT; *U.S. Public*, pg. 249
Brabson, John A., Chm. Bd.--Lykes Brothers Inc., Tampa, FL; *U.S. Private*, pg. 682
Brabson, John A., Jr., Chm. Bd.--Lykes Energy, Inc., Tampa, FL; *U.S. Private*, pg. 682
Bracco, Fulvio, Dr., Chm. Bd.--Bracco S.p.A., Milan, Italy; *Int'l*, pg. 209
Bracewell, Joseph S., Chm. Bd., Pres. & Chief Exec. Officer--Century Bancshares, Inc., Washington, DC; *U.S. Public*, pg. 328
Brack, Reginald K., Chm. Bd.--People, New York, NY; *U.S. Public*, pg. 1613
Bradbury, David, Chm. Bd. & Pres.--Bradbury Company, Inc., Moundridge, KS; *U.S. Private*, pg. 163
Bradbury, Robert J., Chm. Bd.--Dolphin & Bradbury, Inc., Philadelphia, PA; *U.S. Private*, pg. 338
Braddock, James L., Chm. Bd., Pres. & Treas.--Fastec Industrial, Elkhart, IN; *U.S. Private*, pg. 397
Bradford, William E., Chm. Bd. & Chief Exec. Officer--Dresser Industries, Inc., Dallas, TX; *U.S. Public*, pg. 528
Bradley, Charles E., Chm. Bd.--Chatwins Group, Inc., Pittsburgh, PA; *U.S. Private*, pg. 231
Bradley, Charles E., Chm. Bd.--DeVlieg-Bullard Inc., Westport, CT; *U.S. Public*, pg. 502
Bradley, Charles E., Chm. Bd., Pres. & Chief Exec. Officer--Reunion Industries, Inc., Stamford, CT; *U.S. Public*, pg. 1383
Bradley, Henry H., Chm. Bd. & Treas.--News-Press & Gazette Company, Saint Joseph, MO; *U.S. Private*, pg. 797
Bradner, Larry, Chm. Bd.--Syntellect, Inc., Phoenix, AZ; *U.S.* Public, pg. 1550
Bradshaw, David L., Chm. Bd., Pres. & Chief Exec. Officer--Tipperary Corporation, Denver, CO; *U.S. Public*, pg. 1618
Bradshaw, John P., Chm. Bd. & Exec. V.P.--Hayes, Seay, Mattern & Mattern, Inc., Roanoke, VA; *U.S. Private*, pg. 513
Brady, Brian J., Chm. Bd., Pres. & Chief Exec. Officer--Dominguez Services Corporation, Long Beach, CA; *U.S. Public*, pg. 516
Brady, Charles, Chm. Bd.--Invesco Group Asset Management Ltd., London, United Kingdom; *Int'l*, pg. 685
Brady, Jack D., Chm. Bd., Pres. & Chief Exec. & Oper. Officer--Crown Andersen Inc., Peachtree City, GA; *U.S. Public*, pg. 462
Brady, Robert T., Chm. Bd., Pres. & Chief Exec. Officer--Moog Incorporated, East Aurora, NY; *U.S. Public*, pg. 1127
Braitmayer, J.W., Chm. Bd.--Mona Industries, Inc., Paterson, NJ; *U.S. Private*, pg. 756
Braka, Ivor, Chm. Bd. & Pres.--United States Realty & Investment Co., New York, NY; *U.S. Private*, pg. 1125
Brake, W.T., Chm. Bd.--Brake Bros plc, Ashford, United Kingdom; *Int'l*, pg. 210
Brakel, C. J., Chm. Bd.--Wolters Kluwer N.V., Amsterdam, Netherlands; *Int'l*, pg. 1512
Bramble, David A., Chm. Bd. & Chief Exec. Officer--David A. Bramble, Inc., Chestertown, MD; *U.S. Private*, pg. 165
Bran, Al, Chm.-Litton System--Laser Systems, Apopka, FL; *U.S. Public*, pg. 1002
Branca, Ralph M., Chm. Bd.--Quipp, Inc., Hialeah, FL; *U.S. Public*, pg. 1353
Branch, William J., Chm. & Chief Oper. Officer--Masland, Carlisle, PA; *U.S. Public*, pg. 981
Brandli, Hanspeter, Chm. Bd. & Pres.--Danzas Holding Ltd., Basel, Switzerland; *Int'l*, pg. 382
Brandon, David A., Chm. Bd., Pres. & Chief Exec. Officer--Valassis Communications, Inc., Livonia, MI; *U.S. Public*, pg. 1704
Brandrup, Douglas W., Chm. Bd.--Equity Oil Company, Salt Lake City, UT; *U.S. Public*, pg. 590
Brands, Paul A., Chm. Bd. & Chief Exec. Officer--American Management Systems, Inc., Fairfax, VA; *U.S. Public*, pg. 86
Brandt, Charlie, Chm. Bd.--Berryman Products, Inc., Arlington, TX; *U.S. Private*, pg. 138
Brandt, Richard, Chm. Bd.--Trans-Lux Corporation, Norwalk, CT; *U.S. Public*, pg. 1628
Brandt, William F. Jr., Chm. Bd.--American Woodmark Corporation, Winchester, VA; *U.S. Public*, pg. 96
Brann, Alton J., Chm. Bd. & Chief Exec. Officer--UNOVA, Inc., Beverly Hills, CA; *U.S. Public*, pg. 1698
Brann, Alton J., Chm. Bd.--Western Atlas Inc., Houston, TX; *U.S. Public*, pg. 1757
Brannan, Stanley G., Chm. Bd.--Brite Voice Systems, Inc., Heathrow, FL; *U.S. Public*, pg. 257
Brannan, Stanley G., Chm. Bd.--Brite Voice Systems, Canton, MA; *U.S. Public*, pg. 257
Branson, Philip, Chm.--First American Home Buyers Protection Corp., Van Nuys, CA; *U.S. Public*, pg. 625
Branson, Richard, Chm. Bd.--Virgin Hotel, Crathorne, United Kingdom; *Int'l*, pg. 1468
Bratt, John A., Chm. Bd.--Yorktown Tool & Die Corporation, Yorktown, IN; *U.S. Private*, pg. 1196
Bratton, George R., Chm. Bd.--I.C. Thomasson Associates, Inc., Nashville, TN; *U.S. Private*, pg. 1083
Braud, Marcel, Chm. Bd. & Pres.--Manitou BF, Ancenis, France; *Int'l*, pg. 834
Brault, Jean-Louis, Chm. Bd. & Chief Exec. Officer--Groupe GTM, Nanterre, France; *Int'l*, pg. 823
Braun, Warren L., Chm. Bd.--ComSonics, Inc., Harrisonburg, VA; *U.S. Private*, pg. 260
Brauner, Hans U., Chm. Bd.--Rheinmetall Group, Dusseldorf, Germany; *Int'l*, pg. 1108
Bready, Richard L., Chm. Bd. & Chief Exec. Officer--Nortek, Inc., Providence, RI; *U.S. Public*, pg. 1192
Breaker, Richard C., Chm. Bd.--Gerald H. Phipps, Inc., Denver, CO; *U.S. Private*, pg. 862
Breakstone, Myron, Chm. Bd.--Refrigiwear, Inc., Dahlonega, GA; *U.S. Private*, pg. 917
Brecker, Manfred, Chm. Bd.--PharmHouse, Inc., New York, NY; *U.S. Public*, pg. 1286
Breed, Allen K., Chm. Bd. & Chief Exec. Officer--Breed Technologies, Inc., Lakeland, FL; *U.S. Public*, pg. 251
Breen, Daniel A., Chm.--Daniel Breen and Co., Houston, TX; *Int'l*, pg. 313
Breen, John G., Chm. Bd. & Chief Exec. Officer--The Sherwin-Williams Company, Cleveland, OH; *U.S. Public*, pg. 1465
Bregman, Michael, Chm. Bd. & Chief Exec. Officer--The Second Cup, Toronto, Canada; *Int'l*, pg. 266
Bregman, Walter W., Chm. Bd.--Truevision, Inc., Santa Clara, CA; *U.S. Public*, pg. 1642
Brehm, William K., Chm. Bd.--SRA International Inc., Arlington, VA; *U.S. Private*, pg. 957
Breitenbach, E. Allen, Dr., Chm. Bd. & Chief Exec. Officer--Scientific Software-Intercomp, Inc., Denver, CO; *U.S. Public*, pg. 1443
Breitman, Leo R., Chm. Bd. & Chief Exec. Officer--Fleet Bank of Massachusetts, N.A., Boston, MA; *U.S. Public*, pg. 649
Breme, Harold, Chm. Bd.--Otto Junker GmbH Lammersdorf, Simmerath, Germany; *Int'l*, pg. 1014
Bremi, Ulrich, Chm. Bd.--Georg Fischer Ltd., Schaffhausen, Switzerland; *Int'l*, pg. 488
Bremi, Ulrich, Chm. Bd.--Swiss Reinsurance Company, Zurich, Switzerland; *Int'l*, pg. 1332
Bremond, Enrique, Chm. Bd.--El Puerto de Liverpool S.A., Mexico, Mexico; *Int'l*, pg. 435
Bren, Donald, Chm. Bd.--The Irvine Company, Newport Beach, CA; *U.S. Private*, pg. 575
Bren, Donald, Chm. Bd.--Irvine Apartment Communities Incorporated, Newport Beach, CA; *U.S. Private*, pg. 575
Brenan, Michael R., Chm. Bd., Pres. & Chief Exec. Officer--MainStreet BankGroup Incorporated, Martinsville, VA; *U.S. Public*, pg. 1038
Brendsel, Leland C., Chm. Bd. & Chief Exec. Officer--Federal Home Loan Mortgage Corporation, Mc Lean, VA; *U.S. Public*, pg. 615
Brennan, Charles M., III, Chm. Bd. & Chief Exec. Officer--MYR Group Inc., Rolling Meadows, IL; *U.S. Public*, pg. 1029
Brennan, John J., Chm., Pres. & Chief Exec. Officer--The Vanguard Group, Inc., Valley Forge, PA; *U.S. Private*, pg. 1133
Brenner, Karen, Chm. Bd., Pres. & Chief Exec. Officer--Carlyle Industries, Inc., Carlstadt, NJ; *U.S. Public*, pg. 1187
Brentjens, Joep, Chm. Bd.--VNU Verenigde Nederlandse Uitgeversbedrijven B.V., Haarlem, Netherlands; *Int'l*, pg. 1445
Brenton, C. Robert, Chm. Bd.--Brenton Banks, Inc., Des Moines, IA; *U.S. Public*, pg. 251
Bresnahan, William W., Chm. Bd.--Hynes Industries Inc., Youngstown, OH; *U.S. Private*, pg. 552
Bressler, Leon, Chm. Bd. & Chief Exec. Officer--Unibail, Paris, France; *Int'l*, pg. 1431
Breton, Thierry, Chm. Bd.--Thomson Consumer Electronics Inc., Indianapolis, IN; *Int'l*, pg. 1383
Brewer, Jeffrey C., Chm. Bd.--Grandville Printing Company, Grandville, MI; *U.S. Private*, pg. 469
Brewer, Sheldy T., Chm. Bd.--ABB Combustion Engineering Nuclear Power, Windsor, CT; *Int'l*, pg. 3
Brice, Houston A., Jr., Chm. Emeritus--Brice Building Co., Inc., Birmingham, AL; *U.S. Private*, pg. 167

Brickel, Mary L., Chm. Bd.--BEC Inc., Richmond, MI; *U.S. Private*, pg. 106

Bridger, Cedric, Chm. Bd.--Maxus Energy Corporation, Dallas, TX; *Int'l*, pg. 1515

Bridgewater, B.A., Jr., Chm. Bd., Pres., & Chief Exec. Officer--Brown Group, Inc., Saint Louis, MO; *U.S. Public*, pg. 262

Bridgford, Allan L., Chm. Bd.--Bridgford Foods Corporation, Anaheim, CA; *U.S. Public*, pg. 252

Brier, Jack, Chm. Bd.--Kleinert's, Inc., Plymouth Meeting, PA; *U.S. Private*, pg. 625

Brier, Jack, Chm. Bd. & Chief Exec. Officer--Kleinert's, Inc., of Alabama, Elba, AL; *U.S. Private*, pg. 625

Brier, Jack, Chm. Bd. & Chief Exec. Officer--Scott Mills, Gastonia, NC; *U.S. Private*, pg. 625

Brier, Jack, Chm. Bd. & Chief Exec. Officer--Kleinert's Inc. of Florida, Largo, FL; *U.S. Private*, pg. 625

Brierley, Harold M., Chm. Bd. & Pres.--Brierley & Partners, Dallas, TX; *U.S. Private*, pg. 168

Briggs, Karl L., Chm. Bd. & Chief Exec. Officer--Quincy Mutual Fire Insurance Company, Quincy, MA; *U.S. Private*, pg. 901

Briggs, Philip, Chm. Bd.--Empire Blue Cross & Blue Shield, New York, NY; *U.S. Private*, pg. 374

Briggs, Robert S., Chm. Bd., Pres. & Chief Exec. Officer--Bangor Hydro-Electric Company, Bangor, ME; *U.S. Public*, pg. 178

Brigham, James R., Sr., Chm. Bd.--Diagraph Corporation, Earth City, MO; *U.S. Private*, pg. 330

Bright, John, Chm.-Greenalls Inns-In Partnership)--The Greenalls Group PLC, Warrington, United Kingdom; *Int'l*, pg. 558

Brim, A. Eugene, Chm. Bd.--Brim, Inc., Portland, OR; *U.S. Private*, pg. 168

Brinckman, Donald W., Chm. Bd. & Chief Exec. Officer--Safety-Kleen Corp., Elgin, IL; *U.S. Public*, pg. 1425

Brindley, James M., Chm. Bd.--W.A. Roosevelt Co., La Crosse, WI; *U.S. Private*, pg. 943

Brink, William A., Chm. Bd.--The Burton Company, North Haven, CT; *U.S. Public*, pg. 826

Brinker, Norman E., Chm. Bd.--Brinker International, Inc., Dallas, TX; *U.S. Public*, pg. 253

Brinkley, Nicholas B., Chm. Bd. & Chief Exec. Officer--BankAmerica Financial Services System, Inc., San Diego, CA; *U.S. Public*, pg. 181

Brinkman, Lloyd D., Chm. Bd., Chief Exec. & Chief Oper. Officer--LDB Corporation, Kerrville, TX; *U.S. Private*, pg. 639

Brinton, Garrison W., Chm. Bd.--Label-Aire Inc., Fullerton, CA; *U.S. Private*, pg. 641

Briskin, Bernard, Chm. Bd., Pres. & Chief Exec. Officer--Arden Group, Inc., Los Angeles, CA; *U.S. Public*, pg. 128

Britt, William G., Chm. Bd.--Recreational Equipment, Inc., Kent, WA; *U.S. Private*, pg. 914

Britt, William R., Chm. Bd., Pres. & Chief Exec. Officer--Palmer-American National Bank, Danville, IL; *U.S. Public*, pg. 1217

Broad, Eli, Chm. Bd., Pres. & Chief Exec. Officer--SunAmerica Inc., Los Angeles, CA; *U.S. Public*, pg. 1532

Broadbent, J.S.L., Chm. Bd.--Marley Floors (USA) Inc., Tuscumbia, AL; *Int'l*, pg. 843

Broadhead, R., Chm. Bd.--Taylor Woodrow Civil Engineering Ltd., Southall, United Kingdom; *Int'l*, pg. 1358

Broadhead, R., Chm. Bd.--Taylor Woodrow Construction (Southern) Ltd., Southall, United Kingdom; *Int'l*, pg. 1358

Broadhurst, James, Chm. & Chief Exec. Officer--Eat N Park Restaurants, Pittsburgh, PA; *U.S. Private*, pg. 358

Broady, George, Pres. & Chief Exec. Officer--Ultrak Inc., Lewisville, TX; *U.S. Public*, pg. 1663

Brock, J. Don, Chm. Bd. & Pres.--Astec Industries, Inc., Chattanooga, TN; *U.S. Public*, pg. 141

Brock, Milton J., Jr., Chm. Bd.--Nationwide Health Properties Inc., Newport Beach, CA; *U.S. Public*, pg. 1166

Brock, Paul K., Chm. Bd.--Brach & Brock Confections Inc., Chattanooga, TN; *U.S. Private*, pg. 163

Brod, Irven J., Chm. Bd. & Pres.--Empire Diamond Corporation, New York, NY; *U.S. Private*, pg. 374

Brodersen, Norbert, Chm. Bd.--KM-Europa Metal Aktiengesellschaft, Osnabruck, Germany; *Int'l*, pg. 719

Brodersen, Roger R., Chm. Bd. & Chief Exec. Officer--Data Transmission Network Corporation, Omaha, NE; *U.S. Public*, pg. 486

Brodeur, A.W., Chm. Bd., Pres. & Chief Exec. Officer--Cassidy's Ltd., Brossard, Canada; *Int'l*, pg. 275

Brody, Arthur, Chm. Bd. & Chief Exec. Officer--Brodart Company, Williamsport, PA; *U.S. Private*, pg. 170

Brody, Marvin D., Chm. Bd., Pres. & Chief Exec. Officer--Employee Solutions, Inc., Phoenix, AZ; *U.S. Public*, pg. 579

Bromley, Ernest W., Chm. & Chief Exec. Officer--Bromley, Aguilar & Associates, San Antonio, TX; *U.S. Private*, pg. 692

Bronfman, Charles R., Co-Chm. Bd.--The Seagram Company Ltd., Montreal, Canada; *Int'l*, pg. 1214

Bronfman, Edgar M., Chm. Bd.--The Seagram Company Ltd., Montreal, Canada; *Int'l*, pg. 1214

Bronstein, David G., Chm. Bd.--Big V Supermarkets, Inc., Florida, NY; *U.S. Private*, pg. 143

Bront, L. Ray, Chm. Bd.--Resco Products, Inc., Conshohocken, PA; *U.S. Private*, pg. 924

Brooke, Peter A., Chm. Bd.--Advent International, Boston, MA; *U.S. Private*, pg. 22

Brookes, Nick G., Chm. Bd. & Chief Exec. Officer--Brown & Williamson Tobacco Corp., Louisville, KY; *Int'l*, pg. 111

Brookfield, Donald W., Chm. Bd.--Brookfield Engineering Laboratories, Inc., Stoughton, MA; *U.S. Private*, pg. 171

Brooks, A., Chm. Bd.--British Gypsum Ltd., Loughborough, United Kingdom; *Int'l*, pg. 122

Brooks, E.R., Chm. Bd. & Chief Exec. Officer--Central and South West Corporation, Dallas, TX; *U.S. Public*, pg. 324

Brooks, Ed, Chm. Bd.--Foremost Farms USA Cooperative, Baraboo, WI; *U.S. Private*, pg. 418

Brooks, James W., Chm. Bd. & Chief Exec. Officer--Beverage America, Inc., Holland, MI; *U.S. Private*, pg. 141

Brooks, L.E., Chm. Bd. & Chief Exec. Officer--Air Techniques, Inc., Hicksville, NY; *U.S. Private*, pg. 28

Brooks, Mike, Chm. Bd., Pres. & Chief Exec. Officer--Rocky Shoes & Boots, Inc., Nelsonville, OH; *U.S. Public*, pg. 1402

Brooks, Richard E.T., Chm., Pres. & Chief Exec. Officer--ChemDesign Corporation, Fitchburg, MA; *Int'l*, pg. 173

Brookshire, Bruce G., Chm. Bd.--Brookshire Grocery, Tyler, TX; *U.S. Private*, pg. 172

Brookshire, R. A., Chm. Bd. & Pres.--Brookshire Bros., Ltd., Lufkin, TX; *U.S. Private*, pg. 172

Brophy, George T., Chm. Bd., Pres. & Chief Exec. Officer--ABT Building Products Corporation, Neenah, WI; *Int'l*, pg. 20

Brotman, Jeffrey H., Chm. Bd.--Costco Wholesale, Issaquah, WA; *U.S. Public*, pg. 451

Brott, M. Paul, Chm. Bd. & Chief Exec. Officer--Ewing Cole Cherry Brott, Philadelphia, PA; *U.S. Private*, pg. 387

Brown, Allan, Co-Chm. Bd.--Simon Marketing, Inc., Los Angeles, CA; *U.S. Private*, pg. 1001

Brown, Andy F., Chm. Bd.--Calcor Space Facility, Inc., Whittier, CA; *U.S. Private*, pg. 200

Brown, Arthur, Chm. Bd., Pres. & Chief Exec. Officer--Hecla Mining Company, Coeur D'Alene, ID; *U.S. Public*, pg. 803

Brown, Bennett A., Chm. Bd.--NationsBank South, Atlanta, GA; *U.S. Public*, pg. 1163

Brown, Charles, Chm. Bd., Pres. & Chief Exec. Officer--Bayou State Oil Corporation, Shreveport, LA; *U.S. Private*, pg. 125

Brown, Dave M., Chm. Bd.--Homes By Dave Brown, Tempe, AZ; *U.S. Private*, pg. 537

Brown, E. H., Chm. Bd. & Partner--Brown Marketing Communications, Chicago, IL; *U.S. Private*, pg. 174

Brown, Herbert E., Chm. Bd. & Chief Exec. Officer.--Alexander Doll Company, Inc., New York, NY; *U.S. Private*, pg. 33

Brown, Hyatt, J., Chm. Bd., Pres. & Chief Exec. Officer--Poe & Brown, Inc., Daytona Beach, FL; *U.S. Public*, pg. 1312

Brown, J. Bruce, Chm. Bd. & Chief Exec. Officer--Lambert Smith Hampton, London, United Kingdom; *Int'l*, pg. 797

Brown, J. Terrell, Chm. Bd. & Chief Exec. Officer--United Companies Financial Corporation, Baton Rouge, LA; *U.S. Public*, pg. 1675

Brown, Jack, Chm.--J. Brown/LMC Group, Stamford, CT; *U.S. Public*, pg. 764

Brown, Jack E., Chm. Bd. & Chief Exec. Officer--BASES Worldwide, Covington, KY; *U.S. Private*, pg. 120

Brown, Jack H., Chm. Bd., Pres. & Chief Exec. Officer--Stater Bros. Inc., Colton, CA; *U.S. Public*, pg. 456

Brown, Jack W., Chm. Bd., Pres. & Chief Exec. Officer--Gish Biomedical, Inc., Irvine, CA; *U.S. Public*, pg. 745

Brown, Jim, Chm. Bd. & Chief Exec.--Newsquest Media Group, London, United Kingdom; *Int'l*, pg. 927

Brown, John W., Chm. Bd., Pres. & Chief Exec. Officer--Stryker Corporation, Kalamazoo, MI; *U.S. Public*, pg. 1525

Brown, L. Russell, Chm. Bd. & Treas.--Agsco, Inc., Grand Forks, ND; *U.S. Private*, pg. 27

Brown, Louis M., Jr., Chm. Bd.--Planning Systems Inc., Mc Lean, VA; *U.S. Private*, pg. 869

Brown, Louis M., Jr., Chm. Bd.--Micros Systems Inc., Beltsville, MD; *U.S. Public*, pg. 1106

Brown, Milton R., Chm. Bd., Pres. & Chief Exec. Officer--Suntec Industries Inc., Rockford, IL; *U.S. Private*, pg. 1054

Brown, Owsley II, Chm. Bd.--Brown-Forman Beverages Worldwide, Louisville, KY; *U.S. Public*, pg. 261

Brown, Owsley, II, Chm. Bd. & Chief Exec. Officer--Brown-Forman Corporation, Louisville, KY; *U.S. Public*, pg. 261

Brown, Peter, Chm. Bd.--Dawson Holdings PLC, Folkestone, United Kingdom; *Int'l*, pg. 385

Brown, Peter D., Chm. Bd.--Datamarine International, Inc., Mountlake Terrace, WA; *U.S. Public*, pg. 486

Brown, R. Donald, Chm. Bd., Pres. & Chief Exec. Officer--Imperial Tobacco Limited, Montreal, Canada; *Int'l*, pg. 112

Brown, R.J., Chm. Bd.--R.J. Brown and Associates Corporation AG, Zug, Switzerland; *Int'l*, pg. 766

Brown, Richard H., Chm.--Cable & Wireless Communications plc, London, United Kingdom; *Int'l*, pg. 115

Brown, Richard H., Chm.--Cable & Wireless Communications plc, London, United Kingdom; *U.S. Public*, pg. 203

Brown, Richard H., Chm.--Cable & Wireless Communications plc, London, United Kingdom; *Int'l*, pg. 247

Brown, Stephen L., Chm. Bd. & Chief Exec. Officer--John Hancock Mutual Life Insurance Company, Boston, MA; *U.S. Private*, pg. 589

Brown, Stephen L., Chm.--John Hancock Subsidiaries, Inc., Boston, MA; *U.S. Private*, pg. 589

Brown, Thomas G., Chm., Pres. & Chief Exec. Officer--Duncanson & Holt, New York, NY; *U.S. Public*, pg. 1699

Brown, Thomas R., Jr., Chm. Bd.--Burr-Brown Corporation, Tucson, AZ; *U.S. Public*, pg. 270

Brown, Timothy C., Chm. Bd., Pres. & Chief Exec. Officer--Thomas Industries Inc., Louisville, KY; *U.S. Public*, pg. 1598

Brown, Wayne J., Chm. Bd.--Brown Evans Distributing Co., Mesa, AZ; *U.S. Private*, pg. 174

Browning, Roderick H., Chm. Bd.--Bank of Utah, Ogden, UT; *U.S. Private*, pg. 114

Brozman, Jack L., Chm. Bd., Pres. & Chief Exec. Officer--Concorde Career Colleges, Inc., Kansas City, MO; *U.S. Public*, pg. 430

Brubaker, Herman, Chm. Bd.--Mid-America Dairymen, Inc., Springfield, MO; *U.S. Private*, pg. 743

Brubaker, Herman, Chm. Bd.--Milk Marketing Inc., Strongsville, OH; *U.S. Private*, pg. 745

Brubaker, Jerry L., Chm. Bd. & Chief Fin. Officer--Schneller, Inc., Kent, OH; *U.S. Private*, pg. 971

Brubaker, John D., Chm. Bd.--Aqua-Aerobic Systems Inc., Rockford, IL; *U.S. Private*, pg. 78

Brubaker, Robert P., Chm. Bd., Pres. & Chief Exec. Officer--King & Prince Seafood Corporation, Brunswick, GA; *U.S. Private*, pg. 620

Bruce, Frank B., Chm. Bd.--Bruce Industries, Inc., Dayton, NV; *U.S. Private*, pg. 175

Bruce, Leonard J., Chm. Bd.--Vallen Corporation, Houston, TX; *U.S. Public*, pg. 1705

Bruce, Marvin E., Chm. Bd.--TBC Corporation, Memphis, TN; *U.S. Public*, pg. 1553

Bruenger, Leona, Chm. Bd.--M. Bruenger & Co., Inc., Wichita, KS; *U.S. Private*, pg. 175

Bruggink, Herman, Co-Chm.--Reed Elsevier plc, London, United Kingdom; *Int'l*, pg. 1093

Bruggink, Herman, Chm.-Exec. Bd.--Elsevier NV, Amsterdam, Netherlands; *Int'l*, pg. 1093

Bruggink, Herman, Chm.--Reed Elsevier Nederland BV, Amsterdam, Netherlands; *Int'l*, pg. 1100

Bruhn, Richard L., Chm. Bd. & Chief Exec. Officer--Dick Bruhn Incorporated, Salinas, CA; *U.S. Private*, pg. 175

Brumley, Jon, Chm. Bd.--Pioneer Natural Resources Co., Irving, TX; *U.S. Public*, pg. 1299

Brummett, Larry W., Chm. & Chief Exec. Officer--ONEOK Inc., Tulsa, OK; *U.S. Public*, pg. 1226

Brunner, D.G., Chm. Bd.--Waupaca Foundry Inc., Waupaca, WI; *Int'l*, pg. 1389

Brunner, F. J., Chm. Bd.--Brunner & Lay, Inc., Springdale, AR; *U.S. Private*, pg. 176

Brunner, Peter Ch., Chm. Bd.--Desco de Schulthess Ltd., Zurich, Switzerland; *Int'l*, pg. 396

Bruno, Arthur H., Chm. Bd.--White Pine Software, Nashua, NH; *U.S. Private*, pg. 1173

Bruns, George H., Jr., Chm. Bd. & Chief Exec. Officer--Giga-Tronics Incorporated, San Ramon, CA; *U.S. Public*, pg. 742

Brush, Richard F., Chm. Bd.--Sentry Group, Rochester, NY; *U.S. Private*, pg. 984

Brutger, Larry, Chm. Bd. & Pres.--Brutger Equities, Inc., Saint Cloud, MN; *U.S. Private*, pg. 176

Brutsche, H.R., III, Chm. Bd., Pres. & Chief Exec. Officer--Vari-Lite International, Dallas, TX; *U.S. Public*, pg. 1709

Bryan, J. Stewart, III, Chm. Bd., Pres. & Chief Exec. Officer--Media General, Inc., Richmond, VA; *U.S. Public*, pg. 1077

Bryan, John H., Chm. Bd. & Chief Exec. Officer--Sara Lee Corporation, Chicago, IL; *U.S. Public*, pg. 1432

Bryan, R.A., Jr., Chm. Bd.--T.A. Loving Company, Goldsboro, NC; *U.S. Private*, pg. 677

Bryant, A.H. II, Chm. Bd.--O'Sullivan Corporation, Winchester, VA; *U.S. Public*, pg. 1234

Bryant, A.W., Chm. Bd.--Century Fence Company, Pewaukee, WI; *U.S. Private*, pg. 226

Bryant, W. Dexter, Chm. Bd.--Bead Industries Inc., Bridgeport, CT; *U.S. Private*, pg. 126

Bryson, John E., Chm. Bd. & Chief Exec. Officer--Edison International, Rosemead, CA; *U.S. Public*, pg. 564

Bryson, John E., Chm. Bd.--Edison Mission Energy, Irvine, CA; *U.S. Public*, pg. 564

Buaron, Roberto, Chm. Bd.--Berry Plastics Corporation, Evansville, IN; *U.S. Private*, pg. 137

Buccellato, Carl, Chm. Bd., Pres. & Chief Exec. Officer--Homeowners Group, Inc., Sunrise, FL; *U.S. Public*, pg. 832

Buchan, Robert M., Chm. Bd. & Chief Exec. Officer--Kinross Gold Corporation, Toronto, Canada; *Int'l*, pg. 734

Buchanan, David R., Chm. Bd., Pres. & Chief Exec. Officer--Three-Five Systems, Tempe, AZ; *U.S. Public*, pg. 1604

Buchanan, Robert, Chm. Bd.--CPS Corporation, Franklin, TN; *U.S. Private*, pg. 422

Buchanan, Robert C., Chm. Bd. & Pres.--Fox River Paper Company, Appleton, WI; *U.S. Private*, pg. 422

Buchbiner, Henry M., Chm. Bd.--Ardco, Inc., Alsip, IL; *U.S. Private*, pg. 80

Buchwald, James P., Chm. Bd.--Ariel Corporation, Mount Vernon, OH; *U.S. Private*, pg. 81

Buck, Charles T., Chm. Bd., Pres. & Chief Exec. Officer--Buck Knives, Inc., El Cajon, CA; *U.S. Private*, pg. 177

Buckler, Sheldon A., Chm. Bd.--Commonwealth Energy System, Cambridge, MA; *U.S. Public*, pg. 414

Buckman, S. B., Chm. Bd. & Chief Exec. Officer--Buckman Laboratories Inc., Memphis, TN; *U.S. Private*, pg. 180

Bucksbaum, Matthew, Chm. Bd. & Chief Exec. Officer--General Growth Properties Inc., Chicago, IL; *U.S. Public*, pg. 715

Buddenbaum, G., Chm.--Hoogovens Aluminium Walzprodukte GmbH, Koblenz, Germany; *Int'l*, pg. 755

Budin, Gerard, Chm. Bd.--SODIAAL, Paris, France; *Int'l*, pg. 1166

Bueche, Wendell F., Chm. Bd.--IMC Global, Bannockburn, IL; *U.S. Public*, pg. 856

Buehler, Hans, Chm. Bd.--Coastcast Corporation, Gardena, CA; *U.S. Public*, pg. 391

Buennagel, David, Chm. Bd.--Rolock, Inc., Fairfield, CT; *U.S. Private*, pg. 942

Buettner, Thomas W., Dr., Chm. Bd., Pres. & Chief Exec. Officer--Ruetgers-Nease Corporation, State College, PA; *Int'l*, pg. 1148

Bufe, Uwe-Ernst, Dr., Pres. & Chief Exec. Officer--Degussa AG, Frankfurt/Main, Germany; *Int'l*, pg. 388

Buffett, Warren E., Chm. Bd. & Chief Exec. Officer--Berkshire Hathaway Inc., Omaha, NE; *U.S. Public*, pg. 217

Bugg, William, Chm. Bd.--Creation Windows of Indiana, Inc., Elkhart, IN; *U.S. Private*, pg. 287

Buhler, Frank H., Chm. Bd. & Chief Exec. Officer--Old Dominion Box Co., Inc., Madison Heights, VA; *U.S. Private*, pg. 814

Buirski, David, Founder Chm.-Cape Town--Young & Rubicam South Africa, Johannesburg, South Africa; *U.S. Private*, pg. 1198

Buirski, David, Founder Chm.--Young & Rubicam Tholet, Cape Town, South Africa; *U.S. Private*, pg. 1198
Bulcke, Paul, Dr., Chm. Bd. & Gen. Dir.--Nestle Portugal, S.A., Carnaxide, Portugal; *Int'l*, pg. 921
Bulgari, Gianni, Chm.--Fila Sport S.p.A., Biella, Italy; *Int'l*, pg. 484
Bulgari, Paolo, Chm. Bd.--Bulgari SPA, Rome, Italy; *Int'l*, pg. 232
Bull, George J., Chm. Bd.--Grand Metropolitan Plc, London, United Kingdom; *Int'l*, pg. 408
Bull, George J., Sir, Joint Chm.--Diageo Plc, London, United Kingdom; *Int'l*, pg. 408
Bull, Marshall R., Chm. Bd. & Pres.--Industrial Wire Products Corporation, Pomona, CA; *U.S. Private*, pg. 561
Buller, Allan R., Chm. & Treas.--Worthington Foods Inc., Worthington, OH; *U.S. Public*, pg. 1780
Bulmer, J.E., Chm. Bd.--H.P. Bulmer Holdings Plc, Hereford, United Kingdom; *Int'l*, pg. 232
Bumby, John E., Chm. Bd.--Ripon Foods, Inc., Ripon, WI; *U.S. Private*, pg. 931
Bumgarner, John C., Chm. Bd. & Chief Exec. Officer--Apco Argentina Inc., Tulsa, OK; *U.S. Public*, pg. 119
Bunaes, Bard, Chm. Bd.--Constitution Reinsurance Corporation, New York, NY; *Int'l*, pg. 467
Bunn, George R., Chm. Bd.--Bunn-O-Matic Corporation, Springfield, IL; *U.S. Private*, pg. 180
Buntin, Jeffrey, Chm. Bd.--Buntin Out of Home Media, Nashville, TN; *U.S. Private*, pg. 181
Bunting, Christopher, Chm. & Chief Exec. Officer--Continental PIR Communications, Inc., Toronto, Canada; *Int'l*, pg. 1226
Buonanno, Vincent, Chm. & Chief Exec. Officer--Tempel Steel Company, Skokie, IL; *U.S. Private*, pg. 1075
Burd, L.W., Chm. Bd.--Jamieson Film Company, Inc., Dallas, TX; *U.S. Public*, pg. 551
Burda, Hubert, Dr., Chm. Bd.--Burda Holding GmbH & Co., KG, Munich, Germany; *Int'l*, pg. 233
Burdick, Richard L., Chm. Bd., Pres. & Chief Exec. Officer--Thermon Manufacturing Company, San Marcos, TX; *U.S. Private*, pg. 1080
Burford, M.J., Chm. Bd.--First Security Bank of Oregon, Salem, OR; *U.S. Public*, pg. 637
Burger, Paul, Chm. & Chief Exec. Officer--Sony Music Entertainment (UK) Limited, London, United Kingdom; *Int'l*, pg. 1284
Burgess, I.G.R., Chm. Bd.--Australian Mutual Provident, Sydney, Australia; *Int'l*, pg. 100
Burgess, Ian, Chm. Bd.--CSR Limited, Sydney, Australia; *Int'l*, pg. 245
Burgett, William B., Chm. Bd.--Kokosing Construction Company, Inc., Fredericktown, OH; *U.S. Private*, pg. 631
Burguieres, Philip, Chm. Bd.--Weatherford Enterra Incorporated, Houston, TX; *U.S. Public*, pg. 1749
Burkart, Walter, Chm. Bd.--Kingsbury Corporation, Keene, NH; *U.S. Private*, pg. 621
Burke, Lawrence E., Chm. Bd.--Alexander & Alexander Inc., New York, NY; *U.S. Public*, pg. 117
Burkel, Ronald, Chm. Bd.--Smith's Food & Drug Centers, Inc., Salt Lake City, UT; *U.S. Public*, pg. 1103
Burkel, Ronald W., Chm. Bd.--Fred Meyer Incorporated, Portland, OR; *U.S. Public*, pg. 1103
Burkel, Ronald W., Chm. Bd. & Chief Exec. Officer--Fred Meyer Stores, Portland, OR; *U.S. Public*, pg. 1103
Burkhardt, Edward A., Chm. Bd., Pres. & Chief Exec. Officer--Wisconsin Central Transportation Corporation, Rosemont, IL; *U.S. Public*, pg. 1772
Burkle, Joseph, Chm. Bd.--Falley's Inc., Topeka, KS; *U.S. Private*, pg. 1202
Burkle, Ron, Chm. Bd.--Ralphs Grocery Company, Compton, CA; *U.S. Private*, pg. 1202
Burkle, Ron, Chm. Bd. & Chief Exec. Officer--Dominick's Finer Foods, Northlake, IL; *U.S. Private*, pg. 1202
Burkle, Ronald, Mng. Partner--The Yucaipa Companies, Los Angeles, CA; *U.S. Private*, pg. 1202
Burmeister, Helmut, Dr., Chm. Bd.--Kloeckner & Co. AG, Duisburg, Germany; *Int'l*, pg. 737
Burner, David L., Chm. Bd., Pres. & Chief Exec. Officer--The B.F. Goodrich Company, Richfield, OH; *U.S. Public*, pg. 751
Burnet, Steven, Chm.--Harvest States Cooperatives, Saint Paul, MN; *U.S. Private*, pg. 508
Burney, Derek H., Chm., Pres. & Chief Exec. Officer--Bell Canada International, Inc., Montreal, Canada; *Int'l*, pg. 115
Burnham, Duane L., Chm. & Chief Exec. Officer--Abbott Laboratories, Abbott Park, IL; *U.S. Public*, pg. 12
Burnham, Malin, Chm. Bd.--John Burnham & Co., San Diego, CA; *U.S. Private*, pg. 186
Burns, David C., Pres. & Chief Exec. Officer--Ithaco Inc., Ithaca, NY; *U.S. Private*, pg. 576
Burns, Gregory L., Chm. Bd., Pres. & Chief Exec. Officer--O'Charley's Inc., Nashville, TN; *U.S. Public*, pg. 1211
Burns, James W., Chm. Bd.--The Great-West Life Assurance Company, Winnipeg, Canada; *Int'l*, pg. 557
Burns, M. Anthony, Chm. Bd., Pres. & Chief Exec. Officer--Ryder System, Inc., Miami, FL; *U.S. Public*, pg. 1413
Burns, P.D., Chm. Bd.--Confederation Life Insurance and Annuity Company, Atlanta, GA; *Int'l*, pg. 326
Burns, Stephen F., Chm. Bd. & Chief Exec. Officer--Wheaton Van Lines, Inc., Indianapolis, IN; *U.S. Private*, pg. 1171
Burpo, James O., Chm. Bd.--Willis Corroon Corp. of Sacramento, Sacramento, CA; *Int'l*, pg. 1507
Burr, David F., Chm. Bd.--Rollins Leasing Corp., Wilmington, DE; *U.S. Public*, pg. 1405
Burr, Les, Chm.--Galleon Ltd., Woking, United Kingdom; *Int'l*, pg. 114
Burrell, Frank L., Jr., Chm. Bd. & Chief Exec. Officer--Elsinore Corporation, Las Vegas, NV; *U.S. Public*, pg. 570
Burrell, M.W., Chm. Bd.--Lakeside Trading Estate Ltd., Essex, United Kingdom; *Int'l*, pg. 1025
Burrell, Paul M., Chm. Bd., Pres. & Chief Exec. Officer--Outsource International, Deerfield Beach, FL; *U.S. Public*, pg. 1236
Burrell, Thomas J., Chm.--Burrell Communications Group Inc., Chicago, IL; *U.S. Private*, pg. 188
Burris, John E., Chm. Bd.--Burris Foods, Inc., Milford, DE; *U.S. Private*, pg. 188
Burriss, J.D., Chm. Bd., Pres. & Chief Exec. & Oper. Officer--The Alpha Corporation Of Tennessee, Collierville, TN; *U.S. Private*, pg. 44
Burriss, J.D., Chm. Bd. & Pres.--Chroma-Tek, Collierville, TN; *U.S. Private*, pg. 45
Burroughs, Henry F., Jr., Chm. Bd.--First Gray Line Corporation, Beverly Hills, CA; *U.S. Private*, pg. 407
Burrow, Christopher, Chm. Bd.--Woodruff Electric Co-Op, Forrest City, AR; *U.S. Private*, pg. 1187
Burrows, R.W., Jr., Chm. Bd. & Pres.--Burrows Paper Corporation, Little Falls, NY; *U.S. Private*, pg. 188
Bursky, Andrew M., Chm. Bd.--Strategic Distribution Inc., Bensalem, PA; *U.S. Public*, pg. 1523
Burson, Harold, Chm. (New York)--Burson-Marsteller, New York, NY; *U.S. Private*, pg. 1197
Burt, John R., Chm. Bd. & Pres.--Duro-Last Roofing, Inc., Saginaw, MI; *U.S. Private*, pg. 349
Burt, Richard R., Chm. Bd.--Power House Technologies, Inc., Bozeman, MT; *U.S. Public*, pg. 1319
Burt, Richard R., Chm. Bd.--Weirton Steel Corporation, Weirton, WV; *U.S. Public*, pg. 1751
Burt, Robert N., Chm. Bd. & Chief Exec. Officer--FMC Corporation, Chicago, IL; *U.S. Public*, pg. 604
Burton, Robert G., Chm. Bd., Pres. & Chief Exec. Officer--World Color Press, Inc., Greenwich, CT; *U.S. Public*, pg. 1778
Burwell, Rodney P., Chm. Bd.--Xerxes Corporation, Minneapolis, MN; *U.S. Private*, pg. 1194
Bury, Thomas, Chief Exec. Officer & Deputy Chm.-London--Ogilvy & Mather Worldwide, Inc., New York, NY; *Int'l*, pg. 1483
Busby, James L., Chm. Bd.--QMS, Inc., Mobile, AL; *U.S. Public*, pg. 1346
Busch, August A., III, Chm. Bd. & Pres. & V.P.-Mktg.--Anheuser-Busch Companies, Inc., Saint Louis, MO; *U.S. Public*, pg. 113
Busch, Paul L., Dr., Chm. Bd., Pres. & Chief Exec. Officer--Malcolm Pirnie, Inc., White Plains, NY; *U.S. Private*, pg. 867
Busch, Timothy R., Interim Chm. Bd.--Pac Rim Holding Corporation, Woodland Hills, CA; *U.S. Public*, pg. 1246
Buschmann, Siegfried, Chm. Bd. & Chief Exec. Officer--The Budd Company, Troy, MI; *Int'l*, pg. 1388
Bush, Condon, Chm. Bd. & Chief Exec. Officer--Bush Brothers & Company, Knoxville, TN; *U.S. Private*, pg. 189
Bush, Diego Jorge, Chm. Bd.--Sao Paulo Alpargatas S.A., Sao Paulo, Brazil; *Int'l*, pg. 1193
Bush, Jack, Chm. Bd. & Chief Exec. Officer--Jumbo Sports Inc., Tampa, FL; *U.S. Public*, pg. 935
Bush, Paul S., Chm. Bd., Pres. & Chief Exec. Officer--Bush Industries Inc., Jamestown, NY; *U.S. Public*, pg. 270
Bushell, C.J., Chm. & Mng. Dir.--BPB Paper & Packaging Ltd., Northwich, United Kingdom; *Int'l*, pg. 122
Bustillo, Oscar, Jr., Chm. Bd., Pres. & Chief Exec. Officer--Republic National Bank of Miami, Miami, FL; *U.S. Private*, pg. 924
Butcher, Andrew D.W., Chm. Bd. & Chief Exec. Officer--Carat ICG, Los Angeles, CA; *U.S. Private*, pg. 207
Butcher, Charles, Chm. Bd.--The Butcher Company, Marlborough, MA; *U.S. Private*, pg. 189
Butcher, Jonathan, Chm. Bd. & Pres.--Butcher & Co., Inc., Philadelphia, PA; *U.S. Private*, pg. 189
Butcher, McBee, Chm.--The Philadelphia Bourse, Inc., Lanham, MD; *U.S. Private*, pg. 861
Butcko, Joseph A., Chm. Bd.--Crescive Die & Tool, Inc., Saline, MI; *U.S. Private*, pg. 289
Butler, Abbey, Co-Chm.-Bd. & Chief Exec. Officer--Avatex Corporation, Dallas, TX; *U.S. Public*, pg. 151
Butler, Abbey, Co-Chm. Bd. & Co-Chief Exec. Officer--Phar-Mor, Inc., Youngstown, OH; *U.S. Public*, pg. 1284
Butler, Basil, Chm. Bd.--Brown & Root Limited, London, United Kingdom; *U.S. Public*, pg. 775
Butler, Edward F., Chm. Bd., Pres. & Chief Exec. Officer--Regions Bank/Southern Louisiana, New Orleans, LA; *U.S. Public*, pg. 1373
Butler, Lester, Chm. Bd., Pres. & Chief Exec. Officer--SouthTrust Bank of Charleston, Charleston, SC; *U.S. Public*, pg. 1492
Butler, Robert, Chm. Bd.--Subaru Distributor Corp., Orangeburg, NY; *Int'l*, pg. 523
Butler, Sir Richard, The Hon., Chm. Bd.--NatWest Investment Management Limited, London, United Kingdom; *Int'l*, pg. 910
Butler, Stephen, Chm. Bd. & Chief Exec. Officer--KPMG LLP, New York, NY; *U.S. Private*, pg. 603
Butler, Stephen T., Chm. Bd. & Chief Exec. Officer--W.C. Bradley Co., Columbus, GA; *U.S. Private*, pg. 164
Butler, William, Chm. Bd., Pres. & Chief Exec. Officer--Corporex Companies, Inc., Cincinnati, OH; *U.S. Private*, pg. 276
Butler, William T., Chm. Bd.--Lyondell Petrochemical Company, Houston, TX; *U.S. Public*, pg. 1022
Buttenwieser, Lawrence B., Chm. Bd.--General American Investors Company, Inc., New York, NY; *U.S. Public*, pg. 706
Butterfield, Leslie, Chm. Bd., Plng Dir. & New Bus. Contact--Butterfield Day Devito Hockney Ltd., London, United Kingdom; *Int'l*, pg. 237
Butters, David J., Chm. Bd.--EVI, Inc., Houston, TX; *U.S. Public*, pg. 547
Buttner, Jean B., Chm. Bd. & Chief Exec. Officer--Arnold Bernhard & Co., New York, NY; *U.S. Private*, pg. 137
Buttner, Jean B., Chm. Bd. & Chief Exec. Officer--Value Line Publishing, New York, NY; *U.S. Private*, pg. 137
Buttner, Jean Bernhard, Chm. Bd., Pres. & Chief Exec. Officer--Value Line, Inc., New York, NY; *U.S. Private*, pg. 137
Butz, Theophil, Chm. & Creative Dir.--Bosch & Butz, Zollikon, Switzerland; *U.S. Private*, pg. 678
Buxbaum, Paul M., Chm. Bd.--Ames Department Stores, Inc., Rocky Hill, CT; *U.S. Public*, pg. 99
Buxton, Andrew R.W., Chm. Bd. & Pres.--Barclays Bank PLC, London, United Kingdom; *Int'l*, pg. 164
Buxton, C.I., II, Chm. Bd.--Federated Mutual Insurance Company, Owatonna, MN; *U.S. Private*, pg. 399
Buxton, Winslow H., Chm. Bd., Pres. & Chief Exec. Officer--Pentair, Inc., Saint Paul, MN; *U.S. Public*, pg. 1273
Buyers, J. W. A., Chm. Bd.--Mauna Loa Macadamia Nut Corporation, Hilo, HI; *U.S. Private*, pg. 190
Buyers, John W., Chm. Bd. & Chief Exec. Officer--Buyco, Inc., Honolulu, HI; *U.S. Private*, pg. 190
Buyers, John W.A., Chm. Bd. & Chief Exec. Officer--C. Brewer & Company, Limited, Honolulu, HI; *U.S. Private*, pg. 190
Buyers, John W.A., Chm. Bd. & Chief Exec. Officer--Mauna Loa Macadamia Partners, L.P., Honolulu, HI; *U.S. Public*, pg. 1060
Byer, Allan G., Chm. Bd. & Pres.--Byer California, San Francisco, CA; *U.S. Private*, pg. 191
Byland, Peter, Chm. Bd.--St. Lawrence Cement Inc., Montreal, Canada; *Int'l*, pg. 628
Byrd, H.P., Chm. Bd.--Flavor House Products, Inc., Dothan, AL; *U.S. Private*, pg. 410
Byrd, Robert, Chm. Bd., Pres. & Chief Exec. Officer--The Keller Manufacturing Co., Inc., Corydon, IN; *U.S. Private*, pg. 612
Byrne, Arthur, Chm. Bd., Pres. & Chief Exec. Officer--The Wiremold Company, West Hartford, CT; *U.S. Private*, pg. 1184
Byrne, John J., Chm. Bd.--Financial Security Assurance Holdings Ltd., New York, NY; *U.S. Public*, pg. 622
Byrnes, Arthur E., Chm. Bd.--Dravo Corporation, Pittsburgh, PA; *U.S. Public*, pg. 527
Byrnes, James J., Chm. Bd., Pres. & Chief Exec. Officer--Tompkins County Trust Company, Ithaca, NY; *U.S. Public*, pg. 1621
Cabiallavetta, Mathis, Chm. Bd.--Union Bank of Switzerland (Canada), Toronto, Canada; *Int'l*, pg. 1441
Cacciatore, William C., Chm. Bd., Pres. & Chief Exec. Officer--Richey Electronics, Inc., Garden Grove, CA; *U.S. Public*, pg. 1388
Caccini, Gian Paolo, Chm. Bd. & Chief Exec. Officer--Vetrotex CertainTeed Corporation, Wichita Falls, TX; *Int'l*, pg. 1171
Cadbury, Dominic, Exec. Chm.--Cadbury Schweppes p.l.c., London, United Kingdom; *Int'l*, pg. 247
Cadbury, Dominic, Chm. Bd.--The Economist Group Limited., London, United Kingdom; *Int'l*, pg. 1026
Cadieux, Chester, Chm. Bd., Pres. & Chief Exec. Officer--QuikTrip Corporation, Tulsa, OK; *U.S. Private*, pg. 901
Cadogan, William J., Chm. Bd., Pres. & Chief Exec. Officer--ADC Telecommunications, Inc., Minnetonka, MN; *U.S. Public*, pg. 4
Cafaro, William M., Chm. Bd.--The Cafaro Co., Youngstown, OH; *U.S. Private*, pg. 198
Cagle, J. Douglas, Chm. Bd. & Chief Exec. Officer--Cagle's Inc., Atlanta, GA; *U.S. Public*, pg. 291
Cahill, James P., Chm. Bd.-The Wright Group International--Wright Group Publishing, Inc., Bothell, WA; *U.S. Public*, pg. 1636
Cahouet, Frank V., Chm. Bd., Pres. & Chief Exec. Officer--Mellon Bank Corporation, Pittsburgh, PA; *U.S. Public*, pg. 1084
Cain, Herman, Chm. Bd.--Godfather's Pizza, Inc., Omaha, NE; *U.S. Private*, pg. 458
Cain, Richard, Chm. Bd. & Corp. V.P.--West Hudson, Inc. (Healthcare Consulting Services), Dallas, TX; *U.S. Public*, pg. 45
Cainer, Edoardo, Chm.--AGIP (Overseas) Ltd., Saint Helier, United Kingdom; *Int'l*, pg. 428
Cainer, Edoardo, Chm.--AGIP (North Africa & Middle East) Ltd., Saint Helier, United Kingdom; *Int'l*, pg. 428
Cairns, John, Chm. Bd.--Carr Gottstein Foods, Anchorage, AK; *U.S. Public*, pg. 308
Cairns, Lord, Chm. Bd.--British-American Tobacco (Germany) GmbH, Hamburg, Germany; *Int'l*, pg. 111
Cairns, Rt. Hon. Earl, The, Chm. Bd.--B.A.T Industries P.L.C., London, United Kingdom; *Int'l*, pg. 110
Calafati, Gabriel R., Chm. Bd., Pres. & Treas.--Frank Briscoe Co. Inc., Kenilworth, NJ; *U.S. Private*, pg. 169
Calain, Phil, Chm. Bd.--American Classic Voyagers Company, New Orleans, LA; *U.S. Private*, pg. 380
Calamani, Carlo, Chm. Bd.--Crown Cork Company (Italy) S.p.A., Voghera, Italy; *U.S. Public*, pg. 464
Calamari, Herman R., Chm. Bd.--El Dorado Tire Co., Troy, MI; *Int'l*, pg. 1312
Calamati, Mario, Chm. Bd.--Itafinco S.p.A., Milan, Italy; *Int'l*, pg. 138
Calamati, Mario, Chm. Bd.--Finanziaria BTB S.p.A., Trento, Italy; *Int'l*, pg. 138
Calarco, Vincent A., Chm. Bd., Pres. & Chief Exec. Officer--Crompton & Knowles Corporation, Stamford, CT; *U.S. Public*, pg. 459
Caldarone, Anthony J., Chm., Pres. & Chief Exec. Officer--Calton, Inc., Manalapan, NJ; *U.S. Public*, pg. 296
Calder, Clive, Chm. Bd. & Pres.--Zomba Recording Corp., London, United Kingdom; *Int'l*, pg. 1529
Calder, Clive, Chm. Bd. & Pres.--Zomba Group of Companies, New York, NY; *Int'l*, pg. 1529
Caldwell, Howard, Mrs., Chm. Bd.--Thomas L. Green & Co., Inc., Indianapolis, IN; *U.S. Private*, pg. 477
Caldwell, Philip, Chm. Bd.--Mettler-Toledo AG, Greifensee, Switzerland; *U.S. Private*, pg. 4
Caldwell, Robert F., Chm. Bd. & Chief Exec. Officer--Southeastern Michigan Gas Company, Port Huron, MI; *U.S. Public*, pg. 1489
Caldwell, William M., III, Chm. Bd.--King Koil Licensing Company Inc., Saint Paul, MN; *U.S. Private*, pg. 621

Caleffi, Camillo, Chm. Bd.--Caleffi S.p.A., Viadana, Italy; *Int'l*, pg. 252
Calhy, Ronald B., Chm., Pres. & Chief Exec. Officer--United HealthCare Insurance Company, Hartford, CT; *U.S. Public*, pg. 1678
Calicchio, John, Chm. Bd. & Pres.--Delcal Enterprises, Inc., New York, NY; *U.S. Private*, pg. 322
Calicchio, John, Chm. Bd.--Argo International Corp., New York, NY; *U.S. Private*, pg. 322
Call, O. Jay, Chm. Bd.--Flying J. Inc., Brigham City, UT; *U.S. Private*, pg. 415
Call, Robert V., Jr., Chm. Bd.--Curtice Burns Foods, Rochester, NY; *U.S. Private*, pg. 887
Call, William, Chm., Pres. & Chief Exec. Officer--Maverik Country Stores, Inc., Salt Lake City, UT; *U.S. Private*, pg. 715
Callahan, Dennis, Chm. Bd., Pres. & Chief Exec. Officer--Crowley, Milner & Company, Detroit, MI; *U.S. Public*, pg. 461
Callahan, Peter, Chm. Bd., Pres. & Chief Exec. Officer--American Media, Inc., Lake Worth, FL; *U.S. Public*, pg. 87
Callaway, Ely, Chm. Bd.--Callaway Golf Company, Carlsbad, CA; *U.S. Public*, pg. 294
Calleri, Giampiero, Chm. Bd.--Fiscambi Factoring S.p.A., Milan, Italy; *Int'l*, pg. 138
Callier, James T., Jr., Chm. Bd.--Century Products Co., Macedonia, OH; *U.S. Private*, pg. 226
Calligaris, A.E., Chm. Bd., Pres. & Chief Exec. Officer--Stebbins Engineering & Mfg. Co., Watertown, NY; *U.S. Private*, pg. 1037
Calton, Renneth J., Chm. Bd. & Pres.--North Carolina Equipment Co., Raleigh, NC; *U.S. Private*, pg. 804
Calvet, Jacques, Chm.-Mngmt. Bd.--PSA Peugeot Citroen, Paris, France; *Int'l*, pg. 1020
Calvet, Jacques, Chm.-Mngmt. Bd.--Peugeot S.A., Paris, France; *Int'l*, pg. 1020
Calvillo, Ricardo C., Chm. Bd. & Chief Exec. Officer--FerrellCalvillo Communications, Inc., New York, NY; *U.S. Private*, pg. 401
Camargo, Amador, Chm.-Y&R Group--Young & Rubicam Brazil, Sao Paulo, Brazil; *U.S. Private*, pg. 1200
Cambre, Ronald C., Chm. Bd., Pres. & Chief Exec. Officer--Newmont Mining Corporation, Denver, CO; *U.S. Public*, pg. 1178
Camerlo, James P., Jr., Chm. Bd.--Western Dairymen Cooperative, Inc., Thornton, CO; *U.S. Private*, pg. 1165
Cameron, Evan Duff, Chm. Bd.--Crane Group Limited, Epping, Australia; *Int'l*, pg. 340
Cameron, Gerald T., Sr., Chm. Bd. & Chief Exec. Officer--Amray, Inc., Bedford, MA; *U.S. Private*, pg. 67
Cameron, Gerry, Chm. Bd.--U.S. Bancorp, Minneapolis, MN; *U.S. Public*, pg. 1680
Cameron, I.T., Chm.--Senior Colman Limited, Sale, United Kingdom; *Int'l*, pg. 1220
Camosy, Remo E., Chm. Bd.--Camosy, Inc., Russell, IL; *U.S. Private*, pg. 203
Campagna, Harry G., Chm. Bd.--InterDigital Communications Corp., King of Prussia, PA; *U.S. Public*, pg. 889
Campanella, Anton J., Chm. & Chief Exec. Officer--Bell Atlantic Network Services, Inc., Arlington, VA; *U.S. Public*, pg. 202
Campbell, Argyle, Chm. Bd. & Pres.--Cambro Manufacturing Company, Huntington Beach, CA; *U.S. Private*, pg. 203
Campbell, Charles J., Chm. Bd., Pres. & Chief Exec. Officer--Florsheim Group Inc., Chicago, IL; *U.S. Public*, pg. 656
Campbell, James, Chm. Bd., Pres. & Chief Exec. Officer--First Community Bank of Saltville, Saltville, VA; *U.S. Public*, pg. 1039
Campbell, John J., III, Chm. Bd. & Pres.--John J. Campbell Co., Inc., Memphis, TN; *U.S. Private*, pg. 204
Campbell, Keith, Chm. Bd.--Mannington Mills, Inc., Salem, NJ; *U.S. Private*, pg. 700
Campbell, Kenneth L., Mrs., Chm. Bd. & Pres.--Dover Industries Limited, Burlington, Canada; *Int'l*, pg. 417
Campbell, M. Ralph, Chm. Bd.--Montour Bank, Danville, PA; *U.S. Public*, pg. 1222
Campbell, Michael L., Chm. Bd., Pres. & Chief Exec. Officer--Regal Cinemas Inc., Knoxville, TN; *U.S. Public*, pg. 1371
Campbell, Mike, Chm. Bd.--Olin Microelectronic Materials, Inc., Norwalk, CT; *U.S. Public*, pg. 1219
Campbell, Patrick, Chm. Bd.--Campbells/Bewley Group, Dublin, Ireland; *Int'l*, pg. 253
Campbell, Robert H., Chm. Bd., Chief Exec. Officer & Pres.--Sun Company, Inc., Philadelphia, PA; *U.S. Public*, pg. 1530
Campbell, William I., Chm. Bd.--Philip Morris U.S.A., New York, NY; *U.S. Public*, pg. 1289
Campbell, William M., Chm. Bd. & Pres.--Camalloy, Incorporated, Washington, PA; *U.S. Private*, pg. 202
Campion, R. R., Chm. Bd.--Towne Square Furniture, Inc., Hillsboro, TX; *U.S. Private*, pg. 1093
Campo, Richard J., Chm. Bd. & Chief Exec. Officer--Camden Property Trust, Houston, TX; *U.S. Public*, pg. 298
Canavan, Daniel B., Chm. Bd. & Chief Exec. Officer--Triple S Plastics, Inc., Vicksburg, MI; *U.S. Public*, pg. 1639
Candlish, Malcolm, Chm. Bd. & Chief Exec. Officer--First Alert, Inc., Aurora, IL; *U.S. Private*, pg. 406
Canet, Gerardo, Chm. Bd., Pres. & Chief Exec. Officer--IntegraMed America, Purchase, NY; *U.S. Public*, pg. 883
Canfield, Arthur, Sr., Chm. Bd.--Select Canfield, Chicago, IL; *U.S. Private*, pg. 982
Canfield, Brian A., Chm. Bd. & Chief Exec. Officer--BC Telecom Inc., Burnaby, Canada; *U.S. Public*, pg. 697
Cannestra, Kenneth, Chm. Bd.--EA Industries, West Long Branch, NJ; *U.S. Public*, pg. 541
Canno, Jonathon S., Chm. Bd., Pres. & Chief Oper. Officer--Equitable Bag Company, Inc., Florence, KY; *U.S. Private*, pg. 380
Cannon, Dean G., Chm. Bd. & Pres.--Cannon Express Inc., Springdale, AR; *U.S. Public*, pg. 301
Cannon, John D., Chm. Bd.--Cannon, Grand Island, NY; *U.S. Private*, pg. 205
Cannon, Joseph A., Chm. Bd. & Chief Exec. Officer--Geneva Steel, Vineyard, UT; *U.S. Public*, pg. 729
Cantor, Paul, Chm. & Chief Exec. Officer--National Trust Company, Stratford, Canada; *Int'l*, pg. 910
Canzone, Pete, Chm. Bd.--Brylane L.P., New York, NY; *U.S. Public*, pg. 996
Caouette, John B., Chm. Bd. & Chief Exec. Officer--Capital Markets Assurance Corporation, New York, NY; *U.S. Public*, pg. 1023
Capallo, Mark, Chm. Bd. & Chief Exec. Officer--Energy & Process Corp., Tucker, GA; *Int'l*, pg. 1512
Caplan, James A., Chm. Bd., Pres., Treas., Prod. Mgr. & Chief Engr.--Capp, Inc., Clifton Heights, PA; *U.S. Private*, pg. 207
Caplan, L. David, Chm. Bd. & Chief Exec. Officer--Pratt & Whitney Canada Inc., Longueuil, Canada; *U.S. Public*, pg. 1690
Caporella, Nick A., Chm. Bd., Pres., Chief Exec. Officer & Chief Fin. Officer--National Beverage Corp., Plantation, FL; *U.S. Public*, pg. 1153
Capp, William Barret, Chm. Bd.--Sunbeam Victa Holdings Ltd., Campsie, Australia; *Int'l*, pg. 539
Cappelletti, Grace E., Chm. Bd.--Putman Publishing Co., Itasca, IL; *U.S. Private*, pg. 896
Cappiello, William D., Chm. Bd. & Chief Exec. Officer--Parisian, Inc., Birmingham, AL; *U.S. Public*, pg. 1333
Cappis, Marc C., Chm. Bd.--Huber & Suhner AG, Pfaffikon, Switzerland; *Int'l*, pg. 637
Capps, Thomas E., Chm. Bd., Pres. & Chief Exec. Officer--Dominion Resources, Inc., Richmond, VA; *U.S. Public*, pg. 516
Cappy, Joseph E., Chm.--Pentastar Transportation Corp., Tulsa, OK; *U.S. Public*, pg. 354
Capstick, John, Chm. & Chief Exec. Officer--R.R. Donnelley, Limited-York, York, United Kingdom; *U.S. Public*, pg. 519
Carabini, Louis E., Chm. Bd. & Pres.--Monex Deposit Co., Newport Beach, CA; *U.S. Private*, pg. 757
Carberry, Robert L., Chm. Bd., Pres. & Chief Exec. Officer--CyberGuard Corporation, Fort Lauderdale, FL; *U.S. Public*, pg. 470
Carbonari, Bruce A., Chm. & Chief Exec. Officer--Moen Incorporated, North Olmsted, OH; *U.S. Public*, pg. 675
Cardenas, Don Eduardo Monroy, Chm. Bd.--Tablex, S.A. de C.V., Toluca, Mexico; *Int'l*, pg. 1346
Cardoso Salgado, Jose Manuel Pereira, Dr., Chm.--EIVAL, S.A., Lisbon, Portugal; *Int'l*, pg. 1045
Cardy, Robert W., Chm., Pres. & Chief Exec. Officer--Carpenter Technology Corporation, Reading, PA; *U.S. Public*, pg. 307
Carell, Monroe J., Jr., Chm. Bd. & Chief Exec. Officer--Central Parking Corp., Nashville, TN; *U.S. Public*, pg. 326
Carey, C. William, Chm. Bd.--Little Switzerland, Inc., Charlotte Amalie, VI; *U.S. Public*, pg. 1001
Carey, D. John, Chm. Bd.--Integrated Device Technology, Inc., Santa Clara, CA; *U.S. Public*, pg. 884
Carey, William P., Chm. Bd. & Mng. Dir.--W.P. Carey & Co., Inc., New York, NY; *U.S. Private*, pg. 209
Cargile, David L., Chm. Bd., Pres. & Chief Exec. Officer--Centris Group Inc., Costa Mesa, CA; *U.S. Public*, pg. 328
Cargill, Don A., Chm.--Cargill Detroit Corp., Clawson, MI; *U.S. Private*, pg. 210
Caridis, Tony, Chm. Bd. & Pres.--Heat & Control, Inc., Hayward, CA; *U.S. Private*, pg. 518
Carl, Fred, Jr., Chm. Bd., Pres. & Chief Exec. Officer--Viking Range Corp., Greenwood, MS; *U.S. Private*, pg. 1140
Carley, John B., Chm.-Exec. Commitee--Albertson's, Inc., Boise, ID; *U.S. Public*, pg. 38
Carlin, Edward R., Chief Fin. Officer, Exec. V.P. & Sec.--Goody's Family Clothing, Inc., Knoxville, TN; *U.S. Public*, pg. 753
Carlino, Peter M., Chm. Bd. & Chief Exec. Officer--Penn National Gaming, Inc., Wyomissing, PA; *U.S. Public*, pg. 1270
Carlisle, Brian, Chm. Bd. & Chief Exec. Officer--Adept Technology, Inc., San Jose, CA; *U.S. Public*, pg. 19
Carlisle, Tony, Exec. Chm.--Dewe Rogerson Limited, London, United Kingdom; *Int'l*, pg. 408
Carlos, Michael C., Chm. Bd. & Chief Exec. Officer--National Distributing Co., Inc., Atlanta, GA; *U.S. Private*, pg. 781
Carlsen, David R., Chm. Bd., Sec. & Legal Counsel--Upper Midwest Industries, Incorporated, Minneapolis, MN; *U.S. Private*, pg. 1129
Carlson, Curtis L., Chm. Bd. & Chief Exec. Officer--Carlson Companies, Inc., Minnetonka, MN; *U.S. Private*, pg. 211
Carlson, H. Gary, Dr., Chm. Bd., Pres. & Chief Exec. Officer--ElecSys Inc., Peoria, IL; *U.S. Private*, pg. 367
Carlson, Hans, Chm. Bd.--Jarnia AB, Ulricehammn, Sweden; *Int'l*, pg. 188
Carlson, Joseph, Chm. Bd.--Carlson Systems, Omaha, NE; *U.S. Private*, pg. 212
Carlson, LeRoy T., Chm.--Telephone and Data Systems, Inc., Chicago, IL; *U.S. Public*, pg. 1570
Carlson, Neal M., Chm. Bd.--First National Bank of Warsaw, Warsaw, IN; *U.S. Public*, pg. 674
Carlson, Richard N., Chm. Bd.--Park Construction Company, Minneapolis, MN; *U.S. Private*, pg. 839
Carlson, Robert A., Chm. Bd. & Chief Exec. Officer--NAI Technologies, Inc., Huntington, NY; *U.S. Public*, pg. 1144
Carlson, Robert W., Jr., Chm. Bd.--Quadion Corporation, Minneapolis, MN; *U.S. Private*, pg. 898
Carlsson, S., Chm. Bd.--ABB Kent Plc, Luton, United Kingdom; *Int'l*, pg. 2
Carlston, Douglas G., Chm. Bd.--Broderbund Software, Inc., Novato, CA; *U.S. Public*, pg. 258
Carman, Carl D., Chm. Bd.--Symantec Corporation, Cupertino, CA; *U.S. Public*, pg. 1545
Carmichael, Arthur C., Jr., Chm. Bd.--Willis Corroon Corp. of San Jose, San Jose, CA; *Int'l*, pg. 1507
Carmody, Thomas R., Chm. Bd., Pres. & Chief Exec. Officer--American Business Products, Inc., Atlanta, GA; *U.S. Public*, pg. 70
Carnegie, Dorothy, Chm. Bd.--Dale Carnegie Training, New York, NY; *U.S. Private*, pg. 308
Carney, William V., Chm. Bd & Chief Exec. Officer--Porta Systems Corp., Syosset, NY; *U.S. Public*, pg. 1317
Caron, Yvan, Chm. Bd.--Assurance vie Desjardins-Laurentienne, Levis, Canada; *Int'l*, pg. 396
Carota, Richard J., Chm. Bd., Pres. & Chief Exec. Officer--Finch, Pruyn & Co., Inc., Glens Falls, NY; *U.S. Private*, pg. 405
Carpenter, Michael A., Chm. & Chief Exec. Officer--The Travelers Life & Annuity Co., Hartford, CT; *U.S. Public*, pg. 1633
Carr, Greg, Chm. Bd.--Prodigy Inc., White Plains, NY; *U.S. Private*, pg. 888
Carr, Greg C, Chm. Bd.--Comverse Network Systems, Wakefield, MA; *U.S. Public*, pg. 425
Carr, Oliver T., Jr., Chm. Bd.--CarrAmerica Realty, Washington, DC; *U.S. Public*, pg. 308
Carr, Richard, Chm. Bd.--TransTec Plc, Birmingham, United Kingdom; *Int'l*, pg. 1418
Carr, Robert F., III, Chm. & Chief Exec. Officer--Fiduciary Management Associates, Inc., Chicago, IL; *U.S. Public*, pg. 1673
Carrard, Francois, Chm. Bd.--UMS Swiss Metalworks Holding Ltd, Dornach, Switzerland; *Int'l*, pg. 1427
Carrio, Juan Llorens, Chm. Bd.--SEAT, S.A., Barcelona, Spain; *Int'l*, pg. 1475
Carrion, Richard L., Chm. Bd., Pres. & Chief Exec. Officer--Banco Popular de Puerto Rico, San Juan, PR; *U.S. Public*, pg. 175
Carrion, Richard L., Chm. Bd., Pres. & Chief Exec. Officer--BanPonce Corporation, Hato Rey, PR; *U.S. Public*, pg. 176
Carroll, Daniel T., Chm. Bd.--Comshare, Incorporated, Ann Arbor, MI; *U.S. Public*, pg. 425
Carroll, Daniel T., Chm. Bd.--Oshkosh Truck Corporation, Oshkosh, WI; *U.S. Public*, pg. 1233
Carroll, James, Chm. Bd. & Chief Exec. Officer--Wynn's International, Inc., Orange, CA; *U.S. Public*, pg. 1782
Carroll, James, Chm. Bd.--Wynn's-Precision, Inc., Lebanon, TN; *U.S. Public*, pg. 1783
Carruthers, Lynn, Chm. Bd.--Precision Tune Autocare Inc., Leesburg, VA; *U.S. Public*, pg. 1321
Carsey, Marcy, Co-Owner--Carsey-Werner Company, LLC, Studio City, CA; *U.S. Private*, pg. 216
Carson, David E.A., Chm. Bd. & Chief Exec. Officer--People's Bank, Bridgeport, CT; *U.S. Public*, pg. 1274
Carson, James B., Jr., Chm. Bd.--Carter & Associates, Atlanta, GA; *U.S. Private*, pg. 216
Carson, John C., Chm.--Triarc Beverage Group, White Plains, NY; *U.S. Public*, pg. 1635
Carson, Russel L., Chm. Bd.--Quorum Health Group, Inc., Brentwood, TN; *U.S. Public*, pg. 1353
Carson, William C., Chm. Bd. & Chief Exec. Officer--Instrument Specialties Company, Delaware Water Gap, PA; *U.S. Private*, pg. 565
Carson, William G., Chm. Bd.--Boatmen's National Mortgage Inc., Memphis, TN; *U.S. Public*, pg. 1165
Carstarphen, J.M., Chm. Bd., Pres. & Chief Exec. Officer--Stowe-Pharr Mills, Inc., Mc Adenville, NC; *U.S. Private*, pg. 1045
Carte, B. A., Chm. Bd.--Lombard Bank Limited, Enfield, United Kingdom; *Int'l*, pg. 910
Carter, John M., Chm. Bd. & Chief Exec. Officer--Carco Electronics, Menlo Park, CA; *U.S. Private*, pg. 208
Carter, Marshall N., Chm. Bd. & Chief Exec. Officer--State Street Corporation, Boston, MA; *U.S. Public*, pg. 1513
Carter, Mason N., Chm. Bd. & Chief Exec. Officer--Merrimac Industries, Inc., West Caldwell, NJ; *U.S. Public*, pg. 1098
Carter, Sam, Chm. Bd. & Pres.--Carter Companies, Kansas City, MO; *U.S. Private*, pg. 216
Carter, Thomas F., Jr., Chm. Bd. & Chief Exec. Officer--Keck Instruments, Inc., Williamston, MI; *U.S. Public*, pg. 367
Carter, Tim, Chm. Bd. & Chief Exec. Officer--Bell-Carter Foods, Inc., Lafayette, CA; *U.S. Private*, pg. 131
Cartier, Jacques, Chm. Bd.--Agropur, Granby, Canada; *Int'l*, pg. 31
Cartone, Tommaso, Chm. Bd.--Ambro Italia Societa di Intermediazione Mobiliare S.p.A., Milan, Italy; *Int'l*, pg. 138
Cartwright, Peter, Chm. Bd., Pres. & CHief Exec. Officer--Calpine Corporation, San Jose, CA; *U.S. Public*, pg. 296
Carus, M. Blouke, Chm. Bd., Chief Exec. Officer & Chief Oper. Officer--Carus Corporation, Peru, IL; *U.S. Private*, pg. 217
Carver, Martin G., Chm. Bd., Pres. & Chief Exec. Officer--Bandag, Incorporated, Muscatine, IA; *U.S. Public*, pg. 177
Casanas, Luis Miranda, Chm. Bd.--Universal Insurance Co., San Juan, PR; *U.S. Public*, pg. 962
Case, Daniel H., III, Chm. Bd. & Chief Exec. Officer--Hambrecht & Quist LLC., San Francisco, CA; *U.S. Public*, pg. 778
Case, Stephen M., Chm. Bd., Pres, Chief Exec. & Oper. Officer--America Online Incorporated, Dulles, VA; *U.S. Public*, pg. 66
Casella, John W., Chm. Bd., Pres. & Chief Exec. Officer--Casella Waste Systems, Inc., Rutland, VT; *U.S. Public*, pg. 312
Casey-Howell, Bobbi, Exec. V.P. & Dir.-Direct Deutsch--DirectDeutsch, New York, NY; *U.S. Private*, pg. 328
Casey, Aloysius G., Chm. Bd.--National Technical Systems, Inc., Calabasas, CA; *U.S. Public*, pg. 1161
Casey, E. Paul, Chm. Bd.--Metapoint Partners, Peabody, MA; *U.S. Private*, pg. 735
Casey, Jeremiah E., Chm. Bd.--First Maryland Bancorp, Baltimore, MD; *Int'l*, pg. 64
Casey, John A., Chm. Bd.--WGM Safety Corporation, Reading, PA; *Int'l*, pg. 462

Casey, Phillip E., Chm. Bd. & Chief Exec. Officer--AmeriSteel, Tampa, FL; *U.S. Private*, pg. 65
Casey, Richard L., Chm. Bd., Pres. & Chief Exec. Officer--Scios Inc., Mountain View, CA; *U.S. Public*, pg. 1444
Casey, Richard T., Chm. Bd.--F.W. Myers & Co., Inc., Rouses Point, NY; *U.S. Private*, pg. 770
Cash, Francis W., Chm. Bd., Pres. & Chief Exec. Officer--Red Roof Inns, Inc., Hilliard, OH; *U.S. Public*, pg. 1369
Cash, Harvey B., Chm. Bd.--Cyrix Corporation, Richardson, TX; *U.S. Public*, pg. 1160
Cash, R.D., Chm. Bd., Pres. & Chief Exec. Officer--Questar Corporation, Salt Lake City, UT; *U.S. Public*, pg. 1352
Cash, R.D., Chm. Bd.--Questar Development Corporation, Salt Lake City, UT; *U.S. Public*, pg. 1352
Cash, R.D., Chm. Bd.--Questar InfoComm, Salt Lake City, UT; *U.S. Public*, pg. 1352
Cashman, Eugene C., Chm. Bd.--Merchant Capital Group Ltd., Chicago, IL; *U.S. Private*, pg. 732
Casilli, Gerald S., Chm. Bd.--IKOS Systems, Inc., Cupertino, CA; *U.S. Public*, pg. 864
Caspersen, Finn M.W., Chm. Bd. & Chief Exec. Officer--Beneficial Corporation, Wilmington, DE; *U.S. Public*, pg. 211
Caspersen, Finn M.W., Chm. Bd.--Beneficial Management Corporation, Peapack, NJ; *U.S. Public*, pg. 211
Casperson, Finn M.W., Chm. Bd.--Beneficial Management Corporation of America & Affiliated Corps., Wilmington, DE; *U.S. Public*, pg. 211
Cass, Ronald A., Chm. Bd., Pres., Chief Exec. Officer & Treas.--Hospital Staffing Services, Inc., Fort Lauderdale, FL; *U.S. Public*, pg. 840
Cassano, Victor J., Jr., Chm. Bd. & Chief Exec. Officer--Cassano's Inc., Dayton, OH; *U.S. Private*, pg. 218
Cassels, W. T., Jr., Chm. Bd.--Southeastern Freight Lines, Inc., Lexington, SC; *U.S. Private*, pg. 1015
Cassens, Albert, Chm. Bd.--Cassens Transport Company, Edwardsville, IL; *U.S. Private*, pg. 219
Cassese, John J., Chm. Bd., Pres., Chief Oper. & Chief Exec. Officer--Computer Horizons Corp., Mountain Lakes, NJ; *U.S. Public*, pg. 421
Cassese, Patrick J., Chm. Bd., Pres. & Chief Exec. Officer--Antares Group Inc., Cleveland, OH; *U.S. Private*, pg. 76
Cassidy, D., Chm.--Ferguson International Holdings, Banbury, United Kingdom; *Int'l*, pg. 479
Cassidy, D.P., Chm. Bd.--Liberty PLC, London, United Kingdom; *Int'l*, pg. 807
Casteborn, Lars, Chm. Bd.--Brougher Agency, Inc., Indianapolis, IN; *Int'l*, pg. 464
Castellanos, Jaime, Chm. Bd.--S&C Willis Corroon Correduria de Seguros y Reaseguros S.A., Madrid, Spain; *Int'l*, pg. 1509
Castelli, Giulio, Chm. Bd.--Ambrofid Gestioni Fiduciarie S.p.A., Milan, Italy; *Int'l*, pg. 138
Castellini, Clateo, Chm. Bd., Pres. & Chief Exec. Officer--Becton Dickinson & Company, Franklin Lakes, NJ; *U.S. Public*, pg. 199
Castello, John L., Chm. Bd., Chief Exec. Officer & Pres.--XOMA Corporation, Berkeley, CA; *U.S. Public*, pg. 1786
Castle, James, Phd., Chm. Bd. & Chief Exec. Officer--USCS International, Inc., Rancho Cordova, CA; *U.S. Public*, pg. 1659
Castle, John K., Chm. Bd.--Castle-Harlan, Inc., New York, NY; *U.S. Private*, pg. 219
Castle, Joseph L., Chm. Bd., Pres. & Chief Exec. Officer--Castle Energy Corporation, Radnor, PA; *U.S. Public*, pg. 313
Castouguay, Claude, Chm. Bd.--Desjardins Laurentian Life Assurance, Wayne, PA; *Int'l*, pg. 396
Casty, Ronald G., Chm. Bd., Pres., Chief Exec. & Oper. Officer--Chelsea Industries, Inc., Peabody, MA; *U.S. Private*, pg. 231
Catacosinos, William J., Chm. Bd. & Chief Exec. Officer--Long Island Lighting Company, Hicksville, NY; *U.S. Public*, pg. 1013
Cataldo, C.A., Chm. Bd. & Chief Exec. Officer--Hostmark Management Group, Rolling Meadows, IL; *U.S. Private*, pg. 541
Catell, Robert B., Chm. Bd. & Chief Exec. Officer--Brooklyn Union, Brooklyn, NY; *U.S. Public*, pg. 259
Cater, John T., Chm. Bd. & Chief Exec. Officer--River Oaks Trust Company, Houston, TX; *U.S. Public*, pg. 419
Catherwood, H.S.E., Chm.--Lombard and Ulster Limited, Belfast, United Kingdom; *Int'l*, pg. 910
Cato, Wayland H., Jr., Chm. Bd. & Chief Exec. Officer--The Cato Corporation, Charlotte, NC; *U.S. Public*, pg. 318
Caton, Robert J., Chm. Bd. & Pres.--Fay, Spofford & Thorndike, Inc., Burlington, MA; *U.S. Private*, pg. 397
Catsimatidis, John, Chm. Bd. & Chief Exec. Officer--Red Apple Companies, New York, NY; *U.S. Private*, pg. 914
Catsimatidis, John A., Chm. Bd. & Chief Exec. Officer--United Refining Company, Warren, PA; *U.S. Private*, pg. 915
Catsimatidis, John A., Chm. Bd., Chief Exec. Officer & Treas.--Sloan's Supermarkets, Inc., New York, NY; *U.S. Private*, pg. 915
Caunter, Harry K., Chm. Bd.--SPD Technologies, Philadelphia, PA; *U.S. Private*, pg. 957
Cavanaugh, Jim, Chm. Bd., Pres., Chief Exec. Officer & Sec.--Jani King International, Inc., Dallas, TX; *U.S. Private*, pg. 581
Cavender, Lea, Chm. Bd. & Pres.--E-Z Bowz, Inc., Sevierville, TN; *U.S. Private*, pg. 352
Caveney, William V., Chm. Bd.--Southern California Water Company, San Dimas, CA; *U.S. Public*, pg. 1489
Cavoorees, John, Chm.--Chubb Insurance Company of Europe, Brussels, Belgium; *U.S. Public*, pg. 355
Cawley, Charles M., Chm. Bd., Pres. & Chief Exec. Officer--MBNA America Bank N.A., Wilmington, DE; *U.S. Public*, pg. 1023
Cawley, Lawrence J., Chm. Bd.--Kaydon Corporation, Clearwater, FL; *U.S. Public*, pg. 945
Caye, Charles G., Sr., Chm. Bd.--W.C. Caye & Company, Inc., Augusta, GA; *U.S. Private*, pg. 220
Cayre, Joseph, Chm. Bd.--GT Interactive Software Corp., New York, NY; *U.S. Public*, pg. 696
Cayre, Stanley, Chm. Bd.--GoodTimes Entertainment Co., New York, NY; *U.S. Private*, pg. 464
Cecala, Ted T., Chm. Bd. & Chief Exec. Officer--Wilmington Trust Corporation, Wilmington, DE; *U.S. Public*, pg. 1770
Cecan, Ayhan, Chm.--Markom/Leo Burnett A.S., Istanbul, Turkey; *U.S. Private*, pg. 186
Cecchini, Aldo, Chm. Bd.--Bertolli USA, Inc., Secaucus, NJ; *Int'l*, pg. 655
Cecil, Ed, Chm. Bd.--R.W. Beck, Inc., Seattle, WA; *U.S. Private*, pg. 128
Cecil, Robert S., Chm. Bd., Pres. & Chief Exec. Officer--Plantronics Inc., Santa Cruz, CA; *U.S. Public*, pg. 1308
Cedelle, Jean, Chm.-CLINVEST--Credit Lyonnais S.A., Paris, France; *Int'l*, pg. 343
Celentano, Domenick, Chm. Bd. & Pres.--Celentano Bros. Inc., Verona, NJ; *U.S. Private*, pg. 221
Celentano, E., Chm. Bd.--Texaco Interamerican Exploration Co., Bridgetown, Barbados; *U.S. Public*, pg. 1584
Celentano, E., Chm.--Texaco Panama Inc., Panama, Panama; *U.S. Public*, pg. 1584
Celentano, E., Chm. Bd.--Texaco Petroleum Co., Quito, Ecuador; *U.S. Public*, pg. 1584
Celentano, E., Chm.--Texaco Trinidad, Inc., Port of Spain, Trinidad & Tobago; *U.S. Public*, pg. 1584
Celeste, Lino, Chm. Bd.--Avenor, Inc., Montreal, Canada; *Int'l*, pg. 101
Celeste, Lino, Chm. Bd.--Bruncor, Inc., Saint John, Canada; *Int'l*, pg. 230
Celeste, Lino J., Chm. Bd.--Datacor/ISM (Information Systems Management Atlantic Corp.), Moncton, Canada; *Int'l*, pg. 230
Cely, Arquimedos, Chm. Bd.--Industrias Bachoco S.A. de C.V., Celaya, Mexico; *Int'l*, pg. 677
Centofanti, Louis F., Dr., Chm. Bd., Pres. & Chief Exec. Officer--Perma-Fix Environmental Services, Inc., Gainesville, FL; *U.S. Public*, pg. 1279
Certeza, Col., Chm. Bd.--Pasco-Certeza Computer Mapping Corporation, Manila, Philippines; *Int'l*, pg. 1024
Cervieri, John A., Jr., Chm. Bd.--Property Capital Trust, Boston, MA; *U.S. Public*, pg. 1335
Cervinka, James J., Chm. Bd. & Chief Exec. Officer--Arrow Gear Company, Downers Grove, IL; *U.S. Private*, pg. 85
Cervinka, James J., Chm. Bd.--Johnson Gear, Lincoln, NE; *U.S. Private*, pg. 85
Cesarini, Francesco, Chm. Bd.--Banca Popolare di Milano, Milan, Italy; *Int'l*, pg. 137
Chabraja, Nicholas D., Chm. Bd. & Chief Exec. Officer--General Dynamics Corporation, Falls Church, VA; *U.S. Public*, pg. 708
Chadha, Sharon G., Chm. Bd.--Osicom Technologies Inc., Santa Monica, CA; *U.S. Public*, pg. 1233
Chadlington, Lord, Chm. Bd.--Shandwick International Plc, London, United Kingdom; *Int'l*, pg. 1226
Chadwick, Winslow J., Chm. Bd.--Distributors Oil Company, Inc., Baton Rouge, LA; *U.S. Private*, pg. 336
Chaffart, Ferdinand, Dep. Chm.--Banque Generale du Luxembourg SA, Luxembourg, Luxembourg; *Int'l*, pg. 161
Chaffart, Ferdinand, Chm.-Exec. Committee & Mng. Dir.--Generale de Banque S.A., Brussels, Belgium; *Int'l*, pg. 546
Chai, Jay, Chm. Bd.--ITOCHU International Inc., New York, NY; *Int'l*, pg. 694
Chaiken, Eugene B., Chm., Pres. & Chief Exec. Officer--Almo Corp., Philadelphia, PA; *U.S. Private*, pg. 44
Chalmers, David B., Chm. Bd., Pres., Chief Exec. Officer & Treas.--Coral Oil & Gas Inc., Houston, TX; *U.S. Private*, pg. 275
Chaltiel, Victor M.G., Chm. Bd., Pres. & Chief Exec. Officer--Total Renal Care Holdings, Inc., Torrance, CA; *U.S. Public*, pg. 1625
Chamberlain, David M., Chm. Bd.--Genesco Inc., Nashville, TN; *U.S. Public*, pg. 728
Chamberlain, L.N., Deputy Chm.--BNFL, Warrington, United Kingdom; *Int'l*, pg. 120
Chamberlain, Milton, Chm. Bd.--Athens Paper Co. Inc., Nashville, TN; *U.S. Private*, pg. 94
Chamberlain, Peter, Chm. Bd.--Dacon Electronics Plc., Hemel Hempstead, United Kingdom; *U.S. Public*, pg. 395
Chamberlain, Steven R., Chm. Bd. & Chief Exec. Officer--Integral Systems, Inc., Lanham, MD; *U.S. Public*, pg. 883
Chambers, William R., Chm. Bd.--C. B. Fleet Co., Inc., Lynchburg, VA; *U.S. Private*, pg. 410
Champalimaud, Luis, Chm. Bd.--Banco Totta & Acores, Lisbon, Portugal; *Int'l*, pg. 144
Chance, Douglas, Pres. & Chief Exec. Officer--Wyse Technology Inc., San Jose, CA; *U.S. Private*, pg. 1194
Chancey, Malcolm B., Jr., Chm. Bd.--Bank One, Kentucky, NA, Louisville, KY; *U.S. Public*, pg. 173
Chandler, David L., Chm. Bd.--Johnston Industries, Inc., Columbus, GA; *U.S. Public*, pg. 933
Chandler, Richard H., Chm. Bd.,Pres. & Chief Exec. Officer--Sunrise Medical, Inc., Carlsbad, CA; *U.S. Public*, pg. 1535
Chandler, S. R., Chm.--National Westminster Home Loans Limited, Birmingham, United Kingdom; *Int'l*, pg. 910
Chandler, William F., Jr., Chm.-Management Committee, Principal & Mng. Dir.--National Asset Management Corporation, Louisville, KY; *U.S. Public*, pg. 1154
Chandris, John D., Chm.--Celebrity Cruises, Inc., Miami, FL; *U.S. Public*, pg. 1410
Chaney, James R., Chm. Bd. & Chief Exec. Officer--The Coastal Bank of Georgia, Brunswick, GA; *U.S. Public*, pg. 1549
Chaney, John D., Pres. & Chief Exec. Officer--TeleCheck Services, Inc., Houston, TX; *U.S. Public*, pg. 631
Chaney, William R., Chm. Bd. & Chief Exec. Officer--Tiffany & Co., New York, NY; *U.S. Public*, pg. 1608
Chang, Morris, Chm. Bd.--Wyse Technology Inc., San Jose, CA; *U.S. Private*, pg. 1194
Chang, T.Y., Chm. Bd.--Chinese Petroleum Corporation, Taipei, Taiwan; *Int'l*, pg. 286
Chang, Tom, Chm. Bd. & Pres.--H. Salt of Southern California, Inc., Monterey Park, CA; *U.S. Private*, pg. 489
Chano, Takashi, Chm. Bd.--Kayaba Industry Co., Ltd., Tokyo, Japan; *Int'l*, pg. 727
Chant, Dixon S., Chm. Bd.--Versa Services Ltd., Etobicoke, Canada; *U.S. Private*, pg. 79
Chant, Dixon S., Chm. Bd.--Domgroup Ltd., Toronto, Canada; *Int'l*, pg. 631
Chao, Allen Y., Ph.D., Chm. Bd. & Chief Exec. Officer--Watson Pharmaceuticals, Inc., Corona, CA; *U.S. Public*, pg. 1746
Chaplin, Harvey, Chm. Bd.--Southern Wine & Spirits of America Inc., Miami, FL; *U.S. Private*, pg. 1017
Chapman, Keith, Chm. Bd. & Chief Exec. Officer--Fine Art Developments plc, Bradford, United Kingdom; *Int'l*, pg. 485
Chapman, Max C., Jr., Chm. Bd.--Nomura Securities International, Inc., New York, NY; *Int'l*, pg. 956
Chapman, R.N., Chm. Bd. & Chief Exec. Officer--Pneumatic Scale Corporation, Cuyahoga Falls, OH; *U.S. Private*, pg. 118
Chapman, Robert H., Chm. Bd. & Pres.--Barry-Wehmiller Company, Saint Louis, MO; *U.S. Private*, pg. 118
Chapman, Robert H., III, Chm. Bd., Pres., Chief Exec. Officer & Treas.--Inman Mills, Inman, SC; *U.S. Private*, pg. 564
Chapman, Thomas Neal, Chm.--The Southern Life Association Limited, Cape Town, South Africa; *Int'l*, pg. 77
Chapman, Thomas Neal, Chm. Bd.--First National Bank Holdings Limited, Johannesburg, South Africa; *Int'l*, pg. 487
Chapman, Wilford, Chm. Bd., Pres. & Chief Exec. Officer--Idaho Supreme Company, Firth, ID; *U.S. Private*, pg. 557
Chapoton, David, Chm. Bd. & Chief Exec. Officer--Tastee Freez International Inc., Utica, MI; *U.S. Private*, pg. 1069
Chappell, Robert E., Chm. Bd. & Chief Exec. Officer--The Penn Mutual Life Insurance Company, Philadelphia, PA; *U.S. Private*, pg. 849
Chappell, Robert E., Chm. Bd. & Chief Exec. Officer--PNC Bank, Philadelphia, PA; *U.S. Public*, pg. 1243
Charbin, Paul G., Chm. Bd.--J.B. Martin Company, New York, NY; *U.S. Private*, pg. 709
Charles, R., Chm. Bd.--Hydro Group, Inc., Bridgewater, NJ; *U.S. Private*, pg. 552
Charlestein, Gary, Chm. Bd. & Chief Exec. Officer--Premier Dental Products Company, King of Prussia, PA; *U.S. Private*, pg. 881
Charlestein, Morton, Chm. Emeritus--Premier Dental Products Company, King of Prussia, PA; *U.S. Private*, pg. 881
Charpentier, Albert J., Chm. Bd., Pres. & Chief Exec. Officer--Ensoniq, Malvern, PA; *U.S. Private*, pg. 377
Charron, Paul R., Chm. Bd. & Chief Exec. Officer--Liz Claiborne, Inc., New York, NY; *U.S. Public*, pg. 1005
Charton, Steve, Chm. Bd., Pres & Chief Exec. Officer--Don Miguel Mexican Foods, Inc., Anaheim, CA; *U.S. Private*, pg. 339
Chase, Eric T., Chm. Bd., Pres., Chief Exec. Officer & Founder--QC Optics, Inc., Wilmington, MA; *U.S. Public*, pg. 1345
Chase, Malcolm G., III, Chm. Bd.--Mossberg Industries, Inc., Cumberland, RI; *U.S. Private*, pg. 763
Chase, William K., Chm. Bd.--Chase Chevrolet Co., Inc., Stockton, CA; *U.S. Private*, pg. 230
Chasen, Melvin, Chm. Bd., Pres. & Chief Exec. Officer--Transmedia Network Inc., Miami, FL; *U.S. Public*, pg. 1631
Chaus, Josephine, Chm. Bd.--Bernard Chaus, Inc., New York, NY; *U.S. Public*, pg. 342
Chaus, Josephine, Chm. Bd.--Bernard Chaus, Inc., Secaucus, NJ; *U.S. Public*, pg. 342
Chauvallon, G., Chm. Bd.--American Eurocopter Corp., Grand Prairie, TX; *Int'l*, pg. 29
Chavkin, Wallace, Chm. Bd. & Chief Exec. Officer--Biddle Sawyer Corporation, New York, NY; *U.S. Private*, pg. 142
Chavoya, Rene Castro, Chm. Bd.--Compania Siderurgia de Guadalajara, Guadalajara, Mexico; *Int'l*, pg. 576
Chedraui Eguia, Antonio, Chm. Bd.--Grupo Comercial Chedraui S.A. de C.V., Veracruz, Mexico; *Int'l*, pg. 573
Chee Siong, Robert Ng, Chm. Bd.--Yeo Hiap Seng Limited, Singapore, Singapore; *Int'l*, pg. 1008
Cheek, Carl W., Chm. Bd. & Chief Exec. Officer--Specialty Industries, Inc., Red Lion, PA; *U.S. Private*, pg. 1022
Cheema, Jasse, Chm. Bd. & Pres.--Theodore Barry & Associates, Los Angeles, CA; *U.S. Private*, pg. 118
Chehab, Farid, Chm. & Chief Creative Officer--H&C, Leo Burnett, Beirut, Lebanon; *U.S. Private*, pg. 184
Cheit, Earl, Chm. Bd.--Shaklee Corporation, San Francisco, CA; *Int'l*, pg. 1518
Chelberg, Bruce S., Chm. Bd. & Chief Exec. Officer--Whitman Corporation, Rolling Meadows, IL; *U.S. Public*, pg. 1766
Chellgren, Paul W., Chm. Bd. & Chief Exec. Officer--Ashland, Inc., Russell, KY; *U.S. Public*, pg. 138
Chen, Jeffrey C., Chm. Bd., Pres. & Chief Exec. Officer--General Sciences Corp., Laurel, MD; *U.S. Private*, pg. 976
Chen, Pehong, Dr., Chm. Bd., Pres. & Chief Exec. Officer--BroadVision, Inc., Redwood City, CA; *U.S. Public*, pg. 258
Chen, Tu, Chm. Bd.--Komag, Incorporated, San Jose, CA; *U.S. Public*, pg. 966
Cheney, Richard B., Chm. Bd. & Chief Exec. Officer--Halliburton Company, Dallas, TX; *U.S. Public*, pg. 775
Cheney, Richard B., Chm. Bd., Pres. & Chief Exec. Officer--Halliburton Energy Services, Inc., Dallas, TX; *U.S. Public*, pg. 776
Cheney, William J., Chm. Bd., Pres. & Chief Exec. Officer--Steadly Company, Carthage, MO; *U.S. Public*, pg. 986
Cheng Wai Wing, Edmund, Chm.--Singapore Tourist Promotion Board, Singapore, Singapore; *Int'l*, pg. 1253

Cheng, Henry Kar-Shun, Chm. Bd.--Renaissance Hotel Group N.V., Central, Hong Kong; *U.S. Public*, pg. 1048

Cheng, Paul, Chm. Bd.--Inchcape Pacific Ltd., Hong Kong, Hong Kong; *Int'l*, pg. 672

Cheng, Xin, Chm. Bd., Pres. & Chief Exec. Officer--Meret Communications, San Diego, CA; *U.S. Public*, pg. 1233

Cheo-Sakul, Chalerm, Chm. Bd.--Siam City Bank Public Company Limited, Bangkok, Thailand; *Int'l*, pg. 1239

Cherkaoui, A., Chm.--L'Alliance Africaine, Casablanca, Morocco; *Int'l*, pg. 565

Chernick, Aubrey G., Chm. Bd. & Chief Exec. Officer--Candle Corporation, Santa Monica, CA; *U.S. Private*, pg. 204

Chernin, Peter, Chm. Bd.--Twentieth Century Fox Film Corp., Los Angeles, CA; *Int'l*, pg. 926

Cherry, James, Chm. Bd.--Countrymark Cooperative, Inc., Indianapolis, IN; *U.S. Private*, pg. 279

Cherry, Kenneth, Chm. Bd.--American Frozen Foods, Inc., Stratford, CT; *U.S. Private*, pg. 55

Cherry, Peter B., Chm. Bd. & Pres.--Cherry Electrical Products Corporation, Waukegan, IL; *U.S. Public*, pg. 346

Chetsanga, C.J., Prof., Chm. Bd.--Zimbabwe Electricity Supply Authority, Harare, Zimbabwe; *Int'l*, pg. 1528

Chevrier, Robert, Chm. Bd., Pres. & Chief Exec. Officer--Westburne Industrial Enterprises, Ltd., Ville Saint Laurent, Canada; *Int'l*, pg. 1492

Chiba, Kazuo, Chm. Bd.--Oji Paper Co., Ltd., Tokyo, Japan; *Int'l*, pg. 998

Chiba, M., Chm. & Chief Exec. Officer--ING Life Insurance Company, Tokyo, Japan; *Int'l*, pg. 650

Chibata, Ichiro, Ph.D., Chm. Bd., Pres. & Chief Exec. Officer--Tanabe Seiyaku Co., Ltd., Osaka, Japan; *Int'l*, pg. 1354

Chichester, Allen, Chm.-Greater China--Leo Burnett Worldwide Asia/Pacific Hdqtrs., Hong Kong, Hong Kong; *U.S. Private*, pg. 186

Chiesa, Romeo Dalla, Chm.--Banco di Roma, Rome, Italy; *Int'l*, pg. 652

Child, D. M., Chm.--Lombard North Central PLC, Redhill, United Kingdom; *Int'l*, pg. 910

Child, Denis, Chm. Bd.--Orbital Park Limited, London, United Kingdom; *Int'l*, pg. 466

Child, William H., Chm. Bd. & Chief Exec. Officer--R.C. Willey Home Furnishings, Salt Lake City, UT; *U.S. Public, pg. 221*

Childers, Charles E., Chm. Bd., Pres. & Chief Exec. Officer--Potash Corporation of Saskatchewan Inc., Saskatoon, Canada; *Int'l*, pg. 1064

Ching, Chew Lee, Chm. & Pres.--Dentsu Mandate Singapore Pte. Ltd., Singapore, Singapore; *Int'l*, pg. 393

Ching, Han H., Chm. Bd. & Sec.--Aloha Airgroup, Inc., Honolulu, HI; *U.S. Private*, pg. 44

Chinn, Trevor, Sir, Chm. Bd.--Lex Harvey Ltd., Bedworth, United Kingdom; *Int'l*, pg. 599

Chinn, Trevor, Sir, Chm. Bd.--Lex Service PLC, Bourne, United Kingdom; *Int'l*, pg. 806

Chisholm, Samuel J., Chm. & Chief Exec. Officer--The Chisholm-Mingo Group, New York, NY; *U.S. Private*, pg. 237

Chislett, J.H., Chm.--Carolina Builders Corporation, Raleigh, NC; *Int'l*, pg. 1512

Chitayat, Anwar, Chm. Bd. & Chief Exec. Officer--Anorad Corporation, Hauppauge, NY; *U.S. Private*, pg. 75

Chitty, Charles R., Chm. Bd., Pres. & Chief Exec. Officer--IQ Software Corporation, Norcross, GA; *U.S. Public*, pg. 858

Cho, Choong Hoon, Chm. Bd. & Chief Exec. Officer--Korean Airlines Co., Ltd., Seoul, Korea; *Int'l*, pg. 758

Cho, Suck Rae, Chm. Bd.--Hyosung Group, Seoul, Korea; *Int'l*, pg. 640

Choate, Jerry D., Chm. Bd. & Chief Exec. Officer--The Allstate Corporation, Northbrook, IL; *U.S. Public*, pg. 55

Choi, Sung-Rai, Chm. Bd. & Chief Exec. Officer--Samsung Europe Headquarters, Brentford, United Kingdom; *Int'l*, pg. 1183

Chokwatana, Boon-ek, Chm. Bd.--Sahapathanapibul Public Company Limited, Bangkok, Thailand; *Int'l*, pg. 1169

Chokwatana, Boonsithi, Chm. Bd.--International Cosmetics Co., Ltd., Bangkok, Thailand; *Int'l*, pg. 684

Chokwatana, Boonsithi, Chm.-Exec. Committee--Sahapathanapibul Public Company Limited, Bangkok, Thailand; *Int'l*, pg. 1169

Chokwatana, Narong, Chm. & Pres.--Bangkok Athletic Co., Ltd., Bangkok, Thailand; *Int'l*, pg. 146

Chomeau, Douglas B., Chm. Bd.--The Reliable Life Insurance Company, Webster Groves, MO; *U.S. Public*, pg. 1374

Chong, Howe Yoon, Chm. Bd.--The Great Eastern Life Assurance Company Limited, Singapore, Singapore; *Int'l, pg. 557*

Chong, Howe Yoon, Exec. Chm.--Great Eastern Life Assurance Company-Malaysia, Kuala Lumpur, Malaysia; *Int'l*, pg. 557

Choo, Yoon H., Dr., Chm. Bd., Pres. & Chief Exec. Officer--National Micronetics, Inc., Kingston, NY; *Int'l*, pg. 1347

Chookaszian, Dennis H., Chm. Bd. & Chief Exec. Officer--Continental Assurance Company, Chicago, IL; *U.S. Private*, pg. 267

Chookaszian, Dennis H., Chm. Bd. & Chief Exec. Officer--CNA Insurance Companies, Chicago, IL; *U.S. Public*, pg. 1010

Chopra, Ajay, Chm. Bd., V.P. & Gen. Mgr.-Desktop Prods.--Pinnacle Systems, Inc., Mountain View, CA; *U.S. Public*, pg. 1297

Chopra, Deepak, Chm. Bd., Pres. & Chief Exec. Officer--UDT Sensors, Inc., Hawthorne, CA; *U.S. Private*, pg. 1112

Chopra, Deepak, Chm. Bd., Pres. & Chief Exec. Officer--OSI Systems, Inc., Hawthorne, CA; *U.S. Public*, pg. 1208

Choquette, Paul J., Jr., Chm. Bd. & Chief Exec. Officer--Gilbane Building Company, Providence, RI; *U.S. Private*, pg. 452

Chorbajian, Herbert G., Chm. Bd., Pres. & Chief Exec. Officer--Albank Financial Corporation, Albany, NY; *U.S. Public*, pg. 36

Chormann, Richard F., Chm. Bd., Pres. & Chief Exec. Officer--First of America Bank Corporation, Kalamazoo, MI; *U.S. Public*, pg. 636

Chou, Silas K.F., Chm. Bd.--Tommy Hilfiger Corporation, Kowloon, Hong Kong; *Int'l*, pg. 1398

Choufoer, J.H., Chm.-Supvr. Bd.--Royal Pakhoed NV, Rotterdam, Netherlands; *Int'l*, pg. 1147

Choukas, Michael A., Chm. Bd.--Springborn Testing & Research, Inc., Enfield, CT; *U.S. Private*, pg. 1027

Chow, F.C., Chm. Bd.--Gilvin-Terrill Inc., Amarillo, TX; *U.S. Private*, pg. 455

Chowdhary, S.K., Chm. Bd.--Coal India Limited, Calcutta, India; *Int'l*, pg. 298

Chraibi, A., Chm. & Chief Exec. Officer--Al Wataniya, Casablanca, Morocco; *Int'l*, pg. 564

Christ, Alexander, Chm. Bd.--Mackenzie Financial Corporation, Toronto, Canada; *Int'l*, pg. 828

Christen, Peter, Chm. Bd., Pres. & Chief Exec. Officer--Blue Ridge Indemnity Co., Simsbury, CT; *Int'l*, pg. 345

Christen, Peter, Chm. Bd. & Chief Exec. Officer--MassWest Insurance Company, West Springfield, MA; *Int'l*, pg. 345

Christian, Betty S., Chm. Bd., Pres. & Chief Exec. Officer--Central Coca-Cola Bottling Company, Inc., Richmond, VA; *U.S. Private*, pg. 222

Christian, C. Lynch, Jr., Chm. Bd.--Craddock-Terry Inc., Lynchburg, VA; *U.S. Private*, pg. 284

Christiansen, Russell E., Chm. Bd.--MidAmerican Energy Holdings, Des Moines, IA; *U.S. Public*, pg. 1109

Christianson, Stanley D., Vice Chm. & Chief Exec. Officer--Thrall Enterprises, Inc., Chicago, IL; *U.S. Private*, pg. 1084

Christopher, Brian, Chm. Bd.--Astec America Inc., Carlsbad, CA; *Int'l*, pg. 93

Christopher, R., Chm. Bd. & Chief Exec. Officer--IG Autotrim, Inc., Chicago, IL; *Int'l*, pg. 1117

Christopher, Robert A., Chm. Bd. & Chief Exec. Officer--Rieter Automotive North America Inc, Farmington Hills, MI; *Int'l*, pg. 1117

Christophersen, Olaf, Chm. Bd.--Frionor A/S, Lysaker, Norway; *Int'l*, pg. 516

Chu, David Ki Kwan, Chm. Bd.--Toymax International Inc., Plainview, NY; *U.S. Public*, pg. 1626

Chubb, Percy, III, Chm. Bd.--Chubb Insurance Co. of Canada, Toronto, Canada; *U.S. Public*, pg. 355

Chui, David, Chm. Bd.--IWI Holding Limited, Westmont, IL; *U.S. Public*, pg. 861

Chun, Wang Koo Yik, Chm. Emeritus--Johnson Electric Holdings Limited, Tai No, Hong Kong; *Int'l*, pg. 712

Chung, Joseph, Chm. Bd. & Chief Tech. Officer--Art Technology Group, Boston, MA; *U.S. Private*, pg. 86

Chung, M.H., Chm. Bd.--Maxtor Corporation, Milpitas, CA; *Int'l*, pg. 641

Chung, Mong Gyu, Chm.--Hyundai Motor Company, Seoul, Korea; *Int'l*, pg. 641

Chung, Patrick Wang Shui, Chm. Bd. & Chief Exec. Officer--Johnson Electric Holdings Limited, Tai No, Hong Kong; *Int'l*, pg. 712

Chung, Yong, Chm. Bd. & Chief Exec. Officer--Samsung China Headquarters, Beijing, China; *Int'l*, pg. 1183

Churchill, L., Chm. Bd.--National Westminster Unit Trust Managers Limited, Bristol, United Kingdom; *Int'l*, pg. 910

Churchill, Verne B., Chm. Bd.--Market Facts, Inc., Arlington Heights, IL; *U.S. Public*, pg. 1046

Churchill, Verne B., Chm.--Market Facts-New York, Inc., New York, NY; *U.S. Public*, pg. 1047

Churchill, Winston J., Chm. Bd.--Central Sprinkler Corporation, Lansdale, PA; *U.S. Public*, pg. 327

Churm, Peter, Chm. Emeritus--Furon Company, Laguna Niguel, CA; *U.S. Public*, pg. 688

Chute, Robert A., Chm. Bd., Pres. & Chief Exec. Officer--The Gage Company, Pittsburgh, PA; *U.S. Private*, pg. 437

Cifoni, Dario, Chm.--AGIP International B.V., Amsterdam, Netherlands; *Int'l*, pg. 429

Cigarran, Thomas G., Chm. Bd., Pres. & Chief Exec. Officer--American Healthcorp Inc., Nashville, TN; *U.S. Public*, pg. 78

Ciminelli, Louis P., Chm. Bd. & Chief Exec. Officer--Louis P. Ciminelli Construction Co. Inc., Buffalo, NY; *U.S. Private, pg. 239*

Cingano, Francesco, Chm.--Banca Commerciale Italiana S.p.A., Milan, Italy; *Int'l*, pg. 652

Cinnamon, Barry A., Chm. Bd., Pres. & Chief Exec. Officer--Software Publishing Corporation, Fairfield, NJ; *U.S. Public*, pg. 1483

Ciocca, Arthur A., Chm. Bd. & Chief Exec. Officer--The Wine Group, San Francisco, CA; *U.S. Private*, pg. 1182

Cipriani, Robert, Chm.--Cipriani Kremer Design, Boston, MA; *U.S. Private*, pg. 84

Circo, Sebastian A., Chm. Bd.--Precision Industries, Omaha, NE; *U.S. Private*, pg. 879

Cisneros, Gustavo A., Chm. Bd.--Pueblo Xtra International, Inc., Pompano Beach, FL; *U.S. Private*, pg. 894

Cisneros, Marco Antonio Espijel, Chm.--Porcelanite SA de CV, Mexico, Mexico; *Int'l*, pg. 572

Cizik, Robert, Chm. Bd.--Easco Inc., Girard, OH; *U.S. Public*, pg. 548

Clancy, Joseph E., Chm. Bd.--Bridgeport Machines, Inc., Bridgeport, CT; *U.S. Public*, pg. 251

Clariond Garza, Eugenio, Chm. Bd.--Grupo IMSA S.A. de C.V., Garza Garcia, Mexico; *Int'l*, pg. 575

Clarity, Tim B., Pres. & Chief Exec. Officer--Clarity Coverdale Fury Advertising, Minneapolis, MN; *U.S. Private*, pg. 242

Clark, A. James, Chm. Bd. & Pres.--Clark Enterprises, Inc., Bethesda, MD; *U.S. Private*, pg. 242

Clark, C.R.N., Chm.--Cookson Matthey Ceramics PLC, Stoke on Trent, United Kingdom; *Int'l*, pg. 713

Clark, Cyrus Jr., Chm. Bd.--Cyrus Clark Co., Inc., New York, NY; *U.S. Private*, pg. 242

Clark, David, Chm. Bd.--Rinker Materials Corp., West Palm Beach, FL; *Int'l*, pg. 246

Clark, David, Chm. Bd., Pres. & Chief Exec. Officer--Homeland Holding Corp., Oklahoma City, OK; *U.S. Public*, pg. 832

Clark, Donald A., Chm. Bd.--Covington Foods, Inc., Covington, IN; *U.S. Private*, pg. 280

Clark, Donald R., Chm. Bd.--Atlantic Builders Group Inc., Baltimore, MD; *U.S. Private*, pg. 95

Clark, E. Roger, Chm. Bd., Pres. & Chief Exec. Officer--National Forge Company, Irvine, PA; *U.S. Private*, pg. 783

Clark, Edward, Chm. Bd., Pres. & Chief Exec. Officer--American Seating Company, Grand Rapids, MI; *U.S. Private*, pg. 61

Clark, Edwin J., Chm. Bd.--Dwyer Instruments Inc., Michigan City, IN; *U.S. Private*, pg. 350

Clark, George A., Chm. Bd., Pres. & Chief Exec. Officer--Snap-Tite, Inc., Erie, PA; *U.S. Private*, pg. 1010

Clark, Gerald, Chm. Bd--MetLife Capital Holdings, Inc., Bellevue, WA; *U.S. Private*, pg. 737

Clark, Grahame N., Jr., Chm., Pres. & Chief Exec. Officer--BancTec, Inc., Dallas, TX; *U.S. Public*, pg. 176

Clark, Harold J., Chm. Bd. & Chief Exec. Officer--U.S. Aviation Underwriters, Inc., New York, NY; *U.S. Public*, pg. 726

Clark, Howard L., Chm. Bd.--Skandinaviska Enskilda Banken Corporation, New York, NY; *Int'l*, pg. 1259

Clark, James, Chm. Bd.--Netscape Communications Corp., Mountain View, CA; *U.S. Public*, pg. 1168

Clark, James L., Chm. Bd.--Motion Industries (Canada), Inc., Lethbridge, Canada; *U.S. Public*, pg. 732

Clark, Lester, Chm. Bd.--States, Inc., Breckenridge, TX; *U.S. Private*, pg. 1037

Clark, Neil R., Chm. Bd.--Coles Myer Ltd., Tooronga, Australia; *Int'l*, pg. 306

Clark, Richard W., Chm. Bd. & Chief Exec. Officer--Dick Clark Productions, Inc., Burbank, CA; *U.S. Public*, pg. 382

Clark, Robert, Chm. Bd.--Mirror Group plc, London, United Kingdom; *Int'l*, pg. 869

Clark, William P., Chm. Bd. & Chief Exec. Officer--Wall Colmonoy Corp., Madison Heights, MI; *U.S. Private*, pg. 1148

Clarke, David, Chm. Bd.--Goodman Fielder Limited, Sydney, Australia; *Int'l*, pg. 555

Clarke, David H., Chm. Bd. & Chief Exec. Officer--U.S. Industries, Inc., Iselin, NJ; *U.S. Public*, pg. 1683

Clarke, Jeffrey, Chm. Bd., Pres. & Chief Exec. Officer--Coho Energy, Inc., Dallas, TX; *U.S. Public*, pg. 396

Clarke, Kenneth R., Chm. Bd.--Royal LePage Limited, Don Mills, Canada; *Int'l*, pg. 1143

Clarke, Robert F., Chm. Bd., Pres. & Chief Exec. Officer--Hawaiian Electric Industries, Inc., Honolulu, HI; *U.S. Public*, pg. 799

Clarke, Robert F., Chm. Bd.--Hawaiian Electric Company, Inc., Honolulu, HI; *U.S. Public*, pg. 800

Clarke, Robert F., Chm. Bd. & Pres.--Pacific Energy Conservation Services, Inc., Honolulu, HI; *U.S. Public*, pg. 800

Clarke, Roger G., Ph.D., Dr., Chm.--Analytic TSA Global Asset Management Inc., Los Angeles, CA; *U.S. Public*, pg. 1672

Claudon, Jean Gerard, Chm.-Supvr. Bd.--Poliet, Courbevoie, France; *Int'l*, pg. 1177

Clausen, Dick, Chm. Bd., Pres. & Chief Exec. Officer--Verbatim Tape Corporation, San Diego, CA; *Int'l*, pg. 872

Claverie, Roye E., Chm. Bd.--Permanent General Companies, Nashville, TN; *U.S. Private*, pg. 563

Clay, John P., Co-Chm. & Chief Investment Officer--Clay Finlay Inc., New York, NY; *U.S. Public*, pg. 1673

Clay, John W., Jr., Chm. Bd., Pres. & Chief Exec. Officer--SunTrust Banks of Tennessee, Inc., Nashville, TN; *U.S. Public*, pg. 1538

Claypoole, R.E., Chm. Bd.--GATX Terminals Corporation, Chicago, IL; *U.S. Public*, pg. 692

Clayton Lloyd, Donna, Chm. Bd.--Professional Putters Association, Fayetteville, NC; *U.S. Private*, pg. 896

Clayton, Donald W., Chm. Bd. & Chief Exec. Officer--Howell Corporation, Houston, TX; *U.S. Public*, pg. 843

Clayton, J. Brian, Chm. Bd.--Bridon PLC, Doncaster, United Kingdom; *Int'l*, pg. 215

Clayton, James L., Chm. Bd. & Chief Exec. Officer--Clayton Homes, Inc., Knoxville, TN; *U.S. Public*, pg. 382

Clegg, Jack, Chm. Bd., Pres. & Chief Exec. Officer--Nobel Education Dynamics, Inc., Media, PA; *U.S. Public*, pg. 1185

Clegg, Nicholas, Chm.--Daiwa Europe Bank plc, London, United Kingdom; *Int'l*, pg. 375

Cleghorn, John E., Chm. Bd. & Chief Exec. Officer--Royal Bank of Canada, Toronto, Canada; *Int'l*, pg. 1131

Clemenger, Peter G., Chm. Bd.-Clemenger/BBDO (Aust./N.Z.) & Dir.--BBDO Worldwide Inc., New York, NY; *U.S. Public*, pg. 1223

Clement, Gale W., Chm. Bd. & Pres.--Idahoan Foods, Lewisville, ID; *U.S. Private*, pg. 557

Clement, J., Chm. Bd.--Ransomes Plc, Ipswich, United Kingdom; *Int'l*, pg. 1087

Clement, James B., Chm. Bd. & Chief Exec. Officer--Offshore Logistics, Inc., Lafayette, LA; *U.S. Public*, pg. 1212

Clements, Norbert, Chm. Bd.--Willis Corroon Corp. of Orange County, Santa Ana, CA; *Int'l*, pg. 1506

Clements, Richard H., Chm. Bd. & Chief Fin. Officer--Clements Foods Co., Oklahoma City, OK; *U.S. Private*, pg. 245

Clements, Virginia Lee, Chm. Bd.--Golden Eagle Distributors, Inc., Tucson, AZ; *U.S. Private*, pg. 460

Clemons, V. Gordon, Chm. Bd., Pres. & Chief Exec. Officer--CorVel Corporation, Irvine, CA; *U.S. Public*, pg. 451

Clendenin, John L., Chm. Bd.--BellSouth Corporation, Atlanta, GA; *U.S. Public*, pg. 207

Clerici, Paolo, Chm. Bd. & Chief Exec. Officer--Coeclerici Group, Genoa, Italy; *Int'l*, pg. 303

Clerihue, W.R., Chm. Bd.--Spartech Corporation, Clayton, MO; *U.S. Public*, pg. 1495
Cleveland, Russ, Chm. Bd.--Global Environmental Corp., Hagerstown, MD; *U.S. Public*, pg. 747
Clevy, W. Michael, Pres. & Chief Exec. Officer--International Comfort Products, Franklin, TN; *U.S. Public*, pg. 898
Clewlow, Warren A.M., Chm. Bd.--Barlow Ltd., Sandton, South Africa; *Int'l*, pg. 167
Cliff, R.L., Chm.--Alpac Construction & Surveys Limited, Vancouver, Canada; *Int'l*, pg. 114
Cliff, Ronald L., Chm. Bd.--BC Gas Inc., Vancouver, Canada; *Int'l*, pg. 114
Clifford, James, Company Grp. Chm.--HLS Corp., Little Falls, NJ; *Int'l*, pg. 1483
Clifford, Patrick, Chm. Bd.--Mosby-Year Book, Inc., Saint Louis, MO; *U.S. Public*, pg. 1616
Clifford, R. Leigh, Chm. Bd.--Comalco Limited, Brisbane, Australia; *Int'l*, pg. 307
Cline, Morgan E., Chm. Bd.--Cline, Davis & Mann, Inc., New York, NY; *U.S. Private*, pg. 246
Cline, Robert S., Chm. Bd. & Chief Exec. Officer--Airborne Freight Corporation, Seattle, WA; *U.S. Public*, pg. 32
Clinton, Jerry, Chm. Bd.--Grey Eagle Distributors Inc., Maryland Heights, MO; *U.S. Private*, pg. 480
Clitheroe, Lord, Chm. Bd.--Yorkshire Bank, Leeds, United Kingdom; *Int'l*, pg. 906
Cloud, Forrest R., Chm. Bd.--IBT, Inc., Merriam, KS; *U.S. Private*, pg. 553
Cloues, Edward B., II, Chm. Bd.--AMREP Corporation, New York, NY; *U.S. Public*, pg. 104
Cloues, Edward B., II, Chm. Bd. & Chief Exec. Officer--K-Tron International, Inc., Pitman, NJ; *U.S. Public*, pg. 938
Clow, Lee, Chm. & Chief Creative Officer-N.A.--TBWA Chiat/Day, New York, NY; *U.S. Private*, pg. 1062
Clow, Lee, Chm., Chief Creative Officer-N.A.--TBWA Chiat/Day Los Angeles, Venice, CA; *U.S. Private*, pg. 1062
Clubb, I.M., Chm.--B. Elliott plc., London, United Kingdom; *Int'l*, pg. 448
Clulow, Margaretta M., Chm. Bd.--Kingsbury, Inc., Philadelphia, PA; *U.S. Private*, pg. 622
Coady, Todd M., Chm. Bd., Pres. & Chief Exec. Officer--Hicks Oil-Hicks Gas, Inc., Roberts, IL; *U.S. Private*, pg. 526
Coale, William, Chm. Bd. & Chief Exec. Officer--Alcom Printing Group, Inc., Bethlehem, PA; *U.S. Private*, pg. 33
Coape-Arnold, D.A., Chm. Bd. & Chief Exec. Officer--Dunhill Personnel System, Inc., Hauppauge, NY; *U.S. Public*, pg. 1746
Coates, Alan, Chm. Bd.--Brambles Industries Limited, Sydney, Australia; *Int'l*, pg. 210
Coates, Ken H., Chm. Bd.--Meggitt plc, Wimborne Minster, United Kingdom; *Int'l*, pg. 853
Coates, P.C., Chm. Bd.--Davy John Brown PTY Limited, Melbourne, Australia; *Int'l*, pg. 775
Coates, Vincent J., Chm. Bd. & Chief Exec. Officer--Nanometrics Incorporated, Sunnyvale, CA; *U.S. Public*, pg. 1151
Cobb, Timothy S., Chm. Bd., Pres. & Chief Exec. Officer--Salient 3 Communications, Inc., Reading, PA; *U.S. Public*, pg. 1429
Cocchiola, Mark, Chm. Bd., Pres. & Chief Exec. Officer--Suprema Specialties, Inc., Paterson, NJ; *U.S. Public*, pg. 1541
Cocchiola, Mark, Chm. Bd., Pres. & Chief Exec. Officer--Suprema Specialties Northeast, Inc., Ogdensburg, NY; *U.S. Public*, pg. 1541
Cocheteux, Jean-Bernard, Chm. Bd. & Chief Exec. Officer--Microturbo Division, Toulouse, France; *Int'l*, pg. 786
Cochran, John R., Chm. Bd. & Chief Exec. Officer--FirstMerit Corporation, Akron, OH; *U.S. Public*, pg. 646
Cocke, Bartlett, Jr., Chm. Bd.--Bartlett Cocke, Inc., San Antonio, TX; *U.S. Private*, pg. 249
Cockshaw, Alan, Sir, Chm. Bd.--AMEC Plc, Northwich, United Kingdom; *Int'l*, pg. 16
Cody, Roger, Chm. Bd.--Dataram Corporation, Princeton, NJ; *U.S. Public*, pg. 487
Coelho, Anthony, Chm. Bd.--International Thoroughbred Breeders, Inc., Cherry Hill, NJ; *U.S. Public*, pg. 908
Coffin, Sarah R., Chm. Bd. & Chief Exec. Officer--Foster Products Corporation, Minneapolis, MN; *U.S. Public*, pg. 686
Coffman, C. Morris, Chm. Bd., Pres. & Chief Exec. Officer--Farmers Bank & Trust Co., Madisonville, KY; *U.S. Public*, pg. 1217
Cogan, John F., Jr., Chm. Bd. & Pres.--The Pioneer Group, Inc., Boston, MA; *U.S. Public*, pg. 1298
Cogan, Marshall S., Chm. Bd. & Chief Exec. Officer--Trace International Holdings, Inc., New York, NY; *U.S. Private*, pg. 1094
Cogan, Marshall S., Chm. Bd. & Chief Exec. Officer--United Auto Group, Inc., New York, NY; *U.S. Private*, pg. 1095
Coghill, Marvin W., Chm.-Tobacco Div.--Standard Commercial Corporation, Wilson, NC; *U.S. Public*, pg. 1501
Coghlin, Fritzmaurice, Chm. Bd.--Dock Foundry Company, Three Rivers, MI; *U.S. Private*, pg. 337
Cohen Tervaert, Dirk G., Chm. Bd. & Pres.--N.V. Deli-Universal, Rotterdam, Netherlands; *U.S. Public*, pg. 1695
Cohen, Alan, Chm. Bd., Pres. & Chief Exec. Officer--Finish Line, Inc., Indianapolis, IN; *U.S. Public*, pg. 623
Cohen, Alan J., Chm. Bd.--Accurate Perforating Co., Chicago, IL; *U.S. Private*, pg. 12
Cohen, Albert D., Chm. Bd. & Chief Exec. Officer--Gendis Inc., Winnipeg, Canada; *Int'l*, pg. 542
Cohen, Arthur, Chm. Bd. & Chief Exec. Officer--The Arlen Corporation, New York, NY; *U.S. Public*, pg. 131
Cohen, Ben R., Chm. Bd.--Ben & Jerry's Homemade Inc., South Burlington, VT; *U.S. Public*, pg. 210
Cohen, Boris, Chm. Bd.--All-Luminum Products, Inc., Philadelphia, PA; *U.S. Private*, pg. 34
Cohen, Brian, Chm. & Chief Exec. Officer--Technology Solutions Inc., New York, NY; *U.S. Private*, pg. 1157
Cohen, C. Anders, Chm. Bd.--A. Cohen & Co. P.L.C., London, United Kingdom; *Int'l*, pg. 306
Cohen, Donald, Chm. Bd., Pres., Chief Exec. Officer & Chief Fin. Officer--Tool King, Denver, CO; *U.S. Private*, pg. 1091
Cohen, Edward E., Chm. Bd. & Chief Exec. Officer--Resource America, Inc., Philadelphia, PA; *U.S. Public*, pg. 1382
Cohen, Gerald D., Pres.--Information Builders, New York, NY; *U.S. Private*, pg. 561
Cohen, Gordon S., Chm. Bd. & Chief Exec. Officer--Customedix Corporation, Wallingford, CT; *U.S. Private*, pg. 298
Cohen, Irving, Chm. Bd.--Host Apparel, Inc., New York, NY; *U.S. Private*, pg. 540
Cohen, Joseph M., Chm. Bd. & Chief Exec. Officer--Cowen & Company, New York, NY; *U.S. Private*, pg. 280
Cohen, Lawrence M., Chm.-Exec. Committee--Carlyle & Co. Jewelers, Greensboro, NC; *U.S. Private*, pg. 213
Cohen, Melvin S., Chm. Bd.--National Presto Industries, Inc., Eau Claire, WI; *U.S. Public*, pg. 1159
Cohen, Milton L., Chm. Bd. & Pres.--Lifetime Hoan Corp., Westbury, NY; *U.S. Public*, pg. 992
Cohen, Peter J., Chm. Bd., Pres. & Chief Exec. Officer--Periphonics Corp., Bohemia, NY; *U.S. Public*, pg. 1278
Cohen, Robert B., Chm. Bd.--Hudson County News Company, North Bergen, NJ; *U.S. Private*, pg. 545
Cohen, Robert H., Chm. Bd. & Pres.--Beauty Enterprises Inc., Hartford, CT; *U.S. Private*, pg. 128
Cohen, Robert, Dr., Chm. Bd.--Sterling Vision, Inc., East Meadow, NY; *U.S. Public*, pg. 1516
Cohen, Ron, Chm. & Chief Exec. Officer--McDonald's Restaurants of Canada Ltd., Toronto, Canada; *U.S. Public*, pg. 1069
Cohen, Russell, Chm. Bd. & Co-Chief Exec. Officer--Carlyle & Co. Jewelers, Greensboro, NC; *U.S. Private*, pg. 213
Cohen, Sylvan M., Chm. Bd. & Chief Exec. Officer--Pennsylvania Real Estate Investment Trust, Fort Washington, PA; *U.S. Public*, pg. 1272
Cohen, William L., Chm. Bd., Pres. & Chief Exec. Officer--Andover Togs, Inc., New York, NY; *U.S. Public*, pg. 112
Cohenca, Emilia, Chm. Bd.--Jason Industrial, Inc., Fairfield, NJ; *U.S. Private*, pg. 583
Cohn, Mark A., Chm. Bd. & Chief Exec. Officer--Damark International, Inc., Minneapolis, MN; *U.S. Public*, pg. 478
Cohn, Richard, Chm. Bd.--Decorative Crafts, Inc., Greenwich, CT; *U.S. Private*, pg. 320
Cohn, Robert, Chm. Bd. & Chief Exec. Officer--Octel Messaging Division, Milpitas, CA; *U.S. Public*, pg. 1017
Cojuangco, Antonio O., Chm.--Mabuhay Philippines Satellite Corp., Makati, Philippines; *Int'l*, pg. 1051
Coker, Charles W., Chm. Bd. & Chief Exec. Officer--Sonoco Products Company, Hartsville, SC; *U.S. Public*, pg. 1485
Colasacco, Domenic, Chm. Bd. & Pres.--United States Trust Company, Boston, MA; *U.S. Public*, pg. 1660
Colbert, E.M., Chm. Bd.--Data Instruments, Inc., Acton, MA; *U.S. Private*, pg. 312
Colburn, Phil, Chm. Bd.--Allen Telecom Inc., Solon, OH; *U.S. Public*, pg. 45
Colburn, Philip W., Chm. Bd.--Allen Telecom, Inc., Beachwood, OH; *U.S. Public*, pg. 45
Cole, James D., Chm. Bd., Pres., & Chief Exec. Officer--Newpark Resources, Inc., Metairie, LA; *U.S. Public*, pg. 1179
Cole, Jeffrey A., Chm. Bd. & Chief Exec. Officer--Cole National Corporation, Cleveland, OH; *U.S. Public*, pg. 396
Cole, Jeffrey N., Chief Exec. Officer--Ferrous Processing & Trading Co., Detroit, MI; *U.S. Private*, pg. 402
Cole, Kenneth, Chm. Bd. & Pres.--Kenneth Cole Productions, New York, NY; *U.S. Public*, pg. 951
Cole, Lee, Chm. Bd. & Chief Exec. Officer--Calavo Growers of California, Santa Ana, CA; *U.S. Private*, pg. 199
Cole, Louis C., Chm. Bd., Pres. & Chief Exec. Officer--Legato Systems, Inc., Palo Alto, CA; *U.S. Public*, pg. 984
Cole, R.D., Chm. Bd., Pres. & Chief Exec. Officer--The Dosco Corp., Abingdon, VA; *Int'l*, pg. 124
Cole, Richard E., Chm. Bd. & Chief Exec. Officer--Chartwell Re Corporation, Stamford, CT; *U.S. Public*, pg. 336
Cole, Richard E., Jr., Chm. Bd.--The Insurance Corp. of New York, New York, NY; *U.S. Public*, pg. 336
Colehower, William S., Chm. Bd. & Pres.--Jomac, Inc., Warrington, PA; *U.S. Private*, pg. 595
Coleman, Bob, Chm.--Wittnauer International, Inc., New Rochelle, NY; *U.S. Public*, pg. 273
Coleman, Christopher, Chm. Bd.--C.J. Coleman Holdings Ltd., London, United Kingdom; *Int'l*, pg. 306
Coleman, Debi, Chm. Bd., Pres. & Chief Exec. Officer--Merix Corporation, Forest Grove, OR; *U.S. Public*, pg. 1096
Coleman, James W., Jr., Chm. & Chief Exec. Officer--Selective Technical Administrative Services, Inc., Branchville, NJ; *U.S. Public*, pg. 1456
Coleman, Lonzo, Chm. Bd., Pres. & Chief Exec. Officer--ColeJon Corporation, Cleveland, OH; *U.S. Private*, pg. 251
Coleman, Matthew, Chm. Bd.--Escort, Inc., West Chester, OH; *U.S. Private*, pg. 383
Coleman, P. Michael, Chm. Bd., Pres. & Chief Exec. Officer--Integrity Incorporated, Mobile, AL; *U.S. Public*, pg. 886
Coleman, Walter C., Jr., Chm. Bd.--Coleman Dairy LLC, Little Rock, AR; *U.S. Private*, pg. 251
Coleman, William H., Jr., Chm. Bd.--Coleman Cadillac Inc., Bethesda, MD; *U.S. Private*, pg. 251
Coley, Thomas H., Chm. Bd. & Chief Exec. Officer--South Trust Bank of Georgia, Atlanta, GA; *U.S. Public*, pg. 1492
Colgan, Paul, Chm. Bd. & Pres.--Waldo Bros. Company, Boston, MA; *U.S. Private*, pg. 1147
Collert, Goran, Chm. Bd.--Swedbank, Stockholm, Sweden; *Int'l*, pg. 1328
Collins, Don L., Chm. Bd., Pres., Chief Exec. & Oper. Officer--Collins Industries, Inc., Hutchinson, KS; *U.S. Public*, pg. 399
Collins, James A., Chm. Bd.--Sizzler International, Inc., Los Angeles, CA; *U.S. Public*, pg. 1475
Collins, John G., Chm. Bd.--UJB Discount Brokerage, Ridgefield Park, NJ; *U.S. Public*, pg. 1528
Collins, Joseph J., Chm. Bd. & Chief Exec. Officer--Time Warner Cable, Stamford, CT; *U.S. Public*, pg. 1610
Collins, Vernon E., Chm. Bd., Pres. & Chief Exec. Officer--Bliss-Salem, Inc., Salem, OH; *U.S. Private*, pg. 149
Collins, W., III, Chm. Bd. & Pres.--Warren E. Collins, Inc., Braintree, MA; *U.S. Private*, pg. 253
Collman, Nicholas J., Chm. Bd., Pres. & Chief Exec. Officer--Collman Graphics, Inc., Baltimore, MD; *U.S. Private*, pg. 253
Collomb, Bertrand, Chm. Bd. & Chief Exec. Officer--Lafarge S.A., Paris, France; *Int'l*, pg. 788
Colombo, Gianpietro, Chm. Bd.--Immobiliare Maram S.r.l., Milan, Italy; *Int'l*, pg. 138
Colonello, Alex, Chm. Bd.--Bayco Industries, Winnipeg, Canada; *Int'l*, pg. 395
Colonna, Leonard, Chm. Bd.--Colonna Bros., Inc., North Bergen, NJ; *U.S. Private*, pg. 254
Coltman, David A., Chm. Bd. & Pres.--Covia, LLC, Elk Grove Village, IL; *U.S. Public*, pg. 1653
Coltman, David A., Chm. Bd. & Pres.--United Vacations, Inc., Elk Grove Village, IL; *U.S. Public*, pg. 1653
Coltman, David A., Chm. Bd.--Milage Plus, Inc., Rolling Meadows, IL; *U.S. Public*, pg. 1653
Colton, David A., Chm. Bd.--Mileage Plus Holdings, Inc., Elk Grove Village, IL; *U.S. Public*, pg. 1653
Colton, Grant A., Sr., Chm. Bd.--Rodney Hunt Company, Orange, MA; *U.S. Private*, pg. 549
Colton, Sol, Chm. Bd.--Domestic Uniform Rental Co., Farmington Hills, MI; *U.S. Private*, pg. 338
Colwell, Thomas G., Chm. Bd.--Colwell Industries, Inc., Minneapolis, MN; *U.S. Private*, pg. 257
Combe, Ivan D., Chm. Bd.--Combe Incorporated, White Plains, NY; *U.S. Private*, pg. 257
Combes, David, Chm. Bd.--Dietzgen Corporation, Palatine, IL; *U.S. Private*, pg. 332
Comer, Gary C., Chm. Bd.--Lands' End, Inc., Dodgeville, WI; *U.S. Public*, pg. 977
Comey, Dale R., Chm. & Pres.--First State Insurance Company, Boston, MA; *U.S. Public*, pg. 794
Comment, Jeffrey W., Chm. Bd., Pres. & Chief Exec. Officer--Helzberg's Diamond Shops, Inc., Kansas City, MO; *U.S. Public*, pg. 220
Comoli, Jean-Dominique, Chm. Bd. & Chief Exec. Officer--SEITA, Societe Nationale D'Exploitation Industrielle des Tabacs et des Allumettes, Paris, France; *Int'l*, pg. 1219
Compagnie-Portis, Steven, Chm. Bd.--Kettle Restaurants, Houston, TX; *U.S. Private*, pg. 617
Compton, Ronald E., Chm. Bd.--Aetna Inc., Hartford, CT; *U.S. Public*, pg. 26
Compton, William, Chm. Bd. & Chief Exec. Officer--Tropical Sportswear International, Tampa, FL; *U.S. Private*, pg. 1105
Comstock, Harwood B., Chm. Bd. & Pres.--Pratt-Read Corporation, Bridgeport, CT; *U.S. Private*, pg. 879
Conant, Howard R., Chm. Bd.--Interstate Steel Co. Inc., Des Plaines, IL; *Int'l*, pg. 572
Condit, Philip M., Chm. Bd. & Chief Exec. Officer--The Boeing Company, Seattle, WA; *U.S. Public*, pg. 239
Conefry, John J., Jr., Chm. Bd. & Chief Exec. Officer--Long Island Bancorp, Inc., Melville, NY; *U.S. Public*, pg. 1013
Conefry, John J., Jr., Chm. Bd.--Entrust Home Financing, Columbia, MD; *U.S. Public*, pg. 1013
Congdon, Earl E., Chm. Bd. & Chief Exec. Officer--Old Dominion Freight Line, Inc., High Point, NC; *U.S. Public*, pg. 1216
Conger, Harry M., Chm. Bd.--Homestake Mining Company, San Francisco, CA; *U.S. Public*, pg. 832
Conlin, William P., Chm. Bd.--Structural Dynamics Research Corp., Milford, OH; *U.S. Public*, pg. 1525
Conlisk, Raimon, Chm. Bd.--EXAR Corporation, Fremont, CA; *U.S. Public*, pg. 597
Conlon, Harry B., Chm. Bd., Pres. & Chief Exec. Officer--Associated Banc-Corp, Green Bay, WI; *U.S. Public*, pg. 140
Conn, Walter, Chm. Bd. & Owner--Charles Dunn Company, Inc., Los Angeles, CA; *U.S. Private*, pg. 229
Connelly, John E., Chm. Bd. & Chief Exec. Officer--President Casinos, Inc., Saint Louis, MO; *U.S. Public*, pg. 1323
Connelly, Thomas S., Chm. Bd., Pres., Chief Exec. Officer--Connelly Containers, Inc., Bala Cynwyd, PA; *U.S. Private*, pg. 264
Conner, Timothy R., Chm. Bd.--Banner Associates Inc., Laramie, WY; *U.S. Private*, pg. 114
Connolley, John, Chm. Bd. & Chief Exec. Officer--G.E. American Communications, Inc., Princeton, NJ; *U.S. Public*, pg. 711
Connor, John T., Chm. Bd. & Chief Exec. Officer--Transcrypt International, Lincoln, NE; *U.S. Public*, pg. 1630
Connors, Charles W., Chm. Bd. & Chief Exec. Officer--Magneco/Metrel, Inc., Addison, IL; *U.S. Private*, pg. 695
Connors, James J., Chm Bd.--Weiser Inc., Burnaby, Canada; *U.S. Public*, pg. 1055
Conover, Donald E., Pres. & Chm. Bd.--Greystone Realty Corporation, Greenwich, CT; *U.S. Private*, pg. 795
Conrad, Carlton J., Sr., Chm. Bd.--E.H. Titchener & Company, Binghamton, NY; *U.S. Private*, pg. 1089
Conrad, John R., Chm. Bd.--S & C Electric Company, Chicago, IL; *U.S. Private*, pg. 954
Conrades, George H., Chm. Bd., Pres. & Chief Exec. Officer--GTE Internetworking, Cambridge, MA; *U.S. Public*, pg. 696
Conroy, Michael, Co-Chm. & Chief Exec. Officer--FCA!BMZ, Suresnes, France; *Int'l*, pg. 469
Conservo, Salvatore, Chm. Bd.--Banco di Sicilia International S.A., Luxembourg, Luxembourg; *Int'l*, pg. 141

Constantin, Gus, Chm. Bd., Pres. & Chief Exec. Officer--Phoenix American Incorporated, San Rafael, CA; *U.S. Private*, pg. 862

Contadino, Joseph, Chm. Bd., Pres. & Treas.--Del Webb's Coventry Homes, Phoenix, AZ; *U.S. Public*, pg. 495

Conterno, Francesco Michele, Dr., Chm. Bd. & Pres.--Lati Industria Termoplastici S.p.A., Vedano Olona, Italy; *Int'l*, pg. 804

Conway, Christopher J., Chm. Bd. & Chief Exec. Officer--Mentor Corporation, Santa Barbara, CA; *U.S. Public*, pg. 1086

Conway, E. Virgil, Chm. Bd.-MTA--MTA Long Island Rail Road, Jamaica, NY; *U.S. Private*, pg. 739

Conway, E. Virgul, Chm. & Chief Exec. Officer--Metropolitan Transportation Authority, New York, NY; *U.S. Private*, pg. 739

Conway, James F., III, Chm. Bd., Pres., Chief Oper. & Exec. Officer--Courier Corporation, North Chelmsford, MA; *U.S. Public*, pg. 453

Cook, Carl, Chm. Bd. & Chief Exec. Officer--Overland Transportation System, Inc., Indianapolis, IN; *Int'l*, pg. 1469

Cook, E. Gary, Chm. Bd., Pres. & Chief Exec. Officer--Witco Corporation, Greenwich, CT; *U.S. Public*, pg. 1773

Cook, J. Michael, Chm. Bd. & Chief Exec. Officer--Deloitte & Touche LLP, Wilton, CT; *U.S. Private*, pg. 322

Cook, James D., Chm. Bd. & Chief Exec. Officer--Concord Litho Co., Inc., Concord, NH; *U.S. Private*, pg. 261

Cook, L. H., Chm.--Stanbic Bank Zimbabwe Limited, Harare, Zimbabwe; *Int'l*, pg. 1294

Cook, Nicholas H., Chm. Bd. & Chief Exec. Officer--Brauns Fashions Corporation, Plymouth, MN; *U.S. Public*, pg. 251

Cook, Paul, Chm. Bd.--SRI International, Menlo Park, CA; *U.S. Private*, pg. 958

Cook, Peter C., Chm. Bd.--Transnational Motors Inc., Grand Rapids, MI; *U.S. Private*, pg. 1097

Cook, Scott D., Chm. Bd.--Intuit, Inc., Mountain View, CA; *U.S. Public*, pg. 911

Cook, Thomas, Chm. Bd. & Chief Exec. Officer--American Metal & Plastics Inc., Grand Rapids, MI; *U.S. Private*, pg. 59

Cook, William R., Chm. Bd., Pres. & Chief Exec. Officer--BetzDearborn Inc., Trevose, PA; *U.S. Public*, pg. 226

Cook, William R., Chm. Bd., Pres. & Chief Exec. Officer--Jenkins & Associates, Shawnee Mission, KS; *U.S. Private*, pg. 585

Cooke, J.P. Blase, Chm. Bd., Pres. & Chief Exec. Officer--Harkins Builders, Inc., Silver Spring, MD; *U.S. Private*, pg. 502

Cooksey, David, Sir, Chm. Bd.--Bespak plc, Norfolk, United Kingdom; *Int'l*, pg. 193

Cooley, A. Crawford, Chm. Bd.--E.D. Bullard Company, Cynthiana, KY; *U.S. Private*, pg. 180

Cooley, James A., Chm. Bd.--Tri Valley Growers, San Ramon, CA; *U.S. Private*, pg. 1101

Cooley, Raleigh M., Chm. Bd.--Bank of Carroll, Hillsville, VA; *U.S. Public*, pg. 1038

Coombe, V.A., Chm. Bd., Chief Exec. Officer & Treas.--The Wm. Powell Company, Cincinnati, OH; *U.S. Private*, pg. 877

Coon, Kenneth C., Chm. Bd. & Chief Exec. Officer--Acceptance Insurance Co., Inc., Omaha, NE; *U.S. Public*, *pg. 14*

Coon, Max A., Chm. Bd. & Pres.--Maxco, Inc., Lansing, MI; *U.S. Public*, pg. 1061

Coon, Miles A., Chm. Bd.--Red Wing Products, Inc., Plainview, NY; *Int'l*, pg. 480

Cooper, B. William, Chm. Bd. & Chief Exec. Officer--Spectronics Corporation, Westbury, NY; *U.S. Private*, pg. 1024

Cooper, Brian, Chm. Bd.--N.G. Bailey & Co. Ltd., Ilkley, United Kingdom; *Int'l*, pg. 132

Cooper, D.E., Chm. Bd.--C G Smith Ltd., Sandton, South Africa; *Int'l*, pg. 1263

Cooper, Donald M., Chm. Bd., Pres. & Chief Exec. Officer--CoreStates Bank, Lancaster, PA; *U.S. Public*, pg. 446

Cooper, Eric, Chm. Bd. & Chief Exec. Officer--FORE Systems, Inc., Warrendale, PA; *U.S. Public*, pg. 667

Cooper, Fred, Chm. Bd.--Cooper Smith, Inc., Mobile, AL; *U.S. Public*, pg. 547

Cooper, H. Lee, III, Chm. Bd.--CNB Bancshares, Inc., Evansville, IN; *U.S. Public*, pg. 280

Cooper, Joseph V., Chm. Bd. & Pres.--C. Weaver Chevrolet, Inc., New York Mills, NY; *U.S. Private*, pg. 1156

Cooper, Marshall Y., Jr., Chm. Bd., Chief Exec. Officer & Pres.--Harriet & Henderson Yarns, Inc., Henderson, NC; *U.S. Private*, pg. 504

Cooper, Melvin L., Chm. Bd. & Chief Exec. Officer--The Union Corporation, Greenwich, CT; *U.S. Public*, pg. 1667

Cooper, Milton, Chm. Bd. & Chief Exec. Officer--Kimco Realty Corporation, New Hyde Park, NY; *U.S. Public*, pg. 960

Cooper, Robert Gaines, Chm. Bd.--Orthofix International N.V., Curacao, Netherlands Antilles; *Int'l*, pg. 1011

Cooper, Robert Gaines, Chm. Bd.--Orthofix Inc., Richardson, TX; *Int'l*, pg. 1011

Cooper, Stephen E., Chm., Pres. & Chief Exec. Officer--Etec Systems, Inc., Hayward, CA; *U.S. Public*, pg. 594

Cooper, William, Chm. Bd. & Pres.--Allied Industrial Group, Inc., Saint Louis, MO; *U.S. Private*, pg. 39

Cooper, William A., Chm. Bd. & Chief Exec. Officer--TCF Financial Corp., Minneapolis, MN; *U.S. Public*, pg. 1554

Cooper, William E., Chm. Bd.--Chemtech Products Inc., Saint Louis, MO; *U.S. Private*, pg. 39

Coords, Robert H., Chm. Bd. & Chief Exec. Officer--SunTrust Bank, South Florida, N.A., Fort Lauderdale, FL; *U.S. Public*, pg. 1538

Coors, William K., Chm. Bd.--ACX Technologies Inc., Golden, CO; *U.S. Public*, pg. 3

Coors, William K., Chm. Bd. & Pres.--Adolph Coors Company, Golden, CO; *U.S. Public*, pg. 445

Copeland, Daniel M., Chm. Bd.--Ploof Truck Lines, Inc., Jacksonville, FL; *U.S. Private*, pg. 872

Copley, Helen K., Chm. Bd.--The Copley Press, Inc., La Jolla, CA; *U.S. Private*, pg. 275

Coppel Luken, Enrique, Chm. Bd.--Coppel S.A. de C.V., Culiacan, Mexico; *Int'l*, pg. 330

Coppin, Claude, Chm. Bd. & Chief Exec. Officer--Spie Batignolles, Cergy-Pontoise, France; *Int'l*, pg. 16

Copps, Michael W., Chm. Bd. & Chief Exec. Officer--The Copps Corp., Stevens Point, WI; *U.S. Private*, pg. 275

Corasanti, Eugene R., Chm. Bd., Pres. & Chief Exec. Officer--Conmed Corporation, Utica, NY; *U.S. Public*, pg. 431

Corbett, E.M., Jr., Chm. Bd., Pres. & Chief Exec. Officer--Harwick Standard Distribution Corporation, Akron, OH; *U.S. Private*, pg. 509

Corbett, John T., Chm. Bd.--Cigna Life Insurance Australia Limited, Sydney, Australia; *U.S. Public*, pg. 364

Corbett, Luke R., Chm. Bd. & Chief Exec. Officer--Kerr-McGee Corporation, Oklahoma City, OK; *U.S. Public*, pg. 952

Corbett, Richard, Pres.--Crane Manufacturing, Cudahy, WI; *U.S. Private*, pg. 286

Corbett, Thomas W., Chm. Bd. & Chief Exec. Officer--Robert F. Driver Co., Inc., San Diego, CA; *U.S. Private*, pg. 343

Corbin, R.B., Chm. Bd.--Metal Trades, Inc., Hollywood, SC; *U.S. Private*, pg. 734

Corbusier, Dave, Chm. Bd.--Fort Worth Division, Fort Worth, TX; *U.S. Public*, pg. 509

Corcoran, Patrick, Chm. Bd.--Color Arts, Inc., Racine, WI; *U.S. Private*, pg. 254

Corcoran, Philip, Chm. Bd.--Comark, Bloomingdale, IL; *U.S. Private*, pg. 257

Corder, Sidney V., Chm. Bd., Pres. & Chief Exec. Officer--Analytical Surveys, Inc., Colorado Springs, CO; *U.S. Public*, pg. 110

Cordes, J.F., Chm. Bd.--ANR Pipeline Co., Detroit, MI; *U.S. Public*, pg. 389

Cordier, William K., Chm. Bd.--Canton Drop Forge, Canton, OH; *U.S. Private*, pg. 205

Cordner, Tom, Co-Chm. Bd. & Creative Dir.--Team One Advertising, El Segundo, CA; *U.S. Public*, pg. 1422

Cori, C. Tom, Ph.D., Chm. Bd. & Chief Exec. Officer--Sigma-Aldrich Corporation, Saint Louis, MO; *U.S. Public*, pg. 1471

Corkin, Herbert I., Chm. Bd. & Chief Exec. Officer--The Entwistle Company, Hudson, MA; *U.S. Private*, pg. 378

Corley, Carl M., Chm. Bd.--Carco International, Inc., Fort Smith, AR; *U.S. Private*, pg. 208

Cornelio, Albert, Chm. Bd.--Berkshire Life Insurance Company, Pittsfield, MA; *U.S. Private*, pg. 136

Cornelius, James, Chm. Bd.-Guident--Guidant Corporation-Cardiac Rhythm Management Group, Saint Paul, MN; *U.S. Public*, pg. 768

Cornelius, James M., Chm. Bd.--Guidant Corporation, Indianapolis, IN; *U.S. Public*, pg. 768

Cornell, Harry M., Jr., Chm. Bd. & Chief Exec. Officer--Leggett & Platt, Incorporated, Carthage, MO; *U.S. Public*, *pg. 985*

Cornelsen, Paul F., Chm. Bd.--Purina Mills, Inc., Saint Louis, MO; *U.S. Private*, pg. 895

Cornish, David A., Chm. Bd.--Collegeville/Imagineering L.P., Collegeville, PA; *U.S. Private*, pg. 252

Cornog, Robert A., Chm. Bd., Pres. & Chief Exec. Officer--Snap-On Tools Corporation, Kenosha, WI; *U.S. Public*, pg. 1480

Cornstein, David, Chm. Bd.--Finlay Enterprises, Inc., New York, NY; *U.S. Public*, pg. 623

Cornwell, Kevin L., Chm. Bd., Pres. & Chief Exec. Officer--Utah Medical Products, Inc., Midvale, UT; *U.S. Public*, pg. 1700

Cornwell, W. Don, Chm. Bd. & Chief Exec. Officer--Granite Broadcasting Corporation, New York, NY; *U.S. Public*, pg. 759

Corogin, John S., Chm. Bd.--Lake Erie Electric, Inc., Westlake, OH; *U.S. Private*, pg. 643

Corona, Luis Rebollar, Chm. Bd. & Chief Exec. Officer--Grupo Sidek, S.A. de C.V., Guadalajara, Mexico; *Int'l*, pg. 576

Correll, A.D., Chm. Bd. & Chief Exec. Officer--Georgia-Pacific Corporation, Atlanta, GA; *U.S. Public*, pg. 735

Correll, Donald L., Chm. Bd. & Chief Exec. Officer--United Water Resources, Harrington Park, NJ; *U.S. Public*, pg. 1691

Correll, Donald L., Chm. Bd. & Chief Exec. Officer--United Water Management & Services, Harrington Park, NJ; *U.S. Public*, pg. 1692

Corrigan, Wilfred J., Chm. & Chief Exec. Officer--LSI Logic Corp., Milpitas, CA; *U.S. Public*, pg. 971

Corriveau, David O., Co-Chief Exec. Officer & Pres.--Dave & Buster's, Dallas, TX; *U.S. Public*, pg. 488

Corroon, James M., Chm. Bd.--Willis Corroon Corp. of Idaho, Boise, ID; *Int'l*, pg. 1506

Corson, Madeleine G., Chm. Bd.--Guy Gannett Communications, Portland, ME; *U.S. Private*, pg. 439

Cortina, Alfonso, Chm. Bd. & Chief Exec. Officer--Repsol S.A., Madrid, Spain; *Int'l*, pg. 1104

Cortina, R. Martinez, Chm.--Banco NatWest Espana SA, Madrid, Spain; *Int'l*, pg. 911

Corzine, Jon, Chm. Bd. & Chief Exec. Officer--Goldman, Sachs & Co., New York, NY; *U.S. Private*, pg. 462

Cosgrave, Gary D., Chm. Bd. & Chief Exec. Officer--PRO Group, Inc., Englewood, CO; *U.S. Private*, pg. 887

Cosgrove, Howard E., Chm. Bd. & Chief Exec. Officer--Conectiv, Wilmington, DE; *U.S. Public*, pg. 430

Cosgrove, Howard E., Chm. Bd., Pres. & Chief Exec. Officer--Delmarva Power & Light Company, Wilmington, DE; *U.S. Public*, pg. 430

Coslov, Michael, Chm. Bd.--Tube City Inc., Glassport, PA; *U.S. Private*, pg. 1108

Cosman, Les, Chm. Bd.--Genstar Development Company, San Diego, CA; *Int'l*, pg. 112

Coss, Lawrence M., Chm. Bd., Pres. & Chief Exec. & Oper. Officer--Green Tree Financial Corporation, Saint Paul, MN; *U.S. Public*, pg. 761

Costa, Giorgio, Chm. Bd.--Caboto Gestioni Sim S.p.A., Milan, Italy; *Int'l*, pg. 138

Costa, Pat V., Chm. Bd., Pres. & Chief Exec. Officer--Robotic Vision Systems, Inc., Hauppauge, NY; *U.S. Public*, pg. 1395

Costello, Albert J., Chm. Bd., Pres. & Chief Exec. Officer--W.R. Grace & Co., Boca Raton, FL; *U.S. Public*, pg. 754

Coster, Peter, Chm. Bd.--Mercer Management Consulting, Inc., New York, NY; *U.S. Public*, pg. 1049

Costley, Gary E., Ph.D., Chm. Bd., Pres. & Chief Exec. Officer--International Multifoods Corporation, Minneapolis, MN; *U.S. Public*, pg. 900

Cote, Pierre, Chm. Bd.--Celanese Canada, Inc., Montreal, Canada; *Int'l*, pg. 625

Cottam, Harold, Chm. Bd.--Haden Maclellan Holdings plc, Egham, United Kingdom; *Int'l*, pg. 585

Cotter, Daniel A., Chm. Bd. & Chief Exec. Officer--TruServ Corporation, Chicago, IL; *U.S. Private*, pg. 1108

Cotter, James J., Chm. Bd.--Craig Corporation, Los Angeles, CA; *U.S. Public*, pg. 456

Cotter, James J., Chm. Bd.--Citadel Holdings Corp., Los Angeles, CA; *U.S. Public*, pg. 456

Cotterill, D., Chm.--Senior Davis Derby, Derby, United Kingdom; *Int'l*, pg. 1220

Cottet, Gerard, Chm. & Chief Exec. Officer--Essilor International Compagnie Generale d'Optique, Charenton-le-Pont, France; *Int'l*, pg. 462

Cottrell, Comer J., Chm. Bd.--Pro-Line Corporation, Dallas, TX; *U.S. Private*, pg. 887

Cottrell, James L., Chm. Bd.--Cape Coral National Bank, Cape Coral, FL; *U.S. Public*, pg. 607

Cottrell, M.N.F., Chm. Bd.--Matthew Clark Taunton, Ltd., Bristol, United Kingdom; *Int'l*, pg. 848

Cottrell, Michael, Chm. Bd.--Taunton Cider Company P.L.C., Taunton, United Kingdom; *Int'l*, pg. 849

Cottrell, P.J.W., Chm. Bd.--Boral Limited, Sydney, Australia; *Int'l*, pg. 203

Cottrell, P.J.W., Chm. Bd.--Email Limited, Waterloo, Australia; *Int'l*, pg. 450

Cottrell, Peter, Chm. Bd.--Industrial Equity Limited, Sydney, Australia; *Int'l*, pg. 676

Couch, John C., Chm. Bd., Pres. & Chief Exec. Officer--Alexander & Baldwin, Inc., Honolulu, HI; *U.S. Public*, pg. 39

Couch, John C., Chm. Bd.--Matson Navigation Company, Inc., San Francisco, CA; *U.S. Public*, pg. 39

Couch, John C., Chm. Bd. & Pres.--A & B-Hawaii, Inc., Honolulu, HI; *U.S. Public*, pg. 39

Couch, John C., Chm. Bd.--California & Hawaiian Sugar Company Inc., Crockett, CA; *U.S. Public*, pg. 39

Coulon, Jules, Chm. Bd. & Pres.--Moulinex S.A., Bagnolet, France; *Int'l*, pg. 896

Coulson, Robert A., Chm. Bd. & Founder--Restaurant Developers Corp., Independence, OH; *U.S. Private*, pg. 925

Coulter, David, Chm. Bd. & Chief Exec. Officer--BankAmerica Corporation, San Francisco, CA; *U.S. Public*, pg. 179

Councell, Paul S., Chm. & Chief Exec. Officer--Cramer-Krasselt Public Relations, Milwaukee, WI; *U.S. Private*, pg. 286

Counsell, Paul S., Chm. Bd. & Chief Exec. Officer--Cramer-Krasselt, Milwaukee, WI; *U.S. Private*, pg. 285

Countryman, Gary L., Chm. & Chief Exec. Officer--Liberty Mutual Insurance Co., Boston, MA; *U.S. Private*, pg. 666

Couri, George G., Chm. Bd.--Couristan Inc., Fort Lee, NJ; *U.S. Private*, pg. 279

Court, Jean-Francois, Chm.-SOCAPI--Groupe GAN, Paris, France; *Int'l*, pg. 563

Court, Keith William, Chm. Bd.--South West Water PLC, Exeter, United Kingdom; *Int'l*, pg. 1287

Courtin-Clarins, Jacques, Chm. Bd. & Chief Exec. Officer--Clarins, Neuilly-sur-Seine, France; *Int'l*, pg. 295

Cousins, Thomas G., Chm. Bd. & Chief Exec. Officer--Cousins Properties Incorporated, Atlanta, GA; *U.S. Public*, pg. 453

Coutu, Jean, Chm. Bd. & Chief Exec. Officer--The Jean Coutu Group (PJC) Inc., Longueuil, Canada; *Int'l*, pg. 340

Couvelaire, Alexandre, Co-Chm. Bd.--Mooney Aircraft Corporation, Kerrville, TX; *U.S. Private*, pg. 759

Covalt, Robert B., Chm. Bd., Pres. & Chief Exec. Officer--Sovereign Specialty Chemical, Inc., Chicago, IL; *U.S. Private*, pg. 1019

Covey, Roger E., Chm. Bd. & Chief Exec. Officer--System Software Associates, Inc., Chicago, IL; *U.S. Public*, pg. 1552

Covey, Stephen R., Co-Chm. Bd.--Franklin Covey, Salt Lake City, UT; *U.S. Public*, pg. 679

Covington, George, Chm. Bd.--Conway Corporation, Conway, AR; *U.S. Private*, pg. 272

Covino, Charles P., Chm. Bd. & Chief Exec. Officer--General Magnaplate Corporation, Linden, NJ; *U.S. Public*, pg. 717

Cowan, James R., Chm. Bd., Pres. & Chief Exec. Officer--Stonecutter Mills Corp., Spindale, NC; *U.S. Private*, pg. 1044

Cowan, R. Douglas, Chm. Bd., Pres. & Chief Exec. Officer--The Davey Tree Expert Company, Kent, OH; *U.S. Private*, pg. 314

Cowan, Rory, Chm. Bd.--Interleaf, Inc., Waltham, MA; *U.S. Public*, pg. 893

Cowart, Jim C., Chm. Bd. & Chief Exec. Officer--Aurora Electronics, Inc., Irvine, CA; *U.S. Public*, pg. 147

Cowin, John J., Chm. Bd., Pres. & Treas.--Cowin & Company, Inc., Birmingham, AL; *U.S. Private*, pg. 280

Cowles, John, III, Chm. Bd.--Cowles Media Company, Minneapolis, MN; *U.S. Private*, pg. 280

Cowley, George, Chm. Bd.--Alpha One Exchange, New Providence, NJ; *U.S. Private*, pg. 45

Cowpland, Michael, Chm. Bd., Pres. & Chief Exec. Officer--Corel Corporation, Ottawa, Canada; *Int'l*, pg. 331

Cox, Fred B., Chm. Bd.--Emulex Corporation, Costa Mesa, CA; *U.S. Public*, pg. 579

Cox, J.E., Chm. Bd.--Taylor Woodrow-Towell Co. (LLC), Ruwi, Oman; *Int'l*, pg. 1360
Cox, R. Earl, III, Chm. Bd.--Tandycrafts, Inc., Fort Worth, TX; *U.S. Public*, pg. 1561
Cox, William B., Chm. Bd.--Cox Wood Preserving Co., Orangeburg, SC; *U.S. Private*, pg. 283
Coyne, Nancy, Chm. Bd., Chief Exec. Officer & Creative Services Dir.--Serino Coyne Inc., New York, NY; *U.S. Private*, pg. 985
Coyne, Nancy, Chm.--Serino Coyne Public Relations, New York, NY; *U.S. Private*, pg. 985
Crahan, Jack B., Chm. Bd.--Flexsteel Industries, Inc., Dubuque, IA; *U.S. Public*, pg. 653
Craig, David R., Chm. Bd.--Gaston County Dyeing Machine Co., Mount Holly, NC; *U.S. Private*, pg. 441
Craig, John E., Chm. Bd.--Powerscreen International Plc, Dungannon, United Kingdom; *Int'l*, pg. 1066
Craig, Sidney, Chm. Bd. & Chief Exec. Officer--Jenny Craig, Inc., La Jolla, CA; *U.S. Public*, pg. 926
Crain, Keith E., Chm. Bd.--Crain Communications, Inc., Chicago, IL; *U.S. Private*, pg. 284
Cramer, James D., Chm. Bd., Pres. & Chief Exec. Officer--Science & Engineering Associates, Albuquerque, NM; *U.S. Private*, pg. 975
Crandall, David E., Chm. Bd. & Chief Exec. Officer--Premier Metal Products Co., Carrollton, TX; *U.S. Private*, pg. 881
Crandall, Robert L., Chm. Bd. & Chief Exec. Officer--AMR Corporation, Fort Worth, TX; *U.S. Public*, pg. 9
Crane, Douglas P., Chm. Bd.--EMCON, San Mateo, CA; *U.S. Public*, pg. 571
Crane, E.A., Chm. Bd.--California Reconveyance Co., Chatsworth, CA; *U.S. Public*, pg. 1741
Crane, James R., Chm. Bd., Pres. & Chief Exec. Officer--Eagle USA Airfreight, Houston, TX; *U.S. Public*, pg. 547
Crane, Jonathan C., Chm. Bd., Pres. & Chief Exec. Officer--Marcam Solutions, Inc., Newton, MA; *U.S. Public*, pg. 1042
Crane, Lansing, E., Chm. Bd. & Chief Exec. Officer--Crane & Co., Inc., Dalton, MA; *U.S. Private*, pg. 286
Crane, T.R., Jr., Chm. Bd.--Dryden Oil Company, Inc., Baltimore, MD; *Int'l*, pg. 235
Cranford, Wayne, Chm. Emeritus--Cranford Johnson Robinson Woods, Little Rock, AR; *U.S. Private*, pg. 286
Cranor, John M., III, Chm. Bd., Pres. & Chief Exec. Officer--Long John Silver's, Inc., Lexington, KY; *U.S. Private*, pg. 674
Crants, Doctor R., Chm. Bd. & Chief Exec. Officer--Corrections Corporation of America, Nashville, TN; *U.S. Public*, pg. 450
Craven, John, Chm. Bd. & Chief Exec. Officer--Morgan Grenfell Group PLC, London, United Kingdom; *Int'l*, pg. 405
Cravens, William, Chm. Bd.--Alltel Information Services, Inc., Little Rock, AR; *U.S. Public*, pg. 56
Crawford, Bruce, Chm.--Omnicom Group Inc., New York, NY; *U.S. Public*, pg. 1223
Crawford, E.H., Chm. Bd.--The Canada Life Assurance Company, Toronto, Canada; *Int'l*, pg. 254
Crawford, Edward, Chm. Bd.--The Crawford Group, Cleveland, OH; *U.S. Private*, pg. 287
Crawford, Edward, Chm. Bd., Pres & Chief Exec. & Oper. Officer--Park-Ohio Industries, Inc., Cleveland, OH; *U.S. Public*, pg. 1258
Crawford, John D., Chm. Bd., Chief Oper. Officer & Exec. V.P.--Network Long Distance, Inc., Baton Rouge, LA; *U.S. Public*, pg. 1169
Crawford, Mac, Chm. Bd., Pres. & Chief Exec. Officer--Magellan Health Services, Inc., Atlanta, GA; *U.S. Public*, pg. 1033
Crawford, Purdy, Chm. Bd.--Imasco Limited, Montreal, Canada; *Int'l*, pg. 112
Crawford, Purdy, Chm. Bd.--CT Financial Services, Inc., Toronto, Canada; *Int'l*, pg. 112
Crawford, Richard, Chm. Bd. & Chief Exec. Officer--Cambridge Industries Inc., Madison Heights, MI; *U.S. Private*, pg. 202
Cray, Cloud L., Jr., Chm. Bd.--Midwest Grain Products, Inc., Atchison, KS; *U.S. Public*, pg. 1111
Crean, John C., Chm. Emeritus--Fleetwood Enterprises, Inc., Riverside, CA; *U.S. Public*, pg. 650
Creel, Diane C., Chm. Bd., Pres. & Chief Exec. Officer--Earth Technology Corp. USA, Long Beach, CA; *U.S. Public*, pg. 1648
Cresci, Robert, Chm. Bd., Pres. & Chief Exec. Officer--Serv-Tech, Inc., Houston, TX; *U.S. Public*, pg. 1460
Cresimore, James L., Chm. Bd.--The Smithfield Companies, Inc., Portsmouth, VA; *U.S. Public*, pg. 1479
Crespo, J.R., Chm. Bd., Pres. & Chief Exec. Officer--Connecticut Energy Corporation, Bridgeport, CT; *U.S. Public*, pg. 431
Cress, George H., Chm. Bd., Pres. & Chief Exec. Officer--Society Bank, Michigan, Ann Arbor, MI; *U.S. Public*, pg. 954
Cress, Robert G., Chm. Bd.--J.A. Riggs Tractor Co., Little Rock, AR; *U.S. Private*, pg. 930
Cressman, Franklin C., Chm. Bd. & Chief Exec. Officer--Florida Public Utilities Company, West Palm Beach, FL; *U.S. Public*, pg. 655
Crews, Hilliard, Chm. Bd., Pres., Chief Exec. & Chief Fin. Officer--Shelby Group International, Inc., Memphis, TN; *U.S. Private*, pg. 991
Crider, Joe D., Chm. Bd. & Chief Exec. Officer--Reliance Steel & Aluminum Co., Los Angeles, CA; *U.S. Public*, pg. 1375
Crider, Joe D., Chm. Bd. & Chief Exec. Officer--Metalcenter, Inc., Santa Fe Springs, CA; *U.S. Public*, pg. 1375
Crimmins, Michael T., Chm. Bd. & Chief Exec. Officer--Kinark Corporation, Tulsa, OK; *U.S. Public*, pg. 960
Cripps, Robert W.H., Chm. Bd.--Velcro Industries N.V., Willemstad, Netherlands Antilles; *Int'l*, pg. 1462
Crispino, Ralph, Chm. Bd. & Pres.--Plasticrete Block & Supply Corp., North Haven, CT; *U.S. Private*, pg. 871
Critchfield, Jack B., Dr., Chm. Bd. & Chief Exec. Officer--Florida Progress Corporation, Saint Petersburg, FL; *U.S. Public*, pg. 655
Critelli, Michael J., Chm. Bd. & Chief Exec. Officer--Pitney Bowes Inc., Stamford, CT; *U.S. Public*, pg. 1303
Croasdale, William P., Chm.-Media Opers.--Western International Media Corporation, Los Angeles, CA; *U.S. Private*, pg. 1165
Croatti, Aldo A., Chm. Bd.--UniFirst Corporation, Wilmington, MA; *U.S. Public*, pg. 1665
Crocker, Charles, Chm. Bd.--BEI Medical Systems Company, Hackensack, NJ; *U.S. Private*, pg. 106
Crocker, Charles, Chm. Bd., Pres. & Chief Exec. Officer--BEI Technologies, Inc., San Francisco, CA; *U.S. Public*, pg. 160
Croes, Valere, Chm. Bd.--Sabena, Zaventem, Belgium; *Int'l*, pg. 1168
Crombie, David R., Chm. & Chief Exec. Officer--Rayrock Yellowknife Resources Inc., Toronto, Canada; *Int'l*, pg. 1089
Crombie, David R., Chm. Bd. & Chief Exec. Officer--BlackRock Ventures Inc., Toronto, Canada; *Int'l*, pg. 1089
Cromme, Gerhard, Chm. Bd.--Fried. Krupp AG, Essen, Germany; *Int'l*, pg. 507
Cromwell, James J., Chm. Bd.--Potomac Valley Bank, Gaithersburg, MD; *U.S. Public*, pg. 1089
Crona, Joseph S., Chm. Bd.--Compass Bank of the South, N.A., Pensacola, FL; *U.S. Public*, pg. 419
Cronberg, Hakan, Chm. Reg. Bd.--ICA Handlarna Syd AB, Arlov, Sweden; *Int'l*, pg. 643
Crone, W.G., Chm. Bd.--Conley Frog/Switch & Forge Co., Memphis, TN; *U.S. Private*, pg. 263
Cronin, Thomas G., Chm. Bd.--First National Bank of Fort Myers, Fort Myers, FL; *U.S. Public*, pg. 608
Crook, P.L., Chm.--Presstech Controls Limited, Hemel Hempstead, United Kingdom; *U.S. Public*, pg. 789
Crooke, Edward A., Chm. Bd.--Constellation Holdings, Inc., Baltimore, MD; *U.S. Public*, pg. 172
Crooke, Edward A., Chm. Bd.--Constellation Energy Projects & Services, Inc., Baltimore, MD; *U.S. Public*, pg. 172
Crosby, Gordon E., Jr., Chm. Bd. & Chm.-Executive Committee--USLIFE Corporation, New York, NY; *U.S. Public*, pg. 77
Cross, Joe D., Sr., Chm.--Cross Motors Corp., Louisville, KY; *U.S. Private*, pg. 291
Cross, Ray, Chm. Bd., Pres. & Chief Exec. Officer--Krone Casting Corp., North Chicago, IL; *U.S. Private*, pg. 636
Cross, Raymond, Sr., Chm. Bd.--Federal Chicago Corporation, North Chicago, IL; *U.S. Private*, pg. 398
Cross, W. Thomas, Co-Chm.-Prods. Indus. Practice--Price Waterhouse L.L.P. - U.S., New York, NY; *U.S. Private*, pg. 883
Cross, Wilbur J., Chm. Bd., Pres. & Chief Exec. Officer--Catskill Savings Bank, Catskill, NY; *U.S. Public*, pg. 318
Crossingham, James H., Jr., Chm. Bd. & Pres.--Spencer's Inc., Mount Airy, NC; *U.S. Private*, pg. 1025
Crossland, David, Chm.--Airtours Plc, Rossendale, United Kingdom; *Int'l*, pg. 39
Crotty, Gerald R., Chm. Bd. & Chief Exec. Officer--ITT Information Services, Inc., New York, NY; *U.S. Public*, pg. 1512
Crotty, L. William, Chm. & Chief Exec. Officer--Van Dyne-Crotty, Inc., Dayton, OH; *U.S. Private*, pg. 1132
Crowe, A. Derrill, Chm. Bd.--Medical Assurance of West Virginia, Charleston, WV; *U.S. Public*, pg. 1080
Crowe, A. Derrill, M.D., Chm. Bd. & Pres.--Medical Assurance, Inc., Birmingham, AL; *U.S. Public*, pg. 1079
Crowe, Jeffrey C., Chm. Bd., Pres. & Chief Exec. Officer--Landstar Holding, Shelton, CT; *U.S. Public*, pg. 978
Crowe, Kevin E., Chm. & Chief Exec. Officer--Essex Corporation, New York, NY; *U.S. Public*, pg. 320
Crowell, Craven, Chm. Bd.--Tennessee Valley Authority, Knoxville, TN; *U.S. Public*, pg. 1580
Crowell, Raymond E., Chm. Bd.--Glines & Rhodes, Inc., Attleboro, MA; *U.S. Private*, pg. 457
Crowley, Thomas, Jr., Chm. Bd., Pres. & Chief Exec. Officer--Crowley Maritime Corporation, Oakland, CA; *U.S.* Private, pg. 292
Crown, Lester, Chm. Bd.--CC Industries, Inc., Chicago, IL; *U.S. Private*, pg. 192
Crowson, Niel, Chm. Bd., Pres. & Chief Exec. Officer--E.C. Barton & Company, Jonesboro, AR; *U.S. Private*, pg. 119
Crozier, J., Chm. Bd.--Riley Advertising Limited, London, United Kingdom; *Int'l*, pg. 1117
Crozier, William M., Jr., Chm. Bd.--BankBoston Corporation, Boston, MA; *U.S. Public*, pg. 183
Crozier, William M., Jr., Chm. Bd. & Pres.--BayBanks, Inc., Boston, MA, *U.S. Public*, pg. 184
Cruft, Edgar F., Ph.D., Chm. Bd.--Nord Resources Corporation, Albuquerque, NM; *U.S. Public*, pg. 1188
Crump, James G., Chm.-Energy Indus. Practice--Price Waterhouse L.L.P. - U.S., New York, NY; *U.S. Private*, pg. 883
Crutchfield, Bill, Chm. Bd.--State First National Bank, Arkansas, Texarkana, AR; *U.S. Public*, pg. 630
Crutchfield, Bill, Chm. Bd., Pres. & Chief Exec. Officer--State First National Bank, Texas, Texarkana, TX; *U.S. Public*, pg. 630
Crutchfield, Edward E., Jr., Chm. Bd. & Chief Exec. Officer--First Union Corporation, Charlotte, NC; *U.S. Public*, pg. 639
Cruz, Ralph L., Co-Chm. Bd. & Co-Chief Exec. Officer--Omega Research Inc., Miami, FL; *U.S. Public*, pg. 1222
Cruz, William R., Co-Chm. Bd., Pres. & Co-Chief Exec. Officer--Omega Research Inc., Miami, FL; *U.S. Public*, pg. 1222
Csiszar, Ernst N., Chm. Bd. & Chief Exec. Officer--Premium Budget Plan, Inc., Winston Salem, NC; *U.S. Public*, pg. 1453
Csiszar, Ernst N., Chm. Bd. & Chief Exec. Officer--The Innovative Company, Winston Salem, NC; *U.S. Public*, pg. 1454
Csiszar, Ernst N., Chm. Bd. & Chief Exec. Officer--Universal Insurance Co., Winston Salem, NC; *U.S. Public*, pg. 1454
Cubas, Jose M., Chm. & Chief Exec. Officer--SiboneyUSA, Miami, FL; *U.S. Public*, pg. 1641
Cubberly, Walter A., Chm. Bd. & Treas.--Kalas Manufacturing, Inc., Denver, PA; *U.S. Private*, pg. 606
Cudahy, Michael J., Chm. Bd. & Chief Exec. Officer--Marquette Medical Systems, Inc., Milwaukee, WI; *U.S. Public*, pg. 1047
Cude, Richard, Non-Exec. Chm.--Courtaulds Aerospace, Glendale, CA; *Int'l*, pg. 339
Cudlip, Brittain B., Co-Chm. Bd.--Ilsco, Cincinnati, OH; *U.S. Private*, pg. 558
Culea, J.D., Chm., Pres. & Chief Exec. Officer--Northern Labs, Inc., Manitowoc, WI; *U.S. Private*, pg. 805
Cullen, John B., Chm. Bd. & Chief Exec. Officer--King Kullen Grocery Co., Inc., Westbury, NY; *U.S. Private*, pg. 621
Cullingworth, L. Ross, Chm. Bd.--Brookfield Homes Ltd., Toronto, Canada; *Int'l*, pg. 228
Cullingworth, L. Ross, Chm. Bd.--Brookfield Homes, Del Mar, CA; *Int'l*, pg. 228
Cullman, Edgar M., Chm. Bd.--General Cigar Holdings Inc, New York, NY; *U.S. Public*, pg. 707
Cumberlidge, Robert, Chm. Bd.--Texas Utilities Australia, Melbourne, Australia; *U.S. Public*, pg. 1588
Cuming, L.G., Chm. Bd.--McPherson's Limited, Mulgrave, Australia; *Int'l*, pg. 852
Cumming, Ian M., Chm. Bd.--Leucadia National Corporation, New York, NY; *U.S. Public*, pg. 989
Cummings, Jack, Jr., Chm. Bd.--Battey Machinery Company, Rome, GA; *U.S. Private*, pg. 123
Cummings, Thomas L., Jr., Chm. Bd.--Cummings Inc., Nashville, TN; *U.S. Private*, pg. 295
Cunniffe, Maurice J., Chm. Bd.--American Optical Corporation, Greenwich, CT; *U.S. Private*, pg. 60
Cunningham, C. Baker, Chm. Bd., Pres. & Chief Exec. Officer--Belden Inc., Saint Louis, MO; *U.S. Public*, pg. 200
Cunningham, C. Baker, Chm. Bd., Pres. & Chief Exec. Officer--Belden Wire & Cable Company, Richmond, IN; *U.S. Public*, pg. 201
Cunningham, C. Joseph, III, Chm. Bd., Pres. & Chief Exec. Officer--The Fidelity Bank, Frostburg, MD; *U.S. Public*, pg. 1089
Cunningham, William, Chm. Bd. & Chief Exec. Officer--LaundryMart, Inc., Torrance, CA; *U.S. Private*, pg. 222
Cupani, Joseph, Chm. & Chief Creative Dir.--The Chapman Agency, New York, NY; *U.S. Private*, pg. 1197
Curd, Howard R., Chm. Bd. & Chief Exec. Officer--Uniroyal Technology Corporation, Sarasota, FL; *U.S. Public*, pg. 1670
Curley, John J., Chm. Bd. & Chief Exec. Officer--Gannett Company, Inc., Arlington, VA; *U.S. Public*, pg. 698
Curran, D. Patrick, Chm. Bd.--Cook Composites & Polymers Inc., Kansas City, MO; *Int'l*, pg. 1409
Curran, H. Thomas, Chm. Bd.--American Systems Corporation, Chantilly, VA; *U.S. Private*, pg. 63
Curran, John H., Chm. Bd.--Curran Group, Inc., Crystal Lake, IL; *U.S. Private*, pg. 297
Currey, Bradley, Jr., Chm. Bd. & Chief Exec. Officer--Rock-Tenn Company, Norcross, GA; *U.S. Public*, pg. 1396
Currie, James A., Jr., Chm. Bd.--EFCO Inc., Erie, PA; *U.S. Private*, pg. 353
Curry, C. E., Chm. Bd.-Saniserv-Korea--Saniserv-Korea, Seoul, Korea; *U.S. Private*, pg. 965
Curry, John, Chm. Bd.--Knutson Construction Co., Minneapolis, MN; *U.S. Private*, pg. 627
Curtin, Frank T., Chm. Bd., Pres. & Chief Exec. Officer--Brown & Sharpe Manufacturing Company, North Kingstown, RI; *U.S. Public*, pg. 260
Curtin, John D., Jr., Chm. Bd., Pres. & Chief Exec. Officer--Aearo Company, Boston, MA; *U.S. Private*, pg. 23
Curtis, Chuck, Chm. Bd., Pres. & Chief Exec. Officer--Valentine Radford, Inc., Kansas City, MO; *U.S. Private*, pg. 1131
Curtis, Jay, Chm. Bd. & Pres.--Curtis Lumber Company, Ballston Spa, NY; *U.S. Private*, pg. 297
Curtis, Roger William, Chm. Bd., Chief Exec. Officer & Sec.--L.N. Curtis & Sons, Oakland, CA; *U.S. Private*, pg. 297
Cusick, Thomas A., Chm. Bd. & Chief Exec. Officer--TCF Bank Minnesota FSB, Minneapolis, MN; *U.S. Public*, pg. 1554
Custer, John C., Chm. Bd.--Benchmark Electronics Inc., Angleton, TX; *U.S. Public*, pg. 210
Custer, Patrick A., Chm. Bd., Pres. & Chief Exec. Officer--Curtis Mathes Holding Corp., Dallas, TX; *U.S. Public*, pg. 1057
Cusworth, Neville, Chm. & Chief Exec.--Reed Elsevier Legal Division, London, United Kingdom; *Int'l*, pg. 1095
Cutler, Burton, Chm. Bd.--Educational Insights, Inc., Carson, CA; *U.S. Public*, pg. 565
Cutter, W.R., Chm. Bd. & Pres.--Cutter Aviation Albuquerque, Inc, Albuquerque, NM; *U.S. Private*, pg. 298
Cvengros, Joseph, Chm. Bd. & Chief Exec. Officer--Anamet Inc., Waterbury, CT; *U.S. Private*, pg. 70
Cyr, J.V. Raymond, Chm. Bd.--Bell Canada, Montreal, Canada; *Int'l*, pg. 115
D'Agostino, Nicholad, Jr., Chm. Bd.--D'Agostino Supermarkets Inc., Larchmont, NY; *U.S. Private*, pg. 306
D'Agostino, Nicolas, Chm. Bd. & Chief Exec. Officer--Twin County Grocers, Inc., Edison, NJ; *U.S. Private*, pg. 1111
D'Amaro, Louis M., Chm. Bd.--Dennison Stationery Products Company, Holyoke, MA; *U.S. Public*, pg. 153
D'Amour, Donald H., Chm. Bd. & Chief Exec. Officer--Big Y Foods Inc., Springfield, MA; *U.S. Private*, pg. 143
D'Aniello, Daniel A., Chm. Bd.--International Technology Corporation, Monroeville, PA; *U.S. Public*, pg. 907
d'Arbeloff, Alexander, Chm. Bd.--Teradyne, Inc., Boston, MA; *U.S. Public*, pg. 1580

Dabah, Ezra, Chm. Bd., & Chief Exec. Officer--The Children's Place Retail Stores, Inc., West Caldwell, NJ; *U.S. Private*, pg. 237

Dabbagh, Ramzi, Chm. Bd. & Chief Exec. Officer--Communications Instruments Inc., Fairview, NC; *U.S. Private*, pg. 259

Daberko, David A., Chm. Bd. & Chief Exec. Officer--National City Corporation, Cleveland, OH; *U.S. Public*, pg. 1154

Dachowski, Peter R., Chm. Bd.--Ludowici Roof Tile, Inc., New Lexington, OH; *Int'l*, pg. 1171

Dadourian, Haig, Chm. Bd.--Deluxe Storage Systems, Inc., Warren, PA; *U.S. Private*, pg. 323

Dagnan, O.G., Chm. Bd. & Chief Exec. Officer--Centex Construction Products, Inc., Dallas, TX; *U.S. Public*, pg. 322

Dague, Paul, Chm. Bd.--Jones Blair Company, Dallas, TX; *U.S. Private*, pg. 596

Daher, Patrick M., Chm. Bd.--Golden Eagle Group, Inc., Humble, TX; *U.S. Public*, pg. 749

Dahlbaeck, Claes, Chm. Bd.--Stora Kopparbergs Bergslags AB, Falun, Sweden; *Int'l*, pg. 1302

Dahlberg, A.W., Chm. Bd., Pres. & Chief Exec. Officer--Southern Company, Atlanta, GA; *U.S. Public*, pg. 1489

Dahlberg, K. Jeffrey, Chm. Bd.--Grow Biz International, Inc., Minneapolis, MN; *U.S. Public*, pg. 767

Dahlem, Bernard A., Chm. Bd.--Dahlem Company, Inc., Louisville, KY; *U.S. Private*, pg. 306

Dahlsten, Wanda, Chm. Bd.--Dahlsten Truck Line, Inc., Clay Center, NE; *U.S. Private*, pg. 306

Dahms, Christian, Chm. & Mng. Dir.--AON, Jauch & Huebener Gruppe, Hamburg, Germany; *U.S. Public*, pg. 118

Dailey, Peter, Chm., Pres. & Chief Exec. Officer--Memorex Telex N.V., Amsterdam, Netherlands; *Int'l*, pg. 857

Dake, Leland E., Chm. Bd.--Pro-Log Corporation, Monterey, CA; *U.S. Private*, pg. 887

Dalby, Alan J., Chm.--Reckitt & Colman plc, London, United Kingdom; *Int'l*, pg. 1089

Dalessandro, William A., Chm. Bd. & Chief Exec. Officer--MTI/The Image Group, Inc., New York, NY; *U.S. Private*, *pg. 688*

Daley, C. Michael, Chm. & Chief Exec. Officer--LoJack Corporation, Dedham, MA; *U.S. Public*, pg. 1012

Dalhouse, Warner N., Chm. & Chief Exec. Officer--First Union National Bank of Virginia, Roanoke, VA; *U.S. Public*, pg. 640

Dalhouse, Warner N., Chm. Bd.--Shenandoah Life Insurance Company, Roanoke, VA; *U.S. Private*, pg. 992

Dalia, Muhammad Younus, Chm. Bd. & Pres.--Habib Bank Ltd., Karachi, Pakistan; *Int'l*, pg. 584

Dalquist, H. David, Chm. Bd. & Chief Exec. Officer--Nordic Ware, Minneapolis, MN; *U.S. Private*, pg. 806

Dalquist, H. David, Sr., Chm. Bd. & Chief Exec. Officer--Northland Aluminum Products, Inc., Minneapolis, MN; *U.S. Private*, pg. 805

Dalton, George D., Chm. Bd. & Chief Exec. Officer--Fiserv, Inc., Brookfield, WI; *U.S. Public*, pg. 647

Dalton, Parks H., Chm. Bd.--Interstate/Johnson Lane Corporation, Charlotte, NC; *U.S. Public*, pg. 910

Daltoso, Joseph M., Chm. Bd., Pres. & Chief Exec. Officer--Micron Electronics, Inc., Nampa, ID; *U.S. Public*, pg. 1105

Daltry, Robert, Chm. Bd. & Chief Exec. Officer--Flir Systems, Inc., Portland, OR; *U.S. Public*, pg. 654

Daly, Kevin, Chm. Bd., Pres. & Chief Exec. Officer--ATL Products, Inc., Anaheim, CA; *U.S. Public*, pg. 1212

Daly, Leo A., Chm. Bd., Pres. & Treas.--Leo A. Daly Company, Omaha, NE; *U.S. Private*, pg. 309

Daly, Robert, Co-Chm.--Warner Music Group, Inc., New York, NY; *U.S. Public*, pg. 1612

Daly, Robert A., Co-Chm. Bd. & Chief Exec. Officer--Warner Bros. Studios, Inc., Burbank, CA; *U.S. Public*, pg. 1611

Damadian, Raymond, Chm. Bd. & Pres.--Fonar Corporation, Melville, NY; *U.S. Public*, pg. 661

Dammeyer, Rod, Chm. Bd.--Eagle Industries, Inc., Chicago, IL; *U.S. Private*, pg. 473

Damschroder, Robert L., Chm. Bd. & Pres.--Hickman, Williams & Co. Inc., Cincinnati, OH; *U.S. Private*, pg. 525

Danahy, John F.nt, Chm.--Famous-Barr, Saint Louis, MO; *U.S. Public*, pg. 1063

Danbury, Thomas, Chm. Bd.--Survey Sampling, Inc., Fairfield, CT; *U.S. Private*, pg. 1056

Dancker, Paul W., Chm. Bd.--Dancker, Sellew & Douglas, Inc., New York, NY; *U.S. Private*, pg. 309

Dane, John, III, Chm. Bd., Pres. & Chief Exec. Officer--Halter Marine Group, Inc., Gulfport, MS; *U.S. Public*, pg. 778

Daniel, Richard N., Chm. Bd. & Chief Exec. Officer--Handy & Harman, New York, NY; *U.S. Public*, pg. 780

Danieli, Cecilia, Chm. Bd.--Danielli & C. Officine Meccaniche S.p.A., Udine, Italy; *Int'l*, pg. 378

Daniell, Robert F., Chm. Bd.--United Technologies Corporation, Hartford, CT; *U.S. Public*, pg. 1689

Daniels, A.B., Chm. Bd.--Australian National Industries Limited, Pyrmont, Australia; *Int'l*, pg. 100

Daniels, Frank A., Jr., Chm. Bd.--The Associated Press, New York, NY; *U.S. Private*, pg. 92

Daniels, Lee, Chm. Bd.--Daniels Printing Company, Everett, MA; *U.S. Private*, pg. 310

Daniels, Terrence, Chm. Bd.--CAF Holding Company, Dalton, GA; *U.S. Private*, pg. 192

Daniels, Terrence, Chm. Bd.--Collins & Aikman Floorcoverings, Inc., Dalton, GA; *U.S. Private*, pg. 192

Daniels, William D., Chm. Bd. & Chief Exec. Officer--Penn-Daniels, Inc., Quincy, IL; *U.S. Public*, pg. 1467

Dann, Theodore E. Jr., Chm. Bd.--Exolon-Esk Company, Tonawanda, NY; *U.S. Public*, pg. 600

Danna, Leon J., Chm. Bd. & Chief Exec. Officer--Network Real Estate Inc., Capitola, CA; *U.S. Private*, pg. 791

Dannemiller, John C., Chm. Bd., Pres. & Chief Exec. Officer--Applied Industrial Technologies, Cleveland, OH; *U.S. Public*, pg. 122

Dannemiller, John C., Chm. & Chief Exec. Officer--Bruening Bearings, Inc., Cleveland, OH; *U.S. Public*, pg. 122

Dannemiller, John C., Chm. & Chief Exec. Officer--Dixie Bearings, Inc., Cleveland, OH; *U.S. Public*, pg. 122

Dannemiller, John C., Chm. & Chief Exec. Officer--King Bearing, Inc., Cleveland, OH; *U.S. Public*, pg. 122

Danner, George W., Chm. Bd.--Electronic Tele-Communications, Inc., Waukesha, WI; *U.S. Public*, pg. 570

Danuser, Jerry, Chm. Bd.--Danuser Machine Co., Fulton, MO; *U.S. Private*, pg. 310

Danzeisen, John, Chm. Bd.--ICI Americas, Inc., Wilmington, DE; *Int'l*, pg. 663

Darby, O.C., Exec. Chm.--Bass Leisure, Burton on Trent, United Kingdom; *Int'l*, pg. 170

Dardel, Pierre Emmanuel, Chm. Bd.--Sofineti, Paris, France; *Int'l*, pg. 344

Darehshori, Nader, Chm. Bd., Pres. & Chief Exec. Officer--Houghton Mifflin Company, Boston, MA; *U.S. Public*, pg. 841

Dargene, Carl J., Chm. Bd.--Amcore Financial, Inc., Rockford, IL; *U.S. Public*, pg. 64

Darnall, Robert J., Chm. Bd., Pres. & Chief Exec. Officer--Inland Steel Industries, Inc., Chicago, IL; *U.S. Public*, pg. 879

Darnall, Robert J., Chm. Bd. & Chief Exec. Officer--Inland International, Inc., Chicago, IL; *U.S. Public*, pg. 879

Darnis, Pierre, Chm.--CNP Assurances, Paris, France; *Int'l*, pg. 241

Darrigrand, Andre, Chm. Bd.--La Poste Group, Boulogne-Billancourt, France; *Int'l*, pg. 785

Dart, William A., Chm.--Dart Container Corp., Mason, MI; *U.S. Private*, pg. 311

Darwin, Sidney, Chm. Bd.--Cardinal Inc., Rahway, NJ; *U.S. Private*, pg. 208

Darwin, Sidney, Chm. Bd.--Concord Miniatures, Rahway, NJ; *U.S. Private*, pg. 209

Dashper, J.K., Chm. Bd.--Brooke Industrial Holdings Plc, Sheffield, United Kingdom; *Int'l*, pg. 228

Dassault, Serge, Chm. Bd. & Chief Exec. Officer--Dassault Aviation Group, Vaucresson, France; *Int'l*, pg. 383

Dassault, Serge, Chm. Bd.--Dassault Falcon Jet Corp., South Hackensack, NJ; *Int'l*, pg. 383

Date, Yoshihiko, Chm. Bd.--Nitto Denko America, Inc., Fremont, CA; *Int'l*, pg. 950

Daugherty, Jack R., Chm. Bd. & Chief Exec. Officer--Cash America International, Inc., Fort Worth, TX; *U.S. Public*, pg. 312

Daulton, James, Chm. Bd.--Dimco-Gray Company, Centerville, OH; *U.S. Private*, pg. 333

Daunhauer, John R., Jr., Chm. Bd.--Byerly Ford-Nissan Inc., Louisville, KY; *U.S. Private*, pg. 191

Daus, John, Jr., Owner & Chm. Bd.--Anchor Industries Inc., Evansville, IN; *U.S. Private*, pg. 71

Davenport, Gene, Chm. Bd.--Hardware Wholesalers, Inc., Fort Wayne, IN; *U.S. Private*, pg. 502

Davenport, John, Chm. Bd.--Cable & Wireless of North America, Inc., Vienna, VA; *Int'l*, pg. 247

David-Weill, Michel, Chm Bd. & Chief Exec. Officer--Lazard Freres & Co., New York, NY; *Int'l*, pg. 1027

David, Dan, Chm. Bd.--Photo-Me International plc, Bookham, United Kingdom; *Int'l*, pg. 1055

David, Mark M., Chm. Bd. & Chief Exec. Officer--Movie Star, Inc., New York, NY; *U.S. Public*, pg. 1140

David, Morton E., Chm. Bd. & Co-Chief Exec. Officer--Franklin Electronic Publishers, Inc., Burlington, NJ; *U.S. Public*, pg. 679

Davidson, Charles T., Chm. Bd., Pres. & Chief Exec. Officer--J.A. Jones, Inc., Charlotte, NC; *Int'l*, pg. 633

Davidson, Charles T., Chm. Bd., Pres. & Chief Exec. Officer--J. A. Jones Construction Company, Charlotte, NC; *Int'l*, pg. 633

Davidson, Don, Chm. Bd. & Chief Exec. Officer--Outdoor Systems, Inc.-New York, New York, NY; *U.S. Public*, pg. 1235

Davidson, Edward W., Jr., Chm. Bd.--Rosser International, Inc., Atlanta, GA; *U.S. Private*, pg. 946

Davidson, George A., Jr., Chm. Bd. & Chief Exec. Officer--Consolidated Natural Gas Company, Pittsburgh, PA; *U.S. Public*, pg. 435

Davidson, Ian B., Chm. Bd. & Chief Exec. Officer--D.A. Davidson & Co., Great Falls, MT; *U.S. Private*, pg. 314

Davidson, Jeff, Chm. Bd. & Pres.--Michael Weinig, Inc., Statesville, NC; *Int'l*, pg. 1488

Davidson, Kenneth W., Chm. Bd. & Pres.--Maxxim Medical, Inc., Clearwater, FL; *U.S. Public*, pg. 1063

Davidson, Lawrence J., Sr., Co-Chm. Bd.--The Weathervane Retail Corp., New Britain, CT; *U.S. Private*, pg. 1156

Davidson, Phillip T., Co-Chm. Bd.--The Weathervane Retail Corp., New Britain, CT; *U.S. Private*, pg. 1156

Davidson, Richard K., Chm. Bd., Pres. & Chief Exec. Officer--Union Pacific Corporation, Dallas, TX; *U.S. Public*, pg. 1667

Davidson, Robert M., Chm. Bd. & Chief Exec. Officer--Davidson & Associates, Inc., Torrance, CA; *U.S. Public*, pg. 320

Davidson, William, Chm. Bd., Pres., Chief Exec. & Chief Oper. Officer--Guardian Industries Corp., Auburn Hills, MI; *U.S. Private*, pg. 485

Davies, A.M., Chm. Bd.--Simon Engineering plc, London, United Kingdom; *Int'l*, pg. 1251

Davies, D.J., Chm. & Chief Exec.--Johnson Matthey Public Limited Company, London, United Kingdom; *Int'l*, pg. 713

Davies, David J., Chm. Bd.--Sketchley Plc, Hinckley, United Kingdom; *Int'l*, pg. 1261

Davies, Gareth, Chm. Bd.--Glynwed International PLC, Birmingham, United Kingdom; *Int'l*, pg. 554

Davies, George P., Chm. Bd. & Pres.--Trico Electric Co-Op, Tucson, AZ; *U.S. Private*, pg. 1102

Davies, John, Chm. Bd.--Enerfab Inc., Cincinnati, OH; *U.S. Private*, pg. 376

Davies, Noel, Sir, Chm. Bd.--Powell Duffryn PLC, Bracknell, United Kingdom; *Int'l*, pg. 1065

Davies, W.D. L., Chm. Bd.--Amersham Corporation, Arlington Heights, IL; *Int'l*, pg. 992

Davignon, Etienne, Chm. Bd.--Union Miniere, Brussels, Belgium; *Int'l*, pg. 1441

Davis, A. Dano, Chm. Bd. & Principal Exec. Officer--Winn-Dixie Stores, Inc., Jacksonville, FL; *U.S. Public*, pg. 1771

Davis, Alfred M., Chm. Bd.--Halliburton Energy Services, Moorestown, NJ; *U.S. Public*, pg. 776

Davis, Charles E., Sr., Chm. Bd., Pres. & Treas.--Laboratory Supply Company, Inc., Louisville, KY; *U.S. Private*, pg. 641

Davis, Craig, Chm. Bd.--Century Aluminum Company, Monterey, CA; *U.S. Public*, pg. 328

Davis, Craig, Chm.--Ravenswood Aluminum Corp., Ravenswood, WV; *U.S. Public*, pg. 328

Davis, David, Chm. Bd.--Dowty Aerospace Propellers, Gloucester, United Kingdom; *Int'l*, pg. 1337

Davis, DeForest P., Jr., Chm. Bd. & Chief Exec. Officer--Lester B. Knight & Associates, Inc., Chicago, IL; *U.S. Private*, pg. 626

Davis, Donald, Chm. Bd.--First Independence National Bank, Detroit, MI; *U.S. Public*, pg. 635

Davis, Frank, Chm. Bd.--Bardon Group PLC, Solihull, United Kingdom; *Int'l*, pg. 166

Davis, Harold, Chm. Bd. & Chief Exec. Officer--Electrical Wholesale Supply Company, Inc., Idaho Falls, ID; *U.S. Private*, pg. 368

Davis, J. Donald, Chm. Bd.--Davis Wood Products, Inc., Hudson, NC; *U.S. Private*, pg. 315

Davis, J. Roy, Jr., Chm. Bd.--First Charter Corporation, Concord, NC; *U.S. Public*, pg. 627

Davis, Jack, Chm. Bd.--Dataproducts Corporation, Simi Valley, CA; *Int'l*, pg. 620

Davis, James, Chm. Bd. & Chief Exec. Officer--New Balance Athletic Shoe, Inc., Boston, MA; *U.S. Private*, pg. 792

Davis, James L., Chm. Bd.--Davis Paint Company, Kansas City, MO; *U.S. Private*, pg. 315

Davis, James V., Ph.D., Chm. Bd. & Chief Exec. Officer--Willis Corroon Advanced Risk Management Services, Nashville, TN; *Int'l*, pg. 1505

Davis, Jeffrey G., Chm. Bd., Pres. & Chief Exec. Officer--Aetna Plywood, Inc., Barrington, IL; *U.S. Private*, pg. 25

Davis, Jerry, Chm. Bd. & Chief Exec. Officer--Affiliated Foods Southwest, Little Rock, AR; *U.S. Private*, pg. 26

Davis, John H., Chm. Bd.--American Saw & Mfg. Company, East Longmeadow, MA; *U.S. Private*, pg. 61

Davis, L. L., Co.-Chm.--Marley (U.S.A.) Holding Corporation, Johnson City, TN; *Int'l*, pg. 843

Davis, L.L., Chm. & Chief Exec. Officer--Marley Mouldings Inc., Marion, VA; *Int'l*, pg. 843

Davis, Louie R., Chm. Bd.--HDW, Incorporated, Shreveport, LA; *U.S. Private*, pg. 335

Davis, Mark D., Chm. & Chief Exec. Officer--DavisElen Advertising, Inc., Los Angeles, CA; *U.S. Private*, pg. 316

Davis, Mark D., Chm.--Ad Americas, Los Angeles, CA; *U.S. Private*, pg. 316

Davis, Mark D., Chm.--Ingalls Moranville Advertising, San Francisco, CA; *U.S. Private*, pg. 316

Davis, Marvin A., Chm. Bd. & Chief Exec. Officer--Datamax International Corporation, Orlando, FL; *U.S. Private*, pg. 313

Davis, Norwood, Chm. Bd. & Chief Exec. Officer--Trigon Blue Cross & Blue Shield, Richmond, VA; *U.S. Public*, pg. 1637

Davis, Oscar, Chm. Bd.--Hayward Industries, Inc., Elizabeth, NJ; *U.S. Private*, pg. 513

Davis, Peter, Chm. Bd.--Jackson National Life Insurance Company, Lansing, MI; *Int'l*, pg. 1073

Davis, Richard, Chm. Bd.--Davis Industries Inc., Plymouth, MI; *U.S. Private*, pg. 315

Davis, Ronald J., Chm. & Chief Exec. Officer--Biggs Gilmore Communications, Kalamazoo, MI; *U.S. Private*, pg. 143

Davis, Ruth M., Dr., Chm. Bd.--Aerospace Corporation, El Segundo, CA; *U.S. Private*, pg. 24

Davis, Samuel B., Chm. Bd., Chief Exec. Officer & Treas.--Liqui-Box Corporation, Worthington, OH; *U.S. Public*, pg. 1000

Davis, Shelby M.C., Chm. Bd., Pres. & Chief Exec. Officer--Davis Selected Advisors, L.P., Santa Fe, NM; *U.S. Private*, pg. 315

Davis, W. Donald, Chm. Bd., Pres. & Chief Exec. Officer--SouthTrust Bank, Cullman County, Cullman, AL; *U.S. Public*, pg. 1491

Davis, W. Jack, Chm. Bd.--Austin Powder Co., Cleveland, OH; *U.S. Private*, pg. 100

Davis, W. Jack, Chm. Bd.--Rish Equipment Company, Bluefield, WV; *U.S. Private*, pg. 932

Davis, William E., Chm. Bd. & Chief Exec. Offcier--Niagara Mohawk Power Corporation, Syracuse, NY; *U.S. Public*, pg. 1181

Davis, William Jack, Chm. Bd. & Pres.--Davis Mining & Manufacturing, Coeburn, VA; *U.S. Private*, pg. 315

Davis, William L., Chm. Bd. & Chief Exec. Officer--R.R. Donnelley & Sons Company, Chicago, IL; *U.S. Public*, pg. 517

Davis, William L., Chm. Bd. & Chief Exec. Officer--Vermont American Tool Corp., Louisville, KY; *U.S. Public*, pg. 575

Davison, Ian, Chm. Bd.--MDIS Group plc, Hemel Hempstead, United Kingdom; *Int'l*, pg. 826

Davison, Joan, Chm. Bd.--Dacor Corporation, Northfield, IL; *U.S. Private*, pg. 306

Daviss, David B., Chm. Bd.--Luby's Cafeterias, Inc., San Antonio, TX; *U.S. Public*, pg. 1017

Daw, Ronald W., Chm. Bd., Pres. & Chief Exec. Officer--Daw Technologies, Inc., Salt Lake City, UT; *U.S. Public*, pg. 489

Dawdy, Richard A., Chm. Bd. & Chief Exec. Officer--UMB First State Bank of Morrisonville, Morrisonville, IL; *U.S. Public*, pg. 1654

Dawson, Pete, Chm. Bd. & Chief Oper. Officer--Jacob Leinenkugel Brewing Co., Chippewa Falls, WI; *U.S. Public*, pg. 1289

Dawson, Tom, Chm. Bd., Pres. & Chief Exec. Officer--Dawson Construction Co., Inc., Gadsden, AL; *U.S. Private*, pg. 316
Day, Frank, Chm. Bd., Pres. & Chief Exec. Officer--Rock Bottom Restaurants, Louisville, CO; *U.S. Public*, pg. 1396
Day, Frank R., Chm. Bd.--Trustmark Corporation, Jackson, MS; *U.S. Public*, pg. 1643
Day, Frank R., Chm. Bd.--Trustmark National Bank, Jackson, MS; *U.S. Public*, pg. 1643
Day, Graham, Chm. Bd.--Cadbury Beverages North America, Stamford, CT; *Int'l*, pg. 248
Day, James D., Chm. Bd., Pres. & Chief Exec. Officer--Noble Drilling Corporation, Houston, TX; *U.S. Public*, pg. 1186
Day, Joseph P., Chm. Bd.--Vincennes Steel Corp., Vincennes, IN; *U.S. Private*, pg. 1141
Day, Timothy T., Chm. Bd. & Chief Exec. Officer--Bar-S Foods Co., Phoenix, AZ; *U.S. Private*, pg. 114
Dayan, Avi, Chm. Bd.--Bon Jour International Ltd., New York, NY; *U.S. Private*, pg. 156
Dayan, Avi, Chm.--Licensing Div., New York, NY; *U.S. Private*, pg. 156
Dayton, Bruce M., Chm. Bd.--Chancellor Corporation, Boston, MA; *U.S. Public*, pg. 335
De Benedetti, Carlo, Chm. & Chief Exec. Officer--CERUS - Compagnies Europeennes Reunies, Paris, France; *Int'l*, pg. 240
de Boysson, Gaetan, Chm. Bd. & Chief Exec. Officer--Saint Dominique Finance, Paris, France; *Int'l*, pg. 344
De Bree, Simon, Chm. Bd. & Pres.--DSM N.V., Heerlen, Netherlands; *Int'l*, pg. 352
de Bricio Olariaga, Carlos Perez, Chm. Bd.--Compania Espanola de Petroleos, S.A. (CEPSA), Madrid, Spain; *Int'l*, pg. 323
de Bruin, P., Chm.--Vredestein N.V., Velp, Netherlands; *Int'l*, *pg. 1481*
de Carmoy, Herve, Chm. Bd.--Parviland Gerance, Paris, France; *Int'l*, pg. 344
de Chalendar, Pierre Andre, Chm. Bd., Pres. & Chief Exec. Officer--Norton Company, Worcester, MA; *Int'l*, pg. 1173
de Chalon, A. Sauty, Chm. Bd.--Gan Holding Pacifique, Paris, France; *Int'l*, pg. 564
de Clercq, Willy, Chm. Bd.--UCB, S.A., Brussels, Belgium; *Int'l*, pg. 1427
de Croisset, Charles, Chm. Bd. & Chief Exec. Officer--Credit Commercial de France, Paris, France; *Int'l*, pg. 341
De Deo, Joseph E., Chm.-Latin America & Canada--Young & Rubicam Latam (Miami), Miami, FL; *U.S. Private*, pg. 1198
de Geus, Aart J., Chm. Bd. & Chief Exec. Officer--Synopsys, Inc., Mountain View, CA; *U.S. Public*, pg. 1548
de Gier, Johannes, Chm.--SBC Warburg Dillon Read Inc., New York, NY; *Int'l*, pg. 1329
de Janvry, Philippe Choppin, Chm. Bd.--J & L Specialty Products Corp., Pittsburgh, PA; *Int'l*, pg. 572
de Kalbermatte, Bruno, Chm. Bd.--Bobst S.A., Lausanne, Switzerland; *Int'l*, pg. 198
De Keersmaeker, Paul, Chm. Bd.--Kredietbank N.V., Brussels, Belgium; *Int'l*, pg. 760
de Kleuver, W., Chm.--Philips Components B.V., Eindhoven, Netherlands; *Int'l*, pg. 1051
de La Houssaye, E., Chm. Bd.--OCE USA, Inc., Chicago, IL; *Int'l*, pg. 994
de la Parra, Miguel Blesa, Chm., Pres. & Chief Exec. Officer--Caja de Madrid Group, Madrid, Spain; *Int'l*, pg. 251
de la Seigliere, B., Chm. Bd.--Credit Industriel de L'Ouest, Nantes, France; *Int'l*, pg. 564
De Loor, Joop, Dr., Chm. Bd.--Dorbyl Limited, Bedfordview, South Africa; *Int'l*, pg. 416
de Lounoit, Jean-Pierre, Chm.--Royale Belge S.A., Brussels, Belgium; *Int'l*, pg. 562
De Mattos, Carlos D., Chm. Bd. & Pres.--Matthews Studio Equipment, Burbank, CA; *U.S. Public*, pg. 1060
de Mello Brandao, Lazaro, Chm. Bd. & Pres.--Banco Bradesco S.A., Sao Paulo, Brazil; *Int'l*, pg. 139
De Montalivet, Jean Pierre, Chm. Bd.--Henkel France S.A., Boulogne-Billancourt, France; *Int'l*, pg. 612
De Oliveira, Manuel Ferreira, Chm. & Chief Exec. Officer--Petrogal, s.a., Lisbon, Portugal; *Int'l*, pg. 1044
De Oliveira, Manuel Ferreira, Chm.--Petrogal Espanola, S.A., Madrid, Spain; *Int'l*, pg. 1045
De Oliveira, Manuel Ferreira, Chm.--Sacor Maritima, S.A., Lisbon, Portugal; *Int'l*, pg. 1045
De Oliveira, Manuela Ferreira, Chm.--Comp. Logistica Combustiveis, S.A., Lisbon, Portugal; *Int'l*, pg. 1045
de Oriol Ybarra, Inigo, Chm. Bd.--Iberdrola, S.A., Bilbao, Spain; *Int'l*, pg. 657
de Panafieu, G., Chm. Bd.--Westburne Inc., Montreal, Canada; *Int'l*, pg. 1491
de Pear, Ron, Exec. V.P., Exec. Media Dir.-JWT/Europe, Chm.-Global Media Group--J. Walter Thompson Company, New York, NY; *Int'l*, pg. 1483
de Pouzilhac, Alain, Chm. & Chief Exec. Officer--Havas Advertising, Levallois-Perret, France; *Int'l*, pg. 600
De Pretis, Dario, Chm. Bd.--Banca Di Trento e Bolzano S.p.A., Trento, Italy; *Int'l*, pg. 138
de Pury, Simon, Chm. Bd.-Southeby's Europe--Sotheby's Europe, London, United Kingdom; *U.S. Public*, pg. 1487
De Roissard, Henri, Chm. Bd. & Chief Exec. Officer--Dumez-GTM, Nanterre, France; *Int'l*, pg. 823
de Roissard, Henri, Chm. & Chief Exec. Officer--Dumez-GTM, Nanterre, France; *Int'l*, pg. 823
de Rothschild, David, Chm. Bd.--Rothschild North America Inc., New York, NY; *U.S. Private*, pg. 947
de Rothschild, Evelyn, Chm.-Exec. Committee--Rothschild North America Inc., New York, NY; *U.S. Private*, pg. 947
de Ruiter, H., Chm.-Supvr. Bd.--Koninklijke Hoogovens N.V., Ijmuiden, Netherlands; *Int'l*, pg. 753
De Schutter, Richard U., Chm. Bd. & Pres.--Searle & Co., Skokie, IL; *U.S. Public*, pg. 1125
de Spirlet, Louis, Chm. Bd.--Techspace Aero, Milmort, Belgium; *Int'l*, pg. 1166
de Vaucleroy, Gui, Chm. Bd.--Etablissements Delhaize Freres Et Cie "Le Lion" S.A., Brussels, Belgium; *Int'l*, pg. 462
De Vecchi, Francesco, Chm.--Ambroveneto International Bank Ltd., Grand Cayman, Cayman Islands; *Int'l*, pg. 138
De Vecchi, Francesco, Chm. Bd.--Caboto Sim S.p.A., Milan, Italy; *Int'l*, pg. 138
De Vito, Robert A., Chm. Bd., Pres., Chief Exec. & Chief Oper. Officer--Cyber Systems, Inc., Anaheim, CA; *U.S. Private*, pg. 299
de Vlugt, W., Chm. Bd. & Chief Exec. Officer--Royal Packaging Industries Van Leer B.V., Amstelveen, Netherlands; *Int'l*, pg. 1145
De Voto, Richard, Chm. Bd. & Pres.--Canyon Resources Corporation, Golden, CO; *U.S. Public*, pg. 301
de Vries, H. R., Chm.--Grabowsky & Poort International Consultants, Hague, Netherlands; *Int'l*, pg. 607
de Waard, C., Chm. & Dir.-Supervisory Bd.--Van Melle N.V., Breda, Netherlands; *Int'l*, pg. 1450
de Wildt, H.R., Chm.--Hoogovens Aluminium NV, Duffel, Belgium; *Int'l*, pg. 755
De Wit, F.J., Deputy Chm.-Exec. Bd.--KNP BT Nederland B.V., Amsterdam, Netherlands; *Int'l*, pg. 756
Dean, Howard M., Chm. Bd. & Chief Exec. Officer--Dean Foods Company, Franklin Park, IL; *U.S. Public*, pg. 489
Dean, Lester M., Sr., Chm. Bd. & Chief Exec. Officer--Dean Operations Inc., Kansas City, MO; *U.S. Private*, pg. 318
Dean, Ned, Chm. Bd. & Chief Exec. Officer--Chase & Sanborn Coffee, Inc., San Francisco, CA; *Int'l*, pg. 917
Dean, T. Richard, Chm. Bd.--Regions Bank/Middle Tennessee, Nashville, TN; *U.S. Public*, pg. 1372
Deardorff, T.D., Chm. Bd. & Pres.--Deardorff-Jackson Company, Oxnard, CA; *U.S. Private*, pg. 319
DeArment, George S., Co-Chm. Bd.--Channellock, Inc., Meadville, PA; *U.S. Private*, pg. 229
DeArment, William A., Co-Chm. Bd.--Channellock, Inc., Meadville, PA; *U.S. Private*, pg. 229
Deary, Grant, Co.-Chm. Bd. & Pres.--Nor-Cal Beverage Co., Inc., West Sacramento, CA; *U.S. Private*, pg. 801
Deason, Darwin, Chm. Bd. & Chief Exec. Officer--Affiliated Computer Services, Inc., Dallas, TX; *U.S. Public*, pg. 27
Deavenport, Earnest W., Jr,, Chm. Bd. & Chief Exec. Officer--Eastman Chemical Company, Kingsport, TN; *U.S. Public*, pg. 550
DeBard, Daniel L., Chm. Bd.--Clinton State Bank, Clinton, IN; *U.S. Public*, pg. 1217
Debatte, Pierre, Chm. Bd.--W.A. Flick & Co. Pty. Limited, Lane Cove, Australia; *Int'l*, pg. 495
Debenedictis, Nicholas, Chm. Bd., Pres. & Chief Exec. Officer--Philadelphia Suburban Corporation, Bryn Mawr, PA; *U.S. Public*, pg. 1287
Debevoise, Thomas, Chm. Bd.--Woodstock National Bank, Woodstock, VT; *U.S. Public*, pg. 187
DeBruce, Paul, Chm. Bd.--DeBruce Grain Inc., Kansas City, MO; *U.S. Private*, pg. 319
Debrun, Philippe, Chm.--Revima, Roissy, France; *Int'l*, pg. 560
DeCarbonel, Francois, Chm. Bd.--Midial S.A., Paris, France; *Int'l*, pg. 865
DeCesaris, Geaton A., Sr., Chm. Bd.--Washington Homes, Inc., Landover, MD; *U.S. Public*, pg. 1741
Decherd, Robert W., Chm. Bd., Pres. & Chief Exec. Officer--A.H. Belo Corporation, Dallas, TX; *U.S. Public*, pg. 209
Decio, Arthur J., Chm. Bd. & Chief Exec. Officer--Skyline Corporation, Elkhart, IN; *U.S. Public*, pg. 1476
Decker, Jack E., Chm. Bd. & Chief Exec. Officer--Campbell Oil Co., Massillon, OH; *U.S. Private*, pg. 204
Decot, Roger, Chm. Bd.--Eurofip (Madrid), Madrid, Spain; *Int'l*, pg. 163
Decourcelle, Gerard, Chm.--BNP SIM S.P.A., Genoa, Italy; *Int'l*, pg. 164
Dedert, William G., Owner--Dedert Corporation, Olympia Fields, IL; *U.S. Private*, pg. 320
Dedman, Robert H., Sr., Chm. Bd. & Chief Exec. Officer--Club Corporation International, Dallas, TX; *U.S. Private*, pg. 247
Dedman, Robert, Jr., Chm. Bd.--Club Corporation of America, Dallas, TX; *U.S. Private*, pg. 247
Dedman, Robert, Jr., Chm. Bd. & Chief Exec. Officer--Club Corp Realty, Dallas, TX; *U.S. Private*, pg. 247
Dee, Edward, Chm. Bd.--Ce De Candy, Inc., Union, NJ; *U.S. Private*, pg. 220
Deeley, C. Michael, Dr., Chm. Bd.--North Limited, Melbourne, Australia; *Int'l*, pg. 967
Deering, Anthony W., Chm. Bd., Pres. & Chief Exec. Officer--The Rouse Company, Columbia, MD; *U.S. Public*, pg. 1407
Deering, Joseph W., Chm. Bd.--Trion, Inc., Sanford, NC; *U.S. Public*, pg. 1639
Deferrari, Ronald H., Chm. Bd., Chief Exec. Officer, Treas. & Sec.--Plasma-Therm, Inc., Saint Petersburg, FL; *U.S. Public*, pg. 1308
Defibaugh, Patricia J., Chm. Bd., Chief Exec. Officer, & Treas.--Aloette Cosmetics, Inc., West Chester, PA; *U.S. Public*, pg. 57
Dega, Gerard, Chm. Bd. & Pres.--Alcatel Cit (S.A.), Velizy-Villacoublay, France; *Int'l*, pg. 56
Degelman, Wilfred, Chm. Bd. & Pres.--Degelman Industries Ltd., Regina, Canada; *Int'l*, pg. 388
Degen, Alfred P., Chm. Bd., Pres. & Chief Exec. Officer--Valley Resources, Inc., Cumberland, RI; *U.S. Public*, pg. 1706
DeGier, Johannes, Sir, Chm.--SBC Warburg Group plc, London, United Kingdom; *Int'l*, pg. 1330
Degner, Harry, Chm. Bd.--Topa Insurance Company, Los Angeles, CA; *U.S. Private*, pg. 1091
Deguerry, P., Chm. Bd.--Banque Regionale De L'Ain, Bourg-en-Bresse, France; *Int'l*, pg. 563
Deikel, Theodore, Chm. Bd., Pres. & Chief Exec. Officer--Fingerhut Corp., Minnetonka, MN; *U.S. Public*, pg. 623
DeJoris, John Paul, Chm. Bd. & Pres.--John Paul Mitchell Systems, Santa Clarita, CA; *U.S. Private*, pg. 753
DeJulius, Paul, Chm. Bd.--Lavelle Company, Philadelphia, PA; *U.S. Private*, pg. 653
Dekker, Marcel, Chm. Bd. & Chief Eexec. Officer--Marcel Dekker, Inc., New York, NY; *U.S. Private*, pg. 321
Del Giudice, Michael J., Chm. Bd.--Orange and Rockland Utilities, Inc., Pearl River, NY; *U.S. Public*, pg. 1229
Del Guidice, Christopher, Chm. Bd.--Del American Properties, Inc., Maitland, FL; *U.S. Private*, pg. 321
Del Rossi, Paul R., Chm. Bd.--General Cinema Theatres, Inc., Chestnut Hill, MA; *U.S. Public*, pg. 693
Del Vecchio, Leonardo, Chm. Bd. & Pres.--Luxottica Group S.p.A., Agordo, Italy; *Int'l*, pg. 822
Del Vecchio, Leonardo, Prof., Chm. Bd. & Pres.--GS Societa Generale Supermercati, Milan, Italy; *Int'l*, pg. 186
Delahaut, Robert J., Chm. Bd. & Pres.--M K Diamond Products, Inc., Torrance, CA; *U.S. Private*, pg. 684
Delaney, Robert, Chm. Bd.--McMaster Carr Supply Co. Inc., Elmhurst, IL; *U.S. Private*, pg. 724
Delany, Logan, Chm. Bd.--Eastern Air Devices, Inc., Dover, NH; *U.S. Private*, pg. 357
Delendas, Jerome, Exec. Chm.--Allianz General Insurance Company S.A., Athens, Greece; *Int'l*, pg. 59
Delendas, Jerome, Exec. Chm.--Allianz Life Insurance Company S.A., Athens, Greece; *Int'l*, pg. 59
Deleye, A.H.C., Chm. Bd.--Royal Begemann Group, Breda, Netherlands; *Int'l*, pg. 1133
Delgado, Jose Carlos March, Chm. Bd. & Pres.--Banca March S.A., Palma de Mallorca, Spain; *Int'l*, pg. 136
Delgado, Jose Carlos March, Chm.--Banco Urquijo S.A., Madrid, Spain; *Int'l*, pg. 136
Deli, Steven F., Chm. & Chief Exec. Officer--Eaglemark Financial Services, Inc., Chicago, IL; *U.S. Public*, pg. 786
Dell, Michael S., Chm. Bd. & Chief Exec. Officer--Dell Computer Corporation, Round Rock, TX; *U.S. Public*, pg. 495
Della Femina, Jerry, Chm., Chief Exec. Officer & Creative Dir.--Jerry & Ketchum, New York, NY; *U.S. Private*, pg. 616
Dellisola, E., Chm.--European Vinyls Corp. (Holdings) B.V., Amsterdam, Netherlands; *Int'l*, pg. 429
Delmar, Steve, Chm. Bd.--Old Dominion Systems of Maryland, Germantown, MD; *U.S. Public*, pg. 1105
Delmonico, Louis A., Chm. Bd. & Chief Exec. Officer--MacNeal-Schwendler Corp., Costa Mesa, CA; *U.S. Public*, pg. 1031
DeLoache, Frances S., Chm. Bd.--Shealy Electrical Wholesalers, Greenville, SC; *U.S. Private*, pg. 991
Delonis, Robert J., Chm. Bd.--Great Lakes Bancorp, Ann Arbor, MI; *U.S. Public*, pg. 1554
Delpit, Larry, Chm. Bd.--Casey Co., Long Beach, CA; *U.S. Private*, pg. 218
DeLuca, Robert, Chm. Bd., Pres. & Chief Exec. Officer--Aero Data Metal Crafters, Ronkonkoma, NY; *U.S. Private*, pg. 23
DelZotto, Angelo, Chm. & Chief Exec. Officer--Tridel Enterprises Inc., Downsview, Canada; *Int'l*, pg. 1423
DelZotto, Angelo, Chm.--Aluma Systems Corp., Toronto, Canada; *Int'l*, pg. 1423
DeMaria, Joseph A., Sr., Chm. Bd. & Chief Exec. Officer--DeMaria Building Co. Inc., Novi, MI; *U.S. Private*, pg. 323
DeMars, Dan R., Chm. Bd. & Chief Exec. Officer--Geupel DeMars, Inc., Indianapolis, IN; *U.S. Private*, pg. 449
Demel, Herbert, Dr., Chm. Bd.--Audi AG, Ingolstadt, Germany; *Int'l*, pg. 1473
Demere, Robert H., Chm. Bd.--Colonial Oil Industries, Savannah, GA; *U.S. Private*, pg. 253
Deming, Robert H., Chm. Bd. & Chief Exec. Officer--Toastmaster, Inc., Columbia, MO; *U.S. Public*, pg. 1619
Demme, James, Chm. Bd. & Chief Exec. Officer--Bruno's Inc., Birmingham, AL; *U.S. Public*, pg. 265
Demner, Mariusz Jan, Chm. Bd. & Creative Dir.--Demner, Merlicek & Bergmann Werbegesellschaft mbH, Vienna, Austria; *Int'l*, pg. 392
DeMott, George, Chm. Bd.--Carrington Laboratories, Inc., Irving, TX; *U.S. Public*, pg. 309
DeNault, John B., Chm. Bd.--20th Century Industries, Woodland Hills, CA; *U.S. Public*, pg. 1646
Denburg, Robert, Chm. Bd.--Barton Press, Inc., West Orange, NJ; *U.S. Private*, pg. 120
Dench, Robert Graham, Chm. Bd. & Mng. Dir.--Barclays Insurance Brokers International Ltd., London, United Kingdom; *Int'l*, pg. 164
Denieuil, Paul-Henri, Chm.--EULER, Paris, France; *Int'l*, pg. 463
Denise, Robert, Chm. Bd., Pres., Chief Exec. Officer & Chief Fin. Officer--Bucilla Corporation, Hazleton, PA; *U.S. Private*, pg. 352
Denlea, Leo, Chm. Bd. & Chief Exec. Officer--Farmers Group, Inc., Los Angeles, CA; *Int'l*, pg. 110
Denney, George, Chm. Bd.--Cole-Haan, Yarmouth, ME; *U.S. Public*, pg. 1184
Dennis, Daniel R., Jr., Chm. Bd., Pres. & Chief Exec. Officer--Norwich Financial Corp., Norwich, CT; *U.S. Public*, pg. 1203
Dennis, Robert F., Chm. Bd.--United Parking, Inc., Atlanta, GA; *U.S. Private*, pg. 1123
Densen, Alan E., Co-Chm. Bd.--Eastco Industrial Safety Corp., Huntington Station, NY; *U.S. Public*, pg. 548
Dent, Frederick B., Chm. Bd.--Mayfair Mills, Inc., Arcadia, SC; *U.S. Private*, pg. 718
Dent, James R., Chm. Bd & Pres.--Crosby & Overton, Inc., Long Beach, CA; *U.S. Private*, pg. 290
DePaul, John D., Chm. Bd., Pres. & Chief Exec. Officer--The Lehigh Press, Inc., Cherry Hill, NJ; *U.S. Private*, pg. 658
DePiano, Richard, Chm. Bd.--Surgical Laser Technologies, Inc., Montgomeryville, PA; *U.S. Public*, pg. 1542
DePodesta, John F., Chm. Bd.--Iron Road Railways Inc., Washington, DC; *U.S. Private*, pg. 575
DePriest, Donald R., Chm. Bd.--American Telecasting, Inc., Colorado Springs, CO; *U.S. Public*, pg. 93
Deprins, Jacques, Chm.--Bernheim-Comofi, Brussels, Belgium; *Int'l*, pg. 562

Der Torossian, Papken S., Chm. Bd. & Chief Exec. Officer--Silicon Valley Group, Inc., San Jose, CA; *U.S. Public*, pg. 1474
Derbes, Daniel W., Chm. Bd.--San Diego Gas & Electric Company, San Diego, CA; *U.S. Public*, pg. 584
Derham Cato, John P., Vice Chm., Pres. & Chief Oper. Officer--The Cato Corporation, Charlotte, NC; *U.S. Public*, pg. 318
Deroy, Michel, Chm. Bd.--Docks de France S.A., Tours, France; *Int'l*, pg. 98
Derr, Kenneth T., Chm. Bd. & Chief Exec. Officer--Chevron Corporation, San Francisco, CA; *U.S. Public*, pg. 347
Derrow, David D., Chm. Bd.--Ohio Transmission Corporation, Columbus, OH; *U.S. Private*, pg. 813
Derst, Edward J., Jr., Chm. Bd.--Derst Baking Company, Inc., Savannah, GA; *U.S. Private*, pg. 326
Derusha, Roger H., Chm. Bd.--Marinette Marine Corporation, Marinette, WI; *U.S. Private*, pg. 703
DeRusha, William, Chm. Bd.--Heilig Meyers Furniture Co., Richmond, VA; *U.S. Public*, pg. 804
DeRusha, William C., Chm. Bd. & Chief Exec. Officer--Heilig-Meyers Company, Richmond, VA; *U.S. Public*, pg. 804
Derzsi, Andras, Chm. Bd.--Malev Hungarian Airlines, Plc., Budapest, Hungary; *Int'l*, pg. 833
Desai, Rohit M., Chm. Bd. & Pres.--Desai Capital Management Incorporated, New York, NY; *U.S. Private*, pg. 326
DeSanti, Giovanni Grottanelli, Prof., Chm. Bd.--Banca Monte dei Paschi di Siena S.p.A., Siena, Italy; *Int'l*, pg. 136
DeSantis, Carl, Chm. Bd.--Rexall Sundown Inc., Boca Raton, FL; *U.S. Public*, pg. 1384
Descarpentries, Jean-Marie, Chm. Bd. & Chief Exec. Officer--Compagnie des Machines Bull, Louveciennes, France; *Int'l*, pg. 315
DeSimone, L.D., Chm. Bd.--Electronic Products Division, Austin, TX; *U.S. Public*, pg. 1605
DeSimone, Livio D., Chm. Bd. & Chief Exec. Officer--3M, Saint Paul, MN; *U.S. Public*, pg. 1604
DesJardins, Stanley P., Chm. Bd. & Chief Exec. Officer--Simula, Inc., Phoenix, AZ; *U.S. Public*, pg. 1475
Desloge, George B., Chm. Bd.--Watlow Electric Manufacturing Company, Saint Louis, MO; *U.S. Private*, pg. 1153
Desloge, Theodore P., Jr., Co-Chm. Bd.--Valley Forge Corporation, San Rafael, CA; *U.S. Public*, pg. 1705
Desmarais, Andre, Deputy Chm. Bd. & Assoc. Chief Exec. Officer--Southam Inc., Don Mills, Canada; *Int'l*, pg. 631
Desmarest, Thierry, Chm. Bd. & Chief Exec. Officer--Total S.A., Paris, France; *Int'l*, pg. 1408
Desmond, Dermot, Chm. Bd. & Pres.--International Investment & Underwriting Ltd., Dublin, Ireland; *Int'l*, pg. 684
DeSole, Domenico, Chm. Bd.--Gucci America Inc., Secaucus, NJ; *Int'l*, pg. 686
Desperak, Jack, Chm. Bd. & Chief Oper. Officer--New Age Intimates Inc., Long Island City, NY; *U.S. Private*, pg. 792
Despres, Robert, Chm. Bd.--Alliance Forest Products Inc., Montreal, Canada; *Int'l*, pg. 57
Desprez, Martin, Chm. Bd., Pres., Chief Exec. Officer & Dir. General--Editions du Juris-Classeur, Paris, France; *Int'l*, pg. 1095
DeStefano, Daniel A., Chm. Bd.--Initio, Inc., Carson City, NV; *U.S. Public*, pg. 879
Deuss, Walter, Dr., Chm.--Karstadt Aktiengesellschaft, Essen, Germany; *Int'l*, pg. 724
Deuster, Robert G., Chm. Bd., Pres. & Chief Exec. Officer--Newport Corporation, Irvine, CA; *U.S. Public*, pg. 1179
Devarrieux, Benoit, Joint Chm.--Devarrieux Villaret, Paris, France; *Int'l*, pg. 600
Devening, R. Randolph, Chm. Bd., Pres. & Chief Exec. Officer--Foodbrands America, Inc., Oklahoma City, OK; *U.S. Public*, pg. 852
Devers, William J., Jr., Chm. Bd.--Global Turnkey Systems Inc., Parsippany, NJ; *U.S. Private*, pg. 457
Deverse, Frank T., Chm.Bd.--International Microcircuits, Inc., Milpitas, CA; *U.S. Private*, pg. 571
Devlin, Robert M., Chm. Bd. & Chief Exec. Officer--American General Corporation, Houston, TX; *U.S. Public*, *pg. 76*
Devlin, Robert M., Chm. Bd.--The Franklin Life Insurance Company, Springfield, IL; *U.S. Public*, pg. 76
Devlin, Robert M., Chm. Bd. & Chief Exec. Officer--The American Franklin Life Insurance Co., Springfield, IL; *U.S. Public*, pg. 76
Devlin, Robert M., Chm. Bd.--Financial Life Assurance Co. of Canada, Etobicoke, Canada; *U.S. Public*, pg. 77
Dew, Donald H., Chm. Bd., Pres. & Chief Exec. Officer--Diemolding Corp., Canastota, NY; *U.S. Private*, pg. 332
Dew, Jayne, Chm. Bd.--Delta Pride Catfish, Inc., Indianola, MS; *U.S. Private*, pg. 322
Dewan, Derek E., Chm. Bd., Pres. & Chief Exec. Officer--AccuStaff Incorporated, Jacksonville, FL; *U.S. Public*, pg. 15
Dewavrin, Daniel, Chm. Bd. & Chief Exec. Officer--Bertrand Faure, Boulogne, France; *Int'l*, pg. 192
Dewe, Roddy, Chm. Bd.--Dewe Rogerson Limited, London, United Kingdom; *Int'l*, pg. 408
DeWindt, D. Stephen, Chm. Bd. & Chief Exec. Officer--Ameriquest Technologies, Santa Ana, CA; *U.S. Public*, pg. 96
DeWinter, C. Mark, Chm. Bd., Pres. & Chief Exec. Officer--Woodhead Industries, Inc., Buffalo Grove, IL; *U.S. Public*, pg. 1776
Dexeus, C., Chm. & Pres.--SBS Espanan S.A., Madrid, Spain; *Int'l*, pg. 1331
Dhabi, Mohammed, Chm. Bd. & Chief Exec. Officer--Faugere & Jutheau S.A., Paris, France; *U.S. Public*, pg. 1049
Dhanabalan, S., Chm. Bd.--Temasek Holdings Pte. Ltd., Singapore, Singapore; *Int'l*, pg. 1374
Dhanabalan, S., Chm.--Singapore Airlines Ltd., Singapore, Singapore; *Int'l*, pg. 1374
Dhanani, Noorally K. J., Chm. Bd.--Double-Cola Co.-USA, Chattanooga, TN; *U.S. Private*, pg. 341
Dharmasakti, Sanya, Chm. Bd.--The Siam Cement Public Company Limited, Bangkok, Thailand; *Int'l*, pg. 1237
Di Comite, Emilio, Chm. Bd.--Locazioni Finanziarie S.p.A., Brescia, Italy; *Int'l*, pg. 138
Di Giacomo, Thomas A., Chm. Bd.--ManuLife Investment Management Corporation, Toronto, Canada; *Int'l*, pg. 840
Dial, Walter David, III, Chm. Bd., Pres. & Chief Exec. Officer--Plymouth Creameries, Inc., Plymouth, WI; *U.S. Private*, pg. 872
Diamantis, George, Chm. Bd.--National Posters, Inc., Chattanooga, TN; *U.S. Private*, pg. 786
Diamond, Gerald, Chm. Bd. & Chief Exec. Officer--Southern Electronics Corporation, Tucker, GA; *U.S. Public*, pg. 1490
Diamond, Harris, Chm. & Chief Exec. Officer--BSMG Worldwide, New York, NY; *U.S. Public*, pg. 1642
Diamond, Lawrence, Chm. Bd., Pres., Chief Exec. & Chief Oper. Officer & Dir.-Pur.--Triangle Marketing Corp., New York, NY; *U.S. Private*, pg. 1102
Diamond, Rick N., Chm. Bd. & Chief Exec. Officer--ACI Telecentrics, Inc., Minneapolis, MN; *U.S. Public*, pg. 3
Diamond, Walter S., Chm. Bd., Chief Exec. Officer & V.P.--Snyder-Diamond, Santa Monica, CA; *U.S. Private*, pg. 1011
Diassi, Frank, Chm. Bd.--Software Plus Inc., Rutherford, NJ; *U.S. Private*, pg. 1012
Diassi, Frank P., Chm. Bd.--Sterling Chemicals Holdings, Inc., Houston, TX; *U.S. Public*, pg. 1515
Diaz Ceballos, Alejo Peralta y, Chm. Bd.--Grupo Iusacell SA de CV, Mexico, Mexico; *U.S. Public*, pg. 204
Diaz, R., Chm.--Dairy Industries (Jamaica) Ltd., Kingston, Jamaica; *Int'l*, pg. 923
Dibben, David, Chm. Bd.--Carolina Builders Corporation, Raleigh, NC; *Int'l*, pg. 1512
Dibben, David A., Chm.--Ferguson Enterprises, Inc., Newport News, VA; *Int'l*, pg. 1512
DiChio, A., Chm. Bd.--Foster Wheeler Chile, S.A., Santiago, Chile; *U.S. Public*, pg. 677
Dick, Wolfgang, Chm. Bd.--EvoBus GmbH Setra Omnibusse, Ulm, Germany; *Int'l*, pg. 368
Dicke, James, Chm. Bd.--Crown Equipment Corporation, New Bremen, OH; *U.S. Private*, pg. 292
Dickelman, James, Chm. Bd.--Topco Associates, Inc., Skokie, IL; *U.S. Private*, pg. 1091
Dickelman, James H., Chm. Bd., Pres. & Chief Exec. Officer--Schultz Sav-O Stores, Inc., Sheboygan, WI; *U.S. Public*, pg. 1442
Dickerson, Arthur J., Chm. Bd., Pres. & Chief Exec. Officer--Southwestern Petroleum Corporation, Fort Worth, TX; *U.S. Private*, pg. 1019
Dickerson, James H., Chm. Bd.--Bell Atlantic Financial Services, Wilmington, DE; *U.S. Public*, pg. 202
Dickinson, R.H., Chm. Bd.--Northern Rock PLC, Newcastle upon Tyne, United Kingdom; *Int'l*, pg. 968
Dickson, Alan T., Chm. Bd.--Ruddick Corporation, Charlotte, NC; *U.S. Public*, pg. 1412
Dickson, G.G., Chm. Bd.--Scottish Brewers Limited, Edinburgh, United Kingdom; *Int'l*, pg. 1212
Didier, N., Chm.--Schneider Electric S.A., Boulogne-Billancourt, France; *Int'l*, pg. 1207
Didion, James J., Chm. Bd.--CB Commercial Real Estate, Los Angeles, CA; *U.S. Public*, pg. 272
Didion, James J., Co-Chm. Bd.--CB Commercial Real Estate Group, Inc., Los Angeles, CA; *U.S. Public*, pg. 272
Didmer, Fred, Chm.--Radio TV Steiner AG, Bern, Switzerland; *Int'l*, pg. 330
Dieckmann, Karl W., Chm. Bd.--Digital Solutions, Inc., Somerset, NJ; *U.S. Public*, pg. 508
Diedrick, Arthur Hill, Chm. Bd.--Communications International (NY), New York, NY; *U.S. Private*, pg. 259
Diego, Guillermo, Chm., Pres. & Chief Exec. Officer-Y&R Spain--Young & Rubicam, S.A., Madrid, Spain; *U.S. Private*, pg. 1199
Diehl, Neil N., Chm. Bd. Emeritus--Ingram Barge Company, Nashville, TN; *U.S. Private*, pg. 563
Diehl, William, Chm. Bd.--Diehl Specialties International, Defiance, OH; *U.S. Private*, pg. 332
Diehl, William A., Chm. Emeritus--Diehl Inc., Defiance, OH; *U.S. Private*, pg. 332
Diekman, D., Chm. Bd.--Silbrico Corporation, Hodgkins, IL; *U.S. Private*, pg. 1000
Diem, John J., Chm. Bd.--Southern Agricultural Insecticides, Inc., Palmetto, FL; *U.S. Private*, pg. 1015
Dierberg, James, Chm. Bd., Pres. & Chief Exec. Officer--First Banks America, Inc., Clayton, MO; *U.S. Public*, pg. 626
Dierberg, Robert J., Chm. Bd. & Pres.--Dierbergs Markets Inc., Chesterfield, MO; *U.S. Private*, pg. 332
Dieter, Werner H., Chm.-Supervisory Bd.--Krauss-Maffei AG, Munich, Germany; *Int'l*, pg. 836
Dietler, Cortland S., Chm. Bd.--Transmontaigne, Fayetteville, AR; *U.S. Public*, pg. 1631
Dietler, Cortlandt S., Chm. Bd. & Chief Exec. Officer--TransMontaigne Oil Company, Denver, CO; *U.S. Public*, pg. 1631
Dietrich, Wendell, Chm. Bd. & Chief Exec. Officer--Vidar, Inc., New London, MN; *U.S. Private*, pg. 1139
DiFillippo, Thomas D., Chm. Bd. & Pres.--DeVault Foods, Devault, PA; *U.S. Private*, pg. 329
Diggs, Matthew O., Jr., Chm. Bd.--Ripplewood Holdings L.L.C., New York, NY; *U.S. Private*, pg. 931
DiGioia, Anthony M., Jr., Chm. Bd. & Pres.--GAI Consultants, Inc., Monroeville, PA; *U.S. Private*, pg. 433
DiJulio, Christopher, Chm. Bd.--Global Van Lines, Inc., Orange, CA; *U.S. Private*, pg. 458
Dike, Buddy, Chm. Bd.--Willis Corroon, Fort Worth, TX; *Int'l*, *pg. 1504*
Diker, Charles M., Chm. Bd.--Cantel Industries, Inc., Clifton, NJ; *U.S. Public*, pg. 301
Dill, S. L., Chm. Bd.--Coutts & Co Trust Holdings Limited, Nassau, Bahamas; *Int'l*, pg. 911
Dillamore, Ian, Chm. Bd. & Chief Exec. Officer--Doncasters plc, Melbourn, United Kingdom; *Int'l*, pg. 416
Dillard, Henry, III, Chm. Bd. & Pres.--Electronic Drives and Controls, Parsippany, NJ; *U.S. Private*, pg. 370
Dillard, William, Chm. Bd. & Chief Exec. Officer--Dillard's, Inc., Little Rock, AR; *U.S. Public*, pg. 509
Diller, Barry, Chm. Bd. & Chief Exec. Officer--USA Networks, Inc., Saint Petersburg, FL; *U.S. Public*, pg. 1685
Diller, James V., Chm. Bd. & Chief Exec. Officer--Sierra Semiconductor, San Jose, CA; *U.S. Public*, pg. 1470
Dillon, Gary G., Chm. Bd., Pres. & Chief Exec. Officer--Schwitzer, Inc., Indianapolis, IN; *U.S. Public*, pg. 968
Dillon, John T., Chm. Bd. & Chief Exec. Officer--International Paper Company, Purchase, NY; *U.S. Public*, *pg. 901*
DiLorenzo, James E., Chm. Bd., Pres. & Chief Exec. Officer--Quality Pontiac GMC Buick, Albuquerque, NM; *U.S. Private*, pg. 899
Dimitriou, Theodore, Chm. Bd.--Wallace Computer Services, Inc., Lisle, IL; *U.S. Public*, pg. 1735
Dimmick, Henry M., Chm. Bd. & Chief Exec. Officer--AGR International, Inc., Butler, PA; *U.S. Private*, pg. 5
Dimon, Jamie, Co-Chm. & Co-Chief Exec. Officer--Salomon Smith Barney Holdings, Inc., New York, NY; *U.S. Public*, pg. 1633
Dindorf, Joseph L., Chm. Bd., Pres. & Chief Exec. Officer--Hein-Werner Corporation, Waukesha, WI; *U.S. Public*, pg. 805
Dineen, Robert J., Chm. Bd.--Layne Christenson Co., Mission Woods, KS; *U.S. Public*, pg. 981
Dines, Paul, Chm. Bd., Pres. & Chief Exec. Officer--Reyco Industries, Inc., Springfield, MO; *U.S. Private*, pg. 926
Dinger, Frank S., Chm. Bd. & Chief Oper. Officer--William H. Sadlier, Inc., New York, NY; *U.S. Public*, pg. 1422
DiNicola, Robert J., Chm. Bd., Pres. & Chief Exec. Officer--Zale Corporation, Irving, TX; *U.S. Public*, pg. 1789
DiNicola, Robert J., Chm. Bd. & Chief Exec. Officer--Zale Delaware, Inc., Irving, TX; *U.S. Public*, pg. 1789
Dion, Philip J., Chm. Bd. & Chief Exec. Officer--Del Webb Corporation, Phoenix, AZ; *U.S. Public*, pg. 494
Dionne, Joseph L., Chm. Bd. & Chief Exec. Officer--The McGraw-Hill Companies, New York, NY; *U.S. Public*, pg. 1069
Dircks, William, Chm. Bd. & Pres.--Berger Transfer & Storage, Inc., Saint Paul, MN; *U.S. Private*, pg. 135
Dirkes, James V., Sr., Chm. Bd., Chief Exec. Officer & Treas.--Rapid Engineering Inc., Comstock Park, MI; *U.S. Private*, pg. 910
DiRomualdo, Robert, Chm. Bd. & Chief Exec. Officer--Borders Group, Inc., Ann Arbor, MI; *U.S. Public*, pg. 245
Disney, Roy E., Chm. Bd.--Shamrock Holdings, Inc., Burbank, CA; *U.S. Private*, pg. 989
Disney, Roy P., Chm. Bd.--The Apogee Companies, Inc., Lake Oswego, OR; *U.S. Private*, pg. 77
Ditomassi, George R., Chm. Bd.--Milton Bradley Company, East Longmeadow, MA; *U.S. Public*, pg. 797
Dittmer, Thomas H., Chm. Bd.--Refco Group Ltd., Chicago, IL; *U.S. Private*, pg. 917
Diver, Neil, Chm. Bd.--Ameriwood Industries International Inc., Grand Rapids, MI; *U.S. Public*, pg. 98
Dixon, Norval W. Jr., Chm. Bd.--Rockville National Bank, Rockville, IN; *U.S. Public*, pg. 1217
Djalil, Sjahrial, Chm. Bd.--Adwork! EURO RSCG Partnership, Jakarta, Indonesia; *Int'l*, pg. 602
Do Minn, Pyung, Chm. Bd.--Grand Hyatt Seoul, Seoul, Korea; *U.S. Private*, pg. 551
Dobbie, S. J., Chm. Bd.--NatWest Financial Products plc, London, United Kingdom; *Int'l*, pg. 910
Dobrez, John F., Chm. Bd.--Dober Chemical Corp., Midlothian, IL; *U.S. Private*, pg. 337
Dobson, Christopher D., Chm. Bd.--Trikon Technologies Inc., Chatsworth, CA; *U.S. Public*, pg. 1638
Dobson, Grace, Chm. Bd.--Whataburger, Inc., Corpus Christi, TX; *U.S. Private*, pg. 1170
Dockser, William B., Chm. Bd.--CRIIMI MAE, Rockville, MD; *U.S. Public*, pg. 459
Dockser, William B., Chm. Bd.--CRI Liquidating REIT, Inc., Rockville, MD; *U.S. Public*, pg. 459
Doddridge, John, Chm. Bd. & Chief Exec. Officer--Intermet Corporation, Troy, MI; *U.S. Public*, pg. 894
Dodge, Arthur B., Jr., Chm.--Dodge Regupol, Inc., Lancaster, PA; *U.S. Private*, pg. 337
Dodge, James H., Chm. Bd., Pres. & Chief Exec. Officer--Providence Energy Corporation, Providence, RI; *U.S. Public*, pg. 1337
Dodge, John B., Chm. Bd.--Burnham, Lancaster, PA; *U.S. Public*, pg. 270
Dodge, N.P., Jr., Chm. Bd.--Omaha Public Power District, Omaha, NE; *U.S. Private*, pg. 815
Dods, Walter A., Jr., Chm. Bd. & Chief Exec. Officer--First Hawaiian, Inc., Honolulu, HI; *U.S. Public*, pg. 634
Dods, Walter A., Jr., Chm. Bd.--Pacific One Dealer Center, Inc., Costa Mesa, CA; *U.S. Public*, pg. 635
Dods, Walter A., Jr., Chm. Bd. & Chief Exec. Officer--Real Estate Delivery, Inc., Honolulu, HI; *U.S. Public*, pg. 635
Dods, Walter A., Jr., Chm. Bd.--Pacific One Bank, Portland, OR; *U.S. Public*, pg. 635
Dods, Walter A., Jr., Chm. Bd. & Chief Exec. Officer--American Security Properties, Inc., Honolulu, HI; *U.S. Public*, pg. 635
Dods, Walter A., Jr., Chm. & Chief Exec. Officer--First Hawaiian Insurance, Inc., Honolulu, HI; *U.S. Public*, pg. 635
Dodson Macauluy, Cathleen, Chm. Bd. & Chief Exec. Officer--Dodson Group, Kansas City, MO; *U.S. Private*, pg. 338
Doehrman, Dale F., Chm. Bd. & Chief Exec. Officer--The Medical Protective Company, Fort Wayne, IN; *U.S. Private*, pg. 728
Doganiero, Philip, Chm. Bd.--Dataflex Corporation, Clearwater, FL; *U.S. Private*, pg. 313

Doggett, Ron E., Chm. Bd. & Chief Exec. Officer--GoodMark Foods, Inc., Raleigh, NC; *U.S. Public*, pg. 751
Doherty, Edward D., Chm. Bd. & Chief Exec. Officer--Kaneb Pipe Line Partners, L.P., Richardson, TX; *U.S. Public*, pg. 942
Doherty, Robert C., Chm. Bd.--McKinney & Silver, Raleigh, NC; *U.S. Private*, pg. 723
Dohmen, Erwin, Chm. Bd.--The F. Dohmen Company, Germantown, WI; *U.S. Private*, pg. 338
Doi, Masa, Chm. Bd.--Chugai Boyeki Co., Ltd., Tokyo, Japan; *Int'l*, pg. 290
Doi, Sadakane, Chm. Bd.--Daiwa Securities Co. Ltd., Tokyo, Japan; *Int'l*, pg. 374
Dokmo, Harold B., Jr., Chm. Bd., Pres., Owner, Treas. & Sec.--Norcraft Companies, Inc., Saint Paul, MN; *U.S. Private*, pg. 801
Dolan, A. Barr, Chm. Bd.--Heska Corporation, Fort Collins, CO; *U.S. Public*, pg. 812
Dolan, Charles F., Chm. Bd.--Cablevision Systems Corporation, Woodbury, NY; *U.S. Public*, pg. 288
Dolan, Robert E., Chm. & Pres.--Lynch Capital Corporation, Greenwich, CT; *U.S. Public*, pg. 1021
Dolan, William A., II, Chm. Bd.--High Point Financial Corp., Branchville, NJ; *U.S. Public*, pg. 826
Dolcetta, Giovanni, Chm. Bd.--Fiamm S.p.A., Montecchio Maggiore, Italy; *Int'l*, pg. 480
Dolgen, Jonathan, Chm.-Viacom Entertainment Group--Paramount Pictures Corporation, Los Angeles, CA; *U.S. Private*, pg. 776
Doman, H.S., Chm. Bd., Pres. & Chief Exec. Officer--Doman Industries Limited, Duncan, Canada; *Int'l*, pg. 414
Domeniconi, R., Dr., Chm. Bd.--Coutts & Co AG, Zurich, Switzerland; *Int'l*, pg. 911
Don, Robert E., Chm. Bd. & Chief Exec. Officer--Edward Don & Company, North Riverside, IL; *U.S. Private*, pg. 339
Donahue, Daniel W., Jr., Chm. Bd.--Donahue Schriber, Newport Beach, CA; *Int'l*, pg. 253
Donahue, John, Chm. Bd.--Pet Life Foods, Inc., Willowbrook, IL; *U.S. Private*, pg. 856
Donahue, William L., Chm. Bd., Pres., Chief Exec. & Chief Oper. Officer--Dixon Paper Co., Denver, CO; *U.S. Public*, pg. 902
Donal, Maxime, Chm. Bd.--CAP Sesa Hoskyns, Paris, France; *Int'l*, pg. 263
Donald, Jack C., Chm. Bd.--Canadian Western Bank, Edmonton, Canada; *Int'l*, pg. 259
Donald, James L., Chm. Bd., Pres. & Chief Exec. Officer--DSC Communications Corporation, Plano, TX; *U.S. Public*, pg. 475
Donald, Jim, Chm. Bd., Pres. & Chief Exec. Officer--Pathmark Stores Incorporated, Woodbridge, NJ; *U.S. Private*, pg. 843
Donaldson, Nigel, Chm. & Pres.--United Advertising Publications, Inc., Dallas, TX; *Int'l*, pg. 1443
Donelan, Patrick, Chm. Bd.--Kleinwort Benson North America Inc., New York, NY; *Int'l*, pg. 420
Donnell, Barry, Chm. Bd.--Cavalier Homes, Inc., Wichita Falls, TX; *U.S. Public*, pg. 318
Donnell, Thomas B., Chm. Bd.--The Fifth Third Bank of Northwestern Ohio, National Association, Toledo, OH; *U.S. Public*, pg. 622
Donnelly, J., Chm.--Ulster Bank Commercial Services Limited, Dublin, Ireland; *Int'l*, pg. 911
Donner, Michael, Chm. Bd., Pres. & Chief Exec. Officer--Barco of California, Gardena, CA; *U.S. Private*, pg. 115
Donze, B., Chm.--Zenith Vie, Pully, Switzerland; *Int'l*, pg. 565
Doolan, Martin, Chm. Bd.--Nalle Plastics Inc., Austin, TX; *U.S. Private*, pg. 773
Dooner, John J., Jr., Chm. & Chief Exec. Officer--McCann-Erickson Worldwide, New York, NY; *U.S. Public*, pg. 909
Dopkins, Leonard A., Chm. Bd., Treas. & Sec.--Standard Electronics, Inc., Amherst, NY; *U.S. Private*, pg. 1031
Dopp, Paul S., Co-Chm. Bd.--Mooney Aircraft Corporation, Kerrville, TX; *U.S. Private*, pg. 759
Dora, Aysegul, Chm. Bd. & Chief Exec. Officer--Penajans DMB&B Ticaret, Istanbul, Turkey; *U.S. Private*, pg. 305
Doran, Wayne, Chm. Bd.--Ford Motor Land Development Corporation, Dearborn, MI; *U.S. Public*, pg. 663
Dore, William J., Chm. Bd., Pres. & Chief Exec. Officer--Global Industries, Ltd., Lafayette, LA; *U.S. Public*, pg. 748
Dorfman, Henry S., Chm. Bd.--Thorn Apple Valley, Inc., Southfield, MI; *U.S. Public*, pg. 1602
Dormann, Juergen, Chm. Bd.--Hoechst Marion Roussel, Inc., Bridgewater, NJ; *Int'l*, pg. 624
Dorn, J.M., Jr., Chm. Bd. & Pres.--Aiken Electric Cooperative Inc., Aiken, SC; *U.S. Private*, pg. 28
Dorn, J.M., Jr., Chm. Bd. & Pres.--Aiken Electric Satellite, Aiken, SC; *U.S. Private*, pg. 28
Dorn, William L., Chm. Bd.--Forest Oil Corporation, Denver, CO; *U.S. Public*, pg. 670
Dorn, Wolfgang, Chm.--Deutsche Babcock Handel GmbH, Oberhausen, Germany; *Int'l*, pg. 401
Dornau, Peter G., Chm. Bd. & Pres.--Ocean Bio-Chem Inc., Fort Lauderdale, FL; *U.S. Public*, pg. 1211
Dorner, Wolfgang, Chm. Bd. & Chief Exec. Officer--Dorner Manufacturing Corp., Hartland, WI; *U.S. Private*, pg. 340
Dorrian, James, Chm. Bd. & Chief Exec. Officer--Arbor Software Corporation, Sunnyvale, CA; *U.S. Public*, pg. 127
Dorskind, Albert A., Chm. Bd.--Universal Studios Development Co., Universal City, CA; *Int'l*, pg. 1215
Dorval, John, Chm.--Anixter Canada, Mississauga, Canada; *U.S. Public*, pg. 115
Dott, A. Eric, Chm. Bd. & Chief Exec. Officer--Monarch Avalon, Inc., Baltimore, MD; *U.S. Public*, pg. 1123
Doubleday, Nelson, Chm. Bd.--Doubleday Publishing Company, New York, NY; *Int'l*, pg. 191
Douce, Patrice, Chm. Bd.--Sodexho USA, Waltham, MA; *Int'l*, pg. 1274
Douglas, Donald, Chm. Bd.--M&W, Gibson City, IL; *U.S. Public*, pg. 35
Douglas, Jon A., Chm. Bd.--The Prudential - Jon Douglas Company, Los Angeles, CA; *U.S. Private*, pg. 892
Douglas, T. O'Neal, Chm. Bd. & Chief Exec. Officer--American Heritage Life Investment Corp., Jacksonville, FL; *U.S. Public*, pg. 78
Douglas, T. O'Neal, Chm. Bd. & Chief Exec. Officer--American Heritage Life Insurance Co., Jacksonville, FL; *U.S. Public*, pg. 79
Douglas, T. O'Neal, Chm. Bd., Pres. & Chief Exec. Officer--First Colonial Insurance Company, Jacksonville, FL; *U.S. Public*, pg. 79
Douglas, T. O'Neal, Chm. Bd.--Columbia Universal Life Insurance Company, Austin, TX; *U.S. Public*, pg. 79
Douglas, T. O'Neal, Chm. Bd.--Concord General Life Insurance Company, Concord, NH; *U.S. Public*, pg. 79
Douglas, Walter E., Sr., Chm. Bd. & Pres.--Avis Ford Inc., Southfield, MI; *U.S. Private*, pg. 101
Douglass, Don, Chm. Bd.--Alamo Group, Inc., Seguin, TX; *U.S. Public*, pg. 34
Douglass, Steven J., Chm. Bd. & Chief Exec. Officer--Payless ShoeSource, Inc., Topeka, KS; *U.S. Public*, pg. 1268
Douro, Lord, Chm. Bd.--Sun Life and Provincial Holdings plc, London, United Kingdom; *Int'l*, pg. 1318
Doust, Arthur F., Chm. Bd. & Chief Exec. Officer--Chemi-Trol Chemical Co., Gibsonburg, OH; *U.S. Public*, pg. 345
Douville, Jean, Chm. Bd., Pres. & Chief Exec. Officer--UAP, Inc., Montreal, Canada; *Int'l*, pg. 1426
Dove, Grant, Chm. Bd.--Optek Technology, Inc., Carrollton, TX; *U.S. Public*, pg. 1227
Dow, Kerr, Chm. Bd.--Custom Foods Limited, Dundalk, Ireland; *U.S. Public*, pg. 806
Dow, Ngiam Tong, Chm. Bd. & Chief Exec. Officer--DBS Bank Ltd., Singapore, Singapore; *Int'l*, pg. 350
Dow, Robert S., Chm. Bd.--Lord Abbett & Co., New York, NY; *U.S. Private*, pg. 675
Dowdell, Rodger B., Jr., Chm. Bd., Pres. & Chief Exec. Officer--American Power Conversion Corporation, West Kingston, RI; *U.S. Public*, pg. 89
Dowling, James H., Chm. Emeritus, Pres. & Chief Exec. Officer-Lat. Amer. (Miami)--Burson-Marsteller, New York, NY; *U.S. Private*, pg. 1197
Dowling, Shaun C., Chm. Bd.--The Hartstone Group PLC, London, United Kingdom; *Int'l*, pg. 599
Downes, Laurence M., Chm. Bd., Pres. & Chief Exec. Officer--New Jersey Resources Corporation, Wall, NJ; *U.S. Public*, pg. 1172
Downes, Laurence M., Chm. Bd. & Chief Fin. Officer--New Jersey Natural Gas Co., Wall, NJ; *U.S. Public*, pg. 1172
Downes, M., Dr., Chm. Bd.--Gallaher (Dublin) Ltd., Tallaght, Ireland; *Int'l*, pg. 539
Downey, Barry, Chm. Bd.--Sky Network Television Limited, Auckland, New Zealand; *U.S. Public*, pg. 204
Downey, Bruce L., Chm. Bd., Pres. & Chief Exec. Officer--Barr Laboratories Inc., Pomona, NY; *U.S. Public*, pg. 191
Downey, David G., Chm. Bd.--Downey Designs International, Indianapolis, IN; *U.S. Private*, pg. 342
Downs, David, Chm. Bd. & Pres.--Norwest Bank Nevada, N.A., Las Vegas, NV; *U.S. Public*, pg. 1202
Downs, Richard, Chm. Bd. & Chief Exec. Officer--Tony Downs Foods Company, Saint James, MN; *U.S. Private*, pg. 342
Dowsett, William J., Chm. Bd.--East Moline Metal Products Company, East Moline, IL; *U.S. Private*, pg. 357
Doyle White, R., Chm. Bd., Pres. & Chief Exec. Officer--U.S. Filter/Davis Water & Waste Industries, Inc., Thomasville, GA; *U.S. Public*, pg. 1682
Doyle, F. King, Chm. Bd.--King Milling Company, Lowell, MI; *U.S. Private*, pg. 621
Doyle, Kevin, Chm. Bd.--General Cable Corporation, Highland Heights, KY; *Int'l*, pg. 1486
Doyle, M.C., Chm. Bd.--Econolite Control Products, Inc., Anaheim, CA; *U.S. Private*, pg. 361
Doyle, Michael J., Chief Exec. Officer--Care Matrix Corp., Needham, MA; *U.S. Public*, pg. 305
Draime, David M., Chm. Bd.--Stoneridge, Inc., Warren, OH; *U.S. Private*, pg. 1044
Drake, Walter, Chm. Bd. & Chief Exec. Officer--Walter Drake, Inc., Colorado Springs, CO; *U.S. Private*, pg. 421
Draney, Robert, Chm. Bd.--Entertainment Partners, Burbank, CA; *U.S. Private*, pg. 554
Draper, E. Linn, Jr., Chm. Bd. & Chief Exec. Officer--Indiana Michigan Power Company, Fort Wayne, IN; *U.S. Public*, pg. 72
Draper, E. Linn, Jr., Chm. Bd. & Chief Exec. Officer--Ohio Power Company, Canton, OH; *U.S. Public*, pg. 72
Draper, E. Linn, Jr., Chm. Bd. & Chief Exec. Officer--Columbus Southern Power Company, Columbus, OH; *U.S. Public*, pg. 72
Draper, E. Linn, Jr., Chm. Bd. & Chief Exec. Officer--Appalachian Power Company, Roanoke, VA; *U.S. Public*, pg. 72
Draper, E. Linn, Jr., Dr., Chm. Bd., Pres. & Chief Exec. Officer--American Electric Power Company, Inc., Columbus, OH; *U.S. Public*, pg. 71
Draper, E. Linn, Jr., Dr., Chm. Bd., Pres. & Chief Exec. Officer--American Electric Power Service Corp., Columbus, OH; *U.S. Public*, pg. 72
Draper, Paul, Chm. Bd.--Ridge Vineyards Inc., Cupertino, CA; *Int'l*, pg. 1013
Drapkin, Donald G., Chm. Bd.--VIMRx Pharmaceuticals, Inc., Wilmington, DE; *U.S. Public*, pg. 1702
Draxler, Helmut, Dr., Chm.-Bd. of Mngmt.--Osterreichischen Bundesbahnen GmbH, Vienna, Austria; *Int'l*, pg. 1012
Drayer, Phillip M., Chm. Bd., Pres. & Chief Exec. Officer--TelCom Semiconductor, Inc., Mountain View, CA; *U.S. Public*, pg. 1569
Drazin, Avrum I., Chm. Bd.--The Genlyte Group Incorporated, Union, NJ; *U.S. Public*, pg. 729
Dreher, Donald D., Chm. Bd., Pres. & Chief Exec. Officer--DMI Furniture Inc., Louisville, KY; *U.S. Public*, pg. 473
Dreier, R. Chad, Chm. Bd., Pres. & Chief Exec. Officer--The Ryland Group, Inc., Columbia, MD; *U.S. Public*, pg. 1414
Drendel, Frank M., Chm. Bd. & Chief Exec. Officer--CommScope, Inc., Hickory, NC; *U.S. Public*, pg. 415
Drendel, Lee S., Chm. Bd.--Capitol Group, Springfield, IL; *U.S. Private*, pg. 206
Drettmann, Henry, Chm. Bd.--Active Tool & Manufacturing Co., Inc., Roseville, MI; *U.S. Private*, pg. 16
Drexler, Richard A., Chm. Bd., Pres. & Chief Exec. Officer--Allied Products Corporation, Chicago, IL; *U.S. Public*, pg. 48
Dreyer, John W., Chm. Bd., Pres. & Chief Exec. Officer--Harold M. Pitman Co., Inc., Totowa, NJ; *U.S. Private*, pg. 867
Dreyer, Kris, Chm. Bd., Pres. & Chief Exec. Officer--South Bend Stamping, South Bend, IN; *U.S. Private*, pg. 1014
Dreyfuss, Arnold H., Chm. & Interim Chief Exec. Officer--Eskimo Pie Corporation, Richmond, VA; *U.S. Public*, pg. 592
Drinkall, Austin M., Chm. Bd., Pres. & Chief Exec. Officer--South Bend Plastics, Inc., Mishawaka, IN; *U.S. Private*, pg. 1014
Driscoll, Edward C., Chm. Bd., Chief Exec. Officer & Treas.--L.F. Driscoll Co., Bala Cynwyd, PA; *U.S. Private*, pg. 343
Driscoll, Peter, Chm. Bd.--Plastic Suppliers, Inc., Columbus, OH; *U.S. Private*, pg. 871
Driscoll, Thomas, Chm. Bd.--Elof Hansson Inc., Elmsford, NY; *Int'l*, pg. 595
Driver, David A., Chm. Bd.--Driver-Harris Company, Harrison, NJ; *U.S. Public*, pg. 530
Drobis, David, Chm. & Sr. Partner--Prap Japan, Inc., Tokyo, Japan; *U.S. Private*, pg. 617
Drobis, David R., Chm., Sr. Partner & Chief Exec. Officer--Ketchum Public Relations Worldwide, New York, NY; *U.S. Private*, pg. 617
Drossman, Neil, Chm. Bd. & Creative Dir.--Ryan Drossman & Partners, New York, NY; *U.S. Private*, pg. 953
Dru, Jean-Marie, Chm.-BDDP S.A.--BDDP Group, Paris, France; *Int'l*, pg. 116
Drucker, Jean, Chm. & Chief Exec. Officer--M6, Paris, France; *Int'l*, pg. 561
Drucker, Jean, Chm.--Serie Club, Paris, France; *Int'l*, pg. 562
Drury, David, Chm. Bd. & Chief Exec. Officer--The Principal Financial Group, Des Moines, IA; *U.S. Private*, pg. 885
Drury, David, Chm. Bd. & Chief Exec. Officer--Principal Mutual Life Insurance Co., Des Moines, IA; *U.S. Private*, pg. 886
Drury, John E., Chm. Bd.--USA Waste Services, Inc., Houston, TX; *U.S. Public*, pg. 1686
Dryden, Robert C., Chm. Bd.--Caterpillar Industrial Products, Inc., Peoria, IL; *U.S. Public*, pg. 316
Drysdale, Kenneth, Chm. Bd.--Sun Alliance USA, Inc., New York, NY; *Int'l*, pg. 1131
du Rudder, Thierry, Chm. Bd & Pres.--American Cometra, Inc., Fort Worth, TX; *Int'l*, pg. 562
Dubes, Michael J., Chm. Bd.--NWNL Management Corp., Minneapolis, MN; *U.S. Public*, pg. 1375
Dubin, Howard S., Chm. Bd. & Chief Exec. Officer--Manufacturers' News, Inc., Evanston, IL; *U.S. Private*, pg. 700
Dubin, Ronald N., Chm. Bd.--Dubin-Clark & Company, Greenwich, CT; *U.S. Private*, pg. 344
DuBois, Christian, Chm. Bd.--Castorama Italia, Bollate, Italy; *Int'l*, pg. 276
DuBose, E.R., Chm. Bd.--White Electrical Construction Co., Atlanta, GA; *U.S. Private*, pg. 1172
Dubrule, Paul, Co.-Chm. & Co-Pres.--Accor S.A., Evry, France; *Int'l*, pg. 20
Duchossois, C.J., Chm. Bd.--Thrall Car Mfg. Co., Chicago Heights, IL; *U.S. Private*, pg. 344
Duchossois, Richard L., Chm. Bd.--Duchossois Industries, Inc., Elmhurst, IL; *U.S. Private*, pg. 344
Duda, Edward D., Chm. Bd. & Chief Exec. Officer--A. Duda & Sons Inc., Oviedo, FL; *U.S. Private*, pg. 344
Dudhia, Ismael, Chm. Bd.--Mylex Corporation, Fremont, CA; *U.S. Public*, pg. 1143
Duerden, John, Chm. Bd. & Pres.--Stonington Partners Inc., New York, NY; *U.S. Private*, pg. 1045
Duerden, John, Chm. Bd., Pres. & Chief Exec. Officer--Dictaphone Corp., Stratford, CT; *U.S. Private*, pg. 1045
Duff, Charles, Chm. Bd. & Pres.--Farnam Companies, Inc., Phoenix, AZ; *U.S. Private*, pg. 396
Duffy, Edward W., Chm. Bd.--Columbus McKinnon Corp., Amherst, NY; *U.S. Public*, pg. 405
Dugan, Francis R., Chm. Bd. & Chief Exec. Officer--Dugan & Meyers Interests, Inc., Cincinnati, OH; *U.S. Private*, pg. 345
Dugan, Mary E., Chm. Bd., Treas. & Sec.--Dugan Production Corp., Farmington, NM; *U.S. Private*, pg. 345
Dugan, Peter, Chm.--Dugan Valva Contess Inc., Morristown, NJ; *U.S. Private*, pg. 345
Duggan, John, Chm. Bd.--Avonmore Waterford Group plc, Kilkenny, Ireland; *Int'l*, pg. 102
Dunavant, W.B., Jr., Chm. Bd.--Dunavant Enterprises, Inc., Memphis, TN; *U.S. Private*, pg. 346
Dunbar, Dana, Chm. Bd.--Carpenter Industries, Inc., Richmond, IN; *U.S. Private*, pg. 215
Duncan, Dan L., Chm. Bd. & Chief Exec. Officer--Enterprise Products Company, Houston, TX; *U.S. Private*, pg. 377
Duncan, G., Chm. Bd.--Whessoe Plc, Newton Aycliffe, United Kingdom; *Int'l*, pg. 1498
Duncan, George, Chm. Bd.--Laporte plc, Luton, United Kingdom; *Int'l*, pg. 801
Duncan, Richard J., Chm. Bd.--Jerome-Duncan Ford, Sterling Heights, MI; *U.S. Private*, pg. 586
Duncan, Robert, Chm. Bd. & Chief Exec. Officer--Magna Mortgage, Hattiesburg, MS; *U.S. Public*, pg. 1669
Duncan, William A.M., Dr., Chm.--R.W. Johnson Pharmaceutical Research Institute, Raritan, NJ; *U.S. Public*, pg. 928
Dunford, Robert A., Chm. Bd.--Great Lakes Power Inc., Toronto, Canada; *Int'l*, pg. 433
Dunford, Robert A., Chm. Bd.--Unicorp Canada Corporation, Toronto, Canada; *Int'l*, pg. 1433

Dunford, Stanley, Chm. Bd. & Pres.--Contrans Corporation, Woodstock, Canada; Int'l, pg. 328

Dungey, Richard J., Chm. Bd.--Attorneys' Title Insurance Fund, Orlando, FL; U.S. Private, pg. 98

Dunham, Richard L., Chm. Bd. & Acting Chief Exec. Officer--South Jersey Industries, Inc., Folsom, NJ; U.S. Public, pg. 1488

Dunlap, Albert J., Chm. Bd. & Chief Exec. Officer--Sunbeam Corporation, Delray Beach, FL; U.S. Public, pg. 1533

Dunlap, Edward B., Chm Bd., Pres. & Chief Exec. Officer--Centimark Corporation, Canonsburg, PA; U.S. Private, pg. 222

Dunlap, Paul D., Chm. Bd.--Mercantile Bank of Iowa, Des Moines, IA; U.S. Public, pg. 1087

Dunlap, Roy R., Chm. Bd.--SOR Inc., Lenexa, KS; U.S. Private, pg. 957

Dunlap, William D., Chm.--Campbell Mithun Esty, Minneapolis, MN; U.S. Private, pg. 204

Dunlop, Graeme D.S., Chm. Bd.--P&O Scottish Ferries Ltd., Aberdeen, United Kingdom; Int'l, pg. 1034

Dunn, D.J., Chm.--Philips Semiconductors B.V., Eindhoven, Netherlands; Int'l, pg. 1051

Dunn, David J., Chm. Bd.--Iomega Corporation, Roy, UT; U.S. Public, pg. 912

Dunn, Doug, Chm. Bd. & Chief Exec. Officer--Philips Semiconductors, Sunnyvale, CA; Int'l, pg. 1054

Dunn, Jim, Chm.--Shandwick Public Relations Ltd., London, United Kingdom; Int'l, pg. 1226

Dunn, Thomas R., Chm. & Chief Oper. Officer--M & I First American Bank, Wausau, WI; U.S. Public, pg. 1050

Dunn, William H., Sr., Chm. Bd.--Dunn Industries Inc., Kansas City, MO; U.S. Private, pg. 347

Dunne, Robert P., Chm. Bd.--Saztec International, Inc., Billerica, MA; U.S. Public, pg. 1435

Dunne, Thomas P., Chm. Bd. & Chief Exec. Officer--Fred Weber, Inc., Maryland Heights, MO; U.S. Private, pg. 424

Dunnigan, T. Kevin, Chm. Bd. & Chief Exec. Officer--Thomas & Betts Corporation, Memphis, TN; U.S. Public, pg. 1597

Dunphy, T.J. Dermot, Chm. Bd. & Chief Exec. Officer--Sealed Air Corporation, Saddle Brook, NJ; U.S. Public, pg. 1450

Dunst, Laurence D., Co-Chm. & Chief Exec. Officer--Gotham Incorporated, New York, NY; U.S. Private, pg. 677

Dupey, Patricia, Chm. Bd.--Dupey Management Corp., Coppell, TX; U.S. Private, pg. 348

DuPree, Tom E., Jr., Chm. Bd. & Chief Exec. Officer--Apple South, Inc., Madison, GA; U.S. Public, pg. 121

Dupuis, Frank J., Chm. Bd. & Chief Fin. Officer--Your Man Tours, Inc., Inglewood, CA; U.S. Private, pg. 1202

Duques, Henry C., Chm. Bd. & Chief Exec. Officer--First Data Corporation, Hackensack, NJ; U.S. Public, pg. 630

Durfee, John, Chm. Bd., Pres. & Treas.--Bethel Mills, Inc., Bethel, VT; U.S. Private, pg. 141

Durr, Heinz, Chm. Bd., Pres. & Chief Exec. Officer--Deutsche Bahn, Frankfurt/Main, Germany; Int'l, pg. 401

Durrett, William E., Chm. Bd.--American Fidelity Corp., Oklahoma City, OK; U.S. Private, pg. 54

Durward, John C., Chm. Bd.--Duray/J.F. Duncan Industries, Inc., Downey, CA; U.S. Private, pg. 348

Dusenbery, John F., Chm. Bd.--John Dusenbery Co., Inc., Randolph, NJ; U.S. Private, pg. 349

Dusthimer, Thomas L., Chm. Bd. & Chief Exec. Officer--Society National Bank, Elkhart, IN; U.S. Public, pg. 955

Dutia, Suren G., Chm. Bd., Pres. & Chief Exec. Officer--Photomatrix Corporation, San Diego, CA; U.S. Public, pg. 1292

Dutil, Raymond, Chm. Bd.--Faucher Industries Inc., Saint Leonard, Canada; Int'l, pg. 479

Dutka, Solomon, Chm. Bd.--Audits & Surveys Worldwide, New York, NY; U.S. Public, pg. 147

Duvall, Robert, Chm. Bd.--Nobel Insurance Limited, Hamilton, Bermuda; Int'l, pg. 951

Duvall, William A., Chm. Bd. & Chief Exec. Officer--Bliss Manufacturing Company, Youngstown, OH; U.S. Public, pg. 771

Duvar, I.E.H., Chm. Bd. & Chief Exec. Officer--Maritime Telegraph & Telephone Company, Ltd., Halifax, Canada; Int'l, pg. 116

Duvoux, Luc, Chm.--154-Testa, Paris, France; Int'l, pg. 1377

Dwight, Herbert M., Jr., Chm. Bd. & Chief Exec. Officer--Optical Coating Laboratory, Inc., Santa Rosa, CA; U.S. Public, pg. 1227

Dworman, Alvin, Chm. Bd. & Pres.--Lee National Corporation, New York, NY; U.S. Private, pg. 658

Dworman, Alvin, Chm. Bd. & Pres.--Great Universal Capital Corp., New York, NY; U.S. Private, pg. 658

Dwyer, Joe A., Exec. Chm. & Chief Exec. Officer--George Wimpey PLC, London, United Kingdom; Int'l, pg. 1510

Dwyer, Theresa, Chm. Bd.--The Dwyer Group, Inc., Waco, TX; U.S. Public, pg. 537

Dyer, Howard, Chm. Bd. & Chief Exec. Officer--Ascot Holdings Plc, London, United Kingdom; Int'l, pg. 87

Dyer, Lex, III, Chm. Bd., Pres. & Chief Exec. Officer--International Airline Support Group, Inc., Atlanta, GA; U.S. Public, pg. 894

Dyer, Robert, Jr., Chm. Bd. & Chief Exec. Officer--Hickory Farms, Inc., Maumee, OH; U.S. Private, pg. 525

Dyke, Greg, Chm. Bd.--Thames Television Ltd., Teddington, United Kingdom; Int'l, pg. 1026

Dyke, James T., Chm. Bd.--Dyke Industry, Inc., Little Rock, AR; U.S. Private, pg. 350

Dyson, Robert R., Chm. Bd. & Chief Exec. Officer--The Dyson-Kissner-Moran Corporation, New York, NY; U.S. Private, pg. 351

Dyson, Robert R., Chm. Bd.--Kearney-National, Inc., White Plains, NY; U.S. Private, pg. 351

Dzvonik, Michael D., Chm. Bd. & Chief Exec. Officer--Grizzard, Atlanta, GA; U.S. Private, pg. 482

Eacott, James H., Jr., Chm. Bd.--Bartlett Brainard Eacott, Inc., Bloomfield, CT; U.S. Private, pg. 118

Eagle, John M., Chm. Bd. & Chief Exec. Officer--Pipe Fabricating & Supply Company, Santa Fe Springs, CA; U.S. Private, pg. 867

Eagle, Robert M., Chm. Bd. & Chief Exec. Officer--Eagle Lincoln Mercury Inc., Dallas, TX; U.S. Private, pg. 355

Eanes, Jr., Joseph C., Chm Bd.--Fidelity & Deposit Company of Maryland, Baltimore, MD; Int'l, pg. 1530

Earhart, Donald M., Chm. Bd., Pres. & Chief Exec. Officer--I-Flow Corporation, Lake Forest, CA; U.S. Public, pg. 851

Earwood, J. Calvin, Chm. Bd.--Oglethorpe Power Corp., Tucker, GA; U.S. Private, pg. 812

Easley, Ronald L., Chm. Bd. & Chief Exec. Officer--System Planning Corp., Arlington, VA; U.S. Private, pg. 1061

Eastburn, Albert W., Chm. Bd.--Steel of West Virginia, Inc., Huntington, WV; U.S. Public, pg. 1513

Easterly, Clark, Chm. Bd.--Johnstown Knitting Mill Co., Johnstown, NY; U.S. Private, pg. 595

Easton, Robert A., Dr., Chm.--Delta Cables Holdings Ltd., Enfield, United Kingdom; Int'l, pg. 390

Eatman, Roger, Chm. Bd.--Handex Environment Inc., Morganville, NJ; U.S. Private, pg. 498

Eaton, F., Regional Chm.--Barratt Central, Halesowen, United Kingdom; Int'l, pg. 168

Eaton, Henry F., Chm. & Chief Exec. Officer--Dix & Eaton Incorporated, Cleveland, OH; U.S. Private, pg. 336

Eaton, Robert J., Chm. Bd., Pres. & Chief Exec. Officer--Chrysler Corporation, Auburn Hills, MI; U.S. Public, pg. 352

Ebbers, B., Chm. Bd.--LDDS WorldCom, Tulsa, OK; U.S. Public, pg. 1779

Eberhardt, K., Chm. Bd.--Richard Hirschmann GmbH & Co., Neckartenzlingen, Germany; Int'l, pg. 1108

Eberle, Robert W., Chm. Bd.--BMCA Insulation Products, Inc., Ontario, CA; U.S. Private, pg. 433

Eberle, William, Chm. Bd.--Barry's Jewelers, Inc., Monrovia, CA; U.S. Public, pg. 192

Eby, Martin K., Jr., Chm. Bd.--Eby Corporation, Wichita, KS; U.S. Private, pg. 359

Eccles, John, Chm. Bd.--Courtaulds Textiles Plc, London, United Kingdom; Int'l, pg. 339

Eccles, Spencer F., Chm. Bd. & Chief Exec. Officer--First Security Corporation, Salt Lake City, UT; U.S. Public, pg. 637

Echtenkamp, Ronald H., Chm. Bd.--Ballantyne of Omaha, Inc., Omaha, NE; Int'l, pg. 17

Ecke, Paul, III, Chm. Bd., Pres. & Chief Exec. Officer--Paul Ecke Ranch, Encinitas, CA; U.S. Private, pg. 359

Eckelberry, John E., Chm. Bd.--Doremus & Company, New York, NY; U.S. Public, pg. 1223

Eckhouse, Shimon, Chm. Bd., Pres. & Chief Exec. Officer--ESC Medical Systems Ltd., Yokneam, Israel; Int'l, pg. 429

Eddins, Roy A., Chm. Bd.--Friendly Chevrolet Co. Inc., Dallas, TX; U.S. Private, pg. 428

Edelbrock, O. Victor, Jr., Chm. Bd., Pres. & Chief Exec. Officer--Edelbrock Corp., Torrance, CA; U.S. Public, pg. 563

Edelman, Asher B., Chm. Bd. & Chief Exec. Officer--Datapoint Corporation, Paris, France; Int'l, pg. 384

Edelman, Asher B., Chm. Bd. & Chief Exec. Officer--Datapoint Corporation, San Antonio, TX; Int'l, pg. 384

Edelman, Daniel J., Chm. Bd.--Edelman Public Relations Worldwide, Chicago, IL; U.S. Private, pg. 362

Edelman, Thomas J., Chm. Bd., Pres. & Chief Exec. Officer--Patina Oil & Gas Corp., Denver, CO; U.S. Public, pg. 1264

Edelstein, Chaim Y., Chm. Bd.--Hills Stores Co., Canton, MA; U.S. Public, pg. 828

Edelstenne, Charles, Chm. & Chief Exec. Officer--Dassault Systemes, Suresnes, France; Int'l, pg. 383

Edens, Jim B., Chm. Bd. & Pres.--Huttig Sash & Door Co., Chesterfield, MO; U.S. Public, pg. 457

Eder, Robert H., Chm. Bd.--Providence and Worcester Railroad Company, Worcester, MA; U.S. Public, pg. 1336

Edge, Bruce, Chm. Bd.--APEX Specialty Materials, Inc., New Castle, DE; U.S. Private, pg. 77

Edleman, Thomas J., Chm. Bd.--Lomak Petroleum Inc., Fort Worth, TX; U.S. Public, pg. 1012

Edmund, Norman W., Chm. Bd.--Edmund Scientific Company, Barrington, NJ; U.S. Private, pg. 364

Edwards, Benjamin F., III, Chm. Bd., Pres. & Chief Exec. Officer--A.G. Edwards, Inc., Saint Louis, MO; U.S. Public, pg. 565

Edwards, George H., Jr., Chm. Bd.--El Paso Electric Company, El Paso, TX; U.S. Public, pg. 567

Edwards, George W., Jr., Chm. Bd.--Aquarion Company, Bridgeport, CT; U.S. Public, pg. 126

Edwards, James O., Chm. Bd. & Chief Exec. Officer--ICF Kaiser International Inc., Fairfax, VA; U.S. Public, pg. 852

Edwards, Johnathan, Chm. Bd. & Chief Exec. Officer--IPC Interactive, Inc., Novato, CA; Int'l, pg. 651

Edwards, L.A., Chm. Bd. & Chief Exec. Officer--Messier-Dowty, Abingdon, United Kingdom; Int'l, pg. 1340

Edwards, L.A., Chm. Bd. & Chief Exec. Officer--Messier-Dowty International, Velizy-Villacoublay, France; Int'l, pg. 1340

Edwards, Martin H., Chm. Bd. & Pres.--Edwards Brothers, Inc., Ann Arbor, MI; U.S. Private, pg. 365

Edwards, Merle E., Sr., Chm. Bd.--Coastal Wholesale, Inc., Kinston, NC; U.S. Private, pg. 248

Edwards, Murray, Chm. Bd.--Calgary Flames Hockey Club, Calgary, Canada; Int'l, pg. 252

Edwards, N. Murray, Chm. Bd. & Chief Exec. Officer--Magellan Aerospace Corporation, Mississauga, Canada; Int'l, pg. 829

Edwards, Oral W., Chm. Bd.--GES Inc., Marianna, AR; U.S. Private, pg. 434

Edwards, R.C., Chm. Bd.--Edwards Engineering Corporation, Pompton Plains, NJ; U.S. Private, pg. 365

Edwards, William E., Jr., Chm. Bd. & Chief Exec. Officer--Cardinal Aluminum Co., Louisville, KY; U.S. Private, pg. 208

Edwards, William H., Pres. & Chief Exec. Officer--Lockwood Greene Technologies, Oak Ridge, TN; Int'l, pg. 633

Efron, Miles E., Chm. Bd.--ENStar, Inc., Eden Prairie, MN; U.S. Public, pg. 585

Egan, Charles M., Chm. Bd.--CORT Business Services Corporation, Fairfax, VA; U.S. Public, pg. 451

Egan, Michael S., Chm. Bd. & Chief Exec. Officer--Alamo Rent-A-Car Inc., Fort Lauderdale, FL; U.S. Public, pg. 1379

Egan, Richard J., Chm. Bd.--EMC Corporation, Hopkinton, MA; U.S. Public, pg. 545

Egert, Dana, Chm. Bd.--Durst Corporation, Mountainside, NJ; U.S. Private, pg. 349

Egert, Dana, Chm.--Jaclo Inc., Mountainside, NJ; U.S. Private, pg. 349

Egerton, K.R., Chm. Bd. & Mng. Dir.--Taylor Woodrow Property Company Ltd., London, United Kingdom; Int'l, pg. 1359

Egger, Frank, Chm. Bd.--Insight Health Services Corp., Newport Beach, CA; U.S. Public, pg. 880

Egi, Nobutaka, Chm. Bd.--Mitsubishi Logistics Corp., Tokyo, Japan; Int'l, pg. 874

Eglin, Peter B., Chm. Bd., Pres. & Chief Exec. Officer--Mellon Bank, N.A.-Northeastern Region, Wilkes-Barre, PA; U.S. Public, pg. 1085

Eguchi, Hideto, Chm. Bd. & Representative Dir.--Yamaha Motor Co., Ltd., Iwata, Japan; Int'l, pg. 1516

Ehinger, William F., Chm. Bd.--Independent Bank Corporation, Ionia, MI; U.S. Public, pg. 874

Ehlers, William A., Chm. Bd.--Capital Development Co., Lacey, WA; U.S. Private, pg. 205

Ehrlich, Paul, Chm. Bd. & Pres.--Wisconsin Automated Machinery Corp., Oshkosh, WI; U.S. Private, pg. 1184

Ehrlich, Robert S., Chm. Bd.--PSC Inc., Webster, NY; U.S. Public, pg. 1245

Ehrlich, Robert S., Chm. Bd.--A.D. Data Systems, Webster, NY; U.S. Public, pg. 1246

Ehrlinger, Erick, Chm. Bd.--Bitburger Brauerei Th. Simon GmbH, Bitburg, Germany; Int'l, pg. 197

Ehrnrooth, Casimir, Chm. Bd.--Oy Nokia Ab/Nokia Group, Helsinki, Finland; Int'l, pg. 951

Ehrnrooth, Georg, Chm. Bd.--Assa Abloy AB, Stockholm, Sweden; Int'l, pg. 17

Ehrnrooth, Goran J., Chm. Bd.--Fiskars Oy AB, Helsinki, Finland; Int'l, pg. 492

Ehrnrooth, Robert G., Chm. Bd.--Metra Corporation, Helsinki, Finland; Int'l, pg. 862

Eichenberger, J.Y., Chm. Bd.--Sacem, Casablanca, Morocco; Int'l, pg. 662

Eichenfield, Samuel L., Chm. Bd., Pres. & Chief Exec. Officer--The FINOVA Group Inc., Phoenix, AZ; U.S. Public, pg. 624

Eichenfield, Samuel L., Chm. Bd., Pres. & Chief Exec. Officer--FINOVA Capital Corporation, Phoenix, AZ; U.S. Public, pg. 624

Eichner, Ira A., Chm. Bd.--AAR Corp., Wood Dale, IL; U.S. Public, pg. 1

Eichner, Mike, Chm. Bd.--Alpnet Inc., Salt Lake City, UT; U.S. Public, pg. 58

Eie, Olaf, Chm. Bd.--Helly-Hansen A/S, Moss, Norway; Int'l, pg. 1010

Eie, Olaf, Chm.--Helly-Hansen A/S, Moss, Norway; Int'l, pg. 1010

Eigenfeld, F., Chm.-Mngmt. Bd.--Ceteco N.V., Utrecht, Netherlands; Int'l, pg. 279

Eigsti, Roger H., Chm. Bd. & Chief Exec. Officer--SAFECO Corporation, Seattle, WA; U.S. Public, pg. 1423

Eihusen, Robert, Chm. Bd., Pres. & Chief Exec. Officer--Chief Industries, Inc., Grand Island, NE; U.S. Private, pg. 236

Eilledge, Elwyn, Chm. Bd.--BTR plc, London, United Kingdom; Int'l, pg. 124

Einstein, Clifford, Chm. Bd. & Creative Dir.--Dailey & Associates, West Hollywood, CA; U.S. Public, pg. 909

Eisaman, Joe R., Chm. Emeritus--Lois/EJL Los Angeles, Los Angeles, CA; U.S. Private, pg. 673

Eisenberg, Gregg M., Chm. Bd., Pres. & Chief Exec. Officer--Maverick Tube Corporation, Chesterfield, MO; U.S. Public, pg. 1060

Eisenberg, James, Co-Chm. & Chief Exec. Officer--Vienna Sausage Mfg. Co., Chicago, IL; U.S. Private, pg. 1139

Eisenberg, Kenneth, Chm. Bd. & Chief Exec. Officer--Kenwal Products Corp., Dearborn, MI; U.S. Private, pg. 615

Eisenberg, Warren, Chm. Bd., Co-Chief Exec. Officer & Sec.--Bed Bath & Beyond Inc., Union, NJ; U.S. Public, pg. 200

Eisenburg, David, Chm. Bd., Pres. & Chief Exec. Officer--Chief Auto Parts, Dallas, TX; U.S. Private, pg. 236

Eisner, Henry W., Chm. Emeritus--Eisner & Associates, Inc., Baltimore, MD; U.S. Private, pg. 366

Eisner, Michael D., Chm. Bd. & Chief Exec. Officer--The Walt Disney Company, Burbank, CA; U.S. Public, pg. 511

Eisner, Steve, Chm. & Chief Exec. Officer--Eisner, Petrou & Associates, Inc., Baltimore, MD; U.S. Private, pg. 366

Eitan, Shalom, Chm. Bd.--Power Spectrum Technology Ltd., Kiryat Bialick, Israel; U.S. Public, pg. 740

Eitan, Yaron I., Chm. Bd. & Chief Exec. Officer--Geotek Communications, Montvale, NJ; U.S. Public, pg. 739

Ekberg Johnson, Judith, Pres. & Chief Exec. Officer--Meyer Broadcasting Company, Bismarck, ND; U.S. Private, pg. 739

Eklund, Louis, E., Jr., Chm. & Treas.--Fleet Engineers, Inc., Muskegon, MI; U.S. Private, pg. 410

Ekstrom, L.W., Chm. Bd. & Pres.--Samuel Bingham Co, Bloomingdale, IL; U.S. Private, pg. 144

Elbaum, Stephen S., Chm. Bd.--PolyVision Corp., New York, NY; U.S. Public, pg. 1315

Elbaum, Steven S., Chm. Bd. & Chief Exec. Officer--The Alpine Group, Inc., New York, NY; U.S. Public, pg. 58

Elbaum, Steven S., Chm. Bd. & Chief Exec. Officer--Superior Telecommunications, Atlanta, GA; U.S. Public, pg. 58

Elbert, P.O., Chm. Bd.--Pitt-Des Moines, Inc., Pittsburgh, PA; *U.S. Public*, pg. 1304
Elbert, Paul A., Chm. Bd. & Pres.--Michigan Gas Storage Co., Jackson, MI; *U.S. Public*, pg. 280
Elder, William W.R., Chm. Bd.--Genus Inc., Sunnyvale, CA; *U.S. Public*, pg. 732
Eldon Wheeler, M.L., Chm. Bd. & Chief Exec. Officer--Jernberg Industries, Inc., Chicago, IL; *U.S. Private*, pg. 586
Elers, Karl E., Chm. Bd.--Battle Mountain Gold Company, Houston, TX; *U.S. Public*, pg. 193
Elhinney, E. A., Chm. Bd. & Chief Exec. Officer--SAS Holdings Limited, Reading, United Kingdom; *Int'l*, pg. 1152
Elias, Louis, Chm. Bd.--Elias Brothers Restaurants, Inc., Warren, MI; *U.S. Private*, pg. 371
Eliasch, Johan, Owner--Head USA, Inc., Columbia, MD; *U.S. Private*, pg. 514
Elish, Herbert, Chm. Bd.--Kerr Group, Inc., Lancaster, PA; *U.S. Public*, pg. 952
Elisha, Walter Y., Chm. Bd. & Chief Exec. Officer--Springs Industries, Inc., Fort Mill, SC; *U.S. Public*, pg. 1499
Elkin, Jason, Chm. Bd. & Chief Exec. Officer--New Vision Television, Atlanta, GA; *U.S. Private*, pg. 794
Elkins, Robert N., M.D., Chm. Bd. & Chief Exec. Officer--Integrated Health Services, Inc., Owings Mills, MD; *U.S. Public*, pg. 884
Ellenbogen, S. David, Chm. Bd. & Chief Exec. Officer--Hologic, Inc., Waltham, MA; *U.S. Public*, pg. 831
Eller, Karl, Chm. Bd. & Chief Exec. Officer--Eller Media Company, Phoenix, AZ; *U.S. Public*, pg. 383
Ellingson, Chester W., Jr., Chm. Bd. & Pres.--Reese Enterprises, Inc., Rosemount, MN; *U.S. Private*, pg. 916
Elliot, Dennis, Chm. Bd.--STM Wireless, Inc., Irvine, CA; *U.S. Public*, pg. 1421
Elliot, Marion, Chm. Bd.--Denver Wholesale Florists Company, Denver, CO; *U.S. Private*, pg. 326
Elliott, Charles A., Chm. Bd., Pres. & Chief Exec. Officer--Crenlo, Inc., Rochester, MN; *U.S. Private*, pg. 288
Elliott, David H., Chm. Bd. & Chief Exec. Officer--MBIA Inc., Armonk, NY; *U.S. Public*, pg. 1023
Elliott, E.J., Chm. Bd. & Pres.--Gencor Industries, Inc., Orlando, FL; *U.S. Public*, pg. 705
Elliott, J. Mark, Chm. Bd. & Chief Exec. Officer--QST Environmental Inc., Peoria, IL; *U.S. Public*, pg. 367
Elliott, J. Mark, Chm. Bd. & Chief Exec. Officer--QST Energy, Inc., Peoria, IL; *U.S. Public*, pg. 367
Elliott, Michael, Chm. Bd.--WEN Products, Inc., Bensenville, IL; *U.S. Private*, pg. 1144
Elliott, Neal M., Chm. Bd., Pres. & Chief Exec. Officer--Horizon/CMS Healthcare Corporation, Albuquerque, NM; *U.S. Public*, pg. 836
Elliott, R. Keith, Chm. Bd. & Chief Exec. Officer--Hercules Incorporated, Wilmington, DE; *U.S. Public*, pg. 809
Ellis, A.L., Sr. Chm.--NationsBank of Florida Corporation, Fort Lauderdale, FL; *U.S. Public*, pg. 1162
Ellis, Frank P., IV, Chm. Bd.--Associated Equipment Company of Delaware, Mobile, AL; *U.S. Private*, pg. 90
Ellis, G.H.G., Chm. Bd. & Dir.-Lube Mktg.--Mobil Oil Company, Ltd., Milton Keynes, United Kingdom; *U.S. Public*, pg. 1119
Ellis, W.G., Chm. Bd.--Bank of Hazlehurst, Hazlehurst, GA; *U.S. Public*, pg. 1549
Ellis, William D., Chm. Bd. & Chief Exec. Officer--Southern Mills, Inc., Union City, GA; *U.S. Private*, pg. 1016
Ellison, Lawrence J., Chm. Bd. & Chief Exec. Officer--Oracle Corporation, Redwood City, CA; *U.S. Public*, pg. 1227
Ellison, Ray, Chm. Bd.--Kaufman and Broad of Texas, Ltd., San Antonio, TX; *U.S. Public*, pg. 945
Ellison, Richard D., Ph.D.,P.E., Chm. Bd., Pres. & Chief Exec. Officer--TRC Companies, Inc., Windsor, CT; *U.S. Public*, pg. 1557
Ellsworth, Robert F., Chm. Bd.--Howmet Corporation, Greenwich, CT; *U.S. Private*, pg. 213
Ellsworth, Robert F., Chm. Bd.--Howmet Corporation, Greenwich, CT; *U.S. Public*, pg. 1597
Elmaleh, Lou, Chm. Bd. & Chief Exec. Officer--Greyvest Capitol Inc., Toronto, Canada; *Int'l*, pg. 559
Elman, Robert H., Chm. Bd. & Chief Exec. Officer--Desa International, Bowling Green, KY; *U.S. Private*, pg. 326
Elow, David, Chm. Bd.--Chemical Bank Key State, Owosso, MI; *U.S. Public*, pg. 345
Elowitz, Norman, Chm. Bd., Pres. & Chief Exec. Officer--Honey Fashions Ltd., New York, NY; *U.S. Private*, pg. 537
Elrod, William G., Chm. Bd.--Blue Ridge Electric Cooperative Inc., Pickens, SC; *U.S. Private*, pg. 153
Elsberry, Howard W., Chm. Bd., Pres. & Chief Exec. Officer--Westlake Hardware, Inc., Lenexa, KS; *U.S. Private*, pg. 1169
Elsperman, Robert P., P.E., Chm. Bd. & Chief Exec. Officer--Tarlton Corporation, Saint Louis, MO; *U.S. Private*, pg. 1069
Embden, Claus, Co-Chm. Bd.--Krupp Metalurgica Campo Limpo Ltda., Sao Paulo, Brazil; *Int'l*, pg. 508
Emerick, Roger D., Chm. Bd.--Lam Research Corporation, Fremont, CA; *U.S. Public*, pg. 975
Emerson, Barry K., Chm. Bd., Pres. & Chief Exec. Officer--Texas National Bank, Southlake, TX; *U.S. Public*, pg. 633
Emerson, Don, Chm. Bd.--Bank of Lake County, N.A., Lakeport, CA; *U.S. Public*, pg. 1756
Emerson, H. Garfield, Chm.--Rogers Communications, Inc., Toronto, Canada; *Int'l*, pg. 1122
Emigh, Wayne D., Chm. Bd.--Source Services Corporation, Dallas, TX; *U.S. Public*, pg. 1488
Emley, Miles, Chm. Bd.--St. Ives plc, London, United Kingdom; *Int'l*, pg. 1177
Emmerling, John, Chm. Bd. & Chief Creative Officer--Emmerling Post, Inc., New York, NY; *U.S. Private*, pg. 374
Emmi, Michael J., Chm. Bd., Pres. & Chief Exec. Officer--Systems & Computer Technology Corporation, Malvern, PA; *U.S. Public*, pg. 1552
Emmons, Robert, Dr., Chm. Bd.--Smart & Final, Vernon, CA; *Int'l*, pg. 563
Emori, Ryuhara, Chm. Bd.--Amada Co., Ltd., Kanagawa, Japan; *Int'l*, pg. 70
Endres, Michael, Dr., Chm. Bd.--Deutz AG, Cologne, Germany; *Int'l*, pg. 407
Endung, Roar, Chm. Bd.--Kvaerner Ships Equipment AB, Goteborg, Sweden; *Int'l*, pg. 771
Endy, Paul S., Chm. Bd. & Chief Exec. Officer--Paul-Son Gaming Corporation, Las Vegas, NV; *U.S. Public*, pg. 1265
Engebrecht, Richard E., Chm. Bd.--PrimeSource Corporation, Pennsauken, NJ; *U.S. Public*, pg. 1329
Engel, Arthur, Chm. Bd. & Chief Exec. Officer--Southwest Marine, Inc., San Diego, CA; *U.S. Private*, pg. 213
Engel, Clyde W., Chm. Bd. & Pres.--R D I S Corporation, Chicago, IL; *U.S. Private*, pg. 903
Engel, Susan, Chm. Bd., Pres. & Chief Exec. Officer--Department 56 Inc., Eden Prairie, MN; *U.S. Public*, pg. 500
Engelhardt, Irl F., Chm. Bd. & Chief Exec. Officer--Peabody Holding Company, Inc., Saint Louis, MO; *Int'l*, pg. 594
Engelhorn, Curt, Chm. Bd.--Corange Limited, Hamilton, Bermuda; *Int'l*, pg. 330
Engelhorn, Curt, Chm. Supvry. Bd.--Boehringer Mannheim GmbH, Mannheim, Germany; *Int'l*, pg. 331
Engelke, George L., Chm. Bd., Pres. & Chief Exec. Officer--Astoria Financial Corporation, Lake Success, NY; *U.S. Public*, pg. 141
Engelsma, Bruce W., Chm. Bd. & Chief Exec. Officer--Kraus-Anderson Incorporated, Minneapolis, MN; *U.S. Private*, pg. 635
Engelsma, Bruce W., Chm. Bd. & Chief Exec. Officer--Kraus-Anderson, Incorporated, Minneapolis, MN; *U.S. Private*, pg. 635
Engelsted, J.N., Chm. Bd.--O.S. Walker Co. Inc., Worcester, MA; *U.S. Private*, pg. 1147
Engelsted, John N., Chm. Bd. & Chief Exec. Officer--Walker Magnetics Group, Inc., Worcester, MA; *U.S. Private*, pg. 1147
Engelstein, Alec, Chm. Bd., Pres. & Chief Exec. Officer--Engle Homes, Inc., Boca Raton, FL; *U.S. Public*, pg. 583
Engle, Clyde W., Chm. Bd., Pres. & Treas.--GSC Enterprises, Inc., Chicago, IL; *U.S. Private*, pg. 436
Engle, Clyde W., Chm. Bd., Pres. & Chief Exec. Officer--Telco Capital Corporation, Chicago, IL; *U.S. Private*, pg. 1073
Engle, Clyde William, Chm. Bd.--Alba-Waldensian, Inc., Valdese, NC; *U.S. Public*, pg. 35
Engle, Clyde Wm., Chm. Bd. & Pres.--Bank of Lincolnwood, Lincolnwood, IL; *U.S. Private*, pg. 436
Englefield, F.W., III, Chm. Bd.--Englefield, Inc., Newark, OH; *U.S. Private*, pg. 377
Englekirk, Robert E., Chm. Bd., Pres. & Chief Exec. Officer--Robert Englekirk, Inc., Los Angeles, CA; *U.S. Private*, pg. 377
Engler, Paul F., Chm. Bd. & Pres.--Cactus Feeders, Inc., Amarillo, TX; *U.S. Private*, pg. 198
Engles, Gregg L., Chm. Bd. & Chief Exec. Officer--Suiza Foods Corporation, Dallas, TX; *U.S. Public*, pg. 1526
English, David, Sir, Chm.--Harmsworth Media Ltd., London, United Kingdom; *Int'l*, pg. 366
English, David, Sir, Chm.--DMG Exhibition Group Ltd., London, United Kingdom; *Int'l*, pg. 366
English, Floyd L., Chm. Bd., Pres. & Chief Exec. Officer--Andrew Corporation, Orland Park, IL; *U.S. Public*, pg. 112
Ennen, Richard D., Chm. Bd.--NN Ball & Roller, Inc., Erwin, TN; *U.S. Public*, pg. 1146
Ennest, John W., Chm. Bd. & Chief Exec. Officer--Commercial National Bank of Berwyn, Berwyn, IL; *U.S. Public*, pg. 379
Enrico, Roger, Chm. Bd. & Chief Exec. Officer--PepsiCo, Inc., Purchase, NY; *U.S. Public*, pg. 1276
Ensor, Charles E., Sr., Chm. Bd.--Sparks State Bank, Sparks, MD; *U.S. Public*, pg. 1089
Ensor, Clyde F., Sr., Chm. Bd. & Pres.--Hesco Parts Corporation, Louisville, KY; *U.S. Private*, pg. 524
Entringer, James W., Chm. Bd., Pres. & Chief Exec. Officer--Selective Insurance Group, Inc, Branchville, NJ; *U.S. Public*, pg. 1455
Entringer, James W., Chm. Bd., Pres & Chief Exec. Officer--Selective Insurance Company of America, Branchville, NJ; *U.S. Public*, pg. 1455
Entringer, James W., Chm. & Pres.--Niagara Exchange Corporation, Buffalo, NY; *U.S. Public*, pg. 1455
Epley, Tom, Chm. Bd.--Paradyne, Largo, FL; *U.S. Private*, pg. 838
Eppley, Mark, Chm. Bd.--Traveling Software Inc., Bothell, WA; *U.S. Private*, pg. 1098
Epstein, Donald, Chm. Bd., Pres. & Chief Exec. Officer--Vesco Oil Corp., Southfield, MI; *U.S. Private*, pg. 1138
Epstein, Jerome P., Chm. Bd.--Perry Machinery Corporation, Hainesport, NJ; *U.S. Private*, pg. 855
Epstein, Sidney, Chm. Bd.--A. Epstein and Sons, Intl., Inc., Chicago, IL; *U.S. Private*, pg. 379
Erb, Fred A., Chm. Bd., Pres. & Chief Exec. Officer--Amurcon Corporation, Southfield, MI; *U.S. Private*, pg. 69
Erdeljan, Aleksandar, Chm. Bd., Pres. & Co-Chief Exec. Officer--R.P. Scherer Corporation, Troy, MI; *U.S. Public*, pg. 1437
Erdman, Tim, Chm. Bd.--Marshall Erdman and Associates, Inc., Madison, WI; *U.S. Private*, pg. 380
Erdmann, David L., Chm. Bd., Pres. & Chief Exec. Officer--Outlook Group Corporation, Neenah, WI; *U.S. Public*, pg. 1235
Erenberg, Ethan M., Chm. Bd. & Chief Exec. Officer--W. Braun Company, Chicago, IL; *U.S. Private*, pg. 166
Ergas, J.P. M., Chm. Bd. & Chief Exec. Officer--British Alcan Aluminium plc, Gerrards Cross, United Kingdom; *Int'l*, pg. 51
Erickson, Claire L., Chm. Bd.--Erickson Oil Products, Inc., Hudson, WI; *U.S. Private*, pg. 381
Erickson, James W., Chm. Bd., Pres. & Chief Exec. Officer--Anderson Erickson Dairy Company, Des Moines, IA; *U.S. Private*, pg. 72
Erickson, Joe, Chm. Bd.--Andiamo, Inc., Fountain Valley, CA; *U.S. Private*, pg. 73
Erickson, John, Chm. Bd. & Chief Exec. Officer--I.C. System, Inc., Vadnais Heights, MN; *U.S. Private*, pg. 553
Erickson, Richard P., Chm. Bd. & Chief Exec. Officer--Lifetouch, Portrait Studios, Eden Prairie, MN; *U.S. Private*, pg. 667
Erickson, Robert D., Chm. Bd. & Pres.--Amoco Canada Petroleum Company Ltd., Calgary, Canada; *U.S. Public*, pg. 103
Erickson, Ronald A., Chm. Bd.--Holiday Companies, Bloomington, MN; *U.S. Private*, pg. 534
Erickson, Sheldon, Chm. Bd., Pres. & Chief Exec. Officer--Cameron, Houston, TX; *U.S. Public*, pg. 298
Erickson, Stanford, Chm. & Chief Exec. Officer--Farm Journal Inc., Philadelphia, PA; *U.S. Private*, pg. 394
Erikson, George W., Chm. Bd. & Gen. Counsel--CERBCO, Inc., Landover, MD; *U.S. Public*, pg. 330
Erlund, Jan, Chm. Bd.--The East Asiatic Company Ltd. A/S, Copenhagen, Denmark; *Int'l*, pg. 430
Ermatinger, Francis, Chm.--Coop Neuchatel, Neuchatel, Switzerland; *Int'l*, pg. 329
Ernst, Jurgen, Chm. Bd.--Kalifarma S.A., Barcelona, Spain; *Int'l*, pg. 1279
Escandon Cusi, Pablo, Chm. & Dir.--Nadro S.A. de C.V., Mexico, Mexico; *U.S. Public*, pg. 1073
Escarrer, Gabriel, Chm. Bd. & Pres.--Sol Melia, Palma de Mallorca, Spain; *Int'l*, pg. 1277
Escobar, Frank, Chm. & Gen. Mgr.--Joffko Philippines, Inc., Rizal, Philippines; *U.S. Private*, pg. 589
Eskandarian, Ed, Chm. & Chief Exec. Officer--Arnold Communications, Inc., Boston, MA; *U.S. Private*, pg. 83
Esping, P.E., Chm. Bd. & Chief Exec. Officer--BRC Holdings, Dallas, TX; *U.S. Public*, pg. 163
Esposito, Michael J., Chm., Pres. & Chief Exec. Officer--Exel Insurance Co. Ltd., Hamilton, Bermuda; *Int'l*, pg. 467
Esrey, William T., Chm. Bd. & Chief Exec. Officer--Sprint Corporation, Westwood, KS; *U.S. Public*, pg. 1500
Essman, Alyn V., Chm. Bd. & Chief Exec. Officer--CPI Corp., Saint Louis, MO; *U.S. Public*, pg. 283
Estelle, Richard, Chm. Bd.--The Chesapeake Life Insurance Co., Oklahoma City, OK; *U.S. Public*, pg. 1679
Estes, Alexandra H., Chm. Bd. & Pres.--Haeger Industries, Inc., Dundee, IL; *U.S. Private*, pg. 493
Estes, Robey W., Sr., Chm. Bd. & Chief Exec. Officer--Estes Express Lines, Inc., Richmond, VA; *U.S. Private*, pg. 384
Esteve, Manuel, Chm. Bd.--Viva, Madrid, Spain; *Int'l*, pg. 575
Esteverena, Rolando, Chm. Bd. & Pres.--ADFlex Solutions, Inc., Chandler, AZ; *U.S. Public*, pg. 20
Estrin, Melvin, Co-Chm. Bd. & Co-Chief Exec. Officer--Phar-Mor, Inc., Youngstown, OH; *U.S. Public*, pg. 1284
Estrin, Melvyn J., Co-Chm. Bd. & Co-Chief Exec. Officer--Avatex Corporation, Dallas, TX; *U.S. Public*, pg. 151
Etola, Erkki, Deputy Chm.--OY Stockmann AB, Helsinki, Finland; *Int'l*, pg. 1301
Ettenberg, Elliott, Chm. & Chief Exec. Officer--Bozell Retail, Toronto, Canada; *Int'l*, pg. 209
Etter, Richard A., Chm. & Pres.--Bank of America Nevada, Reno, NV; *U.S. Public*, pg. 180
Ettleson, Richard, Chm. Bd. & Pres.--Electro Brand, Inc., Chicago, IL; *U.S. Private*, pg. 368
Eugster, Jack, Chm. Bd., Pres. & Chief Exec. Officer--Musicland Group Inc., Minnetonka, MN; *U.S. Public*, pg. 1142
Eulich, John F., Chm. Bd. & Chief Exec. Officer--Vantage Companies, Dallas, TX; *U.S. Private*, pg. 1134
Evan, Uri, Chm. Bd. & Chief Exec. Officer--USA Detergents, Inc., North Brunswick, NJ; *U.S. Public*, pg. 1685
Evans, Brynley, Chm. Bd.--Grosvenor Marketing Ltd., Paramus, NJ; *Int'l*, pg. 92
Evans, Charles, Chm. Bd.--ECOS Group, Inc., West Palm Beach, FL; *U.S. Public*, pg. 563
Evans, Colin, Chm. Bd.--Austin Reed Limited, London, United Kingdom; *U.S. Public*, pg. 796
Evans, Daniel E., Chm. Bd., Chief Exec. Officer & Sec.--Bob Evans Farms, Inc., Columbus, OH; *U.S. Public*, pg. 596
Evans, David, Chm. & Chief Exec. Officer--Grass Roots Group plc, Tring, United Kingdom; *Int'l*, pg. 1482
Evans, Donald L., Chm. Bd. & Chief Exec. Officer--Tom Brown, Inc., Midland, TX; *U.S. Public*, pg. 262
Evans, Donald L., Chm. Bd. & Chief Exec. Officer--Tom Brown, Inc., Englewood, CO; *U.S. Public*, pg. 262
Evans, Eric P., Chm. Bd.--Integra Resort Management, Inc., Dallas, TX; *U.S. Public*, pg. 778
Evans, Eric P., Chm. Bd.--Condo, Hotel & Resort Management, Dallas, TX; *U.S. Public*, pg. 778
Evans, Handel E., Chm. Bd.--Pharmaceutical Marketing Services Inc., Phoenix, AZ; *U.S. Public*, pg. 1284
Evans, J.C., Chm. Bd.--Gold Medal Products Co., Cincinnati, OH; *U.S. Private*, pg. 459
Evans, John E., Chm. Bd.--Allied Mutual Insurance Company, Des Moines, IA; *U.S. Private*, pg. 39
Evans, John R., Chm. Bd.--Torstar Corporation, Toronto, Canada; *Int'l*, pg. 1402
Evans, John, Dr., Chm. Bd.--Toronto Star Newspapers Ltd., Toronto, Canada; *Int'l*, pg. 1402
Evans, Richard E., Chm. Bd.--Eva-Tone Inc., Clearwater, FL; *U.S. Private*, pg. 384
Evans, Richard W., Jr., Chm. Bd.--Frost National Bank, San Antonio, TX; *U.S. Public*, pg. 467
Evans, Richard W., Jr., Chm. Bd.--Daltex General Agency, San Antonio, TX; *U.S. Public*, pg. 467
Evans, Robert B., Sr., Chm. Bd. & Chief Exec. Officer--Evans Industries, Inc., Detroit, MI; *U.S. Private*, pg. 385

Evans, Robert S., Chm. Bd. & Chief Exec. Officer--Crane Co., Stamford, CT; *U.S. Public*, pg. 456
Evans, Robert S., Chm. Bd. & Chief Exec. Officer--Medusa Corporation, Cleveland, OH; *U.S. Public*, pg. 1084
Evans, Stewart E., Chm. Bd.--Stu Evans Lincoln-Mercury Inc., Southgate, MI; *U.S. Private*, pg. 385
Evans, T.J., Chm. Bd.--Birtley Engineering Ltd., Chesterfield, United Kingdom; *Int'l*, pg. 1139
Evans, T.J., Chm. Bd.--Taylor Woodrow Management & Engineering Limited, Southall, United Kingdom; *Int'l*, pg. 1358
Evans, T.J., Chm. Bd.--Birtley Engineering Ltd., Chesterfield, United Kingdom; *Int'l*, pg. 1359
Evans, William H., Chm. Bd., Pres. & Chief Exec. Officer--SunTrust Bank, North Central Florida, Ocala, FL; *U.S. Public*, pg. 1537
Evanson, Robert E., Chm. Bd.--Hallman & Lorber, Inc., Valley Stream, NY; *U.S. Public*, pg. 783
Everaid, Simon, Chm. Bd.--Alliance & Leicester Building Society, London, United Kingdom; *Int'l*, pg. 57
Everard, Simon, Chm.--Alliance Leicester Building Society, London, United Kingdom; *Int'l*, pg. 57
Everett, Walter A., Chm. Bd.--Met-Pro Corporation, Harleysville, PA; *U.S. Public*, pg. 1100
Everitt, David, Chm. Bd. & Mng. Dir.--John Deere (Pty.) Ltd., Nigel, South Africa; *U.S. Public*, pg. 493
Evert, James, Chm. Bd., Pres. & Chief Exec. Officer--Irvine Sensors Corporation, Costa Mesa, CA; *U.S. Public*, pg. 913
Evins, Dan W., Chm. Bd. & Chief Exec. Officer--Cracker Barrel Old Country Store, Inc., Lebanon, TN; *U.S. Public*, *pg. 455*
Ewaldsen, Kay H., Chm.--WABAG Wassertechnische Anlagen GmbH & Co. KG, Kulmbach, Germany; *Int'l*, pg. 399
Ewart, J.W.D., Chm.--Carclo Engineering Group plc, Sheffield, United Kingdom; *Int'l*, pg. 268
Ewing, William, III, Chm. Bd.--Bowles Fluidics Corporation, Columbia, MD; *U.S. Public*, pg. 248
Eycken, Henri Vander, Prof., Chm. Bd.--Radio Holland Electronics, Almere, Netherlands; *Int'l*, pg. 1151
Eyton, J. Trevor, Sr. Chm.--EdperBrascan Corporation, Toronto, Canada; *Int'l*, pg. 433
Eyton, J. Trevor, Chm. Bd.--Brascade Resources Inc., Toronto, Canada; *Int'l*, pg. 433
Ezell, F. Miles, Sr., Chm. Bd.--Purity Dairies Inc., Nashville, TN; *U.S. Private*, pg. 895
Ezell, John William, Co-Chm. Bd.--Purity Dairies Inc., Nashville, TN; *U.S. Private*, pg. 895
Faber, Esther, Chm. Bd.--Faber Enterprises, Inc., Canoga Park, CA; *U.S. Private*, pg. 390
Fabian, Richard G., Chm. Bd. & Chief Exec. Officer--For Better Living, Inc., Auburn, CA; *U.S. Private*, pg. 417
Fabrikant, Charles, Chm. Bd., Pres. & Chief Exec. Officer--Seacor Smit Inc., Houston, TX; *U.S. Public*, pg. 1449
Fackler, Edwin, Chm. Bd. & Chief Exec. Officer--Byers Industries, Inc., Portland, OR; *U.S. Private*, pg. 191
Fadden, Joe, Chm. Bd.--GTCO Corporation, Columbia, MD; *U.S. Private*, pg. 436
Fahey, Edward D., Chm. Bd.--SI Handling Systems, Inc., Easton, PA; *U.S. Public*, pg. 1418
Fahlbush, Helmut, Chm. Bd.--Gemtron Corporation, Sweetwater, TN; *Int'l*, pg. 1523
Fahlgren, H. Smoot, Chm.--Fahlgren, Dublin, OH; *U.S. Private*, pg. 391
Fahs, John C., Chm. Bd., Pres., Chief Exec. Officer & Treas.--California Panel & Veneer Company, Cerritos, CA; *U.S. Private*, pg. 201
Fain, John H., Chm. Bd., Pres., Chief Exec. Officer & Chief Oper. Officer--Metro Information Services, Virginia Beach, VA; *U.S. Public*, pg. 1102
Fain, Norman M, Chm. Bd.--Teknor Apex Company, Pawtucket, RI; *U.S. Private*, pg. 1073
Fain, Richard D., Chm. Bd. & Chief Exec. Officer--Royal Caribbean Cruises Ltd., Miami, FL; *U.S. Public*, pg. 1410
Fairbank, Richard D., Chm. Bd. & Chief Exec. Officer--Capital One Financial Corporation, Falls Church, VA; *U.S. Public*, pg. 302
Fairchild, John B., Chm. Bd. & Chief Exec. Officer--Fairchild Publications, New York, NY; *U.S. Public*, pg. 513
Fait, George A., Chm. Bd. & Pres.--Capitol Indemnity Corporation, Madison, WI; *U.S. Public*, pg. 302
Fait, George A., Chm. Bd. & Pres.--Capitol Specialty Insurance Corporation, Madison, WI; *U.S. Public*, pg. 302
Faith, Marshall E., Chm. Bd. & Chief Exec. Officer--The Scoular Company, Omaha, NE; *U.S. Private*, pg. 977
Falk, Raymond B., Chm. Bd.--Willis Corroon Corp. of Louisiana, New Orleans, LA; *Int'l*, pg. 1506
Falkman, Edwin G., Chm. Bd.--Waste Management International plc, London, United Kingdom; *U.S. Public*, pg. 1745
Fallon, Donald, Chm. Bd., Pres. & Chief Exec. Officer--S.A. Cimenteries CBR, Brussels, Belgium; *Int'l*, pg. 605
Fallon, Donald M., Chm. Bd.--Lehigh Portland Cement Company, Allentown, PA; *Int'l*, pg. 605
Falls, Glenn, Chm. Bd.--Pay Less Super Markets, Inc., Anderson, IN; *U.S. Private*, pg. 844
Fantone, Stephen D., Chm. Bd.--Benthos, Inc., North Falmouth, MA; *U.S. Public*, pg. 212
Farace, Andrea, Chm. Bd. & Chief Exec. Officer--Foamex International Inc., Linwood, PA; *U.S. Private*, pg. 1094
Farah, Roger N., Chm. Bd. & Chief Exec. Officer--Woolworth Corporation, New York, NY; *U.S. Public*, pg. 1777
Farber, Jack, Chm. Bd., Pres. & Chief Exec. Officer--CSS Industries, Inc., Philadelphia, PA; *U.S. Public*, pg. 283
Farber, John J., Dr., Chm. Bd.--ICC Industries, Inc., New York, NY; *U.S. Private*, pg. 553
Fariello, Frank A., Chm. Bd., Pres. & Chief Exec. Officer--EDO Corporation, New York, NY; *U.S. Public*, pg. 541
Farish, William S., Chm. Bd.--Churchill Downs, Inc., Louisville, KY; *U.S. Public*, pg. 356
Farish, William S., Chm. Bd.--Anderson Park, Inc., Louisville, KY; *U.S. Public*, pg. 356
Farish, William S., Chm. Bd.--Churchill Downs Management Co., Louisville, KY; *U.S. Public*, pg. 356
Farkas, Andrew L., Chm. Bd. & Chief Exec. Officer--Insignia Financial Group, Inc., Greenville, SC; *U.S. Public*, pg. 881
Farley, James N., Chm. Bd.--SpeedFan International, Inc., Chandler, AZ; *U.S. Public*, pg. 1497
Farley, Robert, Chm. Bd.--General Drug Co., Chicago, IL; *U.S. Private*, pg. 1007
Farley, William, Chm. Bd. & Chief Exec. Officer--Fruit of the Loom, Inc., Chicago, IL; *U.S. Public*, pg. 685
Farley, William F., Chm. Bd., Pres. & Chief Exec. Officer--Farley, Inc., Chicago, IL; *U.S. Private*, pg. 394
Farling, Robert J., Chm. Bd. & Chief Exec. Officer--The Toledo Edison Company, Toledo, OH; *U.S. Public*, pg. 645
Farlinger, William, Chm. Bd.--Ontario Hydro, Toronto, Canada; *Int'l*, pg. 1007
Farmer, Bruce, Dr., Chm. Bd.--Allied Colloids Group Plc., Bradford, United Kingdom; *Int'l*, pg. 62
Farmer, John R., Chm. Bd., Pres. & Chief Exec. Officer--SouthTrust Bank, Tuscaloosa County, Tuscaloosa, AL; *U.S. Public*, pg. 1492
Farmer, Phillip W., Chm. Bd., Pres. & Chief Exec. Officer--Harris Corporation, Melbourne, FL; *U.S. Public*, pg. 791
Farmer, Richard T., Chm. Bd.--Cintas Corporation, Mason, OH; *U.S. Public*, pg. 370
Farmer, Roy F., Chm. Bd., Pres., Chief Exec. Officer & Chief Oper. Officer--Farmer Brothers Company, Torrance, CA; *U.S. Public*, pg. 613
Farnam, W.E., Chm. Bd.--The Camden Fire Insurance Assn., Philadelphia, PA; *Int'l*, pg. 543
Farnam, Walter E., Chm. Bd. & Chief Exec. Officer--General Accident Insurance, Philadelphia, PA; *Int'l*, pg. 543
Farnsworth, Ken, Jr., Chm. Bd., Pres. & Exec. V.P.--Rhodes International, Inc., Salt Lake City, UT; *U.S. Private*, pg. 927
Farrah, Pat, Chm. Bd., Pres. & Chief Exec. Officer--MG Products, San Antonio, TX; *U.S. Public*, pg. 1026
Farrar, Donald K., Chm. Bd. & Chief Exec. Officer--IMO Industries Inc., Lawrenceville, NJ; *U.S. Public*, pg. 856
Farrell, Charles, Chm. Bd.--Tropitone Furniture Co. Inc., Irvine, CA; *U.S. Private*, pg. 1105
Farrell, David C., Chm. Bd. & Chief Exec. Officer--The May Department Stores Company, Saint Louis, MO; *U.S. Public*, pg. 1063
Farrell, Frank A., Jr., Chm. Bd., Pres. & Chief Exec. Officer--Hope's Architectural Products Inc., Jamestown, NY; *U.S. Private*, pg. 538
Farrell, James, Chm. Bd.--Kinetic Concepts, Inc., San Antonio, TX; *U.S. Private*, pg. 620
Farrell, W. James, Chm. Bd., Pres. & Chief Exec. Officer--Illinois Tool Works Inc., Glenview, IL; *U.S. Public*, pg. 865
Farrington, Jerry S., Chm. Bd.--Texas Utilities Company, Dallas, TX; *U.S. Public*, pg. 1586
Farver, Herb, Chm. Bd. & Chief Exec. Officer--Blissfield Manufacturing Company, Blissfield, MI; *U.S. Private*, pg. 149
Fassler, Joseph K., Chm. & Chief Exec. Officer--Glacier Park, Inc., Phoenix, AZ; *U.S. Public*, pg. 1718
Fassler, Leonard J., Co-Chm. Bd.--AmeriData Technologies, Inc., Stamford, CT; *U.S. Public*, pg. 711
Faulkner, Henry, Chm. Bd. & Chief Exec. Officer--Faulkner Cadillac Inc., Trevose, PA; *U.S. Private*, pg. 397
Faulkner, Mikel D., Chm. Bd. & Chief Exec. Officer--Harken Energy Corporation, Irving, TX; *U.S. Public*, pg. 785
Faulkner, Richard, Chm. Bd.--Champaign Landmark, Inc., Urbana, OH; *U.S. Private*, pg. 227
Faure, Bertrand, Chm. Bd.--Empress International Ltd., Port Washington, NY; *U.S. Private*, pg. 375
Faure, Jean-Pierre, Chm. & Exec. Mng. Dir.--Faure Vadon Forest, Paris, France; *Int'l*, pg. 601
Faurre, Pierre, Chm. Bd. & Chief Exec. Officer--Societe d'Applications Generales d'Electricite et de Mechanique, Paris, France; *Int'l*, pg. 1273
Faus, Alberto, Chm.--Sharp Electronica Espana S.A. (Barcelona), Barcelona, Spain; *Int'l*, pg. 1229
Faxon, Bradford J., Chm. Bd. & Pres.--Fall River Gas Company, Fall River, MA; *U.S. Public*, pg. 611
Fayer, Elizabeth, Chm. Bd. & Chief Exec. Officer--Alfin, Inc., New York, NY; *U.S. Public*, pg. 40
Fayfield, Robert, Chm. Bd., Pres. & Chief Exec. Officer--Banner Engineering Corp., Minneapolis, MN; *U.S. Private*, pg. 114
Federman, Irwin, Chm. Bd.--QuickLogic Corporation, Sunnyvale, CA; *U.S. Private*, pg. 901
Federman, Joseph R., Chm Bd., Pres. & Chief Exec. Officer--Victor Technology, Addison, IL; *U.S. Private*, pg. 1139
Feely, Martin, Chm.-Mktg. Info. Services--BPI Communications Inc., New York, NY; *Int'l*, pg. 1446
Feerick, John D., Chm. Exec. Committee--American Arbitration Association, New York, NY; *U.S. Private*, pg. 50
Fehsenfeld, Frank B., Chm. Bd.--Crystal Flash Petroleum Corp., Indianapolis, IN; *U.S. Private*, pg. 294
Feil, Thomas E., Chm. Bd. & Chief Exec. Officer--V-Band Corporation, Elmsford, NY; *U.S. Public*, pg. 1701
Feinberg, H., Chm. Bd.--I. Appel Corporation, New York, NY; *U.S. Private*, pg. 78
Feinberg, Henry J., Chm. Bd., Pres. & Chief Exec. Officer--Rand McNally & Company, Skokie, IL; *U.S. Private*, pg. 908
Feinberg, Robert, Chm. Bd.--Duron, Inc., Beltsville, MD; *U.S. Private*, pg. 349
Feinskber, Carl-Erik, Chm. Bd.--Inductus/Industrial Operations, Stockholm, Sweden; *Int'l*, pg. 678
Feld, David, Chm. Bd., Chief Exec. Officer & Founder--Today's Man, Inc., Moorestown, NJ; *U.S. Public*, pg. 1619
Feld, Kenneth, Chm. Bd. & Chief Exec. Officer--Feld Productions, Vienna, VA; *U.S. Private*, pg. 399
Feldberg, Warren D., Chm. Bd. & Chief Exec. Officer--Caldor, Inc., Norwalk, CT; *U.S. Public*, pg. 292
Feldenkreis, George, Chm. Bd. & Chief Exec. Officer--Supreme International Corp., Miami, FL; *U.S. Public*, pg. 1542
Felder, Anton, Chm.--Arni AG, Lyss, Switzerland; *Int'l*, pg. 329
Felder, Anton, Chm.--Nutrex AG, Busswil, Switzerland; *Int'l*, pg. 330
Felder, Anton, Chm.--Panofina AG, Wallisellen, Switzerland; *Int'l*, pg. 330
Felder, Anton, Chm.--Pasta Gala SA, Morges, Switzerland; *Int'l*, pg. 330
Felder, Anton, Chm.--Schweizerische Genpssenschaft fur Gemusebau, Kersers, Switzerland; *Int'l*, pg. 330
Feldman, Lawrence H., Chm. Bd., Pres. & Chief Exec. Officer--Tower Realty Trust, Inc., New York, NY; *U.S. Public*, pg. 1625
Felix, Hans, Chm. Bd. & Mng. Dir.--Scholl AG, Reinach, Switzerland; *Int'l*, pg. 1209
Felken, G. Stephen, Chm. Bd. & Chief Exec. Officer--Avondale Foreign Sales Corporation, Sylacauga, AL; *U.S. Private*, pg. 103
Felker, G. Stephen, Chm. Bd., Pres. & Chief Exec. Officer--Avondale Incorporated, Monroe, GA; *U.S. Private*, pg. 102
Fell, A.S., Chm. Bd. & Chief Exec. Officer--RBC Dominion Securities Ltd., Toronto, Canada; *Int'l*, pg. 1131
Fellheimer, Ronald K., Chm. Bd.--Pontiac Bancorp, Inc., Pontiac, IL; *U.S. Public*, pg. 1316
Fellowes, John, Chm. & Chief Exec. Officer--Fellowes Manufacturing Co., Itasca, IL; *U.S. Private*, pg. 400
Feltenstein, Sidney, Chm. Bd., Pres. & Chief Exec. Officer--A&W Restaurants, Inc., Livonia, MI; *U.S. Private*, pg. 1
Feltenstein, Sidney, Chm. Bd., Chief Exec. Officer & Chief Oper. Officer--A&W Restaurants, Inc.-Carousel Div., Minneapolis, MN; *U.S. Private*, pg. 2
Felton, Edgar C., Chm. & Pres.--Bank of Bermuda (New York) Limited, New York, NY; *Int'l*, pg. 151
Felts, Richard E., Chm. Bd.--Hamilton Mutual Insurance Company Of Cincinnati, Cincinnati, OH; *U.S. Private*, pg. 497
Feniger, William D., Chm. Bd., Pres. & Chief Exec. Officer--Meridian National Corporation, Toledo, OH; *U.S. Public*, pg. 1095
Fenton, C.M., Chm. Bd.--British Mohair Holdings Plc, Bradford, United Kingdom; *Int'l*, pg. 219
Fenwick, Robert, Dr., Chm. Bd. & Chief Exec. Officer--On Command Video, Santa Clara, CA; *U.S. Public*, pg. 138
Ferber, Norman A., Chm. Bd.--Ross Stores, Inc., Newark, CA; *U.S. Public*, pg. 1405
Ferchat, Robert A., Chm., Pres. & Chief Exec. Officer--BCE Mobile Communications Inc., Saint-Laurent, Canada; *Int'l*, pg. 115
Ferdinandtsen, G.R., Chm. Bd. & Pres.--American National Life Insurance Co. of Texas, Galveston, TX; *U.S. Public*, pg. 87
Ferger, Lawrence A., Chm. Bd. & Chief Exec. Officer--Indiana Energy, Inc., Indianapolis, IN; *U.S. Public*, pg. 874
Ferguson, Arthur J., Chm. Bd.--Minerallac Co., Addison, IL; *U.S. Private*, pg. 750
Ferguson, C. David, Chm. Bd., Pres., Chief Exec. & Chief Oper. Officer--Gould Electronics Inc., Eastlake, OH; *U.S. Public*, pg. 1591
Ferguson, Daniel, Chm. Bd.--Mirro Company, Manitowoc, WI; *U.S. Public*, pg. 1177
Ferguson, Daniel C., Chm. Bd.--Newell Co., Freeport, IL; *U.S. Public*, pg. 1176
Ferguson, E., Chm. Bd.--Taylor & Francis Group Ltd., London, United Kingdom; *Int'l*, pg. 1357
Ferguson, Iain, Chm. Bd.--Birds Eye Walls Ltd., Walton-on-Thames, United Kingdom; *Int'l*, pg. 1434
Ferguson, Mark H., Chm. Bd., Pres. & Chief Exec. Officer--Firstbank of Illinois Co., Springfield, IL; *U.S. Public*, pg. 643
Ferguson, Ronald E., Chm. Bd. & Chief Exec. Officer--General Re Corporation, Stamford, CT; *U.S. Public*, pg. 725
Ferguson, Ronald E., Chm. Bd.--General Re Services Corp., Stamford, CT; *U.S. Public*, pg. 725
Ferguson, Thomas G., Chm. & Chief Exec. Officer--CommonHealth USA, Parsippany, NJ; *Int'l*, pg. 1483
Fergusson, Ewen, Sir, Chm.--Coutts & Co., London, United Kingdom; *Int'l*, pg. 910
Ferland, E. James, Chm. Bd., Pres. & Chief Exec. Officer--Public Service Enterprise Group Incorporated, Newark, NJ; *U.S. Public*, pg. 1340
Ferman, James L., Sr., Chm. Bd.--Ferman Oldsmobile, Tampa, FL; *U.S. Private*, pg. 401
Fermon, Joseph C., Chm. Bd. & Chief Exec. Officer--Continental Eagle Corporation, Prattville, AL; *U.S. Private*, pg. 267
Fernandes Salgueiro, Joao Mauricio, Dr., Chm. Bd. & Pres.--Caixa Geral de Depositos, Lisbon, Portugal; *Int'l*, pg. 250
Fernandez Campos, Benito, Chm. Bd.--Sistema Argos S.A., Ciudad Juarez, Mexico; *Int'l*, pg. 1256
Fernandez Rodriguez, Antonio, Chm. & Pres.--Grupo Modelo S.A., Mexico, Mexico; *U.S. Public*, pg. 115
Fernandez, Anthony G., Chm.--ARCO Chemical Co., Newtown Square, PA; *U.S. Public*, pg. 144
Fernandez, Joseph H., Chm. Bd., Pres. & Chief Exec. Officer--Buttrey Food & Drug Company, Great Falls, MT; *U.S. Public*, pg. 271
Ferola, Frank F., Chm. Bd. & Pres.--The Stephan Company, Fort Lauderdale, FL; *U.S. Public*, pg. 1514
Ferran, Xavier, Chm. Bd. & Pres.--Bacardi-Martini Belgium, Brussels, Belgium; *U.S. Private*, pg. 109
Ferrar, Angelo, Chm.--AGIP Petroli International B.V., Amsterdam, Netherlands; *Int'l*, pg. 429
Ferrari, Claudio, Chm. Bd. & Chief Exec. Officer--Foster Wheeler Power Systems, Inc., Clinton, NJ; *U.S. Public*, pg. 677

Ferrarin, E., Chm. & Mng. Dir.--ECP - Enichem Polymers Netherlands B.V., Amsterdam, Netherlands; *Int'l*, pg. 429
Ferre, Antonio Luis, Chm. Bd.--Puerto Rican Cement Co., Inc., Guaynabo, PR; *U.S. Public*, pg. 1341
Ferreira Lima, Manuel Branco, Chm. Bd. & Pres.--Transportes Aereos Portugueses, Lisbon, Portugal; *Int'l*, pg. 1418
Ferreira-Pero, Marta, Chm.--JMCT Publicidad, New York, NY; *U.S. Private*, pg. 599
Ferreira, Fernando Xavier, Chm. Bd., Pres. & Chief Exec. Officer--Telebras S.A., Brasilia, Brazil; *Int'l*, pg. 1362
Ferrell, James E., Chm. Bd. & Chief Exec. Officer--Ferrellgas Partners, L.P., Liberty, MO; *U.S. Public*, pg. 618
Ferrill, Harve A., Chm. Bd.--Advance Ross Corporation, Chicago, IL; *U.S. Public*, pg. 320
Ferrill, Harve A., Chm. Bd.--Europe Tax-Free Shopping Ltd., Chicago, IL; *U.S. Public*, pg. 320
Ferris, Richard, Co-Chm.--Doubletree Corporation, Memphis, TN; *U.S. Public*, pg. 1335
Ferris, Richard P., Chm. & Chief Exec. Officer--Norwest Bank International, Minneapolis, MN; *U.S. Public*, pg. 1202
Ferry, Richard M., Chm. Bd. & Chief Exec. Officer--Korn/Ferry International, Los Angeles, CA; *U.S. Private*, pg. 632
Fertitta, Tilman, Chm. Bd., Pres. & Chief Exec. Officer--Landry's Seafood Restaurants Inc., Houston, TX; *U.S. Public*, pg. 977
Feshbach, Herman, Chm. Bd.--American Science & Engineering, Inc., Billerica, MA; *U.S. Public*, pg. 90
Fesler, John L., Chm. Bd.--Lampert Yards, Inc., Saint Paul, MN; *U.S. Private*, pg. 645
Festa, Angelo Carlo, Chm. Bd. & Pres.--Belfe S.p.A., Marostica, Italy; *Int'l*, pg. 185
Fetherston, James S., Chm. Bd.--Quantic Industries, Inc., San Carlos, CA; *U.S. Private*, pg. 899
Fetridge, Clark W., Chm. Bd. & Chief Exec. Officer--The Dartnell Corporation, Chicago, IL; *U.S. Private*, pg. 312
Fetterman, Annabelle L., Chm. Bd. & Chief Exec. Officer--Lundy Packing Co., Clinton, NC; *U.S. Private*, pg. 681
Feuchter, Robert, Chm. Bd.--American Recreation Centers, Inc., Sacramento, CA; *U.S. Public*, pg. 90
Feuer, Michael, Chm. Bd. & Chief Exec. Officer--OfficeMax, Shaker Heights, OH; *U.S. Public*, pg. 1212
Fevre, Philippe, Chm. Bd.--SEB Internationale, Chemin-du-Petit-Bois, France; *Int'l*, pg. 568
Fey, John T., Chm. Bd.--CertainTeed Corporation, Valley Forge, PA; *Int'l*, pg. 1170
Fialkow, Frederick H., Chm. Bd., Pres. & Chief Exec. Officer--National Home Health Care Corp., Scarsdale, NY; *U.S. Public*, pg. 1157
Fichthorn, Luke E., III, Chm. Bd. & Chief Exec. Officer--Bairnco Corporation, Maitland, FL; *U.S. Public*, pg. 165
Fiddler, Jerry L., Chm. Bd. & Co-Founder--Wind River Systems, Inc., Alameda, CA; *U.S. Public*, pg. 1770
Fiedler, Hanno, Chm. Bd.--Schmalbach-Lubeca AG, Braunschweig, Germany; *Int'l*, pg. 1206
Fiedler, John F., Chm. Bd. & Chief Exec. Officer--Borg Warner Automotive, Inc., Chicago, IL; *U.S. Public*, pg. 245
Fiedler, Paula P., Chm. Bd. & Chief Exec. Officer--Crown Fence Co., Long Beach, CA; *U.S. Private*, pg. 292
Fiedler, Richard D., Chm., Exec. Committee--Crown Fence Co., Long Beach, CA; *U.S. Private*, pg. 292
Fiedler, Richard K., Chm. Bd. & Pres.--Admiral Maintenance Service L.P., Lincolnwood, IL; *U.S. Private*, pg. 17
Field, Eli, Chm. Bd.--Field Container Company, L.P., Elk Grove Village, IL; *U.S. Private*, pg. 403
Field, H. James, Jr., Chm. & Chief Exec. Officer--Fleet Trust Co. of Florida, N.A., Stuart, FL; *U.S. Public*, pg. 649
Field, Robert, Chm. Bd. & Chief Exec. Officer--IA Construction Corp., Concordville, PA; *U.S. Private*, pg. 552
Field, Robert E., Chm. Bd.--Great Lakes Financial Resources, Inc., Matteson, IL; *U.S. Private*, pg. 474
Fields, C.E., Chm. Bd.--Delhi Petroleum Pty. Ltd., Melbourne, Australia; *U.S. Public*, pg. 601
Fields, Gary, Chm. Bd. & Chief Exec. Officer--Banc One-Newark, Newark, OH; *U.S. Public*, pg. 173
Fiesler, Razz, Chm. Bd.--Fort Worth Lumber Company, Fort Worth, TX; *U.S. Private*, pg. 419
Fife, Bernard, Co-Chm. Bd.--Standard Motor Products Inc., Long Island City, NY; *U.S. Public*, pg. 1503
Fife, Kay, Vice Chm.--Cogsdill Tool Products, Inc., Lugoff, SC; *U.S. Private*, pg. 250
Figge, Frederic J., II, Chm.-Credit Policy--NationsBank Corporation, Charlotte, NC; *U.S. Public*, pg. 1162
Figliulo, Robert M., Chm. Bd. & Chief Exec. Officer--SPR, Inc., Oak Brook, IL; *U.S. Public*, pg. 1419
Figueroa, Julie, Chm.--Infocom Technologies, Inc., Pasig, Philippines; *Int'l*, pg. 1051
Fike, John T., Chm. Bd. & Chief Exec. Officer--Pac Paper Inc., Vancouver, WA; *U.S. Private*, pg. 828
Fike, Lester L., Jr., Chm. Bd. & Chief Exec. Officer--Fike Corporation, Blue Springs, MO; *U.S. Private*, pg. 404
Filipacchi, Daniel, Chm. Bd.--Lagardere Groupe North America, New York, NY; *Int'l*, pg. 794
Filipowski, Andrew J., Chm. Bd., Pres. & Chief Exec. Officer--Platinum Technology, Inc., Oak Brook Terrace, IL; *U.S. Public*, pg. 1309
Fill, Dennis, Chm. Bd. & Chief Exec. Officer--ATL Ultrasound, Inc., Bothell, WA; *U.S. Public*, pg. 11
Fimbel, Edward, Jr., Chm. Bd. & Pres.--Fimbel Door Corporation, Whitehouse, NJ; *U.S. Private*, pg. 404
Finck, Thomas G., Chm. Bd. & Chief Exec. Officer--Triton Energy Limited, Dallas, TX; *U.S. Public*, pg. 1640
Findlay, J. Cary, Chm. Bd.--Conso Products Company, Union, SC; *U.S. Public*, pg. 434
Findlay, Roger, Chm. Bd. & Chief Exec. Officer--Modern Medical Modalities Corp., Morristown, NJ; *U.S. Public*, pg. 1121
Fine, Leo, Chm. Bd.--M. Fine & Sons Manufacturing Co., Inc., New York, NY; *U.S. Private*, pg. 405
Fine, Ralph, Chm. Bd.--Triangle Services, Inc., Valley Stream, NY; *U.S. Private*, pg. 1102
Finegold, Aryeh, Chm. Bd.--Mercury Interactive Corp., Sunnyvale, CA; *U.S. Public*, pg. 1093
Fingerson, Leroy M., Chm. Bd.--TSI Incorporated, Shoreview, MN; *U.S. Public*, pg. 1559
Fingleton, Thomas D., Chm.--Hecht's, Arlington, VA; *U.S. Public*, pg. 1063
Fink, H. Bernerd, Chm. Bd.--CGF Industries, Topeka, KS; *U.S. Private*, pg. 194
Fink, Richard, Chm. Bd.--G&K Services, Inc., Minnetonka, MN; *U.S. Public*, pg. 690
Finkelstein, Harold R., Chm. Bd.--Hughes-Treitler Manufacturing Corporation, Garden City, NY; *U.S. Private*, pg. 547
Finkl, Charles W., Chm. Bd. & Chief Exec. Officer--A. Finkl & Sons Co., Chicago, IL; *U.S. Private*, pg. 405
Finlay, Derek, Chm. Bd.--Dawson International PLC, Edinburgh, United Kingdom; *Int'l*, pg. 385
Finlay, Francis, Co-Chm. & Chief Exec. Officer--Clay Finlay Inc., New York, NY; *U.S. Public*, pg. 1673
Finlay, K.M., Chm. Bd.--Exxon Coal Australia Ltd., Sydney, Australia; *U.S. Public*, pg. 602
Finn, Jerome E., Pres.--P/A Industries, Inc., Bloomfield, CT; *U.S. Private*, pg. 825
Finnegan, John D., Chm. Bd.--Integon Corporation, Winston Salem, NC; *U.S. Public*, pg. 719
Finnegan, Lawrence J., Chm. Bd. & Chief Exec. Officer--Boston Mutual Life Insurance Co., Canton, MA; *U.S. Private*, pg. 161
Finocchio, Robert, Pres. & Chief Exec. Officer--Informix Software, Menlo Park, CA; *U.S. Public*, pg. 876
Fiondella, Robert W., Chm. Bd., Pres. & Chief Exec. Officer--Phoenix Home Life Mutual Insurance Company, Hartford, CT; *U.S. Private*, pg. 863
Fiondella, Robert W., Chm. Bd., Pres. & Chief Exec. Officer--Phoenix Home Life Mutual Insurance Co., Hartford, CT; *U.S. Private*, pg. 863
Fiorentino, Gilbert J., Chm. Bd., Pres. & Chief Exec. Officer--Tiger Direct, Inc., Miami, FL; *U.S. Public*, pg. 747
Fiorito, Ricardo, Chm. Bd. & Chief Oper. Officer--Banco Quilmes, Buenos Aires, Argentina; *Int'l*, pg. 142
Fioroni, Daniel J., Chm. Bd.--Thermal Technology Industries, North Kansas City, MO; *U.S. Private*, pg. 1080
Fireman, Paul, Chm. Bd., Pres. & Chief Exec. Officer--Reebok International Ltd., Stoughton, MA; *U.S. Public*, pg. 1369
Firmenich, Fred Henri, Chm. Bd.--Firmenich S.A., Geneva, Switzerland; *Int'l*, pg. 486
Fisch, Michael G., Chm. Bd.--CTB International Corp., Milford, IN; *U.S. Public*, pg. 284
Fischer, Charlotte G., Chm. Bd., Pres. & Chief Exec. Officer--Paul Harris Stores, Inc., Indianapolis, IN; *U.S. Public*, pg. 792
Fischer, Gerhard W., Chm. Bd. & Chief Exec. Officer--Panalpina Welttransport (Holding) AG, Binningen, Switzerland; *Int'l*, pg. 1022
Fischer, Harry A., Jr., Chm. Bd.--Daubert Industries, Inc., Westchester, IL; *U.S. Private*, pg. 313
Fish, Aaron M., Chm. Bd. & Chief Exec. Officer--Unican Security Systems Ltd., Montreal, Canada; *Int'l*, pg. 1432
Fish, Lawrence K., Chm., Pres. & Chief Exec. Officer--Citizens Financial Group, Inc., Providence, RI; *Int'l*, pg. 1132
Fish, Lawrence K., Chm.--Citizens Bank of Massachusetts, Fairhaven, MA; *Int'l*, pg. 1132
Fisher, David I., Chm. Bd.--The Capital Group Companies Inc., Los Angeles, CA; *U.S. Private*, pg. 206
Fisher, David I., Chm. Bd.--The Capital Group International, Los Angeles, CA; *U.S. Private*, pg. 206
Fisher, Donald G., Chm. Bd.--The Gap, Inc., San Francisco, CA; *U.S. Public*, pg. 702
Fisher, Donald G., Chm. Bd. & Chief Exec. Officer--Old Navy Stores, San Francisco, CA; *U.S. Public*, pg. 703
Fisher, George M.C., Chm. Bd. & Chief Exec. Officer--Eastman Kodak Company, Rochester, NY; *U.S. Public*, pg. 550
Fisher, Henry, Chm. Bd. & Chief Fin. Officer--Pyramid Handbags Inc., New York, NY; *U.S. Private*, pg. 896
Fisher, James D., Chm.--Cadbury Chocolate Canada, Inc., Toronto, Canada; *Int'l*, pg. 248
Fisher, Jerome, Chm. Bd.--Nine West Group, Inc., Stamford, CT; *U.S. Public*, pg. 1185
Fisher, John J., Chm. Bd. & Chief Exec. Officer--Corbett HealthConnect, A Frank J. Corbett, Inc., Company, Chicago, IL; *U.S. Public*, pg. 1223
Fisher, Kenneth G., Chm. Bd. & Chief Exec. Officer--Encore Computer Corporation, Fort Lauderdale, FL; *U.S. Public*, pg. 580
Fisher, Larry, Chm. Bd.--Ketchum Public Relations, Los Angeles, CA; *U.S. Private*, pg. 617
Fisher, Paul F., Chm.--The Fifth Third Bank of Western Ohio, National Association, Piqua, OH; *U.S. Public*, pg. 622
Fisher, Phillip W., Chm. Bd.--Durakon Industries, Inc., Lapeer, MI; *U.S. Public*, pg. 537
Fisher, Richard B., Chm.-Exec. Committee--Morgan Stanley Dean Witter & Co., New York, NY; *U.S. Public*, pg. 1132
Fisher, Richard B., Chm. Bd.--Morgan Stanley Group Inc., New York, NY; *U.S. Public*, pg. 1132
Fisher, Ronald D., Chm. Bd.--Phoenix Technologies Ltd., San Jose, CA; *U.S. Public*, pg. 1292
Fisher, Steven, Chm. Bd.--Banner Pharmacaps, Inc., High Point, NC; *Int'l*, pg. 1272
Fisher, Thomas L., Chm. Bd., Pres. & Chief Exec. Officer--NICOR Inc., Naperville, IL; *U.S. Public*, pg. 1182
Fisher, Thomas L., Chm. Bd., Pres. & Chief Exec. Officer--Northern Illinois Gas Company, Naperville, IL; *U.S. Public*, pg. 1183
Fisher, William F., Chm. Bd. & Chief Exec. Officer--Fisher Gauge Limited, Peterborough, Canada; *Int'l*, pg. 491
Fishman, Bernard, Chm.-Exec. Committee--Fishman & Tobin, Inc., Conshohocken, PA; *U.S. Private*, pg. 408
Fishman, Ed, Chm. Bd.--Players International, Inc., Atlantic City, NJ; *U.S. Public*, pg. 1310
Fishman, George, Co-Chm. Bd.--Allied Digital Technologies, Hauppauge, NY; *U.S. Public*, pg. 48
Fishman, Steven S., Chm. Bd., Pres. & Chief Exec. Officer--Pamida Holdings Corporation, Omaha, NE; *U.S. Public*, pg. 1255
Fitch, J. D., Chm. Bd.--Rover Finance Holding Limited, Solihull, United Kingdom; *Int'l*, pg. 911
Fitch, Laura W., Chm. & Pres.--Bank of America New Mexico, Albuquerque, NM; *U.S. Public*, pg. 180
Fites, Donald V., Chm. Bd. & Chief Exec. Officer--Caterpillar Inc., Peoria, IL; *U.S. Public*, pg. 315
Fitzgerald, Edward B., Chm. Bd.--Northern Telecom Japan Inc., Tokyo, Japan; *Int'l*, pg. 970
Fitzgerald, Gale S., Chm. Bd. & Chief Exec. Officer--Computer Task Group, Inc. (CTG), Buffalo, NY; *U.S. Public*, pg. 423
FitzGerald, Niall, Chm. Bd.--Unilever Plc, London, United Kingdom; *Int'l*, pg. 1433
Fitzgerald, William A., Chm Bd. & Chief Exec. Officer--Commercial Federal Corporation, Omaha, NE; *U.S. Public*, pg. 411
Fitzgibbons, James M., Chm. Bd. & Chief Exec. Officer--Fieldcrest Cannon, Inc., Kannapolis, NC; *U.S. Public*, pg. 1296
Fitzpatrick, Barry J., Chm. Bd., Pres. & Chief Exec. Officer--First Virginia Banks, Inc., Falls Church, VA; *U.S. Public*, pg. 641
Fitzpatrick, Daniel B., Chm. Bd., Pres. & Chief Exec. Officer--Quality Dining Inc., Mishawaka, IN; *U.S. Public*, pg. 1349
Fitzsimonds, Roger L., Chm. Bd. & Chief Exec. Officer--Firstar Corporation, Milwaukee, WI; *U.S. Public*, pg. 642
Fizdale, Richard B., Chm. & Chief Exec. Officer--Leo Burnett Company, Inc., Chicago, IL; *U.S. Private*, pg. 183
Flagg, John E., Co.-Chm. Bd.--David Clark Company Incorporated, Worcester, MA; *U.S. Private*, pg. 242
Flaherty, William, Chm. Bd.--Horsehead Resource Development Company, Inc., Palmerton, PA; *U.S. Private*, pg. 540
Flaherty, William, Chm. Bd.--Horsehead Resource Development Co., Inc., New York, NY; *Int'l*, pg. 860
Flaherty, William E., Chm. Bd. & Chief Exec. Officer--Horsehead Industries, Inc., New York, NY; *U.S. Private*, pg. 540
Flanagan, David T., Chm. Bd.--Maine Yankee, Brunswick, ME; *U.S. Public*, pg. 325
Flanagan, John, Chm. Bd., Pres. & Chief Exec. Officer--Goodheart-Willcox Publisher, Tinley Park, IL; *U.S. Private*, pg. 464
Flanders, Don H., Chm. Bd.--Flanders Industries, Inc., Fort Smith, AR; *U.S. Private*, pg. 410
Flanigan, Joseph G., Chm. Bd., Pres. & Chief Exec. Officer--Flanigan's Enterprises, Inc., Fort Lauderdale, FL; *U.S. Public*, pg. 648
Flaschen, Steward S., Ph.D., Chm. Bd.--Telco Systems, Inc., Norwood, MA; *U.S. Public*, pg. 1568
Flatt, W. Pierce, Chm. Bd.--SouthTrust Bank, Dothan, Dothan, AL; *U.S. Public*, pg. 1491
Flax, Larry, Chm. Bd.--California Pizza Kitchen Inc., Los Angeles, CA; *U.S. Public*, pg. 1277
Fleck, James D., Chm. Bd.--Alias Wavefront, Toronto, Canada; *U.S. Public*, pg. 1474
Fleischer, Mathew, Chm. Bd.--Fleischer Manufacturing, Inc., Columbus, NE; *U.S. Private*, pg. 410
Fleischer, Morton H., Chm. Bd., Pres. & Chief Exec. Officer--Franchise Finance Corp. of America, Scottsdale, AZ; *U.S. Public*, pg. 679
Fleischli, Gus, Chm. Bd.--Fleischli Oil Company, Inc., Cheyenne, WY; *U.S. Private*, pg. 410
Fleming, Donald R., Chm. Bd. & Chief Exec. Officer--Zoeller Co., Louisville, KY; *U.S. Private*, pg. 1207
Fleming, J.G., Chm. Bd.--Adason Properties Limited, Toronto, Canada; *Int'l*, pg. 254
Fleming, John, Chm. Bd.--Saab Cars USA, Inc., Norcross, GA; *Int'l*, pg. 687
Fleming, M. Jack, Chm. Bd., Pres., Chief Exec. Officer & Treas.--Merchants Publishing Co., Kalamazoo, MI; *U.S. Private*, pg. 732
Fleming, P.J., Chm. & Pres.--Getty Gas Gathering, Inc., New Orleans, LA; *U.S. Public*, pg. 1583
Fleming, Scott T., Chm. Bd.--Spectrum Asset Management, Inc., Stamford, CT; *U.S. Public*, pg. 1674
Fletcher, Alan, Chm. Bd.--Vector Industries, Ltd., Doncaster, United Kingdom; *Int'l*, pg. 1461
Fletcher, Alan, Chm. Bd.--Vector Marine Holdings, London, United Kingdom; *Int'l*, pg. 1461
Fletcher, Dugald, Chm. Bd.--Binning's Building Products, Inc., Lexington, NC; *U.S. Public*, pg. 67
Fletcher, J.W.S., Chm.--Heavylift Cargo Airlines Limited, Stansted, United Kingdom; *Int'l*, pg. 773
Fletcher, John, Chm.-Trafalgar House-Corp. Devel.--Trafalgar House PLC, London, United Kingdom; *Int'l*, pg. 772
Fletcher, Kenneth W., Chm. Bd., Pres. & Chief Exec. Officer--Roberds, Inc., Carrollton, OH; *U.S. Public*, pg. 1393
Fletcher, Philip B., Chm. Bd.--ConAgra, Inc., Omaha, NE; *U.S. Public*, pg. 425
Fletcher, Robert, J., Chm. Bd.--J.H. Fletcher & Co., Huntington, WV; *U.S. Private*, pg. 412
Fletcher, Winston, Chm.-Europe--Bozell Worldwide, Inc., New York, NY; *U.S. Public*, pg. 1642
Fleury, Jean, Chm. Bd.--CSE Insurance Group, San Francisco, CA; *U.S. Private*, pg. 197
Flicker, Irving, Chm. Bd. & Chief Exec. Officer--Homasote Company, Trenton, NJ; *U.S. Public*, pg. 831
Flint, H. Howard, II, Chm. Bd. & Chief Exec. Officer--Flint Ink Corp., Detroit, MI; *U.S. Private*, pg. 413
Flinton, Richard A., Chm. Bd.--Fluor Constructors International, Inc., Irvine, CA; *U.S. Public*, pg. 660

Flood, A.L., Chm. Bd. & Chief Exec. Officer--Canadian Imperial Bank of Commerce, Toronto, Canada; *Int'l*, pg. 256

Floren, David, Chm. Bd. & Chief Exec. Officer--Martin/ Williams Advertising Inc., Minneapolis, MN; *U.S. Private*, pg. 710

Florence, Leonard, Chm. Bd., Pres. & Chief Exec. Officer--Syratech Corporation, East Boston, MA; *U.S. Private*, pg. 1060

Flores, Rafael Gomez, Chm. Bd.--Motor Coach Industries International, Inc., Phoenix, AZ; *Int'l*, pg. 326

Flores, Rafael Gomez, Sr., Chm. Bd.--Consorcio G. Grupo Dina, S.A. de C.V., Mexico, Mexico; *Int'l*, pg. 326

Flori, Robert D., Chm. Bd. & Treas.--Flori Corp., Phoenix, AZ; *U.S. Private*, pg. 414

Florsheim, Thomas W., Chm. Bd. & Chief Exec. Officer--Weyco Group, Inc., Milwaukee, WI; *U.S. Public*, pg. 1763

Fluor, Peter J., Chm. Bd.--Fluor Corporation, Irvine, CA; *U.S. Public*, pg. 659

Flynn, Patrick, Pres., Chief Exec. Officer, Chief Oper. Officer & Controller--Freeway Corporation, Cleveland, OH; *U.S. Private*, pg. 426

Flynn, Terence M., Chm. Bd.--Devon Publishing Group, Novato, CA; *U.S. Public*, pg. 503

Flynn, William J., Chm. Bd.--Mutual of America Life Insurance Company, New York, NY; *U.S. Private*, pg. 769

Fogel, William, Chm. Bd., Pres. & Chief Exec. Officer--Jordon Commercial Refrigerator Co., Philadelphia, PA; *U.S. Private*, pg. 599

Fogg, F.W., Pres. & Chief Exec. Officer--Southeastern Medequip, Inc., Jacksonville Beach, FL; *U.S. Private*, pg. 1015

Fogg, Janet, Mng. Dir.-London--Interbrand, London, United Kingdom; *U.S. Public*, pg. 1225

Foil, Martin B., Jr., Chm. Bd. & Chief Exec. Officer--Tuscarora Yarns Inc., Mount Pleasant, NC; *U.S. Private*, pg. 1110

Foley, Patrick, Chm. Bd. & Chief Exec. Officer--DHL Worldwide Express, Redwood City, CA; *U.S. Private*, pg. 301

Foley, Thomas C., Chm. Bd.--NTC Group, Greenwich, CT; *U.S. Private*, pg. 772

Foley, Thomas C., Chm. Bd.--TB Wood's Corporation, Chambersburg, PA; *U.S. Public*, pg. 1562

Foley, William A., Chm. Bd., Pres. & Chief Exec. Officer--Lesco, Inc., Rocky River, OH; *U.S. Public*, pg. 989

Foley, William A., II, Chm. Bd. & Chief Exec. Officer--CKE Restaurants Inc., Anaheim, CA; *U.S. Public*, pg. 278

Foley, William P., Chm. Bd.--Star Buffet, Inc., Salt Lake City, UT; *U.S. Public*, pg. 278

Foley, William P., Chm. Bd.--Checkers Drive-In Restaurants, Inc., Clearwater, FL; *U.S. Public*, pg. 342

Foley, William P., II, Chm. Bd. & Chief Exec. Officer--Fidelity National Financial, Inc., Irvine, CA; *U.S. Public*, pg. 620

Foley, William P., II, Chm. Bd.--Rally's Hamburgers, Inc., Louisville, KY; *U.S. Public*, pg. 1359

Folger, Lee M., Chm. Bd.--Folger Nolan Fleming Douglas, Washington, DC; *U.S. Private*, pg. 416

Folkerth, John R., Chm. Bd. & Chief Exec. Officer--Shopsmith, Inc., Dayton, OH; *U.S. Public*, pg. 1467

Foltz, C. Henry, Chm. Bd.--Liggett-Stashower, Inc., Cleveland, OH; *U.S. Private*, pg. 667

Fondren, William M., Chm. Bd.--Distribution America, Des Plaines, IL; *U.S. Private*, pg. 335

Fong, Henry, Chm. Bd., Pres. & Chief Exec. Officer--RDM Sports Group, Atlanta, GA; *U.S. Public*, pg. 1354

Fontaine, Francis, Chm. Bd.--Pain Jacquet S.A., Evry, France; *Int'l*, pg. 1021

Fontana, Omar, Chm. Bd. & Pres.--Transbrasil S.A. Linhas Aereas, Sao Paulo, Brazil; *Int'l*, pg. 1416

Fontanet, Xavier, Vice Chm. & Chief Oper. Officer--Essilor International Compagnie Generale d'Optique, Charenton-le-Pont, France; *Int'l*, pg. 462

Foote, William, Chm. Bd. & Chief Exec. Officer--USG Corporation, Chicago, IL; *U.S. Public*, pg. 1660

Footer, Harold, Chm. Bd.--Easy Day Manufacturing Company, Holliston, MA; *U.S. Private*, pg. 358

Foran, W.J., Chm. Bd.--Cyanamid Canada Inc., Markham, Canada; *U.S. Public*, pg. 80

Forbes, Betty M., Chm. Bd.--Christian Children's Fund, Inc., Richmond, VA; *U.S. Private*, pg. 238

Forbes, Darius, Chm.--Sempell Valves Pvt. Ltd., Pune, India; *Int'l*, pg. 401

Forbes, Malcolm S., Jr., Chm. Bd.--American Heritage Magazine, New York, NY; *U.S. Private*, pg. 417

Forbes, Samuel E., Chm. Bd. & Pres.--Peerless Tyre Co., Denver, CO; *U.S. Private*, pg. 847

Forbes, Walter A., Chm. Bd.--Cendant Corporation, Stamford, CT; *U.S. Public*, pg. 320

Forbes, Walter A., Chm. Bd. & Chief Exec. Officer--CUC International, Inc., Stamford, CT; *U.S. Public*, pg. 320

Ford, Gerald J., Chm. Bd.--California Federal Bank, San Francisco, CA; *U.S. Private*, pg. 690

Ford, James Curtis, Chm. Bd.--Ford Steel Co., Inc., Maryland Heights, MO; *U.S. Private*, pg. 418

Ford, Joe T., Chm. Bd., Pres. & Chief Exec. Officer--ALLTEL Corporation, Little Rock, AR; *U.S. Public*, pg. 55

Fore, James R., Chm. Bd., Pres. & Chief Exec. & Oper. Officer--Communication Cable, Inc., Sanford, NC; *U.S. Public*, pg. 968

Forester, Benjamin, Chm. Bd., Pres. & Chief Exec. Officer--Rex Lumber Company, Acton, MA; *U.S. Private*, pg. 926

Forester, Bernard I., Chm. Bd.--K2 Inc., Los Angeles, CA; *U.S. Public*, pg. 940

Forgione, Anthony, Chm. Bd. & Pres.--Boyer Candy Company Inc., Altoona, PA; *U.S. Private*, pg. 162

Foriel-Destezet, P., Co.-Chm. Bd.--Adecco S.A., Lausanne, Switzerland; *Int'l*, pg. 23

Forissier, Marie-Jose, Chm.-Initiative Media Worldwide & Pres.-Media Communs.--Ammirati Puris Lintas Worldwide, New York, NY; *U.S. Public*, pg. 908

Forman, Paul F., Chm. Bd.--Zygo Corporation, Middlefield, CT; *U.S. Public*, pg. 1795

Forman, Sam, Chm. Bd., Pres. & Chief Exec. Officer--County Seat Stores, Inc., Dallas, TX; *U.S. Private*, pg. 279

Fornear, James R., Chm. Bd.--Res-Care Incorporated, Louisville, KY; *U.S. Public*, pg. 1382

Forster, Peter H., Chm. Bd.--DPL Inc., Dayton, OH; *U.S. Public*, pg. 473

Forster, Peter H., Chm. Bd.--Dayton Power & Light Co., Dayton, OH; *U.S. Public*, pg. 473

Forstmann, Theodore, Chm. Bd. & Chief Exec. Officer--Gulfstream Aerospace Corporation, Savannah, GA; *U.S. Private*, pg. 419

Forstmoser, Peter, Chm. Bd. & Pres.--Hesta Tex AG, Zug, Switzerland; *Int'l*, pg. 617

Forsythe, Gerald, Chm. Bd., Pres. & Chief Exec. Officer--Indeck Power Equipment Company, Wheeling, IL; *U.S. Private*, pg. 559

Forte, Luis Monteiro, Chm.--Galp International Corporation, Panama, Panama; *Int'l*, pg. 1045

Fortgang, Charles, Co.-Chm. Bd.--M. Fabrikant & Sons, Inc., New York, NY; *U.S. Private*, pg. 390

Fortier, Marc G., Chm. Bd., Pres. & Chief Exec. Officer--Societe Generale de Financement du Quebec, Montreal, Canada; *Int'l*, pg. 1274

Foss, Joseph E., Vice Chm.-Business & Fin.--The Orioles, Inc., Baltimore, MD; *U.S. Private*, pg. 819

Foster, Charles H., Jr., Chm. Bd. & Chief Exec. Officer--Lawyers Title Insurance Corporation, Richmond, VA; *U.S. Public*, pg. 981

Foster, E.L., Chm. Bd.--Foster-Miller, Inc., Waltham, MA; *U.S. Private*, pg. 421

Foster, G.A., Jr., Chm. Bd.--Guaranty Corporation, Baton Rouge, LA; *U.S. Private*, pg. 485

Foster, Henry L., Dr., Chm. Bd.--Charles River Laboratories, Inc., Wilmington, MA; *U.S. Public*, pg. 194

Foster, James H., Exec. V.P., Chm.-Brouillard Communications--J. Walter Thompson Company, New York, NY; *Int'l*, pg. 1483

Foster, John H., Chm. Bd.--Foster Management Co., King of Prussia, PA; *U.S. Private*, pg. 421

Foster, John H., Vice Chm.--Malcolm Pirnie, Inc., White Plains, NY; *U.S. Private*, pg. 867

Foster, John H., Chm. Bd.--NovaCare Inc., King of Prussia, PA; *U.S. Public*, pg. 1203

Foster, Kenneth W., Chm. Bd.--First National Bank, McCook, NE; *U.S. Public*, pg. 629

Foster, L.B., Chm. Bd.--Summit Corporation of America, Thomaston, CT; *U.S. Private*, pg. 1050

Foster, Louis W., Chm. Emeritus--20th Century Industries, Woodland Hills, CA; *U.S. Public*, pg. 1646

Foster, Paul L., Chm. Bd. & Chief Exec. Officer--Talley Industries, Inc., Phoenix, AZ; *U.S. Public*, pg. 307

Foster, Ronald H, Sr., Chm. Bd.--The Stellar Group Inc., Jacksonville, FL; *U.S. Private*, pg. 1040

Foster, W. Douglas, Chm. Bd., Pres. & Chief Exec. Officer--Salem Carpet Mills, Inc., Winston Salem, NC; *U.S. Public*, pg. 1464

Foster, William E., Chm. Bd.--Stratus Computer, Inc., Marlborough, MA; *U.S. Public*, pg. 1524

Fothergill, G.P., Chm.--Fisons Consumer Health Plc, Witham, United Kingdom; *Int'l*, pg. 1110

Fouad, Sheikh Abdula, Chm. Bd.--Abdulla Fouad Co. Ltd., Dammam, Saudi Arabia; *Int'l*, pg. 501

Fouche, Yves, Chm. Bd.--Sogitec, Suresnes, France; *Int'l*, pg. 383

Foulds, Jon, Chm. Bd.--Halifax plc, Halifax, United Kingdom; *Int'l*, pg. 589

Fountain, Reginald M., Jr., Chm. Bd., Pres. & Chief Exec. & Oper. Officer--Fountain Powerboat Industries, Inc., Washington, NC; *U.S. Public*, pg. 678

Fournier, Jacques, Chm.-Supervisory Bd.--Carrefour, Paris, France; *Int'l*, pg. 272

Fourtou, Jean-Rene, Chm. Bd. & Chief Exec Officer--Rhone-Poulenc S.A., Courbevoie, France; *Int'l*, pg. 1108

Fowler, Frederick V., Jr., Chm. Bd., Pres. & Chief Exec. Officer--Fred V. Fowler Company, Inc., Newton, MA; *U.S. Private*, pg. 422

Fowler, Walter B., Chm. Bd., Pres. & Chief Exec. Officer--The Carbide/Graphite Group, Inc., Pittsburgh, PA; *U.S. Public*, pg. 304

Fox, Bill, Chm. Bd.--Zoological Society of San Diego, San Diego, CA; *U.S. Private*, pg. 1207

Fox, J. Carter, Chm. Bd.--Chesapeake Corporation, Richmond, VA; *U.S. Public*, pg. 346

Fox, Lawrence J., Chm. Bd. & Chief Exec. Officer--Symix Systems, Inc., Columbus, OH; *U.S. Public*, pg. 1546

Fox, Martin, Chm. Bd.--Deerskin Trading Post, Inc., North Bergen, NJ; *U.S. Public*, pg. 879

Fox, Sam, Chm. Bd. & Chief Exec. Officer--Harbour Group Ltd., Saint Louis, MO; *U.S. Private*, pg. 500

Fox, Wayne F., Chm. Bd. & Chief Exec. Officer--Triple F, Inc., Des Moines, IA; *U.S. Private*, pg. 1104

Foy, Robert W., Chm. Bd.--California Water Service Co., San Jose, CA; *U.S. Public*, pg. 294

Fraefel, Peter, Chm.--Coop Zentralschweiz, Kriens, Switzerland; *Int'l*, pg. 329

Fraenkel, Albert, Chm. Bd.--Fraenkel Company, Baton Rouge, LA; *U.S. Private*, pg. 423

Frahm, Donald R., Chm. & Chief Exec. Officer--Hartford Fire Insurance Co., Hartford, CT; *U.S. Public*, pg. 794

Francis, Florence, Chm. Bd.--We Care Hair, Minneapolis, MN; *U.S. Private*, pg. 115

Francis, Florence F., Chm. Bd.--The Barbers, Hairstyling for Men & Women, Inc., Minneapolis, MN; *U.S. Private*, pg. 115

Francis, Peter T., Chm. Bd., Pres. & Chief Exec. Officer--J.M. Huber Corporation, Edison, NJ; *U.S. Private*, pg. 544

Franck, John M., Chm. Bd.--Tultex Corporation, Martinsville, VA; *U.S. Public*, pg. 1644

Francois, Georges, Chm. Bd. & Chief Exec. Officer--Automotive Wiring Systems Division - Sylea, Montigny-le-Bretonneux, France; *Int'l*, pg. 785

Frandsen, Dennis, Chm. Bd. & Owner--Plastech Corporation, Forest Lake, MN; *U.S. Private*, pg. 870

Frank, Elaine S., Chm. Bd.--Frank Consolidated Enterprises Inc., Des Plaines, IL; *U.S. Private*, pg. 423

Frank, Richard M., Chm. Bd. & Chief Exec. Officer--ShowBiz Pizza Time, Inc., Irving, TX; *U.S. Public*, pg. 1468

Frank, Richard N., Chm. Bd.--Lawry's Restaurants, Inc., Pasadena, CA; *U.S. Private*, pg. 654

Franke, William A., Chm. Bd. & Chief Exec. Officer--America West Holdings Corporation, Phoenix, AZ; *U.S. Public*, pg. 66

Franke, William A., Chm. Bd.--America West Airlines, Inc., Phoenix, AZ; *U.S. Public*, pg. 67

Frankel, Andrew, Chm. Bd. & Chief Exec. Officer--Andal Corp., New York, NY; *U.S. Public*, pg. 111

Frankel, Bernard, Chm. & Chief Exec. Officer--Frankel & Company, Chicago, IL; *U.S. Private*, pg. 424

Frankel, Jerry, Chm. Bd.--Jerell, Inc., Dallas, TX; *U.S. Private*, pg. 586

Frankel, Robert James, Chm. Bd. & Chief Exec. Officer--Construction Counsellors, Inc., Montville, NJ; *U.S. Private*, pg. 266

Frankenberg, Robert J., Chm. Bd.--Wall Data Incorporated, Kirkland, WA; *U.S. Public*, pg. 1734

Frankfort, Lew, Chm. Bd. & Chief Exec. Officer--Coach, New York, NY; *U.S. Public*, pg. 1433

Frankino, Sam J., Chm. Bd. & Chief Exec. Officer--National Auto Credit Inc., Solon, OH; *U.S. Public*, pg. 1152

Franklin, E. Thomas, Chm., Pres. & Treas.--Franklin Baking Co., Inc., Goldsboro, NC; *U.S. Private*, pg. 424

Franklin, Irving H., Chm. Bd. & Treas.--Franklin Sports, Inc., Stoughton, MA; *U.S. Private*, pg. 424

Franklin, Joe P., Chm. Bd. & Chief Exec. Officer--Frequency Electronics, Inc., Uniondale, NY; *U.S. Public*, pg. 681

Franklin, Martin E., Chm. Bd. & Chief Exec. Officer--BEC Group, Inc., Rye, NY; *U.S. Public*, pg. 160

Franklin, Robert M., Chm.--Placer Dome Inc., Vancouver, Canada; *Int'l*, pg. 1060

Franz, Hermann, Chm.-Supervisory Bd.--Siemens AG, Munich, Germany; *Int'l*, pg. 1244

Fraser, Jack, Chm. Bd.--Air Canada, Saint-Laurent, Canada; *Int'l*, pg. 36

Fraser, John S., Chm. Bd. & Chief Exec. Officer--CIBA-GEIGY Plc, Macclesfield, United Kingdom; *Int'l*, pg. 978

Frauenhofer, Victor H., Chm. Bd. & Chief Exec. Officer--CTG Resources, Inc., Hartford, CT; *U.S. Public*, pg. 285

Frauenhofer, Victor H., Chm. Bd. & Chief Exec. Officer--Connecticut Natural Gas Corporation, Hartford, CT; *U.S. Public*, pg. 285

Frauenhofer, Victor H., Chm. Bd. & Chief Exec. Officer--Energy Networks, Inc. (ENI), Hartford, CT; *U.S. Public*, pg. 285

Fravel, J.C., Chm., Pres. & Chief Exec. Officer--Syroco Inc., Peabody, MA; *Int'l*, pg. 844

Frazee, John P., Jr., Chm. Bd., Pres. & Chief Exec. Officer--Paging Network, Inc., Plano, TX; *U.S. Public*, pg. 1252

Frazier, John L.D., Chm. Bd. & Chief Exec. Officer--Full Service Beverage Company, Wichita, KS; *U.S. Private*, pg. 34

Frazier, Warner, Chm. Bd. & Chief Exec. Officer--Simplicity Manufacturing, Inc., Port Washington, WI; *U.S. Private*, pg. 1002

Frederickson, Charles R., Chm. Bd.--Vicorp Restaurants, Inc., Denver, CO; *U.S. Public*, pg. 1719

Freedman, Allen R., Chm. Bd. & Chief Exec. Officer--Fortis, Inc., New York, NY; *Int'l*, pg. 499

Freedman, David, Chm. Bd.--New Brunswick Scientific Co., Inc., Edison, NJ; *U.S. Public*, pg. 1169

Freeland, Robert, Chm. Bd.--Havens Steel Co., Kansas City, MO; *U.S. Private*, pg. 510

Freeman, Carl M., Chm. Bd. & Chief Exec. Officer--Carl M. Freeman Associates, Inc., Potomac, MD; *U.S. Private*, pg. 426

Freeman, Cliff, Chm. & Chief Creative Officer--Cliff Freeman & Partners, New York, NY; *U.S. Public*, pg. 1422

Freeman, D.S., Jr., Chm. Bd. & Chief Exec. Officer--Freeman Decorating Co., Dallas, TX; *U.S. Private*, pg. 426

Freeman, David, Chm. & Chief Exec. Officer--Loctite Corporation, Rocky Hill, CT; *Int'l*, pg. 611

Freeman, Kenneth W., Chm. Bd., Pres. & Chief Exec. Officer--Quest Diagnostics, Inc., Teterboro, NJ; *U.S. Public*, pg. 1351

Freeman, Larry J., Chm. Bd.--Freeman Cosmetic Corp., Los Angeles, CA; *U.S. Private*, pg. 426

Freeman, M W., Chm.--Miller Freeman PTE Ltd., Singapore, Singapore; *Int'l*, pg. 1443

Freeman, Marshall, Chm. Bd.--Miller Freeman PLC, London, United Kingdom; *Int'l*, pg. 1443

Freeman, Marshall W., Chm. Bd., Pres. & Chief Exec. Officer--Miller Freeman Inc., San Francisco, CA; *Int'l*, pg. 1443

Freiherr von Perfall, Eberhard, Dr., Chm. Bd.--Ruetgers A.G., Frankfurt/Main, Germany; *Int'l*, pg. 1147

Freitag, Lothar G., Chm. Bd.--Philipp Holzmann USA, Ltd., Charlotte, NC; *Int'l*, pg. 633

Frem, George N., Chm. Bd. & Chief Exec. Officer--Interstate Resources, Inc., Rosslyn, VA; *U.S. Private*, pg. 573

Fremont, Dominique, Chm. Bd. & Chief Exec. Officer--Fotolabo S.A., Lausanne, Switzerland; *Int'l*, pg. 501

Fremont, Robert S., Chm. Bd. & Chief Exec. Officer--Juno Lighting, Inc., Des Plaines, IL; *U.S. Public*, pg. 935

French, Arthur L., Chm. Bd. & Chief Exec. Officer--Metals USA, Inc., Houston, TX; *U.S. Public*, pg. 1100

French, Morton R., Sr., Chm. Bd.--Commercial Plastics & Supplies Corp., Richmond Hill, NY; *U.S. Private*, pg. 258

Frendigoun, E.R., Chm. Bd.--Jonathan James Limited, Rainham, United Kingdom; *Int'l*, pg. 1358

Frenzel, Michael, Dr., Chm. Bd.--Preussag AG, Hannover, Germany; *Int'l*, pg. 1069

Frere, Albert, Chm. Bd.--Petrofina S.A., Brussels, Belgium; *Int'l*, pg. 1043

Frere, Baron, Chm. Bd. & Mng. Dir.--Groupe Bruxelles Lambert S.A., Brussels, Belgium; *Int'l*, pg. 561
Frere, Baron, Chm.--Electrafina, Brussels, Belgium; *Int'l*, pg. 562
Freston, Thomas, Chm. & Chief Exec. Officer--MTV Networks, New York, NY; *U.S. Private*, pg. 779
Freston, Thomas, Chm. Bd. & Chief Exec. Officer--MTV: Music Television, New York, NY; *U.S. Private*, pg. 779
Freudenberg, Hermann, Chm. Bd.--Freudenberg & Company, Weinheim, Germany; *Int'l*, pg. 505
Freund, Harry I., Chm. Bd.--Publicker Industries Inc., Fairfield, CT; *U.S. Public*, pg. 1341
Frey, Dale F., Chm. Bd. & Pres.--General Electric Investment Corp., Stamford, CT; *U.S. Public*, pg. 712
Frey, Fredric, Chm. Bd.--Great West Casualty Company, South Sioux City, NE; *U.S. Public*, pg. 1218
Frey, John S., Chm. Bd. & Pres.--John S. Frey Enterprises, Los Angeles, CA; *U.S. Private*, pg. 428
Frey, Philip, Jr., Chm. Bd., Pres. & Chief Exec. Officer--Microsemi Corporation, Santa Ana, CA; *U.S. Public*, pg. 1107
Friars, Eileen M., Chm. Bd.--NationsBank Investment Corporation, Richmond, VA; *U.S. Public*, pg. 1163
Fribourg, Paul J., Chm. Bd. & Chief Exec. Officer--Continental Grain Company, New York, NY; *U.S. Private*, *pg. 268*
Fricchione, Frank, Chm. Bd.--Simplex Industries, Inc., Scranton, PA; *U.S. Private*, pg. 1001
Fricke, Klaus, Chm. Bd.--Recaro North America, Inc., Clawson, MI; *U.S. Private*, pg. 914
Fricks, William P., Chm. Bd. & Chief Exec. Officer--Newport News Shipbuilding, Inc., Newport News, VA; *U.S. Public*, pg. 1179
Fried, Albert, Jr., Chm. Bd.--Portec, Inc., Lake Forest, IL; *U.S. Public*, pg. 1317
Friedberg, Thomas H., Chm Bd., Pres. & Chief Exec. Officer--ACCEL International Corporation, Dublin, OH; *U.S. Public*, pg. 14
Friedel, Len, Chm. Bd.--Plastic Engineered Components Inc., Waukesha, WI; *U.S. Private*, pg. 870
Friedland, Louis N., Chm. Bd.--Universal Studios Television Ltd., Universal City, CA; *Int'l*, pg. 1216
Friedlander, Alfred L., Chm. Bd. & Chief Exec. Officer--Rice Food Markets Inc., Houston, TX; *U.S. Private*, pg. 927
Friedlander, Bill, Chm.--Bartlett & Co., Cincinnati, OH; *U.S. Public*, pg. 985
Friedman, Daniel, Chm. Bd.--Kable News Co., Inc., New York, NY; *U.S. Public*, pg. 105
Friedman, Irwin, Chm. Bd. & Mng. Partner--Friedman, Eisenstein, Raemer and Schwartz, LLP, Chicago, IL; *U.S.* Private, pg. 428
Friedman, Isidore, Chm. Bd.--S. Rothchild & Co., Inc., New York, NY; *U.S. Private*, pg. 947
Friedman, Jack, Chm. Bd. & Chief Exec. Officer--Friedman Industries, Inc., Houston, TX; *U.S. Public*, pg. 682
Friedman, Jack, Chm. Bd., Pres. & Chief Exec. Officer--JAKKS Pacific, Inc., Malibu, CA; *U.S. Public*, pg. 923
Friedman, Jack N., Chm. Bd. & Chief Exec. Officer--Florasynth Inc., Teterboro, NJ; *Int'l*, pg. 173
Friedman, Robert, Chm. Bd. & Chief Exec. Officer--Loehmann's, Inc., Bronx, NY; *U.S. Public*, pg. 1010
Friedmann, Jacques, Chm. Bd. & Chief Exec. Officer--Compagnie UAP, Paris, France; *Int'l*, pg. 323
Friedson, Belvin F., Chm. Bd.--Windmere-Durable Holdings, Hialeah, FL; *U.S. Public*, pg. 1771
Frierson, Daniel K., Chm. Bd., Pres. & Chief Exec. Officer--The Dixie Group, Inc., Chattanooga, TN; *U.S. Public*, pg. 514
Frieze, Michael, Chm. Bd. & Chief Exec. Officer--Gordon Brothers Partners Inc., Boston, MA; *U.S. Private*, pg. 465
Frigstad, David, Chm. Bd. & Pres.--Frost & Sullivan, Mountain View, CA; *U.S. Private*, pg. 430
Frings, Jurgen, Chm. Bd.--Radiometer America Inc., Westlake, OH; *Int'l*, pg. 1083
Frisch, Helmut, Chm.--Österreichische Postsparkasse AG, Vienna, Austria; *Int'l*, pg. 1012
Frisinger, Hakan, Chm. Bd.--AB Volvo, Goteborg, Sweden; *Int'l*, pg. 1476
Frist, Thomas F., Jr., Dr., Chm. Bd. & Chief Exec. Officer--Columbia/HCA Healthcare Corporation, Nashville, TN; *U.S. Public*, pg. 403
Frist, Thomas, Jr., Dr., Chm. Bd.--Columbia/HCA Healthcare Corporation, Nashville, TN; *U.S. Public*, pg. 404
Frith, Russell J., Chm. Bd., Pres. & Chief Exec. Officer--Lawn Doctor Inc., Holmdel, NJ; *U.S. Private*, pg. 653
Fritz, Lynn C., Chm. Bd. & Chief Exec. Officer--Fritz Companies, Inc., San Francisco, CA; *U.S. Public*, pg. 683
Fritzky, Edward V., Chm. Bd. & Chief Exec. Officer--Immunex Corporation, Seattle, WA; *U.S. Public*, pg. 871
Fritzky, F. Robert, Chm. & Chief Exec. Officer--MET Solutions, LLC, Morris Plains, NJ; *U.S. Public*, pg. 1642
Froeber, Robert J., Jr., Chm. Bd.--Americal Corporation, Henderson, NC; *U.S. Private*, pg. 49
Frolich, Ottheinrich, Dr., Chm.-Bd. of Mgmnt.--Bayerische Versicherungsbank-AG, Munich, Germany; *Int'l*, pg. 58
Fromm, William M., Chm. & Chief Exec. Officer--Barkley & Evergreen Advertising, Inc., Kansas City, MO; *U.S. Private*, pg. 116
Fromstein, Mitchell S., Chm. Bd., Pres. & Chief Exec. Officer--Manpower Inc., Milwaukee, WI; *U.S. Public*, pg. 1042
Frost, J.P., Chm. Bd.--Renold PLC, Manchester, United Kingdom; *Int'l*, pg. 1103
Frost, Phillip, M.D., Chm. Bd. & Chief Exec. Officer--IVAX Corporation, Miami, FL; *U.S. Public*, pg. 914
Frost, T.C., Sr. Chm. Bd.--Cullen/Frost Bankers, Inc., San Antonio, TX; *U.S. Public*, pg. 467
Frost, T.C., Sr. Chm. Bd.--Frost National Bank, San Antonio, TX; *U.S. Public*, pg. 467
Fruend, Robert A., Chm. Bd.--American National Property & Casualty Co., Springfield, MO; *U.S. Public*, pg. 87
Fruend, Robert A., Chm. Bd.--American National General Insurance Company, Springfield, MO; *U.S. Public*, pg. 88
Fruhauf, Martin, Dr., Chm. Bd.--Hoechst Aktiengesellschaft, Frankfurt/Main, Germany; *Int'l*, pg. 624
Fruman, Albert, Chm. Bd.--Dale Industries Inc., Dearborn, MI; *U.S. Private*, pg. 308
Fry, Darryl D., Chm. Bd. & Chief Exec. Officer--Cytec Industries Inc., West Paterson, NJ; *U.S. Public*, pg. 471
Fryer, C.W.B., Chm. Bd.--ZSR Corporation Ltd., Harare, Zimbabwe; *Int'l*, pg. 1357
Fryer, Robert L., Chm. Bd.--Hopper Soliday & Co., Inc., Lancaster, PA; *Int'l*, pg. 65
Fryling, Victor J., Chm. Bd.--CMS Nomeco, Jackson, MI; *U.S. Public*, pg. 280
Fu, Monty, Chm. Bd.--Syncor International Corporation, Woodland Hills, CA; *U.S. Public*, pg. 1548
Fuchs, Bernard, Chm. Bd.--Stage Stores, Inc., Houston, TX; *U.S. Private*, pg. 1028
Fuchs, David, Chm. Bd. & Chief Exec. Officer--Hampton Industries, Inc., Kinston, NC; *U.S. Public*, pg. 779
Fuchs, G., Chm.-North American Opers.--Hunter Douglas N.V., Rotterdam, Netherlands; *Int'l*, pg. 639
Fuchs, Jerry, Chm. Bd.--Hunter Douglas, Inc., Upper Saddle River, NJ; *Int'l*, pg. 639
Fuchs, K., Chm. Bd.--Erste Bank der oesterreichischen Sparkassen AG, Vienna, Austria; *Int'l*, pg. 459
Fuchs, Manfred, Dr., Chm. Bd.--Fuchs Petrolub AG Oel + Chemie, Mannheim, Germany; *Int'l*, pg. 517
Fudge, S.R., Chm.--Trafalgar House Offshore Fabricators Limited (Port Clarence), Middlesbrough, United Kingdom; *Int'l*, pg. 773
Fudge, S.R., Chm.--Trafalgar House Offshore Fabricators Limited (Linthorpe Dinsdale), Middlesbrough, United Kingdom; *Int'l*, pg. 773
Fudge, S.R., Chm.--Trafalgar House Offshore Fabricators Limited (Methil Works), Buckhaven, United Kingdom; *Int'l*, pg. 773
Fuente, David I., Chm. Bd. & Chief Exec. Officer--Office Depot Inc., Delray Beach, FL; *U.S. Public*, pg. 1212
Fuerbach, W.F., Jr., Chm. Bd., Pres. & Treas.--S.M. Frank & Co., Inc., Peekskill, NY; *U.S. Private*, pg. 423
Fugazy, William D., Chm. Bd.--Fugazy International Corporation, New York, NY; *U.S. Private*, pg. 430
Fuhrman, Robert A., Chm.--Bank of the West, Walnut Creek, CA; *Int'l*, pg. 163
Fujii, Ken, Chm. Bd.--The Mitsui Trust and Banking Company, Limited, Tokyo, Japan; *Int'l*, pg. 882
Fujii, Yoshihiro, Chm. Bd.--Hitachi Zosen Corporation, Osaka, Japan; *Int'l*, pg. 622
Fujimoto, Hidero, Chm. Bd.--Uniden Corporation, Tokyo, Japan; *Int'l*, pg. 1433
Fujimura, Hiroyuki, Chm. Bd.--Ebara Corporation, Tokyo, Japan; *Int'l*, pg. 431
Fujimura, Masaya, Chm. Bd.--Mitsubishi Materials Corp., Tokyo, Japan; *Int'l*, pg. 874
Fujimura, Takuya, Chm. Bd. & Chief Exec. Officer--Tonen Energy International Corp., New York, NY; *Int'l*, pg. 1399
Fujino, Hirotake, Chm.--Takugin Bank (Schweiz) AG, Zurich, Switzerland; *Int'l*, pg. 627
Fujisawa, Tadashi, Chm. Bd.--Asahi Life Investment Europe Ltd., London, United Kingdom; *Int'l*, pg. 85
Fujisawa, Tomokichiro, Chm. Bd.--Fujisawa Pharmaceutical Co. Ltd., Osaka, Japan; *Int'l*, pg. 525
Fujiyoshi, Toshio, Chm. Bd.--The Nikkan Kogyo Shimbun, Ltd., Tokyo, Japan; *Int'l*, pg. 930
Fukada, Atsuo, Chm. Bd.--OYO Corporation, Tokyo, Japan; *Int'l*, pg. 1019
Fukai, Kiyoshi, Chm. Bd.--Otsuka Pakistan Ltd., Karachi, Pakistan; *Int'l*, pg. 1014
Fukisawa, Y., Chm. Bd.--Kotobuki Seating Co., Tokyo, Japan; *Int'l*, pg. 759
Fukunaga, Mark H., Chm. Bd. & Chief Exec. Officer--Servco Pacific Inc., Honolulu, HI; *U.S. Private*, pg. 986
Fukushima, Akira, Chm.--ORIX Auto Leasing Corporation, Tokyo, Japan; *Int'l*, pg. 1008
Fukutake, Soichiro, Chm Bd.--Berlitz International, Inc., Princeton, NJ; *U.S. Public*, pg. 221
Fukutake, Soichiro, Chm. Bd.--Fukutake Publishing Co. Ltd., Okayama, Japan; *U.S. Public*, pg. 222
Fuld, Jr., Richard S., Chm. Bd. & Chief Exec. Officer--Lehman Brothers Holdings Inc., New York, NY; *U.S. Public*, pg. 987
Fuldner, William Terry, Chm. Bd. & Chief Exec. Officer--Efco Corporation, Monett, MO; *U.S. Private*, pg. 353
Fulford, Ronald, Chm. Bd. & Chief Exec. Officer--Liggett Group Inc., Durham, NC; *U.S. Public*, pg. 259
Fuller, A.G.F., Chm. Bd.--Fuller, Smith & Turner Plc, London, United Kingdom; *Int'l*, pg. 529
Fuller, H. Laurance, Chm. Bd. & Chief Exec. Officer--Amoco Corporation, Chicago, IL; *U.S. Public*, pg. 101
Fullmer, John, Chm. Bd.--Welcome Wagon-Intl., Inc., Trumbull, CT; *U.S. Public*, pg. 321
Fulton, John J., Chm. Bd. & Pres.--Delta Power Co., Rockford, IL; *U.S. Private*, pg. 322
Fulton, Paul, Chm. Bd. & Chief Exec. Officer--Bassett Furniture Industries, Incorporated, Bassett, VA; *U.S. Public*, pg. 193
Funk, Dr. Joachim, Chm.-Bd. of Mgmnt.--Mannesmann A.G., Dusseldorf, Germany; *Int'l*, pg. 834
Furlan, Luiz Fernando, Chm. Bd.--Sadia Group, Barueri, Brazil; *Int'l*, pg. 1168
Furman, John R., Chm. Bd.--Furman Lumber Company, Inc., Billerica, MA; *U.S. Private*, pg. 431
Furones, Miguel A., Chm. & Chief Creative Officer--Vitruvio-Leo Burnett, Madrid, Spain; *U.S. Private*, pg. 186
Furst, F.E., Chm .Bd. & Chief Exec. Officer--Furst-McNess Company, Freeport, IL; *U.S. Private*, pg. 432
Furuhashi, Satoru, Chm. Bd. & Pres.--Hosiden Corporation, Yao, Japan; *Int'l*, pg. 635
Furukawa, Masahiko, Chm. Bd.--Mitsubishi Chemical Corporation, Tokyo, Japan; *Int'l*, pg. 870
Furumoto, Jiro, Chm. Bd.--Asahi Glass Co., Ltd., Tokyo, Japan; *Int'l*, pg. 84
Furuta, Norimasa, Chm. Bd.--Mazda Motor Corporation, Hiroshima, Japan; *Int'l*, pg. 849
Furuya, Tetsuo, Chm. Bd.--Fukoku Mutual Life Insurance Company, Tokyo, Japan; *Int'l*, pg. 529
Fusco, Joseph, Chm.--Sweet Life Foods, Inc., Suffield, CT; *U.S. Public*, pg. 1541
Fusz, Louis, Chm. Bd.--Lou Fusz Automotive Network, Saint Louis, MO; *U.S. Private*, pg. 432
Futtaim, M.A., Chm.--Al Futtaim-Wimpey (Pte.) Ltd., Dubai, United Arab Emirates; *Int'l*, pg. 1355
Futterknecht, James O. Jr., Chm. Bd., Pres., & Chief Exec. Officer--Excel Industries, Inc., Elkhart, IN; *U.S. Public*, pg. 598
Gabbert, James D., Chm. Bd. & Chief Exec. Officer--Gabbert's, Inc., Minneapolis, MN; *U.S. Private*, pg. 437
Gabelli, Mario J., Chm. Bd. & Chief Exec. Officer--Lynch Corporation, Greenwich, CT; *U.S. Public*, pg. 1021
Gable, Robert E., Chm. Bd.--Stearns Enterprises, Inc., Lexington, KY; *U.S. Private*, pg. 1037
Gable, Robert E., Chm. Bd.--Stearns Company Limited, Lexington, KY; *U.S. Private*, pg. 1037
Gable, Robert E., Chm. Bd.--Stearns Phoenix Broadway, Lexington, KY; *U.S. Private*, pg. 1037
Gable, Robert L., Chm. Bd. & Chief Exec. Officer--Unitrode Corporation, Merrimack, NH; *U.S. Public*, pg. 1694
Gabor, Andras, Chm. Bd.--G.E. Tungstram Co., Vaciut, Hungary; *U.S. Public*, pg. 713
Gaby, Dan, Chm. & Chief Exec. Officer--Keyes Martin, East Hanover, NJ; *U.S. Private*, pg. 618
Gace, Francis, Joint Chm.--Lewis Gace Bozell Healthcare Worldwide, Fort Lee, NJ; *U.S. Public*, pg. 1642
Gadonneix, Pierre, Chm. Bd.--Gaz de France, Paris, France; *Int'l*, pg. 541
Gaertner, James F., Chm. Bd.--Tandy Brands Accessories, Inc., Arlington, TX; *U.S. Public*, pg. 1560
Gaffey, Eugene E., Chm. Bd.--CFX Bank, Keene, NH; *U.S. Public*, pg. 277
Gaffney, Edward J., Chm. Bd.--Ortho-Kinetics, Inc., Waukesha, WI; *U.S. Private*, pg. 820
Gage, Edwin C., Chm. & Chief Exec. Officer--Gage Marketing Group, Minneapolis, MN; *U.S. Private*, pg. 437
Gahm, W. Dwight, Chm. Bd., Pres. & Chief Exec. Officer--Kitchen Kompact, Inc., Jeffersonville, IN; *U.S. Private*, pg. 624
Gaillard, Jean Philippe, Chm.--CAP Sesa Finance, Paris, France; *Int'l*, pg. 263
Gaines, Howard C., Chm. Bd.--First National Bank of Commerce, New Orleans, LA; *U.S. Public*, pg. 629
Gainey, Harvey N., Chm. Bd.--Lester Coggins Trucking, Okahumpka, FL; *U.S. Private*, pg. 250
Gairard, Jacques, Chm. Bd. & Chief Exec. Officer--Groupe SEB, Ecueille, France; *Int'l*, pg. 568
Gaiswinkler, Chm. Bd.--First Financial Corporation, Stevens Point, WI; *U.S. Public*, pg. 140
Gaiswinkler, Robert, Chm. Bd.--First Financial Bank, FSB, Stevens Point, WI; *U.S. Public*, pg. 140
Gaither, Albert R., Chm. Bd. & Chief Exec. Officer--Ridgeview, Inc., Newton, NC; *U.S. Private*, pg. 930
Gaither, Ann Heafner, Chm. Bd. & Chief Exec. Officer--J.H. Heafner Co. Inc., Lincolnton, NC; *U.S. Private*, pg. 514
Gal, Kenneth, Chm. & Chief Exec. Officer--Italia/Gal Advertising, Los Angeles, CA; *U.S. Private*, pg. 576
Galamba, Richard I., Chm. Bd.--Galamet, Inc., Kansas City, MO; *U.S. Private*, pg. 437
Galamba, Richard I., Chm. Bd.--Galamba Metals, Inc., Kansas City, KS; *U.S. Private*, pg. 437
Galanis, Terry S., Sr., Chm. Bd.--Sealing Devices Inc., Lancaster, NY; *U.S. Private*, pg. 978
Galardi, John N., Chm. Bd.--Galardi Group, Inc., Newport Beach, CA; *U.S. Private*, pg. 437
Galbraith, Evan Griffith, Chm. Bd.--LVMH Moet Hennessy Louis Vuitton, New York, NY; *Int'l*, pg. 781
Galdstone, David, Chm. Bd.--Allied Capital Advisors, Inc., Washington, DC; *U.S. Public*, pg. 47
Galef, Andrew G., Chm. Bd.--MagneTek, Inc., Nashville, TN; *U.S. Public*, pg. 1037
Galesi, Francesco, Chm. Bd. & Pres.--Galesi Group, Schenectady, NY; *U.S. Private*, pg. 437
Gallacher, J.D. Stirling, Chm. Bd. & Mng. Dir.--P&O Vending, London, United Kingdom; *Int'l*, pg. 1034
Gallagher, Hugh, Jr., Chm. Bd.--Consolidated Metal Products, Inc., Cincinnati, OH; *U.S. Private*, pg. 265
Gallagher, John E., Sr., Chm. Bd.--Arrow International, Cleveland, OH; *U.S. Private*, pg. 85
Gallagher, Robert E., Chm. Bd.--Arthur J. Gallagher & Co., Itasca, IL; *U.S. Public*, pg. 698
Gallagher, Thomas J., Chm. Bd.--Everest Insurance Company of Canada, Toronto, Canada; *U.S. Public*, pg. 597
Gallagher, Thomas J., Chm. Bd. & Chief Exec. Officer--Everest Indemnity Insurance Company, Liberty Corner, NJ; *U.S. Public*, pg. 597
Gallen, Herbert, Chm. Bd. & Pres.--Ellen Tracy Inc., New York, NY; *U.S. Private*, pg. 372
Galligan, Thomas J., III, Chm. Bd., Pres. & Chief Exec. Officer--Papa Gino's Inc., Dedham, MA; *U.S. Private*, pg. 837
Gallo, Ernest, Chm. Bd.--E. & J. Gallo Winery, Modesto, CA; *U.S. Private*, pg. 438
Galloway, Bruce, Chm. Bd.--Arthur Treacher's, Inc., Jacksonville, FL; *U.S. Public*, pg. 136
Gallup, Patricia, Chm. Bd. & Chief Exec. Officer--PC Connection, Inc., Milford, MA; *U.S. Private*, pg. 826
Gallus, Gregory F., Chm. Bd. & Pres.--Foodland Distributors, Livonia, MI; *U.S. Public*, pg. 1541
Galpin, Rodney, Chm. Bd.--Alpha Airports Group Plc, Cranford, United Kingdom; *Int'l*, pg. 65
Galt, Barry J., Chm. Bd. & Chief Exec. Officer--Seagull Energy Corporation, Houston, TX; *U.S. Public*, pg. 1450
Galuten, Jerry, Chm. Bd. & Pres.--SGD International Corp., Riverdale, NY; *U.S. Private*, pg. 957
Galvin, E.P., Dr., Chm. Bd.-Crystal Div.--Waterford Crystal Ltd., Kilbarry, Ireland; *Int'l*, pg. 1487

Galvin, Robert W., Chm.-Exec. Committee--Motorola, Inc., Schaumburg, IL; *U.S. Public*, pg. 1136
Gamel, Wendell W., Chm. Bd., Pres. & Chief Exec. Officer--Tech-Sym Corporation, Houston, TX; *U.S. Public*, pg. 1563
Gandois, Jean, Chm. Bd.--Cockerill Sambre, Brussels, Belgium; *Int'l*, pg. 301
Gannon, Robert P., Chm. Bd., Pres. & Chief Exec. Officer--Montana Power Company, Butte, MT; *U.S. Public*, pg. 1126
Gannon, William, Sr., Chm. Bd.--Sentry Technology Group, Westborough, MA; *U.S. Public*, pg. 1425
Gans, Robert J., Chm. Bd.--Gans Ink & Supply Company, Inc., Los Angeles, CA; *U.S. Private*, pg. 440
Gant, Allen E., Jr., Chm. Bd. & Pres.--Glen Raven Mills, Inc., Glen Raven, NC; *U.S. Private*, pg. 456
Gantos, L. Douglas, Chm. Bd.--Gantos Inc., Stamford, CT; *U.S. Public*, pg. 702
Garbacz, Gerald G., Chm. Bd., Pres. & Chief Exec. Officer--Nashua Corporation, Nashua, NH; *U.S. Public*, pg. 1152
Garbagnati, Furio, Chm. & Chief Exec. Officer--Shandwick Corporate Communications S.p.A., Milan, Italy; *Int'l*, pg. 1227
Garber, Bram, Chm. Bd.--Peerless Carpet Corporation, Acton Vale, Canada; *Int'l*, pg. 1032
Garberg, Dennis, Chm. Bd. & Chief Exec. Officer--The Sunflower Group, Overland Park, KS; *U.S. Private*, pg. 1052
Garbi, Gilbert Geraldo, Chm. Bd.--Embraer-Empresa Brasileira de Aeronautica S.A., Sao Jose dos Campos, Brazil; *Int'l*, pg. 452
Garcia Saenz, Miguel, Chm. Bd.--Industrias del Lacado, S.A. (Indulacsa), Logrono, Spain; *U.S. Public*, pg. 1387
Garcia, Alfonso Romo, Chm. Bd. & Chief Exec. Officer--Empressa La Moderna SA de CV, Monterrey, Mexico; *Int'l*, pg. 454
Garcia, Antonio M., Chm. Bd.--Reynolds Philippine Corporation, Manila, Philippines; *U.S. Public*, pg. 1387
Garcia, Ernest C., Chm. Bd. & Chief Exec. Officer--Ugly Duckling Corp., Phoenix, AZ; *U.S. Public*, pg. 1662
Gardiner, Michael R., Chm.--Scott's Restaurants Inc., Markham, Canada; *Int'l*, pg. 1213
Gardner, Bernell Dale, Chm. Bd.--Penninsular Meat Company, Inc., Tampa, FL; *U.S. Private*, pg. 850
Gardner, Betty A., Co-Chm. Bd. & Sec.--Soft Sheen Products, Inc., Chicago, IL; *U.S. Private*, pg. 1012
Gardner, Edward G., Chm. Bd. & Chief Exec. Officer--Soft Sheen Products, Inc., Chicago, IL; *U.S. Private*, pg. 1012
Gardner, Herbert M., Chm. Bd. & Pres.--Supreme Industries, Inc., Goshen, IN; *U.S. Public*, pg. 1541
Gardner, J.L., Chm. Bd.--Invesco Inc., Boston, MA; *Int'l*, pg. 685
Gardner, Rick, Chm. Bd. & Chief Exec. Officer--First Commercial Mortgage Co., Little Rock, AR; *U.S. Public*, pg. 630
Garfield, Eugene, Ph.D., Chm. Bd. & Pres.--Institute For Scientific Information, Philadelphia, PA; *U.S. Public*, pg. 1600
Garfinkel, Lee, Co-Chm. & Chief Creative Officer--Lowe & Partners/SMS, New York, NY; *U.S. Private*, pg. 678
Garman, M.L., Chm. Bd.--ECP Incorporated, Westchester, IL; *U.S. Private*, pg. 313
Garman, Richard E., Chm. Bd.--Merchants Group, Inc., Buffalo, NY; *U.S. Public*, pg. 1090
Garney, Charles A., Chm. Bd.--Garney Holding Company, Inc., Kansas City, MO; *U.S. Private*, pg. 440
Garnier, Anton C., Chm. Bd., Pres. & Chief Exec. Officer--Southwest Water Company, West Covina, CA; *U.S. Public*, pg. 1494
Garrett, D.W.J., Chm. Bd.--Robert Fleming Securities Limited, London, United Kingdom; *Int'l*, pg. 493
Garrett, Nathan T., Chm. Bd.--North Carolina Mutual Life Insurance Co., Durham, NC; *U.S. Private*, pg. 804
Garrett, Scott, Chm. Bd., Pres. & Chief Exec. Officer--Dade Behring Inc., Deerfield, IL; *U.S. Private*, pg. 110
Garrett, Scott, Chm. Bd., Pres. & Chief Exec. Officer--Dade Behring Inc., Deerfield, IL; *Int'l*, pg. 626
Garrison, F.S., Chm. Bd., Pres. & Chief Exec. Officer--American Freightways Corporation, Harrison, AR; *U.S. Public*, pg. 75
Garrison, P. Gregory, Chm.-Entertainment, Media & Communications--Price Waterhouse L.L.P. - U.S., New York, NY; *U.S. Private*, pg. 883
Garrison, Richard C., Chm. Bd. & Chief Exec. Officer--Ingalls, Boston, MA; *U.S. Private*, pg. 562
Garrison, Walter R., Chm. Bd.--CDI Corp., Philadelphia, PA; *U.S. Public*, pg. 276
Garrison, Wayne, Chm. Bd.--J.B. Hunt Transport Services, Inc., Lowell, AR; *U.S. Public*, pg. 849
Garrity, K.R., Chm. Bd.--Fansteel, Inc., North Chicago, IL; *U.S. Public*, pg. 612
Garrott, Thomas M., Chm. Bd., Pres. & Chief Exec. Officer--National Commerce Bancorporation, Memphis, TN; *U.S. Public*, pg. 1154
Garrott, Thomas M., Chm. Bd.--Monroe Properties, Inc., Memphis, TN; *U.S. Public*, pg. 1155
Garvey, John K., Chm. Bd. & Pres.--Petroleum Inc., Wichita, KS; *U.S. Private*, pg. 858
Garvey, Michael D., Co.-Chm. & Co.-Chief Exec. Officer--Totem Resources Corporation, Seattle, WA; *U.S. Private*, *pg. 1092*
Garvey, Robert A., Chm. Bd. & Chief Exec. Officer--Birmingham Steel Corporation, Birmingham, AL; *U.S. Public*, pg. 232
Garvey, Thomas E., Chm. Bd.--DiMark, Inc., Langhorne, PA; *U.S. Public*, pg. 793
Garvey, Willard W., Chm. Bd., Pres. & Chief Exec. Officer--Garvey Industries, Inc., Wichita, KS; *U.S. Private*, pg. 440
Garvin, Andrew P., Chm. Bd., Pres., Chief Exec. Officer & Treas.--Find/SVP, Inc., New York, NY; *U.S. Public*, pg. 623
Garvin, David, Chm. Bd.--Camping World, Inc., Bowling Green, KY; *U.S. Private*, pg. 204
Garvin, Sam S., Chm. Bd. & Chief Exec. Officer--Continental Promotion Group, Tempe, AZ; *U.S. Private*, pg. 269
Garvin, Tom, Chm. Bd.--Edwards Baking Co., Norcross, GA; *U.S. Private*, pg. 365
Gary, Samuel, Chm. Bd.--Gary-Williams Energy Corporation, Denver, CO; *U.S. Private*, pg. 440
Garza Laguera, Eugenio, Chm. Bd.--Bancomer, S.A., Mexico, Mexico; *Int'l*, pg. 145
Gaslow, Lawrence L., Chm. Bd. & Pres.--Empire Office Equipment, Inc., New York, NY; *U.S. Private*, pg. 374
Gasser, Michael J., Chm. Bd. & Chief Exec. Officer--Greif Brothers Corporation, Delaware, OH; *U.S. Public*, pg. 763
Gastman, T.R., Chm. Bd.--Florida Division, Saint Petersburg, FL; *U.S. Public*, pg. 509
Gaston, Gerald N., Chm. Bd. & Chief Oper. Officer--American Bankers Insurance Co. of Florida, Miami, FL; *U.S. Public*, pg. 67
Gaston, Gerald N., Chm. Bd. & Chief Oper. Officer--American Bankers Life Assurance Co. of Florida, Miami, FL; *U.S. Public*, pg. 67
Gaston, Gerald N., Chm. Bd.--American Reliable Insurance Company, Scottsdale, AZ; *U.S. Public*, pg. 67
Gaston, Paul, Chm. Bd. & Chief Exec. Officer--Boston Celtics Limited Partnership, Boston, MA; *U.S. Public*, pg. 246
Gater, Chris, Chm.--Brann Ltd., Cirencester, United Kingdom; *Int'l*, pg. 212
Gates, Charles C., Chm. Bd.--Cody Company, Denver, CO; *U.S. Private*, pg. 249
Gates, E. Jack, Chm. Bd.--Reynolds Metals Company-Troutdale, Troutdale, OR; *U.S. Public*, pg. 1386
Gates, T.J., Chm. Bd. & Pres.--Spfco Erectors, Inc., Cincinnati, OH; *U.S. Private*, pg. 1017
Gates, William H., Chm. Bd. & Chief Exec. Officer--Microsoft Corporation, Redmond, WA; *U.S. Public*, pg. 1107
Gaucher, Michel, Chm. Bd. & Pres.--Socanav Inc., Montreal, Canada; *Int'l*, pg. 1272
Gaugler, Richard L., Chm. Bd.--Macklanburg-Duncan Co., Oklahoma City, OK; *U.S. Private*, pg. 692
Gauldin, John E., III, Chm. Bd.--First Tennessee Bank - Dyersburg, Dyersburg, TN; *U.S. Public*, pg. 639
Gaut, Norman E., Dr., Chm. Bd. & Chief Exec. Officer--PictureTel, Andover, MA; *U.S. Public*, pg. 1294
Gauthier, Henry E., Chm. Bd., Pres. & Chief Oper. Officer--Coherent, Inc., Santa Clara, CA; *U.S. Public*, pg. 395
Gavigan, Michael, Chm. Bd. & Chief Exec. Officer--Pico Products, Inc., Lake View Terrace, CA; *U.S. Public*, pg. 1294
Gavois, Francis, Chm. Bd. & Pres.--Banque Francaise du Commerce Exterieur, Paris, France; *Int'l*, pg. 160
Gavron, Robert, Chm. Bd.--Guardian Media Group plc, Manchester, United Kingdom; *Int'l*, pg. 577
Gay, A.J., Chm.--Cementation Mining Limited, Doncaster, United Kingdom; *Int'l*, pg. 772
Gay, A.J., Chm.--Cemindia Company Limited, Mumbai, India; *Int'l*, pg. 774
Gay, A.J., Chm.--Cemindia Company Limited, Calcutta, India; *Int'l*, pg. 774
Gay, Andrew J., Chm. Bd. & Chief Exec. Officer--Drake & Scull Engineering Ltd., Kew Bridge, United Kingdom; *U.S. Public*, pg. 572
Gaylord, Edson I., Chm. Bd.--Ingersoll International Inc., Rockford, IL; *U.S. Private*, pg. 562
Gaylord, Edson I., Chm. Bd.--The Ingersoll Milling Machine Co., Rockford, IL; *U.S. Private*, pg. 562
Gaylord, Edward L., Chm. Bd.--Broadmoor Hotel, Inc., Colorado Springs, CO; *U.S. Private*, pg. 170
Gaylord, Edward L., Chm. Bd.--Gaylord Entertainment Co., Nashville, TN; *U.S. Public*, pg. 704
Gaylord, Edward L., Chm. Bd. & Chief Exec. Officer--Gaylord Broadcasting Co., Nashville, TN; *U.S. Public*, pg. 704
Gaylord, Edward O., Chm. Bd.--Enron Oil Trading & Transportation Co., Houston, TX; *U.S. Public*, pg. 584
Geaney, Donal J., Chm. Bd. & Chief Exec. Officer--Elan Corporation Plc, Dublin, Ireland; *Int'l*, pg. 435
Gearing, Ian M., Chm. Bd.--Bols Strothmann Brennereien GmbH & Co. KG, Nordrhein-Westfalen, Germany; *Int'l*, pg. 751
Gebler, David B., Chm. Bd., Pres. & Chief Exec. Officer--Airlease Ltd., San Francisco, CA; *U.S. Public*, pg. 33
Gee, Alan, Chm. Bd. & Chief Creative Dir.--Gee, Jeffery & Partners Advertising Inc., Toronto, Canada; *Int'l*, pg. 542
Geer, P. Nicholas, Chm. Bd. & Pres.--Westar Group Ltd., Vancouver, Canada; *Int'l*, pg. 1491
Geginat, Hartwig, Chm. Bd. & Chief Exec. Officer-Zanders--International Paper Company, Purchase, NY; *U.S. Public*, *pg. 901*
Gehl, William D., Chm. Bd., Pres. & Chief Exec. Officer--Gehl Company, West Bend, WI; *U.S. Public*, pg. 704
Geier, Philip H., Jr., Chm. Bd. & Chief Exec. Officer--The Interpublic Group of Companies, Inc., New York, NY; *U.S. Public*, pg. 908
Geiger, Thomas B., Chm. Bd.--Capital Tire, Inc., Toledo, OH; *U.S. Private*, pg. 206
Geir-Sigurgeirsson, Johannes, Chm. Bd.--Landsvirkjun - The National Power Co., Reykjavik, Iceland; *Int'l*, pg. 801
Gelb, Harold S., Chm. Bd.--United Industrial Corporation, New York, NY; *U.S. Public*, pg. 1679
Geller, Larry, Chm. Bd.--URM Stores, Inc., Spokane, WA; *U.S. Private*, pg. 1114
Geller, Sheldon, Chm. Bd.--Key Food Stores Co-operative, Inc., Brooklyn, NY; *U.S. Private*, pg. 617
Geller, Steve, Chm. Bd. & Chief Exec. Officer--Empire of Carolina, Inc., Delray Beach, FL; *U.S. Public*, pg. 579
Gellerman, Jay M., Chm. Bd, Pres. & Chief Exec. Officer--Jaydon Incorporated, Rock Island, IL; *U.S. Private*, pg. 584
Gellert, George G., Chm. Bd. & Pres.--Atalanta Corporation, Elizabeth, NJ; *U.S. Private*, pg. 93
Generali, Claudio, Chm. Bd.--Banca del Gottardo, Lugano, Switzerland; *Int'l*, pg. 1310
Genevray, Henri, Chm. Bd.--N. Schlumberger & Cie, Guebwiller, France; *Int'l*, pg. 1206
Genger, Arie, Chm. Bd.--Trans Resources, Inc., New York, NY; *U.S. Private*, pg. 1096
Genovese, Leonard, Chm. Bd., Pres. & Chief Exec. Officer--Genovese Drug Stores, Inc., Melville, NY; *U.S. Public*, pg. 730
Genovese, Peter J., Co-Chm. Bd. & Co-Chief Exec. Officer--UMB Financial Corporation, Kansas City, MO; *U.S. Public*, pg. 1653
Genovese, Rocco C., Chm. Bd., Pres. & Chief Exec. Officer--Burke Industries, Inc., San Jose, CA; *U.S. Private*, pg. 183
Genshaft, Neil, Chm. Bd. & Chief Exec. Officer--Fresh Mark, Inc., Canton, OH; *U.S. Private*, pg. 427
Gentile, George M., Chm. Bd. & Chief Exec. Officer--Gerber Scientific, Inc., South Windsor, CT; *U.S. Public*, pg. 740
Gentry, Grant, Chm.--Bromar Inc., Newport Beach, CA; *U.S. Private*, pg. 171
Gentry, Jack T., Chm. Bd.--Positronic Industries, Inc., Springfield, MO; *U.S. Private*, pg. 876
Gentry, Marvin D., Chm. Bd. & Pres.--New Fortis Corp., King, NC; *U.S. Public*, pg. 843
Gentzler, Donald W., Chm. Bd.--Spring Grove National Bank, Spring Grove, PA; *U.S. Public*, pg. 1542
George, Boyd, Chm. Bd. & Chief Exec. Officer--Alex Lee, Inc., Hickory, NC; *U.S. Private*, pg. 657
George, Chan Thye Guan, Deputy Grp. Chm.--Batey Ads Singapore, Singapore, Singapore; *Int'l*, pg. 170
George, Joseph A., Chm. Bd.--George & Thomas Cone Co., Hermitage, PA; *U.S. Private*, pg. 448
George, Mary H., Chm. Bd.--Hulman & Company, Terre Haute, IN; *U.S. Private*, pg. 547
George, P.M., Chm. & Chief Exec. Officer--Ladbroke Racing Corporation, Pittsburgh, PA; *Int'l*, pg. 788
George, Richard W., Sir., Chm. & Mng. Dir.--Weetabix Limited, Kettering, United Kingdom; *Int'l*, pg. 1488
George, Sharkey T., Chm. Bd.--Melody Foods, Inc., Farmington Hills, MI; *U.S. Private*, pg. 730
George, Victor E., Jr., Chm. Bd.--Citizens Commercial & Savings Bank, Flint, MI; *U.S. Public*, pg. 379
George, William W., Chm. Bd. & Chief Exec. Officer--Medtronic, Inc., Minneapolis, MN; *U.S. Public*, pg. 1082
Georges-Picot, Bruno, Chm. Bd.--Banque Indosuez Luxembourg, Luxembourg, Luxembourg; *Int'l*, pg. 314
Georges, John A., Chm. Bd. & Chief Exec. Officer--IP Timberlands, Ltd., Purchase, NY; *U.S. Public*, pg. 904
Georgescu, Peter A., Chm. Bd. & Chief Exec. Officer--Young & Rubicam Inc., New York, NY; *U.S. Private*, pg. 1196
Georgine, R.A., Chm. & Chief Exec. Officer--Trust Fund Advisors, Inc., Washington, DC; *U.S. Private*, pg. 1116
Georgine, R.A., Chm. & Chief Exec. Officer--Unioncare, Inc., Washington, DC; *U.S. Private*, pg. 1116
Georgine, R.A., Chm. & Chief Exec. Officer--ULICO Casualty Company, Washington, DC; *U.S. Private*, pg. 1116
Georgine, Robert A., Chm. Bd. & Chief Exec. Officer--ULLICO Inc., Washington, DC; *U.S. Private*, pg. 1115
Georgine, Robert A., Chm. Bd. & Chief Exec. Officer--The Union Labor Life Insurance Co., Washington, DC; *U.S. Private*, pg. 1116
Georgine, Robert A., Chm. Bd. & Chief Exec. Officer--AMI Capital Inc., Bethesda, MD; *U.S. Private*, pg. 1116
Georgoulis, Stratton, Chm. Bd., Pres. & Chief Exec. Officer--TIC United Corporation, Dallas, TX; *U.S. Private*, pg. 1063
Gephart, Thomas, Chm. Bd.--Keystone Brewers, Inc., Pittsburgh, PA; *U.S. Private*, pg. 618
Gerahty, John, Joint Chm.--Chiltem Group SAM, Monaco, Monaco; *Int'l*, pg. 65
Gerald, Patrick N., Chm. Bd.--First National Bank of Sweetwater, Sweetwater, TX; *U.S. Public*, pg. 633
Gerard, Luis, Chm.--Central de Industrias, S.A., Mexico, Mexico; *U.S. Public*, pg. 982
Gerarder, S., Chm. Bd. & Chief Exec. Officer--Crown Lance Italia Srl, Rome, Italy; *U.S. Private*, pg. 155
Gerber, Fritz, Chm. Bd.--Roche Holding Ltd., Basel, Switzerland; *Int'l*, pg. 1119
Gerchenson, Emile H., Chm. Bd. & Chief Exec. Officer--Alva/Amco Pharmacal Companies, Inc., Chicago, IL; *U.S. Private*, pg. 47
Gerdin, Russell A., Chm. Bd., Pres. Chief Exec. Officer, Chief Oper. Officer & Sec.--Heartland Express, Inc., Coralville, IA; *U.S. Public*, pg. 803
Gerdy, Harvey, Chm. Bd., Pres. & Chief Exec. Officer--International Seaway Trading Corporation, Boca Raton, FL; *U.S. Private*, pg. 572
Gerken, Edward, Chm. Bd. & Chief Exec. Officer--Norwalk Furniture Corporation, Norwalk, OH; *U.S. Private*, pg. 807
Gerlach, John B., Jr., Chm. Bd. & Chief Exec. Officer-Lancaster Colony Corp.--Lancaster Colony Automotive Group, Dublin, OH; *U.S. Public*, pg. 977
Germann, Karl, Chm.--Stadtmuhle CMZ Zurich, Zurich, Switzerland; *Int'l*, pg. 330
Gero, James F., Chm. Bd. & Chief Exec. Officer--Sierra Technologies Inc., Buffalo, NY; *U.S. Private*, pg. 999
Geronzi, Cesare, Chm. Bd.--Banca di Roma, Rome, Italy; *Int'l*, pg. 135
Gerrard, Francois, Chm. & Chief Exec. Officer--SIAS - MPA, Paris, France; *Int'l*, pg. 566
Gerretsen, Wob, Chm. Bd. & Mng. Dir.--Costain Engineering & Construction Limited, London, United Kingdom; *Int'l*, pg. 336
Gerrity, Joe W. Jr., Chm. Bd.--Saratoga Equine Sports Center, Saratoga Springs, NY; *U.S. Private*, pg. 965
Gerson, Irwin C., Chm. & Chief Exec. Officer--Lowe McAdams Healthcare, New York, NY; *U.S. Private*, pg. 678
Gerson, Matthew, Chm. Bd. & Pres.--Gerson & Gerson, Inc., New York, NY; *U.S. Private*, pg. 449

Gerson, Samuel J., Chm. Bd. & Chief Exec. Officer--Filene's Basement, Inc., Wellesley, MA; *U.S. Public*, pg. 622

Gerstell, A. Frederick, Chm. Bd. & Chief Exec. Officer--CalMat Co., Los Angeles, CA; *U.S. Public*, pg. 295

Gerstner, Josef, Chm.-Mgmnt. Bd. & Chief Exec. Officer--KSB Aktiengesellschaft, Frankenthal, Germany; *Int'l*, pg. 721

Gertler, Irving, Chm. Bd.--All American Home Center, Downey, CA; *U.S. Private*, pg. 34

Gervasi, Enrico, Chm., Chief Exec. Officer & Fin. Dir.--Young & Rubicam Italia, S.p.A., Milan, Italy; *U.S. Private, pg. 1199*

Gescheider, Bruce A., Chm. Bd. & Chief Exec. Officer--Day-Timers, Inc., East Texas, PA; *U.S. Public*, pg. 674

Gessner, Tom R., Chm. Bd. & Pres.--Al Johnson Construction Co., Bloomington, MN; *U.S. Private*, pg. 590

Gettlefinger, Andrew J., Chm. Bd., Pres. & Chief Exec. Officer--Pride Oil Co., Inc., Knoxville, TN; *U.S. Private*, pg. 613

Gettler, Benjamin, Chm. Bd., Pres., Chief Exec. Officer & Chief Fin. Officer--Vulcan International Corporation, Wilmington, DE; *U.S. Public*, pg. 1725

Getz, T.G., Chm. Bd.--Williams, White & Co., Moline, IL; *U.S. Private*, pg. 1179

Ghaznavi, John, Chm. Bd. & Chief Exec. Officer--Consumers Packaging Inc., Etobicoke, Canada; *Int'l*, pg. 326

Ghaznavi, John, Chm. Bd.--Glenshaw Glass Co. Inc., Allison Park, PA; *U.S. Private*, pg. 457

Ghelfi, Alfred R., Chm. Bd.--Cavco Industries, Inc., Phoenix, AZ; *U.S. Public*, pg. 323

Ghosh, Shikhar, Chm. Bd.--Open Market, Inc., Burlington, MA; *U.S. Public*, pg. 1226

Giacco, Alexander, Chm. Bd. & Pres.--Rheometric Scientific, Piscataway, NJ; *U.S. Public*, pg. 1387

Giacolini, Earl, Chm. Bd.--Sun Diamond Growers of California, Pleasanton, CA; *U.S. Private*, pg. 1051

Giancola, James J., Chm.--Citizens Information Systems, Inc., Evansville, IN; *U.S. Public*, pg. 281

Gianettino, Ronald J., Chm. Bd. & Chief Exec. Officer--Gianettino & Meredith Advertising, Short Hills, NJ; *U.S. Private*, pg. 450

Giasson, Jacques, Chm. Bd.--Tembec Inc., Montreal, Canada; *Int'l*, pg. 1374

Giasson, Jacques J., Chm. Bd.--Uniboard Canada Inc., Laval, Canada; *Int'l*, pg. 1431

Gibara, Samir G., Chm. Bd., Pres. & Chief Exec. Officer--The Goodyear Tire & Rubber Company, Akron, OH; *U.S.* Public, pg. 752

Gibb, Robert, Jr., Chm. Bd. & Pres.--Robert Gibb & Sons, Inc., Fargo, ND; *U.S. Private*, pg. 451

Gibbons, Charles H., Chm. Bd., Pres. & Chief Exec. Officer--Intellisource, Fairfield, CT; *U.S. Public*, pg. 1425

Gibbons, Dr. James, Chm. Bd.--AMATI Communications Corp., San Jose, CA; *U.S. Public*, pg. 1585

Gibbons, John J., Chm. Bd., Pres. & Chief Exec. Officer--Tseng Labs, Norristown, PA; *U.S. Public*, pg. 1643

Gibbs, B.R., Chm. Bd.--Red Wings Inc., Fredonia, NY; *Int'l*, pg. 1398

Gibbs, Charles F., Chm.--Gibbs Wire & Steel Company, Inc., Southington, CT; *U.S. Private*, pg. 451

Gibert, Peter, Chm. Bd. & Chief Exec. Officer--Circle International Group, Inc., San Francisco, CA; *U.S. Public, pg. 370*

Gibson, David W., Chm. Bd.--Wolcott & Lincoln, Inc., Kansas City, MO; *U.S. Private*, pg. 1185

Gibson, Fred D., Jr., Chm. Bd--American Pacific Corporation, Las Vegas, NV; *U.S. Public*, pg. 88

Gibson, Jim, Chm. Bd.--Houchens Industries Inc., Bowling Green, KY; *U.S. Private*, pg. 541

Gibson, Thomas R., Chm. Bd. & Chief Exec. Officer--Asbury Automotive Group, Conshohocken, PA; *U.S. Private*, pg. 87

Gibson, W. Bayne, Chm. Bd.--Staodyn Inc., Longmont, CO; *U.S. Public*, pg. 1509

Gibson, William M., Chm. Bd., Pres. & Chief Exec. Officer--Manugistics Group, Inc., Rockville, MD; *U.S. Public*, pg. 1042

Gidwitz, James G., Chm. Bd. & Chief Exec. Officer--Continental Materials Corporation, Chicago, IL; *U.S. Public*, pg. 441

Gierer, Vincent A., Jr., Chm. Bd., Pres. & Chief Exec. Officer--UST Inc., Greenwich, CT; *U.S. Public*, pg. 1660

Gifford, John F., Chm. Bd., Pres. & Chief Exec. Officer--Maxim Integrated Products, Inc., Sunnyvale, CA; *U.S. Public*, pg. 1061

Gignac, Kenneth, Chm. Bd. & Pres.--Elgin Dairy Foods, Inc., Chicago, IL; *U.S. Private*, pg. 370

Gilbert, Bruce C., Chm. Bd.--Great Lakes Construction Co., Independence, OH; *U.S Private*, pg. 474

Gilbert, E.A., Chm. Bd.--East Kentucky Power Co-op, Winchester, KY; *U.S. Private*, pg. 356

Gilbert, Scott, Co-Chm. Bd. & Chief Exec. Officer--Team One Advertising, El Segundo, CA; *U.S. Public*, pg. 1422

Gilbert, Walter F., Chm. Bd., Pres., Chief Exec. Officer & Treas.--Semco Industries Inc., Stoughton, MA; *U.S. Private*, pg. 983

Gilbert, William B., Chm. Bd.--Lifetime Doors Inc., Farmington, MI; *U.S. Private*, pg. 666

Gildehaus, Thomas A., Chm. Bd. & Chief Exec. Officer--Northwestern Steel & Wire Co., Sterling, IL; *U.S. Public*, pg. 1201

Gilgore, Sheldon G., M.D., Chm. Bd.--AMBI Inc., Tarrytown, NY; *U.S. Public*, pg. 7

Gilkey, Harold B., Chm. Bd. & Chief Exec. Officer--Sterling Financial Corporation, Spokane, WA; *U.S. Public*, pg. 1516

Gill, Ben, Chm. Bd.--Ketchum, Inc., Pittsburgh, PA; *U.S. Private*, pg. 617

Gill, Emanuel, Chm. Bd. & Chief Exec. Officer--Diasonics Ultra Sound, Inc., Santa Clara, CA; *Int'l*, pg. 644

Gill, Emmanuel, Chm. Bd.--Elscint Ltd., Haifa, Israel; *Int'l*, pg. 450

Gill, Merwyn C., Chm. Bd.--M.C. Gill Corporation, El Monte, CA; *U.S. Private*, pg. 453

Gill, Tim, Chm. Bd. & Chief Tech. Officer--Quark Inc., Denver, CO; *U.S. Private*, pg. 900

Gillam, Patrick, Non Executive Chm.--Royal & Sun Alliance Insurance Group plc, London, United Kingdom; *Int'l*, pg. 1130

Gillam, Patrick, Chm. Bd.--Standard Chartered Bank PLC, London, United Kingdom; *Int'l*, pg. 1294

Gillan, Patrick, Chm. Bd.--Asda Group Plc, Leeds, United Kingdom; *Int'l*, pg. 17

Gillen, Richard, Chm. Bd., Pres. & Chief Exec. Officer--Harbor Financial Mortgage Corp., Houston, TX; *U.S. Public*, pg. 644

Gilleran, James E., Chm. Bd. & Chief Exec. Officer--The San Francisco Co., San Francisco, CA; *U.S. Public*, pg. 1430

Gillespie, A.W., Hon., Chm. Bd.--National Westminster Bank of Canada, Toronto, Canada; *Int'l*, pg. 911

Gillespie, R.T.E., Chm. Bd. & Chief Exec. Officer--GE Hydro, Lachine, Canada; *U.S. Public*, pg. 713

Gillespie, Robert W., Chm., Pres. & Chief Exec. Officer--Keycorp, Cleveland, OH; *U.S. Public*, pg. 954

Gillett, George, Chm. Bd.--Packerland Packing Co., Green Bay, WI; *U.S. Private*, pg. 833

Gillette, E. Peter, Chm. Bd. & Pres.--Piper Trust Company, Minneapolis, MN; *U.S. Public*, pg. 1303

Gillette, Lindsay, Chm. Bd.--Computer Power Incorporated, High Bridge, NJ; *U.S. Public*, pg. 421

Gilliam, James H., Jr., Esq., Chm. Bd.--Beneficial National Bank, Wilmington, DE; *U.S. Public*, pg. 211

Gillispie, C. Stephenson, Jr., Chm. Bd., Pres. & Chief Exec. Officer--Cadmus Communications Corporation, Richmond, VA; *U.S. Public*, pg. 290

Gilluly, C.W., Chm. Bd., Pres. & Chief Exec. Officer--Hadron, Inc., Alexandria, VA; *U.S. Public*, pg. 773

Gilman, Steven F., Chm. Bd., Pres, & Chief Exec. Officer--Gilrichco, Inc., Oxnard, CA; *U.S. Private*, pg. 454

Gilmartin, Raymond V., Chm. Bd., Pres. & Chief Exec. Officer--Merck & Co., Inc., Whitehouse Station, NJ; *U.S. Public*, pg. 1090

Gilmour, Everett A., Chm. Bd.--NBT Bancorp Inc., Norwich, NY; *U.S. Public*, pg. 1144

Gilson, Peter W., Chm.-Exec. Committee--Swiss Army Brands, Inc., Shelton, CT; *U.S. Public*; pg. 1544

Gimbel, Roger, Chm. Bd.--RGA and East End Accessories, New York, NY; *U.S. Private*, pg. 903

Gin, Sue Ling, Pres., Chief Exec. Officer & Sole Dir.--Flying Food Fare, Inc., Chicago, IL; *U.S. Private*, pg. 415

Ginebra, Freddy, Chm. Bd. & Pres.--Publicitaria Cumbre, Santo Domingo, Dominican Republic; *U.S. Public*, pg. 1422

Ginn, L.H., III, Chm. Bd.--First Virginia Bank-Colonial, Richmond, VA; *U.S. Public*, pg. 641

Ginn, Russell, Chm. Bd., Pres. & Chief Exec. Officer--The Flexitallic Group, Inc., Houston, TX; *U.S. Private*, pg. 413

Ginns, Daniel, Chm. Bd., Chief Exec. Officer & Corp. Sec.--Datametrics Corporation, Calabasas, CA; *U.S. Public*, pg. 487

Ginsberg, Frank, Co-Chm., Chief Exec. Officer & Creative Dir.--Avrett, Free & Ginsberg, Inc., New York, NY; *U.S. Private*, pg. 103

Ginsberg, Morton A., Chm. Bd.--Ginsberg's Institutional Foods, Inc., Hudson, NY; *U.S. Private*, pg. 455

Ginsburg, Allan, Chm. Bd.--Jaclyn, Inc., West New York, NJ; *U.S. Public*, pg. 920

Ginsburg, Scott K., Chm. Bd. & Chief Exec. Officer--Chancellor Media Corporation, Irving, TX; *U.S. Public*, pg. 335

Giordano, Gilbert R., Chm. Bd.--First Virginia Bank-Maryland, Upper Marlboro, MD; *U.S. Public*, pg. 642

Giordano, Richard V., Chm. Bd. & Chief Exec. Officer--BG Plc, Reading, United Kingdom; *Int'l*, pg. 118

Giordano, Salvatore, Chm. Bd.--Fedders Corp., Liberty Corner, NJ; *U.S. Public*, pg. 614

Girgenti, Steven, Chm. & Chief Exec. Officer--Girgenti, Hughes, Butler & McDowell, New York, NY; *U.S. Private, pg. 455*

Girsky, Joel H., Chm. Bd., Pres. & Treas.--Jaco Electronics, Inc., Hauppauge, NY; *U.S. Public*, pg. 920

Gisi, John J., Chm. Bd. & Chief Exec. Officer--National Bank of Arizona, Tucson, AZ; *U.S. Public*, pg. 1793

Gist, Betty, Chm. Bd., Pres., & Chief Exec. Officer--Dairy Fresh Corp., Greensboro, AL; *U.S. Private*, pg. 307

Gitner, Gerald L., Chm. Bd.--Trans World Airlines, Inc., Saint Louis, MO; *U.S. Public*, pg. 1629

Gittelman, Irving, Chm. Bd.--Triumph Pet Industries, Inc., Warwick, NY; *U.S. Private*, pg. 1104

Giuliano, Louis J., Chm. Bd.--ITT Federal Services Corporation, Colorado Springs, CO; *U.S. Public*, pg. 859

Giumarra, Sal, Chm. Bd. & Pres.--Giumarra Vineyards, Edison, CA; *U.S. Private*, pg. 455

Given, J.B., Chm. Bd.--Fibras Ceramicas, Inc., Ponce, PR; *Int'l*, pg. 893

Givli, Benjamin, Chm. Bd. & Chief Exec. Officer--Laser Industries Ltd., Tel Aviv, Israel; *Int'l*, pg. 429

Gladney, Jim, Chm. Bd.--All Seasons Services, Inc., Braintree, MA; *U.S. Private*, pg. 35

Gladstone, David, Chm. Bd.--Allied Capital Commercial Corporation, Washington, DC; *U.S. Public*, pg. 47

Gladstone, David, Chm. Bd.--Allied Capital Corporation II, Washington, DC; *U.S. Public*, pg. 47

Gladstone, David, Chm. Bd.--Allied Capital Lending Corporation, Washington, DC; *U.S. Public*, pg. 48

Glancy, Alfred R., III, Chm. Bd., Pres. & Chief Exec. Officer--MCN Energy Group, Inc., Detroit, MI; *U.S. Public*, pg. 1024

Glancy, Alfred R., III, Chm. Bd.--MichCon, Detroit, MI; *U.S. Public*, pg. 1025

Glancy, Alfred R., III, Chm. Bd.--MCN Investment, Detroit, MI; *U.S. Public*, pg. 1025

Glas, Don ald A., Co-Chm. & Chief Exec. Officer--First Federal FSB, Hutchinson, MN; *U.S. Public*, pg. 608

Glas, Donald A., Co-Chm. Bd. & Chief Exec. Officer--FSF Financial Corp., Hutchinson, MN; *U.S. Public*, pg. 608

Glaser, Gary A., Chm. Bd.--National City Bank, Cleveland, OH; *U.S. Public*, pg. 1154

Glasgow, Andrew, Chm.--International Water Limited, Manchester, United Kingdom; *Int'l*, pg. 1444

Glasgow, Lloyd, Chm.--Lalique North America, New York, NY; *Int'l*, pg. 797

Glass, Ken, Pres.--Norlen Life Insurance Company, Memphis, TN; *U.S. Public*, pg. 639

Glass, Milton L., Chm. Bd.--Blue Cross and Blue Shield of Massachusetts, Boston, MA; *U.S. Private*, pg. 151

Glass, Sherwin, Chm. Bd., Pres. & Chief Exec. Officer--Warehouse Home Furnishings Distributor, Dublin, GA; *U.S. Private*, pg. 1150

Glass, Walter, Chm. Bd.--American Louver Co., Skokie, IL; *U.S. Private*, pg. 58

Glassman, Daniel, Chm. Bd., Pres. & Chief Exec. Officer--Bradley Pharmaceuticals, Fairfield, NJ; *U.S. Public*, pg. 249

Glassman, Daniel, Chm. Bd., Pres. & Chief Exec. Officer--Doak Dermatologics, Westbury, NY; *U.S. Public*, pg. 250

Glatt, Mitchell S., Chm. Bd.--Magla Products, Morristown, NJ; *U.S. Private*, pg. 695

Glaubinger, Lawrence D., Chm. Bd.--Stern & Stern Industries Inc., New York, NY; *U.S. Private*, pg. 1041

Glazer, Malcolm I., Chm. Bd.--Houlihan's Restaurant Group, Kansas City, MO; *U.S. Public*, pg. 841

Glazer, Malcolm I., Chm. Bd.--Zapata Corporation, Houston, TX; *U.S. Public*, pg. 1789

Glazer, Robert S., Chm. Bd.--Glazer's Wholesale Drug Co. Inc., Dallas, TX; *U.S. Private*, pg. 455

Gleason, James S., Chm. Bd. & Pres.--Gleason Corporation, Rochester, NY; *U.S. Public*, pg. 746

Gleason, Matthew S., Chm. Bd. & Pres.--Gleason/Calise/Associates, Inc., Dallas, TX; *U.S. Private*, pg. 455

Gleason, Thomas, Chm. Bd. & Chief Exec. Officer--PremiumWear, Inc., Minneapolis, MN; *U.S. Public*, pg. 1323

Gleditsch, Odd, Jr., Chm. Bd.--Jotun A/S, Sandefjord, Norway; *Int'l*, pg. 714

Glenn, John J., Chm. Bd. & Chief Exec. Officer--Dunn Reber Glenn Marz, Reno, NV; *U.S. Private*, pg. 347

Glenn, Robert C., DDS, Chm. Bd.--California State Bank-La Habra, La Habra, CA; *U.S. Public*, pg. 294

Glew, David, Chm. Bd.-Epic Records Group--Sony Music Entertainment, Inc., New York, NY; *Int'l*, pg. 1281

Glick, Alvin, Chm. Bd.--Alro Group, Jackson, MI; *U.S. Private*, pg. 45

Glicken, Howard M., Chm. Bd.--Jillian's Entertainment Corporation, Boston, MA; *U.S. Private*, pg. 587

Glickman, Stuart, Chm. Bd., Pres., Chief Exec. Officer & Chief Fin. Officer--Safe Alarm, Inc., Davie, FL; *U.S. Private*, pg. 960

Glidden, Robert, Chm. Bd.--Robert James Sales Inc., Buffalo, NY; *U.S. Private*, pg. 935

Glover, Edmund C., Chm. Bd. & Chief Exec. Officer--Batson-Cook Company, West Point, GA; *U.S. Private*, pg. 123

Gloyd, Lawrence E., Chm. Bd. & Chief Exec. Officer--CLARCOR, Inc., Rockford, IL; *U.S. Public*, pg. 381

Glueck, R., Chm. Bd.--Krupp Robins, Inc., Englewood, CO; *Int'l*, pg. 511

Glynn, Robert D. Jr., Chm. Bd., Pres. & Chief Exec. Officer--PG&E Corporation, San Francisco, CA; *U.S. Public*, pg. 1240

Glynn, Robert D., Jr., Chm. Bd.--Pacific Gas & Electric Company, San Francisco, CA; *U.S. Public*, pg. 1241

Glynn, William C., Pres.--IGI Resources, Inc., Boise, ID; *U.S.* Private, pg. 568

Goad, Fred, Chm. Bd. & Co-Chief Exec. Officer--Envoy Corporation, Nashville, TN; *U.S. Public*, pg. 587

Gobbi, Fausto, Chm. Bd.--I.S.A. Istituto Atesino di Sviluppo S.p.A., Trento, Italy; *Int'l*, pg. 138

Gober, Ira, Chm. Bd. & Chief Exec. Officer--Associated Food Stores, Inc., Jamaica, NY; *U.S. Private*, pg. 90

Gochman, Arthur, Chm. Bd. & Chief Exec. Officer--Academy Corporation, Katy, TX; *U.S. Private*, pg. 11

Goda, Tatsuo, Chm. Bd.--Tosoh Corporation, Tokyo, Japan; *Int'l*, pg. 1407

Godchaux, Frank A., III, Chm. Bd.--Riviana Foods Inc., Houston, TX; *U.S. Public*, pg. 1392

Goddard, Terry, Chm. Bd.--Dimplex UK, Southampton, United Kingdom; *Int'l*, pg. 554

Godden, Tim, Chm.-UK, Mng. Dir.-Europe--Wunderman Worldwide Limited, London, United Kingdom; *U.S. Private*, pg. 1199

Goddu, Roger, Chm. Bd., Pres. & Chief Exec. Officer--Montgomery Ward & Co., Inc., Chicago, IL; *U.S. Private*, pg. 758

Godfrey, Peter, Chm. Bd.--Micro Warehouse, Inc., Norwalk, CT; *U.S. Public*, pg. 1104

Godfrey, William G., Chm. Bd., Pres. & Chief Exec. Officer--Tekra Corporation, New Berlin, WI; *U.S. Private*, pg. 1073

Godfroid, P., Chm. Bd.--Spadel SA, Brussels, Belgium; *Int'l*, pg. 1287

Godomski, Richard, Chm. Bd., Pres. & Chief Exec. Officer--Process Systems Inc., Memphis, TN; *U.S. Private*, pg. 888

Godsoe, Peter C., Chm. Bd. & Chief Exec. Officer--The Bank of Nova Scotia, Toronto, Canada; *Int'l*, pg. 155

Goebert, Donald F.U., Chm. Bd. & Pres.--Relm Wireless Corp., West Chester, PA; *U.S. Public*, pg. 1376

Goedert, Philip H., Pres. & Dir.--RNL Facilities Corporation, Denver, CO; *U.S. Private*, pg. 905

Goehring, Craig, Chm. Bd., Pres. & Chief Exec. Officer--Brown and Caldwell, Pleasant Hill, CA; *U.S. Private*, pg. 173

Goer, Ernest J., Chm. Bd.-Wood Fixture Division--RHC/Spacemaster Corporation, Melrose Park, IL; *U.S. Private, pg. 904*

Goer, Ernest J., Chm. Bd. & Chief Exec. Officer--Goer Manufacturing Co., Charleston, SC; *U.S. Private*, pg. 904
Goergen, Robert B., Chm. Bd., Pres. & Chief Exec. Officer--Blyth Industries, Greenwich, CT; *U.S. Public*, pg. 239
Goergen, Robert B., Chm. Bd.--Xtra Corporation, Boston, MA; *U.S. Public*, pg. 1786
Goergen, Ronald M., Chm. Bd. & Pres.--American Appraisal Associates, Inc., Milwaukee, WI; *U.S. Private*, pg. 49
Goethe, Robert A., Chm. Bd., Pres. & Chief Exec. Officer--Regions Mortgage, Inc., Montgomery, AL; *U.S. Public*, pg. 1373
Goetz, Hannes, Dr., Chm. Bd.--The Swissair Group, Zurich, Switzerland; *Int'l*, pg. 1333
Goff, Charles F., Chm. Bd. & Chief Exec. Officer--Destec Energy, Inc., Houston, TX; *U.S. Public*, pg. 1146
Goff, Walter, Chm. Bd.--Grocers Baking Co., Grand Rapids, MI; *U.S. Private*, pg. 482
Goforth, Charles D., Chm. Bd.--Southwestern Electric Service Co., Dallas, TX; *U.S. Public*, pg. 1588
Goings, Rick, Chm. Bd. & Chief Exec. Officer--Tupperware Corporation, Orlando, FL; *U.S. Public*, pg. 1644
Gold, Larry, Chm. Bd. & Chief Scientific Officer--Nexstar Pharmaceuticals, Inc., Boulder, CO; *U.S. Public*, pg. 1180
Gold, Matthew L., Chm. Bd., Pres. & Chief Exec. Officer--Precision Standard, Inc., Denver, CO; *U.S. Public*, pg. 1321
Gold, Stanley P., Chm. Bd. & Chief Exec. Officer--L.A. Gear, Inc., Santa Monica, CA; *U.S. Public*, pg. 969
Goldammer, Peter, Chm.-Scholz & Friends Hamburg--Scholz & Friends GmbH, Hamburg, Germany; *Int'l*, pg. 1210
Goldband, Shefford S., Chm. Bd.--Totsy Manufacturing Company, Inc., Holyoke, MA; *U.S. Private*, pg. 1093
Goldbath, Raymond, Chm. Bd. & Chief Exec. Officer--Marathon Cheese Corp., Marathon, WI; *U.S. Private*, pg. 701
Goldberg, Arthur, Chm. Bd., Pres. & Chief Exec. Officer--Di Giorgio Corporation, Carteret, NJ; *U.S. Private*, pg. 330
Goldberg, Arthur M., Chm. Bd.--Bally Total Fitness Holdings Corporation, Chicago, IL; *U.S. Public*, pg. 171
Goldberg, Arthur M., Chm. Bd. & Chief Exec. Officer--Bally Total Fitness Corporation, Chicago, IL; *U.S. Public*, pg. 171
Goldberg, Danny, Pres. & Chief Exec. Officer & Chm. Bd.-Mercury Grp.--Polygram N.V., Baarn, Netherlands; *Int'l*, pg. 1051
Goldberg, Donald T., Chm. Bd.--GZA GeoEnvironmental Technologies, Inc., Newton, MA; *U.S. Public*, pg. 697
Goldberg, Fred, Chm. & Chief Exec. Officer--Goldberg Moser O'Neill, San Francisco, CA; *U.S. Private*, pg. 459
Goldberg, Michael C., Chm. Bd., Pres. & Chief Exec. Officer--FDP Corp., Miami, FL; *U.S. Public*, pg. 603
Goldberg, Paul, Chm. Bd.--All American Semiconductor, Inc., Miami, FL; *U.S. Public*, pg. 41
Goldberg, Richard H., Chm. Bd., Pres. & Chief Exec. Officer--Synon Corporation, Larkspur, CA; *U.S. Private*, pg. 1060
Goldberg, Stanley, Chm. Bd., Pres. & Chief Exec. Officer--Ringer Corporation, Bloomington, MN; *U.S. Public*, pg. 1390
Goldberg, Stanley, Chm. Bd., Pres. & Chief Exec. Officer--Dexol, Torrance, CA; *U.S. Public*, pg. 1390
Goldblatt, Lionel, Chm. Bd.--Goldblatt's Department Stores, Chicago, IL; *U.S. Public*, pg. 917
Goldby, Steven, Chm. Bd., Pres. & Chief Exec. Officer--MDL Information Systems, Inc., San Leandro, CA; *Int'l*, pg. 1100
Golden, Donald L., Dr., Chm. Bd.--D.O.C. Optics Corporation, Southfield, MI; *U.S. Private*, pg. 305
Goldenberg, Carl A., Co-Chm.--Goldenberg Candy Company, Philadelphia, PA; *U.S. Private*, pg. 461
Goldenberg, Edgar R., Co-Chm.--Goldenberg Candy Company, Philadelphia, PA; *U.S. Private*, pg. 461
Goldenberg, I. Harry, Chm. Emeritus--Goldenberg Candy Company, Philadelphia, PA; *U.S. Private*, pg. 461
Goldfarb, Aron, Chm. Bd.--G-III Apparel Group, Ltd., New York, NY; *U.S. Public*, pg. 690
Goldfarb, Gene, Chm. Bd.--House of Perfection, Inc., New York, NY; *U.S. Private*, pg. 542
Goldfarb, Martin, Chm. Bd.--Speedy Muffler King, Inc., Toronto, Canada; *U.S. Public*, pg. 1578
Goldfus, Donald W., Chm. Bd.--Apogee Enterprises, Inc., Minneapolis, MN; *U.S. Public*, pg. 120
Goldin, Ken, Chm. Bd., Pres. & Chief Exec. Officer--The Score Board, Inc., Cherry Hill, NJ; *U.S. Public*, pg. 1444
Goldman, Harold A., Chm. Bd.--Iowa Paint Mfg. Company, Inc., Des Moines, IA; *U.S. Private*, pg. 575
Goldman, Jake, Chm. Bd.--Farmland Dairies, Wallington, NJ; *U.S. Private*, pg. 395
Goldman, Siegmund I., Chm. Bd.--S.I. Goldman Co., Longwood, FL; *U.S. Private*, pg. 461
Goldring, Norman M., Chm. Bd.--CPM, Inc., Chicago, IL; *U.S. Private*, pg. 196
Goldsmith, Bram, Chm. Bd.--City National Corporation, Beverly Hills, CA; *U.S. Public*, pg. 380
Goldsmith, Gary, Chm. Bd. & Creative Dir.--Goldsmith/Jeffrey Inc., New York, NY; *U.S. Private*, pg. 462
Goldsmith, John, Chm.--ARC Advertising, London, United Kingdom; *Int'l*, pg. 17
Goldsmith, Russell, Chm. Bd. & Chief Exec. Officer--City National Bank, Beverly Hills, CA; *U.S. Public*, pg. 381
Goldstein, Arthur L., Chm. Bd., Pres. & Chief Exec. Officer--Ionics, Incorporated, Watertown, MA; *U.S. Public*, pg. 912
Goldstein, Harry M., Chm. Bd.--Cohen Furniture Company, Peoria Heights, IL; *U.S. Private*, pg. 250
Goldstein, Jack, Chm. Bd.--OMI Corp., New York, NY; *U.S. Public*, pg. 1208
Goldstein, Jerome, Chm. Bd. & Chief Exec. Officer--Advanced Magnetics, Inc., Cambridge, MA; *U.S. Public*, pg. 20
Goldstein, Jerome J., Chm. Bd.--Scott's Liquid Gold-Inc., Denver, CO; *U.S. Public*, pg. 1447
Goldstein, Stanley, Chm. Bd. & Chief Exec. Officer--CVS Corp., Woonsocket, RI; *U.S. Public*, pg. 287
Goldstone, Steven F., Chm. Bd., Pres. & Chief Exec. Officer--RJR Nabisco Holdings Corp., New York, NY; *U.S. Public*, pg. 1354
Goldwyn, Samuel, Jr., Chm. Bd.--The Samuel Goldwyn Company, Los Angeles, CA; *U.S. Private*, pg. 463
Golemo, Stanley M., Jr., Chm. Bd. & Pres.--Hood & Company, Hamburg, PA; *Int'l*, pg. 572
Golin, Alvin, Chm. Bd.--Golin/Harris Communications, Inc., Chicago, IL; *Int'l*, pg. 1226
Golisano, B. Thomas, Chm. Bd., Pres. & Chief Exec. Officer--Paychex, Inc., Rochester, NY; *U.S. Public*, pg. 1267
Golitz, John T., Chm. Bd. & Chief Exec. Officer--First Financial Building Corporation, Manchester, MO; *U.S. Private*, pg. 407
Gollenbeck, Jurgen, Dr., Chm. Bd.--Howaldtswerke-Deutsche Werft AG, Kiel, Germany; *Int'l*, pg. 1069
Golovin, Jonathan J., Chm. Bd. & Sec.--Consilium, Inc., Mountain View, CA; *U.S. Public*, pg. 434
Golsen, Jack, Chm. Bd.--L & S Bearing Co., Oklahoma City, OK; *U.S. Public*, pg. 970
Golsen, Jack E., Chm. Bd., Pres. & Chief Exec. Officer--LSB Industries, Inc., Oklahoma City, OK; *U.S. Public*, pg. 970
Golub, Harvey, Chm. Bd. & Chief Exec. Officer--American Express Company, New York, NY; *U.S. Public*, pg. 73
Golub, Harvey, Chm. Bd.--American Express Europe Limited, London, United Kingdom; *U.S. Public*, pg. 74
Golub, Lewis, Chm. Bd. & Chief Exec. Officer--Golub Corporation, Schenectady, NY; *U.S. Private*, pg. 463
Gomez, Alain, Chm. Bd. & Chief Exec. Officer--Thomson S.A., Paris, France; *Int'l*, pg. 1381
Gomez, Barry, Chm. Bd.--Ezon Products, Inc., Germantown, TN; *U.S. Private*, pg. 388
Gomez, Consuelo A., Sr. V.P. & Client Services Dir.--Lois/EJL Los Angeles, Los Angeles, CA; *U.S. Public*, pg. 1011
Gomez, Flavio, Chm.--SBG Enterprise, San Francisco, CA; *Int'l*, pg. 1483
Gomez, Oscar J., Jr., Chm. Emeritus--Ezon Products, Inc., Germantown, TN; *U.S. Private*, pg. 388
Gonseth, Denis, Chm. Bd.--HPI Holding S.A., Yverdon, Switzerland; *Int'l*, pg. 579
Gonzales, Adrian Sada, Chm. Bd.--Vitro, Sociedad Anonima, Garza Garcia, Mexico; *Int'l*, pg. 1469
Gonzalez Nova, Carlos, Chm. Bd. & Pres.--Controladora Comercial Mexicana, S.A. de C.V., Mexico, Mexico; *Int'l*, pg. 328
Gonzalez, Sergio Vigil, Chm. Bd.--Industrias Nacobre SA de CV, Mexico, Mexico; *Int'l*, pg. 572
Good, Sheldon F., Chm. Bd. & Chief Exec. Officer--Sheldon Good & Co., Chicago, IL; *U.S. Private*, pg. 463
Goodall, R. William, Chm. Bd.--Carbo Plc, Manchester, United Kingdom; *Int'l*, pg. 268
Goodby, Jeffrey, Co-Chm. & Creative Dir.--Goodby, Silverstein & Partners, San Francisco, CA; *U.S. Public*, pg. 1224
Goodchild, John, Chm. Bd. & Chief Exec. Officer--The Weightman Group, Philadelphia, PA; *U.S. Private*, pg. 1159
Goode, Charles, Chm. Bd.--Australia & New Zealand Banking Group Limited, Melbourne, Australia; *Int'l*, pg. 98
Goode, David R., Chm. Bd., Pres. & Chief Exec. Officer--Norfolk Southern Corporation, Norfolk, VA; *U.S. Public*, pg. 1190
Goode, K. Edward, Chm. Bd.--Bank of Ferrum, Ferrum, VA; *U.S. Public*, pg. 1038
Gooden, C. Michael, Chm. Bd. & Pres.--Integrated Systems Analysts, Inc., Arlington, VA; *U.S. Private*, pg. 566
Goodes, Melvin R., Chm. Bd. & Chief Exec. Officer--Warner-Lambert Company, Morris Plains, NJ; *U.S. Public*, pg. 1738
Goodfriend, Robert M., Chm. Bd. & Chief Exec. Officer--Goody's Family Clothing, Inc., Knoxville, TN; *U.S. Public*, *pg. 753*
Gooding, Terrence, Chm. Bd. & Chief Exec. Officer--Wavetek Corporation, San Diego, CA; *U.S. Private*, pg. 1154
Goodman, Ellis M., Chm. Bd. & Chief Exec. Officer--Barton Incorporated, Chicago, IL; *U.S. Public*, pg. 300
Goodman, Peter A., Chm. & Chief Exec. Officer--Ivy, Vernon, CA; *U.S. Public*, pg. 948
Goodman, Peter A., Chm. & Chief Exec. Officer--A.J. Brandon, Vernon, CA; *U.S. Public*, pg. 948
Goodpasture, Molly, Chm. Bd.--Goodpasture, Inc., Brownfield, TX; *U.S. Private*, pg. 464
Goodrich, Jon, Chm. Bd.--Mace Security International, Inc., Bennington, VT; *U.S. Public*, pg. 1030
Goodstein, Ed, Chm. Bd. & Chief Exec. Officer--Vertex Computer Cable Products, Farmingdale, NY; *U.S. Public*, *pg. 1718*
Goodwin, Daniel L., Chm. Bd. & Chief Exec. Officer--The Inland Group, Inc., Oak Brook, IL; *U.S. Private*, pg. 564
Goodwin, John, Chm. Bd.--The Highland Distilleries Company plc, Glasgow, United Kingdom; *Int'l*, pg. 619
Goodwyn, William, Chm. Bd.--AMF Reece Incorporated, Mechanicsville, VA; *U.S. Private*, pg. 7
Goodyear, William M., Chm. Bd. & Chief Exec. Officer--Bank of America Illinois, Chicago, IL; *U.S. Public*, pg. 180
Goodyear, William M., Chm. & Pres.--Bank of America Illinois Trust Company of Florida, N.A., Boca Raton, FL; *U.S. Public*, pg. 181
Goodyear, William M., Chm. Bd.--Continental Community Development Corp., Chicago, IL; *U.S. Public*, pg. 181
Goosens, Edward, Chm. Bd.--Wayne Wire Cloth Products, Inc., Kalkaska, MI; *U.S. Private*, pg. 1155
Gordon, Barry J., Chm. Bd. & Pres.--American Fund Advisors, Inc., Garden City, NY; *U.S. Private*, pg. 55
Gordon, Bernard M., Chm. Bd. & Chief Exec. Officer--Analogic Corporation, Peabody, MA; *U.S. Public*, pg. 109
Gordon, Beth, Chm. Bd.--BPA International, New York, NY; *U.S. Private*, pg. 107
Gordon, Bruce S., Chm. Bd.--Bell Atlantic TeleProducts Corp., Exton, PA; *U.S. Public*, pg. 203
Gordon, Lloyd, Owner & Chief Exec. Officer--Amcel Corp., Watertown, MA; *U.S. Private*, pg. 48
Gordon, Melvin J., Chm. Bd. & Chief Exec. Officer--Tootsie Roll Industries, Inc., Chicago, IL; *U.S. Public*, pg. 1621
Gordon, Paul, Chm. Bd.--Gordon Food Service Inc., Grand Rapids, MI; *U.S. Private*, pg. 465
Gordon, Peter, Chm. Bd.--Crystal Geyser, Calistoga, CA; *U.S. Private*, pg. 294
Gordon, Peter, Chm. Bd.--Crystal Geyser Water Company, Calistoga, CA; *Int'l*, pg. 1013
Gordon, Robert D., Chm. Bd., Pres. & Chief Exec. Officer--Apertus Technologies Incorporated, Eden Prairie, MN; *U.S. Public*, pg. 119
Gordy, Berry, Chm. Bd.--Motown Record Company, J.P., New York, NY; *Int'l*, pg. 1052
Gorell, Franklyn, Chm. Bd. & Chief Exec. Officer--Season-All Industries, Inc., Indiana, PA; *Int'l*, pg. 267
Gores, Alec, Chm. Bd.--Gores Technology Group, Sherman Oaks, CA; *U.S. Private*, pg. 465
Gorguze, Vincent, Chm. Bd.--Miracle Recreation Equipment Company, Monett, MO; *U.S. Private*, pg. 752
Goris, Paul C., Chm. Bd.--Antwerpse Diamantbank N.V., Antwerp, Belgium; *Int'l*, pg. 147
Gorkuscha, Mischa, Chm. Bd.--Liberty Mortgage Co., Oklahoma City, OK; *U.S. Public*, pg. 174
Gorkuscha, Mischa, Chm. Bd.--Liberty Real Estate Co., Oklahoma City, OK; *U.S. Public*, pg. 175
Gorman, Alvin L., Chm Bd.--Power Contracting & Engineering Corp., Schaumburg, IL; *U.S. Private*, pg. 877
Gorman, James C., Chm. Bd.--The Gorman-Rupp Company, Mansfield, OH; *U.S. Public*, pg. 754
Gorman, Joseph T., Chm. Bd. & Chief Exec. Officer--TRW Inc., Cleveland, OH; *U.S. Public*, pg. 1558
Gorman, Kenneth, Chm. Bd., Pres., & Chief Exec. Officer--IDC Services, Inc., Chicago, IL; *U.S. Private*, pg. 554
Gorman, Kenneth F., Chm. Bd., Pres. & Chief Exec. Officer--Production Payments, Inc., Chicago, IL; *U.S. Private*, pg. 554
Gorman, Kenneth J., Chm. Bd. & Chief Exec. Officer--Atlantic Mutual Companies, New York, NY; *U.S. Private*, pg. 95
Gormly, A.G., Chm.--Trafalgar House Construction Ltd., Croydon, United Kingdom; *Int'l*, pg. 773
Gorra, William, Chm. Bd., Pres. & Chief Exec. Officer--Simoniz USA, Inc., Bolton, CT; *U.S. Private*, pg. 1001
Gorsun, Barry R., Chm. Bd.--Summa Four, Inc., Manchester, NH; *U.S. Public*, pg. 1527
Gortz, Horst, Chm. Bd.--Utimaco Safeware AG, Oberursel, Germany; *Int'l*, pg. 1444
Gosewehr, Carl L., Chm. Bd.--The Oilgear Company, Milwaukee, WI; *U.S. Public*, pg. 1215
Gosman, Abraham D., Chm. Bd. & Chief Exec. Officer--Meditrust Corporation, Needham, MA; *U.S. Public*, pg. 1081
Goss, Howard S., Chm. Bd., Chief Exec. Officer & Treas.--Transco Inc., Chicago, IL; *U.S. Private*, pg. 1096
Gossett, Barry P., Chm. Bd. & Chief Exec. Officer--Williams Scotsman, Inc., Baltimore, MD; *U.S. Private*, pg. 976
Goto, Toyohiko, Chm. Bd.--The Bank of Fukuoka, Ltd., Fukuoka, Japan; *Int'l*, pg. 152
Goto, Yasuo, Chm. Bd.--The Yasuda Fire & Marine Insurance Company Limited, Tokyo, Japan; *Int'l*, pg. 1519
Gottesman, Edward A., Chm.--Derby International Corporation S.A., Luxembourg, Luxembourg; *Int'l*, pg. 394
Gottesman, Jerome, Chm. Bd.--Edison Parking Properties, LLC, Newark, NJ; *U.S. Private*, pg. 364
Gottschalk, Carlos A., Grp. Chm.--Johnson & Johnson Ltda., Sao Paulo, Brazil; *U.S. Public*, pg. 931
Gottwald, Bruce C., Chm. Bd. & Chief Exec. Officer--Ethyl Corporation, Richmond, VA; *U.S. Public*, pg. 595
Gottwald, Floyd D., Jr., Chm. Bd. & Chief Exec. Officer--Albemarle Corporation, Richmond, VA; *U.S. Public*, pg. 37
Gough, Joseph M., Jr., Chm. Bd.--The First National Bank of St. Mary's, Leonardtown, MD; *U.S. Public*, pg. 1089
Gougoux, Yves, Chm. Bd.--BCP Group Ltd., Montreal, Canada; *Int'l*, pg. 116
Goulay, Jean-Claude, Chm. Bd.--Initiative & Finance Investissement, Paris, France; *Int'l*, pg. 344
Gould, F.J., Chm.--Investment Research Company, Rancho Santa Fe, CA; *U.S. Public*, pg. 1673
Gould, Harry E., Jr., Chm. Bd. & Pres.--Gould Paper Corporation, New York, NY; *U.S. Private*, pg. 466
Gould, Margaret Z., Chm. Bd.--Magnetic Analysis Corp., Mount Vernon, NY; *U.S. Private*, pg. 695
Gould, Michael, Chm. Bd.--Bloomingdale's, New York, NY; *U.S. Public*, pg. 617
Gould, Peter G., Chm. Bd.--Old America Stores, Howe, TX; *U.S. Public*, pg. 1215
Gould, Sara K., Chm. Bd.--The Challenge Machinery Co., Grand Haven, MI; *U.S. Private*, pg. 227
Gounot, Denys, Chm. Bd.--Saft Nife Ltd., Hampton, United Kingdom; *Int'l*, pg. 55
Gourgeon, Pierre-Henri, Chm.--Groupe Servair (Compagnie d'Exploitation des Services Auxiliaires Aeriens), Roissy, France; *Int'l*, pg. 560
Goutard, Noel, Chm. Bd. & Chief Exec. Officer--Valeo Research Sooal, Paris, France; *Int'l*, pg. 240
Gower, Roger, Chm. Bd., Pres. & Chief Exec. Officer--Micro Component Technology Inc., Saint Paul, MN; *U.S. Public*, pg. 1104
Gowerie-Smith, Ian Roderick, Chm. Bd.--SkyePharma PLC, London, United Kingdom; *Int'l*, pg. 1262
Gowland, Pablo, Sr., Chm.--Gowland/ADD, Buenos Aires, Argentina; *U.S. Private*, pg. 1200
Graber, Garnel F., Chm. Bd.--Interface Systems, Inc., Ann Arbor, MI; *U.S. Public*, pg. 889

Grace, Barnett, Chm. Bd., Pres. & Chief Exec. Officer--First Commercial Corporation, Little Rock, AR; *U.S. Public*, pg. 630
Grace, Barnett, Chm. Bd. & Chief Exec. Officer--First Commercial Bank, N.A., Little Rock, AR; *U.S. Public*, pg. 630
Grace, John R., Chm. Bd.--SEI Holding Corp., Dallas, TX; *U.S. Private*, pg. 956
Grace, John R., Chm. Bd.--Spring Engineers of Houston Ltd., Houston, TX; *U.S. Private*, pg. 956
Grace, Oliver R., Jr., Chm. Bd.--Andersen Group, Inc., Bloomfield, CT; *U.S. Public*, pg. 111
Grace, Roy, Chm. Bd.--Grace & Rothschild, New York, NY; *U.S. Private*, pg. 468
Grace, W.M., Chm. Bd. & Pres.--W.M. Grace Development, Phoenix, AZ; *U.S. Private*, pg. 468
Grade, Jeffery T., Chm. Bd. & Chief Exec. Officer--Harnischfeger Industries, Inc., Saint Francis, WI; *U.S. Public*, pg. 788
Gradinger, J. Gary, Chm. Bd., Pres. & Chief Exec. Officer--Golden Star Inc., Kansas City, MO; *U.S. Private*, pg. 460
Graebner, Wolfgans, Chm. Bd.--AGIV Group, Frankfurt, Germany; *Int'l*, pg. 14
Graf, W.J., Dr., Chm.--Hoogovens Aluminium Profiltechnik GmbH, Vogt, Germany; *Int'l*, pg. 755
Grafton, W. Robert, Chm. Bd. & Acting Chief Exec. Officer--Andersen Worldwide, New York, NY; *U.S. Private*, pg. 72
Graham, Allister P., Chm. Bd. & Chief Exec. Officer--The Oshawa Group Limited, Etobicoke, Canada; *Int'l*, pg. 1012
Graham, Billy, Chm. Bd.--Christianity Today, Inc., Carol Stream, IL; *U.S. Private*, pg. 238
Graham, Craig, Chm. Bd., Pres. & Chief Exec. Officer--Cashway Building Centres Ltd., Port Hope, Canada; *Int'l*, *pg. 274*
Graham, Donald E., Chm. & Chief Exec. Officer--The Washington Post Company, Washington, DC; *U.S. Public*, pg. 1742
Graham, Kerry, Chm. Bd. & Chief Creative Officer-Buntin Advertising, Inc.--The Buntin Group, Nashville, TN; *U.S. Private*, pg. 181
Graham, Robert A., Chm. Bd.--Bell Atlantic Directory Graphics, Inc., Valley Forge, PA; *U.S. Public*, pg. 203
Graham, Thomas C., Chm. Bd.--Carver Corporation, Lynnwood, WA; *U.S. Public*, pg. 310
Graham, Wallace A., Chm. Bd.--Schenectady International, Inc., Schenectady, NY; *U.S. Private*, pg. 969
Grainger, David W., Chm. Bd.--W.W. Grainger, Inc., Lincolnshire, IL; *U.S. Public*, pg. 758
Gralnick, Marvin, Chm. Bd., Pres. & Chief Exec. Officer--Chico's Fas Inc, Fort Myers, FL; *U.S. Public*, pg. 349
Granat, Kenneth, Chm. Bd.--The Langer Biomechanics Group, Inc., Deer Park, NY; *U.S. Public*, pg. 978
Grangaard, Paul D., Chm. Bd.--Piper Jaffray Ventures Inc., Minneapolis, MN; *U.S. Public*, pg. 1303
Granger, Alton, Chm. Bd. & Pres.--Granger Construction Co., Lansing, MI; *U.S. Private*, pg. 469
Granger, Ronald K., Chm. Bd., Pres. & Chief Exec. Officer--Granger Companies, Lansing, MI; *U.S. Private*, pg. 469
Grant, Alistair, Sir, Chm. Bd.--Scottish & Newcastle plc, Edinburgh, United Kingdom; *Int'l*, pg. 1211
Grant, Donald B., Chm. Bd. & Chief Exec. Officer--Voyager Emblems, Inc., Sanborn, NY; *U.S. Private*, pg. 1143
Grant, Michael, Chm. Bd. & Chief Exec. Officer--Grant-Lydick Beverage Co., San Antonio, TX; *U.S. Private*, pg. 470
Grant, R. Douglas, Chm. Bd., Pres. & Chief Exec. Officer--Lakeland Financial Corporation, Warsaw, IN; *U.S. Public*, *pg. 975*
Grant, Richard H., Jr., Chm.-Steering Committee--The Reynolds and Reynolds Company, Dayton, OH; *U.S. Public*, pg. 1384
Grant, W. Thomas II, Chm. Bd., Pres. & Chief Exec. Officer--Lab One, Lenexa, KS; *U.S. Public*, pg. 1449
Grant, W. Thomas, II, Chm. Bd. & Chief Exec. Officer--Seafield Capital Corporation, Kansas City, MO; *U.S. Public*, pg. 1449
Granum, Robert M., Chm. Bd. & Chief Exec. Officer--Panel Processing, Inc., Alpena, MI; *U.S. Private*, pg. 836
Granzow, Paul H., Chm. Bd.--The Standard Register Company, Dayton, OH; *U.S. Public*, pg. 1505
Grappotte, Francois, Chm. Bd. & Chief Exec. Officer--LeGrand S.A., Limoges, France; *Int'l*, pg. 805
Grass, Martin L., Chm. Bd. & Chief Exec. Officer--Rite Aid Corporation, Camp Hill, PA; *U.S. Public*, pg. 1390
Grassmann, P., Dr., Chm. Bd.--Carl Zeiss, Inc., Thornwood, NY; *Int'l*, pg. 1523
Graupman, Richard, Chm. Bd. & Pres.--South Central Co-Op, Fairfax, MN; *U.S. Private*, pg. 1014
Graves, Earl G., Chm. Bd. & Pres.--Earl G. Graves, Ltd., New York, NY; *U.S. Private*, pg. 471
Graves, Herbert C., Chm. Bd.--Freedom Forge Corporation, Burnham, PA; *U.S. Private*, pg. 425
Gravette, E.T., Chm. Bd. & Chief Exec. Officer--The Turner Corporation, New York, NY; *U.S. Public*, pg. 1645
Gray, Gordon C., Chm. Bd.--Rio Algom Limited, Toronto, Canada; *Int'l*, pg. 1118
Gray, John, S., Sr., Chm. Bd. & Pres.--Jack Gray Transport, Inc., Gary, IN; *U.S. Private*, pg. 471
Gray, Lois Howard, Chm. Bd.--James N. Gray Construction Co., Inc., Lexington, KY; *U.S. Private*, pg. 472
Gray, Melvin, Chm. Bd. & Chief Exec. Officer--Graycor Operating Companies, Homewood, IL; *U.S. Private*, pg. 472
Graybill, V. Lynn, Chm. Bd., Pres. & Chief Exec. Officer--Karts International Inc., Covington, LA; *U.S. Public*, pg. 944
Graziadio, G. Louis, III, Chm. Bd.--Lynx Golf, Inc., City of Industry, CA; *U.S. Private*, pg. 684
Graziadio, G. Louis, III, Chm. Bd. & Chief Exec. Officer--Vista 2000, Inc., Kewanee, IL; *U.S. Private*, pg. 1142
Graziado, George M., Chm. Bd., Pres. & Chief Exec. Officer--Imperial Bancorp, Inglewood, CA; *U.S. Public*, pg. 871
Greaves, Richard W., Dr., Chm. Bd. & Pres.--Vibro-Meter Corp., Long Beach, CA; *U.S. Private*, pg. 1138
Greehey, William E., Chm. Bd. & Chief Exec. Officer--Valero Energy Corporation, San Antonio, TX; *U.S. Public*, pg. 1704
Greehey, William E., Chm. Bd. & Chief Exec. Officer--Valero Refining Company, San Antonio, TX; *U.S. Public*, pg. 1704
Green, A.J., Chm. Bd.--Paterson Zochonis Plc, Stockport, United Kingdom; *Int'l*, pg. 1024
Green, C.H., Chm. Bd.--Rolls-Royce-Commercial Aero Engines Ltd., Derby, United Kingdom; *Int'l*, pg. 1127
Green, Holcombe T., Jr., Chm. Bd. & Chief Exec. Officer--WestPoint Stevens Inc., West Point, GA; *U.S. Public*, pg. 1762
Green, Jeffrey W., Chm. Bd.--Hutchinson Technology Inc., Hutchinson, MN; *U.S. Public*, pg. 850
Green, Jim, Chm. Bd. & Chief Exec. Officer--Active Software, Inc., Santa Clara, CA; *U.S. Private*, pg. 15
Green, R., Chm. Bd. & Chief Exec. Officer--Gan Life and Pensions PLC, Harlow, United Kingdom; *Int'l*, pg. 565
Green, R. Thomas, Jr., Chm. Bd., Pres. & Chief Exec. Officer--Oglebay Norton Company, Cleveland, OH; *U.S. Public*, pg. 1213
Green, Richard C., Jr., Chm. Bd. & Chief Exec. Officer--UtiliCorp United Inc., Kansas City, MO; *U.S. Public*, pg. 1700
Green, Richard L., Chm. Bd., Pres. & Chief Exec. Officer--General Shale Products Corp., Johnson City, TN; *Int'l*, pg. 843
Green, Richard L., Chm. Bd., Pres. & Chief Exec. Officer--General Shale Products Corp., Elizabethton, TN; *Int'l*, pg. 843
Greenberg, Alan C., Chm. Bd. & Sr. Mng. Dir.--The Bear Stearns Companies Inc., New York, NY; *U.S. Public*, pg. 197
Greenberg, Daniel, Chm. Bd. & Chief Exec. Officer--Electro Rent Corporation, Van Nuys, CA; *U.S. Public*, pg. 568
Greenberg, Frank, Chm. Bd.--Burlington Industries, Inc., Greensboro, NC; *U.S. Public*, pg. 268
Greenberg, Jeffrey W., Chm. Bd. & Chief Exec. Officer--Marsh & McLennan Risk Capital Corp., Greenwich, CT; *U.S. Public*, pg. 1049
Greenberg, Lon R., Chm. Bd., Pres. & Chief Exec. Officer--UGI Corporation, King of Prussia, PA; *U.S. Public*, pg. 1653
Greenberg, Lon R., Chm. Bd., Pres. & Chief Exec. Officer--AmeriGas Partners, L.P., Valley Forge, PA; *U.S. Public*, pg. 1653
Greenberg, Maurice, Chm. Bd.--Transatlantic Holdings Inc., New York, NY; *U.S. Public*, pg. 84
Greenberg, Maurice R., Chm. Bd. & Chief Exec. Officer--American International Group, Inc., New York, NY; *U.S. Public*, pg. 83
Greenberg, Robert, Chm. & Chief Exec. Officer--R/GA Interactive, New York, NY; *U.S. Public*, pg. 1641
Greenblatt, Maurice, Chm. Bd.--UniGroup, Inc., Fenton, MO; *U.S. Private*, pg. 1117
Greenbury, Richard, Sir, Chm. Bd.--Marks & Spencer PLC, London, United Kingdom; *Int'l*, pg. 842
Greene, Ronald G., Chm. Bd.--Renaissance Energy Ltd., Calgary, Canada; *Int'l*, pg. 1102
Greener, Anthony, Chm. Bd. & Chief Exec. Officer--Guinness Plc, London, United Kingdom; *Int'l*, pg. 412
Greener, Athony, Joint Chm.--Diageo Plc, London, United Kingdom; *Int'l*, pg. 408
Greener, George, Chm. Bd.--Eagle Star, London, United Kingdom; *Int'l*, pg. 110
Greenfield, Harley J., Chm. & Chief Exec. Officer--Jennifer Convertibles Inc., Woodbury, NY; *U.S. Public*, pg. 926
Greenfield, Harvey, Chm. Bd.--Commonwealth Toy & Novelty Company, New York, NY; *U.S. Private*, pg. 258
Greenfield, Jerry, Vice Chm. & Co-Founder--Ben & Jerry's Homemade Inc., South Burlington, VT; *U.S. Public*, pg. 210
Greenhalgh, W. Edward, Chm.-U.K. Subsidiaries--Krug International Corp., Houston, TX; *U.S. Public*, pg. 967
Greenlees, Michael, Chm.--GGT Advertising Ltd., London, United Kingdom; *Int'l*, pg. 532
Greenman, Stanley, Chm. Bd., Chief Exec. Officer & Treas.--Noodle Kidoodle Inc., Syosset, NY; *U.S. Public*, pg. 1188
Greenstone, Ronald, Chm. & Chief Exec. Officer--Greenstone Roberts Advertising, Melville, NY; *U.S. Public*, pg. 763
Greenstone, Ronald, Chm. & Chief Exec. Officer--Greenstone Roberts/Florida, Orlando, FL; *U.S. Public*, pg. 763
Greenwald, Gerald, Chm. Bd. & Chief Exec. Officer--UAL Corporation, Elk Grove Village, IL; *U.S. Public*, pg. 1652
Greenwald, Martin W., Chm. Bd., Pres. & Chief Exec. Officer--Image Entertainment, Inc., Chatsworth, CA; *U.S. Public*, pg. 870
Greenwood, Daniel B., Chm. Bd.--Specialty Equipment Companies Inc., Aurora, IL; *U.S. Public*, pg. 1496
Greenwood, John, Chm. Bd.--Micron Separations, Inc., Westborough, MA; *U.S. Private*, pg. 742
Greer, Barton, Jr., Chm. Bd.--Autry Greer & Sons, Inc., Prichard, AL; *U.S. Private*, pg. 479
Greer, Tommy D., Chm. Bd.--Catalina Marketing Corporation, Saint Petersburg, FL; *U.S. Public*, pg. 314
Greeson, Tom W., Chm. Bd.--Cohutta Banking Company, Chatsworth, GA; *U.S. Public*, pg. 1549
Grefenstette, Carl G., Chm. Bd. & Chief Exec. Officer--The Hillman Company, Pittsburgh, PA; *U.S. Private*, pg. 530
Gregerson, R.L., Chm. Bd. & Pres.--American Excelsior Company, Arlington, TX; *U.S. Private*, pg. 53
Gregg, F. Browne, Chm. Bd. & Chief Exec. Officer--Florida Crushed Stone Company, Leesburg, FL; *U.S. Private*, pg. 414
Gregor, Thomas C., Chm. Bd., Pres. & Chief Exec. Officer--United National Bancorp, Bridgewater, NJ; *U.S. Public*, pg. 1679
Gregori, S.R., Chm. & Mng. Dir.--Texaco Overseas (Nigeria) Petroleum Co., Lagos, Nigeria; *U.S. Public*, pg. 1584
Gregory, Alan V., Chm. Bd.--SEEQ Technology Inc., Fremont, CA; *U.S. Public*, pg. 1417
Gregory, Robert E., Jr., Chm. Bd. & Chief Exec. Officer--London Fog Industries, Inc., New York, NY; *U.S. Private*, *pg. 673*
Gregory, William R., Chm. Bd.--Northern Tree Service, Inc., Sault Sainte Marie, MI; *U.S. Public*, pg. 592
Greig, Christopher, Chm. Bd.--William Grant & Sons Distillers Ltd., Bellshill, United Kingdom; *Int'l*, pg. 557
Greiner, N. F., Chm.--NatWest Markets Australia Limited, Sydney, Australia; *Int'l*, pg. 911
Grell, Larry, Chm. Bd.--Rice Growers Association of California, West Sacramento, CA; *U.S. Private*, pg. 927
Grenacher, Hans, Chm.--Coop Aargau, Lenzburg, Switzerland; *Int'l*, pg. 329
Gresov, Boris, Chm. Bd., Pres. & Chief Exec. Officer--Standard Metals Corporation, New York, NY; *U.S. Public*, *pg. 1502*
Gressel, Alan, Chm. Bd., Pres., Chief Exec. Officer & Chief Oper. Officer--Research Environmental Industries, Inc., Cleveland, OH; *U.S. Private*, pg. 924
Gressette, L.M., Jr., Chm. Bd. & Chief Exec. Officer--South Carolina Generating Co., Inc., Columbia, SC; *U.S. Public*, *pg. 1436*
Gressier, C., Chm. Bd & Mng. Dir.--CTT Sceta, Paris, France; *Int'l*, pg. 1163
Grey, Richard E., Chm. Bd.--Tyco Toys, Inc., Mount Laurel, NJ; *U.S. Public*, pg. 1058
Gribbin, M.C.D., Chm. Bd. & Chief Exec. Officer--Jardine Insurance Brokers International Limited, London, United Kingdom; *Int'l*, pg. 705
Griebel, R. Nelson, Chm. Bd., Chief Exec. Officer & Pres.--Bank of Boston Connecticut, Hartford, CT; *U.S. Public*, pg. 184
Griffin, Ben Hill, III, Chm. Bd., Pres. & Chief Exec. Officer--Alico, Inc., La Belle, FL; *U.S. Public*, pg. 41
Griffin, Ben Hill, III, Chm. Bd. & Chief Exec. Officer--Orange-Co., Inc., Bartow, FL; *U.S. Public*, pg. 1229
Griffin, Brian E., Chm. Bd.--Irish Cement Ltd., Stillorgan, Ireland; *Int'l*, pg. 242
Griffin, Donald W., Chm. Bd., Pres. & Chief Exec. Officer--Olin Corporation, Norwalk, CT; *U.S. Public*, pg. 1218
Griffin, Gerald D., Chm. Bd.--Comarco, Inc., Yorba Linda, CA; *U.S. Public*, pg. 406
Griffin, Haynes G., Chm. Bd.--Vanguard Cellular Systems, Inc., Greensboro, NC; *U.S. Public*, pg. 1707
Griffin, Jeff, Chm. Bd., Pres. & Chief Exec. Officer--Griffin Transport Services, Inc., Sparks, NV; *U.S. Private*, pg. 481
Griffin, John L., Sr., Chm. Bd.--Griffin Industries, Inc., Cold Spring, KY; *U.S. Private*, pg. 480
Griffin, John W., Chm. Bd., Pres. & Chief Exec. Officer--Griffin Manufacturing Co., Muskogee, OK; *U.S. Private*, pg. 481
Griffin, Mark, Chm. Bd., Pres. & Chief Exec. Officer--Ris Paper Company, Long Island City, NY; *U.S. Private*, pg. 932
Griffin, Mark E., Chm. Bd., Pres. & Chief Exec. Officer--Lewis Drug, Inc., Sioux Falls, SD; *U.S. Private*, pg. 665
Griffin, Marvin W., Chm. Bd.--Brass Eagle Inc., Rogers, AR; *U.S. Public*, pg. 250
Griffin, Merv, Chm. Bd.--Griffin Group, Inc., New York, NY; *U.S. Private*, pg. 480
Griffin, Robert E., Chm. Bd. & Chief Exec. Officer--Escalade Sports, Evansville, IN; *U.S. Public*, pg. 591
Griffin, Rutledge A., Jr., Chm. Bd., Pres. & Chief Exec. Officer--Griffin Corporation, Valdosta, GA; *U.S. Private*, pg. 480
Griffin, Tom, Co-Chm. & Chief Exec. Officer--Griffin Bacal Inc., New York, NY; *U.S. Private*, pg. 480
Griffin, Tom, Chm. Bd.--Griffin Bacal Volny, Toronto, Canada; *U.S. Private*, pg. 480
Griffis, C. Lloyd, Chm. Bd.--Old-First National Bank in Bluffton, Bluffton, IN; *U.S. Public*, pg. 674
Griffith, Alan R., Chm. Bd.--The Bank of New York (Delaware), Newark, DE; *U.S. Public*, pg. 178
Griffith, Dan, Chm. Bd.--Burns Bros. Inc., Portland, OR; *U.S. Private*, pg. 187
Griffith, Dean L., Chm. Bd., Pres. & Chief Exec. Officer--Griffith Laboratories Worldwide, Inc., Alsip, IL; *U.S. Private*, pg. 481
Griffith, P., Chm. Bd.--Standard Products Limited, Huntingdon, United Kingdom; *U.S. Public*, pg. 1505
Griffith, Tom, Chm. Bd.--Downey Printing, Waukee, IA; *U.S. Private*, pg. 342
Griffiths, Anthony, Chm. Bd.--Slater Industries Inc., North York, Canada; *Int'l*, pg. 1262
Griffiths, Anthony F., Chm. Bd.--Vitran Corporation Inc., Toronto, Canada; *Int'l*, pg. 1469
Grigg, Charles W., Chm. Bd., Pres. & Chief Exec. Officer--SPS Technologies, Inc., Jenkintown, PA; *U.S. Public*, pg. 1419
Grigsby, James A., Chm. Bd.--Cigna Worldwide Insurance Company, Wilmington, DE; *U.S. Public*, pg. 365
Grijns, L.C., Chm.--ING (U.S.) Financial Services kk, New York, NY; *Int'l*, pg. 648
Grillo, R., Chm.--AGIP do Brasil S.A., Sao Paulo, Brazil; *Int'l*, pg. 428
Grillo, Robert L., Chm. Bd.--General Office Environments Inc., Rochelle Park, NJ; *U.S. Private*, pg. 445
Grimes, Roy J., Chm. Bd.--St. Louis Division, Saint Louis, MO; *U.S. Public*, pg. 509
Grimmer, James B., Chm. Bd.--Grimmer Realty Co. Inc., Birmingham, AL; *U.S. Private*, pg. 482
Grinberg, Gedalio, Chm. Bd. & Chief Exec. Officer--Movado Group, Inc., Lyndhurst, NJ; *U.S. Public*, pg. 1140
Grinstein, Gerald, Chm. Bd.--Delta Air Lines, Inc., Atlanta, GA; *U.S. Public*, pg. 497
Grinter, Donald W., Chm. Bd. & Chief Exec. Officer--ABC Rail Products Corp., Chicago, IL; *U.S. Public*, pg. 2
Grinzewitsch, George, Chm. Bd. & Pres.--Sacramento Jaguar, Inc., Sacramento, CA; *U.S. Private*, pg. 1143

Grisanti, Eugene P., Chm. Bd., Pres. & Chief Exec. Officer--International Flavors & Fragrances, Inc., New York, NY; *U.S. Public*, pg. 898
Grizzard, Claude T., Jr., Vice Chm.--Grizzard, Atlanta, GA; *U.S. Private*, pg. 482
Groendyke, John, Chm. Bd.--Groendyke Transports, Inc., Enid, OK; *U.S. Private*, pg. 483
Groenenboom, P.J., Chm. Bd.--Internatio-Muller N.V., Rotterdam, Netherlands; *Int'l*, pg. 680
Groenendyk, J., Chm. Bd.--KPN Koninklyke PTT Nederland NV, Groningen, Netherlands; *Int'l*, pg. 720
Groenevelt, Aat, Chm. Bd. & Pres.--Provimi Veal Corporation, Seymour, WI; *U.S. Private*, pg. 892
Grogan, David R., Chm., Pres. & Chief Exec. Officer--Toter Incorporated, Statesville, NC; *U.S. Private*, pg. 1092
Grohe, Charles R., Chm.-Supervisory Bd.--Friedrich Grohe Armaturenfabrik GmbH & Co., Hemer, Germany; *Int'l*, pg. 559
Gromer, Klaus, Chm.--Loher AG, Rott, Germany; *Int'l*, pg. 400
Gropper, Edward, Chm. Bd.--Faber, Coe & Gregg, Inc., Secaucus, NJ; *U.S. Private*, pg. 390
Gros-Pietro, Gian Maria, Chm. Bd. & Chief Exec. Officer--IRI Istituto Ricostruzione Industriale, Rome, Italy; *Int'l*, pg. 652
Grosch, Greg, Chm. Bd., Pres. & Chief Exec. Officer--White Cap Industries, Inc., Costa Mesa, CA; *U.S. Public*, pg. 1765
Gross, Emerick, Chm. Bd.--Dan's Supreme Super Markets Inc., Hempstead, NY; *U.S. Private*, pg. 310
Gross, Howard, Chm. Bd. & Chief Exec. Officer--Snyder Industries, Inc., Lincoln, NE; *U.S. Private*, pg. 1011
Gross, Robert, Chm. Bd. & Chief Exec. Officer--Tops Appliance City, Edison, NJ; *U.S. Public*, pg. 1622
Gross, Ronald M., Chm. Bd. & Chief Exec. Officer--Rayonier Inc., Stamford, CT; *U.S. Public*, pg. 1363
Grossett, Jeff, Chm. Bd.--Owens-Corning Canos S.A., Buenos Aires, Argentina; *U.S. Public*, pg. 1237
Grossi, Richard J., Chm. Bd. & Chief Exec. Officer--United Illuminating Company, New Haven, CT; *U.S. Public*, pg. 1678
Grosskopf, Goran, Chm. Bd.--Tetra Laval Group, Lund, Sweden; *Int'l*, pg. 1377
Grossman, Burton E., Chm. Bd.--Grupo Continental S.A., Tampico, Mexico; *Int'l*, pg. 573
Grossman, Irving J., Chm. & Pres.--Beacon Container Corporation, Birdsboro, PA; *U.S. Private*, pg. 125
Grossman, Larry, Chm. Bd. & Chief Exec. Officer--Trans Leasing International Inc., Northbrook, IL; *U.S. Public*, pg. 1628
Grossman, Louis, Chm. Bd.--Southern Container Corporation, Hauppauge, NY; *U.S. Private*, pg. 1016
Grossman, Robert, Chm. Bd., Pres. & Chief Exec. Officer--Emons Transportation Group, Inc., York, PA; *U.S. Public*, pg. 578
Grossman, Sidney, Chm. Bd.--Grossman Iron & Steel Company, Saint Louis, MO; *U.S. Private*, pg. 483
Grossman, Steve, Chm. Bd.--Democratic National Committee, Washington, DC; *U.S. Private*, pg. 324
Grosvenor, Gilbert M., Chm. Bd.--National Geographic Society, Washington, DC; *U.S. Private*, pg. 783
Grote, Walter F., Jr., Chm. Bd.--Grote Industries, Madison, IN; *U.S. Private*, pg. 483
Grotenfelt, Sten, Chm. Bd.--Sodexi, Roissy, France; *Int'l*, pg. 560
Grove, Andrew S., Chm. Bd. & Chief Exec. Officer--Intel Corporation, Santa Clara, CA; *U.S. Public*, pg. 886
Grubb, David H., Chm. Bd.--Swinerton Inc., San Francisco, CA; *U.S. Private*, pg. 1059
Gruber, Alan R., Chm. Bd.--Orion Capital Companies, Inc., Farmington, CT; *U.S. Public*, pg. 1231
Gruenberg, Paul T., Chm. & Chief Exec. Officer--NYT Video News International, Philadelphia, PA; *U.S. Public*, pg. 1174
Gruhn, Fred, Chm. Bd.--MFA Oil Company, Columbia, MO; *U.S. Private*, pg. 687
Grum, Clifford J., Chm. Bd. & Chief Exec. Officer--Temple-Inland Inc., Diboll, TX; *U.S. Public*, pg. 1574
Grum, Clifford J., Chm. Bd., Pres. & Chief Exec. Officer--Temple-Inland Forest Products Corporation, Diboll, TX; *U.S. Public*, pg. 1575
Grumbacher, M. Thomas (Tim), Chm. Bd.--The Bon Ton Stores, Inc., York, PA; *U.S. Public*, pg. 244
Grundhofer, Jerry A., Chm. Bd., Pres. & Chief Exec. Officer--Starbanc Corporation, Cincinnati, OH; *U.S. Public*, pg. 1510
Grundhofer, Jerry A., Chm. Bd., Pres. & Chief Exec. Officer--Star Bank, N.A., Cincinnati, OH; *U.S. Public*, pg. 1510
Grune, George V., Chm. Bd. & Chief Exec. Officer--The Reader's Digest Association, Inc., Pleasantville, NY; *U.S. Public*, pg. 1367
Gruneisen, Jorg, Chm. Bd., Pres.--Villeroy & Boch AG, Mettlach, Germany; *Int'l*, pg. 1468
Grunnah, Thomas, Chm. Bd.--Reliance Elevator Company, Chicago, IL; *U.S. Private*, pg. 921
Grunzke, Henry R., Chm. Bd.--Standard Wool, Inc., North Oxford, MA; *U.S. Public*, pg. 1502
Gruyters, P., Chm.-Supervisory Bd.--VDL Groep BV, Eindhoven, Netherlands; *Int'l*, pg. 1444
Guccione, Bob, Chm. Bd., Chief Exec. Officer & Publr.--General Media International Inc., New York, NY; *U.S. Private*, pg. 444
Guella, L., Chm.--Montepolimeri Belgio S.A., Nivelles, Belgium; *Int'l*, pg. 429
Guerrovich, Erwin, Chm.--Intermarkets Bahrain, Manama, Bahrain; *Int'l*, pg. 680
Guerrovich, Erwin, Chm.--Intermarkets Lebanon, Beirut, Lebanon; *U.S. Private*, pg. 1062
Guerry, Zan, Chm. Bd. & Chief Exec. Officer--Chattem, Inc., Chattanooga, TN; *U.S. Public*, pg. 341
Guerry, Zan, Chm. Bd.--Chattem, Inc., Consumer Products Division, Chattanooga, TN; *U.S. Public*, pg. 341
Guffey, John W., Jr., Chm. Bd., Pres. & Chief Exec. Officer--Coltec Holdings Inc, Charlotte, NC; *U.S. Public*, pg. 401
Guffey, John, Jr., Chm. Bd. & Chief Exec. Officer--Coltec Industries Inc., Charlotte, NC; *U.S. Public*, pg. 401
Guichard, Antoine, Chm. Bd.--Groupe Casino, Saint Etienne, France; *Int'l*, pg. 562
Guillaume, Marnix L.K., Chm. Bd. & Mgr.-Latin & S. America--Willis Corroon International/Americas, Minneapolis, MN; *Int'l*, pg. 1507
Guinness, J.R.S., Chm. Bd.--BNFL, Warrington, United Kingdom; *Int'l*, pg. 120
Guitron, Jorge Martinez, Chm. Bd.--Grupo Simec, S.A. de C.V., Guadalajara, Mexico; *Int'l*, pg. 576
Gulas, Ivan, Dr., Co-Chm.--Pacific Title/Mirage, Hollywood, CA; *U.S. Public*, pg. 1425
Gulda, Edward J., Chm. Bd. & Chief Exec. Officer--Peregrine Incorporated, Southfield, MI; *U.S. Private*, pg. 852
Gullichsen, Johan, Chm. Bd.--A. Ahlstrom Corporation, Helsinki, Finland; *Int'l*, pg. 32
Gullickson, W.D., Chm. Bd.--McLaughlin Gormley King Company, Minneapolis, MN; *U.S. Private*, pg. 723
Gullotti, Russell A., Chm. Bd., Pres. & Chief Exec. Officer--National Computer Systems, Eden Prairie, MN; *U.S. Public*, pg. 1155
Gumbiner, Anthony J., Chm. Bd. & Chief Exec. Officer--The Hallwood Group Incorporated, Dallas, TX; *U.S. Public*, pg. 777
Gumpertz, Donald G., Chm. Bd., Pres. & Chief Exec. Officer--Industrial Electronic Engineers, Inc., Van Nuys, CA; *U.S. Private*, pg. 561
Gunderson, Richard L., Chm. Bd. & Chief Exec. Officer--Aid Association for Lutherans, Appleton, WI; *U.S. Private*, pg. 27
Gunji, Hiromi, Chm. Bd., Pres. & Chief Exec. Officer--Brother International Corporation, Somerset, NJ; *Int'l*, pg. 229
Gunn, Curtis C., Jr., Chm. Bd.--Curtis C. Gunn, Inc., San Antonio, TX; *U.S. Private*, pg. 488
Guont, James R., Chm., Pres. & Chief Exec. Officer--The Fifth Third Bank of Kentucky, Louisville, Louisville, KY; *U.S. Public*, pg. 621
Gupata, Vinita, Chm. Bd.--Digital Link Corporation, Sunnyvale, CA; *U.S. Public*, pg. 508
Gupta, Narendra K., Chm. Bd., Chief Exec. Officer & Sec.--Integrated Systems, Inc., Sunnyvale, CA; *U.S. Public*, pg. 885
Gupta, Vinod, Chm. Bd.--American Business Advertising, Omaha, NE; *U.S. Private*, pg. 51
Gupta, Vinod, Chm. Bd.--American Business Information, Inc., Omaha, NE; *U.S. Public*, pg. 69
Gurasich, Steve, Chm. Bd.--GSD&M, Austin, TX; *U.S. Private*, pg. 436
Gurbacki, Gerry, Chm. Bd. & Chief Exec. Officer--Pameco Corp., Norcross, GA; *U.S. Public*, pg. 1255
Gurewitz, Richard, Chm. Bd., Pres. & Chief Exec. Officer--Poly Pak America, Inc., Los Angeles, CA; *U.S. Private*, pg. 875
Gurian, Kenneth J., Chm. Bd. & Chief Exec. Officer--BGM Health Communications, Inc., Los Angeles, CA; *U.S. Public*, pg. 1223
Gury, David J., Chm. Bd., Pres. & Chief Exec. Officer--Nabi, Boca Raton, FL; *U.S. Public*, pg. 1148
Gusick, Dennis, Chm. Bd., Pres. & Chief Exec. Officer--Helm, Inc., Detroit, MI; *U.S. Private*, pg. 520
Gussack, Seymour, Chm. Bd.--General Bearing Corp., West Nyack, NY; *U.S. Public*, pg. 706
Gustaferro, Angelo, Chm. Bd., Pres. & Chief Exec. Officer--nVIEW Corporation, Newport News, VA; *U.S. Public*, pg. 1206
Gustafson, F. Edward, Chm. Bd., Pres. & Chief Exec. Officer--Envirodyne Industries, Inc., Oak Brook, IL; *U.S. Public*, pg. 586
Gustafson, James E., Chm. Bd. & Chief Exec. Officer--General Reinsurance Corp., Stamford, CT; *U.S. Public*, pg. 725
Gustin, Abe J., Jr., Chm. Bd. & Chief Exec. Officer--Applebee's International, Inc., Overland Park, KS; *U.S. Public*, pg. 122
Gut, Rainer E., Chm. Bd.--Credit Suisse Group, Zurich, Switzerland; *Int'l*, pg. 345
Guth, John E., Jr., Chm. Bd.--National-Standard Co., Niles, MI; *U.S. Public*, pg. 1160
Guthart, Leo, Chm. Bd.--ADI (Ademco Distribution, Inc.), Syosset, NY; *U.S. Public*, pg. 1306
Guthart, Leo, Chm. Bd.--Cylink Corp., Sunnyvale, CA; *U.S. Public*, pg. 1306
Guthrie, Herbert W., Chm. Bd.--First Virginia Bank-Piedmont, Lynchburg, VA; *U.S. Public*, pg. 642
Guthrie, M. Philip, Chm. Bd., Pres. & Chief Exec. Officer--American Eagle Group, Inc., Dallas, TX; *U.S. Public*, pg. 71
Guthrie, Warren, Chm.--Leo Burnett Company, Ltd.-Taiwan Branch, Taipei, Taiwan; *U.S. Private*, pg. 185
Gutierrez, Graciela, Chm. Bd. & Chief Exec. Officer--Mercantile Bank, Brownsville, TX; *U.S. Private*, pg. 731
Gutierrez, Juan J., Chm. Bd. & Pres.--Kemron Environmental Services, Inc., Vienna, VA; *U.S. Private*, pg. 614
Gutierrez, Ricardo, Chm. Bd.--Grupo Industrial Camesa S.A. de C.V., Mexico, Mexico; *Int'l*, pg. 575
Gutmann, Max, Chm. Bd.--The Elder-Beerman Stores Corp., Dayton, OH; *U.S. Private*, pg. 367
Gutterman, Arthur, Chm. Bd., Pres., Chief Exec. & Chief Oper. Officer--Jelmar Company, Lincolnwood, IL; *U.S. Private*, pg. 585
Guyette, James M, Chm. Bd. & Pres.--Air Canada, New York, NY; *Int'l*, pg. 36
Guzey, John S., Chm. Bd.--Pioneer American Holding Company, Carbondale, PA; *U.S. Public*, pg. 1298
Guzzle, Timothy L., Chm. Bd. & Chief Exec. Officer--TECO Energy, Inc., Tampa, FL; *U.S. Public*, pg. 1565
Gwinn, J. Campbell, Chm. Bd.--National Bank of Summers, Hinton, WV; *U.S. Public*, pg. 836
Gwinn, John Curt, Chm. Bd.--Congaree Construction Co., Inc., Columbia, SC; *U.S. Private*, pg. 263
Gyll, Soren, Chm. Bd.--Pharmacia & Upjohn, Inc., Windsor, United Kingdom; *Int'l*, pg. 1047
Gyllenhammar, Pehr, Chm. Bd.--Pharmacia & Upjohn Biosystems AB, Uppsala, Sweden; *Int'l*, pg. 1047
Gyotoku, Katsumi, Exec. Chm.--The Kyoei Mutual Fire & Marine Insurance Company, Tokyo, Japan; *Int'l*, pg. 777
Haab, Larry, Chm. Bd., Pres. & Chief Exec. Officer--Illinova Inc., Decatur, IL; *U.S. Public*, pg. 869
Haab, Larry D., Chm. Bd., Pres. & Chief Exec. Officer--Illinois Power Company, Decatur, IL; *U.S. Public*, pg. 869
Haab, Larry D., Chm.--Illinova Generating Co., Decatur, IL; *U.S. Public*, pg. 870
Haab, Larry D., Chm.--Illinova Energy Partners, Inc., Oak Brook, IL; *U.S. Public*, pg. 870
Haack, Arthur L., Chm. Bd. & Sec.--Hickman, Williams Canada, Inc., Cambridge, Canada; *U.S. Private*, pg. 525
Haas, Robert B., Chm. Bd.--Haas, Wheat & Partners, Dallas, TX; *U.S. Private*, pg. 492
Haas, Robert B., Chm. Bd.--Playtex Products Inc., Westport, CT; *U.S. Public*, pg. 1310
Haas, Robert D., Chm. Bd. & Chief Exec. Officer--Levi Strauss & Co., San Francisco, CA; *U.S. Private*, pg. 662
Haavisto, Heikki, Chm. Bd.--Raisio Group, Raisio, Finland; *Int'l*, pg. 1085
Haberberger, Arthur A., Chm. Bd.--The Business Outlet, Inc., Reading, PA; *Int'l*, pg. 9
Habgood, Anthony, Chm. Bd.--Bunzl PLC, London, United Kingdom; *Int'l*, pg. 232
Habig, Douglas A., Chm. Bd. & Chief Exec. Oficer--Kimball International, Inc., Jasper, IN; *U.S. Public*, pg. 956
Hacala, John, Chm. & Chief Exec. Officer--Spencer Gifts, Inc., Egg Harbor Township, NJ; *Int'l*, pg. 1216
Hach-Darrow, Kathryn C., Chm. Bd. & Chief Exec. Officer--Hach Company, Loveland, CO; *U.S. Public*, pg. 773
Hackett, Luther F., Chm. Bd.--Banknorth Group Inc., Burlington, VT; *U.S. Public*, pg. 186
Hackett, Roger B., Chm. Bd., Pres., Chief Exec. & Chief Oper. Officer--Go-Video, Inc., Scottsdale, AZ; *U.S. Public*, pg. 748
Hackl, A.J., Chm. Bd.--Herff Jones Inc., Indianapolis, IN; *U.S. Private*, pg. 523
Hackl, Maximilian, Dr., Chm.-Supervisory Bd.--Bayerische Vereinsbank Group, Munich, Germany; *Int'l*, pg. 178
Hackman, Roger, Vice Chm.--Grizzard, Atlanta, GA; *U.S. Private*, pg. 482
Hackney, T. Morris, Chm. Bd. & Chief Exec. Officer--Citation Corporation, Birmingham, AL; *U.S. Public*, pg. 376
Hadawi, Sami, Chm. Bd.--Dena Corporation, Elk Grove Village, IL; *U.S. Private*, pg. 324
Hadfield, F.C., Chm. Bd.--International Center for Entrepreneurial Development, Inc., Cypress, TX; *U.S. Private*, pg. 568
Hadfield, Neil, Chm. Bd., Chief Fin. Officer & Sec.--Western Pacific Data Systems, La Jolla, CA; *U.S. Private*, pg. 1168
Hadjigancheva, Vihra, Chm.--Leo Burnett Advertising, Sofia, Bulgaria; *U.S. Private*, pg. 184
Hadler, Harry G., Chm.--Hadson Corporation, Oklahoma City, OK; *U.S. Public*, pg. 119
Hadley, Leonard A., Chm. Bd. & Chief Exec. Officer--Maytag Corporation, Newton, IA; *U.S. Public*, pg. 1064
Haefner, Walter, Chm. Bd.--Careal Holding AG, Zurich, Switzerland; *Int'l*, pg. 271
Haegele, Jack E., Chm. Bd. & Pres.--TBG Services, Inc., New York, NY; *Int'l*, pg. 1335
Haerther, Daniel P., Chm. Bd.--Semblex Corporation, Elmhurst, IL; *U.S. Private*, pg. 983
Hafer, Fred D., Chm. Bd., Pres. & Chief Exec. Officer--GPU, Inc., Morristown, NJ; *U.S. Public*, pg. 695
Haft, Robert S., Chm. Bd.--Trak Auto West, Inc., Landover, MD; *U.S. Public*, pg. 484
Hagan, J. Michael, Chm. Bd. & Chief Exec. Officer--Furon Company, Laguna Niguel, CA; *U.S. Public*, pg. 688
Hageman, James A., Chm.--May Merchandising Company, Saint Louis, MO; *U.S. Public*, pg. 1064
Hagenlocker, Edward, Chm. Bd.--Ford of Europe, Incorporated, Dearborn, MI; *U.S. Public*, pg. 664
Hager, Edward B., M.D., Chm. Bd. & Chief Exec. Officer--IGI, Inc., Buena, NJ; *U.S. Public*, pg. 855
Haggai, Thomas S., Chm. Bd. & Chief Exec. Officer--IGA, Inc. (Independent Grocers Alliance), Chicago, IL; *U.S. Private*, pg. 555
Haggar, J.M., III, Chm. Bd. & Chief Exec. Officer--Haggar Corporation, Dallas, TX; *U.S. Public*, pg. 774
Haggen, Donald E., Co-Chm. Bd.--Haggen, Inc., Bellingham, WA; *U.S. Private*, pg. 493
Haggen, Richard R., Co-Chm. Bd.--Haggen, Inc., Bellingham, WA; *U.S. Private*, pg. 493
Haggerty, Charles A., Chm. Bd., Pres. & Chief Exec. Officer--Western Digital Corporation, Irvine, CA; *U.S. Public*, pg. 1758
Hagie, R.W., Chm. Bd.--Hagie Manufacturing Co., Clarion, IA; *U.S. Private*, pg. 493
Haglund, Anders, Chm. Bd.--IL Returpapper, Stockholm, Sweden; *Int'l*, pg. 646
Hagood, Benjamin A., Chm. Bd.--William M. Bird & Co., Inc., Charleston, SC; *U.S. Private*, pg. 145
Hahn, Dean L., Chm. Bd. & Chief Exec. Officer--Hawkins Chemical, Inc., Minneapolis, MN; *U.S. Public*, pg. 800
Hahn, Lloyd, Chm. Bd.--Hahn Equipment Co., Evansville, IN; *U.S. Public*, pg. 1624
Hahn, Philip J., Co.-Chm. Bd.--M. Fabrikant & Sons, Inc., New York, NY; *U.S. Private*, pg. 390
Hahn, Warren E., Chm. Bd.--Hahn Systems, Inc., Indianapolis, IN; *U.S. Private*, pg. 493
Haidinger, Robert N., Chm. Bd., Pres. & Chief Exec. Officer--JJI Lighting Group Inc., Greenwich, CT; *Int'l*, pg. 821
Haigh, Robert B., Chm. Bd., Chief Exec. Officer & Treas.--Chicago Tube & Iron Co., Chicago, IL; *U.S. Private*, pg. 235
Haimann, Emilio, Pres.--BDDP S.p.A, Milan, Italy; *Int'l*, pg. 117

Haines, W.K., Sr., Chm. Bd.--Haines & Co., Inc., Canton, OH; *U.S. Private*, pg. 494
Hair, Hugh A., Chm. Bd. & Chief Exec. Officer--Anaren Microwave Inc., East Syracuse, NY; *U.S. Public*, pg. 110
Hajjar, W. Douglas, Chm. Bd.--Control Data Systems, Inc., Arden Hills, MN; *U.S. Public*, pg. 441
Hakes, Ellen H., Chm. Bd.--Construction Specialties, Inc., Cranford, NJ; *U.S. Private*, pg. 266
Hakes, Thomas B., Co-Chm.--Construction Specialties, Inc., Cranford, NJ; *U.S. Private*, pg. 266
Hakim, Joseph E., Chm. Bd.--Bradley Real Estate, Inc., Northbrook, IL; *U.S. Public*, pg. 250
Haking, W., Chm. Bd.--Haking Enterprises, Quarry Bay, Hong Kong; *Int'l*, pg. 586
Halbreich, Stanley I., Chm. Bd. & Chief Exec. Officer--Littlefield, Adams & Company, Huber Heights, OH; *U.S. Public*, pg. 1001
Halbrook, John A., Chm. Bd., Pres. & Chief Exec. Officer--Woodward Governor Company, Rockford, IL; *U.S. Public*, pg. 1776
Hale, John, Chm. Bd., Pres. & Chief Exec. Officer--Telex Communications, Inc., Minneapolis, MN; *U.S. Private*, pg. 1074
Hale, Martin M., Chm. Bd.--Great Lakes Chemical Corporation, West Lafayette, IN; *U.S. Public*, pg. 760
Hale, Roger L., Chm. Bd., Pres. & Chief Exec. Officer--Tennant Company, Minneapolis, MN; *U.S. Public*, pg. 1577
Hale, Roger W., Chm. Bd., Pres. & Chief Exec. Officer--LG & E Energy Corp., Louisville, KY; *U.S. Public*, pg. 970
Hales, Antony J., Chm.--Allied Domecq Retailing Limited, Burton on Trent, United Kingdom; *Int'l*, pg. 63
Haley, Daniel J., Chm. Bd.--Weather Barrier Inc., Conshohocken, PA; *U.S. Private*, pg. 406
Haley, Daniel J., Chm. Bd.--Spring Mill Corp., Conshohocken, PA; *U.S. Private*, pg. 406
Haley, Daniel J., Jr., Chm. Bd.--Finnaren & Haley, Inc., Conshohocken, PA; *U.S. Private*, pg. 405
Haley, John J., Chm. Bd.--NJ Transit, Newark, NJ; *U.S. Private*, pg. 794
Haley, Larry W., Chm. Bd. & Pres.--Midwest Tire & Muffler, Inc., Rapid City, SD; *U.S. Private*, pg. 745
Haley, Mark T., Chm. Bd. & Chief Exec. Officer--Brown & Haley, Tacoma, WA; *U.S. Private*, pg. 173
Haley, Thomas W., Chm. Bd. & Chief Exec. Officer--Innovex, Inc., Hopkins, MN; *U.S. Public*, pg. 880
Hall, Bjorn, Chm. Bd.--Skandia Asia Ltd., Central, Hong Kong; *Int'l*, pg. 1258
Hall, Craig, Chm. Bd.--Hall Financial Group, Inc., Dallas, TX; *U.S. Private*, pg. 495
Hall, Donald J., Chm. Bd.--Hallmark Cards, Inc., Kansas City, MO; *U.S. Private*, pg. 495
Hall, Floyd, Chm. Bd., Pres. & Chief Exec. Officer--Kmart Corporation, Troy, MI; *U.S. Public*, pg. 963
Hall, J.C., Chm. Bd.--RMP Properties Ltd., Crown Mines, South Africa; *Int'l*, pg. 1081
Hall, Kenneth E., Chm. Bd.--Hall Contracting Corp., Louisville, KY; *U.S. Private*, pg. 495
Hall, L.G., Jr., Chm. Bd.--Stackpole Ltd., Newton, MA; *U.S. Private*, pg. 1028
Hall, Phillip G., Chm. Bd.--CH2M Hill, Inc., Greenwood Village, CO; *U.S. Private*, pg. 195
Hall, Robert J., Chm. & Publr.--The Philadelphia Inquirer, Philadelphia, PA; *U.S. Public*, pg. 964
Halla, Brian, Chm. Bd., Pres. & Chief Exec. Officer--National Semiconductor Corporation, Santa Clara, CA; *U.S. Public*, pg. 1159
Hallaker, Rune, Chm. Bd.--Intercontinental Corporation, Indianapolis, IN; *Int'l*, pg. 464
Hallam, John F., Chm. Bd.--Ceiling & Partitions, Inc., Landover, MD; *U.S. Private*, pg. 221
Hallam, Robert, Chm. Bd. & Chief Exec. Officer--Ben E. Keith Company, Fort Worth, TX; *U.S. Private*, pg. 611
Hallden, Lars, Chm. Bd.--Trygg-Hansa, Stockholm, Sweden; *Int'l*, pg. 1425
Halle, Bruce T., Sr., Chm. Bd. & Chief Exec. Officer--Reinalt-Thomas Corp., Ann Arbor, MI; *U.S. Private*, pg. 919
Haller, Peter, Dr., Chm. Bd.--Serviceplan GmbH, Munich, Germany; *Int'l*, pg. 1225
Halley, Paul-Louis, Chm. Bd. & Chief Exec. Officer--Promodes SA, Mondeville, France; *Int'l*, pg. 1071
Halliday, Robert W., Chm. Emeritus--Franchise Finance Corp. of America, Scottsdale, AZ; *U.S. Public*, pg. 679
Halna du Fretay, Amaury, Chm. Bd. & Chief Exec. Officer--Labinal SA, Montigny-le-Bretonneux, France; *Int'l*, pg. 785
Halparin, Scott, Chm. Bd., Chief Exec. Officer & Treas.--Saratoga Brands, Inc., Lakewood, NJ; *U.S. Public*, pg. 1435
Halperin, Thomas C., Chm Bd., Pres. & Chief Exec. Officer--Commercial Light Company, Hillside, IL; *U.S. Private*, pg. 258
Halpern, Merril M., Chm. Bd.--Charterhouse Group International, Inc., New York, NY; *U.S. Private*, pg. 230
Halpern, Richard C., Chm. & Chief Exec. Officer--Schal Bovis Inc., Chicago, IL; *Int'l*, pg. 1033
Halsam, James A., II, Chm. Bd.--Pilot Corporation, Knoxville, TN; *U.S. Private*, pg. 865
Halton, Dale F., Chm. Bd., Pres. & Chief Exec. Officer--Pepsi-Cola Bottling Company of Charlotte Inc., Charlotte, NC; *U.S. Private*, pg. 852
Hamada, Hiroshi, Chm. Bd.--Ricoh Company, Ltd., Tokyo, Japan; *Int'l*, pg. 1114
Hamada, Shohei, Chm. Bd.--NHK Spring Co., Ltd., Yokohama, Japan; *Int'l*, pg. 901
Hamaker, Eugene D., Chm. Bd.--Chemical Bank South, Marshall, MI; *U.S. Public*, pg. 345
Hamann, Donald D., Chm. Bd.--Jewelers Mutual Insurance Company, Neenah, WI; *U.S. Private*, pg. 587
Hamblett, Stephen, Chm. Bd. & Publr.--Providence Journal-Bulletin, Providence, RI; *U.S. Public*, pg. 209
Hambro, Lord, Chm. Bd.--Guardian Royal Exchange Plc, London, United Kingdom; *Int'l*, pg. 577
Hamilton, David R., Chm. Bd., Pres. & Chief Exec. Officer--Chemical Leaman Corporation, Exton, PA; *U.S. Private*, pg. 233
Hamilton, Frederic C., Chm. Bd.--Tejas Gas Corporation, Houston, TX; *Int'l*, pg. 1136
Hamilton, Jack, Chm. Bd. & Chief Exec. Officer--Dunbarton Corporation, Dothan, AL; *U.S. Private*, pg. 194
Hamilton, Richard F., Chm. Bd. & Chief Exec. Officer--Monterey Mechanical Company, Oakland, CA; *U.S. Private*, pg. 758
Hamilton, Thomas M., Chm. Bd., Pres. & Chief Exec. Officer--EEX Corporation, Houston, TX; *U.S. Public*, pg. 542
Hamister, Mark E., Chm. Bd. & Chief Exec. Officer--National Health Care Affiliates, Inc., Buffalo, NY; *U.S. Private*, pg. 784
Hammes, Michael N., Chm. Bd. & Chief Exec. Officer--The Canadian Coleman Co., Ltd., Toronto, Canada; *U.S. Private*, pg. 691
Hammill, Richard D., Chm. Bd., Pres. & Chief Exec. Officer--Hycor Biomedical, Inc., Irvine, CA; *U.S. Public*, pg. 851
Hammond, Daniel D., Chm. Bd. & Chief Exec. Officer--InterVoice, Inc., Dallas, TX; *U.S. Public*, pg. 910
Hammond, Gaines W., Jr., M.D., Chm. Bd.--Maxum Health Corp., Dallas, TX; *U.S. Public*, pg. 881
Hammond, Harvey K., Jr., Chm. Bd., Pres. & Chief Exec. Officer--HNTB Corporation, Kansas City, MO; *U.S. Private*, pg. 492
Hammond, Toby B., Chm. Bd. & Pres.--Hancock Lumber, Inc., Casco, ME; *U.S. Private*, pg. 498
Hampel, Ronald, Sir, Chm. Bd.--Imperial Chemical Industries PLC, London, United Kingdom; *Int'l*, pg. 662
Hampp, Rainer, Chm. & Chief Exec. Officer--Bertelsmann Printing & Manufacturing Corp., Berryville, VA; *Int'l*, pg. 191
Hampson, C., Chm. Bd.--RMC Group p.l.c., Egham, United Kingdom; *Int'l*, pg. 1078
Hampton, John C., Chm. Bd.--Hampton Resources Inc., Portland, OR; *U.S. Private*, pg. 498
Hamrick, Leon C., Chm. Bd.--Mutual Assurance, Inc., Birmingham, AL; *U.S. Public*, pg. 1080
Hanafi bin Ramli, Y.B. Dato' Haji, Chm. Bd.--Malaysia Tourism Promotion Board (MTPB), Kuala Lumpur, Malaysia; *Int'l*, pg. 832
Hand, Elbert O., Chm. Bd. & Chief Exec. Officer--Hartmarx Corporation, Chicago, IL; *U.S. Public*, pg. 795
Handel, Morton E., Chm. Bd.--Concurrent Computer Corporation, Fort Lauderdale, FL; *U.S. Public*, pg. 430
Handleman, David, Chm. Bd.--Handleman Company, Troy, MI; *U.S. Public*, pg. 779
Haney, William M., III, Chm. Bd., Pres. & Chief Exec. Officer--Molten Metal Technology, Inc., Fall River, MA; *U.S. Public*, pg. 1123
Hankin, R.N., Chm. Bd.--House of Fabrics, Inc., Sherman Oaks, CA; *U.S. Public*, pg. 842
Hanley, John J., Chm. Bd. & Chief Exec. Officer--Scientific American, Inc., New York, NY; *Int'l*, pg. 1479
Hanlon, Ted, Chm. Bd.--Computalog Ltd., Calgary, Canada; *Int'l*, pg. 325
Hann, J. David, Chm. Bd.--Digital Sound Corporation, Carpinteria, CA; *U.S. Public*, pg. 508
Hann, James, Sir, Chm. Bd.--Hickson International Plc, Castleford, United Kingdom; *Int'l*, pg. 618
Hann, S.A., Chm. Bd. & Pres.--Medicalodges, Inc., Coffeyville, KS; *U.S. Private*, pg. 728
Hanna, R.G.C., Chm. Bd.--Ervin Amasteel Uk. LP, Tipton, United Kingdom; *U.S. Private*, pg. 382
Hannon, John W., Chm. Bd.--Rollins Hudig Hall of Indiana, Inc., Indianapolis, IN; *U.S. Public*, pg. 117
Hanrahan, Michael, Chm. Bd.--Kerry Group PLC, Tralee, Ireland; *Int'l*, pg. 731
Hansberger, R.V., Chm. Bd.--RAM Golf Corporation, Melrose Park, IL; *U.S. Private*, pg. 908
Hansen, Charles M., Jr., Chm. Bd. & Chief Exec. Officer--Pillowtex Corporation, Dallas, TX; *U.S. Public*, pg. 1296
Hansen, Claire V., Chm. Bd.--Duff & Phelps Utilities Income Inc., Chicago, IL; *U.S. Public*, pg. 534
Hansen, Darryl D., Chm. Bd., Pres. & Chief Exec. Officer--Preferred Risk Mutual Insurance, West Des Moines, IA; *U.S. Private*, pg. 880
Hansen, Donald W., Chm. Bd. & Pres.--Delta Resins & Refractories, Inc., Milwaukee, WI; *U.S. Private*, pg. 323
Hansen, James, Chm. Bd. & Pres.--VideoLabs, Inc., Minneapolis, MN; *U.S. Public*, pg. 1720
Hansen, K.W., Chm. Bd.--Crystal Cream & Butter Company, Sacramento, CA; *U.S. Private*, pg. 294
Hansen, Poul, Chm. Bd.--Chr. Hansen, Inc., Milwaukee, WI; *Int'l*, pg. 288
Hansmeyer, Herbert, Chm. Bd. & Chief Exec. Officer--Allianz of America, Inc., Westport, CT; *Int'l*, pg. 58
Hanson, Charles G., III, Chm. Bd. & Chief Exec. Officer--American Pad and Paper Company, Dallas, TX; *U.S. Public*, pg. 88
Hanson, James, Lord, Chm. Bd.--Hanson PLC, London, United Kingdom; *Int'l*, pg. 592
Hanson, John N., Chm. & Chief Exec. Officer--Beloit Corporation, Beloit, WI; *U.S. Public*, pg. 789
Hanson, Rick, Chm. Bd., Pres. & Chief Exec. Officer--Old Home Foods, Inc., Saint Paul, MN; *U.S. Private*, pg. 814
Hantho, Charles H., Chm. Bd.--DoFasco, Inc., Hamilton, Canada; *Int'l*, pg. 414
Hantho, Charles H., Chm. Bd.--Dominion Textile Inc., Montreal, Canada; *Int'l*, pg. 415
Harad, George J., Chm. Bd. & Chief Exec. Officer--Boise Cascade Corporation, Boise, ID; *U.S. Public*, pg. 242
Harad, George J., Chm. Bd. & Chief Exec. Officer--Boise Cascade Paper Div., Boise, ID; *U.S. Public*, pg. 243
Harary, Ralph, Chm. Bd.--Jacques Moret, Inc., New York, NY; *U.S. Private*, pg. 580
Haratuman, M., Chm. Bd. & Chief Exec. Officer--STV Incorporated, New York, NY; *U.S. Public*, pg. 1421
Haratunian, Michael, Chm. Bd. & Chief Exec. Officer--STV Group, Inc., Douglassville, PA; *U.S. Public*, pg. 1421
Harbin, John P., Chm. Bd. & Chief Exec. Officer--Lone Star Technologies, Inc., Dallas, TX; *U.S. Public*, pg. 1012
Harbison, Gregory A., Pres., Chief Exec. & Trust Officer--Rockville National Bank, Rockville, IN; *U.S. Public*, pg. 1217
Harburg, Lester, Chm. Bd.--Gibson's Discount Centers Inc., Dodge City, KS; *U.S. Private*, pg. 452
Harcum, Joseph A., Chm. & Chief Exec. Officer--Fleet Securities, Inc., New York, NY; *U.S. Public*, pg. 650
Hardaway, L.H., Jr., Chm. Bd.--Hardaway Construction Corp. of Tennessee, Inc., Nashville, TN; *U.S. Private*, pg. 501
Harden, David E., Chm. Bd.--Harden Furniture Company, McConnellsville, NY; *U.S. Private*, pg. 501
Hardie, Jeremy, Chm. Bd.--W.H. Smith Group plc, London, United Kingdom; *Int'l*, pg. 1264
Hardie, Robert, Chm. Bd.--Freedom Communication Inc., Irvine, CA; *U.S. Private*, pg. 425
Harding, Enoch Jr., Chm. Bd.--Kellwood Sportswear, Rutherford, TN; *U.S. Public*, pg. 948
Harding, L. Wayne, Chm. Bd.--Santa Monica Ford Company, Santa Monica, CA; *U.S. Private*, pg. 965
Harding, Richard S., Chm. Emeritus--Harding Lawson Associates Group, Inc., Novato, CA; *U.S. Public*, pg. 785
Harding, Robert J., Chm. Bd.--EdperBrascan Corporation, Toronto, Canada; *Int'l*, pg. 433
Hardis, Stephen R., Chm. Bd. & Chief Exec. Officer--Eaton Corporation, Cleveland, OH; *U.S. Public*, pg. 555
Hardy, Joseph A. Sr., Chm. Bd. & Chief Exec. Officer--84 Lumber Company, Eighty Four, PA; *U.S. Private*, pg. 366
Hardy, R.B., Chm. Bd.--Russell Harrington Cutlery Inc., Southbridge, MA; *U.S. Private*, pg. 551
Hardy, Richard B., Chm. Bd. & Chief Exec. Officer--Hyde Manufacturing Co., Southbridge, MA; *U.S. Private*, pg. 551
Hardymon, James F., Chm. Bd. & Chief Exec. Officer--Textron Inc., Providence, RI; *U.S. Public*, pg. 1588
Harf, Peter, Chm. Bd.--Benckiser Consumer Products Inc., Greenwich, CT; *Int'l*, pg. 185
Harford, Jim, Chm. Bd., Pres. & Chief Exec. Officer--Everfresh Beverages Inc., Chicago, IL; *U.S. Public*, pg. 1153
Hargett, Edd, Chm. Bd.--Texas Electric Cooperatives, Inc., Austin, TX; *U.S. Private*, pg. 1078
Hargrove, G. Thomas, Chm. Bd.--The At-A-Glance Group, Sidney, NY; *U.S. Private*, pg. 295
Hargrove, Jack L., Chm. Bd.--Intercounty Title Co. of Illinois, Chicago, IL; *U.S. Private*, pg. 567
Harig, Hans-Dieter, Dr., Chm.--PreussenElektra Aktiengesellschaft, Hannover, Germany; *Int'l*, pg. 1456
Harker, John V., Chm. Bd., Pres. & Chief Exec. Officer--In Focus Systems, Inc., Wilsonville, OR; *U.S. Public*, pg. 873
Harkins, Frank S., Jr., Chm. Bd. & Chief Exec. Officer--Horizon Bancorp, Inc., Beckley, WV; *U.S. Public*, pg. 836
Harlow, V.R., Chm.-Intl. Mgr.--Sun Company, Inc. (R&M), Philadelphia, PA; *U.S. Public*, pg. 1530
Harmala, Jukka, Chm. Bd., Pres. & Chief Exec. Officer--Enso Oyj, Helsinki, Finland; *Int'l*, pg. 455
Harman, Sidney, Chm. Bd. & Chief Exec. Officer--Harman International Industries, Inc., Woodbury, NY; *U.S. Public*, pg. 787
Harmon, David E., Chm. Bd., Pres., Chief Exec. & Chief Oper. Officer--El Camino Resources, Ltd., Woodland Hills, CA; *U.S. Private*, pg. 366
Harmon, James D., Chm. Bd.--Twin City Die Castings Co., Minneapolis, MN; *U.S. Private*, pg. 1111
Harmon, Lowell D., Chm. Bd. & Pres.--Progressive Driver Services, Inc., Jacksonville, FL; *U.S. Private*, pg. 890
Harmon, Robert E., Chm. Bd.--Harmon Industries, Inc., Blue Springs, MO; *U.S. Public*, pg. 788
Harmon, Terry, Chm. Bd.--Harmon City, Inc., Salt Lake City, UT; *U.S. Private*, pg. 503
Harmon, Timothy, Chm. Bd.--Hercules Engine Company, Canton, OH; *U.S. Private*, pg. 523
Harnett, Gordon D., Chm. Bd., Pres. & Chief Exec. Officer--Brush Wellman Inc., Cleveland, OH; *U.S. Public*, pg. 266
Harp Helu, Alfredo, Chm. Bd.--Grupo Financiero Banamex/Accival, S.A. de C.V., Mexico, Mexico; *Int'l*, pg. 574
Harp, Gerald L., Chm. Bd. & Pres.--Harp's Food Stores, Inc., Springdale, AR; *U.S. Private*, pg. 504
Harper, Daniel R., Chm. Bd. & Pres.--Harper Bros., Inc., Fort Myers, FL; *U.S. Private*, pg. 504
Harper, Marvin, Chm. Bd. & Chief Exec. Officer--General Spring, Inc., Hartsville, TN; *U.S. Private*, pg. 445
Harper, Ronald G., Chm. Bd., Pres. & Chief Exec. Officer--MPSI Systems Inc., Tulsa, OK; *U.S. Public*, pg. 1027
Harpoth, Steffen, Chm. Bd.--SAS Park Royal Hotel, Lysaker, Norway; *Int'l*, pg. 1202
Harr, Ralph P., Chm. Bd.--Tri-City Bank and Trust Company, Blountville, TN; *U.S. Public*, pg. 642
Harreld, M., Chm. Bd. & Chief Exec. Officer--PNC Bank, Louisville, KY; *U.S. Public*, pg. 1242
Harrell, Henry H., Chm. Bd. & Chief Exec. Officer--Universal Corporation, Richmond, VA; *U.S. Public*, pg. 1694
Harrell, James L., III, Chm. Bd.--Camellia Food Stores, Inc., Norfolk, VA; *U.S. Private*, pg. 203
Harrell, Samuel M., Chm. Bd., Pres. & Chief Exec. Officer--EDI International, Inc., Cincinnati, OH; *U.S. Private*, pg. 353
Harrington, Mark G., Chm. Bd. & Chief Exec. Officer--HarCor Energy, Inc., Houston, TX; *U.S. Public*, pg. 782
Harrington, R.L., Chm. Bd.--Dumore Corporation, Mauston, WI; *U.S. Private*, pg. 346
Harris, A., Chm.--Scaw Metal Ltd., Johannesburg, South Africa; *Int'l*, pg. 76
Harris, Alexander W., Chm. Bd.--General Tours Inc., Keene, NH; *U.S. Private*, pg. 445
Harris, D. George, Chm. Bd. & Chief Exec. Officer--Harris Chemical Group, Inc., New York, NY; *U.S. Private*, pg. 505
Harris, D. George, Chm. Bd.--North American Salt Company, Overland Park, KS; *U.S. Private*, pg. 505

Harris, David W., Chm. Bd.--Central United Life Insurance Co., Houston, TX; *U.S. Private*, pg. 225

Harris, Eldon D., Chm. Bd. & Chief Exec. Officer--Manufacturers Railway Company, Saint Louis, MO; *U.S. Public*, pg. 114

Harris, George C., Chm. Bd. & Pres.--Lumber Group Inc., Dothan, AL; *U.S. Private*, pg. 680

Harris, Irving B., Chm.-Exec. Committee--Pittway Corporation, Chicago, IL; *U.S. Public*, pg. 1305

Harris, J. Wayne, Chm. & Chief Exec. Officer-Canada--The Great Atlantic & Pacific Tea Company, Inc., Montvale, NJ; *Int'l*, pg. 1375

Harris, Jack, Chm. Bd.--Harris Steel Co., Cicero, IL; *U.S. Private*, pg. 506

Harris, Jay, Chm. Bd. & Publisher--San Jose Mercury News, San Jose, CA; *U.S. Public*, pg. 964

Harris, King, Chm. Bd.--AptarGroup, Inc., Crystal Lake, IL; *U.S. Public*, pg. 125

Harris, L. Elvon, Chm.--The Manufacturers (Pacific Asia) Insurance Co. Ltd., Hong Kong, Hong Kong; *Int'l*, pg. 841

Harris, Milton E., Chm. Bd. & Chief Exec. Officer--Harris Steel Group Inc., Willowdale, Canada; *Int'l*, pg. 597

Harris, Neison, Chm. Bd.--Pittway Corporation, Chicago, IL; *U.S. Public*, pg. 1305

Harris, Stuart G., Chm. Bd. & Pres.--S&H Citadel, Inc., Hillside, IL; *U.S. Public*, pg. 990

Harris, T.C., Chm. Bd.--P&O Cruises Limited, London, United Kingdom; *Int'l*, pg. 1033

Harris, Titus H., Jr., Chm. Bd.--The GNI Group, Inc., Deer Park, TX; *U.S. Public*, pg. 693

Harris, W.B., Chm.--Barclays Bank of Canada, Toronto, Canada; *Int'l*, pg. 165

Harrison, Donald, Chm. Bd. & Gen. Counsel--PVS Chemicals, Inc., Detroit, MI; *U.S. Private*, pg. 828

Harrison, Ernest, Sir, Chm. Bd.--Vodafone Group PLC, Newbury, United Kingdom; *Int'l*, pg. 1469

Harrison, Frank, Chm. Bd.--Coca-Cola Consolidated, Charlotte, NC; *U.S. Public*, pg. 392

Harrison, J. Frank, III, Chm. Bd. & Chief Exec. Officer--Coca-Cola Bottling Co. Consolidated, Charlotte, NC; *U.S.* Public, pg. 391

Harrison, J. Frank, Jr., Chm. Emeritus--Coca-Cola Bottling Co. Consolidated, Charlotte, NC; *U.S. Public*, pg. 391

Harrison, P., Chm. Bd.--Alpha Airports Group Plc, London, United Kingdom; *Int'l*, pg. 65

Harrison, Sir Ernest, Chm. Bd.--Racal Electronics Plc, Bracknell, United Kingdom; *Int'l*, pg. 1082

Harrison, Stephen E., Chm. Emeritus--Welsco Inc., North Little Rock, AR; *U.S. Private*, pg. 1161

Harrison, Thomas L., Chm.--Harrison & Star, Inc., New York, NY; *U.S. Private*, pg. 506

Harrison, Tom, Chm. & Chief Exec. Officer--Harrison Wilson & Associates, Parsippany, NJ; *U.S. Public*, pg. 1224

Harrison, William B., Jr., Chm., Pres. & Treas.--Chatham Ventures, Inc., New York, NY; *U.S. Public*, pg. 338

Hart, James W., Chm. Bd., Pres., Chief Exec. Officer & Chief Fin. Officer--Hart Holding Company, Inc., Norwalk, CT; *U.S. Private*, pg. 507

Hart, Joe, Chm. Bd.--Subway Franchise Advertising Fund Trust, Milford, CT; *U.S. Private*, pg. 1048

Hart, Milledge A., III, Chm. Bd.--DocuCorp International, Dallas, TX; *U.S. Public*, pg. 1425

Hart, William, Chm. Bd.--Hart Graphics Inc., Austin, TX; *U.S.* Private, pg. 507

Harte, Houston H., Chm. Bd.--Harte-Hanks Communications, Inc., San Antonio, TX; *U.S. Public*, pg. 793

Hartl, Richard, Chm. Bd., Pres. & Chief Exec. Officer--Calmar Inc., City of Industry, CA; *U.S. Private*, pg. 201

Hartley, T.P., Regional Chm.--Barratt Southern, Wallington, United Kingdom; *Int'l*, pg. 168

Hartley, Thomas Y., Chm. Bd.--Southwest Gas Corporation, Las Vegas, NV; *U.S. Public*, pg. 1493

Hartman, Timothy P., Chm. Bd.--NationsBank of Texas, N.A., Dallas, TX; *U.S. Public*, pg. 1163

Hartman, Timothy P., Chm. Bd.--NationsBank Texas Corporation, Dallas, TX; *U.S. Public*, pg. 1163

Hartmann, Andreas, Chm.--Coop Rechtsschutz, Aarau, Switzerland; *Int'l*, pg. 330

Hartmann, Ulrich, Chm. Bd.--Veba AG, Dusseldorf, Germany; *Int'l*, pg. 1454

Hartong, Hendrik J., Jr., Chm. Bd.--Air Express International Corporation, Darien, CT; *U.S. Public*, pg. 30

Hartt, Stanley H., Chm. Bd.--O&Y Properties Corporation, Toronto, Canada; *Int'l*, pg. 993

Hartt, Stanley H., Chm. Bd.--Camdev Properties Inc., Toronto, Canada; *Int'l*, pg. 993

Hartz, Jack, Chm. Bd.--Great Financial Bank FSB, Louisville, KY; *U.S. Private*, pg. 473

Haruna, Kazuo, Chm. Bd.--Marubeni Corporation, Osaka, Japan; *Int'l*, pg. 844

Harvey, David E., Chm. Bd., Pres., Chief Oper. & Chief Exec. Officer--Rome Cable Corporation, Rome, NY; *U.S. Private*, pg. 942

Harvey, J.M., Chm. Bd.--Courtaulds Aerospace, Littleborough, United Kingdom; *Int'l*, pg. 338

Harvey, John J., Chm. Bd.--Artra Group Incorporated, Northfield, IL; *U.S. Public*, pg. 136

Harvey, Joseph H., Jr., Chm. Bd. & Chief Exec. Officer--J.H. Harvey Company, Nashville, GA; *U.S. Private*, pg. 508

Harvey, Niel, Chm.--Amquip (Proprietary) Limited, Isando, South Africa; *Int'l*, pg. 76

Harvey, Tom, Chm. Bd.--Roy F. Weston, Inc., West Chester, PA; *U.S. Public*, pg. 1761

Harvison, John H., Chm. Bd. & Chief Exec. Officer--FFP Marketing Company, Inc., Fort Worth, TX; *U.S. Public*, pg. 604

Harwood, Lowell, Chm. Bd. & Chief Exec Officer--Square Industries, Inc., Jersey City, NJ; *U.S. Public*, pg. 326

Harwood, Sanford, Asst. Chm. & Sec.--Square Industries, Inc., Jersey City, NJ; *U.S. Public*, pg. 326

Hasan, Malik A., M.D., Chm. Bd.--Qual-Med, Inc., Pueblo, CO; *U.S. Public*, pg. 678

Hasan, Malik M., Chm. Bd. & Chief Exec. Officer--Foundation Health Systems, Inc., Pueblo, CO; *U.S. Public*, pg. 678

Hascall, James G., Chm. Bd. & Chief Exec. Officer--Primex Technologies, Inc., Primex Aerospace, Redmond, WA; *U.S. Public*, pg. 1329

Haserjian, Harold, Chm. Bd.--Carpeteria, Inc., Valencia, CA; *U.S. Private*, pg. 215

Hashida, T., Chm. Bd.--General Sekiyu K.K., Tokyo, Japan; *U.S. Public*, pg. 602

Hashimoto, Toru, Chm. Bd.--The Fuji Bank, Limited, Tokyo, Japan; *Int'l*, pg. 519

Haskayne, Richard F., Chm. Bd.--Nova Corporation, Calgary, Canada; *Int'l*, pg. 971

Haskayne, Richard F., Chm. Bd.--Transalta Corporation, Calgary, Canada; *Int'l*, pg. 1416

Haskayne, Richard S., Chm. Bd.--MacMillan Bloedel Limited, Vancouver, Canada; *Int'l*, pg. 828

Haskell, Donald, Chm. Bd.--Tejon Ranch Company, Lebec, CA; *U.S. Public*, pg. 1566

Haskell, Gary W., Chm. Bd. & Chief Exec. Officer--UMB First National Bank, Collinsville, IL; *U.S. Public*, pg. 1654

Haskins, Christopher, Chm. Bd.--Northern Foods plc, Hull, United Kingdom; *Int'l*, pg. 967

Haskins, John H., Chm. Bd., Pres. & Treas.--Arrow Tank & Engineering Co., Minneapolis, MN; *U.S. Private*, pg. 85

Haslam, Charles L., Chm. Bd. & Chief Exec. Officer--Krug International Corp., Houston, TX; *U.S. Public*, pg. 967

Hassard, W.C., Chm. Bd.--Republic Financial Services, Inc., Dallas, TX; *Int'l*, pg. 346

Hassenfeld, Alan G., Chm. & Chief Exec. Officer--Hasbro, Inc., Pawtucket, RI; *U.S. Public*, pg. 797

Hassinger, Norman M., Jr., Chm. Bd., Pres., Chief Exec. & Chief Oper. Officer--The Hassinger Companies Hoffman Homes, Arlington Heights, IL; *U.S. Private*, pg. 510

Hasson, Ray M., Chm. Bd.--AAF Industries Plc, London, United Kingdom; *Int'l*, pg. 1

Hata, Sachio, Chm. Bd.--ORIX Rentec Corporation, Tokyo, Japan; *Int'l*, pg. 1009

Hatcher, David E., Chm. Bd., Pres. & Chief Exec. Officer--Gamma Biologicals Inc., Houston, TX; *U.S. Public*, pg. 698

Hatchett, A.G., Chm. Bd.--P&O Harbours Ltd., Felixstowe, United Kingdom; *Int'l*, pg. 1034

Hatfield, Joe, Chm. Bd. & Chief Exec. Officer--Fieldale Corporation, Baldwin, GA; *U.S. Private*, pg. 403

Hathaway, Derek C., Chm. Bd. & Chief Exec. Officer--Harsco Corporation, Camp Hill, PA; *U.S. Public*, pg. 792

Hathaway, Derek C., Corp. Chm., Pres. & Chief Exec. Officer--Heckett MultiServ, Butler, PA; *U.S. Public*, pg. 793

Hatlen, Roe H., Chm. Bd. & Chief Exec. Officer--Buffets, Inc., Eden Prairie, MN; *U.S. Public*, pg. 267

Hatsopoulos, George N., Chm. Bd. & Chief Exec. Officer--Thermo Electron Corporation, Waltham, MA; *U.S. Public*, *pg. 1591*

Hatt, James R.S., Chm. Bd., Pres. & Chief Exec. Officer--Petersburg Long Distance Inc., Toronto, Canada; *Int'l*, pg. 1040

Hatta, Nobuo, Chm.--Rohm Electronics (U.K.) Limited, Milton Keynes, United Kingdom; *Int'l*, pg. 1125

Hattink, O., Chm.-Supervisory Bd.--Wolters Kluwer N.V., Amsterdam, Netherlands; *Int'l*, pg. 1512

Hattori, Reijiro, Chm. Bd.--Seiko Corporation, Tokyo, Japan; *Int'l*, pg. 1218

Hattori, Reijiro, Chm. Bd.--Seiko Epson Corporation, Nagano, Japan; *Int'l*, pg. 1219

Haub, Erivan, Owner & Chm. Bd.--Tengelmann Warenhandelsgesellschaft, Mulheim, Germany; *Int'l*, pg. 1375

Hauck, John M., Chm. Bd.--Tubular Steel Inc., Saint Louis, MO; *U.S. Private*, pg. 1108

Haumer, Hans, Chm. Bd.--Liechtenstein Global Trust Limited, Vaduz, Liechtenstein; *Int'l*, pg. 809

Haumer, Hans, Dr., Chm. Bd.--LGT Bank in Liechtenstein Aktiengesellschaft, Vaduz, Liechtenstein; *Int'l*, pg. 809

Hauser, Gerard, Chm.-Cables Sector--Alcatel Alsthom Compagnie Generale D'Electricite, Paris, France; *Int'l*, pg. 52

Hauser, Gustave M., Chm. Bd.--Orion Network Systems Incorporated, Rockville, MD; *Int'l*, pg. 218

Hauslein, James N., Chm. Bd., Pres. & Chief Exec. Officer--Sunglass Hut International, Coral Gables, FL; *U.S. Public*, pg. 1535

Hausmann, Carl, Chm. Bd. & Pres.--Central Soya Company, Inc., Fort Wayne, IN; *Int'l*, pg. 324

Hausmann, Ronald L., Vice Chm.--Walbridge Aldinger Company, Detroit, MI; *U.S. Private*, pg. 1146

Hautcoeur, J. L., Chm. Bd.--Assu-Vie, Paris, France; *Int'l*, pg. 563

Hautcoeur, Jean-Louis, Chm.--NATIO-VIE, Paris, France; *Int'l*, pg. 163

Havener, Gary, Chm. Bd.--Antenna Products Corp., Mineral Wells, TX; *U.S. Public*, pg. 289

Haverland, Richard M., Chm. Bd., Pres. & Chief Exec. Officer--Highlands Insurance Co., Houston, TX; *U.S. Public*, pg. 826

Haverty, Rawson, Chm. Bd.--Haverty Furniture Companies, Inc., Atlanta, GA; *U.S. Public*, pg. 799

Haviland, M.M., Chm. Bd.--Haviland Enterprises, Grand Rapids, MI; *U.S. Private*, pg. 511

Hawk, Richard C., Chm. Bd., Pres. & Chief Exec. Officer--Hawk Management Corporation, Overland Park, KS; *U.S.* Private, pg. 511

Hawk, Stephen L., Chm. & Chief Exec. Officer--Northern Capital Management, Inc., Madison, WI; *U.S. Public*, pg. 1673

Hawkes, James B., Chm. Bd., Pres. & Chief Exec. Officer--Eaton Vance Corp., Boston, MA; *U.S. Public*, pg. 559

Hawkins, Andrew, Chm. & Chief Exec. Officer--GGK London Ltd., London, United Kingdom; *Int'l*, pg. 1335

Hawkins, Arthur M., Chm. Bd., Pres. & Chief Exec. Officer--Exide Corporation, Reading, PA; *U.S. Public*, pg. 600

Hawkins, Ken, Chm. Bd.--Raycom Media, Inc., Montgomery, AL; *U.S. Private*, pg. 911

Hawkins, Marvin J., Sr., Chm. Bd.--J.D. Diffenbaugh, Inc., Riverside, CA; *U.S. Private*, pg. 332

Hawkinson, Lowell, Chm. Bd. & Chief Exec. Officer--Gensym Corporation, Cambridge, MA; *U.S. Public*, pg. 731

Hawley, Frank J. Jr., Chm. Bd.--Morgan Products Ltd., Williamsburg, VA; *U.S. Public*, pg. 1132

Hawley, Philip M., Chm. Bd. & Chief Exec. Officer--Krause's Furniture Inc., Brea, CA; *U.S. Public*, pg. 967

Hawn, Van Zandt, Chm. Bd.--Deltak Inc., Plymouth, MN; *U.S. Public*, pg. 924

Haworth, Richard G., Chm. Bd.--Haworth, Inc., Holland, MI; *U.S. Private*, pg. 511

Haws, Terry, Chm. Bd.--Haws Drinking Faucet Co., Berkeley, CA; *U.S. Private*, pg. 512

Hawthorne, Timothy R., Chm. Bd. & Creative Dir.--Hawthorne Communications, Inc., Fairfield, IA; *U.S. Private*, pg. 512

Hayasaki, Hiroshi, Chm. Bd.--The Sumitomo Trust & Banking Co., Ltd., Osaka, Japan; *Int'l*, pg. 1317

Hayashi, Joji, Chm. Bd.--APL Limited, Oakland, CA; *Int'l*, pg. 912

Hayden, J. P., III, Chm. Bd. & Chief Oper. Officer--The Midland Company, Cincinnati, OH; *U.S. Public*, pg. 1110

Hayden, J.P., Jr., Chm.-Exec. Cmmittee--The Midland Company, Cincinnati, OH; *U.S. Public*, pg. 1110

Hayden, John W., Chm. Bd. & Chief Exec. Officer--C S Crable Sportswear, Inc., Batavia, OH; *U.S. Public*, pg. 1111

Hayek, Nicolas G., Chm. Bd. & Chief Exec. Officer--SMH Swiss Corporation for Micro Electronics & Watchmaking Indus. Ltd., Bienne, Switzerland; *Int'l*, pg. 1160

Hayes, Charles A., Chm. Bd. & Chief Exec. Officer--Guilford Mills, Inc., Greensboro, NC; *U.S. Public*, pg. 768

Hayes, Dennis C., Chm. Bd.--Hayes Corporation, Norcross, GA; *U.S. Public*, pg. 800

Hayes, Dennis C., Chm. Bd.--Hayes Microcomputer Products, Inc., Norcross, GA; *U.S. Public*, pg. 801

Hayes, J. Michael, Chm. Bd. & Chief Exec. Officer--C.B. Ragland Company, Nashville, TN; *U.S. Private*, pg. 907

Hayes, John E. Jr., Chm. Bd. & Chief Exec. Officer--Western Resources, Inc., Topeka, KS; *U.S. Public*, pg. 1759

Hayes, Kevin, Chm. Bd.--Cadbury Schweppes Australia Ltd, Melbourne, Australia; *Int'l*, pg. 248

Hayes, R. Dixon, Chm. Bd.--Shenango Industries, Terre Haute, IN; *U.S. Private*, pg. 992

Hayes, William B., Chm. Bd.--Hitox Corporation of America, Corpus Christi, TX; *U.S. Public*, pg. 829

Haymaker, George T., Jr., Chm. Bd. & Chief Exec. Officer--Kaiser Aluminum Corporation, Houston, TX; *U.S. Public*, pg. 1062

Hayne, Richard A., Chm. Bd. & Chief Exec. Officer--Urban Outfitters, Inc., Philadelphia, PA; *U.S. Public*, pg. 1700

Haynes, William E., Chm. Bd., Pres. & Chief Exec. Officer--Innovative Valve Technology, Inc., Houston, TX; *U.S. Public*, pg. 880

Hays, Harry S., Chm. Bd. & Pres.--Allen & Ohara, Inc., Memphis, TN; *U.S. Private*, pg. 36

Hays, Howard H., Jr., Chm. Emeritus--Press Enterprise Company, Riverside, CA; *U.S. Public*, pg. 209

Hays, Raphael S., II, Chm. Bd.--Frog Switch & Manufacturing Company, Carlisle, PA; *U.S. Private*, pg. 429

Hays, Spencer, Chm. Bd.--Tom James Of Atlanta, Inc., Atlanta, GA; *U.S. Private*, pg. 581

Hays, Spencer, Chm. Bd.--Southwestern/Great American Inc., Nashville, TN; *U.S. Private*, pg. 1018

Hays, Thomas C., Chm. Bd. & Chief Exec. Officer--Fortune Brands, Inc., Old Greenwich, CT; *U.S. Public*, pg. 674

Hayward, Thomas M., Chm. Bd.--Southeastern Pennsylvania Transportation Authority, Philadelphia, PA; *U.S. Private*, pg. 1015

Hazelhoff, R., Chm.-Supvry. Bd.--Heineken N.V., Amsterdam, Netherlands; *Int'l*, pg. 608

Hazen, Paul, Chm. Bd. & Chief Exec. Officer--Wells Fargo & Company, San Francisco, CA; *U.S. Public*, pg. 1753

Hazen, Paul, Chm. Bd. & Chief Exec. Officer--Wells Fargo & Company, Los Angeles, CA; *U.S. Public*, pg. 1753

Hazleton, Richard, Chm. Bd. & Chief Exec. Officer--Dow Corning Corporation, Midland, MI; *U.S. Public*, pg. 523

Headrick, Roger, Chm.-Exec. Committee--National Football League Properties, Inc., New York, NY; *U.S. Private*, pg. 783

Heagerty, David A., Chm. Bd. & Chief Exec. Officer--The Coakley Heagerty Advertising & Public Relations Co., San Jose, CA; *U.S. Private*, pg. 248

Heagy, Thomas C., Vice Chm. & Chief Capital Markets Officer--ABN/LaSalle North America Inc., Chicago, IL; *Int'l*, pg. 11

Healey, Brian, Chm. Bd.--National Consolidated, Melbourne, Australia; *Int'l*, pg. 908

Healey, Robert T., Chm. Bd.--Viking Yacht Co., New Gretna, NJ; *U.S. Private*, pg. 1140

Healy, Sondra A., Chm. Bd.--Turtle Wax, Inc., Chicago, IL; *U.S. Private*, pg. 1110

Heap, David A., Chm. Bd.--Daisytek International Corporation, Plano, TX; *U.S. Public*, pg. 477

Heap, David A., Chm. Bd.--Daisytek (Canada) Inc., Toronto, Canada; *U.S. Public*, pg. 477

Heap, David A., Chm. Bd.--Daisytek Latin America, Miami, FL; *U.S. Public*, pg. 477

Heap, David A., Chm. Bd.--Daisytek De Mexico S.A. de C.V., Mexico, Mexico; *U.S. Public*, pg. 477

Heap, David A., Chm. Bd.--Priority Fulfillment Services, Inc., Plano, TX; *U.S. Public*, pg. 477

Heap, David A., Chm. Bd.--Daisytek Australia Pty. Ltd., Alexandria, Australia; *U.S. Public*, pg. 477

Hearin, William J., Chm. Bd.--Mobile Gas Service Corp., Mobile, AL; *U.S. Public*, pg. 1120

Hearn, John, Chm. Bd.--Oxford Instruments-Nuclear Measurements Group, Oak Ridge, TN; *Int'l*, pg. 1018

Hearn, Michael, Chm. Bd. & Pres.--MBT Architecture, San Francisco, CA; *U.S. Private*, pg. 686
Hearn, Richard E., Chm. Bd.--Capital City Press, Inc., Berlin, VT; *U.S. Private*, pg. 205
Hearst, George R., Jr., Chm. Bd.--The Hearst Corporation, New York, NY; *U.S. Private*, pg. 515
Heath, Jinger L., Chm. Bd.--BeautiControl Cosmetics, Inc., Carrollton, TX; *U.S. Public*, pg. 198
Heath, Milton W., Jr., Owner, Chm. Bd. & Treas.--Heath Consultants Incorporated, Houston, TX; *U.S. Private*, pg. 518
Heath, Robert E., Chm. Bd.--Associated Grocers of New England, Inc., Manchester, NH; *U.S. Private*, pg. 91
Hecht, Jack L., Chm. Bd.--Queens Group, Inc., Long Island City, NY; *U.S. Private*, pg. 900
Hecht, William F., Chm. Bd., Pres. & Chief Exec. Officer--PP&L Resources, Allentown, PA; *U.S. Public*, pg. 1244
Hecht, William F., Chm. Bd., Pres. & Chief Exec. Officer--Pennsylvania Power & Light Company-Lehigh Div., Allentown, PA; *U.S. Public*, pg. 1244
Hecht, William F., Chm. Bd. & Chief Exec. Officer--Power Markets Development Company, Allentown, PA; *U.S. Public*, pg. 1244
Heck, Gary, Chm. Bd. & Pres.--F. Korbel Bros. Inc., Guerneville, CA; *U.S. Private*, pg. 632
Heck, Margaret P., Chm. Bd.--Heck Industries, Baton Rouge, LA; *U.S. Private*, pg. 519
Heckmann, Dick, Pres. & Chief Exec. Officer--U.S. Filter, Palm Desert, CA; *U.S. Public*, pg. 61
Hedelius, Tom, Chm. Bd.--Bergman & Beving AB, Stockholm, Sweden; *Int'l*, pg. 188
Hedelius, Tom, Chm. Bd.--Svenska Handelsbanken, Stockholm, Sweden; *Int'l*, pg. 1327
Hedstrom, Bo S., Chm. Bd.--Sodra Skogagarna, Vaxjo, Sweden; *Int'l*, pg. 1275
Heeps. W., Chm. Bd.--Thomson Regional Newspapers Ltd., Watford, United Kingdom; *U.S. Public*, pg. 1601
Heeringa, Donald G., Chm. Bd. & Pres.--Trendway Corporation, Holland, MI; *U.S. Private*, pg. 1099
Heffernan, Gerald R., Chm. Bd.--Texas Industries, Inc., Dallas, TX; *U.S. Public*, pg. 1585
Heffi, H., Dr., Chm. Bd.--Brauerei AG, Zurich, Switzerland; *Int'l*, pg. 479
Heffner, Ralph H., Chm. Bd.--Agway, Inc., De Witt, NY; *U.S.* Private, pg. 27
Hefner, Christie, Chm. Bd. & Chief Exec. Officer--Playboy Enterprises, Inc., Chicago, IL; *U.S. Public*, pg. 1309
Hefty, Thomas R., Chm. Bd., Pres. & Chief Exec. Officer--United Wisconsin Services, Inc., Milwaukee, WI; *U.S. Public*, pg. 1692
Hegarty, John, Chm. Bd. & Creative Dir.--Bartle Bogle Hegarty Limited, London, United Kingdom; *Int'l*, pg. 169
Hegi, Frederick B., Chm. Bd.--United Stationers Inc., Des Plaines, IL; *U.S. Public*, pg. 1689
Heglund, Forrest E., Chm. Bd. & Chief Exec. Officer--Enron Oil & Gas Co., Houston, TX; *U.S. Public*, pg. 584
Hehir, Peter, Chm.--Countrywide Porter/Novelli, Banbury, United Kingdom; *U.S. Public*, pg. 1225
Heiberg, Gerhard, Chm. Bd.--Aker Raj Asa, Oslo, Norway; *Int'l*, pg. 41
Heiberg, Gerhard, Chm. Bd.--Den norske Bank ASA, Oslo, Norway; *Int'l*, pg. 392
Heiden, Bruce, Chm. Bd.--Calcot, Ltd., Bakersfield, CA; *U.S.* Private, pg. 200
Heidrich, James K., Jr., Chm. Bd., Pres. & Chief Exec. Officer--The Miami Margarine Co., Cincinnati, OH; *U.S. Private*, pg. 740
Heigrad, Peter, Reg. Chm. & Chief Exec. Officer--Young & Rubicam Australia/New Zealand, Sydney, Australia; *U.S.* Private, pg. 1198
Heil, William H., Chm. & Chief Exec. Officer--AllEnergy Marketing Company, L.L.C., Waltham, MA; *U.S. Public*, pg. 549
Heiligbrodt, L. William, Pres. & Chief Oper. Officer--Service Corporation International, Houston, TX; *U.S. Public*, pg. 1460
Heiman, Paul, Chm. Bd.--Standard Textile Co., Inc., Cincinnati, OH; *U.S. Private*, pg. 1032
Heimbold, Charles A., Jr., Chm. Bd. & Chief Exec. Officer--Bristol-Myers Squibb Company, New York, NY; *U.S. Public*, pg. 253
Heimendinger, Larry, Chm. Bd. & Pres.--General Kinetics Incorporated, Chantilly, VA; *U.S. Public*, pg. 716
Hein, Nickolas D., Chm. Bd.--Mycogen Corporation, San Diego, CA; *U.S. Public*, pg. 1142
Hein, Raymond, Sir, Chm.--Union Commercial Bank S.A., Antananarivo, Madagascar; *Int'l*, pg. 1294
Heineman, Nicholas A., Chm. Bd.--Conway Import Co. Inc., Franklin Park, IL; *U.S. Private*, pg. 272
Heiniger, Andre, Chm. Bd. & Chief Exec. Officer--Rolex Watch Co. SA, Geneva, Switzerland; *Int'l*, pg. 1126
Heinkel, Karl-Ernst, Chm. Bd.--Heinkel Industriezentrifugen GmbH & Co., Bietigheim-Bissingen, Germany; *Int'l*, pg. 608
Heinrichs, Steve, Chm. Bd. & Chief Fin. Officer--Western Data Systems, Calabasas, CA; *U.S. Private*, pg. 1165
Heinz Durr, Ing. E.h., Dr., Chm.-Supervisory Bd.--Durr AG, Stuttgart, Germany; *Int'l*, pg. 421
Heisley, M.E., Chm. Bd.--Spartan Tool, Mendota, IL; *U.S. Private*, pg. 860
Heisley, Michael E., Chm. Bd. & Chief Exec. Officer--Nutri/System Inc., Horsham, PA; *U.S. Private*, pg. 859
Heisley, Michael Sr., Chm. Bd.--Pettibone Corporation, Lisle, IL; *U.S. Private*, pg. 859
Heist, Charles H., Chm. Bd. & Chief Exec. Officer--C.H. Heist Corp., Clearwater, FL; *U.S. Public*, pg. 807
Heitmann, Fred W., Chm. Bd. & Chief Exec. Officer--LaSalle Northwest National Bank, Chicago, IL; *Int'l*, pg. 10
Heitz, Mark V., Chm. Bd.--Amvestors Financial Corporation, Topeka, KS; *U.S. Private*, pg. 59
Heldman, Julie, Co-Chm. Bd. & Pres.--Signature Eyewear, Inc., Inglewood, CA; *U.S. Public*, pg. 1473
Helford, Irwin, Chm. Bd. & Chief Exec. Officer--Viking Office Products, Torrance, CA; *U.S. Public*, pg. 1720
Helgeson, Donald P., Chm. Bd. & Pres.--JFC Inc., Saint Cloud, MN; *U.S. Private*, pg. 577
Hellberg, Clifford W., Chm. Bd., Pres. & Chief Exec. Officer--Creative Productions, Pittsburgh, PA; *U.S. Private*, pg. 288
Hellenbrand, V.J., Chm. Bd. & Chief Exec. Officer--Research Products Corporation, Madison, WI; *U.S. Private*, pg. 924
Heller, C.M., Jr., Vice Chm. & Treas.--Marquette Coppersmithing Co., Inc., Philadelphia, PA; *U.S. Private*, pg. 706
Heller, James, Chm. Bd.--Heller Bros. Packing Corp., Winter Garden, FL; *U.S. Private*, pg. 520
Heller, John R., Chm. Bd.--Heller Seasonings & Ingredients, Inc., Bedford Park, IL; *U.S. Private*, pg. 520
Heller, Judy, Co-Chm. & Pres.--Cruises Only Inc., Orlando, FL; *U.S. Private*, pg. 293
Hellman, Herman J., Chm. Bd.--Temco Service Industries, New York, NY; *U.S. Public*, pg. 1574
Hellman, William, Chm. Bd., Pres & Chief Exec. Officer--JG Industries, Inc., Chicago, IL; *U.S. Public*, pg. 917
Helmer, Elmer J., Chm. Bd.--The Commercial Bank, Delphos, OH; *U.S. Public*, pg. 410
Helmerich, W.H., III, Chm. Bd.--Helmerich & Payne, Inc., Tulsa, OK; *U.S. Public*, pg. 808
Helmerich, Walter H., III, Chm. Bd.--Atwood Oceanics, Inc., Houston, TX; *U.S. Public*, pg. 146
Helmick, Louis G., Chm. Bd.--Helmick Corporation, Fairmont, WV; *U.S. Private*, pg. 520
Helms, Charles H., Chm. Bd.--Goodwill Industries International, Bethesda, MD; *U.S. Private*, pg. 464
Helms, W. Edd, Jr., Chm. Bd.--Edd Helms Electrical Contracting, Miami, FL; *U.S. Private*, pg. 520
Helpern, David, Chm. Bd.--Joan & David Helpern, Inc., New York, NY; *U.S. Private*, pg. 521
Helton, Bill D., Chm. Bd. & Chief Exec. Officer--New Century Energies, Inc., Denver, CO; *U.S. Public*, pg. 1170
Helton, Bill D., Chm. Bd.--Southwestern Public Service Company, Amarillo, TX; *U.S. Public*, pg. 1170
Helu, Carlos Slim, Chm. Bd.--Telefonos de Mexico S.A. de C.V., Mexico, Mexico; *Int'l*, pg. 1373
Helu, Carlos Slim, Sr., Chm. Bd.--Grupo Carso S.A. de C.V., Mexico, Mexico; *Int'l*, pg. 572
Hemmer, Paul W., Sr., Chm. Bd.--Paul Hemmer Construction Company, Fort Mitchell, KY; *U.S. Private*, pg. 521
Hemminghaus, Roger R., Chm. Bd. & Chief Exec. Officer--Ultramar Diamond Shamrock Corporation, San Antonio, TX; *U.S. Public*, pg. 1663
Hemphill, Robert, Chm. Bd.--Barclay White Incorporated, Berwyn, PA; *U.S. Private*, pg. 115
Hempt, George F., Chm. Bd. & Pres.--Hempt Brothers, Inc., Camp Hill, PA; *U.S. Private*, pg. 521
Hench, Richard F., M.D., Chm. Bd.--Kentucky Medical Insurance Company (KMIC), Louisville, KY; *U.S. Private*, pg. 741
Henderson, Denys H., Chm.--Sinclair/Ameritone Paint Corp., Los Angeles, CA; *Int'l*, pg. 663
Henderson, Denys, Sir, Chm. Bd.--Dalgety Plc, London, United Kingdom; *Int'l*, pg. 376
Henderson, Denys, Sir, Chm. Bd.--The Rank Group PLC, London, United Kingdom; *Int'l*, pg. 1086
Henderson, Donald, Chm. Bd., Pres. & Chief Exec. Officer--Citation National Insurance Company, San Jose, CA; *U.S. Public*, pg. 376
Henderson, Donald, Chm. Bd. & Chief Exec. Officer--Madison Acceptance Corporation, San Jose, CA; *U.S. Public*, pg. 376
Henderson, Donald, Chm. Bd., Pres. & Chief Exec. Officer--Citation Insurance Company, San Jose, CA; *U.S. Public*, pg. 376
Henderson, I. Craig, Dr., Chm. Bd. & Chief Exec. Officer--Sequus Pharmaceuticals, Inc., Menlo Park, CA; *U.S. Public*, pg. 1460
Henderson, James A., Chm. Bd. & Chief Exec. Officer--Cummins Engine Company, Inc., Columbus, IN; *U.S. Public*, pg. 467
Henderson, Robert J., Sr., Chm. Bd., Pres. & Chief Exec. Officer--Ford Development Corporation, Cincinnati, OH; *U.S. Private*, pg. 418
Henderson, Rodney J., Chm. Bd.--Henderson Electric Co., Inc., Louisville, KY; *U.S. Private*, pg. 521
Hendricks, John, Chm. Bd. & Chief Exec. Officer--Discovery Networks, Inc., Bethesda, MD; *U.S. Private*, pg. 334
Hendricks, John S., Chm. Bd. & Chief Exec. Officer--Discovery Communications, Inc., Bethesda, MD; *U.S. Private*, pg. 334
Hendricks, Karen L., Chm. Bd., Pres. & Chief Exec. Officer--Baldwin Piano & Organ Company, Loveland, OH; *U.S. Public*, pg. 169
Hendrickson, Thomas N., Chm. Bd. & Chief Exec. Officer--CPAC, Inc., Leicester, NY; *U.S. Public*, pg. 282
Hendrickson, Tom, Chm. Bd.--The Fuller Brush Company, Great Bend, KS; *U.S. Public*, pg. 282
Hendrix, Tom E., Chm. Bd., Pres. & Chief Exec. Officer--Henco, Inc., Selmer, TN; *U.S. Private*, pg. 521
Hendry, B.W., Chm. Bd.--Taylor Woodrow Construction Corp., New York, NY; *Int'l*, pg. 1359
Hendry, Bruce, Chm. Bd.--Minnesota Brewing Company, Saint Paul, MN; *U.S. Public*, pg. 1115
Henkels, Paul M., Chm. Bd.--Henkels & McCoy, Inc., Blue Bell, PA; *U.S. Private*, pg. 522
Henley, A.B., Jr., Chm. Bd., Pres. & Chief Exec. Officer--Henley Paper Company, Greensboro, NC; *U.S. Private*, pg. 522
Henley, Jerrold T., Chm. Bd.--Sierra West Bancorp, Truckee, CA; *U.S. Public*, pg. 1470
Henley, Lord, Chm. Bd.--Christies International plc, London, United Kingdom; *Int'l*, pg. 289
Henman, Gary, Chm. Bd. & Pres.--Dairy Farmers of America, Inc., Arlington, TX; *U.S. Private*, pg. 307
Hennen, Tim, Chm.--Big River Grille & Brewery Works, Chattanooga, TN; *U.S. Public*, pg. 1396
Hennesberry, William H., Chm. Bd.--Communications Diversified, New York, NY; *U.S. Private*, pg. 259
Hennessey, Frank M., Chm. Bd.--Emco Limited, London, Canada; *Int'l*, pg. 452
Hennessey, Robert J., Chm., Pres. & Chief Exec. Officer--Genome Therapeutics Corporation, Waltham, MA; *U.S. Public*, pg. 730
Hennesy, Dan, Chm. Bd.--Hirsh Company, Skokie, IL; *U.S. Public*, pg. 963
Hennigar, D.J., Chm. Bd.--National Sea Products Limited, Lunenburg, Canada; *Int'l*, pg. 909
Henningsen, Victor W., Jr., Chm. Bd.--Henningsen Foods, Inc., White Plains, NY; *Int'l*, pg. 1074
Henningson, Ray C., Jr., Chm. Bd.--Willis Corroon Corp. of Minnesota, Minneapolis, MN; *Int'l*, pg. 1506
Henriques, Antonio Veiga, Chm.--Carbogal-Carbonos de Portugal, S.A., Lisbon, Portugal; *Int'l*, pg. 1045
Henry, Jerry, Chm. Bd., Pres. & Chief Exec. Officer--Johns Manville Corporation, Denver, CO; *U.S. Public*, pg. 927
Henry, Michael E., Chm. Bd. & Chief Exec. Officer--Jack Henry & Associates, Inc., Monett, MO; *U.S. Public*, pg. 808
Henry, R.E., Sr., Chm. Bd.--Fostoria Industries, Inc., Fostoria, OH; *U.S. Private*, pg. 421
Henselijn, Th.S., Chm. Bd.-Mngmt.--N.V. Koninklijke Bijenkorf Beheer KBB, Amsterdam, Netherlands; *Int'l*, pg. 750
Henson, J. Peter, Chm. Bd. Pres. & Chief Exec. Officer--Flexible Products Company, Marietta, GA; *U.S. Private*, pg. 412
Henson, Richard A., Chm. Bd.--Piedmont Airlines, Inc., Salisbury, MD; *U.S. Public*, pg. 1680
Hentschel, David A., Chm. Bd. & Chief Exec. Officer--Occidental Oil & Gas Corporation, Bakersfield, CA; *U.S. Public*, pg. 1210
Hepher, Michael, Chm. & Chief Exec. Officer--Charterhouse Bank Ltd., London, United Kingdom; *Int'l*, pg. 342
Herb, Marvin J., Chm. Bd. & Chief Exec. Officer--Coca-Cola Bottling Co. of Chicago, Niles, IL; *U.S. Private*, pg. 248
Herbert, M., Chm. Bd.--The Tussauds Group Limited, London, United Kingdom; *Int'l*, pg. 1026
Herbst, Jacob, Chm. Bd. & Chief Exec. Officer--IIS Intelligent Information Systems Ltd., Yokneam, Israel; *Int'l*, pg. 645
Herbster, Charles, Chm. Bd., Pres. & Chief Exec. Officer--Conklin Co. Inc., Shakopee, MN; *U.S. Private*, pg. 263
Herd, Peter, Chm.--GGT Direct Advertising, London, United Kingdom; *Int'l*, pg. 532
Heriard-Dubreuil, Andre, Chm. Bd.--Remy Cointreau, Paris, France; *Int'l*, pg. 1102
Hering, Ralf, Chm.-GCI Europe--GCI Group Inc., New York, NY; *U.S. Public*, pg. 764
Heritage, B., Chm. Bd.--Myton Limited, Hayes, United Kingdom; *Int'l*, pg. 1358
Herkstroter, C.A.J., Chm.-Bd. of Mngmt & Pres.--Royal Dutch/Shell Group of Companies, Hague, Netherlands; *Int'l*, pg. 1135
Herlin, Pekka, Chm. Bd.--Kone Corporation, Helsinki, Finland; *Int'l*, pg. 746
Herlin, Robert M., Chm. Bd. & Chief Exec. Officer--Herlin Press Inc., West Haven, CT; *U.S. Private*, pg. 524
Herlitz, Gunter, Chm.-Supervisory Bd.--Herlitz PBS Aktiengesellschaft, Berlin, Germany; *Int'l*, pg. 616
Herman, Loeb, Jr., Chm. Bd.--Piknik Products Company, Inc., Montgomery, AL; *U.S. Private*, pg. 865
Hermann, Ronald B., Chm. Bd.--BWD Automotive, North Brunswick, NJ; *U.S. Public*, pg. 560
Hermanson, Merril, Chm. Bd.--Mr. Christmas Inc., New York, NY; *U.S. Private*, pg. 765
Hernandez, Robert M., Chm. Bd., Chief Fin. Officer & Exec. V.P.-Fin./USX Corp.--RMI Titanium Company, Niles, OH; *U.S. Public*, pg. 1662
Heroles, Jesus Reyes, Chm. Bd.--Petroleos Mexicanos, Mexico, Mexico; *Int'l*, pg. 1046
Heron, Michael, Chm.--The Post Office, London, United Kingdom; *Int'l*, pg. 1064
Herres, Robert T., Chm. Bd., Chief Exec. & Chief Oper. Officer--USAA (United Services Automobile Association), San Antonio, TX; *U.S. Private*, pg. 1114
Herrick, Kenneth G., Chm. Bd.--Tecumseh Products Company, Tecumseh, MI; *U.S. Public*, pg. 1565
Herring, Sherwin, Pres.--Southco Distributing Company, Goldsboro, NC; *U.S. Private*, pg. 1014
Herringer, Frank, Chm. Bd. & Chief Exec. Officer--Transamerica Corporation, San Francisco, CA; *U.S. Public*, pg. 1629
Herrmann, Raymond H., Chm. Bd.--Sunbelt Beverages, Lutherville, MD; *U.S. Private*, pg. 1051
Herschend, Jack, Chm. Bd.--Silver Dollar City, Inc., Branson, MO; *U.S. Private*, pg. 1000
Hersh, Robert, Chm. Bd., Pres. & Chief Exec. Officer--Catalina Lighting, Inc., Miami, FL; *U.S. Public*, pg. 314
Hershaft, Arthur, Chm. Bd., Pres. & Chief Exec. Officer--PAXAR Corporation, White Plains, NY; *U.S. Public*, pg. 1266
Herst, Douglas J., Chm. Bd. & Pres.--Peerless Lighting Corp., Berkeley, CA; *U.S. Private*, pg. 847
Herteman, Jean-Paul, Chm. Bd.--SNECMA Inc., Dover, DE; *Int'l*, pg. 1166
Hertrich, Adolf, Chm. Bd.--Vanport Manufacturing, Inc., Boring, OR; *U.S. Private*, pg. 1134
Hertz, Arthur, Chm. Bd. & Chief Exec. Officer--Wometco Enterprises, Inc., Coral Gables, FL; *U.S. Private*, pg. 1186
Hertz, Jennings M., Jr., Chm. Bd.--United Distributors, Inc., Smyrna, GA; *U.S. Private*, pg. 1121
Herz, Gunter, Chm. Bd.-Supervisory--Reemtsma Cigarettenfabriken GmbH, Hamburg, Hamburg, Germany; *Int'l*, pg. 1100
Herzer, Richard K., Chm. Bd., Pres. & Chief Exec. Officer--IHOP Corp., Glendale, CA; *U.S. Public*, pg. 862
Hess, J. Robert, Chm. Bd. & Pres.--Lancaster Malleable Castings Company, Lancaster, PA; *U.S. Private*, pg. 645

Hess, Johann T., Chm. Bd.--Hess Engineering Inc., Niles, MI; *U.S. Private*, pg. 524
Hess, John B., Chm. Bd. & Chief Exec. Officer--Amerada Hess Corporation, New York, NY; *U.S. Public*, pg. 65
Hessels, J.M., Chm. Bd. & Pres.--Vendex International N.V., Amsterdam, Netherlands; *Int'l*, pg. 1462
Hesser, Dan, Chm. Bd. & Pres.--Invesco Funds Group, Denver, CO; *Int'l*, pg. 685
Hesser, E. Grant, Chm. Bd.--Maescher Industries, Inc., Cincinnati, OH; *U.S. Private*, pg. 694
Hessler, Pierre, Chm. Bd. & Chief Exec. Officer--Gemini Consulting, Morristown, NJ; *Int'l*, pg. 264
Heston, W. Craig, Chm. Bd. & Chief Exec. Officer--Utica Mutual Insurance Company, New Hartford, NY; *U.S. Private*, pg. 1129
Heth, Meir, Dr., Chm. Bd.--Teva Pharmaceutical Industries Ltd., Petah Tiqwa, Israel; *Int'l*, pg. 1380
Hettinga, Martin, Chm.--HLPB, Amsterdam, Netherlands; *Int'l*, pg. 1377
Hewitt, William B., Chm. Bd.--Capital Credit Corporation, Jacksonville, FL; *U.S. Public*, pg. 1667
Hexham, Rippon of, Lord, Chm. Bd.--Alliance UniChem PLC, Chessington, United Kingdom; *Int'l*, pg. 57
Heye, Willliam B., Jr., Chm. Bd., Pres. & Chief Exec. Officer--SBE, Inc., San Ramon, CA; *U.S. Public*, pg. 1416
Heyer, Andrew R., Chm. Bd.--The Hain Food Group Inc., Uniondale, NY; *U.S. Public*, pg. 774
Heyman, Leonard J., Chm. Bd.--Heyman Corporation, Niles, IL; *U.S. Private*, pg. 524
Heyman, Samuel J., Chm. Bd. & Chief Exec. Officer--GAF Corporation, Wayne, NJ; *U.S. Private*, pg. 433
Heyman, Samuel J., Chm. Bd. & Chief Exec. Officer--G Industries Corporation, Wilmington, DE; *U.S. Private*, pg. 433
Heyman, Samuel J., Chm. Bd. & Chief Exec. Officer--GAF Materials Corporation, Wayne, NJ; *U.S. Private*, pg. 433
Heyman, Samuel J., Chm. Bd. & Chief Exec. Officer--ISP Holdings, Inc., Wayne, NJ; *U.S. Public*, pg. 858
Heywood, J.A., Chm. Bd.--Clayhithe P.L.C., Aylesbury, United Kingdom; *Int'l*, pg. 297
Heyworth, Anthony, Chm. Bd. & Chief Exec. Officer--Society National Bank, Indiana, South Bend, IN; *U.S. Public*, pg. 954
Hiatt, Cliff, Chm. Bd.--Fosters Freeze International, Inc., San Luis Obispo, CA; *U.S. Public*, pg. 677
Hiatt, Robert N., Chm.--Maybelline, Inc., New York, NY; *Int'l*, pg. 819
Hibon, George, Chm. Bd. & Chief Exec. Officer--Connaught Laboratories Limited, Willowdale, Canada; *Int'l*, pg. 1109
Hichens, Antony, Chm. Bd.--Caradon Plc, Weybridge, United Kingdom; *Int'l*, pg. 266
Hickingbotham, Frank D., Chm. Bd. & Chief Exec. Officer--TCBY Enterprises Inc., Little Rock, AR; *U.S. Public*, pg. 1553
Hickman, Waymon L., Chm. Bd. & Chief Exec. Officer--First Farmers & Merchants National Bank, Columbia, TN; *U.S. Private*, pg. 407
Hicks, Donald A., Chm. Bd.--Hicks & Associates Inc., Mc Lean, VA; *U.S. Private*, pg. 976
Hicks, Thomas O., Chm. Bd.--Dallas Stars, Irving, TX; *U.S. Private*, pg. 309
Hicks, Thomas O., Chm. Bd., Chief Exec. Officer & Mng. Dir.--Hicks, Muse, Tate & Furst Inc., Dallas, TX; *U.S. Private*, pg. 526
Hietala, Al, Chm.--Colle & McVoy Marketing Communications, Minneapolis, MN; *U.S. Private*, pg. 252
Hietala, Allan, Chm. Bd.--Colle & McVoy, Inc., Minneapolis, MN; *U.S. Private*, pg. 252
Higgins, Christopher J., Chm. Bd.--James Walker & Co. Limited, Woking, United Kingdom; *Int'l*, pg. 1485
Higgins, David L., Chm. Bd. & Chief Exec. Officer--DVI Business Credit, Inc., Newport Beach, CA; *U.S. Public*, pg. 476
Higgins, James, Chm. Bd., Pres. & Chief Exec. Officer--Charter Builders, Inc., Dallas, TX; *Int'l*, pg. 896
Higgins, Joseph, Jr., Chm. Bd.--J.C. Higgins Corp., Stoughton, MA; *U.S. Public*, pg. 572
Higgins, Larry B., Chm. Bd., Pres. & Chief Exec. Officer--H & H Tube & Manufacturing Co., Vanderbilt, MI; *U.S. Private*, pg. 489
Higgins, Robert J., Chm. Bd., Pres. & Chief Exec. Officer--Trans World Entertainment Corporation, Albany, NY; *U.S. Public*, pg. 1629
Higgins, S.L., Chm. Bd. & Pres.--Air Industries Corporation, Garden Grove, CA; *U.S. Private*, pg. 28
Higgins, Walter M., Chm. Bd., Pres. & Chief Exec. Officer--Sierra Pacific Resources, Reno, NV; *U.S. Public*, pg. 1470
Higgs, Derek, Chm. Bd.--Prudential Portfolio Managers Limited, London, United Kingdom; *Int'l*, pg. 1073
High, S. Dale, Chm. Bd. & Pres.--High Industries, Inc., Lancaster, PA; *U.S. Private*, pg. 528
Higuchi, Hirotaro, Chm. Bd.--Asahi Breweries Ltd., Tokyo, Japan; *Int'l*, pg. 83
Higurashi, Takeshi, Chm. Bd., Pres. & Chief Exec. Officer--Subaru of America, Inc., Cherry Hill, NJ; *Int'l*, pg. 523
Hijikata, Takeshi, Chm. Bd.--Japan Tobacco Inc., Tokyo, Japan; *Int'l*, pg. 703
Hilb, Robert H., Chm. Bd.--Hilb, Rogal and Hamilton Company, Glen Allen, VA; *U.S. Public*, pg. 826
Hilbert, Stephen, Chm. Bd., Pres. & Chief Exec. Officer--CHIC, Carmel, IN; *U.S. Public*, pg. 433
Hilbert, Stephen, Chm. Bd., Pres. & Chief Exec. Officer--Intermediate Holdings, Inc., Carmel, IN; *U.S. Public*, pg. 433
Hilbert, Stephen C., Chm. Bd.--Bankers Life & Casualty Company, Chicago, IL; *U.S. Public*, pg. 433
Hilbert, Steven, Chm. Bd.--American Life Holding Corp., Des Moines, IA; *U.S. Public*, pg. 432
Hilbert, Steven C., Chm. Bd., Pres. & Chief Exec. Officer--Conseco Inc., Carmel, IN; *U.S. Public*, pg. 432
Hildebrandt, Roger, Chm. Bd.--Agripac Inc., Salem, OR; *U.S. Private*, pg. 26
Hildmann, Anton, Chm.-BDDO Germany--BBDO Worldwide Inc., New York, NY; *U.S. Public*, pg. 1223
Hildreth, Charles L., Jr., Chm. Bd.--Emery Waterhouse Company, Portland, ME; *U.S. Private*, pg. 373
Hildreth, Horace A., Jr., Chm. Bd.--Diversified Communications, Portland, ME; *U.S. Private*, pg. 336
Hilfiger, Thomas J., Hon. Chm. Bd.--Tommy Hilfiger Corporation, Kowloon, Hong Kong; *Int'l*, pg. 1398
Hilker, Klaus, Chm. Bd.--STAHLwerke Bremen GmbH, Bremen, Germany; *Int'l*, pg. 79
Hill, Brian, Chm. Bd.--Ajax Magnethermic Corp., Warren, OH; *Int'l*, pg. 113
Hill, Charles, Co.-Chm. Bd.--Town & Country Corporation, Chelsea, MA; *U.S. Public*, pg. 1625
Hill, Dan J., Chm. Bd.--Coastal Oil New England, Inc., Revere, MA; *U.S. Public*, pg. 390
Hill, Dan J., Chm. Bd. & Chief Exec. Officer--Coastal Fuels Marketing, Inc., Miami, FL; *U.S. Public*, pg. 390
Hill, David R., Chm. Bd.--Davel Communications Group, Inc., Jacksonville, IL; *U.S. Public*, pg. 488
Hill, George J., III, Chm. Emeritus--Hill, Holliday, Connors, Cosmopulos, Inc., Boston, MA; *U.S. Private*, pg. 529
Hill, Howard W., Chm. Bd.--Zero Corporation, Los Angeles, CA; *U.S. Public*, pg. 1791
Hill, J. Donald, Chm. Bd., Pres. & Chief Exec. Officer--Excel Technology, Inc., New York, NY; *U.S. Public*, pg. 599
Hill, John, Consultant--Standex Electronics, Cincinnati, OH; *U.S. Public*, pg. 1507
Hill, Lester, Chm. Bd. & Chief Exec. Officer--Pacific Scientific Company, Newport Beach, CA; *U.S. Public*, pg. 1250
Hill, Richard S., Chm. Bd., Pres. & Chief Exec. Officer--Novellus Systems, Inc., San Jose, CA; *U.S. Public*, pg. 1204
Hill, Stephen R., Chm. & Pres.--Tone Commander Systems, Mukilteo, WA; *U.S. Private*, pg. 1090
Hill, William L., Chm. Bd.--Levenson & Hill, Inc., Dallas, TX; *U.S. Private*, pg. 662
Hillege, Jan W., Chm. Bd.--DSM Engineering Plastic Products, Reading, PA; *Int'l*, pg. 354
Hillenbrand, Daniel A., Chm. Bd.--Hillenbrand Industries, Inc., Batesville, IN; *U.S. Public*, pg. 828
Hiller, Stanley, Jr., Chm. Bd.--Key Tronic Corporation, Spokane, WA; *U.S. Public*, pg. 953
Hilliard, Wallace J., Chm. Bd.--American Medical Security Holdings, Inc., Green Bay, WI; *U.S. Public*, pg. 1692
Hillman, Henry, Chm.-Exec. Committee--The Hillman Company, Pittsburgh, PA; *U.S. Private*, pg. 530
Hillman, Herbert, Chm. Bd.--Franklin-Lamoille Bank, Saint Albans, VT; *U.S. Public*, pg. 187
Hillman, Howard B., Chm. Bd., Pres. & Chief Exec. Officer--Auto-trol Technology Corporation, Denver, CO; *U.S. Public*, pg. 148
Hillman, Tommy H., Chm. Bd.--Riceland Foods, Inc., Stuttgart, AR; *U.S. Private*, pg. 928
Hillmyer, Maurice, Chm.--South Florida Land Division, Fort Myers, FL; *U.S. Public*, pg. 1683
Hills, James A., General, Chm. Bd.--Star Food Processing, Inc., San Antonio, TX; *U.S. Private*, pg. 1034
Hilsberg, Marshall, Chm. & Chief Exec. Officer--Lord & Taylor, New York, NY; *U.S. Public*, pg. 1064
Hilsinger, Arthur R., Chm. Bd. & Chief Exec. Officer--The Hilsinger Co. L.P., Plainville, MA; *U.S. Private*, pg. 530
Hilt, John L., Chm. Emeritus--Quality Stores Inc., Muskegon, MI; *U.S. Private*, pg. 899
Hilti, Michael, Chm. Bd.--Hilti AG, Schaan, Liechtenstein; *Int'l*, pg. 619
Hilton, Barron, Chm. Bd.--Hilton Hotels Corporation, Beverly Hills, CA; *U.S. Public*, pg. 828
Himatsingka, B., Chm. Bd.--Assam Carbon Products Limited, Calcutta, India; *Int'l*, pg. 891
Himeles, Martin S., Chm. Bd. & Chief Exec. Officer--Standard Medical Imaging, Inc., Columbia, MD; *U.S. Private*, pg. 1032
Hinchcliffe, Ralph Eric, Chm. Bd.--Heywood Williams Group PLC, Huddersfield, United Kingdom; *Int'l*, pg. 618
Hinckley, Gordon B., Chm. Bd.--Deseret Management Corporation, Salt Lake City, UT; *U.S. Private*, pg. 327
Hinckley, Gordon B., Chm. Bd.--Beneficial Life Insurance, Salt Lake City, UT; *U.S. Private*, pg. 327
Hinckley, Gordon B., Chm. Bd.--Bonneville International Corp., Salt Lake City, UT; *U.S. Private*, pg. 327
Hindman, Don J., Chm. Bd., Pres. & Chief Exec. Officer--Clark Foodservice, Inc., Elk Grove Village, IL; *U.S. Private*, pg. 242
Hindman, Harold, Chm. Bd.--Instron Corporation, Canton, MA; *U.S. Public*, pg. 882
Hindman, Harold, Chm. Bd.--Wilson/Shore Instruments, Canton, MA; *U.S. Public*, pg. 883
Hinds, Thomas M., Chm. Bd., Pres. & Chief Exec. Officer--Regions Bank/Mobile, Mobile, AL; *U.S. Public*, pg. 1372
Hiner, Glen H., Chm. Bd. & Chief Exec. Officer--Owens Corning, Toledo, OH; *U.S. Public*, pg. 1236
Hinge, M.G., Chm. Bd. & Joint Mng. Dir.--Taylor Woodrow Management Ltd., Southall, United Kingdom; *Int'l*, pg. 1359
Hinish, Samuel L., Chm. Bd.--Penn Central National Bank, Huntingdon, PA; *U.S. Public*, pg. 1222
Hinojosa, Santiago, Chm. & Mng. Dir.--DMB&B S.A. de C.V., Mexico, Mexico; *U.S. Private*, pg. 304
Hinson, James N., Jr., Chm. Bd. & Chief Exec. Officer--First Virginia Bank-Southwest, Roanoke, VA; *U.S. Public*, pg. 642
Hinton, James, Chm. Bd.--R.L. Zeigler Co. Inc., Tuscaloosa, AL; *U.S. Private*, pg. 1204
Hipp Hayne, Chm. Bd.--Liberty Life Insurance Company, Greenville, SC; *U.S. Public*, pg. 992
Hipp, W. Hayne, Chm. Bd., Pres. & Chief Exec. Officer--Liberty Corporation, Greenville, SC; *U.S. Public*, pg. 991
Hirano, Toichiro, Chm.--Central Automotive Products, Ltd., Osaka, Japan; *Int'l*, pg. 278
Hirata, Akio, Chm. Bd.--Mitsui Marine & Fire Insurance Co., Ltd., Tokyo, Japan; *Int'l*, pg. 878
Hirayama, S., Chm. Bd. & Pres.--Nippon Fisher Company, Ltd., Tokyo, Japan; *U.S. Public*, pg. 1126
Hirota, Kaoru, Chm. Bd.--Sekisui Chemical Co., Ltd., Osaka, Japan; *Int'l*, pg. 1219
Hirota, Motoo, Chm. Bd.--Japan Aviation Electronics Industry, Ltd., Tokyo, Japan; *Int'l*, pg. 701
Hirsch, Charles L., Chm. Bd. & Pres.--Charles Leonard, Inc., Glendale, NY; *U.S. Private*, pg. 660
Hirsch, Gary D., Chm. Bd.--The Penn Traffic Company, Syracuse, NY; *U.S. Public*, pg. 1270
Hirsch, Laurence E., Chm. Bd. & Chief Exec. Officer--Centex Corporation, Dallas, TX; *U.S. Public*, pg. 322
Hirsch, Leon C., Chm. Bd. & Chief Exec. Officer--U.S. Surgical Corp., Norwalk, CT; *U.S. Public*, pg. 1687
Hirsch, Richard L., Chm. Bd.--Concurrent Industries Group, Inc., New York, NY; *U.S. Private*, pg. 262
Hirschfeld, Daniel J., Chm. Bd.--The Buckle, Inc., Kearney, NE; *U.S. Public*, pg. 267
Hirschfield, Alan J., Co-Chm. Bd. & Co-Chief Exec. Officer--Data Broadcasting Corporation, Jackson, WY; *U.S. Public*, pg. 484
Hirschorn, Martin, Pres. & Chief Exec. Officer--Industrial Acoustics Company, Inc., Bronx, NY; *U.S. Public*, pg. 875
Hiruma, T., Chm. Bd.--Hamamatsu Corp., Bridgewater, NJ; *U.S. Private*, pg. 497
Hishmeh, Basem L., Pres. & Chief Exec. Officer--Aerco International Inc., Northvale, NJ; *U.S. Private*, pg. 23
Hitchcock, Gregory T., Chm. Bd.--Hitchcock Industries, Inc., Bloomington, MN; *U.S. Private*, pg. 531
Hitchcock, Kenneth W., Chm. Bd. & Chief Exec. Officer--The Whyte & Mackay Group Plc., Glasgow, United Kingdom; *U.S. Public*, pg. 675
Hitchens, Stephen, Chm.--BDG/McColl, London, United Kingdom; *Int'l*, pg. 1482
Hite, R. Lee, Chm. Bd., Pres. & Chief Exec. Officer--The Hite Company, Altoona, PA; *U.S. Private*, pg. 531
Hitpas, Terence A., Pres. & Chief Oper. Officer--Union Special Corp., Huntley, IL; *Int'l*, pg. 716
Hixon, Thomas, Chm. Bd., Pres. & Chief Exec. Officer--Gulf South Medical Supply, Inc., Ridgeland, MS; *U.S. Public*, pg. 1294
Hjertberg, Rolf-Erik, Chm. Bd.--ICA Handlarnas AB, Solna, Sweden; *Int'l*, pg. 642
Hlobik, Lawrence S., Chm. Bd. & Pres.--Terra Nitrogen Company, L.P., Tulsa, OK; *U.S. Public*, pg. 1581
Ho, Chan Tai, Chm. Bd.--Playmates Holdings Ltd., Kowloon, Hong Kong; *Int'l*, pg. 1060
Ho, Christopher, Chm. Bd. & Chief Exec. Officer--GrandeTel Technologies Inc., Richmond, Canada; *Int'l*, pg. 556
Ho, Stuart T.K., Chm. Bd.--The Honolulu Advertiser, Honolulu, HI; *U.S. Public*, pg. 701
Hoag, David H., Chm. Bd.--The LTV Corporation, Cleveland, OH; *U.S. Public*, pg. 971
Hoare, David, Chm. Bd.--Pioneer International Ltd., Sydney, Australia; *Int'l*, pg. 1058
Hobbs, Andrew, Chm. Bd.--Kim Eng Securities (London) Limited, London, United Kingdom; *Int'l*, pg. 733
Hobbs, Gerald S., Chm. Bd.--BPI Communications Inc., New York, NY; *Int'l*, pg. 1446
Hochberg, Larry J., Chm. Bd. & Chief Exec. Officer--Sport Mart, Inc., Wheeling, IL; *U.S. Public*, pg. 1499
Hochfelder, J. Gene, Chm. & Chief Exec. Officer--Beldoch Industries, West Hempstead, NY; *U.S. Public*, pg. 519
Hochstadt, Herman R., Chm. Bd.--Neptune Orient Lines Ltd., Singapore, Singapore; *Int'l*, pg. 912
Hock, Conrad, Jr., Chm. Bd. & Chief Exec. Officer--Williams Foods Inc., Lenexa, KS; *U.S. Private*, pg. 1178
Hock, Dato Tan Kay, Chm. Bd.--Jacks International Limited, Singapore, Singapore; *Int'l*, pg. 697
Hockmeyer, Wayne T., Ph.D., Chm. Bd. & Chief Exec. Officer--MedImmune, Inc., Gaithersburg, MD; *U.S. Public*, pg. 1081
Hodapp, Siegfried, Chm. & Chief Exec. Officer--MG Refining & Marketing, Inc., Houston, TX; *Int'l*, pg. 862
Hodes, Harold, Chm. Bd.--DKB & Partners, Inc., Morristown, NJ; *U.S. Private*, pg. 302
Hodgson, Patrick W.E., Chm. Bd. & Chief Exec. Officer--Todd Pacific Shipyards Corp., Seattle, WA; *U.S. Public*, pg. 1619
Hodgson, Tony, Chm. Bd.--Melbourne Port Corporation, Melbourne, Australia; *Int'l*, pg. 856
Hodowal, John R., Chm. Bd. & Pres.--Ipalco Enterprises, Inc., Indianapolis, IN; *U.S. Public*, pg. 912
Hodowal, John R., Chm. Bd. & Chief Exec. Officer--Mid-America Capital Resources, Inc., Indianapolis, IN; *U.S. Public*, pg. 913
Hodowal, John R., Chm. Bd. & Chief Exec. Officer--Cleveland District Cooling Corp., Cleveland, OH; *U.S. Public*, pg. 913
Hodson, Tom, Chm. Bd. & Pres.--Columbia Falls Aluminum Company, Columbia Falls, MT; *U.S. Private*, pg. 255
Hoeft, Jack, Chm. Bd. & Chief Exec. Officer--Bantam Doubleday Dell Publishing Group, Inc., New York, NY; *Int'l*, pg. 191
Hoeft, Leonard C., Chm. Bd.--Ziegler Inc., Minneapolis, MN; *U.S. Private*, pg. 1205
Hoehl, Robert H., Chm. Bd.--IDX Systems Corporation, Burlington, VT; *U.S. Public*, pg. 854
Hoeksema, Timothy E., Chm. Bd. & Chief Exec. Officer--K-C Aviation Inc., Neenah, WI; *U.S. Public*, pg. 959
Hoeksema, Timothy E., Chm. Bd., Pres. & Chief Exec. Officer--Midwest Express Holdings, Inc., Oak Creek, WI; *U.S. Public*, pg. 1111
Hoeksema, Timothy E., Chm. Bd., Pres. & Chief Exec. Officer--Midwest Express Airlines, Inc., Oak Creek, WI; *U.S. Public*, pg. 1111
Hoelzer, Dennis, Chm. Bd., Pres. & Chief Exec. Officer--Sentinel Technologies Inc., Downers Grove, IL; *U.S. Private*, pg. 984
Hoenshell, Craig, Chm. Bd & Chief Exec. Officer--Avis Rent A Car System, Inc., Garden City, NY; *U.S. Public*, pg. 321

Hoenshell, R. Craig, Chm. Bd. & Chief Exec. Officer--Avis Car Leasing, Garden City, NY; *U.S. Public*, pg. 321
Hofer, Dieter, Chm. Bd.--Knurr AG, Munich, Germany; *Int'l*, pg. 739
Hoffman, David, Chm. Bd.--Trophy Holdings Inc., Elmwood Park, NJ; *U.S. Private*, pg. 1105
Hoffman, Ebba C., Chm. Bd., Pres., Chief Exec. Officer & Chief Fin. Officer--Smead Manufacturing Company, Hastings, MN; *U.S. Private*, pg. 1006
Hoffman, Edmund, Chm. Bd.--Coca-Cola Bottling Co. of the Southwest, San Antonio, TX; *U.S. Private*, pg. 248
Hoffman, Eric, Chm. Bd.--Hoffman Corporation, Portland, OR; *U.S. Private*, pg. 532
Hoffman, G.L., Chm. Bd., Pres., Chief Exec. Officer & Sec.--Insignia Systems, Inc., Minnetonka, MN; *U.S. Public*, pg. 881
Hoffman, Jerry V., Chm. Bd., Pres. & Chief Exec. Officer--Berry Petroleum Company, Taft, CA; *U.S. Public*, pg. 223
Hoffman, Michael, Chm. Bd.--FKI Industries. Inc., Fairfield, CT; *Int'l*, pg. 472
Hofmann, Bernard M., Chm. Bd. & Chief Exec. Officer--Hofmann Industries, Inc., Sinking Spring, PA; *U.S. Private*, pg. 533
Hofmann, Richard D., Chm. Bd. & Chief Exec. Officer--Kolmar Laboratories, Inc., Port Jervis, NY; *Int'l*, pg. 239
Hogan, Frank, Chm. Bd. & Pres.--Sullivan Long & Hagerty, Inc., Birmingham, AL; *U.S. Private*, pg. 1050
Hogan, Timothy P., Chm. Bd., Pres. & Chief Exec. Officer--Warmington Homes, Costa Mesa, CA; *U.S. Private*, pg. 1150
Hogbin, W., Chm. Bd.--Taylor Woodrow International Ltd., Southall, United Kingdom; *Int'l*, pg. 1358
Hogg, Christopher, Chm. Bd.--Reuters Holdings PLC, London, United Kingdom; *Int'l*, pg. 1105
Hogg, Christopher, Sir, Chm. Bd.--Allied Domecq PLC, London, United Kingdom; *Int'l*, pg. 62
Hogg, Michael, Chm. Bd. & Chief Exec. Officer--Michael Hogg-Young & Rubicam (Pvt.) Ltd., Harare, Zimbabwe; *U.S. Private*, pg. 1198
Hogg, William T., Jr., Chm. Bd.--Trend Line Corporation, Jackson, MS; *U.S. Private*, pg. 1099
Hoguet, David, Chm. Bd.--Globe Furniture Rentals, Cincinnati, OH; *U.S. Private*, pg. 458
Hoigaard, Conrad, Chm. Bd.--Raven Industries, Inc., Sioux Falls, SD; *U.S. Public*, pg. 1361
Hoke, Joe, Chm. Bd. & Chief Exec. Officer--Mintz & Hoke Inc., Avon, CT; *U.S. Private*, pg. 751
Hokin, Richard, Chm. Bd.--Intermountain Industries, Inc., Boise, ID; *U.S. Private*, pg. 568
Hokin, Richard, Chm. Bd.--III Exploration Co., Boise, ID; *U.S. Private*, pg. 568
Holden, Richmond Y., Jr., Chm. Bd. & Pres.--J.L. Hammett Company, Braintree, MA; *U.S. Private*, pg. 498
Holder, George H., Sr., Chm. Bd.--Hershey Creamery Company, Harrisburg, PA; *U.S. Private*, pg. 524
Holder, Richard G., Chm. & Chief Exec. Officer--Mount Vernon Plastics Company, Sparks, NV; *U.S. Public*, pg. 1386
Holding, Lewis R., Chm. Bd. & Chief Exec. Officer--First Citizens Banc Shares, Inc., Raleigh, NC; *U.S. Public*, pg. 628
Holkeri, Harri, Chm. Bd.--FinnAir Oy, Helsinki, Finland; *Int'l*, pg. 485
Holland, John B., Chm. Bd. & Pres.--Durum Energy Corp., Vancouver, Canada; *Int'l*, pg. 422
Holland, John B., Chm. Bd. & Pres.--Durum Energy Corp., Sucursal Del Peru, Vancouver, Canada; *Int'l*, pg. 422
Holland, John B., Chm. Bd. & Pres.--Durum (Australia) Pty. Ltd., Vancouver, Canada; *Int'l*, pg. 422
Holland, John B., Chm. Bd. & Chief Exec. Officer--Union Underwear Co., Inc., Bowling Green, KY; *U.S. Public*, pg. 686
Holland, Ron, Sr. V.P. & Creative Dir.--Lois/EJL New York, New York, NY; *U.S. Public*, pg. 1011
Holland, Willard R., Chm. Bd. & Chief Exec. Officer--FirstEnergy Corp., Akron, OH; *U.S. Public*, pg. 644
Holland, Willard R., Chm. Bd. & Chief Exec. Officer--Pennsylvania Power Co., New Castle, PA; *U.S. Public*, pg. 645
Holland, William R., Chm. & Chief Exec. Officer--United Dominion Industries, Ltd., Charlotte, NC; *U.S. Public*, pg. 1675
Hollander, Jules A., Chm. Bd. & Treas.--Hartford Distributors Inc., Manchester, CT; *U.S. Private*, pg. 507
Holleman, Matt, Chm. Bd. & Pres.--Capitol Street Corp., Jackson, MS; *U.S. Private*, pg. 207
Hollern, Michael P., Chm. Bd. & Pres.--Brooks Resources Corporation, Bend, OR; *U.S. Private*, pg. 172
Holley, Tom, Chm. Bd. & Owner--Gramex Corporation, Bridgeton, MO; *U.S. Private*, pg. 468
Hollingsworth, B.B., Jr., Chm. Bd., Pres. & Chief Exec. Officer--Group 1 Automotive, Inc., Houston, TX; *U.S. Public*, pg. 767
Hollingsworth, Rodney, Chm. Bd.--Sun Bulb Company, Inc., Arcadia, FL; *U.S. Private*, pg. 1050
Hollins, Arthur, III, Chm. Bd.--The First National Bank of Lake Charles, Lake Charles, LA; *U.S. Public*, pg. 630
Hollis, Samuel B., Owner--Federal Compress & Warehouse Company, Inc., Memphis, TN; *U.S. Private*, pg. 398
Holloway, Caswell F., Jr., Chm. Bd.--Josam Company, Michigan City, IN; *U.S. Private*, pg. 600
Holman, C. Ray, Chm. Bd. & Chief Exec. Officer--Mallinckrodt Inc., Saint Louis, MO; *U.S. Public*, pg. 1039
Holman, Edwin J., Chm. Bd., Pres. & Chief Exec. Officer--Petrie Retail, Inc., Secaucus, NJ; *U.S. Private*, pg. 858
Holman, Joseph S., Chm. Bd.--Holman Enterprises, Pennsauken, NJ; *U.S. Private*, pg. 535
Holman, W.H., Jr., Chm. Bd., Chief Exec. & Oper. Officers--Jitney-Jungle Stores of America, Inc., Jackson, MS; *U.S. Private*, pg. 588
Holman, W.H., Jr., Chm. Bd., Chief Exec. & Chief Oper. Officer--Southern Jitney-Jungle, Inc., Jackson, MS; *U.S. Private*, pg. 588
Holman, W.H., Jr., Chm. Bd., Chief Exec. & Chief Oper. Officer--Jitney-Jungle Bakery, Inc., Jackson, MS; *U.S. Private*, pg. 588
Holmen, Reidar Erik, Chm.--BNP Finans A/S - Norway, Oslo, Norway; *Int'l*, pg. 163
Holmes a Court, J.L., Chm. Bd.--John Holland Group Pty. Ltd., Melbourne, Australia; *Int'l*, pg. 630
Holmes, Arthur, Chm. Bd. & Chief Exec. Officer--Chart Industries, Inc., Cleveland, OH; *U.S. Public*, pg. 336
Holmes, Arthur, Chm. & Chief Exec. Officer--PSI-Process Systems International, Inc., Cleveland, OH; *U.S. Public*, pg. 336
Holmes, Benjamin L., Chm. Bd.--Laserscope Surgical Systems, San Jose, CA; *U.S. Public*, pg. 979
Holmes, David R., Chm., Pres. & Chief Exec. Officer--The Reynolds and Reynolds Company, Dayton, OH; *U.S. Public*, pg. 1384
Holmes, Harold, Co-Chm. Bd. & Owner--Taco John's International, Inc., Cheyenne, WY; *U.S. Private*, pg. 1066
Holmes, Howard S., Chm. Bd.--Chelsea Milling Co., Chelsea, MI; *U.S. Private*, pg. 231
Holmes, Neal H., Chm. Bd. & Chief Exec. Officer--Allied Security, Inc., Pittsburgh, PA; *U.S. Private*, pg. 40
Holmes, Robert M., Chm. Bd.--Oltmans Construction Company, Whittier, CA; *U.S. Private*, pg. 815
Holmqvist, Bjarne, Chm. Bd.--Gunnebo Industrier AB, Gunnebo, Sweden; *Int'l*, pg. 578
Holsapple, E., Chm. Bd.--Welsh Farms, Inc., Long Valley, NJ; *U.S. Private*, pg. 1162
Holscher, Richard H., Chm. Bd.--Firstar Mortgage Corporation, Milwaukee, WI; *U.S. Public*, pg. 643
Holt, Dennis F., Chm. Bd., Pres. & Chief Exec. Officer--Western International Media Corporation, Los Angeles, CA; *U.S. Private*, pg. 1165
Holt, Dennis F., Chm. Bd. & Chief Exec. Officer--Western Motivational Incentives Group, Inc., Los Angeles, CA; *U.S. Private*, pg. 1167
Holt, Henry H., Jr., Chm. Bd.--Denver Chemical (PR) Inc., Humacao, PR; *U.S. Public*, pg. 310
Holt, Ralph M., Jr., Chm. Bd.--Holt Hosiery Mills, Inc., Burlington, NC; *U.S. Private*, pg. 536
Holten, John V., Chm. Bd. & Chief Exec. Officer--Holberg Industries, Inc., Greenwich, CT; *U.S. Private*, pg. 533
Holten, John V., Chm. Bd. & Chief Exec. Officer--Nebco Evans Holding Co., Greenwich, CT; *U.S. Private*, pg. 533
Holter-Sorensen, Erik, Chm. Bd. & Mng. Dir.--A/S Ivaran Rederi, Lysaker, Norway; *Int'l*, pg. 696
Holzer, Edwin H., Chm. Bd., Chief Exec. Officer & Mng. Dir.--Lois/EJL Chicago, Chicago, IL; *U.S. Public*, pg. 1011
Holzer, Jochen, Dr., Chm.-Supervisory Bd.--Viag AG, Bonn, Germany; *Int'l*, pg. 1464
Holzfaster, Ralph, Chm. Bd.--Nebraska Public Power District, Columbus, NE; *U.S. Private*, pg. 789
Holzinger, Pedro, Chm. Bd.--Westag & Getalit AG, Rheda-Wiedenbruck, Germany; *Int'l*, pg. 1491
Holzwasser, Harry A., Chm. Bd.--Arrow Automotive Industries, Inc., Framingham, MA; *U.S. Public*, pg. 133
Homes, W.G., Chm. Bd., Pres. & Treas.--Homes & Son Contractors, Inc., Phoenix, AZ; *U.S. Private*, pg. 537
Honeycutt, V.B., Chm. Bd., Pres. & Chief Exec. Officer--Computer Sciences Corporation, El Segundo, CA; *U.S. Public*, pg. 422
Hong, Yee Jee, Chm.--DBS Computer Services Pte. Ltd., Singapore, Singapore; *Int'l*, pg. 350
Hong, Yee Jee, Chm.--Singapore Factory Development Ltd., Singapore, Singapore; *Int'l*, pg. 351
Hongladarom, Sunthorn, Chm. Bd.--Nakornthon Bank Public Company Limited, Bangkok, Thailand; *Int'l*, pg. 904
Honickman, Harold, Chm. Bd. & Chief Exec. Officer--Honickman Affiliates, Pennsauken, NJ; *U.S. Private*, pg. 537
Hood, Warren, Jr., Chm. Bd.--Atlas Roofing Corp., Meridian, MS; *U.S. Private*, pg. 96
Hoog, Thomas W., Pres. & CEO-USA--Hill and Knowlton, Inc., New York, NY; *Int'l*, pg. 1483
Hooker, Gary R., Chm. Bd.--Hooker Industries, Ontario, CA; *U.S. Private*, pg. 538
Hooker, J. Clyde, Jr., Chm. Bd. & Chief Exec. Officer--Hooker Furniture Corporation, Martinsville, VA; *U.S. Private*, pg. 538
Hooks, B.L., Chm. Bd.--Universal Life Insurance Company, Memphis, TN; *U.S. Private*, pg. 1127
Hooper, Anthony W., Chm. Bd., Pres. & Chief Exec. Officer--Insituform Technologies, Inc., Chesterfield, MO; *U.S. Public*, pg. 881
Hooper, Steven W., Chm. Bd.--Nextlink Communications Inc., Bellevue, WA; *U.S. Public*, pg. 1181
Hooson, Lord, Chm. Bd.--Laura Ashley Holdings Plc, Maidenhead, United Kingdom; *Int'l*, pg. 804
Hope, Colin F.N., Chm. Bd.--Ibstock Plc, Luttorworth, United Kingdom; *Int'l*, pg. 658
Hope, Colin F.N., Sir, Chm. Bd.--T & N Plc, Manchester, United Kingdom; *Int'l*, pg. 1334
Hopkins, James R., Chm. Bd. & Chief Exec. Officer--FirstCity Financial Corporation, Waco, TX; *U.S. Public*, pg. 644
Hopmann, Karl-August, Chm.-Supervisory Bd.--Otto Versand (GmbH & Co.), Hamburg, Germany; *Int'l*, pg. 1014
Hopp, Anthony, Chm. & Chief Exec. Officer--Campbell-Ewald Advertising, Warren, MI; *U.S. Public*, pg. 908
Hoppe, David T., Chm. Bd. & Pres.--CORS, Itasca, IL; *U.S. Private*, pg. 196
Horgen, Chris H., Chm. Bd.--Nichols Research Corporation, Huntsville, AL; *U.S. Public*, pg. 1182
Horie, Yukio, Chm. Bd.--Pentel Co., Ltd., Tokyo, Japan; *Int'l*, pg. 1035
Horn, Donald N., Chm. Bd.--Vicon Industries, Inc., Hauppauge, NY; *U.S. Public*, pg. 1719
Horn, G. Arthur, Chm. Bd.--Horn Packaging Corporation, Ayer, MA; *U.S. Private*, pg. 539
Horn, Jerry D., Chm. Bd.--General Nutrition, Inc., Pittsburgh, PA; *U.S. Public*, pg. 725
Horn, Ralph, Chm. Bd., Pres. & Chief Exec. Officer--First Tennessee National Corporation, Memphis, TN; *U.S. Public*, pg. 638
Horn, Russell E., Sr., Chm. Bd.--Pace Resources, Inc., York, PA; *U.S. Private*, pg. 829
Hornady, Marvel, Chm. Bd.--Hornady Manufacturing Company, Grand Island, NE; *U.S. Private*, pg. 539
Horne, John R., Chm. Bd. & Chief Exec. Officer--Navistar International Corporation, Chicago, IL; *U.S. Public*, pg. 1167
Horne, Timothy P., Chm. Bd. & Chief Exec. Officer--Watts Industries, Inc., North Andover, MA; *U.S. Public*, pg. 1746
Horner, Donald G., Chm. Bd.--First Hawaiian Creditcorp, Inc., Honolulu, HI; *U.S. Public*, pg. 635
Hornery, S.G., Chm. Bd.--Lend Lease Corporation Limited, Sydney, Australia; *Int'l*, pg. 806
Horowitz, Edward D., Chm. & Chief Exec Officer-Viacom New Media--Viacom Broadcasting Inc., New York, NY; *U.S. Private*, pg. 778
Horowitz, Richard A., Chm. Bd., Pres. & Chief Exec. Officer--P & F Industries, Inc., Farmingdale, NY; *U.S. Public*, pg. 1239
Horrigan, J.F., Chm. Bd.--Horrigan American Inc., Reading, PA; *Int'l*, pg. 9
Horrigan, J.F., Chm. Bd.--American Commercial Credit Corp., Reading, PA; *Int'l*, pg. 9
Horrocks, Ray, Chm. Bd.--Chloride Group PLC, London, United Kingdom; *Int'l*, pg. 287
Horstman, A.C.J., Chm. Bd.--Tiel Utrecht, Utrecht, Netherlands; *Int'l*, pg. 647
Horton, D. Vernon, Chm. Bd. & Chief Exec. Officer--Pacific Capital Bancorp, Salinas, CA; *U.S. Public*, pg. 1247
Horton, Donald R., Chm. Bd., Pres., Chief Exec. Officer & Chief Oper. Officer--D.R. Horton, Inc., Arlington, TX; *U.S. Public*, pg. 840
Horton, Gregory L., Chm. Bd., Pres. & Chief Exec. Officer--DDL Electronics, Inc., Newbury Park, CA; *U.S. Public*, pg. 473
Horwitz, Louis B., Chm. Bd. & Pres.--Datum Inc., Irvine, CA; *U.S. Public*, pg. 488
Hosch, Robert F., Chm. Bd. & Pres.--Harris Contracting Co., Saint Paul, MN; *U.S. Private*, pg. 505
Hoskins, John T., Chm. Bd.--Curtis Screw Co., Inc., Buffalo, NY; *U.S. Private*, pg. 298
Hoskins, W. Lee, Chm., Pres. & Chief Exec. Officer--Huntington National Bank, Columbus, OH; *U.S. Public*, pg. 850
Hoskyns, John Austin, Sir, Chm. Bd.--The Burton Group PLC, London, United Kingdom; *Int'l*, pg. 237
Hoskyns, John, Sir, Chm. Bd.--EMAP Plc, Peterborough, United Kingdom; *Int'l*, pg. 451
Hosoda, Tadashi, Chm. Bd.--Mitsubishi Shindoh Co., Ltd., Tokyo, Japan; *Int'l*, pg. 875
Hosokawa, Masuo, Chm. Bd.--Hosokawa Micron Corporation, Osaka, Japan; *Int'l*, pg. 635
Hosoya, Reiji, Chm. Bd.--Futaba Corporation, Mobara, Japan; *Int'l*, pg. 531
Hossack, G.M., Chm. & Mng. Dir.--GKN Chep SA (Pty) Ltd., Wandsbeck, South Africa; *Int'l*, pg. 536
Houck, F. Henry, Chm. Bd.--The Riggs National Bank of Maryland, Rockville, MD; *U.S. Public*, pg. 1390
Hougen, Everett D., Chm. Bd.--Hougen Manufacturing Inc., Swartz Creek, MI; *U.S. Private*, pg. 541
Hough, Richard T., Chm. Bd.--CHEMCENTRAL Corporation, Bedford Park, IL; *U.S. Private*, pg. 231
Houk, Keith D., Chm. Bd.--PSA Airlines, Inc., Vandalia, OH; *U.S. Public*, pg. 1680
Houlihan, Lawrence M., Chm. Bd., Pres., Chief Exec. & Chief Fin. Officer, Treas. & Sec.--Frank B. Ross Co. Inc., Jersey City, NJ; *U.S. Private*, pg. 946
House, David L., Chm. Bd., Pres. & Chief Exec. Officer--Bay Networks, Inc., Santa Clara, CA; *U.S. Public*, pg. 196
House, Frank, Jr., Chm. Bd. & Reg. Construction Mng. Dir.--Willis Corroon Corp. of Birmingham, Birmingham, AL; *Int'l*, pg. 1505
House, Larry R., Chm. Bd. & Chief Exec. Officer--Medpartners Inc., Birmingham, AL; *U.S. Public*, pg. 1082
Housen, Charles B., Chm. Bd., Pres. & Chief Exec. Officer--Erving Industries, Inc., Erving, MA; *U.S. Private*, pg. 382
Houserman, Howard, Chm. Bd. & Pres.--Zetec, Inc., Issaquah, WA; *U.S. Private*, pg. 1205
Housley, Mark, Chm. Bd., Pres. & Chief Exec. Officer--Radius Inc., Sunnyvale, CA; *U.S. Public*, pg. 1358
Housman, Charles J., Chm. Bd. & Pres.--Armatron International, Inc., Melrose, MA; *U.S. Public*, pg. 131
Houssein, Joe S., Chm. Bd., Pres. & Chief Exec. Officer--Intrawest Corporation, Vancouver, Canada; *Int'l*, pg. 685
Houssels, J.K., Chm. Bd.--Showboat, Incorporated, Las Vegas, NV; *U.S. Public*, pg. 1469
Houssels, J.K., Chm. Bd.--Showboat Operating Co., Las Vegas, NV; *U.S. Public*, pg. 1469
Houston, Doug, Chm.--Houston Helm and Company, Los Angeles, CA; *U.S. Private*, pg. 542
Houston, Ivan J., Chm. Bd.--Golden State Mutual Life Insurance Company, Los Angeles, CA; *U.S. Private*, pg. 461
Houston, Paul A., Chm.--Scott's Food Services Inc., Markham, Canada; *Int'l*, pg. 1213
Houston, Robert A., Chm. Bd.--Office Electronics, Inc., Itasca, IL; *U.S. Private*, pg. 812
Hovekamp, George D., Sr., Chm. Bd.--The Kruse Company, Fairfield, OH; *U.S. Private*, pg. 636
Hovers, J.C.M, Dr., Chm. Bd.--Stork N.V., Naarden, Netherlands; *Int'l*, pg. 1304
Hovey, G. Melvin, Chm. Bd.--Maine Public Service Company, Presque Isle, ME; *U.S. Public*, pg. 1038
Hovnanian, Kevork S., Chm. Bd.--Hovnanian Enterprises, Inc., Red Bank, NJ; *U.S. Public*, pg. 843
How, Peter C., Chm. Bd.--How Group Limited, West Bromwich, United Kingdom; *Int'l*, pg. 636
Howard, Bruce, Chm. Bd.--Flint Manufacturing Co., Burton, MI; *U.S. Private*, pg. 413

Howard, Howell H., Chm. Bd.--Southern Mineral Corporation, Houston, TX; *U.S. Public*, pg. 1490
Howard, J.T., Chm.-Emeritus--Howard, Merrell & Partners, Inc., Raleigh, NC; *U.S. Private*, pg. 542
Howard, James J., Chm. Bd., Pres. & Chief Exec. Officer--Northern States Power Company, Minneapolis, MN; *U.S. Public*, pg. 1195
Howard, Jerry A., Chm. Bd., Pres. & Chief Exec. Officer--Atrion Corporation, Arab, AL; *U.S. Public*, pg. 146
Howard, John F., Chm. Bd.--Hawker Siddeley Canada Inc., Mississauga, Canada; *Int'l*, pg. 604
Howard, Ken E., Chm.--Fletcher Merchants Limited, Auckland, New Zealand; *Int'l*, pg. 495
Howard, Mark Fitzalan, Lord, Chm. Bd.--Fleming Investment Trust Management Limited, London, United Kingdom; *Int'l*, pg. 493
Howard, N.G., Chm.-Thermal Ceramics Div.--Morgan Crucible Co. Plc, Windsor, United Kingdom; *Int'l*, pg. 890
Howard, Richard F., Chm. Bd. & Sec.--WSMP, Inc., Claremont, NC; *U.S. Public*, pg. 1729
Howard, Robert, Chm. Bd.--Howtek, Inc., Hudson, NH; *U.S. Public*, pg. 844
Howard, Robert, Chm. Bd.--Presstek, Inc., Hudson, NH; *U.S. Public*, pg. 1324
Howard, Ronald A., Chief Exec. Officer--Hayes Corporation, Regional Office, Gaithersburg, MD; *U.S. Public*, pg. 801
Howard, William G., Chm. Bd.--Mercer Transportation Co., Louisville, KY; *U.S. Private*, pg. 732
Howe, Harold, Jr., Chm. Bd., Chief Exec. Officer & Treas.--Howe Furniture Corporation, Trumbull, CT; *U.S. Private*, pg. 543
Howe, Hubbard C., Chm. Bd. & Interim Chief Exec. Officer--APS Holding Corporation, Houston, TX; *U.S. Public*, pg. 10
Howe, Hubbard C., Chm. Bd., Pres. & Chief Exec. Officer--A.P.S., Inc., Houston, TX; *U.S. Public*, pg. 10
Howe, Hubbard C., Chm. Bd. & Pres.--A.P.S., Memphis, TN; *U.S. Public*, pg. 10
Howe, Michael V., Chm. Bd.--Mileage Plus Marketing, Inc., Elk Grove Village, IL; *U.S. Public*, pg. 1653
Howe, Roger L., Chm. Bd.--U.S. Precision Lens Inc., Cincinnati, OH; *U.S. Public*, pg. 448
Howe, Stan, Chm. Bd.--The HON Co., Muscatine, IA; *U.S. Public*, pg. 772
Howell, Ebert, Chm. Bd., Pres. & Chief Exec. Officer--Trippe Mfg. Co., Chicago, IL; *U.S. Private*, pg. 1104
Howell, Hilton H., Jr., Chm. Bd.--Self-Insurance Administrators, Inc., Stone Mountain, GA; *U.S. Public*, pg. 144
Howell, John R., Chm. Bd., Pres. & Chief Exec. Officer--Summit Bank, Bethlehem, PA; *U.S. Public*, pg. 1528
Howell, John S., Chm. Bd. & Chief Exec. Officer--Howell Instruments Inc., Fort Worth, TX; *U.S. Private*, pg. 543
Howell, Peter C., Chm. Bd.--Signature Brands USA, Inc., Solon, OH; *U.S. Public*, pg. 1472
Howell, S. Oden, Chm. Bd.--United Farm Tools, Inc., Glasgow, KY; *U.S. Private*, pg. 1122
Hoy, Thomas L., Chm. Bd. & Pres.--Arrow Financial Corporation, Glens Falls, NY; *U.S. Public*, pg. 135
Hoyos, Alexander, Chm.-Bd. of Mgmnt.--Wiener Allianz Versicherungs-AG, Vienna, Austria; *Int'l*, pg. 62
Hoyos, Alexander, Dr., Chm.-Bd. of Mngmt.--Wiener Allianz Lebensversicherungs-AG, Vienna, Austria; *Int'l*, pg. 62
Hoyt, Henry H., Jr., Chm. Bd. & Chief Exec. Officer--Carter-Wallace, Inc., New York, NY; *U.S. Public*, pg. 309
Hoz, Maria E., Broker--Century 21 Agmont Real Estate, Inc., Chicago, IL; *U.S. Private*, pg. 226
Hron, Ihor W., Chm. Bd., Pres. & Chief Exec. Officer--Midland Life Insurance Co., Columbus, OH; *U.S. Private*, pg. 744
Hsu, P.T., Chm.--Kuo Hua Inc., Taipei, Taiwan; *Int'l*, pg. 394
Hsui-Chi, Wu, Chm. Bd.--Tainan Spinning Co., Ltd., Tai-nan, Taiwan; *Int'l*, pg. 1347
Hu, Longmen, Chm.--Dentsu (Taiwan) Inc., Taipei, Taiwan; *Int'l*, pg. 394
Huang, K.M., Chm. Bd.--Wei-Chuan Foods Corporation, Taipei, Taiwan; *Int'l*, pg. 1488
Hubbard, J.R., Chm. Bd.--Davies Shephard Pty. Ltd., Keon Park, Australia; *Int'l*, pg. 2
Hubbard, R. D., Chm. Bd. & Chief Exec. Officer--Hollywood Park, Inc., Inglewood, CA; *U.S. Public*, pg. 830
Hubbard, Robert A., Chm. Bd. & Pres.--Wilbur Smith Associates, Columbia, SC; *U.S. Private*, pg. 1009
Hubbard, Stanley S., Chm. Bd., Pres. & Chief Exec. Officer--Hubbard Broadcasting, Inc., Saint Paul, MN; *U.S. Private*, pg. 543
Hubbard, Stanley S., Chm. Bd.--United States Satellite Broadcasting, Co., Saint Paul, MN; *U.S. Private*, pg. 544
Hubbell, Frederick S., Chm. Bd.--Equitable of Iowa Companies, Des Moines, IA; *Int'l*, pg. 647
Hubble, Don W., Chm. Bd., Pres. & Chief Exec. Officer--Angelica Corporation, Chesterfield, MO; *U.S. Public*, pg. 113
Hubble, Don W., Chm. Bd.--National Linen & Uniform Service, Atlanta, GA; *U.S. Public*, pg. 1160
Huber, E. W., Chm. Bd.--Topflight Corp., York, PA; *U.S. Private*, pg. 1091
Huber, Ron, Chm. Bd., Pres. & Chief Exec. Officer--Time Systems, Inc., Phoenix, AZ; *U.S. Private*, pg. 1086
Hubers, David, Chm. Bd., Chief Exec. Officer & Pres.--IDS Financial Services, Inc., Minneapolis, MN; *U.S. Public*, pg. 73
Hubert, Edward, Chm. Bd.--Hubert Company, Harrison, OH; *U.S. Private*, pg. 545
Hubner, Cornelius E., Chm. Bd. & Chief Exec. Officer--American Felt & Filter, Newburgh, NY; *U.S. Private*, pg. 54
Hubner, Donald A., Chm. Bd. & Chief Exec. Officer--Central/Shippee, Inc., Bloomingdale, NJ; *U.S. Private*, pg. 224
Hubner, W., Chm. Bd.--Paramount Fitness Corp., Los Angeles, CA; *U.S. Private*, pg. 838
Hudetz, Frank C., Chm. Bd. & Chief Exec. Officer--Solar Communications, Inc., Naperville, IL; *U.S. Private*, pg. 1012
Hudetz, John F., Chm. Emeritus--Solar Communications, Inc., Naperville, IL; *U.S. Private*, pg. 1012
Hudler, Donald W., Chm. Bd. & Pres.--The Saturn Corporation, Troy, MI; *U.S. Public*, pg. 721
Hudson, C.B., Chm.-Insurance Opers.--Torchmark Corporation, Birmingham, AL; *U.S. Public*, pg. 1622
Hudson, C.B., Chm. & Chief Exec. Officer--Globe Life And Accident Insurance Co., Oklahoma City, OK; *U.S. Public*, pg. 1622
Hudson, Harris W., Vice Chm. & Chm.-Republic Solid Waste & Security Svcs. Div.--Republic Industries, Inc., Fort Lauderdale, FL; *U.S. Public*, pg. 1378
Hudson, John B., Chm.--Hilb, Rogal and Hamilton Company of Victoria, Victoria, TX; *U.S. Public*, pg. 827
Hudson, M.R., Chm. Bd. & Pres.--Fisca Oil Co., Inc., Westwood, KS; *U.S. Private*, pg. 408
Hudson, William A., Chm. Bd. & Pres.--Diversco, Inc., Spartanburg, SC; *U.S. Private*, pg. 336
Huemme, Douglas W., Chm. Bd., Pres. & Chief Exec. Officer--Lilly Industries, Inc., Indianapolis, IN; *U.S. Public*, pg. 994
Huemme, Richard C., Chm. Bd., Pres. & Chief Exec. Officer--Pittsburgh Tube Co., Moon Township, PA; *U.S. Private*, pg. 867
Hueppi, Rolph, Chm. Bd.--Zurich American Insurance Company of Illinois, Schaumburg, IL; *Int'l*, pg. 1530
Huether, Douglas, Chm. Bd.--Independent Can Company, Belcamp, MD; *U.S. Private*, pg. 559
Huff, John R., Chm. Bd., Pres. & Chief Exec. Officer--Oceaneering International, Inc., Houston, TX; *U.S. Public*, pg. 1211
Huff, John R., Chm. Bd., Pres. & Chief Exec. Officer--Oceaneering International, Inc., Morgan City, LA; *U.S. Public*, pg. 1211
Hugenot, Verle, Chm. Bd., Pres. & Chief Exec. Officer--United Missouri Bank Northeast, Monroe City, MO; *U.S. Public*, pg. 1654
Huges, George E., Jr., Chm. Bd.--Hughes Group, Clarksville, IN; *U.S. Private*, pg. 546
Hughes, B. Wayne, Chm. Bd. & Chief Exec. Officer--Public Storage, Inc., Glendale, CA; *U.S. Public*, pg. 1340
Hughes, D.A., Chm. Bd. & Chief Exec. Officer--Hughes Supply Corp., Greenville, OH; *U.S. Private*, pg. 547
Hughes, David H., Chm. Bd. & Chief Exec. Officer--Hughes Supply, Inc., Orlando, FL; *U.S. Public*, pg. 846
Hughes, Francis J., Jr., Chm. Bd.--Texas Micro, Inc., Houston, TX; *U.S. Public*, pg. 1586
Hughes, H.D., Chm. Bd., Pres., Chief Exec. Officer & Dir.-Sls.--Diversified Group, Inc., Harahan, LA; *U.S. Private*, pg. 336
Hughes, Joseph F., Chm. Bd., Pres., Chief Exec. Officer & Treas.--TSR Inc., Hauppauge, NY; *U.S. Public*, pg. 1559
Hughes, Keith W., Chm. Bd. & Chief Exec. Officer--Associates First Capital Corporation, Dallas, TX; *U.S. Public*, pg. 662
Hughes, Keith W., Chm. Bd. & Chief Exec. Officer--Associates Financial Services Corporation, Dallas, TX; *U.S. Public*, pg. 663
Hughes, Kristine F., Chm. Bd.--Nature's Sunshine Products, Inc., Provo, UT; *U.S. Public*, pg. 1166
Hughes, Mark, Chm. Bd., Pres. & Chief Exec. Officer--Herbalife International of America, Inc., Century City, CA; *U.S. Public*, pg. 809
Hughes, Roger K., Chm. Bd.--Hughes Family Markets, Inc., Irwindale, CA; *U.S. Public*, pg. 1349
Hughes, Victor, Chm. Bd. & Chief Exec. Officer--Koger Equity Inc., Jacksonville, FL; *U.S. Public*, pg. 965
Huh, Joon, Chm. Bd.--Daewoo Securities Co., Ltd., Seoul, Korea; *Int'l*, pg. 358
Huibers, S.C., Chm.--The PFH Group, Diemen, Netherlands; *Int'l*, pg. 750
Huisman, Willem, Chm. Bd., Pres. & Chief Exec. Officer--Precision Systems, Inc., Saint Petersburg, FL; *U.S. Public*, pg. 1321
Huitt, E. Larry, Chm. Bd., Exec. V.P., Treas. & Sec.--Huitt-Zollars, Inc., Dallas, TX; *U.S. Private*, pg. 547
Huizenga, H. Wayne, Chm. Bd.--Florida Panthers Holdings, Inc., Fort Lauderdale, FL; *U.S. Public*, pg. 654
Huizenga, H. Wayne, Chm. Bd. & Co-Chief Exec. Officer--Republic Industries, Inc., Fort Lauderdale, FL; *U.S. Public*, pg. 1378
Hull, John C., Chm. Bd. & Chief Exec. Officer--Pratt Casino Corporation, Dallas, TX; *U.S. Public*, pg. 761
Hull, Lewis W., Chm. Bd., Pres. & Chief Exec. Officer--Hull Corporation, Hatboro, PA; *U.S. Private*, pg. 547
Huls, Harrison, Chm. Bd.--Hale-Halsell Company, Tulsa, OK; *U.S. Private*, pg. 494
Hulsey, Neven, Chm. Bd.--Earle M. Jorgensen Company, Brea, CA; *U.S. Private*, pg. 600
Hulstrunk, Rolf, Chm.-Mngmt. Board--Heidelberger Zement A.G., Heidelberg, Germany; *Int'l*, pg. 605
Humann, L. Phillip, Chm. Bd., Pres. & Chief Exec. Officer--SunTrust Banks, Inc., Atlanta, GA; *U.S. Public*, pg. 1537
Hume, William J., Chm. Bd.--Basic American Foods, Walnut Creek, CA; *U.S. Private*, pg. 121
Humke, Ramon L., Chm. Bd.--Meridian Insurance Group, Inc., Indianapolis, IN; *U.S. Public*, pg. 1095
Hummer, Paul F., Chm. Bd., Pres. & Chief Exec. Officer--A.P. Green Industries, Inc., Mexico, MO; *U.S. Public*, pg. 761
Humphrey, G. Watts, Jr., Chm. Bd. & Chief Exec. Officer--The Conair Group, Inc., Pittsburgh, PA; *U.S. Private*, pg. 261
Humphrey, John W., Chm. Bd.--The Forum Corporation, Boston, MA; *U.S. Private*, pg. 420
Humphrey, Robert G., Chm. Bd.--Bulova Watch Company Limited, Toronto, Canada; *U.S. Public*, pg. 1011
Hundley, Franklin M., Chm. Bd.--The Berkshire Gas Company, Pittsfield, MA; *U.S. Public*, pg. 216
Hundley, Monty D., Chm. Bd.--Tollman/Hundley Hotels, Hopewell Junction, NY; *U.S. Private*, pg. 1090
Hung-i, Chiang, Chm. Bd.--China Airlines Ltd., Taipei, Taiwan; *Int'l*, pg. 284
Hunger, Fred M., Chm. Bd.--World Shipping, Inc., Rocky River, OH; *U.S. Private*, pg. 1190
Hunsberger, Ruby Moore, Chm. Bd. Emeritus--Crown International, Inc., Elkhart, IN; *U.S. Private*, pg. 293
Hunt, D.S., Chm.--MFI Furniture Center PLC, London, United Kingdom; *Int'l*, pg. 827
Hunt, E.C., Jr., Chm. Bd. & Chief Exec. Officer--Thermo Industries Inc., Charlotte, NC; *U.S. Private*, pg. 1080
Hunt, Frank M., Chm. Bd. & Pres.--Citrus World Inc., Lake Wales, FL; *U.S. Private*, pg. 241
Hunt, J.B., Sr. Chm. Bd.--J.B. Hunt Transport Services, Inc., Lowell, AR; *U.S. Public*, pg. 849
Hunt, Mitchell W., Jr., Chm. Bd., Pres. & Chief Exec. Officer--SouthTrust Bank of Columbus, Columbus, GA; *U.S. Public*, pg. 1492
Hunt, P.J., Chm. Bd.--Land Securities Properties Limited, London, United Kingdom; *Int'l*, pg. 798
Hunt, P.J., Chm. Bd.--Ravenseft Properties Limited, London, United Kingdom; *Int'l*, pg. 798
Hunt, P.J., Chm. Bd.--Ravenside Investments Limited, London, United Kingdom; *Int'l*, pg. 798
Hunt, P.J., Chm. Bd.--Ravenseft Industrial Estates Limited, London, United Kingdom; *Int'l*, pg. 798
Hunt, P.J., Chm. Bd.--The City of London Real Property Company Limited, London, United Kingdom; *Int'l*, pg. 798
Hunt, Peter, Chm. Bd. & Mng. Dir.--Land Securities Plc, London, United Kingdom; *Int'l*, pg. 798
Hunt, Ray L., Chm. Bd. & Chief Exec. Officer--Hunt Oil Company, Dallas, TX; *U.S. Private*, pg. 548
Hunt, Robert C., Chm. Bd. & Chief Exec. Officer--The Hunt Corporation, Indianapolis, IN; *U.S. Private*, pg. 548
Hunt, W.L., Chm. Bd. & Pres.--Hunt Building Corporation, El Paso, TX; *U.S. Private*, pg. 548
Hunt, William O., Chm. Bd., Pres. & Chief Exec. Officer--Intellicall, Inc., Carrollton, TX; *U.S. Public*, pg. 887
Hunte, Henry F., Chm. Bd. & Pres.--H.G. Fenton Material Company, San Diego, CA; *U.S. Private*, pg. 400
Hunter, B.D., Chm. Bd. & Chief Exec. Officer--Huntco Inc., Town and Country, MO; *U.S. Public*, pg. 849
Hunter, Jerry E., Chm. Bd., Pres. & Chief Exec. Officer--JPS Textile Group, Inc., Greenville, SC; *U.S. Private*, pg. 578
Hunter, John W., Chm. Bd, Pres. & Chief Exec. Officer--Adtec Detention Systems, San Antonio, TX; *U.S. Private*, pg. 18
Hunter, Ronald D., Chm. Bd. & Chief Exec. Officer--Standard Management Corporation, Indianapolis, IN; *U.S. Public*, pg. 1502
Hunting, R.H., Chm. Bd.--Hunting Plc, London, United Kingdom; *Int'l*, pg. 640
Huntington, Lawrence S., Chm. Bd. & Chief Exec. Officer--Fiduciary Trust Company International, New York, NY; *U.S. Public*, pg. 621
Huntington, Tom, Chm. Bd., Pres. & Chief Exec. Officer--EVCON Industries, Wichita, KS; *U.S. Public*, pg. 1788
Huntsman, Jon M., Chm. Bd. & Chief Exec. Officer--Huntsman Corporation, Salt Lake City, UT; *U.S. Private*, pg. 549
Hunziker, Fredy W., Chm. Bd.--LeaRonal S.E. Asia Ltd., Kowloon, Hong Kong; *U.S. Public*, pg. 982
Huppi, Rolf, Chm. Bd. & Chief Exec. Officer--Zurich Insurance Company, Zurich, Switzerland; *Int'l*, pg. 1529
Hurd, Edward T., Chm. Bd.--Moore Products Co., Spring House, PA; *U.S. Public*, pg. 1128
Hurlbut, Wendell P., Chm. Bd. & Chief Exec. Officer--Esterline Technologies Corporation, Bellevue, WA; *U.S. Public*, pg. 594
Hurley, William D., Chm. Bd.--Frequency Engineering Laboratories, Farmingdale, NJ; *U.S. Private*, pg. 427
Hurliman, Ron, Chm. Bd.--Tillamook County Creamery Assn., Tillamook, OR; *U.S. Private*, pg. 1086
Hurn, Roger, Sir, Chm. Bd.--Smiths Industries plc, London, United Kingdom; *Int'l*, pg. 1266
Hurni, Marcel, Chm.--Coop Ostschweiz, Gossau, Switzerland; *Int'l*, pg. 329
Hurvis, Tom, Chm. Bd.--Old World Industries, Inc., Northbrook, IL; *U.S. Private*, pg. 814
Hurwitz, Charles E., Chm. Bd. & Chief Exec. Officer--Maxxam Inc., Houston, TX; *U.S. Public*, pg. 1062
Husseini, Tamer, Chm. Bd., Pres. & Chief Exec. Officer--Celeritek, Inc., Santa Clara, CA; *U.S. Public*, pg. 319
Hussey, Philip W., Jr., Chm. Bd.--Hussey Corporation, North Berwick, ME; *U.S. Private*, pg. 550
Hussman, Walter E., Jr., Chm. Bd., Pres. & Publr.--Wehco Media, Inc., Little Rock, AR; *U.S. Private*, pg. 1159
Hutchings, Gregory F., Exec. Chm. Bd.--Tomkins PLC, London, United Kingdom; *Int'l*, pg. 1395
Hutchins, Burleigh M., Chm. Bd. & Chief Tech. Officer--Zymark Corporation, Hopkinton, MA; *U.S. Private*, pg. 139
Hutchinson, A.M., Chm. Bd.--R & R Marketing, West Caldwell, NJ; *U.S. Private*, pg. 902
Hutchinson, A.M., Chm. Bd.--Royal Division, West Caldwell, NJ; *U.S. Private*, pg. 902
Hutchinson, A.M., Chm. Bd.--Reitman Division, West Caldwell, NJ; *U.S. Private*, pg. 902
Hutchinson, A.M., Chm. Bd.--Spectrum Division, West Caldwell, NJ; *U.S. Private*, pg. 902
Hutchinson, A.M., Chm. Bd.--Raritan Display Division, West Caldwell, NJ; *U.S. Private*, pg. 902
Hutton, Charles R., Chm. Bd.--Chuck Hutton Chevrolet Company, Memphis, TN; *U.S. Private*, pg. 550
Hutton, Edward L., Chm. Bd. & Chief Exec. Officer--Chemed Corporation, Cincinnati, OH; *U.S. Public*, pg. 343
Hutton, Edward L., Chm. Bd.--Omnicare, Inc., Covington, KY; *U.S. Public*, pg. 1223
Hutts, Joseph C., Chm. Bd., Pres. & Chief Exec. Officer--Phycor, Inc., Nashville, TN; *U.S. Public*, pg. 1293
Huyghebaert, Jan, Chm. Bd. & Pres.--Almanij N.V., Antwerp, Belgium; *Int'l*, pg. 65

Huzjak, Thomas J., Chm. Bd. & Chief Exec. Officer--T-NETIX, Inc., Englewood, CO; *U.S. Public*, pg. 1553

Hvide, J. Erik, Chm. Bd. & Chief Exec. Officer--Hvide Marine Incorporated, Fort Lauderdale, FL; *U.S. Public*, pg. 851

Hwang, K. Philip, Dr., Chm. Bd. & Chief Exec. Officer--Televideo, Inc., San Jose, CA; *U.S. Public*, pg. 1572

Hwang, Li-San, Dr., Chm. Bd., Pres. & Chief Exec. Officer--Tetra Tech, Inc., Pasadena, CA; *U.S. Public*, pg. 1582

Hyatt, Frederick, Chm. Bd.--Marshall & Williams Co., Greenville, SC; *U.S. Private*, pg. 708

Hyatt, Kenneth E., Chm. Bd., Pres. & Chief Exec. Officer--Walter Industries, Inc., Tampa, FL; *U.S. Public*, pg. 1736

Hyde, Douglas W., Chm. Bd., Pres. & Chief Exec. Officer--OshKosh B'Gosh, Inc., Oshkosh, WI; *U.S. Public*, pg. 1232

Hyeok, Chang Chi, Chm.--KOHAP Group, Seoul, Korea; *Int'l*, pg. 742

Hyon, Chey Jong, Grp. Chm.--Sunkyong Industries Co., Kyonggi-do, Korea; *Int'l*, pg. 1320

Hyon, Chey Jong, Chm. Bd.--Sunkyong America, Inc., New York, NY; *Int'l*, pg. 1320

Hyung Seole, Suh, Chm. Bd.--Daewoo Corporation, Seoul, Korea; *Int'l*, pg. 357

Iacovelli, Guido, Chm. Bd. & Pres.--Italian Food Manufacturers, Inc., Vestal, NY; *U.S. Private*, pg. 576

Iarossi, Frank J., Chm. Bd.--American Bureau of Shipping, New York, NY; *U.S. Private*, pg. 51

Ibach, Charles R., Jr., Chm. Bd.--Jefferson Mills, Inc., Pulaski, VA; *U.S. Private*, pg. 584

Ibazeta, Jose C., Chm. Bd.--Atlas Consolidated Mining & Development Corporation, Manila, Philippines; *Int'l*, pg. 95

Ibos, Robert J., Chm. Bd., Pres. & Chief Exec. Officer--National Engineering & Contracting Co., Strongsville, OH; *U.S. Private*, pg. 782

Ibsen, Robert, Dr., Chm. Bd., Pres., Chief Exec. Officer & Treas.--Den-Mat Corporation, Santa Maria, CA; *U.S. Private*, pg. 324

Icahn, Carl C., Chm. Bd.--Icahn & Co., Inc., New York, NY; *U.S. Private*, pg. 556

Icahn, Carl C., Chm. Bd.--ACF Industries, Inc., Saint Charles, MO; *U.S. Private*, pg. 556

Icahn, Carl C., Chm. Bd.--Marvel Entertainment Group, New York, NY; *U.S. Public*, pg. 1052

Ide, Masataka, Chm. Bd.--West Japan Railway Company, Osaka, Japan; *Int'l*, pg. 1490

Idemitsu, Shosuke, Chm. Bd.--Idemitsu Kosan Co., Ltd., Tokyo, Japan; *Int'l*, pg. 659

Ienner, Don, Chm. Bd.-Columbia Records Grp.--Sony Music Entertainment, Inc., New York, NY; *Int'l*, pg. 1281

Ihamuotila, Jaakko, Chm. Bd. & Chief Exec. Officer--Neste Oy, Espoo, Finland; *Int'l*, pg. 912

Iibuchi, Shigeru, Chm. Bd.--Hochiki Corporation, Tokyo, Japan; *Int'l*, pg. 623

Iida, Makoto, Chm. Bd., Chief Exec. Officer & Rep. Dir.--Secom Co., Ltd., Tokyo, Japan; *Int'l*, pg. 1217

Ikawa, Takao, Chm. Bd.--Daio Paper Corporation, Tokyo, Japan; *Int'l*, pg. 372

Ikeda, Yasuhiko, Chm. Bd.--Ajinomoto Company Inc., Tokyo, Japan; *Int'l*, pg. 40

Iketani, Masanari, Chm. Bd.--Tamco, Rancho Cucamonga, CA; *U.S. Public*, pg. 99

Ikle, Fred Charles, Dr., Chm. Bd.--Telos Corporation, Ashburn, VA; *U.S. Public*, pg. 1573

Ikuta, Masaki, Chm.--Mikuni American Corporation, Northridge, CA; *Int'l*, pg. 867

Ilardo, Harry, Chm. Bd.--Mamma Ilardo's Corp., Baltimore, MD; *U.S. Private*, pg. 699

Ilaria, Peter V., Chm. Bd. & Pres.--Tropar Mfg. Co., Inc., Florham Park, NJ; *U.S. Private*, pg. 1105

Ilitch, Michael, Chm. Bd. & Pres.--Little Caesar Enterprises, Inc., Detroit, MI; *U.S. Private*, pg. 671

Imamura, Kazusuke, Chm. Bd. & Chief Exec. Officer--Chichibu Onoda Cement Corporation, Tokyo, Japan; *Int'l*, *pg. 284*

Imbert, Yves, Chm. Bd. & Chief Exec. Officer--Hispano-Suiza S.A., Paris, France; *Int'l*, pg. 1165

Imerman, Vivian, Chm. Bd.--Del Monte Royal Corporation, Rivonia, South Africa; *Int'l*, pg. 388

Imerman, Vivian, Chm. Bd.--Del Monte Foods International Limited, Staines, United Kingdom; *Int'l*, pg. 388

Imhoff, Herbert F., Chm. Bd. & Chief Exec. Officer--General Employment Enterprises, Inc., Oak Brook Terrace, IL; *U.S. Public*, pg. 714

Imlay, John P., Jr., Chm. Bd.--Dun & Bradstreet Software Services, Atlanta, GA; *Int'l*, pg. 532

Imose, Mitsuo, Chm. Bd.--The Toyo Trust and Banking Company, Limited, Tokyo, Japan; *Int'l*, pg. 1411

Imperatore, Arthur E., Chm. Bd.--A-P-A Transport Corp., North Bergen, NJ; *U.S. Private*, pg. 2

Inaba, Seiuemon, Dr., Chm. Bd. & Chief Exec. Officer--Fanuc Ltd., Yamanashi, Japan; *Int'l*, pg. 477

Inagaki, Masao, Chm. Bd. & Chief Exec. Officer--Asatsu Inc., Tokyo, Japan; *Int'l*, pg. 85

Inaganti, Prasad, Chm. Bd. & Pres.--Howes Leather Corporation, Curwensville, PA; *U.S. Private*, pg. 543

Inamori, Kazuo, Chm.--Kyocera Corporation, Kyoto, Japan; *Int'l*, pg. 775

Inatome, Joe, Sr. Chm.--American Speedy Printing Centers, Inc., Troy, MI; *U.S. Private*, pg. 62

Inatome, Richard, Co-Chm. Bd.--American Speedy Printing Centers, Inc., Troy, MI; *U.S. Private*, pg. 62

Inatome, Rick, Chm. Bd.--Inacom Corp., Omaha, NE; *U.S. Public*, pg. 873

Indelicato, Vincent, Chm. Bd. & Pres.--Delicato Vineyards, Manteca, CA; *U.S. Private*, pg. 322

Indursky, Harry, Chm. Bd. & Pres.--Cambridge Street Metal Co., Allston, MA; *U.S. Private*, pg. 203

Infanger, Walter, Chm. Bd. & Sr. V.P.--Ferrier Lullin & Cie SA, Geneva, Switzerland; *Int'l*, pg. 480

Infusino, Thomas P., Chm. Bd. & Chief Exec. Officer--Wakefern Food Corporation, Elizabeth, NJ; *U.S. Private*, pg. 1146

Inge, Clifton C., Chm. Bd.--Willis Corroon Corp. of Mobile, Mobile, AL; *Int'l*, pg. 1506

Ingle, Robert P., Chm. Bd. & Chief Exec. Officer--Ingles Markets, Incorporated, Black Mountain, NC; *U.S. Public*, pg. 878

Ingleby, Raymond S., Chm. Bd. & Chief Exec. Officer--Caribiner International, Inc., New York, NY; *U.S. Public*, pg. 305

Ingram, Don V., Chm. Bd.--IMCO Recycling Inc., Irving, TX; *U.S. Public*, pg. 870

Ingram, E.W., III, Chm. Bd., Pres. & Chief Exec. Officer--White Castle System, Inc., Columbus, OH; *U.S. Private*, pg. 1171

Ingram, Jack R., Chm. Bd. & Pres.--XETA Corporation, Tulsa, OK; *U.S. Public*, pg. 1783

Ingram, Richard E., Chm. Bd.--Builder Marts of America, Inc., Greenville, SC; *U.S. Private*, pg. 179

Inkawat, Bhanu, Chm. & Exec. Creative Dir.--Leo Burnett Ltd. Thailand, Bangkok, Thailand; *U.S. Private*, pg. 185

Inman, Frank, Jr., Pres. & Chief Exec. Officer--Inman Construction Corporation, Memphis, TN; *U.S. Private*, pg. 564

Inman, Paul, Chm. Bd.--Paul Inman Associates Inc., Farmington, MI; *U.S. Private*, pg. 564

Inoue, Masayasu, Chm. Bd. & Chief Exec. Officer--Crestbrook Forest Industries Ltd., Cranbrook, Canada; *Int'l*, pg. 348

Inserra, Lawrence, Sr., Chm. Bd.--Inserra Shoprite, Mahwah, NJ; *U.S. Private*, pg. 565

Inui, Tsuneo, Chm. Bd.--Orix Corporation, Tokyo, Japan; *Int'l*, pg. 1008

Iott, Wallace D., Chm. Bd.--Seaway Food Town, Inc., Maumee, OH; *U.S. Public*, pg. 1452

Irala, Xavier, Chm. Bd. & Chief Exec. Officer--Grupo Iberia, Madrid, Spain; *Int'l*, pg. 574

Irani, Dr. Ray R., Chm. Bd.--Canadian Occidental Petroleum Ltd., Calgary, Canada; *U.S. Public*, pg. 1210

Irani, Ray, R., Dr., Chm. Bd. & Chief Exec. Officer--Occidental Petroleum Corporation, Los Angeles, CA; *U.S. Public*, pg. 1210

Ireland, James D., III, Chm. Bd.--Sun Coast Industries, Inc, Dallas, TX; *U.S. Public*, pg. 1529

Ireland, Richard, Chm. Bd.--Severn Trent Plc, Birmingham, United Kingdom; *Int'l*, pg. 1225

Ireland, Richard, Chm. Bd.--Severn Trent Water Ltd., Birmingham, United Kingdom; *Int'l*, pg. 1225

Irvine, Horace H., II, Chm. Bd.--Hadco Corporation, Salem, NH; *U.S. Public*, pg. 773

Irving, Welton L., Chm. Bd.--UHP Healthcare, Inglewood, CA; *U.S. Private*, pg. 1113

Irwin, Ann, Chm. Bd. & Chief Exec. Officer--Labelon Corporation, Canandaigua, NY; *U.S. Private*, pg. 641

Irwin, Arnold B., Co-Chm. Bd.--Irwin Toy Ltd., Toronto, Canada; *Int'l*, pg. 688

Irwin, Richard, Chm. Bd.--PharmChem Laboratories, Inc., Menlo Park, CA; *U.S. Public*, pg. 1285

Irwin, S. Macdonald, Co-Chm. Bd.--Irwin Toy Ltd., Toronto, Canada; *Int'l*, pg. 688

Irwin, Winn, Chm. Bd.--Oliver Products Company, Grand Rapids, MI; *U.S. Private*, pg. 815

Isahikawa, Mr., Chm. Bd. & Pres.--Nissei Sangyo Co., Ltd., Tokyo, Japan; *Int'l*, pg. 945

Isemoto, Larry, Chm. Bd.--Isemoto Contracting Co. Ltd., Hilo, HI; *U.S. Private*, pg. 575

Isenberg, Eugene M., Chm. Bd. & Chief Exec. Officer--Nabors Industries, Inc., Houston, TX; *U.S. Public*, pg. 1148

Isherwood, Robert, Chm. Bd. & Chief Exec. Officer--Ambac International Corp., Columbia, SC; *U.S. Private*, pg. 48

Ishi, Chikashi, Chm.--Showa Aluminum Corp., Sakai, Japan; *Int'l*, pg. 1236

Ishibashi, Kanichiro, Honorary Chm.--Bridgestone Corporation, Tokyo, Japan; *Int'l*, pg. 213

Ishibashi, Shunichi, Chm. Bd.--Daiwa House Industry Co., Ltd., Osaka, Japan; *Int'l*, pg. 374

Ishida, J., Chm. Bd. & Chief Exec. Officer--Sumitomo Sitix Silicon, Inc., Fremont, CA; *Int'l*, pg. 1317

Ishiguro, Seizo, Chm. Bd.--Alpine Electronics of America, Inc., Torrance, CA; *Int'l*, pg. 65

Ishihara, Kenzo, Chm. Bd.--Ishihara Sangyo Kaisha, Ltd., Osaka, Japan; *Int'l*, pg. 689

Ishii, Toshiichi, Chm. & Chief Exec. Officer--NEC Technologies, Inc., Boxboro, MA; *Int'l*, pg. 900

Ishii, Yoshiteru, Chm. Bd.--Anritsu Corporation, Tokyo, Japan; *Int'l*, pg. 77

Ishikawa, Rokuro, Chm. Bd.--Kajima Corporation, Tokyo, Japan; *Int'l*, pg. 721

Ishimoto, Yoshikazu, Chm. Bd.--Descente Ltd., Osaka, Japan; *Int'l*, pg. 395

Ishizaka, Kazuyoshi, Chm. Bd.--Kenwood Corporation, Tokyo, Japan; *Int'l*, pg. 730

Ishizaka, Yasuhiko, Chm.--Matsuya Company Ltd., Tokyo, Japan; *Int'l*, pg. 848

Iskra, Gary, Chm. Bd.--American Home Improvement, Monroeville, PA; *U.S. Private*, pg. 56

Isles, Marvin L., Chm. Bd. & Chief Exec. Officer--Giddings & Lewis, Inc., Fond Du Lac, WI; *Int'l*, pg. 1389

Ismail Bin Mohamed Ali, Tun, Chm. Bd.--Sime Darby Berhad, Kuala Lumpur, Malaysia; *Int'l*, pg. 1249

Ismail, Tan Sin Dato Basir, Chm. Bd.--Cycle & Carriage Industries (1986) Pte. Limited, Singapore, Singapore; *Int'l*, pg. 350

Isobe, Ritsuo, Chm. Bd. & Representative Dir.--Hakuhodo Incorporated, Tokyo, Japan; *Int'l*, pg. 587

Isom, W. Howard, Chm. Bd.--Blue Diamond Growers, Sacramento, CA; *U.S. Private*, pg. 152

Israel, Larry, Chm. Bd., Pres. & Chief Exec. Officer--Telesensory Corporation, Sunnyvale, CA; *U.S. Private*, pg. 1074

Israelson, Chase, Chm. Bd.--The Dorris Lumber & Moulding Co., Sacramento, CA; *U.S. Private*, pg. 341

Issleib, Lutz, Chm. Bd. & Pres.--S & P Company, Mill Valley, CA; *U.S. Private*, pg. 954

Istock, Verne G., Chm. Bd., Pres. & Chief Exec. Officer--First Chicago NBD Corporation, Chicago, IL; *U.S. Public*, *pg. 627*

Itagaki, Hiroshi, Chm. Bd. & Chief Exec. Officer--Teijin Limited, Osaka, Japan; *Int'l*, pg. 1362

Itin, Thomas W., Chm. Bd., Pres. & Chief Exec. Officer--Williams Controls, Inc., Portland, OR; *U.S. Public*, pg. 1769

Itin, Thomas W., Chm. Bd.--Kenco, Middlebury, IN; *U.S. Public*, pg. 1769

Ito, Bill, Chm. Bd.--California Strawberry Commission, Watsonville, CA; *U.S. Private*, pg. 201

Ito, Masatoshi, Chm. Bd.--The Southland Corporation, Dallas, TX; *Int'l*, pg. 693

Itoh, Josei, Chm. Bd.--Nippon Life Insurance Co., Osaka, Japan; *Int'l*, pg. 934

Itoh, Tadashi, Chm. Bd.--Sumitomo Corporation, Tokyo, Japan; *Int'l*, pg. 1312

Iue, Satoshi, Chm. Bd.--Sanyo Electric Co., Ltd., Osaka, Japan; *Int'l*, pg. 1190

Ivans, W.S., Chm. Bd.--Cohu, Inc., San Diego, CA; *U.S. Public*, pg. 396

Iversen, Bruno, Chm. Bd.--Schumann Sasol International AG, Hamburg, Germany; *Int'l*, pg. 1196

Iverson, Ann, Chm. Bd. & Chief Exec. Officer--Laura Ashley (USA) Inc., Boston, MA; *Int'l*, pg. 804

Iverson, F. Kenneth, Chm. Bd.--Nucor Corporation, Charlotte, NC; *U.S. Public*, pg. 1205

Ives, J. Atwood, Chm. Bd. & Chief Exec. Officer--Eastern Enterprises, Weston, MA; *U.S. Public*, pg. 548

Ivester, M. Douglas, Chm. Bd. & Chief Exec. Officer--The Coca-Cola Company, Atlanta, GA; *U.S. Public*, pg. 392

Ivester, M. Douglas, Chm. Bd.--Coca-Cola Enterprises Inc., Atlanta, GA; *U.S. Public*, pg. 393

Iwadare, Koichi, Chm.--Banyu Pharmaceutical Co. Ltd., Tokyo, Japan; *U.S. Public*, pg. 1091

Iwai, I., Chm. Bd.--Amano Corporation, Kanagawa, Japan; *Int'l*, pg. 70

Iwai, Yasushi, Chm.--ORIX Estate Corporation, Osaka, Japan; *Int'l*, pg. 1008

Iwama, Yoichiro, Chm.--Tokio Marine Investment Services, Limited, Hong Kong, Hong Kong; *Int'l*, pg. 1393

Iwasaki, Takuya, Chm. Bd.--The Nikko Securities Co., Ltd., Tokyo, Japan; *Int'l*, pg. 930

Iwasaki, Tetsuo, Chm. Bd.--Applied Materials Japan, Inc., Chiba, Japan; *U.S. Public*, pg. 123

Izuel, Cesareo Alierta, Chm. Bd., Pres. & Chief Exec. Officer--Tabacalera, S.A., Madrid, Spain; *Int'l*, pg. 1345

Jaakkola, Gouko, Chm. Bd.--Tamrock Corp., Tampere, Finland; *Int'l*, pg. 1352

Jackman, Joseph R., Chm. Bd., Pres. & Chief Exec. Officer--Reactive Metals & Alloys Corporation (REMACOR), West Pittsburg, PA; *U.S. Private*, pg. 913

Jackson, Anthony Howland, Chm. Bd.--Bain Hogg Group plc, London, United Kingdom; *Int'l*, pg. 671

Jackson, E.V., Chm. Bd. & Pres.--Reynolds Metals Company-Illinois, Mc Cook, IL; *U.S. Public*, pg. 1385

Jackson, J.B.H., Chm. Bd.--Howden Group Plc, Renfrew, United Kingdom; *Int'l*, pg. 636

Jackson, J.L., Chm. Bd., Pres. & Chief Exec. Officer--Global Industrial Technologies, Dallas, TX; *U.S. Public*, pg. 747

Jackson, John B.H., Chm. Bd.--Ladbroke Group Plc, London, United Kingdom; *Int'l*, pg. 787

Jackson, Marlin, Chm. & Chief Exec. Officer--NationsBank of Conway, Conway, AR; *U.S. Public*, pg. 1164

Jackson, Mary Anne, Chm. Bd., Pres., Chief Oper. & Chief Exec. Officer--My Own Meals, Inc., Deerfield, IL; *U.S. Private*, pg. 770

Jackson, R.A., Chm. Bd., Pres. & Chief Exec. Officer--Nuburn Capital, Calgary, Canada; *Int'l*, pg. 990

Jackson, Richard L., Chm. Bd., Pres. & Chief Exec. Officer--Allegiant Physician Services, Atlanta, GA; *U.S. Public*, pg. 45

Jackson, W. Ronald, Chm. Bd. & Pres.--Jackson Furniture Industries, Cleveland, TN; *U.S. Private*, pg. 579

Jackson, W. Ronald, Chm. Bd. & Pres.--Cleveland Chair Company, Cleveland, TN; *U.S. Private*, pg. 579

Jackson, W.R., Chm. Emeritus--Pitt-Des Moines, Inc., Pittsburgh, PA; *U.S. Public*, pg. 1304

Jacob, Herbert, Chm. Bd. & Chief Exec. Officer--Ajax Paving Industries Inc., Madison Heights, MI; *U.S. Private*, *pg. 29*

Jacob, Norman A., Pres. & Chief Exec. Officer--The Huntington Trust Co., N.A., Columbus, OH; *U.S. Public*, pg. 850

Jacobs, B.E., Chm. Bd.--Grede Transport, Inc., Milwaukee, WI; *U.S. Private*, pg. 476

Jacobs, Bradley S., Chm. Bd. & Chief Exec. Officer--United Waste Systems, Inc., Houston, TX; *U.S. Public*, pg. 1691

Jacobs, Burleigh E., Chm. Bd.--Grede Foundries, Inc., Milwaukee, WI; *U.S. Private*, pg. 476

Jacobs, Charles E., Chm. Bd.--C.S. McKee & Company, Inc., Pittsburgh, PA; *U.S. Public*, pg. 1673

Jacobs, Franklin A., Chm. Bd. & Chief Exec. Officer--Falcon Products, Inc., Saint Louis, MO; *U.S. Public*, pg. 611

Jacobs, Georges, Chm.-Exec. Committee--UCB, S.A., Brussels, Belgium; *Int'l*, pg. 1427

Jacobs, Harry, Chm. Emeritus--The Martin Agency, Richmond, VA; *U.S. Private*, pg. 678

Jacobs, Henry D., Jr., Chm. Bd.--One Price Clothing Stores, Inc., Duncan, SC; *U.S. Public*, pg. 1225

Jacobs, Irwin L., Chm. Bd.--Genmar Holdings, Inc., Minneapolis, MN; *U.S. Private*, pg. 447

Jacobs, Irwin Mark, Chm. Bd. & Chief Exec. Officer--QUALCOMM, San Diego, CA; *U.S. Public*, pg. 1348

Jacobs, J. Jay, Chm. Bd.--Jay Jacobs, Inc., Seattle, WA; *U.S. Public*, pg. 922

Jacobs, Jeremy M., Sr., Chm. Bd. & Chief Exec. Officer--Delaware North Companies, Inc., Buffalo, NY; *U.S. Private*, pg. 321

Jacobs, Klaus J., Co.-Chm. Bd.--Adecco S.A., Lausanne, Switzerland; *Int'l*, pg. 23

Jacobs, Norman, Chm. Bd. & Pres.--Century Publishing Company, Evanston, IL; *U.S. Private*, pg. 226

Jacobs, Peter H., Chm. Bd. & Pres.--Fone America, Inc., Portland, OR; *U.S. Public*, pg. 661
Jacobs, Richard E., Chm. Bd. & Chief Exec. Officer--The Richard E. Jacobs Group, Westlake, OH; *U.S. Private*, pg. 580
Jacobs, Victor, Chm. Bd. & Chief Exec. Officer--Allou Health & Beauty Care, Inc., Brentwood, NY; *U.S. Public*, pg. 55
Jacobsen, Bent, Vice Chm. Bd.--Dansk Industri Syndikat A/S, Herlev, Denmark; *Int'l*, pg. 381
Jacobsen, I., Chm. Bd. & Pres.--Fuller Company, Bethlehem, PA; *Int'l*, pg. 475
Jacobsen, Thomas H., Chm. Bd., Pres. & Chief Exec. Officer--Mercantile Bancorporation Inc., Saint Louis, MO; *U.S. Public*, pg. 1087
Jacobson, Dennis L., Chm. Bd.--RYDS Batindustri AB, Ryds, Sweden; *U.S. Private*, pg. 479
Jacobson, Sidney, Chm. Bd.--Sid Tool Co. Inc., Plainview, NY; *U.S. Private*, pg. 998
Jacobsson, Knut, Chm. Bd.--Atlet AB, Molnlycke, Sweden; *Int'l*, pg. 97
Jacoff, Richard, Chm. Bd.--Great Neck Saw Manufacturers, Inc., Mineola, NY; *U.S. Private*, pg. 475
Jacomb, Martin, Sir, Chm.--Delta plc, London, United Kingdom; *Int'l*, pg. 389
Jacomb, Martin, Sir, Chm. Bd.--Prudential Corporation PLC, London, United Kingdom; *Int'l*, pg. 1073
Jaeger, Joseph A., Chm. Bd. & Pres.--MCC Group, L.L.C., Metairie, LA; *U.S. Private*, pg. 686
Jaeger, Raymond E., Chm. Bd. & Chief Exec. Officer--SpecTran Corporation, Sturbridge, MA; *U.S. Public*, pg. 1497
Jaffe, Elliot S., Chm. Bd & Chief Exec. Officer--The Dress Barn, Inc., Suffern, NY; *U.S. Public*, pg. 528
Jaffe, Richard B., Chm. Bd., Pres. & Chief Exec. Officer--Safeskin Corporation, San Diego, CA; *U.S. Public*, pg. 1425
Jaffee, Richard M., Chm. Bd.--Oil-Dri Corporation of America, Chicago, IL; *U.S. Public*, pg. 1214
Jaffre, Philippe, Chm. Bd., Pres. & Chief Exec. Officer--Elf Aquitane, Paris, France; *Int'l*, pg. 444
Jagger, David M., Jr., Chm. Bd.--Central Maine Power Company, Augusta, ME; *U.S. Public*, pg. 325
Jakes, Clifford, Chm. Bd.--Farm Press, Clarksdale, MS; *U.S.* Public, pg. 1328
Jali, Tajuddin, Dr., Chm.--Reed Exhibition Companies-Malaysia, Kuala Lumpur, Malaysia; *Int'l*, pg. 1097
James, C. Shelton, Chm. Bd. & Chief Exec. Officer--Elcotel, Inc., Sarasota, FL; *U.S. Public*, pg. 568
James, Edward R., Chm. Bd.--James Building Corporation, Northbrook, IL; *U.S. Private*, pg. 580
James, G.W., Jr., Chm. Bd.--T.L. James & Company, Ruston, LA; *U.S. Private*, pg. 580
James, Larry M., Chm. Bd., Pres. & Chief Exec. Officer--USLD Communications Corp., San Antonio, TX; *U.S. Public*, pg. 969
James, R.W.R., Chm. Bd.--Barratt Commercial, Newcastle upon Tyne, United Kingdom; *Int'l*, pg. 168
James, Thomas A., Chm. Bd. & Chief Exec. Officer--Raymond James Financial, Inc., Saint Petersburg, FL; *U.S. Public*, pg. 923
Jamieson, P.L.A., Chm. Bd.--Robert Fleming (Stock Lending) Limited, London, United Kingdom; *Int'l*, pg. 493
Jang, Chull-Hoon, Chm. Bd. & Pres.--Cho Hung Bank, Seoul, Korea; *Int'l*, pg. 287
Janisch, Andrew, Chm. Bd.--Mark Resources Inc., Calgary, Canada; *Int'l*, pg. 842
Janitz, John A., Chm. Bd., Pres. & Chief Exec. Officer--Textron Automotive Company, Troy, MI; *U.S. Public*, pg. 1590
Janney, Stuart S., Chm. Bd.--Bessemer Group, Inc., New York, NY; *U.S. Private*, pg. 139
Jannotta, Lou, Chm. Bd. & Pres.--L&J Technologies, Hillside, IL; *U.S. Private*, pg. 638
Jansen, Henry, Chm. Bd.--Lynden Incorporated, Seattle, WA; *U.S. Private*, pg. 683
Jansen, Peter, Deputy Chm. Bd. & Grp. Chief Exec. Officer--Caradon Plc, Weybridge, United Kingdom; *Int'l*, pg. 266
Janssen, Baron Daniel, Chm.--Solvay S.A., Brussels, Belgium; *Int'l*, pg. 1277
Janssen, Paul-Emmanuel, Chm. Bd.--Generale de Banque S.A., Brussels, Belgium; *Int'l*, pg. 546
Jarmain, W. Edwin, Chm. Bd.--FCA International Ltd., Westmount, Canada; *Int'l*, pg. 470
Jarvis, M.A., Chm.--First Net (Pty.) LTD., Sandton, South Africa; *Int'l*, pg. 487
Jas, Dick, Chm. Bd.--Possehl Electronic Nederland bv, s Hertogenbosch, Netherlands; *Int'l*, pg. 1064
Jaskol, Leonard R., Chm. Bd., Pres. & Chief Exec. Officer--Lydall, Inc., Manchester, CT; *U.S. Public*, pg. 1020
Jaudes, Robert C., Chm. Bd. & Chief Exec. Officer--Laclede Gas Company, Saint Louis, MO; *U.S. Public*, pg. 973
Jaume, Feliciano Fuster, Chm. Bd. & Pres.--ENDESA - Empresa Nacional de Electricidad, S.A., Madrid, Spain; *Int'l*, pg. 1224
Javier, Antero B., Jr., Chm.--Dentsu Young & Rubicam-Alcantara Inc. (Manila), Manila, Philippines; *U.S. Private*, pg. 325
Jaworski, Walter J., Chm. Bd., Chief Exec. Officer & Chief Oper. Officer--Miken Companies, Inc., Cheektowaga, NY; *U.S. Private*, pg. 745
Jay, Morton, Chm. Bd.--Campmor Inc., Upper Saddle River, NJ; *U.S. Private*, pg. 204
Jayson, Joseph M., Chm. Bd., Pres. & Chief Exec. Officer--J.M. Jayson & Co., Inc., Getzville, NY; *U.S. Private*, pg. 584
Jeancourt-Galignani, Antoine, Chm. Bd.--AGF Assurances, Paris, France; *Int'l*, pg. 14
Jeanloz, Claude, Chm. Bd. & Chief Exec. Officer--The Renovator's Supply, Inc., Conway, NH; *U.S. Private*, pg. 923
Jebsen, Finn M., Chm. Bd.--Elkem ASA, Oslo, Norway; *Int'l*, *pg. 446*
Jelenic, Robert M., Chm. Bd., Pres. & Chief Exec. Officer--Journal Register Company, Trenton, NJ; *U.S. Public*, pg. 934
Jelin, Sima, Chm. Bd.--Karnak Corporation, Clark, NJ; *U.S. Private*, pg. 607
Jeney, Evan, Chm. Bd.--National Electric Coil, Columbus, OH; *U.S. Private*, pg. 782
Jenkins, Alan B., Chm. Bd. & Treas.--Felton Brush Inc., Manchester, NH; *U.S. Private*, pg. 400
Jenkins, Brian, Sir, Chm. Bd.--Woolwich Plc, Bexley, United Kingdom; *Int'l*, pg. 1514
Jenkins, David A., Chm. Bd. & Pres.--Arrhythmia Research Technology, Inc., Austin, TX; *U.S. Public*, pg. 133
Jenkins, Howard, Chm. Bd. & Chief Exec. Officer--Publix Supermarkets Inc., Lakeland, FL; *U.S. Private*, pg. 893
Jenkins, Marvin, Chm. Bd.--Concordia Publishing House, Saint Louis, MO; *U.S. Private*, pg. 261
Jenkins, Michael V., Chm.--Delta Encon Ltd., Enfield, United Kingdom; *Int'l*, pg. 391
Jenkins, Robert H., Chm. Bd., Pres. & Chief Exec. Officer--Sundstrand Corporation, Rockford, IL; *U.S. Public*, pg. 1533
Jennings, A. Drue, Chm. Bd., Pres. & Chief Exec. Officer--Kansas City Power & Light Company, Kansas City, MO; *U.S. Public*, pg. 943
Jennings, Eugene, Chm. Bd., Pres. & Chief Exec. Officer--Universal Standard Healthcare, Inc., Southfield, MI; *U.S. Public*, pg. 1697
Jensen, Craig, Chm. Bd. & Chief Exec. Officer--Executive Software, Glendale, CA; *U.S. Private*, pg. 388
Jensen, Gordon, Chm. Bd.--Icicle Seafoods, Inc., Seattle, WA; *U.S. Private*, pg. 556
Jensen, Irving F., Jr., Chm. Bd., Treas. & Sec.--Irving F. Jensen Co., Inc., Sioux City, IA; *U.S. Private*, pg. 586
Jensen, Knud Erik, Chm. Bd.--MD Foods, Viby, Denmark; *Int'l*, pg. 826
Jensen, Loren D., Ph.D., Chm. Bd.--EA Engineering, Science & Technology, Inc., Hunt Valley, MD; *U.S. Public*, pg. 540
Jensen, Robert P., Chm. Bd.--Jostens, Minneapolis, MN; *U.S. Public*, pg. 934
Jensen, Ronald L., Chm. Bd.--United Insurance Companies, Inc., Dallas, TX; *U.S. Public*, pg. 1679
Jenssen, Fred W., Chm.--BBDO Oslo, Oslo, Norway; *U.S. Public*, pg. 1224
Jepson, Jr., Robert S., Chm. Bd. & Chief Exec. Officer--Kuhlman Corporation, Savannah, GA; *U.S. Public*, pg. 968
Jepson, Larry, Chm Bd. & Chief Exec. Officer--First National Bank, Kearney, NE; *U.S. Public*, pg. 629
Jernemyr, Sven-Eric, Chm. Reg. Bd.--ICA Handlarna Mellansverige AB, Vasteras, Sweden; *Int'l*, pg. 642
Jerome, Jerrold V., Chm. Bd.--Unitrin, Inc., Chicago, IL; *U.S.* Public, pg. 1693
Jerome, Wallace H., Chm. Bd.--Jerome Foods Inc., Barron, WI; *U.S. Private*, pg. 586
Jessup, John, Chm. Bd.--British Building & Engineering Appliances Plc, Sandy, United Kingdom; *Int'l*, pg. 219
Jilk, Lawrence T., Jr., Chm. Bd.--National Penn Bank, Boyertown, PA; *U.S. Public*, pg. 1159
Jimenez, Carlos Alvarez, Chm. Bd.--Corporacion MAPFRE, Compania Internacional de Reaseguros, S.A., Madrid, Spain; *Int'l*, pg. 332
Jimenez, Sergio, Chm. Bd.--CODELCO Chile (Corporacion Nacional Del Cobre De Chile), Santiago, Chile; *Int'l*, pg. 302
Jin, Hwang Soo, Chm. Bd.--Singapore Reinsurance Corporation Limited, Singapore, Singapore; *Int'l*, pg. 1253
Joa, Curt G., Chm. Bd.--Curt G. Joa, Inc., Sheboygan Falls, WI; *U.S. Private*, pg. 588
Jobs, Steve, Chm. Bd. & Chief Exec. Officer--Pixar Animation Studios, Richmond, CA; *U.S. Public*, pg. 1307
Jochum, George T., Chm. Bd., Pres. & Chief Exec. Officer--Mid Atlantic Medical Services, Inc., Rockville, MD; *U.S. Public*, pg. 1109
Johann, Heribert Dr., Chm. & Dir.-Corp. Bd.-Fin. Div.--Boehringer Ingelheim GmbH, Ingelheim, Germany; *Int'l*, pg. 199
Johansson, Roger, Chm. Bd.--AMAL AB, Amal, Sweden; *U.S. Public*, pg. 170
Johansson, Ulf J., Chm. Bd.--Agema Infrared Systems AB, Danderyd, Sweden; *Int'l*, pg. 1289
Johansson, Uls J., Chm. Bd.--Spectra-Physics USA, Inc., Blue Bell, PA; *Int'l*, pg. 1289
John, David, Chm. Bd.--The BOC Group plc, Windlesham, United Kingdom; *Int'l*, pg. 121
Johnannessen, Paul, Chm. Bd.--Megapulse, Inc., Bedford, MA; *U.S. Private*, pg. 729
Johnsen, Niels W., Chm. Bd.--International Shipholding Corporation, New Orleans, LA; *U.S. Public*, pg. 907
Johnsen, Niels W., Chm. Bd.--Central Gulf Lines, Inc., New Orleans, LA; *U.S. Public*, pg. 907
Johnson, Antonia Axson, Chm. Bd.--Axel Johnson AB, Stockholm, Sweden; *Int'l*, pg. 707
Johnson, Bob, Chm. Bd. & Exec. V.P.--Southeastern Realty Group Inc., Orlando, FL; *U.S. Private*, pg. 1015
Johnson, Carl, Chm. Bd. & Chief Exec. Officer--II-VI Incorporated, Saxonburg, PA; *U.S. Public*, pg. 1647
Johnson, Charles B., Chm. Bd.--Franklin Advisers, Inc., Fort Lee, NJ; *U.S. Public*, pg. 680
Johnson, Charles Brook, Chm. Bd., Pres. & Chief Exec. Officer--CS Brooks Canada Inc., Greenwich, CT; *U.S. Private*, pg. 197
Johnson, Charles P., Chm. Bd. & Chief Exec. Officer--General Datacomm Industries, Inc., Middlebury, CT; *U.S.* Public, pg. 708
Johnson, Charles P., Chm. Bd.--General DataComm, Inc., Middlebury, CT; *U.S. Public*, pg. 708
Johnson, Clark A., Chm. Bd.--Sunbelt Nursery Group Inc., Fort Worth, TX; *U.S. Public*, pg. 715
Johnson, Clark A., Chm. Bd. & Chief Exec. Officer--Pier 1 Imports, Inc., Fort Worth, TX; *U.S. Public*, pg. 1295
Johnson, Crawford, III, Chm. Bd.--Coca-Cola Bottling Co. United, Inc., Birmingham, AL; *U.S. Private*, pg. 248
Johnson, David, Chm. Bd., Pres. & Chief Exec. Officer--Swanson, Camden, NJ; *U.S. Public*, pg. 299
Johnson, David J., Chm. Bd., Pres. & Chief Exec. Officer--KinderCare Learning Centers, Inc., Portland, OR; *U.S. Public*, pg. 961
Johnson, David W., Chm. Bd.--Campbell Soup Company, Camden, NJ; *U.S. Public*, pg. 298
Johnson, Earl, Jr., Chm. Bd.--Research Triangle Institute, Research Triangle Park, NC; *U.S. Private*, pg. 924
Johnson, Edward C., III, Chm. Bd. & Chief Exec. Officer--Fidelity Investments (FMR Corp.), Boston, MA; *U.S. Private*, pg. 402
Johnson, Franklin P., Jr., Chm. Bd.--Boole & Babbage, Inc., San Jose, CA; *U.S. Public*, pg. 244
Johnson, Glendon E., Chm. Bd., Pres. & Chief Exec. Officer--John Alden Financial Corporation, Miami, FL; *U.S. Public*, pg. 39
Johnson, J. D., Chm. Bd.--Duke Manufacturing Co., Inc., Saint Louis, MO; *U.S. Private*, pg. 346
Johnson, James A., Chm. Bd. & Chief Exec. Officer--Federal National Mortgage Association (Fannie Mae), Washington, DC; *U.S. Public*, pg. 615
Johnson, Joel W., Chm. Bd. & Chief Exec. Officer--Hormel Foods Corp., Austin, MN; *U.S. Public*, pg. 840
Johnson, John, Chm. Bd. & Pres.--Harvest State Feed, Inc., Snohomish, WA; *U.S. Private*, pg. 508
Johnson, John H., Chm. Bd., Chief Exec. Officer & Publisher--Johnson Publishing Company, Inc., Chicago, IL; *U.S. Private*, pg. 591
Johnson, Jon, Chm.--EvansGroup (Public Relations), Salt Lake City, UT; *U.S. Private*, pg. 385
Johnson, Jon, Chm.--GPC International Holdings, Ottawa, Canada; *U.S. Public*, pg. 1225
Johnson, Jon L., Chm. Bd., Chief Exec. Officer & Dir.--EvansGroup, Salt Lake City, UT; *U.S. Private*, pg. 385
Johnson, Jon L., Pres. & Gen. Mgr.--Industrial Construction, Inc., Idaho Falls, ID; *U.S. Private*, pg. 560
Johnson, LaRee K., Chm. Bd.--LeGrand Johnson Construction Co., Logan, UT; *U.S. Private*, pg. 591
Johnson, Lawrence, Chm. Bd., Pres., Chief Exec. Officer & Gen. Counsel--Kelley Company, Inc., Milwaukee, WI; *U.S. Private*, pg. 612
Johnson, Lawrence, Chm. Bd., Pres., Chief Exec. Officer & Gen Counsel--Kelley Dock Systems, Milwaukee, WI; *U.S.* Private, pg. 612
Johnson, Lawrence M., Chm. Bd. & Chief Exec. Officer--Pacific Century Financial Corporation, Honolulu, HI; *U.S. Public*, pg. 1248
Johnson, Lawrence M., Chm. Bd. & Chief Exec. Officer--Bank of Hawaii, Honolulu, HI; *U.S. Public*, pg. 1248
Johnson, Lawrence M., Chm. Bd.--Pacific Century Bank, Phoenix, AZ; *U.S. Public*, pg. 1248
Johnson, Mark, Chm. Bd., Pres. & Chief Exec. Officer--ITEQ, Inc., Houston, TX; *U.S. Public*, pg. 914
Johnson, Mark K., Chm. Bd. & Chief Exec. Officer--Johnson Storage Moving Co, Denver, CO; *U.S. Private*, pg. 594
Johnson, Okey B., Jr., Chm. Bd. & Pres.--Nashville Steel Corp., Nashville, TN; *U.S. Private*, pg. 775
Johnson, Orville D., Chm. Bd.--UFE Incorporated, Stillwater, MN; *U.S. Private*, pg. 1112
Johnson, R.J.V., Chm. & Publisher--Houston Chronicle, Houston, TX; *U.S. Private*, pg. 517
Johnson, Ralph, Chm. Bd. & Pres.--Lake County Press, Waukegan, IL; *U.S. Private*, pg. 643
Johnson, Rebecca, Chm. Bd.--Columbia Farms Inc., Leesville, SC; *U.S. Private*, pg. 255
Johnson, Robert L., Chm. Bd. & Chief Exec. Officer--Black Entertainment Television Holdings Inc., Washington, DC; *U.S. Public*, pg. 235
Johnson, Robert M., Chm. Bd. & Chief Exec. Officer--Bowne & Co., Inc., New York, NY; *U.S. Public*, pg. 248
Johnson, Roger W., Chm. Bd.--General Semiconductor, Inc., Melville, NY; *U.S. Public*, pg. 726
Johnson, S. Curtis, Chm. Bd.-SC Johnson Comml. Markets--S.C. Johnson & Son, Inc., Racine, WI; *U.S. Private*, pg. 592
Johnson, S.A., Chm. Bd.--Dura Automotive Systems, Inc., Minneapolis, MN; *U.S. Public*, pg. 537
Johnson, S.A., Chm. Bd.--Tower Automotive, Inc., Grand Rapids, MI; *U.S. Public*, pg. 1625
Johnson, Samuel C., Chm. Bd.--Johnson Worldwide Associates, Inc., Sturtevant, WI; *U.S. Public*, pg. 932
Johnson, Steven L., Chm. Bd.--Adience Inc., Carnegie, PA; *U.S. Public*, pg. 58
Johnson, Theodore A., Chm. Bd.--International Lottery & Totalizator Systems, Inc., Carlsbad, CA; *U.S. Public*, pg. 900
Johnson, Thomas L., Co-Chm. Bd., Pres. & Chief Exec. Officer--Objective Systems Integrators, Inc., Folsom, CA; *U.S. Public*, pg. 1209
Johnson, Victor L., Chm. Bd.--JCI Data Processing, Inc., Cinnaminson, NJ; *U.S. Private*, pg. 577
Johnson, W.W., Chm. Bd.--NationsBank South Carolina, N.A., Columbia, SC; *U.S. Public*, pg. 1163
Johnson, William, Chm. Bd.--Goshen Rubber Co., Inc., Goshen, IN; *U.S. Private*, pg. 465
Johnson, William B., Chm. Bd. & Chief Exec. Officer--W.B. Johnson Properties, LLC, Atlanta, GA; *U.S. Private*, pg. 594
Johnston, Fred B., II, Chm. Bd. & Chief Exec. Officer--Fred B. Johnston Company, Inc., Chapin, SC; *U.S. Private*, pg. 595
Johnston, Gene, Chm. Bd.--Cass-Clay Creamery, Fargo, ND; *U.S. Private*, pg. 218
Johnston, M. James, Chm. Bd. & Chief Exec. Officer--Fort Wayne National Corporation, Fort Wayne, IN; *U.S. Public*, pg. 673
Johnston, Paul, Chm. Bd.--Cabot Creamery Co-Operative Inc., Cabot, VT; *U.S. Private*, pg. 26
Johnston, Richard M., Chm. Bd.--Metrocall, Inc., Alexandria, VA; *U.S. Public*, pg. 1102

Johson, Urban, Chm. Bd.--Dahl International AB, Stockholm, Sweden; *Int'l*, pg. 359
Joiner, Webb F., Chm.--Bell Helicopter Textron, Hurst, TX; *U.S. Public*, pg. 1588
Jollin, David A., Chm. Bd. & Chief Exec. Officer--Willis Corroon Corp. of Massachusetts, Boston, MA; *Int'l*, pg. 1506
Joly, Alain, Chm. Bd. & Chief Exec. Officer--Air Liquide S.A., Paris, France; *Int'l*, pg. 37
Jones, Alfred W., III, Chm. Bd.--Sea Island Company, Sea Island, GA; *U.S. Private*, pg. 977
Jones, B.R.S., Dr., Chm.-Tech. Ceramics Div.--Morgan Crucible Co. Plc, Windsor, United Kingdom; *Int'l*, pg. 890
Jones, B.R.S., Dr., Chm. Bd.--Archer Technicoat Limited, High Wycombe, United Kingdom; *Int'l*, pg. 893
Jones, Barbara R., Chm. Bd.--Baltimore Stationery Co./ Total Office, Baltimore, MD; *U.S. Private*, pg. 113
Jones, D. Paul, Jr., Chm. Bd. & Chief Exec. Officer--Compass Bancshares, Inc., Birmingham, AL; *U.S. Public, pg. 418*
Jones, D. Paul, Jr., Chm. Bd. & Chief Exec. Officer--Compass Bank, Plano, TX; *U.S. Public*, pg. 419
Jones, D.H., Chm. Bd.--Morgan Matroc S.A., Barcelona, Spain; *Int'l*, pg. 893
Jones, David A., Chm. Bd.--Humana Inc., Louisville, KY; *U.S. Public*, pg. 847
Jones, David A., Chm. Bd., Pres. & Chief Exec. Officer--RAYOVAC Corporation, Madison, WI; *U.S. Private*, pg. 912
Jones, David R., Chm. Bd.--Carver Federal Savings Bank, New York, NY; *U.S. Public*, pg. 310
Jones, Dennis M., Chm., Pres. & Chief Exec. Officer--Jones Medical Industries Inc., Saint Louis, MO; *U.S. Public*, pg. 933
Jones, E.M.T., Chm. Bd.--TCI International Inc., Sunnyvale, CA; *U.S. Public*, pg. 1555
Jones, Glenn R., Chm. Bd., Pres. & Chief Exec. Officer--Jones International, Ltd., Englewood, CO; *U.S. Private*, pg. 597
Jones, J. Larry, Chm. Bd. & Chief Exec. Officer--Addison-Wesley Longman, Inc., Reading, MA; *Int'l*, pg. 1026
Jones, J.C., III, Chm. Bd.--Fuel South, Inc., Hazlehurst, GA; *U.S. Private*, pg. 596
Jones, J.D.P., Chm. Bd.--Wood Group Pressure Control, Houston, TX; *U.S. Public*, pg. 1775
Jones, James, Co. Chm.--ColeJon Corporation, Cleveland, OH; *U.S. Private*, pg. 251
Jones, James C., III, Chm. Bd. & Chief Exec. Officer--Jones Company, Inc., Waycross, GA; *U.S. Private*, pg. 596
Jones, James L., Sr., Chm. Bd. & Chief Exec. Officer--Jones & Jones, Inc., McAllen, TX; *U.S. Private*, pg. 596
Jones, James M., Jr., Chm., Pres. & Chief Exec. Officer--Peoples & Union Bank, Lewisburg, TN; *U.S. Public*, pg. 639
Jones, Jeremy M., Chm. Bd. & Chief Exec. Officer--Apria Healthcare Group Inc., Costa Mesa, CA; *U.S. Public*, pg. 125
Jones, Jerve M., Chm. Bd.--Peck Jones Construction, Los Angeles, CA; *U.S. Private*, pg. 846
Jones, Jesse N., III, Chm. Bd.--Glenroy Construction Co. Inc., Indianapolis, IN; *U.S. Private*, pg. 456
Jones, Leslie A., Chm. Bd.--Dentsply International Inc., York, PA; *U.S. Public*, pg. 498
Jones, Norman T., Chm. Bd.--CF Industries, Inc., Long Grove, IL; *U.S. Private*, pg. 193
Jones, Quincy, Chm. Bd.--Quincy Jones Entertainment, Los Angeles, CA; *U.S. Public*, pg. 1611
Jones, Reese M., Chm. Bd.--Netopia, Inc., Alameda, CA; *U.S. Public*, pg. 1168
Jones, Ronald L., Chm. Bd., Pres. & Chief Exec. Officer--Dawn Food Products, Inc., Jackson, MI; *U.S. Private*, pg. 316
Jones, Russell, Chm. & Mng. Dir.--Batey Couldrey Jones Advertising, Wan Chai, Hong Kong; *Int'l*, pg. 117
Jones, Sir Philip, Chm.--Total Oil Marine p.l.c.-TOM, London, United Kingdom; *Int'l*, pg. 1409
Jones, Steve, Chm. Bd.--Intermountain Farmers Association, Salt Lake City, UT; *U.S. Private*, pg. 568
Jones, Trevor Edward, Chm.--Highveld Steel & Vanadium Corporation, Witbank, South Africa; *Int'l*, pg. 76
Jones, William E., Chm. Bd.--Cummins-Allison Corp., Mount Prospect, IL; *U.S. Private*, pg. 295
Jones, William H., Chm. Bd. & Pres.--Foster Wheeler Energy Corporation, Clinton, NJ; *U.S. Public*, pg. 676
Jones, William H., Jr., Chm. Bd.--Saunders Oil Company, Inc., Richmond, VA; *U.S. Private*, pg. 968
Jongebloed, James T., Chm. Bd., Pres. & Chief Exec. Officer--Pool Energy Services Co., Houston, TX; *U.S. Public*, pg. 1316
Jordan, Don D., Chm. Bd. & Chief Exec. Officer--Houston Industries Incorporated, Houston, TX; *U.S. Public*, pg. 842
Jordan, Don D., Chm. Bd. & Chief Exec. Officer--NorAm Energy Corp., Houston, TX; *U.S. Public*, pg. 843
Jordan, Jerry D., Chm. Bd. & Chief Exec. Officer--CGAS, Inc., Columbus, OH; *U.S. Public*, pg. 585
Jordan, John W., Chm. Bd.--Gear Research Incorporated, Grand Rapids, MI; *U.S. Private*, pg. 598
Jordan, John W., II, Chm. Bd. & Chief Exec. Officer--Jordan Industries, Inc., Deerfield, IL; *U.S. Private*, pg. 598
Jordan, John W., II, Chm. Bd.--The Scott Motors Company, Alamogordo, NM; *U.S. Private*, pg. 598
Jordan, Michael H., Chm. Bd. & Chief Exec. Officer--CBS Corporation, Pittsburgh, PA; *U.S. Public*, pg. 273
Jordan, Michael H., Chm. Bd. & Chief Exec. Officer--CBS, New York, NY; *U.S. Public*, pg. 273
Jordan, Mike, Chm. Bd.--Farmway Co-Op Inc., Beloit, KS; *U.S. Private*, pg. 396
Jordan, Richard E., II, Chm. Bd. & Chief Exec. Officer--L.B. Smith, Inc., Camp Hill, PA; *U.S. Private*, pg. 1009
Joseph, Edwin, Chm. Bd.--The Great Atlantic Management Company, Hampton, VA; *U.S. Private*, pg. 473
Joseph, George, Chm. Bd. & Chief Exec. Officer--Mercury General Corporation, Los Angeles, CA; *U.S. Public*, pg. 1093
Joseph, John B., Chm. Bd., Pres. & Chief Exec. Officer--West Coast Bancorp, Newport Beach, CA; *U.S. Public*, pg. 1755
Joshi, Krishan K., Chm. Bd.--Paravant Computer Systems, Inc., Melbourne, FL; *U.S. Public*, pg. 1257
Jost, Fritz, Chm.--Coop Oberaargau-Thal/Gau, Lagenthal, Switzerland; *Int'l*, pg. 329
Joubert, Peter G., Chm. Bd.--Foodcorp Limited, Bedfordview, South Africa; *Int'l*, pg. 496
Joudrie, Earl, Chm. Bd.--Algoma Steel Inc., Sault Sainte Marie, Canada; *Int'l*, pg. 56
Joudrie, H. Earl, Chm. Bd.--Canadian Tire Corporation Limited, Toronto, Canada; *Int'l*, pg. 259
Joudrie, H. Earl, Chm. Bd.--Gulf Canada Resources Ltd., Calgary, Canada; *Int'l*, pg. 577
Jovanovich, Peter, Chm. Bd.--Harcourt Brace & Company Intl. Corp., Orlando, FL; *U.S. Public*, pg. 783
Jovanovich, Peter, Chm. & Chief Exec. Officer--Addison-Wesley Longman Ltd., Harlow, United Kingdom; *Int'l*, pg. 1027
Joyce, Kevern R., Chm. Bd., Pres., Chief Exec. Officer & Dir.--TNP Enterprises, Inc., Fort Worth, TX; *U.S. Public*, pg. 1557
Joyce, William H., Chm. Bd., Pres. & Chief Exec. Officer--Union Carbide Corporation, Danbury, CT; *U.S. Public*, pg. 1666
Jozoff, Malcolm, Chm. Bd. & Chief Exec. Officer--Lenox, Incorporated, Lawrenceville, NJ; *U.S. Public*, pg. 261
Jozoff, Malcolm, Chm., Pres. & Chief Exec. Officer--The Dial Corporation, Phoenix, AZ; *U.S. Public*, pg. 505
Juday, D.W., Chm. Bd.--Ideal Industries, Inc., Sycamore, IL; *U.S. Private*, pg. 557
Judge, Jerry, Co-Chm.--Lowe Howard-Spink, London, United Kingdom; *U.S. Private*, pg. 678
Judson, Ray W., Chm. Bd.--Parsons Corporation, Pasadena, CA; *U.S. Private*, pg. 841
Juett, J. Lee, Chm. Bd., Pres. & Chief Exec. Officer--J. Lee Hackett Co., Farmington, MI; *U.S. Private*, pg. 492
Juliard, A., Chm. & Chief Exec. Officer--Union Pour Le Financement D'Immeubles Desouetes (UIS), Paris, France; *Int'l*, pg. 565
Julius, Robert P., Chm. Bd., Pres. & Chief Exec. Officer--Nice-Pak Products, Inc., Orangeburg, NY; *U.S. Private*, pg. 798
Jumabhoy, Yusuf, Chm. Bd.--Scotts Holdings Limited, Singapore, Singapore; *Int'l*, pg. 1212
Jumbe, F.A., Chm. Bd. & Pres.--National Bank of Malawi, Blantyre, Malawi; *Int'l*, pg. 1296
Jumonville, Dan, Chm. Bd. & Pres.--Group Insurance Inc. of Louisiana, Baton Rouge, LA; *U.S. Private*, pg. 484
Jungling, Henry C., Jr., Chm. Bd.--Ag Services of America, Inc., Cedar Falls, IA; *U.S. Public*, pg. 6
Junker, Edward P., III, Chm. & Chief Exec. Officer-NW Market--PNC Bank Corp., Pittsburgh, PA; *U.S. Public*, pg. 1242
Jurick, Geoffrey, Chm. Bd. & Pres.--Emerson Radio Corp., Parsippany, NJ; *U.S. Public*, pg. 578
Jurick, Geoffrey, Chm. Bd. & Chief Exec. Officer--Sport Supply Group, Inc., Dallas, TX; *U.S. Public*, pg. 1499
Jusseaume, Rich, Chm. Bd., Pres. & Chief Exec. Officer--Graphic Enterprises of Ohio, Inc., Canton, OH; *U.S. Private*, pg. 471
Justin, John, Chm. Bd. & Chief Exec. Officer--Justin Industries, Inc., Fort Worth, TX; *U.S. Public*, pg. 936
Justiss, James F., Jr., Chm. Bd., Pres. & Chief Exec. Officer--Justiss Oil Co., Inc., Jena, LA; *U.S. Private*, pg. 602
Juszkiewicz, Henry E., Chm. Bd. & Chief Exec. Officer--Gibson Musical Instruments, Inc., Nashville, TN; *U.S. Private*, pg. 451
Juusela, Jyrki, Chm. Bd., Pres. & Chief Exec. Officer--Outokumpu Oyj, Espoo, Finland; *Int'l*, pg. 1015
Kadisha, Neil, Chm. Bd. & Chief Exec. Officer--HPM Corporation, Mount Gilead, OH; *U.S. Private*, pg. 492
Kaemmer, D., Chm. Bd. & Chief Exec. Officer--GEHE AG, Stuttgart, Germany; *Int'l*, pg. 591
Kaempfer, J.W., Jr., Chm. Bd.--The Kaempfer Company, Investment Builders, Washington, DC; *U.S. Private*, pg. 604
Kaeslin, Laura M., Chm. Bd.--Alpine Packing Company, Stockton, CA; *U.S. Private*, pg. 45
Kafadar, Ahmed D., Chm. Bd. & Chief Exec. Officer--OEA, Inc., Aurora, CO; *U.S. Public*, pg. 1206
Kagami, Misao, Chm.--Sanki Engineering Co., Ltd., Tokyo, Japan; *Int'l*, pg. 877
Kagan, Irving, Chm. Bd.--Penobscot Shoe Company, Old Town, ME; *U.S. Public*, pg. 1273
Kage, Yuji, Chm. Bd.--LTCB and F&C Investment Management Co. Limited, London, United Kingdom; *Int'l, pg. 816*
Kahana, Aron, Chm. Bd. & Pres.--Israel Discount Bank of New York, New York, NY; *Int'l*, pg. 645
Kahl, Richard W., Chm. Bd.--Branford Savings Bank, Branford, CT; *U.S. Public*, pg. 250
Kahler, Herman C., Chm. Bd.--The Citizens Savings Bank Company, Pemberville, OH; *U.S. Public*, pg. 1412
Kahlor, Robert A., Chm. Bd. & Chief Exec. Officer--Journal Communications Inc., Milwaukee, WI; *U.S. Private*, pg. 601
Kahn, Alan, Chm. Bd.--M.B. Kahn Construction Co., Inc., Columbia, SC; *U.S. Private*, pg. 604
Kahn, Alfred, Chm.--The Summit Media Group, New York, NY; *U.S. Private*, pg. 1050
Kahn, D. Dan, Chm. Bd. & Chief Exec. Officer--Production Tool Supply Co., Warren, MI; *U.S. Private*, pg. 889
Kahn, Harold D., Chm. Bd. & Chief Exec. Officer--Macy's East, New York, NY; *U.S. Public*, pg. 618
Kahn, Ivor H., Exec. Chm.--Chemrite Southern Africa (Pty) Ltd., Halfway House, South Africa; *U.S. Public*, pg. 1358
Kahn, J. M., Grp. Exec. Chm.--South African Breweries, Ltd., Johannesburg, South Africa; *Int'l*, pg. 1286
Kahn, Myron, Chm. Bd. & Chief Exec. Officer--Croscill, Inc., New York, NY; *U.S. Private*, pg. 290
Kahn, Seymour, Chm. Bd. & Chief Exec. Officer--Mercury Air Group Inc., Los Angeles, CA; *U.S. Public*, pg. 1092
Kaiser, George B., Chm. Bd.--BOK Financial Corp., Tulsa, OK; *U.S. Public*, pg. 163
Kaiser, George B., Chm. Bd--Bank of Oklahoma, N.A., Tulsa, OK; *U.S. Public*, pg. 163
Kaiser, Joseph P., Jr., Chm. Bd.--Gallagher-Kaiser Corp., Detroit, MI; *U.S. Private*, pg. 438
Kakodkar, P.G., Chm. Bd.--State Bank of India, Mumbai, India; *Int'l*, pg. 1297
Kaku, Ryuzaburo, Chm. Bd. & Representative Dir.--Canon Inc., Tokyo, Japan; *Int'l*, pg. 261
Kalainov, Sam, Chm. Bd.--American Mutual Life Holding Co., Des Moines, IA; *U.S. Private*, pg. 59
Kalangis, Ike, Chm. Bd., Pres. & Chief Exec. Officer--NationsBank Sunwest, Inc., Albuquerque, NM; *U.S. Public*, pg. 1165
Kalebic, Thomas V., Chief Oper. Officer & Exec. V.P.--Lane Industries, Inc., Northbrook, IL; *U.S. Private*, pg. 649
Kalff, P.J., Chm. Bd.--ABN-AMRO Holding N.V., Amsterdam, Netherlands; *Int'l*, pg. 8
Kalish, Bernard, Chm. Bd. & Chief Exec. Officer--Lawson Products, Inc., Des Plaines, IL; *U.S. Public*, pg. 980
Kallen, Thomas E., Chm. Bd. & Treas.--Bake-Line Products, Inc., Des Plaines, IL; *U.S. Public*, pg. 657
Kalli, Timo, Chm.-Supvr. Bd.--Kemira Oy, Helsinki, Finland; *Int'l*, pg. 727
Kalma, Ludvik, ing., Chm. Bd.--SKODA, Automobilova a.s., Mlada Boleslav, Czech Republic; *Int'l*, pg. 1475
Kalms, Stanley, Sir, Chm. Bd.--Dixons Group plc, Hemel Hempstead, United Kingdom,; *Int'l*, pg. 413
Kalogirou, Georgios, Chm. Bd.--Olympic Airtours, Athens, Greece; *Int'l*, pg. 1004
Kaloyanides, Steven, Chm. Bd--New England Coffee Company, Malden, MA; *U.S. Private*, pg. 792
Kaltenbacher, Philip D., Chm. Bd. & Chief Exec. Officer--Seton Company, Norristown, PA; *U.S. Private*, pg. 987
Kamai, Goro, Chm. Bd.--Nitto Denko Corporation, Osaka, Japan; *Int'l*, pg. 950
Kaman, Charles H., Chm. Bd., Pres. & Chief Exec. Officer--Kaman Corporation, Bloomfield, CT; *U.S. Public*, pg. 941
Kamberos, Chris, Chm. Bd., Pres. & Chief Oper. Officer--Treasure Island Foodmarts Inc., Chicago, IL; *U.S. Private*, pg. 1098
Kamen, Harry P., Chm. Bd. & Chief Exec. Officer--Metropolitan Life Insurance Co., New York, NY; *U.S. Private*, pg. 737
Kamenstein, Peter, Chm., Pres. & Chief Exec. Officer--M. Kamenstein, Inc., Elmsford, NY; *U.S. Private*, pg. 606
Kamerschen, Robert J., Chm. Bd. & Chief Exec. Officer--ADVO, Inc., Windsor, CT; *U.S. Public*, pg. 23
Kametaka, Sokichi, Chm. Bd.--Kobe Steel, Ltd., Kobe, Japan; *Int'l*, pg. 740
Kamimura, Jiro, Chm. Bd. & Chief Exec. Officer--Aristech Chemical Corporation, Pittsburgh, PA; *Int'l*, pg. 872
Kamins, Philip E., Chm. Bd. & Pres.--PMC, Inc., Sun Valley, CA; *U.S. Private*, pg. 827
Kaminski, Robert S., Chm. Bd. & Chief Exec. Officer--Continental/Midland, Inc., Park Forest, IL; *U.S. Private*, pg. 268
Kaminsky, Larry E., Chm. Bd., Pres. & Chief Exec. Officer--H. R. Kaminsky & Sons, Inc., Fitzgerald, GA; *U.S. Private*, pg. 606
Kaminstein, Merwin F., Chm. Bd.--Brookstone Company, Inc., Nashua, NH; *U.S. Public*, pg. 259
Kamiya, H., Chm.--Nambokusha Inc., Tokyo, Japan; *Int'l*, pg. 904
Kamiya, Soichiro, Chm. Bd. & Pres.--Shizuoka Bank, Ltd., Shizuoka, Japan; *Int'l*, pg. 1236
Kamm, J.O., Chm. & Chief Exec. Officer--Wilkinson Company, Inc., Stow, OH; *U.S. Private*, pg. 368
Kamm, Jacob O., II, Chm. Bd., Pres. & Chief Exec. & Fin. Officer--Electric Furnace Co., Salem, OH; *U.S. Private*, pg. 367
Kammerer, Deiter, Chm. Bd.--AAH plc, Runcorn, United Kingdom; *Int'l*, pg. 591
Kampf, Serge, Chm. Bd. & Chief Exec. Officer--CAP Gemini S.A., Paris, France; *Int'l*, pg. 263
Kampfraath, A.A., Chm.-Supervisory Bd.--Hollandsche Beton Groep NV, Rijswijk, Netherlands; *Int'l*, pg. 630
Kampouris, Emmanuel A., Chm. Bd., Pres. & Chief Exec. Officer--American Standard Inc., Piscataway, NJ; *U.S. Public*, pg. 91
Kamras, Mikael, Chm. Bd.--Aritmos AB, Helsingborg, Sweden; *Int'l*, pg. 1072
Kanary, James R., Chm. Bd., Pres. & Chief Exec. Officer--Grayling State Bank, Grayling, MI; *U.S. Public*, pg. 379
Kanas, John Adam, Chm. Bd., Pres. & Chief Exec. Officer--North Fork Bancorporation, Inc., Melville, NY; *U.S. Public*, pg. 1194
Kanatani, Kunio, Chm. Bd.--Yamato Transport Co., Ltd., Tokyo, Japan; *Int'l*, pg. 1519
Kanchanawat, Prasit, Chm. Bd.--Bangkok Bank Public Company Limited, Bangkok, Thailand; *Int'l*, pg. 146
Kanchanawat, Prasit, Chm. Bd.--Bel (Cayman) Limited, Georgetown, Cayman Islands; *Int'l*, pg. 146
Kane, George F., Chm. Bd.--Trigen Energy Corporation, White Plains, NY; *U.S. Public*, pg. 1637
Kane, John T., Chm. Bd.--Equitrac Corporation, Coral Gables, FL; *U.S. Public*, pg. 590
Kane, Larry I., Chm. Bd. & Chief Exec. Officer--Alternative Resources Corporation, Lincolnshire, IL; *U.S. Public*, pg. 59
Kane, Louis, Co-Chm. Bd.--Au Bon Pain Co., Inc., Boston, MA; *U.S. Public*, pg. 146
Kane, Robert J., Chm. Bd.--Western Regional Off Track Betting, Batavia, NY; *U.S. Private*, pg. 1168
Kane, Sam, Chm. Bd. & Chief Exec. Officer--Sam Kane Beef Processors, Inc., Corpus Christi, TX; *U.S. Private*, pg. 607
Kane, Stanley B., Chm. Bd. & Chief Exec. Officer--Kane-Miller Corp., Tarrytown, NY; *U.S. Private*, pg. 607

Kane, William E., Chm. Bd.--First National Bank in Marlinton, Marlinton, WV; *U.S. Public*, pg. 836
Kaneda, Kozo, Chm.--Nichirei Corporation, Tokyo, Japan; *Int'l*, pg. 928
Kaneda, Yasuyoshi, Chm. Bd.--John O. Butler Co., Chicago, IL; *Int'l*, pg. 1320
Kaneko, Masato, Chm., Pres. & Chief Exec. Officer--Manufacturers Bank, Los Angeles, CA; *Int'l*, pg. 1179
Kaneko, Zenichiro, Pres.--Sakata Seed Corporation, Yokohama, Japan; *Int'l*, pg. 1178
Kang, Jin-Woo, Chm. Bd.--Lotte Shopping Co. Ltd., Seoul, Korea; *Int'l*, pg. 819
Kani, Takeo, Chm. Bd.--Morgan Stanley Japan Ltd., Tokyo, Japan; *U.S. Public*, pg. 1133
Kankowsky, Roland, Dr., Chm. & Chief Exec. Officer--Filterwerk Mann & Hummel GmbH, Ludwigsburg, Germany; *Int'l*, pg. 484
Kann, Peter, Chm. Bd.--Barron's The Dow Jones Business & Financial Weekly, New York, NY; *U.S. Public*, pg. 524
Kann, Peter R., Chm. Bd.--Dow Jones & Company, Inc., New York, NY; *U.S. Public*, pg. 524
Kanner, Robert H., Chm. Bd., Pres., Chief Exec./Fin. Officer & Treas.--Pubco Corporation, Cleveland, OH; *U.S. Public*, pg. 1339
Kanner, Robert H., Chm. Bd. & Chief Exec. Officer--Aspen Imaging International, Inc., Cleveland, OH; *U.S. Public*, pg. 1339
Kano, Eisuke, Chm.--The Bridgeford Group, New York, NY; *Int'l*, pg. 674
Kanter, Burton W., Chm.--Chicago Holdings, Inc., Pittsburgh, PA; *U.S. Private*, pg. 234
Kantor, Martin, Chm. Bd. & Chief Exec. Officer--National Financial Insurance Company, Fort Worth, TX; *U.S. Private*, pg. 782
Kantor, Robert, Chm. & Chief Exec. Officer--Publicis/Bloom, New York, NY; *Int'l*, pg. 470
Kanzaki, Yasutara, Chm. Bd.--Chiyoda Mutual Life Insurance Company, Tokyo, Japan; *Int'l*, pg. 286
Kapcsandy, Lou, Chm. Bd. & Pres.--Baugh Construction Company, Seattle, WA; *U.S. Private*, pg. 123
Kaplan, Burton B., Chm. Bd.--National Bedding Co., Beloit, WI; *U.S. Private*, pg. 780
Kaplan, Edward, Chm., Pres. & Chief Exec. Officer--Zebra Technologies Corporation, Vernon Hills, IL; *U.S. Public*, pg. 1790
Kaplan, Leonard D., Chm. & Treas.--Prime Tanning Co., Inc., Rochester, NH; *U.S. Private*, pg. 884
Kaplanek, Charles, Jr., Chm. Bd., Pres. & Chief Exec. Officer--Floral Glass & Mirror, Inc., Hauppauge, NY; *U.S. Private*, pg. 414
Kapoor, John N., Ph.D., Chm. Bd. & Chief Exec. Officer--Akorn, Inc., Lincolnshire, IL; *U.S. Public*, pg. 34
Kapp, Dennis, Chm. Bd. & Chief Exec. Officer--Martin Universal Design, Inc., Detroit, MI; *U.S. Private*, pg. 709
Kapp, Dennis, Chm. Bd.--Martin/F. Weber Company, Philadelphia, PA; *U.S. Private*, pg. 710
Kappel, Joseph, Chm. Bd.--Coast Manufacturing Company, Yonkers, NY; *U.S. Private*, pg. 248
Kappler, George, Chm. Bd., Pres. & Chief Exec. Officer--Kappler Safety Group, Inc., Guntersville, AL; *U.S. Private*, pg. 607
Kappler, George, Chm. Bd. & Pres.--Kappler USA, Guntersville, AL; *U.S. Private*, pg. 607
Kapson, Jordan H., Chm. Bd.--Jordan Motors, Inc., Mishawaka, IN; *U.S. Private*, pg. 599
Karabots, Nick G., Chm. Bd.--S L C Graphics, LP, Pittston, PA; *U.S. Private*, pg. 955
Karan, Donna, Chm. Bd. & Chief Designer--Donna Karan, New York, NY; *U.S. Public*, pg. 517
Karass, Thomas J., Chm. Bd.--Caristrap International Inc., Laval, Canada; *Int'l*, pg. 271
Karatz, Bruce, Chm. Bd., Pres. & Chief Exec. Officer--Kaufman and Broad Home Corporation, Los Angeles, CA; *U.S. Public*, pg. 944
Kardatzke, E. Stanley, M.D., Chm. Bd. & Chief Exec. Officer--Physician Corporation of America, Miami, FL; *U.S. Public*, pg. 1293
Karelias, Victoria G., Pres.--Karelia Tobacco Company Inc., Kalamata, Greece; *Int'l*, pg. 724
Karges, Edwin, Chm. Bd. & Pres.--The Karges Furniture Company Inc., Evansville, IN; *U.S. Private*, pg. 607
Karinen, Heimo, Chm. & Chief Exec. Officer--Kemira Oy, Helsinki, Finland; *Int'l*, pg. 727
Kariotis, George S., Chm. Bd.--Alpha Industries, Inc., Woburn, MA; *U.S. Public*, pg. 57
Karmanos, Peter, Jr., Chm. Bd. & Chief Exec. Officer--Compuware Corporation, Farmington Hills, MI; *U.S. Public*, pg. 423
Karmazin, Mel, Chm. Bd. & Chief Exec. Officer-CBS Station Grp.--CBS, New York, NY; *U.S. Public*, pg. 273
Karp, Donald M., Chm. Bd. & Chief Exec. Officer--Broad National Bancorporation, Newark, NJ; *U.S. Public*, pg. 257
Karp, Harvey L., Chm. Bd.--Mueller Industries, Inc., Memphis, TN; *U.S. Public*, pg. 1141
Karpen, Roderic B., Chm. Bd. & Chief Exec. Officer--Copes-Vulcan Inc., Lake City, PA; *U.S. Private*, pg. 274
Kasahara, Yukio, Chm. Bd. & Rep. Dir.--Japan Energy Corporation, Tokyo, Japan; *Int'l*, pg. 702
Kasama, Yuichiro, Chm.--Mitsui Toatsu Chemicals, Inc., Tokyo, Japan; *Int'l*, pg. 877
Kaseenhuber, Richard, Vice Chm.--Electric Furnace Co., Salem, OH; *U.S. Private*, pg. 367
Kashi, Akira, Chm. Bd.--ORIX Ireland Limited, Dublin, Ireland; *Int'l*, pg. 1009
Kashio, Toshio, Chm. Bd.--Casio Computer Co., Ltd., Tokyo, Japan; *Int'l*, pg. 274
Kashnow, Richard A., Dr., Chm. Bd., Pres. & Chief Exec. Officer--Raychem Corporation, Menlo Park, CA; *U.S. Public*, pg. 1362
Kaske, Karlheinz, Prof. Dr., Chm.-Supervisory Bd.--MAN Aktiengesellschaft, Munich, Germany; *Int'l*, pg. 824
Kaskel, Roy R., Chm. Bd. & Chief Exec. Officer--Enron Liquid Services Corp., Houston, TX; *U.S. Public*, pg. 584
Kaspar, Don G., Chm. Bd. & Pres.--Kaspar Wire Works, Inc., Shiner, TX; *U.S. Private*, pg. 608
Kasputys, Joseph E., Chm. Bd., Pres. & Chief Exec. Officer--Primark Corporation, Waltham, MA; *U.S. Public*, pg. 1325
Kassab, Charles S., Chm. Bd., Pres., Chief Exec. Officer & Treas.--Huntington Bancshares Michigan, Inc., Troy, MI; *U.S. Public*, pg. 850
Kassab, Edward J., Chm. Bd.--Stainless Incorporated, Deerfield Beach, FL; *U.S. Private*, pg. 1029
Kasschau, Jim, Chm. Bd.--Helikon Furniture Co., Inc., Taftville, CT; *U.S. Private*, pg. 520
Kassel, Robert L., Chm. Bd., Pres., Chief Exec. Officer & Treas.--U.S. Home & Garden Inc., San Francisco, CA; *U.S. Public*, pg. 1682
Kassling, W.E., Chm. Bd. & Chief Exec. Officer--Westinghouse Air Brake Company, Wilmerding, PA; *U.S. Public*, pg. 1760
Kassouf, Elias, Chm. Bd.--Metropolitan Properties Systems, Cleveland, OH; *U.S. Private*, pg. 739
Kasuga, Bill, Chm. Bd.--Kenwood USA, Long Beach, CA; *Int'l*, pg. 730
Katada, Tetsuya, Chm. Bd.--Komatsu Ltd., Tokyo, Japan; *Int'l*, pg. 743
Kathwari, M. Farooq, Chm. Bd., Pres. & Chief Exec. Officer--Ethan Allen Interiors Inc., Danbury, CT; *U.S. Public*, pg. 595
Kato, Keikichi, Chm. Bd.--The Zenshinren Bank, Tokyo, Japan; *Int'l*, pg. 1527
Kato, Masahiko, Chm. & Chief Exec. Officer--Otsuka America, Inc., San Francisco, CA; *Int'l*, pg. 1013
Kato, Masahiko, Chm. Bd.--Otsuka America Pharmaceutical, Inc., Rockville, MD; *Int'l*, pg. 1013
Katsumoto, Malolm T., Chm. Bd.--Toray Composites (America), Inc., Tacoma, WA; *Int'l*, pg. 1400
Katt, Ray, Chm. Bd.--Benjamin Sheridan Co., East Bloomfield, NY; *U.S. Private*, pg. 291
Katz, Alvin, Pres.--Manhattan Store Interiors, Inc., Brooklyn, NY; *U.S. Private*, pg. 699
Katz, Lewis, Chm. Bd.--Kinney System, Inc., New York, NY; *U.S. Private*, pg. 622
Katz, Matthew, Chm. & Gen. Mgr.--EURO RSCG, Warsaw, Poland; *Int'l*, pg. 602
Katz, Ronald C., Chm. Bd. & Chief Exec. Officer--Elkay Manufacturing Company, Oak Brook, IL; *U.S. Private*, pg. 372
Katzenberg, Jeffrey, Chm. Bd.--Walt Disney Pictures and Television, Burbank, CA; *U.S. Public*, pg. 513
Katzman, Lawrence, Chm. Bd. & Chief Exec. Officer--Kaz, Inc., New York, NY; *U.S. Private*, pg. 610
Katzman, Richard, Chm. Bd.--Mastercraft Furniture Corp., Omaha, NE; *U.S. Private*, pg. 714
Kauffman, James B., Jr., Chm. Bd., Pres. & Chief Exec. Officer--Keystone Bank, Horsham, PA; *U.S. Public*, pg. 956
Kauffman, Richard N., Chm. Bd.--H.S. Crocker Co., Inc., Huntley, IL; *U.S. Private*, pg. 290
Kaufman, Alan V., Chm. Bd.--Wall Street Deli, Inc., Birmingham, AL; *U.S. Public*, pg. 1734
Kaufman, Richard F., Chm. Bd. & Chief Exec. Officer--Amstore Corporation, Muskegon, MI; *U.S. Private*, pg. 68
Kaufman, Stephen P., Chm. Bd. & Chief Exec. Officer--Arrow Electronics, Inc., Melville, NY; *U.S. Public*, pg. 133
Kaufman, William H., Chm. Bd.--Kaufman Footwear, Kitchener, Canada; *Int'l*, pg. 725
Kaurisa, C.V., Chm.--Stanbic Bank Namibia Limited, Windhoek, Namibia; *Int'l*, pg. 1293
Kautz, J.H., Chm. Bd. & Chief Exec. Officer--Grain Processing Corp., Muscatine, IA; *U.S. Private*, pg. 1134
Kavanah, John, Chm. Bd., Pres. & Chief Exec. Officer--Marketing Corp. of America, Westport, CT; *U.S. Private*, pg. 704
Kawa, Mae, Chm.--Adaptive Information Systems, Mission Viejo, CA; *Int'l*, pg. 946
Kawabarayashi, Seji, Chm. & Mng. Dir.--Mitsui & Co. (Australia), Brisbane, Australia; *Int'l*, pg. 880
Kawada, Mitsugu, Chm. Bd.--Taiyo Yuden Company Ltd., Tokyo, Japan; *Int'l*, pg. 1349
Kawahara, Shiro, Chm. Bd.--Daido Life Insurance Company, Osaka, Japan; *Int'l*, pg. 363
Kawai, Saburo, Honorary Chm.--The Kyoei Life Insurance Co., Ltd., Tokyo, Japan; *Int'l*, pg. 776
Kawai, Shigeru, Chm. Bd.--Kawai Musical Instruments Mfg. Co., Ltd., Hamamatsu, Japan; *Int'l*, pg. 725
Kawai, Tatsuo, Chm. Bd.--Kyushu Electric Power Co., Inc., Fukuoka, Japan; *Int'l*, pg. 778
Kawai, Tatsuo, Chm. Bd.--Meiji Milk Products Co., Ltd., Tokyo, Japan; *Int'l*, pg. 855
Kawaka, Jiro, Chm. Emeritus--Oji Paper Co., Ltd., Tokyo, Japan; *Int'l*, pg. 998
Kawakami, Tetsuro, Chm. Bd. & Chief Exec. Officer--Sumitomo Electric Industries, Ltd., Osaka, Japan; *Int'l*, pg. 1313
Kawarabayashi, Seiji, Chm.--Mitsui & Co. (N.Z.) Ltd., Wellington, New Zealand; *Int'l*, pg. 882
Kawasaki, Yutaka, Chm. Bd.--Nanto Investment Management Co., Ltd., Nara, Japan; *Int'l*, pg. 905
Kay, Allen, Chm. Bd. & Chief Creative Officer--Korey, Kay & Partners, New York, NY; *U.S. Private*, pg. 632
Kaye, A., Chm.--Longwall International Limited, Worcester, United Kingdom; *U.S. Public*, pg. 789
Kaye, Issac, Chm. Bd. & Chief Exec. Officer--Norton Healthcare Limited, Harlow, United Kingdom; *U.S. Public*, pg. 915
Kayne, Fred, Chm. Bd.--Big Dog Holdings Inc., Santa Barbara, CA; *U.S. Public*, pg. 227
Kazaklaris, Christos, Chm. Bd.--Olympic Catering, Athens, Greece; *Int'l*, pg. 1004
Kealy, Joseph P., Chm. Bd., Pres. & Chief Exec. Officer--International FiberCom, Phoenix, AZ; *U.S. Public*, pg. 898
Kean, John, Chm. Bd.--NUI Corporation, Bedminster, NJ; *U.S. Public*, pg. 1147
Kean, Robert W., Chm. Bd.--E'town Properties Inc., Westfield, NJ; *U.S. Public*, pg. 540
Kean, Stuart B., Chm. Bd.--KCS Energy Inc., Edison, NJ; *U.S. Public*, pg. 938
Keane, John F., Sr., Founder & Chief Exec. Officer--Keane, Inc., Boston, MA; *U.S. Public*, pg. 946
Kearns, T.A., Chm. Bd.--Lancashire Dairies Ltd., Manchester, United Kingdom; *Int'l*, pg. 798
Kearns, Vincent Ed., Chm. Bd.--B.H. Aircraft Co., Inc., Farmingdale, NY; *U.S. Private*, pg. 107
Keating, Daniel J., Jr., Chm. Bd.--Daniel J. Keating Co., Ardmore, PA; *U.S. Private*, pg. 610
Keaveny, Denis J., Pres.--Cains Foods, L.P., Ayer, MA; *U.S. Private*, pg. 199
Kebrdle, Dennis, Chm. Bd.--Domore Corporation, Elkhart, IN; *U.S. Private*, pg. 339
Keck, Brian L., Chm.--Meier & Frank, Portland, OR; *U.S. Public*, pg. 1064
Keen, Jack C., Chm.--Lynch Telephone Corporation, Greenwich, CT; *U.S. Public*, pg. 1022
Keene, Howard, Chm. Bd., Pres.,Chief Exec. & Oper. Officer--Rawlings Sporting Goods Company, Fenton, MO; *U.S. Public*, pg. 1361
Keene, Richard A., Pres.--Holstein Association USA, Inc., Brattleboro, VT; *U.S. Private*, pg. 536
Keene, Robert A., Chm. Bd., Sec. & Treas.--John Roberts Company, Minneapolis, MN; *U.S. Private*, pg. 935
Keener, J.W., Jr., Chm. Bd., Pres., Chief Exec. Officer--The Chardon Rubber Co., Chardon, OH; *U.S. Private*, pg. 229
Keeney, Cecil M., Chm. Bd. & Chief Exec. Officer--Walle Corporation, Harahan, LA; *U.S. Private*, pg. 1148
Keeney, Sean, Asst. Chm. Bd.--Walle Corporation, Harahan, LA; *U.S. Private*, pg. 1148
Keevil, Norman B., Chm. Bd.--Cominco, Ltd., Vancouver, Canada; *Int'l*, pg. 307
Kegel, W.G., Chm. Bd.--Rochester & Pittsburgh Coal Company, Indiana, PA; *U.S. Public*, pg. 1395
Keiler, Richard W., Chm.--Keiler & Company, Farmington, CT; *U.S. Private*, pg. 611
Keimatsu, Shunsuke, Chm. Bd. & Chief Exec. Officer-IMS Cognizant Japan--I.M.S. International, Inc., Totowa, NJ; *U.S. Public*, pg. 395
Keinanen, Eino, Chm. Bd. & Chief Exec. Officer--Postipankki Ltd., Helsinki, Finland; *Int'l*, pg. 1064
Keiper, William C., Chm. Bd. & Chief Exec. Officer--Artisoft, Inc., Tucson, AZ; *U.S. Public*, pg. 136
Keiser, Robert L., Chm. Bd., Pres. & Chief Exec. Officer--Oryx Energy, Dallas, TX; *U.S. Public*, pg. 1232
Keith, Alec, Dr., Chm. Bd.--Polydex Pharmaceuticals Limited, Scarborough, Canada; *Int'l*, pg. 1062
Keith, Colin, Chm. Bd.--Denison Hydraulics, Inc., Marysville, OH; *U.S. Private*, pg. 324
Keith, Edward J., Chm. Bd.--The Failure Group, Inc., Menlo Park, CA; *U.S. Public*, pg. 609
Keith, Edward J., Chm. Bd.--Vectra Technologies, Inc., San Ramon, CA; *U.S. Public*, pg. 1711
Keith, J. Collin, Chm. Bd. & Chief Exec. Officer--Horace Small Apparel Company, Nashville, TN; *Int'l*, pg. 635
Keith, Robert E., Jr., Chm. Bd.--Internet Capital Group, Wayne, PA; *U.S. Public*, pg. 1425
Keith, Roy, Chm. Bd. & Chief Exec. Officer--Carson Products Company, Savannah, GA; *U.S. Public*, pg. 309
Keithley, Joseph P., Chm. Bd., Pres. & Chief Exec. Officer--Keithley Instruments, Inc., Cleveland, OH; *U.S. Public*, pg. 946
Kelb, Edwin D., Chm. Bd.--High Point Oil Co., Indianapolis, IN; *U.S. Private*, pg. 528
Kelleher, Herbert D., Chm. Bd., Pres. & Chief Exec. Officer--Southwest Airlines Co., Dallas, TX; *U.S. Public*, pg. 1493
Kelleher, T. S., Chm. Bd. & Chief Exec. Officer--Clearing-Niagara, Buffalo, NY; *U.S. Private*, pg. 196
Kelleher, T.S., Chm. Bd. & Chief Exec. Officer--CNB International, Inc., Charleston, SC; *U.S. Private*, pg. 196
Kellen, Stephen M., Co-Chm. Bd.--Arnhold and S. Bleichroeder, Inc., New York, NY; *U.S. Private*, pg. 83
Keller, Dennis J., Chm. Bd. & Chief Exec. Officer--DeVry Institutes, Oak Brook Terrace, IL; *U.S. Public*, pg. 503
Keller, Dennis J., Chm. Bd.--Becker CPA Review, Encino, CA; *U.S. Public*, pg. 504
Keller, Fritz, Chm. Bd. & Pres.--Brauerei Eichhof, Lucerne, Switzerland; *Int'l*, pg. 213
Keller, Gary H., Chm. Bd. & Pres.--Hotel Corporation of America, Maple Hill, KS; *U.S. Private*, pg. 541
Keller, George F., Chm. Bd.--Sun Bancorp, Inc., Selinsgrove, PA; *U.S. Public*, pg. 1529
Keller, John, Chm. Bd. & Treas.--Meadville Forging Co., Meadville, PA; *U.S. Private*, pg. 726
Keller, John J., Chm. Bd.--J.J. Keller & Associates, Inc., Neenah, WI; *U.S. Private*, pg. 612
Keller, R. E., Chm.--Principal Portfolio Services, Inc., Costa Mesa, CA; *U.S. Private*, pg. 886
Keller, Thomas E.K., Chm. Bd.--W-B Supply Co., Pampa, TX; *U.S. Private*, pg. 1144
Kelley, Austin P., Chm. Bd. & Chief Exec. Officer--Austin Kelley Advertising, Inc., Atlanta, GA; *U.S. Private*, pg. 100
Kelley, B.O., Chm. Bd.--Dosimeter Corporation of America, Cincinnati, OH; *Int'l*, pg. 892
Kelley, E. W., Chm.--Consolidated Specialty Restaurant, Indianapolis, IN; *U.S. Public*, pg. 436
Kelley, E.W., Chm. Bd. & Chief Exec. Officer--Fairmont Snack Group, Inc., Independence, OH; *U.S. Private*, pg. 392
Kelley, E.W., Chm. Bd.--Consolidated Products, Inc., Indianapolis, IN; *U.S. Public*, pg. 436
Kelley, E.W., Chm. Bd.--SNS Investment Company, Indianapolis, IN; *U.S. Public*, pg. 436
Kelley, E.W., Chm.--Steak 'n Shake, Inc., Indianapolis, IN; *U.S. Public*, pg. 437
Kelley, Gary L., Chm. Bd., Pres. & Chief Exec. Officer--Kelley Bean Co., Inc., Morrill, NE; *U.S. Private*, pg. 612
Kelley, James, Chm. Bd.--La Petite Academy Inc., Overland Park, KS; *U.S. Private*, pg. 640

Kelley, James V., Chm. Bd., Pres. & Chief Exec. Officer--First United Bancshares, Inc., El Dorado, AR; *U.S. Public*, pg. 641
Kelley, Joseph G., Jr., Chm. Bd.--Jordan's Meats, Portland, ME; *U.S. Private*, pg. 599
Kelley, Kevin H., Chm.--Commerce & Industry Insurance Co., New York, NY; *U.S. Public*, pg. 84
Kelley, Robert, Chm. Bd., Pres. & Chief Exec. Officer--Noble Affiliates, Inc., Ardmore, OK; *U.S. Public*, pg. 1186
Kelley, William G., Chm. Bd. & Chief Exec. Officer--Consolidated Stores Corp., Columbus, OH; *U.S. Public*, pg. 437
Kelley, William M., Chm. Bd.--Hill-Rom Company, Inc., Batesville, IN; *U.S. Public*, pg. 828
Kellman, Mildred, Chm. Bd. & Pres.--Globe-Amerada Glass Company, Elk Grove Village, IL; *U.S. Private*, pg. 458
Kellogg, William S., Chm. Bd. & Chief Exec. Officer--Kohl's Corporation, Menomonee Falls, WI; *U.S. Public*, pg. 965
Kells, R.D., Chm.--Ulster Bank Trust Company, Belfast, United Kingdom; *Int'l*, pg. 911
Kelly, B.O., Chm. Bd.--TGM Detectors Inc., Waltham, MA; *Int'l*, pg. 892
Kelly, David M., Chm. Bd., Pres. & Chief Exec. Officer--Matthews International Corp., Pittsburgh, PA; *U.S. Public*, pg. 1059
Kelly, Desmond, M.D., Chm.-Priory Hospitals Group--Community Psychiatric Centers of London (Unlimited), London, United Kingdom; *U.S. Public*, pg. 1716
Kelly, George, Chm. Bd.--Doane Products Co., Joplin, MO; *U.S. Private*, pg. 337
Kelly, James, Chm. Bd.--Kelly Weedon Shute Partnership, London, United Kingdom; *Int'l*, pg. 727
Kelly, James P., Chm. Bd. & Chief Exec. Officer--United Parcel Service of America, Inc., Atlanta, GA; *U.S. Private*, pg. 1123
Kelly, James T., Chm. Bd.--Lincare Holdings Inc., Clearwater, FL; *U.S. Public*, pg. 996
Kelly, John F., Chm. Bd., Pres, Chief Exec. & Oper. Officer--Alaska Air Group, Inc., Seattle, WA; *U.S. Public*, pg. 35
Kelly, Michael, Chm. Bd.--The First Bank of Oak Park, Oak Park, IL; *U.S. Private*, pg. 406
Kelly, Richard M., Chm.--Aubrey G. Lanston & Co. Inc., New York, NY; *Int'l*, pg. 675
Kelly, Stephen J., Chm. Bd., Pres. & Chief Exec. Officer--SouthCo. Inc., Concordville, PA; *U.S. Private*, pg. 1014
Kelly, Thomas J., Chm Bd., Pres., & Chief Exec. Officer--Somerset Savings Bank, Somerville, MA; *U.S. Public*, pg. 1484
Kelman, J.M., Chm. Bd.--Davy International, Canada, Toronto, Canada; *Int'l*, pg. 775
Kelmenson, Leo A., Chm.--Bozell Worldwide, Inc., New York, NY; *U.S. Public*, pg. 1642
Kelmenson, Leo-Arthur, Chm.-Bozell Worldwide--True North Communications Inc., Chicago, IL; *U.S. Public*, pg. 1641
Kelsey, Eugene W. III, Chm. Bd.--Kelsey Construction, Inc., Orlando, FL; *U.S. Private*, pg. 613
Kemmerer, John L., Chm. Bd. & Chief Exec. Officer--Jackson Hole Ski Resort, Teton Village, WY; *U.S. Private*, pg. 579
Kemp, Thomas, Chm. Bd. & Chief Exec. Officer--Penton Publishing, Inc., Cleveland, OH; *U.S. Public*, pg. 1306
Kemp, Wally, Chm. Bd.--Dryper's Corp., Vancouver, WA; *U.S. Private*, pg. 344
Kemper, David W., Chm. Bd., Pres. & Chief Exec. Officer--Commerce Bancshares, Inc., Kansas City, MO; *U.S. Public*, pg. 409
Kemper, Jonathan M., Chm. Bd., Pres. & Chief Exec. Officer--Commerce Bank N.A., Kansas City, MO; *U.S. Public*, pg. 409
Kemper, R. Crosby, Co-Chm. Bd. & Co-Chief Exec. Officer--UMB Financial Corporation, Kansas City, MO; *U.S. Public*, pg. 1653
Kemper, R. Crosby, Chm. Bd. & Chief Exec. Officer--United Missouri Bank N.A., Kansas City, MO; *U.S. Public*, pg. 1654
Kempf, Pat, Chm. Bd.--Moroch & Assoc., Inc., Dallas, TX; *U.S. Private*, pg. 762
Kempner, I.H., III, Chm. Bd.--Imperial Holly Corporation, Sugar Land, TX; *U.S. Public*, pg. 872
Kempner, James C., Chm. Bd.--Holly Sugar Corporation, Sugar Land, TX; *U.S. Public*, pg. 872
Ken, Thai Chee, Deputy Chm.--Inchcape Bdh, Singapore, Singapore; *Int'l*, pg. 672
Kendall, David William, Chm.--Wagon Industrial Holdings PLC, Birmingham, United Kingdom; *Int'l*, pg. 1484
Kendall, Donald S., III, Chm. Bd. & Pres.--Mack Molding Company Inc., Arlington, VT; *U.S. Private*, pg. 691
Kendall, Kennett R., Jr., Chm. Bd. & Chief Exec. Officer--Willis Corroon Corp. of New Hampshire, Rochester, NH; *Int'l*, pg. 1506
Keng, Chew Choo, Chm. Bd.--Khong Guan Flour Milling Limited, Singapore, Singapore; *Int'l*, pg. 732
Kennedy, B., Exec. Chm.-Mining Equip. Div.--Dobson Park Industries Plc, Wigan, United Kingdom; *U.S. Public*, pg. 789
Kennedy, Bernard J., Chm. Bd., Pres. & Chief Exec. Officer--National Fuel Gas Company, Buffalo, NY; *U.S. Public*, pg. 1156
Kennedy, D.P., Chm. Bd.--The First American Financial Corporation, Santa Ana, CA; *U.S. Public*, pg. 624
Kennedy, D.P., Chm. Bd.--First American Title Insurance Co., Santa Ana, CA; *U.S. Public*, pg. 625
Kennedy, James C., Chm. Bd. & Chief Exec. Officer--Cox Enterprises, Inc., Atlanta, GA; *U.S. Private*, pg. 281
Kennedy, John C., Chm. Bd., Pres. & Chief Exec. Officer--Autocam Corporation, Grand Rapids, MI; *U.S. Public*, pg. 148
Kennedy, John M., Chm. Bd., Pres. & Gen. Mgr.--T.H. Rogers Lumber Co., Edmond, OK; *U.S. Private*, pg. 940
Kennedy, K., Chm.--Philips Domestic Appliances and Personal Care B.V., Groningen, Netherlands; *Int'l*, pg. 1051
Kennedy, T.C., Chm. Bd.--BE & K, Inc., Birmingham, AL; *U.S. Private*, pg. 106
Kennedy, William E., Jr., Chm. Bd., Chief Exec. Officer & Treas.--Kennedy Tank & Manufacturing Co., Inc., Indianapolis, IN; *U.S. Private*, pg. 614
Kenney, G. Dickson, Chm. Bd.--Kenney Manufacturing Company, Warwick, RI; *U.S. Private*, pg. 615
Kennon, R. M., Chm. Bd.--First Community Bank of Tifton, Tifton, GA; *U.S. Public*, pg. 1549
Kent, Brian, Chm. Bd.--British Printing Company Ltd., London, United Kingdom; *Int'l*, pg. 220
Kent, Gage A., Chm. Bd.--Precision Foods, Inc., Saint Louis, MO; *U.S. Private*, pg. 1134
Kent, J.H., Chm. Bd. & Chief Exec. Officer--Kent Feeds Inc., Muscatine, IA; *U.S. Private*, pg. 1134
Kent, James H., Chm. Bd.--Blue Seal Feeds, Inc., Londonderry, NH; *U.S. Private*, pg. 1134
Kenter, Louis W., Chm. Bd.--John Boos & Company, Effingham, IL; *U.S. Private*, pg. 156
Keough, Donald R., Chm. Bd.--Excalibur Technologies Corporation, Vienna, VA; *U.S. Public*, pg. 598
Kerkorian, Kirk, Chm. Bd., Pres. & Chief Exec. Officer--Tracinda Corporation, Las Vegas, NV; *U.S. Private*, pg. 1095
Kern, Frank, Jr., Chm. Bd.--Maxitrol Co., Southfield, MI; *U.S. Private*, pg. 716
Kernan, Richard M., Jr., Chm.--NYLIFE Inc., New York, NY; *U.S. Private*, pg. 795
Kerr, David W., Chm. Bd. & Chief Exec. Officer--Noranda Inc., Toronto, Canada; *Int'l*, pg. 433
Kerr, Howard J., Chm. Bd., Pres. & Chief Exec. Officer--Consolidated Pipe & Supply Company, Birmingham, AL; *U.S. Private*, pg. 266
Kerr, Laurence, Chm.--International Public Relations, Pty. Ltd., Melbourne, Australia; *Int'l*, pg. 1227
Kerr, William T., Chm. Bd. & Chief Exec. Officer--Meredith Corporation, Des Moines, IA; *U.S. Public*, pg. 1094
Kershner, Bernard, Chm. Bd.--Health Resources International, West Hartford, CT; *U.S. Private*, pg. 514
Kertzman, Mitchell E., Chm. Bd. & Chief Exec. Officer--Sybase, Inc., Emeryville, CA; *U.S. Public*, pg. 1544
Kervick, Paul J., Chm. Bd.--Kervick Enterprises, Inc., Worcester, MA; *U.S. Private*, pg. 616
Kerzner, Solomon, Chm. Bd. & Chief Exec. Officer--Sun International Hotels Limited, Fort Lauderdale, FL; *U.S. Public*, pg. 1531
Kesselman, Ronald C., Chm.--Wise Foods, Inc., Parsippany, NJ; *U.S. Private*, pg. 157
Kesselman, Ronald C., Chm.--Elmer's Products, Inc., Columbus, OH; *U.S. Private*, pg. 158
Kessels, J.M.J.M., Chm.--Hema B.V., Amsterdam, Netherlands; *Int'l*, pg. 750
Kessler, Frank, Chm. Bd.--Delair Group, L.L.C., Delair, NJ; *U.S. Private*, pg. 47
Kessler, M. Jerome, Partner.--H. Kessler & Company, Atlanta, GA; *U.S. Private*, pg. 616
Kessler, Stwart, Chm. Bd.--American Institute of C.P.A.'s Inc., New York, NY; *U.S. Private*, pg. 57
Kesterson, Tommy, Chm. Bd. & Pres.--Kesterson Food Company, Inc., Paris, TN; *U.S. Private*, pg. 616
Keswick, Henry, Chm. Bd.--Jardine Matheson Holdings Limited, Hamilton, Bermuda; *Int'l*, pg. 703
Keswick, Simon, Chm. Bd.--Dairy Farm International Holdings Limited, Hamilton, Bermuda; *Int'l*, pg. 703
Keswick, Simon, Chm. Bd.--Trafalgar House PLC, London, United Kingdom; *Int'l*, pg. 772
Kett, Herbert J., Vice Chm.--Genovese Drug Stores, Inc., Melville, NY; *U.S. Public*, pg. 730
Ketudat, Sippanondha, Dr., Chm. Bd.--Petroleum Authority of Thailand, Bangkok, Thailand; *Int'l*, pg. 1046
Keudell, Alan, Chm. Bd.--Norpac Foods, Inc., Stayton, OR; *U.S. Private*, pg. 802
Key, Derrick N., Chm. Bd., Pres. & Chief Exec. Officer--Roper Industries, Inc., Bogart, GA; *U.S. Public*, pg. 1405
Keyder, Emine, Chm.--A4 Reklamcilik, Istanbul, Turkey; *U.S. Private*, pg. 1062
Keyes, James H., Chm. Bd. & Chief Exec. Officer--Johnson Controls, Inc., Milwaukee, WI; *U.S. Public*, pg. 932
Keyser, F. Ray, Jr., Chm. Bd.--Central Vermont Public Service Corporation, Rutland, VT; *U.S. Public*, pg. 327
Keysor, Robert E., Chm. Bd.--Keysor Century Corporation, Saugus, CA; *U.S. Private*, pg. 618
Khan, Mohammed, Chm.--Enterprise Nexus Communications, Mumbai, India; *U.S. Private*, pg. 678
Kheng, Oliver TanKok, Chm.--NDC Merchant Bank Ltd., Singapore, Singapore; *Int'l*, pg. 351
Khim, Jay W., Dr., Chm. Bd., Pres. & Chief Exec. Officer--JWK International Corp., Annandale, VA; *U.S. Private*, pg. 579
Khoman, Thanat, Dr., Chm. Bd.--Finance One Public Company Limited, Bangkok, Thailand; *Int'l*, pg. 404
Khoury, Amin, Chm. Bd.--B/E Aerospace, Inc., Wellington, FL; *U.S. Public*, pg. 159
Khoury, Amin J., Chm. Bd.--Applied Extrusion Technologies, Inc., Peabody, MA; *U.S. Public*, pg. 122
Khoury, Tawfig N., Chm. Bd. & Chief Exec. Officer--Monticello Management Co., San Diego, CA; *U.S. Private*, pg. 759
Khulusi, Frank, Chm. Bd., Pres. & Chief Exec. Officer--Creative Computers, Inc., Torrance, CA; *U.S. Public*, pg. 458
Khumalo, M.G., Chm. Bd. & Pres.--JCI Limited, Johannesburg, South Africa; *Int'l*, pg. 696
Kiam, Victor, II, Chm. Bd.--Remington Products Company, L.L.C., Bridgeport, CT; *U.S. Private*, pg. 921
Kiat, Ow Chio, Exec. Chm. Bd.--Hai Sun Hup Group Ltd., Singapore, Singapore; *Int'l*, pg. 586
Kidd, Kenneth, Chm. Bd. & Pres.--Superior Label Systems, Inc., Mason, OH; *U.S. Private*, pg. 1055
Kidder, C. Robert, Chm. Bd. & Chief Exec. Officer--Borden, Inc., Columbus, OH; *U.S. Private*, pg. 157
Kidder, C. Robert, Chm. Bd. & Chief Exec. Officer--Cracker Jack Division, Northbrook, IL; *U.S. Private*, pg. 157
Kiefer, William C., Chm. Bd. & Pres.--Bel-Ray Company, Inc., Farmingdale, NJ; *U.S. Private*, pg. 130
Kier, Ike, Chm. Bd.--Cruise Holdings Ltd., Miami, FL; *U.S. Private*, pg. 293
Kierans, Thomas E., Chm. Bd.--First Marathon Inc., Toronto, Canada; *Int'l*, pg. 486
Kierlin, Robert A., Chm. Bd., Pres. & Chief Exec. Officer--Fastenal Company, Winona, MN; *U.S. Public*, pg. 614
Kiggen, James D., Chm. Bd. & Chief Exec. Officer--Xtek, Inc., Cincinnati, OH; *U.S. Private*, pg. 1194
Kijima, Toshio, Chm. Bd.--Nippon Shinpan Co., Ltd., Tokyo, Japan; *Int'l*, pg. 939
Kikuchi, Kyo, Chm. & Pres.--Yasuda Bank and Trust Company (U.S.A.), New York, NY; *Int'l*, pg. 1520
Kilian, Fredrick P., Chm. Bd.--Welch Foods Inc., A Cooperative, Concord, MA; *U.S. Private*, pg. 784
Kill, Robert H., Chm. Bd., Pres. & Chief Exec. Officer--Ciprico, Inc., Plymouth, MN; *U.S. Public*, pg. 370
Killgallon, William C., Chm. Bd. & Chief Exec. Officer--The Ohio Art Company, Inc., Bryan, OH; *U.S. Public*, pg. 1214
Killian, Raymond L., Jr., Chm. Bd.--Investment Technology Group, Inc., New York, NY; *U.S. Public*, pg. 924
Killinger, Kerry K., Chm. Bd., Pres. & Chief Exec. Officer--Washington Mutual Inc., Seattle, WA; *U.S. Public*, pg. 1741
Killins, David, Chm. Bd. & Chief Exec. Officer--Tecmar Technologies International, Inc., Concord, Canada; *Int'l*, pg. 1361
Killins, David J., Chm. Bd. & Chief Exec. Officer--Legacy Storage Systems Corp., Markham, Canada; *Int'l*, pg. 805
Kilroy, Howard E., Governor--Bank of Ireland, Dublin, Ireland; *Int'l*, pg. 152
Kilts, James M., Chm. Bd., Pres. & Chief Exec. Officer--Nabisco Inc., Parsippany, NJ; *U.S. Public*, pg. 1355
Kim, James J., Chm. Bd. & Chief Exec. Officer--Amkor Electronics, Inc., West Chester, PA; *U.S. Private*, pg. 66
Kim, Ken, Chm. Bd.--Kabuto International Phoenix Inc., San Francisco, CA; *Int'l*, pg. 721
Kim, Kenneth H., Chm., Pres., Chief Exec. Officer, Corp. Sec. & Treas.--Medieval Times Dinner & Tournament, Inc., Buena Park, CA; *U.S. Private*, pg. 728
Kim, Mahn-Je, Dr., Chm. Bd.--Pohang Iron & Steel Co., Ltd., Kyongbuk, Korea; *Int'l*, pg. 1061
Kim, Sonyon, Chm.--Leo Burnett Sonyon Inc., Seoul, Korea; *U.S. Private*, pg. 185
Kim, Suk-Joon, Chm. Bd.--Ssangyong Business Group, Seoul, Korea; *Int'l*, pg. 1291
Kimbell, David A., Chm. Bd. & Pres.--Burk Royalty Co., Wichita Falls, TX; *U.S. Private*, pg. 182
Kimbrell, W. Duke, Chm. Bd. & Chief Exec. Officer--Parkdale Mills, Gastonia, NC; *U.S. Private*, pg. 840
Kimmel, Jerry E., Chm. Bd., Pres. & Chief Exec. Officer--Kevco, Inc., Fort Worth, TX; *U.S. Public*, pg. 952
Kimmel, Sidney, Chm. Bd.--Jones Apparel Group, Inc., Bristol, PA; *U.S. Public*, pg. 933
Kimsey, William L., Deputy Chm. & Chief Oper. Officer--Ernst & Young, LLP, New York, NY; *U.S. Private*, pg. 381
Kimura, Kenichiro, Chm. Bd.--Sapporo U.S.A., Inc., New York, New York, NY; *Int'l*, pg. 1193
Kin, Lai, Chm.--Durable Electrical Metal Factory, Ltd., Hong Kong, Hong Kong; *U.S. Public*, pg. 1771
Kinder, Eric, Chm. Bd.--Smith & Nephew PLC, London, United Kingdom; *Int'l*, pg. 1263
Kindersley, Peter David, Chm. Bd. & Chief Exec. Officer--Dorling Kindersley Holdings plc, London, United Kingdom; *Int'l*, pg. 416
Kindlund, Newton C., Chm. Bd., Pres., Chief Exec. & Chief Oper. Officer--Holiday RV Superstores, Inc., Orlando, FL; *U.S. Public*, pg. 829
King, David C., Chm. Bd., Pres. & Chief Exec. Officer--Proxim, Inc., Mountain View, CA; *U.S. Public*, pg. 1338
King, Edward L., Jr., Chm. Bd. & Chief Exec. Officer--Regions Bank/Okaloosa/Bay County, Fort Walton Beach, FL; *U.S. Public*, pg. 1372
King, G. Edmund, Chm. Bd.--WIC Western International Communications Ltd., Vancouver, Canada; *Int'l*, pg. 1481
King, G.E., Chm. & Chief Exec. Officer--The CIBC Wood Gundy Corporation, Toronto, Canada; *Int'l*, pg. 256
King, George F., Chm. Bd. & Chief Exec. Officer--Kirby Building Systems, Inc., Portland, TN; *Int'l*, pg. 699
King, Graham O., Chm. Bd. & Chief Exec. Officer--US SerVis, West Orange, NJ; *U.S. Public*, pg. 1687
King, H.E., Chm. Bd.--Rentokil Initial plc, East Grinstead, United Kingdom; *Int'l*, pg. 1285
King, John, Chm. Bd.--Greenway Co-Op Service, Rochester, MN; *U.S. Private*, pg. 478
King, Leroy A. Jr., Chm. Bd., Pres. & Chief Exec. Officer--Tighe Industries, Inc., York, PA; *U.S. Private*, pg. 1086
King, Marc, Chm. Bd.--Affiliated Foods Cooperative Inc., Norfolk, NE; *U.S. Private*, pg. 25
King, Olin B., Chm. Bd. & Chief Exec. Officer--SCI Systems, Inc., Huntsville, AL; *U.S. Public*, pg. 1416
King, Peter, Chm. Bd.--Sunrise Leasing Corporation, Golden Valley, MN; *U.S. Public*, pg. 1535
King, Ralph T., Chm. Bd.--Essef Corporation, Chardon, OH; *U.S. Public*, pg. 592
King, Richard S., Chm. Bd. & Pres.--King Industries, Inc., Norwalk, CT; *U.S. Private*, pg. 620
King, Roger, Chm. Bd.--King World Productions, Inc., New York, NY; *U.S. Public*, pg. 961
King, T. Eugene, Chm., Pres. & Chief Exec. Officer--First Security Service Company, Salt Lake City, UT; *U.S. Public*, pg. 638
King, Thomas L., Chm. Bd.--Standex International Corporation, Salem, NH; *U.S. Public*, pg. 1505
King, William C., Chm. Bd. & Chief Exec. Officer--Detrex Corporation, Southfield, MI; *U.S. Public*, pg. 501
Kingma, R.V., Chm.-Exec. Bd.--Delft Instruments N.V., Delft, Netherlands; *Int'l*, pg. 388
Kinney, Douglas M., Sr., Chm. Bd.--Intermatic Inc., Spring Grove, IL; *U.S. Private*, pg. 567

Kinney, Ronald F., Chm. Bd.--All-Phase Electric Supply Co., Benton Harbor, MI; *U.S. Private*, pg. 35
Kinnie, R.H., Chm. Bd. & Pres.--Canada Safeway Limited, Calgary, Canada; *U.S. Public*, pg. 1426
Kinning, Ronald L., Chm. Bd. & Chief Exec. Officer--RK Mechanical, Inc., Denver, CO; *U.S. Private*, pg. 904
Kinnunen, Eero, Chm.--Kesko Ltd., Helsinki, Finland; *Int'l*, pg. 732
Kinsch, Joseph, Chm. Bd., Pres. & Chief Exec. Officer--Arbed S.A., Luxembourg, Luxembourg; *Int'l*, pg. 78
Kinsley, P.H., Chm. Bd., Chief Exec. Officer & Chief Oper. Officer--Permark International (Pty.) Ltd., Johannesburg, South Africa; *Int'l*, pg. 1036
Kinzler, Morton H., Chm. Bd., Pres. & Chief Exec. Officer--Barnwell Industries, Inc., Honolulu, HI; *U.S. Public*, pg. 190
Kiplinger, Austin H., Chm. Bd.--The Kiplinger Washington Editors, Inc., Washington, DC; *U.S. Private*, pg. 623
Kipper, Barbara L., Chm. Bd.--The Chas. Levy Company, Chicago, IL; *U.S. Private*, pg. 664
Kipping, Arthur, Chm. Bd. & Pres.--Ray-Carroll County Grain Co-op, Richmond, MO; *U.S. Private*, pg. 911
Kirac, Suna, Chm. Bd.--Arcelik A.S., Istanbul, Turkey; *Int'l*, pg. 741
Kirby, Dan L., Co.-Chm. Bd., Exec. V.P., Gen. Counsel & Sec.--Western Surety Company, Sioux Falls, SD; *U.S. Public*, pg. 303
Kirby, F.M., Chm. Bd.--Alleghany Corporation, New York, NY; *U.S. Public*, pg. 42
Kirby, Jerry L., Chm. Bd., Pres., & Chief Exec. Officer--CitFed Bancorp, Inc., Dayton, OH; *U.S. Public*, pg. 376
Kirby, Joe P., Co.-Chm. Bd. & Chief Exec. Officer--Western Surety Company, Sioux Falls, SD; *U.S. Public*, pg. 303
Kirby, Robert P., Chm. Bd., Pres. & Chief Exec. Officer--Castleberry/Snow's Brands Inc., Augusta, GA; *U.S. Private*, pg. 219
Kirby, Robert P., Chm. Bd. & Chief Exec. Officer--Bunker Hill Foods Inc., Bedford, VA; *U.S. Private*, pg. 219
Kirchner, King P., Chm. Bd. & Chief Exec. Officer--Unit Corporation, Tulsa, OK; *U.S. Public*, pg. 1672
Kirk, Jesse, Chm. Bd. & Chief Exec. Officer--Dallas Peterbilt, Inc., Irving, TX; *U.S. Private*, pg. 309
Kirk, Larry G., Chm. Bd. & Chief Exec. Officer--Hancock Fabrics, Inc., Tupelo, MS; *U.S. Public*, pg. 779
Kirk, Robert L., Chm. Bd., Pres. & Chief Exec. Officer--British Aerospace Holdings Inc., Chantilly, VA; *Int'l*, pg. 218
Kirkpatrick, Don O., Chm. Bd. & Pres.--Quality Foods Inc., Little Rock, AR; *U.S. Private*, pg. 898
Kirsch, Adam, Mng. Dir.--Bain Capital, Boston, MA; *U.S. Private*, pg. 110
Kirsch, Steven T., Chm. Bd.--Infoseek Corporaton, Sunnyvale, CA; *U.S. Public*, pg. 876
Kirschman, Victor F., Chm. Bd.--Morris Kirschman & Company, Inc., New Orleans, LA; *U.S. Private*, pg. 623
Kirshenbaum, Richard, Co-Chm.--Kirshenbaum, Bond & Partners, New York, NY; *U.S. Private*, pg. 624
Kirshner, Alan I., Chm. Bd. & Chief Exec. Officer--Markel Corporation, Glen Allen, VA; *U.S. Public*, pg. 1046
Kirstien, Ronald D., Chm. Bd., Pres. & Chief Exec. Officer--Davco Restaurants Inc., Crofton, MD; *U.S. Public*, pg. 488
Kirtley, John F., Chm., Pres. & Chief Exec. Officer--Florida Capital Partners, Tampa, FL; *U.S. Private*, pg. 414
Kishida, Shunsuke, Chm. Bd.--The Hiroshima Bank, Ltd., Tokyo, Japan; *Int'l*, pg. 620
Kishimoto, Muneo, Chm. Bd.--Mazda (North America), Inc., Irvine, CA; *Int'l*, pg. 849
Kissner, Charles, Chm. Bd., Pres. & Chief Exec. Officer--Digital Microwave Corporation, San Jose, CA; *U.S. Public*, pg. 508
Kitamura, Toshi, Chm. Bd.--Hitachi America, Ltd., Tarrytown, NY; *Int'l*, pg. 622
Kitchell, Samuel F., Chm. Bd.--Kitchell Corporation, Phoenix, AZ; *U.S. Private*, pg. 624
Kitrosser, Steven, Chm. Bd.--Micronics Computers, Inc., Fremont, CA; *U.S. Public*, pg. 1106
Kiuchi, Takashi, Chm. Bd.--Mitsubishi Electric America, Inc., Cypress, CA; *Int'l*, pg. 872
Kiuchi, Takashioshi, Chm.--Mitsubishi Electronics America, Cypress, CA; *Int'l*, pg. 872
Kives, Philip, Chm. Bd. & Chief Exec. Officer--K-Tel International, Inc., Minneapolis, MN; *U.S. Public*, pg. 937
Kivimaki, Mikko, Chm. Bd., Pres. & Chief Exec. Officer--Rautaruukki Oy, Helsinki, Finland; *Int'l*, pg. 1088
Klapmeier, James E., Chm.--Bluewater, Mora, MN; *U.S. Private*, pg. 153
Klas, Robert C., Chm. Bd. & Chief Exec. Officer--Tapemark, Saint Paul, MN; *U.S. Private*, pg. 1068
Klatsky, Bruce J., Chm. Bd., Pres. & Chief Exec. Officer--Phillips-Van Heusen Corporation, New York, NY; *U.S. Public*, pg. 1291
Klaussner, Hans, Chm. Bd.--Klaussner Corporation, Asheboro, NC; *U.S. Private*, pg. 625
Klaver, P., Chm.--SHV Energy N.V., Utrecht, Netherlands; *Int'l*, pg. 1155
Klein, John, Chm.--Steelcase Financial Services, Inc., Grand Rapids, MI; *U.S. Private*, pg. 1038
Klein, Jonas B., Chm. Bd.--Eastland Shoe Manufacturing Corporation, Freeport, ME; *U.S. Private*, pg. 357
Klein, Lawrence R., Dr., Chm.-Economic Policy Committee & Dir.--W.P. Carey & Co., Inc., New York, NY; *U.S. Private*, pg. 209
Klein, Michael S., Chm. Bd. & Chief Exec. Officer--Klein Tools Inc., Skokie, IL; *U.S. Private*, pg. 625
Klein, Raphael, Chm. Bd. & Pres.--Xicor, Inc., Milpitas, CA; *U.S. Public*, pg. 1785
Klein, Richard M., Dr., Chm. Bd., Pres. & Chief Exec. Officer--Sybron Chemicals Inc., Birmingham, NJ; *U.S. Public*, pg. 1544
Klein, William, Chm. Bd., Pres. & Chief Exec. Officer--The Cerplex Group, Inc., Tustin, CA; *U.S. Public*, pg. 332
Kleinman, Philip, Chm. Bd. & Chief Exec. Officer--AFA Protective Systems, Inc., Syosset, NY; *U.S. Public*, pg. 5
Kleinrock, Leonard, Dr., Chm. Bd. & Chief Exec. Officer--Technology Transfer Institute, Santa Monica, CA; *U.S. Private*, pg. 1072
Kleist, Robert A., Chm. Bd., Pres. & Chief Exec. Officer--Printronix, Inc., Irvine, CA; *U.S. Public*, pg. 1329
Klemer, Richard, Chm. Bd.--Faribault Woolen Mill Co., Faribault, MN; *U.S. Private*, pg. 394
Klenz, Walter, Chm. Bd. & Chief Exec. Officer--Beringer Wine Estates Holdings, Inc., Saint Helena, CA; *U.S. Private*, pg. 1078
Kletjian, Steven C., Chm. Bd. & Chief Exec. Officer--UNICCO Service Company, Boston, MA; *U.S. Private*, pg. 1117
Klevay, Walter S., Sr., Chm., Pres. & Chief Exec. Officer--Kleco Corp., Valley View, OH; *U.S. Private*, pg. 625
Klich, William R., Chm. Bd. & Chief Exec. Officer--SunTrust Bank, Gulf Coast, Sarasota, FL; *U.S. Public*, pg. 1537
Kline, Donald E., Chm. Bd.--Gardner Publications, Inc., Cincinnati, OH; *U.S. Private*, pg. 440
Kling, Richard, Chm. Bd.--IDS Life Insurance Co. of New York, Albany, NY; *U.S. Public*, pg. 73
Kling, Richard, Chm. Bd.--IDS Property Casualty Insurance Company, Minneapolis, MN; *U.S. Public*, pg. 73
Kling, S. Lee, Chm. Bd.--Top Air Manufacturing, Inc., Cedar Falls, IA; *U.S. Public*, pg. 1621
Klinger, Georgette, Chm. Bd.--Georgette Klinger, Inc., New York, NY; *U.S. Private*, pg. 626
Klingle, Ronald E., Chm. Bd. & Chief Exec. Officer--American Waste Services, Inc., Warren, OH; *U.S. Public*, *pg. 94*
Klink, Edwin H., Chm. Bd.--E & A Industries, Inc., Indianapolis, IN; *U.S. Private*, pg. 352
Klipsch, Fred S., Chm. Bd.--Hospital Affiliates Development Corporation, Nashville, TN; *U.S. Private*, pg. 540
Klipsch, Fred S., Chm. Bd.--Klipsch, Inc., Hope, AR; *U.S. Private*, pg. 626
Klosterman, Kenneth, Chm. Bd.--Klosterman Baking Company, Inc., Cincinnati, OH; *U.S. Private*, pg. 626
Kloth, Donald W., Chm. Bd. & Chief Exec. Officer--Busch Agricultural Resources, Inc., Saint Louis, MO; *U.S. Public*, pg. 114
Klotsche, John, Chm.-Exec. Committee--Baker & McKenzie, Attorneys At Law, Chicago, IL; *U.S. Private*, pg. 111
Kluge, John, Chm. Bd.--Metromedia Steakhouses, Inc., Vandalia, OH; *U.S. Private*, pg. 736
Kluge, John W., Chm. & Pres.--Metromedia Company, East Rutherford, NJ; *U.S. Private*, pg. 736
Kluge, John W., Chm. Bd. & Pres.--Metromedia International Group, Inc., East Rutherford, NJ; *U.S. Public*, pg. 1102
Klumpyan, David, Chm. Bd.--Grant Thornton LLP, Chicago, IL; *U.S. Private*, pg. 470
Kluzer, Silvio, Chm. & Pres.--Cerestar Holding B.V., Sas-van-Gent, Netherlands; *Int'l*, pg. 324
Knauer, M., Chm. Bd.--Hoogovens Aluminium GmbH, Dusseldorf, Germany; *Int'l*, pg. 755
Kneeland, Steve, Chm. Bd. & Chief Exec. Officer--Restonic Mattress Corporation, Rosemont, IL; *U.S. Private*, pg. 925
Knick, Gerd, Dr., Chm.-Mng. Bd. & Chief Exec. Officer--Fresenius AG, Bad Hamburg, Germany; *Int'l*, pg. 505
Knight, Andrew, Exec. Chm.--News International plc, London, United Kingdom; *Int'l*, pg. 927
Knight, C.F., Chm. Bd. & Chief Exec. Officer--Emerson Electric Co., Saint Louis, MO; *U.S. Public*, pg. 572
Knight, Charles, Jr., Chm.Bd.--Concrete Technology Corp., Tacoma, WA; *U.S. Private*, pg. 262
Knight, J.A., Chm. Bd., Pres. & Chief Exec. Officer--Heat Controller, Inc., Jackson, MI; *U.S. Private*, pg. 518
Knight, John W., Chm. Bd., Pres. & Chief Exec. Officer--The Fabri-Form Company, Byesville, OH; *U.S. Private*, pg. 390
Knight, Lester B., Chm. Bd. & Chief Exec. Officer--Allegiance Healthcare Corp., McGaw Park, IL; *U.S. Public*, pg. 44
Knight, Michael, Sir, Chm. Bd.--Cobham plc, Wimborne Minster, United Kingdom; *Int'l*, pg. 301
Knight, Philip H., Chm. Bd. & Chief Exec. Officer--Nike, Inc., Beaverton, OR; *U.S. Public*, pg. 1184
Knight, Richard, Chm. Bd., Pres. & Chief Exec. Officer--Greate Bay Casino Corporation, Atlantic City, NJ; *U.S. Public*, pg. 760
Knight, Shirley M., Chm. Emeritus--The Fabri-Form Company, Byesville, OH; *U.S. Private*, pg. 390
Knoebel, F. C., Sr. Chm.--Nobel/Sysco Food Services Company-Denver, Denver, CO; *U.S. Public*, pg. 1551
Knowles, C. Harry, Chm. Bd., Pres. & Chief Exec. Officer--Metrologic Instruments, Inc., Blackwood, NJ; *U.S. Public*, *pg. 1102*
Knox, Boone A., Chm. Bd.--Merry Land & Investment Company, Inc., Augusta, GA; *U.S. Public*, pg. 1098
Knox, Charles E., Jr., Chm. Bd. & Chief Exec. Officer--Knox Oil of Texas Inc., Dallas, TX; *U.S. Private*, pg. 627
Knox, Marion A., Sr., Vice Chm.--Terminix Service, Inc., Columbia, SC; *U.S. Private*, pg. 1077
Knox, T.P, Jr., Chm. Bd.--Terminix Service, Inc., Columbia, SC; *U.S. Private*, pg. 1077
Knox, Tony, Chm. Bd.--Financial Dynamics Ltd., London, United Kingdom; *Int'l*, pg. 117
Knudsen, Bent Hjort, Chm. Bd.--ESS-Food, Copenhagen, Denmark; *Int'l*, pg. 429
Knudtson, Arvid C., Chm. Bd.--Michael Foods, Inc., Minneapolis, MN; *U.S. Public*, pg. 1103
Knurr, Hans, Chm.-Bd. of Mgmnt.--Knurr AG, Munich, Germany; *Int'l*, pg. 739
Knuths, Leroy R., Chm. Bd., Pres. & Chief Exec. Officer--Rosco Manufacturing Co., Madison, SD; *U.S. Private*, pg. 944
Knuts, Per, Chm.--FPB Holding AG, Dusseldorf, Germany; *Int'l*, pg. 1303
Kobauashi, Hiroshi, Chm. Bd.--Lion Henkel Corporation, Tokyo, Japan; *Int'l*, pg. 614
Kobayashi, Hisao, Chm. Bd.--The CIT Group Holdings, Inc., New York, NY; *Int'l*, pg. 360
Kobayashi, Shigeru, Chm. Bd. & Pres.--Shuwa Corporation, Tokyo, Japan; *Int'l*, pg. 1237
Kobayashi, Toshihiro, Chm. Bd.--Rheem Manufacturing Co., New York, NY; *Int'l*, pg. 1022
Kobayashi, Yonezo, Chm. Bd.--Industriebank von Japan (Deutschland) Aktiengesellschaft, Frankfurt/Main, Germany; *Int'l*, pg. 676
Koc, Rahmi M., Chm. Bd.--Koc Holding A.S., Istanbul, Turkey; *Int'l*, pg. 741
Koch-Nielsen, Robert, Chm. Bd--Sophus Berendsen A/S, Soeborg, Denmark; *Int'l*, pg. 1284
Koch, Anthony H., Chm. Bd., Pres. & Chief Exec. Officer--Alamo Industrial Group, San Antonio, TX; *U.S. Private*, pg. 31
Koch, Charles, Chm. Bd.--Koch Engineering Company, Inc., Akron, OH; *U.S. Private*, pg. 628
Koch, Charles G., Chm. Bd. & Chief Exec. Officer--Koch Industries, Incorporated, Wichita, KS; *U.S. Private*, pg. 628
Koch, Charles John, Chm. Bd., Pres. & Chief Exec. Officer--Charter One Financial, Inc., Cleveland, OH; *U.S. Public*, pg. 336
Koch, David A., Chm. Bd.--Graco Inc., Golden Valley, MN; *U.S. Public*, pg. 756
Koch, David C., Chm. Bd. & Chief Exec. Officer--New Era Cap. Co., Derby, NY; *U.S. Private*, pg. 793
Koch, G. Fred, Chm. Bd., Chief Exec. Officer & Treas.--Plywood Plastics Inc., Buffalo, NY; *U.S. Private*, pg. 873
Koch, Klaus, Chm. Bd.--Zimmermann & Jansen GmbH, Duren, Germany; *Int'l*, pg. 1528
Kochheiser, George W., Chm. Bd.--EMC Insurance Group, Inc., Des Moines, IA; *U.S. Public*, pg. 545
Kociszewski, Szymon T., Chm. Bd.--Polskie Linie Lotnicze LOT S.A., Warsaw, Poland; *Int'l*, pg. 1062
Koehl, Hans H., Chm. Bd., Chief Exec. Officer & Chief Engr.--Spirol International Corp., Danielson, CT; *U.S. Private*, pg. 1026
Koehl, Hans H., Chm. Bd.--Prym-Dritz Corporation, Spartanburg, SC; *Int'l*, pg. 1499
Koehler, Rudolph A., Deputy Chm.--Noma Industries Limited, North York, Canada; *Int'l*, pg. 954
Koehn, George W., Chm. Bd., Pres. & Chief Exec. Officer--SunTrust, Orlando, FL; *U.S. Public*, pg. 1537
Koenigs, Erwin, Dr., Chm. Bd.--Software AG, Darmstadt, Germany; *Int'l*, pg. 1276
Koenitzer, John E., Chm. Bd. & Chief Exec. Officer--Helwig Carbon Products, Inc., Milwaukee, WI; *U.S. Private*, pg. 521
Koetters, Ronald A., Chm. Bd. & Chief Exec. Officer--Monarch Construction Company, Cincinnati, OH; *U.S. Private*, pg. 757
Koffel, Martin M., Chm. Bd., Pres. & Chief Exec. Officer--URS Corporation, San Francisco, CA; *U.S. Public*, pg. 1655
Koffman, Burton I., Chm. Bd. & Pres.--Great American Industries, Inc., Vestal, NY; *U.S. Private*, pg. 473
Koga, Kensuke, Chm. Bd.--Nisshin Steel Co., Ltd., Tokyo, Japan; *Int'l*, pg. 946
Kogure, Gohei, Chm. Bd.--Dentsu Inc., Tokyo, Japan; *Int'l*, pg. 392
Kohler, Herbert V., Jr., Chm. Bd. & Pres.--Kohler Company, Kohler, WI; *U.S. Private*, pg. 630
Koivu, Lasse, Chm. Bd.--OY Stockmann AB, Helsinki, Finland; *Int'l*, pg. 1301
Kojima, Akinobu, Chm. Bd.--Quick Corp., Tokyo, Japan; *Int'l*, pg. 929
Kok, W.J., Dr., Chm. Bd.--Escap Limited, Sandton, South Africa; *Int'l*, pg. 459
Kolade, Christopher, Dr., Chm. Bd.--Cadbury Nigeria PLC, Ikeja, Nigeria; *Int'l*, pg. 248
Kolb, David L., Chm. Bd. & Chief Exec. Officer--Mohawk Industries, Inc., Calhoun, GA; *U.S. Public*, pg. 1121
Kolber, Ernest Leo, Chm. Bd. & Dir.--Cineplex Odeon Corporation, Toronto, Canada; *Int'l*, pg. 292
Koldyke, Martin J., Chm. Bd.--WTTW (Channel 11), Chicago, IL; *U.S. Private*, pg. 1145
Koley, James L., Chm. Bd.--Art's-Way Manufacturing Co., Inc., Armstrong, IA; *U.S. Public*, pg. 136
Koll, Donald M., Chm. Bd. & Chief Exec. Officer--Koll Co., Newport Beach, CA; *U.S. Private*, pg. 631
Komai, Shigeharu, Chm. Bd.--Duskin Co., Ltd., Osaka, Japan; *Int'l*, pg. 422
Komai, Yoshiaki, Dep. Chm.--ORIX Australia Corporation Limited, Double Bay, Australia; *Int'l*, pg. 1009
Komansky, David H., Chm. Bd. & Chief Exec. Officer--Merrill Lynch & Co., Inc., New York, NY; *U.S. Public*, pg. 1097
Komen, Richard B., Chm. Bd.--Restaurants Unlimited, Seattle, WA; *U.S. Private*, pg. 925
Komer, Stuart, Chm. Bd.--Artistic Greetings, Inc., Elmira, NY; *U.S. Public*, pg. 136
Komline, Elizabeth M., Chm. Bd.--Komline-Sanderson Engineering Corp., Peapack, NJ; *U.S. Private*, pg. 631
Kommerstad, Robert, Chm. Bd. & Pres.--Provident Investment Counsel, Inc., Pasadena, CA; *U.S. Public*, pg. 1674
Komori, Shuichi, Chm. Bd. & Chief Exec. Officer--Daiwa Securities America Inc., New York, NY; *Int'l*, pg. 375
Komoto, Meizo, Chm.--ORIX Life Insurance Corporation, Tokyo, Japan; *Int'l*, pg. 1009
Kondoh, Akira, Chm. Bd.--Sumitomo Bank Leasing & Finance, Inc., New York, NY; *Int'l*, pg. 1308
Kondoh, Akira, Chm. Bd.--Sumitomo Bank of California, San Francisco, CA; *Int'l*, pg. 1309
Kondziolka, David, Exec. V.P.-Western U.S.--AGRA Earth & Environmental, Inc., Albuquerque, NM; *Int'l*, pg. 31
Kong, Liau Hong, Chm.--NDC Merchant Bank Nominees Pte Ltd., Singapore, Singapore; *Int'l*, pg. 351
Konig, Raimund, Dr., Chm.-Mngmt. Bd.--Triumph Adler Group, Nuremberg, Germany; *Int'l*, pg. 1424
Konigsberg, Max, Chm., Pres. & Chief Exec. Officer--Shirmax Leasing Ltd., Montreal, Canada; *Int'l*, pg. 1235
Kono, Shunji, Chm. Bd.--The Tokio Marine & Fire Insurance Company, Ltd., Tokyo, Japan; *Int'l*, pg. 1391

Konopacki, Benjamin S., Chm. Bd.--Pulse Bancorp, Inc., South River, NJ; *U.S. Public*, pg. 1344
Koo, Bon-Moo, Chm. Bd.--LG Group, Seoul, Korea; *Int'l*, pg. 778
Koo, Cha Kyung, Chm.--Honam Oil Refinery Co. Ltd., Seoul, Korea; *Int'l*, pg. 779
Kopelman, David W., Chm. Bd. & Chief Exec. Officer--The W.B. Wood Company, New Providence, NJ; *U.S. Private*, *pg. 1186*
Kopko, Edward M., Chm. Bd., Pres., Chief Exec. & Chief Oper. Officer--Butler International, Inc., Montvale, NJ; *U.S. Public*, pg. 270
Koplik, Perry, Chm. Bd.--Perry H. Koplik & Sons, New York, NY; *U.S. Private*, pg. 632
Koppelman, Charles, Chm. Bd.--Capitol Industries-EMI Inc., Hollywood, CA; *Int'l*, pg. 427
Kopper, Hilmar, Chm. Bd.--Deutsche Bank AG, Frankfurt/Main, Germany; *Int'l*, pg. 401
Kopper, Hilmar, Chm.-Supervisory Bd.--Mannesmann A.G., Dusseldorf, Germany; *Int'l*, pg. 834
Kopper, Hilmar, Chm. Supervisory Bd.--Kali-Chemie Aktiengesellschaft, Hannover, Germany; *Int'l*, pg. 1278
Koptev, Sergey, Chm. & Chief Exec. Officer--DMB&B St. Petersburg, Saint Petersburg, Russia; *U.S. Private*, pg. 304
Korn, Bernard, Chm. Bd. & Pres.--Colonial Commercial Corp., Levittown, NY; *U.S. Public*, pg. 400
Korn, Carl, Chm. Bd.--Cobra Electronics Corporation, Chicago, IL; *U.S. Public*, pg. 391
Kornberg, Fred, Chm. Bd., Pres. & Chief Exec. Officer--Comtech Telecommunications Corp., Melville, NY; *U.S. Public*, pg. 425
Kornswiet, Neil B., Exec. V.P., Chm. Bd. & Chief Exec. Officer-One Stop Mortgage, Inc--Aames Financial Corporation, Los Angeles, CA; *U.S. Public*, pg. 12
Korphage, George J., Chm. Bd.--Pike & Fischer, Bethesda, MD; *U.S. Private*, pg. 182
Kortbals, Robert W., Chm. Bd.--Co-Steel Inc., Toronto, Canada; *Int'l*, pg. 298
Korth, Harald, Chm. Bd.--Markantstahl GmbH, Hagen, Germany; *Int'l*, pg. 79
Korthoff, Herbert W., Chm. Bd.--Wright Medical Technology, Arlington, TN; *U.S. Private*, pg. 1192
Koshiba, Heiji, Chm. Bd.--Tsudakoma Corp., Kanazawa, Japan; *Int'l*, pg. 1425
Koshiishi, Kazuhide, Chm. Bd.--LTCB Australia Limited, Sydney, Australia; *Int'l*, pg. 816
Koshizawa, Shoji, Chm.--Chuo Senko Advertising Co., Ltd., Tokyo, Japan; *Int'l*, pg. 291
Koss, John C., Chm. Bd.--Koss Corporation, Milwaukee, WI; *U.S. Public*, pg. 966
Kostas, Evans, Chm. Bd. & Chief Exec. Officer--Publishers Equipment Corporation, Dallas, TX; *U.S. Public*, pg. 1341
Kostelni, James C., Chm. Bd., Pres. & Chief Exec. Officer--Georgia-Bonded Fibers, Inc., Newark, NJ; *U.S. Public*, pg. 734
Kostelni, James C., Chm. Bd.--Bontex International (F.S.C.), Buena Vista, VA; *U.S. Public*, pg. 734
Kotick, Robert, Chm. Bd. & Chief Exec. Officer--Activision, Santa Monica, CA; *U.S. Public*, pg. 17
Kotkins, Henry L., Chm. Bd.--Skyway Luggage Co., Seattle, WA; *U.S. Private*, pg. 1005
Kotsatos, Andrew G., Chm. Bd., Chief Exec. Officer & Treas.--Boston Acoustics, Inc., Peabody, MA; *U.S. Public*, pg. 246
Kouchi, Kenji, Chm. Bd--Olympus America Inc., Melville, NY; *Int'l*, pg. 1005
Kourcia, Roger, Chm. Bd.--Gelazur S.A., Nice, France; *U.S. Public*, pg. 429
Kovacevich, Richard M., Chm. Bd., Pres. & Chief Exec. Officer--Norwest Corporation, Minneapolis, MN; *U.S. Public*, pg. 1201
Kovens, Michael L., Chm. Bd.--Universal Security Instruments Inc., Owings Mills, MD; *U.S. Public*, pg. 1697
Kowalski, Michael J., Chm. Bd.--Tiffco Korea, Ltd., Seoul, Korea; *U.S. Public*, pg. 1609
Kozakis, Achilles, Chm. Bd. & Mng. Dir.--Joffko International, Houston, TX; *U.S. Private*, pg. 589
Kozawa, Shozo, Chm. Bd.--Shiseido Company Ltd., Tokyo, Japan; *Int'l*, pg. 1235
Kozlowski, L. Dennis, Chm. Bd., Pres. & Chief Exec. Officer--Tyco International Ltd., Exeter, NH; *U.S. Public*, pg. 1647
Kozlowski, Paul, Chm.--Racal-Datacom, Sunrise, FL; *Int'l*, pg. 1083
Kozuki, Kagemasa, Chm. Bd. & Chief Exec. Officer--Konami Co. Ltd., Tokyo, Japan; *Int'l*, pg. 745
Kraemer, Arthur T., Chm. Bd. & Chief Exec. Officer--M & I Lake Country Bank, Hartland, WI; *U.S. Public*, pg. 1050
Kraft, Harold E., Chm. Bd. & Chief Exec. Officer--Ward Kraft, Inc., Fort Scott, KS; *U.S. Private*, pg. 634
Kraft, Herbert A., Co-Chm. Bd.--American Vanguard Corporation, Newport Beach, CA; *U.S. Public*, pg. 94
Kraft, Marvin E., Chm. Bd. & Chief Exec. Officer--Lario Oil & Gas Company, Calgary, Canada; *U.S. Private*, pg. 651
Kraftsow, Stanley A., Chm. Bd. & Pres.--Craftmatic Industries, Inc., Trevose, PA; *U.S. Private*, pg. 284
Kraftsow, Stanley A., Chm. Bd. & Pres.--Craftmatic Organization, Inc., Trevose, PA; *U.S. Private*, pg. 284
Kragie, Jack, Chm. Bd.--Kragie/Newell, Des Moines, IA; *U.S. Private*, pg. 634
Kraines, Lawrence M., Chm. Bd.--Kraco Enterprises, Inc., Compton, CA; *U.S. Private*, pg. 634
Krakoff, Robert L., Chm. Bd. & Chief Exec. Officer--Advanstar Communications, Cleveland, OH; *U.S. Private*, *pg. 22*
Krall, Norris E., Chm. Bd.--Thomas & Skinner, Inc., Indianapolis, IN; *U.S. Private*, pg. 1082
Kramer, Gordon M., Chm. Bd., Pres. & Chief Exec. Officer--Continental Plastic Card Co., Coral Springs, FL; *U.S. Private*, pg. 269
Kramer, Hans, Dr., Chm. Bd.--AMB Aachener und Muenchener Beteiligungs-AG, Aachen, Germany; *Int'l*, pg. 15
Kramer, Martin B., Chm. Bd.--Trimfit, Inc., Bristol, PA; *U.S. Private*, pg. 1103
Kramer, Richard, Chm. Bd.--Weldotron Corporation, Piscataway, NJ; *U.S. Public*, pg. 1752
Kramer, Richard L., Chm. Bd.--Texfi Industries, Inc., Raleigh, NC; *U.S. Public*, pg. 1588
Kranert, Wolfgang, Dr., Chm. Bd.--Groschopp, Inc., Sioux Center, IA; *Int'l*, pg. 559
Krantz, Andrew, Chm. Bd., Pres. & Chief Oper. Officer--Eagle Iron Works, Des Moines, IA; *U.S. Private*, pg. 354
Krantz, Marie G., Chm. Bd. & Treas.--Fair Grounds Corporation, New Orleans, LA; *U.S. Public*, pg. 609
Krasne, Charles A., Chm. Bd., Pres. & Chief Exec. Officer--Krasdale Foods Inc., White Plains, NY; *U.S. Private*, pg. 635
Krasnoff, Eric, Chm. Bd. & Chief Exec. Officer--Pall Corporation, Greenvale, NY; *U.S. Public*, pg. 1253
Krasnow, Robert, Chm. Bd.--Elektra Entertainment, New York, NY; *U.S. Public*, pg. 1612
Krasny, Michael P., Chm. Bd., Chief Exec. Officer, Treas. & Sec.--CDW Computer Centers, Inc., Vernon Hills, IL; *U.S.* Public, pg. 277
Krass, Robert P., Chm. Bd.--UCAR International Inc., Danbury, CT; *U.S. Public*, pg. 1662
Krat, Gary, Chm. & Chief Exec. Officer--Royal Alliance Associates, Inc., New York, NY; *U.S. Public*, pg. 1533
Krauer, Alex, Dr., Chm. Bd.--Novartis AG, Basel, Switzerland; *Int'l*, pg. 971
Kraus, Eileen, Chm. Bd.--Fleet Bank, N.A., Hartford, CT; *U.S. Public*, pg. 649
Kraus, Eileen S., Chm. Bd.--Fleet National Bank of Connecticut, Hartford, CT; *U.S. Public*, pg. 649
Krauss, Carl W., Chm. Bd.--Lakewood Engineering & Manufacturing Co., Chicago, IL; *U.S. Private*, pg. 644
Krauss, Charles H., Chm. Bd.--Spartan International Inc., Holt, MI; *U.S. Private*, pg. 1020
Krauss, Ingo, Grp. Chm. & Chief Exec. Officer-Y&R Germany--Young & Rubicam GmbH, Frankfurt/Main, Germany; *U.S. Private*, pg. 1199
Krausse, Dan M., Chm. Bd.--Plains Resources Inc., Houston, TX; *U.S. Public*, pg. 1307
Krauter, Hal J., Chm. Bd., Pres. & Chief Exec. Officer--Leasing Solutions, Inc., San Jose, CA; *U.S. Public*, pg. 982
Krebs, Robert D., Chm. Bd., Pres. & Chief Exec. Officer--Burlington Northern Santa Fe Corporation, Fort Worth, TX; *U.S. Public*, pg. 268
Krehbiel, Frederick A., Chm. Bd. & Chief Exec. Officer--Molex Incorporated, Lisle, IL; *U.S. Public*, pg. 1121
Krehbiel, Paul R., Chm. Bd. & Chief Exec. Officer--Kreonite, Inc., Wichita, KS; *U.S. Private*, pg. 635
Kreher, Dr., Chm. Bd.--Durkopp Adler AG, Bielefeld, Germany; *Int'l*, pg. 468
Kreher, Peter-Jurgen, Chm.--FAG Kugelfischer Georg Schafer AG, Schweinfurt, Germany; *Int'l*, pg. 468
Kreher, Peter-Jurgen, Dr., Chm. Bd.--FAG Group, Schweinfurt, Germany; *Int'l*, pg. 468
Kreiter, Harry, Chm. Bd. & Pres.--Castcraft Industries, Inc., Skokie, IL; *U.S. Private*, pg. 219
Kresa, Kent, Chm. Bd., Pres. & Chief Exec. Officer--Northrop Grumman Corporation, Los Angeles, CA; *U.S. Public*, pg. 1197
Kress, James F., Chm. Bd.--Green Bay Packaging Inc., Green Bay, WI; *U.S. Private*, pg. 476
Kreuziger, D., Dr., Chm. Bd.--Ceramtec North America Applications, Inc., Mansfield, MA; *Int'l*, pg. 860
Kriegel, David L., Chm. Bd., Pres. & Chief Exec. Officer--Drug Emporium, Inc., Powell, OH; *U.S. Public*, pg. 530
Kriegel, William, Chm. Bd., Pres. & Chief Exec. Officer--Sithe Energies, Inc., New York, NY; *U.S. Private*, pg. 1004
Krier, B. Bruce, Chm. Bd. & Pres.--Krier Foods, Inc., Brown Deer, WI; *U.S. Private*, pg. 636
Krier, Jean, Chm.-Exec. Bd.--Banque Internationale a Luxembourg S.A., Luxembourg, Luxembourg; *Int'l*, pg. 162
Kriesi, Rolf, Chm. Bd.--Impuls Advertising AG, Kusnacht, Switzerland; *Int'l*, pg. 666
Kriete, Roberto, Chm. Bd.--Taca International Airlines, S. A., San Salvador, El Salvador; *Int'l*, pg. 1346
Krippaehne, William, Jr., Chm. Bd.--Fisher Properties Inc., Seattle, WA; *U.S. Public*, pg. 648
Kristiansen, Kjeld Kirk, Chm. Bd.--LEGO Systems, Inc., Enfield, CT; *Int'l*, pg. 805
Kriwet, Dr. Heinz, Chm. Bd.--Thyssen AG, Dusseldorf, Germany; *Int'l*, pg. 1387
Krneta, Georg, Dr., Chm. Bd.--Landis & Staefa AG, Zug, Switzerland; *Int'l*, pg. 800
Kroef, J.J.A., Chm. Bd.--Electrical Carbon Limited, Sheffield, United Kingdom; *Int'l*, pg. 891
Kroese, John S., Jr., Chm. Bd. & Chief Oper. Officer--Gaffney-Kroese Electrical Supply Corp., Rahway, NJ; *U.S. Private*, pg. 437
Kroetch, Arthur A., Chm. Bd. & Pres.--Krofam Inc., Philip, SD; *U.S. Private*, pg. 636
Kroot, A. Jerome, Chm. Bd.--Foland's Jewelry Brokers, Warren, MI; *U.S. Private*, pg. 416
Kruger, J., II, Chm. Bd. & Chief Exec. Officer--Kruger Inc., Montreal, Canada; *Int'l*, pg. 761
Kruger, Paul, Chm. Bd.--Sasol Limited, Johannesburg, South Africa; *Int'l*, pg. 1196
Krulik, Richard, Chm. Bd. & Chief Oper. Officer--United States Luggage Company, Hauppauge, NY; *U.S. Private*, *pg. 1125*
Krumm, Theodore H., Chm. Bd.--Fidelity & Surety Division, Schaumburg, IL; *U.S. Public*, pg. 215
Krupa, Calvin, Chm. Bd., Pres. & Chief Exec. Officer--Ultra Pac, Inc., Rogers, MN; *U.S. Public*, pg. 1662
Krupp, Douglas, Chm. Bd.--Berkshire Realty Company, Inc., Boston, MA; *U.S. Public*, pg. 221
Kruse, Daniel J., Chm. Bd.--Superior Auctioneers & Marketing, Inc., San Antonio, TX; *U.S. Private*, pg. 1054
Kruse, Dean V., Chm. Bd.--Kruse International, Auburn, IN; *U.S. Private*, pg. 636
Kruse, Ed F., Chm. Bd.--Blue Bell Creameries, L.P., Brenham, TX; *U.S. Private*, pg. 150
Kruse, Ernst Michel, Chm. Bd. & Mng. Dir.--BHF-BANK AG, Frankfurt, Germany; *Int'l*, pg. 119
Kruska, Ken, Chm. Bd.--J.H. Findorff & Son, Inc., Madison, WI; *U.S. Private*, pg. 405
Kruy, Joseph F., Chm. Bd., Pres., Chief Exec. & Chief Oper. Officer--Cambex Corporation, Waltham, MA; *U.S. Public*, pg. 296
Ku, Chenfu, Chm. Bd.--China Synthetic Rubber Corporation, Taipei, Taiwan; *Int'l*, pg. 286
Kuber, Thomas J., Chm. Bd.--Badger Paper Mills, Inc., Peshtigo, WI; *U.S. Public*, pg. 165
Kubly, Raymond, Chm. Bd. & Chief Exec. Officer--The Swiss Colony, Inc, Monroe, WI; *U.S. Private*, pg. 1059
Kubota, Hiroshi, Chm. Bd.--The Nippon Credit Bank, Ltd., Tokyo, Japan; *Int'l*, pg. 932
Kubota, Teruo, Chm. Bd.--The Hokuriku Bank, Ltd., Toyama, Japan; *Int'l*, pg. 627
Kucharski, John M., Chm. Bd. & Chief Exec. Officer--EG & G, Inc., Wellesley, MA; *U.S. Public*, pg. 542
Kuck, Paul, Chm. Bd.--Regal Marine Industries Inc., Orlando, FL; *U.S. Private*, pg. 917
Kudara, Tokuo, Chm. Bd.--Colonial Beef Co., Philadelphia, PA; *U.S. Private*, pg. 253
Kuebler, Christopher A., Chm. Bd. & Chief Exec. Officer--Covance, Inc., Princeton, NJ; *U.S. Public*, pg. 453
Kuebler, Thomas L., Chm. Bd.--Uniflow Manufacturing Co., Erie, PA; *U.S. Private*, pg. 1117
Kuehn, Ronald L., Jr., Chm. Bd. & Chief Exec. Officer--Sonat Inc., Birmingham, AL; *U.S. Public*, pg. 1484
Kuenheim, Eberhard V., Chm. Bd.--Supervisory--Bayerische Motoren Werke Aktiengesellschaft, Munich, Germany; *Int'l*, pg. 177
Kugle, J. Alan, Chm. Bd.--Wailuku Agribusiness Co., Inc., Wailuku, HI; *U.S. Private*, pg. 191
Kugler, Seymour, Chm. Bd., Pres. & Chief Exec. Officer--Winston Resources, Inc., New York, NY; *U.S. Public*, pg. 1772
Kuhlman, Harvey G., Chm. Bd.--Kuhlman, Inc., Menomonee Falls, WI; *U.S. Private*, pg. 636
Kuhn, Robert, Chm. Bd. & Chief Exec. Officer--Goss Graphic Systems, Westmont, IL; *U.S. Private*, pg. 466
Kuhne, Bruno, Chm.--Coop Zurichsee-Linth, Hinwil, Switzerland; *Int'l*, pg. 329
Kuhne, K.M., Chm. Bd. & Chief Exec. Officer--Kuehne & Nagel International AG, Schindellegi, Switzerland; *Int'l*, pg. 763
Kuhnt, Dietmar, Dr., Chm. Bd.--Hochtief AG, Essen, Germany; *Int'l*, pg. 623
Kuhnt, Dietmar, Dr., Chm. Bd., Pres. & Chief Exec. Officer--RWE AG, Essen, Germany; *Int'l*, pg. 1081
Kulicke, C. Scott, Chm. Bd. & Chief Exec. Officer--Kulicke & Soffa Industries, Inc., Willow Grove, PA; *U.S. Public*, pg. 968
Kulkarni, Deepak, Chm. Bd. & Pres.--Wolverine Massachusetts Corporation, Merrimac, MA; *U.S. Private*, pg. 1186
Kullas, Robert H., Chm. Bd. & Chief Oper. Officer--Executive Risk, Inc., Simsbury, CT; *U.S. Public*, pg. 599
Kumagai, Naohiko, Chm. Bd.--Mitsui & Co., Ltd., Tokyo, Japan; *Int'l*, pg. 877
Kumar, U., Chm. Bd. & Mng. Dir.--South Eastern Coalfields Limited, Bilaspur, India; *Int'l*, pg. 299
Kummel, Eugene H., Chm. Emeritus--McCann-Erickson Worldwide, New York, NY; *U.S. Public*, pg. 909
Kummer, Fred S., Chm., Pres., Chief Exec. Officer, Treas. & Founder--HBE Corporation/Design Build Divisions, Saint Louis, MO; *U.S. Private*, pg. 489
Kummer, Glenn F., Chm. Bd. & Chief Exec. Officer--Fleetwood Enterprises, Inc., Riverside, CA; *U.S. Public*, pg. 650
Kummer, Robert W., Jr., Chm. Bd. & Chief Exec. Officer--Mellon First Business Bank, Los Angeles, CA; *U.S. Public*, pg. 1085
Kunin, Myron, Chm. Bd.--Regis Corporation, Minneapolis, MN; *U.S. Public*, pg. 1373
Kunisch, Rolf, Chm. Bd.--Beiersdorf, Inc., Norwalk, CT; *Int'l*, *pg. 182*
Kunisch, Rolf, Dr., Chm.-Exec. Bd.--Beiersdorf Group, Hamburg, Germany; *Int'l*, pg. 182
Kunzler, Christian C., Jr., Chm. Bd. & Pres.--Kunzler & Company, Inc., Lancaster, PA; *U.S. Private*, pg. 636
Kupferman, Ronald J., Chm. Bd., Chief Exec. Officer & Pres.--Global Software, Inc., Raleigh, NC; *U.S. Private*, pg. 457
Kuraishi, Tokuichi, Chm. Bd.--Oriental Motor Co., Ltd., Tokyo, Japan; *Int'l*, pg. 1008
Kuramochi, Choji, Chm. Bd.--Nippon Paper Industries Company Limited, Tokyo, Japan; *Int'l*, pg. 937
Kurland, Rayfield B., Chm. Bd.--Handy Store Fixtures, Inc., Newark, NJ; *U.S. Private*, pg. 499
Kurman, Bernard J., Chm. Bd.--NutraMax Products, Inc., Gloucester, MA; *U.S. Public*, pg. 1206
Kuroda, Shoichi, Chm. Bd.--Kuroda Precision Industries Ltd., Kawasaki, Japan; *Int'l*, pg. 764
Kurosawa, Yoh, Chm. Bd.--The Industrial Bank of Japan, Limited, Tokyo, Japan; *Int'l*, pg. 674
Kurosawa, Yoh, Chm.--The Industrial Bank of Japan, Limited (Canada), Toronto, Canada; *Int'l*, pg. 675
Kurosawa, Yoh, Chm.--The Industrial Bank of Japan (Canada), Toronto, Canada; *Int'l*, pg. 676
Kursman, Daniel R., Chm. Bd. & Treas.--Jetronic Industries, Inc., Philadelphia, PA; *U.S. Public*, pg. 926
Kurtenbach, Aelred J., Chm. Bd., Pres., Chief Exec. & Oper. Officer--Daktronics, Inc., Brookings, SD; *U.S. Public*, pg. 478
Kurtz, Anthony D., Chm. Bd.--Kulite Semiconductor Products, Inc., Leonia, NJ; *U.S. Private*, pg. 636
Kury, Mark C., Chm. Bd.--Marmac Corporation, Vienna, WV; *U.S. Private*, pg. 705
Kurz, Herbert, Chm. Bd., Pres. & Chief Exec. Officer--Presidential Life Corporation, Nyack, NY; *U.S. Public*, pg. 1323

Kurzweg, Victor J., III, Chm. Bd., Chief Exec. Officer & Chief Fin. Officer--Consolidated Companies Inc. (CONCO), Metairie, LA; *U.S. Private*, pg. 265
Kuse, James R., Chm. Bd.--Georgia Gulf Corporation, Atlanta, GA; *U.S. Public*, pg. 734
Kusel, Mr., Chm. Bd.--Rosenthal AG, Selb, Germany; *Int'l*, pg. 1127
Kusumoto, Sadahei, Chm. Bd. & Chief Exec. Officer--Minolta Corporation, Ramsey, NJ; *Int'l*, pg. 869
Kusunoki, Kaneyoshi, Chm. Bd.--Hino Motors, Ltd., Tokyo, Japan; *Int'l*, pg. 620
Kusunoki, Naotaka, Chm. & Chief Exec. Officer--NSK Corporation, Ann Arbor, MI; *Int'l*, pg. 903
Kuttner, Ludwig, Chm. Bd., Pres. & Chief Exec. Officer--Hampshire Group, Ltd., Anderson, SC; *U.S. Public*, pg. 778
Kvamme, Helge, Chm. Bd.--Statoil, Stavanger, Norway; *Int'l*, *pg. 1297*
Kvarmstrom, Jan, Chm. Bd.--Spectra-Physics AB, Stockholm, Sweden; *Int'l*, pg. 1288
Kwa, C.S., Chm. Bd.--Exxon Trading Asia Pacific Private Limited, Singapore, Singapore; *U.S. Public*, pg. 602
Kwak, A.C., Chm.--BolsWessanen Nederland BV, Amstelveen, Netherlands; *Int'l*, pg. 751
Kwan, Yip Kwok, Chm.--DBS Securities Nominees (HK) Ltd., Queensway, Hong Kong; *Int'l*, pg. 351
Kwan, Yip Kwok, Chm.--DBS Securities Philippines, Inc., Manila, Philippines; *Int'l*, pg. 351
Kwok, Walter, Chm. Bd. & Chief Exec.--Sun Hung Kai Properties Ltd., Wan Chai, Hong Kong; *Int'l*, pg. 1318
Kyburz, Jules, Chm. Bd.--Migros, Zurich, Switzerland; *Int'l*, pg. 865
Kyu, Mong, Chm. Bd.--Hyundai Motor Company, Seoul, Korea; *Int'l*, pg. 641
L'Arnaud, J. C., Chm. Bd.--Banque Bonnasse, Marseilles, France; *Int'l*, pg. 563
La Crosse, James E., Chm. Bd. & Chief Exec. Officer--National Wine & Spirits Corp., Indianapolis, IN; *U.S. Private*, pg. 788
La Motta, Joseph M., Chm. Bd.--OppenheimerFunds Distributor, Inc., New York, NY; *U.S. Private*, pg. 818
La Rosa, Donald S., Chm. Bd.--La Rosa's, Inc., Cincinnati, OH; *U.S. Private*, pg. 640
La Tour d'Artaise, Thierry, Chm. Bd.--Calor S.A., Lyon, France; *Int'l*, pg. 568
La Valle, Pier Giorgio, Chm. Bd.--Caboto Holding Societa di Intermediazione Mobiliare S.p.A., Milan, Italy; *Int'l*, pg. 138
LaBarge, Pierre, III, Chm. Bd. & Pres.--LaBarge Pipe & Steel Company, Saint Louis, MO; *U.S. Private*, pg. 641
Labatt, Blair P., Chm. Bd.--Labatt Food Service, San Antonio, TX; *U.S. Private*, pg. 641
Labovitz, George H., Dr., Chm. Bd.--Organizational Dynamics Inc., Burlington, MA; *U.S. Private*, pg. 819
LaBow, Ronald, Chm. Bd.--WHX Corporation, New York, NY; *U.S. Public*, pg. 1726
Lacob, Joe, Chm. Bd.--CellPro, Incorporated, Bothell, WA; *U.S. Public*, pg. 320
Lacourciere, William J., Chm. Bd., Pres. & Chief Exec. Officer--Novametrix Medical Systems Inc., Wallingford, CT; *U.S. Public*, pg. 1203
LaCrosse, Jim, Chm. Bd.--NWS Inc., Chicago, IL; *U.S. Private*, pg. 772
Lacy, Andre B., Chm. Bd., Pres. & Chief Exec. Officer--LDI, Ltd., Indianapolis, IN; *U.S. Private*, pg. 639
Lacy, James, Chm. Bd.--Gilliam Candy Brands, Edwardsville, KS; *U.S. Private*, pg. 454
Lacy, Roane, Chm. Bd.--Plantation Foods Inc., Waco, TX; *U.S. Private*, pg. 869
Lacy, William H., Chm. Bd. & Chief Exec. Officer--Mortgage Guaranty Insurance Corporation, Milwaukee, WI; *U.S. Public*, pg. 1026
Ladd, Jeffrey R., Chm. Bd.--Metra Commuter Rail, Chicago, IL; *U.S. Private*, pg. 919
Ladegaard, Axel, Chm. Bd.--Nykredit, Copenhagen, Denmark; *Int'l*, pg. 993
Ladly, Frederick B., Chm. Bd.--United Health, Inc., Milwaukee, WI; *Int'l*, pg. 468
Lafferty, Cinda, Chm. Bd.--Wheeler Brothers Grain Co., Watonga, OK; *U.S. Private*, pg. 1171
Lafitte, Darrell M., Chm. Bd.--Compass Bank Dallas, Richardson, TX; *U.S. Public*, pg. 419
LaFrance, Stephen, Chm. Bd. & Pres.--Stephen LaFrance Holdings, Inc., Pine Bluff, AR; *U.S. Private*, pg. 642
LaFrance, Stephen L., Chm. Bd. & Pres.--Super D Drugs Acquisition Co., Pine Bluff, AR; *U.S. Private*, pg. 642
Lagaese, John, Chm. Bd.--Central Grocers Co-op, Franklin Park, IL; *U.S. Private*, pg. 223
Lagardere, Jean-Luc, Mng. Partner & Gen. Mgr.--Lagardere Groupe, Paris, France; *Int'l*, pg. 791
Laguera, Eugenio Garza, Chm. Bd.--Fomento Economico Mexicano, S.A. de CV, Monterrey, Mexico; *Int'l*, pg. 496
Lahav, Gideon, Chm. Bd.--Israel Discount Bank Ltd., Tel Aviv, Israel; *Int'l*, pg. 645
LaHaye, Frank W.T., Chm. Bd.--Quarterdeck Corp., Marina Del Rey, CA; *U.S. Public*, pg. 1350
Lahti, Peter H., Chm. Bd., Pres. & Chief Exec. Officer--Kirkpatrick Pettis Smith Polian, Inc., Omaha, NE; *U.S. Private*, pg. 770
Laibe, John, Chm. Bd.--Acheson Industries, Inc., Port Huron, MI; *U.S. Private*, pg. 12
Laing, J.M.K., Sir, Chm. Bd.--John Laing PLC, London, United Kingdom; *Int'l*, pg. 796
Lainson, Hal, Chm. Bd.--Dutton-Lainson Co., Hastings, NE; *U.S. Private*, pg. 350
Lakin, James E., Chm. Bd.--Timpte Industries, Inc., Denver, CO; *U.S. Private*, pg. 1088
Lakin, Lewis, Owner--Lakin General Corporation, Chicago, IL; *U.S. Private*, pg. 644
Lama, Rudolph E., Pres. & Chief Exec. Officer--Tony Lama Co., Inc., El Paso, TX; *U.S. Public*, pg. 937
Lamb, Fritz, Dr., Chm.-Supervisory Bd.--Aesculap Aktiengesellschaft, Tuttlingen, Germany; *Int'l*, pg. 29
Lamb, Isabelle S., Chm. Bd., Pres. & Treas.--Enterprises International Inc., Hoquiam, WA; *U.S. Private*, pg. 377
Lamb, Robert E., II, Chm. Bd.--Robert E. Lamb, Inc., Valley Forge, PA; *U.S. Private*, pg. 644
Lambert, Phelps L., Chm. Bd.--Farmers Bank & Trust Co., Henderson, KY; *U.S. Public*, pg. 1217
Lambert, Robert, Chm. Bd.--Aviall, Inc., Dallas, TX; *U.S. Public*, pg. 154
Lambert, Thomas W., Chm. Bd.--Camtronics Ltd., Hartland, WI; *U.S. Public*, pg. 109
Lamberti, Donald F., Chm. Bd. & Chief Exec. Officer--Casey's General Stores, Inc., Ankeny, IA; *U.S. Public*, pg. 312
Lambesis, Nicholas, Chm. Emeritus & Founder--Lambesis, Del Mar, CA; *U.S. Private*, pg. 644
Lambrinides, Lambert N., Chm. Bd.--Skyline Chili, Inc., Fairfield, OH; *U.S. Public*, pg. 1475
Lammle, Guy M., Chm. Bd., Pres. & Chief Exec. Officer--NxTrend Technology, Inc., Colorado Springs, CO; *U.S. Private*, pg. 809
Lamond, Pierre R., Chm. Bd.--Vitesse Semiconductor Corporation, Camarillo, CA; *U.S. Public*, pg. 1723
Lamoreux, F. Holmes, Chm. Bd., Pres. & Chief Exec. Officer--Sabreliner Corporation, Saint Louis, MO; *U.S. Private*, pg. 959
Lamotte, C., Chm. Bd.--Banque Scalbert Dupont, Lille, France; *Int'l*, pg. 563
Lamoure, Jean-Pierre, Chm. Bd. & Pres.--Forasol S.A., Velizy-Villacoublay, France; *Int'l*, pg. 496
Lamphere, Gilbert H., Chm. Bd.--Illinois Central Corporation, Chicago, IL; *U.S. Public*, pg. 864
Lampl, F.W., Chm. Bd.--Bovis Construction Group, Harrow, United Kingdom; *Int'l*, pg. 1032
Lampl, Frank, Chm. Bd.--Bovis Construction Ltd., Harrow, United Kingdom; *Int'l*, pg. 1032
Lampropoulos, Fred P., Chm. Bd., Pres. & Chief Exec. Officer--Merit Medical Systems, Inc., South Jordan, UT; *U.S. Public*, pg. 1096
Lampton, Leslie B., Sr., Chm. Bd. & Pres.--Ergon, Inc., Jackson, MS; *U.S. Private*, pg. 380
Lan Ma, Sue, Chm. Bd., Pres. & Chief Exec. Officer--Elwell-Parker Limited, Cleveland, OH; *U.S. Private*, pg. 373
Lancaster, Jeremy, Chm. Bd.--Rexam PLC, London, United Kingdom; *Int'l*, pg. 1106
Lancaster, Jeremy, Chm. Bd. & Mng. Dir.--Wolseley Plc., Droitwich, United Kingdom; *Int'l*, pg. 1511
Lancaster, Patrick R., III, Chm. Bd.--Lantech Inc., Louisville, KY; *U.S. Private*, pg. 650
Lance, P., Chm. Bd.--Glaxo Pharmaceuticals UK Ltd., Uxbridge, United Kingdom; *Int'l*, pg. 552
Land, John, Chm. Bd.--M.M. Cohn Co., Inc., Little Rock, AR; *U.S. Private*, pg. 346
Landau, Roy, Chm. Bd.--Landau Building Co., Wexford, PA; *U.S. Private*, pg. 646
Landegger, C.C., Chm. Bd.--The Black Clawson Company, New York, NY; *U.S. Private*, pg. 147
Landegger, George, Chm. Bd.--Parsons & Whittemore, Inc., Rye Brook, NY; *U.S. Private*, pg. 840
Lander, Raymond A., Jr., Chm. Bd.--Cambridge Industries, Inc., Lapeer, MI; *U.S. Private*, pg. 202
Landguth, Daniel P., Chm. Bd. & Chief Exec. Officer--Black Hills Corporation, Rapid City, SD; *U.S. Public*, pg. 235
Landis, Donald, Chm. Bd.--United Credit Corp. & Patroit Funding, New York, NY; *U.S. Private*, pg. 1121
Landon, R. Kirk, Chm. Bd.--American Bankers Insurance Group, Inc., Miami, FL; *U.S. Public*, pg. 67
Landowsky, Klaus, Chm.--Berliner Hypotheken-und Pfandbriefbank AG, Berlin, Germany; *Int'l*, pg. 159
Landsberger, David, Chm. Bd. & Chief Exec. Officer--Bel-Art Products, Pequannock, NJ; *U.S. Private*, pg. 130
Landstrom, Ed, Chm. Bd.--Research, Incorporated, Eden Prairie, MN; *U.S. Public*, pg. 1382
Landuyt, William M., Chm. Bd. & Chief Exec. Officer--Millennium Chemicals Inc., Iselin, NJ; *U.S. Public*, pg. 1111
Lane, Clifford, Chm. Bd., Pres. & Chief Exec. & Chief Oper. Officer--ILC Industries, Inc., Bohemia, NY; *U.S. Private*, pg. 555
Lane, James G., Jr., Chm. Bd., Pres. & Chief Exec. Officer--Synalloy Corporation, Spartanburg, SC; *U.S. Public*, pg. 1547
Lane, William, Chm. Bd. & Chief Exec. Officer--Atlas Electric Devices Co., Chicago, IL; *U.S. Private*, pg. 96
Lane, William N., III, Chm. Bd., Pres. & Chief Exec. Officer--Lane Industries, Inc., Northbrook, IL; *U.S. Private*, pg. 649
Lane, William N., III, Chm. Bd.--General Binding Corporation, Northbrook, IL; *U.S. Public*, pg. 707
Lang, Brien, Chm. Bd.--Span-America Medical Systems Inc., Greenville, SC; *U.S. Public*, pg. 1495
Lang, Frederick W., Chm. Bd.--AIC-FSS Advertising, Minneapolis, MN; *U.S. Private*, pg. 5
Lang, Frederick W., Chm. Bd. & Chief Exec. Officer--Analysts International Corporation, Minneapolis, MN; *U.S. Public*, pg. 110
Lang, Gordon S., Chm. Bd.--CCL Industries, Inc., Willowdale, Canada; *Int'l*, pg. 238
Lang, Henry S., Chm. Bd. & Chief Exec. Officer--Home Juice Co., Melrose Park, IL; *U.S. Private*, pg. 537
Lang, Hugh, Chm. Bd.--Brammer plc, Altrincham, United Kingdom; *Int'l*, pg. 212
Langan, Kevin, Pres.--Northway Motorcar Corporation, Latham, NY; *U.S. Private*, pg. 806
Langbein, Thomas K., Chm. Bd., Pres. & Chief Exec. Officer--Medicore Inc., Hialeah, FL; *U.S. Public*, pg. 1080
Langbein, Thomas K., Chm. Bd. & Chief Exec. Officer--Techdyne, Inc., Hialeah, FL; *U.S. Public*, pg. 1080
Langbo, Arnold G., Chm. Bd. & Chief Exec. Officer--Kellogg Company, Battle Creek, MI; *U.S. Public*, pg. 947
Lange, Paul L., Chm. Bd., Pres. & Chief Exec. Officer--Dynamic Materials Corporation, Lafayette, CO; *U.S. Public*, pg. 539
Langelaang, Rick, Chm.--Communicatie & Design, Wassemaar, Netherlands; *Int'l*, pg. 1335
Langen, Wayne, Chm. Bd.--American Crystal Sugar Company, Moorhead, MN; *U.S. Private*, pg. 52
Langer, Horst, Dr., Chm. Bd.--Siemens Corporation, New York, NY; *Int'l*, pg. 1245
Langman, Harry, Chm. Bd.--Meyer International PLC, London, United Kingdom; *Int'l*, pg. 864
Langner, Jay B., Chm. Bd. & Chief Exec. Officer--Hudson General Corporation, Great Neck, NY; *U.S. Public*, pg. 845
Langone, Kenneth G., Chm. Bd.--Salem National Corporation, Winston Salem, NC; *U.S. Private*, pg. 962
Laniak, Dave, Chm. Bd. & Chief Exec. Officer--ACC Corp., Rochester, NY; *U.S. Public*, pg. 2
Lanier, J.L., Jr., Chm. Bd. & Chief Exec. Officer--Dan River Inc., Danville, VA; *U.S. Public*, pg. 478
Lanigan, John J., Sr., Chm. Bd.--MI-Jack Products, Inc., Hazel Crest, IL; *U.S. Private*, pg. 740
Lanni, J. Terrence, Chm. Bd. & Chief Exec. Officer--MGM Grand, Inc., Las Vegas, NV; *U.S. Public*, pg. 1026
Lansing, Sherry, Chm. Bd., Motion Picture Grp.-Paramount Pictures--National Amusements, Inc., Dedham, MA; *U.S. Private*, pg. 775
Lansing, Sherry, Chm.-Motion Picture Grp.--Paramount Pictures Corporation, Los Angeles, CA; *U.S. Private*, pg. 776
Lanterman, A. Kirk, Chm. Bd.--Holland America Line Westours, Seattle, WA; *U.S. Public*, pg. 306
Lantos, Robert, Chm. Bd. & Chief Exec. Officer--Alliance Communications Corporation, Toronto, Canada; *Int'l*, pg. 57
Lanza, Frank, Chm. Bd. & Chief Exec. Officer--L3 Communications, New York, NY; *U.S. Private*, pg. 638
Lapeyre, Jay, Jr., Chm. & Pres.--The Laitram Corporation, Harahan, LA; *U.S. Private*, pg. 643
Lapides, Robert E., Chm.--United Aluminum Corporation, North Haven, CT, *U.S. Private*, pg. 1120
Lapidot, Zvi, Chm. Bd.--Orbotech Ltd., Yavne, Israel; *Int'l*, pg. 1007
Lapin, Aaron S., Chm. Bd.--Clayton Corporation, Fenton, MO; *U.S. Private*, pg. 244
Lapthorne, Athol, Chm. Bd.--National Mutual Holdings Limited, Melbourne, Australia; *Int'l*, pg. 908
Lapthorne, Athol, Chm. Bd.--The National Mutual Life Association of Australia Limited, Melbourne, Australia; *Int'l*, pg. 909
Lapthorne, R.D., Chm. Bd.--Nycomed Amersham plc, Chalfont Saint Giles, United Kingdom; *Int'l*, pg. 992
Laqerroos, Antii, Chm. Bd.--BTL AB, Goteborg, Sweden; *Int'l*, pg. 123
Laraya, Rogelio G., Chm. Bd.--Benguet Ebara Real Estate Corp., Laguna, Philippines; *Int'l*, pg. 187
LaRoche, W. Walter, Chm. Bd.--LaRoche Industries Inc., Atlanta, GA; *U.S. Private*, pg. 651
LaRosa, Joseph, Chm. Bd. & Co-Chief Exec. Officer--Waring & LaRosa, Inc., New York, NY; *U.S. Private*, pg. 1150
Larsen, Ken, Chm. Bd.--Copley Pharmaceuticals, Inc., Canton, MA; *U.S. Public*, pg. 446
Larsen, Ralph S., Chm. Bd., Pres. & Chief Exec. Officer--Johnson & Johnson, New Brunswick, NJ; *U.S. Public*, pg. 927
Larsen, Terrence A., Chm. Bd., Pres. & Chief Exec. Officer--CoreStates Financial Corp., Philadelphia, PA; *U.S. Public*, pg. 446
Larson, Peter N., Chm. Bd. & Chief Exec. Officer--Brunswick Corporation, Lake Forest, IL; *U.S. Public*, pg. 265
Larson, Richard W., Chm. Bd. & Chief Exec. Officer--Bank of America Alaska, N.A., Anchorage, AK; *U.S. Public*, pg. 180
Larson, Stanley E., Chm. Bd.--High Plains Corporation, Wichita, KS; *U.S. Public*, pg. 825
Larson, William L., Chm. Bd. & Chief Exec. Officer--Network Associates, Inc., Santa Clara, CA; *U.S. Public*, pg. 1168
Lasater, Robert, Chm. Bd.--Cosmolab Div., Lewisburg, TN; *U.S. Private*, pg. 629
Laskawy, Philip A., Chm. Bd. & Chief Exec. Officer--Ernst & Young, LLP, New York, NY; *U.S. Private*, pg. 381
Laskowski, Richard E., Chm. Bd.--Ace Hardware Corporation, Oak Brook, IL; *U.S. Private*, pg. 12
Lasky, David, Chm. Bd. & Pres.--Curtiss-Wright Corp., Lyndhurst, NJ; *U.S. Public*, pg. 469
Lassiter, Phillip B., Chm. Bd., Pres. & Chief Exec. Officer--AMBAC Financial Group, Inc., New York, NY; *U.S. Public*, pg. 62
Lassiter, Ronald C., Chm. Bd. & Chief Exec. Officer--Daniel Industries, Inc., Houston, TX; *U.S. Public*, pg. 482
Latham, Daniel W., Chm. Bd.--Coyote Network Systems, Inc., Westlake Village, CA; *U.S. Public*, pg. 455
Latham, Katherene, Chm. Bd.--The Sands Regent, Reno, NV; *U.S. Public*, pg. 1431
Latner, Albert J., Chm. Bd. & Chief Exec. Officer--Dynacare, Inc., Toronto, Canada; *Int'l*, pg. 425
Latshaw, John, Chm. Bd. & Chief Exec. Officer--Latshaw Enterprises, Inc., Wichita, KS; *U.S. Public*, pg. 979
Latzka, Ernst, Chm.--Leo Burnett & Wirz, Vienna, Austria; *U.S. Private*, pg. 184
Lau, Thomas L.H., Chm. Bd.--Gemstar International Group Limited, Pasadena, CA; *U.S. Public*, pg. 705
Lauder, Estee, Founding Chm. Bd.--Estee Lauder Companies Inc., New York, NY; *U.S. Public*, pg. 594
Lauder, Leonard A., Chm. Bd. & Chief Exec. Officer--Estee Lauder Companies Inc., New York, NY; *U.S. Public*, pg. 594
Laughlin, William, Chm. Bd. & Chief Exec. Officer--Unisource, Minneapolis, MN; *U.S. Public*, pg. 1671
Laughton, A.W., Chm. Bd., Pres. & Mng. Dir.--British Trimmings Ltd., Stockport, United Kingdom; *U.S. Public*, pg. 434
Laughton, H.J., Chm. Bd.--Laughton & Sons, Ltd., Birmingham, United Kingdom; *Int'l*, pg. 804
Laup, Paul, Chm. Bd.--Springfield Precision Instruments, Inc., Wood Ridge, NJ; *U.S. Private*, pg. 1027

Lauren, Ralph, Chm. Bd.--Polo/Ralph Lauren Corporation, New York, NY; *U.S. Private*, pg. 874
Lauren, Ralph, Chm. Bd.--Polo/Ralph Lauren, Lyndhurst, NJ; *U.S. Private*, pg. 875
Lausell, Miguel D., Esq., Chm. Bd.--PonceBank, F.S.B., Ponce, PR; *U.S. Public*, pg. 1316
Lautermilch, Eldon, Chm. Bd.--SaskPower, Regina, Canada; *Int'l*, pg. 1195
Laviec, Gerard, Chm. Bd. & Chief Exec. Officer--CFM International SA, Paris, France; *Int'l*, pg. 1166
Lavin, Leonard H., Chm. Bd.--Alberto-Culver Company, Melrose Park, IL; *U.S. Public*, pg. 37
Law-Smith, David J., Chm. Bd., Pres. & Chief Exec. Officer--Caltex Petroleum Corporation, Irving, TX; *U.S. Public*, pg. 348
Law, Irving D., Jr., Chm. Bd. & Chief Exec. Officer--Broadcast Supply Worldwide, Inc., Tacoma, WA; *U.S. Private*, pg. 170
Law, Jordan, Chm. Bd., Pres. & Chief Exec. Officer--KTI, Orange, CA; *U.S. Public*, pg. 939
LaWarre, William M., Chm. Bd. & Chief Exec. Officer--Northlich Stolley LaWarre, Cincinnati, OH; *U.S. Private*, pg. 806
Lawless, R.E., Chm. Bd.--Central Vermont Railway, Inc., Saint Albans, VT; *Int'l*, pg. 258
Lawrence, David, Dr., Chm. Bd. & Chief Exec. Officer--Kaiser Permanente, Oakland, CA; *U.S. Private*, pg. 605
Lawrence, David, Jr., Chm. Bd. & Publisher--The Miami Herald, Miami, FL; *U.S. Public*, pg. 964
Lawrence, Frederick D., Chm. Bd., Pres. & Chief Exec. Officer--California Microwave, Inc., Sunnyvale, CA; *U.S. Public*, pg. 293
Lawrence, Michael L., Chm. Bd. & Chief Exec. Officer--Ameritruck Distribution Corporation, Fort Worth, TX; *U.S. Private*, pg. 65
Laws, Dean R., Chm.--Lois/EJL Los Angeles, Los Angeles, CA; *U.S. Private*, pg. 673
Laws, Dean R., Chm.--EJL Advertising/Los Angeles, Los Angeles, CA; *U.S. Private*, pg. 673
Laws, Dean R., Chm. Bd.--Lois/EJL Los Angeles, Los Angeles, CA; *U.S. Public*, pg. 1011
Lawson-Johnston, Peter, Chm. Bd.--Zemex Corporation, Toronto, Canada; *Int'l*, pg. 1523
Lawson, A. Lowell, Exec. V.P., Chm. Bd. & Chief Exec. Officer-Raytheon E-Systems--Raytheon Company, Lexington, MA; *U.S. Public*, pg. 1364
Lawson, H. Richard, Chm. Bd.--Lawson Software, Minneapolis, MN; *U.S. Private*, pg. 654
Lawson, Lowell, A., Chm. Bd. & Chief Exec. Officer--Raytheon E-Systems, Greenville, TX; *U.S. Public*, pg. 1365
Lawson, William A., Chm. Bd.--Newcor, Inc., Bloomfield Hills, MI; *U.S. Public*, pg. 1176
Lawson, William H., Chm. Bd. & Chief Exec. Officer--Franklin Electric Co., Inc., Bluffton, IN; *U.S. Public*, pg. 679
Lay, B. Allen, Chm. Bd., Pres. & Chief Exec. Officer--Westbrae Natural, Inc., Carson, CA; *U.S. Public*, pg. 774
Lay, Joe L., Jr., Chm. Bd., Pres. & Chief Exec. Officer--Lay's Fine Foods, Knoxville, TN; *U.S. Private*, pg. 655
Lay, Kenneth L., Chm. Bd. & Chief Exec. Officer--Enron Corp., Houston, TX; *U.S. Public*, pg. 584
Laycock, M., Chm. Bd.--Taylor Woodrow Construction Holdings Limited, Southall, United Kingdom; *Int'l*, pg. 1358
Layden, A.J., Chm. Bd. & Chief Exec. Officer--Allright Corporation, Houston, TX; *U.S. Private*, pg. 42
Lazarini, Gary L., Chm. Bd.--Commerce Investment Corporation, Memphis, TN; *U.S. Public*, pg. 1155
Lazarus, Charles, Chm. Bd.--Toys "R" Us, Inc., Paramus, NJ; *U.S. Public*, pg. 1626
Lazarus, Shelly, Chm. Bd. & Chief Exec. Officer--Ogilvy & Mather Worldwide, Inc., New York, NY; *Int'l*, pg. 1483
Le Clercq, Jacques, Chm. Bd.--Super Discount Markets, Inc., Lithia Springs, GA; *Int'l*, pg. 463
Le Clercq, Jacques, Chm. Bd.--Super Discount Markets, Inc., Lithia Springs, GA; *U.S. Public*, pg. 1540
Lea, George A. Jr., Chm. Bd., Pres. & Chief Exec. Officer--The Mad Butcher, Inc., Pine Bluff, AR; *U.S. Private*, pg. 693
Lea, Scott C., Chm. Bd.--Lance, Inc., Charlotte, NC; *U.S. Public*, pg. 977
Leach, C.G.R., Chm.--Jardine Insurance Services Limited, London, United Kingdom; *Int'l*, pg. 705
Leach, Philip F., Chm. Bd.--Leach & Garner Company, North Attleboro, MA; *U.S. Private*, pg. 655
Leaf, Robert S., Chm.-Intl. (London)--Burson-Marsteller, New York, NY; *U.S. Private*, pg. 1197
Leafstedt, Douglas A., Chm. Bd. & Chief Exec. Officer--AFSA Data Corp., Long Beach, CA; *U.S. Public*, pg. 649
Leahy, John, Sir, Chm. Bd.--Lonrho plc, London, United Kingdom; *Int'l*, pg. 817
Leander, Henry A., Chm. Bd.--Ford Meter Box Company, Wabash, IN; *U.S. Private*, pg. 418
Leatherdale, D.W., Chm. Bd., Pres. & Chief Exec. Officer--The St. Paul Companies, Inc., Saint Paul, MN; *U.S. Public*, pg. 1429
LeBlond, Daniel W., Chm. Bd.--Makino Inc., Mason, OH; *Int'l*, pg. 831
LeBoeuf, Raymond W., Chm. Bd. & Chief Exec. Officer--PPG Industries, Inc., Pittsburgh, PA; *U.S. Public*, pg. 1245
Lebovitz, Charles B., Chm. Bd., Pres. & Chief Exec. Officer--CBL & Associates Properties, Inc., Chattanooga, TN; *U.S. Public*, pg. 273
LeBow, Bennett S., Chm. Bd., Pres. & Chief Exec. Officer--Brooke Group Ltd., Miami, FL; *U.S. Public*, pg. 259
LeBow, Bennett S., Chm. Bd., Pres. & Chief Exec. Officer--BGLS Inc., Miami, FL; *U.S. Public*, pg. 259
Lechler, Howard, Chm. Bd.--Cives Corporation, Roswell, GA; *U.S. Private*, pg. 241
Leclabart, Vincent, Chm. & Pres.--Australie, Levallois-Perret, France; *Int'l*, pg. 600
LeClair, Darryl A., Chm. Bd., Pres. & Chief Exec. Officer--Echelon International Corporation, Saint Petersburg, FL; *U.S. Public*, pg. 560
LeClair, J. Maurice, Chm. Bd.--Sceptre Resources Limited, Calgary, Canada; *Int'l*, pg. 1203
Leclerc, Edouard, Chm. Bd.--Leclerc, Issy-les-Moulineaux, France; *Int'l*, pg. 805
Leclerc, Robert L., Chm. Bd. & Chief Exec. Officer--Echo Bay Mines Ltd., Englewood, CO; *U.S. Public*, pg. 561
Ledecky, Jonathan J., Chm. Bd.--U.S. Office Products Company, Washington, DC; *U.S. Public*, pg. 1686
Lee, Andrew, Chm. Bd., Pres. & Chief Oper. Officer--Daniel Caron Sportswear, New York, NY; *U.S. Private*, pg. 309
Lee, Benjamin C., Jr., Chm. Bd.--KLLM Transport Services, Inc., Jackson, MS; *U.S. Public*, pg. 939
Lee, Cater, Chm. Bd.--Vulcan Inc., Foley, AL; *U.S. Private*, pg. 1144
Lee, Charles, Chm. Bd.--New Tai Milk Products Co. Ltd., Taipei, Taiwan; *Int'l*, pg. 923
Lee, Charles R., Chm. Bd., Chief Exec. Officer & Chief Oper. Officer--GTE Corporation, Stamford, CT; *U.S. Public*, pg. 696
Lee, Chong-Moon, Chm. Bd.--Diamond Multimedia Systems, Inc., San Jose, CA; *U.S. Public*, pg. 505
Lee, Choon Lim, Chm.--Hyundai Heavy Industries Co., Ltd., Ulsan, Korea; *Int'l*, pg. 641
Lee, David B., Chm. Bd. & Chief Exec. Officer--Omega Financial Corporation, State College, PA; *U.S. Public*, pg. 1222
Lee, Frank, Chm. Bd.--Valley Pontiac Buick GMC, Inc., Auburn, WA; *U.S. Private*, pg. 1132
Lee, Gladyce, Chm. Bd.--Lee Grocery Company, Everett, WA; *U.S. Private*, pg. 657
Lee, H.J., Chm. Bd.--Zenith Electronics Corp., Glenview, IL; *U.S. Public*, pg. 1790
Lee, Harry F., Chm. Bd.--C.R. Daniels, Inc., Ellicott City, MD; *U.S. Private*, pg. 310
Lee, James C., Jr., Chm. Bd.--Buffalo Rock Company, Birmingham, AL; *U.S. Private*, pg. 179
Lee, Jane, Chm. Bd.--Red Devil Inc., Union, NJ; *U.S. Private*, pg. 915
Lee, Joe R., Chm. Bd. & Chief Exec. Officer--Darden Restaurants, Inc., Orlando, FL; *U.S. Public*, pg. 483
Lee, John J., Chm. Bd. & Chief Exec. Officer--Hexcel Corporation, Pleasanton, CA; *U.S. Public*, pg. 824
Lee, K., Chm. Bd. & Chief Exec. Officer--CAM International Holdings Ltd., Singapore, Singapore; *Int'l*, pg. 238
Lee, K.J., Chm.--Sharp Korea Corporation (Inchon), Inchon, Korea; *Int'l*, pg. 1230
Lee, Kun-Hee, Chm. Bd.--Samsung Group, Seoul, Korea; *Int'l*, pg. 1181
Lee, Leighton, II, Chm. Bd.--Lee Company, Westbrook, CT; *U.S. Private*, pg. 657
Lee, M.S., Chm. Bd. & Chief Exec. Officer--Houston Fearless 76 Inc., Compton, CA; *U.S. Private*, pg. 542
Lee, Mike, Chm., Pres. & Chief Exec. Officer--Famous Restaurants Inc., Scottsdale, AZ; *U.S. Private*, pg. 393
Lee, Patrick P., Chm. Bd.--Enidine Incorporated, Orchard Park, NY; *U.S. Private*, pg. 377
Lee, Rhoady R., Jr., Chm. Bd. & Chief Exec. Officer--Lakeside Industries, Issaquah, WA; *U.S. Private*, pg. 644
Lee, Richard, Dr., Chm. Bd.--The Apparel Group, Ltd., Louisville, KY; *U.S. Private*, pg. 78
Lee, Robert Y., Chm. Bd. & Chief Exec. Officer--Video City Inc., Bakersfield, CA; *U.S. Public*, pg. 1719
Lee, Ronald G., Chm. Bd. & Pres.--Lee Pharmaceuticals, South El Monte, CA; *U.S. Public*, pg. 984
Lee, Steven J., Chm. Bd. & Chief Exec. Officer--PolyMedica Industries, Inc., Woburn, MA; *U.S. Public*, pg. 1315
Lee, T.P., Chm. Bd.--Jinwoong Inc., San Jose, CA; *Int'l*, pg. 707
Lee, Terry G., Chm. Bd. & Chief Exec. Officer--Bell Sports Corp., San Jose, CA; *U.S. Public*, pg. 207
Lee, Thomas L., Chm. Bd. & Chief Exec. Officer--The Newhall Land And Farming Company, Valencia, CA; *U.S. Public*, pg. 1178
Lee, Yoon Hee, Chm. & Mng. Dir.--Cho Hung Bank Luxembourg S.A., Luxembourg, Luxembourg; *Int'l*, pg. 288
Lee, Yoon-Jae, Chm.--Xiamen Jinwoong Enterprise Co., Ltd., Xiamen, China; *Int'l*, pg. 707
Lee, Yoon-Jae, Chm.--Jinwoong Hong Kong Ltd., Hong Kong, Hong Kong; *Int'l*, pg. 707
Lee, Youn-Jae, Chm. Bd. & Chief Exec. Officer--Jinwoong Inc., Seoul, Korea; *Int'l*, pg. 706
Lee, Youn-Jae, Chm.--Jinwoong Lanka (Pvt) Ltd., Ja-Ela, Sri Lanka; *Int'l*, pg. 707
Lee, Youn-Jae, Chm.--Quest Leisure Products (Aust) Pty. Ltd., Glen Iris, Australia; *Int'l*, pg. 707
Leeb, Peter, Chm. Bd. & Chief Exec. Officer--King Wire Inc., North Chicago, IL; *U.S. Private*, pg. 621
Leebern, Donald, Jr., Chm. Bd.--Georgia Crown Distributing, Columbus, GA; *U.S. Private*, pg. 448
Leebow, Steven, Chm. Bd., Pres. & Chief Exec. Officer--Pacesetter Steel Service, Inc., Kennesaw, GA; *U.S. Private*, pg. 830
Leech, James W., Chm.--Unigas, Calgary, Canada; *Int'l*, pg. 1492
Leedom, John N., Sr., Chm. Bd., Chief Exec. Officer--Wholesale Electronic Supply, Dallas, TX; *U.S. Private*, pg. 1174
Leeds, Gerard G., Co-Chm. Bd.--CMP Media, Inc., Manhasset, NY; *U.S. Public*, pg. 279
Leeds, Lilo J., Co-Chm. Bd.--CMP Media, Inc., Manhasset, NY; *U.S. Public*, pg. 279
Leeds, Richard, Chm. Bd. & Chief Exec. Officer--Global Direct Mail Corp, Port Washington, NY; *U.S. Public*, pg. 747
Leeds, Robert K., Chm. Bd. & Pres.--Jewelmont Corporation, Minneapolis, MN; *U.S. Private*, pg. 587
Leemans, Michel F., Chm. Bd., Pres. & Chief Exec. Officer--IL International Inc., Stratford, CT; *U.S. Public*, pg. 855
Lees, David, Sir, Chm. Bd.--Courtaulds plc, London, United Kingdom; *Int'l*, pg. 338
Lees, David, Sir, Chm. Bd.--GKN plc, Redditch, United Kingdom; *Int'l*, pg. 534
Leever, Harold, Chm. Bd.--MacDermid Incorporated, Waterbury, CT; *U.S. Public*, pg. 1029
Lefebre, H., Chm.--Kali-Chemie Aktiengesellschaft, Hannover, Germany; *Int'l*, pg. 1278
Lefebvre, Richard, Chm. Bd.--Axent Technologies, Rockville, MD; *U.S. Public*, pg. 157
Leff, Joseph, Chm. Bd.--National Spinning Co., Inc., New York, NY; *U.S. Private*, pg. 786
Leff, Martin J., Chm. Bd., Pres. & Chief Fin. Officer--Carole Wren, Inc., New York, NY; *U.S. Private*, pg. 1192
Lefferts, Peter A., Chm. Bd.--IDS Trust Co., Minneapolis, MN; *U.S. Public*, pg. 73
Lefkowitz, Leopold, Chm. Bd.--Crystal Clear Industries, Ridgefield Park, NJ; *U.S. Private*, pg. 293
LeFrak, Samuel J., Chm. Bd.--Lefrak Organization Inc., Rego Park, NY; *U.S. Private*, pg. 658
Leghari, Sardor Noor Ilahi, Chm. Bd.--Pakistan International Airlines Corporation, Karachi, Pakistan; *Int'l*, pg. 1021
Lego, Paul, Chm. Bd.--Commonwealth Industries, Inc., Louisville, KY; *U.S. Public*, pg. 415
Legorreta Chauvet, Eduardo, Chm. Bd.--Grupo Video Visa S.A. de C.V., Mexico, Mexico; *Int'l*, pg. 577
Lehman, Chris, Chm. Bd., Pres. & Chief Exec. Officer--SRDS, Des Plaines, IL; *U.S. Private*, pg. 958
Lehman, Kenneth A., Co-Chm. Bd.--Fel-Pro Incorporated, Skokie, IL; *U.S. Private*, pg. 399
Lehmann, Durwood C., Chm. Bd.--Brance Krachy Company, Inc., Houston, TX; *U.S. Private*, pg. 165
Lehmann, Eckart, Dr., Chm. Bd.--Knorr-Bremse Systeme Fur Schienenfahrzeuge GmbH, Munich, Germany; *Int'l*, pg. 738
Lehmann, John, Chm. Bd.--Butterick Company, Inc., New York, NY; *U.S. Private*, pg. 190
Lehr, Donald A., Chm. Bd., Chief Exec. Officer, Treas. & Sec.--Cubix Corporation, Carson City, NV; *U.S. Private*, pg. 294
Lehr, Gustav J., Chm. Bd.--Shelter Mutual Insurance Company, Columbia, MO; *U.S. Private*, pg. 992
Leibinger, Berthold, Chm. Bd.--Trumpf Inc., Farmington, CT; *U.S. Private*, pg. 1108
Leibler, Ken, Chm. Bd.--Keyport Life Insurance Company, Boston, MA; *U.S. Private*, pg. 666
Leibovitz, Mitchell G., Chm. Bd., Pres. & Chief Exec. Officer--The Pep Boys-Manny, Moe & Jack, Philadelphia, PA; *U.S. Public*, pg. 1276
Leigh, Robert S., Chm. Bd.--Eurodis Electron PLC, Reigate, United Kingdom; *Int'l*, pg. 1247
Leighton, Charles M., Chm. Bd. & Chief Exec. Officer--CML Group, Inc., Acton, MA; *U.S. Public*, pg. 279
Leiser, G. Malcolm, Chm. Bd.--California Custom Foods, Lodi, CA; *U.S. Private*, pg. 831
Leitch, A.P., Chm. Bd.--Eagle Star, Cheltenham, United Kingdom; *Int'l*, pg. 110
Leiting, Denis E., Chm. Bd. & Pres.--Ag Processing Inc., A Cooperative, Omaha, NE; *U.S. Private*, pg. 26
Lekach, Ilia, Chm. Bd.--L. Luria & Son, Inc., Medley, FL; *U.S. Public*, pg. 1020
Lekach, Ilia, Chm. Bd. & Chief Exec. Officer--Parlux Fragrances Inc., Fort Lauderdale, FL; *U.S. Public*, pg. 1264
Leland, David D., Chm. Bd.--Plum Creek Timber Co., L.P., Seattle, WA; *U.S. Public*, pg. 1311
Lemaire, Bernard, Chm. Bd.--The Cascades Group, Kingsey Falls, Canada; *Int'l*, pg. 273
Lemasters, John N., Chm. Bd. & Chief Exec. Officer--Augat, Inc., Mansfield, MA; *U.S. Public*, pg. 1597
Lemieux, Joseph H., Chm. Bd. & Chief Exec. Officer--Owens-Illinois, Inc., Toledo, OH; *U.S. Public*, pg. 1238
Lemke, Paul G., Sr., Chm. Bd.--Thruway Fasteners Inc., North Tonawanda, NY; *U.S. Private*, pg. 1084
Lemley, Jack, Chm. Bd., Pres. & Chief Exec. Officer--American Ecology Corporation, Boise, ID; *U.S. Public*, pg. 71
Lemman, Robert L., Chm. Bd.--North Coast Electric Company, Bellevue, WA; *U.S. Private*, pg. 804
Lemon, James H., Jr., Chm. Bd. & Chief Exec. Officer--Johnston, Lemon & Co. Inc., Washington, DC; *U.S. Private*, pg. 595
Lempka, Arnold, M.D., Chm. Bd.--Physicians Mutual Insurance Co., Omaha, NE; *U.S. Private*, pg. 864
Lengyel, Jeno, Chm.--Petroli Hungary KFT, Budapest, Hungary; *Int'l*, pg. 428
Lenz, Randolph W., Chm. Bd.--FWD/Seagrave Fire Apparatus, Inc., Clintonville, WI; *U.S. Private*, pg. 390
Lenzie, Charles A., Chm. Bd., Pres. & Chief Exec. Officer--Nevada Power Company, Las Vegas, NV; *U.S. Public*, pg. 1169
Leonard, J.L., Dr., Chm. Bd.--Eurotherm plc, Horsham, United Kingdom; *Int'l*, pg. 465
Leone, Lucas J., Chm. Bd.--Eggland's Best, Inc., King of Prussia, PA; *U.S. Private*, pg. 366
Leong, Ng Kim, Chm.--DBS Finance Nominees Pte. Ltd., Singapore, Singapore; *Int'l*, pg. 350
Leong, Ng Kim, Chm.--DBSF Investments Pte. Ltd., Singapore, Singapore; *Int'l*, pg. 351
Leong, Ng Kim, Chm.--DBSF Holdings Pte Ltd., Singapore, Singapore; *Int'l*, pg. 351
Leonhard, Lothar, Chm.-Germany/Frankfurt--Ogilvy & Mather Worldwide, Inc., New York, NY; *Int'l*, pg. 1483
Leonis, John, Chm.Bd. & Chief Exec. Officer--Amecom Div., College Park, MD; *U.S. Public*, pg. 1002
Leonis, John M., Chm. Bd. & Chief Exec. Officer--Litton Industries, Inc., Woodland Hills, CA; *U.S. Public*, pg. 1002
Leonsis, Ted, Chm. Bd., Chief Exec. Officer, Pres. & New Bus. Contact--Redgate Communications Corp., Vero Beach, FL; *U.S. Public*, pg. 66
Leopold, Ernest S., Chm. Bd., Pres. & Chief Exec. Officer--Crown Vantage Inc., Oakland, CA; *U.S. Public*, pg. 465
Lepage, Albert R., Chm. Bd.--Lepage Bakery, Inc., Auburn, ME; *U.S. Private*, pg. 660

LePage, Bernard, Chm. Bd.--Christian Memorial Cultural Center, Rochester Hills, MI; *U.S. Private*, pg. 238

Lepeuple, Gerard, Chm. Bd.--SEP Inc., Wilmington, DE; *Int'l*, pg. 1166

LePore, Patrick G., Chm. Bd., Pres. & Chief Exec. Officer--Boron LePore Group, Fair Lawn, NJ; *U.S. Public*, pg. 246

Leprino, James G., Chm. Bd.--Leprino Foods, Denver, CO; *U.S. Private*, pg. 660

Lerner, Alfred, Chm. Bd. & Chief Exec. Officer--MBNA Corporation, Wilmington, DE; *U.S. Public*, pg. 1023

Lerner, Martin, Chm. Bd., Pres. & Treas.--American List Corporation, Mineola, NY; *U.S. Public*, pg. 1481

Lerner, Michael, Chm. Bd. & Chief Exec. Officer--Safety 1st, Inc., Chestnut Hill, MA; *U.S. Public*, pg. 1425

Lerner, Michael H., Chm. Bd., Pres. & Chief Exec. Officer--Marisa Christina Inc., New Hyde Park, NY; *U.S. Public*, pg. 1044

Lervick, Arne T., Chm. Bd. & Chief Exec. Officer--Twin City Foods, Inc., Stanwood, WA; *U.S. Private*, pg. 1111

LeSaffre, Peter, Chm. Bd. & Pres.--Real World, Andover, MA; *U.S. Private*, pg. 913

LeSage, William A., Chm. Bd & Chief Exec. Officer--General Homes Corporation, Houston, TX; *U.S. Private*, pg. 444

Lesage, Yves, Chm. Bd. & Chief Exec. Officer--CGG Group, Massy, France; *Int'l*, pg. 241

Lesage, Yves, Chm. Bd., Pres. & Chief Exec. Officer--Compagnie Generale de Geophysique, Massy, France; *Int'l*, pg. 241

Lesard, Gilles, Chm. Bd.--McCain U.S.A. Inc., Oak Brook, IL; *Int'l*, pg. 850

Lesch, Donald A., Chm. Bd.--Pinnacle Bank, Valparaiso, IN; *U.S. Public*, pg. 1297

Leser, Lawrence A., Chm. Bd.--The E.W. Scripps Company, Cincinnati, OH; *U.S. Public*, pg. 1447

Lesh, Fred, Chm. Bd. & Chief Exec. Officer--Holcomb & Hoke Mfg. Company, Inc., Indianapolis, IN; *U.S. Private*, pg. 533

Leskys, Algirdas G., Chm. Bd.--The Converse Professional Group, Inc., Monrovia, CA; *U.S. Private*, pg. 271

Lessels, Norman, Chm. Bd.--Standard Life Assurance, Edinburgh, United Kingdom; *Int'l*, pg. 1297

Lesser, Richard, Chm. Bd.--Winners Apparel Ltd., Toronto, Canada; *U.S. Public*, pg. 1557

Lester, Stan, Chm. Bd.--California Fresh Apricot Council, San Francisco, CA; *U.S. Private*, pg. 200

Lester, W. Howard, Chm. Bd. & Chief Exec. Officer--Williams-Sonoma, Inc., San Francisco, CA; *U.S. Public*, pg. 1770

Lestina, Robert L., Chm. Bd.--Spartech Plastics, Portage, WI; *U.S. Public*, pg. 1496

Letaw, Harry, Jr., Chm. Bd., Pres. & Chief Exec. Officer--Essex Corporation, Columbia, MD; *U.S. Public*, pg. 593

Leuenberger, Rolf, Chm.--Argo AG, Mohlin, Switzerland; *Int'l*, pg. 329

Leuenberger, Rolf, Chm.--CWK AG, Winterthur, Switzerland; *Int'l*, pg. 329

Leuenberger, Rolf, Chm.--OK Coop AG, Allschwil, Switzerland; *Int'l*, pg. 330

Leuenberger, Rolf, Chm.--Konsum Verein Zurich AG, Zurich, Switzerland; *Int'l*, pg. 330

Leung Ding-Bong, Ronald, Chm. Bd.--Kwong On Bank, Limited, Central, Hong Kong; *Int'l*, pg. 521

Leuthy, Fritz, Chm.--Coop Bern, Bern, Switzerland; *Int'l*, pg. 329

Leva, J.R., Chm. Bd.--Jersey Central Power & Light Co., Morristown, NJ; *U.S. Public*, pg. 695

Levan, Alan B., Chm. Bd., Pres. & Chief Exec. Officer--BankAtlantic Bancorp, Inc., Fort Lauderdale, FL; *U.S. Public*, pg. 183

LeVan, David M., Chm. Bd., Pres. & Chief Exec. Officer--Conrail, Inc., Philadelphia, PA; *U.S. Public*, pg. 431

Levan, David M., Chm. Bd., Pres. & Chief Exec. Officer--CRR Industries, Inc., Philadelphia, PA; *U.S. Public*, pg. 432

Levantin, Allen M., Chm. Bd. & Chief Exec. Officer--Todays Temporary, Inc., Dallas, TX; *U.S. Public*, pg. 277

Levene, David A., Chm. Bd., Pres. & Chief Exec. Officer--Metropolitan Insurance & Annuity Co., New York, NY; *U.S. Private*, pg. 737

Levene, David A., Chm. Bd., Pres. & Chief Exec. Officer--Metropolitan Tower Life Insurance Co., New York, NY; *U.S. Private*, pg. 737

Levene, David A., Chm. Bd.--Texas Life Insurance Company, Waco, TX; *U.S. Private*, pg. 738

Leventis, Harry K., Chm. Bd.--Southern Pump & Tank Company, Charlotte, NC; *U.S. Private*, pg. 1017

Lever, Roy, Chm. & Chief Exec. Officer--GAN General Insurance Company, Burlington, Canada; *Int'l*, pg. 564

Lever, Roy, Chm. & Chief Exec. Officer--The Gan Company of Canada Ltd., Burlington, Canada; *Int'l*, pg. 564

Levesque, Joseph, Chm. Bd., Pres. & Chief Exec. Officer--Aetrium Inc., Saint Paul, MN; *U.S. Public*, pg. 27

Levesque, Marcel, Chm. Bd.--LaSalle Bank Westmont, Westmont, IL; *Int'l*, pg. 10

Levey, Barry J., Chm. Bd.--First Financial Bancorp, Hamilton, OH; *U.S. Public*, pg. 632

Leviant, Jacques, Chm. Bd.--ICD Group International Inc., New York, NY; *U.S. Private*, pg. 554

Levin, Gerald M., Chm. Bd. & Chief Exec. Officer--Time Warner Inc., New York, NY; *U.S. Public*, pg. 1610

Levin, Gilbert V., Dr., Chm., Pres., Chief Exec. Officer & Treas.--Biospherics Incorporated, Beltsville, MD; *U.S. Public*, pg. 232

Levin, Jerry, Chm. Bd.--The Cosmetic Center Inc., Columbia, MD; *U.S. Private*, pg. 689

Levin, Jerry, Chm. & Chief Exec. Officer--The Coleman Company, Inc., Golden, CO; *U.S. Private*, pg. 690

Levin, Jerry W., Chm.--Revlon, Inc., New York, NY; *U.S. Private*, pg. 689

Levin, Ralph, Chm. Bd. & Pres.--Sturgis Iron & Metal Company, Inc., Sturgis, MI; *U.S. Private*, pg. 1048

Levin, Shlomo, Chm. Bd.--Egged Israel Transport Cooperative Society Ltd., Tel Aviv, Israel; *Int'l*, pg. 435

Levine, Leon, Chm. Bd. & Treas.--Family Dollar Stores, Inc., Matthews, NC; *U.S. Public*, pg. 612

Levine, Sol, Chm.--Revlon Research Center, Inc., Edison, NJ; *U.S. Private*, pg. 690

Levine, William H., Chm. Bd.--Western Corporate Enterprises Inc., Vancouver, Canada; *Int'l*, pg. 1494

Levine, William S., Chm. Bd.--Outdoor Systems, Inc., Phoenix, AZ; *U.S. Public*, pg. 1235

Levins, Buck, Chm. Bd.--Credit Union National Association, Madison, WI; *U.S. Private*, pg. 288

Levy-Lang, Andre, Chm. Bd.--Compagnie Financiere de Paribas, Paris, France; *Int'l*, pg. 319

Levy, Arthur A., Chm. Bd.--Robert Fleming, Inc., New York, NY; *Int'l*, pg. 493

Levy, D.G., Chm. Bd.--Levy Security Corp., Chicago, IL; *U.S. Private*, pg. 664

Levy, Girard, Chm. Bd.--Air Liquide America Corporation, Houston, TX; *Int'l*, pg. 37

Levy, Joe, Chm. Bd. & Chief Exec. Officer--Gottschalks Inc., Fresno, CA; *U.S. Public*, pg. 754

Levy, Kenneth, Chm. Bd.--KLA Tencor Corporation, San Jose, CA; *U.S. Public*, pg. 939

Levy, Laurence S., Chm. Bd.--High Voltage Engineering Corporation, Wakefield, MA; *U.S. Private*, pg. 528

Levy, Lawrence F., Chm. Bd.--The Levy Organization, Chicago, IL; *U.S. Private*, pg. 664

Levy, Leon, Chm. Bd.--Avatar Holdings Inc., Coral Gables, FL; *U.S. Public*, pg. 151

Levy, Lester A., Chm. Bd.--NCH Corporation, Irving, TX; *U.S. Public*, pg. 1145

Levy, Michael R., Chm. Bd. & Publr.--Mediatex Communications Corporation, Austin, TX; *U.S. Private*, pg. 727

Levy, Philip J., Chm. Bd.--Jacob Levy & Bros., Inc., Louisville, KY; *U.S. Private*, pg. 664

Levy, Richard D., Chm. Bd. & Chief Exec. Officer--Oriole Homes Corp., Delray Beach, FL; *U.S. Public*, pg. 1230

Levy, Shemaya, Chm. & Chief Exec. Officer-Renault Group--Renault, Boulogne-Billancourt, France; *Int'l*, pg. 1102

Levys, Isaac A., Chm. Bd.--Level Export Sales Corp., New York, NY; *U.S. Private*, pg. 662

Lewin, Joseph, Chm. Bd., Pres. & Chief Exec. Officer--Health Products Corporation, Yonkers, NY; *U.S. Private*, pg. 514

Lewinton, Christopher, Sir, Chm.--TI Group plc, Abingdon, United Kingdom; *Int'l*, pg. 1337

Lewis, Bill, Chm. Bd. & Chief Exec. Officer--Staffing Solutions, Boulder, CO; *U.S. Private*, pg. 1028

Lewis, Brian, Chm.--Roltra-Morse S.p.A., Turin, Italy; *U.S. Public*, pg. 857

Lewis, Byron E., Chm. Bd. & Chief Exec. Officer--Uniworld Group, Inc., New York, NY; *U.S. Private*, pg. 1128

Lewis, Charles, Chm, Pres, & Chief Exec. Officer--The Check Store, Lakewood, CO; *U.S. Public*, pg. 785

Lewis, Clive, Joint Chm.--Lewis Gace Bozell Healthcare Worldwide, Fort Lee, NJ; *U.S. Public*, pg. 1642

Lewis, David E., Chm. Bd.--Gyyr, Inc., Anaheim, CA; *U.S. Public*, pg. 1212

Lewis, George T., Chm. Bd.--Cogentrix Incorporated, Charlotte, NC; *U.S. Private*, pg. 249

Lewis, Harriet G., Chm. Bd.--Gerber Plumbing Fixtures Corporation, Chicago, IL; *U.S. Private*, pg. 449

Lewis, Harriet G., Chm. Bd.--Kokomo Sanitary Pottery Corp., Kokomo, IN; *U.S. Private*, pg. 449

Lewis, Jewell M., Chm. Bd.--MAC America Communications, Inc., Phoenix, AZ; *U.S. Private*, pg. 685

Lewis, John C., Chm. Bd.--Amdahl Corporation, Sunnyvale, CA; *Int'l*, pg. 527

Lewis, Kevin, Chm. Bd.--Furr's/Bishops, Inc., Lubbock, TX; *U.S. Public*, pg. 689

Lewis, Leslie B., Chm. Bd., Pres. & Chief Exec. Officer--Asahi/America, Inc., Malden, MA; *U.S. Public*, pg. 137

Lewis, Loida Nicolas, Chm. Bd.--TLC Beatrice International Holdings Inc., New York, NY; *U.S. Private*, pg. 1064

Lewis, M.D., Chm. & Chief Exec. Officer--Northwestern Growth Corp., Sioux Falls, SD; *U.S. Public*, pg. 1201

Lewis, M.D., Chm.--Cornerstone Propane G.P. Inc., Watsonville, CA; *U.S. Public*, pg. 1201

Lewis, M.D., Chm. & Chief Exec. Officer--Northwestern Energy Corp., Huron, SD; *U.S. Public*, pg. 1201

Lewis, M.D., Chm. & Chief Exec. Officer--Nekota Resources Inc., Huron, SD; *U.S. Public*, pg. 1201

Lewis, Marilyn Ware, Chm. Bd.--American Water Works Company, Inc., Voorhees, NJ; *U.S. Public*, pg. 95

Lewis, Martin R., Chm. Bd. & Chief Exec. Officer--Williamhouse-Regency, Inc., New York, NY; *U.S. Public*, pg. 89

Lewis, Merle D., Chm. Bd., Pres. & Chief Exec. Officer--Northwestern Public Service, Huron, SD; *U.S. Public*, pg. 1200

Lewis, Peter, Chm.--Ashtead Group PLC, Leatherhead, United Kingdom; *Int'l*, pg. 88

Lewis, Peter B., Chm. Bd., Pres. & Chief Exec. Officer--The Progressive Corporation, Cleveland, OH; *U.S. Public*, pg. 1334

Lewis, R. Jack, Sr., Chm. Bd.--Lewis Brothers Bakeries, Inc., Evansville, IN; *U.S. Private*, pg. 665

Lewis, Ralph M., Chm. Bd.--Lewis Homes Management Corp., Upland, CA; *U.S. Private*, pg. 665

Lewis, Richard H., Chm. Bd., Pres., Chief Exec. & Fin. Officer & Treas.--Prima Energy Corporation, Denver, CO; *U.S. Public*, pg. 1325

Lewis, William, Chm. Bd., Pres. & Chief Exec. Officer--Career Blazers Inc., New York, NY; *U.S. Private*, pg. 209

Lewitt, Wilfred G., Chm. Bd.--MDS Inc., Etobicoke, Canada; *Int'l*, pg. 826

Lexa, M., Chm. & Mng. Dir.--ANTEA SA, Orleans, France; *Int'l*, pg. 607

Ley, Anthony J., Chm. Bd., Pres. & Chief Exec. Officer--Harmonic Lightwaves, Sunnyvale, CA; *U.S. Public*, pg. 788

Leysen, A., Chm. Bd.--Agfa-Gevaert N.V., Antwerp, Belgium; *Int'l*, pg. 174

Lezin, Norman S., Chm. Bd.--Salz Leathers, Inc., Santa Cruz, CA; *U.S. Private*, pg. 963

Lhomme, Pierre, Chm.--Lhomme S.A., Pont-sur-Yonne, France; *U.S. Public*, pg. 1487

Li, David K.P., Chm. Bd.--Oakreed Financial Services Limited, Hong Kong, Hong Kong; *Int'l*, pg. 817

Liang, Goh Cheng, Chm. Bd.--Liang Court Holdings Ltd., Singapore, Singapore; *Int'l*, pg. 807

Liang, Marcel, Chm. Bd. & Chief Exec. Officer--ASI Corp., Fremont, CA; *U.S. Private*, pg. 8

Liao, Duke, Chm. Bd., Pres. & Chief Exec. Officer--Liuski International, Inc., Norcross, GA; *U.S. Public*, pg. 1005

Liautaud, James P., Chm. Bd. & Chief Exec. Officer--Capsonic Group, Inc., Elgin, IL; *U.S. Private*, pg. 207

Liban, G., Chm. Bd. & Chief Exec. Officer--Heresite Protective Coatings Inc., Manitowoc, WI; *U.S. Private*, pg. 523

Libby, Darald R., Co.-Chm. Bd.--David Clark Company Incorporated, Worcester, MA; *U.S. Private*, pg. 242

Libby, Henry G., Chm. Bd. & Pres.--The Disston Co., Greensboro, NC; *U.S. Public*, pg. 950

Libertiny, Attila G., Chm. Bd., Pres. & Chief Exec. Officer--Seneca Falls Technology Group, Seneca Falls, NY; *U.S. Private*, pg. 984

Libonati, Berardino, Chm. Bd.--Banco di Sicilia, Rome, Italy; *Int'l*, pg. 140

Lichtenberger, H. William, Chm. Bd. & Chief Exec. Officer--Praxair Inc., Danbury, CT; *U.S. Public*, pg. 1319

Lichtenstein, Seymour, Chm. Bd.--Garan, Incorporated, New York, NY; *U.S. Public*, pg. 703

Liddy, Richard, Chm. Bd.--Security Mutual Life Insurance Co. of New York, Binghamton, NY; *U.S. Private*, pg. 981

Liddy, Richard A., Chm. Bd., Pres. & Chief Exec. Officer--General American Life Insurance Co., Saint Louis, MO; *U.S. Private*, pg. 443

Lidow, Eric, Chm. Bd., Pres. & Chief Oper. Officer--International Rectifier Corporation, El Segundo, CA; *U.S. Public*, pg. 906

Liebergesell, Rolf K., Chm. Bd., Pres. & Chief Exec. Officer & Chief Oper. Officer--Farrel Corporation, Ansonia, CT; *U.S. Public*, pg. 614

Lieberman, Harvey, Chm. Bd. & Pres.--Esquire Radio & Electronics Inc., Brooklyn, NY; *U.S. Private*, pg. 383

Lieberthal, Gary, Chm. & Chief Exec. Officer--Columbia TriStar Television, Culver City, CA; *Int'l*, pg. 1282

Liebetrau, Bernd, Chm.--Schleicher & Schuell GmbH, Einbeck, Germany; *Int'l*, pg. 1206

Liebherr, Dipl. W. Ing Hans, Chm. Bd.--Liebherr-International AG, Bulle, Switzerland; *Int'l*, pg. 807

Liebowitz, Leo, Chm. Bd. & Chief Exec. Officer--Getty Petroleum Marketing Inc., Jericho, NY; *U.S. Public*, pg. 740

Lienau, Anthony, Chm. Bd. & Chief Exec. Officer--Trend Offset Printing Services, Los Alamitos, CA; *U.S. Private*, pg. 1099

Lienhard, Fredy A., Chm. Bd. & Pres.--Lista Holding AG, Erlen, Switzerland; *Int'l*, pg. 812

Liesen, Klaus, Dr., Chm. Bd.--Ruhrgas Aktiengesellschaft, Essen, Germany; *Int'l*, pg. 1148

Lieske, C.F., Chm. Bd.--Elkins Constructors, Inc., Jacksonville, FL; *U.S. Private*, pg. 372

Lievense, Robert J., Chm. Bd.--A.C. Nielsen Company, Schaumburg, IL; *U.S. Public*, pg. 1183

Light, Nathan, Chm. Bd., Pres. & Chief Exec. Officer--Sterling Inc., Akron, OH; *Int'l*, pg. 1248

Lightfoot, J.R., Chm.--Dowty Aerospace, Wolverhampton, Wolverhampton, United Kingdom; *Int'l*, pg. 1337

Liguori, Frank N., Chm. Bd. & Chief Exec. Officer--Olsten Corporation, Melville, NY; *U.S. Public*, pg. 1220

Liguori, Frank N., Chm. Bd. & Chief Exec. Officer--Olsten Health Services, Melville, NY; *U.S. Public*, pg. 1221

Lilius, Michael, Chm. Bd.--Gambro AB, Lund, Sweden; *Int'l*, pg. 666

Lim, Eric Ang Teik, Chm.--DBS Nominees Pte. Ltd., Singapore, Singapore; *Int'l*, pg. 350

Lim, Eric Ang Teik, Chm.--DBS Trustee Ltd., Singapore, Singapore; *Int'l*, pg. 351

Lima, Manuel Branco Ferreira, Chm. Bd.--TAP Air Portugal, Newark, NJ; *Int'l*, pg. 1418

Limpe, Anthony T., Chm. Bd.--Petro Chem Development Company, New York, NY; *U.S. Private*, pg. 858

Lin, Feng-Liang, Chm. Bd., Pres. & Chief Exec. Officer--Payless Car Rental System, Inc., Saint Petersburg, FL; *U.S. Private*, pg. 844

Lin, Frank C., Chm. Bd., Pres. & Chief Exec. Officer--Trident Microsystems, Inc., Mountain View, CA; *U.S. Public*, pg. 1637

Lin, P.C., Chm.--Qingdao Rolled Glass Co., Ltd., Qingdao, China; *Int'l*, pg. 1348

Lin, P.F., Chm.--Taiwan Autogalss Industries Corp., Taipei, Taiwan; *Int'l*, pg. 1348

Lin, T.S., Dr., Chm. Bd.--Tatung Corporation, Taipei, Taiwan; *Int'l*, pg. 1357

Lin, Y.C., Chm. Bd.--Taiwan Glass Industry Corp., Taipei, Taiwan; *Int'l*, pg. 1348

Lin, Y.C., Chm.--Qingdao Float Glass Co., Ltd., Qingdao, China; *Int'l*, pg. 1348

Lin, Y.C., Chm.--Chang Jiang Float Glass Co., Ltd., Jiangsu, China; *Int'l*, pg. 1348

Linbeck, Leo E., Jr., Chm. Bd. & Chief Exec. Officer--Linbeck Construction Corp, Houston, TX; *U.S. Private*, pg. 667

Lincoln, Howard, Chm. Bd.--Nintendo of America, Redmond, WA; *Int'l*, pg. 932

Lincoln, Lucian A., Chm. & Chief Exec. Officer--Freeman Energy Corporation, Springfield, IL; *U.S. Public*, pg. 709

Lind, Geoffrey E., Chm. Bd. & Chief Exec. Officer--UMB Bank of the West, N.A., Colorado Springs, CO; *U.S. Public*, pg. 1654

Lind, Geoffrey E., Chm Bd. & Chief Oper. Officer--UMB Bank Colorado, Colorado Springs, CO; *U.S. Public*, pg. 1654

Lindahl, John, Chm. Bd. & Chief Exec. Officer--State Industries Inc., Ashland City, TN; *U.S. Private*, pg. 1036

Lindal, Robert W., Chm. Bd. & Chief Exec. Officer--Lindal Cedar Homes, Inc., Seattle, WA; *U.S. Public*, pg. 998
Lindal, Walter, Sir, Chm. Emeritus & Sec.--Lindal Cedar Homes, Inc., Seattle, WA; *U.S. Public*, pg. 998
Lindberg, Neal, Chm. Bd.--Peoples Electric Contractor, Inc., Saint Paul, MN; *U.S. Private*, pg. 851
Lindell, Hans, Chm. Bd.--ACTIVE BioTech AB, Malmo, Sweden; *Int'l*, pg. 23
Lindenbergh, J.H.M., Chm.--Baring Brothers, London, United Kingdom; *Int'l*, pg. 648
Lindenbergh, J.H.M., Chm. Bd. & Chief Exec. Officer--ING Barings, London, United Kingdom; *Int'l*, pg. 650
Lindenbergh, J.M., Chm.--ING Baring Securities, London, United Kingdom; *Int'l*, pg. 649
Linder, James A., Chm. Bd.--Linder & Associates, Inc., Wichita, KS; *U.S. Private*, pg. 668
Lindermann, George L., Chm. Bd. & Chief Exec. Officer--Southern Union Company, Austin, TX; *U.S. Public*, pg. 1491
Lindgren, Bo-Goran, Chm. Reg. Bd.--ICA Handlarna Norr AB, Umea, Sweden; *Int'l*, pg. 642
Lindner, Carl H., Chm. Bd. & Chief Exec. Officer--American Financial Group, Cincinnati, OH; *U.S. Public*, pg. 74
Lindner, Robert D., Sr., Chm. Bd.--United Dairy Farmers, Inc., Cincinnati, OH; *U.S. Private*, pg. 1121
Lindquist, Berthold, Chm. Bd.--COBE Laboratories, Inc., Lakewood, CO; *Int'l*, pg. 667
Lindsay, Winston S., III, Chm. Bd. & Chief Exec. Officer--Lindsay Manufacturing Inc., Ponca City, OK; *U.S. Private, pg. 668*
Lindsey, Paul S., Chm. Bd. & Chief Exec. Officer--All Star Gas Corporation, Lebanon, MO; *U.S. Private*, pg. 35
Lindsey, W. Fred, Chm. Bd.--Dixie Oil Company, Tifton, GA; *U.S. Private*, pg. 337
Lineberger, James E., Chm.-Exec. Committee--Sensormatic Electronics Corporation, Boca Raton, FL; *U.S. Public*, pg. 1457
Ling, W. O., Chm. Bd.--The Derbyshire (Isle of Man) Ltd., Douglas, United Kingdom; *Int'l*, pg. 395
Ling, William O., Chm.--Derbyshire Building Society, Duffield, United Kingdom; *Int'l*, pg. 394
Linier, J. Hicks, Chm. Bd. & Pres.--Oxford Industries, Inc., Atlanta, GA; *U.S. Public*, pg. 1239
Liniger, Dave, Chm. Bd.--RE/MAX International, Inc., Englewood, CO; *U.S. Private*, pg. 912
Link, James F., Chm.--Texaco Capital Inc., White Plains, NY; *U.S. Public*, pg. 1583
Link, Norman, Chm. Bd. & Chief Exec. Officer--O.P. Link Handle Company, Salem, IN; *U.S. Private*, pg. 668
Link, William J., Ph.D., V.P., Chm. & Chief Exec. Officer--Chiron Vision--Chiron Corporation, Emeryville, CA; *U.S. Public*, pg. 349
Linker, Jonathan, Chm. Bd.--Domain Energy Corporation, Houston, TX; *U.S. Public*, pg. 515
Linsalata, Frank, Chm. Bd.--CFA Holding Company, Charlotte, MI; *U.S. Private*, pg. 194
Linsmayer, Robert M., Chm. Bd.--Villaume Industries, Inc., Saint Paul, MN; *U.S. Private*, pg. 1140
Linton, Doug, Chm.--Ambrose Carr Linton Carroll Inc., Toronto, Canada; *Int'l*, pg. 71
Linton, Larry C., Chm. Bd. & Chief Exec. Officer--Landa, Inc., Portland, OR; *U.S. Private*, pg. 646
Lintz, Richard P., Chm. Bd. & Pres.--Busch Properties, Inc., Saint Louis, MO; *U.S. Public*, pg. 114
Lipke, Brian J., Chm. Bd., Pres. & Chief Exec. Officer--Gibraltar Steel Corp., Buffalo, NY; *U.S. Public*, pg. 742
Lipkin, Gerald H., Chm. Bd., Pres. & Chief Exec. Officer--Valley National Bancorp, Wayne, NJ; *U.S. Public*, pg. 1705
Lipman, Ira A., Chm. Bd. & Pres.--Guardsmark, Inc., Memphis, TN; *U.S. Private*, pg. 486
Lipner, William E., Chm. Bd, Pres. & Chief Exec. Officer--NFO Research, Inc., Greenwich, CT; *U.S. Public*, pg. 1146
Lipper, A., Chm. Bd.--Astre Corporate Group, Alexandria, VA; *U.S. Private*, pg. 93
Lippman, Jerome, Chm. Bd.--Go Jo Industries, Cuyahoga Falls, OH; *U.S. Private*, pg. 458
Lipschultz, William H., Chm. Bd.--Bremer Financial Corporation, Saint Paul, MN; *U.S. Private*, pg. 167
Lipson, Mark L., Chm. Bd. & Chief Exec. Officer--Northstar Investment Management Corporation, Greenwich, CT; *U.S. Public*, pg. 1375
Lipstein, Alan S., Chm. Bd.--Advantage Life Products, Inc., Tampa, FL; *U.S. Public*, pg. 22
Liptak, Greg, Chm.--Product Information Network, Englewood, CO; *U.S. Private*, pg. 597
Lipworth, Sidney, Chm. Bd.--Zeneca Group Plc, London, United Kingdom; *Int'l*, pg. 1524
Lisherness, Harley, Chm. Bd. & Pres.--Roofing Wholesale Co., Inc., Phoenix, AZ; *U.S. Private*, pg. 943
Little, Carole, Co-Chm. Bd.--California Fashion Industries Inc., Los Angeles, CA; *U.S. Private*, pg. 200
Little, Chris, Chm. Bd.--Century Pensions Limited, London, United Kingdom; *Int'l*, pg. 685
Little, Roger G., Chm. Bd., Pres. & Chief Exec. Officer--Spire Corporation, Bedford, MA; *U.S. Public*, pg. 1499
Little, William G., Chm. Bd.--Nation's Business, Washington, DC; *U.S. Private*, pg. 788
Little, William G., Chm. Bd., Pres. & Chief Exec. Officer--The West Company, Incorporated, Lionville, PA; *U.S. Public*, pg. 1755
Littlejohn, B.R., Jr., Chm. Bd.--Community Cash Stores, Spartanburg, SC; *U.S. Private*, pg. 259
Littman, Peter, Prof. Dr., Chm. Bd.--Hugo Boss AG, Metzingen, Germany; *Int'l*, pg. 637
Liu, Lee, Chm. Bd. & Chief Exec. Officer--IES Industries Inc., Cedar Rapids, IA; *U.S. Public*, pg. 855
Liu, Lee, Chm. Bd. & Chief Exec. Officer--IES Utilities Inc., Cedar Rapids, IA; *U.S. Public*, pg. 855
Livingston, Phillip K., Chm. Bd. & Chief Exec. Officer--Deposit Guaranty National Bank of Louisiana, Hammond, LA; *U.S. Public*, pg. 500
Livingston, Robert W., Chm. Bd., Pres. & Chief Exec. Officer--GB Holdings, Jurong, Singapore; *Int'l*, pg. 531
Lizerbram, Sol, Dr., Chm. Bd.--FPA Medical Management, Inc., San Diego, CA; *U.S. Public*, pg. 608
Ljungberg, Robert, Chm. Bd., Pres., Chief Exec. & Chief Oper. Officer--Ultra Tool & Plastics, Inc., Amherst, NY; *U.S. Private*, pg. 1116
Llewellyn, J. Bruce, Chm. Bd.--Philadelphia Coca-Cola Bottling Co., Philadelphia, PA; *U.S. Private*, pg. 861
Lloarch, M.E., Chm. Bd.--Firth-Rixson Plc, Sheffield, United Kingdom; *Int'l*, pg. 487
Llowarch, M.E., Chm. Bd.--Transport Development Group Plc, London, United Kingdom; *Int'l*, pg. 1418
Lloyd-Webber, Andrew, Chm. Bd.--Really Useful Holdings Limited, London, United Kingdom; *Int'l*, pg. 1089
Lloyd, Donna Clayton, Chm. Bd.--Putt Putt Golf Courses of America, Inc., Fayetteville, NC; *U.S. Private*, pg. 896
Lloyd, Harold E., Chm. Bd.--Lloyd Controls, Inc., Mountlake Terrace, WA; *U.S. Private*, pg. 672
Lloyd, Jack M., Chm. Bd., Pres. & Chief Exec. Officer--DenAmerica Corp., Scottsdale, AZ; *U.S. Public*, pg. 498
Lloyd, Richard, Sir, Chm. Bd.--Vickers PLC, London, United Kingdom; *Int'l*, pg. 1466
Lo, Victor Chung Wing, Chm. Bd. & Chief Exec. Officer--Gold Peak Industries (Holdings) Limited, Kwai Chung, Hong Kong; *Int'l*, pg. 537
Lo, Yvonne, Chm. Bd. & Pres.--Vitasoy (U.S.A.) Inc., South San Francisco, CA; *Int'l*, pg. 1469
Loback, Donald R., Chm. Bd. & Chief Exec. Officer--Continental Homes Holding Corp., Scottsdale, AZ; *U.S. Public*, pg. 440
Loban, George B., Co-Chm. Bd. & Pres.--FSF Financial Corp., Hutchinson, MN; *U.S. Public*, pg. 608
Loban, George B., Co-Chm. & Pres.--First Federal FSB, Hutchinson, MN; *U.S. Public*, pg. 608
Lobbia, John E., Chm. Bd. & Chief Exec. Officer--DTE Energy Company, Detroit, MI; *U.S. Public*, pg. 475
Lobel, Edith, Chm. Bd.--Smith-Edwards-Dunlap Company, Philadelphia, PA; *U.S. Private*, pg. 1007
Lobo Morales, Humberto, Chm. Bd.--Grupo Protexa S.A. de C.V., Santa Catarina, Mexico; *Int'l*, pg. 576
Lock, David, Chm. Bd.--Militair Aviation Limited, Ringwood, United Kingdom; *Int'l*, pg. 215
Lockhart, J.W., Chm. Bd. & Chief Exec. Officer--Morgan Grenfell Laurie Ltd., London, United Kingdom; *Int'l*, pg. 405
Lockhart, Michael D., Chm. Bd. & Chief Exec. Officer--General Signal Corporation, Stamford, CT; *U.S. Public*, pg. 726
Lockhart, Wilber, Chm. Bd.--Associated Grocers of the South, Inc., Birmingham, AL; *U.S. Private*, pg. 91
Locks, Gene, Chm. Bd.--ROHN Industries, Inc., Peoria, IL; *U.S. Public*, pg. 1404
Lockwood, Earl F., Chm. Bd., Pres. & Chief Exec. Officer--Betac International Corporation, Alexandria, VA; *U.S. Private*, pg. 140
Lodrini, Ron, Chm.--IMG Services, Harrison, NY; *U.S. Private*, pg. 566
Loeb, David S., Chm. Bd.--INMC Mortgage Holdings, Inc., Pasadena, CA; *U.S. Public*, pg. 857
Loeffler, Martin H., Chm. Bd., Pres. & Chief Exec. Officer--Amphenol Corporation, Wallingford, CT; *U.S. Private*, pg. 629
Loeks, Barry, Co-Chm.--Loews Theatre Management Corp., New York, NY; *Int'l*, pg. 1282
Loeks, Jim, Co-Chm.--Loews Theatre Management Corp., New York, NY; *Int'l*, pg. 1282
Loepfe, Otto, Chm. Bd.--Crossair Ltd., Basel, Switzerland; *Int'l*, pg. 1334
Loescher, Dan G., Chm. Bd.--Mattison Technologies, Inc., Rockford, IL; *U.S. Private*, pg. 714
Loewen, Raymond L., Chm. Bd. & Chief Exec. Officer--The Loewen Group, Inc., Burnaby, Canada; *Int'l*, pg. 814
Logan, Frank G., III, Chm. Bd. & Pres.--Nematron Corp., Ann Arbor, MI; *U.S. Private*, pg. 791
Logan, James D., Chm. Bd.--Microtouch Systems, Inc., Methuen, MA; *U.S. Public*, pg. 1108
Lohier, Gerard, Chm Bd.--BNP-Nouvelle Caledonie, Noumea, New Caledonia; *Int'l*, pg. 164
Lohman, Gordon R., Chm. Bd. & Chief Exec. Officer--Amsted Industries Incorporated, Chicago, IL; *U.S. Private*, pg. 68
Lois, George, Chm. Bd. & Co-Chief Exec. Officer--Lois/USA Inc., New York, NY; *U.S. Public*, pg. 1011
Lois, George, Co-Chm. Bd., Chief Exec. Officer & Worldwide Creative Dir.--Lois/EJL New York, New York, NY; *U.S. Public*, pg. 1011
Lomas, Eric, Chm. Bd.--Rexel, Inc., Coral Gables, FL; *Int'l*, pg. 1107
Lomax, Kevin, Chm.--Misys PLC, Worcester, United Kingdom; *Int'l*, pg. 870
Lombardi, Carl A., Chm. Bd. & Chief Exec. Officer--SpaceLabs Medical, Inc., Redmond, WA; *U.S. Public*, pg. 1494
Lombardi, Guido, Chm. Bd.--Ranchers Cotton Oil, Fresno, CA; *U.S. Private*, pg. 908
London, J.P., Dr., Chm. Bd., Pres. & Chief Exec. Officer--CACI International Inc, Arlington, VA; *U.S. Public*, pg. 272
Lonergan, William R., Chm. Bd.--Zitel Corporation, Fremont, CA; *U.S. Public*, pg. 1793
Long, Donald J., Chm. Bd. & Chief Exec. Officer--Imperial, Inc., Green Bay, WI; *U.S. Private*, pg. 558
Long, Robert M., Chm. Bd. & Chief Exec. Officer--Longs Drug Stores Corporation, Walnut Creek, CA; *U.S. Public, pg. 1013*
Long, Robert R., Chm. Bd. & Chief Exec. Officer--SunTrust Banks of Georgia, Inc., Atlanta, GA; *U.S. Public*, pg. 1538
Long, William D., Chm. Bd. & Pres.--Waremart Inc., Boise, ID; *U.S. Private*, pg. 1150
Long, Zelma, Chm. Bd., Pres. & Chief Exec. Officer--Simi Winery, Healdsburg, CA; *Int'l*, pg. 781
Longfield, Craig N., Chm. Bd., Pres. & Chief Exec. Officer--PacifiCorp Financial Services, Inc., Portland, OR; *U.S. Public*, pg. 1252
Longfield, William H., Chm. Bd. & Chief Exec. Officer--C.R. Bard, Inc., Murray Hill, NJ; *U.S. Public*, pg. 189
Longhurst, Andrew, Chm. Bd.--Cheltenham & Gloucester plc, Gloucester, United Kingdom; *Int'l*, pg. 283
Longmire, Dennis B., Chm. Bd. & Chief Exec. Officer--Darling International, Inc, Irving, TX; *U.S. Public*, pg. 484
Loomis, Warren, Chm. Bd.--Logic Associates, Inc., White River Junction, VT; *U.S. Private*, pg. 673
Loon, Goon Kok, Chm. Bd.--CWT Distribution Limited, Singapore, Singapore; *Int'l*, pg. 246
Loon, Oon Kum, Chm.--DBS Trading Pte. Ltd., Singapore, Singapore; *Int'l*, pg. 351
Loonen, P.J.H.M., Chm.-Supervisory Bd.--Campina Melkunie BV, Zaltbommel, Netherlands; *Int'l*, pg. 254
Loos, A.W., Chm. Bd. & Pres.--Loos & Co., Inc., Pomfret, CT; *U.S. Private*, pg. 675
Loos, Arthur E., Chm. Bd.--Evans Adhesive Corp., Columbus, OH; *U.S. Private*, pg. 384
Loosli, Hansueli, Chm.-Exec. Committee--Coop Switzerland, Basel, Switzerland; *Int'l*, pg. 329
Loosli, Hansueli, Chm.--Impo Import Parfumerien AG, Zurich, Switzerland; *Int'l*, pg. 330
Lopez, Francisco Luzon, Chm.--Argentaria Corporacion Bancaria de Espana, S.A., Madrid, Spain; *Int'l*, pg. 80
Lopker, Pamela Meyer, Chm. Bd. & Pres.--QAD Inc, Carpinteria, CA; *U.S. Public*, pg. 1345
Lora, Jose Manuel, Chm. Bd. & Pres.--Editorial Planeta - DeAgostini, S.A., Barcelona, Spain; *Int'l*, pg. 433
Lorch, George A., Chm. Bd. & Chief Exec. Officer--Armstrong World Industries, Inc., Lancaster, PA; *U.S. Public*, pg. 131
Lord, Richard J., Chm.--The Lord Group, New York, NY; *U.S. Private*, pg. 325
Lorentzen, Erling, Chm. Bd.--Aracruz Celulose S.A., Rio de Janeiro, Brazil; *Int'l*, pg. 78
Lorentzen, Erling S., Chm. Bd.--Northern Navigation International Inc., Greenwich, CT; *U.S. Private*, pg. 805
Lorimer, Desmond, Sir, Chm. Bd.--Northern Bank Limited, Belfast, United Kingdom; *Int'l*, pg. 906
Loring, John C., Chm. Bd.--Astrex, Inc., Plainview, NY; *U.S. Public*, pg. 141
Loring, John C., Chm. Bd.--Avest, Inc., Plainview, NY; *U.S. Public*, pg. 141
Loring, Scott R., Chm. Bd., Pres. & Chief Exec. Officer--Heald Colleges, San Francisco, CA; *U.S. Private*, pg. 514
Lortie, Jean-Paul, Chm. Bd.--Sico Inc., Longueuil, Canada; *Int'l*, pg. 1239
Lorton, Robert, Chm. Bd.--World Publishing Company, Tulsa, OK; *U.S. Private*, pg. 1190
Losada Gomez, Angel, Chm. Bd.--Grupo Gigante S.A. de C.V., Mexico, Mexico; *Int'l*, pg. 574
Losh, J. Michael, Chm. Bd.--General Motors Acceptance Corporation (GMAC), Detroit, MI; *U.S. Public*, pg. 719
Lotman, Herbert, Chm. Bd.--Keystone Foods Corporation, Bala Cynwyd, PA; *U.S. Private*, pg. 619
Lotter, John G.H., Chm. Bd. & Chief Exec. Officer--H.C. Miller Company, Milwaukee, WI; *U.S. Private*, pg. 747
Loucks, Vernon R., Jr., Chm. Bd. & Chief Exec. Officer--Baxter International Inc., Deerfield, IL; *U.S. Public*, pg. 196
Loudermilk, R.C., Sr., Chm. Bd.--Aaron Rents, Inc., Atlanta, GA; *U.S. Public*, pg. 12
Loudon, Aarnout A., Chm. Bd.--Akzo Nobel N.V., Arnhem, Netherlands; *Int'l*, pg. 42
Loughney, Pat, Dr., Chm. Bd.--Batchelors (Ireland) Ltd., Dublin, Ireland; *Int'l*, pg. 968
Louis-Dreyfus, Robert, Chm.-Mngmt. Bd.--Adidas AG, Herzogenaurach, Germany; *Int'l*, pg. 24
Louis-Dreyfus, William, Chm. Bd.--Louis Dreyfus Corporation, Wilton, CT; *U.S. Private*, pg. 342
Louttit, William, Chm. & Chief Exec. Officer-Greater N.Y. Metro Region--The Great Atlantic & Pacific Tea Company, Inc., Montvale, NJ; *Int'l*, pg. 1375
Lovaas, Helen Hudson, Chm. Bd.--Hudson, RCI, Temecula, CA; *U.S. Private*, pg. 546
Love, Gay, Chm. Bd.--Printpack Inc., Atlanta, GA; *U.S. Private*, pg. 886
Lovett, Donald R., Chm. Bd., Pres. & Chief Exec. Officer--AMCORE Bank, Rock River Valley, Dixon, IL; *U.S. Public*, pg. 64
Lovette, George R., Chm. Bd.--Omega Bank, N.A., State College, PA; *U.S. Public*, pg. 1222
Lovstrom, Jan T.R., Chm. Bd.--Ecophon CertainTeed, Inc., Valley Forge, PA; *Int'l*, pg. 1171
Low, Fowler H., Chm. & Chief Exec. Officer--Johnston & Murphy Co., Nashville, TN; *U.S. Public*, pg. 728
Low, K. Prescott, Chm. Bd., Pres. & Publr.--George W. Prescott Publishing Co., Quincy, MA; *U.S. Private*, pg. 882
Lowden, Paul W., Chm. Bd. & Chief Exec. Officer--Santa Fe Gaming Corporation, Las Vegas, NV; *U.S. Public*, pg. 1432
Lowder, Robert E., Chm. Bd. & Chief Exec. Officer--The Colonial BancGroup, Inc., Montgomery, AL; *U.S. Public*, pg. 400
Lowder, Robert E., Chm. Bd. & Chief Exec. Officer--Colonial Bank, Montgomery, AL; *U.S. Public*, pg. 400
Lowe, D.C., Chm. Bd.--Barclays Bank Finance Co. (Guernsey) Ltd., Saint Peter Port, United Kingdom; *Int'l*, pg. 165
Lowe, David L., Chm. Bd.--ADAC Laboratories Inc., Milpitas, CA; *U.S. Public*, pg. 3
Lowe, Frank, Chm.--The Lowe Group, New York, NY; *U.S. Private*, pg. 677
Lowe, Phillip A., Chm. Bd.--Yorkshire Chemicals Plc, Leeds, United Kingdom; *Int'l*, pg. 1522
Lowe, Roger, Chm. Bd.--Affiliated Foods, Inc., Amarillo, TX; *U.S. Private*, pg. 25
Lowe, Thomas P., Chm. Bd.--Lyman Lumber Company, Excelsior, MN; *U.S. Private*, pg. 683

Lowenstein, Irwin L., Chm. Bd. & Chief Exec. Officer--Rhodes, Inc., Atlanta, GA; *U.S. Public*, pg. 805

Lowenthal, A.G., Chm. Bd. & Chief Exec. Officer--Fahnestock Viner Holdings Inc., Toronto, Canada; *Int'l*, pg. 476

Lowenthal, A.G., Chm. Bd.--Freedom Investment, Omaha, NE; *Int'l*, pg. 476

Lower, Martin, Chm. Bd.--Vision One, Norwich, CT; *U.S. Private*, pg. 1141

Lower, Martin A., Pres. & Treas.--Ludlow Textiles Co., Inc., Ludlow, MA; *U.S. Private*, pg. 680

Lowery, Lang, Chm. Bd. & Chief Exec. Officer--Anacomp, Inc., Indianapolis, IN; *U.S. Public*, pg. 106

Lowman, George F., Chm. Bd. & Chief Exec. Officer--Farrell Lines Incorporated, New York, NY; *U.S. Private*, pg. 397

Lowrance, Darrell J., Chm. Bd., Pres. & Chief Exec. Officer--Lowrance Electronics, Inc., Tulsa, OK; *U.S. Public*, pg. 1015

Loyd, Paul B. Jr., Chm. Bd., Pres. & Chief Exec. Officer--Reading & Bates Corporation, Houston, TX; *U.S. Public*, pg. 1354

Loyd, Paul B., Jr., Chm. Bd.--R&B Falcon Corporation, Houston, TX; *U.S. Public*, pg. 1354

Loyez, Jean-Hugues, Chm. Bd., Chief Exec. Officer & Mng. Dir.--Castorama Dubois Investissements S.C.A., Templemars, France; *Int'l*, pg. 275

Loynd, Richard B., Chm. Bd.--Furniture Brands International Inc., Saint Louis, MO; *U.S. Public*, pg. 688

Lozyniak, Andrew, Chm. Bd. & Pres.--Dynamics Corporation of America, Greenwich, CT; *U.S. Public*, pg. 286

Lu, Eugene, Chm. Bd., Pres. & Chief Exec. Officer--Advanced Logic Research, Inc., Irvine, CA; *U.S. Public*, pg. 703

Lubar, Sheldon B., Chm. Bd. & Chief Exec. Officer--Christiana Companies, Inc., Milwaukee, WI; *U.S. Public*, pg. 352

Lubin, Michael A., Chm. Bd.--Lexington Precision Corporation, New York, NY; *U.S. Public*, pg. 991

Lubman, Irving, Chm. Bd. & Chief Oper. Officer--Nu Horizons Electronics Corp., Melville, NY; *U.S. Public*, pg. 1205

Lubner, R., Chm. & Chief Exec. Officer--Plate Glass & Shatterprufe Industries Limited, Satonwold, South Africa; *Int'l*, pg. 1287

Luby, Dallas W., Chm. Bd. & Pres.--Herbert Clough, Inc., New York, NY; *U.S. Public*, pg. 726

Lucas, Donald L., Chm. Bd.--Cadence Design Systems, Inc., San Jose, CA; *U.S. Public*, pg. 290

Lucas, George, Chm. Bd. & Chief Exec. Officer--Lucasfilm Ltd., San Rafael, CA; *U.S. Private*, pg. 679

Lucas, Gregory C., Chm. Bd.--NBD Life Insurance Company, Indianapolis, IN; *U.S. Public*, pg. 628

Lucchese, Alphonse M., Chm. Bd. & Chief Exec. Officer--Davox Corp., Westford, MA; *U.S. Public*, pg. 488

Lucchini, Gherarda, Chm.--Shandwick Marketing Communication Srl, Milan, Italy; *Int'l*, pg. 1227

Lucchini, Luigi, Chm. Bd.--Montedison S.p.A., Milan, Italy; *Int'l*, pg. 324

Lucchini, Luigi C., Chm. Bd. & Pres.--Compart SpA, Milan, Italy; *Int'l*, pg. 324

Luciano, Robert P., Chm. Bd.--Schering-Plough Corporation, Madison, NJ; *U.S. Public*, pg. 1438

Luczo, Stephen J., Chm. Bd., Pres. & Chief Oper. Officer--Seagate Technology Inc., Scotts Valley, CA; *U.S. Public*, *pg. 1449*

Ludgate, Lord Stevens of, Chm. Bd.--United News & Media plc, London, United Kingdom; *Int'l*, pg. 1443

Ludington, Ivan, Jr., Chm Bd. & Chief Exec. Officer--Ludington News Co. Inc., Detroit, MI; *U.S. Private*, pg. 679

Ludwig, J.W., Chm.-Mgmnt. Bd.--Ballast Nedam NV, Amstelveen, Netherlands; *Int'l*, pg. 133

Luger, Donald R., Chm., Pres. & Chief Exec. Officer--Lockwood Greene Engineers, Inc., Spartanburg, SC; *Int'l*, pg. 633

Luhrs, Warren R., Chm.--Hunter Marine Corporation, Alachua, FL; *U.S. Private*, pg. 549

Luigs, C. Russell, Chm. Bd.--Global Marine Inc., Houston, TX; *U.S. Public*, pg. 748

Lukash, Seth, Chm. Bd. & Chief Exec. Officer--Ultimate Technology Corporation, Victor, NY; *U.S. Public*, pg. 1637

Lukash, Seth M., Chm. Bd., Pres. & Chief Exec. Officer--Tridex Corporation, Westport, CT; *U.S. Public*, pg. 1637

Luke, John A., Jr., Chm. Bd. & Chief Exec. Officer--Westvaco Corporation, New York, NY; *U.S. Public*, pg. 1762

Lukeman, Gerald C., Chm. Bd.--ASI Market Research, Inc., Stamford, CT; *U.S. Private*, pg. 554

Lukens, Max L., Chm. Bd., Pres. & Chief Exec. Officer--Baker Hughes Incorporated, Houston, TX; *U.S. Public*, pg. 165

Luksch, James A., Chm. Bd., Pres. & Chief Exec. Officer--Blonder-Tongue Laboratories, Inc., Old Bridge, NJ; *U.S. Public*, pg. 237

Lumpkin, Richard A., Chm. Bd.--Consolidated Communications, Mattoon, IL; *U.S. Public*, pg. 1073

Lumwalt, Elmo R., Jr., Adm., Chm. Bd.-Fleet Aerospace Inc.--Aeronca, Inc., Middletown, OH; *Int'l*, pg. 829

Lund, Allan W., Chm. Bd.--Lund International Holdings, Inc., Anoka, MN; *U.S. Public*, pg. 1020

Lund, Olof, Chm.--Celsius Invest AB, Eskilstuna, Sweden; *Int'l*, pg. 276

Lund, Russell T., III, Chm. Bd., Pres. & Chief Exec. Officer--Lund Food Holdings, Inc., Edina, MN; *U.S. Private*, pg. 680

Lund, Victor L., Chm. Bd. & Chief Exec. Officer--American Stores Company, Salt Lake City, UT; *U.S. Public*, pg. 92

Lundberg, Fredrik, Chm. Bd.--Mo och Domsjo AB, Stockholm, Sweden; *Int'l*, pg. 885

Lundgren, Gary, Chm. Bd. & Sec.--Interpacific Investors Services, Seattle, WA; *U.S. Private*, pg. 572

Lundgren, Terry J., Chm.--Federated Merchandising, New York, NY; *U.S. Public*, pg. 618

Lung, Mervin D., Chm. Bd. & Chief Exec. Officer--Patrick Industries Inc., Elkhart, IN; *U.S. Public*, pg. 1264

Lunn, S., Chm.--Lucas Sumitomo Brakes Inc., Lebanon, OH; *Int'l*, pg. 819

Lunsford, W. Bruce, Chm. Bd., Pres. & Chief Exec. Officer--Vencor, Inc., Louisville, KY; *U.S. Public*, pg. 1711

Lunt, Denham C., Jr., Chm. Bd.--Rogers, Lunt & Bowlen Co., Greenfield, MA; *U.S. Private*, pg. 939

Luntz, John R., Chm. Bd.--Luntz Corporation, Canton, OH; *U.S. Private*, pg. 681

Lupberger, Ed, Chm. Bd., Pres. & Chief Exec. Officer--Entergy Corporation, New Orleans, LA; *U.S. Public*, pg. 585

Lupberger, Edwin, Chm. Bd. & Chief Exec. Officer--Entergy Arkansas, Inc., Little Rock, AR; *U.S. Public*, pg. 586

Lupberger, Edwin, Chm. Bd. & Chief Exec. Officer--Entergy Mississippi, Inc., Jackson, MS; *U.S. Public*, pg. 586

Lupberger, Edwin, Chm. Bd.--Entergy Gulf States, Inc., Beaumont, TX; *U.S. Public*, pg. 586

Lupinetti, Alexander R., Chm., Pres. & Chief Exec. Officer--CSP Inc., Billerica, MA; *U.S. Public*, pg. 283

Luptak, Jerry D., Chm. Bd.--Armada Corporation, Detroit, MI; *U.S. Private*, pg. 82

Lupton, John T., Chm. Bd.--The Arnold Palmer Golf Company, Ooltewah, TN; *U.S. Public*, pg. 132

Luscinski, Steven, Chm. Bd., Chief Fin. Officer & V.P.-Fin./Admin.--Accu-Sort Systems, Inc., Telford, PA; *U.S. Private*, pg. 11

Lushkin, Bernard, Chm. Bd.--Bolt Technology Corporation, Norwalk, CT; *U.S. Public*, pg. 244

Luskey, Louis, Chm. Bd.--Luskeys Western Stores, Inc., Fort Worth, TX; *U.S. Private*, pg. 681

Luskin, Jack, Chm. Bd.--Luskin's, Inc., Columbia, MD; *U.S. Private*, pg. 681

Luskin, Meyer, Chm. Bd., Pres. & Chief Exec. Officer--Scope Industries, Santa Monica, CA; *U.S. Public*, pg. 1444

Lussky, R. Fairleigh, Chm. Bd.--Progress Paint Mfg. Co., Louisville, KY; *U.S. Private*, pg. 890

Lussu, Lucio, Chm. Bd.--Nuovo Pignone S.p.a., Florence, Italy; *Int'l*, pg. 990

Lustbader, Edward E., Chm. Bd., Pres., Chief Exec. Officer & Treas.--The P.J. Carlin Construction Company, New Rochelle, NY; *U.S. Private*, pg. 211

Lustine, Burton, Chm. Bd.--Lustine Oldsmobile & Buick, Inc., Hyattsville, MD; *U.S. Private*, pg. 681

Luteijn, David, Chm.-Supvr. Bd.--Heidemij N.V., Arnhem, Netherlands; *Int'l*, pg. 606

Luter, Joseph W., III, Chm. Bd. & Chief Exec. Officer--Smithfield Foods, Inc., Norfolk, VA; *U.S. Public*, pg. 1479

Luter, Joseph W., III, Chm. Bd. & Chief Exec. Officer--Gwaltney of Smithfield, Ltd., Smithfield, VA; *U.S. Public*, pg. 1479

Luter, Joseph W., III, Chm. Bd. & Chief Exec. Officer--The Smithfield Packing Co., Inc., Smithfield, VA; *U.S. Public*, pg. 1479

Luthringshausen, Wayne, Chm. Bd.--Options Clearing Corp., Chicago, IL; *U.S. Private*, pg. 62

Luttmer, Frans P., Chm.-Exec. Bd.--Heidemij N.V., Arnhem, Netherlands; *Int'l*, pg. 606

Lyke, A. Douglas, Chm. Bd.--Lyke Corporation, Ripon, WI; *U.S. Private*, pg. 682

Lyman, James M., Chm. Bd., Pres. & Chief Exec. Officer--G.I. Plastek, Elyria, OH; *U.S. Private*, pg. 435

Lynch, Charles A., Chm. Bd.--Fresh Choice, Inc., Santa Clara, CA; *U.S. Public*, pg. 682

Lynch, Dennis P., Chm. Bd.--Lynch & Mayer, Inc, New York, NY; *U.S. Public*, pg. 998

Lynch, Edward, Chm. Bd.--Pacific Foods, Inc., Kent, WA; *U.S. Private*, pg. 831

Lynch, Harry, Chm. Bd.--Texas Metal Works, Inc., Beaumont, TX; *U.S. Private*, pg. 1078

Lynch, James H., Chm. Bd.--The Sherwood Group, Inc., Jersey City, NJ; *U.S. Public*, pg. 1466

Lynch, John, Chm. Bd. & Chief Exec. Officer--Towers Perrin, New York, NY; *U.S. Private*, pg. 1093

Lynch, Leland T., Chm., Chief Exec. Officer & Mng. Partner--Carmichael Lynch, Inc., Minneapolis, MN; *U.S. Private*, pg. 213

Lynn, C. Stephen, Chm. Bd.--Shoney's, Inc., Nashville, TN; *U.S. Public*, pg. 1467

Lynnes, R. Milton, Chm. & Chief Exec. Officer--Grant/Jacoby, Inc., Chicago, IL; *U.S. Private*, pg. 470

Lynton, Michael, Chm. Bd. & Chief Exec. Officer--Penguin Putnam Inc., New York, NY; *Int'l*, pg. 1027

Lyon, Wayne B., Chm. Bd., Pres. & Chief Exec. Officer--Furnishings International, Inc., Thomasville, NC; *U.S. Private*, pg. 431

Lyon, Wayne B., Chm. Bd., Pres. & Chief Exec. Officer--LifeStyle Furnishings International, Ltd., Thomasville, NC; *U.S. Private*, pg. 431

Lyon, William, Chm. Bd. & Pres.--William Lyon Company, Newport Beach, CA; *U.S. Private*, pg. 684

Lyons, Charles, Chm. Bd. & Chief Exec. Officer--Ascent Entertainment Group, Inc., Denver, CO; *U.S. Public*, pg. 138

Lyons, Donald E., Chm. Bd.--Canisco Resources, Inc., Wilmington, DE; *U.S. Public*, pg. 301

Lyons, Michael J., Chm. Bd. & Chief Exec. Officer--Lyons Lavey Nickel Swift, Inc., New York, NY; *U.S. Public*, pg. 1224

Lyons, W. David, Chm. Bd. & Chief Exec. Officer--Ocelot Energy Inc., Calgary, Canada; *Int'l*, pg. 996

Lyons, Warren R., Chm. Bd.--Avco Financial Services, Costa Mesa, CA; *U.S. Public*, pg. 1589

Lysinger, Rex J., Chm. Bd.--Energen Corporation, Birmingham, AL; *U.S. Public*, pg. 581

Lytel, Ronn K., Chm. Bd. & Chief Exec. Officer--Capstead Mortgage Corporation, Dallas, TX; *U.S. Public*, pg. 303

Lytle, R.D., Chm. Bd., Pres. & Chief Exec. Officer--Star Bronze Company, Alliance, OH; *U.S. Private*, pg. 1034

Maatman, G.L., Chm. Bd.--American Motorists Insurance Co., Long Grove, IL; *U.S. Private*, pg. 614

Maberly, M., Chm. Bd.--Lex Vehicle Leasing Limited, Marlow, United Kingdom; *Int'l*, pg. 910

Mabuchi, Hideo, Chm.--Nippon Sanso Corporation, Tokyo, Japan; *Int'l*, pg. 938

Mac Mahon, Thomas P., Chm. Bd., Pres. & Chief Exec. Office--Laboratory Corp. of America Holdings, Burlington, NC; *U.S. Public*, pg. 973

Mac Phail, B.D., Chm. Bd.--Charlwood Alliance Holdings Ltd., London, United Kingdom; *Int'l*, pg. 1034

Macaleer, R. James, Chm. Bd.--Shared Medical Systems Corporation, Malvern, PA; *U.S. Public*, pg. 1463

MacArthur, Earl W., Dr., Chm. Bd.--Community Bank System, Inc., De Witt, NY; *U.S. Public*, pg. 416

MacArthur, John R., Chm. Bd.--Hammacher, Schlemmer & Co., Inc., Chicago, IL; *U.S. Private*, pg. 497

Macaulay, C.A., Chm. Bd.--Rio Algom Mining Corp., Oklahoma City, OK; *Int'l*, pg. 1118

Maccarone, Roque, Chm. Bd., Pres. & Chief Exec. Officer--Banco de la Nacion Argentina, Buenos Aires, Argentina; *Int'l*, pg. 140

MacCready, Paul, Dr., Chm. Bd. & Chief Exec. Officer--Aerovironment, Inc., Monrovia, CA; *U.S. Private*, pg. 25

MacDonald, David H., Sr. V.P.-Real Estate--The Elder-Beerman Stores Corp., Dayton, OH; *U.S. Private*, pg. 367

MacDonald, E.B., Chm. Bd.--Faribault Foods Inc., Minneapolis, MN; *U.S. Private*, pg. 393

MacDonald, Geoffrey A., Chm. Bd.--Equis Financial Group, Boston, MA; *U.S. Private*, pg. 379

Macdonald, Iain A., Chm. Bd.--SHL Systemhouse Europe Ltd., London, United Kingdom; *Int'l*, pg. 1154

MacDonald, John S., Chm. Bd.--MacDonald Dettwiler & Associates Ltd., Richmond, Canada; *U.S. Public*, pg. 1229

MacDonald, Stewart Gray, Jr., Chm. Bd. & Chief Exec. Officer--Mac-Gray Corporation, Cambridge, MA; *U.S. Public*, pg. 1029

MacDonald, William F., Jr., Chm. Bd., Pres., Chief Exec. & Chief Oper. Officer--Houghton International Inc., Valley Forge, PA; *U.S. Private*, pg. 541

MacDonnell, Russell R., Chm. Bd. & Chief Exec. Officer--Alarmguard Holdings, Inc., Orange, CT; *U.S. Public*, pg. 35

MacDonough, John N., Chm. Bd. & Chief Exec. Officer--Miller Brewing Company, Milwaukee, WI; *U.S. Public*, pg. 1289

MacDougald, James E., Chm. Bd., Chief Exec. Officer & Pres.--ABR Information Services, Inc., Palm Harbor, FL; *U.S. Public*, pg. 2

Maceuzet, Manuel Albarran, Chm. Bd.--Jugos del Valle, S.A. de C.V., Mexico, Mexico; *Int'l*, pg. 716

MacFarlane of Bearsden, Norman, Baron, Chm. Bd.--United Distillers UK Plc, Perth, United Kingdom; *Int'l*, pg. 412

Macfarlane, David K., Chm. Bd.--Spicers Paper Limited, Preston, Australia; *Int'l*, pg. 72

MacFarlane, John C., Chm. Bd., Pres. & Chief Exec. Officer--Otter Tail Power Company, Fergus Falls, MN; *U.S. Public*, pg. 1234

Macfarlane, Peter, Chm. Bd.--Ultra Electronics Holdings plc, Greenford, United Kingdom; *Int'l*, pg. 1431

Machulak, Edward L., Chm. Bd., Pres., Chief Exec. Officer & Chief Oper. Officer--Commerce Group Corp., Milwaukee, WI; *U.S. Public*, pg. 410

MacInnis, Frank T., Chm. Bd. & Chief Exec. Officer--EMCOR Group, Inc., Norwalk, CT; *U.S. Public*, pg. 571

MacIntyre, R. Douglas, Chm. Bd., Pres. & Chief Exec. Officer--Brock International Inc., Atlanta, GA; *U.S. Public*, *pg. 258*

Mack, John E., III, Chm. Bd. & Chief Exec. Officer--Central Hudson Gas & Electric Corporation, Poughkeepsie, NY; *U.S. Public*, pg. 324

Mack, Paul F., Chm. Bd. & Chief Exec. Officer--Mack Printing Company, Easton, PA; *U.S. Private*, pg. 691

Mack, Wolfgang, Chm. Bd.--Wangner Systems Corporation, Greenville, SC; *Int'l*, pg. 1418

MacKenzie, Howard J., Chm. Bd.--Standard Manifold Company, Inc., Chicago, IL; *U.S. Private*, pg. 1031

Mackey, John, Chm. Bd. & Chief Exec. Officer--Whole Foods Market, Inc., Austin, TX; *U.S. Public*, pg. 1767

Mackey, Richard Sr., Chm.--Oliver Oil Company, Inc., Chambersburg, PA; *U.S. Private*, pg. 815

Mackey, William K., Chm. Bd., Pres., Chief Exec. Officer & Treas.--Aqua Care Systems Inc., Coral Springs, FL; *U.S. Public*, pg. 126

Mackie, Greg C., Chm. Bd., Pres. & Chief Exec. Officer--Mackie Designs, Inc., Woodinville, WA; *U.S. Public*, pg. 1030

Mackin, J. Leo, Chm. Bd. & Chief Exec. Officer--Interlock Industries, Inc., Sellersburg, IN; *U.S. Private*, pg. 567

Mackin, J. Stanley, Chm. Bd. & Chief Exec. Officer--Regions Financial Corporation, Birmingham, AL; *U.S. Public*, pg. 1371

Mackin, Joseph L., Chm. Bd.--Metal Sales Manufacturing Corporation, Sellersburg, IN; *U.S. Private*, pg. 567

Mackinlay, J.L., Chm. Bd.--Bradford & Bingley Building Society, Bingley, United Kingdom; *Int'l*, pg. 210

Mackinney, Harold A., Jr., Chm. Bd. & Chief Exec. Officer--Fleet Investment Advisors, Inc., Boston, MA; *U.S. Public*, *pg. 650*

Macklin, Gordon, Chm. Bd.--White River Corporation, White Plains, NY; *U.S. Public*, pg. 1765

MacLaurin, Ian C., Sir, Chm. Bd.--Tesco PLC, Cheshunt, United Kingdom; *Int'l*, pg. 1376

MacLean, Barry L., Chm. Bd., Pres., Chief Exec. & Chief Oper. Officer--Maclean-Fogg Co., Mundelein, IL; *U.S. Private*, pg. 692

Maclean, Donald, Chm. Bd.--Truelove & Maclean Inc., Waterbury, CT; *U.S. Private*, pg. 1107

Macleod, Malcolm W., Chm. Bd., Pres. & Chief Exec. Officer--Jakobson Shipyard, Inc, Greenwich, CT; *U.S. Private*, pg. 760

MacMillan, Whitney, Chm. Bd. & Chief Exec. Officer--Cargill, Wayzata, MN; *U.S. Private*, pg. 210

MacNally, Robert F., Chm.--Tommy Armour Golf, Morton Grove, IL; *U.S. Public,* pg. 1683
MacNeil, M.G., Chm.--Frank R. MacNeill & Son, Inc., Miami, FL; *Int'l,* pg. 705
MacNeil, Norman E., Chm. Bd. & Treas.--Ark-Les Corporation, Stoughton, MA; *U.S. Private,* pg. 82
MacNeill, H. Gordon, Chm. Bd.--Jannock Limited, Toronto, Canada; *Int'l,* pg. 698
MacNeill, H. Gordon, Chm. Bd.--Wajax Limited, Delta, Canada; *Int'l,* pg. 1484
MacPherson, D. C., Chm. Bd.--NatWest Markets Corporate Finance Limited, London, United Kingdom; *Int'l,* pg. 910
MacPherson, Robert W., Chm. Bd. & Chief Exec. Officer--General Latex & Chemical Corporation, Cambridge, MA; *U.S. Private,* pg. 444
Macricostas, Constantine S., Chm. Bd.--Photronics, Inc., Brookfield, CT; *U.S. Public,* pg. 1293
Madanes, Miguel, Chm. Bd. & Pres.--Y.P.F., S.A., Buenos Aires, Argentina; *Int'l,* pg. 1515
Madar, Jean-Philippe, Chm. Bd.--Jean Philippe Fragrances, Inc., New York, NY; *U.S. Public,* pg. 924
Madar, William P., Chm. Bd.--Nordson Corporation, Westlake, OH; *U.S. Public,* pg. 1188
Madarame, Rikihiro, Chm. & Chief Exec. Officer--Nemic-Lambda KK, Tokyo, Japan; *Int'l,* pg. 1242
Maddox, Rod, Chm. Bd.--Tri-State Leasing, Memphis, TN; *U.S. Private,* pg. 1101
Maddox, Rodney A., Chm. Bd.--Tri-State Mack Inc, Memphis, TN; *U.S. Private,* pg. 1101
Maddox, Russell, Chm. Bd.--Taylor Impression, Inc., Nashville, TN; *U.S. Private,* pg. 1070
Madel, Michael, Exec. V.P., Chm., Pres. & Chief Exec. Officer-JWT/Europe--J. Walter Thompson Company, New York, NY; *Int'l,* pg. 1483
Madero, Antonio, Chm. Bd. & Chief Exec. Officer--Corporacion Industrial Sanluis, Mexico, Mexico; *Int'l,* pg. 332
Madigan, John W., Chm. Bd., Pres. & Chief Exec. Officer--Tribune Company, Chicago, IL; *U.S. Public,* pg. 1635
Madigan, Joseph E., Chm. Bd.--Lexford Residential Trust, Columbus, OH; *U.S. Public,* pg. 991
Madison, Harold N., Chm. Bd.--Madison Graham Colorgraphics, Inc., Los Angeles, CA; *U.S. Private,* pg. 694
Madsên, Arne, Chm. Bd.--ISS-International Service System A/S, Holte, Denmark; *Int'l,* pg. 656
Madsen, Richard H., Chm. Bd., Pres. & Chief Exec. Officer--Zions Co-operative Mercantile Institution, Salt Lake City, UT; *U.S. Public,* pg. 1793
Madsen, Sven Dyrlov, Chm. Bd.--Chr. Hansen Holding A/S, Horsholm, Denmark; *Int'l,* pg. 288
Maeda, Katsunosuke, Chm. Bd.--Toray Industries, Inc., Tokyo, Japan; *Int'l,* pg. 1399
Maeda, Kazuo, Chm. Bd.--Mitsui Engineering & Shipbuilding Co., Ltd., Tokyo, Japan; *Int'l,* pg. 878
Maerki, Hans Ulrich, Chm. Bd.--Mikron Holding AG, Biel, Switzerland; *Int'l,* pg. 866
Magasrevy, J., Chm. Bd.--Fibras Ceramicas, C.A., Valencia, Venezuela; *Int'l,* pg. 894
Magee, John F., Chm. Bd.--Arthur D. Little, Inc., Cambridge, MA; *U.S. Private,* pg. 670
Maggiotto, Rocco J., Chm.-Natl. Banking Practice--Coopers & Lybrand, New York, NY; *U.S. Private,* pg. 274
Maghielse, Craig, Chm. Bd., Pres. & Chief Exec. Officer--Maghielse Tool Corporation, Grand Rapids, MI; *U.S. Private,* pg. 694
Magliocco, John, Chm. Bd. & Chief Exec. Officer--Peerless Importers, Inc., Brooklyn, NY; *U.S. Private,* pg. 847
Magnusson, Bernt, Chm. Bd.--NCC AB, Solna, Sweden; *Int'l,* pg. 898
Magowan, Peter A., Chm. Bd.--Safeway Inc., Pleasanton, CA; *U.S. Public,* pg. 1426
Magowan, Peter A., Chm. Bd.--Safeway U.S. Holdings, Inc., Oakland, CA; *U.S. Public,* pg. 1426
Maguire, Bruce J., Jr., Chm. Bd.--Spartan Oil Corp., Lansing, MI; *U.S. Private,* pg. 1021
Maguire, Cary M., Chm. Bd.--Components Corporation Of America, Dallas, TX; *U.S. Private,* pg. 259
Maguire, Cary M., Chm. Bd., Pres. & Chief Exec. Officer--Maguire Oil Co., Dallas, TX; *U.S. Private,* pg. 696
Maguire, D.E., Chm. Bd., Pres. & Chief Exec. Officer--Kemet Corporation, Simpsonville, SC; *U.S. Public,* pg. 949
Mahadeva, Kumar, Chm. Bd. & Chief Exec. Officer--Cognizant Technology Solutions Corp., New York, NY; *U.S. Public,* pg. 395
Mahaney, Larry K., Chm. Bd.--The Erin Company, Bangor, ME; *U.S. Private,* pg. 381
Mahler, Guy, Chm. Bd.--Rhodia-Merieux Chile, Santiago, Chile; *Int'l,* pg. 1112
Mahoney, Gerald F., Chm. Bd. & Chief Exec. Officer--Mail-Well Inc., Englewood, CO, *U.S. Public,* pg. 1037
Mahoney, Gerald F., Chm. Bd. & Chief Exec. Officer--American Mail-Well Envelope, Englewood, CO; *U.S. Public,* pg. 1038
Mahoney, Robert W., Chm. Bd. & Chief Exec. Officer--Diebold, Incorporated, Canton, OH; *U.S. Public,* pg. 506
Maibach, Ben C., Jr., Chm. Bd.--Cloverdale Equipment Co., Oak Park, MI; *U.S. Private,* pg. 247
Maibach, Benjamin C., Jr., Chm. Bd.--Barton Malow Enterprises, Inc., Southfield, MI; *U.S. Private,* pg. 120
Maier, Andrew, Chm. Bd.--Quality Bakers of America Cooperative, Inc., Greenwich, CT; *U.S. Private,* pg. 898
Maier, Gerald J., Chm. Bd.--Transcanada Pipelines Limited, Calgary, Canada; *Int'l,* pg. 1416
Maier, Jack C., Chm. Bd.--Frisch's Restaurants, Inc., Cincinnati, OH; *U.S. Public,* pg. 682
Maier, Russell W., Chm. Bd. & Chief Exec. Officer--Republic Engineered Steels, Inc., Massillon, OH; *U.S. Public,* pg. 1378
Maillan, Jean Claude, Chm.--CAP Sesa Tertiaire, Paris, France; *Int'l,* pg. 263
Mailleret, Michel, Chm. Bd. & Chief Exec. Officer--Filtrauto Division, Montigny-le-Bretonneux, France; *Int'l,* pg. 785
Major, R. Odie, Chm. Bd.--SunTrust Bank, Northeast Tennessee, Johnson City, TN; *U.S. Public,* pg. 1538
Makarechian, Hadi, Chm. Bd.--Capital Pacific Holdings, Newport Beach, CA; *U.S. Public,* pg. 302
Makarechian, Hadi, Chm. Bd.--J.M. Peters Co., Newport Beach, CA; *U.S. Public,* pg. 302
Makhani, Madan P., Chm. Bd., Pres., Chief Oper. & Chief Fin. Officer--American Foundry Group, Inc., Bixby, OK; *U.S. Private,* pg. 54
Malaret, German E., M.D., Chm. Bd.--Firstbank Puerto Rico, Santurce, PR; *U.S. Public,* pg. 644
Malarkey, Michael O., Chm. Bd.--Herbert Malarkey Roofing Company, Portland, OR; *U.S. Private,* pg. 698
Malette, Gaston, Chm. Bd., Pres. & Chief Exec. Officer--Malette Quebec, Inc., Montreal, Canada; *Int'l,* pg. 833
Malette, Gaston, Chm. Bd., Pres. & Chief Exec. Officer--Panneaux Malette-OSB Inc., Saint-Georges, Canada; *Int'l,* pg. 833
Malhotra, I.S., Chm. Bd. & Mng. Dir.--Keystone Valve (India) PVT. Ltd., Baroda, India; *U.S. Public,* pg. 1650
Maljers, F.A., Chm.-Supvr. Bd.--Philips Electronics N.V., Eindhoven, Netherlands; *Int'l,* pg. 1051
Maljers, F.A., Chm. Bd.--Unilever N.V., Rotterdam, Netherlands; *Int'l,* pg. 1434
Malkin, Judd, Chm. Bd.--Amfac, Inc., Chicago, IL; *U.S. Private,* pg. 577
Malkowicz, Edward, Chm. Bd.--Haskel International, Inc., Burbank, CA; *U.S. Public,* pg. 798
Mallary, Richard, Chm. Bd.--The Howard Bank, N.A., Burlington, VT; *U.S. Public,* pg. 187
Mallement, Harvey, Chm. Bd.--Industrial Ceramics, Inc., Lima, NY; *U.S. Private,* pg. 560
Mallement, Harvey P., Chm. Bd.--Burdick, Inc., Milton, WI; *U.S. Private,* pg. 181
Malloy, J.B., Chm.--Smurfit Packaging Corporation, Saint Louis, MO; *Int'l,* pg. 1271
Malloy, W. Manning, Chm. Bd. & Chief Exec. Officer--Cheraw Yarn Mills, Inc., Cheraw, SC; *U.S. Private,* pg. 233
Malone, B.L., Chm. Bd. & Chief Exec. Officer--Malone Advertising, Inc., Akron, OH; *U.S. Private,* pg. 698
Malone, Eduardo, Chm. Bd. & Chief Exec. Officer--Chargeurs, Paris, France; *Int'l,* pg. 280
Malone, James R., Chm. Bd.--Anchor Glass Container Corporation, Tampa, FL; *Int'l,* pg. 327
Malone, Jim, Chm. Bd. & Chief Exec. Officer--HMI Industries, Cleveland, OH; *U.S. Public,* pg. 771
Malone, John C., Chm. Bd.--TCI Communications, Inc., Englewood, CO; *U.S. Public,* pg. 1554
Malone, John C., Chm. Bd.--Liberty Media Corporation, Englewood, CO; *U.S. Public,* pg. 1555
Malone, John C., Chm. Bd.--Liberty Program Investments, Inc., Englewood, CO; *U.S. Public,* pg. 1555
Malpas, Robert, Chm. Bd.--Cookson Group plc, London, United Kingdom; *Int'l,* pg. 328
Malpas, Robert, Non-Exec. Co.-Chm. & Co-Pres.--The Eurotunnel Group, London, United Kingdom; *Int'l,* pg. 466
Malpas, Robert, Chm. Bd.--Eurotunnel Finance Limited, London, United Kingdom; *Int'l,* pg. 466
Malpas, Robert, Chm. Bd.--Le Shuttle Holidays Limited, London, United Kingdom; *Int'l,* pg. 466
Malpass, Frederick, Chm. Bd. & Pres.--East Jordan Iron Works, East Jordan, MI; *U.S. Private,* pg. 356
Maltz, Milton, Chm. Bd. & Chief Exec. Officer--Malrite Communications Group, Inc., Cleveland, OH; *U.S. Private,* pg. 698
Maltzman, Donald, Chm. Bd. & Sec.--Tomco Auto Products, Inc., Los Angeles, CA; *U.S. Private,* pg. 1090
Malzahn, Edwin, Chm. Bd. & Pres.--Charles Machine Works, Inc., Perry, OK; *U.S. Private,* pg. 230
Mamsch, Helmut, Chm. Bd.--Stinnes Corporation, Tarrytown, NY; *Int'l,* pg. 1460
Man-ah, Or, Chm.--CCIC Finance Limited, Central, Hong Kong; *Int'l,* pg. 676
Manabe, Keisaku, Chm. Bd.--Kirin Brewery Co., Ltd., Tokyo, Japan; *Int'l,* pg. 735
Mancuso, Frank G., Chm. Bd. & Chief Exec. Officer--Metro-Goldwyn-Mayer Inc., Santa Monica, CA; *U.S. Public,* pg. 1101
Mandelbaum, Mervyn, Chm. Bd., Pres., Chief Exec. & Chief Oper. Officer--Superba, Inc., Los Angeles, CA; *U.S. Private,* pg. 1054
Mander, Michael, Chm. Bd.--The Dialog Corporation plc, London, United Kingdom; *Int'l,* pg. 412
Mandles, Martinn H., Chm. Bd., Chief Admin. Officer & Exec. V.P.--ABM Industries, San Francisco, CA; *U.S. Public,* pg. 2
Mandor, Leonard, Chm. Bd. & Chief Exec. Officer--Concord Assets Group, Boca Raton, FL; *U.S. Private,* pg. 261
Manford, Tony, Chm. Bd.--Peters & Brownes Foods Ltd., Balcatta, Australia; *Int'l,* pg. 1040
Mangano, Ross, Chm. Bd.--Cerprobe Corporation, Gilbert, AZ; *U.S. Public,* pg. 332
Manigault, Peter, Chm. Bd.--Evening Post Publishing Co., Charleston, SC; *U.S. Private,* pg. 385
Mann, George S., Chm. Bd. & Pres.--Unicorp American Corporation, New York, NY; *Int'l,* pg. 1433
Mann, George S., Chm. Bd.--Union Energy Inc., Toronto, Canada; *Int'l,* pg. 1492
Mann, James L., Chm. Bd., Pres. & Chief Exec. Officer--SunGard Data Systems Inc., Wayne, PA; *U.S. Public,* pg. 1534
Mann, Jerome S., Chm.-House of Seagram--The House of Seagram, New York, NY; *Int'l,* pg. 1217
Mann, Marvin L., Chm. Bd. & Chief Exec. Officer--Lexmark International Group, Inc., Lexington, KY; *U.S. Public,* pg. 991
Mann, Marvin L., Chm. Bd.& Chief Exec. Officer--Lexmark International, Inc., Lexington, KY; *U.S. Public,* pg. 991
Mann, Samuel J., Chm. Bd., Pres. & Chief Exec. Officer--Inverness Corp., Fair Lawn, NJ; *U.S. Private,* pg. 574
Mann, Stephen, Chm. Bd.--Alexander's, Inc., Saddle Brook, NJ; *U.S. Public,* pg. 1725
Manne, Stan, Chm. Bd. & Pres.--Brawney Plastics, Inc., Chicago, IL; *U.S. Private,* pg. 166
Manne, Stanley, Chm. Bd. & Pres.--Brawny Plastics West, Santa Ana, CA; *U.S. Private,* pg. 166
Manning, Burt, Chm. Bd.--J. Walter Thompson Company, New York, NY; *Int'l,* pg. 1483
Manning, James, Chm. Bd. & Pres.--Auburn Hosiery Mills, Inc., Auburn, KY; *U.S. Private,* pg. 98
Manning, James V., Chm. Bd.--COMNET Corporation, Lanham, MD; *U.S. Public,* pg. 416
Manning, Kenneth P., Chm. Bd., Pres. & Chief Exec. Officer--Universal Foods Corporation, Milwaukee, WI; *U.S. Public,* pg. 1695
Manning, Thomas K., Chm. Bd.--The Rival Company, Kansas City, MO; *U.S. Public,* pg. 1391
Mano, T., Chm. Bd.--Nippon Kaiji Kyokai, Tokyo, Japan; *Int'l,* pg. 934
Manoogian, Richard A., Chm. Bd. & Chief Exec. Officer--Masco Corporation, Taylor, MI; *U.S. Public,* pg. 1052
Manoogian, Richard A., Chm. Bd.--TriMas Corporation, Ann Arbor, MI; *U.S. Public,* pg. 1054
Manoogian, Richard A., Chm. Bd. & Chief Exec. Officer--MascoTech, Inc., Taylor, MI; *U.S. Public,* pg. 1055
Manos, Pete L., Chm. Bd., Pres. & Chief Exec. Officer--Giant Food Inc., Landover, MD; *U.S. Public,* pg. 741
Mansell-Jones, R.M., Chm. Bd.--J. Bibby & Sons Plc, London, United Kingdom; *Int'l,* pg. 167
Manser, P.J., Chm. Bd.--Robert Fleming Holdings Ltd., London, United Kingdom; *Int'l,* pg. 493
Manser, P.J., Chm. Bd.--Robert Fleming & Co. Limited, London, United Kingdom; *Int'l,* pg. 493
Mansfield, Michael F., Chm. Bd. & Pres.--Mansfield Oil Company, Gainesville, GA; *U.S. Private,* pg. 700
Mapondera, H.E., Chm. Bd.--T A Holdings Limited, Harare, Zimbabwe; *Int'l,* pg. 1334
Mapplebeck, J. R., Chm.--National Westminster Bank AG, Frankfurt/Main, Germany; *Int'l,* pg. 911
Marbut, Bob, Chm. Bd. & Co-Chief Exec. Officer--Hearst-Argyle Television Incorporated, New York, NY; *U.S. Private,* pg. 516
Marcalus, Robert L., Sr., Chm. Bd.--Marcal Paper Mills, Inc., Elmwood Park, NJ; *U.S. Private,* pg. 701
Marcegaglia, Steno, Chm. Bd.--Marcegaglia SpA, Mantova, Italy; *Int'l,* pg. 841
March, Perrin G., III, Chm. Bd.--Cincinnati Incorporated, Harrison, OH; *U.S. Private,* pg. 240
Marchand, Gerard, Chm. & Chief Exec. Officer--Tessenderlo Chemie, Tessenderlo, Belgium; *Int'l,* pg. 459
Marchesi, G.A., Chm. Bd., Pres. & Chief Exec. Officer--Steiner Co., Inc., Chicago, IL; *U.S. Private,* pg. 1039
Marchioni, Allen, Chm. Bd., Pres. & Chief Exec. Officer--William Morrow & Co., Inc., New York, NY; *U.S. Private,* pg. 515
Marchionne, Henry, Chm. Bd.--Miyano Machinery, Inc., Wood Dale, IL; *U.S. Private,* pg. 754
Marchitto, Al, Chm. Bd. & Chief Exec. Officer--Simmons Juvenile Products, Rutherford, NJ; *U.S. Private,* pg. 1001
Marciano, Maurice, Chm. Bd. & Chief Exec. Officer--Guess ?, Inc., Los Angeles, CA; *U.S. Public,* pg. 768
Marcoux, Remi, Chm. Bd., Pres. & Chief Exec. Officer--G.T.C. Transcontinental Group Ltd., Montreal, Canada; *Int'l,* pg. 538
Marcum, Joseph L., Chm. Bd.--Ohio Casualty Corporation, Hamilton, OH; *U.S. Public,* pg. 1214
Marcum, Joseph L., Chm. Bd.--The Ohio Casualty Insurance Group, Hamilton, OH; *U.S. Public,* pg. 1214
Marcus, Bernard, Chm. Bd.--The Home Depot, Inc., Atlanta, GA; *U.S. Public,* pg. 831
Marcus, Frank W., Chm. Bd.--Harold Leonard & Company, Inc., Union, NJ; *U.S. Private,* pg. 660
Marcus, Jeffrey A., Chm. Bd. & Chief Exec. Officer--Marcus Cable Company, L.P., Dallas, TX; *U.S. Private,* pg. 702
Marcus, Marvin W., Chm. Bd.--Cutco Industries, Inc., Syosset, NY; *U.S. Public,* pg. 470
Marcus, Roger S., Chm. Bd. & Chief Exec. Officer--American Biltrite Inc., Wellesley Hills, MA; *U.S. Public,* pg. 68
Marcus, Samuel, Chm. Bd.--Marcus Brothers Textiles, Inc., New York, NY; *U.S. Private,* pg. 702
Marcus, Stephen, Chm. Bd., Pres. & Chief Exec. Officer--The Marcus Corporation, Milwaukee, WI; *U.S. Public,* pg. 1044
Maree, J.B., Dr., Chm.-Electricity Counsel--Eskom, Sandton, South Africa; *Int'l,* pg. 459
Margalit, Shlomo, Dr., Chm. Bd., Chief Tech. Officer & Sec.--MRV Communications, Inc., Chatsworth, CA; *U.S. Public,* pg. 1027
Margalith, Ethan Harold, Chm. Bd., Chief Exec. Officer & Treas.--Starving Students, Inc., Los Angeles, CA; *U.S. Private,* pg. 1035
Margolis, Jay, Chm. Bd. & Chief Exec. Officer--Esprit de Corp., San Francisco, CA; *U.S. Private,* pg. 383
Margolis, Milton J., Vice Chm.--Host Apparel, Inc., New York, NY; *U.S. Private,* pg. 540
Margolis, Robert, Chm. Bd. & Chief Exec. Officer--Cherokee Inc., Van Nuys, CA; *U.S. Public,* pg. 345
Mariani, Jr., John F., Chm. Bd.--Castello Banfi Srl., Siena, Italy; *U.S. Private,* pg. 113
Marine, Ignacio Bayon, Chm. & Chief Exec. Officer--Citroen Hispana S.A., Pontevedra, Spain; *Int'l,* pg. 1020
Marineau, Phil, Chm. Bd.--Pete's Brewing Company, Palo Alto, CA; *U.S. Public,* pg. 1280
Marini, Robert C., Chm. Bd. & Chief Exec. Officer--Camp Dresser & McKee Inc., Cambridge, MA; *U.S. Private,* pg. 203
Marino, Audrey, Chm. Bd.--Exotic Rubber & Plastics Corp., Farmington Hills, MI; *U.S. Private,* pg. 388
Marino, Frederick, Chm. Bd. & Chief Exec. Officer--The Strober Organization, Inc., Brooklyn, NY; *U.S. Private,* pg. 403
Mario, Ernest, Ph.D., Chm. Bd.--Pharmaceutical Product Development, Inc., Wilmington, NC; *U.S. Public,* pg. 1285

Marion, James P., Jr., Chm. Bd.--Bloomsburg Mills Inc., New York, NY; *U.S. Private*, pg. 150
Maritz, William E., Chm. Bd. & Chief Exec. Officer--Maritz Inc., Fenton, MO; *U.S. Private*, pg. 703
Mark, Kurt, Chm. Bd.--Elof Hansson AB, Goteborg, Sweden; *Int'l*, pg. 595
Mark, Reuben, Chm. Bd. & Chief Exec. Officer--Colgate-Palmolive Company, New York, NY; *U.S. Public*, pg. 397
Markell, Rick, Chm. Bd. & Pres.--Southern Bag Corporation, Madison, MS; *U.S. Private*, pg. 1015
Markin, Allan P., Chm. Bd.--Canadian Natural Resources Limited, Calgary, Canada; *Int'l*, pg. 258
Markin, David R., Chm.--Great Dane Trailers, Inc., Savannah, GA; *U.S. Private*, pg. 1030
Marks, Fred, Chm. Bd.--The Vermont Teddy Bear Company, Inc., Shelburne, VT; *U.S. Public*, pg. 1716
Marks, Marilyn R., Chm. Bd. & Chief Exec. Officer--Dorsey Trailers, Inc., Atlanta, GA; *U.S. Public*, pg. 520
Marks, Mel, Chm. Bd.--Motorcar Parts & Accessories, Torrance, CA; *U.S. Public*, pg. 1136
Marks, Philip, Chm. Bd.--Advertising Display Co., Englewood Cliffs, NJ; *U.S. Private*, pg. 23
Marks, Samuel L., Chm. Bd.--Allied Sporting Goods Inc., Louisville, KY; *U.S. Private*, pg. 41
Marks, William L., Chm. Bd. & Chief Exec. Officer--Whitney Holding Corporation, New Orleans, LA; *U.S. Public*, pg. 1766
Marks, William L., Chm. Bd. & Chief Exec. Officer--Whitney National Bank, New Orleans, LA; *U.S. Public*, pg. 1766
Marlas, James C., Chm. Bd. & Chief Exec. Officer--Mickelberry Communications, Inc., New York, NY; *U.S. Private*, pg. 741
Marlen, James S., Chm. Bd., Pres. & Chief Exec. Officer--Ameron International Corporation, Pasadena, CA; *U.S. Public*, pg. 98
Marley, James E., Chm. Bd.--AMP Incorporated, Harrisburg, PA; *U.S. Public*, pg. 7
Marling, Mark E., Chm. Bd. & Pres.--Ed Marling Stores, Inc., Topeka, KS; *U.S. Private*, pg. 705
Marlon, Anthony M., M.D., Chm. Bd. & Chief Exec. Officer--Sierra Health Services, Inc., Las Vegas, NV; *U.S. Public*, *pg. 1469*
Marnell, Anthony A., II, Chm. Bd. & Chief Exec. Officer--Rio Hotel & Casino Inc., Las Vegas, NV; *U.S. Public*, pg. 1390
Marotta, Thomas S., Chm. Bd., Pres. & Chief Exec. Officer--Marotta Scientific Controls, Inc., Montville, NJ; *U.S. Private*, pg. 706
Marquard, William A., Chm. Bd.--Mosler Inc., Hamilton, OH; *U.S. Private*, pg. 763
Marquardt, Robert J., Chm. Bd.--Gudebrod, Inc., Pottstown, PA; *U.S. Private*, pg. 486
Marquis, Dale, Chm. Bd.--Pacifica Real Estate Group, Santa Barbara, CA; *U.S. Private*, pg. 832
Marram, Edward P., Dr., Chm. Bd., Pres., Chief Exec. Officer & Treas.--Geo-Centers, Inc., Newton, MA; *U.S. Private*, pg. 447
Marriott, J.W., Jr., Chm. Bd. & Chief Exec. Officer--Marriott International, Inc., Washington, DC; *U.S. Public*, pg. 1047
Marriott, J.W., Jr., Chm. Bd.--Marriott Hotels, Resorts, and Suites, Washington, DC; *U.S. Public*, pg. 1048
Marriott, Richard E., Chm. Bd.--Host Marriott Corporation, Bethesda, MD; *U.S. Public*, pg. 841
Marron, Donald B., Chm. Bd. & Chief Exec. Officer--PaineWebber Group Incorporated, New York, NY; *U.S. Public*, pg. 1252
Mars, Forrest E., Jr., Chm. Bd. & Co-Pres.--Mars, Incorporated, Mc Lean, VA; *U.S. Private*, pg. 707
Marsan, Andre, Chm. Bd., Pres. & Chief Exec. Officer--Montrusco Associates, Inc., Montreal, Canada; *Int'l*, pg. 888
Marsden, Brian W.H., Chm. Bd.--Acme Metals Incorporated, Riverdale, IL; *U.S. Public*, pg. 16
Marsh, Don E., Chm. Bd., Pres. & Chief Exec. Officer--Marsh Supermarkets, Inc., Indianapolis, IN; *U.S. Public*, pg. 1049
Marsh, John Allen, Chm. Bd. & Chief Exec. Officer--Marsh Company, Belleville, IL; *U.S. Private*, pg. 707
Marsh, Miles L., Chm. Bd. & Chief Exec. Officer--Fort James Corporation, Richmond, VA; *U.S. Public*, pg. 670
Marsh, Miles L., Chm. Bd.--Consumer Products Business, Norwalk, CT; *U.S. Public*, pg. 671
Marsh, Reid, Chm. Bd.--Marsh Furniture Company, High Point, NC; *U.S. Private*, pg. 708
Marsh, Water G., Chm. Bd. & Chief Exec. Officer--Tapco International Corporation, Plymouth, MI; *U.S. Private*, pg. 1068
Marshall, Gordon S., Chm. Bd.--Marshall Industries, El Monte, CA; *U.S. Public*, pg. 1051
Marshall, Gregory K., Chm. & Chief Exec. Officer--The Sygma Network, Inc.-Denver Central, Lakewood, CO; *U.S. Public*, pg. 1551
Marshall, John, Chm. Bd.-Magneco/Metrel U.K.--Magneco/Metrel, Inc., Addison, IL; *U.S. Private*, pg. 695
Marshall, John L., III, Chm. Bd.--ADP Marshall Contractors Inc., Rumford, RI; *U.S. Public*, pg. 660
Marshall, Joseph W., Chm. Bd. & Chief Exec. Officer--Idaho Power Company, Boise, ID; *U.S. Public*, pg. 861
Marshall, Paul M., Chm. Bd.--Westim Resources Ltd., Vancouver, Canada; *Int'l*, pg. 435
Marshall, Pierce, Chm. Bd. & Chief Exec. Officer--Electron Corp., Littleton, CO; *U.S. Private*, pg. 370
Marshall, Sir Colin, Chm. Bd.--British Airways PLC, London, United Kingdom; *Int'l*, pg. 218
Mart, Marcel, Chm. Bd.--Banque Generale du Luxembourg SA, Luxembourg, Luxembourg; *Int'l*, pg. 161
Martelli, Paolo, Chm. Bd.--Fiscambi Leasing S.p.A., Milan, Italy; *Int'l*, pg. 138
Marten, Randolph L., Chm. Bd., Chief Oper. Officer & Pres.--Marten Transport, Ltd., Mondovi, WI; *U.S. Public*, pg. 1052
Martin Bringas, Francisco Javier, Chm. Bd.--Organizacion Soriana S.A. de C.V., Monterrey, Mexico; *Int'l*, pg. 1008
Martin, Bob, Chm. Bd.--Martin & Bayley Inc., Carmi, IL; *U.S. Private*, pg. 708
Martin, David O., Chm. Bd.--Martin Door Mfg., Inc., Salt Lake City, UT; *U.S. Private*, pg. 708
Martin, Edward, Co-Chm.--The Dunlap Company, Fort Worth, TX; *U.S. Private*, pg. 346
Martin, George J., Chm. Bd.--Washington Scientific Industries, Inc., Long Lake, MN; *U.S. Public*, pg. 1744
Martin, Heino, Chm.--Deutsche Babcock Anlagen GmbH, Oberhausen, Germany; *Int'l*, pg. 398
Martin, Ian, Chm. Bd.--Newmond PLC, Tamworth, United Kingdom; *Int'l*, pg. 924
Martin, Ian, Chm. Bd.--Unigate PLC, London, United Kingdom; *Int'l*, pg. 1433
Martin, J. Landis, Chm. Bd.--Kronos, Inc., Houston, TX; *U.S. Private*, pg. 270
Martin, J. Landis, Chm. Bd., Pres. & Chief Exec. Officer--Tremont Corporation, Denver, CO; *U.S. Private*, pg. 270
Martin, James F., Chm. Bd. & Chief Exec. Officer--Martin Color-Fi, Edgefield, SC; *U.S. Public*, pg. 1052
Martin, James R., Chm. Bd. & Chief Exec. Officer--Plasti-Line, Inc., Knoxville, TN; *U.S. Public*, pg. 1308
Martin, Joe R., Chm. Bd.--Martin Sprocket & Gear, Inc., Arlington, TX; *U.S. Private*, pg. 709
Martin, John, Chm. Bd.--Welbeck Golin/Harris Communications Ltd., London, United Kingdom; *Int'l*, pg. 1226
Martin, L.C., Chm. Bd., Pres. & Chief Exec. Officer--Aztec Manufacturing Co., Crowley, TX; *U.S. Public*, pg. 159
Martin, Larry W., Chm. Bd. & Pres.--Data Dimensions, Inc., Culver City, CA; *U.S. Public*, pg. 485
Martin, Leonard, Chm. Bd.--Mustang Tractor & Equip. Co., Houston, TX; *U.S. Private*, pg. 768
Martin, Michael S., Chm. Bd.--Equitable Financial Consultants, Inc., New York, NY; *U.S. Public*, pg. 589
Martin, Peter, Chm. Bd. & Chief Exec. Officer--Semikron International, GmbH & Co. KG, Nuremberg, Germany; *Int'l*, pg. 1220
Martin, Peter M., Chm. Bd. & Chief Exec. Officer--Provident Bankshares Corporation, Baltimore, MD; *U.S. Public*, pg. 1337
Martin, R. Brad, Chm. Bd. & Chief Exec. Officer--Proffitt's, Inc., Alcoa, TN; *U.S. Public*, pg. 1333
Martin, R.S., Jr., Chm. Bd.--Martin Gas Corporation, Kilgore, TX; *U.S. Private*, pg. 709
Martin, Ray, Chm. Bd. & Chief Exec. Officer--Coast Savings Financial, Inc., Los Angeles, CA; *U.S. Public*, pg. 388
Martin, Reg, Co-Chm.--The Dunlap Company, Fort Worth, TX; *U.S. Private*, pg. 346
Martin, Rex, Chm. Bd., Pres. & Chief Exec. Officer--NIBCO, Inc., Elkhart, IN; *U.S. Private*, pg. 798
Martin, Robert W., Chm. Bd.--Silcorp Limited, Scarborough, Canada; *Int'l*, pg. 1249
Martin, Tom, Chm. Bd. & Chief Exec. Officer--First Commercial Bank, N.A. of Memphis, Memphis, TN; *U.S. Public*, pg. 630
Martin, Vincent L., Chm. Bd. & Chief Exec. Officer--Jason Incorporated, Milwaukee, WI; *U.S. Public*, pg. 923
Martin, W.G., Chm. Bd.--Nitram Energy Inc., Orchard Park, NY; *U.S. Private*, pg. 799
Martin, William H., III, Chm. Bd.--Martin Industries, Inc. (AL), Florence, AL; *U.S. Private*, pg. 709
Martineau, Yvon, Chm. Bd.--Hydro-Quebec, Montreal, Canada; *Int'l*, pg. 640
Martinelli, Alfred W., Chm. Bd. & Chief Exec. Officer--Buckeye Partners, L.P., Allentown, PA; *U.S. Public*, pg. 266
Martinen, John A., Chm. Bd.--Globus & Cosmos, Littleton, CO; *U.S. Private*, pg. 458
Martinez, Arthur C., Chm. Bd. & Chief Exec. Officer--Sears, Roebuck and Co., Hoffman Estates, IL; *U.S. Public*, pg. 1452
Martinez, Julio, Chm. Bd. & Pres.--Chemtex International, Inc., New York, NY; *Int'l*, pg. 872
Martini, E., Chm. Bd.--Bayerische Hypotheken-und Wechsel-Bank Aktiengesellschaft, Munich, Germany; *Int'l*, pg. 175
Martini, Robert E., Chm. Bd.--Bergen Brunswig Corporation, Orange, CA; *U.S. Public*, pg. 213
Martino, Anthony A., Chm. Bd. & Chief Exec. Officer--Maaco Enterprises Inc., King of Prussia, PA; *U.S. Private*, pg. 689
Martins de Jesus, Jose Antonio, Dr., Chm.--Galpgeste, Lda., Lisbon, Portugal; *Int'l*, pg. 1045
Marttinen, Heikki, Chm. Bd., Pres. & Chief Exec. Officer--Imatran Voima Oy, Helsinki, Finland; *Int'l*, pg. 660
Martz, D. Stephen, Chm. Bd., Pres. & Chief Exec. Officer--Hollidaysburg Trust Company, Hollidaysburg, PA; *U.S. Public*, pg. 1222
Marvin, Michael D., Chm. Bd.--MapInfo Corp., Troy, NY; *U.S. Public*, pg. 1042
Marvin, William S., Chm. Bd. & Chief Exec. Officer--Marvin Lumber & Cedar Company, Warroad, MN; *U.S. Private*, pg. 710
Marx, O. B., Chm. Bd.--Pullman Industries, Inc., Pullman, MI; *U.S. Private*, pg. 894
Mas, Jorge L., Sr., Chm. Bd.--MasTec, Inc., Miami, FL; *U.S. Public*, pg. 1055
Mascarin, Ed, Chm. Bd. & Chief Exec. Officer--Crane Carrier Company, Tulsa, OK; *U.S. Private*, pg. 286
Mascia, Frank R., Chm., Pres. & Chief Exec. Officer--United HealthCare of North Carolina, Inc., Greensboro, NC; *U.S. Public*, pg. 1678
Masefield, John, Chm. Bd., Pres. & Chief Exec. Officer--Isomedix Inc., Whippany, NJ; *U.S. Public*, pg. 1515
Maslak, Samuel H., Chm. Bd. & Chief Exec. Officer--Acuson Corporation, Mountain View, CA; *U.S. Public*, pg. 18
Maslow, Lester, Chm. Bd. & Pres.--Best Manufacturing, Inc., New York, NY; *U.S. Private*, pg. 139
Mason, Elvis L., Chm. Bd. & Chief Exec. Officer--Safeguard Business Systems, Inc., Fort Washington, PA; *U.S. Private*, pg. 960
Mason, Raymond A., Chm. Bd., Pres. & Chief Exec. Officer--Legg Mason, Inc., Baltimore, MD; *U.S. Public*, pg. 984
Massacesi, Dr. E., Chm.--Fiat Auto S.p.A., Milan, Italy; *Int'l*, pg. 481
Massaro, Anthony A., Chm. Bd., Pres. & Chief Exec. Officer--The Lincoln Electric Company, Cleveland, OH; *U.S. Public*, pg. 996
Masseu, Jeff, Chm. Bd., Pres. & Chief Exec. Officer--United Design Corporation, Noble, OK; *U.S. Private*, pg. 1121
Massey, Knox, Jr., Chm. Bd. & Chief Exec. Officer--WestWayne, Inc., Atlanta, GA; *U.S. Private*, pg. 1170
Mast, James H., Chm. Bd.--Sunkist Growers, Inc., Sherman Oaks, CA; *U.S. Private*, pg. 1052
Mast, Jim, Chm. Bd.--Fruit Growers Supply Co., Sherman Oaks, CA; *U.S. Private*, pg. 430
Masters, Melvin L., Chm. Bd., Pres. & Chief Exec. Officer--LaserMaster Technologies, Inc., Eden Prairie, MN; *U.S. Public*, pg. 979
Mastracchio, J.A., Company Grp. Chm.--HLS Corp., Little Falls, NJ; *Int'l*, pg. 1483
Masuzawa, Takao, Chm. Bd.--The Long-Term Credit Bank of Japan, Limited, Tokyo, Japan; *Int'l*, pg. 815
Mathes, Heinrich-Wernr, Dr., Chm. Bd.--Lentjes AG, Dusseldorf, Germany; *Int'l*, pg. 861
Mathewson, Charles N., Chm. Bd. & Chief Exec. Officer--International Game Technology, Reno, NV; *U.S. Public*, pg. 900
Mathias, John H., Chm. Bd. & Chief Exec. Officer--The JPM Company, Lewisburg, PA; *U.S. Public*, pg. 919
Mathile, Clay, Chm. Bd. & Chief Exec. Officer--Iams Company, Dayton, OH; *U.S. Private*, pg. 556
Mathis, David B., Chm. Bd. & Chief Exec. Officer--Kemper Insurance Companies, Long Grove, IL; *U.S. Private*, pg. 614
Mathur, R.B., Chm. Bd. & Mng. Dir.--Central Mine Planning & Design Institute Limited, Ranchi, India; *Int'l*, pg. 298
Mathwich, Dale F., Chm. Bd. & Chief Exec. Officer--American Family Mutual Insurance Co., Madison, WI; *U.S. Private*, pg. 53
Matney, R.C., Chm. Bd., Pres. & Chief Exec. Officer--Mark VII, Inc., Memphis, TN; *U.S. Public*, pg. 1046
Matney, R.C., Chm. Bd.--Mark VII Transportation Company, Inc., Greenwood, IN; *U.S. Public*, pg. 1046
Matricaria, Ronald A., Chm. Bd., Pres. & Chief Exec. Officer--St. Jude Medical, Inc., Saint Paul, MN; *U.S. Public*, pg. 1427
Matsaushita, Kanji, Chm. Bd.--Glory Ltd., Himeji, Japan; *Int'l*, pg. 554
Matsuka, Hiromichi, Chm. Bd.--Isuzu Motors Limited, Tokyo, Japan; *Int'l*, pg. 692
Matsukawa, Michiya, Chm.--Nikko International Capital Management Co., Ltd., Tokyo, Japan; *Int'l*, pg. 930
Matsukawa, Yasuo, Chm. Bd.--Tomen Corporation, Osaka, Japan; *Int'l*, pg. 1395
Matsumoto, Seiya, Chm. Bd.--Pioneer Electronic Corporation, Tokyo, Japan; *Int'l*, pg. 1057
Matsushita, Masaharu, Chm. Bd.--Matsushita Electric Industrial Co., Ltd., Kadoma, Japan; *Int'l*, pg. 846
Matsuyama, W. Brian, Chm. Bd. & Chief Exec. Officer--Cascade Natural Gas Corporation, Seattle, WA; *U.S. Public*, pg. 311
Matsuzawa, Mitsuo, Chm. Bd.--INX International, Milwaukee, WI; *Int'l*, pg. 1311
Matt, F.X., II, Chm. Bd. & Corp. Sec.--The F.X. Matt Brewing Co., Utica, NY; *U.S. Private*, pg. 714
Matthaei, Charles W.H., Chm. Bd.--Roman Meal Company, Tacoma, WA; *U.S. Private*, pg. 942
Matthew, Abe J., Chm. Bd.--Custom Accessories Inc., Niles, IL; *U.S. Private*, pg. 298
Matthew, Mike, Chm.--Marketforce (UK) Limited, London, United Kingdom; *Int'l*, pg. 651
Matthew, Robert, Chm. Bd.--Brierley Investments Limited, Wellington, New Zealand; *Int'l*, pg. 215
Matthew, Robert H., Chm. Bd.--Air New Zealand Ltd., Auckland, New Zealand; *Int'l*, pg. 38
Matthews, B.T., Chm. Bd.--Bernard Matthews PLC, Norwich, United Kingdom; *Int'l*, pg. 189
Matthews, George J., Chm. Bd.--Starmet Corporation, Concord, MA; *U.S. Public*, pg. 1511
Matthews, Phillip D., Chm.-Exec. Committee--Wolverine World Wide, Inc., Rockford, MI; *U.S. Public*, pg. 1775
Matthews, Terence H., Chm. Bd. & Chief Exec. Officer--Newbridge Networks Corporation, Kanata, Canada; *Int'l*, pg. 923
Matthews, William D., Chm. Bd. & Chief Exec. Officer--Oneida Ltd., Oneida, NY; *U.S. Public*, pg. 1225
Matthys, Paul, Chm. Bd.--TradeARBED S.A., Luxembourg, Luxembourg; *Int'l*, pg. 79
Mattia, Arthur, Chm. Bd. & Pres.--Action Manufacturing Co., Philadelphia, PA; *U.S. Private*, pg. 15
Mattingly, David, Chm.--Young & Rubicam Mattingly, Richmond, Australia; *U.S. Private*, pg. 1198
Mattioli, Leonard S., Chm. Bd.--American TV & Appliance of Madison, Inc., Madison, WI; *U.S. Private*, pg. 64
Mattson, Brad, Chm. Bd.--Mattson Technology, Inc., Fremont, CA; *U.S. Public*, pg. 1060
Mattsson, Bjorn, Chm. Bd.--Partek Corporation, Helsinki, Finland; *Int'l*, pg. 1024
Matus, Geoffrey, Chm. Bd. & Chief Exec. Officer--Globelle Corporation, Mississauga, Canada; *Int'l*, pg. 554
Maubert, Jean, Chm. Bd.--Robertet Flavors, South Plainfield, NJ; *Int'l*, pg. 1119
Maucher, Helmut, Chm. Bd. & Chief Exec. Officer--Nestle S.A., Vevey, Switzerland; *Int'l*, pg. 915
Maud, Ken E., Chm. Bd.--GTI Corporation, San Diego, CA; *U.S. Public*, pg. 767
Maughan, Deryck, Co-Chm. & Co-Chief Exec. Officer--Salomon Smith Barney Holdings, Inc., New York, NY; *U.S. Public*, pg. 1633
Maughan, Rex, Chm. Bd., Pres. & Chief Exec. Officer--Forever Living Products International, Inc., Scottsdale, AZ; *U.S. Private*, pg. 418
Maulson, Tom, Chm. Bd.--Simpson Electric Co., Elgin, IL; *U.S. Private*, pg. 1002
Maundrell, V.J., Chm.-Specialty Matls. & Tech. Div.--Morgan Crucible Co. Plc, Windsor, United Kingdom; *Int'l*, pg. 890

Mauney, William K., Jr., Chm. Bd.--Mauney Hosiery Mills, Inc., Kings Mountain, NC; *U.S. Private*, pg. 715
Maurer, Donald D., Chm. Bd.--EMPI, Inc., Saint Paul, MN; *U.S. Public*, pg. 545
Maurer, Theodore A., Chm.--HLS Corp., Little Falls, NJ; *Int'l*, pg. 1483
Maurey, Joseph E., Chm. Bd. & Pres.--Maurey Manufacturing Corp., Chicago, IL; *U.S. Private*, pg. 715
Maurin, James E., Chm. Bd.--Maurin-Ogden Properties, New Orleans, LA; *U.S. Private*, pg. 715
Mauser, Helmut, Co-Chm. Bd.--Krupp Metalurgica Campo Limpo Ltda., Sao Paulo, Brazil; *Int'l*, pg. 508
Mautner, Henry, Chm. Bd.--MFRI Inc., Niles, IL; *U.S. Public*, *pg. 1026*
Mautz, Bernhard F., Jr., Chm. Bd. & Pres.--Mautz Paint Co., Madison, WI; *U.S. Private*, pg. 715
Maxheim, John H., Chm. Bd., Pres. & Chief Exec. Officer--Piedmont Natural Gas Co., Inc., Charlotte, NC; *U.S. Public*, pg. 1295
Maxon, Harry R., III, Dr., Chm. Bd.--Maxon Corporation, Muncie, IN; *U.S. Private*, pg. 716
Maxwell, H. James, Chm. Bd. & Chief Exec. Officer--Panaco, Inc., Kansas City, MO; *U.S. Public*, pg. 1255
Maxwell, Hamish, Chm. Bd.--WPP Group plc, London, United Kingdom; *Int'l*, pg. 1482
Maxwell, J.L., Jr., Chm. Bd.--Goldsboro Milling Company, Goldsboro, NC; *U.S. Private*, pg. 462
May, Bill B., Dr., Chm. Bd. & Chief Exec. Officer--ARGOSystems, Inc., Sunnyvale, CA; *U.S. Public*, pg. 240
May, Stan, Chm. & Chief Creative Officer-Leo Burnett/Connaghan & May--Leo Burnett Company, Inc., Chicago, IL; *U.S. Private*, pg. 183
May, T. Michael, Chm. Bd.--Hawaii Electric Light Co., Inc., Hilo, HI; *U.S. Public*, pg. 800
May, T. Michael, Chm. Bd.--Maui Electric Co., Ltd., Kahului, HI; *U.S. Public*, pg. 800
May, Thomas J., Chm. Bd., Pres. & Chief Exec. Officer--Boston Edison Company, Boston, MA; *U.S. Public*, pg. 247
Mayer, Cyrus, Chm. Bd. & Pres.--Mayer/Berkshire Corporation, Wayne, NJ; *U.S. Private*, pg. 717
Mayer, Fred, Chm. Bd.--Commodore Holdings, Hollywood, FL; *U.S. Public*, pg. 414
Mayer, Robert A., Chm. Bd. & Chief Exec. Officer--Standard Security Life Insurance Company of New York, New York, NY; *U.S. Private*, pg. 446
Mayer, Volker, Chm.--ASAL Ingenieure GmbH, Kaiserslautern, Germany; *Int'l*, pg. 608
Mayer, William N., Chm. Bd. & Chief Exec. Officer--Modern Controls, Inc., Minneapolis, MN; *U.S. Public*, pg. 1120
Maynard, James G., Chm. Bd., Chief Exec. Officer & Treas.--Maynard Oil Co., Dallas, TX; *U.S. Public*, pg. 1064
Maynard, James H., Chm. Bd., Pres., Chief Exec. Officer & Treas.--Investors Management Corp., Raleigh, NC; *U.S. Private*, pg. 574
Mayrhuber, Wolfgang, Chm.-Exec. Bd.--Lufthansa Technik AG, Hamburg, Germany; *Int'l*, pg. 407
Mays, L. Lowry, Chm. Bd. & Chief Exec. Officer--Clear Channel Communications, Inc., San Antonio, TX; *U.S. Public*, pg. 383
Maza, Xavier Autrey, Chm. Bd. & Pres.--Altos Hornos de Mexico, S.A., Monclova, Mexico; *Int'l*, pg. 66
Mc Kinney, Craig, Chm. Bd.--Woodchester Investments plc, Dublin, Ireland; *U.S. Public*, pg. 712
McAdam, James, Chm. Bd.--Signet Group plc, London, United Kingdom; *Int'l*, pg. 1248
McAfee, Robert, Pres. & Chief Exec. Officer--Lincoln Foodservice Products, Inc., Fort Wayne, IN; *Int'l*, pg. 188
McAlaine, Robert, Pres.--Namico, Inc., Philadelphia, PA; *U.S. Private*, pg. 773
McAlister, Maurice L., Chm. Bd.--Downey Financial Corp., Newport Beach, CA; *U.S. Public*, pg. 525
McAlister, Maurice L., Chm. Bd.--Downey Savings & Loan Association, F.A., Newport Beach, CA; *U.S. Public*, pg. 526
McAllister, Donald, Jr., Chm. Bd.--Geyer-McAllister Publications, Inc., New York, NY; *U.S. Private*, pg. 450
McAndrew, Nicholas, Chm. Bd.--Murray Johnstone Limited, Glasgow, United Kingdom; *U.S. Public*, pg. 1674
McAulay, Jeffrey J., Chm. Bd. & Pres.--Moran Insurance Company Limited, Greenwich, CT; *U.S. Private*, pg. 760
McAuliffe, John, Chm. Bd. & Pres.--Compendium Systems Corporation, Greenwich, CT; *U.S. Private*, pg. 259
McAvoy, Kenneth J., Chm. Bd. & Chief Exec. Officer--Jameco Industries, Inc., Spindale, NC; *U.S. Public*, pg. 1746
McBeth, Robert D., Chm. Bd., Pres. & Chief Exec. Officer--Associated Industrial Supply, Inc., Columbia, SC; *U.S. Private*, pg. 91
McBride, John H., Chm. Bd.--Porcelain Metals Corp., Louisville, KY; *U.S. Private*, pg. 876
McBride, T. Eugene, Chm. Bd., Pres. & Chief Exec. Officer--Dyersburg Corporation, Dyersburg, TN; *U.S. Public*, pg. 538
McCabe, Edward, Chm. Bd. & Chief Exec. Officer--McCabe & Company, New York, NY; *U.S. Private*, pg. 719
McCabe, William G., Chm. Bd.--CBT Systems USA Ltd., Menlo Park, CA; *U.S. Public*, pg. 275
McCaffray, S.J., Chm. Bd. & Pres.--National Frozen Foods Corp., Seattle, WA; *U.S. Private*, pg. 783
McCague, Beth, Chm. Bd., Pres. & Chief Exec. Officer--First Union National Bank of Tennessee, Nashville, TN; *U.S. Public*, pg. 640
McCaig, J.R., Chm. Bd.--BFC Construction Corporation, Scarborough, Canada; *Int'l*, pg. 118
McCaig, J.R., Chm. Bd.--Trimac Corporation, Calgary, Canada; *Int'l*, pg. 1423
McCain, G. Wallace F., Chm. Bd.--Maple Leaf Foods Inc., Toronto, Canada; *Int'l*, pg. 841
McCain, Harrison, Chm.--McCain Foods Limited, Florenceville, Canada; *Int'l*, pg. 850
McCall, Charles W., Chm. Bd.--HBOC, Atlanta, GA; *U.S. Public*, pg. 770
McCall, Donald, Chm. Bd.--Warner Press, Inc., Anderson, IN; *U.S. Private*, pg. 1150
McCall, Robert H., Chm. Bd., Pres. & Chief Exec. Officer--McCall Oil & Chemical Corp., Portland, OR; *U.S. Private*, *pg. 719*
McCall, Sterling B., Jr., Chm. Bd.--Sterling McCall Toyota Group, Houston, TX; *U.S. Private*, pg. 719
McCallin, John L., Chm. Bd.--Steel, Inc., Commerce City, CO; *U.S. Private*, pg. 1037
McCallum, D., Chm.--NatWest International Trust Holdings Limited, Nassau, Bahamas; *Int'l*, pg. 911
McCallum, John S., Chm. Bd.--Manitoba Hydro, Winnipeg, Canada; *Int'l*, pg. 834
McCann, James F., Chm. Bd.--Conroy's Flowers, Long Beach, CA; *U.S. Private*, pg. 366
McCann, L.D., Chm. Bd., Pres. & Chief Exec. Officer--Standco Industries, Inc., Houston, TX; *U.S. Private*, pg. 1032
McCarragher, B.J., Chm. Bd.--Menasha Corporation, Neenah, WI; *U.S. Private*, pg. 731
McCarthy, C.M., Chm. Bd.--McCain Foods (GB) Limited, Scarborough, United Kingdom; *Int'l*, pg. 850
McCarthy, Leo, Chm. Bd.--Mednet, MPC Corporation, Las Vegas, NV; *U.S. Public*, pg. 1082
McCarthy, Michael M., Chm. Bd. & Chief Exec. Officer--McCarthy Building Companies, Saint Louis, MO; *U.S. Private*, pg. 719
McCartney, Daniel P., Chm. Bd. & Chief Exec. Officer--Healthcare Services Group, Inc., Huntingdon Valley, PA; *U.S. Public*, pg. 803
McCarty, James T., Chm. Bd.--Cigna Compania de Seguros (Chile) S.A., Santiago, Chile; *U.S. Public*, pg. 363
McCauley, Arthur, Chm. Bd. & Pres.--Norwalk Co., Inc., Norwalk, CT; *U.S. Private*, pg. 807
McCausland, Peter, Chm. Bd., Pres. & Chief Exec. Officer--Airgas, Inc., Radnor, PA; *U.S. Public*, pg. 33
McClain, Kenneth D., Chm. Bd., Pres. & Chief Exec. Officer--McClain Industries, Inc., Sterling Heights, MI; *U.S. Public*, pg. 1065
McClean, Murray, Chm. Bd.--Commercial Metals (International) AG, Zug, Switzerland; *U.S. Public*, pg. 414
McClelland, Norman P., Chief Exec. Officer--Shamrock Foods Company, Phoenix, AZ; *U.S. Private*, pg. 989
McClelland, W.C., Chm. Bd. & Chief Exec. Officer--Union Camp Corporation, Wayne, NJ; *U.S. Public*, pg. 1665
McCluggage, Kerry, Chm. Bd., Television Grp.-Viacom Entertainment Grp.--National Amusements, Inc., Dedham, MA; *U.S. Private*, pg. 775
McClung, Jim, Chm. Bd.--National Electrical Manufacturers Association, Arlington, VA; *U.S. Private*, pg. 782
McClure, Thomas R., Chm. & Chief Exec. Officer--The McClure Group, Wayne, PA; *U.S. Private*, pg. 719
McCluskey, Richard T., Chm. Bd., Pres. & Chief Exec. Officer--Fiske Brothers Refining Company, Newark, NJ; *U.S. Private*, pg. 408
McColl, Hugh L., Jr., Chm. Bd. & Chief Exec. Officer--NationsBank Corporation, Charlotte, NC; *U.S. Public*, pg. 1162
McCollum, H.W., Chm.-Fin. Committee--Amerada Hess Corporation, New York, NY; *U.S. Public*, pg. 65
McCollum, James, Chm. Bd. & Chief Exec. Officer--Tingley Rubber Corporation, South Plainfield, NJ; *U.S. Private*, pg. 1088
McComas, Murray K., Chm. Bd. & Pres.--Blair Corporation, Warren, PA; *U.S. Public*, pg. 236
McConnaughy, Tom, Chm. & Chief Creative Officer--McConnaughy Stein Schmidt Brown, Chicago, IL; *U.S. Private*, pg. 720
McConnell, James V., Jr., Chm. Bd.--McConnell Automotive, Mobile, AL; *U.S. Private*, pg. 720
McConnell, John H., Chm. Emeritus & Founder--Worthington Industries, Inc., Columbus, OH; *U.S. Public*, pg. 1780
McConnell, John P., Chm. Bd. & Chief Exec. Officer--Worthington Industries, Inc., Columbus, OH; *U.S. Public*, pg. 1780
McConnell, Michael A., Chm. Bd. & Pres.--Visioneer, Inc., Fremont, CA; *U.S. Public*, pg. 1722
McConnell, Paul R., Chm., Pres. & Chief Exec. Officer--Fleet Bank of Maine, Portland, ME; *U.S. Public*, pg. 649
McConnell, William R., Chm. Bd. & Pres.--McConnell Cabinets, Inc., El Monte, CA; *U.S. Private*, pg. 720
McCord, Herbert W., Chm. Bd., Pres. & Chief Exec. Officer--Granum Communications, Red Bank, NJ; *U.S. Private*, pg. 470
McCormack, John, Chm. Bd.--Visible Changes, Houston, TX; *U.S. Private*, pg. 1141
McCormack, Mark H., Chm. Bd., Pres. & Chief Exec. Officer--IMG, Cleveland, OH; *U.S. Private*, pg. 555
McCormick, Charles P. (Buzz), Jr., Chm. Bd. & Chief Exec. Officer--McCormick/Schilling, Hunt Valley, MD; *U.S. Public*, pg. 1066
McCormick, Charles P., Jr., Chm. Bd.--McCormick & Company, Incorporated, Sparks, MD; *U.S. Public*, pg. 1066
McCormick, R., Jr., Chm. Bd.--American Sweetners, inc., Frazer, PA; *U.S. Private*, pg. 63
McCormick, Richard D., Chm. Bd., Pres. & Chief Exec. Officer--U S West Inc., Englewood, CO; *U.S. Public*, pg. 1688
McCormick, W.T., Jr., Chm. Bd.--Consumers Energy, Jackson, MI; *U.S. Public*, pg. 280
McCormick, William C., Chm. Bd. & Chief Exec. Officer--Precision Castparts Corp., Portland, OR; *U.S. Public*, pg. 1320
McCormick, William T., Jr., Chm. Bd. & Chief Exec. Officer--CMS Energy Corporation, Dearborn, MI; *U.S. Public*, pg. 279
McCourt, David C., Chm. Bd.--Cable Michigan, Inc., Princeton, NJ; *U.S. Public*, pg. 287
McCourt, David C., Chm. Bd.--Commonwealth Telephone Enterprises, Inc., Dallas, PA; *U.S. Public*, pg. 415
McCourt, David C., Chm. Bd. & Chief Exec. Officer--RCN Corporation, Princeton, NJ; *U.S. Public*, pg. 1354
McCoy, John B., Chm. Bd. & Chief Exec. Officer--Banc One Corporation, Columbus, OH; *U.S. Public*, pg. 172
McCoy, R. Michael, Chm. Bd. & Pres.--McCoy Group Inc., Shullsburg, WI; *U.S. Private*, pg. 720
McCracken, Edward R., Chm. Bd. & Chief Exec. Officer--Silicon Graphics, Inc., Mountain View, CA; *U.S. Public*, pg. 1473
McCracken, Thomas, Jr., Chm. Bd.--Regional Transportation Authority (RTA), Chicago, IL; *U.S. Private*, *pg. 918*
McCrady, Kenneth A., Chm. Bd.--Ennis Business Forms, Inc., Ennis, TX; *U.S. Public*, pg. 583
McCulloch, Carolyn H., Chm. Bd.--Bank of Raleigh, Beckley, WV; *U.S. Public*, pg. 836
McCullough, Domhnall, Chm. Bd.--James Crean PLC, Dublin, Ireland; *Int'l*, pg. 340
McCullough, John F., Chm. Bd.--Athey Products Corporation, Wake Forest, NC; *U.S. Public*, pg. 142
McCurdy, Larry W., Chm., Pres. & Chief Exec. Officer--Echlin Inc., Branford, CT; *U.S. Public*, pg. 560
McDaniel, Gary, Chm. Bd. & Pres.--MAC Equipment Inc., Houston, TX; *U.S. Private*, pg. 685
McDermitt, Edward A., Jr., Chm., Pres. & Chief Exec. Officer--National Bulk Carriers, Inc., New York, NY; *U.S. Private*, pg. 780
McDermott, Jeffrey S., Chm. Bd. & Chief Exec. Officer--Bell Atlantic Systems Integration Corp., Arlington, VA; *U.S. Public*, pg. 203
McDonald, Ian, Chm. Bd. & Chief Exec. Officer--Wheaton River Minerals Ltd., Toronto, Canada; *Int'l*, pg. 1498
McDonald, J.M., III, Chm. Bd., Pres. & Chief Exec. Officer--A.Y. McDonald Industries, Inc., Dubuque, IA; *U.S. Private*, pg. 721
McDonald, J.M., III, Chm. Bd. & Chief Exec. Officer--A.Y. McDonald Supply Co. Inc., Dubuque, IA; *U.S. Private*, pg. 721
McDonald, Mike, Chm. Bd.--Texas Holdings Ltd., Manchester, United Kingdom; *Int'l*, pg. 1381
McDonald, R.D., Chm. Bd. & Chief Exec. Officer--A.Y. McDonald Mfg. Co., Dubuque, IA; *U.S. Private*, pg. 721
McDonald, R.D., Chm. Bd. & Chief Exec. Officer--A.Y.M. Inc., Albia, IA; *U.S. Private*, pg. 721
McDonald, T.K., Chm. Bd.--Bank of New Zealand, Wellington, New Zealand; *Int'l*, pg. 906
McDonald, Thomas C., Chm. Bd.--Grindmaster Corporation, Louisville, KY; *U.S. Private*, pg. 482
McDonough, Robert E., Sr., Chm. Bd.--RemedyTemp, Inc., San Juan Capistrano, CA; *U.S. Public*, pg. 1376
McDonough, Russell B., Jr., Chm. Bd. & Chief Exec. Officer--Winrock Enterprises, Inc., Little Rock, AR; *U.S. Private*, pg. 1183
McDowall, John, Chm. Bd.--Avesta Sheffield AB, Stockholm, Sweden; *Int'l*, pg. 221
McDowell, Wallace, Chm. Bd.--Interactive Technologies, Inc., Saint Paul, MN; *U.S. Public*, pg. 888
McEachern, James, Chm. Bd. & Chief Exec. Officer--Tom James Company, Franklin, TN; *U.S. Private*, pg. 580
McElhinny, W.D., Chm. Bd.--Irex Corporation, Lancaster, PA; *U.S. Public*, pg. 913
McEniry, Robert Q., Chm. Bd.--nexAir, Memphis, TN; *U.S. Private*, pg. 797
McEwen, Joseph, Chm. Bd. & Chief Exec. Officer--Modern Group Ltd., Bristol, PA; *U.S. Private*, pg. 754
McEwen, Robert R., Chm. Bd. & Chief Exec. Officer--Goldcorp Inc., Toronto, Canada; *Int'l*, pg. 243
McEwen, Robert R., Chm. & Chief Exec. Officer--Lexam Explorations Inc., Toronto, Canada; *Int'l*, pg. 243
McFadin, Larry, Chm. Bd. & Chief Exec. Officer--Philip Crosby Associates, Inc., Winter Park, FL; *Int'l*, pg. 1072
McFall, Tom, Chm. Bd., Pres. & Chief Exec. Officer--Weatherly Private Capital, Inc., New York, NY; *U.S. Private*, pg. 1156
McFarlane, D.D., Chm. Bd.--Senior Engineering Group, plc., Rickmansworth, United Kingdom; *Int'l*, pg. 1220
McFarling, James W., Chm. Bd.--McFarling Foods, Inc., Indianapolis, IN; *U.S. Private*, pg. 721
McFerson, D. Richard, Chm. Bd. & Chief Exec. Officer--Nationwide Insurance Enterprise, Columbus, OH; *U.S. Private*, pg. 788
McFerson, D.R., Chm. Bd. & Chief Exec Officer--Nationwide Mutual Insurance Co., Columbus, OH; *U.S. Private*, pg. 789
McGehee, Frank S., Co-Chm. Bd. & Co-Chief Exec. Officer--Mac Papers, Inc., Jacksonville, FL; *U.S. Private*, pg. 689
McGehee, Thomas R., Co-Chm Bd. & Chief Exec. Officer--Mac Papers, Inc., Jacksonville, FL; *U.S. Private*, pg. 689
McGettigan, Patrick H., Chm. Bd.--Landmark Systems Corporation, Vienna, VA; *U.S. Private*, pg. 649
McGhan, Donald, Chm. Bd. & Chief Exec. Officer--Inamed Corporation, Las Vegas, NV; *U.S. Public*, pg. 873
McGillicuddy, Dennis, Chm. Bd. & Chief Oper. Officer--CCX, Inc., Charlotte, NC; *U.S. Private*, pg. 193
McGinley, William J., Chm.--Methode Electronics Inc., Chicago, IL; *U.S. Public*, pg. 1101
McGinnis, Arthur J., Sr., Chm. Bd.-Exec. Committee & Chief Exec. Officer--Simmons-Boardman Publishing Corp., New York, NY; *U.S. Private*, pg. 1000
McGinnis, Gerald E., Chm. Bd.--Respironics, Inc., Pittsburgh, PA; *U.S. Public*, pg. 1383
McGinnis, Michael E., Chm. Bd., Pres. & Chief Exec. Officer--American Eco Corporation, Toronto, Canada; *Int'l*, pg. 73
McGlorhlin, James W., Chm. Bd.--Virginia Metal Industries, Inc., Orange, VA; *U.S. Private*, pg. 1141
McGlothlin, James E., Chm. Bd. & Pres.--Quintron Systems, Inc., Santa Maria, CA; *U.S. Private*, pg. 901
McGlynn, Micheal J., Chm. Bd. & Chief Exec. Officer--McGlynn Bakeries Inc., Minneapolis, MN; *U.S. Private*, pg. 721
McGough, George, Chm., Pres. & Chief Exec. Officer--Principal Financial Securities, Dallas, TX; *U.S. Private*, pg. 885

McGovern, Donald A., Chm.-High Tech. Indus. Practice--Price Waterhouse L.L.P. - U.S., New York, NY; *U.S. Private*, pg. 883
McGovern, G., Chm. Bd. & Mng. Dir.--Bovis International Ltd., London, United Kingdom; *Int'l*, pg. 1032
McGovern, Patrick J., Chm. Bd.--International Data Group, Boston, MA; *U.S. Private*, pg. 569
McGowan, Mike, Chm. Bd. & Chief Exec. Officer--N.B.M. Corp., McAlester, OK; *U.S. Private*, pg. 771
McGrath, David J., III, Chm. Bd.--TAD Resources International, Inc., Cambridge, MA; *U.S. Private*, pg. 1062
McGrath, E.B., Chm. Bd.--Bradstock Group plc, London, United Kingdom; *Int'l*, pg. 210
McGrath, Edward A., Chm. Bd.--VWR Scientific Products, West Chester, PA; *U.S. Public*, pg. 1703
McGrath, Eugene R., Chm. Bd., Pres. & Chief Exec. Officer--Consolidated Edison Company of New York, Inc., New York, NY; *U.S. Public*, pg. 434
McGrath, John, Chm. Bd.--Burger King Corporation, Miami, FL; *Int'l*, pg. 411
McGrath, Robert P., Chm. Bd. & Chief Exec. Officer--McGrath RentCorp, Livermore, CA; *U.S. Public*, pg. 1069
McGregor, A. G., Chm. Bd.--James Hardie Industries Ltd., Sydney, Australia; *Int'l*, pg. 596
McGregor, Alan, Chm. Bd.--Burns, Philp & Company Limited, Sydney, Australia; *Int'l*, pg. 236
McGregor, Douglas J., Chm. Bd. & Chief Exec. Officer--M.A. Hanna Company, Cleveland, OH; *U.S. Public*, pg. 780
McGregor, Stewart D., Chm. Bd. & Chief Exec. Officer--Numac Energy Inc., Calgary, Canada; *Int'l*, pg. 990
McGrevin, Gene R., Chm. Bd. & Pres.--Isolyser Company, Inc., Norcross, GA; *U.S. Public*, pg. 914
McGuire, Thomas R., Chm. Bd. & Chief Exec. Officer--The Coast Distribution System, San Jose, CA; *U.S. Public*, pg. 388
McGuire, William W., M.D., Chm. Bd., Pres. & Chief Exec. Officer--United HealthCare Corporation, Minnetonka, MN; *U.S. Public*, pg. 1677
McGuire, William W., M.D., Chm. Bd., Pres. & Chief Exec. Officer--United HealthCare Services, Inc., Minnetonka, MN; *U.S. Public*, pg. 1678
McGuirk, Terence F., Chm. Bd., Pres. & Chief Exec. Officer--Turner Broadcasting System Inc., Atlanta, GA; *U.S. Public*, pg. 1614
McHose, J. Kent, Chm.--Filene's, Boston, MA; *U.S. Public*, pg. 1063
McHugh, C.R., Chm. Bd.--NatWest Futures Inc., Chicago, IL; *Int'l*, pg. 911
McIntyre, James A., Chm. Bd. & Chief Exec. Officer--Fremont General Corporation, Santa Monica, CA; *U.S. Public*, pg. 681
McIntyre, Scott, Jr., Chm. Bd.--United Fire & Casualty Company, Cedar Rapids, IA; *U.S. Public*, pg. 1677
McIntyre, Scott, Jr., Chm. Bd.--Addison Insurance Company, Lombard, IL; *U.S. Public*, pg. 1677
McIntyre, Scott, Jr., Chm.--Lafayette Insurance Company, New Orleans, LA; *U.S. Public*, pg. 1677
McKay, Eugene H., Jr., Chm. Bd.--Archway Cookies, Inc., Battle Creek, MI; *U.S. Private*, pg. 80
Mckay, Keith, Chm.--Von Broembsen Marson Leo Burnett/Harare, Harare, Zimbabwe; *U.S. Private*, pg. 186
McKean, John R., Chm. Bd.--Bay View Capital Corporation, San Mateo, CA; *U.S. Public*, pg. 197
McKearn, Thomas J., Dr., Chm. & Chief Exec. Officer--Cytogen Corporation, Princeton, NJ; *U.S. Public*, pg. 471
McKee, Ellsworth, Chm. Bd.--McKee Foods Corporation, Collegedale, TN; *U.S. Private*, pg. 723
McKeever, Jeffrey D., Chm. Bd. & Chief Exec. Officer--MicroAge, Inc., Tempe, AZ; *U.S. Public*, pg. 1104
McKelvey, Andrew J., Chm. & Chief Exec. Officer--TMP Worldwide, Inc., New York, NY; *U.S. Private*, pg. 1064
Mckenna, Andrew J., Sr., Chm. Bd. & Chief Exec. Officer--Schwarz Paper Company, Morton Grove, IL; *U.S. Private*, pg. 974
McKenna, P.W., Chm. Bd., Pres. & Chief Exec. Officer--Plasti-Kote Company Inc., Medina, OH; *U.S. Private*, pg. 870
McKenna, Robert J., Chm. Bd., Pres. & Chief Exec. Officer--Acme Electric Corporation, East Aurora, NY; *U.S. Public*, pg. 16
McKenna, William J., Chm. Bd.--Kellwood Company, Chesterfield, MO; *U.S. Public*, pg. 948
McKenney, S.S., III, Chm. Bd. & Pres.--W & B Refrigeration Service Co., Dallas, TX; *U.S. Public*, pg. 685
McKennon, Keith R., Chm. Bd.--PacifiCorp, Portland, OR; *U.S. Public*, pg. 1251
McKenzie, John, Chm. Bd. & Chief Exec. Officer--Sleepeezee Limited, London, United Kingdom; *Int'l*, pg. 1263
McKenzie, Michael K., Chm. Bd., Pres. & Chief Exec. Officer--GSC Enterprises, Inc., Sulphur Springs, TX; *U.S. Private*, pg. 436
McKerman, John, Jr., Chm. Bd.--C.F. Hathaway, Waterville, ME; *U.S. Private*, pg. 510
McKiernan, Thomas, Chm. Bd. & Interim Chief Exec. Officer--Moore Corporation Limited, Toronto, Canada; *Int'l*, pg. 888
McKim, Alan S., Chm. Bd., Pres. & Chief Exec. Officer--Clean Harbors, Inc., Braintree, MA; *U.S. Public*, pg. 383
McKinney, Myron W., Chm. Bd., Pres. & Chief Exec. Officer--The Empire District Electric Company, Joplin, MO; *U.S. Public*, pg. 579
McKinney, Reynold, Chm. Bd. & Pres.--McKinney & McKinney Advertising, Redondo Beach, CA; *U.S. Private*, *pg. 723*
McKinney, Robert H., Chm. Bd.--The Somerset Group, Inc., Indianapolis, IN; *U.S. Public*, pg. 1484
McKinney, Robert H., Chm. Bd. & Chief Exec. Officer--First Indiana Corporation, Indianapolis, IN; *U.S. Public*, pg. 1484
McKinniss, Sherman L., Chm. Bd., Pres. & Chief Exec. Officer--Rotonics Manufacturing Inc., Gardena, CA; *U.S. Public*, pg. 1406
McKnight, Andrew D., Chm. Bd., Pres. & Chief Exec. Officer--Tri-Chem, Inc., Harrison, NJ; *U.S. Private*, pg. 1100
McKnight, Robert B., Jr., Chm. Bd. & Chief Exec. Officer--Quiksilver, Inc., Costa Mesa, CA; *U.S. Public*, pg. 1353
McKnight, William M., Chm. Bd.--McKnight Medical Communications Company, Northfield, IL; *U.S. Public*, pg. 1601
McLagan, Donald L., Chm. Bd., Pres. & Chief Exec. Officer--NewsEdge Corporation, Burlington, MA; *U.S. Public*, pg. 1180
McLaughlin, Brian D., Chm. Bd., Pres. & Chief Exec. Officer--Hurco Companies, Inc., Indianapolis, IN; *U.S. Public*, pg. 850
McLaughlin, David, Chm. Bd.--PartnerRe Ltd., Pembroke, Bermuda; *Int'l*, pg. 1024
McLaughlin, R.L., Chm.Bd.--Bee Line Company, Bettendorf, IA; *U.S. Private*, pg. 129
McLaughlin, Robert, Chm. Bd.--Anchor Continental Incorporated, Columbia, SC; *U.S. Private*, pg. 70
McLaurin, Neil H., III, Chm. Bd. & Chief Exec. Officer--E-Z Serve Corp., Houston, TX; *U.S. Public*, pg. 540
McLean, D.G.A., Chm. Bd.--Canadian National Railway Company, Montreal, Canada; *Int'l*, pg. 258
McLean, Gary R., Chm. Bd. & Pres.--Interstate Distributor Company, Tacoma, WA; *U.S. Private*, pg. 573
McLean, William L., III, Chm. Bd. & Pres.--Independent Publications, Inc., Bryn Mawr, PA; *U.S. Private*, pg. 559
McLendon, John A., Chm. Bd.--Nationwide Homes, Inc., Martinsville, VA; *U.S. Private*, pg. 788
McLennan, John T., Chm. Bd. & Chief Exec. Officer--Bell Mobility Paging Inc., Downsview, Canada; *Int'l*, pg. 115
McLennan, Robert G., J.D., Chm. Bd.--Advocate Health Care, Oak Brook, IL; *U.S. Private*, pg. 23
McLeod, Clark, Chm. Bd. & Chief Exec. Officer--McLeodUSA Incorporated, Cedar Rapids, IA; *U.S. Public*, *pg. 1073*
McLeod, John, Chm. Bd.--Lone Star Corrugated Container Corporation, Irving, TX; *U.S. Private*, pg. 674
McLeod, John S., Sr., Chm. Bd.--Mar-Mac Manufacturing Company, Inc., McBee, SC; *U.S. Private*, pg. 701
McMackin, John W., Chm. Bd.--Blessings Corporation, Newport News, VA; *U.S. Private*, pg. 1179
McMahan, John, Chm. Bd.--BRE Properties, Inc., San Francisco, CA; *U.S. Public*, pg. 163
McMahen, Charles E., Chm. Bd. & Chief Exec. Officer--Compass Bancshares, Inc., Houston, TX; *U.S. Public*, pg. 419
McMahon, John J., Chm. Bd.--McWane, Inc., Birmingham, AL; *U.S. Private*, pg. 725
McMahon, John M., Chm. Bd.--Miller & Long Co. Inc., Bethesda, MD; *U.S. Private*, pg. 746
McManus, Michael F., Chm. Bd., Pres. & Chief Exec. Officer--Header Products Inc., Romulus, MI; *U.S. Private*, *pg. 514*
McMaster, Lee P., Chm. Bd.--Union Carbide Asia Pacific Inc., Singapore, Singapore; *U.S. Public*, pg. 1667
McMath, George N., Chm. Bd.--Farmers & Merchants Bank-Eastern Shore, Onley, VA; *U.S. Public*, pg. 1089
McMillan, Douglas, Chm. Bd. & Chief Exec. Officer--Allison-Erwin Co. Inc., Charlotte, NC; *U.S. Private*, pg. 41
McMillan, Steve, Chm. Bd.--Electrolux Corporation, Atlanta, GA; *U.S. Private*, pg. 369
McMillen, Robert B., Co.-Chm. & Co.-Chief Exec. Officer--Totem Resources Corporation, Seattle, WA; *U.S. Private*, *pg. 1092*
McMillen, Russell G., Chm. Bd.--The Eastern Company, Naugatuck, CT; *U.S. Public*, pg. 548
McMorrow, William, Chm. Bd. & Chief Exec. Officer--Kennedy-Wilson, Inc., Santa Monica, CA; *U.S. Public*, pg. 951
McMullen, Walter P., Sr., Chm. Bd. & Chief Exec. Officer--Master Graphic, Inc., Memphis, TN; *U.S. Private*, pg. 713
McMullian, Amos R., Chm. Bd. & Chief Exec. Officer--Flowers Industries, Inc., Thomasville, GA; *U.S. Public*, pg. 656
McMurray, J. Patrick, Chm., Pres. & Chief Exec. Officer--First Security Bank of Idaho, N.A., Boise, ID; *U.S. Public*, *pg. 637*
McMurtrie, James C., Chm. Bd., Chief Exec. Officer & Treas.--E.W. Knauss & Son, Inc., Quakertown, PA; *U.S. Private*, pg. 626
McMurtry, David, Chm. Bd. & Chief Exec. Officer--Renishaw plc, Wotton-under-Edge, United Kingdom; *Int'l*, pg. 1103
McNally, Alan G., Chm. Bd. & Chief Exec. Officer--Harris Bankcorp, Inc., Chicago, IL; *Int'l*, pg. 154
McNally, J., Chm.--Ulster Bank Dublin Trust Company, Dublin, Ireland; *Int'l*, pg. 912
McNamara, Donald J., Chm. Bd.--Bristol Hotels & Resorts, Dallas, TX; *U.S. Public*, pg. 253
McNamee, George C., Chm. Bd.--Mechanical Technology Inc., Latham, NY; *U.S. Public*, pg. 1077
McNamee, James M., Chm. Bd., Pres. & Chief Exec. Officer--Hooper Holmes Corporation, Basking Ridge, NJ; *U.S. Public*, pg. 835
McNaughton, Robert L., Chm. Bd. & Pres.--McNaughton & Gunn, Inc., Saline, MI; *U.S. Private*, pg. 724
McNeal, Larry M., Chm. Bd.--CB & T Bank of Middle Georgia, Warner Robins, GA; *U.S. Public*, pg. 1549
McNealy, Scott G., Chm. Bd., Pres. & Chief Exec. Officer--Sun Microsystems, Inc., Palo Alto, CA; *U.S. Public*, pg. 1531
McNeil, John D., Chm. Bd. & Chief Exec. Officer--Sun Life Assurance Company of Canada, Toronto, Canada; *Int'l*, pg. 1318
McNeil, Manford, Chm.Bd.--Hays Fluid Controls-Division of Romac Industries, Dallas, NC; *U.S. Private*, pg. 942
McNeill, Blair E., Chm.--CoreStates Bank of Delaware NA, Wilmington, DE; *U.S. Public*, pg. 447
McNeill, Bruce, Chm. Bd.--Superior Federal Bank, Fort Smith, AR; *U.S. Private*, pg. 1054
McNeill, Corbin A., Jr., Chm. Bd., Pres. & Chief Exec. Officer--PECO Energy Company, Philadelphia, PA; *U.S. Public*, pg. 1268
McNeilly, Robert E., Jr., Chm. Bd.--First American National Bank, Nashville, TN; *U.S. Public*, pg. 624
McNeilus, Garwin, Chm. Bd.--McNeilus Companies, Dodge Center, MN; *U.S. Private*, pg. 725
McNerney, J. Peter, Chm. Bd.--Seneca Wire & Manufacturing Co., Fostoria, OH; *U.S. Private*, pg. 984
McNicoll, Donald, Chm. Bd.--Willis Corroon Limited, Auckland, New Zealand; *Int'l*, pg. 1509
McNutt, L.W., Jr., Chm. Bd. & Chief Exec. Officer--Collin Street Bakery, Corsicana, TX; *U.S. Private*, pg. 252
McPhail, B.D., Chm. Bd.--P&O Property Holdings Ltd., London, United Kingdom; *Int'l*, pg. 1034
McPhail, B.D., Chm. Bd.--CCL Ltd., London, United Kingdom; *Int'l*, pg. 1034
McPherson, Warren F., Dr., Chm. Bd.--State Volunteer Mutual Insurance Co., Brentwood, TN; *U.S. Private*, pg. 1037
McQueen, Angus, Chm. Bd. & Chief Exec. Officer--Ackerman McQueen, Inc., Oklahoma City, OK; *U.S. Private*, pg. 12
McQuinn, Alvin E., Chm. Bd. & Chief Exec. Officer--Ag-Chem Equipment Co., Inc., Minnetonka, MN; *U.S. Public*, *pg. 6*
McRae, D. Gary, Chm. Bd., Pres. & Chief Exec. Officer--McRae Industries, Inc., Mount Gilead, NC; *U.S. Public*, pg. 1073
McReilly, Robert E., Jr., Chm.--First American Trust Company, N.A., Nashville, TN; *U.S. Public*, pg. 624
McVaney, C. Edward, Pres. & Chief Exec. Officer--J.D. Edwards & Company, Denver, CO; *U.S. Private*, pg. 365
McWane, James R., Chm. Exec. Committee--McWane, Inc., Birmingham, AL; *U.S. Private*, pg. 725
McWhorter, Archer, Chm. Bd.--National Car Rental System, Inc., Minneapolis, MN; *U.S. Public*, pg. 1379
McWhorter, Donald L., Chm. Bd. & Chief Exec. Officer--Banc One Ohio Corporation, Columbus, OH; *U.S. Public*, *pg. 173*
McWilliam, Richard, Chm. Bd. & Chief Exec. Officer--The Upper Deck Company, LLC, Carlsbad, CA; *U.S. Private*, pg. 1129
Mead, Dana, Chm. Bd.--Monroe Auto Equipment Co., Monroe, MI; *U.S. Public*, pg. 1577
Mead, Dana G., Chm. Bd., Pres. & Chief Exec. Officer--Tenneco Inc., Greenwich, CT; *U.S. Public*, pg. 1577
Mead, George W., Chm. Bd.--Consolidated Papers, Inc., Wisconsin Rapids, WI; *U.S. Public*, pg. 436
Meadlock, James W., Chm. Bd., Pres. & Chief Exec. Officer--Intergraph Corporation, Huntsville, AL; *U.S. Public*, pg. 890
Meagher, Richard L., Chm. Bd.--Harza Engineering Co., Chicago, IL; *U.S. Private*, pg. 509
Meakem, John J., Jr., Chm. Bd., Pres. & Chief Exec. Officer--Advanced Polymer Systems, Redwood City, CA; *U.S. Public*, pg. 22
Meanti, Luigi, Chm. & Pres.--ENI S.p.A., Rome, Italy; *Int'l*, pg. 428
Meany, H. Jack, Chm. Bd. & Chief Exec. Officer--Farr Company, El Segundo, CA; *U.S. Public*, pg. 613
Mears, Paul S., Sr., Chm. Bd.--Mears Transportation Group, Orlando, FL; *U.S. Private*, pg. 726
Meazzini, Vittorio, Chm.--Snam International Holding A.G., Zurich, Switzerland; *Int'l*, pg. 429
Mebane, David C., Chm. Bd., Pres., Chief Exec. & Oper. Officer--Madison Gas and Electric Company, Madison, WI; *U.S. Public*, pg. 1032
Mebane, G. Allen, Chm. Bd.--Unifi Inc., Greensboro, NC; *U.S. Public*, pg. 1665
Mechem, Charles S., Jr., Chm. Bd.--Cincinnati Bell Telephone, Cincinnati, OH; *U.S. Public*, pg. 367
Mecklinger, R., Dr., Chm.--Argo Instruments Inc., Winchester, VA; *Int'l*, pg. 839
Medavoy, Mike, Chm. Bd.--TriStar Pictures, Culver City, CA; *Int'l*, pg. 1283
Medina, Agustin, Chm., Pres. & Creative Dir.--La Banda de Agustin Medina S.A., Madrid, Spain; *Int'l*, pg. 783
Medina, Dionisio Garza, Chm. Bd., Pres. & Chief Exec. Officer--Alfa, S.A. de C.V., Garza Garcia, Mexico; *Int'l*, pg. 56
Medina, Dionisio Garza, Chm. Bd.--Hylsamex, S.A. de C.V., San Nicolas, Mexico; *Int'l*, pg. 56
Medina, Robert S., Dr., Chm. Bd.--International Systems & Controls Corp., Houston, TX; *U.S. Private*, pg. 572
Medlin, John G., Jr., Chm. Bd.--Wachovia Corporation, Winston Salem, NC; *U.S. Public*, pg. 1730
Medlock, Jeff, Chm.-Exec. Bd.--Eureko B.V., Amsterdam, Netherlands; *Int'l*, pg. 464
Mee, George, Chm. & Pres.--Mallery Lumber Corp., Emporium, PA; *U.S. Private*, pg. 698
Meek, Paul D., Chm. Bd.--Fina, Inc., Dallas, TX; *Int'l*, pg. 1044
Meeker, Thomas H., Chm. Bd.--Hoosier Park Ltd., Anderson, IN; *U.S. Public*, pg. 356
Meekison, James D., Chm. Bd.--Trimin Enterprises, Inc., Vancouver, Canada; *Int'l*, pg. 1424
Mehdorn, Hartmut, Chm. Bd.--Heidelberger Druckmaschinen A.G., Heidelberg, Germany; *Int'l*, pg. 604
Mehiel, Dennis, Chm. Bd. & Pres.--Four M Corporation, Inc., Valhalla, NY; *U.S. Private*, pg. 421
Mehlis, David L., Chm. Bd., Pres. & Chief Exec. Officer--Cook Communication Ministries, Colorado Springs, CO; *U.S. Private*, pg. 272
Mehner, Edward W., Chm. Bd. & Chief Exec. Officer--The Rugby Group, Inc., Rockville Centre, NY; *Int'l*, pg. 625
Mehta, Dr. A.S., Chm.--John Wyeth (India) Limited, Mumbai, India; *U.S. Public*, pg. 82
Mehta, Shailesh J., Chm. Bd., Pres. & Chief Exec. Officer--Providian Financial Corporation, San Francisco, CA; *U.S. Public*, pg. 1338
Meijer, Doug, Co-Chm.--Meijer, Inc., Grand Rapids, MI; *U.S. Private*, pg. 729

Meijer, Hank, Co-Chm.--Meijer, Inc., Grand Rapids, MI; *U.S. Private*, pg. 729

Meijer, M.C.J., Chm. Bd.--Quaker Chemical S.A., Villeneuve-la-Garonne, France; *U.S. Public*, pg. 1347

Meinhardt, Hans, Dr., Chm.-Executive Bd.--Linde AG, Wiesbaden, Germany; *Int'l*, pg. 810

Meinhardt, Hans, Dr., Chm. Bd.--VARTA AG, Hannover, Germany; *Int'l*, pg. 1451

Meinl, Julius, IV, Chm.-Supervisory Bd.--Julius Meinl AG, Vienna, Austria; *Int'l*, pg. 856

Mele, Edward V., Chm. Bd.--Mele Manufacturing Co., Inc., Utica, NY; *U.S. Private*, pg. 730

Melin, David, Chm. & Chief Exec. Officer--Groupe Saint Louis, Paris, France; *Int'l*, pg. 567

Melin, J., Chm.--Glaxo Wellcome AB, Molndal, Sweden; *Int'l*, pg. 553

Mellon, Timothy, Chm. Bd. & Chief Exec. Officer--Guilford Transportation Industries Inc., Nashua, NH; *U.S. Private*, pg. 487

Mellott, Forrest R., Chm. Bd.--H.B. Mellott Estate, Inc., Warfordsburg, PA; *U.S. Private*, pg. 730

Melnick, Norman, Chm. Bd. & Chief Exec. Officer--Pentech International, Inc., Edison, NJ; *U.S. Public*, pg. 1274

Melnuk, Paul D., Chm. Bd., Pres. & Chief Oper. Officer--Clark Refining & Marketing Inc., Saint Louis, MO; *U.S. Private*, pg. 243

Meloni, Stefano, Chm. Bd., Pres. & Chief Exec. Officer--Eridania Beghin-Say Group, Neuilly-sur-Seine, France; *Int'l*, pg. 324

Meloon, Ralph C., Sr., Chm. Bd.--Correct Craft, Inc., Orlando, FL; *U.S. Private*, pg. 276

Melrose, Kendrick B., Chm. Bd. & Chief Exec. Officer--The Toro Company, Bloomington, MN; *U.S. Public*, pg. 1623

Meltz, Edward E., Chm. Bd., Chief Exec. Officer & Chief Fin. Officer--Carsen Group Inc., Markham, Canada; *U.S. Public*, pg. 301

Meltzer, David B., Chm. Bd.--Evans, Inc., Chicago, IL; *U.S. Public*, pg. 596

Melvyn, London, Chm. Bd.--London Litho Aluminum Co., Inc., Lincolnwood, IL; *U.S. Private*, pg. 673

Menario, John E., Chm. Bd.--Consumers Water Company, Portland, ME; *U.S. Public*, pg. 438

Mendelsohn, Joe, Chm. Bd.--First Team Sports Inc., Anoka, MN; *U.S. Public*, pg. 638

Mendelsohn, Robert V., Chm. Bd., Pres. & Chief Exec. Officer--Royal Insurance, Charlotte, NC; *Int'l*, pg. 1130

Mendelson, Laurans, Chm. Bd., Pres. & Chief Exec. Officer--HEICO Corporation, Hollywood, FL; *U.S. Public*, pg. 804

Mendelson, Murry, Chm. Bd.--Murry's, Inc., Upper Marlboro, MD; *U.S. Private*, pg. 768

Mendik, Bernard H., Chm. Bd.--MENDIK Management Co., Inc., New York, NY; *U.S. Private*, pg. 731

Mendoza Fernandez, Jose, Chm. Bd. & Exec. V.P.--Bufete Industrial S.A. de C.V., Mexico, Mexico; *Int'l*, pg. 232

Mengedoth, Donald R., Chm. Bd., Pres., & Chief Exec. Officer--Community First Bankshares, Inc., Fargo, ND; *U.S. Public*, pg. 416

Menges, Carl B., Chm. Bd. & Chief Exec. Officer--Wood, Struthers & Winthrop Management Corp., New York, NY; *U.S. Public*, pg. 589

Menichetti, Giancarlo, Chm. Bd.--Merloni Elettrodomestici S.A., Madrid, Spain; *Int'l*, pg. 860

Menkel, William C., Chm. Bd. & Pres.--Nashville Bank of Commerce, Nashville, TN; *U.S. Public*, pg. 1155

Mentzer, Carl F., Chm. Bd., Pres. & Chief Exec. Officer--SunTrust Bank, Tampa Bay, Tampa, FL; *U.S. Public*, pg. 1538

Menzies-Gow, Ian, Chm. Bd.--Geest PLC, Spalding, United Kingdom; *Int'l*, pg. 542

Mercer, Robert E., Chm. Bd.--Roadway Express, Inc., Akron, OH; *U.S. Public*, pg. 1392

Mercure, Gilles, Chm. Bd.--Cambior Inc., Montreal, Canada; *Int'l*, pg. 253

Mercurio, Pascal J., Chm. Bd. & Chief Exec. Officer--U.S. Clearing Corp., New York, NY; *U.S. Public*, pg. 650

Merelli, F.H., Chm. Bd., Pres. & Chief Exec. Officer--Key Production Company, Inc., Denver, CO; *U.S. Public*, pg. 953

Meringola, Paul D., Chm. Bd., Pres., Chief Exec. Officer & Chief Oper. Officer--Medical Action Industries Inc., Hauppauge, NY; *U.S. Public*, pg. 1079

Merinoff, Herman I., Chm. Bd.--Charmer Industries, Astoria, NY; *U.S. Private*, pg. 230

Meriwether, J. Bruce, Chm. Bd. & Chief Exec. Officer--Mercantile Bank of Dubuque, N.A., Dubuque, IA; *U.S. Public*, pg. 1088

Merker, Steven, Chm. Bd., Chief Fin. Officer & Treas.--Standard Automotive Corporation, Hillsborough, NJ; *U.S. Private*, pg. 1030

Merkin, A. Barry, Chm. Bd. & Chief Exec. Officer--Dresher, Inc., Carthage, MO; *U.S. Public*, pg. 986

Merloni, Vittorio, Dtre., Chm. Bd., Pres. & Chief Exec. Officer--Merloni Elettrodomestici S.P.A., Fabriano, Italy; *Int'l*, pg. 860

Merriam, David, Chm. Bd.--American Kennel Club, Inc., New York, NY; *U.S. Private*, pg. 58

Merriam, J. Alec, Chm. Bd.--PLM International, Inc., San Francisco, CA; *U.S. Public*, pg. 1241

Merrill, Keniston P., Chm. Bd., Pres. & Chief Exec. Officer--Sentinel Advisors, Inc., Montpelier, VT; *U.S. Private*, pg. 785

Merrill, Keniston P., Chm., Pres. & Chief Exec. Officer--National Life Investment Management Co., Inc., Montpelier, VT; *U.S. Private*, pg. 785

Merriman, Mike, Chm. Bd., Pres. & Chief Exec. Officer--Royal Appliance Mfg. Co., Cleveland, OH; *U.S. Public*, pg. 1410

Merse, Lawrence, Chm. Bd.--Federal Business Products, Inc., Clifton, NJ; *U.S. Private*, pg. 398

Merson, Albert, Chm. Bd.--MacNaughton Einson Graphics, Fair Lawn, NJ; *U.S. Private*, pg. 692

Messier, Jean-Marie, Chm. Bd. & Pres.--Compagnie Generale Des Eaux, Paris, France; *Int'l*, pg. 321

Messmer, Harold M., Jr., Chm. Bd., Pres. & Chief Exec. Officer--Robert Half International Inc., Menlo Park, CA; *U.S. Public*, pg. 774

Messner, James W., Chm. Bd. & Chief Exec. Officer--J.W. Messner, Inc., Grand Rapids, MI; *U.S. Private*, pg. 734

Mestorakis, Emmanuel, Chm. Bd.--Alpha Omikron Limited, Monaco, Monaco; *Int'l*, pg. 65

Mestrallet, Gerard, Chm. Bd. & Chief Exec. Officer--Compagnie de Suez, Paris, France; *Int'l*, pg. 313

Mestrallet, Gerard, Chm. Bd.--Tractebel, Brussels, Belgium; *Int'l*, pg. 1414

Mestre, Fernando Senderos, Chm. Bd. & Chief Exec. Officer--Desc, S.A. de C.V., Mexico, Mexico; *Int'l*, pg. 395

Meton, Sonia, Chm. Bd. & Chief Exec. Officer--Turbomeca Microturbo Division, Bordes, France; *Int'l*, pg. 786

Metropolous, C. Dean, Chm. Bd. & Chief Exec. Officer--The Morning Star Group, Dallas, TX; *U.S. Public*, pg. 1527

Metropoulos, C. Dean, Chm. Bd.--International Home Foods Inc., Parsippany, NJ; *U.S. Private*, pg. 526

Mettler, Ole R., Chm. Bd.--Farmers & Merchants Bank of Central California, Lodi, CA; *U.S. Private*, pg. 394

Mettler, Rollin, Jr., Chm. Bd.--Circuit-Wise, Inc., North Haven, CT; *U.S. Private*, pg. 240

Metz, Gerhard, Chm.--St. Johann Lagerhaus & Schiffahrts-Gesellschaft, Basel, Switzerland; *Int'l*, pg. 330

Metz, Gerhard, Dr., Chm.--CCB Co-op Bank Limited, Basel, Switzerland; *Int'l*, pg. 329

Metz, Gerhard, Dr., Chm.--Coop Bank, Basel, Switzerland; *Int'l*, pg. 329

Metz, Gerhard, Dr., Chm.--Coop Lebensversicherungs Genossenschaft, Basel, Switzerland; *Int'l*, pg. 330

Meulnart, Alain, Chm.--Royal Champignon, Sauitur, France; *Int'l*, pg. 567

Meuser, Stanley, Chm. Bd.--Pride Health Care, Inc., Exeter, PA; *U.S. Private*, pg. 883

Meyer, Edward H., Chm., Chief Exec. Officer & Pres.-Grey Worldwide--Grey Advertising Inc., New York, NY; *U.S. Public*, pg. 764

Meyer, Fred, Chm. Bd., Chief Exec. Officer--Bierbrauerei Fohrenburg, Bludenz, Austria; *Int'l*, pg. 194

Meyer, Frederick R., Chm. Bd. & Chief Exec. Officer--Aladdin Industries, Incorporated, Nashville, TN; *U.S. Private*, pg. 30

Meyer, Henry L., III, Chm. & Chief Exec. Officer--Society National Bank, Cleveland, OH; *U.S. Public*, pg. 954

Meyer, Jerome J., Chm. Bd., Pres. & Chief Exec. Officer--Tektronix, Inc., Wilsonville, OR; *U.S. Public*, pg. 1567

Meyer, Michael, Chm. & Chief Exec. Officer--Emess PLC, London, United Kingdom; *Int'l*, pg. 453

Meyer, Robert, Chm. Bd.--Midwest Mutual Insurance Co., West Des Moines, IA; *U.S. Private*, pg. 881

Meyer, Rolf A., Chm. Bd.--Ciba Specialty Chemicals Holding Inc., Basel, Switzerland; *Int'l*, pg. 291

Meyer, Russell W., Jr., Chm. Bd. & Chief Exec. Officer--The Cessna Aircraft Co., Wichita, KS; *U.S. Public*, pg. 1589

Meyer, W. Darrell, Chm. Bd., Pres. & Chief Exec. Officer--Arkansas Bank & Trust, Hot Springs Village, AR; *U.S. Public*, pg. 630

Meyer, William M., Chm. Bd. & Treas.--Central Sprinkler Company, Lansdale, PA; *U.S. Public*, pg. 327

Meyercord, Wade F., Chm. Bd.--California Micro Devices, Milpitas, CA; *U.S. Public*, pg. 293

Meyers, Howard M., Chm. Bd. & Chief Exec. Officer--Bayou Steel Corporation, La Place, LA; *U.S. Public*, pg. 197

Meyerson, Morton H., Chm. Bd.--Perot Systems Corporation, Dallas, TX; *U.S. Private*, pg. 854

Meyes, Roland, Chm. Bd.--Nestle Industrial e Commercial Ltda., Sao Paulo, Brazil; *Int'l*, pg. 921

Mezzina, John, Chm. & Exec. Creative Dir.--Mezzina/Brown Inc., New York, NY; *U.S. Private*, pg. 739

Mia Je, Patrick Ngiam, Chm. Bd. & Chief Exec. Officer--IPC Corporation Ltd., Singapore, Singapore; *Int'l*, pg. 651

Micali, James, Chm. Bd. & Pres.--Michelin North America, Greenville, SC; *Int'l*, pg. 322

Michael, Gary G., Chm. Bd. & Chief Exec. Officer--Albertson's, Inc., Boise, ID; *U.S. Public*, pg. 38

Michael, Joseph, Chm.--Professional Apartment Management, Inc., Lodi, CA; *U.S. Private*, pg. 889

Michaels, Bill, Chm. Bd.--Pinnacle Automation Inc., Saint Louis, MO; *U.S. Private*, pg. 866

Michaels, Jack D., Chm. Bd., Pres. & Chief Exec. Officer--HON Industries Inc., Muscatine, IA; *U.S. Public*, pg. 772

Michaels, William, Chm. Bd.--The Buschman Co., Cincinnati, OH; *U.S. Private*, pg. 188

Michalek, Richard C., Chm. Bd. & Chief Exec. Officer--Quality Control Corporation, Chicago, IL; *U.S. Private*, pg. 898

Michaud, Pierre, Chm. Bd.--Provigo Inc., Montreal, Canada; *Int'l*, pg. 1072

Michelena, Juan Antonio, Chm. Bd.--Mantex, S.A.C.A., Caracas, Venezuela; *Int'l*, pg. 840

Michels, Lawrence, Chm. Bd.--General Automation, Inc., Irvine, CA; *U.S. Public*, pg. 706

Michielsen, Alois, Chm.-Exec. Committee--Solvay S.A., Brussels, Belgium; *Int'l*, pg. 1277

Mickel, Buck, Chm. Bd. & Chief Exec. Officer--RSI Holdings Inc., Greenville, SC; *U.S. Public*, pg. 1358

Middelmann, Ulrich, Dr., Chm. Bd.--O&K Orenstein & Koppel Aktiengesellschaft, Dortmund, Germany; *Int'l*, pg. 516

Middleton, Charles S., Chm. Bd., Pres & Chief Exec. Officer--Cal-Air Inc., Whittier, CA; *U.S. Private*, pg. 199

Midy, P., Chm. Bd.--Chocoamerican Inc., Cleveland, OH; *Int'l*, pg. 865

Miglio, Daniel J., Chm. Bd. & Chief Exec. Officer--Southern New England Telecommunications Corporation, New Haven, CT; *U.S. Public*, pg. 1490

Miglio, Daniel J., Chm. Bd., Pres. & Chief Exec. Officer--The Southern New England Telephone Company, New Haven, CT; *U.S. Public*, pg. 1491

Mihaylo, Steven G., Chm. Bd. & Chief Exec. Officer--Inter-Tel, Incorporated, Phoenix, AZ; *U.S. Public*, pg. 888

Mikelsons, J. George, Chm. Bd.--Amtran, Inc., Indianapolis, IN; *U.S. Public*, pg. 106

Miki, Hirofumi, Chm. Bd.--Ferro Enamels (Japan) Ltd., Osaka, Japan; *U.S. Public*, pg. 619

Miki, Yoshiharu, Chm.--Miki Pulley Co., Ltd., Kawasaki, Japan; *Int'l*, pg. 866

Mikon, Arnold, Chm., Pres. & Chief Exec. Officer--SmithGroup, Inc., Detroit, MI; *U.S. Private*, pg. 1010

Milch, Bernard, Chm. Bd.--Bermil Industries Corp., Inwood, NY; *U.S. Private*, pg. 136

Milenthal, David, Chm. Bd.--HMS Partners, Columbus, OH; *U.S. Private*, pg. 491

Milenthal, David, Chm. Bd.--HMS Partners-Columbus, Columbus, OH; *U.S. Private*, pg. 492

Miles, Richard F., Chm. Bd.--Syntron, Inc., Houston, TX; *U.S. Public*, pg. 1563

Miles, Richard F., Chm. Bd. & Pres.--CogniSeis Development, Inc., Houston, TX; *U.S. Public*, pg. 1563

Milhaud, Serge, Chm. & Chief Exec. Officer--Societe Generale des Eaux Minerales de Vittel, Vittel, France; *Int'l*, pg. 920

Milhaud, Serge, Chm. Bd. & Chief Exec. Officer--Nestle Sources International S.A., Paris, France; *Int'l*, pg. 921

Milidrag, George, Chm. Bd. & Chief Exec. Officer--Engineering Technology Ltd. (E.T.), Troy, MI; *U.S. Private*, pg. 377

Mill, Victor J., Jr., Chm. Bd.--Lawrence Pumps, Inc., Lawrence, MA; *U.S. Private*, pg. 654

Millard, Dan, Chm. Bd., Pres., Chief Exec. & Chief Oper. Officer--Central Illinois Steel Company, Carlinville, IL; *U.S. Private*, pg. 223

Millard, Suzanne T., Chm. Bd., Pres. & Chief Exec. Officer--Turtle & Hughes, Inc., Linden, NJ; *U.S. Private*, pg. 1110

Miller, Alan, Chm. Bd., Pres. & Chief Exec. Officer--Edison Brothers Stores, Inc., Saint Louis, MO; *U.S. Public*, pg. 563

Miller, Alan B., Chm. Bd., Pres. & Chief Exec. Officer--Universal Health Services, Inc., King of Prussia, PA; *U.S. Public*, pg. 1696

Miller, Alan B., Chm. Bd. & Chief Exec. Officer--Universal Health Realty Income Trust, King of Prussia, PA; *U.S. Public*, pg. 1697

Miller, Bernard J., Jr., Chm. Bd.--Columbian Advertising Inc., Chicago, IL; *U.S. Private*, pg. 256

Miller, C. Douglas, Chm. Bd., Pres. & Chief Oper. Officer--Norrell Corporation, Atlanta, GA; *U.S. Public*, pg. 1192

Miller, C. Edward, Chm. Bd.--Time Oil Company, Seattle, WA; *U.S. Private*, pg. 1086

Miller, Charles D., Chm. Bd. & Chief Exec. Officer--Avery Dennison Corporation, Pasadena, CA; *U.S. Public*, pg. 152

Miller, Charles Q., Exec. V.P., Chm. Bd. & Chief Exec. Officer-Raytheon Engrs.--Raytheon Company, Lexington, MA; *U.S. Public*, pg. 1364

Miller, Charles R., Chm. Bd., Pres. & Chief Exec. Officer--Champion HealthCare Corporation, Houston, TX; *U.S. Public*, pg. 333

Miller, David O., Chm. Bd.--Employers Insurance of Wausau, Wausau, WI; *U.S. Private*, pg. 788

Miller, David P., Chm. Bd.--Atlas Lederer Co., Cleveland, OH; *U.S. Private*, pg. 256

Miller, Donald, Chm. Bd.--H.O. Trerice Company, Oak Park, MI; *U.S. Private*, pg. 1099

Miller, Donald E., Chm. Bd., Pres. & Chief Exec. Officer--Ederer Inc., Seattle, WA; *U.S. Private*, pg. 363

Miller, Donald P., Chm. Bd. & Pres.--Roppe Corp., Fostoria, OH; *U.S. Private*, pg. 944

Miller, Donald R., Chm. Bd.--Nash Finch Company, Edina, MN; *U.S. Public*, pg. 1151

Miller, Douglas H., Chm. Bd. & Chief Exec. Officer--Coda Energy, Inc., Dallas, TX; *U.S. Public*, pg. 584

Miller, Edward D., Chm. Bd. & Chief Exec. Officer--The Equitable Companies Incorporated, New York, NY; *U.S. Public*, pg. 588

Miller, Eugene, Chm. Bd. & Chief Exec. Officer--Ideon Group, Inc., Jacksonville, FL; *U.S. Public*, pg. 320

Miller, Eugene, Chm. Bd.--The Detroit Medical Center, Detroit, MI; *U.S. Private*, pg. 328

Miller, Eugene A., Chm. Bd. & Chief Exec. Officer--Comerica Incorporated, Detroit, MI; *U.S. Public*, pg. 408

Miller, Eugene A., Chm. Bd. & Chief Exec. Officer--Comerica Bank Michigan, Detroit, MI; *U.S. Public*, pg. 409

Miller, F. W., Chm. Bd.--TNT Limited, Redfern, Australia; *Int'l*, pg. 1342

Miller, F.W., Chm. Bd.--Hoechst Australia Ltd., Melbourne, Australia; *Int'l*, pg. 626

Miller, George, Chm. Bd. & Pres.--Peace River Electric Cooperative, Inc., Wauchula, FL; *U.S. Private*, pg. 845

Miller, James D., Chm. Bd.--Wassall Plc, London, United Kingdom; *Int'l*, pg. 1486

Miller, James F., Chm. Bd.--MTI Vacations, Inc., Downers Grove, IL; *U.S. Private*, pg. 688

Miller, James H., Chm. Bd., Pres. & Chief Exec. Officer--Meridian Medical Technology, Inc., Columbia, MD; *U.S. Public*, pg. 1095

Miller, James L., Chm. Bd. & Chief Exec. Officer--JP Foodservice, Inc., Columbia, MD; *U.S. Public*, pg. 918

Miller, James L., Chm. Bd. & Chief Exec. Officer--U.S. Food Service, Wilkes-Barre, PA; *U.S. Public*, pg. 918

Miller, Leonard, Chm. Bd. & Pres.--Lennar Corporation, Miami, FL; *U.S. Public*, pg. 987

Miller, Leonard, Chm. Bd.--Lennar Homes Inc., Miami, FL; *U.S. Public*, pg. 988

Miller, Leonard J., Chm. Bd.--Miller Advertising Agency Inc., New York, NY; *U.S. Private*, pg. 746

Miller, Lester, Chm. Bd.--Contico International, Inc., Saint Louis, MO; *U.S. Private*, pg. 267

Miller, Marvin, Chm. Bd. & Co-Chief Exec. Officer--Prime Source Inc., Carrollton, TX; *U.S. Private*, pg. 884

Miller, Max, Chm. Bd. & Treas.--McInerney-Miller Brothers Inc., Detroit, MI; *U.S. Private*, pg. 722

Miller, Opha H., Chm. Bd.--Miller & Co., Selma, AL; *U.S. Private*, pg. 746

Miller, Paul G., Chm. Bd.--Merrill Corporation, Saint Paul, MN; *U.S. Public*, pg. 1097
Miller, Robert, Chm. Bd.--Monroc, Inc., Salt Lake City, UT; *U.S. Public*, pg. 1124
Miller, Robert S., Chm. Bd. & Chief Exec. Officer--Better Baked Foods, Inc., North East, PA; *U.S. Private*, pg. 141
Miller, Robert S., Chm. Bd., Pres. & Chief Exec. Officer--Waste Management, Inc., Oak Brook, IL; *U.S. Public*, pg. 1744
Miller, Robert V., Chm. Bd.--Miller Meester Advertising Inc., Minneapolis, MN; *U.S. Private*, pg. 747
Miller, Samuel H., Co-Chm. Bd. & Treas.--Forest City Enterprises, Inc., Cleveland, OH; *U.S. Public*, pg. 667
Miller, Sanford, Chm. Bd. & Chief Exec. Officer--Budget Group, Inc., Daytona Beach, FL; *U.S. Private*, pg. 178
Miller, Sanford, Chm. & Chief Exec. Officer--Budget Rent A Car Corporation, Lisle, IL; *U.S. Private*, pg. 178
Miller, Steven, Chm. Bd., Pres. & Chief Exec. Officer--Miller Resources International, Inc., North Brunswick, NJ; *U.S. Private*, pg. 748
Miller, Thomas B., Chm. Bd., Pres. & Chief Exec. & Oper. Officer--Berry Bearing Company, Lyons, IL; *U.S. Public*, pg. 732
Miller, Tod, Chm. Bd. & Chief Exec. Officer--Rosewood Property Company, Dallas, TX; *U.S. Private*, pg. 946
Miller, William J., Chm. Bd. & Chief Exec. Officer--Avid Technology, Inc., Tewksbury, MA; *U.S. Public*, pg. 154
Milley, Alexander M., Chm. Bd., Pres. & Chief Exec. Officer--ELXSI Corporation, Orlando, FL; *U.S. Public*, pg. 545
Milligan, Bruce R., Chm. Bd. & Pres.--Southern County Mutual Insurance Company, Dallas, TX; *Int'l*, pg. 346
Milliken, Roger, Chm. Bd. & Chief Exec. Officer--Milliken & Company, Spartanburg, SC; *U.S. Private*, pg. 748
Milliotte, Jean, Chm. Bd.--Domco Inc., Farnham, Canada; *Int'l*, pg. 415
Millman, James R., Chm. & Chief Exec. Officer--Millsport, Stamford, CT; *U.S. Public*, pg. 1224
Millner, Thomas, Chm. Bd., Pres. & Chief Oper. Officer--Remington Arms Company, Inc., Madison, NC; *U.S. Private*, pg. 921
Mills, Gerald J., Chm. Bd. & Pres.--Mills & Clement Inc., Bakersfield, CA; *U.S. Private*, pg. 749
Mills, Howard, Jr., Chm. Bd.--Maplehurst Farms, Inc., Indianapolis, IN; *U.S. Public*, pg. 490
Mills, James N., Chm. & Chief Exec. Officer--Berg Electronics, Saint Louis, MO; *U.S. Public*, pg. 212
Mills, James S., Co-Chm.--Medline Industries, Inc., Mundelein, IL; *U.S. Private*, pg. 728
Mills, Jon, Co-Chm.--Medline Industries, Inc., Mundelein, IL; *U.S. Private*, pg. 728
Mills, Olan, II, Chm. Bd. & Sec.--Olan Mills, Inc., Chattanooga, TN; *U.S. Private*, pg. 749
Mills, P. Gerald, Chm. Bd., Pres. & Chief Exec. Officer--Jacobson Stores Inc., Jackson, MI; *U.S. Public*, pg. 922
Mills, Walter G., Chm. Bd., Chief Exec. Officer & Treas.--W.G. Mills, Inc., Sarasota, FL; *U.S. Private*, pg. 749
Milmo, Emilio Azcarraga, Chm. Bd. & Grp. Pres.--Grupo Televisa, S.A. de C.V., Mexico, Mexico; *Int'l*, pg. 576
Milnor, George S., Chm. Bd., Pres. & Chief Exec. Officer--Millers Mutual Insurance Assn., Alton, IL; *U.S. Private*, pg. 748
Milo, Yehuda, Chm. Bd.--Makhteshim Chemical Works Ltd., Beersheba, Israel; *Int'l*, pg. 830
Milstein, Howard P., Chm. Bd. & Pres.--Douglas Elliman, New York, NY; *U.S. Private*, pg. 341
Milstein, Monroe G., Chm. Bd., Pres. & Chief Exec. Officer--Burlington Coat Factory Warehouse Corporation, Burlington, NJ; *U.S. Public*, pg. 268
Milstein, Paul, Chm. Bd. & Chief Exec. Officer--Starrett HRH, New York, NY; *U.S. Private*, pg. 1035
Min, Jae-Hong, Chm. Bd. & Chief Exec. Officer--Samsung Asia Headquarters, Singapore, Singapore; *Int'l*, pg. 1183
Minamino, Tuneo, Chm. Bd.--AFG Industries, Inc., Kingsport, TN; *Int'l*, pg. 84
Minarik, William, Chm. Bd.--Minarik Corp, Glendale, CA; *U.S. Private*, pg. 749
Minato, Shungo, Chm. & Mng. Dir.--Pioneer Electronic (Europe) NV, Melsele, Belgium; *Int'l*, pg. 1058
Mindel, Laurence B., Chm. Bd. & Chief Exec. Officer--Il Fornaio America Corporation, Corte Madera, CA; *U.S. Public*, pg. 864
Minetti, Juan G., Chm. Bd.--Juan Minetti S.A., Cordoba, Argentina; *Int'l*, pg. 869
Ming, Hans Peter, Chm. Bd.--Sika Corporation, Lyndhurst, NJ; *Int'l*, pg. 1249
Ming, Nan Chang, Chm.--Beijing Dentsu Advertising Co., Ltd., Beijing, China; *Int'l*, pg. 393
Miniat, Ronald, Chm., Pres. & Chief Exec. Officer Ed Miniat, Inc., Chicago, IL; *U.S. Private*, pg. 750
Mino, Shigekazu, Chm. Bd.--Kubota Corp., Osaka, Japan; *Int'l*, pg. 762
Minor, G. Gilmer III, Chm. Bd., Pres. & Chief Exec. Officer--Owens & Minor Inc., Glen Allen, VA; *U.S. Public*, pg. 1236
Minton, Dwight C., Chm. Bd.--Church & Dwight Co., Inc., Princeton, NJ; *U.S. Public*, pg. 355
Minton, Kenneth J., Chm. Bd.--John Mowlem & Company plc, Isleworth, United Kingdom; *Int'l*, pg. 896
Minyard, Bob L., Chm. Exec. Committee--Minyard Food Stores, Inc., Coppell, TX; *U.S. Private*, pg. 752
Minyard, Lisbeth, Co-Chm. Bd.--Minyard Food Stores, Inc., Coppell, TX; *U.S. Private*, pg. 752
Mirabelli, Mario, Chm. Bd.--Guest Services, Inc., Fairfax, VA; *U.S. Private*, pg. 486
Mirani, C.H., Chm.--Sakura Capital India, Limited, Mumbai, India; *Int'l*, pg. 1180
Mirkos, George, Chm. Bd. & Chief Exec. Officer--National Bank of Greece S.A., Athens, Greece; *Int'l*, pg. 907
Misawa, Tokushiro, Chm.--Asahi Advertising Inc., Tokyo, Japan; *Int'l*, pg. 81
Mishra, R.N., Chm. Bd. & Mng. Dir.--Northern Coalfields Limited, Sidhi, India; *Int'l*, pg. 299
Missett, Judi, Chm. Bd., Pres. & Chief Exec. Officer--Jazzercise, Inc., Carlsbad, CA; *U.S. Private*, pg. 584
Mita, Katsushiga, Chm. Bd.--Hitachi, Ltd., Tokyo, Japan; *Int'l*, pg. 621
Mitchel, Thomas L., Chm. Bd. & Pres.--Mitchel & Scott Machine Co., Inc., Indianapolis, IN; *U.S. Private*, pg. 753
Mitchell, Bradford W., Chm. Bd.--Harleysville Group, Harleysville, PA; *U.S. Public*, pg. 786
Mitchell, Bradford W., Chm. Bd.--Harleysville Mutual Insurance, Harleysville, PA; *U.S. Public*, pg. 787
Mitchell, David E., Chm. Bd.--Chieftain International, Inc., Edmonton, Canada; *Int'l*, pg. 284
Mitchell, David E., Governor--Hudson's Bay Company, Toronto, Canada; *Int'l*, pg. 637
Mitchell, Doug, Chm. Bd. & Pres.--Perryton Equity, Perryton, TX; *U.S. Private*, pg. 855
Mitchell, Edward F., Chm. Bd.--Potomac Electric Power Company, Washington, DC; *U.S. Public*, pg. 1318
Mitchell, George P., Chm. Bd. & Chief Exec. Officer--Mitchell Energy & Development Corp., Spring, TX; *U.S. Public*, pg. 1117
Mitchell, Harvey R., Chm.--Bank One, Texas Corp., Dallas, TX; *U.S. Public*, pg. 173
Mitchell, James, Chm. Bd.--IDS Certificate Company, Minneapolis, MN; *U.S. Public*, pg. 73
Mitchell, John A., III, Chm. Bd.--First Union National Bank of Florida, Jacksonville, FL; *U.S. Public*, pg. 640
Mitchell, Stephen C., Chm. & Chief Exec. Officer--Knight Architects Engineers Planners, Inc., Chicago, IL; *U.S. Private*, pg. 626
Mitchell, William F., Chm. Bd., Pres. & Chief Exec. Officer--Environmental Tectonics Corporation (ETC), Southampton, PA; *U.S. Public*, pg. 587
Mitchell, William F., Chm. Bd., Pres. & Chief Exec. Officer--Mitchell Corporation of Owosso, Owosso, MI; *U.S. Private*, pg. 753
Mitieus, Rene, Chm. Bd., Pres. & Chief Exec. Officer--Imetal, Paris, France; *Int'l*, pg. 661
Mitte, Roy, Chm. Bd., Pres. & Chief Exec. Officer--Financial Industries Corp., Austin, TX; *U.S. Public*, pg. 622
Mitte, Roy, Chm. Bd., Pres. & Chief Exec. Officer--InternContinental Life Corp., Austin, TX; *U.S. Public*, pg. 622
Miura, Mamoru, Chm. & Rep. Dir.--Tokyu Agency Inc., Tokyo, Japan; *Int'l*, pg. 1394
Miura, Tamotsu, Chm. Bd.--Miura Co., Ltd., Matsuyama, Japan; *Int'l*, pg. 884
Miura, Yuichi, Chm. Bd.--A&T Corporation, Tokyo, Japan; *Int'l*, pg. 1393
Mixon, A. Malachi, III, Chm. Bd. & Chief Exec. Officer--Invacare Corporation, Elyria, OH; *U.S. Public*, pg. 911
Miyagi, Kohtaro, Chm. Bd.--Canon Marketing Services Pte. Ltd., Singapore, Singapore; *Int'l*, pg. 263
Miyakawa, Kazuo, Chm.--Dentsu Europe Ltd.-London, London, United Kingdom; *Int'l*, pg. 393
Miyakawa, Kazuo, Chm.--DCA Advertising, Inc., New York, NY; *Int'l*, pg. 393
Miyata, Nagayoshi, Chm.--Daiwa Europe (Deutschland) GmbH, Frankfurt/Main, Germany; *Int'l*, pg. 375
Miyazaki, Isamu, Chm. Bd.--The Kansai Electric Power Co., Inc., Osaka, Japan; *Int'l*, pg. 722
Miyazaki, Kuniji, Chm. Bd.--The Dai-Ichi Kangyo Bank, Limited, Tokyo, Japan; *Int'l*, pg. 359
Miyoshi, Toshio, Chm. Bd.--Matsushita Electric Works, Ltd., Osaka, Japan; *Int'l*, pg. 847
Mizel, Larry A., Chm. Bd., Pres. & Chief Exec. Officer--M.D.C. Holdings, Inc., Denver, CO; *U.S. Public*, pg. 1025
Mizuno, Kenjiro, Chm. Bd.--Mizuno Corporation, Osaka, Japan; *Int'l*, pg. 884
Moakley, Michael, Chm.--Philips Medical Systems North America Company, Shelton, CT; *Int'l*, pg. 1055
Moayedi, Paris, Chm. Bd. & Chief Exec. Officer--Jarvis Plc, Watton-at-Stone, United Kingdom; *Int'l*, pg. 705
Mobley, Paul W., Chm. Bd., Pres. & Chief Exec. Officer--Noble Roman's Inc., Indianapolis, IN; *U.S. Public*, pg. 1187
Mockley, B.A., Chm. Bd. & Pres.--Anchor Gasoline Corporation, Tulsa, OK; *U.S. Private*, pg. 70
Moddrell, Joe, Jr., Chm. Bd.--Insurance Management Associates, Wichita, KS; *U.S. Private*, pg. 565
Modell, William, Chm. Bd.--Henry Modell & Company, Inc., New York, NY; *U.S. Private*, pg. 754
Mody, Russi, Chm. Bd. & Mng. Dir.--The Tata Iron and Steel Co. Ltd., Mumbai, India; *Int'l*, pg. 1356
Moeller, F.H., Chm. Bd. & Chief Exec. Officer--VTEL Corporation, Austin, TX; *U.S. Public*, pg. 1703
Moeller, Gerald, Chm. Bd.--Corange U.S. Holdings, Inc, Indianapolis, IN; *Int'l*, pg. 331
Moessner, Reynold, Chm. Bd. & Pres.--Amana Society, Inc., Amana, IA; *U.S. Private*, pg. 48
Moffat, Brian, Chm. Bd. & Chief Exec. Officer--British Steel Plc, London, United Kingdom; *Int'l*, pg. 220
Moffett, James R., Chm. Bd. & Pres.--Freeport-McMoRan Inc., New Orleans, LA; *U.S. Public*, pg. 680
Moffett, James R., Chm. Bd. & Chief Exec. Officer--Freeport-McMoRan Copper & Gold, Inc., New Orleans, LA; *U.S. Public*, pg. 680
Moffitt, Donald E., Chm. Bd. & Chief Exec. Officer--CNF Transportation Inc., Palo Alto, CA; *U.S. Public*, pg. 281
Mohamed, Ali, Chm. & Exec. Creative Dir.--Leo Burnett Advertising SDN.BHD., Kuala Lumpur, Malaysia; *U.S. Private*, pg. 184
Mohlin, Rune, Chm. Bd.--Aftonbladet AB, Stockholm, Sweden; *Int'l*, pg. 29
Mohn, Richard, Chm. Bd.--Cloister Pure Spring Water Co., Inc., Lancaster, PA; *U.S. Private*, pg. 247
Mohn, Richard, Chm. Bd.--Chester Springs Distribution Point, Chester Springs, PA; *U.S. Private*, pg. 247
Mohn, Richard, Chm. Bd.--Beltsville Distribution Point, Baltimore, MD; *U.S. Private*, pg. 247
Mohn, Richard E., Chm. Bd.--Sovereign Bancorp, Inc., Wyomissing, PA; *U.S. Public*, pg. 1494
Mohri, Yoichi, Chm. Bd.--Toko Inc., Tokyo, Japan; *Int'l*, pg. 1393
Mohrman, LeRoy, Chm. Bd., Pres. & Chief Exec. Officer--Handling Systems Engineering, Jacksonville, FL; *U.S. Private*, pg. 499
Mojden, Wallace W., Chm. Bd.--Fleetwood Systems, Inc., Romeoville, IL; *U.S. Private*, pg. 410
Moldaw, Stuart G., Chm. Emeritus--Ross Stores, Inc., Newark, CA; *U.S. Public*, pg. 1405
Molen, Richard L., Chm. Bd. & Chief Exec. Officer--Huffy Corporation, Miamisburg, OH; *U.S. Public*, pg. 846
Molin, Carl E., Jr., Chm. Bd.--Molin Auto Parts Inc., Buffalo, NY; *U.S. Private*, pg. 756
Molina Sobrino, Enrique, Chm. Bd. & Chief Exec. Officer--Pepsi-Gemex SA de CV, Mexico, Mexico; *Int'l*, pg. 1036
Molinari, D.C., Chm. Bd.--Punch Press Products, Inc., Los Angeles, CA; *U.S. Private*, pg. 895
Molinari, Guy V., Chm. Bd.--Federal Home Loan Bank of New York, New York, NY; *U.S. Private*, pg. 399
Molinari, John B., Chm. Bd.--Norcal Waste Systems, San Francisco, CA; *U.S. Public*, pg. 1188
Molinari, Sandro, Chm. Bd.--Cassa di Risparmio delle Provincie Lombarde SpA (CARIPLO), Milan, Italy; *Int'l*, pg. 274
Molinaria, Alfred A., Jr., Chm. Bd.--Media 100, Inc., Marlborough, MA; *U.S. Public*, pg. 1079
Moll, Curtis E., Chm. Bd. & Chief Exec. Officer--MTD Products, Inc., Valley City, OH; *U.S. Private*, pg. 688
Moller-Racke, Marcus, Pres. & Chm. Bd.--A. Racke GmbH, Bingen, Germany; *Int'l*, pg. 1083
Moller-Racke, Marcus, Chm. Bd.--Racke USA, Sonoma, CA; *Int'l*, pg. 1083
Moller, John J., Chm. Bd.--USA Petroleum Corporation, Agoura Hills, CA; *U.S. Private*, pg. 1125
Moloney, Earl, Chm. Bd. & Chief Exec. Officer--Molon Motor & Coil Corp., Rolling Meadows, IL; *U.S. Private*, pg. 756
Moloney, Thomas F., Chm.--John Hancock Property and Casualty Holding Co., Boston, MA; *U.S. Private*, pg. 590
Molson, Eric H., Chm. Bd.--The Molson Companies Limited, Toronto, Canada; *Int'l*, pg. 887
Molyneux, Richard A., Chm. Bd., Pres. & Chief Exec. Officer--Key Bank of Maine, Portland, ME; *U.S. Public*, pg. 954
Momose, Nobuo, Chm. & Pres.--Dentsu USA Inc.-New York, New York, NY; *Int'l*, pg. 393
Mona, Dave, Chm.-MMMG Group--Shandwick Minneapolis, Minneapolis, MN; *Int'l*, pg. 1227
Monaghan, Thomas S., Chm. Bd., Pres. & Chief Exec. Officer--Domino's Pizza Inc., Ann Arbor, MI; *U.S. Private*, pg. 339
Monahan, William T., Chm. Bd. & Chief Exec. Officer--Imation Corporation, Oakdale, MN; *U.S. Public*, pg. 870
Moncrief, Lee E., Chm. Bd., Pres. & Chief Exec. Officer--SouthTrust Bank, Shoals, Florence, AL; *U.S. Public*, pg. 1492
Mondadori, Leonardo, Chm. Bd.--Arnoldo Mondadori Editore S.p.A., Segrate, Italy; *Int'l*, pg. 887
Mondavi, Robert G., Chm. Bd.--Robert Mondavi Winery, Inc., Oakville, CA; *U.S. Public*, pg. 1393
Monderer, Benjamin, Chm. Bd., Pres. & Chief Tech. Officer--Box Hill Systems Corporation, New York, NY; *U.S. Public*, pg. 249
Monette, Edward A., Chm. Bd., Pres., Chief Exec. Officer & Chief Oper. Officer--St. Croix Press, Inc., New Richmond, WI; *U.S. Private*, pg. 960
Monger, Stephen, Chm. Bd., Pres. & Chief Exec. Officer--Regions Bank/Huntsville, Huntsville, AL; *U.S. Public*, pg. 1372
Monkiewicz, Anthony, Chm. Bd.--Kayem Foods, Inc., Chelsea, MA; *U.S. Private*, pg. 610
Monnoyeur, Baudouin, Chm. Bd. & Pres.--Monnoyeur SCA, Saint Denis, France; *Int'l*, pg. 888
Monod, Jerome, Chm. Bd. & Chief Exec. Officer--Lyonnaise des Eaux S.A., Nanterre, France; *Int'l*, pg. 822
Monson, Robert, Chm. Bd., Pres. & Treas.--Monson Trucking, Inc., Duluth, MN; *U.S. Private*, pg. 758
Monteiro, Antonio Vieira, Chm. Bd.--Banco Luso Espanol S.A., Madrid, Spain; *Int'l*, pg. 251
Montel, Jean-Philippe, Chm. Bd. & Chief Exec. Officer-Aussedat Rey--International Paper Company, Purchase, NY; *U.S. Public*, pg. 901
Montero, Fernan, Chm. & Chief Exec. Officer-Y&R Europe--Young & Rubicam Inc., New York, NY; *U.S. Private*, pg. 1196
Montero, Fernan, Chm. & Chief Exec. Officer-Europe--Young & Rubicam Holdings Ltd., London, United Kingdom; *U.S. Private*, pg. 1199
Montgomery, Joseph S., Chm. Bd., Pres. & Chief Exec. Officer--Cannondale Corporation, Bethel, CT; *U.S. Public*, pg. 301
Montgomery, Walter S., Jr., Chm. Bd. & Chief Exec. Officer--Spartan Mills, Spartanburg, SC; *U.S. Private*, pg. 1020
Montgomery, William, Chm. Bd.--SA-SO Company, Dallas, TX; *U.S. Private*, pg. 955
Montrone, Paul M., Chm. Bd., Pres. & Chief Exec. Officer--Fisher Scientific International, Hampton, NH; *U.S. Private*, pg. 658
Montrone, Paul M., Chm. Bd.--The General Chemical Group, Inc., Hampton, NH; *U.S. Public*, pg. 707
Moo, Johnny, Chm. Bd.--Integral Systems, Inc., Walnut Creek, CA; *Int'l*, pg. 242
Moody, Robert L., Chm. Bd. & Chief Exec. Officer--National Western Life Insurance Company, Austin, TX; *U.S. Public*, pg. 1161
Moody, Ross R., Chm. Bd.--NWL Financial, Inc., Austin, TX; *U.S. Public*, pg. 1161
Moody, Ross R., Chm. Bd. & Chief Exec. Officer--NWL Services, Inc., Austin, TX; *U.S. Public*, pg. 1161
Moomjy, Albert, Chm. Bd.--Einstein Moomjy Inc., Pine Brook, NJ; *U.S. Private*, pg. 366
Moon, Hee Sung, Chm. Bd.--Korea Electric Power Corporation (KEPCO), Seoul, Korea; *Int'l*, pg. 758
Moon, Heon Sang, Chm. Bd. & Pres.--The Export-Import Bank of Korea, Seoul, Korea; *Int'l*, pg. 467

Moon, James B., Chm. Bd., Pres. & Chief Exec. Officer--Protocol Systems, Inc., Beaverton, OR; *U.S. Public*, pg. 1336
Moon, Wayne, Chm. Bd. & Chief Exec. Officer--Blue Shield of California, San Francisco, CA; *U.S. Private*, pg. 153
Mooney, Edward J., Chm. Bd. & Chief Exec. Officer--Nalco Chemical Company, Naperville, IL; *U.S. Public*, pg. 1150
Mooney, James P., Chm. Bd. & Chief Oper. Officer--OM Group, Cleveland, OH; *U.S. Public*, pg. 1208
Mooney, John E., Chm. Bd.--Moscom Corporation, Pittsford, NY; *U.S. Public*, pg. 1136
Moore, Alfred A., Chm. Bd.--Chelsea Moore Company, Loveland, OH; *U.S. Private*, pg. 1164
Moore, Charles, Chm. Bd.--Axiom Inc., Moorestown, NJ; *U.S. Public*, pg. 157
Moore, Clyde W., Chm. Bd.--Crown International, Inc., Elkhart, IN; *U.S. Private*, pg. 293
Moore, D.J., Chm. Bd. & Chief Exec. Officer--ESCO Electronics Corporation, Saint Louis, MO; *U.S. Public*, pg. 546
Moore, Gordon E., Chm. Emeritus--Intel Corporation, Santa Clara, CA; *U.S. Public*, pg. 886
Moore, Harold, Chm. Bd.--Harold Moore & Associates, Inc., Fayetteville, TN; *U.S. Private*, pg. 759
Moore, James E., Chm. Bd. & Chief Exec. Officer--ContiMortgage Corporation, Horsham, PA; *U.S. Public*, pg. 439
Moore, Lee P., Chm. Bd.--Sunniland Corporation, Sanford, FL; *U.S. Private*, pg. 1053
Moore, Leon, Chm. Bd., Pres. & Chief Exec. Officer--Sholodge, Inc., Hendersonville, TN; *U.S. Public*, pg. 1467
Moore, M.R.N., Chm. Bd.--London International Group plc, London, United Kingdom; *Int'l*, pg. 815
Moore, Michael J., Chm. Bd. & Pres.--Southland Industries, Long Beach, CA; *U.S. Private*, pg. 1018
Moore, Nicholas G., Chm. & Chief Exec. Officer--Coopers & Lybrand, New York, NY; *U.S. Private*, pg. 274
Moore, Peter F., Deputy Chm.--Moore Company, Westerly, RI; *U.S. Private*, pg. 759
Moore, Rex, Chm. Bd.--Rex Moore Electrical Contractors & Engineers, West Sacramento, CA; *U.S. Private*, pg. 760
Moore, Sam, Chm. Bd., Pres. & Chief Exec. Officer--Thomas Nelson Inc., Nashville, TN; *U.S. Public*, pg. 1167
Moore, Thomas F., Chm. Bd.--Moore Company, Westerly, RI; *U.S. Private*, pg. 759
Moore, Thomas H., Chm. Bd.--Contractors Supplies, Inc., Lufkin, TX; *U.S. Private*, pg. 270
Moore, Wayne R., Chm. Bd.--Producto Machine Co. Ring Division, Jamestown, NY; *U.S. Private*, pg. 889
Moore, William E., Chm. Bd.--Kelly-Moore Paint Company, Inc., San Carlos, CA; *U.S. Private*, pg. 613
Moore, William M., Jr., Chm. Bd. & Pres.--Trident Financial Corporation, Raleigh, NC; *U.S. Private*, pg. 1103
Moorhouse, Virginia F., Chm. Bd. & Publr.--The Bakersfield Californian, Bakersfield, CA; *U.S. Private*, pg. 112
Moos, J. Clifford, Chm. Bd., Pres. & Chief Exec. Officer--Economy Folding Box Corp., Chicago, IL; *U.S. Private*, pg. 362
Mooty, John, Chm. Bd.--American Dairy Queen Corporation, Minneapolis, MN; *U.S. Public*, pg. 220
Mooty, John W., Chm. Bd.--International Dairy Queen, Inc., Minneapolis, MN; *U.S. Public*, pg. 220
Mooty, John W., Chm. Bd.--Orange Julius of America, Edina, MN; *U.S. Public*, pg. 220
Moquin, Yves, Chm. Bd. & Chief Exec. Officer--Coscient Group Inc., Montreal, Canada; *Int'l*, pg. 335
Moran, Dennis, Chm. Bd. & Chief Exec. Officer--Moran Industries, Inc., Midlothian, IL; *U.S. Private*, pg. 760
Moran, Gordon W., Chm. Bd. & Chief Exec. Officer--Hollingsworth & Vose Co., East Walpole, MA; *U.S. Private*, pg. 534
Moran, Jim M., Chm. Bd.--JM Family Enterprises Inc., Deerfield Beach, FL; *U.S. Private*, pg. 577
Moran, Robert, Chm. Bd.--Sears de Mexico, Mexico, Mexico; *Int'l*, pg. 573
Morbey, R.I., Chm. Bd.--E & D Taylor (Insurance Brokers) Limited, Greenford, United Kingdom; *Int'l*, pg. 1358
Morbey, R.I., Chm. Bd.--Taylor Insurance Brokers Limited, Southall, United Kingdom; *Int'l*, pg. 1358
Morcott, Southwood J., Chm. Bd. & Chief Exec. Officer--Dana Corporation, Toledo, OH; *U.S. Public*, pg. 479
More, Avery, Chm. Bd. & V.P.--Computer City, Fort Worth, TX; *U.S. Public*, pg. 1560
Morean, William, Chm. Bd. & Chief Exec. Officer--Jabil Circuit, Inc., Saint Petersburg, FL; *U.S. Public*, pg. 919
Morel, Bernard, Chm.--Jet Tours, Ivry-sur-Seine, France; *Int'l*, pg. 560
Morelli, Joseph, Chm. Bd., Pres. & Chief Exec. Officer--M.H. Rhodes, Inc., Avon, CT; *U.S. Private*, pg. 927
Moret, Marc, Dr., Chief Exec. Officer and Chm-Bd. Dirs.--Sandoz (Hellas) S.A.C.I., Athens, Greece; *Int'l*, pg. 984
Morgan, Allen, Jr., Chm. Bd. & Chief Exec. Officer--Morgan Keegan, Inc., Memphis, TN; *U.S. Public*, pg. 1131
Morgan, Charles D., Jr., Chm. Bd., Pres. & Chief Exec. Officer--Acxiom Corporation, Conway, AR; *U.S. Public*, pg. 18
Morgan, J.M., Chm. Bd.--Comfort Financieringen Nederland BV, Houten, Netherlands; *Int'l*, pg. 911
Morgan, James C., Chm. Bd. & Chief Exec. Officer--Applied Materials, Inc., Santa Clara, CA; *U.S. Public*, pg. 123
Morgan, Jim, Chm. Bd.--Adra Systems, Inc., Chelmsford, MA; *U.S. Private*, pg. 18
Morgan, John S., Chm. Bd. & Chief Exec. Officer--Morgan Foods, Inc., Austin, IN; *U.S. Private*, pg. 761
Morgan, Louis J., Chm. Bd. & Treas.--PC Quote, Inc., Chicago, IL; *U.S. Public*, pg. 1240
Morgan, Paul S., Chm. Bd.--Morgan Construction Co., Worcester, MA; *U.S. Private*, pg. 761
Morgan, Richard C.E., Chm. Bd.--Quidel Corporation, San Diego, CA; *U.S. Public*, pg. 1352
Morgan, Robert, Chm. Bd.--Aamco Transmissions, Inc., Bala Cynwyd, PA; *U.S. Private*, pg. 9
Morgens, Edwin H., Chm. Bd.--Intrenet, Inc., Milford, OH; *U.S. Public*, pg. 910
Morgridge, John P., Chm. Bd.--Cisco Systems, Inc., San Jose, CA; *U.S. Public*, pg. 375
Mori, Hideo, Chm. Bd.--Sumitomo Chemical Company, Ltd., Tokyo, Japan; *Int'l*, pg. 1310
Mori, Susumu, Chm. Bd. & Pres.--Miyata Industry Co., Ltd., Chigasaki, Japan; *Int'l*, pg. 884
Moriarty, Kevin, Chm. Bd. & Chief Exec. Officer--Del Taco, Inc., Laguna Hills, CA; *U.S. Private*, pg. 321
Morikawa, Toshio, Chm. Bd.--The Sumitomo Bank, Limited, Osaka, Japan; *Int'l*, pg. 1308
Morin-Postel, Christine, Chm.--Indosuez Capital Ltd., London, United Kingdom; *Int'l*, pg. 314
Morini, Angelo S., Chm. Bd., Pres. & Chief Exec. Officer--Galaxy Food Company, Orlando, FL; *U.S. Public*, pg. 697
Morioka, Shigeo, Chm. Bd & Chief Exec. Officer--Yamanouchi Pharmaceutical Co. Ltd., Tokyo, Japan; *Int'l*, pg. 1518
Morita, Katsura, Ph.D., Chm. Bd.--Takeda Chemical Industries, Ltd., Osaka, Japan; *Int'l*, pg. 1350
Morita, Kazuaki, Chm. Bd.--Shikishima Baking Co., Ltd., Nagoya, Japan; *Int'l*, pg. 1231
Morita, Masaaki, Chm. & Chief Exec. Officer--Sony Electronics, Park Ridge, NJ; *Int'l*, pg. 1281
Morley, Harry, Chm. Bd. & Chief Exec. Officer--Taylor-Morley, Inc., Saint Louis, MO; *U.S. Private*, pg. 1071
Morley, John C., Chm. Bd.--Cleveland-Cliffs Inc, Cleveland, OH; *U.S. Public*, pg. 386
Morlock, Ronald, Chm. Bd.--Commercial Testing & Engineering Co., Lombard, IL; *Int'l*, pg. 1153
Morohashi, Shinroku, Chm. Bd.--Mitsubishi Corporation, Tokyo, Japan; *Int'l*, pg. 871
Morokoff, Al, Chm. Bd.--MLC Limited, Sydney, Australia; *Int'l*, pg. 806
Morrill, Robert M., Chm. Bd.--Ardent Software, Inc., Westborough, MA; *U.S. Public*, pg. 129
Morris, Brian R., Chief Exec. Officer & Chm. Bd.-WF Corroon Limited--WF Corroon-United Kingdom & International, London, United Kingdom; *Int'l*, pg. 1501
Morris, Carloss, Chm. Bd. & Co.-Chief Exec. Officer--Stewart Information Services Corporation, Houston, TX; *U.S. Public*, pg. 1518
Morris, Clifton H. Jr., Chm. Bd. & Chief Exec. Officer--AmeriCredit Corp., Fort Worth, TX; *U.S. Public*, pg. 96
Morris, David, Chm. & Chief Exec. Officer--DMB&B/Weekes Morris Osborn, Ultimo, Australia; *U.S. Private*, pg. 304
Morris, Earl L., Chm. Bd.--Acorn Engineering Company, City of Industry, CA; *U.S. Private*, pg. 14
Morris, Lester A., Chm. Emeritus--Mesirow Financial, Chicago, IL; *U.S. Private*, pg. 733
Morris, Michael G., Chm. Bd., Pres. & Chief Exec. Officer--Northeast Utilities, Berlin, CT; *U.S. Public*, pg. 1194
Morris, Michael G., Chm. Bd.--The Connecticut Light & Power Co., Berlin, CT; *U.S. Public*, pg. 1194
Morris, Michael G., Chm. Bd.--Public Service Company of New Hampshire, Manchester, NH; *U.S. Public*, pg. 1195
Morris, Olin, Chm. Bd.--Memphis Light, Gas & Water, Memphis, TN; *U.S. Private*, pg. 731
Morris, Richard, Chm. Bd.--National Fire Protection Association, Quincy, MA; *U.S. Private*, pg. 782
Morris, T.N., Jr., Chm., Pres. & Chief Exec. Officer--Calcasieu Lumber Company, Austin, TX; *U.S. Private*, pg. 200
Morris, W.S., III, Chm. Bd. & Chief Exec. Officer--Athens Newspapers, Inc., Augusta, GA; *U.S. Private*, pg. 996
Morris, W.S., 111, Chm. Bd. & Chief Exec. Officer--Southeastern Newspapers Corporation, Augusta, GA; *U.S. Private*, pg. 996
Morris, William C., Chm. Bd.--Seligman Henderson Co., New York, NY; *Int'l*, pg. 609
Morris, William C., Chm. Bd. & Pres.--J. & W. Seligman & Co., New York, NY; *U.S. Private*, pg. 982
Morris, William C., Chm. Bd.--Tri-Continental Corporation, New York, NY; *U.S. Private*, pg. 982
Morris, William C., Chm. Bd.--Seligman Henderson Co., New York, NY; *U.S. Private*, pg. 982
Morris, William S., III, Chm. Bd. & Chief Exec. Officer--Shivers Trading & Operating Co., Augusta, GA; *U.S. Private*, pg. 994
Morris, William S., III, Chm. Bd. & Chief Exec. Officer--Stauffer Communications, Inc., Augusta, GA; *U.S. Private*, pg. 995
Morrison, A.G., Chm.--Dairy Farm Management Services Limited, Causeway Bay, Hong Kong; *Int'l*, pg. 703
Morrison, Alan, Chm. Bd.--Seed Corporation of America, Baltimore, MD; *U.S. Private*, pg. 981
Morrison, Colin, Chm. Bd.--EMAP Business Communications Division, London, United Kingdom; *Int'l*, pg. 451
Morrison, Colin, Chm. Bd.--EMAP Business Information/EMAP Heighway, London, United Kingdom; *Int'l*, pg. 451
Morrison, J.M., Chm. Bd., Pres. & Sec.--Morrison, Inc., Hammond, IN; *U.S. Private*, pg. 762
Morrison, R.W., Chm. & Chief Exec. Officer--Canada Life Investment Management Limited, Toronto, Canada; *Int'l*, pg. 255
Morrison, Robert K., Co.-Chm. Bd.--Harvey Industries, Inc., Waltham, MA; *U.S. Private*, pg. 508
Morrison, Robert S., Chm. Bd. & Chief Exec. Officer--Kraft Foods Inc., Rye Brook, NY; *U.S. Public*, pg. 1288
Morrison, Robert S., Chm. Bd., Pres. & Chief Exec. Officer--The Quaker Oats Company, Chicago, IL; *U.S. Public*, pg. 1347
Morrison, T. Truxtun, Chm. Bd.--ConAgra International, Omaha, NE; *U.S. Public*, pg. 426
Morrison, William, Chm. Bd., Pres. & Chief Exec. Officer--Northern Trust Bank of Florida, N.A., Miami, FL; *U.S. Public*, pg. 1196
Morrissitte, Clara, Chm. Bd.--Interstate Van Lines, Inc., Springfield, VA; *U.S. Private*, pg. 573
Morrow, Ray, Chm. Bd.--Morrow West Beach, Salem, OR; *U.S. Public*, pg. 1134
Morse, Edward J., Sr., Chm. Bd. & Chief Exec. Officer--Ed Morse Automotive Group, Fort Lauderdale, FL; *U.S. Private*, pg. 763
Mortensen, Peter, Chm. Bd., Pres. & Chief Exec. Officer--F.N.B. Corporation, Hermitage, PA; *U.S. Public*, pg. 607
Mortensen, William S., Chm. Bd.--FirstFed Financial Corp., Santa Monica, CA; *U.S. Public*, pg. 645
Mortenson, G. Russell, Chm. Bd., Pres. & Chief Exec. Officer--Amtech Corporation, Dallas, TX; *U.S. Public*, pg. 105
Mortenson, M.A., Jr., Chm. Bd. & Chief Exec. Officer--M.A. Mortenson Company, Minneapolis, MN; *U.S. Private*, pg. 763
Mortier, Denis, Chm. Bd.--Saint Dominique Participations, Paris, France; *Int'l*, pg. 344
Morton, Dean, Chm. Bd.--Centigram Communications Corporation, San Jose, CA; *U.S. Public*, pg. 323
Morton, Nathan, Co-Chm. & Chief Exec. Officer--Computer City, Fort Worth, TX; *U.S. Public*, pg. 1560
Moscato, Guglielmo, Chm.--AGIP (Africa) Ltd., Saint Helier, United Kingdom; *Int'l*, pg. 428
Moseley, C., Chm. & Chief Exec. Officer--Simpson Investment Co., Seattle, WA; *U.S. Private*, pg. 1003
Moser, Hubertus, Chm.--Landesbank Berlin - Girozentrale, Berlin, Germany; *Int'l*, pg. 160
Mosher, Walter W., Jr., Ph.D., Chm. Bd. & Pres.--Precision Dynamics Corporation, San Fernando, CA; *U.S. Private*, pg. 879
Moskowitz, Joel P., Chm. Bd., Pres. & Chief Exec. Officer--Ceradyne, Inc, Costa Mesa, CA; *U.S. Public*, pg. 330
Moss, Bryan C., Vice Chm.--Gulfstream Aerospace Corporation, Savannah, GA; *U.S. Private*, pg. 419
Moss, Charles W., Chm. Bd.--Hickory Construction Company, Hickory, NC; *U.S. Private*, pg. 525
Moss, Charlie, Chm.--Moss/Dragoti, New York, NY; *Int'l*, pg. 117
Moss, Cruse W., Chm. Bd. & Chief Exec. Officer--General Automotive Corporation, Ann Arbor, MI; *U.S. Private*, pg. 443
Moss, Cruse W., Chm. Bd.--The Flxible Corp., Delaware, OH; *U.S. Private*, pg. 444
Moss, Geo. French, Chm. & Chief Exec. Officer--Western States Envelope Co., Milwaukee, WI; *U.S. Private*, pg. 1168
Mota-Velasco, German Larrea, Chm. & Pres.--Grupo Mexico S.A. de C.V., Mexico, Mexico; *U.S. Public*, pg. 138
Motoyama, Kazuo, Chm. Bd.--The Yokohama Rubber Co., Ltd., Tokyo, Japan; *Int'l*, pg. 1521
Mottard, Jilbert, Chm. Bd.--Credit Communal De Belgique SA, Brussels, Belgium; *Int'l*, pg. 343
Motto, William J., Chm. Bd. & Chief Exec. Officer--Meridian Diagnostics, Inc., Cincinnati, OH; *U.S. Public*, pg. 1094
Mougeot, Robert F., Chm. Bd. & Pres.--HEI Investment Corp., Honolulu, HI; *U.S. Public*, pg. 800
Moulaert, Jacques, Chm. Bd.--Bank Brussels Lambert, Brussels, Belgium; *Int'l*, pg. 146
Moult, Tom, Chm. Bd. & Creative Dir.--EURO RSCG Partnership, Sydney, Australia; *Int'l*, pg. 602
Moult, William, Pres. & Chief Exec. Officer--ASI Market Research, Inc., Stamford, CT; *U.S. Private*, pg. 554
Mourgue, H.G., Chm. Bd.--Kenwood Appliances Plc, Havant, United Kingdom; *Int'l*, pg. 730
Mourry, Dennis, Chm. Bd. & Chief Exec. Officer--Roytex, Inc., New York, NY; *U.S. Private*, pg. 949
Mouton, Michael, Chm. Bd.--Performance Medical Group, Lafayette, LA; *U.S. Private*, pg. 853
Mow, William, Dr., Chm. Bd. & Chief Exec. Officer--Bugle Boy Industries, Inc., Simi Valley, CA; *U.S. Private*, pg. 179
Mower, Eric, Chm. & Chief Exec. Officer--Eric Mower and Associates, Inc., Syracuse, NY; *U.S. Private*, pg. 765
Mower, Eric, Chm. & Chief Exec. Officer--Eric Mower and Associates, Rochester, NY; *U.S. Private*, pg. 765
Moyer, Curtis F., Chm. Bd.--Moyer Packing Company, Souderton, PA; *U.S. Private*, pg. 765
Moyer, William C., Dr., Chm. Bd., Pres. & Chief Exec. Officer--SFA, Inc., Hyattsville, MD; *U.S. Private*, pg. 956
Moyes, Jerry C., Chm. Bd., Pres. & Chief Exec. Officer--Swift Transportation Co., Sparks, NV; *U.S. Public*, pg. 1543
Moylan, James E., Chm. Bd.--Citrus Corp., Houston, TX; *U.S. Public*, pg. 585
Moyse, Hermann, Jr., Chm. Bd.--First Commerce Corporation, New Orleans, LA; *U.S. Public*, pg. 629
Mozilo, Angelo R., Chm. Bd. & Chief Exec. Officer--Countrywide Home Loans Inc., Pasadena, CA; *U.S. Public*, pg. 452
Mrig, G.C., Chm. Bd. & Mng. Dir.--Bharat Coking Coal Limited, Dhanbad, India; *Int'l*, pg. 298
Mrozinski, Walter F., Chm. Bd.--Facemate Corporation, Chicopee, MA; *U.S. Private*, pg. 391
Mueller, Charles W., Chm. Bd., Pres. & Chief Exec. Officer--Ameren Corporation, Saint Louis, MO; *U.S. Public*, pg. 65
Mueller, David R., Chm. Bd. & Chief Exec. Officer--Comair Holdings, Inc., Erlanger, KY; *U.S. Public*, pg. 406
Mueller, J.D., Chm. Bd.--G & W Electric Co., Blue Island, IL; *U.S. Private*, pg. 433
Mueller, John S., Chm. Bd.--Laidlaw Corporation, Scottsdale, AZ; *U.S. Private*, pg. 642
Mueller, Paul, Chm. Bd.--Paul Mueller Company, Springfield, MO; *U.S. Public*, pg. 1141
Mueller, Rand W., Chm. Bd., Pres. & Chief Exec. Officer--Code-Alarm, Inc., Madison Heights, MI; *U.S. Public*, pg. 393
Mueller, Warren A., Chm. Bd. & Treas.--C & M Corporation, Wauregan, CT; *U.S. Private*, pg. 191
Mugnai, Franco, Chm. Bd.--Italfid Italiana Fiduciaria S.p.A., Milan, Italy; *Int'l*, pg. 138
Muhlschlegel, Harry J., Chm. Bd. & Chief Exec. Officer--Jevic Transportation, Inc., Delanco, NJ; *U.S. Public*, pg. 927
Muir, Edward D., Chm. & Chief Exec. Officer--Rapidforms, Inc., Thorofare, NJ; *U.S. Public*, pg. 1171

Mukae, Hisao, Chm. Bd.--Ashikaga Bank, Tochigi, Japan; *Int'l*, pg. 88
Mulder, Lawrence, Chm. Bd. & Pres.--ODL Incorporated, Zeeland, MI; *U.S. Private*, pg. 809
Mull, Jackie, Chm. Bd.--Plains Cotton Co-op Association, Lubbock, TX; *U.S. Private*, pg. 868
Mullen, Edward K., Chm. Bd.--The Newark Group, Inc., Cranford, NJ; *U.S. Private*, pg. 796
Muller, Bernard, Chm. Bd.--Compagnie Bancaire, Paris, France; *Int'l*, pg. 319
Muller, Henry, Chm.--Coop Winterthur, Winterthur, Switzerland; *Int'l*, pg. 329
Muller, Klaus-Jurgen, Co-Chm.--FCA!BMZ, Suresnes, France; *Int'l*, pg. 469
Muller, Klaus-Jurgen, Co-Chm.--BMZ!FCA, Dusseldorf, Germany; *Int'l*, pg. 470
Muller, Norbert, Chm. Bd.--Plettac AG, Plettenberg, Germany; *Int'l*, pg. 1061
Mullet, Roy, Chm. Bd.--Excel Industries, Inc., Hesston, KS; *U.S. Private*, pg. 387
Mullet, Willis, Chm. Bd. & Chief Exec. Officer--Wayne Dalton Corporation, Mount Hope, OH; *U.S. Private*, pg. 1155
Mullett, D.H., Chm. Bd. & Chief Exec. Officer--Bradley Corporation, Menomonee Falls, WI; *U.S. Private*, pg. 164
Mundell, D.E., Chm.--ORIX USA Corporation-San Francisco, San Francisco, CA; *Int'l*, pg. 1009
Mundt, Ray B., Chm. Bd. & Chief Exec. Officer--Unisource Worldwide, Inc., Berwyn, PA; *U.S. Public*, pg. 1670
Mundy, John F., Chm. Bd., Pres. & Chief Exec. Officer--Lava World International/Haggerty Enterprises, Inc., Chicago, IL; *U.S. Private*, pg. 653
Munger, Sharon M., Chm. Bd. & Chief Exec. Officer--The M/A/R/C Group, Irving, TX; *U.S. Public*, pg. 1022
Munk, Peter, Chm. Bd. & Chief Exec. Officer--Barrick Gold Corporation, Toronto, Canada; *Int'l*, pg. 168
Munk, Peter, Chm. Bd. & Chief Exec. Officer--TrizecHahn Corporation, Toronto, Canada; *Int'l*, pg. 1424
Munn, Stephen P., Chm. Bd. & Chief Exec. Officer--Carlisle Companies Incorporated, Syracuse, NY; *U.S. Public*, pg. 305
Munnich, Walter, Chm.--Flender Ishibashi Co. Ltd., Fukuoka, Japan; *Int'l*, pg. 400
Munoz, Angel, Chm. Bd., Pres. & Chief Exec. Officer--Tropic Communications Inc., Columbus, OH; *U.S. Public*, *pg. 1641*
Munro, A.H., Chm. Bd.--Kloof Gold Mining Company Limited, Johannesburg, South Africa; *Int'l*, pg. 738
Munro, Donald, Chm. Bd.--Munro & Company, Inc., Hot Springs National Park, AR; *U.S. Private*, pg. 767
Munro, Donald, Chm. Bd.--Jumping Jacks, Monett, MO; *U.S. Private*, pg. 767
Munro, J. Richard, Chm. Bd.--Genentech, Inc., South San Francisco, CA; *Int'l*, pg. 1120
Munter, Jens, Chm. Bd.--FLS Industries A/S, Valby, Denmark; *Int'l*, pg. 474
Muramoto, Hisao, Chm. Bd.--The Chuo Trust & Banking Co., Ltd., Tokyo, Japan; *Int'l*, pg. 291
Murata, Osamu, Chm. Bd.--Murata Manufacturing Co., Ltd., Kyoto, Japan; *Int'l*, pg. 897
Murch, Maynard H., IV, Chm. Bd.--Robbins & Myers, Inc., Dayton, OH; *U.S. Public*, pg. 1393
Murdoch, H.D., Dr., Exec. Chm.-Indus. Electronics Div.--Dobson Park Industries Plc, Wigan, United Kingdom; *U.S. Public*, pg. 789
Murdoch, K. Rupert, Chm. Bd.--News America Publishing Inc., New York, NY; *Int'l*, pg. 925
Murdoch, Keith Rupert, Chm. Bd.--The New York Post, New York, NY; *Int'l*, pg. 927
Murdock, David H., Chm. Bd. & Chief Exec. Officer--Castle & Cooke Inc., Los Angeles, CA; *U.S. Public*, pg. 313
Murdock, David H., Chm. Bd. & Chief Exec. Officer--Flexi-Van Leasing, Inc., Kenilworth, NJ; *U.S. Private*, pg. 413
Murdock, David H., Chm. Bd. & Chief Exec. Officer--Dole Food Company, Inc., Westlake Village, CA; *U.S. Public*, pg. 515
Murofushi, Minoru, Chm. Bd., Pres. & Chief Exec. Officer--Itochu Corporation, Tokyo, Japan; *Int'l*, pg. 694
Murphy, Charles O., Chm. Bd., Pres. & Chief Exec. Officer--SouthTrust Bank, Suncoast, Sarasota, FL; *U.S. Public*, pg. 1492
Murphy, G.D., Chm. Bd.--Erly Industries, Inc., Los Angeles, CA; *U.S. Public*, pg. 591
Murphy, G.D., Chm. Bd.--Comet American Marketing, Houston, TX; *U.S. Public*, pg. 591
Murphy, Gerald D., Chm. Bd.--American Rice Inc., Houston, TX; *U.S. Public*, pg. 591
Murphy, James R., Chm. Bd., Pres. & Chief Exec. Officer--Bentley Pharmaceuticals, Inc., Tampa, FL; *U.S. Public*, pg. 212
Murphy, Kenneth T., Chm. Bd., Pres. & Chief Exec. Officer--First Financial Bankshares, Inc., Abilene, TX; *U.S. Public*, *pg. 633*
Murphy, Peter, Jr., Chm. Bd., Pres. & Chief Exec. Officer--Murphy Company, Eugene, OR; *U.S. Private*, pg. 768
Murphy, R. Madison, Chm. Bd.--Murphy Oil Corporation, El Dorado, AR; *U.S. Public*, pg. 1141
Murphy, Steve, Chm. Bd. & Pres.--Producers Co-op Association, Inc., Girard, KS; *U.S. Private*, pg. 888
Murphy, Timothy P., Chm. Bd.--Cognitronics Corporation, Danbury, CT; *U.S. Public*, pg. 394
Murphy, Wendell H., Chm.--Murphy Family Farms, Rose Hill, NC; *U.S. Private*, pg. 768
Murray, J. Alec G., Chm. Bd.--Standard Commercial Corporation, Wilson, NC; *U.S. Public*, pg. 1501
Murray, Michael, Chm. Bd. & Pres.--NT Dor-omatic, Harwood Heights, IL; *U.S. Private*, pg. 771
Murray, Robert J., Chm. Bd., Pres. & Chief Exec. Officer--New England Business Service, Inc., Groton, MA; *U.S. Public*, pg. 1170
Murray, Terrence, Chm. Bd., Pres. & Chief Exec. Officer--Fleet Financial Group, Inc., Boston, MA; *U.S. Public*, pg. 648
Murrill, Paul W., Chm. Bd.--Piccadilly Cafeterias, Inc., Baton Rouge, LA; *U.S. Public*, pg. 1294
Murry, Albert B., Chm. Bd., Pres. & Chief Exec. Officer--Keystone Heritage Group, Inc., Lebanon, PA; *U.S. Public*, pg. 687
Muselman, Carl H., Chm. Bd.--E.P. Graphics, Inc., Berne, IN; *U.S. Private*, pg. 354
Muskat, Irwin, Chm. Bd., Pres. & Chief Exec. Officer--Jac Pac Foods, Ltd., Manchester, NH; *U.S. Private*, pg. 579
Musser, Warren V., Chm. Bd. & Chief Exec. Officer--Safeguard Scientifics, Inc., Wayne, PA; *U.S. Public*, pg. 1424
Must, Mike, Chm. Bd.--Detroit City Dairy, Inc., Detroit, MI; *U.S. Private*, pg. 328
Mustain, William G., Chm. Bd., Pres. & Chief Exec. Officer--Comdial Corporation, Charlottesville, VA; *U.S. Public*, pg. 407
Mustain, William G., Chm. Bd. & Chief Exec. Officer--American Telecommunications Corporation, Charlottesville, VA; *U.S. Public*, pg. 407
Mustain, William G., Chm. Bd. & Chief Exec. Officer--Comdial Enterprise Systems, Inc., Charlottesville, VA; *U.S. Public*, pg. 407
Musto, Michael L., Chm. Bd., Pres. & Chief Exec. Officer--Reptron Electronics, Inc., Tampa, FL; *U.S. Public*, pg. 1377
Muth, Peter G., Chm. Bd.--Orco Block Company, Stanton, CA; *U.S. Private*, pg. 819
Mutz, Gregory T., Chm. Bd.--LincAm Properties, Inc., Chicago, IL; *U.S. Public*, pg. 997
Muundrell, P., Chm. Bd.--Chemtronics Inc., Kennesaw, GA; *Int'l*, pg. 892
Muzzy, Richard W., Jr., Chm. Bd. & Chief Exec. Officer--The Holland Hitch Company, Holland, MI; *U.S. Private*, pg. 534
Muzzy, Richard W., Jr., Chm. Bd., Chief Exec. & Chief Oper. Officer--Binkley Company, Warrenton, MO; *U.S. Private*, pg. 534
Mycock, B., Chm. Bd.--Bruntons Areo Product, Musselburgh, United Kingdom; *Int'l*, pg. 268
Myers, A. Maurice, Chm. Bd., Pres. & Chief Exec. Officer--Yellow Corporation, Overland Park, KS; *U.S. Public*, pg. 1788
Myers, Arno R., Chm. Bd.--Airtite Contractors Inc., Chicago, IL; *U.S. Private*, pg. 29
Myers, B., Chm.--Cleveland Structural Engineering Limited, Durham, United Kingdom; *Int'l*, pg. 772
Myers, Chuck, Chm. Bd., Pres. & Chief Exec. Officer--Kitchen Investment Group, Madison, WI; *U.S. Private*, pg. 624
Myers, David L., Chm. Bd.--Fluor Daniel GTI, Inc., Norwood, MA; *U.S. Public*, pg. 660
Myers, Jay E., Chm. Bd. & Chief Exec. Officer--United Southwest Bank, Washington, IN; *U.S. Public*, pg. 1217
Myers, Joseph E., Chm. Bd. & Pres.--Collins Oldsmobile Inc., Indianapolis, IN; *U.S. Private*, pg. 253
Myers, L.G., Pres. & Chief Exec. Officer--LubeCon Systems, Inc., White Cloud, MI; *U.S. Private*, pg. 679
Myers, Paul, Chm. Bd.--Javelin/Young & Rubicam, Dublin, Ireland; *U.S. Private*, pg. 1199
Myers, Robert R., Chm. Bd. & Chief Exec. Officer--Kocolene Oil Corp., Seymour, IN; *U.S. Private*, pg. 629
Myers, Robert R., Chm. Bd.--Shadowood Golf Inc., Seymour, IN; *U.S. Private*, pg. 629
Myers, Stanley T., Chm. Bd.--Mitsubishi Silicon America, Salem, OR; *Int'l*, pg. 875
Myers, Stanley T., Chm. Bd.--Mitsubishi Silicon America, Palo Alto, CA; *Int'l*, pg. 875
Myers, William D., Chm. Bd.--American Dental Technologies, Southfield, MI; *U.S. Public*, pg. 70
Myerson, Robert, Chm. Bd.--Ben Myerson Candy Company, Inc., Los Angeles, CA; *U.S. Private*, pg. 771
Myhre, Leonard A., Chm. Bd.--Hallidie Machinery Company, Inc., Seattle, WA; *U.S. Private*, pg. 495
Myrick, Bobby H., Chm. Bd. & Treas.--Myrick Construction Inc., Biscoe, NC; *U.S. Private*, pg. 771
Myrick, Goodwin L., Chm. Bd. & Pres.--Alfa Corporation, Montgomery, AL; *U.S. Public*, pg. 40
Myrick, Goodwin L., Chm. Bd. & Pres.--Alfa Realty, Inc., Montgomery, AL; *U.S. Public*, pg. 40
Nabers, Drayton, Jr., Chm. Bd. & Chief Exec. Officer--Protective Life Corporation, Birmingham, AL; *U.S. Public*, *pg. 1336*
Nabholz, Robert D., Jr., Chm. Bd. & Chief Exec. Officer--Nabholz Construction Corp., Conway, AR; *U.S. Private*, pg. 772
Nabors, J. Mervyn, Chm. Bd., Pres. & Chief Exec. Officer--Aerosonic Corporation, Clearwater, FL; *U.S. Public*, pg. 25
Naccarato, Vincent A., Chm. Bd., Pres. & Chief Exec. Officer--Wilton Industries, Inc., Woodridge, IL; *U.S. Private*, pg. 1181
Nadhir, Saad J., Co-Chm. & Chief Exec. Officer--Boston Chicken, Inc., Golden, CO; *U.S. Public*, pg. 247
Nadig, Gerald G., Chm. Bd., Pres. & Chief Exec. Officer--Material Sciences Corporation, Elk Grove Village, IL; *U.S. Public*, pg. 1056
Nagai, Atsushi, Chm.--Hitachi Maxell, Ltd., Osaka, Japan; *Int'l*, pg. 621
Nagai, Yasunori, Chm.--IBJ Merchant Bank (Singapore) Limited, Singapore, Singapore; *Int'l*, pg. 676
Nagai, Yataro, Chm. Bd.--Mitsubishi Rayon Co., Ltd., Tokyo, Japan; *Int'l*, pg. 876
Nagamori, S., Chm. Bd.--NIDEC, Canton, MA; *Int'l*, pg. 933
Nagamori, Shigendou, Chm. Bd. & Pres.--Nippon Densan (NIDEC), Kyoto, Japan; *Int'l*, pg. 933
Nagaoka, Takeshi, Chm. Bd.--Nippon Express Co., Ltd., Tokyo, Japan; *Int'l*, pg. 933
Nagara, Akira, Chm. Bd.--Nikkei Business Publications Inc., Tokyo, Japan; *Int'l*, pg. 929
Nagata, Masao, Chm. Bd.--Kanebo, Ltd., Tokyo, Japan; *Int'l*, pg. 722
Nagayama, Tokio, Chm. Bd.--Showa Shell Sekiyu KK, Tokyo, Japan; *Int'l*, pg. 1140
Nagel, Kevin, Chm. Bd., Pres. & Chief Exec. Officer--EBP Life Insurnace Co., Minneapolis, MN; *U.S. Public*, pg. 635
Nagler, Stewart G., Chm. Bd.--Metropolitan Property & Casualty Insurance Co. (Met P&C), Warwick, RI; *U.S. Private*, pg. 737
Nagumo, Shiro, Chm. Bd.--"K" Line (Kawasaki Kisen Kaisha, Ltd.), Tokyo, Japan; *Int'l*, pg. 717
Nagumo, Shiro, Chm. Bd.--Kawasaki Kisen Kaisha, Ltd., Tokyo, Japan; *Int'l*, pg. 726
Nahmad, Albert H., Chm. Bd., Pres. & Chief Exec. Officer--Watsco, Inc., Coconut Grove, FL; *U.S. Public*, pg. 1745
Naify, Marshall, Co-Chm. Bd.--The Todd-AO Corporation, Hollywood, CA; *U.S. Public*, pg. 1619
Naify, Robert A., Co-Chm. Bd.--The Todd-AO Corporation, Hollywood, CA; *U.S. Public*, pg. 1619
Naito, Yuji, Chm. Bd.--Eisai Co., Ltd., Tokyo, Japan; *Int'l*, pg. 435
Nakagawa, Kenzo, Chm. Bd & Mng. Dir.--Showpla Asia Limited, Singapore, Singapore; *Int'l*, pg. 1237
Nakahigashi, Motoo, Chm. Bd.--UBE Industries Ltd., Tokyo, Japan; *Int'l*, pg. 1426
Nakajima, Michio, Chm. Bd.--Citizen Watch Company, Ltd., Tokyo, Japan; *Int'l*, pg. 293
Nakamura, Hirokazu, Chm. Bd.--Mitsubishi Motors Corporation, Tokyo, Japan; *Int'l*, pg. 875
Nakamura, Hisao, Chm. Bd.--Kuraray Co., Ltd., Osaka, Japan; *Int'l*, pg. 764
Nakamura, Kaneo, Chm.--IBJ Asia Limited, Central, Hong Kong; *Int'l*, pg. 676
Nakamura, Kannosuke, Chm. Bd. & Chief Exec. Officer--Kyowa Hakko Kogyo Company, Ltd., Tokyo, Japan; *Int'l*, pg. 778
Nakamura, Kazuhiko, Chm.--Sunstar Inc., Takatsuki, Japan; *Int'l*, pg. 1320
Nakamura, Kunio, Chm. Bd., Chief Exec. Officer & Chief Oper. Officer--Matsushita Electric Corporation of America, Secaucus, NJ; *Int'l*, pg. 847
Nakamura, Masaharie, Chm. & Pres.--Tokio Marine Management Inc., New York, NY; *Int'l*, pg. 1392
Nakamura, Masahide, Chm. Bd.--The Daishi Bank, Ltd., Niigata, Japan; *Int'l*, pg. 372
Nakamura, Masao, Chm. Bd. & Chief Exec. Officer--Hokuriku Electric Industry Co., Ltd., Toyama, Japan; *Int'l*, *pg. 627*
Nakamura, Masaya, Chm. Bd. & Chief Exec. Officer--Namco Ltd., Tokyo, Japan; *Int'l*, pg. 905
Nakamura, Noboru, Chm. Bd.--Kokusai Electric Co., Ltd., Tokyo, Japan; *Int'l*, pg. 743
Nakamura, Teruo, Chm. Bd.--Nippon Kayaku Co. Ltd., Tokyo, Japan; *Int'l*, pg. 934
Nakanishi, T., Chm. Bd.--UGL, Inc., Chicago Heights, IL; *Int'l*, pg. 1117
Nakano, Kozaburo, Chm. Bd.--Kikkoman International, Inc., San Francisco, CA; *Int'l*, pg. 733
Nakano, Mashiko, Chm. Bd.--Kabuto Decom Inc., Sapporo, Japan; *Int'l*, pg. 721
Nakash, Joseph, Chm. Bd. & Pres.--Jordache Enterprises, Inc., New York, NY; *U.S. Private*, pg. 597
Nakashima, Yuichi, Chm. Bd.--Q.P. Corporation, Tokyo, Japan; *Int'l*, pg. 1074
Nakauchi, Isao, Chm. Bd., Pres. & Chief Exec. Officer--The Daiei, Inc., Kobe, Japan; *Int'l*, pg. 364
Nakayama, H., Co-Chm. Bd.--Sega of America Inc., Redwood City, CA; *Int'l*, pg. 1218
Nakayama, Y., Chm. Bd.--Dunlop Tire Corporation, Buffalo, NY; *Int'l*, pg. 1317
Nakazawa, Tadayoshi, Vice Chm.--Itochu Corporation, Tokyo, Japan; *Int'l*, pg. 694
Nam, Dato Tan Chin, Chm. Bd.--Parkway Holdings Limited, Singapore, Singapore; *Int'l*, pg. 1023
Namba, Kunio, Chm. Bd.--Namba Press Works Co., Ltd., Kurashiki, Japan; *Int'l*, pg. 904
Nan, Tan Soo, Chm.--DBS Asia Capital Ltd., Central, Hong Kong; *Int'l*, pg. 351
Nanot, Yves Rene, Chm. Bd., Pres. & Chief Exec. Officer--Ciments Francais, Paris, France; *Int'l*, pg. 292
Napier, James V., Chm. Bd.--Scientific-Atlanta, Inc., Norcross, GA; *U.S. Public*, pg. 1443
Napier, Robert S., Chm. Bd.--The Braas Group, Oberursell, Germany; *Int'l*, pg. 1091
Naples, Ronald J., Chm. Bd., Pres. & Chief Exec. Officer--Quaker Chemical Corporation, Conshohocken, PA; *U.S. Public*, pg. 1346
Naritoni, T.A., Chm. Bd. & Chief Exec. Officer--Steelox Systems Inc., Mason, OH; *U.S. Private*, pg. 1038
Narlinger, Dennis, Chm. Bd., Pres. & Chief Exec. Officer--Shugart Corporation, Mission Viejo, CA; *U.S. Private*, pg. 997
Nashman, Alvin E., Dr., Chm. Bd.--Miltope Group, Inc., Hope Hull, AL; *U.S. Public*, pg. 1114
Nason, Charles T., Chm. Bd., Pres. & Chief Exec. Officer--The Acacia Group - Acacia Life Insurance Co., Bethesda, MD; *U.S. Private*, pg. 10
Nason, Charles W., Chm. Bd. & Pres.--Worzalla Publishing Co., Inc., Stevens Point, WI; *U.S. Private*, pg. 1191
Nasser, Albert, Chm. Bd., Chief Exec. Officer & Chief Oper. Officer--Lady Marlene Sales Corp., New York, NY; *U.S. Private*, pg. 642
Nasu, Shoh, Chm. Bd.--The Tokyo Electric Power Co., Inc., Tokyo, Japan; *Int'l*, pg. 1394
Nathe, Gerald A., Chm. Bd., Pres. & Chief Exec. Officer--Baldwin Technology Company, Inc., Norwalk, CT; *U.S. Public*, pg. 169
Naughton, M.L., Chm. Bd.--The Glen Dimplex Group, Dunleer, Ireland; *Int'l*, pg. 553
Naumann-Etienne, Ruediger, Chm. Bd.--OEC Medical Systems, Inc., Salt Lake City, UT; *U.S. Public*, pg. 1207
Nave, Edward, Chm. Bd.--Mercury Distributing Co., Inc., Chatsworth, CA; *U.S. Private*, pg. 732
Nayar, N.K., Chm. Bd.--IRD Mechanalysis (India) Limited, Mumbai, India; *U.S. Public*, pg. 790
Neal, James L., Chm. Bd.--ABC Packaging Machine Corp., Tarpon Springs, FL; *U.S. Private*, pg. 3

Neal, John R., Chm. Bd. & Pres.--JRN, Inc., Columbia, TN; *U.S. Private*, pg. 578
Neale, Gary L., Chm. Bd., Pres. & Chief Exec. Officer--NIPSCO Industries, Inc., Hammond, IN; *U.S. Public*, pg. 1185
Neally, Phillip, Chm. Bd., Pres. & Chief Exec. Officer--Aldi Food Inc., Batavia, IL; *U.S. Private*, pg. 33
Necker, H.C.T., Dr., Chm.-Supervisory Bd.--IKB Deutsche Industriebank AG, Dusseldorf, Germany; *Int'l*, pg. 645
Nectoux, Georges, Chm. & Chief Exec. Officer--Ricard, Marseilles, France; *Int'l*, pg. 566
Nedblake, Jeff, Chm. Bd.--Package Service Company, LLC., Kansas City, MO; *U.S. Private*, pg. 833
Nederlander, Robert, Chm. Bd.--Riddell Sports, Inc., New York, NY; *U.S. Public*, pg. 1389
Nederlander, Robert E., Chm. Bd.--Riddell Sports, Inc., Chicago, IL; *U.S. Public*, pg. 1389
Needle, Gilbert, Chm. Bd.--Atlantic Plumbing Supply Company, Washington, DC; *U.S. Private*, pg. 95
Negishi, Issac, Chm.--Tokyo Senko International Inc., Tokyo, Japan; *Int'l*, pg. 1394
Negishi, Shigeru, Chm. Bd.--Japan Storage Battery Co., Ltd., Tokyo, Japan; *Int'l*, pg. 702
Neiff, Gerhard, Dr., Chm.-Supervisory Bd.--Ruetgers A.G., Frankfurt/Main, Germany; *Int'l*, pg. 1147
Neilson, Kenneth T., Chm. Bd., Pres. & Chief Exec. Officer--Hubco, Inc., Mahwah, NJ; *U.S. Public*, pg. 845
Neilson, Kenneth T., Chm. Bd. & Chief Exec. Officer--Lafayette American Bank, Union City, NJ; *U.S. Public*, pg. 845
Neister, Martin, Chm. Bd.--Sandoz Pharma Ltd., Eden Terrace, New Zealand; *Int'l*, pg. 985
Nekman, Donald, Chm., Partner & Chief Fin. Officer--EURO RSCG, Copenhagen, Copenhagen, Denmark; *Int'l*, pg. 602
Nekvasil, Jiri, Chm.--Obalex, A.S., Znojmo, Czech Republic; *U.S. Public*, pg. 440
Nelligan, John, Chm. Bd.--Britannia Music Co. Ltd., Ilford, United Kingdom; *Int'l*, pg. 1052
Nelsen, C. Davis, II, Chm. Bd., Pres. & Chief Exec. Officer--Nelsen Steel & Wire Co., Franklin Park, IL; *U.S. Private*, pg. 790
Nelson Ragland, Judith, Chm. Bd.--Duncan Equipment Company, Oklahoma City, OK; *U.S. Private*, pg. 346
Nelson, B.J., Chm. Bd.--Barton Nelson Inc., Kansas City, MO; *U.S. Private*, pg. 120
Nelson, Charles E., Chm. Bd., Pres. & Chief Exec. Officer--Liberty Bancorp, Inc., Oklahoma City, OK; *U.S. Public*, pg. 174
Nelson, Charles E., Chm. Bd., Pres. & Chief Exec. Officer--Liberty Bank & Trust Company of Oklahoma City, Oklahoma City, OK; *U.S. Public*, pg. 174
Nelson, David L., Chm. Bd.--Herman Miller, Inc., Zeeland, MI; *U.S. Public*, pg. 1111
Nelson, Gary R., Chm. Bd. & Chief Exec. Officer--Nelson Photo Supplies, San Diego, CA; *U.S. Private*, pg. 791
Nelson, Jack, Chm. Bd., Chief Exec. Officer & Treas.--Caprius, Inc., Wilmington, MA; *U.S. Public*, pg. 303
Nelson, James D., Chm. Bd. & Chief Exec. Officer--Arbor Acres Farm, Inc., Glastonbury, CT; *Int'l*, pg. 202
Nelson, John C., Chm. Bd. & Chief Exec. Officer--Norwest Bank Colorado N.A., Denver, CO; *U.S. Public*, pg. 1202
Nelson, John F., Chm. Bd.--Golden Gem Growers Inc., Umatilla, FL; *U.S. Private*, pg. 460
Nelson, John M., Chm. Bd.--The TJX Companies, Inc., Framingham, MA; *U.S. Public*, pg. 1556
Nelson, John M., Chm. Bd.--Wyman-Gordon, North Grafton, MA; *U.S. Public*, pg. 1782
Nelson, Keith, Chm. Bd.--Martin Luther Hospital Anaheim, Anaheim, CA; *U.S. Private*, pg. 1118
Nelson, Kurt, Chm. Bd, Pres. & Chief Exec. Officer--Manning & Lewis Engineering Co., Union, NJ; *U.S. Private*, pg. 700
Nelson, Roger R., Deputy Chm.-Consulting Services--Ernst & Young, LLP, New York, NY; *U.S. Private*, pg. 381
Nelson, Ted D., Chm. Bd.--Opal Concepts, Inc., Anaheim, CA; *U.S. Private*, pg. 817
Nelson, W. Peterson, Chm.--Nelson, Benson & Zellmer, Inc., Denver, CO; *U.S. Public*, pg. 1673
Nemirow, Arnold M., Chm. Bd., Pres. & Chief Exec. Officer--Bowater Incorporated, Greenville, SC; *U.S. Public*, pg. 247
Nemoto, Jiro, Chm. Bd.--Nippon Yusen K.K., Tokyo, Japan; *Int'l*, pg. 941
Nerad, John, Chm. Bd.--TimeMed Labeling Systems, Inc., Burr Ridge, IL; *U.S. Private*, pg. 1087
Nesbitt, Gregory L., Chm. Bd., Pres. & Chief Exec. Officer--Central Louisiana Electric Company, Inc., Pineville, LA; *U.S. Public*, pg. 325
Ness, Joseph, Chm. Bd.--Zero-Max, Inc., Minneapolis, MN; *Int'l*, pg. 866
Ness, William G., Chm. Bd.--Arctic Cat Inc., Thief River Falls, MN; *U.S. Public*, pg. 128
Nethercutt, J.B., Chm. Bd.--Merle Norman Cosmetics, Inc., Los Angeles, CA; *U.S. Private*, pg. 733
Netter, Edward, Chm. Bd.--Geneve Corporation, Stamford, CT; *U.S. Private*, pg. 446
Netter, Edward, Chm. Bd. & Chief Exec. Officer--Independence Holding Company, Stamford, CT; *U.S. Private*, pg. 446
Netter, K. Fred, Chm. Bd.--GAF Premium Products, Inc., Wayne, NJ; *U.S. Private*, pg. 433
Netzsch, Thomas, Chm. Bd.--Netzsch Incorporated, Exton, PA; *U.S. Private*, pg. 792
Neubauer, Franz, Chm. Bd.--Bayerische Landesbank, Munich, Germany; *Int'l*, pg. 176
Neubauer, Joseph, Chm. Bd., Pres. & Chief Exec. Officer--Aramark Corp., Philadelphia, PA; *U.S. Private*, pg. 78
Neuber, Friedel, Chm. Bd.--Landesbank Rheinland-Pfalz, Mainz, Germany; *Int'l*, pg. 799
Neuber, Friedel, Chm. Bd.--Westdeutsche Landesbank Girozentrale, Dusseldorf, Germany; *Int'l*, pg. 1492
Neuen, Gottfried, Vice Chm.--Henkel KGaA, Dusseldorf, Germany; *Int'l*, pg. 609
Neukirchen, Kajo, Dr., Chm. Bd.--FAG Bearings Corporation, Danbury, CT; *Int'l*, pg. 469
Neumaier, Gerhard J., Chm. Bd. & Pres.--Ecology and Environment, Inc., Lancaster, NY; *U.S. Public*, pg. 562
Neuwirth, Frank, Chm. Bd. & Pres.--Unex Conveying Systems, Inc., Jackson, NJ; *U.S. Private*, pg. 1117
Neveu, Jean, Chm. Bd.--Quebecor Printing, Inc., Montreal, Canada; *Int'l*, pg. 1076
Neveu, Jean, Chm. Bd. & Chief Exec. Officer--Imprimerie Quebecor Inc., Montreal, Canada; *Int'l*, pg. 1077
Neville, Robert J., Chm. Bd., Pres. & Chief Exec. Officer--The North American Manufacturing Co., Cleveland, OH; *U.S. Private*, pg. 803
Neville, Thomas, Chm. Bd.--Eurocamp Plc, Knutsford, United Kingdom; *Int'l*, pg. 464
New, R.F., Chm. Bd.--Ets. Marshall S.A., Gonesse, France; *Int'l*, pg. 891
Newall, J.E., Chm. Bd.--Methanex Corporation, Vancouver, Canada; *Int'l*, pg. 862
Newberry, Thomas L., Chm. Bd.--American Software, Inc., Atlanta, GA; *U.S. Public*, pg. 91
Newhouse, Samuel I., Jr., Chm. Bd. & Chief Exec. Officer--Advance Publications Inc., Staten Island, NY; *U.S. Private*, pg. 18
Newlin, William R., Chm. Bd.--Kennametal Inc., Latrobe, PA; *U.S. Public*, pg. 950
Newman, Alan, Chm. Bd.--Bristile Clay Tiles, Ltd., Caversham, Australia; *Int'l*, pg. 216
Newman, Dave, Chm. Bd.--Washington State Apple Commission, Wenatchee, WA; *U.S. Private*, pg. 1152
Newman, Frank, Chm. Bd., Pres. & Chief Exec. Officer--Eckerd Corporation, Largo, FL; *U.S. Public*, pg. 917
Newman, Frank N., Chm. Bd., Pres. & Chief Exec. Officer--Bankers Trust New York Corporation, New York, NY; *U.S. Public*, pg. 185
Newman, John W., Exec. Chm.--TT Group PLC, Surrey, United Kingdom; *Int'l*, pg. 1344
Newman, Mark S., Chm. Bd., Pres. & Chief Exec. Officer--DRS Technologies, Inc., Parsippany, NJ; *U.S. Public*, pg. 474
Newman, Stephen H., Chm. Bd. & Chief Exec. Officer--Underwriters Reinsurance, Woodland Hills, CA; *U.S. Public*, pg. 42
Newman, William, Chm. Bd. & Chief Exec. Officer--New Plan Realty Trust, New York, NY; *U.S. Public*, pg. 1172
Newton, William H., III, Chm. Bd.--SATEC Systems Inc., Grove City, PA; *U.S. Private*, pg. 967
Neyer, Jerome C., Chm. Bd. & Chief Exec. Officer--NTH Consultants, Ltd., Farmington, MI; *U.S. Private*, pg. 772
Neyer, Thomas, Sr., Chm. Bd. & Pres.--Al Neyer, Inc., Cincinnati, OH; *U.S. Private*, pg. 797
Nicastro, Louis, Chm. Bd. & Chief Exec. Officer--WHG Resorts & Casinos, Carolina, PR; *U.S. Public*, pg. 1265
Nicastro, Louis J., Chm. Bd.--WMS Industries Inc., Chicago, IL; *U.S. Public*, pg. 1727
Nichel, B., Chm. Bd.--Banque Regionale, Blois, France; *Int'l*, pg. 563
Nichol, David A., Chm., Pres & Chief Exec. Officer--Destination Products International, Inc., Toronto, Canada; *Int'l*, pg. 338
Nicholas, Donna H., Chm. Bd. & Pres.--The Orr Felt Company, Piqua, OH; *U.S. Private*, pg. 820
Nicholas, Peter M., Chm. Bd., Pres. & Chief Exec. Officer--Boston Scientific Corp., Natick, MA; *U.S. Public*, pg. 247
Nicholas, Robert J., Chm. Bd.--Sonoma Valley Bank, Sonoma, CA; *U.S. Public*, pg. 1487
Nichols, Cathy, Chm. Bd. & Chief Exec. Officer--Universal Studios Recreation Services Group, Universal City, CA; *Int'l*, pg. 1216
Nichols, David L., Chm. Bd. & Chief Exec. Officer--Mercantile Stores Company, Inc., Fairfield, OH; *U.S. Public*, pg. 1089
Nichols, Fred R., Chm. Bd., Pres. & Chief Exec. Officer--TCA Cable TV, Inc., Tyler, TX; *U.S. Public*, pg. 1553
Nichols, Fred R., Chm. Bd., Pres. & Chief Exec. Officer--TCA Management Company, Tyler, TX; *U.S. Public*, pg. 1553
Nichols, J.D., Chm. Bd. & Chief Exec. Officer--NTS Development Company, Louisville, KY; *U.S. Private*, pg. 772
Nichols, John W., Chm. Bd.--Devon Energy Corporation, Oklahoma City, OK; *U.S. Public*, pg. 503
Nichols, Steven, Chm. Bd. & Pres.--K-Swiss Inc., Chatsworth, CA; *U.S. Public*, pg. 937
Nichols, W.C., Chm. Bd., Pres. & Chief Exec. Officer--Renfro Corp., Mount Airy, NC; *U.S. Private*, pg. 922
Nicholson, Gary D., Chm. Bd., Pres. & Chief Exec. Officer--Camco International Inc., Houston, TX; *U.S. Public*, pg. 297
Nicholson, James B., Chm. Bd.--Amerisure Companies, Farmington Hills, MI; *U.S. Private*, pg. 65
Nicholson, Paul, Sir, Chm. Bd.--Vaux Group Plc, Sunderland, United Kingdom; *Int'l*, pg. 1453
Nicholson, Will F., Jr., Chm. Bd. & Pres.--Colorado National Bankshares, Inc., Denver, CO; *U.S. Public*, pg. 1680
Nickel, Dieter H., Chm. Bd. & Pres.--Church Mutual Insurance Co., Merrill, WI; *U.S. Private*, pg. 239
Nickell, G.T., Chm. Bd.--AC Corporation, Greensboro, NC; *U.S. Private*, pg. 3
Nickels, William C., Chm. Bd.--Replogle Globes, Inc., Broadview, IL; *U.S. Private*, pg. 923
Nickerson, Joshua A., Jr., Chm. Bd. & Pres.--Nickerson Lumber Company, Orleans, MA; *U.S. Private*, pg. 798
Nickoll, John F., Chm. Bd. & Chief Exec. Officer--The Foothill Group, Inc., Los Angeles, CA; *U.S. Public*, pg. 1201
Nickson, Lord, Chm. Bd.--Clydesdale Bank PLC, Glasgow, United Kingdom; *Int'l*, pg. 906
Nicolai, G.C.A., Chm. Bd.--Karbon Grafit Sanayi A.S., Istanbul, Turkey; *Int'l*, pg. 891
Nicolet, Georges, Chm.--ECIA-Equipments Et Composants Pour L'industrie Automobile, Audincourt, France; *Int'l*, pg. 1021
Nidiffer, Raymond L., Chm. Bd.--C & K Market, Inc., Brookings, OR; *U.S. Private*, pg. 191
Nie, Norman H., Chm. Bd.--SPSS Inc., Chicago, IL; *U.S. Public*, pg. 1420
Nie, Zenon S., Chm. Bd. & Chief Exec. Officer--Simmons Company, Atlanta, GA; *Int'l*, pg. 686
Niederste-Werbeck, Dieter, Chm. Bd.--Jagenberg AG, Neuss, Germany; *Int'l*, pg. 1108
Niehaus, Robert, Chm. Bd.--Waterford Wedgwood UK Plc, Stoke on Trent, United Kingdom; *Int'l*, pg. 1487
Nield, D.A., Chm. Bd.--Canada Life Assurance (Ireland) Ltd., Blackrock, Ireland; *Int'l*, pg. 255
Nields, Morgan W., Chm. Bd. & Chief Exec. Officer--Fischer Imaging Corporation, Denver, CO; *U.S. Public*, pg. 647
Nielsen, Steven B., Chm. Bd.--General Medical Corp., Richmond, VA; *U.S. Public*, pg. 1073
Nielson, John O., Chm. Bd. & Chief Exec. Officer--John Morrell & Co., Cincinnati, OH; *U.S. Public*, pg. 1479
Niemiec, Leo, Chm. Bd.--Ingrid Division of Lawnware, Morton Grove, IL; *U.S. Private*, pg. 654
Nies, Thomas M., Chm. Bd., Pres. & Chief Exec. Officer--Cincom Systems, Inc., Cincinnati, OH; *U.S. Private*, pg. 240
Nilsen, F. O., Chm. Bd.--OCE-Danmark AS, Copenhagen, Denmark; *Int'l*, pg. 994
Nilsen, Leone A., Chm. & Pres.--Inter-Community Telephone Company, Nome, ND; *U.S. Public*, pg. 1022
Nilssen, Cecil Bae, Chm. Bd.--AS OSLO Sporveier, Oslo, Norway; *Int'l*, pg. 1012
Nilsson, Lennart, Vice Chm. Bd.--Cardo AB, Malmo, Sweden; *Int'l*, pg. 268
Nimrodi, Jackob, Chm. Bd. & Pres.--The Israel Land Development Co., Ltd., Tel Aviv, Israel; *Int'l*, pg. 691
Nirenberg, Charles, Chm. Bd.--Dairy Mart Convenience Stores, Inc., Cuyahoga Falls, OH; *U.S. Public*, pg. 476
Nisbet, W. Olin, III, Chm. Bd.--Sterling Capital Management Company, Charlotte, NC; *U.S. Public*, pg. 1674
Nishihachijo, Minoru, Dr., Chm. Bd.--Shimadzu Corporation, Kyoto, Japan; *Int'l*, pg. 1232
Nishimura, Koichi, Ph.D., Chm. Bd., Pres. & Chief Exec. Officer--Solectron Corporation, Milpitas, CA; *U.S. Public*, pg. 1483
Nishina, Kazuo, Chm. Bd.--Takashimaya Company, Limited, Osaka, Japan; *Int'l*, pg. 1349
Nishinaka, Ted, Chm. Bd. & Chief Exec. Officer--Mitsui Foods, Inc., Norwood, NJ; *Int'l*, pg. 879
Nishio, Shinichi, Chm. Bd.--Dai-ichi Mutual Life Insurance Company, Tokyo, Japan; *Int'l*, pg. 362
Niskanen, Yrjo, Chm. Bd.--UPM-Kymmene Corporation, Helsinki, Finland; *Int'l*, pg. 1427
Nissen, William, Chm. Bd. & Pres.--Apache Hose & Belting Company, Inc., Cedar Rapids, IA; *U.S. Private*, pg. 76
Nitsche, F., Chm. Bd.--Treibacher Schleifmittel Corp., Niagara Falls, NY; *U.S. Private*, pg. 1099
Nitti, Raymond M., Chm.--WJW Constructors, LLC, Mesa, AZ; *U.S. Private*, pg. 1187
Niwa, Masaharu, Chm. Bd.--PFU Limited, Ishikawa Pref., Japan; *Int'l*, pg. 526
Nixon, Robert F., Chm. Bd.--Atomic Energy of Canada Ltd., Mississauga, Canada; *Int'l*, pg. 97
Nizam, I., Chm. Bd., Pres. & Chief Exec. Officer--Master International Corp., Santa Monica, CA; *U.S. Private*, pg. 713
Noakes, M., Chm.--Hamworthy Engineering Limited, Poole, United Kingdom; *Int'l*, pg. 1065
Noar, Stephen, Chm. & Mng. Dir.--Denplan Limited, Winchester, United Kingdom; *Int'l*, pg. 1020
Noble, Robert B., Chm. & Chief Exec. Officer--Noble & Associates, Springfield, MO; *U.S. Private*, pg. 800
Noble, Robert B., Chm. & Chief Exec. Officer--Noble & Associates/Chicago, Chicago, IL; *U.S. Private*, pg. 800
Nobles, Bruce R., Chm. Bd., Pres. & Chief Exec. Officer--Hawaiian Airlines, Inc., Honolulu, HI; *U.S. Public*, pg. 799
Noblitt, Niles L., Chm. Bd.--Biomet, Inc., Warsaw, IN; *U.S. Public*, pg. 231
Nobumoto, H., Chm. Bd.--Ambrake Corporation, Elizabethtown, KY; *U.S. Public*, pg. 721
Node-Langois, Patrick, Chm. & Chief Exec. Officer--Lafarge Aluminates, Paris, France; *Int'l*, pg. 789
Noe, Kenneth, Jr., Chm. Bd.--New York Racing Association, Jamaica, NY; *U.S. Private*, pg. 795
Noel, J-C, Chm. Bd., Pres. & Chief Exec. Officer--Hilton Canada Inc., Montreal, Canada; *Int'l*, pg. 788
Noel, John, Chm. Bd. & Pres.--Noel Olson Group, Stevens Point, WI; *U.S. Private*, pg. 800
Noetzli, Hans C., Chm. Bd. & Pres.--Lonza Inc., Fair Lawn, NJ; *Int'l*, pg. 67
Noguchi, Michio, Chm.--Tsubakimoto Chain Co., Osaka, Japan; *Int'l*, pg. 1425
Noha, Edward, Chm. Bd.--CNA Financial Corp., Chicago, IL; *U.S. Public*, pg. 1010
Noiret, Yves, Chm. Bd. & Chief Exec. Officer--Eternit Industries, Vernouillet, France; *Int'l*, pg. 430
Noji, Katsuaki, Chm. Bd.--Citizen Watch Co. of America, Inc., Lyndhurst, NJ; *Int'l*, pg. 294
Nolan, Robert C., Chm. Bd.--Deltic Timber Corporation, El Dorado, AR; *U.S. Public*, pg. 498
Noland, L.U., Jr., Chm. Bd.--Basic Construction Company, Newport News, VA; *U.S. Private*, pg. 121
Noland, Lloyd U., III, Chm. Bd. & Pres.--Noland Company, Newport News, VA; *U.S. Public*, pg. 1187
Nolte, August, Chm.-Supervisory Bd.--Edeka Zentrale AG, Hamburg, Germany; *Int'l*, pg. 433
Nomura, Hisashi, Chm.--Toyo Corporation, Tokyo, Japan; *Int'l*, pg. 1410
Noorda, Raymond, Chm. Bd.--MTI Technology Corporation, Anaheim, CA; *U.S. Public*, pg. 1028
Norberg, Per-Olov, Chm. Bd.--Kanthal AB, Hallstahammar, Sweden; *Int'l*, pg. 723
Norbury, R. L., Chm. Bd.--NatWest Wood MacKenzie & Co Limited, London, United Kingdom; *Int'l*, pg. 911
Nordstrom, Rolf, Chm. Bd.--Fermenta AB, Stockholm, Sweden; *Int'l*, pg. 480

Norelli, Ronald A., Chm. Bd.--CEM Corporation, Matthews, NC; *U.S. Public*, pg. 277
Norgaard, O., Chm. Bd.--Lyons Seafoods Limited, Warminster, United Kingdom; *Int'l*, pg. 824
Norheim, Oddvar, Chm. Bd. & Pres.--American Crane & Equipment Corp., Douglassville, PA; *U.S. Private*, pg. 52
Norrie, K. Peter, Chm. Bd.--FiberMark Inc., Brattleboro, VT; *U.S. Public*, pg. 620
Norris, I.P., Chm.-Carbon Div.--Morgan Crucible Co. Plc, Windsor, United Kingdom; *Int'l*, pg. 890
Norris, James P., Chm. Bd.--Group Maintenance America Corp., Houston, TX; *U.S. Public*, pg. 766
Norris, John W., Jr., Chm. Bd. & Chief Exec. Officer--Lennox International Inc., Richardson, TX; *U.S. Private*, pg. 659
Norris, Thomas C., Chm., Pres. & Chief Exec. Officer--P.H. Glatfelter Company, Spring Grove, PA; *U.S. Public*, pg. 746
Norrod, James D., Chm. Bd.--ITK Telecommunications, Inc., Chelmsford, MA; *U.S. Private*, pg. 556
Norsworthy, Lamar, Chm. Bd. & Chief Exec. Officer--Holly Corporation, Dallas, TX; *U.S. Public*, pg. 830
Norton, David W., Chm. & Chief Exec. Officer--Dresser-Rand Co., Corning, NY; *U.S. Public*, pg. 529
Norton, J. Patrick, Chm. Bd., Pres. & Chief Exec. Officer--Fabreeka International, Inc., Stoughton, MA; *U.S. Private*, pg. 390
Norton, John R., III, Chm. Bd. & Chief Exec. officer--J.R. Norton Company, Phoenix, AZ; *U.S. Private*, pg. 807
Norton, Kenneth R., Chm. Bd. & Chief Exec. Officer--PST Vans, Inc., Salt Lake City, UT; *U.S. Public*, pg. 1246
Norton, M., Regional Chm.--Barratt Northern, Newcastle upon Tyne, United Kingdom; *Int'l*, pg. 168
Norton, Robert R., Chm. Bd., Pres. & Chief Exec. Officer--BeefAmerica Operating Co., Inc., Omaha, NE; *U.S. Private*, pg. 130
Noskwith, R., Chm. Bd.--Charnos plc, Ilkeston, United Kingdom; *Int'l*, pg. 280
Notaro, Thomas R., Asst. Chm. & Information Svcs.--WHX Corporation, New York, NY; *U.S. Public*, pg. 1726
Notebaert, Richard C., Chm. Bd., Pres. & Chief Exec. Officer--Ameritech Corporation, Chicago, IL; *U.S. Public*, pg. 97
Notebaert, Richard C., Chm. Bd. & Chief Exec. Officer--Ameritech Corp., Chicago, IL; *U.S. Public*, pg. 98
Nothburft, Arthur, Chm. Bd. & Pres.--Alno AG, Pfullendorf, Germany; *Int'l*, pg. 65
Noto, Lucio A., Chm. Bd., Pres., Chief Exec. & Chief Oper. Officer--Mobil Oil Corporation, Fairfax, VA; *U.S. Public*, pg. 1118
Novela, Frederick Melville, Chm. Bd. & Pres.--Aviateca, Guatemala, Guatemala; *Int'l*, pg. 102
Noyes, James W., Chm. Bd.--Willis Corroon Corp. of Penn., Radnor, PA; *Int'l*, pg. 1507
Nozko, Henry W., Sr., Chm. Bd., Pres. & Chief Exec. Officer--ACMAT Corporation, New Britain, CT; *U.S. Public*, pg. 16
Nucian, Lew, Chm. Bd.--Norman Levy Associates, Inc., Southfield, MI; *U.S. Private*, pg. 664
Nugent, John H., Chm. Bd.--AT&T Datatek Inc., Dallas, TX; *U.S. Public*, pg. 10
Nugent, Robert, Chm. Bd., Pres. & Chief Exec. Officer--Foodmaker, Inc., San Diego, CA; *U.S. Public*, pg. 661
Nunez, Elpidio, Chm. Bd. & Pres.--Northwestern Meats Inc., Miami, FL; *U.S. Private*, pg. 807
Nunez, Jaine, Chm. Bd. & Pres.--Bagley S.A., Buenos Aires, Argentina; *Int'l*, pg. 379
Nunis, Dick, Chm. Bd.--Disneyland, Anaheim, CA; *U.S. Public*, pg. 511
Nunis, Richard, Chm. Bd.--Walt Disney Attractions Division, Anaheim, CA; *U.S. Public*, pg. 511
Nunis, Richard A., Chm. Bd.--Walt Disney Attractions-Walt Disney World, Lake Buena Vista, FL; *U.S. Public*, pg. 513
Nunley, Richard L., Chm. Bd., Pres. & Treas.--Better Living Inc., Charlottesville, VA; *U.S. Private*, pg. 141
Nunneley, Charles, Chm. Bd.--Nationwide Building Society, Swindon, United Kingdom; *Int'l*, pg. 912
Nunnelly, Mark, Chm. Bd.--EFG Technologies Inc., Saint Paul, MN; *U.S. Public*, pg. 1679
Nurnberger, Thomas S., Chm. Bd. & Chief Policy Officer--ESELCO, Inc., Sault Sainte Marie, MI; *U.S. Public*, pg. 591
Nussbaum, Paul A., Chm. Bd. & Chief Exec. Officer--Patriot American Hospitality, Inc., Dallas, TX; *U.S. Public*, pg. 1265
Nussbaum, Victor M., Jr., Chm. Bd.--Southern Foods, Inc., Greensboro, NC; *U.S. Private*, pg. 1016
Nuzzo, Sal J., Chm. Bd. & Chief Exec. Officer--Datron Incorporated, Windsor, CT; *U.S. Private*, pg. 313
Nuzzo, Salvatore J., Chm. Bd.--SL Industries, Inc., Mount Laurel, NJ; *U.S. Public*, pg. 1418
Nyberg, L.G, Chm.--Philips Communication Systems B.V., Eindhoven, Netherlands; *Int'l*, pg. 1051
Nyberg, Lars, Chm. Bd. & Chief Exec. Officer--NCR Corporation, Dayton, OH; *U.S. Public*, pg. 1146
Nydegger, Peter, Chm. Bd.--Swissair Associated Companies Ltd., Zurich, Switzerland; *Int'l*, pg. 1334
Nye, Erle, Chm. Bd. & Chief Exec. Officer--Texas Utilities Communications Inc., Dallas, TX; *U.S. Public*, pg. 1588
Nye, Erle, Chm. Bd. & Chief Exec. Officer--Texas Utilities Properties Inc., Dallas, TX; *U.S. Public*, pg. 1588
Nygard, Michael, Chm. Bd.--Munck Automation Technology, Newport News, VA; *U.S. Private*, pg. 767
Nyman, Svante, Chm.--ITT Flygt AB, Solna, Sweden; *U.S. Public*, pg. 860
Nysten, Thomas, Chm. Bd.--MD Papier GmbH, Dachau, Germany; *Int'l*, pg. 864
O'Brien, David P., Chm. Bd., Pres. & Chief Exec. Officer--Canadian Pacific Limited, Calgary, Canada; *Int'l*, pg. 258
O'Brien, Gerry B., Chm.--Enfield Holdings Ltd., Bulawayo, Zimbabwe; *Int'l*, pg. 390
O'Brien, Jack, Chm. Bd.--Citizens Insurance Company of America, Howell, MI; *U.S. Public*, pg. 54
O'Brien, John P., Chm. Bd.--Allied Construction Products, Inc., Cleveland, OH; *U.S. Public*, pg. 1339
O'Brien, John V., Chm. Bd.--Allmerica Securities Trust, Worcester, MA; *U.S. Public*, pg. 54
O'Brien, M.V., Chm.--Getty Petroleum Ireland, Ltd., White Plains, NY; *U.S. Public*, pg. 1583
O'Brien, Roy E., Jr., Chm. Bd.--Roy O'Brien Inc., Saint Clair Shores, MI; *U.S. Private*, pg. 810
O'Brien, Thomas H., Chm. Bd. & Chief Exec. Officer--PNC Bank Corp., Pittsburgh, PA; *U.S. Public*, pg. 1242
O'Brien, Vincent, Chm. Bd. & Mng. Dir.--Texaco (Ireland) Ltd., Dublin, Ireland; *U.S. Public*, pg. 1584
O'Brien, William, Chm. Bd.--Frozfruit Corporation, Gardena, CA; *U.S. Private*, pg. 430
O'Connell, Frank J., Chm. Bd., Pres. & Chief Exec. Officer--Gibson Greetings, Inc., Cincinnati, OH; *U.S. Public*, pg. 742
O'Connor, B.P., Chm. Bd.--Dorbyl Structural Engineering (Pty) Ltd., Germiston, South Africa; *Int'l*, pg. 416
O'Connor, James J., Chm. Bd. & Chief Exec. Officer--Unicom Corporation, Chicago, IL; *U.S. Public*, pg. 1664
O'Connor, James J., Chm. Bd. & Chief Exec. Officer--ComEd, Chicago, IL; *U.S. Public*, pg. 1664
O'Connor, Laurence P., Chm. Bd., Pres. & Chief Exec. Officer--Unigard Insurance Co., Bellevue, WA; *Int'l*, pg. 345
O'Connor, Laurence P., Chm. Bd., Pres. & Chief Exec. Officer--Unigard Indemnity Co., Bellevue, WA; *Int'l*, pg. 345
O'Connor, Thomas D., Chm. Bd. & Pres.--Mohawk Paper Mills, Inc., Cohoes, NY; *U.S. Private*, pg. 755
O'Dell, James J., Chm. Bd., Pres. & Chief Exec. Officer--Valley Bank & Trust, Brighton, CO; *U.S. Private*, pg. 1132
O'Donnel, Joe, Chm. Bd. & Chief Exec. Officer--Heurikon Corporation, Madison, WI; *U.S. Public*, pg. 422
O'Donnell, Francis E., Jr., Chm. Bd.--Lasersight Inc., Saint Louis, MO; *U.S. Public*, pg. 979
O'Donnell, James E., Chm. Bd. & Chief Exec. Officer--Wheatland Tube Company, Collingswood, NJ; *U.S. Private*, pg. 1170
O'Donnell, Joseph, Chm. Bd.--Allied Advertising Agency, Public Relations, Boston, MA; *U.S. Private*, pg. 38
O'Donnell, Joseph, Co-Chm. Bd., Pres. & Chief Exec. Officer--Computer Products, Inc., Boca Raton, FL; *U.S. Public*, pg. 422
O'Donnell, Leo, Chm. Bd.--Irish Biscuits, Dublin, Ireland; *Int'l*, pg. 688
O'Donnell, Thomas M., Chm. Bd.--McDonald & Company Investments, Inc., Cleveland, OH; *U.S. Public*, pg. 1068
O'Donnell, William T., Jr., Chm. Bd.--NextHealth Inc., Tucson, AZ; *U.S. Public*, pg. 1181
O'Driscoll, Donnach, Chm.--Country 103.5, London, United Kingdom; *Int'l*, pg. 561
O'Farrell, Dean, Chm. Bd. & Chief Exec. Officer--SouthTrust Bank of Huntsville, Huntsville, AL; *U.S. Public*, pg. 1492
O'Halleran, Michael D., Chm. Bd.--AON Risk Services, Inc., Chicago, IL; *U.S. Public*, pg. 117
O'Hanlon, Michael, Chm. Bd., Pres. & Chief Exec. & Oper. Officer--DVI Financial Services Inc., Newport Beach, CA; *U.S. Public*, pg. 476
O'Hare, Dean R., Chm. Bd. & Chief Exec. Officer--The Chubb Corporation, Warren, NJ; *U.S. Public*, pg. 354
O'Keeffe, Whitney, Chm. Bd. & Chief Exec. Officer--SunTrust Bank, Treasure Coast, N.A., Fort Pierce, FL; *U.S. Public*, pg. 1538
O'Laughlin, Earl T., Chm. Bd.-Aeronca--Aeronca, Inc., Middletown, OH; *Int'l*, pg. 829
O'Leary, Dennis P., Chm. Bd. & Pres.--The F.D. Lawrence Electric Co., Cincinnati, OH; *U.S. Private*, pg. 654
O'Leary, John P., Jr., Chm. Bd., Pres. & Chief Exec. Officer--Tuscarora Incorporated, New Brighton, PA; *U.S. Public*, pg. 1646
O'Leary, Thomas H., Chm. Bd.--Burlington Resources Inc., Houston, TX; *U.S. Public*, pg. 269
O'Mahoney, John P., Chm. Bd. & Chief Exec. Officer--Lawter International, Inc., Kenosha, WI; *U.S. Public*, pg. 980
O'Malley, Thomas D., Chm. Bd. & Chief Exec. Officer--Tosco Corporation, Stamford, CT; *U.S. Public*, pg. 1624
O'Malley, William, Chm. Bd., Pres. & Chief Oper. Officer--Tidewater Inc., New Orleans, LA; *U.S. Public*, pg. 1608
O'Mara, A. James, Chm. Bd., & Chief Exec. Officer--Greenhorne & O'Mara, Inc., Greenbelt, MD; *U.S. Private*, pg. 477
O'Meara, John M., Chm. Bd. & Chief Exec. Officer--First Midwest Bank, N.A., Itasca, IL; *U.S. Public*, pg. 636
O'Neal, Edward A., Chm. Bd.--Chase Manhattan Bank Delaware, Wilmington, DE; *U.S. Public*, pg. 338
O'Neal, Emmet, Chm. Bd.--O'Neal Steel Inc., Birmingham, AL; *U.S. Private*, pg. 817
O'Neil, Bruce P., Chm. Bd. & Chief Exec. Officer--Willis Corroon Corp. of Illinois, Chicago, IL; *Int'l*, pg. 1506
O'Neil, W.E., Chm. Bd.--O'Neil Industries Inc., Chicago, IL; *U.S. Private*, pg. 817
O'Neil, William J., Chm. Bd.--William O'Neil & Co., Inc., Los Angeles, CA; *U.S. Private*, pg. 817
O'Neil, William J., Chm. Bd. & Pres.--O'Neil Data Systems, Inc., Los Angeles, CA; *U.S. Private*, pg. 817
O'Neill, John J., Chm. Bd.--Morrison Textile Machinery Co., Fort Lawn, SC; *U.S. Private*, pg. 762
O'Neill, Paul H., Chm. Bd. & Chief Exec. Officer--Aluminum Company of America, Pittsburgh, PA; *U.S. Public*, pg. 60
O'Neill, W. McKerall, Jr., Chm. Bd.--Berwick Bay Oil Co. Inc., Morgan City, LA; *U.S. Private*, pg. 138
O'Reilly, A.J.F., Non-Exec. Chm.--Waterford Wedgwood Plc, Dublin, Ireland; *Int'l*, pg. 1487
O'Reilly, Anthony J.F., Chm. Bd.--H.J. Heinz Company, Pittsburgh, PA; *U.S. Public*, pg. 805
O'Reilly, Jr., Charlie, Chm. Bd.--O'Reilly Automotive Inc., Springfield, MO; *U.S. Public*, pg. 1230
O'Reilly, Sr., Charlie H., Chm. Emeritus--O'Reilly Automotive Inc., Springfield, MO; *U.S. Public*, pg. 1230
O'Rourke, J. Tracy, Chm. Bd. & Chief Exec. Officer--Varian Associates, Inc., Palo Alto, CA; *U.S. Public*, pg. 1710
O'Shane, Thomas J., Chm. Bd., Pres. & Chief Exec. Officer--First Western Bancorp, Inc., New Castle, PA; *U.S. Public*, pg. 642
O'Shaughnessy, Patrick E., Chm. Bd. & Chief Exec. Officer--Lario Oil & Gas Company, Wichita, KS; *U.S. Private*, pg. 651
O'Shea, Mortimer J., Chm. Bd., Pres. & Chief Exec. Officer--Ramapo Financial Corporation, Wayne, NJ; *U.S. Public*, pg. 1360
O'Sullivan, Dan, Chm. Bd. & Chief Exec. Officer--O'Sullivan Industries Holdings, Lamar, MO; *U.S. Public*, pg. 1234
O'Sullivan, Edward J., Chm. Bd.--Omega Environmental Inc., Bothell, WA; *U.S. Public*, pg. 1221
O'Toole, Robert J., Chm. Bd., Pres. & Chief Exec. Officer--A.O. Smith Corporation, Milwaukee, WI; *U.S. Public*, pg. 1476
O'Toole, Timothy S., Chm. Bd. & Chief Exec. Officer--Patient Care, Inc., West Orange, NJ; *U.S. Public*, pg. 344
Obayashi, Yoshiro, Chm. Bd. & Chief Exec. Officer--Obayashi Corporation, Tokyo, Japan; *Int'l*, pg. 995
Oben, Walter J., Jr., Chm. Bd., Pres., Treas. & Sec.--Southgate Ford Inc., Southgate, MI; *U.S. Private*, pg. 1018
Ober, Douglas G., Chm. Bd. & Chief Exec. Officer--Petroleum & Resources Corp., Baltimore, MD; *U.S. Public*, pg. 1280
Oberg, Lars, Chm. Bd.--Fastighetsaktiebolaget Hufvudstaden, Stockholm, Sweden; *Int'l*, pg. 478
Oberlander, Ronald Y., Chm. Bd.--Abitibi-Consolidated Inc., Montreal, Canada; *Int'l*, pg. 19
Obermeier, Georg, Dr., Chm.-Mngmt. Bd.--Viag AG, Bonn, Germany; *Int'l*, pg. 1464
Obernauer, Marne, Jr., Chm. Bd. & Chief Exec. Officer--Devon Group, Inc., Stamford, CT; *U.S. Public*, pg. 503
Obernier, Robert, Chm. Bd. & Chief Exec. Officer--Horizon Paper Co., Inc., New York, NY; *U.S. Private*, pg. 539
Oberwager, Burn, Chm. Bd.--Western Sky Industries, Inc., Philadelphia, PA; *U.S. Private*, pg. 1168
Oberwelland, Klaus, Chm. Bd.--Storck International GmbH, Halle, Germany; *Int'l*, pg. 1304
Oberwelland, Klaus, Chm. Bd.--Storck U.S.A., L.P., Chicago, IL; *Int'l*, pg. 1304
Oberwortmann, Clarence D., Chm. Bd.--First Midwest Bancorp, Inc., Itasca, IL; *U.S. Public*, pg. 636
Occhipinti, Umberto, Chm. Bd. & Mng. Dir.--Assiprogetti S.p.A., Milan, Italy; *Int'l*, pg. 138
Odienne, Roger, Chm. Bd.--Societe Anonyme Mediterraneene de Salaisons, Biot, France; *U.S. Public*, pg. 429
Odishaw, Edward A., Chm. Bd.--United States Lime & Minerals, Dallas, TX; *U.S. Public*, pg. 1684
Odom, John P., Co-Chm. Bd., Pres. & Chief Exec. Officer--The Odom Corporation, Seattle, WA; *U.S. Private*, pg. 811
Odom, William, Co-Chm. Bd. & Exec. V.P.--The Odom Corporation, Seattle, WA; *U.S. Private*, pg. 811
Oebser, Robert, Chm. Bd.--National Cooperative Refinery Association, Mc Pherson, KS; *U.S. Private*, pg. 781
Oertli, Charles W., Chm. Bd.--Guarantee Electrical Company, Saint Louis, MO; *U.S. Private*, pg. 485
Oesterreicher, James E., Chm. Bd. & Chief Exec. Officer--JC Penney Company, Inc., Plano, TX; *U.S. Public*, pg. 916
Ogasawara, Toshiaki, Chm. Bd. & Pres.--Nifco Inc., Yokohama, Japan; *Int'l*, pg. 928
Ogasawara, Toshiaki, Chm. Bd. & Publisher--The Japan Times, Ltd., Tokyo, Japan; *Int'l*, pg. 928
Ogasawara, Toshiaki, Chm.--Elta Plastics Limited, Stockton on Tees, United Kingdom; *Int'l*, pg. 929
Ogasawara, Toshiaki, Chm. Bd. & Pres.--Simmons Co. Ltd., Zama, Japan; *Int'l*, pg. 929
Ogawa, Tadahiko, Chm. Bd.--Tokai Financial Services, Inc., Berwyn, PA; *Int'l*, pg. 1391
Ogden, J.H., Jr., Chm. Bd., Pres. & Chief Exec. Officer--Conestoga Corporation, Stamford, CT; *U.S. Private*, pg. 262
Oggero, Richard J., Chm. Bd.--The Weitz Company, Inc., Des Moines, IA; *U.S. Private*, pg. 1160
Ogilvie-Thompson, Julian, Chm.--Anglo American Corporation of South Africa Limited, Johannesburg, South Africa; *Int'l*, pg. 76
Ogilvie, Robert M., Chm. Bd., Pres. & Chief Exec. Officer--Toromont Industries Ltd., Concord, Canada; *Int'l*, pg. 1400
Ogle, William E., Chm. Bd. & Chief Exec. Officer--STB Systems, Inc., Richardson, TX; *U.S. Public*, pg. 1421
Ohashi, Hiromu, Chm. & Representative Dir.--Sekisui House, Ltd., Osaka, Japan; *Int'l*, pg. 1219
Ohba, Hiroshi, Chm. & Chief Exec. Officer--Kawasaki Heavy Industries, Ltd., Kobe, Japan; *Int'l*, pg. 725
Ohga, Norio, Chm. Bd. & Chief Exec. Officer--Sony Corporation, Tokyo, Japan; *Int'l*, pg. 1280
Ohinouye, Tsuneo, Chm. & Chief Exec. Officer--Diamond Star Motors, Normal, IL; *Int'l*, pg. 875
Ohlsson, Jan, Chm. Bd.--Karlshamns AB, Karlshamn, Sweden; *Int'l*, pg. 718
Ohlsson, Kenneth, Chm. Reg. Bd.--ICA Handlarna Vast AB, Kungalv, Sweden; *Int'l*, pg. 643
Ohmatsu, S., Chm. Bd.--Leader Instruments Corporation, Hauppauge, NY; *U.S. Private*, pg. 655
Ohnishi, Masafumi, Chm. Bd.--Osaka Gas Co., Ltd., Osaka, Japan; *Int'l*, pg. 1011
Ohnishi, Minoru, Chm. Bd. & Chief Exec. Officer--Fuji Photo Film Co., Ltd., Tokyo, Japan; *Int'l*, pg. 523
Ohno, Akira, Chm. Bd. & Pres.--Morinaga Milk Industry Co., Ltd., Tokyo, Japan; *Int'l*, pg. 895
Ohnuki, Yoshiaki, Chm.--Mitsui & Co. International (Europe) B.V., Amsterdam, Netherlands; *Int'l*, pg. 880
Ohsawa, Hiroshi, Chm. Bd.--Diamond Lease Co., Ltd., Tokyo, Japan; *Int'l*, pg. 413
Ohyama, Rei, Chm. Bd.--Taiyo Life Realty of America, Inc., New York, NY; *Int'l*, pg. 1349

Ohyama, Rei, Chm. Bd.--Taiyo Life International (U.K.), Ltd., London, United Kingdom; *Int'l*, pg. 1349
Ohyama, Rei, Chm. Bd.--Taiyo Life International (H.K.), Ltd., Central, Hong Kong; *Int'l*, pg. 1349
Okabe, Akira, Chm. Bd.--Okabe Company Limited, Tokyo, Japan; *Int'l*, pg. 999
Okada, Musami, Chm. Bd. & Chief Exec. Officer--Fuji Medical Systems USA, Inc., Stamford, CT; *Int'l*, pg. 524
Okada, Takuya, Chm. Bd. & Chief Exec. Officer--JUSCO Co., Ltd., Chiba, Japan; *Int'l*, pg. 28
Okasa, Takuya, Chm. Bd.--AEON Group, Chiba, Japan; *Int'l, pg. 28*
Okawa, Isao, Chm. Bd.--Sega Enterprises Ltd., Tokyo, Japan; *Int'l*, pg. 1218
Okinobu, H., Chm. Bd.--Yamatake-Honeywell Company Ltd., Tokyo, Japan; *U.S. Public*, pg. 835
Okoso, Yoshinori, Chm. Bd. & Pres.--Nippon Meat Packers, Inc., Osaka, Japan; *Int'l*, pg. 936
Oksanen, Antti, Chm. Bd.--Metsa-Serla Corporation, Espoo, Finland; *Int'l*, pg. 863
Okuma, Yoshiyuko, Chm.--Takugin Finance International Ltd., London, United Kingdom; *Int'l*, pg. 627
Okuyama, Takatoshi, Chm.--Daiwa Securities (H.K.) Limited, Hong Kong, Hong Kong; *Int'l*, pg. 376
Okuyama, Tomou, Chm. Bd.--Sure Save Super Market Ltd., Keaau, HI; *U.S. Private*, pg. 1056
Oland, Derek, Chm. Bd.--Nova Scotia Power Inc., Halifax, Canada; *Int'l*, pg. 971
Oland, Thomas E., Chm. Bd., Pres., Chief Exec. Officer & Treas.--Techne Corporation, Minneapolis, MN; *U.S. Public*, pg. 1563
Oland, Thomas E., Chm. Bd.--R&D Systems Inc., Minneapolis, MN; *U.S. Public*, pg. 1564
Oldenburg, Richard, Chm. Bd.--Sotheby's Inc., New York, NY; *U.S. Public*, pg. 1487
Oliver, Robert M., Chm. Bd.--Fair, Isaac and Company, Inc., San Rafael, CA; *U.S. Public*, pg. 609
Olivieri, Icaro, Chm. Bd.--Bauer Sports Inc., Montreal, Canada; *U.S. Public*, pg. 1184
Ollila, Jorma, Pres., Chief Exec. Officer & Chm.-Grp. Exec. Bd.--Oy Nokia Ab/Nokia Group, Helsinki, Finland; *Int'l*, pg. 951
Olsen, J., Chm--Cunard Line Ltd., London, United Kingdom; *Int'l*, pg. 773
Olsen, J., Chm.--The Ritz Hotel (London) Limited, London, United Kingdom; *Int'l*, pg. 773
Olson, Dean A., II, Chm. Bd.--Rockford Acromatic Product Co., Rockford, IL; *U.S. Private*, pg. 938
Olson, Earl B., Chm. Bd.--Jennie-O Foods, Inc., Willmar, MN; *U.S. Public*, pg. 840
Olson, Frank, Chm. & Chief Exec. Officer--Hertz Equipment Rental Corp., Park Ridge, NJ; *U.S. Public*, pg. 664
Olson, Frank A., Chm. Bd. & Chief Exec. Officer--The Hertz Corporation, Park Ridge, NJ; *U.S. Public*, pg. 664
Olson, John M., Chm. Bd. & Chief Exec. Officer--John M. Olson Company, Saint Clair Shores, MI; *U.S. Private*, pg. 815
Olson, Kenneth E., Chm. Bd., Pres. & Chief Exec. Officer--Proxima Corporation, San Diego, CA; *U.S. Public*, pg. 1339
Olson, Ralph J., Chm. Bd., Pres. & Chief Exec. Officer--R.A. Jones & Co. Inc., Covington, KY; *U.S. Private*, pg. 597
Olson, Richard E., Chm. Bd. & Chief Exec. Officer--Champion International Corp., Stamford, CT; *U.S. Public, pg. 333*
Olson, Robert, Chm. Bd.--Excelsior Manufacturing & Supply Corp., Itasca, IL; *U.S. Private*, pg. 387
Olsson, Dan Sten, Chm. Bd.--Stena Line AB, Goteborg, Sweden; *Int'l*, pg. 1300
Olsson, Ingemar, Chm. Bd. & Pres.--Swedish Match do Brasil S/A, Rio de Janeiro, Brazil; *Int'l*, pg. 1328
Olufsen, Peter Skak, Chm. Bd.--Bang & Olufsen A/S, Struer, Denmark; *Int'l*, pg. 145
Omari, Dunstan A., Chm.--East African Cables Ltd., Nairobi, Kenya; *Int'l*, pg. 390
Onaran, Erol, Chm. Bd.--EROL'S Internet, Springfield, VA; *U.S. Private*, pg. 382
Ondis, Albert W., Chm. Bd. & Chief Exec. Officer--Astro-Med, Inc., West Warwick, RI; *U.S. Public*, pg. 141
Onishi, Tohimi, Chm. Bd.--Aichi Steel Works, Ltd., Arao, Japan; *Int'l*, pg. 35
Ono, Masatoshi, Chm. Bd.--Bridgestone/Firestone, Inc., Nashville, TN; *Int'l*, pg. 213
Ono, Masatoshi, Chm. Bd. & Chief Exec. Officer--Bridgestone/Firestone, Inc., Nashville, TN; *Int'l*, pg. 213
Ono, Shigeo, Chm. Bd.--Nikon Corporation, Tokyo, Japan; *Int'l*, pg. 931
Ono, Yoshio, Chm.--ORIX Aviation Systems Limited, Dublin, Ireland; *Int'l*, pg. 1009
Onstead, Robert R., Chm. Bd.--Randalls Food Markets, Inc., Houston, TX; *U.S. Private*, pg. 909
Oort, C.J., Chm. Bd.--KLM Royal Dutch Airlines, Amstelveen, Netherlands; *Int'l*, pg. 719
Opler, Edmond, Jr., Chm. Bd., Pres. & Chief Exec. Officer--World's Finest Chocolate, Inc., Chicago, IL; *U.S. Private, pg. 1191*
Oppenheim, Eytan, Chm. Bd.--Elscint Central & Eastern Europe, Vienna, Austria; *Int'l*, pg. 450
Oram, John L., Chm. Bd.--Pharmaceutical Formulations, Inc., Edison, NJ; *U.S. Public*, pg. 1284
Orban, George P., Chm. Bd. & Chief Exec. Officer--Egghead, Inc., Liberty Lake, WA; *U.S. Public*, pg. 566
Orczyk, Stanley R., Chm. & Chief Oper. Officer--Meenan Oil Co. L.P., Syosset, NY; *U.S. Private*, pg. 729
Orden, Ted, Chm. Bd. & Pres.--Thrifty Oil Co., Santa Fe Springs, CA; *U.S. Private*, pg. 1084
Orders, William H., Chm. Bd., Chief Exec. Officer & Treas--Orders Distributing Co., Greenville, SC; *U.S. Private*, pg. 819
Ordway, Peter S., Chm. Bd., Pres. & Chief Exec. Officer--Union Pump Company, Battle Creek, MI; *U.S. Private*, pg. 1119
Ordway, Ronald D., Chm. Bd. & Chief Exec. Officer--Video Display Corporation, Tucker, GA; *U.S. Public*, pg. 1720
Oren, John R., Chm. Bd. & Chief Exec. Officer--Corporate Express Delivery Systems Southwest, Inc., Houston, TX; *U.S. Public*, pg. 449
Oresman, Roger B., Chm. Bd.--Mississippi Valley Gas Co., Jackson, MS; *U.S. Private*, pg. 753
Orfalea, Paul, Chm. Bd.--Kinko's Corporation, Ventura, CA; *U.S. Private*, pg. 622
Orgill, Joseph, III, Chm. Bd. & Sec.--Orgill Inc., Memphis, TN; *U.S. Private*, pg. 819
Orgill, Joseph, III, Chm. Bd.--West Union Corporation, Memphis, TN; *U.S. Private*, pg. 1163
Oristano, Matthew, Chm. Bd. & Chief Exec. Officer--People's Choice TV Corp., Shelton, CT; *U.S. Public*, pg. 1274
Orleans, Jeffery P., Chm. & Chief Exec. Officer--FPA Corporation, Bensalem, PA; *U.S. Public*, pg. 608
Ormond, Paul A., Chm. Bd., Pres. & Chief Exec. Officer--Health Care & Retirement Corporation, Toledo, OH; *U.S.* Public, pg. 801
Orndorff, Ronald D., Chm. Bd. & Chief Exec. Officer--M & I First National Leasing Corp., Milwaukee, WI; *U.S. Public, pg. 1051*
Orr, Donald C., Chm. Bd., Pres. & Chief Exec. Officer--Nashville Machine Co. Inc., Nashville, TN; *U.S. Private*, pg. 774
Orr, Donald E., Chm. Bd.--The Pollock Corp., Pottstown, PA; *U.S. Private*, pg. 874
Orr, Donald E., Chm. Bd.--Mayer Pollack Steel Corporation, Pottstown, PA; *U.S. Private*, pg. 874
Orr, James F., Chm. Bd. & Chief Exec. Officer--UNUM Life Insurance Company of America, Portland, ME; *U.S. Public*, pg. 1699
Orr, James F., III, Chm. Bd., Pres. & Chief Exec. Officer--UNUM Corporation, Portland, ME; *U.S. Public*, pg. 1699
Orr, James F., III, Chm. Bd. & Chief Exec. Officer--Colonial Life & Accident Insurance Co., Columbia, SC; *U.S. Public*, pg. 1699
Orr, James F., III, Chm. Bd.--Continental National Life Insurance Co., Piscataway, NJ; *U.S. Public*, pg. 1700
Orr, James F., III, Chm. Bd.--Continental International Life Insurance Co., Piscataway, NJ; *U.S. Public*, pg. 1700
Orr, San W., Jr., Chm. Bd.--The Sorg Paper Co., Middletown, OH; *U.S. Public*, pg. 1747
Orrall, Roy E., Chm. Bd. & Pres.--Winthrop Printing Company, Inc., Boston, MA; *U.S. Private*, pg. 1184
Orrico, Eugene, Chm. Bd.--Keeners, Inc., Renton, WA; *U.S. Private*, pg. 611
Orrico, Eugene, Chm. Bd.--Beef Distributors, Inc., Renton, WA; *U.S. Private*, pg. 611
Orrico, Frank A., Chm. Bd.--Winmar Company, Seattle, WA; *U.S. Public*, pg. 1423
Orser, Earl H., Chm. Bd.--London Life Insurance Group, London, Canada; *Int'l*, pg. 435
Orser, Earl H., Chm. Bd.--Spar Aerospace Limited, Toronto, Canada; *Int'l*, pg. 1287
Orsi, Ferruccio Giorgio, Chm. Bd.--Mazzucchelli 1849 S.p.a., Castiglione Olona, Italy; *Int'l*, pg. 849
Orthman, Thomas F., Chm. Bd.--Society First Federal Savings Bank, Fort Myers, FL; *U.S. Public*, pg. 954
Ortolani, Timothy S., Chm. Bd., Pres. & Chief Exec. Officer--Carton-Craft Corporation, Buffalo, NY; *U.S. Private*, pg. 217
Orullian, B. La Rae, Chm. Bd.--Colorado Business Bank, Denver, CO; *U.S. Private*, pg. 255
Orza, Vincent F., Jr., Chm. Bd., Pres. & Chief Exec. Officer--Eateries, Inc., Oklahoma City, OK; *U.S. Public*, pg. 555
Orza, Vincent F., Jr., Chm. Bd., Pres. & Chief Exec. Officer--Pepperoni Grill, Oklahoma City, OK; *U.S. Public*, pg. 555
Osabe, Bunjiro, Chm. Bd., Pres. & Chief Exec. Officer--Ozeki Corporation, Nishinomiya, Japan; *Int'l*, pg. 1019
Osakabe, Norio, Chm. Bd.--Subaru Canada Inc., Mississauga, Canada; *Int'l*, pg. 523
Osatananda, Prasan, Chm.--EURO RSCG Partnership, Bangkok, Thailand; *Int'l*, pg. 602
Osborn, William A., Chm. Bd.--Northern Trust Corporation, Chicago, IL; *U.S. Public*, pg. 1195
Osborn, William A., Chm. Bd. & Chief Exec. Officer--The Northern Trust Company, Chicago, IL; *U.S. Public*, pg. 1197
Osborne, Richard C., Chm. Bd., Pres. & Chief Exec. Officer--Scotsman Industries, Inc., Vernon Hills, IL; *U.S. Public*, pg. 1444
Osborne, Richard de J., Chm. Bd., Pres. & Chief Exec. Officer--Asarco Incorporated, New York, NY; *U.S. Public, pg. 137*
Oshman, Marilyn, Chm. Bd.--Oshman's Sporting Goods, Inc., Houston, TX; *U.S. Public*, pg. 1233
Osterneck, Myles, Chm. Bd., Pres. & Treas.--The Osterneck Co. Inc., Lumberton, NC; *U.S. Private*, pg. 821
Ostler, Clyde W., Vice Chm.--Wells Fargo & Company, San Francisco, CA; *U.S. Public*, pg. 1753
Ostrover, Harvey, Chm. Bd. & Chief Exec. Officer--American Fabrics Company, New York, NY; *U.S. Private*, pg. 53
Ostrow, Barnet D., Chm. Bd.--LeaRonal, Inc., Freeport, NY; *U.S. Public*, pg. 982
Oswald, Robert, Chm., Pres. & Chief Exec. Officer--Robert Bosch Corporation, Broadview, IL; *Int'l*, pg. 204
Oswald, William A., Chm. & Chief Exec. Officer--Ross Roy Communications, Inc., Bloomfield Hills, MI; *U.S. Private*, pg. 946
Otakie, Daniel A., Chm. Bd., Pres., Chief Exec. Officer & Treas.--Futures Personnel Services, Baltimore, MD; *U.S. Private*, pg. 433
Otani, Akiyoshi, Chm. Bd.--Daiwa Bank (Schweiz) AG, Zurich, Switzerland; *Int'l*, pg. 373
Otero, Richard J., Chm. Bd., Pres. & Chief Exec. Officer--RJO Enterprises, Inc., Lanham, MD; *U.S. Private*, pg. 904
Otis, William L., Jr., Chm. Bd.--Columbia Lumber & Manufacturing Co., Columbia, SC; *U.S. Private*, pg. 255
Otsuka, Masatomi, Chm. Bd.--ARS Chemical (Thailand) Co., Ltd., Bangkok, Thailand; *Int'l*, pg. 1014
Otsuka, Masayuki, Chm.--IBJ Espana, Madrid, Spain; *Int'l*, pg. 676
Otsuka, Yoshimitsu, Chm. Bd.--Otsuka Pharmaceutical Co., Ltd., Tokyo, Japan; *Int'l*, pg. 1013
Otsuki, Hiroshi, Chm. Bd.--Yamaichi Bank (Deutschland) GmbH, Frankfurt/Main, Germany; *Int'l*, pg. 1517
Ott, Alan W., Chm. Bd.--Chemical Financial Corporation, Midland, MI; *U.S. Public*, pg. 345
Ott, James H., Chm. Bd.--Novar Electronics, Barberton, OH; *U.S. Private*, pg. 808
Ott, Robert B., Chm. Bd.--The Hennegan Company, Florence, KY; *U.S. Private*, pg. 522
Ottaway, James H. Jr., Sr. V.P. & Chm.-Ottaway Newspapers, Inc.--Dow Jones & Company, Inc., New York, NY; *U.S. Public*, pg. 524
Ottaway, James H., Jr., Chm., Pres. & Chief Exec. Officer--Ottaway Newspapers, Inc., Campbell Hall, NY; *U.S. Public*, pg. 525
Otten, Leslie, Chm. Bd.--American Skiing Company, Bethel, ME; *U.S. Private*, pg. 61
Otto, Dr. Michael, Chm.-Exec. Bd. & Pres.--Otto Versand (GmbH & Co.), Hamburg, Germany; *Int'l*, pg. 1014
Otto, Dr. Michael, Chm. Bd.--Spiegel, Inc., Downers Grove, IL; *U.S. Public*, pg. 1498
Otto, Michael, Chm. Bd.--Postalmarket, Milan, Italy; *Int'l*, pg. 1064
Otto, Richard, Chm. Bd.--Rockbottom Stores, Inc., Lake Success, NY; *U.S. Private*, pg. 938
Otto, Ulrich, Chm.--Trischler und Partner GmbH, Darmstadt, Germany; *Int'l*, pg. 608
Ottosson, David, Chm. Reg. Bd.--ICA Handlarna Ost AB, Arsta, Sweden; *Int'l*, pg. 642
Oung, Margaret, Chm. Bd.--American Sporting Goods Corporation, Irvine, CA; *U.S. Private*, pg. 62
Ounjian, Marilyn J., Chm. Bd. & Chief Exec. Officer--Careers USA Inc., Philadelphia, PA; *U.S. Private*, pg. 209
Ousseime, Khaled, Chm.--Gefinor S.A. Luxembourg, Luxembourg, Luxembourg; *Int'l*, pg. 542
Overholtzer, Durand, Chm. Bd.--Overholtzer Church Furniture, Inc., Modesto, CA; *U.S. Private*, pg. 823
Overton, Carl E., Chm. Bd., Chief Exec. Officer & Treas.--Overton Gear & Tool Corp., Addison, IL; *U.S. Private*, pg. 823
Overton, David, Chm. Bd., Pres. & Chief Exec. Officer--Cheesecake Factory Incorporated, Calabasas Hills, CA; *U.S. Public*, pg. 343
Owen-Jones, Lindsay, Chm. Bd. & Chief Exec. Officer--L'Oreal S.A., Clichy, France; *Int'l*, pg. 818
Owen, Claude B. Jr., Chm. Bd. & Chief Exec. Officer--DIMON, Incorporated, Danville, VA; *U.S. Public*, pg. 509
Owen, Claude B., Jr., Chm. Bd.--Florimex Worldwide, Inc., Danville, VA; *U.S. Public*, pg. 510
Owen, J.M., Dr., Chm.--County NatWest Limited, London, United Kingdom; *Int'l*, pg. 910
Owen, Judy, Chm. Bd.--Norwest Bank Nebraska, N.A., Omaha, NE; *U.S. Public*, pg. 1202
Owen, Robert E., Chm. Bd. & Pres.--Owen Industries, Inc., Carter Lake, IA; *U.S. Private*, pg. 824
Owens, Byron, Chm. Bd.--Vesture Corporation, Asheboro, NC; *U.S. Public*, pg. 192
Owens, Jerry P., Chm. Bd.--Owens Country Sausage, Inc., Richardson, TX; *U.S. Public*, pg. 596
Owens, Patricia, Chm. Bd.--Options and Choices, Inc., Cheyenne, WY; *U.S. Public*, pg. 1699
Owens, Thomas M., Chm. Bd.--Distributed Systems Division, Lisle, IL; *U.S. Public*, pg. 1522
Oyama, Masahiro, Chm. Bd.--Daiwa Overseas Finance Ltd., Central, Hong Kong; *Int'l*, pg. 373
Oyamada, Yutaka, Chm. Bd.--Clarion Co., Ltd., Tokyo, Japan; *Int'l*, pg. 296
Ozaki, Yukiyoshi, Chm. Bd.--Mikuni Corporation, Tokyo, Japan; *Int'l*, pg. 867
Pacchioni, Piermaria, Chm. Bd.--Banca Agricola Mantovana SARL, Mantova, Italy; *Int'l*, pg. 135
Pace, Carlo, Chm.--Banco di Napoli, Naples, Italy; *Int'l*, pg. 140
Pacer, Thomas H., Chm. Bd., Pres. & Chief Exec. Officer--First Union National Bank of Georgia, Atlanta, GA; *U.S. Public*, pg. 640
Pache, Bernard, Chm. Bd.--Bull HN Information Systems Inc., Billerica, MA; *Int'l*, pg. 316
Pache, Bernard, Chm.-Exec. Board--Entreprise Miniere et Chimique, Paris, France; *Int'l*, pg. 458
Pachimsawat, Sukit, Chm.--Sukosol and Mazda Engineering Co., Ltd., Chachoengsao, Thailand; *Int'l*, pg. 849
Pacholder, Asher O., Chm. Bd. & Chief Fin. Officer--ICO, Inc., Houston, TX; *U.S. Public*, pg. 853
Pachulski, Phil, Chm. Bd. & Chief Exec. Officer--Prime Technology, Inc., Grand Rapids, MI; *U.S. Private*, pg. 884
Pacifico, Kerry T., Chm. Bd.--Pacifico Auto Group, Philadelphia, PA; *U.S. Private*, pg. 832
Packard, James, Chm. Bd., Pres. & Chief Exec. Officer--National Twist Drill Div., South Beloit, IL; *U.S. Public*, pg. 1370
Packard, James L., Chm. Bd., Pres. & Chief Exec. Officer--Regal-Beloit Corporation, Beloit, WI; *U.S. Public*, pg. 1370
Paddock, M. David, Chm. Bd., Pres., Chief Exec. & Oper. Officer--Peoples National Bank, Lawrenceville, IL; *U.S. Public*, pg. 1217
Paddock, S.R., Jr., Chm., Chief Exec. Officer & Publr.--Paddock Publications, Inc., Arlington Heights, IL; *U.S. Private*, pg. 833
Paddon, Patrick E., Chm. Bd., Pres. & Chief Exec. Officer--Amplicon, Inc., Santa Ana, CA; *U.S. Public*, pg. 104
Padnos, Seymour K., Chm. Bd.--Louis Padnos Iron & Metal Co., Holland, MI; *U.S. Private*, pg. 834
Page, Carter F., Chm. Bd.--General Communication, Inc., Anchorage, AK; *U.S. Public*, pg. 708
Page, Jack L., Chm. Bd.--Kal Grafx, Kentwood, MI; *U.S. Private*, pg. 387
Page, James, Chm. Bd.--Mission Industries, Las Vegas, NV; *U.S. Private*, pg. 752

Page, Roger B., Chm. Bd., Pres., Chief Exec. Officer & Fin. Officer--Pace Oil Co., Inc., Winston Salem, NC; U.S. Private, pg. 829
Pagesse, Pierre, Chm. Bd.--Groupe Limagrain, Chappes, France; Int'l, pg. 566
Pahidis, Gus P., Chm. Bd.--Cedar Farms Company, Inc., Philadelphia, PA; U.S. Private, pg. 221
Pahl, Charles E., Chm. Bd. & Chief Exec. Officer--J.H. Larson Electrical Company, Golden Valley, MN; U.S. Private, pg. 652
Pai, P.Y., Chm. Bd. & Chief Exec. Officer--The International Commercial Bank of China, Taipei, Taiwan; Int'l, pg. 683
Paige, Norma, Chm. Bd.--Astronautics Corporation of America, Milwaukee, WI; U.S. Private, pg. 93
Painter, Carl, Chm. Bd. & Chief Exec. Officer--BICC Cables Corporation, West Nyack, NY; Int'l, pg. 120
Painter, Howard O. Jr., Chm. Bd.--DSP Technology Inc., Fremont, CA; U.S. Public, pg. 475
Painton, Ira, Chm. Bd.--American National Triflex Fund, Inc., Galveston, TX; U.S. Public, pg. 87
Pala, Gino N., Chm. Bd. & Chief Exec. Officer--Dixon Ticonderoga Company, Heathrow, FL; U.S. Public, pg. 514
Paley, Edward, Chm. Bd. & Chief Exec. Officer--The Texwipe Co., Inc., Upper Saddle River, NJ; U.S. Private, pg. 1079
Palmer, A. Robert, Chm. Bd., Pres. & Chief Exec. Officer--Eastern Color Printing Company, Avon, CT; U.S. Private, pg. 357
Palmer, C. Robert, Chm. Bd., Pres. & Chief Exec. Officer--Rowan Companies, Inc., Houston, TX; U.S. Public, pg. 1409
Palmer, Charles L., Chm. Bd. & Chief Exec. Officer--North American Company, Fort Lauderdale, FL; U.S. Private, pg. 803
Palmer, Dan M., Chm. Bd. & Chief Exec. Officer--Concord EFS, Inc., Memphis, TN; U.S. Public, pg. 429
Palmer, James, Q.C., Chm. Bd.--Telus Corporation, Edmonton, Canada; Int'l, pg. 1374
Palmer, John M., Chm. Bd.--Mobile Telecommunications Technologies Corp., Jackson, MS; U.S. Public, pg. 1120
Palmer, John M., Chm. Bd.--SkyTel Corp., Washington, DC; U.S. Public, pg. 1120
Palmer, Richard F., Chm. Bd.--Palmer Moving & Storage Co., Troy, MI; U.S. Private, pg. 835
Palmer, Richard M., Jr., Chm. Bd. & Pres.--R.M. Palmer Company, Reading, PA; U.S. Private, pg. 835
Palmer, Robert B., Chm. Bd., Pres. & Chief Exec. Officer--Digital Equipment Corporation, Maynard, MA; U.S. Public, pg. 507
Palmer, Robert J., Chm.--R.J. Palmer, Inc., New York, NY; U.S. Private, pg. 835
Palmer, Ron, Chm. Bd.--Horizon Enterprises Group LLC, Taylor, MI; U.S. Private, pg. 539
Palmer, Ron, Chm. Bd. & Chief Exec. Officer--Horizon Investment Group, Taylor, MI; U.S. Private, pg. 539
Palmer, Ron, Chm. Bd.--Horizon Technology Group LLC, Taylor, MI; U.S. Private, pg. 539
Palmer, Stephen T., Jr., Chm. Bd. & Chief Exec. Officer--Palmer International, Inc., Worcester, PA; U.S. Private, pg. 834
Palmstierna, Jacob, Chm. Bd.--Nordbanken AB, Stockholm, Sweden; Int'l, pg. 957
Pamplin, R.B., Jr., Dr., Chm. Bd. & Chief Exec. Officer--Mount Vernon Mills, Inc., Greenville, SC; U.S. Private, pg. 835
Pamplin, Robert B., Sr., Chm. Bd. & Chief Exec. Officer--R.B. Pamplin Corp., Portland, OR; U.S. Private, pg. 835
Pancetti, John A., Chm. Bd. & Chief Exec. Officer--Republic Bank for Savings, New York, NY; U.S. Public, pg. 1380
Pando, Robert T., Chm. Bd. & Pres.--Lynch Machinery, Inc., Bainbridge, GA; U.S. Public, pg. 1022
Panettiere, John M., Chm. Bd.--Frederick Manufacturing Corporation, Kansas City, MO; U.S. Public, pg. 238
Pangburn, A.D., Chm. Bd.--IDenticard Systems, Inc., Lancaster, PA; U.S. Private, pg. 557
Pangestu, Prajogo, Chm. Bd.--United Pulp & Paper Company Limited, Jurong, Singapore; Int'l, pg. 1444
Panic, Milan, Chm. Bd. & Chief Exec. Officer--ICN Pharmaceuticals, Inc., Costa Mesa, CA; U.S. Public, pg. 853
Pantello, Ron, Chm. & Chief Exec. Officer--Lally, McFarland & Pantello Inc., New York, NY; Int'l, pg. 601
Panzica, Ignatius J., Chm. Bd., Pres. & Chief Exec. Officer--Global Motor Sport Group, Inc., Morgan Hill, CA; U.S. Public, pg. 748
Pao, Henry C., Dr., Chm. Bd., Pres. Chief Exec. Officer & Chief Oper. Officer--Supertex, Inc., Sunnyvale, CA; U.S. Public, pg. 1539
Paolercio, Anthony, Jr., Co. Chm. Bd. & Exec. V.P.--Michael Anthony Jewelers, Inc., Mount Vernon, NY; U.S. Public, pg. 1103
Paolercio, Michael W., Co. Chm. Bd. & Chief Exec. Officer--Michael Anthony Jewelers, Inc., Mount Vernon, NY; U.S. Public, pg. 1103
Papada, James M., III, Chm. Bd.--Technitrol, Inc., Trevose, PA; U.S. Public, pg. 1564
Papadakis, Nikolaos, Chm. Bd.--Macedonian Airlines, Athens, Greece; Int'l, pg. 1004
Papadinis, James, Chm. Bd.--Univex Corporation, Salem, NH; U.S. Private, pg. 1128
Papillaud, Pierre, Chm. Bd.--Crystal Geyser Roxane Water L.P., Olancha, CA; Int'l, pg. 1013
Papitto, Ralph R., Chm. Bd. & Chief Exec. Officer--AFC Cable Systems, Inc., Providence, RI; U.S. Public, pg. 6
Pappas, Nicholas, Chm. Bd.--Chemfab Corporation, Merrimack, NH; U.S. Public, pg. 344
Pappas, Ted, Chm. Bd.--The Keyes Company Realtors, Miami, FL; U.S. Private, pg. 618
Parbo, Arvi, Sir, Chm. Bd.--Western Mining Corporation Holdings Limited, Southbank, Australia; Int'l, pg. 1494
Pardus, Donald G., Chm. Bd. & Chief Exec. Officer--Eastern Utilities Associates, Boston, MA; U.S. Public, pg. 549
Paridy, David, Chm. Bd., Pres. & Chief Exec. Officer--Plews/Edelmann, Buffalo Grove, IL; Int'l, pg. 1396
Parisi, Giovanni Battista, Chm. Bd.--Francesco Parisi S.p.A., Trieste, Italy; Int'l, pg. 504
Parizeau, Robert, Chm. Bd.--Gaz Metropolitain & Company, Montreal, Canada; Int'l, pg. 541
Park, J. Leonard, Chm. Bd., Pres., Chief Exec. Officer & Treas.--George W. Park Seed Co., Inc., Greenwood, SC; U.S. Private, pg. 839
Park, Joon, Chm.--Saehan Merchant Banking Corporation, Seoul, Korea; Int'l, pg. 676
Park, Raymond, Chm. Bd. & Pres.--Park Corp., Cleveland, OH; U.S. Private, pg. 839
Park, Sung-Hoon, Chm. Bd. & Pres.--Jaeneung Education Co., Ltd., Seoul, Korea; Int'l, pg. 697
Parke, F.H., Jr., Chm. Bd.--Democrat Printing & Lithograph Company, Little Rock, AR; U.S. Private, pg. 323
Parker, C.C., Chm. Bd.--Reunert Ltd., Sandton, South Africa; Int'l, pg. 1105
Parker, David H., Chm. Bd., Pres & Chief Exec. Officer--Pelican Products, Torrance, CA; U.S. Private, pg. 848
Parker, Gary D., Chm. Bd. Pres. & Chief Exec. Officer--Lindsay Manufacturing Company, Lindsay, NE; U.S. Public, pg. 999
Parker, JoAnn, Chm. Bd.--Omniflight, Inc., Dallas, TX; U.S. Private, pg. 816
Parker, JoAnn, Chm. Bd.--Omniflight Helicopters, Inc., Dallas, TX; U.S. Private, pg. 817
Parker, Leonard F., Chm. Bd.--Hospitality Worldwide Services, Inc., New York, NY; U.S. Public, pg. 841
Parker, Melvin C., Chm. Bd., Pres., Chief Exec. Officer, Chief Fin. Officer & Treas.--Investors Insurance Group, Inc., Boca Raton, FL; U.S. Public, pg. 911
Parker, Patrick S., Chm. Bd.--Parker Hannifin Corporation, Cleveland, OH; U.S. Public, pg. 1259
Parker, Robert L., Sr., Chm. Bd.--Parker Drilling Company, Tulsa, OK; U.S. Public, pg. 1259
Parker, Ronald I., Chm. Bd., Pres. & Chief Exec. Officer--Indian Head Industries Inc., Charlotte, NC; U.S. Private, pg. 559
Parker, Samuel J., Chm. Bd., Pres. & Chief Exec. Officer--PETsMART, Inc., Phoenix, AZ; U.S. Public, pg. 1281
Parker, T.J., Dr., Chm. Bd.--Babcock International Group PLC, Amersham, United Kingdom; Int'l, pg. 130
Parks, Robert M., Chm. Bd.--Parks Products, Inc., Hollywood, CA; U.S. Private, pg. 840
Parrette, William, Pres. & Chief Exec. Officer--Solitec Wafer Processing, Inc., San Jose, CA; U.S. Private, pg. 1013
Parrott, Roy E., Chm. Bd., Pres. & Chief Exec. Officer--Simpson Industries, Inc., Plymouth, MI; U.S. Public, pg. 1474
Parsons, Colin J., Chm. Bd.--Taylor Woodrow plc, London, United Kingdom; Int'l, pg. 1358
Partridge, James E., Chm. Bd. & Pres.--Smith-Emery Company, Los Angeles, CA; U.S. Private, pg. 1007
Parzybok, William G., Jr., Chm. Bd. & Chief Exec. Officer--Fluke Corporation, Everett, WA; U.S. Public, pg. 659
Pascucci, Vito, Chm. Bd. & Chief Exec. Officer--G. Leblanc Corporation, Kenosha, WI; U.S. Private, pg. 656
Pasquel, Alfonso, Chm.--Aerolitoral, Nuevo Leon, Mexico; Int'l, pg. 332
Pasquerilla, Frank J., Chm. Bd. & Chief Exec. Officer--Crown American Realty Trust, Johnstown, PA; U.S. Public, pg. 461
Pasquinelli, Anthony, Chm. Bd.--Beverly Bancorporation Inc., Chicago, IL; U.S. Public, pg. 227
Passano, William M., Jr., Chm. Bd.--Waverly, Inc., Baltimore, MD; U.S. Public, pg. 1748
Paster, Howard, Chm. & Chief Exec. Officer--Hill and Knowlton, Inc., New York, NY; Int'l, pg. 1483
Patch, Glenn E., Chm. Bd.--Patch Communications, Titusville, FL; U.S. Private, pg. 842
Pate, James L., Chm. Bd. & Chief Exec. Officer--Pennzoil Company, Houston, TX; U.S. Public, pg. 1272
Pate, R. Carter, Chm. Bd. & Chief Exec. Officer--Sun TV & Appliances, Inc., Groveport, OH; U.S. Public, pg. 1532
Pate, Sebert L., Chm. Bd. & Chief Exec. Officer--Texas Refinery Corp., Fort Worth, TX; U.S. Private, pg. 1078
Patel, D.S., Chm. Bd., Pres. & Chief Exec. Officer--Circuit Systems, Inc., Elk Grove Village, IL; U.S. Public, pg. 374
Patel, Minaxi, Chm. Bd.--Philway Products, Inc., Ashland, OH; U.S. Private, pg. 862
Patenge, Kenneth E., Chm. Bd., Pres. & Chief Exec. Officer--Wohlert Corp., Lansing, MI; U.S. Private, pg. 1185
Paterek, James L., Chm. Bd.--Comforce Corporation, Lake Success, NY; U.S. Public, pg. 409
Paterna, Salvatore A., Chm. Bd., Pres., Chief Exec. Officer & Chief Oper. Officer--John Solomon, Inc., Somerville, MA; U.S. Private, pg. 1013
Paterson, C.J., Chm.--Macmillan Education Ltd., Basingstoke, United Kingdom; Int'l, pg. 1479
Pathmarajah, Allen Joseph, Chm. Bd.--CSA Holdings Ltd., Singapore, Singapore; Int'l, pg. 242
Patient, William F., Chm. Bd., Pres. & Chief Exec. Officer--The Geon Company, Avon Lake, OH; U.S. Public, pg. 733
Patil, Suhas S., Chm. Emeritus--Cirrus Logic, Inc., Fremont, CA; U.S. Public, pg. 375
Patrick, C.L., Chm. Bd.--Carmike Cinemas, Inc., Columbus, GA; U.S. Public, pg. 305
Patrick, Joseph A., Chm. Bd.--Baird, Patrick & Co., Inc., New York, NY; U.S. Private, pg. 111
Patten, Charles R., Chm. Bd. & Pres.--Colfax Envelope Corporation, Buffalo Grove, IL; U.S. Private, pg. 252
Patterson, Aubrey B., Jr., Chm. Bd. & Chief Exec. Officer--Bancorp South Inc., Tupelo, MS; U.S. Public, pg. 176
Patterson, E. Lynn, Chm. Bd. & Chief Exec. Officer--Digital Courier International Inc., Burnaby, Canada; Int'l, pg. 413
Patterson, Neal L., Chm. Bd. & Chief Exec. Officer--Cerner Corporation, Kansas City, MO; U.S. Public, pg. 331
Patterson, Robert H., Jr., Chm. Bd. & Chief Exec. Officer--Celebrity Incorporated, Tyler, TX; U.S. Public, pg. 319
Pattinson, Mick, Chm. Bd.--Barratt American Inc., Carlsbad, CA; Int'l, pg. 168
Pattison, James A., Chm. Bd., Pres., Chief Exec. Officer & Mng. Dir.--Great Pacific Enterprises Inc., Vancouver, Canada; Int'l, pg. 557
Pattiz, Norman J., Chm. Bd.--Westwood One, Inc., New York, NY; U.S. Public, pg. 1763
Patton, George, Chm. Bd., Pres. & Chief Exec. Officer--Leblanc Communications, Inc., Richardson, TX; U.S. Private, pg. 656
Patton, Jim A., Chm. Bd.--Patton Management, Inc., Atlanta, GA; U.S. Private, pg. 843
Patton, Jim A., Chm. Bd.--Wright & Lopez, Inc., Atlanta, GA; U.S. Private, pg. 843
Patton, T.V., Chm. Bd. & Pres.--Triton Manufacturing, Inc., Atlanta, GA; U.S. Private, pg. 1104
Patton, William A., Chm. Bd. & Chief Exec. Officer--Virginia First Financial Corp., Petersburg, VA; U.S. Public, pg. 1721
Patton, William A., Chm. Bd & Chief Exec. Officer--Virginia First Savings Bank, F.S.B., Petersburg, VA; U.S. Public, pg. 1721
Paty, John C., Jr., Chm. Bd.--The Paty Company, Piney Flats, TN; U.S. Private, pg. 844
Paul, G.W., Chm. Bd.--Pauls plc, Ipswich, United Kingdom; Int'l, pg. 598
Paul, George W., Chm. Bd.--Harrisons & Crosfield plc, London, United Kingdom; Int'l, pg. 598
Paul, George W., Chm. Bd.--Norwich Union Life Insurance, Norwich, United Kingdom; Int'l, pg. 970
Paul, Gerald, Chm. Emeritus--Paul Harris Stores, Inc., Indianapolis, IN; U.S. Public, pg. 792
Paul, Judith A., Chm. Bd.--Advantage Learning Systems, Inc., Wisconsin Rapids, WI; U.S. Public, pg. 22
Paul, Swraj, Chm. Bd.--Caparo Group Ltd., London, United Kingdom; Int'l, pg. 264
Pauley, Stanley F., Chm. Bd. & Chief Exec. Officer--Carpenter Co., Richmond, VA; U.S. Private, pg. 214
Paulsell, Frederick O., Chm. Bd.--TRM Copy Centers Corporation, Portland, OR; U.S. Public, pg. 1558
Paulsen, Stanley K., Chm.--Circle Business Credit, Inc., Indianapolis, IN; U.S. Public, pg. 1785
Pavelich, Daniel L., Chm. Bd.--BDO Seidman, LLP, Chicago, IL; U.S. Private, pg. 106
Paxton, G. Ward, Chm. Bd. & Pres.--ODS Networks, Inc., Richardson, TX; U.S. Public, pg. 1206
Payne, Calvin J., Chm. Bd. & Chief Exec. Officer--Westower Corporation, Vancouver, WA; U.S. Public, pg. 1762
Payne, David, Chm. Bd.--TBWA Payne Stracey, London, United Kingdom; Int'l, pg. 1336
Payne, David L., Chm. Bd., Pres. & Chief Exec. Officer--Westamerica Bancorporation, Fairfield, CA; U.S. Public, pg. 1756
Payne, David L., Chm. Bd., Pres. & Chief Exec. Officer--Westamerica Bank, San Rafael, CA; U.S. Public, pg. 1756
Payne, Donald, Chm. Bd. & Chief Exec. Officer--Willis Corroon Americas, Nashville, TN; Int'l, pg. 1505
Payne, James L., Chm. Bd., Pres. & Chief Exec. Officer--Santa Fe Energy Resources, Inc., Houston, TX; U.S. Public, pg. 1431
Payton, Earl E., Chm. Bd. & Chief Exec. Officer--Cowden Metal Specialties, Inc., Chino, CA; U.S. Private, pg. 280
Peabody, Lester C., Chm. Bd.--Peabody Office Furniture Corporation, Boston, MA; U.S. Private, pg. 844
Peake, David, Chm.--BNP UK Holdings Ltd., London, United Kingdom; Int'l, pg. 164
Peale, Ruth Stafford, Chm. Bd.--Guideposts Associates, Inc., Carmel, NY; U.S. Private, pg. 487
Pearce, David M., Chm.--Donald Brown (Brownall) Ltd., Manchester, United Kingdom; Int'l, pg. 390
Pearce, Louis M., Jr., Chm. Bd.--Pearce Industries Inc., Houston, TX; U.S. Private, pg. 845
Pearlman, Herbert M., Chm. Bd., Pres. & Chief Exec. Officer--Helm Resources Inc., Greenwich, CT; U.S. Public, pg. 808
Pearlman, Herbert M., Chm. Bd.--Seitel, Inc., Houston, TX; U.S. Public, pg. 1454
Pearlman, Herbert M., Chm. Bd.--Unapix Entertainment Inc., New York, NY; U.S. Public, pg. 1664
Pearse, Brian, Sir, Chm. Bd.--LucasVarity plc, London, United Kingdom; Int'l, pg. 819
Pearse, William J., Chm. Bd.--Ultimate Electronics, Thornton, CO; U.S. Public, pg. 1662
Pearson, Andrall E., Chm. Bd. & Chief Exec. Officer--Tricon Global Restaurants, Inc., Louisville, KY; U.S. Public, pg. 1636
Pearson, Harry, Chm. Bd. & Pres.--United Farm Family Life Insurance Co., Indianapolis, IN; U.S. Private, pg. 1122
Pearson, Richard K., Chm. & Chief Exec. Officer--LaSalle Bank Northbrook, Northbrook, IL; Int'l, pg. 10
Pearson, Ronald, Chm. Bd., Pres. & Chief Exec. Officer--Hy-Vee Food Stores Incorporated, West Des Moines, IA; U.S. Private, pg. 550
Pease, David H., Jr., Chm. Bd. & Chief Exec. Officer--Pease Industries, Inc., Fairfield, OH; U.S. Private, pg. 845
Peat, Randall L., Chm. Bd.--Manatron, Inc., Kalamazoo, MI; U.S. Public, pg. 1040
Pebereau, Michel, Chm. Bd. & Chief Exec. Officer--Banque Nationale de Paris, Paris, France; Int'l, pg. 163
Pebereau, Michel, Chm.--CIP, Paris, France; Int'l, pg. 163
Pecci, Alberto, Chm. Bd. & Pres.--Fondiaria S.P.A., Florence, Italy; Int'l, pg. 496
Pecci, D. Alberto, Chm. Bd.--La Fondiaria Assicurazioni S.p.A., Florence, Italy; Int'l, pg. 784
Pechota, Gary, Chm. Bd., Pres., & Chief Exec. Officer--Giant Cement Holding Inc., Summerville, SC; U.S. Public, pg. 741
Pechota, Gary, Chm. Bd. & Chief Exec. Officer--Giant Resource Recovery Company (Grr!), Harleyville, SC; U.S. Public, pg. 741
Pechota, Gary L., Chm. & Chief Exec. Officer--Giant Cement Company, Harleyville, SC; U.S. Public, pg. 741

Peck, Donald E., Chm. Bd.--Pacific Metal Company, Portland, OR; *U.S. Private*, pg. 832

Peckham, Janet G., Chm. Bd.--Peckham Industries, Inc., White Plains, NY; *U.S. Private*, pg. 846

Pedder, Roger A., Chm. Bd.--Clarks International, Street, United Kingdom; *Int'l*, pg. 296

Peebler, Charles D., Jr., Pres.-True North & Chm. & Chief Exec. Officer-TN Div. Cos.--True North Communications Inc., Chicago, IL; *U.S. Public*, pg. 1641

Peebler, Charles D., Jr., Chm. & Chief Exec. Officer--True North Diversified Companies, New York, NY; *U.S. Public*, *pg. 1642*

Peepas, James Z., Chm. Bd.--Selecto-Flash, Inc., West Orange, NJ; *U.S. Private*, pg. 982

Peerbhoy, Bunty, Chm. Bd., Chief Exec. Officer & Mng. Dir.--MAA Communications Bozell, Bangalore, India; *U.S. Public*, pg. 1642

Peerbhoy, Sajid, Chm.--Speer Communications, Mumbai, India; *U.S. Private*, pg. 1063

Peers, Antony, Chm.--Seaforth Maritime Limited, Aberdeen, United Kingdom; *U.S. Public*, pg. 776

Peet, Harrison D., Chm. Bd.--Delta Natural Gas Company, Inc., Winchester, KY; *U.S. Public*, pg. 497

Peladeau, Erik, Chm. Bd. & Chief Exec. Officer--Quebecor Multimedia Inc., Montreal, Canada; *Int'l*, pg. 1076

Peladeau, Pierre, Chm. Bd., Pres. & Chief Exec. Officer--Quebecor Inc., Montreal, Canada; *Int'l*, pg. 1075

Pelisek, Frank J., Chm. Bd.--Stokely USA, Inc., Oconomowoc, WI; *U.S. Public*, pg. 1518

Pelisson, Gerard, Co.-Chm. & Co-Pres.--Accor S.A., Evry, France; *Int'l*, pg. 20

Pellegrino, Anthony, Chm. Bd.--LORAD Corporation, Danbury, CT; *U.S. Public*, pg. 1595

Peller, Joseph A., Chm. Bd.--Andres Wines Ltd., Winona, Canada; *Int'l*, pg. 75

Peltola, Timo, Chm. Bd., Pres. & Chief Exec. Officer--Huhtamaki Oy, Espoo, Finland; *Int'l*, pg. 638

Peltz, Nelson, Chm. Bd. & Chief Exec. Officer--Triarc Companies, Inc., New York, NY; *U.S. Public*, pg. 1634

Peltzer, Martin, Dr., Chm.--Haindl Papier GmbH, Augsburg, Germany; *Int'l*, pg. 586

Pemberton, Gary, Chm. Bd.--Qantas Airways Ltd., Mascot, Australia; *Int'l*, pg. 1074

Pemberton, Gary, Chm. Bd.--Qantas Airways Ltd., El Segundo, CA; *Int'l*, pg. 1075

Pena, Daniel, Chm. Bd.--Success Development International, Jacksonville, FL; *U.S. Private*, pg. 1048

Penberthy, Farrier, Chm. Bd.--Penberthy Lumber Company, Carson, CA; *U.S. Private*, pg. 848

Pence, Ann, Chm. Bd.--Coldwater Creek, Sandpoint, ID; *U.S. Public*, pg. 396

Pencer, Gerald N., Chm. Bd., Pres. & Chief Exec. Officer--Cott Corporation, Pointe-Claire, Canada; *Int'l*, pg. 337

Pendergast, B. Joseph, Chm. Bd. & Chief Exec. Officer--Weatherby Health Care, Norwalk, CT; *U.S. Private*, pg. 1155

Pendleton, Alexander, Chm. Bd. & Chief Exec. Officer--Summit Tool Company, Akron, OH; *U.S. Private*, pg. 1050

Pendleton, Alexander, Chm. Bd. & Chief Exec. Officer--Ken Tool, Akron, OH; *U.S. Private*, pg. 1050

Peng, Ng Soo, Chm.--Morgan Grenfell Asia Limited (Singapore), Singapore, Singapore; *Int'l*, pg. 406

Penisten, Gary D., Chm. Bd.--Acme United Corporation, Fairfield, CT; *U.S. Public*, pg. 17

Penister, Glenn E., Chm. Bd.--Network Peripherals Inc., Milpitas, CA; *U.S. Public*, pg. 1169

Penner, Pete J., Chm. Bd.--Sun-Maid Growers of California, Kingsburg, CA; *U.S. Private*, pg. 1051

Penniman, Allen, Chm. Bd.--Carter Chambers Supply, Inc., Baton Rouge, LA; *U.S. Private*, pg. 216

Penninger, Samuel A., Jr., Chm. Bd.--Serologicals Corporation, Clarkston, GA; *U.S. Public*, pg. 1460

Pennings, Harry, Chm. Bd.--OCE-U.S.A., Itasca, IL; *Int'l*, pg. 994

Pennington, L.D., Chm. Bd.--Centex Forcum-Lannom, Inc., Dyersburg, TN; *U.S. Public*, pg. 322

Penninx, E.G.M., Chm. Bd.--VNU Dagbladengroep B.V., Nijmegen, Netherlands; *Int'l*, pg. 1445

Penske, Richard H., Chm. Bd. & Chief Exec. Officer--Piercing Pagoda, Inc., Bethlehem, PA; *U.S. Public*, pg. 1296

Penske, Roger S., Chm. Bd.--Penske Corporation, Detroit, MI; *U.S. Private*, pg. 850

Penske, Roger S., Chm. Bd.--Detroit Diesel Corp., Detroit, MI; *U.S. Private*, pg. 850

Penske, Roger, Jr., Chm. Bd.--Penske Logistics, Reading, PA; *U.S. Private*, pg. 851

Pentecost, J. Miller, Chm. Bd.--Power & Telephone Supply Company, Memphis, TN; *U.S. Private*, pg. 877

Pepper, John E., Chm. Bd. & Chief Exec. Officer--The Procter & Gamble Company, Cincinnati, OH; *U.S. Public*, *pg. 1330*

Pepper, Richard S., Chm. Bd.--The Pepper Companies, Inc., Chicago, IL; *U.S. Private*, pg. 851

Pepys, Eric, Chm. Bd.--Dot Printer, Inc., Irvine, CA; *U.S. Private*, pg. 341

Peraino, Roy T., Chm. Bd.--Midlantic Bank, N.A., Edison, NJ; *U.S. Public*, pg. 1242

Perakis, James A., Chm. Bd., Pres. & Chief Exec. Officer--Hyperion Software, Stamford, CT; *U.S. Public*, pg. 851

Percival, Richard R., Chm. Bd.--Zieman Manufacturing Company, Whittier, CA; *U.S. Private*, pg. 1205

Percival, Robert, Chm. & Pres.--Intelligent Controls Inc., Lynnwood, WA; *U.S. Private*, pg. 566

Percy, S.W., Chm. Bd. & Chief Exec. Officer--BP America Inc., Cleveland, OH; *Int'l*, pg. 220

Percy, W.A., II, Chm. Bd.--Staple Cotton Cooperative Association, Greenwood, MS; *U.S. Private*, pg. 1033

Perdue, Frank, Chm.-Exec. Committee Bd.--Perdue Farms Incorporated, Salisbury, MD; *U.S. Private*, pg. 852

Perdue, James A., Chm. Bd.--Perdue Farms Incorporated, Salisbury, MD; *U.S. Private*, pg. 852

Perelman, Raymond G., Chm. Bd.--RGP Holding, Inc., Wilmington, DE; *U.S. Private*, pg. 903

Perelman, Ronald O., Chm. Bd. & Chief Exec. Officer--MacAndrews & Forbes Holdings Inc., New York, NY; *U.S. Private*, pg. 689

Perelman, Ronald O., Chm. Bd. & Chief Exec. Officer--Andrews Group, Incorporated, New York, NY; *U.S. Private*, pg. 689

Perenchio, A. Jerrold, Sr. Partner--Chartwell Partners, Los Angeles, CA; *U.S. Private*, pg. 230

Perez, J. Peter, Chm. Bd., Pres., & Chief Exec. Officer--InterBio Inc., Woodlands, TX; *U.S. Private*, pg. 566

Perez, Lombardo, Chm. Bd., Pres. & Chief Oper. Officer--Metro Ford Inc., Miami, FL; *U.S. Private*, pg. 736

Perez, Ricardo, Chm. Bd. & Pres.--Ricardo Perez Asociados, Madrid, Spain; *Int'l*, pg. 1036

Perik, Michael, Chm. Bd. & Chief Exec. Officer--The Learning Co., Inc., Cambridge, MA; *U.S. Public*, pg. 982

Pering, Thomas H., Chm. Bd. & Chief Exec. Officer--Schleicher & Schuell, Inc., Keene, NH; *Int'l*, pg. 1206

Perini, David B., Chm. Bd. & Chief Exec. Officer--Perini Corporation, Framingham, MA; *U.S. Public*, pg. 1278

Perkins, A.D.J., Mng. Dir.--Rolls-Royce Power Engineering plc, Newcastle upon Tyne, United Kingdom; *Int'l*, pg. 1127

Perkins, Lawrence, Chm. Bd. & Treas.--Connecticut Container Corporation, North Haven, CT; *U.S. Private*, pg. 263

Perkins, Leigh H., Chm. Bd.--The Orvis Company, Inc., Manchester, VT; *U.S. Private*, pg. 820

Perkins, Rodney, Chm. Bd.--Resound Corporation, Redwood City, CA; *U.S. Public*, pg. 1382

Perks, A. Campbell, Chm. Bd.--Eclipse Inc., Rockford, IL; *U.S. Private*, pg. 360

Perlegos, George, Chm. Bd., Pres. & Chief Exec. Officer--Atmel Corporation, San Jose, CA; *U.S. Public*, pg. 145

Perlet, Helmot Dr., Chm.--Allianz Versicherungs-AG, Munich, Germany; *Int'l*, pg. 58

Perlman, Lawrence, Chm. Bd., Pres. & Chief Exec. Officer--Ceridian Corporation, Bloomington, MN; *U.S. Public*, pg. 330

Perlmuter, Richard M., Chm. Bd.--Perlmuter Printing Company, Cleveland, OH; *Int'l*, pg. 1177

Perlmutter, Norman, III, Chm. Bd. & Chief Exec. Officer--Heitman Financial Ltd., Chicago, IL; *U.S. Public*, pg. 1673

Perrella, James E., Chm. Bd., Pres. & Chief Exec. Officer--Ingersoll-Rand Company, Woodcliff Lake, NJ; *U.S. Public*, pg. 876

Perrin, C., Chm. Bd.--Bail Equipement, Paris, France; *Int'l*, pg. 563

Perrino, S. Ronald, Chm. Bd., Pres. & Chief Exec. Officer--S.T. Research, Newington, VA; *U.S. Private*, pg. 958

Perrrault, Fernand, Chm.--Cadim, Montreal, Canada; *Int'l*, pg. 249

Perry-Werner, Kathryn M., Chm. Bd. & Treas.--Perry Engineering Company, Inc., Winchester, VA; *U.S. Private*, pg. 854

Perry, Chris N., Chm. Bd. & Chief Exec. Officer--Meldrum & Fewsmith Communications Inc., Cleveland, OH; *U.S. Private*, pg. 730

Perry, J.G.R., Chm.--Meyer Forest Products Ltd, London, United Kingdom; *Int'l*, pg. 864

Perry, M. Dunman, Jr., Chm. Bd., Pres. & Chief Exec. Officer--Perry Equipment Corporation, Mineral Wells, TX; *U.S. Private*, pg. 855

Perry, Michael W., Chm.--Indimac Manufactured Housing Division, San Diego, CA; *U.S. Public*, pg. 857

Perry, Michael W., Chm.--Indimac Third Party Construction Lending Division, Pasadena, CA; *U.S. Public*, pg. 857

Perry, Michael W., Chm.--Warehouse Lending Corporation of America, Pasadena, CA; *U.S. Public*, pg. 857

Perry, Michael W., Chm.--Construction Lending Corporation of America-Builder Division, Pasadena, CA; *U.S. Public*, pg. 857

Perry, Richard, Chm. Bd.--FTD, Inc./Florists Transworld Delivery, Inc., Downers Grove, IL; *U.S. Private*, pg. 389

Perry, Richard E., Chm. Bd.--C-COR Electronics, Inc., State College, PA; *U.S. Public*, pg. 272

Perry, Thomas, Chm. Bd. & Chief Exec. Officer--Perry's Ice Cream Co., Inc., Akron, NY; *U.S. Private*, pg. 855

Persson, Christer, Chm.--Aero Systems Engineering Inc., Saint Paul, MN; *Int'l*, pg. 276

Pesch, Alan J., Chm. Bd., Pres. & Chief Exec. Officer--Ship Analytics, Inc., North Stonington, CT; *U.S. Private*, pg. 994

Peskin, Kenneth G., Chm. Bd. & Chief Exec. Officer--E & B Marine Incorporated, Edison, NJ; *U.S. Public*, pg. 1756

Pester, Jack C., Chm. & Chief Exec. Officer--Coastal Refining & Marketing, Wichita, KS; *U.S. Public*, pg. 390

Peter, Jean D., Chm. Bd.--Union Carbide South Africa (Pty.) Ltd., Johannesburg, South Africa; *U.S. Public*, pg. 1667

Peterkin, George A., Jr., Chm. Bd.--Kirby Corporation, Houston, TX; *U.S. Public*, pg. 961

Peters, Robert L., Chm. Bd., Pres. & Chief Exec. Officer--Holmquist Grain & Lumber Co., Oakland, NE; *U.S. Private*, pg. 535

Petersen, Allen, Chm. Bd. & Chief Exec. Officer--American Tool Companies, Inc., Lincoln, NE; *U.S. Private*, pg. 63

Petersen, Allen D., Chm. Bd. & Chief Exec. Officer--American Tool Companies, Inc., Hoffman Estates, IL; *U.S. Private*, pg. 63

Petersen, Eric, Chm. Bd. & Treas.--Petersen Graphics Group, South Bend, IN; *U.S. Private*, pg. 856

Petersen, James F., Chm. Bd.--Best Software, Inc., Reston, VA; *U.S. Public*, pg. 223

Petersen, Norm, Chm. Bd.--Fujitsu Computer Products of America, Inc., San Jose, CA; *Int'l*, pg. 526

Petersen, R.E., Chm. Emeritus--Petersen Publishing Company, L.L.C., Los Angeles, CA; *U.S. Private*, pg. 856

Peterso, Carl, Chm. Bd.--Agri-Mark, Inc., Lawrence, MA; *U.S. Private*, pg. 26

Peterson, Alfred H., III, Chm. Bd.--Peterson American Corp., Southfield, MI; *U.S. Private*, pg. 857

Peterson, David D., Chm. Bd.--Consolidated-Tomoka Land Co., Daytona Beach, FL; *U.S. Public*, pg. 437

Peterson, David H., Chm. Bd., Pres. & Chief Exec. Officer--NRG Energy, Inc., Minneapolis, MN; *U.S. Public*, pg. 1195

Peterson, Ellsworth L., Chm. Bd. & Chief Exec. Officer--Peterson Builders, Inc., Sturgeon Bay, WI; *U.S. Private*, pg. 857

Peterson, L.N., Founder & Chm. Bd.--Regal Ware, Inc., Kewaskum, WI; *U.S. Private*, pg. 917

Peterson, Lloyd E., Chm. Bd.--Peterson Farms, Decatur, AR; *U.S. Private*, pg. 857

Peterson, Palmer G., Chm. Bd. & Chief Exec. Officer--Bituminous Roadways, Inc., Inver Grove Heights, MN; *U.S. Private*, pg. 146

Peterson, Peter G., Chm. Bd.--The Blackstone Group, New York, NY; *U.S. Private*, pg. 147

Peterson, Robert L., Chm. Bd., Pres. & Chief Exec. Officer--IBP, Inc., Dakota City, NE; *U.S. Public*, pg. 852

Peterson, William L., Chm. Bd.--Alltrista Corporation, Muncie, IN; *U.S. Public*, pg. 56

Petit, Henri, Chm. Bd.--Ecole de Pilotage Amaury de la Grange, Merville, France; *Int'l*, pg. 560

Petit, Parker H., Chm. Bd.--Matria Healthcare, Inc., Marietta, GA; *U.S. Public*, pg. 1057

Petitt, Richard G., Chm. Bd. & Pres.--Colonial Penn Life Insurance Company, Philadelphia, PA; *U.S. Public*, pg. 433

Petitt, Richard G., Chm. Bd. & Pres.--Empire Insurance Group, New York, NY; *U.S. Public*, pg. 990

Petitt, Richard G., Chm. Bd., Pres. & Chief Exec. Officer--Allcity Insurance Co., New York, NY; *U.S. Public*, pg. 990

Petrocelli, A.F., Chm. Bd., Pres. & Chief Exec. Officer--United Capital Corp., Great Neck, NY; *U.S. Public*, pg. 1674

Petroz, Herve, Chm.--Minoterie Coop Rivaz, Puidoux, Switzerland; *Int'l*, pg. 330

Petry, Thomas E., Chm. Bd. & Chief Exec. Officer--Eagle-Picher Industries, Inc., Cincinnati, OH; *U.S. Private*, pg. 355

Pettern, Reinhard, Chm. Bd.--Temca Chemische Union GmbH, Nuremberg, Germany; *U.S. Public*, pg. 1333

Petty, John R., Chm. Bd.--Nippon Credit Trust Company, New York, NY; *Int'l*, pg. 933

Petty, R.B., Chm. Bd., Pres. & Chief Exec. Officer--SouthTrust Bank, Montgomery, Montgomery, AL; *U.S. Public*, pg. 1491

Peugeot, Pierre, Chm.--GEFCO, Courbevoie, France; *Int'l*, pg. 1021

Peugeot, Roland, Chm.-Supervisory Bd.--PSA Peugeot Citroen, Paris, France; *Int'l*, pg. 1020

Peugeot, Roland, Chm. Bd.--Peugeot S.A., Paris, France; *Int'l*, pg. 1020

Pew, Robert C., Chm. Bd.--Steelcase Inc., Grand Rapids, MI; *U.S. Private*, pg. 1038

Peyrelevade, Jean, Chm. Bd., Pres. & Chief Exec. Officer--Credit Lyonnais S.A., Paris, France; *Int'l*, pg. 343

Peyton, Herbert H., Chm. Bd. & Pres.--Gate Petroleum Company, Jacksonville, FL; *U.S. Private*, pg. 441

Peyton, Patrick J., Chm. Bd. & Chief Exec. Officer--Despatch Industries, Minneapolis, MN; *U.S. Private*, pg. 327

Pezzolo, Donald E., Chm. Bd. & Co-Chief Exec. Officer--Diablo Research Corporation, Sunnyvale, CA; *U.S. Public*, pg. 1424

Pfaff, Edward, Chm. Bd.--Anchor Tool & Die Company, Cleveland, OH; *U.S. Private*, pg. 71

Pfaff, Edward, Chm. & Chief Exec. Officer--Condor Tool & Die, Inc., Cleveland, OH; *U.S. Private*, pg. 71

Pfaff, Edward, Chm. Bd.--Anchor Metal Processing, Cleveland, OH; *U.S. Private*, pg. 71

Pfeiffer, D., Chm. Bd.--Groupe GAN, Paris, France; *Int'l*, pg. 563

Pfeiffer, Robert G., Chm. Bd. & Chief Exec. Officer--Neill-LaVielle Supply Co., Louisville, KY; *U.S. Private*, pg. 790

Pfleger, Paul, Chm. Bd.--TIE/Communications, Inc., Overland Park, KS; *U.S. Private*, pg. 1085

Pfleiderer, Ernst-Herbert, Chm. Bd.--Pfleiderer AG, Neumarkt, Germany; *Int'l*, pg. 1046

Phares, Elwood W., II, Chm. Bd. & Pres.--Wechco, Inc., Princeton, NJ; *U.S. Private*, pg. 1158

Phelps, H.T.H.M., Chm. Bd.--Beeton Rumford Ltd., London, United Kingdom; *Int'l*, pg. 1032

Phelps, Isaac E., Chm. Bd.--World Aerospace Corporation, Maple Grove, MN; *U.S. Private*, pg. 1188

Phelps, Michael E.J., Chm. Bd. & Chief Exec. Officer--Westcoast Energy Inc., Vancouver, Canada; *Int'l*, pg. 1492

Phelps, Terry M., Chm. Bd.--Petroleum Marketers, Inc., Roanoke, VA; *U.S. Private*, pg. 859

Phillips, Bert T., Pres. & Chm.--Lehigh Utilities Inc., Apopka, FL; *U.S. Public*, pg. 1116

Phillips, Bradford E., Chm. & Chief Exec. Officer--Totes Incorporated, Loveland, OH; *U.S. Private*, pg. 111

Phillips, David, Chm. Bd. & Chief Exec. Officer--InfoVest, Inc., Chicago, IL; *U.S. Private*, pg. 562

Phillips, Ernie, Chm. Bd.--First American Title Co. of New Mexico, Albuquerque, NM; *U.S. Public*, pg. 625

Phillips, James E., Chm. Bd.--GHM Industries, Inc., Worcester, MA; *U.S. Private*, pg. 435

Phillips, John, Chm.--IBJ Australia Bank Limited, Sydney, Australia; *Int'l*, pg. 676

Phillips, John B., Jr., Chm. Bd. & Chief Exec. Officer--Young-Phillips Sales Co., Clemmons, NC; *U.S. Private*, pg. 1201

Phillips, Ron, Chm. Bd.--Lever Brothers Co., New York, NY; *Int'l*, pg. 1435

Phillips, Thomas L., Chm. Bd., Pres. & Chief Exec. Officer--Phillips Publishing International, Inc., Potomac, MD; *U.S. Private*, pg. 862

Phiri, D.A.R., Chm.--Stanbic Bank Zambia, Lusaka, Zambia; *Int'l*, pg. 1294

Phole, Klaus, Dr., Chm. Bd.--Schering Berlin Inc., Cedar Knolls, NJ; *Int'l*, pg. 1204

Phulpin, Francois, Chm.--CAP Sesa Industrie, Paris, France; *Int'l*, pg. 263

Piasecki, Ronald, Chm. Bd.--Kurdziel Industries, Inc., Muskegon, MI; *U.S. Private*, pg. 637

Picard, Dennis J., Chm. Bd. & Chief Exec. Officer--Raytheon Company, Lexington, MA; *U.S. Public*, pg. 1364

Piccinini, Robert M., Chm. Bd., Chief Exec. Officer & Pres.--Save Mart Supermarkets, Modesto, CA; *U.S. Private*, pg. 968

Pichler, Joseph A., Chm. Bd. & Chief Exec. Officer--The Kroger Co., Cincinnati, OH; *U.S. Public*, pg. 967

Pickard, E.R., Chm. Bd. & Chief Exec. Officer--Sofamor Danek Group, Inc., Memphis, TN; *U.S. Public*, pg. 1482

Pickell, Ira S., Chm. Bd. & Chief Exec. Officer--The Bon Marche, Inc., Seattle, WA; *U.S. Public*, pg. 617

Pickering, Gordon G., Chm. Bd. & Chief Exec. Officer--Pickering Inc., Tacoma, WA; *U.S. Private*, pg. 864

Pickett, George, Jr., Chm. Bd. & Chief Exec. Officer--Atlantic Southeast Airlines Inc., Atlanta, GA; *U.S. Public*, pg. 144

Pickett, Joe K., Chm. Bd. & Chief Exec. Officer--Homeside Lending Company, Jacksonville, FL; *Int'l*, pg. 906

Picknelly, Peter L., Chm. Bd.--Peter Pan Bus Lines, Inc., Springfield, MA; *U.S. Private*, pg. 856

Picower, Jeffrey M., Chm. Bd. & Chief Exec. Officer--Monroe Systems For Business, Inc., Morris Plains, NJ; *U.S. Private*, pg. 757

Picower, Jeffrey M., Chm. Bd.--Physician Computer Network, Inc., Morris Plains, NJ; *U.S. Public*, pg. 1293

Piech, Ferdinand, Dr., Chm.-Mngmt. Bd.--Volkswagen AG, Wolfsburg, Germany; *Int'l*, pg. 1473

Pielenz, Hanns, Chm. Bd.--URS Logistics, Atlanta, GA; *U.S.* Private, pg. 1114

Pierce, James L., Chm. Bd. & Chief Exec. Officer--Arinc Inc. (Consolidated), Annapolis, MD; *U.S. Private*, pg. 81

Pierce, Milton, Chm. Bd.--Guardian Alarm Co., Southfield, MI; *U.S. Private*, pg. 485

Pierce, Willard G., Chm. Bd.--Flexfab Horizons International, Inc., Hastings, MI; *U.S. Private*, pg. 412

Pietrini, Andrew, Chm. Bd., Pres. & Chief Exec. Officer--UIS, Inc., Jersey City, NJ; *U.S. Private*, pg. 1113

Pigott, Mark C., Chm. Bd. & Chief Exec. Officer--Paccar Inc., Bellevue, WA; *U.S. Public*, pg. 1246

Pike, Larry R., Chm., Pres. & Chief Exec. Officer--The Union Central Life Insurance Co., Cincinnati, OH; *U.S. Private*, pg. 1118

Pike, Randy, Chm. Bd.--P.J. Keating Company, Lunenburg, MA; *U.S. Private*, pg. 610

Pikus, Stanton M., Chm. Bd., Pres. & Chief Exec. Officer--Canterbury Corporate Services, Inc., Medford, NJ; *U.S. Public*, pg. 301

Pilgrim, Lonnie A., Chm. Bd. & Chief Exec. Officer--Pilgrim's Pride Corporation, Pittsburg, TX; *U.S. Public*, pg. 1296

Pincus, David, Chm. Bd. & Chief Exec. Officer--Pincus Bros., Inc., Philadelphia, PA; *U.S. Private*, pg. 865

Pineau-Valencienne, Didier, Chm. Bd. & Chief Exec. Officer--Schneider S.A., Boulogne-Billancourt, France; *Int'l*, pg. 1207

Pines, Isidore, Chm. Bd. & Chief Exec. Officer--National Foods Inc., Bronx, NY; *U.S. Public*, pg. 429

Pingel, Paul, Chm. Bd. & Pres.--New Cooperative Inc., Fort Dodge, IA; *U.S. Private*, pg. 792

Pinkerton, Guy C., Chm. Bd., Pres. & Chief Exec. Officer--Washington Federal Savings, Seattle, WA; *U.S. Public*, pg. 1740

Pinner, Douglas K., Chm. Bd., Pres. & Chief Exec. Officer--Tokheim Corporation, Fort Wayne, IN; *U.S. Public*, pg. 1620

Pinola, Richard J., Chm. Bd. & Chief Exec. Officer--Right Management Consultants, Inc., Philadelphia, PA; *U.S. Public*, pg. 1390

Pinquies, J. M., Chm. Bd.--Banque Transatlantique, Paris, France; *Int'l*, pg. 563

Pinsley, Sol, Chm. Bd., Pres., Chief Exec. & Chief Oper. Officer--Espey Mfg. & Electronics Corp., Saratoga Springs, NY; *U.S. Public*, pg. 592

Pinson, Martin S., Chm. Bd. & Chief Exec. Officer--Industrial Distribution Group, Tucker, GA; *U.S. Public*, pg. 875

Pinter, Michael R., Chm. Bd. & Chief Exec. Officer--Kemper Reinsurance Co., Long Grove, IL; *U.S. Private*, pg. 614

Piper, Addison L., Chm. Bd., Pres. & Chief Exec. Officer--Piper Jaffray Companies, Inc., Minneapolis, MN; *U.S. Public*, pg. 1300

Piper, Addison L., Chm. Bd. & Chief Exec. Officer--Piper Jaffray, Inc., Minneapolis, MN; *U.S. Public*, pg. 1303

Pippin, John E., Dr., Chm. Bd.--Electromagnetic Sciences, Inc., Norcross, GA; *U.S. Public*, pg. 569

Pirasteh, Ross, Chm. Bd.--KTI, Inc., Guttenberg, NJ; *U.S. Public*, pg. 939

Pirel, Louis, Chm. & Chief Exec. Officer--Minniti, Noumea, New Caledonia; *Int'l*, pg. 823

Pirie, Robert S, Chm. Bd.--Rothchild Asset Management Inc., New York, NY; *U.S. Private*, pg. 947

Pironnet, J.M., Chm.--AGIP Praha Ltd., Prague, Czech Republic; *Int'l*, pg. 428

Pisa, Michael A., Sr., Chm. Bd. & Chief Exec. Officer--Continental Paper & Supply Co., Detroit, MI; *U.S. Private*, pg. 269

Pischetsrieder, Bernd, Chm. Bd.-Mngmt.--Bayerische Motoren Werke Aktiengesellschaft, Munich, Germany; *Int'l*, pg. 177

Piser, Donald H., Chm. Bd. & Chief Exec. Officer--Morse Diesel International, Inc., New York, NY; *U.S. Private*, pg. 762

Pistilli, Frederick M., Chm. Bd. & Chief Exec. Officer--General Time Corp., Norcross, GA; *U.S. Private*, pg. 445

Pitcher, Desmond, Sir, Chm. Bd.--United Utilities plc, Warrington, United Kingdom; *Int'l*, pg. 1444

Pitcher, Desmond, Sir, Chm.--North West Water Limited, Warrington, United Kingdom; *Int'l*, pg. 1444

Pitman, B.I., Chm. Bd. & Chief Exec. Officer--Lloyds TSB Group PLC, London, United Kingdom; *Int'l*, pg. 812

Pittelkow, Charles R., Chm. Bd. & Pres.--Equitable Savings & Loan Association, Wauwatosa, WI; *U.S. Private*, pg. 380

Pitterich, Michael P., Chm. Bd. & Pres.--Moltrup Steel Products Company, Beaver Falls, PA; *U.S. Private*, pg. 756

Pittman, Gary, Chm. Bd., Pres., Chief Exec., Chief Oper. & Chief Fin. Officer--PCI, Austin, TX; *U.S. Private*, pg. 826

Pitts, Keith B., Chm. Bd., Pres. & Chief Exec. Officer--Paragon Health Network, Inc., Atlanta, GA; *U.S. Public*, pg. 1256

Pivar, Stuart, Chm. Bd.--Chem-Tainer Industries, North Babylon, NY; *U.S. Private*, pg. 231

Pla, Carlos, Chm. Bd., Pres. & Dir.-Opers.--Noblex Argentina S.A.C. e I., Buenos Aires, Argentina; *Int'l*, pg. 951

Placek, Robert A., Chm. Bd., Pres. & Chief Exec. Officer--Wegener Corporation, Duluth, GA; *U.S. Public*, pg. 1751

Plana, Eduardo, Chm. Bd. & Chief Exec. Officer--EURO RSCG, Madrid, Spain; *Int'l*, pg. 602

Plank, Raymond, Chm. Bd. & Chief Exec. Officer--Apache Corporation, Houston, TX; *U.S. Public*, pg. 119

Plaskett, Thomas G., Chm. Bd.--Greyhound Lines, Inc., Dallas, TX; *U.S. Public*, pg. 765

Platt, Lewis E., Chm. Bd., Pres. & Chief Exec. Officer--Hewlett-Packard Company, Palo Alto, CA; *U.S. Public*, pg. 813

Player, J., Chm.--S.O.S. Newall Limited, Stamford, United Kingdom; *Int'l*, pg. 1166

Pledger, Thomas R., Chm. Bd. & Chief Exec. Officer--Dycom Industries, Inc., Palm Beach Gardens, FL; *U.S. Public*, pg. 538

Plotnick, Stanley D., Chm., Chief Exec. Officer & Sec.--Encore Marketing International, Inc., Lanham, MD; *U.S. Public*, pg. 580

Plumbly, Daniel, Chm. Bd. & Corp. Counsel--The Will-Burt Company, Orrville, OH; *U.S. Private*, pg. 1177

Plummer, Lord, Chm. Bd.--Century Employers Life Assurance Company Limited, London, United Kingdom; *Int'l*, pg. 685

Plummer, Walter A., Chm. Bd.--The Zippertubing Co., Los Angeles, CA; *U.S. Private*, pg. 1207

Plunk, Kenneth W., Chm. Bd. & Chief Acctg. Officer--Union Planters Bank, Memphis, TN; *U.S. Public*, pg. 1669

Plunk, Robert, Chm. Emeritus--Preferred Risk Mutual Insurance, West Des Moines, IA; *U.S. Private*, pg. 880

Pocapalia, Dan, Chm. Bd., Pres. & Chief Exec. Officer--Kit Manufacturing Company, Long Beach, CA; *U.S. Public*, pg. 962

Poch, Gerlad A., Co-Chm. Bd., Pres., Chief Exec. Officer & Sec.--AmeriData Technologies, Inc., Stamford, CT; *U.S. Public*, pg. 711

Poelker, John S., Chm. Bd. & Chief Exec. Officer--Fleet Finance, Inc., Atlanta, GA; *U.S. Public*, pg. 650

Poggi, A. Robert, Chm. Bd.--Willis Corroon Corp. of Western Michigan, Grand Rapids, MI; *Int'l*, pg. 1507

Pogue, A. Mack, Chm. Bd. & Chief Exec. Officer--Lincoln Property Company, Dallas, TX; *U.S. Private*, pg. 668

Pogue, David, Chm. Bd. & Chief Exec. Officer--Stackig Advertising and Public Relations, Mc Lean, VA; *U.S. Private*, pg. 1028

Pohlad, Carl R., Chm. Bd.--Mesaba Holdings, Inc., Minneapolis, MN; *U.S. Public*, pg. 1099

Poindexter, Christian H., Chm. Bd. & Chief Exec. Officer--Baltimore Gas and Electric Company, Baltimore, MD; *U.S. Public*, pg. 172

Poinssot, Alain, Chm. Bd., Pres. & Chief Exec. Officer--GEODIS, Paris, France; *Int'l*, pg. 549

Poiree, Alain, Chm.--FCA!BMZ Paris, Suresnes, France; *Int'l*, pg. 469

Poirier, Robert J., Chm. Bd., Pres. & Chief Exec. Officer--USA Floral Products, Inc., Washington, DC; *U.S. Public*, pg. 1685

Poissant, Charles-Albert, Chm. Bd.--Donohue Inc., Quebec, Canada; *Int'l*, pg. 1075

Poitevint, A.L., Chm. Bd. & Pres.--Flint River Mills, Bainbridge, GA; *U.S. Private*, pg. 413

Pol, Steve W., Chm. Bd. & Pres.--Airtrol, Inc., Baton Rouge, LA; *U.S. Private*, pg. 29

Polaner, Leonard, Chm. Bd. & Chief Exec. Officer--B&G Foods, Inc., Roseland, NJ; *U.S. Private*, pg. 105

Poliner, Randall, Chm. Bd.--First American Flood Data Services, Austin, TX; *U.S. Public*, pg. 625

Politzer, Jerald S., Chm. Bd. & Chief Exec. Officer--Salant Corporation, New York, NY; *U.S. Public*, pg. 1429

Polk, Matthew S., Jr., Chm. Bd.--Polk Audio, Inc., Baltimore, MD; *U.S. Public*, pg. 1315

Polk, Stephen R., Chm. Bd. & Chief Exec. Officer--R.L. Polk & Co., Southfield, MI; *U.S. Private*, pg. 874

Pollack, Herbert W., Chm. Bd.--Parlex Corporation, Methuen, MA; *U.S. Public*, pg. 1264

Pollack, John, Chm. Bd.--Grant Geophysical Inc., Houston, TX; *U.S. Private*, pg. 470

Pollak, Martin M., Chm. Bd.--Interferon Sciences, Inc., New Brunswick, NJ; *U.S. Public*, pg. 694

Pollard, C. William, Chm. Bd.--The ServiceMaster Company, Downers Grove, IL; *U.S. Public*, pg. 1461

Pollnow, Charles, Chm. Bd., Chief Exec. & Oper. Officer--The Brulin Corporation, Indianapolis, IN; *U.S. Private*, pg. 176

Pollock, John A., Chm. Bd. & Chief Exec. Officer--Electrohome Ltd., Kitchener, Canada; *Int'l*, pg. 438

Pollock, Kenneth L., Chm. Bd.--Pennsylvania Enterprises Inc., Wilkes-Barre, PA; *U.S. Public*, pg. 1271

Pollock, Kenneth M., Chm.--THETA Land Corporation, Wilkes-Barre, PA; *U.S. Public*, pg. 1272

Pollock, Louis I., Chm. Bd. & Chief Exec. Officer--Morris Coupling Co., Erie, PA; *U.S. Private*, pg. 762

Pollock, Sam, Chm. Bd.--Toronto Blue Jays Baseball Club, Inc., Toronto, Canada; *Int'l*, pg. 680

Pollock, William K., Chm. Bd. & Chief Exec. Officer--Key Industries, Inc., Fort Scott, KS; *U.S. Private*, pg. 618

Pomerantz, John J., Chm. Bd. & Chief Exec. Officer--The Leslie Fay Companies, Inc., New York, NY; *U.S. Public*, pg. 989

Pomerantz, Marvin A., Chm. Bd. & Chief Exec. Officer--Gaylord Container Corporation, Deerfield, IL; *U.S. Public*, pg. 704

Pomeranz, Harold, Chm. Bd., Treas. & Sec.--Stanley Roberts, Inc., Lodi, NJ; *U.S. Private*, pg. 936

Pomeroy, David B., Chm. Bd., Pres. & Chief Exec. Officer--Pomeroy Computer Resources, Hebron, KY; *U.S. Public*, pg. 1315

Pomije, David R., Chm. Bd. & Chief Exec. Officer--Funco, Inc., Eden Prairie, MN; *U.S. Public*, pg. 688

Pond, Byron O., Chm. & Chief Exec. Officer--Arvin Industries, Inc., Columbus, IN; *U.S. Public*, pg. 136

Pong, Cheong Kim, Chm. Bd., Chief Exec. & Oper. Officer--Hong Fok Corporation Ltd., Singapore, Singapore; *Int'l*, pg. 635

Ponsolle, Patrick, Exec. Chm. & Co.-Pres.--The Eurotunnel Group, London, United Kingdom; *Int'l*, pg. 466

Pontet, Philippe, Chm., Pres. & Chief Exec. Officer--Compagnie Generale Maritime et Financiere, Suresnes, France; *Int'l*, pg. 322

Poole-Holmes, Betty J., Chm. Bd. & Chief Exec. Officer--Centrex Corporation, Findlay, OH; *U.S. Private*, pg. 225

Poole, James E., Chm. Bd.--Service Merchandise Company, Inc., Brentwood, TN; *U.S. Public*, pg. 1461

Pope, Mark C., III, Chm. Bd., & Chief Exec. Officer--Graphic Industries, Inc., Atlanta, GA; *U.S. Public*, pg. 1735

Pope, Peter T., Chm. Bd. & Chief Exec. Officer--Pope & Talbot, Inc., Portland, OR; *U.S. Public*, pg. 1316

Popek, Gerald J., Chm. Bd.--Platinum Solutions, Inglewood, CA; *U.S. Public*, pg. 1309

Popoff, Frank P., Chm. Bd.--The Dow Chemical Company, Midland, MI; *U.S. Public*, pg. 522

Popp, John F., Chm. Bd. & Pres.--Perfection Bakeries Inc., Fort Wayne, IN; *U.S. Private*, pg. 852

Porcher, Robert, Chm. Bd.--BGF Industries Inc., Greensboro, NC; *U.S. Private*, pg. 106

Porter, Charles, Chm. & Partner--Crispin Porter & Bogusky, Miami, FL; *U.S. Private*, pg. 290

Porter, Chuck, Chm.--Crispin Porter & Bogusky Advertising, Miami, FL; *U.S. Private*, pg. 290

Porter, Clyde R., Chm. Bd.--P.L. Porter Co., Woodland Hills, CA; *U.S. Private*, pg. 876

Porter, Colin, Chm. Bd.--Coley Porter Bell, London, United Kingdom; *Int'l*, pg. 1482

Porter, James P., Chm. Bd.--CCI/Triad Corporation, Austin, TX; *U.S. Private*, pg. 193

Portillo Acuna, Bernardo, Chm. Bd.--Domicilio Conocido Hercules, Ciudad Camargo, Mexico; *Int'l*, pg. 572

Portman, John C., Jr., Chm. Bd. & Chief Exec. Officer--AMC, Inc., Atlanta, GA; *U.S. Private*, pg. 6

Portno, A.D., Chm. Bd.--Britvic Soft Drinks Ltd., Chelmsford, United Kingdom; *Int'l*, pg. 170

Portno, A.D., Chm. Bd.--Bass International Brewers, Birmingham, United Kingdom; *Int'l*, pg. 170

Portno, A.D., Chm. Bd.--Britvic Soft Drinks Ltd., Chelmsford, United Kingdom; *Int'l*, pg. 1499

Posey, Lee, Chm. Bd. & Chief Exec. Officer--Palm Harbor Homes, Inc., Dallas, TX; *U.S. Public*, pg. 1254

Posnick, Paul, Chm. Bd. & Creative Dir.--Posnick & Kolker, Inc., New York, NY; *U.S. Private*, pg. 876

Posso, Patrick, Chm. Bd. & Pres.--Posso S.A., Paris, France; *Int'l*, pg. 1064

Post, Helen, Chm. Bd. & Chief Exec. Officer--ATHOL Corporation, Butner, NC; *U.S. Private*, pg. 94

Poste, George, Chm. Bd.-Res. & Devel.--SmithKline Beecham Corporation, Philadelphia, PA; *Int'l*, pg. 1264

Potamkin, Allen, Chm. Bd.--Potamkin Company, Miami, FL; *U.S. Private*, pg. 876

Potashner, Kenneth F., Chm. Bd., Pres., Chief Exec. & Chief Oper. Officer--Maxwell Technologies, Inc., San Diego, CA; *U.S. Public*, pg. 1061

Potchen, Peter K., Sr. V.P. & Gen. Auditor--Keycorp, Cleveland, OH; *U.S. Public*, pg. 954

Pote, Hal, Chm. Bd., Pres., Chief Exec. Officer & Sec.--Ambar, Inc., Lafayette, LA; *U.S. Private*, pg. 126

Potila, Antti, Chm.-Bd.of Mgmnt., Pres. & Chief Exec. Officer--FinnAir Oy, Helsinki, Finland; *Int'l*, pg. 485

Potter, David, Chm. Bd.--Guinness Yokohama Leasing Limited, London, United Kingdom; *Int'l*, pg. 159

Potter, Robert G., Chm. Bd. & Chief Exec. Officer--Solutia Inc., Saint Louis, MO; *U.S. Public*, pg. 1483

Potts, Erwin, Chm. Bd.--McClatchy Newspapers Inc., Sacramento, CA; *U.S. Public*, pg. 1065

Pouliot, Adrien D., Chm. Bd.--CF Cable TV Inc., Montreal, Canada; *Int'l*, pg. 240

Pouliot, Adrien D., Chm. Bd.--Reseau de Television Quatre Saisons Inc., Montreal, Canada; *Int'l*, pg. 241

Pouliot, Adrien D., Chm. Bd. & Chief Exec. Officer--Laurentien Cable TV Inc., Montreal, Canada; *Int'l*, pg. 241

Pouliot, Adrien D., Chm. Bd. & Chief Exec. Officer--Northern Cable Holdings Ltd., Montreal, Canada; *Int'l*, pg. 241

Pouliot, Jean A., Chm. Bd.--CFCF Inc., Montreal, Canada; *Int'l*, pg. 240

Poulter, Graham, Chm.--Poulter Communications PLC, Leeds, United Kingdom; *Int'l*, pg. 1065

Pountain, Eric, Sir, Chm. Bd.--IMI Plc, Witton, United Kingdom; *Int'l*, pg. 646

Poure, James A., Chm. Bd., Pres. & Chief Exec. Officer--General Alum & Chemical, Holland, OH; *U.S. Private*, pg. 443

Povah, Eleanor H., Chm. Bd.--Hamilton Stores, Inc., Bozeman, MT; *U.S. Private*, pg. 497

Powell, Don G., Chm. Bd.--Van Kampen/American Capital Inc., Oak Brook Terrace, IL; *U.S. Public*, pg. 1132

Powell, Earl W., Chm. Bd.--Atlantis Plastic, Inc., Atlanta, GA; *U.S. Public*, pg. 145

Powell, Earl W., Chm. Bd. & Chief Exec. Officer--Biscayne Apparel Inc., Clifton, NJ; *U.S. Public*, pg. 232

Powell, Harold H., Chm. Bd.--Powell Electronics Inc., Philadelphia, PA; *U.S. Private*, pg. 877

Powell, Karl C., Jr., Chm. Bd. & Chief Exec. Officer--Sequent Computer Systems, Inc., Beaverton, OR; *U.S. Public*, pg. 1459
Powell, Lawrence M., Chm. Bd.--L. Powell Co., Inc., Culver City, CA; *U.S. Private*, pg. 877
Powell, Phillip E., Chm. Bd. & Chief Exec. Officer--First Cash, Inc., Arlington, TX; *U.S. Public*, pg. 627
Powell, T.E., III, Chm. Bd.--Carolina Biological Supply Co., Burlington, NC; *U.S. Private*, pg. 213
Powell, Thomas W., Chm. Bd., Pres. & Chief Exec. Officer--Powell Industries, Inc., Houston, TX; *U.S. Public*, pg. 1319
Power, James D., III, Chm. Bd.--J.D. Power and Associates, Agoura Hills, CA; *U.S. Private*, pg. 878
Power, John, Chm. Bd.--Vitt Media International, Inc., New York, NY; *U.S. Private*, pg. 1142
Power, Philip H., Chm. Bd.--HomeTown Communications Network, Inc., Livonia, MI; *U.S. Private*, pg. 537
Powers, Frederic B., Jr., Chm. Bd. & Pres.--Powers Fastening, Inc., New Rochelle, NY; *U.S. Private*, pg. 878
Powers, James, Acting Chm.--Canada Ports Corporation, Ottawa, Canada; *Int'l*, pg. 255
Powers, Joe D., Chm. Bd. & Chief Exec. Officer--Merchants National Bank, Fort Smith, AR; *U.S. Public*, pg. 501
Powers, Paul J., Chm. Bd., Pres. & Chief Exec. Officer--Commercial Intertech Corp., Youngstown, OH; *U.S. Public*, pg. 411
Powers, W.O., Chm. Bd.--Powers Construction Co., Inc., Florence, SC; *U.S. Private*, pg. 878
Poynter, Lou Ann, Chm. Bd. & Chief Exec. Officer--UPB of Southern Mississippi, Hattiesburg, MS; *U.S. Public*, pg. 1669
Pozzi, Arthur A., Chm. Bd.--Arthur A. Pozzi Co., Inc., Portland, OR; *U.S. Private*, pg. 878
Prante, Gerhard, Dr., Chm. Bd. & Chief Exec. Officer--AgrEvo GmbH, Berlin, Germany; *Int'l*, pg. 624
Prasad, A.S., Chm. Bd. & Mng. Dir.--Mahanadi Coalfields Limited, Sambalpur, India; *Int'l*, pg. 298
Prate, Alain, Chm.-Supervisory Bd.--CNP Assurances, Paris, France; *Int'l*, pg. 241
Prather, Robert S., Jr., Chm. Bd.--Datasouth Computer Corporation, Charlotte, NC; *U.S. Public*, pg. 267
Pratt, Brian, Chm. Bd., Pres. & Chief Exec. Officer--ARB Inc., Lake Forest, CA; *U.S. Private*, pg. 7
Pratt, Jack E., Chm. Bd. & Chief Exec. Officer--Hollywood Casino Corp, Atlantic City, NJ; *U.S. Public*, pg. 830
Pratt, Richard, Chm. Bd.--Pratt Industries, Melbourne, Australia; *Int'l*, pg. 1066
Pratt, Robert N., Chm. Bd., Pres. & Chief Oper. & Chief Exec. Officer--Alta Gold Co., Henderson, NV; *U.S. Public*, pg. 58
Prautzch, Wolf-Albrecht, Chm.-Supervisory Bd.--Triumph Adler Group, Nuremberg, Germany; *Int'l*, pg. 1424
Preis, Herwig, Co-Owner & Chm.--Select Communications, L.P., New York, NY; *U.S. Private*, pg. 982
Prendergast, G. Joseph, Chm. Bd.--Wachovia Bank of South Carolina, N.A., Columbia, SC; *U.S. Public*, pg. 1730
Prendergast, G. Joseph, Chm. Bd.--Wachovia Bank of South Carolina, Columbia, SC; *U.S. Public*, pg. 1730
Pres., LeRoy J., Chm. Bd.--Madison Paper Industries, Madison, ME; *U.S. Public*, pg. 1174
Present, Randy, Chm. Bd. & Pres.--CH Mortgage Company, Scottsdale, AZ; *U.S. Public*, pg. 441
Pressman, Fred, Chm.-Exec. Committee--Barneys Inc., New York, NY; *U.S. Private*, pg. 116
Pressman, Gene, Co-Chm. Bd. & Co-Chief Exec. Officer--Barneys Inc., New York, NY; *U.S. Private*, pg. 116
Pressman, James R., Chm. Bd., Pres. & Chief Oper. Officer--Pressman Toy Corp., New York, NY; *U.S. Private*, pg. 882
Pressman, Lynn, Chm. Bd.-Emeritus--Pressman Toy Corp., New York, NY; *U.S. Private*, pg. 882
Pressman, Robert, Co-Chm. Bd. & Co-Chief Exec. Officer--Barneys Inc., New York, NY; *U.S. Private*, pg. 116
Pressouyre, Gerard, Chm. Bd.--Seb S.A., Selongey, France; *Int'l*, pg. 569
Prest, Nicholas M., Chm. Bd.--Alvis plc, London, United Kingdom; *Int'l*, pg. 69
Preston, James E., Chm. Bd. & Chief Exec. Officer--Avon Products, Inc., New York, NY; *U.S. Public*, pg. 155
Preston, John M., Ph.D., Chm. Bd.--Merial Ltd., Iselin, NJ; *U.S. Public*, pg. 1092
Preston, John M., Ph.D., Chm. Bd. & Pres.--Merial Ltd., London, United Kingdom; *U.S. Public*, pg. 1092
Preston, John M., Ph.D., Chm. Bd.--Merial Ltd., Iselin, NJ; *Int'l*, pg. 1109
Preston, John M., Ph.D., Chm. Bd. & Pres.--Merial Ltd., London, United Kingdom; *Int'l*, pg. 1110
Preuss, Peter, Chm. Bd.--Network Computing Devices, Inc., Mountain View, CA; *U.S. Public*, pg. 1168
Proviti, James, Chm. Bd, Pres. & Chief Exec. Officer--Forecast Group, Rancho Cucamonga, CA; *U.S. Private*, pg. 418
Price, Charles R., Jr., Chm.--Price/McNabb, Inc., Charlotte, NC; *U.S. Private*, pg. 883
Price, David G., Chm. Bd.--American Golf Corporation, Santa Monica, CA; *U.S. Private*, pg. 55
Price, Michael A., Chm. Bd. & Chief Exec. Officer--T&W Financial Corporation, Tacoma, WA; *U.S. Public*, pg. 1552
Price, Robert, Chm. Bd. & Pres.--Price Communications Corporation, New York, NY; *U.S. Public*, pg. 1324
Price, Robert, Chm. Bd.--Pricellular Corporation, White Plains, NY; *U.S. Public*, pg. 1324
Price, Robert E., Chm. Bd.--Price Enterprises, Inc., San Diego, CA; *U.S. Public*, pg. 1324
Price, Robert E., Chm. Bd., Pres. & Chief Exec. Officer--PriceSmart Inc., San Diego, CA; *U.S. Public*, pg. 1324
Price, Steve, Co-Chm. & Chief Exec. Officer--Publicis/Bloom, Dallas, TX; *Int'l*, pg. 469
Price, Timothy R., Chm. Bd.--Trilon Financial Corp., Toronto, Canada; *Int'l*, pg. 434
Price, William C., Chm. & Chief Exec. Officer--Media That Works, Cincinnati, OH; *U.S. Private*, pg. 727
Priem, Ted, Chm., Pres. & Chief Exec. Officer--Nobles Mfg. Inc., Saint Croix Falls, WI; *U.S. Private*, pg. 800
Priesing, J.W., Chm. Bd.--Russell-Stanley Corporation, Red Bank, NJ; *U.S. Private*, pg. 953
Priester, Wolfgang, Chm. Bd.--Michael Business Machines Corporation, Charleston, SC; *U.S. Private*, pg. 740
Prillaman, Albert L., Chm. Bd., Pres. & Chief Exec. Officer--Stanley Furniture Co. Inc., Stanleytown, VA; *U.S. Public*, pg. 1508
Prince Khaled, H.H., Chm. Bd.--Bondstrand, Ltd., Dammam, Saudi Arabia; *U.S. Public*, pg. 99
Prince, Larry L., Chm. Bd. & Chief Exec. Officer--Genuine Parts Company, Atlanta, GA; *U.S. Public*, pg. 732
Prince, Robert, Chm. Bd. & Pres.--Printing House, Inc., Quincy, FL; *U.S. Private*, pg. 886
Prince, Steven, Chm. Bd. & Chief Exec. Officer--Sempra Energy Trading, Greenwich, CT; *U.S. Public*, pg. 1249
Pringuet, Pierre, Chm. & Chief Exec. Officer--PR Europe, Paris, France; *Int'l*, pg. 566
Prior, James M.L., Rt. Hon. Lord, Chm. Bd.--The General Electric Company, p.l.c., London, United Kingdom; *Int'l*, pg. 543
Prior, Paul W., Chm. Bd.--Ameriana Bancorp, New Castle, IN; *U.S. Public*, pg. 66
Priory, Richard B., Chm. Bd. & Chief Exec. Officer--Duke Energy Corporation, Charlotte, NC; *U.S. Public*, pg. 534
Priory, Richard B., Chm. Bd. & Chief Exec. Officer--Duke Energy International, L.L.C., Houston, TX; *U.S. Public*, pg. 534
Prischak, Joseph J., Chm. Bd. & Pres.--Plastek Group, Erie, PA; *U.S. Private*, pg. 870
Pritt, Frank W., Chm. Bd.--Attachmate, Bellevue, WA; *U.S. Private*, pg. 98
Pritzker, Jay, Chm. Bd.--Hyatt Corporation, Chicago, IL; *U.S. Private*, pg. 551
Pritzker, Jay A., Chm. Bd.--The Marmon Group, Inc., Chicago, IL; *U.S. Private*, pg. 706
Pritzker, Thomas J., Chm. Bd.--First Health Group Corp., Downers Grove, IL; *U.S. Public*, pg. 635
Probst, Lawrence F., III, Chm. Bd. & Chief Exec. Officer--Electronic Arts, San Mateo, CA; *U.S. Public*, pg. 569
Probst, Worth T., Chm. Bd.--Colorbus Inc., Irvine, CA; *U.S. Private*, pg. 255
Probyn, Ed, Chm. Bd.--E.R. Probyn Ltd., New Westminster, Canada; *Int'l*, pg. 1071
Prockow, Eric, Chm. Bd. & Chief Exec. Officer--Sun Data Inc., Norcross, GA; *U.S. Private*, pg. 1050
Proctor, Thomas E., Chm. Bd. & Pres.--American Technical Publishers, Inc., Homewood, IL; *U.S. Private*, pg. 63
Proctor, Truby G., Jr., Chm. Bd.--Lee-Moore Oil Co., Inc., Sanford, NC; *U.S. Private*, pg. 657
Prosser, Ian M.G., Chm. Bd.--Bass PLC, London, United Kingdom; *Int'l*, pg. 169
Prothro, C.V., Chm. Bd., Pres. & Chief Exec. Officer--Dallas Semiconductor Corporation, Dallas, TX; *U.S. Public*, pg. 478
Protze, Gerhard, Chm. Bd., Chief Exec. Officer, Chief Fin. Officer & Mng. Dir.--Traub AG, Reichenbach, Germany; *Int'l*, pg. 1419
Protzman, Jim, Chm. Bd.--FGI Inc., Chapel Hill, NC; *U.S. Private*, pg. 389
Pruim, E.G., Chm. Bd., Pres. & Chief Exec. Officer--Wrought Washer Mfg., Inc., Milwaukee, WI; *U.S. Private*, pg. 1192
Psarouthakis, John, Chm. Bd., Pres. & Chief Exec. Officer--JPE, Inc., Ann Arbor, MI; *U.S. Public*, pg. 919
Psomas, George, Chm. Bd.--Psomas & Associates, Santa Monica, CA; *U.S. Private*, pg. 893
Puckett, Linton B., Chm. Bd.--Willis Corroon Corp. of South Carolina, Greenville, SC; *Int'l*, pg. 1507
Pugh, Graham, Chm. & Mng. Dir.--Datel Technologies Ltd., Preston, United Kingdom; *Int'l*, pg. 384
Pugh, Lawrence R., Chm. Bd.--VF Corporation, Wyomissing, PA; *U.S. Public*, pg. 1702
Puig, Antonio, Chm. Bd.--Antonio Puig SA, Barcelona, Spain; *Int'l*, pg. 1073
Pulitzer, Michael E., Chm. Bd., Pres. & Chief Exec. Officer--Pulitzer Publishing Company, Saint Louis, MO; *U.S. Public*, pg. 1343
Pulliam, Robert F., Chm. Bd. & Pres.--Pulliam Motor Company, Columbia, SC; *U.S. Private*, pg. 894
Pulte, William J., Chm. Bd.--Pulte Corporation, Bloomfield Hills, MI; *U.S. Public*, pg. 1344
Pumpelly, Robert J., Chm. Bd.--Pumpelly Oil, Inc., Westlake, LA; *U.S. Private*, pg. 895
Punches, Dennis G., Chm. Bd.--Payco American Corporation, Brookfield, WI; *U.S. Public*, pg. 1267
Punoose, Salil, Chm. Bd. & Mng. Dir.--Corn Products Co. (India) Ltd., Mumbai, India; *U.S. Public*, pg. 224
Puntillo, Richard D., Chm. Bd.--Harding Lawson Associates Group, Inc., Novato, CA; *U.S. Public*, pg. 785
Puorro, Gerard E., Chm. Bd., Pres. & Chief Exec. Officer--Candela Corporation, Wayland, MA; *U.S. Public*, pg. 300
Purcell, Philip J., Chm. Bd. & Chief Exec. Officer--Morgan Stanley Dean Witter & Co., New York, NY; *U.S. Public*, pg. 1132
Purcell, Philip J., Chm. Bd. & Chief Exec. Officer--Dean Witter, Discover & Co., New York, NY; *U.S. Public*, pg. 1132
Purdam, Robert L., Chm. Bd.--Bucyrus International, South Milwaukee, WI; *U.S. Private*, pg. 177
Purdy, Winifred M., Chm. Bd. & Chief Exec. Officer--The Purdy Corporation, Manchester, CT; *U.S. Private*, pg. 895
Puris, Martin, Chm., Chief Exec. Officer & Chief Creative Officer--Ammirati Puris Lintas Worldwide, New York, NY; *U.S. Public*, pg. 908
Purmort, F. W., III, Chm. Bd. & Pres.--Central Mutual Insurance Co., Van Wert, OH; *U.S. Private*, pg. 223
Purnell, John H., Chm. Bd.--Anheuser-Busch Europe, Inc., London, United Kingdom; *U.S. Public*, pg. 115
Purves, William, Sir, Chm. Bd.--HSBC Holdings plc, London, United Kingdom; *Int'l*, pg. 579
Purvis, G. Frank, Jr., Chm. Bd.--Pan-American Life Insurance Company, New Orleans, LA; *U.S. Private*, pg. 836
Purvis, Kathryn M., Chm. Bd.--A.C. Legg Packing Company, Inc., Birmingham, AL; *U.S. Private*, pg. 658
Puschel, Philip P., Chm. Bd. & Chief Exec. Officer--F. Schumacher & Co., New York, NY; *U.S. Private*, pg. 973
Puskar, Milan, Chm. Bd., Pres. & Chief Exec. Officer--Mylan Laboratories, Inc., Pittsburgh, PA; *U.S. Public*, pg. 1143
Putnam, Frederic L., Jr., Chm. Bd. & Sr. Exec. Officer--Colonial Gas Company, Lowell, MA; *U.S. Public*, pg. 400
Putnam, Thomas, Chm. Bd.--Markem Corporation, Keene, NH; *U.S. Private*, pg. 704
Pyatt, Alan, Chm. Bd., Pres. & Chief Exec. Officer--Sandwell Inc., Vancouver, Canada; *Int'l*, pg. 1188
Pye, Ian, Chm. Bd.--Meridian Technology Leasing Services, Deerfield, IL; *U.S. Private*, pg. 732
Pyle, Byron, Chm. Bd.--Valley National Bank of Cortez, Cortez, CO; *U.S. Public*, pg. 1793
Quadracci, H.R., Chm. Bd.--Quad/Graphics, Inc., Pewaukee, WI; *U.S. Private*, pg. 897
Quarles, John M., Chm. Bd., Pres. & Chief Exec. Officer--Wolverine Tube Inc., Huntsville, AL; *U.S. Public*, pg. 1774
Quasha, Alan G., Chm. Bd. & Chief Exec. Officer--Hanover Direct, Inc., Weehawken, NJ; *U.S. Public*, pg. 782
Quattrocchi, Louis, Chm. Bd.--Philadelphia Reserve Supply Company, Croydon, PA; *U.S. Private*, pg. 861
Quick, Leslie C., Jr., Chm. Bd. & Chief Exec. Officer--The Quick & Reilly Group Inc., Palm Beach, FL; *U.S. Public*, pg. 650
Quier, Myrtle B., Chm. Bd.--Reading Eagle Company, Reading, PA; *U.S. Private*, pg. 913
Quigley, George, Sir, Chm. Bd.--Ulster Bank Limited, Belfast, United Kingdom; *Int'l*, pg. 911
Quinn, Lochlann, Chm. Bd.--Allied Irish Banks, p.l.c., Dublin, Ireland; *Int'l*, pg. 64
Quinn, Thomas H., Chm. Bd.--Welcome Home, Inc., Wilmington, NC; *U.S. Private*, pg. 598
Quinn, Tom, Chm. Bd.--American Safety Razor Company, Verona, VA; *U.S. Private*, pg. 597
Quinnies, Barry C., Chm. Bd.--Independent Metals, Germantown, WI; *U.S. Private*, pg. 559
Quintanilla, Javier Madanes, Chm. Bd.--Fate S.A., San Fernando, Argentina; *Int'l*, pg. 478
Quinto, Harold, Chm. Bd.--California Cedar Products, Inc., Stockton, CA; *U.S. Private*, pg. 200
Qureshey, Safi U., Chm. Bd. & Chief Exec. Officer--AST Research Inc., Irvine, CA; *Int'l*, pg. 1181
Raab, Max L., Chm. Bd. & Chief Exec. Officer--J.G. Hook, Inc., New York, NY; *U.S. Private*, pg. 538
Raab, Simon, Ph.D., Chm. Bd., Pres. & Chief Exec. Officer--FARO Technologies, Inc., Lake Mary, FL; *U.S. Public*, pg. 613
Raasch, Kenneth E., Chm. Bd., Pres. & Chief Exec. Officer--Media Arts Group, Inc., San Jose, CA; *U.S. Public*, pg. 1077
Rabin, Stanley A., Chm. Bd., Pres. & Chief Exec. Officer--Commercial Metals Company, Dallas, TX; *U.S. Public*, pg. 411
Rabinowitz, Leonard, Co-Chm.--California Fashion Industries Inc., Los Angeles, CA; *U.S. Private*, pg. 200
Rabinowitz, Martin J., Chm. Bd., Pres. & Chief Exec. Officer--Thackeray Corporation, New York, NY; *U.S. Public*, pg. 1590
Rabiu, Alhaji I., Chm.--Stanbic Merchant Bank Nigeria Limited, Lagos, Nigeria; *Int'l*, pg. 1294
Rabold, Robert E.H., Chm. Bd., Pres. & Chief Exec. Officer--Motorists Mutual Insurance Co., Columbus, OH; *U.S. Private*, pg. 764
Rabold, Robert E.H., Chm. Bd., Pres. & Chief Exec. Officer--American Hardware Mutual Insurance Co., Columbus, OH; *U.S. Private*, pg. 764
Raburn, Don, Chm. Bd.--Sanden International (U.S.A.), Inc., Wylie, TX; *Int'l*, pg. 1184
Raburn, Vern L., Chm. Bd.--Asymetrix Learning Systems, Inc., Bellevue, WA; *U.S. Private*, pg. 93
Race, David H., Chm. Bd.--CAE Inc., Toronto, Canada; *Int'l*, pg. 237
Rackley, Clifford W., Chm. Bd.--Texas Eastern Products Pipeline Company, L.P., Houston, TX; *U.S. Public*, pg. 535
Raclin, Ernestine M., Chm. Bd.--1st Source Corporation, South Bend, IN; *U.S. Public*, pg. 638
Radford, Lewis C., Jr., Chm. Bd.--National Bank of Walton County, Monroe, GA; *U.S. Public*, pg. 1549
Radler, Louis, Chm. Bd. & Chief Exec. Officer--Chessco Industries, Inc., Westport, CT; *U.S. Private*, pg. 234
Radlinski, David, Chm. Bd. & Chief Exec. Officer--Medstone International, Inc., Aliso Viejo, CA; *U.S. Public*, pg. 1082
Rados, Angie, Chm. Bd.--The Rados Companies, Santa Ana, CA, *U.S. Private*, pg. 907
Radt, Richard L., Vice Chm.--Wausau-Mosinee Paper Corporation, Mosinee, WI; *U.S. Public*, pg. 1747
Radwill, A.R., Chm. Bd.--Master Appliance Corp., Racine, WI; *U.S. Private*, pg. 713
Rady, Ernest S., Chm. Bd., Pres. & Chief Exec. Officer--Westcorp, Irvine, CA; *U.S. Public*, pg. 1756
Rady, Ernest S., Chm. Bd.--Western Financial Bank, Irvine, CA; *U.S. Public*, pg. 1757
Raff, Eytan, Chm. Bd.--Bank Leumi le-Israel B.M., Tel Aviv, Israel; *Int'l*, pg. 150
Raffee, Hans, Chm.--WOB MarketingKommunikation AG, Viernheim, Germany; *Int'l*, pg. 1482
Rafferty, M., Chm.--Ulster Investment Bank Limited, Dublin, Ireland; *Int'l*, pg. 912
Ragsdale, Richard E., Chm. Bd.--Community Health Systems, Inc., Brentwood, TN; *U.S. Private*, pg. 419
Raidl, Claus J., Chm. Bd.--Voest-Alpine International Corporation, New York, NY; *Int'l*, pg. 1470
Raidl, Klaus, Dr., Chm.--Bohler Uddeholm AG, Vienna, Austria; *Int'l*, pg. 1471
Rainer, J., Chm. Bd.--B & R Industrial Automation, Roswell, GA; *U.S. Private*, pg. 105

Rainey, James A., Chm.--Nationsbank/Tennessee, Nashville, TN; *U.S. Public*, pg. 1163

Rainoldi, Joseph C., Chm. Bd.--Rainoldi, Kerzner & Radcliffe, San Francisco, CA; *U.S. Public*, pg. 1224

Raisanen, Walfred R., Chm. Bd.--Arizona Instrument Corporation, Phoenix, AZ; *U.S. Public*, pg. 129

Raker, Gilbert, Chm. Bd.--American Silicon Products, Inc., Providence, RI; *U.S. Public*, pg. 1456

Raker, Gilbert, Chm. Bd.--Retconn, Torrington, CT; *U.S. Public*, pg. 1456

Raker, Gilbert D., Chm. Bd.--Semiconductor Packaging Materials Co., Inc., Armonk, NY; *U.S. Public*, pg. 1456

Rakolta, John, Jr., Chm. Bd. & Chief Exec. Officer--Walbridge Aldinger Company, Detroit, MI; *U.S. Private*, pg. 1146

Rales, Steven M., Chm. Bd.--Danaher Corporation, Washington, DC; *U.S. Public*, pg. 480

Ralph, John, Chm. Bd.--Pacific Dunlop Limited, Melbourne, Australia; *Int'l*, pg. 1021

Ralph, John T., Chm. Bd.--Carlton & United Breweries Ltd., Southbank, Australia; *Int'l*, pg. 500

Ralston, Ken, Chm. Bd.--CM Partners, Inc., Rolling Meadows, IL; *U.S. Private*, pg. 195

Ramat, Charles, Chm. Bd., Pres., Chief Exec. Officer & Asst. Sec.--Aris Industries, Inc., New York, NY; *U.S. Public*, pg. 129

Ramenason, Gaston, Chm.--BMOI, Antananarivo, Madagascar; *Int'l*, pg. 163

Ramos, Gary, Chm. Bd., Pres. & Chief Exec. Officer--Advanced Manufacturing & Development, Willits, CA; *U.S. Private*, pg. 22

Rampone, C. Frank, Chm. Bd.--Hart Engineering Corporation, Greenville, RI; *U.S. Private*, pg. 507

Ramsay, Paul J., Chm. Bd.--Ramsay Health Care, Inc., Coral Gables, FL; *U.S. Public*, pg. 1360

Ramsey, J.C., Chm. Bd. & Chief Exec. Officer--Royle Systems Group, Pompton Lakes, NJ; *U.S. Private*, pg. 949

Ramsey, J.S., Jr., Chm. Bd.--Diamond Hill Plywood Company, Darlington, SC; *U.S. Private*, pg. 311

Ramsey, Roger A., Chm. Bd. & Chief Exec. Officer--Allied Waste Industries, Scottsdale, AZ; *U.S. Public*, pg. 49

Randall, Elizabeth, Chm. Bd.--MBL Life Assurance Corporation, Newark, NJ; *U.S. Private*, pg. 685

Randall, Ronald F., Chm. Bd., Pres. & Chief Exec. Officer--Randall Stores, Inc., Mitchell, SD; *U.S. Private*, pg. 909

Randholm, Gunnar, Chm. Bd.--Eldon AB, Nassjo, Sweden; *Int'l*, pg. 436

Randles, Jan P., Chm. Bd. & Chief Exec. Officer--Thomas Steel Strip Corp., Warren, OH; *Int'l*, pg. 756

Randolph, Jackson H., Chm. Bd.--Cinergy Corp., Cincinnati, OH; *U.S. Public*, pg. 368

Randolph, Jackson H., Chm. Bd. & Chief Exec. Officer--Cinergy, Plainfield, IN; *U.S. Public*, pg. 369

Randolph, Jackson H., Chm. Bd.--Cinergy Investments, Inc., Indianapolis, IN; *U.S. Public*, pg. 369

Randolph, Jackson H., Chm. Bd.--CINergy Services, Inc., Cincinnati, OH; *U.S. Public*, pg. 369

Randolph, Jackson H., Chm. Bd.--KO Transmission Company, Cincinnati, OH; *U.S. Public*, pg. 369

Randolph, Jackson H., Chm. Bd., Pres. & Chief Exec. Officer--Lawrenceburg Gas Co., Cincinnati, OH; *U.S. Public*, pg. 369

Randolph, Jackson H., Chm. Bd.--Cinergy Corp., Cincinnati, OH; *U.S. Public*, pg. 369

Randolph, William, Chm. Bd.--The PBS&J Corporation, Miami, FL; *U.S. Private*, pg. 825

Rankin, Alfred M. Jr., Chm. Bd., Pres. & Chief Exec. Officer--NACCO Industries, Inc., Cleveland, OH; *U.S. Public*, pg. 1149

Ransburg, David P., Chm. Bd. & Chief Exec. Officer--L.R. Nelson Corporation, Peoria, IL; *U.S. Private*, pg. 790

Ransome, Ernest L., III, Chm. Bd.--Giles & Ransome, Inc., Bensalem, PA; *U.S. Private*, pg. 453

Rao, Duane, Chm. Bd. & Chief Exec. Officer--The Rao Group Inc., Sterling Heights, MI; *U.S. Private*, pg. 910

Rapoport, Bernard, Chm. Bd. & Chief Exec. Officer--American Income Holding, Inc., Wilmington, DE; *U.S. Public*, pg. 1622

Rapoport, Bernard, Chm. Bd. & Chief Exec. Officer--American Income Life Insurance Company, Waco, TX; *U.S. Public*, pg. 1622

Rappaport, Allan, Dr., Chm. Bd.--NES Holdings, Inc., Raleigh, NC; *U.S. Private*, pg. 771

Rappaport, Gary B., Chm. Bd. & Chief Exec. Officer--Venturian Corp., Hopkins, MN; *U.S. Public*, pg. 1716

Rappeport, Don, Chm. Bd. & Chief Exec. Officer--Donlen Corp., Northbrook, IL; *U.S. Private*, pg. 340

Rasborg, Steen, Chm. Bd.--Radiometer A/S, Bronshoj, Denmark; *Int'l*, pg. 1083

Raschig, Fr., Dr., Chm. Bd.--Raschig Corp., Richmond, VA; *U.S. Private*, pg. 827

Rasdal, Dan, Chm. Bd. & Chief Exec. Officer--Linfinity Microelectronics Inc., Garden Grove, CA; *U.S. Public*, pg. 1547

Rasdal, William D., Chm. Bd. & Chief Exec. Officer--SymmetriCom, Inc., San Jose, CA; *U.S. Public*, pg. 1547

Rasdal, William D., Chm. Bd. & Chief Exec. Officer-SymmetriCom--Telecom Solutions, San Jose, CA; *U.S. Public*, pg. 1547

Rash, James T., Chm. Bd., Chief Exec. Officer & Chief Fin. Officer--Tidel Technologies, Inc., Houston, TX; *U.S. Public*, pg. 1608

Rasmussen, Erik B., Chm. Bd.--GN Great Nordic Ltd., Copenhagen, Denmark; *Int'l*, pg. 536

Raspino, Louis A., Jr., Chm. Bd.--LL&E Yemen, Ltd., Hamilton, Bermuda; *U.S. Public*, pg. 269

Ratcliffe, G.J., Jr., Chm. Bd., Pres. & Chief Exec. Officer--Hubbell Incorporated, Orange, CT; *U.S. Public*, pg. 844

Rath, F.E., Jr., Chm. Bd., Pres. & Chief Exec. Officer--Today's Kids, Booneville, AR; *U.S. Private*, pg. 1020

Rath, Frank E., Jr., Chm. Bd. & Pres.--Spang & Company, Butler, PA; *U.S. Private*, pg. 1020

Ratican, Peter J., Chm. Bd., Pres. & Chief Exec. Officer--Maxicare Health Plans, Inc., Los Angeles, CA; *U.S. Public*, pg. 1061

Ratliff, Robert J., Chm. Bd., Pres. & Chief Exec. Officer--AGCO Corporation, Duluth, GA; *U.S. Public*, pg. 28

Ratner, Albert B., Co-Chm. Bd.--Forest City Enterprises, Inc., Cleveland, OH; *U.S. Public*, pg. 667

Ratner, Charles, Chm. Bd.--Richter & Ratner Contracting Corporation, Maspeth, NY; *U.S. Private*, pg. 930

Ratner, Phillip, Chm. Bd., Pres. & Chief Exec. Officer--Spaghetti Warehouse, Inc., Garland, TX; *U.S. Public*, pg. 1495

Ratosi, E., Chm.--Dunastyr Polystyr. Manufacturing Co. Ltd., Budapest, Hungary; *Int'l*, pg. 429

Rau Reist, Susanne, Chm. Bd.--Ferag Inc., Bristol, PA; *Int'l, pg. 1484*

Rau, Howard C., Chm. Bd.--Edwin B. Stimpson Company, Inc., Bayport, NY; *U.S. Private*, pg. 1043

Rauch, C. Dixon, III, Chm. Bd. & Chief Exec. Officer--Rundel Products, Inc., Portland, OR; *U.S. Private*, pg. 951

Rauch, Dudley A., Chm. Bd.--InnoServ Technologies, Inc., Arlington, TX; *U.S. Public*, pg. 879

Rauch, Marshall A., Chm. Bd.--Rauch Industries, Inc., Gastonia, NC; *U.S. Private*, pg. 1061

Raudi, Salvatore, Chm.--Telsi Ltd., London, United Kingdom; *Int'l*, pg. 1248

Rauwenhoff, F.C., Chm. Bd.-Supervisory Bd.--KNP BT Nederland B.V., Amsterdam, Netherlands; *Int'l*, pg. 756

Ravich, Mark H., Chm. Bd.--Universal International, Inc., New Hope, MN; *U.S. Public*, pg. 1697

Ravich, Mark H., Chm. Bd.--Only Deals, Inc., New Hope, MN; *U.S. Public*, pg. 1697

Ravin, Richard M., Chm. Bd., Pres. & Chief Exec. Officer--Combined Insurance Company of America, Chicago, IL; *U.S. Public*, pg. 118

Ravizza, Eugene A., Chm. Bd. & Pres.--Synergism, Inc., Sunnyvale, CA; *U.S. Private*, pg. 1060

Rawlins, Benjamin W., Jr., Chm. Bd. & Chief Exec. Officer--Union Planters Corporation, Cordova, TN; *U.S. Public*, pg. 1668

Rawls, Benjamin M., Chm. Bd., Pres. & Chief Exec. Officer--Versar Inc., Springfield, VA; *U.S. Public*, pg. 1717

Rawson, Michael J., Chm. Bd.--Kingsley Machine Co., Downers Grove, IL; *U.S. Public*, pg. 866

Rawson, Thomas C., Chm. Bd. & Chief Exec. Officer--Rawson-Koenig, Inc., Houston, TX; *U.S. Public*, pg. 1362

Ray, C. Eugene, Chm. Bd.--AMCOL International Corp., Arlington Heights, IL; *U.S. Public*, pg. 63

Ray, Merwin J., Chm. Bd. & Chief Exec. Officer--Steel Technologies Inc., Louisville, KY; *U.S. Public*, pg. 1513

Raymond, B. Panet, Chm. Bd.--Manicouagan Power Co., Baie Comeau, Canada; *U.S. Public*, pg. 1387

Raymond, Lee R., Chm. Bd. & Chief Exec. Officer--Exxon Corporation, Irving, TX; *U.S. Public*, pg. 601

Raymonds, John, Chm. Bd. & Chief Exec. Officer--Captive Plastics, Piscataway, NJ; *U.S. Private*, pg. 207

Raymund, Steven A., Chm. Bd. & Chief Exec. Officer--Tech Data Corporation, Clearwater, FL; *U.S. Public*, pg. 1562

Rayner, M.R., Chm. Bd.--National Australia Bank Limited, Melbourne, Australia; *Int'l*, pg. 906

Rayve, Robert G., Chm. Bd., Pres. & Chief Exec. Officer--The Spencer Turbine Co., Windsor, CT; *U.S. Private*, pg. 1025

Reading, Anthony, Chm. Bd.--Tomkins Corporation, Dayton, OH; *Int'l*, pg. 1397

Ready, Robert J., Chm. Bd., Pres. & Chief Exec. Officer--LSI Industries, Inc., Cincinnati, OH; *U.S. Public*, pg. 971

Reagan, Jeanne L., Chm. Bd.--Reagan Equipment Company, Inc., Gretna, LA; *U.S. Private*, pg. 913

Reagan, Mark, Chm. Bd. & Chief Exec. Officer--Willis Corroon Construction Division, Nashville, TN; *Int'l*, pg. 1504

Ream, John K., Chm. Bd. & Chief Exec. Officer--Citibank (Florida) N.A., Dania, FL; *U.S. Public*, pg. 377

Ream, Norman B., Jr., Chm. Bd.--Greenbrier Valley National Bank, Lewisburg, WV; *U.S. Public*, pg. 836

Reardon, O. Ashby, Jr., Chm. Bd.--Reico, Inc., Springfield, VA; *U.S. Private*, pg. 919

Recanati, Raphael, Chm. Bd. & Mng. Dir.--IDB Holding Corporation, Tel Aviv, Israel; *Int'l*, pg. 643

Rechler, Donald, Chm. Bd. & Chief Exec. Officer--Reckson Associates Realty Corp., Melville, NY; *U.S. Public*, pg. 1368

Recordati, Arrigo, Chm. Bd. & Chief Exec. Officer--Recordati Industria Chimica e Farmaceutica S.p.A., Milan, Italy; *Int'l*, pg. 1090

Reddy, N. Damodar, Chm. Bd., Pres. & Chief Exec. Officer--Alliance Semiconductor Corp., San Jose, CA; *U.S. Public*, pg. 47

Reddy, Raj, Chm. Bd.--Telxon Corporation, Akron, OH; *U.S. Public*, pg. 1573

Redfern, J.D., Chm. Bd.--Lafarge Canada Inc., Montreal, Canada; *Int'l*, pg. 789

Redheuil, Alain, Chm. Bd. & Chief Exec. Officer--Rexel, S.A., Paris, France; *Int'l*, pg. 1107

Redies, Robert D., Chm. Bd. & Chief Exec. Officer--R & B Machine Tool Co., Saline, MI; *U.S. Private*, pg. 901

Redmond, Paul A., Chm. Bd.--Itron Inc., Spokane, WA; *U.S. Public*, pg. 914

Redmond, Paul A., Chm. Bd. & Chief Exec. Officer--The Washington Water Power Company, Spokane, WA; *U.S. Public*, pg. 1744

Redmond, William, Pres. & Chief Exec. Officer--Garden Way, Inc., Troy, NY; *U.S. Private*, pg. 440

Redner, Robert P., Chm. Bd.--General Filters, Inc., Novi, MI; *U.S. Private*, pg. 444

Redshaw, P.D., Chm. Bd.--Xerox South Africa, Isando, South Africa; *U.S. Public*, pg. 1785

Redstone, Sumner M., Chm. Bd.--National Amusements, Inc., Dedham, MA; *U.S. Private*, pg. 775

Redstone, Sumner M., Chm. Bd.-Viacom, Inc.--Paramount Pictures Corporation, Los Angeles, CA; *U.S. Private*, pg. 776

Reed, E.C., Chm. Bd., Pres. & Sec.--Utica Boilers Inc., Utica, NY; *U.S. Private*, pg. 1129

Reed, Earl, Chm. Bd. & Pres.--Reed Grain & Bean Company, Buhl, ID; *U.S. Private*, pg. 916

Reed, Frank E., Chm. Bd.--360 Degrees Communications Company, Chicago, IL; *U.S. Public*, pg. 1607

Reed, G.B., Chm. Bd.--John Menzies plc, Edinburgh, United Kingdom; *Int'l*, pg. 707

Reed, John E., Chm. Bd., Pres. & Chief Exec. Officer--Mestek, Inc., Westfield, MA; *U.S. Public*, pg. 1099

Reed, John S., Chm. Bd. & Chief Exec. Officer--Citicorp, New York, NY; *U.S. Public*, pg. 376

Reed, John S., Chm. Bd.--Citibank N.A., Long Island City, NY; *U.S. Public*, pg. 377

Reed, Larry E., Chm. Bd. & Chief Exec. Officer--Horizon Bancorp, Michigan City, IN; *U.S. Private*, pg. 538

Reed, Richard C., Chm. Bd. & Pres.--Kova Fertilizer Inc., Greensburg, IN; *U.S. Private*, pg. 634

Reed, S.L., Jr., Chm. Bd. & Chief Exec. Officer--Ethika Corporation, Hilton Head Island, SC; *U.S. Public*, pg. 595

Reed, Stuart, Chm.-De Vere Hotels--The Greenalls Group PLC, Warrington, United Kingdom; *Int'l*, pg. 558

Reed, Wendy, Chm. Bd. & Chief Exec. Officer--Radix Corporation, Salt Lake City, UT; *U.S. Private*, pg. 906

Reed, William R., Jr., Chm. Bd., Pres. & Chief Exec. Officer--NBC Bank, FSB (Belzoni), Belzoni, MS; *U.S. Public*, pg. 1155

Reese, John R., Chm. Bd.--Owosso Corporation, King of Prussia, PA; *U.S. Public*, pg. 1238

Reese, R. Allan, Ph.D., Chm. Bd. & Pres.--Ace Tank & Equipment Co., Seattle, WA; *U.S. Private*, pg. 12

Reese, Terry, Chm. Bd.--Overly Manufacturing Co., Greensburg, PA; *U.S. Private*, pg. 823

Reese, Thomas W., Chm. Bd.--Hickory Printing Group, Inc., Conover, NC; *U.S. Private*, pg. 525

Reeve, John, Chm. Bd. & Chief Exec. Officer--Willis Corroon Group PLC, London, United Kingdom; *Int'l*, pg. 1501

Reeves, Frances S., Chm. Bd.--Skinner Corp., Lanett, AL; *U.S. Private*, pg. 1005

Reeves, Joseph A., Jr., Chm. Bd. & Chief Exec. Officer--The Meridian Resource Corporation, Houston, TX; *U.S. Public*, pg. 1095

Regal, Melvyn, Chm. Bd.--Foster & Gallagher, Inc., Peoria, IL; *U.S. Private*, pg. 420

Regelbrugge, Roger R., Chm. Bd.--GS Industries, Inc., Charlotte, NC; *U.S. Private*, pg. 435

Rego, Anthony C., Chm. Bd. & Chief Exec. Officer--Riser Foods, Inc., Bedford, OH; *U.S. Private*, pg. 450

Reherman, R.G., Chm. Bd. & Chief Exec. Officer--Energy Systems Group, Inc., Evansville, IN; *U.S. Public*, pg. 1471

Reherman, R.G., Chm. Bd., Pres. & Chief Exec. Officer--ComSource, Inc., Evansville, IN; *U.S. Public*, pg. 1471

Reherman, Ronald G., Chm. Bd., Pres. & Chief Exec. Officer--SIGCORP, Inc., Evansville, IN; *U.S. Public*, pg. 1471

Reherman, Ronald G., Chm. Bd., Pres. & Chief Exec. Officer--Southern Indiana Gas & Electric Co., Evansville, IN; *U.S. Public*, pg. 1471

Rehm, Jack, Chm. Bd.--Country Home Magazine, Des Moines, IA; *U.S. Public*, pg. 1094

Reich, Joseph H., Chm. Bd.--PCA International, Inc., Matthews, NC; *U.S. Public*, pg. 1240

Reichlin, Robert J., Chm. Bd.--Zuckerman-Honickman Inc., King of Prussia, PA; *U.S. Private*, pg. 1207

Reickert, Erick A., Chm. Bd.--Acustar, Inc., Troy, MI; *U.S. Public*, pg. 353

Reid, Alan J., Chm. Bd. & Chief Exec. Officer--Man-Gill Chemical Company, Cleveland, OH; *U.S. Private*, pg. 699

Reid, Bob, Exec. V.P.-Mktg. & Sls.--Outdoor Technologies Group, Spirit Lake, IA; *U.S. Private*, pg. 822

Reid, Bob, Sir, Chm. Bd.--Sears plc, London, United Kingdom; *Int'l*, pg. 1217

Reid, James S., Jr., Chm. Bd.--The Standard Products Company, Dearborn, MI; *U.S. Public*, pg. 1504

Reid, Russ, Chm. Bd. & Chief Exec. Officer--Russ Reid Company, Inc., Pasadena, CA; *U.S. Private*, pg. 952

Reifenhauser, Hans, Chm. Bd.--Reifenhauser GmbH & Co. Maschinenfabrik, Troisdorf, Germany; *Int'l*, pg. 1101

Reifschneider, Darrel, Chm. Bd. & Chief Exec. Officer--Manchester Tank & Equipment Company, Brentwood, TN; *U.S. Private*, pg. 699

Reigle, James D., Chm. Bd.--Regal Ware, Inc., Kewaskum, WI; *U.S. Private*, pg. 917

Reilly, Charles P., Chm. Bd.--PHP Healthcare Corporation, Reston, VA; *U.S. Public*, pg. 1241

Reilly, Conor, Chm. Bd.--Acorn Products, Inc., Columbus, OH; *U.S. Public*, pg. 17

Reilly, Conor, Chm. Bd.--UnionTools, Inc., Columbus, OH; *U.S. Public*, pg. 17

Reilly, Edward T., Chm. Bd.--Columbine JDS Systems, Inc., Denver, CO; *U.S. Public*, pg. 228

Reilly, F. Ward, Jr., Chm. Bd.--Sherman & Reilly, Inc., Chattanooga, TN; *U.S. Private*, pg. 993

Reilly, John P., Chm. Bd.--Figgie International Inc., Cleveland, OH; *U.S. Public*, pg. 622

Reilly, Michael K., Chm. Bd.--Zeigler Coal Holding Company, Fairview Heights, IL; *U.S. Public*, pg. 1790

Reilly, Nick, Chm. Bd. & Mng. Dir.--Vauxhall, Luton, United Kingdom; *U.S. Public*, pg. 724

Reilly, Peter C., Chm. Exec.-Committee--Reilly Industries, Inc., Indianapolis, IN; *U.S. Private*, pg. 919

Reilly, Thomas E., Jr., Chm. Bd., Chief Exec. Officer & Chief Oper. Officer--Reilly Industries, Inc., Indianapolis, IN; *U.S. Private*, pg. 919

Reilly, Wayne R., Chm. Bd. & Chief Exec. Officer--John W. Danforth Co., Buffalo, NY; *U.S. Private*, pg. 309

Reilly, William F., Chm. Bd., Chief Exec. Officer & Chief Oper. Officer--Primedia Inc., New York, NY; *U.S. Public*, pg. 1327

Reily, Timothy, Chm. Bd. & Chief Exec. Officer--Reily Electrical Supply, Inc., Metairie, LA; *U.S. Private*, pg. 919

Reimer, C.M., Chm. & Chief Exec. Officer--Virginia Indonesia Company, Houston, TX; *Int'l*, pg. 804

Reinemund, Steven S., Chm. Bd. & Chief Exec. Officer--Frito-Lay Company, Plano, TX; *U.S. Public*, pg. 1277

Reinhard, Keith L., Chm. Bd. & Chief Exec. Officer--DDB Needham Worldwide Inc., New York, NY; *Int'l*, pg. 357

Reinhard, Keith L., Chm. Bd. & Chief Exec. Officer--DDB Needham Worldwide Inc., New York, NY; *U.S. Public*, pg. 1223

Reinhold, Walter B., Chm. Bd.--Varco International, Inc., Orange, CA; *U.S. Public*, pg. 1709

Reinig, L.P., Chm. Bd. & Chief Exec. Officer--Los Alamos Technical Associates, Inc., Los Alamos, NM; *U.S. Private*, pg. 676

Reinstetle, Harold, Chm. Bd.--Morgan Lumber Sales Co., Columbus, OH; *U.S. Private*, pg. 761

Reisman, S.S., Chm. Bd.--Ranger Oil Limited, Calgary, Canada; *Int'l*, pg. 1086

Reist, Walter, Chm. Bd. & Pres.--WRH Walter Reist Holding AG, Zurich, Switzerland; *Int'l*, pg. 1484

Reiter, William M., M.D., Chm. Bd., Pres. & Chief Exec. Officer--Health Professionals, Inc., Fort Lauderdale, FL; *U.S. Public*, pg. 802

Reitman, Jack, Chm. Bd.--Reitmans (Canada) Limited, Montreal, Canada; *Int'l*, pg. 1102

Reitman, Robert S., Chm. Bd., Pres. & Exec. Officer--The Tranzonic Companies, Pepper Pike, OH; *U.S. Public*, pg. 1632

Rella, William, Chm. Bd., Pres., Chief Exec. & Oper. Officer--LCS Industries, Inc., Clifton, NJ; *U.S. Public*, pg. 970

Rembutsu, Katsuhari, Chm. & Pres.--Daiwa Securities Trust Company, Jersey City, NJ; *Int'l*, pg. 375

Remington, Frederic, Jr., Chm. Bd. & Chief Exec. Officer--Peerless Tube Company, Bloomfield, NJ; *U.S. Public*, pg. 1269

Remmers, Merlin J., Chm. Bd.--Geo. H. Lehleitner & Co., Inc., Kenner, LA; *U.S. Private*, pg. 659

Renneckar, Stephen E., Chm. Bd--New Mexico & Arizona Land Co., Phoenix, AZ; *U.S. Public*, pg. 1172

Rennie, John C., Chm. Bd. & Chief Exec. Officer--Pacer Infotec Inc., Billerica, MA; *U.S. Private*, pg. 830

Renno, Joel Mendes, Chm. Bd. & Pres.--Petrobras - Petroleo Brasileiro S.A., Rio de Janeiro, Brazil; *Int'l*, pg. 1041

Reno, John F., Chm. Bd., Pres. & Chief Exec. Officer--Dynatech Corporation, Burlington, MA; *U.S. Public*, pg. 539

Reno, William J., Chm. Bd. & Chief Exec. Officer--F.B. Wright Co., Dearborn, MI; *U.S. Private*, pg. 1192

Rentenbach, T.J., Chm. Bd.--Rentenbach Engineering Company, Knoxville, TN; *U.S. Private*, pg. 923

Renwick, Robin, Sir, Chm. Bd.--Fluor Daniel Limited, Camberley, United Kingdom; *U.S. Public*, pg. 660

Reny, L. Guy, Chm. Bd. & Pres.--Standard Duplicating Machines Corp., Andover, MA; *U.S. Private*, pg. 1031

Repass, Randy, Chm. Bd.--West Marine, Inc., Watsonville, CA; *U.S. Public*, pg. 1756

Reschke, Michael W., Chm. Bd.--Prime Group Realty Trust, Chicago, IL; *U.S. Public*, pg. 1326

Resnick, Lynda R., Vice Chm.--The Franklin Mint, Franklin Center, PA; *U.S. Private*, pg. 941

Resnick, Stewart, Chm. Bd. & Pres.--Roll International Corporation, Los Angeles, CA; *U.S. Private*, pg. 941

Ressler, Barry, Chm. & Pres., Chief Exec. Officer--Universal Voltronics Corporation, Mount Kisco, NY; *U.S. Public*, pg. 1596

Rethore, Bernard, Chm. Bd. & Chief Exec. Officer--Flowserve Corporation, Dayton, OH; *U.S. Public*, pg. 658

Rethore, Bernard G., Chm. Bd. & Chief Exec. Officer--Flowserve Corporation, Long Beach, CA; *U.S. Public*, pg. 658

Reum, W. Robert, Chm. Bd., Pres. & Chief Exec. Officer--The Interlake Corporation, Lisle, IL; *U.S. Public*, pg. 892

Reuning, J., Chm. Bd. & Gen. Dir.--Otis GmbH, Berlin, Germany; *U.S. Public*, pg. 1690

Reuscher, Richard J., Chm. Bd.--Keystone Powdered Metal Company, Saint Marys, PA; *U.S. Private*, pg. 619

Reuter, Edzard, Chm. Bd.--Bankgesellschaft Berlin, Berlin, Germany; *Int'l*, pg. 159

Reuter, Edzard, Dr., Chm.--Berliner Bank AG, Berlin, Germany; *Int'l*, pg. 159

Reuter, William J., Chm. Bd., Pres. & Chief Exec. Officer--Farmers and Merchants Bank and Trust, Hagerstown, MD; *U.S. Public*, pg. 1542

Reutlinger, Paul, Chm. Bd.--Delta Air Transport N.V., Deurne, Belgium; *Int'l*, pg. 1168

Rex, William J., Chm. Bd., Pres. & Chief Exec. Officer--Rexhall Industries, Inc., Lancaster, CA; *U.S. Public*, pg. 1384

Reynolds, Clarke E., Chm. Bd.--Alpha Microsystems, Santa Ana, CA; *U.S. Public*, pg. 57

Reynolds, James F., Chm. Bd. & Chief Exec. Officer--Croll-Reynolds Company, Inc., Westfield, NJ; *U.S. Private*, pg. 290

Reynolds, James G., Chm. Bd. & Pres.--Portland Food Products Company, Forest Grove, OR; *U.S. Private*, pg. 876

Reynolds, Marshall, Chm. Bd. & Chief Exec. Officer--Broughton Foods Company, Marietta, OH; *U.S. Public*, pg. 259

Reynolds, Marshall T., Chm. Bd., Pres. & Chief Exec. Officer--Champion Industries, Huntington, WV; *U.S. Public*, pg. 333

Reynolds, Randolph N., Chm. Bd.--Aluminium Europe S.A., En Abrege: "Aleurope S.A.", Ghlin, Belgium; *U.S. Public*, pg. 1386

Reznick, Robert, Chm. Bd.--Check Technology Corporation, Minnetonka, MN; *U.S. Public*, pg. 342

Rhein, Paul, Dr., Chm. Bd.--Gebr. Eickhoff Maschinenfabrik und Eisengiesserei mbH, Bochum, Germany; *Int'l*, pg. 542

Rheinfrank, Lamson, Jr., Chm. Bd.--BHA Group Holdings Inc., Kansas City, MO; *U.S. Public*, pg. 161

Rhulen, Walter A., Chm. Bd. & Pres.--Frontier Insurance Group, Inc., Rock Hill, NY; *U.S. Public*, pg. 684

Ribakoff, Eugene, Chm. Bd.--AMI Leasing Corporation, Worcester, MA; *U.S. Private*, pg. 7

Ribe-Anderssen, Svein, Chm. Bd.--Orkla A.S.A., Oslo, Norway; *Int'l*, pg. 1010

Ribolla, Luigi, Chm. Bd.--PLADA S.p.A., Milan, Italy; *U.S. Public*, pg. 807

Riboud, Franck, Chm. Bd. & Chief Exec. Officer--Danone Group, Paris, France; *Int'l*, pg. 379

Ricard, John R., Bishop, Chm. Bd. & Pres.--Catholic Relief Services, Baltimore, MD; *U.S. Private*, pg. 220

Ricard, Patrick, Chm. Bd. & Chief Exec. Officer--Groupe Pernod Ricard, Paris, France; *Int'l*, pg. 566

Riccitiello, John S., Chm. Bd.--MacGregor Golf Company, Alpharetta, GA; *Int'l*, pg. 72

Rice, Charles E., Chm. & Chief Exec. Officer--Barnett Banks, Inc., Jacksonville, FL; *U.S. Public*, pg. 1162

Rice, Don, Chm. Bd.--Rice, Sangalis, Toole & Wilson, Houston, TX; *U.S. Private*, pg. 928

Rice, Joseph L., III, Chm. Bd.--Clayton, Dubilier & Rice, Inc, New York, NY; *U.S. Private*, pg. 244

Rice, Mike, Chm. Bd. & Chief Exec. Officer--Utz Quality Foods, Inc., Hanover, PA; *U.S. Private*, pg. 1130

Rice, Victor A., Chm. Bd. & Chief Exec. Officer--LucasVarity Inc., Buffalo, NY; *Int'l*, pg. 820

Rice, William B., Chm. Bd.--Blue Grass Quality Meats, Crescent Springs, KY; *U.S. Private*, pg. 152

Rich, Alan, Chm. Bd.--Elite Information Systems, Inc., Los Angeles, CA; *U.S. Public*, pg. 258

Rich, Eve A., Chm. Bd. & Chief Exec. Officer--Contempo Casuals, Los Angeles, CA; *U.S. Public*, pg. 1763

Rich, Francis P., Jr., Chm. Bd. & Pres.--Action Equipment, Candia, NH; *U.S. Private*, pg. 14

Rich, John W., Jr., Chm. Bd. & Pres.--Reading Anthracite Co., Pottsville, PA; *U.S. Private*, pg. 913

Rich, Melvin, Chm. Bd.--Great Earth Distribution, Hicksville, NY; *U.S. Private*, pg. 386

Rich, Melvin L., Chm. Bd., Pres. & Treas.--Evergood Products Corporation, Hicksville, NY; *U.S. Private*, pg. 386

Rich, Robert E., Chm. Bd.--Rich Products Corp., Buffalo, NY; *U.S. Private*, pg. 928

Rich, Simon B., Jr., Chm. Bd.--Louis Dreyfus Natural Gas Corp., Oklahoma City, OK; *U.S. Private*, pg. 342

Richard, Oliver G., III, Chm. Bd., Pres. & Chief Exec. Officer--Columbia Energy Group, Reston, VA; *U.S. Public*, pg. 402

Richard, Oliver G., III, Chm. Bd., Pres. & Chief Exec. Officer--Columbia Gas System Service Corp., Wilmington, DE; *U.S. Public*, pg. 403

Richards, Gilbert, Chm. Bd.--Richards Industries, Inc., Cincinnati, OH; *U.S. Private*, pg. 929

Richards, H. Lee, Chm. Bd. & Chief Exec. Officer--Hygeia Dairy Co., Inc., Harlingen, TX; *U.S. Private*, pg. 552

Richards, John D., Acting. Chm. Bd., Pres. & Chief Exec. & Oper. Officer--Granite Furniture Co., Salt Lake City, UT; *U.S. Private*, pg. 469

Richards, John M., Chm. Bd. & Chief Exec. Officer--Potlatch Corporation, Spokane, WA; *U.S. Public*, pg. 1318

Richards, Roy, Chm. Bd. & Chief Exec. Officer--Southwire Company, Carrollton, GA; *U.S. Private*, pg. 1019

Richards, Thomas S., Chm. Bd., Pres. & Chief Exec. Officer--Rochester Gas And Electric Corporation, Rochester, NY; *U.S. Public*, pg. 1395

Richards, William T., Chm. Bd.--Idaho Forest Industry, Inc., Coeur D'Alene, ID; *U.S. Private*, pg. 556

Richardson, David, Sr., Chm. Bd.--Richardson Industries, Inc., Sheboygan Falls, WI; *U.S. Private*, pg. 929

Richardson, Edward J., Chm. Bd. & Chief Exec. Officer--Richardson Electronics, Ltd., Lafox, IL; *U.S. Public*, pg. 1387

Richardson, Gail, Chm. Bd.--Educational Management Group, Scottsdale, AZ; *U.S. Private*, pg. 778

Richardson, J., Chm.--Merchant Bank (Ghana) Limited, Accra, Ghana; *Int'l*, pg. 1293

Richardson, James Craig, Chm. Bd. & Chief Exec. Officer--Richco Inc., Chicago, IL; *U.S. Private*, pg. 929

Richardson, Michael A., Chm. Bd., Pres., Chief Exec. Officer & Chief Oper. Officer--American Consumers, Inc., Fort Oglethorpe, GA; *U.S. Public*, pg. 70

Richardson, R.E., Chm. Bd.--Graystone PLC, Wilmslow, United Kingdom; *Int'l*, pg. 557

Richardson, W.J., Chm. Bd.--Chloride Industrial Batteries Ltd., Manchester, United Kingdom; *Int'l*, pg. 125

Richer, Alvin, Chm., Pres. & Chief Exec. Officer--Arnold Machinery Company, Salt Lake City, UT; *U.S. Private*, pg. 84

Richey, R.K., Chm. Bd.--Vesta Insurance Group, Inc., Birmingham, AL; *U.S. Public*, pg. 1718

Richey, Ronald K., Chm. & Chief Exec. Officer--Torchmark Corporation, Birmingham, AL; *U.S. Public*, pg. 1622

Richey, Steve, Chm. Bd. & Pres.--Precision Parts Corp., Morristown, TN; *U.S. Private*, pg. 879

Richier, Pierre, Chm. Emeritus--Bertrand Faure, Boulogne, France; *Int'l*, pg. 192

Richman, Paul, Chm. Bd. & Chief Exec. Officer--Standard Microsystems Corp., Hauppauge, NY; *U.S. Public*, pg. 1502

Richmond, George, Chm. Bd.--Young Dental Manufacturing, Earth City, MO; *U.S. Private*, pg. 1201

Richmond, Robert L., Chm. Bd. & Chief Exec. Officer--Active Voice Corporation, Seattle, WA; *U.S. Public*, pg. 17

Richter, H.L., Chm. Bd.--Genesis Underwriting Management Company, Stamford, CT; *U.S. Public*, pg. 725

Richter, Irvin E., Chm. Bd. & Chief Exec. Officer--Hill International Inc., Willingboro, NJ; *U.S. Private*, pg. 529

Richter, James A., Chm.-Exec. Committee--Roney & Co., Detroit, MI; *U.S. Private*, pg. 943

Richter, Yochai, Chm. Bd.--Orbotech Inc., Billerica, MA; *Int'l*, pg. 1007

Ricke, David, Chm. Bd. & Chief Exec. Officer--Motek Engineering & Manufacturing Company, Cambridge, MN; *U.S. Private*, pg. 764

Rickershauser, Charles E., Jr., Chm. Bd. & Chief Exec. Officer--PS Group Holdings, San Diego, CA; *U.S. Public*, pg. 1245

Riddell, Tim, Chm.--Sedgwick Oakwood Underwriting Agents Limited, London, United Kingdom; *Int'l*, pg. 1218

Ridder, P. Anthony, Chm. Bd. & Chief Exec. Officer--Knight-Ridder, Inc., Miami, FL; *U.S. Public*, pg. 963

Ridder, Peter, Chm. & Publr.--The Knight Publishing Co., Charlotte, NC; *U.S. Public*, pg. 964

Riddle, H. Marvin, III, Chm. Bd.--Asbury Carbons, Inc., Asbury, NJ; *U.S. Private*, pg. 87

Rider, Robert F., Chm., Chief Exec. Officer & Treas.--O.A. Newton & Son Co., Bridgeville, DE; *U.S. Private*, pg. 797

Riedel, Alan, Chm. Bd.--Gardner Denver Machinery Inc., Quincy, IL; *U.S. Public*, pg. 703

Riedemann, Roger, Chm. Bd.--The Bradford National Bank of Greenville, Greenville, IL; *U.S. Private*, pg. 164

Rieke, Blaine E., Chm. Bd.--First Wisconsin Asset Management, Inc., Madison, WI; *U.S. Public*, pg. 643

Riemel, Fred, Chm. Bd. & Art Dir.--Eiler & Riemel - Testa, Munich, Germany; *Int'l*, pg. 1377

Rifenbergh, Richard, Chm. Bd.--Tristar Corp., San Antonio, TX; *U.S. Public*, pg. 1640

Rifkin, Leonard, Chm. Bd.--Omnisource Corporation, Fort Wayne, IN; *U.S. Private*, pg. 817

Rigas, John, Chm. Bd.--Niagara Frontier Hockey, L.P., Buffalo, NY; *U.S. Private*, pg. 798

Riggio, Leonard, Chm. Bd.--Babbage's Etc. LLC, Grapevine, TX; *U.S. Private*, pg. 108

Riggio, Leonard, Chm. Bd., Pres. & Chief Exec. Officer--Barnes & Noble Inc., New York, NY; *U.S. Public*, pg. 189

Rigoni, Joseph J., Chm. Bd.--Bacco Construction Co., Iron Mountain, MI; *U.S. Private*, pg. 109

Riisager, Birger, Chm. Bd.--Danfoss A/S, Nordborg, Denmark; *Int'l*, pg. 376

Riley, H. John, Jr., Chm. Bd., Pres. & Chief Exec. Officer--Cooper Industries, Inc., Houston, TX; *U.S. Public*, pg. 442

Riley, S., Chm. Bd.--Sedgwick Group plc, London, United Kingdom; *Int'l*, pg. 1217

Riley, William, Chm. Bd. & Chief Exec. Officer--Moore-Handley, Inc., Pelham, AL; *U.S. Public*, pg. 1128

Rincon, Miguel, Chm. Bd. & Chief Exec. Officer--Grupo Industrial Durango S.A. de C.V., Durango, Mexico; *Int'l*, pg. 575

Rindlaub, John V., Chm. Bd. & Chief Exec. Officer--Seafirst Corporation, Seattle, WA; *U.S. Public*, pg. 181

Rinehart, Charles R., Chm. Bd. & Chief Exec. Officer--H.F. Ahmanson & Co., Irwindale, CA; *U.S. Public*, pg. 29

Rinerson, Darrell D., Chm. Bd., Pres. & Sec.--Micron Quantum Devices, Inc., Santa Clara, CA; *U.S. Public*, pg. 1105

Riney, Hal P., Chm. & Chief Exec. Officer--Hal Riney & Partners, Inc., San Francisco, CA; *U.S. Private*, pg. 931

Ringer, Walter M., Jr., Chm. Bd.--Foley-Belsaw Company, Minneapolis, MN; *U.S. Private*, pg. 416

Ringier, Michael, Chm. Bd.--Ringier AG, Zurich, Switzerland; *Int'l*, pg. 1118

Ringler, James M., Chm. Bd., Pres. & Chief Exec. Officer--Premark International, Inc., Deerfield, IL; *U.S. Public*, pg. 1321

Rinkel, Sherman A., Chm. Bd.--General Microwave Corporation, Amityville, NY; *U.S. Public*, pg. 717

Rinker, Michael, Chm. Bd.--Avesta Sheffield East, Inc., Baltimore, MD; *Int'l*, pg. 221

Rinsch, Charles E., Chm. Bd. & Pres.--Argonaut Co., Menlo Park, CA; *U.S. Public*, pg. 129

Riordan, George N., Chm. Bd.--The Macneal-Schwendler Corp., Los Angeles, CA; *U.S. Public*, pg. 1030

Riordan, John F., Chm. Bd., Pres. & Chief Exec. Officer--MidCon Texas Pipeline Operator, Inc., Houston, TX; *U.S. Public*, pg. 1210

Ripley, Barrett F., Chm.Bd., Pres. & Chief exec. Officer--Troy Mills, Inc., Troy, NH; *U.S. Private*, pg. 1106

Ripley, John A., Pres. & Chief Exec. Officer--Precision Tune Autocare Inc., Leesburg, VA; *U.S. Public*, pg. 1321

Risak, Johann, Dr., Chm. Bd.--Agrolinz Melamin GmbH, Lienz, Austria; *Int'l*, pg. 356

Risk, J. Fred, Chm. Bd.--Security Group Inc., Indianapolis, IN; *U.S. Private*, pg. 981

Risley, Larry L., Chm. Bd. & Chief Exec. Officer--Mesa Air Group, Las Vegas, NV; *U.S. Public*, pg. 1098

Rister, Sara, Chm.-New Line Productions--New Line Cinema Corporation, New York, NY; *U.S. Public*, pg. 1614

Ritblat, John, Chm. Bd. & Chief Exec. Officer--The British Land Company PLC, London, United Kingdom; *Int'l*, pg. 219

Ritchie, Alan, Chm. Bd. & Pres.--Marson/Creative Fastener, Inc., Stoughton, MA; *U.S. Private*, pg. 708

Ritchie, Arthur G., Chm. Bd., Pres. & Chief Exec. Officer--Sand Technology Systems, Westmount, Canada; *Int'l*, pg. 1183

Ritchie, David R., Chm. Bd., Pres. & Chief Exec. Officer--Farmers Bank of Maryland, Annapolis, MD; *U.S. Public*, pg. 641

Ritchie, Hale D., Jr., Chm. Bd. & Chief Exec. Officer--Ritchie Corporation, Wichita, KS; *U.S. Private*, pg. 933

Ritter, Alan C., Chm. Bd.--Universal Photonics, Inc., Hicksville, NY; *U.S. Private*, pg. 1127

Rittwage, William R., Chm. Bd., Pres. & Chief Exec. Officer--COP Communications, Glendale, CA; *U.S. Private*, pg. 196

Rittwage, William R., Chm. Bd., Pres. & Chief Exec. Officer--California Offset Printers, Inc., Glendale, CA; *U.S. Private*, pg. 196

Riverin, Bruno, Chm. Bd.--Culinar Inc., Montreal, Canada; *Int'l*, pg. 348

Rivero Larrea, Jose Antonio, Chm. Bd.--Compania Minera Autlan S.A. de C.V., Mexico, Mexico; *Int'l*, pg. 324

Rivett, Ron, Chm. Bd.--Super 8 Motels, Inc., Aberdeen, SD; *U.S. Public*, pg. 322

Rivett, Ron, Chm. Bd.--The Rivet Group L.L.C., Aberdeen, SD; *U.S. Private*, pg. 934
Rizzuto, Leandro P., Chm. Bd. & Pres.--Conair Corporation, Stamford, CT; *U.S. Private*, pg. 261
Roach, Alfred J., Chm. Bd.--TII Industries, Inc., Copiague, NY; *U.S. Public*, pg. 1556
Roach, John V., Chm. Bd. & Chief Exec. Officer--Tandy Corporation, Fort Worth, TX; *U.S. Public*, pg. 1560
Roach, Timothy, Chm. Bd.--TII-Ditel, Hickory, NC; *U.S. Public*, pg. 1556
Roath, Kenneth B., Chm. Bd., Pres. & Chief Exec. Officer--Health Care Property Investors, Inc., Newport Beach, CA; *U.S. Public*, pg. 801
Rob, Joseph M., Chm. Bd. & Chief Exec. Officer--Equity Services, Inc., Montpelier, VT; *U.S. Private*, pg. 785
Robb, Donald H., Chm. Bd. & Chief Exec. Officer--Chittenden & Eastman Co., Burlington, IA; *U.S. Private*, pg. 237
Robb, Donald H., Chm. Bd. & Chief Exec. Officer--Eastman House Of California, Inc., Burlington, IA; *U.S. Private*, pg. 238
Robb, Donald H., Chm. Bd. & Chief Exec. Officer--Eastman House Of Alabama, Inc., Burlington, IA; *U.S. Private*, pg. 238
Robbins, Brian A., Chm. Bd.--TecSyn International, Inc., Saint Catharines, Canada; *Int'l*, pg. 1361
Robbins, Bruce M., Jr., Chm. Bd.--Robbins Manufacturing Company, Tampa, FL; *U.S. Private*, pg. 935
Robbins, James O., Chm. Bd., Pres. & Chief Exec. Officer--Cox Communications, Inc., Atlanta, GA; *U.S. Public*, pg. 454
Robbins, Orem O., Chm. Bd.--Security American Financial Enterprises, Inc., Minnetonka, MN; *U.S. Private*, pg. 980
Robert, Dean E., Jr., Chm. Bd. & Pres.--Roberts Foods, Inc., Springfield, IL; *U.S. Private*, pg. 935
Robert, Serge, Chm.--B.F.C. Ocean Indien, Saint Denis, Reunion; *Int'l*, pg. 315
Robert, Stephen, Chm. Bd. & Co-Chief Exec. Officer--CIBC Oppenheimer Corp., New York, NY; *Int'l*, pg. 257
Robert, Stephen, Chm. Bd.--Oppenheimer Capital, New York, NY; *Int'l*, pg. 257
Roberts, Bert C. Jr., Chm. Bd. & Chief Exec. Officer--MCI Communications Corp., Atlanta, GA; *U.S. Public*, pg. 1023
Roberts, Bert C., Jr., Chm. Bd. & Chief Exec. Officer--MCI Telecommunications Corp., Washington, DC; *U.S. Public*, *pg. 1024*
Roberts, Burnell R., Chm. Bd.--Sweetheart Cup Company Inc., Owings Mills, MD; *U.S. Private*, pg. 1058
Roberts, David J., Chm. & Pres.--Foster Wheeler Trading Co., Ltd., Hamilton, Bermuda; *U.S. Public*, pg. 677
Roberts, Dorothy H., Chm. & Chief Exec. Officer--The Echo Design Group, Inc., New York, NY; *U.S. Private*, pg. 359
Roberts, F. Stone, Co-Chm. & Chief Exec. Officer--Gotham Incorporated, New York, NY; *U.S. Private*, pg. 677
Roberts, John, Chm. Bd. & Pres.--Busch Entertainment Corp., Clayton, MO; *U.S. Public*, pg. 114
Roberts, John H., Chm. Bd.--J.H. Roberts Industries Inc., Des Plaines, IL; *U.S. Private*, pg. 935
Roberts, John, Dr., Chm. Bd.--Expamet International Plc, London, United Kingdom; *Int'l*, pg. 467
Roberts, Joseph, Chm. Bd. & Chief Exec. Officer--Advanced Circuit Technology, Nashua, NH; *U.S. Private*, *pg. 21*
Roberts, Ken, Chm. Bd. & Pres.--Lippincott & Margulies, Inc., New York, NY; *U.S. Public*, pg. 1048
Roberts, M., Chm. Bd.--MetalTech International PLC, Stourbridge, United Kingdom; *Int'l*, pg. 862
Roberts, Madeleine J., Chm. Bd.--E.V. Roberts & Associates, Inc., Culver City, CA; *U.S. Private*, pg. 935
Roberts, Ralph J., Chm. Bd.--Comcast Corporation, Philadelphia, PA; *U.S. Public*, pg. 406
Roberts, Rod, Chm. Bd.--Willis Corroon North Limited, Liverpool, United Kingdom; *Int'l*, pg. 1502
Roberts, T.S., Jr., Chm. Bd. & Chief Exec. Officer--Monticello Drug Co., Jacksonville, FL; *U.S. Private*, pg. 759
Roberts, Thomas S., Chm. Bd.--AmeriPath, Inc., Riviera Beach, FL; *U.S. Public*, pg. 96
Robertson, A., Chm. Bd.--Glaxo Danmark a/s, Copenhagen, Denmark; *Int'l*, pg. 553
Robertson, James C., Chm. Bd., Pres. & Chief Exec. Officer--Consumers Financial Corporation, Camp Hill, PA; *U.S. Public*, pg. 437
Robertson, John C., Chm. Bd.--Market Facts of Canada, Ltd., Toronto, Canada; *U.S. Public*, pg. 1047
Robertson, Timothy B., Chm. Bd. & Pres.--MTM Enterprises, Inc., Studio City, CA; *Int'l*, pg. 927
Robertson, William W., Chm.--Beverage-Air Co., Spartanburg, SC; *U.S. Public*, pg. 1496
Robins, Ralph Sir, Chm. Bd.--Rolls-Royce plc, London, United Kingdom; *Int'l*, pg. 1126
Robinson, E.B., Jr., Chm. Bd. & Chief Exec. Officer--Deposit Guaranty Corp., Jackson, MS; *U.S. Public*, pg. 500
Robinson, Francis Alastair Lavie, Chm. Bd.--Barclays Financial Services Co. Ltd., London, United Kingdom; *Int'l*, pg. 164
Robinson, Gerry, Chm. Bd.--Granada Group PLC, London, United Kingdom; *Int'l*, pg. 556
Robinson, Harry T., Jr., Chm. Bd. & Sec.--Top Flight, Inc., Chattanooga, TN; *U.S. Private*, pg. 1091
Robinson, I., Chm.--John Brown Engineering Limited, Clydebank, United Kingdom; *Int'l*, pg. 772
Robinson, Irwin Z., Chm. & Chief Exec. Officer-Famous Music--Paramount Pictures Corporation, Los Angeles, CA; *U.S. Private*, pg. 776
Robinson, Irwin Z., Chm. & Chief Exec. Officer--Famous Music Corporation, New York, NY; *U.S. Private*, pg. 777
Robinson, J. Mack, Chm. Bd.--Atlantic American Corporation, Atlanta, GA; *U.S. Public*, pg. 143
Robinson, J. Mack, Chm. Bd.--Bull Run Corporation, Atlanta, GA; *U.S. Public*, pg. 267
Robinson, J.M., Chm. Bd., Pres. & Chief Exec. Officer--Footstar Inc., Mahwah, NJ; *U.S. Public*, pg. 661
Robinson, James W., Chm. Bd.--Caldwell Tanks, Inc., Louisville, KY; *U.S. Private*, pg. 200
Robinson, John H., Chm. Emeritus--Circle International Group, Inc., San Francisco, CA; *U.S. Public*, pg. 370
Robinson, Richard, Chm. Bd., Pres. & Chief Exec. Officer--Scholastic Corporation, New York, NY; *U.S. Public*, pg. 1440
Robinson, Ronald, Chm. Bd. & Chief Exec. Officer--Svedala Pumps & Process, Colorado Springs, CO; *Int'l*, pg. 1325
Robinson, Russell M., III, Chm. Bd.--Caraustar Industries, Inc., Austell, GA; *U.S. Public*, pg. 303
Robinson, Samuel C., Chm. Bd.--Robinson Nugent, Inc., New Albany, IN; *U.S. Public*, pg. 1394
Robinson, William B., Chm. & Chief Exec. Officer--AdultCare, Inc., Deerfield Beach, FL; *Int'l*, pg. 499
Robles, Mauro, Chm. Bd.--La Reina, Inc., Los Angeles, CA; *U.S. Private*, pg. 640
Robson, David B., Chm. & Chief Exec. Officer--Veritas DGC Inc., Houston, TX; *U.S. Private*, pg. 1136
Robson, Edward J., Chm. Bd.--Robson Communities, Sun Lakes, AZ; *U.S. Private*, pg. 937
Rocca, Paolo, Chm. Bd.--Tubos de Acero de Mexico, S.A., Mexico, Mexico; *Int'l*, pg. 1426
Roche, George A., Chm. Bd., Pres. & Mng. Dir.--T. Rowe Price Associates, Inc., Baltimore, MD; *U.S. Public*, pg. 1324
Roche, John F., Chm. Bd., Pres. & Chief Exec. Officer--PMC Industries Inc., Wickliffe, OH; *U.S. Private*, pg. 827
Rock, Bradley E., Chm. Bd., Pres. & Chief Exec. Officer--Bank of Smithtown, Smithtown, NY; *U.S. Private*, pg. 114
Rock, Bradley E., Chm. Bd., Pres. & Chief Exec. Officer--Smithtown Bancorp, Inc., Smithtown, NY; *U.S. Public*, pg. 1479
Rock, Douglas L., Chm. Bd., Pres., Chief Exec. & Oper. Officer--Smith International, Inc., Houston, TX; *U.S. Public*, pg. 1478
Rockefeller, Frederic L., Chm. Bd.--Cranston Print Works Company, Cranston, RI; *U.S. Private*, pg. 286
Rockett, Howard, Chm. & Chief Exec. Officer--Rockett, Burkhead, Lewis & Winslow, Raleigh, NC; *U.S. Private*, pg. 938
Rodale, Ardath, Chm. Bd. & Chief Exec. Officer--Rodale Press, Inc., Emmaus, PA; *U.S. Private*, pg. 939
Rodbell, Clyde A., Chm. Bd. & Chief Exec. Officer--Apex Supply Co., Inc., Atlanta, GA; *U.S. Private*, pg. 77
Roddick, Gordon, Chm.--The Body Shop International, Littlehampton, United Kingdom; *Int'l*, pg. 199
Rodgers, B.D., Chm. Bd.--Rodgers Builders, Inc., Charlotte, NC; *U.S. Private*, pg. 939
Rodgers, Charles, Chm. Bd.--Work/Family Directions, Boston, MA; *U.S. Private*, pg. 1188
Rodier, Jean Pierre, Chm. Bd.--Penarroya Metal Europe, Fontenay-sous-Bois, France; *Int'l*, pg. 662
Rodier, Jean-Pierre, Chm. Bd. & Chief Exec. Officer--American National Can Company, Chicago, IL; *Int'l*, pg. 1029
Rodio, Jean-Pierre, Chm. Bd. & Chief Exec. Officer--Pechiney S.A., Courbevoie, France; *Int'l*, pg. 1027
Rodocanachi, Emmanuel, Chm. Bd. & Chief Exec. Officer--Credit Nationale, Paris, France; *Int'l*, pg. 344
Rodocanachi, Emmanuel, Chm. Bd.--Financiere Saint Dominique, Paris, France; *Int'l*, pg. 344
Rodriguez, Francisco Gonzalez, Pres.--Argentaria Corporacion Bancaria de Espana, S.A., Madrid, Spain; *Int'l*, pg. 80
Roe, John H., Chm. Bd. & Chief Exec. Officer--Bemis Company, Inc., Minneapolis, MN; *U.S. Public*, pg. 210
Roe, K. Keith, Chm. Bd., Pres. & Chief Exec. Officer--Burns & Roe Enterprises, Inc., Oradell, NJ; *U.S. Private*, pg. 187
Roehm, MacDonell, Jr., Chm. Bd., Pres. & Chief Exec. Officer--Bill's Dollar Stores, Inc., Ridgeland, MS; *U.S. Private*, pg. 144
Roeller, Dr. Wolfgang, Chm.-Supervisory Board--Heidelberger Zement A.G., Heidelberg, Germany; *Int'l*, pg. 605
Roenigk, Martin A., Chm. Bd., Pres. & Chief Exec. Officer--CompuDyne Corporation, Willimantic, CT; *U.S. Public*, pg. 419
Roese, Dr. Horst, Chm. Bd.--ELSTER AG Mess- und Regeltechnik, Mainz, Germany; *Int'l*, pg. 1148
Roessner, John K., III, Chm. Bd. & Pres.--E.J. Brooks Company, Newark, NJ; *U.S. Private*, pg. 172
Rog, Joseph W., Chm. Bd., Pres. & Chief Exec. Officer--Corrpro Companies, Inc., Medina, OH; *U.S. Public*, pg. 451
Roger, Serge, Chm. Bd. & Pres.--Elscint France S.A., Bagnolet, France; *Int'l*, pg. 450
Rogers, C.B., Jr., Chm. Bd.--Equifax Inc., Atlanta, GA; *U.S. Public*, pg. 588
Rogers, Edward S., Chm. Bd.--Rogers Cantel Mobile Communications Inc., Saint-Laurent, Canada; *Int'l*, pg. 1122
Rogers, G.W., Chm. Bd.--Consolidated Systems, Inc., Columbia, SC; *U.S. Private*, pg. 266
Rogers, Joe, Sr., Chm. Bd.--Waffle House, Incorporated, Norcross, GA; *U.S. Private*, pg. 1146
Rogers, M. Weldon, III, Chm. Bd., Pres. & Chief Exec. Officer--EAC Corporation, Saint Louis, MO; *U.S. Private*, pg. 353
Rogers, N. Stewart, Chm. Bd.--Penford Corp., Bellevue, WA; *U.S. Public*, pg. 1269
Rogers, Richard, Chm. Bd.--Hobie Cat Company, Oceanside, CA; *U.S. Private*, pg. 531
Rogers, Richard R., Chm. Bd.--Mary Kay Corporation, Dallas, TX; *U.S. Private*, pg. 710
Rogers, Samuel H., Jr., Chm. Bd. & Pres.--Wilkins-Rogers Incorporated, Ellicott City, MD; *U.S. Private*, pg. 1176
Rogers, T. Gary, Chm. Bd. & Chief Exec. Officer--Dreyer's Grand Ice Cream, Inc., Oakland, CA; *U.S. Public*, pg. 529
Rogers, W. Murray, Chm.--Kellogg (Aust.) Proprietary Ltd., Pagewood, Australia; *U.S. Public*, pg. 947
Rogerson, Michael, Chm. Bd., Pres. & Chief Exec. Officer--Rogerson Aircraft Corporation, Irvine, CA; *U.S. Private*, pg. 940
Rogowski, Dr. Michael, Chm. Bd.-Mngmt.--J.M. Voith, GmbH, Heidenheim, Germany; *Int'l*, pg. 1472
Rohde, Peter, Dr., Chm.-Mgmt. Bd.--Dyckerhoff AG, Wiesbaden, Germany; *Int'l*, pg. 422
Rohe, Michelle, Chm. Bd.--Shur-Lok Corporation, Irvine, CA; *U.S. Private*, pg. 997
Rohr, Hans Christoph, Dr., Chm. Bd.--Klockner-Werke AG, Duisburg, Germany; *Int'l*, pg. 736
Rohr, James E., Chm. Bd. & Chief Exec. Officer--PNC Bank, N.A., Pittsburgh, PA; *U.S. Public*, pg. 1243
Rohtbart, Markus, Chm. Bd. & Treas.--Cattleman's, Inc., Detroit, MI; *U.S. Public*, pg. 318
Rokop, Joseph, Sr., Chm. Bd.--Rokop Corporation, Bridgeville, PA; *U.S. Private*, pg. 941
Rolf, Randolph K., Chm. Bd., Pres. & Chief Exec. Officer--Unitog Company, Kansas City, MO; *U.S. Public*, pg. 1693
Rolla, M.F., Chm. Bd.--Global Steel Products Corporation, Deer Park, NY; *U.S. Private*, pg. 457
Rolland, Ian M., Chm. Bd., Pres. & Chief Exec. Officer--Lincoln National Corporation, Fort Wayne, IN; *U.S. Public*, pg. 997
Roller, Wolfgang, Dr., Chm. Bd.--Deutsche Lufthansa AG, Cologne, Germany; *Int'l*, pg. 407
Rollhaus, Philip E., Chm.--Energy Absorption Systems, Inc., Chicago, IL; *U.S. Public*, pg. 1353
Rollhaus, Philip E., Jr., Chm. Bd. & Chief Exec. Officer--Quixote Corporation, Chicago, IL; *U.S. Public*, pg. 1353
Rollins, Clark, Jr., Chm. Bd.--Nashville Wire Product Co., Nashville, TN; *U.S. Private*, pg. 775
Rollins, John W., Chm. Bd. & Chief Exec. Officer--Rollins Truck Leasing Corp., Wilmington, DE; *U.S. Public*, pg. 1405
Rollins, John W. Jr., Chm. Bd.--Matlack Systems, Inc., Wilmington, DE; *U.S. Public*, pg. 1057
Rollins, John W., Sr., Chm. Bd.--Brandywine Sports, Inc., Wilmington, DE; *U.S. Private*, pg. 165
Rollins, R. Randall, Chm. Bd. & Chief Exec. Officer--Rollins, Inc., Atlanta, GA; *U.S. Public*, pg. 1404
Rollwagen, John, Chm. Bd.--Computer Network Technology Corporation, Minneapolis, MN; *U.S. Public*, pg. 421
Roloff, Jeffrey J., Chm. Bd. & Chief Exec. Officer--Central Data Corporation, Champaign, IL; *U.S. Private*, pg. 223
Rombouts, F., Chm.--Campina N.V./S.A., Aalst, Belgium; *Int'l*, pg. 254
Romita, Michael, Chm. Bd. & Chief Exec. Officer--Castle Oil Corporation, Harrison, NY; *U.S. Private*, pg. 219
Romney, W. Mitt, Mng. Dir.--Bain Capital, Boston, MA; *U.S. Private*, pg. 110
Rompala, Richard M., Chm. Bd. & Chief Exec. Officer--The Valspar Corporation, Minneapolis, MN; *U.S. Public*, pg. 1707
Romualdez, Benjamin Philip G., Chm. Bd.--Benguet Corporation, Manila, Philippines; *Int'l*, pg. 186
Romulo, Roberto R., Chm. Bd.--Philippine Long Distance Telephone Company, Manila, Philippines; *Int'l*, pg. 1051
Rones, James, Chm. Bd.--Americo Manufacturing Co., Inc., Acworth, GA; *U.S. Private*, pg. 64
Roney, Patrick E., Chm. Bd., Pres. & Chief Exec. Officer--Electro Mechanical Design Services, Inc., Gaithersburg, MD; *U.S. Private*, pg. 369
Roob, R., Chm. Bd.--Benjamin Moore & Co., Montvale, NJ; *U.S. Private*, pg. 133
Roof, William M., Chm. Bd.-Clintock Ltd.--Clintock Limited, Dublin, Ireland; *U.S. Public*, pg. 262
Rooney, Francis, Chm. Bd. & Chief Exec. Officer--H.H. Brown Shoe Company, Inc., Greenwich, CT; *U.S. Public*, pg. 217
Rooney, L.F., III, Chm. Bd. & Pres.--Rooney Brothers Company, Tulsa, OK; *U.S. Private*, pg. 943
Rooney, Patrick W., Chm. Bd., Pres. & Chief Exec. Officer--Cooper Tire & Rubber Company, Findlay, OH; *U.S. Public*, pg. 445
Rooney, Phillip B., Chm. Bd. & Dir.--Rust International Inc., Birmingham, AL; *U.S. Public*, pg. 1366
Rooney, Thomas D., Chm. Bd., Pres. & Chief Exec. Officer--Multigraphics Inc., Mount Prospect, IL; *U.S. Public*, pg. 1141
Root, Andrew, Jr., Chm. Bd.--B&W Co-op, Inc., Breckenridge, MI; *U.S. Private*, pg. 105
Root, John A., Chm. Bd. & Pres.--A.I. Root Company, Medina, OH; *U.S. Private*, pg. 944
Roper, Philip R., III, Chm. Bd.--Roper Bros. Lumber Co., Inc., Petersburg, VA; *U.S. Private*, pg. 944
Roper, William H., Chm. Bd. & Chief Exec. Officer--Ropak Corporation, Fullerton, CA; *Int'l*, pg. 811
Roquelpo, Bruno, Chm. Bd. & Mng. Dir.--Campbell Distillers Limited, Brentford, United Kingdom; *Int'l*, pg. 567
Roquette Riccardi, Antonio Luis, Chm. Bd.--Banco Espirito Santo e Comercial de Lisboa SA, Lisbon, Portugal; *Int'l*, pg. 142
Rorie, Durwood G., Jr., Chm. Bd.--United Air Specialists, Inc., Cincinnati, OH; *U.S. Public*, pg. 382
Rosa, Bruce, Sr. V.P.--T. Marzetti Company, Columbus, OH; *U.S. Public*, pg. 977
Rosanio, Linda, Chm. Bd. & Pres.--RBT/Strum, Cherry Hill, NJ; *U.S. Private*, pg. 902
Rosasco, Nat C., Chm. Bd.--Northwestern Golf Company, Elmhurst, IL; *U.S. Private*, pg. 806
Rose, Edward W., Chm. Bd.--Drew Industries Incorporated, White Plains, NY; *U.S. Public*, pg. 529
Rose, Edward W., III, Chm. Bd.--Leslie Building Products, Inc., White Plains, NY; *U.S. Public*, pg. 989
Rose, Kelly L., Chm. Bd. & Chief Exec. Officer--Starcraft Corporation, Goshen, IN; *U.S. Public*, pg. 1510
Rose, Michael D., Chm. Bd.--Promus Hotel Corporation, Memphis, TN; *U.S. Public*, pg. 1335
Rose, Peter J., Chm. Bd. & Chief Exec. Officer--Expeditors International of Washington, Inc., Seattle, WA; *U.S. Public*, pg. 600
Rose, Porter B., Chm. Bd. & Pres.--Liberty Investment Group, Inc., Greenville, SC; *U.S. Public*, pg. 992

Rose, Stuart, Chm. Bd. & Chief Exec. Officer--Rex Stores Corp., Dayton, OH; *U.S. Public*, pg. 1384

Rose, William R., Chm. Bd., Pres. & Chief Exec. Officer--Rose Packing Company, Barrington, IL; *U.S. Private*, pg. 945

Rose, William T., Jr., Chm. Bd., Pres. & Chief Exec. Officer--Uncle B's Bakery, Inc., Ellsworth, IA; *U.S. Public*, pg. 1664

Rosedale, Miles, Chm. Bd., Pres. & Chief Exec. Officer--Monrovia Nursery Co., Azusa, CA; *U.S. Private*, pg. 757

Rosemore, Fredric M., Chm. Bd.--PMC Capital Inc., Dallas, TX; *U.S. Public*, pg. 1242

Rosen, Benedict P., Chm. Bd., Pres. & Chief Exec. Officer--AVX Corporation, Myrtle Beach, SC; *Int'l*, pg. 775

Rosen, Benjamin M., Chm. Bd.--COMPAQ Computer Corporation, Houston, TX; *U.S. Public*, pg. 417

Rosen, David, Co-Chm. Bd.--Sega of America Inc., Redwood City, CA; *Int'l*, pg. 1218

Rosen, Harry, Chm. Bd. & Chief Exec. Officer--Harry Rosen Inc., Toronto, Canada; *Int'l*, pg. 425

Rosen, Jack, Chm. Bd., Pres. & Chief Exec. Officer--Continental Health Affiliates, Inc., Englewood Cliffs, NJ; *U.S. Public*, pg. 440

Rosen, Jack, Chm. Bd. & Pres.--Hazel Bishop International, Englewood Cliffs, NJ; *U.S. Private*, pg. 514

Rosen, Jonathan P., Chm. Bd.--The First Republic Corporation of America, New York, NY; *U.S. Public*, pg. 637

Rosen, Larry, Chm. Emeritus--GRP Records, New York, NY; *Int'l*, pg. 1215

Rosen, Leon, Chm. Bd.--The Pace Collection, Long Island City, NY; *U.S. Private*, pg. 829

Rosen, Ludwig M., Chm. Bd.--Rosens, Inc., Fairmont, MN; *U.S. Private*, pg. 945

Rosen, Sydney, Chm. Bd.--Rose Art Industries, Livingston, NJ; *U.S. Private*, pg. 945

Rosen, William M., Chm. Bd.--Alaskan Copper Companies, Seattle, WA; *U.S. Private*, pg. 31

Rosen, Yoseph, Chm. Bd.--ECI Telecom Ltd., Petah Tiqwa, Israel; *Int'l*, pg. 643

Rosenbaum, Edward W., Chm. Bd. & Chief Exec. Officer--David Michael & Co. Inc., Philadelphia, PA; *U.S. Private*, pg. 740

Rosenbaum, Jerrold, Pres.--Body Shop of America, Jacksonville, FL; *U.S. Private*, pg. 154

Rosenbaum, Lee, Publisher--Discover, New York, NY; *U.S. Public*, pg. 513

Rosenberg, Charlotte, Chm. Bd.--Rose Printing Company, Inc., Tallahassee, FL; *U.S. Private*, pg. 945

Rosenberg, Gerald, Chm.--Cortec Group, New York, NY; *U.S. Private*, pg. 277

Rosenberg, Harold, Chm. Bd.--Octagon Process Inc., Edgewater, NJ; *U.S. Private*, pg. 811

Rosenberg, Henry A., Jr., Chm. Bd., Pres., Chief Exec. & Oper. Officer--Crown Central Petroleum Corporation, Baltimore, MD; *U.S. Public*, pg. 462

Rosenberg, Kenneth M., Chm. Bd.--Pharmavite Corp., Mission Hills, CA; *U.S. Private*, pg. 860

Rosenberg, Kenneth M., Chm. Bd.--Pharmavite Corporation, Mission Hills, CA; *Int'l*, pg. 1013

Rosenberg, Kurt, Chm. Bd. & Pres.--The Promotion in Motion Companies, Closter, NJ; *U.S. Private*, pg. 890

Rosenberg, Richard, Chm. Bd. & Chief Exec. Officer--Bank of America NT&SA, San Francisco, CA; *U.S. Public*, pg. 180

Rosenberg, Robert, Chm. Bd.--Mister Donut of America, Inc., Randolph, MA; *Int'l*, pg. 63

Rosenblatt, Ed, Chm. & Chief Exec. Officer--Geffen Records, Los Angeles, CA; *Int'l*, pg. 1215

Rosenblatt, Michael, Co-Chm.--Pacific Title/Mirage, Hollywood, CA; *U.S. Public*, pg. 1425

Rosendin, Raymond J., Chm. Bd.--Rosendin Electric, Inc., San Jose, CA; *U.S. Private*, pg. 945

Rosenkranz, Robert, Chm. Bd., Pres. & Chief Exec. Officer--Delphi Financial Group, Inc., Wilmington, DE; *U.S. Public*, pg. 496

Rosenshine, Allen, Chm. Bd., Chief Exec. Officer & Dir.--BBDO Worldwide Inc., New York, NY; *U.S. Public*, pg. 1223

Rosenthal, Alexander B., Chm. Bd.--Greater New York Mutual Insurance Company, New York, NY; *U.S. Private*, pg. 476

Rosenthal, Alexander E., Chm. Bd.--Insurance Company of Greater New York, New York, NY; *U.S. Private*, pg. 476

Rosenthal, George I., Chm. Bd. & Pres.--Raleigh Enterprises, Inc., Santa Monica, CA; *U.S. Private*, pg. 907

Rosenthal, Philip, Chm. Bd.--Rosenthal U.S.A. Limited, Carlstadt, NJ; *Int'l*, pg. 1127

Rosenthal, Richard H., Chm. Bd. & Pres.--F & W Publications, Inc., Cincinnati, OH; *U.S. Private*, pg. 388

Rosenthal, Robert, Co-Chm. Bd.--New York Islanders Hockey Club, Uniondale, NY; *U.S. Private*, pg. 794

Rosner, Carl H., Chm. Bd. & Chief Exec. Officer--Intermagnetics General Corporation, Latham, NY; *U.S. Public*, pg. 893

Ross, Frank, Sr., Chm. Bd. & Chief Oper. Officer--HRH Construction Corp., New York, NY; *U.S. Private*, pg. 1035

Ross, Harold M., Chm. Bd.--Allied Old English, Inc., Port Reading, NJ; *U.S. Private*, pg. 39

Ross, Joseph J., Chm. Bd., Pres. & Chief Exec. Officer--Federal Signal Corporation, Oak Brook, IL; *U.S. Public*, pg. 616

Ross, Lloyd L., Chm. Bd. & Chief Exec. Officer--Tuesday Morning Corporation, Dallas, TX; *U.S. Public*, pg. 1644

Ross, Morton M., Chm. Bd. & Pres.--International Plastics Company, New York, NY; *U.S. Private*, pg. 571

Ross, R. Dale, Chm. Bd. & Chief Exec. Officer--American Oncology Resources, Inc., Houston, TX; *U.S. Public*, pg. 88

Ross, Robert I., Chm. Bd.--Charles Curtain Company, Inc., Dallas, TX; *U.S. Private*, pg. 229

Ross, Robert L., Chm. Bd.--Square Two Golf Incorporated, Fairfield, NJ; *U.S. Public*, pg. 1501

Ross, Stuart B., Chm. Bd.--Xerox Credit Corporation, Stamford, CT; *U.S. Public*, pg. 1785

Rosser, Paul C., Chm.-Exec. Committee--Rosser International, Inc., Atlanta, GA; *U.S. Private*, pg. 946

Rossi, G., Chm.--AGIP (Suisse) S.A., Lausanne, Switzerland; *Int'l*, pg. 428

Rossignolo, G.M., Chm. Bd.--Electrolux San Jose, Pordenone, Italy; *Int'l*, pg. 442

Rossignolo, G.M., Chm. Bd.--Zanussi Italia S.p.A., Pordenone, Italy; *Int'l*, pg. 442

Rossignolo, Gian Mario, Chm.--Telecom Italia S.p.A., Rome, Italy; *Int'l*, pg. 1362

Rosskamm, Alan, Chm. Bd., Pres. & Chief Exec. Officer--Fabri-Centers of America, Inc., Hudson, OH; *U.S. Public*, pg. 609

Rosso, Jean-Pierre, Chm. Bd. & Chief Exec. Officer--Case Corporation, Racine, WI; *U.S. Public*, pg. 311

Rosso, Louis T., Chm. Bd. & Chief Exec. Officer--Beckman Instruments, Inc., Fullerton, CA; *U.S. Public*, pg. 199

Rosson, W.M., Chm. Bd.--Conwood Company L.P., Memphis, TN; *U.S. Private*, pg. 272

Rotelle, John F., Chm.--Rotelle, Inc., West Point, PA; *U.S. Public*, pg. 1389

Roth, Bernard B., Chm. Bd. & Chief Exec. Officer--World Oil Corp., South Gate, CA; *U.S. Private*, pg. 1190

Roth, Michael I., Chm. Bd. & Chief Exec. Officer--The Mutual Life Insurance Company of New York, New York, NY; *U.S. Private*, pg. 769

Roth, Steven, Chm. Bd. & Chief Exec. Officer--Vornado Realty Trust, Saddle Brook, NJ; *U.S. Public*, pg. 1725

Rothenberger, Gunter, Co.-Chm.--Pittler Maschinenfabrik AG, Langen, Germany; *Int'l*, pg. 1128

Rothenberger, Helmut, Chm.-Mngmt. Bd. & Chief Exec. Officer--Rothenberger Group GmbH, Kelheim, Germany; *Int'l*, pg. 1127

Rothenberger, Helmut, Co.-Chm.--Pittler Maschinenfabrik AG, Langen, Germany; *Int'l*, pg. 1128

Rothenberger, Helmut, Chm. Bd.--Ingersoll Equipment Co., Inc., Winneconne, WI; *Int'l*, pg. 1129

Rothensteiner, Walter, Dr., Chm. Bd.--Raiffeisen Zentralbank Osterreich, Vienna, Austria; *Int'l*, pg. 1084

Rothenstreich, Jon W., Chm. & Chief Exec. Officer--TIG Holdings, Inc., New York, NY; *U.S. Public*, pg. 1555

Rothermere, Viscount, The, Chm. Bd.--Daily Mail & General Trust PLC, London, United Kingdom; *Int'l*, pg. 366

Rothwell, Bernard J., III, Chm. Bd.--Bay State Milling Co., Quincy, MA; *U.S. Private*, pg. 124

Rotko, Michael J., Chm. Bd.--MEDIQ Incorporated, Pennsauken, NJ; *U.S. Public*, pg. 1081

Rott, Herbert F., Sr., Chm. Bd. & Chief Exec. Officer--Rott-Keller Supply Co., Fargo, ND; *U.S. Private*, pg. 947

Rotter, Bernard J., Chm. Bd.--The Rottlund Company, Inc., Roseville, MN; *U.S. Public*, pg. 1406

Rotter, Steve H., Chm. Bd.--Towne, Silverstein, Rotter Inc., New York, NY; *U.S. Private*, pg. 1093

Roubos, Gary L., Chm. Bd.--Dover Corporation, New York, NY; *U.S. Public*, pg. 520

Roudebush, James R., Chm. Bd.--Caldwell VanRiper, Inc., Indianapolis, IN; *U.S. Private*, pg. 200

Rouhana, William J., Jr., Chm. Bd. & Chief Exec. Officer--Winstar Communications, New York, NY; *U.S. Public*, pg. 1772

Roulston, Thomas H., II, Chm. Bd.--Defiance, Inc., Cleveland, OH; *U.S. Public*, pg. 493

Rounick, Della, Chm. Bd. & Chief Exec. Officer--The He-Ro Group, Ltd., New York, NY; *U.S. Public*, pg. 801

Rouse, Mitchell, Chm. Bd. & Chief Exec. Officer--Supershuttle Inc., Phoenix, AZ; *U.S. Private*, pg. 1056

Roush, Charles A., Jr., Chm. Bd.--Citizens Bank and Trust of West Georgia, Carrollton, GA; *U.S. Public*, pg. 1549

Roush, David P., Chm. Bd.--Rocor Transportation Companies Inc., Oklahoma City, OK; *U.S. Private*, pg. 938

Roush, Jack, Chm. Bd. & Chief Exec. Officer--Roush Industries Inc., Livonia, MI; *U.S. Private*, pg. 948

Rousseau, David, Chm. Bd.--Salt River Project Agricultural Improvement and Power District, Tempe, AZ; *U.S. Private*, pg. 962

Roussel, Louis J., Jr., Chm. Bd., Pres. & Chief Exec. Officer--Victory Financial Group, Inc., Metairie, LA; *U.S. Private*, pg. 1139

Rousso, Dominic, Chm. Bd., Pres. & Chief Exec. Officer--F.H. Chase, Inc., Mansfield, MA; *U.S. Private*, pg. 230

Routh, Thomas M., Chm. Bd., Pres. & Chief Exec. Officer--J.H. Routh Packing Co., Sandusky, OH; *U.S. Private*, pg. 948

Roux, Ambroise, Chm.-Supervisory Bd.--Pinault Printemps, Paris, France; *Int'l*, pg. 1057

Roux, Ambroise, Chm. Bd.--Pinault Printemps, Paris, France; *Int'l*, pg. 1057

Roverud, Steven M., Chm. Bd. & Chief Exec. Officer--Trunkline Gas Co., Houston, TX; *U.S. Public*, pg. 534

Rovleau, Michael, Chm. Bd.--Aaron Brothers, Inc., City of Commerce, CA; *U.S. Public*, pg. 1104

Rowan, H., Chm. Bd.--Magnetic Metals Corp., Camden, NJ; *U.S. Private*, pg. 560

Rowan, Henry M., Chm. Bd.--Tech-Tran Corporation, Rancocas, NJ; *U.S. Private*, pg. 560

Rowan, Henry M., Jr., Chm. Bd., Pres. & Chief Exec. Officer--Inductotherm Industries, Inc., Rancocas, NJ; *U.S. Private*, pg. 560

Rowe, John W., Chm. Bd.--New England Power Service Co., Westborough, MA; *U.S. Public*, pg. 1171

Rowe, Josiah P., III, Chm. Bd., Pres., Chief Exec. Officer & Gen. Mgr.--The Free Lance-Star Publishing Co., Fredericksburg, VA; *U.S. Private*, pg. 424

Rowe, O. Regan, Jr., Chm. Bd.--The Rowe Corporation, Charlotte, NC; *U.S. Private*, pg. 948

Rowland, L.H., Chm. Bd. & Chief Exec. Officer--Kansas City Southern Industries, Inc., Kansas City, MO; *U.S. Public*, pg. 943

Rowland, Lawrence, Chm., Pres. & Chief Exec. Officer--Lincoln National Administrative Services Corp., Fort Wayne, IN; *U.S. Public*, pg. 998

Rowland, Lawrence, Chm. Bd. & Chief Exec. Officer--Lincoln National Intermediaries, Inc., Fort Wayne, IN; *U.S. Public*, pg. 998

Rowland, Lawrence, Chm. Bd. & Chief Exec. Officer--Lincoln National Reinsurance Company (Bermuda) Limited, Fort Wayne, IN; *U.S. Public*, pg. 998

Rowland, Lawrence, Chm. & Chief Exec. Officer--Lincoln National Risk Management, Inc., Fort Wayne, IN; *U.S. Public*, pg. 998

Rowland, Lawrence, Chm. & Chief Exec. Officer--Lincoln National Structured Settlement, Inc., Fort Wayne, IN; *U.S. Public*, pg. 998

Rowland, Lawrence, Chm. & Chief Exec. Officer--Old Fort Insurance Co., Ltd. (Bermuda), Hamilton, Bermuda; *U.S. Public*, pg. 998

Rowland, Lawrence, Chm. & Chief Exec. Officer--Underwriters & Management Services Inc., Indianapolis, IN; *U.S. Public*, pg. 998

Rowling, Robert, Chm. Bd.--TRT Holdings Inc., Irving, TX; *U.S. Private*, pg. 1065

Rowling, Robert B., Chm. Bd.--Omni Hotels, Irving, TX; *U.S. Private*, pg. 1065

Rowse, James R., Sr., Chm. Bd.--Veryfine Products, Inc., Westford, MA; *U.S. Private*, pg. 1137

Royall, Rovert V., Jr., Chm. Bd. & Chief Exec. Officer--NBSC Corporation, Columbia, SC; *U.S. Public*, pg. 1549

Royer, K.W., Chm. Bd.--Enzopac, Inc., Sheboygan, WI; *U.S. Private*, pg. 379

Royse, John N., Chm. Bd. & Chief Exec. Officer--Old National Bancorp, Evansville, IN; *U.S. Public*, pg. 1217

Royse, John N., Chm. Bd.--Merchants National Bank, Terre Haute, IN; *U.S. Public*, pg. 1217

Rubeli, Paul E., Chm. Bd., Pres. & Chief Exec. Officer--Aztar Corporation, Phoenix, AZ; *U.S. Public*, pg. 158

Rubenstein, Allan E., Chm. Bd.--The Cooper Companies, Inc., Irvine, CA; *U.S. Public*, pg. 442

Rubenstein, Leonard M., Chm. Bd. & Chief Exec. Officer--Conning, Hartford, CT; *U.S. Private*, pg. 443

Rubenzer, Dave, Chm. Bd.--Great Clips, Inc., Minneapolis, MN; *U.S. Private*, pg. 473

Ruberg, Werner, Chm. Bd. & Chief Exec. Officer--Owens-Corning Eternit Rohre GmbH, Aachen, Germany; *U.S. Public*, pg. 1237

Rubin, David, Chm. Bd.--Republic Factors Corp., New York, NY; *U.S. Public*, pg. 1380

Rubin, Donald, Chm. Bd. & Pres.--M. Rubin & Sons Inc., Long Island City, NY; *U.S. Private*, pg. 949

Rubin, Gerald J., Chm. Bd. & Chief Exec. Officer--Helen of Troy Corporation, El Paso, TX; *U.S. Public*, pg. 807

Rubin, Harold R., Chm. Bd.--Stevens-Lee Company, Minneapolis, MN; *U.S. Private*, pg. 1042

Rubin, Joel, Chm. Bd. & Chief Exec. Officer--Phototype Color Graphics, Inc., Pennsauken, NJ; *U.S. Private*, pg. 864

Rubin, Martin, Chm. Bd.--Parsons Brinckerhoff Inc., New York, NY; *U.S. Private*, pg. 841

Rubin, Michael G., Chm. Bd. & Chief Exec. Officer--Ryka Incorporated, King of Prussia, PA; *U.S. Public*, pg. 1414

Rubin, Robert M., Chm. Bd. & Chief Exec. Officer--ERD Waste Corp., Commack, NY; *U.S. Public*, pg. 546

Rubin, Tom, Chm.--Focus Media, Santa Monica, CA; *U.S. Private*, pg. 415

Rubins, Jack, Chm. Bd.--Osprey Park Ltd., London, United Kingdom; *Int'l*, pg. 1012

Ruckelshaus, William D., Chm. Bd.--Browning-Ferris Industries, Inc., Houston, TX; *U.S. Public*, pg. 262

Ruckert, Jurg, Chm.--Reismuhle Brunnen AG, Brunnen, Switzerland; *Int'l*, pg. 330

Rucks, William W., III, Chm. Bd.--The First National Bank of Lafayette, Lafayette, LA; *U.S. Public*, pg. 630

Rudd, Andrew, Chm. Bd. & Chief Exec. Officer--Barra, Inc., Berkeley, CA; *U.S. Public*, pg. 191

Rudd, J.G.R., Chm. Bd.--Thomas Robinson Group Plc, Kilburn, United Kingdom; *Int'l*, pg. 231

Rudd, Nigel, Chm. Bd.--Pilkington Plc, Saint Helens, United Kingdom; *Int'l*, pg. 1056

Rudd, Nigel, Sir, Chm. Bd.--Williams Holdings Plc, Derby, United Kingdom; *Int'l*, pg. 1499

Rudeen, William, Chm. Bd.--Southern Minnesota Beet Sugar Cooperative, Renville, MN; *U.S. Private*, pg. 1016

Rudey, John M., Chm. Bd.--U.S. Timberlands Company, L.P., Klamath Falls, OR; *U.S. Public*, pg. 1688

Rudman, Edward I., Chm.--Rothschild/Pell, Rudman & Co., Inc., Baltimore, MD; *U.S. Public*, pg. 1674

Rudolf, Herbert, Chm. Bd.--Messer Griesheim GmbH, Frankfurt/Main, Germany; *Int'l*, pg. 626

Rudolph, John E., Chm. Bd.--Rudolph Foods Company, Lima, OH; *U.S. Private*, pg. 950

Ruelle, Mark A., Chm. Bd. & Pres.--Westar Energy, Topeka, KS; *U.S. Public*, pg. 1759

Ruen, Richard W., Sr., Chm. Bd.--Cleaners Hangor Co., Palm Harbor, FL; *U.S. Private*, pg. 245

Ruepp, Rene K., Dr., Chm. Bd. & Chief Exec. Officer--Forbo Holding SA, Eglisau, Switzerland; *Int'l*, pg. 496

Ruesch, Ernst, Chm.-Supervisory Committee--The Swiss Life/Rentenanstalt Group, Zurich, Switzerland; *Int'l*, pg. 1332

Ruf, Dave G., Jr., Chm. Bd. & Chief Exec. Officer--Burns & McDonnell Engineers-Architects-Consultants, Kansas City, MO; *U.S. Private*, pg. 187

Ruff, Edward C., Chm. Bd. & Chief Oper. Officer--Interstate/Johnson Lane, Inc., Charlotte, NC; *U.S. Public*, pg. 909

Ruger, William B., Chm. Bd., Chief Exec. Officer & Treas.--Sturm, Ruger & Co., Inc., Southport, CT; *U.S. Public*, pg. 1526

Ruhle, Frank S., Chm. Bd., Pres. & Chief Exec. Officer--Ruhle Companies, Inc., Valhalla, NY; *U.S. Private*, pg. 950

Ruhlman, Jon R., Chm. Bd. & Chief Exec. Officer--Preformed Line Products, Cleveland, OH; *U.S. Public*, pg. 1321

Ruhlman, Terrell L., Chm. Bd. & Chief Exec. Officer--Cade Industries, Inc., Lansing, MI; *U.S. Public*, pg. 289

Rui, Luis, Chm. Bd. & Pres.--RIU International Pan American Ocean Resort Hotel, Miami Beach, FL; *U.S. Private*, pg. 904

Ruiz Nicoli, Pedro, Chm. & Chief Exec. Officer--Ruiz Nicoli Group, Madrid, Spain; *Int'l*, pg. 603

Ruiz, Fred, Chm. Bd. & Chief Exec. Officer--Ruiz Food Products, Inc., Dinuba, CA; *U.S. Private*, pg. 951

Rukeyser, S., Chm. Bd., Chief Exec. Officer & Editor-in-Chief--Whittle Communications L.P., Knoxville, TN; *U.S. Public*, pg. 1614

Rule, Ronald C., Chm. Bd., Pres. & Chief Exec. Officer--The United States Playing Card Company, Cincinnati, OH; *U.S. Private*, pg. 1125

Rullo, Fred P., Chm. Bd. & Chief Exec. Officer--Freedom Chemical Company, Radnor, PA; *U.S. Private*, pg. 425

Rummel, Peter S., Chm. Bd.--Walt Disney Imagineering, Glendale, CA; *U.S. Public*, pg. 513

Rumy, Zsolt, Chm. Bd., Pres. & Chief Exec. Officer--Zoltek Companies, Inc., Saint Louis, MO; *U.S. Public*, pg. 1794

Rund, Tom, Chm. Bd.--Scancem AB, Malmo, Sweden; *Int'l*, pg. 1198

Rundell, C.A., Jr., Chm. Bd.--NCI Building Systems, Inc., Houston, TX; *U.S. Public*, pg. 1145

Rupert, J.P., Chm.--R&R Tobacco Limited, Cape Town, South Africa; *Int'l*, pg. 1129

Rupp, Barry, Chm. Bd. & Chief Exec. Officer--Financial World Partners, New York, NY; *U.S. Private*, pg. 404

Rupp, Glenn R., Chm. Bd., Pres. & Chief Exec. Officer--Converse Inc., North Reading, MA; *U.S. Public*, pg. 441

Ruppman, Charles T., Chm. Bd.--Ruppman Marketing Technologies, Inc., Peoria, IL; *U.S. Private*, pg. 951

Rupprecht, Gerhard, Chm.--Allianz Lebensversicherungs-AG, Stuttgart, Germany; *Int'l*, pg. 58

Rupprecht, Rudolph, Dr., Chm.-Exec. Bd.--MAN Aktiengesellschaft, Munich, Germany; *Int'l*, pg. 824

Rus, Arlyn D., Chm. Bd., Pres. & Chief Exec. Officer--Raritan Bancorp Inc., Bridgewater, NJ; *U.S. Public*, pg. 1361

Rusbridge, Michael, Chm. Bd.--Reed Exhibition Companies-Europe, Paris, France; *Int'l*, pg. 1096

Rusbridge, Michael, Chm. & Chief Exec. Officer--Reed Exhibition Companies, Richmond, United Kingdom; *Int'l*, pg. 1096

Rusch, Freeland, Chm. Bd. & Chief Exec. Officer--M & I Merchants Bank, Rhinelander, WI; *U.S. Public*, pg. 1050

Rusk, Gerald W., Chm. Bd.--Freeman Manufacturing & Supply Company, Avon, OH; *U.S. Private*, pg. 426

Russell, Ed, Chm. Bd., Pres. & Chief Exec. Officer--Minnesota Power, Duluth, MN; *U.S. Public*, pg. 1116

Russell, Frank E., Chm. Bd.--Central Newspapers, Inc., Indianapolis, IN; *U.S. Public*, pg. 326

Russell, George F., Jr., Chm. Bd.--Frank Russell Company, Tacoma, WA; *U.S. Private*, pg. 952

Russell, George F., Jr., Chm.--Frank Russell Securities, Inc., Tacoma, WA; *U.S. Private*, pg. 952

Russell, George F., Jr., Chm.--Frank Russell Trust Co., Tacoma, WA; *U.S. Private*, pg. 952

Russell, George, Sir, Chm. Bd.--3i Group plc, London, United Kingdom; *Int'l*, pg. 1386

Russell, Herman J., Sr., Chm. Bd.--H.J. Russell & Co., Atlanta, GA; *U.S. Private*, pg. 952

Russell, John, Chm. Bd.--Days Inns of America, Inc., Parsippany, NJ; *U.S. Public*, pg. 321

Russell, John, Chm. Bd.--Knights Franchise Systems, Inc., Parsippany, NJ; *U.S. Public*, pg. 321

Russell, John, Jr., Chm., Pres. & Chief Exec. Officer-Hospitality Div.--HFS, Incorporated, Parsippany, NJ; *U.S. Public*, pg. 321

Russell, Richard G., Chm. Bd., Pres. & Chief Exec. Officer--Tech Spray, Inc., Amarillo, TX; *U.S. Private*, pg. 1071

Russell, William K., Chm. Bd.--Knight Equipment International Inc., Costa Mesa, CA; *U.S. Public*, pg. 862

Russo, Anthony J., Chm. Bd. & Pres.--E.C.D., Inc., Hillside, NJ; *U.S. Private*, pg. 353

Rust, Edward B., Jr., Chm. Bd., Pres. & Chief Exec. Officer--State Farm Mutual Automobile Insurance Company, Bloomington, IL; *U.S. Private*, pg. 1036

Rustand, Warren, Chm. Bd. & Chief Exec. Officer--Rural Metro Corporation, Scottsdale, AZ; *U.S. Public*, pg. 1412

Rutherford, Clyde E., Chm. Bd. & Pres.--Dairylea Cooperative Inc., East Syracuse, NY; *U.S. Private*, pg. 307

Rutland, Robert J., Chm. Bd. & Chief Exec. Officer--Allied Holdings, Inc., Decatur, GA; *U.S. Public*, pg. 48

Rutland, Robert J., Chm. Bd. & Chief Exec. Officer--Allied Automotive Group, Decatur, GA; *U.S. Public*, pg. 48

Ruttenberg, Harold, Chm. Bd. & Pres.--Just For Feet, Inc., Pelham, AL; *U.S. Public*, pg. 935

Ruttenberg, Harold J., Chm. Bd., Principal Acctg. Officer, Chief Exec. Officer & Treas.--American Locker Group, Inc., Jamestown, NY; *U.S. Public*, pg. 85

Rutter, William J., Ph.D., Chm. Bd.--Chiron Corporation, Emeryville, CA; *U.S. Public*, pg. 349

Ryan, Arthur F., Chm. Bd. & Chief Exec. Officer--The Prudential Insurance Company of America, Newark, NJ; *U.S. Private*, pg. 892

Ryan, Arthur F., Chm. Bd., Pres. & Chief Exec. Officer--The Prudential Investment Corp., Newark, NJ; *U.S. Private*, pg. 892

Ryan, Brendan, Chm. & Chief Exec. Officer--FCB, New York, NY; *U.S. Private*, pg. 389

Ryan, Brendan, Chm. & Chief Exec. Officer-FCB Worldwide--True North Communications Inc., Chicago, IL; *U.S. Public*, pg. 1641

Ryan, Charles P., Jr., Chm. Bd. & Pres.--Charan Industries, Inc., Garden City, NY; *U.S. Private*, pg. 229

Ryan, David J., Chm. Bd.--EcoScience Corporation, East Brunswick, NJ; *U.S. Public*, pg. 563

Ryan, Frank J., Chm. Bd.--Southdown, Inc., Houston, TX; *U.S. Public*, pg. 1488

Ryan, George T., Chm. Bd.--Thompson Steel Co., Inc., Canton, MA; *U.S. Private*, pg. 1083

Ryan, Gerald A., Chm. Bd.--Rent-Way, Inc., Erie, PA; *U.S. Public*, pg. 1377

Ryan, Gerald A., Chm. Bd.--Spectrum Control, Inc., Erie, PA; *U.S. Public*, pg. 1497

Ryan, James N., Chm. Bd. & Chief Exec. Officer--Petroleum Development Corporation, Bridgeport, WV; *U.S. Public*, pg. 1280

Ryan, Jim, Chm. Bd. & Chief Exec. Officer--BWC Financial Corp., Walnut Creek, CA; *U.S. Public*, pg. 108

Ryan, John G., Chm. Bd. & Chief Exec. Officer--Global Marine Drilling Co., Houston, TX; *U.S. Public*, pg. 748

Ryan, John T., III, Chm. Bd. & Chief Exec. Officer--Mine Safety Appliances Co., Pittsburgh, PA; *U.S. Public*, pg. 1114

Ryan, Patrick G., Chm. Bd., Pres. & Chief Exec. Officer--AON Corporation, Chicago, IL; *U.S. Public*, pg. 117

Ryan, Patrick G., Chm. & Chief Exec. Officer--AON Risk Services Inc. of Illinois, Chicago, IL; *U.S. Public*, pg. 117

Ryan, Russell R., Chm. Bd.--Ryan Construction Company of Minnesota, Inc., Minneapolis, MN; *U.S. Private*, pg. 953

Ryan, T.A., Chm. & Chief Exec. Officer--GPA Group PLC, Shannon, Ireland; *Int'l*, pg. 37

Ryan, William A., Chm. Bd., Pres. & Chief Exec. Officer--Team, Inc., Alvin, TX; *U.S. Public*, pg. 1562

Ryan, William J., Chm. Bd., Pres. & Chief Exec. Officer--Peoples Heritage Financial Group, Inc., Portland, ME; *U.S. Public*, pg. 1275

Rydin, Bo, Chm. Bd.--AB Industrivarden, Stockholm, Sweden; *Int'l*, pg. 678

Rydin, Bo, Chm. Bd.--Svenska Cellulosa Aktiebolaget (SCA), Stockholm, Sweden; *Int'l*, pg. 1326

Rye, Walter L., Chm. Bd. & Chief Exec. Officer--Cincinnati Gear Company, Cincinnati, OH; *U.S. Private*, pg. 240

Rylander, James D., Chm. Bd.--The Tog Shop, Americus, GA; *U.S. Private*, pg. 1090

Rysavy, Jirka, Chm. Bd.--Corporate Express, Inc., Broomfield, CO; *U.S. Public*, pg. 449

Saban, Hiam, Chm. Bd. & Chief Exec. Officer--Saban Entertainment, Los Angeles, CA; *U.S. Private*, pg. 959

Sabanci, Sakip, Chm. Bd.--Sabanci Holding A.S., Istanbul, Turkey; *Int'l*, pg. 1167

Sabatacakis, Petros, Chm. Bd.--Plan International USA, Inc., Warwick, RI; *U.S. Private*, pg. 869

Sabatacakis, Petros K., Chm. Bd.--Chase Manhattan Mortgage Corporation, Worthington, OH; *U.S. Public*, pg. 338

Sabatino, Victor, Chm. Bd., Pres. & Chief Exec. Officer--Family Smacks, Inc., Liberty, MO; *U.S. Private*, pg. 393

Sabbatini, Fabrizio, Chm. & Mng. Dir.--TBWA Italia S.p.A., Milan, Italy; *U.S. Private*, pg. 1063

Sabbeth, Stephen J., Chm. Bd. & Pres.--Sabbeth Industries Ltd, Carle Place, NY; *U.S. Private*, pg. 959

Sabin, David C., Chm. Bd. & Sec.--Salton/Maxim Housewares, Inc., Mount Prospect, IL; *U.S. Public*, pg. 1430

Saca, Tony, Sr. Pres.--Filco, Inc., Sacramento, CA; *U.S. Private*, pg. 404

Sachs, Louis S., Chm. Bd.--Sachs Holding Company, Chesterfield, MO; *U.S. Private*, pg. 959

Sacknoft, Philip, Chm. Bd. & Treas.--XRE Corporation, Littleton, MA; *U.S. Public*, pg. 1595

Sacknoft, Philip, Chm. Bd.--Angiographic Devices, Littleton, MA; *U.S. Public*, pg. 1596

Sacks, Barry, Chm. Bd.--Chorus Line Corporation, Vernon, CA; *U.S. Private*, pg. 238

Sada Gonzalez, Adrian, Chm. Bd.--Banca Serfin, S.A., New York Agency, New York, NY; *Int'l*, pg. 137

Sage, Andrew G.C., II, Chm. Bd.--Robertson-Ceco Corporation, San Ramon, CA; *U.S. Public*, pg. 1394

Sagol, Joseph, Chm. Bd.--Keter Plastic Ltd., Herzliyya, Israel; *Int'l*, pg. 732

Sahakian, Henry D., Chm. Bd. & Chief Exec. Officer--Uni-Marts, Inc., State College, PA; *U.S. Public*, pg. 1664

Sahlberg, Karl Erik, Chm. Bd.--Cardo AB, Malmo, Sweden; *Int'l*, pg. 268

Sahlberg, Karl-Erik, Chm. Bd.--Vattenfall AB, Stockholm, Sweden; *Int'l*, pg. 1452

Sahm, Roland R., Chm. Bd. & Chief Exec. Officer--Elixir Industries, Gardena, CA; *U.S. Private*, pg. 371

Sahm, Volker, Chm. Bd.--Georg Sahm GmbH & Co. KG Maschinenfabrik, Eschwege, Germany; *Int'l*, pg. 1169

Sainsbury, D.J., Chm. & Chief Exec.--J. Sainsbury plc, London, United Kingdom; *Int'l*, pg. 1169

Saint-Geours, Frederic, Chm. Bd.--Peugeot Motor Co. Plc, Coventry, United Kingdom; *Int'l*, pg. 1021

Saint-Pierre, Guy, Chm. Bd.--SNC-Lavalin Group Inc., Montreal, Canada; *Int'l*, pg. 1161

Saito, Hiroshi, Chm. Bd.--Nippon Steel Corporation, Tokyo, Japan; *Int'l*, pg. 939

Saito, Joichi, Chm. Bd. & Chief Exec. Officer--CPB Inc., Honolulu, HI; *U.S. Public*, pg. 282

Saito, Joichi, Chm. Bd. & Chief Exec. Officer--Central Pacific Bank, Honolulu, HI; *U.S. Public*, pg. 283

Saito, Joichi, Chm. Bd.--CPB Properties, Inc., Honolulu, HI; *U.S. Public*, pg. 283

Saito, Kiminori, Chm. Bd.--Daishowa Paper Mfg. Co., Ltd., Fuji, Japan; *Int'l*, pg. 373

Saji, Keizo, Chm. Bd.--Suntory Ltd., Osaka, Japan; *Int'l*, pg. 1321

Sakai, Hirosuke, Chm. Bd.--Nippon Credit International (HK) Limited, Hong Kong, Hong Kong; *Int'l*, pg. 933

Sakai, Kosaku, Chm. Bd.--LTCB Trust Company, New York, NY; *Int'l*, pg. 816

Sakamoto, Katsuro, Chm.--Ikegami Tsushinki Co., Ltd., Tokyo, Japan; *Int'l*, pg. 660

Sakamoto, Michitaka, Chm. Bd.--The Nanto Bank, Ltd., Nara, Japan; *Int'l*, pg. 905

Sakata, Noboru, Chm. Bd.--Nippon Credit (Schweiz) AG, Zurich, Switzerland; *Int'l*, pg. 933

Sakata, Noboru, Chm. Bd.--Eastbridge Holdings Inc., New York, NY; *Int'l*, pg. 933

Sakata, Noboru, Chm. Supervisory Bd.--Nippon Credit Bank AG, Frankfurt/Main, Germany; *Int'l*, pg. 933

Saker, Joseph J., Chm. Bd. & Pres.--Foodarama Supermarkets, Inc., Freehold, NJ; *U.S. Public*, pg. 661

Sakus, Gedas A., Chm. Bd.-Bell Northern Research & Pres.-Nortel Tech.--Northern Telecom Limited, Brampton, Canada; *Int'l*, pg. 968

Saldanha, Stephen, Chm. Bd.--IPAC, Inc., Niagara Falls, NY; *U.S. Private*, pg. 555

Saldanha, Walter, Exec. Chm.--Chaitra Leo Burnett Private Ltd., Mumbai, India; *U.S. Private*, pg. 184

Salim, Soedono, Chm. Bd.--First Pacific Company Limited, Hong Kong, Hong Kong; *Int'l*, pg. 487

Salina Amorini, Elizabeth, Chm. Bd. & Pres.--SGS Societe Generale de Surveillance Holding S.A., Geneva, Switzerland; *Int'l*, pg. 1153

Salinas Pliego, Ricardo B., Chm. Bd. & Pres.--Grupo Elektra S.A. de C.V., Mexico, Mexico; *Int'l*, pg. 573

Sall, Hyman L., Chm. Bd. & Chief Exec. Officer--Atlantic Metals Corporation, Philadelphia, PA; *U.S. Private*, pg. 95

Salles, Pedro Moreira, Chm. Bd.--Uniao de Bancos Brasileiros S.A. (Unibanco), Sao Paulo, Brazil; *Int'l*, pg. 1431

Salmon, John L., Chm. Bd.--TVESCO, Inc., Memphis, TN; *U.S. Private*, pg. 1066

Salmon, Thomas P., Chm. Bd.--Green Mountain Power Corporation, South Burlington, VT; *U.S. Public*, pg. 761

Salmon, Walter J., Chm. Bd.--Hannaford Bros. Co., Scarborough, ME; *U.S. Public*, pg. 781

Salomon, Georges, Chm. Bd.--Salomon S.A., Annecy, France; *Int'l*, pg. 1181

Salwasser, Melvin, Chm. Bd.--Salwasser Manufacturing Company, Inc., Reedley, CA; *U.S. Private*, pg. 963

Salwen, Howard C., Chm. Bd.--Proteon, Inc., Westborough, MA; *U.S. Public*, pg. 1336

Samans, Robert A., Chm. Bd. & Pres.--Scanforms, Inc., Bristol, PA; *U.S. Public*, pg. 228

Samarah, Yasar, Chm. Bd.--DeMert & Dougherty, Inc., Coal City, IL; *U.S. Private*, pg. 323

Samberg, Stephen, Chm. Bd. & Chief Exec. Officer--Nantucket Industries, Inc., Melville, NY; *U.S. Public*, pg. 1151

Samburg, A. Gene, Chm. Bd., Pres. & Chief Exec. Officer--Kastle Systems LLC, Arlington, VA; *U.S. Private*, pg. 608

Sammon, Dr. John W., Jr., Chm. Bd., Pres. & Chief Exec. Officer--PAR Technology Corporation, New Hartford, NY; *U.S. Public*, pg. 1256

Sammons, E.D., Chm. Bd.--Sammons Enterprises, Inc., Dallas, TX; *U.S. Private*, pg. 963

Samouilov, Anatoly, Chm. Bd.--L-Zos Optics, Ltd., Detroit, MI; *U.S. Private*, pg. 639

Sample, David, Chm. Bd., Pres. & Chief Exec. Officer--PSDI, Bedford, MA; *U.S. Private*, pg. 828

Sampson, Curtis A., Chm. Bd., Pres. & Chief Exec. Officer--Communications Systems, Inc., Hector, MN; *U.S. Public*, pg. 415

Sampson, Curtis A., Chm., Pres. & Chief Exec. Officer--Suttle Caribe, Inc., Humacao, PR; *U.S. Public*, pg. 415

Sampson, Gerald A., Chm.--Kaufmann's, Pittsburgh, PA; *U.S. Public*, pg. 1063

Samsill, Mark, Chm. Bd.--Samsill Corporation, Fort Worth, TX; *U.S. Private*, pg. 963

Samson, Bernice, Chm. & Pres.--Sterling Supply Company, Inc., Lisle, IL; *U.S. Private*, pg. 1041

Samuel, Ernie, Chm. Bd.--Samuel Specialty Metals, Parsippany, NJ; *U.S. Private*, pg. 964

San Antonio, Joel, Chm. Bd. & Chief Exec. Officer--Warrantech Corporation, Stamford, CT; *U.S. Public*, pg. 1740

San, Lim Kim, Chm. Bd.--Singapore Press Holdings Ltd., Singapore, Singapore; *Int'l*, pg. 1253

San, Lim Kim, Chm. Bd.--Times Publishing Limited, Singapore, Singapore; *Int'l*, pg. 1390

Sanchez, J.M. Mirazo, Chm. & Gen. Mgr.--Nationale-Nederlanden Spain, Madrid, Spain; *Int'l*, pg. 651

Sanchez, Michael A., Chm. Bd.--Sanchez Computer Associates, Malvern, PA; *U.S. Public*, pg. 1425

Sandberg, Richard A., Chm. Bd.--Dianon Systems, Inc., Stratford, CT; *U.S. Public*, pg. 506

Sanders, E. Craig, Chm. Bd., Pres. & Chief Exec. Officer--Peoples Telephone Company, Inc., Miami, FL; *U.S. Public*, pg. 1275

Sanders, Harvey, Chm. Bd., Pres. & Chief Exec. Officer--Nautica Enterprises, Inc., New York, NY; *U.S. Public*, pg. 1167

Sanders, John W., Chm. Bd.--Creswell, Munsell, Fultz & Zirbel, L.P., Cedar Rapids, IA; *U.S. Private*, pg. 1197

Sanders, Lewis A., Chm. Bd. & Chief Exec. Officer--Sanford C. Bernstein & Co., Inc., New York, NY; *U.S. Private*, pg. 137

Sanders, Max, Chm. Bd.--Memcor Truohm, Huntington, IN; *U.S. Private*, pg. 813

Sanders, Max D., Chm. Bd. & Chief Exec. Officer--Ohmite Manufacturing Company, Skokie, IL; *U.S. Private*, pg. 813

Sanders, O'Neil, Chm. Bd., Pres., Chief Exec. & Chief Oper. Officer--Associated Petroleum Carriers, Spartanburg, SC; *U.S. Private*, pg. 92

Sanders, Steve, Chm. Bd. & Pres.--MMC Corp., Leawood, KS; *U.S. Private*, pg. 687

Sanders, W.J., III, Chm. Bd. & Chief Exec. Officer--Advanced Micro Devices, Inc., Sunnyvale, CA; *U.S. Public*, pg. 21

Sanders, William D., Chm. Bd., Pres. & Chief Exec. Officer--Security Capital Group Incorporated, Santa Fe, NM; *U.S. Private*, pg. 980

Sanderson, Joe Frank, Chm. Bd.--Sanderson Farms, Inc., Laurel, MS; *U.S. Public*, pg. 1430

Sandhu, M.S., Chm. Bd., Pres. & Chief Exec. Officer--SRS Technologies, Newport Beach, CA; *U.S. Private*, pg. 958

Sandifer, Thomas N., Chm. & Chief Exec. Officer--Cain & Bultman, Jacksonville, FL; *U.S. Private*, pg. 199

Sandler, Herbert M., Chm. Bd. & Co-Chief Exec. Officer--Golden West Financial Corporation, Oakland, CA; *U.S. Public*, pg. 750

Sandler, Herbert M., Chm. Bd. & Chief Exec. Officer--World Savings & Loan Association, FSLA, Oakland, CA; *U.S. Public*, pg. 750

Sandler, Herbert M., Chm. Bd. & Chief Exec. Officer--World Savings Bank, FSB, Oakland, CA; *U.S. Public*, pg. 750

Sandler, Marion O., Chm. Bd. & Co-Chief Exec. Officer--Golden West Financial Corporation, Oakland, CA; *U.S. Public*, pg. 750

Sandler, Marion O., Chm. Bd. & Chief Exec. Officer--World Savings Bank, FSB, Oakland, CA; *U.S. Public*, pg. 750

Sandlin, David E., Chm. Bd. & Pres.--The Flight International Group, Inc., Newport News, VA; *U.S. Public*, pg. 654

Sands, Marvin, Chm. Bd.--Canandaigua Wine Company, Inc., Canandaigua, NY; *U.S. Public*, pg. 300

Sanel, Henry, Chm. Bd.--Automotive Supply Associates, Inc., Concord, NH; *U.S. Private*, pg. 101

Sanfilippo, Jasper, Chm. Bd. & Chief Exec. Officer--John B. Sanfilippo & Son, Inc., Elk Grove Village, IL; *U.S. Public*, pg. 1431

Sanford, Bill R., Chm. Bd., Pres. & Treas.--Steris Corporation, Mentor, OH; *U.S. Public*, pg. 1515

Sanford, John T., Chm. Bd.--Trinity-Structural Steel, Montgomery, AL; *U.S. Public*, pg. 1639

Sanford, Mary C., Chm. Bd.--Maui Land & Pineapple Co., Inc., Kahului, HI; *U.S. Public*, pg. 1060

Sanford, Philip H., Chm. Bd. & Chief Exec. Officer--Krystal Company, Chattanooga, TN; *U.S. Private*, pg. 636

Sanford, Richard D., Chm. Bd. & Chief Exec. Officer--Intelligent Electronics, Inc., Exton, PA; *U.S. Public*, pg. 887

Sanger, Stephen W., Chm. Bd. & Chief Exec. Officer--General Mills, Inc., Minneapolis, MN; *U.S. Public*, pg. 717

Sanghi, Steve, Chm. Bd., Pres. & Chief Exec. Officer--Microchip Technology, Inc., Chandler, AZ; *U.S. Public*, pg. 1105

Sankes, Gary, Chm. Bd. & Pres.--Scrufari Construction Co. Inc., Niagara Falls, NY; *U.S. Private*, pg. 977

Sansom, William B., Chm. Bd. & Chief Exec. Officer--The H.T. Hackney Co., Knoxville, TN; *U.S. Private*, pg. 493

Sant, Roger W., Chm. Bd.--AES Corporation, Arlington, VA; *U.S. Public*, pg. 5

Santarlasci, Joseph, Chm. Bd.--Swirl, II LTD, New York, NY; *U.S. Private*, pg. 1059

Santhanam, T. S., Chm.--Brakes India Ltd., Padi, India; *Int'l*, *pg. 820*

Santos, Alberto A., Chm. Bd.--International Bancshares Corp, Laredo, TX; *U.S. Private*, pg. 568

Santos, Jose Castro, Chm. Bd.--FIMA-Productos Alimentares, Lda, Lisbon, Portugal; *Int'l*, pg. 471

Santry, Michael G., Chm. Bd., Pres. & Chief Exec. Officer--ATC Communications Group, Inc., Dallas, TX; *U.S. Public*, pg. 11

Santulli, Richard T., Chm. Bd., Pres. & Chief Exec. Officer--Executive Jet Aviation, Inc., Columbus, OH; *U.S. Private*, *pg. 388*

Saper, Lawrence, Chm. Bd., Pres. & Chief Exec. Officer--Datascope Corp., Montvale, NJ; *U.S. Public*, pg. 487

Saperstein, Alan, Chm. & Creative Dir.--MacNamara, Stewart & Saperstein, New York, NY; *U.S. Private*, pg. 692

Sar, N., Chm. Bd. & Mng. Dir.--Eastern Coalfields Limited, Burdwan, India; *Int'l*, pg. 298

Sarasin, K., Chm. Bd. & Mng. Dir.--Jardine Matheson (Thailand) Ltd., Bangkok, Thailand; *Int'l*, pg. 705

Sarckowsky, Herman, Chm. Bd.--Pace International L.P., Kirkland, WA; *U.S. Private*, pg. 829

Sardas, Jack, Chm. Bd. & Chief Exec. Officer--Dal-Tile International, Dallas, TX; *U.S. Private*, pg. 308

Sargent, Charles L., Chm. Bd. & Chief Exec. Officer--Thetford Corporation, Ann Arbor, MI; *U.S. Private*, pg. 352

Sargent, John, Chm. Bd., Chief Exec. Officer & Editorial Dir.--St. Martins Press, Inc., New York, NY; *Int'l*, pg. 1479

Sargent, Warren B., Chm. Bd.--Todd & Sargent, Inc., Ames, IA; *U.S. Private*, pg. 1089

Sarin, Arun, Chm. Bd.--AirTouch Cellular - Western Region, Bellevue, WA; *U.S. Public*, pg. 34

Sarkes, H. Jay, Chm. Bd., Pres. & Chief Exec. Officer--Fleet Bank, N.A., Jersey City, NJ; *U.S. Public*, pg. 649

Sarkisian, Robert, Chm. Bd., Pres. & Chief Exec. Officer--Marketing Displays International, Farmington Hills, MI; *U.S. Private*, pg. 705

Sarles, H. Jay, Chm. Bd.--Fleet Mortgage Group, Inc., Columbia, SC; *U.S. Public*, pg. 650

Sarmanian, Peter, Chm. Bd. & Chief Exec. Officer--Printed Circuit Corporation, Woburn, MA; *U.S. Private*, pg. 886

Sarmiento, Rogelio, Chm. Bd.--Sarmiento Rappan Industrico, Manila, Philippines; *Int'l*, pg. 1194

Sarnoff, William, Chm. Bd.--Time Warner Trade Publishing, New York, NY; *U.S. Public*, pg. 1614

Sarnow, Greg, Pres.--American Television Time, Inc., Austin, TX; *U.S. Private*, pg. 63

Sarrazin, Jurgen, Chm.-Supervisory Bd.--Bilfinger + Berger Bauaktiengesellschaft, Mannheim, Germany; *Int'l*, pg. 194

Saruwatori, Toshio, Chm.--ORIX Rent-A-Car, Tokyo, Japan; *Int'l*, pg. 1009

Sasai, Akira, Chm. Bd.--Meiji Seika Kaisha, Ltd., Tokyo, Japan; *Int'l*, pg. 855

Sasser, Billy G., Chm. Bd.--Reeves Southeastern Corporation, Tampa, FL; *U.S. Private*, pg. 916

Sato, Fumio, Chm. Bd.--Toshiba Corporation, Tokyo, Japan; *Int'l*, pg. 1402

Sato, Isao, Chm. Bd.--Showa Products Co., Ltd., Osaka, Japan; *U.S. Public*, pg. 1487

Sato, Mitsuo, Chm. Bd. & Pres.--Asian Development Bank, Manila, Philippines; *Int'l*, pg. 88

Sato, Sukekuro, Chm. Bd.--Sato Kogyo Co., Ltd., Tokyo, Japan; *Int'l*, pg. 1197

Satre, Philip G., Chm. Bd., Pres. & Chief Exec. Officer--Harrah's Entertainment, Inc., Memphis, TN; *U.S. Public*, pg. 790

Sattler, Gerhard, Dep. Chm.--Dyckerhoff & Widmann AG, Munich, Germany; *Int'l*, pg. 423

Saubert, Walter, Chm. Bd.--American Red Ball Transit Co. Inc., Indianapolis, IN; *U.S. Private*, pg. 97

Saubert, Walter E., Chm. Bd. & Chief Exec. Officer--Atlas World Group, Inc., Evansville, IN; *U.S. Private*, pg. 97

Saubert, Walter E., Chm. Bd. & Chief Exec. Officer--Atlas Van Lines, Inc., Evansville, IN; *U.S. Private*, pg. 97

Saucer, Willie, Chm. Bd., Pres. & Chief Exec. Officer--Farmers Co-op Market Inc., Frisco City, AL; *U.S. Private*, *pg. 395*

Saudel, Larry, Chm. Bd.--Worldwide Sports & Recreation, Inc., Tulsa, OK; *U.S. Private*, pg. 1191

Sauder, Maynard, Chm. Bd.--Sauder Manufacturing Corporation, Archbold, OH; *U.S. Private*, pg. 967

Sauey, W.R., Chm. Bd., Pres. & Treas.--Flambeau Corporation, Baraboo, WI; *U.S. Private*, pg. 409

Sauey, W.R., Chm. Bd.--Flambeau Products Corp., Middlefield, OH; *U.S. Private*, pg. 409

Sauey, W.R., Chm. Bd.--Seats Incorporated, Reedsburg, WI; *U.S. Private*, pg. 410

Saugman, Per, Chm.--Blackwell Science, Oxford, United Kingdom; *Int'l*, pg. 197

Saul, Andrew, Chm. Bd.--Cache, Inc., New York, NY; *U.S. Public*, pg. 289

Saul, B. Francis, II, Chm. Bd. & Chief Exec. Officer--Saul Centers Inc., Chevy Chase, MD; *U.S. Public*, pg. 1435

Saul, Ralph, Chm. Bd.--Horace Mann Educators Corporation, Springfield, IL; *U.S. Public*, pg. 835

Saul, William J., Chm. Bd.--Remmele Engineering, Inc., New Brighton, MN; *U.S. Private*, pg. 921

Saunders, Bruce T., Chm. Bd.--Saunders Brothers, Westbrook, ME; *U.S. Private*, pg. 968

Saunders, E. Philip, Chm. Bd. & Chief Exec. Officer--Travel Ports of America Inc., Rochester, NY; *U.S. Public*, pg. 1632

Saunders, Fredric M., Chm. Bd. & Chief Exec. Officer--Prime Bancshares Inc., Houston, TX; *U.S. Public*, pg. 1326

Saunders, I.O.S., Chm. Bd.--Fleming Asset Management Limited, London, United Kingdom; *Int'l*, pg. 493

Saunders, J.O., Chm. Bd.--Taywood Homes Ltd., Feltham, United Kingdom; *Int'l*, pg. 1359

Saunders, R.F., Chm. Bd. & Chief Exec. Officer--Dakco Distributors, Inc., Minot, ND; *U.S. Private*, pg. 308

Sautter, Remy, Chm.--CLT UK Radio, London, United Kingdom; *Int'l*, pg. 561

Savage, R.T., Chm. Bd. & Chief Exec. Officer--Modine Manufacturing Company, Racine, WI; *U.S. Public*, pg. 1121

Savage, Richard H., Chm. Bd. & Co-Chief Exec. Officer--Amwest Insurance Group, Inc., Calabasas, CA; *U.S. Public*, pg. 106

Savaiano, N.J., Chm. Bd. & Pres.--United Laboratories, Inc., Saint Charles, IL; *U.S. Private*, pg. 1122

Savarese, Dr. Edward, Chm. Bd., Pres. & Chief Exec. Officer--Imaging Technologies Corp., San Diego, CA; *U.S. Public*, pg. 870

Saviers, F. Grant, Chm. Bd., Pres. & Chief Exec. Officer--Adaptec, Inc., Milpitas, CA; *U.S. Public*, pg. 19

Savitsky, Stephen, Chm. Bd., Pres. & Chief Exec. Officer--Staff Builders Inc., Lake Success, NY; *U.S. Public*, pg. 1501

Sawada, Shigeo, Chm.--Nippon Telegraph and Telephone Corporation, Tokyo, Japan; *Int'l*, pg. 940

Sawaragi, Osamu, Chm. Bd. & Chief Exec. Officer--National Steel Corporation, Mishawaka, IN; *Int'l*, pg. 902

Sawchuk, Arthur R., Chm. Bd., Pres. & Chief Exec. Officer--Du Pont Canada Inc., Mississauga, Canada; *U.S. Public*, pg. 532

Sawyer, Kenneth I., Chm. Bd., Pres. & Chief Exec. Officer--Pharmaceutical Resources, Spring Valley, NY; *U.S. Public*, pg. 1285

Saxton, Paul A., Chm. Bd., Pres. & Chief Exec. Officer--General Housewares Corp., Terre Haute, IN; *U.S. Public*, *pg. 715*

Sbarro, Mario, Chm. Bd. & Pres.--Sbarro, Inc., Commack, NY; *U.S. Public*, pg. 1435

Scaife, Richard M., Chm. Bd. & Publisher--Tribune Review Publishing Co., Greensburg, PA; *U.S. Private*, pg. 1102

Scanlan, Ruth B., Chm. Bd.--Eatelcorp Inc., Gonzales, LA; *U.S. Private*, pg. 358

Scanlon, P.D., Chm.--Tyco Investments (Australia) Limited, Saint Leonards, Australia; *U.S. Public*, pg. 1651

Scanlon, Peter, Joint Chm.--Chiltem Group SAM, Monaco, Monaco; *Int'l*, pg. 65

Scarlett, Joseph, Chm. Bd. & Chief Exec. Officer--Tractor Supply Co., Nashville, TN; *U.S. Public*, pg. 1627

Scattini, James, Chm. Bd. & Chief Exec. Officer--Artichoko Industries, Inc., Castroville, CA; *U.S. Private*, pg. 86

Scelba, David F., Chm. Bd.--SSD&W Integrated Marketing Communications, Montville, NJ; *U.S. Private*, pg. 958

Schaad, E.F., Dr., Chm.--HandelsBank NatWest, Zurich, Switzerland; *Int'l*, pg. 911

Schaaf, Bradford P., Chm. Bd.--Autranet, Inc., New York, NY; *U.S. Public*, pg. 589

Schacht, Henry B., Chm.--Lucent Technologies Inc., Murray Hill, NJ; *U.S. Public*, pg. 1017

Schadt, Dieter, Chm.-Supvr. Bd.--GEHE AG, Stuttgart, Germany; *Int'l*, pg. 591

Schaedler, Thomas J., Sr., Chm. Bd.--Schaedler Brothers, Inc., Harrisburg, PA; *U.S. Private*, pg. 969

Schaefer, George A., Jr., Chm. Bd., Pres. & Chief Exec. Offficer--Fifth Third Bancorp, Cincinnati, OH; *U.S. Public*, *pg. 621*

Schaefer, Rowland, Chm. Bd., Pres. & Chief Exec. Officer-Claire's Stores--Claire's Stores Inc., Pembroke Pines, FL; *U.S. Public*, pg. 381

Schaeffer, John C., Chm. Bd.--Westminster Bank & Trust Co. of Carroll County, Westminster, MD; *U.S. Public*, pg. 1089

Schaeffer, Leonard, Chm. Bd. & Chief Exec. Officer--Blue Cross of California, Woodland Hills, CA; *U.S. Private*, pg. 152

Schaeffer, Leonard D., Chm. Bd.--Wellpoint Health Networks, Inc., Woodland Hills, CA; *U.S. Private*, pg. 152

Schaeffer, Leonard D., Chm. Bd.--UniCARE Financial Corp., Irvine, CA; *U.S. Private*, pg. 152

Schaeffer, Peter, Chm. Bd.--Plibrico Co., Chicago, IL; *U.S. Private*, pg. 872

Schaer, F., Dr., Chm. Bd.--Tetko, Inc., Briarcliff Manor, NY; *U.S. Private*, pg. 1078

Schafer, Gordon, Chm. Bd.--United Hardware Distributing Co., Plymouth, MN; *U.S. Private*, pg. 335

Schafer, Walter, Chm. Bd.--Landesbank Hessen-Thuringen Girozentrale, Frankfurt/Main, Germany; *Int'l*, pg. 798

Schaffler, R.S., Chm. Bd.--Owens Corning/Foamular, Parsippany, NJ; *U.S. Public*, pg. 1237

Schalhamer, Melvin A., Chm. Bd.--Allied Chucker & Engineering Company, Jackson, MI; *U.S. Private*, pg. 38

Schamp, E.D., Chm. Bd. & Chief Exec. Officer--Peco Mfg. Co., Inc., Portland, OR; *U.S. Private*, pg. 846

Schanback, Martin, Chm. Bd.--Friendship Dairies, Inc., Jericho, NY; *U.S. Private*, pg. 429

Schanze, Richard L., Chm. Bd. & Chief Exec. Officer--Pinnacle Financial Services Inc., Saint Joseph, MI; *U.S. Public*, pg. 1297

Schar, Dwight, Chm. Bd. & Chief Exec. Officer--NVR, Inc., Mc Lean, VA; *U.S. Public*, pg. 1148

Schardt, Ronald, Chm. Bd., Chief Exec. Officer & Chief Oper. Officer--Reinke Manufacturing Co., Inc., Deshler, NE; *U.S. Private*, pg. 920

Scharf, Michael J., Chm. Bd., Pres. & Chief Exec. Officer--Niagara Corporation, New York, NY; *U.S. Public*, pg. 1181

Scharlau, Charles E., Chm. Bd. & Chief Exec. Officer--Southwestern Energy Company, Fayetteville, AR; *U.S. Public*, pg. 1494

Scharlau, Charles E., Chm. Bd.--Southwestern Energy Pipeline Company, Fayetteville, AR; *U.S. Public*, pg. 1494

Scharlau, Charles E., Chm. Bd. & Pres.--Arkansas Western Pipeline Company, Fayetteville, AR; *U.S. Public*, pg. 1494

Scharp, Anders, Chm. Bd.--Atlas Copco AB, Stockholm, Sweden; *Int'l*, pg. 95

Scharp, Anders, Chm. Bd.--Electrolux, AB, Stockholm, Sweden; *Int'l*, pg. 438

Scharp, Anders, Chm. Bd.--Saab AB, Linkoping, Sweden; *Int'l*, pg. 686

Scharp, Anders, Chm. Bd.--AB SKF, Goteborg, Sweden; *Int'l*, pg. 1156

Schatz, Douglas S., Pres. & Chief Exec. Officer--Advanced Energy Industry, Fort Collins, CO; *U.S. Public*, pg. 20

Schauer, Ronald L., Chm. Bd., Pres. & Chief Exec. Officer--HMT Technology Corporation, Fremont, CA; *U.S. Public*, pg. 771

Schaufeld, Fred, Chm. Bd., Pres. & Chief Exec. Officer--National Electronics Warranty Corporation, Sterling, VA; *U.S. Private*, pg. 782

Schawbel, William, Co-Chm. Bd.--Town & Country Corporation, Chelsea, MA; *U.S. Public*, pg. 1625

Schawk, Clarence W., Chm. Bd.--Schawk, Inc., Des Plaines, IL; *U.S. Public*, pg. 1437

Schechter, Alvin H., Chm.--Interbrand Schechter, New York, NY; *U.S. Public*, pg. 1224

Schecter, Leroy, Chm. Bd. & Chief Exec. Officer--American Strip Steel Inc., Kearny, NJ; *U.S. Private*, pg. 62

Scheele, Nicholas V., Chm. & Chief Exec. Officer--Jaguar Cars, Mahwah, NJ; *U.S. Public*, pg. 664

Scheffer, H.C., Chm.-Exec. Committee--Royal Gist-Brocades N.V., Delft, Netherlands; *Int'l*, pg. 1142

Scheffer, H.C., Chm. Bd.--Gist-Brocades, Inc., Wilmington, DE; *Int'l*, pg. 1143

Scheib, Donald R., Chm. Bd.--Earl Scheib, Inc., Beverly Hills, CA; *U.S. Public*, pg. 1437

Scheideler, Albert, Chm. Bd., Pres. & Chief Exec. Officer--McNally Industries, Inc., Grantsburg, WI; *U.S. Private*, pg. 724

Schein, Philip S., M.D., Chm. Bd. & Chief Exec. Officer--U.S. Bioscience, Inc., Conshohocken, PA; *U.S. Public*, pg. 1681

Schellenberger, Jean, Chm. Bd. & Chief Exec. Officer--Chantiers Modernes, Pessac, France; *Int'l*, pg. 823

Scheman, Martin, Chm. Bd. & Chief Exec. Officer--Tyco Preschool, New York, NY; *U.S. Public*, pg. 1058

Schenk, Greg F., Chm. Bd. & Pres.--Cookie Tree Inc., Salt Lake City, UT; *U.S. Private*, pg. 273

Schenk, P. Edward, Chm. Bd., Pres. & Chief Exec. Officer--Rymer Foods Inc., Chicago, IL; *U.S. Public*, pg. 1414

Schenkel, Peter, Chm. Bd. & Chief Exec. Officer--Southern Foods Group, Dallas, TX; *U.S. Private*, pg. 1016

Schenz, Richard, Dr., Chm. Bd.--OMV AG, Vienna, Austria; *Int'l*, pg. 995

Scherer, Robert P. Jr., Chm. Bd. & Chief Exec. Officer--Scherer Healthcare, Inc., Atlanta, GA; *U.S. Public*, pg. 1437

Schermer, Lloyd G., Chm. Bd.--Lee Enterprises, Incorporated, Davenport, IA; *U.S. Public*, pg. 983

Scheumann, John B., Chm. Bd. & Chief Exec. Officer--Crossmann Communities, Inc., Indianapolis, IN; *U.S. Public*, pg. 461

Scheuring, Garry, Chm. Bd., Pres. & Chief Exec. Officer--Midlantic Bank, N.A., Philadelphia, PA; *U.S. Public*, pg. 1242

Schiciano, Joseph S., Chm. Bd. & Chief Exec. Officer--The Coon-De Visser Co., Royal Oak, MI; *U.S. Private*, pg. 273

Schiedeknecht, Heyo, Dr., Chm. Bd.--BDAG Balcke-Durr AG, Ratingen, Germany; *Int'l*, pg. 399

Schiefler, Roger, Chm. Bd. & Chief Oper. Officer--Synergis Technologies Group, Grand Rapids, MI; *U.S. Private*, pg. 1060

Schieman, L. Richard, Chm. Bd., Pres., Chief Exec. Officer & Chief Oper. Officer--Hughes-Peters, Inc., Cincinnati, OH; *U.S. Private*, pg. 546
Schieren, Wolfgang, Dr., Chm. Bd.--Allianz Aktiengesellschaft, Munich, Germany; *Int'l*, pg. 58
Schieren, Wolfgang, Dr., Chm.-Supervisory Bd.--Beiersdorf Group, Hamburg, Germany; *Int'l*, pg. 182
Schiff, John J. Jr., Chm. Bd.--Cincinnati Financial Corp., Fairfield, OH; *U.S. Public*, pg. 368
Schifter, Yvonne, Chm. Bd. & Chief Exec. Officer--Squire-Cogswell Company, Gurnee, IL; *U.S. Private*, pg. 1027
Schinas, John P., Chm. Bd.--Digi International Inc., Minnetonka, MN; *U.S. Public*, pg. 506
Schindler, Alfred N., Chm. Bd.--Schindler Holding AG, Hergiswil, Switzerland; *Int'l*, pg. 1204
Schini, Thomas W., Chm. Bd., Pres. & Chief Exec. Officer--First Federal Capital Corp., La Crosse, WI; *U.S. Public*, pg. 632
Schinzler, Hans-Jurgen, Dr., Chm. Bd.--Munchener Ruckversicherungs-Gessellschaft, Munich, Germany; *Int'l*, pg. 897
Schippev, Lionel, Chm. Bd.--The Calgary Sun, Calgary, Canada; *Int'l*, pg. 1320
Schiro, James J., Chm. Bd., Sr. Partner & Chief Exec. Officer--Price Waterhouse L.L.P. - U.S., New York, NY; *U.S. Private*, pg. 883
Schlatermund, D., Chm. Bd.--Riedel-de Haen AG, Seelze, Germany; *Int'l*, pg. 625
Schlatter, H.H., Chm. Bd.--Art Iron, Inc., Toledo, OH; *U.S. Private*, pg. 86
Schlatter, Hans R., Chm. Bd. & Pres.--H.A. Schlatter AG, Schlieren, Switzerland; *Int'l*, pg. 1205
Schlatter, Konrad, Chm. Bd. & Chief Exec. Officer--Corn Products International, Inc., Bedford Park, IL; *U.S. Public*, pg. 447
Schlesinger, Alan, Chm. Bd., Pres. & Chief Exec. Officer--Lamonts Apparel, Inc., Kirkland, WA; *U.S. Public*, pg. 975
Schlesinger, James R., Chm. Bd.--Mitre Corporation, Bedford, MA; *U.S. Private*, pg. 753
Schlosser, Phillip D., Chm. Bd.--Schlosser Forge Company, Rancho Cucamonga, CA; *U.S. Private*, pg. 970
Schmetterer, Bob, Chm. & Chief Exec. Officer-EURO RSCG Worldwide--Havas Advertising, Levallois-Perret, France; *Int'l*, pg. 600
Schmidheimy, Stephan, Dr., Chm. Bd.--Leica A.G., Saint Gallen, Switzerland; *Int'l*, pg. 806
Schmidheiny, Thomas, Chm. Bd. & Pres.--Holderbank Financiere Glaris Ltd., Glaris, Switzerland; *Int'l*, pg. 628
Schmidt-Chiari, Guido, Chm. Bd.--Creditanstalt-Bankverein, Vienna, Austria; *Int'l*, pg. 346
Schmidt-Scheuber, Theodor, Chm. Bd.--Dresdner-NY Inc., New York, NY; *Int'l*, pg. 418
Schmidt, Bernhard, Chm. Bd.--Spar Handels AG, Schenefeld, Germany; *Int'l*, pg. 1288
Schmidt, Dr. Rudolf, Chm. Bd.--Ferngas Nordbayern GmbH, Bramberg, Germany; *Int'l*, pg. 1148
Schmidt, E. Frank, Chm. Bd. & Chief Exec. Officer--SouthTrust Bank of Mobile, Mobile, AL; *U.S. Public*, pg. 1492
Schmidt, Eric, Chm. Bd. & Chief Exec. Officer--Novell, Inc., Orem, UT; *U.S. Public*, pg. 1203
Schmidt, G. Gerry, Chm. Bd. & Pres.--Pacific Handy Cutter, Inc., Costa Mesa, CA; *U.S. Private*, pg. 831
Schmidt, G. Gerry, Chm. Bd. & Pres.--Spectrum Razor Tools, Costa Mesa, CA; *U.S. Private*, pg. 831
Schmidt, Karl-Heinz, Chm. Bd.--Hertie Waren-und Kaufhaus GmbH, Frankfurt/Main, Germany; *Int'l*, pg. 724
Schmidt, Richard K., Chm. Bd.--Aquarion Management Services, Bridgeport, CT; *U.S. Public*, pg. 126
Schmidt, Robert F., Chm. Bd.--Cosco Industries, Spring Valley, NY; *U.S. Private*, pg. 277
Schmidt, Ronald D., Co-Chm. Bd.--Computer Products, Inc., Boca Raton, FL; *U.S. Public*, pg. 422
Schmidt, Werner, Chm. Bd.--SudwestLB, Stuttgart, Germany; *Int'l*, pg. 1304
Schmidt, William B., Chm. Bd., Chief Exec. Officer & Treas--Coca-Cola Bottling Co. of Elizabethtown, Elizabethtown, KY; *U.S. Private*, pg. 248
Schmidtgall, William H., Chm. Bd., Pres., Chief Exec. Officer & Chief Oper. Officer--DMI, Inc., Goodfield, IL; *U.S. Private*, pg. 305
Schmitt, Franz J., Chm.-Supvr. Bd.--Knorr-Bremse AG, Munich, Germany; *Int'l*, pg. 738
Schmitt, Peter C., Chm. Bd.--Atrex Incorporated, Warren, MI; *U.S. Private*, pg. 97
Schmitt, Robert, Chm. Bd.--Paul A. Schmitt Music Company, Minneapolis, MN; *U.S. Private*, pg. 971
Schmitt, Wolfgang R., Chm. Bd. & Chief Exec. Officer--Rubbermaid Incorporated, Wooster, OH; *U.S. Public*, pg. 1411
Schmitz, Michael J., Chm. Bd.--Elan Investment Services, Inc., Milwaukee, WI; *U.S. Public*, pg. 643
Schnabel, James, Chm. Bd., Pres. & Chief Exec. Officer--Sun Electric, Lincolnshire, IL; *U.S. Public*, pg. 1480
Schnatter, John H., Chm. Bd.--Papa John's International Inc., Louisville, KY; *U.S. Public*, pg. 1255
Schneider, Bernard, Chm. Bd. & Gen. Counsel--Swisscom, Bern, Switzerland; *Int'l*, pg. 1334
Schneider, Charles, Chm. Bd.--Future Foam, Inc., Council Bluffs, IA; *U.S. Private*, pg. 433
Schneider, Dr. Manfred, Chm. Bd.--Bayer AG, Leverkusen, Germany; *Int'l*, pg. 171
Schneider, Ernst, Chm. Bd.--PSA International S.A., Geneva, Switzerland; *Int'l*, pg. 1021
Schneider, Herbert J., Chm. Bd.--Schneider Corp., Kitchener, Canada; *Int'l*, pg. 1207
Schneider, Robert, Chm. Bd.--SCM Microsystems, Inc., Los Gatos, CA; *U.S. Public*, pg. 1417
Schneider, Ronald E., Chm. Bd., Pres. & Chief Exec. Officer--First National Bank in Cleburne, Cleburne, TX; *U.S. Public*, pg. 633
Schneider, Theresa Dudek, Chm. Bd.--Dudek & Bock Spring Manufacturing Company, Chicago, IL; *U.S. Private*, pg. 344
Schnitzer, Leonard, Dr., Chm. Bd. & Chief Exec. Officer--Schnitzer Steel Industries, Inc., Portland, OR; *U.S. Public*, pg. 1439
Schnitzer, Leonard, Dr., Chm. Bd. & Chief Exec. Officer--Proler International Corp., Portland, OR; *U.S. Public*, pg. 1440
Schnuck, Craig, Chm. Bd. & Chief Exec. Officer--Schnuck Markets, Inc., Saint Louis, MO; *U.S. Private*, pg. 971
Schoemaker, Hubert J.P., Chm. Bd.--Centocor, Inc., Malvern, PA; *U.S. Public*, pg. 323
Schoen, William J., Chm. Bd. & Chief Exec. Officer--Health Management Associates, Inc., Naples, FL; *U.S. Public*, pg. 802
Schoenberger, Robert G., Chm. & Chief Exec. Officer--Unitil Corporation, Hampton, NH; *U.S. Public*, pg. 1692
Schoenhals, Marvin N., Chm. Bd., Pres. & Chief Exec. Officer--WSFS Financial Corporation, Wilmington, DE; *U.S. Public*, pg. 1728
Schofield, Jonathan M., Chm. Bd. & Chief Exec. Officer--Airbus Industrie of North America, Inc., Herndon, VA; *Int'l*, pg. 39
Scholl, Hermann, Chm.-Mgmnt. Bd. & Pres.--Robert Bosch GmbH, Gerlingen, Germany; *Int'l*, pg. 203
Scholten, J., Chm. Bd.--Tijdschriften Uitgevers Maatschappij, Antwerp, Belgium; *Int'l*, pg. 1447
Scholten, J., Chm. Bd.--Editions Francophones Belges sa (EFB), Brussels, Belgium; *Int'l*, pg. 1447
Schomer, Fred K., Chm. Bd.--Gerber Life Insurance Co., White Plains, NY; *Int'l*, pg. 973
Schoning, Georg, Chm. Bd.--Condea Vista Company, Houston, TX; *Int'l*, pg. 325
Schoning, Peter M., Chm. & Chief Exec. Officer-Scholz & Friends Group--Scholz & Friends GmbH, Hamburg, Germany; *Int'l*, pg. 1210
Schops, Gerhard, Chm. & Mng. Dir.--EURO RSCG, Dusseldorf, Germany; *Int'l*, pg. 602
Schorling, Melker, Chm. Bd.--Skanska AB, Danderyd, Sweden; *Int'l*, pg. 1260
Schornack, John J., Chm. Bd.--Binks Sames Corporation, Franklin Park, IL; *U.S. Public*, pg. 229
Schorner, Jochen, Dr., Chm.--Flender-ATB-Loher Systemtechnik GmbH, Rott, Germany; *Int'l*, pg. 400
Schorr, Marvin G., Chm. Bd.--Helix Technology Corp., Mansfield, MA; *U.S. Public*, pg. 808
Schorr, Marvin G., Chm. Bd.--Landauer, Inc., Glenwood, IL; *U.S. Public*, pg. 977
Schorr, Marvin G., Chm. Bd.--Tech/Ops Sevcon, Inc., Boston, MA; *U.S. Public*, pg. 1563
Schott, Melvin, Chm. Bd.--Schott Brothers, Inc., Perth Amboy, NJ; *U.S. Private*, pg. 972
Schottenstein, Jay, Chm. Bd.--American Eagles Outfitters Inc., Warrendale, PA; *U.S. Private*, pg. 53
Schottenstein, Jay, Chm. Bd. & Chief Exec. Officer--Value City Department Stores, Inc., Columbus, OH; *U.S. Private*, pg. 972
Schottenstein, Jay L., Chm. Bd.--Schottenstein Stores Corporation, Columbus, OH; *U.S. Private*, pg. 972
Schottland, Steve B., Chm. Bd. & Pres.--American Packaging Corporation, Philadelphia, PA; *U.S. Private*, pg. 60
Schrager, Phillip G., Chm. Bd. & Chief Exec. Officer--Pacesetter Corporation, Omaha, NE; *U.S. Private*, pg. 830
Schramm, Bernard C., Jr., Chm. Bd.--The William Cook Agency, Inc., Jacksonville, FL; *U.S. Private*, pg. 273
Schramm, Howard M., Jr., Chm. Bd. & Pres.--Turner Supply Company, Mobile, AL; *U.S. Private*, pg. 1110
Schreiner, Margaret, Chm. Bd--Dakota Electric Association, Farmington, MN; *U.S. Private*, pg. 308
Schrempp, Jurgen E., Dr., Chm. Bd. & Chief Exec. Officer--Daimler-Benz Aktiengesellschaft, Stuttgart, Germany; *Int'l*, pg. 366
Schrimper, Charles, Chm. Bd. & Chie Exec. Officer--Group Dekko, Kendallville, IN; *U.S. Private*, pg. 484
Schroder, Hugo, Chm. Bd.--Danisco A/S, Copenhagen, Denmark; *Int'l*, pg. 378
Schroeder, Gustav Adolf, Chm. Bd.--Stadtsparkasse Koln, Cologne, Germany; *Int'l*, pg. 1293
Schroeder, Horst W., Chm. Bd.--American Italian Pasta Company, Excelsior Springs, MO; *U.S. Public*, pg. 85
Schroeder, John H., Chm. Bd.--Cresline Plastic Pipe Co. Inc., Evansville, IN; *U.S. Private*, pg. 289
Schroeder, William, Chm. Bd. & Chief Exec. Officer--Ireland Coffee Tea, Inc., Pleasantville, NJ; *U.S. Public*, pg. 351
Schroer, Lloyd, Chm. Bd.--National Truck Leasing System, Oak Brook Terrace, IL; *U.S. Private*, pg. 787
Schron, Jack H. Sr., Chm. Bd.--Jergens Inc., Cleveland, OH; *U.S. Private*, pg. 586
Schube, Frank W., Chm. Bd., Pres. & Chief Exec. Officer--Dualite Inc., Williamsburg, OH; *U.S. Private*, pg. 344
Schuchart, John A., Chm. Bd.--MDU Resources Group, Inc., Bismarck, ND; *U.S. Public*, pg. 1025
Schuenke, Donald J., Chm. Bd.--Northern Telecom Limited, Brampton, Canada; *Int'l*, pg. 968
Schuenke, Donald J., Chm. Bd.--MICOM Communications Corp., Simi Valley, CA; *Int'l*, pg. 969
Schuette, Marvin, Chm. Bd., Pres., Chief Exec. Officer & Chief Oper. Officer--Wausau Homes, Inc., Rothschild, WI; *U.S. Private*, pg. 1154
Schuette, Marvin, Chm. Bd., Pres., Chief Exec. Officer & Chief Oper. Officer--Sterling Building Systems, Inc., Rothschild, WI; *U.S. Private*, pg. 1154
Schuff, David A, Chm. Bd.--Schuff Steel Co., Phoenix, AZ; *U.S. Private*, pg. 973
Schuldt, David A., Chm. Bd., Pres. & Chief Exec. Officer--CASI-RUSCO Inc., Boca Raton, FL; *U.S. Private*, pg. 218
Schulhof, Michael P., Chm.--Sony Trans Com Systems Inc., Costa Mesa, CA; *Int'l*, pg. 1281
Schulte-Hillen, Gerd Dr., Chm. Bd.--Gruner + Jahr USA Publishing, Inc., New York, NY; *Int'l*, pg. 190
Schulte-Noelle, Henning, Dr., Chm. Bd.-Mngmt.--Allianz Aktiengesellschaft, Munich, Germany; *Int'l*, pg. 58
Schulte, Susie L., Chm. Bd.--Nixdorff Krein Industries Inc., Saint Louis, MO; *U.S. Private*, pg. 799
Schultz, William, Chm. Bd. & Chief Exec. Officer--Fender Musical Instruments, Scottsdale, AZ; *U.S. Private*, pg. 400
Schulze-Oberlaender, C.R., Chm. Bd. & Pres.--American Barmag Co., Charlotte, NC; *U.S. Private*, pg. 51
Schulze, John B., Chm. Bd., Pres. & Chief Exec. Officer--The Lamson & Sessions Co., Cleveland, OH; *U.S. Public*, pg. 976
Schulze, Richard M., Chm. Bd., Founder & Chief Exec. Officer--Best Buy Co., Inc., Eden Prairie, MN; *U.S. Public*, pg. 223
Schumacher, Donald, Chm. Bd. & Pres.--Schumacher Electric Corporation, Mount Prospect, IL; *U.S. Private*, pg. 973
Schumacher, Hans H., Chm. Bd.--Voest-Alpine Steel Corp., New York, NY; *Int'l*, pg. 1471
Schumaker, Dale H., Chm. Bd.--Appleton Papers Inc., Appleton, WI; *Int'l*, pg. 567
Schuman, Seymour, Chm. Bd. & Sec.--Propper Manufacturing Co., Inc., Long Island City, NY; *U.S. Private*, pg. 891
Schupak, Donald, Chm. Bd.--Danskin Inc., New York, NY; *U.S. Public*, pg. 483
Schupp, Rudy E., Chm. Bd., Pres. & Chief Exec. Officer--Republic Security Financial Corporation, West Palm Beach, FL; *U.S. Public*, pg. 1381
Schuster, Helmut, Dr., Chm.-Supervisory Bd.--Osterreichischen Bundesbahnen GmbH, Vienna, Austria; *Int'l*, pg. 1012
Schwab, Charles, Chm. Bd. & Chief Exec. Officer, Charles Schwab Corporation--Charles Schwab & Co. Inc., San Francisco, CA; *U.S. Public*, pg. 1443
Schwab, Charles R., Chm. Bd. & Chief Exec. Officer--The Charles Schwab Corporation, San Francisco, CA; *U.S. Public*, pg. 1442
Schwab, Les, Chm. Bd.--Les Schwab Tire Centers, Prineville, OR; *U.S. Private*, pg. 974
Schwab, Richard D., Chm. Bd.--S. Schwab Company, Cumberland, MD; *U.S. Private*, pg. 974
Schwan, Al, Chm. Bd. & Chief Exec. Officer--Schwan's Sales Enterprises, Marshall, MN; *U.S. Private*, pg. 974
Schwank, Bernd H., Chm. Bd.--Perfection-Schwank Inc., Waynesboro, GA; *U.S. Private*, pg. 853
Schwartz, Alan, Chm. Bd.--Manhattan Brass & Copper Co., Maspeth, NY; *U.S. Private*, pg. 699
Schwartz, Barry K., Chm. Bd.--Calvin Klein, Inc., New York, NY; *U.S. Private*, pg. 202
Schwartz, Bernard, Chm. Bd.--Jack Schwartz Shoes, Inc., New York, NY; *U.S. Private*, pg. 974
Schwartz, Bernard L., Chm. Bd. & Chief Exec. Officer--K & F Industries Inc., New York, NY; *U.S. Private*, pg. 602
Schwartz, Bernard L., Chm. Bd. & Chief Exec. Officer--Loral Space & Communications, New York, NY; *U.S. Public*, pg. 1014
Schwartz, Gerald W., Chm. Bd., Pres. & Chief Exec. Officer--Onex Corporation, Toronto, Canada; *Int'l*, pg. 1006
Schwartz, H.G., Jr., Chm. Bd. & Pres.--Sverdrup Environmental Inc., Maryland Heights, MO; *U.S. Private*, pg. 1057
Schwartz, Jay, Chm. Bd.--Capital Mercury Shirt, New York, NY; *U.S. Private*, pg. 206
Schwartz, Leonard, Chm. Bd., Pres. & Chief Exec. Officer--Aceto Corporation, Lake Success, NY; *U.S. Public*, pg. 15
Schwartz, M.G., Chm. Bd., Pres. & Chief Exec. Officer--Quaker City Motor Parts Company, Middletown, DE; *U.S.* Private, pg. 898
Schwartz, Richard, Chm. Bd., Pres. & Chief Exec. Officer--Alliant Techsystems, Hopkins, MN; *U.S. Public*, pg. 47
Schwartz, Richard, Chm. Bd.--Boat America Corp., Alexandria, VA; *U.S. Private*, pg. 153
Schwartz, William, Chm. Bd.--UST Corporation, Boston, MA; *U.S. Public*, pg. 1660
Schwarz-Schuette, Patrick, Chm. Bd.--Schwarz Pharma AG, Monheim, Germany; *Int'l*, pg. 1211
Schwarz, H. Marshall, Chm. Bd. & Chief Exec. Officer--U.S. Trust Corporation, New York, NY; *U.S. Public*, pg. 1688
Schwarz, Thomas R., Chm. Bd.--Transact Technologies Incorporated, Wallingford, CT; *U.S. Public*, pg. 1629
Schwebel, Alan, Chm. Bd.--Mennen Medical Inc., Clarence, NY; *Int'l*, pg. 858
Schwedel, Nat N., Chm. Bd.--Amerbelle Corporation, Rockville, CT; *U.S. Private*, pg. 48
Schwegmann, John, Chm. Bd., Pres. & Chief Exec. Officer--Schwegmann Giant Super Markets, New Orleans, LA; *U.S. Private*, pg. 629
Schweitzer, Louis, Grp. Chm. Bd. & Chief Exec. Officer--Renault, Boulogne-Billancourt, France; *Int'l*, pg. 1102
Schweizer, Melvin, Chm. Bd. & Pres.--Prairie Farms Dairy, Inc., Carlinville, IL; *U.S. Private*, pg. 878
Schweizer, Rolf Walter, Dr., Chm. Bd. & Pres.--Clariant International Ltd., Muttenz, Switzerland; *Int'l*, pg. 624
Schwenk, Harold S., Jr., Dr., Chm. Bd., Pres., & Chief Exec. Officer--BGS Systems, Inc., Waltham, MA; *U.S. Public*, pg. 161
Schwerin, Clayton A., Chm. Bd., Pres. & Chief Exec. Officer--Alliance Construction Solutions, Inc., Fort Collins, CO; *U.S. Private*, pg. 38
Schwertfeger, Timothy R., Chm. Bd. & Chief Exec. Officer--The John Nuveen Company, Chicago, IL; *U.S. Public*, pg. 1429
Schwing, Friedrich, Chm. Bd.--Schwing Gmbh, Herne, Germany; *Int'l*, pg. 1211
Sciuto, John J., Chm. Bd., Pres. & Chief Exec. Officer--Comptek Research, Inc., Buffalo, NY; *U.S. Public*, pg. 419
Sclater, John R., Chm. Bd.--Berisford plc, London, United Kingdom; *Int'l*, pg. 188
Scobie, William M., Chm. Bd., Chief Exec. Officer--Mason Shoe Mfg. Co., Chippewa Falls, WI; *U.S. Private*, pg. 712

Scoggin, Daniel R., Chm. Bd. & Chief Exec. Officer--Ground Round Inc., Braintree, MA; *U.S. Public*, pg. 766
Scohier, Pierre, Chm. Bd. & Pres.--GIB Group, Brussels, Belgium; *Int'l*, pg. 532
Scoppechio, Debbie, Chm. Bd. & Chief Exec. Officer--Creative Alliance, Inc., Louisville, KY; *U.S. Private*, pg. 287
Scordato, Emil A., Chm. & Chief Exec. Officer--Medical Laboratory Automation, Inc., Pleasantville, NY; *U.S. Private*, pg. 727
Scoropski, James R., Chm. Bd. & Treas.--Acclaim Entertainment, Inc., Glen Cove, NY; *U.S. Public*, pg. 15
Scotchbrook, Godfrey E., Chm.--Scotchbrook Communications Ltd., Wan Chai, Hong Kong; *U.S. Private*, pg. 411
Scott, Daniel T., Chm. Bd. & Chief Exec. Officer--Scott Printing Corporation, New Providence, NJ; *U.S. Private*, pg. 977
Scott, Dr. B.W., Chm. Bd.--ACI International Ltd., Melbourne, Australia; *Int'l*, pg. 128
Scott, Edward, Chm. Bd.--United States Cold Storage, Inc., Cherry Hill, NJ; *U.S. Private*, pg. 1124
Scott, J.D., Chm. Bd.-ScottPolar Corp.--Toromont Industries Ltd., Concord, Canada; *Int'l*, pg. 1400
Scott, J.D., Chm. Bd.--ScottPolar Corporation, Twin Falls, ID; *Int'l*, pg. 1400
Scott, James T., Chm. Bd., Chief Exec. Officer & Treas.--Norcostco, Inc., Minneapolis, MN; *U.S. Private*, pg. 801
Scott, John S., Chm. & Chief Exec. Officer--XL Vision Inc., Sebastian, FL; *U.S. Public*, pg. 1424
Scott, Robert A., Chm. Bd.--American Educational Products, Boulder, CO; *U.S. Public*, pg. 71
Scott, Sidney Buford, Chm. Bd.--Scott & Stringfellow Financial, Inc., Richmond, VA; *U.S. Public*, pg. 1445
Scott, Steven, Dr., Chm. Bd., Pres. & Chief Exec. Officer--Coastal Physician Group, Inc., Durham, NC; *U.S. Public*, pg. 391
Scott, Stuart L., Chm. Bd. & Chief Exec. Officer--LaSalle Partners, Chicago, IL; *U.S. Public*, pg. 978
Scotti, Anthony J., Chm. Bd. & Chief Exec. Officer--All American Communications, Inc., Santa Monica, CA; *U.S.* Public, pg. 41
Scotti, Anthony J., Chm. Bd.--Scotti Brothers Entertainment Industries, Santa Monica, CA; *U.S. Public*, pg. 41
Scotti, Gavin A., Chm. & Chief Exec. Officer--Klemtner Advertising Inc., New York, NY; *U.S. Public*, pg. 1422
Scraire, Jean-Claude, Chm. Bd. & Chief Exec. Officer--Caisse de depot et placement du Quebec, Montreal, Canada; *Int'l*, pg. 249
Scriba, Ralph D., Chm. Bd. & Chief Exec. Officer--Swift-Cor Tool Engineering, Gardena, CA; *U.S. Private*, pg. 1058
Scribner, Coy J., Chm. Bd.--Enterprise Electronics Corp., Enterprise, AL; *U.S. Public*, pg. 1563
Scruggs, H.E., Jr., Chm. Bd.--American Investment Bank, NA, Salt Lake City, UT; *U.S. Public*, pg. 990
Scrushy, Richard M., Chm. Bd. & Chief Exec. Officer--Healthsouth Corporation, Birmingham, AL; *U.S. Public*, pg. 803
Scudder, Richard B., Chm. Bd.--MediaNews Group Inc., Denver, CO; *U.S. Private*, pg. 727
Scudder, Richard B., Chm. Bd.--Garden State Newspapers, Inc., Denver, CO; *U.S. Private*, pg. 727
Scully, Joseph C., Chm. Bd. & Chief Exec. Officer--St. Paul Bancorp, Inc., Chicago, IL; *U.S. Public*, pg. 1428
Scurlock, Arch C., Dr., Chm. Bd.--Halifax Corporation, Alexandria, VA; *U.S. Public*, pg. 775
Seabrook, James M., Chm. Bd. & Chief Exec. Officer--Seabrook Brothers & Sons, Inc., Seabrook, NJ; *U.S. Private*, pg. 978
Seaman, Jeffrey, Chm. Bd. & Pres.--RTG Furniture Corp., Seffner, FL; *U.S. Private*, pg. 905
Seaton, Kenneth D., Chm. Bd.--D & N Financial Corporation, Hancock, MI; *U.S. Public*, pg. 472
Seaton, Kenneth D., Chm. Bd.--D & N Bank, Hancock, MI; *U.S. Public*, pg. 472
Seaton, Kenneth M., Chm. Bd., Pres. & Chief Exec. Officer--Family Inns of America, Inc., Pigeon Forge, TN; *U.S. Private*, pg. 392
Seaver, Richard, Chm. Bd.--Hydril Company, Houston, TX; *U.S. Private*, pg. 551
Sebire, David J., Chm. Bd.--Bridport-Gundry p.l.c., Dorset, United Kingdom; *Int'l*, pg. 215
Sebree, Gary, Chm. Bd.--Producers Rice Mill Inc., Stuttgart, AR; *U.S. Private*, pg. 888
Secchia, Peter F., Chm. Bd.--Universal Forest Products, Inc., Grand Rapids, MI; *U.S. Public*, pg. 1696
Sechler, Scott I., Chm. Bd. & Pres.--Farmer's Pride, Inc., Fredericksburg, PA; *U.S. Private*, pg. 395
Secrist, Richard, Chm. Bd., Pres. & Chief Exec. Officer--Blue Tee Corporation, New York, NY; *U.S. Private*, pg. 153
Seder, Jeffrey A., Chm. Bd. & Sec.--Craftex Mills Inc. of Pennsylvania, Blue Bell, PA; *U.S. Private*, pg. 284
Seeger, John, Chm. Bd.--Dayton Rogers Mfg. Co., Blaine, MN; *U.S. Private*, pg. 318
Seelbinder, G. Arthur, Chm. Bd. & Chief Exec. Officer--Cooker Restaurant Corporation, West Palm Beach, FL; *U.S. Public*, pg. 442
Seelenfreund, Alan, Chm. Bd.--McKesson Corporation, San Francisco, CA; *U.S. Public*, pg. 1072
Seeley, Raynor M. Jr., Chm. Bd., Pres. & Chief Exec. Officer--PTA Corporation, Oxford, CT; *U.S. Private*, pg. 828
Segal, Myron, Chm. Bd., Pres. & Chief Exec. Officer--Premier Mill Corp., Reading, PA; *U.S. Private*, pg. 881
Segal, Myron, Chm. Bd., Pres. & Chief Exec. Officer--Integrated Press Systems, Reading, PA; *U.S. Private*, pg. 881
Segal, Steven A., Chm. Bd.--North American Products Corp., Jasper, IN; *U.S. Private*, pg. 803
Segal, Zalman, Dr., Chm. Bd. & Chief Exec. Officer--Bank Leumi Trust Company of New York, New York, NY; *Int'l, pg. 150*
Segerdahl, Earl E., Chm. Bd.--The Segerdahl Corp., Wheeling, IL; *U.S. Private*, pg. 981
Seglem, Christopher K., Chm. Bd., Pres. & Chief Exec. Officer--Westmoreland Coal Co., Colorado Springs, CO; *U.S. Public*, pg. 1761
Seibel, Monroe, Chm. Bd.--Seibel & Stern Corp., New York, NY; *U.S. Private*, pg. 981
Seidensticker, Nils, Chm. Bd.--Durriesscharmann, AG, Dusseldorf, Germany; *Int'l*, pg. 860
Seidman, Benson, Chm. Bd.--Cohoes Fashions, Inc., Cohoes, NY; *U.S. Public*, pg. 268
Seidman, Theodore M., Chm. Bd.--Air Conditioning Co., Inc., Glendale, CA; *U.S. Private*, pg. 28
Seiji, Tsutsumi, Chm. Bd.--The Saison Group, Tokyo, Japan; *Int'l*, pg. 1178
Seipp, Walter, Dr., Chm.-Supervisory Bd.--Commerzbank AG, Frankfurt, Germany; *Int'l*, pg. 308
Sejpal, David A., Chm. Bd., Pres., Chief Exec. & Oper. Officer & Sec.--Clothestime Stores, Inc., Anaheim, CA; *U.S. Public*, pg. 387
Sekeres, William, Chm. Bd.--ITT Cannon Sealectro, New Britain, CT; *U.S. Public*, pg. 859
Seki, Hiromasa, Honorary Chm. Bd. & Dir.--Hakuhodo Incorporated, Tokyo, Japan; *Int'l*, pg. 587
Sekimoto, Tadahiro, Chm. Bd.--NEC Corporation, Tokyo, Japan; *Int'l*, pg. 899
Selden, William L., Chm. Bd.--American Buildings Co., Eufaula, AL; *U.S. Public*, pg. 69
Seldin, Marc A., Chm. Bd.--Miss Elaine Inc., Saint Louis, MO; *U.S. Private*, pg. 752
Selecman, Charles E., Chm. Bd., Pres. & Chief Exec. Officer--Input/Output, Inc., Stafford, TX; *U.S. Public*, pg. 880
Self, W.M., Chm. Bd. & Chief Exec. Officer--Greenwood Mills, Inc., Greenwood, SC; *U.S. Private*, pg. 479
Selig, Marvin, Chm. Bd. & Chief Exec. Officer-CMC Steel Grp.--Structural Metals, Inc., Seguin, TX; *U.S. Public*, pg. 412
Seligman, Irving R., Chm. Bd. & Treas.--Seligman & Associates, Inc., Southfield, MI; *U.S. Private*, pg. 982
Selinger, Irwin, Chm. Bd. & Chief Exec. Officer--Graham-Field Health Products, Inc., Hauppauge, NY; *U.S. Public, pg. 757*
Selkowitz, Arthur, Chm. & Chief Exec. Officer-DMB&B Communications--DMB&B Communications, New York, NY; *U.S. Private*, pg. 302
Sellers, Rod, Chm. Bd.--Meristem plc, Wetherby, United Kingdom; *Int'l*, pg. 858
Seltzer, Bernard, Chm. Bd. & Pres.--Hi-Tech Pharmacal Co., Inc., Amityville, NY; *U.S. Public*, pg. 825
Seltzer, Edwin C., Chm. Bd. & Pres.--Roller Derby Skate Corp., Litchfield, IL; *U.S. Private*, pg. 941
Seltzer, Samuel M., Chm. Bd. & Pres.--Allison Corporation, Livingston, NJ; *U.S. Private*, pg. 41
Semel, Terry, Co-Chm.--Warner Music Group, Inc., New York, NY; *U.S. Public*, pg. 1612
Semel, Terry S., Co-Chm. Bd., Pres. & Chief Oper. Officer--Warner Bros. Studios, Inc., Burbank, CA; *U.S. Public*, pg. 1611
Semler, Jerry D., Chm. Bd., Pres. & Chief Exec. Officer--American United Life Insurance Company, Indianapolis, IN; *U.S. Private*, pg. 64
Semmelhack, Henry P., Chm. Bd., Pres. & Chief Exec. Officer--Barrister Information Systems Corporation, Buffalo, NY; *U.S. Public*, pg. 192
Semrod, T. Joseph, Chm. Bd. & Chief Exec. Officer--Summit Bancorp, Princeton, NJ; *U.S. Public*, pg. 1527
Semrod, T. Joseph, Chm. Bd., Pres. & Chief Exec. Officer--United Jersey Bank, Hackensack, NJ; *U.S. Public*, pg. 1528
Semrod, T. Joseph, Chm. Bd. & Chief Exec. Officer--Summit Bank, Chatham, NJ; *U.S. Public*, pg. 1528
Senkler, Robert, Chm. Bd.--The Minnesota Mutual Life Insurance Company, Saint Paul, MN; *U.S. Private*, pg. 750
Senn, Nicholas, Dr., Chm.--Union Bank of Switzerland, Zurich, Switzerland; *Int'l*, pg. 1439
Sennheiser, Dr. Jorg, Professor, Chm. Bd.--Sennheiser Electronic Corp., Old Lyme, CT; *U.S. Private*, pg. 984
Sensing, Wilbur, Jr., Chm. Bd.--Enco Materials, Inc., Nashville, TN; *U.S. Private*, pg. 375
Senty, James A., Chm. Bd. & Pres.--Consolidated Midwest, Inc., La Crosse, WI; *U.S. Private*, pg. 265
Serby, Clay, Chm. Bd.--Saskatchewan Government Insurance, SGI, Regina, Canada; *Int'l*, pg. 1195
Sereviriyakul, Prayuth, Exec. Chm. Bd.--Unicord Public Co. LTD., Bangkok, Thailand; *Int'l*, pg. 1432
Sergeant, Craig C., Chm. Bd., Pres. & Chief Exec. Officer--Cornerstone Construction & Materials, Inc., Neptune, NJ; *Int'l*, pg. 593
Sergel, Richard P., Chm. Bd.--Massachusetts Electric Co., Westborough, MA; *U.S. Public*, pg. 1171
Sergel, Richard P., Chm. Bd.--Narragansett Energy Resources Company, Providence, RI; *U.S. Public*, pg. 1171
Serls, David, Chm. Bd.--Colonial Metals Co., Columbia, PA; *U.S. Private*, pg. 253
Serra Ramoneda, Antoni, Chm. Bd. & Pres.--Caixa d'Estalvis de Catalunya, Barcelona, Spain; *Int'l*, pg. 249
Serra, Matthew D., Chm. & Chief Exec. Officer--Stern's, Paramus, NJ; *U.S. Public*, pg. 618
Serrano Segovia, Jose, Chm. Bd. & Chief Exec. Officer--Transportacion Maritima Mexicana S.A. de C.V., Mexico, Mexico; *Int'l*, pg. 1418
Serruya, Sam, Chm. Bd.--Yogen Fruz Worldwide Inc., Markham, Canada; *Int'l*, pg. 1520
Serulneck, Lester, Chm. Bd.--Allmetal Screw Products Corp., Deer Park, NY; *U.S. Private*, pg. 41
Servaas, Beurt, Chm. Bd. & Pres.--Servaas, Inc., Indianapolis, IN; *U.S. Private*, pg. 986
SerVaas, Cory, M.D., Chm. Bd., Pres. & Chief Exec. Officer--Benjamin Franklin Literary & Medical Society, Inc., Indianapolis, IN; *U.S. Private*, pg. 133
Servatius, Prof. Dr. Bernhard, Chm. Bd.--Axel Springer Verlag AG, Berlin, Germany; *Int'l*, pg. 102
Service, Richard L., Chm. Bd.--Hardwoods Of Michigan, Inc., Clinton, MI; *U.S. Private*, pg. 502
Servitje, Robert, Chm. Bd.--Grupo Industrial Bimbo S.A. de C.V., Mexico, Mexico; *Int'l*, pg. 575
Setubal, Olavo Egydio, Chm. Bd.--Banco Itau S.A., Sao Paulo, Brazil; *Int'l*, pg. 142
Setzer, G.C., Co.-Chm. Bd.--Setzer Forest Products, Sacramento, CA; *U.S. Private*, pg. 987
Setzer, H.C., Co.-Chm. Bd.--Setzer Forest Products, Sacramento, CA; *U.S. Private*, pg. 987
Seuferle, Walter, Dr., Chm. Bd.--Wuestenrot Holding GmbH, Ludwigsburg, Germany; *Int'l*, pg. 1514
Severson, Allan W., Chm. Bd., Pres. & Chief Exec. Officer--Grossmont Bank, San Diego, CA; *U.S. Public*, pg. 1793
Sevier, Helen, Chm. Bd., Pres., Chief Exec. & Chief Oper. Officer--B.A.S.S., Inc., Montgomery, AL; *U.S. Private*, pg. 105
Sevin, Irik, Chm. Bd., Pres. & Chief Exec. Officer--Petroleum Heat & Power Co., Stamford, CT; *U.S. Public, pg. 1281*
Sewell, Cecil W., Jr., Chm. Bd. & Chief Exec. Officer--Centura Banks, Inc., Rocky Mount, NC; *U.S. Public*, pg. 328
Sewell, J. Carl, Jr., Chm. Bd.--Sewell Village Cadillac Co., Dallas, TX; *U.S. Private*, pg. 988
Seydoux, Jerome, Chm. Bd. & Chief Exec. Officer--Pathe, Paris, France; *Int'l*, pg. 1024
Seymour Heatley, Nancy, Chm. Bd. & Pres.--Seymour of Sycamore, Inc., Sycamore, IL; *U.S. Private*, pg. 988
Shackell, K.J., Chm.--NatWest Export Finance Limited, London, United Kingdom; *Int'l*, pg. 910
Shackouls, Bobby S., Chm. Bd., Pres. & Chief Exec. Officer--The Louisiana Land and Exploration Company, New Orleans, LA; *U.S. Public*, pg. 269
Shadek, Laurence A., Chm. Bd.--Pax World Fund Family, Portsmouth, NH; *U.S. Public*, pg. 1266
Shaffer, David H., Chm. Bd. & Chief Exec. Officer--Jostens Learning Corporation, San Diego, CA; *U.S. Private*, pg. 601
Shaffer, Donald, Chm. & Chief Exec. Officer--Western Auto Supply Company, Kansas City, MO; *U.S. Public*, pg. 1452
Shaffer, John, Chm. Bd.--MSI Insurance Companies, Arden Hills, MN; *U.S. Private*, pg. 688
Shah, Ajay B., Chm. Bd., Pres. & Chief Exec. Officer--Smart Modular Technologies, Fremont, CA; *U.S. Public*, pg. 1476
Shah, Harry, Pres.--National Food Stores, Inc., Edison, NJ; *U.S. Private*, pg. 783
Shah, Sanjay, Chm. Bd.--Precision Fasteners Ltd., Thane, India; *U.S. Public*, pg. 1420
Shaheen, John, Chm. Bd.--World Carpets, Inc., Dalton, GA; *U.S. Private*, pg. 1190
Shaheen, John, Chm. Bd.--Sunrise Carpet Ind. Inc., Dalton, GA; *U.S. Private*, pg. 1190
Shaheen, John, Chm. Bd.--White-Crest Dorsett Inc., Dalton, GA; *U.S. Private*, pg. 1190
Shaich, Ron, Co-Chm. Bd. & Chief Exec. Officer--Au Bon Pain Co., Inc., Boston, MA; *U.S. Public*, pg. 146
Shaikh, Humayun N., Chm. Bd.--Burke Mills, Inc., Valdese, NC; *U.S. Public*, pg. 267
Shaker, Joseph R., Chm. Bd.--Shaker Advertising Agency, Oak Park, IL; *U.S. Private*, pg. 988
Shanahan, Michael F., Sr., Chm. Bd.--Engineered Support Systems Inc., Saint Louis, MO; *U.S. Public*, pg. 583
Shanahan, Michael F., Sr., Chm. Bd.--Engineered Specialty Plastics, Hot Springs National Park, AR; *U.S. Public*, pg. 583
Shanback, Martin P., Chm. Bd. & Chief Exec. Officer--Friendship Dairies, Inc., Friendship, NY; *U.S. Private*, pg. 429
Shaneour, Dwight C., Jr., Chm. Bd., Pres. & Chief Exec. Officer--The Shane Group Inc., Hillsdale, MI; *U.S. Private*, pg. 989
Shanes, Abraham, Chm. Bd. & Treas.--Talk-A-Phone Co., Chicago, IL; *U.S. Private*, pg. 1067
Shanklin, Jerry C., Chm. Bd., Pres. & Chief Exec. Officer--Sundowner Offshore Services, Inc., Houston, TX; *U.S. Public*, pg. 1149
Shannahan, Tim, Chm. Bd., Pres. & Chief Exec. Officer--Video Products Distributors, Inc., Sacramento, CA; *U.S. Private*, pg. 1139
Shannon, Joseph, Chm. Bd.--Cape Breton Development Corporation, Glace Bay, Canada; *Int'l*, pg. 265
Shannon, Michael E., Chm. Bd. & Chief Fin. Officer--Ecolab Inc., Saint Paul, MN; *U.S. Public*, pg. 562
Shannon, O John C., Chm., Pres.-Grey Intl. & Chief Exec. Officer-Eur., Mid. E., Afr.--Grey Europe/London, London, United Kingdom; *U.S. Public*, pg. 765
Shapira, David, Chm. Bd. & Chief Exec. Officer--Giant Eagle, Inc., Pittsburgh, PA; *U.S. Private*, pg. 450
Shapira, David, Chm. & Chief Exec. Officer--Giant Eagle Market Co., Pittsburgh, PA; *U.S. Private*, pg. 450
Shapira, David, Chm. & Chief Exec. Officer--Tamarkin Co., Inc., Pittsburgh, PA; *U.S. Private*, pg. 451
Shapiro, L. Dennis, Chm. Bd.--Lifeline Systems, Inc., Cambridge, MA; *U.S. Public*, pg. 992
Shapiro, Marc J., Chm. Bd., Pres. & Chief Exec. Officer--Texas Commerce Bank, Houston, TX; *U.S. Public*, pg. 339
Shapiro, Richard B., Chm. Bd., Pres. & Chief Exec. Officer--Charles River Data Systems, Inc., Framingham, MA; *U.S.* Private, pg. 230
Shapiro, Robert B., Chm. Bd. & Chief Exec. Officer--Monsanto Company, Saint Louis, MO; *U.S. Public*, pg. 1124
Shapiro, Robert E., Chm. Bd.--Presidential Realty Corporation, White Plains, NY; *U.S. Public*, pg. 1323
Sharkey, John, Joint Chm. & Joint Chief Exec. Officer--BST-BDDP, London, United Kingdom; *Int'l*, pg. 117
Sharon, Emanuel, Dr., Chm. Bd.--Bank Hapoalim, Tel Aviv, Israel; *Int'l*, pg. 149

Sharp, Anders, Chm. Bd.--White Consolidated Industries, Inc., Cleveland, OH; *Int'l*, pg. 439

Sharp, Anders, Chm. Bd.--Incentive AB, Stockholm, Sweden; *Int'l*, pg. 666

Sharp, Charles, Chm. Bd., Pres. & Chief Exec. Officer--Clinton State Bank, Clinton, AR; *U.S. Public*, pg. 630

Sharp, Isadore, Chm. Bd. & Chief Exec. Officer--Four Seasons Hotels Inc., Don Mills, Canada; *Int'l*, pg. 502

Sharp, Richard L., Chm. Bd. & Chief Exec. Officer--Circuit City Stores, Inc., Richmond, VA; *U.S. Public*, pg. 374

Sharpe, Louis K., Chm. Bd. & Pres.--Sharpe Dry Goods Co., Inc., Checotah, OK; *U.S. Private*, pg. 990

Sharples, Dr. D. Kent, Chm. Bd.--Peoples Federal Savings & Loan Association, Conway, SC; *U.S. Public*, pg. 634

Shaum, Jack, Chm. Bd.--Associated Food Stores Inc., Salt Lake City, UT; *U.S. Private*, pg. 90

Shaw, L.E., Chm. Bd.--Shaw Industries Ltd., Etobicoke, Canada; *Int'l*, pg. 1231

Shaw, Neil M., Sir, Chm. Bd. & Chief Exec. Officer--Tate & Lyle PLC, London, United Kingdom; *Int'l*, pg. 1356

Shaw, Nicholas Byam, Chm. Bd.--Macmillan Ltd., London, United Kingdom; *Int'l*, pg. 1479

Shaw, Ray, Chm. Bd., Pres., Chief Exec. Officer & Chief Oper. Officer--American City Business Journals, Inc., Charlotte, NC; *U.S. Private*, pg. 19

Shaw, Richard L., Chm. Bd.--Michael Baker Corporation, Pittsburgh, PA; *U.S. Public*, pg. 168

Shaw, Robert, Chm Bd., Pres., & Chief Exec. Officer--Recoton Auto Corporation, Lincolnshire, IL; *U.S. Public*, pg. 1369

Shaw, Robert A., Chm. Bd. & Pres.--Allied Plywood Corp., Alexandria, VA; *U.S. Private*, pg. 40

Shaw, Robert E., Chm. Bd. & Chief Exec. Officer--Shaw Industries, Inc., Dalton, GA; *U.S. Public*, pg. 1464

Shaw, Wayne E., Chm. Bd., Pres. & Chief Exec. Officer--Industra Service Corporation, New Westminster, Canada; *Int'l*, pg. 74

Shaw, William, Chm. Bd.--Host Marriott Services Corporation, Bethesda, MD; *U.S. Public*, pg. 841

Shaw, William, Chm. Bd. & Pres.--Volt Information Sciences, Inc., New York, NY; *U.S. Public*, pg. 1724

Shaw, William, Chm. Bd. & Chief Exec. Officer--Autologic Information International, Inc., Thousand Oaks, CA; *U.S. Public*, pg. 1724

Shaw, William J., Chm. Bd., Pres. & Chief Exec. Officer--U.S. Trails, Dallas, TX; *U.S. Public*, pg. 1688

Shaye, Robert K., Chm. Bd. & Chief Exec. Officer--New Line Cinema Corporation, New York, NY; *U.S. Public*, pg. 1614

Shea, James F., Chm. Bd.--Fairmont Homes, Inc., Nappanee, IN; *U.S. Private*, pg. 391

Shea, Terence J., Chm. Bd. & Chief Exec. Officer--Bradner Central Company, Chicago, IL; *U.S. Private*, pg. 164

Shea, William J., Chm. Bd.--Centennial Technologies, Inc., Wilmington, MA; *U.S. Public*, pg. 322

Shearer, R. Gordon, Chm.--Distrigas of Massachusetts Corporation, Boston, MA; *U.S. Public*, pg. 289

Shearer, William L., III, Chm. Bd. & Treas.--Paine Furniture Co., Natick, MA; *U.S. Private*, pg. 834

Sheehan, Dennis W., Chm. Bd.--Allied Healthcare Products, Inc., Saint Louis, MO; *U.S. Public*, pg. 48

Sheehan, Dennis W., Chm. Bd., Pres. & Chief Exec. Officer--AXIA Incorporated, Lombard, IL; *U.S. Private*, pg. 103

Sheehan, Jeremiah J., Chm. Bd., Pres. & Chief Exec. Officer--Reynolds Metals Company, Richmond, VA; *U.S. Public*, pg. 1385

Sheetz, G. Robert, Co-Chm.--Sheetz, Inc., Altoona, PA; *U.S. Private*, pg. 991

Sheetz, Stephen G., Co-Chm.--Sheetz, Inc., Altoona, PA; *U.S. Private*, pg. 991

Sheffert, Mark W., Chm. Bd.--Medical Graphics Corp., Saint Paul, MN; *U.S. Public*, pg. 1080

Sheffield, J. Julian L.G., Deputy Chm.--Guardian Royal Exchange Plc, London, United Kingdom; *Int'l*, pg. 577

Sheinfeld, David I., Chm. Bd., Chief Exec. Officer & Sec.--Fresh America Corp., Dallas, TX; *U.S. Public*, pg. 681

Sheldon, J.M., Chm. Bd., Pres., Chief Exec. Officer & Chief Oper. Officer--Sheldons' Inc., Antigo, WI; *U.S. Private*, pg. 992

Shell, Earl L., Chm. Bd. & Chief Exec. Officer--Hardin Construction Group, Inc., Atlanta, GA; *U.S. Private*, pg. 501

Shelton, Gene, Chm. Bd. & Pres.--Sunclipse, Inc., Buena Park, CA; *Int'l*, pg. 72

Shelton, James D., Chm., Pres. & Chief Exec. Officer--First Federal Savings, East Hartford, CT; *U.S. Public*, pg. 632

Shepard, Andrew J., Chm. Bd.--Exchange Bank, Santa Rosa, CA; *U.S. Public*, pg. 599

Shepard, Donald J., Chm. Bd., Pres. & Chief Exec. Officer--AEGON USA, Inc., Baltimore, MD; *Int'l*, pg. 26

Shepherd, Donald R., Chm. Bd.--Loomis, Sayles & Co., Boston, MA; *U.S. Private*, pg. 737

Shepherd, William C., Chm. Bd., Pres. & Chief Exec. Officer--Allergan, Inc., Irvine, CA; *U.S. Public*, pg. 46

Sherman, Floyd, Chm. Bd. & Chief Exec. Officer-Triangle Pacific--Bruce Hardwood Floors, Dallas, TX; *U.S. Public*, pg. 1634

Sherman, Floyd F., Chm. Bd. & Chief Exec. Officer--Triangle Pacific Corporation, Dallas, TX; *U.S. Public*, pg. 1634

Sherman, George, Chm. Bd.--Joslyn Corporation, Chicago, IL; *U.S. Public*, pg. 481

Sherman, Glenn, Dr., Chm. Bd. & Chief Exec. Officer--Laser Power Corporation, San Diego, CA; *U.S. Private*, pg. 652

Sherman, Jeffrey, Chm. Bd.--Therapedic Associates, Inc., Middlesex, NJ; *U.S. Private*, pg. 1079

Sherman, Malcolm L., Chm. Bd. & Chief Exec. Officer--Ekco Group, Inc., Nashua, NH; *U.S. Public*, pg. 566

Sherman, Malcolm L., Chm. Bd. & Chief Exec. Officer--Ekco International, Inc., Nashua, NH; *U.S. Public*, pg. 566

Sherman, Peter M., Chm. Bd., Pres. & Chief Exec. Officer--Independence Capital Management, Inc., Horsham, PA; *U.S. Private*, pg. 849

Sherrard, Scott, Chm. Bd.--CDP, London, United Kingdom; *Int'l*, pg. 239

Sherwood, James B., Chm. Bd. & Chief Exec. Officer--Orient-Express Hotels Inc., New York, NY; *Int'l*, pg. 1213

Sherwood, Steven, Co-Chm. Bd. & Pres.--Clayton, Williams & Sherwood, Inc., Newport Beach, CA; *U.S. Private*, pg. 245

Shewmake, C.B., Chm. Bd. & Chief Exec. Officer--Algernon Blair International, Montgomery, AL; *U.S. Private*, pg. 33

Shibata, Taira, Chm. Bd.--Nishimatsu Construction Co., Ltd., Tokyo, Japan; *Int'l*, pg. 942

Shidachi, Takuji, Chm. Bd.--The Mitsubishi Trust and Banking Corporation, Tokyo, Japan; *Int'l*, pg. 876

Shiel, Vincent, Chm. Bd.--The Sportsman's Guide, Inc., Saint Paul, MN; *U.S. Public*, pg. 1499

Shields, Gerald N., Chm. Bd., Pres. & Chief Exec. Officer--Graymills Corp., Chicago, IL; *U.S. Private*, pg. 473

Shields, John, Chm. Bd. & Chief Exec. Officer--TACT Holding, South Pasadena, CA; *U.S. Private*, pg. 1067

Shields, John, Chm. Bd. & Chief Exec. Officer--Trader Joe's Co., South Pasadena, CA; *U.S. Private*, pg. 1067

Shifrin, Kenneth, Chm. Bd.--Prime Medical Services, Inc., Austin, TX; *U.S. Public*, pg. 1327

Shigenari, Hayao, Chm. Bd.--Mitsubishi Cable Industries, Ltd., Tokyo, Japan; *Int'l*, pg. 870

Shih, Stan, Chm. Bd. & Chief Exec. Officer--Acer Incorporated, Taipei, Taiwan; *Int'l*, pg. 22

Shih, Stan, Chm. Bd.--Acer America Corporation, San Jose, CA; *Int'l*, pg. 22

Shiina, Takeo, Chm.--IBM Japan, Ltd., Tokyo, Japan; *U.S. Public*, pg. 897

Shikata, Shiaki, Chm. Bd.--Gunze Sangyo, Inc., Tokyo, Japan; *Int'l*, pg. 578

Shillestad, John G., Chm. Bd. & Chief Exec. Officer--Columbian Mutual Life Insurance Co., Binghamton, NY; *U.S. Private*, pg. 256

Shillington, Colin, Chm. Bd.--Dale Farm Dairies Ltd., Ballymena, United Kingdom; *Int'l*, pg. 968

Shillman, Robert J., Chm. Bd., Pres. & Chief Exec. Officer--Cognex Corporation, Natick, MA; *U.S. Public*, pg. 394

Shilton, Don, Chm. Bd.--Nana Regional Corporation, Inc., Anchorage, AK; *U.S. Private*, pg. 774

Shimada, Yasuo, Chm. Bd.--Nikkeisha, Inc., Tokyo, Japan; *Int'l*, pg. 929

Shimano, Yoshizo, Chm. Bd.--Shimano Inc., Osaka, Japan; *Int'l*, pg. 1232

Shimizu, Shinobu, Chm. Bd. & Pres.--Tokyu Corporation, Tokyo, Japan; *Int'l*, pg. 1394

Shimizu, Toshiaki, Chm.--Kanto Auto Works, Ltd., Yokosuka, Japan; *Int'l*, pg. 1412

Shimoyama, Toshiro, Chm. Bd.--Olympus Optical Co., Ltd., Tokyo, Japan; *Int'l*, pg. 1004

Shingu, Yasuo, Chm. Bd.--Sumitomo Metal Industries, Ltd., Tokyo, Japan; *Int'l*, pg. 1315

Shinn, Richard F., Chm. Bd.--Norbest, Inc., Midvale, UT; *U.S. Private*, pg. 801

Shinozaki, Akihiko, Chm. Bd.--Sumitomo Metal Mining Co., Ltd., Tokyo, Japan; *Int'l*, pg. 1316

Shipley, Walter V., Chm. Bd. & Chief Exec. Officer--The Chase Manhattan Corporation, New York, NY; *U.S. Public*, pg. 337

Shipley, Walter V., Chm. Bd. & Chief Exec. Officer--The Chase Manhattan Bank, New York, NY; *U.S. Public*, pg. 338

Shipley, Walter V., Chm. Bd. & Chief Exec. Officer--Chase Manhattan Bank of Connecticut, Bridgeport, CT; *U.S. Public*, pg. 338

Shipley, William S. II, Chm. Bd. & Chief Exec. Officer--Shipley Companies, York, PA; *U.S. Private*, pg. 994

Shirahata, Ko, Chm. Bd.--Pentax Precision Instrument Corp., Orangeburg, NY; *Int'l*, pg. 85

Shirley, Jon, Chm. Bd.--Mentor Graphics Corporation, Wilsonville, OR; *U.S. Public*, pg. 1086

Shirvanian, Kosti, Chm. Bd., Pres. & Chief Exec. Officer--Western Waste Industries, Torrance, CA; *U.S. Public*, pg. 1686

Shivley, Albert, Chm. Bd.--Farmland Industries, Inc., Kansas City, MO; *U.S. Private*, pg. 395

Shockley, Raymond C., Chm. Bd.--Atlantic Bank, Ocean City, MD; *U.S. Public*, pg. 642

Shoemaker Robinson, Sally, Chm. Bd.--American Bible Society, New York, NY; *U.S. Private*, pg. 51

Shoemate, C.R., Chm. Bd., Pres. & Chief Exec. Officer--Bestfoods, Englewood Cliffs, NJ; *U.S. Public*, pg. 223

Shoen, E.J., Chm. Bd. & Pres.--Amerco, Reno, NV; *U.S. Private*, pg. 48

Shono, Katsuya, Chm. Bd.--Snow Brand Milk Products Co. Ltd., Tokyo, Japan; *Int'l*, pg. 1271

Shore, Jerry, Chm. Bd. & Chief Exec. Officer--Park Electrochemical Corporation, Lake Success, NY; *U.S. Public*, pg. 1258

Shore, Marc P., Chm. Bd., Pres. & Chief Exec. Officer--Shorewood Packaging Corporation, New York, NY; *U.S. Public*, pg. 1468

Shorenstein, Walter H., Chm. Bd.--Shorenstein Company, San Francisco, CA; *U.S. Private*, pg. 996

Shorin, Arthur T., Chm. Bd., Pres. & Chief Exec. Officer--The Topps Company, Inc., New York, NY; *U.S. Public*, pg. 1621

Short, Colin M., Chm. Bd.--United Biscuits (Holdings) Plc, West Drayton, United Kingdom; *Int'l*, pg. 1442

Short, R.J., Chm.--Niedner Limited, Coaticook, Canada; *Int'l*, pg. 1485

Short, William W., Jr., Chm. Bd.--Southern Apparel Corporation, Largo, FL; *U.S. Private*, pg. 1015

Shostack, G. Lynn, Chm. Bd. & Pres.--Joyce International, Inc., New York, NY; *U.S. Private*, pg. 602

Shouldice, S. Patrick, Chm. Bd. & Chief Exec. Officer--Nowsco Well Service Ltd., Calgary, Canada; *Int'l*, pg. 989

Shrachan, I.C., Chm. Bd.--RTZ Pillar Ltd., London, United Kingdom; *Int'l*, pg. 267

Shuey, John H., Chm. Bd., Pres., Chief Exec. & Oper. Officer--Amcast Industrial Corporation, Dayton, OH; *U.S. Public*, pg. 63

Shuford, A. Pope, Chm. Bd.--Shuford Mills, Inc., Hickory, NC; *U.S. Private*, pg. 996

Shuford, Harley F., Jr., Chm. Bd.--Century Furniture Industries, Hickory, NC; *U.S. Private*, pg. 226

Shultz, Gerald, Chm. Bd., Pres. & Chief Exec. Officer--Micro-Met L Corp., Indianapolis, IN; *U.S. Private*, pg. 742

Shum, Martin, Chm. Bd., Pres. & Chief Exec. Officer--ACT Networks, Inc., Camarillo, CA; *U.S. Public*, pg. 3

Shupac, Donald, Chm. Bd.--Pennaco Hosiery, New York, NY; *U.S. Public*, pg. 483

Shure, Myron B., Chm. Bd.--Strombecker Corporation, Chicago, IL; *U.S. Private*, pg. 1047

Sia, David, Exec. V.P., Chm., Chief Exec. Officer, Asia/Pacific & Dir.--BBDO Worldwide Inc., New York, NY; *U.S.* Public, pg. 1223

Sides, James R., Chm. & Chief Exec. Officer--Atlantic Research Corporation, Gainesville, VA; *U.S. Public*, pg. 1458

Sidlik, Thomas W., Chm. Bd., V.P. & Gen. Mgr.-Small Car Opers.--Chrysler Financial Corporation, Southfield, MI; *U.S. Public*, pg. 354

Sidman, Ronald J., Chm. Bd., Pres. & Chief Exec. Officer--The First Years Inc., Avon, MA; *U.S. Public*, pg. 642

Siedentoph, Horst H., Dr., Chm. Bd.--Miller & Co., Chicago, IL; *Int'l*, pg. 1458

Siegal, Michael D., Chm. Bd., Pres. & Chief Exec. Officer--Olympic Steel Inc., Cleveland, OH; *U.S. Public*, pg. 1221

Siegel, Herbert J., Chm. Bd. & Pres.--Chris-Craft Industries, Inc., New York, NY; *U.S. Public*, pg. 351

Siegel, Herbert J., Chm. Bd. & Pres.--BHC Communications, Inc., New York, NY; *U.S. Public*, pg. 352

Siegel, Jerome, Chm. Bd.--The Titan Industrial Corp., New York, NY; *U.S. Private*, pg. 1089

Siegel, Laurence C., Chm. Bd. & Chief Exec. Officer--The Mills Corporation, Arlington, VA; *U.S. Public*, pg. 1113

Siegel, Mace, Chm. Bd.--The Macerich Company, Santa Monica, CA; *U.S. Public*, pg. 1030

Siegel, Mo, Chm. Bd.--Celestial Seasonings, Boulder, CO; *U.S. Public*, pg. 319

Siegel, Owen R., Chm. Bd. & Chief Exec. Officer--R.S. Owens, Chicago, IL; *U.S. Private*, pg. 824

Siegel, Robert, Chm. Bd., Pres. & Chief Exec. Officer--The Stride Rite Corporation, Lexington, MA; *U.S. Public*, pg. 1524

Siegel, Seymour, Chm. Bd. & Chief Exec. Officer--Blue Ridge Farms, Inc., Brooklyn, NY; *U.S. Private*, pg. 153

Siegel, Stuart C., Chm. Bd. & Chief Exec. Officer--S & K Famous Brands, Inc., Glen Allen, VA; *U.S. Public*, pg. 1414

Siegler, Gary N., Chm. Bd.--Medical Resources Inc., Hackensack, NJ; *U.S. Public*, pg. 1080

Siegler, Gary N., Chm. Bd.--National R.V., Inc., Perris, CA; *U.S. Public*, pg. 1159

Siem, Ivar, Chm. Bd.--Grey Wolf, Inc., Houston, TX; *U.S. Public*, pg. 765

Siem, Kristian, Chm. Bd.--Norwegian Cruise Line, Miami, FL; *U.S. Private*, pg. 808

Siemer, Al, Chm. Bd.--Marsh Bellofram Corp., Newell, WV; *U.S. Private*, pg. 707

Siemer, Arnold B., Chm. Bd. & Pres.--Desco Corporation, Columbus, OH; *U.S. Private*, pg. 326

Siemer, J.D., Chm. Bd.--Esso Aktiengesellschaft, Hamburg, Germany; *U.S. Public*, pg. 601

Siener, P. Robert, Jr., Chm. Bd.--Cooley, Inc., Pawtucket, RI; *U.S. Private*, pg. 273

Sierra, Antonio M., Chm. Bd.--Business Mens Insurance Corporation, Coral Gables, FL; *U.S. Private*, pg. 189

Siess, Charles P., Jr., Chm. Bd.--Cabot Oil & Gas Corporation, Houston, TX; *U.S. Public*, pg. 289

Siewert, Reinhart, Chm. Bd. & Pres.--Koenig & Bauer-Albert AG, Wurzburg, Germany; *Int'l*, pg. 742

Sigal, Gerald R., Chm. Bd. & Pres.--SIGAL CONSTRUCTION CORP., Washington, DC; *U.S. Private*, pg. 999

Sigel, Arthur R., Chm. Bd., Pres. & Chief Exec. Officer--Velsicol Chemical Corporation, Rosemont, IL; *U.S. Private*, pg. 1135

Sigler, Russell, Chm. Bd.--Russell Sigler Inc., Phoenix, AZ; *U.S. Private*, pg. 999

Signeski, Leonard L., Chm. Bd., Pres. & Chief Exec. Officer--Syndicate Systems, Inc., Middlebury, IN; *U.S. Private*, pg. 1060

Sigurgeston, Hordur, Chm. Bd.--IceLandAir, Columbia, MD; *Int'l*, pg. 658

Sihler, Helmut, Dr., Chm.-Supervisory Bd.--Deutsche Telekom AG, Bonn, Germany; *Int'l*, pg. 407

Sihler, Helmut, Dr., Chm. Bd.-Suprv. Bd.--Porsche AG, Stuttgart, Germany; *Int'l*, pg. 1063

Silber, Allan, Chm. Bd. & Chief Exec. Officer--Counsel Corporation, Toronto, Canada; *Int'l*, pg. 338

Silber, Allen C., Chm. Bd.--PharMerica, Inc., Tampa, FL; *U.S. Public*, pg. 1286

Siler, J.G., Chm. Bd.--Underground Construction Co., Inc., Benicia, CA; *U.S. Private*, pg. 1116

Sill, Michael R., Chm. Bd. & Chief Exec. Officer--Road Machinery & Supplies Co., Savage, MN; *U.S. Private*, pg. 934

Siller, C.W., Chm. Bd.--Australian Oil & Gas Corporation Limited, Sydney, Australia; *Int'l*, pg. 101

Sills, Nathaniel L., Co-Chm. Bd.--Standard Motor Products Inc., Long Island City, NY; *U.S. Public*, pg. 1503

Silva, Pedro Motas, Chm.-Supervisory Bd.--Petrogal, s.a., Lisbon, Portugal; *Int'l*, pg. 1044

Silver, Bernard, Co-Chm. & Co-Chief Exec. Officer--Allied Bond & Collection Agency, Inc., Trevose, PA; *U.S. Public*, pg. 1667

Silver, Casey, Chm. Bd.--Universal Pictures, Universal City, CA; *Int'l*, pg. 1216

Silver, Herbert R., Co-Chm. & Co-Chief Exec. Officer--Allied Bond & Collection Agency, Inc., Trevose, PA; *U.S. Public*, pg. 1667

Silver, Joel, Chm. Bd., Chief Fin. Officer & Chief Exec. Officer--International Cutlery, LTD, New York, NY; *U.S. Private*, pg. 569
Silver, Martin, Chm. Bd., Pres. & Chief Exec. Officer--Star Industries Inc., Syosset, NY; *U.S. Private*, pg. 1034
Silver, R. Phillip, Chm. Bd. & Co-Chief Exec. Officer--Silgan Corporation, Stamford, CT; *U.S. Public*, pg. 1473
Silver, Richard L., Chm. Bd. & Chief Fin. Officer--Akrochem Corporation, Akron, OH; *U.S. Private*, pg. 30
Silverberg, Joe, Chm. Bd.--Bigsby & Kruthers Companies, Chicago, IL; *U.S. Private*, pg. 143
Silverman, Barry S., Chm. Bd.--The Jaydor Corporation, Millburn, NJ; *U.S. Private*, pg. 584
Silverman, Henry, Chm. Bd. & Chief Exec. Officer--HFS, Incorporated, Parsippany, NJ; *U.S. Public*, pg. 321
Silvers, Brett N., Chm. Bd. & Pres.--First International Bancorp, Inc., Hartford, CT; *U.S. Public*, pg. 635
Silverstein, Elaine, Co-Chm. Bd.--Beber & Silverstein & Partners, Inc., Miami, FL; *U.S. Private*, pg. 128
Silverstein, Richard, Co-Chm. & Creative Dir.--Goodby, Silverstein & Partners, San Francisco, CA; *U.S. Public*, pg. 1224
Sim, Richard G., Chm. Bd. & Chief Exec. Officer--Applied Power Inc., Butler, WI; *U.S. Public*, pg. 124
Simkins, L.J., Chm. Bd., Pres., Chief Exec. & Chief Oper. Officer--Simkins Industries, Inc., New Haven, CT; *U.S. Private*, pg. 1000
Simko, John S., Chm. Bd. & Chief Exec. Officer--Sunshine Mining And Refining Company, Boise, ID; *U.S. Public*, pg. 1536
Simmons, Al H., Chm. Bd.--Pinnacle Bank, Jasper, AL; *U.S.* Public, pg. 1297
Simmons, Edward M., Chm. Bd. & Chief Exec. Officer--McIlhenny Company, Avery Island, LA; *U.S. Private*, pg. 722
Simmons, Glenn, Chm. Bd.--Keystone Steel & Wire Co., Peoria, IL; *U.S. Public*, pg. 955
Simmons, Glenn R., Chm.--Sybra, Inc., Atlanta, GA; *U.S. Private*, pg. 270
Simmons, Glenn R., Chm. Bd.--Keystone Consolidated Industries, Inc., Dallas, TX; *U.S. Public*, pg. 955
Simmons, Harold C., Chm. Bd., Pres. & Chief Exec. Officer--Contran Corporation, Dallas, TX; *U.S. Private*, pg. 270
Simmons, Harold C., Chm. Bd. & Chief Exec. Officer--Valhi, Inc., Dallas, TX; *U.S. Private*, pg. 270
Simmons, Harold C., Chm. Bd.--NL Industries, Inc., Houston, TX; *U.S. Private*, pg. 270
Simmons, Harris H., Chm. Bd.--Zions First National Bank, Salt Lake City, UT; *U.S. Public*, pg. 1793
Simmons, John M., Chm. Bd. & Exec. V.P.--Elberta Crate & Box Company, Bainbridge, GA; *U.S. Private*, pg. 367
Simmons, L.E., Chm. Bd.--Tuboscope Incorporated, Houston, TX; *U.S. Public*, pg. 1643
Simmons, Richard P., Chm. Bd., Pres. & Chief Exec. Officer--Allegheny Teledyne Incorporated, Pittsburgh, PA; *U.S. Public*, pg. 43
Simmons, Roy W., Chm. Bd.--Zions Bancorporation, Salt Lake City, UT; *U.S. Public*, pg. 1792
Simmons, Roy W., Chm. Bd.--Nevada State Bank, Las Vegas, NV; *U.S. Public*, pg. 1793
Simon, Abdallah H., Chm.--Seagram Chateau & Estate Wines Co., New York, NY; *Int'l*, pg. 1215
Simon, Alan D., Chm. Bd. & Chief Exec. Officer--Omaha Steaks, Omaha, NE; *U.S. Private*, pg. 815
Simon, Arthur, Chm. Bd. & Treas.--Eagle Button Co., Inc., Carlstadt, NJ; *U.S. Private*, pg. 354
Simon, David A., Chm. Bd., Pres. & Chief Exec. Officer--Prime Hospitality Corp., Fairfield, NJ; *U.S. Public*, pg. 1326
Simon, Donald R., Chm. Bd., Pres. & Treas.--Contractors Steel Company, Livonia, MI; *U.S. Private*, pg. 270
Simon, Donald, Sr., Chm. Bd.--Serta Mattress Company, Vacaville, CA; *U.S. Private*, pg. 985
Simon, Henry, Dr., Chm. Bd.--Mitel Corporation, Kanata, Canada; *Int'l*, pg. 870
Simon, Herbert, Co-Chm. Bd.--Simon DeBartolo Group, Inc., Indianapolis, IN; *U.S. Public*, pg. 1474
Simon, Leonard S., Chm. Bd. & Chief Exec. Officer--Rochester Community Savings Bank, Rochester, NY; *U.S. Public*, pg. 336
Simon, Melvin, Co-Chm. Bd.--Simon DeBartolo Group, Inc., Indianapolis, IN; *U.S. Public*, pg. 1474
Simon, William E., Jr., Chm. Bd.--International Logistics Limited, Hillside, IL; *U.S. Private*, pg. 571
Simonin, Dominique, Mng. Partner & Chief Edec. Officer-Europe--Conquest Europe S.A.R.L., Neuilly-sur-Seine, France; *Int'l*, pg. 1484
Simons, Carl, Pres.--Gateway Apparel, Inc., Saint Louis, MO; *U.S. Private*, pg. 441
Simons, Paul, Chm. Bd.--Woolworths Limited, Yennora, Australia; *Int'l*, pg. 676
Simonson, Edward A., Chm. Bd.--Mid America Steel, Inc., Fargo, ND; *U.S. Private*, pg. 743
Simonsson, Bengt-Roland, Chm. Reg. Bd.--ICA Handlarna Sydost AB, Vaxjo, Sweden; *Int'l*, pg. 643
Simonyan, Gary, Chm. Emeritus--Wireless Telecom Group, Inc., Paramus, NJ; *U.S. Public*, pg. 1772
Simourian, John A., Chm. Bd. & Chief Exec. Officer--Lily Transportation Corp., Needham, MA; *U.S. Private*, pg. 667
Simpson, Bill, Chm. & Chief Exec. Officer-Periscope Group--Periscope Marketing Communications, Minneapolis, MN; *U.S. Private*, pg. 853
Simpson, Howard, Chm. Bd.--Simpson Gumpertz & Heger Inc., Arlington, MA; *U.S. Private*, pg. 1002
Simpson, Michael, Chm. Bd.--A.M. Castle & Co., Franklin Park, IL; *U.S. Public*, pg. 312
Simpson, Phil, Chm. Bd., Pres. & Chief Exec. Officer--Republic Group Incorporated, Hutchinson, KS; *U.S. Public*, pg. 1378
Simpson, Robert, Chm. Bd. & Chief Exec. Officer--A.G. Simpson Co. Limited, Scarborough, Canada; *Int'l*, pg. 1252
Simpson, Roy, Chm. Bd.--Everfast Inc., Kennett Square, PA; *U.S. Private*, pg. 386
Simpson, Roy, Chm. Bd.--Calico Corners, Kennett Square, PA; *U.S. Private*, pg. 386
Sims, Judy O., Chm. Bd., Pres. & Chief Exec. Officer--Software Spectrum, Inc., Garland, TX; *U.S. Public*, pg. 1483
Simsak, Nathalie, Chm. Bd.--Lanoga Corporation, Redmond, WA; *U.S. Private*, pg. 650
Simson, Wilhelm, Dr., Chm. Bd.--SKW Trostberg Aktiengesellschaft, Trostberg, Germany; *Int'l*, pg. 1464
Sinclair, David R., Chm. Bd.--Vista Gold Corp., Denver, CO; *U.S. Public*, pg. 1723
Sinclair, Desmond, Chm. Bd. & Pres.--DEECO Industries, Hillside, NJ; *U.S. Private*, pg. 320
Sindie, Arnold, Grp. Chm.--BDH Advertising Limited, Manchester, United Kingdom; *Int'l*, pg. 118
Singer, Michael A., Chm. Bd. & Chief Exec. Officer--Medical Manager Corporation, Tampa, FL; *U.S. Public*, pg. 1080
Singer, Nigel, Chm. Bd.--JSB Electrical PLC, Crewe, United Kingdom; *Int'l*, pg. 453
Singleton, Henry E., Chm. Bd.--Argonaut Group, Inc., Los Angeles, CA; *U.S. Public*, pg. 129
Sinnott, Walter B., Chm. Bd.--Hazen & Sawyer, New York, NY; *U.S. Private*, pg. 514
Sinton, Thomas H., Chm. Bd., Pres. & Chief Exec. Officer--ProBusiness Services, Inc., Pleasanton, CA; *U.S. Public*, pg. 1330
Siriratthamrong, Prapan, Chm. Bd.--Bangkok Rubber Public Co., Ltd., Bangkok, Thailand; *Int'l*, pg. 146
Sirois, Charles, Chm. & Chief Exec. Officer--Teleglobe, Inc., Montreal, Canada; *Int'l*, pg. 1373
Sirois, Charles, Chm. Bd. & Chief Exec. Officer--Teleglobe Canada Inc., Montreal, Canada; *Int'l*, pg. 1373
Sirotek, Robert L., Chm. Bd.--Illinois Auto Electric Co., Elmhurst, IL; *U.S. Private*, pg. 557
Sissel, George A., Chm. Bd., Pres. & Chief Exec. Officer--Ball Corporation, Muncie, IN; *U.S. Public*, pg. 170
Sissener, Einar W., Chm. & Chief Exec. Officer--Alpharma Inc., Fort Lee, NJ; *U.S. Public*, pg. 57
Sittason, Charles R., Chm. Bd. & Chief Exec. Officer--Regions Bank/Tuscaloosa, Tuscaloosa, AL; *U.S. Public*, pg. 1373
Siuling, Wong, Deputy Chm.-Fin.--Haking Enterprises, Quarry Bay, Hong Kong; *Int'l*, pg. 586
Sizemore, Dale H., Jr., Chm. Bd. & Chief Exec. Officer--Torotel, Inc., Grandview, MO; *U.S. Public*, pg. 1624
Sjogren, Walter R., Sr., Chm. Bd.--Whibco, Inc., Bridgeton, NJ; *U.S. Private*, pg. 1171
Skaggs, James B., Chm. Bd., Pres. & Chief Exec. Officer--Tracor, Inc., Austin, TX; *U.S. Public*, pg. 1627
Skandrani, N., Chm.--Groupe des Assurances de Tunisie (GAT), Tunis, Tunisia; *Int'l*, pg. 565
Skantze, Bengt, Chm. Bd.--Asea Brown Boveri AG, Vienna, Austria; *Int'l*, pg. 2
Skelsey, Henry F., Chm. Bd.--Berol Corporation, Brentwood, TN; *U.S. Public*, pg. 1178
Skidmore, A. Allan, Vice Chm.--Glentel Inc., Burnaby, Canada; *Int'l*, pg. 1336
Skidmore, James A., Jr., Chm. Bd., Pres. & Chief Exec. Officer--Science Management Corporation, Bridgewater, NJ; *U.S. Public*, pg. 1717
Skidmore, Richard, Chm. Bd.--North American Capacitor Co., Indianapolis, IN; *U.S. Private*, pg. 803
Skidmore, Thomas E., Chm. Bd., Pres. & Chief Exec. Officer--Glentel Inc., Burnaby, Canada; *Int'l*, pg. 1336
Skilling, Jeffrey K., Chm. Bd. & Chief Exec. Officer--Enron Capital & Trade Resources, Houston, TX; *U.S. Public*, pg. 584
Skinner, Claire C., Chm. Bd. & Chief Exec. Officer--Coachmen Industries, Inc., Elkhart, IN; *U.S. Public*, pg. 387
Sklenar, Herbert A., Chm. Bd.--Vulcan Materials Company, Birmingham, AL; *U.S. Public*, pg. 1725
Skuba, William C., Chm. Bd., Pres., Chief Exec. Officer & Sec.--Eastern Environmental Services, Inc., Drums, PA; *U.S. Public*, pg. 549
Skutt, Thomas J., Chm. Bd.--Mutual of Omaha Insurance Company, Omaha, NE; *U.S. Private*, pg. 769
Skutt, Thomas J., Chm. Bd.--United of Omaha Life Insurance Company, Omaha, NE; *U.S. Private*, pg. 770
Slack, John L., Chm. Bd., Pres., Chief Exec. Officer & Acting Treas.--DBA Systems, Inc., Melbourne, FL; *U.S. Public*, pg. 472
Slade, Jarvis J., Chm. Bd.--MCRB Service Bureau, Inc., Chatsworth, CA; *U.S. Private*, pg. 686
Slate, Johnny, Chm. Bd. & Pres.--Affiliated Publishers, Inc., Nashville, TN; *U.S. Private*, pg. 26
Slater, Clifford D., Chm. Bd.--Maui Divers of Hawaii, Honolulu, HI; *U.S. Private*, pg. 715
Slater, Jacqueline R., Chm. Bd.--Catellus Development Corporation, San Francisco, CA; *U.S. Public*, pg. 314
Slater, John, Chm. Bd. & Pres.--Orange Grove Co-operative, Orange Grove, TX; *U.S. Private*, pg. 818
Slater, Michael, Chm. Bd.--Wechsler Coffee Corp., Moonachie, NJ; *U.S. Private*, pg. 1158
Slater, Thomas F., Chm. Bd., Pres. & Chief Exec. Officer--Actron Manufacturing Company, Cleveland, OH; *U.S. Private*, pg. 16
Slattery, Anne, Chm. Bd.--Fleet Bank, F.S.B., Boca Raton, FL; *U.S. Public*, pg. 649
Slattery, John T., Chm. Bd. & Chief Exec. Officer--Lake Business Products, Inc., Willoughby, OH; *U.S. Private*, pg. 643
Slavin, Roy H., Chm. Bd., Pres. & Chief Exec. Officer--Wonderware Corporation, Irvine, CA; *U.S. Public*, pg. 1775
Sledd, Robert C., Chm. Bd. & Chief Exec. Officer--Performance Food Group Company, Richmond, VA; *U.S.* Public, pg. 1278
Sleepec, William, Jr., Chm. Bd.--Sleepeck Printing Company, Bellwood, IL; *U.S. Private*, pg. 1005
Slessman, Donald B., Sr., Chm. Bd.--The Fremont Co., Fremont, OH; *U.S. Private*, pg. 426
Sletten, Ken, Chm. Bd.--Rudolph and Sletten, Inc., Foster City, CA; *U.S. Private*, pg. 950
Slevin, Jack, Chm. Bd., Pres. & Chief Exec. Officer--Comdisco, Inc., Rosemont, IL; *U.S. Public*, pg. 407
Sloan, Morton, Chm. Bd. & Pres.--Inner Secrets, Inc., Harrison, NJ; *U.S. Private*, pg. 564
Sloan, O. Temple, Jr., Chm. Bd. & Chief Exec. Officer--General Parts, Inc., Raleigh, NC; *U.S. Private*, pg. 445
Sloan, Stuart M., Chm. Bd.--Quality Food Centers, Inc., Bellevue, WA; *U.S. Public*, pg. 1349
Sloan, Stuart M., Chm. Bd.--QFC Holding Company, Stamford, CT; *U.S. Public*, pg. 1349
Sloane, A. Richard, Chm. Bd. & Chief Exec. Officer--Softmart, Inc., Downingtown, PA; *U.S. Private*, pg. 1012
Slocum, Ronald A., Chm. & Pres.--Bank of America Idaho, Boise, ID; *U.S. Public*, pg. 180
Sloves, Marvin, Co-Chm.--Lowe & Partners/SMS, New York, NY; *U.S. Private*, pg. 678
Slutzky, Joel, Chm. Bd. & Chief Exec. Officer--Odetics Inc., Anaheim, CA; *U.S. Public*, pg. 1212
Smalley, Robert A., Chm. Bd.--Cruise America, Inc., Mesa, AZ; *U.S. Private*, pg. 178
Smart, Larry, Chm. Bd.--Western Micro Technology, Inc., Campbell, CA; *U.S. Public*, pg. 1759
Smead, H.J., Chm. Bd., Chief Exec. & Chief Fin. Officer & Sec.--Kaiser Aerospace & Electronics Corp., Foster City, CA; *U.S. Private*, pg. 605
Smetana, Joseph C., Jr., Chm. Bd. & Chief Exec. Officer--AIG Risk Management, Inc., New York, NY; *U.S. Public*, pg. 85
Smith, A.J.C., Chm. Bd. & Chief Exec. Officer--Marsh & McLennan Companies, Inc., New York, NY; *U.S. Public*, pg. 1048
Smith, A.J.C., Chm. Bd.--J&H Marsh & McLennan, Inc., New York, NY; *U.S. Public*, pg. 1049
Smith, Alan, Chm. Bd.--Storehouse PLC, London, United Kingdom; *Int'l*, pg. 1304
Smith, Andrew, Chm.--Sedgwick Limited, Melbourne, Australia; *Int'l*, pg. 1218
Smith, Andrew J., Chm. Bd.--Rexene Corporation, Dallas, TX; *U.S. Private*, pg. 549
Smith, Arthur McWilliam, Chm. Bd.--Air Express International (S.A.) (Pty), Ltd., Boksburg, South Africa; *U.S. Public*, pg. 30
Smith, Brian, Chm. Bd. & Chief Exec. Officer--B.C. Hydro, Vancouver, Canada; *Int'l*, pg. 114
Smith, Brian, Chm. Bd.--Hong Kong Telecommunications Limited, Quarry Bay, Hong Kong; *Int'l*, pg. 247
Smith, Bruce A., Chm. Bd., Pres. & Chief Exec. Officer--Tesoro Petroleum Corporation, San Antonio, TX; *U.S. Public*, pg. 1581
Smith, Bruton, Chm. Bd. & Chief Exec. Officer--Speedway Motorsports, Inc., Concord, NC; *U.S. Public*, pg. 1498
Smith, Bruton, Chm. Bd.--Bristol Motor Speedway, Bristol, TN; *U.S. Public*, pg. 1498
Smith, Bruton, Chm. Bd.--Sears Point Raceway, Sonoma, CA; *U.S. Public*, pg. 1498
Smith, Charles H., Jr., Chm. Bd.--Sifco Industries, Inc., Cleveland, OH; *U.S. Public*, pg. 1470
Smith, Craig, Chm. Bd., Pres. & Chief Exec. Officer--Hereford State Bank, Hereford, TX; *U.S. Public*, pg. 633
Smith, Craig, Chm. Bd.--Allomatic Products Company, Sullivan, IN; *U.S. Public*, pg. 1363
Smith, Dan L., Chm. Bd., Pres. & Chief Exec. Officer--Shoreline Financial Corp., Benton Harbor, MI; *U.S. Public*, pg. 1467
Smith, Darrell J., Chm. Bd.--Farmers National Company, Omaha, NE; *U.S. Private*, pg. 738
Smith, David L., Chm. Bd. & Owner--Homestead House Inc., Westminster, CO; *U.S. Private*, pg. 537
Smith, Delford M., Chm. Bd.--Evergreen International Aviation, Inc., McMinnville, OR; *U.S. Private*, pg. 386
Smith, Dennis A., Chm. Bd., Pres. & Chief Exec. Officer--Crawford & Company, Atlanta, GA; *U.S. Public*, pg. 458
Smith, Donald, Chm. Bd. & Chief Exec. Officer--The Restaurant Company, Itasca, IL; *U.S. Private*, pg. 925
Smith, Donald G., Chm. Bd., Pres., Chief Exec. Officer & Treas.--Roanoke Electric Steel Corporation, Roanoke, VA; *U.S. Public*, pg. 1392
Smith, Donald L., Jr., Chm. Bd., Pres. & Chief Exec. Officer--Devcon International Corp., Deerfield Beach, FL; *U.S. Public*, pg. 502
Smith, Donald N., Chm. Bd. & Pres.--Friendly Ice Cream Corp., Wilbraham, MA; *U.S. Public*, pg. 682
Smith, Douglas A., Chm. & Chief Exec. Officer--Borden Foods Corporation, Columbus, OH; *U.S. Private*, pg. 157
Smith, Douglas V., Chm. Bd., Pres. & Chief Exec. Officer--Lufkin Industries, Inc., Lufkin, TX; *U.S. Public*, pg. 1019
Smith, E. Brian, Chm., Pres. & Chief Exec. Officer--Smith Environmental Technologies Corp., Plymouth Meeting, PA; *U.S. Public*, pg. 1477
Smith, E. Brian, Chm. Bd. & Chief Exec. Officer--Smith Technologies Corp., Portland, OR; *U.S. Public*, pg. 1478
Smith, E.G., Chm. Bd.--Terre Hill Concrete Products, Inc., Terre Hill, PA; *U.S. Private*, pg. 1077
Smith, Everett G., Chm. Bd. & Pres.--Everett Smith Group, Ltd., Milwaukee, WI; *U.S. Private*, pg. 1007
Smith, Everett G., Chm. Bd.--Albert Trostel Packings Ltd., Lake Geneva, WI; *U.S. Private*, pg. 1105
Smith, F. Bradford, Chm. Bd.--Environmental Elements Corporation, Baltimore, MD; *U.S. Public*, pg. 586
Smith, Ferdinand, III, Chm. Bd. & Exec. Creative Dir.--Jay Advertising, Inc., Rochester, NY; *U.S. Private*, pg. 583
Smith, Frederick W., Chm. Bd., Pres. & Chief Exec. Officer--FDX Corporation, Memphis, TN; *U.S. Public*, pg. 603
Smith, Gary W., Chm. Bd., Pres. & Chief Exec. Officer--Proto Systems of Atlanta, Alpharetta, GA; *U.S. Private*, pg. 891
Smith, Gordon H., Chm. Bd., Pres. & Chief Exec. Officer--Sargent-Fletcher Inc., El Monte, CA; *Int'l*, pg. 301
Smith, Gordon V., Chm. Bd.--Miller & Smith, Inc., Mc Lean, VA; *U.S. Private*, pg. 746
Smith, Gregory H., Chm. Bd. & Pres.--Maine Potato Growers, Inc., Presque Isle, ME; *U.S. Private*, pg. 697

Smith, H. Kemer, Chm. Bd., Pres. & Chief Exec. Officer--Stone & Webster Engineering & Constructors Corp., Boston, MA; U.S. Public, pg. 1519
Smith, H. Kerner, Chm. Bd., Pres. & Chief Exec. Officer--Stone & Webster, Incorporated, Boston, MA; U.S. Public, pg. 1519
Smith, Hans J., Chm. Bd.--Iscor, Pretoria, South Africa; Int'l, pg. 688
Smith, Harold L., Chm. Bd.--Hilb, Rogal and Hamilton Company of Gainesville, Georgia, Gainesville, GA; U.S. Public, pg. 827
Smith, Harry, Chm. Bd.--Schilling Companies, Inc., Germantown, TN; U.S. Private, pg. 970
Smith, Henry Dale, Chm. Bd.--J.M. Smith Corp., Spartanburg, SC; U.S. Private, pg. 1008
Smith, Howard W., Chm. Bd.--Pawling Corporation, Pawling, NY; U.S. Private, pg. 844
Smith, Hugh S., Jr., Chm. Bd.--Western Bancorp, Newport Beach, CA; U.S. Public, pg. 1757
Smith, Hyrum W., Chm. Bd. & Chief Exec. Officer--Franklin Covey, Salt Lake City, UT; U.S. Public, pg. 679
Smith, J. E., Chm. Bd.--Alabama Electric Cooperative, Inc., Andalusia, AL; U.S. Private, pg. 30
Smith, J. Morse, Chm. Bd.--H.J. Baker & Bro., Inc., Stamford, CT; U.S. Private, pg. 112
Smith, J.R., Chm. Bd. & Mng. Dir.--Taywood Engineering Ltd., Southall, United Kingdom; Int'l, pg. 1359
Smith, Jack, Chm. Bd. & Chief Exec. Officer--The Sports Authority Inc., Fort Lauderdale, FL; U.S. Public, pg. 1499
Smith, Jack B., Chm.--Hoover Treated Wood Products, Inc., Thomson, GA; U.S. Public, pg. 1193
Smith, Jack C., Chm. Bd.--K-VA-T, Abingdon, VA; U.S. Private, pg. 603
Smith, James A., Jr., Chm. Bd.--Smith & Sons Foods, Inc., Macon, GA; U.S. Private, pg. 1006
Smith, James C., Chm. Bd. & Chief Exec. Officer--Webster Financial Corporation, Waterbury, CT; U.S. Public, pg. 1751
Smith, James C., Chm. Bd., Pres. & Chief Exec. Officer--Webster Bank, Waterbury, CT; U.S. Public, pg. 1751
Smith, Jerry, Chm. Bd.--Tennessee Farmers Co-op, La Vergne, TN; U.S. Private, pg. 1076
Smith, Jim, Chm. Bd. & New Bus. Contact--Ground Zero, Santa Monica, CA; U.S. Private, pg. 484
Smith, John F., Jr., Chm. Bd., Pres. & Chief Exec. Officer--General Motors Corporation, Detroit, MI; U.S. Public, pg. 718
Smith, John J., Chm. Bd. & Chief Exec. Officer--Sparton Corporation, Jackson, MI; U.S. Public, pg. 1496
Smith, Joshua I., Chm. Bd. & Chief Exec. Officer--The Maxima Corporation, Lanham, MD; U.S. Private, pg. 716
Smith, L.S., Dr., Chm. Bd., Chief Exec. Officer, Treas. & Sec.--Dallas Gold & Silver Exchange, Inc., Dallas, TX; U.S. Public, pg. 478
Smith, Mark C., Chm. Bd. & Chief Exec. Officer--ADTRAN, Inc., Huntsville, AL; U.S. Public, pg. 20
Smith, Miles J., Jr., Chm. Bd.--Cental Carolina Bank & Trust Company, Salisbury, NC; U.S. Public, pg. 276
Smith, N. Brian, Dr., Chm. Bd.--Cable and Wireless plc, London, United Kingdom; Int'l, pg. 247
Smith, Norman E., Chm. Bd.--North American Metals Distribution Group, Coon Rapids, MN; Int'l, pg. 1118
Smith, O. Bruton, Chm. Bd. & Chief Exec. Officer--Sonic Automotive, Inc., Charlotte, NC; U.S. Public, pg. 1485
Smith, O. Bruton, Chm. Bd.--Atlanta Motor Speedway, Hampton, GA; U.S. Public, pg. 1498
Smith, Orin R., Chm. Bd. & Chief Exec. Officer--Engelhard Corporation, Iselin, NJ; U.S. Public, pg. 582
Smith, Raymond J., Chm. Bd. & Pres.--Lakeland Industries, Inc., Ronkonkoma, NY; U.S. Public, pg. 975
Smith, Raymond W., Chm. Bd. & Chief Exec. Officer--Bell Atlantic Corporation, New York, NY; U.S. Public, pg. 201
Smith, Richard A., Chm., Pres. & Chief Exec. Officer-Real Estate Div.--HFS, Incorporated, Parsippany, NJ; U.S. Public, pg. 321
Smith, Richard A., Chm. Bd.--Century 21 Real Estate Corp., Parsippany, NJ; U.S. Public, pg. 321
Smith, Richard A., Chm. Bd.--Coldwell Banker Real Estate Corporation, Parsippany, NJ; U.S. Public, pg. 321
Smith, Richard A., Chm. Bd. & Chief Exec. Officer--GC Companies, Inc., Chestnut Hill, MA; U.S. Public, pg. 693
Smith, Richard A., Chm. Bd. & Chief Exec. Officer--Harcourt General, Inc., Chestnut Hill, MA; U.S. Public, pg. 782
Smith, Richard E., Chm. Bd. & Chief Exec. Officer--Integrated Brands Inc., Ronkonkoma, NY; U.S. Public, pg. 883
Smith, Robin B., Chm. & Chief Exec. Officer--Publishers Clearing House, Port Washington, NY; U.S. Private, pg. 893
Smith, Rodney, Chm. Bd., Pres. & Chief Exec. Officer--Altera Corporation, San Jose, CA; U.S. Public, pg. 59
Smith, Sheldon E., Chm. Bd., Pres. & Chief Exec. Officer--Old Fashion Foods, Inc., Austell, GA; U.S. Private, pg. 814
Smith, Sherwood H., Jr., Chm. Bd.--Carolina Power & Light Company, Raleigh, NC; U.S. Public, pg. 306
Smith, Sidney L., Chm.--WestWayne, Inc., Atlanta, GA; U.S. Private, pg. 1170
Smith, Sir Roland, Chm. Bd.--Hepworth Plc, London, United Kingdom; Int'l, pg. 614
Smith, Stephen E., Chm. Bd. & Pres.--LSJ Sportswear Inc., Deerfield, WI; U.S. Private, pg. 732
Smith, Steven B., Chm. Bd., Pres. & Chief Exec. Officer--SBS Enterprises Inc., Waco, TX; U.S. Private, pg. 955
Smith, Steven B., Chm. Bd., Pres. & Chief Exec. Officer--Spenco Medical Corporation, Waco, TX; U.S. Private, pg. 955
Smith, Theodore B., Chm. Bd. & Pres.--HITCO, Westbury, NY; U.S. Private, pg. 509
Smith, Theodore B., Chm. Bd.--Cantrock Realty Corp., Hicksville, NY; U.S. Private, pg. 509
Smith, Theodore J., Chm. Bd. & Chief Exec. Officer--FileNet Corporation, Costa Mesa, CA; U.S. Public, pg. 622
Smith, Tim, Chm. & Chief Exec. Officer--Red Sky Interactive, San Francisco, CA; U.S. Public, pg. 1224
Smith, Tom E., Chm. Bd., Pres. & Chief Exec. Officer--Food Lion, Inc., Salisbury, NC; Int'l, pg. 463
Smith, W. Keith, Chm. Bd. & Chief Exec. Officer--The Boston Company, Inc., Boston, MA; U.S. Public, pg. 1085
Smith, W. Keith, Chm. Bd. & Chief Exec. Officer--Boston Safe Deposit & Trust Co., Boston, MA; U.S. Public, pg. 1085
Smith, W.P., Chm. Bd.--Gold Kist, Inc., Atlanta, GA; U.S. Private, pg. 459
Smith, Wayne, Chm. Bd., Pres. & Chief Exec./Fin. Officer--Bekins Distribution Services Co., Saint Louis, MO; U.S. Public, pg. 841
Smith, William H., Co-Chm. Bd.--Allied Digital Technologies, Hauppauge, NY; U.S. Public, pg. 48
Smith, William J., Chm. Bd., Pres. & Chief Exec. Officer--U.S. Can Company, Oak Brook, IL; U.S. Public, pg. 1681
Smithers, Andrew, Chm. Bd.--Whatman plc, Maidstone, United Kingdom; Int'l, pg. 1498
Smithson, John W., Chm. Bd., Pres. & Chief Exec. Officer--PMA Reinsurance Corporation, Philadelphia, PA; U.S. Public, pg. 1272
Smiy, Paul R., Chm. Bd. & Chief Exec. Officer--Elliott Company, Jeannette, PA; U.S. Private, pg. 373
Smorgon, Graham, Chm. Bd.--Smorgon A.R.C., Sunshine, Australia; Int'l, pg. 1269
Smucker, Paul H., Chm.-Exec. Committee--J.M. Smucker Company, Orrville, OH; U.S. Public, pg. 1480
Smucker, Timothy P., Chm. Bd.--J.M. Smucker Company, Orrville, OH; U.S. Public, pg. 1480
Smurfit, M.W.J., Chm. Bd. & Chief Exec. Officer--Jefferson Smurfit Group p.l.c., Dublin, Ireland; Int'l, pg. 1269
Smurfit, M.W.J., Chm.--Jefferson Smurfit Corporation, Saint Louis, MO; Int'l, pg. 1269
Smythe, John, Chm.--Smythe Dorward Lambert, London, United Kingdom; U.S. Public, pg. 1225
Smythe, Thomas M., Chm. Bd. & Pres.--Keller Crescent Co., Evansville, IN; U.S. Private, pg. 612
Snavely, Christian M., Chm. Bd.--Snavely Forest Products, Inc., Pittsburgh, PA; U.S. Private, pg. 1010
Snavely, H. Wayne, Chm. Bd.--Imperial Credit Commercial Mortgage Investment Corp., Los Angeles, CA; U.S. Public, pg. 872
Snavely, Wayne H., Chm. Bd., Pres. & Chief Exec. Officer--Imperial Credit Industries, Inc., Torrance, CA; U.S. Public, pg. 872
Snead, Michael J., Chm. Bd.--Admiral Insurance Company, Cherry Hill, NJ; U.S. Public, pg. 216
Snead, Michael J., Chm. Bd.--Nautilus Insurance Company, Scottsdale, AZ; U.S. Public, pg. 216
Snead, Michael J., Chm. Bd.--Great Divide Insurance Company, Scottsdale, AZ; U.S. Public, pg. 216
Snell, Richard, Chm. Bd. & Chief Exec. Officer--Pinnacle West Capital Corporation, Phoenix, AZ; U.S. Public, pg. 1297
Snell, Richard, Chm. Bd.--APS, Phoenix, AZ; U.S. Public, pg. 1297
Snell, Richard, Chm. Bd.--Suncor Development Company, Phoenix, AZ; U.S. Public, pg. 1298
Snell, Richard, Chm. Bd.--El Dorado Investment Company, Phoenix, AZ; U.S. Public, pg. 1298
Snell, Richard A., Chm. Bd., Pres. & Chief Exec. Officer--Federal-Mogul Corporation, Southfield, MI; U.S. Public, pg. 615
Snelling, Barbara W., Chm. Bd.--Chittenden Corporation, Burlington, VT; U.S. Public, pg. 350
Snelling, Robert O., Sr., Chm. Bd.--Snelling Personnel Services, Dallas, TX; U.S. Private, pg. 1010
Snetzer, Michael A., Chm.--Medite Corporation, Medford, OR; U.S. Private, pg. 999
Snider, Jeffrey A., Chm. Bd., Pres. & Chief Exec. Officer--PAULA Financial, Pasadena, CA; U.S. Public, pg. 1266
Snoddy, L.O., Chm. Bd.--Telsco Industries, Garland, TX; U.S. Private, pg. 1074
Snoekc, H., Chm.--Grabowsky & Poort BV, Hague, Netherlands; Int'l, pg. 607
Snoep, P.P., Chm.-Mngmt. Bd.--Grolsch N.V., Enschede, Netherlands; Int'l, pg. 559
Snow, John W., Chm. Bd., Pres. & Chief Exec. Officer--CSX Corporation, Richmond, VA; U.S. Public, pg. 284
Snowden, Guy B., Chm. Bd.--GTECH Corporation, West Greenwich, RI; U.S. Public, pg. 767
Snowden, William F., Chm. Bd., Pres. & Chief Exec. Officer--Topline Imports, Inc., Bellevue, WA; U.S. Private, pg. 1091
Snowdon, David J., Chm. Bd.--ARC Limited, Chipping Sodbury, United Kingdom; Int'l, pg. 592
Snyder, Daniel M., Chm. Bd., Pres. & Chief Exec. Officer--Snyder Communications, Inc., Bethesda, MD; U.S. Public, pg. 1481
Snyder, John C., Chm. Bd. & Acting Pres.--Snyder Oil Corporation, Fort Worth, TX; U.S. Public, pg. 1481
Snyder, Richard, Chm. Bd.--International Comfort Products, Franklin, TN; U.S. Public, pg. 898
Snyder, Richard E., Chm. Bd. & Chief Exec. Officer--Golden Books Family Entertainment Inc., New York, NY; U.S. Public, pg. 749
Snyder, Richard E., Chm. Bd. & Chief Exec. Officer--Golden Books Publishing, New York, NY; U.S. Public, pg. 749
Snyder, Robert, Chm. Bd.--Lynch Telephone Corporation II, Greenwich, CT; U.S. Public, pg. 1022
Snyder, Robert C., Chm. Bd.--Quanex Corporation, Houston, TX; U.S. Public, pg. 1349
Snyder, Stephen G., Chm. Bd. & Chief Exec. Officer--General Electric Canada Inc., Mississauga, Canada; U.S. Public, pg. 713
Soar, A, Chm. Bd.--Macmillan Distribution Ltd., Basingstoke, United Kingdom; Int'l, pg. 1479
Sobel, Seymour, Chm. Bd.--Land N Sea, Inc., New York, NY; U.S. Private, pg. 645
Sobey, David F., Chm. Bd.--Sobey Inc., Stellarton, Canada; Int'l, pg. 454
Sobey, Donald R., Chm. Bd.--Empire Company Limited, Stellarton, Canada; Int'l, pg. 453
Soderberg, Sven, Chm. Bd.--Skandia Insurance Company Limited, Stockholm, Sweden; Int'l, pg. 1256
Sodini, Pete, Chm. Bd.--Lil'Champ/Food Stores Inc., Jacksonville, FL; U.S. Private, pg. 837
Soenen, Don, Chm. Bd. & Chief Exec. Officer--Sensors, Inc., Saline, MI; U.S. Private, pg. 984
Sohl, John F., Chm. Bd.--Auto Driveaway Co., Chicago, IL; U.S. Private, pg. 100
Sokol, David L., Chm. Bd. & Chief Exec. Officer--CalEnergy Co., Omaha, NE; U.S. Public, pg. 292
Sokol, Si, Chm. Bd., Pres. & Chief Exec. Officer--Bancinsurance Corp., Columbus, OH; U.S. Public, pg. 175
Sola, Jure, Chm. Bd. & Chief Exec. Officer--Sanmina Corporation, San Jose, CA; U.S. Public, pg. 1431
Solari, Richard C., Chm. Bd.--Granite Construction Incorporated, Watsonville, CA; U.S. Public, pg. 759
Solberg, R.A., Chm.--Texaco Indonesia Corp., White Plains, NY; U.S. Public, pg. 1583
Solberg, R.A., Chm.--Texaco Overseas Petroleum Co., White Plains, NY; U.S. Public, pg. 1583
Solberg, R.A., Chm. Bd.--Texaco Natuna Inc., Jakarta, Indonesia; U.S. Public, pg. 1584
Solberg, Robert A., Chm. Bd.--Saudi Arabian Texaco Inc., White Plains, NY; U.S. Public, pg. 1583
Solheim, Louise, Chm. Bd.--Karsten Manufacturing Corporation, Phoenix, AZ; U.S. Private, pg. 608
Soliman, Anwar, Chm. Bd. & Chief Exec. Officer--Grandy's, Inc., Lewisville, TX; U.S. Private, pg. 61
Sollenberger, Samuel K., Chm. Bd.--The Metropolitan Savings Bank of Ohio, Youngstown, OH; U.S. Public, pg. 608
Solley, Larry, Chm. Bd. & Chief Exec. Officer--Fisher Controls International, Inc., Marshalltown, IA; U.S. Public, pg. 573
Soloman, Anthony, Chm. Bd.--Carnegie Holding AB, Stockholm, Sweden; Int'l, pg. 272
Solombrino, Scott, Chm. Bd., Pres. & Chief Exec. Officer--Dav-El Worldwide, Chelsea, MA; U.S. Private, pg. 314
Solomon, Jerry L., Chm. Bd.--American Fluorescent Corporation, Waukegan, IL; U.S. Private, pg. 54
Somerville, Jim, Chm. Bd.--Family Bargain Corporation, San Diego, CA; U.S. Public, pg. 612
Sommer, Jon W., Chm. Bd. & Pres.--Sommer Metalcraft Corporation, Crawfordsville, IN; U.S. Private, pg. 1013
Sommer, Ron, Dr., Chm.-Mngmt. Bd.--Deutsche Telekom AG, Bonn, Germany; Int'l, pg. 407
Sommers, Patrick C., Chm. Bd., Pres. & Chief Exec. Officer--Medicus Systems Corporation, Evanston, IL; U.S. Public, pg. 1080
Son, Masayoshi, Chm. Bd.--Softbank Holdings Inc., Newton, MA; Int'l, pg. 1276
Sondhi, Vir K., Chm. Bd. & Pres.--Nasco Industries Inc., Medina, OH; U.S. Private, pg. 774
Song, Bo-Soon, Chm. Bd. & Chief Exec. Officer--Samsung Electronics North America Inc., Ridgefield Park, NJ; Int'l, pg. 1183
Song, T.B., Chm.-O&M China--Ogilvy & Mather Worldwide, Inc., New York, NY; Int'l, pg. 1483
Sonnabend, Roger, Chm. Bd. & Chief Exec. Officer--Sonesta International Hotels Corporation, Boston, MA; U.S. Public, pg. 1485
Sonnenberg, Willie B., Chm. Bd. & Exec. Creative Dir.--Sonnenberg Murphy Leo Burnett, Sunninghill, South Africa; U.S. Private, pg. 186
Sonstelie, R.R., Chm. Bd. & Chief Exec. Officer--Puget Sound Energy Co., Bellevue, WA; U.S. Public, pg. 1342
Sonstelie, Richard R., Chm. Bd. & Chief Exec. Officer--Puget Sound Energy, Inc., Bellevue, WA; U.S. Public, pg. 1342
Soo, Chang Young, Chm. Bd.--Daewoo Corporation, Seoul, Korea; Int'l, pg. 357
Soo, Han. Seung, Chm. Bd.--Korea Otsuka Pharmaceutical Co., Ltd., Seoul, Korea; Int'l, pg. 1014
Soon, Soh Kim, Chm.--DBS Investment Research Pte. Ltd., Singapore, Singapore; Int'l, pg. 350
Soon, Soh Kim, Chm.--DBS Factors Pte. Ltd., Singapore, Singapore; Int'l, pg. 350
Soon, Soh Kim, Chm.--DBS Securities Singapore Pte. Ltd., Singapore, Singapore; Int'l, pg. 351
Soon, Soh Kim, Chm.--DBS Securities Holding Pte. Ltd., Singapore, Singapore; Int'l, pg. 351
Soon, Soh Kim, Chm.--DBS Securities Nominees Pte. Ltd., Singapore, Singapore; Int'l, pg. 351
Soon, Soh Kim, Chm.--DBS Futures Hong Kong Ltd., Queensway, Hong Kong; Int'l, pg. 351
Soon, Soh Kim, Chm.--DBS Securities Hong Kong Ltd., Queensway, Hong Kong; Int'l, pg. 351
Soon, Soh Kim, Chm.--DBS Securities Malaysia Pte Ltd., Singapore, Singapore; Int'l, pg. 351
Soon, Soh Kim, Chm.--DBS Securities UK Ltd., London, United Kingdom; Int'l, pg. 351
Soong, Raymond, Chm. Bd.--Diodes Incorporated, Westlake Village, CA; U.S. Public, pg. 510
Sopko, Michael D., Chm. Bd. & Chief Exec. Officer--Inco Limited, Toronto, Canada; Int'l, pg. 672
Sopko, W.E., Pres. & Owner--Stamco Industries Inc., Euclid, OH; U.S. Private, pg. 1029
Sorensen, Allan C., Chm. Bd.--Interim Services Inc., Fort Lauderdale, FL; U.S. Public, pg. 892
Sorensen, Robert C., Chm. Bd. & Pres.--Duro-Lite International, Fairfield, NJ; U.S. Private, pg. 349
Soriano, Andres III, Chm. Bd.--La Tondena Distillers, Inc., Manila, Philippines; Int'l, pg. 785
Soriano, Andres, III, Chm. Bd. & Chief Exec. Officer--San Miguel Corp., Manila, Philippines; Int'l, pg. 1183
Soro, Chris, Chm. Bd. & Chief Exec. Officer--Allen & Hoshall, Inc., Memphis, TN; U.S. Private, pg. 36
Soroka, Robert H., Chm.--Robinsons-May, North Hollywood, CA; U.S. Public, pg. 1064
Sorrentino, Stanley L., Chm. Bd.--Uncas Manufacturing Company, Providence, RI; U.S. Private, pg. 1116

Sottile, James, Chm. Bd.--The Goldfield Corporation, Melbourne, FL; *U.S. Public*, pg. 750
Soubliere, J.P., Chm. Bd.--SHL Systemhouse - Canada/ Asia, Ottawa, Canada; *Int'l*, pg. 1154
Soultanian, Sarkis, Chm. Bd. & Pres.--National Utility Service, Inc., Park Ridge, NJ; *U.S. Private*, pg. 787
Southern, R.D., Chm. Bd. & Chief Exec. Officer--ATCO Group Co., Calgary, Canada; *Int'l*, pg. 95
Southgate, Colin, Sir, Chm.--EMI Group plc, London, United Kingdom; *Int'l*, pg. 426
Soviero, J.C., Chm. Bd.--Union Carbide (Europe) S.A., Meyrin, Switzerland; *U.S. Public*, pg. 1667
Sowles, Lawrence H., Chm. Bd.--L.H. Sowles Company, Inc., Minneapolis, MN; *U.S. Private*, pg. 1019
Spadone, Charles D., Chm. Bd.--Spadone Inc., Norwalk, CT; *U.S. Private*, pg. 1019
Spaelti, Peter, Dr., Chm. Bd.--Winterthur Schweizerische Versicherungs Gesellschaft, Winterthur, Switzerland; *Int'l, pg. 345*
Spain, A.J., Chm. Bd.--National Irish Bank Limited, Dublin, Ireland; *Int'l*, pg. 906
Spainhour, J. Patrick, Chm. Bd. & Chief Exec. Officer--AnnTaylor Stores Corporation, New York, NY; *U.S. Public*, pg. 116
Spalding, Phillip E., Jr., Chm.--Molokai Ranch Ltd., Honolulu, HI; *Int'l*, pg. 216
Spangler, C. Gregory, Chm. Bd., Pres. & Chief Exec. Officer--Spangler Candy Company, Bryan, OH; *U.S. Private*, pg. 1020
Spangler, C.D., Jr., Chm. Bd.--National Gypsum Company, Charlotte, NC; *Int'l*, pg. 790
Spangler, David L., Chm. Bd., Pres. & Chief Exec. Officer--First National Bank of Huntington, Huntington, IN; *U.S. Public*, pg. 674
Spanier, Maury L., Chm. Bd. & Chief Oper. Officer--United Aircraft Products, Forest, OH; *U.S. Public*, pg. 1262
Spanos, Alex G., Chm. Bd.--The Spanos Companies, Stockton, CA; *U.S. Private*, pg. 1020
Sparks, K.W., Chm. Bd.--Lucas Automotive GmbH, Koblenz, Germany; *Int'l*, pg. 820
Spatz, D. Dean, Chm. Bd., Pres. & Chief Exec. Officer--Osmonics, Inc., Minnetonka, MN; *U.S. Public*, pg. 1233
Spatz, D.D., Chm. Bd. & Chief Exec. Officer--Autotrol Corporation, Milwaukee, WI; *U.S. Public*, pg. 1234
Spears, Alexander, Chm. Bd. & Chief Exec. Officer--Lorillard Tobacco Company, Greensboro, NC; *U.S. Public*, pg. 1011
Spears, Saul, Chm. Bd.--Premdor Inc., Mississauga, Canada; *Int'l*, pg. 1066
Spector, Martin W., Chm. Bd.--Spec's Music, Inc., Miami, FL; *U.S. Public*, pg. 1497
Spector, Morton, Chm. Bd. & Treas.--D&H Distributing Company, Harrisburg, PA; *U.S. Private*, pg. 300
Speiser, Marvin M., Chm. Bd. & Pres.--Health-Chem Corporation, New York, NY; *U.S. Public*, pg. 802
Speizer, Mark, Chm. Bd. & Chief Exec. Officer--National Insurance Group, South San Francisco, CA; *U.S. Public*, pg. 1157
Speizman, Robert S., Chm. Bd. & Pres.--Speizman Industries, Inc., Charlotte, NC; *U.S. Public*, pg. 1498
Spelde, M.E., Chm. Bd., Pres. & Chief Exec. Officer--Empire Airlines, Coeur D'Alene, ID; *U.S. Private*, pg. 374
Spell, William H., Chm. Bd.--Peerless Industrial Group, Inc., Winona, MN; *U.S. Public*, pg. 1268
Spell, William H., Chm. Bd.--Peerless Chain Company, Winona, MN; *U.S. Public*, pg. 1268
Spence, Jeffrey E., Chm. Bd., Pres., Controller & Chief Exec. & Fin. Officer--Controlled Systems of Wisconsin, Inc., Nashotah, WI; *U.S. Private*, pg. 271
Spence, Robert L., Chm. Bd. & Pres.--Pacific Lumber & Shipping Co., Seattle, WA; *U.S. Private*, pg. 832
Spencer-Arscott, Robin, Chm. Bd. & Chief Exec. Officer--Rollins Burdick Hunter Co. (Bermuda) Ltd., Hamilton, Bermuda; *U.S. Public*, pg. 119
Spencer, Aaron D., Chm. Bd.--Uno Restaurant Corporation, West Roxbury, MA; *U.S. Public*, pg. 1698
Spencer, Guy J., Jr., Chm. Bd., Pres. & Chief Exec. Officer--Spencer Companies Inc., Huntsville, AL; *U.S. Private*, pg. 1024
Spendlove, Rex, Chm. Bd.--HyClone Laboratories Inc., Logan, UT; *Int'l*, pg. 1037
Spenlinhauer, John, III, Chm. Bd.--Spencer Press, Inc., Wells, ME; *U.S. Private*, pg. 1025
Sperber, Burton S., Chm. Bd., Pres. & Chief Exec. Officer--Environmental Industries, Inc., Calabasas, CA; *U.S. Private*, pg. 378
Sperber, Martin, Chm. Bd. & Chief Exec. Officer--Schein Pharmaceutical, Inc., Florham Park, NJ; *U.S. Private*, pg. 969
Sperber, Perry, Chm. Bd. & Pres.--Metal Fab Corporation, Ormond Beach, FL; *U.S. Public*, pg. 658
Sperlich, Harold K., Chm. Bd.--Delco Remy International, Inc., Anderson, IN; *U.S. Public*, pg. 495
Sperlich, Harold K., Chm. Bd.--Delco Remy America, Inc., Anderson, IN; *U.S. Public*, pg. 495
Sperling, John G., Chm. Bd.--Institute for Professional Development, Phoenix, AZ; *U.S. Public*, pg. 120
Sperling, John G., Ph.D., Chm. Bd. & Chief Exec. Officer--Apollo Group, Inc., Phoenix, AZ; *U.S. Public*, pg. 120
Sperry, Allen M., Chm. Bd.--The Turner & Seymour Mfg. Company, Torrington, CT; *U.S. Private*, pg. 1109
Sperry, Bill, Chm. Bd.--Costain Building & Civil Engineering Limited, Maidenhead, United Kingdom; *Int'l*, pg. 336
Speyer, Lester D., Chm. Bd.--Tennsco Corporation, Dickson, TN; *U.S. Private*, pg. 1077
Spicher, Edgar, Chm.--Coop Broye-Fribourg-Moleson, Givisiez, Switzerland; *Int'l*, pg. 329
Spiegel, Herb, Chm. Bd.--Randa Corp., Kinston, NC; *U.S. Private*, pg. 909
Spiegel, Peter, Co-Pres. & Chm. Bd.--Kent & Spiegel Direct, Culver City, CA; *U.S. Private*, pg. 615
Spier, Anthony, Chm. Bd. & Chief Exec. Officer--Wells-Gardner Electronics Corp., Chicago, IL; *U.S. Public*, pg. 1753
Spier, William, Chm. Bd.--DeSoto Inc., Joliet, IL; *U.S. Public, pg. 956*
Spiess, Paul D., Chm. Bd.--CFX Mortgage, Inc., Keene, NH; *U.S. Public*, pg. 278
Spiesshofer, Gunther, Chm. Bd.-Foreign--Triumph International Gruppe Deutschland, Munich, Germany; *Int'l*, pg. 1424
Spiesshofer, Wolfgang, Chm. Bd.-Domestic--Triumph International Gruppe Deutschland, Munich, Germany; *Int'l*, pg. 1424
Spiewak, Gerald, Chm. Emeritus--I. Spiewak & Sons, Inc., New York, NY; *U.S. Private*, pg. 1025
Spiewak, Gerald, Chm. Emeritus--Golden Fleece Outerwear Co., New York, NY; *U.S. Private*, pg. 1025
Spiewak, Michael, Chm. Bd. & Chief Exec. Officer--I. Spiewak & Sons, Inc., New York, NY; *U.S. Private*, pg. 1025
Spiewak, Michael, Chm. Bd. & Chief Exec. Officer--Golden Fleece Outerwear Co., New York, NY; *U.S. Private*, pg. 1025
Spilman, Robert H., Chm. Bd.--Jefferson-Pilot Corporation, Greensboro, NC; *U.S. Public*, pg. 925
Spinetta, Jean Cyril, Chm. Bd.--Groupe Air France, Roissy, France; *Int'l*, pg. 559
Spiro, Walter, Chm.--Earle Palmer Brown Public Relations, New York, NY; *U.S. Private*, pg. 174
Spiro, Walter A., Founder & Chm.--Earle Palmer Brown/ Philadelphia, Philadelphia, PA; *U.S. Private*, pg. 174
Splude, John, Chm. Bd., Pres. & Chief Exec. Officer--HK Systems, Inc., New Berlin, WI; *U.S. Private*, pg. 491
Spogli, Ronald P., Chm. Bd.--EnviroSource, Inc., Horsham, PA; *U.S. Public*, pg. 587
Spolane, Ronald S., Chm. Bd., Pres. & Chief Exec. Officer--Sterling Electronics Corporation, Houston, TX; *U.S. Public*, pg. 1051
Spooner, James, Sir, Chm. Bd.--Morgan Crucible Co. Plc, Windsor, United Kingdom; *Int'l*, pg. 890
Spooner, Robert M., Chm. Bd. & Chief Exec. Officer--Georgia Tent & Awning Inc., Atlanta, GA; *U.S. Private*, pg. 448
Sport, Michael C., Chm. Bd., Pres. & Chief Exec. Officer--Production Management Companies, Inc., Harvey, LA; *U.S. Private*, pg. 888
Spradley, James W., Sr., Chm. Bd.--Standard Candy Co., Inc., Nashville, TN; *U.S. Private*, pg. 1030
Spring, Dryden T., Sir, Chm. Bd.--New Zealand Dairy Board, Wellington, New Zealand; *Int'l*, pg. 923
Sprole, Robert R., II, Chm. Bd. & Chief Exec. Officer--Therm, Inc., Ithaca, NY; *U.S. Private*, pg. 1079
Spruijt, Herman P., Chm. Bd. & Chief Exec. Officer--Elsevier Science (International), Amsterdam, Netherlands; *Int'l*, pg. 1099
Spruill, John, Chm. Bd. & Exec. V.P.--Alcon Systems, Inc., Fort Worth, TX; *Int'l*, pg. 916
Squeri, Charles, Chm. Bd. & Chief Exec. Officer--Squeri Foodservice, Cincinnati, OH; *U.S. Public*, pg. 918
Squires, Nick, Chm.--Squires Robertson Gill, London, United Kingdom; *Int'l*, pg. 1291
Srack, K.S., Chm.--Tarmac (Abu Dhabi) Ltd., Abu Dhabi, United Arab Emirates; *Int'l*, pg. 1355
St. George, Nicholas J., Chm. Bd., Pres. & Chief Exec. Officer--Oakwood Homes Corporation, Greensboro, NC; *U.S. Public*, pg. 1209
St. Laurent, David E., Chm. Bd. & Pres.--Electric Insurance Co., Beverly, MA; *U.S. Private*, pg. 368
Staab, Walter, Chm. Bd.--SFM Media Corporation, New York, NY; *U.S. Private*, pg. 956
Staal, A.J., Chm.--ING (U.S.) Capital Holdings, New York, NY; *Int'l*, pg. 648
Stabler, Donald B., Chm. Bd.--Stabler Companies, Inc., Harrisburg, PA; *U.S. Private*, pg. 1028
Stabler, Donald B., Chm. Bd. & Pres.--Eastern Industries, Harrisburg, PA; *U.S. Private*, pg. 1028
Stabler, Donald B., Chm. Bd. & Pres.--Protection Services, Harrisburg, PA; *U.S. Private*, pg. 1028
Stabler, Donald B., Chm. Bd. & Pres.--Precision Solar Controls, Harrisburg, PA; *U.S. Private*, pg. 1028
Stabler, Donald B., Chm. Bd. & Pres.--Work Area Protection, Harrisburg, PA; *U.S. Private*, pg. 1028
Staby, Ludger W., Chm. Bd.-Mngmt.--Reemtsma Cigarettenfabriken GmbH, Hamburg, Hamburg, Germany; *Int'l*, pg. 1100
Staff, Joel, Chm. Bd., Pres. & Chief Exec. Officer--National-Oilwell Inc., Houston, TX; *U.S. Public*, pg. 1158
Staffa, Donald J., Chm. Bd. & Pres.--Quality Medical Adjudication, Inc., Rancho Cordova, CA; *U.S. Public*, pg. 802
Stafford, John R., Chm. Bd., Pres. & Chief Exec. Officer--American Home Products Corporation, Madison, NJ; *U.S. Public*, pg. 79
Stager, Donald K., Chm. Bd.--Dillingham Construction Corporation, Pleasanton, CA; *U.S. Private*, pg. 333
Staglin, Garen, Chm. Bd.--Safelite AutoGlass, Columbus, OH; *U.S. Private*, pg. 960
Stahlecker, Hans, Chm. Bd.--Spindelfabrik Suessen, Suessen, Germany; *Int'l*, pg. 1290
Stahmann, William J., Chm. Bd.--Stahmann Farms, Inc., La Mesa, NM; *U.S. Private*, pg. 1029
Stainton, Mary, Chm. Bd.--American Journal of Nursing Company, New York, NY; *Int'l*, pg. 1513
Stair, Charles W., Chm. Bd.--ServiceMaster Diversified Health Services, Inc., Memphis, TN; *U.S. Public*, pg. 1462
Stalkamp, William J., Chm. Bd. & Chief Exec. Officer--Mellon PSFS, Philadelphia, PA; *U.S. Public*, pg. 1085
Stamatiade, Pericles P., Grp. Chm.--Johnson & Johnson Hellas S.A., Athens, Greece; *U.S. Public*, pg. 930
Stamm, David A., Chm. Bd.--Clarify Inc., San Jose, CA; *U.S.* Public, pg. 382
Stamp, William M., Jr., Chm. Bd.--Farm Family Casualty Insurance Co., Glenmont, NY; *U.S. Private*, pg. 394
Stamps, E. Roe, IV, Chm. Bd.--Boca Research Inc., Boca Raton, FL; *U.S. Public*, pg. 239
Stanback, W.C., Chm. Bd.--Stanback Company, Salisbury, NC; *U.S. Private*, pg. 1030
Stanchi, E.J., Jr., Chm. Bd.--Kohl & Madden Printing Ink Corp. Div., Fort Lee, NJ; *Int'l*, pg. 370
Standen, Michael, Chm. Bd., Pres. & Chief Exec. Officer--Metallurg, Inc., New York, NY; *U.S. Private*, pg. 735
Standish, Victor J., Chm. Bd., Pres. & Chief Exec. Officer--York Barbell Co., Inc., York, PA; *U.S. Private*, pg. 1196
Stanes, P.J.D., Chm. Bd.--Feltrax International, Inc., Auckland, New Zealand; *Int'l*, pg. 130
Stanford, Alan C., Chm. Bd. & Chief Exec. Officer--Broadway & Seymour, Inc., Charlotte, NC; *U.S. Public*, pg. 258
Stangeland, Roger E., Chm. Bd.--The Grand Union Company, Wayne, NJ; *U.S. Public*, pg. 758
Staniar, Burton, Chm. Bd.--Knoll, Inc., Greenville, PA; *U.S. Private*, pg. 627
Stanley, A. Jack, Chm. Bd. & Chief Exec. Officer--The M.W. Kellogg Company, Houston, TX; *U.S. Public*, pg. 528
Stanley, John C., IV, Chm. Bd. & Chief Exec. Officer--Outdoor Communications, Inc., Corinth, MS; *U.S. Private, pg. 822*
Stanley, John R., Chm. Bd., Pres. & Chief Exec. Officer--Transamerican Natural Gas Corporation, Houston, TX; *U.S. Private*, pg. 1096
Stanley, Richard H., Chm. Bd.--The Stanley Consultants Group, Muscatine, IA; *U.S. Private*, pg. 1032
Stanley, Richard H., Chm. Bd.--Stanley Consultants, Inc., Muscatine, IA; *U.S. Private*, pg. 1033
Stanley, Winford E., Chm. Bd.--First Bank of Stuart, Stuart, VA; *U.S. Public*, pg. 1039
Stanton, Eric, Co-Chm. Bd.--Simon Marketing, Inc., Los Angeles, CA; *U.S. Private*, pg. 1001
Stanton, Ronald, Chm. Bd. & Chief Exec. Officer--Transammonia Inc., New York, NY; *U.S. Private*, pg. 1096
Stanway, W., Chm. & Grp. Mng. Dir.--London & Edinburgh Insurance Group Limited, Worthing, United Kingdom; *U.S. Public*, pg. 795
Stapleton, Nigel, Co-Chm.--Reed Elsevier plc, London, United Kingdom; *Int'l*, pg. 1093
Stapleton, Nigel, Chm.--Reed International P.L.C., London, United Kingdom; *Int'l*, pg. 1093
Stapleton, Nigel, Chm. & Pres.--Reed Elsevier Inc., New York, NY; *Int'l*, pg. 1095
Stapleton, Nigel, Chm.--Reed Technology and Information Services Inc., Horsham, PA; *Int'l*, pg. 1096
Stapleton, Nigel, Chm.--LEXIS-NEXIS, Miamisburg, OH; *Int'l, pg. 1096*
Starkey, A.R., Chm. Bd.--L.A. Rumbold Limited, Camberley, United Kingdom; *Int'l*, pg. 216
Starnes, Michael S., Chm. Bd., Pres. & Chief Exec. Officer--M.S. Carriers, Inc., Memphis, TN; *U.S. Public*, pg. 1027
Stasior, William F., Chm. Bd. & Chief Exec. Officer--Booz, Allen & Hamilton Inc., New York, NY; *U.S. Private*, pg. 157
Stata, Ray, Chm. Bd.--Analog Devices, Inc., Norwood, MA; *U.S. Public*, pg. 107
Stauth, Robert E., Chm. Bd. & Chief Exec. Officer--Fleming Companies, Inc., Oklahoma City, OK; *U.S. Public*, pg. 652
Stayer, Ralph F., Chm. Bd.--Johnsonville Foods, Inc., Kohler, WI; *U.S. Private*, pg. 595
Stead, James, Chm. Bd. & Pres.--GMS Corporation, Woonsocket, RI; *U.S. Private*, pg. 435
Stead, Jerre L., Chm. Bd. & Chief Exec. Officer--Ingram Micro Inc., Santa Ana, CA; *U.S. Public*, pg. 878
Steadman, David R.A., Chm.--Brookwood Companies Inc., New York, NY; *U.S. Public*, pg. 777
Steadman, Jack, Chm. Bd.--Kansas City Chiefs Football Club, Inc., Kansas City, MO; *U.S. Private*, pg. 607
Steck, Brian J., Chm. Bd. & Chief Exec. Officer--The Nesbitt Thomson Corporation Limited, Toronto, Canada; *Int'l*, pg. 153
Stedman, W.R., Chm. Bd.--Pembina Pipeline Corporation, Calgary, Canada; *Int'l*, pg. 1032
Steele, Harold R., Chm. Bd.--Canadian Airlines Corporation, Calgary, Canada; *Int'l*, pg. 255
Steele, Harry R., Chm. Bd. & Chief Exec. Officer--Newfoundland Capital Corporation Limited, Dartmouth, Canada; *Int'l*, pg. 924
Steele, J.R., Chm. Bd.--P&O European Transport Services Ltd., Altrincham, United Kingdom; *Int'l*, pg. 1033
Steele, Loren, Vice Chm. & Chief Exec. Officer--The Rivet Group L.L.C., Aberdeen, SD; *U.S. Private*, pg. 934
Steenberg, W.D., Chm. Bd. & Pres.--Steenberg Homes, Inc., Fond Du Lac, WI; *U.S. Private*, pg. 1039
Steere, William C., Chm. Bd. & Chief Exec. Officer--Pfizer Inc., New York, NY; *U.S. Public*, pg. 1281
Stefanko, Robert A., Chm. Bd. & Chief Fin. Officer--A. Schulman, Inc., Akron, OH; *U.S. Public*, pg. 1441
Steffensen, Dwight A., Chm. Bd. & Chief Exec. Officer--Merisel, Inc., El Segundo, CA; *U.S. Public*, pg. 1095
Steffey, Stewart H., Jr., Chm.--Cigna Insurance Company of Canada, Toronto, Canada; *U.S. Public*, pg. 366
Steigerwaldt, Donna Wolf, Chm. Bd. & Chief Exec. Officer--Jockey International, Inc., Kenosha, WI; *U.S. Private*, pg. 588
Steil, Gordon E., Chm. & Chief Exec. Officer--Harrington & King, Chicago, IL; *U.S. Private*, pg. 504
Stein-Sapir, Leonard, Chm. Bd. & Chief Exec. Officer--Morgan's Foods, Inc., Beachwood, OH; *U.S. Public*, pg. 1133
Stein, Alfred J., Chm. Bd. & Chief Exec. Officer--VLSI Technology, Inc., San Jose, CA; *U.S. Public*, pg. 1703
Stein, C. Jeffrey, Chm. Bd.--Fova, Inc., New York, NY; *U.S. Public*, pg. 764
Stein, Elliot H., Chm. Emeritus--Stifel Financial Corp., Saint Louis, MO; *U.S. Public*, pg. 1518
Stein, Howard, Chm. Bd. & Chief Exec. Officer--The Dreyfus Corporation, New York, NY; *U.S. Public*, pg. 1085
Stein, Jay, Chm. Bd. & Chief Exec. Officer--Stein Mart, Inc., Jacksonville, FL; *U.S. Public*, pg. 1514

Stein, Martin E., Jr., Chm. Bd. & Chief Exec. Officer--Regency Group Inc., Jacksonville, FL; *U.S. Private*, pg. 918

Stein, Sidney J., Dr., Chm. Bd., Chief Exec. Officer--Electro-Science Laboratories, Inc., King of Prussia, PA; *U.S. Private*, pg. 369

Steinback, Kenneth, Chm. Bd. & Chief Exec. Officer--Computer Sales International Inc., Saint Louis, MO; *U.S. Private*, pg. 260

Steinberg, Michael, Chm. Bd.--Macy's West, San Francisco, CA; *U.S. Public*, pg. 618

Steinberg, Phil, Chm. Bd.--Crest Steel Corp., Carson, CA; *Int'l*, pg. 845

Steinberg, Robert M., Chm. Bd. & Chief Exec. Officer--Reliance Insurance Company, Philadelphia, PA; *U.S. Public*, pg. 1374

Steiner, Charles, Chm. Bd. & Chief Exec. Officer--Branch Group Inc., Upper Marlboro, MD; *U.S. Private*, pg. 165

Steiner, Jeffrey J., Chm. Bd. & Chief Exec. Officer--Banner Aerospace, Inc., Washington, DC; *U.S. Public*, pg. 187

Steiner, Jeffrey J., Chm. Bd., Pres. & Chief Exec. Officer--The Fairchild Corporation, Chantilly, VA; *U.S. Public*, pg. 610

Steiner, Thomas A., Chm. Bd.--Advance Business Graphics, Mira Loma, CA; *U.S. Private*, pg. 18

Steinfeld, Manfred, Chm.-Exec. Committee--Shelby Williams Industries, Inc., Morristown, TN; *U.S. Public*, pg. 1464

Steinfeld, Paul N., Chm. Bd. & Chief Exec. Officer--Shelby Williams Industries, Inc., Morristown, TN; *U.S. Public*, pg. 1464

Steinhauer, Frederick C., Chm. Bd. & Pres.--Madison Dairy Produce Company, Madison, WI; *U.S. Private*, pg. 694

Steinmann, Heinrech, Dr., Chm. Bd.--Rieter Holdings, Winterthur, Switzerland; *Int'l*, pg. 1116

Steiny, John O., Chm. Bd.--Steiny & Company, Inc., Baldwin Park, CA; *U.S. Private*, pg. 1039

Stella, Gianni, Chm.--Enichem International Holdings B.V., Amsterdam, Netherlands; *Int'l*, pg. 429

Stemberg, Thomas G., Chm. Bd. & Chief Exec. Officer--Staples, Inc., Westborough, MA; *U.S. Public*, pg. 1509

Stempel, Robert C., Chm. Bd.--Energy Conversion Devices, Inc., Troy, MI; *U.S. Public*, pg. 581

Stempel, Rolf O., Chm. Bd.--Serviceplan GmbH, Munich, Germany; *Int'l*, pg. 1225

Stempler, Gerald L., Chm. Bd.--Textilease Corporation, Beltsville, MD; *U.S. Private*, pg. 1079

Stenbeck, Jan H., Chm. Bd.--Millicom International Cellular SA, Bertrange, Luxembourg; *Int'l*, pg. 867

Stenbeck, Jan Hugo, Chm. Bd.--Korsnas AB, Gavle, Sweden; *Int'l*, pg. 759

Stengel, Ronald, Chm. Bd.--Smith Corona Corp., Cortland, NY; *U.S. Private*, pg. 1007

Stenham, Cob, Chm. Bd.--Arjo Wiggins Appleton plc, Basingstoke, United Kingdom; *Int'l*, pg. 567

Stennett, P., Chm. Bd.--Redland Technologies Ltd., Crawley, United Kingdom; *Int'l*, pg. 1091

Stepan, F. Quinn, Chm. Bd., Pres. & Chief Exec. Officer--Stepan Company, Northfield, IL; *U.S. Public*, pg. 1514

Stephen, Philip, Chm. Bd., Pres., Chief Oper. & Chief Exec. Officer--Aid Auto Stores, Inc., Westbury, NY; *U.S. Public*, *pg. 29*

Stephens, E. Barrie, Chm. Bd.--Siebe plc, Windsor, United Kingdom; *Int'l*, pg. 1240

Stephens, Elton B., Chm. Bd.--EBSCO Industries, Inc., Birmingham, AL; *U.S. Private*, pg. 358

Stephens, Gerald D., Chm. Bd.--RLI Insurance Company, Peoria, IL; *U.S. Public*, pg. 1356

Stephens, Gerald D., Chm. Bd.--Mt. Hawley Insurance Company, Peoria, IL; *U.S. Public*, pg. 1356

Stephens, J.B., Chm. Bd.--Davis Electrical Constructors, Inc., Greenville, SC; *U.S. Private*, pg. 315

Stephenson, E.W., Jr., Sr. Exec. V.P. & Chm. & Chief Exec. Officer-AmSouth Bank FL--AmSouth Bancorporation, Birmingham, AL; *U.S. Public*, pg. 105

Stephenson, William V., Chm. Bd., Pres. & Chief Exec. Officer--First Brands Corporation, Danbury, CT; *U.S. Public*, pg. 626

Stepic, Herbert, Dr., Deputy Chm.--Raiffeisen Zentralbank Osterreich, Vienna, Austria; *Int'l*, pg. 1084

Stepien, Ronald W., Chm. Bd. & Chief Exec. Officer--MidAmerican Capital Company, Des Moines, IA; *U.S. Public*, pg. 1109

Sterling of Plaistow, Lord, Chm. Bd. & Chief Exec. Officer--The Peninsular and Oriental Steam Navigation Company, London, United Kingdom; *Int'l*, pg. 1032

Stern, Charles J., Chm. Bd. & Pres.--The Bionetics Corporation, Newport News, VA; *U.S. Private*, pg. 145

Stern, Herbert L., Jr., Chm.-Exec. Committee & Sec.--T C Manufacturing Company, Inc., Evanston, IL; *U.S. Private*, *pg. 1062*

Stern, Howard S., Chm. Bd.--E-Z-Em, Inc., Westbury, NY; *U.S. Public*, pg. 540

Stern, James, Chm. Bd.--The Cypress Group LLC, New York, NY; *U.S. Private*, pg. 300

Stern, Leonard N., Chm. Bd.--The Hartz Mountain Corp., Secaucus, NJ; *U.S. Private*, pg. 508

Stern, Leonard N., Chm. Bd.--VV Publishing Corp., New York, NY; *U.S. Private*, pg. 1131

Stern, Nelson M., Chm.--Stern Advertising, Inc., Cleveland, OH; *U.S. Private*, pg. 1041

Sternbach, Stephen, Chm. Bd., Pres. & Chief Exec. Officer--Star Multi Care Services Inc., Hicksville, NY; *U.S. Public*, *pg. 1510*

Sternberg, Seymour, Chm. Bd., Pres., Chief Exec. Officer & Chief Oper. Officer--New York Life Insurance Company, New York, NY; *U.S. Private*, pg. 794

Sternberg, Sheldon, Chm. Bd. & Chief Exec. Officer--Bessin Corporation, Chicago, IL; *U.S. Public*, pg. 1433

Sterner, Al G., Chm. & Chief Exec. Officer--M & I Bank of Delavan, Delavan, WI; *U.S. Public*, pg. 1050

Sternheimer, Mark A., Chm. Bd. & Pres.--Sternheimer Brothers Inc., Sandston, VA; *U.S. Private*, pg. 1042

Sternlicht, Barry S., Chm. Bd. & Chief Exec. Officer-Trust--Starwood Hotels & Resorts, Phoenix, AZ; *U.S. Public*, pg. 1512

Sternlisb, Edward, Chm. Bd.--Henry Lee Company, Miami, FL; *U.S. Private*, pg. 657

Stetler, Daniel, Chm. Bd. & Pres.--Louis Allis Company, Milwaukee, WI; *U.S. Private*, pg. 677

Stetson, John B., Chm. Bd.--Commercial Travelers Mutual Insurance Company, Utica, NY; *U.S. Private*, pg. 258

Steurer, Joe, Chm. Bd. & Chief Exec. Officer--Jofco Inc., Jasper, IN; *U.S. Private*, pg. 588

Stevens, Bruce, Chm. Bd.--Rollex Corporation, Elk Grove Village, IL; *U.S. Private*, pg. 941

Stevens, David, Lord, Chm. Bd.--Oak Industries Inc., Waltham, MA; *U.S. Public*, pg. 1209

Stevens, Elizabeth, Chm. Bd.--Cold Heading Co., Warren, MI; *U.S. Private*, pg. 250

Stevens, Lord, of Ludgate, Chm. Bd.--Express Newspapers plc, London, United Kingdom; *Int'l*, pg. 1443

Stevens, Paul I., Chm. Bd. & Chief Exec. Officer--Stevens International, Inc., Fort Worth, TX; *U.S. Public*, pg. 1517

Stevens, William J., Chm. Bd. & Pres.--Motion Industries, Inc., Irondale, AL; *U.S. Public*, pg. 732

Stevenson, Bobby G., Chm. Bd., Chief Exec. Officer & Sec.--Ciber, Inc., Englewood, CO; *U.S. Public*, pg. 356

Stevenson, Charles E., Jr., Chm., Pres. & Chief Exec. Officer--CEBCOR (Consolidated Employment Benefits Corp.), Chicago, IL; *U.S. Private*, pg. 220

Stevenson, Dennis, Chm. Bd.--Pearson plc, London, United Kingdom; *Int'l*, pg. 1025

Stevenson, Derek, Chm. Bd.--The Financial Times Ltd., London, United Kingdom; *Int'l*, pg. 1025

Stevenson, John R., Chm. Bd. & Chief Exec. Officer--McWhorter Technologies, Inc., Carpentersville, IL; *U.S. Public*, pg. 1074

Steves, Marshall T., Sr., Chm. Bd.--Steves & Sons, Inc., San Antonio, TX; *U.S. Private*, pg. 1042

Steward, H.L., Chm. Bd.--LL&E Colombia, Inc., New Orleans, LA; *U.S. Public*, pg. 269

Steward, H.L., Chm. Bd. & Pres.--Inexco Oil Company, New Orleans, LA; *U.S. Public*, pg. 269

Stewart, Andrew K., Chm. Bd., Pres. & Chief Exec. Officer--Computer Methods Corporation, Livonia, MI; *U.S. Private*, pg. 260

Stewart, C. Jim, II, Chm. Bd.--Stewart & Stevenson Services, Inc., Houston, TX; *U.S. Public*, pg. 1517

Stewart, Frank B., Jr., Chm. Bd.--Stewart Enterprises, Inc., Metairie, LA; *U.S. Public*, pg. 1518

Stewart, Gordan Butch, Chm. Bd.--Air Jamaica Ltd., Miami, FL; *U.S. Private*, pg. 28

Stewart, J.W., Chm. Bd., Pres. & Chief Exec. Officer--BJ Services Company, Houston, TX; *U.S. Public*, pg. 161

Stewart, Richard, Chm. Bd. & Chief Exec. Officer--Computer Corporation of America, Framingham, MA; *U.S. Private*, pg. 260

Stewart, S. Jay, Chm. Bd. & Chief Exec. Officer--Morton International Inc., Chicago, IL; *U.S. Public*, pg. 1134

Stewart, Thomas J., Chm. Bd. & Chief Exec. Officer--Services Group of America, Seattle, WA; *U.S. Private*, pg. 987

Stewart, Thomas J., Chm. Bd.--Food Services of America, Seattle, WA; *U.S. Private*, pg. 987

Stewart, W.W., Chm. Bd.--AEGON Financial Services Group (UK) Ltd., London, United Kingdom; *Int'l*, pg. 28

Steyn, C.G., Chm. & Mng. Dir.--Barprop Ltd., Crown Mines, South Africa; *Int'l*, pg. 1081

Stift, Robert C., Chm. Bd. & Chief Exec. Officer--Grove WorldWide, Shady Grove, PA; *Int'l*, pg. 593

Stiles, Terry W., Chm. Bd. & Chief Exec. Officer--Stiles Corporation, Fort Lauderdale, FL; *U.S. Private*, pg. 1043

Stillman, Sheldon, Chm. Bd.--Sage Enterprises, Inc., Des Plaines, IL; *U.S. Private*, pg. 960

Stillman, Walter R., Chm. Bd. & Pres.--Stillman & Hoag, Inc., Englewood, NJ; *U.S. Private*, pg. 1043

Stingel, Russell E., Chm. Bd. & Chief Exec. Officer--IEC Electronics Corp., Newark, NY; *U.S. Public*, pg. 854

Stinson, Kenneth E., Chm. Bd.--Kiewit Construction Group, Inc., Omaha, NE; *U.S. Private*, pg. 619

Stipes, Frank C., Esq., Chm. Bd., Pres. & Chief Exec. Officer--Westernbank of Puerto Rico, Mayaguez, PR; *U.S. Public*, pg. 1760

Stipp, John S., Chm. Bd.--District Petroleum Products, Inc., Sandusky, OH; *U.S. Private*, pg. 336

Stiritz, William P., Chm. Bd.--Ralston Purina Company, Saint Louis, MO; *U.S. Public*, pg. 1359

Stirnemann, Kurt E., Dr., Chm. Bd.--AGIE AG (Fur Industrielle Elektronik), Lausanne, Switzerland; *Int'l*, pg. 488

Stitt, William C., Chm. & Chief Exec. Officer--ICF Kaiser Engineers, Inc., Oakland, CA; *U.S. Public*, pg. 853

Stockham, Herbert, Chm. Bd.--Stockham Valves & Fittings, Inc., Birmingham, AL; *U.S. Private*, pg. 1043

Stockl, Ernst, Chm. Bd.--ElectroCom Automation L.P., Arlington, TX; *Int'l*, pg. 1244

Stockman, David A., Co-Chm.--Collins & Aikman Corporation, Charlotte, NC; *U.S. Public*, pg. 399

Stockman, David A., Chm. Bd.--Haynes International, Inc., Kokomo, IN; *U.S. Public*, pg. 801

Stoddard, John, Chm. Bd.--Pyramid Breweries, Inc.; *U.S. Public*, pg. 1345

Stoddard, Richard E., Chm. Bd. & Chief Exec. Officer--Kaiser Ventures, Inc., Ontario, CA; *U.S. Public*, pg. 941

Stoddart, M.C., Chm. Bd.--Britax International plc, Warwick, United Kingdom; *Int'l*, pg. 216

Stokely, Ted P., Chm. Bd.--Continental Mortgage and Equity Trust, Dallas, TX; *U.S. Public*, pg. 441

Stokes, Patrick T., Chm. Bd. & Chief Exec. Officer--Anheuser-Busch Investment Capital Corporation, Saint Louis, MO; *U.S. Public*, pg. 114

Stollery, A. Gordon, Chm. Bd., Pres. & Chief Exec. Officer--Morrison Petroleums Ltd., Calgary, Canada; *Int'l*, pg. 895

Stolmeier, Robert C., Chm. Bd. & Pres.--KCL Corporation, Shelbyville, IN; *U.S. Private*, pg. 603

Stolt-Nielsen, Jacob, Jr., Chm. Bd. & Chief Exec. Officer--Stolt-Nielsen S.A., London, United Kingdom; *Int'l*, pg. 1301

Stoltz, Bob, Chm. Bd. & Pres.--Tiernay Metals, Redondo Beach, CA; *U.S. Private*, pg. 1085

Stone, Albert, Chm. Bd.--Sterilite Corporation, Townsend, MA; *U.S. Private*, pg. 1040

Stone, Craig, Chm. Bd., Pres. & Chief Exec. Officer--K-D Lamp Company, Cincinnati, OH; *U.S. Private*, pg. 603

Stone, David J., Chm. Bd. & Chief Exec. Officer--Southwestern Financial Corporation, New York, NY; *U.S. Private*, pg. 1018

Stone, David J., Chm. Bd. & Chief Exec. Officer--PennCorp Financial Group, Inc., New York, NY; *U.S. Public*, pg. 1271

Stone, Eugene E., IV, Chm. Bd.--Umbro International, Inc., Greenville, SC; *U.S. Private*, pg. 1116

Stone, James W., Chm. Bd.--Stones, Inc., Bainbridge, GA; *U.S. Private*, pg. 1045

Stone, John McWilliams, Jr., Chm. Bd., Pres., Chief Exec. Officer & Chief Oper. Officer--Dukane Corporation, Saint Charles, IL; *U.S. Private*, pg. 345

Stone, Richard B., Chm. Bd. & Chief Exec. Officer--Dart Group Corporation, Landover, MD; *U.S. Public*, pg. 484

Stone, Richard B., Chm. Bd. & Chief Exec. Officer--Crown Books Corporation, Landover, MD; *U.S. Public*, pg. 484

Stone, Robert M., Chm. Bd. & Pres.--J. A. Jones Applied Research Co., Charlotte, NC; *Int'l*, pg. 633

Stone, Roger W., Chm. Bd., Pres. & Chief Exec. Officer--Stone Container Corporation, Chicago, IL; *U.S. Public*, pg. 1520

Stone, Roger W., Chm. Bd. & Chief Exec. Officer--Stone Forest Industries, Chicago, IL; *U.S. Public*, pg. 1521

Stone, Sherrill, Chm. Bd.,Pres. & Chief Exec. Officer--Peerless Mfg. Co., Dallas, TX; *U.S. Public*, pg. 1268

Stonecipher, Harland C., Chm. Bd. & Chief Exec. Officer--Pre-Paid Legal Services, Inc., Ada, OK; *U.S. Public*, pg. 1320

Stoppelmoor, Wayne H., Chm. Bd. & Chief Exec. Officer--Interstate Power Company, Dubuque, IA; *U.S. Public*, pg. 910

Stork, Wayne A., Chm. & Chief Exec. Officer--Delaware Management Holdings, Inc., Philadelphia, PA; *U.S. Public*, pg. 997

Storm, O.J., Chm.--Brother Norge A.S., Oslo, Norway; *Int'l*, pg. 230

Storr, Hans G., Chm. Bd. & Chief Exec. Officer--Philip Morris Capital Corporation, Rye Brook, NY; *U.S. Public*, pg. 1289

Stott, W.L.B., Chm.--Isle of Man Bank Limited, Douglas, United Kingdom; *Int'l*, pg. 910

Stout, Lonnie J., II, Chm. Bd., Pres. & Chief Exec. Officer--J. Alexanders Corporation, Nashville, TN; *U.S. Public*, pg. 40

Stover, W. Robert, Chm. Bd. & Chief Exec. Officer--Western Staff Services, Walnut Creek, CA; *U.S. Public*, pg. 1760

Stowers, James E., Jr., Chm. Bd.--American Century Companies, Inc., Kansas City, MO; *U.S. Private*, pg. 52

Strachen, John R., Chm. Bd.--Pepsi-Cola Albany Bottling Co., Inc., Latham, NY; *U.S. Private*, pg. 852

Strackbein, Ronald, Chm. Bd.--Chattanooga Group, Inc., Hixson, TN; *U.S. Private*, pg. 231

Strahman, Richard D., Chm. Bd. & Pres.--Strahman Valves, Inc., Florham Park, NJ; *U.S. Private*, pg. 1046

Strahmmer, Peter, Chm. & Pres.--Voest-Alpine Stahl AG, Lienz, Austria; *Int'l*, pg. 1470

Strange, J. Leland, Pres. & Chief Exec. Officer--Intelligent Systems Corp., Norcross, GA; *U.S. Public*, pg. 888

Strano, William J., Chm. Bd.--Strano Syscco Foodservice Limited, Peterborough, Canada; *U.S. Public*, pg. 1552

Stratton, Frederick P., Jr., Chm. Bd. & Chief Exec. Officer--Briggs & Stratton Corporation, Wauwatosa, WI; *U.S. Public*, pg. 252

Stratton, James W., Chm. Bd.--Stratton Management Company, Plymouth Meeting, PA; *U.S. Private*, pg. 1046

Straub, Walter W., Chm. Bd., Pres. & Chief Exec. Officer--Rainbow Technologies, Inc., Irvine, CA; *U.S. Public*, pg. 1359

Straube, Win, Chm. Bd. & Owner--Straube Regional Center LLC, Pennington, NJ; *U.S. Private*, pg. 1046

Straube, Win, Chm. Bd.--Pegasus International Corporation, Pennington, NJ; *U.S. Private*, pg. 1046

Straubmuller, George J., III, Chm. Bd.--Wheaton Inc., Millville, NJ; *Int'l*, pg. 67

Strauch, Charles S., Chm. Bd. & Chief Exec. Officer--PairGain Technologies Inc., Tustin, CA; *U.S. Public*, pg. 1253

Straus, David J., Chm. Bd. & Chief Exec. Officer--STRAFCO, Inc., San Antonio, TX; *U.S. Private*, pg. 1046

Straus, Joseph, Jr., Chm. Bd.--Reuben Organization, Philadelphia, PA; *U.S. Private*, pg. 925

Strauss, C. B., Chm.--Standard Bank London Limited, London, United Kingdom; *Int'l*, pg. 1294

Strauss, C.B., Dr., Chm.--Standard Bank Investment Corporation Limited, Johannesburg, South Africa; *Int'l*, pg. 1293

Strauss, David, Chm. Bd.--Sedgwick Noble Lowndes Group Limited, Croydon, United Kingdom; *Int'l*, pg. 1218

Strauss, David, Chm.--Sedgwick Noble Lowndes Limited, Melbourne, Australia; *Int'l*, pg. 1218

Strauss, Peter, Chm. Bd.--Havatampa, Inc., Tampa, FL; *U.S. Private*, pg. 510

Strauss, Richard H., Pres. & Chief Exec. Officer--Advance Packaging Corporation, Grand Rapids, MI; *U.S. Private*, pg. 18

Stravitz, Russell, Chm.--Rich's/Lazarus/Goldsmith's, Atlanta, GA; *U.S. Public*, pg. 618

Straw, Erwin T., Chm. Bd., Pres. & Chief Exec. Officer--Prime Bancorp, Inc., Fort Washington, PA; *U.S. Public*, pg. 1326

Street, Chriss W., Chm. Bd., Pres. & Chief Exec. & Oper. Officer--Comprehensive Care Corporation, Corona Del Mar, CA; *U.S. Public*, pg. 419

Street, E. Gene, Chm. Bd.--El Chico Restaurants, Inc., Dallas, TX; *U.S. Private*, pg. 283
Street, Gordon P., Jr., Chm. Bd., Pres., Chief Exec. & Chief Oper. Officer--North American Royalties, Inc., Chattanooga, TN; *U.S. Private*, pg. 803
Street, Laurence, Sir, Chm. Bd.--John Fairfax Holdings Limited, Sydney, Australia; *Int'l*, pg. 477
Streety, Keith, Chm. Bd.--Plains Co-op Oil Mill, Lubbock, TX; *U.S. Private*, pg. 868
Stremme, Steffen, Dr., Chm. Bd., Pres. & Chief Exec. Officer--Quelle Group, Furth, Germany; *Int'l*, pg. 1078
Strenger, Hermann J., Chm.-Supervisory Bd.--Linde AG, Wiesbaden, Germany; *Int'l*, pg. 810
Streppel, J.B.M., Chm. Bd.--Labouchere N.V., Amsterdam, Netherlands; *Int'l*, pg. 26
Streur, Harold, Chm. Bd.--Castex Incorporated, Holland, MI; *U.S. Public*, pg. 1577
Strickland, Edward E., Chm. Bd.--Reuter Manufacturing Inc., Hopkins, MN; *U.S. Public*, pg. 1383
Strickland, J.E., Chm. Bd.--The Hongkong and Shanghai Banking Corporation Limited (HongkongBank), Central, Hong Kong; *Int'l*, pg. 583
Strickland, Robert, Chm. Bd. & Chief Exec. Officer--Trust Company Of Georgia, Atlanta, GA; *U.S. Public*, pg. 1538
Strickland, Vernon B., Chm. Bd.--Hawthorne Corp., Charleston, SC; *U.S. Private*, pg. 512
Strickler, R.H., Chm. Bd.--Rocco Inc., Harrisonburg, VA; *U.S. Private*, pg. 937
Strickler, Twig, Chm. Bd.--Shady Brook Farms, Dayton, VA; *U.S. Private*, pg. 937
Strite, Lewis E., Chm. Bd.--Shenandoah Mfg. Co. Inc., Harrisonburg, VA; *U.S. Private*, pg. 992
Strittmatter, Hermann, Chm. & Pres.--TBWA GGK Zurick, Zurich, Switzerland; *Int'l*, pg. 1335
Stronach, Frank, Chm. Bd.--Magna International Inc., Markham, Canada; *Int'l*, pg. 829
Stroud, James A., Co-Chm. Bd., Chief Oper. Officer & Sec.--Capital Senior Living, Inc., Dallas, TX; *U.S. Public*, pg. 302
Stroud, Wilfred C., Chm. Bd. & Pres.--Strouds, Inc., City of Industry, CA; *U.S. Public*, pg. 1525
Strube, Juergen, Dr., Chm. Bd.--BASF AG, Ludwigshafen, Germany; *Int'l*, pg. 103
Struby, Rolf, Chm.--IBM Switzerland, Zurich, Switzerland; *U.S. Public*, pg. 897
Strudler, Robert J., Chm. Bd. & Co.-Chief Exec. Officer--U.S. Home Corporation, Houston, TX; *U.S. Public*, pg. 1682
Strugatz, Arthur, Chm. Bd.--Austin Productions, Inc., Holbrook, NY; *U.S. Private*, pg. 100
Strulovici, Christian, Chm. Bd.--Cofassur Vie, Paris, France; *Int'l*, pg. 564
Stuart, D. Riley, Chm. Bd.--Brice Building Co., Inc., Birmingham, AL; *U.S. Private*, pg. 167
Stuart, James, III, Chm. Bd.--First Commerce Investors, Lincoln, NE; *U.S. Public*, pg. 629
Stuart, James, Jr., Chm. Bd. & Chief Exec. Officer--First Commerce Bancshares, Inc., Lincoln, NE; *U.S. Public*, pg. 629
Stuart, John E., Chm. Bd. & Chief Exec. Officer--Ikon Office Solutions, Inc., Malvern, PA; *U.S. Public*, pg. 862
Stuart, Thomas, Chm. Bd. & Chief Exec. Officer--Bureau of Engraving, Minneapolis, MN; *U.S. Private*, pg. 181
Stubbs, Robert W., Chm. Bd. & Chief Exec. Officer--Bell Atlantic Properties, Inc., Philadelphia, PA; *U.S. Public*, pg. 203
Stubbs, Stoney M., Jr., Chm. Bd., Pres. & Chief Exec. Officer--Frozen Food Express Industries, Inc., Dallas, TX; *U.S. Public*, pg. 685
Stuckey, Charles R., Jr., Chm. Bd., Pres. & Chief Exec. Officer--Security Dynamics Technologies, Bedford, MA; *U.S. Public*, pg. 1453
Stucki, Hans-Rudolf, Dr., Chm. Bd.--Blue Ridge Insurance Co., Simsbury, CT; *Int'l*, pg. 345
Studer, Robert, Chm. Bd.--Union Bank of Switzerland, Zurich, Switzerland; *Int'l*, pg. 1439
Stuesser, Lawrence J., Jr., Chm. Bd.--Curative Health Services, East Setauket, NY; *U.S. Public*, pg. 469
Stull, Roger, Chm. Bd.--Penhall International, Anaheim, CA; *U.S. Private*, pg. 849
Stumpf, John, Chm.--Norwest Bank Texas, N.A., Lubbock, TX; *U.S. Public*, pg. 1203
Stupp, Erwin P., Jr., Chm. Bd.--Stupp Bros, Inc., Saint Louis, MO; *U.S. Private*, pg. 1048
Sturken, Craig, Chm. Bd. & Chief Exec. Officer--Dominion Stores, Etobicoke, Canada; *Int'l*, pg. 1375
Sturken, Craig, Chm. & Chief Exec. Officer-Midwest Region--The Great Atlantic & Pacific Tea Company, Inc., Montvale, NJ; *Int'l*, pg. 1375
Stutz, Rolf, Chm. Bd. & Chief Exec. Officer--Zoll Medical Corporation, Burlington, MA; *U.S. Private*, pg. 1207
Stuzin, Charles B., Chm. Bd., Chief Exec. Officer & Pres.--NationsBank/Miami, Miami, FL; *U.S. Public*, pg. 1162
Styslinger, Lee J., Jr., Chm. Bd.--Altec Industries, Inc., Birmingham, AL; *U.S. Private*, pg. 47
Suarez, Amancio V., Chm. Bd., Pres., Chief Exec. & Chief Fin. Officer--Cosmo Communications Corporation, Miami, FL; *U.S. Public*, pg. 451
Subia, Robert, Chm., Pres. & Chief Exec. Officer--Micron Custom Manufacturing Services, Inc., Nampa, ID; *U.S. Public*, pg. 1105
Subjetzki, Klaus, Chm. Bd.--Schering AG, Berlin, Germany; *Int'l*, pg. 1203
Subramaniam, Shivan S., Chm. Bd., Pres. & Chief Exec. Officer--Allendale Mutual Insurance Co., Johnston, RI; *U.S. Private*, pg. 37
Suda, Hiroshi, Chm. Bd.--Central Japan Railway Company, Nagoya, Japan; *Int'l*, pg. 279
Suddath, Stephen M., Chm. Bd.--The Suddath Companies, Jacksonville, FL; *U.S. Private*, pg. 1049
Suechting, David L., Jr., Chm. Bd.--Track 'n Trail, El Dorado Hills, CA; *U.S. Public*, pg. 1626
Sugar, A.M., Chm. Bd.--Viglen Technology PLC, Alperton, United Kingdom; *Int'l*, pg. 1468
Sugar, Alan, Chm. Bd.--Betacom Plc, Brentwood, United Kingdom; *Int'l*, pg. 193
Sugarman, Joseph, Chm. Bd.--JS&A Group, Inc., Las Vegas, NV; *U.S. Private*, pg. 578
Suggs, Carroll W., Chm. Bd., Pres. & Chief Exec. Officer--Petroleum Helicopters, Inc., Metairie, LA; *U.S. Public*, pg. 1281
Suggs, Leo H., Chm. Bd. & Chief Exec. Officer--Overnite Transportation Co., Richmond, VA; *U.S. Public*, pg. 1668
Sugiura, Go, Chm. Bd. & Chief Exec. Officer--Miller Fluid Power Corp., Bensenville, IL; *U.S. Private*, pg. 747
Sugiura, Takaya, Chm. Bd.--All Nippon Airways Co. Ltd., Tokyo, Japan; *Int'l*, pg. 57
Suissa, David, Chm. Bd. & Exec. Creative Dir.--Suissa Miller Advertising, Inc., Los Angeles, CA; *U.S. Private*, pg. 1049
Suitirong, Pramon, Chm. Bd.--Thai Kabaya Industries Co., Ltd., Chon Buri, Thailand; *Int'l*, pg. 727
Suitt, T. Howard, Chm. Bd. & Chief Exec. Officer--Suitt Construction Company, Inc., Greenville, SC; *U.S. Private*, pg. 106
Sullivan, C. David, Chm. Bd.--National Loss Control Service Corp., Long Grove, IL; *U.S. Private*, pg. 614
Sullivan, Charles, Chm. Bd.--Association of Credit Union League Executives, Madison, WI; *U.S. Private*, pg. 288
Sullivan, Charles A., Chm. Bd. & Chief Exec. Officer--Interstate Bakeries Corporation, Kansas City, MO; *U.S. Public*, pg. 909
Sullivan, Chris T., Chm. Bd. & Chief Exec. Officer--Outback Steakhouse Inc., Tampa, FL; *U.S. Public*, pg. 1235
Sullivan, Daniel J., Chm. Bd., Pres. & Chief Exec. Officer--Caliber System, Inc., Akron, OH; *U.S. Public*, pg. 604
Sullivan, Donald M., Chm. Bd., Pres. & Chief Exec. Officer--MTS Systems Corporation, Eden Prairie, MN; *U.S. Public*, pg. 1028
Sullivan, Fred R., Chm. Bd. & Pres.--Richton International Corporation, Madison, NJ; *U.S. Public*, pg. 1389
Sullivan, G. Craig, Chm. Bd., Pres. & Chief Exec. Officer--The Clorox Company, Oakland, CA; *U.S. Public*, pg. 386
Sullivan, John Fox, Chm., Pres., Chief Exec. Officer & Publr.--National Journal Group, Washington, DC; *U.S. Private*, pg. 785
Sullivan, Joseph P., Chm. Bd.--The Vigoro Corporation, Chicago, IL; *U.S. Public*, pg. 856
Sullivan, Richard S., Chm. Bd.--Sullivan Paper Company, West Springfield, MA; *U.S. Private*, pg. 1050
Sullivan, Thomas C., Chm. Bd. & Chief Exec. Officer--RPM, Inc., Medina, OH; *U.S. Public*, pg. 1356
Sullivan, Thomas C., Chm. Bd.--Mohawk Finishing Products, Inc., Amsterdam, NY; *U.S. Public*, pg. 1357
Sullivan, Thomas C., Chm. Bd.--Radiant Color NV, Houthalen, Belgium; *U.S. Public*, pg. 1357
Sullivan, William H., Jr., Chm. Bd.--National Gas & Oil Company, Newark, OH; *U.S. Public*, pg. 1156
Sulzberger, Arthur Ochs, Chm. Bd. & Chief Exec. Officer--The New York Times Company, New York, NY; *U.S. Public*, pg. 1173
Sulzberger, Arthur Ochs, Chm. Bd. & Chief Exec. Officer--The New York Times, New York, NY; *U.S. Public*, pg. 1174
Sumas, James, Chm. Bd., Chief Oper. Officer, Treas., & Dir.-Adv.--Village Super Market Inc., Springfield, NJ; *U.S.* Public, pg. 1721
Sumiyoshi, Hiroto, Chm. Bd.--Cosmo Oil Co., Ltd., Tokyo, Japan; *Int'l*, pg. 335
Summerill, Jon, Chm. Bd.--Domino, London, United Kingdom; *Int'l*, pg. 415
Summers, R., Chm. Bd.--Home Brewery plc, Nottingham, United Kingdom; *Int'l*, pg. 1211
Sun-Hong, Kim, Chm. Bd.--KIA Motors Corp., Seoul, Korea; *Int'l*, pg. 732
Sundarajan, U., Chm. Bd. & Mng. Dir.--Bharat Petroleum Corporation Ltd., Mumbai, India; *Int'l*, pg. 194
Sundberg, Edward A., Chm. Bd.--Thermo-Mizer Environmental Corp., Rahway, NJ; *U.S. Public*, pg. 1596
Sundberg, Matti, Chm. Bd., Pres. & Chief Exec. Officer--Valmet Corporation, Helsinki, Finland; *Int'l*, pg. 1447
Sunderland, James P., Chm. Bd.--Ash Grove Cement Company, Shawnee Mission, KS; *U.S. Private*, pg. 87
Sunderland, Robert, Chm. Bd.-Honorary--Ash Grove Cement Company, Shawnee Mission, KS; *U.S. Private*, pg. 87
Sundt, H. Wilson, Chm. Bd. & Chief Exec. Officer--Sundt Corp., Tucson, AZ; *U.S. Private*, pg. 1051
Sundt, Petter C.G., Chm. Bd.--Bergesen d.y. A.S., Oslo, Norway; *Int'l*, pg. 188
Sung On, Andrew Ng, Chm. Bd. & Chief Exec. Officer--GP Batteries International Ltd., Singapore, Singapore; *Int'l*, pg. 537
Sung, Kihong, Chm.--Kolon-Met Life Insurance Company Limited, Seoul, Korea; *U.S. Private*, pg. 738
Sushigome, Susumu, Chm.--TYK Refractories Co., Clairton, PA; *Int'l*, pg. 1345
Sutch, P.D.A., Chm. Bd.--Swire Pacific Limited, Central, Hong Kong; *Int'l*, pg. 1328
Sutherland, Donald, Chm. Bd.--The Lion Brewery, Inc., Wilkes-Barre, PA; *U.S. Public*, pg. 1000
Sutowski, Walter, Chm. Bd. & Chief Exec. Officer--Freeway Corporation, Cleveland, OH; *U.S. Private*, pg. 426
Sutton, Kelso F., Chm. Bd.-Time-Warner Books--Time-Life, Inc., Alexandria, VA; *U.S. Public*, pg. 1613
Sutton, Nicholas J., Chm. Bd. & Chief Exec. Officer--HS Resources, San Francisco, CA; *U.S. Public*, pg. 772
Sutton, Thomas C., Chm. Bd. & Chief Exec. Officer--Pacific Life Insurance Company, Newport Beach, CA; *U.S. Private*, pg. 831
Suwyn, Mark A., Chm. Bd. & Chief Exec. Officer--Louisiana Pacific Corporation, Portland, OR; *U.S. Public*, pg. 1015
Suyama, Kiichi, Chm. Bd.--Sun Wave Industrial Co., Tokyo, Japan; *Int'l*, pg. 1320
Suzuki, Chihiro, Chm. Bd.--Oki America Inc., Hackensack, NJ; *Int'l*, pg. 1000
Suzuki, Kaneo, Chm. Bd.--NEC Europe Ltd., London, United Kingdom; *Int'l*, pg. 900
Suzuki, Masashi, Chm. Bd.--The Nomura Securities Co., Ltd., Tokyo, Japan; *Int'l*, pg. 955
Suzuki, Noriyuki, Chm. Bd.--Yamaichi International (H.K.) Ltd., Central, Hong Kong; *Int'l*, pg. 1518
Suzuki, Saburosuke, IV, Chm. Emeritus--Ajinomoto Company Inc., Tokyo, Japan; *Int'l*, pg. 40
Suzuki, Yuji, Chm.--The Industrial Bank of Japan Trust Company, New York, NY; *Int'l*, pg. 675
Svanholm, Poul J., Chm. Bd.--Royal Copenhagen A/S, Frederiksberg, Denmark; *Int'l*, pg. 1134
Svedberg, Bjoern, Dr., Chm. Bd.--Telefonaktiebolaget LM Ericsson, Stockholm, Sweden; *Int'l*, pg. 1363
Svendsen, Arthur, Chm. Bd. & Chief Exec. Officer--Standard Pacific Corp., Costa Mesa, CA; *U.S. Public*, pg. 1503
Swadey, Robert J., Chm. Bd.--Midland Title Security, Inc., Cleveland, OH; *U.S. Public*, pg. 626
Swager, Richard E., Chm. Bd. & Chief Exec. Officer--Reinsurance Alternatives, Inc., Minneapolis, MN; *Int'l*, pg. 1503
Swain, Robert D., Chm. Bd.--Chroma Corporation, McHenry, IL; *U.S. Private*, pg. 238
Swalef, Gijsbert J., Chm.-Supervisory Bd.--Eureko B.V., Amsterdam, Netherlands; *Int'l*, pg. 464
Swam, Robert L., Exec. V.P., Chm. Bd. & Chief Exec. Officer-Raytheon Appliances--Raytheon Company, Lexington, MA; *U.S. Public*, pg. 1364
Swan, Frank J., Chm. Bd.--Mott's Inc., Stamford, CT; *Int'l*, pg. 248
Swanson, Douglas E., Chm. Bd., Pres. & Chief Exec. Officer--Cliffs Drilling Company, Houston, TX; *U.S. Public*, pg. 386
Swanson, William H., Chm. Bd. & Chief Exec. Officer--Raytheon Systems Company, Arlington, VA; *U.S. Public*, pg. 1364
Swanstrom, Kenneth A., Chm. Bd., Pres. & Chief Exec. Officer--Penn Engineering & Manufacturing Corp., Danboro, PA; *U.S. Public*, pg. 1269
Swart, B.J., Chm.--Firstcorp Merchant Bank Limited, Johannesburg, South Africa; *Int'l*, pg. 487
Swart, B.J., Chm.--First National Asset Management & Trust Company (Pty) Ltd., Johannesburg, South Africa; *Int'l*, pg. 487
Swart, B.J., Chm.--First Bowring Insurance Brokers Holdings (Pty.) LTD., Johannesburg, South Africa; *Int'l*, pg. 487
Swart, B.J., Chm.--First National Bank (Asia) LTD., Hong Kong, Hong Kong; *Int'l*, pg. 487
Swartout, Hank B., Chm. Bd., Pres. & Chief Exec. Officer--Precision Drilling Corporation, Calgary, Canada; *Int'l*, pg. 1066
Swartwout, James R., Chm. Bd., Pres. & Chief Fin. Officer--Summa Industries, Torrance, CA; *U.S. Public*, pg. 1527
Swartz, Dr. Jerome, Chm. Bd. & Chief Exec. Officer--Symbol Technologies, Inc., Holtsville, NY; *U.S. Public*, pg. 1546
Swartz, Sidney W., Chm. Bd., Pres. & Chief Exec. Officer--The Timberland Company, Stratham, NH; *U.S. Public*, pg. 1609
Swartz, Thomas B., Chm. Bd. & Chief Exec. Officer--The Sierra Capital Companies, San Francisco, CA; *U.S. Private*, pg. 998
Swaythling, Lord the Rt. Hon., Exec. Chm.--Rothmans UK Holdings Limited, London, United Kingdom; *Int'l*, pg. 1129
Sweasy, William J., Chm. Bd.--Red Wing Shoe Co., Inc., Red Wing, MN; *U.S. Private*, pg. 915
Swedback, James M., Chm. Bd.--Pioneer Mutual Life Insurance Company, Fargo, ND; *U.S. Private*, pg. 866
Sweden, Eric, Chm. Bd.--Vandemoortele N.V., Izegem, Belgium; *Int'l*, pg. 1451
Swee, Foo Kok, Chm. Bd.--International Factors (Singapore) Ltd., Singapore, Singapore; *Int'l*, pg. 684
Sween, Tom, Chm. Bd. & Chief Exec. Officer--E.A. Sween Company, Eden Prairie, MN; *U.S. Private*, pg. 1058
Sweeney, Edward A., Chm. Bd.--Willis Corroon Corp. of New York, New York, NY; *Int'l*, pg. 1506
Swendrowski, John, Chm. Bd. & Chief Exec. Officer--Northland Cranberries, Inc., Wisconsin Rapids, WI; *U.S. Public*, pg. 1197
Swenson, Kurt M., Chm. Bd., Pres. & Chief Exec. Officer--Rock of Ages Corporation, Graniteville, VT; *U.S. Public*, pg. 1396
Swetman, G.D., Chm. Bd.--British & Soviet International Carbon Limited, Windsor, United Kingdom; *Int'l*, pg. 894
Swett, Ralph J., Chm. Bd., Pres. & Chief Exec. Officer--IXC Communications, Inc., Austin, TX; *U.S. Private*, pg. 556
Swift, Charles O., Chm. Bd. & Pres.--Chuck Swift Sales & Leasing, Davis, CA; *U.S. Private*, pg. 1058
Swift, George P., Jr., Chm. Bd. & Chief Exec. Officer--Columbus Mills, Inc., Columbus, GA; *U.S. Private*, pg. 256
Swift, M. Allen, Chm. Bd., Pres. & Treas.--M. Swift & Sons Inc., Hartford, CT; *U.S. Private*, pg. 1059
Swift, Richard J., Chm. Bd., Pres. & Chief Exec. Officer--Foster Wheeler Corporation, Clinton, NJ; *U.S. Public*, pg. 676
Swigert, Henry T., Chm. Bd.--Esco Corporation, Portland, OR; *U.S. Private*, pg. 382
Swindells, William, Jr., Chm. Bd.--Willamette Industries, Inc., Portland, OR; *U.S. Public*, pg. 1768
Swinehart, Keith, Sr., Chm. Bd., Chief Exec. Officer & Chief Fin. Officer--Vanguard Plastics, Inc., Mc Pherson, KS; *U.S. Private*, pg. 1134
Swinimer, William A., Chm. Bd. & Chief Exec. Officer--Uniplast Industries, Inc., Orillia, Canada; *Int'l*, pg. 1424
Swisher, Bill, Chm. Bd. & Chief Exec. Officer--CMI Corporation, Oklahoma City, OK; *U.S. Public*, pg. 278
Swoboda, J. Gus, Chm. Bd.--First Northern Capital Corp., Green Bay, WI; *U.S. Public*, pg. 636
Swope, Samuel G., Chm. Bd.--Sam Swope Auto Group, Inc., Louisville, KY; *U.S. Private*, pg. 1059
Syar, C.M., Chm. Bd.--Syar Industries, Inc., Napa, CA; *U.S. Private*, pg. 1059

Sydnor, Dale, Chm. Bd., Pres. & Chief Exec. Officer--Wireless Telecom Group, Inc., Paramus, NJ; *U.S. Public, pg. 1772*

Sykes, Richard B., Sir, Chm. Bd.--Glaxo Wellcome plc, London, United Kingdom; *Int'l*, pg. 552

Sylva, Eugene R., Chm. Bd. & Pres.--Dimensional Merchandising, Inc., Wharton, NJ; *U.S. Private*, pg. 333

Symonds, J. Taft, Chm. Bd.--Tetra Technologies, Woodlands, TX; *U.S. Public*, pg. 1582

Symons, A.P., Chm. Bd. & Chief Exec. Officer--Canada Life Casualty Insurance Company, Etobicoke, Canada; *Int'l*, pg. 254

Syms, Sy, Chm. Bd.--Syms Corporation, Secaucus, NJ; *U.S. Public*, pg. 1547

Synott, Lee, Chm. Bd., Pres. & Chief Exec. Officer--Ingram Book Company, La Vergne, TN; *U.S. Private*, pg. 563

Syron, M. Bernard, Chm. Bd. & Chief Exec. Officer--Cara Operations Limited, Toronto, Canada; *Int'l*, pg. 266

Syron, Richard F., Chm. Bd. & Chief Exec. Officer--The American Stock Exchange, New York, NY; *U.S. Private*, pg. 62

Syrota, Jean, Chm. & Chief Exec. Officer--COGEMA - Compagnie Generale des Matieres Nucleaires, Velizy-Villacoublay, France; *Int'l*, pg. 304

Szetykiel, George W., Chm. Bd. & Chief Exec. Officer--Spartan Motors, Inc., Charlotte, MI; *U.S. Public*, pg. 1495

Szymaszek, P.G., Chm. Bd. & Pres.--Vilter Manufacturing Corporation, Cudahy, WI; *U.S. Private*, pg. 1140

Tabayashi, Kozo, Honorary Chm.--LTCB Asia Limted, Hong Kong, Hong Kong; *Int'l*, pg. 816

Tabor, Jon K., Chm. Bd., Pres. & Chief Exec. Officer--Allied Mineral Products, Inc., Columbus, OH; *U.S. Private*, pg. 39

Tabor, Maury, Chm. Bd. & Pres.--Condere Corporation, Natchez, MS; *U.S. Private*, pg. 262

Tabuchi, Teruhisa, Chm. Bd. & Pres.--Tabuchi Electric Co., Ltd., Sanda, Japan; *Int'l*, pg. 1346

Tada, Koki, Chm. Bd.--The Chugoku Electric Power Co., Inc., Hiroshima, Japan; *Int'l*, pg. 291

Tadmor, Dov, Chm. Bd.--Scitex Corporation Ltd., Holon, Israel; *Int'l*, pg. 644

Tager, Louise A., Dr., Chm. Bd.--Transnet Group, London, United Kingdom; *Int'l*, pg. 1418

Tager, Louise, Prof., Chm. Bd.--Transnet Ltd., Parkview, South Africa; *Int'l*, pg. 1417

Taguchi, Tadao, Chm. & Chief Exec. Officer--Toshiba America Inc., New York, NY; *Int'l*, pg. 1405

Taguinod, Teodorico C., Chm. Bd. & Chief Exec. Officer--EEI Corporation, Manila, Philippines; *Int'l*, pg. 425

Taittinger-Bonnemison , Claire, Chm. Bd.--Baccarat (Cie des Cristalleries), Paris, France; *Int'l*, pg. 132

Taittinger, Claude, Chm. Bd. & Pres.--Taittinger, Reims, France; *Int'l*, pg. 1348

Taitz, Andrew, Chm. Bd.--Union City Body Company, L.P., Union City, IN; *U.S. Private*, pg. 1118

Takada, Norifumi, Chm.-Mngmt. Bd.--Long-Term Credit Bank of Japan (Deutschland) AG, Frankfurt/Main, Germany; *Int'l*, pg. 816

Takagi, Jotaro, Chm. Bd.--Mitsubishi Estate Co., Ltd., Tokyo, Japan; *Int'l*, pg. 873

Takahashi, Katsuhiko, Chm. Bd.--KG Land California Corporation, Belmont, CA; *Int'l*, pg. 764

Takahashi, Koji, Chm. Bd.--Tekken Corporation, Tokyo, Japan; *Int'l*, pg. 1362

Takahashi, Takemitsu, Chm. Bd. & Pres.--Dainippon Ink & Chemicals, Inc., Tokyo, Japan; *Int'l*, pg. 369

Takaoka, Sueaki, Chm. Bd.--I&S Corp., Tokyo, Japan; *Int'l*, pg. 642

Takaoka, Sueaki, Chm. Bd.--Seiyo, Ltd., Tokyo, Japan; *Int'l, pg. 1178*

Takasaki, Masahiro, Chm. Bd.--The Sakura Bank, Limited, Tokyo, Japan; *Int'l*, pg. 1178

Takasaki, Yoshiro, Chm. Bd.--Toyo Seikan Kaisha, Ltd., Tokyo, Japan; *Int'l*, pg. 1411

Takatta, James, Chm. Bd.--Takatta Inc., Auburn Hills, MI; *U.S. Private*, pg. 528

Takemoto, Yoshiyuki, Chm. & Chief Exec. Officer--Daiwa Europe Limited, London, United Kingdom; *Int'l*, pg. 375

Takenaka, Haruhiko, Chm.--The Industrial Bank of Japan (Luxembourg) S.A., Luxembourg, Luxembourg; *Int'l*, pg. 676

Takeuchi, Takashi, Chm. Bd.--JEOL, Ltd., Tokyo, Japan; *Int'l*, pg. 696

Takizawa, Saburo, Chm. Bd.--Toyobo Co., Ltd., Osaka, Japan; *Int'l*, pg. 1411

Tako, Anthony, Chm. Bd. & Pres.--A.J. Gerrard and Company, Des Plaines, IL; *U.S. Private*, pg. 449

Talbert, J. Michael, Chm. Bd. & Chief Exec. Officer--Transocean Offshore, Inc., Houston, TX; *U.S. Public*, pg. 1631

Talbott, Cloyce A., Chm. Bd. & Chief Exec. Officer--Patterson Energy, Inc., Snyder, TX; *U.S. Public*, pg. 1265

Talbott, Cloyce A., Chm. Bd. & Chief Exec. Officer--Patterson Drilling Co., Snyder, TX; *U.S. Public*, pg. 1265

Talermo, Roger, Chm. Bd.--Wilson Sporting Goods Co., Chicago, IL; *Int'l*, pg. 73

Taliaferro, Scott L., Chm. Bd.--Independent Bankshares, Inc., Abilene, TX; *U.S. Public*, pg. 874

Tallichet, David C., Jr., Chm. Bd., Pres. & Chief Exec. Officer--Specialty Restaurants Corporation, Anaheim, CA; *U.S. Private*, pg. 1022

Tammes, S.J., Chm.-Supvr. Bd.--Ceteco N.V., Utrecht, Netherlands; *Int'l*, pg. 279

Tamzil, Dian P., Chm. Bd.--P.T. Tempo National Life, Jakarta, Indonesia; *Int'l*, pg. 909

Tan, Andrick, Chm. Bd.--Champion Motors (1975) Pte. Ltd., Singapore, Singapore; *Int'l*, pg. 672

Tan, Lucio C., Chm. Bd. & Chief Exec. Officer--Philippine Airlines, Inc., Manila, Philippines; *Int'l*, pg. 1050

Tanaka, Masuo, Chm. Bd.--Kansai Paint Co., Ltd., Osaka, Japan; *Int'l*, pg. 723

Tanaka, Yoshimi, Chm. Bd.--Mercian Corporation, Tokyo, Japan; *Int'l*, pg. 858

Tanaka, Yoshimi, Chm. Bd.--Nichimen Corporation, Tokyo, Japan; *Int'l*, pg. 927

Tananbaum, Stanley, Chm. Bd. & Chief Exec. Officer--Century Business Credit Corporation, New York, NY; *U.S. Private*, pg. 225

Tandou, Sirjang, Chm. Bd.--JTS Corporation, San Jose, CA; *U.S. Public*, pg. 919

Tang, Cyrus, Chm. Bd.--GF Office Furniture Ltd., Gallatin, TN; *U.S. Private*, pg. 434

Tang, Cyrus, Chm. Bd., Pres., & Chief Exec. Officer--Tang Industries Inc., Las Vegas, NV; *U.S. Private*, pg. 1068

Tang, Oscar L., Chm. Bd. & Pres.--KOA Holdings, New York, NY; *U.S. Private*, pg. 603

Tanguay, Louis, Chm. Bd. & Chief Exec. Officer--Telebec Ltee, Anjou, Canada; *Int'l*, pg. 116

Taniguchi, Hidetoshi, Chm. Bd.--Puna Plantation Hawaii Ltd., Hilo, HI; *U.S. Private*, pg. 895

Tanimura, Takashi, Chm. Bd.--JCB International Co., Ltd., Tokyo, Japan; *Int'l*, pg. 696

Tankersley, James I., Chm. Bd. & Chief Exec. Officer--United Foods, Inc., Bells, TN; *U.S. Public*, pg. 1677

Tanklage, Robert C., Chm. Bd., Chief Exec. & Chief Oper. Officer--La Victoria Foods, Inc., City of Industry, CA; *U.S.* Private, pg. 641

Tanner, James T., Chm. Bd.--Tanner Co., Rutherfordton, NC; *U.S. Private*, pg. 1068

Tanner, Paul A., Chm. Bd., Pres. & Chief Exec. Officer--Polyphase Corporation, Dallas, TX; *U.S. Public*, pg. 1315

Tanner, Ray, Chm. Bd. & Chief Exec. Officer--Volunteer Bank, Jackson, TN; *U.S. Public*, pg. 176

Tannova, Narita, Chm.--Mitsui Petrochemical Industries, Ltd., Tokyo, Japan; *Int'l*, pg. 877

Tansky, Burton, Chm. Bd. & Chief Exec. Officer--Bergdorf Goodman, New York, NY; *U.S. Public*, pg. 785

Tansky, Burton, Chm. & Chief Exec. Officer--Neiman Marcus Co., Dallas, TX; *U.S. Public*, pg. 785

Taplett, Rawley F., Chm. Bd.--AirSensors, Inc., Seattle, WA; *U.S. Public*, pg. 33

Tappertzhofen, Werner, Chm.--Flender Getriebewerk Penig GmbH, Penig, Germany; *Int'l*, pg. 400

Taranto, Joseph V., Chm. Bd. & Chief Exec. Officer--Everest Reinsurance Holdings, Liberty Corner, NJ; *U.S. Public*, pg. 597

Taranto, Joseph V., Chm. Bd.--Everest National Insurance Co., Liberty Corner, NJ; *U.S. Public*, pg. 597

Taranto, Joseph V., Chm. Bd. & Chief Exec. Officer--Everest Reinsurance Co., Liberty Corner, NJ; *U.S. Public*, pg. 597

Taranto, Joseph V., Chm. Bd.--Everest Reinsurance, Ltd., London, United Kingdom; *U.S. Public*, pg. 597

Taratoot, Louis J., Chm. Bd. & Chief Exec. Officer--Taracorp, Inc., Atlanta, GA; *U.S. Private*, pg. 1068

Targett, William J., Chm. Bd.--Meier Metal Service Centers, Inc., Hazel Park, MI; *U.S. Public*, pg. 1100

Tarica, James, Chm. Bd.--Jimlar Corporation, Great Neck, NY; *U.S. Private*, pg. 587

Tarlow, Arthur S., Sr., Chm. Bd.--Alden Shoe Co., Inc., Middleboro, MA; *U.S. Private*, pg. 33

Tarrant, R. Lane, Chm. Bd., Pres. & Chief Exec. Officer--Tarrant Service, Inc., Louisville, KY; *U.S. Private*, pg. 1069

Tarrant, Ronald W., Chm. Bd., Pres. & Chief Exec. Officer--Flow International Corporation, Kent, WA; *U.S. Public*, pg. 656

Tarte, Richard R., Chm. Bd.--MetLife Securities, Inc., New York, NY; *U.S. Private*, pg. 738

Tash, Martin E., Chm. Bd., Pres. & Chief Exec. Officer--Gradco Systems, Inc., Las Vegas, NV; *U.S. Public*, pg. 757

Tash, Martin E., Chm. Bd., Pres. & Chief Exec. Officer--Plenum Publishing Corporation, New York, NY; *U.S. Public*, pg. 1311

Tashima, Hideo, Chm. Bd.--Minolta Co., Ltd., Osaka, Japan; *Int'l*, pg. 869

Tat, Philip Ng Chee, Chm. Bd.--Orchard Parade Holdings Limited, Singapore, Singapore; *Int'l*, pg. 1007

Tata, Ratan N, Chm. Bd.--Tata Engineering & Locomotive Co. Ltd. (TELCO), Mumbai, India; *Int'l*, pg. 369

Tatar, Jerome F., Chm. Bd., Pres. & Chief Exec. Officer--The Mead Corporation, Dayton, OH; *U.S. Public*, pg. 1074

Tate, J.C.H., Chm. Bd.--Confederation Pension Investment Management Limited, Stevenage, United Kingdom; *Int'l*, pg. 1319

Tateisi, Nobuo, Chm. Bd. & Dir.--Omron Corporation, Kyoto, Japan; *Int'l*, pg. 1005

Tatman, Richard M., Chm. Bd.--Acme Foundry, Inc., Coffeyville, KS; *U.S. Private*, pg. 13

Tattersall, Keith, Chm. Bd., Pres. & Chief Exec. Officer--Amperif Corporation, Chatsworth, CA; *U.S. Public*, pg. 1523

Tauber, Joel D., Chm. Bd.--Keywell Corporation, Chicago, IL; *U.S. Private*, pg. 619

Taubman, A. Alfred, Chm. Bd.--Sotheby's Holdings Inc., New York, NY; *U.S. Public*, pg. 1487

Taubman, A. Alfred, Chm. Bd.--Taubman Centers, Inc., Bloomfield Hills, MI; *U.S. Public*, pg. 1561

Tauscher, William, Chm. Bd. & Chief Exec. Officer--Vanstar Corporation, Pleasanton, CA; *U.S. Public*, pg. 1708

Tauscher, William Y., Chm. Bd.--Regency Lincoln Mercury, Inc., Dallas, TX; *U.S. Private*, pg. 918

Tavner, Bruce H., Chm. Bd.--Northern Telephone Limited, New Liskeard, Canada; *Int'l*, pg. 115

Tawengwa, S. C., Chm. Bd.--Rio Tinto Zimbabwe Limited, Harare, Zimbabwe; *Int'l*, pg. 1119

Tayama, Yoshio, Chm. Bd.--The Kyoei Life Insurance Co., Ltd., Tokyo, Japan; *Int'l*, pg. 776

Taylor, Cyril J.H., Chm. Bd.--American Institute for Foreign Study, Greenwich, CT; *U.S. Private*, pg. 56

Taylor, Daniel J., Chm. Bd. & Pres.--Advantage Companies, Inc., Wichita, KS; *U.S. Private*, pg. 22

Taylor, Daniel J., Chm. Bd.--Zee Medical, Inc., Irvine, CA; *U.S. Public*, pg. 1073

Taylor, Dian C., Chm. Bd., Pres. & Chief Exec. Officer--Artesian Resources Corporation, Newark, DE; *U.S. Public*, pg. 135

Taylor, Glen A., Chm. Bd. & Chief Exec. Officer--Taylor Corporation, Mankato, MN; *U.S. Private*, pg. 1070

Taylor, Glenn, Chm. & Chief Exec. Officer--Bankhead Enterprises Inc., Atlanta, GA; *U.S. Private*, pg. 114

Taylor, Jack C., Chm. Bd.--Enterprise Rent-A-Car Company, Saint Louis, MO; *U.S. Private*, pg. 377

Taylor, James W., Chm. Bd. & Chief Exec. Officer--Taylor Made Group, Inc., Gloversville, NY; *U.S. Private*, pg. 1070

Taylor, Jeffrey W., Chm. Bd. & Chief Exec. Officer--Taylor Capital Group, Wheeling, IL; *U.S. Private*, pg. 1070

Taylor, Jeffrey W., Chm. Bd.--Cole Taylor Bank, Wheeling, IL; *U.S. Private*, pg. 1070

Taylor, John, Chm. Bd.--Jasper County Farm Bureau Co-op Association, Inc., Rensselaer, IN; *U.S. Private*, pg. 583

Taylor, John A., Chm. Bd.--Taylor Oil Co. Inc., Winston Salem, NC; *U.S. Private*, pg. 1071

Taylor, John N., Jr., Chm. & Chief Exec. Officer--Kurz-Kasch, Inc., Wilmington, OH; *U.S. Private*, pg. 637

Taylor, Jonathan, Chm.--Booker PLC, London, United Kingdom; *Int'l*, pg. 202

Taylor, Kenneth N., Chm. Bd.--Tyndale House Publishers, Inc., Carol Stream, IL; *U.S. Private*, pg. 1112

Taylor, Lucian W., Chm. Bd.--Velcon Filters, Inc., Colorado Springs, CO; *U.S. Private*, pg. 1135

Taylor, M. G., Chm. Bd.--National Westminster Life Assurance Limited, Bristol, United Kingdom; *Int'l*, pg. 910

Taylor, Martin, Chm. Bd.--Inchcape Belgium NV/SA, Brussels, Belgium; *Int'l*, pg. 672

Taylor, Maurice R., Chm. Bd. & Chief Exec. Officer--Chronimed Inc., Minnetonka, MN; *U.S. Public*, pg. 352

Taylor, Roger, Chm. Bd.--Royal & Sun Alliance Insurance Group plc, London, United Kingdom; *Int'l*, pg. 1130

Taylor, Romey A., Chm. Bd.--Southeast Power Corporation, Titusville, FL; *U.S. Public*, pg. 750

Taylor, Volney, Chm. Bd. & Chief Exec. Officer--The Dun & Bradstreet Corporation, Murray Hill, NJ; *U.S. Public*, pg. 535

Taylor, Volney, Chm. Bd.--Dun & Bradstreet, Murray Hill, NJ; *U.S. Public*, pg. 535

Taylor, W. Luther, Chm. Bd. & Pres.--Bank of Pensacola, Pensacola, FL; *U.S. Public*, pg. 1549

Taylor, W.A., Jr., Chm. Bd.--Taylor Machine Works, Inc., Louisville, MS; *U.S. Private*, pg. 1070

Taylor, William, Chm. Bd.--S.E. Huffman Corp., Clover, SC; *U.S. Private*, pg. 546

Taylor, William W., Chm. Bd & Chief Exec. Officer--D.C. Taylor Co., Cedar Rapids, IA; *U.S. Private*, pg. 1070

Taylor, Wilson H., Chm. Bd.--American Enterprise Institute for Public Policy Research, Washington, DC; *U.S. Private*, pg. 53

Tazaki, Kaziaki, Chm. & Mng. Dir.--Brother U.K., Ltd., Manchester, United Kingdom; *Int'l*, pg. 230

Tchuruk, Serge, Chm. Bd. & Chief Exec. Officer--Alcatel Alsthom Compagnie Generale D'Electricite, Paris, France; *Int'l*, pg. 52

Teck, Lee Soon, Chm. Bd.--Lee Kim Tah Holdings Ltd., Singapore, Singapore; *Int'l*, pg. 1346

Tecot, Stephen L., Chm. Bd.--Tecot Electric Supply Company, New Castle, DE; *U.S. Private*, pg. 951

Teel, James E., Co-Chm. Bd.--Raley's & Bel Air, West Sacramento, CA; *U.S. Private*, pg. 907

Teel, Joyce N., Co-Chm. Bd.--Raley's & Bel Air, West Sacramento, CA; *U.S. Private*, pg. 907

Teerlink, Richard F., Chm. Bd.--Harley-Davidson, Inc., Milwaukee, WI; *U.S. Public*, pg. 786

Teeter, Finis F., Chm. Bd. & Co-Chief Exec. Officer--American Homestar Corporation, League City, TX; *U.S. Public*, pg. 83

Tegarden, William H., Chm. Bd., Pres. & Chief Exec. Officer--Citizens Bank of Central Indiana-Orleans Region, Orleans, IN; *U.S. Public*, pg. 280

Teik, Tan Boon, Chm. Bd.--Singapore Petroleum Company Ltd., Singapore, Singapore; *U.S. Public*, pg. 102

Teitelbaum, Irving, Chm. Bd.--The Wet Seal, Inc., Irvine, CA; *U.S. Public*, pg. 1763

Tejuca Suarez, Luis Manuel, Chm. Bd. & Pres.--Hulleras Del Norte, S.A. (HUNOSA), Asturias, Spain; *Int'l*, pg. 639

Tellier, P.M., Chm. Bd.--Grand Trunk Corporation (GTC), Detroit, MI; *Int'l*, pg. 258

Telmer, Frederick H., Chm. Bd.--Stelco Inc., Hamilton, Canada; *Int'l*, pg. 1299

Teltschik, Horst, Dr., Member of Bd.--Bayerische Motoren Werke Aktiengesellschaft, Munich, Germany; *Int'l*, pg. 177

Telyas, Avi, Chm. Bd.--Bayside Motion Group, Port Washington, NY; *U.S. Private*, pg. 125

Temerlin, Liener, Chm. Bd.--Temerlin McClain, Irving, TX; *U.S. Public*, pg. 1642

Tempelsman, Maurice, Chm. Bd.--Lazare Kaplan Intl., Inc., New York, NY; *U.S. Public*, pg. 981

Templeton, John, Chm. Bd.--Templeton, Kenly & Co., Inc., Broadview, IL; *U.S. Private*, pg. 1075

Tendler, Stanley, Chm. Bd. & Chief Exec. Officer--Kennington Ltd., Inc., Van Nuys, CA; *U.S. Private*, pg. 615

Tenenbaum, Joseph M., Chm. Bd.--A. Tenenbaum Co. Inc., North Little Rock, AR; *U.S. Private*, pg. 1076

TenHoopen, Carl A., Jr., Chm. Bd.--The Annapolis Banking & Trust Co., Annapolis, MD; *U.S. Public*, pg. 1088

Tennant, James R., Chm. Bd. & Chief Exec. Officer--Home Products International, Inc., Chicago, IL; *U.S. Public*, pg. 832

Tennant, James R., Chm. Bd. & Chief Exec. Officer--Selfix, Inc., Chicago, IL; *U.S. Public*, pg. 832

Tenneson, P., Chm. & Chief Exec. Officer--Herstal S.A., Herstal, Belgium; *Int'l*, pg. 617

Teo, Ronnie, Chm.--DBS Asset Management (United States) Pte. Ltd., Singapore, Singapore; *Int'l*, pg. 350

Teoh, Steve, Chm.--EURO RSCG Malaysia, Petaling Jaya, Malaysia; *Int'l*, pg. 602

Tepper, Allen, Chm. Bd. & Chief Exec. Officer--PMR Corporation, San Diego, CA; *U.S. Public*, pg. 1242
Teresi, Robert G., Chm Bd., Chief Exec. Officer & Treas.--Caere Corporation, Los Gatos, CA; *U.S. Public*, pg. 291
Terlato, Anthony, Chm. Bd. & Chief Exec. Officer--Paterno Imports Limited, Lake Bluff, IL; *U.S. Private*, pg. 843
Termeer, Henri A., Chm. Bd., Pres. & Chief Exec. Officer--Genzyme Corporation, Cambridge, MA; *U.S. Public*, pg. 733
Terrazas Torres, Federico, Chm. Bd.--Grupo Cementos de Chihuahua S.A. de C.V., Chihuahua, Mexico; *Int'l*, pg. 573
Terry, Richard E., Chm. Bd. & Chief Exec. Officer--Peoples Energy Corporation, Chicago, IL; *U.S. Public*, pg. 1274
Terry, Richard E., Chm. Bd. & Chief Exec. Officer--The Peoples Gas Light & Coke Co., Chicago, IL; *U.S. Public*, pg. 1275
Terry, Richard E., Chm. Bd. & Chief Exec. Officer--Peoples District Energy Corporation, Chicago, IL; *U.S. Public*, pg. 1275
Terry, Richard E., Chm. Bd. & Chief Exec. Officer--Peoples Energy Services Corporation, Chicago, IL; *U.S. Public*, pg. 1275
Terry, Richard E., Chm. Bd. & Chief Exec. Officer--Peoples NGV Corp., Chicago, IL; *U.S. Public*, pg. 1275
Terry, Robert L., Chm. Exec. Committee--Florida Public Utilities Company, West Palm Beach, FL; *U.S. Public*, pg. 655
Teruya, Harold S., Chm. Bd.--Armstrong Produce Ltd., Honolulu, HI; *U.S. Private*, pg. 83
Teruya, Raymond, Chm. Bd., Pres. & Chief Exec. Officer--Teruya Bros., Limited, Honolulu, HI; *U.S. Private*, pg. 1077
Teruzzi, Orlando, Chm. Bd. & Pres.--Precision Resource Inc., Shelton, CT; *U.S. Private*, pg. 880
Terzic, Branco, Chm. Bd., Pres. & Chief Exec. Officer--Yankee Energy System, Inc., Meriden, CT; *U.S. Public*, pg. 1787
Teshoian, Nishan, Chm. Bd.--Anderson, Greenwood & Co., Stafford, TX; *U.S. Public*, pg. 1650
Tesone, Antonio, Chm. Bd. & Pres.--Olivetti SpA, Turin, Italy; *Int'l*, pg. 1002
Tessier, Edward J., Chm., Pres. & Chief Exec. Officer--Amerifoods Inc., Lancaster, PA; *U.S. Private*, pg. 65
Tessler, Allan R., Co-Chm. Bd. & Co-Chief Exec. Officer--Data Broadcasting Corporation, Jackson, WY; *U.S. Public*, pg. 484
Tessler, Allan R., Chm. Bd.--Jackpot Enterprises, Inc., Las Vegas, NV; *U.S. Public*, pg. 920
Testa, Chicco, Chm. Bd.--Ente Nazionale per l'Energia Elettrica SpA (ENEL), Rome, Italy; *Int'l*, pg. 458
Testa, David, Chm. Bd.--Rowe Price-Fleming International Inc., Baltimore, MD; *Int'l*, pg. 493
Testa, Marco, Chm. Bd. & Chief Exec. Officer--Testa International, Milan, Italy; *Int'l*, pg. 1376
Teter, Gordon F., Chm. Bd., Pres. & Chief Oper. Officer--Wendy's International Inc., Dublin, OH; *U.S. Public*, pg. 1754
Teti, Joseph A., Jr., Chm. Bd. & Pres.--La France Corporation, Philadelphia, PA; *U.S. Private*, pg. 640
Tetrault, Roger E., Chm. Bd. & Chief Exec. Officer--McDermott International, Inc., New Orleans, LA; *U.S. Public*, pg. 1067
Tewksbury, Harold V., Chm. Bd.--Solon Manufacturing Company, Solon, ME; *U.S. Private*, pg. 1013
Thacher, Carter P., Chm. Bd.--Wilbur-Ellis Company & Connell Brothers Company, San Francisco, CA; *U.S. Private*, pg. 1175
Thacker, William L., Jr., Chm. Bd., Pres. & Chief Exec. Officer--TEPPCO Partners L.P., Houston, TX; *U.S. Public*, *pg. 534*
Thain, John, Co.-Chm.--Goldman Sachs International Limited, London, United Kingdom; *U.S. Private*, pg. 462
Thalheimer, Louis B., Chm. Bd. & Chief Exec. Officer--American Trading and Production Corporation, Baltimore, MD; *U.S. Private*, pg. 63
Thalheimer, Richard, Chm. Bd. & Chief Exec. Officer--The Sharper Image, San Francisco, CA; *U.S. Public*, pg. 1464
Thammano, Aran, Chm. Bd.--The Industrial Finance Corporation of Thailand, Bangkok, Thailand; *Int'l*, pg. 677
Tharp, James T., Chm. Bd. & Pres.--McCrory Construction Co., Inc., Columbia, SC; *U.S. Private*, pg. 720
Thayer, Stella F., Chm. Bd.--Reflectone, Inc., Tampa, FL; *Int'l*, pg. 218
Theis, Willis C., Chm. Bd.--Simonds-Shields-Theis Grain Co., Kansas City, MO; *U.S. Private*, pg. 1001
Theisen, George, Chm. Bd.--T & S Brass & Bronze Works, Inc., Travelers Rest, SC; *U.S. Private*, pg. 1061
Theofilos, Steve P., Chm. Bd. & Chief Exec. Officer--Theochem Labs., Inc., Tampa, FL; *U.S. Private*, pg. 1079
Thery, Marc, Chm.--Rowenta France S.A., Vernon, France; *Int'l*, pg. 569
Theumim, Moshe, Chm. Bd. & Pres.--Gitam/BBDO, Ramat Gan, Israel; *Int'l*, pg. 552
Thiel, Stephen, Chm. Bd., Pres. & Chief Exec. Officer--Thiel Cheese Co., Hilbert, WI; *U.S. Private*, pg. 1081
Thiele, Heinz Hermann, Chm.-Mng. Bd.--Knorr-Bremse AG, Munich, Germany; *Int'l*, pg. 738
Thiele, Heinz Hermann, Chm. Bd.--Knorr-Bremse Systeme Fur Nutzfahrzeuge GmbH, Munich, Germany; *Int'l*, pg. 738
Thiele, Paul F., Chm. Bd. & Chief Exec. Officer--Thiele Kaolin Co., Sandersville, GA; *U.S. Private*, pg. 1081
Thiemann, Bernd, Dr., Chm. Bd.--DG Bank, Frankfurt/Main, Germany; *Int'l*, pg. 351
Thierstein, Hans, Chm. Bd. & Pres.--Ares-Serono S.A., Geneva, Switzerland; *Int'l*, pg. 80
Thomas, Andrew, Chm. Bd. & Chief Exec.--The Greenalls Group PLC, Warrington, United Kingdom; *Int'l*, pg. 558
Thomas, Charles F., Chm. Bd.--Charlie Thomas Dealerships, Houston, TX; *U.S. Private*, pg. 1082
Thomas, Chris, Chm. Bd.--Seven Seas Limited, Hull, United Kingdom; *Int'l*, pg. 593
Thomas, G. Andes, Chm. Bd., Pres. & Chief Exec. Officer--Magna Group, Inc., Saint Louis, MO; *U.S. Public*, pg. 1037
Thomas, G.N., Chm. Bd., Pres., & Chief Exec. Officer--A. Levy & J. Zentner Co., Sacramento, CA; *U.S. Private*, pg. 663
Thomas, Harold E., Chm. Bd.--Trus Joist MacMillan, Boise, ID; *Int'l*, pg. 829
Thomas, Harold E., Chm. Bd.--TJ International, Inc., Boise, ID; *U.S. Public*, pg. 1556
Thomas, Harold E., Chm. Bd.--Trus Joist MacMillan, Boise, ID; *U.S. Public*, pg. 1556
Thomas, Isiah, Co-Chm. Bd.--American Speedy Printing Centers, Inc., Troy, MI; *U.S. Private*, pg. 62
Thomas, Johnny R., Chm. Bd. & Chief Exec. Officer--AgriBioTech, Inc., Las Vegas, NV; *U.S. Public*, pg. 28
Thomas, Michael E., Chm. Bd.--Chromcraft Corporation, Senatobia, MS; *U.S. Public*, pg. 352
Thomas, Newton B., Chm. Bd. & Pres.--The Newtron Group Inc., Baton Rouge, LA; *U.S. Private*, pg. 797
Thomas, Rick, Chm. Bd. & Chief Exec. Officer--Card Pak, Inc., Cleveland, OH; *U.S. Private*, pg. 208
Thomas, Terence W., Chm. Bd. & Pres.--Arizona Wholesale Supply Company, Phoenix, AZ; *U.S. Private*, pg. 82
Thomas, Terry, Chm. Bd.--National Brands, Inc., Phoenix, AZ; *U.S. Private*, pg. 780
Thomas, Zeb M., Sr., Chm. Bd.--Anchor Financial Corporation, Myrtle Beach, SC; *U.S. Public*, pg. 111
Thomopulos, Gregs G., Chm. Bd. & Pres.--Stanley Design-Build, Inc., Muscatine, IA; *U.S. Private*, pg. 1033
Thomopulos, Gregs G., Chm. Bd.--Stanley Enviromental, Inc., Coralville, IA; *U.S. Private*, pg. 1033
Thompson-Draper, Cheryl, Chm. Bd. & Chief Exec. Officer--Warren Electric Group, Houston, TX; *U.S. Private*, pg. 1151
Thompson, Christopher M.T., Chm. Bd.--Dakota Mining Corporation, Denver, CO; *U.S. Public*, pg. 477
Thompson, David, Chm. Bd. & Chief Exec. Officer--Mikohn Gaming Corporation, Las Vegas, NV; *U.S. Public*, pg. 1111
Thompson, David W., Chm. Bd., Pres. & Chief Exec. Officer--Orbital Sciences Corporation, Dulles, VA; *U.S. Public*, pg. 1229
Thompson, Donald L., Chm. Bd., Pres. & Chief Exec. Officer--Hunt Corporation, Philadelphia, PA; *U.S. Public*, pg. 848
Thompson, F.L., Chm. Bd.--Xebec Corporation, Kansas City, MO; *U.S. Private*, pg. 1194
Thompson, H. Brian, Chm. Bd. & Chief Exec. Officer--LCI International, Inc., Dublin, OH; *U.S. Public*, pg. 969
Thompson, J.F., Chm. Bd.--Burlington Basket Co., Burlington, IA; *U.S. Private*, pg. 183
Thompson, James B., Chm. Bd.--Pacific Coast Building Products Inc., Sacramento, CA; *U.S. Private*, pg. 830
Thompson, James W., Chm. Bd.--NationsBank South Carolina Corporation, Columbia, SC; *U.S. Public*, pg. 1163
Thompson, Jay T., III, Chm. Bd.--Hanover Bank, Mechanicsville, VA; *U.S. Public*, pg. 1039
Thompson, John C., Chm. Bd.--The Hall China Company, East Liverpool, OH; *U.S. Private*, pg. 494
Thompson, Julian Ogilvie, Chm. Bd.--De Beers Consolidated Mines Limited, Kimberley, South Africa; *Int'l*, pg. 76
Thompson, Keith, Chm. Bd. & Treas.--Republic Automotive-AEA Division, Charlotte, NC; *U.S. Public*, pg. 1377
Thompson, Lloyd, Chm. Bd.--Border States Paving, Inc., Fargo, ND; *U.S. Private*, pg. 160
Thompson, P.C.H., Chm.--First National Bank Holdings (Botswana) LTD., Gaborone, Botswana; *Int'l*, pg. 487
Thompson, Paul, Chm. Bd. & Mng. Dir.--Sanderson Technology Ltd., Sheffield, United Kingdom; *Int'l*, pg. 1184
Thompson, Raymon F., Chm. Bd., Pres. & Chief Exec. Officer--Semitool, Inc., Kalispell, MT; *U.S. Public*, pg. 1456
Thompson, Richard M., Chm. Bd.--The Toronto Dominion Bank, Toronto, Canada; *Int'l*, pg. 1401
Thompson, Roger R., Jr., Chm. Bd.--Kennedy Manufacturing Company, Van Wert, OH; *U.S. Private*, pg. 614
Thompson, Ted, Chm. Bd. & Chief Exec. Officer--X-Rite, Incorporated, Grandville, MI; *U.S. Public*, pg. 1783
Thompson, Terry W., Chm. Bd., Pres. & Chief Exec. Officer--State Bank of Standish, Standish, MI; *U.S. Public*, pg. 379
Thompson, Wade F.B., Chm. Bd., Pres. & Chief Exec. Officer--Thor Industries, Inc., Jackson Center, OH; *U.S. Public*, pg. 1602
Thomsen, Craig F., Chm. Bd.--First American Title Co. of Utah, Salt Lake City, UT; *U.S. Public*, pg. 625
Thomson, J.M., Chm. Bd.--Compass Group plc, Chertsey, United Kingdom,; *Int'l*, pg. 324
Thomson, K.R., Chm. Bd.--Thomson U.S. Inc., Stamford, CT; *U.S. Public*, pg. 1601
Thomson, Kenneth R., Chm. Bd.--The Thomson Corporation, Stamford, CT; *U.S. Public*, pg. 1599
Thon, Terje, Chm. Bd.--Telenordia A.B., Stockholm, Sweden; *Int'l*, pg. 223
Thorkildsen, Terje, Chm.--Leo Burnett A/S, Oslo, Norway; *U.S. Private*, pg. 184
Thorn, Gaston, Chm. Bd.--Banque Internationale a Luxembourg S.A., Luxembourg, Luxembourg; *Int'l*, pg. 162
Thorn, Gaston, Chm. Bd.--CLT-UFA, Luxembourg, Luxembourg; *Int'l*, pg. 561
Thorne, Carl F., Chm. Bd., Pres. & Chief Exec. Officer--Ensco International Incorporated (ENSCO), Dallas, TX; *U.S. Public*, pg. 585
Thorner, Peter, Chm. Bd., Chief Exec. Officer & Chief Oper. Officer--Bradlees Inc., Braintree, MA; *U.S. Public*, pg. 249
Thornton, C. John, Chm. Bd.--Thorntons PLC, Darbyshire, United Kingdom; *Int'l*, pg. 1386
Thornton, James H., Chm. Bd.--Thornton Oil Corp., Louisville, KY; *U.S. Private*, pg. 1084
Thornton, John, Co.-Chm.--Goldman Sachs International Limited, London, United Kingdom; *U.S. Private*, pg. 462
Thornton, John M., Chm. Bd.--Mitek Systems, Inc., San Diego, CA; *U.S. Public*, pg. 1117
Thornton, Winfred L., Chm. Bd. & Chief Exec. Officer--St. Joe Corp., Jacksonville, FL; *U.S. Public*, pg. 1426
Thrall, J. Jeffrey, Chm. Bd. & Chief Exec. Officer--Naz-Dar Company, Chicago, IL; *U.S. Private*, pg. 1084
Thrall, Jerome A., Chm. Bd.--Thrall Enterprises, Inc., Chicago, IL; *U.S. Private*, pg. 1084
Threlfall, T.R.B., Chm. Bd.--OCE-Australia Limited, Cheltenham, Australia; *Int'l*, pg. 994
Throop, Robert S., Chm. Bd. & Chief Exec. Officer--Anthem Electronics Inc., San Jose, CA; *U.S. Public*, pg. 134
Thumann, J.R., Chm. Bd.--Hille & Muller, Dusseldorf, Germany; *Int'l*, pg. 754
Thurlow, Juan Gallardo, Chm. Bd. & Chief Exec. Officer--Grupo Embotelladoras Unidas SA de CV, Guadalajara, Mexico; *Int'l*, pg. 574
Thurman, Randy H., Chm. Bd.--Enzon, Inc., Piscataway, NJ; *U.S. Public*, pg. 587
Thyssen-Bornemisza, Georg-Heinrich, Co-Chm. Bd.--TBG Management S.A.M., Monaco, Monaco; *Int'l*, pg. 1335
Thyssen, Hans Heinrich, Co-Chm. Bd.--TBG Management S.A.M., Monaco, Monaco; *Int'l*, pg. 1335
Tibbetts, Linton N., Chm. Bd.--Cox Lumber Co., Saint Petersburg, FL; *U.S. Private*, pg. 283
Tice, Gary L., Chm. Bd.--Customer Service Center of F.N.B., L.L.C., Naples, FL; *U.S. Public*, pg. 607
Tice, Gary L., Chm. Bd.--Southwest Banks, Inc., Naples, FL; *U.S. Public*, pg. 607
Tice, Gary L., Chm. Bd.--First National Bank of Naples, Naples, FL; *U.S. Public*, pg. 607
Tideman, Philip, Chm. Bd. & Pres.--United Power Association, Elk River, MN; *U.S. Private*, pg. 1123
Tilghman, Richard G., Chm. Bd. & Chief Exec. Officer--Crestar Financial Corporation, Richmond, VA; *U.S. Public*, pg. 458
Tilley, C.R., Chm. & Chief Exec. Officer--Columbia Gas Distribution Companies, Columbus, OH; *U.S. Public*, pg. 402
Tilley, Ralph W., Chm. Bd., Pres. & Chief Exec. Officer--Vevay Deposit Bank, Vevay, IN; *U.S. Public*, pg. 633
Tilley, William H., Chm. Bd.--Jacmar Companies, Inc., Alhambra, CA; *U.S. Private*, pg. 580
Tillman, Robert L., Chm. Bd., Pres. & Chief Exec. Officer--Lowe's Companies, Inc., North Wilkesboro, NC; *U.S. Public*, pg. 1015
Tilton, Glenn F., Chm. & Pres.--TRMI Holdings Inc., Houston, TX; *U.S. Public*, pg. 1583
Timbers, Stephen B., Chm. & Chief Exec. Officer--Zurich Kemper Investments, Inc., Chicago, IL; *Int'l*, pg. 1530
Timble, Frank, Chm. Bd.--Bearing Headquarters Co., Broadview, IL; *U.S. Private*, pg. 127
Timken, W.R., Jr., Chm. Bd., Pres. & Chief Exec. Officer--The Timken Company, Canton, OH; *U.S. Public*, pg. 1617
Timmerman, William B., Chm. Bd., Pres., Chief Exec. & Oper. Officer--SCANA Corporation, Columbia, SC; *U.S. Public*, pg. 1436
Timmons, Linda, Chm. Bd.--Bates Container, Inc., North Richland Hills, TX; *U.S. Private*, pg. 122
Timmons, William R., Jr., Chm. Bd.--Carolina First Corporation, Greenville, SC; *U.S. Public*, pg. 306
Tinagero, James J., Chm. Bd.--SLJ Retail LLC, Smyrna, GA; *U.S. Private*, pg. 957
Ting, Dennis, Chm. Bd.--Bachmann Industries, Inc., Philadelphia, PA; *U.S. Private*, pg. 109
Ting, James, Chm.--G.M. Pfaff Aktiengesellschaft, Kaiserslautern, Germany; *Int'l*, pg. 1046
Ting, James H., Chm., Pres. & Chief Exec. Officer--Semi-Tech Corporation, Markham, Canada; *Int'l*, pg. 1220
Tinsley, Sandra C., Chm. Bd.--Tinsley Advertising, Miami, FL; *U.S. Private*, pg. 1088
Tippie, Henry B., Chm.-Exec. Committee & Vice Chm.-Bd.--Rollins Truck Leasing Corp., Wilmington, DE; *U.S. Public*, *pg. 1405*
Tippins, George W., Chm. Bd.--Tippins Incorporated, Pittsburgh, PA; *U.S. Private*, pg. 1088
Tipton, Betty J., Chm. Bd.--Warrens Waller Press, Inc., South San Francisco, CA; *U.S. Private*, pg. 1151
Tisch, Laurence A., Co-Chm. Bd. & Co-Chief Exec. Officer--Loews Corporation, New York, NY; *U.S. Public*, pg. 1010
Tisch, Preston R., Co-Chm. Bd. & Co-Chief Exec. Officer--Loews Corporation, New York, NY; *U.S. Public*, pg. 1010
Tishman, John L., Chm. Bd. & Pres.--Tishman Realty & Construction Co., Inc., New York, NY; *U.S. Private*, pg. 1089
Titley, R.J.W., Chm.--Sedgwick Limited, London, United Kingdom; *Int'l*, pg. 1218
Titus, John, Chm. Bd.--Aero Systems Aviation Corp., Miami, FL; *U.S. Private*, pg. 24
Titus, Roy W., Chm. Bd.--Minuteman Press International, Farmingdale, NY; *U.S. Private*, pg. 752
Tiviluk, George C., Chm. Bd.--Carl-Zeiss-Stiftung, Oberkochen, Germany; *Int'l*, pg. 1522
Toal, Lawrence J., Chm. Bd., Pres. & Chief Exec. Officer--The Dime Savings Bank of New York, New York, NY; *U.S. Public*, pg. 509
Toba, T., Chm. Bd.--Ajinomoto U.S.A., Inc., Teaneck, NJ; *Int'l*, pg. 40
Tober, Donald G., Chm. & Chief Exec. Officer--Sugar Foods Corp, New York, NY; *U.S. Private*, pg. 1049
Tober, Lester V., Chm. Bd. & Chief Exec. Officer--Tober Industries, Inc., Saint Louis, MO; *U.S. Private*, pg. 1089
Tobias, Randall L., Chm. Bd. & Chief Exec. Officer--Eli Lilly and Company, Indianapolis, IN; *U.S. Public*, pg. 992
Tobin, Robert G., Chm. Bd. & Chief Exec. Officer--The Stop & Shop Companies, Inc., Quincy, MA; *Int'l*, pg. 750

Tobin, Sylvan M., Chm. Bd.--Fishman & Tobin, Inc., Conshohocken, PA; U.S. Private, pg. 408
Tochihara, Minoru, Chm. Bd.--Izumi Motor Industries Inc., Kanagawa, Japan; Int'l, pg. 696
Tockarshewsky, Joseph B., Chm. Bd., Pres. & Chief Exec. Officer--Poughkeepsie Financial Corp., Poughkeepsie, NY; U.S. Public, pg. 1319
Tockarshewsky, Joseph B., Chm. Bd., Pres. & Chief Exec. Officer--Bank of the Hudson, Poughkeepsie, NY; U.S. Public, pg. 1319
Todd, J.L., Chm. Bd. & Pres.--J.L. Todd Auction Co., Rome, GA; U.S. Private, pg. 1090
Toft, Richard P., Chm. Bd.--Chicago Title & Trust Co., Chicago, IL; U.S. Public, pg. 42
Togo, Yukiyasu, Chm. Bd.--Toyota Motor Sales, U.S.A., Inc., Torrance, CA; Int'l, pg. 1412
Toigo, Elizabeth, Chm. Bd.--Shato Holdings Ltd., Vancouver, Canada; Int'l, pg. 1230
Tokarz, Michael, Chm. Bd.--Spalding & Evenflo Companies, Inc., Chicopee, MA; U.S. Private, pg. 629
Tolaney, Murli, Chm. Bd., Pres. & Chief Exec. Officer--Montgomery Watson, Pasadena, CA; U.S. Private, pg. 759
Toll, Robert I., Chm. Bd. & Chief Exec. Officer--Toll Brothers, Inc., Huntingdon Valley, PA; U.S. Public, pg. 1620
Tolleson, John C., Chm. Bd.--First USA Paymentech, Inc., Salem, NH; U.S. Public, pg. 174
Tollett, Leland, Chm. Bd. & Chief Exec. Officer--Tyson Foods, Inc., Springdale, AR; U.S. Public, pg. 1652
Tolson, Jay H., Chm. Bd. & Chief Exec. Officer--Bailey, Fischer & Porter Company, Warminster, PA; Int'l, pg. 449
Tolson, Ray H., Chm. Bd., Pres. & Chief Exec. Officer--Pride International, Inc., Houston, TX; U.S. Public, pg. 1324
Toma, Carl D., Chm. Bd.--Haddon Craftsmen, Inc., Scranton, PA; U.S. Public, pg. 518
Tomabechi, Kazou, Chm.--Wako Securities Co., Ltd., Tokyo, Japan; Int'l, pg. 1485
Tomasso, Angelo, Jr., Chm. Bd.--Tilcon, Inc., New Britain, CT; U.S. Private, pg. 1086
Tomasso, Donald C., Chm. Bd. & Chief Exec. Officer--Vitalink Pharmacy Services, Inc., Naperville, IL; U.S. Public, pg. 1041
Tomjack, Thomas J., Chm Bd. & Pres.--North Pacific Lumber Company, Portland, OR; U.S. Private, pg. 805
Tommerdal, Svein, Chm. Bd.--Longva Group, Alesund, Norway; Int'l, pg. 817
Tomomatsu, Kengo, Chm. Bd.--The Furukawa Electric Co., Ltd., Tokyo, Japan; Int'l, pg. 530
Tomono, Kenji, Chm. Bd.--Yamaichi International (Europe) Ltd., London, United Kingdom; Int'l, pg. 1518
Tompe, Istvan, Chm.--Daiwa-MKB (Hungary) Investment and Securities Co. Ltd., Budapest, Hungary; Int'l, pg. 376
Tompkins, J. Richard, Chm. Bd. & Pres.--Middlesex Water Company, Iselin, NJ; U.S. Public, pg. 1110
Tompkins, J. Richard, Chm. Bd.--Tidewater Utilities, Inc., Odessa, DE; U.S. Public, pg. 1110
Tompkins, J. Richard, Chm. Bd.--Pinelands Water & Wastewater Co., Broadway, NJ; U.S. Public, pg. 1110
Toms, Nicholas R.H., Chm., Pres. & Chief Exec. Officer--Peak Technologies Group, Inc., New York, NY; Int'l, pg. 890
Tomsich, Robert J., Chm. Bd.--NESCO, Inc., Cleveland, OH; U.S. Private, pg. 791
Toner, T.C., Chm.--Arnotts plc, Dublin, Ireland; Int'l, pg. 81
Tonnerieux, Guy, Chm. Bd.--Jeumont-Schneider Trenformeteurs, Lyon, France; Int'l, pg. 706
Tonooka, Masao, Chm. Bd.--Achilles Corporation, Tokyo, Japan; Int'l, pg. 22
Tooker, Gary L., Chm. Bd.--Motorola, Inc., Schaumburg, IL; U.S. Public, pg. 1136
Toole, Monte M., Chm. Bd.--GaSonics International, San Jose, CA; U.S. Public, pg. 703
Toolson, Kay L., Chm. Bd., Pres. & Chief Exec. Officer--Monaco Coach Corporation, Coburg, OR; U.S. Public, pg. 1123
Topalidis, Contantinos C., Exec. V.P. & Gen. Mgr.--Teleglobe, Inc., Montreal, Canada; Int'l, pg. 1373
Torchinsky, Benjamin B., Chm. Bd.--Agra Inc., Calgary, Canada; Int'l, pg. 30
Torcivia, Benedict, Chm. Bd. & Chief Exec. Officer--Torcon, Inc., Westfield, NJ; U.S. Private, pg. 1092
Torii, Shin, Chm. Bd.--Suntory International Corp., New York, NY; Int'l, pg. 1321
Torinus, John B., Jr., Chm. Bd. & Chief Exec. Officer--Serigraph, Inc., West Bend, WI; U.S. Private, pg. 985
Torp-Pedersen, Alf, Chm. Bd.--Philipp Holzmann AG, Frankfurt/Main, Germany; Int'l, pg. 632
Torp-Pedersen, Alf, Chm. Bd.--Icopal a/s, Herlev, Denmark; Int'l, pg. 658
Torras, Joseph H., Chm. Bd.--Eastern Fine Paper, Brewer, ME; U.S. Private, pg. 357
Torres, Arturo G., Chm. Bd. & Chief Exec. Officer--Play by Play Toys & Novelties, Inc., San Antonio, TX; U.S. Public, pg. 1309
Torrington, Timothy F., Chm. Bd. & Pres.--Atlapac Trading Company, Inc., Los Angeles, CA; U.S. Private, pg. 96
Torstenson, Robert H., Chm. Bd. & Pres.--Duo-Fast Corporation, Huntley, IL; U.S. Private, pg. 347
Tortoriello, Anthony M., Chm. Bd. & Pres.--Torco Oil Co., Chicago, IL; U.S. Private, pg. 1092
Tory, James M., Chm. Bd.--Cognos Inc., Ottawa, Canada; Int'l, pg. 305
Tory, James M., Chm. Bd.--Inmet Mining Corporation, Toronto, Canada; Int'l, pg. 678
Tory, James M., Chm. Bd.--Metall Mining Corporation, Toronto, Canada; Int'l, pg. 862
Tosaki, Shinobu, Chm. Bd.--Kawasaki Steel Corporation, Tokyo, Japan; Int'l, pg. 726
Toscano, Samuel, Chm. Bd. & Chief Exec. Officer--Neuman Distributors, Inc., Ridgefield, NJ; U.S. Public, pg. 1169
Tosi, Christopher, Chm. Bd.--The Pastene Companies Ltd., Canton, MA; U.S. Private, pg. 842
Toth, Michael C., Chm. Bd., Pres. & New Bus. Contact--Toth Design, Concord, MA; U.S. Private, pg. 1093
Toth, Steve, Jr., Chm. Bd., Pres. & Exec. V.P.--VSI Holdings, Inc., Bloomfield Hills, MI; U.S. Public, pg. 1703
Tourniaire, J.N., Chm. & Mng. Dir.--TIFT SA, Cergy-Pontoise, France; Int'l, pg. 1223
Toussaint, Philippe, Chm. & Chief Exec. Officer--Credit du Nord, Paris, France; Int'l, pg. 319
Tow, Leonard, Chm. Bd. & Chief Exec. Officer--Century Communications Corp., New Canaan, CT; U.S. Public, pg. 329
Tow, Leonard, Chm. Bd. & Chief Exec. & Fin. Officers--Citizens Utilities Company, Stamford, CT; U.S. Public, pg. 379
Tow, Leonard, Chm. Bd., Chief Exec. Officer & Chief Fin. Officer--Citizens Telecommunications, Stamford, CT; U.S. Public, pg. 380
Towell, Anthony P., Co-Chm.--Eastco Industrial Safety Corp., Huntington Station, NY; U.S. Public, pg. 548
Tower, H.L., III, Chm. Bd., Pres. & Chief Exec. Officer--Stanhome Inc., Westfield, MA; U.S. Public, pg. 1508
Townsend, Edwin W., Chm. Bd.--B.M.J. Financial Corp., Bordentown, NJ; U.S. Public, pg. 1528
Townsend, James M., Chm. Bd. & Chief Exec. Officer--First Coast Community Bank & Trust, Fernandina Beach, FL; U.S. Public, pg. 1549
Townsend, Kenneth W., Chm. Bd.--Blue Cross and Blue Shield of Oklahoma, Tulsa, OK; U.S. Private, pg. 151
Townsend, P. Coleman, Jr., Chm. Bd. & Chief Exec. Officer--Townsends, Inc., Wilmington, DE; U.S. Private, pg. 1094
Townsend, Ray T., Chm. Bd.--Townsend Engineering Co., Des Moines, IA; U.S. Private, pg. 1094
Trachtenberg, Joseph M., Chm. Bd. & Chief Exec. Officer--Victaulic Company of America, Easton, PA; U.S. Private, pg. 1138
Tracy, John, Chm.--Sunflower Electric Power Corporation, Hays, KS; U.S. Private, pg. 1052
Traeger, John E., Chm. Bd.--Artistic Carton Company, Elgin, IL; U.S. Private, pg. 87
Trafton, Stephen J., Chm. Bd., Pres., Chief Exec. Officer & Chief Oper. Officer--Glendale Federal Bank, F.S.B., Glendale, CA; U.S. Public, pg. 747
Tragos, Bill, Founder, Chm & Chief Exec. Officer-WW--TBWA Chiat/Day New York, New York, NY; U.S. Private, pg. 1062
Tragos, William G., Founder, Chm. Bd. & Chief Exec. Officer-WW--TBWA Chiat/Day, New York, NY; U.S. Private, pg. 1062
Tran, Thinh Q., Chm. Bd. & Chief Exec. Officer--Sigma Designs, Inc., Fremont, CA; U.S. Public, pg. 1472
Trani, John M., Chm. Bd. & Chief Exec. Officer--The Stanley Works, New Britain, CT; U.S. Public, pg. 1508
Transou, Susan Busch, Chm. Bd. & Chief Exec. Officer--Busch Creative Services Corporation, Saint Louis, MO; U.S. Public, pg. 114
Traskos, Theodore N., Founder & Chm.-Exec. Committee--ACO Inc., Farmington Hills, MI; U.S. Private, pg. 3
Traut, Richard M., Chm. Bd.--Follett Corporation, River Grove, IL; U.S. Private, pg. 416
Trauth, David E., Chm. Bd., Pres. & Chief Exec. Officer--Trauth Dairy Inc., Newport, KY; U.S. Private, pg. 1098
Travaglianti, Edward, Chm. Bd. & Chief Exec. Officer--European American Bank & Trust Co., Uniondale, NY; Int'l, pg. 9
Traylor, W. Leroy, Sr., Chm. Bd.--Traylor Chemical & Supply Co., Orlando, FL; U.S. Private, pg. 1098
Traylor, William F., Chm. Bd.--Traylor Brothers, Inc., Evansville, IN; U.S. Private, pg. 1098
Trbovich, Dr. Nicholas D., Chm. Bd. & Pres.--Servotronics, Inc., Elma, NY; U.S. Public, pg. 1462
Treace, James T., Chm. Bd., Pres. & Cheif Exec. Officer--Xomed Surgical Products, Jacksonville, FL; U.S. Public, pg. 253
Tregoe, Benjamin, Chm. Bd.--Kepner-Tregoe, Inc., Skillman, NJ; U.S. Public, pg. 1659
Tregurtha, Paul R., Chm. Bd.--Moran Transporation Company, Greenwich, CT; U.S. Private, pg. 760
Tregurtha, Paul R., Chm. Bd.--Moran Towing Corporation, Greenwich, CT; U.S. Private, pg. 760
Tregurtha, Paul R., Chm. Bd.--Moran Towing Of Texas Corporation, Greenwich, CT; U.S. Private, pg. 761
Tregurtha, Paul R., Chm. Bd. & Pres.--Mormac Marine Transport, Inc., Stamford, CT; U.S. Private, pg. 762
Treinin, Thomas F., Chm. Bd. & Pres.--Special Devices, Incorporated, Newhall, CA; U.S. Public, pg. 1496
Treis, F. Edward, Chm. Bd. & Chief Exec. Officer--Arandell Corporation, Menomonee Falls, WI; U.S. Private, pg. 79
Treis, F. Edward, Chm. Bd. & Chief Exec. Officer--Arandell-Schmidt, Menomonee Falls, WI; U.S. Private, pg. 79
Tremain, Alan, Chm. Bd.--BFX Hospitality Group, Inc., Fort Worth, TX; U.S. Public, pg. 160
Trerice, Byron W., Jr., Chm. Bd. & Chief Exec. Officer--Trerice Tosto Colliers International, Bingham Farms, MI; U.S. Private, pg. 1099
Trescowthick, Donald, Sir, A.C., K.B.E., Chm. Bd.--Harris Scarfe Holdings Limited, Toorak, Australia; Int'l, pg. 597
Treu, Tiziano, Chm. Bd.--La Centrale Formazione S.r.l., Vicenza, Italy; Int'l, pg. 138
Treves, Vanni, Chm. Bd.--McKechnie PLC, Walsall, United Kingdom; Int'l, pg. 851
Treves, Vanni E., Chm. Bd.--BBA Group plc, London, United Kingdom; Int'l, pg. 112
Trevino, Alex, Jr., Chm. Bd., Pres. & Chief Exec. Officer--ACR Group, Houston, TX; U.S. Public, pg. 3
Trewhella, Stephen W., Chm. & Chief Exec. Officer--Glassmaster Company, Lexington, SC; U.S. Public, pg. 745
Trexler, Terry E., Chm. Bd. & Pres.--Nobility Homes, Inc., Ocala, FL; U.S. Public, pg. 1186
Treyvaud, Jacques, Chm. Bd.--Banque Cantonale Vaudoise, Lausanne, Switzerland; Int'l, pg. 160
Tribble, James L., Chm. Bd. & Chief Exec. Officer--Tribble & Stephens Co., Houston, TX; U.S. Private, pg. 1102
Tribull, Christoph, Chm. Bd., Pres., Chief Exec. Officer & Chief Oper. Officer--Sierracin Corporation, Sylmar, CA; U.S. Private, pg. 999
Tricket, Jean-Claude, Governor--Banque de France, Paris, France; Int'l, pg. 160
Trigano, Serge, Chm.-Supervisory Bd.--Club Mediterranee SA, Paris, France; Int'l, pg. 298
Trimble, Charles R., Chm. Bd., Pres. & Chief Exec. Officer--Trimble Navigation Limited, Sunnyvale, CA; U.S. Public, pg. 1638
Trimingham, Eldon H., Chm. Bd.--The Bank of Bermuda Limited, Hamilton, Bermuda; Int'l, pg. 150
Trimingham, Eldon H., Chm. Bd.--Bank of Bermuda (Guernsey) Limited, Saint Peter Port, United Kingdom; Int'l, pg. 151
Trinchero, Louis, Chm. & Chief Exec. Officer--Sutter Home Winery, Inc., Saint Helena, CA; U.S. Private, pg. 1057
Trip, D. Laman, Chm. Bd.--Postbank Retail Banking, Amsterdam, Netherlands; Int'l, pg. 647
Triplett, William W., Chm. Bd. & Chief Exec. Officer--HDS Services, Farmington Hills, MI; U.S. Private, pg. 490
Trivisonno, Nicholas L., Chm. Bd., Chief Exec. Officer--A.C. Nielsen, Stamford, CT; U.S. Public, pg. 1183
Trogdon, Dewey L., Chm. Bd.--Cone Mills Corporation, Greensboro, NC; U.S. Public, pg. 430
Troike, Frank A., Chm. Bd., Chief Exec. Officer & Treas.--Central Steel & Wire Company, Chicago, IL; U.S. Public, pg. 327
Troncalli, Samuel, Chm. Bd.--Troncalli Motors, Inc., Decatur, GA; U.S. Private, pg. 1104
Tronchetti Provera, Marco, Chm. & Chief Exec. Officer--Pirelli S.p.A., Milan, Italy; Int'l, pg. 1058
Trone, Oliver S. (Lee), III, Chm.--Trone Advertising, Inc., Greensboro, NC; U.S. Private, pg. 1104
Trotman, Alexander J., Chm. Bd., Pres. & Chief Exec. Officer--Ford Motor Company, Dearborn, MI; U.S. Public, pg. 661
Trott, Kenny A., Chm. Bd. & Chief Exec. Officer--Excel Communications, Inc., Dallas, TX; U.S. Public, pg. 598
Trotter, Tim, Deputy Chm.--Weber Public Relations Worldwide, Cambridge, MA; U.S. Private, pg. 1157
Trotter, Tim, Chm. & Chief Exec. Officer--Ludgate Group Limited, London, United Kingdom; U.S. Private, pg. 1157
Trowbridge, C. Robertson, Chm. Bd.--Yankee Publishing Incorporated, Dublin, NH; U.S. Private, pg. 1195
Trozzo, Samuel R., Chm. Bd. & Chief Exec. Officer--Rice, Hall, James & Associates, San Diego, CA; U.S. Public, pg. 1674
Truchard, James J., Chm. Bd., Pres. & Chief Exec. Officer--National Instruments Corp., Austin, TX; U.S. Public, pg. 1157
Trugman, Leonard A., Chm. Bd., Pres. & Chief Exec. Officer--Del Global Technologies, Valhalla, NY; U.S. Public, pg. 493
Trump, Julius, Chm. Bd. & Chief Exec. Officer--The Trump Group, Miami, FL; U.S. Private, pg. 1107
Truslow, Hank, Chm. Bd.--Woolrich, Inc., Woolrich, PA; U.S. Private, pg. 1188
Truslow, Henry, III, Chm. Bd. & Chief Exec. Officer--Sunbury Textiles, Sunbury, PA; U.S. Private, pg. 432
Trygg, Steve, Chm. Bd. & New Bus. Contact--Anderson & Lembke Inc., New York, NY; U.S. Private, pg. 72
Tryon, William A., II, Chm. Bd.--Trayer Products, Inc., Elmira, NY; U.S. Private, pg. 1098
Tschopp, Theodor M., Dr., Chm. Bd.--Alusuisse-Lonza Holding Ltd., Zurich, Switzerland; Int'l, pg. 66
Tsoukanov, Vladimir A., Chm. Bd. & Gen. Dir.--AutotractorExport, Moscow, Russia; Int'l, pg. 101
Tsuchida, Terumichi, Chm. Bd.--Meiji Life Insurance Company, Tokyo, Japan; Int'l, pg. 854
Tsuchihashi, Etsuro, Chm. Bd.--Okuma Corporation, Niwa, Japan; Int'l, pg. 1000
Tsui, Cyrus Y., Chm. Bd., Pres. & Chief Exec. Officer--Lattice Semiconductor Corporation, Hillsboro, OR; U.S. Public, pg. 979
Tsui, John K., Chm. Bd. & Chief Exec. Officer--First Hawaiian Leasing, Inc., Honolulu, HI; U.S. Public, pg. 635
Tsuji, Yoshifumi, Chm. Bd.--Nissan Motor Co., Ltd., Tokyo, Japan; Int'l, pg. 943
Tsukamoto, Koichi, Chm. Bd.--Wacoal Corporation, Kyoto, Japan; Int'l, pg. 1484
Tsumura, Akira, Chm. Bd.--Tsumura & Co., Tokyo, Japan; Int'l, pg. 1425
Tsumura, Monty, Chm. Bd.--Tsumura International, Secaucus, NJ; Int'l, pg. 1426
Tu, Wen-Hu, Chm. Bd., Pres. & Chief Exec. Officer--Transico Incorporated, Santa Ana, CA; U.S. Public, pg. 1630
Tucci, Joseph M., Chm. Bd. & Chief Exec. Officer--Wang Laboratories, Inc., Billerica, MA; U.S. Public, pg. 1737
Tuchman, Martin, Chm. Bd. & Chief Exec. Officer--Interpool, Inc., Princeton, NJ; U.S. Public, pg. 908
Tucker, N.E., Jr., Chm. Bd. & Pres.--Nantahala Power and Light Company, Bryson City, NC; U.S. Public, pg. 534
Tucker, Richard B.C., Sr., Sr. Chm. Bd. & Pres.--Wm. T. Burnett & Co., Inc., Baltimore, MD; U.S. Private, pg. 186
Tugendhat, Christopher, Lord, Chm. Bd.--Abbey National Plc, London, United Kingdom; Int'l, pg. 19
Tugendhat, Lord, Chm. Bd.--CRC, Thame, United Kingdom; Int'l, pg. 241
Tuley, Harry, Chm. Bd.--Scapa Group Plc, Blackburn, United Kingdom; Int'l, pg. 1202
Tuley, Harry, Chm. Bd.--Staveley Industries PLC, Croydon, United Kingdom; Int'l, pg. 1298
Tulin, Marshall, Chm. Bd.--Swank, Inc., Attleboro, MA; U.S. Public, pg. 1543
Turcotte, G.J., Chm. & Chief Exec. Officer--Chauvco Resources Ltd., Calgary, Canada; Int'l, pg. 1424
Turkovich, Tony, Chm. Bd.--Pacific Coast Producers, Lodi, CA; U.S. Private, pg. 830

Turnbull, Malcolm B., Chm. Bd.--OzEmail Limited, Sydney, Australia; *Int'l*, pg. 1019
Turner, Alan, Chm. Bd.--BPB Industries PLC, Slough, United Kingdom; *Int'l*, pg. 122
Turner, Andrew, Chm. Bd., Pres. & Chief Exec. Officer--Sun Healthcare Group Inc., Albuquerque, NM; *U.S. Public*, pg. 1530
Turner, Barry, Chm. Bd., Pres. & Chief Exec. Officer--KTI Fish, Houston, TX; *U.S. Private*, pg. 604
Turner, Bert, Chm. Bd.--Turner Industries, Baton Rouge, LA; *U.S. Private*, pg. 1109
Turner, C.O., III, Chm. Bd. & Pres.--Manufacturers Consolidation Service, Inc., Memphis, TN; *U.S. Private*, pg. 700
Turner, Cal, Jr., Chm. Bd. & Chief Exec. Officer--Dollar General Corporation, Nashville, TN; *U.S. Public*, pg. 515
Turner, Clyde T., Chm. Bd. & Chief Exec. Officer--Circus Circus - Las Vegas, Las Vegas, NV; *U.S. Public*, pg. 374
Turner, Clyde T., Chm. Bd. & Chief Exec. Officer--Circus Circus Hotel Casinos, Inc., Las Vegas, NV; *U.S. Public*, pg. 374
Turner, Edward T., Jr., Chm. Bd. & Chief Exec. Officer--Weston Paper & Manufacturing Co., Terre Haute, IN; *U.S. Private*, pg. 1169
Turner, Fred L., Sr. Chm. Bd.--McDonald's Corporation, Oak Brook, IL; *U.S. Public*, pg. 1068
Turner, Joe Ben, Chm. Bd., Pres. & Chief Exec. Officer--Willis Corroon Corp. of Knoxville, Knoxville, TN; *Int'l*, pg. 1506
Turner, John G., Chm. Bd. & Chief Exec. Officer--ReliaStar Financial Corp., Minneapolis, MN; *U.S. Public*, pg. 1375
Turner, Loyce W., Chm. Bd.--First State Bank and Trust Company, Valdosta, GA; *U.S. Public*, pg. 1549
Turner, R.E., Chm. Bd.--Fox Net, Los Angeles, CA; *Int'l*, pg. 926
Turner, R.E., Chm. Bd.-TBS--The Cartoon Network, Atlanta, GA; *U.S. Public*, pg. 1614
Turner, R.E., Chm. Bd.--Turner Home Entertainment, Atlanta, GA; *U.S. Public*, pg. 1615
Turner, Ted, Vice Chm.--Time Warner Inc., New York, NY; *U.S. Public*, pg. 1610
Turner, William B., Chm.-Exec. Committee--Synovus Financial Corp., Columbus, GA; *U.S. Public*, pg. 1548
Turner, William B., Chm. Bd.--Columbus Bank and Trust Company, Columbus, GA; *U.S. Public*, pg. 1549
Turner, William I.M., Chm. Bd.--Proudfoot plc, Richmond, United Kingdom; *Int'l*, pg. 1071
Turner, William I.M., Chm. Bd.--Proudfoot USA Company, West Palm Beach, FL; *Int'l*, pg. 1072
Turner, William I.M., Chm. Bd.--SNC-Lavalin Inc., Montreal, Canada; *Int'l*, pg. 1162
Turner, William J., Chm. Bd.--Faroudja, Inc., Sunnyvale, CA; *U.S. Public*, pg. 613
Tuttle, C.H., Chm. Bd.--Aerovox Inc., New Bedford, MA; *U.S. Public*, pg. 25
Tuttle, John R., Chm. Bd., Pres. & Treas.--Micron Communications, Inc., Boise, ID; *U.S. Public*, pg. 1105
Tweddle, Michael E., Chm. Bd. & Pres.--Tweddle Litho Company, Clinton Township, MI; *U.S. Private*, pg. 1111
Tweten, Leonard M., Chm. Bd.--Magnolia Hi-Fi, Inc., Kent, WA; *U.S. Private*, pg. 696
Twigg-Smith, Thurston, Chm. Bd. & Chief Exec. Officer--Persis Corporation, Honolulu, HI; *U.S. Private*, pg. 855
Tyabji, Hatim A., Chm. Bd., Pres. & Chief Exec. Officer--VeriFone, Inc., Redwood City, CA; *U.S. Public*, pg. 815
Tyda, William, Chm. Bd. & Chief Exec. Officer--LaSalle-Talman Bank, Chicago, IL; *Int'l*, pg. 11
Tyree, James C., Chm. Bd. & Chief Exec. Officer--Mesirow Financial, Chicago, IL; *U.S. Private*, pg. 733
Tyson, Don, Sr. Chm.-Exec. & Fin. Committee--Tyson Foods, Inc., Springdale, AR; *U.S. Public*, pg. 1652
Tyson, Thomas J., Dr., Chm. Bd., Pres. & Chief Exec. Officer--Energy & Environmental Research Corp., Irvine, CA; *U.S. Private*, pg. 376
Tze, Ker Sin, Dr., Chm. Bd.--Superior Metal Printing Limited, Singapore, Singapore; *Int'l*, pg. 1322
Tzetzo, Jim, Chm. Bd.--Clark Gum Company, Buffalo, NY; *U.S. Private*, pg. 243
Ubaid, M.A., Chm. Bd. & Mng. Dir.--Central Coalfields Limited, Ranchi, India; *Int'l*, pg. 298
Uchida, Shun, Chm. Bd.--Tuta Laboratories (Australia) Pty., Ltd., Lane Cove, Australia; *Int'l*, pg. 1014
Uchida, Shun, Chm. Bd.--Otsuka Pharmaceutical Australia Pty. Ltd., Pymble, Australia; *Int'l*, pg. 1014
Uchtenhagen, Lilian, Dr., Chm.--Coop Zurich, Zurich, Switzerland; *Int'l*, pg. 329
Ude, Christian, Chm. Bd.--Stadtsparkasse Munchen, Munich, Germany; *Int'l*, pg. 1293
Uding, George E., Chm. Bd.--Cement Transit Co., Cleveland, OH; *U.S. Public*, pg. 1084
Uding, George E., Chm. Bd.--Canadian Cement Ltd., Owen Sound, Canada; *U.S. Public*, pg. 1084
Ueberecken, Nicolas, Chm.--AIT - Arbed International Trading S.A., Luxembourg, Luxembourg; *Int'l*, pg. 79
Ueberroth, Peter V., Co-Chm.--Doubletree Corporation, Memphis, TN; *U.S. Public*, pg. 1335
Uehara, Shoji, Chm. Bd.--Taisho Pharmaceutical Co., Ltd., Tokyo, Japan; *Int'l*, pg. 1348
Ueltschi, Albert L., Chm. Bd. & Pres.--FlightSafety International Inc., Flushing, NY; *U.S. Public*, pg. 218
Ueltschi, H.P., Chm. Bd., Pres. & Chief Exec. Officer--Bernina Holding AG, Steckborn, Switzerland; *Int'l*, pg. 189
Ueltschi, H.P., Chm. Bd.--Bernina of America Inc., Aurora, IL; *Int'l*, pg. 189
Ueshima, Seisuke, Chm. Bd.--Yamaha Corporation, Hamamatsu, Japan; *Int'l*, pg. 1515
Uhlmann, Paul, III, Chm. Bd. & Chief Exec. Officer--The Uhlmann Co., Kansas City, MO; *U.S. Private*, pg. 1115
Uhlmann, Paul, Jr., Chm. of Exec. Committee--The Uhlmann Co., Kansas City, MO; *U.S. Private*, pg. 1115
Uhrig, J.A., Chm. Bd.--CRA Limited, Melbourne, Australia; *Int'l*, pg. 1119
Uhrig, John, Chm. Bd.--Westpac Banking Corporation, Sydney, Australia; *Int'l*, pg. 1495
Uihlein, Walter R., Chm. & Chief Exec. Officer--Titleist & Foot-Joy Worldwide, Fairhaven, MA; *U.S. Public*, pg. 675
Uihlein, Walter R., Chm. Bd.--Cobra Golf Incorporated, Carlsbad, CA; *U.S. Public*, pg. 675
Uilarasau, Jose, Chm. Bd.--La Caixa, Barcelona, Spain; *Int'l*, *pg. 784*
Ukon, Hiroshi, Chm. Bd.--Yamaha Motor do Brasil Ltda., Convica, Brazil; *Int'l*, pg. 1516
Ukrop, James E., Chm. Bd. & Chief Exec. Officer--Ukrop's Super Markets, Richmond, VA; *U.S. Private*, pg. 1115
Ulbrich, Frederick C., Jr., Chm. Bd., Pres. & Chief Exec. Officer--Ulbrich Stainless Steels & Special Metals, Inc., North Haven, CT; *U.S. Private*, pg. 1115
Ullo, Phillip D., Chm. Bd.--Ullo International, Inc., Altamonte Springs, FL; *U.S. Private*, pg. 1116
Ullrich, Gunter, Dr., Chm. Bd.-Mngmt.--Deutsche Versicherungs-AG, Berlin, Germany; *Int'l*, pg. 58
Ulrich, Robert J., Chm. Bd. & Chief Exec. Officer--Dayton Hudson Corporation, Minneapolis, MN; *U.S. Public*, pg. 489
Umans, A.R., Chm. Bd. & Chief Exec. Officer--RHC/Spacemaster Corporation, Melrose Park, IL; *U.S. Private*, *pg. 904*
Umphenour, Russell, Jr., Chm. Bd., Pres. & Chief Exec. Officer--R.T.M. Winners, Atlanta, GA; *U.S. Private*, pg. 906
Underwood, Vernon, Chm. Bd., Pres. & Chief Exec. Officer--Young's Holdings Inc., Orange, CA; *U.S. Private*, pg. 1202
Unger, Gerald F., Chm. Bd.--Unger Company, Cleveland, OH; *U.S. Private*, pg. 1117
Ungerman, Steven, Chm. Bd.--Pizza Inn, Inc., Dallas, TX; *U.S. Public*, pg. 1307
Unickel, Jeff, Chm. Bd.--Shapco, Inc., Santa Monica, CA; *U.S. Private*, pg. 989
Unoki, Hajime, Chm. Bd.--Aiwa America, Inc., Mahwah, NJ; *Int'l*, pg. 1280
Unruh, James A., Chm. Bd.--The Franklin Institute, Philadelphia, PA; *U.S. Private*, pg. 424
Unwin, Brian, Sir, Chm. Bd. & Pres.--European Investment Bank, Luxembourg, Luxembourg; *Int'l*, pg. 465
Upbin, Hal, Chm.--American Recreation Products, Inc., Saint Louis, MO; *U.S. Public*, pg. 948
Upfield, James E., Chm. Bd.--Temtex Industries Inc., Dallas, TX; *U.S. Public*, pg. 1575
Upfield, James E., Chm. Bd.--Temco Fireplace Products, Inc., Nashville, TN; *U.S. Public*, pg. 1576
Urakami, Akio, Dr., Chm. Bd. & Pres.--Ryobi Motor Products, Anderson, SC; *Int'l*, pg. 1151
Urban, Thomas N., Chm. Bd.--Pioneer Hi-Bred International, Inc., Des Moines, IA; *U.S. Public*, pg. 1298
Urban, Wolfgang, Dr., Co-Chm.--Metro AG, Cologne, Germany; *Int'l*, pg. 863
Urbanowski, Richard, Chm. Bd. & Pres.--ISK Biotech, Mentor, OH; *Int'l*, pg. 689
Urquhart, Lawrence M., Chm. Bd.--Burmah Castrol plc, Swindon, United Kingdom; *Int'l*, pg. 234
Urquhart, Lawrence M., Chm. Bd.--English China Clays Plc, Theale, United Kingdom; *Int'l*, pg. 455
Urquhart, Lawrence M., Chm. Bd.--Scottish Widows' Fund & Life Assurance Society, Edinburgh, United Kingdom; *Int'l*, *pg. 1212*
Urrutia, Mike, Chm. Bd. & Pres.--Producers Livestock, North Salt Lake, UT; *U.S. Private*, pg. 888
Urso, Joseph, Chm. Bd.--Interstate Engineering, Anaheim, CA; *U.S. Private*, pg. 573
Urstadt, Charles J., Chm. Bd. & Chief Exec. Officer--Urstadt Biddle Properties, Inc., Greenwich, CT; *U.S. Public*, pg. 1700
Urushisako, T., Chm. & Pres.--Sharp Electronics Corporation, Mahwah, NJ; *Int'l*, pg. 1228
Uselton, J.C., Chm. Bd. & Pres.--Sverdrup Investments, Inc., Maryland Heights, MO; *U.S. Private*, pg. 1057
Usher, Thomas J., Chm. Bd. & Chief Exec. Officer--USX Corporation, Pittsburgh, PA; *U.S. Public*, pg. 1661
Usher, Thomas J., Chm. Bd. & Chief Exec. Officer--U.S. Steel International, Inc., Pittsburgh, PA; *U.S. Public*, pg. 1661
Ushigome, Susumu, Chm. Bd. & Pres.--TYK Corporation, Tokyo, Japan; *Int'l*, pg. 1345
Ushikubo, Tomoaki, Chm. Bd.--Sanden Corporation, Tokyo, Japan; *Int'l*, pg. 1184
Usibelli, Joseph E., Chm. Bd.--Usibelli Coal Mine, Inc., Healy, AK; *U.S. Private*, pg. 1129
Usinger, Frederick D., Chm. Bd.--Fred Usinger, Inc., Milwaukee, WI; *U.S. Private*, pg. 1129
Ussery, Richard W., Chm. & Chief Exec. Officer--Total System Services, Inc., Columbus, GA; *U.S. Public*, pg. 1550
Utley, Edward H., Vice Chm.--GEICO Corporation, Washington, DC; *U.S. Public*, pg. 219
Utter, Eero, Chm. Bd.--Cultor Ltd., Helsinki, Finland; *Int'l*, pg. 349
Uyeno, Kimio, Chm. Bd.--Chugai Pharmaceutical Co., Ltd., Tokyo, Japan; *Int'l*, pg. 290
Vague, Richard W., Chm. Bd. & Chief Exec. Officer--First USA, Inc., Dallas, TX; *U.S. Public*, pg. 174
Vague, Richard W., Chm. & Chief Exec. Officer--First USA Bank, Wilmington, DE; *U.S. Public*, pg. 174
Vaight, P.R., Dr., Chm. Bd.--Lamont Holdings Plc, Belfast, United Kingdom; *Int'l*, pg. 797
Vaillaud, Pierre, Chm. Bd. & Chief Exec. Officer--Technip, Paris, France; *Int'l*, pg. 1360
Vainio, Vesa, Chm. Bd. & Chief Exec. Officer--Merita Ltd., Helsinki, Finland; *Int'l*, pg. 858
Vainio, Vesa, Chm. Bd. & Chief Exec. Officer--Merita Bank Ltd., Helsinki, Finland; *Int'l*, pg. 858
Vakil, Usman U., Chm. Bd., Pres. & Treas.--Lights Of America, Inc., Walnut, CA; *U.S. Private*, pg. 667
Valade, Robert C., Chm. Bd. & Chief Exec. Officer--Carhartt, Inc., Dearborn, MI; *U.S. Private*, pg. 210
Valaselis, Ioannis, Chm. Bd.--Galileo Hellas, Athens, Greece; *Int'l*, pg. 1004
Valdiserri, Carl L., Chm. Bd. & Chief Exec. Officer--Rouge Steel Company, Dearborn, MI; *U.S. Public*, pg. 1406
Valente, Dan, Chm. Bd., Pres. & Chief Exec. Officer--Palomar Medical Technologies, Lexington, MA; *U.S. Public*, pg. 1255
Valentin, Pierre, Chm. Bd.--Coflexip S.A., Paris, France; *Int'l*, *pg. 304*
Valentine, Donald T., Chm. Bd.--C-Cube Microsystems, Milpitas, CA; *U.S. Public*, pg. 272
Valentine, Joseph C., Chm. Bd., Pres. & Chief Exec. Officer--Lubrication Engineers, Inc., Fort Worth, TX; *U.S. Private*, pg. 679
Valk, Richard P., Chm. Bd.--Valk Manufacturing Company, New Kingstown, PA; *U.S. Private*, pg. 1131
Valkenaars, C.J., Chm. Bd.--Blydenstein-Willink N.V., Hengelo, Netherlands; *Int'l*, pg. 198
Vallance, Iain D.T., Sir, Chm. Bd.--British Telecommunications plc, London, United Kingdom; *Int'l*, pg. 222
Vallee, Roy, Chm. Bd., Pres. & Chief Exec. & Oper. Officer--Avnet, Inc., Great Neck, NY; *U.S. Public*, pg. 155
Vallely, W.F., Jr., Chm. Bd.--A.T. Clayton & Company, Inc., Greenwich, CT; *U.S. Private*, pg. 244
Valles, Gene, Chm.--Rush Press, San Diego, CA; *U.S. Private*, pg. 268
Valles, Jean-Paul, Chm. Bd. & Chief Exec. Officer--Minerals Technologies, Inc., New York, NY; *U.S. Public*, pg. 1115
Valley, R. Bruce, Chm. Bd., Pres. & Chief Exec. Officer--Piedmont Trust Bank, Martinsville, VA; *U.S. Public*, pg. 1039
Valls, Manuel Malagrida, Chm. Bd.--Tradicion Textil, S.A., Barcelona, Spain; *Int'l*, pg. 1416
Valluzzo, John V., Chm. Bd. & Pres.--DCG Precision Manufacturing Corporation, Bethel, CT; *U.S. Private*, pg. 301
Valmorisco Martin, Manuel, Chm. & Creative Dir.--GGK Madrid, Madrid, Spain; *Int'l*, pg. 1335
Valpey, Ted, Jr., Chm. Bd.--Matec Corporation, Hopkinton, MA; *U.S. Public*, pg. 1056
Valva, George, Chm.--Account Specific Marketing, Inc. (ASM), Morristown, NJ; *U.S. Private*, pg. 345
Van Andel, Steve, Chm. Bd.--Amway Corporation, Ada, MI; *U.S. Private*, pg. 69
van As, Eugene, Chm. Bd. & Chief Exec. Officer--Sappi Limited, Braamfontein, South Africa; *Int'l*, pg. 1193
van As, Eugene, Chm. Bd. & Chief Exec. Officer--S.D. Warren Co., Boston, MA; *Int'l*, pg. 1193
Van Bogan, R., Chm. Bd., Pres. & Chief Exec. Officer--SouthTrust Bank, Orlando, Orlando, FL; *U.S. Public*, pg. 1492
van de Geijn, P., Chm. Bd., Pres. & Chief Exec. Officer--AEGON Nederland N.V., Hague, Netherlands; *Int'l*, pg. 26
Van de Walle, P.L.J., Chm. Bd.--Texaco Italiana SpA, Rome, Italy; *U.S. Public*, pg. 1584
Van Degna, Robert M., Chm. & Chief Exec. Officer--Fleet Equity Partners, Providence, RI; *U.S. Public*, pg. 650
van den Bergh, R.F., Chariman & Chief Exec. Offier--NMU Marketing Information Services, New York, NY; *Int'l*, pg. 1446
Van Den Blink, N. Mooers, Chm. Bd., Chief Exec. Officer, & Treas.--Hilliard Corporation, Elmira, NY; *U.S. Private*, pg. 530
van den Broek, Theo, Chm.--ARA/BDDP, Rotterdam, Netherlands; *Int'l*, pg. 117
van den Hoek, P.C., Chm. Bd.--Ballast Nedam NV, Amstelveen, Netherlands; *Int'l*, pg. 133
van der Driest, C.J., Chm. Bd. of Mngmt.--Koninklijke Van Ommeren NV, Rotterdam, Netherlands; *Int'l*, pg. 758
van der Hagen, E.J., Chm. Bd.--Nutricia BV, Zoetermeer, Netherlands; *Int'l*, pg. 991
van der Heijden, W.A.J.M., Chm. Bd.--FGH Bank N.V., Utrecht, Netherlands; *Int'l*, pg. 26
van der Hoeven, C.H, Chm. Bd.--Koninklijke Ahold NV, Zaandam, Netherlands; *Int'l*, pg. 749
van der Leegte, W., Chm. Bd.--VDL Groep BV, Eindhoven, Netherlands; *Int'l*, pg. 1444
van der Lugt, G.J.A., Chm. Bd.--ING Groep N.V., Amsterdam, Netherlands; *Int'l*, pg. 647
van der Noot, Dino Betti, Chm.--B Communications/GGK, Milan, Italy; *Int'l*, pg. 1335
Van der Plas, H., Chm.--Samas Universal Office Supplies, Utrecht, Netherlands; *Int'l*, pg. 707
van der Walt, L., Chm.--The Lion Match Company Limited, Durban, South Africa; *Int'l*, pg. 1287
van der Wel, Paul, Chm.-European Foods Group--Goodman Fielder Limited, Sydney, Australia; *Int'l*, pg. 555
van Dun, F.J.C.M., Chm.--G&P Starke Diekstra BV, Nieuwegein, Netherlands; *Int'l*, pg. 607
Van Dyke, William G., Chm. Bd., Pres. & Chief Exec. Officer--Donaldson Company, Inc., Minneapolis, MN; *U.S. Public*, pg. 517
Van Elsander, Art, Chm. Bd.--Art Van Furniture Inc., Warren, MI; *U.S. Private*, pg. 86
van Engelshoven, J.M.H., Chm.-Supervisory Bd.--Internatio-Muller N.V., Rotterdam, Netherlands; *Int'l*, pg. 680
van Gels, John J., Chm. Bd.--The Boeing Company Canada Ltd., Toronto, Canada; *U.S. Public*, pg. 242
Van Gilder, Russel, Chm. Bd.--Spartan Stores Inc., Grand Rapids, MI; *U.S. Private*, pg. 1021
Van Hook, Jim, Chm. Bd. & Chief Exec. Officer--Provident Music Group, Brentwood, TN; *Int'l*, pg. 1529
Van Horne, James C., Chm. Bd.--Montgomery St. Income Securities, Inc., San Francisco, CA; *U.S. Public*, pg. 1127
van Kesteren, S.J., Chm. Bd.--BIW Cable Systems, Inc., Franklin, MA; *Int'l*, pg. 417
van Lede, Cees J.A., Chm.-Mgmnt. Bd.--Akzo Nobel N.V., Arnhem, Netherlands; *Int'l*, pg. 42
van Leersum, A.M., Chm. Bd.--McCain Argentina SA, Buenos Aires, Argentina; *Int'l*, pg. 850
van Leersum, Tony, Chm. Bd.--McCain Produce Inc., Florenceville, Canada; *Int'l*, pg. 850

van Leeuwen, J.K., Chm. & Gen. Mgr.--Prumyslovy Penzijni Fond, a.s., Prague, Czech Republic; *Int'l*, pg. 651
van Liemt, H.B., Chm.-Supervisory Bd.--Gamma Holding N.V., Helmond, Netherlands; *Int'l*, pg. 539
van Liemt, H.B., Chm. Bd.-Suprv. Dirs.--Oce-van der Grinten N.V., Venlo, Netherlands; *Int'l*, pg. 993
Van Metre, Albert G., Sr., Chm. Bd.--The Van Metres Companies, Burke, VA; *U.S. Private*, pg. 1132
Van Mollenberg, H., Chm. Bd., Pres. & Chief Exec. Officer--Mollenberg-Betz Inc., Buffalo, NY; *U.S. Private*, pg. 756
Van Oijen, J.G.M., Chm. Bd.-Mngmt.--Gamma Holding N.V., Helmond, Netherlands; *Int'l*, pg. 539
Van Oordt, R.F.W., Chm. Bd.-Exec. Bd.--KNP BT Nederland B.V., Amsterdam, Netherlands; *Int'l*, pg. 756
van Oordt, R.W.F., Chm. Bd.--N.V. Koninklijke KNP BT, Amsterdam, Netherlands; *Int'l*, pg. 756
Van Pelt, David B., Sr., Chm. Bd. & Chief Exec. Officer--Van Pelt Corporation, Detroit, MI; *U.S. Private*, pg. 1133
Van Pelt, David B., Sr., Chm. Bd. & Chief Exec. Officer--Service Steel Division, Detroit, MI; *U.S. Private*, pg. 1133
Van Pelt, Donald C., Sr., Chm. Bd.--Plymouth Tube Company, Warrenville, IL; *U.S. Private*, pg. 873
van Pottelberge, W., Chm.--De Vaderlandsche Insurance, Antwerp, Belgium; *Int'l*, pg. 648
van Royen, O.H.A., Chm.-Supervisory Bd.--Royal Nedlloyd Group N.V., Rotterdam, Netherlands; *Int'l*, pg. 1143
Van Sant, R. William, Chm. Bd. & Chief Exec. Officer--Lukens Inc., Coatesville, PA; *U.S. Public*, pg. 1019
van Schaik, G., Chm. Bd.--AEGON N.V., Hague, Netherlands; *Int'l*, pg. 25
van Schaik, G., Chm.-Supervisory Bd.--Royal Gist-Brocades N.V., Delft, Netherlands; *Int'l*, pg. 1142
Van Smith, D., Chm. Bd.--First Financial Holdings, Inc., Charleston, SC; *U.S. Public*, pg. 634
Van Strydonck, John, Chm. Bd. & Chief Exec. Officer--NAPP Systems Inc, San Marcos, CA; *U.S. Public*, pg. 984
Van Tiem, Donald C., Chm. Bd., Pres. & Treas.--Hoban Foods, Inc., Detroit, MI; *U.S. Private*, pg. 531
Van Tuyl, Cecil L., Chm. Bd., Pres. & Chief Exec. Officer--V.T. Inc., Merriam, KS; *U.S. Private*, pg. 1131
Van Veen, M.C., Chm.-Bd. of Mngmt.--Koninklijke Hoogovens N.V., Ijmuiden, Netherlands; *Int'l*, pg. 753
van Veen, M.C., Chm.-Bd. of Mngmt.--Hoogovens Groep B.V., Ijmuiden, Netherlands; *Int'l*, pg. 753
van Veen, M.C., Chm.-Mngmt. Bd.--Hoogovens Ijmuiden, Ijmuiden, Netherlands; *Int'l*, pg. 753
Van Vleet, Wayne, Chm. Bd.--Trinidad/Benham Corp., Denver, CO; *U.S. Private*, pg. 1103
van Vlissingen, P. Fentener, Chm. Bd.--SHV Holdings N.V., Utrecht, Netherlands; *Int'l*, pg. 1154
van Wachem, L.C., Chm.-Supervisory Bd.--Royal Dutch/Shell Group of Companies, Hague, Netherlands; *Int'l*, pg. 1135
Van Wagenen, Paul G., Chm. Bd., Pres. & Chief Exec. Officer--Pogo Producing Company, Houston, TX; *U.S. Public*, pg. 1312
Van Wagner, Bruce, Chm. Bd.--The Antec Corporation, Rolling Meadows, IL; *U.S. Public*, pg. 116
van Wel, P.W., Chm. Bd.--Wolters Kluwer U.S., Riverwoods, IL; *Int'l*, pg. 1513
van Wensveen, Dr. D.M.N., Chm. Bd.--Mees & Hope Securities Holdings Ltd., London, United Kingdom; *Int'l*, pg. 12
Van Zyl, J.J.M., Chm. Bd.--Distillers Corporation S.A., Stellenbosch, South Africa; *Int'l*, pg. 1129
VanBenthuysen, Walter G., Chm. Bd. & Chief Exec. Officer--Hazelwood Farms Bakeries, Inc., Hazelwood, MO; *U.S. Public*, pg. 1541
Vance, William C., Chm. Bd. & Chief Exec. Officer--Vance Publishing Corporation, Lincolnshire, IL; *U.S. Private*, pg. 1133
Vande Berg, Steve, Chm. Bd.--Best Western International, Inc., Phoenix, AZ; *U.S. Private*, pg. 140
VanDemark, Steven D., Chm. Bd.--Rurban Financial Corp., Defiance, OH; *U.S. Public*, pg. 1412
VanDemark, Steven D., Chm. Bd.--The State Bank and Trust Company, Defiance, OH; *U.S. Public*, pg. 1413
Vandenburgh, David S., Chm. Bd. & Chief Exec. Officer--American Fence & Security Company, Phoenix, AZ; *U.S. Private*, pg. 54
Vander Dussen, Neil, Vice Chm.--Sony Electronics, Park Ridge, NJ; *Int'l*, pg. 1281
Vander Eycken, Henri, Chm. Bd.--SAIT-RadioHolland Group S.A., Brussels, Belgium; *Int'l*, pg. 1151
Vanderbilt, H.B., Chm. Bd.--R.T. Vanderbilt Company, Inc., Norwalk, CT; *U.S. Private*, pg. 1133
Vanderspuy, Peter M., Chm. Bd.--Delta Gold N.L., Sydney, Australia; *Int'l*, pg. 389
Vanderstar, Cornelius C., Chm. Bd. & Chief Exec. Officer--International Aluminum Corporation, Monterey Park, CA; *U.S. Public*, pg. 894
VanDerven, Hans, Chm. Bd.--Hoogovens Aluminium Corp., Secaucus, NJ; *Int'l*, pg. 755
Vanderzee, John B., Chm.--Young & Rubicam Detroit, Detroit, MI; *U.S. Private*, pg. 1198
Vandygriff, Cecil P., Chm. Bd.--Evergreen Mills Inc., Ada, OK; *U.S. Private*, pg. 1134
Vann, James M., Jr., Chm. Bd.--Rea Magnet Wire Company, Inc., Fort Wayne, IN; *U.S. Private*, pg. 913
Vardanega, Roland, Chm. Bd.--Peugeot-Citroen Moteurs (PCM), Nanterre, France; *Int'l*, pg. 1021
Vardeman, J. Rex, Chm. Bd., Pres. & Chief Exec. Officer--Vertex Communications Corporation, Kilgore, TX; *U.S. Public*, pg. 1717
Varel, Daniel W., Chm. Bd., Pres., Chief Exec. Officer & Gen. Mgr.--Varel Manufacturing Co., Dallas, TX; *U.S. Private*, pg. 1134
Vargas, Eduardo, Exec. V.P. & Chm., Chief Exec. Officer-Latin America & Dir.--BBDO Worldwide Inc., New York, NY; *U.S. Public*, pg. 1223
Varma, S.P., Chm. Bd. & Mng. Dir.--Western Coalfields Limited, Nagpur, India; *Int'l*, pg. 299
Varophas, Pairote, Chm.--Krung Thai IBJ Leasing Co., Bangkok, Thailand; *Int'l*, pg. 676
Vassell, William C., Chm. Bd.--Command Security Corporation, Lagrangeville, NY; *U.S. Public*, pg. 409
Vassiliades, Thomas, Chm. Bd. & Chief Exec. Officer--Gandalf Technologies Inc., Nepean, Canada; *Int'l*, pg. 540
Vassort, Francis, Chm. Bd.--Techalloy Co., Inc., Mahwah, NJ; *Int'l*, pg. 572
Vaughan-Lee, Mark A., Chm. Bd.--Danka Business Systems PLC, London, United Kingdom; *Int'l*, pg. 379
Vaughan, Bruce, Chm. Bd.--M.I.M. Holdings Ltd., Brisbane, Australia; *Int'l*, pg. 827
Vaughan, Charles K., Chm. Bd.--Atmos Energy Corporation, Dallas, TX; *U.S. Public*, pg. 145
Vaughan, Curtis, Jr., Chm. Bd.--Vaughan & Sons, Inc., San Antonio, TX; *U.S. Private*, pg. 1134
Vecten, Philippe, Chm. & Chief Exec. Officer--MDPA, Wittelsheim, France; *Int'l*, pg. 459
Velasquez, Arthur R., Chm. Bd., Pres. & Chief Exec. Officer--Azteca Foods, Incorporated, Chicago, IL; *U.S. Private*, pg. 104
Venetis, Petros, Chm. Bd.--Leo Burnett Athens, Athens, Greece; *U.S. Private*, pg. 184
Vengroff, Harvey, Chm. Bd.--Vengroff Williams & Associates, Inc., Commack, NY; *U.S. Private*, pg. 1135
Venier, Gianmarco, Chm. Bd. & Mng. Dir.--Caboto International S.A., Lugano, Switzerland; *Int'l*, pg. 138
Vento, Richard G., Co-Chm. Bd., Pres. & Chief Exec. Officer--Objective Systems Integrators, Inc., Folsom, CA; *U.S. Public*, pg. 1209
Ventre, John, Jr., Chm. Bd., Chief Exec. Officer & Treas.--Ventre Packing Company, Inc., Syracuse, NY; *U.S. Private*, pg. 1135
Vergnes, Bernard P., Sr. V.P. & Chm. Bd.-Microsoft Europe--Microsoft Corporation, Redmond, WA; *U.S. Public*, pg. 1107
Vergon, James F., Chm. Bd.--CILCORP Investment Management Inc., Peoria, IL; *U.S. Public*, pg. 367
Verhaeghe de Naeyer, Thierry, Chm. Bd. & Pres.--N.V. Bekaert S.A., Kortrijk, Belgium; *Int'l*, pg. 183
Verhagen, G., Chm.-Supvr. Bd.--Delft Instruments N.V., Delft, Netherlands; *Int'l*, pg. 388
Verkyk, Robert, Chm. Bd. & Pres.--Misener Marine Construction, Tampa, FL; *U.S. Private*, pg. 752
Verloop, E.J., Chm.-Supvr.--N.V. Koninklijke Bijenkorf Beheer KBB, Amsterdam, Netherlands; *Int'l*, pg. 750
Vermeer, Robert, Chm. Bd. & Chief Exec. Officer--Vermeer Manufacturing Company, Pella, IA; *U.S. Private*, pg. 1137
Vermeeren, A.F.J., Chm. Bd.--Organon Pakistan (Private) Limited, Karachi, Pakistan; *Int'l*, pg. 45
VerMerris, R.C., Chm. Bd. & Pres. & Chief Exec. Officer--Radix Wire Company, Cleveland, OH; *U.S. Private*, pg. 907
Vermonet, J.G., Chm. Bd.--Nyltech North America Inc., Manchester, NH; *Int'l*, pg. 482
Vermylen, Paul A., Chm. Bd.--A. Zeregas Sons, Inc., Fair Lawn, NJ; *U.S. Private*, pg. 1204
Verner, George C., Jr., Chm. Bd. & Chief Exec. Officer--Acousti Engineering Co. of Florida, Orlando, FL; *U.S. Private*, pg. 14
Verni, Ralph F., Chm. Bd., Pres. & Chief Exec. Officer--State Street Research & Management Company, Boston, MA; *U.S. Private*, pg. 738
Verni, Ralph F., Chm. Bd.--State Street Research Investment Services, Inc., Boston, MA; *U.S. Private*, pg. 738
Vernon, Lillian, Chm. Bd. & Chief Exec. Officer--Lillian Vernon Corporation, New Rochelle, NY; *U.S. Public*, pg. 1716
Vernon, W.F., Chm. Bd. & Pres.--The Vernon Company, Newton, IA; *U.S. Private*, pg. 1137
Verplaetse, Alfons, Governor--Banque Nationale de Belgique, Brussels, Belgium; *Int'l*, pg. 162
Veru, Theodore D., Co-Chm. & Co-Chief Exec. Officer--Lois/USA Inc., New York, NY; *U.S. Public*, pg. 1011
Ververs, M., Chm.-Supervisory Bd.--ING Groep N.V., Amsterdam, Netherlands; *Int'l*, pg. 647
Vessey, C.A., Div. Chm.--British Chrome & Chemicals Ltd., Stockton on Tees, United Kingdom; *Int'l*, pg. 598
Vest, Herb D., Chm. Bd., Pres. & Chief Exec. Officer--HD Vest Financial Services, Irving, TX; *U.S. Public*, pg. 770
Vice, H. Anthony, Chm. Bd.--Bowthorpe plc, Crawley, United Kingdom; *Int'l*, pg. 207
Vick, Edward H., Chm. & Chief Exec. Officer-Y&R/Wunderman Partnership--Young & Rubicam Inc., New York, NY; *U.S. Private*, pg. 1196
Vick, Edward H., Chm. & Chief Exec. Officer--Young & Rubicam Inc., New York, NY; *U.S. Private*, pg. 1196
Victoroff, Alexandra, Chm. Bd.--Groupe Strafor Facom, Morangis, France; *Int'l*, pg. 569
Victorri, Marcel, Chm. Bd.--Jouan, Inc., Winchester, VA; *U.S. Private*, pg. 601
Vienot, Marc, Chm. Bd. & Chief Exec. Officer--Societe Generale, Paris, France; *Int'l*, pg. 1273
Viets, Robert O., Chm.--CILCORP Ventures Inc., Peoria, IL; *U.S. Public*, pg. 367
Viets, Robert O., Chm. & Chief Exec. Officer--QST Enterprises Inc., Peoria, IL; *U.S. Public*, pg. 367
Viggiano, Victor A., Chm. Bd. & Chief Exec. Officer--The Okonite Company, Ramsey, NJ; *U.S. Private*, pg. 813
Vigil Gonzalez, Rufino, Chm. Bd.--Industrias CH, S.A. de C.V., Tlalnepantla, Mexico; *Int'l*, pg. 677
Vignau, P., Chm. Bd.--Chevron Chemical S.A., Neuilly-sur-Seine, France; *U.S. Public*, pg. 348
Vignon, Dominique, Chm. Bd. & Pres.--Framatome SA, Paris, France; *Int'l*, pg. 502
Vigo, Aig, Exec. Chm.--Heinemann Educational Nigeria Limited, Ibadan, Nigeria; *Int'l*, pg. 1094
Vile, Joel, D., Chm. Bd.--Vile-Goller, Fine Art Printing & Lithography, Kansas City, KS; *U.S. Private*, pg. 1140
Vilgrain, Jean-Louis, Chm. Bd. & Chief Exec. Officer--Cuisine Solutions, Inc., Alexandria, VA; *U.S. Public*, pg. 466
Villa-Massone, Gilbert, Chm. Bd. & Pres.--Gachot S.A., Montmorency, France; *U.S. Public*, pg. 1650
Villalonga, Juan, Chm. Bd.--Telefonica de Espana, S.A., Madrid, Spain; *Int'l*, pg. 1371
Villanueva, Luis I., Chm. Bd.--AGP Industrial Corporation, Manila, Philippines; *Int'l*, pg. 14
Villares, Paulo Diederichsen, Chm. Bd.--Acos Villares S.A., Sao Paulo, Brazil; *Int'l*, pg. 23
Villaret, Jean-Pierre, Joint Chm.--Devarrieux Villaret, Paris, France; *Int'l*, pg. 600
Villeneuve, Andre F., Chm. Bd.--Instinet Corporation, New York, NY; *Int'l*, pg. 1106
Villiger, Rudolf, Dr., Chm. Bd.--Sika Finanz AG, Baar, Switzerland; *Int'l*, pg. 1248
Vimercati, Piero Angelo, Chm. Bd.--La Centrale Consulenza S.p.A., Milan, Italy; *Int'l*, pg. 138
Vincent, James L., Chm. Bd.--Biogen, Inc., Cambridge, MA; *U.S. Public*, pg. 230
Vinciarelli, Patrizio, Chm. Bd. & Pres.--Vicor Corporation, Andover, MA; *U.S. Public*, pg. 1719
Vine-Lottt, Anthony K., Chm. Bd.--Barclays Bank Trust Co. Ltd., London, United Kingdom; *Int'l*, pg. 164
Vines, Roger A.G., Sir, Chm. Bd.--Alcoa of Australia Limited, Melbourne, Australia; *U.S. Public*, pg. 62
Vink, J.A.J., Dr., Chm. Bd.--CSM N.V., Diemen, Netherlands; *Int'l*, pg. 243
Vinsonneau, M., Chm. Bd. of Dirs.--Ciap S.A., Argenteuil, France; *Int'l*, pg. 994
Viort, Bernard, Chm. Bd.--Gie Amadeus France, Issy-les-Moulineaux, France; *Int'l*, pg. 560
Virtue, Robert A., Chm. Bd., Pres. & Chief Exec. Officer--Virco Mfg. Corporation, Torrance, CA; *U.S. Public*, pg. 1721
Viscusi, E., Chm.--AGIP Petroleum Co., Inc., Dover, DE; *Int'l*, pg. 428
Vitale, A., Chm. Bd.--Crown Publishers, Inc., New York, NY; *U.S. Private*, pg. 21
Vitale, Alberto, Chm. Bd. & Chief Exec. Officer--Random House, Inc., New York, NY; *U.S. Private*, pg. 20
Vitale, Deborah, Chm. Bd.--Europa Cruises Corporation, Saint Petersburg, FL; *U.S. Public*, pg. 595
Vitale, Jody, Chm. Bd. & Pres.--Perfect Fit Industries, Inc., Monroe, NC; *U.S. Private*, pg. 852
Vitito, Robert J., Chm. Bd.--Second National Bank of Saginaw, Saginaw, MI; *U.S. Public*, pg. 379
Vittadini, Adrienne, Chm. Bd.-Adrienne Vittadini Enterprises, Inc.--Marisa Christina Inc., New Hyde Park, NY; *U.S. Public*, pg. 1044
Vittorini, Carlo, Chm. Bd., Publisher, & Chief Exec. Officer--Parade Publications Inc., New York, NY; *U.S. Private*, pg. 20
Vittorini, Carlo, Chm. Bd., Publisher & Chief Exec. Officer--React Magazine, New York, NY; *U.S. Private*, pg. 20
Vituli, Alan, Chm. Bd. & Chief Exec. Officer--Carrols Corporation, Syracuse, NY; *U.S. Private*, pg. 216
Vitulli, Peter J., Chm. Bd. & Chief Exec. Officer--The O'Boise Corporation, Oak Brook, IL; *U.S. Private*, pg. 810
Vivian, H. Melvin, Jr., Chm. Bd.--Vivian Millworks, Forty Fort, PA; *U.S. Private*, pg. 1143
Vivier, John Mary, Chm. Bd.--L'Oreal Technique Professional Div., Brussels, Belgium; *Int'l*, pg. 819
Vivoni, Carlos, Chm. Bd.--Puerto Rico Tourism Company, San Juan, PR; *U.S. Private*, pg. 894
Vlachogiannis, Alexandros, Chm. Bd.--Olympic Aviation, Athens, Greece; *Int'l*, pg. 1004
Vlasic, Richard, Chm. Bd. & Pres.--O/E Automation, Inc., Troy, MI; *U.S. Private*, pg. 809
Vlasman, R.A.M., Chm. Bd.--Strothmann Brennereien G.m.b.H., Minden, Germany; *Int'l*, pg. 751
Vogel, Dieter H., Dr., Chm.- Exec. Bd.--Thyssen AG, Dusseldorf, Germany; *Int'l*, pg. 1387
Vogel, Dieter, Dr., Chm.-Supervisory Bd.--Bertelsmann AG, Gutersloh, Germany; *Int'l*, pg. 189
Vogl, Alexander J., Chm. Bd. & Chief Exec. Officer--Wilton Corporation, Palatine, IL; *U.S. Private*, pg. 1181
Vohs, Dennis V., Chm. Bd. & Chief Exec. Officer--Ross Systems, Inc., Atlanta, GA; *U.S. Public*, pg. 1406
Voigts, H.D., Chm.--First National Bank of Nambia LTD., Windhoek, Namibia; *Int'l*, pg. 487
von Braunmuhl, Hermann W., Dr., Chm.-Exec. Bd.--Delvag Luftfahrtversicherungs-AG, Cologne, Germany; *Int'l*, pg. 407
von Craushner, Joarg, Chm. Bd.--Wella Group, Darmstadt, Germany; *Int'l*, pg. 1489
Von der Ruhr, Garhard, Chm. Bd.--Immtech International, Inc., Evanston, IL; *U.S. Public*, pg. 459
Von der Ruhr, Gerhard J., Chm. Bd., Pres. & Treas.--Criticare Systems, Inc., Waukesha, WI; *U.S. Public*, pg. 459
Von Falkenhausen, Hasso, Dr., Chm. Bd.--DataCard Corporation, Minnetonka, MN; *U.S. Private*, pg. 312
von Freyberg, Karl Ludwig Freiherr, Chm. Bd. of Mngmt.--Frankfurter Versicherungs-AG, Frankfurt/Main, Germany; *Int'l*, pg. 58
von Gruenberg, Hubertus, Dr., Chm.-Exec. Bd.--Continental AG, Hannover, Germany; *Int'l*, pg. 327
von Haeften, Jan, Chm. Bd.--Franz Haniel & Cie, GmbH, Duisburg, Germany; *Int'l*, pg. 591
von Holtzbrinck, Dieter, Chm. Bd. & Pres.--Georg von Holtzbrinck GmbH, Stuttgart, Germany; *Int'l*, pg. 1478
von Matthiessen, Malte, Chm. Bd. & Chief Exec. Officer--YSI Incorporated, Yellow Springs, OH; *U.S. Private*, pg. 1195
von Rickenbach, Josef, Chm. Bd., Pres. & Chief Exec. Officer--PAREXEL International Corporation, Waltham, MA; *U.S. Public*, pg. 1257
von Schack, Wesley W., Chm. Bd., Pres. & Chief Exec. Officer--New York State Electric & Gas Corporation, Binghamton, NY; *U.S. Public*, pg. 1173
von Walderdorf, Hugo Graf, Chm.-Supv. Bd.--Rothenberger Group GmbH, Kelheim, Germany; *Int'l*, pg. 1127
Vonderschmitt, Bernard V., Chm. Bd.--Xilinx, Inc., San Jose, CA; *U.S. Public*, pg. 1786

Vorsten, Erwin G., Chm. Bd.--Jardine Davies Inc., Manila, Philippines; *Int'l*, pg. 705
Voss, Gary, Chm. Bd. & Mng. Dir.--Lever Brothers West Indies Ltd., Champs Fleurs, Trinidad & Tobago; *Int'l*, pg. 1437
Voss, Peter S., Chm. Bd.--Reich & Tang, New York, NY; *U.S. Private*, pg. 737
Voyer, Nil, Chm. Bd. & Pres.--Purdel, Cooperative Agro-Alimentaire, Bic, Canada; *Int'l*, pg. 1073
Vozick, David, Chm. Bd., Treas. & Sec.--AFP Imaging Corporation, Elmsford, NY; *U.S. Public*, pg. 6
Vozick, David, Chm. Bd.--LogEtronics Corporation, Springfield, VA; *U.S. Public*, pg. 6
Vreys, Frans, Chm.--Delimmo S.A., Brussels, Belgium; *Int'l*, pg. 463
Vrins, H.A.M., Chm.--Hoogovens Aluminium BV, Amstelveen, Netherlands; *Int'l*, pg. 753
Vukovich, Robert A., Ph.D., Chm. Bd.--Roberts Pharmaceutical Corporation, Eatontown, NJ; *U.S. Public, pg. 1393*
Vuursteen, Karel, Chm.-Exec. Bd.--Heineken N.V., Amsterdam, Netherlands; *Int'l*, pg. 608
Wachenhut, Richard R., Chm. Bd.--Wackenhut Resources, Inc., Palm Beach Gardens, FL; *U.S. Public*, pg. 1731
Wachner, Brian Gary, Chm. Bd. & Pres.--BGW Systems, Inc., Hawthorne, CA; *U.S. Private*, pg. 107
Wachner, Linda J., Chm. Bd. & Chief Exec. Officer--Authentic Fitness Corp., Los Angeles, CA; *U.S. Public*, pg. 147
Wachner, Linda J., Chm. Bd., Pres. & Chief Exec. Officer--Warnaco Inc., New York, NY; *U.S. Public*, pg. 1738
Wachs, Hartmut, Chm.--Rowenta Werke, Offenbach/Main, Germany; *Int'l*, pg. 569
Wackenhut, George, Chm. Bd.--Wackenhut Corrections Corporation, Palm Beach Gardens, FL; *U.S. Public*, pg. 1731
Wackenhut, George R., Chm. Bd. & Chief Exec. Officer--The Wackenhut Corporation, Palm Beach Gardens, FL; *U.S. Public*, pg. 1731
Wacker, Fred G., Jr., Chm. Bd.--Liquid Controls LLC, Lake Bluff, IL; *U.S. Private*, pg. 669
Waddell, G.H., Chm.--Shanks & McEwan Group Plc, Bourne, United Kingdom; *Int'l*, pg. 1228
Waddell, Robert F., Chm. Bd. & Chief Exec. Officer--Standard Locknut, Inc., Westfield, IN; *U.S. Private*, pg. 1031
Waechter, Klaus, Chm. Bd.--Frankfurter Sparkasse, Frankfurt, Germany; *Int'l*, pg. 504
Wagenhals, Fred W., Chm. Bd., Pres. & Chief Exec. Officer--Action Performance Companies, Inc., Phoenix, AZ; *U.S. Public*, pg. 17
Wagner, Cyril, Jr., Chm. Bd.--Insilco Corporation, Dublin, OH; *U.S. Public*, pg. 881
Wagner, David J., Chm. Bd., Pres. & Chief Exec. Officer--Old Kent Financial Corporation, Grand Rapids, MI; *U.S. Public*, pg. 1216
Wagner, Fernand, Chm. Bd.--Sidmar N.V., Gent, Belgium; *Int'l*, pg. 79
Wagner, Harold A., Chm. Bd., Pres. & Chief Exec. Officer--Air Products and Chemicals, Inc., Allentown, PA; *U.S. Public*, pg. 30
Wagner, N.P., Chm. Bd.--Southern Indiana Properties, Inc., Evansville, IN; *U.S. Public*, pg. 1471
Wagner, Reinhard, Chm. Bd.--BHW Bausparkasse AG, Hameln, Germany; *Int'l*, pg. 120
Wagrodzki, Kezysztof, Chm. Bd.--WWT (Wytwornia Wyrobow Tytoniowych) S.A., Poznan, Poland; *Int'l*, pg. 1101
Wagstaff, David, 111, 2res. & Chief Exec. Officer--Vectura Group, Inc., New Orleans, LA; *U.S. Private*, pg. 1135
Wahedna, Javeed, Chm. & Creative Dir.--Wahedna/DMB&B, Karachi, Pakistan; *U.S. Private*, pg. 305
Wahl, J. H., Chm. Bd.--FABC (New York) Grp., New York, NY; *Int'l*, pg. 163
Wahl, Michael, Chm. Bd., & Chief Exec. Officer--H.M.G. Worldwide Corp., New York, NY; *U.S. Public*, pg. 771
Wahle, John L., Jr., Chm. Bd. & Chief Exec. Officer--The Genesee Brewing Company, Inc., Rochester, NY; *U.S. Public*, pg. 728
Waike, Willi, Chm.-Supervisory Bd.--Norddeutsche Landesbank (NORD/LB), Hannover, Germany; *Int'l*, pg. 957
Wainshal, David, Chm. Bd.--American Israeli Paper Mills Ltd., Hadera, Israel; *Int'l*, pg. 74
Waitt, Ted, Chm. Bd. & Chief Exec. Officer--Gateway 2000, North Sioux City, SD; *U.S. Public*, pg. 703
Wakahara, Yasuyuki, Chm. Bd. & Chief Exec. Officer--Asahi Mutual Life Insurance Company, Tokyo, Japan; *Int'l*, pg. 85
Wakai, Tsuneo, Chm. Bd.--The Bank of Tokyo-Mitsubishi, Ltd., Tokyo, Japan; *Int'l*, pg. 157
Wakefield, G.H.C., Chm. Bd.--Guy Carpenter & Co., Inc, New York, NY; *U.S. Public*, pg. 1048
Wakeley, M.J., Chm. Bd. & Chief Exec. Officer--Jardine Insurance Brokers Ltd., London, United Kingdom; *Int'l*, pg. 705
Waksberg, Joseph, Chm. Bd.--Westat Inc., Rockville, MD; *U.S. Private*, pg. 1163
Walcher, Jack, Chm. Bd. & Chief Exec. Officer--Eddins-Walcher Company, Midland, TX; *U.S. Private*, pg. 362
Waldner, Stephen, Chm. Bd. & Chief Exec. Officer--D. Waldner Company, Inc., Farmingdale, NY; *U.S. Private*, pg. 1147
Waldorf, Robert, Chm. Bd. & Pres.--Idea Man, Inc., Los Angeles, CA; *U.S. Private*, pg. 557
Waldron, William G., Chm. Bd. & Chief Exec. Officer--J.E. Goold & Company, Portland, ME; *U.S. Public*, pg. 229
Waldrop, Thomas E., Chm. Bd. & Pres.--Media General Cable of Fairfax County Inc., Chantilly, VA; *U.S. Public*, pg. 1078
Waldschurz, Gerhard, Chm. Bd., Pres. & Chief Exec. Officer--Optimaxx International, Rockleigh, NJ; *U.S. Private*, pg. 818
Walentas, David C., Chm. Bd.--Builders Transport, Incorporated, Camden, SC; *U.S. Public*, pg. 267
Waley-Cohen, Stephen, Bt, Sir, Chm. Bd.--Willis Faber & Dumas (Agencies) Limited, London, United Kingdom; *Int'l*, pg. 1503
Walgreen, Charles R., III, Chm. Bd. & Chief Exec. Officer--Walgreen Co., Deerfield, IL; *U.S. Public*, pg. 1733
Walker, Claud B., Chm. Bd.--Fibrebond Corporation, Minden, LA; *U.S. Private*, pg. 402
Walker, Dean, Chm. Bd.--Alto Dairy Cooperative, Waupun, WI; *U.S. Private*, pg. 47
Walker, Felix, Dr., Chm. Bd.--Schweizer Verband der Raiffeisenbanken, Saint Gallen, Switzerland; *Int'l*, pg. 1211
Walker, George H., III, Chm. Bd.--Stifel Financial Corp., Saint Louis, MO; *U.S. Public*, pg. 1518
Walker, Guy, Chm.--Van den Bergh Foods Ltd., Crawley, United Kingdom; *Int'l*, pg. 1434
Walker, James D., Jr., Chm. Bd.--Capital Associates, Inc., Lakewood, CO; *U.S. Public*, pg. 302
Walker, John T., Chm. Bd., Pres. & Chief Exec. Officer--St. Paul Metalcraft, Inc., Saint Paul, MN; *U.S. Private*, pg. 961
Walker, Joseph P., Chm. Bd., Pres. & Chief Exec. Officer--CTS Corporation, Elkhart, IN; *U.S. Public*, pg. 285
Walker, K. Grahame, Chm. Bd. & Chief Exec. Officer--The Dexter Corporation, Windsor Locks, CT; *U.S. Public*, pg. 504
Walker, K. Grahame, Chm. Bd.--Life Technologies, Inc., Rockville, MD; *U.S. Public*, pg. 504
Walker, L. Dudley, Chm. Bd.--Bassett-Walker, Martinsville, VA; *U.S. Public*, pg. 1702
Walker, M.D., Chm. Bd.--Taysec Construction Limited, Accra, Ghana; *Int'l*, pg. 1359
Walker, Malcolm C., Chm. Bd. & Chief Exec. Officer--Iceland Group plc, Deeside, United Kingdom; *Int'l*, pg. 658
Walker, Martin J., Chm. Bd & Chief Exec. Officer--Society Asset Mgmt., Inc., Cleveland, OH; *U.S. Public*, pg. 955
Walker, Michael R., Chm. Bd. & Chief Exec. Officer--Genesis Health Ventures, Inc., Kennett Square, PA; *U.S. Public*, pg. 728
Walker, Robert H., Chm. Bd.--Walker Die Casting, Inc., Lewisburg, TN; *U.S. Private*, pg. 1147
Wall, Gloria, Chm. Bd.--Al Larson Boat Shop, Inc., Terminal Island, CA; *U.S. Private*, pg. 652
Wall, John E., Chm. Bd.--Demco Inc., Madison, WI; *U.S. Private*, pg. 323
Wall, Michael A., Chm. Bd.--Alkeremes, Cambridge, MA; *U.S. Public*, pg. 41
Wall, Terrence D., Chm. Bd., Pres. & Chief Exec. Officer--Vital Signs, Inc., Totowa, NJ; *U.S. Public*, pg. 1723
Wallace, David W., Chm. Bd.--Lone Star Industries, Inc., Stamford, CT; *U.S. Public*, pg. 1012
Wallace, Floyd, Chm. Bd.--Cooper Instrument Corp., Middlefield, CT; *U.S. Private*, pg. 274
Wallace, James B., Chm. Bd.--Grease Monkey International Inc., Denver, CO; *U.S. Public*, pg. 759
Wallace, John J., Chm. Bd.--Prab, Inc., Kalamazoo, MI; *U.S. Public*, pg. 1319
Wallace, Milton J., Chm. Bd.--Med/Waste, Inc., Hialeah, FL; *U.S. Public*, pg. 1077
Wallace, Milton J., Chm. Bd.--Renex Corp., Coral Gables, FL; *U.S. Public*, pg. 1377
Wallace, Timothy R., Chm.--Trinity Railcar Leasing, Dallas, TX; *U.S. Public*, pg. 1639
Wallace, W. Ray, Chm. Bd., Pres. & Chief Exec. Officer--Trinity Industries Inc., Dallas, TX; *U.S. Public*, pg. 1638
Wallach, Ira D., Chm. Bd.--Central National-Gottesman Inc., Purchase, NY; *U.S. Private*, pg. 224
Wallbridge, Van, Chm. Bd., Pres. & Chief Exec. Officer--Mobil Tool International, Westminster, CO; *Int'l*, pg. 1486
Wallenberg, Jacob, Chm. Bd.--Skandinaviska Enskilda Banken, Stockholm, Sweden; *Int'l*, pg. 1258
Wallenberg, Peter, Chm. Bd.--Investor AB, Stockholm, Sweden; *Int'l*, pg. 686
Waller, Frank S., Chm. Bd.--Woodward-Clyde Group, Inc., Denver, CO; *U.S. Public*, pg. 1655
Waller, Jim, Chm. Bd. & Chief Exec. Officer--Ithaca Industries, Inc., Wilkesboro, NC; *U.S. Private*, pg. 576
Waller, Joel N., Chm. Bd. & Chief Exec. Officer--Wilsons The Leather Experts Inc., Brooklyn Park, MN; *U.S. Private*, pg. 1181
Wallingford, Thomas R., Chm. Bd.--Trans Financial, Inc., Bowling Green, KY; *U.S. Public*, pg. 1628
Wallis, Norma, Chm. Bd.--Livernois Engineering Company, Dearborn, MI; *U.S. Private*, pg. 672
Wallis, S., Chm. Bd.--Scholl Plc, Newton, United Kingdom; *Int'l*, pg. 1209
Wallis, Stan D.M., Chm. Bd.--Amcor Limited, Melbourne, Australia; *Int'l*, pg. 71
Walls, Stephen, Chm. Bd.--The Albert Fisher Group PLC, Stoke Poges, United Kingdom; *Int'l*, pg. 491
Walmsley, Jerry T., Chm. Bd.--Oxarc Inc., Spokane, WA; *U.S. Private*, pg. 825
Walser, Robert J., Chm. Bd.--Walser Automotive Group, Bloomington, MN; *U.S. Private*, pg. 1148
Walsh, Gary, Chm. Bd.--Core-Mark International, South San Francisco, CA; *U.S. Private*, pg. 275
Walsh, L., Dr., Chm. Bd.--Dulmison Inc., Lawrenceville, GA; *Int'l*, pg. 893
Walsh, Mathew, Jr., Chm. Bd.--Walsh Construction Co. of Illinois, Chicago, IL; *U.S. Private*, pg. 1148
Walsh, Matthew, Jr., Chm. Bd.--Walsh Group, Chicago, IL; *U.S. Private*, pg. 1148
Walsh, Peter, Chm. Bd.--Premier Power Ltd., Antrim, United Kingdom; *Int'l*, pg. 119
Walsh, Steve, Co-Chm. Bd.--New York Islanders Hockey Club, Uniondale, NY; *U.S. Private*, pg. 794
Walsh, Steve, Chm. Bd. & Chief Exec. Officer--Signal Apparel Company, Inc., Chattanooga, TN; *U.S. Public*, pg. 1472
Walsh, T.W.N., Chm.--Ulster Bank (Isle of Man) Limited, Douglas, United Kingdom; *Int'l*, pg. 911
Walsh, William D., Chm. Bd.--Consolidated Freightways Corp., Menlo Park, CA; *U.S. Public*, pg. 435
Walshe, G., Chm.--Brother International (NZ) Limited, Petone, New Zealand; *Int'l*, pg. 229
Walske, Steven C., Chm. Bd.--Parametric Technology Corporation, Waltham, MA; *U.S. Public*, pg. 1257
Walter, Manfred, Chm. Bd. & Chief Exec. Officer--Traub-Hermle Corporation, Menomonee Falls, WI; *Int'l*, pg. 1419
Walter, Paul F., Chm. Bd., Pres. & Chief Exec. Officer--Thermo Electric Co., Inc., Saddle Brook, NJ; *U.S. Private*, pg. 1080
Walter, Reinhard, Dr., Chm. Exec. Bd.--B.U.S. Berzelius Umwelt-Service GmbH, Frankfurt/Main, Germany; *Int'l*, pg. 860
Walter, Richard A., Chm. Bd. & Chief Exec. Officer--Scicom Data Services, Ltd., Minnetonka, MN; *U.S. Private*, pg. 975
Walter, Robert D., Chm. Bd. & Chief Exec. Officer--Cardinal Health Inc., Dublin, OH; *U.S. Public*, pg. 304
Walters, Charles D., Chm. Bd. & Chief Exec. Officer--World Acceptance Corporation, Greenville, SC; *U.S. Public*, pg. 1778
Walters, Paul S., Chm. Bd. & Chief Exec. Officer--Sears Canada, Inc., Toronto, Canada; *U.S. Public*, pg. 1452
Walters, Peter, Sir, Chm. Bd.--SmithKline Beecham plc, Brentford, United Kingdom; *Int'l*, pg. 1264
Walters, Peter, Sir., Deputy Chm.-Non-Exec.--EMI Group plc, London, United Kingdom; *Int'l*, pg. 426
Walters, Roger A., Chm. Bd.--Harrison Paint Corp., Canton, OH; *U.S. Private*, pg. 506
Waltman, Howard L., Chm. Bd.--Express Scripts, Inc., Maryland Heights, MO; *U.S. Public*, pg. 600
Walton, James H., Chm. Bd. & Chief Exec. Officer--ITC Learning Corp., Herndon, VA; *U.S. Public*, pg. 859
Walton, R.O., Chm. Bd.--Crested Butte Mountain Resort, Inc., Crested Butte, CO; *U.S. Private*, pg. 289
Walton, S. Robson, Chm. Bd.--Wal-Mart Stores, Inc., Bentonville, AR; *U.S. Public*, pg. 1732
Walton, William, Chm. Bd. & Chief Exec. Officer--Allied Capital Corporation, Washington, DC; *U.S. Public*, pg. 47
Waltrip, Robert L., Chm. Bd. & Chief Exec. Officer--Service Corporation International, Houston, TX; *U.S. Public*, pg. 1460
Waltrip, William H., Chm. Bd.--Bausch & Lomb Incorporated, Rochester, NY; *U.S. Public*, pg. 194
Waltrip, William H., Chm.--Technology Solutions Company (TSC), Chicago, IL; *U.S. Public*, pg. 1564
Wampler, B.C., Chm. Bd.--Pulaski Furniture Corporation, Pulaski, VA; *U.S. Public*, pg. 1342
Wampler, Charles W., Jr., Chm. Bd.--WLR Foods, Inc., Timberville, VA; *U.S. Public*, pg. 1727
Wamser, Carl H., Chm. Bd.--Everbrite, Inc., Greenfield, WI; *U.S. Private*, pg. 386
Waney, Arjun C., Chm. Bd.--Niches, Inc., San Diego, CA; *U.S. Public*, pg. 1181
Wang, C.Y., Chm. Bd.--China Steel Corporation, Kao-hsiung, Taiwan; *Int'l*, pg. 285
Wang, Charles B., Chm. Bd. & Chief Exec. Officer--Computer Associates International, Inc., Islandia, NY; *U.S. Public*, pg. 420
Wang, Charles B., Chm. Bd. & Chief Exec. Officer--Cheyenne, Roslyn Heights, NY; *U.S. Public*, pg. 420
Wang, Charles B., Chm. Bd. & Chief Exec. Officer--ACCPAC International, Santa Clara, CA; *U.S. Public*, pg. 420
Wang, Charles B., Chm. Bd. & Chief Exec. Officer--Acacia Technologies, Lisle, IL; *U.S. Public*, pg. 420
Wang, Charles B., Chm. Bd. & Chief Exec. Officer--NetHaven, Islandia, NY; *U.S. Public*, pg. 420
Wang, Charles B., Chm. Bd. & Chief Exec. Officer--Computer Associates International, Inc., Islandia, NY; *U.S. Public*, pg. 420
Wang, Charles B., Chm. Bd. & Chief Exec. Officer--MK Group, Islandia, NY; *U.S. Public*, pg. 420
Wang, Charles B., Chm. Bd. & Chief Exec. Officer--Infresco Corporation, Sarasota, FL; *U.S. Public*, pg. 420
Wang, Herbert, Chm. Bd.--Tech Industries, Inc., Woonsocket, RI; *U.S. Private*, pg. 1071
Wang, Xuebing, Chm. Bd. & Pres.--Bank of China, Beijing, China; *Int'l*, pg. 152
Wang, Yungching, Chm. Bd.--Formosa Plastics Corporation, Kao-hsiung, Taiwan; *Int'l*, pg. 498
Wanjui, J.B., Chm.--Stanbic Bank Kenya Limited, Nairobi, Kenya; *Int'l*, pg. 1293
Wansbrough, J.C.C., Chm. Bd.--National Trustco Inc., Toronto, Canada; *Int'l*, pg. 909
Warburton, Richard, Chm. Bd.--David Jones Limited, Sydney, Australia; *Int'l*, pg. 714
Ward, G. William, Chm. Bd.--Ward Trucking Corp., Altoona, PA; *U.S. Private*, pg. 1149
Ward, Harold M., Dr., Chm. Bd.--Indian Rocks National Bank, Largo, FL; *U.S. Public*, pg. 608
Ward, John, Chm. Bd. & Chief Exec. Officer--American Express Bank Ltd., New York, NY; *U.S. Public*, pg. 73
Ward, Milton H., Chm. Bd., Pres. & Chief Exec. Officer--Cyprus Amax Minerals Company, Englewood, CO; *U.S. Public*, pg. 470
Ward, Milton H., Chm. Bd. & Chief Exec. Officer--Amax Gold Inc., Englewood, CO; *U.S. Public*, pg. 470
Ward, V. A., Chm. Bd.--NatWest Futures Limited, London, United Kingdom; *Int'l*, pg. 910
Ward, W.F., Jr., Chm. Bd.--The Ward Machinery Company, Hunt Valley, MD; *U.S. Private*, pg. 1149
Ward, William, Chm. Bd. & Pres.--Ashley F. Ward, Inc., Mason, OH; *U.S. Private*, pg. 1149
Wardeberg, George E., Chm. Bd. & Chief Exec. Officer--WICOR, Inc., Milwaukee, WI; *U.S. Public*, pg. 1767
Wardeberg, George E., Chm. Bd.--Shurflo Pump Manufacturing Co., Santa Ana, CA; *U.S. Public*, pg. 1767
Wardeberg, George E., Chm. Bd.--Hypro Corporation, New Brighton, MN; *U.S. Public*, pg. 1767
Warden, William G., III, Chm. Bd.--Superior Group, Inc., Radnor, PA; *U.S. Private*, pg. 1055

Wardrop, Richard, Chm. Bd., Pres. & Chief Exec. Officer--AK Steel Corporation, Middletown, OH; *U.S. Public,* pg. 7

Warehime, John A., Chm. Bd., Pres. & Chief Exec. Officer--Hanover Foods Corporation, Hanover, PA; *U.S. Private,* pg. 499

Warehime, Michael, Chm. Bd.--Snyder's of Hanover, Inc., Hanover, PA; *U.S. Private,* pg. 1011

Warm, Alexander D., Chm. Bd.--Warm Brothers Construction Company, Cincinnati, OH; *U.S. Private,* pg. 1150

Warner, Douglas A., III, Chm. Bd. & Chief Exec. Officer--J.P. Morgan Co. Incorporated, New York, NY; *U.S. Public,* pg. 1129

Warner, John W., Jr., Chm. Bd.--Gulf States Paper Corporation, Tuscaloosa, AL; *U.S. Private,* pg. 487

Warnock, John E., Chm. & Chief Exec. Officer--Adobe Systems Incorporated, San Jose, CA; *U.S. Public,* pg. 20

Warren, Everett, Chm. Bd. & Pres.--American Manufacturing Company, Chattanooga, TN; *U.S. Private,* pg. 58

Warren, J.R., Chm. Bd.--Compressor Systems, Inc., Midland, TX; *Int'l,* pg. 1027

Warren, John C., Chm. Bd., Pres. & Chief Exec. Officer--Washington Trust Bancorp, Inc., Westerly, RI; *U.S. Public,* pg. 1744

Warren, Michael P., Chm. Bd.--International Murex Technologies Corporation, Guelph, Canada; *Int'l,* pg. 684

Warren, Paul B., Chm. Bd. & Pres.--UVP, Inc., Upland, CA; *U.S. Private,* pg. 1115

Warrillow, James K., Chm. Bd.--Maclean Hunter Publishing Ltd., Toronto, Canada; *Int'l,* pg. 1123

Waruhiu, S.N., Chm. Bd.--Barclays Bank of Kenya Ltd., Nairobi, Kenya; *Int'l,* pg. 165

Washington, Dennis R., Chm. Bd.--Morrison Knudsen Corporation, Boise, ID; *U.S. Public,* pg. 1133

Washington, R. Peter, Chm. Bd. & Chief Exec. Officer--L & D Group, Aurora, IL; *U.S. Private,* pg. 638

Washington, R. Peter, Chm. Bd. & Chief Exec. Officer--Lyon Metal Products, Inc., Montgomery, IL; *U.S. Private,* pg. 638

Wasp, Tricia, Chm. Bd. & Pres.--Ronco Communications & Electronics Inc., Tonawanda, NY; *U.S. Private,* pg. 943

Wass, Tom, Chm. & Chief Exec. Officer--Tequila UK Ltd., London, United Kingdom; *Int'l,* pg. 118

Wasserstein, Bruce, Chm. Bd.--Wasserstein Perella Group, Inc., New York, NY; *Int'l,* pg. 956

Wassong, D.K., Chm. Bd., Pres. & Chief Exec. Officer--Sally Hansen, Farmingdale, NY; *U.S. Public,* pg. 494

Wassong, Dan K., Chm. Bd., Pres. & Chief Exec. Officer--Del Laboratories, Inc., Farmingdale, NY; *U.S. Public,* pg. 494

Watanabe, Eiji, Chm. Bd.--JGC Corporation, Tokyo, Japan; *Int'l,* pg. 697

Watanabe, Haruro, Chm. Bd. & Chief Exec. Officer--Marubeni America Corporation, New York, NY; *Int'l,* pg. 844

Watanabe, Hiroshi, Chm. Bd.--The Sanwa Bank Limited, Osaka, Japan; *Int'l,* pg. 1189

Watanabe, Hiroshi, Chm. Bd.--Tokyo Gas Co., Ltd., Tokyo, Japan; *Int'l,* pg. 1394

Watanabe, Tomoyoshi, Chm.--Brother Corporation (Asia) Ltd., Kowloon, Hong Kong; *Int'l,* pg. 229

Watase, Frank W., Chm. Bd.--Yum Yum Donut Shop, Inc., City of Industry, CA; *U.S. Private,* pg. 1203

Waterfield, Harry Lee II, Chm. Bd., Pres. & Chief Exec. Officer--Kentucky Investors, Inc., Frankfort, KY; *U.S. Public,* pg. 951

Waterhouse, Lawrence M., Jr., Chm. Bd.--Waterhouse Investor Services, New York, NY; *Int'l,* pg. 1401

Waters, Louis A., Chm. Bd.--Tyler Corporation, Dallas, TX; *U.S. Public,* pg. 1651

Waters, Warner S., Jr., Chm., Pres. & Chief Exec. Officer--Mellon Bank (DE) National Association, Wilmington, DE; *U.S. Public,* pg. 1085

Waterson, E.R., Chm.--Senior Engineering (Pty) Limited-South Africa, Vereeniging, South Africa; *Int'l,* pg. 1223

Wathen, Thomas, Chm. Bd.--Pinkerton's Inc., Encino, CA; *U.S. Public,* pg. 1296

Watkins, Dean A., Dr., Chm. Bd.--Watkins-Johnson Company, Palo Alto, CA; *U.S. Public,* pg. 1745

Watkins, Edward G., Chm. Bd., Pres. & Chief Exec. Officer--Simplex Time Recorder Co., Gardner, MA; *U.S. Private,* pg. 1002

Watkins, James H., Chm. Bd. & Chief Oper. Officer--ATCOM, Inc., Research Triangle Park, NC; *U.S. Private,* pg. 94

Watkins, Lee, Chm. Bd. & Chief Exec. Officer--SouthTrust Bank of Marion County, Hamilton, AL; *U.S. Public,* pg. 1492

Watkins, Robert G., Jr., Chm. Bd.--Watkins System Inc., Concordville, PA; *U.S. Private,* pg. 1153

Watkins, Ted, Pres.--McCrory Stores Div., York, PA; *U.S. Private,* pg. 721

Watsa, V. Prem, Chm. Bd. & Chief Exec. Officer--Fairfax Financial Holdings Limited, Toronto, Canada; *Int'l,* pg. 476

Watson, Chuck, Chm. Bd. & Chief Exec. Officer--NGC Corporation, Houston, TX; *U.S. Public,* pg. 1146

Watson, J.H., Chm., Pres. & Chief Exec. Officer--Confed Investment Counselling Limited, Toronto, Canada; *Int'l,* pg. 325

Watson, John C., Chm. Bd., Pres. & Chief Exec. Officer--NACOLAH Holding Corp. Inc., Chicago, IL; *U.S. Private,* pg. 963

Watson, Max P., Jr., Chm. Bd., Pres. & Chief Exec. Officer--BMC Software, Inc., Houston, TX; *U.S. Public,* pg. 162

Watt, Donald G., Chm. Bd.--The Watt Design Group Inc., Toronto, Canada; *Int'l,* pg. 338

Watt, James W., Pres.--Watt Publishing Co., Mount Morris, IL; *U.S. Private,* pg. 1154

Watt, Leslie A., Chm. Emeritus--Watt Publishing Co., Mount Morris, IL; *U.S. Private,* pg. 1154

Watt, Ronald W., Chm. & Chief Exec. Officer--Watt, Roop & Co., Cleveland, OH; *U.S. Private,* pg. 1154

Wattelet, Paul L., Chm. Bd. & Chief Exec. Officer--Sargent & Lundy, Chicago, IL; *U.S. Private,* pg. 965

Wax, Edward L., Chm.--Saatchi & Saatchi Advertising Worldwide, New York, NY; *U.S. Public,* pg. 1422

Waxman, Melvin, Chm. Bd. & Co-Chief Exec. Officer--Waxman Industries, Inc., Bedford, OH; *U.S. Public,* pg. 1748

Waxman, Melvin, Chm. Bd. & Co-Chief Exec. Officer--WOC Inc., Bedford, OH; *U.S. Public,* pg. 1748

Way, Alva O., Chm. Bd.--IBJ Schroder Bank & Trust Company, New York, NY; *Int'l,* pg. 674

Way, Charles D., Chm. Bd., Pres. & Chief Exec. Officer--Ryan's Family Steak Houses, Inc., Greer, SC; *U.S. Public,* pg. 1413

Way, Kenneth L., Chm. Bd. & Chief Exec. Officer--Lear Corporation, Southfield, MI; *U.S. Public,* pg. 981

Weaner, Frank A., Chm. Bd.--Paradise, Inc., Plant City, FL; *U.S. Public,* pg. 1256

Weatherby, Ed, Chm. Bd. & Pres.--Weatherby, Inc., Atascadero, CA; *U.S. Private,* pg. 1155

Weathersby, H.J., Sr. V.P.--Dunavant Enterprises, Inc., Memphis, TN; *U.S. Private,* pg. 346

Weatherup, Craig, Chm. Bd. & Chief Exec. Officer--Pepsi-Cola Company, Somers, NY; *U.S. Public,* pg. 1277

Weaver, J.C., Chm. Bd.--Aircraft of Canada Ltd., Calgary, Canada; *U.S. Public,* pg. 1365

Weaver, John C., Exec. V.P. & Chm. Bd. & Chief Exec. Officer-Raytheon Intl., Inc.--Raytheon Company, Lexington, MA; *U.S. Public,* pg. 1364

Weaver, Welcome I., Chm. Bd.--Weaver Popcorn Company, Inc., Van Buren, IN; *U.S. Private,* pg. 1156

Webb, Barrie P., Chm. & Chief Exec. Officer--R.P. Scherer Holdings Pty. Ltd., Braeside, Australia; *U.S. Public,* pg. 1438

Webb, George H., Chm. Bd., Pres. & Chief Exec. Officer--Jervis B. Webb Company, Farmington Hills, MI; *U.S. Private,* pg. 1156

Webb, Harley D., Chm. Bd. & Pres.--Webb Builders Hardware, Arlington, TX; *U.S. Private,* pg. 1156

Webb, J.S., Chm. Bd.--The Titan Corporation, San Diego, CA; *U.S. Public,* pg. 1618

Webb, Jervis C., Chm. Bd. Emeritus--Jervis B. Webb Company, Farmington Hills, MI; *U.S. Private,* pg. 1156

Webb, O. Glenn, Chm. Bd.--ADM/GROWMARK, Bloomington, IL; *U.S. Public,* pg. 128

Webb, O. Glenn, Chm. Bd.--Federal Farm Credit Banks Funding Corporation, Jersey City, NJ; *U.S. Private,* pg. 398

Webb, O. Glenn, Chm. Bd. & Pres.--Growmark, Inc., Bloomington, IL; *U.S. Private,* pg. 484

Webber, Randall M., Chm. Bd. & Chief Exec. Officer--Humphrey Products Company, Kalamazoo, MI; *U.S. Private,* pg. 547

Weber, Alfred, Chm. Bd., Pres. & Chief Exec. Officer--C&D Charter Power Systems, Blue Bell, PA; *U.S. Public,* pg. 271

Weber, Alfred, Chm. Bd., Pres. & Chief Exec. Officer--C & D Technologies, Inc., Blue Bell, PA; *U.S. Public,* pg. 272

Weber, Joseph A., Jr., Chm. Bd. Chief Exec. Officer--Weber Marking Systems, Inc., Arlington Heights, IL; *U.S. Private,* pg. 1157

Weber, Jurgen, Chm.-Exec. Bd. & Chief Exec. Officer--Deutsche Lufthansa AG, Cologne, Germany; *Int'l,* pg. 407

Weber, Larry, Chm. Bd. & Chief Exec. Officer--Drug Emporium of Arizona, Scottsdale, AZ; *U.S. Private,* pg. 343

Weber, Larry, Chm. & Chief Exec. Officer--Weber Public Relations Worldwide, Cambridge, MA; *U.S. Private,* pg. 1157

Weber, Robert, Chm. Bd.--Osmose Wood Preserving, Inc., Buffalo, NY; *U.S. Private,* pg. 821

Webster, Colin W., Chm. Bd.--International Paints (Canada) Ltd., Montreal, Canada; *Int'l,* pg. 339

Webster, David, Chm. Bd.--Safeway PLC, Hayes, United Kingdom; *Int'l,* pg. 1169

Webster, Elroy, Chm. Bd.--CENEX, Inc., Inver Grove Heights, MN; *U.S. Private,* pg. 221

Wechsler, Bradley J., Chm. Bd. & Co-Chief Exec. Officer--Imax Corporation, Mississauga, Canada; *Int'l,* pg. 661

Weeder, Charles E., Chm. Bd., Pres. & Chief Exec. Officer--Homes of Merit Inc., Bartow, FL; *U.S. Private,* pg. 537

Weeks, Charles R., Chm. Bd.--Citizens Banking Corporation, Flint, MI; *U.S. Public,* pg. 379

Weeks, Sinclair, Chm. Bd.--Reed & Barton Corporation, Taunton, MA; *U.S. Private,* pg. 916

Wegner, Arthur E., Exec. V.P., Chm. Bd. & Chief Exec. Officer-Raytheon Aircraft Co.--Raytheon Company, Lexington, MA; *U.S. Public,* pg. 1364

Wegner, Arthur E., Chm. Bd., Chief Exec. Officer & Sr. V.P.--Raytheon Aircraft Company, Wichita, KS; *U.S. Public,* pg. 1365

Wegner, Charles T., IV, Chm. Bd.--The Jel Sert Co., West Chicago, IL; *U.S. Private,* pg. 585

Wehle, John L., Jr., Chm. Bd. & Chief Exec. Officer--Genesee Corporation, Rochester, NY; *U.S. Public,* pg. 728

Wehrle, Gary, Chm. Bd. & Chief Exec. Officer--Pacific Crest Capital, Inc., Agoura Hills, CA; *U.S. Public,* pg. 1248

Wehrle, Henry B., Jr., Chm. Bd.--McJunkin Corporation, Charleston, WV; *U.S. Private,* pg. 722

Wehrli, Robert L., Chm. Bd.--Siliconix, Inc., Santa Clara, CA; *Int'l,* pg. 367

Weibel, Fred E., Jr., Chm. Bd., Pres. & Chief Exec. Officer--Weibel Winery, Lodi, CA; *U.S. Private,* pg. 1159

Weider, Joe, Chm. Emeritus--Weider Publications, Inc., Woodland Hills, CA; *U.S. Private,* pg. 1159

Weigandt, Fritz, Chm. Bd.--Tri-State Armature & Electric Works, Memphis, TN; *U.S. Private,* pg. 1100

Weigel, Dr. Hanns-Juergen, Chm. Bd.--Alte Leipziger Versicherung Aktiengesellschaft, Oberursel, Germany; *Int'l,* pg. 66

Weil, A. Lorne, Chm. Bd. & Chief Exec. Officer--Autotote Corporation, Newark, DE; *U.S. Public,* pg. 150

Weil, Robert, Chm. Bd.--Proventus AB, Stockholm, Sweden; *Int'l,* pg. 1072

Weil, Robert S., Sr., Chm. Bd. & Chief Exec. Officer--Weil Brothers Cotton Inc., Montgomery, AL; *U.S. Private,* pg. 1159

Weill, Sanford I., Chm. Bd. & Chief Exec. Officer--Travelers Group, New York, NY; *U.S. Public,* pg. 1632

Wein, Bernard J., Chm. Bd., Pres. & Chief Exec. Officer--Catherines Stores Corporation, Memphis, TN; *U.S. Public,* pg. 317

Weinbach, Lawrence A., Chm. & Chief Exec. Officer--Unisys Corporation, Blue Bell, PA; *U.S. Public,* pg. 1671

Weinberg, David A., Co-Chm. Bd.--Fel-Pro Incorporated, Skokie, IL; *U.S. Private,* pg. 399

Weinberg, Mark, Sir, Chm.--St. James's Place Capital plc., London, United Kingdom; *Int'l,* pg. 1177

Weinberg, Mark, Sir, Chm.--J. Rothschild Assurance Holdings, Gloucester, United Kingdom; *Int'l,* pg. 1178

Weinberg, Marsha, Chm. Bd.--Coast Grain Company, Inc., Ontario, CA; *U.S. Private,* pg. 248

Weinberg, Ronald, Chm. Bd.--Hawk Corp., Cleveland, OH; *U.S. Private,* pg. 511

Weinberg, Ronald, Chm. Bd.--The S.K. Wellman Friction Products Co., Brook Park, OH; *U.S. Private,* pg. 511

Weinberg, Serge, Chm.-Mngmt. Bd.--Pinault Printemps, Paris, France; *Int'l,* pg. 1057

Weinberger, Caspar W., Chm. Bd.--Forbes, Inc., New York, NY; *U.S. Private,* pg. 417

Weinberger, Paul, Co-Chm. & Creative Dir.--Lowe Howard-Spink, London, United Kingdom; *U.S. Private,* pg. 678

Weiner, David L., Chm. & Chief Exec. Officer--Marketing Support, Incorporated, Chicago, IL; *U.S. Private,* pg. 705

Weiner, Leon, Co-Chm. Bd.--Weiners Stores, Inc., Houston, TX; *U.S. Private,* pg. 1160

Weiner, Sol B., Co-Chm. Bd.--Weiners Stores, Inc., Houston, TX; *U.S. Private,* pg. 1160

Weiner, Walter H., Chm. Bd. & Chief Exec. Officer--Republic New York Corporation, New York, NY; *U.S. Public,* pg. 1380

Weinhardt, J.W., Chm. Bd. & Chief Exec. Officer--SJW Corp., San Jose, CA; *U.S. Public,* pg. 1418

Weinig, Dr. Sheldon, Chm. Bd.--Materials Research Corporation, Gilbert, AZ; *Int'l,* pg. 1283

Weinstein, Alvin, Chm. Bd.--Concord Fabrics Inc., New York, NY; *U.S. Public,* pg. 429

Weinstein, Bob, Co-Chm. Bd.--Miramax Films, Inc., New York, NY; *U.S. Public,* pg. 514

Weinstein, Gerald, Chm. Bd.--General Tools Mfg., Co. Inc., New York, NY; *U.S. Private,* pg. 445

Weinstein, Harvey, Co-Chm. Bd.--Miramax Films, Inc., New York, NY; *U.S. Public,* pg. 514

Weinstein, Harvey, Chm. Bd. & Treas.--West Mill Clothes, Inc., Woodside, NY; *U.S. Private,* pg. 1163

Weinstein, Howard J., Chm. Bd., Pres. & Chief Exec. Officer--Adams Wine Co., Atlanta, GA; *U.S. Private,* pg. 17

Weinstein, Ira P., Chm. Bd. & Acct. Exec.--Temkin & Temkin, Northbrook, IL; *U.S. Private,* pg. 1074

Weintraub, Allen, Chm. Bd. & Chief Exec. Officer--The Advest Group, Inc., Hartford, CT; *U.S. Public,* pg. 23

Weintraub, Allen, Chm. Bd. & Chief Exec. Officer--Advest, Inc., Hartford, CT; *U.S. Public,* pg. 23

Weir, Kevin, Chm. Bd.--Framesi USA, Inc./Roffler Industries, Inc./Casa di Colore, Inc., Coraopolis, PA; *U.S. Private,* pg. 419

Weir, Lord, Sir, Chm Bd.--BICC plc, London, United Kingdom; *Int'l,* pg. 120

Weir, Vicount, Chm. Bd.--Weir Group PLC, Glasgow, United Kingdom; *Int'l,* pg. 1488

Weirsoe, Steen, Chm.--Danisco Ingredients USA, Inc., New Century, KS; *Int'l,* pg. 378

Weis, Konrad M., Ph.D., Chm. Bd.--Bayer Corporation/Consumer Care Division, Morristown, NJ; *Int'l,* pg. 173

Weis, Robert F., Chm. Bd. & Treas.--Weis Markets, Inc., Sunbury, PA; *U.S. Public,* pg. 1751

Weisbach, Lou, Chm. Bd., Pres. & Chief Exec. Officer--Ha-Lo Industries, Inc., Niles, IL; *U.S. Public,* pg. 773

Weisberg, A.A., Chm. Bd. & Treas.--Technic Incorporated, Cranston, RI; *U.S. Private,* pg. 1071

Weisberg, Arthur, Chm. Bd.--State Electric Supply Co., Huntington, WV; *U.S. Private,* pg. 1036

Weisbrod, Carl B., Chm. Bd.--National Income Realty Trust, New York, NY; *U.S. Public,* pg. 1157

Weisel, Tom, Chm. Bd. & Chief Exec. Officer--NationsBank Montgomery Securities LLC, San Francisco, CA; *U.S. Public,* pg. 1162

Weisenburger, Randall, Co-Chm.--Collins & Aikman Corporation, Charlotte, NC; *U.S. Public,* pg. 399

Weisend, C. Frederick, Chm. Bd., Pres. & Chief Exec. Officer--Fritz Industries Inc., Mesquite, TX; *U.S. Private,* pg. 429

Weiser, Irving, Chm. Bd., Pres. & Chief Exec. Officer--Dain Rauscher Corporation, Minneapolis, MN; *U.S. Public,* pg. 476

Weiser, Ralph R., Chm. Bd.--International Recovery Corp., Miami Springs, FL; *U.S. Public,* pg. 906

Weiser, Sherwood M., Chm. Bd. & Chief Exec. Officer--Carnival Hotels & Casinos, Miami, FL; *U.S. Public,* pg. 1265

Weisfield, William M., Chm. Bd.--UTILX Corporation, Kent, WA; *U.S. Public,* pg. 1701

Weisiger, Ed, Sr., Chm. Bd.--Carolina Tractor & Equipment Co., Charlotte, NC; *U.S. Private,* pg. 214

Weiss, Bernard, Co-Chm. Bd. & Chief Exec. Officer--Signature Eyewear, Inc., Inglewood, CA; *U.S. Public,* pg. 1473

Weiss, David E., Chm. Bd., Pres. & Chief Exec. Officer--Storage Technology Corporation, Louisville, CO; *U.S. Public,* pg. 1522

Weiss, Heinrich, Chm.-Supervisory Bd.--Altana AG, Bad Homburg, Germany; *Int'l,* pg. 65

Weiss, Larry, Chm. Bd., Pres., Chief Exec. Officer & Sec.--Fresh Food, Inc., Hobart, IN; *U.S. Private,* pg. 427

Weiss, Morry, Chm. Bd. & Chief Exec. Officer--American Greetings Corporation, Cleveland, OH; *U.S. Public*, pg. 77
Weiss, Sam, Chm. Bd., Pres. & Chief Exec. Officer--United Receptical, Inc., Pottsville, PA; *U.S. Private*, pg. 1123
Weiss, Steven L., Chm.--Quest Futures Group, Inc., Naples, FL; *U.S. Public*, pg. 909
Weiss, Ulrich, Chm. Bd.--Continental AG, Hannover, Germany; *Int'l*, pg. 327
Weissberg, Ron, Chm. Bd.--I.L.D. Insurance Co. Ltd., Tel Aviv, Israel; *Int'l*, pg. 691
Weisshaar, Klaus, Chm.-Exec. Bd.--Friedrich Grohe Armaturenfabrik GmbH & Co., Hemer, Germany; *Int'l*, pg. 559
Weissman, Morris, Chm. Bd. & Chief Exec. Officer--American Banknote Corp., New York, NY; *U.S. Public*, pg. 68
Weissman, Robert E., Chm. Bd. & Chief Exec. Officer--Cognizant Corporation, Westport, CT; *U.S. Public*, pg. 395
Welch, Jerry R., Chm. Bd. & Chief Exec. Officer--Glacier Water Services Inc., Carlsbad, CA; *U.S. Public*, pg. 745
Welch, John F., Jr., Chm. Bd. & Chief Exec. Officer--General Electric Company, Fairfield, CT; *U.S. Public*, pg. 709
Welch, Joseph F., Chm. Bd., Pres. & Chief Exec. Officer--Bachman Company, Reading, PA; *U.S. Private*, pg. 109
Welch, Patrick, Chm. Bd. & Chief Exec. Officer--National Life Insurance Company, Montpelier, VT; *U.S. Private*, pg. 785
Welch, Patrick E., Chm. Bd., Pres. & Chief Exec. Officer--The Life Insurance Co. of Virginia, Richmond, VA; *U.S. Public*, pg. 712
Welch, Robin, Chm. Bd.--NYLIFE Administration Corp., Austin, TX; *U.S. Private*, pg. 795
Welka, Gene, Chm. Bd. & Chief Exec. Officer--Frozen Specialties, Inc., Archbold, OH; *U.S. Public*, pg. 378
Welkamp, Darwin L., Chm. Bd.--Valley American Bank, South Bend, IN; *U.S. Public*, pg. 674
Welke, Robert H., Chm. & Chief Creative Officer--EURO RSCG Tatham, Chicago, IL; *Int'l*, pg. 601
Wellek, Richard L., Chm. Bd. & Chief Exec. Officer--Varlen Corporation, Naperville, IL; *U.S. Public*, pg. 1710
Wellens, Leroy, Chm. Bd., Pres., Chief Exec. & Chief Fin. Officer & Treas.--Wellens & Co., Inc., Minneapolis, MN; *U.S. Private*, pg. 1161
Welles, D.K., Sr., Founder--Therma-Tru Corp., Maumee, OH; *U.S. Private*, pg. 1079
Wellesley-Wesley, Michael, Chm. Bd.--Chyron Corp., Melville, NY; *Int'l*, pg. 1372
Wells, Calvin B., Chm. Bd., Pres. & Chief Exec. Officer--North Carolina Natural Gas Corporation, Fayetteville, NC; *U.S. Public*, pg. 1194
Wells, J.M., Jr., Chm. Bd. & Chief Exec. Officer--The Homer Laughlin China Company, Newell, WV; *U.S. Private*, pg. 653
Wells, Mark, Chm. Bd. & Pres.--Case France S.A., Paris, France; *U.S. Public*, pg. 1579
Welsby, John, Chm. Bd. & Chief Exec. Officer--British Railways Board, London, United Kingdom; *Int'l*, pg. 220
Welter, Edward P., Chm. Bd.--Fabwel Inc., Elkhart, IN; *U.S. Private*, pg. 390
Welty, John, Chm. Bd., Pres. & Dir.-Mktg. & Adv.--Swensen's Ice Cream Co., Ronkonkoma, NY; *U.S. Public*, pg. 883
Wenaas, Eric P., Ph.D., Chm. Bd., Pres. & Chief Exec. Officer--Jaymark, Inc., San Diego, CA; *U.S. Private*, pg. 584
Wendel, W. Hall, Jr., Chm. Bd. & Chief Exec. Officer--Polaris Industries, Inc., Minneapolis, MN; *U.S. Public*, pg. 1313
Wender, Herbert, Chm. Bd.--CMAC Investment Corporation, Philadelphia, PA; *U.S. Public*, pg. 278
Wender, Herbert, Chm. Bd. & Chief Exec. Officer--Commonwealth Land Title Insurance Company, Philadelphia, PA; *U.S. Public*, pg. 1374
Wendlandt, Gary E., Chm. Bd.--Massmutual Corporate Investors, Springfield, MA; *U.S. Public*, pg. 1055
Wendt, Richard, Chm. Bd.--Jeld-Wen, Inc., Klamath Falls, OR; *U.S. Private*, pg. 585
Wenger, Jerry, Chm. Bd.--Wenger Corporation, Owatonna, MN; *U.S. Private*, pg. 1162
Wenger, Walter, Chm. Bd.--Coop Bern Oberland, Thun, Switzerland; *Int'l*, pg. 329
Wenninger, Walter, Dr., Chm. Bd.--Bayer Corporation, Pittsburgh, PA; *Int'l*, pg. 172
Wenzinger, Carl J., Jr., Chm. Bd.--Doron Precision Systems, Inc., Binghamton, NY; *U.S. Private*, pg. 341
Werhahn, Michael, Dr., Chm. Bd.--D.A. Stuart Company, Warrenville, IL; *U.S. Private*, pg. 1048
Werner, B.K., Chm. Bd. & Chief Exec. Officer--Safety National Casualty Corp., Saint Louis, MO; *U.S. Public*, pg. 496
Werner, Clarence L., Chm. Bd. & Chief Exec. Officer--Werner Enterprises, Inc., Omaha, NE; *U.S. Public*, pg. 1754
Werner, Jack S., Chm., Pres. & Chief Exec. Officer--Second National Bank of Bay City, Bay City, MI; *U.S. Public*, pg. 379
Werner, Seth, Co-Chm. & Chief Oper. Officer-Dallas--Publicis/Bloom Inc., New York, NY; *Int'l*, pg. 470
Werner, Tom, Co-Owner--Carsey-Werner Company, LLC, Studio City, CA; *U.S. Private*, pg. 216
Werra, Robert, Chm. Bd. & Chief Exec. Officer--Univesco Inc., Dallas, TX; *U.S. Private*, pg. 1128
Werries, E. Dean, Chm. Bd.--Sonic Corporation, Oklahoma City, OK; *U.S. Public*, pg. 1485
Wertz, Richard L., Chm. Bd. & Pres.--Amos-Hill Associates, Inc., Edinburgh, IN; *U.S. Private*, pg. 67
Wesley, Norman H., Chm. Bd. & Chief Exec. Officer--ACCO World Corporation, Lincolnshire, IL; *U.S. Public*, pg. 674
Wesley, Norman H., Chm. Bd. & Chief Exec. Officer--MasterBrand Industries, Inc., Lincolnshire, IL; *U.S. Public*, pg. 675
West, Alfred P., Jr., Chm. Bd. & Chief Exec. Officer--SEI Investments, Oaks, PA; *U.S. Public*, pg. 1417
West, Doyle D., Chm. Bd., Pres. & Chief Exec. Officer--Matrix Service Company, Tulsa, OK; *U.S. Public*, pg. 1057
West, G. Vincent, Chm. Bd.--West Building Materials, Atlanta, GA; *U.S. Private*, pg. 1163
West, Gary, Chm. Bd.--Valley National Gasses Inc., Wheeling, WV; *U.S. Private*, pg. 1132
West, John C., Chm. Bd.--The Seibels Bruce Group, Inc., Columbia, SC; *U.S. Public*, pg. 1453
West, John C., Chm. Bd.--Consolidated American Insurance Co., Columbia, SC; *U.S. Public*, pg. 1454
West, John C., Chm. Bd.--Catawba Insurance Co., Columbia, SC; *U.S. Public*, pg. 1454
West, John C., Chm. Bd.--Investors National Life Insurance Co., Columbia, SC; *U.S. Public*, pg. 1454
West, John C., Chm. Bd.--Kentucky Insurance Co., Louisville, KY; *U.S. Public*, pg. 1454
West, John C., Chm. Bd.--Forest Lake Travel Service, Inc., Columbia, SC; *U.S. Public*, pg. 1454
West, Neil S., Chm. Bd.--Stone Fort National Bank, Nacogdoches, Nacogdoches, TX; *U.S. Public*, pg. 630
West, Neil S., Chm. Bd. & Chief Exec. Officer--Tyler Bank & Trust, Tyler, TX; *U.S. Public*, pg. 630
West, Richard E., Chm. Bd. & Chief Exec. Officer--D & N Mortgage Corporation, Hancock, MI; *U.S. Public*, pg. 472
West, Robert H., Chm. Bd. & Chief Exec. Officer--Butler Manufacturing Company, Kansas City, MO; *U.S. Public*, pg. 271
West, Rowland L., Chm. Bd.--United Missouri Bank of Warrensburg, Warrensburg, MO; *U.S. Public*, pg. 1655
West, Sally, Chm. Bd.--Preservative Paint Company, Seattle, WA; *U.S. Private*, pg. 613
West, Thomas L., Jr., Chm. Bd. & Chief Exec. Officer--Western National Corporation, Houston, TX; *U.S. Public*, pg. 76
West, William G., Chm. Bd. & Pres.--Stanchem Inc., East Berlin, CT; *U.S. Private*, pg. 1030
West, William H., Dr., Chm. Bd.--Response Oncology, Inc., Memphis, TN; *U.S. Public*, pg. 1449
Westdijk, N.J., Chm.-Exec. Bd.--Royal Pakhoed NV, Rotterdam, Netherlands; *Int'l*, pg. 1147
Westdyk, N. J., Chm. Bd.--Furness BV, Rotterdam, Netherlands; *Int'l*, pg. 530
Westerbeke, John H., Jr., Chm. Bd. & Pres.--Westerbeke Corporation, Avon, MA; *U.S. Public*, pg. 1757
Westerberg, Bengt, Chm. Bd.--Telia AB, Farsta, Sweden; *Int'l*, pg. 1373
Westerberg, John R., Chm. Bd. & Chief Exec. Officer--Nelson Westerberg, Inc., Elk Grove Village, IL; *U.S. Private*, pg. 1163
Westerberg, John R., Chm. Bd. & Chief Exec. Officer--Nelson Westerberg International Inc., Elk Grove Village, IL; *U.S. Private*, pg. 1164
Westerberg, John R., Chm. Bd. & Chief Exec. Officer--Commercial Record Center, Elk Grove Village, IL; *U.S. Private*, pg. 1164
Westerboe, Lage, Chm. Bd.--Norske Skogindustrier A.S, Skogn, Norway; *Int'l*, pg. 965
Westerfeld, William A., Chm. Bd., Pres., Chief Exec. Officer & Treas.--The Westerfelds, Inc., Pittsford, NY; *U.S. Private*, pg. 1164
Westin, Richard S., Chm. Bd. & Chief Exec. Officer--Westin, Inc., Omaha, NE; *U.S. Private*, pg. 1169
Westlie, Charles, Chm. Bd.--Westlie Motor Company, Minot, ND; *U.S. Private*, pg. 1169
Weston, Christopher J., Chm. Bd. & Pres.--Phillips Fine Art Auctioneers, New York, NY; *U.S. Private*, pg. 861
Weston, Donald E., Chm. Bd.--Gradison Division, Cincinnati, OH; *U.S. Public*, pg. 1068
Weston, G.H., Chm. Bd.--Associated British Foods plc, London, United Kingdom; *Int'l*, pg. 92
Weston, Garry H., Chm. Bd.--Fortnum & Mason PLC, London, United Kingdom; *Int'l*, pg. 500
Weston, Josh S., Chm. Bd.--Automatic Data Processing, Inc., Roseland, NJ; *U.S. Public*, pg. 150
Weston, Roger L., Chm. Bd., Pres. & Chief Exec. Officer--GreatBanc, Inc., Aurora, IL; *U.S. Public*, pg. 760
Weston, W. Galen, Chm. Bd.--George Weston Limited, Toronto, Canada; *Int'l*, pg. 1494
Westrick, George A., Chm. Bd.--Sangamon Industries, Taylorville, IL; *U.S. Private*, pg. 965
Wexler, Lewis P., Chm. Bd., Pres., Chief Exec. Officer & Chief Oper. Officer--Free Service Tire Company, Inc., Johnson City, TN; *U.S. Private*, pg. 425
Wexner, Leslie H., Chm. Bd.--The Limited, Inc., Columbus, OH; *U.S. Public*, pg. 995
Wexner, Leslie H., Chm. Bd.--Victoria's Secret Stores, Reynoldsburg, OH; *U.S. Public*, pg. 995
Weyerhaeuser, George H., Chm. Bd.--Weyerhaeuser Company, Federal Way, WA; *U.S. Public*, pg. 1764
Weyers, Larry L., Chm. Bd., Pres. & Chief Exec. Officer--WPS Resources Corp., Green Bay, WI; *U.S. Public*, pg. 1728
Weyers, Larry L., Chm. Bd. & Chief Exec. Officer--Wisconsin Public Service Corporation, Green Bay, WI; *U.S. Public*, pg. 1728
Weyforth, Frank G., Jr., Chm. Bd., Pres. & Chief Exec. Officer--MRA, An Integrated Marketing Communications Agency, Overland Park, KS; *U.S. Private*, pg. 687
Weymuller, Bruno, Chm. Bd. & Pres.--Elf Aquitaine, Inc., New York, NY; *Int'l*, pg. 445
Whalen, John D., Chm. Bd.--Pennsylvania Crusher Corp., Broomall, PA; *U.S. Private*, pg. 850
Whaling, George, Chm. Bd.--Petty Company, Inc., Effingham, IL; *U.S. Private*, pg. 860
Whalley, Jeff, Chm.--FKI Plc, Halifax, United Kingdom; *Int'l*, pg. 471
Wheat, Allen D., Chm. Bd., Pres. & Chief Exec. Officer--Credit Suisse First Boston, Inc., New York, NY; *Int'l*, pg. 345
Wheeler, Dennis E., Chm., Pres. & Chief Exec. Officer--Coeur D'Alene Mines Corporation, Coeur D'Alene, ID; *U.S. Public*, pg. 394
Wheeler, Harry B., Chm. & Chief Exec. Officer--Cabre Exploration Ltd., Calgary, Canada; *Int'l*, pg. 247
Wheeler, R.C.P., Chm. Bd.--J. Jarvis & Sons P.L.C., London, United Kingdom; *Int'l*, pg. 705
Wheeler, Thomas B., Chm. Bd. & Chief Exec. Officer--Massachusetts Mutual Life Insurance Co., Springfield, MA; *U.S. Private*, pg. 712
Whelan, Denis, Chm. Bd.--Rentokil Initial USA, Atlanta, GA; *Int'l*, pg. 1286
Whelan, William N., Chm. Bd.--Spaulding & Slye, Boston, MA; *U.S. Private*, pg. 1021
Whitacre, Edward E., Jr., Chm. Bd. & Chief Exec. Officer--SBC Communications Inc., San Antonio, TX; *U.S. Public*, pg. 1415
Whitacre, John J., Chm. Bd.--Nordstrom, Inc., Seattle, WA; *U.S. Public*, pg. 1190
White, Art, Chm. Bd.--Rite-Hite Corporation (WI), Milwaukee, WI; *U.S. Private*, pg. 933
White, Arthur K., Chm. Bd.--Rite-Hite Corporation, Milwaukee, WI; *U.S. Private*, pg. 933
White, Carter H., Chm. Bd.--The Record-Journal Publishing Company, Meriden, CT; *U.S. Private*, pg. 914
White, Charles W., Chm. Bd.--NewTel Enterprises Limited, Saint Johns, Canada; *Int'l*, pg. 115
White, Edward A., Chm. Bd.--Bowmar Instrument Corporation, Phoenix, AZ; *U.S. Public*, pg. 248
White, Guillermo Canedo, Chm. & Chief Corp. Officer--Grupo Televisa, S.A. de C.V., Mexico, Mexico; *Int'l*, pg. 576
White, John C., Chm. Bd.--Brunswick Mining & Smelting Corp. Ltd., Bathurst, Canada; *Int'l*, pg. 434
White, John F., Chm. Bd., Pres. & Chief Exec. Officer--Haemonetics Corporation, Braintree, MA; *U.S. Public*, pg. 773
White, John H., Sr., Chm. Bd.--Taco Incorporated, Cranston, RI; *U.S. Private*, pg. 1066
White, Lawrence D., Chm. Bd., Pres., & Chief Exec. Officer--Menley & James Laboratories, Inc., Horsham, PA; *U.S. Public*, pg. 1086
White, Lord, KBE, Chm. Bd.--Hanson North America, Woodbridge, NJ; *Int'l*, pg. 593
White, Peter G., Chm. Bd.--Unimedia Inc., Montreal, Canada; *Int'l*, pg. 632
White, Phillip E., Chm. Bd.--Informix Software, Menlo Park, CA; *U.S. Public*, pg. 876
White, Randall W., Chm. Bd., Pres. & Treas.--Educational Development Corporation, Tulsa, OK; *U.S. Public*, pg. 564
White, Richard, Chm. Bd.--Premier Investment Advisors, L.C., New Orleans, LA; *U.S. Public*, pg. 173
White, Robert G., Chm. Bd.--New England Frozen Foods, Inc., Southborough, MA; *U.S. Private*, pg. 793
White, Stuart, Chm. Bd.--Cogsdill Tool Products, Inc., Lugoff, SC; *U.S. Private*, pg. 250
White, Tom, Chm. Bd. & Chief Exec. Officer--Enron Operations Corp., Houston, TX; *U.S. Public*, pg. 584
White, Tony L., Chm. Bd., Pres. & Chief Exec. Officer--The Perkin-Elmer Corporation, Norwalk, CT; *U.S. Public*, pg. 1279
White, Tony L., Chm. Bd., Pres. & Chief Exec. Officer--Applied Biosystems, Foster City, CA; *U.S. Public*, pg. 1279
White, Victoria, Chm. Bd. & Co-Chief Exec. Officer--Tork, Inc., Mount Vernon, NY; *U.S. Private*, pg. 1092
White, William J., Chm. Bd.--Bell & Howell Holdings, Skokie, IL; *U.S. Public*, pg. 201
White, William S., Chm. Bd.--United States Sugar Corporation, Clewiston, FL; *U.S. Private*, pg. 1126
White, Willis S., Chm. Bd.--Battelle Memorial Institute, Columbus, OH; *U.S. Private*, pg. 123
Whiteley, B.R., Chm. Bd.--Standard Insurance Co., Portland, OR; *U.S. Private*, pg. 1031
Whiteman, John O., Chm. Bd. & Chief Exec. Officer--Empire Southwest Co., Mesa, AZ; *U.S. Private*, pg. 374
Whitescarver, William A., Chm. Bd.--McCain Bindery Systems, Inc., Chicago, IL; *U.S. Private*, pg. 719
Whitfield, L.B., III, Chm. Bd.--Whitfield Foods, Inc., Montgomery, AL; *U.S. Private*, pg. 1173
Whiting, A. Milton, Chm. Bd. & Chief Exec. Officer--Kaibab Industries, Phoenix, AZ; *U.S. Private*, pg. 605
Whitley, Michael R., Chm. Bd., Pres. & Chief Exec. Officer--Kentucky Utilities Company, Lexington, KY; *U.S. Public*, pg. 941
Whitman, Christine, Chm. Bd., Pres. & Chief Exec. Officer--CVC Products, Inc., Rochester, NY; *U.S. Private*, pg. 197
Whitman, Martin J., Chm. Bd. & Chief Exec. & Investment Officer--Danielson Holding Corporation, New York, NY; *U.S. Public*, pg. 483
Whitman, William F., Jr., Chm. Bd.--The Middleby Corporation, Rolling Meadows, IL; *U.S. Public*, pg. 1109
Whitmire, J.L., Chm. Bd. & Chief Exec. Officer--Union Texas Petroleum Holdings, Houston, TX; *U.S. Public*, pg. 1669
Whitney, Dickson L., Sr., Chm. Bd.--McGean-Rohco, Inc., Cleveland, OH; *U.S. Private*, pg. 721
Whitney, H.N., Chm. Bd.--Colonial Pipeline Company, Atlanta, GA; *U.S. Private*, pg. 254
Whitney, John K., Chm. Bd.--Gaymar Industries, Inc., Orchard Park, NY; *U.S. Private*, pg. 442
Whitney, Michael, Chm. Bd., Pres. & Chief Exec. Officer--Fleet Bank-NH, Nashua, NH; *U.S. Public*, pg. 649
Whitney, Michael C., Jr., Chm. Bd., Pres. & Chief Exec. Officer--Fleet Bank NH, Manchester, NH; *U.S. Public*, pg. 649
Whitsell, Helen J., Chm. Bd., Chief Exec. Officer & Treas.--Copeland Lumber Yard, Inc., Portland, OR; *U.S. Private*, pg. 274
Whittle, John J., Chm. Bd., Pres. & Chief Exec. Officer--Farmers and Traders Life Insurance Co., Syracuse, NY; *U.S. Private*, pg. 394

Whitwam, David R., Chm. Bd. & Chief Exec. Officer--Whirlpool Corporation, Benton Harbor, MI; *U.S. Public*, pg. 1764
Whyte, George C., Jr., Chm. Bd., Pres. & Chief Exec. Officer--Dakotah, Inc., Webster, SD; *U.S. Public*, pg. 477
Whyte, R., Chm.--Fortune Communication Holdings Ltd., Sydney, Australia; *Int'l*, pg. 500
Wichelow, P.A., Chm. Bd.--Robert Fleming Management Services Limited, London, United Kingdom; *Int'l*, pg. 493
Wick, John F., Chm. Bd.--Wick Building Systems, Mazomanie, WI; *U.S. Private*, pg. 1174
Wickersham, Lysle, Chm. & Chief Creative Officer--Wickersham Hunt Schwantner, Boston, MA; *U.S. Private, pg. 84*
Wicki, Hans, Chm. Bd.--Coop Switzerland, Basel, Switzerland; *Int'l*, pg. 329
Wickland, John A. III, Chm. Bd.--Wickland Corporation, Sacramento, CA; *U.S. Private*, pg. 1174
Widdrington, Peter N.T., Chm. Bd.--Talisman Energy Inc., Calgary, Canada; *Int'l*, pg. 1352
Widmer, Hans, Dr., Chm. Bd., Pres., Chief Exec. & Oper. Officer--Oerlikon-Buhrle Holding AG, Zurich, Switzerland; *Int'l*, pg. 996
Wiedeking, Wendelin, Chm. Bd. of Porsche AG-Germany--Porsche Cars North America, Inc., Reno, NV; *Int'l*, pg. 1063
Wiedemann, George S., Chm. & Chief Exec. Officer--Grey Direct, New York, NY; *U.S. Public*, pg. 764
Wiedenbeck, Roger D., Chm. Bd.--The Johnson Corporation, Three Rivers, MI; *U.S. Private*, pg. 591
Wiedenhaupt, Kurt, Chm. Bd. & Pres.--American Precision Industries Inc., Buffalo, NY; *U.S. Public*, pg. 90
Wiedenhues, Heribert J., Chm. Bd.--Krupp Fordertechnik GmbH, Duisburg, Germany; *Int'l*, pg. 511
Wiedmann, Bernd, Chm. Bd.--ZF Friedrichshafen A.G., Friedrichshafen, Germany; *Int'l*, pg. 1522
Wiegand, Bruce, Chm. Bd.--T.W. Phillips Gas and Oil Co., Butler, PA; *U.S. Private*, pg. 862
Wiegandt, Klaus, Co-Chm.--Metro AG, Cologne, Germany; *Int'l*, pg. 863
Wieland, Eckart, Chm.--Flender-Himmelwerk GmbH, Tubingen, Germany; *Int'l*, pg. 400
Wieland, John F., Chm. Bd., Pres. & Chief Exec. Officer--John Wieland Homes Inc., Atlanta, GA; *U.S. Private*, pg. 1175
Wiemers, Norbert, Dr., Chm.-Supervisory Bd.--Rohm GmbH, Darmstadt, Germany; *Int'l*, pg. 1454
Wiener, Louis, Chm. Bd.--Lone Star Equities Inc., Lynbrook, NY; *U.S. Private*, pg. 674
Wiese-Hansen, Torre, Chm. Bd.--Air Products A/S-Gardner Cryogenics Div., Kristiansand, Norway; *U.S. Public*, pg. 31
Wiesner, John J., Chm. Bd. & Chief Exec. Officer--C.R. Anthony Company, Oklahoma City, OK; *U.S. Private*, pg. 1029
Wietecki, Keith H., Chm.-Cenerprise Unit--Northern States Power Company, Minneapolis, MN; *U.S. Public*, pg. 1195
Wiethoff, E., Chm. Bd.--Copeland Corporation Ltd., Thatcham, United Kingdom; *U.S. Public*, pg. 576
Wigdale, J.B., Chm. Bd. & Chief Exec. Officer--Marshall & Ilsley Corporation, Milwaukee, WI; *U.S. Public*, pg. 1049
Wigdale, J.B., Chm. Bd. & Chief Exec. Officer--M & I Marshall & Ilsley Bank, Milwaukee, WI; *U.S. Public*, pg. 1050
Wiggin, Blanton C., Chm. Bd.--Advanced Instruments, Inc., Norwood, MA; *U.S. Private*, pg. 22
Wiggins, Robert S., Chm. Bd., Chief Exec. Officer & Sec.--Technology Research Corporation, Clearwater, FL; *U.S. Public*, pg. 1564
Wiggins, Stephen F., Chm. Bd.--Oxford Health Plans Inc., Norwalk, CT; *U.S. Public*, pg. 1238
Wight, Robin, Chm. Bd.--WCRS, London, United Kingdom; *Int'l*, pg. 603
Wigley, Robert J., Chm. Bd.--Great Plains Companies, Inc., Roseville, MN; *U.S. Private*, pg. 475
Wikander, Sten, Chm. Bd.--Celsius AB, Stockholm, Sweden; *Int'l*, pg. 276
Wikerson, Kenneth L., Chm.--Foley's, Houston, TX; *U.S. Public*, pg. 1063
Wiking, Gosta, Chm. Bd.--Perstorp AB, Perstorp, Sweden; *Int'l*, pg. 1036
Wikman, Ulf, Chm. Bd.--Morgardshammar AB, Smedjebacken, Sweden; *Int'l*, pg. 378
Wilcock, James W., Chm. Bd.--L.B. Foster Company, Pittsburgh, PA; *U.S. Public*, pg. 675
Wild, Floyd, Chm. Bd. & Pres.--Lyon County Co-op Oil Co., Marshall, MN; *U.S. Private*, pg. 684
Wildauer, Werner K., Chm. Bd. & Pres.--Leupold & Stevens, Inc., Beaverton, OR; *U.S. Private*, pg. 662
Wilder, Duane, Chm. Bd., Pres. & Treas.--Wilder Deem, Inc., New York, NY; *U.S. Private*, pg. 1176
Wilder, Susan P., Chm. Bd.--Sealing Equipment Products Co., Inc., Pelham, AL; *U.S. Private*, pg. 978
Wilding, Ernest L., Chm. Bd., Pres. & Chief Exec. Officer--Spray-Tech, Inc., Longwood, FL; *U.S. Private*, pg. 1026
Wildman, Donald C., Chm. Bd.--Scoville Press, Inc., Minneapolis, MN; *U.S. Private*, pg. 977
Wildrick, Robert N., Chm. Bd., Pres. & Chief Exec. Officer--Venture Stores, Inc., O Fallon, MO; *U.S. Public*, pg. 1716
Wilensky, Alvin, Chm. Bd.--CV Reit, Inc., West Palm Beach, FL; *U.S. Public*, pg. 286
Wiley, Bradford, II, Chm. Bd.--John Wiley & Sons, Inc., New York, NY; *U.S. Public*, pg. 1768
Wilhelm, Marcus, Chm. Bd., Chief Exec. Officer & Chief Oper. Officer--Doubleday Direct, Garden City, NY; *Int'l*, pg. 191
Wilk, John J., Chm. Bd. & Treas.--TransNet Corporation, Somerville, NJ; *U.S. Public*, pg. 1631
Wilkerson, L. John, Chm. Bd.--Vencare, Incorporated, Alpharetta, GA; *U.S. Public*, pg. 1715
Wilkie, M.L., Chm. Bd.--Continental Machines, Inc., Savage, MN; *U.S. Private*, pg. 268
Wilkie, Michael L., Chm. Bd., Pres., Chief Exec. & Chief Oper. Officer--DOALL Company, Des Plaines, IL; *U.S. Private*, pg. 337
Wilkinson, Bruce W., Chm. Bd. & Chief Exec. Officer--CRSS Inc., Houston, TX; *Int'l*, pg. 1415
Wilkinson, Eugene R., Chm. Bd., Pres., & Chief Exec. Officer--Hanson Engineers Inc., Springfield, IL; *U.S. Private*, pg. 500
Wilkinson, Frank S., Jr., Chm. Bd. & Chief Exec. Officer--E.W. Blanch Capital Risk Solutions, Inc., Minneapolis, MN; *U.S. Public*, pg. 236
Wilkinson, Michael, Chm. Bd. & Pres.--DSC Ltd., Trenton, MI; *U.S. Private*, pg. 305
Wilkinson, Paul, Chm. Bd.--Ranks Hovis McDougall Limited, Marlow, United Kingdom; *Int'l*, pg. 1395
Wilkinson, Trevor S., Chm. Bd.--Butler Lutos Sutton Wilkinson, London, United Kingdom; *Int'l*, pg. 237
Will, James F., Chm. Bd., Pres. & Chief Exec. Officer--Armco Inc., Pittsburgh, PA; *U.S. Public*, pg. 131
Willard, Larry, Chm. & Pres.--Norwest Bank New Mexico, N.A., Albuquerque, NM; *U.S. Public*, pg. 1202
Willert, August W., Jr., Chm. Bd. & Treas.--Willert Home Products, Inc., Saint Louis, MO; *U.S. Private*, pg. 1177
Willes, Mark, Chm. Bd., Pres. & Chief Exec. Officer--The Times Mirror Company, Los Angeles, CA; *U.S. Public*, pg. 1615
Willet, Richard H., Chm. Bd., Pres. & Chief Exec. Officer--Consoltex Group Inc., Ville Saint Laurent, Canada; *Int'l*, pg. 326
Williams, Andrew W., Chm. Bd. & Chief Exec. Officer--Florafax International, Inc., Vero Beach, FL; *U.S. Public*, pg. 654
Williams, Barry, Chm.--Kinney Shoe Corporation, New York, NY; *U.S. Public*, pg. 1777
Williams, Byron, Co-Chm. Bd. & Sec.--Clayton, Williams & Sherwood, Inc., Newport Beach, CA; *U.S. Private*, pg. 245
Williams, Clarke M., Chm. Bd.--Century Telephone Enterprises, Inc., Monroe, LA; *U.S. Public*, pg. 329
Williams, David F., Chm.--The W.W. Williams Company, Columbus, OH; *U.S. Private*, pg. 1178
Williams, Don, Chm. Bd.--Trammell Crow Company, Dallas, TX; *U.S. Public*, pg. 1628
Williams, Don E., Chm. Bd.--Don E. Williams Co., Rock Island, IL; *U.S. Private*, pg. 1177
Williams, Donald, Chm. Bd. & Chief Exec. Officer--First Banks, Inc., Sacramento, CA; *U.S. Public*, pg. 626
Williams, F. Everett, Chm. Bd.--Sea Island Bank, Statesboro, GA; *U.S. Public*, pg. 1549
Williams, Francis M., Chm. Bd., Pres. & Chief Exec. Officer--Kimmins Corp., Tampa, FL; *U.S. Public*, pg. 960
Williams, Frank E., III, Chm. Bd., Pres. & Chief Exec. Officer--Williams Industries, Inc., Falls Church, VA; *U.S. Public*, pg. 1769
Williams, George C., Chm. Bd.--Allied Capital Financial Corporation, Washington, DC; *U.S. Public*, pg. 48
Williams, Glenn, Chm. Bd. & Pres.--Heritage Co-op, Rushville, IN; *U.S. Private*, pg. 524
Williams, Gretchen, Co-Chm. Bd.--Minyard Food Stores, Inc., Coppell, TX; *U.S. Private*, pg. 752
Williams, Harmon C., Jr., Chm. Bd.--United Dominion Realty Trust, Inc., Richmond, VA; *U.S. Public*, pg. 1677
Williams, J. Kelley, Chm. Bd. & Chief Exec. Officer--ChemFirst Inc., Jackson, MS; *U.S. Public*, pg. 344
Williams, James E., Chm. Bd. & Chief Exec. Officer--Golden State Foods, Irvine, CA; *U.S. Private*, pg. 460
Williams, James F., Chm. Bd. & Chief Exec. Officer--Integrated Waste Services, Inc., Buffalo, NY; *U.S. Public, pg. 886*
Williams, John, Chm. Bd.--H.E. Williams, Inc., Carthage, MO; *U.S. Private*, pg. 1178
Williams, John A., Chm. Bd.--Aero Electronics Incorporated, Memphis, TN; *U.S. Private*, pg. 731
Williams, John B., Chm. Bd.--Firstar Community Investment Corp., Milwaukee, WI; *U.S. Public*, pg. 643
Williams, Kenneth, Chm. Bd. & Chief Exec. Officer--Sierra On-Line, Inc., Bellevue, WA; *U.S. Public*, pg. 321
Williams, Mathew, Chm. Bd.--Liberty Fabrics, Inc., New York, NY; *Int'l*, pg. 340
Williams, Peter, Dr., Chm. Bd.--Oxford Instruments plc, Witney, United Kingdom; *Int'l*, pg. 1018
Williams, Robert M., Chm., Chief Exec. Officer & Treas.--Genova Products, Inc., Davison, MI; *U.S. Private*, pg. 447
Williams, S.B., Chm. Bd.--Williams-Rolls, Inc., Walled Lake, MI; *U.S. Private*, pg. 1178
Williams, Sam B., Dr., Chm. Bd. & Chief Exec. Officer--Williams International, Walled Lake, MI; *U.S. Private*, pg. 1178
Williams, Sterling L., Chm. Bd.--Sterling Commerce, Inc., Dublin, OH; *U.S. Public*, pg. 1515
Williams, Theodore, Chm. Bd.--Bell Industries, Inc., El Segundo, CA; *U.S. Public*, pg. 204
Williams, Thomas A., Chm. Bd.--Pagoda, Saint Louis, MO; *U.S. Public*, pg. 262
Williams, Thomas C., Chm. Bd. & Chief Exec. Officer--The Peoples Banking Company, Findlay, OH; *U.S. Public*, pg. 1413
Williams, Thomas C., Chm. Bd.--Rurban Life Insurance Company, Defiance, OH; *U.S. Public*, pg. 1413
Williams, Thomas C., Chm. Bd.--Rurbanc Data Services, Inc., Defiance, OH; *U.S. Public*, pg. 1413
Williams, William J., Chm. Bd.--The Western and Southern Life Insurance Company, Cincinnati, OH; *U.S. Private*, pg. 1164
Williams, Willis, Chm. Bd. & Chief Exec. Officer--Monticello Bank, Jacksonville, FL; *U.S. Private*, pg. 759
Williamson, Philip C., Chm. Bd., Pres. & Chief Exec. Officer--Williamson-Dickie Mfg. Co., Fort Worth, TX; *U.S. Private*, pg. 1179
Williamson, Richard B., Chm. Bd., Pres. & Chief Exec. Officer--T.D. Williamson, Inc., Tulsa, OK; *U.S. Private*, pg. 1179
Willig, Leslie A., Chm. Bd.--Photo Control Corporation, Minneapolis, MN; *U.S. Public*, pg. 1292
Willitts, William, Chm. Bd.--Willitts Design, Petaluma, CA; *U.S. Private*, pg. 1180
Wills, J. Blacklock, Chm. Bd.--Wills Group, Inc., La Plata, MD; *U.S. Private*, pg. 1180
Wilmers, Robert G., Chm. Bd. & Chief Exec. Officer--First Empire State Corporation, Buffalo, NY; *U.S. Public*, pg. 631
Wilmsen, Wolfgang, Chm. Bd.--Michael Weinig AG, Tauberbischofsheim, Germany; *Int'l*, pg. 1488
Wilnai, Amos, Chm. Bd. & Exec. V.P.-Bus. Devel.--MMC Networks, Inc., Sunnyvale, CA; *U.S. Public*, pg. 1027
Wilsey, Michael W., Chm. Bd. & Pres.--Wilsey Bennett Co., San Francisco, CA; *U.S. Private*, pg. 1180
Wilson, A.C., Chm. Bd. & Chief Exec. Officer--Ernest Paper Products, Inc., Los Angeles, CA; *U.S. Private*, pg. 381
Wilson, David W., Chm. Bd. & Pres.--Wilson Products Co., Salt Lake City, UT; *U.S. Private*, pg. 1181
Wilson, Diane M., Chm. Bd., Pres. & Chief Exec. Officer--Trend Laboratories Inc., Atlanta, GA; *U.S. Public*, pg. 1634
Wilson, Diane M., Chm. Bd. & Chief Exec. Officer--Trend Media, Atlanta, GA; *U.S. Public*, pg. 1634
Wilson, Frank, Chm. Bd.--New Brunswick Power Corporation, Fredericton, Canada; *Int'l*, pg. 923
Wilson, G. Larry, Chm. Bd., Pres. & Chief Exec. Officer--Policy Management Systems Corporation, Blythewood, SC; *U.S. Public*, pg. 1314
Wilson, Gary L., Chm. Bd.--Northwest Airlines Corp., Saint Paul, MN; *U.S. Public*, pg. 1199
Wilson, Gregory L., Chm. Bd., Pres & Chief Exec. Officer--Mity-Lite, Inc., Orem, UT; *U.S. Public*, pg. 1118
Wilson, Ian R., Chm. Bd., Pres., & Chief Exec. Officer--Dartford Partnership, San Francisco, CA; *U.S. Private*, pg. 312
Wilson, J. Lawrence, Chm. Bd. & Chief Exec. Officer--Rohm and Haas Company, Philadelphia, PA; *U.S. Public*, pg. 1403
Wilson, J. Steven, Chm. Bd., Pres. & Chief Exec. Officer--Riverside Group, Inc., Jacksonville, FL; *U.S. Public*, pg. 1391
Wilson, J. Steven, Chm. Bd. & Chief Exec. Officer--Wickes Inc., Vernon Hills, IL; *U.S. Public*, pg. 1391
Wilson, James, Chm. Bd.--Huck International, Inc., Tucson, AZ; *U.S. Public*, pg. 1597
Wilson, James R., Chm. Bd., Pres. & Chief Exec. Officer--Thiokol Corporation, Ogden, UT; *U.S. Public*, pg. 1596
Wilson, Johnny, Chm. Bd.--SF Services, North Little Rock, AR; *U.S. Private*, pg. 956
Wilson, Kemmons, Sr., Chm. Bd. & Owner--Kemmons Wilson, Inc., Memphis, TN; *U.S. Private*, pg. 613
Wilson, L.A., Chm. Bd.--Wilson Connolly, Northampton, United Kingdom; *Int'l*, pg. 1510
Wilson, L.R., Chm Bd.--Montreal Trustco, Montreal, Canada; *Int'l*, pg. 155
Wilson, Larry T., Chm. Bd.--CUNA Mutual Insurance Society, Madison, WI; *U.S. Private*, pg. 296
Wilson, Lynton R., Chm. Bd.--BCE Inc., Montreal, Canada; *Int'l*, pg. 114
Wilson, P.M., Chm. Bd. & Chief Exec. Officer--Gallaher Tobacco Ltd., Weybridge, United Kingdom; *Int'l*, pg. 539
Wilson, Peter, Chm. Bd. & Chief Exec.--Gallaher Limited, Weybridge, United Kingdom; *Int'l*, pg. 539
Wilson, R.P., Chm. Bd.-RTZ--Rio Tinto PLC, London, United Kingdom; *Int'l*, pg. 1118
Wilson, Ralph C., Jr., Chm. Bd. & Pres.--Ralph C. Wilson Enterprises, Detroit, MI; *U.S. Private*, pg. 1181
Wilson, Rich, Jr., Chm. Bd., Pres. & Chief Exec. Officer--Heavy Machines, Inc., Memphis, TN; *U.S. Private*, pg. 518
Wilson, Thomas D., Chm. Bd., Pres. & Chief Exec. Officer--Helian Health Group, Inc., Monterey, CA; *U.S. Public*, pg. 1715
Wilson, Thomas W., Jr., Chm. Bd.--Information Resources, Inc., Chicago, IL; *U.S. Public*, pg. 875
Wilson, W., Chm. Bd.--Fletcher Challenge Limited, Auckland, New Zealand; *Int'l*, pg. 494
Wilson, W. David, Chm. & Chief Exec. Officer--ScotiaMcLeod Inc., Toronto, Canada; *Int'l*, pg. 156
Wilson, W. David, Chm. & Chief Exec. Officer--Scotia Capital Markets, Toronto, Canada; *Int'l*, pg. 156
Wilson, W. Scott, Chm. Bd.--Bank of Coweta, Newnan, GA; *U.S. Public*, pg. 1549
Wilson, Wallace S., Chm. Bd., Pres. & Chief Exec. Officer--Wilson Industries Inc., Houston, TX; *U.S. Private*, pg. 1181
Wilson, William M., Chm.--Alexander & Alexander Services (UK) Plc, London, United Kingdom; *U.S. Public*, pg. 118
Wiltshire, Richard W., Chm. Bd.--Home Beneficial Corporation, Richmond, VA; *U.S. Public*, pg. 76
Wilzig, Siggi B., Chm. Bd. & Chief Exec. Officer--The Trustcompany Bancorporation, Jersey City, NJ; *U.S. Public*, pg. 1643
Winch, Harold, Chm. Bd. & Chief Exec. Officer--The Minster Machine Company, Minster, OH; *U.S. Private*, pg. 751
Windsor, W.M., Chm. Bd.--BWI Plc, Altrincham, United Kingdom; *Int'l*, pg. 130
Winfrey, Oprah, Chm. Bd. & Chief Exec. Officer--Harpo Entertainment Group, Chicago, IL; *U.S. Private*, pg. 504
Wing, John A., Chm. Bd. & Chief Exec. Officer--ABN AMRO Chicago Corporation, Chicago, IL; *Int'l*, pg. 10
Wing, John B., Chm. Bd.--The Wing Group, Woodlands, TX; *U.S. Public*, pg. 1760
Wingate, David A., Chm. Bd., Pres. & Chief Exec. Officer--Hi-Shear Industries Inc., New Hyde Park, NY; *U.S. Public*, pg. 824
Winiger, Rolf, Chm. Bd.--Balair/CTA Ltd., Geneva, Switzerland; *Int'l*, pg. 1333
Winn, Francis W., Chm. Bd.--Computer Language Research, Inc., Carrollton, TX; *U.S. Public*, pg. 421
Winokur, Herbert S., Chm. Bd.--Mrs. Fields' Original Cookies, Inc., Salt Lake City, UT; *U.S. Private*, pg. 688

Winship, Patricia C., Chm. Bd.--Transus Intermodal L.L.C., Atlanta, GA; *U.S. Private*, pg. 1097
Winstead, George, Chm. Bd.--Universal Cooperatives, Inc., Minneapolis, MN; *U.S. Private*, pg. 1127
Winterbottom, Clare, Chm. & Chief Exec. Officer--Anchor Lamina Inc., Windsor, Canada; *Int'l*, pg. 75
Wintermute, Glenn A., Co-Chm. Bd.--American Vanguard Corporation, Newport Beach, CA; *U.S. Public*, pg. 94
Winters, Steve D., Chm. Bd. & Pres.--Bepco, Inc., Winston Salem, NC; *U.S. Private*, pg. 134
Wintsch, O., Pres. of the Bd.--Oerlikon Buhrle Immobilien AG, Zurich, Switzerland; *Int'l*, pg. 998
Wintz, George L., Jr., Chm. Bd.--Wintz Companies, Saint Paul, MN; *U.S. Private*, pg. 1184
Wirth, M.F., Chm. Bd.--Wirth Ltd., Montreal, Canada; *Int'l*, pg. 1150
Wise, Brion G., Chm. Bd. & Chief Exec. Officer--Western Gas Resources, Inc., Denver, CO; *U.S. Public*, pg. 1758
Wise, P.J.S., Chm. Bd.--NatWest Capital Markets Limited, London, United Kingdom; *Int'l*, pg. 910
Wise, William A., Chm. Bd., Pres. & Chief Exec. Officer--El Paso Natural Gas Co., Houston, TX; *U.S. Public*, pg. 567
Wishnack, Marshall B., Chm. Bd. & Chief Exec. Officer--Wheat First Butcher Singer, Inc., Richmond, VA; *U.S. Public*, pg. 640
Wisne, Anthony, Chm. Bd.--Progressive Tool & Industries Co., Southfield, MI; *U.S. Private*, pg. 890
Wisotsky, Helen E., Chm. Bd., Sec. & Treas.--Imperial Litho & Dryography, Inc., Phoenix, AZ; *U.S. Private*, pg. 558
Wiss, Ronald A., Chm. Bd. & Chief Exec. Officer--Edwards and Kelcey, Inc., Boston, MA; *U.S. Private*, pg. 364
Withall, William E., Chm. Bd.--Miner Enterprises Inc., Geneva, IL; *U.S. Private*, pg. 749
Witkowski, Johannes, Chm.--Babcock Feuerungssysteme GmbH, Oberhausen, Germany; *Int'l*, pg. 398
Witt, Howard B., Chm. Bd., Pres. & Chief Exec. Officer--Littelfuse, Inc., Des Plaines, IL; *U.S. Public*, pg. 1001
Witt, Ray H., Chm. Bd.--CMI International Inc., Southfield, MI; *U.S. Private*, pg. 195
Witte, Margaret K., Chm., Pres. & Chief Exec. Officer--Royal Oak Mines Inc., Kirkland, WA; *U.S. Public*, pg. 1410
Wittlin, Felix, Dr., Chm. Bd.--Ascom Holding AG, Bern, Switzerland; *Int'l*, pg. 86
Wobst, Frank, Chm. Bd. & Chief Exec. Officer--Huntington Bancshares Inc., Columbus, OH; *U.S. Public*, pg. 849
Woeste, Albrecht, Chm. Bd.--Henkel KGaA, Dusseldorf, Germany; *Int'l*, pg. 609
Wohland, Helmut, Dr., Chm. Bd. & Pres.--Suspa Compart AG, Altdorf, Germany; *Int'l*, pg. 1322
Woit, Erik P., Chm.--Sea Containers America Inc., New York, NY; *Int'l*, pg. 1213
Wojciechowski, Peter, Chm. Bd.--Anoka Electric Cooperative, Ramsey, MN; *U.S. Private*, pg. 75
Wolcott, Arthur S., Chm. Bd.--Seneca Foods Corporation, Pittsford, NY; *U.S. Public*, pg. 1456
Wolcott, James D., Jr., Chm. Bd. & Pres.--Weldon, Williams & Lick, Inc., Fort Smith, AR; *U.S. Private*, pg. 1161
Wolcott, L.H., Chm. Bd.--Microdyne Corporation, Alexandria, VA; *U.S. Public*, pg. 1105
Wolf, Albert E., Chm. Bd.--Checkpoint Systems Inc., Thorofare, NJ; *U.S. Public*, pg. 343
Wolf, Hans, Chm. Bd.--Network Equipment Technologies, Inc., Redwood City, CA; *U.S. Public*, pg. 1168
Wolf, Hans A., Chm. Bd.--Tab Products Co., Palo Alto, CA; *U.S. Public*, pg. 1559
Wolf, Melvin Lee, Chm. Bd. & Chief Exec. Officer--Star Furniture Company, Houston, TX; *U.S. Public*, pg. 221
Wolf, Stephen M., Chm. Bd. & Chief Exec. Officer--US Airways Group, Inc., Arlington, VA; *U.S. Public*, pg. 1680
Wolf, Tom, Chm. Bd., Pres. & Chief Exec. Officer--STS Consultants, Inc., Deerfield, IL; *U.S. Private*, pg. 959
Wolfe, Kenneth L., Chm. Bd. & Chief Exec. Officer--Hershey Foods Corporation, Hershey, PA; *U.S. Public*, pg. 811
Wolfe, Thomas E., Chm. Bd, Pres. & Chief Exec. Officer--Ziebart International Corporation, Troy, MI; *U.S. Private*, pg. 1205
Wolff, Hans-Joachim, Dr. Ing., Chm. Bd. & Pres.--Dyckerhoff & Widmann AG, Munich, Germany; *Int'l*, pg. 423
Wolfington, John F., Chm. Bd.--Wolfington Body Company, Exton, PA; *U.S. Private*, pg. 1186
Wolford, David G., Chm. Bd.--Commtek Communications, Corp., Vienna, VA; *U.S. Private*, pg. 258
Wolfson, David, Hon. Lord, Chm.--The Great Universal Stores P.L.C., London, United Kingdom; *Int'l*, pg. 557
Wollenberg, Richard P., Chm. Bd., Pres. & Chief Exec. Officer--Longview Fibre Company, Longview, WA; *U.S. Public*, pg. 1013
Wollschlager, Klaus, Dr., Chm.--Aral AG, Bochum, Germany; *Int'l*, pg. 1460
Wolohan, James L., Chm. Bd., Pres & Chief Exec. Officer--Wolohan Lumber Co., Saginaw, MI; *U.S. Public*, pg. 1774
Wolstein, Scott A., Chm. Bd., Pres. & Chief Exec. Officer--Developers Diversified Realty Corporation, Moreland Hills, OH; *U.S. Public*, pg. 502
Woltz, Howard O., Jr., Chm. Bd.--Insteel Industries, Inc., Mount Airy, NC; *U.S. Public*, pg. 882
Womack, James S., Chm. Bd.--Sheldahl, Inc., Northfield, MN; *U.S. Public*, pg. 1465
Womack, Robert R., Chm. Bd. & Chief Exec. Officer--Zurn Industries, Inc., Erie, PA; *U.S. Public*, pg. 1794
Wood, Andrew L., Chm. Bd. & Chief Exec. Officer--Burnham, Atlanta, GA; *Int'l*, pg. 686
Wood, Bruce, Chm. Bd., Pres. & Chief Exec. Officer--Agromac International, Inc., Gering, NE; *U.S. Private*, pg. 27
Wood, David C., Chm. Bd. & Chief Exec. Officer--Norwest Financial, Inc., Des Moines, IA; *U.S. Public*, pg. 1202
Wood, E.L., IV, Chm. Bd.--Southeastern Steel Company, Florence, SC; *U.S. Private*, pg. 1015
Wood, James, Chm. Bd.--Bentley & Bentley, Fremont, CA; *U.S. Private*, pg. 1186
Wood, James, Chm. Bd.--Big Valley Marketing Corp., Fremont, CA; *U.S. Private*, pg. 1186
Wood, James, Chm. Bd. & Co-Chief Exec. Officer--The Great Atlantic & Pacific Tea Company, Inc., Montvale, NJ; *Int'l*, pg. 1375
Wood, John W., Jr., Chm. Bd. & Chief Exec. Officer--Thermo Cardiosystems Inc., Woburn, MA; *U.S. Public*, pg. 1592
Wood, Lan, Sir, Chm. Bd.--Scottish Enterprise, Glasgow, United Kingdom; *Int'l*, pg. 1212
Wood, R. Ray, Chm. Bd., Pres., Chief Exec. & Oper. Officer--Rockford Products Corp., Rockford, IL; *U.S. Private*, pg. 938
Wood, R.D., Jr., Chm. Bd.--PQ Corporation, Berwyn, PA; *U.S. Private*, pg. 827
Wood, T., Chm. Bd. & Mng. Dir.--GKN Driveshafts Ltd., Walsall, United Kingdom; *Int'l*, pg. 534
Wood, Willis B., Jr., Chm. Bd. & Chief Exec. Officer--Pacific Enterprises, Los Angeles, CA; *U.S. Public*, pg. 1249
Woodbeck, Milford E., Chm. Bd. & Chief Exec. Officer--Overhead Conveyor Co., Ferndale, MI; *U.S. Private*, pg. 822
Woodhall, J.A., Jr., Chm. Bd. Chief Exec. Officer--Central Allied Enterprises, Canton, OH; *U.S. Private*, pg. 222
Woodhouse, John F., Chm. Bd.--Sysco Corporation, Houston, TX; *U.S. Public*, pg. 1550
Wooding, Norman, Sir, Chm.--EIS Group Plc, London, United Kingdom; *Int'l*, pg. 426
Woodrick, Bob, Chm. Bd.--D & W Food Centers, Inc., Grand Rapids, MI; *U.S. Private*, pg. 300
Woodruff, Paul H., Chm. Bd.--Environmental Resources Management, Exton, PA; *U.S. Private*, pg. 378
Woods, Joe E., Chm. Bd., Pres. & Chief Exec. Officer--Joe E. Woods, Inc., Mesa, AZ; *U.S. Private*, pg. 1187
Woods, John W., Chm. Bd.--AmSouth Bancorporation, Birmingham, AL; *U.S. Public*, pg. 105
Woods, Kenneth W., Chm. Bd.--Cravens, Dargan & Company, Pacific Coast of Illinois, Inc., Chicago, IL; *U.S. Public*, pg. 366
Woods, Ronald, Chm. Bd.--Associated Grocers, Inc., Baton Rouge, LA; *U.S. Private*, pg. 90
Woods, Shelby, Chm. Bd. & Chm.-Exec. Committee--Cranford Johnson Robinson Woods, Little Rock, AR; *U.S. Private*, pg. 286
Woods, Thomas C., III, Chm. Bd.--Aliant Communications Inc., Lincoln, NE; *U.S. Public*, pg. 40
Woods, Ward W., Chm. Bd.--Stant Corporation, Denver, CO; *Int'l*, pg. 1396
Woodson, James, Co-Chm. Bd. & Owner--Taco John's International, Inc., Cheyenne, WY; *U.S. Private*, pg. 1066
Woodward, Nancy R., Chm. Bd.--Pervasive Software Inc., Austin, TX; *U.S. Public*, pg. 1280
Woolard, Edgar S., Jr., Chm. Bd.--Du Pont (E.I. Du Pont De Nemours & Co.), Wilmington, DE; *U.S. Public*, pg. 530
Wooley, John C., Chm. Bd. & Pres.--Schlotzsky's, Inc., Austin, TX; *U.S. Public*, pg. 1439
Woolf, Jack, Chm. Bd.--William L. Crow Construction Co., New York, NY; *Int'l*, pg. 633
Woolley, Moger, Non-Exec. Chm.--Brunel Holdings Plc, Chippenham, United Kingdom; *Int'l*, pg. 230
Woolworth, Richard, Chm. Bd.--Regence BlueCross BlueShield of Oregon, Portland, OR; *U.S. Private*, pg. 917
Woolworth, Richard L., Chm. Bd.--HMO Oregon, Salem, OR; *U.S. Private*, pg. 918
Wooten, Robert E., Chm. Bd.--Brown Wooten Mills, Inc., Burlington, NC; *U.S. Private*, pg. 174
Wordeman, Mike, Chm. Bd. & Chief Exec. Officer--Sodak Gaming, Inc., Rapid City, SD; *U.S. Public*, pg. 1482
Wordsworth, Jerry, Chm. Bd. & Pres.--MBM, Rocky Mount, NC; *U.S. Private*, pg. 685
Worely, Floyd L., Chm. Bd. & Chief Exec. Officer--B-Line Systems, Inc., Highland, IL; *U.S. Public*, pg. 1471
Work, Harold K., Chm. Bd., Pres. & Chief Exec. Officer--Elcor Corporation, Dallas, TX; *U.S. Public*, pg. 567
Worrell, Thomas E., Jr., Chm. Bd.--Worrell Enterprises, Inc., Boca Raton, FL; *U.S. Private*, pg. 1191
Worsley, Walter C., Jr., Chm. Bd.--Entrepreneur, Inc., Wilmington, NC; *U.S. Private*, pg. 1191
Wortberg, Ernst J., Chm. Bd. & Pres.--L. Possehl & Co. mbH, Lubeck, Germany; *Int'l*, pg. 1063
Wortel, T.M., Chm. Bd. & Exec. V.P.--Esso N.V./S.A., Maasmechelen, Belgium; *U.S. Public*, pg. 602
Wortell, M.R., Chm. Bd.--Triton Industries, Inc., Chicago, IL; *U.S. Private*, pg. 1104
Wray, Marc F., Chm. Bd.--Joy Mining Machinery, Warrendale, PA; *U.S. Public*, pg. 789
Wren, John, Chm. Bd. & Chief Exec Officer--Diversified Agency Services, New York, NY; *U.S. Public*, pg. 1223
Wrey, Benjamin H.B., Chm. Bd.--Henderson Administration Group PLC, London, United Kingdom, *Int'l*, pg. 609
Wright, A.D.B., Chm.--Stanbic Bank Uganda Limited, Kampala, Uganda; *Int'l*, pg. 1294
Wright, James O., Chm. Bd.--Badger Meter, Inc., Milwaukee, WI; *U.S. Public*, pg. 164
Wright, Joseph, Chm. Bd.--GRC International, Inc., Vienna, VA; *U.S. Public*, pg. 695
Wright, Leon, Chm. Bd.--Levmark Capital Corporation, Atlanta, GA; *U.S. Private*, pg. 663
Wright, Michael W., Chm. Bd.--ShopKo Stores, Inc., Green Bay, WI; *U.S. Public*, pg. 1467
Wright, Michael W., Chm. Bd., Pres. & Chief Exec. Officer--SuperValu, Inc., Eden Prairie, MN; *U.S. Public*, pg. 1540
Wright, Phillip E., Chm. Bd. & Chief Exec. Officer--SunTrust Bank, North Florida, N.A., Jacksonville, FL; *U.S. Public*, pg. 1537
Wright, Richard W., Chm. Bd.--Front Royal, Inc., Morrisville, NC; *U.S. Private*, pg. 430
Wright, Roy A., Chm. Bd.--Iwerks Entertainment, Burbank, CA; *U.S. Public*, pg. 915
Wright, Thomas C., Chm. Bd. & Chief Exec. Officer--Wright Group Publishing, Inc., Bothell, WA; *U.S. Public*, pg. 1636
Wright, Warren E., Chm Bd. & Chief Oper. Officer--Renosol Corp., Saline, MI; *U.S. Private*, pg. 922
Wrigley, William, Chm. Bd., Pres. & Chief Oper. Officer--Wm. Wrigley Jr. Company, Chicago, IL; *U.S. Public*, pg. 1781
Wu, Hsiuchi, Chm. Bd.--President Enterprises Corp., Tainan, Taiwan; *Int'l*, pg. 1068
Wulf, Walter H., Chm. Bd.--Monarch Cement Co., Humboldt, KS; *U.S. Public*, pg. 1123
Wunderman, Lester, Chm. Bd. Worldwide--Wunderman Cato Johnson, New York, NY; *U.S. Private*, pg. 1197
Wurm, Robert J., Chm. Bd., Pres. & Chief Exec. Officer--Quest Technologies, Inc., Oconomowoc, WI; *U.S. Private*, pg. 900
Wurtele, C. Angus, Chm. Bd.--Valspar Paints, Minneapolis, MN; *U.S. Public*, pg. 1707
Wyandt, Steven P., Chm., Pres. & Chief Exec. Officer--Body Drama, Inc., Culver City, CA; *U.S. Public*, pg. 1182
Wyatt, Jame A., Chm. Bd. & Chief Oper. officer--ICM Holdings Inc., New York, NY; *U.S. Private*, pg. 554
Wyatt, W. Whitlow, Chm. Bd., Pres. & Chief Exec. Officer--Altama Delta Corporation, Atlanta, GA; *U.S. Private*, pg. 47
Wyckaert, Luke, Chm. Bd., Pres. & Chief Exec. Officer--Intertrade Industries, Huntington Beach, CA; *U.S. Private*, pg. 573
Wydman, Marcy R., Chm. Bd. & Chief Exec. Officer--Witt Company, Cincinnati, OH; *U.S. Private*, pg. 1185
Wygod, Martin, Chm. Bd.--Synetic, Inc., Elmwood Park, NJ; *U.S. Public*, pg. 1548
Wygod, Martin J., Chm. Bd.--MEDCO Containment Services, Inc., Montvale, NJ; *U.S. Public*, pg. 1091
Wyle, F. Stephen, Chm. Bd. & Chief Exec. Officer--Wyle Laboratories, Inc., El Segundo, CA; *U.S. Private*, pg. 1193
Wylie, R.M., OBE, Chm. Bd.--Q.U.F. Industries Ltd., Brisbane, Australia; *Int'l*, pg. 1074
Wylie, Torrance, Chm.--GPC Government Policy Consultants (Federal), Ottawa, Canada; *U.S. Public*, pg. 1225
Wyly, Sam, Chm. Bd.--Michaels Stores, Inc., Irving, TX; *U.S. Public*, pg. 1104
Wyly, Sam, Chm. Bd.--Sterling Software, Inc., Dallas, TX; *U.S. Public*, pg. 1516
Wyman, Robert, Chm. Bd.--Suncor Inc., Calgary, Canada; *Int'l*, pg. 1320
Wyndham, Henry, Chm. Bd.-Sotheby's U.K.--Sotheby's Europe, London, United Kingdom; *U.S. Public*, pg. 1487
Wynn, Stephen A., Chm. Bd., Pres. & Chief Exec. Officer--Mirage Resorts Incorporated, Las Vegas, NV; *U.S. Public*, pg. 1116
Wynne, John W., Chm. Bd.--Duke Realty Investments, Inc., Indianapolis, IN; *U.S. Public*, pg. 535
Wyse, Marc A., Chm. & Chief Exec. Officer--Wyse Advertising, Cleveland, OH; *U.S. Private*, pg. 1193
Ximenes Alves Ferreira, Paulo Cesar, Chm. Bd. & Pres.--Banco do Brasil, Brasilia, Brazil; *Int'l*, pg. 141
Xing, Xu Fu, Chm.--Dentsu Young & Rubicam Advertising Co., Ltd. (Beijing), Beijing, China; *U.S. Private*, pg. 325
Yaboshi, Kokichi, Chm. Bd.--Ibiden Co., Ltd., Gifu, Japan; *Int'l*, pg. 878
Yaeger, Philip C., Chm. Bd.--Hub Group, Inc., Lombard, IL; *U.S. Public*, pg. 844
Yamada, Kikuo, Chm. Bd.--Mitsubishi Oil Co. Ltd., Tokyo, Japan; *Int'l*, pg. 876
Yamada, Kiyomi, Chm. Bd.--Chemoil, San Francisco, CA; *U.S. Private*, pg. 233
Yamada, Yasuhiro, Chm. Bd. & Chief Exec. Officer--Mentholatum Company, Buffalo, NY; *Int'l*, pg. 1126
Yamada, Yasuhiro, Chm. Bd.--Josephine Cosmetics, Inc., Osaka, Japan; *Int'l*, pg. 1126
Yamaguchi, Hajime, Chm. Bd. & Pres.--Teac America, Inc., Montebello, CA; *Int'l*, pg. 1360
Yamaguchi, Nobuo, Chm. Bd.--Asahi Chemical Industry Co., Ltd., Tokyo, Japan; *Int'l*, pg. 83
Yamaji, Hiroyuki, Chm. Bd.--Daiwa Bank Canada, Toronto, Canada; *Int'l*, pg. 373
Yamaji, Susumo, Chm Bd.--Japan Airlines Company, Ltd., Tokyo, Japan; *Int'l*, pg. 699
Yamakoshi, Noby, Chm. Bd. & Chief Exec. Officer--Nobart, Inc., Chicago, IL; *U.S. Private*, pg. 800
Yamamoto, Shigeo, Chm. Bd.--Shizuki Electric Corporation, Nishinomiya, Japan; *Int'l*, pg. 1236
Yamamoto, Yoshihide, Chm. Bd., Pres. & Chief Exec. Officer--Sumikin Bussan Corporation, Osaka, Japan; *Int'l*, pg. 1308
Yamamshina, Makoto, Chm. Bd.--Bandai Co., Ltd., Tokyo, Japan; *Int'l*, pg. 145
Yamanaka, Takashi, Chm. Bd.--Yokogawa Electric Corporation, Tokyo, Japan; *Int'l*, pg. 1520
Yamane, George, Sr. V.P.--Shannon & Wilson, Inc., Seattle, WA; *U.S. Private*, pg. 989
Yamanouchi, Shuichiro, Chm. Bd.--East Japan Railway Company, Tokyo, Japan; *Int'l*, pg. 431
Yamauchi, Naoyuki, Chm. Bd.--New Hong Kong Tunnel Co., Ltd., Hong Kong, Hong Kong; *Int'l*, pg. 764
Yanai, H., Chm. Bd.--Waterville TG Inc., Waterville, Canada; *Int'l*, pg. 1487
Yanai, Yural, Chm. Bd.--Elscint Espana S.A., Barcelona, Spain; *Int'l*, pg. 450
Yano, Kiyoshi, Chm. Bd.--Oversea Courier Service Co., Ltd., Tokyo, Japan; *Int'l*, pg. 929
Yanover, Robert A., Chm. Bd.--Lason, Inc., Troy, MI; *U.S. Public*, pg. 979
Yanowitz, Irwin M., Chm. Bd.--Sharon Tube Company, Sharon, PA; *U.S. Private*, pg. 990
Yansouni, Cyril J., Chm. Bd. & Chief Exec. Officer--Read-Rite Corporation, Milpitas, CA; *U.S. Public*, pg. 1366
Yantis, John M., Chm. Bd.--Yantis Corporation, San Antonio, TX; *U.S. Private*, pg. 1195
Yarbrough, Jerry A., Chm. Bd. & Chief Exec. Officer--Integrated Distributions, Inc., Little Rock, AR; *U.S. Public*, pg. 131

Yardley, John, Chm.--Camden Motors Ltd., Leighton Buzzard, United Kingdom; *Int'l*, pg. 165
Yarhi, Henry, Chm. Bd.--Bufkor, Inc., Clearwater, FL; *U.S. Private*, pg. 179
Yariv, Amnon, Ph.D., Chm. Bd.--Ortel Corporation, Alhambra, CA; *U.S. Public*, pg. 1232
Yarnell, John R., Chm. Bd.--Poco Petroleums Ltd., Calgary, Canada; *Int'l*, pg. 1061
Yarom, Artzi, Chm.--Produtos Medico Hospitalares Elscint Ltda., Sao Paulo, Brazil; *Int'l*, pg. 450
Yarom, Artzi, Chm. Bd.--Elscint GmbH, Wiesbaden, Germany; *Int'l*, pg. 450
Yasinsky, John B., Chm. Bd., Pres. & Chief Exec. Officer--GenCorp Inc., Fairlawn, OH; *U.S. Public*, pg. 705
Yassukovich, Stanislas, Chm. Bd.--Flextech p.l.c., London, United Kingdom; *Int'l*, pg. 495
Yasuda, H., Chm. Bd.--Jardine Matheson K.K., Tokyo, Japan; *Int'l*, pg. 705
Yasue, Motoi, Chm. Bd.--Daido Steel Co., Ltd., Nagoya, Japan; *Int'l*, pg. 364
Yasufuku, Teruyoshi, Chm. Bd.--Sanwa Bank California, Los Angeles, CA; *Int'l*, pg. 1189
Yasui, Kenji, Chm. Bd.--Daiwa Bank (Capital Management) Ltd., London, United Kingdom; *Int'l*, pg. 373
Yates, B.H., Chm. Bd.--SAE Engineering, Inc., Santa Clara, CA; *U.S. Private*, pg. 955
Yates, E.J., Chm. Bd. & Mng. Dir.--Kodak Limited, Hemel Hempstead, United Kingdom; *U.S. Public*, pg. 553
Yates, Jim, Chm. Bd.--E-Z Mart Stores, Inc., Texarkana, TX; *U.S. Private*, pg. 353
Yau-Lai, Winston, Exec. Chm. & Mng. Dir.--Vitasoy International Holdings Ltd., Tuen Mun, Hong Kong; *Int'l*, pg. 1468
Yau, Sam, Chm. Bd.--ICS Learning Systems, Inc., Scranton, PA; *U.S. Public*, pg. 783
Yau, Sam, Chm. Bd.--ICS Intangibles Holding Company, Irvine, CA; *U.S. Public*, pg. 783
Yau, Sam, Chm. Bd. & Pres.--National Education Payroll Corp., Irvine, CA; *U.S. Public*, pg. 784
Yau, Sam, Chm. Bd.--Steck-Vaughn Publishing Corporation, Austin, TX; *U.S. Public*, pg. 784
Yaw, Wee Cho, Chm. Bd.--Haw Par Brothers International Limited, Singapore, Singapore; *Int'l*, pg. 603
Yaw, Wee Cho, Chm. Bd.--Tiger Medicals Ltd., Singapore, Singapore; *Int'l*, pg. 603
Yaw, Wee Cho, Chm. Bd.--Singapore Land Limited, Singapore, Singapore; *Int'l*, pg. 1252
Yaw, Wee Cho, Chm. Bd.--United Overseas Land Limited, Singapore, Singapore; *Int'l*, pg. 1443
Yearley, Douglas C., Chm. Bd. & Chief Exec. Officer--Phelps Dodge Corporation, Phoenix, AZ; *U.S. Public*, pg. 1286
Yellowlees, Robert A., Chm. Bd. & Chief Exec. Officer--National Data Corporation, Atlanta, GA; *U.S. Public*, pg. 1155
Yelverton, William F., Chm. & Chief Exec. Officer--New York Life Worldwide Holding, Inc., New York, NY; *U.S. Private*, pg. 795
Yenkin, Bernard, Chm. Bd.--Yenkin-Majestic Paint Corporation, Columbus, OH; *U.S. Private*, pg. 1195
Yeo, Dennis G., Chm. & Founder--Multigen Inc., San Jose, CA; *U.S. Public*, pg. 1425
Yerant, Gene S., Chm. Bd. & Pres.--Transport Insurance Co., Dallas, TX; *U.S. Public*, pg. 75
Yeshoua, Marco, Chm. Bd.--Lucky Winner, Inc., New York, NY; *U.S. Private*, pg. 679
Yew, Gloria Lee Kim, Chm. Bd.--Kim Eng Holdings Limited, Singapore, Singapore; *Int'l*, pg. 733
Yocam, Delbert W., Chm. & Chief Exec. Officer--Borland International, Inc., Scotts Valley, CA; *U.S. Public*, pg. 246
Yoder, G.L., Chm. Bd.--Yoder Oil Company Inc., Elkhart, IN; *U.S. Private*, pg. 1196
Yoh, Harold L., Jr., Chm. Bd. & Chief Exec. Officer--Day & Zimmermann, Inc., Philadelphia, PA; *U.S. Private*, pg. 316
Yohman, Edward J., Chm. Bd. & Chief Exec. Officer--Cyberex, Inc., Mentor, OH; *U.S. Public*, pg. 481
Yohn, George, Chm. Bd.--Items International/Airwalk, Inc., Altoona, PA; *U.S. Private*, pg. 576
Yokoi, Tasuku, Chm. Bd.--Sumitomo Rubber Industries Ltd., Kobe, Japan; *Int'l*, pg. 1316
Yokokawa, Tadashi, Chm. Bd.--Skylark Co., Ltd., Tokyo, Japan; *Int'l*, pg. 1262
Yokote, Kosuke, Chm. Bd.--The Asahi Bank, Ltd., Tokyo, Japan; *Int'l*, pg. 81
Yoneyama, Takanori, Chm. Bd.--Konica Corporation, Tokyo, Japan; *Int'l*, pg. 748
Yong, Lee Howe, Chm. Bd.--Transmarco Limited, Singapore, Singapore; *Int'l*, pg. 1417
Yontz, Kenneth F., Chm. Bd., Pres., & Chief Exec. Officer--Sybron International Corporation, Milwaukee, WI; *U.S. Public*, pg. 1544
Yoon, Myung-Yee, Chm. Bd.--Daehong Advertising Inc., Seoul, Korea; *Int'l*, pg. 357
York, Denise DeBartolo, Chm. Bd.--Louisiana Downs, Bossier City, LA; *U.S. Private*, pg. 319
York, Roy B., Chm. Bd. & Chief Exec. Officer--Martin Electronics, Inc., Perry, FL; *U.S. Private*, pg. 709
Yoshida, Tadashi, Chm. Bd.--NEC Industries (UK) Plc., London, United Kingdom; *Int'l*, pg. 900
Yoshihara, Saburo, Chm. Bd.--Chiba Kogyo Bank, Chiba, Japan; *Int'l*, pg. 283
Yoshimatsu, T., Chm. Bd.--Mizuno USA, Inc., Norcross, GA; *Int'l*, pg. 885
Yoshimura, Shintaro, Chm. Bd.--Shima Trading Co. Ltd., Osaka, Japan; *Int'l*, pg. 1231
Yoshino, Yoshihiko, Governor--The Japan Development Bank, Tokyo, Japan; *Int'l*, pg. 701
Yost, Frank A., Chm. Bd.--Hopkinsville Milling Co., Hopkinsville, KY; *U.S. Private*, pg. 538
Yost, Larry D., Chm. Bd. & Chief Exec. Officer--Meritor Automotive, Inc., Troy, MI; *U.S. Public*, pg. 1096
Yost, Wallace H., Chm. Bd. & Chief Exec. Officer--D.S.U.-Peterbilt & GMC, Inc., Portland, OR; *U.S. Private*, pg. 306
Young, Dan E., Chm. Bd.--Young Automotive Group, Indianapolis, IN; *U.S. Private*, pg. 1095
Young, Edward, Chm. Bd.--Munroe, Inc., Pittsburgh, PA; *U.S. Private*, pg. 767
Young, Edward S., Chm. Bd.--Ken-Mac Metals, Inc., Cleveland, OH; *Int'l*, pg. 1388
Young, J. Givens, Chm. Bd.--Young Pecan Company (A Partnership), Florence, SC; *U.S. Private*, pg. 1201
Young, Jack, Chm. Bd., Pres., Chief Exec. & Chief Fin. Officer--Jack Young Associates, Hazleton, PA; *U.S. Private*, pg. 1201
Young, Jane H., Chm. Bd.--General Wholesale Company, Inc., Atlanta, GA; *U.S. Private*, pg. 445
Young, John A., Jr., Chm. Bd. & Chief Exec. Officer--Burd & Fletcher Company, Kansas City, MO; *U.S. Private*, pg. 181
Young, Mary, Chm. Bd.--Sealaska Corporation, Juneau, AK; *U.S. Private*, pg. 978
Young, Neil, Chm. Bd. & Chief Exec. Officer--Grubb & Ellis Company, Northbrook, IL; *U.S. Public*, pg. 767
Young, R.J., Chm. Bd.--Harvey Plant Limited, Bedworth, United Kingdom; *Int'l*, pg. 910
Young, R.J., Chm. Bd.--Jaguar Cars Finance Limited, Coventry, United Kingdom; *Int'l*, pg. 910
Young, R.J., Chm. Bd.--Transfleet Services Limited, Coventry, United Kingdom; *Int'l*, pg. 911
Young, Richard F., Chm. Bd., Pres. & Chief Exec. Officer--Sues, Young & Brown Inc., Baldwin Park, CA; *U.S. Private*, pg. 1049
Young, Robert A., Chm. Bd.--Data-Tronics Corp., Fort Smith, AR; *U.S. Public*, pg. 130
Young, Robert H., Chm. Bd.--Vermont Yankee Nuclear Power Corp., Brattleboro, VT; *U.S. Public*, pg. 328
Young, Roger, Chm.-Greenalls Inns-Retail--The Greenalls Group PLC, Warrington, United Kingdom; *Int'l*, pg. 558
Young, Roger A., Chm. Bd. & Chief Exec. Officer--Bay State Gas Company, Westborough, MA; *U.S. Public*, pg. 196
Young, Thomas, Jr., Chm. Bd.--Young Electric Sign Company, Salt Lake City, UT; *U.S. Private*, pg. 1201
Young, Victor L., Chm. Bd. & Chief Exec. Officer--Fishery Products International Ltd., Saint Johns, Canada; *Int'l*, pg. 492
Young, Walter R., Jr., Chm. Bd., Pres. & Chief Exec. Officer--Champion Enterprises, Inc., Auburn Hills, MI; *U.S. Public*, pg. 332
Young, Warren V., Vice Chm.--Manheim Auctions, Inc., Atlanta, GA; *U.S. Private*, pg. 282
Young, William J., Chm. Bd., Pres. & Chief Exec. Officer--Advanced Machine Vision Corp., Medford, OR; *U.S. Public*, pg. 20
Young, William P., Chm. Bd.--Plastipak Packaging Inc., Plymouth, MI; *U.S. Private*, pg. 872
Younger, The Rt. Hon. Viscount, of Lechie, Chm. Bd.--The Royal Bank of Scotland plc, Edinburgh, United Kingdom; *Int'l*, pg. 1132
Yount, G. Stuart, Chm. Bd. & Chief Exec. Officer--Fortifiber Corporation, Incline Village, NV; *U.S. Private*, pg. 419
Yu-Tung, Cheng, Dr., Chm. Bd.--New World Development Co. Ltd., Hong Kong, Hong Kong; *Int'l*, pg. 923
Yu, Philip, Chm. Bd. & Chief Exec. Officer-Nortel China--Northern Telecom Limited, Brampton, Canada; *Int'l*, pg. 968
Yuasa, Hisao, Chm. & Chief Exec. Officer--Ricoh Corporation, West Caldwell, NJ; *Int'l*, pg. 1114
Yukihira, Tsugio, Chm. Bd.--Yamaichi Securities Co., Ltd., Tokyo, Japan; *Int'l*, pg. 1516
Yull, Melbourne F., Chm. Bd. & Chief Exec. Officer--Intertape Polymer Group Inc., Saint-Laurent, Canada; *Int'l*, pg. 684
Yun, Jong-Yong, Chm. Bd. & Chief Exec. Officer--Samsung Japan Corporation, Tokyo, Japan; *Int'l*, pg. 1183
Yutaka, Masaru, Chm.--ORIX Alpha Corporation, Tokyo, Japan; *Int'l*, pg. 1008
Yuzon, Virgilio A., Chm.--Hemisphere-Leo Burnett, Inc., Manila, Philippines; *U.S. Private*, pg. 184
Zable, Walter J., Chm. Bd., Pres. & Chief Exec. Officer--Cubic Corporation, San Diego, CA; *U.S. Public*, pg. 466
Zaccaglin, Victor, Chm. Bd. & Chief Exec. Officer--Calprop Corporation, Marina Del Rey, CA; *U.S. Public*, pg. 296
Zachry, H.B., Jr., Chm. Bd. & Chief Exec. Officer--H.B. Zachry, San Antonio, TX; *U.S. Private*, pg. 1203
Zacks, Gordon, Chm. Bd., Pres. & Chief Exec. Officer--R.G. Barry Corporation, Pickerington, OH; *U.S. Public*, pg. 192
Zadel, C. William, Chm. Bd., Pres. & Chief Exec. Officer--Millipore Corporation, Bedford, MA; *U.S. Public*, pg. 1112
Zades, Stephen H., Chm. & Chief Exec. Officer--Long Haymes Carr, Inc., Winston Salem, NC; *U.S. Public*, pg. 909
Zafiropoulo, Arthur W., Chm. Bd., Pres. & Chief Exec. Officer--Ultratech Stepper, Inc., San Jose, CA; *U.S. Public*, pg. 1663
Zain, Tan S.A.A.B., Chm. Bd.--Teamwork Corporation Sdn Bhd, Kuala Lumpur, Malaysia; *Int'l*, pg. 1360
Zamoiski, Calman, Chm. Bd. & Pres.--The Zamoiski Co., Baltimore, MD; *U.S. Private*, pg. 1203
Zandano, Gianni, Chm. Bd.--Istituto Bancario San Paolo Di Torino S.p.A., Turin, Italy; *Int'l*, pg. 691
Zandman, Dr. Felix, Chm. Bd.--Dale Electronics, Inc., Columbus, NE; *U.S. Public*, pg. 1722
Zandman, Felix, Dr., Chm. Bd., Pres. & Chief Exec. Officer--Vishay Intertechnology, Inc., Malvern, PA; *U.S. Public*, pg. 1721
Zantop, Duane A., Chm. Bd. & Chief Exec. Officer--Zantop International Airlines, Inc., Ypsilanti, MI; *U.S. Private*, pg. 1204
Zarkin, Herbert J., Chm. Bd.--BJ's Wholesale Club, Inc., Natick, MA; *U.S. Public*, pg. 162
Zarkin, Herbert J., Chm. Bd.--HomeBase, Inc., Irvine, CA; *U.S. Public*, pg. 832
Zax, Stanley R., Chm. Bd. & Pres.--Zenith National Insurance Corp., Woodland Hills, CA; *U.S. Public*, pg. 1790
Zech, Ronald H., Chm. Bd. & Chief Exec. Officer--GATX Corporation, Chicago, IL; *U.S. Public*, pg. 690
Zegarski, Ronald, Chm. Bd.--System Sensor Division, Saint Charles, IL; *U.S. Public*, pg. 1306
Zeidler, Gerhard, Chm. Bd.--Wandel & Goltermann GmbH & Co., Elektronische Messtechnik, Eningen, Germany; *Int'l*, pg. 1485
Zeien, Alfred M., Chm. Bd. & Chief Exec. Officer--The Gillette Company, Boston, MA; *U.S. Public*, pg. 743
Zeigler, Charles E., Chm. Bd.--PSNC Cardinal Pipeline Company, Gastonia, NC; *U.S. Public*, pg. 1340
Zeigler, Charles E., Jr., Chm. Bd., Pres. & Chief Exec. Officer--Public Service Company of North Carolina, Inc., Gastonia, NC; *U.S. Public*, pg. 1340
Zeitoun, Raymond, Chm. Bd.--SMH France S.A., Paris, France; *Int'l*, pg. 1161
Zell, Samuel, Chm. Bd.--Anixter International, Chicago, IL; *U.S. Public*, pg. 115
Zell, Samuel, Chm. Bd. & Chief Exec. Officer--Capsure Holdings Corp., Chicago, IL; *U.S. Public*, pg. 303
Zell, Samuel, Chm. Bd.--Equity Group Investments, Chicago, IL; *U.S. Private*, pg. 380
Zell, Samuel, Chm. Bd.--Great American Management & Investment, Inc., Chicago, IL; *U.S. Private*, pg. 473
Zell, Samuel, Chm. Bd.--First Capital Financial Corp., Troy, MI; *U.S. Private*, pg. 473
Zell, Samuel, Chm. Bd.--Equity Residential Properties Trust, Chicago, IL; *U.S. Public*, pg. 590
Zell, Samuel, Chm. Bd.--Jacor Communications, Inc., Covington, KY; *U.S. Public*, pg. 922
Zenk, Barbara, Chm. Bd.--Monico Alloys, Inc., Los Angeles, CA; *U.S. Private*, pg. 757
Zensen, Dennis C., Chm. Bd., Pres. & Chief Exec. Officer--Sylvan Inc., Saxonburg, PA; *U.S. Public*, pg. 1545
Zensen, Dennis C., Chm. Bd.--Quincy Corp., Quincy, FL; *U.S. Public*, pg. 1545
Zenz, Barbara E., Chm. Bd., Pres. & New Bus. Contact--The Stephenz Group, Inc., San Jose, CA; *U.S. Private*, pg. 1040
Zicarelli, Jim, Chm. Bd., Chief Exec. Officer & Chief Oper. Officer--Cramer Inc., Kansas City, KS; *U.S. Private*, pg. 285
Ziegenbein, Klaus, Chm. Bd., Pres. & Chief Exec. Officer--Koh-I-Noor, Inc., Bloomsbury, NJ; *U.S. Private*, pg. 629
Zieger, Claus D., Chm. Bd., Pres., Chief Exec. Officer & Treas.--Interbath, Inc., City of Industry, CA; *U.S. Private*, pg. 566
Ziegler, Fritz, Chm.-Supvr. Bd.--Harpen AG, Dortmund, Germany; *Int'l*, pg. 597
Ziegler, John K., Chm. Bd. & Chief Exec. Officer--Willcox & Gibbs, Inc., Carteret, NJ; *U.S. Private*, pg. 1177
Ziegler, R.D., Chm. Bd.--The Ziegler Companies, Inc., West Bend, WI; *U.S. Public*, pg. 1791
Ziegler, R.D., Chm. Bd.--B.C. Ziegler & Co., West Bend, WI; *U.S. Public*, pg. 1792
Ziegler, R.D., Chm.--Ziegler Asset Management, Inc., West Bend, WI; *U.S. Public*, pg. 1792
Ziegler, Willam, III, Chm. Bd. & Chief Exec. Officer--Swisher International Group, Inc., Darien, CT; *U.S. Public*, pg. 1543
Ziering, Sigi, Ph.D., Chm. Bd. & Chief Exec. Officer--Diagnostic Products Corporation, Los Angeles, CA; *U.S. Public*, pg. 505
Zietlow, Donald P., Chm. Bd.--Kwik Trip Inc., La Crosse, WI; *U.S. Private*, pg. 637
Zilber, Joseph J., Chm. Bd.--Zilber, Ltd., Milwaukee, WI; *U.S. Private*, pg. 1206
Zildjian, Armand, Chm. Bd. & Pres.--Avedis Zildjian Company, Norwell, MA; *U.S. Private*, pg. 1206
Zimdar, William L., Chm. Bd., Chief Exec. Officer, Chief Fin. Officer & V.P.--Zimdar Enterprises/Frames Unlimited, Wyoming, MI; *U.S. Private*, pg. 1206
Zimlich, Albert L., Chm. Bd.--Blue Grass Cooperage Co., Louisville, KY; *U.S. Public*, pg. 261
Zimmer, Edward M., Jr., Chm. Bd. & Chief Exec. Officer--Telonic Berkeley, Inc., Laguna Beach, CA; *U.S. Private*, pg. 1074
Zimmer, George, Chm. Bd. & Chief Exec. Officer--Men's Wearhouse, Fremont, CA; *U.S. Public*, pg. 1086
Zimmer, William R., Chm. Bd.--Reeds Jewelers, Inc., Wilmington, NC; *U.S. Public*, pg. 1370
Zimmerli, Kurt, Chm. Bd.--Kusters Corporation, Spartanburg, SC; *U.S. Private*, pg. 637
Zimmerli, Kurt, Chm. Bd., Pres., & Chief Exec. Officer--Zima Corporation, Spartanburg, SC; *U.S. Private*, pg. 637
Zimmerman, Adam H., Chm. Bd. & Chief Exec. Officer--Noranda Forest Inc., Toronto, Canada; *Int'l*, pg. 434
Zimmerman, James M., Chm. Bd. & Chief Exec. Officer--Federated Department Stores, Inc., Cincinnati, OH; *U.S. Public*, pg. 617
Zimmerman, John, Chm. Bd.--Sunline Coach Co., Inc., Denver, PA; *U.S. Private*, pg. 1053
Zimmerman, Jordan, Chm. Bd., Pres. & New Bus. Contact--Zimmerman & Partners Advertising, Inc., Fort Lauderdale, FL; *U.S. Private*, pg. 1206
Zimmerman, Martin E., Chm. Bd. & Chief Exec. Officer--LINC Capital Group, Chicago, IL; *U.S. Public*, pg. 996
Zimmermann, F.N., Chm. Bd. & Pres.--March Manufacturing Inc., Glenview, IL; *U.S. Private*, pg. 702
Zinkin, Peter, Chm.--BICC Developments Ltd., London, United Kingdom; *Int'l*, pg. 120
Zirkle, David H., Chm. Bd.--FTP Software Inc., Andover, MA; *U.S. Public*, pg. 609
Zissman, Lorin, Chm. Bd. & Chief Exec. Officer--Total Research Corporation, Princeton, NJ; *U.S. Public*, pg. 1625
Zissu, Frederick, Chm. Emeritus--General Microwave Corporation, Amityville, NY; *U.S. Public*, pg. 717
Zizza, Salvatore, Chm. Bd. & Chief Exec. Officer--The Bethlehem Corporation, Easton, PA; *U.S. Public*, pg. 225

Zizza, Salvatore J., Chm. Bd., Pres. & Chief Exec. Officer--First Medical Group Inc., Stamford, CT; *U.S. Public*, pg. 636

Zoeller, Robert F., Chm. Emeritus--Zoeller Co., Louisville, KY; *U.S. Private*, pg. 1207

Zondervan, A.M., Chm. Bd.--Koninklijke BolsWessanen nv, Amstelveen, Netherlands; *Int'l*, pg. 750

Zook, Woodrow J., Chm. Bd.--The Wooster Brush Company, Wooster, OH; *U.S. Private*, pg. 1188

Zucaro, Aldo C., Chm. Bd., Pres. & Chief Exec. Officer--Old Republic International Corporation, Chicago, IL; *U.S. Public*, pg. 1218

Zuccotti, John E., Chm. Bd. & Chief Exec. Officer--World Financial Properties, Inc., New York, NY; *Int'l*, pg. 1004

Zucker, Jerry, Chm. & Pres.--The Intertech Group Inc., Charleston, SC; *Int'l*, pg. 113

Zuckerman, Mortimer, Chm. Bd.--The Atlantic Monthly Magazine, Boston, MA; *U.S. Private*, pg. 95

Zuckerman, Mortimer B., Chm. Bd. & Editor-in-Chief--U.S. News & World Report, New York, NY; *U.S. Private*, pg. 1125

Zuckerman, Ronald K., Chm. Bd.--Grist Mill Company, Lakeville, MN; *U.S. Public*, pg. 766

Zuckerwar, Richard J., Chm. Bd. & Chief Exec. Officer--The Grandoe Corp., Gloversville, NY; *U.S. Private*, pg. 469

Zufferey, Rene, Chm.--Coop Valais/Wallis, Sion, Switzerland; *Int'l*, pg. 329

Zuhlsdorff, Peter, Chm.-Intl. Div.--MacAndrews & Forbes Holdings Inc., New York, NY; *U.S. Private*, pg. 689

Zuk, Ben, Chm. Bd. & Pres.--Plastic Reel Corp. of America, Lyndhurst, NJ; *U.S. Private*, pg. 871

Zumbaum, Jong, Chm. Bd.--Groschopp & Co. GmbH EMW Elektromotoren-Feinbauwerk, Viersen, Germany; *Int'l*, pg. 559

Zumwinkel, Klaus, Dr., Chm. Bd.--Deutsche Post AG, Bonn, Germany; *Int'l*, pg. 407

ZurSchmiede, W.T., Jr., Chm. Bd., Chief Exec. & Chief Fin. Officer--Federal Screw Works, Detroit, MI; *U.S. Public*, pg. 616

Zweifel, H.H., Chm. Bd.--Cruspi S.A., Dallikon, Switzerland; *Int'l*, pg. 348

Zylstra, Stan, Chm. Bd.--Land O'Lakes, Inc., Arden Hills, MN; *U.S. Private*, pg. 645

CHIEF EXECUTIVE OFFICER

Aagaard, A. Kim, Pres. & Chief Exec. Officer--Synergistics Industries Limited, Mississauga, Canada; *U.S. Public*, pg. 734

Aal, Irv, Pres. & Chief Exec. Officer--Tyler Industries, Benson, MN; *U.S. Private*, pg. 1112

Aanderud, Stephen A., Pres. & Chief Exec. Officer--Thrustmaster, Inc., Hillsboro, OR; *U.S. Public*, pg. 1607

Aaser, Svein, Deputy Chief Exec. Officer--Nycomed Amersham, Oslo, Norway; *Int'l*, pg. 993

Abate, Joseph A., Pres. & Exec. Oper. Officer--Tilcon, Inc., New Britain, CT; *U.S. Private*, pg. 1086

Abbey, Nelson D., III, Pres. & Chief Exec. Officer--Abbey Etna Machine Company, Perrysburg, OH; *U.S. Private*, pg. 9

Abbott, Catherine Good, Pres. & Chief Exec. Officer--Columbia Gas Transmission Corp., Charleston, WV; *U.S. Public*, pg. 403

Abbott, Catherine Good, Chief Exec. Officer--Columbia Gulf Transmission Co., Charleston, WV; *U.S. Public*, pg. 403

Abbott, David L., Pres. & Chief Exec. Officer--Purina Mills, Inc., Saint Louis, MO; *U.S. Private*, pg. 895

Abbott, Michael E., Chm. Bd. & Chief Exec. Officer--American Republic Insurance Co., Des Moines, IA; *U.S. Private*, pg. 61

Abbott, Robert T., Chief Exec. & Chief Oper. Officer--NeoRx Corporation, Seattle, WA; *U.S. Private*, pg. 791

Abbott, Steven R., Pres. & Chief Exec. Officer--Essex International, Inc., Fort Wayne, IN; *U.S. Public*, pg. 593

Abdalla, Herbert A., Pres. & Chief Exec. Officer--Abdalla's Lafayette, Inc., Lafayette, LA; *U.S. Private*, pg. 10

Abdel-Malek, Refaat A., Pres. & Chief Exec. Officer--Harza Engineering Co., Chicago, IL; *U.S. Private*, pg. 509

Abdelmalak, George, Chief Exec. Officer--GAM/DMB&B Beirut, Beirut, Lebanon; *U.S. Private*, pg. 304

Abdoo, Richard A., Chm. Bd., Pres. & Chief Exec. Officer--Wisconsin Energy Corporation, Milwaukee, WI; *U.S. Public*, pg. 1773

Abe, Tomohide, Chief Oper. Officer--Makita Benelux B.V., Son, Netherlands; *Int'l*, pg. 832

Abe, Yoshitaka, Pres & Chief Exec. Officer--Dentsu Young & Rubicam Inc. (Tokyo), Tokyo, Japan; *U.S. Private*, pg. 325

Abelman, Steve, Pres. & Chief Exec. Officer--Oxford Automotive, Inc., Troy, MI; *U.S. Private*, pg. 825

Abelman, Steven M., Deputy Chief Exec.--Bundy International, Warren, MI; *Int'l*, pg. 1340

Abelmann, Ronald A., Pres. & Chief Exec. Officer--Wind River Systems, Inc., Alameda, CA; *U.S. Public*, pg. 1770

Abene, William, Chief Exec. Officer & Sec.--Davidson Printing Company, Duluth, MN; *U.S. Private*, pg. 314

Abernathy, Gary N., Pres. & Chief Exec. Officer--Saztec International, Inc., Billerica, MA; *U.S. Public*, pg. 1435

Ablon, R. Richard, Chm. Bd., Pres. & Chief Exec. Officer--Ogden Corporation, New York, NY; *U.S. Public*, pg. 1213

Ablon, R. Richard, Chm. Bd. & Chief Exec. Officer--Ogden Energy Group, Inc., Fairfield, NJ; *U.S. Public*, pg. 1213

Aboumrad, Alejandro, Chief Exec. Officer--Porcelanite SA de CV, Mexico, Mexico; *Int'l*, pg. 572

Abplanalp, Robert H., Chm. Bd., Pres. & Chief Exec. Officer--Precision Valve Corporation, Yonkers, NY; *U.S. Private*, pg. 880

Abraham, G.M., Chief Exec. Officer & Gen. Mgr.--Screw Conveyor Corp., Hammond, IN; *U.S. Private*, pg. 977

Abraham, Seth G., Pres. & Chief Exec. Officer--Time Warner Sports, New York, NY; *U.S. Public*, pg. 1611

Abrahams, B., Chm. Bd. & Chief Exec. Officer--Greenham Trading Limited, Isleworth, United Kingdom; *Int'l*, pg. 1358

Abrahamson, David A., Pres. & Chief Exec. Officer--Medicine Shoppe International, Inc., Saint Louis, MO; *U.S. Public*, pg. 304

Abram, J. Adam, Pres. & Chief Exec. Officer--Front Royal, Inc., Morrisville, NC; *U.S. Private*, pg. 430

Abrams, Allan, Chm. Bd., Pres., Chief Exec. Officer & Chief Oper. Officer--Arrow Fastener Co., Inc., Saddle Brook, NJ; *U.S. Private*, pg. 85

Abrams, Bernard, Chm. Bd. & Chief Exec. Officer--Three D Departments, Inc., Costa Mesa, CA; *U.S. Public*, pg. 1604

Abrams, Ellen J., Pres. & Chief Exec. Officer--National City Trust Company, West Palm Beach, FL; *U.S. Public*, pg. 1154

Abrams, Leigh J., Pres. & Chief Exec. Officer--Drew Industries Incorporated, White Plains, NY; *U.S. Public*, pg. 529

Abrams, Leigh J., Pres. & Chief Exec. Officer--Leslie Building Products, Inc., White Plains, NY; *U.S. Public*, pg. 989

Abrams, Lloyd R., Pres. & Chief Exec. Officer--Bentley International, Inc., Saint Louis, MO; *U.S. Public*, pg. 212

Abramson, Earl, Chm. Bd. & Pres.--Rapid Mounting & Finishing Co., Chicago, IL; *U.S. Private*, pg. 910

Abramson, Morrie K., Chm. Bd., Pres. & Chief Exec. Officer--Kent Electronics Corp., Houston, TX; *U.S. Public*, pg. 951

Abruzzo, Cloyd J., Pres. & Chief Exec. Officer--Stoneridge, Inc., Warren, OH; *U.S. Private*, pg. 1044

Abu Bakar, Abdul Rahim bin, Chief Exec. Officer & Mng. Dir.--Petroliam Nasional Berhad (Petronas), Kuala Lumpur, Malaysia; *Int'l*, pg. 1046

Ach, Roger W., II, Chm. Bd., Pres. & Chief Exec. Officer--Chicago West Pullman Corporation, Cincinnati, OH; *U.S. Private*, pg. 235

Ackerley, Barry A., Co-Chm. Bd. & Chief Exec. Officer--The Ackerley Group, Seattle, WA; *U.S. Public*, pg. 15

Ackerman, A., Dr., Chief Exec. Officer--Ascom Immobilien AG, Bern, Switzerland; *Int'l*, pg. 86

Ackerman, F. Duane, Pres. & Chief Exec. Officer--BellSouth Corporation, Atlanta, GA; *U.S. Public*, pg. 207

Ackerman, John T., Chm. Bd.--Public Service Company of New Mexico, Albuquerque, NM; *U.S. Public*, pg. 1339

Ackerman, Roger G., Chm. Bd. & Chief Exec. Officer--Corning Incorporated, Corning, NY; *U.S. Public*, pg. 448

Ackerman, Roy A., Chief Exec. Officer--Astre Corporate Group, Alexandria, VA; *U.S. Private*, pg. 93

Ackert, Robert C., Chm. Bd. & Chief Exec. Officer--SouthTrust Bank, Southwest Florida, Fort Myers, FL; *U.S. Public*, pg. 1492

Acridge, James E., Chm. Bd., Pres. & Chief Exec. Officer--Giant Industries Inc., Scottsdale, AZ; *U.S. Public*, pg. 741

Adam, A., Pres. & Chief Exec. Officer--Algoma Steel Inc., Sault Sainte Marie, Canada; *Int'l*, pg. 56

Adam, Klaus G., Chief Exec. Officer--Landesbank Rheinland-Pfalz, Mainz, Germany; *Int'l*, pg. 799

Adam, P.J., Chm. Bd. & Chief Exec. Officer--Black & Veatch, Kansas City, MO; *U.S. Private*, pg. 146

Adams, Charles R., Chm. Bd. & Chief Exec. Officer--Chad Therapeutics, Chatsworth, CA; *U.S. Public*, pg. 332

Adams, Donald E., Pres. & Chief Exec. Officer--SouthTrust Mobile Services, Birmingham, AL; *U.S. Public*, pg. 1492

Adams, Frank A., Pres. & Chief Exec. Officer--Grotech Capital Group, Inc., Timonium, MD; *U.S. Private*, pg. 483

Adams, Fred, Chief Exec. Officer--Cal-Maine Foods, Inc., Jackson, MS; *U.S. Public*, pg. 292

Adams, Jacob, Chm. Bd., Pres. & Chief Exec. Officer--Arctic Slope Regional Corporation, Barrow, AK; *U.S. Private*, pg. 80

Adams, John, Chm. & Chief Exec. Officer--The Martin Agency, Richmond, VA; *U.S. Private*, pg. 678

Adams, John B., Jr., Chm. & Chief Exec. Officer--The Martin Agency, Richmond, VA; *U.S. Private*, pg. 678

Adams, John B., Jr., Chm. & Chief Exec. Officer--The Martin Agency, Richmond, VA; *U.S. Public*, pg. 909

Adams, John C., Chm. Bd., Pres. & Chief Exec. Officer--Russell Corporation, Alexander City, AL; *U.S. Public*, pg. 1413

Adams, John W., Chm. Bd. & Chief Exec. Officer--Harvard Industries, Inc., Tampa, FL; *U.S. Public*, pg. 796

Adams, Johnston C., Chm. Bd. & Chief Exec. Officer--AutoZone, Inc., Memphis, TN; *U.S. Public*, pg. 150

Adams, K.S., Jr., Chm. Bd., Pres. & Chief Exec. Officer--Adams Resources & Energy, Inc., Houston, TX; *U.S. Public*, pg. 18

Adams, Ken, Chief Exec. Officer--SunGard Technology Systems Group, Wayne, PA; *U.S. Public*, pg. 1535

Adams, Kenneth R., Grp. Chief Exec. Officer-SunGard Healthcare Information Systems--SunGard Data Systems Inc., Wayne, PA; *U.S. Public*, pg. 1534

Adams, Peter D., Chm. Bd. & Chief Exec. Officer--Adams Rite Manufacturing Co., City of Industry, CA; *U.S. Private*, pg. 17

Adams, R. Dale, Pres. & Chief Exec. Officer--First National Bank of Marshall, Marshall, IL; *U.S. Public*, pg. 634

Adams, Richard B., Pres., Chief Exec. Officer & Treas.--R.P. Adams Company, Inc., Tonawanda, NY; *U.S. Public*, pg. 19

Adams, Richard M., Chm. Bd. & Chief Exec. Officer--United Bankshares, Inc., Parkersburg, WV; *U.S. Public*, pg. 1674

Adams, Robert E., Pres. & Chief Exec. Officer--MidSouth Ice Co., Huntsville, AL; *U.S. Private*, pg. 1025

Adams, W Randolph, Chief Exec. Officer--Mississippi Valley Advisors Inc., Saint Louis, MO; *U.S. Public*, pg. 1087

Adams, W. Randolph, Chm. Bd. & Chief Exec. Officer--Mercantile Bank of St. Louis N.A., Saint Louis, MO; *U.S. Public*, pg. 1087

Adams, W. Randolph, Chief Exec. Officer--Mercantile Investment Services, Inc., Saint Louis, MO; *U.S. Public*, pg. 1087

Adamson, James B., Chm. Bd., Pres. & Chief Exec. Officer--Advantica Restaurant Group, Inc., Spartanburg, SC; *U.S. Public*, pg. 22

Adamson, Tom, Chief Exec. Officer--Commercial Construction Div., Bloomington, MN; *U.S. Public*, pg. 120

Adderley, Terence E., Pres. & Chief Exec. Officer--Kelly Services, Inc., Troy, MI; *U.S. Public*, pg. 949

Addison, E. Christopher, Chm. Bd.--Addison Steel Inc., Albany, GA; *U.S. Private*, pg. 17

Adereth, Jonathan, Pres. & Chief Exec. Officer--Elscint Ltd., Haifa, Israel; *Int'l*, pg. 450

Ades, Alan, Chm. Bd., Pres. & Chief Exec. Officer--A&E Stores, Inc., Teterboro, NJ; *U.S. Private*, pg. 1

Adikes, Park T., Chm. Bd. & Chief Exec. Officer--JSB Financial, Lynbrook, NY; *U.S. Public*, pg. 919

Adkins, Ralph J., Chm. Bd. & Chief Exec. Officer--Chesapeake Utilities Corporation, Dover, DE; *U.S. Public*, pg. 347

Adkinson, C. Wayne, Pres. & Chief Exec. Officer--Regions Investments, Inc., Birmingham, AL; *U.S. Public*, pg. 1371

Adkison, Peter, Pres. & Chief Exec. Officer--Wizards of the Coast, Renton, WA; *U.S. Private*, pg. 1185

Adkison, Peter, Pres. & Chief Exec. Officer--TSR, Inc., Renton, WA; *U.S. Private*, pg. 1185

Adler, Larry M., Pres. & Chief Exec. Officer--Adler Boschetto Peebles & Partners, Inc., New York, NY; *U.S. Private*, pg. 17

Adler, Michael F., Chm. Bd. & Chief Exec. Officer--Moto Photo, Inc., Dayton, OH; *U.S. Public*, pg. 1136

Adler, Myron, Pres. & Chief Exec. Officer--Myron Manufacturing Corporation, Maywood, NJ; *U.S. Private*, pg. 771

Adler, Robert, Pres. & Chief Exec. Officer--Vintage Blue, Arleta, CA; *U.S. Public*, pg. 948

Adler, Robert W., Pres. & Chief Exec. Officer--Halmode Apparel, Inc., New York, NY; *U.S. Public*, pg. 948

Adolff, Peter, Dr., Chief Exec. Officer--Allianz Versicherungs-AG, Stuttgart, Germany; *Int'l*, pg. 58

Adorjan, J. Joe, Chm. Bd., Pres. & Chief Exec. Officer--Borg-Warner Security Corporation, Chicago, IL; *U.S. Public*, pg. 245

Adrean, Lee, Pres. & Chief Exec. Officer--Peoples Security Insurance Company, Durham, NC; *Int'l*, pg. 27

Aerne, Bruno, Chief Exec.--Morning Star Cement Ltd., Ho Chi Minh City, Vietnam; *Int'l*, pg. 629

Afeyan, Noubar B., Chm. Bd. & Chief Exec. Officer--PerSeptive Biosystems, Inc., Framingham, MA; *U.S. Public*, pg. 1279

Agan, R.E., Chm. Bd., & Chief Exec. Officer--Hardings, Inc., Elmira, NY; *U.S. Private*, pg. 502

Agarow, Uma N., Pres. & Chief Exec. Officer--Allied Healthcare Products, Inc., Saint Louis, MO; *U.S. Public*, pg. 48

Aginian, Richard D., Pres. & Chief Exec. Officer--HomeTown Communications Network, Inc., Livonia, MI; *U.S. Private*, pg. 537

Aginsky, Phillip C., Chm. Bd. & Chief Exec. Officer--Tekgraf, Inc., Norcross, GA; *U.S. Private*, pg. 1073

Aglialoro, John, Chm. Bd. & Chief Exec. Officer--U.M. Holding Limited, Haddonfield, NJ; *U.S. Private*, pg. 1113

Agresti, Jack J., Pres. & Chief Exec. Officer--Atkinson, San Bruno, CA; *U.S. Public*, pg. 143

Aguilar, Estuardo, Pres. & Chief Exec. Officer--Dos:Puntos, Guatemala, Guatemala; *U.S. Private*, pg. 304

Aguilar, Pedro, Pres. & Chief Exec. Officer-DMB&B/Spain--D'Arcy Masius Benton & Bowles, S.A., Madrid, Spain; *U.S. Private*, pg. 304

Aguirre, A., Chief Exec. Officer--Zurich Insurance (Guam), Inc., Agana, GU; *Int'l*, pg. 1532

Aguirre, Carlos E., Chm. Bd., Pres. & Chief Exec. Officer--Oregon Metallurgical Corporation, Albany, OR; *U.S. Public*, pg. 43

Aguirre, G., Chief Exec. Officer--Compania de Seguros La Chilena Consolidada, Santiago, Chile; *Int'l*, pg. 1531

Aharonian, Steve, M.D., Chief Exec. Officer--Facey Medical Foundation, Mission Hills, CA; *U.S. Private*, pg. 1118

Ahearn, Joseph M., Pres. & Chief Exec. Officer--Toy Biz, Inc., New York, NY; *U.S. Public*, pg. 1625

Ahearn, Lance W., Chm. Bd. & Chief Exec. Officer--RMT, Inc., Madison, WI; *U.S. Public*, pg. 1728

Ahearn, Lance W., Pres. & Chief Exec. Officer--ENSERV, Inc., Madison, WI; *U.S. Public*, pg. 1728

Ahearn, Lance W., Pres. & Chief Exec. Officer--Heartland Development Corporation, Madison, WI; *U.S. Public*, pg. 1728

Ahern, John E., Chm. Bd. & Chief Exec. Officer--J.F. Ahern Co., Fond Du Lac, WI; *U.S. Private*, pg. 27

Ahern, Joseph M., Pres. & Chief Exec. Officer--Colorforms, Ramsey, NJ; *U.S. Public*, pg. 1625

Ahlmann, Kaj, Chm., Pres. & Chief Exec. Officer--Employers Reinsurance Corp., Overland Park, KS; *U.S. Public*, pg. 711

Ahlstrom, Krister, Pres. & Chief Exec. Officer--A. Ahlstrom Corporation, Helsinki, Finland; *Int'l*, pg. 32

Ahrens, Jay, Chm. Bd., Pres. & Chief Exec. Officer--Holly's Inc., Grand Rapids, MI; *U.S. Private*, pg. 535

Ahs, Bjorn, Pres. & Chief Exec. Officer--Kvaerner Pulping Technologies AB, Goteborg, Sweden; *Int'l*, pg. 768

Aiken, Hugh, Chm. Bd. & Chief Exec. Officer--Prospect Foundry, Inc., Minneapolis, MN; *U.S. Public*, pg. 142

Aiken, Hugh H., Chm. Bd., Pres. & Chief Exec. Officer--Atchison Casting Corporation, Atchison, KS; *U.S. Public*, pg. 142

Aiken, William, Chm. Bd. & Chief Exec. Officer--ACO Inc., Farmington Hills, MI; *U.S. Private*, pg. 3

Aikens, P., Chief Exec. Officer--Matthew Clark Taunton, Ltd., Bristol, United Kingdom; *Int'l*, pg. 848

Aikens, Peter, Chief Exec.--Taunton Cider Company P.L.C., Taunton, United Kingdom; *Int'l*, pg. 849

Ailleret, Francois, Chief Exec. Officer--Electricite de France, Paris, France; *Int'l*, pg. 437

Ain, Mark S., Chm. Bd. & Chief Exec. Officer--Kronos Incorporated, Waltham, MA; *U.S. Public*, pg. 967

Ainsworth, A.J., Chief Exec. Officer-European Engineered Fabrics--Scapa Group Plc, Blackburn, United Kingdom; *Int'l*, pg. 1202

Aitken, Timothy M., Chm. Bd. & Chief Exec. Officer--Transworld Home Healthcare, Inc., New York, NY; *U.S. Public*, pg. 1632
Akers, William C., II, Pres. & Chief Exec. Officer--Akers Packaging Service Inc., Middletown, OH; *U.S. Private*, pg. 29
Akerson, Daniel F., Chm. Bd. & Chief Exec. Officer--Nextel Communications, Mc Lean, VA; *U.S. Public*, pg. 1180
Akhtar, M. Saleem, Chief Exec. Officer & Sr. Exec. V.P.--Habib Credit & Exchange Bank Ltd., Karachi, Pakistan; *Int'l*, pg. 584
Akin, Bruce, Exec. V.P. & Chief Exec. Officer-Oxmoor House Books--Southern Progress Corporation, Birmingham, AL; *U.S. Public*, pg. 1612
Akizawa, Takashi, Pres. & Chief Exec. Officer--Ishihara Sangyo Kaisha, Ltd., Osaka, Japan; *Int'l*, pg. 689
Akton, Richard A., Pres. & Chief Exec. Officer--Bell Atlantic TeleProducts Corp., Exton, PA; *U.S. Public*, pg. 203
Alagen, Beny, Chm. Bd., Pres. & Chief Exec. Officer--Packard Bell NEC, Sacramento, CA; *U.S. Private*, pg. 833
Albani, Thomas, Pres. & Chief Exec. Officer--Electrolux Corporation, Atlanta, GA; *U.S. Private*, pg. 369
Albarran, Roberto, Chief Exec. Officer--Jugos del Valle, S.A. de C.V., Mexico, Mexico; *Int'l*, pg. 716
Albert, Andrew B., Co-Chm. Bd. & Co-Chief Exec. Officer--Rittenhouse Inc., Park Ridge, IL; *U.S. Private*, pg. 933
Albert, Carl, Chm. Bd. & Chief Exec. Officer--Fairchild Aerospace Corporation, San Antonio, TX; *U.S. Private*, pg. 391
Albert, Carl A., Chm. Bd. & Chief Exec. Officer--Fairchild Dornier USA, San Antonio, TX; *U.S. Private*, pg. 391
Albert, Frita, Chief Exec. Officer--Mueller's Muehle GmbH, Gelsenkirchen, Germany; *Int'l*, pg. 896
Albert, Michael P., Chm. Bd. & Pres.--The Harodite Finishing Company Inc., North Dighton, MA; *U.S. Private*, *pg. 503*
Alberthal, Lester M., Jr., Chm. Bd. & Chief Exec. Officer--Electronic Data Systems Corporation, Plano, TX; *U.S. Public*, pg. 569
Albrecht, Arlin, Pres. & Chief Exec. Officer--Red Wing Publishing Company, Red Wing, MN; *U.S. Private*, pg. 915
Albrecht, Steven, Chm. Bd., Pres. & Chief Exec. Officer--The Fred W. Albrecht Grocery Co., Akron, OH; *U.S. Private*, pg. 32
Alcock, G.L., Jr., Pres. & Chief Exec. Officer--S. Bent & Brothers, Inc., Gardner, MA; *U.S. Private*, pg. 134
Alcone, Matt, Chm. Bd. & Chief Exec. Officer--Alcone Marketing Group, Irvine, CA; *U.S. Public*, pg. 1223
Alcorn, David S., Chm. Bd. & Chief Exec. Officer--Donlee Technologies Inc., York, PA; *U.S. Private*, pg. 339
Aldinger, William F., Chm. Bd. & Chief Exec. Officer--Household International, Inc., Prospect Heights, IL; *U.S. Public*, pg. 842
Aldred, P.J., Pres. & Chief Exec. Officer--Enerflex Systems Ltd., Calgary, Canada; *Int'l*, pg. 1400
Aldridge, Edward C., Pres. & Chief Exec. Officer--Aerospace Corporation, El Segundo, CA; *U.S. Private*, pg. 24
Aldwinckle, Richard, Deputy Chief Exec.--Scope Ketchum Communications Ltd., London, United Kingdom; *U.S. Private*, pg. 617
Alejandro, Gerardo F., Chief Exec. Officer--Avia EURO RSCG, Manila, Philippines; *Int'l*, pg. 602
Aleu, Dr. Fernando, Chief Exec. Officer--Paco Rabanne Compar, New York, NY; *Int'l*, pg. 1073
Alewine, Betty C., Pres. & Chief Exec. Officer--COMSAT Corporation, Bethesda, MD; *U.S. Public*, pg. 424
Alexander, Helen, Pres. & Chief Exec. Officer--The Economist Group Limited., London, United Kingdom; *Int'l*, pg. 1026
Alexander, Kobi, Chm. Bd., Pres. & Chief Exec. Officer--Comverse Technology, Inc., Woodbury, NY; *U.S. Public*, pg. 425
Alexander, Margo N., Chief Exec. Officer--Mitchell Hutchins Asset Management Inc., New York, NY; *U.S. Public*, pg. 1253
Alexander, Michael, Chm. Bd. & Chief Exec. Officer--Intermetrics, Inc., Burlington, MA; *U.S. Private*, pg. 567
Alexander, Norman E., Chm. Bd. & Chief Exec. Officer--Sequa Corporation, New York, NY; *U.S. Public*, pg. 1458
Alexander, Patrick D., Chm. Bd. & Chief Exec. Officer--Cold Spring Granite Company, Cold Spring, MN; *U.S. Private*, pg. 250
Alexander, Stanford, Chm. Bd. & Chief Exec. Officer--Weingarten Realty Investors, Houston, TX; *U.S. Public*, pg. 1751
Alexander, William B., Chm. Bd. & Chief Exec. Officer--Turnbull Enterprises, Inc., Baltimore, MD; *U.S. Private*, pg. 1109
Alexy, R. James, Pres. & Chief Exec. Officer--Network Services Company, Mount Prospect, IL; *U.S. Private*, pg. 791
Aley, Paul N., Pres. & Chief Exec. Officer--National Machinery, Tiffin, OH; *U.S. Private*, pg. 785
Alfano, James C., Pres. & Chief Exec. Officer--Stelco Inc., Hamilton, Canada; *Int'l*, pg. 1299
Alfi, Moataz Al, Chm. & Chief Exec. Officer--Cairo Foods Industries SAE, Cairo, Egypt; *U.S. Public*, pg. 806
Alfiero, Sal H., Chm. Bd. & Chief Exec. Officer--Mark IV Industries Inc., Amherst, NY; *U.S. Public*, pg. 1044
Alger, David D., Pres. & Chief Exec. Officer--Castle Convertible Fund, Inc., New York, NY; *U.S. Public*, pg. 313
Alibrandi, Joseph F., Chm. Bd., Pres. & Chief Exec. Officer--Whittaker Corporation, Simi Valley, CA; *U.S. Public*, pg. 1766
Alkis, H., Pres. & Chief Exec. Officer--Kusters Corporation, Spartanburg, SC; *U.S. Private*, pg. 637
Allain, Lee, Chief Exec. Officer--Micro Networks Corp., Worcester, MA; *U.S. Private*, pg. 969
Allaire, Paul A., Chm. Bd., Chief Exec. Officer & Chm.-Exec. Committee--Xerox Corporation, Stamford, CT; *U.S. Public*, pg. 1783
Allard, Jean Marc, Chm. Bd., Pres. & Chief Exec. Officer--Hubbard Construction Co., Winter Park, FL; *U.S. Private*, *pg. 544*
Allard, John, Chief Exec. Officer--Granite State Manufacturing Co., Manchester, NH; *U.S. Private*, pg. 36
Allard, John R., Pres. & Chief Exec. Officer--The Jewell Electrical Instruments Co., Manchester, NH; *U.S. Private*, *pg. 36*
Allbritton, J.L., Chm. Bd. & Chief Exec. Officer--Riggs National Corporation, Washington, DC; *U.S. Public*, pg. 1389
Allbritton, Joe L., Chm. Bd. & Chief Exec. Officer--Perpetual Corporation, Washington, DC; *U.S. Private*, pg. 854
Allemand, Jacques, Chm. Bd. & Chief Exec. Officer--GTM Construction, Nanterre, France; *Int'l*, pg. 823
Allen, Bill, Chief Exec. Officer--Koo Koo Roo, Inc., Los Angeles, CA; *U.S. Public*, pg. 966
Allen, Bob D., Pres. & Chief Exec. Officer--Consolidated-Tomoka Land Co., Daytona Beach, FL; *U.S. Public*, pg. 437
Allen, Brent, Chm. Bd. & Chief Exec. Officer--Lifetime Products Inc., Clearfield, UT; *U.S. Private*, pg. 667
Allen, Charles, Chief Exec.--Granada Group PLC, London, United Kingdom; *Int'l*, pg. 556
Allen, Charles S., Pres. & Chief Exec. Officer--Sloan Valve Company, Franklin Park, IL; *U.S. Private*, pg. 1006
Allen, Darryl F., Chm. Bd., Pres. & Chief Exec. Officer--Aeroquip-Vickers, Inc., Maumee, OH; *U.S. Public*, pg. 24
Allen, David, Chm. Bd., Pres., Chief Exec. Officer & Chief Fin. Officer--AMD Industries Inc., Cicero, IL; *U.S. Private*, *pg. 6*
Allen, David, Chief Exec.--Sampson Tyrrell Enterprise, London, United Kingdom; *Int'l*, pg. 1482
Allen, Delbert E., Jr., Pres. & Chief Exec. Officer--Allen Canning Company, Siloam Springs, AR; *U.S. Private*, pg. 36
Allen, G.J., Chief Exec. Officer & Mng. Dir.--IMI Plc, Witton, United Kingdom; *Int'l*, pg. 646
Allen, Herbert A., Pres. & Chief Exec. Officer--Allen & Company Incorporated, New York, NY; *U.S. Private*, pg. 36
Allen, J. William Jr., Pres. & Chief Exec. Officer--J.W. Allen & Company, Wheeling, IL; *U.S. Private*, pg. 37
Allen, Leon, Chm. Bd. & Chief Exec. Officer--The Tetley Group Limited, Greenford, United Kingdom; *Int'l*, pg. 1377
Allen, Robert, Chief Exec. Officer--Core-Mark International, South San Francisco, CA; *U.S. Private*, pg. 275
Allen, Roderick L., Chm. Bd. & Chief Exec. Officer--Allen Canning Company, Siloam Springs, AR; *U.S. Private*, pg. 36
Allen, Ronald, Chm. Bd., Pres. & Chief Exec. Officer--American Foodservice Corp., King of Prussia, PA; *U.S. Private*, pg. 54
Allen, Thomas W., Chm. Bd. & Chief Exec. Officer--First Midwest Trust Company, N.A., Joliet, IL; *U.S. Public*, pg. 636
Allen, Thomas W., Pres. & Chief Exec. Officer--Vernay Laboratories, Inc., Yellow Springs, OH; *U.S. Private*, pg. 1137
Allen, W.W., Chm. Bd. & Chief Exec. Officer--Phillips Petroleum Company, Bartlesville, OK; *U.S. Public*, pg. 1290
Allender, Richard C., Chm. Bd., Pres. & Chief Exec. Officer--Farah Incorporated, El Paso, TX; *U.S. Public*, pg. 612
Allenspach, W., Chief Exec. Officer--Zurich International de Venezuela C.A. de Corretaje de Reaseguros, Caracas, Venezuela; *Int'l*, pg. 1532
Allington, Robert W., Chm. Bd. & Chief Exec. Officer--Isco, Inc., Lincoln, NE; *U.S. Public*, pg. 913
Allione, Miro, Chief Exec. Officer--Stream, Rome, Italy; *Int'l*, pg. 1363
Allison, Gerald L., Chief Exec. Officer--AJC International, Inc., Atlanta, GA; *U.S. Private*, pg. 6
Allison, John A., Chm. Bd. & Chief Exec. Officer--BB&T Corporation, Winston Salem, NC; *U.S. Public*, pg. 159
Allison, Robert J., Jr., Chm. Bd., Pres. & Chief Exec. Officer--Anadarko Petroleum Corporation, Houston, TX; *U.S. Public*, pg. 107
Allred, Barry L., Pres. & Chief Exec. Officer--Elkins Constructors, Inc., Jacksonville, FL; *U.S. Private*, pg. 372
Almeida Garcia, Victor D., Vice Chm. & Chief Exec. Officer--Internacional de Ceramica S.A. de C.V., Chihuahua, Mexico; *Int'l*, pg. 680
Almeida, Richard J., Chm. Bd., Pres. & Chief Exec. Officer--Heller International Corporation, Chicago, IL; *Int'l*, pg. 519
Almeida, Richard J., Chm. & Chief Exec. Officer--Heller International Group, Inc., Chicago, IL; *Int'l*, pg. 519
Almeida, Richard J., Chm. Bd., Pres. & Chief Exec. Officer--Heller International, Chicago, IL; *U.S. Private*, pg. 520
Alonso, Jose Garcia, Chief Exec. Officer-Fin. Corp.--Caja de Madrid Group, Madrid, Spain; *Int'l*, pg. 251
Aloukos, Alexandrou, Dir. Gen.--Olympic Airtours, Athens, Greece; *Int'l*, pg. 1004
Alper, Martin, Pres. & Chief Exec. Officer--Virgin Interactive Entertainment Inc., Irvine, CA; *U.S. Private*, pg. 776
Alperin, Jeff, Chief Exec. Officer-Western Div.--Grey Advertising Inc., Western Div., Los Angeles, CA; *U.S. Public*, pg. 764
Alpert, Norman R., Chm. Bd., Pres. & Chief Exec. Officer--Bio-Tek Instruments, Inc., Winooski, VT; *U.S. Private*, pg. 144
Alred, Michael W., Chm. Bd. & Chief Exec. Officer--SouthTrust Bank of Marshall County, Boaz, AL; *U.S. Public*, pg. 1492
Alter, Dennis, Chm. Bd. & Chief Exec. Officer--Advanta Corp., Spring House, PA; *U.S. Public*, pg. 22
Althaver, Lambert E., Chm. Bd. & Chief Exec. Officer--Walbro Corporation, Cass City, MI; *U.S. Public*, pg. 1733
Altheim, Philip, Chief Exec. Officer--Forest Electric Corp., New York, NY; *U.S. Public*, pg. 571
Altman, Robert, Pres. & Chief Exec. Officer--General Media International Inc., New York, NY; *U.S. Private*, pg. 444
Alton, John W., Pres.--Minerallac Co., Addison, IL; *U.S. Private*, pg. 750
Altorfer, Rolf, Pres. & Chief Exec. officer--Panalpina, Inc., Jersey City, NJ; *Int'l*, pg. 1022
Alvarez Perez, Angel, Pres. & Chief Exec. Officer--Firstbank Puerto Rico, Santurce, PR; *U.S. Public*, pg. 644
Alvarez, Antonio, III, Chief Exec. Officer--Long MFG. NC, Inc., Tarboro, NC; *U.S. Private*, pg. 674
Alvarez, Eduardo R., Pres. & Chief Exec. Officer--Consolidated ORIX Leasing and Finance Corporation, Manila, Philippines; *Int'l*, pg. 1009
Alvarez, Marcial Portela, Chief Exec. Officer-Telefonica Internacional S.A.--Telefonica de Espana, S.A., Madrid, Spain; *Int'l*, pg. 1371
Alvarez, Tony, Chm. Bd., Pres. & Chief Exec. Officer--Wherehouse Entertainment, Inc., Torrance, CA; *U.S. Private*, pg. 1171
Amaral, Donald J., Chm. Bd. & Chief Exec. Officer--Coram Healthcare Corporation, Denver, CO; *U.S. Public*, pg. 446
Amemiya, M., Chm. Bd. & Chief Exec. Officer--Interkal, Inc., Kalamazoo, MI; *Int'l*, pg. 759
Amenduni, Michele, Chief Exec. Officer & Gen. Mgr.--Fiscambi Leasing Sud S.p.A., Bari, Italy; *Int'l*, pg. 138
Amerman, John, Chief Exec. Officer--Mattel Games/Puzzles, El Segundo, CA; *U.S. Public*, pg. 1058
Amerson, Robert, Pres. & Chief Exec. Officer--Flanders Corp., Washington, NC; *U.S. Public*, pg. 648
Ames, A. Gary, Pres. & Chief Exec. Officer-Intl.--U S West Inc., Englewood, CO; *U.S. Public*, pg. 1688
Ames, Richard S., Chm. Bd., Pres. & Chief Exec. Officer--Command Plastic Corporation, Akron, OH; *U.S. Private*, pg. 257
Ames, Roger, Chm. Bd. & Chief Exec. Officer--PolyGram International Ltd., London, United Kingdom; *Int'l*, pg. 1053
Amin, Mark S., Chm. Bd. & Chief Exec. Officer--Trimark Holdings, Inc., Santa Monica, CA; *U.S. Public*, pg. 1638
Aminian, Gary, Pres. & Chief Exec. Officer--BIW Cable Systems, Inc., Franklin, MA; *Int'l*, pg. 417
Amman, Robert J., Chm., Pres. & Chief Exec. Officer--John H. Harland Company, Decatur, GA; *U.S. Public*, pg. 785
Ammerman, Robert T., Chief Exec. Officer--American Buildings Co., Eufaula, AL; *U.S. Public*, pg. 69
Amos, Daniel P., Pres. & Chief Exec. Officer--AFLAC Incorporated, Columbus, GA; *U.S. Public*, pg. 28
Amsbaugh, Jeffry K., Pres. & Chief Exec. Officer--Nobel Insurance Limited, Hamilton, Bermuda; *Int'l*, pg. 951
Amster, Harry S., Chief Exec. Officer--A S H, Inc., Phoenix, AZ; *U.S. Private*, pg. 2
Anagnostopolous, Georgios, Chief Exec. Officer & Dir. Gen.--Olympic Catering, Athens, Greece; *Int'l*, pg. 1004
Anchel, Edward, Chm. Bd. & Pres.--Altec Lansing Technologies, Inc., Milford, PA; *U.S. Private*, pg. 479
Ancira Elizondo, Alonso, Vice Chm. & Chief Exec. Officer--Grupo Acerero del Norte S.A. de C.V. (GAN), Mexico, Mexico; *Int'l*, pg. 572
Andereck, Michael D., Pres. & Chief Exec. Officer--DocuCorp International, Dallas, TX; *U.S. Public*, pg. 1425
Anderson, A. Scott, Pres. & Chief Exec. Officer--Zions First National Bank, Salt Lake City, UT; *U.S. Public*, pg. 1793
Anderson, Alan, Pres. & Chief Exec. Officer--Quintus Corporation, Fremont, CA; *U.S. Private*, pg. 901
Anderson, Bruce, Pres. & Chief Exec. Officer--IWI Holding Limited, Westmont, IL; *U.S. Public*, pg. 861
Anderson, Carl H., Pres. & Chief Exec. Officer--Paragon Life Insurance Co., Saint Louis, MO; *U.S. Private*, pg. 443
Anderson, Clyde, Pres. & Chief Exec. Officer--Books-A-Million, Inc., Birmingham, AL; *U.S. Public*, pg. 244
Anderson, Craig, Pres.--The Hercules Tire & Rubber Company, Findlay, OH; *U.S. Private*, pg. 523
Anderson, Curtis, Chm. & Chief Exec. Officer--Arrow Tru-Line, Inc., Archbold, OH; *U.S. Private*, pg. 85
Anderson, Davis G., Chief Exec. Officer--Chicago Extruded Metals Co., Cicero, IL; *U.S. Private*, pg. 234
Anderson, Donald C., Pres. & Chief Exec. Officer--Norwest Agricultural Credit, Inc., Sioux Falls, SD; *U.S. Public*, pg. 1201
Anderson, Doug, Pres. & Chief Exec. Officer--Rent-A-Center, Inc., Wichita, KS; *Int'l*, pg. 1385
Anderson, Doug, Pres. & Chief Exec. Officer--Remco America, Inc., Wichita, KS; *Int'l*, pg. 1385
Anderson, Edward R., Pres. & Chief Exec. Officer--CompuCom Systems, Inc., Dallas, TX; *U.S. Public*, pg. 1424
Anderson, Edward, R., Chm. Bd., Pres. & Chief Exec. Officer--Rose's Stores, Inc., Henderson, NC; *U.S. Public*, *pg. 1405*
Anderson, Eric E., Pres. & Chief Exec. Officer--Aviall, Inc., Dallas, TX; *U.S. Public*, pg. 154
Anderson, Frank O., Pres. & Chief Exec. Officer--Hobart Brothers Co., Troy, OH; *U.S. Public*, pg. 866
Anderson, Fred, Pres. & Chief Exec. Officer--Stewart Smith West, Inc., Los Angeles, CA; *Int'l*, pg. 1508
Anderson, G.D., Jr., Pres. & Chief Exec. Officer--Sherley Grain Company, Bovina, TX; *U.S. Private*, pg. 993
Anderson, Gary, Pres. & Chief Exec. Officer--IDS Trust Co., Minneapolis, MN; *U.S. Public*, pg. 73
Anderson, Gavin, Chm. Bd. & Chief Exec. Officer--Gavin Anderson & Company, New York, NY; *U.S. Public*, pg. 1223
Anderson, Gordon M., Chm. Bd. & Chief Exec. Officer--Santa Fe International Corporation, Dallas, TX; *Int'l*, pg. 765
Anderson, Ivan V., Jr., Pres.--Evening Post Publishing Co., Charleston, SC; *U.S. Private*, pg. 385
Anderson, James, Chm. Bd., Chief Exec. Officer & Pres.--Anderson Brothers Construction Brainerd, Brainerd, MN; *U.S. Private*, pg. 72

Anderson, Jeff, Pres. & Chief Exec. Officer--Gerry Sportswear Company, Mercer Island, WA; *U.S. Private*, pg. 449
Anderson, John H., Chm. Bd. & Chief Exec. Officer--BT Financial Corporation, Johnstown, PA; *U.S. Public*, pg. 163
Anderson, Kent T., Chm. Bd., Pres. & Chief Exec. Officer--B.B. Walker Company, Asheboro, NC; *U.S. Public*, pg. 1734
Anderson, Lee R., Sr., Chm. Bd. & Chief Exec. Officer--API Group Inc., Saint Paul, MN; *U.S. Private*, pg. 7
Anderson, Lowell C., Chm. Bd., Pres. & Chief Exec. Officer--Allianz Life Insurance Company of North America, Minneapolis, MN; *Int'l*, pg. 58
Anderson, Mac, Chief Exec. Officer--Successories, Inc., Aurora, IL; *U.S. Private*, pg. 1049
Anderson, Michael H., Chm. Bd., Pres. & Chief Exec. Officer--Hogan Systems, Inc., Dallas, TX; *U.S. Public*, pg. 422
Anderson, R. John, Chief Exec. Officer, Ladbroke Group Properties--Ladbroke Group Plc, London, United Kingdom; *Int'l*, pg. 787
Anderson, Ralph, Chm Bd., Pres., & Chief Exec. Officer--Belcan Corporation, Cincinnati, OH; *U.S. Private*, pg. 131
Anderson, Ray C., Chm. Bd. & Chief Exec. Officer--Interface Inc., Atlanta, GA; *U.S. Public*, pg. 889
Anderson, Richard E., Chm. Bd. & Chief Exec. Officer--Cadet Manufacturing Company, Vancouver, WA; *U.S. Private*, pg. 198
Anderson, Richard P., Chm. Bd. & Chief Exec. Officer--The Andersons Incorporated, Maumee, OH; *U.S. Public*, pg. 111
Anderson, Ronald G., Pres. & Chief Exec. Officer--GretagMacbeth LLC, New Windsor, NY; *U.S. Public*, pg. 965
Anderson, Ruel L., Jr., Pres. & Chief Exec. Officer--Anco Insulations, Inc., Baton Rouge, LA; *U.S. Private*, pg. 71
Anderson, T.I., Pres. & Chief Exec. Officer--W.J. & Dennis Co., Elgin, IL; *U.S. Private*, pg. 1144
Anderson, Winston H., Chief Exec. Officer--Piedmont Mechanical, Inc., Spartanburg, SC; *U.S. Private*, pg. 865
Andersson, Alf, Chief Officer--Juvelbagerierna AB, Stockholm, Sweden; *Int'l*, pg. 718
Andison, R.G., Chief Exec. Officer--Powell Equipment Ltd., Winnipeg, Canada; *Int'l*, pg. 1066
Andraside, James S., Pres. & Chief Exec. Officer--Mauna Loa Macadamia Nut Corporation, Hilo, HI; *U.S. Private*, pg. 190
Andrea, Frank A.D., Jr., Chm. Bd. & Chief Exec. Officer--Andrea Electronics Corporation, Long Island City, NY; *U.S. Public*, pg. 112
Andreas, David L., Chm. Bd. & Chief Exec. Officer--National City Bancorp, Minneapolis, MN; *U.S. Public*, pg. 1153
Andreas, G. Allen, Pres. & Chief Exec. Officer--Archer Daniels Midland Company (ADM), Decatur, IL; *U.S. Public*, pg. 127
Andress, Jim, Chief Exec. Officer--Warner-Chilcott Laboratories, Inc., Rockaway, NJ; *Int'l*, pg. 436
Andretta, Vincent J., Pres., Chief Exec. Officer & Treas.--Colony Liquor Distributors, Inc., Kingston, NY; *U.S. Private*, pg. 254
Andrews, Charles E., Pres. & Chief Exec. Officer--Sunbelt Beverages, Lutherville, MD; *U.S. Private*, pg. 1051
Andrews, Dennis, Chief Exec. Officer & V.P.--Electronic Systems Packaging Corp., Rancho Dominguez, CA; *U.S. Private*, pg. 370
Andrews, Gerald B., Chief Exec. Officer--Opp Micolas Mills Inc., Opp, AL; *U.S. Public*, pg. 933
Andrews, Michael, Chief Exec. Officer-Energy--Fletcher Challenge Limited, Auckland, New Zealand; *Int'l*, pg. 494
Andrews, R. Bruce, Pres. & Chief Exec. Officer--Nationwide Health Properties Inc., Newport Beach, CA; *U.S. Public*, pg. 1166
Andrusterich, Thomas A., Pres. & Chief Exec. Officer--Henry Birks & Sons (1993) Inc., Montreal, Canada; *Int'l*, pg. 196
Andrzejewski, John R., Pres. & Chief Exec. Officer--Anson Industries, Inc., Melrose Park, IL; *U.S. Private*, pg. 76
Anfield, Frank, Pres. & Chief Exec. Officer-Special Communications Group--Young & Rubicam Inc., New York, NY; *U.S. Private*, pg. 1196
Angel, David L., Chm. Bd. & Chief Exec. Officer--Information Storage Devices, San Jose, CA; *U.S. Public*, pg. 876
Angelich, Samuel M., Chm. Bd. & Pres.--Amelco Corporation, Gardena, CA; *U.S. Public*, pg. 65
Angelillo, Tom, Pres. & Chief Exec. Officer--Southern Progress Corporation, Birmingham, AL; *U.S. Public*, pg. 1612
Angelo, Stanley, Chief Exec. Officer--Angelo Brothers Co., Philadelphia, PA; *U.S. Private*, pg. 74
Angelos, Peter, Chm. Bd. & Chief Oper. Officer--The Orioles, Inc., Baltimore, MD; *U.S. Private*, pg. 819
Angle, William S., III, Pres. & Chief Exec. Officer--Oak Industries Inc., Waltham, MA; *U.S. Public*, pg. 1209
Anixter, Scott C., Chm. Bd. & Chief Exec. Officer--Anicom, Inc., Rosemont, IL; *U.S. Public*, pg. 115
Ansary, Hushang, Chm. Bd. & Chief Exec. Officer--IRI International Corporation, Houston, TX; *U.S. Public*, pg. 858
Anschutz, Philip, Pres.--Anschutz Corporation, Denver, CO; *U.S. Private*, pg. 75
Anselmi, Beniamino, Deputy Chief Exec.--Cassa di Risparmio delle Provincie Lombarde SpA (CARIPLO), Milan, Italy; *Int'l*, pg. 274
Ansin, Arthur, Chief Exec. Officer--Lauriat Inc., Canton, MA; *U.S. Private*, pg. 195
Anthony, John E., Chm. Bd., Pres. & Chief Exec. Officer--Bearden Lumber Company, Inc., Bearden, AR; *U.S. Private*, pg. 127
Anthony, John Lee, Pres. & Chief Exec. Officer--Anthony Forest Products Co., Inc., El Dorado, AR; *U.S. Private*, pg. 76
Anthony, Michael, Pres. & Chief Exec. Officer--Brookstone Company, Inc., Nashua, NH; *U.S. Public*, pg. 259
Antink, Grant S., Pres. & Chief Exec. Officer--Technical Image Products, Inc./DGI, Elk Grove Village, IL; *U.S. Private*, pg. 1072
Antioco, John, Chief Exec. Officer--Blockbuster Entertainment Group, Dallas, TX; *U.S. Private*, pg. 775
Anton, Tom, Chief Exec. Officer--WEN Products, Inc., Bensenville, IL; *U.S. Private*, pg. 1144
Antonini, Richard L., Chm. Bd., Pres. & Chief Exec. Officer--Foremost Corporation of America, Caledonia, MI; *U.S. Public*, pg. 667
Aoki, Akira, Pres. & Chief Exec. Officer--Japan Securities Finance Co. Ltd., Tokyo, Japan; *Int'l*, pg. 702
Aoki, Hiroshi, Chm. Bd. & Chief Exec. Officer--Daido Hoxan Inc., Tokyo, Japan; *Int'l*, pg. 363
Applebaum, Arnold N., Chm. Bd., Pres. & Chief Exec. Officer--Solid State Devices, Inc., La Mirada, CA; *U.S. Private*, pg. 1012
Applebaum, Eugene, Chm. Bd., Pres. & Chief Exec. Officer--Arbor Drugs, Inc., Troy, MI; *U.S. Public*, pg. 126
Applegate, Leslie T., Chm. Bd. & Chief Exec. Officer--Surgical Appliance Industries, Inc., Cincinnati, OH; *U.S. Private*, pg. 1056
Applequist, Roy, Pres. & Chief Exec. Officer--Great Plains Manufacturing, Inc., Salina, KS; *U.S. Private*, pg. 475
Appleton, Steve, Chm. Bd., Pres. & Chief Exec. Officer--Micron Technology Inc., Boise, ID; *U.S. Public*, pg. 1105
Appleton, Stuart, Chief Exec. Officer--Metro Group, London, United Kingdom; *Int'l*, pg. 1482
Appold, James, Chm. Bd., Pres. & Chief Exec. Officer--Consolidated Biscuit Co., Mc Comb, OH; *U.S. Private*, pg. 265
Appoloni, Peter, Chief Exec. Officer--Ascom Zelcom AG, Hombrechtikon, Switzerland; *Int'l*, pg. 86
Aquirre, Pam, Chief Exec. Officer--Mexican Industries in Michigan, Detroit, MI; *U.S. Private*, pg. 739
Arabia, James R., Chm. Bd., Pres. & Chief Exec. Officer--I.C.H. Corporation, La Jolla, CA; *U.S. Public*, pg. 853
Arai, Kentaro, Pres. & Chief Exec. Officer--Calsonic International, Inc., Irvine, CA; *Int'l*, pg. 944
Arai, Kimio, Pres. & Chief Exec. Officer--Tokyu Agency Inc., Tokyo, Japan; *Int'l*, pg. 1394
Arai, Takao, Pres. & Chief Exec. Officer--Nippon Life Insurance Company of the Philippines, Inc., Makati, Philippines; *Int'l*, pg. 936
Aramani, Ronald A., Pres. & Chief Exec. Officer--Allegheny Airlines, Inc., Middletown, PA; *U.S. Public*, pg. 1680
Araskog, Rand V., Chm. Bd. & Chief Exec. Officer--ITT Corporation, New York, NY; *U.S. Public*, pg. 1512
Arch, D.C., Chm. Bd. & Chief Exec. Officer--Blistex, Inc., Oak Brook, IL; *U.S. Private*, pg. 149
Archer, James P., Chm. Bd. & Chief Exec. Officer--Jackson Paper Company, Jackson, MS; *U.S. Private*, pg. 579
Archibald, Nolan D., Chm. Bd., Pres. & Chief Exec. Officer--The Black & Decker Corporation, Towson, MD; *U.S. Public*, pg. 233
Archuleta, Celestino E., Pres. & Chief Exec. Officer--National Systems & Research Co., Colorado Springs, CO; *U.S. Private*, pg. 787
Archuleta, George, Chm., Pres. & Chief Exec. Officer--Alantec Corp., San Jose, CA; *U.S. Public*, pg. 667
Ardia, Stephen V., Chm. Bd., Pres. & Chief Exec. Officer--Environment/One Corporation, Niskayuna, NY; *U.S. Public*, pg. 586
Arditi, David, Pres. & Chief Exec. Officer--Peerless Carpet Corporation, Acton Vale, Canada; *Int'l*, pg. 1032
Arduini, Giovanni, Chm. Bd., Pres., Chief Exec. & Oper. Officer--I.B.I.S.-S.p.A., Busseto, Italy; *Int'l*, pg. 642
Arenberg, William D., Pres. & Chief Exec. Officer--Columbia Pipe & Supply Company, Chicago, IL; *U.S. Private*, pg. 256
Arend, John R., Chm. Bd. & Chief Exec. Officer--International Chemical Company, Tulsa, OK; *U.S. Private*, pg. 568
Arends, H.J., Chm. Bd. & Chief Exec. Officer--Auto-Owners Insurance, Lansing, MI; *U.S. Private*, pg. 100
Argov, Gideon, Chm. Bd., Pres. & Chief Exec. Officer--Kollmorgen Corporation, Waltham, MA; *U.S. Public*, pg. 965
Arguetty, Isaac, Chm. Bd., Pres. & Chief Exec. Officer--Jan Bell Marketing Inc., Sunrise, FL; *U.S. Public*, pg. 207
Argus, D.R., Chief Exec. Officer & Mng. Dir.--National Australia Bank Limited, Melbourne, Australia; *Int'l*, pg. 906
Arison, Micky, Chm. Bd. & Chief Exec. Officer/Carnival Corp.--Carnival Corporation, Miami, FL; *U.S. Public*, pg. 306
Aristides, George, Chief Exec. Officer--Graco Inc., Golden Valley, MN; *U.S. Public*, pg. 756
Arkin, Moshe, Chm. Bd., Pres. & Chief Exec. Officer--Agis Industries Ltd., Bnei-Brak, Israel; *Int'l*, pg. 30
Arledge, David A., Chm. Bd, Pres. & Chief Exec. Officer--The Coastal Corporation, Houston, TX; *U.S. Public*, pg. 389
Arlen, John R., Pres. & Chief Exec. Officer--Thetford Corporation, Ann Arbor, MI; *U.S. Private*, pg. 352
Armour, James A., Pres. & Chief Exec. Officer--AM General Corporation, South Bend, IN; *U.S. Private*, pg. 922
Armstrong, Arthur O., Chief Exec. Officer--Merle Norman Cosmetics, Inc., Los Angeles, CA; *U.S. Private*, pg. 733
Armstrong, C. J., Jr., Pres. & Chief Exec. Officer--Omniflight Helicopters, Inc., Dallas, TX; *U.S. Private*, pg. 817
Armstrong, C. Michael, Chm. & Chief Exec. Officer--AT&T Corporation, Basking Ridge, NJ; *U.S. Public*, pg. 10
Armstrong, C.J., Jr., Pres. & Chief Exec. Officer--Omniflight, Inc., Dallas, TX; *U.S. Private*, pg. 816
Armstrong, Greg L., Pres. & Chief Exec. Officer--Plains Resources Inc., Houston, TX; *U.S. Public*, pg. 1307
Armstrong, Greg L., Pres. & Chief Exec. Officer--Plains Illinois, Inc., Bridgeport, IL; *U.S. Public*, pg. 1308
Armstrong, J. Hord, III, Chm. Bd. & Chief Exec. Officer--D & K Healthcare Resources, Inc., Saint Louis, MO; *U.S. Public*, pg. 471
Armstrong, M.H., Chm., Pres. & Chief Exec. Officer--Armstrong International, Inc., Three Rivers, MI; *U.S. Private*, pg. 83
Armstrong, Mark, Chief Exec. Officer--The Monarch Company, Inc., Atlanta, GA; *U.S. Private*, pg. 756
Armstrong, Peter, Mng. Dir.--Young & Rubicam (Zambia) Ltd., Lusaka, Zambia; *U.S. Private*, pg. 1198
Armstrong, Rich, Chief Exec. Officer--Gallo/Galileo Salame, San Lorenzo, CA; *U.S. Public*, pg. 1433
Arnault, Bernard, Chm. Bd. & Chief Exec. Officer--LVMH Moet Hennessy Louis Vuitton, Paris, France; *Int'l*, pg. 779
Arnault, Bernard, Chm. Bd. & ChiefExec. Officer--Guerlain S.A., Paris, France; *Int'l*, pg. 780
Arnberg, Henry, Chm. Bd., Pres. & Chief Exec. Officer--Hirsch International Corp., Hauppauge, NY; *U.S. Public*, pg. 829
Arnell, Gordon E., Chm. Bd. & Chief Exec. Officer--Brookfield Properties Corporation, Toronto, Canada; *Int'l*, pg. 228
Arnett, E. James, Pres. & Chief Exec. Officer--The Molson Companies Limited, Toronto, Canada; *Int'l*, pg. 887
Arnette, F. Davis, Pres. & Chief Exec. Officer--Regions Bank/Elbert County, Elberton, GA; *U.S. Public*, pg. 1372
Arnof, Ian, Pres. & Chief Exec. Officer--First Commerce Corporation, New Orleans, LA; *U.S. Public*, pg. 629
Arnold-Baker, James, Chief Exec. Officer--Oxford University Press, Oxford, United Kingdom; *Int'l*, pg. 1018
Arnold, E.H., Chm. Bd., Pres. & Chief Exec. Officer--Arnold Industries, Inc., Lebanon, PA; *U.S. Public*, pg. 132
Arnold, George L., Pres.-Dallas & Dir.--EvansGroup, Salt Lake City, UT; *U.S. Private*, pg. 385
Arnold, Paul N., Pres. & Chief Exec. Officer--CORT Business Services Corporation, Fairfax, VA; *U.S. Public*, pg. 451
Arnold, Truman, Chm. Bd. & Chief Exec. Officer--Truman Arnold Companies, Texarkana, TX; *U.S. Private*, pg. 84
Aron, Adam, Chm. Bd. & Chief Exec. Officer--Vail Resorts, Inc., Vail, CO; *U.S. Public*, pg. 1704
Aronoff, Leona, Chief Exec. Officer--Gate City Beverage Distributors, San Bernardino, CA; *U.S. Private*, pg. 441
Arpin, Paul G., Chm. Bd. & Chief Exec. Officer--Paul Arpin Vanlines, Inc., West Warwick, RI; *U.S. Private*, pg. 85
Arranz, Gonzalo, Chief Exec.--Banco Santander, Shanghai, China; *Int'l*, pg. 144
Arrington, Michael B., Pres. & Chief Exec. Officer--Arrington Travel Center Inc., Chicago, IL; *U.S. Private*, pg. 85
Arriola, Joe, Chm. Bd. & Chief Exec. Officer--Avanti Press Inc., Miami, FL; *U.S. Private*, pg. 101
Arst, Rodger M., Chief Exec. Officer--Goldsmiths, Inc., Wichita, KS; *U.S. Private*, pg. 462
Arth, Lawrence J., Chm. Bd. & Chief Exec. Officer--Ameritas Life Insurance Corp., Lincoln, NE; *U.S. Private*, pg. 65
Artigas, Ricardo, Pres. & Chief Exec. Officer-G.E. Power Controls--G.E. Electric Distribution & Control Manufacturing, Plainville, CT; *U.S. Public*, pg. 710
Aruffo, A. James, Chief Exec. Officer--Zenith Products Corp., New Castle, DE; *U.S. Public*, pg. 1054
Asada, Junzo, Choef Oper. Officer--Dolmar GmbH, Hamburg, Germany; *Int'l*, pg. 831
Asanuma, Jun, Chief Officer-Electronic Matls.--Japan Energy Corporation, Tokyo, Japan; *Int'l*, pg. 702
Asaumi, Naoaki, Pres. & Chief Exec. Officer--The Sakura Bank (Canada), Toronto, Canada; *Int'l*, pg. 1180
Asch, Arthur L., Chm. Bd. & Chief Exec. Officer--Rexx Environmental Corp., New York, NY; *U.S. Public*, pg. 1384
Asch, Peter, Pres. & Chief Exec. Officer--Twincraft, Inc., Winooski, VT; *U.S. Private*, pg. 1111
Aschinger, Carl J., Jr., Chm. Bd., Pres. & Chief Exec. Officer--Columbus Show Case Company, Columbus, OH; *U.S. Private*, pg. 257
Aschkenasy, Herbert, Pres. & Chief Exec. Officer--Oregon Freeze Dry, Inc., Albany, OR; *U.S. Private*, pg. 819
Asford, Les, Chief Exec. Officer--SLD Holdings Ltd., Stevenage, United Kingdom; *Int'l*, pg. 1160
Ash, Allie, Pres. & Chief Exec. Officer--National Information Corporation, Mc Lean, VA; *U.S. Private*, pg. 784
Ash, Richard, Chief Exec. Officer--Sam Ash Music Corp., Hicksville, NY; *U.S. Private*, pg. 88
Ash, Thomas G., Chief Exec. Officer--SunTrust Service Corporation, Atlanta, GA; *U.S. Public*, pg. 1538
Ashcroft, Ian, Chief Exec. Officer-Manchester Div.--Guardian Media Group plc, Manchester, United Kingdom; *Int'l*, pg. 577
Ashford, Jim, Chief Exec. Officer--AP North American Aftermarket Division, Goldsboro, NC; *U.S. Private*, pg. 230
Ashkenazi, Ely, Chm. Bd. & Chief Exec. Officer--SDI Technologies Inc., Rahway, NJ; *U.S. Private*, pg. 956
Ashkettle, Phillip D., Pres. & Chief Exec. Officer--Reichhold Chemicals, Inc., Durham, NC; *Int'l*, pg. 370
Ashton, Harris J., Chm. Bd., Pres. & Chief Exec. Officer--General Host Corporation, Stamford, CT; *U.S. Public*, pg. 715
Ashton, James, Ph.D., Chief Exec. Officer--Cytec Fiberite Inc., Tempe, AZ; *U.S. Public*, pg. 471
Asinari, Matthew, Pres & Chief Exec. Officer-Singapore--Dentsu Young & Rubicam Partnerships, New York, NY; *U.S. Private*, pg. 325
Asinari, Matthew, Pres. & Chief Exec. Officer--Dentsu Young & Rubicam brand communications (Network Center), Singapore, Singapore; *U.S. Private*, pg. 325
Askin, Richard H., Jr., Pres. & Chief Exec. Officer--Tribune Entertainment Company, Los Angeles, CA; *U.S. Public*, pg. 1636
Asphahani, Aziz, Pres. & Chief Exec. Officer--Carus Chemical Company, Chemical Div., Peru, IL; *U.S. Private*, pg. 217
Assumma, Frank, Vice Chm.-BDDP Worldwide, Chm. & CEO-Wells BDDP-NY--BDDP Group, Paris, France; *Int'l*, pg. 116

Atanasoff, John V., II, Chm. Bd., Pres. & Chief Exec. Officer--Colorado MEDtech, Inc., Boulder, CO; *U.S. Public*, pg. 401
Ates, Luther A., Pres. & Chief Exec. Officer--Regions Bank/Walton/Holmes County, De Funiak Springs, FL; *U.S. Public*, pg. 1373
Atkin, Edward, Mng. Dir.--Cannon Rubber Ltd., London, United Kingdom; *Int'l*, pg. 261
Atkin, Jerry C., Chm. Bd., Pres. & Chief Exec. Officer--SkyWest Inc., Saint George, UT; *U.S. Public*, pg. 1476
Atkins, E. Larry, Pres. & Chief Exec. Officer--Insight Health Services Corp., Newport Beach, CA; *U.S. Public*, pg. 880
Atkins, Jeffrey A., Chief Exec. Officer--Pete's Brewing Company, Palo Alto, CA; *U.S. Public*, pg. 1280
Atkinson, R. Jay, Pres. & Chief Exec. Officer--Jannock Limited, Toronto, Canada; *Int'l*, pg. 698
Atkinson, Richard Westaway, Chief Exec. Officer--Eurocamp Plc, Knutsford, United Kingdom; *Int'l*, pg. 464
Atman, Robert, Pres. & Chief Exec. Officer--General Media Automotive Group Inc., New York, NY; *U.S. Private*, pg. 444
Atman, Robert, Pres. & Chief Exec. Officer--General Media Communications Group Inc., New York, NY; *U.S. Private*, *pg. 444*
Atman, Robert, Pres. & Chief Exec. Officer--General Media Entertainment Group Inc., New York, NY; *U.S. Private*, pg. 444
Atman, Robert, Pres. & Chief Exec. Officer--General Media Films Group Inc., New York, NY; *U.S. Private*, pg. 444
Atman, Robert, Pres. & Chief Exec. Officer--The General Media Group Inc., New York, NY; *U.S. Private*, pg. 444
Atols, John M., Chm. Bd. & Chief Exec. Officer--Atols Tool and Mold Corp., Schiller Park, IL; *U.S. Private*, pg. 97
Attuissimo, Andrew M., Chm. Bd. & Chief Exec. Officer--First Central Financial Corporation, Lynbrook, NY; *U.S. Private*, pg. 406
Aubuchon, William E., III, Chief Exec. Officer & V.P.-Mktg. & Adv.--W.E. Aubuchon Co., Inc., Westminster, MA; *U.S. Private*, pg. 98
Auch, Fred J., Jr., Chm. Bd. & Chief Exec. Officer--George W. Auch Co., Pontiac, MI; *U.S. Private*, pg. 98
Augustsson, Peter, Chief Exec. Officer & Mng. Dir.--AB SKF, Goteborg, Sweden; *Int'l*, pg. 1156
Auhll, Richard, Chm. & Chief Exec. Officer--Circon ACMI, Stamford, CT; *U.S. Public*, pg. 373
Auhll, Richard A., Chm. Bd., Pres. & Chief Exec. Officer--Circon Corporation, Santa Barbara, CA; *U.S. Public*, pg. 373
Ault, Lee A., III, Chief Exec. Officer--Equifax Check Service, Brea, CA; *U.S. Public*, pg. 588
Aurichio, Joseph L., Pres. & Chief Exec. Officer--Kearney-National, Inc., White Plains, NY; *U.S. Private*, pg. 351
Ausburn, Ross B., Chm. Bd. & Chief Exec. Officer--Southern Missouri Containers Inc., Springfield, MO; *U.S. Private*, pg. 1017
Auslander, Norman L., Chm. Bd. & Chief Exec. Officer--Lander Co., Inc., Englewood, NJ; *U.S. Private*, pg. 647
Austad, Dave, Chm. Bd. & Chief Exec. Officer--The Austad Company, San Diego, CA; *U.S. Public*, pg. 782
Austin, Aubrey L., Chm. Bd., Pres. & Chief Exec. Officer--Santa Monica Bank, Santa Monica, CA; *U.S. Public*, pg. 1757
Austin, Michael, Pres. & Chief Exec. Officer--Haynes International, Inc., Kokomo, IN; *U.S. Public*, pg. 801
Austin, William F., Chm. Bd. & Chief Exec. Officer--Starkey Laboratories, Inc., Eden Prairie, MN; *U.S. Private*, pg. 1035
Autrey Maza, Sergio M., Pres. & Chief Exec. Officer--Grupo Casa Autrey, Mexico, Mexico; *Int'l*, pg. 573
Autry, Gene, Chm. Bd., Pres. & Chief Exec. Officer--Golden West Broadcasters, Los Angeles, CA; *U.S. Private*, pg. 461
Avchen, Daniel L., Chief Exec. Officer--Hammel, Green & Abrahamson, Inc., Minneapolis, MN; *U.S. Private*, pg. 497
Avchen, Malvin, Chm. Bd. & Chief Exec. Officer--Sun City Industries, Inc., Fort Lauderdale, FL; *U.S. Public*, pg. 1529
Aveling, Tony, Chief Exec. Officer--Australian Guarantee Corporation Limited, Sydney, Australia; *Int'l*, pg. 1496
Aveni, Joseph T., Chm. Bd. & Chief Exec. Officer--Realty One, Cleveland, OH; *U.S. Private*, pg. 914
Averill, M.C.E., Grp. Chief Exec. Officer--Shanks & McEwan Group Plc, Bourne, United Kingdom; *Int'l*, pg. 1228
Aversano, John, Pres. & Chief Exec. Officer--Air Conditioning Co., Inc., Glendale, CA; *U.S. Private*, pg. 28
Avery, John M., Pres. & Chief Exec. Officer--Government Employees Financial Corporation, Washington, DC; *U.S. Public*, pg. 220
Avery, Nathan, Chief Exec. Officer--GH Hensley Industries, Inc., Dallas, TX; *U.S. Private*, pg. 439
Avery, Nathan M., Chm. Bd., Pres. & Chief Exec. Officer--Galveston-Houston Company, Houston, TX; *U.S. Private*, *pg. 438*
Avery, William J., Chm. Bd. & Chief Exec. Officer--Crown Cork & Seal Company, Inc., Philadelphia, PA; *U.S. Public*, pg. 462
Avida, Dan, Pres. & Chief Exec. Officer--Electronics For Imaging, Inc., San Mateo, CA; *U.S. Public*, pg. 570
Awad, Sandra, Chief Exec. Officer--Zack Electronics, San Jose, CA; *U.S. Private*, pg. 1203
Awrey, Robert C., Chm. Bd. & Chief Exec. Officer--Awrey Bakeries, Inc., Livonia, MI; *U.S. Private*, pg. 103
Axelrod, Norman, Chm. Bd., Pres. & Chief Exec. Officer--Linens 'n Things, Inc., Clifton, NJ; *U.S. Private*, pg. 668
Ayers, Robert L., Pres. & Chief Exec. Officer--Sulzer Bingham Pumps Inc., Portland, OR; *Int'l*, pg. 1305
Ayling, Robert, Chief Exec. Officer--British Airways PLC, London, United Kingdom; *Int'l*, pg. 218
Ayre, Miller, Chief Exec. Officer & Grp. Publisher--The Evening Telegram, Saint Johns, Canada; *Int'l*, pg. 631
Aznar, Enrique Used, Chief Exec. Officer--Telefonica Publicidad e Informac., Madrid, Spain; *Int'l*, pg. 1372
Azrielant, Ofer, Chm. Bd. & Chief Exec. Officer--Andin International Inc., New York, NY; *U.S. Private*, pg. 73
Azzoli, Val, Co-Chm. & Co-Chief Exec. Officer--Atlantic Recording Corporation, New York, NY; *U.S. Public*, pg. 1611
Baba, Hisao, Pres. & Chief Exec. Officer--Oki Semiconductor Group, Sunnyvale, CA; *Int'l*, pg. 1000
Babcock, James F., Chm. Bd. & Chief Exec. Officer--First Virginia Bank of Tidewater, Norfolk, VA; *U.S. Public*, pg. 642
Babcock, John B., Jr., Pres. & Chief Exec. Officer--BPI Communications Inc., New York, NY; *Int'l*, pg. 1446
Babcock, John Jr., Pres. & Chief Exec. Officer--A/S/M Communications, Inc., New York, NY; *Int'l*, pg. 1446
Bach, Andrew, Pres. & Chief Exec. Officer--AVO International, Dallas, TX; *Int'l*, pg. 1335
Bach, Kenneth W., Chm. Bd., Pres. & Chief Exec. Officer--Electro Metrics, Inc., Johnstown, NY; *U.S. Private*, pg. 369
Bachand, Stephen E., Pres. & Chief Exec. Officer--Canadian Tire Corporation Limited, Toronto, Canada; *Int'l*, pg. 259
Bachhuber, Carl, Chm. Bd., Pres. & Chief Exec. Officer--Mayville Engineering Co., Inc., Mayville, WI; *U.S. Private*, *pg. 718*
Bachman, James E., Chief Exec. Officer--New Hampshire Insurance Group, New York, NY; *U.S. Public*, pg. 84
Bachman, Todd L., Chm. Bd. & Chief Exec. Officer--Bachman's, Inc., Minneapolis, MN; *U.S. Private*, pg. 109
Bacon, Donald G., Chm. Bd., Pres. & Chief Exec. Officer--West Kootenay Power, Trail, Canada; *U.S. Public*, pg. 1701
Bacot, J. Carter, Chm. Bd. & Chief Exec. Officer--The Bank of New York Company, Inc., New York, NY; *U.S. Public*, pg. 178
Badcook, Ben M., Chm. Bd., Pres. & Chief Exec. Officer--W.S. Badcock Corporation, Mulberry, FL; *U.S. Private*, pg. 109
Bader, Ronald L., Pres. & Chief Exec. Officer--Bader Rutter & Assoc., Inc., Brookfield, WI; *U.S. Private*, pg. 110
Badger, Susan, Pres. & Chief Exec. Officer--Wadsworth Publishing Co., Belmont, CA; *U.S. Public*, pg. 1600
Baena, Richard, Chief Exec. Officer--Olaer Group, Colombes, France; *Int'l*, pg. 467
Baer, Albert, Chm. Bd. & Chief Exec. Officer--Imperial Schrade Corp., Ellenville, NY; *U.S. Private*, pg. 559
Baer, Robert E., Pres. & Chief Exec. Officer--Efficient Engineering Co., Troy, MI; *U.S. Private*, pg. 365
Baggett, W. Les, Pres. & Chief Exec. Officer--LePage's, Inc., Pittsburgh, PA; *U.S. Private*, pg. 598
Bagley, George D., Pres. & Chief Exec. Officer--Horizon Air Industries, Seattle, WA; *U.S. Public*, pg. 35
Bagley, James, Chief Exec. Officer--Lam Research Corporation, Fremont, CA; *U.S. Public*, pg. 975
Bagwell, Larry, Pres. & Chief Exec. Officer--Rea Magnet Wire Company, Inc., Fort Wayne, IN; *U.S. Private*, pg. 913
Bahre, Everett, Pres. & Chief Exec. Officer--Lambda Advanced Analog, Santa Clara, CA; *Int'l*, pg. 1241
Bahrenburg, D. Claeys, Chief Exec. Officer--Petersen Publishing Company, L.L.C., Los Angeles, CA; *U.S. Private*, pg. 856
Bailey, Albert C., Jr., Pres. & Chief Exec. Officer--Lavelle Company, Philadelphia, PA; *U.S. Private*, pg. 653
Bailey, Colin, Pres., Chief Exec. Officer & V.P.--Calgon Carbon Corporation, Pittsburgh, PA; *U.S. Public*, pg. 292
Bailey, Don M., Pres. & Chief Exec. Officer--Comarco, Inc., Yorba Linda, CA; *U.S. Public*, pg. 406
Bailey, Dustin L., Chief Exec. Officer & Sr. V.P.-Special Services Div.--Diversco, Inc., Spartanburg, SC; *U.S. Private*, pg. 336
Bailey, Harry J., Pres. & Chief Exec. Officer--Ameriana Bancorp, New Castle, IN; *U.S. Public*, pg. 66
Bailey, J.H., Chm. Bd. & Chief Exec. Officer--The Cretex Companies, Elk River, MN; *U.S. Private*, pg. 289
Bailey, John, Chm. Bd., Pres., Chief Exec. & Fin. Officer & Treas.--Cal Emblem Labels, Inc., Fresno, CA; *U.S. Private*, pg. 199
Bailey, John H., Chm. Bd., Pres., Chief Exec. & Chief Oper. Officer--The Climatic Corp., Columbia, SC; *U.S. Private*, pg. 246
Bailey, Keith E., Chm. Bd., Pres. & Chief Exec. Officer--The Williams Companies, Inc., Tulsa, OK; *U.S. Public*, pg. 1769
Bailey, Robert L., Chm. Bd. & Chief Exec. Officer--State Automobile Mutual Insurance Co., Columbus, OH; *U.S. Private*, pg. 1036
Bailey, Robert L., Pres. & Chief Exec. Officer--PMC Sierra, Inc., Burnaby, Canada; *U.S. Public*, pg. 1470
Bailey, Ted, Chief Oper. Officer, V.P. & Treas.--Heavy Machines, Inc., Memphis, TN; *U.S. Private*, pg. 518
Bailey, Timothy P., Pres. & Chief Exec. Officer--TCF Bank Wisconsin, Milwaukee, WI; *U.S. Public*, pg. 1554
Baileys, Alvin M., Chief Exec. Officer--Safeguard Health Plans, Inc., Anaheim, CA; *U.S. Public*, pg. 1424
Baileys, Steven J., D.D.S., Chm. Bd., Pres. & Chief Exec. Officer--Safeguard Health Enterprises, Inc., Anaheim, CA; *U.S. Public*, pg. 1424
Baillie, A. Charles, Pres. & Chief Exec. Officer--The Toronto Dominion Bank, Toronto, Canada; *Int'l*, pg. 1401
Bailly, Jeff, Pres. & Chief Exec. Officer--UFP Technology, Georgetown, MA; *U.S. Private*, pg. 1112
Bain, Lorne D., Chm. Bd. & Chief Exec. Officer--Sanifill, Inc., Houston, TX; *U.S. Public*, pg. 1686
Baines, P.G., Chief Exec. Officer--AEGON Financial Services Group (UK) Ltd., London, United Kingdom; *Int'l*, *pg. 28*
Bainsfair, Paul, Joint Chm., Joint Chief Exec. Officer & Pres.--BST-BDDP, London, United Kingdom; *Int'l*, pg. 117
Bainton, Donald J., Chm. Bd. & Chief Exec. Officer--Continental Can Co., Norwalk, CT; *U.S. Public*, pg. 439
Bainum, Stewart, Jr., Chief Exec. Officer--Manor Care, Inc., Gaithersburg, MD; *U.S. Public*, pg. 1041
Baione, Dominick, Owner & Chief Exec. Officer--Universal Molding Company, Lynwood, CA; *U.S. Private*, pg. 1127
Baird, William J., Jr., Pres. & Chief Exec. Officer--Willis Corroon Corp. of Maryland, Hunt Valley, MD; *Int'l*, pg. 1506
Baird, William S., Pres. & Chief Exec. Officer--Alabama Metal Industries Corporation, Birmingham, AL; *U.S. Private*, pg. 30
Baker, Andrew H., Chm. Bd., Pres. & Chief Exec. Officer--Unilab Corporation, Tarzana, CA; *U.S. Public*, pg. 1352
Baker, C.E., Jr., Chm. Bd. & Chief Exec. Officer--Arch Communications Group, Inc., Westborough, MA; *U.S. Public*, pg. 127
Baker, Charles A., Chm. Bd. & Chief Exec. Officer--The Liposome Company, Inc., Princeton, NJ; *U.S. Public*, pg. 1000
Baker, Dale, Pres. & Chief Exec. Officer--Aviation Sales Company, Miami, FL; *U.S. Public*, pg. 154
Baker, Daniel, Chm. Bd., Pres. & Chief Exec. Officer--Tate Access Floors, Inc., Jessup, MD; *U.S. Private*, pg. 1069
Baker, David, Chief Exec. Officer--Advertising Investment Services Pty. Ltd., Surrey Hills, Australia; *Int'l*, pg. 394
Baker, F.C. "Buzz", Pres. & Chief Exec. Officer--Creswell, Munsell, Fultz & Zirbel, L.P., Cedar Rapids, IA; *U.S. Private*, pg. 1197
Baker, Francis E., Pres. & Chief Exec. Officer--Andersen Group, Inc., Bloomfield, CT; *U.S. Public*, pg. 111
Baker, George F., Chm. Bd. & Chief Exec. Officer--Whitehall Corporation, Dallas, TX; *U.S. Public*, pg. 1765
Baker, J.R., Chief Exec. Officer--Rolls-Royce Power Engineering plc, Newcastle upon Tyne, United Kingdom; *Int'l*, pg. 1127
Baker, Jack, Chm. & Chief Exec. Officer--Baker's Supermarkets, Inc., Omaha, NE; *U.S. Public*, pg. 652
Baker, John D. II, Pres. & Chief Exec. Officer--Florida Rock Industries, Inc., Jacksonville, FL; *U.S. Public*, pg. 655
Baker, Kenneth D., Pres. & Chief Exec. Officer--NewAge Industries Inc., Willow Grove, PA; *U.S. Private*, pg. 796
Baker, Kenneth D., Chief Exec. Officer--Newage Industries Inc., Testing Instruments Group, Willow Grove, PA; *U.S. Private*, pg. 796
Baker, L.M., Jr., Pres. & Chief Exec. Officer--Wachovia Corporation, Winston Salem, NC; *U.S. Public*, pg. 1730
Baker, Maurice W., Pres. & Chief Exec. Officer--Madison Grocery Co., Inc., Richmond, KY; *U.S. Private*, pg. 694
Baker, Robert, Chief Exec. Officer--The Chamberlain Group, Inc., Elmhurst, IL; *U.S. Private*, pg. 344
Baker, Ronald L., Chief Exec. Officer--Harris Scarfe Holdings Limited, Toorak, Australia; *Int'l*, pg. 597
Baker, Wilder D., Chm. Bd. & Chief Exec. Officer--Warwick Baker O'Neill, New York, NY; *U.S. Private*, pg. 1152
Baker, William C., Chm. Bd., Pres. & Chief Exec. Officer--The Santa Anita Companies, Arcadia, CA; *U.S. Public*, pg. 1081
Baker, William C., Chm. Bd. & Chief Exec. Officer--Santa Anita Enterprises, Inc., Arcadia, CA; *U.S. Public*, pg. 1081
Bakke, Dennis W., Pres. & Chief Exec. Officer--AES Corporation, Arlington, VA; *U.S. Public*, pg. 5
Bakke, Richard M., Pres. & Chief Exec. Officer--PG Vinyl Windows/PG Proglass Construction, Westbrook, ME; *U.S. Private*, pg. 826
Balachowski, T.J., Chief Exec. Officer--ING Investment Management Inc., Atlanta, GA; *Int'l*, pg. 648
Balaji, T.K., Chief Oper. Officer--Lucas-TVS Ltd., Padi, India; *Int'l*, pg. 820
Balaz, Joe K., Pres. & Chief Exec. Officer--Flinn & Dreffein Engineering Co., Northbrook, IL; *U.S. Private*, pg. 413
Balch, Alan, Chm. Bd. & Chief Exec. Officer--Lane Limited, Tucker, GA; *Int'l*, pg. 1129
Baldwin, H. Furlong, Chm. Bd., Pres. & Chief Exec. Officer--Mercantile Bankshares Corporation, Baltimore, MD; *U.S. Public*, pg. 1088
Baldwin, Sandra Kaye, Pres. & Treas.--H & H Distributing Company, Inc., West Union, IA; *U.S. Private*, pg. 489
Bale, James K., Chief Exec. Officer--Bale Of Kentucky, Inc., Horse Cave, KY; *U.S. Private*, pg. 112
Balkanski, Alexandre A., Pres. & Chief Exec. Officer--C-Cube Microsystems, Milpitas, CA; *U.S. Public*, pg. 272
Balkind, Aubrey, Chm. & Chief Exec. Officer--Frankfurt Balkind Partners, New York, NY; *U.S. Private*, pg. 424
Ball, Anna C., Chm. Bd., Pres. & Chief Exec. Officer--Ball Horticultural Company, West Chicago, IL; *U.S. Private*, pg. 112
Ball, John H., Chm. Bd. & Chief Exec. Officer--R.M. Shoemaker Co., West Conshohocken, PA; *U.S. Private*, pg. 996
Ball, Robert L., Pres.--Alcan Aluminum Corporation, Cleveland, OH; *Int'l*, pg. 50
Ballantine, Brent, Chief Exec. Officer--Mrs. Alison's Cookie Company, Saint Louis, MO; *U.S. Private*, pg. 765
Ballard, Dale H., Chm. Bd., Pres. & Chief Exec. Officer--Ballard Medical Products, Draper, UT; *U.S. Public*, pg. 171
Ballard, John W., Pres. & Chief Exec. Officer--TCI International Inc., Sunnyvale, CA; *U.S. Public*, pg. 1555
Ballard, Larry, Chief Exec. Officer--Middlesex Insurance, Westford, MA; *U.S. Private*, pg. 985
Ballentine, Brent, Chief Exec. Officer--Troyer Foods, Inc., Goshen, IN; *Int'l*, pg. 619
Ballew, Glenn, Pres. & Chief Exec. Officer--Midwest Mutual Insurance Co., West Des Moines, IA; *U.S. Private*, pg. 881
Ballin, Robert, Pres. & Chief Exec. Officer--Willis Corroon Corp. of Eugene, Eugene, OR; *Int'l*, pg. 1505
Ballou, F. Remington, Chief Exec. Officer--B.A. Ballou & Co. Inc., East Providence, RI; *U.S. Private*, pg. 112
Balloun, James S., Chm. Bd., Pres. & Chief Exec. Officer--National Service Industries, Inc., Atlanta, GA; *U.S. Public*, pg. 1160
Balmas, Bruce B., Pres. & Chief Exec. Officer--D & N Mortgage Corporation, Hancock, MI; *U.S. Public*, pg. 472
Balmuth, Marc, Chm. Bd. & Chief Exec. Officer--Bob's Stores, Inc., Meriden, CT; *U.S. Public*, pg. 287

Balmuth, Michael, Vice Chm. & Chief Exec. Officer--Ross Stores, Inc., Newark, CA; U.S. Public, pg. 1405
Balogh, Alex G., Chm. Bd. & Chief Exec. Officer--Falconbridge Limited, Toronto, Canada; Int'l, pg. 433
Balsamo, Salvatore, Chm. Bd. & Chief Exec. Officer--Technical Aid Corporation, Newton, MA; U.S. Private, pg. 1072
Balson, Patrick, Pres. & Chief Exec. Officer--Aetna Bearing Company, Chicago, IL; U.S. Private, pg. 25
Banchini, Saverio A., Chief Exec.--HISALBA - Hornos Ibericos Alba S.A., Madrid, Spain; Int'l, pg. 629
Bancroft, Charles, Pres. & Chief Exec. Officer--Citation Insurance Group, San Jose, CA; U.S. Public, pg. 376
Bandi, Lawrence E., Pres. & Chief Exec. Officer--Valley National Gasses Inc., Wheeling, WV; U.S. Private, pg. 1132
Bandolik, Keith A., Pres. & Chief Exec. Officer--Switchcraft, Inc., Chicago, IL; U.S. Public, pg. 1366
Bankes, James R., Pres. & Chief Exec. Officer--Samsill Corporation, Fort Worth, TX; U.S. Private, pg. 963
Banks, Charles A., Pres. & Chief Exec. Officer--Ferguson Enterprises, Inc., Newport News, VA; Int'l, pg. 1512
Banks, David R., Chm. Bd. & Chief Exec. Officer--Beverly Enterprises, Inc., Fort Smith, AR; U.S. Public, pg. 227
Bankston, James G., Chm. Bd., Pres. & Chief Exec. Officer--W.O. Bankston Enterprises Inc., Dallas, TX; U.S. Public, pg. 1379
Bankuty, Geza E., Chm. Bd., Pres. & Chief Exec. Officer--New England Machinery, Inc., Bradenton, FL; U.S. Private, pg. 793
Bannon, George, Pres. & Chief Exec. Officer--Handex Environment Inc., Morganville, NJ; U.S. Private, pg. 498
Bannon, Robert G., Pres. & Chief Exec. Officer--First American Title Insurance Co. of N.Y., New York, NY; U.S. Public, pg. 626
Banucci, Gene G., Ph.D., Chm. Bd., Pres. & Chief Exec. Officer--ATMI, Inc., Danbury, CT; U.S. Public, pg. 12
Baptista, Carlos M., Chief Exec. Officer, Dir.-Mfg. & Fin.--Apolo Produtos de Aco S.A., Rio de Janeiro, Brazil; Int'l, pg. 78
Barad, Jill Elikann, Chm. Bd. & Chief Exec. Officer--Mattel, Inc., El Segundo, CA; U.S. Public, pg. 1057
Baranski, Dennis A., Chm. Bd., Pres. & Chief Exec. Officer--Barancorp, Lecompton, KS; U.S. Private, pg. 115
Barba, Guillermo, Chief Exec. Officer--Betancourt Barba EURO RSCG, Mexico, Mexico; Int'l, pg. 603
Barba, J. Brendan, Chm. Bd., Pres. & Chief Exec. Officer--AEP Industries, Inc., South Hackensack, NJ; U.S. Public, pg. 4
Barbakow, Jeffrey C., Chm. Bd. & Chief Exec. Officer--Tenet Healthcare Corporation, Santa Barbara, CA; U.S. Public, pg. 1576
Barbarossa, Franco, Chief Exec. Officer--Redi, Bologna, Italy; Int'l, pg. 430
Barbarossa, Franco, Chief Exec. Officer--Europlast, Treviso, Italy; Int'l, pg. 430
Barbee, Robert P., Chm. Bd. & Chief Exec. Officer--Pneumafil Corporation, Charlotte, NC; U.S. Private, pg. 873
Barber, Albert F., Chm. Bd. & Chief Exec. Officer--Stuart Entertainment Inc., Council Bluffs, IA; U.S. Public, pg. 1526
Barber, Irving K., Chm. Bd., Pres. & Chief Exec. Officer--Slocan Forest Products Ltd., Richmond, Canada; Int'l, pg. 1263
Barber, Peter, Chief Exec. Officer--Accurate Perforating Co., Chicago, IL; U.S. Private, pg. 12
Barber, Walter, Pres. & Chief Exec. Officer--Fluor Daniel GTI, Inc., Norwood, MA; U.S. Public, pg. 660
Barbero, Emilio, Chief Exec. Officer--Barbero 1891 SpA, Canale, Italy; Int'l, pg. 164
Barbookles, James, Pres. & Chief Exec. Officer--Orion Research Inc., Boston, MA; U.S. Public, pg. 1592
Barclay, John P., Jr., Chm. Bd. & Chief Exec. Officer--Wire Rope Corporation of America, Inc., Saint Joseph, MO; U.S. Private, pg. 1184
Barclay, Richard D., Pres. & Chief Exec. Officer--First National Bank of Central Illinois, Springfield, IL; U.S. Public, pg. 644
Bard, I. Gary, Chm. Bd. & Chief Exec. Officer--Aydin Corporation, Horsham, PA; U.S. Public, pg. 158
Bard, Shannon, Pres. & Chief Exec. Officer--Aquapore Moisture Systems, Inc., Phoenix, AZ; Int'l, pg. 1066
Barden, Thomas, Chief Exec. Officer & Exec. V.P.--Barden & Robeson Corporation, Middleport, NY; U.S. Private, pg. 116
Bardis, John A., Pres. & Chief Exec. Officer--Vencare, Incorporated, Alpharetta, GA; U.S. Public, pg. 1715
Barefoot, Gerald, Pres. & Chief Exec. Officer--Rieter Automotive North America Inc, Farmington Hills, MI; Int'l, pg. 1117
Barensfeld, David E., Chief Exec. Officer--Ellwood Group, Inc., Ellwood City, PA; U.S. Private, pg. 373
Bares, W.G., Chm. Bd., Pres. & Chief Exec. Officer--The Lubrizol Corporation, Wickliffe, OH; U.S. Public, pg. 1016
Barger, John William, Sr., Pres. & Chief Exec. Officer--Barger Builders, Saint Petersburg, FL; U.S. Private, pg. 116
Barguirdjian, Henri, Pres. & Chief Exec. Officer--Van Cleef & Arpels, Inc., New York, NY; U.S. Private, pg. 1132
Barkalow, Lynn, Chief Exec. Officer--Nor-Cal Beverage Co., Inc., West Sacramento, CA; U.S. Private, pg. 801
Barkeley, Norman A., Chm. Bd. & Chief Exec. Officer--Ducommun Incorporated, Carson, CA; U.S. Public, pg. 533
Barker, G. Carlton, Chm. Bd., Pres. & Chief Exec. Officer--Regions Bank/Montgomery/Alexander City, Montgomery, AL; U.S. Public, pg. 1372
Barker, G. V., Chief Exec. Officer--National Westminster Life Assurance Limited, Bristol, United Kingdom; Int'l, pg. 910
Barkhurst, Ross, Pres. & Chief Exec. Officer--Vermont Yankee Nuclear Power Corp., Brattleboro, VT; U.S. Public, pg. 328
Barksdale, James L., Pres. & Chief Exec. Officer--Netscape Communications Corp., Mountain View, CA; U.S. Public, pg. 1168
Barlas, Mehr A., Chief Exec. Officer--National Bank of Pakistan, Karachi, Pakistan; Int'l, pg. 907
Barlow, John, Pres. & Chief Exec. Officer--Safelite AutoGlass, Columbus, OH; U.S. Private, pg. 960
Barnaby, Richard G., Pres. & Chief Oper. Officer--Kaiser Permanente, Oakland, CA; U.S. Private, pg. 605
Barnes, Andrew, Chm. Bd., Chief Exec. Officer & Editor--The Times Publishing Co., Saint Petersburg, FL; U.S. Private, pg. 1087
Barnes, Bradford, Chm. Bd. & Chief Exec. Officer--Crouch Supply Company, Inc., Fort Worth, TX; U.S. Private, pg. 291
Barnes, Daniel F., Chief Exec. Officer--Republic Fastener Products Corp., Great Falls, SC; U.S. Private, pg. 923
Barnes, Galen, Pres. & Chief Oper. Officer--Employers Insurance of Wausau, Wausau, WI; U.S. Private, pg. 788
Barnes, Geoffrey, Chief Oper. Officer--Novo Nordisk Entotech, Inc., Davis, CA; Int'l, pg. 987
Barnes, James E., Chm. Bd., Pres. & Chief Exec. Officer--Mapco Inc., Tulsa, OK; U.S. Public, pg. 1042
Barnes, John E., Chief Exec. Officer--Small Parts, Inc., Logansport, IN; U.S. Private, pg. 1006
Barnes, John R., Chm. Bd., Pres. & Chief Exec. Officer--Kaneb Services, Inc., Richardson, TX; U.S. Public, pg. 942
Barnes, Richard J., Chief Exec. Officer--MelloButtercup Ice Cream Inc., Wilson, NC; U.S. Private, pg. 730
Barnes, Robert, Chief Exec. Officer--Belle Tire Distributor Inc., Allen Park, MI; U.S. Private, pg. 132
Barnes, T.J.O., Chief Exec. Officer--National Bank of Malawi, Blantyre, Malawi; Int'l, pg. 1296
Barnet, Bruce, Pres. & Chief Exec. Officer--Reed Elsevier Business Information, Newton, MA; Int'l, pg. 1095
Barnett, Cecil C., Chm. Bd., Pres. & Chief Exec. Officer--Algood Food Company, Louisville, KY; U.S. Private, pg. 34
Barnett, Dana G., Chm. Bd. & Chief Exec. Officer--Somerset Pharmaceuticals Inc., Tampa, FL; U.S. Public, pg. 1143
Barnett, John, Pres. & Chief Exec. Officer--Molson Breweries, Toronto, Canada; Int'l, pg. 500
Barnett, John, Pres. & Chief Exec. Officer--Molson Breweries, Toronto, Canada; U.S. Public, pg. 1289
Barnett, Richard M., Chm. Bd., Pres. & Chief Exec. Officer--Reliable Stores, Inc., Columbia, MD; U.S. Private, pg. 920
Barnett, T., Chm. Bd. & Chief Exec. Officer--CIBA-GEIGY (Pty.) Ltd., Isando, South Africa; Int'l, pg. 978
Barnette, Joseph D. Jr., Pres. & Chief Exec. Officer--Bank One, Indiana, N.A., Indianapolis, IN; U.S. Public, pg. 173
Barnettte, Curtis H., Chm. Bd. & Chief Exec. Officer--Bethlehem Steel Corporation, Bethlehem, PA; U.S. Public, pg. 226
Barney, R.L., Chief Exec. Officer--National Electrical Carbon Canada, Mississauga, Canada; Int'l, pg. 892
Barnhardt, T.L., Pres. & Chief Exec. Officer--Barnhardt Manufacturing Co., Charlotte, NC; U.S. Private, pg. 116
Barnhill, Robert B., Jr., Chm. Bd., Pres. & Chief Exec. Officer--Tessco Technologies, Inc., Sparks, MD; U.S. Public, pg. 1582
Barnum, T.B., Chm. Bd., Pres. & Chief Exec. Officer--Max & Erma's Restaurants, Columbus, OH; U.S. Public, pg. 1060
Baroni, Giovanni, Deputy Chief Exec.--Cassa di Risparmio delle Provincie Lombarde SpA (CARIPLO), Milan, Italy; Int'l, pg. 274
Barouh, Victor, Chief Exec. Officer--Barouh Eaton Allen Corporation, Brooklyn, NY; U.S. Private, pg. 117
Barouh, Victor, Chief Exec. Officer--Ko-Rec-Type, Brooklyn, NY; U.S. Private, pg. 117
Barowsky, Andrew P., Chief Exec. Officer--Lepage Bakery, Inc., Auburn, ME; U.S. Private, pg. 660
Barr, Donald M., Pres.--Barr & Barr, Inc., New York, NY; U.S. Private, pg. 117
Barr, Edward, Chm. Bd. & Chief Exec. Officer--Sun Chemical Corp., Fort Lee, NJ; Int'l, pg. 370
Barr, J. James, Pres. & Chief Exec. Officer--American Water Works Company, Inc., Voorhees, NJ; U.S. Public, pg. 95
Barr, Lynn E., Pres. & Chief Exec. Officer--Underground Construction Co., Inc., Benicia, CA; U.S. Private, pg. 1116
Barragan, Napoleon, Pres. & Chief Exec. Officer--Dial A Mattress USA, Long Island City, NY; U.S. Private, pg. 330
Barral, Gervasio, Pres. & Chief Exec. Officer--Unitros, Madrid, Spain; Int'l, pg. 603
Barrans, Terry, Pres. & Chief Exec. Officer--Fisher Mills, Inc., Seattle, WA; U.S. Public, pg. 640
Barre, Stephen A., Chm. Bd., Pres., Chief Exec. Officer & Sec.--Servo Corporation of America, Westbury, NY; U.S. Private, pg. 987
Barrett, James H., Pres. & Chief Exec. Officer--Duchesne Bank, Saint Peters, MO; U.S. Public, pg. 643
Barrett, John F., Pres. & Chief Exec. Officer--The Western and Southern Life Insurance Company, Cincinnati, OH; U.S. Private, pg. 1164
Barrett, John F., Pres. & Chief Exec. Officer--Western-Southern Life Assurance Co., Cincinnati, OH; U.S. Private, pg. 1164
Barrett, Matthew W., Chm. Bd. & Chief Exec. Officer--Bank of Montreal, Toronto, Canada; Int'l, pg. 153
Barringer, Paul B., II, Chm. Bd. & Chief Exec. Officer--Coastal Lumber Company, Weldon, NC; U.S. Private, pg. 248
Barrington, William J., Pres. & Chief Exec. Officer--Sea Ray, Knoxville, TN; U.S. Public, pg. 266
Barrios Sanchez, Luis, Pres. & Chief Exec. Officer--Grupo Posadas S.A. de C.V., Mexico, Mexico; Int'l, pg. 576
Barry, Herbert, Chm. Bd. & Chief Exec. Officer--Uniflex, Inc., Hicksville, NY; U.S. Public, pg. 1665
Barsoum, Khalil, Pres. & Chief Exec. Officer--IBM Canada Limited, Markham, Canada; U.S. Public, pg. 897
Bartell, George D., Pres. & Chief Oper. Officer--The Bartell Drug Company, Seattle, WA; U.S. Private, pg. 118
Bartelli, James, Chm. Bd., Pres. & Chief Exec. Officer--Mercury Computer Systems, Inc., Chelmsford, MA; U.S. Private, pg. 732
Bartels, Bill, Pres. & Chief Exec. Officer--Spar Marketing Force, Inc., Rochester Hills, MI; U.S. Public, pg. 23
Bartels, Juergen, Chm. Bd. & Chief Exec. Officer--Westin Hotels & Resorts, Seattle, WA; U.S. Public, pg. 1512
Bartels, Peter, Chief Exec. Officer & Mng. Dir.--Coles Myer Ltd., Tooronga, Australia; Int'l, pg. 306
Bartenbach, Klaus G., Pres. & Chief Exec. Officer--Ford, Bacon & Davis Companies Inc., Duluth, GA; Int'l, pg. 401
Bartenbach, Klaus G., Pres. & Chief Exec. Officer--Ford, Bacon & Davis Companies, Inc., Duluth, GA; Int'l, pg. 401
Bartges, Hans, Pres. & Chief Exec. Officer--Auto Lenders Acceptance Corp., Atlanta, GA; Int'l, pg. 499
Barth, Edgar, Chief Oper. Officer--Himmelwerk GmbH & Co., Tubingen, Germany; Int'l, pg. 400
Barth, James, Pres. & Chief Exec. Officer--Shurfine International, Inc., Northlake, IL; U.S. Private, pg. 997
Barth, Steve, Pres. & Chief Exec. Officer--Challenger Electrical Equipment Corp., Pittsburgh, PA; U.S. Public, pg. 558
Barth, William, Pres. & Chief Exec. Officer--Packaged Products Division, McAllen, TX; U.S. Private, pg. 1191
Bartlett, Robert A., Chm. Bd. & Chief Exec. Officer--The F.A. Bartlett Tree Expert Co., Stamford, CT; U.S. Private, pg. 119
Bartlett, Thomas A., Pres. & Chief Exec. Officer-Intl. Wireless Unit--Bell Atlantic Corporation, New York, NY; U.S. Public, pg. 201
Bartlett, Tom, Pres. & Chief Exec. Officer--Grupo Iusacell SA de CV, Mexico, Mexico; U.S. Public, pg. 204
Bartlett, Vivian Wade, Chief Exec. Officer & Mng. Dir.--First National Bank Holdings Limited, Johannesburg, South Africa; Int'l, pg. 487
Bartling, John B., Pres. & Chief Exec. Officer--Lexford Residential Trust, Columbus, OH; U.S. Public, pg. 991
Bartoli, Henry E., Chm. & Chief Exec. Officer--Foster Wheeler Energy International, Inc., Clinton, NJ; U.S. Public, pg. 676
Barton, A.P., Jr., Chm. Bd., Pres. & Chief Exec. Officer--Mutual Manufacturing & Supply Co., Cincinnati, OH; U.S. Private, pg. 769
Barton, Francis J., Chm. & Chief Exec. Officer--Wahlstrom & Company, Stamford, CT; U.S. Public, pg. 1641
Barton, John, Chief Exec. Officer--JIB Group plc, London, United Kingdom; Int'l, pg. 705
Barton, John A., Pres. & Chief Exec. Officer--Southwestern Electric Service Co., Dallas, TX; U.S. Public, pg. 1588
Barton, R.J.O., Chief Exec. Officer--Jardine Insurance Services Limited, London, United Kingdom; Int'l, pg. 705
Barton, Richard D., Pres. & Chief Exec. Officer--The Paper Magic Group, Inc., Scranton, PA; U.S. Public, pg. 284
Barton, Richard S., Pres. & Chief Exec. Officer--Xerox Canada Holdings Inc., North York, Canada; U.S. Public, pg. 1785
Barton, Robert, Pres. & Chief Exec. Officer--National Electric Coil, Columbus, OH; U.S. Private, pg. 782
Bartscht, Karl G., Chm. Bd. & Chief Exec. Officer--Chi Systems Division, Ann Arbor, MI; U.S. Public, pg. 1539
Bartz, Carol, Chm. Bd. & Chief Exec. Officer--Autodesk, Inc., San Rafael, CA; U.S. Public, pg. 148
Baruch, Jack, Chief Exec. Officer--Coast Business Credit, Los Angeles, CA; U.S. Public, pg. 872
Barwick, Allen, Pres. & Chief Exec. Officer--Shuford Mills, Inc., Hickory, NC; U.S. Private, pg. 996
Baschera, Pius, Dr., Chief Exec. Officer--Hilti AG, Schaan, Liechtenstein; Int'l, pg. 619
Basham, B.H., Pres. & Chief Exec. Officer--Industrial Rubber Products Company, Charleston, WV; U.S. Private, pg. 561
Basile, Peter A., Chief Exec. Officer--Peter A. Basile Sons Inc., Livonia, MI; U.S. Private, pg. 121
Basinait, Martin C., Pres. & Chief Exec. Officer--Western Regional Off Track Betting, Batavia, NY; U.S. Private, pg. 1168
Baskind, Barry, Pres., Chief Exec. Officer & Dir.-Cash Mngmt.--Mott's Holdings, Inc., Glastonbury, CT; U.S. Private, pg. 764
Basler, William L., Chm. Bd., Chief Exec. Officer & Treas.--Basler Electric Company, Highland, IL; U.S. Private, pg. 121
Basserman, Michael, Chm. Bd. & Chief Exec. Officer--Mercedes-Benz of North America, Inc., Montvale, NJ; Int'l, pg. 368
Basset, Christian, Pres. & Chief Exec. Officer--Coronado Paint Company, Edgewater, FL; Int'l, pg. 1488
Bassett, Douglas G., O.C., Vice Chm. & Chief Exec. Officer--Baton Broadcasting Incorporated, Scarborough, Canada; Int'l, pg. 170
Bassett, William A., Chm. Bd., Pres. & Chief Exec. Officer--Decorator Industries, Inc., Pembroke Pines, FL; U.S. Public, pg. 491
Bastable, Colum P., Pres. & Chief Exec. Officer--Royal LePage Limited, Don Mills, Canada; Int'l, pg. 1143
Bastian, Michael, Pres. & Chief Exec. Officer--Royal Bank Action Direct Inc., Richmond Hill, Canada; Int'l, pg. 1131
Baszucki, Paul, Chm. Bd. & Chief Exec. Officer--Norstan, Inc., Plymouth, MN; U.S. Public, pg. 1192
Bateman, Walter R., Pres. & Chief Exec. Officer--Harleysville Group, Harleysville, PA; U.S. Public, pg. 786
Bateman, Walter R., Chm. Bd. & Chief Exec. Officer--Great Oaks Insurance Company, Dublin, OH; U.S. Public, pg. 786
Bateman, Walter R., Pres. & Chief Exec. Officer--Harleysville Mutual Insurance, Harleysville, PA; U.S. Public, pg. 787

Bateman, Walter R., Pres. & Chief Exec. Officer--Minnesota Fire & Casualty Company, Minnetonka, MN; *U.S. Public,* pg. 787

Bates, Ernest A., M.D., Chm. Bd., Pres., Chief Exec. & Oper. Officer--American Shared Hospital Services, San Francisco, CA; *U.S. Public,* pg. 91

Bates, John C., Chm. of Bd., Pres. & Chief Exec. Officer--Heidtman Steel Products, Inc., Toledo, OH; *U.S. Private,* pg. 519

Bates, Robert D., Chm. Bd., Pres. & Chief Exec. Officer--Guarantee Life Insurance Co., Omaha, NE; *U.S. Public,* pg. 768

Bates, Thomas R., Pres. & Chief Exec. Officer--Weatherford Enterra Incorporated, Houston, TX; *U.S. Public,* pg. 1749

Batinovich, Robert, Chm. Bd. & Chief Exec. Officer--Glenborough Realty Trust Incorporated, San Mateo, CA; *U.S. Public,* pg. 747

Batkin, Sanford L., Chm. Bd, Chief Exec. Officer & Treas.--Universal Folding Box Company, Inc., Hoboken, NJ; *U.S. Private,* pg. 1127

Batt, James M., Pres., Chief Exec. Officer & Controller--Peck Spring Company, Plainville, CT; *U.S. Private,* pg. 846

Batten, Michael E., Chm. Bd. & Chief Exec. Officer--Twin Disc, Incorporated, Racine, WI; *U.S. Public,* pg. 1646

Batterton, John C., Pres. & Chief Exec. Officer--CalComp Technology, Inc., Anaheim, CA; *U.S. Public,* pg. 1007

Batting, Robert T., Pres. & Chief Exec. Officer--Kenney Manufacturing Company, Warwick, RI; *U.S. Private,* pg. 615

Battista, G.A., Chief Exec. Officer--Network Solutions, Inc., Herndon, VA; *U.S. Private,* pg. 976

Battista, Gabe, Chief Exec. Officer--Cable & Wireless of North America, Inc., Vienna, VA; *Int'l,* pg. 247

Battista, Gabriel, Pres. & Chief Exec. Officer--Cable & Wireless Communications Inc., Vienna, VA; *Int'l,* pg. 247

Battjer, Bruce H., Grp. Chief Exec. Officer-SunGard Computer Services--SunGard Data Systems Inc., Wayne, PA; *U.S. Public,* pg. 1534

Bauer, Charles, Chief Exec. Officer--Aim Family of Funds, Houston, TX; *Int'l,* pg. 685

Bauer, Charles, Chief Exec. Officer--Aim Equity Funds, Inc., Houston, TX; *Int'l,* pg. 685

Bauer, Chris M., Chm. Bd. & Chief Exec. Officer--Firstar Milwaukee Bank, N.A., Milwaukee, WI; *U.S. Public,* pg. 643

Bauer, Fred T., Chm. Bd. & Chief Exec. Officer--Gentex Corporation, Zeeland, MI; *U.S. Public,* pg. 731

Baughman, Gary, Pres. & Chief Exec. Officer--Fisher-Price, Inc., East Aurora, NY; *U.S. Public,* pg. 1058

Baum, Charles C., Chm. & Chief Exec. Officer--The Morgan Group, Inc., Elkhart, IN; *U.S. Public,* pg. 1022

Baum, David, Chm. Bd., Pres. & Chief Exec. Officer--Arcon Construction Co., Inc., Harris, MN; *U.S. Private,* pg. 80

Baum, Herbert M., Chm. Bd. & Chief Exec. Officer--Quaker State Corporation, Irving, TX; *U.S. Public,* pg. 1348

Baum, Michael H., Chief Exec. Officer--Advantage Learning Systems, Inc., Wisconsin Rapids, WI; *U.S. Public,* pg. 22

Baum, Nick, Chief Exec. Officer-Europe--EURO RSCG Institutionnel, Levallois-Perret, France; *Int'l,* pg. 600

Baum, Stephen L., Chm. Bd. & Chief Exec. Officer--Enova Corp, San Diego, CA; *U.S. Public,* pg. 583

Bauman, James J., Co-President & Co-Chief Exec. Officer--Eastbridge Capital Inc., New York, NY; *Int'l,* pg. 933

Bauman, Robert L., Chm. Bd., Pres. & Chief Exec. Officer--Hickok Incorporated, Cleveland, OH; *U.S. Public,* pg. 825

Baumeister, Rosemarie, Chief Exec. Officer--Tengelmann Warenhandelsgesellschaft, Mulheim, Germany; *Int'l,* pg. 1375

Baumgardner, J. Dwane, Ph.D., Chm. Bd., Pres. & Chief Exec. Officer--Donnelly Corporation, Holland, MI; *U.S. Public,* pg. 519

Baumhauer, William H., Chm. Bd. & Chief Exec. Officer--Unique Casual Restaurants, inc., Danvers, MA; *Int'l,* pg. 324

Baunton, Michael J., Grp. Chief Exec.--Varity Perkins, Peterborough, United Kingdom; *Int'l,* pg. 820

Baxter, Frank E., Chm. Bd., Pres. & Chief Exec. Officer--Jefferies Group, Inc., Los Angeles, CA; *U.S. Public,* pg. 924

Baxter, Harold J., Chm. Bd. & Chief Exec. Officer--Pilgram Baxter & Associates, Wayne, PA; *U.S. Public,* pg. 1673

Baxter, Keith G., Pres. & Chief Exec. Officer--Cornerstone Propane G.P. Inc., Watsonville, CA; *U.S. Public,* pg. 1201

Baxter, Peter J., Pres. & Chief Exec. Officer--CFX Bank, Keene, NH; *U.S. Public,* pg. 277

Baxter, Raymond A., Pres. & Chief Oper. Officer--Interbake Foods Inc., Richmond, VA; *Int'l,* pg. 1495

Baxter, Rick, Pres. & Chief Exec. Officer--J.H. Baxter & Company, San Mateo, CA; *U.S. Private,* pg. 124

Bay, Mogens C., Chm. Bd. & Chief Exec. Officer--Valmont Industries, Inc., Valley, NE; *U.S. Public,* pg. 1706

Bayer, Ian D., Pres. & Chief Exec. Officer--Battle Mountain Gold Company, Houston, TX; *U.S. Public,* pg. 193

Bayer, Robert, Chm. Bd., Pres. & Chief Exec. Officer--Bayer Clothing Group, New York, NY; *U.S. Private,* pg. 124

Bayless, Charles E., Chm. Bd., Pres. & Chief Exec. Officer--UniSource Energy Corporation, Tucson, AZ; *U.S. Public,* pg. 1670

Bayless, Charles E., Chm. Bd., Pres. & Chief Exec. Officer--Tucson Electric Power Company, Tucson, AZ; *U.S. Public,* pg. 1670

Bayley, Robert E., Chm. Bd. & Chief Exec. Officer--Robert E. Bayley Construction, Seattle, WA; *U.S. Private,* pg. 125

Bayly, George V., Pres. & Chief Exec. Officer--Ivex Packaging Corporation, Lincolnshire, IL; *U.S. Public,* pg. 915

Bayman, James L., Chm. Bd. & Chief Exec. Officer--Pioneer-Standard Electronics, Inc., Cleveland, OH; *U.S. Public,* pg. 1300

Bayman, Scott R., Pres. & Chief Exec. Officer-G.E. India--General Electric International Operations, London, United Kingdom; *U.S. Public,* pg. 713

Bazet, James R., Pres., Chief Exec. Officer & Chief Oper. Officer--Cobra Electronics Corporation, Chicago, IL; *U.S. Public,* pg. 391

Bazzani, Palmira, Chief Exec. Officer--Marcegaglia SpA, Mantova, Italy; *Int'l,* pg. 841

Beach, Roger C., Chm. Bd. & Chief Exec. Officer--Unocal Corporation, El Segundo, CA; *U.S. Public,* pg. 1698

Beach, William H., Chm. Bd., Pres., Chief Exec. & Oper. Officer--Beach Mold & Tool Inc., New Albany, IN; *U.S. Private,* pg. 125

Beale, Samuel E., Chm. Bd. & Chief Exec. Officer--Ruby Tuesday, Inc., Mobile, AL; *U.S. Public,* pg. 1411

Beall, Robert M., II, Chief Exec. Officer--Beall's, Inc., Bradenton, FL; *U.S. Private,* pg. 126

Beam, Alan M., Pres. & Chief Exec. Officer--F.W. Woolworth Co. Limited, Canada, Weston, Canada; *U.S. Public,* pg. 1778

Bean, Delcie D., Pres., Chief Exec. Officer & Treas.--D.D. Bean & Sons Co., Jaffrey, NH; *U.S. Private,* pg. 126

Beard, Frederick K., Exec. V.P. & Chm. Bd., Pres. & Chief Exec. Officer-Mellon Bank--Mellon Bank Corporation, Pittsburgh, PA; *U.S. Public,* pg. 1084

Beard, Frederick K., Chm. Bd., Pres. & Chief Exec. Officer--Mellon Bank (MD), Rockville, MD; *U.S. Public,* pg. 1085

Beard, Thomas G., Chm. Bd., Pres. & Chief Exec. Officer--Palmer Electric Co., Winter Park, FL; *U.S. Private,* pg. 834

Beardall, James C., Chm. Bd., Pres. & Chief Exec. Officer--Anderson Lumber Company, Ogden, UT; *U.S. Private,* pg. 72

Beardsley, John R., Chm. Bd. & Chief Exec. Officer--Padilla Speer Beardsley Inc., Minneapolis, MN; *U.S. Private,* pg. 833

Beasley, Robert E., Jr., Pres. & Chief Exec. Officer--Hunter Fan Company, Memphis, TN; *U.S. Private,* pg. 549

Beaton, Bradford, Chm. Bd., Pres. & Chief Exec. Officer--New England Newspaper Supply Company, Inc., Millbury, MA; *U.S. Private,* pg. 793

Beattie, Don, Chief Exec.-Personnel--The BOC Group plc, Windlesham, United Kingdom; *Int'l,* pg. 121

Beattie, Ted, Pres. & Chief Exec. Officer--John G. Shedd Aquarium, Chicago, IL; *U.S. Private,* pg. 991

Beatty, Greg, Chief Exec. Officer-Able Pryda Group--National Consolidated, Melbourne, Australia; *Int'l,* pg. 908

Beauchamp, Guy-R., Pres. & Chief Oper. Officer--CF Cable TV Inc., Montreal, Canada; *Int'l,* pg. 240

Beaudoin, Laurent, Chm. Bd. & Chief Exec. Officer--Bombardier Inc., Montreal, Canada; *Int'l,* pg. 199

Beaudoin, Pierre, Pres. & Chief Exec. Officer--Bombardier Motorized Consumer Products Group, Montreal, Canada; *Int'l,* pg. 200

Beaumont, Ronald R., Pres. & Chief Exec. Officer--MFS Telecom Companies, Oak Brook, IL; *U.S. Public,* pg. 1779

Beavers, Shirley, Pres. & Chief Exec. Officer--First Virginia Life Insurance Company, Falls Church, VA; *U.S. Public,* pg. 642

Beben, Henry, Pres. & Chief Exec. Officer--Principal Marques Inc., Toronto, Canada; *Int'l,* pg. 599

Beben, Henry, Pres. & Chief Exec. Officer--Principal Marques Meat Co., Etobicoke, Canada; *Int'l,* pg. 841

Bechat, Jean-Paul, Chm. & Chief Exec. Officer--SNECMA - Societe Nationale d'Etude et de Construction de Moteurs d'Aviation, Paris, France; *Int'l,* pg. 1165

Bechen, Peter F., Pres. & Chief Exec. Officer--M & T Partners, Portland, OR; *U.S. Private,* pg. 684

Becher, F. James, Jr., Chm. Bd., Pres. & Chief Exec. Officer--Geneva Corporation, Greensboro, NC; *U.S. Private,* pg. 446

Becherer, Hans W., Chm. Bd. & Chief Exec. Officer--Deere & Company, Moline, IL; *U.S. Public,* pg. 491

Bechtel, Riley, Chm. Bd. & Chief Exec. Officer--Bechtel Group, Inc., San Francisco, CA; *U.S. Private,* pg. 128

Beck, H. Thomas, Chm. Bd. & Chief Exec. Officer--Noma Industries Limited, North York, Canada; *Int'l,* pg. 954

Beck, Jeffrey L., Co-Chm. Bd. & Chief Exec. Officer--Capital Senior Living, Inc., Dallas, TX; *U.S. Public,* pg. 302

Beck, Paul D., Chief Exec. Officer--Tecknit Incorporated, Cranford, NJ; *U.S. Private,* pg. 1072

Becker, B. Frederick, Chm. Bd. & Chief Exec. Officer--MMI Companies, Inc., Deerfield, IL; *U.S. Public,* pg. 1027

Becker, Christopher, Pres. & Chief Exec. Officer--GeneTrace Systems, Inc., Menlo Park, CA; *U.S. Private,* pg. 958

Becker, Eugene E., Chief Exec. Officer--American Bankers Life Assurance Co. of Florida, Miami, FL; *U.S. Public,* pg. 67

Becker, Gene, Chief Exec. Officer--American Bankers Insurance Co. of Florida, Miami, FL; *U.S. Public,* pg. 67

Becker, John C., Pres., Chief Exec. Officer & Chief Oper. Officer--Axent Technologies, Rockville, MD; *U.S. Public,* pg. 157

Becker, Norbert, Pres. & Chief Exec. Officer--Renaissance Cosmetics, Inc., New York, NY; *U.S. Private,* pg. 922

Becker, Norbert, Pres. & Chief Exec. Officer--Dana Perfumes Corp., New York, NY; *U.S. Private,* pg. 922

Becker, Richard, Pres. & Chief Exec. Officer--M & I Bank of Menomonee Falls, Menomonee Falls, WI; *U.S. Public,* pg. 1050

Becker, W. Marston, Chm. Bd. & Chief Exec. Officer--Orion Capital Corporation, New York, NY; *U.S. Public,* pg. 1231

Becker, W. Marston, Chief Exec. Officer--Orion Capital Companies, Inc., Farmington, CT; *U.S. Public,* pg. 1231

Beckerman, David, Chm. Bd. & Chief Exec. Officer--Starter Corp., New Haven, CT; *U.S. Public,* pg. 1511

Beckerman, David R., Pres. & Chief Exec. Officer--Polyfibron Technologies Corp., Billerica, MA; *U.S. Private,* pg. 875

Beckord, Michael, Chief Exec. Officer--Allianz Versicherungs-AG, Berlin, Germany; *Int'l,* pg. 58

Beckwith, Brian, Pres. & Chief Exec. Officer--Primedia Inc., Peoria, IL; *U.S. Public,* pg. 1328

Beckwith, F.W., Chm. Bd. & Chief Exec. Officer--Fareway Stores, Inc., Boone, IA; *U.S. Private,* pg. 393

Beckwith, G. Nicholas, III, Pres. & Chief Exec. Officer--Beckwith Machinery Company, Murrysville, PA; *U.S. Private,* pg. 129

Bedford, Bryan K., Pres. & Chief Exec. Officer--Mesaba Holdings, Inc., Minneapolis, MN; *U.S. Public,* pg. 1099

Beebe, Stephen A., Pres. & Chief Exec. Officer--J.R. Simplot Company, Boise, ID; *U.S. Private,* pg. 1002

Beers, John, Pres. & Chief Exec. Officer--World Finer Foods, Inc., Bloomfield, NJ; *U.S. Private,* pg. 1190

Beeston, Paul, Pres. & Chief Exec. Officer--Toronto Blue Jays Baseball Club, Inc., Toronto, Canada; *Int'l,* pg. 680

Beffa, Jean-Louis, Chm. Bd. & Chief Exec. Officer--Saint-Gobain, Courbevoie, France; *Int'l,* pg. 1170

Beg, Mohammad Yousuf, Mng. Dir.--National Refinery Limited, Karachi, Pakistan; *Int'l,* pg. 909

Begel, Thomas M., Chm. Bd., Pres, & Chief Exec. Officer--Johnstown America Industries, Chicago, IL; *U.S. Public,* pg. 933

Beggington, Andrew, Chief Exec. Officer--NESLAB Instruments, Inc., Newington, NH; *U.S. Public,* pg. 1595

Begnone, Piero, Deputy Chm. & Chief Exec. Officer--Hunter Engineering Co., Inc., Riverside, CA; *Int'l,* pg. 474

Behan, Patrick J., Pres. & Chief Exec. Officer--Hill-Behan Lumber Company, Saint Louis, MO; *U.S. Private,* pg. 529

Behr, Richard, Pres. & Chief Exec. Officer--Joseph Behr & Sons Inc., Rockford, IL; *U.S. Private,* pg. 130

Behrakis, George D., Pres., Chief Exec. Officer & Treas.--Muro Pharmaceutical, Inc., Tewksbury, MA; *U.S. Private,* pg. 767

Behrendt, Peter D., Chm. Bd., Pres. & Chief Exec. Officer--Exabyte Corporation, Boulder, CO; *U.S. Public,* pg. 597

Behrens, Fred H., Chm. Bd., Chief Exec. Officer & Chief Fin. Officer--Amcor Capital Corporation, Coachella, CA; *U.S. Public,* pg. 64

Beisenherz, Robert L., Chief Exec. Officer--Constitution Life Insurance Co., Dallas, TX; *U.S. Private,* pg. 1018

Beissinger, Frederick W., Chm. Bd., Pres. & Chief Exec. Officer--American General Finance, Inc., Evansville, IN; *U.S. Public,* pg. 76

Beitzel, George, Chm. Bd. & Chief Exec. Officer--Blue Anchor, Inc., Dinuba, CA; *U.S. Private,* pg. 150

Belanger, Bernard, Pres. & Chief Exec. Officer--Premier CDN Enterprises Ltd., Dorval, Canada; *Int'l,* pg. 1067

Belanger, Charles, Pres. & Chief Exec. Officer-Brdcst. Group--CFCF Inc., Montreal, Canada; *Int'l,* pg. 240

Belanger, Charles, Vice Chm., Pres. & Chief Exec. Officer--Reseau de Television Quatre Saisons Inc., Montreal, Canada; *Int'l,* pg. 241

Belanger, Charles, Vice Chm. & Chief Exec. Officer--Champlain Productions Inc., Montreal, Canada; *Int'l,* pg. 241

Belatti, Frank J., Chm. Bd. & Chief Exec. Officer--AFC Enterprises, Atlanta, GA; *U.S. Private,* pg. 5

Belcher, Donald D., Chm. Bd., Pres. & Chief Exec. Officer--Banta Corporation, Menasha, WI; *U.S. Public,* pg. 187

Belden, Dennnis D., Chief Exec. Officer--Target Oilfield Pipe & Supply Company (TOPS), Canton, OH; *U.S. Private,* pg. 1078

Belden, Sanford A., Pres. & Chief Exec. Officer--Community Bank System, Inc., De Witt, NY; *U.S. Public,* pg. 416

Belden, Sanford A., Pres. & Chief Exec. Officer--Community Bank N.A., De Witt, NY; *U.S. Public,* pg. 416

Belgrad, D.A., Chm. Bd., Pres. & Chief Exec. Officer--Schnadig Corporation, Des Plaines, IL; *U.S. Private,* pg. 971

Belk, John M., Chm. Bd. & Chief Exec. Officer--Belk Stores Services Inc., Charlotte, NC; *U.S. Private,* pg. 131

Bell, A. Quinn, Pres. & Chief Exec. Officer--The Suddath Companies, Jacksonville, FL; *U.S. Private,* pg. 1049

Bell, Alan R., Pres. & Chief Exec. Officer--Dakota Mining Corporation, Denver, CO; *U.S. Public,* pg. 477

Bell, David, Pres. & Chief Exec. Officer-Bozell Worldwide--True North Communications Inc., Chicago, IL; *U.S. Public,* pg. 1641

Bell, David, Pres. & Chief Exec. Officer--Bozell Worldwide, Inc., New York, NY; *U.S. Public,* pg. 1642

Bell, Gene, Pres. & Chief Exec. Officer--San Diego Union Tribune, San Diego, CA; *U.S. Private,* pg. 275

Bell, George, Pres. & Chief Exec. Officer--Excite, Inc., Redwood City, CA; *U.S. Public,* pg. 599

Bell, Glenn R., Chief Exec. Officer--Simpson Gumpertz & Heger Inc., Arlington, MA; *U.S. Private,* pg. 1002

Bell, Larry, Pres. & Chief Exec. Officer--Shato Holdings Ltd. Vancouver, Canada; *Int'l,* pg. 1230

Bell, Ray, Pres.--Ray Bell Construction Co. Inc., Brentwood, TN; *U.S. Private,* pg. 131

Bell, Ray L., Pres. & Chief Exec. Officer--Bell Gas, Inc., Roswell, NM; *U.S. Private,* pg. 131

Bell, Richard E., Pres. & Chief Exec. Officer--Riceland Foods, Inc., Stuttgart, AR; *U.S. Private,* pg. 928

Bell, Thomas D., Jr., Pres. & Chief Exec. Officer (New York)--Burson-Marsteller, New York, NY; *U.S. Private,* pg. 1197

Bell, Tom, Pres. & Chief Exec. Officer-Burson-Marsteller--Young & Rubicam Inc., New York, NY; *U.S. Private,* pg. 1196

Belle, Thomas V., Pres. & Chief Exec. Officer--Carlson Learning Company, Minneapolis, MN; *U.S. Private,* pg. 212

Bellini, Francesco, Ph.D., Pres. & Chief Exec. Officer--BioChem Pharma Inc., Laval, Canada; *Int'l,* pg. 196

Bellis, Marc, Chief Exec. Officer--Generale Bank - London, London, United Kingdom; *Int'l,* pg. 547

Bello, Regis, Chm. & Chief Exec. Officer--De Dietrich & Co., Niederbronn-les-Bains, France; *Int'l,* pg. 386

Bello, Regis, Chm. & Chief Exec. Officer--Cogifer SA, Croissy-sur-Seine, France; *Int'l,* pg. 386

Bellon, Pierre, Chm. Bd. & Chief Exec. Officer--Sodexho S.A., Montigny-le-Bretonneux, France; *Int'l*, pg. 1274

Bellut, Jacques, Chief Exec. Officer--Credit Agricole Asset Management - Southeast Asia, Central, Hong Kong; *Int'l, pg. 341*

Belmonte, Dennis R., Pres. & Chief Exec. Officer--Benguet Corporation, Manila, Philippines; *Int'l*, pg. 186

Belot, Thomas G., Pres. & Chief Exec. Officer--The Vollrath Company, L.L.C., Sheboygan, WI; *U.S. Private*, pg. 1143

Beltranana, Enrique, Chief Exec. Officer--Aviateca, Guatemala, Guatemala; *Int'l*, pg. 102

Belzberg, Brent S., Pres. & Chief Exec. Officer--Harrowston Corporation, Toronto, Canada; *Int'l*, pg. 599

Belzer, Burton E., Chm. Bd., Chief Exec. Officer, Chief Fin. Officer & Treas.--TCI Aluminum, Gardena, CA; *U.S. Private*, pg. 1063

Belzer, Burton E., Chm. Bd., Chief Exec. Officer, Cheif Fin. Officer & Treas.--E-Z Lok, Gardena, CA; *U.S. Private*, pg. 1063

Benaroya, Raphael, Chm. Bd., Pres. & Chief Exec. Officer--United Retail Group, Inc., Rochelle Park, NJ; *U.S. Public, pg. 1679*

Benassi, Peter, Pres. & Chief Exec. Officer--MRI Los Angeles, Santa Monica, CA; *U.S. Private*, pg. 727

Benassi, Peter M., Pres. & Chief Exec. Officer--Media Resources International, New York, NY; *U.S. Private*, pg. 727

Bender, A. Thomas, Pres. & Chief Exec. Officer--The Cooper Companies, Inc., Irvine, CA; *U.S. Public*, pg. 442

Bender, Miles, Pres. & Chief Exec. Officer--National Energy Group, Inc., Dallas, TX; *U.S. Public*, pg. 1156

Bender, Robert L., Chm., Pres., Chief Exec. Officer & Chief Oper. Officer--Lord, Sullivan & Yoder Inc. Marketing Communications, Columbus, OH; *U.S. Private*, pg. 676

Bender, Thomas B., Jr., Chm. Bd., Pres. & Chief Exec. Officer--Bender Shipbuilding & Repair Company, Inc., Mobile, AL; *U.S. Private*, pg. 132

Benderson, Randall, Pres. & Chief Exec. Officer--Benderson Development Co., Inc., Buffalo, NY; *U.S. Private*, pg. 132

Bendheim, Ralf E., Chief Exec.--A.M.A. Asset Management Advisors of Dresdner Bank, Frankfurt/Main, Germany; *Int'l*, pg. 418

Benedict, Robert, Chief Exec. Officer, Chief Fin. Officer & V.P.--Real World, Andover, MA; *U.S. Private*, pg. 913

Benefield, Jerry L., Pres. & Chief Exec. Officer--Nissan Motor Mfg. Corp., U.S.A., Smyrna, TN; *Int'l*, pg. 945

Benesch, Valli, Chm. Bd. & Chief Exec. Officer--Fritzi of California Manufacturing Corp., San Francisco, CA; *U.S. Private*, pg. 429

Benhamou, Eric A., Chm. Bd., Pres. & Chief Exec. Officer--3Com Corporation, Santa Clara, CA; *U.S. Public*, pg. 1603

Benhamou, Guy, Chm. Bd., Pres. & Chief Exec. Officer--Oroamerica, Inc., Burbank, CA; *U.S. Public*, pg. 1232

Beningson, Robert M., Chm. Bd., Pres. & Chief Exec. Officer--York Research Corporation, New York, NY; *U.S. Public*, pg. 1789

Benjamin, Douglas, Exec. V.P. & Chief Exec. Officer-FJB Fashions--F. J. Benjamin Holdings Ltd., Singapore, Singapore; *Int'l*, pg. 187

Benjamin, Douglas, Chief Exec. Officer--F.J. Benjamin Fashions (Singapore) Pte. Ltd., Singapore, Singapore; *Int'l*, pg. 187

Benjamin, Frank, Pres. & Chief Exec. Officer--F. J. Benjamin Holdings Ltd., Singapore, Singapore; *Int'l*, pg. 187

Benjamin, Larry, Pres. & Chief Exec. Officer--Stella Foods, Inc., Green Bay, WI; *U.S. Private*, pg. 1040

Benjamin, Lawrence, Pres. & Chief Exec. Officer--Specialty Foods Corporation, Deerfield, IL; *U.S. Private*, pg. 1022

Benjamin, Mark, Pres. & Chief Exec. Officer--Morley Builders, Santa Monica, CA; *U.S. Private*, pg. 761

Benjamin, Mark, Pres. & Chief Exec. Officer--Benchmark Contractors, Inc., Santa Monica, CA; *U.S. Private*, pg. 761

Benjaminsen, P., Chief Exec. Officer--Zurich Forsikring, Oslo, Norway; *Int'l*, pg. 1531

Bennack, Frank, Pres. & Chief Exec. Officer-Hearst Corp.--Cosmopolitan, New York, NY; *U.S. Private*, pg. 517

Bennack, Frank A., Jr., Pres. & Chief Exec. Officer--The Hearst Corporation, New York, NY; *U.S. Private*, pg. 515

Bennack, Frank A., Jr., Pres. & Chief Exec. Officer--Hearst Realty Development Co., Inc., New York, NY; *U.S. Private*, pg. 515

Benner, Mike, Chief Exec. Officer--Stewart Warner Instruments Corporation, Des Plaines, IL; *U.S. Private*, pg. 1042

Bennet, Richard W., III, Pres. & Chief Exec. Officer--Kaufmann's, Pittsburgh, PA; *U.S. Public*, pg. 1063

Bennett, Gary P., Chm. Bd., Pres. & Chief Exec. Officer--Analysis & Technology, Inc., North Stonington, CT, *U.S. Public*, pg. 109

Bennett, Jeffrey, Pres. & Chief Exec. Officer--Nature's Recipe Pet Foods, Corona, CA; *U.S. Private*, pg. 789

Bennett, Paul F., Chm. Bd. & Chief Exec. Officer--Utility Trailer Manufacturing Co., City of Industry, CA; *U.S. Private*, pg. 1130

Bennett, Robert J., Chm. Bd., Pres. & Chief Exec. Officer--ONBANCorp, Inc., Syracuse, NY; *U.S. Public*, pg. 631

Bennett, Robert R., Pres. & Chief Exec. Officer--Liberty Media Corporation, Englewood, CO; *U.S. Public*, pg. 1555

Bennett, Stephen D., Pres. & Chief Exec. & Oper. Officer--Acme Metals Incorporated, Riverdale, IL; *U.S. Public*, pg. 16

Bennion, Richard E., Pres. & Chief Exec. Officer--The Rowe Corporation, Charlotte, NC; *U.S. Private*, pg. 948

Benoit, David C., Chief Exec. Officer--Key Plastics, Inc., Novi, MI; *U.S. Private*, pg. 618

Benon, Alain, Chief Oper. Officer & Gen. Mgr.--Unibail, Paris, France; *Int'l*, pg. 1431

Benosik, Doris D., Pres. & Chief Oper. Officer--Datapoint Corporation, Paris, France; *Int'l*, pg. 384

Bensabat, Elias Zerbib, Exec. Pres.--Mantex, S.A.C.A., Caracas, Venezuela; *Int'l*, pg. 840

Bensabat, Paul, Pres. & Chief Exec. Officer--Sorrento Cheese Company, Inc., Buffalo, NY; *Int'l*, pg. 323

Benson, Donald W., Pres. & Chief Exec. Officer--Associated Grocers, Inc., Seattle, WA; *U.S. Private*, pg. 90

Benson, Kevin E., Pres., Chief Exec. & Fin. Officer--Canadian Airlines Corporation, Calgary, Canada; *Int'l*, pg. 255

Benson, Kevin E., Pres. & Chief Exec. Officer--Canadian Airlines International Ltd., Calgary, Canada; *Int'l*, pg. 256

Benson, M., Chief Exec. Officer-Pacific--Invesco Group Asset Management Ltd., London, United Kingdom; *Int'l*, pg. 685

Benson, Tom, Chm. Bd. & Chief Exec. Officer--Benson Motors Corporation, Metairie, LA; *U.S. Private*, pg. 134

Benstock, Gerald M., Chm. Bd. & Chief Exec. Officer--Superior Surgical Mfg. Co., Inc., Seminole, FL; *U.S. Public*, pg. 1539

Bentley, Keith, Chief Exec. Officer--Bentley Systems, Inc., Exton, PA; *U.S. Private*, pg. 134

Bentley, Peter J.G., Chm. Bd. & Chief Exec. Officer--Canfor Corporation, Vancouver, Canada; *Int'l*, pg. 260

Bently, Donald E., Chm. Bd. & Chief Exec. Officer--Bently Nevada Corporation, Minden, NV; *U.S. Private*, pg. 134

Benton, A.E., Chm. Bd. & Pres.--Benton Oil & Gas Company, Carpinteria, CA; *U.S. Public*, pg. 212

Benton, Michael K., Exec. Dir.--Irving Convention & Visitors Bureau, Irving, TX; *U.S. Private*, pg. 575

Benton, Virgil, II., Chm. Bd. & Chief Exec. Officer--Keystone Automotive Industries, Inc., Pomona, CA; *U.S. Public*, pg. 955

Benton, William B., Chm. Bd., Chief Exec. Officer & Chief Fin. Officer--Mid South Sales, Helena, AR; *U.S. Private*, pg. 744

Benwell, Peter D., Chief Exec. Officer--The Cardwell Machine Company, Richmond, VA; *U.S. Private*, pg. 209

Benz, Charles, Chief Exec. Officer--American Technology Corporation, Hudson, MA; *U.S. Private*, pg. 63

Beppu, Masakatsu, Chief Oper. Officer--Nittsu Real Estate Co., Ltd., Tokyo, Japan; *Int'l*, pg. 934

Berard, Andre, Chm. Bd. & Chief Exec. Officer--National Bank of Canada, Montreal, Canada; *Int'l*, pg. 907

Berard, Dailey J., Chm. Bd., Pres. & Chief Exec. Officer--Unifab International Inc., New Iberia, LA; *U.S. Public*, pg. 1665

Berdin, Jerry, Chm. Bd. & Chief Exec. Officer--Allied Office Supplies, Hasbrouck Heights, NJ; *U.S. Private*, pg. 39

Bere, David, Pres. & Chief Exec. Officer--McCain Foods Inc., Oak Brook, IL; *Int'l*, pg. 850

Beren, S.O., Chm. Bd., Pres. & Chief Exec. Officer--Misco Industries, Wichita, KS; *U.S. Private*, pg. 752

Berenzweig, Stanley, Chm. Bd. & Chief Exec. Officer--Rag Shops, Inc., Hawthorne, NJ; *U.S. Public*, pg. 1358

Berer, Stanley H., Co.-Chm. & Co.-Chief Exec. Officer--Totem Resources Corporation, Seattle, WA; *U.S. Private, pg. 1092*

Berg, Carl E., Pres. & Chief Exec. Officer--Mission West Properties, Cupertino, CA; *U.S. Public*, pg. 1117

Berg, Jack H., Pres., Chief Exec. Officer & Treas.--Serfilco, Ltd., Northbrook, IL; *U.S. Private*, pg. 985

Berg, Jeffrey, Pres. & Chief Exec. Officer--ICM Holdings Inc., New York, NY; *U.S. Private*, pg. 554

Berg, John A., Pres. & Chief Exec. Officer--Norwest Bank Minnesota North, N.A., Duluth, MN; *U.S. Public*, pg. 1202

Berg, Kenneth, Chm. Bd. & Chief Exec. Officer--Koo Koo Roo, Inc., Los Angeles, CA; *U.S. Public*, pg. 966

Berg, Lars, Pres. & Chief Exec. Officer--Telia AB, Farsta, Sweden; *Int'l*, pg. 1373

Berge, Paul M., Chm. & Chief Exec. Officer--M & I Madison Bank, Madison, WI; *U.S. Public*, pg. 1050

Berger, Charles M., Chm. Bd., Pres. & Chief Exec. Officer--The Scotts Company, Marysville, OH; *U.S. Public*, pg. 1446

Berger, Ron, Chm. Bd., Pres., Chief Exec. Officer--Rentrak Corporation, Portland, OR; *U.S. Public*, pg. 1377

Bergeson, Jim, Chief Exec. Officer & New Bus. Contact--Colle & McVoy Marketing Communications, Minneapolis, MN; *U.S. Private*, pg. 252

Berghash, Robert, Chief Exec. Officer--Brimms Inc., Tonawanda, NY; *U.S. Private*, pg. 169

Bergman, Ake, Chief Officer--City Stormarknad, Stockholm, Sweden; *Int'l*, pg. 718

Bergman, David R., Pres. & Treas.--Processed Plastic Company, Montgomery, IL; *U.S. Private*, pg. 888

Bergman, Stanley M., Chm. Bd., Pres. & Chief Exec. Officer--Henry Schein, Inc., Melville, NY; *U.S. Public*, pg. 1437

Bergmann, Horst A., Chm. Bd., Pres. & Chief Exec. Officer--Jeppesen Sanderson, Englewood, CO; *U.S. Public*, pg. 1616

Bergmann, Horst A., Chm. Bd., Pres. & Chief Exec. Officer--Jeppesen and Co. GmbH, Frankfurt/Main, Germany; *U.S. Public*, pg. 1617

Bergmann, Horst A., Chm., Pres. & Chief Exec. Officer--Achieve Global, Tampa, FL; *U.S. Public*, pg. 1617

Bergquist, Carl R., Jr., Chm. Bd., Pres. & Chief Exec. Officer--The Bergquist Company, Minneapolis, MN; *U.S. Private*, pg. 135

Bergsma, David P., Pres. & Chief Oper. Officer--Levy Security Corp., Chicago, IL; *U.S. Private*, pg. 664

Bergson, Jim, Chief Exec. Officer--Colle & McVoy, Inc., Minneapolis, MN; *U.S. Private*, pg. 252

Bergstein, Melvyn E., Chm. Bd. & Chief Exec. Officer--Diamond Technology Partners, Chicago, IL; *U.S. Public*, pg. 1424

Berk, Fred, Pres., & Chief Exec. Officer--Huffman Koos, River Edge, NJ; *U.S. Private*, pg. 546

Berkeley, Frederick D., Chm. Bd. & Chief Exec. Officer--Graham Corporation, Batavia, NY; *U.S. Public*, pg. 757

Berkeley, Virginia K., Pres. & Chief Exec. Officer--Colorado Business Bank, Denver, CO; *U.S. Private*, pg. 255

Berkins, S.J., Chief Exec. Officer--Senior Flexonics Ltd., Oldbury, United Kingdom; *Int'l*, pg. 1221

Berkley, William, Chm. Bd. & Chief Exec. Officer--Interlaken Capital, Inc., Greenwich, CT; *U.S. Private*, pg. 567

Berkley, William, Pres. & Chief Exec. Officer--Tension Envelope Corp., Kansas City, MO; *U.S. Private*, pg. 1077

Berkley, William R., Chm. Bd. & Chief Exec. Officer--W.R. Berkley Corporation, Greenwich, CT; *U.S. Public*, pg. 215

Berkowitz, David H., Chm. Bd. & Chief Exec. Officer--Central Lewmar, Newark, NJ; *U.S. Private*, pg. 223

Berkowitz, Ivan, Chief Exec. Officer--PolyVision Corp., New York, NY; *U.S. Public*, pg. 1315

Berman, Lyle, Chm. Bd. & Chief Exec. Officer--Grand Casinos, Inc., Minnetonka, MN; *U.S. Public*, pg. 758

Berman, Michael, Chief Exec. Officer--Nomura Holding America, Inc., New York, NY; *Int'l*, pg. 956

Berman, Michael A., Chief Exec. Officer--Nomura Securities International, Inc., New York, NY; *Int'l*, pg. 956

Berman, Richard N., Chm. Bd., Pres. & Chief Exec. Officer--R&B, Inc., Colmar, PA; *U.S. Public*, pg. 1354

Berman, Robert A., Pres. & Chief Exec. Officer--Hospitality Worldwide Services, Inc., New York, NY; *U.S. Public*, pg. 841

Bern, Dorrit J., Chm. Bd., Pres. & Chief Exec. Officer--Charming Shoppes, Inc., Bensalem, PA; *U.S. Public*, pg. 335

Bernard, Norman, Chm. Bd. & Chief Exec. Officer--Master Industries Corp., New York, NY; *U.S. Private*, pg. 713

Bernards, Douglas, Chm. Bd., Pres. & Chief Exec. Officer--Bernards Brothers, Inc., San Fernando, CA; *U.S. Private, pg. 136*

Bernhardt, Alex, Sr., Chief Exec. Officer--Bernhardt Furniture Co., Lenoir, NC; *U.S. Private*, pg. 137

Bernick, Howard B., Pres. & Chief Exec. Officer--Alberto-Culver Company, Melrose Park, IL; *U.S. Public*, pg. 37

Bernick, Howard B., Pres. & Chief Exec. Officer--Alberto-Culver USA, Inc., Melrose Park, IL; *U.S. Public*, pg. 38

Bernon, Peter M., Chm. Bd. & Chief Exec. Officer--Garelick Farms, Inc., Franklin, MA; *U.S. Public*, pg. 1527

Bernstein, Allen J., Chm. Bd., Pres. & Chief Exec. Officer--Morton's Restaurant Group, Inc., New Hyde Park, NY; *U.S. Public*, pg. 1136

Bernstein, Elliot, Chm. Bd. & Chief Exec. Officer--Bel Fuse Inc., Jersey City, NJ; *U.S. Public*, pg. 200

Bernstein, George, Pres. & Chief Exec. Officer--AVC/Nu-Vision, Inc., Flint, MI; *U.S. Private*, pg. 9

Bernstein, Harvey, Pres. & Chief Exec. Officer--Spirite Industries, Inc., Englewood, NJ; *U.S. Private*, pg. 1026

Bernstein, Michael H., Pres. & Chief Exec. Officer--Crown Crafts, Inc., Atlanta, GA; *U.S. Public*, pg. 465

Bernstein, Robert, Chm. Bd., Pres. & Chief Exec. Officer--Bernstein-Rein Advertising, Inc., Kansas City, MO; *U.S. Private*, pg. 137

Bernstein, S.J., Chm. Bd. & Chief Exec. Officer--The Biltrite Corporation, Waltham, MA; *U.S. Private*, pg. 144

Bero, Robert D., Pres. & Chief Exec. Officer--Menasha Corporation, Neenah, WI; *U.S. Private*, pg. 731

Berouard, Gilles, Chief Exec. Officer--EURO RSCG, Praha, Prague, Czech Republic; *Int'l*, pg. 602

Berrard, Steven R., Pres. & Co-Chief Exec. Officer--Republic Industries, Inc., Fort Lauderdale, FL; *U.S. Public*, pg. 1378

Berrie, Russell, Chm. Bd. & Chief Exec. Officer--Russ Berrie and Company, Inc., Oakland, NJ; *U.S. Public*, pg. 222

Berry, Dan W., Chm. Bd., Pres. & Chief Exec. Officer--American Trouser, Inc., Columbus, MS; *U.S. Private*, pg. 64

Berry, Dennis, Pres. & Chief Exec. Officer--Manheim Auctions, Inc., Atlanta, GA; *U.S. Private*, pg. 282

Berry, Robert E., Chm. Bd. & Chief Exec. Officer--Berry-Brown Advertising, Inc., Dallas, TX; *U.S. Private*, pg. 137

Bershad, Stephen W., Chm. Bd. & Chief Exec. Officer--Axsys Technologies, Inc., New York, NY; *U.S. Public*, pg. 157

Bersoff, Edward H., Dr., Chm. Bd., Pres. & Chief Exec. Officer--BTG, Inc., Fairfax, VA; *U.S. Public*, pg. 164

Bersticker, Albert C., Chm. Bd. & Chief Exec. Officer--Ferro Corporation, Cleveland, OH; *U.S. Public*, pg. 618

Berta, Michael A., Ph.D., Pres. & Chief Exec. Officer--RMS Information Systems, Inc., Lanham, MD; *U.S. Public*, pg. 1425

Berta, Mike, Pres. & Chief Exec. Officer--RMS Techs, Inc., Lanham, MD; *U.S. Private*, pg. 905

Berta, Vince A., Pres. & Chief Exec. Officer--Trans Financial, Inc., Bowling Green, KY; *U.S. Public*, pg. 1628

Bertani, A., Chief Exec. Officer--Zurigo Compagnia di Assicurazioni Sulla Vita, Milan, Italy; *Int'l*, pg. 1530

Bertani, A., Chief Exec. Officer--Zurigo Compagnia di Assicurazioni, Milan, Italy; *Int'l*, pg. 1531

Bertarelli, Ernesto, Chief Exec. Officer--Ares-Serono S.A., Geneva, Switzerland; *Int'l*, pg. 80

Berthelot, Barry F., Pres. & Chief Exec. Officer--The First National Bank of Lafayette, Lafayette, LA; *U.S. Public*, pg. 630

Berthelot, Michael J., Chm. Bd. & Chief Exec. Officer--TransTechnology Corporation, Liberty Corner, NJ; *U.S. Public*, pg. 1632

Berthelsen, Bruce, Pres. & Chief Exec. Officer--Willis Corroon Corp. of Georgia, Atlanta, GA; *Int'l*, pg. 1506

Berthiaume, Douglas A., Chm. Bd., Pres. & Chief Exec. Officer--Waters Corporation, Milford, MA; *U.S. Public*, pg. 1745

Bertmar, Lars, Chief Exec. Officer--Carnegie Holding AB, Stockholm, Sweden; *Int'l*, pg. 272

Beshouri, Peter, Chm. Bd., Pres. & Chief Exec. Officer--Sound Advice, Inc., Dania, FL; *U.S. Public*, pg. 1488

Besnier, Michel, Chief Exec. Officer--Compagnie Laitiere BESNIER, Laval, France; *Int'l*, pg. 322

Besse, William C., Chief Exec. Officer--Coleman Powermate Compressors, Springfield, MN; *U.S. Private*, pg. 691

Best, Russell, Pres. & Chief Exec. Officer--Best Access Systems, Indianapolis, IN; *U.S. Public*, pg. 223

Bestgen, Guenter, Chief Exec. Officer & Gen. Mgr.--Lowe & Partners, Frankfurt/Main, Germany; *U.S. Private*, pg. 678

Betancourt, Jose Luis, Chief Exec. Officer--Betancourt Barba EURO RSCG, Mexico, Mexico; *Int'l*, pg. 603

Bethea, David, Chief Exec. Officer & Exec. V.P.--E.K. Williams, Waco, TX; *U.S. Public*, pg. 538
Bethune, Gordon, Chm. Bd. & Chief Exec. Officer--Continental Airlines, Houston, TX; *U.S. Public*, pg. 439
Bethurum, George M., Chm. Bd., Pres. & Chief Exec. Officer--Bethurum Research & Development, Inc., Texas City, TX; *U.S. Private*, pg. 141
Bettendorf, Larry, Pres. & Chief Exec. Officer--ECP Incorporated, Westchester, IL; *U.S. Private*, pg. 313
Beumer, R.E., Chm. Bd. & Chief Exec. Officer--Sverdrup Corporation, Maryland Heights, MO; *U.S. Private*, pg. 1057
Beveridge, Crawford, Pres. & Chief Exec. Officer--Scottish Enterprise, Glasgow, United Kingdom; *Int'l*, pg. 1212
Bevier, Deborah L., Chm. Bd. & Chief Exec. Officer--Key Bank of Washington, Tacoma, WA; *U.S. Public*, pg. 954
Bevilaqua, Steven K., Pres. & Chief Exec. Officer--KLLM Transport Services, Inc., Jackson, MS; *U.S. Public*, pg. 939
Bew, R.E., Chief Exec. Officer--ICI Chemicals & Polymers Ltd., Runcorn, United Kingdom; *Int'l*, pg. 663
Bewkes, Jeffrey L, Chm. Bd., Pres. & Chief Exec. Officer--Home Box Office, Inc., New York, NY; *U.S. Public*, pg. 1612
Beyer, Sonya Z., Chm. Bd. & Chief Exec. Officer--Midco International Inc., Chicago, IL; *U.S. Private*, pg. 744
Beyland, Mark, Chief Exec. Officer--Reed Technology and Information Services Inc., Horsham, PA; *Int'l*, pg. 1096
Beyster, J.R., Chm. Bd. & Chief Exec. Officer--Science Applications International Corp., San Diego, CA; *U.S. Private*, pg. 975
Bezos, Jeffrey P., Chm. Bd., Pres. & Chief Exec. Officer--Amazon.com, Inc., Seattle, WA; *U.S. Public*, pg. 62
Bhargava, Rai P.K., Pres. & Chief Exec. Officer--MCN Investment, Detroit, MI; *U.S. Public*, pg. 1025
Bhutani, Raj, Dr., Pres. & Chief Exec. Officer--Alra Laboratories, Inc., Gurnee, IL; *U.S. Private*, pg. 45
Bible, Geoffrey C., Chm. Bd. & Chief Exec. Officer--Philip Morris Companies Inc., New York, NY; *U.S. Public*, pg. 1287
Bibler, James, Chm. Bd. & Chief Exec. Officer--Bibler Brothers, Inc., Russellville, AR; *U.S. Private*, pg. 142
Bich, Bruno, Chm. Bd. & Chief Exec. Officer--Societe BIC S.A., Clichy, France; *Int'l*, pg. 1272
Bich, Bruno, Chm. Bd. & Chief Exec. Officer--BIC Corporation, Milford, CT; *Int'l*, pg. 1273
Bicknell, O. Gene, Chm. Bd. & Chief Exec. Officer--NPC International, Inc., Pittsburg, KS; *U.S. Public*, pg. 1146
Bickner, Bruce P., Chm. Bd. & Chief Exec. Officer--Dekalb Genetics Corporation, De Kalb, IL; *U.S. Public*, pg. 493
Biddinger, Clay M., Pres. & Chief Exec. Officer--Sun Financial Group, Inc., Tampa, FL; *U.S. Public*, pg. 691
Biddle, James, Sr, Pres. & Chief Exec. Officer--Mader Construction Corp, Elma, NY; *U.S. Private*, pg. 693
Bidwell, Donald, Sr., Pres. & Chief Exec. Officer--Bidwell Industrial Group, Inc., Middletown, CT; *U.S. Private*, pg. 142
Bidwell, Donald, Sr., Pres. & Chief Exec. Officer--Power-Dyne, Middletown, CT; *U.S. Private*, pg. 142
Bidwell, Donald, Sr., Pres. & Chief Exec. Officer--Rapid Print, Middletown, CT; *U.S. Private*, pg. 142
Biegler, David W., Chm. Bd. & Chief Exec. Officer--Lone Star Gas Co., Dallas, TX; *U.S. Public*, pg. 1587
Bierer, William, Chm. Bd. & Chief Exec. Officer--Essex Grain Products, Inc., Frazer, PA; *U.S. Private*, pg. 383
Bieri, Robert K., Chief Exec. Officer--Barnett Recovery Corporation, Jacksonville, FL; *U.S. Public*, pg. 1162
Bierman, C.J.M., Chief Exec. Officer--Swiss Bank Corporation Nederland N.V., Amsterdam, Netherlands; *Int'l*, pg. 1332
Biggar, James M., Pres. & Chief Exec. Officer--Nestle Holdings, Inc., Stamford, CT; *Int'l*, pg. 916
Biggs, John H., Chm. Bd., Pres. & Chief Exec. Officer--Teachers Insurance and Annuity Association, New York, NY; *U.S. Private*, pg. 1071
Biggs, Stanley D., Chief Exec. Officer--The Rival Company, Kansas City, MO; *U.S. Public*, pg. 1391
Bignami, Franco, Chief Exec. Officer & Mng. Dir.--Foster Wheeler Italiana S.P.A. (Italy), Milan, Italy; *U.S. Public*, pg. 677
Bigum, Jens, Grp. Mng. Dir.--MD Foods, Viby, Denmark; *Int'l*, pg. 826
Bijur, Peter I., Chm. Bd. & Chief Exec. Officer--Texaco Inc., White Plains, NY; *U.S. Public*, pg. 1582
Bikard, Jean Luc, Chief Exec. Officer--Clestra Hauserman, Inc., Solon, OH; *Int'l*, pg. 569
Bilger, J.P.H., Chief Exec. Officer--GEC Alsthom N.V., Amsterdam, Netherlands; *Int'l*, pg. 56
Billett, James F., Jr., Chm. Bd., Pres. & Chief Exec. Officer--Trenwick Group Inc., Stamford, CT; *U.S. Public*, pg. 1634
Billing, Grant D., Pres. & Chief Exec. Officer--Norcen Energy Resources Limited, Calgary, Canada; *Int'l*, pg. 434
Billmaier, James A., Pres. & Chief Exec. Officer--Asymetrix Learning Systems, Inc., Bellevue, WA; *U.S. Private*, pg. 93
Billotti, Nicholas, Chief Exec. Officer--Turner Steiner International, New York, NY; *U.S. Public*, pg. 1646
bin Haji Zakaria, Datuk Ismail, Chief Exec. Officer--Sime Bank Berhad, Kuala Lumpur, Malaysia; *Int'l*, pg. 1250
bin Marican, Dato' Mohd Hassan, Chm. Bd.--Petroliam Nasional Berhad (Petronas), Kuala Lumpur, Malaysia; *Int'l*, pg. 1046
Binder, Gordon M., Chm. Bd. & Chief Exec. Officer--Amgen Inc., Thousand Oaks, CA; *U.S. Public*, pg. 100
Binder, Stanley S., Chm. Bd., Pres & Chief Exec. Officer--Barringer Technologies Inc., New Providence, NJ; *U.S. Public*, pg. 191
Bindley, William E., Chm. Bd. & Chief Exec. Officer--Bindley Western Industries, Inc., Indianapolis, IN; *U.S. Public*, pg. 228
Binswanger, David R., Pres. & Chief Exec. Officer--Binswanger, Philadelphia, PA; *U.S. Private*, pg. 144
Biondi, Frank J., Jr., Chm. Bd. & Chief Exec. Officer--Universal Studios, Inc., Universal City, CA; *Int'l*, pg. 1215
Birch, Eric N., Pres. & Chief Exec. Officer--Intertek Testing Services, Andover, MA; *Int'l*, pg. 672
Birch, Peter, Chief Exec. Officer--Abbey National Plc, London, United Kingdom; *Int'l*, pg. 19
Birck, Michael J., Pres. & Chief Exec. Officer-Tellabs, Inc.--Tellabs Operations, Inc., Lisle, IL; *U.S. Public*, pg. 1572
Bird, Gerg, Chief Exec. Officer--Horizon Enterprises Group LLC, Taylor, MI; *U.S. Private*, pg. 539
Bird, Greg, Chief Exec. Officer--Horizon Technology Group LLC, Taylor, MI; *U.S. Private*, pg. 539
Birkholz, Ray, Pres. & Chief Exec. Officer--Republic Storage Systems Company Inc., Canton, OH; *U.S. Private*, pg. 924
Birnbach, Gerald, Chm. Bd., Pres. & Chief Exec. Officer--Rowe Furniture Corp., Mc Lean, VA; *U.S. Public*, pg. 1410
Birrell, N., Dr., Chief Exec.--County NatWest Australia Investment, Melbourne, Australia; *Int'l*, pg. 911
Bisang, Frank, Pres. & Chief Exec. Officer--Garnac Grain Co., Inc., Overland Park, KS; *U.S. Private*, pg. 802
Bischoff, Manfred, Chief Exec.--Daimler-Benz Aerospace AG, Bremen, Germany; *Int'l*, pg. 367
Bishop, Benjamin M., Chm. Bd. & Chief Exec. Officer--The Western Group, Saint Louis, MO; *U.S. Private*, pg. 1165
Bishop, F., Chief Exec. Officer-U.S.--Invesco Group Asset Management Ltd., London, United Kingdom; *Int'l*, pg. 665
Bishop, Thomas A., Chm. Bd. & Chief Exec. Officer--California State Bank, West Covina, CA; *U.S. Public*, pg. 294
Bishop, Vernon, Chm. Bd. & Chief Exec. Officer--Lebanon Seaboard Corporation, Lebanon, PA; *U.S. Private*, pg. 656
Bissell, Mark J., Pres. & Chief Exec. Officer--Bissell Inc., Grand Rapids, MI; *U.S. Private*, pg. 145
Bisson, Edwin, Pres. & Chief Exec. Officer--Crowe Rope Industries L.L.C., Waterville, ME; *U.S. Private*, pg. 291
Bither, Richard A., PE, Chm. Bd., Pres. & Chief Exec. Officer--Giffels Associates, Inc., Southfield, MI; *U.S. Private*, pg. 452
Bither, Richard A., PE, Chief Exec. Officer--Giffels Strategic Consultants, L.L.C., Southfield, MI; *U.S. Private*, pg. 452
Bittner, Thomas, Pres. & Chief Exec. Officer--Polychrome Corp. Div., Fort Lee, NJ; *Int'l*, pg. 370
Bixby, Walter E., Vice Chm., Pres. & Chief Exec. Officer--Kansas City Life Insurance Co., Kansas City, MO; *U.S. Public*, pg. 942
Bixby, Walter E., Chm. Bd. & Chief Exec. Officer--Old American Insurance Co., Kansas City, MO; *U.S. Public*, pg. 943
Bize, Pierre, Pres. & Chief Exec. Officer--CSE Insurance Group, San Francisco, CA; *U.S. Private*, pg. 197
Bjerrum, C. A., Chief Exec. Officer--Sea Containers Asia Ltd., Hong Kong, Hong Kong; *Int'l*, pg. 1214
Bjork, Claes, Pres. & Grp. Chief Exec. Officer--Skanska AB, Danderyd, Sweden; *Int'l*, pg. 1260
Black, Conrad M., Chm. Bd. & Chief Exec. Officer--Hollinger Inc., Vancouver, Canada; *Int'l*, pg. 630
Black, Conrad M., Chm. Bd. & Chief Exec. Officer--Southam Inc., Don Mills, Canada; *Int'l*, pg. 631
Black, L. David, Chm. Bd., Pres., & Chief Exec. Officer--JLG Industries, Inc., McConnellsburg, PA; *U.S. Public*, pg. 918
Black, Philip, Chief Exec. Officer--Box Hill Systems Corporation, New York, NY; *U.S. Public*, pg. 249
Black, Scott, Chm. & Chief Exec. Officer--Black Rogers Sullivan Goodnight, Inc., Houston, TX; *U.S. Private*, pg. 147
Blackburn, J.M., Pres. & Chief Exec. Officer--Halifax plc, Halifax, United Kingdom; *Int'l*, pg. 589
Blackwell, E. Scott, Pres. & Chief Exec. Officer--eMerge Vision Systems, Sebastian, FL; *U.S. Public*, pg. 1425
Blaeser, Jack, Pres. & Chief Exec. Officer--Concord Communications, Inc., Marlborough, MA; *U.S. Public*, pg. 429
Blagge, Timothy J., Pres. & Chief Exec. Officer--Blagge Enterprises, Rancho Cordova, CA; *U.S. Private*, pg. 148
Blair, Don, Chief Exec. Officer-Henderson's Automotive Group--National Consolidated, Melbourne, Australia; *Int'l*, *pg. 908*
Blair, Douglas, Pres. & Chief Exec. Officer--The Thermos Company, Schaumburg, IL; *Int'l*, pg. 938
Blair, Michael D., Chm. Bd. & Chief Exec. Officer--Cyborg Systems, Inc., Chicago, IL; *U.S. Private*, pg. 299
Blair, R. Cary, Chm. Bd., Pres. & Chief Exec. Officer--Westfield Companies, Westfield Center, OH; *U.S. Private*, pg. 1169
Blajsczak, Richard J., Pres. & Chief Exec. Officer--RCB Baking Company, Fargo, ND; *U.S. Public*, pg. 1354
Blake, Norman P., Jr., Chm. Bd., Pres. & Chief Exec. Officer--USF&G Corporation, Baltimore, MD; *U.S. Public*, pg. 1659
Blake, Richard, Chief Exec. Officer--Transistor Devices, Inc., Cedar Knolls, NJ; *U.S. Private*, pg. 1097
Blake, Steven B., Chief Exec. Officer & Mng. Dir.--Geraghty & Miller, Inc., Denver, CO; *Int'l*, pg. 607
Blanch, E.W., Jr., Chief Exec. Officer--E.W. Blanch International, Inc., Minneapolis, MN; *U.S. Public*, pg. 236
Blanch, E.W., Jr., Chm. Bd. & Chief Exec. Officer--E.W. Blanch Wholesale Insurance Services Inc., Minneapolis, MN; *U.S. Public*, pg. 236
Blanch, Edgar W., Jr., Chm. Bd., Chief Exec. Officer--E.W. Blanch Holdings, Inc., Minneapolis, MN; *U.S. Public*, pg. 236
Blanchard, Charles H., Pres. & Chief Exec. Officer--First National Bank of Russellville, Russellville, AR; *U.S. Public*, pg. 630
Blanchard, J.A.(Gus), III, Chm. Bd., Pres. & Chief Exec. Officer--Deluxe Corporation, Shoreview, MN; *U.S. Public*, *pg. 498*
Blanchard, James H., Chm. Bd. & Chief Exec. Officer--Synovus Financial Corp., Columbus, GA; *U.S. Public*, pg. 1548
Blanchard, Kenneth E., Chm. Bd., Pres. & Chief Exec. Officer--Phonetics, Inc., Aston, PA; *U.S. Private*, pg. 863
Blanco, Rafael, Esq., Pres., Chief Exec. & Oper. Officer--PonceBank, F.S.B., Ponce, PR; *U.S. Public*, pg. 1316
Bland, W. Greg, Pres. & Chief Exec. Officer--Tasco Sales Inc., Miramar, FL; *U.S. Private*, pg. 928
Blanding, Robert, Chief Exec. Officer--Loomis, Sayles & Co., Boston, MA; *U.S. Private*, pg. 737
Blank, Arthur M., Pres., Chief Exec. Officer & Chief Oper. Officer--The Home Depot, Inc., Atlanta, GA; *U.S. Public*, pg. 831
Blank, Arthur M., Chief Exec. Officer--The Home Depot, Inc., Atlanta, GA; *U.S. Public*, pg. 831
Blank, Matthew, Chm. Bd. & Chief Exec. Officer-Showtime Networks, Inc.--National Amusements, Inc., Dedham, MA; *U.S. Private*, pg. 775
Blankenship, Joseph M., Pres. & Chief Exec. Officer--National Bank of Summers, Hinton, WV; *U.S. Public*, pg. 836
Blankenship, Truman, Pres., Chief Exec. Officer & Chief Oper. Officer--Berryman Products, Inc., Arlington, TX; *U.S. Private*, pg. 138
Blankley, Walter E., Chm. Bd. & Chief Exec. Officer--AMETEK, Inc., Paoli, PA; *U.S. Public*, pg. 99
Blattner, Simon J., Jr., Co-Chm. Bd. & Co-Chief Exec. Officer--Rittenhouse Inc., Park Ridge, IL; *U.S. Private*, pg. 933
Blattner, William H., Jr., Chief Exec. Officer--D.H. Blattner & Sons, Inc., Avon, MN; *U.S. Private*, pg. 148
Blau, Barry, Chm. Bd. & Chief Exec. Officer--Blau Marketing Technologies, Inc., Wilton, CT; *U.S. Private*, pg. 148
Blau, Harvey R., Chm. Bd. & Chief Exec. Officer--Aeroflex Incorporated, Plainview, NY; *U.S. Public*, pg. 23
Blauer, Charles, Chm. Bd., Pres.,Chief Exec. Officer & Treas.--Blauer Manufacturing Co., Inc., Boston, MA; *U.S.* Private, pg. 149
Blaugrund, Lee S., Pres. & Chief Exec. Officer--American Furniture Company, Albuquerque, NM; *U.S. Private*, pg. 55
Blethen, Frank A., Chm. Bd., Chief Exec. Officer & Publr.--Seattle Times Company, Seattle, WA; *U.S. Private*, pg. 980
Blethen, Roger W., Pres. & Chief Exec. Officer--LTX Corporation, Westwood, MA; *U.S. Public*, pg. 972
Bleustein, Jeffrey, Pres. & Chief Exec. Officer--Harley-Davidson, Inc., Milwaukee, WI; *U.S. Public*, pg. 786
Blevins, James W., Pres. & Chief Exec Officer--Blevins Inc., Nashville, TN; *U.S. Private*, pg. 149
Bleyer, Klaus, Chief Exec. Officer--ZF Friedrichshafen A.G., Friedrichshafen, Germany; *Int'l*, pg. 1522
Bliss, David C., Chm. Bd., Pres. & Chief Exec. Oficer--Quality Stores Inc., Muskegon, MI; *U.S. Private*, pg. 899
Blitzer, Charles N., Pres. & Chief Exec. Officer--MGI PHARMA INC., Minneapolis, MN; *U.S. Public*, pg. 1026
Bloch, Federico, Pres. & Chief Exec. Officer--Taca International Airlines, S. A., San Salvador, El Salvador; *Int'l*, pg. 1346
Block, Edward L., Pres. & Chief Exec. Officer--Block Distributing Company, San Antonio, TX; *U.S. Private*, pg. 149
Blockus, G., Chief Exec. Office--Zurich Ubezpieczenie Service Sp. z o.o., Warsaw, Poland; *Int'l*, pg. 1532
Blodgett, Mark, Chm. Bd. & Chief Exec. Officer--Stocker & Yale, Inc., Salem, NH; *U.S. Public*, pg. 1518
Blogh, Julian, Dr., Chief Exec. Officer--Ultra Electronics Holdings plc, Greenford, United Kingdom; *Int'l*, pg. 1431
Blomqvist, Kaj, Chief Exec. Officer--DMB&B Helsinki, Helsinki, Finland; *U.S. Private*, pg. 303
Blomstrom, Bruce, Chief Exec. Officer--Clinishare, Chatsworth, CA; *U.S. Private*, pg. 1118
Blondeau, Gilles, Chm. Bd. & Chief Exec. Officer--Domtar Inc., Montreal, Canada; *Int'l*, pg. 416
Blondeau, Jacques, Chm. Bd. & Chief Exec. Officer--SCOR, Paris, France; *Int'l*, pg. 1152
Bloom, Donald, Pres. & Chief Exec. Officer--Bloom Electric Services, Inc., Oklahoma City, OK; *U.S. Private*, pg. 150
Bloom, Geoffrey B., Chm. Bd. & Chief Exec. Officer--Wolverine World Wide, Inc., Rockford, MI; *U.S. Public*, pg. 1775
Bloom, Robert H., Chm. Bd. & Chief Exec. Officer--Publicis/Bloom Inc., New York, NY; *Int'l*, pg. 470
Bloomberg, Lawrence S., Pres. & Chief Exec. Officer--First Marathon Inc., Toronto, Canada; *Int'l*, pg. 486
Bloomer, Michael, Chief Exec. Officer-TNT Vacations--TNT Vacations, Boston, MA; *U.S. Private*, pg. 1065
Blossom, Donald M., Pres. & Chief Exec. Officer--The First National Bank of Ottawa, Ottawa, OH; *U.S. Public*, pg. 1413
Blow, Warner C., Pres. & Chief Exec. Officer--Sterling Commerce, Inc., Dublin, OH; *U.S. Public*, pg. 1515
Blue, Dale, Pres. & Chief Exec. Officer--The Chase Manhattan Bank of Canada, Toronto, Canada; *U.S. Public*, pg. 340
Blue, David S., Pres. & Chief Exec. Officer--Louisville Scrap Material Co., Inc., Louisville, KY; *U.S. Private*, pg. 677
Blue, J. Neal, Chm. Bd., Pres. & Chief Exec. Officer--General Atomics, San Diego, CA; *U.S. Private*, pg. 443
Bluestone, Stanton J., Chm. Bd. & Chief Exec. Officer--Carson Pirie Scott & Co., Milwaukee, WI; *U.S. Public*, pg. 309
Bluhm, Jurgen, Chief Exec. Officer--Eiler & Riemel - Testa, Munich, Germany; *Int'l*, pg. 1377
Blum, Bruce, Chief Exec. Officer--Doral Hotel & Resorts Management Co., New York, NY; *U.S. Private*, pg. 340
Blum, G., Grp. Chief Exec. Officer--Schweizerischer Bankverein, Basel, Switzerland; *Int'l*, pg. 1329
Blumberg, Armin W., Pres. & Chief Exec. Officer--Nautilus Insurance Company, Scottsdale, AZ; *U.S. Public*, pg. 216
Blumberg, Armin W., Pres. & Chief Exec. Officer--Great Divide Insurance Company, Scottsdale, AZ; *U.S. Public*, pg. 216

Blumberg, David, Pres. & Chief Exec. Officer--Blumberg Communications Inc., Minneapolis, MN; *U.S. Public*, pg. 305
Blume, Robert L., Pres. & Chief Exec. Officer--Capital Development Co., Lacey, WA; *U.S. Private*, pg. 205
Blumenthal, Herman, Chm. Bd. & Chief Exec. Officer--Radiator Specialty Company, Charlotte, NC; *U.S. Private*, *pg. 906*
Blystone, John B., Chm. Bd., Pres. & Chief Exec. Officer--SPX Corporation, Muskegon, MI; *U.S. Public*, pg. 1420
Blyth, James, Lord, Chief Exec. Officer--The Boots Company PLC, Nottingham, United Kingdom; *Int'l*, pg. 202
Bober, David, Pres. & Chief Exec. Officer--American Beverage Corp. Inc., Akron, OH; *Int'l*, pg. 752
Bobin, Alan, Pres. & Chief Exec. Officer--The Generra Company, Seattle, WA; *U.S. Private*, pg. 446
Bobins, Norman, Pres. & Chief Exec. Officer--LaSalle National Bank, Chicago, IL; *Int'l*, pg. 10
Bobit, Edward J., Chm. Bd. & Chief Exec. Officer--Bobit Publishing Company, Torrance, CA; *U.S. Private*, pg. 154
Bocek, J., Chief Exec. Officer--Zurich Pojistovna, Prague, Czech Republic; *Int'l*, pg. 1531
Bockerstette, Joe, Pres. & Chief Exec. Officer--Seyfert Foods, Inc., Fort Wayne, IN; *U.S. Private*, pg. 988
Bodager, Brian R., Pres. & Chief Exec. Officer--Banc Life Insurance Corporation, Phoenix, AZ; *U.S. Public*, pg. 140
Boddie, William L., Pres. & Chief Exec. Officer--Boddie-Noell Enterprises Inc., Rocky Mount, NC; *U.S. Private*, pg. 154
Bodine, John R., Pres. & Chief Exec. Officer--Bodine Electric Company, Chicago, IL; *U.S. Private*, pg. 154
Bodine, Richard P., Jr., Chief Exec. Officer--Bodine Assembly and Test Systems, Bridgeport, CT; *U.S. Private*, pg. 154
Bodman, James W., Co-Chm. & Chief Exec. Officer--Vienna Sausage Mfg. Co., Chicago, IL; *U.S. Private*, pg. 1139
Bodman, Samuel W., Chm. Bd. & Chief Exec. Officer--Cabot Corporation, Boston, MA; *U.S. Public*, pg. 288
Bodnar, J. Michael, Pres. & Chief Exec. Officer--Shoney's, Inc., Nashville, TN; *U.S. Public*, pg. 1467
Boehm, William J., Chm. Bd., Pres. & Chief Exec. Officer--Connector Manufacturing Company, Hamilton, OH; *U.S. Private*, pg. 264
Boerger, Dick G., Pres. & Chief Exec. Officer--Southwestern Bell Printing Company, Houston, TX; *U.S. Public*, pg. 1415
Boetticher, Jeffrey M., Chm. Bd. & Chief Exec. Officer--Black Box Corporation of PA, Lawrence, PA; *U.S. Public*, *pg. 235*
Bogie, Bill, Dr., Chief Exec. Officer--Medeva PLC, London, United Kingdom; *Int'l*, pg. 852
Bogle, Donald E., Pres. & Chief Exec. Officer--Moore Products Co., Spring House, PA; *U.S. Public*, pg. 1128
Bogle, Nigel, Joint Chief Exec.--Bartle Bogle Hegarty Limited, London, United Kingdom; *Int'l*, pg. 169
Bognanno, P. F., Pres. & Chief Exec. Officer--Principal Residential Mortgage, Inc., Des Moines, IA; *U.S. Private*, *pg. 886*
Bogni, R., Chief Exec. Officer--Swiss Bank Corporation, London, United Kingdom; *Int'l*, pg. 1330
Boh, Robert S., Pres. & Chief Exec. Officer--Boh Bros. Construction Co., LLC, New Orleans, LA; *U.S. Private*, pg. 154
Bohannon, Robert H., Chm. Bd., Pres. & Chief Exec. Officer--Viad Corp, Phoenix, AZ; *U.S. Public*, pg. 1718
Bohbot, Allen J., Chm. & Chief Exec. Officer--Quantum Media International, Inc., New York, NY; *U.S. Private*, pg. 899
Bohlander, Frans A.C.M., Chief Exec.--Sulzer Infra Nederland B.V., Tilburg, Netherlands; *Int'l*, pg. 1306
Bohlen, Urs, Chief Exec.--Holderbank Cement & Beton, Eclepens, Switzerland; *Int'l*, pg. 628
Bohlund, Kjell, Chief Officer--Raben & Sjogren AB, Stockholm, Sweden; *Int'l*, pg. 718
Bohman, Terrance, Pres. & Chief Exec. Officer--Universal Cooperatives, Inc., Minneapolis, MN; *U.S. Private*, pg. 1127
Bohn, Peter, Chief Exec. Officer--Utimaco Safeware AG, Oberursel, Germany; *Int'l*, pg. 1444
Bohn, Robert G., Chm. Bd. & Chief Exec. Officer--Preferred Utilities Manufacturing Corp., Danbury, CT; *U.S. Private*, pg. 881
Bohn, Robert G., Chm. Bd. & Chief Exec. Officer--Preferred Instruments, Danbury, CT; *U.S. Private*, pg. 881
Bohn, Robert G., Pres. & Chief Exec. Officer--Oshkosh Truck Corporation, Oshkosh, WI; *U.S. Public*, pg. 1233
Bohorques, Juan Cristobal Ferrer, Chief Exec. Officer--Publicidad Ferrer y Asociados, S.A. de C.V., Mexico, Mexico; *Int'l*, pg. 1073
Bohren, Kevin, Pres. & Chief Exec. Officer--Traveling Software Inc., Bothell, WA; *U.S. Private*, pg. 1098
Boklund, Thomas B., Chm. Bd. & Chief Exec. Officer--Oregon Steel Mills Inc., Portland, OR; *U.S. Public*, pg. 1230
Bokser, Stephen R., Pres. & Chief Oper. Officer--White Rose Food, Carteret, NJ; *U.S. Private*, pg. 330
Boland, David, Chm. Bd., Pres. & Chief Exec. Officer--David Boland, Inc., Titusville, FL; *U.S. Private*, pg. 154
Boland, John A., III, Pres. & Chief Exec. Officer--Dominion Textile Inc., Montreal, Canada; *Int'l*, pg. 415
Bolander, Glen S., Pres. & Chief Exec. Officer--Grist Mill Company, Lakeville, MN; *U.S. Public*, pg. 766
Bolch, Carl, Jr., Chm. Bd. & Chief Exec. Officer--Racetrac Petroleum, Inc., Smyrna, GA; *U.S. Private*, pg. 906
Bolinger, Robert S., Pres. & Chief Exec. Officer--Susquehanna Bancshares, Inc., Lititz, PA; *U.S. Public*, pg. 1542
Bolinger, Robert S., Chm. Bd. & Chief Exec. Officer--Farmers First Bank, Lititz, PA; *U.S. Public*, pg. 1542
Bollenbach, Stephen F., Pres. & Chief Exec. Officer--Hilton Hotels Corporation, Beverly Hills, CA; *U.S. Public*, pg. 828
Bollerer, Fred L., Chm. Bd. & Chief Exec. Officer--First American Metro Corp., Mc Lean, VA; *U.S. Public*, pg. 640
Bollinger, Don M., Chm. Bd. & Chief Exec. Officer--The John C. Groub Company Inc., Seymour, IN; *U.S. Private*, *pg. 484*
Bollinger, Donald T., Chm. Bd. & Chief Exec. Officer--Bollinger Shipyards, Inc., Lockport, LA; *U.S. Private*, pg. 155
Bollinger, Donald T., Chief Exec. Officer--Bollinger Algiers Inc., New Orleans, LA; *U.S. Private*, pg. 155
Bollinger, Glenn D., Chm. Bd. & Chief Exec. Officer--Bollinger Industries Inc., Grand Prairie, TX; *U.S. Public*, pg. 243
Bolton, Tom, Chief Exec. Officer-Goodman Fielder NZ--Goodman Fielder Limited, Sydney, Australia; *Int'l*, pg. 555
Bonczyk, Robert, Pres. & Chief Exec. Officer--U.S. Can Company, Newnan, GA; *U.S. Public*, pg. 1681
Bond, Bruce, Pres. & Chief Exec. Officer-ANS Communications--America Online Incorporated, Dulles, VA; *U.S. Public*, pg. 66
Bonderman, David, Chief Exec. Officer--Texas Pacific Group, Fort Worth, TX; *U.S. Private*, pg. 1078
Bondi, Enrico, Chief Exec. Officer & Mng. Dir.--Compart SpA, Milan, Italy; *Int'l*, pg. 324
Bondi, Enrico, Chief Exec. Officer--Montedison S.p.A., Milan, Italy; *Int'l*, pg. 324
Bonfante, Michael, Pres. & Chief Exec. Officer--Nob Hill General Store, Inc., Gilroy, CA; *U.S. Private*, pg. 799
Bonfield, Peter, Sir, Chief Exec.--British Telecommunications plc, London, United Kingdom; *Int'l*, pg. 222
Bonfigli, G., Chief Exec. Officer--SASIB Railway S.p.A., Bologna, Italy; *Int'l*, pg. 1194
Bonifacio, Gerard, Chm Bd.--Societe Scholtes S.A., Thionville, France; *Int'l*, pg. 860
Bonifazio, J., Chief Exec. Officer--Jamison Plastic Corporation, Allentown, PA; *U.S. Private*, pg. 581
Bonk, James E., Pres. & Chief Exec. Officer--Camelot Music, Inc., Canton, OH; *U.S. Private*, pg. 203
Bonke, Neil R., Chief Exec. Officer--Electroglas, Inc., Santa Clara, CA; *U.S. Public*, pg. 727
Bonn, Neal F., Pres. & Chief Exec. Officer--F.H. Bonn Company, Springfield, OH; *U.S. Private*, pg. 156
Bonner, Joel, Pres. & Chief Exec. Officer--Hydrotex Inc., Dallas, TX; *Int'l*, pg. 892
Bonnet, Denis, Chm. & Chief Exec. Officer-OgilvyOne worldwide Paris--Ogilvy & Mather Worldwide, Inc., New York, NY; *Int'l*, pg. 1483
Bono, Al J., Pres. & Chief Exec. Officer--Favorite Brands International, Inc., Lincolnshire, IL; *U.S. Private*, pg. 397
Bonse-Geisking, Wilhelm, Chief Exec. Officer--VEBA OEL AG, Gelsenkirchen, Germany; *Int'l*, pg. 1460
Bonsignore, Michael R., Chm. Bd. & Chief Exec. Officer--Honeywell Inc., Minneapolis, MN; *U.S. Public*, pg. 833
Boodjeh, Doug, Chief Exec. Officer--Imediate Pharmaceutical Services Inc., Medina, OH; *U.S. Private*, pg. 334
Boodjeh, Parviz, Chief Exec. Officer--Discount Drug Mart Inc., Medina, OH; *U.S. Private*, pg. 334
Booker, Noel, Pres. & Chief Exec. Officer--K.C.I. Coatings, Inc., Louisville, KY; *U.S. Private*, pg. 890
Boomer, Walter E., Pres. & Chief Exec. Officer--Rogers Corporation, Rogers, CT; *U.S. Public*, pg. 1402
Boone, Thomas H., Chm. Bd. & Chief Oper. Officer--Countrywide Title Corporation, Pasadena, CA; *U.S. Public*, pg. 453
Booth, John J., Acting Chm. Bd., Pres. & Chief Exec. Officer--INCSTAR Corporation, Stillwater, MN; *Int'l*, pg. 483
Borchardt, Robert L., Co-Chm. Bd, Pres. & Chief Exec. Officer--Recoton Corporation, Lake Mary, FL; *U.S. Public*, pg. 1369
Borchardt, Robert L., Chm. Bd. & Chief Exec. Officer--Interact Accessories, Inc., Hunt Valley, MD; *U.S. Public*, pg. 1369
Borchardt, Robert L., Chm. Bd. & Chief Exec. Officer--Christie Design, Chatsworth, CA; *U.S. Public*, pg. 1369
Borck, Judith L., Pres. & Chief Exec. Officer--Country Home Bakery, Inc., Bridgeport, CT; *U.S. Private*, pg. 278
Bord, Michel, Pres. & Chief Exec. Officer--Austin Nichols & Co. Inc., New York, NY; *Int'l*, pg. 566
Bordelais, Jacques, Pres. & Chief Exec. Officer-BL/LB Group--Bordelais, Lemeunier-Leo Burnett Paris, Levallois-Perret, France; *U.S. Private*, pg. 184
Borden, Lorraine, Chm. Bd., Chief Exec. Officer, Chief Fin. Officer, Pres.--Great Scott Advertising Co. Inc., New York, NY; *U.S. Private*, pg. 475
Boren, L.E., Chm. Bd. & Chief Exec. Officer--Badger Equipment Co., Winona, MN; *U.S. Private*, pg. 102
Boren, Leland E., Chm. Bd., Pres. & Chief Exec. Officer--Avis Industrial Corporation, Upland, IN; *U.S. Private*, pg. 102
Borg, Malcolm A., Chm. Bd., Pres. & Chief Exec. Officer--Macromedia Incorporated, Hackensack, NJ; *U.S. Private*, *pg. 693*
Borg, Malcom A., Chief Exec. Officer--Gremac Inc., Hackensack, NJ; *U.S. Private*, pg. 693
Borgersen, Bjarne, Chief Exec. Officer & Mng. Dir.--Fokus Bank A/S, Trondheim, Norway; *Int'l*, pg. 496
Boris, James R., Chm. & Chief Exec. Officer--EVEREN Securities, Inc., Chicago, IL; *U.S. Public*, pg. 597
Borislow, Daniel, Chm. Bd. & Chief Exec. Officer--Tel-Save Holdings, Inc., New Hope, PA; *U.S. Public*, pg. 1568
Borjesson, Anders, Pres. & Chief Exec. Officer--Bergman & Beving AB, Stockholm, Sweden; *Int'l*, pg. 188
Borjesson, Rolf, Chief Exec. Officer & Mng. Dir.--Rexam PLC, London, United Kingdom; *Int'l*, pg. 1106
Borland, Clifford R., Chm. Bd. & Chief Exec. Officer--NS Group, Inc., Newport, KY; *U.S. Public*, pg. 1147
Born, Allen, Chm. Bd. & Chief Exec. Officer--Alumax Inc., Atlanta, GA; *U.S. Public*, pg. 59
Bornhuetter, Ronald L., Chm. Bd. & Chief Exec. Officer--NAC Re Corp., Greenwich, CT; *U.S. Public*, pg. 1144
Borzino, Leo, Pres. & Chief Exec. Officer--Petite Sophisticate Outlet, Enfield, CT; *U.S. Private*, pg. 219
Boschsler, Karl, Chief Exec.--Sulzer Infra Deutschland GmbH., Stuttgart, Germany; *Int'l*, pg. 1306
Boscov, Albert, Chm. Bd. & Chief Exec. Officer--Boscov's Department Store, Inc., Reading, PA; *U.S. Private*, pg. 160
Bosley, James R., Pres. & Chief Exec. Officer--First Parke State Bank, Rockville, IN; *U.S. Public*, pg. 634
Boss, Russell A., Pres. & Chief Exec. Officer--A.T. Cross Co., Lincoln, RI; *U.S. Public*, pg. 460
Bossett, Barry P., Chm. Bd. & Chief Exec. Officer--Scotsman Holding Inc., Baltimore, MD; *U.S. Private*, pg. 976
Bossidy, Lawrence A., Chm. Bd. & Chief Exec. Officer--AlliedSignal Inc., Morristown, NJ; *U.S. Public*, pg. 49
Bossidy, Lawrence A., Chief Exec. Officer--AlliedSignal Aerospace, Stratford, CT; *U.S. Public*, pg. 50
Bossier, Albert L., Jr., Chm. Bd., Pres. & Chief Exec. Officer--Avondale Industries, Inc., Avondale, LA; *U.S. Public*, pg. 156
Bostock, Roy J., Chm. & Chief Exec. Officer--The MacManus Group, Inc., New York, NY; *U.S. Private*, pg. 692
Boswell, Robert S., Pres. & Chief Exec. Officer--Forest Oil Corporation, Denver, CO; *U.S. Public*, pg. 670
Bosworth, Michael F., Chm. Bd., Pres. & Chief Exec. Officer--OrCAD Inc., Beaverton, OR; *U.S. Public*, pg. 1230
Botelho, Mauricio, Pres. & Chief Exec. Officer--Embraer-Empresa Brasileira de Aeronautica S.A., Sao Jose dos Campos, Brazil; *Int'l*, pg. 452
Bothwell, David, Pres. & Chief Exec. Officer--Howtek, Inc., Hudson, NH; *U.S. Public*, pg. 844
Botin, Emilio, Chm. Bd. & Chief Exec. Officer--Banco Santander, Madrid, Spain; *Int'l*, pg. 143
Botnar, Octave, Chm. Bd. & Chief Exec. Officer--Nissan Motor Manufacturing (UK) Ltd., Sunderland, United Kingdom; *Int'l*, pg. 945
Bottorff, Dennis C., Chm. Bd., Pres. & Chief Exec. Officer--First American Corporation, Nashville, TN; *U.S. Public*, pg. 624
Botts, Tom, Chief Exec. Officer--NES Holdings, Inc., Raleigh, NC; *U.S. Private*, pg. 771
Botts, William W., Chm. Bd., Pres. & Chief Exec. Officer--O.I. Corporation, College Station, TX; *U.S. Public*, pg. 1208
Botvin, George B., Chm. Bd., Chief Exec. Officer & Treas.--ACS Industries, Inc., Woonsocket, RI; *U.S. Private*, pg. 3
Bouchard, Alain, Chief Exec. Officer--Alimentation Couche Tard Inc., Vimont, Canada; *Int'l*, pg. 57
Bouchard, Roger, Chief Exec. Officer--Green Mountain Steel Erectors Inc., Bennington, VT; *U.S. Private*, pg. 133
Bouckaert, Carl, Pres. & Chief Exec. Officer--Beaulieu Group, Dalton, GA; *U.S. Private*, pg. 127
Bouckaert, G.P., Chm. Bd. & Chief Exec. Officer--Nooter Corporation, Saint Louis, MO; *U.S. Private*, pg. 801
Bougie, Jacques, Pres. & Chief Exec. Officer--Alcan Aluminium Limited, Montreal, Canada; *Int'l*, pg. 50
Bouhelier, Jacques, Chm. Bd. & Chief Exec. Officer--Messier-Dowty SAS, Velizy-Villacoublay, France; *Int'l*, pg. 1340
Boulet, Jean-Claude, Pres. & Chief Exec. Officer-BDDP S.A.--BDDP Group, Paris, France; *Int'l*, pg. 116
Bouley, Bruno, Chm. Bd. & Chief Exec. Officer--Dumez Construction, Malakoff, France; *Int'l*, pg. 823
Boulis, Gus, Chm. Bd., Pres. & Chief Exec. Officer--Miami Subs Corporation, Fort Lauderdale, FL; *U.S. Public*, pg. 1103
Boundy, K. A., Chief Exec.--Goodman Fielder Asia Holdings Ltd., Singapore, Singapore; *Int'l*, pg. 555
Bouras, Nicholas J., Chief Exec. Officer--Bouras Industries, Summit, NJ; *U.S. Private*, pg. 161
Bourgeois, Steven J., Pres. & Chief Exec. Officer--Franklin-Lamoille Bank, Saint Albans, VT; *U.S. Public*, pg. 187
Bourke, Thomas J., Pres. & Chief Exec. Officer--Tele-Direct (Publications) Inc., Montreal, Canada; *Int'l*, pg. 116
Bourland, Curtis F., Chm. Bd., Pres. & Chief Exec. Officer--Continental Graphics Holdings, Inc., Los Angeles, CA; *U.S. Private*, pg. 268
Bourven, Monique J., Chm. Bd. & Chief Exec. Officer--State Street Banque S.A., Paris, France; *U.S. Public*, pg. 1513
Bouts, Larry, Chm. & Chief Exec. Officer--Six Flags Theme Parks Inc., Parsippany, NJ; *U.S. Public*, pg. 1611
Bouts, Larry, Pres. & Chief Exec. Officer-Six Flags Theme Parks Inc.--Six Flags Magic Mountain & Six Flags Hurricane Harbor, Valencia, CA; *U.S. Public*, pg. 1611
Bouts, Larry D., Chm. Bd. & Chief Exec. Officer--Six Flags Great Adventure Theme Park & Wild Safari Animal Park, Jackson, NJ; *U.S. Public*, pg. 1611
Boutwell, Wayne A., Pres. & Chief Exec. Officer--Southern States Cooperative, Inc., Richmond, VA; *U.S. Private*, pg. 1017
Bouygues, Martin, Chm. Bd. & Chief Exec. Officer--Bouygues, Saint Quentin-en-Yvelines, France; *Int'l*, pg. 206
Bova, Anthony F., Pres. & Chief Exec. Officer--Atlantis Plastic, Inc., Atlanta, GA; *U.S. Public*, pg. 145
Bovaird, W.J., Chm. Bd., Pres. & Chief Exec. Officer--Bovaird Supply Co., Tulsa, OK; *U.S. Private*, pg. 162
Bowden, Al, Pres. & Chief Exec. Officer--Sencore, Inc., Sioux Falls, SD; *U.S. Private*, pg. 983
Bowe, Peter A., Pres. & Chief Exec. Officer--Ellicott Machine Corporation International, Baltimore, MD; *U.S. Private*, pg. 372
Bowen, Charles, Chief Exec.--Booker PLC, London, United Kingdom; *Int'l*, pg. 202
Bowen, Kevin C., Pres. & Chief Exec. Officer--K-Tron America, Inc., Pitman, NJ; *U.S. Public*, pg. 938
Bowen, Robert, Pres. & Chief Exec. Officer--COMNET Corporation, Lanham, MD; *U.S. Public*, pg. 416

Bowen, Robert, Chm. Bd. & Chief Exec. Officer--Group 1 Software, Inc., Lanham, MD; *U.S. Public*, pg. 417

Bowen, Stephen T., Pres. & Chief Exec. Officer--Polymer Composites Inc., Winona, MN; *Int'l*, pg. 624

Bowers, Alan J., Pres. & Chief Exec. Officer--MBL Life Assurance Corporation, Newark, NJ; *U.S. Private*, pg. 685

Bowers, D.D., Pres. & Chief Exec. Officer--Makino Inc., Mason, OH; *Int'l*, pg. 831

Bowers, John, Pres. & Chief Exec. Officer--Southwestern Financial Services Corp., Dallas, TX; *U.S. Private*, pg. 1018

Bowkett, Alan, Chief Exec. Officer--Berisford plc, London, United Kingdom; *Int'l*, pg. 188

Bowler, G.J., Chief Exec. Officer--Kwik Save Group plc, Prestatyn, United Kingdom; *Int'l*, pg. 704

Bowles, Robert, Chief Exec. Officer-Chartered Health Plans--PHP Healthcare Corporation, Reston, VA; *U.S. Public*, pg. 1241

Bowles, Robert L., Pres. & Chief Exec. Officer--D.C. Chartered Health Plan, Washington, DC; *U.S. Public*, pg. 1241

Bowles, Timothy, Chief Exec. Officer--MRB Group, Inc., New York, NY; *Int'l*, pg. 1483

Bowlin, John D., Chief Exec. Officer-Kraft Foods Intl.--Philip Morris Companies Inc., New York, NY; *U.S. Public*, pg. 1287

Bowlin, John D., Pres. & Chief Exec. Officer--Kraft Foods International, Rye Brook, NY; *U.S. Public*, pg. 1288

Bowlin, Mike R., Chm. Bd. & Chief Exec. Officer--Atlantic Richfield Company, Los Angeles, CA; *U.S. Public*, pg. 144

Bowlus, Brad A., Pres. & Chief Exec. Officer--PacifiCare of California, Cypress, CA; *U.S. Public*, pg. 1251

Bowman, A. Blaine, Pres. & Chief Exec. Officer--Dionex Corporation, Sunnyvale, CA; *U.S. Public*, pg. 510

Bowman, Harry W., Chm. Bd., Pres. & Chief Exec. Officer--Outboard Marine Corporation, Waukegan, IL; *U.S. Private*, pg. 478

Bowmer, John, Chief Exec. Officer--Adecco S.A., Lausanne, Switzerland; *Int'l*, pg. 23

Bowmer, John P., Chief Exec. Officer--Adecco Employment Services, Redwood City, CA; *Int'l*, pg. 24

Bowra, David, Chief Exec. Officer--Skeena Cellulose Inc., Vancouver, Canada; *Int'l*, pg. 1261

Box, Sam W., Chm. Bd., Pres. & Chief Exec. Officer--Foster Wheeler Environmental Corporation, Livingston, NJ; *U.S. Public*, pg. 677

Boxall, Gerald, Chm. & Chief Exec. Officer--Vickers Defence Systems, Armstrong Works, Newcastle upon Tyne, United Kingdom; *Int'l*, pg. 1467

Boyadjieff, George, Pres. & Chief Exec. Officer--Varco International, Inc., Orange, CA; *U.S. Public*, pg. 1709

Boyce, Donald N., Chm. Bd., Pres. & Chief Exec. Officer--IDEX Corporation, Northbrook, IL; *U.S. Public*, pg. 862

Boyce, G. H., Pres. & Chief Exec. Officer--Kennecott Energy and Coal Company, Salt Lake City, UT; *Int'l*, pg. 1119

Boyd, Dennis, Pres. & Chief Exec. Officer--Royal Waterbeds, Maryland Heights, MO; *U.S. Private*, pg. 949

Boyd, Michael L., Pres. & Chief Exec. Officer--San Angelo National Bank, San Angelo, TX; *U.S. Public*, pg. 633

Boyd, Stephen D., Pres. & Chief Exec. Officer-Mktg. Resources Grp.--U S West Inc., Englewood, CO; *U.S. Public*, pg. 1688

Boyd, Steve, Pres. & Chief Exec. Officer--U S West DEX, Denver, CO; *U.S. Public*, pg. 1689

Boyd, William S., Chm. Bd. & Chief Exec. Officer--Boyd Gaming Corporation, Las Vegas, NV; *U.S. Public*, pg. 249

Boyea, Bruce W., Pres. & Chief Exec. Officer--Security Mutual Life Insurance Co. of New York, Binghamton, NY; *U.S. Private*, pg. 981

Boyer, David S., Pres. & Chief Exec. Officer--Teleflex Incorporated, Plymouth Meeting, PA; *U.S. Public*, pg. 1569

Boyer, Lucien, Chief Exec. Officer, Bus. Dir. & Information--LMG (Lifestyle Marketing Group), Neuilly-sur-Seine, France; *U.S. Public*, pg. 1422

Boyer, Rahn, Pres. & Chief Exec. Officer--Gem-Dandy, Inc., Madison, NC; *U.S. Private*, pg. 442

Boyer, Richard, Pres. & Chief Exec. Officer--Stoneville Furniture Co. Inc., Stoneville, NC; *U.S. Private*, pg. 1045

Boyette, John V., Chief Exec. Officer--Piedmont Olsen Hensley, Inc., Greenville, SC; *Int'l*, pg. 607

Boyle, Matt, Pres. & Chief Exec. Officer--Tech/Ops Sevcon, Inc., Boston, MA; *U.S. Public*, pg. 1563

Boyle, P.J., Chief Exec. Officer--Schulze & Burch Biscuit Company, Chicago, IL; *U.S. Private*, pg. 973

Boyle, R.E., Chm. Bd., Pres. & Chief Exec. Officer--Ormet Corporation, Wheeling, WV; *U.S. Private*, pg. 820

Boyle, Richard, Chm. Bd. & Chief Exec. Officer--Spinnaker Industries, Inc., Dallas, TX; *U.S. Public*, pg. 1022

Boze, Jimmy R., Chm. Bd., Pres. & Chief Exec. Officer--The Security Bank, Harrison, Harrison, AR; *U.S. Public*, pg. 630

Bozic, Michael, Chm. Bd. & Chief Exec. Officer--Levitz Furniture Incorporated, Boca Raton, FL; *U.S. Public*, pg. 990

Bozic, Michael, Chief Exec. Officer--Levitz Furniture Corporation, Boca Raton, FL; *U.S. Public*, pg. 990

Bozic, Michael, Chm. Bd. & Chief Exec. Officer--John M. Smyth Co., Downers Grove, IL; *U.S. Public*, pg. 990

Bozzuto, Michael A., Pres., Chief Exec. Officer & Treas.--Bozzuto's Inc., Cheshire, CT; *U.S. Public*, pg. 249

Bracco, Diana, Dr., Chief Exec. Officer & Mng. Dir.--Bracco S.p.A., Milan, Italy; *Int'l*, pg. 209

Bracco, Sergio, Chief Exec. Officer--Astra Veicoli Industriali S.p.A., Piacenza, Italy; *Int'l*, pg. 94

Bracewell, Joseph S., Chm. Bd., Pres. & Chief Exec. Officer--Century Bancshares, Inc., Washington, DC; *U.S. Public*, pg. 328

Bracken, Peter A., Pres. & Chief Exec. Officer--Computer Data Systems, Inc., Rockville, MD; *U.S. Public*, pg. 28

Bradburd, Arnold W., Chief Exec. Officer--Interstate Steel Supply Company, Philadelphia, PA; *U.S. Public*, pg. 1100

Bradbury, George, Chief Exec. Officer--Computer Power Group Limited, Melbourne, Australia; *Int'l*, pg. 325

Bradford, William E., Chm. Bd. & Chief Exec. Officer--Dresser Industries, Inc., Dallas, TX; *U.S. Public*, pg. 528

Bradley, Charles E., Chm. Bd., Pres. & Chief Exec. Officer--Reunion Industries, Inc., Stamford, CT; *U.S. Public*, pg. 1383

Bradly, Glen, Dr., Pres. & Chief Exec. Officer--CIBA Vision AG, Niederwangen, Switzerland; *Int'l*, pg. 972

Bradshaw, David L., Chm. Bd., Pres. & Chief Exec. Officer--Tipperary Corporation, Denver, CO; *U.S. Public*, pg. 1618

Brady, Brian J., Chm. Bd., Pres. & Chief Exec. Officer--Dominguez Services Corporation, Long Beach, CA; *U.S. Public*, pg. 516

Brady, Frank, Pres. & Chief Exec. Officer--Brady Marketing Company, Pacheco, CA; *U.S. Private*, pg. 165

Brady, Jack D., Chm. Bd., Pres. & Chief Exec. & Oper. Officer--Crown Andersen Inc., Peachtree City, GA; *U.S. Public*, pg. 462

Brady, John, Chief Exec. Officer & Pres.--Excelsior Manufacturing & Supply Corp., Itasca, IL; *U.S. Private*, pg. 387

Brady, Patrick J., Pres. & Chief Exec. Officer--Semiconductor Equipment Group, Scotts Valley, CA; *U.S. Public*, pg. 1745

Brady, Philip T., Pres. & Chief Exec. Officer-Thomas Ferguson Associates--CommonHealth USA, Parsippany, NJ; *Int'l*, pg. 1483

Brady, Robert, Pres. & Chief Exec. Officer--First NH Mortgage Corp., Hooksett, NH; *Int'l*, pg. 153

Brady, Robert T., Chm. Bd., Pres. & Chief Exec. Officer--Moog Incorporated, East Aurora, NY; *U.S. Public*, pg. 1127

Bragdon, Serge, Pres. & Chief Exec. Officer--Uniboard Canada Inc., Laval, Canada; *Int'l*, pg. 1431

Bragiel, Jerry, Pres. & Chief Exec. Officer--Champion Parts, Inc., Glen Ellyn, IL; *U.S. Public*, pg. 334

Bragman, Barbro, Chief Officer--Fakta, Stockholm, Sweden; *Int'l*, pg. 718

Braithwaite, J. Lorne, Pres. & Chief Exec. Officer--Cambridge Shopping Centres Limited, Toronto, Canada; *Int'l*, pg. 253

Brake, Frank, Grp. Chief Exec.--Brake Bros plc, Ashford, United Kingdom; *Int'l*, pg. 210

Brambilla, Roberto, Deputy Chief Exec.--Cassa di Risparmio delle Provincie Lombarde SpA (CARIPLO), Milan, Italy; *Int'l*, pg. 274

Bramble, David A., Chm. Bd. & Chief Exec. Officer--David A. Bramble, Inc., Chestertown, MD; *U.S. Private*, pg. 165

Bramble, Frank P., Pres. & Chief Exec. Officer--First Maryland Bancorp, Baltimore, MD; *Int'l*, pg. 64

Bramley, Christopher, Pres. & Chief Exec. Officer--Safety Fund National Bank, Fitchburg, MA; *U.S. Public*, pg. 278

Bramwell, Jerry L., Chief Exec. Officer--Medite Corporation, Medford, OR; *U.S. Private*, pg. 999

Branch, William J., Chm. & Chief Oper. Officer--Masland, Carlisle, PA; *U.S. Public*, pg. 981

Branche, Francois, Pres. & Chief Exec. Officer--Calberson, Paris, France; *Int'l*, pg. 549

Brand, B., Chief Exec. Officer--Kobra International Ltd, New York, NY; *U.S. Private*, pg. 628

Brandenberg, Frank, Pres. & Chief Exec. Officer--EA Industries, West Long Branch, NJ; *U.S. Public*, pg. 541

Brandon, David A., Chm. Bd., Pres. & Chief Exec. Officer--Valassis Communications, Inc., Livonia, MI; *U.S. Public*, pg. 1704

Brands, Paul A., Chm. Bd. & Chief Exec. Officer--American Management Systems, Inc., Fairfax, VA; *U.S. Public*, pg. 86

Brandt, David N., Pres. & Chief Exec. Officer--Dresdner Bank Canada, Toronto, Canada; *Int'l*, pg. 419

Brandt, William A., Jr., Pres. & Chief Exec. Officer--Mercury Finance Co., Lake Forest, IL; *U.S. Public*, pg. 1093

Brann, Alton J., Chm. Bd. & Chief Exec. Officer--UNOVA, Inc., Beverly Hills, CA; *U.S. Public*, pg. 1698

Brant, D.G., Dep. Chief Exec. & Grp. Mng. Dir.--George Wimpey PLC, London, United Kingdom; *Int'l*, pg. 1510

Brasser, Wayne E., Pres. & Chief Exec. Officer--Chemtech Products Inc., Saint Louis, MO; *U.S. Private*, pg. 39

Braswell, Gary, Pres. & Chief Exec. Officer--MPD, Inc., Owensboro, KY; *U.S. Private*, pg. 687

Bratt, John, Chief Exec. Officer--Hoffco/Comet Industries, Inc., Richmond, IN; *U.S. Private*, pg. 532

Brault, Jean-Louis, Chm. Bd. & Chief Exec. Officer--Groupe GTM, Nanterre, France; *Int'l*, pg. 823

Braun, Edward H., Pres. & Chief Exec. Officer--Veeco Instruments, Inc., Plainview, NY; *U.S. Public*, pg. 1711

Braun, Hartmut, Chief Oper. Officer--Skandia Versicherungs Mgmt und Serv GmbH, Berlin, Germany; *Int'l*, pg. 1258

Braun, Stanley, Pres., Chief Exec. Officer & Chief Oper. Officer--Pac Rim Holding Corporation, Woodland Hills, CA; *U.S. Public*, pg. 1246

Brays Haw, Nicholas Paul, Grp. Chief Exec.--Wagon Industrial Holdings PLC, Birmingham, United Kingdom; *Int'l*, pg. 1484

Brayton, Roswell, Jr., Pres., Chief Exec. Officer & Chief Fin. Officer--Woolrich, Inc., Woolrich, PA; *U.S. Private*, pg. 1188

Braznell, Gerald, Pres. & Chief Exec. Officer--Heritage Inks International, Edison, NJ; *U.S. Private*, pg. 524

Braznell, Gerald K., Chief Exec. Officer--Acme Printing Ink Co., Inc., Elk Grove Village, IL; *Int'l*, pg. 1311

Bready, Richard L., Chm. Bd. & Chief Exec. Officer--Nortek, Inc., Providence, RI; *U.S. Public*, pg. 1192

Breakstone, Kay S., Chief Exec. Officer--Ludgate Communications, Inc., New York, NY; *U.S. Private*, pg. 1157

Bredthauer, Patrick, Chief Exec.--La Cemento Nacional C.A., Guayaquil, Ecuador; *Int'l*, pg. 630

Breed, Allen K., Chm. Bd. & Chief Exec. Officer--Breed Technologies, Inc., Lakeland, FL; *U.S. Public*, pg. 251

Breen, Donald D., Pres. & Chief Exec. Officer--Brothers Gourmet Coffees, Inc., Boca Raton, FL; *U.S. Public*, pg. 259

Breen, John G., Chm. Bd. & Chief Exec. Officer--The Sherwin-Williams Company, Cleveland, OH; *U.S. Public*, pg. 1465

Bregman, Michael, Chm. Bd. & Chief Exec. Officer--The Second Cup, Toronto, Canada; *Int'l*, pg. 266

Breitenbach, E. Allen, Dr., Chm. Bd. & Chief Exec. Officer--Scientific Software-Intercomp, Inc., Denver, CO; *U.S. Public*, pg. 1443

Breitenstein, Heinz, Dr., Chief Oper. Officer--DVO-Datenverabeitungs-Service Oberhausen GmbH, Oberhausen, Germany; *Int'l*, pg. 401

Breitman, Leo R., Chm. Bd. & Chief Exec. Officer--Fleet Bank of Massachusetts, N.A., Boston, MA; *U.S. Public*, pg. 649

Bremner, Ron, Pres. & Chief Exec. Officer--Calgary Flames Hockey Club, Calgary, Canada; *Int'l*, pg. 252

Brenan, Michael R., Chm. Bd., Pres. & Chief Exec. Officer--MainStreet BankGroup Incorporated, Martinsville, VA; *U.S. Public*, pg. 1038

Brendsel, Leland C., Chm. Bd. & Chief Exec. Officer--Federal Home Loan Mortgage Corporation, Mc Lean, VA; *U.S. Public*, pg. 615

Brennan, Charles M., III, Chm. Bd. & Chief Exec. Officer--MYR Group Inc., Rolling Meadows, IL; *U.S. Public*, pg. 1029

Brennan, J.H., Pres. & Chief Exec. Officer--Commemorative Brands, Inc., Austin, TX; *U.S. Private*, pg. 258

Brennan, John J., Chm., Pres. & Chief Exec. Officer--The Vanguard Group, Inc., Valley Forge, PA; *U.S. Private*, pg. 1133

Brennan, Michael P., Pres. & Chief Exec. Officer--Deer Park Federal Savings and Loan Association, Cincinnati, OH; *U.S. Public*, pg. 66

Brennan, Robert B., Pres. & Chief Exec. Officer--Manitoba Hydro, Winnipeg, Canada; *Int'l*, pg. 834

Brenner, Karen, Chm. Bd., Pres. & Chief Exec. Officer--Carlyle Industries, Inc., Carlstadt, NJ; *U.S. Public*, pg. 1187

Brenninkmeyer, Roland, Pres. & Chief Exec. Officer--American Retail Group, New York, NY; *U.S. Private*, pg. 61

Brenton, Donald L., Chief Exec. Officer--Autoswage Products, Inc., Shelton, CT; *U.S. Private*, pg. 101

Bressler, Leon, Chm. Bd. & Chief Exec. Officer--Unibail, Paris, France; *Int'l*, pg. 1431

Bretz, Jon, Chief Exec. Officer--Alimed, Inc., Dedham, MA; *U.S. Private*, pg. 34

Breuer, Linda S., Pres. & Chief Exec. Officer--Breuer/Tornado, Chicago, IL; *U.S. Private*, pg. 167

Brewton, Kenneth, Jr., Pres. & Chief Exec. Officer--Clariant Corporation, Charlotte, NC; *Int'l*, pg. 624

Brian, William A., Pres. & Chief Exec. Officer--Brian Unlimited Distribution Company, Inc., Detroit, MI; *U.S. Private*, pg. 167

Brice, Joni, Chief Exec. Officer--Heil-Brice Retail Advertising, Newport Beach, CA; *U.S. Private*, pg. 519

Brick, Frank E., Pres., Chief Oper. Officer & Chief Exec. Officer--Telxon Corporation, Akron, OH; *U.S. Public*, pg. 1573

Brickel, Jack W., Pres., Chief Exec. & Chief Oper. Officer--BEC Inc., Richmond, MI; *U.S. Private*, pg. 106

Bridges, Barton, Chief Exec. Officer--Diamond Products Company, Seffner, FL; *U.S. Private*, pg. 510

Bridges, L. Michael, Pres. & Chief Exec. Officer--Columbia LNG Corp., Wilmington, DE; *U.S. Public*, pg. 403

Bridgewater, Allan, Grp. Chief Exec.--Norwich Union Life Insurance, Norwich, United Kingdom; *Int'l*, pg. 970

Bridgewater, B.A., Jr., Chm. Bd., Pres., & Chief Exec. Officer--Brown Group, Inc., Saint Louis, MO; *U.S. Public*, pg. 262

Bridgman, Tim, Pres. & Chief Exec. Officer--United States Cold Storage, Inc., Cherry Hill, NJ; *U.S. Private*, pg. 1124

Brieger, M. L., Chief Exec. Officer--OCE-Brasil Comercio e Industria Ltda., Sao Paulo, Brazil; *Int'l*, pg. 994

Brien, Nick, Chief Exec. Officer--Leo Burnett Limited, London, United Kingdom; *U.S. Private*, pg. 185

Brier, Jack, Chm. Bd. & Chief Exec. Officer--Kleinert's, Inc., of Alabama, Elba, AL; *U.S. Private*, pg. 625

Brier, Jack, Chm. Bd. & Chief Exec. Officer--Scott Mills, Gastonia, NC; *U.S. Private*, pg. 625

Brier, Jack, Chm. Bd. & Chief Exec. Officer--Kleinert's Inc. of Florida, Largo, FL; *U.S. Private*, pg. 625

Briggs, Karl L., Chm. Bd. & Chief Exec. Officer--Quincy Mutual Fire Insurance Company, Quincy, MA; *U.S. Private*, pg. 901

Briggs, Robert S., Chm. Bd., Pres. & Chief Exec. Officer--Bangor Hydro-Electric Company, Bangor, ME; *U.S. Public*, pg. 178

Bright, Harvey W., Pres. & Chief Exec. Officer--Engineered Specialty Plastics, Hot Springs National Park, AR; *U.S. Public*, pg. 583

Bright, Stanley J., Pres. & Chief Exec. Officer--MidAmerican Energy Holdings, Des Moines, IA; *U.S. Public*, pg. 1109

Brilliant, James, Chief Exec. Officer & Chief Oper. Officer--Sporto Corp., Boston, MA; *U.S. Private*, pg. 1026

Brinckman, Donald W., Chm. Bd. & Chief Exec. Officer--Safety-Kleen Corp., Elgin, IL; *U.S. Public*, pg. 1425

Brindell, Charlie, Chief Exec. Officer-Southeast Region--Trammell Crow Company, Dallas, TX; *U.S. Public*, pg. 1628

Brindle, A.W., Pres. & Chief Exec. Officer--Wards Cove Packing Company, Seattle, WA; *U.S. Private*, pg. 1149

Brining, David R., Pres., Chief Oper. & Chief Exec. Officer--Valley Forge Corporation, San Rafael, CA; *U.S. Public*, pg. 1705

Brink, Jay, Chief Exec. Officer--Brink Electric Construction Company, Rapid City, SD; *U.S. Private*, pg. 169

Brinkley, Nicholas B., Chm. Bd. & Chief Exec. Officer--BankAmerica Financial Services System, Inc., San Diego, CA; *U.S. Public*, pg. 181

Brinkman, Lloyd D., Chm. Bd., Chief Exec. & Chief Oper. Officer--LDB Corporation, Kerrville, TX; *U.S. Private*, pg. 639

Brinzo, John S., Pres. & Chief Exec. Officer--Cleveland-Cliffs Inc, Cleveland, OH; *U.S. Public*, pg. 386

Briscoe, John R., Chief Exec. Officer--Bergelectric Corporation, Los Angeles, CA; *U.S. Private*, pg. 135

Briskin, Bernard, Chm. Bd., Pres. & Chief Exec. Officer--Arden Group, Inc., Los Angeles, CA; *U.S. Public*, pg. 128

Britt, William R., Chm. Bd., Pres. & Chief Exec. Officer--Palmer-American National Bank, Danville, IL; *U.S. Public*, *pg. 1217*

Brizzolara, Bruce J., Pres. & Chief Exec. Officer--Eversharp Pen Co., Franklin Park, IL; *U.S. Private*, pg. 386

Broad, Eli, Chm. Bd., Pres. & Chief Exec. Officer--SunAmerica Inc., Los Angeles, CA; *U.S. Public*, pg. 1532

Broad, John W., Pres. & Chief Exec. Officer--Broad, Vogt & Conant, Inc., Detroit, MI; *U.S. Private*, pg. 170

Broadhurst, James, Chm. & Chief Exec. Officer--Eat N Park Restaurants, Pittsburgh, PA; *U.S. Private*, pg. 358

Broady, George, Pres. & Chief Exec. Officer--Ultrak Inc., Lewisville, TX; *U.S. Public*, pg. 1663

Broccoli, Henry, Chief Exec. Officer--Best Manufacturing, Inc., New York, NY; *U.S. Private*, pg. 139

Brocteur, A., Chief Oper. Officer--S.A. Centre d'Enfouissement Technique de Mont-Saint-Guibert C.E.Te.M., Mont-Saint Guibert, Belgium; *Int'l*, pg. 301

Brode, Harold, Chief Exec. Officer--Broder Bros. Co., Plymouth, MI; *U.S. Private*, pg. 170

Brodersen, Roger R., Chm. Bd. & Chief Exec. Officer--Data Transmission Network Corporation, Omaha, NE; *U.S. Public*, pg. 486

Brodeur, A.W., Chm. Bd., Pres. & Chief Exec. Officer--Cassidy's Ltd., Brossard, Canada; *Int'l*, pg. 275

Brodie, Jim, Chief Exec. Officer--Flavor House Products, Inc., Dothan, AL; *U.S. Private*, pg. 410

Brody, Arthur, Chm. Bd. & Chief Exec. Officer--Brodart Company, Williamsport, PA; *U.S. Private*, pg. 170

Brody, Marvin D., Chm. Bd., Pres. & Chief Exec. Officer--Employee Solutions, Inc., Phoenix, AZ; *U.S. Public*, pg. 579

Brogan, R. Alan, Pres. & Chief Exec. Officer--North American Van Lines, Inc., Fort Wayne, IN; *U.S. Public*, pg. 1191

Bromley, Ernest W., Chm. & Chief Exec. Officer--Bromley, Aguilar & Associates, San Antonio, TX; *U.S. Private*, pg. 692

Bromley, Wayne L., Jr., Pres. & Chief Exec. Officer--Giles & Ransome, Inc., Bensalem, PA; *U.S. Private*, pg. 453

Brondum, L., Chief Exec. Officer--B&C Danmark A/S, Moldrup, Denmark; *Int'l*, pg. 1091

Bronner, Michael, Chief Exec. Officer--Bronner Slosberg Humphrey/Strategic Interactive Group, Boston, MA; *U.S.* Private, pg. 171

Bronstein, Kathy, Vice Chm. & Chief Exec. Officer--The Wet Seal, Inc., Irvine, CA; *U.S. Public*, pg. 1763

Brookes, Nicholas K., Chief Exec. Officer--Bowthorpe plc, Crawley, United Kingdom; *Int'l*, pg. 207

Brookes, Nick G., Chm. Bd. & Chief Exec. Officer--Brown & Williamson Tobacco Corp., Louisville, KY; *Int'l*, pg. 111

Brookman, Amber M., Pres. & Chief Exec. Officer--Brookwood Companies Inc., New York, NY; *U.S. Public*, pg. 777

Brooks, Craig, Pres. & Chief Exec. Officer--Key Mortgage Services, Inc., Cleveland, OH; *U.S. Public*, pg. 954

Brooks, Diana D., Pres. & Chief Exec. Officer--Sotheby's Holdings Inc., New York, NY; *U.S. Public*, pg. 1487

Brooks, Diana D., Pres. & Chief Exec. Officer--Sotheby's Inc., New York, NY; *U.S. Public*, pg. 1487

Brooks, E.R., Chm. Bd. & Chief Exec. Officer--Central and South West Corporation, Dallas, TX; *U.S. Public*, pg. 324

Brooks, James R., Pres. & Chief Exec. Officer--Global Special Risks, Inc. Holdings, Metairie, LA; *Int'l*, pg. 1503

Brooks, James R., Pres. & Chief Exec. Officer--Global Special Risks, Inc. of Houston, Houston, TX; *Int'l*, pg. 1503

Brooks, James W., Chm. Bd. & Chief Exec. Officer--Beverage America, Inc., Holland, MI; *U.S. Private*, pg. 141

Brooks, L.E., Chm. Bd. & Chief Exec. Officer--Air Techniques, Inc., Hicksville, NY; *U.S. Private*, pg. 28

Brooks, Mike, Chm. Bd., Pres. & Chief Exec. Officer--Rocky Shoes & Boots, Inc., Nelsonville, OH; *U.S. Public*, pg. 1402

Brooks, Richard E.T., Chm., Pres. & Chief Exec. Officer--ChemDesign Corporation, Fitchburg, MA; *Int'l*, pg. 173

Brooks, Roger, Pres. & Chief Exec. Officer--American Mutual Life Holding Co., Des Moines, IA; *U.S. Private*, pg. 59

Brooks, Roger, Chief Exec. Officer--AmerUS Life, Des Moines, IA; *U.S. Private*, pg. 59

Brophy, George T., Chm. Bd., Pres. & Chief Exec. Officer--ABT Building Products Corporation, Neenah, WI; *Int'l*, pg. 20

Brosnan, Daryl, Chief Exec. Offic.--Bel-Ray Company, Inc., Farmingdale, NJ; *U.S. Private*, pg. 130

Brost, Jay, Pres. & Chief Exec. Officer--Miniature Precision Components, Walworth, WI; *U.S. Private*, pg. 750

Brott, M. Paul, Chm. Bd. & Chief Exec. Officer--Ewing Cole Cherry Brott, Philadelphia, PA; *U.S. Private*, pg. 387

Broughton, Martin Faulkner, Grp. Chief Exec. & Dep. Chm.--B.A.T Industries P.L.C., London, United Kingdom; *Int'l*, pg. 110

Brouse, John S., Pres. & Chief Exec. Officer--Highmark Inc., Pittsburgh, PA; *U.S. Private*, pg. 528

Brown, Alex, Chief Exec. Officer--AAF Industries Plc, London, United Kingdom; *Int'l*, pg. 1

Brown, Arthur, Chm. Bd., Pres. & Chief Exec. Officer--Hecla Mining Company, Coeur D'Alene, ID; *U.S. Public*, pg. 803

Brown, C., Chief Exec. Officer--Scholl Plc, Newton, United Kingdom; *Int'l*, pg. 1209

Brown, C. Terry, Pres. & Chief Exec. Officer--Atlas Hotels, Inc., San Diego, CA; *U.S. Private*, pg. 96

Brown, Carter, Pres. & Chief Exec. Officer--Omega Performance Group, Sausalito, CA; *U.S. Private*, pg. 816

Brown, Charles, Chm. Bd., Pres. & Chief Exec. Officer--Bayou State Oil Corporation, Shreveport, LA; *U.S. Private*, pg. 125

Brown, Denis, Pres. & Chief Exec. Officer--Pinkerton's Inc., Encino, CA; *U.S. Public*, pg. 1296

Brown, Douglas R., Pres. & Chief Exec. Officer--Advent International, Boston, MA; *U.S. Private*, pg. 22

Brown, Edgar L., Pres. & Chief Exec. Officer--Bell Atlanticom Systems, Inc., Princeton, NJ; *U.S. Public*, pg. 203

Brown, Herbert E., Chm. Bd. & Chief Exec. Officer--Alexander Doll Company, Inc., New York, NY; *U.S. Private*, pg. 33

Brown, Hyatt, J., Chm. Bd., Pres. & Chief Exec. Officer--Poe & Brown, Inc., Daytona Beach, FL; *U.S. Public*, pg. 1312

Brown, I. Larry, Pres. & Chief Exec. Officer--Rollins Leasing Corp., Wilmington, DE; *U.S. Public*, pg. 1405

Brown, J. Bruce, Chm. Bd. & Chief Exec. Officer--Lambert Smith Hampton, London, United Kingdom; *Int'l*, pg. 797

Brown, J. Terrell, Chm. Bd. & Chief Exec. Officer--United Companies Financial Corporation, Baton Rouge, LA; *U.S. Public*, pg. 1675

Brown, Jack E., Chm. Bd. & Chief Exec. Officer--BASES Worldwide, Covington, KY; *U.S. Private*, pg. 120

Brown, Jack H., Chm. Bd., Pres. & Chief Exec. Officer--Stater Bros. Inc., Colton, CA; *U.S. Public*, pg. 456

Brown, Jack W., Chm. Bd., Pres. & Chief Exec. Officer--Gish Biomedical, Inc., Irvine, CA; *U.S. Public*, pg. 745

Brown, James, Pres. & Chief Exec. Officer--Union Planters Bank of Mississippi, Grenada, MS; *U.S. Public*, pg. 1669

Brown, James E., Chief Exec. Officer--Brown Industries, Inc., Dalton, GA; *U.S. Private*, pg. 174

Brown, Jay W., Pres. & Chief Exec. Officer--Du Pont Protein Technologies International, Saint Louis, MO; *U.S. Public*, *pg. 531*

Brown, Jim, Chm. Bd. & Chief Exec.--Newsquest Media Group, London, United Kingdom; *Int'l*, pg. 927

Brown, John, Chief Exec. Officer--Blockhouse Co., Inc., York, PA; *U.S. Private*, pg. 150

Brown, John W., Chm. Bd., Pres. & Chief Exec. Officer--Stryker Corporation, Kalamazoo, MI; *U.S. Public*, pg. 1525

Brown, Joseph W., Chm. Bd., Pres. & Chief Exec. Officer--Talegen Corporation, Seattle, WA; *U.S. Public*, pg. 1784

Brown, Kathye W., Pres., Chief Exec. Officer, V.P. & Corp. Sec.--Brown Evans Distributing Co., Mesa, AZ; *U.S. Private*, pg. 174

Brown, Ken, Chief Exec.-Materials Handling Div.--J. Bibby & Sons Plc, London, United Kingdom; *Int'l*, pg. 167

Brown, Marvin P., Pres. & Chief Exec. Officer--Mace Security International, Inc., Bennington, VT; *U.S. Public*, pg. 1030

Brown, Michael A., Chief Exec. Officer--Quantum Corporation, Milpitas, CA; *U.S. Public*, pg. 1350

Brown, Milton R., Chm. Bd., Pres. & Chief Exec. Officer--Suntec Industries Inc., Rockford, IL; *U.S. Private*, pg. 1054

Brown, Nicholas M., Jr., Pres. & Chief Exec. Officer--NAC Reinsurance Corporation, Greenwich, CT; *U.S. Public*, pg. 1144

Brown, Nicholas M., Jr., Vice Chm. & Chief Exec. Officer--Greenwich Insurance Company, Greenwich, CT; *U.S. Public*, pg. 1144

Brown, Nicholas M., Jr., Vice Chm. & Chief Exec. Officer--Indian Harbor Insurance Company, Greenwich, CT; *U.S. Public*, pg. 1144

Brown, Owsley, II, Chm. Bd. & Chief Exec. Officer--Brown-Forman Corporation, Louisville, KY; *U.S. Public*, pg. 261

Brown, R. Donald, Chm. Bd., Pres. & Chief Exec. Officer--Imperial Tobacco Limited, Montreal, Canada; *Int'l*, pg. 112

Brown, R. Frank, Pres. & Chief Exec. Officer--Arthur Treacher's, Inc., Jacksonville, FL; *U.S. Public*, pg. 136

Brown, Randy, Pres. & Chief Exec. Officer--Agsco, Inc., Grand Forks, ND; *U.S. Private*, pg. 27

Brown, Richard H., Chief Exec. Officer--Cable and Wireless plc, London, United Kingdom; *Int'l*, pg. 247

Brown, Richard L., Pres. & Chief Exec. Officer--Houston General Insurance Co., Fort Worth, TX; *Int'l*, pg. 1392

Brown, Robert W., Jr., Exec. V.P., Gen. Mgr. & Sec.--Brown Motors, Toledo, OH; *U.S. Private*, pg. 174

Brown, Ronald A., Pres. & Chief Exec. Officer--Calcor Space Facility, Inc., Whittier, CA; *U.S. Private*, pg. 200

Brown, Ronald D., Pres. & Chief Exec. Officer--Sales Technologies, Atlanta, GA; *U.S. Public*, pg. 395

Brown, Stephen L., Chm. Bd. & Chief Exec. Officer--John Hancock Mutual Life Insurance Company, Boston, MA; *U.S. Private*, pg. 589

Brown, Stewart, Chief Exec. Officer & Mng. Dir.--BWI Plc, Altrincham, United Kingdom; *Int'l*, pg. 130

Brown, Thomas G., Chm., Pres. & Chief Exec. Officer--Duncanson & Holt, New York, NY; *U.S. Public*, pg. 1699

Brown, Thomas V., Pres. & Chief Exec. Officer--Caraustar Industries, Inc., Austell, GA; *U.S. Public*, pg. 303

Brown, Timothy C., Chm. Bd., Pres. & Chief Exec. Officer--Thomas Industries Inc., Louisville, KY; *U.S. Public*, pg. 1598

Brown, W.C., Pres. & Chief Exec. Officer--B C Sugar Refinery, Ltd., Vancouver, Canada; *Int'l*, pg. 103

Brown, Wayne W., Pres. & Chief Exec. Officer--Willis Corroon Corp. of Louisiana, New Orleans, LA; *Int'l*, pg. 1506

Brown, William, Chief Exec. Officer--Columbia Health Care, Inc., Toronto, Canada; *U.S. Public*, pg. 1531

Brown, Woods R., Pres., Chief Exec. Officer & Treas.--Kingsbury, Inc., Philadelphia, PA; *U.S. Private*, pg. 622

Browne, David M., Pres. & Chief Exec. Officer--Lenscrafters, Cincinnati, OH; *Int'l*, pg. 822

Browne, E.J.P., Chief Exec. Officer--The British Petroleum Company P.L.C., London, United Kingdom; *Int'l*, pg. 219

Browne, Stephen B., Pres. & Chief Exec. Officer--All American Bottling Corp., Oklahoma City, OK; *U.S. Private*, pg. 34

Browne, Stephen B., Pres. & Chief Exec. Officer--All-American Bottling Financial Corp., Oklahoma City, OK; *U.S. Private*, pg. 34

Brualdi, Ulysses J., Jr., Pres. & Chief Exec. Officer--ADT Security Services, Inc., Aurora, CO; *U.S. Public*, pg. 1649

Brubaker, Robert P., Chm. Bd., Pres. & Chief Exec. Officer--King & Prince Seafood Corporation, Brunswick, GA; *U.S.* Private, pg. 620

Bruell, Pierre, Pres. & Chief Exec. Officer--Polarome International, Jersey City, NJ; *U.S. Private*, pg. 874

Bruggeman, William L., Chief Exec. Officer--Diversified Dynamics Corporation, Minneapolis, MN; *U.S. Private*, pg. 336

Bruhn, Richard L., Chm. Bd & Chief Exec. Officer--Dick Bruhn Incorporated, Salinas, CA; *U.S. Private*, pg. 175

Brumback, Emerson L., Pres. & Chief Exec. Officer--Bank One, Cincinnati, Cincinnati, OH; *U.S. Public*, pg. 173

Brummett, Larry W., Chm. & Chief Exec. Officer--ONEOK Inc., Tulsa, OK; *U.S. Public*, pg. 1226

Brunel, Jerome, Chief Exec. Officer-Credit Lyonnais-Americas--Credit Lyonnais Americas, New York, NY; *Int'l*, pg. 344

Brunetti, Wayne H., Vice Chm. & Chief Exec. Officer--Southwestern Public Service Company, Amarillo, TX; *U.S. Public*, pg. 1170

Brunetti, Wayne H., Pres. & Chief Exec. Officer--Public Service Company of Colorado, Denver, CO; *U.S. Public*, pg. 1170

Brunner, L. Douglas, Pres. & Chief Exec. Officer--ACI Holding Inc., Baltimore, MD; *Int'l*, pg. 464

Bruno, Joseph M., Chm. Bd & Chief Exec. Officer--Dixie Brewing Co., Inc., New Orleans, LA; *U.S. Private*, pg. 336

Bruns, George H., Jr., Chm. Bd. & Chief Exec. Officer--Giga-Tronics Incorporated, San Ramon, CA; *U.S. Public*, pg. 742

Bruns, Rainer, Deputy Chief Exec. Officer--Filterwerk Mann & Hummel GmbH, Ludwigsburg, Germany; *Int'l*, pg. 484

Brunton, Ann, Chief Exec. Officer--Welbeck Golin/Harris Communications Ltd., London, United Kingdom; *Int'l*, pg. 1226

Brutsche, H.R., III, Chm. Bd., Pres. & Chief Exec. Officer--Vari-Lite International, Dallas, TX; *U.S. Public*, pg. 1709

Brutsche, Peter, Chief Exec. Officer & Exec. V.P.-Japan--Union Bank of Switzerland, Zurich, Switzerland; *Int'l*, pg. 1439

Bruzelius, Jan, Pres. & Chief Exec. Officer--IL Returpapper, Stockholm, Sweden; *Int'l*, pg. 646

Bruzelius, Jan, Pres. & Chief Exec. Officer--IL Sekretess, Stockholm, Sweden; *Int'l*, pg. 646

Bryan, David, Chief Exec. Officer--Avedis Zildjian Company, Norwell, MA; *U.S. Private*, pg. 1206

Bryan, F. Sibley, Jr., Pres. & Chief Exec. Officer--Chipman-Union, Inc., Union Point, GA; *U.S. Private*, pg. 237

Bryan, J. Stewart, III, Chm. Bd., Pres. & Chief Exec. Officer--Media General, Inc., Richmond, VA; *U.S. Public*, pg. 1077

Bryan, J.P., Pres. & Chief Exec. Officer--Gulf Canada Resources Ltd., Calgary, Canada; *Int'l*, pg. 577

Bryan, John H., Chm. Bd. & Chief Exec. Officer--Sara Lee Corporation, Chicago, IL; *U.S. Public*, pg. 1432

Bryan, John H., III, Pres. & Chief Exec. Officer--Bryan Foods, West Point, MS; *U.S. Public*, pg. 1433

Bryan, L. Merill, Jr., Pres. & Chief Exec. Officer--Union Pacific Technologies, Saint Louis, MO; *U.S. Public*, pg. 1668

Bryan, Robert, Chief Exec. Officer--Midwest Petroleum Co., Saint Louis, MO; *U.S. Private*, pg. 745

Bryant, Dudley E., Pres. & Chief Exec. Officer--Advanced Separation Technologies Incorporated, Lakeland, FL; *U.S. Public*, pg. 655

Bryce, Hamish, Chief Exec. Officer--Thorn Lighting Group Plc, Borehamwood, United Kingdom; *Int'l*, pg. 1385

Bryfonski, Dedria, Pres. & Chief Exec. Officer--Gale Research Inc., Detroit, MI; *U.S. Public*, pg. 1600

Brymer, Charles, Chief Exec. Officer--Interbrand Schechter, New York, NY; *U.S. Public*, pg. 1224

Bryson, John E., Chm. Bd. & Chief Exec. Officer--Edison International, Rosemead, CA; *U.S. Public*, pg. 564

Buccellato, Carl, Chm. Bd., Pres. & Chief Exec. Officer--Homeowners Group, Inc., Sunrise, FL; *U.S. Public*, pg. 832

Bucci, Anthony L., Pres. & Chief Exec. Officer--MARC, Pittsburgh, PA; *U.S. Private*, pg. 701

Buchan, Robert M., Chm. Bd & Chief Exec. Officer--Kinross Gold Corporation, Toronto, Canada; *Int'l*, pg. 734

Buchanan, David R., Chm. Bd., Pres. & Chief Exec. Officer--Three-Five Systems, Tempe, AZ; *U.S. Public*, pg. 1604

Buchanan, R.D., Chief Exec. Officer-North American Engineered Fabrics--Scapa Group Plc, Blackburn, United Kingdom; *Int'l*, pg. 1202

Buchanan, Robert C., Pres. & Chief Exec. Officer--Fox Valley Corporation, Appleton, WI; *U.S. Private*, pg. 422

Buchel, Andre P., Pres. & Chief Exec. Officer--Sulzermedica USA Inc., Angleton, TX; *Int'l*, pg. 1307

Buck, Charles T., Chm. Bd., Pres. & Chief Exec. Officer--Buck Knives, Inc., El Cajon, CA; *U.S. Private*, pg. 177

Buck, Manfred, Pres. & Chief Exec. Officer--Maison Mathieu, S.A., Antwerp, Belgium; *Int'l*, pg. 846

Buckee, James W., Dr., Pres. & Chief Exec. Officer--Talisman Energy Inc., Calgary, Canada; *Int'l*, pg. 1352

Buckland, Arthur R., Pres. & Chief Exec. Officer--C.P. Clare Corporation, Beverly, MA; *U.S. Public*, pg. 382

Buckland, Ross, Chief Exec. Officer--Unigate PLC, London, United Kingdom; *Int'l*, pg. 1433

Buckley, Bob, Pres. & Chief Exec. Officer--Meridian Neuro Care, Newport Beach, CA; *U.S. Public*, pg. 839

Buckley, Charles, Pres. & Chief Exec. Officer--John Brown Plastics Machinery, Attleboro, MA; *Int'l*, pg. 773

Buckley, James J., Pres. & Chief Exec. Officer--CBT Systems USA Ltd., Menlo Park, CA; *U.S. Public*, pg. 275

Buckley, Maurice, Pres. & Chief Exec. Officer--Pamarco Technologies, Inc., New Providence, NJ; *U.S. Private,* pg. 835

Buckley, Walter W., III, Pres. & Chief Exec. Officer--Internet Capital Group, Wayne, PA; *U.S. Public,* pg. 1425

Buckman, Frederick W., Pres. & Chief Exec. Officer--PacifiCorp, Portland, OR; *U.S. Public,* pg. 1251

Buckman, Robert H., Pres. & Chief Exec. Officer--Bulab Holdings, Inc., Memphis, TN; *U.S. Private,* pg. 180

Buckman, S. B., Chm. Bd. & Chief Exec. Officer--Buckman Laboratories Inc., Memphis, TN; *U.S. Private,* pg. 180

Buckmaster, A.C., Chief Exec. Officer--Longwall International Limited, Worcester, United Kingdom; *U.S. Public,* pg. 789

Buckner, Steve, Chief Exec. & Chief Fin. Officer--Johnson County Farm Bureau Co-op, Franklin, IN; *U.S. Private,* pg. 591

Bucksbaum, Matthew, Chm. Bd. & Chief Exec. Officer--General Growth Properties Inc., Chicago, IL; *U.S. Public, pg. 715*

Budd, Richard, Chief Exec. Officer--Lofts Seed, Inc., Winston Salem, NC; *U.S. Public,* pg. 29

Buddemeyer, David, Pres., Chief Exec. Officer & Chief Oper. Officer--Servico, Inc., West Palm Beach, FL; *U.S. Public,* pg. 1462

Budialim, Rahardjo, Chief Exec.--PT. KONE Indo Elevator, Java, Indonesia; *Int'l,* pg. 747

Buechler, Bradley B., Pres. & Chief Exec. Officer--Spartech Corporation, Clayton, MO; *U.S. Public,* pg. 1495

Buell, Dick, Pres. & Chief Exec. Officer--The Griffith Laboratories Ltd., Scarborough, Canada; *U.S. Private,* pg. 481

Buettner, Thomas W., Dr., Chm. Bd., Pres. & Chief Exec. Officer--Ruetgers-Nease Corporation, State College, PA; *Int'l,* pg. 1148

Bufe, Uwe-Ernst, Dr., Pres. & Chief Exec. Officer--Degussa AG, Frankfurt/Main, Germany; *Int'l,* pg. 388

Buffett, Warren E., Chm. Bd. & Chief Exec. Officer--Berkshire Hathaway Inc., Omaha, NE; *U.S. Public,* pg. 217

Buford, E.R., Pres. & Chief Exec. Officer--Temtex Industries Inc., Dallas, TX; *U.S. Public,* pg. 1575

Buford, E.R., Pres. & Chief Exec. Officer--Temco Fireplace Products, Inc., Nashville, TN; *U.S. Public,* pg. 1576

Buhler, Alfred P., Chm., Pres. & Chief Exec. Officer--Bank of America Canada, Toronto, Canada; *U.S. Public,* pg. 182

Buhler, Frank H., Chm. Bd. & Chief Exec. Officer--Old Dominion Box Co., Inc., Madison Heights, VA; *U.S. Private,* pg. 814

Buhlmann, G., Chief Exec. Officer--Schiedel GmbH & Co., Munich, Germany; *Int'l,* pg. 1091

Buitoni, G.L.L., Pres. & Chief Exec. Officer--Ferrari North America, Inc., Englewood Cliffs, NJ; *Int'l,* pg. 483

Bull, William H., Pres. & Chief Exec. Officer--McNaughton-McKay Electric Co., Madison Heights, MI; *U.S. Private,* pg. 724

Bullard, Edward D., Pres. & Chief Exec. Officer--E.D. Bullard Company, Cynthiana, KY; *U.S. Private,* pg. 180

Bullock, B.L., Pres. & Chief Exec. Officer--Intera Information Technologies Corp., Calgary, Canada; *Int'l,* pg. 1424

Bullock, Jim, Pres. & Chief Exec. Officer--Laidlaw Inc., Burlington, Canada; *Int'l,* pg. 259

Bullock, Thomas, Pres. & Chief Exec. Officer--Ocean Spray Cranberries, Inc., Middleboro, MA; *U.S. Private,* pg. 811

Bumby, Edward W., Pres. & Chief Exec. Officer--Ripon Foods, Inc., Ripon, WI; *U.S. Private,* pg. 931

Bumgarner, John C., Chm. Bd. & Chief Exec. Officer--Apco Argentina Inc., Tulsa, OK; *U.S. Public,* pg. 119

Bunaes, Bard, Chief Exec. Officer--Constitution Re Corp., New York, NY; *Int'l,* pg. 467

Bundy, Dennis, Chief Exec. Officer & Chief Fin. Officer--Hood Lumber Co., Mill City, OR; *U.S. Private,* pg. 538

Bundy, Terry L., Pres. & Chief Exec. Officer--Lincoln Electric Systems, Lincoln, NE; *U.S. Private,* pg. 668

Bunkers, E.W., Chief Exec. Officer & Exec. V.P.-Fin.--Mueller Industries, Inc., Memphis, TN; *U.S. Public,* pg. 1141

Bunn, Arthur H., Pres. & Chief Exec. Officer--Bunn-O-Matic Corporation, Springfield, IL; *U.S. Private,* pg. 180

Bunn, Richard C., Pres. & Chief Exec. Officr--UGI Utilities, Inc., Reading, PA; *U.S. Public,* pg. 1653

Bunte, Brent, Chief Exec. Officer & Gen. Mgr.--New Cooperative Inc., Fort Dodge, IA; *U.S. Private,* pg. 792

Buntin, Jeffrey W., Pres. & Chief Exec. Officer--The Buntin Group, Nashville, TN; *U.S. Private,* pg. 181

Buonanno, Vincent, Chm. & Chief Exec. Officer--Tempel Steel Company, Skokie, IL; *U.S. Private,* pg. 1075

Burchi, Giorgio, Chief Exec. Officer & Gen. Mgr.--Fiscambi Factoring S.p.A., Milan, Italy; *Int'l,* pg. 138

Burd, Steve, Pres. & Chief Exec. Officer--Safeway Inc., Pleasanton, CA; *U.S. Public,* pg. 1426

Burdick, Richard L., Chm. Bd., Pres. & Chief Exec. Officer--Thermon Manufacturing Company, San Marcos, TX; *U.S. Private,* pg. 1080

Burenga, Kenneth, Chief Exec. Officer--Dow Jones Markets, Jersey City, NJ; *U.S. Public,* pg. 525

Burenga, Kenneth L., Pres., Chief Exec. Officer & Chief Oper. Officer-Dow Jones Market--Dow Jones & Company, Inc., New York, NY; *U.S. Public,* pg. 524

Burenga, Kenneth L., Chief Exec. Officer--Dow Jones Telerate Holdings, Inc., Jersey City, NJ; *U.S. Public,* pg. 525

Burford, Jeffrey, Pres. & Chief Exec. Officer--Fibrebond Corporation, Minden, LA; *U.S. Private,* pg. 402

Burgdorff, Peter, Pres. & Chief Exec. Officer--ERA Real Estate, Parsippany, NJ; *U.S. Public,* pg. 321

Burger, Paul, Chm. & Chief Exec. Officer--Sony Music Entertainment (UK) Limited, London, United Kingdom; *Int'l,* pg. 1284

Burgess, John K., Pres. & Chief Exec. Officer--BAT Office Products, Zion, IL; *U.S. Public,* pg. 1686

Burgess, Robert K., Pres. & Chief Exec. Officer--Pulte Corporation, Bloomfield Hills, MI; *U.S. Public,* pg. 1344

Burgett, W. Brian, Pres. & Chief Exec. Officer--Kokosing Construction Company, Inc., Fredericktown, OH; *U.S. Private,* pg. 631

Burgin, Urs, Chief Exec. Officer--Kunz & Dietfurt, Windisch, Switzerland; *Int'l,* pg. 998

Burgis, Alan, Chief Exec. Officer & Mng. Dir.--EURO RSCG Partnership, Sydney, Australia; *Int'l,* pg. 602

Burhmaster, Robert C., Pres. & Chief Exec. Officer--Jostens, Minneapolis, MN; *U.S. Public,* pg. 934

Burke, Andrew J., Pres. & Chief Exec. Officer--Degussa Corporation, Ridgefield Park, NJ; *Int'l,* pg. 388

Burke, Gary W., Pres. & Chief Exec. Officer--Burke Engineering Company, South El Monte, CA; *U.S. Private, pg. 183*

Burke, John J., Chief Exec. Officer & Mng. Dir.--Bristol & West Building Society, Bristol, United Kingdom; *Int'l,* pg. 216

Burke, Larry W., Pres. & Chief Exec. Officer--Robinson Nugent, Inc., New Albany, IN; *U.S. Public,* pg. 1394

Burke, Paul B., Chm. Bd., Pres. & Chief Exec. Officer--BMC Industries, Inc., Minneapolis, MN; *U.S. Public,* pg. 162

Burke, Steven F., Pres. & Chief Exec. Officer--North American Outdoor Group, Inc., Minnetonka, MN; *U.S. Public,* pg. 321

Burke, W.R., Pres. & Chief Exec. Officer--White Cap, Inc., Downers Grove, IL; *Int'l,* pg. 1207

Burke, William J., Chm. Bd. & Chief Exec. Officer--Osco Industries Inc., Portsmouth, OH; *U.S. Private,* pg. 820

Burkel, Ronald W., Chm. Bd. & Chief Exec. Officer--Fred Meyer Stores, Portland, OR; *U.S. Public,* pg. 1103

Burkhardt, Edward A., Chm. Bd., Pres. & Chief Exec. Officer--Wisconsin Central Transportation Corporation, Rosemont, IL; *U.S. Public,* pg. 1772

Burkhardt, William C., Pres. & Chief Exec. Officer--Austin Quality Foods, Cary, NC; *U.S. Private,* pg. 100

Burkle, Ron, Chm. Bd. & Chief Exec. Officer--Dominick's Finer Foods, Northlake, IL; *U.S. Private,* pg. 1202

Burleigh, William R., Pres. & Chief Exec. Officer--The E.W. Scripps Company, Cincinnati, OH; *U.S. Public,* pg. 1447

Burleson, Gene, Chief Exec. Officer--Vitalink Pharmacy Services, Inc., Naperville, IL; *U.S. Public,* pg. 1041

Burleson, Gene, Chief Exec. Officer--Vitalink Pharmacy Services, Inc., Atlanta, GA; *U.S. Public,* pg. 1042

Burnay, Luis, Chief Exec.--Sulzer Infra Portugal, Ltda., Lisbon, Portugal; *Int'l,* pg. 1306

Burner, David L., Chm. Bd., Pres. & Chief Exec. Officer--The B.F. Goodrich Company, Richfield, OH; *U.S. Public,* pg. 751

Burnett, Steven, Chief Exec. Officer--Healthsource Connecticut, Farmington, CT; *U.S. Public,* pg. 360

Burney, Derek H., Chm., Pres. & Chief Exec. Officer--Bell Canada International, Inc., Montreal, Canada; *Int'l,* pg. 115

Burnham, Duane L., Chm. & Chief Exec. Officer--Abbott Laboratories, Abbott Park, IL; *U.S. Public,* pg. 12

Burns, David C., Pres. & Chief Exec. Officer--Ithaco Inc., Ithaca, NY; *U.S. Private,* pg. 576

Burns, Gregory L., Chm. Bd., Pres. & Chief Exec. Officer--O'Charley's Inc., Nashville, TN; *U.S. Public,* pg. 1211

Burns, Harry A., Pres. & Chief Exec. Officer--Cargill Salt Inc., Minneapolis, MN; *Int'l,* pg. 48

Burns, J. A., Chief Exec. Officer--TSB Hill Samuel Bank Holding Co Plc, London, United Kingdom; *Int'l,* pg. 813

Burns, John J., Jr., Pres. & Chief Exec. Officer--Alleghany Corporation, New York, NY; *U.S. Public,* pg. 42

Burns, Jullius, Pres. & Chief Exec. Officer--MMI Products, Inc., Houston, TX; *U.S. Private,* pg. 687

Burns, M. Anthony, Chm. Bd., Pres. & Chief Exec. Officer--Ryder System, Inc., Miami, FL; *U.S. Public,* pg. 1413

Burns, R. Patrick, Pres. & Chief Exec. Officer--The Vermont Teddy Bear Company, Inc., Shelburne, VT; *U.S. Public,* pg. 1716

Burns, Stephen F., Chm. Bd. & Chief Exec. Officer--Wheaton Van Lines, Inc., Indianapolis, IN; *U.S. Private,* pg. 1171

Burrell, Frank L., Jr., Chm. Bd. & Chief Exec. Officer--Elsinore Corporation, Las Vegas, NV; *U.S. Public,* pg. 570

Burrell, Paul M., Chm. Bd., Pres. & Chief Exec. Officer--Outsource International, Deerfield Beach, FL; *U.S. Public,* pg. 1236

Burriss, J.D., Chm. Bd., Pres. & Chief Exec. & Oper. Officer--The Alpha Corporation Of Tennessee, Collierville, TN; *U.S. Private,* pg. 44

Burrow, Grady, Pres. & Chief Exec. Officer--National Computer Print, Inc., Birmingham, AL; *U.S. Private,* pg. 780

Burrows, John, Pres. & Chief Exec. Officer--SPI Polyols, Inc., New Castle, DE; *Int'l,* pg. 599

Burrows, P.J., Dr., Chief Exec.--GKN Westland Technologies Limited, Yeovil, United Kingdom; *Int'l,* pg. 535

Burrows, Peter, Chief Exec. Officer--Chiltem Group SAM, Monaco, Monaco; *Int'l,* pg. 65

Burt, James, Pres. & Chief Exec. Officer--Wisconsin Pharmacal Co., Inc., Jackson, WI; *U.S. Private,* pg. 1185

Burt, Robert N., Chm. Bd. & Chief Exec. Officer--FMC Corporation, Chicago, IL; *U.S. Public,* pg. 604

Burtman, Charles, Pres. & Chief Exec. Officer--Burtman Iron Works, Inc., Readville, MA; *U.S. Private,* pg. 188

Burton, Raymond C., Jr., Pres. & Chief Exec. Officer--TTX Co., Chicago, IL; *U.S. Private,* pg. 1066

Burton, Robert G., Chm. Bd., Pres. & Chief Exec. Officer--World Color Press, Inc., Greenwich, CT; *U.S. Public,* pg. 1778

Bury, Thomas, Chief Exec. Officer & Deputy Chm.-London--Ogilvy & Mather Worldwide, Inc., New York, NY; *Int'l,* pg. 1483

Burzycki, Thomas, Pres. & Chief Exec. Officer--The Selmer Co., Inc., Elkhart, IN; *U.S. Public,* pg. 1514

Busby, Jheryl, Pres. & Chief Exec. Officer--Motown Record Company, J.P., New York, NY; *Int'l,* pg. 1052

Busch, Paul L., Dr., Chm. Bd., Pres. & Chief Exec. Officer--Malcolm Pirnie, Inc., White Plains, NY; *U.S. Private,* pg. 867

Buschmann, Siegfried, Chm. Bd. & Chief Exec. Officer--The Budd Company, Troy, MI; *Int'l,* pg. 1388

Bush, Condon, Chm. Bd. & Chief Exec. Officer--Bush Brothers & Company, Knoxville, TN; *U.S. Private,* pg. 189

Bush, Jack, Chm. Bd. & Chief Exec. Officer--Jumbo Sports Inc., Tampa, FL; *U.S. Public,* pg. 935

Bush, John, Chief Exec. Officer--International Dessert Partners, Miami, FL; *U.S. Public,* pg. 447

Bush, Paul S., Chm. Bd., Pres. & Chief Exec. Officer--Bush Industries Inc., Jamestown, NY; *U.S. Public,* pg. 270

Busti, Dennis, Pres. & Chief Exec. Officer--Reliance National Insurance Company, New York, NY; *U.S. Public,* pg. 1374

Butcher, Andrew D.W., Chm. Bd. & Chief Exec. Officer--Carat ICG, Los Angeles, CA; *U.S. Private,* pg. 207

Butcher, C. Preston, Pres. & Chief Exec. Officer--Lincoln Property Co., Northern California, Foster City, CA; *U.S. Private,* pg. 668

Butcko, James M., Chief Exec. Officer--Crescive Die & Tool, Inc., Saline, MI; *U.S. Private,* pg. 289

Buterbaugh, Noel L., Pres. & Chief Exec. Officer--BioWhittaker, Inc., Walkersville, MD; *U.S. Public,* pg. 297

Butler-Wheelhouse, Keith, Chief Exec. Officer--Smiths Industries plc, London, United Kingdom; *Int'l,* pg. 1266

Butler, Abbey, Co-Chm.-Bd. & Chief Exec. Officer--Avatex Corporation, Dallas, TX; *U.S. Public,* pg. 151

Butler, Abbey, Co-Chm. Bd. & Co-Chief Exec. Officer--Phar-Mor, Inc., Youngstown, OH; *U.S. Public,* pg. 1284

Butler, Andrew, Pres.--Butler Automatic, Inc., Canton, MA; *U.S. Private,* pg. 189

Butler, Bryn, Grp. Chief Exec. Officer--BDH Advertising Limited, Manchester, United Kingdom; *Int'l,* pg. 118

Butler, Dan, Chief Exec. Officer--CSC United States, Wilmington, DE; *U.S. Private,* pg. 197

Butler, Edward F., Chm. Bd., Pres. & Chief Exec. Officer--Regions Bank/Southern Louisiana, New Orleans, LA; *U.S. Public,* pg. 1373

Butler, Fred M., Pres. & Chief Exec. Officer--The Manitowoc Company, Inc., Manitowoc, WI; *U.S. Public,* pg. 1040

Butler, Fred M., Chief Exec. Officer--Manitowoc Ice, Inc., Manitowoc, WI; *U.S. Public,* pg. 1041

Butler, Lester, Chm. Bd., Pres. & Chief Exec. Officer--SouthTrust Bank of Charleston, Charleston, SC; *U.S. Public,* pg. 1492

Butler, Martin, Joint Chief Exec. Officer--Butler Lutos Sutton Wilkinson, London, United Kingdom; *Int'l,* pg. 237

Butler, Norton L., Pres. & Chief Oper. Officer--Chittenden & Eastman Co., Burlington, IA; *U.S. Private,* pg. 237

Butler, Robert F., Pres. & Chief Exec. Officer--Holtzman's Little Folk Shop, Inc., City of Industry, CA; *U.S. Public,* pg. 1777

Butler, Stephen, Chm. Bd. & Chief Exec. Officer--KPMG LLP, New York, NY; *U.S. Private,* pg. 603

Butler, Stephen T., Chm. Bd. & Chief Exec. Officer--W.C. Bradley Co., Columbus, GA; *U.S. Private,* pg. 164

Butler, William, Chm. Bd., Pres. & Chief Exec. Officer--Corporex Companies, Inc., Cincinnati, OH; *U.S. Private,* pg. 276

Butta, Tom, Chief Exec. Officer--FGI Inc., Chapel Hill, NC; *U.S. Private,* pg. 389

Butta, Tom, Chief Exec. Officer--FGI New York, New York, NY; *U.S. Private,* pg. 389

Butterworth, Edward L., Pres. & Chief Exec. Officer--Fedco, Inc., Santa Fe Springs, CA; *U.S. Private,* pg. 398

Buttner, Jean B., Chm. Bd & Chief Exec. Officer--Value Line Publishing, New York, NY; *U.S. Private,* pg. 137

Buttner, Jean Bernhard, Chm. Bd., Pres. & Chief Exec. Officer--Value Line, Inc., New York, NY; *U.S. Private,* pg. 137

Butvilas, George J., Pres. & Chief Exec. Officer--D & N Financial Corporation, Hancock, MI; *U.S. Public,* pg. 472

Buxbaum, Matthew, Chief Exec. Officer--GGP/Homart, Inc., Chicago, IL; *U.S. Public,* pg. 715

Buxton, Winslow H., Chm. Bd., Pres. & Chief Exec. Officer--Pentair, Inc., Saint Paul, MN; *U.S. Public,* pg. 1273

Buyers, John W., Chm. Bd. & Chief Exec. Officer--Buyco, Inc., Honolulu, HI; *U.S. Private,* pg. 190

Buyers, John W.A., Chm. Bd. & Chief Exec. Officer--Mauna Loa Macadamia Partners, L.P., Honolulu, HI; *U.S. Public, pg. 1060*

Bylin, Art, Chief Exec. Officer--Fitz & Floyd, Dallas, TX; *U.S. Private,* pg. 409

Byrd, Robert, Chm. Bd., Pres. & Chief Exec. Officer--The Keller Manufacturing Co., Inc., Corydon, IN; *U.S. Private, pg. 612*

Byrne, Arthur, Chm. Bd., Pres. & Chief Exec. Officer--The Wiremold Company, West Hartford, CT; *U.S. Private,* pg. 1184

Byrnes, Edward G., Pres. & Chief Exec. Officer--Byrnes & Kiefer Company, Callery, PA; *U.S. Private,* pg. 191

Byrnes, James J., Chm. Bd., Pres. & Chief Exec. Officer--Tompkins County Trust Company, Ithaca, NY; *U.S. Public,* pg. 1621

Cabeke, Gui, Pres. & Chief Exec. Officer--Porcelanite, Inc., Lexington, NC; *Int'l,* pg. 573

Caberlotto, Giovanni, Chief Exec. Officer--Lotto S.p.A., Montebelluna, Italy; *Int'l,* pg. 819

Cabot, Samuel, III, Pres. & Chief Exec. Officer--Samuel Cabot, Inc., Newburyport, MA; *U.S. Private,* pg. 198

Cacciatore, William C., Chm. Bd., Pres. & Chief Exec. Officer--Richey Electronics, Inc., Garden Grove, CA; *U.S. Public,* pg. 1388

Caccini, Gian Paolo, Vice Chm., Pres., Chief Exec. & Chief Oper. Officer--CertainTeed Corporation, Valley Forge, PA; *Int'l,* pg. 1170

Caccini, Gian Paolo, Chm. Bd. & Chief Exec. Officer--Vetrotex CertainTeed Corporation, Wichita Falls, TX; *Int'l,* pg. 1171

Cadbury, Dominic, Chief Exec. Officer--Cadbury Beverages North America, Stamford, CT; *Int'l,* pg. 248

Cadena, Alvaro, Pres. & Chief Oper. Officer--Graham Corporation, Batavia, NY; *U.S. Public*, pg. 757
Cadieux, Chester, Chm. Bd., Pres. & Chief Exec. Officer--QuikTrip Corporation, Tulsa, OK; *U.S. Private*, pg. 901
Cadogan, William J., Chm. Bd., Pres. & Chief Exec. Officer--ADC Telecommunications, Inc., Minnetonka, MN; *U.S. Public*, pg. 4
Cadwell, Marvin S., Pres. & Chief Exec. Officer--Shared Medical Systems Corporation, Malvern, PA; *U.S. Public*, pg. 1463
Cady, Lyle, Pres. & Chief Exec. Officer--Jouan, Inc., Winchester, VA; *U.S. Private*, pg. 601
Cafferata, Patricia A., Pres. & Chief Exec. Officer--Young & Rubicam Chicago, Chicago, IL; *U.S. Private*, pg. 1198
Caffery, Patrick, Pres. & Chief Exec. Officer--Edgewater Steel Company, Oakmont, PA; *U.S. Private*, pg. 364
Caffi, Alain, Chief Exec. Officer--Sofineti, Paris, France; *Int'l*, *pg. 344*
Caffrey, Hugh R., Pres. & Chief Exec. Officer--Hilb, Rogal and Hamilton Company of Atlanta, Inc., Atlanta, GA; *U.S. Public*, pg. 827
Cagle, J. Douglas, Chm. Bd. & Chief Exec. Officer--Cagle's Inc., Atlanta, GA; *U.S. Public*, pg. 291
Cahouet, Frank V., Chm. Bd., Pres. & Chief Exec. Officer--Mellon Bank Corporation, Pittsburgh, PA; *U.S. Public*, pg. 1084
Cain, Phillip W., Chief Exec. Officer & Exec. V.P.--First National Bank in Marlinton, Marlinton, WV; *U.S. Public*, pg. 836
Cain, Vernon W., Chief Exec. Officer--The Faxon Company, Inc., Westwood, MA; *Int'l*, pg. 385
Caizza, Donald, Pres. & Chief Exec. Officer--CSC, Ltd., Warren, OH; *U.S. Private*, pg. 924
Calabro, Joseph A., Pres. & Chief Exec. Officer--Artistic Greetings, Inc., Elmira, NY; *U.S. Public*, pg. 136
Calapp, David, Chief Exec. Officer--Morrow West Beach, Salem, OR; *U.S. Public*, pg. 1134
Calarco, Vincent A., Chm. Bd., Pres. & Chief Exec. Officer--Crompton & Knowles Corporation, Stamford, CT; *U.S. Public*, pg. 459
Calarco, Vincent A., Pres. & Chief Exec. Officer--Uniroyal Chemical Company, Inc., Middlebury, CT; *U.S. Public*, pg. 460
Calburn, Keith W., Chief Exec. Officer--Consolidated Electrical Distributors, Westlake Village, CA; *U.S. Private*, *pg. 265*
Caldarone, Anthony J., Chm., Pres. & Chief Exec. Officer--Calton, Inc., Manalapan, NJ; *U.S. Public*, pg. 296
Caldwell, John E., Pres. & Chief Exec. Officer--CAE Inc., Toronto, Canada; *Int'l*, pg. 237
Caldwell, Robert F., Chm. Bd. & Chief Exec. Officer--Southeastern Michigan Gas Company, Port Huron, MI; *U.S. Public*, pg. 1489
Calerno, Catherine, Pres. & Chief Exec. Officer--Rainoldi, Kerzner & Radcliffe, San Francisco, CA; *U.S. Public*, pg. 1224
Caletti, Cesare, Chief Exec. Officer & Gen. Mgr.--Banco di Sicilia, Rome, Italy; *Int'l*, pg. 140
Calhoun, David, Pres. & Chief Exec. Officer--G.E. Lighting Division, Cleveland, OH; *U.S. Public*, pg. 710
Calhoun, David L., Pres. & Chief Exec. Officer--GE Transportation Systems, Erie, PA; *U.S. Public*, pg. 711
Calhy, Ronald B., Chm., Pres. & Chief Exec. Officer--United HealthCare Insurance Company, Hartford, CT; *U.S. Public*, pg. 1678
Calise, Charles J., Chief Exec. Officer & New Bus. Contact--Gleason/Calise/Associates, Inc., Dallas, TX; *U.S. Private*, pg. 455
Calkins, Harlan D., Chm. Bd. & Chief Exec. Officer--Rochester Midland Corporation, Rochester, NY; *U.S. Private*, pg. 937
Call, Ralph, Pres. & Chief Exec. Officer--Dyna Technology Incorporated, Le Center, MN; *U.S. Private*, pg. 350
Call, Ralph, Pres. & Chief Exec. Officer--WINCO, Le Center, MN; *U.S. Private*, pg. 350
Call, William, Chm., Pres. & Chief Exec. Officer--Maverik Country Stores, Inc., Salt Lake City, UT; *U.S. Private*, pg. 715
Callaghan, Howard, Pres.--Plastic Suppliers, Inc., Columbus, OH; *U.S. Private*, pg. 871
Callahan, Dennis, Chm. Bd., Pres. & Chief Exec. Officer--Crowley, Milner & Company, Detroit, MI; *U.S. Public*, pg. 461
Callahan, Dennis, Pres. & Chief Exec. Officer--Steinbach Stores, Inc., Detroit, MI; *U.S. Public*, pg. 461
Callahan, Peter, Chm. Bd., Pres. & Chief Exec. Officer--American Media, Inc., Lake Worth, FL; *U.S. Public*, pg. 87
Callaway, Howard Bo, Chief Exec. Officer--Crested Butte Mountain Resort, Inc., Crested Butte, CO; *U.S. Private*, pg. 289
Calligaris, A.E., Chm. Bd., Pres. & Chief Exec. Officer--Stebbins Engineering & Mfg. Co., Watertown, NY; *U.S. Private*, pg. 1037
Callon, Fred L., Pres. & Chief Exec. Officer--Callon Petroleum Company, Natchez, MS; *U.S. Public*, pg. 295
Calvillo, Ricardo C., Chm. Bd. & Chief Exec. Officer--FerrellCalvillo Communications, Inc., New York, NY; *U.S.* Private, pg. 401
Calzolari, Michele, Chief Exec. Officer & Gen. Mgr.--Caboto Sim S.p.A., Milan, Italy; *Int'l*, pg. 138
Cambre, Ronald C., Chm. Bd., Pres. & Chief Exec. Officer--Newmont Mining Corporation, Denver, CO; *U.S. Public*, pg. 1178
Camelio, Cosmo, Pres. & Chief Exec. Officer--Freudenberg Nonwovens, Durham, NC; *Int'l*, pg. 505
Cameron, Gerald T., Sr., Chm. Bd. & Chief Exec. Officer--Amray, Inc., Bedford, MA; *U.S. Private*, pg. 67
Cameron, William M., Pres. & Chief Exec. Officer--American Fidelity Corp., Oklahoma City, OK; *U.S. Private*, pg. 54
Cammarata, Bernard, Pres. & Chief Exec. Officer--The TJX Companies, Inc., Framingham, MA; *U.S. Public*, pg. 1556
Camosy, Raymond J., Pres. & Chief Exec. Officer--Camosy, Inc., Russell, IL; *U.S. Private*, pg. 203
Camp, Michael, Pres. & Chief Exec. Officer--Olicom, Inc., Marlborough, MA; *Int'l*, pg. 1001
Campanella, Anton J., Chm. & Chief Exec. Officer--Bell Atlantic Network Services, Inc., Arlington, VA; *U.S. Public*, pg. 202
Campbell, Charles J., Chm. Bd., Pres. & Chief Exec. Officer--Florsheim Group Inc., Chicago, IL; *U.S. Public*, pg. 656
Campbell, David, Pres. & Chief Exec. Officer--Master Lock Company, Milwaukee, WI; *U.S. Public*, pg. 675
Campbell, David J., Pres. & Chief Exec. Officer--The Detroit Medical Center, Detroit, MI; *U.S. Private*, pg. 328
Campbell, Edward P., Pres. & Chief Exec. Officer--Nordson Corporation, Westlake, OH; *U.S. Public*, pg. 1188
Campbell, George M., Pres. & Chief Exec. Officer--Regions Bank/North Louisiana, Monroe, LA; *U.S. Public*, pg. 1372
Campbell, Gregor A., Dr., Chief Exec. Officer--Trikon Technologies Inc., Chatsworth, CA; *U.S. Public*, pg. 1638
Campbell, J.H., Jr., Pres. & Chief Exec. Officer--Associated Grocers, Inc., Baton Rouge, LA; *U.S. Private*, pg. 90
Campbell, James, Chm. Bd., Pres. & Chief Exec. Officer--First Community Bank of Saltville, Saltville, VA; *U.S. Public*, pg. 1039
Campbell, James R., Pres. & Chief Exec. Officer--Norwest Bank Minnesota N.A., Minneapolis, MN; *U.S. Public*, pg. 1202
Campbell, John A., Pres. & Chief Exec. Officer--The Pacific Lumber Company, Scotia, CA; *U.S. Public*, pg. 1062
Campbell, Jon R., Pres. & Chief Exec. Officer--Norwest Bank Arizona, N.A., Phoenix, AZ; *U.S. Public*, pg. 1202
Campbell, Lewis B., Pres. & Chief Oper. Officer--Textron Inc., Providence, RI; *U.S. Public*, pg. 1588
Campbell, Michael L., Chm. Bd., Pres. & Chief Exec. Officer--Regal Cinemas Inc., Knoxville, TN; *U.S. Public*, pg. 1371
Campbell, P.D., Pres. & Chief Exec. Officer--Dunlop Tire Corporation, Buffalo, NY; *Int'l*, pg. 1317
Campbell, R.S., Pres. & Chief Exec. Officer--Marlite, Dover, OH; *U.S. Private*, pg. 705
Campbell, Richard J., Chief Exec. Officer--Benjamin Obdyke, Inc., Warminster, PA; *U.S. Private*, pg. 810
Campbell, Robert H., Chm. Bd., Chief Exec. Officer & Pres.--Sun Company, Inc., Philadelphia, PA; *U.S. Public*, pg. 1530
Campbell, Robert J., Jr., Chief Exec. Officer--Bridgestone Multi-Media Group, Chandler, AZ; *U.S. Private*, pg. 168
Campbell, Robert J., Jr., Chief Exec. Officer--Alpha Omega Publications, Chandler, AZ; *U.S. Private*, pg. 168
Campbell, William V., Pres. & Chief Exec. Officer--Intuit, Inc., Mountain View, CA; *U.S. Public*, pg. 911
Camperi, S., Pres.--SAE Engineering, Inc., Santa Clara, CA; *U.S. Private*, pg. 955
Campo, Richard J., Chm. Bd. & Chief Exec. Officer--Camden Property Trust, Houston, TX; *U.S. Public*, pg. 298
Camuto, Vincent, Chief Exec. Officer--Nine West Group, Inc., Stamford, CT; *U.S. Public*, pg. 1185
Canada, Ronald G., Chief Exec. Officer--Computational Systems Inc., Knoxville, TN; *U.S. Public*, pg. 572
Canavan, Daniel B., Chm. Bd & Chief Exec. Officer--Triple S Plastics, Inc., Vicksburg, MI; *U.S. Public*, pg. 1639
Candela, Peter R., Pres. & Chief Exec. Officer--Pinnacle Bank, Valparaiso, IN; *U.S. Public*, pg. 1297
Candell, Thomas M., Pres. & Chief Exec. Officer--Rocor Transportation Companies Inc., Oklahoma City, OK; *U.S.* Private, pg. 938
Candlish, Malcolm, Chm. Bd. & Chief Exec. Officer--First Alert, Inc., Aurora, IL; *U.S. Private*, pg. 406
Canet, Gerardo, Chm. Bd., Pres. & Chief Exec. Officer--IntegraMed America, Purchase, NY; *U.S. Public*, pg. 883
Canfield, Brian A., Chm. Bd. & Chief Exec. Officer--BC Telecom Inc., Burnaby, Canada; *U.S. Public*, pg. 697
Cannatelli, Vincenzo, Chief Exec. Officer & Mng. Dir.--ELSAG Bailey Process Automation N.V., Schiphol, Netherlands; *Int'l*, pg. 449
Canning, Charles F., Jr., Chief Exec. Officer--Pine State Trading Company, Augusta, ME; *U.S. Private*, pg. 865
Canning, Simon, Pres. & Chief Exec. Officer--SBC Warburg Dillon Read Inc., Boston, MA; *Int'l*, pg. 1329
Canning, Simon, Pres. & Chief Exec. Officer--SBC Warburg Dillon Read Inc., New York, NY; *Int'l*, pg. 1329
Cannon, Joseph A., Chm. Bd. & Chief Exec. Officer--Geneva Steel, Vineyard, UT; *U.S. Public*, pg. 729
Cantalupo, James R., Pres. & Chief Exec. Officer-Intl.--McDonald's Corporation, Oak Brook, IL; *U.S. Public*, pg. 1068
Cantor, Paul, Chief Exec. Officer--National Trustco Inc., Toronto, Canada; *Int'l*, pg. 909
Cantor, Paul G.S., Pres. & Chief Exec. Officer--Confederation Life Insurance Company, Toronto, Canada; *Int'l*, pg. 325
Cantrell, Wesley, Pres. & Chief Exec. Officer--Lanier Worldwide Inc., Atlanta, GA; *U.S. Public*, pg. 791
Cantu, Carlos, Chief Exec. Officer--American Home Shield Corporation, Memphis, TN; *U.S. Public*, pg. 1461
Cantu, Carlos H., Pres. & Chief Exec. Officer--The ServiceMaster Company, Downers Grove, IL; *U.S. Public*, pg. 1461
Caouette, John B., Chm. Bd. & Chief Exec. Officer--Capital Markets Assurance Corporation, New York, NY; *U.S. Public*, pg. 1023
Capaldini, Mark, Pres. & Chief Exec. Officer--Congressional Information Service (CIS), Bethesda, MD; *Int'l*, pg. 1096
Capallo, Mark, Chm. Bd. & Chief Exec. Officer--Energy & Process Corp., Tucker, GA; *Int'l*, pg. 1512
Capitanno, Tommaso, Chief Exec. Officer--Crediop Overseas Bank Ltd., Georgetown, Cayman Islands; *Int'l*, pg. 341
Caplan, L. David, Chm. Bd. & Chief Exec. Officer--Pratt & Whitney Canada Inc., Longueuil, Canada; *U.S. Public*, pg. 1690
Caplea, George C., Pres. & Chief Exec. Officer--Trelleborg YSH, Inc., South Haven, MI; *Int'l*, pg. 1422
Capone, Daniel J., Jr., Pres. & Chief Exec. Officer--Proteon, Inc., Westborough, MA; *U.S. Public*, pg. 1336
Caporaletti, Amedeo, Chief Exec. Officer & Mng. Dir.--Agusta S.P.A., Varese, Italy; *Int'l*, pg. 32
Caporella, Nick A., Chm. Bd., Pres., Chief Exec. Officer & Chief Fin. Officer--National Beverage Corp., Plantation, FL; *U.S. Public*, pg. 1153
Cappello, Vito, Chief Exec. Officer & Gen. Mgr.--Foster Wheeler Andina, S.A., Bogota, Colombia; *U.S. Public*, pg. 677
Cappiello, William D., Chm. Bd. & Chief Exec. Officer--Parisian, Inc., Birmingham, AL; *U.S. Public*, pg. 1333
Capps, Thomas E., Chm. Bd., Pres. & Chief Exec. Officer--Dominion Resources, Inc., Richmond, VA; *U.S. Public*, pg. 516
Capriotti, Laurence, Pres. & Chief Exec. Officer--Intercounty Title Co. of Illinois, Chicago, IL; *U.S. Private*, pg. 567
Capstick, John, Chm. & Chief Exec. Officer--R.R. Donnelley, Limited-York, York, United Kingdom; *U.S. Public*, pg. 519
Capuano, Ken, Chief Officer--Novo Nordisk Pharmaceuticals, Inc., Princeton, NJ; *Int'l*, pg. 987
Carberry, Robert L., Chm. Bd., Pres. & Chief Exec. Officer--CyberGuard Corporation, Fort Lauderdale, FL; *U.S. Public*, pg. 470
Carbonari, Bruce A., Chm. & Chief Exec. Officer--Moen Incorporated, North Olmsted, OH; *U.S. Public*, pg. 675
Carbonell, Robert J., Pres. & Chief Exec. Officer--Tetley USA Inc., Shelton, CT; *Int'l*, pg. 1377
Cardarelli, Donald P., Pres. & Chief Exec. Officer--Agway, Inc., De Witt, NY; *U.S. Private*, pg. 27
Cardin, R. Larry, Pres. & Chief Exec. Officer--Regions Bank/Columbus, Columbus, GA; *U.S. Public*, pg. 1372
Cardinal, Claus, Pres. & Chief Exec. Officer--Jefferson Insurance Company of New York, Jersey City, NJ; *Int'l*, pg. 59
Cardwell, Paul, Chief Exec. Officer--GGK London Ltd., London, United Kingdom; *Int'l*, pg. 1335
Cardy, Robert W., Chm., Pres. & Chief Exec. Officer--Carpenter Technology Corporation, Reading, PA; *U.S. Public*, pg. 307
Carell, Monroe J., Jr., Chm. Bd. & Chief Exec. Officer--Central Parking Corp., Nashville, TN; *U.S. Public*, pg. 326
Carendi, Jan R., Chief Exec. Officer--American Skandia Investment Holding Corporation, Shelton, CT; *Int'l*, pg. 1257
Carette, Bruno, Chief Exec. Officer--LG Seeds Inc., Peoria, IL; *Int'l*, pg. 566
Carfora, Alfred, Pres. & Chief Exec. Officer--Duty Free International, Inc., Ridgefield, CT; *Int'l*, pg. 103
Cargile, David L., Chm. Bd., Pres. & Chief Exec. Officer--Centris Group Inc., Costa Mesa, CA; *U.S. Public*, pg. 328
Cariani, Paul R., Pres. & Chief Exec. Officer--Maine Public Service Company, Presque Isle, ME; *U.S. Public*, pg. 1038
Caridis, Andrew, Chief Exec. Officer--Heat & Control, Inc., Hayward, CA; *U.S. Private*, pg. 518
Carlberg, W. Charles, Pres. & Chief Exec. Officer--Rives Carlberg, Houston, TX; *U.S. Private*, pg. 934
Carlbom, Chuck, Pres., Chief Exec. Officer & Sec.--United Grocers Inc., Portland, OR; *U.S. Private*, pg. 1122
Carlino, Peter M., Chm. Bd. & Chief Exec. Officer--Penn National Gaming, Inc., Wyomissing, PA; *U.S. Public*, pg. 1270
Carlisle, Brian, Chm. Bd. & Chief Exec. Officer--Adept Technology, Inc., San Jose, CA; *U.S. Public*, pg. 19
Carlisle, Van, Pres. & Chief Exec. Officer--Fire King International, Inc., New Albany, IN; *U.S. Private*, pg. 406
Carlos, Michael C., Chm. Bd. & Chief Exec. Officer--National Distributing Co., Inc., Atlanta, GA; *U.S. Private*, pg. 781
Carlson, Curtis L., Chm. Bd. & Chief Exec. Officer--Carlson Companies, Inc., Minnetonka, MN; *U.S. Private*, pg. 211
Carlson, Cynthia, Pres. & Chief Exec. Officer--American Enterprise Investment Services, Inc., Minneapolis, MN; *U.S. Public*, pg. 73
Carlson, D.A., Jr., Pres., Chief Exec. Officer & Treas.--Ziegler Securities Division, Chicago, IL; *U.S. Public*, pg. 1792
Carlson, E. Jerome, Chief Exec. Officer--The Instant Web Companies, Chanhassen, MN; *U.S. Private*, pg. 565
Carlson, H. Gary, Dr., Chm. Bd., Pres. & Chief Exec. Officer--ElecSys Inc., Peoria, IL; *U.S. Private*, pg. 367
Carlson, LeRoy T., Jr., Pres. & Chief Exec. Officer--Telephone and Data Systems, Inc., Chicago, IL; *U.S. Public*, pg. 1570
Carlson, Robert A., Chm. Bd. & Chief Exec. Officer--NAI Technologies, Inc., Huntington, NY; *U.S. Public*, pg. 1144
Carlson, Victor E., Pres., Chief Oper. Officer, Chief Exec. Officer--Foga Systems, Oxnard, CA; *Int'l*, pg. 496
Carlson, W. Pierce, Chief Exec. Officer--Nord Pacific Limited, Albuquerque, NM; *U.S. Public*, pg. 1188
Carlton, Donald M., Pres. & Chief Exec. Officer--Radian International LLC, Austin, TX; *U.S. Public*, pg. 522
Carlton, Edward, Jr., Pres. & Chief Exec. Officer--Corrugated Metals, Inc., Bedford Park, IL; *U.S. Private*, pg. 277
Carlucci, Paul, Chief Exec. Officer--TV Guide Magazine, Radnor, PA; *Int'l*, pg. 925
Carmazzi, Frank, Pres. & Chief Exec. Officer--Persingers, Inc., Charleston, WV; *U.S. Private*, pg. 855
Carmody, Thomas R., Chm. Bd., Pres. & Chief Exec. Officer--American Business Products, Inc., Atlanta, GA; *U.S. Public*, pg. 70
Carneiro, J. Lamy, Chief Exec. Officer--Lusoceram-Empreendimentos Ceramicos, S.A., Lisbon, Portugal; *Int'l*, pg. 1092
Carnevale, A.R., Pres. & Chief Exec. Officer--Bradford-White Corporation, Ambler, PA; *U.S. Private*, pg. 164
Carney, William V., Chm. Bd & Chief Exec. Officer--Porta Systems Corp., Syosset, NY; *U.S. Public*, pg. 1317
Carni, Giora, Pres. & Chief Exec. Officer--Clay-Park Labs, Inc., Bronx, NY; *Int'l*, pg. 30

Carota, Richard J., Chm. Bd., Pres. & Chief Exec. Officer--Finch, Pruyn & Co., Inc., Glens Falls, NY; *U.S. Private*, pg. 405
Carpenter, Alvin R., Pres. & Chief Exec. Officer--CSX Transportation, Inc., Jacksonville, FL; *U.S. Public*, pg. 284
Carpenter, Dave, Pres. & Chief Exec. Officer--UniHealth, Burbank, CA; *U.S. Private*, pg. 1117
Carpenter, Larry, Pres. & Chief Exec. Officer--Spring Arbor Distributors, Belleville, MI; *U.S. Private*, pg. 563
Carpenter, Michael A., Chm. & Chief Exec. Officer--The Travelers Life & Annuity Co., Hartford, CT; *U.S. Public*, pg. 1633
Carpenter, Richard W., Pres. & Chief Exec. Officer--Leisure Technology, Inc., Atlanta, GA; *U.S. Private*, pg. 659
Carpenter, Terry R., Pres. & Chief Exec. Officer--Indiana Lawrence Bank, North Manchester, IN; *U.S. Public*, pg. 633
Carpenter, William M., Pres. & Chief Exec. Officer--Bausch & Lomb Incorporated, Rochester, NY; *U.S. Public*, pg. 194
Carper, Howell P., Pres. & Chief Exec. Officer--Iceland Seafood Corporation, Newport, VA; *U.S. Private*, pg. 556
Carr, Jeremiah, Chief Exec. Officer--Rochester Telephone Corp., Rochester, NY; *U.S. Public*, pg. 684
Carr, John, III, Pres. & Chief Exec. Officer--Central Supply Co., Inc., Indianapolis, IN; *U.S. Private*, pg. 225
Carr, Michael T., Pres. & Chief Exec. Officer--Weider Publications, Inc., Woodland Hills, CA; *U.S. Private*, pg. 1159
Carr, Robert F., III, Chm. & Chief Exec. Officer--Fiduciary Management Associates, Inc., Chicago, IL; *U.S. Public*, pg. 1673
Carr, Roger, Chief Exec. Officer--Williams Holdings Plc, Derby, United Kingdom; *Int'l*, pg. 1499
Carr, Thomas A., Pres. & Chief Exec. Officer--CarrAmerica Realty, Washington, DC; *U.S. Public*, pg. 308
Carraher, Richard, Pres. & Chief Exec. Officer--Fragrance Resources, Inc., Clifton, NJ; *U.S. Private*, pg. 423
Carrillo, Luis Miguel Monroy, Chief Exec. Officer--Tablex, S.A. de C.V., Toluca, Mexico; *Int'l*, pg. 1346
Carrion, Richard L., Chm. Bd., Pres. & Chief Exec. Officer--Banco Popular de Puerto Rico, San Juan, PR; *U.S. Public*, pg. 175
Carrion, Richard L., Chm. Bd., Pres. & Chief Exec. Officer--BanPonce Corporation, Hato Rey, PR; *U.S. Public*, pg. 176
Carroll, Esme, Pres. & Chief Exec. Officer--Ambrose Carr Linton Carroll Inc., Toronto, Canada; *Int'l*, pg. 71
Carroll, James, Chm. Bd. & Chief Exec. Officer--Wynn's International, Inc., Orange, CA; *U.S. Public*, pg. 1782
Carroll, Jane, Chief Exec. Officer-Forum Europe & Forum Asia--The Forum Corporation, Boston, MA; *U.S. Private*, pg. 420
Carroll, Loren, Pres. & Chief Exec. Officer--M-I L.L.C., Houston, TX; *U.S. Public*, pg. 776
Carroll, Paul, Chief Exec. Officer & V.P.--Mountain States Pipe & Supply Company, Colorado Springs, CO; *U.S. Private*, pg. 764
Carroll, Philip J., Pres. & Chief Exec. Officer--Shell Oil Company, Houston, TX; *Int'l*, pg. 1136
Carroll, Thomas E., Pres. & Chief Exec. Officer--MEDIQ Incorporated, Pennsauken, NJ; *U.S. Public*, pg. 1081
Carruthers, G.D., Chief Exec. Officer--Canterbury Timber Products Limited, Rangiora, New Zealand; *U.S. Public*, pg. 905
Carruthers, George, Pres., Chief Exec. & Chief Fin. Officer--Polycoat Systems, Inc., Hudson Falls, NY; *U.S. Private*, pg. 875
Carson, David E.A., Chm. Bd. & Chief Exec. Officer--People's Bank, Bridgeport, CT; *U.S. Public*, pg. 1274
Carson, W. Pierce, Ph.D., Pres. & Chief Exec. Officer--Nord Resources Corporation, Albuquerque, NM; *U.S. Public*, pg. 1188
Carson, William C., Chm. Bd. & Chief Exec. Officer--Instrument Specialties Company, Delaware Water Gap, PA; *U.S. Private*, pg. 565
Carstarphen, J.M., Chm. Bd., Pres. & Chief Exec. Officer--Stowe-Pharr Mills, Inc., Mc Adenville, NC; *U.S. Private*, pg. 1045
Carstens, Donald, Chief Exec. Officer--United Steel & Wire Co., Battle Creek, MI; *U.S. Private*, pg. 1126
Cartagine, Anthony L., Chief Exec. Officer--Reeves Brothers Inc., New York, NY; *U.S. Private*, pg. 507
Carte, B.A., Chief Exec. Officer--Lombard North Central PLC, Redhill, United Kingdom; *Int'l*, pg. 910
Carter, Frank H., Pres. & Chief Exec. Officer--Wellington Industries Inc., Madison, GA; *U.S. Private*, pg. 1161
Carter, J.D., Chief Exec.--Hepworth Heating Ltd., Belper, United Kingdom; *Int'l*, pg. 615
Carter, J.G.T., Chief Exec. Officer--Commercial Union plc, London, United Kingdom; *Int'l*, pg. 308
Carter, John, Chief Exec. Officer--Hepworth Plc, London, United Kingdom; *Int'l*, pg. 614
Carter, John M., Chm. Bd. & Chief Exec. Officer--Carco Electronics, Menlo Park, CA; *U.S. Private*, pg. 208
Carter, Marshall N., Chm. Bd. & Chief Exec. Officer--State Street Corporation, Boston, MA; *U.S. Public*, pg. 1513
Carter, Mason N., Chm. Bd. & Chief Exec. Officer--Merrimac Industries, Inc., West Caldwell, NJ; *U.S. Public*, pg. 1098
Carter, Philip L., Pres. & Chief Exec. Officer--Mac Frugal's Bargains Close-Outs Inc., Rancho Dominguez, CA; *U.S. Public*, pg. 437
Carter, Stephen, Pres. & Chief Exec. Officer--Concordia Publishing House, Saint Louis, MO; *U.S. Private*, pg. 261
Carter, Stephen M., Pres. & Chief Exec. Officer--Southwestern Bell Telecom, Dallas, TX; *U.S. Public*, pg. 1416
Carter, Thomas F., Jr., Chm. Bd. & Chief Exec. Officer--Keck Instruments, Inc., Williamston, MI; *U.S. Public*, pg. 367
Carter, Tim, Chm. Bd. & Chief Exec. Officer--Bell-Carter Foods, Inc., Lafayette, CA; *U.S. Private*, pg. 131
Cartwright, G., Chief Exec.-Automotive Brake--BBA Group plc, London, United Kingdom; *Int'l*, pg. 112
Cartwright, Peter, Chm. Bd., Pres. & CHief Exec. Officer--Calpine Corporation, San Jose, CA; *U.S. Public*, pg. 296
Carus, M. Blouke, Chm. Bd., Chief Exec. Officer & Chief Oper. Officer--Carus Corporation, Peru, IL; *U.S. Private*, pg. 217
Caruso, Stephen M., Chief Exec. Officer--Citrus World Inc., Lake Wales, FL; *U.S. Private*, pg. 241
Carvelli, A.J., Vice Chm. & Chief Exec. Officer--Pannier Corporation, Pittsburgh, PA; *U.S. Private*, pg. 837
Carver, Martin G., Chm. Bd., Pres. & Chief Exec. Officer--Bandag, Incorporated, Muscatine, IA; *U.S. Public*, pg. 177
Case, Daniel H., III, Chm. Bd. & Chief Exec. Officer--Hambrecht & Quist LLC., San Francisco, CA; *U.S. Public*, pg. 778
Case, R.I., Chief Exec.--GKN Westland Helicopters Limited, Yeovil, United Kingdom; *Int'l*, pg. 535
Case, Stephen M., Chm. Bd., Pres, Chief Exec. & Oper. Officer--America Online Incorporated, Dulles, VA; *U.S. Public*, pg. 66
Casebeer, Scott, Pres. & Chief Exec. Officer--Capitol Chevrolet Cadillac GEO Subaru Inc., Salem, OR; *U.S. Private*, pg. 206
Casella, John W., Chm. Bd., Pres. & Chief Exec. Officer--Casella Waste Systems, Inc., Rutland, VT; *U.S. Public*, pg. 312
Caserta, Marco, Chief Exec. Officer--BDDP S.p.A, Milan, Italy; *Int'l*, pg. 117
Casey, Edward F., Pres. & Chief Exec. Officer--Stewart Smith Group, Inc., Nashville, TN; *Int'l*, pg. 1508
Casey, Jeremiah E., Chief Exec.-USA Div.--Allied Irish Banks, p.l.c., Dublin, Ireland; *Int'l*, pg. 64
Casey, Phillip E., Chm. Bd. & Chief Exec. Officer--AmeriSteel, Tampa, FL; *U.S. Private*, pg. 65
Casey, Richard L., Chm. Bd., Pres. & Chief Exec. Officer--Scios Inc., Mountain View, CA; *U.S. Public*, pg. 1444
Casey, Shawn M., Vice Chm., Pres. & Chief Exec. Officer--Success Development International, Jacksonville, FL; *U.S. Private*, pg. 1048
Cash, Francis W., Chm. Bd., Pres. & Chief Exec. Officer--Red Roof Inns, Inc., Hilliard, OH; *U.S. Public*, pg. 1369
Cash, R.D., Chm. Bd., Pres. & Chief Exec. Officer--Questar Corporation, Salt Lake City, UT; *U.S. Public*, pg. 1352
Caspersen, Finn M.W., Chm. Bd. & Chief Exec. Officer--Beneficial Corporation, Wilmington, DE; *U.S. Public*, pg. 211
Cass, Ronald A., Chm. Bd., Pres., Chief Exec. Officer & Treas.--Hospital Staffing Services, Inc., Fort Lauderdale, FL; *U.S. Public*, pg. 840
Cassano, Victor J., Jr., Chm. Bd. & Chief Exec. Officer--Cassano's Inc., Dayton, OH; *U.S. Private*, pg. 218
Cassese, John J., Chm. Bd., Pres., Chief Oper. & Chief Exec. Officer--Computer Horizons Corp., Mountain Lakes, NJ; *U.S. Public*, pg. 421
Cassese, Patrick J., Chm. Bd., Pres. & Chief Exec. Officer--Antares Group Inc., Cleveland, OH; *U.S. Private*, pg. 76
Cassetty, Fred, Chm. Bd., Pres. & Chief Exec. Officer--Alley-Cassetty Coal Co., Nashville, TN; *U.S. Private*, pg. 37
Cassidy, Frank, Pres. & Chief Exec. Officer--Energis Resources Incorporated, Edison, NJ; *U.S. Public*, pg. 1340
Cassner, Alvin B., Pres. & Chief Exec. Officer--Rotary Forms Press, Inc., Hillsboro, OH; *U.S. Private*, pg. 947
Castaner, Francisco, Chief Exec. Officer--Sociedad Nestle A.E.P.A., Barcelona, Spain; *Int'l*, pg. 922
Castell, W.M., Chief Exec.-Amersham Pharmacia Biotech--Nycomed Amersham plc, Chalfont Saint Giles, United Kingdom; *Int'l*, pg. 992
Castellani, Lawrence, Pres. & Chief Exec. Officer--Tops Markets, Inc., Amherst, NY; *Int'l*, pg. 750
Castellini, Clateo, Chm. Bd., Pres. & Chief Exec. Officer--Becton Dickinson & Company, Franklin Lakes, NJ; *U.S. Public*, pg. 199
Castello, John L., Chm. Bd., Chief Exec. Officer & Pres.--XOMA Corporation, Berkeley, CA; *U.S. Public*, pg. 1786
Castells, Fernando, Chief Exec. Officer--Targor GmbH, Mainz, Germany; *Int'l*, pg. 105
Casten, Thomas R., Pres. & Chief Exec. Officer--Trigen Energy Corporation, White Plains, NY; *U.S. Public*, pg. 1637
Castle, Frank E., Pres. & Chief Exec. Officer--Components Corporation Of America, Dallas, TX; *U.S. Private*, pg. 259
Castle, James, Phd., Chm. Bd. & Chief Exec. Officer--USCS International, Inc., Rancho Cordova, CA; *U.S. Public*, pg. 1659
Castle, Jim, Pres. & Chief Exec. Officer--D.A. Stuart Company, Warrenville, IL; *U.S. Private*, pg. 1048
Castle, Joseph L., Chm. Bd., Pres. & Chief Exec. Officer--Castle Energy Corporation, Radnor, PA; *U.S. Public*, pg. 313
Castle, Robert L., Pres. & Chief Exec. Officer--VideoServer, Inc., Burlington, MA; *U.S. Public*, pg. 1720
Castleberry, W. Thomas, Chief Exec. Officer--RezSolutions, Inc., Phoenix, AZ; *Int'l*, pg. 1098
Castor, Joe D., Pres. & Chief Exec. Officer--Westco Products, Inc., Pico Rivera, CA; *Int'l*, pg. 244
Castor, Tony, Chief Exec. Officer--Hayward Industries, Inc., Elizabeth, NJ; *U.S. Private*, pg. 513
Castro, Adolfo, Chief Exec. Officer--Lowe MBAC, Barcelona, Spain; *U.S. Private*, pg. 678
Castro, John W., Pres. & Chief Exec. Officer--Merrill Corporation, Saint Paul, MN; *U.S. Public*, pg. 1097
Casty, Ronald G., Chm. Bd., Pres., Chief Exec. & Oper. Officer--Chelsea Industries, Inc., Peabody, MA; *U.S. Private*, pg. 231
Catacosinos, William J., Chm. Bd. & Chief Exec. Officer--Long Island Lighting Company, Hicksville, NY; *U.S. Public*, pg. 1013
Catala, Alain, Chief Exec. Officer--Groupe Limagrain, Chappes, France; *Int'l*, pg. 566
Cataldo, C.A., Chm. Bd. & Chief Exec. Officer--Hostmark Management Group, Rolling Meadows, IL; *U.S. Private*, pg. 541
Catell, Robert B., Chm. Bd. & Chief Exec. Officer--Brooklyn Union, Brooklyn, NY; *U.S. Public*, pg. 259
Cater, John T., Chm. Bd. & Chief Exec. Officer--River Oaks Trust Company, Houston, TX; *U.S. Public*, pg. 419
Cates, Steven T., Pres. & Chief Exec. Officer--Texas Life Insurance Company, Waco, TX; *U.S. Private*, pg. 738
Catherwood, Charles E., Chief Exec. Officer, V.P. & Treas.--Independent Publications, Inc., Bryn Mawr, PA; *U.S. Private*, pg. 559
Cathey, Peter, Pres. & Chief Exec. Officer--DFI/Inflight, Inc., Ridgefield, CT; *Int'l*, pg. 103
Cato, Glenn P., Pres. & Chief Exec. Officer--Maxum Health Corp., Dallas, TX; *U.S. Public*, pg. 881
Cato, Wayland H., Jr., Chm. Bd. & Chief Exec. Officer--The Cato Corporation, Charlotte, NC; *U.S. Public*, pg. 318
Catsimatidis, John, Chm. Bd. & Chief Exec. Officer--Red Apple Companies, New York, NY; *U.S. Private*, pg. 914
Catsimatidis, John A., Chm. Bd. & Chief Exec. Officer--United Refining Company, Warren, PA; *U.S. Private*, pg. 915
Catsimatidis, John A., Chm., Chief Exec. Officer & Treas.--Sloan's Supermarkets, Inc., New York, NY; *U.S. Private*, pg. 915
Caulfield, E. Michael, Chief Exec. Officer--Prudential Defined Contribution Services, Florham Park, NJ; *U.S. Private*, pg. 892
Caulfield, E.Michael, Chief Exec. Officer-Money Mngmnt. Grp.--The Prudential Insurance Company of America, Newark, NJ; *U.S. Private*, pg. 892
Causey, James D., Chief Exec. Officer--Cadmus Custom Publishing, Boston, MA; *U.S. Public*, pg. 291
Cavalier, John C., Pres. & Chief Exec. Officer--MapInfo Corp., Troy, NY; *U.S. Public*, pg. 1042
Cavaliere, Phyllis, Pres. & Chief Exec. Officer--Sunday Magazine Network, New York, NY; *U.S. Private*, pg. 739
Cavanaugh, Jim, Chm. Bd., Pres., Chief Exec. Officer & Sec.--Jani King International, Inc., Dallas, TX; *U.S. Private*, pg. 581
Cavanaugh, William, III, Pres. & Chief Exec. Officer--Carolina Power & Light Company, Raleigh, NC; *U.S. Public*, pg. 306
Cavaricci, Jim, Chief Exec. Officer--Z. Cavaricci Inc., Los Angeles, CA; *U.S. Private*, pg. 1203
Cave, Douglas G., Chief Exec. Officer--Practice Patterns Science, Maryland Heights, MO; *U.S. Public*, pg. 601
Cave, N.D., Chief Exec. Officer--Morganite Electrical Carbon Limited, Morriston, United Kingdom; *Int'l*, pg. 891
Cavell, Charles G., Pres. & Chief Exec. Officer--Quebecor Printing, Inc., Montreal, Canada; *Int'l*, pg. 1076
Cavender, Lea, Chm. Bd. & Pres.--E-Z Bowz, Inc., Sevierville, TN; *U.S. Private*, pg. 352
Cawley, Charles M., Chm. Bd., Pres. & Chief Exec. Officer--MBNA America Bank N.A., Wilmington, DE; *U.S. Public*, pg. 1023
Cawly, Robert H., Pres. & Chief Exec. Officer--Sentry Technology Group, Westborough, MA; *U.S. Public*, pg. 1425
Cayne, James E., Pres., Chief Exec. Officer & Sr. Mng. Dir.--The Bear Stearns Companies Inc., New York, NY; *U.S. Public*, pg. 197
Cayzac, Alain, Chief Exec. Officer--EURO RSCG Institutionnel, Levallois-Perret, France; *Int'l*, pg. 600
Cecala, Ted T., Chm. Bd. & Chief Exec. Officer--Wilmington Trust Corporation, Wilmington, DE; *U.S. Public*, pg. 1770
Cecchi, Giuseppe, Pres. & Chief Exec. Officer--The IDI Group Companies, Arlington, VA; *U.S. Private*, pg. 554
Cecil, Robert S., Chm. Bd., Pres. & Chief Exec. Officer--Plantronics Inc., Santa Cruz, CA; *U.S. Public*, pg. 1308
Ceiley, Glen, Pres. & Chief Exec. Officer--Bisco Industries, Inc, Orange, CA; *U.S. Private*, pg. 145
Cela, J., Chief Exec. Officer--Zurich Compania de Seguros sobre la Vida, Barcelona, Spain; *Int'l*, pg. 1529
Cela, J., Chief Exec. Officer--Zurich Compania de Seguros, Barcelona, Spain; *Int'l*, pg. 1531
Cela, J., Chief Exec. Officer--Caudal S.A. de Seguros y Reaseguros, Madrid, Spain; *Int'l*, pg. 1531
Cella, Frank C., Pres. & Chief Exec. Officer--Nestle Canada Inc., North York, Canada; *Int'l*, pg. 921
Centanni, Ross, Pres. & Chief Exec. Officer--Gardner Denver Machinery Inc., Quincy, IL; *U.S. Public*, pg. 703
Centofanti, Louis F., Dr., Chm. Bd., Pres. & Chief Exec. Officer--Perma-Fix Environmental Services, Inc., Gainesville, FL; *U.S. Public*, pg. 1279
Cerillo, Peter, Pres. & Chief Exec. Officer--Shape Inc., Kennebunk, ME; *U.S. Private*, pg. 990
Cerini, F. Brian, Pres. & Chief Exec. Officer--Sierra Capital Management, Northridge, CA; *U.S. Public*, pg. 1742
Cervenka, Robert, Chief Exec. Officer--Phillips Plastics Corporation, Phillips, WI; *U.S. Private*, pg. 862
Cervinka, James J., Chm. Bd. & Chief Exec. Officer--Arrow Gear Company, Downers Grove, IL; *U.S. Private*, pg. 85
Cesarman, Carlos, Chief Exec. Officer--Industrias CH, S.A. de C.V., Tlalnepantla, Mexico; *Int'l*, pg. 677
Chabraja, Nicholas D., Chm. Bd. & Chief Exec. Officer--General Dynamics Corporation, Falls Church, VA; *U.S. Public*, pg. 708
Chadwick, Bruce, Chief Exec. Officer--Kelley Advertising Inc., Hamilton, Canada; *U.S. Public*, pg. 765
Chadwick, Bruce A., Chief Exec. Officer--Kelley Advertising Inc., Toronto, Canada; *U.S. Public*, pg. 765
Chadwick, Rodney L., Mng. Dir. & Chief Exec. Officer--Pacific Dunlop Limited, Melbourne, Australia; *Int'l*, pg. 1021
Chadwick, Simon, Chief Exec. Officer--Winona Research, Phoenix, AZ; *Int'l*, pg. 1483
Chadwick, William H., Pres. & Chief Exec. Officer--Banknorth Group Inc., Burlington, VT; *U.S. Public*, pg. 186
Chaffringeon, Andre, Chief Exec. Officer--Banque Nationale de Paris (Canada), Montreal, Canada; *Int'l*, pg. 164

Chaiken, Eugene B., Chm., Pres. & Chief Exec. Officer--Almo Corp., Philadelphia, PA; *U.S. Private*, pg. 44
Chaimowitz, Ronald, Pres. & Chief Exec. Officer--GT Interactive Software Corp., New York, NY; *U.S. Public*, pg. 696
Chakkaphak, Pin, Pres. & Chief Exec. Officer--Finance One Public Company Limited, Bangkok, Thailand; *Int'l*, pg. 484
Chalmers, David B., Chm. Bd., Pres., Chief Exec. Officer & Treas.--Coral Oil & Gas Inc., Houston, TX; *U.S. Private*, pg. 275
Chaltiel, Victor M.G., Chm. Bd., Pres. & Chief Exec. Officer--Total Renal Care Holdings, Inc., Torrance, CA; *U.S. Public*, pg. 1625
Chamberlain, Steven R., Chm. Bd. & Chief Exec. Officer--Integral Systems, Inc., Lanham, MD; *U.S. Public*, pg. 883
Chambers, John T., Pres. & Chief Exec. Officer--Cisco Systems, Inc., San Jose, CA; *U.S. Public*, pg. 375
Chambers, Raymond, Co-Chief Exec. Officer--Dryper's Corp., Vancouver, WA; *U.S. Private*, pg. 344
Chambre, Peter, Chief Exec. Officer--Bespak plc, Norfolk, United Kingdom; *Int'l*, pg. 193
Chamillard, George W., Chief Exec. Officer--Teradyne, Inc., Boston, MA; *U.S. Public*, pg. 1580
Champagne, Gilles, Pres. & Chief Exec. Officer--Oceanex, Montreal, Canada; *Int'l*, pg. 924
Champel, Louis, Chief Exec. Officer--Merial Ltd., Iselin, NJ; *U.S. Public*, pg. 1092
Champel, Louis, Chief Exec. Officer--Merial Ltd., London, United Kingdom; *U.S. Public*, pg. 1092
Champel, Louis, Chief Exec. Officer--Merial Ltd., Iselin, NJ; *Int'l*, pg. 1109
Champel, Louis, Chief Exec. Officer--Merial Ltd., London, United Kingdom; *Int'l*, pg. 1110
Champion, James K., Pres. & Chief Exec. Officer--Riverdale Chemical Co., Glenwood, IL; *U.S. Private*, pg. 934
Chan, Kwok C., Chief Exec. Officer--LaFehr Chan Technologies, Houston, TX; *U.S. Private*, pg. 642
Chance, Douglas, Pres. & Chief Exec. Officer--Wyse Technology Inc., San Jose, CA; *U.S. Private*, pg. 1194
Chanda, Par, Dr., Chief Exec. Officer--Osicom Technologies Inc., Santa Monica, CA; *U.S. Public*, pg. 1233
Chandler, Colin, Sir, Chief Exec. Officer--Vickers PLC, London, United Kingdom; *Int'l*, pg. 1466
Chandler, J. Harold, Pres. & Chief Exec. Officer--Provident Companies, Inc., Chattanooga, TN; *U.S. Public*, pg. 1337
Chandler, Richard, Chief Exec. Officer--Joern's Sunrise Medical, Stevens Point, WI; *U.S. Public*, pg. 1536
Chandler, Richard H., Chm. Bd.,Pres. & Chief Exec. Officer--Sunrise Medical, Inc., Carlsbad, CA; *U.S. Public*, pg. 1535
Chandler, S. R., Deputy Chief Exec.--NatWest U.K., London, United Kingdom; *Int'l*, pg. 910
Chandler, Scott C., Pres. & Chief Exec. Officer--C-COR Electronics, Inc., State College, PA; *U.S. Public*, pg. 272
Chandramohan, Satchy, Chief Exec. Officer--Ford Graphics, South Pasadena, CA; *U.S. Private*, pg. 418
Chandran, Robert V., Pres. & Chief Exec. Officer--Chemoil, San Francisco, CA; *U.S. Private*, pg. 233
Chaney, Andrew, Chm. Bd. & Chief Exec. Officer--Barnett Bank N.A., Jacksonville, FL; *U.S. Public*, pg. 1162
Chaney, E. Thomas, Pres. & Chief Exec. Officer--Community Health Systems, Inc., Brentwood, TN; *U.S. Private*, pg. 419
Chaney, James R., Chm. Bd. & Chief Exec. Officer--The Coastal Bank of Georgia, Brunswick, GA; *U.S. Public*, pg. 1549
Chaney, John D., Pres. & Chief Exec. Officer--TeleCheck Services, Inc., Houston, TX; *U.S. Public*, pg. 631
Chaney, William R., Chm. Bd. & Chief Exec. Officer--Tiffany & Co., New York, NY; *U.S. Public*, pg. 1608
Chao, Allen Y., Ph.D., Chm. Bd. & Chief Exec. Officer--Watson Pharmaceuticals, Inc., Corona, CA; *U.S. Public*, pg. 1746
Chapin, Jere D., Chm. & Chief Exec. Officer--M & I Central State Bank, Ripon, WI; *U.S. Public*, pg. 1050
Chapman, Christopher, Pres. & Chief Exec. Officer--North Central Life Insurance Company, Saint Paul, MN; *U.S. Private*, pg. 404
Chapman, Gary, Pres. & Chief Exec. Officer--LIN Central Broadcasting Corporation (WOTV), Providence, RI; *U.S. Public*, pg. 11
Chapman, Hugh M., Pres. & Chief Exec. Officer--NationsBank South, Atlanta, GA; *U.S. Public*, pg. 1163
Chapman, Jerry B., Chief Exec. Officer--Chapman Automotive Group Inc., Scottsdale, AZ; *U.S. Private*, pg. 229
Chapman, Keith, Chm. Bd. & Chief Exec. Officer--Fine Art Developments plc, Bradford, United Kingdom; *Int'l*, pg. 485
Chapman, Lawrence, Pres. & Chief Exec. Officer--Manna Pro Corporation, Saint Louis, MO; *U.S. Private*, pg. 700
Chapman, Lynn, Pres. & Chief Exec. Officer--Netrix, Corp., Herndon, VA; *U.S. Private*, pg. 791
Chapman, Paul, Pres. & Chief Exec. Officer--Chattanooga Group, Inc., Hixson, TN; *U.S. Private*, pg. 231
Chapman, R.N., Chm. Bd. & Chief Exec. Officer--Pneumatic Scale Corporation, Cuyahoga Falls, OH; *U.S. Private*, pg. 118
Chapman, Robert H., III, Chm. Bd., Pres., Chief Exec. Officer & Treas.--Inman Mills, Inman, SC; *U.S. Private*, pg. 564
Chapman, Roy, Chief Exec. Officer--Chapman Management Group, Berwyn, PA; *U.S. Private*, pg. 229
Chapman, Steven G., Pres. & Chief Exec. Officer--ITA Group Inc., West Des Moines, IA; *U.S. Private*, pg. 555
Chapman, Wilford, Chm. Bd., Pres. & Chief Exec. Officer--Idaho Supreme Company, Firth, ID; *U.S. Private*, pg. 557
Chapoton, David, Chm. Bd. & Chief Exec. Officer--Tastee Freez International Inc., Utica, MI; *U.S. Private*, pg. 1069
Chappell, Robert E., Chm. Bd. & Chief Exec. Officer--The Penn Mutual Life Insurance Company, Philadelphia, PA; *U.S. Private*, pg. 849
Chappell, Robert E., Chm. Bd. & Chief Exec. Officer--PNC Bank, Philadelphia, PA; *U.S. Public*, pg. 1243
Chareyre, P., Chief Exec. Officer--Sogem, Brussels, Belgium; *Int'l*, pg. 1442
Charles, Barry, Joint Chief Exec. Officer--Eurodis Electron PLC, Reigate, United Kingdom; *Int'l*, pg. 1247
Charlestein, Gary, Chm. Bd. & Chief Exec. Officer--Premier Dental Products Company, King of Prussia, PA; *U.S. Private*, pg. 881
Charlton-Perrin, Geoffrey, Pres. & Chief Exec. Officer--DFM/TATHAM, Chicago, IL; *Int'l*, pg. 601
Charlton, Russell T., Pres. & Chief Exec. Officer--Transamerica Real Estate Information Companies, Dallas, TX; *U.S. Public*, pg. 1630
Charnley, Hal, Pres. & Chief Exec. Officer--Artel Video Systems, Inc., Marlborough, MA; *U.S. Private*, pg. 86
Charpentier, Albert J., Chm. Bd., Pres. & Chief Exec. Officer--Ensoniq, Malvern, PA; *U.S. Private*, pg. 377
Charrier, John P., Jr., Pres. & Chief Exec. Officer--Atlantic Bank, Ocean City, MD; *U.S. Public*, pg. 642
Charron, Paul R., Chm. Bd. & Chief Exec. Officer--Liz Claiborne, Inc., New York, NY; *U.S. Public*, pg. 1005
Charton, Steve, Chm. Bd., Pres & Chief Exec. Officer--Don Miguel Mexican Foods, Inc., Anaheim, CA; *U.S. Private*, pg. 339
Chase, Eric T., Chm. Bd., Pres., Chief Exec. Officer & Founder--QC Optics, Inc., Wilmington, MA; *U.S. Public*, pg. 1345
Chase, Howard E., Pres. & Chief Exec. Officer--Trident Rowand Group, Inc., Somerset, NJ; *U.S. Private*, pg. 1103
Chasen, Melvin, Chm. Bd., Pres. & Chief Exec. Officer--Transmedia Network Inc., Miami, FL; *U.S. Public*, pg. 1631
Chauvin, Dominique, Grp. Chief Exec. Officer-Varity-Kelsey-Hayes--LucasVarity Inc., Buffalo, NY; *Int'l*, pg. 820
Chauvin, Dominique, Grp. Chief Exec. Officer--Varity Kelsey Hayes, Livonia, MI; *Int'l*, pg. 820
Chavez, Lloyd G., Pres. & Chief Exec. Officer--LGC Management, Englewood, CO; *U.S. Private*, pg. 639
Chavez, Robert B., Pres. & Chief Exec. Officer--Etienne Aigner, New York, NY; *U.S. Private*, pg. 384
Chavkin, Wallace, Chm. Bd. & Chief Exec. Officer--Biddle Sawyer Corporation, New York, NY; *U.S. Private*, pg. 142
Checketts, David W., Pres. & Chief Exec. Officer--Madison Square Garden Corporation, New York, NY; *U.S. Public*, pg. 288
Checketts, David W., Pres. & Chief Exec. Officer--Madison Square Garden Network, New York, NY; *U.S. Public*, pg. 288
Cheek, Carl W., Chm. Bd. & Chief Exec. Officer--Specialty Industries, Inc., Red Lion, PA; *U.S. Private*, pg. 1022
Chehebar, J., Pres. & Chief Exec. Officer--Rainbow Apparel Distribution Center, Brooklyn, NY; *U.S. Private*, pg. 907
Chelberg, Bruce S., Chm. Bd. & Chief Exec. Officer--Whitman Corporation, Rolling Meadows, IL; *U.S. Public*, pg. 1766
Chellgren, Paul W., Chm. Bd. & Chief Exec. Officer--Ashland, Inc., Russell, KY; *U.S. Public*, pg. 138
Chemello, Roberto, Co-Chief Exec. Officer & Mng. Dir.--Luxottica Group S.p.A., Agordo, Italy; *Int'l*, pg. 822
Chen, Jeffrey C., Chm. Bd., Pres. & Chief Exec. Officer--General Sciences Corp., Laurel, MD; *U.S. Private*, pg. 976
Chen, Joe, Dr., Pres. & Chief Exec. Officer--Micropolis Corporation, Chatsworth, CA; *U.S. Private*, pg. 742
Chen, Pehong, Dr., Chm. Bd., Pres. & Chief Exec. Officer--BroadVision, Inc., Redwood City, CA; *U.S. Public*, pg. 258
Chen, Sai-Sin, Pres., Chief Exec. Officer & Dir.-Fin.--Seika Electric Co., Ltd., Taipei, Taiwan; *Int'l*, pg. 1218
Chenery, R.J., Chief Exec. Officer--Redland Properties Ltd., Reigate, United Kingdom; *Int'l*, pg. 1091
Cheney, Richard B., Chm. Bd. & Chief Exec. Officer--Halliburton Company, Dallas, TX; *U.S. Public*, pg. 775
Cheney, Richard B., Chm. Bd., Pres. & Chief Exec. Officer--Halliburton Energy Services, Inc., Dallas, TX; *U.S. Public*, *pg. 776*
Cheney, William J., Chm. Bd., Pres. & Chief Exec. Officer--Steadly Company, Carthage, MO; *U.S. Public*, pg. 986
Cheng, L.W., Chief Exec. Officer--Zurich International (Bermuda) Ltd., Hamilton, Bermuda; *Int'l*, pg. 1532
Cheng, Mei-Wei, Pres. & Chief Exec. Officer-G.E. China--General Electric (USA) China Company, Ltd., Hong Kong, Hong Kong; *U.S. Public*, pg. 713
Cheng, Xin, Chm. Bd., Pres. & Chief Exec. Officer--Meret Communications, San Diego, CA; *U.S. Public*, pg. 1233
Cherlouche, Y., Pres. & Chief Exec. Officer--Scitex Corporation Ltd., Holon, Israel; *Int'l*, pg. 644
Chernick, Aubrey G., Chm. Bd. & Chief Exec. Officer--Candle Corporation, Santa Monica, CA; *U.S. Private*, pg. 204
Cherone, Patrick F., Pres. & Chief Exec. Officer--Wisconsin Machine and Tool Corporation, Milwaukee, WI; *U.S. Private*, pg. 1185
Chertkow, Louis, Pres. & Chief Exec. Officer--Elkay Plastics Company, Inc., Los Angeles, CA; *U.S. Private*, pg. 372
Chesterton, James D., Pres. & Chief Exec. Officer--A.W. Chesterton Company, Stoneham, MA; *U.S. Private*, pg. 234
Chestnov, Robert, Pres. & Chief Exec. Officer--Jaclyn, Inc., West New York, NJ; *U.S. Public*, pg. 920
Cheung, Linus W.L., Chief Exec. Officer--Hong Kong Telecommunications Limited, Quarry Bay, Hong Kong; *Int'l*, pg. 247
Chevrier, Robert, Vice Chm., Pres. & Chief Exec. Officer--Westburne Inc., Montreal, Canada; *Int'l*, pg. 1491
Chevrier, Robert, Chm. Bd., Pres. & Chief Exec. Officer--Westburne Industrial Enterprises, Ltd., Ville Saint Laurent, Canada; *Int'l*, pg. 1492
Chiaraluce, Marshall T., Pres. & Chief Exec. Officer--Connecticut Water Service, Inc., Clinton, CT; *U.S. Public*, *pg. 431*
Chiba, Koji, Pres. & Chief Exec. Officer--Duskin Co., Ltd., Osaka, Japan; *Int'l*, pg. 422
Chiba, M., Chm. & Chief Exec. Officer--ING Life Insurance Company, Tokyo, Japan; *Int'l*, pg. 650
Chibata, Ichiro, Ph.D., Chm. Bd., Pres. & Chief Exec. Officer--Tanabe Seiyaku Co., Ltd., Osaka, Japan; *Int'l*, pg. 1354
Chichester, Richard H.L., Chief Exec. Officer & Gen. Mgr.--Select Sires, Inc., Plain City, OH; *U.S. Private*, pg. 982
Chiganze, T.N., Chief Exec.--T A Holdings Limited, Harare, Zimbabwe; *Int'l*, pg. 1334
Child, William H., Chm. Bd. & Chief Exec. Officer--R.C. Willey Home Furnishings, Salt Lake City, UT; *U.S. Public*, *pg. 221*
Childers, Charles E., Chm. Bd., Pres. & Chief Exec. Officer--Potash Corporation of Saskatchewan Inc., Saskatoon, Canada; *Int'l*, pg. 1064
Ching, Ho, Pres. & Chief Exec. Officer--Singapore Technologies Pte. Ltd., Singapore, Singapore; *Int'l*, pg. 1253
Chirichigno, Francesco, Chief Exec. Officer--TELECOM ITALIA S.p.A., Rome, Italy; *Int'l*, pg. 1363
Chisholm, Samuel J., Chm. & Chief Exec. Officer--The Chisholm-Mingo Group, New York, NY; *U.S. Private*, pg. 237
Chiste, R., Pres. & Chief Exec. Officer--Philip Industrial Services Group, Houston, TX; *Int'l*, pg. 1050
Chitayat, Anwar, Chm. Bd. & Chief Exec. Officer--Anorad Corporation, Hauppauge, NY; *U.S. Private*, pg. 75
Chitty, Charles R., Chm. Bd., Pres. & Chief Exec. Officer--IQ Software Corporation, Norcross, GA; *U.S. Public*, pg. 858
Chivari, George A., Pres. & Chief Exec. Officer--Bil Mar Foods, Inc., Zeeland, MI; *U.S. Public*, pg. 1433
Cho, Choong Hoon, Chm. Bd. & Chief Exec. Officer--Korean Airlines Co., Ltd., Seoul, Korea; *Int'l*, pg. 758
Choate, Jerry D., Chm. Bd. & Chief Exec. Officer--The Allstate Corporation, Northbrook, IL; *U.S. Public*, pg. 55
Chocola, J. Christopher, Pres. & Chief Exec. Officer--CTB International Corp., Milford, IN; *U.S. Public*, pg. 284
Choel, Patrick J., Pres. & Chief Exec. Officer--Chesebrough-Pond's USA Co., Greenwich, CT; *Int'l*, pg. 1435
Choi, James K.C., Pres. & Chief Exec. Officer--Renaissance Hotel Group N.V., Central, Hong Kong; *U.S. Public*, pg. 1048
Choi, Sung-Rai, Chm. Bd. & Chief Exec. Officer--Samsung Europe Headquarters, Brentford, United Kingdom; *Int'l*, pg. 1183
Chomeau, Douglas B., Chm. Bd.--The Reliable Life Insurance Company, Webster Groves, MO; *U.S. Public*, pg. 1374
Choo, Yoon H., Dr., Chm. Bd., Pres. & Chief Exec. Officer--National Micronetics, Inc., Kingston, NY; *Int'l*, pg. 1347
Chookaszian, Dennis H., Chm. Bd. & Chief Exec. Officer--Continental Assurance Company, Chicago, IL; *U.S. Private*, pg. 267
Chookaszian, Dennis H., Chm. Bd. & Chief Exec. Officer--CNA Insurance Companies, Chicago, IL; *U.S. Public*, pg. 1010
Choong Kong, Cheong, Chief Exec. Officer--Singapore Airlines, Los Angeles, CA; *Int'l*, pg. 1374
Chopra, Deepak, Chm. Bd., Pres. & Chief Exec. Officer--UDT Sensors, Inc., Hawthorne, CA; *U.S. Private*, pg. 1112
Chopra, Deepak, Chm. Bd., Pres. & Chief Exec. Officer--OSI Systems, Inc., Hawthorne, CA; *U.S. Public*, pg. 1208
Choquette, Paul J., Jr., Chm. Bd. & Chief Exec. Officer--Gilbane Building Company, Providence, RI; *U.S. Private*, pg. 452
Choquette, Pierre, Pres. & Chief Exec. Officer--Methanex Corporation, Vancouver, Canada; *Int'l*, pg. 862
Chorbajian, Herbert G., Chm. Bd., Pres. & Chief Exec. Officer--Albank Financial Corporation, Albany, NY; *U.S. Public*, pg. 36
Chorbajian, Herbert G., Chief Exec. Officer--Albany Savings Bank, Albany, NY; *U.S. Public*, pg. 36
Chormann, Richard F., Chm. Bd., Pres. & Chief Exec. Officer--First of America Bank Corporation, Kalamazoo, MI; *U.S. Public*, pg. 636
Chow, C.K., Chief Exec. Officer--GKN plc, Redditch, United Kingdom; *Int'l*, pg. 534
Chraibi, A., Chm. & Chief Exec. Officer--Al Wataniya, Casablanca, Morocco; *Int'l*, pg. 564
Christ, Clifford C., Pres. & Chief Exec. Officer--NavCom Defense Electronics, Inc., El Monte, CA; *U.S. Private*, pg. 789
Christen, Peter, Pres. & Chief Exec. Officer--Blue Ridge Insurance Co., Simsbury, CT; *Int'l*, pg. 345
Christen, Peter, Chm. Bd., Pres. & Chief Exec. Officer--Blue Ridge Indemnity Co., Simsbury, CT; *Int'l*, pg. 345
Christen, Peter, Chm. Bd. & Chief Exec. Officer--MassWest Insurance Company, West Springfield, MA; *Int'l*, pg. 345
Christensen, David A., Pres. & Chief Exec. Officer--Raven Industries, Inc., Sioux Falls, SD; *U.S. Public*, pg. 1361
Christensen, Gary M., Pres. & Chief Exec. Officer--Pella Corporation, Pella, IA; *U.S. Private*, pg. 848
Christensen, Mahlon, Pres. & Chief Exec. Officer--Muska Electric Company, Roseville, MN; *U.S. Private*, pg. 768
Christian, Betty S., Chm. Bd., Pres. & Chief Exec. Officer--Central Coca-Cola Bottling Company, Inc., Richmond, VA; *U.S. Private*, pg. 222
Christian, Nathan, Pres. & Chief Exec. Officer--Norwest Bank El Paso, N.A., El Paso, TX; *U.S. Public*, pg. 1201
Christianson, Stanley D., Vice Chm. & Chief Exec. Officer--Thrall Enterprises, Inc., Chicago, IL; *U.S. Private*, pg. 1084
Christie, Jane M., Pres. & Chief Exec. Officer--General Automation, Inc., Irvine, CA; *U.S. Public*, pg. 706
Christie, John, Chief Exec. Officer--Hoppe's A Brunswick Company, Coatesville, PA; *U.S. Public*, pg. 266
Christie, Ron, Chief Exec. Officer--Novo Nordisk (Pty) Ltd., Woodmead, South Africa; *Int'l*, pg. 988
Christmas, James W., Pres. & Chief Exec. Officer--KCS Energy Inc., Edison, NJ; *U.S. Public*, pg. 938

Christopher, R., Chm. Bd. & Chief Exec. Officer--IG Autotrim, Inc., Chicago, IL; *Int'l*, pg. 1117
Christopher, Robert A., Chm. Bd. & Chief Exec. Officer--Rieter Automotive North America Inc, Farmington Hills, MI; *Int'l*, pg. 1117
Christopher, Socrates, Chief Oper. Officer--Jacobs Sirrine Engineers, Inc., Greenville, SC; *U.S. Public*, pg. 921
Christopher, Todd, Pres. & Chief Exec. Officer--Physician Sales & Services Inc., Beaumont, TX; *U.S. Public*, pg. 1294
Chryst, Steven L., Pres. & Chief Exec. Officer--Anchor Financial Corporation, Myrtle Beach, SC; *U.S. Public*, pg. 111
Chun-Hak, Ahn, Pres.--Korea Heavy Industries & Construction Co., Ltd., Seoul, Korea; *Int'l*, pg. 758
Chung, Doo-Young, Chief Officer--Ssangyong Singapore PTE., Ltd., Singapore, Singapore; *Int'l*, pg. 1291
Chung, Patrick Wang Shui, Chm. Bd. & Chief Exec. Officer--Johnson Electric Holdings Limited, Tai No, Hong Kong; *Int'l*, pg. 712
Chung, Yong, Chm. Bd. & Chief Exec. Officer--Samsung China Headquarters, Beijing, China; *Int'l*, pg. 1183
Church, John F., Jr., Pres. & Chief Exec. Officer--The Cincinnati Cordage & Paper Company, Cincinnati, OH; *U.S. Private*, pg. 239
Church, Walter G., Sr., Pres. & Chief Exec. Officer--BB&T Savings Bank, SSB, Valdese, NC; *U.S. Public*, pg. 160
Chute, Robert A., Chm. Bd., Pres. & Chief Exec. Officer--The Gage Company, Pittsburgh, PA; *U.S. Private*, pg. 437
Chwang, Ronald, Pres. & Chief Exec. Officer--Acer America Corporation, San Jose, CA; *Int'l*, pg. 22
Ciffone, Donald L., Jr., Pres. & Chief Exec. Officer--EXAR Corporation, Fremont, CA; *U.S. Public*, pg. 597
Cigarran, Thomas G., Chm. Bd., Pres. & Chief Exec. Officer--American Healthcorp Inc., Nashville, TN; *U.S. Public*, pg. 78
Cignarella, Robert, Pres. & Chief Exec. Officer--BMW, Flushing, NY; *U.S. Private*, pg. 107
Cilurzo, Joseph W., Pres. & Chief Exec. Officer--Mobile Technology Inc., Los Angeles, CA; *U.S. Private*, pg. 754
Ciminelli, Frank L., Chief Exec. Officer--Ciminelli Development Company, Inc., Williamsville, NY; *U.S. Private*, pg. 239
Ciminelli, Louis P., Chm. Bd & Chief Exec. Officer--Louis P. Ciminelli Construction Co. Inc., Buffalo, NY; *U.S. Private*, *pg. 239*
Cimino, Jay, Pres. & Chief Exec. Officer--Phil Long Ford, Colorado Springs, CO; *U.S. Private*, pg. 675
Cinnamon, Barry A., Chm. Bd., Pres. & Chief Exec. Officer--Software Publishing Corporation, Fairfield, NJ; *U.S. Public*, pg. 1483
Ciocca, Arthur A., Chm. Bd. & Chief Exec. Officer--The Wine Group, San Francisco, CA; *U.S. Private*, pg. 1182
Circo, Dennis P., Pres. & Chief Exec. Officer--Precision Industries, Omaha, NE; *U.S. Private*, pg. 879
Cirello, John, Exec. V.P. & Pres. & Chief Exec. Officer-Florida Water Services--Minnesota Power, Duluth, MN; *U.S. Public*, pg. 1116
Clack, Ian, Chief Exec. Officer & Mng. Dir.--Burns, Philp & Company Limited, Sydney, Australia; *Int'l*, pg. 236
Cladianos, Pete, Jr., Pres. & Chief Exec. Officer--The Sands Regent, Reno, NV; *U.S. Public*, pg. 1431
Clain, G., Chief Exec. Officer--Gerber International Inc., New York, NY; *U.S. Private*, pg. 448
Clain, G., Pres. & Chief Exec. Officer--J. Gerber & Co. Inc., New York, NY; *U.S. Private*, pg. 449
Clancey, John, Pres. & Chief Exec. Officer--Sea-Land Service, Inc., Charlotte, NC; *U.S. Public*, pg. 284
Claprood, Pierre, Pres. & Chief Exec. Officer--Natrel Inc., Longueuil, Canada; *Int'l*, pg. 32
Clare, John, Grp. Chief Exec.--Dixons Group plc, Hemel Hempstead, United Kingdom,; *Int'l*, pg. 413
Clariond Reyes, Eugenio, Chief Exec. Officer & Sec.--Grupo IMSA S.A. de C.V., Garza Garcia, Mexico; *Int'l*, pg. 575
Clarity, Tim B., Pres. & Chief Exec. Officer--Clarity Coverdale Fury Advertising, Minneapolis, MN; *U.S. Private*, pg. 242
Clark, Cyrus, III, Pres. & Chief Exec. Officer--Cyrus Clark Co., Inc., New York, NY; *U.S. Private*, pg. 242
Clark, David, Chm. Bd., Pres. & Chief Exec. Officer--Homeland Holding Corp., Oklahoma City, OK; *U.S. Public*, pg. 832
Clark, David, Pres. & Chief Exec. Officer--Homeland Stores, Inc., Oklahoma City, OK; *U.S. Public*, pg. 832
Clark, Don, Pres. & Chief Exec. Officer--Mid America Steel, Inc., Fargo, ND; *U.S. Private*, pg. 743
Clark, Donald, Chief Exec. Officer--Dempster Industries Inc., Beatrice, NE; *U.S. Private*, pg. 324
Clark, E. Roger, Chm. Bd., Pres. & Chief Exec. Officer--National Forge Company, Irvine, PA; *U.S. Private*, pg. 783
Clark, Edward, Chm. Bd., Pres. & Chief Exec. Officer--American Seating Company, Grand Rapids, MI; *U.S. Private*, pg. 61
Clark, Fred, Pres. & Chief Exec. Officer--The Clark Group, Mission, Canada; *Int'l*, pg. 296
Clark, Gary, Pres. & Chief Exec. Officer--Indimac Third Party Construction Lending Division, Pasadena, CA; *U.S.* Public, pg. 857
Clark, Gary O., Pres. & Chief Exec. Officer--Commercial National Bank of Berwyn, Berwyn, IL; *U.S. Public*, pg. 379
Clark, George A., Chm. Bd., Pres. & Chief Exec. Officer--Snap-Tite, Inc., Erie, PA; *U.S. Private*, pg. 1010
Clark, Grahame N., Jr., Chm., Pres. & Chief Exec. Officer--BancTec, Inc., Dallas, TX; *U.S. Public*, pg. 176
Clark, Harold J., Chm. Bd. & Chief Exec. Officer--U.S. Aviation Underwriters, Inc., New York, NY; *U.S. Public*, pg. 726
Clark, Jeff C., Pres.--Covington Foods, Inc., Covington, IN; *U.S. Private*, pg. 280
Clark, Joseph T., Pres. & Chief Exec. Officer--Response Oncology, Inc., Memphis, TN; *U.S. Public*, pg. 1449
Clark, Katherine K., Pres. & Chief Exec. Officer--Landmark Systems Corporation, Vienna, VA; *U.S. Private*, pg. 649
Clark, Kevin, Chief Exec. Officer--Poppe Tyson, New York, NY; *U.S. Public*, pg. 1642
Clark, L. Hill, Pres. & Chief Oper. Officer--Crane Co., Stamford, CT; *U.S. Public*, pg. 456
Clark, R.M., Chief Exec. Officer--Zurich International (Belgique) S.A., Brussels, Belgium; *Int'l*, pg. 1532
Clark, Richard W., Chm. Bd. & Chief Exec. Officer--Dick Clark Productions, Inc., Burbank, CA; *U.S. Public*, pg. 382
Clark, Robert W., Pres. & Chief Exec. Officer--Shenandoah Life Insurance Company, Roanoke, VA; *U.S. Private*, pg. 992
Clark, Stephen S., Pres. & Chief Exec. Officer--Dwyer Instruments Inc., Michigan City, IN; *U.S. Private*, pg. 350
Clark, Steven, Pres. & Chief Exec. Officer--Taco Cabana, San Antonio, TX; *U.S. Public*, pg. 1559
Clark, Thomas B., Pres. & Chief Exec. Officer--Alltrista Corporation, Muncie, IN; *U.S. Public*, pg. 56
Clark, Thomas L., Pres. & Chief Exec. Officer--Carver Federal Savings Bank, New York, NY; *U.S. Public*, pg. 310
Clark, William P., Chm. Bd. & Chief Exec. Officer--Wall Colmonoy Corp., Madison Heights, MI; *U.S. Private*, pg. 1148
Clark, William S., Pres. & Chief Exec. Officer--First Bank of Stuart, Stuart, VA; *U.S. Public*, pg. 1039
Clarke, D.C., Chief Exec. Officer--MLC Limited, Sydney, Australia; *Int'l*, pg. 806
Clarke, David H., Deputy Chm. & Chief Exec. Officer--Hanson North America, Woodbridge, NJ; *Int'l*, pg. 593
Clarke, David H., Chm. Bd. & Chief Exec. Officer--U.S. Industries, Inc., Iselin, NJ; *U.S. Public*, pg. 1683
Clarke, J.W., Chief Exec. Officer--Monier Inc., Orange, CA; *Int'l*, pg. 1091
Clarke, Jeffrey, Chm. Bd., Pres. & Chief Exec. Officer--Coho Energy, Inc., Dallas, TX; *U.S. Public*, pg. 396
Clarke, Kenneth R., Pres. & Chief Exec. Officer--Trilon Financial Corp., Toronto, Canada; *Int'l*, pg. 434
Clarke, Robert F., Chm. Bd., Pres. & Chief Exec. Officer--Hawaiian Electric Industries, Inc., Honolulu, HI; *U.S. Public*, pg. 799
Clarke, Roger C., Chief Exec. Officer, V.P. & Exec. Asst. to Pres.--LucasVarity Inc., Buffalo, NY; *Int'l*, pg. 820
Clary, John P., Pres. & Chief Exec. Officer--Modcomp, Fort Lauderdale, FL; *U.S. Public*, pg. 283
Clausen, Dick, Chm. Bd., Pres. & Chief Exec. Officer--Verbatim Tape Corporation, San Diego, CA; *Int'l*, pg. 872
Clausen, Jorgen M., Pres. & Chief Exec. Officer--Danfoss A/S, Nordborg, Denmark; *Int'l*, pg. 376
Clay, John W., Jr., Chm. Bd., Pres. & Chief Exec. Officer--SunTrust Banks of Tennessee, Inc., Nashville, TN; *U.S. Public*, pg. 1538
Clay, John W., Jr., Chm. & Chief Exec. Officer--SunTrust Bank, Nashville, N.A., Nashville, TN; *U.S. Public*, pg. 1538
Clay, Larry D., Pres. & Chief Exec. Officer--Pacific Coast Producers, Lodi, CA; *U.S. Private*, pg. 830
Clayton, Donald W., Chm. Bd. & Chief Exec. Officer--Howell Corporation, Houston, TX; *U.S. Public*, pg. 843
Clayton, F.O., Pres. & Chief Exec. Officer--Shand Mining Inc., Indianapolis, IN; *Int'l*, pg. 281
Clayton, James L., Chm. Bd. & Chief Exec. Officer--Clayton Homes, Inc., Knoxville, TN; *U.S. Public*, pg. 382
Cleary, Martin J., Pres. & Chief Oper. Officer--The Richard E. Jacobs Group, Westlake, OH; *U.S. Private*, pg. 580
Cleary, Robert T., Chief Exec. Officer, Treas. & Sec.--KineticSystems Corporation, Lockport, IL; *U.S. Private*, pg. 620
Cleave, James H., Pres. & Chief Exec. Officer--HSBC Americas, Buffalo, NY; *Int'l*, pg. 580
Cleave, James H., Pres. & Chief Exec. Officer--Marine Midland Bank, Buffalo, NY; *Int'l*, pg. 581
Cleaver, A. B., Chief Exec. Officer--IBM United Kingdom Holdings Limited, Portsmouth, United Kingdom; *U.S. Public*, pg. 897
Cleberg, Harry C., Pres. & Chief Exec. Officer--Farmland Industries, Inc., Kansas City, MO; *U.S. Private*, pg. 395
Clegg, Jack, Chm. Bd., Pres. & Chief Exec. Officer--Nobel Education Dynamics, Inc., Media, PA; *U.S. Public*, pg. 1185
Cleghorn, John E., Chm. Bd. & Chief Exec. Officer--Royal Bank of Canada, Toronto, Canada; *Int'l*, pg. 1131
Clemens, Jack S., Pres. & Chief Exec. Officer--Clemens Markets Inc., Kulpsville, PA; *U.S. Private*, pg. 245
Clemens, Philip A., Pres. & Chief Exec. Officer--Hatfield Quality Meats, Hatfield, PA; *U.S. Private*, pg. 510
Clemens, Richard E., Pres. & Chief Exec. Officer--The Monarch Machine Tool Company, Sidney, OH; *U.S. Public*, pg. 1123
Clement, James B., Chm. Bd. & Chief Exec. Officer--Offshore Logistics, Inc., Lafayette, LA; *U.S. Public*, pg. 1212
Clement, James W., Pres. & Chief Exec. Officer--Bank of Carroll, Hillsville, VA; *U.S. Public*, pg. 1038
Clements, Edward B., Pres. & Chief Exec. Officer--Clements Foods Co., Oklahoma City, OK; *U.S. Private*, pg. 245
Clements, Ronald L., Chief Exec. & Oper. Officer--Belden & Blake Corporation, Canton, OH; *U.S. Private*, pg. 1078
Clemons, V. Gordon, Chm. Bd., Pres. & Chief Exec. Officer--CorVel Corporation, Irvine, CA; *U.S. Public*, pg. 451
Clenenti, D.C., Joint Chief Exec. Officer--Kleinwort Benson Ltd., London, United Kingdom; *Int'l*, pg. 420
Clerici, Paolo, Chm. Bd. & Chief Exec. Officer--Coeclerici Group, Genoa, Italy; *Int'l*, pg. 303
Clerval, Pierre, Pres. & Chief Exec. Officer--Hutchenson Seal Corporation, Downey, CA; *U.S. Private*, pg. 550
Clerval, Pierre, Pres. & Chief Exec. Officer--Stillman Seal, Carlsbad, CA; *U.S. Private*, pg. 550
Cleveland, James R., Jr., Pres. & Chief Exec. Officer--Cleveland Group, Inc., Atlanta, GA; *U.S. Private*, pg. 246
Cleveland, Jay W., Sr., Pres. & Chief Exec. Officer--Cleveland Brothers Equipment Co., Inc., Harrisburg, PA; *U.S. Private*, pg. 245
Clevy, W. Michael, Pres. & Chief Exec. Officer--International Comfort Products, Franklin, TN; *U.S. Public*, pg. 898
Click, James, Chief Exec. Officer & Partner--Tuttle-Click Automobile Group, Irvine, CA; *U.S. Private*, pg. 1111
Clifford, John, Pres. & Chief Exec. Officer--Clifford Paper Inc., Upper Saddle River, NJ; *U.S. Private*, pg. 246
Cliggott, Richard T., Sr., Chief Exec. Officer--Cliggott Publishing, Greenwich, CT; *U.S. Private*, pg. 246
Cline, Robert S., Chm. Bd. & Chief Exec. Officer--Airborne Freight Corporation, Seattle, WA; *U.S. Public*, pg. 32
Clinton, Stephen P., Chief Oper. Officer & Sr. V.P.--Hayes, Seay, Mattern & Mattern, Inc., Roanoke, VA; *U.S. Private*, pg. 513
Clode, P.M., Pres. & Chief Exec. Officer--Grosvenor Marketing Ltd., Paramus, NJ; *Int'l*, pg. 92
Clodfelter, Gary N., Pres. & Chief Exec. Officer--White Electrical Construction Co., Atlanta, GA; *U.S. Private*, pg. 1172
Close, Allyn D., Pres., Chief Exec. Officer & Mgr.-Sls. & Mktg.--Interpacific Investors Services, Seattle, WA; *U.S. Private*, pg. 572
Close, Carl Zane, Pres. & Chief Exec. Officer--Cerprobe Corporation, Gilbert, AZ; *U.S. Public*, pg. 332
Clothier, Richard J., Chief Exec. Officer--Dalgety Plc, London, United Kingdom; *Int'l*, pg. 376
Cloud, Ronald E., Pres. & Chief Exec. Officer--E.V. Roberts & Associates, Inc., Culver City, CA; *U.S. Private*, pg. 935
Cloud, Stephen R., Pres. & Chief Exec. Officer--IBT, Inc., Merriam, KS; *U.S. Private*, pg. 553
Cloues, Edward B., II, Chm. Bd. & Chief Exec. Officer--K-Tron International, Inc., Pitman, NJ; *U.S. Public*, pg. 938
Clough, Stephen K., Pres. & Chief Exec. Officer--Kaydon Corporation, Clearwater, FL; *U.S. Public*, pg. 945
Clowe, Tom, Pres. & Chief Exec. Officer--Missouri Gas Energy, Kansas City, MO; *U.S. Public*, pg. 1491
Cluss, Chris, Pres. & Chief Exec. Officer--O.C. Cluss Lumber Co., Uniontown, PA; *U.S. Private*, pg. 248
Clutterbuck, Howard C., Pres. & Chief Exec. Officer--American Journal of Nursing Company, New York, NY; *Int'l*, pg. 1513
Coady, Todd M., Chm. Bd., Pres. & Chief Exec. Officer--Hicks Oil-Hicks Gas, Inc., Roberts, IL; *U.S. Private*, pg. 526
Coakley, P.J., Chief Exec. Officer--Best-Wood Limited, Auckland, New Zealand; *U.S. Public*, pg. 905
Coale, William, Chm. Bd. & Chief Exec. Officer--Alcom Printing Group, Inc., Bethlehem, PA; *U.S. Private*, pg. 33
Coan, Gaylord O., Chief Exec. Officer--Gold Kist, Inc., Atlanta, GA; *U.S. Private*, pg. 459
Coape-Arnold, D.A., Chm. Bd. & Chief Exec. Officer--Dunhill Personnel System, Inc., Hauppauge, NY; *U.S. Public*, pg. 1746
Coates, Jon P., Pres. & Chief Exec. Officer--Key Bank of Colorado, Fort Collins, CO; *U.S. Public*, pg. 954
Coates, Vincent J., Chm. Bd. & Chief Exec. Officer--Nanometrics Incorporated, Sunnyvale, CA; *U.S. Public*, pg. 1151
Coath, J. Douglas, Jr., Pres. & Chief Exec. Officer--Frank W. Winne & Son, Inc., Philadelphia, PA; *U.S. Private*, pg. 1183
Coatney, Doyle, Pres. & Chief Exec. Officer--Acme Truck Line, Inc., Harvey, LA; *U.S. Private*, pg. 14
Cobb, Timothy S., Chm. Bd., Pres. & Chief Exec. Officer--Salient 3 Communications, Inc., Reading, PA; *U.S. Public*, pg. 1429
Coccari, Greg, Pres. & Chief Exec. Officer--Teleflora, LLC, Los Angeles, CA; *U.S. Private*, pg. 941
Cocchiola, Mark, Chm. Bd., Pres. & Chief Exec. Officer--Suprema Specialties, Inc., Paterson, NJ; *U.S. Public*, pg. 1541
Cocchiola, Mark, Chm. Bd., Pres. & Chief Exec. Officer--Suprema Specialties Northeast, Inc., Ogdensburg, NY; *U.S. Public*, pg. 1541
Cocheteux, Jean-Bernard, Chm. Bd. & Chief Exec. Officer--Microturbo Division, Toulouse, France; *Int'l*, pg. 786
Cochran, John R., Chm. Bd. & Chief Exec. Officer--FirstMerit Corporation, Akron, OH; *U.S. Public*, pg. 646
Cochran, Robert P., Pres. & Chief Exec. Officer--Financial Security Assurance Holdings Ltd., New York, NY; *U.S. Public*, pg. 622
Cochran, Russell G., Chm. Bd., Pres. & Chief Exec. Officer--United Missouri Bank of Joplin, Joplin, MO; *U.S. Public*, pg. 1655
Cochrane, Jr., Haywood D., Pres. & Chief Exec. Officer--Allied Clinical Laboratories, Inc., Nashville, TN; *U.S. Public*, pg. 973
Cocker, Victor, Grp. Chief Exec.--Severn Trent Plc, Birmingham, United Kingdom; *Int'l*, pg. 1225
Cocker, Victor, Group Chief Exec.--Severn Trent Water Ltd., Birmingham, United Kingdom; *Int'l*, pg. 1225
Cockwell, Jack L., Pres. & Chief Exec. Officer--EdperBrascan Corporation, Toronto, Canada; *Int'l*, pg. 433
Cocquyt, Marie-Jose, Pres. & Chief Exec. Officer--Kompass International Neuenschwander SA, Cruet, France; *Int'l*, pg. 745
Cody, John T., Jr., Pres. & Chief Oper. Officer-Domestic--JC Penney Company, Inc., Plano, TX; *U.S. Public*, pg. 916
Coe, Dennis R., Pres. & Chief. Exec. Officer--Lois/EJL Los Angeles, Los Angeles, CA; *U.S. Public*, pg. 1011
Coelho, J.M., Chief Exec. Officer--Zurich Life Insurance Company, Lisbon, Portugal; *Int'l*, pg. 1530
Coelho, J.M., Chief Exec. Officer--Companhia de Seguros Metropole S.A., Lisbon, Portugal; *Int'l*, pg. 1531
Coffeng, Hans, Pres. & Chief Exec. Officer--Fremont Indemnity Corp., Santa Monica, CA; *U.S. Public*, pg. 681
Coffin, Sarah R., Chm. Bd. & Chief Exec. Officer--Foster Products Corporation, Minneapolis, MN; *U.S. Public*, pg. 686
Coffin, Sarah R., Chief Exec. Officer--TEC Incorporated, Palatine, IL; *U.S. Public*, pg. 687

Coffman, C. Morris, Chm. Bd., Pres. & Chief Exec. Officer--Farmers Bank & Trust Co., Madisonville, KY; *U.S. Public, pg. 1217*
Coffman, Vance D., Vice Chm. & Chief Exec. Officer--Lockheed Martin Corporation, Bethesda, MD; *U.S. Public*, pg. 1006
Cogan, Marshall S., Chm. Bd. & Chief Exec. Officer--Trace International Holdings, Inc., New York, NY; *U.S. Private*, pg. 1094
Cogan, Marshall S., Chm. Bd. & Chief Exec. Officer--United Auto Group, Inc., New York, NY; *U.S. Private*, pg. 1095
Coggin, Luther, Pres. & Chief Exec. Officer--Coggin Automotive Group, Jacksonville, FL; *U.S. Private*, pg. 250
Cohan, Norman H., Pres. & Chief Exec. Officer--Security Plastics, Inc., Hialeah, FL; *U.S. Private*, pg. 981
Cohen, Alan, Chm. Bd., Pres. & Chief Exec. Officer--Finish Line, Inc., Indianapolis, IN; *U.S. Public*, pg. 623
Cohen, Albert D., Chm. Bd. & Chief Exec. Officer--Gendis Inc., Winnipeg, Canada; *Int'l*, pg. 542
Cohen, Arthur, Chm. Bd. & Chief Exec. Officer--The Arlen Corporation, New York, NY; *U.S. Public*, pg. 131
Cohen, Barney J., Chief Exec. Officer--Valley Record Distributors, Inc., Woodland, CA; *U.S. Private*, pg. 1132
Cohen, Brian, Chm. & Chief Exec. Officer--Technology Solutions Inc., New York, NY; *U.S. Private*, pg. 1157
Cohen, Donald, Chm. Bd., Pres., Chief Exec. Officer & Chief Fin. Officer--Tool King, Denver, CO; *U.S. Private*, pg. 1091
Cohen, Edward E., Chm. Bd. & Chief Exec. Officer--Resource America, Inc., Philadelphia, PA; *U.S. Public*, pg. 1382
Cohen, Gordon S., Chm. Bd. & Chief Exec. Officer--Customedix Corporation, Wallingford, CT; *U.S. Private*, pg. 298
Cohen, James, Pres. & Chief Exec. Officer--Hudson County News Company, North Bergen, NJ; *U.S. Private*, pg. 545
Cohen, Joseph M., Chm. Bd. & Chief Exec. Officer--Cowen & Company, New York, NY; *U.S. Private*, pg. 280
Cohen, Leonard, Pres. & Chief Exec. Officer--Kelly, Scott And Madison, Inc., Chicago, IL; *U.S. Private*, pg. 613
Cohen, Lewis M., Pres. & Chief Exec. Officer--Acme Canvas Co., Inc., Malden, MA; *U.S. Private*, pg. 13
Cohen, Louis D., Pres. & Chief Exec. Officer--Sheplers, Inc., Wichita, KS; *U.S. Private*, pg. 993
Cohen, Maryjo, Pres., Chief Exec. Officer & Chief Fin. Officer--National Presto Industries, Inc., Eau Claire, WI; *U.S. Public*, pg. 1159
Cohen, Peter J., Chm. Bd., Pres. & Chief Exec. Officer--Periphonics Corp., Bohemia, NY; *U.S. Public*, pg. 1278
Cohen, Ron, Chm. & Chief Exec. Officer--McDonald's Restaurants of Canada Ltd., Toronto, Canada; *U.S. Public*, pg. 1069
Cohen, Russell, Chm. Bd. & Co-Chief Exec. Officer--Carlyle & Co. Jewelers, Greensboro, NC; *U.S. Private*, pg. 213
Cohen, Steven, Pres. & Chief Exec. Officer--Hasselblad USA, Inc., Fairfield, NJ; *Int'l*, pg. 1468
Cohen, Sylvan M., Chm. Bd. & Chief Exec. Officer--Pennsylvania Real Estate Investment Trust, Fort Washington, PA; *U.S. Public*, pg. 1272
Cohen, W.C., Jr., Chief Exec. Officer--Insurance Management Associates, Wichita, KS; *U.S. Private*, pg. 565
Cohn, Jeffrey, Chief Exec. Officer & Pres.--Decorative Crafts, Inc., Greenwich, CT; *U.S. Private*, pg. 320
Cohn, Mark A., Chm. Bd. & Chief Exec. Officer--Damark International, Inc., Minneapolis, MN; *U.S. Public*, pg. 478
Cohn, Robert, Chm. Bd. & Chief Exec. Officer--Octel Messaging Division, Milpitas, CA; *U.S. Public*, pg. 1017
Coil, Lawrence, Pres. & Chief Exec. Officer--Pinkerton & Laws Inc., Atlanta, GA; *U.S. Private*, pg. 865
Cojuangco, Antonio, Pres. & Chief Exec. Officer--Philippine Long Distance Telephone Company, Manila, Philippines; *Int'l*, pg. 1051
Coker, Charles W., Chm. Bd. & Chief Exec. Officer--Sonoco Products Company, Hartsville, SC; *U.S. Public*, pg. 1485
Colaccino, Frank, Pres. & Chief Exec. Officer--Dairy Mart, Inc., Enfield, CT; *U.S. Public*, pg. 476
Colangelo, Larry A., Pres. & Chief Exec. Officer--SPD Technologies, Philadelphia, PA; *U.S. Private*, pg. 957
Colaninno, Roberto, Chief Exec. Officer & Mng. Dir.--Olivetti SpA, Turin, Italy; *Int'l*, pg. 1002
Colaou, Hadzini, Chief Exec. Officer & Chief Fin. Officer--CCF Athens, Athens, Greece; *Int'l*, pg. 342
Colby, Donald L., Pres. & Chief Exec. Officer--BNY Holdings (New Jersey) Corp., West Paterson, NJ; *U.S. Public*, pg. 178
Cole, Alan, Chief Exec. Officer--Transport Development Group Plc, London, United Kingdom; *Int'l*, pg. 1418
Cole, Christopher C., Chief Exec. Officer--The Buschman Co., Cincinnati, OH; *U.S. Private*, pg. 188
Cole, Crawford, Pres. & Chief Exec. Officer--West Marine, Inc., Watsonville, CA; *U.S. Public*, pg. 1756
Cole, Gregory W., Pres. & Chief Exec. Officer--Inland Detroit Diesel Allison Co., Butler, WI; *U.S. Private*, pg. 564
Cole, James D., Chm. Bd., Pres., & Chief Exec. Officer--Newpark Resources, Inc., Metairie, LA; *U.S. Public*, pg. 1179
Cole, Jeffrey A., Chm. Bd. & Chief Exec. Officer--Cole National Corporation, Cleveland, OH; *U.S. Public*, pg. 396
Cole, Jeffrey N., Chief Exec. Officer--Ferrous Processing & Trading Co., Detroit, MI; *U.S. Private*, pg. 402
Cole, Lee, Chm. Bd. & Chief Exec. Officer--Calavo Growers of California, Santa Ana, CA; *U.S. Private*, pg. 199
Cole, Louis C., Chm. Bd., Pres. & Chief Exec. Officer--Legato Systems, Inc., Palo Alto, CA; *U.S. Public*, pg. 984
Cole, R.D., Chm. Bd., Pres. & Chief Exec. Officer--The Dosco Corp., Abingdon, VA; *Int'l*, pg. 124
Cole, Richard E., Chm. Bd. & Chief Exec. Officer--Chartwell Re Corporation, Stamford, CT; *U.S. Public*, pg. 336
Coleman, Debi, Chm. Bd., Pres. & Chief Exec. Officer--Merix Corporation, Forest Grove, OR; *U.S. Public*, pg. 1096
Coleman, Donald A., Pres. & Chief Exec. Officer--Don Coleman Advertising, Inc., Southfield, MI; *U.S. Private*, pg. 251
Coleman, James W., Jr., Chm. & Chief Exec. Officer--Selective Technical Administrative Services, Inc., Branchville, NJ; *U.S. Public*, pg. 1456
Coleman, Jim, Pres. & Chief Exec. Officer--Coleman Cable Systems, Inc., North Chicago, IL; *U.S. Public*, pg. 968
Coleman, Lonzo, Chm. Bd., Pres. & Chief Exec. Officer--ColeJon Corporation, Cleveland, OH; *U.S. Private*, pg. 251
Coleman, P. Michael, Chm. Bd., Pres. & Chief Exec. Officer--Integrity Incorporated, Mobile, AL; *U.S. Public*, pg. 886
Coleman, Steve, Chief Exec. Officer--Pergament Home Centers, Inc., Melville, NY; *U.S. Private*, pg. 853
Coleon, Yves, Pres. & Chief Exec. Officer--Lalique North America, Carlstadt, NJ; *Int'l*, pg. 797
Coley, Thomas H., Chm. Bd. & Chief Exec. Officer--South Trust Bank of Georgia, Atlanta, GA; *U.S. Public*, pg. 1492
Collantes, Francisco Javier Salas, Chm. & Chief Exec. Officer--Sepi, Madrid, Spain; *Int'l*, pg. 1224
Collette, Craig D., Pres. & Chief Exec. Officer--California State Bank-La Habra, La Habra, CA; *U.S. Public*, pg. 294
Collings, Charles L., Chief Exec. Officer--Raley's & Bel Air, West Sacramento, CA; *U.S. Private*, pg. 907
Collins, Bert, Pres. & Chief Exec. Officer--North Carolina Mutual Life Insurance Co., Durham, NC; *U.S. Private*, pg. 804
Collins, C.A., Pres. & Chief Exec. Officer--Adams Rite Sabre International, Glendale, CA; *U.S. Private*, pg. 1203
Collins, Charles F., Pres. & Chief Exec. Officer--Industrial Maintenance Overflow Corporation, Fletcher, NC; *U.S. Private*, pg. 561
Collins, Christopher C., Chm. Bd., Pres. & Chief Exec. Officer--Nuttall Gear Corporation, Niagara Falls, NY; *U.S.* Private, pg. 809
Collins, Don L., Chm. Bd., Pres., Chief Exec. & Oper. Officer--Collins Industries, Inc., Hutchinson, KS; *U.S. Public*, pg. 399
Collins, Duane E., Pres. & Chief Exec. Officer--Parker Hannifin Corporation, Cleveland, OH; *U.S. Public*, pg. 1259
Collins, Francis A., Pres. & Chief Exec. Officer--The Imperial Electric Company, Akron, OH; *U.S. Private*, pg. 598
Collins, Joseph J., Chm. Bd. & Chief Exec. Officer--Time Warner Cable, Stamford, CT; *U.S. Public*, pg. 1610
Collins, Keith, Chief Exec. Officer--ChubbHealth New York/New Jersey, New York, NY; *U.S. Public*, pg. 360
Collins, Kevin, Chief Oper. Officer & V.P.--Bill Collins Ford Inc., Louisville, KY; *U.S. Private*, pg. 253
Collins, Marshall J., Jr., Pres. & Chief Exec. Officer--BI-LO Inc., Greenville, SC; *Int'l*, pg. 749
Collins, Michael J., Dr., Pres. & Chief Exec. Officer--CEM Corporation, Matthews, NC; *U.S. Public*, pg. 277
Collins, Paul, Chief Exec.--Brierley Investments Limited, Wellington, New Zealand; *Int'l*, pg. 215
Collins, Richard B., Pres. & Chief Exec. Officer--First Massachusettes Bank, N.A., Worcester, MA; *U.S. Public, pg. 187*
Collins, Ron, Pres. & Chief Exec. Officer--Stone Fort National Bank, Nacogdoches, Nacogdoches, TX; *U.S. Public*, pg. 630
Collins, Russell A., Pres. & Chief Exec. Officer--Fattal & Collins (F&C), Marina Del Rey, CA; *U.S. Public*, pg. 765
Collins, Timothy C., Chief Exec. Officer & Sr. Mng. Dir.--Ripplewood Holdings L.L.C., New York, NY; *U.S. Private, pg. 931*
Collins, Vernon E., Chm. Bd., Pres. & Chief Exec. Officer--Bliss-Salem, Inc., Salem, OH; *U.S. Private*, pg. 149
Collins, William L., III, Pres. & Chief Exec. Officer--Metrocall, Inc., Alexandria, VA; *U.S. Public*, pg. 1102
Collman, Nicholas J., Chm. Bd., Pres. & Chief Exec. Officer--Collman Graphics, Inc., Baltimore, MD; *U.S. Private*, pg. 253
Collomb, Bertrand, Chm. Bd. & Chief Exec. Officer--Lafarge S.A., Paris, France; *Int'l*, pg. 788
Colman, James A., Pres. & Chief Exec. Officer--Acme Mills Co. Inc., Detroit, MI; *U.S. Private*, pg. 13
Colman, John, Chief Exec. Officer--Mother Earth News, New York, NY; *U.S. Private*, pg. 1056
Colonna, Peter, Pres., Chief Exec. Officer & Mng. Dir.--Colonna Bros., Inc., North Bergen, NJ; *U.S. Private*, pg. 254
Coltart, Michael, Pres. & Chief Exec. Officer--Andes Candies Inc., Delavan, WI; *U.S. Private*, pg. 163
Colton, Bruce L., Pres. & Chief Exec. Officer--Domestic Uniform Rental Co., Farmington Hills, MI; *U.S. Private*, pg. 338
Colwell, J. Bart, Pres. & Chief Exec. Officer--First State Bank, Brazil, IN; *U.S. Public*, pg. 634
Combs, William H., III, Pres. & Chief Exec. Officer--Tamaqua Cable Products Corp., Schuylkill Haven, PA; *Int'l*, pg. 417
Comer, Clarence C., Pres. & Chief Exec. Officer--Southdown, Inc., Houston, TX; *U.S. Public*, pg. 1488
Comment, Jeffrey W., Chm. Bd., Pres. & Chief Exec. Officer--Helzberg's Diamond Shops, Inc., Kansas City, MO; *U.S. Public*, pg. 220
Commonte, Sheridan W.A., Joint Chief Exec.--TT Group PLC, Surrey, United Kingdom; *Int'l*, pg. 1344
Comoli, Jean-Dominique, Chm. Bd. & Chief Exec. Officer--SEITA, Societe Nationale D'Exploitation Industrielle des Tabacs et des Allumettes, Paris, France; *Int'l*, pg. 1219
Compton, Franklin, Pres., Chief Exec. Officer & New Bus. Contact--Sawyer Riley Compton Inc., Atlanta, GA; *U.S. Private*, pg. 969
Compton, James, Pres. & Chief Exec. Officer--Stewart Smith Southeast, Inc., Tampa, FL; *Int'l*, pg. 1508
Compton, Thomas A., Pres. & Chief Exec. Officer--EnviroSource-International Mill Service, Inc., Horsham, PA; *U.S. Public*, pg. 587
Compton, William, Chm. Bd. & Chief Exec. Officer--Tropical Sportswear International, Tampa, FL; *U.S. Private*, pg. 1105
Compton, William F., Pres. & Chief Oper. Officer--Trans World Airlines, Inc., Saint Louis, MO; *U.S. Public*, pg. 1629
Comstock, Harwood B., Chm. Bd. & Pres.--Pratt-Read Corporation, Bridgeport, CT; *U.S. Private*, pg. 879
Conant, Victor, Pres. & Chief Exec. Officer--Nightingale-Conant Corp., Niles, IL; *U.S. Private*, pg. 799
Concannon, Bill, Chief Exec. Officer-Corp. Services & Exec. V.P.--Trammell Crow Company, Dallas, TX; *U.S. Public*, pg. 1628
Conde, Cristobal I., Grp. Chief Exec. Officer-SunGard Trading Systems--SunGard Data Systems Inc., Wayne, PA; *U.S. Public*, pg. 1534
Condit, Philip M., Chm. Bd., Pres. & Chief Exec. Officer--The Boeing Company, Seattle, WA; *U.S. Public*, pg. 239
Condo, Patrick C., Pres. & Chief Exec. Officer--Excalibur Technologies Corporation, Vienna, VA; *U.S. Public*, pg. 598
Condron, Christopher M., Chief Exec. Officer--The Dreyfus Corporation, New York, NY; *U.S. Public*, pg. 1085
Conefry, John J., Jr., Chm. Bd. & Chief Exec. Officer--Long Island Bancorp, Inc., Melville, NY; *U.S. Public*, pg. 1013
Conforti, Fred, Pres. & Chief Exec. Officer--Pittway Systems Technology Grp., Naperville, IL; *U.S. Public*, pg. 1306
Congdon, Earl E., Chm. Bd. & Chief Exec. Officer--Old Dominion Freight Line, Inc., High Point, NC; *U.S. Public*, pg. 1216
Conklin, Charles E., Pres. & Chief Exec. Officer--Conklin Instrument Corporation, Pleasant Valley, NY; *U.S. Private*, pg. 263
Conley, Joseph H., Jr., Pres. & Chief Exec. Officer--Cook Moving Systems, Inc., Buffalo, NY; *U.S. Private*, pg. 272
Conley, Michael E., Pres. & Chief Exec. Officer--General Life Insurance Company Of America, Edwardsville, IL; *U.S. Private*, pg. 443
Conlon, Denis, Chief Exec. Officer--CRC Industries, Inc., Warminster, PA; *U.S. Private*, pg. 138
Conlon, Harry B., Chm. Bd., Pres. & Chief Exec. Officer--Associated Banc-Corp, Green Bay, WI; *U.S. Public*, pg. 140
Connell, William F., Chm. Bd. & Chief Exec. Officer--Connell Limited Partnership, Boston, MA; *U.S. Private*, pg. 264
Connelly, Jerry, Pres. & Chief Exec. Officer--Pfaudler, Inc., Rochester, NY; *U.S. Public*, pg. 1393
Connelly, John E., Chm. Bd. & Chief Exec. Officer--President Casinos, Inc., Saint Louis, MO; *U.S. Public*, pg. 1323
Connelly, Thomas S., Chm. Bd., Pres., Chief Exec. Officer--Connelly Containers, Inc., Bala Cynwyd, PA; *U.S. Private*, pg. 264
Connolley, John, Chm. Bd. & Chief Exec. Officer--G.E. American Communications, Inc., Princeton, NJ; *U.S. Public*, pg. 711
Connolly, Daryl, Pres. & Chief Exec. Officer--HCO Energy Ltd., Calgary, Canada; *U.S. Public*, pg. 782
Connor, Alan M., Pres. & Chief Exec. Officer--Cornerstone Real Estate, Hartford, CT; *U.S. Private*, pg. 712
Connor, John T., Chm. Bd. & Chief Exec. Officer--Transcrypt International, Lincoln, NE; *U.S. Public*, pg. 1630
Connors, Charles W., Chm. Bd. & Chief Exec. Officer--Magneco/Metrel, Inc., Addison, IL; *U.S. Private*, pg. 695
Connors, James H., Chief Exec. Officer--Plastics Manufacturing Company, Dallas, TX; *U.S. Public*, pg. 1530
Connors, James J., Pres. & Chief Exec. Officer--Century Products Co., Macedonia, OH; *U.S. Private*, pg. 226
Connors, John M., Jr., Chief Exec. Officer--Hill, Holliday, Connors, Cosmopulos, Inc., Boston, MA; *U.S. Private*, pg. 529
Conomikes, John G., Pres. & Co-Chief Exec. Officer--Hearst-Argyle Television Incorporated, New York, NY; *U.S. Private*, pg. 516
Conrad, Carlton J., Jr., Pres. & Chief Exec. Officer--E.H. Titchener & Company, Binghamton, NY; *U.S. Private*, pg. 1089
Conrad, William C., Pres. & Chief Exec. Officer--First American Capital Management, Inc., Newport Beach, CA; *U.S. Public*, pg. 625
Conrades, George H., Chm. Bd., Pres. & Chief Exec. Officer--GTE Internetworking, Cambridge, MA; *U.S. Public*, pg. 696
Conroy, Michael, Co-Chm. & Chief Exec. Officer--FCA!BMZ, Suresnes, France; *Int'l*, pg. 469
Constable, P.S., Chief Exec. Officer--Black Horse Agencies Ltd., Hatfield, United Kingdom, *Int'l*, pg. 813
Constantin, Gus, Chm. Bd., Pres. & Chief Exec. Officer--Phoenix American Incorporated, San Rafael, CA; *U.S. Private*, pg. 862
Conte, Leo, Pres. & Chief Exec. Officer--Montebello Brands Inc., Baltimore, MD; *U.S. Private*, pg. 758
Contino, Frederick, Chief Exec. Officer--Swing-N-Slide Corp., Janesville, WI; *U.S. Public*, pg. 1543
Conway, Christopher J., Chm. Bd. & Chief Exec. Officer--Mentor Corporation, Santa Barbara, CA; *U.S. Public*, pg. 1086
Conway, E. Virgul, Chm. & Chief Exec. Officer--Metropolitan Transportation Authority, New York, NY; *U.S. Private*, pg. 739
Conway, James F., III, Chm. Bd., Pres., Chief Oper. & Exec. Officer--Courier Corporation, North Chelmsford, MA; *U.S.* Public, pg. 453
Cook, C. Thomas, Pres. & Chief Exec. Officer--First Security Information Technology, Inc., Salt Lake City, UT; *U.S. Public*, pg. 637
Cook, Carl, Chm. Bd. & Chief Exec. Officer--Overland Transportation System, Inc., Indianapolis, IN; *Int'l*, pg. 1469

Cook, E. Gary, Chm. Bd., Pres. & Chief Exec. Officer--Witco Corporation, Greenwich, CT; *U.S. Public*, pg. 1773
Cook, J. Michael, Chm. Bd. & Chief Exec. Officer--Deloitte & Touche LLP, Wilton, CT; *U.S. Private*, pg. 322
Cook, James D., Chm. Bd. & Chief Exec. Officer--Concord Litho Co., Inc., Concord, NH; *U.S. Private*, pg. 261
Cook, Kenneth C., Pres. & Chief Exec. Officer--Potomac Valley Bank, Gaithersburg, MD; *U.S. Public*, pg. 1089
Cook, Nicholas H., Chm. Bd. & Chief Exec. Officer--Brauns Fashions Corporation, Plymouth, MN; *U.S. Public*, pg. 251
Cook, Roger, Chief Exec. Officer--Heating Oil Partners L.P., Darien, CT; *U.S. Private*, pg. 518
Cook, Roger A., Chief Exec. Officer--Colliers Jardine Holdings Ltd., Hong Kong, Hong Kong; *Int'l*, pg. 705
Cook, Thomas, Chm. Bd. & Chief Exec. Officer--American Metal & Plastics Inc., Grand Rapids, MI; *U.S. Private*, pg. 59
Cook, William R., Chm. Bd., Pres. & Chief Exec. Officer--BetzDearborn Inc., Trevose, PA; *U.S. Public*, pg. 226
Cook, William R., Chm. Bd., Pres. & Chief Exec. Officer--Jenkins & Associates, Shawnee Mission, KS; *U.S. Private*, pg. 585
Cooke, Gordon R., Pres. & Chief Exec. Officer--DM Management Company, Hingham, MA; *U.S. Public*, pg. 473
Cooke, J.P. Blase, Chm. Bd., Pres. & Chief Exec. Officer--Harkins Builders, Inc., Silver Spring, MD; *U.S. Private*, pg. 502
Cooklin, Lawrence, Chief Exec. Officer--Signet Group plc, London, United Kingdom; *Int'l*, pg. 1248
Cookson, Michael, Chief Exec. Officer--Wham-O, Inc., San Francisco, CA; *U.S. Private*, pg. 1170
Coolidge, E. David, III, Chief Exec. Officer--William Blair & Company L.L.C., Chicago, IL; *U.S. Private*, pg. 148
Coombe, V.A., Chm. Bd., Chief Exec. Officer & Treas.--The Wm. Powell Company, Cincinnati, OH; *U.S. Private*, pg. 877
Coon, Kenneth C., Chm. Bd. & Chief Exec. Officer--Acceptance Insurance Co., Inc., Omaha, NE; *U.S. Public*, *pg. 14*
Cooney, Jack, Pres. & Chief Exec. Officer--Advance Machine Company, Plymouth, MN; *Int'l*, pg. 932
Coopat, E. Thomas, Pres., Chief Exec. Officer & Rep. Dir.--Avon Products Co., Ltd., Tokyo, Japan; *U.S. Public*, pg. 156
Cooper, B. E., Pres. & Chief Exec. Officer--Kennecott Holdings Corporation, Magna, UT; *Int'l*, pg. 1119
Cooper, B. William, Chm. Bd. & Chief Exec. Officer--Spectronics Corporation, Westbury, NY; *U.S. Private*, pg. 1024
Cooper, B. William, Chief Exec. Officer--Tracer Products, Westbury, NY; *U.S. Private*, pg. 1024
Cooper, Donald M., Chm. Bd., Pres. & Chief Exec. Officer--CoreStates Bank, Lancaster, PA; *U.S. Public*, pg. 446
Cooper, Eric, Chm. Bd. & Chief Exec. Officer--FORE Systems, Inc., Warrendale, PA; *U.S. Public*, pg. 667
Cooper, Jane, Pres. & Chief Exec. Officer--Paramount Parks, Charlotte, NC; *U.S. Private*, pg. 776
Cooper, Jerry A., Pres. & Chief Exec. Officer--Defiance, Inc., Cleveland, OH; *U.S. Public*, pg. 493
Cooper, M. Lynn, Chm. Bd., Pres. & Chief Exec. Officer--Citizens Bank of Illinois, Mount Vernon, IL; *U.S. Public*, pg. 280
Cooper, Marshall Y., Jr., Chm. Bd., Chief Exec. Officer & Pres.--Harriet & Henderson Yarns, Inc., Henderson, NC; *U.S. Private*, pg. 504
Cooper, Melvin L., Chm. Bd. & Chief Exec. Officer--The Union Corporation, Greenwich, CT; *U.S. Public*, pg. 1667
Cooper, Milton, Chm. Bd. & Chief Exec. Officer--Kimco Realty Corporation, New Hyde Park, NY; *U.S. Public*, pg. 960
Cooper, Norton J., Pres. & Chief Exec. Officer--Charles Jacquin et Cie, Inc., Philadelphia, PA; *U.S. Private*, pg. 580
Cooper, Ronald, Pres. & Chief Exec. Officer--Delta Foremost Chemical Corp., Memphis, TN; *U.S. Private*, pg. 322
Cooper, Stephen E., Chm., Pres. & Chief Exec. Officer--Etec Systems, Inc., Hayward, CA; *U.S. Public*, pg. 594
Cooper, William, Grp. Chief Exec.--Dorbyl Limited, Bedfordview, South Africa; *Int'l*, pg. 416
Cooper, William A., Chm. Bd. & Chief Exec. Officer--TCF Financial Corp., Minneapolis, MN; *U.S. Public*, pg. 1554
Cooperstone, Elliot S., Pres. & Chief Exec. Officer--Alexander & Alexander Inc., New York, NY; *U.S. Public*, pg. 117
Coords, Robert H., Chm. Bd. & Chief Exec. Officer--SunTrust Bank, South Florida, N.A., Fort Lauderdale, FL; *U.S. Public*, pg. 1538
Coors, Jeffrey H., Co-Pres. & Co-Chief Exec. Officer--ACX Technologies Inc., Golden, CO; *U.S. Public*, pg. 3
Coors, Joseph, Jr., Co-Pres. & Co-Chief Exec. Officer--ACX Technologies Inc., Golden, CO; *U.S. Public*, pg. 3
Coors, Joseph, Jr., Pres. & Chief Exec. Officer--Coors Ceramics Company, Golden, CO; *U.S. Public*, pg. 3
Coors, Peter H., Chief Exec. Officer--Adolph Coors Company, Golden, CO; *U.S. Public*, pg. 445
Cope, Larry W., Pres. & Chief Exec. Officer--Clear Springs Foods, Inc., Buhl, ID; *U.S. Private*, pg. 245
Copeland, Clare, Pres. & Chief Exec. Officer--Peoples Jewellers Corporation, Don Mills, Canada; *Int'l*, pg. 1036
Copeland, Stewart, Chief Exec. Officer--Liberty PLC, London, United Kingdom; *Int'l*, pg. 807
Copland, James R., III, Pres., Chief Exec. Officer & Treas.--Copland Fabrics, Inc., Burlington, NC; *U.S. Private*, pg. 274
Copley, David C., Pres. & Chief Exec. Officer--The Copley Press, Inc., La Jolla, CA; *U.S. Private*, pg. 275
Coppin, Claude, Chm. Bd. & Chief Exec. Officer--Spie Batignolles, Cergy-Pontoise, France; *Int'l*, pg. 16
Coppinger, Jack, Pres. & Chief Exec. Officer--Super Discount Markets, Inc., Lithia Springs, GA; *Int'l*, pg. 463
Coppinger, Jack, Pres. & Chief Exec. Officer--Super Discount Markets, Inc., Lithia Springs, GA; *U.S. Public*, pg. 1540
Coppola, Arthur, Pres. & Chief Exec. Officer--The Macerich Company, Santa Monica, CA; *U.S. Public*, pg. 1030
Copps, Michael W., Chm. Bd. & Chief Exec. Officer--The Copps Corp., Stevens Point, WI; *U.S. Private*, pg. 275
Corasanti, Eugene R., Chm. Bd., Pres. & Chief Exec. Officer--Conmed Corporation, Utica, NY; *U.S. Public*, pg. 431
Corazzin, Antonio, Chief Exec. Officer & Gen. Mgr.--La Centrale Formazione S.r.l., Vicenza, Italy; *Int'l*, pg. 138
Corbett, E.M., Jr., Chm. Bd., Pres. & Chief Exec. Officer--Harwick Standard Distribution Corporation, Akron, OH; *U.S. Private*, pg. 509
Corbett, Luke R., Chm. Bd. & Chief Exec. Officer--Kerr-McGee Corporation, Oklahoma City, OK; *U.S. Public*, pg. 952
Corbett, Richard, Pres.--Crane Manufacturing, Cudahy, WI; *U.S. Private*, pg. 286
Corbett, Thomas W., Chm. Bd. & Chief Exec. Officer--Robert F. Driver Co., Inc., San Diego, CA; *U.S. Private*, pg. 343
Corbin, J. E., Jr., Chief Exec. Officer--Metal Trades, Inc., Hollywood, SC; *U.S. Private*, pg. 734
Cordemans, Jan, Chief Exec. Officer-Creation & Production--Quattro DMB&B, Brussels, Brussels, Belgium; *U.S. Private*, pg. 305
Corder, Sidney, Pres. & Chief Exec. Officer--MSC Corporation, Indianapolis, IN; *U.S. Public*, pg. 110
Corder, Sidney V., Chm. Bd., Pres. & Chief Exec. Officer--Analytical Surveys, Inc., Colorado Springs, CO; *U.S. Public*, pg. 110
Corder, Sidney V., Chief Exec. Officer--ASI Landmark, Inc., Cary, NC; *U.S. Public*, pg. 110
Corey, Allen, Pres. Chief Exec. Officer--Big River Grille & Brewery Works, Chattanooga, TN; *U.S. Public*, pg. 1396
Cori, C. Tom, Ph.D., Chm. Bd. & Chief Exec. Officer--Sigma-Aldrich Corporation, Saint Louis, MO; *U.S. Public*, pg. 1471
Corkin, Herbert I., Chm. Bd. & Chief Exec. Officer--The Entwistle Company, Hudson, MA; *U.S. Private*, pg. 378
Corley, James W., Co-Chief Exec. Officer & Chief Oper. Officer--Dave & Buster's, Dallas, TX; *U.S. Public*, pg. 488
Cornelis, Francois, Vice Chm., Chief Exec. Officer & Mng. Dir.--Petrofina S.A., Brussels, Belgium; *Int'l*, pg. 1043
Cornelius, Charles, Pres. & Chief Exec. Officer--Atlanta Life Insurance Company, Atlanta, GA; *U.S. Private*, pg. 94
Cornell, Andrew, Pres. & Chief Exec. Officer--Cornell Iron Works, Inc., Mountain Top, PA; *U.S. Private*, pg. 276
Cornell, Harry M., Jr., Chm. Bd. & Chief Exec. Officer--Leggett & Platt, Incorporated, Carthage, MO; *U.S. Public*, *pg. 985*
Cornog, Robert A., Chm. Bd., Pres. & Chief Exec. Officer--Snap-On Tools Corporation, Kenosha, WI; *U.S. Public*, pg. 1480
Cornwall, John R., Pres. & Chief Exec. Officer--MetLife Capital Holdings, Inc., Bellevue, WA; *U.S. Private*, pg. 737
Cornwell, Kevin L., Chm. Bd., Pres. & Chief Exec. Officer--Utah Medical Products, Inc., Midvale, UT; *U.S. Public*, pg. 1700
Cornwell, W. Don, Chm. Bd. & Chief Exec. Officer--Granite Broadcasting Corporation, New York, NY; *U.S. Public*, pg. 759
Corogin, Peter J., Pres. & Chief Exec. Officer--Lake Erie Electric, Inc., Westlake, OH; *U.S. Private*, pg. 643
Corona, Luis Rebollar, Chm. Bd. & Chief Exec. Officer--Grupo Sidek, S.A. de C.V., Guadalajara, Mexico; *Int'l*, pg. 576
Corona, Luis Rebollar, Chief Exec. Officer--Grupo Situr SA de CV, Guadalajara, Mexico; *Int'l*, pg. 576
Corp, William, Pres. & Chief Exec. Officer--Comstock Canada Ltd., Burlington, Canada; *U.S. Public*, pg. 572
Corr, Thomas L., Pres. & Chief Exec. Officer--George E. Warren Corporation, Vero Beach, FL; *U.S. Private*, pg. 1151
Corrao, Michael J., Pres. & Chief Exec. Officer--Gingiss International, Addison, IL; *U.S. Private*, pg. 455
Correll, A.D., Chm. Bd. & Chief Exec. Officer--Georgia-Pacific Corporation, Atlanta, GA; *U.S. Public*, pg. 735
Correll, Donald L., Chm. Bd. & Chief Exec. Officer--United Water Resources, Harrington Park, NJ; *U.S. Public*, pg. 1691
Correll, Donald L., Chm. Bd. & Chief Exec. Officer--United Water Management & Services, Harrington Park, NJ; *U.S. Public*, pg. 1692
Correnti, John D., Co-Vice Chm., Pres. & Chief Exec. Officer--Nucor Corporation, Charlotte, NC; *U.S. Public*, pg. 1205
Corrigan, Wilfred J., Chm. & Chief Exec. Officer--LSI Logic Corp., Milpitas, CA; *U.S. Public*, pg. 971
Corriveau, David O., Co-Chief Exec. Officer & Pres.--Dave & Buster's, Dallas, TX; *U.S. Public*, pg. 488
Corsentino, Charles J., Pres. & Chief Exec. Officer--Exhibitgroup/Giltspur, Roselle, IL; *U.S. Public*, pg. 1718
Corsiglia, Robert, Pres. & Chief Exec. officer--Hyre Electric Company of Indiana, Inc., Highland, IN; *U.S. Public*, pg. 572
Corsini, John M., Pres., Chief Exec. Officer & Treas.--Uncas Manufacturing Company, Providence, RI; *U.S. Private*, pg. 1116
Cortazzi, William, Chief Exec. Officer--Dalgety Food Ingredients Ltd., London, United Kingdom; *Int'l*, pg. 376
Cortina, Alfonso, Chm. Bd. & Chief Exec. Officer--Repsol S.A., Madrid, Spain; *Int'l*, pg. 1104
Corzine, Jon, Chm. Bd. & Chief Exec. Officer--Goldman, Sachs & Co., New York, NY; *U.S. Private*, pg. 462
Cosgrave, Gary D., Chm. Bd. & Chief Exec. Officer--PRO Group, Inc., Englewood, CO; *U.S. Private*, pg. 887
Cosgrove, Howard E., Chm. Bd. & Chief Exec. Officer--Conectiv, Wilmington, DE; *U.S. Public*, pg. 430
Cosgrove, Howard E., Chm. Bd., Pres. & Chief Exec. Officer--Delmarva Power & Light Company, Wilmington, DE; *U.S. Public*, pg. 430
Cosner, Melvin, Pres. & Chief Exec. Officer--Lady Baltimore Foods, Inc., Kansas City, KS; *U.S. Public*, pg. 975
Coss, Lawrence M., Chm. Bd., Pres. & Chief Exec. & Oper. Officer--Green Tree Financial Corporation, Saint Paul, MN; *U.S. Public*, pg. 761
Costa, Pat V., Chm. Bd., Pres. & Chief Exec. Officer--Robotic Vision Systems, Inc., Hauppauge, NY; *U.S. Public*, pg. 1395
Costanzo, Gian Luigi, Chief Exec. & Gen. Mgr.--Caboto Gestioni Sim S.p.A., Milan, Italy; *Int'l*, pg. 138
Coste, Thierry, Deputy Chief Exec. Officer-Capital Mkts.--Credit Agricole, Bonvin, France; *Int'l*, pg. 341
Costello, Albert J., Chm. Bd., Pres. & Chief Exec. Officer--W.R. Grace & Co., Boca Raton, FL; *U.S. Public*, pg. 754
Costello, Robert L., Pres., Chief Exec. & Chief Oper. Officer--URS Greiner Engineering, Inc., Denver, CO; *U.S.* Public, pg. 1658
Costley, Gary E., Ph.D., Chm. Bd., Pres. & Chief Exec. Officer--International Multifoods Corporation, Minneapolis, MN; *U.S. Public*, pg. 900
Cote, David M., Pres. & Chief Exec. Officer--G.E. Appliances, Louisville, KY; *U.S. Public*, pg. 710
Cotter, Daniel A., Chm. Bd. & Chief Exec. Officer--TruServ Corporation, Chicago, IL; *U.S. Private*, pg. 1108
Cotter, William R., Chief Exec. Officer--Bank of Ireland Asset Management Limited, Dublin, Ireland; *Int'l*, pg. 152
Cotterill, D., Chief Exec. Officer--Renold PLC, Manchester, United Kingdom; *Int'l*, pg. 1103
Cottet, Gerard, Chm. & Chief Exec. Officer--Essilor International Compagnie Generale d'Optique, Charenton-le-Pont, France; *Int'l*, pg. 462
Cottier, Marius, Dr., Pres. & Chief Exec. Officer--Schweizer Verband der Raiffeisenbanken, Saint Gallen, Switzerland; *Int'l*, pg. 1211
Couch, John C., Chm. Bd., Pres. & Chief Exec. Officer--Alexander & Baldwin, Inc., Honolulu, HI; *U.S. Public*, pg. 39
Coughlin, Christopher J., Pres. & Chief Exec. Officer--Nabisco Inc., Parsippany, NJ; *U.S. Public*, pg. 1355
Coughlin, John, Pres. & Chief Exec. Officer--Benthos, Inc., North Falmouth, MA; *U.S. Public*, pg. 212
Couillaud, Bernard J., Ph.D., Pres. & Chief Exec. Officer--Coherent, Inc., Santa Clara, CA; *U.S. Public*, pg. 395
Coulombe, Dennis N., Pres. & Chief Oper. Officer--White Rock Distilleries Inc., Lewiston, ME; *U.S. Private*, pg. 1173
Coulombe, Paul G., Chief Exec. Officer & Chief Fin. Officer--White Rock Distilleries Inc., Lewiston, ME; *U.S. Private*, pg. 1173
Coultas, Jeffrey B., Pres. & Chief Exec. Officer--Elliott State Bank, Jacksonville, IL; *U.S. Public*, pg. 643
Coulter, David, Chm. Bd. & Chief Exec. Officer--BankAmerica Corporation, San Francisco, CA; *U.S. Public*, pg. 179
Coulter, David A., Pres. & Chief Exec. Officer--Bank of America NT&SA, San Francisco, CA; *U.S. Public*, pg. 180
Coulter, David A., Pres. & Chief Exec. Officer--Bank of America California, San Francisco, CA; *U.S. Public*, pg. 180
Councell, Paul S., Chm. & Chief Exec. Officer--Cramer-Krasselt Public Relations, Milwaukee, WI; *U.S. Private*, pg. 286
Counsell, Paul S., Chm. Bd. & Chief Exec. Officer--Cramer-Krasselt, Milwaukee, WI; *U.S. Private*, pg. 285
Countryman, Gary L., Chm. & Chief Exec. Officer--Liberty Mutual Insurance Co., Boston, MA; *U.S. Private*, pg. 666
Couri, Ronald J., Pres. & Chief Exec. Officer--Couristan Inc., Fort Lee, NJ; *U.S. Private*, pg. 279
Courtin-Clarins, Jacques, Chm. Bd. & Chief Exec. Officer--Clarins, Neuilly-sur-Seine, France; *Int'l*, pg. 295
Courtney, Eugene W., Pres. & Chief Exec. Officer--HEI, Inc., Victoria, MN; *U.S. Public*, pg. 770
Cousins, Thomas G., Chm. Bd. & Chief Exec. Officer--Cousins Properties Incorporated, Atlanta, GA; *U.S. Public*, pg. 453
Coutu, Jean, Chm. Bd. & Chief Exec. Officer--The Jean Coutu Group (PJC) Inc., Longueuil, Canada; *Int'l*, pg. 340
Couture, Jacques, Dir. & Advisor to the Chm. & Chief Exec. Officer--COGEMA - Compagnie Generale des Matieres Nucleaires, Velizy-Villacoublay, France; *Int'l*, pg. 304
Covalt, Robert B., Chm. Bd., Pres. & Chief Exec. Officer--Sovereign Specialty Chemical, Inc., Chicago, IL; *U.S. Private*, pg. 1019
Covey, Roger E., Chm. Bd. & Chief Exec. Officer--System Software Associates, Inc., Chicago, IL; *U.S. Public*, pg. 1552
Covino, Charles P., Chm. Bd. & Chief Exec. Officer--General Magnaplate Corporation, Linden, NJ; *U.S. Public*, pg. 717
Cowan, James R., Chm. Bd., Pres. & Chief Exec. Officer--Stonecutter Mills Corp., Spindale, NC; *U.S. Private*, pg. 1044
Cowan, R. Douglas, Chm. Bd., Pres. & Chief Exec. Officer--The Davey Tree Expert Company, Kent, OH; *U.S. Private*, pg. 314
Cowart, Jim, Chief Exec. Officer--Aurora Electronics, Marina Del Rey, CA; *U.S. Public*, pg. 147
Cowart, Jim C., Chm. Bd. & Chief Exec. Officer--Aurora Electronics, Inc., Irvine, CA; *U.S. Public*, pg. 147
Cowles, Alfred, Jr., Pres. & Chief Exec. Officer--Bluff City Distributing Co., Inc., Memphis, TN; *U.S. Private*, pg. 153
Cowpland, Michael, Chm. Bd., Pres. & Chief Exec. Officer--Corel Corporation, Ottawa, Canada; *Int'l*, pg. 331
Cox, David C., Pres. & Chief Exec. Officer--Cowles Media Company, Minneapolis, MN; *U.S. Private*, pg. 280
Cox, Frank, Pres. & Chief Exec. Officer--Cranford Johnson Robinson Woods, Little Rock, AR; *U.S. Private*, pg. 286
Cox, P.V., Chief Exec. Officer--Polifin Limited, Randburg, South Africa; *Int'l*, pg. 1197

Cox, Pieter, Mng. Dir. & Chief Exec. Officer--Sasol Limited, Johannesburg, South Africa; *Int'l*, pg. 1196
Cox, Ron, Pres. & Chief Exec. Officer--Learning International, Stamford, CT; *U.S. Public*, pg. 1617
Cox, Ron, Chief Exec. Officer-Times Mirror Training Grp.--Zenger-Miller, San Jose, CA; *U.S. Public*, pg. 1617
Cox, William B., Jr., Pres. & Chief Exec. Officer--Cox Wood Preserving Co., Orangeburg, SC; *U.S. Private*, pg. 283
Coy, Doug, Chief Exec. Officer--Bridgeman's Restaurants Inc., Minnetonka, MN; *U.S. Private*, pg. 167
Coyne, Frank J., Pres. & Chief Oper. Officer--General Assurance Company, Melville, NY; *Int'l*, pg. 543
Coyne, John, Chief Exec. Officer--Acacia Federal Mortgage Corp., Annandale, VA; *U.S. Private*, pg. 11
Coyne, Nancy, Chm. Bd., Chief Exec. Officer & Creative Services Dir.--Serino Coyne Inc., New York, NY; *U.S. Private*, pg. 985
Coyne, William P., Chief Exec. Officer--Coyne Beahm Inc., Colfax, NC; *U.S. Private*, pg. 283
Coyte, C.A., Chief Exec. Officer--Carter Holt Harvey Wood Products Limited, Auckland, New Zealand; *U.S. Public*, pg. 904
Cozzani, Gian Carlo, Pres. & Chief Exec. Officer--Vesuvius U.S.A., Champaign, IL; *Int'l*, pg. 329
Craft, Gary, Chief Exec. Officer--Spar (UK) Ltd., Harrow, United Kingdom; *Int'l*, pg. 1288
Craig, George, Pres. & Chief Exec. Officer--HarperCollins Publishers, New York, NY; *Int'l*, pg. 926
Craig, Jack, Chief Exec. Officer--PTS Electronics Corporation, Bloomington, IN; *U.S. Private*, pg. 828
Craig, Sidney, Chm. Bd. & Chief Exec. Officer--Jenny Craig, Inc., La Jolla, CA; *U.S. Public*, pg. 926
Cramer, James D., Chm. Bd., Pres. & Chief Exec. Officer--Science & Engineering Associates, Albuquerque, NM; *U.S. Private*, pg. 975
Cramer, Larry, Pres. & Chief Exec. Officer--Laser Diode Products, New Brunswick, NJ; *Int'l*, pg. 892
Cramer, Stephen W., Chief Exec. Officer--Octagon Process Inc., Edgewater, NJ; *U.S. Private*, pg. 811
Crandall, David E., Chm. Bd. & Chief Exec. Officer--Premier Metal Products Co., Carrollton, TX; *U.S. Private*, pg. 881
Crandall, Robert L., Chm. Bd. & Chief Exec. Officer--AMR Corporation, Fort Worth, TX; *U.S. Public*, pg. 9
Crane, Ann B., Pres. & Chief Exec. Officer--Crane Plastics Company, Columbus, OH; *U.S. Private*, pg. 286
Crane, James R., Chm. Bd., Pres. & Chief Exec. Officer--Eagle USA Airfreight, Houston, TX; *U.S. Public*, pg. 547
Crane, Jonathan C., Pres. & Chief Exec. Officer--Bogen Communications, Inc., Ramsey, NJ; *U.S. Public*, pg. 739
Crane, Jonathan C., Chm. Bd., Pres. & Chief Exec. Officer--Marcam Solutions, Inc., Newton, MA; *U.S. Public*, pg. 1042
Crane, Lansing, E., Chm. Bd. & Chief Exec. Officer--Crane & Co., Inc., Dalton, MA; *U.S. Private*, pg. 286
Cranor, John M., III, Chm. Bd., Pres. & Chief Exec. Officer--Long John Silver's, Inc., Lexington, KY; *U.S. Private*, pg. 674
Cranston, John, Chief Exec. Officer & V.P.-Opers.--Philips Speech Processing, Atlanta, GA; *Int'l*, pg. 1055
Crants, Doctor R., Chm. Bd. & Chief Exec. Officer--Corrections Corporation of America, Nashville, TN; *U.S. Public*, pg. 450
Craven, John, Chm. Bd. & Chief Exec. Officer--Morgan Grenfell Group PLC, London, United Kingdom; *Int'l*, pg. 405
Cravit, David, Chief Exec. Officer--David Cravit & Associates Advertising, Chicago, IL; *U.S. Private*, pg. 287
Crawford, Edward, Chm. Bd., Pres & Chief Exec. & Oper. Officer--Park-Ohio Industries, Inc., Cleveland, OH; *U.S. Public*, pg. 1258
Crawford, Mac, Chm. Bd., Pres. & Chief Exec. Officer--Magellan Health Services, Inc., Atlanta, GA; *U.S. Public*, pg. 1033
Crawford, Paul, III, Pres. & Chief Exec. Officer--Interstate Billing Service, Inc., Decatur, AL; *U.S. Public*, pg. 1373
Crawford, Richard, Chm. Bd. & Chief Exec. Officer--Cambridge Industries Inc., Madison Heights, MI; *U.S. Private*, pg. 202
Crawford, William P., Pres. & Chief Exec. Officer-Steelcase Design Partnership--Steelcase Inc., Grand Rapids, MI; *U.S. Private*, pg. 1038
Creasman, Kevin L., Pres. & Chief Oper. Officer-SC Johnson Comml. Markets--S.C. Johnson & Son, Inc., Racine, WI; *U.S. Private*, pg. 592
Creel, Diane C., Chm. Bd., Pres. & Chief Exec. Officer--Earth Technology Corp. USA, Long Beach, CA; *U.S. Public*, pg. 1648
Creighton, John W., Pres. & Chief Exec. Officer--Weyerhaeuser Company, Federal Way, WA; *U.S. Public*, pg. 1761
Crenshaw, Bruce, Pres. & Chief Exec. Officer--Royal Rubber & Manufacturing Co., South Gate, CA; *U.S. Private*, pg. 949
Cresci, Robert, Chm. Bd., Pres. & Chief Exec. Officer--Serv-Tech, Inc., Houston, TX; *U.S. Public*, pg. 1460
Crespo, J.R., Chm. Bd., Pres. & Chief Exec. Officer--Connecticut Energy Corporation, Bridgeport, CT; *U.S. Public*, pg. 431
Cress, George H., Chm. Bd., Pres. & Chief Exec. Officer--Society Bank, Michigan, Ann Arbor, MI; *U.S. Public*, pg. 954
Cressman, Franklin C., Chm. Bd. & Chief Exec. Officer--Florida Public Utilities Company, West Palm Beach, FL; *U.S. Public*, pg. 655
Crichfield, Douglas, Pres. & Chief Exec. Officer--Concord Savings Bank, Concord, NH; *U.S. Public*, pg. 278
Crichley, Keith, Pres. & Chief Exec. Officer--Printwest Communications Ltd., Regina, Canada; *Int'l*, pg. 1195
Crider, Joe D., Chm. Bd. & Chief Exec. Officer--Reliance Steel & Aluminum Co., Los Angeles, CA; *U.S. Public*, pg. 1375
Crider, Joe D., Chm. Bd. & Chief Exec. Officer--Metalcenter, Inc., Santa Fe Springs, CA; *U.S. Public*, pg. 1375
Crimmins, Michael T., Chm. Bd. & Chief Exec. Officer--Kinark Corporation, Tulsa, OK; *U.S. Public*, pg. 960
Cringan, Drew, Pres. & Chief Exec. Officer--McKim Communications Limited, Winnipeg, Canada; *U.S. Private*, pg. 104
Crippa, Alberto, Deputy Chief Exec.--Cassa di Risparmio delle Provincie Lombarde SpA (CARIPLO), Milan, Italy; *Int'l*, pg. 274
Crisman, Craig D., Chm. Bd., Pres., Chief Exec. & Fin. Officer--Applied Magnetics Corporation, Goleta, CA; *U.S. Public*, pg. 123
Crisp, Donald W., Pres. & Chief Exec. Officer--Caroline Hunt Trust Estate, Dallas, TX; *U.S. Private*, pg. 548
Crispin, Andre A., Chief Exec. Officer--The Crispin Company, Houston, TX; *U.S. Private*, pg. 290
Crist, Robert, Pres. & Chief Exec. & Chief Oper. Officer--American Recreation Centers, Inc., Sacramento, CA; *U.S. Public*, pg. 90
Cristiano, Joseph P., Pres. & Chief Exec. Officer--Kelly-Moore Paint Company, Inc., San Carlos, CA; *U.S. Private*, pg. 613
Critchfield, Jack B., Dr., Chm. Bd. & Chief Exec. Officer--Florida Progress Corporation, Saint Petersburg, FL; *U.S. Public*, pg. 655
Critelli, Michael J., Chm. Bd. & Chief Exec. Officer--Pitney Bowes Inc., Stamford, CT; *U.S. Public*, pg. 1303
Croatti, Ronald D., Vice Chm., Pres. & Chief Exec. Officer--UniFirst Corporation, Wilmington, MA; *U.S. Public*, pg. 1665
Crocker, Charles, Chm. Bd., Pres. & Chief Exec. Officer--BEI Technologies, Inc., San Francisco, CA; *U.S. Public*, pg. 160
Crocker, Douglas, II, Pres. & Chief Exec. Officer--Equity Residential Properties Trust, Chicago, IL; *U.S. Public*, pg. 590
Crocker, Will, Pres. & Chief Exec. Officer--Amot Controls Corporation, Richmond, CA; *U.S. Public*, pg. 1405
Crockett, R.J., Pres. & Chief Exec. Officer--Dexter Company, Fairfield, IA; *U.S. Private*, pg. 329
Croen, Ronald A., Pres. & Chief Exec. Officer--Nuance Communications, Menlo Park, CA; *U.S. Private*, pg. 958
Crom, J. Oliver, Pres. & Chief Exec. Officer--Dale Carnegie Training, New York, NY; *U.S. Private*, pg. 308
Crombie, David R., Chm. & Chief Exec. Officer--Rayrock Yellowknife Resources Inc., Toronto, Canada; *Int'l*, pg. 1089
Crombie, David R., Chm. Bd. & Chief Exec. Officer--BlackRock Ventures Inc., Toronto, Canada; *Int'l*, pg. 1089
Cronin, Edmund B., Jr., Pres. & Chief Exec. Officer--Washington Real Estate Investment Trust, Kensington, MD; *U.S. Public*, pg. 1743
Cronin, Robert J., Pres. & Chief Exec. Officer--Wallace Computer Services, Inc., Lisle, IL; *U.S. Public*, pg. 1735
Cronin, Timothy E., Co-Pres. & Co-Chief Exec. Officer--The Nikko Securities Co. International Inc., New York, NY; *Int'l*, pg. 930
Croom, Judson H., Pres. & Chief Exec. Officer--CTX Mortgage Co., Inc., Dallas, TX; *U.S. Public*, pg. 323
Cropper, Stephen L., Pres. & Chief Exec. Officer--Williams Pipe Line Co., Tulsa, OK; *U.S. Public*, pg. 1769
Cross, Jim, Pres. & Chief Exec. Officer--Thaw & Walrus, Inc., Seattle, WA; *U.S. Private*, pg. 914
Cross, Ray, Chm. Bd., Pres. & Chief Exec. Officer--Krone Casting Corp., North Chicago, IL; *U.S. Private*, pg. 636
Cross, Timothy E., Pres. & Chief Exec. Officer--M & I Bank of Shawano, N.A., Shawano, WI; *U.S. Public*, pg. 1050
Cross, Wilbur J., Chm. Bd., Pres. & Chief Exec. Officer--Catskill Savings Bank, Catskill, NY; *U.S. Public*, pg. 318
Crossen, Mark, Pres. & Chief Exec. Officer--Amrion Inc., Boulder, CO; *U.S. Public*, pg. 1767
Crosta, Edward A., Chief Exec. Officer & Exec. V.P. & Sec.--West Building Materials, Atlanta, GA; *U.S. Private*, pg. 1163
Crotty, L. William, Chm. & Chief Exec. Officer--Van Dyne-Crotty, Inc., Dayton, OH; *U.S. Private*, pg. 1132
Crowder, Otis A., Pres. & Chief Exec. Officer--Crowder Construction Co., Charlotte, NC; *U.S. Private*, pg. 291
Crowe, J., Chief Exec. Officer--Ascom Hasler Mailing Systems AG, Bern, Switzerland; *Int'l*, pg. 86
Crowe, James Q., Pres. & Chief Exec. Officer--Kiewit Construction Group, Inc., Omaha, NE; *U.S. Private*, pg. 619
Crowe, Jeffrey C., Chm. Bd., Pres. & Chief Exec. Officer--Landstar Holding, Shelton, CT; *U.S. Public*, pg. 978
Crowe, Kevin E., Chm. & Chief Exec. Officer--Essex Corporation, New York, NY; *U.S. Public*, pg. 320
Crowe, Maureen, Pres. & Chief Exec. Officer--Carl Byoir & Associates, Inc., New York, NY; *Int'l*, pg. 1483
Crowell, Steven H., Pres., Chief Oper. Officer, Chief Exec. Officer & Treas.--East Coast Steel, Inc., Claremont, NH; *U.S. Private*, pg. 356
Crowley, Frank J., Pres. & Chief Oper. Officer--Commercial Union Life Assurance Company of Canada, Scarborough, Canada; *Int'l*, pg. 308
Crowley, Thomas, Jr., Chm. Bd., Pres. & Chief Exec. Officer--Crowley Maritime Corporation, Oakland, CA; *U.S. Private*, pg. 292
Crown, William, Pres. & Chief Exec. Officer--CC Industries, Inc., Chicago, IL; *U.S. Private*, pg. 192
Crowser, John C., Chief Exec. Officer--Hart Crowser, Inc., Seattle, WA; *U.S. Private*, pg. 507
Crowson, Dan, Chief Oper. Officer--United Supermarkets Inc., Lubbock, TX; *U.S. Private*, pg. 1126
Crowson, Niel, Chm. Bd., Pres. & Chief Exec. Officer--E.C. Barton & Company, Jonesboro, AR; *U.S. Private*, pg. 119
Crowther, P., Chief Exec. Officer--Redland Distribution Limited, Worksop, United Kingdom; *Int'l*, pg. 1090
Croxton, G. Duke, Chief Exec. Officer--Magnus Software Corporation, Smyrna, GA; *U.S. Private*, pg. 795
Cruiscshanks, Douglas, Pres. & Chief Exec. Officer--NationsBank Virginia, Richmond, VA; *U.S. Public*, pg. 1163
Crum, David H., Pres., Chief Exec. & Chief Fin. Officer--Crum Electric Supply Co., Inc., Casper, WY; *U.S. Private*, pg. 293
Crutchfield, Bill, Chm. Bd., Pres. & Chief Exec. Officer--State First National Bank, Texas, Texarkana, TX; *U.S. Public*, pg. 630
Crutchfield, Edward E., Jr., Chm. Bd. & Chief Exec. Officer--First Union Corporation, Charlotte, NC; *U.S. Public*, pg. 639
Cruz, Ralph L., Co-Chm. Bd. & Co-Chief Exec. Officer--Omega Research Inc., Miami, FL; *U.S. Public*, pg. 1222
Cruz, William R., Co-Chm. Bd., Pres. & Co-Chief Exec. Officer--Omega Research Inc., Miami, FL; *U.S. Public*, pg. 1222
Crystal, Richard C., Chief Exec. Officer--Lerner New York, New York, NY; *U.S. Public*, pg. 995
Csabai, B., Chief Exec. Officer--Bramac Kft, Veszprem, Hungary; *Int'l*, pg. 1092
Csiszar, Ernst N., Pres. & Chief Exec. Officer--The Seibels Bruce Group, Inc., Columbia, SC; *U.S. Public*, pg. 1453
Csiszar, Ernst N., Chief Exec. Officer--South Carolina Insurance Company, Columbia, SC; *U.S. Public*, pg. 1453
Csiszar, Ernst N., Chm. Bd. & Chief Exec. Officer--Premium Budget Plan, Inc., Winston Salem, NC; *U.S. Public*, pg. 1453
Csiszar, Ernst N., Pres. & Chief Exec. Officer--Consolidated American Insurance Co., Columbia, SC; *U.S. Public*, pg. 1454
Csiszar, Ernst N., Pres. & Chief Exec. Officer--Catawba Insurance Co., Columbia, SC; *U.S. Public*, pg. 1454
Csiszar, Ernst N., Pres. & Chief Exec. Officer--Investors National Life Insurance Co., Columbia, SC; *U.S. Public*, pg. 1454
Csiszar, Ernst N., Pres. & Chief Exec. Officer--Kentucky Insurance Co., Louisville, KY; *U.S. Public*, pg. 1454
Csiszar, Ernst N., Pres. & Chief Exec. Officer--Seibels, Bruce & Co., Columbia, SC; *U.S. Public*, pg. 1454
Csiszar, Ernst N., Pres. & Chief Exec. Officer--Agency Specialty Inc., Columbia, SC; *U.S. Public*, pg. 1454
Csiszar, Ernst N., Pres. & Chief Exec. Officer--Forest Lake Travel Service, Inc., Columbia, SC; *U.S. Public*, pg. 1454
Csiszar, Ernst N., Chm. Bd. & Chief Exec. Officer--The Innovative Company, Winston Salem, NC; *U.S. Public*, pg. 1454
Csiszar, Ernst N., Chm. Bd. & Chief Exec. Officer--Universal Insurance Co., Winston Salem, NC; *U.S. Public*, pg. 1454
Csomor, Laszlo, Mng. Dir.--EURO RSCG, Budapest, Hungary; *Int'l*, pg. 602
Cubas, Jose M., Chm. & Chief Exec. Officer--SiboneyUSA, Miami, FL; *U.S. Public*, pg. 1641
Cucuz, Ron, Pres. & Chief Exec. Officer--Hayes Wheels International, Inc., Romulus, MI; *U.S. Private*, pg. 513
Cudahy, Michael J., Chm. Bd. & Chief Exec. Officer--Marquette Medical Systems, Inc., Milwaukee, WI; *U.S. Public*, pg. 1047
Culea, J.D., Chm., Pres. & Chief Exec. Officer--Northern Labs, Inc., Manitowoc, WI; *U.S. Private*, pg. 805
Cullen, J. Russell, Jr., Pres. & Chief Exec. Officer--Nason and Cullen Group Incorporated, King of Prussia, PA; *U.S. Private*, pg. 775
Cullen, John B., Chm. Bd. & Chief Exec. Officer--King Kullen Grocery Co., Inc., Westbury, NY; *U.S. Private*, pg. 621
Cullman, Edgar M., Jr., Pres. & Chief Exec. Officer--General Cigar Holdings Inc, New York, NY; *U.S. Public*, pg. 707
Culp, Robert G., III, Chm. Bd. & Chief Exec. Officer--Culp, Inc., High Point, NC; *U.S. Public*, pg. 467
Culver, Mike, Chief Exec. Officer--National Airmotive Corporation, Oakland, CA; *U.S. Private*, pg. 775
Cummings, Terry M., Pres. & Chief Exec. Officer--Bremer Financial Corporation, Saint Paul, MN; *U.S. Private*, pg. 167
Cummings, Thomas L., III, Pres. & Chief Exec.--Cummings Inc., Nashville, TN; *U.S. Private*, pg. 295
Cunningham, C. Baker, Chm. Bd., Pres. & Chief Exec. Officer--Belden Inc., Saint Louis, MO; *U.S. Public*, pg. 200
Cunningham, C. Baker, Chm. Bd., Pres. & Chief Exec. Officer--Belden Wire & Cable Company, Richmond, IN; *U.S. Public*, pg. 201
Cunningham, C. Joseph, III, Chm. Bd., Pres. & Chief Exec. Officer--The Fidelity Bank, Frostburg, MD; *U.S. Public*, pg. 1089
Cunningham, Douglas L., Pres. & Chief Exec. Officer--Rexair, Inc., Troy, MI; *U.S. Public*, pg. 1684
Cunningham, Philip T., Pres. & Chief Exec. Officer--Microdyne Corporation, Alexandria, VA; *U.S. Public*, pg. 1105
Cunningham, William, Chm. Bd. & Chief Exec. Officer--LaundryMart, Inc., Torrance, CA; *U.S. Private*, pg. 222
Cuny, Jean-Pierre, Deputy Grp. Chief Exec.--BPB Industries PLC, Slough, United Kingdom; *Int'l*, pg. 122
Curcio, Mark, Chief Exec. Officer--LIVE Entertainment Inc., Van Nuys, CA; *U.S. Private*, pg. 671
Curcio, Mark, Chief Exec. Officer--LIVE Film & Mediaworks, Van Nuys, CA; *U.S. Private*, pg. 671
Curd, Howard R., Chm. Bd. & Chief Exec. Officer--Uniroyal Technology Corporation, Sarasota, FL; *U.S. Public*, pg. 1670
Curi, Maurico, Superintendent-Mktg.--Fiat Automisveis S.A., Sao Paulo, Brazil; *Int'l*, pg. 483
Curley, John J., Chm. Bd. & Chief Exec. Officer--Gannett Company, Inc., Arlington, VA; *U.S. Public*, pg. 698
Curran, James J, Chief Executive Officer-N.E. Region--First Interstate Bank of Washington, N.A., Seattle, WA; *U.S. Public*, pg. 1753
Curran, Michael F., Chief Exec. Officer--Michael Curran & Associates, Houston, TX; *U.S. Private*, pg. 297
Curran, William, Pres. & Chief Exec. Officer--Curran Group, Inc., Crystal Lake, IL; *U.S. Private*, pg. 297
Currey, Bradley, Jr., Chm. Bd. & Chief Exec. Officer--Rock-Tenn Company, Norcross, GA; *U.S. Public*, pg. 1396

Currie, Jerry N., Pres. & Chief Exec. Officer--Curries Company, Mason City, IA; *Int'l*, pg. 18

Currie, William G., Chief Exec. Officer--Universal Forest Products, Inc., Grand Rapids, MI; *U.S. Public*, pg. 1696

Curry, Peter, Chief Exec. Officer--Unitech Plc, Reading, United Kingdom; *Int'l*, pg. 1241

Curry, Thomas C., Pres. & Chief Exec. Officer--The Macneal-Schwendler Corp., Los Angeles, CA; *U.S. Public*, pg. 1030

Curry, W. Roger, Pres. & Chief Exec. Officer--Consolidated Freightways Corp., Menlo Park, CA; *U.S. Public*, pg. 435

Curtin, Frank T., Chm. Bd., Pres. & Chief Exec. Officer--Brown & Sharpe Manufacturing Company, North Kingstown, RI; *U.S. Public*, pg. 260

Curtin, John D., Jr., Chm. Bd., Pres. & Chief Exec. Officer--Aearo Company, Boston, MA; *U.S. Private*, pg. 23

Curtin, Thomas J., Pres. & Chief Exec. Officer--Princeton Bank & Trust Company National Association, East Brunswick, NJ; *U.S. Public*, pg. 338

Curtis, Charlie, Pres. & Chief Exec. Officer--Nana Regional Corporation, Inc., Anchorage, AK; *U.S. Private*, pg. 774

Curtis, Chuck, Chm. Bd., Pres. & Chief Exec. Officer--Valentine Radford, Inc., Kansas City, MO; *U.S. Private*, pg. 1131

Curtis, Roger William, Chm. Bd., Chief Exec. Officer & Sec.--L.N. Curtis & Sons, Oakland, CA; *U.S. Private*, pg. 297

Curto, Richard S., Pres. & Chief Exec. Officer--Prime Group Realty Trust, Chicago, IL; *U.S. Public*, pg. 1326

Cusack, Thomas J., Pres. & Chief Exec. Officer--Transamerica Life Companies, Los Angeles, CA; *U.S. Public*, pg. 1630

Cushing, Robert, Pres. & Chief Exec. Officer--Pepsi-Cola General Bottlers, Inc., Rolling Meadows, IL; *U.S. Public*, pg. 1277

Cusick, C. Robert, Vice Chm., Pres. & Chief Exec. Officer--International Murex Technologies Corporation, Guelph, Canada; *Int'l*, pg. 684

Cusick, Thomas A., Chm. Bd. & Chief Exec. Officer--TCF Bank Minnesota FSB, Minneapolis, MN; *U.S. Public*, pg. 1554

Custer, Patrick A., Chm. Bd., Pres. & Chief Exec. Officer--Curtis Mathes Holding Corp., Dallas, TX; *U.S. Public*, pg. 1057

Cusworth, Neville, Chm. & Chief Exec.--Reed Elsevier Legal Division, London, United Kingdom; *Int'l*, pg. 1095

Cutler, Benjamin, Chief Exec. Officer--Time Insurance, Milwaukee, WI; *Int'l*, pg. 499

Cutler, James M., Chief Exec. Officer--Continental Paper Recycling LLC, Portland, OR; *U.S. Private*, pg. 269

Cuvelier, Joseph, Pres. & Chief Exec. Officer--Gie ETEX Gestion, Vernouillet, France; *Int'l*, pg. 430

Cvengros, Joseph, Chm. Bd. & Chief Exec. Officer--Anamet Inc., Waterbury, CT; *U.S. Private*, pg. 70

Cvengros, William D., Chief Exec. Officer--PIMCO Advisors L.P., Newport Beach, CA; *U.S. Private*, pg. 832

Cvengros, William D., Pres. & Chief Exec. Officer--PIMCO Advisors, Stamford, CT; *U.S. Public*, pg. 1296

Cynamon, David, Chief Exec. Oficer--KIK Corporation Holdings Inc., Concord, Canada; *U.S. Private*, pg. 222

Cypher, Victor, Pres. & Chief Exec. Officer--Caldwell Manufacturing Company, Rochester, NY; *U.S. Private*, pg. 200

Czerwinski, Eugene, Chief Exec. Officer--Cerwin Vega, Inc., Simi Valley, CA; *U.S. Private*, pg. 227

Cziraky, Debra Adray, Pres. & Chief Exec. Officer--Adray Appliance & Photo Center, Inc., Dearborn, MI; *U.S. Private*, pg. 18

Czura, Antony, Pres. & Chief Exec. Officer--SGS North America Inc., New York, NY; *Int'l*, pg. 1153

D'Agostino, Nicolas, Chm. Bd. & Chief Exec. Officer--Twin County Grocers, Inc., Edison, NJ; *U.S. Private*, pg. 1111

D'Alessandro, Dominic, Pres. & Chief Exec. Officer--Manulife Financial (The Manufacturers Life Insurance Company), Toronto, Canada; *Int'l*, pg. 840

D'Alessandro, Dominic, Pres. & Chief Exec. Officer--Manulife Financial, Toronto, Canada; *Int'l*, pg. 840

D'Alessio, Frederick D., Pres. & Chief Exec. Officer--Bell Atlantic-MD, Baltimore, MD; *U.S. Public*, pg. 202

D'Amour, Donald H., Chm. Bd. & Chief Exec. Officer--Big Y Foods Inc., Springfield, MA; *U.S. Private*, pg. 143

D'Arcy, Thomas P., Pres. & Chief Exec. Officer--Bradley Real Estate, Inc., Northbrook, IL; *U.S. Public*, pg. 250

D'Urso, Giorgio, Pres. & Chief Exec. Officer--Diamedix Corporation, Miami, FL; *U.S. Public*, pg. 914

Daage, Didier Colmet, Chief Exec. Officer-Media Opers.--Havas Advertising, Levallois-Perret, France; *Int'l*, pg. 600

Dabah, Ezra, Chm. Bd., & Chief Exec. Officer--The Children's Place Retail Stores, Inc., West Caldwell, NJ; *U.S. Private*, pg. 237

Dabbagh, Ramzi, Chm. Bd. & Chief Exec. Officer--Communications Instruments Inc., Fairview, NC; *U.S. Private*, pg. 259

Daberko, David A., Chm. Bd. & Chief Exec. Officer--National City Corporation, Cleveland, OH; *U.S. Public*, pg. 1154

Dackow, Orest T., Pres. & Chief Exec. Officer--The Great-West Life Assurance Company, Winnipeg, Canada; *Int'l*, pg. 557

Dadd, Ronald F., Pres. & Chief Exec. Officer--Construction Specialties, Inc., Cranford, NJ; *U.S. Private*, pg. 266

Dagnan, O.G., Chm. Bd. & Chief Exec. Officer--Centex Construction Products, Inc., Dallas, TX; *U.S. Public*, pg. 322

Dahlberg, A.W., Chm. Bd., Pres. & Chief Exec. Officer--Southern Company, Atlanta, GA; *U.S. Public*, pg. 1489

Dahlmann, David S., Pres. & Chief Exec. Officer--Southwest National Corporation, Greensburg, PA; *U.S. Public*, pg. 1493

Dahnke, Scott, Chief Exec. Officer--American Business Information, Inc., Omaha, NE; *U.S. Public*, pg. 69

Dailey, Peter, Chm., Pres. & Chief Exec. Officer--Memorex Telex N.V., Amsterdam, Netherlands; *Int'l*, pg. 857

Dailey, T.E., Chief Exec. Officer--Claritas, Inc., Arlington, VA; *Int'l*, pg. 1447

Dalal, Ashok, Chief Exec. Officer--NewCare Health Corporation, Atlanta, GA; *U.S. Public*, pg. 1176

Dalessandro, William A., Chm. Bd. & Chief Exec. Officer--MTI/The Image Group, Inc., New York, NY; *U.S. Private*, pg. 688

Daley, C. Michael, Chm. & Chief Exec. Officer--LoJack Corporation, Dedham, MA; *U.S. Public*, pg. 1012

Dalhouse, Warner N., Chm. & Chief Exec. Officer--First Union National Bank of Virginia, Roanoke, VA; *U.S. Public*, pg. 640

Dalquist, H. David, Chm. Bd. & Chief Exec. Officer--Nordic Ware, Minneapolis, MN; *U.S. Private*, pg. 806

Dalquist, H. David, Sr., Chm. Bd. & Chief Exec. Officer--Northland Aluminum Products, Inc., Minneapolis, MN; *U.S. Private*, pg. 805

Dalton, Charles E., Pres. & Chief Exec. Officer--Blue Ridge Electric Cooperative Inc., Pickens, SC; *U.S. Private*, pg. 153

Dalton, George D., Chm. Bd. & Chief Exec. Officer--Fiserv, Inc., Brookfield, WI; *U.S. Public*, pg. 647

Dalton, James E., Jr., Pres. & Chief Exec. Officer--Quorum Health Group, Inc., Brentwood, TN; *U.S. Public*, pg. 1353

Dalton, William R.P., Chief Exec. Officer--Midland Bank PLC, London, United Kingdom; *Int'l*, pg. 580

Dalton, William R.P., Pres. & Chief Exec. Officer--HongKong Bank of Canada, Vancouver, Canada; *Int'l*, pg. 583

Daltoso, Joseph M., Chm. Bd., Pres. & Chief Exec. Officer--Micron Electronics, Inc., Nampa, ID; *U.S. Public*, pg. 1105

Daltry, Robert, Chm. Bd. & Chief Exec. Officer--Flir Systems, Inc., Portland, OR; *U.S. Public*, pg. 654

Daly, Kevin, Chm. Bd., Pres. & Chief Exec. Officer--ATL Products, Inc., Anaheim, CA; *U.S. Public*, pg. 1212

Daly, Robert A., Co-Chm. Bd. & Chief Exec. Officer--Warner Bros. Studios, Inc., Burbank, CA; *U.S. Public*, pg. 1611

Dambra, Barton, Pres. & Chief Exec. Officer--Markin Tubing, Inc., Wyoming, NY; *U.S. Private*, pg. 705

Damm, Karl Hans, Chief Exec. Officer--AEG Hausgerate AG, Nuremberg, Germany; *Int'l*, pg. 442

Dammeyer, Rod F., Pres. & Chief Exec. Officer--Great American Management & Investment, Inc., Chicago, IL; *U.S. Private*, pg. 473

Dan, Michael T., Pres. & Chief Exec. Officer--The Pittston Company, Glen Allen, VA; *U.S. Public*, pg. 1305

Dan, Michael T., Pres. & Chief Exec. Officer--Brink's, Inc., Darien, CT; *U.S. Public*, pg. 1305

Danahy, J. Patrick, Pres. & Chief Exec. Officer--Cone Mills Corporation, Greensboro, NC; *U.S. Public*, pg. 430

Dane, John, III, Chm. Bd., Pres. & Chief Exec. Officer--Halter Marine Group, Inc., Gulfport, MS; *U.S. Public*, pg. 778

Dangerfield, W.F., Chief Exec. Officer--New Zealand Starch, Auckland, New Zealand; *Int'l*, pg. 555

Daniel, Charles, Pres. & Chief Exec. Officer--UPB of Girardeau Co., Cape Girardeau, MO; *U.S. Public*, pg. 1669

Daniel, Richard N., Chm. Bd. & Chief Exec. Officer--Handy & Harman, New York, NY; *U.S. Public*, pg. 780

Daniels, William D., Chm. Bd. & Chief Exec. Officer--Penn-Daniels, Inc., Quincy, IL; *U.S. Public*, pg. 1467

Danilson, Ron, Pres. & Chief Exec. Officer--Delaware Charter Guarantee & Trust Co., Wilmington, DE; *U.S. Private*, pg. 885

Danis, Peter G., Jr., Pres. & Chief Exec. Officer-Boise Cascade Office Prods.--Boise Cascade Corporation, Boise, ID; *U.S. Public*, pg. 242

Danna, Leon J., Chm. Bd. & Chief Exec. Officer--Network Real Estate Inc., Capitola, CA; *U.S. Private*, pg. 791

Dannemiller, John C., Chm. Bd., Pres. & Chief Exec. Officer--Applied Industrial Technologies, Cleveland, OH; *U.S. Public*, pg. 122

Dannemiller, John C., Chm. & Chief Exec. Officer--Bruening Bearings, Inc., Cleveland, OH; *U.S. Public*, pg. 122

Dannemiller, John C., Chm. & Chief Exec. Officer--Dixie Bearings, Inc., Cleveland, OH; *U.S. Public*, pg. 122

Dannemiller, John C., Chm. & Chief Exec. Officer--King Bearing, Inc., Cleveland, OH; *U.S. Public*, pg. 122

Danner-Duroc, Bernard J., Pres. & Chief Exec. Officer--EVI, Inc., Houston, TX; *U.S. Public*, pg. 547

Danner, Dean W., Pres. & Chief Exec. Officer--Electronic Tele-Communications, Inc., Waukesha, WI; *U.S. Public*, pg. 570

Danner, Paul, Pres. & Chief Exec. Officer--Regions Bank/Citrus County, Inverness, FL; *U.S. Public*, pg. 1372

Danzinger, Eric A., Pres. & Chief Exec. Officer-Corp.--Starwood Hotels & Resorts, Phoenix, AZ; *U.S. Public*, pg. 1512

Dapper, G. Steven, Pres. & Chief Exec. Officer--Rapp Collins Worldwide, New York, NY; *U.S. Public*, pg. 1224

Darbelnet, Robert L., Pres. & Chief Exec. Officer--American Automobile Association, Heathrow, FL; *U.S. Private*, pg. 50

Darby, Christopher, Pres. & Chief Exec. Officer--Caronet LLC, Raleigh, NC; *U.S. Public*, pg. 307

Darby, Jim, Chief Exec. Officer--Kearney Company, Fayetteville, AR; *U.S. Public*, pg. 444

Darby, Joseph, Chief Exec. Officer--LASMO plc, London, United Kingdom; *Int'l*, pg. 803

Darby, Kenneth M., Pres. & Chief Exec. & Oper. Officer--Vicon Industries, Inc., Hauppauge, NY; *U.S. Public*, pg. 1719

Darcey, John, Chief Exec. Officer--Laminaire Corporation, Rahway, NJ; *U.S. Public*, pg. 1596

Darcy, Jon J., Pres., Chief Exec. Officer & Treas.--Thermo-Mizer Environmental Corp., Rahway, NJ; *U.S. Public*, pg. 1596

Dardel, Pierre Emmanuel, Chief Exec. Officer--Saint Dominique Participations, Paris, France; *Int'l*, pg. 344

Dardick, Steve, Chief Exec. Officer--DARCOM Technologies, Inc., Nashua, NH; *U.S. Private*, pg. 311

Darehshori, Nader, Chm. Bd., Pres. & Chief Exec. Officer--Houghton Mifflin Company, Boston, MA; *U.S. Public*, pg. 841

Dariano, Joseph, Chief Exec. Officer--Reed Technology and Information Services-Government Services, Horsham, PA; *Int'l*, pg. 1096

Darling, Darrell, Pres. & Chief Exec. Officer--First National Bank of Crossville, Crossville, TN; *U.S. Public*, pg. 1669

Darling, Robert M., Pres. & Chief Exec. Officer--Ampco Metal Incorporated, Milwaukee, WI; *U.S. Private*, pg. 67

Darling, W., Pres. & Chief Exec. Officer--General Railway Signal Corp., Rochester, NY; *Int'l*, pg. 1194

Darmisch, Hans E., Chief Exec.--Unternehmensbeteilgungs-gesellschaft fur die deutsche Wirtschaft, Frankfurt/Main, Germany; *Int'l*, pg. 418

Darnall, Robert J., Chm. Bd., Pres. & Chief Exec. Officer--Inland Steel Industries, Inc., Chicago, IL; *U.S. Public*, pg. 879

Darnall, Robert J., Chm. Bd. & Chief Exec. Officer--Inland International, Inc., Chicago, IL; *U.S. Public*, pg. 879

Darvish, John, Pres. & Chief Exec. Officer--Darcars Ltd., Lanham, MD; *U.S. Private*, pg. 311

Dasburg, John H., Pres. & Chief Exec. Officer--Northwest Airlines Corp., Saint Paul, MN; *U.S. Public*, pg. 1199

Dassault, Serge, Chm. Bd. & Chief Exec. Officer--Dassault Aviation Group, Vaucresson, France; *Int'l*, pg. 383

Dauch, Richard E., Pres. & Chief Exec. Officer--American Axle & Manufacturing, Detroit, MI; *U.S. Private*, pg. 51

Daugherty, Jack R., Chm. Bd. & Chief Exec. Officer--Cash America International, Inc., Fort Worth, TX; *U.S. Public*, pg. 312

Daul, Robert, Chief Exec. Officer--Mahlo GmbH & Co. KG, Saal, Germany; *Int'l*, pg. 830

Davatzes, Nicholas, Pres. & Chief Exec. Officer--The History Channel, New York, NY; *U.S. Public*, pg. 512

Davatzes, Nickolas, Pres. & Chief Exec. Officer--Arts & Entertainment Network/ABC/NBC, New York, NY; *U.S. Public*, pg. 512

Davatzes, Nickolas, Pres. & Chief Exec. Officer--A&E Television Networks, New York, NY; *U.S. Private*, pg. 515

Davatzes, Nickolas, Pres. & Chief Exec. Officer--Arts & Entertainment Network/ABC/NBC, New York, NY; *U.S. Private*, pg. 516

Davenport, Glenn A., Pres. & Chief Exec. Officer--Morrison Health Care Inc., Smyrna, GA; *U.S. Public*, pg. 1133

Davenport, Timothy A., Pres. & Chief Exec. Officer--Best Software, Inc., Reston, VA; *U.S. Public*, pg. 223

David-Weill, Michel, Chm Bd. & Chief Exec. Officer--Lazard Freres & Co., New York, NY; *Int'l*, pg. 1027

David, George A., Pres. & Chief Exec. Officer--United Technologies Corporation, Hartford, CT; *U.S. Public*, pg. 1689

David, Mark M., Chm. Bd. & Chief Exec. Officer--Movie Star, Inc., New York, NY; *U.S. Public*, pg. 1140

David, Morton E., Chm. Bd. & Co-Chief Exec. Officer--Franklin Electronic Publishers, Inc., Burlington, NJ; *U.S. Public*, pg. 679

David, P. J., Chief Exec. Officer--Pig Improvement Group Ltd., Abingdon, United Kingdom; *Int'l*, pg. 376

Davidge, C.M., Chief Exec. Officer--Christies International plc, London, United Kingdom; *Int'l*, pg. 289

Davids, Bob, Chief Exec. Officer--Radica USA Limited, Dallas, TX; *U.S. Private*, pg. 906

Davidson, Charles T., Chm. Bd., Pres. & Chief Exec. Officer--J.A. Jones, Inc., Charlotte, NC; *Int'l*, pg. 633

Davidson, Charles T., Chm. Bd., Pres. & Chief Exec. Officer--J. A. Jones Construction Company, Charlotte, NC; *Int'l*, pg. 633

Davidson, Don, Chm. Bd. & Chief Exec. Officer--Outdoor Systems, Inc.-New York, New York, NY; *U.S. Public*, pg. 1235

Davidson, F. Lee, Pres. & Chief Exec. Officer--Parks Corporation, Fall River, MA; *U.S. Private*, pg. 840

Davidson, George A., Jr., Chm. Bd. & Chief Exec. Officer--Consolidated Natural Gas Company, Pittsburgh, PA; *U.S. Public*, pg. 435

Davidson, Ian B., Chm. Bd. & Chief Exec. Officer--D.A. Davidson & Co., Great Falls, MT; *U.S. Private*, pg. 314

Davidson, Lawrence J., Jr., Pres., Chief Exec.,Oper. & Fin. Officer--The Weathervane Retail Corp., New Britain, CT; *U.S. Private*, pg. 1156

Davidson, Richard K., Chm. Bd., Pres. & Chief Exec. Officer--Union Pacific Corporation, Dallas, TX; *U.S. Public*, pg. 1667

Davidson, Robert M., Chm. Bd. & Chief Exec. Officer--Davidson & Associates, Inc., Torrance, CA; *U.S. Public*, pg. 320

Davidson, Spencer, Pres. & Chief Exec. Officer--General American Investors Company, Inc., New York, NY; *U.S. Public*, pg. 706

Davidson, William, Chm. Bd., Pres., Chief Exec. & Chief Oper. Officer--Guardian Industries Corp., Auburn Hills, MI; *U.S. Private*, pg. 485

Davies, C.W., Jr., Pres. & Chief Exec. Officer--Tultex Corporation, Martinsville, VA; *U.S. Public*, pg. 1644

Davies, Craig E., Pres. & Chief Exec. Officer--UTILX Corporation, Kent, WA; *U.S. Public*, pg. 1701

Davies, D.J., Chm. & Chief Exec.--Johnson Matthey Public Limited Company, London, United Kingdom; *Int'l*, pg. 713

Davies, Mike, Chief Exec. Officer--Newmond PLC, Tamworth, United Kingdom; *Int'l*, pg. 924

Davies, Paul T., Pres. & Chief Exec. Officer--F.W. Woolworth Co., New York, NY; *U.S. Public*, pg. 1777

Davies, Robert A., III, Pres. & Chief Exec. Officer--Church & Dwight Co., Inc., Princeton, NJ; *U.S. Public*, pg. 355

Davies, Robert A., III, Chief Exec. Officer--Arm & Hammer Consumer Products, Princeton, NJ; *U.S. Public*, pg. 356

Davies, Tudor, Chief Exec. Officer--Hicking Pentecost Plc, Penarth, United Kingdom; *Int'l*, pg. 618

Davis, A. Dano, Chm. Bd. & Principal Exec. Officer--Winn-Dixie Stores, Inc., Jacksonville, FL; *U.S. Public*, pg. 1771

Davis, Allen L., Pres. & Chief Exec. Officer--Provident Financial Group, Inc., Cincinnati, OH; *U.S. Public*, pg. 1338

Davis, Brian, Pres. & Chief Exec. Officer--Nationwide Building Society, Swindon, United Kingdom; *Int'l*, pg. 912
Davis, Charles E., Sr., Chm. Bd., Pres. & Treas.--Laboratory Supply Company, Inc., Louisville, KY; *U.S. Private*, pg. 641
Davis, DeForest P., Jr., Chm. Bd. & Chief Exec. Officer--Lester B. Knight & Associates, Inc., Chicago, IL; *U.S. Private*, pg. 626
Davis, Edwin V., II, Pres. & Chief Exec. Officer--First Security Bank of Oregon, Salem, OR; *U.S. Public*, pg. 637
Davis, Erroll B. Jr., Pres. & Chief Exec. Officer--WPL Holdings, Inc., Madison, WI; *U.S. Public*, pg. 1727
Davis, Gareth, Chief Exec. Officer--Imperial Tobacco Group, Ltd., Bristol, United Kingdom; *Int'l*, pg. 666
Davis, Harold, Chm. Bd. & Chief Exec. Officer--Electrical Wholesale Supply Company, Inc., Idaho Falls, ID; *U.S. Private*, pg. 368
Davis, Jack, Pres. & Chief Exec. Officer--Ventura Foods LLC, City of Industry, CA; *Int'l*, pg. 879
Davis, James, Chm. Bd. & Chief Exec. Officer--New Balance Athletic Shoe, Inc., Boston, MA; *U.S. Private*, pg. 792
Davis, James B., Jr., Chief Exec. Officer--Jimmy Davis Enterprises, Inc., Madison, FL; *U.S. Private*, pg. 315
Davis, James C., Pres. & Chief Exec. Officer--FFG Trust, Inc., Springfield, IL; *U.S. Public*, pg. 644
Davis, James S., Pres. & Chief Exec. Officer--TAD Resources International, Inc., Cambridge, MA; *U.S. Private*, pg. 1062
Davis, James V., Ph.D., Chm. Bd. & Chief Exec. Officer--Willis Corroon Advanced Risk Management Services, Nashville, TN; *Int'l*, pg. 1505
Davis, Jay M., Pres. & Chief Exec. Officer--National Distributing Co., Inc., Atlanta, GA; *U.S. Private*, pg. 781
Davis, Jeffrey G., Chm. Bd., Pres. & Chief Exec. Officer--Aetna Plywood, Inc., Barrington, IL; *U.S. Private*, pg. 25
Davis, Jerry, Chm. Bd. & Chief Exec. Officer--Affiliated Foods Southwest, Little Rock, AR; *U.S. Private*, pg. 26
Davis, Joe, Chief Exec. Officer--Consolidated Graphics, Inc., Houston, TX; *U.S. Private*, pg. 265
Davis, John, Pres. & Chief Exec. Officer--Thomson Book/Reference Group, Stamford, CT; *U.S. Public*, pg. 1600
Davis, John S., Pres. & Chief Exec. Officer--Mobile Gas Service Corp., Mobile, AL; *U.S. Public*, pg. 1120
Davis, Kenneth A., Pres., Chief Exec. Officer & Chief Oper. Officer--PharmHouse, Inc., New York, NY; *U.S. Public*, pg. 1286
Davis, L.L., Chm. & Chief Exec. Officer--Marley Mouldings Inc., Marion, VA; *Int'l*, pg. 843
Davis, Leon A., Mng. Dir. & Chief Executive--CRA Limited, Melbourne, Australia; *Int'l*, pg. 1119
Davis, Mark D., Chm. & Chief Exec. Officer--DavisElen Advertising, Inc., Los Angeles, CA; *U.S. Private*, pg. 316
Davis, Marvin A., Chm. Bd. & Chief Exec. Officer--Datamax International Corporation, Orlando, FL; *U.S. Private*, pg. 313
Davis, Norwood, Chm. Bd. & Chief Exec. Officer--Trigon Blue Cross & Blue Shield, Richmond, VA; *U.S. Public*, pg. 1637
Davis, Pat, Pres. & Chief Exec. Officer--UPB of Northeast MS, New Albany, MS; *U.S. Public*, pg. 1669
Davis, Peter, Sir, Grp. Chief Exec.--Prudential Corporation PLC, London, United Kingdom; *Int'l*, pg. 1073
Davis, Richard A., Pres. & Chief Exec. Officer--Treibacher Schleifmittel Corp., Niagara Falls, NY; *U.S. Private*, pg. 1099
Davis, Richard A., Pres. & Chief Exec. Officer--Pentzer Corporation, Spokane, WA; *U.S. Public*, pg. 1744
Davis, Ronald D., Pres. & Chief Exec. Officer--Monroc, Inc., Salt Lake City, UT; *U.S. Public*, pg. 1124
Davis, Ronald J., Chm. & Chief Exec. Officer--Biggs Gilmore Communications, Kalamazoo, MI; *U.S. Private*, pg. 143
Davis, Samuel B., Chm. Bd., Chief Exec. Officer & Treas.--Liqui-Box Corporation, Worthington, OH; *U.S. Public*, pg. 1000
Davis, Shelby M.C., Chm. Bd., Pres. & Chief Exec. Officer--Davis Selected Advisors, L.P., Santa Fe, NM; *U.S. Private*, pg. 315
Davis, Thomas A., Pres., Chief Exec. Officer & Asst. Sec.--United HealthCare of Utah, Salt Lake City, UT; *U.S. Public*, pg. 1678
Davis, W. Donald, Chm. Bd., Pres. & Chief Exec. Officer--SouthTrust Bank, Cullman County, Cullman, AL; *U.S. Public*, pg. 1491
Davis, Wes, Pres. & Chief Exec. Officer--Microtouch Systems, Inc., Methuen, MA; *U.S. Public*, pg. 1108
Davis, William E., Chm. Bd. & Chief Exec. Offcier--Niagara Mohawk Power Corporation, Syracuse, NY; *U.S. Public*, pg. 1181
Davis, William H., Chief Exec. Officer & New Bus. Contact--Holland Mark Martin, Boston, MA; *U.S. Private*, pg. 534
Davis, William L., Chm. Bd. & Chief Exec. Officer--R.R. Donnelley & Sons Company, Chicago, IL; *U.S. Public*, pg. 517
Davis, William L., Chm. Bd & Chief Exec. Officer--Vermont American Tool Corp., Louisville, KY; *U.S. Public*, pg. 575
Davison, William H., Chm. Bd. & Chief Exec. Officer--SunTrust Bank, East Central Florida, Daytona Beach, FL; *U.S. Public*, pg. 1537
Davisson, W. Gene, Pres. & Chief Exec. Officier--Bank of Hundred, Hundred, WV; *U.S. Public*, pg. 850
Davoli, Pier Paolo, Chief Exec. Officer--Finsiel, Rome, Italy; *Int'l*, pg. 654
Davutoglu, Nesteren, Chief Exec. Officer--Lowe Adam, Istanbul, Turkey; *U.S. Private*, pg. 678
Daw, Ronald W., Chm. Bd., Pres. & Chief Exec. Officer--Daw Technologies, Inc., Salt Lake City, UT; *U.S. Public*, pg. 489
Dawdy, Richard A., Chm. Bd. & Chief Exec. Officer--UMB First State Bank of Morrisonville, Morrisonville, IL; *U.S. Public*, pg. 1654
Dawson, James A., Pres. & Chief Exec. Officer--Quebecor Printing (USA) Corp., Boston, MA; *Int'l*, pg. 1076
Dawson, Laurence A., Jr., Pres. & Co.-Chief Exec. Officer--American Homestar Corporation, League City, TX; *U.S. Public*, pg. 83
Dawson, Tom, Chm. Bd., Pres. & Chief Exec. Officer--Dawson Construction Co., Inc., Gadsden, AL; *U.S. Private*, pg. 316
Day, Frank, Chm. Bd., Pres. & Chief Exec. Officer--Rock Bottom Restaurants, Louisville, CO; *U.S. Public*, pg. 1396
Day, James D., Chm. Bd., Pres. & Chief Exec. Officer--Noble Drilling Corporation, Houston, TX; *U.S. Public*, pg. 1186
Day, John T., Pres. & Chief Exec. Officer--Mining Services International, Inc., Sandy, UT; *U.S. Public*, pg. 1115
Day, Joseph C., Pres. & Chief Exec. Officer--Freudenberg-NOK, Plymouth, MI; *U.S. Private*, pg. 427
Day, Timothy T., Chm. Bd. & Chief Exec. Officer--Bar-S Foods Co., Phoenix, AZ; *U.S. Private*, pg. 114
Dayan, Charles, Pres. & Chief Exec. Officer--Bon Jour International Ltd., New York, NY; *U.S. Private*, pg. 156
Dayan, Charles, Pres. & Chief Exec. Officer--Licensing Div., New York, NY; *U.S. Private*, pg. 156
de Argumosa, A. Arnaz, Chief Exec. Officer--OCE-Espana S.A., Barcelona, Spain; *Int'l*, pg. 994
de Bakker, Ferry, Pres. & Chief Exec. Officer-Europe (London)--Burson-Marsteller, New York, NY; *U.S. Private*, pg. 1197
de Beausse, Xavier, Chief Exec.--BNP-Dresdner Bank (Bulgaria) A.D., Sofia, Bulgaria; *Int'l*, pg. 418
De Benedetti, Carlo, Chm. & Chief Exec. Officer--CERUS - Compagnies Europeennes Reunies, Paris, France; *Int'l*, pg. 240
De Biase, Dean, Pres. & Chief Exec. Officer--The Imagination Network, Burlingame, CA; *U.S. Public*, pg. 66
de Boysson, Gaetan, Chm. Bd. & Chief Exec. Officer--Saint Dominique Finance, Paris, France; *Int'l*, pg. 344
de Buhr, Ted, Pres. & Chief Exec. Officer--Fox Photo, Inc., Saint Louis, MO; *U.S. Public*, pg. 283
De Carlo, Romano, Chief Exec. Officer & Gen. Mgr.--C.S.O. Centrale Supporti Operativi S.p.A., Torri di Quartesolo, Italy; *Int'l*, pg. 138
de Carvalho Dias, Roberto Marques, Pres. & Chief Exec. Officer--LPC Industrias Alimenticias S.A., Vila Jaguara, Brazil; *Int'l*, pg. 380
de Chalendar, Pierre Andre, Chm. Bd., Pres. & Chief Exec. Officer--Norton Company, Worcester, MA; *Int'l*, pg. 1173
de Cima, Ernesto Zaragoza, Pres. & Chief Exec. & Chief Fin. Officer--Inversiones De Guaymas S.A. De C.V., Guaymas, Mexico; *Int'l*, pg. 685
de Col, Renato, Chief Exec. Officer & Gen. Mgr.--Itafinco S.p.A., Milan, Italy; *Int'l*, pg. 138
De Crescenzo, Tony, Chief Oper. Officer & Exec. V.P.--Marlite, Dover, OH; *U.S. Private*, pg. 705
de Croisset, Charles, Chm. Bd. & Chief Exec. Officer--Credit Commercial de France, Paris, France; *Int'l*, pg. 341
De Deo, Joe, Chief Exec. Officer--Young & Rubicam, S.A. de C.V., Mexico, Mexico; *U.S. Private*, pg. 1200
De Forrest, Sean B., Pres. & Chief Exec. Officer--American Security Distribution, Anaheim, CA; *U.S. Private*, pg. 61
de Geus, Aart J., Chm. Bd. & Chief Exec. Officer--Synopsys, Inc., Mountain View, CA; *U.S. Public*, pg. 1548
De Graffenreidt, James H., Jr., Pres. & Chief Exec. Officer--Washington Gas Light Co., Springfield, VA; *U.S. Public*, pg. 1740
de Jong, H., Chief Exec. Officer--Aluminium Delfzijl BV, Delfzijl, Netherlands; *Int'l*, pg. 753
De Jonge, Max, Pres. & Chief Exec. Officer--O'Neal Steel Inc., Birmingham, AL; *U.S. Private*, pg. 817
de la Cruz, Rene, Pres. & Chief Exec. Officer--de la Cruz & Associates, San Juan, PR; *U.S. Private*, pg. 318
de la Parra, Miguel Blesa, Chm., Pres. & Chief Exec. Officer--Caja de Madrid Group, Madrid, Spain; *Int'l*, pg. 251
de Labouchere, Pierre, Pres. & Chief Exec. Officer--R.J. Reynolds Tobacco Intl., Inc., Geneva, Switzerland; *U.S. Public*, pg. 1355
de Lima Mayer, Th., Chief Exec. Officer--OCE-Lima Mayer S.A., Lisbon, Portugal; *Int'l*, pg. 994
De Montgailhard, William Desazars, Chief Exec. Officer--Cycles Europe, Romilly-sur-Seine, France; *Int'l*, pg. 350
de Oliveira, Manuel, Chief Exec. Officer--Cimianto Sth SA, Vila Franca de Xira, Portugal; *Int'l*, pg. 430
De Oliveira, Manuel Ferreira, Chm. & Chief Exec. Officer--Petrogal, s.a., Lisbon, Portugal; *Int'l*, pg. 1044
de Pouzilhac, Alain, Chm. & Chief Exec. Officer--Havas Advertising, Levallois-Perret, France; *Int'l*, pg. 600
de Puzo, Julio J., Jr., Pres. & Chief Exec. Officer--Source Capital, Inc., Los Angeles, CA; *U.S. Public*, pg. 1488
de Puzo, Julio J., Jr., Chief Exec. Officer--First Pacific Advisors, Inc., Los Angeles, CA; *U.S. Public*, pg. 1673
De Roissard, Henri, Chm. Bd. & Chief Exec. Officer--Dumez-GTM, Nanterre, France; *Int'l*, pg. 823
de Roissard, Henri, Chm. & Chief Exec. Officer--Dumez-GTM, Nanterre, France; *Int'l*, pg. 823
De Santis, Nunzio, Chief Exec. Officer--International Thoroughbred Breeders, Inc., Cherry Hill, NJ; *U.S. Public*, pg. 908
De Schutter, Richard U., Chief Exec. Officer--Searle Laboratories, Skokie, IL; *U.S. Public*, pg. 1125
de Severac, Jean, Chief Exec. Officer--Parviland Gerance, Paris, France; *Int'l*, pg. 344
De Stigter, Glenn H., Pres. & Chief Exec. Officer--The Weitz Company, Inc., Des Moines, IA; *U.S. Private*, pg. 1160
de Sus Auria, E., Chief Exec. Officer--OCE-Renting S.A., Barcelona, Spain; *Int'l*, pg. 995
de Thieusies, Etienne Orbert, Vice. Chm. & Chief Exec. Officer--Peugeot Talbot Espana, Madrid, Spain; *Int'l*, pg. 1021
De Titta, Louis, Jr., Chief Exec. Officer--SSD&W Integrated Marketing Communications, Montville, NJ; *U.S. Private*, pg. 958
de Visser, R.J.L., Chief Exec.--DSM Elastomers, Sittard, Netherlands; *Int'l*, pg. 353
De Vito, Robert A., Chm. Bd., Pres., Chief Exec. & Chief Oper. Officer--Cyber Systems, Inc., Anaheim, CA; *U.S. Private*, pg. 299
Deal, Frederick A., Pres. & Chief Exec. Officer--Society First Federal Savings Bank, Fort Myers, FL; *U.S. Public*, pg. 954
Dean, Henry E., III, Pres. & Chief Exec. Officer--The Monticello Companies, Inc., Jacksonville, FL; *U.S. Private*, pg. 759
Dean, Howard M., Chm. Bd. & Chief Exec. Officer--Dean Foods Company, Franklin Park, IL; *U.S. Public*, pg. 489
Dean, Lester M., Sr., Chm. Bd & Chief Exec. Officer--Dean Operations Inc., Kansas City, MO; *U.S. Private*, pg. 318
Dean, Ned, Chm. Bd. & Chief Exec. Officer--Chase & Sanborn Coffee, Inc., San Francisco, CA; *Int'l*, pg. 917
Dearden, Douglas E., Chief Exec. Officer--Dearden's, Los Angeles, CA; *U.S. Private*, pg. 319
Dearlove, A. James, Pres. & Chief Exec. Officer--Penn Virginia Corporation, Radnor, PA; *U.S. Public*, pg. 1271
DeArment, W.S., Pres. & Chief Exec. Officer--Hold-E-Zee, Ltd., Meadville, PA; *U.S. Private*, pg. 229
DeArment, William S., Pres. & Chief Exec. Officer--Channellock, Inc., Meadville, PA; *U.S. Private*, pg. 229
Deason, Darwin, Chm. Bd. & Chief Exec. Officer--Affiliated Computer Services, Inc., Dallas, TX; *U.S. Public*, pg. 27
Deasy, William J., Vice Chm., Pres. & Chief Exec. Officer--T.L. James & Company, Ruston, LA; *U.S. Private*, pg. 580
Deavenport, Earnest W., Jr,, Chm. Bd. & Chief Exec. Officer--Eastman Chemical Company, Kingsport, TN; *U.S. Public*, pg. 550
DeBartolo, Edward J., Jr., Pres. & Chief Exec. Officer--The Edward J. DeBartolo Corporation, Youngstown, OH; *U.S.* Private, pg. 319
Debenedictis, Nicholas, Chm. Bd., Pres. & Chief Exec. Officer--Philadelphia Suburban Corporation, Bryn Mawr, PA; *U.S. Public*, pg. 1287
deBest, Cess, Pres. & Chief Exec. Officer--Verkerke Reprodukties, N.V., Ede, Netherlands; *U.S. Private*, pg. 496
Debonny, Mike, Pres. & Chief Exec. Officer--OMNI Products, Inc., Portland, OR; *U.S. Private*, pg. 816
Decaluwe, Rafael, Chief Exec. Officer--N.V. Bekaert S.A., Kortrijk, Belgium; *Int'l*, pg. 183
DeCamp, D.A., Pres. & Chief Exec. Officer--Flexfab Horizons International, Inc., Hastings, MI; *U.S. Private*, pg. 412
DeCarlo, Anthony J., Pres. & Chief Exec. Officer--Lumbermens Merchandising Corporation, Wayne, PA; *U.S. Private*, pg. 680
DeCesaris, Geaton A., Jr., Pres. & Chief Exec. Officer--Washington Homes, Inc., Landover, MD; *U.S. Public*, pg. 1741
Decherd, Robert W., Chm. Bd., Pres. & Chief Exec. Officer--A.H. Belo Corporation, Dallas, TX; *U.S. Public*, pg. 209
Decio, Arthur J., Chm. Bd. & Chief Exec. Officer--Skyline Corporation, Elkhart, IN; *U.S. Public*, pg. 1476
Decker, Jack E., Chm. Bd. & Chief Exec. Officer--Campbell Oil Co., Massillon, OH; *U.S. Private*, pg. 204
Dedgo, Harry, Chief Exec. Officer--Essence Communications Inc., New York, NY; *U.S. Private*, pg. 383
Dedman, Robert H., Sr., Chm. Bd. & Chief Exec. Officer--Club Corporation International, Dallas, TX; *U.S. Private*, pg. 247
Dedman, Robert, Jr., Chm. Bd. & Chief Exec. Officer--Club Corp Realty, Dallas, TX; *U.S. Private*, pg. 247
Dee, John T., Pres. & Chief Exec. Officer--Service America Corporation, Stamford, CT; *U.S. Private*, pg. 986
Dee, Robert, Chief Exec. Officer--Dee Paper Company, Chester, PA; *U.S. Private*, pg. 320
Deeney, Gerald D., Chief Fin. Officer--United States Satellite Broadcasting, Co., Saint Paul, MN; *U.S. Private, pg. 544*
Deering, Anthony W., Chm. Bd., Pres. & Chief Exec. Officer--The Rouse Company, Columbia, MD; *U.S. Public*, pg. 1407
DeFabis, Mike, Pres. & Chief Exec. Officer--Associated Wholesale Grocers, Inc., Kansas City, KS; *U.S. Private*, pg. 93
DeFeo, Ronald M., Pres. & Chief Exec. Officer--Terex Corporation, Westport, CT; *U.S. Public*, pg. 1581
Deferrari, Ronald H., Chm. Bd., Chief Exec. Officer, Treas. & Sec.--Plasma-Therm, Inc., Saint Petersburg, FL; *U.S. Public*, pg. 1308
Defibaugh, Patricia J., Chm. Bd., Chief Exec. Officer, & Treas.--Aloette Cosmetics, Inc., West Chester, PA; *U.S. Public*, pg. 57
Defline, Louis, Chief Exec. Officer & Mng. Dir.--ECIA-Equipments Et Composants Pour L'industrie Automobile, Audincourt, France; *Int'l*, pg. 1021
Degan, Robert A., Pres. & Chief Exec. Officer--Summa Four, Inc., Manchester, NH; *U.S. Public*, pg. 1527
Degen, Alfred P., Chm. Bd., Pres. & Chief Exec. Officer--Valley Resources, Inc., Cumberland, RI; *U.S. Public*, pg. 1706
DeGiglio, Michael A., Pres. & Chief Exec. Officer--EcoScience Corporation, East Brunswick, NJ; *U.S. Public*, pg. 563
Dehmlow, Steven L., Pres., Chief Exec. & Chief Oper. Officer--GLS Corporation, Arlington Heights, IL; *U.S. Private*, pg. 435
Deieso, Donald A., Ph.D., Pres. & Chief Exec. Officer--EA Engineering, Science & Technology, Inc., Hunt Valley, MD; *U.S. Public*, pg. 540
Deikel, Theodore, Chm. Bd., Pres. & Chief Exec. Officer--Fingerhut Corp., Minnetonka, MN; *U.S. Public*, pg. 623

Deinhammer, Robert L., Chief Exec. Officer--Applied Microsystems Corporation, Redmond, WA; *U.S. Public*, pg. 123
deJaray, Steven A.W., Pres. & Chief Exec. Officer--AIM Safety Company Inc., Delta, Canada; *Int'l*, pg. 36
Dekker, Marcel, Chm. Bd. & Chief Eexec. Officer--Marcel Dekker, Inc., New York, NY; *U.S. Private*, pg. 321
Dekker, Russell, Chief Pub. Officer--Marcel Dekker, Inc., New York, NY; *U.S. Private*, pg. 321
Del Ninno, Giulio, Chief Exec. Officer--Edison S.p.A., Milan, Italy; *Int'l*, pg. 324
del Peral, Javier Revuelta, Chief Exec. Officer--Telefonica de Espana, S.A., Madrid, Spain; *Int'l*, pg. 1371
del Rivero, Eduardo, Pres. & Chief Exec. Officer--del Rivero Messianu Advertising, Ltd., Coral Gables, FL; *U.S. Private*, pg. 321
del Rosal, Roberto, Pres. & Chief Exec. Officer--Bacardi Corporation, San Juan, PR; *Int'l*, pg. 131
Del Vecchio, Claudio, Pres. & Chief Exec. Officer--Casual Corner Group, Inc., Enfield, CT; *U.S. Private*, pg. 219
Del Vecchio, Claudio, Pres. & Chief Exec. Officer--Casual Corner Outlet, Enfield, CT; *U.S. Private*, pg. 219
Del Vecchio, Claudio, Co-Chief Exec. Officer--Luxottica Group S.p.A., Agordo, Italy; *Int'l*, pg. 822
del Vecchio, Leonardo, Chm. Bd.--Casual Corner Group, Inc., Enfield, CT; *U.S. Private*, pg. 219
Delahanty, P., Chief Oper. Officer--J & B Products, Inc., South Bend, IN; *U.S. Private*, pg. 399
Delahousse, Michel, Chief Exec. Officer--Credit Mutuel, Paris, France; *Int'l*, pg. 344
DeLap, Mike, Pres. & Chief Exec. Officer--Schlosser Forge Company, Rancho Cucamonga, CA; *U.S. Private*, pg. 970
Delattre, Philippe, Deputy Chief Exec. Officer-Fin.--Credit Agricole, Bonvin, France; *Int'l*, pg. 341
Delaunois, Philippe, Vice Chm. & Chief Exec. Officer--Cockerill Sambre, Brussels, Belgium; *Int'l*, pg. 301
Delavan, John P., Pres. & Chief Exec. Officer--Intrenet, Inc., Milford, OH; *U.S. Public*, pg. 910
Delfosse, J., Chief Exec. Officer--Redland Koramic Bricks N.V., Malle, Belgium; *Int'l*, pg. 1093
Deli, Steven F., Chm. & Chief Exec. Officer--Eaglemark Financial Services, Inc., Chicago, IL; *U.S. Public*, pg. 786
Dell, Michael S., Chm. Bd. & Chief Exec. Officer--Dell Computer Corporation, Round Rock, TX; *U.S. Public*, pg. 495
Dell'Oca, Conrad J., Ph.D., Pres. & Chief Exec. Officer--Aspec Technology, Inc., Sunnyvale, CA; *U.S. Private*, pg. 89
Della Femina, Jerry, Chm., Chief Exec. Officer & Creative Dir.--Jerry & Ketchum, New York, NY; *U.S. Private*, pg. 616
Dellamano, Patricia, Pres. & Chief Exec. & Chief Fin. Officer--Patson's Press, Sunnyvale, CA; *U.S. Private*, pg. 843
DelliBovi, Alfred A., Pres. & Chief Exec. Officer--Federal Home Loan Bank of New York, New York, NY; *U.S. Private*, pg. 399
Delmonico, Louis A., Chm. Bd. & Chief Exec. Officer--MacNeal-Schwendler Corp., Costa Mesa, CA; *U.S. Public*, pg. 1031
DeLong, Dan, Pres. & Chief Exec. Officer--Triplett Corporation, Bluffton, OH; *U.S. Private*, pg. 1104
Delorme, J.P., Pres. & Chief Exec. Officer--U.S. Divers Co., Inc., Santa Ana, CA; *U.S. Private*, pg. 1125
Delp, R. Lee, Pres. & Chief Exec. Officer--Moyer Packing Company, Souderton, PA; *U.S. Private*, pg. 765
DeLuca, Anthony J., Pres. & Chief Exec. Officer--International Technology Corporation, Monroeville, PA; *U.S. Public*, pg. 907
DeLuca, Robert, Chm. Bd., Pres. & Chief Exec. Officer--Aero Data Metal Crafters, Ronkonkoma, NY; *U.S. Private*, pg. 23
DeLuca, Robert, Pres. & Chief Exec. Officer--Air Crafters Inc., Ronkonkoma, NY; *U.S. Private*, pg. 24
DeLuca, Roberta, Pres. & Chief Exec. Officer--Lab Crafters Inc., Ronkonkoma, NY; *U.S. Private*, pg. 24
DeLue, Robert S., Pres. & Chief Exec. Officer--ACSIA, Burlingame, CA; *Int'l*, pg. 499
Delusinne, Philippe, Pres., Mng. Dir. & Chief Exec. Officer--Young & Rubicam Belgium S.A., Brussels, Belgium; *U.S. Private*, pg. 1199
DelZotto, Angelo, Chm. & Chief Exec. Officer--Tridel Enterprises Inc., Downsview, Canada; *Int'l*, pg. 1423
DeMaria, Joseph A., Sr., Chm. Bd. & Chief Exec. Officer--DeMaria Building Co. Inc., Novi, MI; *U.S. Private*, pg. 323
DeMarines, Victor A., Pres. & Chief Eexec. Officer--Mitre Corporation, Bedford, MA; *U.S. Private*, pg. 753
DeMars, Dan R., Chm. Bd. & Chief Exec. Officer--Geupel DeMars, Inc., Indianapolis, IN; *U.S. Private*, pg. 449
Demarthe, J.M., Pres. & Chief Exec. Officer--Minemet Recherche, Trappes, France; *Int'l*, pg. 661
Dembinski, Jan A., Pres., Chief Exec. Officer & Treas.--M.J. Daly & Sons, Inc., Waterbury, CT; *U.S. Private*, pg. 309
Demere, Robert H., Jr., Pres. & Chief Exec. Officer--Colonial Oil Industries, Savannah, GA; *U.S. Private*, pg. 253
Demeritt, Stephen R., Chief Exec. Officer--Cereal Partners Worldwide, Morges, Switzerland; *U.S. Public*, pg. 718
Demeritt, Stephen R., Chief Exec. Officer--Cereal Partners Worldwide, Morges, Switzerland; *Int'l*, pg. 916
DeMerritt, Ted C., Chief Exec. Officer--Olsy North America Inc., Liberty Lake, WA; *Int'l*, pg. 1002
DeMeulenaere, Robert L., Pres. & Chief Exec. Officer--Brenton Banks, Inc., Des Moines, IA; *U.S. Public*, pg. 251
DeMeulenaere, Robert L., Chief Exec. Officer--Brenton Bank, Des Moines, IA; *U.S. Public*, pg. 251
Deming, Claiborne P., Pres. & Chief Exec. Officer--Murphy Oil Corporation, El Dorado, AR; *U.S. Public*, pg. 1141
Deming, Robert H., Chm. Bd. & Chief Exec. Officer--Toastmaster, Inc., Columbia, MO; *U.S. Public*, pg. 1619
Demjan, Zoltan, Chief Exec.--Hirocem a.s., Rohoznik, Slovenia; *Int'l*, pg. 629
Demme, James, Chm. Bd. & Chief Exec. Officer--Bruno's Inc., Birmingham, AL; *U.S. Public*, pg. 265
Demmer, John E., Chief Exec. Officer--Jack Demmer Ford, Inc., Wayne, MI; *U.S. Private*, pg. 323
Demms, Terry D., Pres. & Chief Exec. Officer--CSW Energy, Inc., Dallas, TX; *U.S. Public*, pg. 324
Demone, Henry E., Pres. & Chief Exec. Officer--National Sea Products Limited, Lunenburg, Canada; *Int'l*, pg. 909
Demone, Henry E., Pres. & Chief Exec. Officer--National Sea Products Incorporated, Portsmouth, NH; *Int'l*, pg. 909
DeMoulas, Telemachus A., Pres. & Chief Exec. Officer--Demoulas Market Basket, Tewksbury, MA; *U.S. Private*, pg. 324
Dempster, Alastair C., Chief Exec. Officer--TSB Bank Scotland Plc, Edinburgh, United Kingdom; *Int'l*, pg. 813
Denburg, Edmund, Pres. & Chief Exec. Officer--Barton Press, Inc., West Orange, NJ; *U.S. Private*, pg. 120
Denig, Thomas H., Pres. & Chief Exec. Officer--TJ International, Inc., Boise, ID; *U.S. Public*, pg. 1556
Denisco, Ralph, Pres. & Chief Exec. Officer--Norse Dairy Systems, Columbus, OH; *U.S. Private*, pg. 802
Denisco, Ralph A., Chief Exec. Officer--Noise Dairy Systems, LP, Columbus, OH; *U.S. Private*, pg. 249
Denise, Robert, Chm. Bd., Pres., Chief Exec. Officer & Chief Fin. Officer--Bucilla Corporation, Hazleton, PA; *U.S. Private*, pg. 352
Denlea, Leo, Chm. Bd. & Chief Exec. Officer--Farmers Group, Inc., Los Angeles, CA; *Int'l*, pg. 110
Dennis, Daniel R., Jr., Chm. Bd., Pres. & Chief Exec. Officer--Norwich Financial Corp., Norwich, CT; *U.S. Public*, pg. 1203
Denny, Charles W., Pres. & Chief Exec. Officer-N. American Division/Schneider Elec.--Schneider S.A., Boulogne-Billancourt, France; *Int'l*, pg. 1207
Denotte, Gianfranco, Deputy Chief Exec.--Cassa di Risparmio delle Provincie Lombarde SpA (CARIPLO), Milan, Italy; *Int'l*, pg. 274
DePaul, John D., Chm. Bd., Pres. & Chief Exec. Officer--The Lehigh Press, Inc., Cherry Hill, NJ; *U.S. Private*, pg. 658
Der Torossian, Papken S., Chm. Bd. & Chief Exec. Officer--Silicon Valley Group, Inc., San Jose, CA; *U.S. Public*, pg. 1474
Dermul, Walter, Chief Exec. Officer-Organization & Fin.--Quattro DMB&B, Brussels, Brussels, Belgium; *U.S. Private*, pg. 305
DeRoeck, Walter A., Chm. Bd. & Chief Exec. Officer--TCC Industries, Austin, TX; *U.S. Public*, pg. 1554
DeRosa, Paul R., Pres. & Chief Exec. Officer--Eastbridge Holdings Inc., New York, NY; *Int'l*, pg. 933
Derr, Kenneth T., Chm. Bd. & Chief Exec. Officer--Chevron Corporation, San Francisco, CA; *U.S. Public*, pg. 347
Derrick, John M., Jr., Pres. & Chief Exec. Officer--Potomac Electric Power Company, Washington, DC; *U.S. Public*, pg. 1318
Derrick, Mark E., Pres. & Chief Exec. Officer--Perry & Derrick Co., Cincinnati, OH; *U.S. Private*, pg. 854
Derschow, Feico, Chief Exec. Officer & Art Dir.--Eiler & Riemel - Testa, Munich, Germany; *Int'l*, pg. 1377
Derst, Edward J., III, Pres. & Chief Exec. Officer--Derst Baking Company, Inc., Savannah, GA; *U.S. Private*, pg. 326
DeRusha, William C., Chm. Bd. & Chief Exec. Officer--Heilig-Meyers Company, Richmond, VA; *U.S. Public*, pg. 804
Desbiens, Michel, Pres. & Chief Exec. Officer--Donohue Inc., Quebec, Canada; *Int'l*, pg. 1075
Descarpentries, Jean-Marie, Chm. Bd. & Chief Exec. Officer--Compagnie des Machines Bull, Louveciennes, France; *Int'l*, pg. 315
Deschenes, Jean-Pierre, Chief Exec. Officer--Cooperative Federee de Quebec, Montreal, Canada; *Int'l*, pg. 330
DeSimone, Livio D., Chm. Bd. & Chief Exec. Officer--3M, Saint Paul, MN; *U.S. Public*, pg. 1604
DesJardins, Stanley P., Chm. Bd. & Chief Exec. Officer--Simula, Inc., Phoenix, AZ; *U.S. Public*, pg. 1475
Desmarais, Andre, Deputy Chm. Bd. & Assoc. Chief Exec. Officer--Southam Inc., Don Mills, Canada; *Int'l*, pg. 631
Desmarest, Thierry, Chm. Bd. & Chief Exec. Officer--Total S.A., Paris, France; *Int'l*, pg. 1408
Desor, Klaus, Chief Exec.--Europa Bank AG, Luxembourg, Luxembourg; *Int'l*, pg. 420
Desprez, Martin, Chm. Bd., Pres., Chief Exec. Officer & Dir. General--Editions du Juris-Classeur, Paris, France; *Int'l*, pg. 1095
Desproges, Patrick, Chief Exec. Officer--Comark Communications, Inc., Chalfont, PA; *Int'l*, pg. 1383
Desriac, J. L., Chief Exec. Officer--OCE Graphics France S.A., Creteil, France; *Int'l*, pg. 994
Dessimoz, Richard E., Chief Exec. Officer--Wabash National Finance Corp., Arlington Heights, IL; *U.S. Public*, pg. 1730
DeStefanis, John, Pres. & Chief Exec. Officer-Charter--Magellan Health Services, Inc., Atlanta, GA; *U.S. Public*, pg. 1033
DeStefano, James L., Pres. & Chief Exec. Officer--Emcee Broadcast Products, Inc., White Haven, PA; *U.S. Public*, pg. 570
Detsch, Hanspeter, Chief Exec. Officer--Impuls Advertising AG, Kusnacht, Switzerland; *Int'l*, pg. 666
Detsch, Hanspeter, Chief Exec. Officer--Impuls Advertising, Bern, Switzerland; *Int'l*, pg. 666
Detter, Gerald L., Pres. & Chief Exec. Officer--Con-Way Transportation Services, Palo Alto, CA; *U.S. Public*, pg. 281
Deulofeu, Julio, Pres.-San Francisco & Dir.--EvansGroup, Salt Lake City, UT; *U.S. Private*, pg. 385
Deuster, Robert G., Chm. Bd., Pres. & Chief Exec. Officer--Newport Corporation, Irvine, CA; *U.S. Public*, pg. 1179
Deutsch, Donny, Chief Exec. Officer--Deutsch, Inc., New York, NY; *U.S. Private*, pg. 328
Devencenzi, Mark, Chief Exec. Officer--Harmony Foods Corporation, Santa Cruz, CA; *U.S. Private*, pg. 503
Devening, R. Randolph, Chm. Bd., Pres. & Chief Exec. Officer--Foodbrands America, Inc., Oklahoma City, OK; *U.S. Public*, pg. 852
DeVesto, Thomas J., Pres. & Chief Exec. Officer--Cambridge Soundworks, Inc., Newton, MA; *U.S. Private*, pg. 202
Devlin, Mike, Pres. & Chief Exec. Officer--Rational Software Corporation, Cupertino, CA; *U.S. Public*, pg. 1361
Devlin, Robert M., Chm. Bd. & Chief Exec. Officer--American General Corporation, Houston, TX; *U.S. Public*, pg. 76
Devlin, Robert M., Chm. Bd. & Chief Exec. Officer--The American Franklin Life Insurance Co., Springfield, IL; *U.S. Public*, pg. 76
DeVore, Ron, Chief Exec. Officer--Terumo Medical Corporation, Somerset, NJ; *Int'l*, pg. 1376
DeVries, William L., Pres. & Chief Exec. Officer-Athletic Footwear & Apparel--Woolworth Corporation, New York, NY; *U.S. Public*, pg. 1777
Devroy, Floyd, Chief Exec. Officer--Intermark World Products, Ltd., Kenilworth, IL; *U.S. Private*, pg. 567
Dew, Donald H., Chm. Bd., Pres. & Chief Exec. Officer--Diemolding Corp., Canastota, NY; *U.S. Private*, pg. 332
Dewan, Derek E., Chm. Bd., Pres. & Chief Exec. Officer--AccuStaff Incorporated, Jacksonville, FL; *U.S. Public*, pg. 15
Dewavrin, Daniel, Chm. Bd. & Chief Exec. Officer--Bertrand Faure, Boulogne, France; *Int'l*, pg. 192
DeWindt, D. Stephen, Chm. Bd. & Chief Exec. Officer--Ameriquest Technologies, Santa Ana, CA; *U.S. Public*, pg. 96
DeWinter, C. Mark, Chm. Bd., Pres. & Chief Exec. Officer--Woodhead Industries, Inc., Buffalo Grove, IL; *U.S. Public*, pg. 1776
di Comite, Emilio, Chief Exec. Officer & Gen. Mgr.--Fiscambi Leasing S.p.A., Milan, Italy; *Int'l*, pg. 138
di Vignano, Tomaso Tommasi, Chief Exec. Officer--Telecom Italia S.p.A., Rome, Italy; *Int'l*, pg. 1362
Dial, Neil, Chief Exec. Officer & V.P.--ADFlex Solutions, Inc., Chandler, AZ; *U.S. Public*, pg. 20
Dial, Walter David, III, Chm. Bd., Pres. & Chief Exec. Officer--Plymouth Creameries, Inc., Plymouth, WI; *U.S. Private*, pg. 872
Diamond, Chris, Pres., Chief Oper. Officer & Chief Exec. Officer--Haystack Ski Resort at Mount Snow, Wilmington, VT; *U.S. Private*, pg. 61
Diamond, Gerald, Chm. Bd. & Chief Exec. Officer--Southern Electronics Corporation, Tucker, GA; *U.S. Public*, pg. 1490
Diamond, Harris, Chm. & Chief Exec. Officer--BSMG Worldwide, New York, NY; *U.S. Public*, pg. 1642
Diamond, Lawrence, Chm. Bd., Pres., Chief Exec. & Chief Oper. Officer & Dir.-Pur.--Triangle Marketing Corp., New York, NY; *U.S. Private*, pg. 1102
Diamond, Rick N., Chm. Bd. & Chief Exec. Officer--ACI Telecentrics, Inc., Minneapolis, MN; *U.S. Public*, pg. 3
Diamond, Walter S., Chm. Bd., Chief Exec. Officer & V.P.--Snyder-Diamond, Santa Monica, CA; *U.S. Private*, pg. 1011
DiBui, William J., Pres., Chief Exec. Office & Chief Oper. Officer--Rumsey Electric Company, Conshohocken, PA; *U.S. Private*, pg. 951
DiCamillo, Gary T., Chm. & Chief Exec. Officer--Polaroid Corporation, Cambridge, MA; *U.S. Public*, pg. 1313
Dicapo, Rick, Chief Exec. Officer--Medical Center of Baton Rouge, Baton Rouge, LA; *U.S. Public*, pg. 405
Dick, David E., Chief Exec. Officer--Dick Corporation, Large, PA; *U.S. Private*, pg. 331
Dickelman, James H., Chm. Bd., Pres. & Chief Exec. Officer--Schultz Sav-O Stores, Inc., Sheboygan, WI; *U.S. Public*, pg. 1442
Dickerson, Arthur J., Chm. Bd., Pres. & Chief Exec. Officer--Southwestern Petroleum Corporation, Fort Worth, TX; *U.S. Private*, pg. 1019
Dickerson, James H., Jr., Chief Exec. Officer--Bell Atlantic Investment Development Corporation, Philadelphia, PA; *U.S. Public*, pg. 202
Dickerson, Michael A., Pres. & Chief Exec. Officer--High Point Financial Corp., Branchville, NJ; *U.S. Public*, pg. 826
Dickson, Harold A., Jr., Chm. Bd., Pres. & Chief Exec. Officer--SouthTrust Bank, Sylacauga, Sylacauga, AL; *U.S. Public*, pg. 1492
Dickson, Thomas W., Pres.--Ruddick Corporation, Charlotte, NC; *U.S. Public*, pg. 1412
Diego, Guillermo, Chm., Pres. & Chief Exec. Officer-Y&R Spain--Young & Rubicam, S.A., Madrid, Spain; *U.S. Private*, pg. 1199
Diehl, Peter, Pres. & Chief Exec. Officer--Diehl Inc., Defiance, OH; *U.S. Private*, pg. 332
Dierberg, James, Chm. Bd., Pres. & Chief Exec. Officer--First Banks America, Inc., Clayton, MO; *U.S. Public*, pg. 626
Dietler, Cortlandt S., Chm. Bd. & Chief Exec. Officer--TransMontaigne Oil Company, Denver, CO; *U.S. Public*, pg. 1631
Dietrich, Thomas W., Pres. & Chief Exec. Officer--Dietrich's Milk Products, Inc., Reading, PA; *U.S. Private*, pg. 332
Dietrich, Wendell, Chm. Bd. & Chief Exec. Officer--Vidar, Inc., New London, MN; *U.S. Private*, pg. 1139
Dietz, Klaus, Chief Exec. Officer--Hoechst Roussel Vet GmbH, Wiesbaden, Germany; *Int'l*, pg. 626
DiGeso, Amy, Pres. & Chief Exec. Officer-MaryKay, Inc.--Mary Kay Corporation, Dallas, TX; *U.S. Private*, pg. 710
Diggins, John, Pres. & Chief Exec. Officer--Foresight Software, Inc., Atlanta, GA; *U.S. Private*, pg. 872
Diggins, John, Pres. & Chief Exec. Officer--Pilot Software, Cambridge, MA; *U.S. Private*, pg. 872
DiGiovanna, Charles, Pres. & Chief Exec. Officer--Continental Plastic Containers, Inc., Norwalk, CT; *U.S. Public*, pg. 440
DiGiusto, Walter, Pres., Chief Exec. Officer & Treas.--ESA, Inc., Chelmsford, MA; *U.S. Private*, pg. 354

Dilda, Roland, Pres. & Chief Exec. Officer--Aero Systems Engineering Inc., Saint Paul, MN; *Int'l*, pg. 276
Dill, John, Pres. & Chief Exec. Officer--McGraw-Hill Ryerson, Ltd., Whitby, Canada; *U.S. Public*, pg. 1072
Dillamore, Ian, Chm. & Chief Exec. Officer--Doncasters plc, Melbourn, United Kingdom; *Int'l*, pg. 416
Dillard, William, Chm. Bd. & Chief Exec. Officer--Dillard's, Inc., Little Rock, AR; *U.S. Public*, pg. 509
Diller, Barry, Chm. Bd. & Chief Exec. Officer--USA Networks, Inc., Saint Petersburg, FL; *U.S. Public*, pg. 1685
Diller, James V., Chm. Bd. & Chief Exec. Officer--Sierra Semiconductor, San Jose, CA; *U.S. Public*, pg. 1470
Dillman, Ron, Chief Exec. Officer & Gen. Mgr.--The Virgin Islands Daily News, Saint Thomas, VI; *U.S. Public*, pg. 702
Dillon, Daniel P., Pres. & Chief Exec. Officer--Welch Foods Inc., A Cooperative, Concord, MA; *U.S. Private*, pg. 784
Dillon, Gary G., Chm. Bd., Pres. & Chief Exec. Officer--Schwitzer, Inc., Indianapolis, IN; *U.S. Public*, pg. 968
Dillon, John T., Chm. Bd. & Chief Exec. Officer--International Paper Company, Purchase, NY; *U.S. Public*, *pg. 901*
Dillon, John T., Chief Exec. Officer--Hammermill Papers, Memphis, TN; *U.S. Public*, pg. 902
DiLorenzo, James E., Chm. Bd., Pres. & Chief Exec. Officer--Quality Pontiac GMC Buick, Albuquerque, NM; *U.S. Private*, pg. 899
DiMeglio, S.J., Chief Exec. Officer--Guest Services, Inc., Fairfax, VA; *U.S. Private*, pg. 486
Dimeo, Thomas P., Pres. & Chief Exec. Officer--Dimeo Construction Company, Providence, RI; *U.S. Private*, pg. 333
Dimitriou, A., Chief Exec. Officer--B&D Instruments and Avionics, Inc., Valley Center, KS; *Int'l*, pg. 208
Dimmick, Henry M., Chm. Bd. & Chief Exec. Officer--AGR International, Inc., Butler, PA; *U.S. Private*, pg. 5
Dimon, Jamie, Co-Chm. & Co-Chief Exec. Officer--Salomon Smith Barney Holdings, Inc., New York, NY; *U.S. Public*, pg. 1633
Dindorf, Joseph L., Chm. Bd., Pres. & Chief Exec. Officer--Hein-Werner Corporation, Waukesha, WI; *U.S. Public*, pg. 805
Dines, Paul, Chm. Bd., Pres. & Chief Exec. Officer--Reyco Industries, Inc., Springfield, MO; *U.S. Private*, pg. 926
Dinetz, Steven, Pres. & Chief Exec. Officer--Chancellor Radio Broadcasting Co., Dallas, TX; *U.S. Public*, pg. 335
DiNicola, Robert J., Chm. Bd., Pres. & Chief Exec. Officer--Zale Corporation, Irving, TX; *U.S. Public*, pg. 1789
DiNicola, Robert J., Chm. Bd. & Chief Exec. Officer--Zale Delaware, Inc., Irving, TX; *U.S. Public*, pg. 1789
Dinstein, Stanford M., Vice Chm. & Chief Exec. Officer--Builders Transport, Incorporated, Camden, SC; *U.S. Public*, pg. 267
Dion, Philip J., Chm. Bd. & Chief Exec. Officer--Del Webb Corporation, Phoenix, AZ; *U.S. Public*, pg. 494
Dionne, Joseph L., Chm. Bd. & Chief Exec. Officer--The McGraw-Hill Companies, New York, NY; *U.S. Public*, pg. 1069
DiPasqua, Louis S., Pres. & Chief Exec. Officer--TBC Corporation, Memphis, TN; *U.S. Public*, pg. 1553
Dirkes, James V., Sr., Chm. Bd., Chief Exec. Officer & Treas.--Rapid Engineering Inc., Comstock Park, MI; *U.S. Private*, pg. 910
DiRomualdo, Robert, Chm. Bd & Chief Exec. Officer--Borders Group, Inc., Ann Arbor, MI; *U.S. Public*, pg. 245
Dirti, Arnold, Chief Exec. Officer--Hedstrom Holding Co., Mount Prospect, IL; *U.S. Private*, pg. 526
Disbrow, Bruce, Pres. & Chief Exec. Officer--DonTech, Chicago, IL; *U.S. Public*, pg. 98
Dischler, Ralph, Pres. & Chief Exec. Officer--Maplehurst Farms, Inc., Indianapolis, IN; *U.S. Public*, pg. 490
Dishinger, C.W., Chief Exec. Officer--Richmond Screw Anchor Company, Fort Worth, TX; *U.S. Private*, pg. 932
Ditri, Arnold, Chief Exec. Officer--Hedstrom Corporation, Mount Prospect, IL; *U.S. Private*, pg. 526
Ditri, Arnold, Chief Exec. Officer--ERO, Inc., Mount Prospect, IL; *U.S. Private*, pg. 526
Ditri, Arnold, Chief Exec. Officer--ERO Industries, Inc., Mount Prospect, IL; *U.S. Private*, pg. 526
Ditto, Arthur H., Pres. & Chief Oper. Officer--Kinross Gold Corporation, Toronto, Canada; *Int'l*, pg. 734
Divin, Rolland, Pres. & Chief Exec. Officer--Tom's Foods, Inc., Columbus, GA; *U.S. Private*, pg. 1090
Divird, D. Thomas, Pres. & Chief Exec. Officer--Anchor Continental Incorporated, Columbia, SC; *U.S. Private*, pg. 70
Dix, Jan, Chief Exec. Officer--OCE-U.S.A., Itasca, IL; *Int'l*, pg. 994
Dix, Jan F., Pres. & Chief Exec. Officer--OCE USA, Inc., Chicago, IL; *Int'l*, pg. 994
Dixon, John, Pres. & Chief Exec. Officer--Mutual Service Corporation, North Palm Beach, FL; *U.S. Private*, pg. 831
Dixon, Stephen, Pres. & Chief Exec. Officer--Martin Luther Hospital Anaheim, Anaheim, CA; *U.S. Private*, pg. 1118
Dixon, Steve, Chief Exec. Officer--La Palma Intercommunity Hospital, La Palma, CA; *U.S. Private*, pg. 1118
Dixson, M.C.S., Dr., Chief Exec. Officer--Simon Engineering plc, London, United Kingdom; *Int'l*, pg. 1251
Djumaeva, Stora V., Chief Exec.--Novo Nordisk A/S, Tashkent, Uzbekistan; *Int'l*, pg. 987
do Carmo, Jorge, Chief Oper. Officer--Sharp do Brasil S.A. Industria de Equipamentos Electronicos, Manaus, Brazil; *Int'l*, pg. 1229
Dobbin, Alvin, Pres. & Chief Exec. Officer--Giant of Salisbury, Inc., Hyattsville, MD; *U.S. Public*, pg. 741
Dobbin, Alvin, Pres. & Chief Exec. Officer--Shaw Community Supermarket, Hyattsville, MD; *U.S. Public*, pg. 741
Dobby, L. M., Grp. Chief Exec.--Meyer International PLC, London, United Kingdom; *Int'l*, pg. 864
Dobson, Thomas, Pres. & Chief Exec. Officer--Whataburger, Inc., Corpus Christi, TX; *U.S. Private*, pg. 1170
Dockweiler, Thomas L., Pres. & Chief Exec. Officer--First National Bank of Blue Island, Blue Island, IL; *U.S. Private*, pg. 474
Doctor, Louis J., Pres. & Chief Exec. Officer--Truevision, Inc., Santa Clara, CA; *U.S. Public*, pg. 1642
Dodd, David A., Pres. & Chief Exec. Officer--Solvay Pharmaceuticals, Inc., Marietta, GA; *Int'l*, pg. 1278
Doddridge, John, Chm. Bd. & Chief Exec. Officer--Intermet Corporation, Troy, MI; *U.S. Public*, pg. 894
Dodds, Douglas W., Vice Chm., Pres. & Chief Exec. Officer--Schneider Corp., Kitchener, Canada; *Int'l*, pg. 1207
Dodge, Arthur B., III, Pres. & Chief Exec. Officer--Dodge Regupol, Inc., Lancaster, PA; *U.S. Private*, pg. 337
Dodge, E.V., Pres. & Chief Exec. Officer--Canadian Pacific Railway, Minneapolis, MN; *Int'l*, pg. 259
Dodge, James H., Chm. Bd., Pres. & Chief Exec. Officer--Providence Energy Corporation, Providence, RI; *U.S. Public*, pg. 1337
Dodig, Victor G., Pres. & Chief Exec. Officer--Atlas Asset Management Inc., Toronto, Canada; *Int'l*, pg. 865
Dods, Walter A., Jr., Chm. Bd. & Chief Exec. Officer--First Hawaiian, Inc., Honolulu, HI; *U.S. Public*, pg. 634
Dods, Walter A., Jr., Chm. Bd. & Chief Exec. Officer--First Hawaiian Bank, Honolulu, HI; *U.S. Public*, pg. 634
Dods, Walter A., Jr., Chm. Bd. & Chief Exec. Officer--Real Estate Delivery, Inc., Honolulu, HI; *U.S. Public*, pg. 635
Dods, Walter A., Jr., Chm. Bd. & Chief Exec. Officer--American Security Properties, Inc., Honolulu, HI; *U.S. Public*, pg. 635
Dods, Walter A., Jr., Chm. & Chief Exec. Officer--First Hawaiian Insurance, Inc., Honolulu, HI; *U.S. Public*, pg. 635
Dodson Macaulay, Cathleen, Chm. Bd. & Chief Exec. Officer--Dodson Group, Kansas City, MO; *U.S. Private*, pg. 338
Dodson, David, Chm. Bd. & Chief Exec. Officer--ADAP Inc., Brockton, MA; *U.S. Private*, pg. 4
Doehrman, Dale F., Chm. Bd. & Chief Exec. Officer--The Medical Protective Company, Fort Wayne, IN; *U.S. Private*, pg. 728
Doepper, Walter, Prof. Dr., Chief Exec. Officer--Kennametal Hertel AG, Furth, Germany; *U.S. Public*, pg. 951
Doeren, William B., Pres. & Chief Exec. Officer--General Cinema Theatres, Inc., Chestnut Hill, MA; *U.S. Public*, pg. 693
Doering, John H., Chief Exec. Officer-Dover Mills Ltd. & V.P.--Dover Industries Limited, Burlington, Canada; *Int'l*, pg. 417
Doerner, Ewald, Chief Exec.--DSB-Dresdner Bank, Santiago, Chile; *Int'l*, pg. 419
Doggett, Ron E., Chm. Bd. & Chief Exec. Officer--GoodMark Foods, Inc., Raleigh, NC; *U.S. Public*, pg. 751
Doherty, Edward D., Chm. Bd. & Chief Exec. Officer--Kaneb Pipe Line Partners, L.P., Richardson, TX; *U.S. Public*, pg. 942
Doherty, Phillip H., Pres. & Chief Exec. Officer--Star Data Systems Inc., Markham, Canada; *U.S. Public*, pg. 1077
Dohmen, John, Pres. & Chief Exec. Officer--The F. Dohmen Company, Germantown, WI; *U.S. Private*, pg. 338
Dohrman, Fred, Pres. & Chief Exec. Officer--Winnebago Acceptance Corp., Forest City, IA; *U.S. Public*, pg. 1772
Dohrmann, Fred G., Chief Exec. Officer--Winnebago Industries, Inc., Forest City, IA; *U.S. Public*, pg. 1772
Doig, George, Pres. & Chief Exec. Officer--Johnson Yokogawa Corporation, Newnan, GA; *Int'l*, pg. 1521
Dolan, James L., Chief Exec. Officer--Cablevision Systems Corporation, Woodbury, NY; *U.S. Public*, pg. 288
Dolan, Ronald V., Pres. & Chief Exec. Officer--First Colony Life Insurance Co., Lynchburg, VA; *U.S. Public*, pg. 711
Dolgen, Jonathan L., Chm. Bd. & Chief Exec. Officer-Viacom Entertainment Grp.--National Amusements, Inc., Dedham, MA; *U.S. Private*, pg. 775
Dollens, Ronald W., Pres. & Chief Exec. Officer--Guidant Corporation, Indianapolis, IN; *U.S. Public*, pg. 768
Dollens, Ronald W., Chief Exec. Officer-Guident--Guidant Corporation-Cardiac Rhythm Management Group, Saint Paul, MN; *U.S. Public*, pg. 768
Dolson, Robert A., Pres. & Chief Exec. Officer--Continental Water Company, Saint Louis, MO; *U.S. Private*, pg. 269
Doman, H.S., Chm. Bd., Pres. & Chief Exec. Officer--Doman Industries Limited, Duncan, Canada; *Int'l*, pg. 414
Dominioni, A.M., Chief Exec. Officer--Cucina Classica Italiana, Inc., Lakewood, NJ; *U.S. Public*, pg. 1435
Dominioni, Angelo M., Pres. & Chief Exec. Officer--Cucina Classica Italiana Inc., Lakewood, NJ; *U.S. Public*, pg. 1435
Dominski, Matthew S., Chief Exec. Officer--Urban Shopping Centers, Inc., Chicago, IL; *U.S. Public*, pg. 1700
Domuracki, Mary Ann, Chief Exec. Officer--Danskin Inc., New York, NY; *U.S. Public*, pg. 483
Domuracki, Mary Ann, Pres. & Chief Exec. Officer--Pennaco Hosiery, New York, NY; *U.S. Public*, pg. 483
Don, Robert E., Chm. Bd. & Chief Exec. Officer--Edward Don & Company, North Riverside, IL; *U.S. Private*, pg. 339
Donahue, Dennis, Pres. & Chief Exec. Officer & Chief Oper. Officer--The Will-Burt Company, Orrville, OH; *U.S. Private*, pg. 1177
Donahue, William L., Chm. Bd., Pres., Chief Exec. & Chief Oper. Officer--Dixon Paper Co., Denver, CO; *U.S. Public*, *pg. 902*
Donald, James L., Chm. Bd., Pres. & Chief Exec. Officer--DSC Communications Corporation, Plano, TX; *U.S. Public*, pg. 475
Donald, Jim, Chm. Bd., Pres. & Chief Exec. Officer--Pathmark Stores Incorporated, Woodbridge, NJ; *U.S. Private*, pg. 843
Donaldson, Darrell, Pres. & Chief Exec. Officer--Hot Shot Delivery Inc., Houston, TX; *U.S. Private*, pg. 541
Donaldson, Hugh, Chief Exec. Officer--Spillers Foods, New Malden, United Kingdom; *Int'l*, pg. 376
Donaldson, J. Harold, Pres. & Chief Exec. Officer--Regions Bank/Marianna, Marianna, FL; *U.S. Public*, pg. 1372
Donaldson, Jerry, Exec. V.P. & Chief Exec. Officer--First National Bank of Saxton, Allentown, PA; *U.S. Public*, pg. 1222
Donaway, Carl D., Pres. & Chief Exec. Officer--ABX Air, Inc., Wilmington, OH; *U.S. Public*, pg. 33
Donawho, James L., Acting Chief Exec. Officer--Howell Instruments Inc., Fort Worth, TX; *U.S. Private*, pg. 543
Donnell, Thomas, V.P. & Pres. & Chief Exec. Officer-Cain's Coffee Co.--Chock Full O' Nuts Corporation, New York, NY; *U.S. Public*, pg. 351
Donnelly, Thomas, Pres. & Chief Exec. Officer--Camping World, Inc., Bowling Green, KY; *U.S. Private*, pg. 204
Donner, Michael, Chm. Bd., Pres. & Chief Exec. Officer--Barco of California, Gardena, CA; *U.S. Private*, pg. 115
Donohue, Thomas J., Pres. & Chief Exec. Officer--Nation's Business, Washington, DC; *U.S. Private*, pg. 788
Dooley, Larry W., Pres. & Chief Exec. Officer--Regions Bank-Cedartown/Rockmart, Cedartown, GA; *U.S. Public*, *pg. 1372*
Dooner, John J., Jr., Chm. & Chief Exec. Officer--McCann-Erickson Worldwide, New York, NY; *U.S. Public*, pg. 909
Dora, Aysegul, Chm. Bd. & Chief Exec. Officer--Penajans DMB&B Ticaret, Istanbul, Turkey; *U.S. Private*, pg. 305
Dordelman, Bill, Chief Exec. Officer--Colorado Prime Corporation, Farmingdale, NY; *U.S. Private*, pg. 255
Dore, William J., Chm. Bd., Pres. & Chief Exec. Officer--Global Industries, Ltd., Lafayette, LA; *U.S. Public*, pg. 748
Doretti, Robert L., Pres. & Chief Exec. Officer--Thinking Machines Corporation, Burlington, MA; *U.S. Private*, pg. 1081
Dorfer, Manfred, Chief Exec. Officer--Dorfer Dialogue GmbH, Frankfurt/Main, Germany; *U.S. Private*, pg. 304
Dorfman, Joel, Pres. & Chief Exec. Officer--Thorn Apple Valley, Inc., Southfield, MI; *U.S. Public*, pg. 1602
Dorfman, Larry I., Pres. & Chief Exec. Officer--Automobile Protection Corporation-APCO, Atlanta, GA; *U.S. Public*, pg. 150
Doria, Joseph, Pres. & Chief Exec. Officer--The Lincoln Electric Co. of Canada Ltd., Toronto, Canada; *U.S. Public*, pg. 997
Dorio, Martin, Pres. & Chief Exec. Officer--Clark Material Handling Company, Lexington, KY; *U.S. Private*, pg. 243
Doris, Kevin, Pres. & Chief Exec. Officer--Gerland Corp., Houston, TX; *U.S. Private*, pg. 449
Dorner, Wolfgang, Chm. Bd. & Chief Exec. Officer--Dorner Manufacturing Corp., Hartland, WI; *U.S. Private*, pg. 340
Dorrian, James, Chm. Bd. & Chief Exec. Officer--Arbor Software Corporation, Sunnyvale, CA; *U.S. Public*, pg. 127
Dorris, Al, Pres. & Chief Exec. Officer--Xerxes Corporation, Minneapolis, MN; *U.S. Private*, pg. 1194
Dorval, Remi, Chief Exec. Officer--Forasol S.A., Velizy-Villacoublay, France; *Int'l*, pg. 496
dos Santos, Elisio Alexandre Soares, Chief Exec. Officer--YMR, Lisbon, Portugal; *Int'l*, pg. 750
Dott, A. Eric, Chm. Bd. & Chief Exec. Officer--Monarch Avalon, Inc., Baltimore, MD; *U.S. Public*, pg. 1123
Dotterweich, Helmut, Pres. & Chief Exec. Officer--Spar Handels AG, Schenefeld, Germany; *Int'l*, pg. 1288
Dottori, Frank A., Pres. & Chief Exec. Officer--Tembec Inc., Montreal, Canada; *Int'l*, pg. 1374
Doucet, John, Pres. & Chief Oper. Officer--Day & Ross Inc., Hartland, Canada; *Int'l*, pg. 850
Dougan, Paul M., Pres. & Chief Exec. Officer--Equity Oil Company, Salt Lake City, UT; *U.S. Public*, pg. 590
Doughan, James, Pres. & Chief Exec. Officer--Abitibi-Consolidated Inc., Montreal, Canada; *Int'l*, pg. 19
Dougherty, David F., Pres. & Chief Exec. Officer--MATRIXX Marketing Inc., Cincinnati, OH; *U.S. Public*, pg. 368
Douglas, Herbert, Pres. & Chief Exec. Officer--Weiners Stores, Inc., Houston, TX; *U.S. Private*, pg. 1160
Douglas, T. O'Neal, Chm. Bd. & Chief Exec. Officer--American Heritage Life Investment Corp., Jacksonville, FL; *U.S. Public*, pg. 78
Douglas, T. O'Neal, Chm. Bd. & Chief Exec. Officer--American Heritage Life Insurance Co., Jacksonville, FL; *U.S. Public*, pg. 79
Douglas, T. O'Neal, Chm. Bd., Pres. & Chief Exec. Officer--First Colonial Insurance Company, Jacksonville, FL; *U.S.* Public, pg. 79
Douglass, Steven J., Chm. Bd. & Chief Exec. Officer--Payless ShoeSource, Inc., Topeka, KS; *U.S. Public*, pg. 1268
Douroux, Lucien, Chief Exec. Officer--Credit Agricole, Bonvin, France; *Int'l*, pg. 341
Doust, Arthur F., Chm. Bd. & Chief Exec. Officer--Chemi-Trol Chemical Co., Gibsonburg, OH; *U.S. Public*, pg. 345
Douville, Jean, Chm. Bd., Pres. & Chief Exec. Officer--UAP, Inc., Montreal, Canada; *Int'l*, pg. 1426
Dow, Ngiam Tong, Chm. Bd. & Chief Exec. Officer--DBS Bank Ltd., Singapore, Singapore; *Int'l*, pg. 350
Dow, Paul A., Chief Exec. Officer & Chief Inv. Officer--Piper Capital Management, Incorporated, Minneapolis, MN; *U.S. Public*, pg. 1303
Dow, William J., Chief Oper. Officer--Daily Racing Form, Inc., Phoenix, AZ; *U.S. Public*, pg. 1327
Dowd, James F., Chief Exec. Officer--Odyssey Reinsurance Corporation, New York, NY; *Int'l*, pg. 1258
Dowd, Kevin P., Pres., Chief Exec. Officer & Chief Oper. Officer--Checkpoint Systems Inc., Thorofare, NJ; *U.S. Public*, pg. 343
Dowd, Philip L., Grp. Chief Exec. Officer-SunGard Trust & Shareholder Systems--SunGard Data Systems Inc., Wayne, PA; *U.S. Public*, pg. 1534
Dowdell, Rodger B., Jr., Chm. Bd., Pres. & Chief Exec. Officer--American Power Conversion Corporation, West Kingston, RI; *U.S. Public*, pg. 89
Dowdle, James C., Pres. & Chief Exec. Officer--CLTV News, Oak Brook, IL; *U.S. Public*, pg. 1635
Dowell, Gary R., Pres. & Chief Exec. Officer--Reistertown Federal Savings Bank, Baltimore, MD; *U.S. Public*, pg. 1543

Dowers, Dale, Chief Exec. Officer--J.M. Peters Co., Newport Beach, CA; *U.S. Public,* pg. 302
Dowling, James H., Chm. Emeritus, Pres. & Chief Exec. Officer-Lat. Amer. (Miami)--Burson-Marsteller, New York, NY; *U.S. Private,* pg. 1197
Downes, Laurence M., Chm. Bd., Pres. & Chief Exec. Officer--New Jersey Resources Corporation, Wall, NJ; *U.S. Public,* pg. 1172
Downey, Bruce L., Chm. Bd., Pres. & Chief Exec. Officer--Barr Laboratories Inc., Pomona, NY; *U.S. Public,* pg. 191
Downing, Kathryn, Pres. & Chief Exec. Officer--Matthew Bender & Company, Incorporated, New York, NY; *U.S. Public,* pg. 1616
Downing, Kathryn M., Pres. & Chief Exec. Officer--Mosby-Year Book, Inc., Saint Louis, MO; *U.S. Public,* pg. 1616
Downs, Richard, Chm. Bd. & Chief Exec. Officer--Tony Downs Foods Company, Saint James, MN; *U.S. Private,* pg. 342
Dowsett, Patrick W., Pres. & Chief Exec. Officer--East Moline Metal Products Company, East Moline, IL; *U.S. Private,* pg. 357
Doyle White, R., Chm. Bd., Pres. & Chief Exec. Officer--U.S. Filter/Davis Water & Waste Industries, Inc., Thomasville, GA; *U.S. Public,* pg. 1682
Doyle, Dan, Chief Exec. Officer--Danka Business Systems, Saint Petersburg, FL; *Int'l,* pg. 379
Doyle, Dan M., Chief Exec. & Exec. Dir.--Danka Business Systems PLC, London, United Kingdom; *Int'l,* pg. 379
Doyle, Lawrence P., Pres. & Chief Exec. Officer--ASC Incorporated, Southgate, MI; *U.S. Private,* pg. 8
Doyle, Patrick J., Pres. & Chief Exec. Officer--Willis Corroon Corp. of Missouri, Saint Louis, MO; *Int'l,* pg. 1506
Draeger, Kenneth, Pres.--AGFA EPS Division, Wilmington, MA; *Int'l,* pg. 172
Draheim, Edward R., Chief Exec. Officer--Faultless Caster, Evansville, IN; *Int'l,* pg. 473
Drake, Walter, Chm. Bd. & Chief Exec. Officer--Walter Drake, Inc., Colorado Springs, CO; *U.S. Private,* pg. 421
Draper, E. Linn, Jr., Chm. Bd. & Chief Exec. Officer--Indiana Michigan Power Company, Fort Wayne, IN; *U.S. Public,* pg. 72
Draper, E. Linn, Jr., Chm. Bd. & Chief Exec. Officer--Ohio Power Company, Canton, OH; *U.S. Public,* pg. 72
Draper, E. Linn, Jr., Chm. Bd. & Chief Exec. Officer--Columbus Southern Power Company, Columbus, OH; *U.S. Public,* pg. 72
Draper, E. Linn, Jr., Chm. Bd. & Chief Exec. Officer--Appalachian Power Company, Roanoke, VA; *U.S. Public, pg. 72*
Draper, E. Linn, Jr., Dr., Chm. Bd., Pres. & Chief Exec. Officer--American Electric Power Company, Inc., Columbus, OH; *U.S. Public,* pg. 71
Draper, E. Linn, Jr., Dr., Chm. Bd., Pres. & Chief Exec. Officer--American Electric Power Service Corp., Columbus, OH; *U.S. Public,* pg. 72
Drasner, Fred, Vice Chm. & Chief Exec. Officer--The Atlantic Monthly Magazine, Boston, MA; *U.S. Private,* pg. 95
Drasner, Fred, Chief Exec. Officer--U.S. News & World Report, New York, NY; *U.S. Private,* pg. 1125
Drayer, Phillip M., Chm. Bd., Pres. & Chief Exec. Officer--TelCom Semiconductor, Inc., Mountain View, CA; *U.S. Public,* pg. 1569
Drebes, Charles F., Pres. & Chief Exec. Officer--Gaylord Printing, Inc., Detroit, MI; *U.S. Private,* pg. 441
Dreher, Donald D., Chm. Bd., Pres. & Chief Exec. Officer--DMI Furniture Inc., Louisville, KY; *U.S. Public,* pg. 473
Dreier, R. Chad, Chm. Bd., Pres. & Chief Exec. Officer--The Ryland Group, Inc., Columbia, MD; *U.S. Public,* pg. 1414
Dreimann, Leonhard, Pres. & Chief Exec. Officer--Salton/Maxim Housewares, Inc., Mount Prospect, IL; *U.S. Public,* pg. 1430
Drendel, Frank M., Chm. Bd. & Chief Exec. Officer--CommScope, Inc., Hickory, NC; *U.S. Public,* pg. 415
Drennen, Felix, III, Pres. & Chief Exec. Officer--Brice Building Co., Inc., Birmingham, AL; *U.S. Private,* pg. 167
Dresnick, Stephen J., M.D., Pres. & Chief Exec. Officer--Sterling Healthcare Group, Inc., Miami, FL; *U.S. Public,* pg. 608
Drexler, Millard S., Pres. & Chief Exec. Officer--The Gap, Inc., San Francisco, CA; *U.S. Public,* pg. 702
Drexler, Millard S., Pres. & Chief Exec. Officer--Old Navy Stores, San Francisco, CA; *U.S. Public,* pg. 703
Drexler, Richard A., Chm. Bd., Pres. & Chief Exec. Officer--Allied Products Corporation, Chicago, IL; *U.S. Public,* pg. 48
Dreyer, John W., Chm. Bd., Pres. & Chief Exec. Officer--Harold M. Pitman Co., Inc., Totowa, NJ; *U.S. Private,* pg. 867
Dreyer, Kris, Chm. Bd., Pres. & Chief Exec. Officer--South Bend Stamping, South Bend, IN; *U.S. Private,* pg. 1014
Dreyfuss, Arnold H., Chm. & Interim Chief Exec. Officer--Eskimo Pie Corporation, Richmond, VA; *U.S. Public,* pg. 592
Drimal, Charles E., Jr., Pres., Chief Exec. Officer & Chief Oper. Officer--PrimeEnergy Corporation, Stamford, CT; *U.S. Public,* pg. 1328
Drinkall, Austin M., Chm. Bd., Pres. & Chief Exec. Officer--South Bend Plastics, Inc., Mishawaka, IN; *U.S. Private,* pg. 1014
Drinkward, Cecil W., Chief Exec. Officer--Hoffman Corporation, Portland, OR; *U.S. Private,* pg. 532
Driscoll, Edward C., Chm. Bd., Chief Exec. Officer & Treas.--L.F. Driscoll Co., Bala Cynwyd, PA; *U.S. Private,* pg. 343
Driscoll, Mike, Chief Exec. Officer--IPC Technologies, Inc., Austin, TX; *Int'l,* pg. 651
Driscoll, W. Michael, Pres. & Chief Exec. Officer--Smith Corona Corp., Cortland, NY; *U.S. Private,* pg. 1007
Driver, Frank L., IV, Pres. & Chief Exec. Officer--Driver-Harris Company, Harrison, NJ; *U.S. Public,* pg. 530
Drnevich, Ronald J., Pres. & Chief Exec. Officer--Gannett Fleming Affiliates, Inc., Camp Hill, PA; *U.S. Private,* pg. 439
Drobis, David R., Chm., Sr. Partner & Chief Exec. Officer--Ketchum Public Relations Worldwide, New York, NY; *U.S. Private,* pg. 617
Drongowski, Steve, Chief Exec. Officer--Fahlgren, Dublin, OH; *U.S. Private,* pg. 391
Drook, Gary, Chief Exec. Officer--Ruppman Marketing Technologies, Inc., Peoria, IL; *U.S. Private,* pg. 951
Drossaert, Jacques, Chief Exec. Officer--PanEuroLife, Luxembourg, Luxembourg; *Int'l,* pg. 323
Dru, Jean-Marie, Chm.-BDDP S.A.--BDDP Group, Paris, France; *Int'l,* pg. 116
Drucker, Jean, Chm. & Chief Exec. Officer--M6, Paris, France; *Int'l,* pg. 561
Drummond, Garry N., Chief Exec. Officer--Drummond Company, Inc., Jasper, AL; *U.S. Private,* pg. 343
Drummond, Jere, Pres. & Chief Exec. Officer-BellSouth Communications Grp.--BellSouth Corporation, Atlanta, GA; *U.S. Public,* pg. 207
Drummond, Jere A., Pres. & Chief Exec. Officer--BellSouth Telecommunications, Inc., Atlanta, GA; *U.S. Public,* pg. 209
Drummond, Robert J., Pres. & Chief Exec. Officer--Epsilon, Burlington, MA; *U.S. Public,* pg. 74
Drury, David, Chm. Bd. & Chief Exec. Officer--The Principal Financial Group, Des Moines, IA; *U.S. Private,* pg. 885
Drury, David, Chm. Bd. & Chief Exec. Officer--Principal Mutual Life Insurance Co., Des Moines, IA; *U.S. Private,* pg. 886
du Boullay, E., Chief Exec. Officer--Zurich Compagnie d'assurances sur la vie, Paris, France; *Int'l,* pg. 1529
du Boullay, E., Chief Exec. Officer--Zurich Epargne, Paris, France; *Int'l,* pg. 1531
du Boullay, E., Chief Exec. Officer--Zurich International (France) S.A., Paris, France; *Int'l,* pg. 1532
Dubach, Werner, Chief Exec. Officer--Brauerei Eichhof, Lucerne, Switzerland; *Int'l,* pg. 213
Dubes, Michael J., Pres. & Chief Exec. Officer--Northern Life Insurance Company, Seattle, WA; *U.S. Public,* pg. 1375
Dubey, Prabhat K., Pres. & Chief Exec. Officer--MMC Networks, Inc., Sunnyvale, CA; *U.S. Public,* pg. 1027
Dubiel, Robert S., Pres. & Chief Exec. Officer--Cobra Golf Incorporated, Carlsbad, CA; *U.S. Public,* pg. 675
Dubin, Dan, Chief Exec. Officer--Penguin Air Conditioning Corp., Brooklyn, NY; *U.S. Public,* pg. 572
Dubin, Howard S., Chm. Bd. & Chief Exec. Officer--Manufacturers' News, Inc., Evanston, IL; *U.S. Private,* pg. 700
Dubinsky, Peter, Pres. & Chief Exec. Officer--Accurate Bushing Co., Inc., Garwood, NJ; *U.S. Private,* pg. 11
Duch-Pedersen, Alf, Pres. & Chief Exec. Officer--Danisco A/S, Copenhagen, Denmark; *Int'l,* pg. 378
Ducharme, Ron, Chief Exec. Officer & Dir.-Fin.--Speedrack Products Group, Ltd., Sparta, MI; *U.S. Private,* pg. 1024
Duchossois, Craig J., Pres. & Chief Exec. Officer--Duchossois Industries, Inc., Elmhurst, IL; *U.S. Private,* pg. 344
Duda, Edward D., Chm. Bd. & Chief Exec. Officer--A. Duda & Sons Inc., Oviedo, FL; *U.S. Private,* pg. 344
Duda, Ferdinand S., Pres. & Chief Exec. Officer--A. Duda & Sons Inc., Oviedo, FL; *U.S. Private,* pg. 344
Dudek, Walter, Pres. & Chief Exec. Officer--Dudek & Bock Spring Manufacturing Company, Chicago, IL; *U.S. Private,* pg. 344
Duerden, John, Chm. Bd., Pres. & Chief Exec. Officer--Dictaphone Corp., Stratford, CT; *U.S. Private,* pg. 1045
Dueser, F. Scott, Pres. & Chief Exec. Officer--First National Bank of Abilene, Abilene, TX; *U.S. Public,* pg. 633
Dueser, Fred F., Chief Exec. Officer & Dir.--States, Inc., Breckenridge, TX; *U.S. Private,* pg. 1037
Duff, Philip N., Pres. & Chief Exec. Officer--Van Kampen/American Capital Inc., Oak Brook Terrace, IL; *U.S. Public,* pg. 1132
Duff, Thomas M., Pres. & Chief Exec. Officer--Wellman, Inc., Shrewsbury, NJ; *U.S. Public,* pg. 1752
Duffey, W.E., Owner & Chief Exec. Officer--Driv-Lok, Inc., Sycamore, IL; *U.S. Private,* pg. 343
Duffield, David, Pres. & Chief Exec. Officer--PeopleSoft, Inc., Pleasanton, CA; *U.S. Public,* pg. 1276
Dugan, Francis R., Chm. Bd. & Chief Exec. Officer--Dugan & Meyers Interests, Inc., Cincinnati, OH; *U.S. Private,* pg. 345
Dugan, Thomas A., Pres., Chief Exec. Officer & Chief Fin. Officer--Dugan Production Corp., Farmington, NM; *U.S. Private,* pg. 345
Duignan, J. J., Chief Exec. Officer--Arnotts plc, Dublin, Ireland; *Int'l,* pg. 81
Duke, Timothy R., Pres. & Chief Exec. Officer--Steel of West Virginia, Inc., Huntington, WV; *U.S. Public,* pg. 1513
Dull, David, Pres. & Chief Exec. Officer--Fluidrive Inc., Brookston, IN; *U.S. Private,* pg. 415
Dull, William H., Pres. & Chief Exec. Officer--Tamura Corporation of America, Temecula, CA; *U.S. Private,* pg. 1067
Dulwell, David, Chief Exec. Officer--Gorges/Quik-To-Fix Foods, Dallas, TX; *U.S. Private,* pg. 465
Dunbar, Bill, Pres. & Chief Exec. Officer--Northwestel Inc., Whitehorse, Canada; *Int'l,* pg. 115
Dunbar, Bill, Pres. & Chief Exec. Officer--CellularVision Canada Ltd., Vancouver, Canada; *Int'l,* pg. 1482
Dunbar, John, Chief Exec. Officer--Hampton Print Works, Inc., Johnson City, TN; *U.S. Private,* pg. 498
Dunbar, William F., Pres. & Chief Oper. Officer--Allied Capital Corporation II, Washington, DC; *U.S. Public,* pg. 47
Duncan, Dan L., Chm. Bd. & Chief Exec. Officer--Enterprise Products Company, Houston, TX; *U.S. Private,* pg. 377
Duncan, Gregory A., Pres. & Chief Exec. Officer--Citizens National Bank of Southern Pennsylvania, Greencastle, PA; *U.S. Public,* pg. 1542
Duncan, Robert, Chm. Bd. & Chief Exec. Officer--Magna Mortgage, Hattiesburg, MS; *U.S. Public,* pg. 1669
Duncan, Ronald A., Pres. & Chief Exec. Officer--General Communication, Inc., Anchorage, AK; *U.S. Public,* pg. 708
Duncan, William W., Jr., Pres. & Chief Exec. Officer--St. Michaels Bank, Saint Michaels, MD; *U.S. Public,* pg. 1089
Dunham, Archie, Chief Exec. Officer--Conoco, Houston, TX; *U.S. Public,* pg. 531
Dunham, Michael D., Pres. & Chief Exec. Officer--Effective Management Systems, Milwaukee, WI; *U.S. Public,* pg. 565
Dunham, Richard L., Chm. Bd. & Acting Chief Exec. Officer--South Jersey Industries, Inc., Folsom, NJ; *U.S. Public,* pg. 1488
Dunlap, Albert J., Chm. Bd. & Chief Exec. Officer--Sunbeam Corporation, Delray Beach, FL; *U.S. Public,* pg. 1533
Dunlap, Edward B., Chm Bd., Pres. & Chief Exec. Officer--Centimark Corporation, Canonsburg, PA; *U.S. Private,* pg. 222
Dunn, Al, Chief Exec. Officer & Mng. Dir.--McDonald's System of New Zealand Ltd., Freeman's Bay, New Zealand; *U.S. Public,* pg. 1069
Dunn, Charles O., Pres. & Chief Exec. Officer--Mississippi Chemical Corporation, Yazoo City, MS; *U.S. Public,* pg. 1117
Dunn, David M., Chief Exec. Officer--Scapa Group Plc, Blackburn, United Kingdom; *Int'l,* pg. 1202
Dunn, Doug, Chm. Bd. & Chief Exec. Officer--Philips Semiconductors, Sunnyvale, CA; *Int'l,* pg. 1054
Dunn, James W., Pres. & Chief Exec. Officer--Willis Corroon Corp. of Florida, Tampa, FL; *Int'l,* pg. 1505
Dunn, Stephen D., Pres., Chief Exec. Officer & Treas.--Dunn Reality, Inc., Kansas City, MO; *U.S. Private,* pg. 347
Dunn, Terrence P., Pres. & Chief Exec. Officer--Dunn Industries Inc., Kansas City, MO; *U.S. Private,* pg. 347
Dunne, Thomas P., Chm. Bd. & Chief Exec. Officer--Fred Weber, Inc., Maryland Heights, MO; *U.S. Private,* pg. 424
Dunnigan, T. Kevin, Chm. Bd. & Chief Exec. Officer--Thomas & Betts Corporation, Memphis, TN; *U.S. Public,* pg. 1597
Dunning, Richard, Pres. & Chief Exec. Officer--VIMRx Pharmaceuticals, Inc., Wilmington, DE; *U.S. Public,* pg. 1702
Dunphy, T.J. Dermot, Chm. Bd. & Chief Exec. Officer--Sealed Air Corporation, Saddle Brook, NJ; *U.S. Public,* pg. 1450
Dunst, Laurence D., Co-Chm. & Chief Exec. Officer--Gotham Incorporated, New York, NY; *U.S. Private,* pg. 677
Dupey, Michael, Chief Exec. Officer--Dupey Management Corp., Coppell, TX; *U.S. Private,* pg. 348
DuPont, F.I., Pres.& Chief Exec. Officer--SouthTrust Bank of Jacksonville, Jacksonville, FL; *U.S. Public,* pg. 1492
Dupont, P., Chief Exec. Officer--Coverland S.A., Rueil-Malmaison, France; *Int'l,* pg. 1092
DuPree, Tom E., Jr., Chm. Bd. & Chief Exec. Officer--Apple South, Inc., Madison, GA; *U.S. Public,* pg. 121
Dupuis, Lenore, Chief Exec. Officer & Treas.--Your Man Tours, Inc., Inglewood, CA; *U.S. Private,* pg. 1202
Dupuis, Pierre, Pres. & Chief Exec. Officer--Sico Inc., Longueuil, Canada; *Int'l,* pg. 1239
Duques, Henry C., Chm. Bd. & Chief Exec. Officer--First Data Corporation, Hackensack, NJ; *U.S. Public,* pg. 630
Durant, James E., Pres. & Chief Exec. Officer--Trautman & Shreve, Inc., Denver, CO; *U.S. Public,* pg. 572
Durham, Michael J., Pres. & Chief Exec. Officer--The SABRE Group Holdings, Inc., Fort Worth, TX; *U.S. Public,* pg. 10
Durham, Timothy S., Pres. & Chief Exec. Officer--Carpenter Industries, Inc., Richmond, IN; *U.S. Private,* pg. 215
Durhan, Michael D., Chm., Pres. & Chief Exec. Officer--SunTrust Bank, West Florida, Pensacola, FL; *U.S. Public,* pg. 1538
Durr, Heinz, Chm. Bd., Pres. & Chief Exec. Officer--Deutsche Bahn, Frankfurt/Main, Germany; *Int'l,* pg. 401
Durrett, Joseph P., Chief Exec. Officer--Broderbund Software, Inc., Novato, CA; *U.S. Public,* pg. 258
Durrett, R. Lamar, Pres. & Chief Exec. Officer--Air Canada, Saint-Laurent, Canada; *Int'l,* pg. 36
Durwood, Stanley H., Chm. Bd. & Chief Exec. Officer--AMC Entertainment, Inc., Kansas City, MO; *U.S. Private,* pg. 6
Dusa, Jerry A., Pres. & Chief Exec. Officer--Digi International Inc., Minnetonka, MN; *U.S. Public,* pg. 506
Dusthimer, Thomas L., Chm. Bd. & Chief Exec. Officer--Society National Bank, Elkhart, IN; *U.S. Public,* pg. 955
Dutia, Suren G., Chm. Bd., Pres. & Chief Exec. Officer--Photomatrix Corporation, San Diego, CA; *U.S. Public,* pg. 1292
Dutmers, James E., Jr., Chief Exec. Officer--Empire National Bank, Traverse City, MI; *U.S. Private,* pg. 374
Dutton, Christopher L., Pres. & Chief Exec. Officer--Green Mountain Power Corporation, South Burlington, VT; *U.S. Public,* pg. 761
Duval, Daniel W., Pres. & Chief Exec. Officer--Robbins & Myers, Inc., Dayton, OH; *U.S. Public,* pg. 1393
Duvar, I.E.H., Chm. Bd. & Chief Exec. Officer--Maritime Telegraph & Telephone Company, Ltd., Halifax, Canada; *Int'l,* pg. 116
Duyser, Peter A., Chief Exec. Officer--OCE-Australia Limited, Cheltenham, Australia; *Int'l,* pg. 994
Dwight, Herbert M., Jr., Chm. Bd. & Chief Exec. Officer--Optical Coating Laboratory, Inc., Santa Rosa, CA; *U.S. Public,* pg. 1227
Dworkin, David, Pres. & Chief Exec. Officer-Uptons Inc.--American Retail Group, New York, NY; *U.S. Private,* pg. 61
Dwyer, Joe A., Exec. Chm. & Chief Exec. Officer--George Wimpey PLC, London, United Kingdom; *Int'l,* pg. 1510
Dwyer, M.A., Pres. & Chief Exec. Officer--Daubert Chemical Company, Inc., Chicago, IL; *U.S. Private,* pg. 313
Dye, Donald H., Pres. & Chief Exec. Officer--Callaway Golf Company, Carlsbad, CA; *U.S. Public,* pg. 294

Dye, Michael H., Pres. & Chief Exec. Officer--The PBS&J Corporation, Miami, FL; *U.S. Private*, pg. 825
Dye, William, Pres. & Chief Exec. Officer--Unidigital Inc., New York, NY; *U.S. Public*, pg. 1664
Dyer, Colin, Chief Exec.-Clothing--Courtaulds Textiles Plc, London, United Kingdom; *Int'l*, pg. 339
Dyer, Howard, Chm. Bd. & Chief Exec. Officer--Ascot Holdings Plc, London, United Kingdom; *Int'l*, pg. 87
Dyer, Lex, III, Chm. Bd., Pres. & Chief Exec. Officer--International Airline Support Group, Inc., Atlanta, GA; *U.S. Public*, pg. 894
Dyer, Robert, Jr., Chm. Bd. & Chief Exec. Officer--Hickory Farms, Inc., Maumee, OH; *U.S. Private*, pg. 525
Dyke, Greg, Chief Exec. Officer--Pearson Television Ltd., Teddington, United Kingdom; *Int'l*, pg. 1026
Dyment, F.J., Pres. & Chief Exec. Officer--Ranger Oil Limited, Calgary, Canada; *Int'l*, pg. 1086
Dymond, Robert C.J., Pres. & Chief Exec. Officer--ANGUS Chemical Company, Buffalo Grove, IL; *U.S. Private*, pg. 75
Dyson, Robert R., Chm. Bd. & Chief Exec. Officer--The Dyson-Kissner-Moran Corporation, New York, NY; *U.S. Private*, pg. 351
Dyszkiewicz, Tom, Pres. & Chief Exec. Officer--The National Super Service Co., Toledo, OH; *U.S. Private*, pg. 787
Dzvonik, Michael D., Chm. Bd. & Chief Exec. Officer--Grizzard, Atlanta, GA; *U.S. Private*, pg. 482
Eadie, Douglas M., Grp. Mng. Dir.--Henderson Administration Group PLC, London, United Kingdom; *Int'l*, pg. 609
Eagle, John M., Chm. Bd. & Chief Exec. Officer--Pipe Fabricating & Supply Company, Santa Fe Springs, CA; *U.S. Private*, pg. 867
Eagle, Robert M., Chm. Bd. & Chief Exec. Officer--Eagle Lincoln Mercury Inc., Dallas, TX; *U.S. Private*, pg. 355
Earhart, Donald M., Chm. Bd., Pres. & Chief Exec. Officer--I-Flow Corporation, Lake Forest, CA; *U.S. Public*, pg. 851
Earnheart, Aubrey, Pres. & Chief Exec. Officer--First State Bank, Brownsville, TN; *U.S. Public*, pg. 1669
Easley, Ronald L., Chm. Bd. & Chief Exec. Officer--System Planning Corp., Arlington, VA; *U.S. Private*, pg. 1061
East, Charles, Pres. & Chief Exec. Officer--Regions Bank/Rockdale County, Conyers, GA; *U.S. Public*, pg. 1372
Eastin, Raymond, Exec. V.P. & Chief Exec. Officer--Blue Circle America Inc., Marietta, GA; *Int'l*, pg. 197
Eastland, Woods E., Pres. & Chief Exec. Officer--Staple Cotton Cooperative Association, Greenwood, MS; *U.S. Private*, pg. 1033
Eaton, F., Chief Exec. Officer--Barratt Developments Plc, Newcastle upon Tyne, United Kingdom; *Int'l*, pg. 167
Eaton, Henry F., Chm. & Chief Exec. Officer--Dix & Eaton Incorporated, Cleveland, OH; *U.S. Private*, pg. 336
Eaton, Robert J., Chm. Bd., Pres. & Chief Exec. Officer--Chrysler Corporation, Auburn Hills, MI; *U.S. Public*, pg. 352
Ebbers, Bernard J., Pres. & Chief Exec. Officer--WorldCom, Inc., Jackson, MS; *U.S. Public*, pg. 1779
Ebbers, Bernard J., Pres. & Chief Exec. Officer--LDDS/WorldCom Communications, Revere, MA; *U.S. Public*, pg. 1779
Ebert, John H., Pres. & Chief Exec. Officer--M & I Bank South Central, Watertown, WI; *U.S. Public*, pg. 1050
Ebihara, Yushi, Mng. Partner & Chief Exec. Officer--Kovel Kresser & Partners, Santa Monica, CA; *U.S. Private*, pg. 634
Ebrahimi, Fred, Pres. & Chief Exec. Officer--Quark Inc., Denver, CO; *U.S. Private*, pg. 900
Eccles, Spencer F., Chm. Bd. & Chief Exec. Officer--First Security Corporation, Salt Lake City, UT; *U.S. Public*, pg. 637
Echeverria, Matt J., Sr. V.P. & Acting Chief Exec. Officer--Tejon Ranch Company, Lebec, CA; *U.S. Public*, pg. 1566
Echolds, Mike, Chief Exec. Officer--Tropitone Furniture Co. Inc., Irvine, CA; *U.S. Private*, pg. 1105
Echols, Rebecca S., Pres. & Chief Exec. Officer--Regions Bank/Douglas County, Douglasville, GA; *U.S. Public*, pg. 1372
Ecke, Paul, III, Chm. Bd., Pres. & Chief Exec. Officer--Paul Ecke Ranch, Encinitas, CA; *U.S. Private*, pg. 359
Eckert, Michael J., Pres. & Chief Exec. Officer--Broadcast and Video Enterprises Div., Atlanta, GA; *U.S. Private*, pg. 647
Eckert, Michael J., Chief Exec. Officer--The Weather Channel, Atlanta, GA; *U.S. Private*, pg. 647
Eckert, P., Chief Exec. Officer--Zurich Insurance Company, Glattbrugg, Switzerland; *Int'l*, pg. 1529
Eckert, R. Andrew, Chief Exec. Officer--ADAC Laboratories Inc., Milpitas, CA; *U.S. Public*, pg. 3
Eckert, Wesley, Pres. & Chief Exec. Officer--Darigold, Inc., Seattle, WA; *U.S. Private*, pg. 311
Eckhoff, Gilbert B., Pres. & Chief Exec. Officer--Henningsen Foods, Inc., White Plains, NY; *Int'l*, pg. 1074
Eckhouse, Shimon, Chm. Bd., Pres. & Chief Exec. Officer--ESC Medical Systems Ltd., Yokneam, Israel; *Int'l*, pg. 429
Edamoto, Kenzo, Pres. & Chief Exec. Officer--Sapporo Breweries Ltd., Tokyo, Japan; *Int'l*, pg. 1193
Eddings, J. Carson, Pres. & Chief Exec. Officer--The William Cook Agency, Inc., Jacksonville, FL; *U.S. Private*, pg. 273
Eddins, Mark A., Pres. & Chief Exec. Officer--Friendly Chevrolet Co. Inc., Dallas, TX; *U.S. Private*, pg. 428
Edell, David, Pres. & Chief Exec. Officer--CCA Industries, Inc., East Rutherford, NJ; *U.S. Public*, pg. 276
Edelman, Asher B., Chm. Bd. & Chief Exec. Officer--Datapoint Corporation, Paris, France; *Int'l*, pg. 384
Edelman, Asher B., Chm. Bd. & Chief Exec. Officer--Datapoint Corporation, San Antonio, TX; *Int'l*, pg. 384
Edelman, Keith, Grp. Chief Exec.--Storehouse PLC, London, United Kingdom; *Int'l*, pg. 1304
Edelman, Richard, Pres. & Chief Exec. Officer--Edelman Public Relations Worldwide, Chicago, IL; *U.S. Private*, pg. 362
Edelman, Richard W., Pres. & Chief Exec. Officer--Edelman Worldwide, Inc., New York, NY; *U.S. Private*, pg. 362
Edelman, Thomas J., Chm. Bd., Pres. & Chief Exec. Officer--Patina Oil & Gas Corp., Denver, CO; *U.S. Public*, pg. 1264
Edelstenne, Charles, Chm. & Chief Exec. Officer--Dassault Systemes, Suresnes, France; *Int'l*, pg. 383
Edenfield, J. Michael, Chief Exec. Officer--Logility, Inc., Atlanta, GA; *U.S. Public*, pg. 91
Edenfield, James C., Pres., Chief Exec. Officer & Treas.--American Software, Inc., Atlanta, GA; *U.S. Public*, pg. 91
Edmund, Robert M., Chief Exec. Officer--Edmund Scientific Company, Barrington, NJ; *U.S. Private*, pg. 364
Edwards, Alasdair, Chief Exec. Officer--IRPC Hinton Limited, Hinckley, United Kingdom; *Int'l*, pg. 1502
Edwards, Benjamin F., III, Chm. Bd., Pres. & Chief Exec. Officer--A.G. Edwards, Inc., Saint Louis, MO; *U.S. Public*, pg. 565
Edwards, D.J., Chief Exec. Officer--Readymix Gulf Ltd., Sharjah, United Arab Emirates; *Int'l*, pg. 1092
Edwards, Jack, Pres. & Chief Exec. Officer--Danzas Corporation, Bellevue, WA; *Int'l*, pg. 382
Edwards, James O., Chm. Bd. & Chief Exec. Officer--ICF Kaiser International Inc., Fairfax, VA; *U.S. Public*, pg. 852
Edwards, Jeffrey B., Pres. & Chief Exec. Officer-MICROS-Fidelio Software GmbH & Co. KG--Micros Systems Inc., Beltsville, MD; *U.S. Public*, pg. 1106
Edwards, Johnathan, Chm. Bd. & Chief Exec. Officer--IPC Interactive, Inc., Novato, CA; *Int'l*, pg. 651
Edwards, Joseph, Pres. & Chief Exec. Officer--Superior Federal Bank, Fort Smith, AR; *U.S. Private*, pg. 1054
Edwards, L.A., Chief Exec. Officer--Dowty Aerospace, Abingdon, United Kingdom; *Int'l*, pg. 1337
Edwards, L.A., Chm. Bd. & Chief Exec. Officer--Messier-Dowty, Abingdon, United Kingdom; *Int'l*, pg. 1340
Edwards, L.A., Chm. Bd. & Chief Exec. Officer--Messier-Dowty International, Velizy-Villacoublay, France; *Int'l*, pg. 1340
Edwards, Larry, Pres. & Chief Exec. Officer--Reliability Incorporated, Houston, TX; *U.S. Public*, pg. 1373
Edwards, Merle W., Jr., Pres. & Chief Exec. Officer--Coastal Wholesale, Inc., Kinston, NC; *U.S. Private*, pg. 248
Edwards, N. Murray, Chm. Bd. & Chief Exec. Officer--Magellan Aerospace Corporation, Mississauga, Canada; *Int'l*, pg. 829
Edwards, Paul, Chief Exec. Officer--The Henley Centre, London, United Kingdom; *Int'l*, pg. 1482
Edwards, William E., Jr., Chm. Bd. & Chief Exec. Officer--Cardinal Aluminum Co., Louisville, KY; *U.S. Private*, pg. 208
Eeg, David A., Pres. & Chief Exec. Officer--Storage Dimensions, Inc., Milpitas, CA; *U.S. Public*, pg. 1522
Egan, Gerald L., Pres. & Chief Exec. Officer--Egan Cos., Minneapolis, MN; *U.S. Private*, pg. 365
Egan, Jack, Pres. & Chief Exec. Officer--RehabWorks Inc., Clearwater, FL; *U.S. Public*, pg. 839
Egan, Jack, Chief Exec. Officer--CMS Therapies, Inc., Charlotte, NC; *U.S. Public*, pg. 839
Egan, John M., Pres. & Chief Exec. Officer--The Antec Corporation, Rolling Meadows, IL; *U.S. Public*, pg. 116
Egan, John, Sir, Chief Exec.--BAA plc, London, United Kingdom; *Int'l*, pg. 103
Egan, Michael A., Pres. & Chief Exec. Officer--CheckRite International, Midvale, UT; *U.S. Public*, pg. 484
Egan, Michael S., Chm. Bd. & Chief Exec. Officer--Alamo Rent-A-Car Inc., Fort Lauderdale, FL; *U.S. Public*, pg. 1379
Egart, John J., Pres. & Chief Exec. Officer--First Team Sports Inc., Anoka, MN; *U.S. Public*, pg. 638
Egizii, Robert, Pres. & Chief Exec. Officer--Egizii Electric, Inc., Springfield, IL; *U.S. Private*, pg. 366
Eglin, Peter B., Chm. Bd., Pres. & Chief Exec. Officer--Mellon Bank, N.A.-Northeastern Region, Wilkes-Barre, PA; *U.S. Public*, pg. 1085
Ehlers, Kurt-Peters, Chief Oper. Officer--Stolberger Metallwerke GmbH & Co. KG, Stolberg, Germany; *Int'l*, pg. 719
Ehmke, B.S., Pres. & Chief Exec. Officer--Forney Corporation, Carrollton, TX; *Int'l*, pg. 1500
Ehrlich, Donald J., Pres. & Chief Exec. Officer--Wabash National Corp., Lafayette, IN; *U.S. Public*, pg. 1730
Ehrnrooth, Georg, Pres. & Chief Exec. Officer--Metra Corporation, Helsinki, Finland; *Int'l*, pg. 862
Eibner, W.P., Pres. & Chief Exec. Officer--Fostoria Industries, Inc., Fostoria, OH; *U.S. Private*, pg. 421
Eichenfield, Samuel L., Chm. Bd., Pres. & Chief Exec. Officer--The FINOVA Group Inc., Phoenix, AZ; *U.S. Public*, pg. 624
Eichenfield, Samuel L., Chm. Bd., Pres. & Chief Exec. Officer--FINOVA Capital Corporation, Phoenix, AZ; *U.S. Public*, pg. 624
Eichhorn, Gary, Pres. & Chief Exec. Officer--Open Market, Inc., Burlington, MA; *U.S. Public*, pg. 1226
Eichmann, M., Chief Exec. Officer--Zurich Insurance Company, Tokyo, Japan; *Int'l*, pg. 1531
Eigsti, Roger H., Chm. Bd. & Chief Exec. Officer--SAFECO Corporation, Seattle, WA; *U.S. Public*, pg. 1423
Eihusen, Robert, Chm. Bd., Pres. & Chief Exec. Officer--Chief Industries, Inc., Grand Island, NE; *U.S. Private*, pg. 236
Eiler, Frank, Intl. Chief Exec. Officer--Eiler & Riemel - Testa, Munich, Germany; *Int'l*, pg. 1377
Einstein, Clifford, Chm. Bd. & Creative Dir.--Dailey & Associates, West Hollywood, CA; *U.S. Public*, pg. 909
Eisele, Ed, Pres. & Chief Exec. Officer--Holsum Bakery, Inc., Phoenix, AZ; *U.S. Private*, pg. 536
Eisenberg, Gregg M., Chm. Bd., Pres. & Chief Exec. Officer--Maverick Tube Corporation, Chesterfield, MO; *U.S. Public*, pg. 1060
Eisenberg, James, Co-Chm. & Chief Exec. Officer--Vienna Sausage Mfg. Co., Chicago, IL; *U.S. Private*, pg. 1139
Eisenberg, Kenneth, Chm. Bd. & Chief Exec. Officer--Kenwal Products Corp., Dearborn, MI; *U.S. Private*, pg. 615
Eisenberg, Warren, Chm. Bd., Co-Chief Exec. Officer & Sec.--Bed Bath & Beyond Inc., Union, NJ; *U.S. Public*, pg. 200
Eisenburg, David, Chm. Bd., Pres. & Chief Exec. Officer--Chief Auto Parts, Dallas, TX; *U.S. Private*, pg. 236
Eisner, Michael D., Chm. Bd. & Chief Exec. Officer--The Walt Disney Company, Burbank, CA; *U.S. Public*, pg. 511
Eisner, Steve, Chm. & Chief Exec. Officer--Eisner, Petrou & Associates, Inc., Baltimore, MD; *U.S. Private*, pg. 366
Eisner, Steven C., Pres. & Chief Exec. Officer--Eisner & Associates, Inc., Baltimore, MD; *U.S. Private*, pg. 366
Eitan, Yaron I., Chm. Bd. & Chief Exec. Officer--Geotek Communications, Montvale, NJ; *U.S. Public*, pg. 739
Ejabat, Mory, Pres. & Chief Exec. Officer--Ascend Communications, Inc., Alameda, CA; *U.S. Public*, pg. 138
Eke, Michael R., Joint Chief Exec.--TT Group PLC, Surrey, United Kingdom; *Int'l*, pg. 1344
Ekins, W. Leo, Pres. & Chief Exec. Officer--AgrEvo USA Company, Wilmington, DE; *Int'l*, pg. 1203
Eklund, George, Pres. & Chief Exec. Officer--Digital Solutions, Inc., Somerset, NJ; *U.S. Public*, pg. 508
Eklund, Helge, Pres. & Chief Exec. Officer--Sodra Cell AB, Vaxjo, Sweden; *Int'l*, pg. 1275
Elbaum, Steven S., Chm. Bd. & Chief Exec. Officer--The Alpine Group, Inc., New York, NY; *U.S. Public*, pg. 58
Elbaum, Steven S., Chm. Bd. & Chief Exec. Officer--Superior Telecommunications, Atlanta, GA; *U.S. Public*, pg. 58
Eldon Wheeler, M.L., Chm. Bd. & Chief Exec. Officer--Jernberg Industries, Inc., Chicago, IL; *U.S. Private*, pg. 586
Eldon, D.G., Chief Exec. Officer--The Hongkong and Shanghai Banking Corporation Limited (HongkongBank), Central, Hong Kong; *Int'l*, pg. 583
Elgas, Devere L., Pres., Chief Exec. Officer & Chief Oper. Officer--Citizens Gas Fuel Company, Adrian, MI; *U.S. Public*, pg. 1025
Elhinney, E. A., Chm. Bd. & Chief Exec. Officer--SAS Holdings Limited, Reading, United Kingdom; *Int'l*, pg. 1152
Elia, Michael A., Pres. & Chief Exec. Officer--Sevenson Environmental Services, Inc., Niagara Falls, NY; *U.S. Public*, pg. 1462
Elias, Elmer J., Pres. & Chief Exec. Officer--B.M.J. Financial Corp., Bordentown, NJ; *U.S. Public*, pg. 1528
Elisha, Walter Y., Chm. Bd. & Chief Exec. Officer--Springs Industries, Inc., Fort Mill, SC; *U.S. Public*, pg. 1499
Elizondo, Alonso Ancira, Chief Exec. Officer & Exec. V.P.--Altos Hornos de Mexico, S.A., Monclova, Mexico; *Int'l*, pg. 66
Elkhatib, Hasan M., Pres. & Chief Exec. Officer--Dena Corporation, Elk Grove Village, IL; *U.S. Private*, pg. 324
Elkin, Alan S., Chief Exec. Officer--Active International, Pearl River, NY; *U.S. Private*, pg. 15
Elkin, Jason, Chm. Bd. & Chief Exec. Officer--New Vision Television, Atlanta, GA; *U.S. Private*, pg. 794
Elkin, Kenneth, Pres. & Chief Exec. Officer--SGS U.S. Testing Company, Inc., Fairfield, NJ; *Int'l*, pg. 1153
Elkins, Robert N., M.D., Chm. Bd. & Chief Exec. Officer--Integrated Health Services, Inc., Owings Mills, MD; *U.S. Public*, pg. 884
Ellenberger, Richard G., Pres. & Chief Exec. Officer--Cincinnati Bell Telephone Company, Cincinnati, OH; *U.S. Public*, pg. 367
Ellenbogen, S. David, Chm. Bd. & Chief Exec. Officer--Hologic, Inc., Waltham, MA; *U.S. Public*, pg. 831
Eller, Karl, Chm. Bd. & Chief Exec. Officer--Eller Media Company, Phoenix, AZ; *U.S. Public*, pg. 383
Ellett, Phil D., Pres. & Chief Exec. Officer--Gates/Arrow Commercial Systems Div., Greenville, SC; *U.S. Public*, pg. 133
Ellingford, A.J., Chief Exec. Officer--Reunert Ltd., Sandton, South Africa; *Int'l*, pg. 1105
Elliott, Charles A., Chm. Bd., Pres. & Chief Exec. Officer--Crenlo, Inc., Rochester, MN; *U.S. Private*, pg. 288
Elliott, David H., Chm. Bd. & Chief Exec. Officer--MBIA Inc., Armonk, NY; *U.S. Public*, pg. 1023
Elliott, J. Mark, Chm. Bd. & Chief Exec. Officer--QST Environmental Inc., Peoria, IL; *U.S. Public*, pg. 367
Elliott, J. Mark, Chief Exec. Officer--QST Communications, Inc., Peoria, IL; *U.S. Public*, pg. 367
Elliott, J. Mark, Chm. Bd. & Chief Exec. Officer--QST Energy, Inc., Peoria, IL; *U.S. Public*, pg. 367
Elliott, James V., Pres. & Chief Exec. Officer--Investors Trust Company, Wyomissing, PA; *U.S. Public*, pg. 1159
Elliott, Neal M., Chm. Bd., Pres. & Chief Exec. Officer--Horizon/CMS Healthcare Corporation, Albuquerque, NM; *U.S. Public*, pg. 836
Elliott, Perry, Pres. & Chief Exec. Officer--Stephenville Bank & Trust Co., Stephenville, TX; *U.S. Public*, pg. 633
Elliott, R. Keith, Chm. Bd. & Chief Exec. Officer--Hercules Incorporated, Wilmington, DE; *U.S. Public*, pg. 809
Elliott, Robert D., Pres. & Chief Exec. Officer--Aerovox Inc., New Bedford, MA; *U.S. Public*, pg. 25
Ellis, Charles R., Pres. & Chief Exec. Officer--John Wiley & Sons, Inc., New York, NY; *U.S. Public*, pg. 1768
Ellis, E. Addison, III, Pres. & Chief Exec. Officer--Glencoe/Mc-Graw Hill, Westerville, OH; *U.S. Public*, pg. 1070
Ellis, Fred K., Pres. & Chief Inv. Officer--Skandia Investment Management, Inc., New York, NY; *Int'l*, pg. 1257
Ellis, J. Ronald, Pres. & Chief Exec. Officer--Willis Corroon Corp. of Nashville, Nashville, TN; *Int'l*, pg. 1506
Ellis, Jerry K., Chief Exec. Officer & Exec. Gen. Mgr.--BHP Minerals, Melbourne, Australia; *Int'l*, pg. 223
Ellis, William D., Chm. Bd. & Chief Exec. Officer--Southern Mills, Inc., Union City, GA; *U.S. Private*, pg. 1016
Ellison, Lawrence J., Chm. Bd. & Chief Exec. Officer--Oracle Corporation, Redwood City, CA; *U.S. Public*, pg. 1227

Ellison, Richard D., Ph.D.,P.E., Chm. Bd., Pres. & Chief Exec. Officer--TRC Companies, Inc., Windsor, CT; *U.S. Public*, pg. 1557

Ellspermann, W.R., Pres. & Chief Exec. Officer--Security Pacific Information Services Corporation, San Diego, CA; *U.S. Public*, pg. 182

Ellstrom, Olof W., Jr., Pres. & Chief Exec. Officer--Dearborn Gage Company, Garden City, MI; *U.S. Private*, pg. 319

Elmaleh, Lou, Chm. Bd. & Chief Exec. Officer--Greyvest Capitol Inc., Toronto, Canada; *Int'l*, pg. 559

Elman, Robert H., Chm. Bd. & Chief Exec. Officer--Desa International, Bowling Green, KY; *U.S. Private*, pg. 326

Elowitz, Norman, Chm. Bd., Pres. & Chief Exec. Officer--Honey Fashions Ltd., New York, NY; *U.S. Private*, pg. 537

Elsberry, Howard W., Chm. Bd., Pres. & Chief Exec. Officer--Westlake Hardware, Inc., Lenexa, KS; *U.S. Private*, pg. 1169

Elsbury, D.C., Chief Exec. Officer--Racal Electronics Plc, Bracknell, United Kingdom; *Int'l*, pg. 1082

Elsener, Frank, Chief Exec. Officer--Tree Top, Inc., Selah, WA; *U.S. Private*, pg. 1098

Elsperman, Robert P., P.E., Chm. Bd. & Chief Exec. Officer--Tarlton Corporation, Saint Louis, MO; *U.S. Private*, pg. 1069

Emerson, Barry K., Chm. Bd., Pres. & Chief Exec. Officer--Texas National Bank, Southlake, TX; *U.S. Public*, pg. 633

Emerson, Thomas E., Chief Exec. Officer--Norwest Audit Services, Inc., Minneapolis, MN; *U.S. Public*, pg. 1201

Emich, Fred, III, Pres. & Chief Exec. Officer--Emich Oldsmobile, Inc., Golden, CO; *U.S. Private*, pg. 373

Emmi, Michael J., Chm. Bd., Pres. & Chief Exec. Officer--Systems & Computer Technology Corporation, Malvern, PA; *U.S. Public*, pg. 1552

Emsermann, M., Dr., Chief Exec. Officer--Ascom Frako GmbH, Teningen, Germany; *Int'l*, pg. 87

Enders, A.T., Mng. Partner & Chief Exec. Officer--Brown Brothers Harriman & Co., New York, NY; *U.S. Private*, pg. 173

Enders, Larry J., Pres. & Chief Exec. Officer--Oliver Rubber Co., Athens, GA; *U.S. Public*, pg. 1504

Endy, Paul S., Chm. Bd. & Chief Exec. Officer--Paul-Son Gaming Corporation, Las Vegas, NV; *U.S. Public*, pg. 1265

Eng, Lua Cheng, Chief Exec. Officer--Neptune Orient Lines Ltd., Singapore, Singapore; *Int'l*, pg. 912

Engel, Arthur, Chm. Bd. & Chief Exec. Officer--Southwest Marine, Inc., San Diego, CA; *U.S. Private*, pg. 213

Engel, Susan, Chm. Bd., Pres. & Chief Exec. Officer--Department 56 Inc., Eden Prairie, MN; *U.S. Public*, pg. 500

Engelke, George L., Chm. Bd., Pres. & Chief Exec. Officer--Astoria Financial Corporation, Lake Success, NY; *U.S. Public*, pg. 141

Engels, Karl G., Pres. & Chief Exec. Officer--Hoechst Marion Roussel, Inc., Bridgewater, NJ; *Int'l*, pg. 624

Engelsma, Bruce W., Chm. Bd. & Chief Exec. Officer--Kraus-Anderson Incorporated, Minneapolis, MN; *U.S. Private*, pg. 635

Engelsma, Bruce W., Chm. Bd. & Chief Exec. Officer--Kraus-Anderson, Incorporated, Minneapolis, MN; *U.S. Private*, pg. 635

Engelsted, John N., Chm. Bd. & Chief Exec. Officer--Walker Magnetics Group, Inc., Worcester, MA; *U.S. Private*, pg. 1147

Engelstein, Alec, Chm. Bd., Pres. & Chief Exec. Officer--Engle Homes, Inc., Boca Raton, FL; *U.S. Public*, pg. 583

Enger, Ole, Pres. & Chief Exec. Officer--Elkem ASA, Oslo, Norway; *Int'l*, pg. 446

Engibous, Thomas J., Pres. & Chief Exec. Officer--Texas Instruments Incorporated, Dallas, TX; *U.S. Public*, pg. 1585

England, C.M., Pres. & Chief Exec. Officer--Logan Corporation, Huntington, WV; *U.S. Private*, pg. 672

England, Neil M., Grp. Chief Exec.--The Albert Fisher Group PLC, Stoke Poges, United Kingdom; *Int'l*, pg. 491

England, Peter W., Pres. & Chief Exec. Officer--Elizabeth Arden Company, New York, NY; *Int'l*, pg. 1435

Engle, Clyde W., Chm. Bd., Pres. & Chief Exec. Officer--Telco Capital Corporation, Chicago, IL; *U.S. Private*, pg. 1073

Engle, Gary D., Pres. & Chief Exec. Officer--Equis Financial Group, Boston, MA; *U.S. Private*, pg. 379

Englefield, F.W., IV, Co-Pres., Chief Exec., Chief Fin. Officer & Sec.--Englefield, Inc., Newark, OH; *U.S. Private*, pg. 377

Englekirk, Robert E., Chm. Bd., Pres. & Chief Exec. Officer--Robert Englekirk, Inc., Los Angeles, CA; *U.S. Private*, pg. 377

Engles, Gregg L., Chm. Bd. & Chief Exec. Officer--Suiza Foods Corporation, Dallas, TX; *U.S. Public*, pg. 1526

English, Floyd L., Chm. Bd., Pres. & Chief Exec. Officer--Andrew Corporation, Orland Park, IL; *U.S. Public*, pg. 112

English, Marc A., Pres. & Chief Exec. Officer--Cleo Inc., Memphis, TN; *U.S. Public*, pg. 284

Ennen, Richard, Pres. & Chief Exec. Officer--Universal International, Inc., New Hope, MN; *U.S. Public*, pg. 1697

Ennerfelt, Goran, Pres. & Chief Exec. Officer--Axel Johnson AB, Stockholm, Sweden; *Int'l*, pg. 707

Ennest, John W., Chm. Bd. & Chief Exec. Officer--Commercial National Bank of Berwyn, Berwyn, IL; *U.S. Public*, pg. 379

Enrico, Roger, Chm. Bd. & Chief Exec. Officer--PepsiCo, Inc., Purchase, NY; *U.S. Public*, pg. 1276

Entringer, James W., Chm. Bd., Pres. & Chief Exec. Officer--Selective Insurance Group, Inc, Branchville, NJ; *U.S. Public*, pg. 1455

Epprecht, Hans, Pres. & Chief Exec. Officer--The Great Lakes Cheese Co., Newbury, OH; *U.S. Private*, pg. 473

Epstein, Donald, Chm. Bd., Pres. & Chief Exec. Officer--Vesco Oil Corp., Southfield, MI; *U.S. Private*, pg. 1138

Erb, Fred A., Chm. Bd., Pres. & Chief Exec. Officer--Amurcon Corporation, Southfield, MI; *U.S. Private*, pg. 69

Erdeljan, Aleksandar, Chm. Bd., Pres. & Co-Chief Exec. Officer--R.P. Scherer Corporation, Troy, MI; *U.S. Public*, pg. 1437

Erdmann, David L., Chm. Bd., Pres. & Chief Exec. Officer--Outlook Group Corporation, Neenah, WI; *U.S. Public*, pg. 1235

Erenberg, Ethan M., Chm. Bd. & Chief Exec. Officer--W. Braun Company, Chicago, IL; *U.S. Private*, pg. 166

Erener, Serdar, Chief Exec. Officer & Mng. Dir.--Young & Rubicam Turkey, Istanbul, Turkey; *U.S. Private*, pg. 1200

Erenmalm, Stattan, Pres. & Chief Exec. Officer--Akerlund & Rausing, Leerdam, Netherlands; *Int'l*, pg. 33

Erennalm, Stattan, Pres. & Chief Exec. Officer--AB Akerlund & Rausing Group, Lund, Sweden; *Int'l*, pg. 33

Ergas, J.P. M., Chm. Bd. & Chief Exec. Officer--British Alcan Aluminium plc, Gerrards Cross, United Kingdom; *Int'l*, pg. 51

Erickson, James W., Chm. Bd., Pres. & Chief Exec. Officer--Anderson Erickson Dairy Company, Des Moines, IA; *U.S.* Private, pg. 72

Erickson, John, Chm. Bd. & Chief Exec. Officer--I.C. System, Inc., Vadnais Heights, MN; *U.S. Private*, pg. 553

Erickson, Richard P., Chm. Bd. & Chief Exec. Officer--Lifetouch, Portrait Studios, Eden Prairie, MN; *U.S. Private*, pg. 667

Erickson, Robert M., Pres. & Chief Fin. Officer--Madison Acceptance Corporation, San Jose, CA; *U.S. Public*, pg. 376

Erickson, Sheldon, Chm. Bd., Pres. & Chief Exec. Officer--Cameron, Houston, TX; *U.S. Public*, pg. 298

Erickson, Stanford, Chm. & Chief Exec. Officer--Farm Journal Inc., Philadelphia, PA; *U.S. Private*, pg. 394

Ericson, James D., Pres. & Chief Exec. Officer--Northwestern Mutual Life Insurance Co., Milwaukee, WI; *U.S. Private*, pg. 807

Erkeneff, Richard R., Pres. & Chief Exec. Officer--United Industrial Corporation, New York, NY; *U.S. Public*, pg. 1679

Erkeneff, Richard R., Pres. & Chief Exec. Officer--AAI Corporation, Hunt Valley, MD; *U.S. Public*, pg. 1679

Ernst, Paul W., Pres. & Chief Exec. Officer--Carter Day International, Minneapolis, MN; *U.S. Private*, pg. 216

Erokan, Dennis, Pres. & Editor-in-Chief--Bam Media, Pleasant Hill, CA; *U.S. Private*, pg. 113

Erskine, David, Pres. & Chief Exec. Officer--Scott Paper Limited, Mississauga, Canada; *Int'l*, pg. 762

Erskine, John E., Jr., Pres. & Chief Exec. Officer--Racine Federated, Inc., Racine, WI; *U.S. Private*, pg. 906

Ertun, Aybars, Chief Exec.--KONE Asansor Sanayi ve Ticaret A.S., Istanbul, Turkey; *Int'l*, pg. 747

Erxleben, William, Pres. & Chief Exec. Officer--Data I/O Corporation, Redmond, WA; *U.S. Public*, pg. 486

Esak, J. Ronald, Pres. & Chief Exec. Officer--Nexus Plastics, Inc., Hawthorne, NJ; *U.S. Private*, pg. 797

Escarrer, Sebastian, Chief Exec. Officer--Sol Melia, Palma de Mallorca, Spain; *Int'l*, pg. 1277

Eschrich, Robert W., Pres. & Chief Exec. Officer--WM Life Insurance Company, Seattle, WA; *U.S. Public*, pg. 1742

Eshelman, Fred N., Ph.D., Chief Exec. Officer--Pharmaceutical Product Development, Inc., Wilmington, NC; *U.S. Public*, pg. 1285

Eskandarian, Ed, Chm. & Chief Exec. Officer--Arnold Communications, Inc., Boston, MA; *U.S. Private*, pg. 83

Esping, P.E., Chm. Bd. & Chief Exec. Officer--BRC Holdings, Dallas, TX; *U.S. Public*, pg. 163

Espino, Alberto N., Pres. & Chief Oper. Officer--Coastal Fuels Marketing, Inc., Miami, FL; *U.S. Public*, pg. 390

Espinosa, Herberto, Pres. & Chief Exec. Officer--Amtrade International Bank, Miami, FL; *U.S. Private*, pg. 68

Esposito, Chris, Pres. & Chief Exec. Officer--Four Seasons Solar Products Corp., Holbrook, NY; *U.S. Private*, pg. 422

Esposito, Michael J., Chm., Pres. & Chief Exec. Officer--Exel Insurance Co. Ltd., Hamilton, Bermuda; *Int'l*, pg. 467

Esrey, William T., Chm. Bd. & Chief Exec. Officer--Sprint Corporation, Westwood, KS; *U.S. Public*, pg. 1500

Essenberg, Henry, Chief Exec. Officer--Air UK Ltd., Stansted, United Kingdom; *Int'l*, pg. 38

Essig, Armand J., Chief Exec. Officer--Allied Sporting Goods Inc., Louisville, KY; *U.S. Private*, pg. 41

Essman, Alyn V., Chm. Bd. & Chief Exec. Officer--CPI Corp., Saint Louis, MO; *U.S. Public*, pg. 283

Esson, J. Douglas, Chief Exec. Officer--King Cotton Foods, Memphis, TN; *U.S. Public*, pg. 1433

Estenson, Noel, Pres. & Chief Exec. Officer--CENEX, Inc., Inver Grove Heights, MN; *U.S. Private*, pg. 221

Estes, Bill, Pres. & Chief Exec. Officer--McKesson Corporation, Carrollton, TX; *U.S. Public*, pg. 1073

Estes, Robey W., Sr., Chm. Bd. & Chief Exec. Officer--Estes Express Lines, Inc., Richmond, VA; *U.S. Private*, pg. 384

Estey, John W., Pres. & Chief Exec. Officer--S & C Electric Company, Chicago, IL; *U.S. Private*, pg. 954

Estrin, Melvin, Co-Chm. Bd. & Co-Chief Exec. Officer--Phar-Mor, Inc., Youngstown, OH; *U.S. Public*, pg. 1284

Estrin, Melvyn J., Co-Chm. Bd. & Co-Chief Exec. Officer--Avatex Corporation, Dallas, TX; *U.S. Public*, pg. 151

Ethridge, J.B., Pres.--Struthers Industries Inc., Gulfport, MS; *U.S. Private*, pg. 1048

Ettore, Joseph R., Pres. & Chief Exec. Officer--Ames Department Stores, Inc., Rocky Hill, CT; *U.S. Public*, pg. 99

Eubanks, Gordon E., Jr., Pres. & Chief Exec. Officer--Symantec Corporation, Cupertino, CA; *U.S. Public*, pg. 1545

Eugster, Jack, Chm. Bd., Pres. & Chief Exec. Officer--Musicland Group Inc., Minnetonka, MN; *U.S. Public*, pg. 1142

Eulich, John F., Chm. Bd. & Chief Exec. Officer--Vantage Companies, Dallas, TX; *U.S. Private*, pg. 1134

Evan, Uri, Chm. Bd. & Chief Exec. Officer--USA Detergents, Inc., North Brunswick, NJ; *U.S. Public*, pg. 1685

Evans, C.L., Jr., Pres. & Chief Exec. Officer--Unisource, Doraville, GA; *U.S. Public*, pg. 1671

Evans, Daniel E., Chm. Bd., Chief Exec. Officer & Sec.--Bob Evans Farms, Inc., Columbus, OH; *U.S. Public*, pg. 596

Evans, Donald L., Chm. Bd. & Chief Exec. Officer--Tom Brown, Inc., Midland, TX; *U.S. Public*, pg. 262

Evans, Donald L., Chm. Bd. & Chief Exec. Officer--Tom Brown, Inc., Englewood, CO; *U.S. Public*, pg. 262

Evans, Dwight H., Pres. & Chief Exec. Officer--Mississippi Power Co., Gulfport, MS; *U.S. Public*, pg. 1490

Evans, G., Chief Exec. Officer--Woolworths (New Zealand) Ltd., Auckland, New Zealand; *Int'l*, pg. 704

Evans, George W., Pres. & Chief Exec. Officer--Regions Bank/Banks County, Homer, GA; *U.S. Public*, pg. 1371

Evans, Gorton M., Pres. & Chief Exec. Officer--Consolidated Papers, Inc., Wisconsin Rapids, WI; *U.S. Public*, pg. 436

Evans, Jim, Pres. & Chief Exec. Officer--Evans, Hardy & Young, Inc., Santa Barbara, CA; *U.S. Private*, pg. 384

Evans, R.H., Chief Exec. Officer--British Aerospace p.l.c., Farnborough, United Kingdom; *Int'l*, pg. 217

Evans, Richard E., Chm. Bd.--Eva-Tone Inc., Clearwater, FL; *U.S. Private*, pg. 384

Evans, Richard W., Jr., Chief Exec. Officer--Cullen/Frost Bankers, Inc., San Antonio, TX; *U.S. Public*, pg. 467

Evans, Robert B., Sr., Chm. Bd. & Chief Exec. Officer--Evans Industries, Inc., Detroit, MI; *U.S. Private*, pg. 385

Evans, Robert S., Chm. Bd. & Chief Exec. Officer--Crane Co., Stamford, CT; *U.S. Public*, pg. 456

Evans, Robert S., Chm. Bd. & Chief Exec. Officer--Medusa Corporation, Cleveland, OH; *U.S. Public*, pg. 1084

Evans, Ronald A., Pres. & Chief Exec. Officer--Best Western International, Inc., Phoenix, AZ; *U.S. Private*, pg. 140

Evans, Ronald C., Pres. & Chief Exec. Officer--Nationwide Homes, Inc., Martinsville, VA; *U.S. Private*, pg. 788

Evans, Stuart M., Pres. & Chief Exec. Officer--Amtech Europe Limited, Cambridge, United Kingdom; *U.S. Public*, pg. 106

Evans, William H., Chm. Bd., Pres. & Chief Exec. Officer--SunTrust Bank, North Central Florida, Ocala, FL; *U.S. Public*, pg. 1537

Evert, James, Chm. Bd., Pres. & Chief Exec. Officer--Irvine Sensors Corporation, Costa Mesa, CA; *U.S. Public*, pg. 913

Evins, Dan W., Chm. Bd. & Chief Exec. Officer--Cracker Barrel Old Country Store, Inc., Lebanon, TN; *U.S. Public*, *pg. 455*

Ewing, John H., Dr., Exec. Dir.--American Mathematical Society, Inc., Providence, RI; *U.S. Private*, pg. 59

Ewing, P., Chief Exec. Officer--Ferguson Publishing Company, Chicago, IL; *U.S. Private*, pg. 401

Ewing, Stephen E., Pres. & Chief Exec. Officer--MichCon, Detroit, MI; *U.S. Public*, pg. 1025

Eyler, John, Pres. & Chief Exec. Officer--F.A.O. Schwarz, New York, NY; *Int'l*, pg. 750

Ezrin, Hershell, Chief Exec. Officer--Speedy Muffler King, Inc., Toronto, Canada; *U.S. Public*, pg. 1578

Fabian, John M., Pres. & Chief Exec. Officer--ANSER (Analytic Services Inc.), Arlington, VA; *U.S. Private*, pg. 75

Fabian, Richard G., Chm. Bd. & Chief Exec. Officer--For Better Living, Inc., Auburn, CA; *U.S. Private*, pg. 417

Fabrikant, Charles, Chm. Bd., Pres. & Chief Exec. Officer--Seacor Smit Inc., Houston, TX; *U.S. Public*, pg. 1449

Facchina, Robert, Pres. & Chief Exec. Officer--Johanna Foods Inc., Flemington, NJ; *U.S. Private*, pg. 589

Facchinetti, Giovanni, Chief Exec. Officer--Intermarine S.p.A., Sarzana, Italy; *Int'l*, pg. 324

Fackier, Edwin, Chief Exec. Officer--Byers Portland Willamette, Portland, OR; *U.S. Private*, pg. 191

Fackler, Edwin, Chm. Bd. & Chief Exec. Officer--Byers Industries, Inc., Portland, OR; *U.S. Private*, pg. 191

Fadel, Mitch, Pres. & Chief Exec. Officer--ColorTyme, Inc., Irving, TX; *U.S. Private*, pg. 255

Faeller, Kurt, Pres. & Chief Exec. Officer--Rieter Holdings, Winterthur, Switzerland; *Int'l*, pg. 1116

Fagel, Harold, Chief Exec. Officer--Aurora Packing Co., Inc., North Aurora, IL; *U.S. Private*, pg. 99

Fahey, John, Pres. & Chief Exec. Officer--National Geographic Society, Washington, DC; *U.S. Private*, pg. 783

Fahlin, Roland, Pres. & Chief Exec. Officer--ICA Handlarnas AB, Solna, Sweden; *Int'l*, pg. 642

Fahnenstich, Heiner, Chief Officer--Deutsche Babcock International Vetriebs-GmbH, Oberhausen, Germany; *Int'l*, pg. 401

Fahrni, Fritz, Pres. & Chief Exec. Officer--Sulzer Ltd., Winterthur, Switzerland; *Int'l*, pg. 1305

Fahs, John C., Chm. Bd., Pres., Chief Exec. Officer & Treas.--California Panel & Veneer Company, Cerritos, CA; *U.S. Private*, pg. 201

Fain, John H., Chm. Bd., Pres., Chief Exec. Officer & Chief Oper. Officer--Metro Information Services, Virginia Beach, VA; *U.S. Public*, pg. 1102

Fain, Richard D., Chm. Bd. & Chief Exec. Officer--Royal Caribbean Cruises Ltd., Miami, FL; *U.S. Public*, pg. 1410

Fair, C.B., III, Pres. & Chief Exec. Officer--Regions Bank/Paulding County, Dallas, TX; *U.S. Public*, pg. 1372

Fairbank, Richard D., Chm. Bd. & Chief Exec. Officer--Capital One Financial Corporation, Falls Church, VA; *U.S. Public*, pg. 302

Fairbanks, J. Nelson, Chief Exec. Officer--United States Sugar Corporation, Clewiston, FL; *U.S. Private*, pg. 1126

Fairbanks, J. Nelson, Pres. & Chief Exec. Officer--United States Corrulite Corporation, Clewiston, FL; *U.S. Private*, *pg. 1126*

Fairbanks, J. Nelson, Pres. & Chief Exec. Officer--South Central Florida Express, Inc., Clewiston, FL; *U.S. Private*, *pg. 1126*

Fairbanks, J. Nelson, Pres. & Chief Exec. Officer--Southern Garden Citrus Processing, Clewiston, FL; *U.S. Private*, pg. 1126
Fairchild, John B., Chm. Bd. & Chief Exec. Officer--Fairchild Publications, New York, NY; *U.S. Public*, pg. 513
Fairchild, Ronald, Pres. & Chief Exec. Officer--Paul Inman Associates Inc., Farmington, MI; *U.S. Private*, pg. 564
Fairfield, Bill, Pres. & Chief Exec. Officer--Inacom Corp., Omaha, NE; *U.S. Public*, pg. 873
Faith, Marshall E., Chm. Bd. & Chief Exec. Officer--The Scoular Company, Omaha, NE; *U.S. Private*, pg. 977
Falk, Lloyd, Pres., Chief Exec. Officer & Chief Oper. Officer--Fort Lock Corporation, River Grove, IL; *U.S. Private*, pg. 419
Falk, Steve, Pres. & Chief Exec. Officer--San Francisco Newspaper Agency, San Francisco, CA; *U.S. Private*, pg. 239
Falkenberg, J., Chief Exec. Officer--Dan Tegl Tag A/S, Aalborg, Denmark; *Int'l*, pg. 1092
Fallon, Donald, Chm. Bd., Pres. & Chief Exec. Officer--S.A. Cimenteries CBR, Brussels, Belgium; *Int'l*, pg. 605
Falsetti, Emilio, Chief Exec. Officer & V.P.--Costa Container Lines S.p.A., Genoa, Italy; *Int'l*, pg. 336
Famalette, Joseph P., Pres. & Chief Exec. Officer--Tri Valley Growers, San Ramon, CA; *U.S. Private*, pg. 1101
Fancher, Mac, Chief Exec. Officer--Taylor & Francis, Washington, DC; *Int'l*, pg. 1358
Fanelli, Richard G., Pres. & Chief Exec. Officer--Enthone-OMI, Inc., West Haven, CT; *U.S. Public*, pg. 138
Fanfani, Marco, Chief Exec. Officer--Ata Tonic, Milan, Italy; *Int'l*, pg. 602
Fantom, Lynn, Chief Exec. Officer--Lowe Direct, New York, NY; *U.S. Private*, pg. 678
Farace, Andrea, Chm. Bd. & Chief Exec. Officer--Foamex International Inc., Linwood, PA; *U.S. Private*, pg. 1094
Farah, Roger N., Chm. Bd. & Chief Exec. Officer--Woolworth Corporation, New York, NY; *U.S. Public*, pg. 1777
Farb, Martin N., Pres. & Chief Exec. Officer--Brinkmann Instruments, Inc., Westbury, NY; *U.S. Private*, pg. 169
Farber, Bill, Chief Exec. Officer--Major Pharmaceuticals Corp., Auburn Hills, MI; *U.S. Private*, pg. 475
Farber, Jack, Chm. Bd., Pres. & Chief Exec. Officer--CSS Industries, Inc., Philadelphia, PA; *U.S. Public*, pg. 283
Farber, Sam, Chief Exec. Officer--OXO International, New York, NY; *U.S. Public*, pg. 716
Fargo, Brian, Chief Exec. Officer--Interplay Productions, Inc., Irvine, CA; *U.S. Private*, pg. 572
Fariello, Frank A., Chm. Bd., Pres. & Chief Exec. Officer--EDO Corporation, New York, NY; *U.S. Public*, pg. 541
Faris, Mustapha, Chief Exec. Officer--BMCI Morocco, Casablanca, Morocco; *Int'l*, pg. 163
Farkas, Andrew L., Chm. Bd. & Chief Exec. Officer--Insignia Financial Group, Inc., Greenville, SC; *U.S. Public*, pg. 881
Farley, William, Chief Exec. Officer--Acme Boot Co., Inc., El Paso, TX; *U.S. Private*, pg. 394
Farley, William, Chm. Bd. & Chief Exec. Officer--Fruit of the Loom, Inc., Chicago, IL; *U.S. Public*, pg. 685
Farley, William, Chief Exec. Officer--Gitano Fashions Ltd., Bowling Green, KY; *U.S. Public*, pg. 686
Farley, William F., Chm. Bd., Pres. & Chief Exec. Officer--Farley, Inc., Chicago, IL; *U.S. Private*, pg. 394
Farling, Robert J., Chm. Bd. & Chief Exec. Officer--The Toledo Edison Company, Toledo, OH; *U.S. Public*, pg. 645
Farmer, Bruce J., Pres. & Chief Exec. Officer--Four Winds Investment Corp., Galveston, TX; *U.S. Private*, pg. 422
Farmer, Bruce J., Pres. & Chief Exec. Officer--Farmers Marine Copper Works, Galveston, TX; *U.S. Private*, pg. 422
Farmer, John R., Chm. Bd., Pres. & Chief Exec. Officer--SouthTrust Bank, Tuscaloosa County, Tuscaloosa, AL; *U.S. Public*, pg. 1492
Farmer, Phillip W., Chm. Bd., Pres. & Chief Exec. Officer--Harris Corporation, Melbourne, FL; *U.S. Public*, pg. 791
Farmer, Roy F., Chm. Bd., Pres., Chief Exec. Officer & Chief Oper. Officer--Farmer Brothers Company, Torrance, CA; *U.S. Public*, pg. 613
Farnam, Walter E., Chm. Bd. & Chief Exec. Officer--General Accident Insurance, Philadelphia, PA; *Int'l*, pg. 543
Farnsworth, Jack, Pres. & Chief Exec. Officer--Primedia Informatin Group, New York, NY; *U.S. Public*, pg. 1328
Farnsworth, Jack, Pres. & Chief Exec. Officer--Primedia Workplace Learning, Carrollton, TX; *U.S. Public*, pg. 1328
Farr, David, Chief Exec. Officer--Astec International Limited, Wan Chai, Hong Kong; *Int'l*, pg. 92
Farrah, Pat, Chm. Bd., Pres. & Chief Exec. Officer--MG Products, San Antonio, TX; *U.S. Public*, pg. 1026
Farrar, David, Chief Exec.--Allied Colloids Group Plc., Bradford, United Kingdom; *Int'l*, pg. 62
Farrar, David, Chief Exec. Officer--Allied Colloids Ltd., Bradford, United Kingdom; *Int'l*, pg. 62
Farrar, Donald K., Chm. Bd. & Chief Exec. Officer--IMO Industries Inc., Lawrenceville, NJ; *U.S. Public*, pg. 856
Farrell, David C., Chm. Bd. & Chief Exec. Officer--The May Department Stores Company, Saint Louis, MO; *U.S. Public*, pg. 1063
Farrell, Frank A., Jr., Chm. Bd., Pres. & Chief Exec. Officer--Hope's Architectural Products Inc., Jamestown, NY; *U.S. Private*, pg. 538
Farrell, Roger A., Pres. & Chief Exec. Officer--Enogex Inc., Oklahoma City, OK; *U.S. Public*, pg. 1207
Farrell, W. James, Chm. Bd., Pres. & Chief Exec. Officer--Illinois Tool Works Inc., Glenview, IL; *U.S. Public*, pg. 865
Farren, Owen, Pres. & Chief Exec. Officer--SL Industries, Inc., Mount Laurel, NJ; *U.S. Public*, pg. 1418
Farrington, Hugh G., Pres. & Chief Exec. Officer--Hannaford Bros. Co., Scarborough, ME; *U.S. Public*, pg. 781
Farris, Allen, Pres. & Chief Exec. Officer--United Missouri Bank N.A., Kansas City, MO; *U.S. Public*, pg. 1654
Farris, David J., Pres. & Chief Exec. Officer--Beneficial Management Corporation, Peapack, NJ; *U.S. Public*, pg. 211
Farris, David J., Pres. & Chief Exec. Officer--Beneficial Management Corporation of America & Affiliated Corps., Wilmington, DE; *U.S. Public*, pg. 211
Farris, Michael R., Pres. & Chief Exec. Officer--Lasersight Inc., Saint Louis, MO; *U.S. Public*, pg. 979
Farris, William P., Pres. & Chief Exec. Officer--Mattison Technologies, Inc., Rockford, IL; *U.S. Private*, pg. 714
Farver, Herb, Chm. Bd. & Chief Exec. Officer--Blissfield Manufacturing Company, Blissfield, MI; *U.S. Private*, pg. 149
Fassinotti, Antonio Ello, Chief Exec. Officer & Exec. V.P.--Ferrero U.S.A., Inc., Somerset, NJ; *Int'l*, pg. 480
Fassler, Joseph K., Chm. & Chief Exec. Officer--Glacier Park, Inc., Phoenix, AZ; *U.S. Public*, pg. 1718
Fassler, Joseph K., Pres. & Chief Exec. Officer--Restaura, Inc., Phoenix, AZ; *U.S. Public*, pg. 1718
Faulkner, Henry, Chm. Bd. & Chief Exec. Officer--Faulkner Cadillac Inc., Trevose, PA; *U.S. Private*, pg. 397
Faulkner, Mikel D., Chm. Bd. & Chief Exec. Officer--Harken Energy Corporation, Irving, TX; *U.S. Public*, pg. 785
Faurre, Pierre, Chm. Bd. & Chief Exec. Officer--Societe d'Applications Generales d'Electricite et de Mechanique, Paris, France; *Int'l*, pg. 1273
Favish, Michael, Pres. & Chief Exec. Officer--FOTOBALL USA, Inc., San Diego, CA; *U.S. Public*, pg. 678
Fayer, Elizabeth, Chm. Bd. & Chief Exec. Officer--Alfin, Inc., New York, NY; *U.S. Public*, pg. 40
Fayfield, Robert, Chm. Bd., Pres. & Chief Exec. Officer--Banner Engineering Corp., Minneapolis, MN; *U.S. Private*, pg. 114
Fearnhead, Ivan J., Chief Exec. Officer-Engineered Rolls--Scapa Group Plc, Blackburn, United Kingdom; *Int'l*, pg. 1202
Federman, Joseph R., Chm Bd., Pres. & Chief Exec. Officer--Victor Technology, Addison, IL; *U.S. Private*, pg. 1139
Fedrick, C. Richard, Chief Exec. Officer--C.R. Fedrick, Inc., Novato, CA; *U.S. Private*, pg. 1052
Fee, P.S., Pres. & Chief Exec. Officer--BOVAR Inc., Calgary, Canada; *Int'l*, pg. 1424
Feehrer, E. Ross, Pres. & Chief Exec. Officer--F.N. Burt Company, Inc., Buffalo, NY; *U.S. Private*, pg. 188
Feeney, James H., Pres. & Chief Exec. Officer--Trone Advertising, Inc., Greensboro, NC; *U.S. Private*, pg. 1104
Fees, Samuel E., Pres. & Chief Exec. Officer--Woodstuff Manufacturing, Inc., Phoenix, AZ; *U.S. Private*, pg. 1187
Fehr, Robert, Pres. & Chief Exec. Officer--Cox Lumber Co., Saint Petersburg, FL; *U.S. Private*, pg. 283
Fehrman, Roger A., Pres. & Chief Exec. Officer--The Felters Company, Roebuck, SC; *U.S. Private*, pg. 400
Fehsenfeld, Mac, Chief Exec. Officer--Crystal Flash Petroleum Corp., Indianapolis, IN; *U.S. Private*, pg. 294
Feigenbutz, Gary, Pres. & Chief Exec. Officer--Miracle Recreation Equipment Company, Monett, MO; *U.S. Private*, pg. 752
Feil, Thomas E., Chm. Bd. & Chief Exec. Officer--V-Band Corporation, Elmsford, NY; *U.S. Public*, pg. 1701
Feinberg, Henry J., Chm. Bd., Pres. & Chief Exec. Officer--Rand McNally & Company, Skokie, IL; *U.S. Private*, pg. 908
Feinberg, Hill, Pres. & Chief Exec. Officer--First Southwest Company, Dallas, TX; *U.S. Private*, pg. 407
Feinstein, Leonard, Pres. & Co-Chief Exec. Officer--Bed Bath & Beyond Inc., Union, NJ; *U.S. Public*, pg. 200
Feinstein, Ronald, Pres. & Chief Exec. Officer--Lifeline Systems, Inc., Cambridge, MA; *U.S. Public*, pg. 992
Felber, Ronald, Pres., Chief Exec. & Chief Oper. Officer--Oakite Products, Inc., Berkeley Heights, NJ; *Int'l*, pg. 861
Feld, David, Chm. Bd., Chief Exec. Officer & Founder--Today's Man, Inc., Moorestown, NJ; *U.S. Public*, pg. 1619
Feld, Kenneth, Chm. Bd. & Chief Exec. Officer--Feld Productions, Vienna, VA; *U.S. Private*, pg. 399
Feld, Kenneth, Pres. & Chief Exec. Officer--Ringling Bros., Barnum & Bailey Combined Shows, Inc., Vienna, VA; *U.S. Private*, pg. 400
Feldberg, Warren D., Chm. Bd. & Chief Exec. Officer--Caldor, Inc., Norwalk, CT; *U.S. Public*, pg. 292
Feldenkreis, George, Pres.--Carfel, Inc., Miami, FL; *U.S. Private*, pg. 210
Feldenkreis, George, Chm. Bd. & Chief Exec. Officer--Supreme International Corp., Miami, FL; *U.S. Public*, pg. 1542
Feldman, Gerald, Pres. & Chief Exec. Officer--Allied Advertising Agency, Public Relations, Boston, MA; *U.S. Private*, pg. 38
Feldman, Jerome I., Pres. & Chief Exec. Officer--GP Strategies Corporation, New York, NY; *U.S. Public*, pg. 694
Feldman, Joseph, Pres. & Chief Exec. Officer--Isfel Company, Inc., Rahway, NJ; *U.S. Private*, pg. 576
Feldman, Lawrence H., Chm. Bd., Pres. & Chief Exec. Officer--Tower Realty Trust, Inc., New York, NY; *U.S. Public*, pg. 1625
Feldman, Robert, Pres. & Chief Exec. Officer-GCI Group, Inc.--GCI Group Inc., New York, NY; *U.S. Public*, pg. 764
Felken, G. Stephen, Chm. Bd. & Chief Exec. Officer--Avondale Foreign Sales Corporation, Sylacauga, AL; *U.S. Private*, pg. 103
Felker, G. Stephen, Chm. Bd., Pres. & Chief Exec. Officer--Avondale Incorporated, Monroe, GA; *U.S. Private*, pg. 102
Fellowes, John, Chm. & Chief Exec. Officer--Fellowes Manufacturing Co., Itasca, IL; *U.S. Private*, pg. 400
Fellows, George, Pres. & Chief Exec. Officer--Revlon, Inc., New York, NY; *U.S. Private*, pg. 689
Fellows, James, Pres. & Chief Exec. Officer--Evans Adhesive Corp., Columbus, OH; *U.S. Private*, pg. 384
Felsenthal, Donald, Chief Exec. Officer--Earle Industries, Inc., Earle, AR; *U.S. Private*, pg. 356
Feltenstein, Sidney, Chm. Bd., Pres. & Chief Exec. Officer--A&W Restaurants, Inc., Livonia, MI; *U.S. Private*, pg. 1
Feltenstein, Sidney, Chm. Bd., Chief Exec. Officer & Chief Oper. Officer--A&W Restaurants, Inc.-Carousel Div., Minneapolis, MN; *U.S. Private*, pg. 2
Felts, Jeffrey E., Pres. & Chief Exec. Officer--Hamilton Mutual Insurance Company Of Cincinnati, Cincinnati, OH; *U.S. Private*, pg. 497
Feniger, William D., Chm. Bd., Pres. & Chief Exec. Officer--Meridian National Corporation, Toledo, OH; *U.S. Public*, pg. 1095
Fenton, Jim, Pres., Chief Exec. Officer & Treas.--Southeastern Steel Company, Florence, SC; *U.S. Private*, pg. 1015
Fenwick, Robert, Dr., Chm. Bd. & Chief Exec. Officer--On Command Video, Santa Clara, CA; *U.S. Public*, pg. 138
Ferchat, Robert A., Chm., Pres. & Chief Exec. Officer--BCE Mobile Communications Inc., Saint-Laurent, Canada; *Int'l*, pg. 115
Ferfer, Gottfried, Chief Officer--Generale Bank & Co., Monchengladbach, Germany; *Int'l*, pg. 548
Ferger, Lawrence A., Chm. Bd. & Chief Exec. Officer--Indiana Energy, Inc., Indianapolis, IN; *U.S. Public*, pg. 874
Fergus, M.P., Chief Exec. Officer--Allied Van Lines, Inc., Naperville, IL; *Int'l*, pg. 901
Ferguson, C. David, Chm. Bd., Pres., Chief Exec. & Chief Oper. Officer--Gould Electronics Inc., Eastlake, OH; *U.S. Public*, pg. 1591
Ferguson, David, Pres. & Chief Exec. Officer--McCourt Label Co., Lewis Run, PA; *U.S. Private*, pg. 720
Ferguson, Gerry, Pres., Chief Exec. Officer & Chief Oper. Officer--Binning's Building Products, Inc., Lexington, NC; *U.S. Public*, pg. 67
Ferguson, J.T., Pres. & Chief Exec. Officer--Cormier Rice Milling Company, Inc., De Witt, AR; *U.S. Private*, pg. 276
Ferguson, James, Pres. & Chief Exec. Officer--Span-America Medical Systems Inc., Greenville, SC; *U.S. Public*, pg. 1495
Ferguson, Mark H., Chm. Bd., Pres. & Chief Exec. Officer--Firstbank of Illinois Co., Springfield, IL; *U.S. Public*, pg. 643
Ferguson, Ronald E., Chm. Bd. & Chief Exec. Officer--General Re Corporation, Stamford, CT; *U.S. Public*, pg. 725
Ferguson, Sam, Pres., Chief Exec. & Chief Oper. Officer--Ferguson International, Inc., Dallas, TX; *U.S. Private*, pg. 401
Ferguson, Thomas G., Chm. & Chief Exec. Officer--CommonHealth USA, Parsippany, NJ; *Int'l*, pg. 1483
Ferguson, W.A. III, Pres. & Chief Exec. Officer--Setco, Cincinnati, OH; *U.S. Private*, pg. 987
Ferland, E. James, Chm. Bd., Pres. & Chief Exec. Officer--Public Service Enterprise Group Incorporated, Newark, NJ; *U.S. Public*, pg. 1340
Fermon, Joseph C., Chm. Bd. & Chief Exec. Officer--Continental Eagle Corporation, Prattville, AL; *U.S. Private*, pg. 267
Fernandes, Meguel, Chief Exec. Officer--EURO RSCG, Oeiras, Portugal; *Int'l*, pg. 602
Fernandez Carbajal, Jose Antonio, Chief Exec. Officer--Fomento Economico Mexicano, S.A. de CV, Monterrey, Mexico; *Int'l*, pg. 496
Fernandez, Jesus, Chief Exec. & Chief Oper. Officer--Tradicion Textil, S.A., Barcelona, Spain; *Int'l*, pg. 1416
Fernandez, Joseph H., Chm. Bd., Pres. & Chief Exec. Officer--Buttrey Food & Drug Company, Great Falls, MT; *U.S. Public*, pg. 271
Fernandez, Nestor, Chief Exec. Officer & V.P.--Condal Distributors Inc., Bronx, NY; *U.S. Private*, pg. 262
Fernandez, Nestor, Pres. & Chief Exec. Officer--Digitron Tool Co., Inc., Miamisburg, OH; *U.S. Private*, pg. 332
Ferolie, Lawrence J., Chief Exec. Officer--Ferolie Group, Montvale, NJ; *U.S. Private*, pg. 401
Ferrari, Claudio, Chm. Bd. & Chief Exec. Officer--Foster Wheeler Power Systems, Inc., Clinton, NJ; *U.S. Public*, pg. 677
Ferreira, Fernando Xavier, Chm. Bd., Pres. & Chief Exec. Officer--Telebras S.A., Brasilia, Brazil; *Int'l*, pg. 1362
Ferreira, K., Chief Exec. Officer--The Simba Group, Isando, South Africa; *Int'l*, pg. 496
Ferrell, James E., Chm. Bd. & Chief Exec. Officer--Ferrellgas Partners, L.P., Liberty, MO; *U.S. Public*, pg. 618
Ferrentino, Michael, Chief Exec. Officer--Comforce/Uniforce Staffing Services, Woodbury, NY; *U.S. Public*, pg. 409
Ferries, Chuck, Pres. & Chief Exec. Officer--Scott Sports Group, Ketchum, ID; *U.S. Private*, pg. 977
Ferries, Chuck, Pres. & Chief Exec. Officer--Scott U.S.A., Ketchum, ID; *U.S. Private*, pg. 977
Ferris, Richard P., Chm. & Chief Exec. Officer--Norwest Bank International, Minneapolis, MN; *U.S. Public*, pg. 1202
Ferron, Rosendo, Pres. & Chief Exec. Officer--Halsey Drug Company, Brooklyn, NY; *U.S. Private*, pg. 496
Ferry, Richard M., Chm. Bd. & Chief Exec. Officer--Korn/Ferry International, Los Angeles, CA; *U.S. Private*, pg. 632
Ferry, William, Pres. & Chief Exec. Officer--Banyan Systems Inc., Westborough, MA; *U.S. Public*, pg. 189
Fertitta, Tilman, Chm. Bd., Pres. & Chief Exec. Officer--Landry's Seafood Restaurants Inc., Houston, TX; *U.S. Public*, pg. 977
Feshbach, Andrew D., Pres. & Chief Exec. Officer--Big Dog Holdings Inc., Santa Barbara, CA; *U.S. Public*, pg. 227
Feske, Thomas, Chief Exec.--Banco Santander, Frankfurt/Main, Germany; *Int'l*, pg. 144
Festa, Oscar, Chief Exec. Officer--EURO RSCG, Buenos Aires, Argentina; *Int'l*, pg. 602
Fetridge, Clark W., Chm. Bd. & Chief Exec. Officer--The Dartnell Corporation, Chicago, IL; *U.S. Private*, pg. 312
Fetterman, Annabelle L., Chm. Bd. & Chief Exec. Officer--Lundy Packing Co., Clinton, NC; *U.S. Private*, pg. 681

Feuer, Michael, Chm. Bd. & Chief Exec. Officer--OfficeMax, Shaker Heights, OH; *U.S. Public*, pg. 1212
Feuerstein, Aaron, Pres. & Chief Exec. Officer--Malden Mills Industries, Inc., Lawrence, MA; *U.S. Private*, pg. 698
Feury, Robert, Pres. & Chief Exec. Officer--Allied Building Products Corporation, East Rutherford, NJ; *U.S. Private*, pg. 38
Fialkow, Frederick H., Chm. Bd., Pres. & Chief Exec. Officer--National Home Health Care Corp., Scarsdale, NY; *U.S. Public*, pg. 1157
Fibery, Donald C., Pres. & Chief Exec. Officer--Central DuPage Health System, Winfield, IL; *U.S. Private*, pg. 223
Fichthorn, Luke E., III, Chm. Bd. & Chief Exec. Officer--Bairnco Corporation, Maitland, FL; *U.S. Public*, pg. 165
Fidler, Jay W., Pres. & Chief Exec. Officer--Hercules Chemical Co., Inc., Passaic, NJ; *U.S. Private*, pg. 523
Fiebig, Phil, Chief Exec. Officer--Leo Burnett Advertising SDN.BHD., Kuala Lumpur, Malaysia; *U.S. Private*, pg. 184
Fiebiger, James R., Pres. & Chief Exec. Officer--Gatefield Corporation, Fremont, CA; *U.S. Public*, pg. 703
Fiedler, Howard A., Chief Exec. Officer--Black Dot Graphics, Inc., Crystal Lake, IL; *U.S. Public*, pg. 503
Fiedler, John F., Chm. Bd. & Chief Exec. Officer--Borg Warner Automotive, Inc., Chicago, IL; *U.S. Public*, pg. 245
Fiedler, Paula P., Chm. Bd. & Chief Exec. Officer--Crown Fence Co., Long Beach, CA; *U.S. Private*, pg. 292
Field, H. James, Jr., Chm. & Chief Exec. Officer--Fleet Trust Co. of Florida, N.A., Stuart, FL; *U.S. Public*, pg. 649
Field, Kenneth W., Pres. & Chief Exec. Officer--Continental Web Press, Inc., Itasca, IL; *U.S. Private*, pg. 269
Field, Kenneth W., Sr., Pres. & Chief Exec. Officer--Continental Web Press Of Kentucky, Walton, KY; *U.S. Private*, pg. 269
Field, Lawrence, Pres. & Chief Exec. Officer--Field Container Company, L.P., Elk Grove Village, IL; *U.S. Private*, pg. 403
Field, Robert, Chm. Bd. & Chief Exec. Officer--IA Construction Corp., Concordville, PA; *U.S. Private*, pg. 552
Fields, Catherine M., Pres. & Chief Exec. Officer--P.S. International Inc., Durham, NC; *U.S. Private*, pg. 827
Fields, F.W., Pres. & Chief Exec. Officer--The Coe Manufacturing Company, Painesville, OH; *U.S. Private*, pg. 249
Fields, Gary, Chm. Bd. & Chief Exec. Officer--Banc One-Newark, Newark, OH; *U.S. Public*, pg. 173
Fields, William R., Pres. & Chief Exec. Officer--Hudson's Bay Company, Toronto, Canada; *Int'l*, pg. 637
Fierman, Gerald Shea, Pres. & Chief Exec. Officer--ANESCO, Kingston, PA; *U.S. Private*, pg. 74
Fife, Scott, Pres. & Chief Exec. Officer--Citizens First Bank, Fordyce, AR; *U.S. Public*, pg. 630
Figeac, Michel, Chief Exec. Officer (Southern Europe)--McCain Alimentaire SA, Harnes, France; *Int'l*, pg. 850
Figliulo, Robert M., Chm. Bd. & Chief Exec. Officer--SPR, Inc., Oak Brook, IL; *U.S. Public*, pg. 1419
Figoff, Michael, Pres. & Chief Exec. Officer--Puroflow Incorporated, Van Nuys, CA; *U.S. Public*, pg. 1345
Fike, John T., Chm. Bd. & Chief Exec. Officer--Pac Paper Inc., Vancouver, WA; *U.S. Private*, pg. 828
Fike, Lester L., Jr., Chm. Bd. & Chief Exec. Officer--Fike Corporation, Blue Springs, MO; *U.S. Private*, pg. 404
Fike, William T., Pres. & Chief Exec. Officer--Sierra West Bancorp, Truckee, CA; *U.S. Public*, pg. 1470
Filesi, Thomas R., Pres. & Chief Exec. Officer--Optek Technology, Inc., Carrollton, TX; *U.S. Public*, pg. 1227
Filho, Walter Fontana, Pres. & Chief Exec. Officer--Sadia Group, Barueri, Brazil; *Int'l*, pg. 1168
Filipowski, Andrew J., Chm. Bd., Pres. & Chief Exec. Officer--Platinum Technology, Inc., Oak Brook Terrace, IL; *U.S. Public*, pg. 1309
Filipps, Frank P., Pres. & Chief Exec. Officer--CMAC Investment Corporation, Philadelphia, PA; *U.S. Public*, pg. 278
Fill, Dennis, Chm. Bd. & Chief Exec. Officer--ATL Ultrasound, Inc., Bothell, WA; *U.S. Public*, pg. 11
Fillippo, Thomas A., Pres., Chief Exec. Officer & Corp. Sec.--DeVault Foods, Devault, PA; *U.S. Private*, pg. 329
Fillmer, Larry, Pres. & Chief Exec. Officer--Antares Alliance Group, Dallas, TX; *Int'l*, pg. 528
Filomeni, T., Chief Exec. Officer--Caffaro S.p.A., Milan, Italy; *Int'l*, pg. 248
Filosa, Nicholas A., Pres. & Chief Exec. Officer--Union Bank & Trust Co., North Vernon, IN; *U.S. Public*, pg. 633
Filter, Eunice M., Pres. & Chief Exec. Officer--Xerox Credit Corporation, Stamford, CT; *U.S. Public*, pg. 1785
Finch, David B., Pres. & Chief Exec. Officer--ATCOM, Inc., Research Triangle Park, NC; *U.S. Private*, pg. 94
Fincher, Jim V., Pres. & Chief Exec. Officer--Commercial Bank at Alma, Alma, AR; *U.S. Public*, pg. 641
Finck, Thomas G., Chm. Bd. & Chief Exec. Officer--Triton Energy Limited, Dallas, TX; *U.S. Public*, pg. 1640
Findlay, Roger, Chm. Bd. & Chief Exec. Officer--Modern Medical Modalities Corp., Morristown, NJ; *U.S. Public*, pg. 1121
Fink, Marvin H., Pres. & Chief Exec. Officer--Teledyne Electronic Technologies, Los Angeles, CA; *U.S. Public*, pg. 43
Finkelstein, Paul D., Pres. & Chief Exec. Officer--Regis Corporation, Minneapolis, MN; *U.S. Public*, pg. 1373
Finkl, Charles W., Chm. Bd. & Chief Exec. Officer--A. Finkl & Sons Co., Chicago, IL; *U.S. Private*, pg. 405
Finlay, Francis, Co-Chm. & Chief Exec. Officer--Clay Finlay Inc., New York, NY; *U.S. Public*, pg. 1673
Finn, L.P., Chief Exec. Officer & Chief Oper. Officer--Northern Rock PLC, Newcastle upon Tyne, United Kingdom; *Int'l*, pg. 968
Finn, Richard H., Pres. & Chief Exec. Officer--Transamerica Finance Group, Inc., Los Angeles, CA; *U.S. Public*, pg. 1630
Finnegan, Lawrence J., Chm. Bd. & Chief Exec. Officer--Boston Mutual Life Insurance Co., Canton, MA; *U.S. Private*, pg. 161
Finnegan, Neal, Pres. & Chief Exec. Officer--UST Corporation, Boston, MA; *U.S. Public*, pg. 1660
Finocchio, Robert, Pres. & Chief Exec. Officer--Informix Software, Menlo Park, CA; *U.S. Public*, pg. 876
Fiondella, Robert W., Chm. Bd., Pres. & Chief Exec. Officer--Phoenix Home Life Mutual Insurance Company, Hartford, CT; *U.S. Private*, pg. 863
Fiondella, Robert W., Chm. Bd., Pres. & Chief Exec. Officer--Phoenix Home Life Mutual Insurance Co., Hartford, CT; *U.S. Private*, pg. 863
Fiorentino, Gilbert J., Chm. Bd., Pres. & Chief Exec. Officer--Tiger Direct, Inc., Miami, FL; *U.S. Public*, pg. 747
Fircetz, Michael J., Chief Exec. Officer--First Virginia Bank-Clinch Valley, Richlands, VA; *U.S. Public*, pg. 641
Fireman, Paul, Chm. Bd., Pres. & Chief Exec. Officer--Reebok International Ltd., Stoughton, MA; *U.S. Public*, pg. 1369
Firestone, Sue, Pres.--Sue Firestone & Assoc., Santa Barbara, CA; *U.S. Private*, pg. 406
Firmenich, Pierre Yves, Chief Exec. Officer--Firmenich S.A., Geneva, Switzerland; *Int'l*, pg. 486
Fisch, Michael J., Pres. & Chief Exec. Officer--The Bakersfield Californian, Bakersfield, CA; *U.S. Private*, pg. 112
Fischbach, Gregory E., Chief Exec. Officer--Acclaim Entertainment, Inc., Glen Cove, NY; *U.S. Public*, pg. 15
Fischer, Charlotte G., Chm. Bd., Pres. & Chief Exec. Officer--Paul Harris Stores, Inc., Indianapolis, IN; *U.S. Public*, pg. 792
Fischer, Christian O., Dr., Chief Officer--Tela Versicherung AG, Munich, Germany; *Int'l*, pg. 58
Fischer, Daniel J., Pres., Chief Exec. Officer & Gen. Counsel--Manhattan Life Insurance Company, Cincinnati, OH; *U.S. Private*, pg. 1118
Fischer, Douglas J., Chief Exec. Officer--J. Richard Industries, L.P., Toledo, OH; *U.S. Private*, pg. 249
Fischer, Gerhard W., Chm. Bd. & Chief Exec. Officer--Panalpina Welttransport (Holding) AG, Binningen, Switzerland; *Int'l*, pg. 1022
Fischer, Heinrich, Chief Exec. Officer--Saurer AG, Arbon, Switzerland; *Int'l*, pg. 1198
Fischer, Stephen H., Pres. & Chief Exec. Officer--PrimeVest Financial Services, Inc., Saint Cloud, MN; *U.S. Public*, pg. 1376
Fischer, Thomas R., Dr., Chief Exec. Officer--Landesgirokasse Bank, Stuttgart, Germany; *Int'l*, pg. 799
Fish, Aaron M., Chm. Bd. & Chief Exec. Officer--Unican Security Systems Ltd., Montreal, Canada; *Int'l*, pg. 1432
Fish, Lawrence K., Chm., Pres. & Chief Exec. Officer--Citizens Financial Group, Inc., Providence, RI; *Int'l*, pg. 1132
Fisher, Donald G., Chm. Bd. & Chief Exec. Officer--Old Navy Stores, San Francisco, CA; *U.S. Public*, pg. 703
Fisher, George M.C., Chm. Bd. & Chief Exec. Officer--Eastman Kodak Company, Rochester, NY; *U.S. Public*, pg. 550
Fisher, Jeffrey, Pres. & Chief Exec. Officer--Pyramid Handbags Inc., New York, NY; *U.S. Private*, pg. 896
Fisher, John, Pres. & Chief Exec. Officer--Hyde Athletic Industries, Inc., Peabody, MA; *U.S. Public*, pg. 851
Fisher, John J., Chm. Bd. & Chief Exec. Officer--Corbett HealthConnect, A Frank J. Corbett, Inc., Company, Chicago, IL; *U.S. Public*, pg. 1223
Fisher, Joseph V., Pres. & Chief Exec. Officer--Big V Supermarkets, Inc., Florida, NY; *U.S. Private*, pg. 143
Fisher, Kenneth G., Chm. Bd. & Chief Exec. Officer--Encore Computer Corporation, Fort Lauderdale, FL; *U.S. Public*, pg. 580
Fisher, Rayburn J., Jr., Pres. & Chief Exec. Officer--Regions Bank/Atlanta, Sandy Springs, GA; *U.S. Public*, pg. 1371
Fisher, Thomas L., Chm. Bd., Pres. & Chief Exec. Officer--NICOR Inc., Naperville, IL; *U.S. Public*, pg. 1182
Fisher, Thomas L., Chm. Bd., Pres. & Chief Exec. Officer--Northern Illinois Gas Company, Naperville, IL; *U.S. Public*, pg. 1183
Fisher, William E., Pres. & Chief Exec. Officer--Applied Communications, Inc., Omaha, NE; *U.S. Public*, pg. 1629
Fisher, William F., Chm. Bd. & Chief Exec. Officer--Fisher Gauge Limited, Peterborough, Canada; *Int'l*, pg. 491
Fisherkeller, Paul F., Pres. & Chief Exec. Officer--Taco John's International, Inc., Cheyenne, WY; *U.S. Private*, pg. 1066
Fishman, Jerald G., Pres. & Chief Exec. Officer--Analog Devices, Inc., Norwood, MA; *U.S. Public*, pg. 107
Fishman, Steven S., Chm. Bd., Pres. & Chief Exec. Officer--Pamida Holdings Corporation, Omaha, NE; *U.S. Public*, pg. 1255
Fisler, B., Chief Exec. Officer--Societa Italiana Assicurazioni e Reassicurazioni S.p.A., Rome, Italy; *Int'l*, pg. 1531
Fites, Donald V., Chm. Bd. & Chief Exec. Officer--Caterpillar Inc., Peoria, IL; *U.S. Public*, pg. 315
Fitzgerald, Dave, Chief Exec. Officer--The Botsford Group, Atlanta, GA; *U.S. Private*, pg. 409
Fitzgerald, Duane D., Pres. & Chief Exec. Officer--Bath Iron Works Corporation, Bath, ME; *U.S. Public*, pg. 709
Fitzgerald, Gale S., Chm. Bd. & Chief Exec. Officer--Computer Task Group, Inc. (CTG), Buffalo, NY; *U.S. Public*, pg. 423
Fitzgerald, Mark, Pres. & Chief Exec. Officer--Willis Corroon Construction Services Corp., New Hyde Park, NY; *Int'l*, pg. 1504
Fitzgerald, Peter D., Pres.--Qualex Inc., Durham, NC; *U.S. Public*, pg. 551
Fitzgerald, Raymond N., Chief Exec. Officer--Atlantic Aviation Corp., New Castle, DE; *U.S. Private*, pg. 94
Fitzgerald, William A., Chm Bd. & Chief Exec. Officer--Commercial Federal Corporation, Omaha, NE; *U.S. Public*, pg. 411
Fitzgibbons, James M., Chm. Bd. & Chief Exec. Officer--Fieldcrest Cannon, Inc., Kannapolis, NC; *U.S. Public*, pg. 1296
Fitzpatrick, Barry J., Chm. Bd., Pres. & Chief Exec. Officer--First Virginia Banks, Inc., Falls Church, VA; *U.S. Public*, pg. 641
Fitzpatrick, Daniel B., Chm. Bd., Pres. & Chief Exec. Officer--Quality Dining Inc., Mishawaka, IN; *U.S. Public*, pg. 1349
Fitzpatrick, Richard J., Pres. & Chief Exec. Officer--The Howard Bank, N.A., Burlington, VT; *U.S. Public*, pg. 187
Fitzsimonds, Roger L., Chm. Bd. & Chief Exec. Officer--Firstar Corporation, Milwaukee, WI; *U.S. Public*, pg. 642
Fizdale, Richard B., Chm. & Chief Exec. Officer--Leo Burnett Company, Inc., Chicago, IL; *U.S. Private*, pg. 183
Flaherty, William E., Chm. Bd. & Chief Exec. Officer--Horsehead Industries, Inc., New York, NY; *U.S. Private*, pg. 540
Flakoll, Thomas J., Pres. & Chief Exec. & Oper. Officer--Technitrol, Inc., Trevose, PA; *U.S. Public*, pg. 1564
Flam, Seth, Dr., Pres. & Chief Exec. Officer--FPA Medical Management, Inc., San Diego, CA; *U.S. Public*, pg. 608
Flamingo, Joseph, Pres. & Chief Exec. Officer--International Wire Group Inc., Saint Louis, MO; *U.S. Private*, pg. 526
Flamingo, Joseph, Pres. & Chief Exec. Officer--Harness Division, Saint Louis, MO; *U.S. Private*, pg. 526
Flamingo, Joseph, Pres. & Chief Exec. Officer--Non-Insulated Division, Camden, NY; *U.S. Private*, pg. 526
Flamingo, Joseph, Pres. & Chief Exec. Officer--Insulated Division, Avilla, IN; *U.S. Private*, pg. 526
Flanagan, David T., Pres. & Chief Exec. Officer--Central Maine Power Company, Augusta, ME; *U.S. Public*, pg. 325
Flanagan, Dennis, Pres. & Chief Exec. Officer--Okidata Group, Mount Laurel, NJ; *Int'l*, pg. 1000
Flanagan, John, Chm. Bd., Pres. & Chief Exec. Officer--Goodheart-Willcox Publisher, Tinley Park, IL; *U.S. Private*, pg. 464
Flanagan, Terry M., Ph.D., Pres. & Chief Exec. Officer--Jacor Networks Inc., San Diego, CA; *U.S. Private*, pg. 584
Flanigan, Joseph G., Chm. Bd., Pres. & Chief Exec. Officer--Flanigan's Enterprises, Inc., Fort Lauderdale, FL; *U.S. Public*, pg. 648
Flaten, Alfred N., Chief Exec. Officer--Nash Finch Company, Edina, MN; *U.S. Public*, pg. 1151
Flatgard, Bjorn, Pres. & Chief Exec. Officer--Nycomed Pharma AS, Oslo, Norway; *Int'l*, pg. 993
Flatow, Mike, Pres. & Chief Exec. Officer--Champion Products Inc., Winston Salem, NC; *U.S. Public*, pg. 1433
Flaum, Sander A., Pres. & Chief Exec. Officer--Robert A. Becker, New York, NY; *Int'l*, pg. 601
Flechtner, Richard D., Pres. & Chief Exec. Officer--Car-Freshner Corporation, Watertown, NY; *U.S. Private*, pg. 207
Fleetwood, Christopher J., Chief Exec. Officer--Whessoe Plc, Newton Aycliffe, United Kingdom; *Int'l*, pg. 1498
Fleischer, J., Chief Exec. Officer--Neumeyer Fliesspressen GmbH, Nuremberg, Germany; *Int'l*, pg. 755
Fleischer, Morton H., Chm. Bd., Pres. & Chief Exec. Officer--Franchise Finance Corp. of America, Scottsdale, AZ; *U.S. Public*, pg. 679
Fleischhackei, M., Chief Exec. Officer--Zurich Poistovna sluzby s.r.o., Bratislava, Slovakia; *Int'l*, pg. 1532
Fleischhacker, Joe F., Jr., Chief Exec. Officer & Exec. V.P.--Lake Region Manufacturing, Inc., Chaska, MN; *U.S. Private*, pg. 643
Fleishman, Stanley, Chief Exec. Officer--Jetro Holdings, Inc., College Point, NY; *U.S. Private*, pg. 587
Fleishman, Stanley, Chief Exec. Officer--Jetro Cash & Carry, Philadelphia, PA; *U.S. Private*, pg. 587
Fleissner, Chief Exec. Officer--Fleissner GmbH & Co. Maschinenfabrik, Egelsbach, Germany; *Int'l*, pg. 493
Fleming, Cecil, Chief Exec. Officer--BDO Seidman, LLP, Chicago, IL; *U.S. Private*, pg. 106
Fleming, Donald R., Chm. Bd. & Chief Exec. Officer--Zoeller Co., Louisville, KY; *U.S. Private*, pg. 1207
Fleming, Larry A., Pres. & Chief Exec. Officer--Knoxville Utilities Board, Knoxville, TN; *U.S. Private*, pg. 627
Fleming, M. Jack, Chm. Bd., Pres., Chief Exec. Officer & Treas.--Merchants Publishing Co., Kalamazoo, MI; *U.S. Private*, pg. 732
Fleming, Robert W., Pres. & Chief Exec. Officer--Folger Nolan Fleming Douglas, Washington, DC; *U.S. Private*, pg. 416
Flenniken, Tom, Pres. & Chief Exec. Officer--UPB of Chattanooga, Chattanooga, TN; *U.S. Public*, pg. 1669
Fletcher, Andrew, Pres. & Chief Exec. Officer--Tausche Martin Lonsdorf, Atlanta, GA; *U.S. Private*, pg. 1069
Fletcher, Donald J., Pres.--George S. May International Company, Park Ridge, IL; *U.S. Private*, pg. 717
Fletcher, Hugh A., Chief Exec. Officer--Fletcher Challenge Limited, Auckland, New Zealand; *Int'l*, pg. 494
Fletcher, John, Chief Exec. Officer--Brambles Industries Limited, Sydney, Australia; *Int'l*, pg. 210
Fletcher, Kenneth W., Chm. Bd., Pres. & Chief Exec. Officer--Roberds, Inc., Carrollton, OH; *U.S. Public*, pg. 1393
Fletcher, William, Pres. & Chief Exec. Officer--Teva USA - Biocraft, Fair Lawn, NJ; *Int'l*, pg. 1381
Flicker, Irving, Chm. Bd. & Chief Exec. Officer--Homasote Company, Trenton, NJ; *U.S. Public*, pg. 831
Flint, H. Howard, II, Chm. Bd. & Chief Exec. Officer--Flint Ink Corp., Detroit, MI; *U.S. Private*, pg. 413
Fliss, Michael C., Pres. & Chief Exec. Officer--AMCORE Bank N.A., Rock River Valley, Sterling, IL; *U.S. Public*, pg. 64
Flocken, Jeff, Chief Exec. Officer--Northridge Hospital-Roscoe Blvd. Campus, Northridge, CA; *U.S. Private*, pg. 1118
Floeckher, Peter W., Pres. & Chief Exec. Officer--The Citizens National Bank, Laurel, MD; *U.S. Public*, pg. 1089
Flood, A.L., Chm. Bd. & Chief Exec. Officer--Canadian Imperial Bank of Commerce, Toronto, Canada; *Int'l*, pg. 256

Flood, Peter E., Pres. & Chief Exec. Officer--The Flood Company, Hudson, OH; *U.S. Private*, pg. 414
Floren, David, Chm. Bd. & Chief Exec. Officer--Martin/Williams Advertising Inc., Minneapolis, MN; *U.S. Private*, pg. 710
Florence, Leneord, Chief Exec. Officer-Syratech--Carvel Hall, Crisfield, MD; *U.S. Private*, pg. 1061
Florence, Leonard, Chm. Bd., Pres. & Chief Exec. Officer--Syratech Corporation, East Boston, MA; *U.S. Private*, pg. 1060
Florescue, Barry, Pres. & Chief Exec. Officer--Marietta Corporation, Cortland, NY; *U.S. Private*, pg. 702
Flori, John R., Pres. & Chief. Exec. Officer--Flori Corp., Phoenix, AZ; *U.S. Private*, pg. 414
Florio, Steven, Pres. & Chief Exec. Officer--The Conde Nast Publications Inc., New York, NY; *U.S. Private*, pg. 20
Florsheim, Thomas W., Chm. Bd. & Chief Exec. Officer--Weyco Group, Inc., Milwaukee, WI; *U.S. Public*, pg. 1763
Flowers, L.C., Chief Oper. Officer--Casa Export Limited, Smithfield, NC; *U.S. Public*, pg. 1695
Floyd, James G., Pres. & Chief Exec. Officer--The Houston Exploration Company, Houston, TX; *U.S. Public*, pg. 259
Floyd, William R., Pres. & Chief Exec. Officer--Choice Hotels International, Inc., Silver Spring, MD; *U.S. Public*, pg. 351
Flynn, Patrick, Pres., Chief Exec. Officer, Chief Oper. Officer & Controller--Freeway Corporation, Cleveland, OH; *U.S. Private*, pg. 426
Focke, H., Chief Exec. Officer--Zurich Lebenversicherungs-Gesellschaft, Frankfurt/Main, Germany; *Int'l*, pg. 1529
Focke, H., Chief Exec. Officer--Zurich Versicherungs-Gesellschaft, Frankfurt/Main, Germany; *Int'l*, pg. 1531
Focke, H., Chief Exec. Officer--Agrippina Lebensversicherung Aktiengesellschaft, Cologne, Germany; *Int'l*, pg. 1531
Focke, H., Chief Exec. Officer--Agrippina Rechtsschutzversicherung AG, Cologne, Germany; *Int'l*, pg. 1531
Focke, H., Chief Exec. Officer--Agrippina Versicherung Aktiengesellschaft, Cologne, Germany; *Int'l*, pg. 1531
Focke, H., Chief Exec. Officer--DA Deutsche Allgemeine Versicherungs-Aktiengellschaft, Frankfurt/Main, Germany; *Int'l*, pg. 1531
Focke, H., Chief Exec. Officer--Patria Versicherung Aktiengesellschaft, Cologne, Germany; *Int'l*, pg. 1531
Focke, H., Chief Exec. Officer--Zeta Finanza S.p.A., Milan, Italy; *Int'l*, pg. 1531
Focke, H., Chief Exec. Officer--Zurich International (Deutschland) Versicherungs-Aktiengesellschaft, Frankfurt/Main, Germany; *Int'l*, pg. 1532
Focke, H., Chief Exec. Officer--Zurich Kautions-und Kreditversicherungs-Aktiengesellschaft, Frankfurt/Main, Germany; *Int'l*, pg. 1532
Focke, H., Chief Exec. Officer--Zurich Rechtsschutzversicherungs-Aktiengesellschaft, Frankfurt/Main, Germany; *Int'l*, pg. 1532
Fogel, William, Chm. Bd., Pres. & Chief Exec. Officer--Jordon Commercial Refrigerator Co., Philadelphia, PA; *U.S. Private*, pg. 599
Fogg, F.W., Pres. & Chief Exec. Officer--Southeastern Medequip, Inc., Jacksonville Beach, FL; *U.S. Private*, pg. 1015
Fohrman, Neal, Pres. & Chief Exec. Officer--Red Calliope & Associates, Inc., Los Angeles, CA; *U.S. Public*, pg. 465
Foil, Martin B., Jr., Chm. Bd. & Chief Exec. Officer--Tuscarora Yarns Inc., Mount Pleasant, NC; *U.S. Private*, pg. 1110
Fojtasek, Randall S., Pres. & Chief Exec. Officer--Atrium Companies, Inc., Dallas, TX; *U.S. Private*, pg. 98
Foley, Charles R., Pres. & Chief Exec. Officer--Ameriwood Industries International Inc., Grand Rapids, MI; *U.S. Public*, pg. 98
Foley, Frank M., Pres. & Chief Exec. Officer--CHF Industries, Inc., New York, NY; *U.S. Private*, pg. 1094
Foley, J. Michael, Pres. & Chief Exec. Officer--Midwest Employer's Casualty Company, Maryland Heights, MO; *U.S. Public*, pg. 215
Foley, Patrick, Chm. Bd. & Chief Exec. Officer--DHL Worldwide Express, Redwood City, CA; *U.S. Private*, pg. 301
Foley, Stephen X., Jr., Chief Oper. Officer--Steve Foley Cadillac, Northbrook, IL; *U.S. Private*, pg. 416
Foley, William, Chief Exec. Officer--Fidelity National Title Insurance Company of Tennessee, Knoxville, TN; *U.S. Public*, pg. 621
Foley, William A., Chm. Bd., Pres. & Chief Exec. Officer--Lesco, Inc., Rocky River, OH; *U.S. Public*, pg. 989
Foley, William A., II, Chm. Bd. & Chief Exec. Officer--CKE Restaurants Inc., Anaheim, CA; *U.S. Public*, pg. 278
Foley, William P., II, Chm. Bd. & Chief Exec. Officer--Fidelity National Financial, Inc., Irvine, CA; *U.S. Public*, pg. 620
Foley, William P., II, Chief Exec. Officer Fidelity National Title Insurance Company, Irvine, CA; *U.S. Public*, pg. 620
Folger, Roger, Pres., Chief Exec. Officer & Chief Oper. Officer--Punch Press Products, Inc., Los Angeles, CA; *U.S. Private*, pg. 895
Folino, Paul F., Pres. & Chief Exec. Officer--Emulex Corporation, Costa Mesa, CA; *U.S. Public*, pg. 579
Folkert, Rod, Pres. & Chief Exec. Officer--Grocers Baking Co., Grand Rapids, MI; *U.S. Private*, pg. 482
Folkerth, John R., Chm. Bd. & Chief Exec. Officer--Shopsmith, Inc., Dayton, OH; *U.S. Public*, pg. 1467
Folley, K., Chief Exec. Officer--CV Home Furnishings Limited, Manchester, United Kingdom; *Int'l*, pg. 299
Folwell, G.J., Deputy Chief Exec.--Halifax plc, Halifax, United Kingdom; *Int'l*, pg. 589
Folz, Theo, Pres. & Chief Exec. Officer--Consolidated Cigar Corp., Fort Lauderdale, FL; *U.S. Private*, pg. 690
Folz, Theo W., Pres. & Chief Exec. Officer--Mafco Consolidated Group Inc., New York, NY; *U.S. Private*, pg. 690
Folz, Theodore W., Pres. & Chief Exec. Officer--Consolidated Cigar Corporation, Fort Lauderdale, FL; *U.S. Private*, pg. 690
Fonataine, R. Richard, Chief Exec. Officer--Babbage's Etc. LLC, Grapevine, TX; *U.S. Private*, pg. 108
Fondevik, O., Chief Exec. Officer--OCE-Norge A/S, Oslo, Norway; *Int'l*, pg. 994
Fong, Henry, Chm. Bd., Pres. & Chief Exec. Officer--RDM Sports Group, Atlanta, GA; *U.S. Public*, pg. 1354
Fontaine, Peter J., Chief Exec. Officer--Discount Auto Parts, Inc., Lakeland, FL; *U.S. Public*, pg. 510
Fontana, Victor, Pres., Chief Exec. Officer & Treas.--Autranet, Inc., New York, NY; *U.S. Public*, pg. 589
Fontenot, Chip, Chief Exec. Officer--Home Innovations, Inc., New York, NY; *U.S. Private*, pg. 536
Foose, Ralph G., Chief Exec. Officer--IRD Mechanalysis, Inc. (U.S.A.), Columbus, OH; *U.S. Public*, pg. 789
Foote, John, Chief Exec. Officer--Du Pont (Australia) Ltd., Sydney, Australia; *U.S. Public*, pg. 532
Foote, Robert, Pres. & Chief Exec. Officer--David White, L.L.C., Germantown, WI; *U.S. Public*, pg. 1765
Foote, Robert, Pres. & Chief Exec. Officer--David White, L.L.C., Germantown, WI; *U.S. Private*, pg. 1765
Foote, William, Chm. Bd. & Chief Exec. Officer--USG Corporation, Chicago, IL; *U.S. Public*, pg. 1660
Footman, John W., Chief Exec. Officer-Building Distr. UK--Wolseley Plc., Droitwich, United Kingdom; *Int'l*, pg. 1511
Footman, John W., Chief Exec. Officer--Wolseley Building Distribution - Europe, Droitwich, United Kingdom; *Int'l*, pg. 1511
Forbes, James L., Pres. & Chief Exec. Officer--Badger Meter, Inc., Milwaukee, WI; *U.S. Public*, pg. 164
Forbes, Malcolm S., Jr., Pres., Chief Exec. & Editor-in-Chief--Forbes, Inc., New York, NY; *U.S. Private*, pg. 417
Forbes, Walter A., Chm. Bd. & Chief Exec. Officer--CUC International, Inc., Stamford, CT; *U.S. Public*, pg. 320
Ford, Joe T., Chm. Bd., Pres. & Chief Exec. Officer--ALLTEL Corporation, Little Rock, AR; *U.S. Public*, pg. 55
Ford, Richard Q., Chief Exec. Officer-Life & Health Programs Div.--Willis Corroon Administrative Services, Inc., Nashville, TN; *Int'l*, pg. 1504
Ford, Tom, Pres. & Chief Exec. Officer--Grossman's, Inc., Stoughton, MA; *U.S. Private*, pg. 585
Forde, W.D., Chief Exec. Officer--Readymix Qatar WLL & The Quatar Quarry Co. WLL, Doha, Qatar; *Int'l*, pg. 1092
Fore, James R., Chm. Bd., Pres. & Chief Exec. & Oper. Officer--Communication Cable, Inc., Sanford, NC; *U.S. Public*, pg. 968
Forester, Benjamin, Chm. Bd., Pres. & Chief Exec. Officer--Rex Lumber Company, Acton, MA; *U.S. Private*, pg. 926
Forgione, Anthony, Chm. Bd. & Pres.--Boyer Candy Company Inc., Altoona, PA; *U.S. Private*, pg. 162
Forjaz, Duarte, Chief Exec. Officer--DMB&B Lisbon, Lisbon, Portugal; *U.S. Private*, pg. 304
Forlig, Paolo, Chief Exec. Officer--Arnoldo Mondadori Editore S.p.A., Segrate, Italy; *Int'l*, pg. 887
Forman, Sam, Chm. Bd., Pres. & Chief Exec. Officer--County Seat Stores, Inc., Dallas, TX; *U.S. Private*, pg. 279
Forman, Willis M., Pres., Chief Exec. Officer & Treas.--Paper Calmenson & Co., Saint Paul, MN; *U.S. Private*, pg. 837
Formica, Mark J., Pres. & Chief Exec. Officer--Citizens Savings Bank, Providence, RI; *Int'l*, pg. 1132
Formica, Mark J., Pres. & Chief Exec. Officer--Citizens Trust Company, Providence, RI; *Int'l*, pg. 1132
Formica, Mark J., Chm. & Chief Exec. Officer--Citizens Mortgage Corporation, Atlanta, GA; *Int'l*, pg. 1132
Fornataro, A.A., Pres. & Chief Exec. Officer--Salem Group, Inc., Pittsburgh, PA; *U.S. Private*, pg. 961
Fornataro, A.A., Pres. & Chief Exec. Officer--Salem Corporation, Pittsburgh, PA; *U.S. Private*, pg. 961
Forneri, Jean-Marc, Chief Exec. Officer--Rossignol S.A., Voiron, France; *Int'l*, pg. 1127
Forrest, Gregory J., Pres. & Chief Exec. Officer--Bank of America Capital, Costa Mesa, CA; *U.S. Public*, pg. 180
Fors, Borje, Chief Officer--Akademibokhandelsgruppen, Stockholm, Sweden; *Int'l*, pg. 718
Forster, Frank L., Chief Oper. Officer & Sr. V.P.--Hawaiian Airlines, Inc., Honolulu, HI; *U.S. Public*, pg. 799
Forster, Peter H., Chm. Bd.--Dayton Power & Light Co., Dayton, OH; *U.S. Public*, pg. 473
Forstmann, Theodore, Chm. Bd. & Chief Exec. Officer--Gulfstream Aerospace Corporation, Savannah, GA; *U.S. Private*, pg. 419
Forsythe, Daryl R., Pres. & Chief Exec. Officer--NBT Bancorp Inc., Norwich, NY; *U.S. Public*, pg. 1144
Forsythe, Gerald, Chm. Bd., Pres. & Chief Exec. Officer--Indeck Power Equipment Company, Wheeling, IL; *U.S. Private*, pg. 559
Forterre, Bernard, Pres.-France & Chief Exec. Officer--Anjou International Company, New York, NY; *Int'l*, pg. 321
Fortier, Marc G., Chm. Bd., Pres. & Chief Exec. Officer--Societe Generale de Financement du Quebec, Montreal, Canada; *Int'l*, pg. 1274
Fortino, Joe, Chief Exec. Officer--Champion Products, Winston Salem, NC; *U.S. Public*, pg. 1433
Fortkiewicz, Victor A., Pres. & Chief Exec. Officer--Elizabethtown Gas Co., Union, NJ; *U.S. Public*, pg. 1147
Fortun, Wayne M., Pres., Chief Exec. Officer & Chief Oper. Officer--Hutchinson Technology Inc., Hutchinson, MN; *U.S. Public*, pg. 850
Fortune, Ronald F., Pres. & Chief Exec. Officer--Computer Curriculum Corporation, Sunnyvale, CA; *U.S. Private*, pg. 778
Forward, Gordon E., Pres. & Chief Exec. Officer--Chaparral Steel Co., Midlothian, TX; *U.S. Public*, pg. 1585
Foshee, Douglas L., Pres. & Chief Exec. Officer--Nuevo Energy Company, Houston, TX; *U.S. Public*, pg. 1206
Fosmire, John C., Pres. & Chief Exec. Officer--Anderson Lithograph Company, Los Angeles, CA; *U.S. Private*, pg. 72
Foster, Charles H., Jr., Chm. Bd. & Chief Exec. Officer--Lawyers Title Insurance Corporation, Richmond, VA; *U.S. Public*, pg. 981
Foster, Dennis, Pres. & Chief Exec. Officer--360 Degrees Communications Company, Chicago, IL; *U.S. Public*, pg. 1607
Foster, James H., Exec. V.P., Chm.-Brouillard Communications--J. Walter Thompson Company, New York, NY; *Int'l*, pg. 1483
Foster, Lee B., II, Pres. & Chief Exec. Officer--L.B. Foster Company, Pittsburgh, PA; *U.S. Public*, pg. 675
Foster, Leland, Ph.D., Pres. & Chief Exec. Officer--HyClone Laboratories Inc., Logan, UT; *Int'l*, pg. 1037
Foster, Matthew, Reg. Chief Exec Officer--Milk Products Holdings (Australia) Pty Ltd, Rowville, Australia; *Int'l*, pg. 923
Foster, Michael, Pres. & Chief Exec. Officer--Moorman's Inc., Quincy, IL; *U.S. Private*, pg. 760
Foster, Mike, Chief Exec. Officer--Inntrepreneur Pub Company Limited, Thame, United Kingdom; *Int'l*, pg. 956
Foster, Neil, Pres. & Chief Exec. Officer--Star Sales Co., Inc., Knoxville, TN; *U.S. Private*, pg. 1035
Foster, Paul L., Chm. Bd. & Chief Exec. Officer--Talley Industries, Inc., Phoenix, AZ; *U.S. Public*, pg. 307
Foster, S.R., Chief Exec. Officer--Toyota (Great Britain) Limited, Redhill, United Kingdom; *Int'l*, pg. 1414
Foster, Steven L., Pres. & Chief Exec. Officer--Jillian's Entertainment Corporation, Boston, MA; *U.S. Private*, pg. 587
Foster, Timothy E., Chief Exec. Officer--NovaCare Inc., King of Prussia, PA; *U.S. Public*, pg. 1203
Foster, W. Douglas, Chm. Bd., Pres. & Chief Exec. Officer--Salem Carpet Mills, Inc., Winston Salem, NC; *U.S. Public*, pg. 1464
Foster, Willett S., IV, Pres. & Chief Exec. Officer--Edlund Company, Inc., Burlington, VT; *U.S. Private*, pg. 364
Foujlhac, Charles, Chief Exec. Officer--Credit Agricole (CNCA) Madrid, Madrid, Spain; *Int'l*, pg. 341
Foulkes-Jones, Robert, Chief Exec. Officer--Brammer plc, Altrincham, United Kingdom; *Int'l*, pg. 212
Fountain, Larry, Pres. & Chief Exec. Officer--Stanley Stores, Inc., Vidor, TX; *U.S. Private*, pg. 1033
Fountain, Reginald M., Jr., Chm. Bd., Pres. & Chief Exec. & Oper. Officer--Fountain Powerboat Industries, Inc., Washington, NC; *U.S. Public*, pg. 678
Fournier, Ronald P., Vice Chm. & Deputy Chief Exec. Officer--Co-Steel Inc., Toronto, Canada; *Int'l*, pg. 298
Fourtou, Jean-Rene, Chm. Bd. & Chief Exec Officer--Rhone-Poulenc S.A., Courbevoie, France; *Int'l*, pg. 1108
Foust, David D., Pres. & Chief Exec. Officer--Seneca Wire & Manufacturing Co., Fostoria, OH; *U.S. Private*, pg. 984
Fowler, Frederick V., Jr., Chm. Bd., Pres. & Chief Exec. Officer--Fred V. Fowler Company, Inc., Newton, MA; *U.S. Private*, pg. 422
Fowler, John, Joint Chief Exec. Officer--Westcan Chromalox, Cambridge, Canada; *Int'l*, pg. 554
Fowler, Paul, Chief Exec. Officer-Solid Wood Forestry--Fletcher Challenge Limited, Auckland, New Zealand; *Int'l*, pg. 494
Fowler, Robert E., Jr., Pres. & Chief Exec. & Oper. Officer--IMC Global, Bannockburn, IL; *U.S. Public*, pg. 856
Fowler, Robert E., Jr., Pres. & Chief Exec. Officer--The Vigoro Corporation, Chicago, IL; *U.S. Public*, pg. 856
Fowler, Walter B., Chm. Bd., Pres. & Chief Exec. Officer--The Carbide/Graphite Group, Inc., Pittsburgh, PA; *U.S. Public*, pg. 304
Fox, Alan B., Chief Exec. Officer--Iveco-Ford Truck Ltd., Watford, United Kingdom; *Int'l*, pg. 484
Fox, Bob, Pres. & Chief Exec. Officer--Foster Farms, Livingston, CA; *U.S. Private*, pg. 421
Fox, David M., Pres. & Chief Exec. Officer--Unapix Entertainment Inc., New York, NY; *U.S. Public*, pg. 1664
Fox, Herbert C., Pres. & Chief Exec. Officer--Active Electrical Supply Company, Chicago, IL; *U.S. Private*, pg. 15
Fox, Jeff, Pres. & Chief Exec. Officer--Alltel Information Services, Inc., Little Rock, AR; *U.S. Public*, pg. 56
Fox, Jonathan E., Chief Exec. Officer, Exec. V.P.-Intl. & Reg. Dir.-Asia Pacific--Grey Asia Pacific, Quarry Bay, Hong Kong; *U.S. Public*, pg. 765
Fox, Lawrence J., Chm. Bd. & Chief Exec. Officer--Symix Systems, Inc., Columbus, OH; *U.S. Public*, pg. 1546
Fox, Murray L., Pres. & Chief Exec. Officer--Consolidated Carma Corporation, Calgary, Canada; *Int'l*, pg. 229
Fox, Sam, Chm. Bd. & Chief Exec. Officer--Harbour Group Ltd., Saint Louis, MO; *U.S. Private*, pg. 500
Fox, Wayne F., Chm. Bd. & Chief Exec. Officer--Triple F, Inc., Des Moines, IA; *U.S. Private*, pg. 1104
Foy, Thomas, Pres. & Chief Exec. Officer--Action Industries, Inc., Tupelo, MS; *U.S. Public*, pg. 688
Frachey, Enrico, Chief Exec. Officer--Fila Sport S.p.A., Biella, Italy; *Int'l*, pg. 484
Frahm, Donald R., Chm. & Chief Exec. Officer--Hartford Fire Insurance Co., Hartford, CT; *U.S. Public*, pg. 794
Frame, Paul A., Pres. & Chief Exec. Officer--Seitel, Inc., Houston, TX; *U.S. Public*, pg. 1454
Frances, Philippe, Chief Exec.-KERL--Kingfisher plc, London, United Kingdom; *Int'l*, pg. 733
Francesconi, Joseph J., Pres. & Chief Exec. Officer--Network Equipment Technologies, Inc., Redwood City, CA; *U.S. Public*, pg. 1168
Francis, Peter T., Chm. Bd., Pres. & Chief Exec. Officer--J.M. Huber Corporation, Edison, NJ; *U.S. Private*, pg. 544
Francis, Philip L., Pres. & Chief Exec. Officer--Shaw's Supermarkets, Inc., East Bridgewater, MA; *Int'l*, pg. 1170
Franco, Christopher P., Chief Exec. Officer--Comforce Corporation, Lake Success, NY; *U.S. Public*, pg. 409
Francoeur, M., Pres. & Chief Exec. Officer--Stelco-McMaster Ltee, Contrecoeur, Canada; *Int'l*, pg. 1299
Francois, Emile, Pres. & Chief Exec. Officer--Poliet, Courbevoie, France; *Int'l*, pg. 1177
Francois, Georges, Chm. Bd. & Chief Exec. Officer--Automotive Wiring Systems Division - Sylea, Montigny-le-Bretonneux, France; *Int'l*, pg. 785

Frangenberg, Bernd, Pres. & Chief Exec. Officer--Continental General Tire, Inc., Charlotte, NC; *Int'l*, pg. 327
Franich, Steven, Pres. & Chief Exec. Officer--Marty Franich Auto Center, Watsonville, CA; *U.S. Private*, pg. 423
Frank, D.P., Pres. & Chief Exec. Officer--Ziegler Thrift Trading, Inc., Minneapolis, MN; *U.S. Public*, pg. 1792
Frank, H. Alan, Chief Exec. Officer--Admiral Packaging, Inc., Providence, RI; *U.S. Private*, pg. 1119
Frank, John B., Pres. & Chief Exec. Officer--SunTrust Bank, Middle Georgia, N.A., Macon, GA; *U.S. Public*, pg. 1538
Frank, Richard M., Chm. Bd. & Chief Exec. Officer--ShowBiz Pizza Time, Inc., Irving, TX; *U.S. Public*, pg. 1468
Frank, Richard R., Pres. & Chief Exec. Officer--Lawry's Restaurants, Inc., Pasadena, CA; *U.S. Private*, pg. 654
Franke, J.P., Pres. & Chief Exec. Officer--Syndesis Development Corp., Milwaukee, WI; *U.S. Public*, pg. 1773
Franke, Peter, Chief Exec. Officer--Lufthansa Systems GmbH, Kelsterbach, Germany; *Int'l*, pg. 407
Franke, William A., Chm. Bd. & Chief Exec. Officer--America West Holdings Corporation, Phoenix, AZ; *U.S. Public*, pg. 66
Frankel, Andrew, Chm. Bd. & Chief Exec. Officer--Andal Corp., New York, NY; *U.S. Public*, pg. 111
Frankel, Bernard, Chm. & Chief Exec. Officer--Frankel & Company, Chicago, IL; *U.S. Private*, pg. 424
Frankel, Robert James, Chm. Bd. & Chief Exec. Officer--Construction Counsellors, Inc., Montville, NJ; *U.S. Private*, pg. 266
Frankel, Steven T., Pres. & Chief Exec. Officer--Quidel Corporation, San Diego, CA; *U.S. Public*, pg. 1352
Frankenberg, Jay, Pres. & Chief Exec. Officer--Graphic Technology, Inc., New Century, KS; *Int'l*, pg. 950
Frankfort, Lew, Chm. Bd. & Chief Exec. Officer--Coach, New York, NY; *U.S. Public*, pg. 1433
Frankino, Sam J., Chm. Bd. & Chief Exec. Officer--National Auto Credit Inc., Solon, OH; *U.S. Public*, pg. 1152
Franklin, Beth, Pres. & Chief Exec. Officer--Star Transportation, Inc., Nashville, TN; *U.S. Private*, pg. 1035
Franklin, H. Allen, Pres. & Chief Exec. Officer--Georgia Power Co., Atlanta, GA; *U.S. Public*, pg. 1490
Franklin, Joe P., Chm. Bd. & Chief Exec. Officer--Frequency Electronics, Inc., Uniondale, NY; *U.S. Public*, pg. 681
Franklin, Larry, Pres. & Chief Exec. Officer--Harte-Hanks Communications, Inc., San Antonio, TX; *U.S. Public*, pg. 793
Franklin, Martin E., Chm. Bd. & Chief Exec. Officer--BEC Group, Inc., Rye, NY; *U.S. Public*, pg. 160
Franzone, John B., Pres. & Chief Exec. Officer--Fawn Industries, Inc., Hunt Valley, MD; *U.S. Private*, pg. 397
Franzutti, Brunello, Chief Exec. Officer & Gen. Mgr.--Publifactoring S.p.A., Milan, Italy; *Int'l*, pg. 138
Franzutti, Brunello, Chief Exec. Officer & Gen. Mgr.--Publicfactoring S.p.A., Milan, Italy; *Int'l*, pg. 138
Frasca, Giorgio, Pres. & Chief Exec. Officer--Iveco France S.A., Trappes, France; *Int'l*, pg. 696
Frasco, Pat, Chief Exec. Officer--B&W Co-op, Inc., Breckenridge, MI; *U.S. Private*, pg. 105
Fraser, Alan, Pres. & Chief Exec. Officer--Digital Link Corporation, Sunnyvale, CA; *U.S. Public*, pg. 508
Fraser, John S., Chm. Bd. & Chief Exec. Officer--CIBA-GEIGY Plc, Macclesfield, United Kingdom; *Int'l*, pg. 978
Fraser, Robert, Chief Oper. Officer--Engine Control Systems, Ltd., Newmarket, Canada; *U.S. Public*, pg. 1016
Frauenfelder, Lew, Pres. & Chief Exec. Officer--Fujitsu Computer Products of America, Inc., San Jose, CA; *Int'l, pg. 526*
Frauenhofer, Victor H., Chm. Bd. & Chief Exec. Officer--CTG Resources, Inc., Hartford, CT; *U.S. Public*, pg. 285
Frauenhofer, Victor H., Chm. Bd. & Chief Exec. Officer--Connecticut Natural Gas Corporation, Hartford, CT; *U.S. Public*, pg. 285
Frauenhofer, Victor H., Chm. Bd. & Chief Exec. Officer--Energy Networks, Inc. (ENI), Hartford, CT; *U.S. Public*, pg. 285
Fravel, J.C., Chm., Pres. & Chief Exec. Officer--Syroco Inc., Peabody, MA; *Int'l*, pg. 844
Frawley, Steve, Pres. & Chief Exec. Officer--Emery Waterhouse Company, Portland, ME; *U.S. Private*, pg. 373
Frazee, John P., Jr., Chm. Bd., Pres. & Chief Exec. Officer--Paging Network, Inc., Plano, TX; *U.S. Public*, pg. 1252
Frazier, James H., Pres. & Chief Exec. Officer--Building Plastics, Inc., Memphis, TN; *U.S. Private*, pg. 180
Frazier, John L.D., Chm. Bd. & Chief Exec. Officer--Full Service Beverage Company, Wichita, KS; *U.S. Private*, pg. 34
Frazier, Warner, Chm. Bd. & Chief Exec. Officer--Simplicity Manufacturing, Inc., Port Washington, WI; *U.S. Private*, pg. 1002
Frechette, Peter L., Pres. & Chief Exec. Officer--Patterson Dental Company, Saint Paul, MN; *U.S. Public*, pg. 1265
Frederic, Rand, Chief Exec. Officer--Frederic Printing Company, Aurora, CO; *U.S. Private*, pg. 265
Frediani, Steve, Pres. & Chief Exec. Officer--Ancra International LLC, Hawthorne, CA; *U.S. Private*, pg. 71
Fredriksson, Ake, Pres. & Chief Exec. Officer--Perstorp AB, Perstorp, Sweden; *Int'l*, pg. 1036
Freedman, Allen R., Chm. Bd. & Chief Exec. Officer--Fortis, Inc., New York, NY; *Int'l*, pg. 499
Freeman, Carl M., Chm. Bd. & Chief Exec. Officer--Carl M. Freeman Associates, Inc., Potomac, MD; *U.S. Private*, pg. 426
Freeman, D.S., Jr., Chm. Bd. & Chief Exec. Officer--Freeman Decorating Co., Dallas, TX; *U.S. Private*, pg. 426
Freeman, David, Chm. & Chief Exec. Officer--Loctite Corporation, Rocky Hill, CT; *Int'l*, pg. 611
Freeman, Kenneth W., Chm. Bd., Pres. & Chief Exec. Officer--Quest Diagnostics, Inc., Teterboro, NJ; *U.S. Public*, pg. 1351
Freeman, Mark S., Pres. & Chief Exec. Officer--Freeman Cosmetic Corp., Los Angeles, CA; *U.S. Private*, pg. 426
Freeman, Marshall W., Chm. Bd., Pres. & Chief Exec. Officer--Miller Freeman Inc., San Francisco, CA; *Int'l*, pg. 1443
Freeman, William M., Pres. & Chief Exec. Officer--Bell Atlantic-Washington, D.C., Inc., Washington, DC; *U.S. Public*, pg. 203
Frega, Ben, Pres. & Chief Exec. Officer--Comstock Michigan Fruit, Rochester, NY; *U.S. Private*, pg. 887
Frem, George N., Chm. Bd. & Chief Exec. Officer--Interstate Resources, Inc., Rosslyn, VA; *U.S. Private*, pg. 573
Fremes, Charles, Co-Chief Exec. Officer-Canada--Edelman Public Relations Worldwide, Toronto, Canada; *U.S. Private*, pg. 363
Fremont, Dominique, Chm. Bd. & Chief Exec. Officer--Fotolabo S.A., Lausanne, Switzerland; *Int'l*, pg. 501
Fremont, Robert S., Chm. Bd. & Chief Exec. Officer--Juno Lighting, Inc., Des Plaines, IL; *U.S. Public*, pg. 935
French, Arthur L., Chm. Bd. & Chief Exec. Officer--Metals USA, Inc., Houston, TX; *U.S. Public*, pg. 1100
French, D.J, Chief Oper. Officer--Universal Woods, Incorporated, Smithfield, NC; *U.S. Public*, pg. 1695
French, James S.M., Pres. & Chief Exec. Officer--Dunn Investment Co., Birmingham, AL; *U.S. Private*, pg. 347
French, Morton R., Jr., Pres., Chief Exec. Officer, Chief Fin. Officer & Treas.--Commercial Plastics & Supplies Corp., Richmond Hill, NY; *U.S. Private*, pg. 258
Frericks, Peter, Chief Exec. Officer & Gen. Mgr.--Sandoz Pharma Ltd., Eden Terrace, New Zealand; *Int'l*, pg. 985
Freston, Thomas, Chm. & Chief Exec. Officer--MTV Networks, New York, NY; *U.S. Private*, pg. 779
Freston, Thomas, Chm. Bd. & Chief Exec. Officer--MTV: Music Television, New York, NY; *U.S. Private*, pg. 779
Freston, Thomas E., Chm. Bd. & Chief Exec. Officer-MTV Networks--National Amusements, Inc., Dedham, MA; *U.S. Private*, pg. 775
Frew, Bud L., Pres. & Chief Exec Officer--MFA Incorporated, Columbia, MO; *U.S. Private*, pg. 686
Frey, Charles, Chief Exec. Officer--Turkey Hill Dairy, Inc., Conestoga, PA; *U.S. Private*, pg. 1109
Frey, Philip, Jr., Chm. Bd., Pres. & Chief Exec. Officer--Microsemi Corporation, Santa Ana, CA; *U.S. Public*, pg. 1107
Freyou, Ernest, Pres. & Chief Exec. Officer--Regions Bank/New Iberia, New Iberia, LA; *U.S. Public*, pg. 1372
Fribourg, Paul J., Chm. Bd. & Chief Exec. Officer--Continental Grain Company, New York, NY; *U.S. Private, pg. 268*
Fricks, William P., Chm. Bd. & Chief Exec. Officer--Newport News Shipbuilding, Inc., Newport News, VA; *U.S. Public*, pg. 1179
Friedberg, Thomas H., Chm Bd., Pres. & Chief Exec. Officer--ACCEL International Corporation, Dublin, OH; *U.S. Public*, pg. 14
Friederich, Jan, Chief Exec. Officer--Furr's Supermarkets, Albuquerque, NM; *U.S. Private*, pg. 432
Friedheim, Louis, Pres. & Chief Exec. Officer--Cougle Commission Company, Inc., Chicago, IL; *U.S. Private*, pg. 278
Friedland, Scott, Pres. & Chief Exec. Officer--Friedland Jacobs Communications, Burbank, CA; *U.S. Private*, pg. 428
Friedland, Thomas S., Pres. & Chief Exec. Officer--Harcrest International, Ltd., Clark, NJ; *U.S. Private*, pg. 500
Friedlander, Alfred L., Chm. Bd. & Chief Exec. Officer--Rice Food Markets Inc., Houston, TX; *U.S. Private*, pg. 927
Friedline, William, Chief Exec. Officer--Somerset Steel, Stoystown, PA; *U.S. Private*, pg. 930
Friedman, Dr. Alan, Pres. & Chief Exec. Officer--Planning Systems Inc., Mc Lean, VA; *U.S. Private*, pg. 869
Friedman, J. Roger, Pres. & Chief Exec. Officer--Lebhar-Friedman, Inc., New York, NY; *U.S. Private*, pg. 656
Friedman, Jack, Chm. Bd., Pres. & Chief Exec. Officer--JAKKS Pacific, Inc., Malibu, CA; *U.S. Public*, pg. 923
Friedman, Jack N., Chm. Bd. & Chief Exec. Officer--Florasynth Inc., Teterboro, NJ; *Int'l*, pg. 173
Friedman, Joe, Co-Chief Exec. Officer--J & R Music World, New York, NY; *U.S. Private*, pg. 576
Friedman, Rachelle, Co-Chief Exec. Officer--J & R Music World, New York, NY; *U.S. Private*, pg. 576
Friedman, Robert, Chm. Bd. & Chief Exec. Officer--Loehmann's, Inc., Bronx, NY; *U.S. Public*, pg. 1010
Friedman, William S., Pres. & Chief Exec. Officer--National Income Realty Trust, New York, NY; *U.S. Public*, pg. 1157
Friedman, William S., Pres. & Chief Exec. Officer--Tarragon Realty Investors, Dallas, TX; *U.S. Public*, pg. 1561
Friedmann, Daniel E., Pres. & Chief Exec. Officer--MacDonald Dettwiler & Associates Ltd., Richmond, Canada; *U.S. Public*, pg. 1229
Friedmann, Jacques, Chm. Bd. & Chief Exec. Officer--Compagnie UAP, Paris, France; *Int'l*, pg. 323
Friedrich, Doug, Pres. & Chief Exec. Officer--Capital Graphics Inc., Wheeling, IL; *U.S. Private*, pg. 206
Friedrich, Doug, Chief Exec. Officer--The Clarinda Company, Atlantic, IA; *U.S. Private*, pg. 206
Friedson, David M., Pres. & Chief Exec. Officer--Windmere-Durable Holdings, Hialeah, FL; *U.S. Public*, pg. 1771
Friend, Howard, Pres.--On-Cor Frozen Foods Inc., Northbrook, IL; *U.S. Private*, pg. 817
Friend, Sol, Chief Exec. Officer--On-Cor Frozen Foods Inc., Northbrook, IL; *U.S. Private*, pg. 817
Frierson, Daniel K., Chm. Bd., Pres. & Chief Exec. Officer--The Dixie Group, Inc., Chattanooga, TN; *U.S. Public*, pg. 514
Frieze, Michael, Chm. Bd. & Chief Exec. Officer--Gordon Brothers Partners Inc., Boston, MA; *U.S. Private*, pg. 465
Frings, Jurgen, Chief Exec. Officer--Radiometer International A/S, Roedovre, Denmark; *Int'l*, pg. 1083
Frisell, William, Pres. & Chief Exec. Officer--Diners Club Inc., Chicago, IL; *U.S. Public*, pg. 377
Frist, Thomas F., Jr., Dr., Chm. Bd. & Chief Exec. Officer--Columbia/HCA Healthcare Corporation, Nashville, TN; *U.S. Public*, pg. 403
Frith, Russell J., Chm. Bd., Pres. & Chief Exec. Officer--Lawn Doctor Inc., Holmdel, NJ; *U.S. Private*, pg. 653
Fritscher, Hans-Peter, Chief Exec. Officer--Procter & Gamble AG, Geneva, Switzerland; *U.S. Public*, pg. 1332
Fritz, James P., Chm. Bd. & Chief Exec. Officer--Fritz Co. Inc., Newport, MN; *U.S. Private*, pg. 429
Fritz, Lynn C., Chm. Bd. & Chief Exec. Officer--Fritz Companies, Inc., San Francisco, CA; *U.S. Public*, pg. 683
Fritzky, Edward V., Chm. Bd. & Chief Exec. Officer--Immunex Corporation, Seattle, WA; *U.S. Public*, pg. 871
Fritzky, F. Robert, Chm. & Chief Exec. Officer--MET Solutions, LLC, Morris Plains, NJ; *U.S. Public*, pg. 1642
Froidevaux, Pierre A., Chief Exec.--Apasco S.A. de C.V., Mexico, Mexico; *Int'l*, pg. 629
Froissant, Andre, Pres. & Chief Exec. Officer--Credit Lyonnais Canada, Montreal, Canada; *Int'l*, pg. 344
Fromm, Ronald A., Chief Exec. Officer--Famous Footwear, Madison, WI; *U.S. Public*, pg. 262
Fromm, William M., Chm. & Chief Exec. Officer--Barkley & Evergreen Advertising, Inc., Kansas City, MO; *U.S. Private*, pg. 116
Fromstein, Mitchell S., Chm. Bd., Pres. & Chief Exec. Officer--Manpower Inc., Milwaukee, WI; *U.S. Public*, pg. 1042
Fronert, Herbert, Chief Oper. Officer--Volksfursorge Krankenversicherung AG, Hamburg, Germany; *Int'l*, pg. 16
Frost, Mike, Pres. & Chief Exec. Officer--Cleveland Capital Holdings, Cliffside, NC; *U.S. Private*, pg. 246
Frost, Phillip, M.D., Chm. Bd. & Chief Exec. Officer--IVAX Corporation, Miami, FL; *U.S. Public*, pg. 914
Fry, Charles A., Chief Exec. Officer--Johnson Fry Holdings PLC, London, United Kingdom; *Int'l*, pg. 713
Fry, Darryl D., Chm. Bd. & Chief Exec. Officer--Cytec Industries Inc., West Paterson, NJ; *U.S. Public*, pg. 471
Fry, Jonathan M., Chief Exec. Officer--Burmah Castrol plc, Swindon, United Kingdom; *Int'l*, pg. 234
Frye, M.J.E., Chief Exec. Officer & Mng. Dir.--B. Elliott plc., London, United Kingdom; *Int'l*, pg. 448
Fryml, J.S., Pres. & Chief Exec. Officer--American Fast Print, Limited, Spartanburg, SC; *U.S. Private*, pg. 53
Fuchs, David, Chm. Bd. & Chief Exec. Officer--Hampton Industries, Inc., Kinston, NC; *U.S. Public*, pg. 779
Fuente, David I., Chm. Bd. & Chief Exec. Officer--Office Depot Inc., Delray Beach, FL; *U.S. Public*, pg. 1212
Fugelsang, George N., Chief Exec. Officer--Dresdner Bank AG, New York, NY; *Int'l*, pg. 418
Fuhrmann, Charles J., II, Pres., Chief Exec. Officer & Chief Fin. Officer--Lot$ Off Corporation, San Antonio, TX; *U.S. Public*, pg. 1014
Fujii, Hiro, Pres. & Chief Exec. Officer--Minolta Corporation, Ramsey, NJ; *Int'l*, pg. 869
Fujii, Juntaro, Chief Exec. Offier & Mng. Dir.--Tokyo-Mitsubishi International plc, London, United Kingdom; *Int'l*, pg. 158
Fujii, T., Chief Oper. Officer--NHK Gasket Singapore Co. (Pte.) Ltd., Jurong, Singapore; *Int'l*, pg. 948
Fujimura, Takuya, Chm. Bd. & Chief Exec. Officer--Tonen Energy International Corp., New York, NY; *Int'l*, pg. 1399
Fujisawa, Yoshihiro, Pres. & Chief Exec. Officer--Daiwa-MKB (Hungary) Investment and Securities Co. Ltd., Budapest, Hungary; *Int'l*, pg. 376
Fujiwara, Kikuo, Pres. & Chief Exec. Officer--Shimadzu Corporation, Kyoto, Japan; *Int'l*, pg. 1232
Fujiwara, Yasuyuki, Chief Oper. Officer--Makita Singapore PTE. LTD., Singapore, Singapore; *Int'l*, pg. 832
Fujiyama, Akira, Pres. & Chief Exec. Officer--Fujisawa Pharmaceutical Co. Ltd., Osaka, Japan; *Int'l*, pg. 525
Fukatsu, Seiji, Pres. & Chief Exec. Officer--All Nippon Airways Co. Ltd., Tokyo, Japan; *Int'l*, pg. 57
Fukuchi, Hideo, Pres. & Chief Exec. Officer--Nikon Inc., Melville, NY; *Int'l*, pg. 931
Fukuda, Kazuhiko, Chief Exec.--Nittetsu Shoji Co., Ltd., Tokyo, Japan; *Int'l*, pg. 939
Fukunaga, Mark H., Chm. Bd. & Chief Exec. Officer--Servco Pacific Inc., Honolulu, HI; *U.S. Private*, pg. 986
Fukunaka, Sohta, Chief Exec. Officer--Daihatsu America, Inc., Los Alamitos, CA; *Int'l*, pg. 365
Fukushima, Sumio, Chief Exec. Officer--Sumitomo Finance International plc, London, United Kingdom; *Int'l*, pg. 1310
Fuld, Jr., Richard S., Chm. Bd. & Chief Exec. Officer--Lehman Brothers Holdings Inc., New York, NY; *U.S. Public*, pg. 987
Fuld, Richard S., Pres. & Co-Chief Exec. Officer--Lehman Brothers, New York, NY; *U.S. Public*, pg. 987
Fuldner, William Terry, Chm. Bd. & Chief Exec. Officer--Efco Corporation, Monett, MO; *U.S. Private*, pg. 353
Fulford, Greg, Chief Exec. Officer--Fleming Packaging Corp., Peoria, IL; *U.S. Private*, pg. 411
Fulford, Ronald, Chm. Bd. & Chief Exec. Officer--Liggett Group Inc., Durham, NC; *U.S. Public*, pg. 259
Fulgoni, Gian M., Chief Exec. Officer--Information Resources, Inc., Chicago, IL; *U.S. Public*, pg. 875
Fullagar, E.J., Chief Exec. Officer--Sandoz Pharmaceuticals Corp., East Hanover, NJ; *Int'l*, pg. 974
Fuller, D. Ward, Pres. & Chief Exec. Officer--General American Transportation Corporation, Chicago, IL; *U.S. Public*, pg. 692
Fuller, Gary T., Pres. & Chief Exec. Officer--Woolworth Overseas Corp., New York, NY; *U.S. Public*, pg. 1778
Fuller, H. Laurance, Chm. Bd. & Chief Exec. Officer--Amoco Corporation, Chicago, IL; *U.S. Public*, pg. 101
Fuller, John, Pres. & Chief Exec. Officer-Automotive Fin. Corp.--Minnesota Power, Duluth, MN; *U.S. Public*, pg. 1116
Fuller, Lawrence R., Pres. & Publr.--The Honolulu Advertiser, Honolulu, HI; *U.S. Public*, pg. 701

Fuller, Michael, Pres. & Chief Exec. Officer--Management Dynamics, New Providence, NJ; *U.S. Public*, pg. 1040
Fuller, Richard S., Pres. & Chief Exec. Officer--The Smithfield Companies, Inc., Portsmouth, VA; *U.S. Public*, *pg. 1479*
Fullerton, James H., Pres. & Chief Exec. Officer--M & I Bank of LaCrosse, La Crosse, WI; *U.S. Public*, pg. 1050
Fulton, James, Pres. & Chief Exec. Officer--FKI Industries, Inc., Fairfield, CT; *Int'l*, pg. 472
Fulton, Paul, Chm. Bd. & Chief Exec. Officer--Bassett Furniture Industries, Incorporated, Bassett, VA; *U.S. Public*, pg. 193
Fulton, Rufus J., Jr., Pres. & Chief Exec. Officer--Fulton Financial Corp., Lancaster, PA; *U.S. Public*, pg. 687
Fulton, Sandy M., Pres. & Chief Exec. Officer-Pacific Forest Products Ltd.--Avenor, Inc., Montreal, Canada; *Int'l*, pg. 101
Fulton, Thomas M., Pres. & Chief Exec. Officer--Landauer, Inc., Glenwood, IL; *U.S. Public*, pg. 977
Fulwiler, Terrance, Chief Exec. Officer--Wisconsin Label Corporation, Algoma, WI; *U.S. Private*, pg. 1184
Funari, Robert, Pres. & Chief Exec. Officer--Syncor International Corporation, Woodland Hills, CA; *U.S. Public*, pg. 1548
Funk, Joe, Pres. & Chief Exec. Officer--Allen-Rogers Co., Laconia, NH; *U.S. Private*, pg. 315
Furlong, Edward V., Jr., Pres. & Chief Exec. Officer--WWF Paper Corporation, Bala Cynwyd, PA; *U.S. Private*, pg. 1145
Furness, Terence N., Chief Exec. Officer--Isolyser Company, Inc., Norcross, GA; *U.S. Public*, pg. 914
Furst, F.E., Chm .Bd. & Chief Exec. Officer--Furst-McNess Company, Freeport, IL; *U.S. Private*, pg. 432
Furuhata, Masayoshi, Pres. & Chief Exec. Officer--Mitsui & Co. (U.S.A.), Inc., New York, NY; *Int'l*, pg. 879
Futch, Tom, Chief Exec. Officer--Golden Care Inc., Indianapolis, IN; *U.S. Public*, pg. 1531
Futerman, Mike, Chief Exec. Officer--Hahn Automotive Warehouse, Inc., Rochester, NY; *U.S. Public*, pg. 774
Futerman, Mike, Chief Exec. Officer--Professional Auto Warehouse, Rochester, NY; *U.S. Public*, pg. 774
Futter, Bernard, Pres. & Chief Exec. Officer--Futter Lumber Corporation, Rockville Center, NY; *U.S. Private*, pg. 432
Futterknecht, James O. Jr., Chm. Bd., Pres., & Chief Exec. Officer--Excel Industries, Inc., Elkhart, IN; *U.S. Public*, pg. 598
Fuyuno, K., Chief Exec. Officer--Nippon Monier Co. Ltd., Osaka, Japan; *Int'l*, pg. 1092
Gabbert, James D., Chm. Bd. & Chief Exec. Officer--Gabbert's, Inc., Minneapolis, MN; *U.S. Private*, pg. 437
Gabelli, Mario J., Chm. Bd. & Chief Exec. Officer--Lynch Corporation, Greenwich, CT; *U.S. Public*, pg. 1021
Gable, Robert L., Chm. Bd. & Chief Exec. Officer--Unitrode Corporation, Merrimack, NH; *U.S. Public*, pg. 1694
Gabriel, George S., Chief Exec. Officer--Lab Products, Inc., Seaford, DE; *U.S. Private*, pg. 641
Gabriel, N., Chief Exec. Officer--OCE (Far East) Pte. Ltd., Singapore, Singapore; *Int'l*, pg. 994
Gabrielson, Bo, Chief Exec. Officer--Waste Management International plc, London, United Kingdom; *U.S. Public*, pg. 1745
Gaby, Dan, Chm. & Chief Exec. Officer--Keyes Martin, East Hanover, NJ; *U.S. Private*, pg. 618
Gaddy, Bob L., Chief Exec. Officer--Pace Industries, Inc., Fayetteville, AR; *U.S. Public*, pg. 986
Gaeng, J. Brian, Pres. & Chief Exec. Officer--Fredericktown Bank & Trust Co., Frederick, MD; *U.S. Public*, pg. 1089
Gage, Edwin C., Chm. & Chief Exec. Officer--Gage Marketing Group, Minneapolis, MN; *U.S. Private*, pg. 437
Gagin, David, Chief Exec. Officer--Kevlin Corporation, Wilmington, MA; *U.S. Public*, pg. 953
Gagne, Paul E., Pres. & Chief Exec. Officer--Avenor, Inc., Montreal, Canada; *Int'l*, pg. 101
Gagnier, Charles E., Pres. & Chief Exec. Officer--AMCORE Bank N.A., Rockford, Rockford, IL; *U.S. Public*, pg. 64
Gahm, W. Dwight, Chm. Bd., Pres. & Chief Exec. Officer--Kitchen Kompact, Inc., Jeffersonville, IN; *U.S. Private*, pg. 624
Gaillard, Roger R., Pres. & Chief Exec. Officer--Williams & Company, Inc., Pittsburgh, PA; *U.S. Private*, pg. 1055
Gains, John C., Chief Exec. Officer--John Mowlem & Company plc, Isleworth, United Kingdom; *Int'l*, pg. 896
Gairard, Jacques, Chm. Bd. & Chief Exec. Officer--Groupe SEB, Ecueille, France; *Int'l*, pg. 568
Gaites, Robert, Chief Exec. Officer--Architectural Wall Systems, LLC, Edison, NJ; *U.S. Private*, pg. 403
Gaither, Albert R., Chm. Bd. & Chief Exec. Officer--Ridgeview, Inc., Newton, NC; *U.S. Private*, pg. 930
Gaither, Ann Heafner, Chm. Bd. & Chief Exec. Officer--J.H. Heafner Co. Inc., Lincolnton, NC; *U.S. Private*, pg. 514
Gal, Kenneth, Chm. & Chief Exec. Officer--Italia/Gal Advertising, Los Angeles, CA; *U.S. Private*, pg. 576
Gale, Michael G., Chief Exec.--Hong Kong Telephone Company Ltd., Wan Chai, Hong Kong; *Int'l*, pg. 247
Galeandro, Carlo, Chief Exec. Officer & Gen. Mgr.--Ambrofid Gestioni Fiduciarie S.p.A., Milan, Italy; *Int'l*, pg. 138
Galef, James M., Chief Exec. Officer--Acme Tube Inc., Somerset, NJ; *U.S. Private*, pg. 14
Gallagher, J. Patrick, Jr., Pres. & Chief Exec. Officer--Arthur J. Gallagher & Co., Itasca, IL; *U.S. Public*, pg. 698
Gallagher, Michael, Chief Exec. Officer--Playtex Beauty Care, Inc., Westport, CT; *U.S. Public*, pg. 1311
Gallagher, Michael R., Chief Exec. Officer--Playtex Products Inc., Westport, CT; *U.S. Public*, pg. 1310
Gallagher, Thomas J., Chm. Bd. & Chief Exec. Officer--Everest Indemnity Insurance Company, Liberty Corner, NJ; *U.S. Public*, pg. 597
Gallaher, Edward W., Sr., Pres., Chief Exec. Officer & Treas.--Phoenix Medical Technology, Inc., Andrews, SC; *U.S. Public*, pg. 1292
Gallant, Ben J., Pres. & Chief Exec. Officer--American Dental Technologies, Southfield, MI; *U.S. Public*, pg. 70
Gallemore, William II, Chief Oper. Officer--National Banner Company, Inc., Dallas, TX; *U.S. Private*, pg. 780
Galligan, Thomas J., III, Chm. Bd., Pres. & Chief Exec. Officer--Papa Gino's Inc., Dedham, MA; *U.S. Private*, pg. 837
Gallo, Eugenio, Pres. & Chief Exec. Officer--Italia Di Navigazione S.p.A., Genoa, Italy; *Int'l*, pg. 653
Gallois, Louis, Pres. & Chief Exec. Officer--SNCF, Paris, France; *Int'l*, pg. 1163
Galloway, David A., Pres. & Chief Exec. Officer--Torstar Corporation, Toronto, Canada; *Int'l*, pg. 1402
Gallup, Patricia, Chm. Bd. & Chief Exec. Officer--PC Connection, Inc., Milford, MA; *U.S. Private*, pg. 826
Galme, Ralf, Chief Exec. Officer--Europe Tax-Free Shopping Ltd., Chicago, IL; *U.S. Public*, pg. 320
Galt, Barry J., Chm. Bd. & Chief Exec. Officer--Seagull Energy Corporation, Houston, TX; *U.S. Public*, pg. 1450
Galvan, Alberto, Chief Exec. Officer--FEMSA Empaque, S.A. de CV, Monterrey, Mexico; *Int'l*, pg. 496
Galvin, Christopher B., Chief Exec. Officer--Motorola, Inc., Schaumburg, IL; *U.S. Public*, pg. 1136
Gama, Alejandre, Co-Exec. Officer & Creative Dir.--Young & Rubicam Brazil, Sao Paulo, Brazil; *U.S. Private*, pg. 1200
Gamberale, Vito, Chief Exec. Officer--Telecom Italia Mobile, Rome, Italy; *Int'l*, pg. 1363
Gamble, Neil H., Chief Exec. Officer-Australian Opers.--Showboat, Incorporated, Las Vegas, NV; *U.S. Public*, pg. 1469
Gamble, Richard, Pres. & Grp. Chief Exec.--Royal & Sun Alliance Insurance Group plc, London, United Kingdom; *Int'l*, pg. 1130
Gambrill, Anthony, Chief Exec. Officer & Bus. Devel./Information--CGR Communications, Kingston, Jamaica; *U.S. Public*, pg. 1422
Gamel, Wendell W., Chm. Bd., Pres. & Chief Exec. Officer--Tech-Sym Corporation, Houston, TX; *U.S. Public*, pg. 1563
Gandrud, Robert P., Pres. & Chief Exec. Officer--Lutheran Brotherhood, Minneapolis, MN; *U.S. Private*, pg. 681
Gann, Kenneth W., Pres. & Chief Exec. Officer--CCAIR, Inc., Charlotte, NC; *U.S. Public*, pg. 276
Gannon, Robert P., Chm. Bd., Pres. & Chief Exec. Officer--Montana Power Company, Butte, MT; *U.S. Public*, pg. 1126
Ganster, Dennis G., Pres. & Chief Exec. Officer--Comshare, Incorporated, Ann Arbor, MI; *U.S. Public*, pg. 425
Gantcher, Nathan, Pres. & Co-Chief Exec. Officer--CIBC Oppenheimer Corp., New York, NY; *Int'l*, pg. 257
Gantert, F., Dr., Chief Exec. Officer--Ascom Autelca AG, Gumligen, Switzerland; *Int'l*, pg. 86
Garbacz, Gerald G., Chm. Bd., Pres. & Chief Exec. Officer--Nashua Corporation, Nashua, NH; *U.S. Public*, pg. 1152
Garbagnati, Furio, Chm. & Chief Exec. Officer--Shandwick Corporate Communications S.p.A., Milan, Italy; *Int'l*, pg. 1227
Garber, George E., Pres. & Chief Exec. Officer--The St. George Group, Inc., Pittsburgh, PA; *U.S. Private*, pg. 960
Garberg, Dennis, Chm. Bd. & Chief Exec. Officer--The Sunflower Group, Overland Park, KS; *U.S. Private*, pg. 1052
Garcea, Pier Luigi, Chief Exec. Officer--Estee Lauder S.R.L., Milan, Italy; *U.S. Public*, pg. 594
Garcia-Planas, R., Chief Oper. Officer--Hilana C.A., Guarenas, Venezuela; *Int'l*, pg. 947
Garcia, Alfonso Romo, Chm. Bd. & Chief Exec. Officer--Empressa La Moderna SA de CV, Monterrey, Mexico; *Int'l*, pg. 454
Garcia, Diego Alonso, Chief Exec. Officer--Union Naval de Levante, S.A., Madrid, Spain; *Int'l*, pg. 1442
Garcia, Ernest C., Chm. Bd. & Chief Exec. Officer--Ugly Duckling Corp., Phoenix, AZ; *U.S. Public*, pg. 1662
Garcia, Jose Luis, Chief Oper. & Exec. Officer--Agropecuaria de Guissona, S. Coop. Ltda., Guisona, Spain; *Int'l*, pg. 31
Garcia, Pete, Pres. & Chief Exec. Officer--University Mechanical & Engineering Contractors, Inc., San Diego, CA; *U.S. Public*, pg. 572
Gardner, David E., Pres. & Chief Exec. Officer--Alfred Nickles Bakery, Inc., Navarre, OH; *U.S. Private*, pg. 799
Gardner, Edward G., Chm. Bd. & Chief Exec. Officer--Soft Sheen Products, Inc., Chicago, IL; *U.S. Private*, pg. 1012
Gardner, Herbert M., Chm. Bd. & Pres.--Supreme Industries, Inc., Goshen, IN; *U.S. Public*, pg. 1541
Gardner, Rick, Chm. Bd. & Chief Exec. Officer--First Commercial Mortgage Co., Little Rock, AR; *U.S. Public*, pg. 630
Gardner, Roy, Chief Exec.--Centrica Plc, Slough, United Kingdom; *Int'l*, pg. 279
Gardner, William, Pres. & Chief Exec. Officer--Wisconsin & Southern Railroad Co., Milwaukee, WI; *U.S. Private*, pg. 1184
Garel, John R., Pres. & Chief Exec. Officer--Cadmus Journal Services, Inc., Linthicum Heights, MD; *U.S. Public*, pg. 291
Garges, Thomas W. Jr., Pres.--Rochester & Pittsburgh Coal Company, Indiana, PA; *U.S. Public*, pg. 1395
Garman, D.N.C., Chief Exec.-Allied Bakeries Limited--Associated British Foods plc, London, United Kingdom; *Int'l*, pg. 92
Garman, M. Lawrence, Pres. & Chief Exec. Officer--Daubert Industries, Inc., Westchester, IL; *U.S. Private*, pg. 313
Garner, H. Richard, Chief Exec. Officer--Haviland Enterprises, Grand Rapids, MI; *U.S. Private*, pg. 511
Garnett, Gerald, Chief Exec. Officer & Exec. V.P.--Southern Farm Bureau Casualty Insurance Company, Ridgeland, MS; *U.S. Private*, pg. 1016
Garnier, Anton C., Chm. Bd., Pres. & Chief Exec. Officer--Southwest Water Company, West Covina, CA; *U.S. Public*, pg. 1494
Garofalo, Donald R., Pres. & Chief Exec. Officer--Andersen Corporation, Bayport, MN; *U.S. Private*, pg. 71
Garrett, J. Patrick, Chief Exec. Officer--Windsor Quality Food Co., Ltd., Houston, TX; *U.S. Private*, pg. 1182
Garrett, Scott, Chm. Bd., Pres. & Chief Exec. Officer--Dade Behring Inc., Deerfield, IL; *U.S. Private*, pg. 110
Garrett, Scott, Chm. Bd., Pres. & Chief Exec. Officer--Dade Behring Inc., Deerfield, IL; *Int'l*, pg. 626
Garrett, William, Grp. Chief Exec.--Robert Fleming Holdings Ltd., London, United Kingdom; *Int'l*, pg. 493
Garrick, Ronald, Sir, Chief Exec. Officer & Mng. Dir.--Weir Group PLC, Glasgow, United Kingdom; *Int'l*, pg. 1488
Garrison, F.S., Chm. Bd., Pres. & Chief Exec. Officer--American Freightways Corporation, Harrison, AR; *U.S. Public*, pg. 75
Garrison, F.S., Pres. & Chief Exec. Officer--American Freightways, Inc., Harrison, AR; *U.S. Public*, pg. 76
Garrison, John, Pres. & Chief Exec. Officer--SBS Holdings, Inc., Saginaw, MI; *U.S. Private*, pg. 955
Garrison, Richard C., Chm. Bd. & Chief Exec. Officer--Ingalls, Boston, MA; *U.S. Private*, pg. 562
Garrott, Thomas M., Chm. Bd., Pres. & Chief Exec. Officer--National Commerce Bancorporation, Memphis, TN; *U.S. Public*, pg. 1154
Garvey, Michael D., Co.-Chm. & Co.-Chief Exec. Officer--Totem Resources Corporation, Seattle, WA; *U.S. Private*, *pg. 1092*
Garvey, Robert A., Chm. Bd. & Chief Exec. Officer--Birmingham Steel Corporation, Birmingham, AL; *U.S. Public*, pg. 232
Garvey, Willard W., Chm. Bd., Pres. & Chief Exec. Officer--Garvey Industries, Inc., Wichita, KS; *U.S. Private*, pg. 440
Garvin, Andrew P., Chm. Bd., Pres., Chief Exec. Officer & Treas.--Find/SVP, Inc., New York, NY; *U.S. Public*, pg. 623
Garvin, Sam S., Chm. Bd. & Chief Exec. Officer--Continental Promotion Group, Tempe, AZ; *U.S. Private*, pg. 269
Garvin, Thomas M., Pres. & Chief Exec. Officer--UB Foods U.S., Inc., Elmhurst, IL; *Int'l*, pg. 1442
Gasser, Michael J., Chm. Bd. & Chief Exec. Officer--Greif Brothers Corporation, Delaware, OH; *U.S. Public*, pg. 763
Gassner, Rudi, Pres. & Chief Exec. Officer-BMG Intl.--Bertelsmann Music Group, Wilmington, DE; *Int'l*, pg. 191
Gast, Warren E., Pres., Chief Exec. Officer & Gen. Mgr.--Gast Mfg. Corp., Benton Harbor, MI; *U.S. Private*, pg. 440
Gaston, Gerald N., Vice Chm., Pres. & Chief Exec. Officer--American Bankers Insurance Group, Inc., Miami, FL; *U.S. Public*, pg. 67
Gaston, Paul, Chm. Bd. & Chief Exec. Officer--Boston Celtics Limited Partnership, Boston, MA; *U.S. Public*, pg. 246
Gates, Walter, Pres. & Chief Exec. Officer--THORN Americas, Wichita, KS; *Int'l*, pg. 1385
Gates, William H., Chm. Bd. & Chief Exec. Officer--Microsoft Corporation, Redmond, WA; *U.S. Public*, pg. 1107
Gathright, Richard E., Pres. & Chief Exec. Officer--Transmontaigne, Fayetteville, AR; *U.S. Public*, pg. 1631
Gattuso, Joseph, Pres. & Chief Exec. Officer-Ferguson 2000--CommonHealth USA, Parsippany, NJ; *Int'l*, pg. 1483
Gaughn, Peter, Pres. & Chief Exec. Officer--Pip Printing, Agoura Hills, CA; *U.S. Private*, pg. 423
Gaulke, Michael, Pres. & Chief Exec. Officer--The Failure Group, Inc., Menlo Park, CA; *U.S. Public*, pg. 609
Gaunt, Bobbie, Pres. & Chief Exec. Officer--Ford Motor Co. of Canada Ltd, Oakville, Canada; *U.S. Public*, pg. 666
Gauss, Cal, Pres. & Chief Exec. Officer--Wm. E. Wright Limited Partnership, West Warren, MA; *U.S. Private*, pg. 1192
Gaut, Norman E., Dr., Chm. Bd. & Chief Exec. Officer--PictureTel, Andover, MA; *U.S. Public*, pg. 1294
Gautier, Jean Francois, Pres. & Chief Exec. Officer--Salomon S.A., Annecy, France; *Int'l*, pg. 1181
Gavigan, Michael, Chm. Bd. & Chief Exec. Officer--Pico Products, Inc., Lake View Terrace, CA; *U.S. Public*, pg. 1294
Gay, Andrew J., Chm. Bd. & Chief Exec. Officer--Drake & Scull Engineering Ltd., Kew Bridge, United Kingdom; *U.S. Public*, pg. 572
Gayle, Norman W., III, Pres. & Chief Exec. Officer--The Shelby Insurance Companies, Shelby, OH; *U.S. Public*, pg. 1718
Gaylord, Edward L., Chm. Bd. & Chief Exec. Officer--Gaylord Broadcasting Co., Nashville, TN; *U.S. Public*, pg. 704
Geaney, Donal J., Chm. Bd. & Chief Exec. Officer--Elan Corporation Plc, Dublin, Ireland; *Int'l*, pg. 435
Geary, Ronald G., Pres. & Chief Exec. Officer--Res-Care Incorporated, Louisville, KY; *U.S. Public*, pg. 1382
Gebauer, Rüdiger, Pres. & Chief Exec. Officer--Springer-Verlag New York Inc., New York, NY; *Int'l*, pg. 1291
Geber, C., Chief Exec. Officer--Kuehne & Nagel (AG & Co.), Bremen, Germany; *Int'l*, pg. 763
Gebhardt, Scott W., Pres. & Chief Exec. Officer--PG&E Energy Services, San Francisco, CA; *U.S. Public*, pg. 1241
Gebler, David B., Chm. Bd., Pres. & Chief Exec. Officer--Airlease Ltd., San Francisco, CA; *U.S. Public*, pg. 33
Gee, David, Pres. & Chief Exec. Officer--Marsulex Inc., North York, Canada; *Int'l*, pg. 599
Geener, Anthony, Chief Exec. Officer--Guinness Enterprises Ltd., London, United Kingdom; *Int'l*, pg. 412
Geer, Carlton L., Pres. & Chief Exec. Officer-Las Vegas Showboat--Showboat, Incorporated, Las Vegas, NV; *U.S. Public*, pg. 1469
Geginat, Hartwig, Chm. Bd. & Chief Exec. Officer-Zanders--International Paper Company, Purchase, NY; *U.S. Public*, *pg. 901*
Gehl, William D., Chm. Bd., Pres. & Chief Exec. Officer--Gehl Company, West Bend, WI; *U.S. Public*, pg. 704
Gehlhaar, H., Chief Exec. Officer--Hoogovens Aluminium Bausysteme GmbH, Koblenz, Germany; *Int'l*, pg. 755

Geier, Philip H., Jr., Chm. Bd. & Chief Exec. Officer--The Interpublic Group of Companies, Inc., New York, NY; *U.S. Public*, pg. 908

Geiger, Ron, Pres. & Chief Exec. Officer--Harker's Distribution, Inc., Le Mars, IA; *U.S. Private*, pg. 502

Geijer, Reinhold, Pres. & Chief Exec. Officer--Swedbank, Stockholm, Sweden; *Int'l*, pg. 1328

Geise, David N., Pres. & Chief Exec. Officer--Furman Foods, Inc., Northumberland, PA; *U.S. Private*, pg. 431

Geissinger, Frederick W., Chm. Bd., Pres. & Chief Exec. Officer--Yosemite Insurance Co., Evansville, IN; *U.S. Public*, pg. 77

Gelardi, Ronald N., Chief Oper. Officer, Mng. Dir. & Sec.--Barr Brothers & Co., Inc., New York, NY; *U.S. Private*, pg. 117

Gelb, Richard, Chief Exec. Officer & Gen. Mgr.-Staff--Bristol-Myers Squibb International, Princeton, NJ; *U.S. Public*, pg. 254

Gelfond, Richard L., Vice Chm. & Co-Chief Exec. Officer--Imax Corporation, Mississauga, Canada; *Int'l*, pg. 661

Geli, Giorgio, Chief Exec. Officer--Ideal Form Team S.r.L., Monsano, Italy; *Int'l*, pg. 659

Gelinas, J. Arthur, Pres. & Chief Exec. Officer--Davie Industries Inc., Levis, Canada; *Int'l*, pg. 385

Geller, Larry, Pres. & Chief Exec. Officer--Rosauers Supermarkets, Inc., Spokane, WA; *U.S. Private*, pg. 944

Geller, Steve, Chm. Bd. & Chief Exec. Officer--Empire of Carolina, Inc., Delray Beach, FL; *U.S. Public*, pg. 579

Gellerman, Jay M., Chm. Bd, Pres. & Chief Exec. Officer--Jaydon Incorporated, Rock Island, IL; *U.S. Private*, pg. 584

Gellerstedt, L.L., III, Chm. & Chief Exec. Officer--Beers Construction Company, Atlanta, GA; *Int'l*, pg. 1261

Gellert, Jay M., Pres. & Chief Oper Officer--Foundation Health Systems, Inc., Pueblo, CO; *U.S. Public*, pg. 678

Genadiev, Nikola, Chief Exec. Officer--International Media Concepts/DMB&B, Sofia, Bulgaria; *U.S. Private*, pg. 304

Gencarelli, Louis A., Sr., Pres. & Chief Exec. Officer--Bess Eaton Donut Flour Co., Inc., Westerly, RI; *U.S. Private*, pg. 139

Genger, Arie, Chm. Bd.--Trans Resources, Inc., New York, NY; *U.S. Private*, pg. 1096

Genovese, Leonard, Chm. Bd., Pres. & Chief Exec. Officer--Genovese Drug Stores, Inc., Melville, NY; *U.S. Public*, pg. 730

Genovese, Peter J., Co-Chm. Bd. & Co-Chief Exec. Officer--UMB Financial Corporation, Kansas City, MO; *U.S. Public*, pg. 1653

Genovese, Rocco C., Chm. Bd., Pres. & Chief Exec. Officer--Burke Industries, Inc., San Jose, CA; *U.S. Private*, pg. 183

Genovese, Rocco C., Pres. & Chief Exec. Officer--Burke Flooring Products Div., San Jose, CA; *U.S. Private*, pg. 183

Genovese, Rocco C., Pres. & Chief Exec. Officer--Custom Process, San Jose, CA; *U.S. Private*, pg. 183

Genshaft, Neil, Chm. Bd. & Chief Exec. Officer--Fresh Mark, Inc., Canton, OH; *U.S. Private*, pg. 427

Gentile, George M., Chm. Bd. & Chief Exec. Officer--Gerber Scientific, Inc., South Windsor, CT; *U.S. Public*, pg. 740

Gentine, Louis P., Chief Exec. Officer--Sargento Foods Inc., Plymouth, WI; *U.S. Private*, pg. 966

Gentry, Robert T., Pres. & Chief Exec. Officer--Penn Central National Bank, Huntingdon, PA; *U.S. Public*, pg. 1222

Genuardi, Charles A., Pres. & Chief Exec. Officer--Genuardi Family Markets Inc., Norristown, PA; *U.S. Private*, pg. 447

Geoppinger, William A., Pres. & Chief Exec. Officer--Hillshire Farm & Kahn's, Cincinnati, OH; *U.S. Public*, pg. 1433

George, Boyd, Chm. Bd. & Chief Exec. Officer--Alex Lee, Inc., Hickory, NC; *U.S. Private*, pg. 657

George, P.M., Chm. & Chief Exec. Officer--Ladbroke Racing Corporation, Pittsburgh, PA; *Int'l*, pg. 788

George, Peter M., Vice Chm. & Grp. Chief Exec. Officer--Ladbroke Group Plc, London, United Kingdom; *Int'l*, pg. 787

George, Richard L., Pres. & Chief Exec. Officer--Suncor Inc., Calgary, Canada; *Int'l*, pg. 1320

George, Robert C., Pres. & Chief Exec. Officer--Indian Rocks National Bank, Largo, FL; *U.S. Public*, pg. 608

George, Ross, Pres. & Chief Exec. Officer--Simonds Industries Inc., Fitchburg, MA; *U.S. Private*, pg. 1001

George, William W., Chm. Bd. & Chief Exec. Officer--Medtronic, Inc., Minneapolis, MN; *U.S. Public*, pg. 1082

Georgehead, Christopher W., II, Pres. & Chief Exec. Officer--Gateway Press, Inc., Louisville, KY; *U.S. Private*, pg. 441

Georges, Jean-Francois, Chief Exec. Officer--Dassault Falcon Jet Corp., South Hackensack, NJ; *Int'l*, pg. 383

Georges, John A., Chm. Bd. & Chief Exec. Officer--IP Timberlands, Ltd., Purchase, NY; *U.S. Public*, pg. 904

Georgescu, Peter, Chief Exec. Officer--Young & Rubicam, S.A. de C.V., Mexico, Mexico; *U.S. Private*, pg. 1200

Georgescu, Peter A., Chm. Bd. & Chief Exec. Officer--Young & Rubicam Inc., New York, NY; *U.S. Private*, pg. 1196

Georgine, Robert A., Chm. Bd. & Chief Exec. Officer--ULLICO Inc., Washington, DC; *U.S. Private*, pg. 1115

Georgine, Robert A., Chm. Bd. & Chief Exec. Officer--AMI Capital Inc., Bethesda, MD; *U.S. Private*, pg. 1116

Georgoulis, Stratton, Chm. Bd., Pres. & Chief Exec. Officer--TIC United Corporation, Dallas, TX; *U.S. Private*, pg. 1063

Geppi, Stephen A., Pres. & Chief Exec. Officer--Diamond Comic Distributors, Inc., Timonium, MD; *U.S. Private*, pg. 330

Geraghty, James, Chief Exec. Officer--TSI Corporation, Milford, MA; *U.S. Public*, pg. 733

Geraghy, James A., Pres. & Chief Exec. Officer--Genzyme Transgenics, Framingham, MA; *U.S. Public*, pg. 733

Gerbig, Robert L., Pres. & Chief Exec. Officer--Gerbig, Snell/Weisheimer & Assoc., Inc., Columbus, OH; *U.S. Private*, pg. 449

Gerchenson, Emile H., Chm. Bd. & Chief Exec. Officer--Alva/Amco Pharmacal Companies, Inc., Chicago, IL; *U.S. Private*, pg. 47

Gerdin, Russell A., Chm. Bd., Pres. Chief Exec. Officer, Chief Oper. Officer & Sec.--Heartland Express, Inc., Coralville, IA; *U.S. Public*, pg. 803

Gerdy, Harvey, Chm. Bd., Pres. & Chief Exec. Officer--International Seaway Trading Corporation, Boca Raton, FL; *U.S. Private*, pg. 572

Geresi, Joseph, Chief Exec. Officer--Paisano Publications, Inc., Agoura, CA; *U.S. Private*, pg. 834

Gergacz, David, Pres. & Chief Exec. Officer--Brite Voice Systems, Inc., Heathrow, FL; *U.S. Public*, pg. 257

Gergacz, David, Pres. & Chief Exec. Officer--Brite Voice Systems, Canton, MA; *U.S. Public*, pg. 257

Geringer, Steven I., Pres. & Chief Exec. Officer--PCS Health Systems, Inc., Scottsdale, AZ; *U.S. Public*, pg. 993

Gerken, Edward, Chm. Bd. & Chief Exec. Officer--Norwalk Furniture Corporation, Norwalk, OH; *U.S. Private*, pg. 807

Gerlach, John B., Jr., Pres., Chief Exec. Officer, Chief Oper. Officer & Sec.--Lancaster Colony Corporation, Columbus, OH; *U.S. Public*, pg. 976

Gerlach, John B., Jr., Chm. Bd. & Chief Exec. Officer-Lancaster Colony Corp.--Lancaster Colony Automotive Group, Dublin, OH; *U.S. Public*, pg. 977

Gerlach, N.E., Chief Exec. Officer--Braas GmbH, Oberursell, Germany; *Int'l*, pg. 1091

Gero, James F., Chm. Bd. & Chief Exec. Officer--Sierra Technologies Inc., Buffalo, NY; *U.S. Private*, pg. 999

Gerrard, Francois, Chm. & Chief Exec. Officer--SIAS - MPA, Paris, France; *Int'l*, pg. 566

Gerson, Irwin C., Chm. & Chief Exec. Officer--Lowe McAdams Healthcare, New York, NY; *U.S. Private*, pg. 678

Gerson, Samuel J., Chm. Bd. & Chief Exec. Officer--Filene's Basement, Inc., Wellesley, MA; *U.S. Public*, pg. 622

Gerstell, A. Frederick, Chm. Bd. & Chief Exec. Officer--CalMat Co., Los Angeles, CA; *U.S. Public*, pg. 295

Gerstner, Josef, Chm.-Mgmnt. Bd. & Chief Exec. Officer--KSB Aktiengesellschaft, Frankenthal, Germany; *Int'l*, pg. 721

Gerstner, Louis V., Jr., Chm. Bd. & Chief Exec. Officer--International Business Machines Corporation, Armonk, NY; *U.S. Public*, pg. 895

Gerston, Kenneth, Chief Exec. Officer--Continental Coin Corporation, Van Nuys, CA; *U.S. Private*, pg. 267

Gervasi, Enrico, Chm. & Chief Exec. Officer-Milan--Young & Rubicam Roma SRL, Rome, Italy; *U.S. Private*, pg. 1199

Gescheider, Bruce A., Pres. & Chief Exec. Officer--ACCO Brands, Inc., Wheeling, IL; *U.S. Public*, pg. 674

Gescheider, Bruce A., Chm. Bd. & Chief Exec. Officer--Day-Timers, Inc., East Texas, PA; *U.S. Public*, pg. 674

Geske, Larry D., Pres. & Chief Exec. Officer--Energy West Inc., Great Falls, MT; *U.S. Public*, pg. 581

Gettier, Glenn H., Jr., Pres. & Chief Exec. Officer--Southwestern Life Insurance Company, Dallas, TX; *U.S. Private*, pg. 1018

Gettlefinger, Andrew J., Chm. Bd., Pres. & Chief Exec. Officer--Pride Oil Co., Inc., Knoxville, TN; *U.S. Private*, pg. 613

Gettler, Benjamin, Chm. Bd., Pres., Chief Exec. Officer & Chief Fin. Officer--Vulcan International Corporation, Wilmington, DE; *U.S. Public*, pg. 1725

Ghafari, Yousif B., Pres. & Chief Exec. Officer--Ghafari Associates, Inc., Dearborn, MI; *U.S. Private*, pg. 450

Ghaznavi, John, Chm. Bd. & Chief Exec. Officer--Consumers Packaging Inc., Etobicoke, Canada; *Int'l*, pg. 326

Ghelfi, Al, Chief Exec. Officer--SunBuilt Homes, Inc., Phoenix, AZ; *U.S. Public*, pg. 323

Ghelfi, Brent, Pres. & Chief Exec. Officer--Cavco Industries, Inc., Phoenix, AZ; *U.S. Public*, pg. 323

Gherty, John E., Pres. & Chief Exec. Officer--Land O'Lakes, Inc., Arden Hills, MN; *U.S. Private*, pg. 645

Gholson, Robert L., Pres. & Chief Exec. Officer--Universal Life Insurance Company, Memphis, TN; *U.S. Private*, pg. 1127

Giancola, James, Pres. & Chief Exec. Officer--CNB Bancshares, Inc., Evansville, IN; *U.S. Public*, pg. 280

Gianettino, Ronald J., Chm. Bd. & Chief Exec. Officer--Gianettino & Meredith Advertising, Short Hills, NJ; *U.S. Private*, pg. 450

Giannopoulos, A.L., Pres. & Chief Exec. Officer--Micros Systems Inc., Beltsville, MD; *U.S. Public*, pg. 1106

Gibara, Samir G., Chm. Bd., Pres. & Chief Exec. Officer--The Goodyear Tire & Rubber Company, Akron, OH; *U.S. Public*, pg. 752

Gibb, M.W. Bindloss, Chief Exec. Officer--Osprey Park Ltd., London, United Kingdom; *Int'l*, pg. 1012

Gibbons, Charles H., Chm. Bd., Pres. & Chief Exec. Officer-Intellisource, Fairfield, CT; *U.S. Public*, pg. 1425

Gibbons, John J., Chm. Bd., Pres. & Chief Exec. Officer--Tseng Labs, Norristown, PA; *U.S. Public*, pg. 1643

Gibbons, Robert J., Pres. & Chief Exec. Officer--The Franklin Life Insurance Company, Springfield, IL; *U.S. Public*, pg. 76

Gibbons, Ronald W., Pres. & Chief Exec. Officer--First National Bank, Harrisburg, IL; *U.S. Public*, pg. 1217

Gibbs, James R., Pres. & Chief Exec. Officer--Wainoco Oil Corporation, Houston, TX; *U.S. Public*, pg. 1732

Gibert, Peter, Chm. Bd. & Chief Exec. Officer--Circle International Group, Inc., San Francisco, CA; *U.S. Public*, *pg. 370*

Gibson, John R., Pres. & Chief Exec. Officer--American Pacific Corporation, Las Vegas, NV; *U.S. Public*, pg. 88

Gibson, R.E.G., Chief Exec.--Bradstock Group plc, London, United Kingdom; *Int'l*, pg. 210

Gibson, S. Baily, Chief Exec. Officer--Zurich Life Insurance Company, Dubai, United Arab Emirates; *Int'l*, pg. 1529

Gibson, Thomas R., Chm. Bd. & Chief Exec. Officer--Asbury Automotive Group, Conshohocken, PA; *U.S. Private*, pg. 87

Gibson, Timothy P.S., Chief Exec. Officer--Alexander & Alexander (Hong Kong) Holdings Ltd., Central, Hong Kong; *U.S. Public*, pg. 117

Gibson, William M., Chm. Bd., Pres. & Chief Exec. Officer--Manugistics Group, Inc., Rockville, MD; *U.S. Public*, pg. 1042

Gidwitz, James G., Chm. Bd. & Chief Exec. Officer--Continental Materials Corporation, Chicago, IL; *U.S. Public*, pg. 441

Gidwitz, Ronald J., Pres. & Chief Exec. Officer--Helene Curtis Industries, Inc., Chicago, IL; *Int'l*, pg. 1434

Gieg, L. Frederick, Jr., Pres. & Chief Exec. Officer--RMI Titanium Company, Niles, OH; *U.S. Public*, pg. 1662

Gierer, Vincent A., Jr., Chm. Bd., Pres. & Chief Exec. Officer--UST Inc., Greenwich, CT; *U.S. Public*, pg. 1660

Giersdorf, David, Chief Exec. Officer--CF2GS, Seattle, WA; *U.S. Private*, pg. 194

Gieskes, Hans, Pres. & Chief Exec. Officer--LEXIS-NEXIS, Miamisburg, OH; *Int'l*, pg. 1096

Gietzen, Jeff, Pres. & Chief Exec. Officer--D & W Food Centers, Inc., Grand Rapids, MI; *U.S. Private*, pg. 300

Gifford, Charles K., Chief Exec. Officer--BankBoston Corporation, Boston, MA; *U.S. Public*, pg. 183

Gifford, Dale, Chief Exec. Officer--Hewitt Associates LLC, Lincolnshire, IL; *U.S. Private*, pg. 524

Gifford, Gary L., Pres. & Chief Exec. Officer--Maui Land & Pineapple Co., Inc., Kahului, HI; *U.S. Public*, pg. 1060

Gifford, John F., Chm. Bd., Pres. & Chief Exec. Officer--Maxim Integrated Products, Inc., Sunnyvale, CA; *U.S. Public*, pg. 1061

Gignac, Louis P., Pres. & Chief Exec. Officer--Cambior Inc., Montreal, Canada; *Int'l*, pg. 253

Gignac, Pierre, Pres. & Chief Exec. Officer--Ultima Foods, Brossard, Canada; *Int'l*, pg. 32

Gigou, Michel, Pres. & Chief Exec. Officer--Mack Trucks, Inc., Allentown, PA; *Int'l*, pg. 1102

Gilardi, Carlo, Chief Exec. Officer & Mng. Dir.--Benetton Group S.p.A., Ponzano Veneto, Italy; *Int'l*, pg. 186

Gilbert, Carl A., Pres. & Chief Exec. Officer--Dravo Corporation, Pittsburgh, PA; *U.S. Public*, pg. 527

Gilbert, Jeffrey, Chief Exec.--Melbourne Port Corporation, Melbourne, Australia; *Int'l*, pg. 856

Gilbert, Rodney C., Pres. & Chief Exec. Officer--Rust International Inc., Birmingham, AL; *U.S. Public*, pg. 1366

Gilbert, Scott, Co-Chm. Bd. & Chief Exec. Officer--Team One Advertising, El Segundo, CA; *U.S. Public*, pg. 1422

Gilbert, Walter F., Chm. Bd., Pres., Chief Exec. Officer & Treas.--Semco Industries Inc., Stoughton, MA; *U.S. Private*, pg. 983

Gilbertsen, Robert G., Pres. & Chief Exec. Officer--Network Computing Devices, Inc., Mountain View, CA; *U.S. Public*, pg. 1168

Gildehaus, Thomas A., Chm. Bd. & Chief Exec. Officer--Northwestern Steel & Wire Co., Sterling, IL; *U.S. Public*, pg. 1201

Giles, Don, Pres. & Chief Exec. Officer--Icicle Seafoods, Inc., Seattle, WA; *U.S. Private*, pg. 556

Gilkey, Harold B., Chm. Bd. & Chief Exec. Officer--Sterling Financial Corporation, Spokane, WA; *U.S. Public*, pg. 1516

Gill, Emanuel, Chm. Bd. & Chief Exec. Officer--Diasonics Ultra Sound, Inc., Santa Clara, CA; *Int'l*, pg. 644

Gill, Robert, Pres. & Chief Exec. Officer--Matec Corporation, Hopkinton, MA; *U.S. Public*, pg. 1056

Gill, Stephen E., Pres. & Chief Exec. Officer--M.C. Gill Corporation, El Monte, CA; *U.S. Private*, pg. 453

Gillen, Richard, Chm. Bd., Pres. & Chief Exec. Officer--Harbor Financial Mortgage Corp., Houston, TX; *U.S. Public*, pg. 644

Gillenwater, Kelso, Pres. & Publr.--The News Tribune, Tacoma, WA; *U.S. Public*, pg. 1066

Gilleran, James E., Chm. Bd. & Chief Exec. Officer--The San Francisco Co., San Francisco, CA; *U.S. Public*, pg. 1430

Gilles, Perrot, Chief Exec. Officer--Cook Composites & Polymers Inc., Kansas City, MO; *Int'l*, pg. 1409

Gillespie, James J., Chief Exec. Officer--Checkers Drive-In Restaurants, Inc., Clearwater, FL; *U.S. Public*, pg. 342

Gillespie, James J., Pres. & Chief Exec. Officer--Rally's Hamburgers, Inc., Louisville, KY; *U.S. Public*, pg. 1359

Gillespie, R.T.E., Chm. Bd. & Chief Exec. Officer--GE Hydro, Lachine, Canada; *U.S. Public*, pg. 713

Gillespie, Robert W., Chm., Pres. & Chief Exec. Officer--Keycorp, Cleveland, OH; *U.S. Public*, pg. 954

Gilliam, John, Pres. & Chief Exec. Officer--Anderson Wholesale Company, Muskogee, OK; *U.S. Private*, pg. 73

Gillis, Daniel F., Pres. & Chief Exec. Officer--Software AG Americas, Inc., Reston, VA; *U.S. Public*, pg. 1482

Gillispie, C. Stephenson, Jr., Chm. Bd., Pres. & Chief Exec. Officer--Cadmus Communications Corporation, Richmond, VA; *U.S. Public*, pg. 290

Gilluly, C.W., Chm. Bd., Pres. & Chief Exec. Officer--Hadron, Inc., Alexandria, VA; *U.S. Public*, pg. 773

Gillum, Jack, Pres. & Chief Exec. Officer--BCS Wireless, New Glarus, WI; *U.S. Public*, pg. 609

Gilman, Alan B., Pres. & Chief Exec. Officer--Consolidated Products, Inc., Indianapolis, IN; *U.S. Public*, pg. 436

Gilman, Steven F., Chm. Bd., Pres. & Chief Exec. Officer--Gilrichco, Inc., Oxnard, CA; *U.S. Private*, pg. 454

Gilmartin, Raymond V., Chm. Bd., Pres. & Chief Exec. Officer--Merck & Co., Inc., Whitehouse Station, NJ; *U.S. Public*, pg. 1090

Gilmore, Howard N., Jr., Chief Exec. Officer--Gilmore Envelope Corp., Los Angeles, CA; *U.S. Private*, pg. 454

Gilway, B., Chief Exec. Officer--Assurance Company of America, Baltimore, MD; *Int'l*, pg. 1530

Gilway, B., Chief Exec. Officer--Maine Bonding & Casualty Company, Baltimore, MD; *Int'l*, pg. 1530

Gilway, B., Chief Exec. Officer--Maryland Insurance Company, Baltimore, MD; *Int'l*, pg. 1530

Gilway, B., Chief Exec. Officer--National Standard Insurance Company, Baltimore, MD; *Int'l*, pg. 1530
Gilway, B., Chief Exec. Officer--Valiant Insurance Company, Baltimore, MD; *Int'l*, pg. 1530
Gilway, Barry John, Chief Exec. Officer--Maryland Casualty Co., Baltimore, MD; *Int'l*, pg. 1530
Gin, Sue Ling, Pres., Chief Exec. Officer & Sole Dir.--Flying Food Fare, Inc., Chicago, IL; *U.S. Private*, pg. 415
Gingl, Manfred, Pres. & Chief Exec. Officer--Tesma International Inc., Concord, Canada; *Int'l*, pg. 830
Ginn, Russell, Chm. Bd., Pres. & Chief Exec. Officer--The Flexitallic Group, Inc., Houston, TX; *U.S. Private*, pg. 413
Ginns, Daniel, Chm. Bd., Chief Exec. Officer & Corp. Sec.--Datametrics Corporation, Calabasas, CA; *U.S. Public*, pg. 487
Ginsberg, David M., Pres. & Chief Exec. Officer--Ginsberg's Institutional Foods, Inc., Hudson, NY; *U.S. Private*, pg. 455
Ginsberg, Frank, Co-Chm., Chief Exec. Officer & Creative Dir.--Avrett, Free & Ginsberg, Inc., New York, NY; *U.S. Private*, pg. 103
Ginsburg, Scott K., Chm. Bd. & Chief Exec. Officer--Chancellor Media Corporation, Irving, TX; *U.S. Public*, pg. 335
Giordano, Richard V., Chm. Bd. & Chief Exec. Officer--BG Plc, Reading, United Kingdom; *Int'l*, pg. 118
Giordano, Robert R., Pres. & Chief Exec. Officer--EnergyNorth, Inc., Manchester, NH; *U.S. Public*, pg. 581
Giordano, Salvatore, Jr., Vice Chm., Pres. & Chief Exec. Officer--Fedders Corp., Liberty Corner, NJ; *U.S. Public*, pg. 614
Giovannetti, Gary, Pres. & Chief Exec. Officer--Co-Steel Sayreville Inc., Sayreville, NJ; *Int'l*, pg. 298
Gipson, Hayward R., Pres. & Chief Exec. Officer--Playtex Apparel, Inc., Stamford, CT; *U.S. Public*, pg. 1433
Girard, Chris, Pres. & Chief Exec. Officer--Plaid Pantries, Inc., Beaverton, OR; *U.S. Private*, pg. 868
Girard, Francis E., Pres. & Chief Exec. Officer--Comverse Network Systems, Wakefield, MA; *U.S. Public*, pg. 425
Girgenti, Steven, Chm. & Chief Exec. Officer--Girgenti, Hughes, Butler & McDowell, New York, NY; *U.S. Private*, pg. 455
Gisi, John J., Chm. Bd. & Chief Exec. Officer--National Bank of Arizona, Tucson, AZ; *U.S. Public*, pg. 1793
Gist, Betty, Chm. Bd., Pres., & Chief Exec. Officer--Dairy Fresh Corp., Greensboro, AL; *U.S. Private*, pg. 307
Gittelman, Milton, Chief Exec. Officer, V.P, Treas. & Sec.--Triumph Pet Industries, Inc., Warwick, NY; *U.S. Private*, pg. 1104
Gitter, David J., Pres. & Chief Exec. Officer--M & I Bank Fox Valley, Appleton, WI; *U.S. Public*, pg. 1050
Givli, Benjamin, Chm. Bd. & Chief Exec. Officer--Laser Industries Ltd., Tel Aviv, Israel; *Int'l*, pg. 429
Gladchun, Marshall D., Pres. & Chief Exec. Officer--Advanced Accessories Systems, LLC., Sterling Heights, MI; *U.S. Private*, pg. 21
Gladys, Kendall, Chief Exec. Officer--International Tool & Supply, PLC, New Malden, United Kingdom; *Int'l*, pg. 684
Glancy, Alfred R., III, Chm. Bd., Pres. & Chief Exec. Officer--MCN Energy Group, Inc., Detroit, MI; *U.S. Public*, pg. 1024
Glarbo, Henrik, Chief Exec.--Novo Nordisk A/S (Tianjin) Biotechnology Co. Ltd., Beijing, China; *Int'l*, pg. 988
Glas, Don ald A., Co-Chm. & Chief Exec. Officer--First Federal FSB, Hutchinson, MN; *U.S. Public*, pg. 608
Glas, Donald A., Co-Chm. Bd. & Chief Exec. Officer--FSF Financial Corp., Hutchinson, MN; *U.S. Public*, pg. 608
Glaske, Paul E., Chm. Bd., Pres. & Chief Exec. Officer--Blue Bird Corporation, Macon, GA; *U.S. Private*, pg. 151
Glass, David D., Pres. & Chief Exec. Officer--Wal-Mart Stores, Inc., Bentonville, AR; *U.S. Public*, pg. 1732
Glass, Sherwin, Chm. Bd., Pres. & Chief Exec. Officer--Warehouse Home Furnishings Distributor, Dublin, GA; *U.S. Private*, pg. 1150
Glassman, Daniel, Chm. Bd., Pres. & Chief Exec. Officer--Bradley Pharmaceuticals, Fairfield, NJ; *U.S. Public*, pg. 249
Glassman, Daniel, Chm. Bd., Pres. & Chief Exec. Officer--Doak Dermatologics, Westbury, NY; *U.S. Public*, pg. 250
Glazer, Avram A., Pres. & Chief Exec. Officer--Zapata Corporation, Houston, TX; *U.S. Public*, pg. 1789
Glazer, Michael, Pres. & Chief Exec. Officer--Kay-Bee Toy & Hobby Shops, Inc., Pittsfield, MA; *U.S. Public*, pg. 437
Glazner, Wayne D., Pres. & Chief Exec. Officer--Valley National Bank of Cortez, Cortez, CO; *U.S. Public*, pg. 1793
Gleason, Thomas, Chm. Bd. & Chief Exec. Officer--PremiumWear, Inc., Minneapolis, MN; *U.S. Public*, pg. 1323
Gleed, William H., Chief Exec. Officer--The Citadel Assurance Companies, Toronto, Canada; *Int'l*, pg. 346
Glenn, Clyde A., Jr., Pres. & Treas.--Potter-Shackelford Construction Co., Greenville, SC; *U.S. Private*, pg. 877
Glenn, John J., Chm. Bd. & Chief Exec. Officer--Dunn Reber Glenn Marz, Reno, NV; *U.S. Private*, pg. 347
Glickman, Marshall L., Pres. & Chief Exec. Officer--Ruslander & Sons, Inc., Buffalo, NY; *U.S. Private*, pg. 952
Glickman, Stuart, Vice Chm. & Chief Exec. Officer--Carsey-Werner Company, LLC, Studio City, CA; *U.S. Private*, pg. 216
Glover, Bruce, Chief Exec. Officer--Vinyl Plastics Incorporated, Sheboygan, WI; *U.S. Private*, pg. 1141
Glover, Edmund C., Chm. Bd. & Chief Exec. Officer--Batson-Cook Company, West Point, GA; *U.S. Private*, pg. 123
Glover, Keith, Pres. & Gen. Mgr.--Producers Rice Mill Inc., Stuttgart, AR; *U.S. Private*, pg. 888
Glover, Vernon, Pres. & Chief Exec. Officer--Tennessee Farmers Co-op, La Vergne, TN; *U.S. Private*, pg. 1076
Gloyd, Lawrence E., Chm. Bd. & Chief Exec. Officer--CLARCOR, Inc., Rockford, IL; *U.S. Public*, pg. 381
Gluckman, Michael J., Pres. & Chief Exec. Officer--TriStar Ventures Corporation, Wilmington, DE; *U.S. Public*, pg. 403
Glynn, Robert D. Jr., Chm. Bd., Pres. & Chief Exec. Officer--PG&E Corporation, San Francisco, CA; *U.S. Public*, pg. 1240
Glynn, W.J., Chief Exec.--Ulster Bank Commercial Services Limited, Dublin, Ireland; *Int'l*, pg. 911
Goad, Fred, Chm. Bd. & Co-Chief Exec. Officer--Envoy Corporation, Nashville, TN; *U.S. Public*, pg. 587
Gober, Ira, Chm. Bd. & Chief Exec. Officer--Associated Food Stores, Inc., Jamaica, NY; *U.S. Private*, pg. 90
Gochman, Arthur, Chm. Bd. & Chief Exec. Officer--Academy Corporation, Katy, TX; *U.S. Private*, pg. 11
Goda, Kohei, Pres. & Chief Exec. Officer--Haseko Corporation, Tokyo, Japan; *Int'l*, pg. 599
Godbersen, Byron, Chief Exec. Officer--Midwest Industries, Inc., Ida Grove, IA; *U.S. Private*, pg. 744
Godbold, Wilford D., Jr., Pres. & Chief Exec. Officer--Zero Corporation, Los Angeles, CA; *U.S. Public*, pg. 1791
Goddard, John H., Jr., Pres. & Chief Exec. Officer--Momentum, Seattle, WA; *U.S. Public*, pg. 1329
Goddu, Roger, Chm. Bd., Pres. & Chief Exec. Officer--Montgomery Ward & Co., Inc., Chicago, IL; *U.S. Private*, pg. 758
Godfrey, Paul, Pres. & Chief Exec. Officer--Sun Media Corporation, Toronto, Canada; *Int'l*, pg. 1320
Godfrey, William G., Chm. Bd., Pres. & Chief Exec. Officer--Tekra Corporation, New Berlin, WI; *U.S. Private*, pg. 1073
Godomski, Richard, Chm. Bd., Pres. & Chief Exec. Officer--Process Systems Inc., Memphis, TN; *U.S. Private*, pg. 888
Godsoe, Peter C., Chm. Bd. & Chief Exec. Officer--The Bank of Nova Scotia, Toronto, Canada; *Int'l*, pg. 155
Godson, Don, Chief Exec. Officer--CRH, plc, Dublin, Ireland; *Int'l*, pg. 242
Goebel, Christopher J., Pres. & Chief Exec. Officer--Star Lumber & Supply Company, Inc., Wichita, KS; *U.S. Private*, pg. 1034
Goehring, Craig, Chm. Bd., Pres. & Chief Exec. Officer--Brown and Caldwell, Pleasant Hill, CA; *U.S. Private*, pg. 173
Goekjian, Christopher, Chief Exec. Officer--Credit Suisse Financial Products, London, United Kingdom; *Int'l*, pg. 345
Goeller, William A., Pres. & Chief Exec. Officer--Hatzel & Buehler, Inc., Wilmington, DE; *U.S. Private*, pg. 266
Goergen, Robert B., Chm. Bd., Pres. & Chief Exec. Officer--Blyth Industries, Greenwich, CT; *U.S. Public*, pg. 239
Goerner, Rick, Pres. & Chief Exec. Officer--Silicon Systems, Inc., Tustin, CA; *U.S. Public*, pg. 1585
Goers, Charles, Pres., Chief Exec. Officer & Treas.--T O Plastics, Inc., Minneapolis, MN; *U.S. Private*, pg. 1065
Goethe, Robert A., Chm. Bd., Pres. & Chief Exec. Officer--Regions Mortgage, Inc., Montgomery, AL; *U.S. Public*, pg. 1373
Goetz, Lew, Pres. & Chief Exec. Officer--SOR Inc., Lenexa, KS; *U.S. Private*, pg. 957
Goff, Charles F., Chm. Bd. & Chief Exec. Officer--Destec Energy, Inc., Houston, TX; *U.S. Public*, pg. 1146
Goffloo, Klaus, Dr., Chief Exec. Officer--Heraeus Holding GmbH, Hanau, Germany; *Int'l*, pg. 615
Gogan, James W., Pres. & Chief Exec. Officer--Empire Company Limited, Stellarton, Canada; *Int'l*, pg. 453
Goh, R., Chief Exec. Officer--OCE Systems (Malaysia) Sdn. Bhd., Petaling Jaya, Malaysia; *Int'l*, pg. 995
Goh, R., Chief Exec. Officer--Sirah Sdn. Bhd., Petaling Jaya, Malaysia; *Int'l*, pg. 995
Goings, Rick, Chm. Bd. & Chief Exec. Officer--Tupperware Corporation, Orlando, FL; *U.S. Public*, pg. 1644
Gokal, Ramesh, Pres. & Chief Exec. Officer--Knights Franchise Systems, Inc., Parsippany, NJ; *U.S. Public*, pg. 321
Gold, Matthew L., Chm. Bd., Pres. & Chief Exec. Officer--Precision Standard, Inc., Denver, CO; *U.S. Public*, pg. 1321
Gold, Stanley P., Chm. Bd. & Chief Exec. Officer--L.A. Gear, Inc., Santa Monica, CA; *U.S. Public*, pg. 969
Goldbath, Raymond, Chm. Bd. & Chief Exec. Officer--Marathon Cheese Corp., Marathon, WI; *U.S. Private*, pg. 701
Goldberg, Arthur, Chm. Bd., Pres. & Chief Exec. Officer--Di Giorgio Corporation, Carteret, NJ; *U.S. Private*, pg. 330
Goldberg, Arthur M., Chm. Bd. & Chief Exec. Officer--Bally Total Fitness Corporation, Chicago, IL; *U.S. Public*, pg. 171
Goldberg, Bruce M., Pres. & Chief Oper. Officer--All American Semiconductor, Inc., Miami, FL; *U.S. Public*, pg. 41
Goldberg, Danny, Pres. & Chief Exec. Officer & Chm. Bd. Mercury Grp.--Polygram N.V., Baarn, Netherlands; *Int'l*, pg. 1051
Goldberg, Fred, Chm. & Chief Exec. Officer--Goldberg Moser O'Neill, San Francisco, CA; *U.S. Private*, pg. 459
Goldberg, Howard A., Pres. & Chief Exec. Officer--Players International, Inc., Atlantic City, NJ; *U.S. Public*, pg. 1310
Goldberg, Linda P., Pres. & Chief Exec. Officer--Dental Health Alliance, L.L.C., New York, NY; *Int'l*, pg. 499
Goldberg, Michael C., Chm. Bd., Pres. & Chief Exec. Officer--FDP Corp., Miami, FL; *U.S. Public*, pg. 603
Goldberg, Neil, Pres. & Chief Exec. Officer--Raymour and Flanigan Furniture Co., Liverpool, NY; *U.S. Private*, pg. 912
Goldberg, Richard H., Chm. Bd., Pres. & Chief Exec. Officer--Synon Corporation, Larkspur, CA; *U.S. Private*, pg. 1060
Goldberg, Stanley, Chm. Bd., Pres. & Chief Exec. Officer--Ringer Corporation, Bloomington, MN; *U.S. Public*, pg. 1390
Goldberg, Stanley, Chm. Bd., Pres. & Chief Exec. Officer--Dexol, Torrance, CA; *U.S. Public*, pg. 1390
Goldberger, Robert D., Pres. & Chief Exec. Officer--GFI America, Minneapolis, MN; *U.S. Private*, pg. 435
Goldby, Steven, Chm. Bd., Pres. & Chief Exec. Officer--MDL Information Systems, Inc., San Leandro, CA; *Int'l*, pg. 1100
Golden, Richard S., Pres. & Chief Exec. Officer--D.O.C. Optics Corporation, Southfield, MI; *U.S. Private*, pg. 305
Golden, Terence C., Pres., Chief Exec. Officer & Dir.--Cousins Properties Incorporated, Atlanta, GA; *U.S. Public*, pg. 453
Golden, Terence C., Pres., Chief Exec. Officer--Host Marriott Corporation, Bethesda, MD; *U.S. Public*, pg. 841
Goldfarb, Andrew, Pres. & Chief Exec. Officer--HCC Industries, Rosemead, CA; *U.S. Private*, pg. 490
Goldin, Ken, Chm. Bd., Pres. & Chief Exec. Officer--The Score Board, Inc., Cherry Hill, NJ; *U.S. Public*, pg. 1444
Goldman, Marc, Pres. & Chief Exec. Officer--Farmland Dairies, Wallington, NJ; *U.S. Private*, pg. 395
Goldman, Mark D., Pres. & Chief Exec. Officer--Galoob Toys, Inc., South San Francisco, CA; *U.S. Public*, pg. 698
Goldman, Steve, Pres. & Chief Exec. Officer--Power-One, Inc., Camarillo, CA; *U.S. Private*, pg. 878
Goldsmith, Russell, Chief Exec. Officer--City National Corporation, Beverly Hills, CA; *U.S. Public*, pg. 380
Goldsmith, Russell, Chm. Bd. & Chief Exec. Officer--City National Bank, Beverly Hills, CA; *U.S. Public*, pg. 381
Goldstein, Arthur L., Chm. Bd., Pres. & Chief Exec. Officer--Ionics, Incorporated, Watertown, MA; *U.S. Public*, pg. 912
Goldstein, Jerome, Chm. Bd. & Chief Exec. Officer--Advanced Magnetics, Inc., Cambridge, MA; *U.S. Public*, pg. 20
Goldstein, K.T., Pres. & Chief Exec. Officer--Universal Underwriters Insurance Co., Overland Park, KS; *Int'l*, pg. 1530
Goldstein, K.T., Chief Exec. Officer--Universal Underwriters of Texas, Overland Park, KS; *Int'l*, pg. 1530
Goldstein, Mark E., Pres. & Chief Exec. Officer--Scott's Liquid Gold-Inc., Denver, CO; *U.S. Public*, pg. 1447
Goldstein, Marry, Pres. & Chief Exec. Officer--Alliance Gaming Corporation, Las Vegas, NV; *U.S. Public*, pg. 46
Goldstein, Michael, Vice Chm. & Chief Exec. Officer--Toys "R" Us, Inc., Paramus, NJ; *U.S. Public*, pg. 1626
Goldstein, Richard A., Pres. & Chief Exec. Officer--Unilever United States Inc., New York, NY; *Int'l*, pg. 1435
Goldstein, Ronald, Chief Exec. Officer--Flexible Flyer Toys, West Point, MS; *U.S. Private*, pg. 412
Goldstein, Stanley, Chm. Bd. & Chief Exec. Officer--CVS Corp., Woonsocket, RI; *U.S. Public*, pg. 287
Goldston, Mark, Pres. & Chief Exec. Officer--Einstein/Noah Bagel Corp., Golden, CO; *U.S. Public*, pg. 247
Goldstone, Mark, Chief Exec. Officer--EURO RSCG Healthcare, London, United Kingdom; *Int'l*, pg. 603
Goldstone, Steven F., Chm. Bd., Pres. & Chief Exec. Officer--RJR Nabisco Holdings Corp., New York, NY; *U.S. Public*, pg. 1354
Goldwater, Charles, Pres. & Chief Exec. Officer--Mann Theatres, Encino, CA; *U.S. Private*, pg. 239
Golias, Tipton L., Pres. & Chief Exec. Officer--Helena Laboratories Corporation, Beaumont, TX; *U.S. Private*, pg. 519
Golisano, B. Thomas, Chm. Bd., Pres. & Chief Exec. Officer--Paychex, Inc., Rochester, NY; *U.S. Public*, pg. 1267
Golitz, John T., Chm. Bd. & Chief Exec. Officer--First Financial Building Corporation, Manchester, MO; *U.S. Private*, pg. 407
Golleher, George, Chief Exec. Officer--Ralphs Grocery Company, Compton, CA; *U.S. Private*, pg. 1202
Golsen, Jack E., Chm. Bd., Pres. & Chief Exec. Officer--LSB Industries, Inc., Oklahoma City, OK; *U.S. Public*, pg. 970
Golub, Harvey, Chm. Bd. & Chief Exec. Officer--American Express Company, New York, NY; *U.S. Public*, pg. 73
Golub, Lewis, Chm. Bd. & Chief Exec. Officer--Golub Corporation, Schenectady, NY; *U.S. Private*, pg. 463
Gomer, David W., Pres. & Chief Exec. Officer--Cape Coral National Bank, Cape Coral, FL; *U.S. Public*, pg. 607
Gomez, Alain, Chm. Bd. & Chief Exec. Officer--Thomson S.A., Paris, France; *Int'l*, pg. 1381
Gomez, Alain, Chief Exec. Officer--Cryotechnologies SA, Blagnac, France; *Int'l*, pg. 1383
Gondola, Donna, Chief Exec. Officer--Tasha, Fremont, CA; *U.S. Private*, pg. 1069
Gongaware, Donald F., Pres. & Chief Exec. Officer--Bankers Life & Casualty Company, Chicago, IL; *U.S. Public*, pg. 433
Gonzalez Elizondo, Jesus, Chief Exec. Officer--Grupo SYR, S.A. de C.V., Mexico, Mexico; *Int'l*, pg. 576
Gonzalez Zabalegui, Carlos, Chief Exec. Officer--Controladora Comercial Mexicana, S.A. de C.V., Mexico, Mexico; *Int'l*, pg. 328
Gonzalez, Rodolfo Fernandez, Chief Oper. Officer & Gen. Dir.--Vitromex, S.A., Saltillo, Mexico; *Int'l*, pg. 1469
Good, Sheldon F., Chm. Bd. & Chief Exec. Officer--Sheldon Good & Co., Chicago, IL; *U.S. Private*, pg. 463
Goodchild, John, Chm. Bd. & Chief Exec. Officer--The Weightman Group, Philadelphia, PA; *U.S. Private*, pg. 1159
Goode, David R., Chm. Bd., Pres. & Chief Exec. Officer--Norfolk Southern Corporation, Norfolk, VA; *U.S. Public*, pg. 1190
Goodes, Melvin R., Chm. Bd. & Chief Exec. Officer--Warner-Lambert Company, Morris Plains, NJ; *U.S. Public*, pg. 1738
Goodfriend, Robert M., Chm. Bd. & Chief Exec. Officer--Goody's Family Clothing, Inc., Knoxville, TN; *U.S. Public*, pg. 753
Gooding, Terrence, Chm. Bd. & Chief Exec. Officer--Wavetek Corporation, San Diego, CA; *U.S. Private*, pg. 1154
Goodman, Ellis, Exec. V.P. & Chief Exec. Officer-Spirits & Beers--Canandaigua Wine Company, Inc., Canandaigua, NY; *U.S. Public*, pg. 300

Goodman, Ellis M., Chm. Bd. & Chief Exec. Officer--Barton Incorporated, Chicago, IL; *U.S. Public*, pg. 300

Goodman, Fredric, Chief Exec. Officer--Welsbach Electric Corp., College Point, NY; *U.S. Public*, pg. 572

Goodman, Gilbert, Chief Exec. Officer--J. Josephson, Inc., South Hackensack, NJ; *U.S. Private*, pg. 601

Goodman, John M., Chief Exec. Officer & Sr. V.P.--Lewis Homes Management Corp., Upland, CA; *U.S. Private*, pg. 665

Goodman, Louis J., Pres. & Chief Exec. Officer--J.C. Higgins Corp., Stoughton, MA; *U.S. Public*, pg. 572

Goodman, Peter, Chief Exec. Officer--Goodman Knitting Company, Brockton, MA; *U.S. Public*, pg. 948

Goodman, Peter A., Chm. & Chief Exec. Officer--Ivy, Vernon, CA; *U.S. Public*, pg. 948

Goodman, Peter A., Chm. & Chief Exec. Officer--A.J. Brandon, Vernon, CA; *U.S. Public*, pg. 948

Goodmanson, Richard R., Pres. & Chief Exec. Officer--America West Airlines, Inc., Phoenix, AZ; *U.S. Public*, pg. 67

Goodmon, James F., Pres. & Chief Exec. Officer--Capitol Broadcasting Co., Inc., Raleigh, NC; *U.S. Private*, pg. 206

Goodnight, James H., Pres., Chief Exec. Officer & Co-Founder--SAS Institute Inc., Cary, NC; *U.S. Private*, pg. 966

Goodrich, T.M., Pres. & Chief Exec. Officer--BE & K, Inc., Birmingham, AL; *U.S. Private*, pg. 106

Goodson, W.A., Chief Oper. Officer--Winston Leaf Tobacco Co., Winston Salem, NC; *U.S. Public*, pg. 1695

Goodspeed, Paul, Chief Exec. Officer--Safer, Ltd., Scarborough, Canada; *U.S. Public*, pg. 1390

Goodstein, Ed, Chm. Bd. & Chief Exec. Officer--Vertex Computer Cable Products, Farmingdale, NY; *U.S. Public*, *pg. 1718*

Goodwin, Carl, Pres. & Chief Exec. Officer--Bijur Lubricating Corporation, Bennington, VT; *U.S. Private*, pg. 143

Goodwin, F., Chief Exec. Officer--Yorkshire Bank, Leeds, United Kingdom; *Int'l*, pg. 906

Goodwin, F.A., Chief Exec. Officer--Clydesdale Bank PLC, Glasgow, United Kingdom; *Int'l*, pg. 906

Goodwin, H. Clark, Pres. & Chief Exec. Officer--Bank of Union, Monroe, NC; *U.S. Public*, pg. 627

Goodyear, William M., Chm. Bd. & Chief Exec. Officer--Bank of America Illinois, Chicago, IL; *U.S. Public*, pg. 180

Goolsby, John L., Pres. & Chief Exec. Officer--Howard Hughes Corporation, Las Vegas, NV; *U.S. Public*, pg. 1407

Gorder, Mark S., V.P., Pres.& Chief Exec. Officer-Resistance Technology, Inc.--Selas Corporation of America, Dresher, PA; *U.S. Public*, pg. 1454

Gorder, Mark S., Pres. & Chief Exec. Officer--Resistance Technology Inc., Arden Hills, MN; *U.S. Public*, pg. 1455

Gordon, Bernard M., Chm. Bd. & Chief Exec. Officer--Analogic Corporation, Peabody, MA; *U.S. Public*, pg. 109

Gordon, Dan, Pres. & Chief Exec. Officer--Gordon Food Service Inc., Grand Rapids, MI; *U.S. Private*, pg. 465

Gordon, Lloyd, Owner & Chief Exec. Officer--Amcel Corp., Watertown, MA; *U.S. Private*, pg. 48

Gordon, Melvin J., Chm. Bd. & Chief Exec. Officer--Tootsie Roll Industries, Inc., Chicago, IL; *U.S. Public*, pg. 1621

Gordon, Melvin S., Pres. & Chief Exec. Officer--Paradise, Inc., Plant City, FL; *U.S. Public*, pg. 1256

Gordon, Richard, Pres. & Chief Exec. Officer--American Aircraft Parts Manufacturing Co., Fraser, MI; *U.S. Private*, pg. 49

Gordon, Robert D., Chm. Bd., Pres. & Chief Exec. Officer--Apertus Technologies Incorporated, Eden Prairie, MN; *U.S. Public*, pg. 119

Gore, James L., V.P. & Pres. & Chief Exec. Officer-Coventry HealthCare Mngmt.--Coventry Corporation, Nashville, TN; *U.S. Public*, pg. 454

Gore, Robert W., Pres. & Chief Exec. Officer--W.L. Gore & Associates, Inc., Newark, DE; *U.S. Private*, pg. 465

Gore, Stephen J., Pres. & Chief Exec. Officer--DT Industries Inc., Springfield, MO; *U.S. Public*, pg. 475

Gorell, Franklyn, Chm. Bd. & Chief Exec. Officer--Season-All Industries, Inc., Indiana, PA; *Int'l*, pg. 267

Gores, Tom, Pres. & Chief Exec. Officer--Platinum Equity Holdings, LLC, Los Angeles, CA; *U.S. Private*, pg. 872

Gorga, J.L., Chief Exec. Officer--CMI Industries, Inc., Columbia, SC; *U.S. Private*, pg. 195

Gorguze, Vincent, Chief Exec. Officer--Carco Electronics, Menlo Park, CA; *U.S. Private*, pg. 208

Gorham, Brian L., Pres. & Chief Exec. Officer--Hilb, Rogal and Hamilton Insurance Services of Central California, Inc., Fresno, CA; *U.S. Public*, pg. 827

Gorman, Joseph T., Chm. Bd. & Chief Exec. Officer--TRW Inc., Cleveland, OH; *U.S. Public*, pg. 1558

Gorman, Kenneth F., Chm. Bd., Pres. & Chief Exec. Officer--Production Payments, Inc., Chicago, IL; *U.S. Private*, pg. 554

Gorman, Kenneth J., Chm. Bd. & Chief Exec. Officer--Atlantic Mutual Companies, New York, NY; *U.S. Private*, pg. 95

Gorra, William, Chm. Bd., Pres. & Chief Exec. Officer--Simoniz USA, Inc., Bolton, CT; *U.S. Private*, pg. 1001

Gosa, James J., Pres. & Chief Exec. Officer--American Woodmark Corporation, Winchester, VA; *U.S. Public*, pg. 96

Gosman, Abraham D., Chm. Bd. & Chief Exec. Officer--Meditrust Corporation, Needham, MA; *U.S. Public*, pg. 1081

Gosnell, Robert A., Chief Exec. Officer--Pointe Group Ltd., Phoenix, AZ; *U.S. Private*, pg. 873

Gosnell, Robert A., Chief Exec. Officer--Gosnell Builders, Phoenix, AZ; *U.S. Private*, pg. 873

Gosper, Brett, Chief Exec. Officer--EURO RSCG Wnek Gosper, London, United Kingdom; *Int'l*, pg. 603

Goss, Howard S., Chm. Bd., Chief Exec. Officer & Treas.--Transco Inc., Chicago, IL; *U.S. Private*, pg. 1096

Gosselink, Jerry D., Pres.-Natl. Div. & Chief Oper. Officer--The Weitz Company, Inc., Des Moines, IA; *U.S. Private*, pg. 1160

Gossett, Barry P., Chm. Bd. & Chief Exec. Officer--Williams Scotsman, Inc., Baltimore, MD; *U.S. Private*, pg. 976

Gossner, Alfred, Dr., Chief Exec. Officer--Allianz Versicherungs-AG, Hamburg, Germany; *Int'l*, pg. 58

Gotschall, Jeffrey P., Pres. & Chief Exec. Officer--Sifco Industries, Inc., Cleveland, OH; *U.S. Public*, pg. 1470

Gottlieb, Richard D., Pres. & Chief Exec. Officer--Lee Enterprises, Incorporated, Davenport, IA; *U.S. Public*, pg. 983

Gottwald, Bruce C., Chm. Bd. & Chief Exec. Officer--Ethyl Corporation, Richmond, VA; *U.S. Public*, pg. 595

Gottwald, Floyd D., Jr., Chm. Bd. & Chief Exec. Officer--Albemarle Corporation, Richmond, VA; *U.S. Public*, pg. 37

Gottwald, John D., Pres. & Chief Exec. Officer--Tredegar Industries Inc., Richmond, VA; *U.S. Public*, pg. 1633

Gougoux, Yves, Pres. & Chief Exec. Officer--Publicis BCP Montreal Inc., Montreal, Canada; *Int'l*, pg. 116

Goulard, F. Eric, Chief Exec. Officer--Castorama Italia, Bollate, Italy; *Int'l*, pg. 276

Gould, Peter J., Pres. & Chief Exec. Officer--Aldine Technologies Industries Inc., Carlstadt, NJ; *U.S. Private*, pg. 33

Gould, Steven, Pres. & Chief Exec. Officer--Gould Packaging, Inc., Vancouver, WA; *U.S. Private*, pg. 466

Gould, William S., III, Pres.--Magnetic Analysis Corp., Mount Vernon, NY; *U.S. Private*, pg. 695

Goupil, Eric, Chief Exec. Officer--Polive/Tricosteril, Courbevoie, France; *U.S. Public*, pg. 673

Gourd, Alain, Pres. & Chief Exec. Officer--Canadian Satellite Communications Inc., Mississauga, Canada; *Int'l*, pg. 1481

Gourd, Alain, Pres. & Chief Exec. Officer--CSC, Ottawa, Ottawa, Canada; *Int'l*, pg. 1482

Gournay, Patrick, Pres. & Chief Exec. Officer--The Dannon Co., Tarrytown, NY; *Int'l*, pg. 379

Goutard, Noel, Chm. Bd. & Chief Exec. Officer--Valeo Research Sooal, Paris, France; *Int'l*, pg. 240

Gowan, Damon, Pres. & Chief Exec. Officer--Gowan, Inc., Houston, TX; *U.S. Public*, pg. 572

Gowdy, Bob G., Pres. & Chief Exec. Officer--Commercial Union Corporation, Boston, MA; *Int'l*, pg. 308

Gower, Roger, Chm. Bd., Pres. & Chief Exec. Officer--Micro Component Technology Inc., Saint Paul, MN; *U.S. Public*, pg. 1104

Gozali, H., Chief Oper. Officer--P.T. Toyo Kanetsu Indonesia, Jakarta, Indonesia; *Int'l*, pg. 949

Grabowski, Jerry W., Pres., Chief Exec. Officer, Chief Fin. Officer & Treas.--Waters Instruments, Inc., Rochester, MN; *U.S. Public*, pg. 1745

Grace, Barnett, Chm. Bd., Pres. & Chief Exec. Officer--First Commercial Corporation, Little Rock, AR; *U.S. Public*, pg. 630

Grace, Barnett, Chm. Bd. & Chief Exec. Officer--First Commercial Bank, N.A., Little Rock, AR; *U.S. Public*, pg. 630

Grace, Howard T., Chief Exec. Officer, V.P. & Dir.-Leasing--W.M. Grace Development, Phoenix, AZ; *U.S. Private*, pg. 468

Grade, Jeffery T., Chm. Bd. & Chief Exec. Officer--Harnischfeger Industries, Inc., Saint Francis, WI; *U.S. Public*, pg. 788

Gradinger, J. Gary, Chm. Bd., Pres. & Chief Exec. Officer--Golden Star Inc., Kansas City, MO; *U.S. Private*, pg. 460

Grady, John, Pres. & Chief Exec. Officer--XRE Corporation, Littleton, MA; *U.S. Public*, pg. 1595

Graf, John A., Pres. & Chief Exec. Officer--Western National Life Insurance Co., Houston, TX; *U.S. Public*, pg. 76

Graf, Mel, Pres. & Chief Exec. Officer--Baris Shoe Company, Inc., New York, NY; *U.S. Private*, pg. 116

Graf, Paul E., Pres. & Chief Exec. Officer--Axel Johnson Inc., Stamford, CT; *Int'l*, pg. 709

Grafton, W. Robert, Chm. Bd. & Acting Chief Exec. Officer--Andersen Worldwide, New York, NY; *U.S. Private*, pg. 72

Graham, Allister P., Chm. Bd. & Chief Exec. Officer--The Oshawa Group Limited, Etobicoke, Canada; *Int'l*, pg. 1012

Graham, Craig, Chm. Bd., Pres. & Chief Exec. Officer--Cashway Building Centres Ltd., Port Hope, Canada; *Int'l*, *pg. 274*

Graham, Donald E., Chm. & Chief Exec. Officer--The Washington Post Company, Washington, DC; *U.S. Public*, pg. 1742

Graham, Gordon, Pres., Chief Exec. Officer & Chief Oper. Officer--Bell Industries, Inc., El Segundo, CA; *U.S. Public*, *pg. 204*

Graham, James, Pres. & Chief Exec. Officer--Versa Services Ltd., Etobicoke, Canada; *U.S. Private*, pg. 79

Graham, John, Chief Exec. Officer--Fleishman-Hillard, Saint Louis, MO; *U.S. Private*, pg. 411

Graham, Kenneth, Pres. & Chief Exec. Officer--Thyssen Inc., Detroit, MI; *Int'l*, pg. 1389

Graham, Stedman, Chief Exec. Officer--Graham Gregory Bozell, Inc., New York, NY; *U.S. Public*, pg. 1642

Graham, Stedman, Chief Exec. Officer--Graham Gregory Bozell, Inc., Chicago, IL; *U.S. Public*, pg. 1642

Graham, Stuart, Pres. & Chief Exec. Officer--Skanska E&C, Carmel, IN; *Int'l*, pg. 1261

Grahman-Helwig, Roland, Chief Exec. Officer--Willis Corroon Corp. of San Jose, San Jose, CA; *Int'l*, pg. 1507

Grahn, Gary L., Pres. & Chief Exec. Officer--The Langer Biomechanics Group, Inc., Deer Park, NY; *U.S. Public*, pg. 978

Gralnick, Marvin, Chm. Bd., Pres. & Chief Exec. Officer--Chico's Fas Inc, Fort Myers, FL; *U.S. Public*, pg. 349

Grandin, Michael A., Pres. & Chief Exec. Officer--Sceptre Resources Limited, Calgary, Canada; *Int'l*, pg. 1203

Grandy, Fred, Pres. & Chief Exec. Officer--Goodwill Industries International, Bethesda, MD; *U.S. Private*, pg. 464

Granger, Ronald K., Chm. Bd., Pres. & Chief Exec. Officer--Granger Companies, Lansing, MI; *U.S. Private*, pg. 469

Granjean, Michel, chief Exec. Offcier--Mediapolis France, Puteaux, France; *U.S. Private*, pg. 1199

Grant, Berl, Pres. & Chief Exec. Officer--Seymour Manufacturing Company, Seymour, IN; *U.S. Private*, pg. 988

Grant, Donald B., Chm. Bd. & Chief Exec. Officer--Voyager Emblems, Inc., Sanborn, NY; *U.S. Private*, pg. 1143

Grant, John E., Chief Exec. Officer--Delta Pride Catfish, Inc., Indianola, MS; *U.S. Private*, pg. 322

Grant, Michael, Chm. Bd. & Chief Exec. Officer--Grant-Lydick Beverage Co., San Antonio, TX; *U.S. Private*, pg. 470

Grant, R. Douglas, Chm. Bd., Pres. & Chief Exec. Officer--Lakeland Financial Corporation, Warsaw, IN; *U.S. Public*, *pg. 975*

Grant, W. Thomas II, Chm. Bd., Pres. & Chief Exec. Officer--Lab One, Lenexa, KS; *U.S. Public*, pg. 1449

Grant, W. Thomas, II, Chm. Bd. & Chief Exec. Officer--Seafield Capital Corporation, Kansas City, MO; *U.S. Public*, pg. 1449

Granum, Robert M., Chm. Bd. & Chief Exec. Officer--Panel Processing, Inc., Alpena, MI; *U.S. Private*, pg. 836

Grappotte, Francois, Chm. Bd. & Chief Exec. Officer--LeGrand S.A., Limoges, France; *Int'l*, pg. 805

Grass, Martin L., Chm. Bd. & Chief Exec. Officer--Rite Aid Corporation, Camp Hill, PA; *U.S. Public*, pg. 1390

Gravenhorst, Ted, Sr., Pres. & Chief Exec. Officer--John Boos & Company, Effingham, IL; *U.S. Private*, pg. 156

Graves, Earl G., Jr., Chief Exec. Officer & Exec. V.P.--Earl G. Graves, Ltd., New York, NY; *U.S. Private*, pg. 471

Gravette, E.T., Chm. Bd. & Chief Exec. Officer--The Turner Corporation, New York, NY; *U.S. Public*, pg. 1645

Grawert, Ron, Chief Exec. Officer--MobileComm, Ridgefield Park, NJ; *U.S. Public*, pg. 1120

Gray, H.M.V., Chief Exec.--NatWest U.K., London, United Kingdom; *Int'l*, pg. 910

Gray, J. Douglas, Chief Exec. Officer--CSC Index, Inc., Cambridge, MA; *U.S. Public*, pg. 422

Gray, Melvin, Chm. Bd. & Chief Exec. Officer--Graycor Operating Companies, Homewood, IL; *U.S. Private*, pg. 472

Gray, Robert, Chief Exec. Officer--St. John Knits, Irvine, CA; *U.S. Private*, pg. 960

Gray, Robert A., Pres. & Chief Exec. Officer--Gray Printing Co., Fostoria, OH; *U.S. Private*, pg. 472

Gray, Roger L., Pres. & Chief Exec. Officer--Gray Kirk/VanSant Advertising, Inc., Baltimore, MD; *U.S. Private*, pg. 472

Graybill, V. Lynn, Chm. Bd., Pres. & Chief Exec. Officer--Karts International Inc., Covington, LA; *U.S. Public*, pg. 944

Grazer, Brian, Co-Chief Exec. Officer--Imagine Entertainment, Los Angeles, CA; *U.S. Private*, pg. 558

Graziadio, G. Louis, III, Chm. Bd. & Chief Exec. Officer--Vista 2000, Inc., Kewanee, IL; *U.S. Private*, pg. 1142

Graziado, George M., Chm. Bd., Pres. & Chief Exec. Officer--Imperial Bancorp, Inglewood, CA; *U.S. Public*, pg. 871

Greathouse, Steve, Pres. & Chief Exec. Officer--Casino Electronics, Inc., Las Vegas, NV; *U.S. Public*, pg. 47

Greaves, R. Malcolm, Chief Exec. Officer & Pres.-Haskel Intl.--Haskel International, Inc., Burbank, CA; *U.S. Public*, *pg. 798*

Greco, James, Chief Exec. Officer--FieldBrook Farms, Inc., Dunkirk, NY; *U.S. Private*, pg. 403

Greco, Rosemarie B., Pres. & Chief Exec. Officer--CoreStates Bank, N.A., Philadelphia, PA; *U.S. Public*, pg. 446

Greczyn, Robert, Chief Exec. Officer--Healthsource North Carolina, Inc., Morrisville, NC; *U.S. Public*, pg. 360

Greehey, William E., Chm. Bd. & Chief Exec. Officer--Valero Energy Corporation, San Antonio, TX; *U.S. Public*, pg. 1704

Greehey, William E., Chm. Bd. & Chief Exec. Officer--Valero Refining Company, San Antonio, TX; *U.S. Public*, pg. 1704

Greely, F.J., Jr., Pres. & Chief Exec. Officer--Regions Bank/Central Louisiana, New Roads, LA; *U.S. Public*, pg. 1372

Greely, William C., Pres. & Chief Exec. Officer--Keeneland Assoc., Inc., Lexington, KY; *U.S. Private*, pg. 611

Green, Bruce, Co-Chief Exec. Officer--Maurice Electric Supply Company, Washington, DC; *U.S. Private*, pg. 715

Green, C.N., Chief Exec.--Paterson Zochonis Plc, Stockport, United Kingdom; *Int'l*, pg. 1024

Green, Clay S., Pres. & Chief Exec. Officer--First Midwest Mortgage Corporation, Joliet, IL; *U.S. Public*, pg. 636

Green, Frederick M., Pres. & Chief Exec. Officer--Ault Incorporated, Minneapolis, MN; *U.S. Public*, pg. 147

Green, Henry, Pres. & Chief Exec. Officer--Physician Computer Network, Inc., Morris Plains, NJ; *U.S. Public*, pg. 1293

Green, Holcombe T., Jr., Chm. Bd. & Chief Exec. Officer--WestPoint Stevens Inc., West Point, GA; *U.S. Public*, pg. 1762

Green, Howard, Chief Exec. Officer--Quartet Manufacturing Co., Skokie, IL; *U.S. Public*, pg. 707

Green, J. B., Pres. & Chief Exec. Officer--Marigold Foods, Inc., Minneapolis, MN; *Int'l*, pg. 752

Green, James M., Pres. & Chief Exec. Officer--FWD/Seagrave Fire Apparatus, Inc., Clintonville, WI; *U.S. Private*, pg. 390

Green, Jim, Chm. Bd. & Chief Exec. Officer--Active Software, Inc., Santa Clara, CA; *U.S. Private*, pg. 15

Green, Johnathan D., Pres. & Chief Exec. Officer--Rockefeller Center Management Corporation, New York, NY; *Int'l*, pg. 873

Green, Mike, Pres. & Chief Exec. Officer-Inpower--Integral Systems, Inc., Walnut Creek, CA; *Int'l*, pg. 242

Green, R., Chm. Bd. & Chief Exec. Officer--Gan Life and Pensions PLC, Harlow, United Kingdom; *Int'l*, pg. 565
Green, R. Thomas, Jr., Chm. Bd., Pres. & Chief Exec. Officer--Oglebay Norton Company, Cleveland, OH; *U.S. Public*, pg. 1213
Green, Richard C., Jr., Chm. Bd. & Chief Exec. Officer--UtiliCorp United Inc., Kansas City, MO; *U.S. Public*, pg. 1700
Green, Richard L., Chm. Bd., Pres. & Chief Exec. Officer--General Shale Products Corp., Johnson City, TN; *Int'l*, pg. 843
Green, Richard L., Chm. Bd., Pres. & Chief Exec. Officer--General Shale Products Corp., Elizabethton, TN; *Int'l*, pg. 843
Green, Stanley, Pres. & Chief Exec. Officer--DAQ Electronics Inc., Piscataway, NJ; *U.S. Private*, pg. 300
Green, Tim, Co-Chief Exec. Officer--Maurice Electric Supply Company, Washington, DC; *U.S. Private*, pg. 715
Greenberg, Daniel, Chm. Bd. & Chief Exec. Officer--Electro Rent Corporation, Van Nuys, CA; *U.S. Public*, pg. 568
Greenberg, Jack M., Vice Chm. & Chief Exec. Officer--McDonald's Corporation, Oak Brook, IL; *U.S. Public*, pg. 1068
Greenberg, Jeffrey W., Chm. Bd. & Chief Exec. Officer--Marsh & McLennan Risk Capital Corp., Greenwich, CT; *U.S. Public*, pg. 1049
Greenberg, Lon R., Chm. Bd., Pres. & Chief Exec. Officer--UGI Corporation, King of Prussia, PA; *U.S. Public*, pg. 1653
Greenberg, Lon R., Chm. Bd., Pres. & Chief Exec. Officer--AmeriGas Partners, L.P., Valley Forge, PA; *U.S. Public*, pg. 1653
Greenberg, Marvin, Chief Exec. Officer--Baltic Linen Company, Inc., Valley Stream, NY; *U.S. Private*, pg. 113
Greenberg, Maurice R., Chm. Bd. & Chief Exec. Officer--American International Group, Inc., New York, NY; *U.S. Public*, pg. 83
Greenberg, Robert, Chm. & Chief Exec. Officer--R/GA Interactive, New York, NY; *U.S. Public*, pg. 1641
Greenbury, R., Chief Exec. Officer--Marks & Spencer US Holdings Inc., New York, NY; *Int'l*, pg. 843
Greene, Marc J., Pres. & Chief Exec. Officer--Regions Bank/White County, Cleveland, GA; *U.S. Public*, pg. 1373
Greene, Warren E., Pres. & Chief Exec. Officer--Adair Greene Advertising, Atlanta, GA; *U.S. Private*, pg. 16
Greener, Anthony, Chm. Bd. & Chief Exec. Officer--Guinness Plc, London, United Kingdom; *Int'l*, pg. 412
Greenfield, Harley J., Chm. & Chief Exec. Officer--Jennifer Convertibles Inc., Woodbury, NY; *U.S. Public*, pg. 926
Greenlee, Stewart M., Pres. & Chief Exec. Officer--The Fifth Third Bank of Southern Ohio, Hillsboro, OH; *U.S. Public*, pg. 622
Greenman, Stanley, Chm. Bd., Chief Exec. Officer & Treas.--Noodle Kidoodle Inc., Syosset, NY; *U.S. Public*, pg. 1188
Greenspun, Daniel Allen, Chief Exec. Officer--Las Vegas Sun, Las Vegas, NV; *U.S. Private*, pg. 652
Greenstone, Ronald, Chm. & Chief Exec. Officer--Greenstone Roberts Advertising, Melville, NY; *U.S. Public*, pg. 763
Greenstone, Ronald, Chm. & Chief Exec. Officer--Greenstone Roberts/Florida, Orlando, FL; *U.S. Public*, pg. 763
Greenwald, Gerald, Chm. Bd. & Chief Exec. Officer--UAL Corporation, Elk Grove Village, IL; *U.S. Public*, pg. 1652
Greenwald, Martin W., Chm. Bd., Pres. & Chief Exec. Officer--Image Entertainment, Inc., Chatsworth, CA; *U.S. Public*, pg. 870
Greer, Carol G., Pres. & Chief Exec. Officer-Specialty Footwear--Woolworth Corporation, New York, NY; *U.S. Public*, pg. 1777
Grefenstette, Carl G., Chm. Bd. & Chief Exec. Officer--The Hillman Company, Pittsburgh, PA; *U.S. Private*, pg. 530
Gregg, F. Browne, Chm. Bd. & Chief Exec. Officer--Florida Crushed Stone Company, Leesburg, FL; *U.S. Private*, pg. 414
Gregor, Thomas C., Chm. Bd., Pres. & Chief Exec. Officer--United National Bancorp, Bridgewater, NJ; *U.S. Public*, pg. 1679
Gregory, William R., Pres. & Chief Exec. Officer--ESELCO, Inc., Sault Sainte Marie, MI; *U.S. Public*, pg. 591
Gremillion, Robert, Pres. & Chief Exec. Officer--Sun-Sentinel Company, Fort Lauderdale, FL; *U.S. Public*, pg. 1636
Gremmo, Giovanni, Chief Exec. Officer--Bozzalla & Lesna S.p.A., Coggiola, Italy; *Int'l*, pg. 209
Grenouillaud, J., Chief Exec.--Union Commercial Bank S.A., Antananarivo, Madagascar; *Int'l*, pg. 1294
Gresov, Boris, Chm. Bd., Pres. & Chief Exec. Officer--Standard Motals Corporation, New York, NY; *U.S. Public*, pg. 1502
Gressel, Alan, Chm. Bd., Pres., Chief Exec. Officer & Chief Oper. Officer--Research Environmental Industries, Inc., Cleveland, OH; *U.S. Private*, pg. 924
Gressette, L.M., Jr., Chm. Bd. & Chief Exec. Officer--South Carolina Generating Co., Inc., Columbia, SC; *U.S. Public*, pg. 1436
Gressette, L.M., Jr., Chm. Bd. & Chief Exec. Officer--SCANA Resources, Inc., Columbia, SC; *U.S. Public*, pg. 1436
Gresty, Alan, Chief Exec.-Indus. Div.--J. Bibby & Sons Plc, London, United Kingdom; *Int'l*, pg. 167
Gribbin, M.C.D., Chm. Bd. & Chief Exec. Officer--Jardine Insurance Brokers International Limited, London, United Kingdom; *Int'l*, pg. 705
Griebel, R. Nelson, Chm. Bd., Chief Exec. Officer & Pres.--Bank of Boston Connecticut, Hartford, CT; *U.S. Public*, pg. 184
Grier, James R., III, Pres. & Chief Exec. Officer--Eby Corporation, Wichita, KS; *U.S. Private*, pg. 359
Grier, James R., III, Pres. & Chief Exec. Officer--Martin K. Eby Construction Company, Inc., Wichita, KS; *U.S. Private*, pg. 359
Griesdorn, Donald E., Chief Exec. Officer--BKM Enterprises, Inc., East Hartford, CT; *U.S. Private*, pg. 107
Griesedieck, Chris R., Pres. & Chief Exec. Officer--Colonial Bank, Des Peres, MO; *U.S. Public*, pg. 643
Griffin, Ben Hill, III, Chm. Bd., Pres. & Chief Exec. Officer--Alico, Inc., La Belle, FL; *U.S. Public*, pg. 41
Griffin, Ben Hill, III, Chm. Bd. & Chief Exec. Officer--Orange-Co., Inc., Bartow, FL; *U.S. Public*, pg. 1229
Griffin, Dennis B., Pres. & Chief Exec. Officer--Griffin Industries, Inc., Cold Spring, KY; *U.S. Private*, pg. 480
Griffin, Donald W., Chm. Bd., Pres. & Chief Exec. Officer--Olin Corporation, Norwalk, CT; *U.S. Public*, pg. 1218
Griffin, G. Lee, Chief Exec. Officer--Bank One, Louisiana, Baton Rouge, LA; *U.S. Public*, pg. 173
Griffin, G. Lee, Chief Exec. Officer--Premier Bank N.A., Baton Rouge, LA; *U.S. Public*, pg. 173
Griffin, Gary, Chief Exec. Officer--Interstate Engineering, Anaheim, CA; *U.S. Private*, pg. 573
Griffin, Jeff, Chm. Bd., Pres. & Chief Exec. Officer--Griffin Transport Services, Inc., Sparks, NV; *U.S. Private*, pg. 481
Griffin, John W., Chm. Bd., Pres. & Chief Exec. Officer--Griffin Manufacturing Co., Muskogee, OK; *U.S. Private*, pg. 481
Griffin, Mark, Chm. Bd., Pres. & Chief Exec. Officer--Ris Paper Company, Long Island City, NY; *U.S. Private*, pg. 932
Griffin, Mark E., Chm. Bd., Pres. & Chief Exec. Officer--Lewis Drug, Inc., Sioux Falls, SD; *U.S. Private*, pg. 665
Griffin, Robert E., Chm. Bd. & Chief Exec. Officer--Escalade Sports, Evansville, IN; *U.S. Public*, pg. 591
Griffin, Rutledge A., Jr., Chm. Bd., Pres. & Chief Exec. Officer--Griffin Corporation, Valdosta, GA; *U.S. Private*, pg. 480
Griffin, Tom, Co-Chm. & Chief Exec. Officer--Griffin Bacal Inc., New York, NY; *U.S. Private*, pg. 480
Griffith, Dan L., Pres. & Chief Exec. Officer--Bridgeport Machines, Inc., Bridgeport, CT; *U.S. Public*, pg. 251
Griffith, Dean L., Chm. Bd., Pres. & Chief Exec. Officer--Griffith Laboratories Worldwide, Inc., Alsip, IL; *U.S. Private*, pg. 481
Griffith, Gerald P., Pres. & Chief Exec. Officer--Alpha/Owens Corning LLC, Collierville, TN; *U.S. Private*, pg. 45
Grigelevich, Joseph, Pres. & Chief Exec. Officer--American Modular Technologies, Liberty, NC; *U.S. Public*, pg. 69
Grigg, Charles W., Chm. Bd., Pres. & Chief Exec. Officer--SPS Technologies, Inc., Jenkintown, PA; *U.S. Public*, pg. 1419
Griggs, David, Pres., Chief Exec. & Chief Fin. Officer & Treas.--Jack Griggs Inc., Exeter, CA; *U.S. Private*, pg. 482
Grillo, Steven G., Pres., Chief Exec. Officer & Chief Oper. Officer--General Office Environments Inc., Rochelle Park, NJ; *U.S. Private*, pg. 445
Grinberg, Gedalio, Chm. Bd. & Chief Exec. Officer--Movado Group, Inc., Lyndhurst, NJ; *U.S. Public*, pg. 1140
Grinder, Dan, Pres. & Chief Exec. Officer--Hood Communications, Inc., Grand Terrace, CA; *U.S. Private*, pg. 673
Grinter, Donald W., Chm. Bd. & Chief Exec. Officer--ABC Rail Products Corp., Chicago, IL; *U.S. Public*, pg. 2
Grisanti, Eugene P., Chm. Bd., Pres. & Chief Exec. Officer--International Flavors & Fragrances, Inc., New York, NY; *U.S. Public*, pg. 898
Grisanti, Michael J., Pres. & Chief Exec. Officer--Grisanti, Inc., Louisville, KY; *U.S. Private*, pg. 482
Griver, Michael A., Pres. & Chief Exec. Officer--American Health and Life Insurance Co., Fort Worth, TX; *U.S. Public*, pg. 1633
Grobman, Frank, Pres. & Chief Exec. Officer--Dan's Supreme Super Markets Inc., Hempstead, NY; *U.S. Private*, pg. 310
Groendyke, Jay, Pres. & Chief Exec. Officer--Synergis Technologies Group, Grand Rapids, MI; *U.S. Private*, pg. 1060
Groenewold, Ken, Chief Exec. Officer--Kentile Operting Co., Chicago, IL; *U.S. Private*, pg. 615
Grogan, David R., Chm., Pres. & Chief Exec. Officer--Toter Incorporated, Statesville, NC; *U.S. Private*, pg. 1092
Grojean, Tom, Chief Exec. Officer--Burlington Motor Holdings Inc., Daleville, IN; *U.S. Private*, pg. 183
Gromek, Josheph, Pres. & Chief Exec. Officer--Brooks Brothers, New York, NY; *Int'l*, pg. 843
Gronchi, Divo, Chief Exec. & Oper. Officers--Banca Monte dei Paschi di Siena S.p.A., Siena, Italy; *Int'l*, pg. 136
Grongvist, Erkki, Chief Oper. Officer--Neste Oy, Shipping, Espoo, Finland; *Int'l*, pg. 913
Grontzki, Werner, Chief Exec.--Dresdner Vermogensberatungs-gesellschaft mbH, Frankfurt/Main, Germany; *Int'l*, pg. 418
Gros-Pietro, Gian Maria, Chm. Bd. & Chief Exec. Officer--IRI Istituto Ricostruzione Industriale, Rome, Italy; *Int'l*, pg. 652
Grosch, Greg, Chm. Bd., Pres. & Chief Exec. Officer--White Cap Industries, Inc., Costa Mesa, CA; *U.S. Public*, pg. 1765
Grosman, Abraham D., Chief Exec. Officer--Meditrust Operating Company, West Palm Beach, FL; *U.S. Public*, pg. 1081
Gross, Howard, Chm. Bd. & Chief Exec. Officer--Snyder Industries, Inc., Lincoln, NE; *U.S. Private*, pg. 1011
Gross, Robert, Chm. Bd. & Chief Exec. Officer--Tops Appliance City, Edison, NJ; *U.S. Public*, pg. 1622
Gross, Ronald M., Chm. Bd. & Chief Exec. Officer--Rayonier Inc., Stamford, CT; *U.S. Public*, pg. 1363
Grossi, Richard J., Chm. Bd. & Chief Exec. Officer--United Illuminating Company, New Haven, CT; *U.S. Public*, pg. 1678
Grossman, Andrew, Chief Exec. Officer--Bernard Chaus, Inc., New York, NY; *U.S. Public*, pg. 342
Grossman, Andrew, Chief Exec. Officer--Bernard Chaus, Inc., Secaucus, NJ; *U.S. Public*, pg. 342
Grossman, Larry, Chm. Bd. & Chief Exec. Officer--Trans Leasing International Inc., Northbrook, IL; *U.S. Public*, pg. 1628
Grossman, Robert, Chm. Bd., Pres. & Chief Exec. Officer--Emons Transportation Group, Inc., York, PA; *U.S. Public*, pg. 578
Grosso, John, Pres. & Chief Exec. Officer--PCA International, Inc., Matthews, NC; *U.S. Public*, pg. 1240
Grove, Andrew S., Chm. Bd. & Chief Exec. Officer--Intel Corporation, Santa Clara, CA; *U.S. Public*, pg. 886
Grubbs, R., Pres. & Chief Exec. Officer--Anixter Inc., Skokie, IL; *U.S. Public*, pg. 115
Gruber, David P., Pres. & Chief Exec. Officer--Wyman-Gordon, North Grafton, MA; *U.S. Public*, pg. 1782
Gruber, Evan M., Pres. & Chief Exec. Officer--Modtech, Inc., Perris, CA; *U.S. Public*, pg. 1121
Gruenberg, Paul T., Chm. & Chief Exec. Officer--NYT Video News International, Philadelphia, PA; *U.S. Public*, pg. 1174
Grum, Clifford J., Chm. Bd. & Chief Exec. Officer--Temple-Inland Inc., Diboll, TX; *U.S. Public*, pg. 1574
Grum, Clifford J., Chm. Bd., Pres. & Chief Exec. Officer--Temple-Inland Forest Products Corporation, Diboll, TX; *U.S. Public*, pg. 1575
Grumbach, Didier, Chief Oper. Officer--Mugler Triumvirat, Paris, France; *Int'l*, pg. 295
Grundhofer, Jerry A., Chm. Bd., Pres. & Chief Exec. Officer--Starbanc Corporation, Cincinnati, OH; *U.S. Public*, pg. 1510
Grundhofer, Jerry A., Chm. Bd., Pres. & Chief Exec. Officer--Star Bank, N.A., Cincinnati, OH; *U.S. Public*, pg. 1510
Grundhofer, John F., Pres. & Chief Exec. Officer--U.S. Bancorp, Minneapolis, MN; *U.S. Public*, pg. 1680
Grune, George V., Chm. Bd. & Chief Exec. Officer--The Reader's Digest Association, Inc., Pleasantville, NY; *U.S. Public*, pg. 1367
Grybauskas, Roland, Chief Exec. Officer & Exec. Creative Dir.--Grybauskas Beatrice, New York, NY; *U.S. Private*, pg. 485
Grzelak, Dave, Pres. & Chief Exec. Officer--Komatsu America International Company, Vernon Hills, IL; *Int'l*, pg. 744
Guccione, Bob, Chm. Bd., Chief Exec. Officer & Publr.--General Media International Inc., New York, NY; *U.S. Private*, pg. 444
Guerrovich, Erwin, Chief Exec. Officer--Intermarkets Advertising, Beirut, Lebanon; *Int'l*, pg. 680
Guerry, Zan, Chm. Bd. & Chief Exec. Officer--Chattem, Inc., Chattanooga, TN; *U.S. Public*, pg. 341
Guffey, John W., Jr., Chm. Bd., Pres. & Chief Exec. Officer--Coltec Holdings Inc, Charlotte, NC; *U.S. Public*, pg. 401
Guffey, John, Jr., Chm. Bd. & Chief Exec. Officer--Coltec Industries Inc., Charlotte, NC; *U.S. Public*, pg. 401
Gugino, Carmelo, Jr., Pres. & Chief Exec. Officer--Dinaire Corp., Buffalo, NY; *U.S. Private*, pg. 334
Guillin, Pierre, Pres. & Chief Exec. Officer--Sanders, Athis-Mons, France; *Int'l*, pg. 459
Guinchord, Gilles, Pres. & Chief Exec. Officer--Rexel, Inc., Coral Gables, FL; *Int'l*, pg. 1107
Guiral, Philippe, Deputy Chief Exec. Officer-Corp. & Intl.--Credit Agricole, Bonvin, France; *Int'l*, pg. 341
Guise, Kenneth E., Chief Exec. Officer & Gen. Mgr.--Knouse Foods Inc., Peach Glen, PA; *U.S. Private*, pg. 627
Guizzetti, Joseph, Chief Exec. Officer & Gen. Mgr.--Buffelen Woodworking Company, Tacoma, WA; *U.S. Private*, pg. 179
Gula, Allen J., Jr., Pres. & Chief Exec. Officer--Key Services Corporation, Cleveland, OH; *U.S. Public*, pg. 954
Gulbas, Bruce, Pres. & Chief Exec. Officer--National Restaurant Supply Company, El Paso, TX; *U.S. Private*, pg. 786
Gulda, Edward J., Chm. Bd. & Chief Exec. Officer--Peregrine Incorporated, Southfield, MI; *U.S. Private*, pg. 852
Gulesci, Hasan, Chief Exec. Officer--Sabanci Holding A.S., Istanbul, Turkey; *Int'l*, pg. 1167
Gulett, Michael, Pres. & Chief Exec. Officer--Paradigm Technology, Inc., San Jose, CA; *U.S. Public*, pg. 1256
Gullickson, W.D., Jr., Pres. & Chief Exec. Officer--McLaughlin Gormley King Company, Minneapolis, MN; *U.S. Private*, pg. 723
Gulling, Daniel L., Pres. & Chief Exec. Officer--Marinette Marine Corporation, Marinette, WI; *U.S. Private*, pg. 703
Gullotti, Russell A., Chm. Bd., Pres. & Chief Exec. Officer--National Computer Systems, Eden Prairie, MN; *U.S. Public*, pg. 1155
Gumbiner, Anthony J., Chm. Bd. & Chief Exec. Officer--The Hallwood Group Incorporated, Dallas, TX; *U.S. Public*, pg. 777
Gummer, Charles L., Pres. & Chief Exec. Officer--Comerica Bank Texas, Dallas, TX; *U.S. Public*, pg. 409
Gumpertz, Donald G., Chm. Bd., Pres. & Chief Exec. Officer--Industrial Electronic Engineers, Inc., Van Nuys, CA; *U.S. Private*, pg. 561
Gumucio, Marcelo, Pres. & Chief Exec. Officer--Memorex Telex Corp., Irving, TX; *Int'l*, pg. 857
Gunderson, Richard L., Chm. Bd. & Chief Exec. Officer--Aid Association for Lutherans, Appleton, WI; *U.S. Private*, pg. 27
Gunji, Hiromi, Chm. Bd., Pres. & Chief Exec. Officer--Brother International Corporation, Somerset, NJ; *Int'l*, pg. 229
Gunst, Robert A., Pres. & Chief Exec. Officer--The Good Guys, Inc., Brisbane, CA; *U.S. Public*, pg. 750
Guont, James R., Chm., Pres. & Chief Exec. Officer--The Fifth Third Bank of Kentucky, Louisville, Louisville, KY; *U.S. Public*, pg. 621
Gupta, Narendra K., Chm. Bd., Chief Exec. Officer & Sec.--Integrated Systems, Inc., Sunnyvale, CA; *U.S. Public*, pg. 885
Gurbacki, Gerry, Chm. Bd. & Chief Exec. Officer--Pameco Corp., Norcross, GA; *U.S. Public*, pg. 1255

Gurewitz, Richard, Chm. Bd., Pres. & Chief Exec. Officer--Poly Pak America, Inc., Los Angeles, CA; U.S. Private, pg. 875

Gurgovits, Stephen J., Pres. & Chief Exec. Officer--First National Bank of Pennsylvania, Hermitage, PA; U.S. Public, pg. 607

Gurian, Kenneth J., Chm. Bd. & Chief Exec. Officer--BGM Health Communications, Inc., Los Angeles, CA; U.S. Public, pg. 1223

Gurrieri, John, Mng. Dir.-South Pacific Tires--Pacific Dunlop Limited, Melbourne, Australia; Int'l, pg. 1021

Gury, David J., Chm. Bd., Pres. & Chief Exec. Officer--Nabi, Boca Raton, FL; U.S. Public, pg. 1148

Gusick, Dennis, Chm. Bd., Pres. & Chief Exec. Officer--Helm, Inc., Detroit, MI; U.S. Private, pg. 520

Gustaferro, Angelo, Chm. Bd., Pres. & Chief Exec. Officer--nVIEW Corporation, Newport News, VA; U.S. Public, pg. 1206

Gustafson, James E., Pres. & Chief Exec. Officer--General Re Services Corp., Stamford, CT; U.S. Public, pg. 725

Gustafson, James E., Chm. Bd. & Chief Exec. Officer--General Reinsurance Corp., Stamford, CT; U.S. Public, pg. 725

Gustar, Chris, Chief Exec.--GKN Westland Aerospace Limited, East Cowes, United Kingdom; Int'l, pg. 535

Gustavsen, John C., Pres. & Chief Exec. Officer--Amspec Chemical Corporation, Gloucester City, NJ; U.S. Private, pg. 67

Gustin, Abe J., Jr., Chm. Bd. & Chief Exec. Officer--Applebee's International, Inc., Overland Park, KS; U.S. Public, pg. 122

Guthart, Leo, Chief Exec. Officer--Alarm Device Manufacturing Company, Syosset, NY; U.S. Public, pg. 1306

Guthrie, Bob, Chief Exec. Officer--Willis Corroon Limited, Kingston upon Thames, United Kingdom; Int'l, pg. 1502

Guthrie, M. Philip, Chm. Bd., Pres. & Chief Exec. Officer--American Eagle Group, Inc., Dallas, TX; U.S. Public, pg. 71

Gutierrez, Graciela, Chm. Bd. & Chief Exec. Officer--Mercantile Bank, Brownsville, TX; U.S. Private, pg. 731

Gutierrez, Julian Serrano, Chief Exec. Officer--Cadena Comercial Oxxo, S.A. de CV, Monterrey, Mexico; Int'l, pg. 496

Gutierrez, Tom, Pres. & Chief Exec. Officer--Exide Electronics Group, Inc., Raleigh, NC; Int'l, pg. 126

Gutterman, Arthur, Chm. Bd., Pres., Chief Exec. & Chief Oper. Officer--Jelmar Company, Lincolnwood, IL; U.S. Private, pg. 585

Guttman, Alan R., Chief Exec. Officer--The Guttman Group, Belle Vernon, PA; U.S. Private, pg. 488

Guttman, Steven J., Pres. & Chief Exec. Officer--Federal Realty Investment Trust, Rockville, MD; U.S. Public, pg. 616

Guyer, Ray, Pres. & Chief Exec. Officer--PetCare Plus, Inc., Aurora, IL; U.S. Private, pg. 856

Guzman, Samuel, Pres. & Chief Exec. Officer--Young & Rubicam Bogota, Bogota, Colombia; U.S. Private, pg. 1200

Guzzetti, Louis A., Jr., Pres. & Chief Exec. Officer--EnviroSource, Inc., Horsham, PA; U.S. Public, pg. 587

Guzzle, Timothy L., Chm. Bd. & Chief Exec. Officer--TECO Energy, Inc., Tampa, FL; U.S. Public, pg. 1565

Gyenes, Peter, Pres. & Chief Exec. Officer--Ardent Software, Inc., Westborough, MA; U.S. Public, pg. 129

Gyllstrom, Gregory, Pres. & Chief Exec. Officer--Industrial Coatings Group, Inc., Chicago, IL; U.S. Private, pg. 434

Gynne, Goran, Chief Officer--AB Tidningen Vi, Stockholm, Sweden; Int'l, pg. 718

Haab, Larry, Chm. Bd., Pres. & Chief Exec. Officer--Illinova Inc., Decatur, IL; U.S. Public, pg. 869

Haab, Larry D., Chm. Bd., Pres. & Chief Exec. Officer--Illinois Power Company, Decatur, IL; U.S. Public, pg. 869

Haag, Herbert, Pres. & Chief Fin. Officer--PartnerRe Ltd., Pembroke, Bermuda; Int'l, pg. 1024

Haank, Derk, Chief Exec.--Bonaventura, Amsterdam, Netherlands; Int'l, pg. 1099

Haank, Derk, Chief Exec. Officer--Elsevier Bedrijfinformatie B.V., Doetinchem, Netherlands; Int'l, pg. 1099

Haank, Derk J., Chief Exec. Officer--Elsevier Business Information, Amsterdam, Netherlands; Int'l, pg. 1099

Haas, Marvin I., Pres. & Chief Exec. Officer--Chock Full O' Nuts Corporation, New York, NY; U.S. Public, pg. 351

Haas, Robert D., Chm. Bd. & Chief Exec. Officer--Levi Strauss & Co., San Francisco, CA; U.S. Private, pg. 662

Habecker, Eugene B., Pres., Chief Exec. Officer & Sec.--American Bible Society, New York, NY; U.S. Private, pg. 51

Habegger, Fred, Pres. & Chief Exec. Officer--The Habegger Corporation, Cincinnati, OH; U.S. Private, pg. 492

Habgood, Martyn A., Chief Exec. Officer-JCPE--John Crane Polymer Division, Abingdon, United Kingdom; Int'l, pg. 1338

Habig, Douglas A., Chm. Bd. & Chief Exec. Oficer--Kimball International, Inc., Jasper, IN; U.S. Public, pg. 956

Hacala, John, Chm. & Chief Exec. Officer--Spencer Gifts, Inc., Egg Harbor Township, NJ; Int'l, pg. 1216

Hach-Darrow, Kathryn C., Chm. Bd. & Chief Exec. Officer--Hach Company, Loveland, CO; U.S. Public, pg. 773

Hachiya, H., Chief Oper. Officer--Otto Sumisho Inc., Tokyo, Japan; Int'l, pg. 1015

Hackerman, Willard, Pres., Chief Exec. Officer & Treas.--The Whiting-Turner Contracting Co., Baltimore, MD; U.S. Private, pg. 1174

Hackett, James P., Pres. & Chief Exec. Officer--Steelcase Inc., Grand Rapids, MI; U.S. Private, pg. 1038

Hackett, Roger B., Chm. Bd., Pres., Chief Exec. & Chief Oper. Officer--Go-Video, Inc., Scottsdale, AZ; U.S. Public, pg. 748

Hackney, T. Morris, Chm. Bd. & Chief Exec. Officer--Citation Corporation, Birmingham, AL; U.S. Public, pg. 376

Hackworth, Michael L., Pres. & Chief Exec. Officer--Cirrus Logic, Inc., Fremont, CA; U.S. Public, pg. 375

Haddix, Woody, Chief Exec. Officer--Lovejoy Inc., Downers Grove, IL; U.S. Private, pg. 677

Haddock, Ron W., Pres. & Chief Exec. Officer--Fina, Inc., Dallas, TX; Int'l, pg. 1044

Haddrill, Richard M., Pres., Chief Exec. Officer & Treas.--Power House Technologies, Inc., Bozeman, MT; U.S. Public, pg. 1319

Hadeler, David, Pres., Chief Exec. Officer & Founder--Hadeler Sullivan Ewing, Dallas, TX; U.S. Private, pg. 493

Hadfield, Frederick W., Pres. & Chief Exec. Officer--Ingersoll-Dresser Pump Company, Liberty Corner, NJ; U.S. Public, pg. 529

Hadley, Leonard A., Chm. Bd. & Chief Exec. Officer--Maytag Corporation, Newton, IA; U.S. Public, pg. 1064

Hadley, Leornard, Chief Exec. Officer-Maytag Corp.--Jenn-Air, Newton, IA; U.S. Public, pg. 1064

Haeng, Cho-Kwan, Chief Exec. Officer--POSAM New York Office, New York, NY; Int'l, pg. 1062

Hafer, Fred D., Chm. Bd., Pres. & Chief Exec. Officer--GPU, Inc., Morristown, NJ; U.S. Public, pg. 695

Hafner, J.A., Jr., Pres. & Chief Exec. Officer--Riviana International Inc., Houston, TX; U.S. Public, pg. 1392

Hafner, Joseph A., Jr., Pres. & Chief Exec. Officer--Riviana Foods Inc., Houston, TX; U.S. Public, pg. 1392

Hagan, J. Michael, Chm. Bd. & Chief Exec. Officer--Furon Company, Laguna Niguel, CA; U.S. Public, pg. 688

Hageman, William M., Chief Exec. Officer--Conway Corporation, Conway, AR; U.S. Private, pg. 272

Hagen, Cliff, Pres. & Chief Exec. Officer--Cass-Clay Creamery, Fargo, ND; U.S. Private, pg. 218

Hager, Edward B., M.D., Chm. Bd. & Chief Exec. Officer--IGI, Inc., Buena, NJ; U.S. Public, pg. 855

Hager, J.L., Pres. & Chief Exec. Officer--WRR Environmental Services Co., Inc., Eau Claire, WI; U.S. Public, pg. 1792

Haggai, Thomas S., Chm. Bd. & Chief Exec. Officer--IGA, Inc. (Independent Grocers Alliance), Chicago, IL; U.S. Private, pg. 555

Haggar, J.M., III, Chm. Bd. & Chief Exec. Officer--Haggar Corporation, Dallas, TX; U.S. Public, pg. 774

Haggarty, Michael C., Pres. & Chief Exec. Officer--The Auburn State Bank, Auburn, IN; U.S. Public, pg. 674

Haggerty, Charles A., Chm. Bd., Pres. & Chief Exec. Officer--Western Digital Corporation, Irvine, CA; U.S. Public, pg. 1758

Haggerty, Daniel J., Pres. & Chief Exec. Officer--Norwest Venture Capital Management, Inc., Minneapolis, MN; U.S. Public, pg. 1202

Hahn, Dean L., Chm. Bd. & Chief Exec. Officer--Hawkins Chemical, Inc., Minneapolis, MN; U.S. Public, pg. 800

Hahn, Horst, Pres., Chief Exec. Officer & Gen. Mgr.--Multimatic Corporation, Northvale, NJ; U.S. Private, pg. 767

Hahn, Norman, Chief Exec. Officer--Conestoga Wood Specialties Corp., East Earl, PA; U.S. Private, pg. 262

Hai, Hong, Dr., Pres. & Chief Exec. Officer--Haw Par Brothers International Limited, Singapore, Singapore; Int'l, pg. 603

Hai, Hong, Dr., Pres. & Chief Exec. Officer--Tiger Medicals Ltd., Singapore, Singapore; Int'l, pg. 603

Haidlmair, J., Chief Exec. Officer--Schiedel Kaminwerke GmbH, Wartberg, Austria; Int'l, pg. 1092

Haigh, Robert B., Chm. Bd., Chief Exec. Officer & Treas.--Chicago Tube & Iron Co., Chicago, IL; U.S. Private, pg. 235

Haile, William B., Pres. & Chief Exec. Officer--SunTrust Bank, Savannah, N.A., Savannah, GA; U.S. Public, pg. 1538

Haimovitz, Jules, Pres. & Chief Oper. Officer--King World Productions, Inc., New York, NY; U.S. Public, pg. 961

Haines, Bruce, Chief Exec.--CME KHBB, London, United Kingdom; Int'l, pg. 241

Haines, James S., Jr., Pres. & Chief Exec. Officer--El Paso Electric Company, El Paso, TX; U.S. Public, pg. 567

Haines, Peter, Pres. & Chief Exec. Officer--Cybex International, Inc., Medway, MA; U.S. Private, pg. 1114

Haines, Terry L., Pres. & Chief Exec. Officer--A. Schulman, Inc., Akron, OH; U.S. Public, pg. 1441

Haiplik, T.W., Pres. & Chief Exec. Officer--MacMillan Bathurst Inc., Mississauga, Canada; Int'l, pg. 20

Hair, Hugh A., Chm. Bd. & Chief Exec. Officer--Anaren Microwave Inc., East Syracuse, NY; U.S. Public, pg. 110

Hakala, Heikki, Pres. & Chief Exec. Officer-Rauma Oy--UPM-Kymmene Corporation, Helsinki, Finland; Int'l, pg. 1427

Hakala, Heikki, Pres. & Chief Exec. Officer--Rauma Ltd., Helsinki, Finland; Int'l, pg. 1428

Halano, Hiroshi, Chief Exec. Officer--GS Battery (U.S.A.), Inc., City of Industry, CA; Int'l, pg. 702

Halbreich, Stanley I., Chm. Bd. & Chief Exec. Officer--Littlefield, Adams & Company, Huber Heights, OH; U.S. Public, pg. 1001

Halbrook, John A., Chm. Bd., Pres. & Chief Exec. Officer--Woodward Governor Company, Rockford, IL; U.S. Public, pg. 1776

Hale, John, Chm. Bd., Pres. & Chief Exec. Officer--Telex Communications, Inc., Minneapolis, MN; U.S. Private, pg. 1074

Hale, Roger L., Chm. Bd., Pres. & Chief Exec. Officer--Tennant Company, Minneapolis, MN; U.S. Public, pg. 1577

Hale, Roger W., Chm. Bd., Pres. & Chief Exec. Officer--LG & E Energy Corp., Louisville, KY; U.S. Public, pg. 970

Hales, Antony J., Chief Exec.--Allied Domecq PLC, London, United Kingdom; Int'l, pg. 62

Haley, Mark T., Chm. Bd. & Chief Exec. Officer--Brown & Haley, Tacoma, WA; U.S. Private, pg. 173

Haley, Robert A., Jr., Chief Exec. Officer--Finnaren & Haley, Inc., Conshohocken, PA; U.S. Private, pg. 405

Haley, Robert, Jr., Chief Exec. Officer--Weather Barrier Inc., Conshohocken, PA; U.S. Private, pg. 406

Haley, Robert, Jr., Chief Exec. Officer--Spring Mill Corp., Conshohocken, PA; U.S. Private, pg. 406

Haley, Roy W., Pres. & Chief Exec. Officer--WESCO Distribution, Inc., Pittsburgh, PA; U.S. Private, pg. 244

Haley, Thomas W., Chm. Bd. & Chief Exec. Officer--Innovex, Inc., Hopkins, MN; U.S. Public, pg. 880

Hall, Alvin D., Pres. & Chief Exec. Officer--Miller & Smith, Inc., Mc Lean, VA; U.S. Private, pg. 746

Hall, Bob, Chief Exec. Officer--Upstate Milk Cooperatives Inc., Le Roy, NY; U.S. Private, pg. 1129

Hall, Conrad M., Pres. & Chief Exec. Officer--Trader Publishing Company, Norfolk, VA; U.S. Private, pg. 649

Hall, David J., Chief Exec. Officer--Firth-Rixson Plc, Sheffield, United Kingdom; Int'l, pg. 487

Hall, Floyd, Chm. Bd., Pres. & Chief Exec. Officer--Kmart Corporation, Troy, MI; U.S. Public, pg. 963

Hall, James C., Pres. & Chief Exec. Officer--Fidelity Federal Savings Bank, Marion, IN; U.S. Public, pg. 632

Hall, Larry D., Chm. Bd., Pres. & Chief Exec. Officer--K N Energy, Inc., Lakewood, CO; U.S. Public, pg. 937

Hall, Rob, Chief Exec.-Broadcasting Dataservices Ltd.--BBC Magazines, London, United Kingdom; Int'l, pg. 114

Hall, Rob, Chief Exec. Officer--Shoe Pavilion, Richmond, CA; U.S. Private, pg. 996

Halla, Brian, Chm. Bd., Pres. & Chief Exec. Officer--National Semiconductor Corporation, Santa Clara, CA; U.S. Public, pg. 1159

Hallam, Robert, Chm. Bd. & Chief Exec. Officer--Ben E. Keith Company, Fort Worth, TX; U.S. Private, pg. 611

Hallam, Stuart, Chief Exec. Officer-European, Middle East & Asia--Brite Voice Systems, Inc., Heathrow, FL; U.S. Public, pg. 257

Hallam, Stuart, Chief Exec. Officer--Brite Voice Systems Europe, Cambridge, United Kingdom; U.S. Public, pg. 257

Halle, Bruce T., Sr., Chm. Bd. & Chief Exec. Officer--Reinalt-Thomas Corp., Ann Arbor, MI; U.S. Private, pg. 919

Haller, J., Pres. & Chief Exec. Officer--PNC Bank, Cincinnati, OH; U.S. Public, pg. 1242

Hallet, Jim, Pres. & Chief Exec. Officer--Adesa Inc., Indianapolis, IN; U.S. Public, pg. 1116

Hallett, James P., Pres. & Chief Exec. Officer-ADESA--Minnesota Power, Duluth, MN; U.S. Public, pg. 1116

Halley, Paul-Louis, Chm. Bd. & Chief Exec. Officer--Promodes SA, Mondeville, France; Int'l, pg. 1071

Halligan, Joe, Pres. & Chief Exec. Officer--PharmChem Laboratories, Inc., Menlo Park, CA; U.S. Public, pg. 1285

Halloway, Michael, Pres. & Chief Exec. Officer--American Credit Services Inc., Rochester, NY; U.S. Public, pg. 336

Halna du Fretay, Amaury, Chm. Bd. & Chief Exec. Officer--Labinal SA, Montigny-le-Bretonneux, France; Int'l, pg. 785

Halparin, Scott, Chm. Bd., Chief Exec. Officer & Treas.--Saratoga Brands, Inc., Lakewood, NJ; U.S. Public, pg. 1435

Halperin, Thomas C., Chm Bd., Pres. & Chief Exec. Officer--Commercial Light Company, Hillside, IL; U.S. Private, pg. 258

Halpern, Richard C., Chm. & Chief Exec. Officer--Schal Bovis Inc., Chicago, IL; Int'l, pg. 1033

Halpin, James F., Pres. & Chief Exec. Officer--CompUSA, Dallas, TX; U.S. Public, pg. 420

Halton, Dale F., Chm. Bd., Pres. & Chief Exec. Officer--Pepsi-Cola Bottling Company of Charlotte Inc., Charlotte, NC; U.S. Private, pg. 852

Hamaberg, Bob, Chief Exec. Officer--BTR Aerspace Group, Winnipeg, Canada; Int'l, pg. 127

Hamada, Yasuyuki, Pres. & Chief Exec. Officer--Nisshin Steel Co., Ltd., Tokyo, Japan; Int'l, pg. 946

Hamer, M.D., Chief Exec. Officer--Centre Reinsurance Representative Limited, London, United Kingdom; Int'l, pg. 1530

Hamer, M.D., Chief Exec. Officer--Centre Reinsurance International Company, Dublin, Ireland; Int'l, pg. 1531

Hamilburg, Maurice J., Pres. & Chief Exec. Officer--Plymouth Rubber Company, Inc., Canton, MA; U.S. Public, pg. 1311

Hamilton, David R., Chm. Bd., Pres. & Chief Exec. Officer--Chemical Leaman Corporation, Exton, PA; U.S. Private, pg. 233

Hamilton, David R., Pres. & Chief Exec. Officer-Chemical Leaman Corp.--Chemical Leaman Tank Lines, Inc., Exton, PA; U.S. Private, pg. 233

Hamilton, Jack, Chm. Bd. & Chief Exec. Officer--Dunbarton Corporation, Dothan, AL; U.S. Private, pg. 194

Hamilton, Jack H., Chief Exec. Officer--CGF Industries, Topeka, KS; U.S. Private, pg. 194

Hamilton, Richard, Chief Exec. Officer--Zenith Media Services, Inc., New York, NY; U.S. Private, pg. 1204

Hamilton, Richard F., Chm. Bd. & Chief Exec. Officer--Monterey Mechanical Company, Oakland, CA; U.S. Private, pg. 758

Hamilton, Thomas M., Chm. Bd., Pres. & Chief Exec. Officer--EEX Corporation, Houston, TX; U.S. Public, pg. 542

Hamister, Mark E., Chm. Bd. & Chief Exec. Officer--National Health Care Affiliates, Inc., Buffalo, NY; U.S. Private, pg. 784

Hamlin, Craig, Pres. & Chief Exec. Officer--ADM Milling Co., Overland Park, KS; U.S. Public, pg. 128

Hamlyn, Richard, Chief Exec. Officer & V.P.--Elias Brothers Restaurants, Inc., Warren, MI; U.S. Private, pg. 371

Hammachek, Todd, Pres. & Chief Exec. Officer--Penford Corp., Bellevue, WA; U.S. Public, pg. 1269

Hammer, Paul F., Chief Exec. Officer--Lodgistix, Inc., Phoenix, AZ; U.S. Public, pg. 1527

Hammes, Michael N., Chm. Bd. & Chief Exec. Officer--The Canadian Coleman Co., Ltd., Toronto, Canada; U.S. Private, pg. 691

Hammill, Richard D., Chm. Bd., Pres. & Chief Exec. Officer--Hycor Biomedical, Inc., Irvine, CA; U.S. Public, pg. 851

Hammond, Daniel D., Chm. Bd. & Chief Exec. Officer--InterVoice, Inc., Dallas, TX; U.S. Public, pg. 910

Hammond, Harvey K., Jr., Chm. Bd., Pres. & Chief Exec. Officer--HNTB Corporation, Kansas City, MO; *U.S. Private*, pg. 492
Hammond, Peter W., Chief Exec. Officer & Mng. Dir.--Spicers Paper Limited, Preston, Australia; *Int'l*, pg. 72
Hammond, Terry, Pres. & Chief Exec. Officer--Crown International, Inc., Elkhart, IN; *U.S. Private*, pg. 293
Hampel, Bernard, Ph.D., Pres. & Chief Exec. Officer--Eon Labs Manufacturing, Inc., Laurelton, NY; *U.S. Private*, pg. 379
Hampp, Rainer, Chm. & Chief Exec. Officer--Bertelsmann Printing & Manufacturing Corp., Berryville, VA; *Int'l*, pg. 191
Hampton, Charles, Pres. & Chief Exec. Officer--American Louver Co., Skokie, IL; *U.S. Private*, pg. 58
Hanasaki, Takenori, Pres. & Chief Exec. Officer--Oki Telecom Group, Suwanee, GA; *Int'l*, pg. 1000
Hancock, George, Pres. & Chief Exec. Officer--Pyramid Breweries, Inc.; *U.S. Public*, pg. 1345
Hand, Elbert O., Chm. Bd. & Chief Exec. Officer--Hartmarx Corporation, Chicago, IL; *U.S. Public*, pg. 795
Hand, Kerry, Pres. & Chief Exec. Officer--Communicorp, Inc., Columbus, GA; *U.S. Public*, pg. 28
Handover, Richard, Chief Exec. Officer--W.H. Smith Group plc, London, United Kingdom; *Int'l*, pg. 1264
Haney, David C., Pres. & Chief Exec.Officer--Willis Corroon Corp. of Penn., Radnor, PA; *Int'l*, pg. 1507
Haney, William M., III, Chm. Bd., Pres. & Chief Exec. Officer--Molten Metal Technology, Inc., Fall River, MA; *U.S. Public*, pg. 1123
Hanggi, Rolf, Pres. & Co-Chief Exec. Officer--Zurich Insurance Company, Zurich, Switzerland; *Int'l*, pg. 1529
Hanka, Erina, Pres.--Suspa, Inc., Grand Rapids, MI; *Int'l*, pg. 1322
Hankinson, James F., Pres. & Chief Exec. Officer--New Brunswick Power Corporation, Fredericton, Canada; *Int'l*, *pg. 923*
Hanley, John J., Chm. Bd. & Chief Exec. Officer--Scientific American, Inc., New York, NY; *Int'l*, pg. 1479
Hanley, William T., Pres. & Chief Exec. Officer--Galileo Corp., Sturbridge, MA; *U.S. Public*, pg. 698
Hanlin, Russell L., Pres., Chief Exec. & Chief Oper. Officer--Sunkist Growers, Inc., Sherman Oaks, CA; *U.S. Private*, pg. 1052
Hanman, Gary, Pres. & Chief Exec. Officer--Mid-America Dairymen, Inc., Springfield, MO; *U.S. Private*, pg. 743
Hanna, Allan C., Pres. & Chief Exec. Officer--Zephyr Inc., Muskegon, MI; *U.S. Private*, pg. 1204
Hanna, J.M., Mng. Dir. & Chief Exec. Officer--Email Limited, Waterloo, Australia; *Int'l*, pg. 450
Hannah, Thomas E., Pres. & Chief Exec. Officer--Collins & Aikman Corporation, Charlotte, NC; *U.S. Public*, pg. 399
Hannay, Roger A., Pres., Chief Exec. Officer & Chief Fin. Officer--Hannay Reels, Westerlo, NY; *U.S. Private*, pg. 499
Hannigan, Raymond R., Pres. & Chief Exec. Officer--Kinetic Concepts, Inc., San Antonio, TX; *U.S. Private*, pg. 620
Hanning, Franz, Pres. & Chief Exec. Officer--Vacation Break USA, Fort Lauderdale, FL; *U.S. Public*, pg. 611
Hanon, John, Pres. & Chief Exec. Officer--Berks Products Corporation, Reading, PA; *U.S. Private*, pg. 136
Hansberger, James R., Pres. & Chief Exec. Officer--RAM Golf Corporation, Melrose Park, IL; *U.S. Private*, pg. 908
Hansel, Stephen A., Pres. & Chief Exec. Officer--Hibernia Corporation, New Orleans, LA; *U.S. Public*, pg. 825
Hansen, Charles M., Jr., Chm. Bd. & Chief Exec. Officer--Pillowtex Corporation, Dallas, TX; *U.S. Public*, pg. 1296
Hansen, Darryl D., Chm. Bd., Pres. & Chief Exec. Officer--Preferred Risk Mutual Insurance, West Des Moines, IA; *U.S. Private*, pg. 880
Hansen, Darryl D., Pres. & Chief Exec. Officer--Central Property & Casualty Insurance Company, West Des Moines, IA; *U.S. Private*, pg. 880
Hansen, Jean-Pierre, Chief Exec. Officer--Electrabel S.A., Brussels, Belgium; *Int'l*, pg. 436
Hansen, Paul, Pres. & Chief Exec. Officer--Penobscot Shoe Company, Old Town, ME; *U.S. Public*, pg. 1273
Hansmeyer, Herbert, Chm. Bd. & Chief Exec. Officer--Allianz of America, Inc., Westport, CT; *Int'l*, pg. 58
Hanson, Charles G., III, Chm. Bd. & Chief Exec. Officer--American Pad and Paper Company, Dallas, TX; *U.S. Public*, pg. 88
Hanson, David M., Chm. & Chief Exec. Officer--M & I Bank S.S.B., Sheboygan, WI; *U.S. Public*, pg. 1050
Hanson, John N., Chm. & Chief Exec. Officer--Beloit Corporation, Beloit, WI; *U.S. Public*, pg. 789
Hanson, John N., Pres. & Chief Exec. Officer--Joy Mining Machinery, Warrendale, PA; *U.S. Public*, pg. 789
Hanson, Rick, Chm. Bd., Pres. & Chief Exec. Officer--Old Home Foods, Inc., Saint Paul, MN; *U.S. Private*, pg. 814
Hantila, I., Chief Exec. Officer--Ascom Energy Systems, Bern, Switzerland; *Int'l*, pg. 86
Hanvik, O., Chief Exec. Officer--OCE Svenska AB, Stockholm, Sweden; *Int'l*, pg. 995
Harad, George J., Chm. Bd. & Chief Exec. Officer--Boise Cascade Corporation, Boise, ID; *U.S. Public*, pg. 242
Harad, George J., Chm. Bd. & Chief Exec. Officer--Boise Cascade Paper Div., Boise, ID; *U.S. Public*, pg. 243
Haranger, M., Chief Exec. Officer--OCE-France Financement S.A., Saint Cloud, France; *Int'l*, pg. 994
Haratuman, M., Chm. Bd. & Chief Exec. Officer--STV Incorporated, New York, NY; *U.S. Public*, pg. 1421
Haratuman, M., Chief Exec. Officer--STV Construction Services, Douglassville, PA; *U.S. Public*, pg. 1421
Haratuman, M., Chief Exec. Officer--STV International, New York, NY; *U.S. Public*, pg. 1421
Haratunian, M., Pres. & Chief Exec. Officer--STV Architects, Douglassville, PA; *U.S. Public*, pg. 1421
Haratunian, Michael, Chm. Bd. & Chief Exec. Officer--STV Group, Inc., Douglassville, PA; *U.S. Public*, pg. 1421
Harbin, Henry, Pres. & Chief Exec. Officer--Merit Behavioral Care Corp., Park Ridge, NJ; *U.S. Public*, pg. 1036
Harbin, John P., Chm. Bd. & Chief Exec. Officer--Lone Star Technologies, Inc., Dallas, TX; *U.S. Public*, pg. 1012
Harbing, Lars-Peter, Pres. & Chief Exec. Officer--Getinge/Castle Inc., Rochester, NY; *Int'l*, pg. 551
Harbison, Gregory A., Pres., Chief Exec. & Trust Officer--Rockville National Bank, Rockville, IN; *U.S. Public*, pg. 1217
Harcourt, John P., Jr., Pres. & Chief Exec. Officer--Healthcare America, Inc., Austin, TX; *U.S. Private*, pg. 515
Harcum, Joseph A., Chm. & Chief Exec. Officer--Fleet Securities, Inc., New York, NY; *U.S. Public*, pg. 650
Hardage, Samuel A., Pres. & Chief Exec. Officer--The Woodfin Suite Hotels, San Diego, CA; *U.S. Private*, pg. 1187
Harden, Gregory, Chief Exec. Officer--Harden Furniture Company, McConnellsville, NY; *U.S. Private*, pg. 501
Harder, Ronald R., Pres. & Chief Exec. Officer--Jewelers Mutual Insurance Company, Neenah, WI; *U.S. Private*, pg. 587
Hardie, David, Chm. & Chief Exec. Officer--International Distillers & Vintners Ltd., London, United Kingdom; *Int'l*, pg. 409
Hardin, James, Pres. & Chief Exec. Officer--Brookshire Grocery, Tyler, TX; *U.S. Private*, pg. 172
Hardin, Joseph, Jr., Pres. & Chief Exec. Officer--Kinko's Corporation, Ventura, CA; *U.S. Private*, pg. 622
Harding, Jack, Chief Exec. Officer--Cadence Design Systems, Inc., San Jose, CA; *U.S. Public*, pg. 290
Hardis, Stephen R., Chm. Bd. & Chief Exec. Officer--Eaton Corporation, Cleveland, OH; *U.S. Public*, pg. 555
Hardy, Joseph A. Sr., Chm. Bd. & Chief Exec. Officer--84 Lumber Company, Eighty Four, PA; *U.S. Private*, pg. 366
Hardy, Richard B., Chm. Bd. & Chief Exec. Officer--Hyde Manufacturing Co., Southbridge, MA; *U.S. Private*, pg. 551
Hardy, Russell, Chief Exec. Officer--Dolland & Aitchison Ltd., Birmingham, United Kingdom; *Int'l*, pg. 414
Hardymon, James F., Chm. Bd. & Chief Exec. Officer--Textron Inc., Providence, RI; *U.S. Public*, pg. 1588
Harf, Peter, Dr., Pres. & Chief Exec. Officer--Joh. A. Benckiser GmbH, Ludwigshafen, Germany; *Int'l*, pg. 185
Harford, Jim, Chm. Bd., Pres. & Chief Exec. Officer--Everfresh Beverages Inc., Chicago, IL; *U.S. Public*, pg. 1153
Harg, Morten, Chief Exec. Officer--D'Arcy Masius Benton & Bowles, Oslo, Norway; *U.S. Private*, pg. 304
Hargrave, Robert L., Chief Exec. & Fin. Officer & Treas.--Stewart & Stevenson Services, Inc., Houston, TX; *U.S. Public*, pg. 1517
Hargrove, Basil, Chief Exec. Officer--McCain Foods (Australia) Pty, Ltd., Ballarat, Australia; *Int'l*, pg. 850
Harker, John V., Chm. Bd., Pres. & Chief Exec. Officer--In Focus Systems, Inc., Wilsonville, OR; *U.S. Public*, pg. 873
Harkins, Frank S., Jr., Chm. Bd. & Chief Exec. Officer--Horizon Bancorp, Inc., Beckley, WV; *U.S. Public*, pg. 836
Harkins, Frank S., Jr., Pres. & Chief Exec. Officer--Bank of Raleigh, Beckley, WV; *U.S. Public*, pg. 836
Harlacher, Meredith, Pres. & Chief Exec. Officer--Atlantic Electric Co., Pleasantville, NJ; *U.S. Public*, pg. 430
Harmala, Jukka, Chm. Bd., Pres. & Chief Exec. Officer--Enso Oyj, Helsinki, Finland; *Int'l*, pg. 455
Harman, Sidney, Chm. Bd. & Chief Exec. Officer--Harman International Industries, Inc., Woodbury, NY; *U.S. Public*, pg. 787
Harmon, David E., Chm. Bd., Pres., Chief Exec. & Chief Oper. Officer--El Camino Resources, Ltd., Woodland Hills, CA; *U.S. Private*, pg. 366
Harmon, Steven J., Pres. & Chief Exec. Officer--Twin City Die Castings Co., Minneapolis, MN; *U.S. Private*, pg. 1111
Harmon, W. Henry, Pres. & Chief Exec. Officer--Columbia Natural Resources, Inc., Charleston, WV; *U.S. Public*, pg. 403
Harms, Ronald, Chief Exec. Officer--Healthsource New York, De Witt, NY; *U.S. Public*, pg. 360
Harnett, Gordon D., Chm. Bd., Pres. & Chief Exec. Officer--Brush Wellman Inc., Cleveland, OH; *U.S. Public*, pg. 266
Harper, Charles, Chief Exec. Officer--ConAgra Fruen Milling Co., Omaha, NE; *U.S. Public*, pg. 428
Harper, Marvin, Chm. Bd. & Chief Exec. Officer--General Spring, Inc., Hartsville, TN; *U.S. Private*, pg. 445
Harper, Ronald G., Chm. Bd., Pres. & Chief Exec. Officer--MPSI Systems Inc., Tulsa, OK; *U.S. Public*, pg. 1027
Harreld, M., Chm. Bd. & Chief Exec. Officer--PNC Bank, Louisville, KY; *U.S. Public*, pg. 1242
Harrell, H.H, Chief Oper. Officer--Latco, Inc., Richmond, VA; *U.S. Public*, pg. 1695
Harrell, H.H., Chief Oper. Officer--Southern Processors, Inc., Danville, VA; *U.S. Public*, pg. 1695
Harrell, H.H., Chief Oper. Officer--J.P. Taylor Co., Inc., Henderson, NC; *U.S. Public*, pg. 1695
Harrell, H.H., Chief Oper. Officer--Universal Leaf Export Company, Inc., Richmond, VA; *U.S. Public*, pg. 1695
Harrell, Henry H., Chm. Bd. & Chief Exec. Officer--Universal Corporation, Richmond, VA; *U.S. Public*, pg. 1694
Harrell, Samuel M., Chm. Bd., Pres. & Chief Exec. Officer--EDI International, Inc., Cincinnati, OH; *U.S. Private*, pg. 353
Harries, David, Pres. & Chief Exec. Officer--DMB&B Montreal, Montreal, Canada; *U.S. Private*, pg. 304
Harrigan, W. Brian, Pres. & Chief Exec. Officer--United Insurance Companies, Inc., Dallas, TX; *U.S. Public*, pg. 1679
Harrington, Douglas, M.D., Chief Exec. Officer--ChromaVision Medical Systems, Inc., San Juan Capistrano, CA; *U.S. Public*, pg. 1424
Harrington, Mark G., Chm. Bd. & Chief Exec. Officer--HarCor Energy, Inc., Houston, TX; *U.S. Public*, pg. 782
Harrington, Richard J., Pres., Chief Exec. & Oper. Officer--The Thomson Corporation, Stamford, CT; *U.S. Public*, pg. 1599
Harris, Ben T., Pres. & Chief Exec. Officer--Genesco Inc., Nashville, TN; *U.S. Public*, pg. 728
Harris, D. George, Chm. Bd. & Chief Exec. Officer--Harris Chemical Group, Inc., New York, NY; *U.S. Private*, pg. 505
Harris, David J., Pres. & Chief Exec. Officer--M & I Bank Northeast, Green Bay, WI; *U.S. Public*, pg. 1050
Harris, Eldon D., Chm. Bd. & Chief Exec. Officer--Manufacturers Railway Company, Saint Louis, MO; *U.S. Public*, pg. 114
Harris, Elmer B., Pres. & Chief Exec. Officer--Alabama Power Co., Birmingham, AL; *U.S. Public*, pg. 1489
Harris, George, Chief Exec. Officer--Thoro, Jacksonville, FL; *U.S. Private*, pg. 505
Harris, J. Wayne, Chief Exec. Officer--The Grand Union Company, Wayne, NJ; *U.S. Public*, pg. 758
Harris, J. Wayne, Chm. & Chief Exec. Officer-Canada--The Great Atlantic & Pacific Tea Company, Inc., Montvale, NJ; *Int'l*, pg. 1375
Harris, James A., Pres. & Chief Exec. Officer--Eljer Plumbingware, Dallas, TX; *U.S. Public*, pg. 1794
Harris, Jeffery, Chief Exec. Officer--Alliance UniChem PLC, Chessington, United Kingdom; *Int'l*, pg. 57
Harris, Jerrold B., Pres. & Chief Exec. Officer--VWR Scientific Products, West Chester, PA; *U.S. Public*, pg. 1703
Harris, John, Chief Exec. Officer-Auto Trader Div.--Guardian Media Group plc, Manchester, United Kingdom; *Int'l*, pg. 577
Harris, John M., Chief Exec. Officer--The Forum Corporation, Boston, MA; *U.S. Private*, pg. 420
Harris, King, Pres. & Chief Exec. Officer--Pittway Corporation, Chicago, IL; *U.S. Public*, pg. 1305
Harris, Larry J., Chief Exec. Officer--Pollo Tropical, Inc., Miami, FL; *U.S. Public*, pg. 1315
Harris, Leon, Chief Exec. Officer--Sulcus Computer Corp., Greensburg, PA; *U.S. Public*, pg. 1527
Harris, Michael S., Pres. & Chief Exec. Officer--Deck House Inc., Acton, MA; *U.S. Private*, pg. 320
Harris, Michael S., Pres. & Chief Exec. Officer--Acorn Structures, Acton, MA; *U.S. Private*, pg. 320
Harris, Milton E., Chm. Bd. & Chief Exec. Officer--Harris Steel Group Inc., Willowdale, Canada; *Int'l*, pg. 597
Harris, Robert M., Pres. & Chief Exec. Officer--GFA Brands, Inc., Cresskill, NJ; *U.S. Private*, pg. 435
Harris, Ron R., Pres. & Chief Exec. Officer--Pervasive Software Inc., Austin, TX; *U.S. Public*, pg. 1280
Harris, Thomas E., Pres. & Chief Exec. Officer--Commonwealth Gas Services, Inc., Richmond, VA; *U.S. Public*, pg. 403
Harris, Tim, Pres. & Chief Oper. Officer--Witt Company, Cincinnati, OH; *U.S. Private*, pg. 1185
Harris, William B., Pres. & Chief Exec. Officer--Trevira, Charlotte, NC; *Int'l*, pg. 626
Harrison, Andrew, Chief Exec. Officer--Lex Service PLC, Bourne, United Kingdom; *Int'l*, pg. 806
Harrison, Angela E., Pres. & Chief Exec. Officer--Welsco Inc., North Little Rock, AR; *U.S. Private*, pg. 1161
Harrison, Barry W., Pres. & Chief Exec. Officer--Mark Resources Inc., Calgary, Canada; *Int'l*, pg. 842
Harrison, David, Pres. & Chief Exec. Officer--Harrison, Young, Pesonen & Newell Inc., Toronto, Canada; *Int'l*, pg. 598
Harrison, Frank, III, Vice Chm. & Chief Exec. Officer--Coca-Cola Consolidated, Charlotte, NC; *U.S. Public*, pg. 392
Harrison, J. Frank, III, Chm. Bd. & Chief Exec. Officer--Coca-Cola Bottling Co. Consolidated, Charlotte, NC; *U.S.* Public, pg. 391
Harrison, John, Pres. & Chief Exec. Officer--Chemical Bank Key State, Owosso, MI; *U.S. Public*, pg. 345
Harrison, John C., Jr., Pres. & Chief Exec. Officer--Harrison Construction Corp., Miami, FL; *U.S. Private*, pg. 506
Harrison, N.A., Pres. & Chief Exec. Officer--BFC Construction Corporation, Scarborough, Canada; *Int'l*, pg. 118
Harrison, Paul, Chief Exec.--Alpha Airports Group Plc, Cranford, United Kingdom; *Int'l*, pg. 65
Harrison, Ridgley, III, Pres. & Chief Exec. Officer--The Thompson-Minwax Company, Upper Saddle River, NJ; *U.S. Public*, pg. 1466
Harrison, Robert E., Pres., Chief Exec. & Fin. Officer--Standard Commercial Corporation, Wilson, NC; *U.S. Public*, pg. 1501
Harrison, Tom, Chm. & Chief Exec. Officer--Harrison Wilson & Associates, Parsippany, NJ; *U.S. Public*, pg. 1224
Harshman, Richard R., Pres. & Chief Exec. Officer--Storck U.S.A., L.P., Chicago, IL; *Int'l*, pg. 1304
Hart, David, Chief Exec. Officer--Hart Graphics Inc., Austin, TX; *U.S. Private*, pg. 507
Hart, E. Thomas, Pres. & Chief Exec. Officer--QuickLogic Corporation, Sunnyvale, CA; *U.S. Private*, pg. 901
Hart, James W., Chm. Bd., Pres., Chief Exec. Officer & Chief Fin. Officer--Hart Holding Company, Inc., Norwalk, CT; *U.S. Private*, pg. 507
Hart, William, Chief Exec. Officer--Fairfield Electric Cooperative, Winnsboro, SC; *U.S. Private*, pg. 391
Harten, P., Chief Exec.--DSM Limburg B.V., Geleen, Netherlands; *Int'l*, pg. 353
Hartin, Terry, Chief Oper. Officer--The Body Shop Inc., Wake Forest, NC; *Int'l*, pg. 199
Hartiss, B.S., Chief Exec. Officer--Powell Duffryn PLC, Bracknell, United Kingdom; *Int'l*, pg. 1065
Hartl, Richard, Chm. Bd., Pres. & Chief Exec. Officer--Calmar Inc., City of Industry, CA; *U.S. Private*, pg. 201
Hartman, Carl C., Pres., Chief Exec. Officer & Chief Oper. Officer--Trinidad/Benham Corp., Denver, CO; *U.S. Private*, pg. 1103
Hartman, Jack, Pres. & Chief Exec. Officer--SunTrust Bank, Southeast Georgia, N.A., Brunswick, GA; *U.S. Public*, pg. 1538
Hartmann, Edward G., Pres. & Chief Exec. Officer--BA Investment Managers, Los Angeles, CA; *U.S. Public*, pg. 180
Hartog, Jack B., Sr., Chief Exec. Officer--Hartog Rahil Foods, Inc., New York, NY; *U.S. Private*, pg. 508

Hartzmark, Michael, Pres. & Chief Exec. Officer--Cragar Industries, Inc., Phoenix, AZ; *U.S. Public*, pg. 456
Harvey, David E., Chm. Bd., Pres., Chief Oper. & Chief Exec. Officer--Rome Cable Corporation, Rome, NY; *U.S. Private*, pg. 942
Harvey, Joseph H., Jr., Chm. Bd. & Chief Exec. Officer--J.H. Harvey Company, Nashville, GA; *U.S. Private*, pg. 508
Harvison, John H., Chm. Bd. & Chief Exec. Officer--FFP Marketing Company, Inc., Fort Worth, TX; *U.S. Public*, pg. 604
Harwood, Jim, Chief Exec. Officer--City National Bank of Fort Smith, Fort Smith, AR; *U.S. Public*, pg. 641
Harwood, Lowell, Chm. Bd. & Chief Exec Officer--Square Industries, Inc., Jersey City, NJ; *U.S. Public*, pg. 326
Harzenski, Eugene S., Pres. & Chief Exec. Officer--Alloy Technology International Inc., West Nyack, NY; *U.S. Private*, pg. 42
Hasan, Malik M., Chm. Bd. & Chief Exec. Officer--Foundation Health Systems, Inc., Pueblo, CO; *U.S. Public*, pg. 678
Hascall, James G., Chm. Bd. & Chief Exec. Officer--Primex Technologies, Inc., Primex Aerospace, Redmond, WA; *U.S. Public*, pg. 1329
Haseldonckx, Paul, Pres. & Chief Exec. Officer--Deminex-Deutsche GmbH, Essen, Germany; *Int'l*, pg. 1460
Hashagen, John D., Jr., Pres. & Chief Exec. Officer--Vermont Financial Services Corp., Brattleboro, VT; *U.S. Public*, pg. 1716
Hashim, Dato' Razman M., Dep. Chief Exec. Officer--Standard Chartered Bank Malaysia Berhad, Kuala Lumpur, Malaysia; *Int'l*, pg. 1295
Haskell, Gary W., Chm. Bd. & Chief Exec. Officer--UMB First National Bank, Collinsville, IL; *U.S. Public*, pg. 1654
Haskell, George, Pres. & Chief Exec. Officer--Organizational Dynamics Inc., Burlington, MA; *U.S. Private*, pg. 819
Haslam, Charles L., Chm. Bd. & Chief Exec. Officer--Krug International Corp., Houston, TX; *U.S. Public*, pg. 967
Haslam, James A., III, Chief Exec. Officer & Chief Oper. Officer--Pilot Corporation, Knoxville, TN; *U.S. Private*, pg. 865
Haslehurst, Peter, Chief Exec.--EIS Group Plc, London, United Kingdom; *Int'l*, pg. 426
Hassan, Fred, Pres. & Chief Exec. Officer--Pharmacia & Upjohn, Inc., Windsor, United Kingdom; *Int'l*, pg. 1047
Hassanein, Salah M., Pres. & Chief Exec. Officer--The Todd-AO Corporation, Hollywood, CA; *U.S. Public*, pg. 1619
Hassenfeld, Alan G., Chm. & Chief Exec. Officer--Hasbro, Inc., Pawtucket, RI; *U.S. Public*, pg. 797
Hassinger, Norman M., Jr., Chm. Bd., Pres., Chief Exec. & Chief Oper. Officer--The Hassinger Companies Hoffman Homes, Arlington Heights, IL; *U.S. Private*, pg. 510
Hasten, Michael, Pres., Chief Exec. Officer & Chief Oper. Officer--Downey Designs International, Indianapolis, IN; *U.S. Private*, pg. 342
Hatcher, David E., Chm. Bd., Pres. & Chief Exec. Officer--Gamma Biologicals Inc., Houston, TX; *U.S. Public*, pg. 698
Hatfield, Joe, Chm. Bd. & Chief Exec. Officer--Fieldale Corporation, Baldwin, GA; *U.S. Private*, pg. 403
Hatfield, Joe, Chief Exec. Officer--Best Aviation, Baldwin, GA; *U.S. Private*, pg. 403
Hathaway, Derek C., Chm. Bd. & Chief Exec. Officer--Harsco Corporation, Camp Hill, PA; *U.S. Public*, pg. 792
Hathaway, Derek C., Corp. Chm., Pres. & Chief Exec. Officer--Heckett MultiServ, Butler, PA; *U.S. Public*, pg. 793
Hatlen, Roe H., Chm. Bd. & Chief Exec. Officer--Buffets, Inc., Eden Prairie, MN; *U.S. Public*, pg. 267
Hatsopoulos, George N., Chm. Bd. & Chief Exec. Officer--Thermo Electron Corporation, Waltham, MA; *U.S. Public*, *pg. 1591*
Hatt, James R.S., Chm. Bd., Pres. & Chief Exec. Officer--Petersburg Long Distance Inc., Toronto, Canada; *Int'l*, pg. 1040
Hattersley, Peter, Deputy Chief Exec. Officer--Willis Corroon Risk Consulting Limited, London, United Kingdom; *Int'l*, pg. 1503
Hattori, Hideaki, Pres. & Chief Exec. Officer--Pacific Guardian Life Insurance, Honolulu, HI; *Int'l*, pg. 854
Hattori, Satoshi, Chief Oper. Officer--Tosoh Medics, Inc., Foster City, CA; *Int'l*, pg. 1407
Haub, Christian W.E., Pres. & Co-Chief Exec. Officer--The Great Atlantic & Pacific Tea Company, Inc., Montvale, NJ; *Int'l*, pg. 1375
Hauck, L. Christian, Pres. & Chief Exec. Officer--Sunflower Electric Power Corporation, Hays, KS; *U.S. Private*, pg. 1052
Haugen, Rolf E., Pres. & Chief Exec. Officer--Farm Credit Leasing Services Corporation, Minneapolis, MN; *U.S. Private*, pg. 398
Haun, G. Richard, Jr., Chief Exec. Officer--Sterner Lighting Systems Incorporated, Eden Prairie, MN; *U.S. Private*, pg. 1042
Hauser, Joshua A., Pres. & Chief Exec. Officer--Lambda Electronics Inc., Melville, NY; *Int'l*, pg. 1241
Hauslein, James N., Chm. Bd., Pres. & Chief Exec. Officer--Sunglass Hut International, Coral Gables, FL; *U.S. Public*, pg. 1535
Hauss, John, Pres. & Chief Exec. Officer--Lifetime Doors Inc., Farmington, MI; *U.S. Private*, pg. 666
Havener, Gary W., Pres. & Chief Exec. Officer--Cabre Corp., Wilmington, DE; *U.S. Public*, pg. 289
Haverkate, Mark, Pres. & Chief Exec. Officer--Cable Michigan, Inc., Princeton, NJ; *U.S. Public*, pg. 287
Haverland, Richard M., Chm. Bd., Pres. & Chief Exec. Officer--Highlands Insurance Co., Houston, TX; *U.S. Public*, pg. 826
Haverty, Michael R., Pres. & Chief Exec. Officer--The Kansas City Southern Railway Co., Kansas City, MO; *U.S. Public*, pg. 944
Hawk, David W., Pres. & Chief Exec. Officer--Gertrude Hawk Chocolates, Inc., Dunmore, PA; *U.S. Private*, pg. 449
Hawk, Richard C., Chm. Bd., Pres. & Chief Exec. Officer--Hawk Management Corporation, Overland Park, KS; *U.S. Private*, pg. 511
Hawk, Robert, Pres. & Chief Exec. Officer--Hale-Halsell Company, Tulsa, OK; *U.S. Private*, pg. 494
Hawk, Stephen L., Chm. & Chief Exec. Officer--Northern Capital Management, Inc., Madison, WI; *U.S. Public*, pg. 1673
Hawkes, James B., Chm. Bd., Pres. & Chief Exec. Officer--Eaton Vance Corp., Boston, MA; *U.S. Public*, pg. 559
Hawkins, Andrew, Chm. & Chief Exec. Officer--GGK London Ltd., London, United Kingdom; *Int'l*, pg. 1335
Hawkins, Arthur M., Chm. Bd., Pres. & Chief Exec. Officer--Exide Corporation, Reading, PA; *U.S. Public*, pg. 600
Hawkins, Dan, Pres. & Chief Exec. Officer--Bank of Goodlettsville, Goodlettsville, TN; *U.S. Public*, pg. 1669
Hawkins, James T., Pres. & Chief Exec. Officer--Weasler Engineering Inc., West Bend, WI; *U.S. Private*, pg. 249
Hawkins, Phillip E., Pres. & Chief Exec. Officer--The Penn Traffic Company, Syracuse, NY; *U.S. Public*, pg. 1270
Hawkinson, Lowell, Chm. Bd. & Chief Exec. Officer--Gensym Corporation, Cambridge, MA; *U.S. Public*, pg. 731
Hawley, Edmund, Chief Exec. Officer & Sr. V.P.--Skyway Freight Systems, Inc., Watsonville, CA; *U.S. Private*, pg. 1005
Hawley, Philip M., Chm. Bd. & Chief Exec. Officer--Krause's Furniture Inc., Brea, CA; *U.S. Public*, pg. 967
Hawthorne, James T., Chief Exec. Officer--Hawthorne Machinery Company, San Diego, CA; *U.S. Private*, pg. 512
Hayden, John W., Chm. Bd. & Chief Exec. Officer--C S Crable Sportswear, Inc., Batavia, OH; *U.S. Public*, pg. 1111
Hayden, Robert W., Pres. & Chief Exec. Officer--The Midland Company, Cincinnati, OH; *U.S. Public*, pg. 1110
Hayek, Nicolas G., Chm. Bd. & Chief Exec. Officer--SMH Swiss Corporation for Micro Electronics & Watchmaking Indus. Ltd., Bienne, Switzerland; *Int'l*, pg. 1160
Hayes, Charles A., Chm. Bd. & Chief Exec. Officer--Guilford Mills, Inc., Greensboro, NC; *U.S. Public*, pg. 768
Hayes, J. Michael, Chm. Bd. & Chief Exec. Officer--C.B. Ragland Company, Nashville, TN; *U.S. Private*, pg. 907
Hayes, John, Pres. & Chief Exec. Officer--Raycom Media, Inc., Montgomery, AL; *U.S. Private*, pg. 911
Hayes, John E. Jr., Chm. Bd. & Chief Exec. Officer--Western Resources, Inc., Topeka, KS; *U.S. Public*, pg. 1759
Hayes, Michael, Chief Exec. Officer--Petroferm Inc., Fernandina Beach, FL; *U.S. Private*, pg. 858
Hayes, Michael J., Pres. & Chief Exec. Officer--Fred's Inc., Memphis, TN; *U.S. Public*, pg. 680
Haymaker, George T., Jr., Chm. Bd. & Chief Exec. Officer--Kaiser Aluminum Corporation, Houston, TX; *U.S. Public*, pg. 1062
Haymon, Monte R., Pres. & Chief Exec. Officer--S.D. Warren Co., Boston, MA; *Int'l*, pg. 1193
Hayne, Richard A., Chm. Bd. & Chief Exec. Officer--Urban Outfitters, Inc., Philadelphia, PA; *U.S. Public*, pg. 1700
Haynes, Michael C., Pres. & Chief Exec. Officer--GT Bicycles, Inc., Santa Ana, CA; *U.S. Public*, pg. 695
Haynes, Peter, Pres. & Chief Exec. Officer--Consumers Water Company, Portland, ME; *U.S. Public*, pg. 438
Haynes, William E., Chm. Bd., Pres. & Chief Exec. Officer--Innovative Valve Technology, Inc., Houston, TX; *U.S. Public*, pg. 880
Haynes, William E., Pres. & Chief Exec. Officer--Lyondell-Citgo Refining Company, Ltd., Houston, TX; *U.S. Public*, pg. 1022
Hays, George G., Pres. & Chief Exec. Officer--Arizona Instrument Corporation, Phoenix, AZ; *U.S. Public*, pg. 129
Hays, Michael D., Pres. & Chief Exec. Officer--National Research Corporation, Lincoln, NE; *U.S. Public*, pg. 1159
Hays, Thomas C., Chm. Bd. & Chief Exec. Officer--Fortune Brands, Inc., Old Greenwich, CT; *U.S. Public*, pg. 674
Hays, William, Sr., Pres. & Chief Exec. Officer--Town & Country Ford Inc., Louisville, KY; *U.S. Private*, pg. 1093
Hayt, John T., Chief Exec. Officer--EquiCredit Corporation, Jacksonville, FL; *U.S. Public*, pg. 1162
Hayward, Brian, Chief Exec. Officer--United Grain Growers Ltd., Winnipeg, Canada; *Int'l*, pg. 1442
Hayward, Lawrence, Pres. & Chief Exec. Officer--Carr Gottstein Foods, Anchorage, AK; *U.S. Public*, pg. 308
Hazard, Glenn C., Pres. & Chief Exec. Officer--FTP Software Inc., Andover, MA; *U.S. Public*, pg. 609
Hazen, Paul, Chm. Bd. & Chief Exec. Officer--Wells Fargo & Company, San Francisco, CA; *U.S. Public*, pg. 1753
Hazen, Paul, Chm. Bd. & Chief Exec. Officer--Wells Fargo & Company, Los Angeles, CA; *U.S. Public*, pg. 1753
Hazen, Thomas, Pres. & Chief Exec. Officer--Hazen Paper Company, Holyoke, MA; *U.S. Private*, pg. 514
Hazleton, Richard, Chm. Bd. & Chief Exec. Officer--Dow Corning Corporation, Midland, MI; *U.S. Public*, pg. 523
Heagerty, David A., Chm. Bd. & Chief Exec. Officer--The Coakley Heagerty Advertising & Public Relations Co., San Jose, CA; *U.S. Private*, pg. 248
Healey, William J., Pres. & Chief Exec. Officer--Viking Yacht Co., New Gretna, NJ; *U.S. Private*, pg. 1140
Healy, James T., Pres. & Chief Exec. Officer--Genus Inc., Sunnyvale, CA; *U.S. Public*, pg. 732
Healy, Thomas, Pres.--Owen-Ames-Kimball Co., Grand Rapids, MI; *U.S. Private*, pg. 823
Healy, Tim, Pres. & Chief Exec. Officer--Select Beverages, Inc., Darien, IL; *U.S. Private*, pg. 982
Hearn, David, Chief Exec. Officer--Goodman Fielder Limited, Sydney, Australia; *Int'l*, pg. 555
Heath, Alan, Pres. & Chief Exec. Officer--The Vendo Company, Fresno, CA; *Int'l*, pg. 1184
Heath, Richard W., Pres. & Chief Exec. Officer--BeautiControl Cosmetics, Inc., Carrollton, TX; *U.S. Public*, pg. 198
Heaton, Larry A., Pres. & Chief Exec. Officer--Bank of Ferrum, Ferrum, VA; *U.S. Public*, pg. 1038
Heavenridge, David L., Pres. & Chief Exec. Officer--Dominion Capital, Inc., Richmond, VA; *U.S. Public*, pg. 516
Hebe, James L., Pres. & Chief Exec. Officer--Freightliner Corp., Portland, OR; *Int'l*, pg. 368
Hechler, Robert, Pres. & Chief Exec. Officer--Waddell & Reed, Inc., Shawnee Mission, KS; *U.S. Public*, pg. 1623
Hecht, Robert, Chief Exec. Officer--Trumbull Corporation/ P.J. Dick, Inc., West Mifflin, PA; *U.S. Private*, pg. 1107
Hecht, William F., Chm. Bd., Pres. & Chief Exec. Officer--PP&L Resources, Allentown, PA; *U.S. Public*, pg. 1244
Hecht, William F., Chm. Bd., Pres. & Chief Exec. Officer--Pennsylvania Power & Light Company-Lehigh Div., Allentown, PA; *U.S. Public*, pg. 1244
Hecht, William F., Chm. Bd. & Chief Exec. Officer--Power Markets Development Company, Allentown, PA; *U.S. Public*, pg. 1244
Heckmann, Dick, Pres. & Chief Exec. Officer--U.S. Filter, Palm Desert, CA; *U.S. Public*, pg. 61
Heckmann, Richard J., Pres. & Chief Exec. Officer--United States Filter Corporation, Palm Desert, CA; *U.S. Public*, pg. 1681
Hedfors, Bo, Chief Exec. Officer--Telefonaktiebolaget LM Ericsson, Stockholm, Sweden; *Int'l*, pg. 1363
Hedrick, K.L., Pres. & Chief Exec. Officer--Phillips Gas Company, Bartlesville, OK; *U.S. Public*, pg. 1291
Hedstrom, Clas Ake, Pres. & Chief Exec. Officer--Sandvik AB, Sandviken, Sweden; *Int'l*, pg. 1185
Hedstrom, Jan, Pres. & Chief Exec. Officer--Gunnebo Industrier AB, Gunnebo, Sweden; *Int'l*, pg. 578
Heenan, D.A., Pres. & Chief Exec. Officer--Theo. H. Davies & Co., Ltd, Honolulu, HI; *Int'l*, pg. 704
Heffer, John, Pres. & Chief Exec. Officer--Republic Factors Corp., New York, NY; *U.S. Public*, pg. 1380
Hefner, Christie, Chm. Bd. & Chief Exec. Officer--Playboy Enterprises, Inc., Chicago, IL; *U.S. Public*, pg. 1309
Hefner, Thomas L., Pres. & Chief Exec. Officer--Duke Realty Investments, Inc., Indianapolis, IN; *U.S. Public*, pg. 535
Hefty, Thomas R., Chm. Bd., Pres. & Chief Exec. Officer--United Wisconsin Services, Inc., Milwaukee, WI; *U.S. Public*, pg. 1692
Hegener, Peter W., Pres. & Chief Exec. Officer--Peterson's Guides, Inc., Princeton, NJ; *U.S. Private*, pg. 858
Heglund, Forrest E., Chm. Bd. & Chief Exec. Officer--Enron Oil & Gas Co., Houston, TX; *U.S. Public*, pg. 584
Heider, David, Pres. & Chief Exec. Officer--United Hardware Distributing Co., Plymouth, MN; *U.S. Private*, pg. 335
Heidrich, James K., Jr., Chm. Bd., Pres. & Chief Exec. Officer--The Miami Margarine Co., Cincinnati, OH; *U.S. Private*, pg. 740
Heigrad, Peter, Reg. Chm. & Chief Exec. Officer--Young & Rubicam Australia/New Zealand, Sydney, Australia; *U.S. Private*, pg. 1198
Heil, William H., Chm. & Chief Exec. Officer--AllEnergy Marketing Company, L.L.C., Waltham, MA; *U.S. Public*, pg. 549
Heim, Greg, Chief Exec. Officer--Modern Drop Forge Co., Blue Island, IL; *U.S. Private*, pg. 754
Heiman, Gary, Pres. & Chief Exec. Officer--Standard Textile Co., Inc., Cincinnati, OH; *U.S. Private*, pg. 1032
Heimbinder, Isaac, Pres., Co.-Chief Exec. Officer & Chief Oper. Officer--U.S. Home Corporation, Houston, TX; *U.S. Public*, pg. 1682
Heimbold, Charles A., Jr., Chm. Bd. & Chief Exec. Officer--Bristol-Myers Squibb Company, New York, NY; *U.S. Public*, pg. 253
Heimbuch, Babette, Chief Exec. Officer--Seaside Financial Corporation, Santa Monica, CA; *U.S. Public*, pg. 646
Heimbuch, Babette E., Pres. & Chief Exec. Officer--FirstFed Financial Corp., Santa Monica, CA; *U.S. Public*, pg. 645
Heimendinger, Larry, Chm. Bd. & Pres.--General Kinetics Incorporated, Chantilly, VA; *U.S. Public*, pg. 716
Heinen, Jeffrey, Pres. & Chief Exec. Officer--Heinen's Inc., Cleveland, OH; *U.S. Private*, pg. 519
Heiner, Clyde M., Pres. & Chief Exec. Officer--Interstate Land Corp., Salt Lake City, UT; *U.S. Public*, pg. 1352
Heiner, Clyde M., Pres. & Chief Exec. Officer--Questar Development Corporation, Salt Lake City, UT; *U.S. Public*, pg. 1352
Heiner, Clyde M., Pres. & Chief Exec. Officer--Questar InfoComm, Salt Lake City, UT; *U.S. Public*, pg. 1352
Heiniger, Andre, Chm. Bd. & Chief Exec. Officer--Rolex Watch Co. SA, Geneva, Switzerland; *Int'l*, pg. 1126
Heins, John, Pres. & Chief Exec. Officer--Gruner + Jahr USA Publishing, Inc., New York, NY; *Int'l*, pg. 190
Heins, John, Pres. & Chief Exec. Officer--Parents Magazine, New York, NY; *Int'l*, pg. 191
Heisley, Michael E., Chm. Bd. & Chief Exec. Officer--Nutri/System Inc., Horsham, PA; *U.S. Private*, pg. 859
Heisley, Michael E., Vice Chm. & Chief Exec. Officer--Robertson-Ceco Corporation, San Ramon, CA; *U.S. Public*, pg. 1394
Heist, Charles H., Chm. Bd. & Chief Exec. Officer--C.H. Heist Corp., Clearwater, FL; *U.S. Public*, pg. 807
Heitmann, Fred W., Chm. Bd. & Chief Exec. Officer--LaSalle Northwest National Bank, Chicago, IL; *Int'l*, pg. 10
Hejmelaeus, Hannu, Chief Oper. Officer--Tampere EPS Plant, Tampere, Finland; *Int'l*, pg. 863
Held, James G., Pres. & Chief Exec. Officer--Home Shopping Network, Inc., Saint Petersburg, FL; *U.S. Public*, pg. 1685
Held, James G., Pres. & Chief Exec. Officer--America's Store, Saint Petersburg, FL; *U.S. Public*, pg. 1685
Heldrich, John, Pres. & Chief Exec. Officer--Swift Textiles, Inc., Atlanta, GA; *Int'l*, pg. 415
Helford, Irwin, Chm. Bd. & Chief Exec. Officer--Viking Office Products, Torrance, CA; *U.S. Public*, pg. 1720
Helgason, Sigurdur, Pres. & Chief Exec. Officer--Icelandair, Reykjavik, Iceland; *Int'l*, pg. 658
Helgason, Sigurdur, Pres. & Chief Exec. Officer--IceLandAir, Columbia, MD; *Int'l*, pg. 658
Helgeson, Michael, Chief Oper. Officer--JFC Inc., Saint Cloud, MN; *U.S. Private*, pg. 577

Helgeson, Mike, Chief Exec. Officer--Gold'n Plump Poultry, Saint Cloud, MN; *U.S. Private*, pg. 577

Hellberg, Clifford W., Chm. Bd., Pres. & Chief Exec. Officer--Creative Productions, Pittsburgh, PA; *U.S. Private*, pg. 288

Hellenbrand, V.J., Chm. Bd. & Chief Exec. Officer--Research Products Corporation, Madison, WI; *U.S. Private*, pg. 924

Heller, Chester M., Sr., Dr., Chm. Bd., Pres., Chief Exec. Officer & Chief Engr.--Marquette Coppersmithing Co., Inc., Philadelphia, PA; *U.S. Private*, pg. 706

Heller, Robert W., Pres. & Chief Exec. Officer--Advance Circuits, Inc., Minnetonka, MN; *Int'l*, pg. 713

Heller, Wayne, Chief Exec. Officer--Cruises Only Inc., Orlando, FL; *U.S. Private*, pg. 293

Hellman, Wayne R., Chief Exec. Officer--Advanced Lighting Technologies, Inc., Twinsburg, OH; *U.S. Public*, pg. 20

Hellman, William, Chm. Bd., Pres & Chief Exec. Officer--JG Industries, Inc., Chicago, IL; *U.S. Public*, pg. 917

Helmen, John R., Pres., Chief Exec. Officer & Chief Oper. Officer--Photo Control Corporation, Minneapolis, MN; *U.S. Public*, pg. 1292

Helmerich, Hans, Pres. & Chief Exec. Officer--Helmerich & Payne, Inc., Tulsa, OK; *U.S. Public*, pg. 808

Helmetag, Carl, Pres. & Chief Exec. Officer--Head USA, Inc., Columbia, MD; *U.S. Private*, pg. 514

Helppie, Richard D., Pres. & Chief Exec. Officer--Superior Consultant Company, Inc., Southfield, MI; *U.S. Public*, pg. 1539

Helppie, Richard D., Jr., Pres. & Chief Exec. Officer--Superior Consultant Holdings Corp., Southfield, MI; *U.S. Public*, pg. 1538

Helton, Bill D., Chm. Bd. & Chief Exec. Officer--New Century Energies, Inc., Denver, CO; *U.S. Public*, pg. 1170

Helton, James E., Pres. & Chief Exec. Officer--M & M Precision Systems Corporation, Carrollton, OH; *U.S. Public*, pg. 482

Helton, Raymond E., Pres. & Chief Exec. Officer--Sterling Electric, Inc., Irvine, CA; *U.S. Private*, pg. 1041

Helzer, James A., Pres. & Chief Exec. Officer--Unicover Corporation, Cheyenne, WY; *U.S. Private*, pg. 1117

Hemer, Douglas L., Pres. & Chief Exec. Officer--San Diego Division, San Diego, CA; *U.S. Public*, pg. 27

Hemmer, Paul W., Jr., Pres. & Chief Exec. Officer--Paul Hemmer Construction Company, Fort Mitchell, KY; *U.S. Private*, pg. 521

Hemmerle, Glenn, Pres. & Chief Exec. Officer--The Johnny Rockets Group, Inc, Irvine, CA; *U.S. Private*, pg. 222

Hemmerle, Glenn, Pres. & Chief Exec. Officer--Pearle Vision, Inc., Dallas, TX; *U.S. Public*, pg. 397

Hemminghaus, Roger R., Chm. Bd. & Chief Exec. Officer--Ultramar Diamond Shamrock Corporation, San Antonio, TX; *U.S. Public*, pg. 1663

Hemminghaus, Roger R., Chief Exec. Officer--Diamond Shamrock Credit Card Center, Amarillo, TX; *U.S. Public*, pg. 1663

Henderson, D.A., Chief Exec. Officer--Scottisch Equitable, Edinburgh, United Kingdom; *Int'l*, pg. 28

Henderson, Donald, Chm. Bd., Pres. & Chief Exec. Officer--Citation National Insurance Company, San Jose, CA; *U.S. Public*, pg. 376

Henderson, Donald, Chm. Bd. & Chief Exec. Officer--Madison Acceptance Corporation, San Jose, CA; *U.S. Public*, pg. 376

Henderson, Donald, Chm. Bd., Pres. & Chief Exec. Officer--Citation Insurance Company, San Jose, CA; *U.S. Public*, pg. 376

Henderson, Donald E., Chief Exec. Officer & Exec. V.P.--United Farm Family Life Insurance Co., Indianapolis, IN; *U.S. Private*, pg. 1122

Henderson, George W., Pres. & Chief Exec. Officer--Burlington Industries, Inc., Greensboro, NC; *U.S. Public*, pg. 268

Henderson, Greer F., Vice Chm. & Chief Exec. Officer--USLIFE Corporation, New York, NY; *U.S. Public*, pg. 77

Henderson, I. Craig, Dr., Chm. Bd. & Chief Exec. Officer--Sequus Pharmaceuticals, Inc., Menlo Park, CA; *U.S. Public*, pg. 1460

Henderson, James A., Chm. Bd. & Chief Exec. Officer--Cummins Engine Company, Inc., Columbus, IN; *U.S. Public*, pg. 467

Henderson, Louis C., Jr., Pres. & Chief Exec. Officer--Wall Street Deli, Inc., Birmingham, AL; *U.S. Public*, pg. 1734

Henderson, Michael L., Pres. & Chief Exec. Officer--Joseph J. Henderson & Son, Inc., Gurnee, IL; *U.S. Private*, pg. 521

Henderson, Mike, Chief Exec. Officer & Chief Fin. Officer--Gibson's Discount Centers Inc., Dodge City, KS; *U.S. Private*, pg. 452

Henderson, Robert J., Sr., Chm. Bd., Pres. & Chief Exec. Officer--Ford Development Corporation, Cincinnati, OH; *U.S. Private*, pg. 418

Hendrick, J., Chief Exec. Officer--RBB NV, Tessenderlo, Belgium; *Int'l*, pg. 1092

Hendricks, John, Chm. Bd. & Chief Exec. Officer--Discovery Networks, Inc., Bethesda, MD; *U.S. Private*, pg. 334

Hendricks, John S., Chm. Bd. & Chief Exec. Officer--Discovery Communications, Inc., Bethesda, MD; *U.S. Private*, pg. 334

Hendricks, Karen L., Chm. Bd., Pres. & Chief Exec. Officer--Baldwin Piano & Organ Company, Loveland, OH; *U.S. Public*, pg. 169

Hendricks, Kenneth A., Pres. & Chief Exec. Officer--ABC Supply Company, Inc., Beloit, WI; *U.S. Private*, pg. 3

Hendrickson, Susan, Chief Exec. Officer--Horizon Specialty Hospital - Wichita, Wichita, KS; *U.S. Public*, pg. 837

Hendrickson, Thomas N., Chm. Bd. & Chief Exec. Officer--CPAC, Inc., Leicester, NY; *U.S. Public*, pg. 282

Hendrix, Bill, Chief Exec. Officer--Remington Arms Company, Inc., Madison, NC; *U.S. Private*, pg. 921

Hendrix, Tom E., Chm. Bd., Pres. & Chief Exec. Officer--Henco, Inc., Selmer, TN; *U.S. Private*, pg. 521

Hendry, Robert, Pres. & Chief Exec. Officer--Saab Automobile AB, Nykoping, Sweden; *Int'l*, pg. 687

Hendry, Robert, Pres. & Chief Exec. Officer--Saab Automobile AB, Nykoping, Sweden; *U.S. Public*, pg. 725

Henein, Rafick, Ph.D., Pres. & Chief Exec. Officer--Zenith Goldline Pharmaceuticals, Miami, FL; *U.S. Public*, pg. 915

Heng, Yeo Yong, Chief Exec. Officer--Singapore Reinsurance Corporation Limited, Singapore, Singapore; *Int'l*, pg. 1253

Henican, Joseph P., III, Vice Chm. & Chief Exec. Officer--Stewart Enterprises, Inc., Metairie, LA; *U.S. Public*, pg. 1518

Henley, A.B., Jr., Chm. Bd., Pres. & Chief Exec. Officer--Henley Paper Company, Greensboro, NC; *U.S. Private*, pg. 522

Henley, Dale, Pres. & Chief Exec. Officer--Haggen, Inc., Bellingham, WA; *U.S. Private*, pg. 493

Hennessey, Mike J., Pres. & Chief Exec. Officer--Jumping Jacks, Monett, MO; *U.S. Private*, pg. 767

Hennessey, Robert J., Chm., Pres. & Chief Exec. Officer--Genome Therapeutics Corporation, Waltham, MA; *U.S. Public*, pg. 730

Hennessy, Michael, Pres. & Chief Exec. Officer--Munro & Company, Inc., Hot Springs National Park, AR; *U.S. Private*, pg. 767

Henning, John R., Chief Exec. Officer--Columbia Coal Gasification Corp., Ashland, KY; *U.S. Public*, pg. 402

Henning, Peter H., Pres. & Chief Exec. Officer--Plano Molding Co., Plano, IL; *U.S. Private*, pg. 869

Henricks, Susan L., Pres. & Chief Exec. Officer--Metromail Corporation, Lombard, IL; *U.S. Public*, pg. 1102

Henry, James C., III, Pres. & Chief Exec. Officer--E.P. Henry Corporation, Woodbury, NJ; *U.S. Private*, pg. 522

Henry, Jerry, Chm. Bd., Pres. & Chief Exec. Officer--Johns Manville Corporation, Denver, CO; *U.S. Public*, pg. 927

Henry, Michael E., Chm. Bd. & Chief Exec. Officer--Jack Henry & Associates, Inc., Monett, MO; *U.S. Public*, pg. 808

Henry, William L., Pres. & Chief Exec. Officer--The Stroh Brewery Company, Detroit, MI; *U.S. Private*, pg. 1047

Hensley, Thomas L., Pres. & Chief Exec. Officer--Dairy Queen Corporate Store, Louisville, KY; *U.S. Public*, pg. 220

Henson, J. Peter, Chm. Bd. Pres. & Chief Exec. Officer--Flexible Products Company, Marietta, GA; *U.S. Private*, pg. 412

Hentschel, David A., Chm. Bd. & Chief Exec. Officer--Occidental Oil & Gas Corporation, Bakersfield, CA; *U.S. Public*, pg. 1210

Hepburn, Jim, Chief Exec. Officer--Milk Products Holdings (North America) Inc., Santa Rosa, CA; *Int'l*, pg. 923

Hepburn, Robin, Chief Exec. Officer--Ludgate Communications, London, United Kingdom; *U.S. Private*, pg. 1157

Hepher, Michael, Chm. & Chief Exec. Officer--Charterhouse Bank Ltd., London, United Kingdom; *Int'l*, pg. 342

Herb, Marvin J., Chm. Bd. & Chief Exec. Officer--Coca-Cola Bottling Co. of Chicago, Niles, IL; *U.S. Private*, pg. 248

Herbst, Jacob, Chm. Bd. & Chief Exec. Officer--IIS Intelligent Information Systems Ltd., Yokneam, Israel; *Int'l*, pg. 645

Herbster, Charles, Chm. Bd., Pres. & Chief Exec. Officer--Conklin Co. Inc., Shakopee, MN; *U.S. Private*, pg. 263

Herdemian, Gregory, Chief Exec. Officer & Chief Oper. Officer--Empire Diamond Corporation, New York, NY; *U.S. Private*, pg. 374

Herder, Gary A., Pres. & Chief Exec. Officer--Prab, Inc., Kalamazoo, MI; *U.S. Public*, pg. 1319

Herlaar, Will, Chief Exec.--Sulzer Metco (Benelux) B.V., Breda, Netherlands; *Int'l*, pg. 1308

Herlihy, Michael, Pres. & Chief Exec. Officer--Advest Bank, Hartford, CT; *U.S. Public*, pg. 23

Herlin, Antti, Deputy Chm. Bd. & Chief Exec. Officer--Kone Corporation, Helsinki, Finland; *Int'l*, pg. 746

Herlin, Robert M., Chm. Bd. & Chief Exec. Officer--Herlin Press Inc., West Haven, CT; *U.S. Private*, pg. 524

Herman, Jay A., Pres. & Chief Exec. Officer--Check Technology Corporation, Minnetonka, MN; *U.S. Public*, pg. 342

Hermida, Hector, Chief Exec. Officer--Juan Minetti S.A., Cordoba, Argentina; *Int'l*, pg. 869

Hernandez, Mike Acosta, Pres. & Chief Exec. Officer--Camino Real Chevrolet & Geo, Monterey Park, CA; *U.S. Private*, pg. 203

Hernandez, Roland, Pres. & Chief Exec. Officer--Telemundo Group, Inc., Hialeah, FL; *U.S. Public*, pg. 1570

Herndon, Hubert G., Pres. & Chief Exec. Officer--Bank of Morgan County, Madison, GA; *U.S. Public*, pg. 1371

Herrera, Carlos, Chief Exec. Officer--DNA Plant Technology Corp., Oakland, CA; *Int'l*, pg. 454

Herrero, Javier, Mng. Dir.--Iberdrola, S.A., Bilbao, Spain; *Int'l*, pg. 657

Herres, Robert T., Chm. Bd., Chief Exec. & Chief Oper. Officer--USAA (United Services Automobile Association), San Antonio, TX; *U.S. Private*, pg. 1114

Herrick, Todd W., Pres. & Chief Exec. Officer--Tecumseh Products Company, Tecumseh, MI; *U.S. Public*, pg. 1565

Herring, James, Pres. & Chief Exec. Officer--Friona Industries, L.P., Amarillo, TX; *U.S. Private*, pg. 429

Herring, Sherwin, Pres.--Southco Distributing Company, Goldsboro, NC; *U.S. Private*, pg. 1014

Herringer, Frank, Chm. Bd. & Chief Exec. Officer--Transamerica Corporation, San Francisco, CA; *U.S. Public*, pg. 1629

Herrmann, Dick, Pres. & Chief Exec. Officer--Health Economics Corporation, Dallas, TX; *U.S. Public*, pg. 588

Herrmann, John A., Pres. & Chief Exec. Officer--The Bridgeford Group, New York, NY; *Int'l*, pg. 674

Hersh, Harry, Pres. & Chief Exec. Officer--Suntory Water Group, Inc., Marietta, GA; *Int'l*, pg. 1321

Hersh, Robert, Chm. Bd., Pres. & Chief Exec. Officer--Catalina Lighting, Inc., Miami, FL; *U.S. Public*, pg. 314

Hershaft, Arthur, Chm. Bd., Pres. & Chief Exec. Officer--PAXAR Corporation, White Plains, NY; *U.S. Public*, pg. 1266

Herslow, John H., Pres. & Chief Exec. Officer--Sillcocks Plastics, Inc., Berkeley Heights, NJ; *U.S. Private*, pg. 63

Herson, Eugene E., Pres. & Chief Exec. Officer--EMCON, San Mateo, CA; *U.S. Public*, pg. 571

Herson, Gerald, Pres. & Chief Exec. Officer--Delair Group, L.L.C., Delair, NJ; *U.S. Private*, pg. 47

Herstrum, Al, Pres. & Chief Exec. Officer--Yazoo Power Equipment, LLC, Jackson, MS; *U.S. Private*, pg. 1195

Hertz, Arthur, Chm. Bd. & Chief Exec. Officer--Wometco Enterprises, Inc., Coral Gables, FL; *U.S. Private*, pg. 1186

Herzer, Richard K., Chm. Bd., Pres. & Chief Exec. Officer--IHOP Corp., Glendale, CA; *U.S. Public*, pg. 862

Herzig, Ron F., Pres. & Chief Exec. Officer--Fremont Indemnity Co./Medical Professional Liab. Div., Santa Monica, CA; *U.S. Public*, pg. 681

Hess, Gary, Pres. & Chief Exec. Officer--Vacu-Dry Company, Sebastopol, CA; *U.S. Public*, pg. 1704

Hess, John B., Chm. Bd. & Chief Exec. Officer--Amerada Hess Corporation, New York, NY; *U.S. Public*, pg. 65

Hesse, James D., Chief Oper. Officer & Exec. V.P.-Commercial--WHX Corporation, New York, NY; *U.S. Public*, pg. 1726

Hesse, Jay C., Pres. & Chief Exec. Officer--Automatic Equipment Mfg. Co., Pender, NE; *U.S. Private*, pg. 101

Hesser, Grant V., Pres. & Chief Exec. Officer--Maescher Industries, Inc., Cincinnati, OH; *U.S. Private*, pg. 694

Hessler, Kurt, Pres., Chief Exec. Officer & Chief Fin. Officer--Quarterdeck Corp., Marina Del Rey, CA; *U.S. Public*, pg. 1350

Hessler, Pierre, Chm. Bd. & Chief Exec. Officer--Gemini Consulting, Morristown, NJ; *Int'l*, pg. 264

Heston, W. Craig, Chm. Bd. & Chief Exec. Officer--Utica Mutual Insurance Company, New Hartford, NY; *U.S. Private*, pg. 1129

Hewson, Jeffrey, Pres. & Chief Exec. Officer--Beckley Cardy Group, Mansfield, OH; *U.S. Private*, pg. 190

Heye, Willliam B., Jr., Chm. Bd., Pres. & Chief Exec. Officer--SBE, Inc., San Ramon, CA; *U.S. Public*, pg. 1416

Heyerdahl d.y., Jens P., Pres. & Chief Exec. Officer--Orkla A.S.A., Oslo, Norway; *Int'l*, pg. 1010

Heyman, Lawrence S., Pres. & Chief Exec. Officer--Heyman Corporation, Niles, IL; *U.S. Private*, pg. 524

Heyman, Samuel J., Chm. Bd. & Chief Exec. Officer--GAF Corporation, Wayne, NJ; *U.S. Private*, pg. 433

Heyman, Samuel J., Chm. Bd. & Chief Exec. Officer--G Industries Corporation, Wilmington, DE; *U.S. Private*, pg. 433

Heyman, Samuel J., Chm. Bd. & Chief Exec. Officer--GAF Materials Corporation, Wayne, NJ; *U.S. Private*, pg. 433

Heyman, Samuel J., Chm. Bd. & Chief Exec. Officer--ISP Holdings, Inc., Wayne, NJ; *U.S. Public*, pg. 858

Heyman, Samuel J., Chief Exec. Officer--ISP Chemicals Inc., Calvert City, KY; *U.S. Public*, pg. 858

Heyman, Samuel J., Chief Exec. Officer--ISP Technologies Inc., Texas City, TX; *U.S. Public*, pg. 859

Heyworth, Anthony, Chm. Bd. & Chief Exec. Officer--Society National Bank, Indiana, South Bend, IN; *U.S. Public*, pg. 954

Hibon, George, Chm. Bd. & Chief Exec. Officer--Connaught Laboratories Limited, Willowdale, Canada; *Int'l*, pg. 1109

Hickey, Brian, Chief Exec. Officer--Silhouette Books, New York, NY; *Int'l*, pg. 1402

Hickey, Brian E., Pres. & Chief Exec. Officer--Harlequin Enterprises Ltd., Don Mills, Canada; *Int'l*, pg. 1402

Hickey, William M., Pres. & Chief Exec. Officer--Lapham-Hickey Steel Corp., Chicago, IL; *U.S. Private*, pg. 651

Hickingbotham, Frank D., Chm. Bd. & Chief Exec. Officer--TCBY Enterprises Inc., Little Rock, AR; *U.S. Public*, pg. 1553

Hickman, Waymon L., Chm. Bd. & Chief Exec. Officer--First Farmers & Merchants National Bank, Columbia, TN; *U.S. Private*, pg. 407

Hicks, Joseph D., Pres. & Chief Exec. Officer--Siecor Corporation, Saskatoon, Canada; *U.S. Public*, pg. 449

Hicks, Thomas O., Chm. Bd., Chief Exec. Officer & Mng. Dir.--Hicks, Muse, Tate & Furst Inc., Dallas, TX; *U.S. Private*, pg. 526

Hickson, Richard G., Pres. & Chief Exec. Officer--Trustmark Corporation, Jackson, MS; *U.S. Public*, pg. 1643

Hickson, Richard G., Vice Chm. & Chief Exec. Officer--Trustmark National Bank, Jackson, MS; *U.S. Public*, pg. 1643

Hiemstra, R.J.J., Chief Exec. Officer--Oremco Inc., New York, NY; *Int'l*, pg. 754

Higginbotham, Alton, Chief Exec. Officer & Gen. Mgr.--First Electric Cooperative, Corp., Jacksonville, AR; *U.S. Private*, pg. 407

Higginbotham, Richard A., Pres. & Chief Exec. Officer--Fleet Bank, N.A., Hartford, CT; *U.S. Public*, pg. 649

Higginbotham, Richard A., Pres. & Chief Exec. Officer--Fleet National Bank of Connecticut, Hartford, CT; *U.S. Public*, pg. 649

Higginbotham, Tommy, Chief Exec. Officer--Ozark Motor Lines, Memphis, TN; *U.S. Private*, pg. 825

Higgins, Bill, Pres. & Chief Exec. Officer--Dillingham Construction Corporation, Pleasanton, CA; *U.S. Private*, pg. 333

Higgins, Clark, Chief Exec. Officer--Jonathan Manufacturing Corp., Fullerton, CA; *U.S. Private*, pg. 595

Higgins, David L., Chm. Bd. & Chief Exec. Officer--DVI Business Credit, Inc., Newport Beach, CA; *U.S. Public*, pg. 476

Higgins, Larry B., Chm. Bd., Pres. & Chief Exec. Officer--H & H Tube & Manufacturing Co., Vanderbilt, MI; *U.S. Private*, pg. 489

Higgins, Robert J., Pres. & Chief Exec. Officer--Fleet National Bank, Providence, RI; *U.S. Public*, pg. 649

Higgins, Robert J., Chm. Bd., Pres. & Chief Exec. Officer--Trans World Entertainment Corporation, Albany, NY; *U.S. Public*, pg. 1629

Higgins, Walter M., Chm. Bd., Pres. & Chief Exec. Officer--Sierra Pacific Resources, Reno, NV; *U.S. Public*, pg. 1470

Highland, Glenn W., Pres. & Chief Exec. Officer--DataCard Corporation, Minnetonka, MN; *U.S. Private*, pg. 312

Hightower, Lloyd A., Pres. & Chief Exec. Officer--Williams Field Services, Tulsa, OK; *U.S. Public*, pg. 1769

Hightower, Sr., Neil H., Pres. & Chief Exec. Officer--Thomaston Mills, Inc., Thomaston, GA; *U.S. Public*, pg. 1599

Higuchi, Tatsuo, Pres. & Chief Exec. Officer--Pharmavite Corp., Mission Hills, CA; *U.S. Private*, pg. 860

Higuchi, Tatsuo, Pres. & Chief Exec. Officer--Pharmavite Corporation, Mission Hills, CA; *Int'l*, pg. 1013

Higurashi, Takeshi, Chm. Bd., Pres. & Chief Exec. Officer--Subaru of America, Inc., Cherry Hill, NJ; *Int'l*, pg. 523

Hikansson, Bo, Chief Exec. Officer--ACTIVE BioTech AB, Malmo, Sweden; *Int'l*, pg. 23

Hilbert, Stephen, Chm. Bd., Pres. & Chief Exec. Officer--CHIC, Carmel, IN; *U.S. Public*, pg. 433

Hilbert, Stephen, Chm. Bd., Pres. & Chief Exec. Officer--Intermediate Holdings, Inc., Carmel, IN; *U.S. Public*, pg. 433

Hilbert, Steve, Chief Exec. Officer--Conseco Capital Partners II, L.P., New York, NY; *U.S. Public*, pg. 432

Hilbert, Steven C., Chm. Bd., Pres. & Chief Exec. Officer--Conseco Inc., Carmel, IN; *U.S. Public*, pg. 432

Hilbert, William M., Pres. & Chief Exec. Officer--PHB Die Casting, Fairview, PA; *U.S. Private*, pg. 826

Hilbert, William M., Sr., Pres. & Chief Exec. Officer--PHB Machining Division, Fairview, PA; *U.S. Private*, pg. 826

Hilbert, William M., Sr., Pres. & Chief Exec. Officer--PHB Plastic & Rubber Molding Division, Fairview, PA; *U.S. Private*, pg. 826

Hildebrand, Willard R., Pres. & Chief Exec. Officer--Bucyrus International, South Milwaukee, WI; *U.S. Private*, pg. 177

Hill, Allen M., Pres. & Chief Exec. Officer--DPL Inc., Dayton, OH; *U.S. Public*, pg. 473

Hill, Allen M., Pres. & Chief Exec. Officer--Dayton Power & Light Co., Dayton, OH; *U.S. Public*, pg. 473

Hill, Brice E., Pres. & Chief Exec. Officer--Centex Construction Group, Inc., Dallas, TX; *U.S. Public*, pg. 322

Hill, Dan J., Chm. Bd. & Chief Exec. Officer--Coastal Fuels Marketing, Inc., Miami, FL; *U.S. Public*, pg. 390

Hill, Edward G., Jr., Pres. & Chief Exec. Officer--Abco Markets, Inc., Phoenix, AZ; *U.S. Private*, pg. 10

Hill, Elmer W., Pres. & Chief Exec. Officer--GEC Precision Corp., Wellington, KS; *Int'l*, pg. 545

Hill, George M., Chief Exec. Officer--McGuffey's Restaurants, Inc., Asheville, NC; *U.S. Private*, pg. 721

Hill, J. Donald, Chm. Bd., Pres. & Chief Exec. Officer--Excel Technology, Inc., New York, NY; *U.S. Public*, pg. 599

Hill, J.S., Chief Exec. Officer--MG Natural Gas Corporation, Houston, TX; *Int'l*, pg. 862

Hill, Lester, Chm. Bd. & Chief Exec. Officer--Pacific Scientific Company, Newport Beach, CA; *U.S. Public*, pg. 1250

Hill, R.G., Grp. Gen. Mgr. & Dir.--Q.U.F. Industries Ltd., Brisbane, Australia; *Int'l*, pg. 1074

Hill, Richard S., Chm. Bd., Pres. & Chief Exec. Officer--Novellus Systems, Inc., San Jose, CA; *U.S. Public*, pg. 1204

Hill, Robert D., Pres. & Chief Exec. Officer--Davel Communications Group, Inc., Jacksonville, IL; *U.S. Public*, pg. 488

Hill, Roger W., Pres. & Chief Exec. Officer--Holly Sugar Corporation, Sugar Land, TX; *U.S. Public*, pg. 872

Hill, Stephen, Chief Exec. Officer--The Financial Times Ltd., London, United Kingdom; *Int'l*, pg. 1025

Hill, William R., Pres. & Chief Exec. Officer--OAO Technology Solutions, Inc., Greenbelt, MD; *U.S. Public*, pg. 1425

Hillenbrand, W August, Pres. & Chief Exec. Officer--Hillenbrand Industries, Inc., Batesville, IN; *U.S. Public*, pg. 828

Hillerich, John A., III, Pres. & Chief Exec. Officer--Hillerich & Bradsby Co., Louisville, KY; *U.S. Private*, pg. 530

Hillgarth, Tristan, Chief Exec. Officer-Europe--Invesco Group Asset Management Ltd., London, United Kingdom; *Int'l*, pg. 685

Hillis, Kelly, Pres. & Chief Exec. Officer--Regions Bank/Carroll County, Carrollton, GA; *U.S. Public*, pg. 1372

Hillman, Howard B., Chm. Bd., Pres. & Chief Exec. Officer--Auto-trol Technology Corporation, Denver, CO; *U.S. Public*, pg. 148

Hillman, Lee S., Pres. & Chief Exec. Officer--Bally Total Fitness Holdings Corporation, Chicago, IL; *U.S. Public*, pg. 171

Hilsabeck, Frank H., Pres. & Chief Exec. Officer--Aliant Communications Inc., Lincoln, NE; *U.S. Public*, pg. 40

Hilsberg, Marshall, Chm. & Chief Exec. Officer--Lord & Taylor, New York, NY; *U.S. Public*, pg. 1064

Hilsinger, Arthur R., Chm. Bd. & Chief Exec. Officer--The Hilsinger Co. L.P., Plainville, MA; *U.S. Private*, pg. 530

Hilz, Mark T., Pres. & Chief Exec. Officer--PC Service Source, Inc., Dallas, TX; *U.S. Public*, pg. 1240

Himeles, Martin S., Chm. Bd. & Chief Exec. Officer--Standard Medical Imaging, Inc., Columbia, MD; *U.S. Private*, pg. 1032

Himes, Michael, Chief Exec. Officer--Petroleum Traders Corporation, Fort Wayne, IN; *U.S. Private*, pg. 859

Hinchliffe, Allan, Chief Oper. Officer--Mikron Corp. Anderson, Anderson, SC; *Int'l*, pg. 866

Hinden, Milton, Chief Exec. Officer--Duro Dyne Corporation, Farmingdale, NY; *U.S. Private*, pg. 349

Hindery, Leo, Jr., Pres. & Chief Exec. Officer--TCI Communications, Inc., Englewood, CO; *U.S. Public*, pg. 1554

Hindman, Don J., Chm. Bd., Pres. & Chief Exec. Officer--Clark Foodservice, Inc., Elk Grove Village, IL; *U.S. Private*, pg. 242

Hinds, Thomas M., Chm. Bd., Pres. & Chief Exec. Officer--Regions Bank/Mobile, Mobile, AL; *U.S. Public*, pg. 1372

Hiner, Glen H., Chm. Bd. & Chief Exec. Officer--Owens Corning, Toledo, OH; *U.S. Public*, pg. 1236

Hinfey, John K., Pres. & Chief Exec. Officer--United Planners' Financial Services of America, Scottsdale, AZ; *U.S. Private*, pg. 831

Hinkle, Max E., Chief Exec. Officer--R.O. Whitesell & Associates, Inc, Indianapolis, IN; *U.S. Private*, pg. 1173

Hinman, Kirk, Pres., Chief Exec. Officer, Chief Fin. Officer & Treas.--Rome Strip Steel Co., Inc., Rome, NY; *U.S. Private*, pg. 942

Hinshaw, W. Eric, Pres. & Chief Exec. Officer--Kingsdown, Inc., Mebane, NC; *U.S. Private*, pg. 622

Hinson, James N., Jr., Chm. Bd. & Chief Exec. Officer--First Virginia Bank-Southwest, Roanoke, VA; *U.S. Public*, pg. 642

Hinton, Leslie, Chief Exec. Officer--News America Publishing Inc., New York, NY; *Int'l*, pg. 925

Hipp, Frederick R., Pres. & Chief Exec. Officer--Houlihan's Restaurant Group, Kansas City, MO; *U.S. Public*, pg. 841

Hipp, Ray, Pres. & Chief Exec. Officer--ITI Marketing Services, Inc., Omaha, NE; *U.S. Private*, pg. 555

Hipp, W. Hayne, Chm. Bd., Pres. & Chief Exec. Officer--Liberty Corporation, Greenville, SC; *U.S. Public*, pg. 991

Hippler, John D., Pres. & Chief Exec. Officer--Bank of America, Coeur D'Alene, ID; *U.S. Public*, pg. 180

Hirai, Katsuhiko, Pres. & Chief Exec. Officer--Toray Industries, Inc., Tokyo, Japan; *Int'l*, pg. 1399

Hiranandani, Hiro, Pres. & Chief Exec. Officer--Computer Power Incorporated, High Bridge, NJ; *U.S. Public*, pg. 421

Hirano, Sadayoshi, Chief Oper. Officer--Makita Sp. Z O.O., Bielsko-Biala, Poland; *Int'l*, pg. 832

Hirano, Sadayoshi, Chief Oper. Officer--Makita S.R.O., Brno, Czech Republic; *Int'l*, pg. 832

Hirlinger, Franz-Hermann, Chief Rep.--Bayerische Landesbank Girozentrale, Tokyo, Japan; *Int'l*, pg. 177

Hirsch, Laurence E., Chm. Bd. & Chief Exec. Officer--Centex Corporation, Dallas, TX; *U.S. Public*, pg. 322

Hirsch, Leon C., Chm. Bd. & Chief Exec. Officer--U.S. Surgical Corp., Norwalk, CT; *U.S. Public*, pg. 1687

Hirsch, Nathan, Pres. & Chief Exec. Officer--Junior Gallery Ltd., New York, NY; *U.S. Private*, pg. 602

Hirsch, Robert F., Chief Exec. Officer--Gold Eagle Company, Chicago, IL; *U.S. Private*, pg. 459

Hirsch, Ruth, Chief Exec. Officer--Dubek Ltd., Tel Aviv, Israel; *Int'l*, pg. 421

Hirsch, Sheldon, Chief Exec. Officer--The Summit Media Group, New York, NY; *U.S. Private*, pg. 1050

Hirsch, William B., Pres. & Chief Exec. Officer--Keystone Powdered Metal Company, Saint Marys, PA; *U.S. Private*, pg. 619

Hirschfeld, David L., Pres., Chief Exec. Officer & Treas.--Hirschfeld, Inc., San Angelo, TX; *U.S. Private*, pg. 530

Hirschfield, Alan J., Co-Chm. Bd. & Co-Chief Exec. Officer--Data Broadcasting Corporation, Jackson, WY; *U.S. Public*, pg. 484

Hirschorn, Martin, Pres. & Chief Exec. Officer--Industrial Acoustics Company, Inc., Bronx, NY; *U.S. Public*, pg. 875

Hirshman, Karl J., Pres. & Chief Oper. Officer--Doron Precision Systems, Inc., Binghamton, NY; *U.S. Private*, pg. 341

Hirsig, Alan R., Pres. & Chief Exec. Officer--ARCO Chemical Co., Newtown Square, PA; *U.S. Public*, pg. 144

Hirt, David J., Pres. & Chief Exec. Officer--Batesville Casket Company, Inc., Batesville, IN; *U.S. Public*, pg. 828

Hishmeh, Basem L., Pres. & Chief Exec. Officer--Aerco International Inc., Northvale, NJ; *U.S. Private*, pg. 23

Hislof, Ian, Pres. & Chief Exec. Officer--Capital Controls Company Inc., Colmar, PA; *Int'l*, pg. 1226

Hitchcock, Fritz, Pres. & Chief Exec. Officer--Hitchcock Automotive Resources, City of Industry, CA; *U.S. Private*, pg. 531

Hitchcock, Kenneth W., Chm. Bd. & Chief Exec. Officer--The Whyte & Mackay Group Plc., Glasgow, United Kingdom; *U.S. Public*, pg. 675

Hitchcock, Timothy R., Pres. & Chief Exec. Officer--Hitchcock Industries, Inc., Bloomington, MN; *U.S. Private*, pg. 531

Hitchens, Roy, Chief Exec.--Staveley Industries PLC, Croydon, United Kingdom; *Int'l*, pg. 1298

Hite, R. Lee, Chm. Bd., Pres. & Chief Exec. Officer--The Hite Company, Altoona, PA; *U.S. Private*, pg. 531

Hixon, Thomas, Chm. Bd., Pres. & Chief Exec. Officer--Gulf South Medical Supply, Inc., Ridgeland, MS; *U.S. Public*, pg. 1294

Hjartland, Gunnar, Pres. & Chief Exec. Officer--Jotun A/S, Sandefjord, Norway; *Int'l*, pg. 714

Ho, Anthony, Chief Exec. Officer--The Universal Hardware and Plastic Fty. Ltd., Kowloon, Hong Kong; *Int'l*, pg. 430

Ho, Christopher, Chm. Bd. & Chief Exec. Officer--GrandeTel Technologies Inc., Richmond, Canada; *Int'l*, pg. 556

Hoag, James, Chief Exec. Officer--Meridian Sports/Water Sports Group, New York, NY; *U.S. Private*, pg. 689

Hoare, David, Chief Exec. Officer--Laura Ashley Holdings Plc, Maidenhead, United Kingdom; *Int'l*, pg. 804

Hoare, Toby, Chief Exec. Officer-Y&R London--Young & Rubicam Holdings Ltd., London, United Kingdom; *U.S. Private*, pg. 1199

Hobbins, Jeremy P.E., Chief Exec. Officer--Inchcape Bdh, Singapore, Singapore; *Int'l*, pg. 672

Hobbs, Eamonn P., Pres. & Chief Exec. Officer--AngioDynamics, Queensbury, NY; *U.S. Public*, pg. 540

Hobbs, Gerald S., Pres. & Chief Exec. Officer--VNU USA, Inc., New York, NY; *Int'l*, pg. 1447

Hobbs, Jerry, Chief Exec. Officer--Billboard Magazine, New York, NY; *Int'l*, pg. 1446

Hobbs, Peter, Chief Exec. Officer--Tollycraft Yacht Corporation, San Diego, CA; *U.S. Public*, pg. 1620

Hobday, Charles W., Exec. V.P. & Gen. Mgr.--Lancaster Malleable Castings Company, Lancaster, PA; *U.S. Private*, pg. 645

Hochberg, Larry J., Chm. Bd. & Chief Exec. Officer--Sport Mart, Inc., Wheeling, IL; *U.S. Public*, pg. 1499

Hochberg, Mitchell C., Pres. & Chief Exec. Officer--Spectrum Skanska Inc., Greenwich, CT; *Int'l*, pg. 1261

Hochfelder, J. Gene, Chm. & Chief Exec. Officer--Beldoch Industries, West Hempstead, NY; *U.S. Public*, pg. 519

Hock, Conrad, Jr., Chm. Bd. & Chief Exec. Officer--Williams Foods Inc., Lenexa, KS; *U.S. Private*, pg. 1178

Hockaday, Irvine O., Jr., Pres. & Chief Exec. Officer--Hallmark Cards, Inc., Kansas City, MO; *U.S. Private*, pg. 495

Hockmeyer, Wayne T., Ph.D., Chm. Bd. & Chief Exec. Officer--MedImmune, Inc., Gaithersburg, MD; *U.S. Public*, *pg. 1081*

Hod, Nathan, Pres. & Chief Exec. Officer--DSP Communications Inc., Cupertino, CA; *U.S. Public*, pg. 475

Hodes, Alan, Chief Exec. Officer--Pen-Tab Industries, Inc., Front Royal, VA; *U.S. Private*, pg. 848

Hodges, Larry, Pres. & Chief Exec. Officer--Pretzel Time Inc., Salt Lake City, UT; *U.S. Private*, pg. 688

Hodges, Nicholas R., Chief Exec.--London International Group plc, London, United Kingdom; *Int'l*, pg. 815

Hodgson, Patrick W.E., Chm. Bd. & Chief Exec. Officer--Todd Pacific Shipyards Corp., Seattle, WA; *U.S. Public*, pg. 1619

Hodnik, David F., Pres. & Chief Exec. Officer--Ace Hardware Corporation, Oak Brook, IL; *U.S. Private*, pg. 12

Hodowal, John R., Chm. Bd. & Pres.--Ipalco Enterprises, Inc., Indianapolis, IN; *U.S. Public*, pg. 912

Hodowal, John R., Chm. Bd. & Chief Exec. Officer--Cleveland District Cooling Corp., Cleveland, OH; *U.S. Public*, pg. 913

Hoeft, Jack, Chm. Bd. & Chief Exec. Officer--Bantam Doubleday Dell Publishing Group, Inc., New York, NY; *Int'l*, pg. 191

Hoeksema, Timothy E., Chm. Bd. & Chief Exec. Officer--K-C Aviation Inc., Neenah, WI; *U.S. Public*, pg. 959

Hoeksema, Timothy E., Chm. Bd., Pres. & Chief Exec. Officer--Midwest Express Holdings, Inc., Oak Creek, WI; *U.S. Public*, pg. 1111

Hoeksema, Timothy E., Chm. Bd., Pres. & Chief Exec. Officer--Midwest Express Airlines, Inc., Oak Creek, WI; *U.S. Public*, pg. 1111

Hoelzer, Dennis, Chm. Bd., Pres. & Chief Exec. Officer--Sentinel Technologies Inc., Downers Grove, IL; *U.S. Private*, pg. 984

Hoen-Saric, Christopher, R., Chief Exec. Officer--Sylvan Learning Systems Inc., Baltimore, MD; *U.S. Public*, pg. 1545

Hoenshell, Craig, Chm. Bd. & Chief Exec. Officer--Avis Rent A Car System, Inc., Garden City, NY; *U.S. Public*, pg. 321

Hoenshell, R. Craig, Chm. Bd. & Chief Exec. Officer--Avis Car Leasing, Garden City, NY; *U.S. Public*, pg. 321

Hoerner, John Lee, Grp. Chief Exec.--The Burton Group PLC, London, United Kingdom; *Int'l*, pg. 237

Hoeven, John, Pres. & Chief Exec. Officer--Bank Of North Dakota, Bismarck, ND; *U.S. Private*, pg. 114

Hoey, John J., Pres. & Chief Exec. Officer--Hondo Oil & Gas Company, Roswell, NM; *Int'l*, pg. 818

Hofer, Judith K., Pres. & Chief Exec. Officer--Filene's, Boston, MA; *U.S. Public*, pg. 1063

Hoffer, Robert A., Sr., Pres. & Chief Exec. Officer--Hoffer Plastics Corporation, South Elgin, IL; *U.S. Private*, pg. 532

Hoffman, Al, Jr., Chief Exec. Officer--WCI Communities, Inc., Bonita Springs, FL; *U.S. Private*, pg. 1144

Hoffman, Donald, Chief Exec. Officer--Creative Playthings Ltd., Framingham, MA; *U.S. Private*, pg. 287

Hoffman, Ebba C., Chm. Bd., Pres., Chief Exec. Officer & Chief Fin. Officer--Smead Manufacturing Company, Hastings, MN; *U.S. Private*, pg. 1006

Hoffman, G.L., Chm. Bd., Pres., Chief Exec. Officer & Sec.--Insignia Systems, Inc., Minnetonka, MN; *U.S. Public*, pg. 881

Hoffman, Gary T., Chief Exec. Officer--MML Investors Services, Inc., Springfield, MA; *U.S. Private*, pg. 712

Hoffman, Harvey, Pres. & Chief Exec. Officer--Fraenkel Company, Baton Rouge, LA; *U.S. Private*, pg. 423

Hoffman, Jerry V., Chm. Bd., Pres. & Chief Exec. Officer--Berry Petroleum Company, Taft, CA; *U.S. Public*, pg. 223

Hoffman, Jerry V., Chief Exec. Officer--Berry Petroleum Company-Coastal Operations, Oxnard, CA; *U.S. Public*, pg. 223

Hoffman, Jerry V., Chief Exec. Officer--Berry Oil Trading and Transportation, Taft, CA; *U.S. Public*, pg. 223

Hoffman, Mark S., Pres. & Chief Exec. Officer--A.P.S., Memphis, TN; *U.S. Public*, pg. 10

Hoffman, Martin, Pres., Chief Exec. & Fin. Officer, Treas.--Designatronics, Inc., New Hyde Park, NY; *U.S. Private*, pg. 327

Hoffmeyer, Stig, Chief Exec. Officer--Dansk Industri Syndikat A/S, Herlev, Denmark; *Int'l*, pg. 381

Hofmann, Bernard M., Chm. Bd. & Chief Exec. Officer--Hofmann Industries, Inc., Sinking Spring, PA; *U.S. Private*, pg. 533

Hofmann, George B., II, Pres. & Chief Exec. Officer--Nevada State Bank, Las Vegas, NV; *U.S. Public*, pg. 1793

Hofmann, Herbert C., Pres. & Chief Exec. Officer--Bulova Corporation, Woodside, NY; *U.S. Public*, pg. 1010

Hofmann, Richard D., Chm. Bd. & Chief Exec. Officer--Kolmar Laboratories, Inc., Port Jervis, NY; *Int'l*, pg. 239

Hogan, Dan W., Pres. & Chief Exec. Officer--NBC Bank, FSB (Knoxville), Knoxville, TN; *U.S. Public*, pg. 1155

Hogan, Frank J., Pres. & Chief Exec. Officer--Overseas Service Corporation, West Palm Beach, FL; *U.S. Private*, *pg. 823*

Hogan, Thomas J., Pres. & Chief Exec. Officer--Foley's, Houston, TX; *U.S. Public*, pg. 1063

Hogan, Timothy P., Chm. Bd., Pres. & Chief Exec. Officer--Warmington Homes, Costa Mesa, CA; *U.S. Private*, pg. 1150
Hogarty, Daniel J. Jr., Pres. & Chief Exec. Officer--The Troy Savings Bank, Troy, NY; *U.S. Private*, pg. 1106
Hoge, Ronald N., Pres. & Chief Exec. Officer--MagneTek, Inc., Nashville, TN; *U.S. Public*, pg. 1037
Hogg, Michael, Chm. Bd. & Chief Exec. Officer--Michael Hogg-Young & Rubicam (Pvt.) Ltd., Harare, Zimbabwe; *U.S. Private*, pg. 1198
Hogg, Robert H., III, Chief Exec. Officer & Pres.--Better Brands Of Atlanta, Inc., Atlanta, GA; *U.S. Private*, pg. 141
Hoglund, Ray G., Chief Exec. Officer--ESAB Welding & Cutting Products, Hanover, PA; *Int'l*, pg. 281
Hoke, Joe, Chm. Bd. & Chief Exec. Officer--Mintz & Hoke Inc., Avon, CT; *U.S. Private*, pg. 751
Hokin, Myron, Pres. & Chief Exec. Officer--Century America Corporation, Chicago, IL; *U.S. Private*, pg. 225
Holas, Frank W., Pres. & Chief Exec. Officer--Rich SeaPak Corp., Saint Simons Island, GA; *U.S. Private*, pg. 928
Holbrook, George T., Jr., Pres. & Chief Exec. Officer--Reliance Surety Corp., Philadelphia, PA; *U.S. Public*, pg. 1374
Holder, Richard G., Chm. & Chief Exec. Officer--Mount Vernon Plastics Company, Sparks, NV; *U.S. Public*, pg. 1386
Holder, Thomas M., Chief Exec. Officer--Holder Construction Company, Atlanta, GA; *U.S. Private*, pg. 534
Holding, Lewis R., Chm. Bd. & Chief Exec. Officer--First Citizens Banc Shares, Inc., Raleigh, NC; *U.S. Public*, pg. 628
Holding, R. Earl, Chief Exec. Officer--Little America Hotels, Salt Lake City, UT; *U.S. Private*, pg. 1003
Holding, R.E., Pres. & Chief Exec. Officer--Sinclair Oil Corp., Salt Lake City, UT; *U.S. Private*, pg. 1003
Holdt, Terry N., Pres. & Chief Exec. Officer--S3 Incorporated, Santa Clara, CA; *U.S. Public*, pg. 1415
Holguin, Juan, Chief Exec. Officer--Aero Peru Corporation, Coral Gables, FL; *U.S. Private*, pg. 24
Holland, D.J., Chief Exec. Officer--Wimpey Homes Holdings Ltd., London, United Kingdom; *Int'l*, pg. 1510
Holland, G. Ed, Jr., Pres. & Chief Exec. Officer--Savannah Electric & Power Co., Savannah, GA; *U.S. Public*, pg. 1490
Holland, James T., Pres. & Chief Exec. Officer--O'Sullivan Corporation, Winchester, VA; *U.S. Public*, pg. 1234
Holland, John B., Chm. Bd. & Chief Exec. Officer--Union Underwear Co., Inc., Bowling Green, KY; *U.S. Public*, pg. 686
Holland, Michael C., Pres. & Chief Exec. Officer--Mojave Pipeline Company, Bakersfield, CA; *U.S. Public*, pg. 567
Holland, Richard F., Pres. & Chief Exec. Officer--D/B Cameras Microcheck Division, Fullerton, CA; *U.S. Private*, pg. 5
Holland, Richard F., Pres. & Chief Exec. Officer--Electro-Mechanical Instruments Div., Fullerton, CA; *U.S. Private*, pg. 5
Holland, Richard F., Pres. & Chief Exec. Officer--Precision Power Div., Fullerton, CA; *U.S. Private*, pg. 5
Holland, Willard R., Chm. Bd. & Chief Exec. Officer--FirstEnergy Corp., Akron, OH; *U.S. Public*, pg. 644
Holland, Willard R., Chm. Bd. & Chief Exec. Officer--Pennsylvania Power Co., New Castle, PA; *U.S. Public*, pg. 645
Holland, William R., Chm. & Chief Exec. Officer--United Dominion Industries, Ltd., Charlotte, NC; *U.S. Public*, pg. 1675
Hollander, Milton B., Chief Exec. Officer--Newport Electronics, Inc., Santa Ana, CA; *U.S. Private*, pg. 816
Holleman, Matthew, Pres. & Chief Exec. Officer--Mississippi Valley Gas Co., Jackson, MS; *U.S. Private*, pg. 753
Holler, J., Pres. & Chief Exec. Officer--PNC Bank, Cincinnati, OH; *U.S. Public*, pg. 1242
Holley, Rick R., Pres. & Chief Exec. Officer--Plum Creek Timber Co., L.P., Seattle, WA; *U.S. Public*, pg. 1311
Hollick, Clive, Lord, Chief Exec. Officer--United News & Media plc, London, United Kingdom; *Int'l*, pg. 1443
Hollick, Roger E., Chief Exec. Officer--Derbyshire Building Society, Duffield, United Kingdom; *Int'l*, pg. 394
Holliday, Charles O., Pres. & Chief Exec. Officer--Du Pont (E.I. Du Pont De Nemours & Co.), Wilmington, DE; *U.S. Public*, pg. 530
Holliman, W.G., Pres. & Chief Exec. Officer--Furniture Brands International Inc., Saint Louis, MO; *U.S. Public*, pg. 688
Hollingsworth, B.B., Jr., Chm. Bd., Pres. & Chief Exec. Officer--Group 1 Automotive, Inc., Houston, TX; *U.S. Public*, pg. 767
Hollister, Dean, Pres. & Chief Exec. Officer--Hollister Advertising, New Providence, NJ; *U.S. Public*, pg. 830
Holloran, John, Chief Exec.--Reed Books, London, United Kingdom; *Int'l*, pg. 1093
Holloway, Gary, Chief Exec. Officer-Global Debt Markets--National Westminster Bank PLC, London, United Kingdom; *Int'l*, pg. 910
Holloway, J.G., Chief Exec. Officer--Humberside Holdings Ltd, Grimsby, United Kingdom; *Int'l*, pg. 1065
Holly, Brian, Pres. & Chief Exec. Officer--ITK Telecommunications, Inc., Chelmsford, MA; *U.S. Private*, pg. 556
Holman, C. Ray, Chm. Bd. & Chief Exec. Officer--Mallinckrodt Inc., Saint Louis, MO; *U.S. Public*, pg. 1039
Holman, Edwin J., Chm. Bd., Pres. & Chief Exec. Officer--Petrie Retail, Inc., Secaucus, NJ; *U.S. Private*, pg. 858
Holman, W.H., Jr., Chm. Bd., Chief Exec. & Oper. Officers--Jitney-Jungle Stores of America, Inc., Jackson, MS; *U.S.* Private, pg. 588
Holman, W.H., Jr., Chm. Bd., Chief Exec. & Chief Oper. Officer--Southern Jitney-Jungle, Inc., Jackson, MS; *U.S. Private*, pg. 588
Holman, W.H., Jr., Chm. Bd., Chief Exec. & Chief Oper. Officer--Jitney-Jungle Bakery, Inc., Jackson, MS; *U.S. Private*, pg. 588
Holmes, Arthur, Chm. Bd. & Chief Exec. Officer--Chart Industries, Inc., Cleveland, OH; *U.S. Public*, pg. 336
Holmes, Arthur, Chm. & Chief Exec. Officer--PSI-Process Systems International, Inc., Cleveland, OH; *U.S. Public*, pg. 336
Holmes, Carl, Chief Exec. Officer--Chemical Bank Thumb Area, Caro, MI; *U.S. Public*, pg. 345
Holmes, David R., Chm., Pres. & Chief Exec. Officer--The Reynolds and Reynolds Company, Dayton, OH; *U.S. Public*, pg. 1384
Holmes, Frank E., Dr., Exec. V.P., Chief Oper. Officer & Sec.--Semi-Tech Corporation, Markham, Canada; *Int'l*, pg. 1220
Holmes, George B., Pres., Chief Exec. & Chief Fin. Officer--Dombrowski & Holmes, Inc., Hammond, IN; *U.S. Private*, *pg. 338*
Holmes, Martin, Pres. & Chief Exec. Officer--Belvedere Company, Belvidere, IL; *U.S. Private*, pg. 1008
Holmes, Neal H., Chm. Bd. & Chief Exec. Officer--Allied Security, Inc., Pittsburgh, PA; *U.S. Private*, pg. 40
Holmstrom, Tom, Pres. & Chief Exec. Officer--Corporate Express Office Products, Arden Hills, MN; *U.S. Public*, pg. 449
Holness, Gordon V.R., Pres. & Chief Exec. Officer--Albert Kahn Associates, Inc., Detroit, MI; *U.S. Private*, pg. 604
Holsapple, Jerry L., Pres. & Chief Exec. Officer--Bright National Bank, Flora, IN; *U.S. Public*, pg. 633
Holsworth, William C., Pres. & Chief Exec. Officer--FINAST, Maple Heights, OH; *Int'l*, pg. 750
Holt, Dennis F., Chm. Bd., Pres. & Chief Exec. Officer--Western International Media Corporation, Los Angeles, CA; *U.S. Private*, pg. 1165
Holt, Dennis F., Chm. Bd. & Chief Exec. Officer--Western Motivational Incentives Group, Inc., Los Angeles, CA; *U.S. Private*, pg. 1167
Holt, Stephen L., Chief Exec. Officer-IL Weeklies--O'Fallon Progress, O Fallon, IL; *U.S. Public*, pg. 964
Holten, John V., Chm. Bd. & Chief Exec. Officer--Holberg Industries, Inc., Greenwich, CT; *U.S. Private*, pg. 533
Holten, John V., Chm. Bd. & Chief Exec. Officer--Nebco Evans Holding Co., Greenwich, CT; *U.S. Private*, pg. 533
Holton, Rick, Chief Oper. Officer--Automation Finishing Inc., Cleveland, OH; *U.S. Private*, pg. 426
Holtschlag, Steve, Pres. & Chief Exec. Officer--Consolidated Systems, Inc., Columbia, SC; *U.S. Private*, pg. 266
Holtz, Harry L., Pres. & Chief Exec. Officer--Great Northern Iron Ore Properties, Saint Paul, MN; *U.S. Public*, pg. 760
Holtzman, Seymour, Pres. & Chief Exec. Officer--Jewelcor Companies, Wilkes-Barre, PA; *U.S. Private*, pg. 587
Holveck, David P., Chief Exec. Officer--Centocor, Inc., Malvern, PA; *U.S. Public*, pg. 323
Holzer, Edwin H., Chm. Bd., Chief Exec. Officer & Mng. Dir.--Lois/EJL Chicago, Chicago, IL; *U.S. Public*, pg. 1011
Holzhey, Fritz, Chief Exec. Officer--Haindl Papier GmbH, Augsburg, Germany; *Int'l*, pg. 586
Holzhey, Georg, Dr., Chief Exec. Officer--Haindl Papier GmbH, Augsburg, Germany; *Int'l*, pg. 586
Homan, Charles I., Pres. & Chief Exec. Officer--Michael Baker Corporation, Pittsburgh, PA; *U.S. Public*, pg. 168
Homan, Paul M., Pres. & Chief Exec. Office--Riggs Bank N.A., Washington, DC; *U.S. Public*, pg. 1390
Homer, C.R., Pres. & Chief Exec. Officer--GSW Inc., Guelph, Canada,; *Int'l*, pg. 538
Hone, L. Michael, Pres. & Chief Exec. Officer--Centennial Technologies, Inc., Wilmington, MA; *U.S. Public*, pg. 322
Honeycutt, V.B., Chm. Bd., Pres. & Chief Exec. Officer--Computer Sciences Corporation, El Segundo, CA; *U.S. Public*, pg. 422
Hong, Wooshik, Pres. & Chief Exec. Officer--Seoul DMB&B, Inc., Seoul, Korea; *Int'l*, pg. 1223
Honickman, Harold, Chm. Bd. & Chief Exec. Officer--Honickman Affiliates, Pennsauken, NJ; *U.S. Private*, pg. 537
Honroth, Dale K., Pres. & Chief Exec. Officer--Kendale Industries, Inc., Valley View, OH; *U.S. Private*, pg. 614
Hood, A. Thomas, Pres. & Chief Exec. Officer--First Financial Holdings, Inc., Charleston, SC; *U.S. Public*, pg. 634
Hood, Jim, Chief Exec. Officer--The Lord Group, New York, NY; *U.S. Private*, pg. 325
Hood, John, Chief Exec. Officer-Pulp & Paper--Fletcher Challenge Limited, Auckland, New Zealand; *Int'l*, pg. 494
Hooever, Claude, Chief Exec. Officer--Delicato Vineyards, Manteca, CA; *U.S. Private*, pg. 322
Hooker, J. Clyde, Jr., Chm. Bd. & Chief Exec. Officer--Hooker Furniture Corporation, Martinsville, VA; *U.S. Private*, pg. 538
Hooker, Robert J., Jr., Chief Oper. Officer--Purity Products Inc., Miami, FL; *U.S. Private*, pg. 896
Hooker, Robert L., Vice Chm. & Chief Exec. Officer--Transnational Motors Inc., Grand Rapids, MI; *U.S. Private*, pg. 1097
Hooley, John H., V.P. & Pres. & Chief Exec. Officer-Cub Foods--SuperValu, Inc., Eden Prairie, MN; *U.S. Public*, pg. 1540
Hooley, John H., Pres. & Chief Exec. Officer--Cub Foods Stores, Stillwater, MN; *U.S. Public*, pg. 1541
Hooper, Anthony W., Chm. Bd., Pres. & Chief Exec. Officer--Insituform Technologies, Inc., Chesterfield, MO; *U.S. Public*, pg. 881
Hoops, Alan, Pres. & Chief Exec. Officer--PacifiCare Health Systems, Inc., Cypress, CA; *U.S. Public*, pg. 1250
Hope, William, Chief Exec. Officer--G&K Services, Inc., Minnetonka, MN; *U.S. Public*, pg. 690
Hopkins, James R., Chm. Bd. & Chief Exec. Officer--FirstCity Financial Corporation, Waco, TX; *U.S. Public*, pg. 644
Hopp, Anthony, Chm. & Chief Exec. Officer--Campbell-Ewald Advertising, Warren, MI; *U.S. Public*, pg. 908
Hopper, Duane B., Pres. & Chief Exec. Officer--Graphic Controls Corporation, Buffalo, NY; *U.S. Private*, pg. 470
Hopper, Thomas H., Chief Exec. Officer--Hardwick Clothes Inc., Cleveland, TN; *U.S. Private*, pg. 502
Hopson, Jim, Pres. & Chief Exec. Officer--The Advocate, Newark, OH; *U.S. Private*, pg. 23
Hord, Fenton N., Pres. & Chief Exec. Officer--Carolina Builders Corporation, Raleigh, NC; *Int'l*, pg. 1512
Horn, Ralph, Chm. Bd., Pres. & Chief Exec. Officer--First Tennessee National Corporation, Memphis, TN; *U.S. Public*, pg. 638
Horn, Ralph, Chm. Bd., Pres., Chief Exec. & Oper. Officer--First Tennessee Bank National Association, Memphis, TN; *U.S. Public*, pg. 639
Hornbuckley, William J., Pres. & Chief Exec. Officer--GNL, Corp., Laughlin, NV; *U.S. Public*, pg. 1116
Horne, John R., Chm. Bd. & Chief Exec. Officer--Navistar International Corporation, Chicago, IL; *U.S. Public*, pg. 1167
Horne, Timothy B., Chief Exec. Officer-Charbroil Div.--W.C. Bradley Co., Columbus, GA; *U.S. Private*, pg. 164
Horne, Timothy P., Chm. Bd. & Chief Exec. Officer--Watts Industries, Inc., North Andover, MA; *U.S. Public*, pg. 1746
Horner, Donald G., Pres. & Chief Exec. Officer--Pacific One Dealer Center, Inc., Costa Mesa, CA; *U.S. Public*, pg. 635
Horner, Maurice O., Pres. & Chief Exec. Officer--Willis Corroon Corp. of Chattanooga, Chattanooga, TN; *Int'l*, pg. 1505
Horner, Nick, Pres. & Chief Exec. Officer--Citizens First Bank, El Dorado, AR; *U.S. Public*, pg. 630
Hornstein, Richard, Chief Exec. Officer--Norel Paper Corporation, Little Ferry, NJ; *U.S. Public*, pg. 1671
Hornyak, George T., Jr., Pres. & Chief Exec. Officer--Pulse Bancorp, Inc., South River, NJ; *U.S. Public*, pg. 1344
Hornyak, George T., Jr., Pres. & Chief Exec. Officer--Pulse Savings Bank, South River, NJ; *U.S. Public*, pg. 1344
Horowitz, Edward D., Chm. & Chief Exec Officer-Viacom New Media--Viacom Broadcasting Inc., New York, NY; *U.S. Private*, pg. 778
Horowitz, Joel J., Pres. & Chief Exec. Officer--Tommy Hilfiger Corporation, Kowloon, Hong Kong; *Int'l*, pg. 1398
Horowitz, Richard A., Chm. Bd., Pres. & Chief Exec. Officer--P & F Industries, Inc., Farmingdale, NY; *U.S. Public*, pg. 1239
Horrick, James, Pres. & Chief Exec. Officer--Reed Stenhouse Companies Ltd., Toronto, Canada; *U.S. Public*, pg. 118
Horrigan, D. Greg, Pres. & Co-Chief Exec. Officer--Silgan Corporation, Stamford, CT; *U.S. Public*, pg. 1473
Horton, D. Vernon, Chm. Bd. & Chief Exec. Officer--Pacific Capital Bancorp, Salinas, CA; *U.S. Public*, pg. 1247
Horton, Donald R., Chm. Bd., Pres., Chief Exec. Officer & Chief Oper. Officer--D.R. Horton, Inc., Arlington, TX; *U.S.* Public, pg. 840
Horton, Gregory L., Chm. Bd., Pres. & Chief Exec. Officer--DDL Electronics, Inc., Newbury Park, CA; *U.S. Public*, pg. 473
Horton, L. Thomas, Pres. & Chief Exec. Officer--Courtaulds Coatings Inc., Louisville, KY; *Int'l*, pg. 338
Horton, Vern, Chief Exec. Officer--First National Bank of Central California, Salinas, CA; *U.S. Public*, pg. 1248
Horwitz, Dan, Pres. & Chief Exec. Officer--Thompson Medical Company, Inc., West Palm Beach, FL; *U.S. Private*, pg. 1083
Horwitz, Martin, Pres. & Chief Exec. Officer--Stewart Smith Mid America, Inc., Chicago, IL; *Int'l*, pg. 1508
Horwitz, Susan, Pres. & Chief Exec. Officer--Aurora National Bank, Aurora, IL; *U.S. Public*, pg. 760
Hoser, Albert, Pres. & Chief Exec. Officer--Siemens Corporation, New York, NY; *Int'l*, pg. 1245
Hoshino, Toshio, Chief Exec. Officer--Goldwell Cosmetics (USA) Inc., Linthicum Heights, MD; *Int'l*, pg. 718
Hoskins, W. Lee, Chm., Pres. & Chief Exec. Officer--Huntington National Bank, Columbus, OH; *U.S. Public*, pg. 850
Hosler, David, Pres. & Chief Exec. Officer--Old Guard Insurance Group, Lancaster, PA; *U.S. Public*, pg. 1216
Hoster, George, Chief Exec. Officer--Evans Adhesive Corp., Columbus, OH; *U.S. Private*, pg. 384
Hostetler, Robert D., Pres. & Chief Exec. Officer--American Telecasting, Inc., Colorado Springs, CO; *U.S. Public*, pg. 93
Hottinger, Edwin, Chief Exec. Officer--Careal Holding AG, Zurich, Switzerland; *Int'l*, pg. 271
Houck, Peter, Pres. & Chief Exec. Officer--Houck Industries, Inc., Visalia, CA; *U.S. Private*, pg. 541
Hougen, Randall, Pres. & Chief Exec. Officer--Hougen Manufacturing Inc., Swartz Creek, MI; *U.S. Private*, pg. 541
Hough, Lawrence A., Pres. & Chief Exec. Officer--SLM Holding Corp., Washington, DC; *U.S. Public*, pg. 1419
Hough, S. Lachlan, Pres. & Chief Exec. Officer--Security Pacific Asian Bank, Ltd., Central, Hong Kong; *U.S. Public*, pg. 183
Houlihan, Lawrence M., Chm. Bd., Pres., Chief Exec. & Chief Fin. Officer, Treas. & Sec.--Frank B. Ross Co. Inc., Jersey City, NJ; *U.S. Private*, pg. 946
House, David L., Chm. Bd., Pres. & Chief Exec. Officer--Bay Networks, Inc., Santa Clara, CA; *U.S. Public*, pg. 196
House, Larry R., Chm. Bd. & Chief Exec. Officer--Medpartners Inc., Birmingham, AL; *U.S. Public*, pg. 1082
Housen, Charles B., Chm. Bd., Pres. & Chief Exec. Officer--Erving Industries, Inc., Erving, MA; *U.S. Private*, pg. 382
Housley, Mark, Chm. Bd., Pres. & Chief Exec. Officer--Radius Inc., Sunnyvale, CA; *U.S. Public*, pg. 1358
Houssein, Joe S., Chm. Bd., Pres. & Chief Exec. Officer--Intrawest Corporation, Vancouver, Canada; *Int'l*, pg. 685
Houssels, J. Kell, III, Pres. & Chief Exec. Officer--Showboat, Incorporated, Las Vegas, NV; *U.S. Public*, pg. 1469
Houston, Paul A., Pres. & Chief Exec. Officer--Scott's Restaurants Inc., Markham, Canada; *Int'l*, pg. 1213

Houston, W. Tennent, Pres. & Chief Exec. Officer--Merry Land & Investment Company, Inc., Augusta, GA; *U.S. Public*, pg. 1098

Hovekamp, George D., Jr., Pres. & Chief Exec. Officer--The Kruse Company, Fairfield, OH; *U.S. Private*, pg. 636

Hovnanian, Ara K., Pres. & Chief Exec. Officer--Hovnanian Enterprises, Inc., Red Bank, NJ; *U.S. Public*, pg. 843

Howalt, F. Harvey, Jr., Pres. & Chief Exec. Officer--Textile Rubber & Chemical Company, Dalton, GA; *U.S. Private*, pg. 1079

Howard, Clarisa F., Pres. & Chief Exec. Officer--bd Systems, Inc, Torrance, CA; *U.S. Private*, pg. 106

Howard, Elaine, Pres. & Chief Exec. Officer--Army Times Publishing Co., Springfield, VA; *U.S. Public*, pg. 699

Howard, Gary L., Pres. & Chief Exec. Officer--McRae's, Inc., Jackson, MS; *U.S. Public*, pg. 1333

Howard, Gerald T., Pres., & Chief Exec. Officer--D.C.I., Inc., Saint Cloud, MN; *U.S. Private*, pg. 301

Howard, H.N., Jr., Chief Oper. Officer--R.P. Watson Co., Richmond, VA; *U.S. Public*, pg. 1695

Howard, James J., Chm. Bd., Pres. & Chief Exec. Officer--Northern States Power Company, Minneapolis, MN; *U.S. Public*, pg. 1195

Howard, Jerry A., Chm. Bd., Pres. & Chief Exec. Officer--Atrion Corporation, Arab, AL; *U.S. Public*, pg. 146

Howard, Ron, Co-Chief Exec. Officer--Imagine Entertainment, Los Angeles, CA; *U.S. Private*, pg. 558

Howard, Ron, Chief Exec. Officer--Hayes Corporation, Norcross, GA; *U.S. Public*, pg. 800

Howard, Ronald A., Chief Exec. Officer--Hayes Corporation, Regional Office, Gaithersburg, MD; *U.S. Public*, pg. 801

Howard, Sean, Chief Exec. Officer--OzEmail Limited, Sydney, Australia; *Int'l*, pg. 1019

Howe, Harold, Jr., Chm. Bd., Chief Exec. Officer & Treas.--Howe Furniture Corporation, Trumbull, CT; *U.S. Private*, pg. 543

Howe, Hubbard C., Chm. Bd. & Interim Chief Exec. Officer--APS Holding Corporation, Houston, TX; *U.S. Public*, pg. 10

Howe, Hubbard C., Chm. Bd., Pres. & Chief Exec. Officer--A.P.S., Inc., Houston, TX; *U.S. Public*, pg. 10

Howell-Davies, Peter D., Dep. Chief Exec. Officer--Hong Kong Telecommunications Limited, Quarry Bay, Hong Kong; *Int'l*, pg. 247

Howell, Ebert, Chm. Bd., Pres. & Chief Exec. Officer--Trippe Mfg. Co., Chicago, IL; *U.S. Private*, pg. 1104

Howell, Hilton H., Jr., Pres. & Chief Exec. Officer--Atlantic American Corporation, Atlanta, GA; *U.S. Public*, pg. 143

Howell, John R., Chm. Bd., Pres. & Chief Exec. Officer--Summit Bank, Bethlehem, PA; *U.S. Public*, pg. 1528

Howell, John S., Chm. Bd. & Chief Exec. Officer--Howell Instruments Inc., Fort Worth, TX; *U.S. Private*, pg. 543

Howells, Daniel P., Pres. & Chief Exec. Officer--Nature's Sunshine Products, Inc., Provo, UT; *U.S. Public*, pg. 1166

Howells, Robert L., Pres. & Chief Exec. Officer--Mendoza, Dillon & Asociados, Inc., Newport Beach, CA; *Int'l*, pg. 1483

Hoyle, Donald A., Jr., Pres. & Chief Exec. Officer--Pioneer American Holding Company, Carbondale, PA; *U.S. Public*, pg. 1298

Hoyle, John, Chief Oper. Officer--United Eco Systems, High Point, NC; *Int'l*, pg. 74

Hoyne, W., Chief Exec. Officer--Brinks-Allied, Dublin, Ireland; *Int'l*, pg. 81

Hoyt, Brad, Chief Oper. Officer--Hoyt Development, Plymouth, MN; *U.S. Private*, pg. 543

Hoyt, Henry H., Jr., Chm. Bd. & Chief Exec. Officer--Carter-Wallace, Inc., New York, NY; *U.S. Public*, pg. 309

Hoyt, Steven B., Chief Exec. Officer--Complast, Inc., Bloomington, MN; *U.S. Private*, pg. 259

Hozik, John, Pres. & Chief Exec. Officer--The Philadelphia Bourse, Inc., Lanham, MD; *U.S. Private*, pg. 861

Hroblak, Gerald, Pres. & Chief Exec. Officer--United Broadcasting L.P., Bethesda, MD; *U.S. Private*, pg. 1121

Hron, Ihor W., Chm. Bd., Pres. & Chief Exec. Officer--Midland Life Insurance Co., Columbus, OH; *U.S. Private*, pg. 744

Hubbard, James W., Pres. & Chief Exec. Officer--Herff Jones Inc., Indianapolis, IN; *U.S. Private*, pg. 523

Hubbard, R. D., Chm. Bd. & Chief Exec. Officer--Hollywood Park, Inc., Inglewood, CA; *U.S. Public*, pg. 830

Hubbard, R.D., Pres. & Chief Exec. Officer--Turf Paradise, Inc., Phoenix, AZ; *U.S. Public*, pg. 831

Hubbard, Samuel T., Jr., Pres. & Chief Exec. Officer--The Ailing & Cory Company, Rochester, NY; *U.S. Public*, pg. 1666

Hubbard, Stanley E., Pres. & Chief Exec. Officer--United States Satellite Broadcasting, Co., Saint Paul, MN; *U.S. Private*, pg. 544

Hubbard, Stanley S., Chm. Bd., Pres. & Chief Exec. Officer--Hubbard Broadcasting, Inc., Saint Paul, MN; *U.S. Private*, pg. 543

Hubble, Don W., Chm. Bd., Pres. & Chief Exec. Officer--Angelica Corporation, Chesterfield, MO; *U.S. Public*, pg. 113

Huber, Michael S., Chief Fin. Officer, Sr. V.P. & Treas.--Andal Corp., New York, NY; *U.S. Public*, pg. 111

Huber, Richard L., Pres. & Chief Exec. Officer--Aetna Inc., Hartford, CT; *U.S. Public*, pg. 26

Huber, Ron, Chm. Bd., Pres. & Chief Exec. Officer--Time Systems, Inc., Phoenix, AZ; *U.S. Private*, pg. 1086

Hubers, David, Chm. Bd., Chief Exec. Officer & Pres.--IDS Financial Services, Inc., Minneapolis, MN; *U.S. Public*, pg. 73

Hubers, David R., Pres. & Chief Exec. Officer--American Express Financial Advisor, Minneapolis, MN; *U.S. Public*, pg. 73

Hubner, Cornelius E., Chm. Bd. & Chief Exec. Officer--American Felt & Filter, Newburgh, NY; *U.S. Private*, pg. 54

Hubner, Donald A., Chm. Bd. & Chief Exec. Officer--Central/Shippee, Inc., Bloomingdale, NJ; *U.S. Private*, pg. 224

Huddleston, Ray, Pres. & Chief Exec. Officer--Citizens First Bank, Springhill, LA; *U.S. Public*, pg. 630

Hudetz, Frank C., Chm. Bd. & Chief Exec. Officer--Solar Communications, Inc., Naperville, IL; *U.S. Private*, pg. 1012

Hudson, C.B., Chm. Bd. & Chief Exec. Officer--Globe Life And Accident Insurance Co., Oklahoma City, OK; *U.S. Public*, pg. 1622

Hudson, J. Clifford, Pres. & Chief Exec. Officer--Sonic Corporation, Oklahoma City, OK; *U.S. Public*, pg. 1485

Hudson, Kathy M., Pres. & Chief Exec. Officer--W.H. Brady Co., Milwaukee, WI; *U.S. Public*, pg. 250

Hudson, Kent O., Pres. & Chief Exec. Officer--SRS, Raleigh, NC; *U.S. Public*, pg. 307

Hudson, S. Michael, Pres. & Chief Exec. Officer--Allison Engine Company Inc., Indianapolis, IN; *Int'l*, pg. 1127

Hudson, Stephen R., Pres. & Chief Exec. Officer--Nyltech North America Inc., Manchester, NH; *Int'l*, pg. 482

Hudson, Steven K., Pres. & Chief Exec. Officer--Newcourt Credit Group Inc., Toronto, Canada; *Int'l*, pg. 924

Hudson, Tom, Pres. & Chief Exec. Officer--Computer Network Technology Corporation, Minneapolis, MN; *U.S. Public*, pg. 421

Hudson, William J., Pres. & Chief Exec. Officer--AMP Incorporated, Harrisburg, PA; *U.S. Public*, pg. 7

Huebler, F., Chief Exec. Officer--Bramac Dachsysteme International GmbH, Pochlarn, Austria; *Int'l*, pg. 1092

Huemer, David A., Chief Exec. Officer--New York Switch Corporation, Fort Lee, NJ; *U.S. Public*, pg. 339

Huemme, Douglas W., Chm. Bd., Pres. & Chief Exec. Officer--Lilly Industries, Inc., Indianapolis, IN; *U.S. Public*, pg. 994

Huemme, Richard C., Chm. Bd., Pres. & Chief Exec. Officer--Pittsburgh Tube Co., Moon Township, PA; *U.S. Private*, pg. 867

Huff, Jackson, Pres. & Chief Exec. Officer--UPB of Louisiana, Baton Rouge, LA; *U.S. Public*, pg. 1669

Huff, John R., Chm. Bd., Pres. & Chief Exec. Officer--Oceaneering International, Inc., Houston, TX; *U.S. Public*, pg. 1211

Huff, John R., Chm. Bd., Pres. & Chief Exec. Officer--Oceaneering International, Inc., Morgan City, LA; *U.S. Public*, pg. 1211

Huff, Wayne, Pres. & Chief Exec. Officer--Cegelec AEG Automation Systems Corp., Canonsburg, PA; *Int'l*, pg. 52

Huffer, Russell, Pres. & Chief Exec. Officer--Apogee Enterprises, Inc., Minneapolis, MN; *U.S. Public*, pg. 120

Huffman, Robert T., Pres. & Chief Exec. Officer--Vesta Insurance Group, Inc., Birmingham, AL; *U.S. Public*, pg. 1718

Hug, Klaus, Chief Exec.--Protek GmbH, Freiburg, Germany; *Int'l*, pg. 1307

Hugenot, Verle, Chm. Bd., Pres. & Chief Exec. Officer--United Missouri Bank Northeast, Monroe City, MO; *U.S. Public*, pg. 1654

Huggins, Frederick A., Jr., Pres. & Chief Exec. Officer--The Barbers, Hairstyling for Men & Women, Inc., Minneapolis, MN; *U.S. Private*, pg. 115

Huggins, Frederick A., Jr., Pres. & Chief Exec. Officer--We Care Hair, Minneapolis, MN; *U.S. Private*, pg. 115

Hughes, B. Wayne, Chm. Bd. & Chief Exec. Officer--Public Storage, Inc., Glendale, CA; *U.S. Public*, pg. 1340

Hughes, Catherine, Chief Exec. Officer--Radio One Inc., Lanham, MD; *U.S. Private*, pg. 906

Hughes, D.A., Chm. Bd. & Chief Exec. Officer--Hughes Supply Corp., Greenville, OH; *U.S. Private*, pg. 547

Hughes, David H., Chm. Bd. & Chief Exec. Officer--Hughes Supply, Inc., Orlando, FL; *U.S. Public*, pg. 846

Hughes, H.D., Chm. Bd., Pres., Chief Exec. Officer & Dir.-Sls.--Diversified Group, Inc., Harahan, LA; *U.S. Private*, pg. 336

Hughes, Hugh, Chief Exec. Officer--Societe Generale Equities International, London, United Kingdom; *Int'l*, pg. 1274

Hughes, John, Pres. & Chief Exec. Officer--AMCOL International Corp., Arlington Heights, IL; *U.S. Public*, pg. 63

Hughes, John, Pres. & Chief Exec. Officer--Volclay Standard Pty. Ltd., Geelong, Australia; *U.S. Public*, pg. 64

Hughes, Joseph F., Chm. Bd., Pres., Chief Exec. Officer & Treas.--TSR Inc., Hauppauge, NY; *U.S. Public*, pg. 1559

Hughes, Keith W., Chm. Bd. & Chief Exec. Officer--Associates First Capital Corporation, Dallas, TX; *U.S. Public*, pg. 662

Hughes, Keith W., Chm. Bd. & Chief Exec. Officer--Associates Financial Services Corporation, Dallas, TX; *U.S. Public*, pg. 663

Hughes, Malcolm, Chief Exec. Officer--Proudfoot plc, Richmond, United Kingdom; *Int'l*, pg. 1071

Hughes, Malcolm, Chief Exec. Officer--Proudfoot USA Company, West Palm Beach, FL; *Int'l*, pg. 1072

Hughes, Mark, Chm. Bd., Pres. & Chief Exec. Officer--Herbalife International of America, Inc., Century City, CA; *U.S. Public*, pg. 809

Hughes, Stephen B., Pres. & Chief Exec. Officer--Celestial Seasonings, Boulder, CO; *U.S. Public*, pg. 319

Hughes, T.D., Chief Exec. & Chief Fin. Officer--La Rosa's, Inc., Cincinnati, OH; *U.S. Private*, pg. 640

Hughes, Terry, Pres. & Chief Exec. Officer--InfoWorks, Mississauga, Canada; *U.S. Public*, pg. 1225

Hughes, Victor, Chm. Bd. & Chief Exec. Officer--Koger Equity Inc., Jacksonville, FL; *U.S. Public*, pg. 965

Hugo-Martinez, Albert J., Pres. & Chief Exec. Officer--GTI Corporation, San Diego, CA; *U.S. Public*, pg. 767

Hugo-Martinez, Albert J., Pres. & Chief Exec. Officer--Valor Electronics, Inc., San Diego, CA; *U.S. Public*, pg. 768

Huisman, Dick, Pres. & Chief Exec. Officer--Greyhound Lines of Canada Ltd., Calgary, Canada; *Int'l*, pg. 559

Huisman, Willem, Chm. Bd., Pres. & Chief Exec. Officer--Precision Systems, Inc., Saint Petersburg, FL; *U.S. Public*, pg. 1321

Huizenga, Donald, Pres. & Chief Exec. Officer--Kurdziel Industries, Inc., Muskegon, MI; *U.S. Private*, pg. 637

Huizenga, H. Wayne, Chm. Bd. & Co-Chief Exec. Officer--Republic Industries, Inc., Fort Lauderdale, FL; *U.S. Public*, pg. 1378

Hulber, Loren J., Pres. & Chief Exec. Officer--NovaCare Employee Services, Inc., Norristown, PA; *U.S. Public*, pg. 1203

Hull, John C., Chm. Bd. & Chief Exec. Officer--Pratt Casino Corporation, Dallas, TX; *U.S. Public*, pg. 761

Hull, Kenneth J., Pres. & Chief Exec. Officer--Follett Corporation, River Grove, IL; *U.S. Private*, pg. 416

Hull, Lewis W., Chm. Bd., Pres. & Chief Exec. Officer--Hull Corporation, Hatboro, PA; *U.S. Private*, pg. 547

Hulseman, Robert L., Pres.--Solo Cup Company, Highland Park, IL; *U.S. Private*, pg. 1013

Hultman, C.A., Chief Exec. Officer--Eurotherm plc, Horsham, United Kingdom; *Int'l*, pg. 465

Humann, L. Phillip, Chm. Bd., Pres. & Chief Exec. Officer--SunTrust Banks, Inc., Atlanta, GA; *U.S. Public*, pg. 1537

Humer, Franz, Chief Exec. Officer--Roche Holding Ltd., Basel, Switzerland; *Int'l*, pg. 1119

Hummer, Paul F., Chm. Bd., Pres. & Chief Exec. Officer--A.P. Green Industries, Inc., Mexico, MO; *U.S. Public*, pg. 761

Humphrey, G. Watts, Jr., Chm. Bd. & Chief Exec. Officer--The Conair Group, Inc., Pittsburgh, PA; *U.S. Private*, pg. 261

Humphreys, Johnny M., Pres. & Chief Exec. Officer--Itron Inc., Spokane, WA; *U.S. Public*, pg. 914

Humphreys, Steven, Pres. & Chief Exec. Officer--SCM Microsystems, Inc., Los Gatos, CA; *U.S. Public*, pg. 1417

Humphries, Ian E., Chief Exec. Officer-Agricultural & Tech. services--Wolseley Plc., Droitwich, United Kingdom; *Int'l*, pg. 1511

Hung, Wendell, Pres. & Chief Exec. Officer--Deltak Inc., Plymouth, MN; *U.S. Public*, pg. 924

Hunger, Armin, Chief Exec. Officer & V.P.--Hunger Hydraulics, Limited, Rossford, OH; *Int'l*, pg. 639

Hunt, Bruce W., Pres. & Chief Exec. Officer--Petro-Hunt Corporation, Dallas, TX; *U.S. Private*, pg. 858

Hunt, E.C., Jr., Chm. Bd. & Chief Exec. Officer--Thermo Industries Inc., Charlotte, NC; *U.S. Private*, pg. 1080

Hunt, James H., Chief Exec. Officer--Barnett Bank of Southeast Georgia, N.A., Brunswick, GA; *U.S. Public*, pg. 1162

Hunt, Joseph A., Pres.--Westat Inc., Rockville, MD; *U.S. Private*, pg. 1163

Hunt, M.L., Chief Exec. Officer--Hunt Building Corporation, El Paso, TX; *U.S. Private*, pg. 548

Hunt, Rocklyn, Pres. & Chief Exec. Officer--Regions Bank/Forsyth County, Cumming, GA; *U.S. Public*, pg. 1372

Hunt, Terrill E., Pres. & Chief Exec. Officer--Allied Security, International, Spokane, WA; *U.S. Private*, pg. 41

Hunt, William O., Chm. Bd., Pres. & Chief Exec. Officer--Intellicall, Inc., Carrollton, TX; *U.S. Public*, pg. 887

Hunter, B.D., Chm. Bd. & Chief Exec. Officer--Huntco Inc., Town and Country, MO; *U.S. Public*, pg. 849

Hunter, James L., Pres. & Chief Exec. Officer--Mackenzie Financial Corporation, Toronto, Canada; *Int'l*, pg. 828

Hunter, Jerry E., Chm. Bd., Pres. & Chief Exec. Officer--JPS Textile Group, Inc., Greenville, SC; *U.S. Private*, pg. 578

Hunter, John W., Chm. Bd, Pres. & Chief Exec. Officer--Adtec Detention Systems, San Antonio, TX; *U.S. Private*, pg. 18

Hunter, Richard, Pres. & Chief Exec. Officer--Pace International L.P., Kirkland, WA; *U.S. Private*, pg. 829

Hunter, Ronald D., Chm. Bd. & Chief Exec. Officer--Standard Management Corporation, Indianapolis, IN; *U.S. Public*, pg. 1502

Hunter, Samuel P., Pres. & Chief Exec. Officer--T.A. Loving Company, Goldsboro, NC; *U.S. Private*, pg. 677

Huntington, Lawrence S., Chm. Bd. & Chief Exec. Officer--Fiduciary Trust Company International, New York, NY; *U.S. Public*, pg. 621

Huntington, Tom, Chm. Bd., Pres. & Chief Exec. Officer--EVCON Industries, Wichita, KS; *U.S. Public*, pg. 1788

Huntsman, Jon M., Chm. Bd. & Chief Exec. Officer--Huntsman Corporation, Salt Lake City, UT; *U.S. Private*, pg. 549

Hunziker, Eugen, Chief Exec. Officer--Migros, Zurich, Switzerland; *Int'l*, pg. 865

Huppi, Rolf, Chm. Bd. & Chief Exec. Officer--Zurich Insurance Company, Zurich, Switzerland; *Int'l*, pg. 1529

Hurlbut, Wendell P., Chm. Bd. & Chief Exec. Officer--Esterline Technologies Corporation, Bellevue, WA; *U.S. Public*, pg. 594

Hurley, K., Chief Exec. Officer--Kaye Instruments, Inc., Bedford, MA; *Int'l*, pg. 208

Hurrelbrink, Richard A., Chief Exec. Officer--Cash Plus, Inc., Minneapolis, MN; *U.S. Private*, pg. 218

Hurvitz, Eli, Pres. & Chief Exec. Officer--Teva Pharmaceutical Industries Ltd., Petah Tiqwa, Israel; *Int'l*, pg. 1380

Hurwitz, Charles E., Chm. Bd. & Chief Exec. Officer--Maxxam Inc., Houston, TX; *U.S. Public*, pg. 1062

Husseini, Tamer, Chm. Bd., Pres. & Chief Exec. Officer--Celeritek, Inc., Santa Clara, CA; *U.S. Public*, pg. 319

Hussey, Tim, Pres. & Chief Exec. Officer--Hussey Seating Company, North Berwick, ME; *U.S. Private*, pg. 550

Huta, Henry N., Pres. & Chief Exec. Officer--Califia Company, San Diego, CA; *U.S. Public*, pg. 584

Hutchinson, Lew C., Pres. & Chief Exec. Offcier--Co-Steel Inc., Toronto, Canada; *Int'l*, pg. 298

Hutchison, Craig, Pres. & Chief Exec. Officer--Perry Graphic Communications, Inc., Waterloo, WI; *U.S. Private*, pg. 855

Hutnick, Larry, Interim Chief Exec. Officer--Consilium, Inc., Mountain View, CA; *U.S. Public*, pg. 434

Hutson, Billy, Chief Oper. Officer--River Ranch Southwest, Inc., Dallas, TX; *U.S. Private*, pg. 934

Hutton, Edward B., Jr., Pres. & Chief Exec. Officer--Waverly, Inc., Baltimore, MD; *U.S. Public*, pg. 1748

Hutton, Edward L., Chm. Bd. & Chief Exec. Officer--Chemed Corporation, Cincinnati, OH; *U.S. Public*, pg. 343

Hutts, Joseph C., Chm. Bd., Pres. & Chief Exec. Officer--Phycor, Inc., Nashville, TN; *U.S. Public*, pg. 1293
Huzjak, Thomas J., Chm. Bd. & Chief Exec. Officer--T-NETIX, Inc., Englewood, CO; *U.S. Public*, pg. 1553
Hvide, J. Erik, Chm. Bd. & Chief Exec. Officer--Hvide Marine Incorporated, Fort Lauderdale, FL; *U.S. Public*, pg. 851
Hvistendahl, Finn A., Pres. & Cheif Exec. officer--Den norske Bank ASA, Oslo, Norway; *Int'l*, pg. 392
Hwang, K. Philip, Dr., Chm. Bd. & Chief Exec. Officer--Televideo, Inc., San Jose, CA; *U.S. Public*, pg. 1572
Hwang, Li-San, Dr., Chm. Bd., Pres. & Chief Exec. Officer--Tetra Tech, Inc., Pasadena, CA; *U.S. Public*, pg. 1582
Hwee, Koh Boon, Chief Exec. Officer & Mng. Dir.--Liang Court Holdings Ltd., Singapore, Singapore; *Int'l*, pg. 807
Hyatt, Arnold, Pres. & Chief Exec. Officer--Stride Rite Footwear, Inc., Lawrence, MA; *U.S. Public*, pg. 1525
Hyatt, Kenneth E., Chm. Bd., Pres. & Chief Exec. Officer--Walter Industries, Inc., Tampa, FL; *U.S. Public*, pg. 1736
Hyde, Douglas W., Chm. Bd., Pres. & Chief Exec. Officer--OshKosh B'Gosh, Inc., Oshkosh, WI; *U.S. Public*, pg. 1232
Hydorn, Vernon H., Pres. & Chief Exec. Officer--Barber Dairies, Inc., Birmingham, AL; *U.S. Private*, pg. 115
Hyjek, Ed, Pres. & Chief Exec. Officer--Bridgestone/Firestone Canada Inc., Mississauga, Canada; *Int'l*, pg. 214
Hyland, Geoffrey F., Pres. & Chief Exec. Officer--Shaw Industries Ltd., Etobicoke, Canada; *Int'l*, pg. 1231
Hylbert, Paul, Pres. & Co-Chief Exec. Officer--Prime Source Inc., Carrollton, TX; *U.S. Private*, pg. 884
Hyman, Morton P., Pres.--Overseas Shipholding Group, Inc., New York, NY; *U.S. Public*, pg. 1236
Hyman, Richard, Chief Oper. Officer & Exec. V.P.--Milgray/New England, Inc., Wilmington, MA; *U.S. Public*, pg. 206
Hyslop, Charles N., Pres. & Chief Exec. Officer--Sybra, Inc., Atlanta, GA; *U.S. Private*, pg. 270
Ianuzzi, L., Chief Exec. Officer--OCE-Italia S.p.A., Milan, Italy; *Int'l*, pg. 994
Ibos, Robert J., Chm. Bd., Pres. & Chief Exec. Officer--National Engineering & Contracting Co., Strongsville, OH; *U.S. Private*, pg. 782
Ibsen, Robert, Dr., Chm. Bd., Pres., Chief Exec. Officer & Treas.--Den-Mat Corporation, Santa Maria, CA; *U.S. Private*, pg. 324
Idelson, Charles K., Pres. & Chief Exec. Officer--SunTrust Bank, Southwest Florida, Fort Myers, FL; *U.S. Public*, pg. 1538
Idol, John, Chief Exec. Officer--Donna Karan, New York, NY; *U.S. Public*, pg. 517
Iglesias, R., Chief Exec. Officer--SBS Ibersuizas S.A., Madrid, Spain; *Int'l*, pg. 1332
Ihamuotila, Jaakko, Chm. Bd. & Chief Exec. Officer--Neste Oy, Espoo, Finland; *Int'l*, pg. 912
Iida, Makoto, Chm. Bd., Chief Exec. Officer & Rep. Dir.--Secom Co., Ltd., Tokyo, Japan; *Int'l*, pg. 1217
Iida, Yozo, Pres. & Chief Exec. Officer--Descente Ltd., Osaka, Japan; *Int'l*, pg. 395
Ill, Richard C., Pres. & Chief Exec. Officer--Triumph Group, Inc., Wayne, PA; *U.S. Public*, pg. 1640
Imamura, Kazusuke, Chm. Bd. & Chief Exec. Officer--Chichibu Onoda Cement Corporation, Tokyo, Japan; *Int'l, pg. 284*
Imbert, Yves, Chm. Bd. & Chief Exec. Officer--Hispano-Suiza S.A., Paris, France; *Int'l*, pg. 1165
Imbimbo, Victor, Jr., Pres. & Chief Exec. Officer--Cohn & Wells, New York, NY; *Int'l*, pg. 601
Imbler, Martin R., Pres. & Chief Exec. Officer--Berry Plastics Corporation, Evansville, IN; *U.S. Private*, pg. 137
Imhoff, Herbert F., Chm. Bd. & Chief Exec. Officer--General Employment Enterprises, Inc., Oak Brook Terrace, IL; *U.S. Public*, pg. 714
Inaba, Seiuemon, Dr., Chm. Bd. & Chief Exec. Officer--Fanuc Ltd., Yamanashi, Japan; *Int'l*, pg. 477
Inagaki, Masao, Chm. Bd. & Chief Exec. Officer--Asatsu Inc., Tokyo, Japan; *Int'l*, pg. 85
Inagaki, Y., Chief Oper. Officer--P.T. Sarinitokyu Hotel Corp., Jakarta, Indonesia; *Int'l*, pg. 949
Inerney, Michael M., Pres. & Chief Exec. Officer--Gibson Electric Co., Oak Brook, IL; *U.S. Public*, pg. 572
Infusino, Thomas P., Chm. Bd. & Chief Exec. Officer--Wakefern Food Corporation, Elizabeth, NJ; *U.S. Private*, pg. 1146
Ingle, Robert P., Chm. Bd. & Chief Exec. Officer--Ingles Markets, Incorporated, Black Mountain, NC; *U.S. Public*, pg. 878
Ingleby, Raymond S., Chm. Bd. & Chief Exec. Officer--Caribiner International, Inc., New York, NY; *U.S. Public*, pg. 305
Ingram, E.W., III, Chm. Bd., Pres. & Chief Exec. Officer--White Castle System, Inc., Columbus, OH; *U.S. Private*, pg. 1171
Ingram, Robert, Chief Exec. Officer--Glaxo Wellcome plc, London, United Kingdom; *Int'l*, pg. 552
Ingram, Robert A., Pres. & Chief Exec. Officer--Glaxo Wellcome Inc., Research Triangle Park, NC; *Int'l*, pg. 552
Inman, Frank, Jr., Pres. & Chief Exec. Officer--Inman Construction Corporation, Memphis, TN; *U.S. Private*, pg. 564
Inoue, Masayasu, Chm. Bd. & Chief Exec. Officer--Crestbrook Forest Industries Ltd., Cranbrook, Canada; *Int'l*, pg. 348
Insetta, Victor, Pres. & Chief Exec. Officer--American Technical Ceramics Corp., Huntington Station, NY; *U.S. Public*, pg. 93
Inskeep, C., Chief Exec. Officer--Monitor Products Company Inc., Oceanside, CA; *Int'l*, pg. 208
Inwood, Albert, Chief Exec. Officer--Calumet Carton Company, South Holland, IL; *U.S. Private*, pg. 201
Ioannou, Kyriakos, Chief Exec. Officer--Gnomi Advertising, Nicosia, Cyprus; *U.S. Private*, pg. 304
Iochpe, Daniel, Chief Exec. Officer--Iochpe-Maxion S.A., Sao Paulo, Brazil; *Int'l*, pg. 688
Iogi, Shigeru, Chief Exec. Officer--Meiwa Trading Co., Tokyo, Japan; *Int'l*, pg. 871
Iordanou, C., Pres. & Chief Exec. Officer--Zurich American Insurance Company of Illinois, Schaumburg, IL; *Int'l*, pg. 1530
Iordanou, C., Chief Exec. Officer--American Guarantee & Liability Insurance Company, Schaumburg, IL; *Int'l*, pg. 1530
Iordanou, C., Chief Exec. Officer--American Zurich Insurance Company, Schaumburg, IL; *Int'l*, pg. 1530
Iordanou, C., Chief Exec. Officer--Steadfast Insurance Company, Schaumburg, IL; *Int'l*, pg. 1530
Iordanou, C., Chief Exec. Officer--Zurich American Insurance Company of Illinois, Schaumburg, IL; *Int'l*, pg. 1530
Iordanou, C., Chief Exec. Officer--Zurich American Lloyds, Schaumburg, IL; *Int'l*, pg. 1530
Iordanou, Constantine P., Chief Exec. Officer--Zurich Insurance Company, Schaumburg, IL; *Int'l*, pg. 1530
Iott, Richard B., Pres. & Chief Exec. Officer--Seaway Food Town, Inc., Maumee, OH; *U.S. Public*, pg. 1452
Irala, Xavier, Chm. Bd. & Chief Exec. Officer--Grupo Iberia, Madrid, Spain; *Int'l*, pg. 574
Irani, Ray, R., Dr., Chm. Bd. & Chief Exec. Officer--Occidental Petroleum Corporation, Los Angeles, CA; *U.S. Public*, pg. 1210
Ireland, Rob J., Pres. & Chief Exec. Officer--Roquette America Inc., Keokuk, IA; *U.S. Private*, pg. 944
Irvine, R., Chief Exec. Officer--Zurich Insurance Company, Dublin, Ireland; *Int'l*, pg. 1531
Irving, W.R., Chief Exec. Officer--Ferguson International Holdings, Banbury, United Kingdom; *Int'l*, pg. 479
Irwin, Ann, Chm. Bd. & Chief Exec. Officer--Labelon Corporation, Canandaigua, NY; *U.S. Private*, pg. 641
Irwin, George M., Pres. & Chief Exec. Officer--Irwin Toy Ltd., Toronto, Canada; *Int'l*, pg. 688
Irwin, John R., Pres. & Chief Exec. Officer--Atwood Oceanics, Inc., Houston, TX; *U.S. Public*, pg. 146
Irwin, Michael L., Pres. & Chief Exec. Officer--Cadmus Direct Marketing, Inc., Charlotte, NC; *U.S. Public*, pg. 290
Isaacs, Bob, Chief Exec. Officer--The Fuller Brush Company, Great Bend, KS; *U.S. Public*, pg. 282
Isenberg, Eugene M., Chm. Bd. & Chief Exec. Officer--Nabors Industries, Inc., Houston, TX; *U.S. Public*, pg. 1148
Isenberg, Howard, Pres. & Chief Exec. Officer--CCL Custom Manufacturing, Niles, IL; *Int'l*, pg. 238
Isherwood, Robert, Chm. Bd. & Chief Exec. Officer--Ambac International Corp., Columbia, SC; *U.S. Private*, pg. 48
Ishida, J., Chm. Bd. & Chief Exec. Officer--Sumitomo Sitix Silicon, Inc., Fremont, CA; *Int'l*, pg. 1317
Ishii, Takafumi, Pres. & Chief Exec. Officer--Nippon Credit Trust Company, New York, NY; *Int'l*, pg. 933
Ishii, Toshiichi, Chm. & Chief Exec. Officer--NEC Technologies, Inc., Boxboro, MA; *Int'l*, pg. 900
Ishimaru, Tsuneo, Pres. & Chief Exec. Officer--Nippondenso Co., Ltd., Kariya, Japan; *Int'l*, pg. 1412
Ishizaka, Yoshio, Pres. & Chief Exec. Officer--Toyota Motor Sales, U.S.A., Inc., Torrance, CA; *Int'l*, pg. 1412
Isles, Marvin L., Chm. Bd. & Chief Exec. Officer--Giddings & Lewis, Inc., Fond Du Lac, WI; *Int'l*, pg. 1389
Israel, Larry, Chm. Bd., Pres. & Chief Exec. Officer--Telesensory Corporation, Sunnyvale, CA; *U.S. Private*, pg. 1074
Issakainen, Markku, Chief Exec. Officer--VPV EURO RSCG, Helsinki, Finland; *Int'l*, pg. 603
Istock, Verne G., Chm. Bd., Pres. & Chief Exec. Officer--First Chicago NBD Corporation, Chicago, IL; *U.S. Public, pg. 627*
Itagaki, Hiroshi, Chm. & Chief Exec. Officer--Teijin Limited, Osaka, Japan; *Int'l*, pg. 1362
Itagaki, Osamu, Chief Oper. Officer--S.A. Makita N.V., Vilvoorde, Belgium; *Int'l*, pg. 832
Itin, Thomas W., Pres. & Chief Exec. Officer--Ajay Sports Inc., Delavan, WI; *U.S. Public*, pg. 34
Itin, Thomas W., Chm. Bd., Pres. & Chief Exec. Officer--Williams Controls, Inc., Portland, OR; *U.S. Public*, pg. 1769
Ito, M., Pres. & Chief Exec. Officer--Sankosha Corporation, Tokyo, Japan; *Int'l*, pg. 1189
Itoh, Kiyoshi, Pres. & Chief Exec. Officer--Seiko Instruments Inc., Chiba, Japan; *Int'l*, pg. 1219
Ivanier, Paul, Pres. & Chief Exec. Officer--The Ivaco Group, Montreal, Canada; *Int'l*, pg. 695
Iverson, Ann, Chm. Bd. & Chief Exec. Officer--Laura Ashley (USA) Inc., Boston, MA; *Int'l*, pg. 804
Ives, J. Atwood, Chm. Bd. & Chief Exec. Officer--Eastern Enterprises, Weston, MA; *U.S. Public*, pg. 548
Ivester, M. Douglas, Chm. Bd. & Chief Exec. Officer--The Coca-Cola Company, Atlanta, GA; *U.S. Public*, pg. 392
Ivey, J.C., Chief Exec. Officer--The Davis Service Group Plc., London, United Kingdom; *Int'l*, pg. 385
Ivy, Jim, Pres. & Chief Exec. Officer--Savin Corporation, Stamford, CT; *Int'l*, pg. 1114
Iwata, Saiji, Chief Oper. Officer--Makita Werkzeug GmbH, Duisburg, Germany; *Int'l*, pg. 832
Ix, Douglas, Chief Exec. Officer--Frank IX & Sons, Inc., Charlottesville, VA; *U.S. Private*, pg. 423
Ix, Douglas, Chief Exec. Officer--Frank IX & Sons, Inc., Lexington, NC; *U.S. Private*, pg. 423
Izuel, Cesareo Alierta, Chm. Bd., Pres. & Chief Exec. Officer--Tabacalera, S.A., Madrid, Spain; *Int'l*, pg. 1345
Jack, Barbara, Worldwide Chief Exec. Officer--Wunderman Cato Johnson, New York, NY; *U.S. Private*, pg. 1197
Jackman, Joseph R., Chm. Bd., Pres. & Chief Exec. Officer--Reactive Metals & Alloys Corporation (REMACOR), West Pittsburg, PA; *U.S. Private*, pg. 913
Jackson, Christopher, Pres. & Chief Exec. Officer--DynetCom, Guyancourt, France; *Int'l*, pg. 425
Jackson, J.L., Chm. Bd., Pres. & Chief Exec. Officer--Global Industrial Technologies, Dallas, TX; *U.S. Public*, pg. 747
Jackson, John, Chief Exec. Officer--Sketchley Plc, Hinckley, United Kingdom; *Int'l*, pg. 1261
Jackson, Kenneth, Chief Exec. Officer--Carbo Plc, Manchester, United Kingdom; *Int'l*, pg. 268
Jackson, Margaret A., Pres.--Western Pacific Data Systems, La Jolla, CA; *U.S. Private*, pg. 1168
Jackson, Marlin, Chm. & Chief Exec. Officer--NationsBank of Conway, Conway, AR; *U.S. Public*, pg. 1164
Jackson, Mary Anne, Chm. Bd., Pres., Chief Oper. & Chief Exec. Officer--My Own Meals, Inc., Deerfield, IL; *U.S. Private*, pg. 770
Jackson, P.J., Chief Exec.-British Sugar--Associated British Foods plc, London, United Kingdom; *Int'l*, pg. 92
Jackson, Peter, Chief Exec. Officer--British Sugar plc, Peterborough, United Kingdom; *Int'l*, pg. 92
Jackson, Quintin, Pres. & Chief Exec. Officer--Alfa Laval Inc., Kenosha, WI; *Int'l*, pg. 1378
Jackson, R.A., Chm. Bd., Pres. & Chief Exec. Officer--Nuburn Capital, Calgary, Canada; *Int'l*, pg. 990
Jackson, Richard L., Chm. Bd., Pres. & Chief Exec. Officer--Allegiant Physician Services, Atlanta, GA; *U.S. Public*, pg. 45
Jackson, Robert, Interim Pres. & Chief Exec. Officer--The Bombay Company, Inc., Fort Worth, TX; *U.S. Public*, pg. 244
Jackson, Robert, Interim Pres. & Chief Exec. Officer--The Bombay Company, Fort Worth, TX; *U.S. Public*, pg. 244
Jacob, Herbert, Chm. Bd. & Chief Exec. Officer--Ajax Paving Industries Inc., Madison Heights, MI; *U.S. Private, pg. 29*
Jacobi, C.M., Pres. & Chief Exec. Officer--Timex Corporation, Middlebury, CT; *U.S. Private*, pg. 1088
Jacobs, Bradley S., Chm. Bd. & Chief Exec. Officer--United Waste Systems, Inc., Houston, TX; *U.S. Public*, pg. 1691
Jacobs, Bruce, Pres. & Chief Exec. Officer--Grede-Pryor, Inc., Pryor, OK; *U.S. Private*, pg. 476
Jacobs, Bruce E., Pres. & Chief Exec. Officer--Grede Foundries, Inc., Milwaukee, WI; *U.S. Private*, pg. 476
Jacobs, Franklin A., Chm. Bd. & Chief Exec. Officer--Falcon Products, Inc., Saint Louis, MO; *U.S. Public*, pg. 611
Jacobs, Irwin Mark, Chm. Bd. & Chief Exec. Officer--QUALCOMM, San Diego, CA; *U.S. Public*, pg. 1348
Jacobs, Jeremy M., Sr., Chm. Bd. & Chief Exec. Officer--Delaware North Companies, Inc., Buffalo, NY; *U.S. Private*, pg. 321
Jacobs, Jerry, Pres. & Chief Exec. Officer--First National Bank, Nashville, Nashville, AR; *U.S. Public*, pg. 630
Jacobs, Joseph J., Dr., Chm. Bd.--Jacobs Engineering Group Inc., Pasadena, CA; *U.S. Public*, pg. 921
Jacobs, Mark L., Pres. & Chief Exec. Officer--Watkins Incorporated, Winona, MN; *U.S. Private*, pg. 1153
Jacobs, Paul, Pres. & Chief Exec. Officer--IsoQuest, Inc., Fairfax, VA; *U.S. Private*, pg. 958
Jacobs, Richard E., Chm. Bd. & Chief Exec. Officer--The Richard E. Jacobs Group, Westlake, OH; *U.S. Private*, pg. 580
Jacobs, Victor, Chm. Bd. & Chief Exec. Officer--Allou Health & Beauty Care, Inc., Brentwood, NY; *U.S. Public*, pg. 55
Jacobs, William, Chief Exec. Officer--Guaranty Asset Protection Services, Inc., West Hills, CA; *U.S. Public*, pg. 857
Jacobsen, Thomas H., Chm. Bd., Pres. & Chief Exec. Officer--Mercantile Bancorporation Inc., Saint Louis, MO; *U.S. Public*, pg. 1087
Jacobson, Edwin, Pres. & Chief Exec. Officer--Avatar Holdings Inc., Coral Gables, FL; *U.S. Public*, pg. 151
Jacobson, Harvey, Pres., Chief Exec. Officer & Sec.--Glencraft Lingerie, Inc., New York, NY; *U.S. Private*, pg. 456
Jacobson, Mitchell, Pres. & Chief Exec. Officer--Sid Tool Co. Inc., Plainview, NY; *U.S. Private*, pg. 998
Jacobson, Mitchell, Pres. & Chief Exec. Officer--MSC Industrial Supply Co., Plainview, NY; *U.S. Private*, pg. 998
Jacobson, Rick, Pres. & Chief Exec. Officer--Norpac Foods, Inc., Stayton, OR; *U.S. Private*, pg. 802
Jaeger, Raymond E., Chm. Bd. & Chief Exec. Officer--SpecTran Corporation, Sturbridge, MA; *U.S. Public*, pg. 1497
Jaffe, Elliot S., Chm. Bd. & Chief Exec. Officer--The Dress Barn, Inc., Suffern, NY; *U.S. Public*, pg. 528
Jaffe, Richard B., Chm. Bd., Pres. & Chief Exec. Officer--Safeskin Corporation, San Diego, CA; *U.S. Public*, pg. 1425
Jaffee, Daniel S., Pres. & Chief Exec. Officer--Oil-Dri Corporation of America, Chicago, IL; *U.S. Public*, pg. 1214
Jaffre, Philippe, Chm. Bd., Pres. & Chief Exec. Officer--Elf Aquitane, Paris, France; *Int'l*, pg. 444
Jaffri, Shafeeg H., Chief Exec. Officer--Habib Bank Ltd., New York, NY; *Int'l*, pg. 581
Jager, Durk I., Pres. & Chief Oper. Officer--Richardson-Vicks, Inc., Health Care Products, Cincinnati, OH; *U.S. Public*, pg. 1331
Jakobsen, Ole, Chief Exec. Officer--Nilfisk A/S, Brondby, Denmark; *Int'l*, pg. 932
Jakowsky, Richard H., Pres., Chief Exec. Officer & Chief Oper. Officer--Anderson Electric, Inc., Springfield, IL; *U.S. Private*, pg. 72
Jamar, John P., Pres. & Chief Exec. Officer--Cable Constructors, Inc., Iron Mountain, MI; *U.S. Private*, pg. 197
James, Artis E., Jr., Pres. & Chief Exec. Officer--Purcell Co., Inc., Diamondhead, MS; *U.S. Private*, pg. 895
James, C. Shelton, Chm. Bd. & Chief Exec. Officer--Elcotel, Inc., Sarasota, FL; *U.S. Public*, pg. 568
James, Donald M., Pres. & Chief Exec. Officer--Vulcan Materials Company, Birmingham, AL; *U.S. Public*, pg. 1725
James, Guo Jin Zhi, Chief Exec. Officer--KONE Elevators (Shenzhen) Co. Ltd., Shenzhen, China; *Int'l*, pg. 747
James, Larry M., Chm. Bd., Pres. & Chief Exec. Officer--USLD Communications Corp., San Antonio, TX; *U.S. Public*, pg. 969

James, Patrick M., Pres. & Chief Exec. Officer--Rio Algom Limited, Toronto, Canada; *Int'l*, pg. 1118
James, Sean, Pres. & Chief Exec. Officer--Wagner Spray Tech Corp., Plymouth, MN; *U.S. Private*, pg. 1146
James, Thomas A., Chm. Bd. & Chief Exec. Officer--Raymond James Financial, Inc., Saint Petersburg, FL; *U.S. Public*, pg. 923
James, William, Pres. & Chief Exec. Officer--Inmet Mining Corporation, Toronto, Canada; *Int'l*, pg. 678
Jandernoa, Michael, Chm. Bd., Chief Exec. Officer--L. Perrigo Company, Allegan, MI; *U.S. Public*, pg. 1280
Janik, Richard A., Pres. & Chief Exec. Officer--Janik & Associates, Inc., Los Angeles, CA; *U.S. Private*, pg. 582
Janitz, John A., Chm. Bd., Pres. & Chief Exec. Officer--Textron Automotive Company, Troy, MI; *U.S. Public*, pg. 1590
Jankovic, Paul, Pres., Chief Exec. & Chief Oper. Officer--GHM Industries, Inc., Worcester, MA; *U.S. Private*, pg. 435
Jansen, James H., Pres., Chief Exec. & Oper. Officer--Lynden Incorporated, Seattle, WA; *U.S. Private*, pg. 683
Jansen, Peter, Deputy Chm. Bd. & Grp. Chief Exec. Officer--Caradon Plc, Weybridge, United Kingdom; *Int'l*, pg. 266
Jansen, Raymond A., Pres., Chief Exec. Officer & Publr.--Newsday, Melville, NY; *U.S. Public*, pg. 1616
Jansen, W. David, Pres.& Chief Exec. Officer--WJW Constructors, LLC, Mesa, AZ; *U.S. Private*, pg. 1187
Janson, Nils-Erik, Chief Exec. Officer--Aftonbladet AB, Stockholm, Sweden; *Int'l*, pg. 29
Jansson, Urban, Chief Exec. Officer--Forvaltnings AB Ratos, Stockholm, Sweden; *Int'l*, pg. 500
Janzem, Glen N., Pres. & Chief Exec. Officer--Ranchers Cotton Oil, Fresno, CA; *U.S. Private*, pg. 908
Jardine, Larry L., Chief Exec. Officer--LeGrand Johnson Construction Co., Logan, UT; *U.S. Private*, pg. 591
Jarke, D.W., Chief Exec. Officer--Jarke Corporation, Niles, IL; *U.S. Private*, pg. 583
Jarosz, William D., Pres. & Chief Exec. Officer--Fansteel, Inc., North Chicago, IL; *U.S. Public*, pg. 612
Jarritt, I. A., Chief Exec. Officer--Isle of Man Bank Limited, Douglas, United Kingdom; *Int'l*, pg. 910
Jarvis, D., Chief Exec. Officer--Hilton International Co., Coral Gables, FL; *Int'l*, pg. 787
Jarvis, Peter J., Chief Exec. Officer--Whitbread PLC, London, United Kingdom; *Int'l*, pg. 1498
Jaskol, Leonard R., Chm. Bd., Pres. & Chief Exec. Officer--Lydall, Inc., Manchester, CT; *U.S. Public*, pg. 1020
Jasper, Charles, Pres. & Chief Exec. Officer--Espey Huston Associates, Inc., Austin, TX; *U.S. Private*, pg. 826
Jastrow, Kenneth M., II, Pres. & Chief Exec. Officer--Guaranty F.S.B., Dallas, TX; *U.S. Public*, pg. 1575
Jatusipitak, Som, Dr., Pres. & Chief Exec. Officer--Siam City Bank Public Company Limited, Bangkok, Thailand; *Int'l*, pg. 1239
Jaudes, Robert C., Chm. Bd. & Chief Exec. Officer--Laclede Gas Company, Saint Louis, MO; *U.S. Public*, pg. 973
Jaworski, Walter J., Chm. Bd., Chief Exec. Officer & Chief Oper. Officer--Miken Companies, Inc., Cheektowaga, NY; *U.S. Private*, pg. 745
Jay, Dan, Pres., Chief Exec. Officer & Chief Fin. Officer--Campmor Inc., Upper Saddle River, NJ; *U.S. Private*, pg. 204
Jayson, Joseph M., Chm. Bd., Pres. & Chief Exec. Officer--J.M. Jayson & Co., Inc., Getzville, NY; *U.S. Private*, pg. 584
Jean, Emilio Azcarraga, Pres. & Chief Exec. Officer--Grupo Televisa, S.A. de C.V., Mexico, Mexico; *Int'l*, pg. 576
Jean, R.L., Chief Exec. Officer--Indiana Insurance Company, Indianapolis, IN; *Int'l*, pg. 648
Jeanloz, Claude, Chm. Bd. & Chief Exec. Officer--The Renovator's Supply, Inc., Conway, NH; *U.S. Private*, pg. 923
Jedlinski, Ronald T., Pres. & Chief Exec. Officer--Roman, Inc., Roselle, IL; *U.S. Private*, pg. 942
Jefferson, E. Jeff, Pres. & Chief Exec. Officer--Fresh Choice, Inc., Santa Clara, CA; *U.S. Public*, pg. 682
Jeffery, Kim, Pres. & Chief Exec. Officer--The Perrier Group of America, Greenwich, CT; *Int'l*, pg. 919
Jeffery, Kim, Pres. & Chief Exec. Officer--Great Bear Spring Company, Greenwich, CT; *Int'l*, pg. 919
Jelenic, Robert M., Chm. Bd., Pres. & Chief Exec. Officer--Journal Register Company, Trenton, NJ; *U.S. Public*, pg. 934
Jenkins, David, Group Exec. Officer--Millward Brown International, Warwick, United Kingdom; *Int'l*, pg. 1482
Jenkins, Francis, Chief Exec. Officer--Royster-Clark, Inc., Tarboro, NC; *U.S. Private*, pg. 949
Jenkins, Howard, Chm. Bd. & Chief Exec. Officer--Publix Supermarkets Inc., Lakeland, FL; *U.S. Private*, pg. 893
Jenkins, J. Michael, Pres. & Chief Exec. Officer--Vicorp Restaurants, Inc., Denver, CO; *U.S. Public*, pg. 1719
Jenkins, J.S.B., Pres. & Chief Exec. Officer--Tandy Brands Accessories, Inc., Arlington, TX; *U.S. Public*, pg. 1560
Jenkins, Joseph R., Chief Exec. Officer & Exec. V.P.--Heilig Meyers Furniture Co., Richmond, VA; *U.S. Public*, pg. 804
Jenkins, Robert H., Chm. Bd., Pres. & Chief Exec. Officer--Sundstrand Corporation, Rockford, IL; *U.S. Public*, pg. 1533
Jennings, A. Drue, Chm. Bd., Pres. & Chief Exec. Officer--Kansas City Power & Light Company, Kansas City, MO; *U.S. Public*, pg. 943
Jennings, Eugene, Chm. Bd., Pres. & Chief Exec. Officer--Universal Standard Healthcare, Inc., Southfield, MI; *U.S. Public*, pg. 1697
Jennings, Glenn R., Pres. & Chief Exec. Officer--Delta Natural Gas Company, Inc., Winchester, KY; *U.S. Public*, *pg. 497*
Jenny, Charles W., Pres. & Chief Exec. Officer-N.A. Div.--Schneider Electric S.A., Boulogne-Billancourt, France; *Int'l*, pg. 1207
Jenny, Klaus, Chief Exec. Officer-Credit Suisse Private Banking--Credit Suisse Group, Zurich, Switzerland; *Int'l*, pg. 345
Jensen, Craig, Chm. Bd. & Chief Exec. Officer--Executive Software, Glendale, CA; *U.S. Private*, pg. 388
Jensen, Erik A., Chief Exec. Officer--E.J. Bartells Co., Renton, WA; *U.S. Private*, pg. 118
Jensen, Steven R., Pres. & Chief Exec. Officer--Norbest, Inc., Midvale, UT; *U.S. Private*, pg. 801
Jepson, Jr., Robert S., Chm. Bd. & Chief Exec. Officer--Kuhlman Corporation, Savannah, GA; *U.S. Public*, pg. 968
Jepson, Larry, Chm Bd. & Chief Exec. Officer--First National Bank, Kearney, NE; *U.S. Public*, pg. 629
Jepson, Mark, Pres. & Chief Exec. Officer--First National Bank, McCook, NE; *U.S. Public*, pg. 629
Jerge, Pat, Pres. Chief Exec. Officer--First Commerce Technologies, Lincoln, NE; *U.S. Public*, pg. 629
Jernstedt, Rich, Chief Exec. Officer--Golin/Harris Communications, Inc., Chicago, IL; *Int'l*, pg. 1226
Jesse, W.C., Pres. & Chief Exec. Officer--Tangram Enterprise Solutions, Inc., Cary, NC; *U.S. Public*, pg. 1424
Jester, John R., Pres. & Chief Exec. Officer--Muzak Limited Partnership, Seattle, WA; *U.S. Private*, pg. 222
Jett, Dan, Pres.--Hunter Marine Corporation, Alachua, FL; *U.S. Private*, pg. 549
Jett, Dennis D., Pres. & Chief Exec. Officer--Oklahoma National Bank of Duncan, Duncan, OK; *U.S. Public*, pg. 630
Jewell, Everett G., Chm. Bd., Pres., Chief Exec. Officer & Treas.--Jewell Building Systems, Dallas, NC; *U.S. Private*, pg. 587
Jilk, Lawrence T., Jr., Pres. & Chief Exec. Officer--National Penn Bancshares, Inc., Boyertown, PA; *U.S. Public*, pg. 1158
Jilot, Dennis L., Pres. & Chief Exec. Officer--Springborn Testing & Research, Inc., Enfield, CT; *U.S. Private*, pg. 1027
Jinghall, Kent, Pres. & Chief Exec. Officer--Fermenta AB, Stockholm, Sweden; *Int'l*, pg. 480
Jiu, Xu Yong, Chief Officer--Shanghai Pulong Concrete Products Co., Ltd., Shanghai, China; *Int'l*, pg. 1293
Job, P., Chief Exec. Officer--Reuters Holdings PLC, London, United Kingdom; *Int'l*, pg. 1105
Jobs, Steve, Chm. Bd. & Chief Exec. Officer--Pixar Animation Studios, Richmond, CA; *U.S. Public*, pg. 1307
Jochum, George T., Chm. Bd., Pres. & Chief Exec. Officer--Mid Atlantic Medical Services, Inc., Rockville, MD; *U.S. Public*, pg. 1109
Johanneson, Gerald B., Pres. & Chief Exec. Officer--Haworth, Inc., Holland, MI; *U.S. Private*, pg. 511
Johansen, Richard W., Pres. & Chief Exec. Officer--Hudson, RCI, Temecula, CA; *U.S. Private*, pg. 546
Johanson, Nancy, Pres. & Chief Exec. Officer--Johanson Manufacturing Corporation, Boonton, NJ; *U.S. Private*, pg. 589
Johansson, Leif, Chief Exec. Officer--AB Volvo, Goteborg, Sweden; *Int'l*, pg. 1476
Johansson, Ulf, Pres. & Chief Exec. Officer--Spectra-Physics AB, Stockholm, Sweden; *Int'l*, pg. 1288
John, Edward F., Pres. & Chief Exec. Officer--Gudebrod, Inc., Pottstown, PA; *U.S. Private*, pg. 486
John, Francis D., Pres., Chief Exec. Officer & Chief Fin. Officer--Key Energy Group Inc., East Brunswick, NJ; *U.S. Public*, pg. 953
Johnsen, K.W.M., Deputy Chm. & Chief Executive Officer--Howden Group Plc, Renfrew, United Kingdom; *Int'l*, pg. 636
Johnsen, Walter C., Pres. & Chief Exec. Officer--Acme United Corporation, Fairfield, CT; *U.S. Public*, pg. 17
Johnsey, Walter F., Pres. & Chief Exec. Officer--Jasper Corp., Birmingham, AL; *U.S. Private*, pg. 583
Johnson, Andrew F., Co-Chief Exec. Officer & Pres.-Opers.--Hastings Manufacturing Company, Hastings, MI; *U.S. Public*, pg. 798
Johnson, Bill, Chief Exec. Officer--Farnam Companies, Inc., Phoenix, AZ; *U.S. Private*, pg. 396
Johnson, Carl, Chm. Bd. & Chief Exec. Officer--II-VI Incorporated, Saxonburg, PA; *U.S. Public*, pg. 1647
Johnson, Carl A., Pres., Chief Exec. & Chief Oper. Officer--The Berlin Steel Construction Company, Berlin, CT; *U.S. Private*, pg. 136
Johnson, Charles B., Pres. & Chief Exec. Officer--Franklin Resources, Inc., San Mateo, CA; *U.S. Public*, pg. 679
Johnson, Charles Brook, Chm. Bd., Pres. & Chief Exec. Officer--CS Brooks Canada Inc., Greenwich, CT; *U.S. Private*, pg. 197
Johnson, Charles P., Chm. Bd. & Chief Exec. Officer--General Datacomm Industries, Inc., Middlebury, CT; *U.S. Public*, pg. 708
Johnson, Charles S., Pres. & Chief Exec. Officer--Pioneer Hi-Bred International, Inc., Des Moines, IA; *U.S. Public*, pg. 1298
Johnson, Clark A., Chm. Bd. & Chief Exec. Officer--Pier 1 Imports, Inc., Fort Worth, TX; *U.S. Public*, pg. 1295
Johnson, Claude, Pres, Chief Exec. Officer & Chief Fin. Officer--Research, Incorporated, Eden Prairie, MN; *U.S. Public*, pg. 1382
Johnson, Craig T., Pres. & Chief Exec. Officer--Crabar Business Systems, Dayton, OH; *U.S. Private*, pg. 283
Johnson, D., Pres. & Chief Exec. Officer--Blandin Paper Company, Grand Rapids, MN; *Int'l*, pg. 495
Johnson, David, Chm. Bd., Pres. & Chief Exec. Officer--Swanson, Camden, NJ; *U.S. Public*, pg. 299
Johnson, David J., Chm. Bd., Pres. & Chief Exec. Officer--KinderCare Learning Centers, Inc., Portland, OR; *U.S. Public*, pg. 961
Johnson, David W., Pres. & Chief Exec. Officer--Campbell Sales Company, Camden, NJ; *U.S. Public*, pg. 299
Johnson, Dennis A., Pres. & Chief Exec. Officer--St. Paul Bank for Cooperatives, Saint Paul, MN; *U.S. Private*, pg. 398
Johnson, Dennis R., Pres. & Chief Exec. Officer--XATA Corporation, Burnsville, MN; *U.S. Public*, pg. 1783
Johnson, Donald R., Pres. & Chief Oper. Officer--Modine Manufacturing Company, Racine, WI; *U.S. Public*, pg. 1121
Johnson, Douglas W., Chief Exec. Officer--Blue Ridge Electric Membership Corp., Lenoir, NC; *U.S. Private*, pg. 153
Johnson, Edward C., III, Chm. Bd. & Chief Exec. Officer--Fidelity Investments (FMR Corp.), Boston, MA; *U.S. Private*, pg. 402
Johnson, Eldon, Pres. & Chief Exec. Officer--Dakota Electric Association, Farmington, MN; *U.S. Private*, pg. 308
Johnson, Gary S., Pres. & Chief Exec. Officer--Superior Oil Co. Inc., Indianapolis, IN; *U.S. Private*, pg. 1055
Johnson, Glendon E., Chm. Bd., Pres. & Chief Exec. Officer--John Alden Financial Corporation, Miami, FL; *U.S. Public*, pg. 39
Johnson, Gregory, Pres. & Chief Exec. Officer--Waccamaw Corporation, Myrtle Beach, SC; *U.S. Private*, pg. 1145
Johnson, James A., Chm. Bd. & Chief Exec. Officer--Federal National Mortgage Association (Fannie Mae), Washington, DC; *U.S. Public*, pg. 615
Johnson, Jim, Pres. & Chief Exec. Officer--Anspach Grossman Enterprise, New York, NY; *Int'l*, pg. 1483
Johnson, Joel W., Chm. Bd. & Chief Exec. Officer--Hormel Foods Corp., Austin, MN; *U.S. Public*, pg. 840
Johnson, John D., Pres. & Chief Exec. Officer--Harvest States Cooperatives, Saint Paul, MN; *U.S. Private*, pg. 508
Johnson, John H., Chm. Bd., Chief Exec. Officer & Publisher--Johnson Publishing Company, Inc., Chicago, IL; *U.S. Private*, pg. 591
Johnson, Jon L., Chm. Bd., Chief Exec. Officer & Dir.--EvansGroup, Salt Lake City, UT; *U.S. Private*, pg. 385
Johnson, Jon L., Pres. & Gen. Mgr.--Industrial Construction, Inc., Idaho Falls, ID; *U.S. Private*, pg. 560
Johnson, Kevin, Pres. & Chief Exec. Officer--Dianon Systems, Inc., Stratford, CT; *U.S. Public*, pg. 506
Johnson, Lawrence, Chm. Bd., Pres., Chief Exec. Officer & Gen. Counsel--Kelley Company, Inc., Milwaukee, WI; *U.S. Private*, pg. 612
Johnson, Lawrence, Chm. Bd., Pres., Chief Exec. Officer & Gen Counsel--Kelley Dock Systems, Milwaukee, WI; *U.S.* Private, pg. 612
Johnson, Lawrence M., Chm. Bd. & Chief Exec. Officer--Pacific Century Financial Corporation, Honolulu, HI; *U.S. Public*, pg. 1248
Johnson, Lawrence M., Chm. Bd. & Chief Exec. Officer--Bank of Hawaii, Honolulu, HI; *U.S. Public*, pg. 1248
Johnson, Linda E., Pres. & Chief Exec. Officer--JCI Data Processing, Inc., Cinnaminson, NJ; *U.S. Private*, pg. 577
Johnson, Lynn, Chief Exec. Officer--Johnson Brothers Wholesale Liquor, Saint Paul, MN; *U.S. Private*, pg. 591
Johnson, Mark, Chm. Bd., Pres. & Chief Exec. Officer--ITEQ, Inc., Houston, TX; *U.S. Public*, pg. 914
Johnson, Mark K., Chm. Bd. & Chief Exec. Officer--Johnson Storage Moving Co, Denver, CO; *U.S. Private*, pg. 594
Johnson, Mark R.S., Co-Chief Exec. Officer & Pres.-Mktg.--Hastings Manufacturing Company, Hastings, MI; *U.S. Public*, pg. 798
Johnson, Peter, Pres. & Chief Exec. Officer--Agouron Pharmaceuticals, Inc., La Jolla, CA; *U.S. Public*, pg. 28
Johnson, R.K. Peter, Pres. & Chief Exec. Officer--Faribault Woolen Mill Co., Faribault, MN; *U.S. Private*, pg. 394
Johnson, Richard E., Pres. & Chief Exec. Officer--The Stratevest Group, N.A., Burlington, VT; *U.S. Public*, pg. 187
Johnson, Robert, Pres. & Chief Exec. Officer-Dry Bulk Services--Chemical Leaman Tank Lines, Inc., Exton, PA; *U.S. Private*, pg. 233
Johnson, Robert L., Chm. Bd. & Chief Exec. Officer--Black Entertainment Television Holdings Inc., Washington, DC; *U.S. Public*, pg. 235
Johnson, Robert L., Pres. & Chief Exec. Officer--Action Pay-Per-View, Washington, DC; *U.S. Public*, pg. 235
Johnson, Robert M., Chm. Bd. & Chief Exec. Officer--Bowne & Co., Inc., New York, NY; *U.S. Public*, pg. 248
Johnson, Stephen C., Pres. & Chief Exec. Officer--Komag, Incorporated, San Jose, CA; *U.S. Public*, pg. 966
Johnson, Steve, Chief Exec. Officer & Pres.--Komag Incorporated, Milpitas, CA; *Int'l*, pg. 84
Johnson, Thomas, Pres. & Chief Exec. Officer--Chesapeake Corporation, Richmond, VA; *U.S. Public*, pg. 346
Johnson, Thomas L., Co-Chm. Bd., Pres. & Chief Exec. Officer--Objective Systems Integrators, Inc., Folsom, CA; *U.S. Public*, pg. 1209
Johnson, Van, Pres. & Chief Exec. Officer--First Citizens Bank of Hohenwald, Hohenwald, TN; *U.S. Public*, pg. 1669
Johnson, Van R., Pres. & Chief Exec. Officer--Sutter Health, Sacramento, CA; *U.S. Private*, pg. 1057
Johnson, Virland, Pres. & Chief Exec. Officer--Solidex, Scottsdale, AZ; *U.S. Public*, pg. 1672
Johnson, Walter D., Pres. & Chief Exec. Officer--Johnson Bros. Corporation, Litchfield, MN; *U.S. Private*, pg. 590
Johnson, William B., Chm. Bd. & Chief Exec. Officer--W.B. Johnson Properties, LLC, Atlanta, GA; *U.S. Private*, pg. 594
Johnson, William L., Pres. & Chief Exec. Officer--Southeastern Michigan Gas Enterprises, Inc., Port Huron, MI; *U.S. Public*, pg. 1489
Johnson, William R., Pres. & Chief Exec. Officer--H.J. Heinz Company, Pittsburgh, PA; *U.S. Public*, pg. 805
Johnson, Willis J., Chief Exec. Officer--Copart, Inc., Benicia, CA; *U.S. Public*, pg. 446
Johnston, Brian G., Pres. & Chief Exec. Officer--Cigna Insurance Company of Canada, Toronto, Canada; *U.S. Public*, pg. 366
Johnston, Chap, Pres. & Chief Exec. Officer--Tanner Co., Rutherfordton, NC; *U.S. Private*, pg. 1068
Johnston, Dennis, Chief Exec. Officer--Cornerstone Health Management, Dallas, TX; *U.S. Public*, pg. 1257

Johnston, Fred B., II, Chm. Bd. & Chief Exec. Officer--Fred B. Johnston Company, Inc., Chapin, SC; *U.S. Private*, pg. 595
Johnston, Fred B., II, Chief Exec. Officer--Weisz Graphics, Chapin, SC; *U.S. Private*, pg. 595
Johnston, M. James, Chm. Bd. & Chief Exec. Officer--Fort Wayne National Corporation, Fort Wayne, IN; *U.S. Public*, pg. 673
Johnston, Summerfield K., Jr., Vice Chm. & Chief Exec. Officer--Coca-Cola Enterprises Inc., Atlanta, GA; *U.S. Public*, pg. 393
Johnstone, Michael B., Pres. & Chief Exec. Officer--TCF Bank Illinois, Oak Brook, IL; *U.S. Public*, pg. 1554
Jollin, David A., Chm. Bd. & Chief Exec. Officer--Willis Corroon Corp. of Massachusetts, Boston, MA; *Int'l*, pg. 1506
Jolly, Mike, Chief Exec. Officer--The Tussauds Group Limited, London, United Kingdom; *Int'l*, pg. 1026
Joly, Alain, Chm. Bd. & Chief Exec. Officer--Air Liquide S.A., Paris, France; *Int'l*, pg. 37
Jonas, Donald L., Vice Chm., Chief Exec. Officer & Dir.-Mktg.--Lechters, Inc., Harrison, NJ; *U.S. Public*, pg. 983
Jonas, Hilton, Pres. & Chief Exec. Officer--A.P. Wyott, Dallas, TX; *U.S. Private*, pg. 1193
Jones, Alan, Chief Exec. Officer--BICC plc, London, United Kingdom; *Int'l*, pg. 120
Jones, Chester, Pres. & Chief Exec. Officer--Hunter Corp., Portage, IN; *U.S. Private*, pg. 549
Jones, Christopher, Chief Exec. Officer--J. Walter Thompson Company, New York, NY; *Int'l*, pg. 1483
Jones, D. Paul, Jr., Chm. Bd. & Chief Exec. Officer--Compass Bancshares, Inc., Birmingham, AL; *U.S. Public*, *pg. 418*
Jones, D. Paul, Jr., Chm. Bd. & Chief Exec. Officer--Compass Bank, Plano, TX; *U.S. Public*, pg. 419
Jones, D.C., Mng. Trustee & Chief Exec.--Tattersalls, Melbourne, Australia; *Int'l*, pg. 1357
Jones, David A., Chm. Bd., Pres. & Chief Exec. Officer--RAYOVAC Corporation, Madison, WI; *U.S. Private*, pg. 912
Jones, David R., Pres. & Chief Exec. Officer--AGL Resources, Atlanta, GA; *U.S. Public*, pg. 6
Jones, Dennis M., Chm., Pres. & Chief Exec. Officer--Jones Medical Industries Inc., Saint Louis, MO; *U.S. Public*, pg. 933
Jones, Don, Pres.--Mainship Corporation, Saint Augustine, FL; *U.S. Private*, pg. 697
Jones, Fletcher, Jr., Pres. & Chief Exec. Officer--Fletcher Jones Management Group, Las Vegas, NV; *U.S. Private*, *pg. 597*
Jones, Glenn R., Chm. Bd., Pres. & Chief Exec. Officer--Jones International, Ltd., Englewood, CO; *U.S. Private*, pg. 597
Jones, Gordon, Pres. & Chief Exec. Officer--Arcade Inc., Chattanooga, TN; *U.S. Private*, pg. 79
Jones, J. Larry, Chm. Bd. & Chief Exec. Officer--Addison-Wesley Longman, Inc., Reading, MA; *Int'l*, pg. 1026
Jones, James C., III, Chm. Bd. & Chief Exec. Officer--Jones Company, Inc., Waycross, GA; *U.S. Private*, pg. 596
Jones, James L., Sr., Chm. Bd. & Chief Exec. Officer--Jones & Jones, Inc., McAllen, TX; *U.S. Private*, pg. 596
Jones, James M., Jr., Chm., Pres. & Chief Exec. Officer--Peoples & Union Bank, Lewisburg, TN; *U.S. Public*, pg. 639
Jones, Jeremy M., Chm. Bd. & Chief Exec. Officer--Apria Healthcare Group Inc., Costa Mesa, CA; *U.S. Public*, pg. 125
Jones, John W., Pres. & Chief Exec. Officer--Modern Welding Co., Inc., Owensboro, KY; *U.S. Private*, pg. 755
Jones, Keith, Chief Exec.--Reed Business Information, Sutton, United Kingdom; *Int'l*, pg. 1094
Jones, Lloyd T., Pres. & Chief Exec. Officer--The Bank of North Arkansas, Melbourne, AR; *U.S. Public*, pg. 641
Jones, Norman T., Chief Exec. Officer--Growmark, Inc., Bloomington, IL; *U.S. Private*, pg. 484
Jones, Paul, Pres. & Chief Exec. Officer--Rule Industries, Inc., Gloucester, MA; *U.S. Public*, pg. 950
Jones, Richard H., Pres. & Chief Exec. Officer--Group Health Plan, Inc., Saint Louis, MO; *U.S. Public*, pg. 454
Jones, Robert L., Pres. & Chief Exec. Officer--First National Bank of Magnolia, Magnolia, AR; *U.S. Public*, pg. 641
Jones, Robert L., Pres. & Chief Exec. Officer--Southeast Power Corporation, Titusville, FL; *U.S. Public*, pg. 750
Jones, Ronald, Pres. & Chief Exec. Officer--Sealy Corporation, Cleveland, OH; *U.S. Private*, pg. 978
Jones, Ronald, Pres. & Chief Exec. Officer--Royal Doulton USA Inc., Somerset, NJ; *Int'l*, pg. 1135
Jones, Ronald L., Chm. Bd., Pres. & Chief Exec. Officer--Dawn Food Products, Inc., Jackson, MI; *U.S. Private*, pg. 316
Jones, Russell G., Jr., Vice Chm. & Chief Exec. Officer--Package Service Company, LLC., Kansas City, MO; *U.S. Private*, pg. 833
Jones, Stanley, Pres., Chief Exec. Officer & Gen. Mgr.--Buhrman-Pharr Hardware Company, Texarkana, AR; *U.S. Private*, pg. 179
Jones, Wallace A., Pres. & Chief Exec. Officer--El Chico Restaurants, Inc., Dallas, TX; *U.S. Private*, pg. 283
Jones, Wilbur S., Jr., Pres. & Chief Exec. Officer--Stone & Thomas, Wheeling, WV; *U.S. Private*, pg. 1044
Jones, William W., Jr., Pres. & Chief Exec. Officer--Baltimore Stationery Co./Total Office, Baltimore, MD; *U.S. Private*, pg. 113
Jongebloed, James T., Chm. Bd., Pres. & Chief Exec. Officer--Pool Energy Services Co., Houston, TX; *U.S. Public*, pg. 1316
Jordan, A. J., Chief Exec. Officer--Ulster Bank (Isle of Man) Limited, Douglas, United Kingdom; *Int'l*, pg. 911
Jordan, Don D., Chm. Bd. & Chief Exec. Officer--Houston Industries Incorporated, Houston, TX; *U.S. Public*, pg. 842
Jordan, Don D., Chm. Bd. & Chief Exec. Officer--NorAm Energy Corp., Houston, TX; *U.S. Public*, pg. 843
Jordan, Jerry D., Chm. Bd. & Chief Exec. Officer--CGAS, Inc., Columbus, OH; *U.S. Public*, pg. 585
Jordan, John W., II, Chm. Bd. & Chief Exec. Officer--Jordan Industries, Inc., Deerfield, IL; *U.S. Private*, pg. 598
Jordan, Michael H., Chm. Bd. & Chief Exec. Officer--CBS Corporation, Pittsburgh, PA; *U.S. Public*, pg. 273
Jordan, Michael H., Chm. Bd. & Chief Exec. Officer--CBS, New York, NY; *U.S. Public*, pg. 273
Jordan, Michael L., Pres. & Chief Exec. Officer--SI/Baker, Inc., Easton, PA; *U.S. Public*, pg. 1418
Jordan, Richard E., II, Chm. Bd. & Chief Exec. Officer--L.B. Smith, Inc., Camp Hill, PA; *U.S. Private*, pg. 1009
Jordan, Roger, Chief Exec. Officer--Hanson Amalgamated Industries, Stevenage, United Kingdom; *Int'l*, pg. 592
Jorden, Edwin W., Pres. & Chief Exec. Officer--Barclay White Incorporated, Berwyn, PA; *U.S. Private*, pg. 115
Jordi, Walter, Chief Exec. Officer--Maloya Fredestein, Gelterkinden, Switzerland; *Int'l*, pg. 505
Jorgenson, Don, Pres. & Chief Exec. Officer--Hypro Corporation, New Brighton, MN; *U.S. Public*, pg. 1767
Joseph, George, Chm. Bd. & Chief Exec. Officer--Mercury General Corporation, Los Angeles, CA; *U.S. Public*, pg. 1093
Joseph, John B., Chm. Bd., Pres. & Chief Exec. Officer--West Coast Bancorp, Newport Beach, CA; *U.S. Public*, pg. 1755
Joshi, Krishan K., Pres. & Chief Exec. Officer--UES, Inc., Dayton, OH; *U.S. Private*, pg. 1112
Joslin, Donald E., Pres. & Chief Exec. Officer--Monitor Life Insurance Company of New York, Utica, NY; *U.S. Private*, pg. 258
Joss, Robert, Chief Exec. Officer & Mng. Dir.--Westpac Banking Corporation, Sydney, Australia; *Int'l*, pg. 1495
Jovanovich, Peter, Chm. & Chief Exec. Officer--Addison-Wesley Longman Ltd., Harlow, United Kingdom; *Int'l*, pg. 1027
Joy, Frank R., Jr., Pres. & Chief Exec. Officer--The Bradford National Bank of Greenville, Greenville, IL; *U.S. Private*, pg. 164
Joy, Ronald, Chief Exec. Officer, V.P.-Fin. & Controller--MacNaughton Einson Graphics, Fair Lawn, NJ; *U.S. Private*, pg. 692
Joyce, Burton M., Pres. & Chief Exec. Officer--Terra Industries, Inc., Sioux City, IA; *U.S. Public*, pg. 1581
Joyce, James R., Pres. & Chief Exec., Fin. & Acctg. Officer--Magellan Petroleum Corporation, Madison, CT; *U.S. Public*, pg. 1036
Joyce, Kevern R., Chm. Bd., Pres., Chief Exec. Officer & Dir.--TNP Enterprises, Inc., Fort Worth, TX; *U.S. Public*, pg. 1557
Joyce, William H., Chm. Bd., Pres. & Chief Exec. Officer--Union Carbide Corporation, Danbury, CT; *U.S. Public*, pg. 1666
Jozoff, Malcolm, Chm. Bd. & Chief Exec. Officer--Lenox, Incorporated, Lawrenceville, NJ; *U.S. Public*, pg. 261
Jozoff, Malcolm, Chm., Pres. & Chief Exec. Officer--The Dial Corporation, Phoenix, AZ; *U.S. Public*, pg. 505
Juanarena, Douglas B., Pres. & Chief Exec. Officer--Pressure Systems, Inc., Hampton, VA; *Int'l*, pg. 1130
Judge, Fred, Pres. & Chief Exec. Officer--Titan Information Systems, San Diego, CA; *U.S. Public*, pg. 1618
Juett, J. Lee, Chm. Bd., Pres. & Chief Exec. Officer--J. Lee Hackett Co., Farmington, MI; *U.S. Private*, pg. 492
Juilfs, George, Pres. & Chief Exec. Officer--SENCORP, Newport, KY; *U.S. Private*, pg. 983
Juliard, A., Chm. & Chief Exec. Officer--Union Pour Le Financement D'Immeubles Desouetes (UIS), Paris, France; *Int'l*, pg. 565
Julius, Robert P., Chm. Bd., Pres. & Chief Exec. Officer--Nice-Pak Products, Inc., Orangeburg, NY; *U.S. Private*, pg. 798
Jumani, Abbas, Chief Exec. Officer--Russell Corp. UK Limited, Livingston, United Kingdom; *U.S. Public*, pg. 1413
Junck, Mary, Chief Exec. Officer & Publisher--The Baltimore Sun Newspapers, Baltimore, MD; *U.S. Public*, pg. 1616
Junel, Staffan, Chief Exec. Officer--Victor Hasselblad AB, Goteborg, Sweden; *Int'l*, pg. 1468
Junker, Edward P., III, Chm. & Chief Exec. Officer-NW Market--PNC Bank Corp., Pittsburgh, PA; *U.S. Public*, pg. 1242
Jurick, Geoffrey, Chm. Bd. & Chief Exec. Officer--Sport Supply Group, Inc., Dallas, TX; *U.S. Public*, pg. 1499
Jusseaume, Rich, Chm. Bd., Pres. & Chief Exec. Officer--Graphic Enterprises of Ohio, Inc., Canton, OH; *U.S. Private*, pg. 471
Justin, John, Chm. Bd. & Chief Exec. Officer--Justin Industries, Inc., Fort Worth, TX; *U.S. Public*, pg. 936
Justin, John, Chief Exec. Officer--Justin Boot Company, Fort Worth, TX; *U.S. Public*, pg. 937
Justiss, James F., Jr., Chm. Bd., Pres. & Chief Exec. Officer--Justiss Oil Co., Inc., Jena, LA; *U.S. Private*, pg. 602
Juszkiewicz, Henry E., Chm. Bd. & Chief Exec. Officer--Gibson Musical Instruments, Inc., Nashville, TN; *U.S. Private*, pg. 451
Juusela, Jyrki, Chm. Bd., Pres. & Chief Exec. Officer--Outokumpu Oyj, Espoo, Finland; *Int'l*, pg. 1015
Kabala, Stanely J., Chief Exec. Officer--Rogers Cantel Mobile Communications Inc., Saint-Laurent, Canada; *Int'l*, pg. 1122
Kable, Mark, Chief Exec. Officer--Setzer Forest Products, Sacramento, CA; *U.S. Private*, pg. 987
Kabus, Alan S., Pres. & Chief Exec. Officer--Bentley Mills, Inc., City of Industry, CA; *U.S. Public*, pg. 889
Kachapis, Paul, Pres. & Chief Exec. Officer--Alden Auto Parts Warehouse, Inc., Somerset, MA; *U.S. Private*, pg. 33
Kacin, William L., Pres. & Chief Exec. Officer--Met-Pro Corporation, Harleysville, PA; *U.S. Public*, pg. 1100
Kadiri, Hamid, Chief Exec. Officer--Klem EURO RSCG, Casablanca, Morocco; *Int'l*, pg. 603
Kadisha, Neil, Chm. Bd. & Chief Exec. Officer--HPM Corporation, Mount Gilead, OH; *U.S. Private*, pg. 492
Kaemmer, D., Chm. Bd. & Chief Exec. Officer--GEHE AG, Stuttgart, Germany; *Int'l*, pg. 591
Kafadar, Ahmed D., Chm. Bd. & Chief Exec. Officer--OEA, Inc., Aurora, CO; *U.S. Public*, pg. 1206
Kahl, James, Pres. & Chief Exec. Officer--La Petite Academy Inc., Overland Park, KS; *U.S. Private*, pg. 640
Kahler, John S., Pres. & Chief Exec. Officer--Cincinnati Incorporated, Harrison, OH; *U.S. Private*, pg. 240
Kahlor, Robert A., Chm. Bd. & Chief Exec. Officer--Journal Communications Inc., Milwaukee, WI; *U.S. Private*, pg. 601
Kahn, D. Dan, Chm. Bd. & Chief Exec. Officer--Production Tool Supply Co., Warren, MI; *U.S. Private*, pg. 889
Kahn, Harold D., Chm. Bd. & Chief Exec. Officer--Macy's East, New York, NY; *U.S. Public*, pg. 618
Kahn, Myron, Chm. Bd. & Chief Exec. Officer--Croscill, Inc., New York, NY; *U.S. Private*, pg. 290
Kahn, Seymour, Chm. Bd. & Chief Exec. Officer--Mercury Air Group Inc., Los Angeles, CA; *U.S. Public*, pg. 1092
Kaiser, Marshall J., Pres. & Chief Exec. Officer--Safe Harbor Water Power Corp., Conestoga, PA; *U.S. Public*, pg. 172
Kaiser, Marshall J., Pres. & Chief Exec. Officer--Pennsylvania Power & Light Company-Northeast Div., Wilkes-Barre, PA; *U.S. Public*, pg. 1244
Kaiser, Marshall J., Pres. & Chief Exec. Officer--Safe Harbor Water Power Corp., Conestoga, PA; *U.S. Public*, pg. 1244
Kaiser, Steven, Pres. & Chief Exec. Officer--Baume Mercier, Inc., New York, NY; *U.S. Private*, pg. 124
Kaitz, Ben B., Pres. & Chief Exec. Officer--Palm Beach Beauty Products Co., Minneapolis, MN; *U.S. Private*, pg. 834
Kakiage, Masatoshi, Pres. & Chief Exec. Officer--Mitsui Fudosan (USA), Inc., New York, NY; *Int'l*, pg. 882
Kalangis, Ike, Chm. Bd., Pres. & Chief Exec. Officer--NationsBank Sunwest, Inc., Albuquerque, NM; *U.S. Public*, pg. 1165
Kalb, Jeffrey C., Pres. & Chief Exec. Officer--California Micro Devices, Milpitas, CA; *U.S. Public*, pg. 293
Kalbermatter, E., Chief Exec. Officer--Ascom Business Systems AG, Solothurn, Switzerland; *Int'l*, pg. 86
Kaldellis, Emanuel, Chm. Bd., Pres. & Chief Exec. Officer--Copais Food & Beverage Company S.A., Athens, Greece; *U.S. Public*, pg. 806
Kalin, Edward L., Pres.--Kalin Enterprises, Inc., Sarasota, FL; *U.S. Private*, pg. 606
Kalinske, Thomas, Pres. & Chief Exec. Officer--Sega of America Inc., Redwood City, CA; *Int'l*, pg. 1218
Kalish, Bernard, Chm. Bd. & Chief Exec. Officer--Lawson Products, Inc., Des Plaines, IL; *U.S. Public*, pg. 980
Kalitta, Conrad, Pres. & Chief Exec. Officer--American International Airways, Ypsilanti, MI; *U.S. Private*, pg. 57
Kalkhoven, Kevin, Pres. & Chief Exec. Officer--Uniphase Corporation, San Jose, CA; *U.S. Public*, pg. 1670
Kalpala, Asmo, Chief Exec. Officer--Tapiola-Yhtiot, Espoo, Finland; *Int'l*, pg. 1354
Kaltenbacher, Philip D., Chm. Bd. & Chief Exec. Officer--Seton Company, Norristown, PA; *U.S. Private*, pg. 987
Kaltman, Eric, Chief Exec. Officer--Queens Group, Inc., Long Island City, NY; *U.S. Private*, pg. 900
Kaman, Charles H., Chm. Bd., Pres. & Chief Exec. Officer--Kaman Corporation, Bloomfield, CT; *U.S. Public*, pg. 941
Kamatsu, T., Chief Oper. Officer--Asian Transmission Corp., Manila, Philippines; *Int'l*, pg. 947
Kambayashi, Akio, Pres. & Chief Exec. Officer--Kasumi Co., Ltd., Tsuchiura, Japan; *Int'l*, pg. 724
Kamberos, Chris, Chm. Bd., Pres. & Chief Oper. Officer--Treasure Island Foodmarts Inc., Chicago, IL; *U.S. Private*, pg. 1098
Kamen, Harry P., Chm. Bd. & Chief Exec. Officer--Metropolitan Life Insurance Co., New York, NY; *U.S. Private*, pg. 737
Kamenstein, Peter, Chm., Pres. & Chief Exec. Officer--M. Kamenstein, Inc., Elmsford, NY; *U.S. Private*, pg. 606
Kamerschen, Robert J., Chm. Bd. & Chief Exec. Officer--ADVO, Inc., Windsor, CT; *U.S. Public*, pg. 23
Kamimura, Jiro, Chm. Bd. & Chief Exec. Officer--Aristech Chemical Corporation, Pittsburgh, PA; *Int'l*, pg. 872
Kaminow, Edward S., Pres. & Chief Exec. Officer--West Mill Clothes, Inc., Woodside, NY; *U.S. Private*, pg. 1163
Kaminski, Mark V., Pres. & Chief Exec. Officer--Commonwealth Industries, Inc., Louisville, KY; *U.S. Public*, pg. 415
Kaminski, Mark V., Pres. & Chief Exec. Officer--Alflex, Long Beach, CA; *U.S. Public*, pg. 415
Kaminski, Robert M., Chief Exec. Officer--Leiner Health Products, Inc., Carson, CA; *U.S. Private*, pg. 659
Kaminski, Robert S., Chm. Bd. & Chief Exec. Officer--Continental/Midland, Inc., Park Forest, IL; *U.S. Private*, pg. 268
Kaminsky, Larry E., Chm. Bd., Pres. & Chief Exec. Officer--H. R. Kaminsky & Sons, Inc., Fitzgerald, GA; *U.S. Private*, pg. 606
Kamm, Jacob O., II, Chm. Bd., Pres. & Chief Exec. & Fin. Officer--Electric Furnace Co., Salem, OH; *U.S. Private*, pg. 367
Kampf, Serge, Chm. Bd. & Chief Exec. Officer--CAP Gemini S.A., Paris, France; *Int'l*, pg. 263
Kampouris, Emmanuel A., Chm. Bd., Pres. & Chief Exec. Officer--American Standard Inc., Piscataway, NJ; *U.S. Public*, pg. 91
Kamras, Mikael, Chief Exec. Officer--Proventus AB, Stockholm, Sweden; *Int'l*, pg. 1072
Kanagawa, Chihiro, Pres. & Chief Exec. Officer--Shin-Etsu Chemical Co. ltd., Tokyo, Japan; *Int'l*, pg. 1234
Kanary, James R., Chm. Bd., Pres. & Chief Exec. Officer--Grayling State Bank, Grayling, MI; *U.S. Public*, pg. 379
Kanas, John Adam, Chm. Bd., Pres. & Chief Exec. Officer--North Fork Bancorporation, Inc., Melville, NY; *U.S. Public*, pg. 1194
Kane, Alfie, Chief Exec. Officer--Telecom Eireann, Dublin, Ireland; *Int'l*, pg. 1362

Kane, Dennis B., Pres. & Chief Exec. Officer--ABC/Kane Productions International, Inc., Washington, DC; *U.S. Public*, pg. 511

Kane, Joseph R., Jr., Pres. & Chief Exec. Officer--Days Inns of America, Inc., Parsippany, NJ; *U.S. Public*, pg. 321

Kane, Larry I., Chm. Bd. & Chief Exec. Officer--Alternative Resources Corporation, Lincolnshire, IL; *U.S. Public*, pg. 59

Kane, Sam, Chm. Bd. & Chief Exec. Officer--Sam Kane Beef Processors, Inc., Corpus Christi, TX; *U.S. Private*, pg. 607

Kane, Stanley B., Chm. Bd. & Chief Exec. Officer--Kane-Miller Corp., Tarrytown, NY; *U.S. Private*, pg. 607

Kaneb, John, Chief Exec. Officer--Gulf Oil Limited Partnership, Chelsea, MA; *U.S. Private*, pg. 487

Kaneko, Zenichiro, Pres.--Sakata Seed Corporation, Yokohama, Japan; *Int'l*, pg. 1178

Kanfer, Joseph, Pres. & Chief Exec. Officer--Go Jo Industries, Cuyahoga Falls, OH; *U.S. Private*, pg. 458

Kankowsky, Roland, Dr., Chm. & Chief Exec. Officer--Filterwerk Mann & Hummel GmbH, Ludwigsburg, Germany; *Int'l*, pg. 484

Kanner, Robert H., Chm. Bd., Pres., Chief Exec./Fin. Officer & Treas.--Pubco Corporation, Cleveland, OH; *U.S. Public*, pg. 1339

Kanner, Robert H., Chm. Bd. & Chief Exec. Officer--Aspen Imaging International, Inc., Cleveland, OH; *U.S. Public*, pg. 1339

Kantor, Martin, Chm. Bd. & Chief Exec. Officer--National Financial Insurance Company, Fort Worth, TX; *U.S. Private*, pg. 782

Kantor, Robert, Chm. & Chief Exec. Officer--Publicis/Bloom, New York, NY; *Int'l*, pg. 470

Kantz, Phil, Pres. & Chief Exec. Officer--Tab Products Co., Palo Alto, CA; *U.S. Public*, pg. 1559

Kanzaki, Yasuhiko, Chief Oper. Officer--Euro Makita Corporation B.V., Amsterdam, Netherlands; *Int'l*, pg. 831

Kanzaki, Yasuhiko, Chief Oper. Officer--Makita International Europe Ltd., Milton Keynes, United Kingdom; *Int'l*, pg. 832

Kaplan, Edward, Chm., Pres. & Chief Exec. Officer--Zebra Technologies Corporation, Vernon Hills, IL; *U.S. Public*, pg. 1790

Kaplan, Jerome, Chief Oper. Officer--Transilwrap Company, Inc., Chicago, IL; *U.S. Private*, pg. 1097

Kaplan, Larry, Chief Exec. Officer-Americas--Shandwick International Plc, London, United Kingdom; *Int'l*, pg. 1226

Kaplan, Larry, Chief Exec. Officer--Shandwick Americas, New York, NY; *Int'l*, pg. 1226

Kaplan, Samuel, Pres., Chief Exec. Officer, Sec. & Dir.-Sls. & Pur.--Admiration Hosiery Mills, Inc., Charlotte, NC; *U.S. Private*, pg. 528

Kaplanek, Charles, Jr., Chm. Bd., Pres. & Chief Exec. Officer--Floral Glass & Mirror, Inc., Hauppauge, NY; *U.S. Private*, pg. 414

Kapoor, John N., Ph.D., Chm. Bd. & Chief Exec. Officer--Akorn, Inc., Lincolnshire, IL; *U.S. Public*, pg. 34

Kapp, Dennis, Chm. Bd. & Chief Exec. Officer--Martin Universal Design, Inc., Detroit, MI; *U.S. Private*, pg. 709

Kappler, George, Chm. Bd., Pres. & Chief Exec. Officer--Kappler Safety Group, Inc., Guntersville, AL; *U.S. Private*, pg. 607

Kappler, George P., Jr., Chief Exec. Officer--Kappler Safety Group, Inc., Guntersville, AL; *U.S. Private*, pg. 607

Kappler, George P., Jr., Chief Exec. Officer--Kappler USA, Guntersville, AL; *U.S. Private*, pg. 607

Kar, Maharaj, Chief Exec.--Sulzer Flovel Hydro Ltd., New Delhi, India; *Int'l*, pg. 1308

Karake, Timo, Deputy Chief Exec. Officer & Exec. V.P.-Foodstuffs--Kesko Ltd., Helsinki, Finland; *Int'l*, pg. 732

Karam, Thomas F., Pres. & Chief Exec. Officer--Pennsylvania Enterprises Inc., Wilkes-Barre, PA; *U.S. Public*, pg. 1271

Karatz, Bruce, Chm. Bd., Pres. & Chief Exec. Officer--Kaufman and Broad Home Corporation, Los Angeles, CA; *U.S. Public*, pg. 944

Karatzas, Jordan, Chief Exec. Officer--Olympic Airways, New York, NY; *Int'l*, pg. 1004

Kardatzke, E. Stanley, M.D., Chm. Bd. & Chief Exec. Officer--Physician Corporation of America, Miami, FL; *U.S. Public*, pg. 1293

Kardos, Paul J., Pres., Chief Exec. Officer & Chief Oper. Officer--Horace Mann Educators Corporation, Springfield, IL; *U.S. Public*, pg. 835

Karinen, Heimo, Chm. & Chief Exec. Officer--Kemira Oy, Helsinki, Finland; *Int'l*, pg. 727

Karis, William G., Pres. & Chief Exec. Officer--Consol, Pittsburgh, PA; *U.S. Public*, pg. 531

Karis, William G., Pres. & Chief Exec. Officer--Consol, Pittsburgh, PA; *Int'l*, pg. 1081

Karl, Susan Gamson, Pres. & Chief Exec. Officer--Annabelle Candy Company, Inc., Hayward, CA; *U.S. Private*, pg. 75

Karl, Wolfgang, Chief Exec.--Sulzermedica GmbH, Cologne, Germany; *Int'l*, pg. 1307

Karlan, Mark S., Pres. & Chief Exec. Officer--Imperial Credit Commercial Mortgage Investment Corp., Los Angeles, CA; *U.S. Public*, pg. 872

Karlsson, Tommy, Chief Exec. Officer--CarnaudMetalbox, Paris, France; *U.S. Public*, pg. 463

Karman, James B., Pres. & Chief Exec. Officer--Spaulding & Slye, Boston, MA; *U.S. Private*, pg. 1021

Karmanos, Peter, Jr., Chm. Bd. & Chief Exec. Officer--Compuware Corporation, Farmington Hills, MI; *U.S. Public*, pg. 423

Karmazin, Mel, Chm. Bd. & Chief Exec. Officer-CBS Station Grp.--CBS, New York, NY; *U.S. Public*, pg. 273

Karmazin, Mel, Chief Exec. Officer--Westwood One, Inc., New York, NY; *U.S. Public*, pg. 1763

Karol, Steven E., Pres. & Chief Exec. Officer--H M K Enterprises, Inc., Waltham, MA; *U.S. Private*, pg. 489

Karp, Allen, Pres. & Chief Exec. Officer--Cineplex Odeon Corporation, Toronto, Canada; *Int'l*, pg. 292

Karp, Donald M., Chm. Bd. & Chief Exec. Officer--Broad National Bancorporation, Newark, NJ; *U.S. Public*, pg. 257

Karp, Leonard, Chief Exec. Officer, V.P. & Treas.--Best Provision Co., Inc., Newark, NJ; *U.S. Private*, pg. 140

Karp, Mark E., Pres. & Chief Exec. Officer--Moore Medical Corp., New Britain, CT; *U.S. Public*, pg. 1128

Karpen, Roderic B., Chm. Bd. & Chief Exec. Officer--Copes-Vulcan Inc., Lake City, PA; *U.S. Private*, pg. 274

Karrick, Robert, Pres. & Chief Exec. Officer--Gelco Information Network, Inc., Eden Prairie, MN; *U.S. Private*, pg. 442

Karter, Jerome, Pres. & Chief Exec. Officer--SCOR U.S. Corporation, New York, NY; *Int'l*, pg. 1152

Kashnow, Richard A., Dr., Chm. Bd., Pres. & Chief Exec. Officer--Raychem Corporation, Menlo Park, CA; *U.S. Public*, pg. 1362

Kaske, Wolfgang, Dr., Pres. & Chief Exec. Officer--AMB Aachener und Muenchener Beteiligungs-AG, Aachen, Germany; *Int'l*, pg. 15

Kaskel, Roy R., Chm. Bd. & Chief Exec. Officer--Enron Liquid Services Corp., Houston, TX; *U.S. Public*, pg. 584

Kasle, Don, Pres. & Chief Exec. Officer--Western Financial Bank, Irvine, CA; *U.S. Public*, pg. 1757

Kasle, Roger, Chief Exec. Officer--Kasle Steel Corporation, Dearborn, MI; *U.S. Private*, pg. 608

Kasputys, Joseph E., Chm. Bd., Pres. & Chief Exec. Officer--Primark Corporation, Waltham, MA; *U.S. Public*, pg. 1325

Kass, Ron, Chief Exec. Officer--Robert Allen Ametek, Mansfield, MA; *U.S. Private*, pg. 432

Kass, Ron, Chief Exec. Officer--Ametex Fabrics, Inc., Mansfield, MA; *U.S. Private*, pg. 432

Kassab, Charles S., Chm. Bd., Pres., Chief Exec. Officer & Treas.--Huntington Bancshares Michigan, Inc., Troy, MI; *U.S. Public*, pg. 850

Kassab, Gregory E., Chief Exec. Officer--Stainless Incorporated, Deerfield Beach, FL; *U.S. Private*, pg. 1029

Kassel, Robert L., Chm. Bd., Pres., Chief Exec. Officer & Treas.--U.S. Home & Garden Inc., San Francisco, CA; *U.S. Public*, pg. 1682

Kassling, W.E., Chm. Bd. & Chief Exec. Officer--Westinghouse Air Brake Company, Wilmerding, PA; *U.S. Public*, pg. 1760

Kassouf, James, Pres., Chief Exec. Officer & Treas.--Metropolitan Properties Systems, Cleveland, OH; *U.S. Private*, pg. 739

Kataoka, Masataka, Pres. & Chief Exec. Officer--Alps Electric Co., Ltd., Tokyo, Japan; *Int'l*, pg. 65

Katayama, Shozo, Pres. & Chief Exec. Officer--Toyo Tire & Rubber Co., Ltd., Osaka, Japan; *Int'l*, pg. 1411

Kathwari, M. Farooq, Chm. Bd., Pres. & Chief Exec. Officer--Ethan Allen Interiors Inc., Danbury, CT; *U.S. Public*, pg. 595

Kathwari, M. Farooq, Chm., Pres. & Chief Exec. Officer--Ethan Allen, Inc., Danbury, CT; *U.S. Public*, pg. 595

Kato, Masahiko, Chm. & Chief Exec. Officer--Otsuka America, Inc., San Francisco, CA; *Int'l*, pg. 1013

Kato, Yoshiyuki, Chief Exec. Officer--LTCB International Limited, London, United Kingdom; *Int'l*, pg. 816

Katoh, Motoaki, Pres.--Colonial Beef Co., Philadelphia, PA; *U.S. Private*, pg. 253

Katopodis, Louis, Pres. & Chief Exec. Officer--Fiesta Mart Inc., Houston, TX; *U.S. Private*, pg. 403

Katz, Joel, Pres. & Chief Exec. Officer--Boatmen's National Mortgage Inc., Memphis, TN; *U.S. Public*, pg. 1165

Katz, Ronald C., Chm. Bd. & Chief Exec. Officer--Elkay Manufacturing Company, Oak Brook, IL; *U.S. Private*, pg. 372

Katz, Solomon, Treas. & Sec.--Manhattan Store Interiors, Inc., Brooklyn, NY; *U.S. Private*, pg. 699

Katzen, Cyrus, Dr., Pres. & Chief Exec. Officer--Mozel Development Corp., Baileys Crossroads, VA; *U.S. Private*, pg. 765

Katzman, Lawrence, Chm. Bd. & Chief Exec. Officer--Kaz, Inc., New York, NY; *U.S. Private*, pg. 610

Kauffman, James B., Jr., Chm. Bd., Pres. & Chief Exec. Officer--Keystone Bank, Horsham, PA; *U.S. Public*, pg. 956

Kaufman, Bruce J., Pres. & Chief Exec. Officer--Kaufel Group Ltd., Dorval, Canada; *Int'l*, pg. 724

Kaufman, Derek, Chief Exec. Officer--Diesel Technology Company, Wyoming, MI; *Int'l*, pg. 205

Kaufman, Herbert W., Pres. & Chief Exec. Officer--H.W. Kaufman Financial Group, Inc., Farmington, MI; *U.S. Private*, pg. 609

Kaufman, Jerry, Pres. & Chief Exec. Officer--Nationwide Credit Inc., Marietta, GA; *U.S. Private*, pg. 788

Kaufman, Richard F., Chm. Bd. & Chief Exec. Officer--Amstore Corporation, Muskegon, MI; *U.S. Private*, pg. 68

Kaufman, Stephen P., Chm. Bd. & Chief Exec. Officer--Arrow Electronics, Inc., Melville, NY; *U.S. Public*, pg. 133

Kaufmann, Joachim, Chief Exec. & Chief Oper. Officer--Feintool International Holding AG, Lyss, Switzerland; *Int'l*, pg. 479

Kaufmann, Luiz, Pres. & Chief Exec. Officer--Aracruz Celulose S.A., Rio de Janeiro, Brazil; *Int'l*, pg. 78

Kaul, Rakesh K., Pres. & Chief Exec. Officer--Hanover Direct, Inc., Weehawken, NJ; *U.S. Public*, pg. 782

Kauranen, Timo, Chief Exec. Officer & Mng. Dir.--Foster Wheeler Energia Oy, Helsinki, Finland; *U.S. Public*, pg. 677

Kavanagh, J.P., Pres. & Chief Exec. Officer--Schieffelin & Somerset Co., New York, NY; *Int'l*, pg. 412

Kavanah, John, Chm. Bd., Pres. & Chief Exec. Officer--Marketing Corp. of America, Westport, CT; *U.S. Private*, pg. 704

Kawakami, Fumio, Chief Exec.--Sulzer Metco (Japan) Ltd., Tokyo, Japan; *Int'l*, pg. 1308

Kawakami, Tetsuro, Chm. Bd. & Chief Exec. Officer--Sumitomo Electric Industries, Ltd., Osaka, Japan; *Int'l*, pg. 1313

Kawamoto, Nobuhiko, Pres. & Chief Exec. Officer--Honda Motor Co., Ltd., Tokyo, Japan; *Int'l*, pg. 634

Kawamoto, Toshio, Chief Exec. Officer--Willis Corroon Japan Limited, Tokyo, Japan; *Int'l*, pg. 1509

Kawamura, Koji, Chief Oper. Officer--Makita (New Zealand) Ltd., Auckland, New Zealand; *Int'l*, pg. 832

Kay, Brian, Pres. & Chief Exec. Officer--Connecting Point Computer Services, Canton, OH; *U.S. Private*, pg. 471

Kay, Jack, Pres. & Chief Exec. Officer--Phoenix Technologies Ltd., San Jose, CA; *U.S. Public*, pg. 1292

Kaye, Alan, Chm. & Chief Exec. Officer--Dobson Park Industries Plc, Wigan, United Kingdom; *U.S. Public*, pg. 789

Kaye, Isaac, Deputy Chief Exec. Officer--IVAX Corporation, Miami, FL; *U.S. Public*, pg. 914

Kaye, Issac, Chm. Bd. & Chief Exec. Officer--Norton Healthcare Limited, Harlow, United Kingdom; *U.S. Public*, pg. 915

Kayne, Fred, Chief Exec. Officer--Fortune Fashion Inc., City of Commerce, CA; *U.S. Private*, pg. 419

Kayser, Kraig H., Pres. & Chief Exec. Officer--Seneca Foods Corporation, Pittsford, NY; *U.S. Public*, pg. 1456

Kazmaier, Dick, Chief Exec. Officer--Bike Athletic Co., Knoxville, TN; *U.S. Private*, pg. 143

Kealy, Joseph P., Chm. Bd., Pres. & Chief Exec. Officer--International FiberCom, Phoenix, AZ; *U.S. Public*, pg. 898

Kean, John, Jr., Pres. & Chief Exec. Officer--NUI Corporation, Bedminster, NJ; *U.S. Public*, pg. 1147

Keane, John F., Sr., Founder & Chief Exec. Officer--Keane, Inc., Boston, MA; *U.S. Public*, pg. 946

Kearney, Joseph P., Pres. & Chief Exec. Officer--U.S. Generating Company, Bethesda, MD; *U.S. Public*, pg. 1241

Kearney, Joseph P., Pres. & Chief Exec. Officer--PG&E Gas Transmission, San Francisco, CA; *U.S. Public*, pg. 1241

Kearns, Joseph G., Chief Exec. Officer--Daniel F. Young, Inc., New York, NY; *U.S. Private*, pg. 1200

Kearns, Walter J., Pres. & Chief Exec. Officer--Data Documents Holdings, Inc., Omaha, NE; *U.S. Public*, pg. 449

Keat, Tony Tan Choon, Chief Exec. Officer--Parkway Holdings Limited, Singapore, Singapore; *Int'l*, pg. 1023

Keating, Pierce J., Pres. & Chief Exec. Officer--Daniel J. Keating Co., Ardmore, PA; *U.S. Private*, pg. 610

Keating, Susan, Pres. & Chief Exec. Officer--Dauphin Deposit Bank and Trust Company, Harrisburg, PA; *Int'l*, pg. 64

Kebrdle, Dennis, Chief Exec. Officer--Sican Corp., Elkhart, IN; *U.S. Private*, pg. 997

Kee, Lim Ho, Chief Exec. Officer & Exec. V.P.-Far East--Union Bank of Switzerland, Zurich, Switzerland; *Int'l*, pg. 1439

Keehan, Ed, Chief Exec. Officer--Damart, Rollinsford, NH; *Int'l*, pg. 376

Keeler, James L., Pres. & Chief Exec. Officer--WLR Foods, Inc., Timberville, VA; *U.S. Public*, pg. 1727

Keenan, Jack, Chief Exec. Officer-Drinks--Grand Metropolitan Plc, London, United Kingdom; *Int'l*, pg. 408

Keene, Howard, Chm. Bd., Pres.,Chief Exec. & Oper. Officer--Rawlings Sporting Goods Company, Fenton, MO; *U.S. Public*, pg. 1361

Keener, J.W., Jr., Chm. Bd., Pres., Chief Exec. Officer--The Chardon Rubber Co., Chardon, OH; *U.S. Private*, pg. 229

Keener, Wayne, Pres. & Chief Exec. Officer--Keeners, Inc., Renton, WA; *U.S. Private*, pg. 611

Keener, Wayne, Pres. & Chief Exec. Officer--Beef Distributors, Inc., Renton, WA; *U.S. Private*, pg. 611

Keeney, Cecil M., Chm. Bd. & Chief Exec. Officer--Walle Corporation, Harahan, LA; *U.S. Private*, pg. 1148

Keersmaeker, Charles A., Pres.--The John Johnson Co., Detroit, MI; *U.S. Private*, pg. 591

Kefalas, Paul T., Pres. & Chief Exec. Officer--ABB in Canada, Saint-Laurent, Canada; *Int'l*, pg. 7

Keimatsu, Shunsuke, Chm. Bd. & Chief Exec. Officer-IMS Cognizant Japan--I.M.S. International, Inc., Totowa, NJ; *U.S. Public*, pg. 395

Keinanen, Eino, Chm. Bd. & Chief Exec. Officer--Postipankki Ltd., Helsinki, Finland; *Int'l*, pg. 1064

Keiper, William C., Chm. Bd. & Chief Exec. Officer--Artisoft, Inc., Tucson, AZ; *U.S. Public*, pg. 136

Keiser, Donald M., Pres. & Chief Exec. Officer--SunTrust Bank, Northwest Georgia, N.A., Rome, GA; *U.S. Public*, pg. 1538

Keiser, Robert L., Chm. Bd., Pres. & Chief Exec. Officer--Oryx Energy, Dallas, TX; *U.S. Public*, pg. 1232

Keith, J. Collin, Chm. Bd. & Chief Exec. Officer--Horace Small Apparel Company, Nashville, TN; *Int'l*, pg. 635

Keith, Robert, Pres. & Chief Exec. Officer--ServiceMaster Management Services Corporation, Downers Grove, IL; *U.S. Public*, pg. 1462

Keith, Robert E., Pres. & Chief Exec. Officer--TL Ventures, Wayne, PA; *U.S. Public*, pg. 1424

Keith, Roy, Chm. Bd. & Chief Exec. Officer--Carson Products Company, Savannah, GA; *U.S. Public*, pg. 309

Keithley, Joseph P., Chm. Bd., Pres. & Chief Exec. Officer--Keithley Instruments, Inc., Cleveland, OH; *U.S. Public*, pg. 946

Kelleher, Herbert D., Chm. Bd., Pres. & Chief Exec. Officer--Southwest Airlines Co., Dallas, TX; *U.S. Public*, pg. 1493

Kelleher, Kevin, Pres. & Chief Exec. Officer--HFS Mobility Services, Danbury, CT; *U.S. Public*, pg. 321

Kelleher, Richard M., Pres. & Chief Exec. Officer--Doubletree Corporation, Memphis, TN; *U.S. Public*, pg. 1335

Kelleher, T. S., Chm. Bd. & Chief Exec. Officer--Clearing-Niagara, Buffalo, NY; *U.S. Private*, pg. 196

Kelleher, T.S., Chm. Bd. & Chief Exec. Officer--CNB International, Inc., Charleston, SC; *U.S. Private*, pg. 196

Keller, Charles E., Chief Exec. Officer--Acordia Northeast, Boston, MA; *Int'l*, pg. 671

Keller, David, Pres. & Chief Exec. Officer--UPB of Mid-Missouri, Columbia, MO; *U.S. Public*, pg. 1669

Keller, Dennis J., Chm. Bd. & Chief Exec. Officer--DeVry Institutes, Oak Brook Terrace, IL; *U.S. Public*, pg. 503

Keller, Larry, Chief Exec. Officer--Dewberry Design Group, Oklahoma City, OK; *U.S. Private*, pg. 329
Keller, Richard D., Pres. & Chief Exec. Officer--Electric Fuel Corp., Saint Petersburg, FL; *U.S. Public*, pg. 655
Keller, Robert L., Pres. & Chief Exec. Officer--J.J. Keller & Associates, Inc., Neenah, WI; *U.S. Private*, pg. 612
Kellermeyer, Donald V., Pres., Chief Exec. Officer & Treas.--Kellermeyer Co., Toledo, OH; *U.S. Private*, pg. 612
Kelley, Austin P., Chm. Bd. & Chief Exec. Officer--Austin Kelley Advertising, Inc., Atlanta, GA; *U.S. Private*, pg. 100
Kelley, Brian J., Pres. & Chief Exec. Officer--Cognitronics Corporation, Danbury, CT; *U.S. Public*, pg. 394
Kelley, Bruce G., Pres., Chief Exec. Officer & Treas.--EMC Insurance Group, Inc., Des Moines, IA; *U.S. Public*, pg. 545
Kelley, E.W., Chm. Bd. & Chief Exec. Officer--Fairmont Snack Group, Inc., Independence, OH; *U.S. Private*, pg. 392
Kelley, Gary L., Chm. Bd., Pres. & Chief Exec. Officer--Kelley Bean Co., Inc., Morrill, NE; *U.S. Private*, pg. 612
Kelley, James V., Chm. Bd., Pres. & Chief Exec. Officer--First United Bancshares, Inc., El Dorado, AR; *U.S. Public*, pg. 641
Kelley, Joe, Pres. & Chief Exec. Officer--AGC Life Insurance Co., Nashville, TN; *U.S. Public*, pg. 76
Kelley, Joe, Pres. & Chief Exec. Officer--American General Life & Accident Insurance Co., Nashville, TN; *U.S. Public*, pg. 76
Kelley, Larry I., Pres. & Chief Exec. Officer--One Price Clothing Stores, Inc., Duncan, SC; *U.S. Public*, pg. 1225
Kelley, Robert, Chm. Bd., Pres. & Chief Exec. Officer--Noble Affiliates, Inc., Ardmore, OK; *U.S. Public*, pg. 1186
Kelley, William G., Chm. Bd. & Chief Exec. Officer--Consolidated Stores Corp., Columbus, OH; *U.S. Public*, pg. 437
Kellogg, Charles T., Pres., Chief Exec. Officer & Treas.--Hubbard Hall Inc., Waterbury, CT; *U.S. Private*, pg. 544
Kellogg, Martin N., Pres. & Chief Exec. Officer--UFE Incorporated, Stillwater, MN; *U.S. Private*, pg. 1112
Kellogg, William S., Chm. Bd. & Chief Exec. Officer--Kohl's Corporation, Menomonee Falls, WI; *U.S. Public*, pg. 965
Kells, R. D., Chief Exec. Officer--Ulster Bank Limited, Belfast, United Kingdom; *Int'l*, pg. 911
Kelly, Anthony O., Pres. & Chief Exec. Officer--Mannington Mills, Inc., Salem, NJ; *U.S. Private*, pg. 700
Kelly, David M., Chm. Bd., Pres. & Chief Exec. Officer--Matthews International Corp., Pittsburgh, PA; *U.S. Public*, *pg. 1059*
Kelly, Fred W., Jr., Pres. & Chief Exec. Officer--Sun Bancorp, Inc., Selinsgrove, PA; *U.S. Public*, pg. 1529
Kelly, J. Fredrick, Jr., Pres. & Chief Exec. Officer--Aeroglide Corporation, Cary, NC; *U.S. Private*, pg. 24
Kelly, James P., Chm. Bd. & Chief Exec. Officer--United Parcel Service of America, Inc., Atlanta, GA; *U.S. Private*, pg. 1123
Kelly, John, Pres. & Chief Exec. Officer--Biederman, Kelly & Shaffer, Inc., New York, NY; *U.S. Private*, pg. 142
Kelly, John D., Pres. & Chief Exec. Officer--Na-Churs Plant Food Company, Marion, OH; *U.S. Private*, pg. 1096
Kelly, John F., Chm. Bd., Pres, Chief Exec. & Oper. Officer--Alaska Air Group, Inc., Seattle, WA; *U.S. Public*, pg. 35
Kelly, John J., Pres. & Chief Exec. Officer--Willis Corroon Corp. of New York, New York, NY; *Int'l*, pg. 1506
Kelly, Michael, Chief Exec. Officer & Chief Fin. Officer--Regency Savings Bank, Naperville, IL; *U.S. Private*, pg. 406
Kelly, Patrick, Pres. & Chief Exec. Officer--Physician Sales and Services Inc., Jacksonville, FL; *U.S. Public*, pg. 1293
Kelly, Robert, Pres. & Chief Exec. Officer--Eagle Food Centers, Inc., Milan, IL; *U.S. Public*, pg. 547
Kelly, Robert, Pres. & Chief Exec. Officer--Nicklaus Golf Company, L.C., West Palm Beach, FL; *U.S. Private*, pg. 799
Kelly, Stephen J., Chm. Bd., Pres. & Chief Exec. Officer--SouthCo. Inc., Concordville, PA; *U.S. Private*, pg. 1014
Kelly, Thomas J., Chm Bd., Pres., & Chief Exec. Officer--Somerset Savings Bank, Somerville, MA; *U.S. Public*, pg. 1484
Kelly, Tom, Publr. & Chief Exec. Officer--Catholic Digest, Saint Paul, MN; *U.S. Private*, pg. 220
Kelly, Tom, Chief Exec. Officer--Hawthorne Communications, Inc., Fairfield, IA; *U.S. Private*, pg. 512
Kelly, Tony, Pres. & Chief Exec. Officer, Mannington Mills--Mannington Resilient Floors, Salem, NJ; *U.S. Private*, pg. 700
Kelso, Richard W., Pres. & Chief Exec. Officer--PQ Corporation, Berwyn, PA; *U.S. Private*, pg. 827
Kemeny, Robert A., Pres. & Chief Exec. Officer--This End Up Furniture, Richmond, VA; *U.S. Private*, pg. 1081
Kemmerer, John L., Chm. Bd. & Chief Exec. Officer--Jackson Hole Ski Resort, Teton Village, WY; *U.S. Private*, pg. 579
Kemp, K. Thomas, Pres. & Chief Exec. Officer--Fund American Enterprises Holdings, Inc., Hanover, NH; *U.S. Public*, pg. 688
Kemp, Melvin T., Pres. & Chief Exec. Officer--B & K Steel & Supply, Inc., Ogden, UT; *U.S. Private*, pg. 105
Kemp, Steven E., Pres. & Chief Exec. Officer--Regions Bank/Rome, Rome, GA; *U.S. Public*, pg. 1372
Kemp, Thomas, Chm. Bd. & Chief Exec. Officer--Penton Publishing, Inc., Cleveland, OH; *U.S. Public*, pg. 1306
Kemper, David W., Chm. Bd., Pres. & Chief Exec. Officer--Commerce Bancshares, Inc., Kansas City, MO; *U.S. Public*, pg. 409
Kemper, Jonathan M., Chm. Bd., Pres. & Chief Exec. Officer--Commerce Bank N.A., Kansas City, MO; *U.S. Public*, pg. 409
Kemper, Michael J., Pres. & Chief Exec. Officer--Northern Pipeline Construction Co., Phoenix, AZ; *U.S. Public*, pg. 1493
Kemper, R. Crosby, Co-Chm. Bd. & Co-Chief Exec. Officer--UMB Financial Corporation, Kansas City, MO; *U.S. Public*, pg. 1653
Kemper, R. Crosby, Chm. Bd. & Chief Exec. Officer--United Missouri Bank N.A., Kansas City, MO; *U.S. Public*, pg. 1654
Kempner, James C., Pres. & Chief Exec. Officer--Imperial Holly Corporation, Sugar Land, TX; *U.S. Public*, pg. 872
Kendall, Kennett R., Jr., Chm. Bd. & Chief Exec. Officer--Willis Corroon Corp. of New Hampshire, Rochester, NH; *Int'l*, pg. 1506
Kendall, Stephen F., Pres. & Chief Exec. Officer--Aluminum Shapes, LLC, Delair, NJ; *U.S. Private*, pg. 47
Kendall, Steve, Pres. & Chief Exec. Officer--Electrical Insulation Suppliers, Atlanta, GA; *U.S. Private*, pg. 368
Kendell, Ross E., Pres. & Chief Exec. Officer--Key Bank of Utah, Salt Lake City, UT; *U.S. Public*, pg. 954
Kennealy, Dave P., Chief Exec. Officer--Foodcorp Limited, Bedfordview, South Africa; *Int'l*, pg. 496
Kennedy, B., Deputy Chief Exec.--Longwall International Limited, Worcester, United Kingdom; *U.S. Public*, pg. 789
Kennedy, Bernard J., Chm. Bd., Pres. & Chief Exec. Officer--National Fuel Gas Company, Buffalo, NY; *U.S. Public*, pg. 1156
Kennedy, D., Chief Exec. Officer--Bowthorpe Thermometrics, Taunton, United Kingdom; *Int'l*, pg. 207
Kennedy, James C., Chm. Bd. & Chief Exec. Officer--Cox Enterprises, Inc., Atlanta, GA; *U.S. Private*, pg. 281
Kennedy, John C., Chm. Bd., Pres. & Chief Exec. Officer--Autocam Corporation, Grand Rapids, MI; *U.S. Public*, pg. 148
Kennedy, John M., Chm. Bd., Pres. & Gen. Mgr.--T.H. Rogers Lumber Co., Edmond, OK; *U.S. Private*, pg. 940
Kennedy, John R., Pres. & Chief Exec. Officer--Federal Paper Board Company, Inc., Montvale, NJ; *U.S. Public*, pg. 903
Kennedy, W. Keith, Jr., Dr., Pres. & Chief Exec. Officer--Watkins-Johnson Company, Palo Alto, CA; *U.S. Public*, pg. 1745
Kennedy, William E., Jr., Chm. Bd., Chief Exec. Officer & Treas.--Kennedy Tank & Manufacturing Co., Inc., Indianapolis, IN; *U.S. Private*, pg. 614
Kennelly, P.E.M., Chief Exec. Officer--Delmon Ready Mixed Concrete & Products Co. W.L.L. (Bahrain), Manama, Bahrain; *Int'l*, pg. 1092
Kenny, James R., Pres., Chief Exec. Officer & Sec.--SJNB Financial Corp., San Jose, CA; *U.S. Public*, pg. 1418
Kent, J.H., Chm. Bd. & Chief Exec. Officer--Kent Feeds Inc., Muscatine, IA; *U.S. Private*, pg. 1134
Kent, Marsha, Co-Pres. & Chief Exec. Officer--Kent & Spiegel Direct, Culver City, CA; *U.S. Private*, pg. 615
Kenyon, Bruce D., Pres. & Chief Exec. Officer-Nuclear--Northeast Utilities, Berlin, CT; *U.S. Public*, pg. 1194
Keon, William T., III, Pres. & Chief Exec. Officer--Pueblo Xtra International, Inc., Pompano Beach, FL; *U.S. Private*, pg. 894
Keret, M., Pres. & Chief Exec. Officer--Israel Aircraft Industries Ltd., Israel; *Int'l*, pg. 689
Kerkorian, Kirk, Chm. Bd., Pres. & Chief Exec. Officer--Tracinda Corporation, Las Vegas, NV; *U.S. Private*, pg. 1095
Kerman, Harold M., Chief Exec. Officer--Steiner Electric Company, Elk Grove Village, IL; *U.S. Private*, pg. 1039
Kerr, Bill, Pres. & Chief Exec. Officer--Country Home Magazine, Des Moines, IA; *U.S. Public*, pg. 1094
Kerr, David W., Chm. Bd. & Chief Exec. Officer--Noranda Inc., Toronto, Canada; *Int'l*, pg. 433
Kerr, Donald J., Pres. & Chief Exec. Officer--Crestar Food Products, Inc., Brentwood, TN; *U.S. Public*, pg. 805
Kerr, Howard J., Chm. Bd., Pres. & Chief Exec. Officer--Consolidated Pipe & Supply Company, Birmingham, AL; *U.S. Private*, pg. 266
Kerr, Richard L., Pres. & Chief Exec. Officer--IMCO Recycling Inc., Irving, TX; *U.S. Public*, pg. 870
Kerr, Stephen R., Chief Exec. Officer--Holstein Association USA, Inc., Brattleboro, VT; *U.S. Private*, pg. 536
Kerr, William T., Chm. Bd. & Chief Exec. Officer--Meredith Corporation, Des Moines, IA; *U.S. Public*, pg. 1094
Kersulis, Bernard J., Pres., Chief Exec. Officer & Chief Oper. Officer--Standun, Inc., Inglewood, CA; *U.S. Private*, *pg. 1032*
Kertzman, Mitchell E., Chm. Bd. & Chief Exec. Officer--Sybase, Inc., Emeryville, CA; *U.S. Public*, pg. 1544
Kerzner, Solomon, Chm. Bd. & Chief Exec. Officer--Sun International Hotels Limited, Fort Lauderdale, FL; *U.S. Public*, pg. 1531
Kesl, James R., Pres. & Chief Exec. Officer--Willis Corroon Corp. of Seattle, Seattle, WA; *Int'l*, pg. 1507
Ketcham, Henry, III, Pres. & Chief Exec. Officer--West Fraser Timber Co. Ltd., Vancouver, Canada; *Int'l*, pg. 1490
Ketesledger, Roger, Pres. & Chief Exec. Officer--Yale/Chase Materials Handling, Inc., City of Industry, CA; *U.S. Private*, pg. 1195
Kever, Jim, Pres. & Co-Chief Exec. Officer--Envoy Corporation, Nashville, TN; *U.S. Public*, pg. 587
Kevtko, Colleen, Pres. & Chief Exec. Officer--Fifth-Third Trust Co. & Savings Bank, FSB, Naples, FL; *U.S. Public*, *pg. 622*
Key, Derrick N., Chm. Bd., Pres. & Chief Exec. Officer--Roper Industries, Inc., Bogart, GA; *U.S. Public*, pg. 1405
Key, James Richard, Pres. & Chief Exec. Officer--Regions Bank/Chilton County, Thorsby, AL; *U.S. Public*, pg. 1372
Key, John, Pres. & Chief Exec. Officer--Clinton State Bank, Clinton, IN; *U.S. Public*, pg. 1217
Keyes, James H., Chm. Bd. & Chief Exec. Officer--Johnson Controls, Inc., Milwaukee, WI; *U.S. Public*, pg. 932
Keyser, Richard L., Pres. & Chief Exec. Officer--W.W. Grainger, Inc., Lincolnshire, IL; *U.S. Public*, pg. 758
Khan, Sultan W., Pres. & Chief Exec. Officer--Newcom, Inc., Westlake Village, CA; *U.S. Public*, pg. 147
Kheng, Gwee Lian, Pres. & Chief Exec. Officer--United Overseas Land Limited, Singapore, Singapore; *Int'l*, pg. 1443
Khoo, Richard, Chief Exec. Officer & Gen. Mgr.--SATS Passenger Services Pte. Ltd., Singapore, Singapore; *Int'l*, pg. 1374
Khoury, Robert, Vice Chm. & Chief Exec. Officer--B/E Aerospace, Inc., Wellington, FL; *U.S. Public*, pg. 159
Khoury, Tawfiq N., Chm. Bd. & Chief Exec. Officer--Monticello Management Co., San Diego, CA; *U.S. Private*, pg. 759
Khulusi, Frank, Chm. Bd., Pres. & Chief Exec. Officer--Creative Computers, Inc., Torrance, CA; *U.S. Public*, pg. 458
Kidd, Kenneth, Chm. Bd. & Pres.--Superior Label Systems, Inc., Mason, OH; *U.S. Private*, pg. 1055
Kidder, C. Robert, Chm. Bd. & Chief Exec. Officer--Borden, Inc., Columbus, OH; *U.S. Private*, pg. 157
Kidder, C. Robert, Chm. Bd. & Chief Exec. Officer--Cracker Jack Division, Northbrook, IL; *U.S. Private*, pg. 157
Kidder, Norman, Pres. & Chief Exec. Officer--Rauland-Borg Corporation, Skokie, IL; *U.S. Private*, pg. 911
Kielholz, Walter B., Pres. & Chief Exec. Officer--Swiss Reinsurance Company, Zurich, Switzerland; *Int'l*, pg. 1332
Kierlin, Robert A., Chm. Bd., Pres. & Chief Exec. Officer--Fastenal Company, Winona, MN; *U.S. Public*, pg. 614
Kies, A.M., Pres. & Chief Exec. Officer--Erico International, Solon, OH; *U.S. Private*, pg. 381
Kiesinger, Fred, Chief Exec. Officer--Muench-Kreuzer Candle Company, Syracuse, NY; *U.S. Private*, pg. 766
Kiggen, James D., Chm. Bd. & Chief Exec. Officer--Xtek, Inc., Cincinnati, OH; *U.S. Private*, pg. 1194
Kiil, Leevi, Chief Exec. Officer & Sr. Mng. Partner--HLW International LLP, New York, NY; *U.S. Private*, pg. 491
Kikkawa, Akikazu, Pres. & Chief Exec. Officer--Ajinomoto U.S.A., Inc., Teaneck, NJ; *Int'l*, pg. 40
Kikkawa, Hideaki, Dep. Chief Exec.-Intl. Div.--Wako Securities Co., Ltd., Tokyo, Japan; *Int'l*, pg. 1485
Kilcollin, T. Eric, Pres. & Chief Exec. Officer--Chicago Mercantile Exchange, Chicago, IL; *U.S. Private*, pg. 235
Kilgore, Tom D., Pres. & Chief Exec. Officer--Georgia Transmission Corporation, Tucker, GA; *U.S. Private*, pg. 448
Kilgore, Tom D., Pres. & Chief Exec. Officer--Oglethorpe Power Corp., Tucker, GA; *U.S. Private*, pg. 812
Kill, Robert H., Chm. Bd., Pres. & Chief Exec. Officer--Ciprico, Inc., Plymouth, MN; *U.S. Public*, pg. 370
Killgallon, William C., Chm. Bd. & Chief Exec. Officer--The Ohio Art Company, Inc., Bryan, OH; *U.S. Public*, pg. 1214
Killian, Raymond L., Jr., Chm. Bd.--Investment Technology Group, Inc., New York, NY; *U.S. Public*, pg. 924
Killinger, Kerry K., Chm. Bd., Pres. & Chief Exec. Officer--Washington Mutual Inc., Seattle, WA; *U.S. Public*, pg. 1741
Killins, David, Chm. Bd. & Chief Exec. Officer--Tecmar Technologies International, Inc., Concord, Canada; *Int'l*, pg. 1361
Killins, David J., Chm. Bd. & Chief Exec. Officer--Legacy Storage Systems Corp., Markham, Canada; *Int'l*, pg. 805
Killoran, F.J., Pres. & Chief Exec. Officer--Taro Industries Limited, Calgary, Canada; *Int'l*, pg. 1424
Kilpatrick, J.F., Chief Exec.-Matls. Div.--Cookson Matthey Ceramics, West Chester, PA; *Int'l*, pg. 714
Kilts, James M., Chm. Bd., Pres. & Chief Exec. Officer--Nabisco Inc., Parsippany, NJ; *U.S. Public*, pg. 1355
Kim, Chang Hee, Pres. & Chief Exec. Officer--Daewoo Securities Co., Ltd., Seoul, Korea; *Int'l*, pg. 358
Kim, Edward, Pres., Chief Oper. & Chief Exec. Officer--Pantech Construction Co., Lanham, MD; *U.S. Private*, pg. 837
Kim, Jae Koo, Pres. & Chief Exec. Officer--Cho Hung Bank of Canada, Toronto, Canada; *Int'l*, pg. 288
Kim, James J., Chm. Bd. & Chief Exec. Officer--Amkor Electronics, Inc., West Chester, PA; *U.S. Private*, pg. 66
Kim, Kenneth H., Chm., Pres., Chief Exec. Officer, Corp. Sec. & Treas.--Medieval Times Dinner & Tournament, Inc., Buena Park, CA; *U.S. Private*, pg. 728
Kim, Moo N., Chief Exec. Officer, Exec. V.P. & Mgr.-Mfg.--Crown Confectionery Co., Ltd., Seoul, Korea; *Int'l*, pg. 348
Kim, Seung-Hwan, Chief Officer--Qingdao Ssangyong Apparel Co., Ltd., Qingdao, China; *Int'l*, pg. 1291
Kim, W.K., Pres. & Chief Exec. Officer--Kia Motors America, Inc., Irvine, CA; *Int'l*, pg. 733
Kim, Young Han, Pres. & Chief Oper. Officer--Daewoo Securities (America) Inc., New York, NY; *Int'l*, pg. 359
Kimball, L. Robert, Chief Exec. Officer & Treas.--L. Robert Kimball & Associates, Ebensburg, PA; *U.S. Private*, pg. 619
Kimbell, John S., Pres. & Chief Exec. Officer--Vermont Gas Systems, Inc., South Burlington, VT; *Int'l*, pg. 542
Kimbrell, W. Duke, Chm. Bd. & Chief Exec. Officer--Parkdale Mills, Gastonia, NC; *U.S. Private*, pg. 840
Kimbrough, James H., Pres. & Chief Exec. Officer--SunTrust Bank, Nature Coast, Brooksville, FL; *U.S. Public*, pg. 1537
Kimbrough, Lawrence M., Pres. & Chief Exec. Officer--First Charter Corporation, Concord, NC; *U.S. Public*, pg. 627
Kimmel, Jerry E., Chm. Bd., Pres. & Chief Exec. Officer--Kevco, Inc., Fort Worth, TX; *U.S. Public*, pg. 952
Kimmell, Lee, Chief Exec. Officer--American Marine Holdings Inc., Sarasota, FL; *U.S. Private*, pg. 58
Kimmell, Lee, Chief Exec. Officer--Donzi Marine Corporation, Sarasota, FL; *U.S. Private*, pg. 58
Kimura, Seishi "Woody", Pres.--Sanden International (U.S.A.), Inc., Wylie, TX; *Int'l*, pg. 1184
Kimura, Ted, Pres. & Chief Exec. Officer--Yamaha Motor Corp., U.S.A., Cypress, CA; *Int'l*, pg. 1516
Kincaid, Brent B., Pres. & Chief Exec. Officer--Broyhill Furniture Industries, Inc., Saint Louis, MO; *U.S. Public*, pg. 688
Kincaid, John, Pres. & Chief Exec. Officer--Schaake Corporation, Ellensburg, WA; *U.S. Private*, pg. 969

Kindersley, Peter David, Chm. Bd. & Chief Exec. Officer--Dorling Kindersley Holdings plc, London, United Kingdom; *Int'l*, pg. 416
Kindig, Karl K., Pres. & Chief Exec. Officer--Pittston Minerals Group, Inc., Lebanon, VA; *U.S. Public*, pg. 1305
Kindlund, Newton C., Chm. Bd., Pres., Chief Exec. & Chief Oper. Officer--Holiday RV Superstores, Inc., Orlando, FL; *U.S. Public*, pg. 829
King, Burt, Pres. & Chief Exec. Officer--Gibson County Bank, Princeton, IN; *U.S. Public*, pg. 1217
King, David C., Chm. Bd., Pres. & Chief Exec. Officer--Proxim, Inc., Mountain View, CA; *U.S. Public*, pg. 1338
King, Dennis, M., Pres. & Chief Exec. Officer--Harley Ellington Design, Southfield, MI; *U.S. Private*, pg. 503
King, Desmond B., Chief Exec. Officer--Premier Power Ltd., Antrim, United Kingdom; *Int'l*, pg. 119
King, Edward L., Jr., Chm. Bd. & Chief Exec. Officer--Regions Bank/Okaloosa/Bay County, Fort Walton Beach, FL; *U.S. Public*, pg. 1372
King, G.E., Chm. & Chief Exec. Officer--The CIBC Wood Gundy Corporation, Toronto, Canada; *Int'l*, pg. 256
King, George F., Pres. & Chief Exec. Officer--Associated Building Systems, Portland, TN; *Int'l*, pg. 699
King, George F., Chm. Bd. & Chief Exec. Officer--Kirby Building Systems, Inc., Portland, TN; *Int'l*, pg. 699
King, Gilman R., Pres. & Chief Exec. Officer--AEC/Application Automation, Inc., Wood Dale, IL; *U.S. Private*, pg. 1041
King, Graham O., Chm. Bd. & Chief Exec. Officer--US SerVis, West Orange, NJ; *U.S. Public*, pg. 1687
King, Jack H., Pres. & Chief Exec. Officer--Zitel Corporation, Fremont, CA; *U.S. Public*, pg. 1793
King, Leroy A. Jr., Chm. Bd., Pres. & Chief Exec. Officer--Tighe Industries, Inc., York, PA; *U.S. Private*, pg. 1086
King, Michael, Chief Exec. Officer--King World Productions, Inc., New York, NY; *U.S. Public*, pg. 961
King, Michael, Pres. & Chief Exec. Officer--King World Productions Los Angeles, CA; *U.S. Public*, pg. 961
King, Olin B., Chm. Bd. & Chief Exec. Officer--SCI Systems, Inc., Huntsville, AL; *U.S. Public*, pg. 1416
King, Richard C., Chm., Pres. & Chief Exec. Officer-MBK & MBKC--Mercantile Bancorporation Inc., Saint Louis, MO; *U.S. Public*, pg. 1087
King, Ronald F., Pres. & Chief Exec. Officer--Blue Cross and Blue Shield of Oklahoma, Tulsa, OK; *U.S. Private*, pg. 151
King, T. Eugene, Chm., Pres. & Chief Exec. Officer--First Security Service Company, Salt Lake City, UT; *U.S. Public*, pg. 638
King, William C., Chm. Bd. & Chief Exec. Officer--Detrex Corporation, Southfield, MI; *U.S. Public*, pg. 501
Kingham, David, Chief Exec. Officer--Wydawnictwa Prawnicze PWN, Warsaw, Poland; *Int'l*, pg. 1095
Kingsbury, Peter, Pres. & Chief Exec. Officer-Asia/Pacific (Singapore)--Burson-Marsteller, New York, NY; *U.S. Private*, pg. 1197
Kinlein, David, Pres. & Chief Exec. Officer--Optic Graphics, Inc., Glen Burnie, MD; *U.S. Private*, pg. 818
Kinney, Steven, Pres. & Chief Exec. Officer--Weslock National, Inc., Los Angeles, CA; *U.S. Private*, pg. 1163
Kinning, Ronald L., Chm. Bd. & Chief Exec. Officer--RK Mechanical, Inc., Denver, CO; *U.S. Private*, pg. 904
Kinsch, Joseph, Chm. Bd., Pres. & Chief Exec. Officer--Arbed S.A., Luxembourg, Luxembourg; *Int'l*, pg. 78
Kinsella, John J., Pres. & Chief Exec. Officer--Admiral Insurance Company, Cherry Hill, NJ; *U.S. Public*, pg. 216
Kinsley, P.H., Chm. Bd., Chief Exec. Officer & Chief Oper. Officer--Permark International (Pty.) Ltd., Johannesburg, South Africa; *Int'l*, pg. 1036
Kinzel, Richard L., Pres. & Chief Exec. Officer--Cedar Fair, L.P., Sandusky, OH; *U.S. Public*, pg. 319
Kinzel, Richard L., Pres & Chief Exec. Officer--The Cedar Point Transportation Co., Sandusky, OH; *U.S. Public*, pg. 319
Kinzler, Morton H., Chm. Bd., Pres. & Chief Exec. Officer--Barnwell Industries, Inc., Honolulu, HI; *U.S. Public*, pg. 190
Kipec, Anita, Pres. & Chief Exec. Officer--Steck-Vaughn Publishing Corporation, Austin, TX; *U.S. Public*, pg. 784
Kipp, David, Chief Exec. Officer--Kipp Group, Ontario, CA; *U.S. Private*, pg. 623
Kirac, Inan, Chief Exec. Officer--Koc Holding A.S., Istanbul, Turkey; *Int'l*, pg. 741
Kirby, Jerry L., Chm. Bd., Pres., & Chief Exec. Officer--CitFed Bancorp, Inc., Dayton, OH; *U.S. Public*, pg. 376
Kirby, Joe P., Co.-Chm. Bd. & Chief Exec. Officer--Western Surety Company, Sioux Falls, SD; *U.S. Public*, pg. 303
Kirby, Robert P., Chm. Bd., Pres. & Chief Exec. Officer--Castleberry/Snow's Brands Inc., Augusta, GA; *U.S. Private*, pg. 219
Kirby, Robert P., Chm. Bd. & Chief Exec. Officer--Bunker Hill Foods Inc., Bedford, VA; *U.S. Private*, pg. 219
Kirchner, King P., Chm. Bd. & Chief Exec. Officer--Unit Corporation, Tulsa, OK; *U.S. Public*, pg. 1672
Kirdar, Nemir A., Pres. & Chief Exec. Officer--Investcorp International, Manama, Bahrain; *Int'l*, pg. 686
Kirk, James D., Pres. & Chief Exec. Officer--AgAmerica, FCB, Spokane, WA; *U.S. Private*, pg. 398
Kirk, James L., Chm. Bd., Pres. & Chief Exec. Officer--OHM Corporation, Findlay, OH; *U.S. Public*, pg. 1207
Kirk, Jesse, Chm. Bd. & Chief Exec. Officer--Dallas Peterbilt, Inc., Irving, TX; *U.S. Private*, pg. 309
Kirk, Larry G., Chm. Bd. & Chief Exec. Officer--Hancock Fabrics, Inc., Tupelo, MS; *U.S. Public*, pg. 779
Kirk, P., Chief Exec.--Dalgety Agriculture, Limited, Bristol, United Kingdom; *Int'l*, pg. 376
Kirk, Robert L., Chm. Bd., Pres. & Chief Exec. Officer--British Aerospace Holdings Inc., Chantilly, VA; *Int'l*, pg. 218
Kirk, Spencer F., Pres. & Chief Exec. Officer--Megahertz Holding Inc., Salt Lake City, UT; *U.S. Public*, pg. 1604
Kirpalani, Andrew, Pres. & Chief Exec. Officer--Andrew Sports Club Inc., Secaucus, NJ; *U.S. Private*, pg. 73
Kirshner, Alan I., Chm. Bd. & Chief Exec. Officer--Markel Corporation, Glen Allen, VA; *U.S. Public*, pg. 1046
Kirshner, Hal, Pres. & Chief Exec. Officer--Trex Medical Corporation, Danbury, CT; *U.S. Public*, pg. 1595
Kirstien, Ronald D., Chm. Bd., Pres. & Chief Exec. Officer--Davco Restaurants Inc., Crofton, MD; *U.S. Public*, pg. 488
Kirtley, John F., Chm., Pres. & Chief Exec. Officer--Florida Capital Partners, Tampa, FL; *U.S. Private*, pg. 414
Kis, Peter, Deputy Chief Exec. Officer--Malev Hungarian Airlines, Plc., Budapest, Hungary; *Int'l*, pg. 833
Kissling, Walter, Pres. & Chief Exec. Officer--H.B. Fuller Company, Saint Paul, MN; *U.S. Public*, pg. 686
Kissner, Charles, Chm. Bd., Pres. & Chief Exec. Officer--Digital Microwave Corporation, San Jose, CA; *U.S. Public*, pg. 508
Kissner, Matthew, Pres.--Pitney Bowes Financial Services, Norwalk, CT; *U.S. Public*, pg. 1303
Kissner, Matthew, Pres. & Chief Exec. Officer--Pitney Bowes Real Estate Financing Corporation, Norwalk, CT; *U.S. Public*, pg. 1303
Kitajima, Yoshitoshi, Pres. & Chief Exec. Officer--Dai Nippon Printing Co., Ltd., Tokyo, Japan; *Int'l*, pg. 363
Kitashiro, Kakutaroh, Pres. & Chief Exec. Officer--IBM Japan, Ltd., Tokyo, Japan; *U.S. Public*, pg. 897
Kitazo, Hiroyki, Pres. & Chief Oper. Officer--JRC Canida, Inc., Fort Worth, TX; *U.S. Private*, pg. 578
Kitchen, Michael B., Pres. & Chief Exec. Officer--CUNA Mutual Insurance Society, Madison, WI; *U.S. Private*, pg. 296
Kivenko, Ken, Pres. & Chief Exec. Officer--NBS Technologies, Inc., Mississauga, Canada; *Int'l*, pg. 898
Kivenko, Ken, Pres. & Chief Exec. Officer--NBS Technologies Inc., Mississauga, Canada; *Int'l*, pg. 898
Kives, Philip, Chm. Bd. & Chief Exec. Officer--K-Tel International, Inc., Minneapolis, MN; *U.S. Public*, pg. 937
Kivimaki, Mikko, Chm. Bd., Pres. & Chief Exec. Officer--Rautaruukki Oy, Helsinki, Finland; *Int'l*, pg. 1088
Kizer, Robert, Pres. & Chief Exec. Officer--Arkansas Lime Co., Batesville, AR; *U.S. Public*, pg. 1685
Kizer, Robert, Pres. & Chief Exec. Officer--Texas Lime Co., Cleburne, TX; *U.S. Public*, pg. 1685
Kizirakos, Nikolaos, Chief Exec. Officer--Galileo Hellas, Athens, Greece; *Int'l*, pg. 1004
Klas, Robert C., Chm. Bd. & Chief Exec. Officer--Tapemark, Saint Paul, MN; *U.S. Private*, pg. 1068
Klasson, Eric, Chief Exec. Officer--River Ranch - Salinas, Salinas, CA; *Int'l*, pg. 491
Klatsky, Bruce J., Chm. Bd., Pres. & Chief Exec. Officer--Phillips-Van Heusen Corporation, New York, NY; *U.S. Public*, pg. 1291
Klaus, Robert, Pres. & Chief Exec. Officer--Klaus Radio Inc., Peoria, IL; *U.S. Private*, pg. 625
Klee, Rainer, Pres. & Chief Exec. Officer--Deutsche Babcock Technologies, Inc., Duluth, GA; *Int'l*, pg. 401
Klein, Calvin, Pres. & Chief Exec. Officer--Calvin Klein, Inc., New York, NY; *U.S. Private*, pg. 202
Klein, John E., Chief Exec. Officer--MDIS Group plc, Hemel Hempstead, United Kingdom; *Int'l*, pg. 826
Klein, Michael S., Chm. Bd. & Chief Exec. Officer--Klein Tools Inc., Skokie, IL; *U.S. Private*, pg. 625
Klein, Richard M., Dr., Chm. Bd., Pres. & Chief Exec. Officer--Sybron Chemicals Inc., Birmingham, NJ; *U.S. Public*, pg. 1544
Klein, William, Chm. Bd., Pres. & Chief Exec. Officer--The Cerplex Group, Inc., Tustin, CA; *U.S. Public*, pg. 332
Kleinman, Philip, Chm. Bd. & Chief Exec. Officer--AFA Protective Systems, Inc., Syosset, NY; *U.S. Public*, pg. 5
Kleinrock, Leonard, Dr., Chm. Bd. & Chief Exec. Officer--Technology Transfer Institute, Santa Monica, CA; *U.S. Private*, pg. 1072
Kleist, Robert A., Chm. Bd., Pres. & Chief Exec. Officer--Printronix, Inc., Irvine, CA; *U.S. Public*, pg. 1329
Klenz, Walter, Chm. Bd. & Chief Exec. Officer--Beringer Wine Estates Holdings, Inc., Saint Helena, CA; *U.S. Private*, pg. 1078
Kletjian, Steven C., Chm. Bd. & Chief Exec. Officer--UNICCO Service Company, Boston, MA; *U.S. Private*, pg. 1117
Klevay, Walter S., Sr., Chm., Pres. & Chief Exec. Officer--Kleco Corp., Valley View, OH; *U.S. Private*, pg. 625
Klibert, Jeffery M., Pres. & Chief Exec. Officer--Lift-All Co., Inc., Manheim, PA; *U.S. Private*, pg. 667
Klich, William R., Chm. Bd. & Chief Exec. Officer--SunTrust Bank, Gulf Coast, Sarasota, FL; *U.S. Public*, pg. 1537
Kline, J. Peter, Pres. & Chief Exec. Officer--Bristol Hotels & Resorts, Dallas, TX; *U.S. Public*, pg. 253
Kline, Jerome C., Pres. & Chief Exec. Officer--Kline Iron & Steel Co., Inc., Columbia, SC; *U.S. Private*, pg. 626
Klingle, Ronald E., Chm. Bd. & Chief Exec. Officer--American Waste Services, Inc., Warren, OH; *U.S. Public*, *pg. 94*
Klink, Patricia de Blank, Pres. & Chief Exec. Officer--Advisers Capital Management Inc., New York, NY; *U.S. Private*, pg. 23
Klopfer, George M., Chief Exec. Officer--Polk Audio, Inc., Baltimore, MD; *U.S. Public*, pg. 1315
Kloss, Robert W., Pres. & Chief Exec. Officer--Provident Mutual Life Insurance Company, Berwyn, PA; *U.S. Private*, pg. 891
Kloster, Carol G., Pres. & Chief Exec. Officer--The Chas. Levy Company, Chicago, IL; *U.S. Private*, pg. 664
Kloth, Donald W., Chm. Bd. & Chief Exec. Officer--Busch Agricultural Resources, Inc., Saint Louis, MO; *U.S. Public*, pg. 114
Klotsche, Allan J., Pres. & Chief Exec. Officer--Willis Corroon Corp. of Minnesota, Minneapolis, MN; *Int'l*, pg. 1506
Kluger, Neal, Chief Exec. Officer--Eagle Electric Mfg. Co., Inc., Long Island City, NY; *U.S. Private*, pg. 354
Klym, Richard W., Pres. & Chief Exec. Officer--Kirkwood Industries, Inc., Cleveland, OH; *U.S. Private*, pg. 623
Klym, Richard W., Chief Exec. Officer--Toledo Commutator Co., Owosso, MI; *U.S. Private*, pg. 623
Knaur, Hans-Juergen, Dr., Chief Exec. Officer--Stinnes AG, Mulheim, Germany; *Int'l*, pg. 1458
Kneeland, Steve, Chm. Bd. & Chief Exec. Officer--Restonic Mattress Corporation, Rosemont, IL; *U.S. Private*, pg. 925
Kneip, Robert C., Chief Exec. Officer--Wackenhut Resources, Inc., Palm Beach Gardens, FL; *U.S. Public*, pg. 1731
Knepper, Barry, Pres. & Chief Exec. Officer--Unitel Video, Inc., New York, NY; *U.S. Public*, pg. 1692
Knetzger, Edwin L., III, Pres. & Chief Exec. Officer--Greenwich Capital Markets, Inc., Greenwich, CT; *Int'l*, pg. 911
Knick, Gerd, Dr., Chm.-Mng. Bd. & Chief Exec. Officer--Fresenius AG, Bad Hamburg, Germany; *Int'l*, pg. 505
Knight, C.F., Chm. Bd. & Chief Exec. Officer--Emerson Electric Co., Saint Louis, MO; *U.S. Public*, pg. 572
Knight, J.A., Chm. Bd., Pres. & Chief Exec. Officer--Heat Controller, Inc., Jackson, MI; *U.S. Private*, pg. 518
Knight, John W., Chm. Bd., Pres. & Chief Exec. Officer--The Fabri-Form Company, Byesville, OH; *U.S. Private*, pg. 390
Knight, Lester B., Chm. Bd. & Chief Exec. Officer--Allegiance Healthcare Corp., McGaw Park, IL; *U.S. Public*, pg. 44
Knight, Lyle R., Pres. & Chief Exec. Officer--US Bank, Las Vegas, NV; *U.S. Public*, pg. 181
Knight, Philip H., Chm. Bd. & Chief Exec. Officer--Nike, Inc., Beaverton, OR; *U.S. Public*, pg. 1184
Knight, Richard, Chm. Bd., Pres. & Chief Exec. Officer--Greate Bay Casino Corporation, Atlantic City, NJ; *U.S. Public*, pg. 760
Knopfel, Thomas, Chief Exec.--Cementos Boyaca S.A., Bogota, Colombia; *Int'l*, pg. 629
Knowles, C. Harry, Chm. Bd., Pres. & Chief Exec. Officer--Metrologic Instruments, Inc., Blackwood, NJ; *U.S. Public*, *pg. 1102*
Knowles, Roger E., Pres. & Chief Exec. Officer--Willis Corroon Corp. of Texas, Dallas, TX; *Int'l*, pg. 1507
Knox, Charles E., Jr., Chm. Bd. & Chief Exec. Officer--Knox Oil of Texas Inc., Dallas, TX; *U.S. Private*, pg. 627
Knuths, Leroy R., Chm. Bd., Pres. & Chief Exec. Officer--Rosco Manufacturing Co., Madison, SD; *U.S. Private*, pg. 944
Knutsen, Anders, Pres. & Chief Exec. Officer--Bang & Olufsen A/S, Struer, Denmark; *Int'l*, pg. 145
Kobayashi, Kazamasa, Pres. & Chief Exec. Officer--Kobayashi Pharmaceutical Co., Ltd., Osaka, Japan; *Int'l*, pg. 740
Kobylarek, Thomas, Pres. & Chief Exec. Officer--IMI Cash Valve, Inc., Cullman, AL; *Int'l*, pg. 646
Koch, Anthony H., Chm. Bd., Pres. & Chief Exec. Officer--Alamo Industrial Group, San Antonio, TX; *U.S. Private*, pg. 31
Koch, Charles G., Chm. Bd. & Chief Exec. Officer--Koch Industries, Incorporated, Wichita, KS; *U.S. Private*, pg. 628
Koch, Charles John, Chm. Bd., Pres. & Chief Exec. Officer--Charter One Financial, Inc., Cleveland, OH; *U.S. Public*, pg. 336
Koch, David, Chief Exec. & Chief Oper. Officer--Koch Engineering Company, Inc., Akron, OH; *U.S. Private*, pg. 628
Koch, David C., Chm. Bd. & Chief Exec. Officer--New Era Cap. Co., Derby, NY; *U.S. Private*, pg. 793
Koch, G. Fred, Chm. Bd., Chief Exec. Officer & Treas.--Plywood Plastics Inc., Buffalo, NY; *U.S. Private*, pg. 873
Koch, Hans-Wolfgang, Pres. & Chief Exec. Officer--BDAG Balcke-Durr AG, Ratingen, Germany; *Int'l*, pg. 399
Koch, John E., Pres. & Chief Exec. Officer--M & I Citizens American Bank, Merrill, WI; *U.S. Public*, pg. 1050
Koch, Robert L. II, Pres. & Chief Exec. Officer--George Koch Sons, Inc., Evansville, IN; *U.S. Private*, pg. 628
Koch, Robert M., Pres. & Chief Exec. Officer--First Stuttgart Bank & Trust, Stuttgart, AR; *U.S. Public*, pg. 641
Koch, William I., Pres. & Chief Exec. Officer--Oxbow Corporation, West Palm Beach, FL; *U.S. Private*, pg. 825
Koechlein, Gregg, Pres. & Chief Exec. Officer--Mallory, Inc., Carson City, NV; *U.S. Private*, pg. 698
Koehl, Hans H., Chm. Bd., Chief Exec. Officer & Chief Engr.--Spirol International Corp., Danielson, CT; *U.S. Private*, pg. 1026
Koehn, George W., Chm. Bd., Pres. & Chief Exec. Officer--SunTrust, Orlando, FL; *U.S. Public*, pg. 1537
Koehn, Michael, Pres. & Chief Exec. Officer--Analytic TSA Global Asset Management Inc., Los Angeles, CA; *U.S. Public*, pg. 1672
Koeller, David, Pres.-Grp. Practice--HBO & Company/Cycare Business Group, Scottsdale, AZ; *U.S. Public*, pg. 770
Koenig, Steve E., Dr., Chief Exec. Officer--Bioproducts, Inc., Fairlawn, OH; *U.S. Private*, pg. 145
Koenig, Walter E., Chief Exec. Officer--Gummiwerke Fulda, Fulda, Germany; *U.S. Public*, pg. 753
Koenitzer, John E., Chm. Bd. & Chief Exec. Officer--Helwig Carbon Products, Inc., Milwaukee, WI; *U.S. Private*, pg. 521
Koeppel, Martin, Chief Exec. Officer & Gen. Mgr.--Hughes-Treitler Manufacturing Corporation, Garden City, NY; *U.S. Private*, pg. 547
Koertner, William A., Pres. & Chief Exec. Officer--CIPSCO Investment Company, Springfield, IL; *U.S. Public*, pg. 66
Koetters, Ronald A., Chm. Bd. & Chief Exec. Officer--Monarch Construction Company, Cincinnati, OH; *U.S. Private*, pg. 757
Koffel, Martin M., Chm. Bd., Pres. & Chief Exec. Officer--URS Corporation, San Francisco, CA; *U.S. Public*, pg. 1655
Koffman, Robert G., Pres. & Chief Exec. Officer--United Properties, Bay City, MI; *U.S. Private*, pg. 1123
Kogan, Richard J., Pres. & Chief Exec. Officer--Schering-Plough Corporation, Madison, NJ; *U.S. Public*, pg. 1438
Koh, Katsuo, Pres. & Chief Exec. Officer--Marubeni America Corporation, New York, NY; *Int'l*, pg. 844

Kohler, John T., Pres. & Chief Exec. Officer--Technology Solutions Company (TSC), Chicago, IL; *U.S. Public*, pg. 1564
Kohlhaupt, Fritz, Chief Exec.--Sulzer Escher Wyss Kaltetchnik G.m.b.H., Lauterach, Austria; *Int'l*, pg. 1306
Kohlhepp, Robert J., Chief Exec. Officer--Cintas Corporation, Mason, OH; *U.S. Public*, pg. 370
Kojabashian, C., Pres. & Chief Exec. Officer--Foster-Miller, Inc., Waltham, MA; *U.S. Private*, pg. 421
Kojima, Tsugumasa, Mng. Dir. & Chief Exec. Officer--Sakura Finance International Limited, London, United Kingdom; *Int'l*, pg. 1180
Kolb, David L., Chm. Bd. & Chief Exec. Officer--Mohawk Industries, Inc., Calhoun, GA; *U.S. Public*, pg. 1121
Kolen, Joel, Pres. & Chief Exec. Officer--Empress International Ltd., Port Washington, NY; *U.S. Private*, pg. 375
Kolikof, Robert A., Pres., Chief Exec. Officer & Treas.--Prudential Metal Supply Corp., East Dedham, MA; *U.S. Private*, pg. 893
Koll, Donald M., Chm. Bd. & Chief Exec. Officer--Koll Co., Newport Beach, CA; *U.S. Private*, pg. 631
Koloszar, G., Chief Exec. Officer--Zurich Biztosito Rt., Budapest, Hungary; *Int'l*, pg. 1532
Kolowratnik, P., Chief Exec. Officer--Braas Italia S.p.A., Bolzano, Italy; *Int'l*, pg. 1092
Komansky, David H., Chm. Bd. & Chief Exec. Officer--Merrill Lynch & Co., Inc., New York, NY; *U.S. Public*, pg. 1097
Komansky, David H., Pres. & Chief Exec. Officer--Merrill Lynch, Pierce, Fenner & Smith, Inc., New York, NY; *U.S. Public*, pg. 1098
Komar, Charles E., Pres. & Chief Exec. Officer--Charles Komar & Sons, Inc., New York, NY; *U.S. Private*, pg. 631
Komar, David L., Exec. V.P.--Charles Komar & Sons, Inc., New York, NY; *U.S. Private*, pg. 631
Kominami, Shigeharu, Chief Oper. Officer--Makita S.p.A., San Vittore Olona, Italy; *Int'l*, pg. 832
Komisarjevsky, Chris, Pres. & Chief Exec. Officer-U.S. (New York)--Burson-Marsteller, New York, NY; *U.S. Private*, pg. 1197
Koncelik, David G., Pres. & Chief Exec. Officer--California & Hawaiian Sugar Company Inc., Crockett, CA; *U.S. Public*, *pg. 39*
Konig, Gerhard, Pres. & Chief Exec. Officer--Quanterra Environmental Services, Englewood, CO; *U.S. Private*, pg. 899
Konig, Thomas, Pres. & Chief Exec. Officer--Meritcare, Inc., Sewickley, PA; *U.S. Private*, pg. 733
Konigsberg, Max, Chm., Pres. & Chief Exec. Officer--Shirmax Leasing Ltd., Montreal, Canada; *Int'l*, pg. 1235
Kontos, Arthur, Pres. & Chief Exec. Officer--The Sherwood Group, Inc., Jersey City, NJ; *U.S. Public*, pg. 1466
Konuntakiet, Phornpun, Pres. & Chief Exec. Officer--Unicord Public Co. LTD., Bangkok, Thailand; *Int'l*, pg. 1432
Koogle, Tim, Pres. & Chief Exec. Officer--Yahoo!, Inc., Santa Clara, CA; *U.S. Public*, pg. 1787
Kooijn, N. W., Chief Exec. Officer--OCE (Hong Kong China) Ltd., Hong Kong, Hong Kong; *Int'l*, pg. 994
Kookootsedes, John, Pres. & Chief Exec. Officer--Willis Corroon Corp. of Orange County, Santa Ana, CA; *Int'l*, pg. 1506
Koon, Richard D., Pres. & Chief Exec. Officer--Cubic Worldwide Technical Services, Inc., San Diego, CA; *U.S. Public*, pg. 466
Koons, James E., Chief Exec. Officer--Jim Koons Management, Vienna, VA; *U.S. Private*, pg. 632
Koontz, James L., Pres. & Chief Exec. Officer--Kingsbury Corporation, Keene, NH; *U.S. Private*, pg. 621
Koopmann, Andreas, Chief Exec. Officer--Bobst S.A., Lausanne, Switzerland; *Int'l*, pg. 198
Kopelman, David W., Chm. Bd. & Chief Exec. Officer--The W.B. Wood Company, New Providence, NJ; *U.S. Private*, *pg. 1186*
Kopko, Edward M., Chm. Bd., Pres., Chief Exec. & Chief Oper. Officer--Butler International, Inc., Montvale, NJ; *U.S. Public*, pg. 270
Koplik, Michael, Pres. & Chief Exec. Officer--Perry H. Koplik & Sons, New York, NY; *U.S. Private*, pg. 632
Kopp, Charles G., Chief Exec. Officer--Wolf, Block, Schorr & Solis-Cohen, Philadelphia, PA; *U.S. Private*, pg. 1185
Koptev, Sergey, Chief Exec. Officer, Mng. Dir.--DMB&B Moscow, Moscow, Russia; *U.S. Private*, pg. 304
Korman, Scott, Pres. & Chief Exec. Officer--Welsh Farms, Inc., Long Valley, NJ; *U.S. Private*, pg. 1162
Kornberg, Fred, Chm. Bd., Pres. & Chief Exec. Officer--Comtech Telecommunications Corp., Melville, NY; *U.S. Public*, pg. 425
Kornstein, Don R., Pres. & Chief Exec. Officer--Jackpot Enterprises, Inc., Las Vegas, NV; *U.S. Public*, pg. 920
Kornswiet, Neil, Pres. & Chief Exec. Officer--One Stop Mortgage, Inc., Costa Mesa, CA; *U.S. Public*, pg. 12
Kornswiet, Neil B., Exec. V.P., Chm. Bd. & Chief Exec. Officer-One Stop Mortgage, Inc--Aames Financial Corporation, Los Angeles, CA; *U.S. Public*, pg. 12
Korpan, Richard, Pres. & Chief Exec. Officer--Florida Progress Corporation, Saint Petersburg, FL; *U.S. Public*, pg. 655
Korpan, Richard, Pres. & Chief Exec. Officer--Progress Capital Holdings, Inc., Saint Petersburg, FL; *U.S. Public*, pg. 655
Korsmeier, Gary, Chief Exec. Officer--California Milk Producers, Artesia, CA; *U.S. Private*, pg. 201
Korssjoem, Y. Jam Erek, Chief Exec. Officer--Simrad Norge AF, Horten, Norway; *Int'l*, pg. 1252
Koss, Michael J., Pres., Chief Exec., Oper. & Fin. Officer--Koss Corporation, Milwaukee, WI; *U.S. Public*, pg. 966
Koss, Michael J., Pres., Chief Exec. Officer & Chief Fin. Officer--Koss Classics Ltd., Milwaukee, WI; *U.S. Public*, pg. 966
Kostadinov, Peter, Chief Exec.--Sulzer Praha s.r.o., Prague, Czech Republic; *Int'l*, pg. 1306
Kostas, Evans, Chm. Bd. & Chief Exec. Officer--Publishers Equipment Corporation, Dallas, TX; *U.S. Public*, pg. 1341
Kostelni, James C., Chm. Bd., Pres. & Chief Exec. Officer--Georgia-Bonded Fibers, Inc., Newark, NJ; *U.S. Public*, pg. 734
Kostelni, Jeffrey C., Chief Exec. Officer--Bontex, Buena Vista, VA; *U.S. Public*, pg. 734
Kostusiak, Karl, Pres. & Chief Exec. Officer--Detection Systems, Inc., Fairport, NY; *U.S. Public*, pg. 501
Kotani, Y., Pres., Chief Exec. & Oper. Officer--Waterville TG Inc., Waterville, Canada; *Int'l*, pg. 1487
Kotek, William, Pres. & Chief Exec. Officer--Raffi & Swanson, Inc., Wilmington, MA; *U.S. Private*, pg. 907
Kotick, Robert, Chm. Bd. & Chief Exec. Officer--Activision, Santa Monica, CA; *U.S. Public*, pg. 17
Kotsatos, Andrew G., Chm. Bd., Chief Exec. Officer & Treas.--Boston Acoustics, Inc., Peabody, MA; *U.S. Public*, pg. 246
Kottmann, Bernd, Chief Officer--Deutsche Babcock Bau GmbH, Oberhausen, Germany; *Int'l*, pg. 401
Koury, James N., Chm. Bd. & Chief Exec. Officer--Security Pacific State Bank, Irvine, CA; *U.S. Public*, pg. 182
Kouzuma, Makoto, Pres. & Chief Exec. Officer--SpeedFan International, Inc., Chandler, AZ; *U.S. Public*, pg. 1497
Kovacevich, Richard M., Chm. Bd., Pres. & Chief Exec. Officer--Norwest Corporation, Minneapolis, MN; *U.S. Public*, pg. 1201
Kowalski, John, Pres. & Chief Exec. Officer--Pulse Engineering, Inc., San Diego, CA; *U.S. Public*, pg. 1564
Kowalski, Michael, Pres. & Chief Exec. Officer--Kowalski Sausage Co., Inc., Hamtramck, MI; *U.S. Private*, pg. 634
Kozlowski, L. Dennis, Chm. Bd., Pres. & Chief Exec. Officer--Tyco International Ltd., Exeter, NH; *U.S. Public*, pg. 1647
Kozlowski, M., Chief Exec. Officer--OCE-Poland Limited, Sp. z o.o., Warsaw, Poland; *Int'l*, pg. 995
Kozuki, Kagemasa, Chm. Bd. & Chief Exec. Officer--Konami Co. Ltd., Tokyo, Japan; *Int'l*, pg. 745
Kraehe, G.J., Chief Exec. Officer & Mng. Dir.--Southcorp Holdings Ltd., Adelaide, Australia; *Int'l*, pg. 1287
Kraemer, Arthur T., Chm. Bd. & Chief Exec. Officer--M & I Lake Country Bank, Hartland, WI; *U.S. Public*, pg. 1050
Kraft, Marvin E., Chm. Bd. & Chief Exec. Officer--Lario Oil & Gas Company, Calgary, Canada; *U.S. Private*, pg. 651
Kraines, Maurice H., Chief Exec. Officer--Kraco Enterprises, Inc., Compton, CA; *U.S. Private*, pg. 634
Krakoff, Robert L., Chm. Bd. & Chief Exec. Officer--Advanstar Communications, Cleveland, OH; *U.S. Private*, *pg. 22*
Krall, George F., Pres. & Chief Exec. Officer--Mebane Packaging Group, Mebane, NC; *U.S. Private*, pg. 726
Krall, George F., Pres. & Chief Exec. Officer--Mebane Packaging Group., Kearny, NJ; *U.S. Private*, pg. 726
Kramer, Arnold A., Pres. & Chief Exec. Officer--Trimfit, Inc., Bristol, PA; *U.S. Private*, pg. 1103
Kramer, Dale, Pres. & Chief Exec. Officer--ShopKo Stores, Inc., Green Bay, WI; *U.S. Public*, pg. 1467
Kramer, Earl, Pres., Chief Exec. & Chief Oper. Officer--Concord Fabrics Inc., New York, NY; *U.S. Public*, pg. 429
Kramer, Gordon M., Chm. Bd., Pres. & Chief Exec. Officer--Continental Plastic Card Co., Coral Springs, FL; *U.S. Private*, pg. 269
Kramer, Hans B., Dr., Pres. & Chief Exec. Officer--Solvay Performance Chemicals, Greenwich, CT; *Int'l*, pg. 1278
Kramzar, G., Chief Exec. Officer-Commercial--NIPA Hardwicke, Inc., Wilmington, DE; *U.S. Private*, pg. 771
Kran, Kjell O., Pres. & Chief Exec. Officer--Union Bank of Norway, Oslo, Norway; *Int'l*, pg. 1439
Krantz, John F., Chief Exec. Officer & Treas.--Adventure Lands of America, Inc., Des Moines, IA; *U.S. Private*, pg. 22
Krasne, Charles A., Chm. Bd., Pres. & Chief Exec. Officer--Krasdale Foods Inc., White Plains, NY; *U.S. Private*, pg. 635
Krasnoff, Eric, Chm. Bd. & Chief Exec. Officer--Pall Corporation, Greenvale, NY; *U.S. Public*, pg. 1253
Krasny, Michael P., Chm. Bd., Chief Exec. Officer, Treas. & Sec.--CDW Computer Centers, Inc., Vernon Hills, IL; *U.S. Public*, pg. 277
Krat, Gary, Chm. & Chief Exec. Officer--Royal Alliance Associates, Inc., New York, NY; *U.S. Public*, pg. 1533
Krat, Gary W., Chm. & Chief Exec. Officer--SunAmerica Securities, Inc., Phoenix, AZ; *U.S. Public*, pg. 1533
Krattli, E., Chief Exec. Officer--Ascom Finanz AG, Bern, Switzerland; *Int'l*, pg. 86
Kraus, Dieter, Chief Exec. Officer & Exec. V.P.--Union Air Transport GmbH, Dusseldorf, Germany; *U.S. Private*, pg. 1120
Kraus, Margery, Pres. & Chief Exec. Officer-APCO Associates--GCI Group Inc., New York, NY; *U.S. Public*, pg. 764
Krauter, Hal J., Chm. Bd., Pres. & Chief Exec. Officer--Leasing Solutions, Inc., San Jose, CA; *U.S. Public*, pg. 982
Kravec, Rafael, Pres. & Chief Exec. Officer--French Fragrances Inc., Miami, FL; *U.S. Public*, pg. 681
Krebel, Albert D., Pres. & Chief Exec. Officer--Reed & Barton Corporation, Taunton, MA; *U.S. Private*, pg. 916
Krebs, Robert D., Chm. Bd., Pres. & Chief Exec. Officer--Burlington Northern Santa Fe Corporation, Fort Worth, TX; *U.S. Public*, pg. 268
Kreh, Gordon W., Pres. & Chief Exec. Officer--The Hartford Steam Boiler Inspection & Insurance Co., Hartford, CT; *U.S. Public*, pg. 795
Kreh, Kent, Chief Exec. Officer--Cardio-Fitness Corporation, New York, NY; *U.S. Public*, pg. 806
Kreh, Kent, Chief Exec. Officer--The Fitness Institute, Willowdale, Canada; *U.S. Public*, pg. 806
Kreh, Kent Q., Pres. & Chief Exec. Officer--Weight Watchers International, Inc., Woodbury, NY; *U.S. Public*, pg. 806
Krehbiel, Frederick A., Chm. Bd. & Chief Exec. Officer--Molex Incorporated, Lisle, IL; *U.S. Public*, pg. 1121
Krehbiel, Paul R., Chm. Bd. & Chief Exec. Officer--Kreonite, Inc., Wichita, KS; *U.S. Private*, pg. 635
Kreis, W., Chief Exec. Officer--Ascom Ericsson Transmission AG, Bern, Switzerland; *Int'l*, pg. 86
Krempa, Frank S., Pres. & Chief Exec. Officer--Lenape Forge, Inc., West Chester, PA; *U.S. Private*, pg. 659
Kresa, Kent, Chm. Bd., Pres. & Chief Exec. Officer--Northrop Grumman Corporation, Los Angeles, CA; *U.S. Public*, pg. 1197
Kretzer, William T., Pres. & Chief Exec. Officer--Unifi Inc., Greensboro, NC; *U.S. Public*, pg. 1665
Kretzmer, Anthony, Pres. & Chief Exec. Officer--Angeles Housing Concepts, Canoga Park, CA; *U.S. Private*, pg. 74
Kreusch, Paul P., Chief Exec. Officer--Leonard Kreusch, Inc., Northvale, NJ; *U.S. Private*, pg. 635
Kricfalusi, Michael C., Pres. & Chief Exec. Officer--Key Clearing Corp., Brooklyn, OH; *U.S. Public*, pg. 955
Kriegel, David L., Chm. Bd., Pres. & Chief Exec. Officer--Drug Emporium, Inc., Powell, OH; *U.S. Public*, pg. 530
Kriegel, William, Chm. Bd., Pres. & Chief Exec. Officer--Sithe Energies, Inc., New York, NY; *U.S. Private*, pg. 1004
Kries, W., Chief Exec. Officer--Ascom Hasler AG, Bern, Switzerland; *Int'l*, pg. 86
Krihak, Paul R., Chief Exec. Officer & Treas.--Holbrook Lumber Company, Albany, NY; *U.S. Private*, pg. 533
Krippaehne, William W., Jr., Pres. & Chief Exec. Officer--Fisher Companies Inc., Seattle, WA; *U.S. Public*, pg. 647
Kroll, Robert D., Pres. & Chief Exec. Officer--The B. Manischewitz Company, Jersey City, NJ; *U.S. Private*, pg. 699
Kromorl, Wolfgang, Dr., Chief Exec. Officer--Groschopp & Co. GmbH EMW Elektromotoren-Feinbauwerk, Viersen, Germany; *Int'l*, pg. 559
Kronenberger, Robert, Pres. & Chief Exec. Officer--Petty Company, Inc., Effingham, IL; *U.S. Private*, pg. 860
Kronick, Susan, Chm. Bd. & Chief Exec. Officer--Burdines, Miami, FL; *U.S. Public*, pg. 618
Kronk, Claude F., Pres. & Chief Exec. Officer--J & L Specialty Products Corp., Pittsburgh, PA; *Int'l*, pg. 572
Kropf, Omer G., Pres. & Chief Exec. Officer--Supreme Corporation, Goshen, IN; *U.S. Public*, pg. 1542
Krueger, Robert A., Pres., Chief Exec. Officer & Treas.--Tri-Mark Metal Corp., Shelby, MI; *U.S. Private*, pg. 1100
Kruger, J., II, Chm. Bd. & Chief Exec. Officer--Kruger Inc., Montreal, Canada; *Int'l*, pg. 761
Kruger, Konrad R., Co-Pres. & Co-Chief Exec. Officer--Greenwich Capital Markets, Inc., Greenwich, CT; *Int'l*, pg. 911
Kruit, J. H., Chief Exec.--DSM Hydrocarbons, Sittard, Netherlands; *Int'l*, pg. 353
Krum, Frank, Chief Exec. Officer--Golden Cat Corporation, Saint Louis, MO; *U.S. Public*, pg. 1360
Krupa, Calvin, Chm. Bd., Pres. & Chief Exec. Officer--Ultra Pac, Inc., Rogers, MN; *U.S. Public*, pg. 1662
Kruse, Howard W., Pres. & Chief Exec. Officer--Blue Bell Creameries, L.P., Brenham, TX; *U.S. Private*, pg. 150
Kruse, Mitchell, Pres., Chief Exec. Officer & Auctioneer--Kruse International, Auburn, IN; *U.S. Private*, pg. 636
Kruy, Joseph F., Chm. Bd., Pres., Chief Exec. & Chief Oper. Officer--Cambex Corporation, Waltham, MA; *U.S. Public*, pg. 296
Kuban, William G., Pres., Chief Exec. Officer & Treas.--Kurt Manufacturing Co. Inc., Fridley, MN; *U.S. Private*, pg. 637
Kubicek, R.T., Pres. & Chief Exec. Officer--AppleTree Markets, Houston, TX; *U.S. Private*, pg. 78
Kubly, Raymond, Chm. Bd. & Chief Exec. Officer--The Swiss Colony, Inc, Monroe, WI; *U.S. Private*, pg. 1059
Kucharski, John M., Chm. Bd. & Chief Exec. Officer--EG & G, Inc., Wellesley, MA; *U.S. Public*, pg. 542
Kuck, Duane, Pres. & Chief Exec. Officer--Regal Marine Industries Inc., Orlando, FL; *U.S. Private*, pg. 917
Kuczwanski, John, Chief Exec. Officer--Loan America Financial Corp., Jacksonville, FL; *U.S. Public*, pg. 1162
Kuebler, Christopher A., Chm. Bd. & Chief Exec. Officer--Covance, Inc., Princeton, NJ; *U.S. Public*, pg. 453
Kuebler, J. Clarke, Pres. & Chief Exec. Officer--Uniflow Manufacturing Co., Erie, PA; *U.S. Private*, pg. 1117
Kuehn, Ronald L., Jr., Chm. Bd. & Chief Exec. Officer--Sonat Inc., Birmingham, AL; *U.S. Public*, pg. 1484
Kuehne, Carl, Chief Exec. Officer--American Foods Group, Green Bay, WI; *U.S. Private*, pg. 54
Kuehne, Carl W., Pres. & Chief Exec. Officer--American Foods Group, Inc., Green Bay, WI; *U.S. Private*, pg. 54
Kuehne, W., Chief Oper. Officer--BPC Division, Bristol, IN; *Int'l*, pg. 618
Kueng, Bernard, Chief Exec. Officer--St. Lawrence Cement Inc., Montreal, Canada; *Int'l*, pg. 628
Kugler, Seymour, Chm. Bd., Pres. & Chief Exec. Officer--Winston Resources, Inc., New York, NY; *U.S. Public*, pg. 1772
Kuhlmann, A., Chief Exec. Officer & Gen. Mgr.--ING Trust Company of Canada, North York, Canada; *Int'l*, pg. 650
Kuhlmann, William, Pres., Chief Oper. & Exec. Officer--General Physics Corporation, Columbia, MD; *U.S. Public*, *pg. 694*
Kuhn, Robert, Chm. Bd. & Chief Exec. Officer--Goss Graphic Systems, Westmont, IL; *U.S. Private*, pg. 466
Kuhne, K.M., Chm. Bd. & Chief Exec. Officer--Kuehne & Nagel International AG, Schindellegi, Switzerland; *Int'l*, pg. 763
Kuhnt, Dietmar, Dr., Chm. Bd., Pres. & Chief Exec. Officer--RWE AG, Essen, Germany; *Int'l*, pg. 1081
Kuijvenhoven, Pieter, Chief Exec. Officer--ARA/BDDP, Rotterdam, Netherlands; *Int'l*, pg. 117
Kujovich, Larry, Pres. & Chief Exec. Officer--Dietzgen Corporation, Palatine, IL; *U.S. Private*, pg. 332
Kukk, Toomas J., Pres. & Chief Exec. Officer--Chempower, Inc., Akron, OH; *Int'l*, pg. 74
Kulek, Maurice, Pres. & Chief Exec. Officer--DeMert & Dougherty, Inc., Coal City, IL; *U.S. Private*, pg. 323

Kulenkampf, Arnfred, Pres. & Chief Exec. Officer--TLT-Babcock, Inc., Akron, OH; *Int'l*, pg. 401
Kulenkampff, Georg, Chief Exec. Officer--Raab Karcher AG, Essen, Germany; *Int'l*, pg. 1457
Kulicke, C. Scott, Chm. Bd. & Chief Exec. Officer--Kulicke & Soffa Industries, Inc., Willow Grove, PA; *U.S. Public*, pg. 968
Kulle, Richard J., Pres. & Chief Exec. Officer--Siliconix, Inc., Santa Clara, CA; *Int'l*, pg. 367
Kulp, Frank E., III, Pres. & Chief Exec. Officer--Younkers, Inc., Des Moines, IA; *U.S. Public*, pg. 1334
Kumamoto, Masahiro, Pres. & Chief Exec. Officer--Kobe Steel, Ltd., Kobe, Japan; *Int'l*, pg. 740
Kummer, Fred S., Chm., Pres., Chief Exec. Officer, Treas. & Founder--HBE Corporation/Design Build Divisions, Saint Louis, MO; *U.S. Private*, pg. 489
Kummer, Glenn F., Chm. Bd. & Chief Exec. Officer--Fleetwood Enterprises, Inc., Riverside, CA; *U.S. Public*, pg. 650
Kummer, Robert W., Jr., Chm. Bd. & Chief Exec. Officer--Mellon First Business Bank, Los Angeles, CA; *U.S. Public*, pg. 1085
Kunisch, Robert D., Pres. & Chief Exec. Officer--PHH Corporation, Hunt Valley, MD; *U.S. Public*, pg. 321
Kunk, Stephen E., Pres. & Chief Exec. Officer--Provident Bank of Florida, Sarasota, FL; *U.S. Public*, pg. 1338
Kunkel, Edward T., Pres. & Chief Exec. Officer--Foster's Brewing Group Limited, Southbank, Australia; *Int'l*, pg. 500
Kuperhand, J., Chief Exec. Officer--Autronics Corporation, Arcadia, CA; *Int'l*, pg. 208
Kuperman, Bob, Pres., Chief Exec. Officer-West--TBWA Chiat/Day Los Angeles, Venice, CA; *U.S. Private*, pg. 1062
Kuperman, Robert, Pres. & Chief Exec. Officer-West--TBWA Chiat/Day, New York, NY; *U.S. Private*, pg. 1062
Kupferman, Ronald J., Chm. Bd., Chief Exec. Officer & Pres.--Global Software, Inc., Raleigh, NC; *U.S. Private*, pg. 457
Kupiec, Russel, Pres. & Chief Exec. Officer--Wells Aluminum Corp., Baltimore, MD; *U.S. Private*, pg. 1161
Kupperman, Melvin, Pres. & Chief Exec. Officer--A. Epstein and Sons, Intl., Inc., Chicago, IL; *U.S. Private*, pg. 379
Kursman, Peter J., Pres.--Jetronic Industries, Inc., Philadelphia, PA; *U.S. Public*, pg. 926
Kurtenbach, Aelred J., Chm. Bd., Pres., Chief Exec. & Oper. Officer--Daktronics, Inc., Brookings, SD; *U.S. Public*, pg. 478
Kurtz, Philip D., Chief Exec. Officer--CIS Technologies, Inc., Tulsa, OK; *U.S. Public*, pg. 1155
Kurtzman, Zvi, Pres. & Chief Exec. Officer--Aura Systems, Inc., El Segundo, CA; *U.S. Public*, pg. 147
Kurz, Herbert, Chm. Bd., Pres. & Chief Exec. Officer--Presidential Life Corporation, Nyack, NY; *U.S. Public*, pg. 1323
Kurz, Kelli McDonald, Pres. & Chief Oper. Officer-Denver & Dir.--EvansGroup, Salt Lake City, UT; *U.S. Private*, pg. 385
Kurz, Milton, Chief Exec. Officer--Apex Mills Corporation, Inwood, NY; *U.S. Private*, pg. 77
Kurz, Mitch, Pres. & Chief Oper. Officer-Y&R Wunderman Partnership--Young & Rubicam Inc., New York, NY; *U.S. Private*, pg. 1196
Kurzinger, Armin, Chief Exec.--Bank for Europe Ltd., Luxembourg, Luxembourg; *Int'l*, pg. 419
Kurzweg, Victor J., III, Chm. Bd., Chief Exec. Officer & Chief Fin. Officer--Consolidated Companies Inc. (CONCO), Metairie, LA; *U.S. Private*, pg. 265
Kushlick, W.J., Pres. & Chief Exec. Officer--Weiser Inc., Burnaby, Canada; *U.S. Public*, pg. 1055
Kusumi, Gary, Pres. & Chief Exec. Officer--Leader National Insurance Company, Dallas, TX; *U.S. Public*, pg. 75
Kusumoto, Sadahei, Chm. Bd. & Chief Exec. Officer--Minolta Corporation, Ramsey, NJ; *Int'l*, pg. 869
Kutner, Jack P., Pres. & Chief Exec. Officer--Investors Services Group, Boston, MA; *U.S. Public*, pg. 631
Kuttner, Ludwig, Chm. Bd., Pres. & Chief Exec. Officer--Hampshire Group, Ltd., Anderson, SC; *U.S. Public*, pg. 778
Kuzmich, Richard, Pres. & Chief Exec. Officer--Associated Merchandising Corp. (AMC), New York, NY; *U.S. Private*, pg. 91
Kvamme, Mark D., Pres. & Chief Exec. Officer--CKS Group, Cupertino, CA; *U.S. Private*, pg. 195
Kwader, Alex, Pres. & Chief Exec. Officer--FiberMark Inc., Brattleboro, VT; *U.S. Public*, pg. 620
Kwasek, Matthew J., Jr., Pres. & Chief Exec. Officer--Freezer Queen Foods Inc., Buffalo, NY; *Int'l*, pg. 340
Kwok, Walter, Chm. Bd. & Chief Exec.--Sun Hung Kai Properties Ltd., Wan Chai, Hong Kong; *Int'l*, pg. 1318
Kyman, Larry, Pres. & Chief Exec. Officer--Ultimo Ltd., Chicago, IL; *U.S. Private*, pg. 1116
La Crosse, James E., Chm. Bd. & Chief Exec. Officer--National Wine & Spirits Corp., Indianapolis, IN; *U.S. Private*, pg. 788
Laas, Madis, Chief Exec. Officer & Mng. Dir.--Kontuur-Leo Burnett/Estonia, Tallinn, Estonia; *U.S. Private*, pg. 184
LaBarge, Craig E., Pres. & Chief Exec. Officer--LaBarge, Inc., Saint Louis, MO; *U.S. Public*, pg. 973
Labatt, Blair P., Jr., Pres. & Chief Exec. Officer--Labatt Food Service, San Antonio, TX; *U.S. Private*, pg. 641
Laboon, Jr., James L., Chm. Bd. & Chief Exec. Officer--Athens First Bank & Trust Co., Athens, GA; *U.S. Public*, pg. 1549
LaBorde, Ronald A., Pres. & Chief Exec. Officer--Piccadilly Cafeterias, Inc., Baton Rouge, LA; *U.S. Public*, pg. 1294
Labrecque, Richard J., Pres. & Chief Exec. Officer--ITT Fluid Technology Corporation, Midland Park, NJ; *U.S. Public*, pg. 860
Labrecque, Richard J., Pres. & Chief Exec. Officer--ITT Fluid Handling, Morton Grove, IL; *U.S. Public*, pg. 860
Labreque, Richard J., Pres. & Chief Exec. Officer--Goulds Pumps, Incorporated, Fairport, NY; *U.S. Public*, pg. 860
Labroue, Jean-Noel, Pres. & Chief Exec. Officer--Le Groupe Darty, Bondy, France; *Int'l*, pg. 734
Lacey, Dennis J., Pres. & Chief Exec. Officer--Capital Associates, Inc., Lakewood, CO; *U.S. Public*, pg. 302
Lacey, John S., Pres. & Chief Exec. Officer--WIC Western International Communications Ltd., Vancouver, Canada; *Int'l*, pg. 1481
Lachenmayer, Greg, Pres. & Chief Exec. Officer--Collegeville Flag & Mfg. Company, Collegeville, PA; *U.S. Private*, pg. 252
Lacomis, Bernard J., Pres. & Chief Exec. Officer--Arthur D. Little Enterprises, Inc., Cambridge, MA; *U.S. Private*, pg. 670
Lacourciere, Paul A., Pres. & Chief Oper. Officer--Jameco Industries, Inc., Spindale, NC; *U.S. Public*, pg. 1746
Lacourciere, William J., Chm. Bd., Pres. & Chief Exec. Officer--Novametrix Medical Systems Inc., Wallingford, CT; *U.S. Public*, pg. 1203
LaCross, David, Chief Exec. Officer--Risk Management Technologies, Berkeley, CA; *U.S. Public*, pg. 610
Lacy, Andre B., Chm. Bd., Pres. & Chief Exec. Officer--LDI, Ltd., Indianapolis, IN; *U.S. Private*, pg. 639
Lacy, Bill, Vice Chm. & Chief Exec. Officer--Gilliam Candy Brands, Edwardsville, KS; *U.S. Private*, pg. 454
Lacy, Linwood A., Pres. & Chief Exec. Officer--Micro Warehouse, Inc., Norwalk, CT; *U.S. Public*, pg. 1104
Lacy, Roane, Jr., Chief Exec. Officer--Plantation Foods Inc., Waco, TX; *U.S. Private*, pg. 869
Lacy, William H., Pres. & Chief Exec. Officer--MGIC Investment Corporation, Milwaukee, WI; *U.S. Public*, pg. 1026
Lacy, William H., Chm. Bd. & Chief Exec. Officer--Mortgage Guaranty Insurance Corporation, Milwaukee, WI; *U.S. Public*, pg. 1026
Ladds, H.P., Jr., Pres. & Chief Exec. Officer--Columbus McKinnon Corp., Amherst, NY; *U.S. Public*, pg. 405
Ladly, Frederick B., Deputy Chm. & Chief Exec. Officer--Extendicare Inc., Markham, Canada; *Int'l*, pg. 468
Laemgrich, Norbert, Pres. & Chief Exec. Officer--Embedded Performance, Inc., Milpitas, CA; *U.S. Private*, pg. 373
Lagardere, Arnaud, Chief Exec. Officer--Grolier Inc., Danbury, CT; *Int'l*, pg. 794
Lagardere, Jean-Luc, Mng. Partner & Gen. Mgr.--Lagardere Groupe, Paris, France; *Int'l*, pg. 791
Lagorce, Michel, Chief Exec. Officer--Fabrications Mecaniques de l'Atlantique (FAMAT SA), Saint Nazaire, France; *Int'l*, pg. 1166
Lagstaff, David H., Pres. & Chief Exec. Officer--Calspan SRL Corporation, Washington, DC; *U.S. Private*, pg. 1136
Lahdesmaki, Tuomo, Pres. & Chief Exec. Officer--Leiras Oy, Turku, Finland; *Int'l*, pg. 639
LaHowchic, Nicholas J., Pres. & Chief Exec. Officer--Limited Distribution Services, Columbus, OH; *U.S. Public*, pg. 995
Lahr, Bill, Chief Exec. Officer--Midwest Auto Parts Distributors, Inc., Saint Paul, MN; *U.S. Private*, pg. 744
Lahti, Peter H., Chm. Bd., Pres. & Chief Exec. Officer--Kirkpatrick Pettis Smith Polian, Inc., Omaha, NE; *U.S. Private*, pg. 770
Lai, Cal, Adv. Chief Exec. Officer--LVL Interactive, Palo Alto, CA; *U.S. Private*, pg. 640
Lai, Calbert, Chief Exec. Officer--LVL Advertising, Palo Alto, CA; *U.S. Private*, pg. 640
Laible, Charles, Chief Exec. Officer--Willis Corroon Aerospace, New York, NY; *Int'l*, pg. 1505
Laing, Bert, Pres. & Chief Exec. Officer--LINC Anthem Inc., Chicago, IL; *U.S. Public*, pg. 996
Laird, Larrie W., Pres. & Chief Exec. Officer--Laird & Company, Eatontown, NJ; *U.S. Private*, pg. 642
Laird, Thomas, Pres. & Chief Exec. Officer--Woods Equipment Company, Oregon, IL; *U.S. Private*, pg. 249
Laitt, Graham, Chief Exec. Officer--Peters & Brownes Foods Ltd., Balcatta, Australia; *Int'l*, pg. 1040
Lake, R. D., Chief Exec. Officer-N. America--NFC plc, London, United Kingdom; *Int'l*, pg. 901
Lama, Rudolph E., Pres. & Chief Exec. Officer--Tony Lama Co., Inc., El Paso, TX; *U.S. Public*, pg. 937
LaMacchia, John T., Pres. & Chief Exec. Officer--Cincinnati Bell Telephone, Cincinnati, OH; *U.S. Public*, pg. 367
LaMantia, Charles R., Pres. & Chief Exec. Officer--Arthur D. Little, Inc., Cambridge, MA; *U.S. Private*, pg. 670
LaMarche, Ann, Chief Exec. Officer--Ortho-Kinetics, Inc., Waukesha, WI; *U.S. Private*, pg. 820
Lamarre, Jacques, Pres. & Chief Exec. Officer--SNC-Lavalin Group Inc., Montreal, Canada; *Int'l*, pg. 1161
Lamattina, Larry, Pres. & Chief Exec. Officer--All American Television, Inc., New York, NY; *U.S. Public*, pg. 41
Lambert, D.N., Chief Exec. Officer--La Garantie Generale Marocaine (G.G.M.), Casablanca, Morocco; *Int'l*, pg. 1531
Lambert, Henry A., Pres. & Chief Exec. Officer--Reliance Development Group Inc., New York, NY; *U.S. Public*, pg. 1374
Lambert, Jean-Michel, Chief Exec. Officer & Dir.--Nicoll, Cholet, France; *Int'l*, pg. 430
Lambert, Robert, Chm. Bd.--Aviall, Inc., Dallas, TX; *U.S. Public*, pg. 154
Lamberti, Donald F., Chm. Bd. & Chief Exec. Officer--Casey's General Stores, Inc., Ankeny, IA; *U.S. Public*, pg. 312
Lambrechts, Antoon, Chief Exec. Officer--Considar Europe S.A., Luxembourg, Luxembourg; *Int'l*, pg. 79
Lamer, Gerald P., Pres., Chief Exec. & Chief Oper. Officer--Marine Travelift, Inc., Sturgeon Bay, WI; *U.S. Private*, pg. 703
Lammle, Guy M., Chm. Bd., Pres. & Chief Exec. Officer--NxTrend Technology, Inc., Colorado Springs, CO; *U.S. Private*, pg. 809
Lamoreux, F. Holmes, Chm. Bd., Pres. & Chief Exec. Officer--Sabreliner Corporation, Saint Louis, MO; *U.S. Private*, pg. 959
Lampe, Jerry, Chief Exec. Officer--Innovative Health Alliances, Overland Park, KS; *U.S. Public*, pg. 839
Lamping, Mark, Pres. & Chief Exec. Officer--St. Louis National Baseball Club L.P., Saint Louis, MO; *U.S. Private*, pg. 961
Lampropoulos, Fred P., Chm. Bd., Pres. & Chief Exec. Officer--Merit Medical Systems, Inc., South Jordan, UT; *U.S. Public*, pg. 1096
Lan Ma, Sue, Chm. Bd., Pres. & Chief Exec. Officer--Elwell-Parker Limited, Cleveland, OH; *U.S. Private*, pg. 373
Lan, S., Chief Exec. Officer--Zurich Insurance Company (Asia) Limited, Quarry Bay, Hong Kong; *Int'l*, pg. 1532
Lancaster, B. Allen, Pres. & Chief Exec. Officer--Regions Bank/Raybun County, Clayton, GA; *U.S. Public*, pg. 1372
Lancaster, James J., Pres. & Chief Exec. Officer--Lantech Inc., Louisville, KY; *U.S. Private*, pg. 650
Landan, Amnon, Pres. & Chief Exec. Officer--Mercury Interactive Corp., Sunnyvale, CA; *U.S. Public*, pg. 1093
Lande, James R., Chief Exec. Officer--Quadion Corporation, Minneapolis, MN; *U.S. Private*, pg. 898
Landel, Michael, Pres. & Chief Exec. Officer--Sodexho USA, Waltham, MA; *Int'l*, pg. 1274
Landes, Gary, Pres. & Chief Exec. Officer--Meco Corporation, Greeneville, TN; *U.S. Private*, pg. 726
Landgraf, Kurt, Pres. & Chief Exec. Officer--The Du Pont Merck Pharmaceutical Company, Wilmington, DE; *U.S. Public*, pg. 531
Landguth, Daniel P., Chm. Bd. & Chief Exec. Officer--Black Hills Corporation, Rapid City, SD; *U.S. Public*, pg. 235
Landrum, Jim, Chief Exec. Officer--Esco Elevator Corp., Fort Worth, TX; *U.S. Private*, pg. 383
Landry, Richard, Pres. & Chief Exec. Officer--Hypermedia Communications, Inc., San Mateo, CA; *U.S. Public*, pg. 851
Landsberger, David, Chm. Bd. & Chief Exec. Officer--Bel-Art Products, Pequannock, NJ; *U.S. Private*, pg. 130
Landuyt, William M., Chm. Bd. & Chief Exec. Officer--Millennium Chemicals Inc., Iselin, NJ; *U.S. Public*, pg. 1111
Landy, Thomas M., Pres. & Chief Exec. Officer--Convair Cooler Corp., Phoenix, AZ; *U.S. Private*, pg. 271
Lane, Clifford, Chm. Bd., Pres. & Chief Exec. & Chief Oper. Officer--ILC Industries, Inc., Bohemia, NY; *U.S. Private*, pg. 555
Lane, Daniel D.(Ron), Chief Exec. Officer--Boston Pacific, Inc., Anaheim, CA; *U.S. Public*, pg. 278
Lane, Davina C., Pres. & Chief Exec. Officer--HealthCare USA, Jacksonville, FL; *U.S. Public*, pg. 454
Lane, James G., Jr., Chm. Bd., Pres. & Chief Exec. Officer--Synalloy Corporation, Spartanburg, SC; *U.S. Public*, pg. 1547
Lane, Joseph C., Pres. & Chief Exec. Officer--GATX Capital Corporation, San Francisco, CA; *U.S. Public*, pg. 690
Lane, Timothy, Pres. & Chief Exec. Officer--Bass PLC, London, United Kingdom; *Int'l*, pg. 169
Lane, William N., III, Chm. Bd., Pres. & Chief Exec. Officer--Lane Industries, Inc., Northbrook, IL; *U.S. Private*, pg. 649
Lang, Daniel, Pres. & Chief Exec. Officer--American Decal & Mfg. Co., Chicago, IL; *U.S. Private*, pg. 53
Lang, Everett, Pres. & Chief Exec. Officer--National Discount Brokers, New York, NY; *U.S. Public*, pg. 1467
Lang, Frederick W., Chm. Bd. & Chief Exec. Officer--Analysts International Corporation, Minneapolis, MN; *U.S. Public*, pg. 110
Lang, Henry S., Chm. Bd. & Chief Exec. Officer--Home Juice Co., Melrose Park, IL; *U.S. Private*, pg. 537
Lang, Robert H., Jr., Pres. & Chief Exec. Officer--Horn Packaging Corporation, Ayer, MA; *U.S. Private*, pg. 539
Langan, Kevin, Pres.--Northway Motorcar Corporation, Latham, NY; *U.S. Private*, pg. 806
Langbein, Thomas K., Chm. Bd., Pres. & Chief Exec. Officer--Medicore Inc., Hialeah, FL; *U.S. Public*, pg. 1080
Langbein, Thomas K., Chm. Bd. & Chief Exec. Officer--Techdyne, Inc., Hialeah, FL; *U.S. Public*, pg. 1080
Langbo, Arnold G., Chm. Bd. & Chief Exec. Officer--Kellogg Company, Battle Creek, MI; *U.S. Public*, pg. 947
Lange, Chadwick S., Pres.--Owatonna Canning Company, Owatonna, MN; *U.S. Public*, pg. 349
Lange, Paul L., Chm. Bd., Pres. & Chief Exec. Officer--Dynamic Materials Corporation, Lafayette, CO; *U.S. Public*, pg. 539
Langeheine, Jurgen, Dr., Pres. & Chief Exec. Officer--EMTEC Magnetics GmbH, Ludwigshafen, Germany; *Int'l*, pg. 743
Langer, Jack, Pres. & Chief Exec. Officer--City Gas Company of Florida, Hialeah, FL; *U.S. Public*, pg. 1147
Langford, Dean, Pres. & Chief Exec. Officer--Osram Sylvania Inc., Malvern, PA; *Int'l*, pg. 1245
Langner, Jay B., Chm. Bd. & Chief Exec. Officer--Hudson General Corporation, Great Neck, NY; *U.S. Public*, pg. 845
Langstaff, David H., Chief Exec. Officer--Veridian, Alexandria, VA; *U.S. Private*, pg. 1136
Langston, John, Deputy Chief Exec.--Bundy International, Warren, MI; *Int'l*, pg. 1340
Langston, John, Deputy Chief Exec. Officer--Bundy Group, Abingdon, United Kingdom; *Int'l*, pg. 1341
Langton, Bryan D., Chm. Bd. & Chief Exec. Officer--Holiday Inn Worldwide, Atlanta, GA; *Int'l*, pg. 170
Laniak, Dave, Chm. Bd. & Chief Exec. Officer--ACC Corp., Rochester, NY; *U.S. Public*, pg. 2
Lanier, J.L., Jr., Chm. Bd. & Chief Exec. Officer--Dan River Inc., Danville, VA; *U.S. Public*, pg. 478
Lanigan, John J., Jr., Pres. & Chief Exec. Officer Lanco Intl.--MI-Jack Products, Inc., Hazel Crest, IL; *U.S. Private*, pg. 740
Lanktree, Charles T., Pres., Chief Exec. Officer & Chief Oper. Officer--Eggland's Best, Inc., King of Prussia, PA; *U.S. Private*, pg. 366
Lanni, J. Terrence, Chm. Bd. & Chief Exec. Officer--MGM Grand, Inc., Las Vegas, NV; *U.S. Public*, pg. 1026
Lantis, B.T., Pres. & Chief Exec. Officer--Mooney Aircraft Corporation, Kerrville, TX; *U.S. Private*, pg. 759

Lantos, Robert, Chm. Bd. & Chief Exec. Officer--Alliance Communications Corporation, Toronto, Canada; *Int'l*, pg. 57
Lanza, Frank, Chm. Bd. & Chief Exec. Officer--L3 Communications, New York, NY; *U.S. Private*, pg. 638
Lanzagorta, Javier, Pres. & Chief Exec. Officer--The Walworth Company USA, Houston, TX; *U.S. Private*, pg. 1149
Lapin, Byron R., Pres. & Chief Exec. Officer--Clayton Corporation, Fenton, MO; *U.S. Private*, pg. 244
Lapin, Jay F., Pres. & Chief Exec. Officer-Japan--General Electric International Operations, London, United Kingdom; *U.S. Public*, pg. 713
LaPointe, William J., Pres. & Chief Exec. Officer--Andover Controls, Andover, MA; *U.S. Private*, pg. 73
Lappes, Constantine T., Pres. & Chief Exec. Officer--NYLIFE Administration Corp., Austin, TX; *U.S. Private*, pg. 795
Laptewicz, Joseph E., Jr., Pres. & Chief Exec. Officer--EMPI, Inc., Saint Paul, MN; *U.S. Public*, pg. 545
Laraway, Steven D., Pres. & Chief Exec. Officer--First American Trust Company of Minnesota, Saint Cloud, MN; *U.S. Private*, pg. 167
Larcombe, Brian, Chief Exec. Officer--3i Group plc, London, United Kingdom; *Int'l*, pg. 1386
Larison, H.H., Pres. & Chief Exec. Officer--Columbia Paint & Coatings, Spokane, WA; *U.S. Private*, pg. 256
Larkin, Carl, Pres. & Chief Exec. Officer--Larkin Meeder & Schweidel, Dallas, TX; *U.S. Private*, pg. 651
LaRoche, Calvin, Pres. & Chief Exec. Officer-Mtel. International--MTel International, Washington, DC; *U.S. Public*, pg. 1120
LaRoche, Calvin C., Chief Exec. Officer-Mtel Intl.--Mobile Telecommunications Technologies Corp., Jackson, MS; *U.S. Public*, pg. 1120
Larochelle, Richard, Pres. & Chief Exec. Officer--Irving Tanning Co., Hartland, ME; *U.S. Private*, pg. 575
LaRosa, Charles, Pres. & Chief Exec. Officer--Pharmaceutical Formulations, Inc., Edison, NJ; *U.S. Public*, pg. 1284
LaRosa, Joseph, Chm. Bd. & Co-Chief Exec. Officer--Waring & LaRosa, Inc., New York, NY; *U.S. Private*, pg. 1150
Larrimore, Randall W., Pres. & Chief Exec. Officer--United Stationers Inc., Des Plaines, IL; *U.S. Public*, pg. 1689
Larsen, Asbjorn, Pres. & Chief Exec. Officer--Saga Petroleum ASA, Sandvika, Norway; *Int'l*, pg. 1169
Larsen, Ralph S., Chm. Bd., Pres. & Chief Exec. Officer--Johnson & Johnson, New Brunswick, NJ; *U.S. Public*, pg. 927
Larsen, Terrence A., Chm. Bd., Pres. & Chief Exec. Officer--CoreStates Financial Corp., Philadelphia, PA; *U.S. Public*, pg. 446
Larson, Greg, Pres. & Chief Exec. Officer--Demco Inc., Madison, WI; *U.S. Private*, pg. 323
Larson, Jack, Pres. & Chief Exec. Officer--Career Education Corporation, Hoffman Estates, IL; *U.S. Private*, pg. 209
Larson, John D., Pres. & Chief Exec. Officer--National Guardian Life Insurance Company, Madison, WI; *U.S. Private*, pg. 784
Larson, Peter N., Chm. Bd. & Chief Exec. Officer--Brunswick Corporation, Lake Forest, IL; *U.S. Public*, pg. 265
Larson, Richard W., Chm. Bd. & Chief Exec. Officer--Bank of America Alaska, N.A., Anchorage, AK; *U.S. Public*, pg. 180
Larson, Stephen C., Chief Exec. Officer--InterLake Papers, Inc., Stamford, CT; *U.S. Public*, pg. 436
Larson, Steve, Pres. & Chief Exec. Officer--Repap Enterprises Inc., Montreal, Canada; *Int'l*, pg. 1104
Larson, Steve, Pres. & Chief Exec. Officer--Repap New Brunswick Inc., Montreal, Canada; *Int'l*, pg. 1104
Larson, William L., Chm. Bd. & Chief Exec. Officer--Network Associates, Inc., Santa Clara, CA; *U.S. Public*, pg. 1168
Larsson, Hakan, Chief Exec. Officer--BTL AB, Goteborg, Sweden; *Int'l*, pg. 123
Laskawy, Philip A., Chm. Bd. & Chief Exec. Officer--Ernst & Young, LLP, New York, NY; *U.S. Private*, pg. 381
Lassiter, Phillip B., Chm. Bd., Pres. & Chief Exec. Officer--AMBAC Financial Group, Inc., New York, NY; *U.S. Public*, pg. 62
Lassiter, Ronald C., Chm. Bd. & Chief Exec. Officer--Daniel Industries, Inc., Houston, TX; *U.S. Public*, pg. 482
Laster, Ralph W., Jr., Pres. & Chief Exec. Officer--Amvestors Financial Corporation, Topeka, KS; *U.S. Private*, pg. 59
Latham, John, Pres. & Chief Exec. Officer--Colony Insurance Company, Richmond, VA; *U.S. Private*, pg. 430
Lathan, Barry R., Pres. & Chief Exec. Officer--Xerox Colorgraphics, San Jose, CA; *U.S. Public*, pg. 1784
Lathrop, Thomas C., Pres. & Chief Exec. Officer--M & I Thunderbird Bank, Phoenix, AZ; *U.S. Public*, pg. 1050
Latimer, John A., III, Pres. & Chief Exec. Officer--Jamison Door Company, Hagerstown, MD; *U.S. Private*, pg. 581
Latiolais, Rene L., Pres. & Chief Exec. Officer--Freeport-McMoRan Inc., New Orleans, LA; *U.S. Public*, pg. 680
Latner, Albert J., Chm. Bd. & Chief Exec. Officer--Dynacare, Inc., Toronto, Canada; *Int'l*, pg. 425
Latshaw, John, Chm. Bd. & Chief Exec. Officer--Latshaw Enterprises, Inc., Wichita, KS; *U.S. Public*, pg. 979
Lau, John C.S., Chief Exec. Officer--Husky Oil Ltd., Calgary, Canada; *Int'l*, pg. 640
Lau, John C.S., Chief Exec. Officer--Husky Oil Intl. Ltd., Calgary, Canada; *Int'l*, pg. 640
Laucirica, Louis, Pres., Chief Exec. Officer & Chief Oper. Officer--Norton Performance Plastics, Wayne, NJ; *Int'l*, pg. 1174
Lauder, Leonard A., Chm. Bd. & Chief Exec. Officer--Estee Lauder Companies Inc., New York, NY; *U.S. Public*, pg. 594
Lauff, H., Chief Exec. Officer--Ruppkeramik GmbH, Buchen, Germany; *Int'l*, pg. 1093
Laughlin, William, Chm. Bd. & Chief Exec. Officer--Unisource, Minneapolis, MN; *U.S. Public*, pg. 1671
Laule, William J., Chief Exec. Officer-Bundy--TI Group plc, Abingdon, United Kingdom; *Int'l*, pg. 1337
Laule, William J., Chief Exec. Officer--Bundy International, Warren, MI; *Int'l*, pg. 1340
Lauletta, John F., Pres. & Chief Exec. Officer--Tuboscope Incorporated, Houston, TX; *U.S. Public*, pg. 1643
Lauren, Ralph, Chm. Bd.--Polo/Ralph Lauren Corporation, New York, NY; *U.S. Private*, pg. 874
Laurent, Jean, Deputy Chief Exec. Officer-Devel. & Mkts.--Credit Agricole, Bonvin, France; *Int'l*, pg. 341
Lauritsen, K. Bruce, Pres. & Chief Exec. Officer--Flexsteel Industries, Inc., Dubuque, IA; *U.S. Public*, pg. 653
Lauzon, D.A., Pres. & Chief Exec. Officer--Dow Chemical Canada, Inc., Sarnia, Canada; *U.S. Public*, pg. 523
Laver, Kenneth G., Chief Exec. Officer--de Havilland Inc., Downsview, Canada; *Int'l*, pg. 200
Laverty, Roger M., III, Pres. & Chief Exec. Officer--Smart & Final, Vernon, CA; *Int'l*, pg. 563
Laviec, Gerard, Chm. Bd. & Chief Exec. Officer--CFM International SA, Paris, France; *Int'l*, pg. 1166
Lavington, Mike, Pres. & Chief Exec. Officer--Resorts USA Inc., Bushkill, PA; *Int'l*, pg. 1087
Law-Smith, David J., Chm. Bd., Pres. & Chief Exec. Officer--Caltex Petroleum Corporation, Irving, TX; *U.S. Public*, pg. 348
Law, Irving D., Jr., Chm. Bd. & Chief Exec. Officer--Broadcast Supply Worldwide, Inc., Tacoma, WA; *U.S. Private*, pg. 170
Law, Jordan, Chm. Bd., Pres. & Chief Exec. Officer--KTI, Orange, CA; *U.S. Public*, pg. 939
LaWarre, William M., Chm. Bd. & Chief Exec. Officer--Northlich Stolley LaWarre, Cincinnati, OH; *U.S. Private*, pg. 806
Lawernce, W. Larry Jr., Pres. & Chief Exec. Officer--Sunline Coach Co., Inc., Denver, PA; *U.S. Private*, pg. 1053
Lawless, Robert J., Pres. & Chief Exec. Officer--McCormick & Company, Incorporated, Sparks, MD; *U.S. Public*, pg. 1066
Lawrence, David, Dr., Chm. Bd. & Chief Exec. Officer--Kaiser Permanente, Oakland, CA; *U.S. Private*, pg. 605
Lawrence, Frederick D., Chm. Bd., Pres. & Chief Exec. Officer--California Microwave, Inc., Sunnyvale, CA; *U.S. Public*, pg. 293
Lawrence, Fredrick D., Chief Exec. Officer--Comstream Corporation, San Diego, CA; *Int'l*, pg. 1288
Lawrence, Julien, Chief Exec. Officer--Logica Plc, London, United Kingdom; *Int'l*, pg. 814
Lawrence, Julien, Chief Exec. Officer--Logica UK Ltd., London, United Kingdom; *Int'l*, pg. 814
Lawrence, Michael L., Chm. Bd. & Chief Exec. Officer--Ameritruck Distribution Corporation, Fort Worth, TX; *U.S.* Private, pg. 65
Lawson, A. Lowell, Exec. V.P., Chm. Bd. & Chief Exec. Officer-Raytheon E-Systems--Raytheon Company, Lexington, MA; *U.S. Public*, pg. 1364
Lawson, Charles E., Pres. & Chief Exec. Officer--The Lion Brewery, Inc., Wilkes-Barre, PA; *U.S. Public*, pg. 1000
Lawson, G.B., Dr., Chief Exec. Officer--Watts Blake Bearne & Co. Plc, Newton Abbot, United Kingdom; *Int'l*, pg. 1487
Lawson, William, Pres. & Chief Exec. Officer--Lawson Software, Minneapolis, MN; *U.S. Private*, pg. 654
Lawson, William H., Chm. Bd. & Chief Exec. Officer--Franklin Electric Co., Inc., Bluffton, IN; *U.S. Public*, pg. 679
Lawyer, Joseph C., Pres. & Chief Exec. Officer--Chatwins Group, Inc., Pittsburgh, PA; *U.S. Private*, pg. 231
Lay, B. Allen, Chm. Bd., Pres. & Chief Exec. Officer--Westbrae Natural, Inc., Carson, CA; *U.S. Public*, pg. 774
Lay, Charles, Pres. & Chief Exec. Officer--Geneva Pharmaceuticals, Inc., Broomfield, CO; *Int'l*, pg. 973
Lay, Joe L., Jr., Chm. Bd., Pres. & Chief Exec. Officer--Lay's Fine Foods, Knoxville, TN; *U.S. Private*, pg. 655
Lay, Kenneth L., Chm. Bd. & Chief Exec. Officer--Enron Corp., Houston, TX; *U.S. Public*, pg. 584
Layden, A.J., Chm. Bd. & Chief Exec. Officer--Allright Corporation, Houston, TX; *U.S. Private*, pg. 42
Layton, Mark, Chief Exec. Officer--Daisytek Incorporated, Plano, TX; *U.S. Public*, pg. 477
Layton, Mark C., Pres., Chief Exec. & Oper. Officer--Daisytek International Corporation, Plano, TX; *U.S. Public*, pg. 477
Layton, Mark C., Pres., Chief Exec. & Oper. Officer--Daisytek (Canada) Inc., Toronto, Canada; *U.S. Public*, pg. 477
Layton, Mark C., Pres., Chief Exec. & Oper. Officer--Daisytek Latin America, Miami, FL; *U.S. Public*, pg. 477
Layton, Mark C., Pres., Chief Exec. & Oper. Officer--Daisytek De Mexico S.A. de C.V., Mexico, Mexico; *U.S. Public*, pg. 477
Layton, Mark C., Pres., Chief Exec. & Oper. Officer--Priority Fulfillment Services, Inc., Plano, TX; *U.S. Public*, pg. 477
Layton, Mark C., Pres., Chief Exec. & Oper. Officer--Daisytek Australia Pty. Ltd., Alexandria, Australia; *U.S. Public*, pg. 477
Lazarchick, Robert, Pres. & Chief Exec. Officer--Terre Hill Concrete Products, Inc., Terre Hill, PA; *U.S. Private*, pg. 1077
Lazarus, Shelly, Chm. Bd. & Chief Exec. Officer--Ogilvy & Mather Worldwide, Inc., New York, NY; *Int'l*, pg. 1483
Le Chatelier, Nicolas, Chief Exec. Officer--SODIAAL, Paris, France; *Int'l*, pg. 1166
Le Mener, Georges, Pres. & Chief Exec. Officer--Motel 6 Operating L.P., Dallas, TX; *Int'l*, pg. 21
Lea, George A. Jr., Chm. Bd., Pres. & Chief Exec. Officer--The Mad Butcher, Inc., Pine Bluff, AR; *U.S. Private*, pg. 693
Leahy, Terry, Pres. & Chief Exec. Officer--Stream International Holdings Inc., Canton, MA; *U.S. Public*, pg. 518
Leahy, Terry, Chief Exec.--Tesco PLC, Cheshunt, United Kingdom; *Int'l*, pg. 1376
Leary, William, Chief Fin. Officer & V.P.--Pen-Tab Industries, Inc., Front Royal, VA; *U.S. Private*, pg. 848
Leasure, George, Pres., Chief Exec. Officer, Chief Fin. Officer & Treas.--Ghent Manufacturing, Inc., Lebanon, OH; *U.S. Private*, pg. 450
Leatherby, Russell E., Pres. & Chief Exec. Officer--UniCARE Financial Corp., Irvine, CA; *U.S. Private*, pg. 152
Leatherdale, D.W., Chm. Bd., Pres. & Chief Exec. Officer--The St. Paul Companies, Inc., Saint Paul, MN; *U.S. Public*, pg. 1429
Leaverton, Robert, Chief Exec. Officer--Eagle Iron Works, Des Moines, IA; *U.S. Private*, pg. 354
Lebel, Andre, Pres. & Chief Exec. Officer--Teleglobe Canada Inc., Montreal, Canada; *Int'l*, pg. 1373
LeBoeuf, Raymond W., Chm. Bd. & Chief Exec. Officer--PPG Industries, Inc., Pittsburgh, PA; *U.S. Public*, pg. 1245
Lebovitz, Charles B., Chm. Bd., Pres. & Chief Exec. Officer--CBL & Associates Properties, Inc., Chattanooga, TN; *U.S. Public*, pg. 273
LeBow, Bennett S., Chm. Bd., Pres. & Chief Exec. Officer--Brooke Group Ltd., Miami, FL; *U.S. Public*, pg. 259
LeBow, Bennett S., Chm. Bd., Pres. & Chief Exec. Officer--BGLS Inc., Miami, FL; *U.S. Public*, pg. 259
LeClair, Darryl A., Chm. Bd., Pres. & Chief Exec. Officer--Echelon International Corporation, Saint Petersburg, FL; *U.S. Public*, pg. 560
Leclerc, Robert L., Chm. Bd. & Chief Exec. Officer--Echo Bay Mines Ltd., Englewood, CO; *U.S. Public*, pg. 561
Lee, Charles R., Chm. Bd., Chief Exec. Officer & Chief Oper. Officer--GTE Corporation, Stamford, CT; *U.S. Public*, pg. 696
Lee, Ching-Rong, Div. Chief--Taiwan Power Company, Taipei, Taiwan; *Int'l*, pg. 1348
Lee, Chong Haee, Chief Exec. Officer--C.I. Holdings Berhad, Kuala Lumpur, Malaysia; *Int'l*, pg. 1092
Lee, Dan K., Pres. & Chief Exec. Officer--Willis Corroon Property & Casualty Programs Div., Nashville, TN; *Int'l*, pg. 1508
Lee, David B., Chm. Bd. & Chief Exec. Officer--Omega Financial Corporation, State College, PA; *U.S. Public*, pg. 1222
Lee, David B., Pres. & Chief Exec. Officer--Omega Bank, N.A., State College, PA; *U.S. Public*, pg. 1222
Lee, David B., Pres. & Chief Exec. Officer--Montour Bank, Danville, PA; *U.S. Public*, pg. 1222
Lee, Do-Hee, Exec. Dir.--Daehong Advertising Inc., Seoul, Korea; *Int'l*, pg. 357
Lee, Doyle, Pres. & Chief Exec. Officer--Weatherford National Bank, Weatherford, TX; *U.S. Public*, pg. 633
Lee, Hun Jo, Vice Chm. & Chief Exec. Officer--LG Group, Seoul, Korea; *Int'l*, pg. 778
Lee, James C., III, Pres.--Buffalo Rock Company, Birmingham, AL; *U.S. Private*, pg. 179
Lee, Joe R., Chm. Bd. & Chief Exec. Officer--Darden Restaurants, Inc., Orlando, FL; *U.S. Public*, pg. 483
Lee, John E., Pres. & Chief Exec. Officer--Carver, Inc., Savannah, GA; *U.S. Private*, pg. 217
Lee, John J., Chm. Bd. & Chief Exec. Officer--Hexcel Corporation, Pleasanton, CA; *U.S. Public*, pg. 824
Lee, K., Chm. Bd. & Chief Exec. Officer--CAM International Holdings Ltd., Singapore, Singapore; *Int'l*, pg. 238
Lee, M.S., Chm. Bd. & Chief Exec. Officer--Houston Fearless 76 Inc., Compton, CA; *U.S. Private*, pg. 542
Lee, Mike, Chm., Pres. & Chief Exec. Officer--Famous Restaurants Inc., Scottsdale, AZ; *U.S. Private*, pg. 393
Lee, Rhoady R., Jr., Chm. Bd. & Chief Exec. Officer--Lakeside Industries, Issaquah, WA; *U.S. Private*, pg. 644
Lee, Richard G., Chief Exec. Officer & Dir.--Zung Fu Company Ltd., Hong Kong, Hong Kong; *Int'l*, pg. 704
Lee, Robert, Chief Exec. Officer--Country Coach, Inc., Junction City, OR; *U.S. Public*, pg. 1159
Lee, Robert E., Pres. & Chief Exec. Officer--Millennium Inorganic Chemicals, Hunt Valley, MD; *Int'l*, pg. 593
Lee, Robert E., Pres. & Chief Exec. Officer--Millennium Inorganic Chemicals, Hunt Valley, MD; *U.S. Public*, pg. 1111
Lee, Robert H., Chief Exec. Officer & Gen. Mgr.--Wagstaff Inc., Spokane, WA; *U.S. Private*, pg. 1146
Lee, Robert Y., Chm. Bd. & Chief Exec. Officer--Video City Inc., Bakersfield, CA; *U.S. Public*, pg. 1719
Lee, Ronald G., Chm. Bd. & Pres.--Lee Pharmaceuticals, South El Monte, CA; *U.S. Public*, pg. 984
Lee, Steven J., Chm. Bd. & Chief Exec. Officer--PolyMedica Industries, Inc., Woburn, MA; *U.S. Public*, pg. 1315
Lee, Tan Beng, Chief Exec. Officer--The Great Eastern Life Assurance Company Limited, Singapore, Singapore; *Int'l*, pg. 557
Lee, Terry G., Chm. Bd. & Chief Exec. Officer--Bell Sports Corp., San Jose, CA; *U.S. Public*, pg. 207
Lee, Thomas L., Chm. Bd. & Chief Exec. Officer--The Newhall Land And Farming Company, Valencia, CA; *U.S.* Public, pg. 1178
Lee, Y.I., Pres. & Chief Exec. Officer--Hyundai Motor America, Fountain Valley, CA; *Int'l*, pg. 641
Lee, Youn-Jae, Chm. Bd. & Chief Exec. Officer--Jinwoong Inc., Seoul, Korea; *Int'l*, pg. 706
Lee, Young C., Chief Oper. Officer--Novo Nordisk Bioindustrial, Korea, Seoul, Korea; *Int'l*, pg. 989
Leeb, Peter, Chm. Bd. & Chief Exec. Officer--King Wire Inc., North Chicago, IL; *U.S. Private*, pg. 621
Leech, James W., Pres. & Chief Exec. Officer--Union Energy Inc., Toronto, Canada; *Int'l*, pg. 1492
Leedom, John N., Sr., Chm. Bd., Chief Exec. Officer--Wholesale Electronic Supply, Dallas, TX; *U.S. Private*, pg. 1174
Leeds, Michael S., Pres. & Chief Exec. Officer--CMP Media, Inc., Manhasset, NY; *U.S. Public*, pg. 279
Leeds, Richard, Chm. Bd. & Chief Exec. Officer--Global Direct Mail Corp, Port Washington, NY; *U.S. Public*, pg. 747
Leemans, Michel F., Chm. Bd., Pres. & Chief Exec. Officer--IL International Inc., Stratford, CT; *U.S. Public*, pg. 855

Leeming, R., Chief Exec. Officer--Pilkington Australasia Limited, Melbourne, Australia; Int'l, pg. 1057

Leer, Steven F., Pres. & Chief Exec. Officer--Arch Coal, Inc., Saint Louis, MO; U.S. Public, pg. 139

Leever, Daniel H., Pres. & Chief Exec. Officer--MacDermid Incorporated, Waterbury, CT; U.S. Public, pg. 1029

Lefelle, Philippe, Chief Exec. Officer--Euromezzanine Gestion, Paris, France; Int'l, pg. 344

Lefkof, Alan B., Pres. & Chief Exec. Officer--Netopia, Inc., Alameda, CA; U.S. Public, pg. 1168

Lefkowitz, Abraham, Chief Exec. Officer--Crystal Clear Industries, Ridgefield Park, NJ; U.S. Private, pg. 293

Lefton, Al Paul, Jr., Pres. & Chief Exec. Officer--Al Paul Lefton Co., Inc., Philadelphia, PA; U.S. Private, pg. 658

Leger, J.C., Pres. & Chief Exec. Officer--CGTX Inc., Mississauga, Canada; Int'l, pg. 604

Legum, Jeffrey A., Pres. & Chief Exec. Officer--The Park Circle Motor Co., Baltimore, MD; U.S. Private, pg. 839

Lehman, Chris, Chm. Bd., Pres. & Chief Exec. Officer--SRDS, Des Plaines, IL; U.S. Private, pg. 958

Lehmer, Thomas W., Chief Exec. Officer--Snack America, Los Angeles, CA; U.S. Private, pg. 1010

Lehn, Jacques, Pres.--Lagardere Groupe, Paris, France; Int'l, pg. 791

Lehr, Donald A., Chm. Bd., Chief Exec. Officer, Treas. & Sec.--Cubix Corporation, Carson City, NV; U.S. Private, pg. 294

Leibovitz, Mitchell G., Chm. Bd., Pres. & Chief Exec. Officer--The Pep Boys-Manny, Moe & Jack, Philadelphia, PA; U.S. Public, pg. 1276

Leibowitz, Jerry, Chief Exec. Officer--Konica Medical Corporation, Wayne, NJ; Int'l, pg. 749

Leicht, Richard F., Jr., Pres. & Chief Exec. Officer--Eclipse Manufacturing Company, Sheboygan, WI; U.S. Private, pg. 361

Leiff, Ann Spector, Pres. & Chief Exec. Officer--Spec's Music, Inc., Miami, FL; U.S. Public, pg. 1497

Leighton, Allan, Deputy Chief Exec. Officer & Dir.-Retail--Asda Group Plc, Leeds, United Kingdom; Int'l, pg. 17

Leighton, Charles M., Chm. Bd. & Chief Exec. Officer--CML Group, Inc., Acton, MA; U.S. Public, pg. 279

Leinweber, John L., Pres. & Chief Exec. Officer--Danka Business Systems, La Grange, IL; Int'l, pg. 379

Leistner, Ralph, Pres. & Chief Exec. Officer--McAlear Associates, Inc., Grand Rapids, MI; Int'l, pg. 1508

Lekach, Ilia, Chm. Bd. & Chief Exec. Officer--Parlux Fragrances Inc., Fort Lauderdale, FL; U.S. Public, pg. 1264

Lekach, Rachmil, Chief Exec. Officer--L. Luria & Son, Inc., Medley, FL; U.S. Public, pg. 1020

Lemaire, Alain, Pres. & Chief Exec. Officer--Rolland Inc., Saint-Jerome, Canada; Int'l, pg. 273

Lemaire, Laurent, Pres. & Chief Exec. Officer--The Cascades Group, Kingsey Falls, Canada; Int'l, pg. 273

Lemaire, Laurent, Pres. & Chief Exec. Offficer--Cascades, Inc., Kingsey Falls, Canada; Int'l, pg. 273

Lemasters, John N., Chm. Bd. & Chief Exec. Officer--Augat, Inc., Mansfield, MA; U.S. Public, pg. 1597

Lemieux, Joseph H., Chm. Bd. & Chief Exec. Officer--Owens-Illinois, Inc., Toledo, OH; U.S. Public, pg. 1238

Lemke, Ronald A.H., Pres. & Chief Exec. Officer--McLean McCarthy Limited, Toronto, Canada; Int'l, pg. 405

Lemley, Jack, Chm. Bd., Pres. & Chief Exec. Officer--American Ecology Corporation, Boise, ID; U.S. Public, pg. 71

Lemmon, David, Pres. & Chief Exec. Officer--Colonial Pipeline Company, Atlanta, GA; U.S. Private, pg. 254

Lemmon, George B., Jr., Pres. & Chief Exec. Officer--Owosso Corporation, King of Prussia, PA; U.S. Public, pg. 1238

Lemon, James H., Jr., Chm. Bd. & Chief Exec. Officer--Johnston, Lemon & Co. Inc., Washington, DC; U.S. Private, pg. 595

Leng, James W., Chief Exec. Officer & Mng. Dir.--Laporte plc, Luton, United Kingdom; Int'l, pg. 801

Lenhart, Miles L., Chief Exec. Officer--Reeves Southeastern Corporation, Tampa, FL; U.S. Private, pg. 916

Lenhart, Ronald G., Pres.-Mount Morris Facility--AMCORE Bank, Rock River Valley, Mount Morris, IL; U.S. Public, pg. 64

Lenig, Larry, Pres. & Chief Exec. Officer--Grant Geophysical Inc., Houston, TX; U.S. Private, pg. 470

Lennox, Gregory P., Pres. & Chief Exec. Officer--P.L. Porter Co., Woodland Hills, CA; U.S. Private, pg. 876

Lenoci, V. William, Pres. & Chief Exec. Officer--Industrial Coated Fabrics Group, Spartanburg, SC; U.S. Private, pg. 507

Lenox, John W., Pres. & Chief Exec. Officer--Shelter Mutual Insurance Company, Columbia, MO; U.S. Private, pg. 992

Lentzsch, Craig, Pres. & Chief Exec. Officer--Greyhound Lines, Inc., Dallas, TX; U.S. Public, pg. 765

Lenzie, Charles A., Chm. Bd., Pres. & Chief Exec. Officer--Nevada Power Company, Las Vegas, NV; U.S. Public, pg. 1169

Leonard, Thomas C., Pres. & Chief Exec. Officer--Alpha Industries, Inc., Woburn, MA; U.S. Public, pg. 57

Leone, John A., Pres. & Chief Exec. Officer--Bonney Forge Corporation, Allentown, PA; U.S. Private, pg. 156

Leong, Wong Chee, Pres. & Chief Exec. Officer--Bangkok Bank Berhad, Kuala Lumpur, Malaysia; Int'l, pg. 146

Leonhardt, Thomas C., Pres. & Chief Exec. Officer--Rust Environment & Infrastructure, Inc., Greenville, SC; U.S. Public, pg. 1745

Leonis, John, Chm.Bd. & Chief Exec. Officer--Amecom Div., College Park, MD; U.S. Public, pg. 1002

Leonis, John M., Chm. Bd. & Chief Exec. Officer--Litton Industries, Inc., Woodland Hills, CA; U.S. Public, pg. 1002

Leonsis, Ted, Chm. Bd., Chief Exec. Officer, Pres. & New Bus. Contact--Redgate Communications Corp., Vero Beach, FL; U.S. Public, pg. 66

Leonsis, Theodore, Pres. & Chief Exec. Officer-AOL Studios--America Online Incorporated, Dulles, VA; U.S. Public, pg. 66

Leopold, Ernest S., Chm. Bd., Pres. & Chief Exec. Officer--Crown Vantage Inc., Oakland, CA; U.S. Public, pg. 465

Lepofsky, Robert J., Pres. & Chief Exec. Officer--Helix Technology Corp., Mansfield, MA; U.S. Public, pg. 808

Lepore, Donald, Pres. & Chief Exec. Officer--NutraMax Products, Inc., Gloucester, MA; U.S. Public, pg. 1206

LePore, Patrick G., Chm. Bd., Pres. & Chief Exec. Officer--Boron LePore Group, Fair Lawn, NJ; U.S. Public, pg. 246

Lepp, H.J., Pres. & Chief Exec. Officer--AltaSteel Ltd., Edmonton, Canada; Int'l, pg. 1299

Lerenius, Bo, Pres. & Chief Exec. Officer--Stena Line AB, Goteborg, Sweden; Int'l, pg. 1300

Lerner, Alfred, Chm. Bd. & Chief Exec. Officer--MBNA Corporation, Wilmington, DE; U.S. Public, pg. 1023

Lerner, Bernard J., Chief Exec. Officer--Beco Engineering Company, Oakmont, PA; U.S. Private, pg. 129

Lerner, Michael, Chm. Bd. & Chief Exec. Officer--Safety 1st, Inc., Chestnut Hill, MA; U.S. Public, pg. 1425

Lerner, Michael H., Chm. Bd., Pres. & Chief Exec. Officer--Marisa Christina Inc., New Hyde Park, NY; U.S. Public, pg. 1044

Lervick, Arne T., Chm. Bd. & Chief Exec. Officer--Twin City Foods, Inc., Stanwood, WA; U.S. Private, pg. 1111

LeSage, William A., Chm. Bd & Chief Exec. Officer--General Homes Corporation, Houston, TX; U.S. Private, pg. 444

Lesage, Yves, Chm. Bd. & Chief Exec. Officer--CGG Group, Massy, France; Int'l, pg. 241

Lesage, Yves, Chm. Bd., Pres. & Chief Exec. Officer--Compagnie Generale de Geophysique, Massy, France; Int'l, pg. 241

Lesar, David J., Pres. & Chief Exec. Officer--Brown & Root Inc., Alhambra, CA; U.S. Public, pg. 775

Leschly, Jan, Chief Exec. Officer--SmithKline Beecham plc, Brentford, United Kingdom; Int'l, pg. 1264

Lesh, Fred, Chm. Bd. & Chief Exec. Officer--Holcomb & Hoke Mfg. Company, Inc., Indianapolis, IN; U.S. Private, pg. 533

LeSieur, James G., III, Pres. & Chief Exec. Officer--Sunwest Bank, Tustin, CA; U.S. Public, pg. 1755

Leskys, Algirdas G., Chm. Bd.--The Converse Professional Group, Inc., Monrovia, CA; U.S. Private, pg. 271

Leslie, James K., Pres. & Chief Exec. Officer--Pharmakinetics Laboratories, Inc., Baltimore, MD; U.S. Public, pg. 1285

Lesok, Eddie, Pres. & Chief Exec. Officer--Sun Coast Industries, Inc, Dallas, TX; U.S. Public, pg. 1529

Lessard, Claude, Pres. & Chief Exec. Officer--Cossette Communication Marketing, Quebec, Canada; Int'l, pg. 335

Lester, W. Howard, Chm. Bd. & Chief Exec. Officer--Williams-Sonoma, Inc., San Francisco, CA; U.S. Public, pg. 1770

Letaw, Harry, Jr., Chm. Bd., Pres. & Chief Exec. Officer--Essex Corporation, Columbia, MD; U.S. Public, pg. 593

Letica, Illija, Pres. & Chief Exec. Officer--Letica Corporation, Rochester, MI; U.S. Private, pg. 661

Letters, Jerry, Pres. & Chief Exec. Officer--Farmers Union Marketing & Processing Association, Redwood Falls, MN; U.S. Private, pg. 395

Leuliette, Timothy D., Pres. & Chief Oper. Officer--Penske Corporation, Detroit, MI; U.S. Private, pg. 850

Leung, Brian, Chief Exec. Officer--Seattle Pacific Industries, Inc., Seattle, WA; U.S. Private, pg. 980

Levan, Alan B., Chm. Bd., Pres. & Chief Exec. Officer--BankAtlantic Bancorp, Inc., Fort Lauderdale, FL; U.S. Public, pg. 183

LeVan, David M., Chm. Bd., Pres. & Chief Exec. Officer--Conrail, Inc., Philadelphia, PA; U.S. Public, pg. 431

Levan, David M., Chm. Bd., Pres. & Chief Exec. Officer--CRR Industries, Inc., Philadelphia, PA; U.S. Public, pg. 432

Levantin, Allen M., Chm. Bd. & Chief Exec. Officer--Todays Temporary, Inc., Dallas, TX; U.S. Public, pg. 277

Levene, David A., Chm. Bd., Pres. & Chief Exec. Officer--Metropolitan Insurance & Annuity Co., New York, NY; U.S. Private, pg. 737

Levene, David A., Chm. Bd., Pres. & Chief Exec. Officer--Metropolitan Tower Life Insurance Co., New York, NY; U.S. Private, pg. 737

Levenick, Mark, Pres. & Chief Exec. Officer--Tidel Engineering, Inc., Carrollton, TX; U.S. Public, pg. 1608

Levenson, Barbara L., Pres. & Chief Exec. Officer--Levenson & Hill, Inc., Dallas, TX; U.S. Private, pg. 662

Lever, Roy, Chm. & Chief Exec. Officer--GAN General Insurance Company, Burlington, Canada; Int'l, pg. 564

Lever, Roy, Chm. & Chief Exec. Officer--The Gan Company of Canada Ltd., Burlington, Canada; Int'l, pg. 564

Levesque, Joseph, Chm. Bd., Pres. & Chief Exec. Officer--Aetrium Inc., Saint Paul, MN; U.S. Public, pg. 27

Levin, Gerald M., Chm. Bd. & Chief Exec. Officer--Time Warner Inc., New York, NY; U.S. Public, pg. 1610

Levin, Gilbert V., Dr., Chm., Pres., Chief Exec. Officer & Treas.--Biospherics Incorporated, Beltsville, MD; U.S. Public, pg. 232

Levin, Jerry, Chm. & Chief Exec. Officer--The Coleman Company, Inc., Golden, CO; U.S. Private, pg. 690

Levin, Michael S., Pres. & Chief Exec. Officer--The Titan Industrial Corp., New York, NY; U.S. Private, pg. 1089

Levine, Jesse, Pres. & Chief Exec. Officer--Los Angeles Times Syndicate, Los Angeles, CA; U.S. Public, pg. 1616

Levine, Jules B., Pres. & Chief Exec. Officer--Pick Quick Foods, Jamaica, NY; U.S. Private, pg. 864

Levine, Leon, Chm. Bd. & Treas.--Family Dollar Stores, Inc., Matthews, NC; U.S. Public, pg. 612

Levine, Martin, Pres. & Chief Exec. Officer--MarketSource Corporation, Cranbury, NJ; U.S. Private, pg. 705

Levine, Stuart, Chief Exec. Officer--Dale Carnegie & Associates, Garden City, NY; U.S. Private, pg. 308

Levinson, Arthur D., Ph.D., Pres. & Chief Exec. Officer--Genentech, Inc., South San Francisco, CA; Int'l, pg. 1120

Levit, Milton, Chief Exec. Officer--Grocers Supply Co. Inc., Houston, TX; U.S. Private, pg. 483

Leviton, Howard, Pres. & Chief Exec. Officer--Leviton Mfg. Co., Inc., Little Neck, NY; U.S. Private, pg. 663

Levitt, Richard, Pres. & Chief Exec. Officer--Lillie Rubin Fashions Inc., Miami, FL; U.S. Private, pg. 667

Levy, Elio, Pres. & Chief Exec. Officer--Tech Data Canada, Inc., Mississauga, Canada; U.S. Public, pg. 1562

Levy, Frank L., Pres. & Chief Exec. Officer--L & L Oil Company, Inc., Metairie, LA; U.S. Private, pg. 638

Levy, Frank L., Pres. & Chief Exec. Officer--L & L Environmental Services, Metairie, LA; U.S. Private, pg. 638

Levy, Gerard, Chief Exec. Officer--Air Liquide S.A., Paris, France; Int'l, pg. 37

Levy, Joe, Chm. Bd. & Chief Exec. Officer--Gottschalks Inc., Fresno, CA; U.S. Public, pg. 754

Levy, Lew, Chief Exec. Officer--United States Luggage Company, Hauppauge, NY; U.S. Private, pg. 1125

Levy, Richard D., Chm. Bd. & Chief Exec. Officer--Oriole Homes Corp., Delray Beach, FL; U.S. Public, pg. 1230

Levy, Robert, Pres., Chief Exec. Officer & Chief Oper. Officer--Norman Levy Associates, Inc., Southfield, MI; U.S. Private, pg. 664

Levy, Shemaya, Chm. & Chief Exec. Officer-Renault Group--Renault, Boulogne-Billancourt, France; Int'l, pg. 1102

Levy, Steve, Pres. & Chief Exec. Officer--Jacob Levy & Bros., Inc., Louisville, KY; U.S. Private, pg. 664

Levys, Nessim, Pres. & Chief Exec. Officer--Level Export Sales Corp., New York, NY; U.S. Private, pg. 662

Lewin, Joseph, Chm. Bd., Pres. & Chief Exec. Officer--Health Products Corporation, Yonkers, NY; U.S. Private, pg. 514

Lewis-Gordon, Danna, Pres. & Chief Exec. Officer--Surfer Publications, Inc., Dana Point, CA; U.S. Private, pg. 417

Lewis, Alan G., Chief Exec. Officer--Gerber Plumbing Fixtures Corporation, Chicago, IL; U.S. Private, pg. 449

Lewis, Alan G., Chief Exec. Officer--Kokomo Sanitary Pottery Corp., Kokomo, IN; U.S. Private, pg. 449

Lewis, Bill, Chm. Bd. & Chief Exec. Officer--Staffing Solutions, Boulder, CO; U.S. Private, pg. 1028

Lewis, Byron E., Chm. Bd. & Chief Exec. Officer--Uniworld Group, Inc., New York, NY; U.S. Private, pg. 1128

Lewis, Charles, Chm, Pres, & Chief Exec. Officer--The Check Store, Lakewood, CO; U.S. Public, pg. 785

Lewis, David J., Chief Exec. Officer--Cogentrix Incorporated, Charlotte, NC; U.S. Private, pg. 249

Lewis, Edward, Chief Exec. Officer--Essence Communications Inc., New York, NY; U.S. Private, pg. 383

Lewis, Freida Z., Pres. & Chief Exec. Officer--Fleet Brokerage Securities Corp., New York, NY; U.S. Public, pg. 649

Lewis, Jerald P., Pres. & Chief Exec. Officer--First American Trust Co., Santa Ana, CA; U.S. Public, pg. 626

Lewis, Leslie B., Chm. Bd., Pres. & Chief Exec. Officer--Asahi/America, Inc., Malden, MA; U.S. Public, pg. 137

Lewis, M.D., Chm. & Chief Exec. Officer--Northwestern Growth Corp., Sioux Falls, SD; U.S. Public, pg. 1201

Lewis, M.D., Chm. & Chief Exec. Officer--Northwestern Energy Corp., Huron, SD; U.S. Public, pg. 1201

Lewis, M.D., Chm. & Chief Exec. Officer--Nekota Resources Inc., Huron, SD; U.S. Public, pg. 1201

Lewis, Martin R., Chm. Bd. & Chief Exec. Officer--Williamhouse-Regency, Inc., New York, NY; U.S. Public, pg. 89

Lewis, Merle D., Chm. Bd., Pres. & Chief Exec. Officer--Northwestern Public Service, Huron, SD; U.S. Public, pg. 1200

Lewis, Michael, Pres. & Chief Exec. Officer--ILD Communications, Inc., Carrollton, TX; U.S. Public, pg. 887

Lewis, Paul, Chief Exec. Officer--Tate & Lyle Inc., Wilmington, DE; Int'l, pg. 1357

Lewis, Peter B., Chm. Bd., Pres. & Chief Exec. Officer--The Progressive Corporation, Cleveland, OH; U.S. Public, pg. 1334

Lewis, R. Jack, Jr., Pres. & Chief Exec. Officer--Lewis Brothers Bakeries, Inc., Evansville, IN; U.S. Private, pg. 665

Lewis, R. Jack, Jr., Pres., Chief Oper. & Exec. Officer--Hartford Bakery, Inc., Evansville, IN; U.S. Private, pg. 665

Lewis, Richard H., Chm. Bd., Pres., Chief Exec. & Fin. Officer & Treas.--Prima Energy Corporation, Denver, CO; U.S. Public, pg. 1325

Lewis, William, Chm. Bd., Pres. & Chief Exec. Officer--Career Blazers Inc., New York, NY; U.S. Private, pg. 209

Lewton, Larry L., Pres. & Chief Exec. Officer--Boulevard Bancorp, Inc., Chicago, IL; U.S. Public, pg. 1680

Lewton, Marvin, Chief Exec. Officer--Lewtan Industries Corp., Hartford, CT; U.S. Private, pg. 666

Lewy, Glen S., Chief Exec. Officer--Fuji-Wolfensohn International, New York, NY; Int'l, pg. 519

Ley, Anthony J., Chm. Bd., Pres. & Chief Exec. Officer--Harmonic Lightwaves, Sunnyvale, CA; U.S. Public, pg. 788

Ley, James A., Pres. & Chief Exec. Officer--First Vantage-Tennessee, Knoxville, TN; U.S. Public, pg. 641

Lezin, Jeremy, Pres. & Chief Exec. Officer--Salz Leathers, Inc., Santa Cruz, CA; U.S. Private, pg. 963

Liang, Marcel, Chm. Bd. & Chief Exec. Officer--ASI Corp., Fremont, CA; U.S. Private, pg. 8

Liao, Duke, Chm. Bd., Pres. & Chief Exec. Officer--Liuski International, Inc., Norcross, GA; U.S. Public, pg. 1005

Liautaud, James P., Chm. Bd & Chief Exec. Officer--Capsonic Group, Inc., Elgin, IL; U.S. Private, pg. 207

Liban, G., Chm. Bd. & Chief Exec. Officer--Heresite Protective Coatings Inc., Manitowoc, WI; U.S. Private, pg. 523

Libertiny, Attila G., Chm. Bd., Pres. & Chief Exec. Officer--Seneca Falls Technology Group, Seneca Falls, NY; *U.S. Private*, pg. 984

Licht, J.M., Pres. & Chief Exec. Officer--Duraco Products, Inc., Streamwood, IL; *U.S. Private*, pg. 348

Lichtenberger, H. William, Chm. Bd. & Chief Exec. Officer--Praxair Inc., Danbury, CT; *U.S. Public*, pg. 1319

Lichtenberger, Rudi, Pres. & Chief Exec. Officer--EDS Fides, Zurich, Switzerland; *U.S. Public*, pg. 570

Lick, Fred, Jr., Chm. Bd., Pres. & Chief Exec. Officer--Central Reserve Life of North America Insurance Co., Strongsville, OH; *U.S. Public*, pg. 326

Liddell, W.K., Pres., Chief Exec. & Chief Oper. Officer--Irex Corporation, Lancaster, PA; *U.S. Public*, pg. 913

Liddy, Richard A., Chm. Bd., Pres. & Chief Exec. Officer--General American Life Insurance Co., Saint Louis, MO; *U.S. Private*, pg. 443

Lidow, Alexander, Co-Chief Exec. Officer--International Rectifier Corporation, El Segundo, CA; *U.S. Public*, pg. 906

Lidow, Derek B., Co-Chief Exec. Officer--International Rectifier Corporation, El Segundo, CA; *U.S. Public*, pg. 906

Liebau, F. Jack, Pres. & Chief Exec. Officer--Patriot American Hospitality Operating Company, San Mateo, CA; *U.S. Public*, pg. 1265

Liebenow, Larry, Pres. & Chief Exec. Officer--Quaker Fabric Corporation, Fall River, MA; *U.S. Public*, pg. 1347

Lieberg, Eric N., Pres., Chief Fin. Officer & Exec. V.P.--Rundel Products, Inc., Portland, OR; *U.S. Private*, pg. 951

Liebergesell, Rolf K., Chm. Bd., Pres. & Chief Exec. Officer & Chief Oper. Officer--Farrel Corporation, Ansonia, CT; *U.S. Public*, pg. 614

Lieberthal, Gary, Chm. & Chief Exec. Officer--Columbia TriStar Television, Culver City, CA; *Int'l*, pg. 1282

Liebowitz, Leo, Chm. Bd. & Chief Exec. Officer--Getty Petroleum Marketing Inc., Jericho, NY; *U.S. Public*, pg. 740

Liee, Chi, Chief Exec. Officer--Tainan Spinning Co., Ltd., Tai-nan, Taiwan; *Int'l*, pg. 1347

Lienau, Anthony, Chm. Bd. & Chief Exec. Officer--Trend Offset Printing Services, Los Alamitos, CA; *U.S. Private*, pg. 1099

Lieppe, Charles, Pres. & Chief Exec. Officer--DBT Online, Inc., Las Vegas, NV; *U.S. Public*, pg. 472

Lieppe, Charles, Pres. & Chief Exec. Officer--Berol Corporation, Brentwood, TN; *U.S. Public*, pg. 1178

Lietz, Andrew E., Pres. & Chief Exec. Officer--Hadco Corporation, Salem, NH; *U.S. Public*, pg. 773

Light, Nathan, Chm. Bd., Pres. & Chief Exec. Officer--Sterling Inc., Akron, OH; *Int'l*, pg. 1248

Liguori, Frank N., Chm. Bd. & Chief Exec. Officer--Olsten Corporation, Melville, NY; *U.S. Public*, pg. 1220

Liguori, Frank N., Chm. Bd. & Chief Exec. Officer--Olsten Health Services, Melville, NY; *U.S. Public*, pg. 1221

Likarish, John, Chief Exec. Officer--Encycle/Texas, Inc., Corpus Christi, TX; *U.S. Public*, pg. 138

Lilius, Mikael, Pres. & Chief Exec. Officer--Incentive AB, Stockholm, Sweden; *Int'l*, pg. 666

Lillis, Charles, Pres. & Chief Exec. Officer--U S West Media Group, Englewood, CO; *U.S. Public*, pg. 1689

Lilly, Ed, Pres. & Chief Exec. Officer--Serta, Inc., Itasca, IL; *U.S. Private*, pg. 985

Lim, Barry, Chief Exec.--Esselte Meto (Malaysia) SDN BHD, Kuala Lumpur, Malaysia; *Int'l*, pg. 461

Lim, H.P., Pres. & Chief Exec. Officer--Baker Engineering, NY, Inc., Elmsford, NY; *U.S. Public*, pg. 168

Lima, Marcos, Pres. & Chief Exec. Officer--CODELCO Chile (Corporacion Nacional Del Cobre De Chile), Santiago, Chile; *Int'l*, pg. 302

Lin, Feng-Liang, Chm. Bd., Pres. & Chief Exec. Officer--Payless Car Rental System, Inc., Saint Petersburg, FL; *U.S. Private*, pg. 844

Lin, Frank C., Chm. Bd., Pres. & Chief Exec. Officer--Trident Microsystems, Inc., Mountain View, CA; *U.S. Public*, pg. 1637

Lin, Jack, Pres. & Chief Exec. Officer--National Technical Systems, Inc., Calabasas, CA; *U.S. Public*, pg. 1161

Lin, Zhang Fu, Chief Exec.--Suzhou Hongda Enzyme Co. Ltd., Jiangsu, China; *Int'l*, pg. 989

Linbeck, Leo E., Jr., Chm. Bd. & Chief Exec. Officer--Linbeck Construction Corp, Houston, TX; *U.S. Private*, pg. 667

Lincoln, H.G.Y., Chief Exec. Officer-Europe--Howden Group Plc, Renfrew, United Kingdom; *Int'l*, pg. 636

Lincoln, John, Pres. & Chief Exec. Officer--Revenue Collection Group World Headquarters, San Diego, CA; *U.S. Public*, pg. 466

Lincoln, Larry W., Pres. & Chief Exec. Officer--Mark III Industries, Ocala, FL; *U.S. Private*, pg. 704

Lincoln, Lucian A., Chm. & Chief Exec. Officer--Freeman Energy Corporation, Springfield, IL; *U.S. Public*, pg. 709

Lind, Geoffrey E., Chm. Bd. & Chief Exec. Officer--UMB Bank of the West, N.A., Colorado Springs, CO; *U.S. Public*, pg. 1654

Lind, Steven R., Pres. & Chief Exec. Officer--Top Air Manufacturing, Inc., Cedar Falls, IA; *U.S. Public*, pg. 1621

Lindahl, Goran, Pres. & Chief Exec. Officer--ABB Asea Brown Boveri (Holding) Ltd., Zurich, Switzerland; *Int'l*, pg. 1

Lindahl, John, Chm. Bd. & Chief Exec. Officer--State Industries Inc., Ashland City, TN; *U.S. Private*, pg. 1036

Lindal, Robert W., Chm. Bd. & Chief Exec. Officer--Lindal Cedar Homes, Inc., Seattle, WA; *U.S. Public*, pg. 998

Linde, K., Pres. & Chief Exec. Officer--Principal Health Care, Inc., Rockville, MD; *U.S. Private*, pg. 885

Lindegaard, Jorgen, Pres. & Chief Exec. Officer--GN Great Nordic Ltd., Copenhagen, Denmark; *Int'l*, pg. 536

Lindelow, Jan, Pres. & Chief Exec. Officer--Trivoli Systems Inc., Austin, TX; *U.S. Public*, pg. 896

Lindelow, Jan, Pres. & Chief Exec. Officer--Trivoli Systems, Indianapolis, IN; *U.S. Public*, pg. 896

Lindemann, D.L., Pres. & Chief Exec. Officer--Citizens Gas & Coke Utility, Indianapolis, IN; *U.S. Private*, pg. 241

Lindemann, Glen W., Pres. & Chief Exec. Officer--Figgie International Inc., Cleveland, OH; *U.S. Public*, pg. 622

Lindenbergh, J.H.M., Chm. Bd. & Chief Exec. Officer--ING Barings, London, United Kingdom; *Int'l*, pg. 650

Lindermann, George L., Chm. Bd. & Chief Exec. Officer--Southern Union Company, Austin, TX; *U.S. Public*, pg. 1491

Lindig, Bill M., Pres. & Chief Exec. Officer--Sysco Corporation, Houston, TX; *U.S. Public*, pg. 1550

Lindner, Carl H., Chm. Bd. & Chief Exec. Officer--American Financial Group, Cincinnati, OH; *U.S. Public*, pg. 74

Lindquist, Berthold, Pres. & Chief Exec. Officer--Gambro AB, Lund, Sweden; *Int'l*, pg. 666

Lindquist, Sonny, Chief Exec. Officer-Forsheda--John Crane Polymer Division, Abingdon, United Kingdom; *Int'l*, pg. 1338

Lindsay, James W., Chief Exec. Officer--Ag Processing Inc., A Cooperative, Omaha, NE; *U.S. Private*, pg. 26

Lindsay, Tim, Chief Exec. Officer--Lowe Howard-Spink, London, United Kingdom; *U.S. Private*, pg. 678

Lindsay, Winston S., III, Chm. Bd. & Chief Exec. Officer--Lindsay Manufacturing Inc., Ponca City, OK; *U.S. Private*, pg. 668

Lindsey, Paul S., Chm. Bd. & Chief Exec. Officer--All Star Gas Corporation, Lebanon, MO; *U.S. Private*, pg. 35

Linford, Jim, Pres. & Chief Exec. Officer--Gulf States, Inc., Freeport, TX; *U.S. Private*, pg. 487

Ling, John, Pres. & Chief Exec. Officer--Bettcher Manufacturing Corp., Cleveland, OH; *U.S. Private*, pg. 169

Ling, Zhi, Co-Chief Exec. Officer--Bank of China, Beijing, China; *Int'l*, pg. 152

Linier, J. Hicks, Chm. Bd. & Pres.--Oxford Industries, Inc., Atlanta, GA; *U.S. Public*, pg. 1239

Liniger, Gail, Chief Exec. Officer--RE/MAX International, Inc., Englewood, CO; *U.S. Private*, pg. 912

Link, Norman, Chm. Bd. & Chief Exec. Officer--O.P. Link Handle Company, Salem, IN; *U.S. Private*, pg. 668

Link, William J., Ph.D., V.P., Chm. & Chief Exec. Officer--Chiron Vision--Chiron Corporation, Emeryville, CA; *U.S. Public*, pg. 349

Linsalata, Frank, Chief Exec. Officer--Kathabar Incorporated, Somerset, NJ; *U.S. Private*, pg. 609

Linsmayer, J. Nicholas, Pres.--Villaume Industries, Inc., Saint Paul, MN; *U.S. Private*, pg. 1140

Linster, John, Pres. & Chief Exec. Officer--Pentech International, Inc., Edison, NJ; *U.S. Public*, pg. 1274

Linton, Larry C., Chm. Bd. & Chief Exec. Officer--Landa, Inc., Portland, OR; *U.S. Private*, pg. 646

Lipke, Brian J., Chm. Bd., Pres. & Chief Exec. Officer--Gibraltar Steel Corp., Buffalo, NY; *U.S. Public*, pg. 742

Lipkin, Gerald H., Chm. Bd., Pres. & Chief Exec. Officer--Valley National Bancorp, Wayne, NJ; *U.S. Public*, pg. 1705

Lipner, William E., Chm. Bd, Pres. & Chief Exec. Officer--NFO Research, Inc., Greenwich, CT; *U.S. Public*, pg. 1146

Lippe, George, Pres. & Chief Exec. Officer--Trammell Crow Company, Dallas, TX; *U.S. Public*, pg. 1628

Lipps, Ben, Dr., Pres. & Chief Exec. Officer--Fresenius Medical Care, Inc., Lexington, MA; *Int'l*, pg. 505

Lipscomb, Michael S., Pres. & Chief Exec. Officer--Argo-Tech Corporation, Cleveland, OH; *U.S. Private*, pg. 81

Lipson, David S., Pres. & Chief Exec. Officer--Integrated Systems Consulting Group, Wayne, PA; *U.S. Public*, pg. 1425

Lipson, Mark L., Chm. Bd. & Chief Exec. Officer--Northstar Investment Management Corporation, Greenwich, CT; *U.S. Public*, pg. 1375

Lipton, Ivan, Pres. & Chief Exec. Officer--Strawberries Inc., Milford, MA; *U.S. Private*, pg. 1046

Lisanke, Vincent P., Pres. & Chief Exec. Officer--American Express Credit Corporation, Wilmington, DE; *U.S. Public*, pg. 74

Lisauskas, A.J., Pres. & Chief Exec. Officer--Spartech Plastics, Portage, WI; *U.S. Public*, pg. 1496

Lisker, Lawrence, Chief Exec. Officer & Treas.--Antwerp Diamond Distributors Inc., New York, NY; *U.S. Private*, pg. 76

Liskowski, Fred J., Pres. & Chief Exec. Officer--First Western Trust Services Co., New Castle, PA; *U.S. Public*, pg. 642

Liss, Victor, Vice Chm., Pres. & Chief Exec. Officer--Trans-Lux Corporation, Norwalk, CT; *U.S. Public*, pg. 1628

Lister, Richard L., Pres. & Chief Exec. Officer--Zemex Corporation, Toronto, Canada; *Int'l*, pg. 1523

Liszt, Howard, Chief Exec. Officer--Campbell Mithun Esty, Minneapolis, MN; *U.S. Private*, pg. 204

Little, C.A., Chief Exec. Officer & Mng. Dir.--British Mohair Spinners Limited, Bradford, United Kingdom; *Int'l*, pg. 219

Little, Chris, Chief Exec. Officer--Century Life, London, United Kingdom; *Int'l*, pg. 685

Little, Roger G., Chm. Bd., Pres. & Chief Exec. Officer--Spire Corporation, Bedford, MA; *U.S. Public*, pg. 1499

Little, William G., Chm. Bd., Pres. & Chief Exec. Officer--The West Company, Incorporated, Lionville, PA; *U.S. Public*, pg. 1755

Littlejohn, Peter J., Chief Exec. Officer--BHP Information Technology, Melbourne, Australia; *Int'l*, pg. 225

Litwinski, Jan, Pres. & Chief Exec. Officer--Polskie Linie Lotnicze LOT S.A., Warsaw, Poland; *Int'l*, pg. 1062

Liu, Lee, Chm. Bd. & Chief Exec. Officer--IES Industries Inc., Cedar Rapids, IA; *U.S. Public*, pg. 855

Liu, Lee, Chm. Bd. & Chief Exec. Officer--IES Utilities Inc., Cedar Rapids, IA; *U.S. Public*, pg. 855

Liu, Steve, Pres. & Chief Exec. Officer--Esprit Systems, Inc., San Jose, CA; *U.S. Private*, pg. 383

Liuzzi, R.C., Pres. & Chief Exec. Officer--CF Industries, Inc., Long Grove, IL; *U.S. Private*, pg. 193

Livermore, Curtis, Chief Exec. Officer--Laidlaw Corporation, Scottsdale, AZ; *U.S. Private*, pg. 642

Livingston, Phillip K., Chm. Bd. & Chief Exec. Officer--Deposit Guaranty National Bank of Louisiana, Hammond, LA; *U.S. Public*, pg. 500

Livingston, Robert W., Chm. Bd., Pres. & Chief Exec. Officer--GB Holdings, Jurong, Singapore; *Int'l*, pg. 531

Livingston, Robert W., Chief Exec. Officer--Grand Banks Yachts Sdn. Bhd., Pasir Gudang, Malaysia; *Int'l*, pg. 531

Livingston, W. Curtis, III, Pres., Chief Exec. Officer--Pacific American Income Shares, Inc., Pasadena, CA; *U.S. Public*, pg. 1247

Lizza, Joseph R., Pres. & Chief Exec. Officer--Fairfax Savings Bank, Baltimore, MD; *U.S. Public*, pg. 1543

Ljungberg, Robert, Chm. Bd., Pres., Chief Exec. & Chief Oper. Officer--Ultra Tool & Plastics, Inc., Amherst, NY; *U.S. Private*, pg. 1116

Lloyd, Carmen L., Pres. & Chief Exec. Officer--Canadian Marconi Company, Montreal, Canada; *Int'l*, pg. 545

Lloyd, D.W., Chief Exec.-Ceramic Div.--Cookson Matthey Ceramics, West Chester, PA; *Int'l*, pg. 714

Lloyd, Jack M., Chm. Bd., Pres. & Chief Exec. Officer--DenAmerica Corp., Scottsdale, AZ; *U.S. Public*, pg. 498

Lo Alker, Pauline, Pres. & Chief Exec. Officer--Network Peripherals Inc., Milpitas, CA; *U.S. Public*, pg. 1169

Lo, Victor Chung Wing, Chm. Bd. & Chief Exec. Officer--Gold Peak Industries (Holdings) Limited, Kwai Chung, Hong Kong; *Int'l*, pg. 537

Loback, Donald R., Chm. Bd. & Chief Exec. Officer--Continental Homes Holding Corp., Scottsdale, AZ; *U.S. Public*, pg. 440

Lobanoff, Mark, Pres. & Chief Exec. Officer--NSK-Autoliv, Inc., Bloomfield Hills, MI; *Int'l*, pg. 439

Lobbia, John E., Chm. Bd. & Chief Exec. Officer--DTE Energy Company, Detroit, MI; *U.S. Public*, pg. 475

Lockhart, J.W., Chm. Bd. & Chief Exec. Officer--Morgan Grenfell Laurie Ltd., London, United Kingdom; *Int'l*, pg. 405

Lockhart, Michael D., Chm. Bd. & Chief Exec. Officer--General Signal Corporation, Stamford, CT; *U.S. Public*, pg. 726

Lockwood, Earl F., Chm. Bd., Pres. & Chief Exec. Officer--Betac International Corporation, Alexandria, VA; *U.S. Private*, pg. 140

Lockwood, Robert, Pres. & Chief Exec. Officer--Our Sunday Visitor, Inc., Huntington, IN; *U.S. Private*, pg. 821

Locurto, Wayne W., Pres. & Chief Exec. Officer--News America Marketing, Norwalk, CT; *Int'l*, pg. 925

Loden, D. John, Pres. & Chief Exec. Officer--FCB HealthCare, San Francisco, CA; *U.S. Public*, pg. 1641

Loeb, Thomas F., Chief Exec. Officer--Mellon Capital Management Corporation (MFSC 1085

Loeffler, Martin H., Chm. Bd., Pres. & Chief Exec. Officer--Amphenol Corporation, Wallingford, CT; *U.S. Private*, pg. 629

Loewen, Don, Chief Exec. Officer--Saskatchewan Wheat Pool, Regina, Canada; *Int'l*, pg. 1195

Loewen, Raymond L., Chm. Bd. & Chief Exec. Officer--The Loewen Group, Inc., Burnaby, Canada; *Int'l*, pg. 814

Logan, Don, Pres. & Chief Exec. Officer--People, New York, NY; *U.S. Public*, pg. 1613

Logan, Oran, Chief Exec. Officer--M&W, Gibson City, IL; *U.S. Public*, pg. 35

Loghry, Gerald, Chief Exec. Officer--Fleischli Oil Company, Inc., Cheyenne, WY; *U.S. Private*, pg. 410

Loghry, Richard M., Pres. & Chief Exec. Officer--Mason & Hanger Corporation, Inc., Lexington, KY; *U.S. Private*, pg. 711

Lohaus, Peter, Pres. & Chief Exec. Officer--Tetko, Inc., Briarcliff Manor, NY; *U.S. Private*, pg. 1078

Lohman, Gordon R., Chm. Bd. & Chief Exec. Officer--Amsted Industries Incorporated, Chicago, IL; *U.S. Private*, pg. 68

Lois, George, Chm. Bd. & Co-Chief Exec. Officer--Lois/USA Inc., New York, NY; *U.S. Public*, pg. 1011

Lois, George, Co-Chm. Bd., Chief Exec. Officer & Worldwide Creative Dir.--Lois/EJL New York, New York, NY; *U.S. Public*, pg. 1011

Lokey, James, Pres. & Chief Exec. Officer--Downey Financial Corp., Newport Beach, CA; *U.S. Public*, pg. 525

Lokey, James W., Pres. & Chief Exec. Officer--Downey Savings & Loan Association, F.A., Newport Beach, CA; *U.S. Public*, pg. 526

Lombard, George E., Pres. & Chief Exec. Officer--Lombard Architectural Precast Prod. Co, Alsip, IL; *U.S. Private*, pg. 673

Lombardi, Carl A., Chm. Bd. & Chief Exec. Officer--SpaceLabs Medical, Inc., Redmond, WA; *U.S. Public*, pg. 1494

Lombardi, Paul V., Pres. & Chief Exec. Officer--DynCorp, Reston, VA; *U.S. Private*, pg. 351

Lomelin Guillen, Jaime, Pres. & Chief Exec. Officer--Industrias Penoles S.A. de C.V., Cuauhtemoc, Mexico; *Int'l*, pg. 677

Lomelin, Carlos Salazar, Chief Exec. Officer--Femsa Cerveza S.A. de CV, Monterrey, Mexico; *Int'l*, pg. 496

Loncharich, Tim, Pres. & Chief Exec. Officer--Snelling Personnel Services, Dallas, TX; *U.S. Private*, pg. 1010

Londchal, Marc, Pres. & Chief Exec. Officer--Tredi, Paris, France; *Int'l*, pg. 459

London, J.P., Dr., Chm. Bd., Pres. & Chief Exec. Officer--CACI International Inc, Arlington, VA; *U.S. Public*, pg. 272

London, Terry E., Pres. & Chief Exec. Officer--Gaylord Entertainment Co., Nashville, TN; *U.S. Public*, pg. 704

Long, David R., Pres. & Chief Exec. Officer--Snokist Growers, Yakima, WA; *U.S. Private*, pg. 1011

Long, Donald J., Chm. Bd. & Chief Exec. Officer--Imperial, Inc., Green Bay, WI; *U.S. Private*, pg. 558

Long, Jonathan R., Pres., Chief Exec. Officer & Chief Fin. Officer--J.E. Higgins Lumber Co., Concord, CA; *U.S. Private*, pg. 527

Long, Robert A., Pres. & Chief Exec. Officer--J.E. Dunn Equities, Inc., Kansas City, MO; *U.S. Private*, pg. 347

Long, Robert M., Chm. Bd. & Chief Exec. Officer--Longs Drug Stores Corporation, Walnut Creek, CA; *U.S. Public, pg. 1013*
Long, Robert R., Chm. Bd. & Chief Exec. Officer--SunTrust Banks of Georgia, Inc., Atlanta, GA; *U.S. Public*, pg. 1538
Long, Ronald C., Pres. & Chief Exec. Officer--Independent Bank-East Michigan, Caro, MI; *U.S. Public*, pg. 874
Long, William J., Pres. & Chief Exec. Officer--Sprayroq, Inc., Birmingham, AL; *U.S. Public*, pg. 882
Long, Yeo Khee, Asst. Chief Exec.-Corp. Svcs. & Mktg.--Singapore Tourist Promotion Board, Singapore, Singapore; *Int'l*, pg. 1253
Long, Zelma, Chm. Bd., Pres. & Chief Exec. Officer--Simi Winery, Healdsburg, CA; *Int'l*, pg. 781
Longaberger, Dave, Chief Exec. Officer--The Longaberger Company, Dresden, OH; *U.S. Private*, pg. 675
Longacre, Kenneth A., Chief Exec. Officer--Farm & Home Oil Company, Telford, PA; *U.S. Private*, pg. 394
Longee, Robert, Chief Oper. Officer--Univar Europe N.V., Croydon, United Kingdom; *Int'l*, pg. 1147
Longfield, Craig N., Chm. Bd., Pres. & Chief Exec. Officer--PacifiCorp Financial Services, Inc., Portland, OR; *U.S. Public*, pg. 1252
Longfield, William H., Chm. Bd. & Chief Exec. Officer--C.R. Bard, Inc., Murray Hill, NJ; *U.S. Public*, pg. 189
Longley, Charles, Chief Exec. Officer--DHL International (Hong Kong) Ltd., Wan Chai, Hong Kong; *U.S. Private*, pg. 302
Longmire, Dennis B., Chm. Bd. & Chief Exec. Officer--Darling International, Inc, Irving, TX; *U.S. Public*, pg. 484
Longstaff, G. Geoffrey, Pres. & Chief Exec. Officer--Regions Bank/Orlando, Longwood, FL; *U.S. Public*, pg. 1372
Looby, Philip, Chief Oper. Officer--Bayer Clothing Group, New York, NY; *U.S. Private*, pg. 124
Loop, Gary, Chief Oper. Officer--Neste Polyester Inc., Fort Smith, AR; *Int'l*, pg. 913
Lopker, Karl F., Chief Exec. Officer & Sec.--QAD Inc, Carpinteria, CA; *U.S. Public*, pg. 1345
Lorberbaum, Jeffery, Pres. & Chief Exec. Officer--Aladdin Mills, Dalton, GA; *U.S. Public*, pg. 1121
Lorch, George A., Chm. Bd. & Chief Exec. Officer--Armstrong World Industries, Inc., Lancaster, PA; *U.S. Public*, pg. 131
LoRe, Linda, Pres. & Chief Exec. Officer--Giorgio Beverly Hills, Santa Monica, CA; *U.S. Public*, pg. 1331
Lorenzo, Jorge, Chief Exec. Officer--Bagley S.A., Buenos Aires, Argentina; *Int'l*, pg. 379
Lorenzoni, Mario, V.P. & Chief Exec. Officer-Chiron Biocine S.p.A.--Chiron Corporation, Emeryville, CA; *U.S. Public*, pg. 349
Loring, Scott R., Chm. Bd., Pres. & Chief Exec. Officer--Heald Colleges, San Francisco, CA; *U.S. Private*, pg. 514
Lotan, Noam, Pres. & Chief Exec. Officer--MRV Communications, Inc., Chatsworth, CA; *U.S. Public*, pg. 1027
Lotter, Charles R., Exec. V.P., Gen. Counsel & Sec.--JC Penney Company, Inc., Plano, TX; *U.S. Public*, pg. 916
Lotter, John G.H., Chm. Bd. & Chief Exec. Officer--H.C. Miller Company, Milwaukee, WI; *U.S. Private*, pg. 747
Loubet, Henry R., Chief Exec. Officer--United HealthCare of Nevada, Inc., Las Vegas, NV; *U.S. Public*, pg. 1678
Loubet, Henry R., Chief Exec. Officer--United HealthCare of Oregon, Inc., Minnetonka, MN; *U.S. Public*, pg. 1678
Loucks, Vernon R., Jr., Chm. Bd. & Chief Exec. Officer--Baxter International Inc., Deerfield, IL; *U.S. Public*, pg. 196
Loudemilk, Billy R., Pres. & Chief Exec. Officer--Regions Bank/Gilmer County, Ellijay, GA; *U.S. Public*, pg. 1372
Louttit, William, Chm. & Chief Exec. Officer-Greater N.Y. Metro Region--The Great Atlantic & Pacific Tea Company, Inc., Montvale, NJ; *Int'l*, pg. 1375
Lovejoy, W. Scott, Chief Exec. Officer--Paramount Petroleum Corp., Paramount, CA; *U.S. Private*, pg. 838
Lovell, Alan, Chief Exec. Officer--Costain Group PLC, London, United Kingdom; *Int'l*, pg. 336
Lovett, David F.G., Chief Exec.-Heavy Bldg. Materials International--Blue Circle Industries PLC, London, United Kingdom; *Int'l*, pg. 197
Lovett, Donald R., Chm. Bd., Pres. & Chief Exec. Officer--AMCORE Bank, Rock River Valley, Dixon, IL; *U.S. Public*, pg. 64
Low, Fowler H., Chm. & Chief Exec. Officer--Johnston & Murphy Co., Nashville, TN; *U.S. Public*, pg. 728
Lowden, Paul W., Chm. Bd. & Chief Exec. Officer--Santa Fe Gaming Corporation, Las Vegas, NV; *U.S. Public*, pg. 1432
Lowder, Robert E., Chm. Bd. & Chief Exec. Officer--The Colonial BancGroup, Inc., Montgomery, AL; *U.S. Public*, pg. 400
Lowder, Robert E., Chm. Bd. & Chief Exec. Officer--Colonial Bank, Montgomery, AL; *U.S. Public*, pg. 400
Lowe, Don, Chief Exec. Officer--Franchise Services, Inc., Mission Viejo, CA; *U.S. Private*, pg. 423
Lowe, Don F., Chief Exec. Officer--Sir Speedy, Inc., Mission Viejo, CA; *U.S. Private*, pg. 423
Lowell, David, Pres. & Chief Exec. Officer--Diversified Communications, Portland, ME; *U.S. Private*, pg. 336
Lowenstein, Irwin L., Chm. Bd. & Chief Exec. Officer--Rhodes, Inc., Atlanta, GA; *U.S. Public*, pg. 805
Lowenthal, A.G., Chm. Bd. & Chief Exec. Officer--Fahnestock Viner Holdings Inc., Toronto, Canada; *Int'l*, pg. 476
Lower, James, Pres. & Chief Exec. Officer--Vision One, Norwich, CT; *U.S. Private*, pg. 1141
Lowery, Lang, Chm. Bd. & Chief Exec. Officer--Anacomp, Inc., Indianapolis, IN; *U.S. Public*, pg. 106
Lowman, George F., Chm. Bd. & Chief Exec. Officer--Farrell Lines Incorporated, New York, NY; *U.S. Private*, pg. 397
Lowrance, Darrell J., Chm. Bd., Pres. & Chief Exec. Officer--Lowrance Electronics, Inc., Tulsa, OK; *U.S. Public*, pg. 1015
Loyd, Paul B. Jr., Chm. Bd., Pres. & Chief Exec. Officer--Reading & Bates Corporation, Houston, TX; *U.S. Public*, pg. 1354
Loyez, Jean-Hugues, Chm. Bd., Chief Exec. Officer & Mng. Dir.--Castorama Dubois Investissements S.C.A., Templemars, France; *Int'l*, pg. 275
Lozier, Allan, Chief Exec. Officer--Lozier Corporation, Omaha, NE; *U.S. Private*, pg. 679
Lu, Eugene, Chm. Bd., Pres. & Chief Exec. Officer--Advanced Logic Research, Inc., Irvine, CA; *U.S. Public*, pg. 703
Luard, Roger, Grp. Chief Exec.--Flextech p.l.c., London, United Kingdom; *Int'l*, pg. 495
Lubar, Sheldon B., Chm. Bd. & Chief Exec. Officer--Christiana Companies, Inc., Milwaukee, WI; *U.S. Public*, pg. 352
Lubin, William J., Chief Exec. Officer & Exec. V.P.-Commercial Managed Care--PHP Healthcare Corporation, Reston, VA; *U.S. Public*, pg. 1241
Lubner, R., Chm. & Chief Exec. Officer--Plate Glass & Shutterprufe Industries Limited, Satonwold, South Africa; *Int'l*, pg. 1287
Luborsky, Brian, Pres. & Chief Exec. Officer--Premier Salons International, Edina, MN; *U.S. Private*, pg. 881
Luca, Raymond J., Pres. & Chief Exec. Officer--LogEtronics Corporation, Springfield, VA; *U.S. Public*, pg. 6
Lucas, George, Chm. Bd. & Chief Exec. Officer--Lucasfilm Ltd., San Rafael, CA; *U.S. Private*, pg. 679
Lucchese, Alphonse M., Chm. Bd. & Chief Exec. Officer--Davox Corp., Westford, MA; *U.S. Public*, pg. 488
Lucchetti, David J., Pres. & Chief Exec. Officer--Pacific Coast Building Products Inc., Sacramento, CA; *U.S. Private*, pg. 830
Luddy, Robert, Pres. & Chief Exec. Officer--Captive-Aire Systems, Inc., Youngsville, NC; *U.S. Private*, pg. 207
Ludes, John T., Chm. Bd. & Chief Exec. Officer--ABCO, Inc., Old Greenwich, CT; *U.S. Public*, pg. 674
Ludington, Ivan, Jr., Chm Bd. & Chief Exec. Officer--Ludington News Co. Inc., Detroit, MI; *U.S. Private*, pg. 679
Ludlow, Stephen J., Pres. & Chief Exec. Officer--Veritas DGC Inc, Houston, TX; *U.S. Private*, pg. 1136
Ludt, Steve G., Pres., Chief Exec. Officer & Treas.--Columbian Rope Company, Guntown, MS; *U.S. Private*, pg. 256
Ludwig, William, Pres. & Chief Exec. Officer--Rice Growers Association of California, West Sacramento, CA; *U.S. Private*, pg. 927
Luecke, David A., Pres. & Chief Exec. Officer--Riemeier Lumber Company, Inc., Cincinnati, OH; *U.S. Private*, pg. 930
Lugash, Murray, Chief Exec. Officer--Maxon Industries, Inc., Huntington Park, CA; *U.S. Private*, pg. 717
Luger, Donald R., Chm., Pres. & Chief Exec. Officer--Lockwood Greene Engineers, Inc., Spartanburg, SC; *Int'l*, pg. 633
Lukash, Seth, Chm. Bd. & Chief Exec. Officer--Ultimate Technology Corporation, Victor, NY; *U.S. Public*, pg. 1637
Lukash, Seth M., Chm. Bd., Pres. & Chief Exec. Officer--Tridex Corporation, Westport, CT; *U.S. Public*, pg. 1637
Luke, John A., Jr., Chm. Bd. & Chief Exec. Officer--Westvaco Corporation, New York, NY; *U.S. Public*, pg. 1762
Lukens, Max L., Chm. Bd., Pres. & Chief Exec. Officer--Baker Hughes Incorporated, Houston, TX; *U.S. Public*, pg. 165
Luksch, James A., Chm. Bd., Pres. & Chief Exec. Officer--Blonder-Tongue Laboratories, Inc., Old Bridge, NJ; *U.S. Public*, pg. 237
Lumme, Larry, Pres. & Chief Exec. Officer--Republic Automotive-AEA Division, Charlotte, NC; *U.S. Public*, pg. 1377
Lund, James E., Pres. & Chief Exec. Officer--BHA Group Holdings Inc., Kansas City, MO; *U.S. Public*, pg. 161
Lund, Olof, Pres. & Chief Exec. Officer--Celsius AB, Stockholm, Sweden; *Int'l*, pg. 276
Lund, Peter A., Pres. & Chief Exec. Officer--CBS Broadcast Group, New York, NY; *U.S. Public*, pg. 274
Lund, Peter A., Pres. & Chief Exec. Officer-CBS Television & Cable Grp.--CBS Television Network, New York, NY; *U.S. Public*, pg. 274
Lund, Richard, Pres. & Chief Exec. Officer--Farmington National Bank, Farmington, NH; *U.S. Public*, pg. 187
Lund, Russell T., III, Chm. Bd., Pres. & Chief Exec. Officer--Lund Food Holdings, Inc., Edina, MN; *U.S. Private*, pg. 680
Lund, Russell T., III, Pres. & Chief Exec. Officer--Lund's Inc., Edina, MN; *U.S. Private*, pg. 680
Lund, Soren H., Chief Exec. Officer--Novo Nordisk A/S, Kuala Lumpur, Malaysia; *Int'l*, pg. 989
Lund, Thomas C., Chief Exec. Officer--Customer Development Corporation, Peoria, IL; *U.S. Private*, pg. 298
Lund, Victor L., Chm. Bd. & Chief Exec. Officer--American Stores Company, Salt Lake City, UT; *U.S. Public*, pg. 92
Lundberg, Fredrik, Pres. & Chief Exec. Officer--L E Lundbergforetagen AB, Stockholm, Sweden; *Int'l*, pg. 820
Lundeen, Kenneth C., Pres. & Chief Exec. Officer--C.J. Langenfelder & Son, Inc., Baltimore, MD; *U.S. Private*, pg. 650
Lundgren, Per S., Chief Exec.--Novo Nordisk Pharmaceuticals, Inc., Plantation, FL; *Int'l*, pg. 987
Lundholm, Lars-Arne, Pres. & Chief Exec. Officer--Modernfold, Inc., New Castle, IN; *U.S. Private*, pg. 755
Lundin, Richard, Pres. & Chief Exec. Officer--Da-Lite Screen Company, Inc., Warsaw, IN; *U.S. Private*, pg. 306
Lundquist, Bo, Pres. & Chief Exec. Officer--Esselte AB, Solna, Sweden; *Int'l*, pg. 459
Lundstedt, David, Pres. & Chief Exec. Officer--Prestone Products Corporation, Danbury, CT; *U.S. Public*, pg. 51
Lundstrom, Edward L., Chief Exec. Officer--Sheldahl, Inc., Northfield, MN; *U.S. Public*, pg. 1465
Lundy, Larry E., Pres. & Chief Exec. Officer--Lundy Enterprises, Inc., New Orleans, LA; *U.S. Private*, pg. 681
Lung, Mervin D., Chm. Bd. & Chief Exec. Officer--Patrick Industries Inc., Elkhart, IN; *U.S. Public*, pg. 1264
Lunsford, W. Bruce, Chm. Bd., Pres. & Chief Exec. Officer--Vencor, Inc., Louisville, KY; *U.S. Public*, pg. 1711
Lupberger, Ed, Chm. Bd., Pres. & Chief Exec. Officer--Entergy Corporation, New Orleans, LA; *U.S. Public*, pg. 585
Lupberger, Edwin, Chm. Bd. & Chief Exec. Officer--Entergy Arkansas, Inc., Little Rock, AR; *U.S. Public*, pg. 586
Lupberger, Edwin, Chm. Bd. & Chief Exec. Officer--Entergy Mississippi, Inc., Jackson, MS; *U.S. Public*, pg. 586
Lupberger, Edwin, Chm. Bd. & Chief Exec. Officer--Entergy New Orleans, Inc., New Orleans, LA; *U.S. Public*, pg. 586
Lupient, James, Chief Exec. Officer--Lupient Automotive Group, Minneapolis, MN; *U.S. Private*, pg. 681
Lupinetti, Alexander R., Chm., Pres. & Chief Exec. Officer--CSP Inc., Billerica, MA; *U.S. Public*, pg. 283
Lurcott, Robert A., Pres. & Chief Exec. Officer--Henkel Corporation, King of Prussia, PA; *Int'l*, pg. 610
Luscher, B., Dr., Chief Exec. Officer--Ascom Tech AG, Bern, Switzerland; *Int'l*, pg. 86
Lusic, Ronald, Pres. & Chief Exec. Officer--Fleming Company, Waukesha, WI; *U.S. Public*, pg. 653
Luskin, Meyer, Chm. Bd., Pres. & Chief Exec. Officer--Scope Industries, Santa Monica, CA; *U.S. Public*, pg. 1444
Lussier, Gaetan, Pres. & Chief Exec. Officer--Culinar Inc., Montreal, Canada; *Int'l*, pg. 348
Lustbader, Edward E., Chm. Bd., Pres., Chief Exec. Officer & Treas.--The P.J. Carlin Construction Company, New Rochelle, NY; *U.S. Private*, pg. 211
Luter, Joseph W., III, Chm. Bd. & Chief Exec. Officer--Smithfield Foods, Inc., Norfolk, VA; *U.S. Public*, pg. 1479
Luter, Joseph W., III, Chm. Bd. & Chief Exec. Officer--Gwaltney of Smithfield, Ltd., Smithfield, VA; *U.S. Public*, pg. 1479
Luter, Joseph W., III, Chm. Bd. & Chief Exec. Officer--The Smithfield Packing Co., Inc., Smithfield, VA; *U.S. Public*, pg. 1479
Lutos, Matthew, Joint Chief Exec. Officer--Butler Lutos Sutton Wilkinson, London, United Kingdom; *Int'l*, pg. 237
Lutz, John C., Pres., Chief Exec. Officer & Chief Oper. Officer--Elco Textron, Rockford, IL; *U.S. Public*, pg. 1590
Lybarger, Stanley A., Pres. & Chief Exec. Officer--BOK Financial Corp., Tulsa, OK; *U.S. Public*, pg. 163
Lyman, James M., Chm. Bd., Pres. & Chief Exec. Officer--G.I. Plastek, Elyria, OH; *U.S. Private*, pg. 435
Lynaugh, N., Dr., Chief Exec. Officer--VG Analytical Ltd., Manchester, United Kingdom; *Int'l*, pg. 1110
Lynch, Alexander P., Co. Pres. & Co-Chief Exec. Officer--The Bridgeford Group, New York, NY; *Int'l*, pg. 674
Lynch, John, Chm. Bd. & Chief Exec. Officer--Towers Perrin, New York, NY; *U.S. Private*, pg. 1093
Lynch, John H., Pres. & Chief Exec. Officer--Knoll, Inc., Greenville, PA; *U.S. Private*, pg. 627
Lynch, Leland T., Chm., Chief Exec. Officer & Mng. Partner--Carmichael Lynch, Inc., Minneapolis, MN; *U.S. Private*, pg. 213
Lynn, Jeffrey G., Pres. & Chief Exec. Officer--Dunham's Athleisure Corporation, Waterford, MI; *U.S. Private*, pg. 346
Lynnes, R. Milton, Chm. & Chief Exec. Officer--Grant/Jacoby, Inc., Chicago, IL; *U.S. Private*, pg. 470
Lynton, Michael, Chm. Bd. & Chief Exec. Officer--Penguin Putnam Inc., New York, NY; *Int'l*, pg. 1027
Lyon, Wayne B., Chm. Bd., Pres. & Chief Exec. Officer--Furnishings International, Inc., Thomasville, NC; *U.S. Private*, pg. 431
Lyon, Wayne B., Chm. Bd., Pres. & Chief Exec. Officer--LifeStyle Furnishings International, Ltd., Thomasville, NC; *U.S. Private*, pg. 431
Lyons, Charles, Chm. Bd. & Chief Exec. Officer--Ascent Entertainment Group, Inc., Denver, CO; *U.S. Public*, pg. 138
Lyons, Edward M., Pres. & Chief Exec. Officer--Conley Frog/Switch & Forge Co., Memphis, TN; *U.S. Private*, pg. 263
Lyons, James F., Pres. & Chief Exec. Officer--GenRad, Inc., Westford, MA; *U.S. Public*, pg. 731
Lyons, James F., Pres. & Chief Exec. Officer--GenRad Electronic Manufacturing Tests Systems, Westford, MA; *U.S. Public*, pg. 731
Lyons, Michael J., Chm. Bd. & Chief Exec. Officer--Lyons Lavey Nickel Swift, Inc., New York, NY; *U.S. Public*, pg. 1224
Lyons, Richard, Chief Exec. Officer--Northridge Hospital-Sherman Way Campus, Van Nuys, CA; *U.S. Private*, pg. 1118
Lyons, Stuart, Pres. & Chief Exec. Officer--Royal Doulton Plc., Stoke on Trent, United Kingdom; *Int'l*, pg. 1135
Lyons, W. David, Chm. Bd. & Chief Exec. Officer--Ocelot Energy Inc., Calgary, Canada; *Int'l*, pg. 996
Lyons, Wayne, Pres. & Chief Exec. Officer--Lafarge Construction Materials, Canfield, OH; *Int'l*, pg. 788
Lytel, Ronn K., Chm. Bd. & Chief Exec. Officer--Capstead Mortgage Corporation, Dallas, TX; *U.S. Public*, pg. 303
Lytle, L. Ben, Pres. & Chief Exec. Officer--Anthem, Inc., Indianapolis, IN; *U.S. Private*, pg. 76
Lytle, R.D., Chm. Bd., Pres. & Chief Exec. Officer--Star Bronze Company, Alliance, OH; *U.S. Private*, pg. 1034
Maag, J.G., Chief Exec. Officer--Zurich Insurance Services (Middle East) E.C., Manama, Bahrain; *Int'l*, pg. 1532
Maaloe, Jens, Pres. & Chief Exec. Officer--GN Nettest, Telecom Division, Brondby, Denmark; *Int'l*, pg. 536
Maatman, G.L., Chm. Bd.--American Motorists Insurance Co., Long Grove, IL; *U.S. Private*, pg. 614
Mac Mahon, Thomas P., Chm. Bd., Pres. & Chief Exec. Officer--Laboratory Corp. of America Holdings, Burlington, NC; *U.S. Public*, pg. 973
Maca, Allen Leigh, Chief Exec. Officer--Sommer & Maca Industries, Inc., Cicero, IL; *U.S. Private*, pg. 1013

Macaskill, Bridget, Pres. & Chief Exec. Officer--Oppenheimer Funds, Inc., New York, NY; *U.S. Private*, pg. 712
Macaskill, Bridget A., Pres. & Chief Exec. Officer--OppenheimerFunds Distributor, Inc., New York, NY; *U.S. Private*, pg. 818
Maccarone, Roque, Chm. Bd., Pres. & Chief Exec. Officer--Banco de la Nacion Argentina, Buenos Aires, Argentina; *Int'l*, pg. 140
MacCready, Paul, Dr., Chm. Bd. & Chief Exec. Officer--Aerovironment, Inc., Monrovia, CA; *U.S. Private*, pg. 25
Macdonald, Dave, Pres. & Chief Exec. Officer--New Haven Mfg. Corp., New Haven, CT; *U.S. Private*, pg. 793
MacDonald, James B., Pres. & Chief Exec. Officer--WIC Television Ltd., Vancouver, Canada; *Int'l*, pg. 1482
Macdonald, James B., Pres. & Chief Exec. Officer--WIC Entertainment Ltd., Vancouver, Canada; *Int'l*, pg. 1482
MacDonald, Jay C., Pres. & Chief Exec. Officer--MacDonald Communications, New York, NY; *U.S. Private*, pg. 691
MacDonald, K., Chief Exec. Officer--Franklins Holdings Ltd., Chullora, Australia; *Int'l*, pg. 703
MacDonald, Mary, Chief Exec. Officer & Mng. Dir.--DMB&B/Yellow Pages, Northbrook, IL; *U.S. Private*, pg. 303
MacDonald, Reid V., Pres. & Chief Exec. Officer--Faribault Foods Inc., Minneapolis, MN; *U.S. Private*, pg. 393
MacDonald, Stewart Gray, Jr., Chm. Bd. & Chief Exec. Officer--Mac-Gray Corporation, Cambridge, MA; *U.S. Public*, pg. 1029
MacDonald, William F., Jr., Chm. Bd., Pres., Chief Exec. & Chief Oper. Officer--Houghton International Inc., Valley Forge, PA; *U.S. Private*, pg. 541
MacDonnell, Russell R., Chm. Bd. & Chief Exec. Officer--Alarmguard Holdings, Inc., Orange, CT; *U.S. Public*, pg. 35
MacDonough, John N., Chm. Bd. & Chief Exec. Officer--Miller Brewing Company, Milwaukee, WI; *U.S. Public*, pg. 1289
MacDougald, James E., Chm. Bd., Chief Exec. Officer & Pres.--ABR Information Services, Inc., Palm Harbor, FL; *U.S. Public*, pg. 2
Mace, Garry M., Chief Exec. Officer-Energy--Fletcher Challenge Limited, Auckland, New Zealand; *Int'l*, pg. 494
MacFarlane, John C., Chm. Bd., Pres. & Chief Exec. Officer--Otter Tail Power Company, Fergus Falls, MN; *U.S. Public*, pg. 1234
MacFarlane, Phil, Pres. & Chief Exec. Officer--OmniTRAX Inc., Chicago, IL; *U.S. Private*, pg. 171
Machado, Gus, Pres. & Chief Exec. Officer--Gus Machado Enterprises, Hialeah, FL; *U.S. Private*, pg. 691
Macher, F., Chief Exec. Officer--Kuehne & Nagel GmbH, Vienna, Austria; *Int'l*, pg. 763
Machida, Tetsuo, Pres. & Chief Exec. Officer--DCA Advertising, Inc., New York, NY; *Int'l*, pg. 393
Machulak, Edward L., Chm. Bd., Pres., Chief Exec. Officer & Chief Oper. Officer--Commerce Group Corp., Milwaukee, WI; *U.S. Public*, pg. 410
MacInnis, Frank T., Chm. Bd. & Chief Exec. Officer--EMCOR Group, Inc., Norwalk, CT; *U.S. Public*, pg. 571
MacIntyre, R. Douglas, Chm. Bd., Pres. & Chief Exec. Officer--Brock International Inc., Atlanta, GA; *U.S. Public*, *pg. 258*
MacIntyre, R. Douglas, Pres. & Chief Exec. Officer--Dun & Bradstreet Software Services, Atlanta, GA; *Int'l*, pg. 532
Mack, James A., Pres. & Chief Exec. Officer--Cambrex Corporation, East Rutherford, NJ; *U.S. Public*, pg. 297
Mack, John, Pres. & Chief Exec. Officer--Morgan Stanley Group Inc., New York, NY; *U.S. Public*, pg. 1132
Mack, John E., III, Chm. Bd. & Chief Exec. Officer--Central Hudson Gas & Electric Corporation, Poughkeepsie, NY; *U.S. Public*, pg. 324
Mack, Paul F., Chm. Bd. & Chief Exec. Officer--Mack Printing Company, Easton, PA; *U.S. Private*, pg. 691
Mackay, Charles, Vice Chm. & Chief Exec. Officer--Inchcape PLC, London, United Kingdom; *Int'l*, pg. 671
Mackay, F.H., Deputy Chm. & Chief Exec. Officer--Compass Group plc, Chertsey, United Kingdom.; *Int'l*, pg. 324
MacKenzie, Brian S., Pres. & Chief Exec. Officer--Builder Marts of America, Inc., Greenville, SC; *U.S. Private*, pg. 179
MacKenzie, Norman, Pres. & Chief Exec. Officer--Agripac Inc., Salem, OR; *U.S. Private*, pg. 26
MacKenzie, Thomas D., Pres. & Chief Exec. Officer--Everest Insurance Company of Canada, Toronto, Canada; *U.S. Public*, pg. 597
Mackey, John, Chm. Bd. & Chief Exec. Officer--Whole Foods Market, Inc., Austin, TX; *U.S. Public*, pg. 1767
Mackey, Paul N., Pres. & Chief Exec. Officer--Prym-Dritz Corporation, Spartanburg, SC; *Int'l*, pg. 1499
Mackey, William K., Chm. Bd., Pres., Chief Exec. Officer & Treas.--Aqua Care Systems Inc., Coral Springs, FL; *U.S. Public*, pg. 126
Mackie, D.B., Pres. & Chief Exec. Officer--Great Lakes Dredge & Dock Co., Oak Brook, IL; *U.S. Private*, pg. 474
Mackie, Greg C., Chm. Bd., Pres. & Chief Exec. Officer--Mackie Designs, Inc., Woodinville, WA; *U.S. Public*, pg. 1030
Mackin, J. Leo, Chm. Bd. & Chief Exec. Officer--Interlock Industries, Inc., Sellersburg, IN; *U.S. Private*, pg. 567
Mackin, J. Stanley, Chm. Bd. & Chief Exec. Officer--Regions Financial Corporation, Birmingham, AL; *U.S. Public*, pg. 1371
Mackin, John H., Pres. & Chief Exec. Officer--SouthTrust Bank, Gadsden, Gadsden, AL; *U.S. Public*, pg. 1491
Mackinney, Harold A., Jr., Chm. Bd. & Chief Exec. Officer--Fleet Investment Advisors, Inc., Boston, MA; *U.S. Public*, *pg. 650*
Mackler, Paul, Co.-Chief Exec. Officer--Ullo International, Inc., Altamonte Springs, FL; *U.S. Private*, pg. 1116
Maclay, G.G., Jr., Pres. & Chief Exec. Officer--Ziegler Asset Management, Inc., West Bend, WI; *U.S. Public*, pg. 1792
MacLean, Barry L., Chm. Bd., Pres., Chief Exec. & Chief Oper. Officer--Maclean-Fogg Co., Mundelein, IL; *U.S. Private*, pg. 692
MacLeod, Malcolm W., Pres. & Chief Exec. Officer--Moran Transporation Company, Greenwich, CT; *U.S. Private*, pg. 760
MacLeod, Malcolm W., Pres. & Chief Exec. Officer--Moran Towing Corporation, Greenwich, CT; *U.S. Private*, pg. 760
Macleod, Malcolm W., Chm. Bd., Pres. & Chief Exec. Officer--Jakobson Shipyard, Inc, Greenwich, CT; *U.S. Private*, pg. 760
MacLeod, Malcolm W., Pres. & Chief Exec. Officer, CT--Moran Towing of Maryland, Baltimore, MD; *U.S. Private*, pg. 761
MacMillan, Whitney, Chm. Bd. & Chief Exec. Officer--Cargill, Wayzata, MN; *U.S. Private*, pg. 210
MacNeill, Brian F., Pres. & Chief Exec. Officer--IPL Energy Inc., Calgary, Canada; *Int'l*, pg. 651
MacNeill, Brian F., Pres. & Chief Exec. Officer--Interprovincial Pipe Line Inc., Edmonton, Canada; *Int'l*, pg. 652
Macozoma, Saki, Mng. Dir.--Transnet Ltd., Parkview, South Africa; *Int'l*, pg. 1417
MacPhail, Andrew B., Pres. & Chief Exec. Officer--Chicago National League Ball Club, Inc. (Chicago Cubs), Chicago, IL; *U.S. Public*, pg. 1635
MacPherson, Donald R., Pres. & Chief Exec. Officer--Red Devil Inc., Union, NJ; *U.S. Private*, pg. 915
MacPherson, Robert W., Chm. Bd. & Chief Exec. Officer--General Latex & Chemical Corporation, Cambridge, MA; *U.S. Private*, pg. 444
MacVittie, Paula R., Pres. & Chief Exec. Officer--Caldwell VanRiper, Inc., Indianapolis, IN; *U.S. Private*, pg. 200
Madarame, Rikihiro, Chm. & Chief Exec. Officer--Nemic-Lambda KK, Tokyo, Japan; *Int'l*, pg. 1242
Madavi, Syrus P., Pres. & Chief Exec. Officer--Burr-Brown Corporation, Tucson, AZ; *U.S. Public*, pg. 270
Maddox, Gary, Pres. & Chief Exec. Officer--A. Pomerantz & Company, Philadelphia, PA; *U.S. Private*, pg. 875
Maddox, L.E., Pres. & Chief Exec. Officer--PG&E Energy Trading, Houston, TX; *U.S. Public*, pg. 1241
Maddrey, E.E., II, Pres. & Chief Exec. Officer--Delta Woodside Industries, Inc., Greenville, SC; *U.S. Public*, pg. 497
Madel, Michael, Exec. V.P., Chm., Pres. & Chief Exec. Officer-JWT/Europe--J. Walter Thompson Company, New York, NY; *Int'l*, pg. 1483
Madero, Antonio, Chm. Bd. & Chief Exec. Officer--Corporacion Industrial Sanluis, Mexico, Mexico; *Int'l*, pg. 332
Madigan, John W., Chm. Bd., Pres. & Chief Exec. Officer--Tribune Company, Chicago, IL; *U.S. Public*, pg. 1635
Madison, D. Raymond, Chm. Bd. & Chief Exec. Officer--Dynamic Homes, Inc., Detroit Lakes, MN; *U.S. Public*, pg. 538
Madison, Thomas R., Jr., Pres. & Chief Exec. Officer--CSC Financial Services Group, Austin, TX; *U.S. Public*, pg. 422
Madsen, Richard H., Chm. Bd., Pres. & Chief Exec. Officer--Zions Co-operative Mercantile Institution, Salt Lake City, UT; *U.S. Public*, pg. 1793
Madson, Paul C., Pres. & Chief Exec. Officer--Border States Industries, Inc., Fargo, ND; *U.S. Private*, pg. 160
Maeda, Noburo, Pres. & Chief Exec. Officer--Fujisawa U.S.A., Deerfield, IL; *Int'l*, pg. 525
Maeda, Noburu, Pres. & Chief Exec. Officer--Fujisawa U.S.A. Inc., Deerfield, IL; *Int'l*, pg. 525
Maenpaa, Richard, Chief Exec. Officer--Peace River Electric Cooperative, Inc., Wauchula, FL; *U.S. Private*, pg. 845
Maestroni, M., Chief Exec. Officer--General Railway Signal Corp., Rochester, NY; *Int'l*, pg. 1194
Maffic, Michael O., Pres. & Chief Exec. Officer--Carson Water Co., Las Vegas, NV; *U.S. Public*, pg. 1493
Maffie, Michael O., Pres. & Chief Exec. Officer--Southwest Gas Corporation, Las Vegas, NV; *U.S. Public*, pg. 1493
Maffie, Michael O., Chief Exec. Officer--Utility Financial Corp., Las Vegas, NV; *U.S. Public*, pg. 1493
Maffie, Michael O., Pres. & Chief Exec. Officer--LNG Energy, Inc., Phoenix, AZ; *U.S. Public*, pg. 1493
Magee, Michael M., Jr., Pres. & Chief Exec. Officer--Independent Bank, Ionia, MI; *U.S. Public*, pg. 874
Maghielse, Craig, Chm. Bd., Pres. & Chief Exec. Officer--Maghielse Tool Corporation, Grand Rapids, MI; *U.S. Private*, pg. 694
Magliocco, John, Chm. Bd. & Chief Exec. Officer--Peerless Importers, Inc., Brooklyn, NY; *U.S. Private*, pg. 847
Magnan, Larry, Pres. & Chief Exec. Officer--Cruise Holdings Ltd., Miami, FL; *U.S. Private*, pg. 293
Magnano, Louis A., Pres. & Chief Exec. Officer--Blue Bird Coach Lines Inc., Olean, NY; *U.S. Private*, pg. 150
Maguire, Cary M., Chm. Bd., Pres. & Chief Exec. Officer--Maguire Oil Co., Dallas, TX; *U.S. Private*, pg. 696
Maguire, D.E., Chm. Bd., Pres. & Chief Exec. Officer--Kemet Corporation, Simpsonville, SC; *U.S. Public*, pg. 949
Mahadeva, Kumar, Chm. Bd. & Chief Exec. Officer--Cognizant Technology Solutions Corp., New York, NY; *U.S. Public*, pg. 395
Mahaffey, Paul F., Pres. & Chief Exec. Officer--PLUM, Eden Prairie, MN; *Int'l*, pg. 1504
Mahaffy, Patrick J., Pres. & Chief Exec. Officer--Nexstar Pharmaceuticals, Inc., Boulder, CO; *U.S. Public*, pg. 1180
Mahaney, Kevin P., Chief Exec. Officer--The Erin Company, Bangor, ME; *U.S. Private*, pg. 381
Maher, M. Brian, Chief Exec. Officer--Maher Terminals Inc., Jersey City, NJ; *U.S. Private*, pg. 697
Mahoney, Gerald F., Chm. Bd. & Chief Exec. Officer--Mail-Well Inc., Englewood, CO; *U.S. Public*, pg. 1037
Mahoney, Gerald F., Chm. Bd. & Chief Exec. Officer--American Mail-Well Envelope, Englewood, CO; *U.S. Public*, pg. 1038
Mahoney, Michael, Chief Exec. Officer--Access Industries, Grandview, MO; *U.S. Private*, pg. 11
Mahoney, Robert W., Chm. Bd. & Chief Exec. Officer--Diebold, Incorporated, Canton, OH; *U.S. Public*, pg. 506
Mahr, Rene, Pres. & Chief Exec. Officer--Paul Wurth S.A., Luxembourg, Luxembourg; *Int'l*, pg. 80
Mai, Vincent, Pres. & Chief Exec. Officer--AEA Investors Inc., New York, NY; *U.S. Private*, pg. 4
Maier, Craig F., Pres. & Chief Exec. Officer--Frisch's Restaurants, Inc., Cincinnati, OH; *U.S. Public*, pg. 682
Maier, Russell W., Chm. Bd. & Chief Exec. Officer--Republic Engineered Steels, Inc., Massillon, OH; *U.S. Public*, pg. 1378
Mailleret, Michel, Chm. Bd. & Chief Exec. Officer--Filtrauto Division, Montigny-le-Bretonneux, France; *Int'l*, pg. 785
Maire, Jacques, Pres. & Chief Exec. Officer--Gaz de France, Paris, France; *Int'l*, pg. 541
Maitrepierre, Philippe, Chief Exec. Officer--Techalloy Co., Inc., Mahwah, NJ; *Int'l*, pg. 572
Makay, David J., Chief Exec. Officer--John Menzies plc, Edinburgh, United Kingdom; *Int'l*, pg. 707
Makin, Ed, Pres. & Chief Exec. Officer--Domino Sugar Corporation, New York, NY; *Int'l*, pg. 1356
Makinen, Heimo, Pres. & Chief Exec. Officer--Montgomery KONE Inc., Moline, IL; *Int'l*, pg. 746
Makitalo, Osten, Chief Exec. Officer--Telia Research AB, Haninge, Sweden; *Int'l*, pg. 1374
Makowski, Karen, Pres. & Chief Exec. Officer--Key Bank of Vermont, Burlington, VT; *U.S. Public*, pg. 954
Malamatinas, Dennis, Chief Exec. Officer--Burger King Corporation, Miami, FL; *Int'l*, pg. 411
Malette, Gaston, Chm. Bd., Pres. & Chief Exec. Officer--Malette Quebec, Inc., Montreal, Canada; *Int'l*, pg. 833
Malette, Gaston, Chm. Bd., Pres. & Chief Exec. Officer--Panneaux Malette-OSB Inc., Saint-Georges, Canada; *Int'l*, pg. 833
Malixi, Conrado R., Pres. & Chief Exec. Officer--La Tondena Distillers, Inc., Manila, Philippines; *Int'l*, pg. 785
Malkani, Roma, Pres. & Chief Exec. Officer--Information Systems & Network Corporation, Bethesda, MD; *U.S. Private*, pg. 561
Malkin, Roger, Chief Exec. Officer--Delta & Pine Land Company, Scott, MS; *U.S. Public*, pg. 497
Mall, Hans-Peter, Dr., Chief Exec. Officer--Pfleiderer AG, Neumarkt, Germany; *Int'l*, pg. 1046
Mallachuk, Allan, Chief Exec. Officer--KBA-Planeta North America Inc., Williston, VT; *Int'l*, pg. 742
Mallet, Thierry, Pres. & Chief Exec. Officer--Air & Water Technologies Corporation, Branchburg, NJ; *U.S. Public*, pg. 29
Malloy, W. Manning, Chm. Bd. & Chief Exec. Officer--Cheraw Yarn Mills, Inc., Cheraw, SC; *U.S. Private*, pg. 233
Malm, Goran S., Pres. & Chief Exec. Officer--GE Medical Systems Asia Ltd., Tokyo, Japan; *U.S. Public*, pg. 713
Malms, Christoph, Pres. & Chief Exec. Officer--ISL Marketing A.G., Lucerne, Switzerland; *Int'l*, pg. 394
Malone, B.L., Chm. Bd. & Chief Exec. Officer--Malone Advertising, Inc., Akron, OH; *U.S. Private*, pg. 698
Malone, Eduardo, Chm. Bd. & Chief Exec. Officer--Chargeurs, Paris, France; *Int'l*, pg. 280
Malone, Eduardo, Vice Chm. & Chief Exec. Officer--Pathe, Paris, France; *Int'l*, pg. 1024
Malone, Jim, Chm. Bd. & Chief Exec. Officer--HMI Industries, Cleveland, OH; *U.S. Public*, pg. 771
Malone, Robert A., Pres., Chief Exec. & Oper. Officer--Alyeska Pipeline Service Company, Anchorage, AK; *U.S. Private*, pg. 47
Malone, Wallace D., Jr., Pres. & Chief Exec. Officer--SouthTrust Corporation, Birmingham, AL; *U.S. Public*, pg. 1491
Maloney, Irvin W., Pres. & Chief Exec. Officer--Dataproducts Corporation, Simi Valley, CA; *Int'l*, pg. 620
Maloney, Raymond, Pres. & Chief Exec. Officer--Intertec Publishing, Atlanta, GA; *U.S. Public*, pg. 1328
Maloney, Raymond E., Pres. & Chief Exec. Officer--Intertec Publishing, Overland Park, KS; *U.S. Public*, pg. 1327
Maloney, Richard A., Pres. & Chief Exec. Officer--Meier & Frank, Portland, OR; *U.S. Public*, pg. 1064
Malott, T.J, Pres. & Chief Exec. Officer--Siemens Energy & Automation Inc., Alpharetta, GA; *Int'l*, pg. 1245
Maltz, Milton, Chm. Bd. & Chief Exec. Officer--Malrite Communications Group, Inc., Cleveland, OH; *U.S. Private*, pg. 698
Mamsch, Helmut, Chief Exec. Officer--BRENNTAG Eurochem GmbH, Essen, Germany; *Int'l*, pg. 1458
Manby, Joel, Pres. & Chief Exec. Officer--Saab Cars USA, Inc., Norcross, GA; *Int'l*, pg. 687
Manchester, David E., Pres. & Chief Exec. Officer--J.E. Baker Co., York, PA; *U.S. Private*, pg. 112
Manchester, Eli, Pres. & Chief Exec. Officer--Kewaunee Scientific Corporation, Statesville, NC; *U.S. Public*, pg. 953
Mancini, Brooks T., Pres. & Treas.--B.T. Mancini Co., Inc., Milpitas, CA; *U.S. Private*, pg. 699
Mancuso, Frank G., Chm. Bd. & Chief Exec. Officer--Metro-Goldwyn-Mayer Inc., Santa Monica, CA; *U.S. Public*, pg. 1101
Mandelbaum, Lawrence, Pres. & Chief Exec. Officer--Big M, Inc., Totowa, NJ; *U.S. Private*, pg. 143
Mandelbaum, Mervyn, Chm. Bd., Pres., Chief Exec. & Chief Oper. Officer--Superba, Inc., Los Angeles, CA; *U.S. Private*, pg. 1054
Mandell, Lester, Chief Exec. Officer--Greater Construction Corp., Altamonte Springs, FL; *U.S. Private*, pg. 476
Mandeville, Reba, Chief Exec. Officer--First National Bank of Clifton Forge, Clifton Forge, VA; *U.S. Public*, pg. 1039
Mandor, Leonard, Chm. Bd. & Chief Exec. Officer--Concord Assets Group, Boca Raton, FL; *U.S. Private*, pg. 261
Maney, Steven R., Pres. & Chief Exec. Officer--Regions Bank/Barrow County, Winder, GA; *U.S. Public*, pg. 1371
Mang, Robert, Chief Exec. Officer--The Monet Group, Inc., New York, NY; *U.S. Private*, pg. 757
Mang, W.P.E., Pres. & Chief Exec. Officer--Fedmet International Inc., Mississauga, Canada; *Int'l*, pg. 1150
Mangin, Joseph A., Pres. & Chief Exec. Officer--Barr Brothers & Co., Inc., New York, NY; *U.S. Private*, pg. 117

Mangold, J., Dr., Pres. & Chief Exec. Officer--Daimler-Benz InterServices (debis) AG, Berlin, Germany; *Int'l*, pg. 367
Mangold, Klaus, Chief Exec.--Daimler-Benz InterServices (debis) AG, Stuttgart, Germany; *Int'l*, pg. 367
Mangwengwende, S.E., Chief Exec. Officer--Zimbabwe Electricity Supply Authority, Harare, Zimbabwe; *Int'l*, pg. 1528
Mann, David, Pres. & Chief Exec. Officer--Nova Scotia Power Inc., Halifax, Canada; *Int'l*, pg. 971
Mann, Howard, Pres. & Chief Exec. Officer--McCain Foods Limited, Florenceville, Canada; *Int'l*, pg. 850
Mann, James L., Chm. Bd., Pres. & Chief Exec. Officer--SunGard Data Systems Inc., Wayne, PA; *U.S. Public*, pg. 1534
Mann, John K., Pres. & Chief Exec. Officer--Chelsea State Bank, Chelsea, MI; *U.S. Private*, pg. 231
Mann, Marvin L., Chm. Bd. & Chief Exec. Officer--Lexmark International Group, Inc., Lexington, KY; *U.S. Public*, pg. 991
Mann, Marvin L., Chm. Bd.& Chief Exec. Officer--Lexmark International, Inc., Lexington, KY; *U.S. Public*, pg. 991
Mann, Myron, Chief Exec. Officer--Sheridan Australia Ltd., Woodville, Australia; *U.S. Private*, pg. 197
Mann, Samuel J., Chm. Bd., Pres. & Chief Exec. Officer--Inverness Corp., Fair Lawn, NJ; *U.S. Private*, pg. 574
Manna, Daniel C., Pres. & Chief Exec. Officer--Paul Mueller Company, Springfield, MO; *U.S. Public*, pg. 1141
Manning, Frank B., Pres. & Chief Exec. Officer--Zoom Telephonics, Inc., Boston, MA; *U.S. Public*, pg. 1794
Manning, William R., Pres. & Chief Exec. Officer--Statewide Mortgage Company, Birmingham, AL; *U.S. Public*, pg. 1202
Manomaiphibul, C., Chief Oper. Officer--Glory Kawasaki Motors Co., Ltd., Bangkok, Thailand; *Int'l*, pg. 947
Manoogian, Richard A., Chm. Bd. & Chief Exec. Officer--Masco Corporation, Taylor, MI; *U.S. Public*, pg. 1052
Manoogian, Richard A., Chm. Bd. & Chief Exec. Officer--MascoTech, Inc., Taylor, MI; *U.S. Public*, pg. 1055
Manos, John, Pres., Chief Exec. Officer & New Bus. Contact--DKB & Partners, Inc., Morristown, NJ; *U.S. Private*, pg. 302
Manos, Pete L., Chm. Bd., Pres. & Chief Exec. Officer--Giant Food Inc., Landover, MD; *U.S. Public*, pg. 741
Manos, Pete L., Pres. & Chief Exec. Officer--Leco Inc., Hyattsville, MD; *U.S. Public*, pg. 741
Mantegazza, Paolo, Pres. & Chief Exec. Officer--Globus & Cosmos, Littleton, CO; *U.S. Private*, pg. 458
Maor, Galia, Chief Exec. Officer & Gen. Mgr.--Bank Leumi le-Israel B.M., Tel Aviv, Israel; *Int'l*, pg. 150
Maples, Gary D., Pres. & Chief Exec. Officer--M & I Bank, Superior, WI; *U.S. Public*, pg. 1050
Maraffy, Patrick J., Chief Exec. Officer--Nexstar Pharmaceuticals, Inc., Boulder, CO; *U.S. Public*, pg. 1180
Marah, Edward A., Chief Exec. Officer--Irish Intercontinental Bank, Ltd., Dublin, Ireland; *Int'l*, pg. 761
Maraia, A.O., Pres. & Chief Exec. Officer--National Gypsum Company, Charlotte, NC; *Int'l*, pg. 790
Marberg, Edwin, Owner, Pres. & Chief Exec. Officer--MCM Enterprises, Inc., Crawfordsville, IN; *U.S. Private*, pg. 686
Marberg, William, Pres. & Chief Exec. Officer--Wilcox Electric, Inc., Kansas City, MO; *Int'l*, pg. 1384
Marble, C.E., Chief Exec. Officer-Mfg.--NIPA Hardwicke, Inc., Wilmington, DE; *U.S. Private*, pg. 771
Marble, Stephen C., Pres. & Chief Exec. Officer--Nielsen Dillingham Builders, Inc., San Diego, CA; *U.S. Private*, pg. 333
Marbut, Bob, Chm. Bd. & Co-Chief Exec. Officer--Hearst-Argyle Television Incorporated, New York, NY; *U.S. Private*, pg. 516
Marcalus, Nicholas R., Pres. & Chief Exec. Officer--Marcal Paper Mills, Inc., Elmwood Park, NJ; *U.S. Private*, pg. 701
Marcegaglia, Antonio, Chief Exec. Officer--Marcegaglia SpA, Mantova, Italy; *Int'l*, pg. 841
Marcegaglia, Antonio, Dr., Pres. & Chief Exec. Officer--Damascus Bishop Tube Co., Greenville, PA; *Int'l*, pg. 842
Marcegaglia, Emma, Chief Exec. Officer--Marcegaglia SpA, Mantova, Italy; *Int'l*, pg. 841
Marcemmi, Romano, Chief Exec. Officer--CCF Milan, Milan, Italy; *Int'l*, pg. 342
Marchand, Gerard, Chm. & Chief Exec. Officer--Tessenderlo Chemie, Tessenderlo, Belgium; *Int'l*, pg. 459
Marchesano, Michael, Pres. & Chief Exec. Officer--BPA International, New York, NY; *U.S. Private*, pg. 107
Marchesi, G.A., Chm. Bd., Pres. & Chief Exec. Officer--Steiner Co., Inc., Chicago, IL; *U.S. Private*, pg. 1039
Marchioni, Allen, Chm. Bd., Pres. & Chief Exec. Officer--William Morrow & Co., Inc., New York, NY; *U.S. Private*, pg. 515
Marchionne, Sergio, Deputy Chief Exec. Officer & Chief Oper. Officer--Alusuisse-Lonza Holding Ltd., Zurich, Switzerland; *Int'l*, pg. 66
Marchitto, Al, Chm. Bd. & Chief Exec. Officer--Simmons Juvenile Products, Rutherford, NJ; *U.S. Private*, pg. 1001
Marciano, Maurice, Chm. Bd. & Chief Exec. Officer--Guess ?, Inc., Los Angeles, CA; *U.S. Public*, pg. 768
Marcil, William C., Pres., Chief Exec. Officer, & Publr. of The Forum--Forum Communications Company, Fargo, ND; *U.S. Private*, pg. 420
Marconi, Robert C., Chief Exec. Officer & Owner--RCM Industries, Franklin Park, IL; *U.S. Private*, pg. 902
Marcoux, Remi, Chm. Bd., Pres. & Chief Exec. Officer--G.T.C. Transcontinental Group Ltd., Montreal, Canada; *Int'l*, pg. 538
Marcus, Jeffrey A., Chm. Bd. & Chief Exec. Officer--Marcus Cable Company, L.P., Dallas, TX; *U.S. Private*, pg. 702
Marcus, Roger S., Chm. Bd. & Chief Exec. Officer--American Biltrite Inc., Wellesley Hills, MA; *U.S. Public*, pg. 68
Marcus, Roger S., Pres. & Chief Exec. Officer--Congoleum Corporation, Mercerville, NJ; *U.S. Public*, pg. 69
Marcus, Stephen, Chm. Bd., Pres. & Chief Exec. Officer--The Marcus Corporation, Milwaukee, WI; *U.S. Public*, pg. 1044
Marcy, Charles F., Pres. & Chief Exec. Officer--Sealright Company, Inc., De Soto, KS; *U.S. Public*, pg. 1451
Marcy, Ray, Pres. & Chief Exec. Officer--Interim Services Inc., Fort Lauderdale, FL; *U.S. Public*, pg. 892
Margalith, Ethan Harold, Chm. Bd., Chief Exec. Officer & Treas.--Starving Students, Inc., Los Angeles, CA; *U.S. Private*, pg. 1035
Marge, Guy, Pres. & Chief Exec. Officer--Millhouse Group, Glendora, CA; *U.S. Private*, pg. 748
Margherio, Martin J., Pres. & Chief Exec. Officer--Crowley Foods, Inc., Binghamton, NY; *Int'l*, pg. 752
Margolis, Jay, Chm. Bd. & Chief Exec. Officer--Esprit de Corp., San Francisco, CA; *U.S. Private*, pg. 383
Margolis, Michael L., Pres. & Chief Exec. Officer--Tekelec, Calabasas, CA; *U.S. Public*, pg. 1566
Margolis, Robert, Chm. Bd. & Chief Exec. Officer--Cherokee Inc., Van Nuys, CA; *U.S. Public*, pg. 345
Margus, Albert F., Chief Exec. Officer--Kitchens Of The Oceans, Inc., Deerfield Beach, FL; *U.S. Private*, pg. 625
Mariani, John, Chief Exec. Officer--Banfi Product Corp, Old Brookville, NY; *U.S. Private*, pg. 113
Mariani, John F., Chief Exec. Officer--Castello Banfi Srl., Siena, Italy; *U.S. Private*, pg. 113
Mariano, Robert, Pres. & Chief Exec. Officer--Dominick's Finer Foods, Northlake, IL; *U.S. Private*, pg. 1202
Mariano, Robert J., Pres. & Chief Exec. Officer--Branford Savings Bank, Branford, CT; *U.S. Public*, pg. 250
Marine, Ignacio Bayon, Chm. & Chief Exec. Officer--Citroen Hispana S.A., Pontevedra, Spain; *Int'l*, pg. 1020
Marineau, Philip A., Pres. & Chief Exec. Officer/Pepsi-Cola N. America--Pepsi-Cola Company, Somers, NY; *U.S. Public*, pg. 1277
Marini, Robert C., Chm. Bd. & Chief Exec. Officer--Camp Dresser & McKee Inc., Cambridge, MA; *U.S. Private*, pg. 203
Marino, Frederick, Chm. Bd. & Chief Exec. Officer--The Strober Organization, Inc., Brooklyn, NY; *U.S. Private*, pg. 403
Marino, Peter, Chief Exec. Officer--Firearms Training Systems, Inc., Suwanee, GA; *U.S. Private*, pg. 222
Marino, Raymond V., Pres. & Chief Exec. Officer--Pacific Gateway Properties, San Francisco, CA; *U.S. Public*, pg. 1250
Marino, Robert J., Pres. & Chief Exec. Officer--Cincinnati Bell Information Systems Inc., Cincinnati, OH; *U.S. Public*, pg. 367
Mario, Ernest, Chief Exec. Officer--Alza Corporation, Palo Alto, CA; *U.S. Public*, pg. 62
Marion, James P., III, Pres. & Chief Exec. Officer--Bloomsburg Mills Inc., New York, NY; *U.S. Private*, pg. 150
Maritz, William E., Chm. Bd. & Chief Exec. Officer--Maritz Inc., Fenton, MO; *U.S. Private*, pg. 703
Mark, Michael, Chief Exec. Officer--Software Plus Inc., Rutherford, NJ; *U.S. Private*, pg. 1012
Mark, Reuben, Chm. Bd. & Chief Exec. Officer--Colgate-Palmolive Company, New York, NY; *U.S. Public*, pg. 397
Markham, Richard J., Chief Exec. Officer--Hoechst Marion Roussel AG, Frankfurt/Main, Germany; *Int'l*, pg. 624
Marklund, Lena, Chief Officer--B&W Stormarknader AB, Stockholm, Sweden; *Int'l*, pg. 718
Markoff, Steven, Pres. & Chief Exec. Officer--A-Mark Financial, Santa Monica, CA; *U.S. Private*, pg. 2
Markos, Dennis, Chief Exec. Officer--TriEnda Corporation, Portage, WI; *U.S. Private*, pg. 1103
Marks, Marilyn R., Chm. Bd. & Chief Exec. Officer--Dorsey Trailers, Inc., Atlanta, GA; *U.S. Public*, pg. 520
Marks, Steven L., Pres. & Chief Exec. Officer--Advertising Display Co., Englewood Cliffs, NJ; *U.S. Private*, pg. 23
Marks, William L., Chm. Bd. & Chief Exec. Officer--Whitney Holding Corporation, New Orleans, LA; *U.S. Public*, pg. 1766
Marks, William L., Chm. Bd. & Chief Exec. Officer--Whitney National Bank, New Orleans, LA; *U.S. Public*, pg. 1766
Markwick, Jim, Chief Exec. Officer--Guardian & Observer, London, United Kingdom; *Int'l*, pg. 577
Marlantes, Lorian L., Pres. & Chief Exec. Officer--Rockefeller Group, Inc., New York, NY; *Int'l*, pg. 873
Marlas, James C., Chm. Bd. & Chief Exec. Officer--Mickelberry Communications, Inc., New York, NY; *U.S. Private*, pg. 741
Marlen, James S., Chm. Bd., Pres. & Chief Exec. Officer--Ameron International Corporation, Pasadena, CA; *U.S. Public*, pg. 98
Marlon, Anthony M., M.D., Chm. Bd. & Chief Exec. Officer--Sierra Health Services, Inc., Las Vegas, NV; *U.S. Public*, pg. 1469
Marlow, John L., Sr. Exec. Officer--Advanswers Media/Programming, Saint Louis, MO; *Int'l*, pg. 117
Marnell, Anthony A., II, Chm. Bd. & Chief Exec. Officer--Rio Hotel & Casino Inc., Las Vegas, NV; *U.S. Public*, pg. 1390
Marold, Ronald, Pres. & Chief Exec. Officer--Maxcor Manufacturing, Inc., Colorado Springs, CO; *U.S. Private*, pg. 716
Marotta, Thomas S., Chm. Bd., Pres. & Chief Exec. Officer--Marotta Scientific Controls, Inc., Montville, NJ; *U.S. Private*, pg. 706
Marquis, Doug, Pres. & Chief Exec. Officer--Handgards Inc., Northbrook, IL; *U.S. Private*, pg. 499
Marr, Malcolm, Pres. & Chief Exec. Officer--Imperial Litho & Dryography, Inc., Phoenix, AZ; *U.S. Private*, pg. 558
Marram, Edward P., Dr., Chm. Bd., Pres., Chief Exec. Officer & Treas.--Geo-Centers, Inc., Newton, MA; *U.S. Private*, pg. 447
Marriott, J.W., Jr., Chm. Bd. & Chief Exec. Officer--Marriott International, Inc., Washington, DC; *U.S. Public*, pg. 1047
Marron, Donald B., Chm. Bd. & Chief Exec. Officer--PaineWebber Group Incorporated, New York, NY; *U.S. Public*, pg. 1252
Mars, John F., Co-Pres. & Chief Exec. Officer--Mars, Incorporated, Mc Lean, VA; *U.S. Private*, pg. 707
Marsal, Bryan, Pres. & Chief Exec. Officer--Arrow Shirt Company, New York, NY; *Int'l*, pg. 194
Marsan, Andre, Chm. Bd., Pres. & Chief Exec. Officer--Montrusco Associates, Inc., Montreal, Canada; *Int'l*, pg. 888
Marsh, Don E., Chm. Bd., Pres. & Chief Exec. Officer--Marsh Supermarkets, Inc., Indianapolis, IN; *U.S. Public*, pg. 1049
Marsh, John Allen, Chm. Bd. & Chief Exec. Officer--Marsh Company, Belleville, IL; *U.S. Private*, pg. 707
Marsh, Miles L., Chm. Bd. & Chief Exec. Officer--Fort James Corporation, Richmond, VA; *U.S. Public*, pg. 670
Marsh, Water G., Chm. Bd. & Chief Exec. Officer--Tapco International Corporation, Plymouth, MI; *U.S. Private*, pg. 1068
Marshall, David, Pres. & Chief Exec. Officer--Berkshire Realty Company, Inc., Boston, MA; *U.S. Public*, pg. 221
Marshall, David D., Chief Exec. Officer--DQE Inc., Coraopolis, PA; *U.S. Public*, pg. 474
Marshall, Gregory K., Sr. V.P. & Chm. & Chief Exec. Officer-The SYGMA Network--Sysco Corporation, Houston, TX; *U.S. Public*, pg. 1550
Marshall, Gregory K., Chm. & Chief Exec. Officer--The Sygma Network, Inc.-Denver Central, Lakewood, CO; *U.S. Public*, pg. 1551
Marshall, Griffith M., Pres., Chief Exec. Officer & Chief Oper. Officer--Herbert Malarkey Roofing Company, Portland, OR; *U.S. Private*, pg. 698
Marshall, Jeffrey, Pres. & Chief Exec. Officer--Aluma Systems Corp., Toronto, Canada; *Int'l*, pg. 1423
Marshall, Jeremy, Chief Exec.--Delarue Systems Limited Plc, Havant, United Kingdom; *Int'l*, pg. 388
Marshall, Joseph W., Chm. Bd. & Chief Exec. Officer--Idaho Power Company, Boise, ID; *U.S. Public*, pg. 861
Marshall, Pierce, Chm. Bd. & Chief Exec. Officer--Electron Corp., Littleton, CO; *U.S. Private*, pg. 370
Marshall, Raymond, Chief Exec. Officer--AmeriServe Food Distribution, Inc., Dallas, TX; *U.S. Private*, pg. 533
Marsiello, Lawrence A., Pres. & Chief Exec. Officer--The CIT Group/Commercial Services, New York, NY; *Int'l*, pg. 360
Marsilius, Newman M., III, Pres. & Chief Exec. Officer--The Producto Machine Co., Bridgeport, CT; *U.S. Private*, pg. 889
Marsilius, Newman M., III, Pres. & Chief Exec. Officer--Producto Machine Co. Ring Division, Jamestown, NY; *U.S. Private*, pg. 889
Marsilius, Newman M., III, Pres. & Chief Exec. Officer--Moore Tool Company, Inc., Bridgeport, CT; *U.S. Private*, pg. 889
Marston, Theodore U., Dr., Pres. & Chief Exec. Officer--P and G Specialty Insurance Services, Newport Beach, CA; *U.S. Private*, pg. 354
Martel, Curtis W., Pres. & Chief Exec. Officer--United Farm Tools, Inc., Glasgow, KY; *U.S. Private*, pg. 1122
Martens, Herbert R., Pres. & Chief Exec. Officer--NatCity Investments, Inc., Cleveland, OH; *U.S. Public*, pg. 1154
Martens, Richard A., Chm. Bd. & Chief Exec. Officer--Security Pacific Oregon Bancorp, Portland, OR; *U.S. Public*, pg. 182
Martensson, Arne, Pres. & Chief Exec. Officer--Svenska Handelsbanken, Stockholm, Sweden; *Int'l*, pg. 1327
Martenyi, Karoly, Deputy Chief Exec. Officer--Malev Hungarian Airlines, Plc., Budapest, Hungary; *Int'l*, pg. 833
Martin-Lof, Sverker, Pres. & Chief Exec. Officer--Svenska Cellulosa Aktiebolaget (SCA), Stockholm, Sweden; *Int'l*, pg. 1326
Martin, Anthony J., Chief Exec. Officer--Bundy Asia Pacific, Adelaide, Australia; *Int'l*, pg. 1341
Martin, C.G., Jr., Chief Oper. Officer--Lancaster Leaf Tobacco Co. of Pennsylvania, Lancaster, PA; *U.S. Public*, pg. 1695
Martin, Craig, Publisher & Chief Exec. Officer--The Edmonton Sun, Edmonton, Canada; *Int'l*, pg. 1320
Martin, Dennis, Chief Exec. Officer-ITW Welding Prods. Grp.--Miller Electric Manufacturing Co., Appleton, WI; *U.S. Public*, pg. 867
Martin, Frederick J., Pres. & Chief Exec. Officer--Dobbs International Services, Inc., Memphis, TN; *U.S. Public*, pg. 1718
Martin, J. Landis, Chm. Bd., Pres. & Chief Exec. Officer--Tremont Corporation, Denver, CO; *U.S. Private*, pg. 270
Martin, J. Landis, Pres. & Chief Exec. Officer--Titanium Metals Corporation, Denver, CO; *U.S. Private*, pg. 270
Martin, James F., Chm. Bd. & Chief Exec. Officer--Martin Color-Fi, Edgefield, SC; *U.S. Public*, pg. 1052
Martin, James R., Chm. Bd. & Chief Exec. Officer--Plasti-Line, Inc., Knoxville, TN; *U.S. Public*, pg. 1308
Martin, Jim, Pres. & Chief Exec. Officer--UPB of the Cumberlands, Cookeville, TN; *U.S. Public*, pg. 1669
Martin, Ken, Chm. & Chief Exec. Officer--Sedgwick Noble Lowndes, Memphis, TN; *Int'l*, pg. 1218
Martin, L.C., Chm. Bd., Pres. & Chief Exec. Officer--Aztec Manufacturing Co., Crowley, TX; *U.S. Public*, pg. 159
Martin, Peter, Chm. Bd. & Chief Exec. Officer--Semikron International, GmbH & Co. KG, Nuremberg, Germany; *Int'l*, pg. 1220
Martin, Peter M., Chm. Bd. & Chief Exec. Officer--Provident Bankshares Corporation, Baltimore, MD; *U.S. Public*, pg. 1337
Martin, R. Brad, Chm. Bd. & Chief Exec. Officer--Proffitt's, Inc., Alcoa, TN; *U.S. Public*, pg. 1333
Martin, Ralph J., Pres. & Chief Exec. Officer--Community Newspaper Holdings Inc., Lexington, KY; *U.S. Private*, pg. 259
Martin, Ray, Chm. Bd. & Chief Exec. Officer--Coast Savings Financial, Inc., Los Angeles, CA; *U.S. Public*, pg. 388
Martin, Richard O., Pres. & Chief Exec. Officer--Physio-Control Corporation, Redmond, WA; *U.S. Public*, pg. 1294

Martin, Rodney O., Pres. & Chief Exec. Officer--American General Life Insurance Company of New York, Syracuse, NY; *U.S. Public*, pg. 76

Martin, Roy C., Sr., Chief Exec. Officer & Sec.--Triangle Electric Company, Madison Heights, MI; *U.S. Private*, pg. 1102

Martin, Ruben S., III, Pres. & Chief Exec. Officer--Martin Gas Corporation, Kilgore, TX; *U.S. Private*, pg. 709

Martin, Theodore E., Pres. & Chief Exec. Officer--Barnes Group Inc., Bristol, CT; *U.S. Public*, pg. 189

Martin, Tom, Chm. Bd. & Chief Exec. Officer--First Commercial Bank, N.A. of Memphis, Memphis, TN; *U.S. Public*, pg. 630

Martin, Vincent L., Chm. Bd. & Chief Exec. Officer--Jason Incorporated, Milwaukee, WI; *U.S. Public*, pg. 923

Martin, Wayne, Pres. & Chief Exec. Officer--Plains Co-op Oil Mill, Lubbock, TX; *U.S. Private*, pg. 868

Martineau, James, Pres. & Chief Exec. Officer--Viracon, Inc., Owatonna, MN; *U.S. Public*, pg. 120

Martinelli, Alfred W., Chm. Bd. & Chief Exec. Officer--Buckeye Partners, L.P., Allentown, PA; *U.S. Public*, pg. 266

Martinez, Arthur C., Chm. Bd. & Chief Exec. Officer--Sears, Roebuck and Co., Hoffman Estates, IL; *U.S. Public*, pg. 1452

Martinez, Jose Manuel Martinez, Mng. Dir. & Chief Exec. Officer--Corporacion MAPFRE, Compania Internacional de Reaseguros, S.A., Madrid, Spain; *Int'l*, pg. 332

Martinez, Larry, Chief Exec. Officer--Crop Growers Insurance, Overland Park, KS; *Int'l*, pg. 59

Martinez, Norma, Pres. & Chief Exec. Officer--Southwestern Bell Messaging Services, San Antonio, TX; *U.S. Public*, pg. 1416

Martino, Anthony A., Chm. Bd. & Chief Exec. Officer--Maaco Enterprises Inc., King of Prussia, PA; *U.S. Private*, pg. 689

Marto, Robert, Pres. & Chief Exec. Officer--White River Corporation, White Plains, NY; *U.S. Public*, pg. 1765

Marton, R.E.C., Chief Exec. Officer--Britax International plc, Warwick, United Kingdom; *Int'l*, pg. 216

Marttinen, Heikki, Chm. Bd., Pres. & Chief Exec. Officer--Imatran Voima Oy, Helsinki, Finland; *Int'l*, pg. 660

Martz, D. Stephen, Chm. Bd., Pres. & Chief Exec. Officer--Hollidaysburg Trust Company, Hollidaysburg, PA; *U.S. Public*, pg. 1222

Maruyama, N., Chief Oper. Officer--The Masan Steel Tube Works Co. Ltd., Masan, Korea; *Int'l*, pg. 948

Marvin, William S., Chm. Bd. & Chief Exec. Officer--Marvin Lumber & Cedar Company, Warroad, MN; *U.S. Private*, pg. 710

Mas, Frederico, Chief Exec.--Sulzer Hydro S.A. de C.V., Morelia, Mexico; *Int'l*, pg. 1308

Mas, Jorge, Pres. & Chief Exec. Officer--MasTec, Inc., Miami, FL; *U.S. Public*, pg. 1055

Mascarin, Ed, Chm. Bd. & Chief Exec. Officer--Crane Carrier Company, Tulsa, OK; *U.S. Private*, pg. 286

Mascia, Frank R., Chm., Pres. & Chief Exec. Officer--United HealthCare of North Carolina, Inc., Greensboro, NC; *U.S. Public*, pg. 1678

Masefield, John, Chm. Bd., Pres. & Chief Exec. Officer--Isomedix Inc., Whippany, NJ; *U.S. Public*, pg. 1515

Masenthin, Gregg, Chief Exec. Officer & Chief Fin. Officer--Jami, Inc., Shawnee Mission, KS; *U.S. Private*, pg. 581

Masini, Massimo, Chief Exec. Officer--Stet International, Rome, Italy; *Int'l*, pg. 1363

Maslak, Samuel H., Chm. Bd. & Chief Exec. Officer--Acuson Corporation, Mountain View, CA; *U.S. Public*, pg. 18

Mason, Bruce, Chief Exec. Officer-True North Communications Inc.--True North Communications Inc., Chicago, IL; *U.S. Public*, pg. 1641

Mason, Chris, Chief Exec. Officer--World Brands Duty Free, Brentford, United Kingdom; *Int'l*, pg. 567

Mason, David D. S., Pres., Chief Exec. & Chief Fin. Officer & Treas.--Toms Sierra Company, Ione, CA; *U.S. Private*, pg. 1090

Mason, Douglas L., Pres. & Chief Exec. Officer--Clearly Canadian Beverage Corp., Vancouver, Canada; *Int'l*, pg. 297

Mason, Elvis L., Chm. Bd. & Chief Exec. Officer--Safeguard Business Systems, Inc., Fort Washington, PA; *U.S. Private*, pg. 960

Mason, James L., Pres. & Chief Exec. Officer--Wampler Foods, Timberville, VA; *U.S. Public*, pg. 1727

Mason, L. Mike, Pres. & Chief Exec. Officer--Telsco Industries, Garland, TX; *U.S. Private*, pg. 1074

Mason, Peter, Chief Exec. Officer--AMEC Plc, Northwich, United Kingdom; *Int'l*, pg. 16

Mason, Peter I., Pres. & Chief Exec. Officer--May & Speh, Inc., Downers Grove, IL; *U.S. Public*, pg. 1063

Mason, Raymond A., Chm. Bd., Pres. & Chief Exec. Officer--Legg Mason, Inc., Baltimore, MD; *U.S. Public*, pg. 984

Mason, Scott P., Pres. & Chief Exec. Officer--Investment Technology Group, Inc., New York, NY; *U.S. Public*, pg. 924

Mason, Tom, Pres. & Chief Exec. Officer--Schwinn Holdings, Boulder, CO; *U.S. Private*, pg. 975

Mason, Tom, Pres. & Chief Exec. Officer--Schwinn Cycling & Fitness Inc., Boulder, CO; *U.S. Private*, pg. 975

Massaro, Anthony A., Chm. Bd., Pres. & Chief Exec. Officer--The Lincoln Electric Company, Cleveland, OH; *U.S. Public*, pg. 996

Masseu, Jeff, Chm. Bd., Pres. & Chief Exec. Officer--United Design Corporation, Noble, OK; *U.S. Private*, pg. 1121

Massey, D.E., Chief Exec. Officer--Crest Cadillac, Inc., Nashville, TN; *U.S. Private*, pg. 712

Massey, D.E., Chief Exec. Officer--Massey Cadillac, Inc., Downey, CA; *U.S. Private*, pg. 713

Massey, D.E., Pres. & Chief Exec. Officer--Massey Cadillac, Inc., Detroit, MI; *U.S. Private*, pg. 713

Massey, D.E., Pres. & Chief Exec. Officer--Massey Cadillac, Inc., Dallas, TX; *U.S. Private*, pg. 713

Massey, Donald E., Pres. & Chief Exec. Officer--Don Massey Cadillac Inc., Plymouth, MI; *U.S. Private*, pg. 712

Massey, Knox, Jr., Chm. Bd. & Chief Exec. Officer--WestWayne, Inc., Atlanta, GA; *U.S. Private*, pg. 1170

Massey, Stewart R., Pres. & Chief Exec. Officer--Robert Fleming, Inc., New York, NY; *Int'l*, pg. 493

Mastandrea, James C., Chm. Bd., Pres. & Chief Exec. Officer--First Union Real Estate Investments, Cleveland, OH; *U.S. Public*, pg. 640

Masters, Melvin L., Chm. Bd., Pres. & Chief Exec. Officer--LaserMaster Technologies, Inc., Eden Prairie, MN; *U.S. Public*, pg. 979

Matchett, Ken, Chief Exec. Officer--XCAN Grain Pool Ltd., Winnipeg, Canada; *Int'l*, pg. 1195

Mathewson, Charles N., Chm. Bd. & Chief Exec. Officer--International Game Technology, Reno, NV; *U.S. Public*, pg. 900

Mathewson, George R., Dr., Chief Exec. Officer--The Royal Bank of Scotland plc, Edinburgh, United Kingdom; *Int'l*, pg. 1132

Mathewson, John, Pres. & Chief Exec. Officer--AGA Catalog Marketing & Design, New York, NY; *U.S. Private*, pg. 5

Mathias, John H., Chm. Bd. & Chief Exec. Officer--The JPM Company, Lewisburg, PA; *U.S. Public*, pg. 919

Mathieson, Joe, Chief Exec.--Thorn Security Group, Ltd., Sunbury, United Kingdom; *Int'l*, pg. 1386

Mathieson, Joe, Chief Exec.--ADT Phone & Modern Security, Northwood, United Kingdom; *U.S. Public*, pg. 1649

Mathile, Clay, Chm. Bd. & Chief Exec. Officer--Iams Company, Dayton, OH; *U.S. Private*, pg. 556

Mathis, David B., Chm. Bd. & Chief Exec. Officer--Kemper Insurance Companies, Long Grove, IL; *U.S. Private*, pg. 614

Mathwich, Dale F., Chm. Bd. & Chief Exec. Officer--American Family Mutual Insurance Co., Madison, WI; *U.S. Private*, pg. 53

Matney, R.C., Chm. Bd., Pres. & Chief Exec. Officer--Mark VII, Inc., Memphis, TN; *U.S. Public*, pg. 1046

Matricaria, Ronald A., Chm. Bd., Pres. & Chief Exec. Officer--St. Jude Medical, Inc., Saint Paul, MN; *U.S. Public*, pg. 1427

Matson, Ronald, Pres. & Chief Exec. Officer--Cerberus Pyrotronics Inc., Cedar Knolls, NJ; *Int'l*, pg. 1246

Matsue, Shigeki, Pres. & Chief Exec. Officer--NEC Electronics Inc., Santa Clara, CA; *Int'l*, pg. 900

Matsunaga, Yutaka, Chief Oper. Officer--Nippon Shipping Co., Ltd., Tokyo, Japan; *Int'l*, pg. 934

Matsuura, Isao, Pres. & Chief Exec. Officer--Sanwa Bank California, San Francisco, CA; *Int'l*, pg. 1189

Matsuyama, W. Brian, Chm. Bd. & Chief Exec. Officer--Cascade Natural Gas Corporation, Seattle, WA; *U.S. Public*, pg. 311

Matthaei, William L., Pres. & Chief Exec. Officer--Roman Meal Company, Tacoma, WA; *U.S. Private*, pg. 942

Matthew, Mike, Chief Exec.--IPC Magazines Limited, London, United Kingdom; *Int'l*, pg. 651

Matthews, Chris, Chief Exec.--Shandwick Consultants Ltd., London, United Kingdom; *Int'l*, pg. 1227

Matthews, Clark J. II, Pres., Chief Exec. Officer & Sec.--The Southland Corporation, Dallas, TX; *Int'l*, pg. 693

Matthews, Gary, Pres. & Chief Exec. Officer--Guinness Import Company, Stamford, CT; *Int'l*, pg. 412

Matthews, Jack, Pres. & Chief Exec. Officer--Environetx, Itasca, IL; *U.S. Private*, pg. 378

Matthews, Terence H., Chm. Bd. & Chief Exec. Officer--Newbridge Networks Corporation, Kanata, Canada; *Int'l*, pg. 923

Matthews, William D., Chm. Bd. & Chief Exec. Officer--Oneida Ltd., Oneida, NY; *U.S. Public*, pg. 1225

Matthewson, Edwin, Pres. & Chief Exec. Officer--Pullman Industries, Inc., Pullman, MI; *U.S. Private*, pg. 894

Matthies, Helmut, Pres. & Chief Exec. Officer-WCJ Europe (Frankfurt HQ)--Wunderman Cato Johnson, New York, NY; *U.S. Private*, pg. 1197

Mattingly, Thomas J., Pres. & Chief Exec. Officer--Metro Foods, Inc., Olive Branch, MS; *U.S. Private*, pg. 736

Mattis, David S., Pres. & Chief Exec. Officer--Ausco Products, Inc., Benton Harbor, MI; *U.S. Private*, pg. 299

Mattsson, Bjorn, Pres. & Chief Exec. Officer--Cultor Ltd., Helsinki, Finland; *Int'l*, pg. 349

Matus, Geoffrey, Chm. Bd. & Chief Exec. Officer--Globelle Corporation, Mississauga, Canada; *Int'l*, pg. 554

Matveld, H. Edward, Pres. & Chief Exec. Officer--Alpha Therapeutic Corp., Los Angeles, CA; *Int'l*, pg. 558

Maucher, Helmut, Chm. Bd. & Chief Exec. Officer--Nestle S.A., Vevey, Switzerland; *Int'l*, pg. 915

Mauer, David, Chief Exec. Officer--Riddell Sports, Inc., New York, NY; *U.S. Public*, pg. 1389

Mauer, David M., Chief Exec. Officer--Riddell Sports, Inc., Chicago, IL; *U.S. Public*, pg. 1389

Mauersberger, P., Chief Exec. Officer--Zurich Life Insurance Company Ltd., Quarry Bay, Hong Kong; *Int'l*, pg. 1530

Maughan, Deryck, Co-Chm. & Co-Chief Exec. Officer--Salomon Smith Barney Holdings, Inc., New York, NY; *U.S. Public*, pg. 1633

Maughan, Rex, Chm. Bd., Pres. & Chief Exec. Officer--Forever Living Products International, Inc., Scottsdale, AZ; *U.S. Private*, pg. 418

Mauldin, Earle, Pres. & Chief Exec. Officer--BellSouth Enterprises, Inc., Atlanta, GA; *U.S. Public*, pg. 208

Mauldin, Larry D., Chm., Pres. & Chief Exec. Officer--SunTrust Bank, East Tennessee, N.A., Knoxville, TN; *U.S. Public*, pg. 1538

Maunder, Andrew, Pres. & Chief Exec. Officer--Axiom Inc., Moorestown, NJ; *U.S. Public*, pg. 157

Mauney, William K., III, Pres.--Mauney Hosiery Mills, Inc., Kings Mountain, NC; *U.S. Private*, pg. 715

Maurer, Don, Pres. & Chief Exec. Officer--McKinney & Silver, Raleigh, NC; *U.S. Private*, pg. 723

Maurer, Thomas, Chief Oper. Officer--Auburn Hosiery Mills, Inc., Auburn, KY; *U.S. Private*, pg. 98

Mauri, Alberto, Deputy Chief Exec.--Cassa di Risparmio delle Provincie Lombarde SpA (CARIPLO), Milan, Italy; *Int'l*, pg. 274

Maurice, Samuel, Pres. & Chief Exec. Officer--London House, Rosemont, IL; *U.S. Public*, pg. 1070

Maus, Manfred, Pres. & Chief Exec. Officer--OBI Bau-und Heimwerkermaerkte GmbH & Co. KG, Wermelskirchen, Germany; *Int'l*, pg. 993

Mavel, James C., Chm. Bd., Pres. & Chief Exec. Officer--Scan-Optics, Inc., Manchester, CT; *U.S. Public*, pg. 1436

Maxheim, John H., Chm. Bd., Pres. & Chief Exec. Officer--Piedmont Natural Gas Co., Inc., Charlotte, NC; *U.S. Public*, pg. 1295

Maxwell, H. James, Chm. Bd. & Chief Exec. Officer--Panaco, Inc., Kansas City, MO; *U.S. Public*, pg. 1255

Maxwell, R.L., Pres. & Chief Exec. Officer--The Lathrop Company, Toledo, OH; *U.S. Public*, pg. 1645

Maxwell, Robert O., Pres. & Chief Exec. Officer--Security American Financial Enterprises, Inc., Minnetonka, MN; *U.S. Private*, pg. 980

May, Andrew, Pres. & Chief Exec. Officer--Paradyne, Largo, FL; *U.S. Private*, pg. 838

May, Bill B., Dr., Chm. Bd. & Chief Exec. Officer--ARGOSystems, Inc., Sunnyvale, CA; *U.S. Public*, pg. 240

May, T. Michael, Pres. & Chief Exec. Officer--Hawaiian Electric Company, Inc., Honolulu, HI; *U.S. Public*, pg. 800

May, Thomas J., Chm. Bd., Pres. & Chief Exec. Officer--Boston Edison Company, Boston, MA; *U.S. Public*, pg. 247

May, Van, Pres. & Chief Exec. Officer--Plains Cotton Co-op Association, Lubbock, TX; *U.S. Private*, pg. 868

Mayben, William R., Pres. & Chief Exec. Officer--Nebraska Public Power District, Columbus, NE; *U.S. Private*, pg. 789

Mayberry, John T., Pres. & Chief Exec. Officer--DoFasco, Inc., Hamilton, Canada; *Int'l*, pg. 414

Mayer, Bert, Chief Exec. Officer--Gunnebo Fastening Corp., Lonoke, AR; *U.S. Private*, pg. 488

Mayer, Girard H., Pres. & Chief Exec. Officer--Benefit Plans Administrative Services, Inc., Utica, NY; *U.S. Public*, pg. 416

Mayer, Robert A., Chm. Bd. & Chief Exec. Officer--Standard Security Life Insurance Company of New York, New York, NY; *U.S. Private*, pg. 446

Mayer, Robert H., Pres. & Chief Exec Officer--Danisco Ingredients USA, Inc., New Century, KS; *Int'l*, pg. 378

Mayer, Robert L., Pres.--Cole Hersee Company, Boston, MA; *U.S. Private*, pg. 251

Mayer, William N., Chm. Bd. & Chief Exec. Officer--Modern Controls, Inc., Minneapolis, MN; *U.S. Public*, pg. 1120

Maynard, James G., Chm. Bd., Chief Exec. Officer & Treas.--Maynard Oil Co., Dallas, TX; *U.S. Public*, pg. 1064

Maynard, James H., Chm. Bd., Pres., Chief Exec. Officer & Treas.--Investors Management Corp., Raleigh, NC; *U.S. Private*, pg. 574

Maynard, Otto, Pres. & Chief Exec. Officer--Wolf Creek Nuclear Operating Corp., Burlington, KS; *U.S. Public*, pg. 1759

Maynard, Robert E., Pres. & Chief Exec. Officer--Allianz Canada, Toronto, Canada; *Int'l*, pg. 59

Mays, L. Lowry, Chm. Bd. & Chief Exec. Officer--Clear Channel Communications, Inc., San Antonio, TX; *U.S. Public*, pg. 383

Mays, Mark Pitman, Pres. & Chief Oper. Officer--Clear Channel Communications, Inc., San Antonio, TX; *U.S. Public*, pg. 383

Maziarka, Donald, Pres., Chief Exec. & Chief Oper. Officer--George Sollitt Construction, Wood Dale, IL; *U.S. Private*, pg. 1013

Mazur, Jack M., Pres. & Chief Exec. Officer--PHP Healthcare Corporation, Reston, VA; *U.S. Public*, pg. 1241

Mazzaiupi, Giulio, Pres. & Chief Exec. Officer--Atlas Copco AB, Stockholm, Sweden; *Int'l*, pg. 95

Mazzarello, Giuseppe, Chief Exec. Officer--Istituto Bancario San Paolo Di Torino S.p.A., Turin, Italy; *Int'l*, pg. 691

Mazzella, David G., Pres. & Chief Exec. Officer--Moscom Corporation, Pittsford, NY; *U.S. Public*, pg. 1136

Mazzotta-Green, Joanne, Co-Pres. & Chief Exec. Officer--Friendly Holidays Inc., Lake Success, NY; *U.S. Private*, pg. 428

Mazzotta, Dorothy, Pres. & Chief Exec. Officer--Friendly Holidays Inc., Lake Success, NY; *U.S. Private*, pg. 428

McAfee, Dwayne L., Pres. & Chief Exec. Officer--First Image Management Co., Atlanta, GA; *U.S. Public*, pg. 631

McAliley, Kevin, Pres. & Chief Exec. Officer--Films for the Humanities & Sciences, Inc., Monmouth Junction, NJ; *U.S. Public*, pg. 1327

McAllen, David D., Pres.--Geupel DeMars, Inc., Indianapolis, IN; *U.S. Private*, pg. 449

McAllen, Robert, Chief Exec. Officer--Press Communications, LLC, Wall, NJ; *U.S. Private*, pg. 882

McAllister, Dan, Pres. & Chief Exec. Officer--Kilovac Corporation, Carpinteria, CA; *U.S. Private*, pg. 259

McAllister, Ian, Chief Exec. Officer--Ford Motor Company Limited, Brentwood, United Kingdom; *U.S. Public*, pg. 666

McAmis, K. Wayne, Chief Oper. Officer & Exec. V.P.--Southwire Company, Carrollton, GA; *U.S. Private*, pg. 1019

McArdle, P. A., Chief Exec. Officer--Lombard and Ulster Banking Limited, Dublin, Ireland; *Int'l*, pg. 911

McAuley, Thomas H., Pres. & Chief Exec. Officer--IRT Property Company, Atlanta, GA; *U.S. Public*, pg. 858

McAuliff, Timothy M., Pres. & Chief Exec. Officer--Blair Television, New York, NY; *U.S. Private*, pg. 148

McAvoy, Kenneth J., Chm. Bd. & Chief Exec. Officer--Jameco Industries, Inc., Spindale, NC; *U.S. Public*, pg. 1746

McBeth, Robert D., Chm. Bd., Pres. & Chief Exec. Officer--Associated Industrial Supply, Inc., Columbia, SC; *U.S. Private*, pg. 91

McBride, T. Eugene, Chm. Bd., Pres. & Chief Exec. Officer--Dyersburg Corporation, Dyersburg, TN; *U.S. Public,* pg. 538
McBride, T. Eugene, Pres. & Chief Exec. Officer--Dyersburg Fabric, Dyersburg, TN; *U.S. Public,* pg. 538
McBride, Teresa N., Pres. & Chief Exec. Officer--McBride and Associates, Inc., Albuquerque, NM; *U.S. Private,* pg. 719
McCabe, Edward, Chm. Bd. & Chief Exec. Officer--McCabe & Company, New York, NY; *U.S. Private,* pg. 719
McCabe, Robert L., Pres. & Chief Exec. Officer--Narragansett Energy Resources Company, Providence, RI; *U.S. Public,* pg. 1171
McCafferty, Michael, Pres. & Chief Exec. Officer--TTC Illinois Inc., Kankakee, IL; *U.S. Private,* pg. 1066
McCague, Beth, Chm. Bd., Pres. & Chief Exec. Officer--First Union National Bank of Tennessee, Nashville, TN; *U.S. Public,* pg. 640
McCaig, Jeffrey J., Pres. & Chief Exec. Officer--Trimac Corporation, Calgary, Canada; *Int'l,* pg. 1423
McCain, Allison, Chief Exec. Officer & Mng. Dir.--McCain Foods (GB) Limited, Scarborough, United Kingdom; *Int'l,* pg. 850
McCall, R.H., Pres. & Chief Exec. Officer--McCall Oil Real Estate Corporation, Portland, OR; *U.S. Private,* pg. 719
McCall, Robert H., Chm. Bd., Pres. & Chief Exec. Officer--McCall Oil & Chemical Corp., Portland, OR; *U.S. Private, pg. 719*
McCall, Ronald L., Vice Chm., Chief Exec. Officer, Chief Fin. Officer & Treas.--M.B. Kahn Construction Co., Inc., Columbia, SC; *U.S. Private,* pg. 604
McCallum, Craig L., Pres. & Chief Exec. Officer--Mission Viejo Company, Mission Viejo, CA; *U.S. Public,* pg. 1289
McCallum, Craig L., Pres. & Chief Exec. Officer-Mission Viejo Company--Philip Morris Capital Corporation, Rye Brook, NY; *U.S. Public,* pg. 1289
McCallum, Elkin, Pres. & Chief Exec. Officer--Joan Fabrics Corp., Tyngsboro, MA; *U.S. Private,* pg. 588
McCallum, William T., Pres. & Chief Exec. Officer-U.S.--The Great-West Life Assurance Company, Winnipeg, Canada; *Int'l,* pg. 557
McCann, John P., Pres. & Chief Exec. Officer--United Dominion Realty Trust, Inc., Richmond, VA; *U.S. Public,* pg. 1677
McCann, L.D., Chm. Bd., Pres. & Chief Exec. Officer--Standco Industries, Inc., Houston, TX; *U.S. Private,* pg. 1032
McCarten, William, Pres. & Chief Exec. Officer--Host Marriott Services Corporation, Bethesda, MD; *U.S. Public,* pg. 841
McCarter, William J., Pres. & Chief Exec. Officer--WTTW (Channel 11), Chicago, IL; *U.S. Private,* pg. 1145
McCarthy, Daniel J., Pres. & Chief Exec. Officer--American Crystal Sugar Company, Moorhead, MN; *U.S. Private,* pg. 52
McCarthy, Michael M., Chm. Bd. & Chief Exec. Officer--McCarthy Building Companies, Saint Louis, MO; *U.S. Private,* pg. 719
McCartney, Daniel P., Chm. Bd. & Chief Exec. Officer--Healthcare Services Group, Inc., Huntingdon Valley, PA; *U.S. Public,* pg. 803
McCartney, J.J., Chief Exec. Officer--Empire Fire & Marine Insurance Co., Omaha, NE; *Int'l,* pg. 1530
McCartney, William G., Pres. & Chief Exec. Officer--TSC Shannock Corporation, Burnaby, Canada; *Int'l,* pg. 1343
McCaskey, Raymond F., Pres. & Chief Exec. Officer--Blue Cross & Blue Shield of Illinois, Chicago, IL; *U.S. Private,* pg. 151
McCaslin, T.A., IV, Chief Exec. Officer--J. Fegely Inc., Pottstown, PA; *U.S. Private,* pg. 399
McCaslin, T.A., IV, Chief Exec. Officer--Carey Division, Baltimore, MD; *U.S. Private,* pg. 399
McCausland, Peter, Chm. Bd., Pres. & Chief Exec. Officer--Airgas, Inc., Radnor, PA; *U.S. Public,* pg. 33
McCausland, Thomas, Pres. & Chief Exec. Officer--Siemens Medical Systems, Inc., Iselin, NJ; *Int'l,* pg. 1246
McClain, Kenneth D., Chm. Bd., Pres. & Chief Exec. Officer--McClain Industries, Inc., Sterling Heights, MI; *U.S. Public,* pg. 1065
McClatchy, Kevin S., Chief Exec. Officer & Mng. Gen. Partner--Pittsburgh Pirates, Pittsburgh, PA; *U.S. Private,* pg. 867
McCleary, James K., Chief Exec. Officer--GE Capital/IT Solutions, Minneapolis, MN; *U.S. Public,* pg. 711
McClellan, John, Pres. & Chief Exec. Officer--ASCG, Inc., Anchorage, AK; *U.S. Private,* pg. 80
McClelland, Mike, Pres. & Chief Exec. Officer--Hardware Wholesalers, Inc., Fort Wayne, IN; *U.S. Private,* pg. 502
McClelland, Norman P., Chief Exec. Officer--Shamrock Foods Company, Phoenix, AZ; *U.S. Private,* pg. 989
McClelland, W.C., Chm. Bd. & Chief Exec. Officer--Union Camp Corporation, Wayne, NJ; *U.S. Public,* pg. 1665
McClellen, Robert E., Jr., Pres. & Chief Exec. Officer--Florists' Mutual Insurance Co., Edwardsville, IL; *U.S. Private,* pg. 415
McCloskey, John A., Pres. & Chief Exec. Officer--The Barden Corporation, Danbury, CT; *Int'l,* pg. 468
McClure, Allan, Pres. & Chief Exec. Officer--First National Bank, West Point, NE; *U.S. Public,* pg. 629
McClure, Thomas R., Chm. & Chief Exec. Officer--The McClure Group, Wayne, PA; *U.S. Private,* pg. 719
McClurg, Douglas G., Pres. & Chief Exec. Officer--Mossberg Industries, Inc., Cumberland, RI; *U.S. Private,* pg. 763
McCluskey, Richard T., Chm. Bd., Pres. & Chief Exec. Officer--Fiske Brothers Refining Company, Newark, NJ; *U.S. Private,* pg. 408
McCoin, O.B., Pres. & Chief Exec. Officer--Hospital Affiliates Development Corporation, Nashville, TN; *U.S. Private,* pg. 540
McColl, Hugh L., Jr., Chm. Bd. & Chief Exec. Officer--NationsBank Corporation, Charlotte, NC; *U.S. Public,* pg. 1162
McCollum, James, Chm. Bd. & Chief Exec. Officer--Tingley Rubber Corporation, South Plainfield, NJ; *U.S. Private,* pg. 1088
McCollum, Jr., L. Gwaltney, Pres. & Chief Exec. Officer--First National Bank, Jasper, AL; *U.S. Public,* pg. 1549
McCollum, Robert, Pres. & Chief Exec. Officer--R.S. Hughes Co., Inc., Sunnyvale, CA; *U.S. Private,* pg. 547
McCombs, Red, Chief Exec. Officer--McCombs Automotive, San Antonio, TX; *U.S. Private,* pg. 720
McConnell, James, Pres. & Chief Exec.Officer--Wilson/Shore Instruments, Canton, MA; *U.S. Public,* pg. 883
McConnell, James M., Pres. & Chief Exec. Officer--Instron Corporation, Canton, MA; *U.S. Public,* pg. 882
McConnell, John, Pres. & Chief Exec. Officer--Medic Computer Systems, Inc., Raleigh, NC; *Int'l,* pg. 870
McConnell, John P., Chm. Bd. & Chief Exec. Officer--Worthington Industries, Inc., Columbus, OH; *U.S. Public,* pg. 1780
McConnell, John W., Pres. & Chief Exec. Officer--Fairfield Communities, Inc., Little Rock, AR; *U.S. Public,* pg. 610
McConnell, Paul R., Chm., Pres. & Chief Exec. Officer--Fleet Bank of Maine, Portland, ME; *U.S. Public,* pg. 649
McCord, Herbert W., Chm. Bd., Pres. & Chief Exec. Officer--Granum Communications, Red Bank, NJ; *U.S. Private,* pg. 470
McCorkell, M.W., Non-Exec. Dir.--Pauls plc, Ipswich, United Kingdom; *Int'l,* pg. 598
McCormack, Mark H., Chm. Bd., Pres. & Chief Exec. Officer--IMG, Cleveland, OH; *U.S. Private,* pg. 555
McCormick, Charles P. (Buzz), Jr., Chm. Bd. & Chief Exec. Officer--McCormick/Schilling, Hunt Valley, MD; *U.S. Public,* pg. 1066
McCormick, Douglas W., Chief Exec. Officer Officer--Lifetime Television/ABC, New York, NY; *U.S. Public,* pg. 512
McCormick, Douglas W., Chief Exec. Officer Officer--Lifetime Television/ABC, New York, NY; *U.S. Private,* pg. 516
McCormick, Ed, Chief Exec. Officer--Tri-State Motor Transit Co., Joplin, MO; *U.S. Private,* pg. 1101
McCormick, G. Roger, Pres. & Chief Exec. Officer--People's Bank & Trust Co., Mount Vernon, IN; *U.S. Public,* pg. 1217
McCormick, Richard D., Chm. Bd., Pres. & Chief Exec. Officer--U S West Inc., Englewood, CO; *U.S. Public,* pg. 1688
McCormick, Rick M., Chief Oper. Officer--Corporate Express Delivery Systems Southwest, Inc., Houston, TX; *U.S. Public,* pg. 449
McCormick, Robert A., Pres. & Chief Exec. Officer--TrustCo Bank Corp., NY, Schenectady, NY; *U.S. Public,* pg. 1643
McCormick, Robert V., Pres. & Chief Exec. Officer--Laserscope Inc., San Jose, CA; *Int'l,* pg. 616
McCormick, Robert V., Pres. & Chief Exec. Officer--Laserscope Surgical Systems, San Jose, CA; *U.S. Public,* pg. 979
McCormick, Thomas P., Pres. & Chief Exec. Officer--Horizon Bancorp, Michigan City, IN; *U.S. Private,* pg. 538
McCormick, William, Pres. & Chief Exec. Officer--Riverside Cement Co., Diamond Bar, CA; *Int'l,* pg. 1293
McCormick, William C., Chm. Bd. & Chief Exec. Officer--Precision Castparts Corp., Portland, OR; *U.S. Public,* pg. 1320
McCormick, William T., Jr., Chm. Bd. & Chief Exec. Officer--CMS Energy Corporation, Dearborn, MI; *U.S. Public,* pg. 279
McCourt, David C., Chm. Bd. & Chief Exec. Officer--RCN Corporation, Princeton, NJ; *U.S. Public,* pg. 1354
McCourt, Kenneth W., Pres. & Chief Exec. Officer--Buffalo Color Corporation, Parsippany, NJ; *U.S. Private,* pg. 178
McCoy, John B., Chm. Bd. & Chief Exec. Officer--Banc One Corporation, Columbus, OH; *U.S. Public,* pg. 172
McCracken, Edward R., Chm. Bd. & Chief Exec. Officer--Silicon Graphics, Inc., Mountain View, CA; *U.S. Public,* pg. 1473
McCrady, Kenneth A., Chm. Bd.--Ennis Business Forms, Inc., Ennis, TX; *U.S. Public,* pg. 583
McCrary, Dennie L., Pres. & Chief Exec. Officer--Sea Island Company, Sea Island, GA; *U.S. Private,* pg. 977
McCrea, James, Chief Exec. Officer & Mng. Dir.--Air New Zealand Ltd., Auckland, New Zealand; *Int'l,* pg. 38
McCree, Donald H., Jr., Pres. & Chief Exec. Officer--IBJ Schroder Bank & Trust Company, New York, NY; *Int'l,* pg. 674
McCroskey, V.D., Pres. & Chief Exec. Officer--WGM Safety Corporation, Reading, PA; *Int'l,* pg. 462
McCullar, Cecil R., Pres. & Chief Exec. Officer--First American Federal Savings Bank, Bristol, VA; *U.S. Public, pg. 624*
McCulloch, Dave, Pres. & Chief Exec. Officer--Garland Commercial Ranges, Ltd., Mississauga, Canada; *Int'l,* pg. 189
McCullough, J.E., Pres. & Chief Exec. Officer--South Jersey Energy Co., Folsom, NJ; *U.S. Public,* pg. 1488
McCurdy, Larry, Chief Exec. Officer--Steering and Suspension Division, Saint Louis, MO; *U.S. Public,* pg. 443
McCurdy, Larry W., Chm., Pres. & Chief Exec. Officer--Echlin Inc., Branford, CT; *U.S. Public,* pg. 560
McDaniel, Gary P., Chief Exec. Officer--Chateau Communities, Inc., Englewood, CO; *U.S. Public,* pg. 341
McDermitt, Edward A., Jr., Chm., Pres. & Chief Exec. Officer--National Bulk Carriers, Inc., New York, NY; *U.S. Private,* pg. 780
McDermott, Jeffrey S., Chm. Bd. & Chief Exec. Officer--Bell Atlantic Systems Integration Corp., Arlington, VA; *U.S. Public,* pg. 203
McDonald, Fred A., Pres. & Chief Exec. Officer--Cadmus Marketing Services, Atlanta, GA; *U.S. Public,* pg. 291
McDonald, Ian, Chm. Bd. & Chief Exec. Officer--Wheaton River Minerals Ltd., Toronto, Canada; *Int'l,* pg. 1498
McDonald, Ian, Chief Exec. Officer--Willis Corroon Hinton Limited, Abingdon, United Kingdom; *Int'l,* pg. 1502
McDonald, J.M., III, Chm. Bd. & Chief Exec. Officer--A.Y. McDonald Supply Co. Inc., Dubuque, IA; *U.S. Private,* pg. 721
McDonald, James F., Pres. & Chief Exec. Officer--Scientific-Atlanta, Inc., Norcross, GA; *U.S. Public,* pg. 1443
McDonald, John J., Pres. & Chief Exec. Officer--Casio, Inc., Dover, NJ; *Int'l,* pg. 274
McDonald, Mackey J., Pres., Chief Exec. Officer & Chief Oper. Officer--VF Corporation, Wyomissing, PA; *U.S. Public,* pg. 1702
McDonald, R.D., Chm. Bd. & Chief Exec. Officer--A.Y. McDonald Mfg. Co., Dubuque, IA; *U.S. Private,* pg. 721
McDonald, R.D., Chm. Bd. & Chief Exec. Officer--A.Y.M. Inc., Albia, IA; *U.S. Private,* pg. 721
McDonald, Robert B., Pres. & Chief Exec. Officer--Great Lakes Chemical Corporation, West Lafayette, IN; *U.S. Public,* pg. 760
McDonald, Roy K., Pres. & Chief Exec. Officer--Connectix Corporation, San Mateo, CA; *U.S. Private,* pg. 264
McDonald, Scott, Pres. & Chief Exec. Officer--McDonald Equipment Co., Willoughby, OH; *U.S. Private,* pg. 721
McDonald, Stuart R., Pres., Chief Exec. Officer & Treas.--Marshall & Williams Co., Greenville, SC; *U.S. Private,* pg. 708
McDonald, Tom, Pres. & Chief Exec. Officer--Keller Kitchen Cabinets, De Land, FL; *U.S. Private,* pg. 612
McDonald, William E., Pres. & Chief Exec. Officer--National City Bank, Cleveland, OH; *U.S. Public,* pg. 1154
McDonnell, Dennis, Pres. & Chief Exec. Officer--Trace Mountain Products, San Jose, CA; *U.S. Private,* pg. 1095
McDonnell, Kevin R., Pres. & Chief Exec. Officer--Skyline Chili, Inc., Fairfield, OH; *U.S. Public,* pg. 1475
McDonnell, Terrence, Vice Chm. & Chief Exec. Officer--Connors Bros. Limited, Blacks Harbour, Canada; *Int'l,* pg. 1495
McDonnell, Thomas A., Pres. & Chief Exec. Officer--DST Systems, Inc., Kansas City, MO; *U.S. Public,* pg. 943
McDonough, Myles, Chief Exec. Officer--Flexcon Co., Inc., Spencer, MA; *U.S. Private,* pg. 412
McDonough, Russell B., Jr., Chm. Bd. & Chief Exec. Officer--Winrock Enterprises, Inc., Little Rock, AR; *U.S. Private,* pg. 1183
McDougall, Ronald A., Pres. & Chief Exec. Officer--Brinker International, Inc., Dallas, TX; *U.S. Public,* pg. 253
McDowell, Frank, Pres. & Chief Exec. Officer--BRE Properties, Inc., San Francisco, CA; *U.S. Public,* pg. 163
McDowell, Patrick W., Chief Exec. Officer-Retail Div.--Bank of Ireland, Dublin, Ireland; *Int'l,* pg. 152
McDowell, Robert, Pres. & Chief Exec. Officer--Olan Mills, Inc., Chattanooga, TN; *U.S. Private,* pg. 749
McEachern, James, Chm. Bd. & Chief Exec. Officer--Tom James Company, Franklin, TN; *U.S. Private,* pg. 580
McEachern, Ron, Pres. & Chief Exec. Officer--Pepsi-Cola Canada, Ltd., Toronto, Canada; *U.S. Public,* pg. 1277
McElnea, Jeffrey K., Pres. & Chief Exec. Officer--Einson Freeman Inc., Paramus, NJ; *Int'l,* pg. 1483
McEntire, J. Edward, Chief Exec. Officer--Ultimate Electronics, Thornton, CO; *U.S. Public,* pg. 1662
McEvoy, E. Bruce, Chief Exec. Officer--Sealed-Sweet Growers, Inc., Vero Beach, FL; *U.S. Private,* pg. 978
McEwen, Joseph, Chm. Bd. & Chief Exec. Officer--Modern Group Ltd., Bristol, PA; *U.S. Private,* pg. 754
McEwen, Robert R., Chm. & Chief Exec. Officer--CSA Management Inc., Toronto, Canada; *Int'l,* pg. 243
McEwen, Robert R., Chm. Bd. & Chief Exec. Officer--Goldcorp Inc., Toronto, Canada; *Int'l,* pg. 243
McEwen, Robert R., Chm. & Chief Exec. Officer--Lexam Explorations Inc., Toronto, Canada; *Int'l,* pg. 243
McFadgen, Terry, Chief Exec. Officer-Building--Fletcher Challenge Limited, Auckland, New Zealand; *Int'l,* pg. 494
McFadin, Larry, Chm. Bd. & Chief Exec. Officer--Philip Crosby Associates, Inc., Winter Park, FL; *Int'l,* pg. 1072
McFall, Tom, Chm. Bd., Pres. & Chief Exec. Officer--Weatherly Private Capital, Inc., New York, NY; *U.S. Private,* pg. 1156
McFarland, Julie, Chief Exec. Officer--McNaughton & Gunn, Inc., Saline, MI; *U.S. Private,* pg. 724
McFarland, Mike, Pres. & Chief Exec. Officer--Citizens First Bank, Arkadelphia, AR; *U.S. Public,* pg. 630
McFarlane, Roger, Joint Chief Exec. Officer--Union-Transport Corporation, Rancho Dominguez, CA; *U.S. Private,* pg. 1119
McFeetors, Raymond L., Pres. & Chief Exec. Officer-Canada--The Great-West Life Assurance Company, Winnipeg, Canada; *Int'l,* pg. 557
McFerson, D. Richard, Chm. Bd. & Chief Exec. Officer--Nationwide Insurance Enterprise, Columbus, OH; *U.S. Private,* pg. 788
McFerson, D.R., Chm. Bd. & Chief Exec Officer--Nationwide Mutual Insurance Co., Columbus, OH; *U.S. Private,* pg. 789
McGann, Gary, Group Chief Exec. Officer--Aer Lingus, Dublin, Ireland; *Int'l,* pg. 28
McGarland, William H., Pres. & Chief Exec. Officer--Irvine Apartment Communities Incorporated, Newport Beach, CA; *U.S. Private,* pg. 575
McGeehan, Robert L., Pres. & Chief Exec. Officer--Kennametal Inc., Latrobe, PA; *U.S. Public,* pg. 950
McGehee, Frank S., Co-Chm. Bd. & Co-Chief Exec. Officer--Mac Papers, Inc., Jacksonville, FL; *U.S. Private,* pg. 689
McGehee, Scott, Pres. & Chief Exec. Officer--Fort Wayne Newspapers, Inc., Fort Wayne, IN; *U.S. Public,* pg. 964
McGehee, Thomas R., Co-Chm Bd. & Chief Exec. Officer--Mac Papers, Inc., Jacksonville, FL; *U.S. Private,* pg. 689
McGhan, Donald, Chm. Bd. & Chief Exec. Officer--Inamed Corporation, Las Vegas, NV; *U.S. Public,* pg. 873
McGhie, Austin, Pres. & Chief Exec. Officer--Young & Rubicam San Francisco, San Francisco, CA; *U.S. Private,* pg. 1198
McGillivary, C.J., Chief Exec. Officer-U.S.A.--Waterford Wedgwood Plc, Dublin, Ireland; *Int'l,* pg. 1487
McGinley, Nigel Stephen, Chief Exec. Officer--Tie Rack plc, Brentford, United Kingdom; *Int'l,* pg. 1389

McGinn, Richard A., Pres. & Chief Exec. Officer--Lucent Technologies Inc., Murray Hill, NJ; *U.S. Public*, pg. 1017

McGinnis, Arthur J., Sr., Chm. Bd.-Exec. Committee & Chief Exec. Officer--Simmons-Boardman Publishing Corp., New York, NY; *U.S. Private*, pg. 1000

McGinnis, Daniel L., Chief Exec. Officer--Coherent Communications Systems Corp., Ashburn, VA; *U.S. Public*, pg. 1424

McGinnis, Michael E., Chm. Bd., Pres. & Chief Exec. Officer--American Eco Corporation, Toronto, Canada; *Int'l*, pg. 73

McGinnis, Michael E., Pres. & Chief Exec. Officer--American Eco Corporation, Houston, TX; *Int'l*, pg. 74

McGinnis, Patrick W., Co-Pres. & Co-Chief Exec. Officer--Ralston Purina Company, Saint Louis, MO; *U.S. Public*, pg. 1359

McGinty, Fredaerick W., Chief Exec. Officer--Hilb, Rogal and Hamilton Company of Savannah, Inc., Savannah, GA; *U.S. Public*, pg. 827

McGinty, Frederick W., Chief Exec.--Hilb, Rogal and Hamilton Company of St. Simons Island, Saint Simons Island, GA; *U.S. Public*, pg. 827

McGlaughlin, D.W., Vice Chm. & Chief Exec. Officer--Equifax Inc., Atlanta, GA; *U.S. Public*, pg. 588

McGlothlin, James W., Chm. Bd. & Chief Exec. Officer--The United Company, Bristol, VA; *U.S. Private*, pg. 1121

McGlynn, Micheal J., Chm. Bd. & Chief Exec. Officer--McGlynn Bakeries Inc., Minneapolis, MN; *U.S. Private*, pg. 721

McGonagle, Patrick J., Pres. & Chief Exec. Officer--National Gas & Oil Company, Newark, OH; *U.S. Public*, pg. 1156

McGough, George, Chm., Pres. & Chief Exec. Officer--Principal Financial Securities, Dallas, TX; *U.S. Private*, pg. 885

McGoun, Sam H., Pres. & Chief Exec. Officer--Willis Corroon Corp. of Michigan, Livonia, MI; *Int'l*, pg. 1506

McGovern, Terrence J., Pres. & Chief Exec. Officer--Liggett-Stashower, Inc., Cleveland, OH; *U.S. Private*, pg. 667

McGowan, David, Chief Exec. Officer--Bank of Ireland Corporate & International Banking, Belfast, United Kingdom; *Int'l*, pg. 153

McGowan, James, Pres. & Chief Exec. Officere--EIS International Inc., Herndon, VA; *U.S. Public*, pg. 544

McGowan, Mike, Chm. Bd. & Chief Exec. Officer--N.B.M. Corp., McAlester, OK; *U.S. Private*, pg. 771

McGrath, Don J., Pres. & Chief Exec. Officer--Bank of the West, Walnut Creek, CA; *Int'l*, pg. 163

McGrath, Eugene R., Chm. Bd., Pres. & Chief Exec. Officer--Consolidated Edison Company of New York, Inc., New York, NY; *U.S. Public*, pg. 434

McGrath, J.B., Group Chief Exec.--Diageo Plc, London, United Kingdom; *Int'l*, pg. 408

McGrath, J.B., Chief Exec. Officer--Grand Metropolitan Plc, London, United Kingdom; *Int'l*, pg. 408

McGrath, John P., Pres. & Chief Exec. Officer--Hilb, Rogal and Hamilton Company of Pittsburgh, Inc., Pittsburgh, PA; *U.S. Public*, pg. 827

McGrath, Margaret H., Pres. & Chief Oper. Officer--PPG Canada Inc., Mississauga, Canada; *U.S. Public*, pg. 1245

McGrath, Patrick J., Pres. & Chief Exec. Officer--Jordan, McGrath, Case & Taylor Inc., New York, NY; *U.S. Private*, pg. 598

McGrath, Robert P., Chm. Bd. & Chief Exec. Officer--McGrath RentCorp, Livermore, CA; *U.S. Public*, pg. 1069

McGraw, Richard D., Pres. & Chief Exec. Officer--Vitran Corporation Inc., Toronto, Canada; *Int'l*, pg. 1469

McGregor, Douglas J., Chm. Bd. & Chief Exec. Officer--M.A. Hanna Company, Cleveland, OH; *U.S. Public*, pg. 780

McGregor, G. W., Chief Exec. Officer & Exec. Gen. Mgr.--BHP Service Companies, Melbourne, Australia; *Int'l*, pg. 225

McGregor, I.C., Chief Exec. Officer--Redland Quarries Inc., Hamilton, Canada; *Int'l*, pg. 1093

McGregor, Stewart D., Chm. Bd. & Chief Exec. Officer--Numac Energy Inc., Calgary, Canada; *Int'l*, pg. 990

McGrory, Jack, Pres. & Chief Exec. Officer--Price Enterprises, Inc., San Diego, CA; *U.S. Public*, pg. 1324

McGuire, Gerald A., Corp. V.P., Pres. & Chief Exec. Officer-Pepsi Cola Gen. Bottlers--Whitman Corporation, Rolling Meadows, IL; *U.S. Public*, pg. 1766

McGuire, James, Chief Exec. Officer--Twinco Services, Inc., Edison, NJ; *U.S. Private*, pg. 1111

McGuire, James, Chief Exec. Officer--Twinco Graphics, Edison, NJ; *U.S. Private*, pg. 1111

McGuire, Michael, Pres. & Chief Exec. Officer--Astrex, Inc., Plainview, NY; *U.S. Public*, pg. 141

McGuire, Michael, Pres. & Chief Exec. Officer--Progress International Limited, Plainview, NY; *U.S. Public*, pg. 141

McGuire, Thomas R., Chm. Bd. & Chief Exec. Officer--The Coast Distribution System, San Jose, CA; *U.S. Public*, pg. 388

McGuire, William W., M.D., Chm. Bd., Pres. & Chief Exec. Officer--United HealthCare Corporation, Minnetonka, MN; *U.S. Public*, pg. 1677

McGuire, William W., M.D., Chm. Bd., Pres. & Chief Exec. Officer--United HealthCare Services, Inc., Minnetonka, MN; *U.S. Public*, pg. 1678

McGuirk, Terence F., Chm. Bd., Pres. & Chief Exec. Officer--Turner Broadcasting System Inc., Atlanta, GA; *U.S. Public*, pg. 1614

McHale, Hank P., Pres. & Chief Exec. Officer--TransPro, Inc., New Haven, CT; *U.S. Public*, pg. 1631

McHugh, James P., Pres. & Chief Exec. Officer--James McHugh Construction Co., Chicago, IL; *U.S. Private*, pg. 721

McIlnay, Donald, Pres. & Chief Exec. Officer--The Gibson-Homans Company, Twinsburg, OH; *U.S. Private*, pg. 451

McInerney, James S., Pres. & Chief Exec. Officer--Aquarion Management Services, Bridgeport, CT; *U.S. Public*, pg. 126

McInerney, Joseph A., Pres. & Chief Exec. Officer--Travelodge, El Cajon, CA; *U.S. Public*, pg. 322

McInnes, Allen, Pres. & Chief Exec. Officer--Tetra Technologies, Woodlands, TX; *U.S. Public*, pg. 1582

McInnis, Buck, Chief Exec. Officer--Tampa Bay Steel, Tampa, FL; *U.S. Private*, pg. 1067

McIntyre, James A., Chm. Bd. & Chief Exec. Officer--Fremont General Corporation, Santa Monica, CA; *U.S. Public*, pg. 681

McIntyre, Patrick, Chief Exec. Officer--Outdoor Technologies Group, Spirit Lake, IA; *U.S. Private*, pg. 822

McIntyre, William D., Pres. & Chief Exec. Officer--American Speedy Printing Centers, Inc., Troy, MI; *U.S. Private*, pg. 62

McKane, Tom, Pres. & Chief Exec. Officer--S-B Power Tool Company, Chicago, IL; *Int'l*, pg. 205

McKay, Carl, Pres. & Chief Exec. Officer--Sioux Manufacturing Corp., Fort Totten, ND; *U.S. Private*, pg. 1003

McKay, Frank J., Chief Exec.-Blue Circle Heating--Blue Circle Industries PLC, London, United Kingdom; *Int'l*, pg. 197

McKay, Frederick, M.D., Chief Exec. Officer--Huntington Provider Management Services, Pasadena, CA; *U.S. Private*, pg. 1118

McKay, Robert C., Pres. & Chief Exec. Officer--Tenera, Inc., San Francisco, CA; *U.S. Public*, pg. 1576

McKearn, Thomas J., Dr., Chm. & Chief Exec. Officer--Cytogen Corporation, Princeton, NJ; *U.S. Public*, pg. 471

McKee, Ernest H., Pres. & Chief Exec. Officer--Westwood Corporation, Tulsa, OK; *U.S. Public*, pg. 1763

McKee, Jack C., Pres. & Chief Exec. Officer--McKee Foods Corporation, Collegedale, TN; *U.S. Private*, pg. 723

McKee, Paul, Chief Exec. Officer & Exec. V.P.--The Martin Agency, Richmond, VA; *U.S. Private*, pg. 678

McKee, Paul, Chief Exec. Officer & Exec. V.P.--The Martin Agency, Richmond, VA; *U.S. Public*, pg. 909

McKee, W.W., Pres., Chief Exec. & Chief Oper. Officer--Pitt-Des Moines, Inc., Pittsburgh, PA; *U.S. Public*, pg. 1304

McKeever, Jeffrey D., Chm. Bd. & Chief Exec. Officer--MicroAge, Inc., Tempe, AZ; *U.S. Public*, pg. 1104

McKellar, Christopher S., Chief Exec. Officer--McKellar Companies, San Diego, CA; *U.S. Private*, pg. 723

McKelvey, Andrew J., Chm. & Chief Exec. Officer--TMP Worldwide, Inc., New York, NY; *U.S. Private*, pg. 1064

Mckenna, Andrew J., Sr., Chm. Bd. & Chief Exec. Officer--Schwarz Paper Company, Morton Grove, IL; *U.S. Private*, pg. 974

McKenna, John A., Jr., Pres. & Chief Exec. Officer--Entex Information Services, Rye Brook, NY; *U.S. Private*, pg. 378

McKenna, P.W., Chm. Bd., Pres. & Chief Exec. Officer--Plasti-Kote Company Inc., Medina, OH; *U.S. Private*, pg. 870

McKenna, Robert J., Chm. Bd., Pres. & Chief Exec. Officer--Acme Electric Corporation, East Aurora, NY; *U.S. Public*, pg. 16

MCKenzie, Ian S.V., Chief Exec.-Blue Circle Cement Europe--Blue Circle Industries PLC, London, United Kingdom; *Int'l*, pg. 197

McKenzie, James, Pres. & Chief Exec. Officer-Canada--Leo Burnett Company, Inc., Chicago, IL; *U.S. Private*, pg. 183

McKenzie, James, Pres. & Chief Exec. Officer--Leo Burnett Company Ltd., Toronto, Canada; *U.S. Private*, pg. 185

Mckenzie, John, Chm. Bd. & Chief Exec. Officer--Sleepeezee Limited, London, United Kingdom; *Int'l*, pg. 1263

McKenzie, Michael K., Chm. Bd., Pres. & Chief Exec. Officer--GSC Enterprises, Inc., Sulphur Springs, TX; *U.S. Private*, pg. 436

McKenzie, R.W., Chief Exec. Officer--TIC, Steamboat Springs, CO; *U.S. Private*, pg. 1064

McKeown, S., Chief Exec. Officer--Powerscreen International Plc, Dungannon, United Kingdom; *Int'l*, pg. 1066

McKiernan, Thomas, Chm. Bd. & Interim Chief Exec. Officer--Moore Corporation Limited, Toronto, Canada; *Int'l*, pg. 888

McKim, Alan S., Chm. Bd., Pres. & Chief Exec. Officer--Clean Harbors, Inc., Braintree, MA; *U.S. Public*, pg. 383

McKinney, John B., Pres. & Chief Exec. Officer--Laclede Steel Company, Saint Louis, MO; *U.S. Public*, pg. 974

McKinney, Marni, Pres. & Chief Exec. Officer--The Somerset Group, Inc., Indianapolis, IN; *U.S. Public*, pg. 1484

McKinney, Myron W., Chm. Bd., Pres. & Chief Exec. Officer--The Empire District Electric Company, Joplin, MO; *U.S. Public*, pg. 579

McKinney, William H., Pres. & Chief Exec. Officer--The Royal China & Porcelain Companies Inc., Moorestown, NJ; *U.S. Private*, pg. 948

McKinniss, Sherman L., Chm. Bd., Pres. & Chief Exec. Officer--Rotonics Manufacturing Inc., Gardena, CA; *U.S. Public*, pg. 1406

McKinnon, Bob E., Pres. & Chief Exec. Officer--Century Furniture Industries, Hickory, NC; *U.S. Private*, pg. 226

McKinnon, R., Chief Exec.-Bus. & Trustee Superannuation--MLC Limited, Sydney, Australia; *Int'l*, pg. 806

McKitrick, James T., Pres. & Chief Exec. Officer--Central Tractor Farm & Country, Inc., Des Moines, IA; *U.S. Private*, pg. 237

McKnight, Andrew D., Chm. Bd., Pres. & Chief Exec. Officer--Tri-Chem, Inc., Harrison, NJ; *U.S. Private*, pg. 1100

McKnight, Robert B., Jr., Chm. Bd. & Chief Exec. Officer--Quiksilver, Inc., Costa Mesa, CA; *U.S. Public*, pg. 1353

McKnight, William B., Jr., Pres. & Chief Exec. Officer--Wise Foods, Inc., Parsippany, NJ; *U.S. Private*, pg. 157

McKone, F.L., Pres. & Chief Exec. Officer--Albany International Corp., Albany, NY; *U.S. Public*, pg. 36

McLagan, Donald L., Chm. Bd., Pres. & Chief Exec. Officer--NewsEdge Corporation, Burlington, MA; *U.S. Public*, pg. 1180

McLain, Mike A., Pres. & Chief Exec. Officer--DowBrands, L.P., Indianapolis, IN; *U.S. Public*, pg. 523

McLane, Tim, Pres. & Chief Exec. Officer--Skinner Corp., Lanett, AL; *U.S. Private*, pg. 1005

McLaughlin, Brian D., Chm. Bd., Pres. & Cbief Exec. Officer--Hurco Companies, Inc., Indianapolis, IN; *U.S. Public*, pg. 850

McLaughlin, J.J., Pres. & Chief Exec. Officer--DAP Inc., Tipp City, OH; *Int'l*, pg. 1486

McLaughlin, Paul, Pres. & Chief Exec. Officer--The Butcher Company, Marlborough, MA; *U.S. Private*, pg. 189

McLaughlin, Philip L., Pres. & Chief Exec. Officer--Greenbrier Valley National Bank, Lewisburg, WV; *U.S. Public*, pg. 836

McLaughlin, William F., Pres. & Chief Exec. Officer--Sweetheart Cup Company Inc., Owings Mills, MD; *U.S. Private*, pg. 1058

McLaurin, Neil H., III, Chm. Bd. & Chief Exec. Officer--E-Z Serve Corp., Houston, TX; *U.S. Public*, pg. 540

McLean, Archie D., Vice Chm. & Chief Exec. Officer--Maple Leaf Foods Inc., Toronto, Canada; *Int'l*, pg. 841

McLean, Robert H., Chief Exec. Officer--BFX Hospitality Group, Inc., Fort Worth, TX; *U.S. Public*, pg. 160

McLeod, Clark, Chm. Bd. & Chief Exec. Officer--McLeodUSA Incorporated, Cedar Rapids, IA; *U.S. Public*, pg. 1073

McLeod, D.A., Pres. & Chief Exec. Officer--Newhawk Gold Mines LTD., Vancouver, Canada; *U.S. Public*, pg. 833

McLeod, Wayne M.E., Pres. & Chief Exec. Officer--CCL Industries, Inc., Willowdale, Canada; *Int'l*, pg. 238

McLoughlin, Raymond J., Chief Exec. Officer--James Crean PLC, Dublin, Ireland; *Int'l*, pg. 340

McMahen, Charles E., Chm. Bd. & Chief Exec. Officer--Compass Bancshares, Inc., Houston, TX; *U.S. Public*, pg. 419

McMahon, Patrick, Pres. & Chief Exec. Officer--Virginia Tourism Corp., Richmond, VA; *U.S. Private*, pg. 1141

McMahon, Richard A., Pres. & Chief Exec. Officer--Minnesota Brewing Company, Saint Paul, MN; *U.S. Public*, pg. 1115

McMahon, William J., Pres. & Chief Exec. Officer--Lund International Holdings, Inc., Anoka, MN; *U.S. Public*, pg. 1020

McManus, James A., Pres. & Chief Exec. Officer--Radio City Productions, New York, NY; *Int'l*, pg. 873

McManus, Michael F., Chm. Bd., Pres. & Chief Exec. Officer--Header Products Inc., Romulus, MI; *U.S. Private*, pg. 514

McMillan, Douglas, Chm. Bd. & Chief Exec. Officer--Allison-Erwin Co. Inc., Charlotte, NC; *U.S. Private*, pg. 41

McMillen, John, Pres. & Chief Exec. Officer--The Garber Company, Ashland, OH; *U.S. Public*, pg. 303

McMillen, Robert B., Co.-Chm. & Co.-Chief Exec. Officer--Totem Resources Corporation, Seattle, WA; *U.S. Private*, pg. 1092

McMorris, Jerry, Pres. & Chief Exec. Officer--NW Transport Service, Inc., Denver, CO; *U.S. Private*, pg. 772

McMorrow, William, Chm. Bd. & Chief Exec. Officer--Kennedy-Wilson, Inc., Santa Monica, CA; *U.S. Public*, pg. 951

McMullen, Walter P., Sr., Chm. Bd. & Chief Exec. Officer--Master Graphic, Inc., Memphis, TN; *U.S. Private*, pg. 713

McMullian, Amos R., Chm. Bd. & Chief Exec. Officer--Flowers Industries, Inc., Thomasville, GA; *U.S. Public*, pg. 656

McMurtrie, James C., Chm. Bd., Chief Exec. Officer & Treas.--E.W. Knauss & Son, Inc., Quakertown, PA; *U.S. Private*, pg. 626

McMurtry, David, Chm. Bd. & Chief Exec. Officer--Renishaw plc, Wotton-under-Edge, United Kingdom; *Int'l*, pg. 1103

McNable, John, Pres. & Chief Exec. Officer--NVF Company, Yorklyn, DE; *U.S. Private*, pg. 772

McNair, Joe, Pres. & Chief Exec. Officer--Whitfield Foods, Inc., Montgomery, AL; *U.S. Private*, pg. 1173

McNally, Alan G., Chm. Bd. & Chief Exec. Officer--Harris Bankcorp, Inc., Chicago, IL; *Int'l*, pg. 154

McNamara, Austin T., Pres. & Chief Exec. Officer--General Cigar Company, Inc., Bloomfield, CT; *U.S. Public*, pg. 708

Mcnamara, Daniel F., Pres. & Chief Exec. Officer--URS Logistics, Atlanta, GA; *U.S. Private*, pg. 1114

McNamara, James, Pres. & Chief Exec. Officer--New World Entertainment, Inc., Los Angeles, CA; *Int'l*, pg. 926

McNamara, Robert, Chief Exec. Officer--ADP Marshall Contractors Inc., Rumford, RI; *U.S. Public*, pg. 660

McNamee, James M., Chm. Bd., Pres. & Chief Exec. Officer--Hooper Holmes Corporation, Basking Ridge, NJ; *U.S. Public*, pg. 835

McNamee, Rick, Chm. Bd., Pres. & Chief Exec. Officer--Continental Circuits Corp., Phoenix, AZ; *U.S. Public*, pg. 440

McNealy, Scott G., Chm. Bd., Pres. & Chief Exec. Officer--Sun Microsystems, Inc., Palo Alto, CA; *U.S. Public*, pg. 1531

McNeil, John D., Chm. Bd. & Chief Exec. Officer--Sun Life Assurance Company of Canada, Toronto, Canada; *Int'l*, pg. 1318

McNeill, Corbin A., Jr., Chm. Bd., Pres. & Chief Exec. Officer--PECO Energy Company, Philadelphia, PA; *U.S. Public*, pg. 1268

McNeill, Michael, Pres. & Chief Exec. Officer--Gifford-Hill Company, Dallas, TX; *Int'l*, pg. 593

McNeilly, R.J., Exec. Gen. Mgr. & Chief Exec. Officer--BHP Steel, Melbourne, Australia; *Int'l*, pg. 225

McNeilly, Robert E., III, Chm., Pres. & Chief Exec. Officer--SunTrust Bank, Alabama, N.A., Florence, AL; *U.S. Public*, pg. 1538

McNelis, Michael F., Pres. & Chief Exec. Officer--Equitable Financial Consultants, Inc., New York, NY; *U.S. Public*, pg. 589

McNerney, W. James, Pres. & Chief Exec. Officer--Greenwich Air Services, Miami, FL; *U.S. Public*, pg. 710

McNulty, Dermot, Chief Exec. Officer--Shandwick International Plc, London, United Kingdom; *Int'l*, pg. 1226

McNulty, James F., Pres. & Chief Exec. Officer--Parsons Corporation, Pasadena, CA; U.S. Private, pg. 841
McNutt, L.W., Jr., Chm. Bd. & Chief Exec. Officer--Collin Street Bakery, Corsicana, TX; U.S. Private, pg. 252
McPhail, Douglas J., Pres., Chief Exec. & Fin. Officer & Treas.--Indiana Records Managers, Fishers, IN; U.S. Private, pg. 560
McPherson, Karen, Chief Exec. Officer--TMP Worldwide Pty Limited, Sydney, Australia; Int'l, pg. 1342
McPheters, Rebecca, Pres. & Chief Exec. Officer--Simmons, New York, NY; Int'l, pg. 1483
McQueen, Angus, Chm. Bd. & Chief Exec. Officer--Ackerman McQueen, Inc., Oklahoma City, OK; U.S. Private, pg. 12
McQuillen, Harry A., Pres. & Chief Exec. Officer--K-III Media Group, New York, NY; U.S. Public, pg. 1328
McQuinn, Alvin E., Chm. Bd. & Chief Exec. Officer--Ag-Chem Equipment Co., Inc., Minnetonka, MN; U.S. Public, pg. 6
McRae, D. Gary, Chm. Bd., Pres. & Chief Exec. Officer--McRae Industries, Inc., Mount Gilead, NC; U.S. Public, pg. 1073
McShane, Brian, Pres. & Chief Exec. Officer--Advertising Checking Bureau Incorporated, New York, NY; U.S. Private, pg. 23
McTeer, Robert D., Jr., Pres. & Chief Exec. Officer--Federal Reserve Bank of Dallas, Dallas, TX; U.S. Private, pg. 399
McVaney, C. Edward, Pres. & Chief Exec. Officer--J.D. Edwards & Company, Denver, CO; U.S. Private, pg. 365
McWhorter, Donald L., Chm. Bd. & Chief Exec. Officer--Banc One Ohio Corporation, Columbus, OH; U.S. Public, pg. 173
McWilliam, Richard, Chm. Bd. & Chief Exec. Officer--The Upper Deck Company, LLC, Carlsbad, CA; U.S. Private, pg. 1129
Mead, Dana G., Chm. Bd., Pres. & Chief Exec. Officer--Tenneco Inc., Greenwich, CT; U.S. Public, pg. 1577
Mead, Gary L., Pres. & Chief Exec. Officer--La Quinta Inns, Inc., San Antonio, TX; U.S. Public, pg. 972
Meade, David C., Chief Exec. Officer & Mgr.-Adv.--The Journal, Williamston, SC; U.S. Private, pg. 601
Meade, H.S., Chief Oper. Officer--Virginia Tobacco Co., Inc., Danville, VA; U.S. Public, pg. 1695
Meade, H.S., Chief Oper. Officer--Virsa, Inc., Danville, VA; U.S. Public, pg. 1695
Meade, John, Pres. & Chief Exec. Officer--Hanover Bank, Mechanicsville, VA; U.S. Public, pg. 1039
Meader, Peggy, Pres. & Chief Exec. Officer--Inland Associates, Olathe, KS; U.S. Private, pg. 563
Meader, Scott, Pres. & Chief Exec. Officer--The Milnot Company, Saint Louis, MO; U.S. Private, pg. 749
Meadlock, James W., Chm. Bd., Pres. & Chief Exec. Officer--Intergraph Corporation, Huntsville, AL; U.S. Public, pg. 890
Meagher, Joseph B., Pres. & Chief Exec. Officer--Yankee Publishing Incorporated, Dublin, NH; U.S. Private, pg. 1195
Meagher, Michael J., Chief Exec. Officer-Corp. & Treas. Div.--Bank of Ireland, Dublin, Ireland; Int'l, pg. 152
Meakem, John J., Jr., Chm. Bd., Pres. & Chief Exec. Officer--Advanced Polymer Systems, Redwood City, CA; U.S. Public, pg. 22
Meany, H. Jack, Chm. Bd. & Chief Exec. Officer--Farr Company, El Segundo, CA; U.S. Public, pg. 613
Mears, Paul S., Jr., Chief Exec. Officer--Mears Transportation Group, Orlando, FL; U.S. Private, pg. 726
Mebane, David C., Chm. Bd., Pres., Chief Exec. & Oper. Officer--Madison Gas and Electric Company, Madison, WI; U.S. Public, pg. 1032
Mechura, Frank, Pres. & Chief Exec. Officer--Crown Cork of Canada Ltd., Concord, Canada; U.S. Public, pg. 464
Mechura, Frank J., Pres. & Chief Exec. Officer--Crown Cork & Seal Canada, Inc., Concord, Canada; U.S. Public, pg. 464
Medary, William, Pres. & Chief Exec. Officer--Bass Enterprises Production Company, Fort Worth, TX; U.S. Private, pg. 122
Medina, Dionisio Garza, Chm. Bd., Pres. & Chief Exec. Officer--Alfa, S.A. de C.V., Garza Garcia, Mexico; Int'l, pg. 56
Meeker, Thomas H., Pres. & Chief Exec. Officer--Churchill Downs, Inc., Louisville, KY; U.S. Public, pg. 356
Meelia, Richard D., Pres. & Chief Exec. Officer--The Kendall Company, Mansfield, MA; U.S. Public, pg. 1647
Meerstadt, Bert, Pres. & Chief Exec. Officer--PMSVW/Young & Rubicam B.V., Amsterdam, Netherlands; U.S. Private, pg. 1199
Meeuwsen, Michael D., Pres. & Chief Exec. Officer--First Northern Capital Corp., Green Bay, WI; U.S. Public, pg. 636
Mefford, Dean A., Pres. & Chief Exec. Officer--Viskase Corporation, Chicago, IL; U.S. Public, pg. 586
Mehlis, David L., Chm. Bd., Pres. & Chief Exec. Officer--Cook Communication Ministries, Colorado Springs, CO; U.S. Private, pg. 272
Mehner, Edward W., Chm. Bd. & Chief Exec. Officer--The Rugby Group, Inc., Rockville Centre, NY; Int'l, pg. 625
Mehta, Shailesh J., Chm. Bd., Pres. & Chief Exec. Officer--Providian Financial Corporation, San Francisco, CA; U.S. Public, pg. 1338
Mehta, V.K., Chief Exec. Officer--WAGO & Controls (India) Ltd., Nolda, India; Int'l, pg. 209
Meier, Norman M., Pres. & Chief Exec. Officer--Columbia Laboratories, Inc., Miami, FL; U.S. Public, pg. 405
Meier, Paul, Chief Exec. Officer--Credit Suisse First Boston, Zurich, Switzerland; Int'l, pg. 345
Meier, Paul Gerhard, Chief Exec.--Sulzer Metco (Deutschland) GmbH, Hattersheim, Germany; Int'l, pg. 1307
Meinert, K.J., Pres. & Chief Exec. Officer--CGC Inc., Mississauga, Canada; U.S. Public, pg. 1660
Meinig, Peter, Pres. & Chief Exec. Officer--HM International, Tulsa, OK; U.S. Private, pg. 491
Meister, James, Pres. & Chief Exec. Officer--Kings Super Markets Inc., West Caldwell, NJ; Int'l, pg. 843
Melancon, Barry C., Pres. & Chief Exec. Officer--American Institute of C.P.A.'s Inc., New York, NY; U.S. Private, pg. 57
Melbourn, J. W., Deputy Grp. Chief Exec. Officer--National Westminster Bank PLC, London, United Kingdom; Int'l, pg. 910
Melia, Kevin, Pres. & Chief Exec. Officer--Manufacturers' Services Ltd., Concord, MA; U.S. Private, pg. 701
Melin, David, Chm. & Chief Exec. Officer--Groupe Saint Louis, Paris, France; Int'l, pg. 567
Mellen, Harold J., Jr., Pres. & Chief Exec. Officer--MDU Resources Group, Inc., Bismarck, ND; U.S. Public, pg. 1025
Mellick, William L., Pres. & Chief Exec. Officer--20th Century Industries, Woodland Hills, CA; U.S. Public, pg. 1646
Melling, A. Frederick, Pres. & Chief Exec. Officer--Willis Corroon Melling Inc., Montreal, Canada; Int'l, pg. 1509
Mellon, Timothy, Chm. Bd. & Chief Exec. Officer--Guilford Transportation Industries Inc., Nashua, NH; U.S. Private, pg. 487
Mellott, Paul C., Chief Exec. Officer--H.B. Mellott Estate, Inc., Warfordsburg, PA; U.S. Private, pg. 730
Melman, Richard, Chief Exec. Officer--Lettuce Entertain You Enterprises, Inc., Chicago, IL; U.S. Private, pg. 661
Melnick, Norman, Chm. Bd. & Chief Exec. Officer--Pentech International, Inc., Edison, NJ; U.S. Public, pg. 1274
Meloni, Stefano, Chm. Bd., Pres. & Chief Exec. Officer--Eridania Beghin-Say Group, Neuilly-sur-Seine, France; Int'l, pg. 324
Meloon, Walter N., Pres. & Chief Exec. Officer--Correct Craft, Inc., Orlando, FL; U.S. Private, pg. 276
Melrose, Kendrick B., Chm. Bd. & Chief Exec. Officer--The Toro Company, Bloomington, MN; U.S. Public, pg. 1623
Melsop, J. William, Pres. & Chief Exec. Officer--The Austin Company, Cleveland, OH; U.S. Private, pg. 99
Meltz, Edward E., Chm. Bd., Chief Exec. Officer & Chief Fin. Officer--Carsen Group Inc., Markham, Canada; U.S. Public, pg. 301
Meltzer, Robert K., Pres. & Chief Exec. Officer--Evans, Inc., Chicago, IL; U.S. Public, pg. 596
Meltzner, Sidney, Chief Exec. Officer--Condor Pacific Industries, Inc., Westlake Village, CA; U.S. Private, pg. 262
Melucci, Thomas, Pres. & Chief Exec. Officer--Priority Finishing Corp., Fall River, MA; U.S. Private, pg. 887
Melvin, Joseph, Pres. & Chief Oper. Officer--Finlay Fine Jewelry Corporation, New York, NY; U.S. Public, pg. 624
Melzer, Robert M., Pres. & Chief Exec. Officer--Property Capital Trust, Boston, MA; U.S. Public, pg. 1335
Menard, R. Claude, Chief Exec. Officer--Agropur, Granby, Canada; Int'l, pg. 31
Mendelsohn, Robert V., Chm. Bd., Pres. & Chief Exec. Officer--Royal Insurance, Charlotte, NC; Int'l, pg. 1130
Mendelson, Eric A., Chief Exec. Officer--Jet Avion Corporation, Hollywood, FL; U.S. Public, pg. 804
Mendelson, Ira, Pres. & Chief Exec. Officer--Murry's, Inc., Upper Marlboro, MD; U.S. Private, pg. 768
Mendelson, Laurans, Chm. Bd., Pres. & Chief Exec. Officer--HEICO Corporation, Hollywood, FL; U.S. Public, pg. 804
Mendoza, V., Chief Fin. Officer, Chief Information Officer & Treas.--Gator Industries Inc., Hialeah, FL; U.S. Private, pg. 441
Meng Wah, Alex Chan, Chief Exec. Officer & Mng. Dir--Yeo Hiap Seng Limited, Singapore, Singapore; Int'l, pg. 1008
Mengedoth, Donald R., Chm. Bd., Pres., & Chief Exec. Officer--Community First Bankshares, Inc., Fargo, ND; U.S. Public, pg. 416
Menges, Carl B., Chm. Bd. & Chief Exec. Officer--Wood, Struthers & Winthrop Management Corp., New York, NY; U.S. Public, pg. 589
Mentzer, Carl F., Chm. Bd., Pres. & Chief Exec. Officer--SunTrust Bank, Tampa Bay, Tampa, FL; U.S. Public, pg. 1538
Menzies-Gow, R. Ian, Chief Exec. Officer--ARC Limited, Chipping Sodbury, United Kingdom; Int'l, pg. 592
Menzler, Jurgen, Dr., Chief Exec. Officer--Pittler Maschinenfabrik AG, Langen, Germany; Int'l, pg. 1128
Mercer, Don P., Chief Exec. Officer--Australia & New Zealand Banking Group Limited, Melbourne, Australia; Int'l, pg. 98
Mercer, William, Pres. & Chief Exec. Officer--ALARIS Medical Systems, Inc., San Diego, CA; U.S. Public, pg. 35
Mercer, William J., Pres. & Chief Exec. Officer--ALARIS Medical, Inc., San Diego, CA; U.S. Public, pg. 35
Merchant, Keith, Chief Exec. Officer--B & P Manufacturing, Cadillac, MI; U.S. Private, pg. 105
Mercurio, Pascal J., Chm. Bd. & Chief Exec. Officer--U.S. Clearing Corp., New York, NY; U.S. Public, pg. 650
Merelli, F.H., Chm. Bd., Pres. & Chief Exec. Officer--Key Production Company, Inc., Denver, CO; U.S. Public, pg. 953
Meringola, Paul D., Chm. Bd., Pres., Chief Exec. Officer & Chief Oper. Officer--Medical Action Industries Inc., Hauppauge, NY; U.S. Public, pg. 1079
Merkel, F.G., Chief Exec. Officer--HealthAmerica Pennsylvania, Inc., Pittsburgh, PA; U.S. Public, pg. 454
Merkel, F.G. Chip, V.P. & Chief Exec. Officer--HealthAmerica of Central Pennsylvania, Harrisburg, PA; U.S. Public, pg. 454
Merkin, A. Barry, Chm. Bd. & Chief Exec. Officer--Dresher, Inc., Carthage, MO; U.S. Public, pg. 986
Merksamer, Samuel J., Pres. & Chief Exec. Officer--Barry's Jewelers, Inc., Monrovia, CA; U.S. Public, pg. 192
Merloni, Vittorio, Dtre., Chm. Bd., Pres. & Chief Exec. Officer--Merloni Elettrodomestici S.P.A., Fabriano, Italy; Int'l, pg. 860
Mermelstein, Bernard, Chief Exec. Officer--Elgin Watch Company, Long Island City, NY; U.S. Private, pg. 371
Merrell, John K., Pres., Chief Exec. Officer & Chief Oper. Officer--Industrial Dielectrics, Inc., Noblesville, IN; U.S. Private, pg. 560
Merrell, W.M., Pres. & Chief Exec. Officer--Howard, Merrell & Partners, Inc., Raleigh, NC; U.S. Private, pg. 542
Merrill, Keniston P., Chm. Bd., Pres. & Chief Exec. Officer--Sentinel Advisors, Inc., Montpelier, VT; U.S. Private, pg. 785
Merrill, Keniston P., Chm., Pres. & Chief Exec. Officer--National Life Investment Management Co., Inc., Montpelier, VT; U.S. Private, pg. 785
Merriman, Mike, Chm. Bd., Pres. & Chief Exec. Officer--Royal Appliance Mfg. Co., Cleveland, OH; U.S. Public, pg. 1410
Merritts, Glenn, Pres. & Chief Exec. Officer--Mednet, MPC Corporation, Las Vegas, NV; U.S. Public, pg. 1082
Merry, Bob, Pres. & Chief Exec. Officer--USDATA Corporation, Richardson, TX; U.S. Public, pg. 1425
Mersereau, Stephen C., Chief Exec. Officer--Infinicom, Chatham, NJ; U.S. Private, pg. 561
Merson, Robert, Pres. & Chief Exec. Officer--Southern Electric Supply Co., Inc., Meridian, MS; Int'l, pg. 1107
Mertens, Lynne, Pres. & Chief Exec. Officer--Warrens Waller Press, Inc., South San Francisco, CA; U.S. Private, pg. 1151
Mertes, Wayne M., Pres. & Chief Exec. Officer--National R.V., Inc., Perris, CA; U.S. Public, pg. 1159
Meshberg, Emil, Chief Exec. Officer--Emson, Inc., Bridgeport, CT; U.S. Private, pg. 375
Meshon, Louis P., Chief Exec. Officer--CV Reit, Inc., West Palm Beach, FL; U.S. Public, pg. 286
Messer, John R., Pres. & Chief Exec. Officer--SaskPower, Regina, Canada; Int'l, pg. 1195
Messina, Dana, Pres. & Chief Exec. Officer--Utilimaster Corp., Wakarusa, IN; U.S. Private, pg. 1130
Messina, George, Pres. & Chief Exec. Officer--Burdick, Inc., Milton, WI; U.S. Private, pg. 181
Messino, Frank, Pres. & Chief Exec. Officer--Carme' Cosmeceutical Sciences, Inc., Napa, CA; U.S. Private, pg. 213
Messmer, Harold M., Jr., Chm. Bd., Pres. & Chief Exec. Officer--Robert Half International Inc., Menlo Park, CA; U.S. Public, pg. 774
Messner, James W., Chm. Bd. & Chief Exec. Officer--J.W. Messner, Inc., Grand Rapids, MI; U.S. Private, pg. 734
Mestrallet, Gerard, Chm. Bd. & Chief Exec. Officer--Compagnie de Suez, Paris, France; Int'l, pg. 313
Mestre, Fernando Senderos, Chm. Bd. & Chief Exec. Officer--Desc, S.A. de C.V., Mexico, Mexico; Int'l, pg. 395
Metcalf, Micheal, Chief Exec.--Thorn plc, Chertsey, United Kingdom; Int'l, pg. 1385
Metcalfe, Jeremy W., Pres. & Chief Exec. Officer--Millicom International Cellular SA, Bertrange, Luxembourg; Int'l, pg. 867
Meteny, Dennis S., Pres. & Chief Exec. Officer--Respironics, Inc., Pittsburgh, PA; U.S. Public, pg. 1383
Meton, Sonia, Chm. Bd. & Chief Exec. Officer--Turbomeca Microturbo Division, Bordes, France; Int'l, pg. 786
Metropolous, C. Dean, Chm. Bd. & Chief Exec. Officer--The Morning Star Group, Dallas, TX; U.S. Public, pg. 1527
Metzger, Michael, Pres. & Chief Exec. Officer--Willis Corroon Corp. of Arizona, Phoenix, AZ; Int'l, pg. 1505
Meuleman, Robert J., Pres. & Chief Exec. Officer--Amcore Financial, Inc., Rockford, IL; U.S. Public, pg. 64
Meuser, Philip, Chief Exec. Officer--Riker Products, Inc., Toledo, OH; U.S. Private, pg. 300
Meuser, Scott, Pres. & Chief Exec. Officer--Pride Health Care, Inc., Exeter, PA; U.S. Private, pg. 883
Meyer-Galow, Erhard, Dr., Chief Exec. Officer--Huls AG, Marl, Germany; Int'l, pg. 1454
Meyer, Edward H., Chm., Chief Exec. Officer & Pres.-Grey Worldwide--Grey Advertising Inc., New York, NY; U.S. Public, pg. 764
Meyer, Fred, Chm. Bd., Chief Exec. Officer--Bierbrauerei Fohrenburg, Bludenz, Austria; Int'l, pg. 194
Meyer, Frederick R., Chm. Bd. & Chief Exec. Officer--Aladdin Industries, Incorporated, Nashville, TN; U.S. Private, pg. 30
Meyer, George G., Chief Exec. Officer, Treas. & Sec.--Central Sprinkler Corporation, Lansdale, PA; U.S. Public, pg. 327
Meyer, Henry L., III, Chm. & Chief Exec. Officer--Society National Bank, Cleveland, OH; U.S. Public, pg. 954
Meyer, Herbert, Dr., Co-Chief Exec. Officer--Heidelberger Druckmaschinen A.G., Heidelberg, Germany; Int'l, pg. 604
Meyer, Jeffrey C., Chief Exec. Officer--Bemrose USA, Inc., Fort Wayne, IN; Int'l, pg. 185
Meyer, Jerome J., Chm. Bd., Pres. & Chief Exec. Officer--Tektronix, Inc., Wilsonville, OR; U.S. Public, pg. 1567
Meyer, Jerry, Chief Exec. Officer--Pinnacle Brands, Inc., Dallas, TX; U.S. Private, pg. 866
Meyer, Jerry, Chief Exec. Officer--Donruss Trading Card Co., Dallas, TX; U.S. Private, pg. 866
Meyer, Michael, Chm. & Chief Exec. Officer--Emess PLC, London, United Kingdom; Int'l, pg. 453
Meyer, Mike, Pres. & Chief Exec. Officer--CAP Gemini America, New York, NY; Int'l, pg. 263
Meyer, Rockford G., Pres. & Chief Exec. Officer--Citrus Corp., Houston, TX; U.S. Public, pg. 585
Meyer, Russell W., Jr., Chm. Bd. & Chief Exec. Officer--The Cessna Aircraft Co., Wichita, KS; U.S. Public, pg. 1589
Meyer, W. Darrell, Chm. Bd., Pres. & Chief Exec. Officer--Arkansas Bank & Trust, Hot Springs Village, AR; U.S. Public, pg. 630
Meyers, Howard M., Chm. Bd. & Chief Exec. Officer--Bayou Steel Corporation, La Place, LA; U.S. Public, pg. 197
Meyers, Howard M., Chm. Bd., Pres. & Chief Exec. Officer--Quexco Incorporated, Dallas, TX; U.S. Private, pg. 900
Meyers, John R., Pres. & Chief Exec. Officer--Treadco, Inc., Fort Smith, AR; U.S. Public, pg. 131
Meyerson, A. Jay, Chief Exec. Officer--Key Bank USA N.A., Cleveland, OH; U.S. Public, pg. 954

Mia Je, Patrick Ngiam, Chm. Bd. & Chief Exec. Officer--IPC Corporation Ltd., Singapore, Singapore; *Int'l*, pg. 651
Michael, Edward A., Pres. & Chief Exec. Officer--Diamond Brands, Inc., Cloquet, MN; *U.S. Private*, pg. 330
Michael, Gary G., Chm. Bd. & Chief Exec. Officer--Albertson's, Inc., Boise, ID; *U.S. Public*, pg. 38
Michael, Jeffrey J., Pres. & Chief Exec. Officer--ENStar, Inc., Eden Prairie, MN; *U.S. Public*, pg. 585
Michael, Jonathan E., Pres. & Chief Exec. Officer--RLI Insurance Company, Peoria, IL; *U.S. Public*, pg. 1356
Michael, Jonathan E., Pres. & Chief Exec. Officer--Mt. Hawley Insurance Company, Peoria, IL; *U.S. Public*, pg. 1356
Michael, Robert W., Pres. & Chief Oper. Officer--Jim Walter Homes, Inc., Tampa, FL; *U.S. Public*, pg. 1737
Michaels, J. David, Chief Exec. Officer--Michaels Development Group, Inc., Clifton Park, NY; *U.S. Private*, pg. 740
Michaels, Jack, Chief Exec. Officer--The HON Co., Muscatine, IA; *U.S. Public*, pg. 772
Michaels, Jack D., Chm. Bd., Pres. & Chief Exec. Officer--HON Industries Inc., Muscatine, IA; *U.S. Public*, pg. 772
Michaels, Randy, Chief Exec. Officer--Jacor Communications, Inc., Covington, KY; *U.S. Public*, pg. 922
Michalek, Richard C., Chm. Bd. & Chief Exec. Officer--Quality Control Corporation, Chicago, IL; *U.S. Private*, pg. 898
Michalko, M. Mark, Pres. & Chief Exec. Officer--International Lottery & Totalizator Systems, Inc., Carlsbad, CA; *U.S. Public*, pg. 900
Michel, Peter A., Pres. & Chief Exec. Officer--Brink's Home Security, Inc., Irving, TX; *U.S. Public*, pg. 1305
Michel, Philippe, Pres. & Chief Exec. Officer--Bobst Group Inc., Roseland, NJ; *Int'l*, pg. 198
Micheletto, Joe R., Pres. & Chief Exec. Officer--Ralcorp Holdings Inc., Saint Louis, MO; *U.S. Public*, pg. 1359
Michell, S., Pres. & Chief Exec. Officer--Jardine Davies Inc., Manila, Philippines; *Int'l*, pg. 705
Michelson, Alan P., Chief Exec. Officer--Easy Day Manufacturing Company, Holliston, MA; *U.S. Private*, pg. 358
Michils, Marc, Chief Exec. Officer-Strategy & Creation--Quattro DMB&B, Brussels, Brussels, Belgium; *U.S. Private*, pg. 305
Mickel, Buck, Chm. Bd. & Chief Exec. Officer--RSI Holdings Inc., Greenville, SC; *U.S. Public*, pg. 1358
Midash, Michael, Chief Officer--Heraeus Electro-Nite Co., Philadelphia, PA; *Int'l*, pg. 616
Midden, Louis E., Chief Exec. Officer-Property & Casualty Programs Div.--Willis Corroon Administrative Services, Inc., Nashville, TN; *Int'l*, pg. 1504
Middleton, Charles S., Chm. Bd., Pres. & Chief Exec. Officer--Cal-Air Inc., Whittier, CA; *U.S. Private*, pg. 199
Middleton, Frank, Dr., Chief Exec. Officer--Healthsource South Carolina, Inc., Charleston, SC; *U.S. Public*, pg. 360
Middleton, R., Chief Exec. Officer--Wessex Advanced Switching Products Ltd., Havant, United Kingdom; *Int'l*, pg. 208
Midgley, Graham, Pres. & Chief Exec. Officer--Heath Consultants Incorporated, Houston, TX; *U.S. Private*, pg. 518
Might, Thomas O., Pres. & Chief Exec. Officer--Post-Newsweek Cable Division, Phoenix, AZ; *U.S. Public*, pg. 1743
Miglio, Daniel J., Chm. Bd. & Chief Exec. Officer--Southern New England Telecommunications Corporation, New Haven, CT; *U.S. Public*, pg. 1490
Miglio, Daniel J., Chm. Bd., Pres. & Chief Exec. Officer--The Southern New England Telephone Company, New Haven, CT; *U.S. Public*, pg. 1491
Migliori, Richard J., M.D., Pres. & Chief Exec. Officer--United HealthCare Plans of New England, Inc., Warwick, RI; *U.S. Public*, pg. 1678
Mignanelli, James, Chief Exec. & Oper. Officer & Treas.--Plastic Engineering Co. Inc., Haverhill, MA; *U.S. Private*, pg. 871
Mignault, Pierre L., Pres. & Chief Exec. Officer--Provigo Inc., Montreal, Canada; *Int'l*, pg. 1072
Mignault, Pierre L., Pres. & Chief Exec. Officer--Loeb Inc., Ottawa, Canada; *Int'l*, pg. 1073
Mihaichuk, Garry P., Pres. & Chief Exec. Officer--TransCanada International Ltd., Calgary, Canada; *Int'l*, pg. 1417
Mihaly, Gabe, Pres. & Chief Exec. Officer--Acorn Products, Inc., Columbus, OH; *U.S. Public*, pg. 17
Mihaly, Gabe, Pres. & Chief Exec. Officer--UnionTools, Inc., Columbus, OH; *U.S. Public*, pg. 17
Mihaylo, Steven G., Chm. Bd. & Chief Exec. Officer--Inter-Tel, Incorporated, Phoenix, AZ; *U.S. Public*, pg. 888
Mikel, Steve H., Chief Exec., Oper. & Fin. Officers--Southern Mineral Corporation, Houston, TX; *U.S. Public*, pg. 1490
Mikimoto, Toyohiko, Chief Exec. Officer--K. Mikimoto & Co., Ltd., Tokyo, Japan; *Int'l*, pg. 866
Miklas, Robert, Pres. & Chief Exec. Officer--National Fiberstock Corporation, Norristown, PA; *U.S. Private*, pg. 782
Mikon, Arnold, Chm., Pres. & Chief Exec. Officer--SmithGroup, Inc., Detroit, MI; *U.S. Private*, pg. 1010
Mikos, Paul W., Pres. & Chief Exec. Officer--RemedyTemp, Inc., San Juan Capistrano, CA; *U.S. Public*, pg. 1376
Mikulsky, Philip M., Pres. & Chief Exec. Officer--WPS Energy Services, Inc., Green Bay, WI; *U.S. Public*, pg. 1728
Milan, Nigel, Chief Exec. Officer--Australian Radio Network, Seven Hills, Australia; *U.S. Public*, pg. 386
Milenthal, Rick, Chief Exec. Officer--HMS Partners, Columbus, OH; *U.S. Private*, pg. 491
Miles, John C., II, Vice Chm. & Chief Exec. Officer--Dentsply International Inc., York, PA; *U.S. Public*, pg. 498
Miles, Lyn, Chief Exec.--Barnett Merchant Services Corp., Jacksonville, FL; *U.S. Public*, pg. 1162
Miles, Nick, Chief Exec. Officer--Financial Dynamics Ltd., London, United Kingdom; *Int'l*, pg. 117
Milhaud, Serge, Chm. & Chief Exec. Officer--Societe Generale des Eaux Minerales de Vittel, Vittel, France; *Int'l*, pg. 920
Milhaud, Serge, Chm. Bd. & Chief Exec. Officer--Nestle Sources International S.A., Paris, France; *Int'l*, pg. 921
Milidrag, George, Chm. Bd. & Chief Exec. Officer--Engineering Technology Ltd. (E.T.), Troy, MI; *U.S. Private*, pg. 377
Miliou, Elana, Chief Exec. Officer, Mng. Dir.--International Marketing & Promotions, Athens, Greece; *U.S. Private*, pg. 304
Mill, Mick, Chief Exec. Officer--EWA Ltd., Chelmsford, United Kingdom; *Int'l*, pg. 1482
Mill, Victor J., III, Pres. & Chief Exec. Officer--Lawrence Pumps, Inc., Lawrence, MA; *U.S. Private*, pg. 654
Millard, Dan, Chm. Bd., Pres., Chief Exec. & Chief Oper. Officer--Central Illinois Steel Company, Carlinville, IL; *U.S. Private*, pg. 223
Millard, Donald R., Pres., Chief Exec. Officer & Chief Fin. Officer--Matria Healthcare, Inc., Marietta, GA; *U.S. Public*, pg. 1057
Millard, J.B., Dr., Pres. & Chief Exec. Officer-Mitel Corp.--Mitel, Inc., Herndon, VA; *Int'l*, pg. 870
Millard, John B., Dr., Pres. & Chief Exec. Officer--Mitel Corporation, Kanata, Canada; *Int'l*, pg. 870
Millard, Suzanne T., Chm. Bd., Pres. & Chief Exec. Officer--Turtle & Hughes, Inc., Linden, NJ; *U.S. Private*, pg. 1110
Millen, Lewis, Pres. & Chief Exec. Officer--Industrial Ceramics, Inc., Lima, NY; *U.S. Private*, pg. 560
Miller, Alan, Chm. Bd., Pres. & Chief Exec. Officer--Edison Brothers Stores, Inc., Saint Louis, MO; *U.S. Public*, pg. 563
Miller, Alan B., Chm. Bd., Pres. & Chief Exec. Officer--Universal Health Services, Inc., King of Prussia, PA; *U.S.* Public, pg. 1696
Miller, Alan B., Chm. Bd. & Chief Exec. Officer--Universal Health Realty Income Trust, King of Prussia, PA; *U.S. Public*, pg. 1697
Miller, Bill, Pres., Chief Exec. & Chief Oper. Officer--Contico International, Inc., Saint Louis, MO; *U.S. Private*, pg. 267
Miller, Brian, Pres. & Chief Exec. Officer--Willis Corroon Corp. of Wash. D.C., Bethesda, MD; *Int'l*, pg. 1507
Miller, Bryce, Chief Exec. Officer-Central Texas--Trammell Crow Company, Dallas, TX; *U.S. Public*, pg. 1628
Miller, Charles D., Chm. Bd. & Chief Exec. Officer--Avery Dennison Corporation, Pasadena, CA; *U.S. Public*, pg. 152
Miller, Charles Q., Exec. V.P., Chm. Bd. & Chief Exec. Officer-Raytheon Engrs.--Raytheon Company, Lexington, MA; *U.S. Public*, pg. 1364
Miller, Charles R., Chm. Bd., Pres. & Chief Exec. Officer--Champion HealthCare Corporation, Houston, TX; *U.S. Public*, pg. 333
Miller, Craig, Pres. & Chief Exec. Officer--Uno Restaurant Corporation, West Roxbury, MA; *U.S. Public*, pg. 1698
Miller, D., Chief Exec. Officer--Zurich Pacific Insurance Pty. Ltd., Port Moresby, Papua New Guinea; *Int'l*, pg. 1532
Miller, Dane A., Ph.D., Pres. & Chief Exec. Officer--Biomet, Inc., Warsaw, IN; *U.S. Public*, pg. 231
Miller, Dave, Pres. & Chief Exec. Officer--Consumers Markets Inc., Springfield, MO; *U.S. Public*, pg. 653
Miller, David, Pres. & Chief Exec. Officer--H.L. Bouton Company Inc., Buzzards Bay, MA; *U.S. Private*, pg. 162
Miller, David, Pres. & Chief Exec. Officer--Lensclean, Inc., Buzzards Bay, MA; *U.S. Private*, pg. 162
Miller, David P., Pres. & Chief Exec. Officer--Columbia National Group, Inc., Cleveland, OH; *U.S. Private*, pg. 255
Miller, Dennis K., Pres.-Seattle & Dir.--EvansGroup, Salt Lake City, UT; *U.S. Private*, pg. 385
Miller, Donald E., Chm. Bd., Pres. & Chief Exec. Officer--Ederer Inc., Seattle, WA; *U.S. Private*, pg. 363
Miller, Douglas H., Chm. Bd. & Chief Exec. Officer--Coda Energy, Inc., Dallas, TX; *U.S. Public*, pg. 584
Miller, Duane L., Chief Exec. Officer & Exec. V.P.--Country Life Insurance Company, Bloomington, IL; *U.S. Private*, pg. 278
Miller, Edward D., Chm. Bd. & Chief Exec. Officer--The Equitable Companies Incorporated, New York, NY; *U.S. Public*, pg. 588
Miller, Elwood M., Pres. & Chief Exec. Officer--Blessings Corporation, Newport News, VA; *U.S. Private*, pg. 1179
Miller, Eugene, Chm. Bd. & Chief Exec. Officer--Ideon Group, Inc., Jacksonville, FL; *U.S. Public*, pg. 320
Miller, Eugene A., Chm. Bd. & Chief Exec. Officer--Comerica Incorporated, Detroit, MI; *U.S. Public*, pg. 408
Miller, Eugene A., Chm. Bd. & Chief Exec. Officer--Comerica Bank Michigan, Detroit, MI; *U.S. Public*, pg. 409
Miller, Gary R., Chief Exec. Officer--Cannon, Grand Island, NY; *U.S. Private*, pg. 205
Miller, Gaylen D., Pres. & Chief Exec. Officer--Ag Services of America, Inc., Cedar Falls, IA; *U.S. Public*, pg. 6
Miller, George D., Pres. & Chief Exec. Officer--National Fire Protection Association, Quincy, MA; *U.S. Private*, pg. 782
Miller, George E., Pres. & Chief Exec. Officer--Peter Piper, Inc., Phoenix, AZ; *Int'l*, pg. 157
Miller, Henry E., Jr., Chief Exec. Officer--Miller Building Corp., Wilmington, NC; *U.S. Private*, pg. 746
Miller, Howard, Chief Exec. Officer--Dynamic Metal Products Company, Manchester, CT; *U.S. Private*, pg. 350
Miller, J. Christopher, Chief Exec. Officer--Wassall Plc, London, United Kingdom; *Int'l*, pg. 1486
Miller, J.H., Pres. & Chief Exec. Officer--Howard Miller, Zeeland, MI; *U.S. Private*, pg. 747
Miller, Jack, Pres. & Chief Exec. Officer--Industrial Indemnity Company, San Francisco, CA; *U.S. Public*, pg. 681
Miller, James A., Pres. & Chief Exec. Officer--Alliant Foodservice, Inc., Deerfield, IL; *U.S. Private*, pg. 244
Miller, James H., Chm. Bd., Pres. & Chief Exec. Officer--Meridian Medical Technology, Inc., Columbia, MD; *U.S. Public*, pg. 1095
Miller, James L., Chm. Bd. & Chief Exec. Officer--JP Foodservice, Inc., Columbia, MD; *U.S. Public*, pg. 918
Miller, James L., Pres. & Chief Exec. Officer--JP Foodservice Distributors, Inc., Columbia, MD; *U.S. Public*, pg. 918
Miller, James L., Chm. Bd. & Chief Exec. Officer--U.S. Food Service, Wilkes-Barre, PA; *U.S. Public*, pg. 918
Miller, Jay, Pres. & Chief Exec. Officer--TargetCom, Inc., Chicago, IL; *U.S. Private*, pg. 1069
Miller, Jeff, Pres. & Chief Exec. Officer--Aqua-Chem Inc., Milwaukee, WI; *Int'l*, pg. 824
Miller, John C., Pres. & Chief Exec. Officer--Miller-St. Nazianz, Inc., Saint Nazianz, WI; *U.S. Private*, pg. 748
Miller, John C., Pres., Chief Exec. Officer & Chief Oper. Officer--Badger Farm Systems, Inc., Saint Nazianz, WI; *U.S. Private*, pg. 748
Miller, John S., Pres. & Chief Exec. Officer--Tencarva Machinery Co., Inc., Greensboro, NC; *U.S. Private*, pg. 1075
Miller, John T., Pres. & Chief Exec. Officer--Pacific Generation Company, Portland, OR; *U.S. Public*, pg. 1252
Miller, Jon, Pres. & Chief Exec. Officer-USA Broadcasting--USA Networks, Inc., Saint Petersburg, FL; *U.S. Public*, pg. 1685
Miller, Jon, Pres. & Chief Exec. Officer--USA Broadcasting, New York, NY; *U.S. Public*, pg. 1686
Miller, K.W., Chief Exec. Officer--Hunting Plc, London, United Kingdom; *Int'l*, pg. 640
Miller, Lewis, Chief Exec. Officer-Virginia Banking--Wachovia Bank, Richmond, VA; *U.S. Public*, pg. 1730
Miller, Mark J., Chief Oper. Officer & Exec. V.P.--Atlantic City Showboat, Atlantic City, NJ; *U.S. Public*, pg. 1469
Miller, Marlin J., Jr., Pres. & Chief Exec. Officer--Arrow International, Inc., Reading, PA; *U.S. Public*, pg. 135
Miller, Marvin, Chm. Bd. & Co-Chief Exec. Officer--Prime Source Inc., Carrollton, TX; *U.S. Private*, pg. 884
Miller, Michael A., Pres. & Chief Exec. Officer--Firestone Financial, Newton, MA; *U.S. Public*, pg. 1660
Miller, Paul A., Pres. & Chief Exec. Officer--Lawrence Savings Bank, North Andover, MA; *U.S. Public*, pg. 980
Miller, Richard J., Chief Exec. Officer--Walnut Street Securities, Inc., Saint Louis, MO; *U.S. Private*, pg. 443
Miller, Robert G., Pres. & Chief Exec. Officer--Fred Meyer Incorporated, Portland, OR; *U.S. Public*, pg. 1103
Miller, Robert G., Pres. & Chief Exec. Officer--Smith's Food & Drug Centers, Inc., Salt Lake City, UT; *U.S. Public*, pg. 1103
Miller, Robert S., Chm. Bd. & Chief Exec. Officer--Better Baked Foods, Inc., North East, PA; *U.S. Private*, pg. 141
Miller, Robert S., Chm. Bd., Pres. & Chief Exec. Officer--Waste Management, Inc., Oak Brook, IL; *U.S. Public*, pg. 1744
Miller, Robin, Chief Exec. Officer--EMAP Plc, Peterborough, United Kingdom; *Int'l*, pg. 451
Miller, Sanford, Chm. Bd. & Chief Exec. Officer--Budget Group, Inc., Daytona Beach, FL; *U.S. Private*, pg. 178
Miller, Sanford, Chm. & Chief Exec. Officer--Budget Rent A Car Corporation, Lisle, IL; *U.S. Private*, pg. 178
Miller, Steven, Chief Exec. Officer--Resort Condominiums International, Indianapolis, IN; *U.S. Public*, pg. 322
Miller, Steven, Chm. Bd., Pres. & Chief Exec. Officer--Miller Resources International, Inc., North Brunswick, NJ; *U.S. Private*, pg. 748
Miller, Steven, Chief Exec. Officer--Miller Temporaries, Inc., North Brunswick, NJ; *U.S. Private*, pg. 748
Miller, Steven, Chief Exec. Officer--Miller Scientific, Inc., North Brunswick, NJ; *U.S. Private*, pg. 748
Miller, Thomas, Pres. & Chief Exec. Officer--Carl Zeiss, Inc., Thornwood, NY; *Int'l*, pg. 1523
Miller, Thomas B., Chm. Bd., Pres. & Chief Exec. & Oper. Officer--Berry Bearing Company, Lyons, IL; *U.S. Public*, pg. 732
Miller, Tod, Chm. Bd. & Chief Exec. Officer--Rosewood Property Company, Dallas, TX; *U.S. Private*, pg. 946
Miller, Victor J., Pres. & Chief Exec. Officer--Mill-Rose Company, Mentor, OH; *U.S. Private*, pg. 746
Miller, William J., Chm. Bd. & Chief Exec. Officer--Avid Technology, Inc., Tewksbury, MA; *U.S. Public*, pg. 154
Milley, Alexander M., Chm. Bd., Pres. & Chief Exec. Officer--ELXSI Corporation, Orlando, FL; *U.S. Public*, pg. 545
Millgard, V. Dennis, Pres. & Chief Exec. Officer--The Millgard Corp., Livonia, MI; *U.S. Private*, pg. 748
Milligan, Bruce R., Pres. & Chief Exec. Officer--Republic Diversified Services, Inc., Dallas, TX; *Int'l*, pg. 346
Milligan, Patrick M., Pres. & Chief Exec. Officer--Willis Corroon Corp. of Northern Ohio, Dublin, OH; *Int'l*, pg. 1506
Milliken, R.A., Chief Exec. Officer--Lamont Holdings Plc, Belfast, United Kingdom; *Int'l*, pg. 797
Milliken, Roger, Chm. Bd. & Chief Exec. Officer--Milliken & Company, Spartanburg, SC; *U.S. Private*, pg. 748
Millinor, J. Patrick, Jr., Chief Exec. Officer--Group Maintenance America Corp., Houston, TX; *U.S. Public*, pg. 766
Mills, Charlie, Chief Exec. Officer--Medline Industries, Inc., Mundelein, IL; *U.S. Private*, pg. 728
Mills, Howard C., Pres. & Chief Exec. Officer--Halifax Corporation, Alexandria, VA; *U.S. Public*, pg. 775
Mills, Howard C., Pres. & Chief Exec. Officer--Halifax Engineering, Inc., Alexandria, VA; *U.S. Public*, pg. 775
Mills, Howard C., Pres. & Chief Exec. Officer--Halifax Technical Services, Alexandria, VA; *U.S. Public*, pg. 775
Mills, James, Chief Exec. Officer--Mills & Partners, Saint Louis, MO; *U.S. Private*, pg. 526
Mills, James N., Chm. & Chief Exec. Officer--Berg Electronics, Saint Louis, MO; *U.S. Public*, pg. 212
Mills, P. Gerald, Chm. Bd., Pres. & Chief Exec. Officer--Jacobson Stores Inc., Jackson, MI; *U.S. Public*, pg. 922

Mills, Walter G., Chm. Bd., Chief Exec. Officer & Treas.--W.G. Mills, Inc., Sarasota, FL; *U.S. Private*, pg. 749

Millstein, Jack H., Jr., Pres.--Millstein Industries, Youngwood, PA; *U.S. Private*, pg. 749

Millwee, Robert, Pres. & Chief Exec. Officer--Garney Holding Company, Inc., Kansas City, MO; *U.S. Private*, pg. 440

Milne, David, Chief Exec. Officer--Willis Corroon Risk Consulting Limited, London, United Kingdom; *Int'l*, pg. 1503

Milne, David S., Jr., Pres. & Chief Exec. Officer--Gas Energy Inc., Brooklyn, NY; *U.S. Public*, pg. 296

Milne, G., Chief Exec. Officer--Milk Products Holdings (Europe) Ltd., Reigate, United Kingdom; *Int'l*, pg. 923

Milne, Stephen A., Pres., Chief Exec. Officer--Erie Family Life Insurance Company, Erie, PA; *U.S. Public*, pg. 590

Milner, Stanley A., Pres. & Chief Exec. Officer--Chieftain International, Inc., Edmonton, Canada; *Int'l*, pg. 284

Milnor, George S., Chm. Bd., Pres. & Chief Exec. Officer--Millers Mutual Insurance Assn., Alton, IL; *U.S. Private*, pg. 748

Milstein, Monroe G., Chm. Bd., Pres. & Chief Exec. Officer--Burlington Coat Factory Warehouse Corporation, Burlington, NJ; *U.S. Public*, pg. 268

Milstein, Paul, Chm. Bd. & Chief Exec. Officer--Starrett HRH, New York, NY; *U.S. Private*, pg. 1035

Milstein, Philip, Pres. & Chief Exec. Officer--Emigrant Savings Bank, New York, NY; *U.S. Private*, pg. 373

Min, Jae-Hong, Chm. Bd. & Chief Exec. Officer--Samsung Asia Headquarters, Singapore, Singapore; *Int'l*, pg. 1183

Mincheva, Juliana, Chief Exec. Officer--International Media Concepts/DMB&B, Sofia, Bulgaria; *U.S. Private*, pg. 304

Minchk, Frederick, Pres. & Chief Oper. Officer--National Loss Control Service Corp., Long Grove, IL; *U.S. Private*, *pg. 614*

Mindel, Laurence B., Chm. Bd. & Chief Exec. Officer--Il Fornaio America Corporation, Corte Madera, CA; *U.S. Public*, pg. 864

Minear, David, Vice Chm. & Grp. Chief Exec.-Melbourne--Y&R Mattingly, Richmond, Australia; *U.S. Private*, pg. 325

Minelli, J., Chief Oper. Officer--Bristolipe Division, Bristol, IN; *Int'l*, pg. 618

Minerva, Daniel O., Co-Pres. & Co-Chief Exec. Officer--Eastbridge Capital Inc., New York, NY; *Int'l*, pg. 933

Ming, Hans Peter, Dr., Chief Exec. Officer--Sika Finanz AG, Baar, Switzerland; *Int'l*, pg. 1248

Miniat, Ronald, Chm., Pres. & Chief Exec. Officer--Ed Miniat, Inc., Chicago, IL; *U.S. Private*, pg. 750

Minihan, John M., Pres. & Chief Exec. Officer--Louisville Bedding Company, Louisville, KY; *U.S. Private*, pg. 677

Minor, G. Gilmer III, Chm. Bd., Pres. & Chief Exec. Officer--Owens & Minor Inc., Glen Allen, VA; *U.S. Public*, pg. 1236

Minor, Henry H., Jr., Chief Exec. Officer--P.W. Minor & Son, Inc., Batavia, NY; *U.S. Private*, pg. 751

Minotto, Gene J., Pres. & Chief Exec. Officer--Basic American Medical Products, Inc., Atlanta, GA; *U.S. Public*, pg. 758

Minty, C.J., Deputy Chm. & Chief Exec. Officer--Henry Ansbacher Holding PLC, London, United Kingdom; *Int'l*, pg. 487

Mira, Sal E., Pres. & Chief Exec. Officer--KDI Precision Products, Inc., Cincinnati, OH; *U.S. Private*, pg. 603

Miranda, Guillermo, Jr., Chm., Chief Exec. Officer & Pres.--Gator Industries Inc., Hialeah, FL; *U.S. Private*, pg. 441

Miranda, Richard, Chief Exec. Officer--ORIX Auto Finance (India) Limited, Mumbai, India; *Int'l*, pg. 1009

Mirante, Arthur J., II, Pres. & Chief Exec. Officer--Cushman & Wakefield, Inc., New York, NY; *Int'l*, pg. 873

Mirkos, George, Chm. Bd. & Chief Exec. Officer--National Bank of Greece S.A., Athens, Greece; *Int'l*, pg. 907

Misch, Donald L., Chief Exec. Officer & Gen. Mgr.--Jasper County Farm Bureau Co-op Association, Inc., Rensselaer, IN; *U.S. Private*, pg. 583

Mischinski, Paul, Pres. & Chief Exec. Officer-Bali Brand--Bali Company, Winston Salem, NC; *U.S. Public*, pg. 1433

Misdanitis, Kostas, Chief Exec.--Novo Nordisk Maroc, Casablanca, Morocco; *Int'l*, pg. 988

Misitano, Anthony, Pres. & Chief Exec. Officer--Continental Medical Systems, Inc., Mechanicsburg, PA; *U.S. Public*, pg. 839

Misrasi, John, Pres. & Chief Exec. Officer--Commtek Communications, Corp., Vienna, VA; *U.S. Private*, pg. 258

Missett, Judi, Chm. Bd., Pres. & Chief Exec. Officer--Jazzercise, Inc., Carlsbad, CA; *U.S. Private*, pg. 584

Misumi, Yoshio, Pres. & Chief Exec. Officer--Pioneer/Eclipse Corp., Sparta, NC; *Int'l*, pg. 71

Misunas, Kathy, Chief Exec.--Reed Travel Group, Dunstable, United Kingdom; *Int'l*, pg. 1097

Misunas, Kathy, Chief Exec. Officer--Reed Travel Group, Secaucus, NJ; *Int'l*, pg. 1097

Mitchell, Andrew, Chief Exec. Officer--Miller Patterson Aldred Mitchell, London, United Kingdom; *U.S. Private*, pg. 1152

Mitchell, Bo, Pres. & Chief Exec. Officer--Marshall Jaccoma Mitchell Advertising, New York, NY; *U.S. Private*, pg. 708

Mitchell, Charlie, Chief Exec. Officer--Heckethorn Mfg. Company, Inc., Dyersburg, TN; *U.S. Private*, pg. 519

Mitchell, George P., Chm. Bd. & Chief Exec. Officer--Mitchell Energy & Development Corp., Spring, TX; *U.S. Public*, pg. 1117

Mitchell, John M., Pres., Chief Exec. & Chief Oper. Officer--Pluess-Staufer Industries, Inc., Proctor, VT; *Int'l*, pg. 1061

Mitchell, Lee Roy, Chief Exec. Officer--Cinemark USA, Inc., Dallas, TX; *U.S. Private*, pg. 240

Mitchell, Stephen C., Chm. & Chief Exec. Officer--Knight Architects Engineers Planners, Inc., Chicago, IL; *U.S. Private*, pg. 626

Mitchell, Thomas, Pres. & Chief Exec. Officer--Davenport Insulation, Inc, Upper Marlboro, MD; *U.S. Private*, pg. 314

Mitchell, William A., Jr., Pres. & Chief Exec. Officer--Carter & Associates, Atlanta, GA; *U.S. Private*, pg. 216

Mitchell, William F., Chm. Bd., Pres. & Chief Exec. Officer--Environmental Tectonics Corporation (ETC), Southampton, PA; *U.S. Public*, pg. 587

Mitchell, William F., Chm. Bd., Pres. & Chief Exec. Officer--Mitchell Corporation of Owosso, Owosso, MI; *U.S. Private*, pg. 753

Mitchum, John, Pres. & Chief Exec. Officer--Tricord Systems, Inc., Plymouth, MN; *U.S. Public*, pg. 1637

Mitieus, Rene, Chm. Bd., Pres. & Chief Exec. Officer--Imetal, Paris, France; *Int'l*, pg. 661

Mitsui, Kouhei, Pres. & Chief Exec. Officer--Kubota Corp., Osaka, Japan; *Int'l*, pg. 762

Mittag, Michael T., Chief Exec. Officer--Electrovert, Grand Prairie, TX; *Int'l*, pg. 328

Mitte, Roy, Chm. Bd., Pres. & Chief Exec. Officer--Financial Industries Corp., Austin, TX; *U.S. Public*, pg. 622

Mitte, Roy, Chm. Bd., Pres. & Chief Exec. Officer--InternContinental Life Corp., Austin, TX; *U.S. Public*, pg. 622

Mittelstadt, Eric, Pres. & Chief Exec. Officer--FANUC Robotics North America, Inc., Rochester Hills, MI; *Int'l*, pg. 477

Mixon, A. Malachi, III, Chm. Bd. & Chief Exec. Officer--Invacare Corporation, Elyria, OH; *U.S. Public*, pg. 911

Miyauchi, Yoshihiko, Pres. & Grp. Chief Exec. Officer--Orix Corporation, Tokyo, Japan; *Int'l*, pg. 1008

Mizel, Larry A., Chm. Bd., Pres. & Chief Exec. Officer--M.D.C. Holdings, Inc., Denver, CO; *U.S. Public*, pg. 1025

Mizoguchi, Isao, Pres. & Chief Exec. Officer--The Nikkan Kogyo Shimbun, Ltd., Tokyo, Japan; *Int'l*, pg. 930

Mlnarik, Robert F., Pres. & Chief Exec. Officer--MACtac Morgan Adhesive Company, Stow, OH; *U.S. Public*, pg. 210

Moakley, Michael, Pres. & Chief Exec. Officer--Philips Electronics North America Corporation, New York, NY; *Int'l*, pg. 1053

Moayedi, Paris, Chm. Bd. & Chief Exec. Officer--Jarvis Plc, Watton-at-Stone, United Kingdom; *Int'l*, pg. 705

Mobley, Paul W., Chm. Bd., Pres. & Chief Exec. Officer--Noble Roman's Inc., Indianapolis, IN; *U.S. Public*, pg. 1187

Modell, Mitchell B., Co-Pres. & Chief Exec. Officer--Henry Modell & Company, Inc., New York, NY; *U.S. Private*, pg. 754

Modrovich, Ivan, Chief Exec. Officer--Medical Analysis Systems Inc., Camarillo, CA; *U.S. Private*, pg. 727

Moe, Henrik, Pres., Chief Oper. & Exec. Officer--DEC International, Inc., Madison, WI; *U.S. Private*, pg. 301

Moeller, F.H., Chm. Bd. & Chief Exec. Officer--VTEL Corporation, Austin, TX; *U.S. Public*, pg. 1703

Moenkhaus, James E., Pres. & Chief Exec. Officer--Willis Corroon Corp. of Northern Ohio, Cleveland, OH; *Int'l*, pg. 1506

Moersch, Kevin P., Pres. & Chief Exec. Officer--MFS Network Technologies, Inc., Omaha, NE; *U.S. Public*, pg. 1779

Moersdorf, Gerard B., Jr., Pres., Chief Exec. Officer & Treas.--Applied Innovation Inc., Dublin, OH; *U.S. Public*, pg. 123

Moffat, Brian, Chm. Bd. & Chief Exec. Officer--British Steel Plc, London, United Kingdom; *Int'l*, pg. 220

Moffett, James R., Chm. Bd. & Chief Exec. Officer--Freeport-McMoRan Copper & Gold, Inc., New Orleans, LA; *U.S. Public*, pg. 680

Moffitt, Donald E., Chm. Bd. & Chief Exec. Officer--CNF Transportation Inc., Palo Alto, CA; *U.S. Public*, pg. 281

Mogas, V. Louis, Pres. & Chief Exec. Officer--Mogas Industries, Inc., Houston, TX; *U.S. Private*, pg. 755

Mogelgaard, Michael, Vice Chm., Chief Creative Officer & Dir.--EvansGroup, Salt Lake City, UT; *U.S. Private*, pg. 385

Mogren, Hakan, Pres. & Chief Exec. Officer--Astra AB, Sodertalje, Sweden; *Int'l*, pg. 93

Mohrman, LeRoy, Chm. Bd., Pres. & Chief Exec. Officer--Handling Systems Engineering, Jacksonville, FL; *U.S. Private*, pg. 499

Moilanen, Thomas A., Pres. & Chief Exec. Officer--Cloverdale Equipment Co., Oak Park, MI; *U.S. Private*, pg. 247

Molen, Richard L., Chm. Bd. & Chief Exec. Officer--Huffy Corporation, Miamisburg, OH; *U.S. Public*, pg. 846

Moles, Robert T., Pres. & Chief Exec. Officer--Century 21 Real Estate Corp., Parsippany, NJ; *U.S. Public*, pg. 321

Molin, Per, Pres. & Chief Exec. Officer--Avesta Sheffield AB, Stockholm, Sweden; *Int'l*, pg. 221

Molina Sobrino, Enrique, Chm. Bd. & Chief Exec. Officer--Pepsi-Gemex SA de CV, Mexico, Mexico; *Int'l*, pg. 1036

Molinari, John, Pres. & Chief Exec. Officer--Media 100, Inc., Marlborough, MA; *U.S. Public*, pg. 1079

Moll, Curtis E., Chm. Bd. & Chief Exec. Officer--MTD Products, Inc., Valley City, OH; *U.S. Private*, pg. 688

Molloy, Patrick, Chief Exec. Officer--Bank of Ireland, Dublin, Ireland; *Int'l*, pg. 152

Moloney, Earl, Chm. Bd. & Chief Exec. Officer--Molon Motor & Coil Corp., Rolling Meadows, IL; *U.S. Private*, pg. 756

Moloney, John, Chief Exec.-Food Ingredients--Avonmore Waterford Group plc, Kilkenny, Ireland; *Int'l*, pg. 102

Moloney, Tom, Chief Exec. Officer--EMAP Elan, London, United Kingdom; *Int'l*, pg. 451

Moloney, Tom, Chief Exec. Officer--EMAP Consumer Magazines, London, United Kingdom; *Int'l*, pg. 451

Monaghan, Thomas S., Chm. Bd., Pres. & Chief Exec. Officer--Domino's Pizza Inc., Ann Arbor, MI; *U.S. Private*, *pg. 339*

Monahan, Pierre, Pres. & Chief Exec. Officer--Alliance Forest Products Inc., Montreal, Canada; *Int'l*, pg. 57

Monahan, William D., Pres. & Chief Exec. Officer--The Monahan Company, Eastpointe, MI; *U.S. Private*, pg. 756

Monahan, William T., Chm. Bd. & Chief Exec. Officer--Imation Corporation, Oakdale, MN; *U.S. Public*, pg. 870

Monark, Ronald, Pres. & Chief Exec. Officer--Mitchell International, San Diego, CA; *U.S. Public*, pg. 1601

Monastear, Chris, Chief Exec. Officer--Polyphase Instruments Co., Fort Washington, PA; *U.S. Public*, pg. 1315

Moncrief, Lee E., Chm. Bd., Pres. & Chief Exec. Officer--SouthTrust Bank, Shoals, Florence, AL; *U.S. Public*, pg. 1492

Mondavi, R. Michael, Pres. & Chief Exec. Officer--Robert Mondavi Winery, Inc., Oakville, CA; *U.S. Public*, pg. 1393

Monette, Edward A., Chm. Bd., Pres., Chief Exec. Officer & Chief Oper. Officer--St. Croix Press, Inc., New Richmond, WI; *U.S. Private*, pg. 960

Monger, Stephen, Chm. Bd., Pres. & Chief Exec. Officer--Regions Bank/Huntsville, Huntsville, AL; *U.S. Public*, pg. 1372

Mongkol, Suchest Suwan, Chief Exec. Officer--Siam City Charoen Hire-Purchase (Hat Yai) Co., Ltd., Songkhla, Thailand; *Int'l*, pg. 1239

Monitto, Douglas, Chief Exec. Officer--Monitor Aerospace Corporation, Amityville, NY; *U.S. Private*, pg. 757

Monk, Albert C., III, Pres. & Chief Exec. Officer--DIMON, International, Inc., Farmville, NC; *U.S. Public*, pg. 510

Monk, Brian, Chief Exec. Officer-Engrng.-Electrical & Plastics--Wolseley Plc., Droitwich, United Kingdom; *Int'l*, pg. 1511

Monker, Josephine, Chief Exec. Officer--Elsevier Opleidingen BV, Zwijndrecht, Netherlands; *Int'l*, pg. 1094

Monker, Josephine, Chief Exec. Officer--Koninklijke PBNA BV, Arnhem, Netherlands; *Int'l*, pg. 1100

Monker, Josephine, Chief Exec. Officer--CBBM BV, Zwijndrecht, Netherlands; *Int'l*, pg. 1100

Monker, Josephine, Chief Exec. Officer--Nederlands Studiecentrum, Vlaardingen, Netherlands; *Int'l*, pg. 1100

Monkiewicz, Ray, Pres. & Chief Exec. Officer--Kayem Foods, Inc., Chelsea, MA; *U.S. Private*, pg. 610

Monod, Jerome, Chm. Bd. & Chief Exec. Officer--Lyonnaise des Eaux S.A., Nanterre, France; *Int'l*, pg. 822

Monoley, Ed, Pres. & Chief Exec. Officer--Ridley Canada Limited, Winnipeg, Canada; *Int'l*, pg. 1116

Monroe, Bruce B., Pres. & Chief Exec. Officer--The Johnson Corporation, Three Rivers, MI; *U.S. Private*, pg. 591

Monroe, Frank, Chief Exec. Officer--Columbia Farms Inc., Leesville, SC; *U.S. Private*, pg. 255

Monroe, Gary L., Chief Exec. Officer--Lason, Inc., Troy, MI; *U.S. Public*, pg. 979

Monroe, Mark E., Pres. & Chief Exec. Officer--Louis Dreyfus Natural Gas Corp., Oklahoma City, OK; *U.S. Private*, pg. 342

Monroe, William, Pres. & Chief Exec. Officer--Bertolli USA, Inc., Secaucus, NJ; *Int'l*, pg. 655

Monson, Mike, Chief Exec. Officer--Monson Trucking, Inc., Duluth, MN; *U.S. Private*, pg. 758

Montani, Anthony A., Pres. & Chief Oper. Officer--McInnes Steel Company, Corry, PA; *U.S. Private*, pg. 722

Montel, Jean-Philippe, Chm. Bd. & Chief Exec. Officer-Aussedat Rey--International Paper Company, Purchase, NY; *U.S. Public*, pg. 901

Montella, Luigi, Chief Exec. Officer--Sirti, Milan, Italy; *Int'l*, pg. 1362

Montero, Fernan, Chm. & Chief Exec. Officer-Y&R Europe--Young & Rubicam Inc., New York, NY; *U.S. Private*, pg. 1196

Montgomery, David, Chief Exec. Officer--Mirror Group plc, London, United Kingdom; *Int'l*, pg. 869

Montgomery, George, Pres. & Chief Exec. Officer--Taylor Made Golf Co. Inc., Carlsbad, CA; *Int'l*, pg. 1181

Montgomery, Joseph S., Chm. Bd., Pres. & Chief Exec. Officer--Cannondale Corporation, Bethel, CT; *U.S. Public*, *pg. 301*

Montgomery, Walter S., Jr., Chm. Bd. & Chief Exec. Officer--Spartan Mills, Spartanburg, SC; *U.S. Private*, pg. 1020

Monti, Roberto, Chief Exec. Officer--Y.P.F., S.A., Buenos Aires, Argentina; *Int'l*, pg. 1515

Montoya, Benjamin F., Pres. & Chief Exec. Officer--Public Service Company of New Mexico, Albuquerque, NM; *U.S. Public*, pg. 1339

Montrone, Paul M., Chm. Bd., Pres. & Chief Exec. Officer--Fisher Scientific International, Hampton, NH; *U.S. Private*, pg. 658

Montross, Albert E., Pres. & Chief Exec. Officer--Mylex Corporation, Fremont, CA; *U.S. Public*, pg. 1143

Monty, Jean, Chief Exec. Officer--Northern Telecom, Nashville, TN; *Int'l*, pg. 969

Monty, Jean C., Pres. & Chief Exec. & Oper. Officer--BCE Inc., Montreal, Canada; *Int'l*, pg. 114

Moodie, J.C., Chief Exec. Officer-South Africa--Howden Group Plc, Renfrew, United Kingdom; *Int'l*, pg. 636

Moody, Robert L., Chm. Bd. & Chief Exec. Officer--National Western Life Insurance Company, Austin, TX; *U.S. Public*, pg. 1161

Moody, Ross R., Chm. Bd. & Chief Exec. Officer--NWL Services, Inc., Austin, TX; *U.S. Public*, pg. 1161

Moon, James B., Chm. Bd., Pres. & Chief Exec. Officer--Protocol Systems, Inc., Beaverton, OR; *U.S. Public*, pg. 1336

Moon, Wayne, Chm. Bd. & Chief Exec. Officer--Blue Shield of California, San Francisco, CA; *U.S. Private*, pg. 153

Moone, Michael J., Pres. & Chief Exec. Officer--Faroudja, Inc., Sunnyvale, CA; *U.S. Public*, pg. 613

Mooney, Edward J., Chm. Bd. & Chief Exec. Officer--Nalco Chemical Company, Naperville, IL; *U.S. Public*, pg. 1150

Mooney, J., Pres. & Chief Exec. Officer--A&W Food Services of Canada Inc., North Vancouver, Canada; *Int'l*, *pg. 1*

Mooney, Michael M., Pres. & Chief Exec. Officer--Key Bank of Idaho, Boise, ID; *U.S. Public*, pg. 954

Mooney, Tim, Chief Exec. Officer--HIH America, Irvine, CA; *U.S. Private*, pg. 153

Moore, B.L., Pres. & Chief Exec. Officer--Chep USA, Orlando, FL; *Int'l*, pg. 211

Moore, Bradley G., Pres. & Chief Exec. Officer--Sparks State Bank, Sparks, MD; *U.S. Public*, pg. 1089

Moore, D.J., Chm. Bd. & Chief Exec. Officer--ESCO Electronics Corporation, Saint Louis, MO; *U.S. Public*, pg. 546

Moore, Dan, Chief Exec. Officer--SEE Technologies Inc., Fremont, CA; *U.S. Public*, pg. 1421

Moore, Daniel E., Chief Exec. Officer--SSE Telecom, Inc., Vienna, VA; *U.S. Public*, pg. 1421

Moore, James E., Pres. & Chief Exec. Officer--ContiFinancial Corporation, New York, NY; *U.S. Public*, pg. 439

Moore, James E., Chm. Bd. & Chief Exec. Officer--ContiMortgage Corporation, Horsham, PA; *U.S. Public*, pg. 439

Moore, John, Pres., Chief Exec. & Oper. Officer--Mindscape, Inc., Novato, CA; *Int'l*, pg. 1026

Moore, John O., Mng. Dir.--Duncan Equipment Company, Oklahoma City, OK; *U.S. Private*, pg. 346

Moore, John R., Corp. V.P., Pres. & Chief Exec. Officer-Midas Intl. Corp.--Whitman Corporation, Rolling Meadows, IL; *U.S. Public*, pg. 1766

Moore, Keith F., Pres. & Chief Exec. Officer--Hawker Siddeley Canada Inc., Mississauga, Canada; *Int'l*, pg. 604

Moore, Leon, Chm. Bd., Pres. & Chief Exec. Officer--Sholodge, Inc., Hendersonville, TN; *U.S. Public*, pg. 1467

Moore, Nicholas G., Chm. & Chief Exec. Officer--Coopers & Lybrand, New York, NY; *U.S. Private*, pg. 274

Moore, Peter, Pres. & Chief Exec. Officer--Adidas International, Portland, OR; *Int'l*, pg. 24

Moore, Richard L., Pres. & Chief Exec. Officer--Grant Marketing Communications, Ardmore, PA; *U.S. Private*, pg. 470

Moore, Richard L., Pres. & Chief Exec. Officer--Kingswood Advertising, Inc., Ardmore, PA; *U.S. Private*, pg. 622

Moore, Richard L., Pres. & Chief Exec. Officer--Kingswood Interactive, Ardmore, PA; *U.S. Private*, pg. 622

Moore, Sam, Chm. Bd., Pres. & Chief Exec. Officer--Thomas Nelson Inc., Nashville, TN; *U.S. Public*, pg. 1167

Moore, Steven E., Chm. Bd., Pres. & Chief Exec. Officer--OGE Energy Corp., Oklahoma City, OK; *U.S. Public*, pg. 1207

Moore, Thomas R., Pres. & Chief Exec. Officer--Remmele Engineering, Inc., New Brighton, MN; *U.S. Private*, pg. 921

Moore, William B., Vice Chm. & Chief Tech. Officer--Moore Products Co., Spring House, PA; *U.S. Public*, pg. 1128

Moorhouse, Jim, Chief Exec. Officer--Expamet Building Products, Hartlepool, United Kingdom; *Int'l*, pg. 467

Moos, J. Clifford, Chm. Bd., Pres. & Chief Exec. Officer--Economy Folding Box Corp., Chicago, IL; *U.S. Private*, pg. 362

Moquin, Yves, Chm. Bd. & Chief Exec. Officer--Coscient Group Inc., Montreal, Canada; *Int'l*, pg. 335

Mora, Eugene A., Chief Exec. Officer--ATC Healthcare, Tucson, AZ; *U.S. Private*, pg. 8

Mora, Richard, Pres. & Chief Exec. Officer--Coastcast Corporation, Gardena, CA; *U.S. Public*, pg. 391

Moralez, Abelardo, Pres. & Chief Exec. Officer--Banca Serfin, S.A., New York Agency, New York, NY; *Int'l*, pg. 137

Moran, Dennis, Chm. Bd. & Chief Exec. Officer--Moran Industries, Inc., Midlothian, IL; *U.S. Private*, pg. 760

Moran, Gordon W., Chm. Bd. & Chief Exec. Officer--Hollingsworth & Vose Co., East Walpole, MA; *U.S. Private*, pg. 534

Moran, Keenan, Pres. & Chief Exec. Officer--Tuffy Associates Corp., Toledo, OH; *U.S. Private*, pg. 1109

Moran, Patricia, Pres. & Chief Exec. Officer--JM Family Enterprises Inc., Deerfield Beach, FL; *U.S. Private*, pg. 577

Moran, Robert J., Pres. & Chief Exec. Officer--Ludlow Composites Corporation, Fremont, OH; *U.S. Private*, pg. 680

Moran, Thomas J., Pres. & Chief Exec. Officer--Mutual of America Life Insurance Company, New York, NY; *U.S. Private*, pg. 769

Moran, Thomas J., Pres. & Chief Exec. Officer--American Life Insurance Company of New York, New York, NY; *U.S. Private*, pg. 769

Moran, William M., Jr., Pres. & Chief Exec. Officer--Moran Foods, Inc./Save-A-Lot Ltd., Saint Louis, MO; *U.S. Public*, pg. 1541

Moravec, Frank, Pres. & Chief Exec. Officer--INX International, Milwaukee, WI; *Int'l*, pg. 1311

Morcott, Southwood J., Chm. Bd. & Chief Exec. Officer--Dana Corporation, Toledo, OH; *U.S. Public*, pg. 479

Morden, Reid, Pres. & Chief Exec. Officer--Atomic Energy of Canada Ltd., Mississauga, Canada; *Int'l*, pg. 97

Moreau, Gary, Chief Exec. Officer--Lionel LLC, Chesterfield, MI; *U.S. Private*, pg. 669

Morelli, Joseph, Chm. Bd., Pres. & Chief Exec. Officer--M.H. Rhodes, Inc., Avon, CT; *U.S. Private*, pg. 927

Moreno, Arthur R., Pres. & Chief Exec. Officer--Outdoor Systems, Inc., Phoenix, AZ; *U.S. Public*, pg. 1235

Moret, Marc, Dr., Chief Exec. Officer and Chm-Bd. Dirs.--Sandoz (Hellas) S.A.C.I., Athens, Greece; *Int'l*, pg. 984

Moreton, John, Chief Exec. Officer--Sun Healthcare Group International Ltd., Windsor, United Kingdom; *U.S. Public*, pg. 1531

Morgan-Stubbe, Jaime, Chief Exec. Officer--Rums of Puerto Rico, New York, NY; *U.S. Private*, pg. 951

Morgan, A.J., Chief Exec. Officer--Eskom, Sandton, South Africa; *Int'l*, pg. 459

Morgan, Allen, Jr., Chm. Bd. & Chief Exec. Officer--Morgan Keegan, Inc., Memphis, TN; *U.S. Public*, pg. 1131

Morgan, Charles D., Jr., Chm. Bd., Pres. & Chief Exec. Officer--Acxiom Corporation, Conway, AR; *U.S. Public*, pg. 18

Morgan, David, Chief Exec. Officer--Standard Chartered Bank Malaysia Berhad, Kuala Lumpur, Malaysia; *Int'l*, pg. 1295

Morgan, Frank R., Pres. & Chief Exec. Officer--Star Fine Foods, Inc., Fresno, CA; *U.S. Private*, pg. 1034

Morgan, Gwyn, Pres. & Chief Exec. Officer--Alberta Energy Company, Ltd., Calgary, Canada; *Int'l*, pg. 48

Morgan, Hugh M., Chief Exec. Officer--Western Mining Corporation Holdings Limited, Southbank, Australia; *Int'l*, pg. 1494

Morgan, James C., Chm. Bd. & Chief Exec. Officer--Applied Materials, Inc., Santa Clara, CA; *U.S. Public*, pg. 123

Morgan, James H., Pres. & Chief Exec. Officer--Interstate/Johnson Lane, Inc., Charlotte, NC; *U.S. Public*, pg. 909

Morgan, James H., Pres. & Chief Exec. Officer--Interstate/Johnson Lane Corporation, Charlotte, NC; *U.S. Public*, pg. 910

Morgan, Jim, Chief Exec. Officer--Adra Systems, Inc., Chelmsford, MA; *U.S. Private*, pg. 18

Morgan, John S., Chm. Bd. & Chief Exec. Officer--Morgan Foods, Inc., Austin, IN; *U.S. Private*, pg. 761

Morgan, Keith, Chief Exec. Officer--Aamco Transmissions, Inc., Bala Cynwyd, PA; *U.S. Private*, pg. 9

Morgan, Phillip R., Pres. & Chief Exec. Officer--Morgan Construction Co., Worcester, MA; *U.S. Private*, pg. 761

Morgan, Robert B., Pres. & Chief Exec. Officer--Cincinnati Financial Corp., Fairfield, OH; *U.S. Public*, pg. 368

Morgan, Thomas I., Pres. & Chief Exec. Officer--U.S. Office Products Company, Washington, DC; *U.S. Public*, pg. 1686

Morgenstern, William E., Pres. & Chief Exec. Officer--Rent-Way, Inc., Erie, PA; *U.S. Public*, pg. 1377

Mori, Reijiro, Pres. & Chief Exec. Officer--Sumitomo Sitix Corporation, Amagasaki, Japan; *Int'l*, pg. 1317

Moriarty, Kevin, Chm. Bd. & Chief Exec. Officer--Del Taco, Inc., Laguna Hills, CA; *U.S. Private*, pg. 321

Morikawa, Shigeru, Chief Oper. Officer--Makita (U.K.) LTD., Milton Keynes, United Kingdom; *Int'l*, pg. 832

Morin, Curtis L., Pres., Treas. & Sec.--Bennington Iron Works, Inc., Bennington, VT; *U.S. Private*, pg. 133

Morini, Angelo S., Chm. Bd., Pres. & Chief Exec. Officer--Galaxy Food Company, Orlando, FL; *U.S. Public*, pg. 697

Morioka, Shigeo, Chm. Bd. & Chief Exec. Officer--Yamanouchi Pharmaceutical Co. Ltd., Tokyo, Japan; *Int'l*, pg. 1518

Morishige, Naoki, Deputy Chief Exec. & Chief Gen. Mgr.--IBJ Australia Bank Limited, Melbourne, Australia; *Int'l*, pg. 676

Morison, John H., III, Pres. & Chief Exec. Officer--Hitchiner Manufacturing Company, Inc., Milford, NH; *U.S. Private*, pg. 531

Morison, Stephen G., Vice Chm., Pres. & Chief Exec. Officer--Chancellor Corporation, Boston, MA; *U.S. Public*, *pg. 335*

Morita, Masaaki, Chm. & Chief Exec. Officer--Sony Electronics, Park Ridge, NJ; *Int'l*, pg. 1281

Moritz, Donald I., Pres. & Interim Chief Exec. Officer--Equitable Resources, Inc., Pittsburgh, PA; *U.S. Public*, pg. 589

Mork, Richard G., Pres., Chief Exec. Officer & Chief Oper. Officer--A.M. Castle & Co., Franklin Park, IL; *U.S. Public*, *pg. 312*

Morley, Harry, Chm. Bd. & Chief Exec. Officer--Taylor-Morley, Inc., Saint Louis, MO; *U.S. Private*, pg. 1071

Moroch, Thomas F., Chief Exec. Officer--Moroch & Assoc., Inc., Dallas, TX; *U.S. Private*, pg. 762

Morreo, Phillip A., Pres. & Chief Exec. Officer--Emergi-Lite, Inc., Westbrook, CT; *Int'l*, pg. 725

Morris, Brian R., Chief Exec. Officer & Chm. Bd.-WF Corroon Limited--WF Corroon-United Kingdom & International, London, United Kingdom; *Int'l*, pg. 1501

Morris, Carloss, Chm. Bd. & Co.-Chief Exec. Officer--Stewart Information Services Corporation, Houston, TX; *U.S. Public*, pg. 1518

Morris, Clifton H. Jr., Chm. Bd. & Chief Exec. Officer--AmeriCredit Corp., Fort Worth, TX; *U.S. Public*, pg. 96

Morris, David, Chm. & Chief Exec. Officer--DMB&B/Weekes Morris Osborn, Ultimo, Australia; *U.S. Private*, pg. 304

Morris, Donald E., Pres. & Chief Exec. Officer--Acorn Engineering Company, City of Industry, CA; *U.S. Private*, pg. 14

Morris, G. Ronald, Pres. & Chief Exec. Officer--Western Industries, Inc., Milwaukee, WI; *U.S. Private*, pg. 1165

Morris, Herman, Pres. & Chief Exec. Officer--Memphis Light, Gas & Water, Memphis, TN; *U.S. Private*, pg. 731

Morris, James T., Pres. & Chief Exec. Officer--IWC Resources Corporation, Indianapolis, IN; *U.S. Public*, pg. 1185

Morris, Mark L., Pres. & Chief Exec. Officer--First National Bank of Fort Myers, Fort Myers, FL; *U.S. Public*, pg. 608

Morris, Michael, Pres. & Chief Exec. Officer--Consumers Energy, Jackson, MI; *U.S. Public*, pg. 280

Morris, Michael G., Chm. Bd., Pres. & Chief Exec. Officer--Northeast Utilities, Berlin, CT; *U.S. Public*, pg. 1194

Morris, Stewart, Pres. & Co.-Chief Exec. Officer Stewart Information Services Corporation, Houston, TX; *U.S. Public*, pg. 1518

Morris, T.N., Jr., Chm., Pres. & Chief Exec. Officer--Calcasieu Lumber Company, Austin, TX; *U.S. Private*, pg. 200

Morris, Thomas E., Pres. & Chief Exec. Officer--Scotty's, Inc., Winter Haven, FL; *Int'l*, pg. 533

Morris, W.S., III, Chm. Bd. & Chief Exec. Officer--Athens Newspapers, Inc., Augusta, GA; *U.S. Private*, pg. 996

Morris, W.S., 111, Chm. Bd. & Chief Exec. Officer--Southeastern Newspapers Corporation, Augusta, GA; *U.S. Private*, pg. 996

Morris, William S., III, Chm. Bd. & Chief Exec. Officer--Shivers Trading & Operating Co., Augusta, GA; *U.S. Private*, pg. 994

Morris, William S., III, Chm. Bd. & Chief Exec. Officer--Stauffer Communications, Inc., Augusta, GA; *U.S. Private*, pg. 995

Morrison, Albert, III, Pres. & Chief Exec. Officer--Burnham, Lancaster, PA; *U.S. Public*, pg. 270

Morrison, Dale F., Pres. & Chief Exec. Officer--Campbell Soup Company, Camden, NJ; *U.S. Public*, pg. 298

Morrison, Dennis R., Pres. & Chief Exec. Officer--Norwest Bank Illinois, N.A., Galesburg, IL; *U.S. Public*, pg. 1202

Morrison, Keith, Pres. & Chief Exec. Officer--Western Broadcast Sales Ltd., Toronto, Canada; *Int'l*, pg. 1482

Morrison, R.W., Chm. & Chief Exec. Officer--Canada Life Investment Management Limited, Toronto, Canada; *Int'l*, pg. 255

Morrison, Richard S., Pres. & Chief Exec. Officer--Molded Fiber Glass Companies, Ashtabula, OH; *U.S. Private*, pg. 755

Morrison, Robert, Chief Exec. Officer-Kraft Foods N. America--Philip Morris Companies Inc., New York, NY; *U.S. Public*, pg. 1287

Morrison, Robert S., Chm. & Chief Exec. Officer--Kraft Foods, Inc., Northfield, IL; *U.S. Public*, pg. 1287

Morrison, Robert S., Chm. Bd. & Chief Exec. Officer--Kraft Foods Inc., Rye Brook, NY; *U.S. Public*, pg. 1288

Morrison, Robert S., Chm. Bd., Pres. & Chief Exec. Officer--The Quaker Oats Company, Chicago, IL; *U.S. Public*, pg. 1347

Morrison, William, Chm. Bd., Pres. & Chief Exec. Officer--Northern Trust Bank of Florida, N.A., Miami, FL; *U.S. Public*, pg. 1196

Morrod, James, Pres. & Chief Exec. Officer--ITK International, Inc., Chelmsford, MA; *U.S. Private*, pg. 556

Morschel, John, Chief Exec. Officer & Mng. Dir.--Lend Lease Corporation Limited, Sydney, Australia; *Int'l*, pg. 806

Morse, Edward J., Sr., Chm. Bd. & Chief Exec. Officer--Ed Morse Automotive Group, Fort Lauderdale, FL; *U.S. Private*, pg. 763

Mortensen, Peter, Chm. Bd., Pres. & Chief Exec. Officer--F.N.B. Corporation, Hermitage, PA; *U.S. Public*, pg. 607

Mortenson, G. Russell, Chm. Bd., Pres. & Chief Exec. Officer--Amtech Corporation, Dallas, TX; *U.S. Public*, pg. 105

Mortenson, Lee N., Pres. & Chief Exec. Officer--Alba-Waldensian, Inc., Valdese, NC; *U.S. Public*, pg. 35

Mortenson, Lee N., Pres. & Chief Exec. Officer--Pilot Research Corp., Valdese, NC; *U.S. Public*, pg. 36

Mortenson, Lee N., Pres. & Chief Exec. Officer--Sunstates Corporation, Raleigh, NC; *U.S. Public*, pg. 1536

Mortenson, M.A., Jr., Chm. Bd. & Chief Exec. Officer--M.A. Mortenson Company, Minneapolis, MN; *U.S. Private*, pg. 763

Mortham, Karen, Acting Chief Exec. Officer--Geonex Corporation, Saint Petersburg, FL; *U.S. Private*, pg. 447

Mortier, Denis, Chief Exec. Officer--Financiere Saint Dominique, Paris, France; *Int'l*, pg. 344

Morton, David L., Pres. & Chief Exec. Officer--U.S. & Canadian Food Products, Chicago, IL; *U.S. Public*, pg. 1347

Morton, David L., Pres. & Chief Exec. Officer--The Quaker Oats Co. of Canada Ltd., Peterborough, Canada; *U.S. Public*, pg. 1348

Morton, Jay W., Pres. & Chief Exec. Officer--United Engines, Inc., Oklahoma City, OK; *U.S. Private*, pg. 1122

Morton, Nathan, Co-Chm. & Chief Exec. Officer--Computer City, Fort Worth, TX; *U.S. Public*, pg. 1560

Mosack, Carl L., Pres. & Chief Exec. Officer--Conbraco Industries Inc., Matthews, NC; *U.S. Private*, pg. 261

Mosco, Robert M., Pres. & Chief Exec. Officer-Mdsg.--Proffitt's, Inc., Alcoa, TN; *U.S. Public*, pg. 1333

Moseley, C., Chm. & Chief Exec. Officer--Simpson Investment Co., Seattle, WA; *U.S. Private*, pg. 1003

Moses, Reg, Chief Exec. Officer--SSB Advertising Sydney, Sydney, Australia; *Int'l*, pg. 394

Moskowitz, Joel P., Chm. Bd., Pres. & Chief Exec. Officer--Ceradyne, Inc, Costa Mesa, CA; *U.S. Public*, pg. 330

Mosley, Ralph, Chief Exec. Officer--Southwestern/Great American Inc., Nashville, TN; *U.S. Private*, pg. 1018

Moss, Cruse W., Chm. Bd. & Chief Exec. Officer--General Automotive Corporation, Ann Arbor, MI; *U.S. Private*, pg. 443

Moss, Geo. French, Chm. & Chief Exec. Officer--Western States Envelope Co., Milwaukee, WI; *U.S. Private*, pg. 1168

Moss, Victor, Pres. & Chief Exec. Officer--Tomco Auto Products, Inc., Los Angeles, CA; *U.S. Private*, pg. 1090

Mossberg, Alan I., Pres., Chief Exec. & Chief Oper. Officer & Treas.--O.F. Mossberg & Sons, Inc., North Haven, CT; *U.S. Private*, pg. 764

Motley, Lyle, Pres. & Chief Exec. Officer--Miami Div., Hialeah, FL; *U.S. Public*, pg. 1148

Motomatsu, Yukuto, Chief Exec. Officer--Ascom Hasler (Japan) Ltd., Tokyo, Japan; *Int'l*, pg. 87

Motro, Harry M., Chief Exec. Officer--Infoseek Corporaton, Sunnyvale, CA; *U.S. Public*, pg. 876

Motta, James, Chief Exec. Officer--Arvida, Boca Raton, FL; *U.S. Private*, pg. 578

Motto, William J., Chm. Bd. & Chief Exec. Officer--Meridian Diagnostics, Inc., Cincinnati, OH; *U.S. Public*, pg. 1094

Mougeot, Robert F., Chief Oper. Officer & Chief Fin. Officer--HEI Diversified, Inc., Honolulu, HI; *U.S. Public*, pg. 800

Moulter, Larry, Pres. & Chief Exec. Officer--Woolf Associates, Boston, MA; *U.S. Private*, pg. 84

Mount, John M., Pres. & Chief Exec. Officer--Service America Systems, Inc., Deerfield Beach, FL; *U.S. Public*, *pg. 344*

Mourry, Dennis, Chm. Bd. & Chief Exec. Officer--Roytex, Inc., New York, NY; *U.S. Private*, pg. 949

Mow, William, Dr., Chm. Bd. & Chief Exec. Officer--Bugle Boy Industries, Inc., Simi Valley, CA; *U.S. Private*, pg. 179

Mower, Eric, Chm. & Chief Exec. Officer--Eric Mower and Associates, Inc., Syracuse, NY; *U.S. Private*, pg. 765

Mower, Eric, Chm. & Chief Exec. Officer--Eric Mower and Associates, Rochester, NY; *U.S. Private*, pg. 765

Moyan, Francois, Pres. & Chief Exec. Officer--Companhia Siderurgica Belgo-Mineira, Belo Horizonte, Brazil; *Int'l*, pg. 79

Moyer, William C., Dr., Chm. Bd., Pres. & Chief Exec. Officer--SFA, Inc., Hyattsville, MD; *U.S. Private*, pg. 956

Moyes, Jerry C., Chm. Bd., Pres. & Chief Exec. Officer--Swift Transportation Co., Sparks, NV; *U.S. Public*, pg. 1543
Moynahan, Stephen R., Pres. & Chief Exec. Officer--Dolphin & Bradbury, Inc., Philadelphia, PA; *U.S. Private*, pg. 338
Moynan, John H., Pres. & Chief Exec. Officer--FCA International Ltd., Westmount, Canada; *Int'l*, pg. 470
Moynihan, James J., AIA, Pres. & Chief Exec. Officer--Heery International, Inc., Atlanta, GA; *U.S. Private*, pg. 519
Mozilo, Angelo R., Chm. Bd. & Chief Exec. Officer--Countrywide Home Loans Inc., Pasadena, CA; *U.S. Public*, pg. 452
Mozilo, Angelo R., Vice Chm. & Chief Exec. Officer--INMC Mortgage Holdings, Inc., Pasadena, CA; *U.S. Public*, pg. 857
Mruz, Michael J., Pres. & Chief Exec. & Oper. Officer--Nichols Research Corporation, Huntsville, AL; *U.S. Public*, pg. 1182
Much, Ian F.R., Chief Exec.-Opers.--T & N Plc, Manchester, United Kingdom; *Int'l*, pg. 1334
Muck, Philip F., Pres., Chief Exec. Officer & Treas.--Munroe, Inc., Pittsburgh, PA; *U.S. Private*, pg. 767
Mueller, Charles W., Chm. Bd., Pres. & Chief Exec. Officer--Ameren Corporation, Saint Louis, MO; *U.S. Public*, pg. 65
Mueller, Charles W., Pres. & Chief Exec. Officer--AmerenUE, Saint Louis, MO; *U.S. Public*, pg. 66
Mueller, David R., Chm. Bd. & Chief Exec. Officer--Comair Holdings, Inc., Erlanger, KY; *U.S. Public*, pg. 406
Mueller, Ed, Pres. & Chief Exec. Officer--Pacific Bell, San Ramon, CA; *U.S. Public*, pg. 1416
Mueller, Ed, Pres. & Chief Exec. Officer--Pacific Bell, San Francisco, CA; *U.S. Public*, pg. 1416
Mueller, Jack J., Pres. & Chief Exec. Officer--Cincinnati Bell Directory Inc., Cincinnati, OH; *U.S. Public*, pg. 367
Mueller, Rand W., Chm. Bd., Pres. & Chief Exec. Officer--Code-Alarm, Inc., Madison Heights, MI; *U.S. Public*, pg. 393
Mueller, Robert W., Pres. & Chief Exec. Officer--Victoria Financial Corporation, Cleveland, OH; *U.S. Public*, pg. 1660
Mueller, Robert W., Pres. & Chief Exec. Officer--Victoria Fire & Casualty, Cleveland, OH; *U.S. Public*, pg. 1660
Mugnai, Franco, Chief Exec. Officer & Gen. Mgr.--La Centrale Fondi S.p.A., Milan, Italy; *Int'l*, pg. 138
Muhlemann, Lukas, Grp. Chief Exec. Officer--Credit Suisse Group, Zurich, Switzerland; *Int'l*, pg. 345
Muhlschlegel, Harry J., Chm. Bd. & Chief Exec. Officer--Jevic Transportation, Inc., Delanco, NJ; *U.S. Public*, pg. 927
Muir, Edward D., Chm. & Chief Exec. Officer--Rapidforms, Inc., Thorofare, NJ; *U.S. Public*, pg. 1171
Mukunda, Ram, Pres., Chief Exec. Officer & Treas.--Startec Global Communications Corporation, Bethesda, MD; *U.S. Public*, pg. 1511
Mulcahy, Geoffrey, Sir, Chief Exec.--Kingfisher plc, London, United Kingdom; *Int'l*, pg. 733
Mulcahy, J. Patrick, Co-Pres. & Co-Chief Exec. Officer--Ralston Purina Company, Saint Louis, MO; *U.S. Public*, pg. 1359
Mulcahy, Thomas P., Grp. Chief Exec.--Allied Irish Banks, p.l.c., Dublin, Ireland; *Int'l*, pg. 64
Muldowney, P., Pres. & Chief Exec. Officer--Morgan Chemical Products Inc., Tucker, GA; *Int'l*, pg. 892
Muldrow, Ken, Pres. & Chief Exec. Officer--Goodpasture, Inc., Brownfield, TX; *U.S. Private*, pg. 464
Mulholland, C. Bradley, Pres. & Chief Exec. Officer--Matson Navigation Company, Inc., San Francisco, CA; *U.S. Public*, pg. 39
Mulholland, Michael F., Grp. Chief Exec. Officer-SunGard Recovery Services--SunGard Data Systems Inc., Wayne, PA; *U.S. Public*, pg. 1534
Mullagh, Michael, Pres. & Chief Exec. Officer--Whisper Communications, Sunnyvale, CA; *U.S. Public*, pg. 1425
Mullan, James F., Pres. & Chief Exec. Officer--PrimeSource Corporation, Pennsauken, NJ; *U.S. Public*, pg. 1329
Mullen, David P., Pres. & Chief Exec. Officer--Robinsons-May, North Hollywood, CA; *U.S. Public*, pg. 1064
Mullen, Dennis M., Pres. & Chief Exec. Officer--Curtice Burns Foods, Rochester, NY; *U.S. Private*, pg. 887
Mullen, Dennis M., Pres. & Chief Exec. Officer--Agrilink Foods, Inc., Rochester, NY; *U.S. Private*, pg. 887
Mullen, James X., Principal & Chief Exec. Officer--Mullen Advertising, Inc., Wenham, MA; *U.S. Private*, pg. 766
Mullen, Paul B., Pres. & Chief Exec. Officer--GES Exposition Services, Inc., Las Vegas, NV; *U.S. Public*, pg. 1718
Muller-Eschenbach, Peter, Dr., Chief Exec. Officer--O&K Orenstein & Koppel Aktiengesellschaft, Dortmund, Germany; *Int'l*, pg. 516
Muller, Dennis M., Pres. & Chief Exec. Officer--Southern Frozen Foods, Montezuma, GA; *U.S. Private*, pg. 887
Muller, Edward R., Pres. & Chief Exec. Officer--Edison Mission Energy, Irvine, CA; *U.S. Public*, pg. 564
Muller, H., Pres. & Chief Exec. Officer--Voith Sulzer Papiertechnik GmbH, Heidenheim, Germany; *Int'l*, pg. 1307
Muller, Jurgen, Dr., Exec. Bd. Member & Chief Exec. Officer-Sandoz Technology Ltd.--Sandoz (Hellas) S.A.C.I., Athens, Greece; *Int'l*, pg. 984
Mullet, Willis, Chm. Bd. & Chief Exec. Officer--Wayne Dalton Corporation, Mount Hope, OH; *U.S. Private*, pg. 1155
Mullett, D.H., Chm. Bd. & Chief Exec. Officer--Bradley Corporation, Menomonee Falls, WI; *U.S. Private*, pg. 164
Mulligan, Gerald T., Pres. & Chief Exec. Officer--Andover Bancorp, Inc., Andover, MA; *U.S. Public*, pg. 111
Mullin, Leo F., Pres. & Chief Exec. Officer--Delta Air Lines, Inc., Atlanta, GA; *U.S. Public*, pg. 497
Mullins, Roy L., Jr., Pres. & Chief Exec. Officer--Beacon Sales Corporation, Jacksonville, FL; *U.S. Private*, pg. 126
Munaf, Triawan, Pres., Chief Exec. Officer & Creative Dir.--Adwork! EURO RSCG Partnership, Jakarta, Indonesia; *Int'l*, pg. 602
Munafo, Samuel J., Pres. & Chief Exec. Officer--Clyde Savings Bank Company, Clyde, OH; *U.S. Public*, pg. 632
Mundschau, Walter J., Pres.--Kalmbach Publishing Co., Waukesha, WI; *U.S. Private*, pg. 606
Mundt, G. Henry, III, Pres. & Chief Exec. Officer--MasterCard International-Cirrus Brand, Purchase, NY; *U.S. Private*, pg. 714
Mundt, Ray B., Chm. Bd. & Chief Exec. Officer--Unisource Worldwide, Inc., Berwyn, PA; *U.S. Public*, pg. 1670
Mundy, John F., Chm. Bd., Pres. & Chief Exec. Officer--Lava World International/Haggerty Enterprises, Inc., Chicago, IL; *U.S. Private*, pg. 653
Munger, Sharon M., Chm. Bd. & Chief Exec. Officer--The M/A/R/C Group, Irving, TX; *U.S. Public*, pg. 1022
Mungo, Frank, Chief Exec. Officer--Temperature Equipment Corporation, Lansing, IL; *U.S. Private*, pg. 1075
Munk, Peter, Chm. Bd. & Chief Exec. Officer--Barrick Gold Corporation, Toronto, Canada; *Int'l*, pg. 168
Munk, Peter, Chm. Bd. & Chief Exec. Officer--TrizecHahn Corporation, Toronto, Canada; *Int'l*, pg. 1424
Munkley, Ronald, Pres. & Chief Exec. Officer--The Consumers' Gas Company Ltd., Scarborough, Canada; *Int'l*, pg. 652
Munn, Stephen P., Chm. Bd. & Chief Exec. Officer--Carlisle Companies Incorporated, Syracuse, NY; *U.S. Public*, pg. 305
Munoz, Angel, Chm. Bd., Pres. & Chief Exec. Officer--Tropic Communications Inc., Columbus, OH; *U.S. Public*, *pg. 1641*
Munro, Scott, Pres. & Chief Exec. Officer--Western Micro Technology, Inc., Campbell, CA; *U.S. Public*, pg. 1759
Munshani, Shanker, Pres. & Chief Exec. Officer--Micronics Computers, Inc., Fremont, CA; *U.S. Public*, pg. 1106
Murakami, Yasufumi, Chief Oper. Officer--Makita Do Brasil Ferramentas Eletricas LTDA., Sao Bernardo do Campo, Brazil; *Int'l*, pg. 832
Murase, Haruo, Pres. & Chief Exec. Officer--Canon U.S.A., Inc., Lake Success, NY; *Int'l*, pg. 262
Murata, Junichi, Pres. & Chief Exec. Officer--Murata Machinery, Ltd., Kyoto, Japan; *Int'l*, pg. 897
Muratore, Michael K., Grp. Chief Exec. Officer-SunGard Fin. Systems--SunGard Data Systems Inc., Wayne, PA; *U.S. Public*, pg. 1534
Muratore, Robert, Pres. & Chief Exec. Officer--KPR, New York, NY; *U.S. Public*, pg. 1224
Muratore, Robert P., Pres. & Chief Exec. Officer-Ferguson Direct--CommonHealth USA, Parsippany, NJ; *Int'l*, pg. 1483
Murayama, Takayoshi, Pres. & Chief Exec. Officer--Asahi Advertising Inc., Tokyo, Japan; *Int'l*, pg. 81
Murdoch, Keith Rupert, Chm. Bd. & Chief Exec. Officer--The News Corporation Limited, Sydney, Australia; *Int'l*, pg. 925
Murdock, David H., Chm. Bd. & Chief Exec. Officer--Castle & Cooke Inc., Los Angeles, CA; *U.S. Public*, pg. 313
Murdock, David H., Chm. Bd. & Chief Exec. Officer--Flexi-Van Leasing, Inc., Kenilworth, NJ; *U.S. Private*, pg. 413
Murdock, David H., Chm. Bd. & Chief Exec. Officer--Dole Food Company, Inc., Westlake Village, CA; *U.S. Public*, pg. 515
Murdock, David H., Pres. & Chief Exec. Officer--Pacific Holding Corporation, Los Angeles, CA; *U.S. Private*, pg. 831
Murdock, Richard D., Pres. & Chief Exec. Officer--CellPro, Incorporated, Bothell, WA; *U.S. Public*, pg. 320
Murdza, Gretchen Curran, Chief Exec. Officer-HomeCall, Inc. & HomeCall Infusion--Mid Atlantic Medical Services, Inc., Rockville, MD; *U.S. Public*, pg. 1109
Murgolo, Joseph, Pres., Chief Exec. Officer & Chief Oper. Officer--Friendship Dairies, Inc., Friendship, NY; *U.S. Private*, pg. 429
Muro, Roy A., Chief Exec. Officer--Vitt Media International, Inc., New York, NY; *U.S. Private*, pg. 1142
Murofushi, Minoru, Chm. Bd., Pres. & Chief Exec. Officer--Itochu Corporation, Tokyo, Japan; *Int'l*, pg. 694
Murphy, Christopher J., III, Pres. & Chief Exec. Officer--1st Source Corporation, South Bend, IN; *U.S. Public*, pg. 638
Murphy, Christopher J., III, Pres & Chief Exec. Officer--1st Source Bank Consolidated, South Bend, IN; *U.S. Public*, pg. 638
Murphy, Douglas A., Pres. & Chief Exec. Officer--American Rice Inc., Houston, TX; *U.S. Public*, pg. 591
Murphy, E. M., Chief Exec. Officer--NFC plc, London, United Kingdom; *Int'l*, pg. 901
Murphy, G.D., Chm. Bd.--Erly Industries, Inc., Los Angeles, CA; *U.S. Public*, pg. 591
Murphy, Henry, Chief Exec. Officer--Americo Manufacturing Co., Inc., Acworth, GA; *U.S. Private*, pg. 64
Murphy, James, Pres. & Chief Exec. Officer--Willis Corroon Corp. of Los Angeles, Glendale, CA; *Int'l*, pg. 1506
Murphy, James R., Chm. Bd., Pres. & Chief Exec. Officer--Bentley Pharmaceuticals, Inc., Tampa, FL; *U.S. Public*, pg. 212
Murphy, John, Joint Chief Exec.Officer--Westcan Chromalox, Cambridge, Canada; *Int'l*, pg. 554
Murphy, Kenneth T., Chm. Bd., Pres. & Chief Exec. Officer--First Financial Bankshares, Inc., Abilene, TX; *U.S. Public*, *pg. 633*
Murphy, Noel, Pres. & Chief Exec. Officer--True Life, Dublin, Ireland; *Int'l*, pg. 1425
Murphy, Patrick F., Pres. & Chief Exec. Officer--AGA Gas, Inc., Independence, OH; *Int'l*, pg. 13
Murphy, Peter J., Pres. & Chief Exec. Officer--Parlex Corporation, Methuen, MA; *U.S. Public*, pg. 1264
Murphy, Peter, Jr., Chm. Bd., Pres. & Chief Exec. Officer--Murphy Company, Eugene, OR; *U.S. Private*, pg. 768
Murphy, William, Chief Exec.-Agricultural Trading--Avonmore Waterford Group plc, Kilkenny, Ireland; *Int'l*, pg. 102
Murray, Frank, Chief Exec. Officer--Goodman Manufacturing, Houston, TX; *U.S. Private*, pg. 464
Murray, James C., Pres. & Chief Exec. Officer--Utilities Construction Co., Inc. Of South Carolina, Charleston, SC; *U.S. Private*, pg. 1130
Murray, N. Leight, Pres. & Chief Exec. Officer--The Airolite Company, Marietta, OH; *U.S. Private*, pg. 29
Murray, Robert J., Chm. Bd., Pres. & Chief Exec. Officer--New England Business Service, Inc., Groton, MA; *U.S. Public*, pg. 1170
Murray, Robert W., Pres., Chief Exec. Officer & Chief Fin. Officer--Mercantile Bank of Iowa, Des Moines, IA; *U.S. Public*, pg. 1087
Murray, Terrence, Chm. Bd., Pres & Chief Exec. Officer--Fleet Financial Group, Inc., Boston, MA; *U.S. Public*, pg. 648
Murrell, R., Pres. & Chief Exec. Officer--Birdsall, Inc., Riviera Beach, FL; *U.S. Public*, pg. 1182
Murry, Albert B., Chm. Bd., Pres. & Chief Exec. Officer--Keystone Heritage Group, Inc., Lebanon, PA; *U.S. Public*, pg. 687
Muscat, Robert, Chief Exec. Officer--John Fairfax Holdings Limited, Sydney, Australia; *Int'l*, pg. 477
Muse, Albert C., Pres. & Chief Exec. Officer--Crown Coal & Coke Co. Inc., Pittsburgh, PA; *U.S. Private*, pg. 292
Muskat, Irwin, Chm. Bd., Pres. & Chief Exec. Officer--Jac Pac Foods, Ltd., Manchester, NH; *U.S. Private*, pg. 579
Musser, Warren V., Chm. Bd. & Chief Exec. Officer--Safeguard Scientifics, Inc., Wayne, PA; *U.S. Public*, pg. 1424
Mustain, William G., Chm. Bd., Pres. & Chief Exec. Officer--Comdial Corporation, Charlottesville, VA; *U.S. Public*, pg. 407
Mustain, William G., Chm. Bd. & Chief Exec. Officer--American Telecommunications Corporation, Charlottesville, VA; *U.S. Public*, pg. 407
Mustain, William G., Chm. Bd. & Chief Exec. Officer--Comdial Enterprise Systems, Inc., Charlottesville, VA; *U.S. Public*, pg. 407
Musto, Michael L., Chm. Bd., Pres. & Chief Exec. Officer--Reptron Electronics, Inc., Tampa, FL; *U.S. Public*, pg. 1377
Musu, Rumengan, Pres. & Chief Exec. Officer--P.T. International Nickel Indonesia, Jakarta, Indonesia; *Int'l*, pg. 947
Musumeci, Ernesto, Chief Exec. Officer--Fiamm S.p.A., Montecchio Maggiore, Italy; *Int'l*, pg. 480
Muzzy, Richard W., Jr., Chm. Bd. & Chief Exec. Officer--The Holland Hitch Company, Holland, MI; *U.S. Private*, pg. 534
Muzzy, Richard W., Jr., Chm. Bd., Chief Exec. & Chief Oper. Officer--Binkley Company, Warrenton, MO; *U.S. Private*, pg. 534
Myers, A. Maurice, Chm. Bd., Pres. & Chief Exec. Officer--Yellow Corporation, Overland Park, KS; *U.S. Public*, pg. 1788
Myers, Chuck, Chm. Bd., Pres. & Chief Exec. Officer--Kitchen Investment Group, Madison, WI; *U.S. Private*, pg. 624
Myers, Chuck, Pres. & Chief Exec. Officer--Country Kitchen International, Inc., Madison, WI; *U.S. Private*, pg. 624
Myers, D. Fredric, Pres. & Chief Exec. Officer--Fournier Furniture, Saint Paul, VA; *U.S. Private*, pg. 422
Myers, Garry C., Chief Exec. Officer--Highlights for Children, Inc., Columbus, OH; *U.S. Private*, pg. 528
Myers, Jay, Pres. & Chief Exec. Officer--Andiamo, Inc., Fountain Valley, CA; *U.S. Private*, pg. 73
Myers, Jay E., Chm. Bd. & Chief Exec. Officer--United Southwest Bank, Washington, IN; *U.S. Public*, pg. 1217
Myers, Kurt J., Pres. & Chief Exec. Officer & Treas.--Amalgamated Automotive Industries, Inc., Enola, PA; *U.S. Private*, pg. 48
Myers, L.G., Pres. & Chief Exec. Officer--LubeCon Systems, Inc., White Cloud, MI; *U.S. Private*, pg. 679
Myers, Myrtle Q., Chief Exec. Officer--Chicago Machine Tool Company, Elk Grove Village, IL; *U.S. Private*, pg. 235
Myers, Norman S., Pres., Chief Exec. & Fin. Officers & Treas.--IDM Controls, Houston, TX; *U.S. Private*, pg. 554
Myers, Robert R., Chm. Bd. & Chief Exec. Officer--Kocolene Oil Corp., Seymour, IN; *U.S. Private*, pg. 629
Myers, Stephen E., Pres. & Chief Exec. Officer--Myers Industries, Inc., Akron, OH; *U.S. Public*, pg. 1143
Myklebust, Egil, Pres. & Chief Exec. Officer--Norsk Hydro a.s, Oslo, Norway; *Int'l*, pg. 959
Myra, Harold, Pres. & Chief Exec. Officer--Christianity Today, Inc., Carol Stream, IL; *U.S. Private*, pg. 238
Mywng-Kwan, Hyun, Chief Oper. Officer--Hotel Shilla Co. Ltd., Seoul, Korea; *Int'l*, pg. 947
Nabers, Drayton, Jr., Chm. Bd. & Chief Exec. Officer--Protective Life Corporation, Birmingham, AL; *U.S. Public*, *pg. 1336*
Nabholz, Robert D., Jr., Chm. Bd. & Chief Exec. Officer--Nabholz Construction Corp., Conway, AR; *U.S. Private*, pg. 772
Nabors, J. Mervyn, Chm. Bd., Pres. & Chief Exec. Officer--Aerosonic Corporation, Clearwater, FL; *U.S. Public*, pg. 25
Nabuurs, P.J.J.G., Chief Exec. Officer--OCE-Belgium N.V./S.A., Brussels, Belgium; *Int'l*, pg. 994
Naccarato, Vincent A., Chm. Bd., Pres. & Chief Exec. Officer--Wilton Industries, Inc., Woodridge, IL; *U.S. Private*, pg. 1181
Nadata, Arthur, Pres. & Chief Exec. Officer--Nu Horizons Electronics Corp., Melville, NY; *U.S. Public*, pg. 1205
Nadel, Herbert, Pres. & Chief Exec. Officer--Nadel Architects, Inc., Los Angeles, CA; *U.S. Private*, pg. 773
Nadel, Herbert, Pres. & Chief Exec. Officer--Nadel Architects, PC Nevada, Las Vegas, NV; *U.S. Private*, pg. 773
Nadhir, Saad J., Co-Chm. & Chief Exec. Officer--Boston Chicken, Inc., Golden, CO; *U.S. Public*, pg. 247
Nadig, Gerald G., Chm. Bd., Pres. & Chief Exec. Officer--Material Sciences Corporation, Elk Grove Village, IL; *U.S. Public*, pg. 1056

Nady, John, Pres. & Chief Exec. Officer--Nady Systems, Inc., Emeryville, CA; *U.S. Private*, pg. 773
Nafilyan, Guy, Pres. & Chief Exec. Officer--Kaufman and Broad, France, Paris, France; *U.S. Public*, pg. 945
Nagai, Hidetake, Chief Oper. Officer--Joyama Kaihatsu Ltd., Hoi-gun, Japan; *Int'l*, pg. 831
Nagel, Daryl D., Pres. & Chief Exec. Officer--Lanoga Corporation, Redmond, WA; *U.S. Private*, pg. 650
Nagel, Kevin, Chm. Bd., Pres. & Chief Exec. Officer--EBP Life Insurnace Co., Minneapolis, MN; *U.S. Public*, pg. 635
Nahey, Brian L., Pres. & Chief Exec. Officer--Venturedyne, Ltd., Milwaukee, WI; *U.S. Private*, pg. 1136
Nahm, Sang-Jo, Pres. & Chief Exec. Officer--Daehong Advertising Inc., Seoul, Korea; *Int'l*, pg. 357
Nahmad, Albert H., Chm. Bd., Pres. & Chief Exec. Officer--Watsco, Inc., Coconut Grove, FL; *U.S. Public*, pg. 1745
Nail, Matt, Chief Oper. Officer-Design Build Div.--HBE Corporation/Design Build Divisions, Saint Louis, MO; *U.S. Private*, pg. 489
Naito, Haruo, Pres. & Chief Exec. Officer--Eisai Co., Ltd., Tokyo, Japan; *Int'l*, pg. 435
Najjar, Edward, Pres. & Chief Exec. Officer--Hampshire Chemical Corp., Lexington, MA; *U.S. Private*, pg. 498
Nakai, Ken-ichiro, Chief Oper. Officer--Makita (China) Co., Ltd., Jiangyin, China; *Int'l*, pg. 832
Nakajima, Kenkichi, Mng. Dir. & Chief Exec.--Yamaichi International (Europe) Ltd., London, United Kingdom; *Int'l*, pg. 1518
Nakamura, Kannosuke, Chm. Bd. & Chief Exec. Officer--Kyowa Hakko Kogyo Company, Ltd., Tokyo, Japan; *Int'l*, pg. 778
Nakamura, Kunio, Chm. Bd., Chief Exec. Officer & Chief Oper. Officer--Matsushita Electric Corporation of America, Secaucus, NJ; *Int'l*, pg. 847
Nakamura, Masao, Chm. Bd. & Chief Exec. Officer--Hokuriku Electric Industry Co., Ltd., Toyama, Japan; *Int'l*, *pg. 627*
Nakamura, Masaya, Chm. Bd. & Chief Exec. Officer--Namco Ltd., Tokyo, Japan; *Int'l*, pg. 905
Nakamura, Minoru, Pres. & Chief Exec. Officer--Nissan Motor Corporation in U.S.A., Gardena, CA; *Int'l*, pg. 945
Nakamura, Takaaki, Chief Oper. Officer--Daiko Pacific International Advertising Co., Beijing, China; *Int'l*, pg. 366
Nakatsugawa, Naoaki, Pres. & Chief Exec. Officer--The Industrial Bank of Japan Trust Company, New York, NY; *Int'l*, pg. 675
Nakauchi, Isao, Chm. Bd., Pres. & Chief Exec. Officer--The Daiei, Inc., Kobe, Japan; *Int'l*, pg. 364
Nakayama, Hayao, Pres. & Chief Exec. Officer--Sega Enterprises Ltd., Tokyo, Japan; *Int'l*, pg. 1218
Nakayama, Tsunehiro, Mng. Dir. & Chief Exec.--IBJ International plc, London, United Kingdom; *Int'l*, pg. 676
Nalle, Alan, Pres. & Chief Exec. Officer--Nalle Plastics Inc., Austin, TX; *U.S. Private*, pg. 773
Nam, Tan Chin, Chief Exec.--Singapore Tourist Promotion Board, Singapore, Singapore; *Int'l*, pg. 1253
Namiot, Milton, Pres. & Chief Exec. Officer--Deering Ice Cream, Inc., Portland, ME; *U.S. Private*, pg. 403
Naney, Charles H., Chief Exec. Officer--Rogers Bridge Company, Inc., Atlanta, GA; *U.S. Private*, pg. 993
Nanot, Yves Rene, Chm. Bd., Pres. & Chief Exec. Officer--Ciments Francais, Paris, France; *Int'l*, pg. 292
Napier, R.S., Chief Exec. Officer--Redland PLC, Reigate, United Kingdom; *Int'l*, pg. 1090
Naples, Ronald J., Chm. Bd., Pres. & Chief Exec. Officer--Quaker Chemical Corporation, Conshohocken, PA; *U.S. Public*, pg. 1346
Naporano, Joseph, Chief Exec. Officer--Naporano Iron & Metal, Newark, NJ; *U.S. Private*, pg. 774
Naqvi, Saiyid T., Pres. & Chief Exec. Officer--PNC Mortgage Corporation of America, Vernon Hills, IL; *U.S. Public*, pg. 1243
Nardelli, Robert L., Pres. & Chief Exec. Officer--G.E. Power Systems, Schenectady, NY; *U.S. Public*, pg. 711
Nardin, J.P., Dr., Chief Exec. Officer--Elektro-Apparatebau Olten AG, Olten, Switzerland; *Int'l*, pg. 444
Nardoni, Dennis, Pres. & Chief Exec. Officer--Chicago Steel Tape, Bradley, IL; *U.S. Private*, pg. 235
Narimatsu, Masayushi, Chief Exec. Officer--Sony Corporation of Panama, Panama, Panama; *Int'l*, pg. 1284
Naritoni, T.A., Chm. Bd. & Chief Exec. Officer--Steelox Systems Inc., Mason, OH; *U.S. Private*, pg. 1038
Narlinger, Dennis, Chm. Bd., Pres. & Chief Exec. Officer--Shugart Corporation, Mission Viejo, CA; *U.S. Private*, pg. 997
Nasella, Henry, Pres. & Chief Exec. Officer--Star Markets Company, Inc., Cambridge, MA; *U.S. Private*, pg. 1035
Nash, Craig M., Chief Exec. Officer--Interval International Inc., Miami, FL; *U.S. Public*, pg. 320
Nason, Charles T., Chm. Bd., Pres. & Chief Exec. Officer--The Acacia Group - Acacia Life Insurance Co., Bethesda, MD; *U.S. Private*, pg. 10
Nason, Charles T., Pres. & Chief Exec. Officer--Acacia Financial Corporation, Bethesda, MD; *U.S. Private*, pg. 11
Nason, Charles T., Pres. & Chief Exec. Officer--Acacia National Life Ins. Co., Bethesda, MD; *U.S. Private*, pg. 11
Nason, Tucker, Pres. & Chief Exec. Officer--Burbank Aircraft Supply Inc., Sun Valley, CA; *U.S. Public*, pg. 187
Nason, Tucker, Pres. & Chief Exec. Officer--Harco, El Segundo, CA; *U.S. Public*, pg. 187
Nasr, Youssef, Deputy Chief Exec. Officer--HongKong Bank of Canada, Vancouver, Canada; *Int'l*, pg. 583
Nasser, Albert, Chm. Bd., Chief Exec. Officer & Chief Oper. Officer--Lady Marlene Sales Corp., New York, NY; *U.S. Private*, pg. 642
Nast, Chris, Chief Exec. Officer--Thompson Nutritional Products, Boca Raton, FL; *U.S. Public*, pg. 1384
Nast, Christian, Pres. & Chief Exec. Officer--Rexall Sundown Inc., Boca Raton, FL; *U.S. Public*, pg. 1384
Nathe, Gerald A., Chm. Bd., Pres. & Chief Exec. Officer--Baldwin Technology Company, Inc., Norwalk, CT; *U.S. Public*, pg. 169
Nation, Jim, Pres. & Chief Exec. Officer--The Spring Air Company, Des Plaines, IL; *U.S. Private*, pg. 1027
Nauert, Peter W., Chief Exec. Officer--Pioneer Life Insurance Co. of Illinois, Rockford, IL; *U.S. Public*, pg. 434
Navolio, Margaret, Pres., Chief Exec. Officer & New Bus. Contact--CPM, Inc., Chicago, IL; *U.S. Private*, pg. 196
Nawrocki, Richard A., Pres. & Chief Exec. Officer--CMI International Inc., Southfield, MI; *U.S. Private*, pg. 195
Nazario, Miguel A., Pres. & Chief Exec. Officer--Puerto Rican Cement Co., Inc., Guaynabo, PR; *U.S. Public*, pg. 1341
Neal, Gary M., Pres. & Chief Exec. Officer--Watlow Electric Manufacturing Company, Saint Louis, MO; *U.S. Private*, pg. 1153
Neal, William, Chief Exec. Officer--Elite Information Systems, Inc., New York, NY; *U.S. Public*, pg. 258
Neal, William, Chief Exec. Officer--Elite Information Systems, Inc., London, United Kingdom; *U.S. Public*, pg. 258
Neale, Gary L., Chm. Bd., Pres. & Chief Exec. Officer--NIPSCO Industries, Inc., Hammond, IN; *U.S. Public*, pg. 1185
Neally, Phillip, Chm. Bd., Pres. & Chief Exec. Officer--Aldi Food Inc., Batavia, IL; *U.S. Private*, pg. 33
Nectoux, Georges, Chm. & Chief Exec. Officer--Ricard, Marseilles, France; *Int'l*, pg. 566
Neff, L., Chief Exec. Officer--American Foundry Group, Inc., Bixby, OK; *U.S. Private*, pg. 54
Neff, Phillip R., Pres. & Chief Exec. Officer--Willis Corroon Corp. of Kansas, Wichita, KS; *Int'l*, pg. 1506
Neil, Donald, Dr., Chief Exec. Officer--Meristem plc, Wetherby, United Kingdom; *Int'l*, pg. 858
Neill, Donald M., Pres. & Chief Exec. Officer--Lufkin National Bank, Lufkin, TX; *U.S. Public*, pg. 630
Neill, John M., Chief Exec. Officer--Unipart Group Limited, Cowley, United Kingdom; *Int'l*, pg. 218
Neill, William J., Publisher & Chief Exec. Officer--The Ottawa Sun, Ottawa, Canada; *Int'l*, pg. 1320
Neilson, Kenneth T., Chm. Bd., Pres. & Chief Exec. Officer--Hubco, Inc., Mahwah, NJ; *U.S. Public*, pg. 845
Neilson, Kenneth T., Chm. Bd. & Chief Exec. Officer--Lafayette American Bank, Union City, NJ; *U.S. Public*, pg. 845
Neira, Sergio, Chief Exec.--KONE Elevadores, S.A., Madrid, Spain; *Int'l*, pg. 747
Neisel, Peter, Chief Exec. Officer--Schwab Corp., Lafayette, IN; *U.S. Private*, pg. 974
Nelsen, C. Davis, II, Chm. Bd., Pres. & Chief Exec. Officer--Nelsen Steel & Wire Co., Franklin Park, IL; *U.S. Private*, pg. 790
Nelson, Barry E., Pres. & Chief Exec. Officer--Cincinnati Bell Long Distance Inc., Cincinnati, OH; *U.S. Public*, pg. 367
Nelson, Charles E., Chm. Bd., Pres. & Chief Exec. Officer--Liberty Bancorp, Inc., Oklahoma City, OK; *U.S. Public*, pg. 174
Nelson, Charles E., Chm. Bd., Pres. & Chief Exec. Officer--Liberty Bank & Trust Company of Oklahoma City, Oklahoma City, OK; *U.S. Public*, pg. 174
Nelson, Dennis H., Pres. & Chief Exec. Officer--The Buckle, Inc., Kearney, NE; *U.S. Public*, pg. 267
Nelson, Gary R., Chm. Bd. & Chief Exec. Officer--Nelson Photo Supplies, San Diego, CA; *U.S. Private*, pg. 791
Nelson, H. Donald, Pres. & Chief Exec. Officer--United States Cellular Corporation, Chicago, IL; *U.S. Public*, pg. 1572
Nelson, Jack, Chm. Bd., Chief Exec. Officer & Treas.--Caprius, Inc., Wilmington, MA; *U.S. Public*, pg. 303
Nelson, James D., Chm. Bd. & Chief Exec. Officer--Arbor Acres Farm, Inc., Glastonbury, CT; *Int'l*, pg. 202
Nelson, Jim, Pres. & Chief Exec. Officer--Time Publishing Ventures, Inc., Los Angeles, CA; *U.S. Public*, pg. 1613
Nelson, John C., Chm. Bd. & Chief Exec. Officer--Norwest Bank Colorado N.A., Denver, CO; *U.S. Public*, pg. 1202
Nelson, Jonathan, Chief Exec. Officer--Organic Online, San Francisco, CA; *U.S. Public*, pg. 1224
Nelson, Kirk N., Pres. & Chief Exec. Officer--Federated Mutual Insurance Company, Owatonna, MN; *U.S. Private*, pg. 399
Nelson, Kurt, Chm. Bd, Pres. & Chief Exec. Officer--Manning & Lewis Engineering Co., Union, NJ; *U.S. Private*, pg. 700
Nelson, M.C., Pres. & Chief Exec. Officer--Radisson Hotel Corporation, Minneapolis, MN; *U.S. Private*, pg. 212
Nelson, Maurice F., Pres. & Chief Exec. Officer--Earle M. Jorgensen Company, Brea, CA; *U.S. Private*, pg. 600
Nelson, Peter C., Pres. & Chief Exec. Officer--California Water Service Co., San Jose, CA; *U.S. Public*, pg. 294
Nemirow, Arnold M., Chm. Bd., Pres. & Chief Exec. Officer--Bowater Incorporated, Greenville, SC; *U.S. Public*, pg. 247
Nemschoff, Mark, Pres., Chief Exec. Officer & Treas.--Nemschoff Chairs, Inc., Sheboygan, WI; *U.S. Private*, pg. 791
Nennecker, Werner G., Pres. & Chief Exec. Officer--Pegasus Gold Corporation, Spokane, WA; *U.S. Public*, pg. 1269
Nero, Robert A., Pres. & Chief Exec. Officer--Interface Systems, Inc., Ann Arbor, MI; *U.S. Public*, pg. 889
Nesbitt, Arthur, Chief Exec. Officer--Nasco Modesto, Modesto, CA; *U.S. Private*, pg. 446
Nesbitt, Arthur, Pres. & Chief Exec. Officer--Nasco International, Inc., Fort Atkinson, WI; *U.S. Private*, pg. 446
Nesbitt, Gregory L., Chm. Bd., Pres. & Chief Exec. Officer--Central Louisiana Electric Company, Inc., Pineville, LA; *U.S. Public*, pg. 325
NeSmith, Joseph Q., Chief Exec. Officer & Treas.--Continental Dynamics, Inc., Herndon, VA; *U.S. Public*, pg. 110
Ness, Steven, Pres. & Chief Exec. Officer--Ness Holding Co., Portland, OR; *U.S. Private*, pg. 791
Nester, Dallas G., Pres. & Chief Exec. Officer--Brown Wooten Mills, Inc., Burlington, NC; *U.S. Private*, pg. 174
Nestrick, Dwight, Chief Exec. Officer--Citizens Bank of Kentucky, Madisonville, KY; *U.S. Public*, pg. 280
Netter, Alfred E., Pres. & Chief Exec. Officer--GAF Premium Products, Inc., Wayne, NJ; *U.S. Private*, pg. 433
Netter, Edward, Chm. Bd. & Chief Exec. Officer--Independence Holding Company, Stamford, CT; *U.S. Private*, pg. 446
Neubauer, Joseph, Chm. Bd., Pres. & Chief Exec. Officer--Aramark Corp., Philadelphia, PA; *U.S. Private*, pg. 78
Neuenschwander, Paul A., Pres. & Chief Exec. Officer--Zions Mortgage Company, Salt Lake City, UT; *U.S. Public*, pg. 1793
Neumann, Hans Jorgen, Acting Chief Exec. Officer--Berendsen PMC AB, Stockholm, Sweden; *Int'l*, pg. 1285
Neuvile, Patrick Martin, Pres. & Chief Exec. Officer--Calberson Overseas, Roissy, France; *Int'l*, pg. 549
Neveu, Jean, Pres. & Chief Exec. Officer--Quebecor Inc., Montreal, Canada; *Int'l*, pg. 1075
Neveu, Jean, Chm. Bd. & Chief Exec. Officer--Imprimerie Quebecor Inc., Montreal, Canada; *Int'l*, pg. 1077
Neville, Robert J., Chm. Bd., Pres. & Chief Exec. Officer--The North American Manufacturing Co., Cleveland, OH; *U.S. Private*, pg. 803
Nevin, John J., Pres. & Chief Exec. Officer--Broadcast Electronics, Inc., Quincy, IL; *U.S. Private*, pg. 531
New, James C., Pres. & Chief Exec. Officer--AmeriPath, Inc., Riviera Beach, FL; *U.S. Public*, pg. 96
Newall, J.E. (Ted), Vice Chm. & Chief Exec. Officer--Nova Corporation, Calgary, Canada; *Int'l*, pg. 971
Newcomb, Jonathan, Pres. & Chief Exec. Officer--Simon & Schuster, New York, NY; *U.S. Private*, pg. 777
Newell, Liz, Pres., Chief Exec. Officer & New Bus. Contact--Kragie/Newell, Des Moines, IA; *U.S. Private*, pg. 634
Newhart, Larry, Chief Exec. Officer--Storeroom Solutions Inc., Montrose, PA; *U.S. Private*, pg. 1045
Newhouse, Samuel I., Jr., Chm. Bd. & Chief Exec. Officer--Advance Publications Inc., Staten Island, NY; *U.S. Private*, pg. 18
Newland, Richard, Pres. & Chief Exec. Officer--Anoka Electric Cooperative, Ramsey, MN; *U.S. Private*, pg. 75
Newman, Craig, Chief Officer--Callahan Enterprises, Westfield, IN; *Int'l*, pg. 566
Newman, Frank, Chm. Bd., Pres. & Chief Exec. Officer--Eckerd Corporation, Largo, FL; *U.S. Public*, pg. 917
Newman, Frank N., Chm. Bd., Pres. & Chief Exec. Officer--Bankers Trust New York Corporation, New York, NY; *U.S. Public*, pg. 185
Newman, Mark S., Chm. Bd., Pres. & Chief Exec. Officer--DRS Technologies, Inc., Parsippany, NJ; *U.S. Public*, pg. 474
Newman, R. Stephen, Pres. & Chief Exec. Officer--Bacon's Information, Inc., Chicago, IL; *U.S. Public*, pg. 1327
Newman, Stephen H., Chm. Bd. & Chief Exec. Officer--Underwriters Reinsurance, Woodland Hills, CA; *U.S. Public*, pg. 42
Newman, William, Chm. Bd. & Chief Exec. Officer--New Plan Realty Trust, New York, NY; *U.S. Public*, pg. 1172
Newnham, Dennis, Pres. & Chief Exec. Officer--Tsumura International, Secaucus, NJ; *Int'l*, pg. 1426
Newton, B., Chief Exec. Officer--Booker Tate Ltd., Thame, United Kingdom; *Int'l*, pg. 1357
Newton, Paul E., Pres. & Chief Exec. Officer--Boole & Babbage, Inc., San Jose, CA; *U.S. Public*, pg. 244
Newtow, David, Chief Exec. Officer--Shaer Shoe Corporation, Bedford, NH; *U.S. Private*, pg. 988
Neyer, Jerome C., Chm. Bd. & Chief Exec. Officer--NTH Consultants, Ltd., Farmington, MI; *U.S. Private*, pg. 772
Neyer, Thomas, Sr., Chm. Bd. & Pres.--Al Neyer, Inc., Cincinnati, OH; *U.S. Private*, pg. 797
Ng, Hubert, Chief Exec.-SmarTone Telecomm. Holdings Ltd.--Sun Hung Kai Properties Ltd., Wan Chai, Hong Kong; *Int'l*, pg. 1318
Nho, Byung-Yong, Chief Exec. Officer--Lotte Shopping Co. Ltd., Seoul, Korea; *Int'l*, pg. 819
Nicastro, Louis, Chm. Bd. & Chief Exec. Officer--WHG Resorts & Casinos, Carolina, PR; *U.S. Public*, pg. 1265
Nicastro, Neil D., Pres. & Chief Exec. Officer--WMS Industries Inc., Chicago, IL; *U.S. Public*, pg. 1727
Nicely, Olza M., Pres. & Chief Exec. Officer-Insurance Opers.--GEICO Corporation, Washington, DC; *U.S. Public*, pg. 219
Nichol, David A., Chm., Pres & Chief Exec. Officer--Destination Products International, Inc., Toronto, Canada; *Int'l*, pg. 338
Nicholas, Dimitri M., Chief Exec. Officer & V.P.--The Orr Felt Company, Piqua, OH; *U.S. Private*, pg. 820
Nicholas, Peter M., Chm. Bd., Pres. & Chief Exec. Officer--Boston Scientific Corp., Natick, MA; *U.S. Public*, pg. 247
Nichols, Cathy, Chm. Bd. & Chief Exec. Officer--Universal Studios Recreation Services Group, Universal City, CA; *Int'l*, pg. 1216
Nichols, David L., Chm. Bd. & Chief Exec. Officer--Mercantile Stores Company, Inc., Fairfield, OH; *U.S. Public*, pg. 1089
Nichols, Fred R., Chm. Bd., Pres. & Chief Exec. Officer--TCA Management Company, Tyler, TX; *U.S. Public*, pg. 1553
Nichols, George H., Chief Exec. Officer--The Arnold Palmer Golf Company, Ooltewah, TN; *U.S. Public*, pg. 132
Nichols, Grace, Pres. & Chief Exec. Officer--Victoria's Secret Stores, Reynoldsburg, OH; *U.S. Public*, pg. 995
Nichols, J. Larry, Pres. & Chief Exec. Officer--Devon Energy Corporation, Oklahoma City, OK; *U.S. Public*, pg. 503
Nichols, J.D., Chm. Bd. & Chief Exec. Officer--NTS Development Company, Louisville, KY; *U.S. Private*, pg. 772
Nichols, James T., Pres. & Chief Exec. Officer--InterTAN Inc., Fort Worth, TX; *U.S. Public*, pg. 910
Nichols, W.C., Chm. Bd., Pres. & Chief Exec. Officer--Renfro Corp., Mount Airy, NC; *U.S. Private*, pg. 922

Nicholson, Gary D., Chm. Bd., Pres. & Chief Exec. Officer--Camco International Inc., Houston, TX; *U.S. Public*, pg. 297

Nicholson, Gary D., Pres. & Chief Exec. Officer--Camco International Inc., Houston, TX; *U.S. Public*, pg. 298

Nicholson, James B., Pres. & Chief Exec. Officer--PVS Chemicals, Inc., Detroit, MI; *U.S. Private*, pg. 828

Nicholson, Thomas J., Pres. & Chief Exec. Officer--Central Bank of Monroe, Monroe, LA; *U.S. Public*, pg. 629

Nicholson, Will F., Jr., Chm. Bd. & Pres.--Colorado National Bankshares, Inc., Denver, CO; *U.S. Public*, pg. 1680

Nick, Jeffrey J., Pres. & Chief Exec. Officer-Lincoln National Investment Companies--Lincoln National Corporation, Fort Wayne, IN; *U.S. Public*, pg. 997

Nickel, Jeffrey V., Chief Exec. Officer--Familian Corp., Van Nuys, CA; *Int'l*, pg. 1512

Nickel, Mark A., Chief Exec. Officer & Exec. Publr.--Sampler Publications Inc., Saint Charles, IL; *U.S. Private*, pg. 963

Nickels, William F., Pres. & Chief Exec. Officer--Replogle Globes, Inc., Broadview, IL; *U.S. Private*, pg. 923

Nickly, John, Pres. & Chief Exec. Officer--Regence Life & Health Insurance Co., Portland, OR; *U.S. Private*, pg. 918

Nickoll, John F., Chm. Bd. & Chief Exec. Officer--The Foothill Group, Inc., Los Angeles, CA; *U.S. Public*, pg. 1201

Nicolette, Thomas A., Pres. & Chief Exec. Officer--Sentry Technology Corp., Hauppauge, NY; *U.S. Public*, pg. 1458

Nicoletti, William, Chief Officer--Dolisos, Las Vegas, NV; *Int'l*, pg. 566

Nicoli, E.L., Chief Exec. Officer--United Biscuits (Holdings) Plc, West Drayton, United Kingdom; *Int'l*, pg. 1442

Nicolosi, Richard R., Pres. & Chief Exec. Officer--Samsonite Corporation, Denver, CO; *U.S. Public*, pg. 1430

Nicosia, Joseph A., Pres. & Chief Exec. Officer--GATX Logistics, Inc., Jacksonville, FL; *U.S. Public*, pg. 691

Nidiffer, Douglas A., Pres. & Chief Exec. Officer--C & K Market, Inc., Brookings, OR; *U.S. Private*, pg. 191

Nie, Zenon S., Chm. Bd. & Chief Exec. Officer--Simmons Company, Atlanta, GA; *Int'l*, pg. 686

Niederske-Werbeck, Dieter, Chief Exec.--Rheinmetall Group, Dusseldorf, Germany; *Int'l*, pg. 1108

Nield, David A., Pres. & Chief Exec. Officer--The Canada Life Assurance Company, Toronto, Canada; *Int'l*, pg. 254

Nields, Morgan W., Chm. Bd. & Chief Exec. Officer--Fischer Imaging Corporation, Denver, CO; *U.S. Public*, pg. 647

Nielsen, Claude B., Pres. & Chief Exec. Officer--Coca-Cola Bottling Co. United, Inc., Birmingham, AL; *U.S. Private*, pg. 248

Nielson, Bruce, Chief Exec. Officer, Treas. & Gen. Mgr.--Producers Livestock, North Salt Lake, UT; *U.S. Private*, pg. 888

Nielson, John O., Chm. Bd. & Chief Exec. Officer--John Morrell & Co., Cincinnati, OH; *U.S. Public*, pg. 1479

Nielsson, Tommie, Chief Exec. Officer--KappAhl AB, Goteborg, Sweden; *Int'l*, pg. 718

Niemann, H.C., Chief Exec. Officer--Paul Hellermann GmbH, Pinneberg, Germany; *Int'l*, pg. 209

Niemela, Juha, Pres. & Chief Exec. Officer--UPM-Kymmene Corporation, Helsinki, Finland; *Int'l*, pg. 1427

Niemeyer, W. Pil, Chief Fin. Officer & Exec. V.P.--Nasco, Fort Atkinson, WI; *U.S. Private*, pg. 446

Niemiec, Leo P., Pres. & Chief Exec. Officer--Lawnware Products, Inc., Morton Grove, IL; *U.S. Private*, pg. 653

Nienow, Lance, Chief Exec. Officer--Weinbrenner Shoe Company, Inc., Merrill, WI; *U.S. Private*, pg. 1160

Nierenberg, Nico, Pres. & Chief Exec. Officer--Actuate Software Corporation, San Mateo, CA; *U.S. Private*, pg. 16

Nies, Thomas M., Chm. Bd., Pres. & Chief Exec. Officer--Cincom Systems, Inc., Cincinnati, OH; *U.S. Private*, pg. 240

Nieto, Fernando, Chief Exec. Officer--Grupo Barro Testa, Madrid, Spain; *Int'l*, pg. 1377

Nigbor, Donald E., Pres. & Chief Exec. Officer--Benchmark Electronics Inc., Angleton, TX; *U.S. Public*, pg. 210

Nikolaev, Richard D., Pres. & Chief Exec. Officer--Wright Medical Technology, Arlington, TN; *U.S. Private*, pg. 1192

Niles, Lou, Pres. & Chief Exec. Officer--Benson Industries, Inc., Portland, OR; *U.S. Private*, pg. 133

Niles, Nicholas H., Pres. & Chief Exec. Officer--The Sporting News Publishing Company, Saint Louis, MO; *U.S. Public*, pg. 1616

Nilsson, Ingemar, Chief Officer--Obs! Stormarknaden AB, Stockholm, Sweden; *Int'l*, pg. 718

Nilsson, Kjell, Pres. & Chief Exec. Officer--Trelleborg AB, Trelleborg, Sweden; *Int'l*, pg. 1419

Nimrodi, Ofer, Chief Exec. Officer & Dir.--The Israel Land Development Co., Ltd., Tel Aviv, Israel; *Int'l*, pg. 691

Nipp, Heinz, Chief Exec. Officer & Exec. V.P.-Fin.--Liechtenstein Global Trust Limited, Vaduz, Liechtenstein; *Int'l*, pg. 809

Nipp, Heinz, Dr., Pres. & Chief Exec. Officer--LGT Bank in Liechtenstein Aktiengesellschaft, Vaduz, Liechtenstein; *Int'l*, pg. 809

Nishiguchi, Hiroshi, Chief Oper. Officer--Makita (Taiwan) LTD., Taipei, Taiwan; *Int'l*, pg. 832

Nishimuro, Taizo, Pres. & Chief Exec. Officer--Toshiba Corporation, Tokyo, Japan; *Int'l*, pg. 1402

Nishinaka, Ted, Chm. Bd. & Chief Exec. Officer--Mitsui Foods, Inc., Norwood, NJ; *Int'l*, pg. 879

Nishio, Masaharu, Pres. & Chief Exec. Officer--Muratech America, Inc., Plano, TX; *Int'l*, pg. 897

Nislick, Stephen, Chief Exec. Officer--Edison Parking Properties, LLC, Newark, NJ; *U.S. Private*, pg. 364

Nixon, J. L., Mng. Dir. & Chief Exec. Officer--Rio Tinto Zimbabwe Limited, Harare, Zimbabwe; *Int'l*, pg. 1119

Nixon, P. Andrews, Pres. & Chief Exec. Officer--Dead River Company, Portland, ME; *U.S. Private*, pg. 318

Nizam, I., Chm. Bd., Pres. & Chief Exec. Officer--Master International Corp., Santa Monica, CA; *U.S. Private*, pg. 713

Noble, Robert B., Chm. & Chief Exec. Officer--Noble & Associates, Springfield, MO; *U.S. Private*, pg. 800

Noble, Robert B., Pres. & Chief Exec. Officer--Noble & Associates Promotion Group, Springfield, MO; *U.S. Private*, pg. 800

Nobles, Bruce R., Chm. Bd., Pres. & Chief Exec. Officer--Hawaiian Airlines, Inc., Honolulu, HI; *U.S. Public*, pg. 799

Node-Langois, Patrick, Chm. & Chief Exec. Officer--Lafarge Aluminates, Paris, France; *Int'l*, pg. 789

Noe, Greg, Pres. & Chief Exec. Officer--Pilliod Furniture, Greensboro, NC; *U.S. Public*, pg. 974

Noel, J-C, Chm. Bd., Pres. & Chief Exec. Officer--Hilton Canada Inc., Montreal, Canada; *Int'l*, pg. 788

Noel, Marc, Chief Exec. Officer--Nomaco, Inc., Zebulon, NC; *U.S. Private*, pg. 801

Noel, T. Howard, Pres. & Chief Exec. Officer--Hayes, Seay, Mattern & Mattern, Inc., Roanoke, VA; *U.S. Private*, pg. 513

Noels, Jacques, Pres., Chief Exec. Officer & Chief Oper. Officer--Zenith Data Systems, Deerfield, IL; *Int'l*, pg. 317

Noelting, Jean, Pres. & Chief Exec. Officer--Parmalat Canada Ltd., Etobicoke, Canada; *Int'l*, pg. 1023

Noer, John A., Chm., Pres. & Chief Exec. Officer--Northern States Power Co. (Wis.), Eau Claire, WI; *U.S. Public*, pg. 1195

Noia, Alan J., Pres. & Chief Exec. Officer--Allegheny Power System, Inc., Hagerstown, MD; *U.S. Public*, pg. 42

Noiret, Yves, Chm. Bd. & Chief Exec. Officer--Eternit Industries, Vernouillet, France; *Int'l*, pg. 430

Noiret, Yves, Chief Exec. Officer--Edilit, Padua, Italy; *Int'l*, pg. 430

Nolan, Cary J., Pres. & Chief Exec. Officer--Picker International, Inc., Cleveland, OH; *Int'l*, pg. 545

Noll, Gregory P., Pres. & Chief Exec. Officer--The Provident Bank of Kentucky, Cincinnati, OH; *U.S. Public*, pg. 1338

Noonan, Edward J., Pres. & Chief Exec. Officer--American Re Corporation, Princeton, NJ; *Int'l*, pg. 897

Noonan, Edward J., Pres. & Chief Exec. Officer--American Re-Insurance Company, Princeton, NJ; *Int'l*, pg. 897

Noonan, Jack, Pres. & Chief Exec. Officer--SPSS Inc., Chicago, IL; *U.S. Public*, pg. 1420

Nordin, Ronald H., Pres. & Chief Exec. Officer--SQA, Inc., Burlington, MA; *U.S. Public*, pg. 1361

Nordin, Stig, Chief Exec. & Oper. Officer--Korsnas AB, Gavle, Sweden; *Int'l*, pg. 759

Nordloh, Gary L., Pres. & Chief Exec. Officer--Wexpro Company, Salt Lake City, UT; *U.S. Public*, pg. 1352

Nordloh, Gary L., Pres. & Chief Exec. Officer--Celsius Energy Company, Salt Lake City, UT; *U.S. Public*, pg. 1352

Nordloh, Gary L., Pres. & Chief Exec. Officer--Universal Resources Corporation, Salt Lake City, UT; *U.S. Public*, pg. 1352

Norman, Archie, Chief Exec. Officer--Asda Group Plc, Leeds, United Kingdom; *Int'l*, pg. 17

Norris, David W., Pres. & Chief Exec. Officer--PCC Flow Technologies, Inc., Houston, TX; *U.S. Public*, pg. 1320

Norris, J.C., Pres. & Chief Exec. Officer--Turner Foods Corporation, Punta Gorda, FL; *U.S. Public*, pg. 608

Norris, John W., Jr., Chm. Bd. & Chief Exec. Officer--Lennox International Inc., Richardson, TX; *U.S. Private*, pg. 659

Norris, Thomas C., Chm., Pres. & Chief Exec. Officer--P.H. Glatfelter Company, Spring Grove, PA; *U.S. Public*, pg. 746

Norsworthy, Lamar, Chm. Bd. & Chief Exec. Officer--Holly Corporation, Dallas, TX; *U.S. Public*, pg. 830

Norton, David W., Chm. & Chief Exec. Officer--Dresser-Rand Co., Corning, NY; *U.S. Public*, pg. 529

Norton, J. Patrick, Chm. Bd., Pres. & Chief Exec. Officer--Fabreeka International, Inc., Stoughton, MA; *U.S. Private*, pg. 390

Norton, John R., III, Chm. Bd. & Chief Exec. officer--J.R. Norton Company, Phoenix, AZ; *U.S. Private*, pg. 807

Norton, Kenneth R., Chm. Bd. & Chief Exec. Officer--PST Vans, Inc., Salt Lake City, UT; *U.S. Public*, pg. 1246

Norton, Michael, Deputy Chief Exec.--Barratt Developments Plc, Newcastle upon Tyne, United Kingdom; *Int'l*, pg. 167

Norton, Robert, Pres. & Chief Exec. Officer--FTD, Inc./ Florists Transworld Delivery, Inc., Downers Grove, IL; *U.S. Private*, pg. 389

Norton, Robert R., Chm. Bd., Pres. & Chief Exec. Officer--BeefAmerica Operating Co., Inc., Omaha, NE; *U.S. Private*, pg. 130

Norvik, Harald, Pres. & Chief Exec. Officer--Statoil, Stavanger, Norway; *Int'l*, pg. 1297

Nosaki, G., Chief Exec. Officer--Tokio Marine Management Inc., New York, NY; *Int'l*, pg. 1392

Nosler, Peter, Chief Exec. Officer--DPR Construction, Inc., Redwood City, CA; *U.S. Private*, pg. 305

Notebaert, Edmond F., Pres. & Chief Exec. Officer--The Children's Hospital of Philadelphia, Philadelphia, PA; *U.S. Private*, pg. 236

Notebaert, Richard C., Chm. Bd., Pres. & Chief Exec. Officer--Ameritech Corporation, Chicago, IL; *U.S. Public*, pg. 97

Notebaert, Richard C., Chm. Bd. & Chief Exec. Officer--Ameritech Corp., Chicago, IL; *U.S. Public*, pg. 98

Notley, J.P.W., Chief Exec. Officer--ABB Kent Plc, Luton, United Kingdom; *Int'l*, pg. 2

Noto, Lucio A., Chm. Bd., Pres., Chief Exec. & Chief Oper. Officer--Mobil Oil Corporation, Fairfax, VA; *U.S. Public*, pg. 1118

Nova, Gianluigi, Pres., Chief Exec. Officer & Controller--Itam Tech Italimplianti, Inc., Coraopolis, PA; *Int'l*, pg. 655

Novak, Mark, Pres. & Chief Exec. Officer--Arrowhead Mills, Inc., Hereford, TX; *U.S. Private*, pg. 86

Novello, R.J., Chief Exec. Officer--Copeland Corporation, Sidney, OH; *U.S. Public*, pg. 573

Novelly, P. A., Chief Exec. Officer--Apex Oil Company, Inc., Saint Louis, MO; *U.S. Private*, pg. 77

Novich, Neil S., Pres. & Chief Exec. Officer--Ryerson Tull, Chicago, IL; *U.S. Public*, pg. 879

Nowak, Larry, Chief Exec. Officer--American Paper Group, Inc., Youngstown, OH; *U.S. Private*, pg. 60

Nowak, Larry, Chief Exec. Officer--American Church, Youngstown, OH; *U.S. Private*, pg. 60

Nowak, Larry, Chief Exec. Officer--American Church, Richmond, VA; *U.S. Private*, pg. 60

Nozko, Henry W., Sr., Chm. Bd., Pres. & Chief Exec. Officer--ACMAT Corporation, New Britain, CT; *U.S. Public*, pg. 16

Nugent, Michael, Chief Exec. Officer--Five Star Foods Incorporated, Dalton, GA; *U.S. Private*, pg. 409

Nugent, Robert, Chm. Bd., Pres. & Chief Exec. Officer--Foodmaker, Inc., San Diego, CA; *U.S. Public*, pg. 661

Numauchi, Motohiko, Pres. & Chief Exec. Officer--Mitsubishi International Corporation, New York, NY; *Int'l*, pg. 871

Nunez, Elpidio, Chm. Bd. & Pres.--Northwestern Meats Inc., Miami, FL; *U.S. Private*, pg. 807

Nunez, Ramon A., Pres. & Chief Exec. Officer--IKOS Systems, Inc., Cupertino, CA; *U.S. Public*, pg. 864

Nunn, Kent G., Pres. & Chief Exec. Officer-One Sys. Grp. LLC--Farmland Industries, Inc., Kansas City, MO; *U.S. Private*, pg. 395

Nusbaum, W., Pres. & Chief Exec. Officer--Long Manufacturing, Ltd., Oakville, Canada; *Int'l*, pg. 815

Nussbaum, Irving, Chief Exec. Officer--New York Carpet World, Dalton, GA; *U.S. Public*, pg. 1464

Nussbaum, Paul A., Chm. Bd. & Chief Exec. Officer--Patriot American Hospitality, Inc., Dallas, TX; *U.S. Public*, pg. 1265

Nuzzo, Sal J., Chm. Bd. & Chief Exec. Officer--Datron Incorporated, Windsor, CT; *U.S. Private*, pg. 313

Nyberg, Lars, Chm. Bd. & Chief Exec. Officer--NCR Corporation, Dayton, OH; *U.S. Public*, pg. 1146

Nybo, Svein G., Pres. & Chief Exec. Officer--Frionor A/S, Lysaker, Norway; *Int'l*, pg. 516

Nye, Erle, Pres. & Chief Exec. Officer--Texas Utilities Company, Dallas, TX; *U.S. Public*, pg. 1586

Nye, Erle, Chm. Bd. & Chief Exec. Officer--Texas Utilities Communications Inc., Dallas, TX; *U.S. Public*, pg. 1588

Nye, Erle, Chm. Bd. & Chief Exec. Officer--Texas Utilities Properties Inc., Dallas, TX; *U.S. Public*, pg. 1588

Nyland, Robert M., Pres. & Chief Exec. Officer--Outdoor Services, San Francisco, CA; *U.S. Private*, pg. 1166

Nyquist, Carl-Erik, Pres. & Chief Exec. Officer--Vattenfall AB, Stockholm, Sweden; *Int'l*, pg. 1452

O'Brien, Charles J., Pres. & Chief Exec. Officer--MTL Inc., Plant City, FL; *U.S. Public*, pg. 1028

O'Brien, Charles P., Pres. & Chief Exec. Officer--Reliance Standard Life Insurance Company, Philadelphia, PA; *U.S. Public*, pg. 496

O'Brien, Coby, Pres. & Chief Exec. Officer--Darwin Digital, New York, NY; *U.S. Public*, pg. 1422

O'Brien, Daniel R., Pres. & Chief Exec. Officer--Beneficial Insurance Group, Inc., Peapack, NJ; *U.S. Public*, pg. 211

O'Brien, David P., Chm. Bd., Pres. & Chief Exec. Officer--Canadian Pacific Limited, Calgary, Canada; *Int'l*, pg. 258

O'Brien, John F., Pres. & Chief Exec. Officer--Allmerica Financial Corporation, Worcester, MA; *U.S. Public*, pg. 54

O'Brien, Ken, Pres. & Chief Exec. Officer--R.W. Beck, Inc., Seattle, WA; *U.S. Private*, pg. 128

O'Brien, Michael J., Chief Exec. Officer--Salick Health Care, Inc., Los Angeles, CA; *Int'l*, pg. 1524

O'Brien, Terry, Vice Chm. & Chief Exec. Officer--Ryan Herco Products Corp., Burbank, CA; *U.S. Private*, pg. 953

O'Brien, Thomas H., Chm. Bd. & Chief Exec. Officer--PNC Bank Corp., Pittsburgh, PA; *U.S. Public*, pg. 1242

O'Callaghan, R.A., Chief Exec. Officer--Universal Builders Supply, Inc., Mount Vernon, NY; *U.S. Private*, pg. 1126

O'Connell, Frank J., Chm. Bd., Pres. & Chief Exec. Officer--Gibson Greetings, Inc., Cincinnati, OH; *U.S. Public*, pg. 742

O'Connell, Mark, Chief Exec. Officer--Adra Systems, Inc., Chelmsford, MA; *U.S. Private*, pg. 18

O'Connor-Vos, Lynn, Pres. & Chief Exec. Officer-GHG--Grey Healthcare Group, New York, NY; *U.S. Public*, pg. 765

O'Connor, J.F., Chief Exec.-Corp. Devel.--BBA Group plc, London, United Kingdom; *Int'l*, pg. 112

O'Connor, James, Chief Exec. Officer--G.F. Wright Steel & Wire Company, Worcester, MA; *U.S. Private*, pg. 1192

O'Connor, James J., Chm. Bd. & Chief Exec. Officer--Unicom Corporation, Chicago, IL; *U.S. Public*, pg. 1664

O'Connor, James J., Chm. Bd. & Chief Exec. Officer--ComEd, Chicago, IL; *U.S. Public*, pg. 1664

O'Connor, John, Chief Exec. Officer & Exec. Gen. Mgr.--BHP Petroleum, Melbourne, Australia; *Int'l*, pg. 224

O'Connor, Laurence P., Chm. Bd., Pres. & Chief Exec. Officer--Unigard Insurance Co., Bellevue, WA; *Int'l*, pg. 345

O'Connor, Laurence P., Chm. Bd., Pres. & Chief Exec. Officer--Unigard Indemnity Co., Bellevue, WA; *Int'l*, pg. 345

O'Connor, Tom, Chief Exec. Officer--Saul Bros. & Company, Inc., Norcross, GA; *U.S. Private*, pg. 968

O'Connor, William Y., Pres. & Chief Exec. Officer--GTECH Corporation, West Greenwich, RI; *U.S. Public*, pg. 767

O'Dell, James J., Chm. Bd., Pres. & Chief Exec. Officer--Valley Bank & Trust, Brighton, CO; *U.S. Private*, pg. 1132

O'Donnel, Joe, Chm. Bd. & Chief Exec. Officer--Heurikon Corporation, Madison, WI; *U.S. Public*, pg. 422

O'Donnell, Christopher, Deputy Chief Exec. Officer--Smith & Nephew PLC, London, United Kingdom; *Int'l*, pg. 1263

O'Donnell, James E., Chm. Bd. & Chief Exec. Officer--Wheatland Tube Company, Collingswood, NJ; *U.S. Private*, pg. 1170

O'Donnell, Joseph, Co-Chm. Bd., Pres. & Chief Exec. Officer--Computer Products, Inc., Boca Raton, FL; *U.S. Public*, pg. 422

O'Donoghue, P.R., Chief Exec. Officer-Crystal Div.--Waterford Wedgwood Plc, Dublin, Ireland; *Int'l*, pg. 1487

O'Donoghue, P.R., Chief Exec. Officer--Waterford Crystal Ltd., Kilbarry, Ireland; *Int'l*, pg. 1487
O'Donovan, Timothy J., Pres. & Chief Oper. Officer--Wolverine World Wide, Inc., Rockford, MI; *U.S. Public*, pg. 1775
O'Farrell, Dean, Chm. Bd. & Chief Exec. Officer--SouthTrust Bank of Huntsville, Huntsville, AL; *U.S. Public*, pg. 1492
O'Groman, Joseph, Chief Exec. Officer--RenoAir Inc., Reno, NV; *U.S. Private*, pg. 922
O'Halleran, Michael D., Pres. & Chief Oper. Officer--Alexander & Alexander Services Inc., New York, NY; *U.S. Public*, pg. 117
O'Halloran, Martin, Pres. & Chief Exec. Officer--ISS International Service System, Inc., Atlanta, GA; *Int'l*, pg. 656
O'Hanlon, Michael, Chm. Bd., Pres. & Chief Exec. & Oper. Officer--DVI Financial Services Inc., Newport Beach, CA; *U.S. Public*, pg. 476
O'Hara, Brian M., Chief Exec. Officer--X.L. Insurance Company, Ltd., Hamilton, Bermuda; *Int'l*, pg. 467
O'Hare, Dean R., Chm. Bd. & Chief Exec. Officer--The Chubb Corporation, Warren, NJ; *U.S. Public*, pg. 354
O'Keefe, Daniel, Pres. & Chief Exec. Officer--Thermotron Industries, Holland, MI; *U.S. Private*, pg. 1136
O'Keeffe, Whitney, Chm. Bd. & Chief Exec. Officer--SunTrust Bank, Treasure Coast, N.A., Fort Pierce, FL; *U.S. Public*, pg. 1538
O'Leary, Dennis P., Chm. Bd. & Pres.--The F.D. Lawrence Electric Co., Cincinnati, OH; *U.S. Private*, pg. 654
O'Leary, Edward T., Pres. & Chief Exec. Officer--First Security Bank of New Mexico, Albuquerque, NM; *U.S. Public*, pg. 637
O'Leary, John P., Jr., Chm. Bd., Pres. & Chief Exec. Officer--Tuscarora Incorporated, New Brighton, PA; *U.S. Public*, pg. 1646
O'Mahoney, John P., Chm. Bd. & Chief Exec. Officer--Lawter International, Inc., Kenosha, WI; *U.S. Public*, pg. 980
O'Mahoney, Rory, Chief Exec.-Consumer Foods Grp.--Avonmore Waterford Group plc, Kilkenny, Ireland; *Int'l*, pg. 102
O'Mahony, Liam, Chief Exec. Officer-Oldcastle--CRH, plc, Dublin, Ireland; *Int'l*, pg. 242
O'Malia, Daniel J., Pres. & Chief Exec. Officer--O'Malia Food Markets Inc., Carmel, IN; *U.S. Private*, pg. 816
O'Malley, Thomas D., Chm. Bd. & Chief Exec. Officer--Tosco Corporation, Stamford, CT; *U.S. Public*, pg. 1624
O'Malley, William, Chm. Bd., Pres. & Chief Oper. Officer--Tidewater Inc., New Orleans, LA; *U.S. Public*, pg. 1608
O'Mara, A. James, Chm. Bd., & Chief Exec. Officer--Greenhorne & O'Mara, Inc., Greenbelt, MD; *U.S. Private*, pg. 477
O'Meara, John M., Chm. Bd. & Chief Exec. Officer--First Midwest Bank, N.A., Itasca, IL; *U.S. Public*, pg. 636
O'Meara, Robert P., Pres. & Chief Exec. Officer--First Midwest Bancorp, Inc., Itasca, IL; *U.S. Public*, pg. 636
O'Neal, James, Pres. & Chief Exec. Officer-Intl. Bus.--Frito-Lay Company, Plano, TX; *U.S. Public*, pg. 1277
O'Neil, Bruce P., Chm. Bd. & Chief Exec. Officer--Willis Corroon Corp. of Illinois, Chicago, IL; *Int'l*, pg. 1506
O'Neill, D. J., Chief Exec. Officer--Ulster Bank Group Treasury Limited, Dublin, Ireland; *Int'l*, pg. 912
O'Neill, Donald F., Chm. Bd. & Chief Exec. Officer--Perfecseal Company, Philadelphia, PA; *U.S. Public*, pg. 210
O'Neill, Paul H., Chm. Bd. & Chief Exec. Officer--Aluminum Company of America, Pittsburgh, PA; *U.S. Public*, pg. 60
O'Neill, Stephen, Pres. & Chief Exec. Officer--Alvey Systems, Inc, Saint Louis, MO; *U.S. Private*, pg. 47
O'Neill, Steve, Pres. & Chief Exec. Officer--Pinnacle Automation Inc., Saint Louis, MO; *U.S. Private*, pg. 866
O'Neill, Thomas J., Pres. & Chief Exec. Officer--Parsons Brinckerhoff Inc., New York, NY; *U.S. Private*, pg. 841
O'Neill, W., Chief Exec. Officer--Times Newspapers Ltd., London, United Kingdom; *Int'l*, pg. 927
O'Rahilly, Patrick J., Pres. & Chief Exec. Officer--Creative Marketing International Corp., West Chicago, IL; *U.S. Private*, pg. 287
O'Reilly, David, Pres. & Chief Exec. Officer--O'Reilly Automotive Inc., Springfield, MO; *U.S. Public*, pg. 1230
O'Rourke, J. Tracy, Chm. Bd. & Chief Exec. Officer--Varian Associates, Inc., Palo Alto, CA; *U.S. Public*, pg. 1710
O'Shane, Thomas J., Chm. Bd., Pres. & Chief Exec. Officer--First Western Bancorp, Inc., New Castle, PA; *U.S. Public*, pg. 642
O'Shaughnessy, Patrick E., Chm. Bd. & Chief Exec. Officer--Lario Oil & Gas Company, Wichita, KS; *U.S. Private*, pg. 651
O'Shea, Mortimer J., Chm. Bd., Pres. & Chief Exec. Officer--Ramapo Financial Corporation, Wayne, NJ; *U.S. Public*, pg. 1360
O'Shea, Stephen R., Chief Exec. Officer--Halma p.l.c., Amersham, United Kingdom; *Int'l*, pg. 589
O'Sullivan, Dan, Chm. Bd. & Chief Exec. Officer--O'Sullivan Industries Holdings, Lamar, MO; *U.S. Public*, pg. 1234
O'Tool, Michael, Pres. & Chief Exec. Officer--Templeton, Kenly & Co., Inc., Broadview, IL; *U.S. Private*, pg. 1075
O'Toole, Robert J., Chm. Bd., Pres. & Chief Exec. Officer--A.O. Smith Corporation, Milwaukee, WI; *U.S. Public*, pg. 1476
O'Toole, Timothy S., Chm. Bd. & Chief Exec. Officer--Patient Care, Inc., West Orange, NJ; *U.S. Public*, pg. 344
Oakes, Gary E., Pres., Chief Exec. & Oper. Officer--American Precast Concrete, Inc., Indianapolis, IN; *U.S. Private*, pg. 60
Oatway, Francis C., Pres. & Chief Exec. Officer--Hargro Enterprises, Inc., Stamford, CT; *U.S. Private*, pg. 502
Obayashi, Yoshiro, Chm. Bd. & Chief Exec. Officer--Obayashi Corporation, Tokyo, Japan; *Int'l*, pg. 995
Ober, Douglas G., Chm. Bd. & Chief Exec. Officer--Petroleum & Resources Corp., Baltimore, MD; *U.S. Public*, pg. 1280
Obermueller, G., Chief Exec. Officer--Bramac Dachsysteme International GmbH, Pochlarn, Austria; *Int'l*, pg. 1092
Obernauer, Marne, Jr., Chm. Bd. & Chief Exec. Officer--Devon Group, Inc., Stamford, CT; *U.S. Public*, pg. 503
Obernier, Robert, Chm. Bd. & Chief Exec. Officer--Horizon Paper Co., Inc., New York, NY; *U.S. Private*, pg. 539
Obletter, P., Chief Exec. Officer--Braas Italia S.p.A., Bolzano, Italy; *Int'l*, pg. 1092
Ochs, Ronald K., Chm. Bd. & Chief Exec. Officer--M & I Bank of Janesville, Janesville, WI; *U.S. Public*, pg. 1050
Ockels, Theodore S., Pres., Chief Exec. Officer, Chief Fin. Officer & Treas.--Up-Right Work Platforms Division, Selma, CA; *U.S. Private*, pg. 1128
Oda, Yasuyuki, Chief Exec.--KONE Japan Co. Ltd., Tokyo, Japan; *Int'l*, pg. 747
Odak, Perry, Chief Exec. Officer--Ben & Jerry's Homemade Inc., South Burlington, VT; *U.S. Public*, pg. 210
Oddis, Alvo M., Pres. & Chief Exec. Officer--Clayton Group, Inc., Tampa, FL; *U.S. Private*, pg. 244
Odeen, Phillip, Pres. & Chief Exec. Officer--BDM International, Inc., Mc Lean, VA; *U.S. Public*, pg. 1558
Oden, Clyde W., Dr., Pres. & Chief Exec. Officer--UHP Healthcare, Inglewood, CA; *U.S. Private*, pg. 1113
Odermatt, Ernst, Chief Exec. Officer--Oerlikon-Contraves AG, Zurich, Switzerland; *Int'l*, pg. 998
Odom, F.A., Pres. & Chief Exec. Officer--United States National Bank, Galveston, TX; *U.S. Public*, pg. 467
Odom, Howard, Pres. & Chief Exec. Officer--Ortronics, Inc., Pawcatuck, CT; *Int'l*, pg. 806
Odom, John P., Co-Chm. Bd., Pres. & Chief Exec. Officer--The Odom Corporation, Seattle, WA; *U.S. Private*, pg. 811
Oechsle, Vernon E., Pres. & Chief Exec. Officer--Quanex Corporation, Houston, TX; *U.S. Public*, pg. 1349
Oehlke, Jack W., Pres. & Chief Exec. Officer--Key Tronic Corporation, Spokane, WA; *U.S. Public*, pg. 953
Oesterreicher, James E., Chm. Bd. & Chief Exec. Officer--JC Penney Company, Inc., Plano, TX; *U.S. Public*, pg. 916
Off, George W., Pres. & Chief Exec. Officer--Catalina Marketing Corporation, Saint Petersburg, FL; *U.S. Public*, pg. 314
Offen, Robert, Chief Exec. Officer--Mediapolis, London, United Kingdom; *Int'l*, pg. 853
Offray, Claude, Jr., Pres. & Chief Exec. Officer--C.M. Offray & Son Inc., Chester, NJ; *U.S. Private*, pg. 812
Ogata, Keith, Pres., Chief Exec. Officer & Treas.--National Education Credit Corporation, Irvine, CA; *U.S. Public*, pg. 784
Ogden, J.H., Jr., Chm. Bd., Pres. & Chief Exec. Officer--Conestoga Corporation, Stamford, CT; *U.S. Private*, pg. 262
Ogier, Michael O., Pres. & Chief Exec. Officer--Pioneer Concrete of America, Houston, TX; *Int'l*, pg. 1058
Ogilvie, Robert M., Chm. Bd., Pres. & Chief Exec. Officer--Toromont Industries Ltd., Concord, Canada; *Int'l*, pg. 1400
Ogle, William E., Chm. Bd. & Chief Exec. Officer--STB Systems, Inc., Richardson, TX; *U.S. Public*, pg. 1421
Ohayon, Michel, Pres. & Chief Exec. Officer--VKO, Inc., Taunton, MA; *U.S. Private*, pg. 1130
Ohba, Hiroshi, Chm. & Chief Exec. Officer--Kawasaki Heavy Industries, Ltd., Kobe, Japan; *Int'l*, pg. 725
Ohga, Norio, Chm. Bd. & Chief Exec. Officer--Sony Corporation, Tokyo, Japan; *Int'l*, pg. 1280
Ohinouye, Tsuneo, Chm. & Chief Exec. Officer--Diamond Star Motors, Normal, IL; *Int'l*, pg. 875
Ohlsson, Sven, Pres. & Chief Exec. Officer--Scancem AB, Malmo, Sweden; *Int'l*, pg. 1198
Ohnishi, Minoru, Chm. Bd. & Chief Exec. Officer--Fuji Photo Film Co., Ltd., Tokyo, Japan; *Int'l*, pg. 523
Ohtani, Yukio, Chief Exec. Officer & Mng. Dir.--Japan Airlines American Region, New York, NY; *Int'l*, pg. 700
Ohya, Satoru, Pres.--OYO Corporation, Tokyo, Japan; *Int'l*, pg. 1019
Okada, Musami, Chm. Bd. & Chief Exec. Officer--Fuji Medical Systems USA, Inc., Stamford, CT; *Int'l*, pg. 524
Okada, Takuya, Chm. Bd. & Chief Exec. Officer--JUSCO Co., Ltd., Chiba, Japan; *Int'l*, pg. 28
Okagaki, Sam, Pres. & Chief Exec. Officer--Amano Cincinnati, Inc., Roseland, NJ; *Int'l*, pg. 70
Okano, Jun, Chief Exec. Officer & Mng. Dir.--Nikko Europe Plc, London, United Kingdom; *Int'l*, pg. 930
Okazaki, Y., Pres. & Chief Exec. Officer--ITOCHU International Inc., New York, NY; *Int'l*, pg. 694
Okumura, Ariyoshi, Pres. & Chief Exec. Officer--IBJ NW Asset Management Co., Ltd., Tokyo, Japan; *Int'l*, pg. 1485
Okumura, Roy H., Chief Exec. Officer--Valley Isle Produce, V.I.P. Food Service, Kahului, HI; *U.S. Private*, pg. 1132
Okuyama, Carl, Pres. & Chief Exec. Officer--Sure Save Super Market Ltd., Keaau, HI; *U.S. Private*, pg. 1056
Oland, Thomas E., Chm. Bd., Pres., Chief Exec. Officer & Treas.--Techne Corporation, Minneapolis, MN; *U.S. Public*, pg. 1563
Olbrich, F., Chief Exec. Officer--Ziegelwerke Gleinstatten GmbH & Co. KG, Gleinstatten, Austria; *Int'l*, pg. 1092
Olcott, Emery G., Pres. & Chief Exec. Officer--Packard BioScience Company, Meriden, CT; *U.S. Private*, pg. 833
Oldenburg, Wayne C., Pres. & Chief Exec. Officer--The Oldenburg Group Companies, Milwaukee, WI; *U.S. Private*, pg. 814
Older, Thomas, Pres. & Chief Exec. Officer--Svedala Industri AB, Malmo, Sweden; *Int'l*, pg. 1323
Oleson, Douglas E., Dr., Pres. & Chief Exec. Officer--Battelle Memorial Institute, Columbus, OH; *U.S. Private*, pg. 123
Olida, Carmine T., Pres. & Chief Exec. Officer--Microtel International Inc., Ontario, CA; *U.S. Public*, pg. 1108
Oliver, Aloysius J., Pres. & Chief Exec. Officer--Chemical Financial Corporation, Midland, MI; *U.S. Public*, pg. 345
Oliver, Gene, Pres. & Chief Exec. Officer--SouthTrust Bank, West Florida, Saint Petersburg, FL; *U.S. Public*, pg. 1492
Ollila, Jorma, Pres., Chief Exec. Officer & Chm.-Grp. Exec. Bd.--Oy Nokia Ab/Nokia Group, Helsinki, Finland; *Int'l*, pg. 951
Olsen, Dave, Chief Exec. Officer--Lost Arrow Corporation, Ventura, CA; *U.S. Private*, pg. 676
Olsen, Donald, Pres. & Chief Exec. Officer--United States Ceramic Tile Co., East Sparta, OH; *U.S. Private*, pg. 1124
Olsen, Frank A., Chief Exec. Officer--Hertz Corporation, Trenton, NJ; *U.S. Public*, pg. 664
Olsen, Frank O., Chief Exec. Officer--Hertz Corporation, Newark, NJ; *U.S. Public*, pg. 664
Olsen, John, Chief Exec. Officer--Cunard Line Ltd., New York, NY; *Int'l*, pg. 773
Olson, Dave, Chief Exec. Officer--Bing Steel Inc., Detroit, MI; *U.S. Private*, pg. 144
Olson, Frank, Chm. & Chief Exec. Officer--Hertz Equipment Rental Corp., Park Ridge, NJ; *U.S. Public*, pg. 664
Olson, Frank A., Chm. Bd. & Chief Exec. Officer--The Hertz Corporation, Park Ridge, NJ; *U.S. Public*, pg. 664
Olson, John M., Chm. Bd. & Chief Exec. Officer--John M. Olson Company, Saint Clair Shores, MI; *U.S. Private*, pg. 815
Olson, Kenneth E., Chm. Bd., Pres. & Chief Exec. Officer--Proxima Corporation, San Diego, CA; *U.S. Public*, pg. 1339
Olson, Paul M., Pres. & Chief Exec. Officer--Cable Design Technologies Corporation, Pittsburgh, PA; *U.S. Public*, pg. 287
Olson, Ralph J., Chm. Bd., Pres. & Chief Exec. Officer--R.A. Jones & Co. Inc., Covington, KY; *U.S. Private*, pg. 597
Olson, Richard E., Chm. Bd. & Chief Exec. Officer--Champion International Corp., Stamford, CT; *U.S. Public*, pg. 333
Olson, Ronald G., Pres. & Chief Exec. Officer--Grow Biz International, Inc., Minneapolis, MN; *U.S. Public*, pg. 767
Olson, Ronald G., Pres. & Chief Exec. Officer--Grow Biz Games, Inc., Minneapolis, MN; *U.S. Public*, pg. 767
Olson, Tom, Pres. & Chief Exec. Officer--Katz Media Group, Inc., New York, NY; *U.S. Public*, pg. 335
Olsson, Bjorn E., Pres. & Chief Exec. Officer--Harmon Industries, Inc., Blue Springs, MO; *U.S. Public*, pg. 788
Olvey, Daniel R., Pres. & Chief Exec. Officer--Wausau-Mosinee Paper Corporation, Mosinee, WI; *U.S. Public*, pg. 1747
Omachinski, Dave, Chief Fin. Officer--Men's Wear, Oshkosh, WI; *U.S. Public*, pg. 1233
Oman, Mark C., Pres. & Chief Exec. Officer--Norwest Mortgage, Inc., Des Moines, IA; *U.S. Public*, pg. 1202
Oman, Norma J., Pres. & Chief Exec. Officer--Meridian Insurance Group, Inc., Indianapolis, IN; *U.S. Public*, pg. 1095
Oman, Norma J., Pres. & Cheif Exec. Officer--Meridian Security Insurance Company, Indianapolis, IN; *U.S. Public*, pg. 1095
Omote, Koji, Chief Oper. Officer--Makita Mexico, S.A. De C.V., Mexico, Mexico; *Int'l*, pg. 832
Onda, Tsuneo, Pres. & Chief Exec. Officer--Sumitomo Bank of California, San Francisco, CA; *Int'l*, pg. 1309
Ondis, Albert W., Chm. Bd. & Chief Exec. Officer--Astro-Med, Inc., West Warwick, RI; *U.S. Public*, pg. 141
Oni, Bunmi, Chief Exec. & Mng. Dir.--Cadbury Nigeria PLC, Ikeja, Nigeria; *Int'l*, pg. 248
Ono, Kozo, Chief Exec. & Mng. Dir.--Yamaichi Bank (U.K.) Plc, London, United Kingdom; *Int'l*, pg. 1517
Ono, Masatoshi, Chm. Bd. & Chief Exec. Officer--Bridgestone/Firestone, Inc., Nashville, TN; *Int'l*, pg. 213
Onofrio, P., Chief Exec. Officer--Ficut S.p.A., Milan, Italy; *Int'l*, pg. 994
Onstead, R. Randall, Jr., Pres. & Chief Exec. Officer--Randalls Food Markets, Inc., Houston, TX; *U.S. Private*, pg. 909
Onzik, John, Pres. & Chief Exec. Officer--Dickten & Masch Manufacturing Co., Nashotah, WI; *U.S. Private*, pg. 331
Opler, Edmond, Jr., Chm. Bd., Pres. & Chief Exec. Officer--World's Finest Chocolate, Inc., Chicago, IL; *U.S. Private*, pg. 1191
Oppedahl, John E., Publr. & Chief Exec. Officer--Phoenix Newspapers, Inc., Phoenix, AZ; *U.S. Public*, pg. 326
Oppegaard, Grant E., Pres. & Chief Exec. Officer--Genmar Holdings, Inc., Minneapolis, MN; *U.S. Private*, pg. 447
Orban, George P., Chm. Bd. & Chief Exec. Officer--Egghead, Inc., Liberty Lake, WA; *U.S. Public*, pg. 566
Orbon, Leif, Chief Exec. Officer--Kvarn AB Juvel, Goteborg, Sweden; *Int'l*, pg. 718
Orders, William H., Chm. Bd., Chief Exec. Officer & Treas--Orders Distributing Co., Greenville, SC; *U.S. Private*, pg. 819
Ordway, Peter S., Chm. Bd., Pres. & Chief Exec. Officer--Union Pump Company, Battle Creek, MI; *U.S. Private*, pg. 1119
Ordway, Ronald D., Chm. Bd. & Chief Exec. Officer--Video Display Corporation, Tucker, GA; *U.S. Public*, pg. 1720
Oreck, David, Chief Exec. Officer--Oreck Corporation, New Orleans, LA; *U.S. Private*, pg. 819
Oren, John R., Chm. Bd. & Chief Exec. Officer--Corporate Express Delivery Systems Southwest, Inc., Houston, TX; *U.S. Public*, pg. 449
Orfao, David, Pres. & Chief Exec. Officer--Allaire Corporation, Cambridge, MA; *U.S. Private*, pg. 36
Oristano, Matthew, Chm. Bd. & Chief Exec. Officer--People's Choice TV Corp., Shelton, CT; *U.S. Public*, pg. 1274
Orleans, Jeffery P., Chm. & Chief Exec. Officer--FPA Corporation, Bensalem, PA; *U.S. Public*, pg. 608
Orlich, Robert F., Pres. & Chief Exec. Officer--Transatlantic Holdings Inc., New York, NY; *U.S. Public*, pg. 84
Orloff, Malcolm, Dr., Chief Exec. Officer--Moore & Munger Marketing Inc., Shelton, CT; *Int'l*, pg. 1197
Orlowski, Henry, Pres. & Chief Exec. Officer--Emtec Products Corporation, Coldwater, MI; *U.S. Public*, pg. 968
Ormond, Paul A., Chm. Bd., Pres. & Chief Exec. Officer--Health Care & Retirement Corporation, Toledo, OH; *U.S.* Public, pg. 801

Orndorff, Ronald D., Chm. Bd. & Chief Exec. Officer--M & I First National Leasing Corp., Milwaukee, WI; *U.S. Public, pg. 1051*
Orr, Bruce, Pres. & Chief Exec. Officer--TLPartnership, Dallas, TX; *U.S. Public*, pg. 1224
Orr, Charles L., Pres. & Chief Exec. Officer--Shaklee Corporation, San Francisco, CA; *Int'l*, pg. 1518
Orr, David, Pres. & Chief Exec. Officer--Alcatel Telecom, Richardson, TX; *Int'l*, pg. 55
Orr, Donald C., Chm. Bd., Pres. & Chief Exec. Officer--Nashville Machine Co. Inc., Nashville, TN; *U.S. Private*, pg. 774
Orr, James F., Chm. Bd. & Chief Exec. Officer--UNUM Life Insurance Company of America, Portland, ME; *U.S. Public*, pg. 1699
Orr, James F., III, Chm. Bd., Pres. & Chief Exec. Officer--UNUM Corporation, Portland, ME; *U.S. Public*, pg. 1699
Orr, James F., III, Chm. Bd. & Chief Exec. Officer--Colonial Life & Accident Insurance Co., Columbia, SC; *U.S. Public*, pg. 1699
Orrell-Jones, Keith, Chief Exec.--Blue Circle Industries PLC, London, United Kingdom; *Int'l*, pg. 197
Orshinsky, Stanford R., Chief Exec. Officer--Ovonic Battery Company, Inc., Troy, MI; *U.S. Public*, pg. 581
Orsino, Philip, Pres. & Chief Exec. Officer--Premdor Inc., Mississauga, Canada; *Int'l*, pg. 1066
Ortolani, Timothy S., Chm. Bd., Pres. & Chief Exec. Officer--Carton-Craft Corporation, Buffalo, NY; *U.S. Private*, pg. 217
Orza, Vincent F., Jr., Chm. Bd., Pres. & Chief Exec. Officer--Eateries, Inc., Oklahoma City, OK; *U.S. Public*, pg. 555
Orza, Vincent F., Jr., Chm. Bd., Pres. & Chief Exec. Officer--Pepperoni Grill, Oklahoma City, OK; *U.S. Public*, pg. 555
Osborn, William A., Chm. Bd. & Chief Exec. Officer--The Northern Trust Company, Chicago, IL; *U.S. Public*, pg. 1197
Osborne, Richard C., Chm. Bd., Pres. & Chief Exec. Officer--Scotsman Industries, Inc., Vernon Hills, IL; *U.S. Public*, pg. 1444
Osborne, Richard de J., Chm. Bd., Pres. & Chief Exec. Officer--Asarco Incorporated, New York, NY; *U.S. Public, pg. 137*
Osborne, Ronald, Pres. & Chief Exec. Officer--Bell Canada, Montreal, Canada; *Int'l*, pg. 115
Osborne, Thomas C., Chief Exec. Officer--ICI Paints, Cleveland, OH; *Int'l*, pg. 664
Osbourne, James, Pres. & Chief Exec. Officer--Selectone, Inc., Hayward, CA; *U.S. Private*, pg. 982
Oshima, Yuji, Pres. & Chief Exec. Officer--Yasuda Mutual Life Insurance Co., Tokyo, Japan; *Int'l*, pg. 1519
Oskin, D. W., Chief Exec. Officer & Mng. Dir.--Carter Holt Harvey Limited, Auckland, New Zealand; *U.S. Public*, pg. 904
Osment, Jim L., Pres. & Chief Exec. Officer--Arrow Automotive Industries, Inc., Framingham, MA; *U.S. Public*, pg. 133
Ospel, Marcel, Grp. Chief Exec. Officer--Swiss Bank Corporation, Basel, Switzerland; *Int'l*, pg. 1329
Ospel, Marcel, Deputy Chm. & Chief Exec. Officer--SBC Warburg Group plc, London, United Kingdom; *Int'l*, pg. 1330
Osswald, Dr. Rainer, Chief Oper. Officer--Ernst Michalke GmbH, Langweid, Germany; *Int'l*, pg. 624
Ost, Michael, Chief Exec. Officer--Coats Viyella plc, Manchester, United Kingdom; *Int'l*, pg. 299
Oster, Richard, Chief Exec. Officer--Cookson Group plc, London, United Kingdom; *Int'l*, pg. 328
Ostergard, Tonn, Pres. & Chief Exec. Officer--Crete Carrier Corp., Lincoln, NE; *U.S. Private*, pg. 289
Ostertag, Robert A., Jr., Pres. & Chief Exec. Officer--Foster & Gallagher, Inc., Peoria, IL; *U.S. Private*, pg. 420
Ostertag, Ronald A., Pres. & Chief Exec. Officer--General Semiconductor, Inc., Melville, NY; *U.S. Public*, pg. 726
Ostrander, Gregg A., Pres. & Chief Exec. Officer--Michael Foods, Inc., Minneapolis, MN; *U.S. Public*, pg. 1103
Ostroff, Michael I., Dr., Pres. & Chief Exec. Officer--GraphLine Inc., Tamarac, FL; *U.S. Private*, pg. 471
Ostrover, Harvey, Chm. Bd. & Chief Exec. Officer--American Fabrics Company, New York, NY; *U.S. Private*, pg. 53
Ostrovsky, Steven N., Chief Exec. Officer--VTA Management Services, Inc., Brooklyn, NY; *U.S. Public*, pg. 839
Oswald, Robert, Chm., Pres. & Chief Exec. Officer--Robert Bosch Corporation, Broadview, IL; *Int'l*, pg. 204
Oswald, William A., Chm. & Chief Exec. Officer--Ross Roy Communications, Inc., Bloomfield Hills, MI; *U.S. Private*, pg. 946
Otaki, Katsuhiko, Pres. & Chief Exec. Officer--The Industrial Bank of Japan (Canada), Toronto, Canada; *Int'l*, pg. 676
Otakie, Daniel A., Chm. Bd., Pres., Chief Exec. Officer & Treas.--Futures Personnel Services, Baltimore, MD; *U.S. Private*, pg. 433
Otero, Richard J., Chm. Bd., Pres. & Chief Exec. Officer--RJO Enterprises, Inc., Lanham, MD; *U.S. Private*, pg. 904
Ottaway, James H., Jr., Chm., Pres. & Chief Exec. Officer--Ottaway Newspapers, Inc., Campbell Hall, NY; *U.S. Public*, pg. 525
Otten, Leslie B., Owner & Chief Exec. Officer--Killington Limited, Killington, VT; *U.S. Private*, pg. 61
Ottink, G., Chief Exec. Officer--Hoogovens Handel BV, Amsterdam, Netherlands; *Int'l*, pg. 754
Otto, Doug, Pres. & Chief Exec. Officer--Deckers Outdoor Corporation, Goleta, CA; *U.S. Public*, pg. 491
Otto, Tim, Pres. & Chief Exec. Officer--Sid Harvey Industries, Valley Stream, NY; *U.S. Private*, pg. 998
Ouf, Hazem, Pres., Chief Exec. Officer & Sr. V.P.--Lyon's Restaurants, Inc., Foster City, CA; *U.S. Private*, pg. 684
Ounjian, Marilyn J., Chm. Bd. & Chief Exec. Officer--Careers USA Inc., Philadelphia, PA; *U.S. Private*, pg. 209
Ourisman, Mandell J., Chief Exec. Officer--Ourisman Chevrolet, Marlow Heights, MD; *U.S. Private*, pg. 821
Ousley, James E., Pres. & Chief Exec. Officer--Control Data Systems, Inc., Arden Hills, MN; *U.S. Public*, pg. 441
Overton, Carl E., Chm. Bd., Chief Exec. Officer & Treas.--Overton Gear & Tool Corp., Addison, IL; *U.S. Private*, pg. 823
Overton, David, Chm. Bd., Pres. & Chief Exec. Officer--Cheesecake Factory Incorporated, Calabasas Hills, CA; *U.S. Public*, pg. 343
Ovlisen, Mads, Pres. & Chief Exec. Officer--Novo Nordisk A/S, Bagsvaerd, Denmark; *Int'l*, pg. 987
Ovshinsky, Stanford R., Pres. & Chief Exec. Officer--Energy Conversion Devices, Inc., Troy, MI; *U.S. Public*, pg. 581
Ovshinsky, Stanford R., Pres. & Chief Exec. Officer--United Solar Systems Corp., Troy, MI; *U.S. Public*, pg. 581
Owen-Jones, Lindsay, Chm. Bd. & Chief Exec. Officer--L'Oreal S.A., Clichy, France; *Int'l*, pg. 818
Owen, Claude B. Jr., Chm. Bd. & Chief Exec. Officer--DIMON, Incorporated, Danville, VA; *U.S. Public*, pg. 509
Owen, Mark, Pres., Chief Exec. Officer & Gen. Mgr.--Aero Corporation, Lake City, FL; *U.S. Public*, pg. 1766
Owen, Peter, Chief Exec. Officer--PPP hc, Tunbridge Wells, United Kingdom; *Int'l*, pg. 1020
Owen, Richard F., Pres.-Southern Divisions & Exec. V.P.--Owen Industries, Inc., Carter Lake, IA; *U.S. Private*, pg. 824
Owens, Bobby, Pres.-Putt-Putt Golf & Chief Exec. Officer--Putt Putt Golf Courses of America, Inc., Fayetteville, NC; *U.S. Private*, pg. 896
Owings, Frank, Jr., Chief Exec. Officer--Service Supply Co. Inc. of Indiana, Indianapolis, IN; *U.S. Private*, pg. 987
Oyler, James R., Pres. & Chief Exec. Officer--Evans & Sutherland Computer Corporation, Salt Lake City, UT; *U.S. Public*, pg. 595
Ozawa, Mitoshi, Pres. & Chief Exec. Officer--Sumitomo Heavy Industries, Ltd., Tokyo, Japan; *Int'l*, pg. 1314
Ozur, Mark, Pres.--Digital Sound Corporation, Carpinteria, CA; *U.S. Public*, pg. 508
Ozveren, Bulend, Chief Exec. Officer--Penajans DMB&B Ticaret, Istanbul, Turkey; *U.S. Private*, pg. 305
Pace, George, Chief Exec. Officer--Rocco Inc., Harrisonburg, VA; *U.S. Private*, pg. 937
Pace, George, Chief Exec. Officer--Shady Brook Farms, Dayton, VA; *U.S. Private*, pg. 937
Pacer, Thomas H., Chm. Bd., Pres. & Chief Exec. Officer--First Union National Bank of Georgia, Atlanta, GA; *U.S. Public*, pg. 640
Pacholder, Sylvia A., Pres. & Chief Exec. Officer--ICO, Inc., Houston, TX; *U.S. Public*, pg. 853
Pachulski, Phil, Chm. Bd. & Chief Exec. Officer--Prime Technology, Inc., Grand Rapids, MI; *U.S. Private*, pg. 884
Packard Thomas M., Pres. & Chief Exec. Officer--Land O'Lakes Fluid Dairy Division, Arden Hills, MN; *U.S. Private*, pg. 646
Packard, James, Chm. Bd., Pres. & Chief Exec. Officer--National Twist Drill Div., South Beloit, IL; *U.S. Public*, pg. 1370
Packard, James L., Chm. Bd., Pres. & Chief Exec. Officer--Regal-Beloit Corporation, Beloit, WI; *U.S. Public*, pg. 1370
Paddock, James S., Pres. & Chief Exec. Officer--Titanium Industries, Inc., Morristown, NJ; *U.S. Public*, pg. 43
Paddock, M. David, Chm. Bd., Pres., Chief Exec. & Oper. Officer--Peoples National Bank, Lawrenceville, IL; *U.S. Public*, pg. 1217
Paddock, S.R., Jr., Chm., Chief Exec. Officer & Publr.--Paddock Publications, Inc., Arlington Heights, IL; *U.S. Private*, pg. 833
Paddon, Patrick E., Chm. Bd., Pres. & Chief Exec. Officer--Amplicon, Inc., Santa Ana, CA; *U.S. Public*, pg. 104
Padilla Longoria, Pedro, Chief Exec. Officer--Grupo Elektra S.A. de C.V., Mexico, Mexico; *Int'l*, pg. 573
Paetzold, David, Pres. & Chief Exec. Officer--SouthTrust Bank, Southwest Florida, Fort Myers, FL; *U.S. Public*, pg. 1492
Paffard, Roger, Chief Exec. Officer--Thorntons PLC, Darbyshire, United Kingdom; *Int'l*, pg. 1386
Page, G.F., Chief Exec. Officer--Cobham plc, Wimborne Minster, United Kingdom; *Int'l*, pg. 301
Page, Richard, Pres. & Chief Exec. Officer--Grand Holdings, Inc., Edina, MN; *U.S. Private*, pg. 468
Page, Robert B., Pres. & Chief Exec. Officer--Romacorp, Inc., Dallas, TX; *U.S. Public*, pg. 1147
Page, Robert L., Pres. & Chief Exec. Officer--Replacements, Ltd., Mc Leansville, NC; *U.S. Private*, pg. 923
Page, Roger B., Chm. Bd., Pres., Chief Exec. Officer & Fin. Officer--Pace Oil Co., Inc., Winston Salem, NC; *U.S. Private*, pg. 829
Pahidis, Peter, Pres. & Chief Exec. Officer--Cedar Farms Company, Inc., Philadelphia, PA; *U.S. Private*, pg. 221
Pahl, Charles E., Chm. Bd. & Chief Exec. Officer--J.H. Larson Electrical Company, Golden Valley, MN; *U.S. Private*, pg. 652
Pai, P.Y., Chm. Bd. & Chief Exec. Officer--The International Commercial Bank of China, Taipei, Taiwan; *Int'l*, pg. 683
Paidas, George P., Pres. & Chief Exec. Officer--The Old Phoenix National Bank of Medina, Medina, OH; *U.S. Public*, pg. 646
Painchaud, Francois, Chief Exec. Officer--Nouveler, Montreal, Canada; *Int'l*, pg. 640
Painter, Carl, Chm. Bd. & Chief Exec. Officer--BICC Cables Corporation, West Nyack, NY; *Int'l*, pg. 120
Pajak, Andrewd P., Pres. & Chief Exec. Officer--GZA GeoEnvironmental Technologies, Inc., Newton, MA; *U.S.* Public, pg. 697
Pak, Kua Hong, Pres. & Chief Exec. Officer--Times Publishing Limited, Singapore, Singapore; *Int'l*, pg. 1390
Pala, Gino N., Chm. Bd. & Chief Exec. Officer--Dixon Ticonderoga Company, Heathrow, FL; *U.S. Public*, pg. 514
Palermo, John P., Pres. & Chief Exec. Officer--Victor Corporation, West Warwick, RI; *U.S. Private*, pg. 1138
Paley, Edward, Chm. Bd. & Chief Exec. Officer--The Texwipe Co., Inc., Upper Saddle River, NJ; *U.S. Private*, pg. 1079
Paliughi, Ronald D., Chief Exec. Officer--National Propane Corp., Cedar Rapids, IA; *U.S. Public*, pg. 1635
Palk, Eun Hak, Pres. & Chief Exec. Officer--California Cho Hung Bank, Los Angeles, CA; *Int'l*, pg. 287
Palk, Roy, Pres. & Chief Exec. Officer--East Kentucky Power Co-op, Winchester, KY; *U.S. Private*, pg. 356
Pallitto, Richard, Chief Exec. Officer--Key Food Stores Co-operative, Inc., Brooklyn, NY; *U.S. Private*, pg. 617
Palm, M.D., Chief Exec. Officer--Centre Reinsurance (Bermuda) Ltd., Hamilton, Bermuda; *Int'l*, pg. 1531
Palmer, A. Robert, Chm. Bd., Pres. & Chief Exec. Officer--Eastern Color Printing Company, Avon, CT; *U.S. Private, pg. 357*
Palmer, C. Robert, Chm. Bd., Pres. & Chief Exec. Officer--Rowan Companies, Inc., Houston, TX; *U.S. Public*, pg. 1409
Palmer, Charles L., Chm. Bd. & Chief Exec. Officer--North American Company, Fort Lauderdale, FL; *U.S. Private*, pg. 803
Palmer, Dan M., Chm. Bd. & Chief Exec. Officer--Concord EFS, Inc., Memphis, TN; *U.S. Public*, pg. 429
Palmer, Dan M., Chief Exec. Officer--Concord National Bank, Inc., Memphis, TN; *U.S. Public*, pg. 429
Palmer, Eldon D., Pres. & Chief Exec. Officer--Kenworth of Indianapolis Inc., Indianapolis, IN; *U.S. Private*, pg. 615
Palmer, Frank, Pres. & Chief Exec. Officer--Palmer Jarvis Communications, Vancouver, Canada; *Int'l*, pg. 1022
Palmer, H.A., Chief Exec. Officer--Taylor Woodrow plc, London, United Kingdom; *Int'l*, pg. 1358
Palmer, Jon, Chief Exec. Officer--Wellspring Resources, LLC, Jacksonville, FL; *U.S. Private*, pg. 1154
Palmer, Jon, Chief Exec. Officer--Wellspring Resources, LLC, Jacksonville, FL; *U.S. Public*, pg. 1513
Palmer, Jonathan J., Chief Exec. Officer--Barnett Technologies, Inc., Jacksonville, FL; *U.S. Public*, pg. 1162
Palmer, Robert B., Chm. Bd., Pres. & Chief Exec. Officer--Digital Equipment Corporation, Maynard, MA; *U.S. Public*, pg. 507
Palmer, Ron, Chm. Bd. & Chief Exec. Officer--Horizon Investment Group, Taylor, MI; *U.S. Private*, pg. 539
Palmer, Ron, Pres. & Chief Exec. Officer--Business Air, Grosse Ile, MI; *U.S. Private*, pg. 539
Palmer, Stephen T., Jr., Chm. Bd. & Chief Exec. Officer--Palmer International, Inc., Worcester, PA; *U.S. Private*, pg. 834
Palmer, Steven L., Pres. & Chief Exec. Officer--Intermountain Farmers Association, Salt Lake City, UT; *U.S. Private*, pg. 568
Palmer, Terry, Chief Exec. Officer--Comalco Limited, Brisbane, Australia; *Int'l*, pg. 307
Palonen, Gary L., Chief Exec. Officer--Veda Systems, Incorporated, California, MD; *U.S. Private*, pg. 1136
Paluck, Robert J., Chief Exec. Officer--Convex Technology Center - Hewlett-Packard, Richardson, TX; *U.S. Public*, pg. 815
Pamplin, R.B., Jr., Dr., Chm. Bd. & Chief Exec. Officer--Mount Vernon Mills, Inc., Greenville, SC; *U.S. Private*, pg. 835
Pamplin, R.B., Jr., Dr., Pres. & Chief Exec. Officer--K.F. Jacobson Co., Portland, OR; *U.S. Private*, pg. 836
Pamplin, Robert B., Sr., Chm. Bd. & Chief Exec. Officer--R.B. Pamplin Corp., Portland, OR; *U.S. Private*, pg. 835
Pancetti, John A., Chm. Bd. & Chief Exec. Officer--Republic Bank for Savings, New York, NY; *U.S. Public*, pg. 1380
Pancio, Alfonso Gomez, Pres. & Chief Exec. Officer--Anchor Glass Container Corporation, Tampa, FL; *Int'l*, pg. 327
Panettiere, John, Chief Exec. Officer--Blount, Inc. Sporting Equipment Group, Lewiston, ID; *U.S. Public*, pg. 238
Panettiere, John M., Pres. & Chief Exec. Officer--Blount International, Inc., Montgomery, AL; *U.S. Public*, pg. 237
Panettiere, John M., Pres. & Chief Exec. Officer--Blount, Inc., Montgomery, AL; *U.S. Public*, pg. 238
Pangilinan, Manuel V., Chief Exec. Officer & Mng. Dir.--First Pacific Company Limited, Hong Kong, Hong Kong; *Int'l*, pg. 487
Panic, Milan, Chm. Bd. & Chief Exec. Officer--ICN Pharmaceuticals, Inc., Costa Mesa, CA; *U.S. Public*, pg. 853
Pankow, Charles J., Jr., Chief Exec. Officer--Charles Pankow Builders, Ltd., Altadena, CA; *U.S. Private*, pg. 836
Pannell, Derek, Pres. & Chief Exec. Officer--Brunswick Mining & Smelting Corp. Ltd., Bathurst, Canada; *Int'l*, pg. 434
Pantano, Bruce, Pres. & Chief Oper. Officer--Publishers Clearing House, Port Washington, NY; *U.S. Private*, pg. 893
Pantello, Ron, Chm. & Chief Exec. Officer--Lally, McFarland & Pantello Inc., New York, NY; *Int'l*, pg. 601
Panyeko, Stephen H., Pres. & Chief Exec. Officer--United Jersey Leasing Company, Princeton, NJ; *U.S. Public*, pg. 1528
Panzica, Ignatius J., Chm. Bd., Pres. & Chief Exec. Officer--Global Motor Sport Group, Inc., Morgan Hill, CA; *U.S. Public*, pg. 748
Pao, Henry C., Dr., Chm. Bd., Pres. Chief Exec. Officer & Chief Oper. Officer--Supertex, Inc., Sunnyvale, CA; *U.S. Public*, pg. 1539
Paolercio, Michael W., Co. Chm. Bd. & Chief Exec. Officer--Michael Anthony Jewelers, Inc., Mount Vernon, NY; *U.S.* Public, pg. 1103
Papetti, Arthur, Chief Exec. Officer--Papetti Hygrade Egg Products, Elizabeth, NJ; *U.S. Public*, pg. 1104
Papit, Ted J., Pres. & Chief Exec. Officer--Furr's/Bishops, Inc., Lubbock, TX; *U.S. Public*, pg. 689
Papitto, Ralph R., Chm. Bd. & Chief Exec. Officer--AFC Cable Systems, Inc., Providence, RI; *U.S. Public*, pg. 6
Pappenthenasi, Arthur J., Pres. & Chief Exec. Officer--Scangas Brothers Holdings, Inc., Lynn, MA; *U.S. Private, pg. 969*
Pardo, Jaime Chico, Chief Exec. Officer--Telefonos de Mexico S.A. de C.V., Mexico, Mexico; *Int'l*, pg. 1373

Pardum, Thomas E., Pres. & Chief Exec. Officer--Multimedia Communications--U S West Inc., Englewood, CO; *U.S. Public*, pg. 1688
Pardus, Donald G., Chm. Bd. & Chief Exec. Officer--Eastern Utilities Associates, Boston, MA; *U.S. Public*, pg. 549
Paredes, Jaime, Chief Oper. Officer--Skandia Holding de Colombia S.A., Bogota, Colombia; *Int'l*, pg. 1258
Paredes, Jaime, Chief Oper. Officer--Skandia Sociedad Fiduciaria SA, Bogota, Colombia; *Int'l*, pg. 1258
Paredes, Jaime, Chief Oper. Officer--Skandia Seguros De Vida S.A., Bogota, Colombia; *Int'l*, pg. 1258
Parham, Richard D., Chief Exec. Officer--Peugeot Motor Co. Plc, Coventry, United Kingdom; *Int'l*, pg. 1021
Parham, W.E., Chief Oper. Officer--K.R. Edwards Leaf Tobacco Co., Inc., Smithfield, NC; *U.S. Public*, pg. 1694
Paridy, David, Chm. Bd., Pres. & Chief Exec. Officer--Plews/Edelmann, Buffalo Grove, IL; *Int'l*, pg. 1396
Park, C.S., Dr., Pres. & Chief Exec. Officer--Maxtor Corporation, Milpitas, CA; *Int'l*, pg. 641
Park, J. Leonard, Chm. Bd., Pres., Chief Exec. Officer & Treas.--George W. Park Seed Co., Inc., Greenwood, SC; *U.S. Private*, pg. 839
Park, James C., Pres. & Chief Exec. Officer--Besser Company, Alpena, MI; *U.S. Private*, pg. 139
Parker, Barry J.C., Pres. & Chief Exec. Officer--Luby's Cafeterias, Inc., San Antonio, TX; *U.S. Public*, pg. 1017
Parker, David H., Chm. Bd., Pres. & Chief Exec. Officer--Pelican Products, Torrance, CA; *U.S. Private*, pg. 848
Parker, Gary D., Chm. Bd. Pres. & Chief Exec. Officier--Lindsay Manufacturing Company, Lindsay, NE; *U.S. Public*, pg. 999
Parker, Melvin C., Chm. Bd., Pres., Chief Exec. Officer, Chief Fin. Officer & Treas.--Investors Insurance Group, Inc., Boca Raton, FL; *U.S. Public*, pg. 911
Parker, Richard, Pres. & Chief Exec. Officer--Artco-Bell Corporation, Temple, TX; *U.S. Private*, pg. 86
Parker, Robert A., Pres. & Chief Exec. Officer--Regions Bank/Stephens County, Toccoa, GA; *U.S. Public*, pg. 1373
Parker, Ron, Pres. & Chief Exec. Officer--Hampton Resources Inc., Portland, OR; *U.S. Private*, pg. 498
Parker, Ronald I., Chm. Bd., Pres. & Chief Exec. Officer--Indian Head Industries Inc., Charlotte, NC; *U.S. Private*, pg. 559
Parker, Samuel J., Chm. Bd., Pres. & Chief Exec. Officer--PETsMART, Inc., Phoenix, AZ; *U.S. Public*, pg. 1281
Parker, Scott S., Pres. & Chief Exec. Officer--Intermountain Health Care Inc., Salt Lake City, UT; *U.S. Private*, pg. 568
Parker, T.C., Chief Exec. Officer--Kenwood Appliances Plc, Havant, United Kingdom; *Int'l*, pg. 730
Parker, Timothy, Chief Exec. Officer--Clarks International, Street, United Kingdom; *Int'l*, pg. 296
Parkinson, Richard, Pres., Chief Exec. Officer & Gen Mgr.--Associated Food Stores Inc., Salt Lake City, UT; *U.S. Private*, pg. 90
Parks, Delton C., Pres. & Chief Exec. Officer--Country Fresh, Inc., Grand Rapids, MI; *U.S. Public*, pg. 1526
Parks, John R., Pres. & Chief Exec. Officer--Parks Products, Inc., Hollywood, CA; *U.S. Private*, pg. 840
Parks, Ralph T., Pres. & Chief Exec. Officer--FootAction USA, Irving, TX; *U.S. Public*, pg. 661
Parmacek, Robert, Chief Exec. Officer--Carlisle Food Service Products, Oklahoma City, OK; *U.S. Public*, pg. 305
Parodi, Janet, Chief Exec. Officer--Long Beach Community Hospital, Long Beach, CA; *U.S. Private*, pg. 1118
Parrette, William, Pres. & Chief Exec. Officer--Solitec Wafer Processing, Inc., San Jose, CA; *U.S. Private*, pg. 1013
Parrish, John W., Jr., Pres. & Chief Exec. Officer--Loxcreen Company, West Columbia, SC; *U.S. Private*, pg. 679
Parrott, Roy E., Chm. Bd., Pres. & Chief Exec. Officer--Simpson Industries, Inc., Plymouth, MI; *U.S. Public*, pg. 1474
Parsley, Harry, Pres. & Chief Exec. Officer--Racke USA, Sonoma, CA; *Int'l*, pg. 1083
Parsley, Harry, Pres. & Chief Exec. Officer--Buena Vista Winery, Sonoma, CA; *Int'l*, pg. 1083
Parten, Steve, Pres. & Chief Exec. Officer--Bromar Inc., Newport Beach, CA; *U.S. Private*, pg. 171
Partridge, Keith J., Chief Exec. Officer & Mng. Dir.--Carlton Paper Corp. Ltd., Johannesburg, South Africa; *U.S. Public*, pg. 959
Parzybok, William G., Jr., Chm. Bd. & Chief Exec. Officer--Fluke Corporation, Everett, WA; *U.S. Public*, pg. 659
Pascoa Martins, Joaquim, Chief Oper. Officer--Banco Totta & Acores, Lisbon, Portugal; *Int'l*, pg. 144
Pascucci, Vito, Chm. Bd. & Chief Exec. Officer--G. Leblanc Corporation, Kenosha, WI; *U.S. Private*, pg. 656
Paskins, I., Chief Exec. Officer--OCE (U.K.) Finance Limited, Loughton, United Kingdom; *Int'l*, pg. 995
Pasquarello, Theodore, Pres. & Chief Exec. Officer--Chiswick Trading Inc., Sudbury, MA; *U.S. Private*, pg. 237
Pasquelale, Doug, Pres. & Chief Exec. Officer--Richfield Hospitality Services, Englewood, CO; *U.S. Private*, pg. 929
Pasquerilla, Frank J., Chm. Bd. & Chief Exec. Officer--Crown American Realty Trust, Johnstown, PA; *U.S. Public*, pg. 461
Passera, Corrado, Chief Exec. Officer, Mng. Dir. & Gen. Mgr.--Banco Ambrosiano Veneto S.p.A., Milan, Italy; *Int'l, pg. 138*
Passow, Rolf, Chief Exec.--Deutscher Investment-Trust Gesellschaft fur Wertpapieranlagen mbH, Frankfurt/Main, Germany; *Int'l*, pg. 418
Paster, Howard, Chm. & Chief Exec. Officer--Hill and Knowlton, Inc., New York, NY; *Int'l*, pg. 1483
Pastore, Dalton, Chief Exec. Officer--Carillo, Pastore EURO RSCG, Sao Paulo, Brazil; *Int'l*, pg. 603
Patch, Lauren N., Pres. & Chief Exec. Officer--Ohio Casualty Corporation, Hamilton, OH; *U.S. Public*, pg. 1214
Pate, James L., Chm. Bd. & Chief Exec. Officer--Pennzoil Company, Houston, TX; *U.S. Public*, pg. 1272
Pate, R. Carter, Chm. Bd. & Chief Exec. Officer--Sun TV & Appliances, Inc., Groveport, OH; *U.S. Public*, pg. 1532
Pate, Sebert L., Chm. Bd. & Chief Exec. Officer--Texas Refinery Corp., Fort Worth, TX; *U.S. Private*, pg. 1078
Patel, D.S., Chm. Bd., Pres. & Chief Exec. Officer--Circuit Systems, Inc., Elk Grove Village, IL; *U.S. Public*, pg. 374
Patel, Ken N., Pres. & Chief Exec. Officer--Carrier Vibrating Equipment, Inc., Louisville, KY; *U.S. Private*, pg. 215
Patel, Mahendra, Pres., Chief Exec. Officer & Gen. Mgr.--Philway Products, Inc., Ashland, OH; *U.S. Private*, pg. 862
Patenge, Kenneth E., Chm. Bd., Pres. & Chief Exec. Officer--Wohlert Corp., Lansing, MI; *U.S. Private*, pg. 1185
Paterna, Salvatore A., Chm. Bd., Pres., Chief Exec. Officer & Chief Oper. Officer--John Solomon, Inc., Somerville, MA; *U.S. Private*, pg. 1013
Patient, William F., Chm. Bd., Pres. & Chief Exec. Officer--The Geon Company, Avon Lake, OH; *U.S. Public*, pg. 733
Patinella, John, Pres. & Chief Exec. Officer--Homestead Publishing, Bel Air, MD; *U.S. Public*, pg. 1616
Paton, John, Publisher & Chief Exec. Officer--The London Free Press, London, Canada; *Int'l*, pg. 1320
Patrick, Michael W., Pres. & Chief Exec. Officer--Carmike Cinemas, Inc., Columbus, GA; *U.S. Public*, pg. 305
Patrick, Stuart K., Pres. & Chief Exec. Officer--Baird, Patrick & Co., Inc., New York, NY; *U.S. Private*, pg. 111
Patrikeev, A., Chief Exec. Officer--L-Zos Optics, Ltd., Detroit, MI; *U.S. Private*, pg. 639
Patsley, Pamela H., Pres. & Chief Exec. Officer--First USA Paymentech, Inc., Salem, NH; *U.S. Public*, pg. 174
Patten, Joseph P., Pres.--LeFebure Corp., Cedar Rapids, IA; *Int'l*, pg. 387
Patterson, Aubrey B., Jr., Chm. Bd. & Chief Exec. Officer--Bancorp South Inc., Tupelo, MS; *U.S. Public*, pg. 176
Patterson, Bill, Chief Exec. Officer--Lansdown Conquest, London, United Kingdom; *Int'l*, pg. 1482
Patterson, Charles, Pres., Chief Exec. Officer & Chief Oper. Officer--Walman Optical Company, Minneapolis, MN; *U.S. Private*, pg. 1148
Patterson, Donald A.W., Pres. & Chief Exec. Officer--Home Federal Bank, Hamilton, OH; *U.S. Public*, pg. 633
Patterson, E. Lynn, Chm. Bd. & Chief Exec. Officer--Digital Courier International Inc., Burnaby, Canada; *Int'l*, pg. 413
Patterson, Jeff, Pres. & Chief Exec. Officer--F.W. Myers & Co., Inc., Rouses Point, NY; *U.S. Private*, pg. 770
Patterson, Neal L., Chm. Bd. & Chief Exec. Officer--Cerner Corporation, Kansas City, MO; *U.S. Public*, pg. 331
Patterson, Robert H., Jr., Chm. Bd. & Chief Exec. Officer--Celebrity Incorporated, Tyler, TX; *U.S. Public*, pg. 319
Patterson, Terry, Pres. & Chief Exec. Officer--Strauss Discount Auto, South River, NJ; *U.S. Private*, pg. 1046
Patterson, Terry W., Pres. & Chief Exec. Officer--Frederick's of Hollywood, Inc., Hollywood, CA; *U.S. Private*, pg. 424
Pattillo, Bob, Pres. & Chief Exec. Officer--Shop 'n Save Warehouse Foods, Inc., Kirkwood, MO; *U.S. Public*, pg. 1541
Pattis, Mark R., Pres. & Chief Exec. Officer--NTC/Contemporary Publishing Group, Lincolnwood, IL; *U.S. Public*, pg. 1635
Pattison, James A., Chm. Bd., Pres., Chief Exec. Officer & Mng. Dir.--Great Pacific Enterprises Inc., Vancouver, Canada; *Int'l*, pg. 557
Patton, George, Chm. Bd., Pres. & Chief Exec. Officer--Leblanc Communications, Inc., Richardson, TX; *U.S. Private*, pg. 656
Patton, William A., Chm. Bd. & Chief Exec. Officer--Virginia First Financial Corp., Petersburg, VA; *U.S. Public*, pg. 1721
Patton, William A., Chm. Bd & Chief Exec. Officer--Virginia First Savings Bank, F.S.B., Petersburg, VA; *U.S. Public*, pg. 1721
Patz, Lawrence C., Pres. & Chief Exec. Officer--Concord General Life Insurance Company, Concord, NH; *U.S. Public*, pg. 79
Pauek, Tommy, Pres., Chief Exec. & Oper. Officer--Alabama Farmers Co-op, Decatur, AL; *U.S. Private*, pg. 30
Paul, Akash, Co-Chief Exec. Officer--Caparo Group Ltd., London, United Kingdom; *Int'l*, pg. 264
Paul, Akash, Co-Chief Exec. Officer--Caparo Industries Plc, Walsall, United Kingdom; *Int'l*, pg. 264
Paul, Ambar, Co-Chief Exec. Officer--Caparo Group Ltd., London, United Kingdom; *Int'l*, pg. 264
Paul, Ambar, Co-Chief Exec. Officer--Caparo Industries Plc, Walsall, United Kingdom; *Int'l*, pg. 264
Paul, Bob, Chief Exec. Officer--Allen Telecom Inc., Solon, OH; *U.S. Public*, pg. 45
Paul, G., Chief Exec. Officer--Thomson Regional Newspapers Ltd., Watford, United Kingdom; *U.S. Public*, pg. 1601
Paul, Robert A., Pres. & Chief Exec. Officer--Ampco-Pittsburgh Corporation, Pittsburgh, PA; *U.S. Public*, pg. 103
Paul, Robert G., Pres. & Chief Exec. Officer--Allen Telecom, Inc., Beachwood, OH; *U.S. Public*, pg. 45
Paul, Thomas A., Pres. & Chief Exec. Officer--International Thomson Publishing Limited, London, United Kingdom; *U.S. Public*, pg. 1600
Pauley, Stanley F., Chm. Bd. & Chief Exec. Officer--Carpenter Co., Richmond, VA; *U.S. Private*, pg. 214
Paulson, Bernard, Chief Exec. Officer--Hitox Corporation of America, Corpus Christi, TX; *U.S. Public*, pg. 829
Pavilla, Adrian, Chief Exec. Officer--Jetro Cash & Carry, Long Beach, CA; *U.S. Private*, pg. 587
Paxton, Gary, Pres. & Chief Exec. Officer--Dollar Rent A Car, Tulsa, OK; *U.S. Public*, pg. 354
Payne, Calvin J., Chm. Bd. & Chief Exec. Officer--Westower Corporation, Vancouver, WA; *U.S. Public*, pg. 1762
Payne, David L., Chm. Bd., Pres. & Chief Exec. Officer--Westamerica Bancorporation, Fairfield, CA; *U.S. Public*, pg. 1756
Payne, David L., Chm. Bd., Pres. & Chief Exec. Officer--Westamerica Bank, San Rafael, CA; *U.S. Public*, pg. 1756
Payne, Donald, Chm. Bd. & Chief Exec. Officer--Willis Corroon Americas, Nashville, TN; *Int'l*, pg. 1505
Payne, James L., Chm. Bd., Pres. & Chief Exec. Officer--Santa Fe Energy Resources, Inc., Houston, TX; *U.S. Public*, pg. 1431
Payne, Thomas H., Pres. & Chief Exec. Officer--Market Facts, Inc., Arlington Heights, IL; *U.S. Public*, pg. 1046
Payne, Walter F., Pres. & Chief Exec. Officer--Blue Diamond Growers, Sacramento, CA; *U.S. Private*, pg. 152
Payton, Earl E., Chm. Bd., Pres. & Chief Exec. Officer--Cowden Metal Specialties, Inc., Chino, CA; *U.S. Private*, pg. 280
Payton, Earl E., Pres., Chief Exec. Officer & Chief Fin. Officer--Cowden Metal-San Jose, San Jose, CA; *U.S. Private*, pg. 280
Payton, Roger, Pres. & Chief Exec. Officer--International Logistics Limited, Hillside, IL; *U.S. Private*, pg. 571
Peacock, G., Chief Exec. Officer--Bentalls plc, Kingston upon Thames, United Kingdom; *Int'l*, pg. 187
Peacock, Gary, Chief Exec. Officer--Barnett Bank of Southwest Georgia, Columbus, GA; *U.S. Public*, pg. 1162
Pearce, John, Chief Exec. Officer--Healthsource Georgia, Atlanta, GA; *U.S. Public*, pg. 360
Pearce, Ron L., Pres. & Chief Exec. Officer--Deltic Timber Corporation, El Dorado, AR; *U.S. Public*, pg. 498
Pearce, W. McFall, Pres. & Chief Exec. Officer--PYA/Monarch, Inc., Greenville, SC; *U.S. Public*, pg. 1433
Peardon, Thomas, Pres. & Chief Exec. Officer--Brunschwig & Fils, Inc., White Plains, NY; *U.S. Private*, pg. 176
Pearlman, Earl, Pres. & Chief Exec. Officer--MTI Technology Corporation, Anaheim, CA; *U.S. Public*, pg. 1028
Pearlman, Herbert M., Chm. Bd., Pres. & Chief Exec. Officer--Helm Resources Inc., Greenwich, CT; *U.S. Public*, pg. 808
Pearson, Andrall E., Chm. Bd. & Chief Exec. Officer--Tricon Global Restaurants, Inc., Louisville, KY; *U.S. Public*, pg. 1636
Pearson, C., Pres. & Chief Exec. Officer--PNC Bank, Camp Hill, PA; *U.S. Public*, pg. 1243
Pearson, Joseph, Chm. Bd. & Chief Exec. Officer--National Real Estate Services, Inc., Vancouver, Canada; *Int'l*, pg. 909
Pearson, Richard K., Chm. & Chief Exec. Officer--LaSalle Bank Northbrook, Northbrook, IL; *Int'l*, pg. 10
Pearson, Ronald, Chm. Bd., Pres. & Chief Exec. Officer--Hy-Vee Food Stores Incorporated, West Des Moines, IA; *U.S. Private*, pg. 550
Pease, David H., Jr., Chm. Bd. & Chief Exec. Officer--Pease Industries, Inc., Fairfield, OH; *U.S. Private*, pg. 845
Peavey, Hartley D., Chief Exec. Officer--Peavey Electronics Corp., Meridian, MS; *U.S. Private*, pg. 845
Pebereau, Michel, Chm. Bd. & Chief Exec. Officer--Banque Nationale de Paris, Paris, France; *Int'l*, pg. 163
Pechota, Gary, Chm. Bd., Pres., & Chief Exec. Officer--Giant Cement Holding Inc., Summerville, SC; *U.S. Public, pg. 741*
Pechota, Gary, Chm. Bd. & Chief Exec. Officer--Giant Resource Recovery Company (Grr!), Harleyville, SC; *U.S. Public*, pg. 741
Pechter, Richard H., Chief Exec. Officer--Pershing Division, Jersey City, NJ; *U.S. Public*, pg. 589
Pecker, David J., Pres. & Chief Exec. Officer--Hachette Filipacchi Magazines Inc., New York, NY; *Int'l*, pg. 794
Pedersen, Calvin J., Pres. & Chief Exec. Officer--Duff & Phelps Utilities Income Inc., Chicago, IL; *U.S. Public*, pg. 534
Pedersen, Jens Lind, Chief Exec.--Novo Nordisk de Mexico S.A. de C.V., Mexico, Mexico; *Int'l*, pg. 989
Pedone, Michael F., Pres. & Chief Exec. Officer--Pedone & Partners Adv., Inc., New York, NY; *U.S. Private*, pg. 846
Peebler, Charles D., Jr., Pres.-True North & Chm. & Chief Exec. Officer-TN Div. Cos.--True North Communications Inc., Chicago, IL; *U.S. Public*, pg. 1641
Peebler, Charles D., Jr., Chm. & Chief Exec. Officer--True North Diversified Companies, New York, NY; *U.S. Public, pg. 1642*
Peebler, Robert P., Pres. & Chief Exec. Officer--Landmark Graphics Corporation, Houston, TX; *U.S. Public*, pg. 776
Peeler, John R., Pres. & Chief Exec. Officer--Telecommunications Techniques Corp., Germantown, MD; *U.S. Public*, pg. 539
Peerbhoy, Bunty, Chm. Bd., Chief Exec. Officer & Mng. Dir.--MAA Communications Bozell, Bangalore, India; *U.S. Public*, pg. 1642
Peifer, Charles, Pres. & Chief Exec. Officer--Prince Sports Group Inc., Bordentown, NJ; *U.S. Private*, pg. 884
Peifer, Charles, Chief Exec. Officer--Ektelon, Bordentown, NJ; *U.S. Private*, pg. 884
Peladeau, Erik, Chm. Bd. & Chief Exec. Officer--Quebecor Multimedia Inc., Montreal, Canada; *Int'l*, pg. 1076
Peladeau, Pierre, Chm. Bd., Pres. & Chief Exec. Officer--Quebecor Inc., Montreal, Canada; *Int'l*, pg. 1075
Pele, J. P., Chief Exec. Officer--OCE-Hungaria Kft., Budapest, Hungary; *Int'l*, pg. 994
Peled, Rafi, Pres. & Chief Exec. Officer--The Israel Electric Corporation Ltd., Haifa, Israel; *Int'l*, pg. 690
Peled, Zvi, Pres. & Chief Exec. Officer--Bogen Communications, Inc., Ramsey, NJ; *U.S. Public*, pg. 739
Peline, Val P., Jr., Pres. & Chief Exec. Officer--Stanford Telecommunications, Sunnyvale, CA; *U.S. Public*, pg. 1508
Pellegrino, John B., Pres. & Chief Exec. Offcier--Ridg-U-Rak, Inc., North East, PA; *U.S. Private*, pg. 930
Peller, John E., Pres. & Chief Exec. Officer--Andres Wines Ltd., Winona, Canada; *Int'l*, pg. 75
Pelletier, Peter, Pres. & Chief Exec. Officer--Robertson Factories, Inc., Taunton, MA; *U.S. Private*, pg. 936
Peltola, Timo, Chm. Bd., Pres. & Chief Exec. Officer--Huhtamaki Oy, Espoo, Finland; *Int'l*, pg. 638

Peltz, Nelson, Chm. Bd. & Chief Exec. Officer--Triarc Companies, Inc., New York, NY; *U.S. Public*, pg. 1634

Pemberton, Brian, Pres. & Chief Exec. Officer--ROHN Industries, Inc., Peoria, IL; *U.S. Public*, pg. 1404

Pena, Luis X., Pres., Chief Exec. Officer & Chief Fin. Officer--Gulf States Asphalt Company, Inc., South Houston, TX; *U.S. Private*, pg. 487

Pence, Dennis, Vice Chm., Pres. & Chief Exec. Officer--Coldwater Creek, Sandpoint, ID; *U.S. Public*, pg. 396

Pencer, Gerald N., Chm. Bd., Pres. & Chief Exec. Officer--Cott Corporation, Pointe-Claire, Canada; *Int'l*, pg. 337

Pendergast, B. Joseph, Chm. Bd. & Chief Exec. Officer--Weatherby Health Care, Norwalk, CT; *U.S. Private*, pg. 1155

Pendleton, Alexander, Chm. Bd. & Chief Exec. Officer--Summit Tool Company, Akron, OH; *U.S. Private*, pg. 1050

Pendleton, Alexander, Chm. Bd. & Chief Exec. Officer--Ken Tool, Akron, OH; *U.S. Private*, pg. 1050

Penfold, Richard, Pres. & Chief Exec. Officer--Buffalo Truck Center, Buffalo, NY; *U.S. Private*, pg. 179

Penhoet, Edward E., Ph.D., Pres. & Chief Exec. Officer--Chiron Corporation, Emeryville, CA; *U.S. Public*, pg. 349

Penland, James J., Pres. & Chief Exec. Officer--Regions Bank/Winchester, Winchester, TN; *U.S. Public*, pg. 1373

Penman, James A., Pres. & Chief Exec. Officer--Stephenson Equipment, Inc., Harrisburg, PA; *U.S. Private*, pg. 1040

Penn, Daniel A., Pres. & Chief Exec. Officer--Peck Jones Construction, Los Angeles, CA; *U.S. Private*, pg. 846

Penney, C. Bradford, Pres. & Chief Exec. Officer--Streamlight Inc., Norristown, PA; *U.S. Private*, pg. 1047

Pennings, J.V.H., Dr., Pres. & Chief Exec. Officer--Oce-van der Grinten N.V., Venlo, Netherlands; *Int'l*, pg. 993

Penske, Richard H., Chm. Bd. & Chief Exec. Officer--Piercing Pagoda, Inc., Bethlehem, PA; *U.S. Public*, pg. 1296

Peoples, D. Louis, Vice Chm. & Chief Exec. Officer--Pike County Light & Power Co., Milford, PA; *U.S. Public*, pg. 1229

Peoples, D. Louis, Vice. Chm. & Chief Exec. Officer--Rockland Electric Co., Saddle River, NJ; *U.S. Public*, pg. 1229

Peoples, Louis, D., Vice Chm. & Chief Exec. Officer--Orange and Rockland Utilities, Inc., Pearl River, NY; *U.S.* Public, pg. 1229

Pepe, Frederico, Chief Exec. Officer--Banco di Napoli, Naples, Italy; *Int'l*, pg. 140

Pepper, J. Stanley, Pres. & Chief Exec. Officer--The Pepper Companies, Inc., Chicago, IL; *U.S. Private*, pg. 851

Pepper, Joe, Pres. & Chief Exec. Officer--OEC Medical Systems, Inc., Salt Lake City, UT; *U.S. Public*, pg. 1207

Pepper, John E., Chm. Bd. & Chief Exec. Officer--The Procter & Gamble Company, Cincinnati, OH; *U.S. Public*, *pg. 1330*

Pepys, Shirley, Pres. & Chief Exec. Officer--Noel Joanna, Inc., Rancho Santa Margarita, CA; *U.S. Public*, pg. 465

Per Longva, John, Chief Exec. Officer & Gen. Mgr.--Longva Group, Alesund, Norway; *Int'l*, pg. 817

Perakis, James A., Chm. Bd., Pres. & Chief Exec. Officer--Hyperion Software, Stamford, CT; *U.S. Public*, pg. 851

Peralta-Ramos, Arturo H., III, Co-Chief Exec. Officer--Medtech Inc., Jackson, WY; *U.S. Private*, pg. 728

Percelay, David, Pres. & Chief Exec. Officer--Scripps Howard Productions, Santa Monica, CA; *U.S. Public*, pg. 1448

Perconti, Paul J., Pres. & Chief Exec. Officer--Thornton Oil Corp., Louisville, KY; *U.S. Private*, pg. 1084

Percy, S.W., Chm. Bd. & Chief Exec. Officer--BP America Inc., Cleveland, OH; *Int'l*, pg. 220

Percy, Steven, Chief Exec. Officer & Pres.--BP Oil Co., Cleveland, OH; *Int'l*, pg. 220

Perelman, Ronald O., Chm. Bd. & Chief Exec. Officer--MacAndrews & Forbes Holdings Inc., New York, NY; *U.S. Private*, pg. 689

Perelman, Ronald O., Chm. Bd. & Chief Exec. Officer--Andrews Group, Incorporated, New York, NY; *U.S. Private*, pg. 689

Perez, Alana S., Pres. & Chief Exec. Officer--OFC/DMB&B Bucharest, Bucharest, Romania; *U.S. Private*, pg. 305

Perez, Angel Alvarez, Pres. & Chief Exec. Officer--First Federal Finance Corporation, Santurce, PR; *U.S. Public*, pg. 644

Perez, Angel Alvarez, Pres. & Chief Exec. Officer--First Leasing & Rental Corporation, Toa Baja, PR; *U.S. Public*, pg. 644

Perez, J. Peter, Chm. Bd., Pres., & Chief Exec. Officer--InterBio Inc., Woodlands, TX; *U.S. Private*, pg. 566

Perez, John D., Pres. & Chief Exec. Officer--Perez Trading Co. Inc., Miami, FL; *U.S. Private*, pg. 852

Perez, William D., Pres. & Chief Exec. Officer--S.C. Johnson & Son, Inc., Racine, WI; *U.S. Private*, pg. 592

Perham, Leonard C., Pres. & Chief Exec. Officer--Integrated Device Technology, Inc., Santa Clara, CA; *U.S. Public*, pg. 884

Periard, Ronal W., Pres., Chief Exec. Officer & Sec. of the Bd.--Central National Bank of Mattoon, Mattoon, IL; *U.S.* Public, pg. 643

Perik, Michael, Chm. Bd. & Chief Exec. Officer--The Learning Co., Inc., Cambridge, MA; *U.S. Public*, pg. 982

Pering, Thomas H., Chm. Bd. & Chief Exec. Officer--Schleicher & Schuell, Inc., Keene, NH; *Int'l*, pg. 1206

Perini, David B., Chm. Bd. & Chief Exec. Officer--Perini Corporation, Framingham, MA; *U.S. Public*, pg. 1278

Perkins, Jim, Pres. & Chief Exec. Officer--Hendrick Automotive Group, Charlotte, NC; *U.S. Private*, pg. 522

Perkins, Kevin, Pres. & Chief Exec. Officer--Sizzler International, Inc., Los Angeles, CA; *U.S. Public*, pg. 1475

Perkins, Kevin, Pres. & Chief Exec. Officer--CFI Pty., Ltd., Los Angeles, CA; *U.S. Public*, pg. 1475

Perkins, Leigh H., Jr., Pres. & Chief Exec. Officer--The Orvis Company, Inc., Manchester, VT; *U.S. Private*, pg. 820

Perks, Douglas,, Pres. & Chief Exec. Officer--Eclipse Inc., Rockford, IL; *U.S. Private*, pg. 360

Perlegos, George, Chm. Bd., Pres. & Chief Exec. Officer--Atmel Corporation, San Jose, CA; *U.S. Public*, pg. 145

Perlis, Morris, Pres. & Chief Exec. Officer--Stadtlander Drug Company, Inc., Pittsburgh, PA; *Int'l*, pg. 338

Perlis, Morris, Pres. & Chief Exec. Officer--Health Management, Inc., Ronkonkoma, NY; *Int'l*, pg. 338

Perlman, Lawrence, Chm. Bd., Pres. & Chief Exec. Officer--Ceridian Corporation, Bloomington, MN; *U.S. Public*, pg. 330

Perlmutter, Norman, III, Chm. Bd. & Chief Exec. Officer--Heitman Financial Ltd., Chicago, IL; *U.S. Public*, pg. 1673

Perot, Ross, Interim Pres. & Chief Exec. Officer--Perot Systems Corporation, Dallas, TX; *U.S. Private*, pg. 854

Perott, Edward J., Pres. & Chief Exec. Officer--Chip Supply Inc., Orlando, FL; *U.S. Private*, pg. 237

Perrault, Paul A., Pres. & Chief Exec. Officer--Chittenden Corporation, Burlington, VT; *U.S. Public*, pg. 350

Perrella, James E., Chm. Bd., Pres. & Chief Exec. Officer--Ingersoll-Rand Company, Woodcliff Lake, NJ; *U.S. Public*, pg. 876

Perriello, Alex, Pres. & Chief Exec. Officer--Coldwell Banker Real Estate Corporation, Parsippany, NJ; *U.S. Public*, pg. 321

Perrino, S. Ronald, Chm. Bd., Pres. & Chief Exec. Officer--S.T. Research, Newington, VA; *U.S. Private*, pg. 958

Perrotto, Larry J., Pres. & Chief Exec. Officer--American Publishing Management Services Inc., West Frankfort, IL; *Int'l*, pg. 632

Perry, Allan E., Pres. & Chief Exec. Officer--Knape & Vogt Mfg. Co., Grand Rapids, MI; *U.S. Public*, pg. 963

Perry, Chris N., Chm. Bd. & Chief Exec. Officer--Meldrum & Fewsmith Communications Inc., Cleveland, OH; *U.S. Private*, pg. 730

Perry, George, Pres. & Chief Exec. Officer--Siemens Automotive Corporation, Auburn Hills, MI; *Int'l*, pg. 1245

Perry, M. Dunman, Jr., Chm. Bd., Pres. & Chief Exec. Officer--Perry Equipment Corporation, Mineral Wells, TX; *U.S. Private*, pg. 855

Perry, Michael W., Pres. & Chief Exec. Officer--Indimac, Inc., Pasadena, CA; *U.S. Public*, pg. 857

Perry, Thomas, Chm. Bd. & Chief Exec. Officer--Perry's Ice Cream Co., Inc., Akron, NY; *U.S. Private*, pg. 855

Perry, Wayne M., Vice Chm. & Chief Exec. Officer--Nextlink Communications Inc., Bellevue, WA; *U.S. Public*, pg. 1181

Perry, William H., Chief Exec. Officer--Cardinal Scale Manufacturing Company, Webb City, MO; *U.S. Private*, pg. 209

Perry, William H., Chief Exec. Officer--Detecto Scale Company, Webb City, MO; *U.S. Private*, pg. 209

Persson, B., Chief Exec. Officer--Zanda AB, Sennan, Sweden; *Int'l*, pg. 1092

Persson, B., Chief Exec. Officer--Zanda A/S, Slemmestad, Norway; *Int'l*, pg. 1092

Pertz, Douglas A., Pres. & Chief Exec. Officer--Culligan International Company, Northbrook, IL; *U.S. Public*, pg. 467

Peruzzi, Christian, Chief Exec. Officer--Fiat Auto Ireland Ltd., Dublin, Ireland; *Int'l*, pg. 481

Pesch, Alan J., Chm. Bd., Pres. & Chief Exec. Officer--Ship Analytics, Inc., North Stonington, CT; *U.S. Private*, pg. 994

Peskin, Kenneth G., Chm. Bd. & Chief Exec. Officer--E & B Marine Incorporated, Edison, NJ; *U.S. Public*, pg. 1756

Pester, Jack C., Chm. & Chief Exec. Officer--Coastal Refining & Marketing, Wichita, KS; *U.S. Public*, pg. 390

Pesut, Gerry, Pres. & Chief Exec. Officer--Distributed Systems Division, Lisle, IL; *U.S. Public*, pg. 1522

Peters, Donald J., Pres. & Chief Oper. Officer--American Stone-Mix, Inc., Towson, MD; *U.S. Private*, pg. 62

Peters, Earl W., Pres. & Chief Exec. Officer--Farmers Bank & Trust Co., Henderson, KY; *U.S. Public*, pg. 1217

Peters, Jan, Chief Exec. Officer--MediaOne, Boston, MA; *U.S. Public*, pg. 1688

Peters, Jon, Co-Chief Exec. Officer--The Guber Peters Entertainment Company, Los Angeles, CA; *Int'l*, pg. 1283

Peters, Robert L., Chm. Bd., Pres. & Chief Exec. Officer--Holmquist Grain & Lumber Co., Oakland, NE; *U.S. Private*, pg. 535

Petersen, Allen, Chm. Bd. & Chief Exec. Officer--American Tool Companies, Inc., Lincoln, NE; *U.S. Private*, pg. 63

Petersen, Allen D., Chm. Bd. & Chief Exec. Officer--American Tool Companies, Inc., Hoffman Estates, IL; *U.S. Private*, pg. 63

Petersen, Fred M., Pres. & Chief Exec. Officer--Omaha Public Power District, Omaha, NE; *U.S. Private*, pg. 815

Petersen, Ronald J., Chief Exec. Officer--Bridon PLC, Doncaster, United Kingdom; *Int'l*, pg. 215

Petersen, Sheldon C., Governor & Chief Exec. Officer--National Rural Utilities Cooperative Finance Corporation, Herndon, VA; *U.S. Private*, pg. 786

Peterson, Carl, Pres., Chief Exec. Officer & Gen. Mgr.--Kansas City Chiefs Football Club, Inc., Kansas City, MO; *U.S. Private*, pg. 607

Peterson, David H., Chm. Bd., Pres. & Chief Exec. Officer--NRG Energy, Inc., Minneapolis, MN; *U.S. Public*, pg. 1195

Peterson, Donald V., Chief Exec. Officer--North Carolina Mutual Wholesale Drug Co., Durham, NC; *U.S. Private*, pg. 804

Peterson, Ellsworth L., Chm. Bd. & Chief Exec. Officer--Peterson Builders, Inc., Sturgeon Bay, WI; *U.S. Private*, pg. 857

Peterson, Jim, Pres. & Chief Exec. Officer--Bojangles' Restaraunts, Inc., Charlotte, NC; *U.S. Private*, pg. 154

Peterson, Norman A., Pres. & Chief Exec. Officer--Willis Corroon Corp. of Wisconsin, Milwaukee, WI; *Int'l*, pg. 1507

Peterson, O. James, III, Pres. & Chief Exec. Officer--Dominion Capital, Inc., Richmond, VA; *U.S. Public*, pg. 516

Peterson, Palmer G., Chm. Bd. & Chief Exec. Officer--Bituminous Roadways, Inc., Inver Grove Heights, MN; *U.S. Private*, pg. 146

Peterson, Ralph R., Pres. & Chief Exec. Officer--CH2M Hill, Inc., Greenwood Village, CO; *U.S. Private*, pg. 195

Peterson, Robert L., Chm. Bd., Pres. & Chief Exec. Officer--IBP, Inc., Dakota City, NE; *U.S. Public*, pg. 852

Peterson, William P., Pres. & Chief Exec. Officer--Clarin, Lake Bluff, IL; *U.S. Private*, pg. 242

Petersson, Lars-Eric, Pres. & Chief Exec. Officer--Skandia Insurance Company Limited, Stockholm, Sweden; *Int'l*, pg. 1256

Petitt, Richard G., Chm. Bd., Pres. & Chief Exec. Officer--Allcity Insurance Co., New York, NY; *U.S. Public*, pg. 990

Petras, Gregory J., Pres. & Chief Exec. Officer--National Health Enhancement Systems, Inc., Phoenix, AZ; *U.S. Public*, pg. 1157

Petrie, William, Chief Exec. Officer--Boler Company, Itasca, IL; *U.S. Private*, pg. 155

Petrilli, Frank, Pres., Chief Exec. Officer & Chief Oper. Officer--Waterhouse Investor Services, New York, NY; *Int'l*, pg. 1401

Petrocelli, A.F., Chm. Bd., Pres. & Chief Exec. Officer--United Capital Corp., Great Neck, NY; *U.S. Public*, pg. 1674

Petroni, Mario, Chief Exec. Officer & Gen. Mgr.--Banca Agricola Mantovana SARL, Mantova, Italy; *Int'l*, pg. 135

Petry, Thomas E., Chm. Bd. & Chief Exec. Officer--Eagle-Picher Industries, Inc., Cincinnati, OH; *U.S. Private*, pg. 355

Petsche, Rudolf, Dr., Chief Exec. Officer--Asea Brown Boveri AG, Vienna, Austria; *Int'l*, pg. 2

Pettapiece, Jay, CLU, Pres. & Chief Exec. Officer--Vision Financial Corporation, Keene, NH; *U.S. Private*, pg. 1141

Petterson, Bengt, Pres. & Chief Exec. Officer--Mo och Domsjo AB, Stockholm, Sweden; *Int'l*, pg. 885

Petty, George K., Pres. & Chief Exec. Officer--Telus Corporation, Edmonton, Canada; *Int'l*, pg. 1374

Petty, J.W., Pres. & Chief Exec. Officer--Orval Kent Food Co., Wheeling, IL; *U.S. Private*, pg. 820

Petty, R.B., Chm. Bd., Pres. & Chief Exec. Officer--SouthTrust Bank, Montgomery, Montgomery, AL; *U.S. Public*, pg. 1491

Peyrelevade, Jean, Chm. Bd., Pres. & Chief Exec. Officer--Credit Lyonnais S.A., Paris, France; *Int'l*, pg. 343

Peyrelongue, Guy, Pres. & Chief Exec. Officer--Cosmair, Inc., New York, NY; *Int'l*, pg. 818

Peyton, Patrick J., Chm. Bd. & Chief Exec. Officer--Despatch Industries, Minneapolis, MN; *U.S. Private*, pg. 327

Pezzolo, Donald E., Chm. Bd. & Co-Chief Exec. Officer--Diablo Research Corporation, Sunnyvale, CA; *U.S. Public*, pg. 1424

Pfaff, Edward, Chm. & Chief Exec. Officer--Condor Tool & Die, Inc., Cleveland, OH; *U.S. Private*, pg. 71

Pfaff, Frederick A., Pres. & Chief Exec. Officer--Anchor Tool & Die Company, Cleveland, OH; *U.S. Private*, pg. 71

Pfannschmidt, Utz O., Chief Exec.--Hardy & Co Privatbankiers, Frankfurt/Main, Germany; *Int'l*, pg. 418

Pfeiffer, Eckhard, Pres. & Chief Exec. Officer--COMPAQ Computer Corporation, Houston, TX; *U.S. Public*, pg. 417

Pfeiffer, Michael, Pres. & Chief Exec. Officer--Aircraft of Canada Ltd., Calgary, Canada; *U.S. Public*, pg. 1365

Pfeiffer, Robert G., Chm. Bd. & Chief Exec. Officer--Neill-LaVielle Supply Co., Louisville, KY; *U.S. Private*, pg. 790

Pfister, Jacques, Pres. & Chief Exec. Officer--Orangina France, Aix-en-Provence, France; *Int'l*, pg. 566

Pfizenmaier, Wolfgang, Co-Chief Exec. Officer--Heidelberger Druckmaschinen A.G., Heidelberg, Germany; *Int'l*, pg. 604

Pharris, Walter, Pres. & Chief Exec. Officer--Fairfield Industries, Inc., Houston, TX; *U.S. Private*, pg. 391

Phelps, Isaac E., II, Pres. & Chief Exec. Officer--World Aerospace Corporation, Maple Grove, MN; *U.S. Private*, pg. 1188

Phelps, Michael E.J., Chm. Bd. & Chief Exec. Officer--Westcoast Energy Inc., Vancouver, Canada; *Int'l*, pg. 1492

Pherigo, William L., Pres. & Chief Exec. Officer--The National Bank of South Carolina, Sumter, SC; *U.S. Public*, pg. 1549

Phillips, Bradford E., Chm. & Chief Exec. Officer--Totes Incorporated, Loveland, OH; *U.S. Private*, pg. 111

Phillips, Dave, Chm. Bd. & Chief Exec. Officer--CCC Information Services, Chicago, IL; *U.S. Private*, pg. 562

Phillips, David, Chm. Bd. & Chief Exec. Officer--InfoVest, Inc., Chicago, IL; *U.S. Private*, pg. 562

Phillips, Donald C., Pres. & Chief Exec. Officer--Bank of Coweta, Newnan, GA; *U.S. Public*, pg. 1549

Phillips, John B., Jr., Chm. Bd. & Chief Exec. Officer--Young-Phillips Sales Co., Clemmons, NC; *U.S. Private*, pg. 1201

Phillips, John H., Acting Pres. & Chief Exec. Officer--Cadmus, Sandston, VA; *U.S. Public*, pg. 290

Phillips, Michael J., Pres. & Chief Exec. Officer--Frank Russell Company, Tacoma, WA; *U.S. Private*, pg. 952

Phillips, R., Chief Exec. Officer--Ascom Timeplex, Woodcliff Lake, NJ; *Int'l*, pg. 86

Phillips, Raymond A., Pres. & Chief Exec. Officer--Cives Corporation, Roswell, GA; *U.S. Private*, pg. 241

Phillips, Richard, Pres. & Chief Exec. Officer--Pilot Air Freight Corp., Lima, PA; *U.S. Private*, pg. 865

Phillips, Robert G., Chief Exec. Officer--Eastex Energy Inc., Houston, TX; *U.S. Public*, pg. 567

Phillips, Thomas L., Chm. Bd., Pres. & Chief Exec. Officer--Phillips Publishing International, Inc., Potomac, MD; *U.S. Private*, pg. 862

Phillips, Tony, Chief Exec.-Capital Equip. Div.--J. Bibby & Sons Plc, London, United Kingdom; *Int'l*, pg. 167

Phillis, Bob, Chief Exec. Officer--Guardian Media Group plc, Manchester, United Kingdom; *Int'l*, pg. 577

Philosophe, Isidore, Pres. & Chief Exec. Officer--Cinram Ltd., Scarborough, Canada; *Int'l*, pg. 293

Phipps, Allen, Pres. & Chief Exec. Officer--SRI Consulting, Menlo Park, CA; *U.S. Private*, pg. 958

Picard, Dennis J., Chm. Bd. & Chief Exec. Officer--Raytheon Company, Lexington, MA; *U.S. Public*, pg. 1364

Piccinini, Robert M., Chm. Bd., Chief Exec. Officer & Pres.--Save Mart Supermarkets, Modesto, CA; *U.S. Private*, pg. 968

Piccirilli, Joseph, Vice Chm., Pres. & Chief Exec. Officer--Keystone Brewers, Inc., Pittsburgh, PA; *U.S. Private*, pg. 618

Piccolo, C.A. Lance, Chief Exec. Officer--Caremark International Inc, Northbrook, IL; *U.S. Public*, pg. 1082

Pichler, Joseph A., Chm. Bd. & Chief Exec. Officer--The Kroger Co., Cincinnati, OH; *U.S. Public*, pg. 967

Pickard, E.R., Chm. Bd. & Chief Exec. Officer--Sofamor Danek Group, Inc., Memphis, TN; *U.S. Public*, pg. 1482

Pickell, Ira S., Chm. Bd. & Chief Exec. Officer--The Bon Marche, Inc., Seattle, WA; *U.S. Public*, pg. 617

Pickering, Gordon G., Chm. Bd. & Chief Exec. Officer--Pickering Inc., Tacoma, WA; *U.S. Private*, pg. 864

Pickett, George, Jr., Chm. Bd. & Chief Exec. Officer--Atlantic Southeast Airlines Inc., Atlanta, GA; *U.S. Public*, pg. 144

Pickett, Joe K., Chm. Bd. & Chief Exec. Officer--Homeside Lending Company, Jacksonville, FL; *Int'l*, pg. 906

Pickle, Kirby G., Pres. & Chief Exec. Officer--MFS Intelenet Companies, Jersey City, NJ; *U.S. Public*, pg. 1779

Picknelly, Peter A., Jr., Pres. & Chief Exec. Officer--Peter Pan Bus Lines, Inc., Springfield, MA; *U.S. Private*, pg. 856

Picower, Jeffrey M., Chm. Bd. & Chief Exec. Officer--Monroe Systems For Business, Inc., Morris Plains, NJ; *U.S. Private*, pg. 757

Piecuch, J.M., Pres. & Chief Exec. Officer--Lafarge Canada Inc., Montreal, Canada; *Int'l*, pg. 789

Pierce, Brian, Pres. & Chief Exec. Officer--Peirce-Phelps, Inc., Philadelphia, PA; *U.S. Private*, pg. 847

Pierce, Douglas, Chief Exec. Officer & V.P.--Guardian Alarm Co., Southfield, MI; *U.S. Private*, pg. 485

Pierce, Garrett E., Pres. & Chief Exec. Officer--Materials Research Corporation, Gilbert, AZ; *Int'l*, pg. 1283

Pierce, J.L., Pres. & Chief Exec. Officer--Mid-Continent Casualty Company, Tulsa, OK; *U.S. Public*, pg. 75

Pierce, James L., Chm. Bd. & Chief Exec. Officer--Arinc Inc. (Consolidated), Annapolis, MD; *U.S. Private*, pg. 81

Pieros, Larry, Pres. & Chief Exec. Officer--Armor All Products Group, Oakland, CA; *U.S. Public*, pg. 387

Pietrafesa, Richard C., Jr., Chief Exec. Officer--Jos. J. Pietrafesa Co., Liverpool, NY; *U.S. Private*, pg. 865

Pietrini, Andrew, Chm. Bd., Pres. & Chief Exec. Officer--UIS, Inc., Jersey City, NJ; *U.S. Private*, pg. 1113

Pigott, Mark C., Chm. Bd. & Chief Exec. Officer--Paccar Inc., Bellevue, WA; *U.S. Public*, pg. 1246

Pike, Gregory, Pres. & Chief Exec. Officer--First County Bank, Chardon, OH; *U.S. Public*, pg. 607

Pike, Larry R., Chm., Pres. & Chief Exec. Officer--The Union Central Life Insurance Co., Cincinnati, OH; *U.S. Private*, pg. 1118

Pikus, Stanton M., Chm. Bd., Pres. & Chief Exec. Officer--Canterbury Corporate Services, Inc., Medford, NJ; *U.S. Public*, pg. 301

Pilcher, Dave, Pres. & Chief Exec. Officer--Interform Corporation, Bridgeville, PA; *U.S. Public*, pg. 333

Pilgrim, Lonnie A., Chm. Bd. & Chief Exec. Officer--Pilgrim's Pride Corporation, Pittsburg, TX; *U.S. Public*, pg. 1296

Pincus, David, Chm. Bd. & Chief Exec. Officer--Pincus Bros., Inc., Philadelphia, PA; *U.S. Private*, pg. 865

Pinder, M., Chief Exec.--National Australia Life, London, United Kingdom; *Int'l*, pg. 906

Pineau-Valencienne, Didier, Chm. Bd. & Chief Exec. Officer--Schneider S.A., Boulogne-Billancourt, France; *Int'l*, pg. 1207

Pines, Isidore, Chm. Bd. & Chief Exec. Officer--National Foods Inc., Bronx, NY; *U.S. Public*, pg. 429

Pink, Alan, Chief Exec. Officer--Zeneca Agrochemicals and Seeds, Maidstone, United Kingdom; *Int'l*, pg. 1524

Pinkert, Michael, Pres. & Chief Exec. Officer--MHM Services Inc., Vienna, VA; *U.S. Public*, pg. 1027

Pinkerton, Guy C., Chm. Bd., Pres. & Chief Exec. Officer--Washington Federal Savings, Seattle, WA; *U.S. Public*, pg. 1740

Pinkerton, John H., Pres. & Chief Exec. Officer--Lomak Petroleum Inc., Fort Worth, TX; *U.S. Public*, pg. 1012

Pinkerton, John H., Pres. & Chief Exec. Officer--Lomak Operating Company, Hartville, OH; *U.S. Public*, pg. 1012

Pinkham, Mike, Pres. & Chief Exec. Officer--Columbia Universal Life Insurance Company, Austin, TX; *U.S. Public*, pg. 79

Pinneker, R.V., Pres. & Chief Exec. Officer--Security Pacific Services Corporation, San Diego, CA; *U.S. Public*, pg. 182

Pinner, Douglas K., Chm. Bd., Pres. & Chief Exec. Officer--Tokheim Corporation, Fort Wayne, IN; *U.S. Public*, pg. 1620

Pino, John A., Pres. & Chief Exec. Officer--ACT Manufacturing, Hudson, MA; *U.S. Public*, pg. 3

Pinola, Richard J., Chm. Bd. & Chief Exec. Officer--Right Management Consultants, Inc., Philadelphia, PA; *U.S. Public*, pg. 1390

Pinsley, Sol, Chm. Bd., Pres., Chief Exec. & Chief Oper. Officer--Espey Mfg. & Electronics Corp., Saratoga Springs, NY; *U.S. Public*, pg. 592

Pinson, Martin S., Chm. Bd. & Chief Exec. Officer--Industrial Distribution Group, Tucker, GA; *U.S. Public*, pg. 875

Pinter, Michael R., Chm. Bd. & Chief Exec. Officer--Kemper Reinsurance Co., Long Grove, IL; *U.S. Private*, pg. 614

Pinto, Fernando, Pres. & Chief Exec. Officer--Varig Brazilian Airlines S.A., Rio de Janeiro, Brazil; *Int'l*, pg. 1451

Pinto, James J., Pres. & Chief Exec. Officer--Action Instruments, Inc., San Diego, CA; *U.S. Private*, pg. 15

Pinto, Joao Costa, Chief Exec.--Banco de Comercio E Industria, S.A., Lisbon, Portugal; *Int'l*, pg. 144

Pinzino, Thomas F., Pres. & Chief Exec. Officer--Sunnyland Refining Co., Inc., Birmingham, AL; *U.S. Private*, pg. 607

Piouro, Mario, Chief Exec. Officer--Crediop-Credito Per Le Imprese e le Opere Pubbliche SpA, Rome, Italy; *Int'l*, pg. 341

Piouro, Mario, Chief Exec. Officer--SPF Promotio Sim SPA, Milan, Italy; *Int'l*, pg. 341

Piper, Addison L., Chm. Bd., Pres. & Chief Exec. Officer--Piper Jaffray Companies, Inc., Minneapolis, MN; *U.S. Public*, pg. 1300

Piper, Addison L., Chm. Bd. & Chief Exec. Officer--Piper Jaffray, Inc., Minneapolis, MN; *U.S. Public*, pg. 1303

Pippin, M. Lenny, Pres. & Chief Exec. Officer--Lykes Brothers Inc., Tampa, FL; *U.S. Private*, pg. 682

Pirel, Louis, Chm. & Chief Exec. Officer--Minniti, Noumea, New Caledonia; *Int'l*, pg. 823

Pirkner, Gabor, Chief Exec.--Sulzer Infra Anlagen- und Gebaudetechnik Gesellschaft m.b.H, Vienna, Austria; *Int'l*, pg. 1306

Pirrung, Mark, Chief Exec. Officer--Atlanta Beverage Co., Atlanta, GA; *U.S. Private*, pg. 94

Pisa, Michael A., Sr., Chm. Bd. & Chief Exec. Officer--Continental Paper & Supply Co., Detroit, MI; *U.S. Private*, pg. 269

Piser, Donald H., Chm. Bd. & Chief Exec. Officer--Morse Diesel International, Inc., New York, NY; *U.S. Private*, pg. 762

Pistilli, Frederick M., Chm. Bd. & Chief Exec. Officer--General Time Corp., Norcross, GA; *U.S. Private*, pg. 445

Pitman, B.I., Chm. Bd. & Chief Exec. Officer--Lloyds TSB Group PLC, London, United Kingdom; *Int'l*, pg. 812

Pitsch, Karl-Heinz, Chm. Bd., Pres. & Chief Exec. Officer--The Wella Corporation, Montvale, NJ; *Int'l*, pg. 1489

Pittman, Bob, Pres. & Chief Exec. Officer--AOL Networks--America Online Incorporated, Dulles, VA; *U.S. Public*, pg. 66

Pittman, Gary, Chm. Bd., Pres., Chief Exec., Chief Oper. & Chief Fin. Officer--PCI, Austin, TX; *U.S. Private*, pg. 826

Pittman, Robert W., Pres. & Chief Exec. Officer--Time Warner Enterprises, New York, NY; *U.S. Public*, pg. 1611

Pitts, Keith B., Chm. Bd., Pres. & Chief Exec. Officer--Paragon Health Network, Inc., Atlanta, GA; *U.S. Public*, pg. 1256

Pizzagalli, James, Chief Exec. Officer--Pizzagalli Construction Co., South Burlington, VT; *U.S. Private*, pg. 868

Pla, Roberto, Vice Chm. & Chief Oper. Officer--Noblex Argentina S.A.C. e I., Buenos Aires, Argentina; *Int'l*, pg. 951

Placek, Robert A., Chm. Bd., Pres. & Chief Exec. Officer--Wegener Corporation, Duluth, GA; *U.S. Public*, pg. 1751

Plamann, Alfred A., Pres. & Chief Exec. Officer--Certified Grocers of California, Los Angeles, CA; *U.S. Private*, pg. 226

Plana, Eduardo, Chm. Bd. & Chief Exec. Officer--EURO RSCG, Madrid, Spain; *Int'l*, pg. 602

Planes, John, Pres., Chief Exec. Officer & Sec.--Planes Moving And Storage, Inc., Cincinnati, OH; *U.S. Private*, pg. 869

Planes, John J., Chief Exec. Officer--Planes Moving & Storage Company Of Columbus, Columbus, OH; *U.S. Private*, pg. 869

Plank, Raymond, Chm. Bd. & Chief Exec. Officer--Apache Corporation, Houston, TX; *U.S. Public*, pg. 119

Plassat, Georges, Vice Chm. & Chief Exec. Officer--Groupe Casino, Saint Etienne, France; *Int'l*, pg. 562

Platt, Lewis E., Chm. Bd., Pres. & Chief Exec. Officer--Hewlett-Packard Company, Palo Alto, CA; *U.S. Public*, pg. 813

Platz, Jens Lykke, Chief Exec. Officer--Novo Nordisk Ferment Ltd., Dittingen, Switzerland; *Int'l*, pg. 989

Pledger, Ray, Chief Exec. Officer--Lakeside Trading Estate Ltd., Essex, United Kingdom; *Int'l*, pg. 1025

Pledger, Thomas R., Chm. Bd. & Chief Exec. Officer--Dycom Industries, Inc., Palm Beach Gardens, FL; *U.S. Public*, pg. 538

Plonzke, Klaus C., Chief Exec. Officer--CSC Ploenzke, Kliedrich, Germany; *U.S. Public*, pg. 423

Plotnick, Stanley D., Chm., Chief Exec. Officer & Sec.--Encore Marketing International, Inc., Lanham, MD; *U.S. Public*, pg. 580

Plumeri, Joseph J., II, Chm. & Chief Exec. Officer--Primerica Financial Services, Duluth, GA; *U.S. Public*, pg. 1633

Pocapalia, Dan, Chm. Bd., Pres. & Chief Exec. Officer--Kit Manufacturing Company, Long Beach, CA; *U.S. Public*, pg. 962

Poch, Gerlad A., Co-Chm. Bd., Pres., Chief Exec. Officer & Sec.--AmeriData Technologies, Inc., Stamford, CT; *U.S. Public*, pg. 711

Pochick, Daniel T., Pres. & Chief Exec. Officer--Rish Equipment Company, Bluefield, WV; *U.S. Private*, pg. 932

Poe, John D., Pres. & Chief Exec. Officer--Semtech Corporation, Newbury Park, CA; *U.S. Public*, pg. 1456

Poe, Ronald F., Chief Exec. Officer--Dorman & Wilson, Inc., White Plains, NY; *U.S. Public*, pg. 985

Poe, Thomas R., Pres. & Chief Exec. Officer--National City Commercial Finance, Inc., Cleveland, OH; *U.S. Public*, pg. 1154

Poehlmann, Karl M., Pres. & Chief Exec. Officer--George Uhe Co., Inc., Paramus, NJ; *U.S. Private*, pg. 1115

Poehner, Michael, Pres. & Chief Exec. Officer--DMR Group, Inc., Montreal, Canada; *Int'l*, pg. 527

Poetsch, Hans Dieter, Chief Exec.--Durr AG, Stuttgart, Germany; *Int'l*, pg. 421

Pogge, Kirk, Chief Exec. Officer & V.P.--Grassland Equipment & Irrigation Corp., Latham, NY; *U.S. Private*, pg. 471

Poggi, Michael J., Pres. & Chief Exec. Officer--Willis Corroon Corp. of Western Michigan, Grand Rapids, MI; *Int'l*, pg. 1507

Pogmore, James W., Pres. & Chief Exec. Officer--Cramer Company, Old Saybrook, CT; *U.S. Public*, pg. 1238

Pogue, A. Mack, Chm. Bd. & Chief Exec. Officer--Lincoln Property Company, Dallas, TX; *U.S. Private*, pg. 668

Pogue, David, Chm. Bd. & Chief Exec. Officer--Stackig Advertising and Public Relations, Mc Lean, VA; *U.S. Private*, pg. 1028

Pohl, David, Chief Oper. Officer--Dentsply (Australia) Pty. Ltd., Abbotsford, Australia; *U.S. Public*, pg. 499

Pohlad, Carl R., Chm. Bd.--Mesaba Holdings, Inc., Minneapolis, MN; *U.S. Public*, pg. 1099

Pohs, Arnold C., Pres. & Chief Exec. Officer--CommNet Cellular Inc., Englewood, CO; *U.S. Public*, pg. 414

Poindexter, Christian H., Chm. Bd. & Chief Exec. Officer--Baltimore Gas and Electric Company, Baltimore, MD; *U.S. Public*, pg. 172

Poinssot, Alain, Chm. Bd., Pres. & Chief Exec. Officer--GEODIS, Paris, France; *Int'l*, pg. 549

Poirier, Robert J., Chm. Bd., Pres. & Chief Exec. Officer--USA Floral Products, Inc., Washington, DC; *U.S. Public*, pg. 1685

Poirier, Victor L., Pres., Chief Exec. & Oper. Officer--Thermo Cardiosystems Inc., Woburn, MA; *U.S. Public*, pg. 1592

Poist, William G., Pres. & Chief Exec. Officer--Commonwealth Energy System, Cambridge, MA; *U.S. Public*, pg. 414

Pokelwaldt, Robert N., Chm. Bd., Pres. & Chief Exec. Officer--York International Corporation, York, PA; *U.S. Public*, pg. 1788

Poland, William F., Pres. & Chief Exec. Officer--Willis Corroon Corp. of California, San Francisco, CA; *Int'l*, pg. 1505

Polaner, Leonard, Chm. Bd. & Chief Exec. Officer--B&G Foods, Inc., Roseland, NJ; *U.S. Private*, pg. 105

Polgar, Marina, Chief Exec. Officer & Creative Dir.--Equipe, Milan, Italy; *Int'l*, pg. 602

Politzer, Jerald S., Chm. Bd. & Chief Exec. Officer--Salant Corporation, New York, NY; *U.S. Public*, pg. 1429

Polk, Stephen R., Chm. Bd. & Chief Exec. Officer--R.L. Polk & Co., Southfield, MI; *U.S. Private*, pg. 874

Pollack, Mayer, II, Chief Exec. Officer--Mayer Pollack Steel Corporation, Pottstown, PA; *U.S. Private*, pg. 874

Polley, R. Stephen, Chm. Bd., Pres. & Chief Exec. Officer--Interphase Corporation, Dallas, TX; *U.S. Public*, pg. 908

Pollinger, Stanley H., Chief Exec. Officer--Stapo Hollander Industries, Lakewood, NJ; *U.S. Private*, pg. 1033

Pollnow, Charles, Chm. Bd., Chief Exec. & Oper. Officer--The Brulin Corporation, Indianapolis, IN; *U.S. Private*, pg. 176

Pollock, John, Pres. & Chief Exec. Officer--General Casualty Company of Illinois, Freeport, IL; *Int'l*, pg. 346

Pollock, John A., Chm. Bd. & Chief Exec. Officer--Electrohome Ltd., Kitchener, Canada; *Int'l*, pg. 438

Pollock, John R., Pres. & Chief Exec. Officer--General Casualty Company of Wisconsin, Sun Prairie, WI; *Int'l*, pg. 345

Pollock, Larry M., Pres. & Chief Exec. Officer--Canadian Western Bank, Edmonton, Canada; *Int'l*, pg. 259

Pollock, Louis I., Chm. Bd. & Chief Exec. Officer--Morris Coupling Co., Erie, PA; *U.S. Private*, pg. 762

Pollock, Mayer, II, Pres., Chief Exec. Officer & Chief Oper. Officer--The Pollock Corp., Pottstown, PA; *U.S. Private*, pg. 874

Pollock, Robert B., Pres. & Chief Exec. Officer--Fortis Benefits Insurance Company, Kansas City, MO; *Int'l*, pg. 499

Pollock, W.A., V.P. & Chief Exec. Officer--Ercon Development Co., Houston, TX; *U.S. Public*, pg. 769

Pollock, William K., Chm. Bd. & Chief Exec. Officer--Key Industries, Inc., Fort Scott, KS; *U.S. Private*, pg. 618

Pollux, P.M.J., Chief Exec. Officer--OCE-Czech-Republic s.r.o., Prague, Czech Republic; *Int'l*, pg. 994

Polychronopoulos, Ioannis, Dir. Gen.--Macedonian Airlines, Athens, Greece; *Int'l*, pg. 1004

Pomerantz, John J., Chm. Bd. & Chief Exec. Officer--The Leslie Fay Companies, Inc., New York, NY; *U.S. Public*, pg. 989

Pomerantz, Marvin A., Chm. Bd. & Chief Exec. Officer--Gaylord Container Corporation, Deerfield, IL; *U.S. Public*, pg. 704

Pomeroy, David B., Chm. Bd., Pres. & Chief Exec. Officer--Pomeroy Computer Resources, Hebron, KY; *U.S. Public*, pg. 1315

Pomije, David R., Chm. Bd. & Chief Exec. Officer--Funco, Inc., Eden Prairie, MN; *U.S. Public*, pg. 688

Pond, Byron O., Chm. & Chief Exec. Officer--Arvin Industries, Inc., Columbus, IN; *U.S. Public*, pg. 136

Pond, Gerry, Pres. & Chief Exec. Officer--Bruncor, Inc., Saint John, Canada; *Int'l*, pg. 230

Pond, Gerry, Pres. & Chief Exec. Officer--The New Brunswick Telephone Company, Limited (NBTel), Saint John, Canada; *Int'l*, pg. 230

Pong, Cheong Kim, Chm. Bd., Chief Exec. & Oper. Officer--Hong Fok Corporation Ltd., Singapore, Singapore; *Int'l*, pg. 635

Ponman, Steve, Chief Exec.--KPI Elevators, Inc., Makati, Philippines; *Int'l*, pg. 747

Pontet, Philippe, Chm., Pres. & Chief Exec. Officer--Compagnie Generale Maritime et Financiere, Suresnes, France; *Int'l*, pg. 322

Pontius, Stanley N., Pres. & Chief Exec. Officer--First Financial Bancorp, Hamilton, OH; *U.S. Public*, pg. 632

Poole-Holmes, Betty J., Chm. Bd. & Chief Exec. Officer--Centrex Corporation, Findlay, OH; *U.S. Private*, pg. 225

Pope, Mark C., III, Chm. Bd., & Chief Exec. Officer--Graphic Industries, Inc., Atlanta, GA; *U.S. Public*, pg. 1735

Pope, Peter T., Chm. Bd. & Chief Exec. Officer--Pope & Talbot, Inc., Portland, OR; *U.S. Public*, pg. 1316

Pope, William A., Pres. & Chief Exec. Officer--New Mexico & Arizona Land Co., Phoenix, AZ; *U.S. Public*, pg. 1172

Pops, Richard F., Chief Exec. Officer--Alkeremes, Cambridge, MA; *U.S. Public*, pg. 41
Porter, Donald E., Pres., Chief Exec. Officer & Treas.--The Woodbury Telephone Company, Woodbury, CT; *U.S. Public*, pg. 1491
Porter, Ivan, Pres. & Chief Exec. Officer--Canron Inc., Rexdale, Canada; *Int'l*, pg. 695
Porter, Jim, Pres. & Chief Exec. Officer--Higginbotham-Bartlett Co., Lubbock, TX; *U.S. Private*, pg. 527
Porter, Michael, Pres. & Chief Exec. Officer--Acheson Industries, Inc., Port Huron, MI; *U.S. Private*, pg. 12
Portillo, Bernardo, Chief Oper. Officer--Minera del Norte, Chihuahua, Mexico; *Int'l*, pg. 66
Portman, John C., Jr., Chm. Bd. & Chief Exec. Officer--AMC, Inc., Atlanta, GA; *U.S. Private*, pg. 6
Posen, L.M., Pres. & Chief Exec. Officer--Beltone Electronics Corporation, Chicago, IL; *U.S. Private*, pg. 132
Posencheg, Alan N., Pres. & Chief Exec. Officer--UJB Discount Brokerage, Ridgefield Park, NJ; *U.S. Public*, pg. 1528
Posey, Billy, Pres. & Chief Exec. Officer--Univest Financial Services, LLC, Atlanta, GA; *U.S. Private*, pg. 1128
Posey, Lee, Chm. Bd. & Chief Exec. Officer--Palm Harbor Homes, Inc., Dallas, TX; *U.S. Public*, pg. 1254
Posey, Richard E., Pres. & Chief Exec. Officer--Hamilton Beach/Proctor-Silex, Inc., Glen Allen, VA; *U.S. Public*, pg. 1149
Post, Glen F., III, Vice Chm., Pres. & Chief Exec. Officer--Century Telephone Enterprises, Inc., Monroe, LA; *U.S. Public*, pg. 329
Post, Helen, Chm. Bd. & Chief Exec. Officer--ATHOL Corporation, Butner, NC; *U.S. Private*, pg. 94
Post, William J., Pres. & Chief Exec. Officer--APS, Phoenix, AZ; *U.S. Public*, pg. 1297
Postl, James J., Chief Exec. Officer--Nabisco International Incorporated, New York, NY; *U.S. Public*, pg. 1355
Potashner, Kenneth F., Chm. Bd., Pres., Chief Exec. & Chief Oper. Officer--Maxwell Technologies, Inc., San Diego, CA; *U.S. Public*, pg. 1061
Pote, Hal, Chm. Bd., Pres., Chief Exec. Officer & Sec.--Ambar, Inc., Lafayette, LA; *U.S. Private*, pg. 126
Potila, Antti, Chm.-Bd.of Mgmnt., Pres. & Chief Exec. Officer--FinnAir Oy, Helsinki, Finland; *Int'l*, pg. 485
Potter, John W., Chief Exec. Officer--John Crane Mechanical Seals, Morton Grove, IL; *Int'l*, pg. 1339
Potter, Robert G., Chm. Bd. & Chief Exec. Officer--Solutia Inc., Saint Louis, MO; *U.S. Public*, pg. 1483
Potter, Robert J., Pres. & Chief Exec. Officer--Construction Equip. Div., Lubbock, TX; *U.S. Private*, pg. 355
Potthast, Ulrich, Chief Exec. Officer--VEBA Kraftwerke Ruhr AG, Gelsenkirchen, Germany; *Int'l*, pg. 1460
Pottow, Geoffrey W.J., Pres. & Chief Exec. Officer--Becker Milk Co. Ltd., Scarborough, Canada; *Int'l*, pg. 182
Potts, Gary, Chief Exec. Officer--Maxoptix Corp., Fremont, CA; *Int'l*, pg. 762
Pouget, Philippe, Chief Exec. Officer--Crehalet Pouget Poussielgues, Paris, France; *U.S. Private*, pg. 1152
Pouliot, Adrien D., Pres. & Chief Exec. Officer--CFCF Inc., Montreal, Canada; *Int'l*, pg. 240
Pouliot, Adrien D., Chm. Bd. & Chief Exec. Officer--Laurentien Cable TV Inc., Montreal, Canada; *Int'l*, pg. 241
Pouliot, Adrien D., Chm. Bd. & Chief Exec. Officer--Northern Cable Holdings Ltd., Montreal, Canada; *Int'l*, pg. 241
Poulos, Lori J., Chief Exec. Officer--Bridgewater Resources Corporation, Los Angeles, CA; *U.S. Private*, pg. 168
Poulson, Howard, Grp. Chief Exec.--Premier Farnell plc, Wetherby, United Kingdom; *Int'l*, pg. 1068
Poure, James A., Chm. Bd., Pres. & Chief Exec. Officer--General Alum & Chemical, Holland, OH; *U.S. Private*, pg. 443
Pouyat, Alain, Chief Exec. Officer--E.P.I., Villeneuve-le-Roi, France; *Int'l*, pg. 206
Powch, George, Pres. & Chief Exec. Officer--Champlain Cable Corp., Colchester, VT; *Int'l*, pg. 637
Powell, Daniel E., Chief Exec. Officer--Mathews & Boucher, Rochester, NY; *U.S. Private*, pg. 714
Powell, Earl W., Chm. Bd. & Chief Exec. Officer--Biscayne Apparel Inc., Clifton, NJ; *U.S. Public*, pg. 232
Powell, Hugo, Pres. & Chief Exec. Officer--Labatt Brewing Company Limited, Toronto, Canada; *Int'l*, pg. 679
Powell, John A., Pres. & Chief Exec. Officer--Wajax Limited, Delta, Canada; *Int'l*, pg. 1484
Powell, Karl C., Jr., Chm. Bd. & Chief Exec. Officer--Sequent Computer Systems, Inc., Beaverton, OR; *U.S. Public*, pg. 1459
Powell, Phillip E., Chm. Bd. & Chief Exec. Officer--First Cash, Inc., Arlington, TX; *U.S. Public*, pg. 627
Powell, R. Edward, Pres. & Chief Exec. Officer--CAIRE, Inc., Burnsville, MN; *U.S. Private*, pg. 751
Powell, Richard M., Pres. & Chief Exec. Officer--L. Powell Co., Inc., Culver City, CA; *U.S. Private*, pg. 877
Powell, Susan F., Chief Oper. Officer--Investors Insurance Corp., Jacksonville, FL; *U.S. Public*, pg. 912
Powell, Thomas W., Chm. Bd., Pres. & Chief Exec. Officer--Powell Industries, Inc., Houston, TX; *U.S. Public*, pg. 1319
Powell, William, Pres. & Chief Exec. Officer--Union Planters Bank of Alabama, Decatur, AL; *U.S. Public*, pg. 1669
Power, Edward, Chief Exec.-Meat Div.--Avonmore Waterford Group plc, Killkenny, Ireland; *Int'l*, pg. 102
Powers, Joe D., Chm. Bd. & Chief Exec. Officer--Merchants National Bank, Fort Smith, AR; *U.S. Public*, pg. 501
Powers, Larry, Pres. & Chief Exec. Officer--The Genlyte Group Incorporated, Union, NJ; *U.S. Public*, pg. 729
Powers, Paul J., Chm. Bd., Pres. & Chief Exec. Officer--Commercial Intertech Corp., Youngstown, OH; *U.S. Public*, pg. 411
Poynter, James J., Chief Exec. Officer--GN Nettest Fiber Optic Division, Utica, NY; *Int'l*, pg. 536
Pozza, Duane C., Pres., Chief Exec. Officer & Treas.--Bartlett Cocke, Inc., San Antonio, TX; *U.S. Private*, pg. 249
Prairie, Duane, Pres. & Chief Exec. Officer--Park Construction Company, Minneapolis, MN; *U.S. Private*, pg. 839
Prann, John R., Jr., Pres. & Chief Exec. Officer--Katy Industries, Inc., Englewood, CO; *U.S. Public*, pg. 944
Prante, Gerhard, Dr., Chm. Bd. & Chief Exec. Officer--AgrEvo GmbH, Berlin, Germany; *Int'l*, pg. 624
Pratesi, Roberto, Chief Exec. Officer--Tecnimont Spa, Milan, Italy; *Int'l*, pg. 324
Prather, Robert S., Pres. & Chief Exec. Officer--Bull Run Corporation, Atlanta, GA; *U.S. Public*, pg. 267
Pratt, Brian, Chm. Bd., Pres. & Chief Exec. Officer--ARB Inc., Lake Forest, CA; *U.S. Private*, pg. 7
Pratt, Jack E., Chm. Bd. & Chief Exec. Officer--Hollywood Casino Corp, Atlantic City, NJ; *U.S. Public*, pg. 830
Pratt, Michael G., Pres. & Chief Exec. Officer--Coats & Clark Inc., Greenville, SC; *Int'l*, pg. 300
Pratt, Robert N., Chm. Bd., Pres. & Chief Oper. & Chief Exec. Officer--Alta Gold Co., Henderson, NV; *U.S. Public*, pg. 58
Pratt, Steven D., Pres. & Chief Exec. Officer--Esco Corporation, Portland, OR; *U.S. Private*, pg. 382
Pratt, Tomn, Pres. & Chief Exec. Officer--Florida Tile Industries, Inc., Lakeland, FL; *U.S. Public*, pg. 1322
Precourt, Jay A., Vice Chm., Pres. & Chief Exec. Officer--Tejas Gas Corporation, Houston, TX; *Int'l*, pg. 1136
Preis, Albert, Dr., Chief Exec.--DMC Dresdner Management Consult GmbH, Frankfurt/Main, Germany; *Int'l*, pg. 418
Prendergast, Thomas J., Chief Exec. Officer & Exec. V.P.--R.P. Scherer Korea Limited, Seoul, Korea; *U.S. Public*, pg. 1438
Prescott, J.B., Mng. Dir. & Chief Exec. Officer--The Broken Hill Proprietary Company Limited, Melbourne, Australia; *Int'l*, pg. 223
Pressman, Gene, Co-Chm. Bd. & Co-Chief Exec. Officer--Barneys Inc., New York, NY; *U.S. Private*, pg. 116
Pressman, Robert, Co-Chm. Bd. & Co-Chief Exec. Officer--Barneys Inc., New York, NY; *U.S. Private*, pg. 116
Preston, Frank J., Chief Exec. Officer--Masland, Carlisle, PA; *U.S. Public*, pg. 981
Preston, James E., Chm. Bd. & Chief Exec. Officer--Avon Products, Inc., New York, NY; *U.S. Public*, pg. 155
Preston, P.S., Pres. & Chief Exec. Officer--McDonald's Hamburgers Limited, London, United Kingdom; *U.S. Public*, pg. 1069
Previti, James, Chm. Bd, Pres. & Chief Exec. Officer--Forecast Group, Rancho Cucamonga, CA; *U.S. Private*, pg. 418
Prible, Larry L., Pres. & Chief Exec. Officer--Indianapolis Life Insurance Co., Indianapolis, IN; *U.S. Private*, pg. 560
Price, Francis, Pres. & Chief Exec. Officer--Q3 Stamped Metal, Columbus, OH; *U.S. Private*, pg. 897
Price, Fredric D., Pres., Chief Exec. Officer & Acting Chief Fin. Officer--AMBI Inc., Tarrytown, NY; *U.S. Public*, pg. 7
Price, Gayle B., Jr., Pres. & Chief Exec. Officer--Price Brothers Co., Dayton, OH; *U.S. Private*, pg. 883
Price, Michael A., Chm. Bd. & Chief Exec. Officer--T&W Financial Corporation, Tacoma, WA; *U.S. Public*, pg. 1552
Price, Robert E., Chm. Bd., Pres. & Chief Exec. Officer--PriceSmart Inc., San Diego, CA; *U.S. Public*, pg. 1324
Price, Steve, Co-Chm. & Chief Exec. Officer--Publicis/Bloom, Dallas, TX; *Int'l*, pg. 469
Price, Steven, Pres., Chief Oper. & Exec. Officer--Pricellular Corporation, White Plains, NY; *U.S. Public*, pg. 1324
Price, Thomas P., Jr., Pres. & Chief Exec. Officer--Sabin Robbins Paper Co., Cincinnati, OH; *U.S. Private*, pg. 959
Price, Westcott W., III, Pres. & Chief Exec. Officer--Pacificare Health Systems, Santa Ana, CA; *U.S. Public*, pg. 1251
Price, William C., Chm. & Chief Exec. Officer--Media That Works, Cincinnati, OH; *U.S. Private*, pg. 727
Priem, Ted, Chm., Pres. & Chief Exec. Officer--Nobles Mfg. Inc., Saint Croix Falls, WI; *U.S. Private*, pg. 800
Prieszol, Jozsef, Chief Exec.--Holderbank Ungarn GmbH, Budapest, Hungary; *Int'l*, pg. 629
Prillaman, Albert L., Chm. Bd., Pres. & Chief Exec. Officer--Stanley Furniture Co. Inc., Stanleytown, VA; *U.S. Public*, pg. 1508
Prince, Larry L., Chm. Bd. & Chief Exec. Officer--Genuine Parts Company, Atlanta, GA; *U.S. Public*, pg. 732
Prince, Steven, Chm. Bd. & Chief Exec. Officer--Sempra Energy Trading, Greenwich, CT; *U.S. Public*, pg. 1249
Pringle, Hamish, Chief Exec. Officer--K Advertising, London, United Kingdom; *U.S. Public*, pg. 1422
Pringle, W.J., Pres. & Chief Exec. Officer--Brookfield Homes, Del Mar, CA; *Int'l*, pg. 228
Pringle, William J., Pres. & Chief Exec. Officer--Brookfield Homes Ltd., Toronto, Canada; *Int'l*, pg. 228
Pringuet, Pierre, Chm. & Chief Exec. Officer--PR Europe, Paris, France; *Int'l*, pg. 566
Priory, Richard B., Chm. Bd. & Chief Exec. Officer--Duke Energy Corporation, Charlotte, NC; *U.S. Public*, pg. 534
Priory, Richard B., Chm. Bd. & Chief Exec. Officer--Duke Energy International, L.L.C., Houston, TX; *U.S. Public*, pg. 534
Pritzker, Robert A., Pres. & Chief Exec. Officer--The Marmon Group, Inc., Chicago, IL; *U.S. Private*, pg. 706
Proano, Stephan, Chief Exec. Officer & Chief Oper. Officer--Punto Aparte Publicidad, S.A., Panama, Panama; *U.S. Private*, pg. 305
Probst, Lawrence F., III, Chm. Bd. & Chief Exec. Officer--Electronic Arts, San Mateo, CA; *U.S. Public*, pg. 569
Prockow, Eric, Chm. Bd. & Chief Exec. Officer--Sun Data Inc., Norcross, GA; *U.S. Private*, pg. 1050
Proctor, Dominic, Exec. V.P., CEO-JWT/London & Area Dir.-UK & Ireland--J. Walter Thompson Company, New York, NY; *Int'l*, pg. 1483
Proiss, Mike, Chief Exec. Officer/Taren--Cole of California, Los Angeles, CA; *U.S. Public*, pg. 148
Prosser, D.J., Grp. Chief Exec.--Legal & General Group PLC, London, United Kingdom; *Int'l*, pg. 805
Proteau, Jocelyn, Pres. & Chief Exec. Officer--Federation des caisses populaires Desjardins, Montreal, Canada; *Int'l*, pg. 479
Prothro, C.V., Chm. Bd., Pres. & Chief Exec. Officer--Dallas Semiconductor Corporation, Dallas, TX; *U.S. Public*, pg. 478
Protze, Gerhard, Chm. Bd., Chief Exec. Officer, Chief Fin. Officer & Mng. Dir.--Traub AG, Reichenbach, Germany; *Int'l*, pg. 1419
Prout, Stephen, Pres. & Chief Exec. Officer--Alpha Q, Inc., Colchester, CT; *U.S. Private*, pg. 45
Prueter, Williams R., Pres. & Chief Exec. Officer--Metropolitan Life Insurance Company Of Canada, Ottawa, Canada; *U.S. Private*, pg. 738
Pruitt, Gary B., Pres. & Chief Exec. Officer--McClatchy Newspapers Inc., Sacramento, CA; *U.S. Public*, pg. 1065
Prum Jr., P., Chief Exec. Officer--Zurich-Anglo Seguradora S.A., Sao Paulo, Brazil; *Int'l*, pg. 1532
Pruniaux, Bernard, Dr., Chief Exec. Officer-Atmel ES2--Atmel Corporation, San Jose, CA; *U.S. Public*, pg. 145
Psarouthakis, John, Chm. Bd., Pres. & Chief Exec. Officer--JPE, Inc., Ann Arbor, MI; *U.S. Public*, pg. 919
Pucci, Mark, Pres. & Chief Exec. Officer--Walker Group/CNI Inc., New York, NY; *Int'l*, pg. 1483
Pudil, Michael J., Pres. & Chief Exec. Officer--Washington Scientific Industries, Inc., Long Lake, MN; *U.S. Public*, pg. 1744
Puente, E. A., Pres. & Chief Exec. Officer--Tree of Life, Inc., Saint Augustine, FL; *Int'l*, pg. 752
Puette, Bob, Pres. & Chief Exec. Officer--Centigram Communications Corporation, San Jose, CA; *U.S. Public*, pg. 323
Pulgar, Juan J., Pres. & Chief Exec. Officer--BITOR America Corp., Boca Raton, FL; *Int'l*, pg. 1045
Pulido, Mark A., Pres. & Chief Exec. Officer--McKesson Corporation, San Francisco, CA; *U.S. Public*, pg. 1072
Pulido, Mike, Pres. & Chief Exec. Officer--McKesson U.S. Health Care, San Francisco, CA; *U.S. Public*, pg. 1073
Pulitzer, Michael E., Chm. Bd., Pres. & Chief Exec. Officer--Pulitzer Publishing Company, Saint Louis, MO; *U.S. Public*, pg. 1343
Puls, Michael G., Pres. & Chief Exec. Officer--InnoServ Technologies, Inc., Arlington, TX; *U.S. Public*, pg. 879
Pundyk, Bernard, Chief Exec. Officer--Glamorise Foundations, Inc., New York, NY; *U.S. Private*, pg. 455
Puno, Jimmy, Pres., Chief Exec. Officer & Chief Oper. Officer--Dentsu Young & Rubicam-Alcantara Inc. (Manila), Manila, Philippines; *U.S. Private*, pg. 325
Puorro, Gerard E., Chm. Bd., Pres. & Chief Exec. Officer--Candela Corporation, Wayland, MA; *U.S. Public*, pg. 300
Purcell, Philip J., Chm. Bd. & Chief Exec. Officer--Morgan Stanley Dean Witter & Co., New York, NY; *U.S. Public*, pg. 1132
Purcell, Philip J., Chm. Bd. & Chief Exec. Officer--Dean Witter, Discover & Co., New York, NY; *U.S. Public*, pg. 1132
Purdy, Winifred M., Chm. Bd. & Chief Exec. Officer--The Purdy Corporation, Manchester, CT; *U.S. Private*, pg. 895
Puris, Martin, Pres. & Chief Exec. Officer--Ammirati, Puris & Lintas, Inc., New York, NY; *U.S. Private*, pg. 66
Puris, Martin, Chm., Chief Exec. Officer & Chief Creative Officer--Ammirati Puris Lintas Worldwide, New York, NY; *U.S. Public*, pg. 908
Purkiss, D., Chief Exec. Officer--Turegum Insurance Company, London, United Kingdom; *Int'l*, pg. 1530
Purkiss, D., Chief Exec. Officer--Zurich Re (UK) Limited, London, United Kingdom; *Int'l*, pg. 1532
Pursell, Taylor, Pres. & Chief Exec. Officer--Pursell Industries, Sylacauga, AL; *U.S. Private*, pg. 896
Purser, Lat W., III, Pres. & Chief Exec. Officer--Lat Purser & Associates, Charlotte, NC; *U.S. Private*, pg. 896
Puschel, Philip P., Chm. Bd. & Chief Exec. Officer--F. Schumacher & Co., New York, NY; *U.S. Private*, pg. 973
Puskar, Milan, Chm. Bd., Pres. & Chief Exec. Officer--Mylan Laboratories, Inc., Pittsburgh, PA; *U.S. Public*, pg. 1143
Putnam, Carl E., Pres. & Chief Oper. Officer--Anicom, Inc., Rosemont, IL; *U.S. Public*, pg. 115
Putnam, Frederic L., III, Pres. & Chief Exec. Officer--Colonial Gas Company, Lowell, MA; *U.S. Public*, pg. 400
Putter, Robyn, Chief Exec. Officer.-O&M Rightford, South Africa--Ogilvy & Mather Worldwide, Inc., New York, NY; *Int'l*, pg. 1483
Pyatt, Alan, Chm. Bd., Pres. & Chief Exec. Officer--Sandwell Inc., Vancouver, Canada; *Int'l*, pg. 1188
Pyette, Les, Publisher & Chief Exec. Officer--The Calgary Sun, Calgary, Canada; *Int'l*, pg. 1320
Pyne, J.H., Pres. & Chief Exec. Officer--Kirby Corporation, Houston, TX; *U.S. Public*, pg. 961
Pyott, David, Pres. & Chief Exec. Officer--Novartis Nutrition Corporation, Saint Louis Park, MN; *Int'l*, pg. 974
Quadracci, H.V., Pres. & Chief Exec. Officer--Quad/Graphics, Inc., Pewaukee, WI; *U.S. Private*, pg. 897
Quarles, John M., Chm. Bd., Pres. & Chief Exec. Officer--Wolverine Tube Inc., Huntsville, AL; *U.S. Public*, pg. 1774
Quarta, Roberto, Chief Exec. Officer--BBA Group plc, London, United Kingdom; *Int'l*, pg. 112
Quasha, Alan G., Chm. Bd. & Chief Exec. Officer--Hanover Direct, Inc., Weehawken, NJ; *U.S. Public*, pg. 782
Quick, J. Douglas, Pres. & Chief Exec. Officer--Lakeside Foods, Inc., Manitowoc, WI; *U.S. Private*, pg. 643
Quick, Leslie C., Jr., Chm. Bd. & Chief Exec. Officer--The Quick & Reilly Group Inc., Palm Beach, FL; *U.S. Public*, pg. 650
Quinlan, Mary Lou, Pres. & Chief Exec. Officer--N.W. Ayer & Partners, New York, NY; *U.S. Private*, pg. 103
Quinlan, Michael R., Chm. & Chief Exec. Officer--McDonald's Corporation, Oak Brook, IL; *U.S. Public*, pg. 1068
Quinlan, William, Pres. & Chief Exec. Officer--Processed Products Division, Cincinnati, OH; *U.S. Private*, pg. 1191
Quinn, Larry, Pres. & Chief Exec. Officer--Niagara Frontier Hockey, L.P., Buffalo, NY; *U.S. Private*, pg. 798

Quinn, Thomas H., Chief Exec. Officer--Archibald Candy Company, Chicago, IL; *U.S. Private*, pg. 597
Quintanilla, Rafael F., Deputy Chief Exec. Officer--Banco Santander (Suisse), S.A., Geneva, Switzerland; *Int'l*, pg. 144
Quirk, John E., Pres. & Chief Exec. Officer--Village Car Company, Bangor, ME; *U.S. Private*, pg. 1140
Quirk, Peter R., Pres. & Chief Exec. Officer--Walk, Haydel & Associates, Inc., New Orleans, LA; *Int'l*, pg. 624
Qureshey, Safi U., Chm. Bd. & Chief Exec. Officer--AST Research Inc., Irvine, CA; *Int'l*, pg. 1181
Raab, Max L., Chm. Bd. & Chief Exec. Officer--J.G. Hook, Inc., New York, NY; *U.S. Private*, pg. 538
Raab, Simon, Ph.D., Chm. Bd., Pres. & Chief Exec. Officer--FARO Technologies, Inc., Lake Mary, FL; *U.S. Public*, pg. 613
Raasch, Kenneth E., Chm. Bd., Pres. & Chief Exec. Officer--Media Arts Group, Inc., San Jose, CA; *U.S. Public*, pg. 1077
Rabaut, Thomas W., Pres. & Chief Exec. Officer--United Defense L.P., Arlington, VA; *U.S. Private*, pg. 213
Rabin, Stanley A., Chm. Bd., Pres. & Chief Exec. Officer--Commercial Metals Company, Dallas, TX; *U.S. Public*, pg. 411
Rabinowitz, Martin J., Chm. Bd., Pres. & Chief Exec. Officer--Thackeray Corporation, New York, NY; *U.S. Public*, pg. 1590
Rabinowitz, Stephen, Pres. & Chief Exec. Officer--General Cable Corporation, Highland Heights, KY; *Int'l*, pg. 1486
Rabold, Robert E.H., Chm. Bd., Pres. & Chief Exec. Officer--Motorists Mutual Insurance Co., Columbus, OH; *U.S. Private*, pg. 764
Rabold, Robert E.H., Pres. & Chief Exec. Officer--MICO Insurance Company, Columbus, OH; *U.S. Private*, pg. 764
Rabold, Robert E.H., Chm. Bd., Pres. & Chief Exec. Officer--American Hardware Mutual Insurance Co., Columbus, OH; *U.S. Private*, pg. 764
Rabut, Jean-Eudes, Chief Exec. Officer--Air Charter, Rungis, France; *Int'l*, pg. 560
Radecke, Albrecht C., Chief Exec.--Deutsch-Sudamerikanische Bank AG, Hamburg, Germany; *Int'l*, pg. 418
Rademacher, Rolf Dieter, Chief Exec. Officer--Tuchenhagen GmbH, Buchen, Germany; *Int'l*, pg. 1426
Radler, Louis, Chm. Bd. & Chief Exec. Officer--Chessco Industries, Inc., Westport, CT; *U.S. Private*, pg. 234
Radlinski, David, Chm. Bd. & Chief Exec. Officer--Medstone International, Inc., Aliso Viejo, CA; *U.S. Public*, pg. 1082
Radtke, H. Helmut, Pres. & Chief Exec. Officer--Melitta U.S.A., Inc., Clearwater, FL; *Int'l*, pg. 857
Radus, Philip, Pres. & Chief Exec. Officer--Ribbon Narrow Fabric Company, Secaucus, NJ; *U.S. Private*, pg. 927
Radwill, Scott, Pres., Chief Exec., Oper. & Fin. Officer--Master Appliance Corp., Racine, WI; *U.S. Private*, pg. 713
Rady, Ernest S., Chm. Bd., Pres. & Chief Exec. Officer--Westcorp, Irvine, CA; *U.S. Public*, pg. 1756
Rady, Paul M., Pres. & Chief Exec. Officer--Barrett Resources Corporation, Denver, CO; *U.S. Public*, pg. 191
Radzievsky, Yuri, Pres. & Chief Exec. Officer--YAR Communications, New York, NY; *U.S. Private*, pg. 1195
Raeber, Robert, Chief Exec. Officer--Nestle Deutschland AG, Frankfurt/Main, Germany; *Int'l*, pg. 921
Raese, John R., Chief Exec. Officer--Greer Steel Co., Dover, OH; *U.S. Private*, pg. 479
Raetzel, Dr. Henner, Chief Exec. Officer--Serviceplan GmbH, Munich, Germany; *Int'l*, pg. 1225
Raftery, Joseph P., Chm. Bd. & Chief Exec. Officer--Bank of America Business Credit, San Diego, CA; *U.S. Public*, pg. 180
Ragland, David, Pres. & Chief Exec. Officer--Duncan Equipment Company, Oklahoma City, OK; *U.S. Private*, pg. 346
Ragland, Ron, Chm. Bd. & Chief Exec. Officer--Remec, Inc., San Diego, CA; *U.S. Public*, pg. 1376
Ragland, Ron, Chief Exec. Officer--Humphrey, Inc., San Diego, CA; *U.S. Public*, pg. 1376
Ragsdale, T. Smith, III, Pres. & Chief Exec. Officer--Embers Charcoal Company, Inc., Conway, SC; *U.S. Private*, pg. 373
Rahr, Stewart, Pres., Chief Exec. Officer & Chief Fin. Officer--Kinray Inc., Whitestone, NY; *U.S. Private*, pg. 622
Raimondo, A.F., Pres. & Chief Exec. Officer--Behlen Mfg. Co., Columbus, NE; *U.S. Private*, pg. 130
Rainwater, Gary L., Pres. & Chief Exec. Officer--AmerenCIPS, Springfield, IL; *U.S. Public*, pg. 65
Raisbeck, Peter, Pres. & Chief Exec. Officer--Institutional Financing Services, Benicia, CA; *U.S. Public*, pg. 1652
Raissig, Peter, Mng. Dir.--Impuls Direct, Kusnacht, Switzerland; *Int'l*, pg. 666
Rakolta, John, Jr., Chm. Bd. & Chief Exec. Officer--Walbridge Aldinger Company, Detroit, MI; *U.S. Private*, pg. 1146
Rakow, Thomas S., Pres., Chief Exec. Officer & Treas.--IHC Group, Inc., South Elgin, IL; *U.S. Private*, pg. 555
Ramacher, W.G.Y., Chief Exec. Officer--Advanced Metal Forming CV, Zwolle, Netherlands; *Int'l*, pg. 753
Ramaekers, Lawrence, Acting Chief Exec. Officer--Medical Resources Inc., Hackensack, NJ; *U.S. Public*, pg. 1080
Ramaker, David B., Pres. & Chief Exec. Officer--Chemical Bank & Trust Company, Midland, MI; *U.S. Public*, pg. 345
Ramat, Charles, Chm. Bd., Pres., Chief Exec. Officer & Asst. Sec.--Aris Industries, Inc., New York, NY; *U.S. Public*, pg. 129
Rambo, Larry, Pres. & Chief Exec. Officer--PrimeCare Health Plan, Inc., Milwaukee, WI; *U.S. Public*, pg. 1678
Ramirez-Isava, Daniel, Pres. & Chief Exec. Officer--BITOR Europe, Brentford, United Kingdom; *Int'l*, pg. 1046
Ramirez, Ernesto, Chief Exec. Officer--Asland do Brasil Ltda., Sao Paulo, Brazil; *Int'l*, pg. 790
Ramos, Gary, Chm. Bd., Pres. & Chief Exec. Officer--Advanced Manufacturing & Development, Willits, CA; *U.S. Private*, pg. 22
Ramsey, J.C., Chm. Bd. & Chief Exec. Officer--Royle Systems Group, Pompton Lakes, NJ; *U.S. Private*, pg. 949
Ramsey, Roger A., Chm. Bd. & Chief Exec. Officer--Allied Waste Industries, Scottsdale, AZ; *U.S. Public*, pg. 49
Ranck, Bruce E., Pres. & Chief Exec. Officer--Browning-Ferris Industries, Inc., Houston, TX; *U.S. Public*, pg. 262
Rand, Albert, Pres. & Chief Exec. Officer--Dynamics Research Corporation, Andover, MA; *U.S. Public*, pg. 539
Randal, J.D., Mng. Dir. & Chief Exec. Officer--MFI Furniture Center PLC, London, United Kingdom; *Int'l*, pg. 827
Randall, James H., Pres.--Allfast Fastening Systems, Inc., City of Industry, CA; *U.S. Private*, pg. 37
Randall, Ronald F., Chm. Bd., Pres. & Chief Exec. Officer--Randall Stores, Inc., Mitchell, SD; *U.S. Private*, pg. 909
Randi, Salvatore, Chief Exec. Officer--Italtel, Milan, Italy; *Int'l*, pg. 1363
Randles, Jan P., Chm. Bd. & Chief Exec. Officer--Thomas Steel Strip Corp., Warren, OH; *Int'l*, pg. 756
Randolph, Jackson H., Chm. Bd.--Cinergy Corp., Cincinnati, OH; *U.S. Public*, pg. 368
Randolph, Jackson H., Chm. Bd. & Chief Exec. Officer--Cinergy, Plainfield, IN; *U.S. Public*, pg. 369
Randolph, Jackson H., Chm. Bd., Pres. & Chief Exec. Officer--Lawrenceburg Gas Co., Cincinnati, OH; *U.S. Public*, pg. 369
Randolph, Ron, Pres. & Chief Exec. Officer--Associated Grocers of the South, Inc., Birmingham, AL; *U.S. Private*, pg. 91
Rands, Tara, Pres. & Chief Exec. Officer--Brush Research Manufacturing Company, Los Angeles, CA; *U.S. Private*, pg. 176
Rangen, Chirstopher, Chief Exec. Officer--Rangen, Inc., Buhl, ID; *U.S. Private*, pg. 909
Rankin, Alfred M. Jr., Chm. Bd., Pres. & Chief Exec. Officer--NACCO Industries, Inc., Cleveland, OH; *U.S. Public*, pg. 1149
Ransburg, David P., Chm. Bd. & Chief Exec. Officer--L.R. Nelson Corporation, Peoria, IL; *U.S. Private*, pg. 790
Rantanen, Juha, Chief Oper. Officer--Borealis Holding A/S, Lyngby, Denmark; *Int'l*, pg. 914
Rao, Duane, Chm. Bd. & Chief Exec. Officer--The Rao Group Inc., Sterling Heights, MI; *U.S. Private*, pg. 910
Rao, Duane, Chief Exec. Officer--Metro Cell, Inc., Sterling Heights, MI; *U.S. Private*, pg. 910
Rao, Duane, Chief Exec. Officer--Metro 25 Tire Centers, Sterling Heights, MI; *U.S. Private*, pg. 910
Rapelje, Ronald D., Pres. & Chief Exec. Officer--Ebeling & Reuss Company, Allentown, PA; *U.S. Private*, pg. 358
Rapoport, Bernard, Chm. Bd. & Chief Exec. Officer--American Income Holding, Inc., Wilmington, DE; *U.S. Public*, pg. 1622
Rapoport, Bernard, Chm. Bd. & Chief Exec. Officer--American Income Life Insurance Company, Waco, TX; *U.S. Public*, pg. 1622
Rapoport, M., Pres. & Chief Exec. Officer--Mosler Inc., Hamilton, OH; *U.S. Private*, pg. 763
Rapp, C.J., Pres. & Chief Exec. Officer--Global Beverage Co., Rochester, NY; *U.S. Private*, pg. 457
Rapp, William M., Pres. & Chief Exec. Officer--Vance Industries, Inc., Chicago, IL; *U.S. Private*, pg. 1133
Rappaport, Gary B., Chm. Bd. & Chief Exec. Officer--Venturian Corp., Hopkins, MN; *U.S. Public*, pg. 1716
Rappeport, Don, Chm. Bd. & Chief Exec. Officer--Donlen Corp., Northbrook, IL; *U.S. Private*, pg. 340
Rasdal, Dan, Chm. Bd. & Chief Exec. Officer--Linfinity Microelectronics Inc., Garden Grove, CA; *U.S. Public*, pg. 1547
Rasdal, William D., Chm. Bd. & Chief Exec. Officer--SymmetriCom, Inc., San Jose, CA; *U.S. Public*, pg. 1547
Rasdal, William D., Chm. Bd. & Chief Exec. Officer-SymmetriCom--Telecom Solutions, San Jose, CA; *U.S. Public*, pg. 1547
Rash, James T., Chm. Bd., Chief Exec. Officer & Chief Fin. Officer--Tidel Technologies, Inc., Houston, TX; *U.S. Public*, pg. 1608
Rask, Jan, Pres. & Chief Exec. Officer--Marine Drilling Companies, Inc., Sugar Land, TX; *U.S. Public*, pg. 1044
Rasmussen, Mogems, Grp. Chief Exec. Officer--Nykredit, Copenhagen, Denmark; *Int'l*, pg. 993
Ratcliffe, G.J., Jr., Chm. Bd., Pres. & Chief Exec. Officer--Hubbell Incorporated, Orange, CT; *U.S. Public*, pg. 844
Rath, F.E., Jr., Chm. Bd., Pres. & Chief Exec. Officer--Today's Kids, Booneville, AR; *U.S. Private*, pg. 1020
Rathman, George, Chief Exec. Officer--The Prudential - Jon Douglas Company, Los Angeles, CA; *U.S. Private*, pg. 892
Ratican, Peter J., Chm. Bd., Pres. & Chief Exec. Officer--Maxicare Health Plans, Inc., Los Angeles, CA; *U.S. Public*, pg. 1061
Ratliff, Robert J., Chm. Bd., Pres. & Chief Exec. Officer--AGCO Corporation, Duluth, GA; *U.S. Public*, pg. 28
Ratner, Charles A., Pres. & Chief Exec. Officer--Forest City Enterprises, Inc., Cleveland, OH; *U.S. Public*, pg. 667
Ratner, Dennis, Chief Exec. Officer--Creative Hairdressers, Falls Church, VA; *U.S. Private*, pg. 287
Ratner, James A., Pres. & Chief Exec. Officer--Forest City Commercial Construction Company, Inc., Cleveland, OH; *U.S. Public*, pg. 668
Ratner, James A., Pres. & Chief Exec. Officer--Forest City Rental Properties Corporation, Cleveland, OH; *U.S. Public*, pg. 668
Ratner, Phillip, Chm. Bd., Pres. & Chief Exec. Officer--Spaghetti Warehouse, Inc., Garland, TX; *U.S. Public*, pg. 1495
Ratner, Ronald A., Pres. & Chief Exec. Officer--Forest City Residential Development Inc., Cleveland, OH; *U.S. Public*, pg. 669
Ratton, Jean Pierre, Chief Exec.--Industria Nacional de Cemento S.A., San Jose, Costa Rica; *Int'l*, pg. 630
Rau Reist, Susanne, Chief Exec. Officer & Exec. V.P.--WRH Walter Reist Holding AG, Zurich, Switzerland; *Int'l*, pg. 1484
Rau, Jerome E., Pres. & Chief Exec. Officer--Minuteman International, Inc., Addison, IL; *Int'l*, pg. 587
Rau, John, Pres. & Chief Exec. Officer--ABN/LaSalle North America Inc., Chicago, IL; *Int'l*, pg. 11
Rau, John, Pres. & Chief Exec. Officer--Chicago Title & Trust Co., Chicago, IL; *U.S. Public*, pg. 42
Rau, John, Pres. & Chief Exec. Officer--Chicago Title Insurance Co., Chicago, IL; *U.S. Public*, pg. 42
Rau, Ralph E., Jr., Pres.--Edwin B. Stimpson Company, Inc., Bayport, NY; *U.S. Private*, pg. 1043
Rau, Robert H., Pres. & Chief Exec. Officer--Rohr, Inc., Chula Vista, CA; *U.S. Public*, pg. 751
Rauch, C. Dixon, III, Chm. Bd. & Chief Exec. Officer--Rundel Products, Inc., Portland, OR; *U.S. Private*, pg. 951
Rauch, Donald, Pres. & Chief Exec. Officer--M & C Specialties Company, Southampton, PA; *U.S. Private*, pg. 684
Rauch, Peter, Pres. & Chief Exec. Officer--Rauch Industries, Inc., Gastonia, NC; *U.S. Private*, pg. 1061
Rauenhorst, Mark, Pres. & Chief Exec. Officer--OPUS Corp., Minnetonka, MN; *U.S. Private*, pg. 818
Rauenhorst, Neil, Pres. & Chief Exec. Officer--Opus South Corporation, Tampa, FL; *U.S. Private*, pg. 818
Raven, Gregory, Pres. & Chief Exec. Officer--Hills Stores Co., Canton, MA; *U.S. Public*, pg. 828
Ravin, Richard M., Chm. Bd., Pres. & Chief Exec. Officer--Combined Insurance Company of America, Chicago, IL; *U.S. Public*, pg. 118
Raviv, Gabriel, Ph.D., Pres. & Chief Exec. Officer--Bio-Logic Systems Corp., Mundelein, IL; *U.S. Public*, pg. 230
Rawlins, Ben, Chief Exec. Officer--Union Planters Bank, Memphis, TN; *U.S. Public*, pg. 1669
Rawlins, Benjamin W., Jr., Chm. Bd. & Chief Exec. Officer--Union Planters Corporation, Cordova, TN; *U.S. Public*, pg. 1668
Rawls, Benjamin M., Chm. Bd., Pres. & Chief Exec. Officer--Versar Inc., Springfield, VA; *U.S. Public*, pg. 1717
Rawn, Stanley R., Jr., Chief Exec. Officer--Noel Group, Inc., New York, NY; *U.S. Public*, pg. 1187
Rawson, Thomas C., Chm. Bd. & Chief Exec. Officer--Rawson-Koenig, Inc., Houston, TX; *U.S. Public*, pg. 1362
Ray, Gene W., Pres. & Chief Exec. Officer--The Titan Corporation, San Diego, CA; *U.S. Public*, pg. 1618
Ray, J.W., Chief Exec. Officer--Pillar Electrical plc, London, United Kingdom; *Int'l*, pg. 267
Ray, Merwin J., Chm. Bd. & Chief Exec. Officer--Steel Technologies Inc., Louisville, KY; *U.S. Public*, pg. 1513
Ray, Russell L., Jr., Pres. & Chief Exec. Officer--World Airways, Inc., Herndon, VA; *U.S. Public*, pg. 1780
Raymond, Lee R., Chm. Bd. & Chief Exec. Officer--Exxon Corporation, Irving, TX; *U.S. Public*, pg. 601
Raymonds, John, Chm. Bd. & Chief Exec. Officer--Captive Plastics, Piscataway, NJ; *U.S. Private*, pg. 207
Raymund, Steven A., Chm. Bd. & Chief Exec. Officer--Tech Data Corporation, Clearwater, FL; *U.S. Public*, pg. 1562
Rayner, Tom, Chief Exec. Officer--Expanded Metal Industrial, Hartlepool, United Kingdom; *Int'l*, pg. 467
Rayner, Tom, Chief Exec. Officer--Industrial Building Components Ltd., Hartlepool, United Kingdom; *Int'l*, pg. 467
Rayve, Robert G., Chm. Bd., Pres. & Chief Exec. Officer--The Spencer Turbine Co., Windsor, CT; *U.S. Private*, pg. 1025
Ready, Robert J., Chm. Bd., Pres. & Chief Exec. Officer--LSI Industries, Inc., Cincinnati, OH; *U.S. Public*, pg. 971
Reagan, Mark, Chm. Bd. & Chief Exec. Officer--Willis Corroon Construction Division, Nashville, TN; *Int'l*, pg. 1504
Realf, A.D., Chief Exec. Officer--AMI, Crawley, United Kingdom; *Int'l*, pg. 707
Ream, John K., Chm. Bd. & Chief Exec. Officer--Citibank (Florida) N.A., Dania, FL; *U.S. Public*, pg. 377
Reamer, Norton H., Pres. & Chief Exec. Officer--United Asset Management Corporation, Boston, MA; *U.S. Public*, pg. 1672
Reardon, Philip H., Pres. & Chief Exec. Officer--Essex County Gas Company, Amesbury, MA; *U.S. Public*, pg. 593
Reardon, Philip H., Pres. & Chief Exec. Officer--LNG Storage Inc., Amesbury, MA; *U.S. Public*, pg. 593
Reasor, Robert A., Pres. & Chief Exec. Officer--Security Bank & Trust Co., Mount Carmel, IL; *U.S. Public*, pg. 1217
Rebello, Anthony J., Pres. & Chief Exec. Officer--Park Foods L.P., Barrington, IL; *U.S. Private*, pg. 839
Rechler, Donald, Chm. Bd. & Chief Exec. Officer--Reckson Associates Realty Corp., Melville, NY; *U.S. Public*, pg. 1368
Recordati, Arrigo, Chm. Bd. & Chief Exec. Officer--Recordati Industria Chimica e Farmaceutica S.p.A., Milan, Italy; *Int'l*, pg. 1090
Redding, Peter S., Pres. & Chief Exec. Officer--The Standard Register Company, Dayton, OH; *U.S. Public*, pg. 1505
Reddy, Govi C., Pres. & Chief Exec. Officer--General Binding Corporation, Northbrook, IL; *U.S. Public*, pg. 707
Reddy, N. Damodar, Chm. Bd., Pres. & Chief Exec. Officer--Alliance Semiconductor Corp., San Jose, CA; *U.S. Public*, pg. 47
Redheuil, Alain, Chm. Bd. & Chief Exec. Officer--Rexel, S.A., Paris, France; *Int'l*, pg. 1107
Redies, Robert D., Chm. Bd. & Chief Exec. Officer--R & B Machine Tool Co., Saline, MI; *U.S. Private*, pg. 901
Rediker, Dennis L., Chief Exec. Officer--English China Clays Plc, Theale, United Kingdom; *Int'l*, pg. 455
Redmond, Donald P., Pres. & Chief Exec. Officer--Integon Corporation, Winston Salem, NC; *U.S. Public*, pg. 719
Redmond, Donald P., Pres. & Chief Exec. Officer--Integon National Insurance Co., Winston Salem, NC; *U.S. Public*, pg. 720

Redmond, Donald P., Pres. & Chief Exec. Officer--Integon Indemnity Corporation, Winston Salem, NC; *U.S. Public*, pg. 720

Redmond, Donald P., Pres. & Chief exec. Officer--Integon General Insurance Corporation, Winston Salem, NC; *U.S. Public*, pg. 720

Redmond, Donald P., Pres. & Chief Exec. Officer--New South Insurance Company, Winston Salem, NC; *U.S. Public*, pg. 720

Redmond, Donald P., Pres. & Chief Exec. Officer--Integon Specialty Insurance Company, Winston Salem, NC; *U.S. Public*, pg. 720

Redmond, Donald P., Pres. & Chief Exec. Officer--Integon Preferred Insurance Company, Winston Salem, NC; *U.S. Public*, pg. 720

Redmond, Donald P., Pres. & Chief Exec. Officer--Integon Casualty Insurance Company, Winston Salem, NC; *U.S. Public*, pg. 720

Redmond, John, Pres. & Chief Exec. Officer--Hoover Group, Inc., Alpharetta, GA; *U.S. Private*, pg. 538

Redmond, Paul A., Chm. Bd. & Chief Exec. Officer--The Washington Water Power Company, Spokane, WA; *U.S. Public*, pg. 1744

Rednayne, Nicolas, Sir, Joint Chief Exec. Officer--Kleinwort Benson Ltd., London, United Kingdom; *Int'l*, pg. 420

Reeb, William, Pres. & Chief Exec. Officer--Wilsonart International, Inc., Temple, TX; *U.S. Public*, pg. 1322

Reece, Bill, Chief Exec. Officer--HealthGate Data Corp., Malden, MA; *U.S. Public*, pg. 1182

Reece, Thomas, Pres. & Chief Exec. Officer--Dover Corporation, New York, NY; *U.S. Public*, pg. 520

Reed, Don, Pres. & Chief Exec. Officer--SA-SO Company, Dallas, TX; *U.S. Private*, pg. 955

Reed, Donald B., Pres. & Chief Exec. Officer--Cabletron Systems, Inc., Rochester, NH; *U.S. Public*, pg. 288

Reed, Grant O., Pres. & Chief Exec. Officer--LaRoche Industries Inc., Atlanta, GA; *U.S. Private*, pg. 651

Reed, Jackie L., Pres. & Chief Exec. Officer--Regions Bank/Heard County, Franklin, GA; *U.S. Public*, pg. 1372

Reed, John E., Chm. Bd., Pres. & Chief Exec. Officer--Mestek, Inc., Westfield, MA; *U.S. Public*, pg. 1099

Reed, John S., Chm. Bd. & Chief Exec. Officer--Citicorp, New York, NY; *U.S. Public*, pg. 376

Reed, Larry E., Chm. Bd. & Chief Exec. Officer--Horizon Bancorp, Michigan City, IN; *U.S. Private*, pg. 538

Reed, Martin, Dr., Chief Exec. Officer--Logica, Inc., Lexington, MA; *Int'l*, pg. 814

Reed, S.L., Jr., Chm. Bd. & Chief Exec. Officer--Ethika Corporation, Hilton Head Island, SC; *U.S. Public*, pg. 595

Reed, Sam, Chief Exec. Officer--Sunshine Biscuits, Inc., Woodbridge, NJ; *U.S. Private*, pg. 434

Reed, Sam, Pres. & Chief Exec. Officer--Keebler Company, Elmhurst, IL; *U.S. Public*, pg. 657

Reed, Sam, Chief Exec. Officer--Sunshine Biscuits, Inc., Woodbridge, NJ; *U.S. Public*, pg. 657

Reed, Wendy, Chm. Bd. & Chief Exec. Officer--Radix Corporation, Salt Lake City, UT; *U.S. Private*, pg. 906

Reed, William R., Jr., Chm. Bd., Pres. & Chief Exec. Officer--NBC Bank, FSB (Belzoni), Belzoni, MS; *U.S. Public*, pg. 1155

Reeder, Phil, Grp. Chief Exec.--Expamet International Plc, London, United Kingdom; *Int'l*, pg. 467

Rees, Barry, Chief Exec. Officer-Ajax Fasteners Group--National Consolidated, Melbourne, Australia; *Int'l*, pg. 908

Reese, Richard B., Pres. & Chief Exec. Officer--JBB Worldwide, Inc., Deerfield, IL; *U.S. Public*, pg. 675

Reeth, George P., Jr., Exec. V.P. & Chief Exec. Officer-Marine, Aviation & Intl. Div.--Willis Faber North America, Inc.-New York, New York, NY; *Int'l*, pg. 1503

Reeve, John, Chm. Bd. & Chief Exec. Officer--Willis Corroon Group PLC, London, United Kingdom; *Int'l*, pg. 1501

Reeves, Joseph A., Jr., Chm. Bd. & Chief Exec. Officer--The Meridian Resource Corporation, Houston, TX; *U.S. Public*, pg. 1095

Regan, Harold, Pres. & Chief Exec. Officer--The H.W. Wilson Co., Bronx, NY; *U.S. Private*, pg. 1180

Regan, Lynda, Chief Exec. Officer--Legacy Marketing Group, Petaluma, CA; *U.S. Private*, pg. 658

Regelin, Eric G., Pres. & Chief Exec. Officer--Atlantic Builders Group Inc., Baltimore, MD; *U.S. Private*, pg. 95

Rego, Anthony C., Chm. Bd. & Chief Exec. Officer--Riser Foods, Inc., Bedford, OH; *U.S. Private*, pg. 450

Reherman, R.G., Chm. Bd. & Chief Exec. Officer--Energy Systems Group, Inc., Evansville, IN; *U.S. Public*, pg. 1471

Reherman, R.G., Chm. Bd., Pres. & Chief Exec. Officer--ComSource, Inc., Evansville, IN; *U.S. Public*, pg. 1471

Reherman, Ronald G., Chm. Bd., Pres. & Chief Exec. Officer--SIGCORP, Inc., Evansville, IN; *U.S. Public*, pg. 1471

Reherman, Ronald G., Chm. Bd., Pres. & Chief Exec. Officer--Southern Indiana Gas & Electric Co., Evansville, IN; *U.S. Public*, pg. 1471

Reich, Kenneth I., Chief Oper. Officer--Kendall Regional Medical Center, Miami, FL; *U.S. Public*, pg. 405

Reichman, Joel H., Pres. & Chief Exec. Officer--Designs, Inc., Needham, MA; *U.S. Public*, pg. 501

Reichmann, Charles, Chief Exec. Officer--Dri Mark Products, Inc., Port Washington, NY; *U.S. Private*, pg. 342

Reichmann, Philip, Chief Exec. Officer--O&Y Properties Corporation, Toronto, Canada; *Int'l*, pg. 993

Reid, Alan J., Chm. Bd. & Chief Exec. Officer--Man-Gill Chemical Company, Cleveland, OH; *U.S. Private*, pg. 699

Reid, I.M., Chief Exec. Officer--Redland Aggregates Ltd., Groby, United Kingdom; *Int'l*, pg. 1090

Reid, I.M., Chief Exec. Officer--Redland Readymix Ltd., Groby, United Kingdom; *Int'l*, pg. 1091

Reid, M. Bagley, Pres. & Chief Exec. Officer--Scott & Stringfellow Capital Management, Inc., Richmond, VA; *U.S. Public*, pg. 1445

Reid, Russ, Chm. Bd. & Chief Exec. Officer--Russ Reid Company, Inc., Pasadena, CA; *U.S. Private*, pg. 952

Reid, William P., Pres. & Chief Exec. Officer--Gundle/SLT Environmental, Inc., Houston, TX; *U.S. Public*, pg. 769

Reid, William P., Pres. & Chief Exec. Officer--GSE Living Technology, Inc., Houston, TX; *U.S. Public*, pg. 770

Reiff, Doug, Pres. & Chief Exec. Officer--Otsuka America Pharmaceutical, Inc., Rockville, MD; *Int'l*, pg. 1013

Reifschneider, Darrel, Chm. Bd. & Chief Exec. Officer--Manchester Tank & Equipment Company, Brentwood, TN; *U.S. Private*, pg. 699

Reigle, Jeffrey A., Pres. & Chief Exec. Officer--Regal Ware, Inc., Kewaskum, WI; *U.S. Private*, pg. 917

Reiland, Nicholas, Chief Exec. Officer--Healthsource Arkansas, Inc., Little Rock, AR; *U.S. Public*, pg. 360

Reilly, Edward T., Pres. & Chief Exec. Officer--Big Flower Press Holdings, Inc., New York, NY; *U.S. Public*, pg. 228

Reilly, James P., Pres. & Chief Exec. Officer--Cantel Industries, Inc., Clifton, NJ; *U.S. Public*, pg. 301

Reilly, John, Pres. & Chief Exec. Officer--Stant Corporation, Denver, CO; *Int'l*, pg. 1396

Reilly, Kevin, Jr., Pres. & Chief Exec. Officer--Lamar Corporation, Baton Rouge, LA; *U.S. Private*, pg. 644

Reilly, Lawrence J., Pres. & Chief Exec. Officer--Narragansett Electric Co., Providence, RI; *U.S. Public*, pg. 1171

Reilly, Thomas E., Jr., Chm. Bd., Chief Exec. Officer & Chief Oper. Officer--Reilly Industries, Inc., Indianapolis, IN; *U.S. Private*, pg. 919

Reilly, Wayne R., Chm. Bd. & Chief Exec. Officer--John W. Danforth Co., Buffalo, NY; *U.S. Private*, pg. 309

Reilly, William F., Chm. Bd., Chief Exec. Officer & Chief Oper. Officer--Primedia Inc., New York, NY; *U.S. Public*, pg. 1327

Reily, Timothy, Chm. Bd. & Chief Exec. Officer--Reily Electrical Supply, Inc., Metairie, LA; *U.S. Private*, pg. 919

Reiman, Stephen W., Pres., Chief Exec. Officer & Mgr.-Sls.--W.A. Roosevelt Co., La Crosse, WI; *U.S. Private*, pg. 943

Reimer, C.M., Chm. & Chief Exec. Officer--Virginia Indonesia Company, Houston, TX; *Int'l*, pg. 804

Reinas, Jan, Pres. & Chief Exec. Officer--Norske Skogindustrier A.S, Skogn, Norway; *Int'l*, pg. 965

Reinemund, Steven S., Chm. Bd. & Chief Exec. Officer--Frito-Lay Company, Plano, TX; *U.S. Public*, pg. 1277

Reiner, Arthur E., Vice Chm., Pres. & Chief Exec. Officer--Finlay Enterprises, Inc., New York, NY; *U.S. Public*, pg. 623

Reiner, Arthur E., Chief Exec. Officer--Finlay Fine Jewelry Corporation, New York, NY; *U.S. Public*, pg. 624

Reiners, T.P., Chief Exec. Officer & Fin. Mgr.--EURO RSCG, Oslo, Norway; *Int'l*, pg. 602

Reinhard, Keith L., Chm. Bd. & Chief Exec. Officer--DDB Needham Worldwide Inc., New York, NY; *Int'l*, pg. 357

Reinhard, Keith L., Chm. Bd. & Chief Exec. Officer--DDB Needham Worldwide Inc., New York, NY; *U.S. Public*, pg. 1223

Reinig, L.P., Chm. Bd. & Chief Exec. Officer--Los Alamos Technical Associates, Inc., Los Alamos, NM; *U.S. Private*, pg. 676

Reinke, Jerome, Pres. & Chief Exec. Officer--Armada Corporation, Detroit, MI; *U.S. Private*, pg. 82

Reinke, Jerome, Pres. & Chief Exec. Officer--Hoskins Mfg. Co., Detroit, MI; *U.S. Private*, pg. 83

Reinking, C. William, Pres. & Chief Exec. Officer--Exchange Bank, Santa Rosa, CA; *U.S. Public*, pg. 599

Reischl, Hans, Chief Exec. Officer--Rewe-Handelsgruppe, Cologne, Germany; *Int'l*, pg. 1106

Reiss, Jeffrey, Chief Exec. Officer--CareerTrack Inc., Boulder, CO; *U.S. Public*, pg. 1555

Reister, Mark S., Chief Oper. Officer & V.P.--Wohlert Corp., Lansing, MI; *U.S. Private*, pg. 1185

Reiter, William M., M.D., Chm. Bd., Pres. & Chief Exec. Officer--Health Professionals, Inc., Fort Lauderdale, FL; *U.S. Public*, pg. 802

Reith, James N., Pres. & Chief Exec. Officer--Jennie-O Foods, Inc., Willmar, MN; *U.S. Public*, pg. 840

Reitz, William, Pres. & Chief Exec. Officer--Scott's Food Stores Inc., Fort Wayne, IN; *U.S. Public*, pg. 1541

Rella, William, Chm. Bd., Pres., Chief Exec. & Oper. Officer--LCS Industries, Inc., Clifton, NJ; *U.S. Public*, pg. 970

Rellis, G., Chief Exec. Officer--OCE-Ireland Ltd., Dublin, Ireland; *Int'l*, pg. 994

Relyea, K.S., Pres. & Chief Exec. Officer--Family Restaurants, Inc., Irvine, CA; *U.S. Private*, pg. 393

Remley, William L., Vice Chm. & Chief Exec Officer--Texfi Industries, Inc., Raleigh, NC; *U.S. Public*, pg. 1588

Rempen, Thomas, Chief Exec. Officer-Campus--Havas Advertising, Levallois-Perret, France; *Int'l*, pg. 600

Rene, Jean-Guy, Chief Exec. Officer--Societe d'energie de la Baie James, Montreal, Canada; *Int'l*, pg. 640

Rennert, Ira Leon, Pres. & Chief Exec. Officer--Renco Group, New York, NY; *U.S. Private*, pg. 922

Rennie, John C., Chm. Bd. & Chief Exec. Officer--Pacer Infotec Inc., Billerica, MA; *U.S. Private*, pg. 830

Rennie, Stephen, Chief Exec. Officer--Glynwed Consumer & Construction Products Ltd., Royal Leamington Spa, United Kingdom; *Int'l*, pg. 554

Reno, John F., Chm. Bd., Pres. & Chief Exec. Officer--Dynatech Corporation, Burlington, MA; *U.S. Public*, pg. 539

Reno, William J., Chm. Bd. & Chief Exec. Officer--F.B. Wright Co., Dearborn, MI; *U.S. Private*, pg. 1192

Renollet, Lewis R., Pres. & Chief Exec. Officer--The Citizens Savings Bank Company, Pemberville, OH; *U.S. Public*, pg. 1412

Renschler, C. Arnold, M.D., Pres. & Chief Exec. Officer--PharMerica, Inc., Tampa, FL; *U.S. Public*, pg. 1286

Rensi, Edward H., Pres. & Chief Exec. Officer--McDonald's U.S.A., Oak Brook, IL; *U.S. Public*, pg. 1069

Rentenbach, T.M., Pres. & Chief Exec. Officer--Rentenbach Engineering Company, Knoxville, TN; *U.S. Private*, pg. 923

Renwick, Ken, Pres. & Chief Exec. Officer--All-Phase Electric Supply Co., Benton Harbor, MI; *U.S. Private*, pg. 35

Resnick, Jack, Pres. & Chief Exec. Officer--Transkrit Corporation, Roanoke, VA; *U.S. Private*, pg. 782

Ressler, Barry, Chm. & Pres., Chief Exec. Officer--Universal Voltronics Corporation, Mount Kisco, NY; *U.S. Public*, pg. 1596

Resweber, Louis J., Pres. & Chief Exec. Officer--Network Acquisition Corp., Baton Rouge, LA; *U.S. Public*, pg. 1169

Rethore, Bernard, Chm. Bd. & Chief Exec. Officer--Flowserve Corporation, Dayton, OH; *U.S. Public*, pg. 658

Rethore, Bernard G., Chm. Bd. & Chief Exec. Officer--Flowserve Corporation, Long Beach, CA; *U.S. Public*, pg. 658

Rettani, Roberto, Chief Exec. Officer--Antibioticos S.p.A., Milan, Italy; *Int'l*, pg. 324

Rettani, Roberto, Chief Exec. Officer--Antibioticos S.A., Madrid, Spain; *Int'l*, pg. 324

Reuben, Ronald, Chief Exec. Officer--Pennsylvania Real Estate Investment Trust, Fort Washington, PA; *U.S. Public*, pg. 1272

Reuland, Noel, Pres. & Chief Exec. Officer--Reuland Electric Company, City of Industry, CA; *U.S. Private*, pg. 925

Reum, W. Robert, Chm. Bd., Pres. & Chief Exec. Officer--The Interlake Corporation, Lisle, IL; *U.S. Public*, pg. 892

Reuter, Chlodwig, Chief Exec.--Dresdner Bank (Ireland) plc, Dublin, Ireland; *Int'l*, pg. 419

Reuter, William J., Chm. Bd., Pres. & Chief Exec. Officer--Farmers and Merchants Bank and Trust, Hagerstown, MD; *U.S. Public*, pg. 1542

Reuterskiold, Clas, Pres. & Chief Exec. Officer--AB Industrivarden, Stockholm, Sweden; *Int'l*, pg. 678

Reutlinger, Paul, Pres. & Chief Exec. Officer--Sabena, Zaventem, Belgium; *Int'l*, pg. 1168

Revely, Thomas, III, Pres. & Chief Exec. Officer--Cincinnati Bell Supply Company, Cincinnati, OH; *U.S. Public*, pg. 367

Rey, Alfonso, Chief Exec. Officer--Milk Products Holdings (Latin America) Ltd., Fort Lauderdale, FL; *Int'l*, pg. 923

Reynolds, Byron, Jr., Chief Exec. Officer--Bandini Fertilizer Company, Los Angeles, CA; *U.S. Private*, pg. 113

Reynolds, James F., Chm. Bd. & Chief Exec. Officer--Croll-Reynolds Company, Inc., Westfield, NJ; *U.S. Private*, pg. 290

Reynolds, Jim, Chief Exec. Officer--Reynolds Machine Tool Corp., Melrose Park, IL; *U.S. Private*, pg. 926

Reynolds, Marshall, Chm. Bd. & Chief Exec. Officer--Broughton Foods Company, Marietta, OH; *U.S. Public*, pg. 259

Reynolds, Marshall T., Chm. Bd., Pres. & Chief Exec. Officer--Champion Industries, Huntington, WV; *U.S. Public*, pg. 333

Rezzo, Kathleen, Pres. & Chief Exec. Officer--Construction Lending Corporation of America-Builder Division, Pasadena, CA; *U.S. Public*, pg. 857

Rhein, Timothy J., Pres. & Chief Exec. Officer--APL Limited, Oakland, CA; *Int'l*, pg. 912

Rhines, Wally, Pres. & Chief Exec. Officer--Mentor Graphics Corporation, Wilsonville, OR; *U.S. Public*, pg. 1086

Rhoads, Mitchel, Chm. Bd., Pres. & Chief Exec. Officer--Le Peep's Grill Inc., Littleton, CO; *U.S. Private*, pg. 655

Rhodes, Richard G., Pres. & Chief Exec. Officer--Regions Bank/Dalton/Cartersville/Chattanooga, Dalton, GA; *U.S. Public*, pg. 1372

Riboud, Franck, Chm. Bd. & Chief Exec. Officer--Danone Group, Paris, France; *Int'l*, pg. 379

Ricard, Patrick, Chm. Bd. & Chief Exec. Officer--Groupe Pernod Ricard, Paris, France; *Int'l*, pg. 566

Ricciardi, Salvatore, Pres. & Chief Exec. Officer--Purity Wholesale Grocers, Boca Raton, FL; *U.S. Private*, pg. 896

Rice, Bruce C., Pres. & Chief Exec. Officer--Buster Brown Apparel, Inc., Chattanooga, TN; *U.S. Private*, pg. 189

Rice, Charles A., Pres. & Chief Exec. Officer--Dey Laboratories Inc., Napa, CA; *Int'l*, pg. 812

Rice, Charles E., Chm. & Chief Exec. Officer--Barnett Banks, Inc., Jacksonville, FL; *U.S. Public*, pg. 1162

Rice, Mike, Chm. Bd. & Chief Exec. Officer--Utz Quality Foods, Inc., Hanover, PA; *U.S. Private*, pg. 1130

Rice, Thomas E., Pres. & Chief Exec. Officer--Suburban Newspapers of Greater St. Louis, Saint Louis, MO; *U.S. Public*, pg. 935

Rice, V.A., Chief Exec. Officer--LucasVarity plc, London, United Kingdom; *Int'l*, pg. 819

Rice, Victor A., Chm. Bd. & Chief Exec. Officer--LucasVarity Inc., Buffalo, NY; *Int'l*, pg. 820

Rich, Eve A., Chm. Bd. & Chief Exec. Officer--Contempo Casuals, Los Angeles, CA; *U.S. Public*, pg. 1763

Rich, Nigel, Chief Exec. Officer--Trafalgar House PLC, London, United Kingdom; *Int'l*, pg. 772

Rich, Robert E., Jr., Pres.--Rich Products Corp., Buffalo, NY; *U.S. Private*, pg. 928

Richard, David, Pres. & Chief Exec. Officer--Norstan, Inc., Plymouth, MN; *U.S. Public*, pg. 1192

Richard, Gary, Pres. & Chief Exec. Officer--P.C. Richard & Son, Farmingdale, NY; *U.S. Private*, pg. 928

Richard, Oliver G., III, Chm. Bd., Pres. & Chief Exec. Officer--Columbia Energy Group, Reston, VA; *U.S. Public*, pg. 402

Richard, Oliver G., III, Chm. Bd., Pres. & Chief Exec. Officer--Columbia Gas System Service Corp., Wilmington, DE; *U.S. Public*, pg. 403

Richards, Craig M., Chief Exec. Officer--Baker & Taylor, Inc., Charlotte, NC; *U.S. Private*, pg. 111

Richards, David L., Chief Exec. Officer & Mng. Dir.--Warwick International Ltd., Flintshire, United Kingdom; *U.S. Public*, pg. 1459

Richards, H. Lee, Chm. Bd. & Chief Exec. Officer--Hygeia Dairy Co., Inc., Harlingen, TX; *U.S. Private*, pg. 552

Richards, John D., Acting. Chm. Bd., Pres. & Chief Exec. & Oper. Officer--Granite Furniture Co., Salt Lake City, UT; *U.S. Private*, pg. 469
Richards, John M., Chm. Bd. & Chief Exec. Officer--Potlatch Corporation, Spokane, WA; *U.S. Public*, pg. 1318
Richards, Roy, Chm. Bd. & Chief Exec. Officer--Southwire Company, Carrollton, GA; *U.S. Private*, pg. 1019
Richards, Thomas P., Pres. & Chief Exec. Officer--Grey Wolf, Inc., Houston, TX; *U.S. Public*, pg. 765
Richardson, Edward J., Chm. Bd. & Chief Exec. Officer--Richardson Electronics, Ltd., Lafox, IL; *U.S. Public*, pg. 1387
Richardson, James C., Jr., Vice Chm. & Chief Exec. Officer--WSMP, Inc., Claremont, NC; *U.S. Public*, pg. 1729
Richardson, James Craig, Chm. Bd. & Chief Exec. Officer--Richco Inc., Chicago, IL; *U.S. Private*, pg. 929
Richardson, Joe E., Chief Exec. Officer--Clayson Knitting Co. Inc., Star, NC; *U.S. Private*, pg. 244
Richardson, John, Chief Exec. Officer--Power Conversion, Inc., Elmwood Park, NJ; *Int'l*, pg. 127
Richardson, John G., Pres., Chief Exec. & Chief Fin. Officer--Sugar Creek Packing Co., Washington Court House, OH; *U.S. Private*, pg. 1049
Richardson, Joseph H., Pres. & Chief Exec. Officer--Florida Power Corporation, Saint Petersburg, FL; *U.S. Public*, pg. 655
Richardson, Larry L., Chief Exec. Officer--First Virginia Bank-Mountain Empire, Abingdon, VA; *U.S. Public*, pg. 642
Richardson, Michael A., Chm. Bd., Pres., Chief Exec. Officer & Chief Oper. Officer--American Consumers, Inc., Fort Oglethorpe, GA; *U.S. Public*, pg. 70
Richardson, Michael J., Pres. & Chief Exec. Officer--ADT Automotive, Inc., Nashville, TN; *U.S. Public*, pg. 1648
Richardson, Rodney, Chief Exec. Officer--Roth SA, Mions, France; *Int'l*, pg. 467
Richer, Alvin, Chm., Pres. & Chief Exec. Officer--Arnold Machinery Company, Salt Lake City, UT; *U.S. Private*, pg. 84
Richers, Burckhard W., Chief Oper. Officer--North German Branch, Hamburg, Germany; *Int'l*, pg. 645
Richey, Don, Pres. & Chief Exec. Officer--House of Fabrics, Inc., Sherman Oaks, CA; *U.S. Public*, pg. 842
Richey, Ronald K., Chm. & Chief Exec. Officer--Torchmark Corporation, Birmingham, AL; *U.S. Public*, pg. 1622
Richey, Van L., Pres. & Chief Exec. Officer--American Cast Iron Pipe Co., Birmingham, AL; *U.S. Private*, pg. 51
Richings, Michael B., Pres. & Chief Exec. Officer--Vista Gold Corp., Denver, CO; *U.S. Public*, pg. 1723
Richman, Joshua V., Pres. & Chief Exec. Officer--Straw Hat Cooperative Corp., Dublin, CA; *U.S. Private*, pg. 1046
Richman, Paul, Chm. Bd. & Chief Exec. Officer--Standard Microsystems Corp., Hauppauge, NY; *U.S. Public*, pg. 1502
Richmond, Robert L., Chm. Bd. & Chief Exec. Officer--Active Voice Corporation, Seattle, WA; *U.S. Public*, pg. 17
Richoz, Andre, Chief Exec. Officer--AGIE Charmilles Group, Zug, Switzerland; *Int'l*, pg. 488
Richoz, Andre, Dr., Chief Exec. Officer & Dir.--AGIE AG (Fur Industrielle Elektronik), Lausanne, Switzerland; *Int'l*, pg. 488
Richter, Garrett S., Pres. & Chief Exec. Officer--First National Bank of Naples, Naples, FL; *U.S. Public*, pg. 607
Richter, Irvin E., Chm. Bd. & Chief Exec. Officer--Hill International Inc., Willingboro, NJ; *U.S. Private*, pg. 529
Richter, Juergen, Dr., Chief Exec. Officer--Axel Springer Verlag AG, Berlin, Germany; *Int'l*, pg. 102
Richter, Yochai, Pres. & Chief Exec. Officer--Orbotech Ltd., Yavne, Israel; *Int'l*, pg. 1007
Ricke, David, Chm. Bd. & Chief Exec. Officer--Motek Engineering & Manufacturing Company, Cambridge, MN; *U.S. Private*, pg. 764
Rickershauser, Charles E., Jr., Chm. Bd. & Chief Exec. Officer--PS Group Holdings, San Diego, CA; *U.S. Public*, pg. 1245
Rickert, Lynn, Pres. & Chief Exec. Officer--Union Trust Bank, Union City, IN; *U.S. Public*, pg. 633
Ricoy, Martin, Pres. & Chief Exec. Officer--Grupo Synkro, S.A. de C.V., Mexico, Mexico; *Int'l*, pg. 576
Ridder, P. Anthony, Chm. Bd. & Chief Exec. Officer--Knight-Ridder, Inc., Miami, FL; *U.S. Public*, pg. 963
Ridderstrale, Carl-Erik, Pres. & Chief Exec. Officer--BT Industries AB, Mjolby, Sweden; *Int'l*, pg. 123
Riddleberger, Hensel D., Jr., Chief Exec. Officer--Riddleberger Bros.. Inc., Mount Crawford, VA; *U.S. Private*, pg. 930
Rider, Robert F., Chm., Chief Exec. Officer & Treas.--O.A. Newton & Son Co., Bridgeville, DE; *U.S. Private*, pg. 797
Ridge, Garry O., Pres. & Chief Exec. Officer--WD-40 Company, San Diego, CA; *U.S. Public*, pg. 1726
Ridgley, Robert L., Pres. & Chief Exec. Officer--Northwest Natural Gas Company, Portland, OR; *U.S. Public*, pg. 1200
Ridings, Louis, Pres. & Chief Exec. Officer--Quixx Corporation, Amarillo, TX; *U.S. Public*, pg. 1170
Ridler, Peter, Chief Exec. Officer--Savia S.A., Bielsko-Biala, Poland; *Int'l*, pg. 1376
Ridling, Jim L., Pres. & Chief Exec. Officer--Southern Guaranty Insurance Companies, Montgomery, AL; *Int'l*, pg. 346
Ridout, Derek M., Pres. & Chief Exec. Officer--Silcorp Limited, Scarborough, Canada; *Int'l*, pg. 1249
Ridsdale, B.P., Chief Exec. Officer--Zurich Life Assurance Company Limited, Portsmouth, United Kingdom; *Int'l*, pg. 1532
Riedel, Bob, Chief Exec. Officer--Michael Stevens Ltd., Sayreville, NJ; *U.S. Private*, pg. 1042
Riedel, Dan, Chief Exec. Officer--Benchmark Industries, Brookville, OH; *U.S. Private*, pg. 132
Riederer, Richard K., Pres. & Chief Exec. Officer--Weirton Steel Corporation, Weirton, WV; *U.S. Public*, pg. 1751
Riedman, James, Chief Exec. Officer--Daniel Green Co., Dolgeville, NY; *U.S. Private*, pg. 477
Rieger, Robert, Pres. & Chief Exec. Officer--Exolon-Esk Company, Tonawanda, NY; *U.S. Public*, pg. 600
Riepenhausen, Peter, Pres. & Chief Exec. Officer--Resound Corporation, Redwood City, CA; *U.S. Public*, pg. 1382
Rieson, Dean A., Pres. & Chief Exec. Officer--Carlson Real Estate Company, Minnetonka, MN; *U.S. Private*, pg. 212
Riess, J.M., Chief Exec. Officer--The Gates Corporation, Denver, CO; *Int'l*, pg. 1396
Rieth, Robert, Pres. & Chief Exec. Officer--Wyle Laboratories, Inc., El Segundo, CA; *U.S. Private*, pg. 1193
Rigaud, Jacques, Chief Exec. Officer--RTL, Paris, France; *Int'l*, pg. 561
Rigberg, Allen, Chief Exec. Officer--Just Toys, New York, NY; *U.S. Private*, pg. 903
Riggio, Leonard, Chm. Bd., Pres. & Chief Exec. Officer--Barnes & Noble Inc., New York, NY; *U.S. Public*, pg. 189
Riggs, Louis V., Pres. & Chief Exec. Officer--A. Teichert & Son, Inc., Sacramento, CA; *U.S. Private*, pg. 1072
Rigoulot, Pierre, Chief Exec. Officer--Beaud-Challes-Solap S.A., Rumilly, France; *Int'l*, pg. 430
Rigsby, James H., Jr., Pres. & Chief Exec. Officer--Allied Bank of Georgia, Thomson, GA; *U.S. Public*, pg. 1373
Rihani, D.N., Dr., Chief Exec. Officer--Kinetics Technology India Ltd., New Delhi, India; *Int'l*, pg. 837
Rihm, Walter F., Chief Exec. Officer--Rihm Motor Company, Saint Paul, MN; *U.S. Private*, pg. 931
Riisager, Birger, Pres. & Chief Exec. Officer--FLS Industries A/S, Valby, Denmark; *Int'l*, pg. 474
Rijnberg, Witte L., Chief Oper. Officer--Novo Nordisk A/S, Vienna, Austria; *Int'l*, pg. 987
Riklis, Meshulam, Chm. Bd. & Chief Exec. Officer--McCrory Corporation, New York, NY; *U.S. Private*, pg. 720
Riley, David K., Vice Chm. & Chief Exec. Officer--Community First Bank & Trust, Celina, OH; *U.S. Public*, pg. 633
Riley, David P., Pres. & Chief Exec. Officer--The Middleby Corporation, Rolling Meadows, IL; *U.S. Public*, pg. 1109
Riley, H. John, Jr., Chm. Bd., Pres. & Chief Exec. Officer--Cooper Industries, Inc., Houston, TX; *U.S. Public*, pg. 442
Riley, Robert E., Chief Exec. Officer--Mandarin Oriental International Limited, Hamilton, Bermuda; *Int'l*, pg. 704
Riley, William, Chm. Bd. & Chief Exec. Officer--Moore-Handley, Inc., Pelham, AL; *U.S. Public*, pg. 1128
Rimbey, Robert A., Pres. & Chief Exec. Officer--Reeves Bank, Beaver Falls, PA; *U.S. Public*, pg. 607
Rimel III, William P., Pres. & Chief Exec. Officer--American Inks & Coatings Corp., Phoenixville, PA; *U.S. Private*, pg. 56
Rimer, Harlan L., Pres. & Chief Exec. Officer--Four-S Baking Company, Los Angeles, CA; *U.S. Private*, pg. 422
Rinaldi, Richard A., Pres. & Chief Exec. Officer--CCX, Inc., Charlotte, NC; *U.S. Private*, pg. 193
Rincon, Miguel, Chm. Bd. & Chief Exec. Officer--Grupo Industrial Durango S.A. de C.V., Durango, Mexico; *Int'l*, pg. 575
Rindlaub, John V., Chm. Bd. & Chief Exec. Officer--Seafirst Corporation, Seattle, WA; *U.S. Public*, pg. 181
Rinehart, Charles R., Chm. Bd. & Chief Exec. Officer--H.F. Ahmanson & Co., Irwindale, CA; *U.S. Public*, pg. 29
Riney, Hal P., Chm. & Chief Exec. Officer--Hal Riney & Partners, Inc., San Francisco, CA; *U.S. Private*, pg. 931
Ringler, James M., Chm. Bd., Pres. & Chief Exec. Officer--Premark International, Inc., Deerfield, IL; *U.S. Public*, pg. 1321
Ringo, Philip J., Pres. & Chief Exec. Officer--Chemical Leaman Tank Lines, Inc., Exton, PA; *U.S. Private*, pg. 233
Rinsch, Charles E., Pres. & Chief Exec. Officer--Argonaut Group, Inc., Los Angeles, CA; *U.S. Public*, pg. 129
Ripich, Lawrence, Chief Exec. Officer--American Tank & Fabricating Co., Cleveland, OH; *U.S. Private*, pg. 63
Ripley, Barrett F., Chm.Bd., Pres. & Chief exec. Officer--Troy Mills, Inc., Troy, NH; *U.S. Private*, pg. 1106
Ripley, John A., Pres. & Chief Exec. Officer--Precision Tune Autocare Inc., Leesburg, VA; *U.S. Public*, pg. 1321
Ripps, Harold A., Pres. & Chief Exec. Officer--Dairyland Greyhound Park, Inc., Kenosha, WI; *U.S. Private*, pg. 307
Risdall, Charles A., Pres. & Chief Exec. Officer--Smith System Manufacturing Company, Plano, TX; *U.S. Private*, pg. 1009
Rising, Nelson C., Pres. & Chief Exec. Officer--Catellus Development Corporation, San Francisco, CA; *U.S. Public*, pg. 314
Risinger, James A., Pres. & Chief Exec. Officer--Old National Bank, Evansville, IN; *U.S. Public*, pg. 1217
Risk, Richard R., Pres. & Chief Exec. Officer--Advocate Health Care, Oak Brook, IL; *U.S. Private*, pg. 23
Riskind, Kenneth J., Pres. & Chief Exec. Officer--Fullerton Metals Co., Northbrook, IL; *U.S. Private*, pg. 431
Risley, Larry L., Chm. Bd. & Chief Exec. Officer--Mesa Air Group, Las Vegas, NV; *U.S. Public*, pg. 1098
Risse, K. H., Ph.D., Pres. & Chief Exec. Officer--Bayer Corporation/Diagnostics Division, Tarrytown, NY; *Int'l*, pg. 173
Ritblat, John, Chm. Bd. & Chief Exec. Officer--The British Land Company PLC, London, United Kingdom; *Int'l*, pg. 219
Ritchason, Marvin, Chief Exec. Officer--Ray-Carroll County Grain Co-op, Richmond, MO; *U.S. Private*, pg. 911
Ritchie, Arthur G., Chm. Bd., Pres. & Chief Exec. Officer--Sand Technology Systems, Westmount, Canada; *Int'l*, pg. 1183
Ritchie, Clark, Pres. & Chief Exec. Officier--B & J Operations Company, Inc., Fairmont, WV; *U.S. Public*, pg. 850
Ritchie, David R., Chm. Bd., Pres. & Chief Exec. Officer--Farmers Bank of Maryland, Annapolis, MD; *U.S. Public*, pg. 641
Ritchie, Hale D., Jr., Chm. Bd. & Chief Exec. Officer--Ritchie Corporation, Wichita, KS; *U.S. Private*, pg. 933
Ritchie, Malcom, Chief Exec. Officer & Mng. Dir.--H.J. Heinz Company, Limited, Hayes, United Kingdom; *U.S. Public*, pg. 806
Ritchie, R., Pres. & Chief Exec. Officer--Canadian Pacific Railway, Calgary, Canada; *Int'l*, pg. 258
Ritchie, Robert D., Pres. & Chief Exec. Officer--Vox Medica Corporation, Philadelphia, PA; *U.S. Private*, pg. 1143
Ritsema, Larry J., Pres. & Chief Exec. Officer--The Challenge Machinery Co., Grand Haven, MI; *U.S. Private*, pg. 227
Ritter, C. Dowd, Pres. & Chief Exec. Officer--AmSouth Bancorporation, Birmingham, AL; *U.S. Public*, pg. 105
Rittwage, William R., Chm. Bd., Pres. & Chief Exec. Officer--COP Communications, Glendale, CA; *U.S. Private*, pg. 196
Rittwage, William R., Chm. Bd., Pres. & Chief Exec. Officer--California Offset Printers, Inc., Glendale, CA; *U.S. Private*, pg. 196
Rivera, Raul, Pres. & Chief Oper. Officer--National Benefit Life Insurance Co., New York, NY; *U.S. Public*, pg. 1633
Riviere, Charles J., Sr. V.P. & Dir. Gen.-SRA Europe--SRA International Inc., Arlington, VA; *U.S. Private*, pg. 957
Roach, John V., Chm. Bd. & Chief Exec. Officer--Tandy Corporation, Fort Worth, TX; *U.S. Public*, pg. 1560
Roach, Timothy J., Vice Chm., Pres. & Chief Exec. Officer--TII Industries, Inc., Copiague, NY; *U.S. Public*, pg. 1556
Roake, Andrew, Chief Exec.--Welbilt Corporation, Stamford, CT; *Int'l*, pg. 188
Roark, Martin, Chief Exec. Officer--Ferag Inc., Bristol, PA; *Int'l*, pg. 1484
Roath, Kenneth B., Chm. Bd., Pres. & Chief Exec. Officer--Health Care Property Investors, Inc., Newport Beach, CA; *U.S. Public*, pg. 801
Roave, Robert C., Pres. & Chief Exec. Officer--The Riggs National Bank of Virginia, Merrifield, VA; *U.S. Public*, pg. 1390
Rob, Joseph M., Chm. Bd. & Chief Exec. Officer--Equity Services, Inc., Montpelier, VT; *U.S. Private*, pg. 785
Robb, Donald H., Chm. Bd. & Chief Exec. Officer--Chittenden & Eastman Co., Burlington, IA; *U.S. Private*, pg. 237
Robb, Donald H., Chm. Bd. & Chief Exec. Officer--Eastman House Of California, Inc., Burlington, IA; *U.S. Private*, pg. 238
Robb, Donald H., Chm. Bd. & Chief Exec. Officer--Eastman House Of Alabama, Inc., Burlington, IA; *U.S. Private*, pg. 238
Robbins, James O., Chm. Bd., Pres. & Chief Exec. Officer--Cox Communications, Inc., Atlanta, GA; *U.S. Public*, pg. 454
Robbins, James O., Pres. & Chief Exec. Officer-Cox Communications--Arizona Sports Programming Network, Phoenix, AZ; *U.S. Public*, pg. 455
Robbins, L.C., Pres. & Chief Exec. Officer--Star Food Processing, Inc., San Antonio, TX; *U.S. Private*, pg. 1034
Roberson, David A., Pres. & Chief Exec. Officer--Cavalier Homes, Inc., Wichita Falls, TX; *U.S. Public*, pg. 318
Robert, Stephen, Chm. Bd. & Co-Chief Exec. Officer--CIBC Oppenheimer Corp., New York, NY; *Int'l*, pg. 257
Roberts, Bert C. Jr., Chm. Bd. & Chief Exec. Officer--MCI Communications Corp., Atlanta, GA; *U.S. Public*, pg. 1023
Roberts, Bert C., Jr., Chm. Bd. & Chief Exec. Officer--MCI Telecommunications Corp., Washington, DC; *U.S. Public*, pg. 1024
Roberts, Charles, Jr., Chief Exec. Officer--Chas Roberts Air Conditioning, Inc., Phoenix, AZ; *U.S. Private*, pg. 935
Roberts, David J., Chm. Bd., Pres. & Chief Exec. Officer--Foster Wheeler Real Estate Development Corp., Clinton, NJ; *U.S. Public*, pg. 677
Roberts, Derek F., Chief Exec. Officer--Yorkshire Building Society, Bradford, United Kingdom; *Int'l*, pg. 1522
Roberts, Dorothy H., Chm. & Chief Exec. Officer--The Echo Design Group, Inc., New York, NY; *U.S. Private*, pg. 359
Roberts, F. Stone, Co-Chm. & Chief Exec. Officer--Gotham Incorporated, New York, NY; *U.S. Private*, pg. 677
Roberts, Gary J., Pres. & Chief Exec. Officer--The Metropolitan Savings Bank of Ohio, Youngstown, OH; *U.S. Public*, pg. 608
Roberts, John, Chief Exec. Officer--The Post Office, London, United Kingdom; *Int'l*, pg. 1064
Roberts, John K., Jr., Pres. & Chief Exec. Officer--Pan-American Life Insurance Company, New Orleans, LA; *U.S. Private*, pg. 836
Roberts, Joseph, Chm. Bd. & Chief Exec. Officer--Advanced Circuit Technology, Nashua, NH; *U.S. Private*, pg. 21
Roberts, Kevin J., Chief Exec. Officer--American Golf Corporation, Santa Monica, CA; *U.S. Private*, pg. 55
Roberts, Kevin J., Chief Exec. Officer--Saatchi & Saatchi Advertising Worldwide, New York, NY; *U.S. Public*, pg. 1422
Roberts, Seth, Chief Exec. Officer--Total Holdings (Australia) Pty. Ltd., Sydney, Australia; *Int'l*, pg. 1409
Roberts, Stephen M., Pres., Chief Exec. Officer & Treas.--F.L. Roberts & Co. Inc., Springfield, MA; *U.S. Private*, pg. 935
Roberts, T.S., Jr., Chm. Bd. & Chief Exec. Officer--Monticello Drug Co., Jacksonville, FL; *U.S. Private*, pg. 759
Roberts, William Ted, Pres. & Chief Exec. Officer--SouthTrust Bank of Elba, Elba, AL; *U.S. Public*, pg. 1492
Robertson, Chuck, Chief Exec. Officer--VeriBest Inc., Boulder, CO; *U.S. Public*, pg. 891
Robertson, Dennis, Chief Exec. Officer & Exec. V.P.--Arkansas Farm Bureau Federation, Little Rock, AR; *U.S. Private*, pg. 82
Robertson, G. Bruce, Pres. & Chief Exec. Officer--Robertson Marketing Inc., Charlotte, NC; *U.S. Private*, pg. 936

Robertson, G. Bruce, Pres. & Chief Exec. Officer--RMI Educational Services, Charlotte, NC; *U.S. Private*, pg. 936

Robertson, James C., Chm. Bd., Pres. & Chief Exec. Officer--Consumers Financial Corporation, Camp Hill, PA; *U.S. Public*, pg. 437

Robertson, Robert G., Pres. & Chief Exec. Officer--White Hen Pantry, Inc., Elmhurst, IL; *U.S. Private*, pg. 1172

Robertson, Scott V., Pres. & Chief Exec. Officer--Robertson's Auto Salvage, Wareham, MA; *U.S. Private*, pg. 936

Robertson, William L., Pres. & Chief Exec. Officer--Roy F. Weston, Inc., West Chester, PA; *U.S. Public*, pg. 1761

Robimarga, Davide, Chief Exec. Officer & Gen. Mgr.--Ambro Italia Societa di Intermediazione Mobiliare S.p.A., Milan, Italy; *Int'l*, pg. 138

Robinette, Douglas, Chief Fin. Officer--Employers Insurance of Wausau, Wausau, WI; *U.S. Private*, pg. 788

Robinette, Larry R., Pres. & Chief Exec. Officer--Morgan Products Ltd., Williamsburg, VA; *U.S. Public*, pg. 1132

Robins, John V., Chief Exec. Officer--Guardian Royal Exchange Plc, London, United Kingdom; *Int'l*, pg. 577

Robinson, Bill, Pres. & Chief Exec. Officer--Pacific Mutual Distributors, Newport Beach, CA; *U.S. Private*, pg. 831

Robinson, Bob, Pres. & Chief Exec. Officer--Doane Products Co., Joplin, MO; *U.S. Private*, pg. 337

Robinson, Claude D., Pres. & Chief Exec. Officer--Sivyer Steel Corporation, Bettendorf, IA; *U.S. Private*, pg. 1008

Robinson, Douglas F., Pres. & Chief Exec. Officer--Computalog Ltd., Calgary, Canada; *Int'l*, pg. 325

Robinson, E.B., Jr., Chm. Bd. & Chief Exec. Officer--Deposit Guaranty Corp., Jackson, MS; *U.S. Public*, pg. 500

Robinson, Edward, Chief Exec.-UK Agribusiness--Booker PLC, London, United Kingdom; *Int'l*, pg. 202

Robinson, Gary J., Pres. & Chief Exec. Officer--Columbia Gas of Maryland, Inc., Columbus, OH; *U.S. Public*, pg. 403

Robinson, Gary J., Pres. & Chief Exec. Officer--Columbia Gas of Pennsylvania, Inc., Columbus, OH; *U.S. Public*, pg. 403

Robinson, Hugh C. III, Pres., Chief Exec. Officer & Chief Oper. Officer--Presto Food Stores, Inc., Plant City, FL; *U.S. Private*, pg. 882

Robinson, Irwin Z., Chm. & Chief Exec. Officer-Famous Music--Paramount Pictures Corporation, Los Angeles, CA; *U.S. Private*, pg. 776

Robinson, J.M., Chm. Bd., Pres. & Chief Exec. Officer--Footstar Inc., Mahwah, NJ; *U.S. Public*, pg. 661

Robinson, John, Chief Exec. Officer--House of White Birches, Inc., Berne, IN; *U.S. Private*, pg. 542

Robinson, John H., Grp. Chief Exec. Officer--Smith & Nephew PLC, London, United Kingdom; *Int'l*, pg. 1263

Robinson, Richard, Chm. Bd., Pres. & Chief Exec. Officer--Scholastic Corporation, New York, NY; *U.S. Public*, pg. 1440

Robinson, Ronald, Chm. Bd. & Chief Exec. Officer--Svedala Pumps & Process, Colorado Springs, CO; *Int'l*, pg. 1325

Robinson, Scott S., Pres. & Chief Exec. Officer--The Berkshire Gas Company, Pittsfield, MA; *U.S. Public*, pg. 216

Robinson, William B., Chm. & Chief Exec. Officer--AdultCare, Inc., Deerfield Beach, FL; *Int'l*, pg. 499

Robinson, William B., Jr., Pres. & Chief Exec. Officer--George & Lynch, Inc., New Castle, DE; *U.S. Private*, pg. 448

Robledo, Rafael Miranda, Chief Exec. Officer--ENDESA - Empresa Nacional de Electricidad, S.A., Madrid, Spain; *Int'l*, pg. 1224

Robson, David B., Chm. & Chief Exec. Officer--Veritas DGC Inc., Houston, TX; *U.S. Private*, pg. 1136

Roccaforte, J., Pres. & Chief Exec. Officer--Thomas Pipe & Steel, Inc., Baton Rouge, LA; *U.S. Private*, pg. 508

Roche, David H., Pres. & Chief Oper. Officer--Michigan Sugar Company, Saginaw, MI; *U.S. Public*, pg. 873

Roche, David H., Pres. & Chief Exec. Officer--Great Lakes Sugar Company, Fremont, OH; *U.S. Public*, pg. 873

Roche, John F., Chm. Bd., Pres. & Chief Exec. Officer--PMC Industries Inc., Wickliffe, OH; *U.S. Private*, pg. 827

Rocheleau, Donald, Chief Exec. Officer--Attwood Corporation, Lowell, MI; *U.S. Private*, pg. 1038

Rochelleau, Paul, Dr., Chief Exec. Officer--Albright & Wilson plc, Oldbury, United Kingdom; *Int'l*, pg. 49

Rochon, John P., Pres. & Chief Exec. Officer--Mary Kay Corporation, Dallas, TX; *U.S. Private*, pg. 710

Rock, Bradley E., Chm. Bd., Pres. & Chief Exec. Officer--Bank of Smithtown, Smithtown, NY; *U.S. Private*, pg. 114

Rock, Bradley E., Chm. Bd., Pres. & Chief Exec. Officer--Smithtown Bancorp, Inc., Smithtown, NY; *U.S. Public*, pg. 1479

Rock, Douglas L., Chm. Bd., Pres., Chief Exec. & Oper. Officer--Smith International, Inc., Houston, TX; *U.S. Public*, pg. 1478

Rocker, Kirk B., Pres. & Chief Exec. Officer--Bank of Millen, Millen, GA; *U.S. Public*, pg. 1371

Rockett, Howard, Chm. & Chief Exec. Officer--Rockett, Burkhead, Lewis & Winslow, Raleigh, NC; *U.S. Private*, pg. 938

Rodale, Ardath, Chm. Bd. & Chief Exec. Officer--Rodale Press, Inc., Emmaus, PA; *U.S. Private*, pg. 939

Rodbell, Clyde A., Chm. Bd. & Chief Exec. Officer--Apex Supply Co., Inc., Atlanta, GA; *U.S. Private*, pg. 77

Rodde, Anton, PhD, Pres. & Chief Exec. Officer--Western Data Systems, Calabasas, CA; *U.S. Private*, pg. 1165

Roddick, Anita, Founder & Chief Exec.--The Body Shop International, Littlehampton, United Kingdom; *Int'l*, pg. 199

Roden, Donald R., Pres., Chief Exec. Officer & Chief Oper. Officer--Bergen Brunswig Corporation, Orange, CA; *U.S. Public*, pg. 213

Roden, Steven L., Chief Exec. Officer--ComSkill Learning Centers, Inc., Herndon, VA; *U.S. Public*, pg. 859

Rodet, Jacques H., Chief Exec. Officer--Roger Cleveland Golf Company, Paramount, CA; *Int'l*, pg. 1127

Rodgers, Fran Sussner, Chief Exec. Officer--Work/Family Directions, Boston, MA; *U.S. Private*, pg. 1188

Rodgers, T.J., Pres. & Chief Exec. Officer--Cypress Semiconductor Corporation, San Jose, CA; *U.S. Public*, pg. 470

Rodier, Jean-Pierre, Chm. Bd. & Chief Exec. Officer--American National Can Company, Chicago, IL; *Int'l*, pg. 1029

Rodin, Robert, Pres. & Chief Exec. Officer--Marshall Industries, El Monte, CA; *U.S. Public*, pg. 1051

Rodio, Jean-Pierre, Chm. Bd. & Chief Exec. Officer--Pechiney S.A., Courbevoie, France; *Int'l*, pg. 1027

Rodocanachi, Emmanuel, Chm. Bd. & Chief Exec. Officer--Credit Nationale, Paris, France; *Int'l*, pg. 344

Rodrigues, Christopher, Chief Exec. Officer--Bradford & Bingley Building Society, Bingley, United Kingdom; *Int'l*, pg. 210

Rodriguez, Jorge, Chief Exec. Officer-Miami--Young & Rubicam Latam (Miami), Miami, FL; *U.S. Private*, pg. 1198

Rodriguez, M., Chief Exec. Officer--Great Brands of Europe, Stamford, CT; *Int'l*, pg. 381

Rodstein, Richard M., Pres. & Chief Exec. Officer--K2 Inc., Los Angeles, CA; *U.S. Public*, pg. 940

Roe, David H., Pres. & Chief Exec. Officer--Bankers Security Life Insurance Society, Woodbury, NY; *U.S. Public*, pg. 1375

Roe, John H., Chm. Bd. & Chief Exec. Officer--Bemis Company, Inc., Minneapolis, MN; *U.S. Public*, pg. 210

Roe, K. Keith, Chm. Bd., Pres. & Chief Exec. Officer--Burns & Roe Enterprises, Inc., Oradell, NJ; *U.S. Private*, pg. 187

Roehm, MacDonell, Jr., Chm. Bd., Pres. & Chief Exec. Officer--Bill's Dollar Stores, Inc., Ridgeland, MS; *U.S. Private*, pg. 144

Roelandts, Willem P., Pres. & Chief Exec. Officer--Xilinx, Inc., San Jose, CA; *U.S. Public*, pg. 1786

Roell, R., Pres. & Chief Exec. Officer--Ceramtec North America Applications, Inc., Mansfield, MA; *Int'l*, pg. 860

Roenigk, Martin A., Chm. Bd., Pres. & Chief Exec. Officer--CompuDyne Corporation, Willimantic, CT; *U.S. Public*, pg. 419

Roeser, Robert R., Pres. & Chief Exec. Officer--Elo TouchSystems, Inc., Fremont, CA; *U.S. Public*, pg. 1362

Roesing, Jim, Pres. & Chief Exec. Officer--Super Sky Products, Inc., Mequon, WI; *U.S. Private*, pg. 1054

Roessler, E.C., Pres. & Chief Exec. Officer--CCB Financial Corporation, Durham, NC; *U.S. Public*, pg. 276

Rog, Joseph W., Chm. Bd., Pres. & Chief Exec. Officer--Corrpro Companies, Inc., Medina, OH; *U.S. Public*, pg. 451

Rogal, Andrew L., Pres. & Chief Exec. Officer--Hilb, Rogal and Hamilton Company, Glen Allen, VA; *U.S. Public*, pg. 826

Rogan, T.B., Chief Exec. Officer--Horan Goldman Companies Inc., Wayne, PA; *Int'l*, pg. 705

Rogel, Steven R., Pres. & Chief Exec. Officer--Willamette Industries, Inc., Portland, OR; *U.S. Public*, pg. 1768

Rogers, Bill, Pres. & Chief Exec. Officer--Weather Tec Corporation, Fresno, CA; *U.S. Private*, pg. 1155

Rogers, C. Jeffrey, Pres. & Chief Exec. Officer--Pizza Inn, Inc., Dallas, TX; *U.S. Public*, pg. 1307

Rogers, Edward S., Chief Exec. Officer--Rogers Cable Systems, Etobicoke, Canada; *Int'l*, pg. 1123

Rogers, Gary L., Pres. & Chief Exec. Officer--G.E. Plastics, Pittsfield, MA; *U.S. Public*, pg. 710

Rogers, Hugh P., Deputy Chief Exec. Officer--Derbyshire Building Society, Duffield, United Kingdom; *Int'l*, pg. 394

Rogers, James E., Vice Chm. & Chief Exec. Officer--Cinergy Investments, Inc., Indianapolis, IN; *U.S. Public*, pg. 369

Rogers, James E., Vice Chm., Pres. & Chief Exec. Officer--CINergy Services, Inc., Cincinnati, OH; *U.S. Public*, pg. 369

Rogers, James E., Vice Chm. & Chief Exec. Officer--KO Transmission Company, Cincinnati, OH; *U.S. Public*, pg. 369

Rogers, James E., Vice Chm. & Chief Exec. Officer--Lawrenceburg Gas Co., Cincinnati, OH; *U.S. Public*, pg. 369

Rogers, James E., Vice Chm. & Chief Exec. Officer--Miami Power Corp., Cincinnati, OH; *U.S. Public*, pg. 369

Rogers, James E., Vice Chm. & Chief Exec. Officer--Tri-State Improvement Co., Cincinnati, OH; *U.S. Public*, pg. 369

Rogers, James E., Vice Chm. & Chief Exec. Officer--Union Light, Heat and Power Co., Cincinnati, OH; *U.S. Public*, pg. 369

Rogers, Joe W., Jr., Pres. & Chief Exec. Officer--Waffle House, Incorporated, Norcross, GA; *U.S. Private*, pg. 1146

Rogers, John, Pres. & Chief Exec. Officer--MDS Inc., Etobicoke, Canada; *Int'l*, pg. 826

Rogers, M. Weldon, III, Chm. Bd., Pres. & Chief Exec. Officer--EAC Corporation, Saint Louis, MO; *U.S. Private*, pg. 353

Rogers, P.G., Pres. & Chief Exec. Officer--Cashco, Inc., Ellsworth, KS; *U.S. Private*, pg. 218

Rogers, Robert D., Pres. & Chief Exec. Officer--Texas Industries, Inc., Dallas, TX; *U.S. Public*, pg. 1585

Rogers, T. Gary, Chm. Bd. & Chief Exec. Officer--Dreyer's Grand Ice Cream, Inc., Oakland, CA; *U.S. Public*, pg. 529

Rogers, Ted, Pres. & Chief Exec. Officer--Rogers Communications, Inc., Toronto, Canada; *Int'l*, pg. 1122

Rogers, Thomas W., Pres. & Chief Exec. Officer--Apollo Colors Inc., Northbrook, IL; *U.S. Private*, pg. 77

Rogers, Tony, Chief Exec. Officer--Smorgon A.R.C., Sunshine, Australia; *Int'l*, pg. 1269

Rogers, W., Chief Exec.-Traditional Life--MLC Limited, Sydney, Australia; *Int'l*, pg. 806

Rogers, Yandell, Jr., Pres., Chief Exec. Officer & Gen. Counsel--YRJ Corporation, Houston, TX; *U.S. Private*, pg. 1176

Rogerson, Michael, Chm. Bd., Pres. & Chief Exec. Officer--Rogerson Aircraft Corporation, Irvine, CA; *U.S. Private*, pg. 940

Rogulic, Rob, Chief Exec. Officer--K & R Express Systems Inc., Hinsdale, IL; *U.S. Private*, pg. 602

Rohde, Bruce, Vice Chm., Pres., & Chief Exec. Officer--ConAgra, Inc., Omaha, NE; *U.S. Public*, pg. 425

Roher, Charles, Pres. Chief Exec. & Fin. Officer--C. Roher Inc., Fleetwood, PA; *U.S. Private*, pg. 940

Rohle, Michael, Chief Exec. Officer-DMB&B-Germany--DMB&B Frankfurt, Frankfurt/Main, Germany; *U.S. Private*, pg. 303

Rohle, Michael, Chief Exec. Officer (Out of Frankfurt)--DMB&B Dusseldorf, Dusseldorf, Germany; *U.S. Private*, pg. 303

Rohleder, Michael J., Pres. & Chief Exec. Officer--Wyle Electronics, Irvine, CA; *Int'l*, pg. 1457

Rohr, James E., Chm. Bd. & Chief Exec. Officer--PNC Bank, N.A., Pittsburgh, PA; *U.S. Public*, pg. 1243

Rohrbasser, Markus, Chief Exec. Officer & Exec. V.P.-N. America--Union Bank of Switzerland, Zurich, Switzerland; *Int'l*, pg. 1439

Rohrmann, Guenter, Pres. & Chief Exec. Officer--Air Express International Corporation, Darien, CT; *U.S. Public*, pg. 30

Rohs, Thomas W., Chm. Bd. & Chief Exec. Officer--American Modern Home Insurance Group, Amelia, OH; *U.S. Public*, pg. 1110

Rohtbart, David S., Pres. & Chief Exec. Officer--Cattleman's, Inc., Detroit, MI; *U.S. Public*, pg. 318

Roland, Donald E., Pres. & Chief Exec. Officer--Treasure Chest Advertising Co., Inc., Glendora, CA; *U.S. Public*, pg. 228

Roland, Frank, Pres., Chief Exec. Officer & Chief Oper. Officer--Rubatex Corporation, Roanoke, VA; *U.S. Private*, *pg. 56*

Rolenberg, Greg, Chief Exec. Officer--Express Scripts Vision, Earth City, MO; *U.S. Public*, pg. 601

Rolf, Randolph K., Chm. Bd., Pres. & Chief Exec. Officer--Unitog Company, Kansas City, MO; *U.S. Public*, pg. 1693

Rolland, Ian M., Chm. Bd., Pres. & Chief Exec. Officer--Lincoln National Corporation, Fort Wayne, IN; *U.S. Public*, pg. 997

Rolland, Jan, Mng. Dir., Chief Exec. Officer--Clarion I.M.P. A/S, Oslo, Norway; *U.S. Private*, pg. 303

Roller, Donald E., Pres. & Chief Exec. Officer--United States Gypsum Co., Chicago, IL; *U.S. Public*, pg. 1660

Rollhaus, Philip E., Jr., Chm. Bd. & Chief Exec. Officer--Quixote Corporation, Chicago, IL; *U.S. Public*, pg. 1353

Rollins, David, Pres. & Chief Exec. Officer--Nashville Wire Product Co., Nashville, TN; *U.S. Private*, pg. 775

Rollins, John W., Chm. Bd. & Chief Exec. Officer--Rollins Truck Leasing Corp., Wilmington, DE; *U.S. Public*, pg. 1405

Rollins, R. Randall, Chm. Bd. & Chief Exec. Officer--Rollins, Inc., Atlanta, GA; *U.S. Public*, pg. 1404

Roloff, Jeffrey J., Chm. Bd. & Chief Exec. Officer--Central Data Corporation, Champaign, IL; *U.S. Private*, pg. 223

Rolston, David W., Dr., Pres. & Chief Exec. Officer--Multigen Inc., San Jose, CA; *U.S. Public*, pg. 1425

Romano, Donald, Chief Exec. Officer--Heritage Air Systems, Inc., Deer Park, NY; *U.S. Public*, pg. 572

Romano, Joe, Pres. & Chief Exec. Officer--Advantage Life Products, Inc., Tampa, FL; *U.S. Public*, pg. 22

Romanowski, Thomas S., Pres. & Chief Exec. Officer--CILCORP Investment Management Inc., Peoria, IL; *U.S. Public*, pg. 367

Romanowski, Thomas S., Pres. & Chief Exec. Officer--CILCORP Ventures Inc., Peoria, IL; *U.S. Public*, pg. 367

Romero, Antonio J., V.P.-Blockbuster & Chief Exec. Officer-NewLeaf Corp.--Blockbuster Entertainment Group, Dallas, TX; *U.S. Private*, pg. 775

Romita, Michael, Chm. Bd. & Chief Exec. Officer--Castle Oil Corporation, Harrison, NY; *U.S. Private*, pg. 219

Rompala, Richard M., Chm. Bd. & Chief Exec. Officer--The Valspar Corporation, Minneapolis, MN; *U.S. Public*, pg. 1707

Rompala, Richard M., Pres. & Chief Exec. Officer--Valspar Paints, Minneapolis, MN; *U.S. Public*, pg. 1707

Ronca, Michael, Pres. & Chief Exec. Officer--Domain Energy Corporation, Houston, TX; *U.S. Public*, pg. 515

Roney, Patrick E., Chm. Bd., Pres. & Chief Exec. Officer--Electro Mechanical Design Services, Inc., Gaithersburg, MD; *U.S. Private*, pg. 369

Roney, Walter E., Pres. & Chief Exec. Officer--Willis Corroon Corp. of Mobile, Mobile, AL; *Int'l*, pg. 1506

Rongen, G., Chief Exec. Officer--OCE (Singapore) Pte. Ltd., Singapore, Singapore; *Int'l*, pg. 995

Ronkko, Tuomo, Chief Exec. Officer-Ahlstrom Machinery--A. Ahlstrom Corporation, Helsinki, Finland; *Int'l*, pg. 32

Ronner, Oskar K., Pres. & Chief Exec. Officer--Electrowatt Ltd., Zurich, Switzerland; *Int'l*, pg. 1246

Rooney, Francis, Chm. Bd. & Chief Exec. Officer--H.H. Brown Shoe Company, Inc., Greenwich, CT; *U.S. Public*, pg. 217

Rooney, Patrick W., Chm. Bd., Pres. & Chief Exec. Officer--Cooper Tire & Rubber Company, Findlay, OH; *U.S. Public*, pg. 445

Rooney, Thomas D., Chm. Bd., Pres. & Chief Exec. Officer--Multigraphics Inc., Mount Prospect, IL; *U.S. Public*, pg. 1141

Roos, Jef, Chief Exec. Officer-Stainless Steel Div.--Sidmar N.V., Gent, Belgium; *Int'l*, pg. 79

Root, L.D., Jr., Chief Exec. Officer--New York Wire Co., Mount Wolf, PA; *U.S. Private*, pg. 795

Roper, John L. III, Pres. & Chief Exec. Officer--Norfolk Shipbuilding & Drydock Corporation, Norfolk, VA; *U.S. Private*, pg. 802

Roper, William H., Chm. Bd. & Chief Exec. Officer--Ropak Corporation, Fullerton, CA; *Int'l*, pg. 811

Roquero, Angel, Chief Exec. Officer--Ruiz Nicoli Group, Madrid, Spain; *Int'l*, pg. 603

Rosane, Edwin L., Pres. & Chief Exec. Officer--USAA Life Insurance Co., San Antonio, TX; *U.S. Private*, pg. 1115

Rosati, Robert S., Pres. & Chief Exec. Officer--Transtar Holdings, L.P., Monroeville, PA; *U.S. Private*, pg. 1097
Roscoe, Michael R., Pres. & Chief Exec. Officer--Distribution Services, Inc., Lantana, FL; *U.S. Public*, pg. 87
Rose, D.N., Pres. & Chief Exec. Officer--Mountain Fuel Supply Company, Salt Lake City, UT; *U.S. Public*, pg. 1352
Rose, D.N., Pres. & Chief Exec. Officer--Questar Pipeline Company, Salt Lake City, UT; *U.S. Public*, pg. 1352
Rose, F., Chief Exec. Officer--Clare Rose Inc./Clare Rose of Nassau, Patchogue, NY; *U.S. Private*, pg. 945
Rose, John E.V., Chief Exec. Officer--Rolls-Royce plc, London, United Kingdom; *Int'l*, pg. 1126
Rose, Kelly L., Chm. Bd. & Chief Exec. Officer--Starcraft Corporation, Goshen, IN; *U.S. Public*, pg. 1510
Rose, Kenneth L., Pres. & Chief Exec. Officer--Henkels & McCoy, Inc., Blue Bell, PA; *U.S. Private*, pg. 522
Rose, Peter J., Chm. Bd. & Chief Exec. Officer--Expeditors International of Washington, Inc., Seattle, WA; *U.S. Public*, pg. 600
Rose, Richard, Chief Exec. Officer--Dataflex Corporation, Clearwater, FL; *U.S. Private*, pg. 313
Rose, Robert E., Pres. & Chief Exec. Officer--Diamond Offshore Drilling, Inc., Houston, TX; *U.S. Public*, pg. 1011
Rose, Stuart, Chm. Bd. & Chief Exec. Officer--Rex Stores Corp., Dayton, OH; *U.S. Public*, pg. 1384
Rose, William R., Chm. Bd., Pres. & Chief Exec. Officer--Rose Packing Company, Barrington, IL; *U.S. Private*, pg. 945
Rose, William T., Jr., Chm. Bd., Pres. & Chief Exec. Officer--Uncle B's Bakery, Inc., Ellsworth, IA; *U.S. Public*, pg. 1664
Roseberry, Thomas D., Pres. & Chief Exec. Officer--Willis Corroon Corp. of Utah, Salt Lake City, UT; *Int'l*, pg. 1507
Rosebrough, Walter M., Jr., Pres. & Chief Exec. Officer--Hill-Rom Company, Inc., Batesville, IN; *U.S. Public*, pg. 828
Rosedale, Miles, Chm. Bd., Pres. & Chief Exec. Officer--Monrovia Nursery Co., Azusa, CA; *U.S. Private*, pg. 757
Rosemore, Lance B., Pres., Chief Exec. Officer & Sec.--PMC Capital Inc., Dallas, TX; *U.S. Public*, pg. 1242
Rosen, Benedict P., Chm. Bd., Pres. & Chief Exec. Officer--AVX Corporation, Myrtle Beach, SC; *Int'l*, pg. 775
Rosen, David, Pres. & Chief Exec. Officer--CB North America, Inc., Saratoga Springs, NY; *U.S. Private*, pg. 192
Rosen, Frederick D., Pres. & Chief Exec. Officer--Ticketmaster Corporation, West Hollywood, CA; *U.S. Private*, pg. 1084
Rosen, Gerald, Chief Exec. Officer--Sunnydale Farms, Brooklyn, NY; *U.S. Private*, pg. 1053
Rosen, Harry, Chm. Bd. & Chief Exec. Officer--Harry Rosen Inc., Toronto, Canada; *Int'l*, pg. 425
Rosen, Jack, Chm. Bd., Pres. & Chief Exec. Officer--Continental Health Affiliates, Inc., Englewood Cliffs, NJ; *U.S. Public*, pg. 440
Rosen, Lawrence, Pres. & Chief Exec. Officer--Rose Art Industries, Livingston, NJ; *U.S. Private*, pg. 945
Rosen, Mike, Chief Exec. Officer & Exec. V.P.-Corp Devel Mktg.--Herbalife International of America, Inc., Century City, CA; *U.S. Public*, pg. 809
Rosenbaum, Edward W., Chm. Bd. & Chief Exec. Officer--David Michael & Co. Inc., Philadelphia, PA; *U.S. Private*, pg. 740
Rosenberg, Alan, Pres. & Chief Exec. Officer--Seaman Furniture Company, Inc., Woodbury, NY; *U.S. Public*, pg. 1452
Rosenberg, Burton M., Chief Exec. Officer--Henry I. Siegel Company, Inc., New York, NY; *U.S. Private*, pg. 998
Rosenberg, Henry A., Jr., Chm. Bd., Pres., Chief Exec. & Oper. Officer--Crown Central Petroleum Corporation, Baltimore, MD; *U.S. Public*, pg. 462
Rosenberg, Kenneth B., Pres., Chief Exec. Officer & Sec.--Eastern Smelting & Refining Corporation, Lynn, MA; *U.S. Private*, pg. 357
Rosenberg, Michael G., Chief Exec. Officer--The Promotion in Motion Companies, Closter, NJ; *U.S. Private*, pg. 890
Rosenberg, Robert, Pres. & Chief Exec. Officer--Baskin-Robbins Incorporated, Glendale, CA; *Int'l*, pg. 63
Rosenberg, Shelly, Pres. & Chief Exec. Officer--Equity Group Investments, Chicago, IL; *U.S. Private*, pg. 380
Rosenberger, Larry E., Pres. & Chief Exec. Officer--Fair, Isaac and Company, Inc., San Rafael, CA; *U.S. Public*, pg. 609
Rosenblatt, Ed, Chm. & Chief Exec. Officer--Geffen Records, Los Angeles, CA; *Int'l*, pg. 1215
Rosenkranz, Danny, Chief Exec. Officer--The BOC Group plc, Windlesham, United Kingdom; *Int'l*, pg. 121
Rosenkranz, Robert, Chm. Bd., Pres. & Chief Exec. Officer--Delphi Financial Group, Inc., Wilmington, DE; *U.S. Public*, pg. 496
Rosenshine, Allen, Chm. Bd., Chief Exec. Officer & Dir.--BBDO Worldwide Inc., New York, NY; *U.S. Public*, pg. 1223
Rosensteel, John W., Pres. & Chief Exec. Officer--Keyport Life Insurance Company, Boston, MA; *U.S. Private*, pg. 666
Rosenthal, Marvin, Chief Exec. Officer--National Lumber Co., Warren, MI; *U.S. Private*, pg. 785
Rosenthal, Reuben, Pres. & Chief Exec. Officer--Quala Systems, Inc., Exton, PA; *U.S. Private*, pg. 233
Rosenthal, Robert, Ph.D, Pres., Chief Exec. Officer & Chief Oper. Officer--Thermo Jarrell Ash Corporation, Franklin, MA; *U.S. Public*, pg. 1594
Rosier, Grady, Pres. & Chief Exec. Officer-McLane Co., Inc.--Wal-Mart Stores, Inc., Bentonville, AR; *U.S. Public*, pg. 1732
Rosier, William G., Pres. & Chief Exec. Officer--McLane Company, Inc., Temple, TX; *U.S. Public*, pg. 1733
Rosner, Carl H., Chm. Bd. & Chief Exec. Officer--Intermagnetics General Corporation, Latham, NY; *U.S. Public*, pg. 893
Ross, Fred C., Pres. & Chief Exec. Officer--Allied Old English, Inc., Port Reading, NJ; *U.S. Private*, pg. 39
Ross, Gerald, Pres., Chief Exec. & Chief Fin. Officer--MGR Equipment Corp., Inwood, NY; *U.S. Private*, pg. 687
Ross, Joseph, Chief Exec. Officer--Entron Industries Limited Partnership, Forest Hills, NY; *U.S. Private*, pg. 378
Ross, Joseph J., Chm. Bd., Pres. & Chief Exec. Officer--Federal Signal Corporation, Oak Brook, IL; *U.S. Public*, pg. 616
Ross, Mike, Grp. Chief Exec.--Scottish Widows' Fund & Life Assurance Society, Edinburgh, United Kingdom; *Int'l*, pg. 1212
Ross, R. Dale, Chm. Bd. & Chief Exec. Officer--American Oncology Resources, Inc., Houston, TX; *U.S. Public*, pg. 88
Ross, Robert, Chief Exec. Officer--Swiss-M-Tex, L.P., Travelers Rest, SC; *U.S. Private*, pg. 1059
Ross, Ron, Chief Exec. Officer--Cameron Ashley Building Products, Inc., Dallas, TX; *U.S. Public*, pg. 298
Rosse, James N., Pres. & Chief Exec. Officer--Freedom Communication Inc., Irvine, CA; *U.S. Private*, pg. 425
Rossi, L., Chief Exec. Officer--EL. BO. MEC. Thermalloy Srl., Bologna, Italy; *Int'l*, pg. 209
Rosskamm, Alan, Chm. Bd., Pres. & Chief Exec. Officer--Fabri-Centers of America, Inc., Hudson, OH; *U.S. Public*, pg. 609
Rosso, Jean-Pierre, Chm. Bd. & Chief Exec. Officer--Case Corporation, Racine, WI; *U.S. Public*, pg. 311
Rosso, Louis T., Chm. Bd. & Chief Exec. Officer--Beckman Instruments, Inc., Fullerton, CA; *U.S. Public*, pg. 199
Rosso, Mario, Chief Exec. Officer--Maxus Energy Corporation, Dallas, TX; *Int'l*, pg. 1515
Rossow, Merlin, Chief Exec. Officer--Howden Fluid Systems, Santa Barbara, CA; *U.S. Public*, pg. 1045
Roten, Robert W., Pres. & Chief Exec. Officer--Sterling Chemicals Holdings, Inc., Houston, TX; *U.S. Public*, pg. 1515
Roten, Robert W., Pres. & Chief Exec. Officer--Sterling Chemicals, Inc., Houston, TX; *U.S. Public*, pg. 1515
Roth, Bernard B., Chm. Bd. & Chief Exec. Officer--World Oil Corp., South Gate, CA; *U.S. Private*, pg. 1190
Roth, Christian, Chief Exec. Officer--Bilfinger + Berger Bauaktiengesellschaft, Mannheim, Germany; *Int'l*, pg. 194
Roth, Clarence, Chirf Exec. Officer--Prince Rupert Grain Ltd., Vancouver, Canada; *Int'l*, pg. 1195
Roth, Jim, Pres. & Chief Exec. Officer--GRC International, Inc., Vienna, VA; *U.S. Public*, pg. 695
Roth, John A., Chief Exec. & Oper. Officer & Pres.-Nortel North America--Northern Telecom Limited, Brampton, Canada; *Int'l*, pg. 968
Roth, John A., Pres. & Chief Exec. Officer--MICOM Communications Corp., Simi Valley, CA; *Int'l*, pg. 969
Roth, Michael I., Chm. Bd. & Chief Exec. Officer--The Mutual Life Insurance Company of New York, New York, NY; *U.S. Private*, pg. 769
Roth, Michael JC, Pres. & Chief Exec. Officer--USAA Investment Management Co., San Antonio, TX; *U.S. Private*, pg. 1114
Roth, Steven, Chm. Bd. & Chief Exec. Officer--Vornado Realty Trust, Saddle Brook, NJ; *U.S. Public*, pg. 1725
Roth, Steven, Chief Exec. Officer--Alexander's, Inc., Saddle Brook, NJ; *U.S. Public*, pg. 1725
Rothbaum, Michael, Pres. & Chief Exec. Officer--The Harwood Companies, Inc., Fort Lauderdale, FL; *U.S. Public*, pg. 1433
Rothenberger, Helmut, Chm.-Mngmt. Bd. & Chief Exec. Officer--Rothenberger Group GmbH, Kelheim, Germany; *Int'l*, pg. 1127
Rothenstreich, Jon W., Chm. & Chief Exec. Officer--TIG Holdings, Inc., New York, NY; *U.S. Public*, pg. 1555
Rothwell, Brian G., Pres. & Chief Exec. Officer--Bay State Milling Co., Quincy, MA; *U.S. Private*, pg. 124
Rott, Herbert F., Sr., Chm. Bd. & Chief Exec. Officer--Rott-Keller Supply Co., Fargo, ND; *U.S. Private*, pg. 947
Rotter, David H., Pres., Chief Exec. Officer & Sec.--The Rottlund Company, Inc., Roseville, MN; *U.S. Public*, pg. 1406
Rouanne, Guy, Chief Exec. Officer--SAGEM, Osny, France; *Int'l*, pg. 1273
Roudebush, Ronald L., Vice Chm. & Chief Exec. Officer--The Standard Products Company, Dearborn, MI; *U.S. Public*, pg. 1504
Rouhana, William J., Jr., Chm. Bd. & Chief Exec. Officer--Winstar Communications, New York, NY; *U.S. Public*, pg. 1772
Rouleau, Mark, Pres. & Chief Exec. Officer--Associated Hosts, Inc., Indianapolis, IN; *Int'l*, pg. 215
Rouleau, Michael, Chief Exec. Officer--Michaels Stores, Inc., Irving, TX; *U.S. Public*, pg. 1104
Rounick, Della, Chm. Bd. & Chief Exec. Officer--The He-Ro Group, Ltd., New York, NY; *U.S. Public*, pg. 801
Rounick, Marvin, Pres., Chief Exec. Officer & Chief Oper. Officer--Deb Shops, Inc., Philadelphia, PA; *U.S. Public*, pg. 491
Rouse, Mitchell, Chm. Bd. & Chief Exec. Officer--Supershuttle Inc., Phoenix, AZ; *U.S. Private*, pg. 1056
Roush, Jack, Chm. Bd. & Chief Exec. Officer--Roush Industries Inc., Livonia, MI; *U.S. Private*, pg. 948
Roussel, Louis J., Jr., Chm. Bd., Pres. & Chief Exec. Officer--Victory Financial Group, Inc., Metairie, LA; *U.S. Private*, pg. 1139
Rousso, Dominic, Chm. Bd., Pres. & Chief Exec. Officer--F.H. Chase, Inc., Mansfield, MA; *U.S. Private*, pg. 230
Routh, Thomas M., Chm. Bd., Pres. & Chief Exec. Officer--J.H. Routh Packing Co., Sandusky, OH; *U.S. Private*, pg. 948
Roux, Michel, Pres. & Chief Exec. Officer--Carillon Importers, Ltd., Fort Lee, NJ; *Int'l*, pg. 409
Roverud, Steven M., Chm. Bd. & Chief Exec. Officer--Trunkline Gas Co., Houston, TX; *U.S. Public*, pg. 534
Rowan, Frederick J., Pres. & Chief Exec. Officer--The William Carter Company, Morrow, GA; *U.S. Private*, pg. 217
Rowan, Henry M., Jr., Chm. Bd., Pres. & Chief Exec. Officer--Inductotherm Industries, Inc., Rancocas, NJ; *U.S. Private*, pg. 560
Rowe, James W., Pres. & Chief Exec. Officer--Defense Credit Union Council, Washington, DC; *U.S. Private*, pg. 288
Rowe, John W., Pres. & Chief Exec. Officer--New England Electric System, Westborough, MA; *U.S. Public*, pg. 1171
Rowe, Josiah P., III, Chm. Bd., Pres., Chief Exec. Officer & Gen. Mgr.--The Free Lance-Star Publishing Co., Fredericksburg, VA; *U.S. Private*, pg. 424
Rowe, William J., Pres., Chief Exec. Officer & Publr.--Greenwich Times, Greenwich, CT; *U.S. Public*, pg. 1616
Rowen, Harold C., Pres. & Chief Exec. Officer--Kinney Shoe Corporation, New York, NY; *U.S. Public*, pg. 1777
Rowland, L.H., Chm. Bd. & Chief Exec. Officer--Kansas City Southern Industries, Inc., Kansas City, MO; *U.S. Public*, pg. 943
Rowland, Lawrence, Pres. & Chief Exec. Officer-Reinsurance--Lincoln National Corporation, Fort Wayne, IN; *U.S. Public*, pg. 997
Rowland, Lawrence, Chm., Pres. & Chief Exec. Officer--Lincoln National Administrative Services Corp., Fort Wayne, IN; *U.S. Public*, pg. 998
Rowland, Lawrence, Chm. Bd. & Chief Exec. Officer--Lincoln National Intermediaries, Inc., Fort Wayne, IN; *U.S. Public*, pg. 998
Rowland, Lawrence, Chm. Bd. & Chief Exec. Officer--Lincoln National Reinsurance Company (Bermuda) Limited, Fort Wayne, IN; *U.S. Public*, pg. 998
Rowland, Lawrence, Chm. & Chief Exec. Officer--Lincoln National Risk Management, Inc., Fort Wayne, IN; *U.S. Public*, pg. 998
Rowland, Lawrence, Chm. & Chief Exec. Officer--Lincoln National Structured Settlement, Inc., Fort Wayne, IN; *U.S. Public*, pg. 998
Rowland, Lawrence, Chm. & Chief Exec. Officer--Old Fort Insurance Co., Ltd. (Bermuda), Hamilton, Bermuda; *U.S. Public*, pg. 998
Rowland, Lawrence, Chm. & Chief Exec. Officer--Underwriters & Management Services Inc., Indianapolis, IN; *U.S. Public*, pg. 998
Rowley, Ivan R., Pres. & Chief Exec. Officer--Astra USA, Inc., Westborough, MA; *Int'l*, pg. 93
Rowley, Ronald L., Pres. & Chief Exec. Officer--BCP Technical Service, Inc., Gretna, LA; *U.S. Private*, pg. 106
Roy, Louise, Pres. & Chief Exec. Officer--Telemedia Inc., Montreal, Canada; *Int'l*, pg. 1373
Roy, Xavier, Chief Exec.--Reed MIDEM Organisation S.A., Paris, France; *Int'l*, pg. 1097
Royall, Rovert V., Jr., Chm. Bd. & Chief Exec. Officer--NBSC Corporation, Columbia, SC; *U.S. Public*, pg. 1549
Royse, John N., Chm. Bd. & Chief Exec. Officer--Old National Bancorp, Evansville, IN; *U.S. Public*, pg. 1217
Rozar, Rick L., Pres. & Chief Exec. Officer--CDB Infotec Inc., Santa Ana, CA; *U.S. Private*, pg. 193
Rubeli, Paul E., Chm. Bd., Pres. & Chief Exec. Officer--Aztar Corporation, Phoenix, AZ; *U.S. Public*, pg. 158
Rubenstein, Leonard M., Chm. Bd. & Chief Exec. Officer--Conning, Hartford, CT; *U.S. Private*, pg. 443
Rubenstein, Stephen, Pres. & Chief Exec. Officer--JB Oxford Holdings Inc., Beverly Hills, CA; *U.S. Public*, pg. 916
Ruberg, Werner, Chm. Bd. & Chief Exec. Officer--Owens-Corning Eternit Rohre GmbH, Aachen, Germany; *U.S. Public*, pg. 1237
Rubin, Gerald J., Chm. Bd. & Chief Exec. Officer--Helen of Troy Corporation, El Paso, TX; *U.S. Public*, pg. 807
Rubin, Gerrold R., Pres. & Chief Exec. Officer--Rubin Postaer & Associates, Santa Monica, CA; *U.S. Private*, pg. 949
Rubin, Joel, Chm. Bd. & Chief Exec. Officer--Phototype Color Graphics, Inc., Pennsauken, NJ; *U.S. Private*, pg. 864
Rubin, Joseph H., Pres. & Chief Exec. Officer--Abrams Industries, Inc., Atlanta, GA; *U.S. Public*, pg. 14
Rubin, Lewis, Pres. & Chief Exec. Officer--Xtra Corporation, Boston, MA; *U.S. Public*, pg. 1786
Rubin, Michael G., Chm. Bd. & Chief Exec. Officer--Ryka Incorporated, King of Prussia, PA; *U.S. Public*, pg. 1414
Rubin, Robert M., Chm. Bd. & Chief Exec. Officer--ERD Waste Corp., Commack, NY; *U.S. Public*, pg. 546
Rubner, David, Pres. & Chief Exec. Officer--ECI Telecom Ltd., Petah Tiqwa, Israel; *Int'l*, pg. 643
Rubow, Steven, Pres. & Chief Exec. Officer--Topco Associates, Inc., Skokie, IL; *U.S. Private*, pg. 1091
Ruckmar, J., Chief Exec. Officer--Zurich Insurance (Malaysia) Sdn. Bhd., Kuala Lumpur, Malaysia; *Int'l*, pg. 1532
Ruckriegel, Robert, Pres.--BR Associates, Inc., Jasper, IN; *U.S. Private*, pg. 107
Ruda, Kevin, Pres. & Chief Exec. Officer--Beatrice Cheese Co., Waukesha, WI; *U.S. Public*, pg. 426
Rudd, Andrew, Chm. Bd. & Chief Exec. Officer--Barra, Inc., Berkeley, CA; *U.S. Public*, pg. 191
Rude, Antone J., Chief Exec. Officer, Exec. V.P. & Gen. Mgr.--United Power Association, Elk River, MN; *U.S. Private*, pg. 1123
Rudgard, J.K., Chief Exec. Officer--H.P. Bulmer Holdings Plc, Hereford, United Kingdom; *Int'l*, pg. 232
Rudge, Alan W., Dr., Deputy Chief Exec.--British Telecommunications plc, London, United Kingdom; *Int'l*, pg. 222
Rudis, Jim, Pres. & Chief Exec. Officer--Overhill Farms, Inc., Culver City, CA; *U.S. Public*, pg. 1315
Rudloff, Jean, Chief Exec. Officer--Jallatte S.A., Saint Hippolyte-du-Fort, France; *Int'l*, pg. 430
Rudolph, Frederick W., Chief Exec. Officer--Rudolph/Libbe, Inc., Walbridge, OH; *U.S. Private*, pg. 950
Rudolph, James E., Pres. & Chief Exec. Officer--Rudolph Foods Company, Lima, OH; *U.S. Private*, pg. 950
Rudolph, Scott, Chm. Bd., Pres., Chief Exec. Officer & Chief Oper. Officer--Nature's Bounty Inc., Bohemia, NY; *U.S. Public*, pg. 1166

Rudston, Tony, Chief Exec. Officer--British Printing Company Ltd., London, United Kingdom; *Int'l*, pg. 220
Ruegg, Hans R., Pres. & Chief Exec. Officer--Baumann Federn AG, Ruti, Switzerland; *Int'l*, pg. 171
Ruepp, Rene K., Dr., Chm. Bd. & Chief Exec. Officer--Forbo Holding SA, Eglisau, Switzerland; *Int'l*, pg. 496
Ruettgers, Michael C., Pres. & Chief Exec. Officer--EMC Corporation, Hopkinton, MA; *U.S. Public*, pg. 545
Ruf, Dave G., Jr., Chm. Bd. & Chief Exec. Officer--Burns & McDonnell Engineers-Architects-Consultants, Kansas City, MO; *U.S. Private*, pg. 187
Rufeh, Firooz, Chief Exec. Officer--Thermolase, San Diego, CA; *U.S. Public*, pg. 1595
Ruffolo, Ugo, Chief Exec. Officer & Dir. Gen.--Banca Fideuran S.p.A., Rome, Italy; *Int'l*, pg. 692
Ruger, William B., Chm. Bd., Chief Exec. Officer & Treas.--Sturm, Ruger & Co., Inc., Southport, CT; *U.S. Public*, pg. 1526
Ruhle, Frank S., Chm. Bd., Pres. & Chief Exec. Officer--Ruhle Companies, Inc., Valhalla, NY; *U.S. Private*, pg. 950
Ruhlman, Jon R., Chm. Bd. & Chief Exec. Officer--Preformed Line Products, Cleveland, OH; *U.S. Public*, pg. 1321
Ruhlman, Terrell L., Chm. Bd. & Chief Exec. Officer--Cade Industries, Inc., Lansing, MI; *U.S. Public*, pg. 289
Ruiz Nicoli, Pedro, Chm. & Chief Exec. Officer--Ruiz Nicoli Group, Madrid, Spain; *Int'l*, pg. 603
Ruiz, Fred, Chm. Bd. & Chief Exec. Officer--Ruiz Food Products, Inc., Dinuba, CA; *U.S. Private*, pg. 951
Rukeyser, S., Chm. Bd., Chief Exec. Officer & Editor-in-Chief--Whittle Communications L.P., Knoxville, TN; *U.S. Public*, pg. 1614
Rule, Ronald C., Chm. Bd., Pres. & Chief Exec. Officer--The United States Playing Card Company, Cincinnati, OH; *U.S. Private*, pg. 1125
Rullo, Fred P., Chm. Bd. & Chief Exec. Officer--Freedom Chemical Company, Radnor, PA; *U.S. Private*, pg. 425
Rumble, R.M., Pres. & Chief Exec. Officer--MediVators, Inc., Eagan, MN; *U.S. Public*, pg. 301
Rummell, Grant D., Pres. & Chief Exec. Officer--Linear Corporation, Carlsbad, CA; *U.S. Public*, pg. 1193
Rumy, Zsolt, Chm. Bd., Pres. & Chief Exec. Officer--Zoltek Companies, Inc., Saint Louis, MO; *U.S. Public*, pg. 1794
Rundell, C.A., Jr., Pres. & Chief Exec. Officer--Tyler Corporation, Dallas, TX; *U.S. Public*, pg. 1651
Rupp, Barry, Chm. Bd. & Chief Exec. Officer--Financial World Partners, New York, NY; *U.S. Private*, pg. 404
Rupp, Glenn R., Chm. Bd., Pres. & Chief Exec. Officer--Converse Inc., North Reading, MA; *U.S. Public*, pg. 441
Ruppel, Ferdinand A., Jr., Pres. & Chief Exec. Officer--Westminster Bank & Trust Co. of Carroll County, Westminster, MD; *U.S. Public*, pg. 1089
Rus, Arlyn D., Chm. Bd., Pres. & Chief Exec. Officer--Raritan Bancorp Inc., Bridgewater, NJ; *U.S. Public*, pg. 1361
Rusbridge, Michael, Chm. & Chief Exec. Officer--Reed Exhibition Companies, Richmond, United Kingdom; *Int'l*, pg. 1096
Rusch, Freeland, Chm. Bd. & Chief Exec. Officer--M & I Merchants Bank, Rhinelander, WI; *U.S. Public*, pg. 1050
Rush, Carl V., Jr., Pres. & Chief Exec. Officer--The GNI Group, Inc., Deer Park, TX; *U.S. Public*, pg. 693
Rush, William J., Chief Exec. Officer, Publr. & V.P.--Journal Register Company, Trenton, NJ; *U.S. Public*, pg. 934
Rush, William J., Chief Exec. Officer & Publr.--New Haven Register, Inc., New Haven, CT; *U.S. Public*, pg. 935
Russ, Jim, Chief Exec. Officer--Bardon USA Inc., Greenbelt, MD; *Int'l*, pg. 166
Russ, Robert, Pres. & Co-Chief Exec. Officer--Diablo Research Corporation, Sunnyvale, CA; *U.S. Public*, pg. 1424
Russek, Michael, Chief Oper. & Fin. Officer--Astronautics Corporation of America, Milwaukee, WI; *U.S. Private*, pg. 93
Russel, Terence A., Pres. & Chief Exec. Officer--Morgan Drive Away, Inc., Elkhart, IN; *U.S. Public*, pg. 1022
Russell, Ed, Chm. Bd., Pres. & Chief Exec. Officer--Minnesota Power, Duluth, MN; *U.S. Public*, pg. 1116
Russell, John R., Pres. & Chief Exec. Officer--Western Atlas Inc., Houston, TX; *U.S. Public*, pg. 1757
Russell, John, Jr., Chm., Pres. & Chief Exec. Officer-Hospitality Div.--HFS, Incorporated, Parsippany, NJ; *U.S. Public*, pg. 321
Russell, Richard, Chief Oper. Officer--General Chemical (Soda Ash) Partners, Parsippany, NJ; *Int'l*, pg. 1407
Russell, Richard C., Pres. & Chief Exec. Officer--The Danis Companies, Dayton, OH; *U.S. Private*, pg. 310
Russell, Richard F., Pres. & Chief Exec. Officer--Amerisure Companies, Farmington Hills, MI; *U.S. Private*, pg. 65
Russell, Richard G., Chm. Bd., Pres. & Chief Exec. Officer--Tech Spray, Inc., Amarillo, TX; *U.S. Private*, pg. 1071
Russell, Richard R., Pres., Chief Exec. Officer & Mng. Dir.--The General Chemical Group, Inc., Hampton, NH; *U.S. Public*, pg. 707
Russell, Wayland, Chief Exec. Officer--Rainbow Rentals, Inc., Canfield, OH; *U.S. Private*, pg. 907
Russo, Thomas, Pres. & Chief Exec. Officer--Fyrnetics, Inc., Roselle, IL; *Int'l*, pg. 1499
Rust, Edward B., Jr., Chm. Bd., Pres. & Chief Exec. Officer--State Farm Mutual Automobile Insurance Company, Bloomington, IL; *U.S. Private*, pg. 1036
Rust, Lois, Pres. & Chief Exec. Officer--Rose Acre Farms, Seymour, IN; *U.S. Private*, pg. 944
Rustand, Warren, Chm. Bd. & Chief Exec. Officer--Rural Metro Corporation, Scottsdale, AZ; *U.S. Public*, pg. 1412
Rutherford, J. Larry, Pres. & Chief Exec. Officer--Atlantic Gulf Communities Corporation, Miami, FL; *U.S. Public*, pg. 144
Rutland, Robert J., Chm. Bd. & Chief Exec. Officer--Allied Holdings, Inc., Decatur, GA; *U.S. Public*, pg. 48
Rutland, Robert J., Chm. Bd. & Chief Exec. Officer--Allied Automotive Group, Decatur, GA; *U.S. Public*, pg. 48
Rutledge, A. Bradley, Pres. & Chief Exec. Officer--Regions Bank/Pickens County, Jasper, GA; *U.S. Public*, pg. 1372
Rutledge, Phillip, Pres. & Chief Exec. Officer-Pizza Hut Grp.--Lundy Enterprises, Inc., New Orleans, LA; *U.S. Private*, pg. 681
Rutledge, William A., Pres. & Chief Exec. Officer--Farmers Mutual Hail Insurance Co. of Iowa, Des Moines, IA; *U.S. Private*, pg. 395
Ruttenberg, Harold J., Chm. Bd., Principal Acctg. Officer, Chief Exec. Officer & Treas.--American Locker Group, Inc., Jamestown, NY; *U.S. Public*, pg. 85
Ruud, Tom, Pres. & Chief Exec. Officer--Aker Raj Asa, Oslo, Norway; *Int'l*, pg. 41
Ruud, Tom, Pres. & Chief Exec. Officer--Christiania Bank og Kreditkasse ASA, Oslo, Norway; *Int'l*, pg. 289
Ryan, Arthur F., Chm. Bd. & Chief Exec. Officer--The Prudential Insurance Company of America, Newark, NJ; *U.S. Private*, pg. 892
Ryan, Arthur F., Chm. Bd., Pres. & Chief Exec. Officer--The Prudential Investment Corp., Newark, NJ; *U.S. Private*, pg. 892
Ryan, Ashton J., Jr., Pres. & Chief Exec. Officer--First National Bank of Commerce, New Orleans, LA; *U.S. Public*, pg. 629
Ryan, Brendan, Chm. & Chief Exec. Officer--FCB, New York, NY; *U.S. Private*, pg. 389
Ryan, Brendan, Chm. & Chief Exec. Officer-FCB Worldwide--True North Communications Inc., Chicago, IL; *U.S. Public*, pg. 1641
Ryan, Edward R., Pres. & Chief Exec. Officer--Sandusky International Inc., Sandusky, OH; *U.S. Private*, pg. 964
Ryan, James N., Chm. Bd. & Chief Exec. Officer--Petroleum Development Corporation, Bridgeport, WV; *U.S. Public*, pg. 1280
Ryan, Jim, Chm. Bd. & Chief Exec. Officer--BWC Financial Corp., Walnut Creek, CA; *U.S. Private*, pg. 108
Ryan, Jim, Chief Exec. Officer--Ryan Construction Company of Minnesota, Inc., Minneapolis, MN; *U.S. Private*, pg. 953
Ryan, John D., Pres. & Chief Exec. Officer--Worldvision Enterprises, New York, NY; *U.S. Private*, pg. 776
Ryan, John G., Chm. Bd. & Chief Exec. Officer--Global Marine Drilling Co., Houston, TX; *U.S. Public*, pg. 748
Ryan, John T., III, Chm. Bd. & Chief Exec. Officer--Mine Safety Appliances Co., Pittsburgh, PA; *U.S. Public*, pg. 1114
Ryan, Kevin, Pres. & Chief Exec. Officer--Wesley-Jessen, Des Plaines, IL; *U.S. Private*, pg. 111
Ryan, Kevin, Pres. & Chief Exec. Officer--Pilkington Barnes Hind (PBH), San Diego, CA; *U.S. Private*, pg. 111
Ryan, Matthew, Pres. & Chief Exec. Officer--Ryan Drossman & Partners, New York, NY; *U.S. Private*, pg. 953
Ryan, Patrick G., Chm. Bd., Pres. & Chief Exec. Officer--AON Corporation, Chicago, IL; *U.S. Public*, pg. 117
Ryan, Patrick G., Chm. & Chief Exec. Officer--AON Risk Services Inc. of Illinois, Chicago, IL; *U.S. Public*, pg. 117
Ryan, Patrick M.A., Chief Exec. Officer--Bank of Ireland International Services Limited, Dublin, Ireland; *Int'l*, pg. 152
Ryan, Stephen F., Pres. & Chief Exec. Officer--Selas Corporation of America, Dresher, PA; *U.S. Public*, pg. 1454
Ryan, T.A., Chm. & Chief Exec. Officer--GPA Group PLC, Shannon, Ireland; *Int'l*, pg. 37
Ryan, Thomas M., Vice Chm., Pres., Chief Exec. Officer & Chief Oper. Officer-CVS--CVS Corp., Woonsocket, RI; *U.S. Public*, pg. 287
Ryan, W.P., Chief Exec. Officer--Rothmans UK Holdings Limited, London, United Kingdom; *Int'l*, pg. 1129
Ryan, William A., Chm. Bd., Pres. & Chief Exec. Officer--Team, Inc., Alvin, TX; *U.S. Public*, pg. 1562
Ryan, William J., Chm. Bd., Pres. & Chief Exec. Officer--Peoples Heritage Financial Group, Inc., Portland, ME; *U.S. Public*, pg. 1275
Ryder, Robert G., Pres. & Chief Exec. Officer--The First National Bank of Lake Charles, Lake Charles, LA; *U.S. Public*, pg. 630
Rydholm, Ralph W., Chief Exec. Officer--EURO RSCG Tatham, Chicago, IL; *Int'l*, pg. 601
Rye, Walter L., Chm. Bd. & Chief Exec. Officer--Cincinnati Gear Company, Cincinnati, OH; *U.S. Private*, pg. 240
Ryker, Gary E., Pres. & Chief Exec. Officer--Union Switch & Signal Inc., Pittsburgh, PA; *Int'l*, pg. 77
Rynone, Thomas E., Chief Exec. Officer--Rynone Manufacturing Corporation, Sayre, PA; *U.S. Private*, pg. 953
Ryzman, Zvi, Pres. & Chief Exec. Officer--American International Industries, City of Commerce, CA; *U.S. Private*, pg. 57
Ryzman, Zvi, Pres. & Chief Exec. Officer--Andrea International, City of Commerce, CA; *U.S. Private*, pg. 57
Ryzman, Zvi, Pres. & Chief Exec. Officer--All Clubman, City of Commerce, CA; *U.S. Private*, pg. 57
Ryzman, Zvi, Pres. & Chief Exec. Officer--Delore, City of Commerce, CA; *U.S. Private*, pg. 57
Ryzman, Zvi, Pres. & Chief Exec. Officer--GiGi, City of Commerce, CA; *U.S. Private*, pg. 57
Ryzman, Zvi, Pres. & Chief Exec. Officer--SuperNail, City of Commerce, CA; *U.S. Private*, pg. 57
Ryzman, Zvi, Pres. & Chief Exec. Officer--Ardell International, Inc., City of Industry, CA; *U.S. Private*, pg. 57
Saban, Haim, Chief Exec. Officer--Fox Kids Worldwide, Los Angeles, CA; *Int'l*, pg. 927
Saban, Hiam, Chm. Bd. & Chief Exec. Officer--Saban Entertainment, Los Angeles, CA; *U.S. Private*, pg. 959
Sabatino, Victor, Chm. Bd., Pres. & Chief Exec. Officer--Family Smacks, Inc., Liberty, MO; *U.S. Private*, pg. 393
Sacco, Donald, Pres. & Chief Exec. Officer--Regence BlueCross BlueShield of Oregon, Portland, OR; *U.S. Private*, pg. 917
Sachs, Bruce I., Pres. & Chief Exec. Officer--Stratus Computer, Inc., Marlborough, MA; *U.S. Public*, pg. 1524
Sachs, Philip E., Pres. & Chief Exec. Officer--Legg Mason Capital Management Inc., Baltimore, MD; *U.S. Public*, pg. 985
Sachse, Rich, Pres. & Chief Exec. Officer--Woodcraft Industries, Inc., Saint Cloud, MN; *U.S. Private*, pg. 1187
Sack, Han, Pres. & Chief Exec. Officer--Latrobe Steel Company, Latrobe, PA; *U.S. Public*, pg. 1617
Sack, Thomas F., Pres., Chief Exec. Officer & Chief Oper. Officer--Haddon Craftsmen, Inc., Scranton, PA; *U.S. Public*, pg. 518
Sada, Tomas Gonzalez, Chief Exec. Officer--CYDSA S.A., Garza Garcia, Mexico; *Int'l*, pg. 246
Sada, Tomas Gonzalez, Chief Exec. Officer--Grupo Cydsa, S.A. de C.V., Garza Garcia, Mexico; *Int'l*, pg. 246
Sadler, Mike, Pres. & Chief Exec. Officer--SF Services, North Little Rock, AR; *U.S. Private*, pg. 956
Sadler, Robert L., Pres. & Chief Exec. Officer--Old Kent Bank, Grand Rapids, MI; *U.S. Public*, pg. 1216
Sage, G.H., Chief Oper. Officer--RTZ Pillar Ltd., London, United Kingdom; *Int'l*, pg. 267
Sahakian, Henry D., Chm. Bd. & Chief Exec. Officer--Uni-Marts, Inc., State College, PA; *U.S. Public*, pg. 1664
Sahm, Roland R., Chm. Bd. & Chief Exec. Officer--Elixir Industries, Gardena, CA; *U.S. Private*, pg. 371
Sai, E. Wang Tong, Chief Exec. Offficer-China--The Hongkong and Shanghai Banking Corporation Limited (HongkongBank), Central, Hong Kong; *Int'l*, pg. 583
Sainsbury, D.J., Chm. & Chief Exec.--J. Sainsbury plc, London, United Kingdom; *Int'l*, pg. 1169
Saint-Pierre, Guy, Pres. & Chief Exec. Officer--SNC-Lavalin Inc., Montreal, Canada; *Int'l*, pg. 1162
Sainz, Pedro L., Chief Oper. Officer--Baumann Muelles, S.A., Legutiano, Spain; *Int'l*, pg. 171
Saito, Hiroyuki, Chief Exec. Officer--Novo Nordisk Bioindustry Ltd, Chiba, Japan; *Int'l*, pg. 989
Saito, Joichi, Chm. Bd. & Chief Exec. Officer--CPB Inc., Honolulu, HI; *U.S. Public*, pg. 282
Saito, Joichi, Chm. Bd. & Chief Exec. Officer--Central Pacific Bank, Honolulu, HI; *U.S. Public*, pg. 283
Saito, Shichiro, Pres. & Chief Exec. Officer--Mitsui & Co. (Canada), Montreal, Canada; *Int'l*, pg. 880
Saiz, Guillermo, Chief Exec.--Banco Santander, Buenos Aires, Argentina; *Int'l*, pg. 144
Sakai, Hideki, Pres. & Chief Exec. Officer--Hirose Electric Co., Ltd., Tokyo, Japan; *Int'l*, pg. 620
Sakai, Hiro, Chief Exec. Officer--Mutoh America Inc., Phoenix, AZ; *Int'l*, pg. 897
Sakami, Tomio, Chief Oper. Officer--Kabushiki Kaisha TMK, Toyohashi, Japan; *Int'l*, pg. 831
Saker, Joseph J., Chm. Bd. & Pres.--Foodarama Supermarkets, Inc., Freehold, NJ; *U.S. Public*, pg. 661
Sakogawa, Ridai, Pres. & Chief Exec. Officer--TOHO Mutual Life Insurance Company, Tokyo, Japan; *Int'l*, pg. 1390
Salameh, Samer, Pres. & Chief Exec. Officer--Prodigy Inc., White Plains, NY; *U.S. Private*, pg. 888
Salamone, Anthony, Pres.--Sunroc Corporation, Dover, DE; *U.S. Private*, pg. 1053
Salazar, Rogelio C., Pres. & Chief Exec. Officer--Atlas Consolidated Mining & Development Corporation, Manila, Philippines; *Int'l*, pg. 95
Salizzoni, Frank L., Pres. & Chief Exec. Officer--H & R Block, Inc., Kansas City, MO; *U.S. Public*, pg. 770
Sall, Hyman L., Chm. Bd. & Chief Exec. Officer--Atlantic Metals Corporation, Philadelphia, PA; *U.S. Private*, pg. 95
Salles, Paulo, Pres. & Chief Exec. Officer--Salles/DMB&B Publicidade S.A., Sao Paulo, Brazil; *U.S. Private*, pg. 305
Salman, Steven L., Pres. & Chief Exec. Officer--Kentucky Medical Insurance Company (KMIC), Louisville, KY; *U.S. Private*, pg. 741
Salminen, Matti, Chief Exec. Officer--Raisio Group, Raisio, Finland; *Int'l*, pg. 1085
Salsbury, Phillip J., Dr., Pres. & Chief Exec. Officer--SEEQ Technology Inc., Fremont, CA; *U.S. Public*, pg. 1417
Saltzman, Robert, Pres. & Chief Exec. Officer--Jackson National Life Insurance Company, Lansing, MI; *Int'l*, pg. 1073
Salvatori, Carlo, Chief Exec. Officer--Cassa di Risparmio delle Provincie Lombarde SpA (CARIPLO), Milan, Italy; *Int'l*, pg. 274
Samberg, Stephen, Chm. Bd. & Chief Exec. Officer--Nantucket Industries, Inc., Melville, NY; *U.S. Public*, pg. 1151
Sambol, David, Pres. & Chief Exec. Officer--Countrywide Capital Markets, Inc., Pasadena, CA; *U.S. Public*, pg. 453
Samburg, A. Gene, Chm. Bd., Pres. & Chief Exec. Officer--Kastle Systems LLC, Arlington, VA; *U.S. Private*, pg. 608
Samis, Michael S., Pres. & Chief Exec. Officer--Macklanburg-Duncan Co., Oklahoma City, OK; *U.S. Private*, pg. 692
Sammon, Dr. John W., Jr., Chm. Bd., Pres. & Chief Exec. Officer--PAR Technology Corporation, New Hartford, NY; *U.S. Public*, pg. 1256
Sample, David, Chm. Bd., Pres. & Chief Exec. Officer--PSDI, Bedford, MA; *U.S. Private*, pg. 828
Sampson, Curtis A., Chm. Bd., Pres. & Chief Exec. Officer--Communications Systems, Inc., Hector, MN; *U.S. Public*, pg. 415
Sampson, Curtis A., Chm., Pres. & Chief Exec. Officer--Suttle Caribe, Inc., Humacao, PR; *U.S. Public*, pg. 415
San Antonio, Joel, Chm. Bd. & Chief Exec. Officer--Warrantech Corporation, Stamford, CT; *U.S. Public*, pg. 1740
San, Lim Hock, Pres. & Chief Exec. Officer--Singapore Land Limited, Singapore, Singapore; *Int'l*, pg. 1252
Sanborn, Bruce, Chm. Bd. & Chief Exec. Officer--Financial Life Companies, Inc., Saint Paul, MN; *U.S. Private*, pg. 404
Sanders, E. Craig, Chm. Bd., Pres. & Chief Exec. Officer--Peoples Telephone Company, Inc., Miami, FL; *U.S. Public*, pg. 1275

Sanders, Harvey, Chm. Bd., Pres. & Chief Exec. Officer--Nautica Enterprises, Inc., New York, NY; *U.S. Public*, pg. 1167
Sanders, James N., Mng. Dir. & Chief Exec. Officer--Ansaldo Signal N.V., Amsterdam, Netherlands; *Int'l*, pg. 77
Sanders, Lewis A., Chm. Bd. & Chief Exec. Officer--Sanford C. Bernstein & Co., Inc., New York, NY; *U.S. Private*, pg. 137
Sanders, Mark, Pres. & Chief Exec. Officer--Pinnacle Systems, Inc., Mountain View, CA; *U.S. Public*, pg. 1297
Sanders, Max D., Chm. Bd. & Chief Exec. Officer--Ohmite Manufacturing Company, Skokie, IL; *U.S. Private*, pg. 813
Sanders, O'Neil, Chm. Bd., Pres., Chief Exec. & Chief Oper. Officer--Associated Petroleum Carriers, Spartanburg, SC; *U.S. Private*, pg. 92
Sanders, Tom, Chief Exec. Officer--MMC Corp., Leawood, KS; *U.S. Private*, pg. 687
Sanders, W.J., III, Chm. Bd. & Chief Exec. Officer--Advanced Micro Devices, Inc., Sunnyvale, CA; *U.S. Public*, pg. 21
Sanders, Wayne R., Chm. Bd. & Chief Exec. Officer--Kimberly-Clark Corporation, Dallas, TX; *U.S. Public*, pg. 958
Sanders, William D., Chm. Bd., Pres. & Chief Exec. Officer--Security Capital Group Incorporated, Santa Fe, NM; *U.S.* Private, pg. 980
Sanderson, Joe F., Jr., Pres. & Chief Exec. Officer--Sanderson Farms, Inc., Laurel, MS; *U.S. Public*, pg. 1430
Sanderson, Jr., Robert C., Pres. & Chief Exec. Officer--Citizens Bank Of Connecticut, New London, CT; *Int'l*, pg. 1132
Sanderson, Michael, Pres. & Chief Exec. Officer--Instinet Corporation, New York, NY; *Int'l*, pg. 1106
Sanderson, Mike, Pres. & Chief Exec. Officer--Chronos Richardson, Fairfield, NJ; *Int'l*, pg. 1299
Sanderson, Sandra B., Pres. & Chief Exec. Officer--Sanderson Plumbing Products Inc., Columbus, MS; *U.S. Private*, pg. 964
Sandhu, M.S., Chm. Bd., Pres. & Chief Exec. Officer--SRS Technologies, Newport Beach, CA; *U.S. Private*, pg. 958
Sandifer, Thomas N., Chm. & Chief Exec. Officer--Cain & Bultman, Jacksonville, FL; *U.S. Private*, pg. 199
Sandifur, C. Paul, Jr., Pres. & Chief Exec. Officer--Metropolitan Mortgage & Securities Co., Inc., Spokane, WA; *U.S. Private*, pg. 738
Sandkuyl, A., Chief Exec. Officer--Zurich Levensverzekering-Maatschappij, Hague, Netherlands; *Int'l*, pg. 1529
Sandkuyl, A., Chief Exec. Officer--Zurich Verzekeringen, Leidschendam, Netherlands; *Int'l*, pg. 1531
Sandkuyl, A., Chief Exec. Officer--Zurich International (Nederland) N.V., Leidschendam, Netherlands; *Int'l*, pg. 1532
Sandler, Herbert M., Chm. Bd. & Co-Chief Exec. Officer--Golden West Financial Corporation, Oakland, CA; *U.S. Public*, pg. 750
Sandler, Herbert M., Chm. Bd. & Chief Exec. Officer--World Savings & Loan Association, FSLA, Oakland, CA; *U.S. Public*, pg. 750
Sandler, Herbert M., Chm. Bd. & Chief Exec. Officer--World Savings Bank, FSB, Oakland, CA; *U.S. Public*, pg. 750
Sandler, Marion O., Chm. Bd. & Co-Chief Exec. Officer--Golden West Financial Corporation, Oakland, CA; *U.S. Public*, pg. 750
Sandler, Marion O., Chm. Bd. & Chief Exec. Officer--World Savings Bank, FSB, Oakland, CA; *U.S. Public*, pg. 750
Sandor, Thomas L., Pres. & Chief Exec. Officer--Superior Group, Inc., Radnor, PA; *U.S. Private*, pg. 1055
Sands, Richard, Pres. & Chief Exec. Officer--Canandaigua Wine Company, Inc., Canandaigua, NY; *U.S. Public*, pg. 300
Sanfilippo, Jasper, Chm. Bd. & Chief Exec. Officer--John B. Sanfilippo & Son, Inc., Elk Grove Village, IL; *U.S. Public*, pg. 1431
Sanford, Philip H., Chm. Bd. & Chief Exec. Officer--Krystal Company, Chattanooga, TN; *U.S. Private*, pg. 636
Sanford, Richard D., Chm. Bd. & Chief Exec. Officer--Intelligent Electronics, Inc., Exton, PA; *U.S. Public*, pg. 887
Sanger, Stephen W., Chm. Bd. & Chief Exec. Officer--General Mills, Inc., Minneapolis, MN; *U.S. Public*, pg. 717
Sanghi, Steve, Chm. Bd., Pres. & Chief Exec. Officer--Microchip Technology, Inc., Chandler, AZ; *U.S. Public*, pg. 1105
Sangiacomo, Michael J., Pres. & Chief Exec. Officer--Norcal Waste Systems, San Francisco, CA; *U.S. Public*, pg. 1188
Sankey, Vernon L., Chief Exec.--Reckitt & Colman plc, London, United Kingdom; *Int'l*, pg. 1089
Sankpill, L. Alan, Pres. & Chief Exec. Officer--U.S. Safety, Lenexa, KS; *U.S. Private*, pg. 1125
Sansom, William B., Chm. Bd. & Chief Exec. Officer--The H.T. Hackney Co., Knoxville, TN; *U.S. Private*, pg. 493
Sansone, Paul, Pres. & Chief Exec. Officer--Sansone Auto Mall, Avenel, NJ; *U.S. Private*, pg. 965
Sant, Stephen R., Pres. & Chief Exec. Officer--First Western Bank, National Association, New Castle, PA; *U.S. Public*, pg. 642
Santamarina, R., Chief Exec. Officer--Zurich Compania de Seguros, Buenos Aires, Argentina; *Int'l*, pg. 1531
Santamarina, R., Chief Exec. Officer--Iguazu Compania de Seguros, Buenos Aires, Argentina; *Int'l*, pg. 1531
Santhidej, S., Chief Exec. Officer--OCE (Thailand) Ltd., Bangkok, Thailand; *Int'l*, pg. 995
Santos, Everaldo N., Pres. & Chief Exec. Officer--Alcan Empreendimentos Ltda., Sao Paulo, Brazil; *Int'l*, pg. 50
Santry, Michael G., Chm. Bd., Pres. & Chief Exec. Officer--ATC Communications Group, Inc., Dallas, TX; *U.S. Public*, pg. 11
Santulli, Richard T., Chm. Bd., Pres. & Chief Exec. Officer--Executive Jet Aviation, Inc., Columbus, OH; *U.S. Private*, *pg. 388*
Saper, Lawrence, Chm. Bd., Pres. & Chief Exec. Officer--Datascope Corp., Montvale, NJ; *U.S. Public*, pg. 487
Sapos, Mary Ann, Pres. & Chief Exec. Officer--Hutchins/Young & Rubicam, Rochester, NY; *U.S. Private*, pg. 1197
Sappington, Donald, Pres. & Chief Exec. Officer--C.F. Hathaway, Waterville, ME; *U.S. Private*, pg. 510
Sardas, Jack, Chm. Bd. & Chief Exec. Officer--Dal-Tile International, Dallas, TX; *U.S. Private*, pg. 308
Sardas, Jack, Chief Exec. Officer--Dal-Tile Corp., Dallas, TX; *U.S. Private*, pg. 308
Sardas, Jack, Chief Exec. Officer--Dal Keystone, Gettysburg, PA; *U.S. Private*, pg. 308
Sardina, Eduardo M., Pres. & Chief Exec. Officer--Bacardi-Martini U.S.A., Inc., Miami, FL; *Int'l*, pg. 131
Sardina, Edvardo, Pres. & Chief Exec. Officer--Bacardi-Martini, USA, Inc., Miami, FL; *U.S. Private*, pg. 109
Sargent, Charles L., Chm. Bd. & Chief Exec. Officer--Thetford Corporation, Ann Arbor, MI; *U.S. Private*, pg. 352
Sargent, John, Pres. & Chief Exec. Officer--DK Publishing, New York, NY; *Int'l*, pg. 417
Sargent, John, Chm. Bd., Chief Exec. Officer & Editorial Dir.--St. Martins Press, Inc., New York, NY; *Int'l*, pg. 1479
Sargent, Joseph D., Pres. & Chief Exec. Officer--The Guardian Life Insurance Company of America, New York, NY; *U.S. Private*, pg. 486
Sargent, Lee M., Pres. & Chief Exec. Officer--Todd & Sargent, Inc., Ames, IA; *U.S. Private*, pg. 1089
Sarkes, H. Jay, Chm. Bd., Pres. & Chief Exec. Officer--Fleet Bank, N.A., Jersey City, NJ; *U.S. Public*, pg. 649
Sarkisian, Norman,, Owner, Pres. & Chief Exec. Officer--Beacon Group, Bloomfield, CT; *U.S. Private*, pg. 126
Sarkisian, Robert, Chm. Bd., Pres. & Chief Exec. Officer--Marketing Displays International, Farmington Hills, MI; *U.S. Private*, pg. 705
Sarmanian, Peter, Chm. Bd. & Chief Exec. Officer--Printed Circuit Corporation, Woburn, MA; *U.S. Private*, pg. 886
Sarrat, Fernand B., Pres. & Chief Exec. Officer--Cylink Corp., Sunnyvale, CA; *U.S. Public*, pg. 1306
Sassenrath, Bernd, Chief Exec. Officer--Ticona Polymerwerke GmbH, Kelsterbach, Germany; *Int'l*, pg. 624
Sasso, John, Pres. & Chief Exec. Officer--Fire Burglary Instruments, Inc., Syosset, NY; *U.S. Public*, pg. 1306
Sasson, Ori, Chief Exec. Officer--Scopus Technology, Inc., Emeryville, CA; *U.S. Public*, pg. 1444
Sassos, Thomas P., Chief Exec. Officer--VSM, Inc., New York, NY; *U.S. Private*, pg. 1130
Satcher, James R., Pres. & Chief Exec. Officer--Southland Oil Company, Jackson, MS; *U.S. Private*, pg. 1018
Sato, Hiroshi, Pres.--TDK Corporation, Tokyo, Japan; *Int'l*, pg. 1336
Sato, Isao, Pres. & Chief Exec. Officer--Hosokawa Micron International Inc., New York, NY; *Int'l*, pg. 635
Sato, Tetsuya, Chief Exec. Officer--Toshoku Ltd., Tokyo, Japan; *Int'l*, pg. 1407
Satre, Philip G., Chm. Bd., Pres. & Chief Exec. Officer--Harrah's Entertainment, Inc., Memphis, TN; *U.S. Public*, pg. 790
Satrum, Jerry R., Chief Exec. Officer--Georgia Gulf Corporation, Atlanta, GA; *U.S. Public*, pg. 734
Saubert, Walter E., Chm. Bd. & Chief Exec. Officer--Atlas World Group, Inc., Evansville, IN; *U.S. Private*, pg. 97
Saubert, Walter E., Chm. Bd. & Chief Exec. Officer--Atlas Van Lines, Inc., Evansville, IN; *U.S. Private*, pg. 97
Saucer, Willie, Chm. Bd., Pres. & Chief Exec. Officer--Farmers Co-op Market Inc., Frisco City, AL; *U.S. Private*, *pg. 395*
Sauder, Maynard, Pres. & Chief Exec. Officer--Sauder Woodworking Co., Archbold, OH; *U.S. Private*, pg. 967
Sauers, Laurence C., Pres. & Chief Exec. Officer--Meier Metal Service Centers, Inc., Hazel Park, MI; *U.S. Public*, pg. 1100
Sauey, Craig, Chief Exec. Officer--Flambeau Corporation, Baraboo, WI; *U.S. Private*, pg. 409
Saul, B. Francis, II, Chm. Bd. & Chief Exec. Officer--Saul Centers Inc., Chevy Chase, MD; *U.S. Public*, pg. 1435
Saunders, E. Philip, Chm. Bd. & Chief Exec. Officer--Travel Ports of America Inc., Rochester, NY; *U.S. Public*, pg. 1632
Saunders, Fredric M., Chm. Bd. & Chief Exec. Officer--Prime Bancshares Inc., Houston, TX; *U.S. Public*, pg. 1326
Saunders, R.F., Chm. Bd. & Chief Exec. Officer--Dakco Distributors, Inc., Minot, ND; *U.S. Private*, pg. 308
Saunders, Richard D., Pres. & Chief Exec. Officer--Kenetech Corp., San Francisco, CA; *U.S. Public*, pg. 950
Saurel, Paul, Chief Exec.--Banco Santander (Suisse), S.A., Geneva, Switzerland; *Int'l*, pg. 144
Sautter, Remy, Pres. & Chief Exec. Officer--CLT-UFA, Luxembourg, Luxembourg; *Int'l*, pg. 561
Sauvanet, Guy, Chief Exec. Officer--Nigbel Merchant Bank (Nigeria) Ltd., Lagos, Nigeria; *Int'l*, pg. 548
Savage, G.P., Chief Exec. Officer--Northern Bank Limited, Belfast, United Kingdom; *Int'l*, pg. 906
Savage, Grahame, Chief Exec.--National Irish Bank Limited, Dublin, Ireland; *Int'l*, pg. 906
Savage, John E., Pres., Chief Oper. Officer, Co-Chief Exec. Officer & Sec.--Amwest Insurance Group, Inc., Calabasas, CA; *U.S. Public*, pg. 106
Savage, Peter P., Pres. & Chief Exec. Officer--Applied Digital Access, San Diego, CA; *U.S. Public*, pg. 122
Savage, R.T., Chm. Bd. & Chief Exec. Officer--Modine Manufacturing Company, Racine, WI; *U.S. Public*, pg. 1121
Savage, Richard H., Chm. Bd. & Co-Chief Exec. Officer--Amwest Insurance Group, Inc., Calabasas, CA; *U.S. Public*, pg. 106
Savarese, Dr. Edward, Chm. Bd., Pres. & Chief Exec. Officer--Imaging Technologies Corp., San Diego, CA; *U.S. Public*, pg. 870
Savel, Bill, Pres. & Chief Exec. Officer--Alta-Dena Certified Dairy, City of Industry, CA; *Int'l*, pg. 201
Saviers, F. Grant, Chm. Bd., Pres. & Chief Exec. Officer--Adaptec, Inc., Milpitas, CA; *U.S. Public*, pg. 19
Savitsky, Stephen, Chm. Bd., Pres. & Chief Exec. Officer--Staff Builders Inc., Lake Success, NY; *U.S. Public*, pg. 1501
Sawaragi, Osamu, Chm. Bd. & Chief Exec. Officer--National Steel Corporation, Mishawaka, IN; *Int'l*, pg. 902
Sawchuk, Arthur R., Chm. Bd., Pres. & Chief Exec. Officer--Du Pont Canada Inc., Mississauga, Canada; *U.S. Public*, pg. 532
Sawin, Craiges B., Chm. & Chief Exec. Officer--Drake Beam Morin, Inc., New York, NY; *U.S. Public*, pg. 783
Sawyer, Kenneth I., Chm. Bd., Pres. & Chief Exec. Officer--Pharmaceutical Resources, Spring Valley, NY; *U.S. Public*, pg. 1285
Saxton, John, Chief Exec. Officer--The Sheridan Group, Hanover, PA; *U.S. Private*, pg. 993
Saxton, Paul A., Chm. Bd., Pres. & Chief Exec. Officer--General Housewares Corp., Terre Haute, IN; *U.S. Public*, *pg. 715*
Sayle, John G., Pres., Chief Exec. Officer & Treas.--The Hall China Company, East Liverpool, OH; *U.S. Private*, pg. 494
Scaliei, Sam A., Jr., Pres. & Chief Exec. Officer--Regions Bank/Blount County, Oneonta, AL; *U.S. Public*, pg. 1372
Scanlan, Arthur G., II, Chief Exec. Officer & Treas.--Eatelcorp Inc., Gonzales, LA; *U.S. Private*, pg. 358
Scarlett, Joseph, Chm. Bd. & Chief Exec. Officer--Tractor Supply Co., Nashville, TN; *U.S. Public*, pg. 1627
Scaroni, Paolo, Group Chief Exec.--Pilkington Plc, Saint Helens, United Kingdom; *Int'l*, pg. 1056
Scattini, James, Chm. Bd. & Chief Exec. Officer--Artichoke Industries, Inc., Castroville, CA; *U.S. Private*, pg. 86
Schachter, William, Pres. & Chief Exec. Officer--CSI International Corporation, New York, NY; *U.S. Private*, pg. 197
Schadt, Dieter, Chief Exec. Officer--Franz Haniel & Cie, GmbH, Duisburg, Germany; *Int'l*, pg. 591
Schaefer, George A., Jr., Chm. Bd., Pres. & Chief Exec. Offficer--Fifth Third Bancorp, Cincinnati, OH; *U.S. Public*, *pg. 621*
Schaefer, Rowland, Chm. Bd., Pres. & Chief Exec. Officer-Claire's Stores--Claire's Stores Inc., Pembroke Pines, FL; *U.S. Public*, pg. 381
Schamp, E.D., Chm. Bd. & Chief Exec. Officer--Peco Mfg. Co., Inc., Portland, OR; *U.S. Private*, pg. 846
Schanze, Richard L., Chm. Bd. & Chief Exec. Officer--Pinnacle Financial Services Inc., Saint Joseph, MI; *U.S. Public*, pg. 1297
Schar, Dwight, Chm. Bd. & Chief Exec. Officer--NVR, Inc., Mc Lean, VA; *U.S. Public*, pg. 1148
Schardt, Ronald, Chm. Bd., Chief Exec. Officer & Chief Oper. Officer--Reinke Manufacturing Co., Inc., Deshler, NE; *U.S. Private*, pg. 920
Scharf, Michael J., Chm. Bd., Pres. & Chief Exec. Officer--Niagara Corporation, New York, NY; *U.S. Public*, pg. 1181
Scharlau, Charles E., Chm. Bd. & Chief Exec. Officer--Southwestern Energy Company, Fayetteville, AR; *U.S. Public*, pg. 1494
Schatteman, S., Pres. & Chief Exec. Officer--PNC Bank, Ohio National Assoc., Fort Mitchell, KY; *U.S. Public*, pg. 1243
Schatteman, S., Pres. & Chief Exec. Officer--PNC Bank, Northern Kentucky, Union, KY; *U.S. Public*, pg. 1243
Schatz, Douglas S., Pres. & Chief Exec. Officer--Advanced Energy Industry, Fort Collins, CO; *U.S. Public*, pg. 20
Schauer, Ronald L., Chm. Bd., Pres. & Chief Exec. Officer--HMT Technology Corporation, Fremont, CA; *U.S. Public*, pg. 771
Schauerman, Chris L., Pres. & Chief Exec. Officer--Capital Lending Services, Inc., Roswell, GA; *U.S. Private*, pg. 206
Schaufeld, Fred, Chm. Bd., Pres. & Chief Exec. Officer--National Electronics Warranty Corporation, Sterling, VA; *U.S. Private*, pg. 782
Schawk, David A., Pres. & Chief Exec. Officer--Schawk, Inc., Des Plaines, IL; *U.S. Public*, pg. 1437
Scheafer, David, Pres. & Chief Exec. Officer--Lynx Golf, Inc., City of Industry, CA; *U.S. Private*, pg. 684
Schecter, Leroy, Chm. Bd. & Chief Exec. Officer--American Strip Steel Inc., Kearny, NJ; *U.S. Private*, pg. 62
Scheele, Nicholas V., Chm. & Chief Exec. Officer--Jaguar Cars, Mahwah, NJ; *U.S. Public*, pg. 664
Scheessele, John R., Chief Exec. Officer--Wheeling-Pittsburgh Steel Corporation, Wheeling, WV; *U.S. Public*, *pg. 1727*
Scheffler, Gustavo, Chief Exec.-Latin America--Skandia S.A., Mexico, Mexico; *Int'l*, pg. 1256
Scheideler, Albert, Chm. Bd., Pres. & Chief Exec. Officer--McNally Industries, Inc., Grantsburg, WI; *U.S. Private*, pg. 724
Schein, Philip S., M.D., Chm. Bd. & Chief Exec. Officer--U.S. Bioscience, Inc., Conshohocken, PA; *U.S. Public*, pg. 1681
Scheinman, Tom, Pres. & Chief Exec. Officer--The Unimax Corporation, New York, NY; *U.S. Private*, pg. 1118
Schelfhaudt, Peter, Partner & Chief Fin. Officer--Earle Palmer Brown Public Relations, New York, NY; *U.S. Private*, pg. 174
Schellenberger, Jean, Chm. Bd. & Chief Exec. Officer--Chantiers Modernes, Pessac, France; *Int'l*, pg. 823
Schelling, P., Chief Exec. Officer--P.T. Zurich Insurance Indonesia, Jakarta, Indonesia; *Int'l*, pg. 1532
Scheman, Martin, Chm. Bd. & Chief Exec. Officer--Tyco Preschool, New York, NY; *U.S. Public*, pg. 1058
Schemmer, Neil, Pres. & Chief Exec. Officer--Security National Bank & Trust Co. of Norman, Norman, OK; *U.S.* Public, pg. 630

Schengili, Josef, Pres. & Chief Exec. Officer--Numetrix Ltd., Toronto, Canada; *Int'l*, pg. 990

Schenk, Douglas, Pres. & Chief Exec. Officer--Maui Pineapple Co., Ltd., Kahului, HI; *U.S. Public*, pg. 1060

Schenk, P. Edward, Chm. Bd., Pres. & Chief Exec. Officer--Rymer Foods Inc., Chicago, IL; *U.S. Public*, pg. 1414

Schenkel, Peter, Chm. Bd. & Chief Exec. Officer--Southern Foods Group, Dallas, TX; *U.S. Private*, pg. 1016

Schennet, G., Chief Exec. Officer--OCE Osterreich Ges.m.b.H., Vienna, Austria; *Int'l*, pg. 995

Scherer, Peter, Pres. & Chief Exec. Officer--Scherer Bros. Lumber Company, Minneapolis, MN; *U.S. Private*, pg. 970

Scherer, Robert P. Jr., Chm. Bd. & Chief Exec. Officer--Scherer Healthcare, Inc., Atlanta, GA; *U.S. Public*, pg. 1437

Scherer, Robert P., Jr., Chm. Bd. & Chief Exec. Officer--Vital Signs, Englewood, CO; *U.S. Public*, pg. 1723

Scherzer, D. J., Pres. & Chief Exec. Officer--NMI Corporation, Dallas, TX; *Int'l*, pg. 900

Scheumann, John B., Chm. Bd. & Chief Exec. Officer--Crossmann Communities, Inc., Indianapolis, IN; *U.S. Public*, pg. 461

Scheuring, G.J., Pres. & Chief Exec. Officer--Midlantic Bank, N.A., Edison, NJ; *U.S. Public*, pg. 1242

Scheuring, Garry, Chm. Bd., Pres. & Chief Exec. Officer--Midlantic Bank, N.A., Philadelphia, PA; *U.S. Public*, pg. 1242

Schiano, Tony, Pres. & Chief Oper. Officer--Edwards Super Food Stores, Carlisle, PA; *Int'l*, pg. 749

Schiavone, Phillip, Pres. & Chief Exec. Officer--E.W. Howell Company, Inc., Port Washington, NY; *Int'l*, pg. 995

Schiavone, Ronald, Chief Exec. Officer--Schiavone Construction Co., Secaucus, NJ; *U.S. Private*, pg. 970

Schiavuzzi, Gianantonio, Chief Exec. Officer & Gen. Mgr.--Banca Di Trento e Bolzano S.p.A., Trento, Italy; *Int'l*, pg. 138

Schibuola, Dino, Pres. & Chief Exec. Officer--Costa Cruise Lines, N.V., Miami, FL; *U.S. Private*, pg. 278

Schiciano, Joseph S., Chm. Bd. & Chief Exec. Officer--The Coon-De Visser Co., Royal Oak, MI; *U.S. Private*, pg. 273

Schiefer, D., Chief Exec. Officer--Braas Schweiz AG, Villmergen, Switzerland; *Int'l*, pg. 1092

Schieman, L. Richard, Chm. Bd., Pres., Chief Exec. Officer & Chief Oper. Officer--Hughes-Peters, Inc., Cincinnati, OH; *U.S. Private*, pg. 546

Schifter, Yvonne, Chm. Bd. & Chief Exec. Officer--Squire-Cogswell Company, Gurnee, IL; *U.S. Private*, pg. 1027

Schikorra, G.E., P.E., Pres. & Chief Exec. Officer--Jagenberg, Inc., Enfield, CT; *Int'l*, pg. 1108

Schild, Harold, Pres. & Chief Exec. Officer--Tillamook County Creamery Assn., Tillamook, OR; *U.S. Private*, pg. 1086

Schilling, Ernie, Pres. & Chief Exec. Officer--Powell Electronics Inc., Philadelphia, PA; *U.S. Private*, pg. 877

Schimmelbusch, Heinz, Ph.D., Pres. & Chief Exec. Officer--Safeguard International Group, Wayne, PA; *U.S. Public*, pg. 1424

Schindler, Andrew J., Pres. & Chief Exec. Officer-RJR Nabisco--R.J. Reynolds Tobacco Company, Winston Salem, NC; *U.S. Public*, pg. 1355

Schini, Thomas W., Chm. Bd., Pres. & Chief Exec. Officer--First Federal Capital Corp., La Crosse, WI; *U.S. Public*, pg. 632

Schinler, Richard J., Pres. & Chief Exec. Officer--Integrity Mutual Insurance Company, Appleton, WI; *U.S. Private*, pg. 566

Schiro, James J., Chm. Bd., Sr. Partner & Chief Exec. Officer--Price Waterhouse L.L.P. - U.S., New York, NY; *U.S. Private*, pg. 883

Schlatter, Donald A., Pres., Chief Exec. Officer & Gen. Counsel--Art Iron, Inc., Toledo, OH; *U.S. Private*, pg. 86

Schlatter, Konrad, Chm. Bd. & Chief Exec. Officer--Corn Products International, Inc., Bedford Park, IL; *U.S. Public*, pg. 447

Schlegel, Bill, Pres. & Chief Exec. Officer, Medical Economics Data--Medical Economics Company Inc., Montvale, NJ; *U.S. Public*, pg. 1601

Schlegel, G., Chief Exec. Officer--Ascom Infrasys AG, Solothurn, Switzerland; *Int'l*, pg. 86

Schlesinger, Alan, Chm. Bd., Pres. & Chief Exec. Officer--Lamonts Apparel, Inc., Kirkland, WA; *U.S. Public*, pg. 975

Schlotfeldt, Walter, Pres. & Chief Exec. Officer--Badger Air Brush Company, Franklin Park, IL; *U.S. Private*, pg. 110

Schlott, Robert, Chief Exec. Officer--Warren Distribution, Inc., Omaha, NE; *U.S. Private*, pg. 1151

Schlotthauer, Karl-Heinz, Co-Chief Oper. Officer--Helaba Trust Beratungs-und Management Gesellschaft mbH, Frankfurt/Main, Germany; *Int'l*, pg. 799

Schlueter, Don, Chief Exec. Officer--Production Tool Corporation, Chicago, IL; *U.S. Private*, pg. 889

Schmalhofer, Bruno, Chief Exec. Officer & Gen. Mgr.--Farmer's Pride, Inc., Fredericksburg, PA; *U.S. Private*, pg. 395

Schmdl, Franz W., Chief Exec. Officer--OSV Partners, Greenwich, CT; *U.S. Public*, pg. 1673

Schmeider, Luke R., Pres., Treas. & Chief Exec. Officer--Mesa Laboratories, Inc., Wheat Ridge, CO; *U.S. Public*, pg. 1099

Schmelzer, Randy, Chief Oper. Officer--River Ranch Northeast, Inc., Buffalo, NY; *U.S. Private*, pg. 934

Schmetterer, Bob, Chm. & Chief Exec. Officer-EURO RSCG Worldwide--Havas Advertising, Levallois-Perret, France; *Int'l*, pg. 600

Schmid, C., Chief Exec. Officer--Ascom Zeag, Spreitenbach, Switzerland; *Int'l*, pg. 86

Schmid, James A., Chief Exec. Officer--Crescent Electric Supply Co., East Dubuque, IL; *U.S. Private*, pg. 289

Schmideknecht, Heyo, Dr., Chief Exec. Officer--Deutsche Babcock AG, Oberhausen, Germany; *Int'l*, pg. 398

Schmidt-Holtz, Rolf, Pres. & Chief Exec. Officer--CLT-UFA, Luxembourg, Luxembourg; *Int'l*, pg. 561

Schmidt, E. Frank, Chm. Bd. & Chief Exec. Officer--SouthTrust Bank of Mobile, Mobile, AL; *U.S. Public*, pg. 1492

Schmidt, Eric, Chm. Bd. & Chief Exec. Officer--Novell, Inc., Orem, UT; *U.S. Public*, pg. 1203

Schmidt, Eric, Chief Exec. Officer--Novell Inc., San Jose, CA; *U.S. Public*, pg. 1203

Schmidt, Marcus, Pres. & Chief Exec. Officer--Atlas Tool Inc., Roseville, MI; *U.S. Private*, pg. 97

Schmidt, Peter G., Pres. & Chief Exec. Officer--Marine Construction & Design Co., Seattle, WA; *U.S. Private*, pg. 703

Schmidt, Richard K., Chief Exec. Officer--Hydrocorp, Inc., Bridgeport, CT; *U.S. Public*, pg. 126

Schmidt, Richard K., Chief Exec. Officer--IEA, Inc., Research Triangle Park, NC; *U.S. Public*, pg. 126

Schmidt, Richard K., Ph.D., Pres. & Chief Exec. Officer--Aquarion Company, Bridgeport, CT; *U.S. Public*, pg. 126

Schmidt, Robert, Pres. & Chief Exec. Officer--M & I Mid-State Bank, Stevens Point, WI; *U.S. Public*, pg. 1050

Schmidt, Robert T., Pres. & Chief Exec. Officer--Iron Road Railways Inc., Washington, DC; *U.S. Private*, pg. 575

Schmidt, Ronald, Pres. & Chief Exec. Officer--I.B. Diffusion, LP, Chicago, IL; *U.S. Private*, pg. 553

Schmidt, Uwe, Pres. & Chief Exec. Officer--Olympic Continental Resources, LLC, Pepper Pike, OH; *U.S. Public*, pg. 1221

Schmidt, Waldemar, Pres. & Chief Exec. Officer--ISS-International Service System A/S, Holte, Denmark; *Int'l*, pg. 656

Schmidt, William B., Chm. Bd., Chief Exec. Officer & Treas--Coca-Cola Bottling Co. of Elizabethtown, Elizabethtown, KY; *U.S. Private*, pg. 248

Schmidtgall, William H., Chm. Bd., Pres., Chief Exec. Officer & Chief Oper. Officer--DMI, Inc., Goodfield, IL; *U.S. Private*, pg. 305

Schmitt, Andrew, Pres. & Chief Exec. Officer--Layne Christenson Co., Mission Woods, KS; *U.S. Public*, pg. 981

Schmitt, Thomas M., Pres. & Chief Exec. Officer--Paul A. Schmitt Music Company, Minneapolis, MN; *U.S. Private*, pg. 971

Schmitt, Wolfgang R., Chm. Bd. & Chief Exec. Officer--Rubbermaid Incorporated, Wooster, OH; *U.S. Public*, pg. 1411

Schnabel, Brian T., Pres. & Chief Exec. Officer--Elmer's Products, Inc., Columbus, OH; *U.S. Private*, pg. 158

Schnabel, James, Chm. Bd., Pres. & Chief Exec. Officer--Sun Electric, Lincolnshire, IL; *U.S. Public*, pg. 1480

Schnack, Uwe, Chief Oper. Officer--TSC Shannock Corporation, Calgary, Canada; *Int'l*, pg. 1343

Schnack, Uwe, Chief Oper. Officer--TSC Shannock Corporation, Don Mills, Canada; *Int'l*, pg. 1343

Schnack, Uwe, Chief Oper. Officer--TSC Shannock Corporation, Saskatoon, Canada; *Int'l*, pg. 1343

Schnack, Uwe, Chief Oper. Officer--TSC Shannock Corporation, Mississauga, Canada; *Int'l*, pg. 1343

Schnack, Uwe, Chief Oper. Officer--TSC Shannock Corporation, Edmonton, Canada; *Int'l*, pg. 1343

Schnaidt, Kay E., Chief Exec. Officer & Exec. V.P.--American Barmag Co., Charlotte, NC; *U.S. Private*, pg. 51

Schneider, Bruce, Pres. & Chief Exec. Officer--Future Foam, Inc., Council Bluffs, IA; *U.S. Private*, pg. 433

Schneider, Charles R., Pres. & Chief Exec. Officer--U.S. Security Associates, Inc., Roswell, GA; *U.S. Private*, pg. 1126

Schneider, Milton, Pres. & Chief Exec. Officer--I. Appel Corporation, New York, NY; *U.S. Private*, pg. 78

Schneider, Ronald E., Chm. Bd., Pres. & Chief Exec. Officer--First National Bank in Cleburne, Cleburne, TX; *U.S. Public*, pg. 633

Schneider, Steven L., Pres. & Chief Exec. Officer--Trion, Inc., Sanford, NC; *U.S. Public*, pg. 1639

Schneuwly, Peter, Pres. & Chief Exec. Officer--UMS Swiss Metalworks Holding Ltd, Dornach, Switzerland; *Int'l*, pg. 1427

Schnitzer, Leonard, Dr., Chm. Bd. & Chief Exec. Officer--Schnitzer Steel Industries, Inc., Portland, OR; *U.S. Public*, pg. 1439

Schnitzer, Leonard, Dr., Chm. Bd. & Chief Exec. Officer--Proler International Corp., Portland, OR; *U.S. Public*, pg. 1440

Schoen, Fred, Chief Exec. Officer--Active Tool & Manufacturing Co., Inc., Roseville, MI; *U.S. Private*, pg. 16

Schoen, William J., Chm. Bd. & Chief Exec. Officer--Health Management Associates, Inc., Naples, FL; *U.S. Public*, pg. 802

Schoenberger, Robert G., Chm. & Chief Exec. Officer--Unitil Corporation, Hampton, NH; *U.S. Public*, pg. 1692

Schoenecker, Guy, Pres. & Chief Exec. Officer--Schoeneckers, Inc., Minneapolis, MN; *U.S. Private*, pg. 971

Schoenhals, Marvin N., Chm. Bd., Pres. & Chief Exec. Officer--WSFS Financial Corporation, Wilmington, DE; *U.S. Public*, pg. 1728

Schoenwitz, Frank, Pres. & Chief Exec. Officer--Weldun International, Inc., Bridgman, MI; *Int'l*, pg. 205

Schofield, Jonathan M., Chm. Bd. & Chief Exec. Officer--Airbus Industrie of North America, Inc., Herndon, VA; *Int'l*, pg. 39

Schofield, Michael, Chief Exec.-Blue Circle Bathrooms--Blue Circle Industries PLC, London, United Kingdom; *Int'l*, pg. 197

Scholl, Thomas, Pres. & Chief Exec. Officer--Scholls Inc., Arden Hills, MN; *U.S. Private*, pg. 972

Scholler, Ray, Pres. & Chief Exec. Officer--Times Printing Company, Inc., Random Lake, WI; *U.S. Private*, pg. 1087

Schollmaier, Edgar H., Chm. Bd., Pres. & Chief Exec. Officer--Alcon Laboratories, Inc., Fort Worth, TX; *Int'l*, pg. 916

Scholobhm, Roy, Pres.--National Corset Supply House, Los Angeles, CA; *U.S. Private*, pg. 781

Scholtz, Ed, Pres. & Chief Exec. Officer--The Murray Ohio Mfg. Co., Brentwood, TN; *Int'l*, pg. 1397

Scholz, Manfred, Dr., Chief Exec. Officer--Haindl Papier GmbH, Augsburg, Germany; *Int'l*, pg. 586

Schoning, Peter M., Chm. & Chief Exec. Officer-Scholz & Friends Group--Scholz & Friends GmbH, Hamburg, Germany; *Int'l*, pg. 1210

Schonmeier, Manfred, Pres. & Chief Exec. Officer--F.W. Woolworth GmbH Co. (Germany), Frankfurt/Main, Germany; *U.S. Public*, pg. 1778

Schort, Donald, Chief Exec. Officer--Neutrogena Corporation, Los Angeles, CA; *U.S. Public*, pg. 928

Schott, Owen W., Pres. & Chief Exec. Officer--Schott Corporation, Wayzata, MN; *U.S. Private*, pg. 972

Schottenstein, Jay, Chm. Bd. & Chief Exec. Officer--Value City Department Stores, Inc., Columbus, OH; *U.S. Private*, pg. 972

Schouwenburg, P., Chief Exec. Officer--Redland Dakprodukten B.V., Montfoort, Netherlands; *Int'l*, pg. 1093

Schrader, Robert E., Chm. Bd., Pres. & Chief Exec. Officer--Zing Technologies, Inc., Valhalla, NY; *U.S. Public*, pg. 1792

Schrager, Phillip G., Chm. Bd. & Chief Exec. Officer--Pacesetter Corporation, Omaha, NE; *U.S. Private*, pg. 830

Schrempp, Jurgen E., Dr., Chm. Bd. & Chief Exec. Officer--Daimler-Benz Aktiengesellschaft, Stuttgart, Germany; *Int'l*, pg. 366

Schreuder, Donald L., Pres. & Chief Exec. Officer--Harding Lawson Associates Group, Inc., Novato, CA; *U.S. Public*, pg. 785

Schrier, Eric, Pres. & Chief Exec. Officer--Time Inc. Health, San Francisco, CA; *U.S. Public*, pg. 1613

Schrimper, Charles, Chm. Bd. & Chie Exec. Officer--Group Dekko, Kendallville, IN; *U.S. Private*, pg. 484

Schriver, Donald, Chief Exec. Officer & Exec. V.P.--Milk Marketing Inc., Strongsville, OH; *U.S. Private*, pg. 745

Schroder, Johan, Pres. & Chief Exec. Officer--Radiometer A/S, Bronshoj, Denmark; *Int'l*, pg. 1083

Schroeder, Charles, Chief Exec. Officer--National Cattlemen's Beef Association, Chicago, IL; *U.S. Private*, pg. 780

Schroeder, Haus-Ulrich, Pres. & Chief Exec. Officer--Ascom Holding AG, Bern, Switzerland; *Int'l*, pg. 86

Schroeder, Leonhard, Chief Exec. Officer--Royal Copenhagen A/S, Frederiksberg, Denmark; *Int'l*, pg. 1134

Schroeder, Manfred F., Pres. & Chief Exec. Officer--VAW of America, Inc., Ellenville, NY; *Int'l*, pg. 1466

Schroeder, William, Chm. Bd. & Chief Exec. Officer--Ireland Coffee Tea, Inc., Pleasantville, NJ; *U.S. Public*, pg. 351

Schroeder, William J., Pres. & Chief Exec. Officer--Diamond Multimedia Systems, Inc., San Jose, CA; *U.S. Public*, pg. 505

Schroeter, Heimar, Chief Exec. Officer--Michael Conrad & Leo Burnett GmbH, Frankfurt/Main, Germany; *U.S. Private*, pg. 184

Schrum, E.P., Pres., Chief Exec. Officer & Treas.--Carolina Mills, Inc., Maiden, NC; *U.S. Private*, pg. 214

Schrushy, Richard, Pres. & Chief Exec. Officer--Healthsouth Corporation, Sunnyvale, CA; *U.S. Public*, pg. 803

Schube, Frank W., Chm. Bd., Pres. & Chief Exec. Officer--Dualite Inc., Williamsburg, OH; *U.S. Private*, pg. 344

Schube, Greg, Pres. & Chief Exec. Officer--Dualite Sales & Service, Inc., Williamsburg, OH; *U.S. Private*, pg. 344

Schubert, John, Chief Exec. Officer & Mng. Dir.--Pioneer International Ltd., Sydney, Australia; *Int'l*, pg. 1058

Schubert, William C., Pres., Chief Exec. Officer & Treas.--Kitchell Corporation, Phoenix, AZ; *U.S. Private*, pg. 624

Schuermann, Fred L., Jr., Pres. & Chief Exec. Officer--Ladd Furniture, Inc., Greensboro, NC; *U.S. Public*, pg. 974

Schuette, Marvin, Chm. Bd., Pres., Chief Exec. Officer & Chief Oper. Officer--Wausau Homes, Inc., Rothschild, WI; *U.S. Private*, pg. 1154

Schuette, Marvin, Chm. Bd., Pres., Chief Exec. Officer & Chief Oper. Officer--Sterling Building Systems, Inc., Rothschild, WI; *U.S. Private*, pg. 1154

Schuff, Scott, Pres. & Chief Exec. Officer--Schuff Steel Co., Phoenix, AZ; *U.S. Private*, pg. 973

Schuh, Dale R., Pres. & Chief Exec. Officer--Sentry Insurance, A Mutual Company, Stevens Point, WI; *U.S. Private*, pg. 984

Schuldt, David A., Chm. Bd., Pres. & Chief Exec. Officer--CASI-RUSCO Inc., Boca Raton, FL; *U.S. Private*, pg. 218

Schulein, S., Chief Exec. Officer--Oce-Credit Corporation, Purchase, NY; *Int'l*, pg. 994

Schuler, C., Chief Exec. Officer--Zurich Compagnie d'Assurances, Luxembourg, Luxembourg; *Int'l*, pg. 1531

Schuler, C., Chief Exec. Officer--Zurich International Services (Luxembourg) S.A., Luxembourg, Luxembourg; *Int'l*, pg. 1532

Schuler, Michael, Pres. & Chief Exec. Officer--Zippo Manufacturing Company, Bradford, PA; *U.S. Private*, pg. 1207

Schulmeyer, Gerhard, Chief Oper. Officer--Siemens-Nixdorf Informationssysteme AG, Paderborn, Germany; *Int'l*, pg. 1245

Schult, Alex, Pres. & Chief Exec. Officer--The Chinet Co., Norwalk, CT; *Int'l*, pg. 1146

Schulte, Johnie, Pres. & Chief Exec. Officer--NCI Building Systems, Inc., Houston, TX; *U.S. Public*, pg. 1145

Schultz, Howard, Pres. & Chief Exec. Officer--Starbucks Coffee Company, Seattle, WA; *U.S. Public*, pg. 1510

Schultz, James, Chief Exec. Officer--PREPLINK, Cleveland, OH; *U.S. Private*, pg. 475

Schultz, James R., Pres. & Chief Exec. Officer--Great Lakes Lithograph Co., Cleveland, OH; *U.S. Private*, pg. 474

Schultz, Ray, Pres. & Chief Exec. Officer--Promus Hotel Corporation, Memphis, TN; *U.S. Public*, pg. 1335

Schultz, Robert B., Pres. & Chief Exec. Officer--Midland Walwyn Inc., Toronto, Canada; *Int'l*, pg. 865

Schultz, William, Chm. Bd. & Chief Exec. Officer--Fender Musical Instruments, Scottsdale, AZ; *U.S. Private,* pg. 400
Schulze, John B., Chm. Bd., Pres. & Chief Exec. Officer--The Lamson & Sessions Co., Cleveland, OH; *U.S. Public,* pg. 976
Schulze, Richard M., Chm. Bd., Founder & Chief Exec. Officer--Best Buy Co., Inc., Eden Prairie, MN; *U.S. Public,* pg. 223
Schuman, Allan L., Pres. & Chief Exec. Officer--Ecolab Inc., Saint Paul, MN; *U.S. Public,* pg. 562
Schuman, G.E., Chief Exec. Officer--Schuman Carriage Company, Honolulu, HI; *Int'l,* pg. 523
Schuster, R.W., Pres. & Chief Exec. Officer--Global Environmental Corp., Hagerstown, MD; *U.S. Public,* pg. 747
Schwab, Anthony, Pres. & Chief Exec. Officer--Claire Manufacturing Co., Addison, IL; *U.S. Private,* pg. 462
Schwab, Anthony, Pres. & Chief Exec. Officer--Sprayway, Inc., Addison, IL; *U.S. Private,* pg. 462
Schwab, Charles, Chm. Bd. & Chief Exec. Officer, Charles Schwab Corporation--Charles Schwab & Co. Inc., San Francisco, CA; *U.S. Public,* pg. 1443
Schwab, Charles R., Chm. Bd. & Chief Exec. Officer--The Charles Schwab Corporation, San Francisco, CA; *U.S. Public,* pg. 1442
Schwab, Frederick J., Pres. & Chief Exec. Officer--Porsche Cars North America, Inc., Reno, NV; *Int'l,* pg. 1063
Schwab, Jim, Pres. & Chief Exec. Officer--Gramex Corporation, Bridgeton, MO; *U.S. Private,* pg. 468
Schwab, Samuel C., Pres. & Chief Exec. Officer--S. Schwab Company, Cumberland, MD; *U.S. Private,* pg. 974
Schwade, Hans, Pres. & Chief Exec. Officer--Bergemann USA, Inc., Atlanta, GA; *Int'l,* pg. 401
Schwager, John L., Pres. & Chief Exec. Officer--Alamco, Inc., Charleston, WV; *U.S. Public,* pg. 403
Schwan, Al, Chm. Bd. & Chief Exec. Officer--Schwan's Sales Enterprises, Marshall, MN; *U.S. Private,* pg. 974
Schwan, Charles A., Pres. & Chief Exec. Officer--Cohu, Inc., San Diego, CA; *U.S. Public,* pg. 396
Schwartz, Bernard L., Chm. Bd. & Chief Exec. Officer--K & F Industries Inc., New York, NY; *U.S. Private,* pg. 602
Schwartz, Bernard L., Chm. Bd. & Chief Exec. Officer--Loral Space & Communications, New York, NY; *U.S. Public,* pg. 1014
Schwartz, David, Pres. & Chief Exec. Officer--Bio-Rad Laboratories, Inc., Hercules, CA; *U.S. Public,* pg. 230
Schwartz, Dennis, Pres. & Chief Exec. Officer--Valley American Bank, South Bend, IN; *U.S. Public,* pg. 674
Schwartz, Gerald W., Chm. Bd., Pres. & Chief Exec. Officer--Onex Corporation, Toronto, Canada; *Int'l,* pg. 1006
Schwartz, Larry, V.P.-Fin. & Admin.--RTG Furniture Corp., Seffner, FL; *U.S. Private,* pg. 905
Schwartz, Leonard, Chm. Bd., Pres. & Chief Exec. Officer--Aceto Corporation, Lake Success, NY; *U.S. Public,* pg. 15
Schwartz, Lonn R., Chief Fin. Officer--Auto Glass Specialists, Madison, WI; *U.S. Private,* pg. 100
Schwartz, M.G., Chm. Bd., Pres. & Chief Exec. Officer--Quaker City Motor Parts Company, Middletown, DE; *U.S. Private,* pg. 898
Schwartz, Richard, Chm. Bd., Pres. & Chief Exec. Officer--Alliant Techsystems, Hopkins, MN; *U.S. Public,* pg. 47
Schwarz, Guenther, Pres. & Chief Exec. Officer--Agrolinz Melamin GmbH, Lienz, Austria; *Int'l,* pg. 356
Schwarz, H. Marshall, Chm. Bd. & Chief Exec. Officer--U.S. Trust Corporation, New York, NY; *U.S. Public,* pg. 1688
Schwarz, John H., Chief Exec. Officer--Perini Land and Development Co., Framingham, MA; *U.S. Public,* pg. 1278
Schwarzer, Fred, Pres. & Chief Exec. Officer--Heska Corporation, Fort Collins, CO; *U.S. Public,* pg. 812
Schwarzman, Stephen A., Pres. & Chief Exec. & Oper. Officer--The Blackstone Group, New York, NY; *U.S. Private,* pg. 147
Schwarzwalder, Daniel, Pres. & Chief Exec. Officer--Chernin's Shoes, Inc., Chicago, IL; *U.S. Private,* pg. 233
Schwegmann, John, Chm. Bd., Pres. & Chief Exec. Officer--Schwegmann Giant Super Markets, New Orleans, LA; *U.S. Private,* pg. 629
Schweitzer, Louis, Grp. Chm. Bd. & Chief Exec. Officer--Renault, Boulogne-Billancourt, France; *Int'l,* pg. 1102
Schwenk, Harold S., Jr., Dr., Chm. Bd., Pres., & Chief Exec. Officer--BGS Systems, Inc., Waltham, MA; *U.S. Public,* pg. 161
Schwericke, Jurgen, Dr., Chief Exec.--Plettac AG, Plettenberg, Germany; *Int'l,* pg. 1061
Schwerin, Clayton A., Chm. Bd., Pres. & Chief Exec. Officer--Alliance Construction Solutions, Inc., Fort Collins, CO; *U.S. Private,* pg. 38
Schwertfeger, Timothy R., Chm. Bd. & Chief Exec. Officer--The John Nuveen Company, Chicago, IL; *U.S. Public,* pg. 1429
Sciame, Frank, Pres., Treas., Chief Exec. & Chief Fin. Officer--F.J. Sciame Construction Co. Inc., New York, NY; *U.S. Private,* pg. 975
Scibelli, R. M., Pres. & Chief Exec. Officer--Ener-Tek International Corporation, Pawcatuck, CT; *U.S. Private,* pg. 376
Scibelli, R.M., Pres. & Chief Exec. Officer--Yardney Technical Products, Inc., Pawcatuck, CT; *U.S. Private,* pg. 376
Sciuto, John J., Chm. Bd., Pres. & Chief Exec. Officer--Comptek Research, Inc., Buffalo, NY; *U.S. Public,* pg. 419
Scobie, William M., Chm. Bd., Chief Exec. Officer--Mason Shoe Mfg. Co., Chippewa Falls, WI; *U.S. Private,* pg. 712
Scoggin, Daniel R., Chm. Bd. & Chief Exec. Officer--Ground Round Inc., Braintree, MA; *U.S. Public,* pg. 766
Scoppechio, Debbie, Chm. Bd. & Chief Exec. Officer--Creative Alliance, Inc., Louisville, KY; *U.S. Private,* pg. 287
Scordato, Emil A., Chm. Bd. & Chief Exec. Officer--Medical Laboratory Automation, Inc., Pleasantville, NY; *U.S. Private,* pg. 727
Scott-Hansen, Peter, Chief Exec. Officer--Applied Industrial Materials Corporation, Stamford, CT; *U.S. Public,* pg. 1736
Scott-Maxwell, J., Chief Exec. Officer--Delta plc, London, United Kingdom; *Int'l,* pg. 389
Scott, Allan, Pres. & Chief Oper. Officer--TELUS Marketing Communications, Edmonton, Canada; *Int'l,* pg. 1374
Scott, Benjamin, Pres. & Chief Exec. Officer-PCS PrimeCo--Bell Atlantic Corporation, New York, NY; *U.S. Public,* pg. 201
Scott, Daniel T., Chm. Bd. & Chief Exec. Officer--Scott Printing Corporation, New Providence, NJ; *U.S. Private,* pg. 977
Scott, Dave, Pres. & Chief Exec. Officer--Dimco-Gray Company, Centerville, OH; *U.S. Private,* pg. 333
Scott, E. Lynn, Pres. & Chief Exec. Officer--Brass Eagle Inc., Rogers, AR; *U.S. Public,* pg. 250
Scott, Geoff, Grp. Chief Exec. Officer--Frontline- Distribution Division, Peterborough, United Kingdom; *Int'l,* pg. 451
Scott, Harry, Pres. & Chief Exec. Oper.--Corporate Travel Services, San Francisco, CA; *U.S. Private,* pg. 276
Scott, J.B., Chief Exec. Officer--Zurich Life Insurance Company of America, Schaumburg, IL; *Int'l,* pg. 1530
Scott, James T., Chm. Bd., Chief Exec. Officer & Treas.--Norcostco, Inc., Minneapolis, MN; *U.S. Private,* pg. 801
Scott, John S., Chm. & Chief Exec. Officer--XL Vision Inc., Sebastian, FL; *U.S. Public,* pg. 1424
Scott, P., Chief Exec.-Superannuation & Investments--MLC Limited, Sydney, Australia; *Int'l,* pg. 806
Scott, Patrick, Pres. & Chief Exec. Officer--Fisher Broadcasting Inc., Seattle, WA; *U.S. Public,* pg. 648
Scott, R.A., Grp. Chief Exec.--General Accident Fire and Life Assurance Corporation p.l.c., Perth, United Kingdom; *Int'l,* pg. 542
Scott, Robert, Pres. & Chief Exec. Officer--NewBold Corporation, Rocky Mount, VA; *U.S. Private,* pg. 796
Scott, Roland, Pres. & Chief Exec. Officer--Whitney Blake Company of Vermont, Inc., Bellows Falls, VT; *U.S. Private,* pg. 148
Scott, Steven, Dr., Chm. Bd., Pres. & Chief Exec. Officer--Coastal Physician Group, Inc., Durham, NC; *U.S. Public,* pg. 391
Scott, Stuart L., Chm. Bd. & Chief Exec. Officer--LaSalle Partners, Chicago, IL; *U.S. Public,* pg. 978
Scotti, Anthony J., Chm. Bd. & Chief Exec. Officer--All American Communications, Inc., Santa Monica, CA; *U.S. Public,* pg. 41
Scotti, Gavin A., Chm. & Chief Exec. Officer--Klemtner Advertising Inc., New York, NY; *U.S. Public,* pg. 1422
Scraire, Jean-Claude, Chm. Bd. & Chief Exec. Officer--Caisse de depot et placement du Quebec, Montreal, Canada; *Int'l,* pg. 249
Scriba, Ralph D., Chm. Bd. & Chief Exec. Officer--Swift-Cor Tool Engineering, Gardena, CA; *U.S. Private,* pg. 1058
Scribner, Robert K., Chief Exec.--Esselte Corporation, Garden City, NY; *Int'l,* pg. 460
Scrushy, Richard M., Chm. Bd. & Chief Exec. Officer--Healthsouth Corporation, Birmingham, AL; *U.S. Public,* pg. 803
Scull, Jorge, Chief Exec. Officer--EURO RSCG-Venezuela, Caracas, Venezuela; *Int'l,* pg. 603
Scully, Joseph C., Chm. Bd. & Chief Exec. Officer--St. Paul Bancorp, Inc., Chicago, IL; *U.S. Public,* pg. 1428
Seaberg, Ladd M., Pres. & Chief Exec. Officer--Midwest Grain Products, Inc., Atchison, KS; *U.S. Public,* pg. 1111
Seabolt, Stephen J., Pres. & Chief Exec. Officer--Sunset Publishing Corporation, Menlo Park, CA; *U.S. Public,* pg. 1613
Seabrook, Francis G., Chief Exec. Officer--Barnett Mortgage Company, Jacksonville, FL; *U.S. Public,* pg. 1162
Seabrook, James H., Jr., Pres. & Chief Exec. Officer--Seabrook Wallcoverings, Inc., Memphis, TN; *U.S. Private,* pg. 978
Seabrook, James M., Chm. Bd. & Chief Exec. Officer--Seabrook Brothers & Sons, Inc., Seabrook, NJ; *U.S. Private,* pg. 978
Seal, Thomas F., Pres. & Chief Exec. Officer--Alpnet Inc., Salt Lake City, UT; *U.S. Public,* pg. 58
Seaman, James D., Pres. & Chief Exec. Officer--Seaman Timber Company, Inc., Montevallo, AL; *U.S. Private,* pg. 979
Seardino, Marjorie, Chief Exec. Officer--Pearson plc, London, United Kingdom; *Int'l,* pg. 1025
Seaton, Kenneth M., Chm. Bd., Pres. & Chief Exec. Officer--Family Inns of America, Inc., Pigeon Forge, TN; *U.S. Private,* pg. 392
Seaver, Christopher T., Pres. & Chief Exec. Officer--Hydril Company, Houston, TX; *U.S. Private,* pg. 551
Seaver, Roger, Chief Exec. Officer--Glendale Memorial Hospital and Medical Center, Glendale, CA; *U.S. Private,* pg. 1118
Secrist, Richard, Chm. Bd., Pres. & Chief Exec. Officer--Blue Tee Corporation, New York, NY; *U.S. Private,* pg. 153
Sedler, Herbert L., Pres. & Chief Exec. Officer--Paper Enterprises, Inc., Bronx, NY; *U.S. Private,* pg. 837
Seelbinder, G. Arthur, Chm. Bd. & Chief Exec. Officer--Cooker Restaurant Corporation, West Palm Beach, FL; *U.S. Public,* pg. 442
Seeley, Donald L., Pres. & Chief Exec. Officer--The Alexander Consulting Group Inc., Lyndhurst, NJ; *U.S. Public,* pg. 117
Seeley, Raynor M. Jr., Chm. Bd., Pres. & Chief Exec. Officer--PTA Corporation, Oxford, CT; *U.S. Private,* pg. 828
Segal, David, Chief Exec. Officer--Steven Manufacturing Co., Hermann, MO; *U.S. Private,* pg. 1042
Segal, Gordon I., Chief Exec. Officer--Euromarket Designs, Inc., Northbrook, IL; *U.S. Private,* pg. 384
Segal, Myron, Chm. Bd., Pres. & Chief Exec. Officer--Premier Mill Corp., Reading, PA; *U.S. Private,* pg. 881
Segal, Myron, Chm. Bd., Pres. & Chief Exec. Officer--Integrated Press Systems, Reading, PA; *U.S. Private,* pg. 881
Segal, Zalman, Dr., Chm. Bd. & Chief Exec. Officer--Bank Leumi Trust Company of New York, New York, NY; *Int'l,* pg. 150
Segel, Richard M., Pres. & Chief Exec. Officer--Dunmore Corporation, Newtown, PA; *U.S. Private,* pg. 346
Seglem, Christopher K., Chm. Bd., Pres. & Chief Exec. Officer--Westmoreland Coal Co., Colorado Springs, CO; *U.S. Public,* pg. 1761
Sehgal, R.K., Vice Chm. & Chief Exec. Officer--H.J. Russell & Co., Atlanta, GA; *U.S. Private,* pg. 952
Seidenberg, Otto, Pres. & Chief Exec. Officer--Hoffer's Inc., Schofield, WI; *U.S. Private,* pg. 239
Seigel, Dan, Pres. & Chief Exec. Officer--Earl Scheib, Inc., Beverly Hills, CA; *U.S. Public,* pg. 1437
Seinsheimer, J. Fellman, III, Pres. & Chief Exec. Officer--American Indemnity Financial Corp., Galveston, TX; *U.S. Public,* pg. 83
Seinsheimer, J. Fellman, III, Pres. & Chief Exec. Officer--American Indemnity Company, Galveston, TX; *U.S. Public,* pg. 83
Seinsheimer, J.F., III, Pres. & Chief Exec. Officer--Texas General Indemnity Co., Galveston, TX; *U.S. Public,* pg. 83
Sejpal, David A., Chm. Bd., Pres., Chief Exec. & Oper. Officer & Sec.--Clothestime Stores, Inc., Anaheim, CA; *U.S. Public,* pg. 387
Sekeres, Charles E., Chief Exec. Officer--Form-You-3 International, Inc., Akron, OH; *U.S. Private,* pg. 418
Sekeres, Charles E., Pres. & Chief Exec. Officer--Physicians Weight Loss Centers, Inc., Akron, OH; *U.S. Private,* pg. 864
Sekeres, Charles E., Pres. & Chief Exec. Officer--Diet Center Worldwide, Inc., Akron, OH; *U.S. Private,* pg. 864
Seko, Akira, Pres. & Chief Exec. Officer--ORIX USA Corporation-San Francisco, San Francisco, CA; *Int'l,* pg. 1009
Selander, Lennart, Pres. & Chief Exec. Officer--AGA AB, Lidingo, Sweden; *Int'l,* pg. 12
Selander, Robert, Pres. & Chief Exec. Officer--Mastercard International, Inc., Purchase, NY; *U.S. Private,* pg. 714
Selby, Alan, Chief Exec. Officer--Mando Marketing Limited, Aylesbury, United Kingdom; *Int'l,* pg. 1482
Selders, Wim, H.J., Pres. & Chief Exec. Officer--Ortel Corporation, Alhambra, CA; *U.S. Public,* pg. 1232
Seldin, Marc A., Chm. Bd.--Miss Elaine Inc., Saint Louis, MO; *U.S. Private,* pg. 752
Sele, J., Chief Exec. Officer--Zurich Versicherungs-Gesellschaft, Vaduz, Liechtenstein; *Int'l,* pg. 1531
Selebai, Milan, Chief Oper. Officer--Suspa France SARL, Barbizon, France; *Int'l,* pg. 1322
Selecman, Charles E., Chm. Bd., Pres. & Chief Exec. Officer--Input/Output, Inc., Stafford, TX; *U.S. Public,* pg. 880
Self, W.M., Chm. Bd. & Chief Exec. Officer--Greenwood Mills, Inc., Greenwood, SC; *U.S. Private,* pg. 479
Selig, Marvin, Chm. Bd. & Chief Exec. Officer-CMC Steel Grp.--Structural Metals, Inc., Seguin, TX; *U.S. Public,* pg. 412
Selinger, Irwin, Chm. Bd. & Chief Exec. Officer--Graham-Field Health Products, Inc., Hauppauge, NY; *U.S. Public,* pg. 757
Selkowitz, Arthur, Chm. & Chief Exec. Officer-DMB&B Communications--DMB&B Communications, New York, NY; *U.S. Private,* pg. 302
Sellman, Michael B., Pres. & Chief Exec. Officer--Maine Yankee, Brunswick, ME; *U.S. Public,* pg. 325
Selvey, Anthony R., Pres. & Chief Exec. Officer--Taylor & Francis Group Ltd., London, United Kingdom; *Int'l,* pg. 1357
Semler, Jerry D., Chm. Bd., Pres. & Chief Exec. Officer--American United Life Insurance Company, Indianapolis, IN; *U.S. Private,* pg. 64
Semmelhack, Henry P., Chm. Bd., Pres. & Chief Exec. Officer--Barrister Information Systems Corporation, Buffalo, NY; *U.S. Public,* pg. 192
Semrod, T. Joseph, Chm. Bd. & Chief Exec. Officer--Summit Bancorp, Princeton, NJ; *U.S. Public,* pg. 1527
Semrod, T. Joseph, Chm. Bd., Pres. & Chief Exec. Officer--United Jersey Bank, Hackensack, NJ; *U.S. Public,* pg. 1528
Semrod, T. Joseph, Chm. Bd. & Chief Exec. Officer--Summit Bank, Chatham, NJ; *U.S. Public,* pg. 1528
Sendlmeier, Helmut, Chief Exec. Officer--TBWA Dusseldorf GmbH, Dusseldorf, Germany; *U.S. Private,* pg. 1063
Seng, Ong Poh, Dr., Chief Exec. Officer--Milk Products Holdings (SEA), Singapore, Singapore; *Int'l,* pg. 923
Senie, Kevin, Pres. & Chief Exec. Officer--The Travel Channel, Atlanta, GA; *U.S. Private,* pg. 647
Senlmeier, Helmut, Chief Exec. Officer--TBWA Germany, Frankfurt/Main, Germany; *U.S. Private,* pg. 1063
Senlmeier, Helmut, Chief Exec. Officer--TBWA Munich, Munich, Germany; *U.S. Private,* pg. 1063
Serafini, Claudio, Chief Exec. Officer & Mng. Dir.--Heinz Food Service S.r.l., Commessaggio, Italy; *U.S. Public,* pg. 806
Serafini, Claudio, Chief Exec. Officer & Mng. Dir.--PLADA S.p.A., Milan, Italy; *U.S. Public,* pg. 807
Seramur, John C., Pres., Chief Exec. Officer & Chief Oper. Officer--First Financial Corporation, Stevens Point, WI; *U.S. Public,* pg. 140
Sergey, John M., Pres. & Chief Exec. Officer--Strategic Distribution Inc., Bensalem, PA; *U.S. Public,* pg. 1523
Serra, Matthew D., Chm. & Chief Exec. Officer--Stern's, Paramus, NJ; *U.S. Public,* pg. 618
Serrano Segovia, Jose, Chm. Bd. & Chief Exec. Officer--Transportacion Maritima Mexicana S.A. de C.V., Mexico, Mexico; *Int'l,* pg. 1418
Serruya, Michael, Pres. & Chief Exec. Officer--Yogen Fruz Worldwide Inc., Markham, Canada; *Int'l,* pg. 1520

SerVaas, Cory, M.D., Chm. Bd., Pres. & Chief Exec. Officer--Benjamin Franklin Literary & Medical Society, Inc., Indianapolis, IN; *U.S. Private*, pg. 133

Servitje, Daniel, Chief Exec. Officer--Grupo Industrial Bimbo S.A. de C.V., Mexico, Mexico; *Int'l*, pg. 575

Setubal, Roberto Egydio, Pres. & Chief Exec. Officer--Banco Itau S.A., Sao Paulo, Brazil; *Int'l*, pg. 142

Sevensson, Roland, Chief Exec. Officer & Mng. Dir.--KF/Konsum Coop Group, Stockholm, Sweden; *Int'l*, pg. 718

Severson, Allan W., Chm. Bd., Pres. & Chief Exec. Officer--Grossmont Bank, San Diego, CA; *U.S. Public*, pg. 1793

Sevier, Helen, Chm. Bd., Pres., Chief Exec. & Chief Oper. Officer--B.A.S.S., Inc., Montgomery, AL; *U.S. Private*, pg. 105

Sevin, Irik, Chm. Bd., Pres. & Chief Exec. Officer--Petroleum Heat & Power Co., Stamford, CT; *U.S. Public*, *pg. 1281*

Seward, John E., Jr., Pres. & Chief Exec. Officer--The Paty Company, Piney Flats, TN; *U.S. Private*, pg. 844

Sewell, Cecil W., Jr., Chm. Bd. & Chief Exec. Officer--Centura Banks, Inc., Rocky Mount, NC; *U.S. Public*, pg. 328

Sewell, D.J., Chief Exec. Officer--Clayhithe P.L.C., Aylesbury, United Kingdom; *Int'l*, pg. 297

Seya, Hiromichi, Pres. & Chief Exec. Officer--Asahi Glass Co., Ltd., Tokyo, Japan; *Int'l*, pg. 84

Seydoux, Jerome, Chm. Bd. & Chief Exec. Officer--Pathe, Paris, France; *Int'l*, pg. 1024

Shacklett, James, III, Chief Exec. Officer--National Label Company, Lafayette Hill, PA; *U.S. Private*, pg. 785

Shacknai, Jonah, Chief Exec. Officer--Medicis Pharmaceutical Corp., Phoenix, AZ; *U.S. Public*, pg. 1080

Shackouls, Bobby S., Pres. & Chief Exec. Officer--Burlington Resources Inc., Houston, TX; *U.S. Public*, pg. 269

Shackouls, Bobby S., Pres. & Chief Exec. Officer--Meridian Oil Holding Inc., Houston, TX; *U.S. Public*, pg. 269

Shackouls, Bobby S., Chm. Bd., Pres. & Chief Exec. Officer--The Louisiana Land and Exploration Company, New Orleans, LA; *U.S. Public*, pg. 269

Shafer, Byron A., Pres. & Chief Exec. Officer--Shafer Commercial Seating Inc., Denver, CO; *U.S. Private*, pg. 988

Shafer, Chip, Chief Exec. Officer & New Bus. Contact--Shafer, Irvine, CA; *U.S. Private*, pg. 988

Shaffer, David H., Chm. Bd. & Chief Exec. Officer--Jostens Learning Corporation, San Diego, CA; *U.S. Private*, pg. 601

Shaffer, James B., Pres. & Chief Exec. Officer--Guy Gannett Communications, Portland, ME; *U.S. Private*, pg. 439

Shaffer, Lee P., Pres. & Chief Exec. Officer--Kenan Transport Company, Chapel Hill, NC; *U.S. Public*, pg. 949

Shaftman, Frederick A., Chief Exec. Officer--BellSouth Communication Systems, Inc., Roanoke, VA; *U.S. Public*, *pg. 209*

Shafto, Robert A., Pres. & Chief Exec. Officer--The New England, Boston, MA; *U.S. Private*, pg. 737

Shah, Ajay B., Chm. Bd., Pres. & Chief Exec. Officer--Smart Modular Technologies, Fremont, CA; *U.S. Public*, pg. 1476

Shah, Harry, Pres.--National Food Stores, Inc., Edison, NJ; *U.S. Private*, pg. 783

Shah, Satish, Pres. & Chief Exec. Officer--Accra Pac Group, Elkhart, IN; *U.S. Private*, pg. 11

Shaheen, David, Vice Chm. & Chief Exec. Officer--World Carpets, Inc., Dalton, GA; *U.S. Private*, pg. 1190

Shaheen, Gabriel L., Pres. & Chief Exec. Officer--Lincoln National Reinsurance Company (Barbados) Limited, Fort Wayne, IN; *U.S. Public*, pg. 998

Shaich, Ron, Co-Chm. Bd. & Chief Exec. Officer--Au Bon Pain Co., Inc., Boston, MA; *U.S. Public*, pg. 146

Shake, Ed, Pres. & Chief Exec. Officer--Roadmaster/Brunswick, Olney, IL; *U.S. Public*, pg. 265

Shanback, Martin P., Chm. Bd. & Chief Exec. Officer--Friendship Dairies, Inc., Friendship, NY; *U.S. Private*, pg. 429

Shaneour, Dwight C., Jr., Chm. Bd., Pres. & Chief Exec. Officer--The Shane Group Inc., Hillsdale, MI; *U.S. Private*, pg. 989

Shank, Glen L., Pres. & Chief Exec. Officer--Duckwall-Alco Stores, Inc., Abilene, KS; *U.S. Public*, pg. 533

Shankar, R. Sam, Pres., Chief Oper. Officer & Co-Chief Exec. Officer--Tork, Inc., Mount Vernon, NY; *U.S. Private*, pg. 1092

Shanklin, Jerry C., Chm. Bd., Pres. & Chief Exec. Officer--Sundowner Offshore Services, Inc., Houston, TX; *U.S. Public*, pg. 1149

Shannon, O John C., Chm., Pres.-Grey Intl. & Chief Exec. Officer-Eur., Mid. E., Afr.--Grey Europe/London, London, United Kingdom; *U.S. Public*, pg. 765

Shapell, Nathan, Chm. Bd., Pres. & Chief Exec. Officer--Shapell Industries, Inc., Beverly Hills, CA; *U.S. Private*, pg. 990

Shapira, David, Chm. Bd. & Chief Exec. Officer--Giant Eagle, Inc., Pittsburgh, PA; *U.S. Private*, pg. 450

Shapira, David, Chm. & Chief Exec. Officer--Giant Eagle Market Co., Pittsburgh, PA; *U.S. Private*, pg. 450

Shapira, David, Chm. & Chief Exec. Officer--Tamarkin Co., Inc., Pittsburgh, PA; *U.S. Private*, pg. 451

Shapiro, Marc J., Chm. Bd., Pres. & Chief Exec. Officer--Texas Commerce Bank, Houston, TX; *U.S. Public*, pg. 339

Shapiro, Richard B., Chm. Bd., Pres. & Chief Exec. Officer--Charles River Data Systems, Inc., Framingham, MA; *U.S. Private*, pg. 230

Shapiro, Robert B., Chm. Bd. & Chief Exec. Officer--Monsanto Company, Saint Louis, MO; *U.S. Public*, pg. 1124

Sharkey, John, Joint Chm. & Joint Chief Exec. Officer--BST-BDDP, London, United Kingdom; *Int'l*, pg. 117

Sharoky, Melvin, Pres. & Chief Exec. Officer--Circa Pharmaceuticals, Inc., Copiague, NY; *U.S. Public*, pg. 1746

Sharon, Thomas E., Dr., Pres. & Chief Exec. Officer--Electromagnetic Sciences, Inc., Norcross, GA; *U.S. Public*, pg. 569

Sharp, Charles, Chm. Bd., Pres. & Chief Exec. Officer--Clinton State Bank, Clinton, AR; *U.S. Public*, pg. 630

Sharp, Isadore, Chm. Bd. & Chief Exec. Officer--Four Seasons Hotels Inc., Don Mills, Canada; *Int'l*, pg. 502

Sharp, Richard L., Chm. Bd. & Chief Exec. Officer--Circuit City Stores, Inc., Richmond, VA; *U.S. Public*, pg. 374

Shaughnessy, Keith C., Pres. & Chief Exec. Officer--Metapoint Partners, Peabody, MA; *U.S. Private*, pg. 735

Shaughnessy, Tom, Chief Exec. Officer & Adv. Dir.--Unidigital/Cardinal Corp., New York, NY; *U.S. Public*, pg. 1664

Shaughnessy, William J., Pres. & Chief Exec. Officer--Wilbur Chocolate Co., Inc., Lititz, PA; *U.S. Private*, pg. 210

Shaw Jr,., William D, Pres. & Chief Exec. Officer--Aubrey G. Lanston & Co. Inc., New York, NY; *Int'l*, pg. 675

Shaw, James R., Jr., Pres. & Chief Exec. Officer--Regions Bank/Jackson County, Jefferson, GA; *U.S. Public*, pg. 1372

Shaw, Neil M., Sir, Chm. Bd. & Chief Exec. Officer--Tate & Lyle PLC, London, United Kingdom; *Int'l*, pg. 1356

Shaw, Ray, Chm. Bd., Pres., Chief Exec. Officer & Chief Oper. Officer--American City Business Journals, Inc., Charlotte, NC; *U.S. Private*, pg. 19

Shaw, Robert, Chm Bd., Pres., & Chief Exec. Officer--Recoton Auto Corporation, Lincolnshire, IL; *U.S. Public*, pg. 1369

Shaw, Robert, Pres. & Chief Exec. Officer--NHT, Benicia, CA; *U.S. Public*, pg. 1369

Shaw, Robert E., Chm. Bd. & Chief Exec. Officer--Shaw Industries, Inc., Dalton, GA; *U.S. Public*, pg. 1464

Shaw, Wayne E., Chm. Bd., Pres. & Chief Exec. Officer--Industra Service Corporation, New Westminster, Canada; *Int'l*, pg. 74

Shaw, William, Chm. Bd. & Chief Exec. Officer--Autologic Information International, Inc., Thousand Oaks, CA; *U.S. Public*, pg. 1724

Shaw, William J., Chm. Bd., Pres. & Chief Exec. Officer--U.S. Trails, Dallas, TX; *U.S. Public*, pg. 1688

Shaye, Robert K., Chm. Bd. & Chief Exec. Officer--New Line Cinema Corporation, New York, NY; *U.S. Public*, pg. 1614

Shea, Charlie, Chief Exec. Officer--The Fifth Third Bank of Northeastern Ohio, Cleveland, OH; *U.S. Public*, pg. 621

Shea, James P., Pres. & Chief Exec. Officer--Renex Corp., Coral Gables, FL; *U.S. Public*, pg. 1377

Shea, Terence J., Chm. Bd. & Chief Exec. Officer--Bradner Central Company, Chicago, IL; *U.S. Private*, pg. 164

Shearer, Martin P., Pres. & Chief Exec. Officer--Southern Belle Dairy Company, Somerset, KY; *U.S. Private*, pg. 1015

Sheed, James C., Chief Exec. Officer--Hastings Deering (Australia) Limited, Archerfield, Australia; *Int'l*, pg. 1250

Sheehan, Dennis W., Chm. Bd., Pres. & Chief Exec. Officer--AXIA Incorporated, Lombard, IL; *U.S. Private*, pg. 103

Sheehan, Jeremiah J., Chm. Bd., Pres. & Chief Exec. Officer--Reynolds Metals Company, Richmond, VA; *U.S. Public*, pg. 1385

Sheehy, Robert J., Pres. & Chief Exec. Officer--United HealthCare of Ohio, Inc., Columbus, OH; *U.S. Public*, pg. 1678

Sheets, Mary J., Pres. & Chief Exec. Officer--Rapid Industries, Inc., Louisville, KY; *U.S. Private*, pg. 910

Sheetz, Stanton R., Pres. & Chief Exec. Officer--Sheetz, Inc., Altoona, PA; *U.S. Private*, pg. 991

Sheffield, Scott, Pres. & Chief Exec. Officer--Pioneer Natural Resources Co., Irving, TX; *U.S. Public*, pg. 1299

Sheffler, Dudley P., Pres. & Chief Exec. Officer--RELTEC Corporation, Cleveland, OH; *U.S. Private*, pg. 921

Sheinfeld, David I., Chm. Bd., Chief Exec. Officer & Sec.--Fresh America Corp., Dallas, TX; *U.S. Public*, pg. 681

Sheldon, J.M., Chm. Bd., Pres., Chief Exec. Officer & Chief Oper. Officer--Sheldons' Inc., Antigo, WI; *U.S. Private*, pg. 992

Sheley, G. Michael, Chief Exec. Officer--National Health Plans, Modesto, CA; *U.S. Public*, pg. 1577

Shell, Earl L., Chm. Bd. & Chief Exec. Officer--Hardin Construction Group, Inc., Atlanta, GA; *U.S. Private*, pg. 501

Shellenbarger, David, Pres. & Chief Exec. Officer--Macro Computer Products Inc., Rochester Hills, MI; *U.S. Private*, pg. 693

Shelton, Darold E., Pres. & Chief Exec. Officer--United Missouri Bank of Cass County, Peculiar, MO; *U.S. Public*, pg. 1655

Shelton, James D., Chm., Pres. & Chief Exec. Officer--First Federal Savings, East Hartford, CT; *U.S. Public*, pg. 632

Shemesh, Jacob, Exec. V.P.-Sls.--IIS Intelligent Information Systems Ltd., Yokneam, Israel; *Int'l*, pg. 645

Shenkenburg, W.J., Pres. & Chief Exec. Officer--M & I Bank of Racine, Racine, WI; *U.S. Public*, pg. 1050

Shepard, Donald J., Chm. Bd., Pres. & Chief Exec. Officer--AEGON USA, Inc., Baltimore, MD; *Int'l*, pg. 26

Shepard, Jeffrey A., Pres. & Chief Exec. Officer--Meldisco, Mahwah, NJ; *U.S. Public*, pg. 661

Shepherd, J. Harold, Chief Exec. Officer--Shepherd Construction Co., Inc., Atlanta, GA; *U.S. Private*, pg. 993

Shepherd, James M., Pres. & Chief Exec. Officer-Japan Johnson & V.P.-SC Johnson & Son--S.C. Johnson & Son, Inc., Racine, WI; *U.S. Private*, pg. 592

Shepherd, William C., Chm. Bd., Pres. & Chief Exec. Officer--Allergan, Inc., Irvine, CA; *U.S. Public*, pg. 46

Sheridan, Gregory C., Pres. & Chief Exec. Officer--Huntington Bancshares Indiana, Inc., Indianapolis, IN; *U.S. Public*, pg. 850

Sheridan, Ralph S., Pres. & Chief Exec. Officer--American Science & Engineering, Inc., Billerica, MA; *U.S. Public*, pg. 90

Sherin, L., Chief Exec. Officer--Zurich International Services (Ireland) Limited, Dublin, Ireland; *Int'l*, pg. 1532

Sherling, George L., Pres. & Chief Exec. Officer--Compass Bank Dallas, Richardson, TX; *U.S. Public*, pg. 419

Sherman, Floyd, Chm. Bd. & Chief Exec. Officer-Triangle Pacific--Bruce Hardwood Floors, Dallas, TX; *U.S. Public*, pg. 1634

Sherman, Floyd F., Chm. Bd. & Chief Exec. Officer--Triangle Pacific Corporation, Dallas, TX; *U.S. Public*, pg. 1634

Sherman, George M., Pres. & Chief Exec. Officer--Danaher Corporation, Washington, DC; *U.S. Public*, pg. 480

Sherman, Glenn, Dr., Chm. Bd. & Chief Exec. Officer--Laser Power Corporation, San Diego, CA; *U.S. Private*, pg. 652

Sherman, John, Jr., Pres. & Chief Exec. Officer--Scott & Stringfellow Financial, Inc., Richmond, VA; *U.S. Public*, pg. 1445

Sherman, John, Jr., Pres. & Chief Exec. Officer--Scott & Stringfellow, Inc., Richmond, VA; *U.S. Public*, pg. 1445

Sherman, Malcolm L., Chm. Bd. & Chief Exec. Officer--Ekco Group, Inc., Nashua, NH; *U.S. Public*, pg. 566

Sherman, Malcolm L., Chm. Bd. & Chief Exec. Officer--Ekco International, Inc., Nashua, NH; *U.S. Public*, pg. 566

Sherman, Peter M., Chm. Bd., Pres. & Chief Exec. Officer--Independence Capital Management, Inc., Horsham, PA; *U.S. Private*, pg. 849

Sherman, Stanley, Pres. & Chief Exec. Officer--Ciba Specialty Chemicals, Tarrytown, NY; *Int'l*, pg. 291

Sherwood, James B., Chm. Bd. & Chief Exec. Officer--Orient-Express Hotels Inc., New York, NY; *Int'l*, pg. 1213

Sherwood, Simon, Chief Exec. Officer--B.B.H. Asia Pacific, Singapore, Singapore; *Int'l*, pg. 169

Sheth, Viren, Pres. & Chief Exec. Officer--Tristar Corp., San Antonio, TX; *U.S. Public*, pg. 1640

Shetrit, Yoram, Chief Exec. Officer--Carmel Container Systems Ltd., Petah Tiqwa, Israel; *Int'l*, pg. 75

Shettle, John F., Jr., Pres. & Chief Exec. Officer--Avemco Corporation, Frederick, MD; *U.S. Public*, pg. 151

Shevack, Brett, Chief Exec. Officer--Partners & Shevack, Inc., New York, NY; *U.S. Private*, pg. 842

Shewmake, C.B., Chm. Bd. & Chief Exec. Officer--Algernon Blair International, Montgomery, AL; *U.S. Private*, pg. 33

Shields, Gerald N., Chm. Bd., Pres. & Chief Exec. Officer--Graymills Corp., Chicago, IL; *U.S. Private*, pg. 473

Shields, John, Chm. Bd. & Chief Exec. Officer--TACT Holding, South Pasadena, CA; *U.S. Private*, pg. 1067

Shields, John, Chm. Bd. & Chief Exec. Officer--Trader Joe's Co., South Pasadena, CA; *U.S. Private*, pg. 1067

Shiells, W., Chief Exec. Officer--Transport Fuel Systems (N.Z.) Limited, Auckland, New Zealand; *U.S. Public*, pg. 905

Shih, Stan, Chm. Bd. & Chief Exec. Officer--Acer Incorporated, Taipei, Taiwan; *Int'l*, pg. 22

Shillestad, John G., Chm. Bd. & Chief Exec. Officer--Columbian Mutual Life Insurance Co., Binghamton, NY; *U.S. Private*, pg. 256

Shillman, Robert J., Chm. Bd., Pres. & Chief Exec. Officer--Cognex Corporation, Natick, MA; *U.S. Public*, pg. 394

Shimizu, Takuji, Pres., Chief Exec. Officer & Chief Oper. Officer--Meitsu Inc., Tokyo, Japan; *Int'l*, pg. 856

Shipley, Walter V., Chm. Bd. & Chief Exec. Officer--The Chase Manhattan Corporation, New York, NY; *U.S. Public*, pg. 337

Shipley, Walter V., Chm. Bd. & Chief Exec. Officer--The Chase Manhattan Bank, New York, NY; *U.S. Public*, pg. 338

Shipley, Walter V., Chm. Bd. & Chief Exec. Officer--Chase Manhattan Bank of Connecticut, Bridgeport, CT; *U.S. Public*, pg. 338

Shipley, William S. II, Chm. Bd. & Chief Exec. Officer--Shipley Companies, York, PA; *U.S. Private*, pg. 994

Shiraishi, Shozo, Pres. & Chief Exec. Officer--Miura Co., Ltd., Matsuyama, Japan; *Int'l*, pg. 884

Shirvanian, Kosti, Chm. Bd., Pres. & Chief Exec. Officer--Western Waste Industries, Torrance, CA; *U.S. Public*, pg. 1686

Shlomm, Boris, Pres. & Chief Exec. Officer--Amicale Industries, Inc., New York, NY; *U.S. Private*, pg. 66

Shoemate, C.R., Chm. Bd., Pres. & Chief Exec. Officer--Bestfoods, Englewood Cliffs, NJ; *U.S. Public*, pg. 223

Shoham, Y., Pres. & Chief Exec. Officer--Onyx Technologies Ltd., Tel Aviv, Israel; *Int'l*, pg. 1007

Shoham, Y., Pres. & Chief Exec. Officer--Onyx Interactive Multimedia Ltd., Tel Aviv, Israel; *Int'l*, pg. 1007

Shoji, Takashi, Pres. & Chief Exec. Officer--Hakuhodo Incorporated, Tokyo, Japan; *Int'l*, pg. 587

Shokrgozar, Hamid, Pres. & Chief Exec. Officer--Bowmar Instrument Corporation, Phoenix, AZ; *U.S. Public*, pg. 248

Shon, Mark S., Pres. & Chief Exec. Officer--E-C Apparatus Corp., Saint Petersburg, FL; *U.S. Public*, pg. 1595

Shore, Jerry, Chm. Bd. & Chief Exec. Officer--Park Electrochemical Corporation, Lake Success, NY; *U.S. Public*, pg. 1258

Shore, Marc P., Chm. Bd., Pres. & Chief Exec. Officer--Shorewood Packaging Corporation, New York, NY; *U.S. Public*, pg. 1468

Shorenstein, Douglas W., Pres. & Chief Exec. Officer--Shorenstein Company, San Francisco, CA; *U.S. Private*, pg. 996

Shorin, Arthur T., Chm. Bd., Pres. & Chief Exec. Officer--The Topps Company, Inc., New York, NY; *U.S. Public*, pg. 1621

Short, Alan L., Pres. & Chief Exec. Officer--Peoples Bank & Trust Company, Sunman, IN; *U.S. Public*, pg. 633

Shorts, Gary K., Publisher & Chief Exec. Officer--The Morning Call, Allentown, PA; *U.S. Public*, pg. 1616

Shouldice, S. Patrick, Chm. Bd. & Chief Exec. Officer--Nowsco Well Service Ltd., Calgary, Canada; *Int'l*, pg. 989

Shoup, Allen C., Pres. & Chief Exec. Officer--Stimson Lane Ltd., Woodinville, WA; *U.S. Public*, pg. 1661

Shoup, Andrew J., Jr., Pres. & Chief Exec. Officer--The Wiser Oil Company, Dallas, TX; *U.S. Public*, pg. 1773

Shoushanian, Hraut, Chief Oper. Officer--Technic Incorporated, Cranston, RI; *U.S. Private*, pg. 1071
Showalter, Robert, Pres. & Chief Exec. Officer--National City Processing, Inc., Louisville, KY; *U.S. Public*, pg. 1154
Shrader, Joseph M., Chief Exec. Officer--Urban Retail Properties, Inc., Chicago, IL; *U.S. Public*, pg. 1700
Shreiber, Gerald B., Chm. Bd., Pres. & Chief Exec. Officer--J & J Snack Foods Corporation, Pennsauken, NJ; *U.S. Public*, pg. 916
Shuen, Loo Heng, Chief Exec. Officer--Scotts Holdings Limited, Singapore, Singapore; *Int'l*, pg. 1212
Shuey, John H., Chm. Bd., Pres., Chief Exec. & Oper. Officer--Amcast Industrial Corporation, Dayton, OH; *U.S. Public*, pg. 63
Shufeldt, R. Charles, Chief Exec. Officer--SunTrust Securities, Inc., Atlanta, GA; *U.S. Public*, pg. 1538
Shultz, Gerald, Chm. Bd., Pres. & Chief Exec. Officer--Micro-Met L Corp., Indianapolis, IN; *U.S. Private*, pg. 742
Shultz, L.E., Pres. & Chief Exec. Officer--Smith & Wesson Corp., Springfield, MA; *Int'l*, pg. 1397
Shum, Martin, Chm. Bd., Pres. & Chief Exec. Officer--ACT Networks, Inc., Camarillo, CA; *U.S. Public*, pg. 3
Shundman, Bart C., Pres. & Chief Exec. Officer--Transact Technologies Incorporated, Wallingford, CT; *U.S. Public*, pg. 1629
Shure, Daniel B., Pres. & Chief Exec. Officer--Strombecker Corporation, Chicago, IL; *U.S. Private*, pg. 1047
Shuster, George, Pres. & Chief Exec. Officer--Cranston Print Works Company, Cranston, RI; *U.S. Private*, pg. 286
Shute, David, Chief Exec. Officer--Kelly Weedon Shute Partnership, London, United Kingdom; *Int'l*, pg. 727
Shwed, Gil, Pres., Chief Exec. Officer & Co-Founder--Check Point Software Technologies Ltd., Redwood City, CA; *U.S. Public*, pg. 342
Shydlowski, L. Michael, Pres. & Chief Exec. Officer--Master Builders Inc., Cleveland, OH; *Int'l*, pg. 1465
Sia, David, Exec. V.P., Chm., Chief Exec. Officer, Asia/Pacific & Dir.--BBDO Worldwide Inc., New York, NY; U.S. Public, pg. 1223
Sias, John, Chief Exec. Officer--Chronicle Publishing Co. Inc., San Francisco, CA; *U.S. Private*, pg. 239
Sicola, Tom, Pres. & Chief Exec. Officer--SicolaMartin Inc., Austin, TX; *U.S. Private*, pg. 998
Sides, James R., Chm. & Chief Exec. Officer--Atlantic Research Corporation, Gainesville, VA; *U.S. Public*, pg. 1458
Sidgmore, John W., Chief Exec. Officer--UUNET Technologies, Inc., Fairfax, VA; *U.S. Public*, pg. 1779
Sidhu, Jay S., Pres. & Chief Exec. Officer--Sovereign Bancorp, Inc., Wyomissing, PA; *U.S. Public*, pg. 1494
Sidman, Ronald J., Chm. Bd., Pres. & Chief Exec. Officer--The First Years Inc., Avon, MA; *U.S. Public*, pg. 642
Siebel, Carl, Pres. & Chief Exec. Officer--AptarGroup, Inc., Crystal Lake, IL; *U.S. Public*, pg. 125
Siegal, Michael D., Chm. Bd., Pres. & Chief Exec. Officer--Olympic Steel Inc., Cleveland, OH; *U.S. Public*, pg. 1221
Siegel, Clifford A., Chief Exec. Officer--Jefferies International Limited, London, United Kingdom; *U.S. Public*, pg. 925
Siegel, E. Courtney, Pres. & Chief Exec. Officer--Concurrent Computer Corporation, Fort Lauderdale, FL; *U.S. Public*, pg. 430
Siegel, Edward M., Jr., Pres. & Chief Exec. Officer--Russel Metals Inc., Mississauga, Canada; *Int'l*, pg. 1149
Siegel, Laurence C., Chm. Bd. & Chief Exec. Officer--The Mills Corporation, Arlington, VA; *U.S. Public*, pg. 1113
Siegel, Mo, Chief Exec. Officer--Celestial Beverages, Inc., Boulder, CO; *U.S. Public*, pg. 320
Siegel, Owen R., Chm. Bd. & Chief Exec. Officer--R.S. Owens, Chicago, IL; *U.S. Private*, pg. 824
Siegel, Robert, Chm. Bd., Pres. & Chief Exec. Officer--The Stride Rite Corporation, Lexington, MA; *U.S. Public*, pg. 1524
Siegel, Seymour, Chm. Bd. & Chief Exec. Officer--Blue Ridge Farms, Inc., Brooklyn, NY; *U.S. Private*, pg. 153
Siegel, Stuart C., Chm. Bd. & Chief Exec. Officer--S & K Famous Brands, Inc., Glen Allen, VA; *U.S. Public*, pg. 1414
Siemer, Richard C., Pres. & Chief Exec. Officer--Siemer Milling Company, Teutopolis, IL; *U.S. Private*, pg. 998
Sierk, James, Acting Pres. & Chief Exec. Officer--Iomega Corporation, Roy, UT; *U.S. Public*, pg. 912
Sierra, Anthony, Pres.--Business Mens Insurance Corporation, Coral Gables, FL; *U.S. Private*, pg. 189
Sigel, Arthur R., Chm. Bd., Pres. & Chief Exec. Officer--Velsicol Chemical Corporation, Rosemont, IL; *U.S. Private*, pg. 1135
Sigman, Robert, Chief Exec. Officer--Republic Entertainment, Inc., Los Angeles, CA; *U.S. Private*, pg. 776
Signeski, Leonard L., Chm. Bd., Pres. & Chief Exec. Officer--Syndicate Systems, Inc., Middlebury, IN; *U.S. Private*, pg. 1060
Sigrist, R., Chief Exec. Officer--Buss AG, Pratteln, Switzerland; *Int'l*, pg. 490
Silber, Allan, Chm. Bd. & Chief Exec. Officer--Counsel Corporation, Toronto, Canada; *Int'l*, pg. 338
Sill, Michael R., Chm. Bd. & Chief Exec. Officer--Road Machinery & Supplies Co., Savage, MN; *U.S. Private*, pg. 934
Sillard, Benoit, Chief Exec. Officer--Fun Radio, Neuilly-sur-Seine, France; *Int'l*, pg. 561
Sills, Lawrence I., Pres. & Chief Exec. & Oper. Officer--Standard Motor Products Inc., Long Island City, NY; *U.S. Public*, pg. 1503
Sills, Stephen J., Pres. & Chief Exec. Officer--Executive Risk, Inc., Simsbury, CT; *U.S. Public*, pg. 599
Silva Salgado, Ricardo Espirito Santo, Vice Chm., Pres. & Chief Exec. Officer--Banco Espirito Santo e Comercial de Lisboa SA, Lisbon, Portugal; *Int'l*, pg. 142
Silver, Bernard, Co-Chm. & Co-Chief Exec. Officer--Allied Bond & Collection Agency, Inc., Trevose, PA; *U.S. Public*, pg. 1667
Silver, Herbert R., Co-Chm. & Co-Chief Exec. Officer--Allied Bond & Collection Agency, Inc., Trevose, PA; *U.S. Public*, pg. 1667
Silver, Joel, Chm. Bd., Chief Fin. Officer & Chief Exec. Officer--International Cutlery, LTD, New York, NY; *U.S. Private*, pg. 569
Silver, R. Phillip, Chm. Bd. & Co-Chief Exec. Officer--Silgan Corporation, Stamford, CT; *U.S. Public*, pg. 1473
Silver, Walton A., Pres. & Chief Exec. Officer--Akrochem Corporation, Akron, OH; *U.S. Private*, pg. 30
Silverberg, H. Gene, Chief Exec. Officer--Bigsby & Kruthers Companies, Chicago, IL; *U.S. Private*, pg. 143
Silverman, Henry, Chm. Bd. & Chief Exec. Officer--HFS, Incorporated, Parsippany, NJ; *U.S. Public*, pg. 321
Silverman, Henry R., Pres. & Chief Exec. Officer--Cendant Corporation, Stamford, CT; *U.S. Public*, pg. 320
Silverman, Joel, Acting Chief Exec. Officer--Galyan's Trading Co., Plainfield, IN; *U.S. Public*, pg. 995
Silverstein, Robert, Pres. & Chief Exec. Officer--Arch Aluminium & Glass L.C., Tamarac, FL; *U.S. Private*, pg. 79
Sim, Richard G., Chm. Bd. & Chief Exec. Officer--Applied Power Inc., Butler, WI; *U.S. Public*, pg. 124
Simkins, L.J., Chm. Bd., Pres., Chief Exec. & Chief Oper. Officer--Simkins Industries, Inc., New Haven, CT; *U.S. Private*, pg. 1000
Simko, John S., Chm. Bd. & Chief Exec. Officer--Sunshine Mining And Refining Company, Boise, ID; *U.S. Public*, pg. 1536
Simmons, D. Ramsay, Jr., Pres. & Chief Exec. Officer--Elberta Crate & Box Company, Bainbridge, GA; *U.S. Private*, pg. 367
Simmons, Edward M., Chm. Bd. & Chief Exec. Officer--McIlhenny Company, Avery Island, LA; *U.S. Private*, pg. 722
Simmons, Gaylan, Pres. & Chief Exec. Officer--Pacific Northern Inc., Seattle, WA; *U.S. Private*, pg. 832
Simmons, Hardwick, Pres. & Chief Exec. Officer-Prudential Securities, Inc.--The Prudential Insurance Company of America, Newark, NJ; *U.S. Private*, pg. 892
Simmons, Hardwick, Pres. & Chief Exec. Officer--Prudential Securities Inc., New York, NY; *U.S. Private*, pg. 892
Simmons, Harold C., Chm. Bd., Pres. & Chief Exec. Officer--Contran Corporation, Dallas, TX; *U.S. Private*, pg. 270
Simmons, Harold C., Chm. Bd. & Chief Exec. Officer--Valhi, Inc., Dallas, TX; *U.S. Private*, pg. 270
Simmons, Harris H., Pres. & Chief Exec. Officer--Zions Bancorporation, Salt Lake City, UT; *U.S. Public*, pg. 1792
Simmons, Paul, Chm. Bd. & Pres.--Simons Palmer Denton Clemmow & Johnson Ltd., London, United Kingdom; *Int'l*, pg. 1252
Simmons, Richard E., III, Pres. & Chief Exec. Officer--Hilb, Rogal and Hamilton Company of Alabama, Inc., Birmingham, AL; *U.S. Public*, pg. 827
Simmons, Richard P., Chm. Bd., Pres. & Chief Exec. Officer--Allegheny Teledyne Incorporated, Pittsburgh, PA; *U.S. Public*, pg. 43
Simms, G. S., Chief Exec.--Lombard and Ulster Limited, Belfast, United Kingdom; *Int'l*, pg. 910
Simms, Neville, Dep. Chm. & Chief Exec. Officer--Tarmac plc, Wolverhampton, United Kingdom; *Int'l*, pg. 1355
Simon, Alan D., Chm. Bd. & Chief Exec. Officer--Omaha Steaks, Omaha, NE; *U.S. Private*, pg. 815
Simon, David, Chief Exec. Officer--Simon DeBartolo Group, Inc., Indianapolis, IN; *U.S. Public*, pg. 1474
Simon, David A., Chm. Bd., Pres. & Chief Exec. Officer--Prime Hospitality Corp., Fairfield, NJ; *U.S. Public*, pg. 1326
Simon, Irwin D., Pres. & Chief Exec. Officer--The Hain Food Group Inc., Uniondale, NY; *U.S. Public*, pg. 774
Simon, Leonard S., Chm. Bd. & Chief Exec. Officer--Rochester Community Savings Bank, Rochester, NY; *U.S. Public*, pg. 336
Simon, Martin, Pres.--Triangle Brass Manufacturing, Los Angeles, CA; *U.S. Private*, pg. 1101
Simon, Ralph, Dr., Pres. & Chief Exec. Officer--QT Optoelectronics, Sunnyvale, CA; *U.S. Private*, pg. 897
Simonds, Christopher E., Pres. & Chief Exec. Officer--Genelco, Inc., Saint Louis, MO; *U.S. Private*, pg. 443
Simonil, D.F., Chief Oper. Officer--Northwest Alloys, Inc., Addy, WA; *U.S. Public*, pg. 61
Simonin, Dominique, Mng. Partner & Chief Edec. Officer-Europe--Conquest Europe S.A.R.L., Neuilly-sur-Seine, France; *Int'l*, pg. 1484
Simourian, John A., Chm. Bd. & Chief Exec. Officer--Lily Transportation Corp., Needham, MA; *U.S. Private*, pg. 667
Simpson, Bill, Chm. & Chief Exec. Officer-Periscope Group--Periscope Marketing Communications, Minneapolis, MN; *U.S. Private*, pg. 853
Simpson, Jack, Pres., Chief Exec. Officer & Chief Oper. Officer--Advance Seed Co., Fulton, KY; *Int'l*, pg. 566
Simpson, John, Pres. & Chief Exec. Officer--H.E. Sargent, Inc., Stillwater, ME; *U.S. Private*, pg. 966
Simpson, Louis A., Pres. & Chief Exec. Officer-Capital Opers.--GEICO Corporation, Washington, DC; *U.S. Public*, pg. 219
Simpson, Phil, Chm. Bd., Pres. & Chief Exec. Officer--Republic Group Incorporated, Hutchinson, KS; *U.S. Public*, pg. 1378
Simpson, Robert, Chm. Bd. & Chief Exec. Officer--A.G. Simpson Co. Limited, Scarborough, Canada; *Int'l*, pg. 1252
Simpson, Sam, Pres. & Chief Exec. Officer--Cable Car Beverage Corporation, Denver, CO; *U.S. Public*, pg. 1635
Simpson, William, Chief Exec. Officer--The Pfaltzgraff Co., York, PA; *U.S. Private*, pg. 860
Simpson, William, Chief Exec. Officer--Silentnight Holdings Plc, Colne, United Kingdom; *Int'l*, pg. 1249
Sims, Douglas D., Pres. & Chief Exec. Officer--CoBank, Englewood, CO; *U.S. Private*, pg. 398
Sims, James K., Pres. & Chief Exec. Officer--Cambridge Technology Partners, Cambridge, MA; *U.S. Public*, pg. 1424
Sims, Judy O., Chm. Bd., Pres. & Chief Exec. Officer--Software Spectrum, Inc., Garland, TX; *U.S. Public*, pg. 1483
Sims, Larry D., Pres. & Chief Exec. Officer--Marley Floors (USA) Inc., Tuscumbia, AL; *Int'l*, pg. 843
Sims, Willis D., Pres. & Chief Exec. Officer--SunTrust Bank, South Georgia, N.A., Albany, GA; *U.S. Public*, pg. 1538
Simunek, Tom, Pres. & Chief Exec. Officer--Bradley Printing Company, Des Plaines, IL; *U.S. Public*, pg. 1778
Sinclair, C.J.F., Chief Exec. Officer--Daily Mail & General Trust PLC, London, United Kingdom; *Int'l*, pg. 366
Sinclair, Christopher A., Pres. & Chief Exec. Officer--Quality Food Centers, Inc., Bellevue, WA; *U.S. Public*, pg. 1349
Sinclair, Christopher D., Pres. & Chief Exec. Officer--QFC Holding Company, Stamford, CT; *U.S. Public*, pg. 1349
Sinclair, Desmond, Chm. Bd. & Pres.--DEECO Industries, Hillside, NJ; *U.S. Private*, pg. 320
Sincoff, Jerome J., Pres.--Hellmuth, Obata & Kassabaum, Inc., Saint Louis, MO; *U.S. Private*, pg. 520
Sinegal, James D., Pres. & Chief Exec. Officer--Costco Wholesale, Issaquah, WA; *U.S. Public*, pg. 451
Singer, Garold G., Pres. & Chief Exec. Officer--Alpine Packing Company, Stockton, CA; *U.S. Private*, pg. 45
Singer, Michael A., Chm. Bd. & Chief Exec. Officer--Medical Manager Corporation, Tampa, FL; *U.S. Public*, pg. 1080
Singer, Robert W., Pres., Chief Exec. Officer & Chief Oper. Officer--Keystone Consolidated Industries, Inc., Dallas, TX; *U.S. Public*, pg. 955
Singh, Jeet, Pres. & Chief Exec. Officer--Art Technology Group, Boston, MA; *U.S. Private*, pg. 86
Singh, Karmjit, Chief Exec. Officer & Gen. Mgr.--SATS Apron Services Pte., Ltd., Singapore, Singapore; *Int'l*, pg. 1374
Singleton, R.L., Pres. & Chief Exec. Officer--Russell-Stanley Corporation, Red Bank, NJ; *U.S. Private*, pg. 953
Singleton, William Dean, Pres. & Chief Exec. Officer--MediaNews Group Inc., Denver, CO; *U.S. Private*, pg. 727
Singleton, William Dean, Vice Chm., Pres. & Chief Exec. Officer--Garden State Newspapers, Inc., Denver, CO; *U.S. Private*, pg. 727
Sinnott, John T., Chief Exec. Officer--J&H Marsh & McLennan, Inc., New York, NY; *U.S. Public*, pg. 1049
Sinton, Thomas H., Chm. Bd., Pres. & Chief Exec. Officer--ProBusiness Services, Inc., Pleasanton, CA; *U.S. Public*, pg. 1330
Sirois, Charles, Chm. & Chief Exec. Officer--Teleglobe, Inc., Montreal, Canada; *Int'l*, pg. 1373
Sirois, Charles, Chm. Bd. & Chief Exec. Officer--Teleglobe Canada Inc., Montreal, Canada; *Int'l*, pg. 1373
Sison, B.I., Chief Oper. Officer--APEX Motor Mfg. Corp., Manila, Philippines; *Int'l*, pg. 947
Sissel, George A., Chm. Bd., Pres. & Chief Exec. Officer--Ball Corporation, Muncie, IN; *U.S. Public*, pg. 170
Sissener, Einar W., Chm. & Chief Exec. Officer--Alpharma Inc., Fort Lee, NJ; *U.S. Public*, pg. 57
Sittason, Charles R., Chm. Bd. & Chief Exec. Officer--Regions Bank/Tuscaloosa, Tuscaloosa, AL; *U.S. Public*, pg. 1373
Sivan, Amiran, Chief Exec. Officer & Chm.-Mgmnt. Bd.--Bank Hapoalim, Tel Aviv, Israel; *Int'l*, pg. 149
Sivitz, William, Chief Exec. Officer--Wicks 'n Sticks, Ltd, Houston, TX; *U.S. Private*, pg. 1175
Sizemore, Dale H., Jr., Chm. Bd. & Chief Exec. Officer--Torotel, Inc., Grandview, MO; *U.S. Public*, pg. 1624
Sjoberg, Bjorn, Chief Officer--KF Fastigheter AB, Stockholm, Sweden; *Int'l*, pg. 718
Sjoqvist, Jan, Pres. & Chief Exec. Officer--NCC AB, Solna, Sweden; *Int'l*, pg. 898
Skaggs, James B., Chm. Bd., Pres. & Chief Exec. Officer--Tracor, Inc., Austin, TX; *U.S. Public*, pg. 1627
Skaggs, Robert C., Jr., Pres. & Chief Exec. Officer--Columbia Gas of Kentucky, Inc., Columbus, OH; *U.S. Public*, pg. 403
Skaggs, Robert C., Jr., Pres. & Chief Exec. Officer--Columbia Gas of Ohio, Inc., Columbus, OH; *U.S. Public*, pg. 403
Skandalaris, Robert J., Pres. & Chief Exec. Officer--Noble International Ltd., Bloomfield Hills, MI; *U.S. Public*, pg. 1187
Skates, Ronald L., Pres. & Chief Exec. Officer--Data General Corporation, Westborough, MA; *U.S. Public*, pg. 485
Skelly, Jim, Chief Exec. Officer--Thermalloy, Inc., Farmers Branch, TX; *Int'l*, pg. 208
Skeppner, Ake, Chief Exec. Officer & Mng. Dir.--Eldon AB, Nassjo, Sweden; *Int'l*, pg. 436
Skidmore, A. Allan, Vice Chm., Pres. & Chief Exec. Officer-Automotive Grp.--TCG International Inc., Burnaby, Canada; *Int'l*, pg. 1336
Skidmore, Arthur, Chm. Bd. & Chief Exec. Officer--TCG International Inc., Burnaby, Canada; *Int'l*, pg. 1336
Skidmore, James A., Jr., Chm. Bd., Pres. & Chief Exec. Officer--Science Management Corporation, Bridgewater, NJ; *U.S. Public*, pg. 1717
Skidmore, Thomas E., Vice Chm.-Fin. & Investments & Chief Exec. Officer-Communications--TCG International Inc., Burnaby, Canada; *Int'l*, pg. 1336
Skidmore, Thomas E., Chm. Bd., Pres. & Chief Exec. Officer--Glentel Inc., Burnaby, Canada; *Int'l*, pg. 1336
Skillern, Frank J., Jr., Chief Exec. Officer-American Express Centurion Bank & Deposit Cor--American Express Company, New York, NY; *U.S. Public*, pg. 73
Skilton, Harry I., Pres. & Chief Exec. Officer--American Meter Company, Horsham, PA; *Int'l*, pg. 1149
Skinner, Claire C., Chm. Bd. & Chief Exec. Officer--Coachmen Industries, Inc., Elkhart, IN; *U.S. Public*, pg. 387

Skirka, Kenneth John, Pres., Chief Exec. & Oper. Officer, Mng. Dir.--Australian Oil & Gas Corporation Limited, Sydney, Australia; *Int'l*, pg. 101

Skraning, Gyrd, Pres. & Chief Exec. Officer--Helly-Hansen A/S, Moss, Norway; *Int'l*, pg. 1010

Skuba, William C., Chm. Bd., Pres., Chief Exec. Officer & Sec.--Eastern Environmental Services, Inc., Drums, PA; *U.S. Public*, pg. 549

Slack, John L., Chm. Bd., Pres., Chief Exec. Officer & Acting Treas.--DBA Systems, Inc., Melbourne, FL; *U.S. Public*, pg. 472

Slade, Vic, Chief Exec. Officer--Printpac-UEB Carton Group, Auckland, New Zealand; *U.S. Public*, pg. 905

Slaine, Mason P., Pres. & Chief Exec. Officer--Thomson Financial Services, Stamford, CT; *U.S. Public*, pg. 1601

Slama, Thomas G., Pres. & Chief Exec. Officer--National Infusion Services, Inc., Indianapolis, IN; *U.S. Public*, pg. 229

Slamecka, Thomas A., Pres. & Chief Oper. Officer--ConAgra Poultry Company, El Dorado, AR; *U.S. Public*, pg. 427

Slate, William K., II, Pres. & Chief Exec. Officer--American Arbitration Association, New York, NY; *U.S. Private*, pg. 50

Slater, Chuck, Chief Exec. Officer--Healthsource North Texas, Inc., Fort Worth, TX; *U.S. Public*, pg. 360

Slater, James K., Chief Exec. Officer--Barnett Banks Services Insurance, Inc., Jacksonville, FL; *U.S. Public*, pg. 1162

Slater, John E., Jr., Pres. & Chief Exec. Officer--Haverty Furniture Companies, Inc., Atlanta, GA; *U.S. Public*, pg. 799

Slater, Thomas F., Chm. Bd., Pres. & Chief Exec. Officer--Actron Manufacturing Company, Cleveland, OH; *U.S. Private*, pg. 16

Slattery, John T., Chm. Bd. & Chief Exec. Officer--Lake Business Products, Inc., Willoughby, OH; *U.S. Private*, pg. 643

Slattery, Robert, Chief Exec. Officer--The Rockport Company, Marlborough, MA; *U.S. Public*, pg. 1370

Slavin, Roy H., Chm. Bd., Pres. & Chief Exec. Officer--Wonderware Corporation, Irvine, CA; *U.S. Public*, pg. 1775

Slayton, Maurice, Pres.--Conning, Hartford, CT; *U.S. Private*, *pg. 443*

Sledd, Robert C., Chm. Bd. & Chief Exec. Officer--Performance Food Group Company, Richmond, VA; *U.S.* Public, pg. 1278

Sleewuwenhoek, Hans, Pres. & Chief Exec. Officer--Tactyl Technologies, Inc., Vista, CA; *U.S. Public*, pg. 1425

Sleigh, Ron, Pres. & Chief Exec. Officer--UPB of North Central Tennessee, Erin, TN; *U.S. Public*, pg. 1669

Slevin, Jack, Chm. Bd., Pres. & Chief Exec. Officer--Comdisco, Inc., Rosemont, IL; *U.S. Public*, pg. 407

Slifka, Alfred A., Pres. & Chief Exec. Officer--Global Petroleum Corp., Waltham, MA; *U.S. Private*, pg. 457

Sloan, Morton, Chief Exec. Officer--Secretly Yours Inc., Harrison, NJ; *U.S. Private*, pg. 565

Sloan, Morton, Chief Exec. Officer--Allegria Inc., Harrison, NJ; *U.S. Private*, pg. 565

Sloan, O. Temple, Jr., Chm. Bd. & Chief Exec. Officer--General Parts, Inc., Raleigh, NC; *U.S. Private*, pg. 445

Sloane, A. Richard, Chm. Bd. & Chief Exec. Officer--Softmart, Inc., Downingtown, PA; *U.S. Private*, pg. 1012

Sloss, Lynes, Pres. & Chief Exec. Officer--Bellwether Technology Corporation, New Orleans, LA; *U.S. Private*, pg. 132

Slowik, Lawrence, Pres. & Chief Exec. Officer--AR Accessories Group, Inc., Milwaukee, WI; *U.S. Private*, pg. 7

Slusarchuk, William A., Pres. & Chief Exec. Officer--AGRA Earth & Environmental Limited, Calgary, Canada; *Int'l*, pg. 30

Slutzky, Joel, Chm. Bd. & Chief Exec. Officer--Odetics Inc., Anaheim, CA; *U.S. Public*, pg. 1212

Small, A., Chief Exec. Officer--Zurich Australian Insurance Limited, Sydney, Australia; *Int'l*, pg. 1531

Small, A., Chief Exec. Officer--Zurich Australian Life Insurance Limited, Sydney, Australia; *Int'l*, pg. 1531

Small, Robert, Pres. & Chief Exec. Officer--The Fairmont Hotels, San Francisco, CA; *U.S. Private*, pg. 391

Smalley, Randall S., Pres. & Chief Exec. Officer--Cruise America, Inc., Mesa, AZ; *U.S. Private*, pg. 178

Smead, H.J., Chm. Bd., Chief Exec. & Chief Fin. Officer & Sec.--Kaiser Aerospace & Electronics Corp., Foster City, CA; *U.S. Private*, pg. 605

Smeller, Carl J., Pres. & Chief Exec. Officer--Buckeye Corrugated Inc., Wooster, OH; *U.S. Private*, pg. 177

Smetana, Joseph C., Jr., Chm. Bd. & Chief Exec. Officer--AIG Risk Management, Inc., New York, NY; *U.S. Public*, pg. 85

Smialek, Robert, Chief Exec. Officer--American Protection Insurance Co., Long Grove, IL; *U.S. Private*, pg. 614

Smialek, Robert L., Pres. & Chief Exec. Officer--Insilco Corporation, Dublin, OH; *U.S. Public*, pg. 881

Smillie, Scott, Chief Exec. Officer--Hennells, Inc., Ferndale, MI; *U.S. Private*, pg. 522

Smit, James H., Pres. & Chief Exec. Officer--Spartan Oil Corp., Lansing, MI; *U.S. Private*, pg. 1021

Smith, A.J.C., Chm. Bd. & Chief Exec. Officer--Marsh & McLennan Companies, Inc., New York, NY; *U.S. Public*, pg. 1048

Smith, A.W., Jr., Pres. & Chief Exec. Officer--Watson Wyatt Worldwide, Bethesda, MD; *U.S. Private*, pg. 1154

Smith, Adrian J.R., Chief Exec. Officer--Grant Thornton LLP, Chicago, IL; *U.S. Private*, pg. 470

Smith, Albert A., Pres. & Chief Exec. Officer--Utility Engineering Corporation, Amarillo, TX; *U.S. Public*, pg. 1170

Smith, Allen J., Pres. & Chief Exec. Officer--Oriel Instruments Corporation, Stratford, CT; *U.S. Private*, pg. 819

Smith, Archie W., III, Chief Exec. Officer--Universal Construction Company, Inc., Kansas City, KS; *U.S. Private*, pg. 1127

Smith, Arthur O., Chief Exec. Officer--Smith Investment Company, Milwaukee, WI; *U.S. Private*, pg. 1008

Smith, Brian, Chm. Bd. & Chief Exec. Officer--B.C. Hydro, Vancouver, Canada; *Int'l*, pg. 114

Smith, Bruce A., Chm. Bd., Pres. & Chief Exec. Officer--Tesoro Petroleum Corporation, San Antonio, TX; *U.S. Public*, pg. 1581

Smith, Bruton, Chm. Bd. & Chief Exec. Officer--Speedway Motorsports, Inc., Concord, NC; *U.S. Public*, pg. 1498

Smith, Charles Miller, Chief Exec. Officer--Imperial Chemical Industries PLC, London, United Kingdom; *Int'l*, pg. 662

Smith, Clifton L., Pres. & Chief Exec. Officer--Corning Asahi Video Products Company, Corning, NY; *Int'l*, pg. 84

Smith, Clifton L., Pres. & Chief Exec. Officer--Corning Asahi Video Products Company, Corning, NY; *U.S. Public*, pg. 449

Smith, Colin, Chief Exec. Officer--Safeway Stores plc, Hayes, United Kingdom; *Int'l*, pg. 1169

Smith, Colin D., Chief Exec. Officer--Safeway PLC, Hayes, United Kingdom; *Int'l*, pg. 1169

Smith, Craig, Chm. Bd., Pres. & Chief Exec. Officer--Hereford State Bank, Hereford, TX; *U.S. Public*, pg. 633

Smith, Craig R., Pres. & Chief Exec. Officer--Raytech Corporation, Shelton, CT; *U.S. Public*, pg. 1363

Smith, Cullen F., Pres. & Chief Exec. Officer--Bergen Brunswig Medical Corporation, Orange, CA; *U.S. Public*, pg. 214

Smith, Dan F., Pres. & Chief Exec. Officer--Lyondell Petrochemical Company, Houston, TX; *U.S. Public*, pg. 1022

Smith, Dan L., Chm. Bd., Pres. & Chief Exec. Officer--Shoreline Financial Corp., Benton Harbor, MI; *U.S. Public*, pg. 1467

Smith, Darrell, Pres. & Chief Exec. Officer--Hickory Printing Group, Inc., Conover, NC; *U.S. Private*, pg. 525

Smith, Daryl D., Pres. & Chief Exec. Officer--Troy Corporation, Florham Park, NJ; *U.S. Private*, pg. 1105

Smith, David, Pres. & Chief Exec. Officer--American Eurocopter Corp., Grand Prairie, TX; *Int'l*, pg. 29

Smith, David, Chief Exec. Officer--Healthsource Indiana, Indianapolis, IN; *U.S. Public*, pg. 360

Smith, David, Chief Exec. Officer--Healthsource Kentucky, Louisville, KY; *U.S. Public*, pg. 360

Smith, David, Pres. & Chief Exec. Officer--Quad Systems Corporation, Willow Grove, PA; *U.S. Private*, pg. 898

Smith, David D., Chief Fin. Officer--Material Handling Equipment Division, Oak Creek, WI; *U.S. Public*, pg. 788

Smith, David, Ph.D, Chief Exec. Officer--Whatman plc, Maidstone, United Kingdom; *Int'l*, pg. 1498

Smith, Dennis A., Chm. Bd., Pres. & Chief Exec. Officer--Crawford & Company, Atlanta, GA; *U.S. Public*, pg. 458

Smith, Donald, Chm. Bd. & Chief Exec. Officer--The Restaurant Company, Itasca, IL; *U.S. Private*, pg. 925

Smith, Donald E., Pres. & Chief Exec. Officer--First Financial Corporation, Terre Haute, IN; *U.S. Public*, pg. 633

Smith, Donald E., Pres. & Chief Exec. Officer--Terre Haute First National Bank, Terre Haute, IN; *U.S. Public*, pg. 634

Smith, Donald G., Chm. Bd., Pres., Chief Exec. Officer & Treas.--Roanoke Electric Steel Corporation, Roanoke, VA; *U.S. Public*, pg. 1392

Smith, Douglas A., Chm. & Chief Exec. Officer--Borden Foods Corporation, Columbus, OH; *U.S. Private*, pg. 157

Smith, Douglas V., Chm. Bd., Pres. & Chief Exec. Officer--Lufkin Industries, Inc., Lufkin, TX; *U.S. Public*, pg. 1019

Smith, E. Brian, Chm., Pres. & Chief Exec. Officer--Smith Environmental Technologies Corp., Plymouth Meeting, PA; *U.S. Public*, pg. 1477

Smith, E. Brian, Chm. Bd. & Chief Exec. Officer--Smith Technologies Corp., Portland, OR; *U.S. Public*, pg. 1478

Smith, E. Warren, Jr., Pres. & Chief Exec. Officer--Regions Bank/Middle Tennessee, Nashville, TN; *U.S. Public*, pg. 1372

Smith, Frederick W., Chm. Bd., Pres. & Chief Exec. Officer--FDX Corporation, Memphis, TN; *U.S. Public*, pg. 603

Smith, Gary B., Pres. & Chief Exec. Officer--Glenayre Technologies, Inc., Charlotte, NC; *U.S. Public*, pg. 746

Smith, Gary W., Chm. Bd., Pres. & Chief Exec. Officer--Proto Systems of Atlanta, Alpharetta, GA; *U.S. Private*, pg. 891

Smith, George E., Pres. & Chief Exec. Officer--Alco Industries, Inc., Valley Forge, PA; *U.S. Private*, pg. 32

Smith, Gordon H., Chm. Bd., Pres. & Chief Exec. Officer--Sargent-Fletcher Inc., El Monte, CA; *Int'l*, pg. 301

Smith, Gordon R., Pres. & Chief Exec. Officer--Pacific Gas & Electric Company, San Francisco, CA; *U.S. Public*, pg. 1241

Smith, H. Kemer, Chm. Bd., Pres. & Chief Exec. Officer--Stone & Webster Engineering & Constructors Corp., Boston, MA; *U.S. Public*, pg. 1519

Smith, H. Kerner, Chm. Bd., Pres. & Chief Exec. Officer--Stone & Webster, Incorporated, Boston, MA; *U.S. Public*, *pg. 1519*

Smith, Henry B., Pres. & Chief Exec. Officer--The Bank of Bermuda Limited, Hamilton, Bermuda; *Int'l*, pg. 150

Smith, Hyrum W., Chm. Bd. & Chief Exec. Officer--Franklin Covey, Salt Lake City, UT; *U.S. Public*, pg. 679

Smith, J. Edward, Pres. & Chief Exec. Officer--WIC Radio Ltd., Vancouver, Canada; *Int'l*, pg. 1482

Smith, J. Morse, Chm. Bd.--H.J. Baker & Bro., Inc., Stamford, CT; *U.S. Private*, pg. 112

Smith, J.E., Chief Exec. Officer--Waters Coal Company, Andalusia, AL; *U.S. Private*, pg. 30

Smith, J.E., Chief Exec. Officer--United Energy Corporation, Andalusia, AL; *U.S. Private*, pg. 30

Smith, J.E., Chief Exec. Officer--Lakeside Coal Company, Andalusia, AL; *U.S. Private*, pg. 30

Smith, J.E., Chief Exec. Officer--Andalusia & Conecuh Railroad, Inc., Andalusia, AL; *U.S. Private*, pg. 30

Smith, J.E., Chief Exec. Officer--Power South, Andalusia, AL; *U.S. Private*, pg. 30

Smith, J.H., III, Chief Oper. Officer--Maclin-Zimmer McGill Tobacco Company, Inc., Petersburg, VA; *U.S. Public*, pg. 1695

Smith, J.L., Pres. & Chief Exec. Officer--J.R. Smith Manufacturing Company, Montgomery, AL; *U.S. Private*, pg. 1008

Smith, Jack, Pres. & Chief Exec. Officer--Pharmacists Public Relations Bureau, Wichita, KS; *U.S. Private*, pg. 295

Smith, Jack, Pres. & Chief Exec. Officer--Pharmacists Public Relations Bureau, New York, NY; *U.S. Private*, pg. 295

Smith, Jack, Chm. Bd. & Chief Exec. Officer--The Sports Authority Inc., Fort Lauderdale, FL; *U.S. Public*, pg. 1499

Smith, James C., Pres. & Chief Exec. Officer--First Health Group Corp., Downers Grove, IL; *U.S. Public*, pg. 635

Smith, James C., Chm. Bd. & Chief Exec. Officer--Webster Financial Corporation, Waterbury, CT; *U.S. Public*, pg. 1751

Smith, James C., Chm. Bd., Pres. & Chief Exec. Officer--Webster Bank, Waterbury, CT; *U.S. Public*, pg. 1751

Smith, James Keith, II, Pres. & Chief Exec. Officer--Keith Smith Company, Hot Springs National Park, AR; *U.S. Private*, pg. 1008

Smith, Jay L., Pres. & Chief Exec. Officer--Smith Industries, Inc., Montgomery, AL; *U.S. Private*, pg. 1008

Smith, John F., Jr., Chm. Bd., Pres. & Chief Exec. Officer--General Motors Corporation, Detroit, MI; *U.S. Public*, pg. 718

Smith, John J., Chm. Bd. & Chief Exec. Officer--Sparton Corporation, Jackson, MI; *U.S. Public*, pg. 1496

Smith, Joshua I., Chm. Bd. & Chief Exec. Officer--The Maxima Corporation, Lanham, MD; *U.S. Private*, pg. 716

Smith, L.S., Dr., Chm. Bd., Chief Exec. Officer, Treas. & Sec.--Dallas Gold & Silver Exchange, Inc., Dallas, TX; *U.S. Public*, pg. 478

Smith, Londeo A., Vice Chm.-The Hartford & Pres. & Chief Exec. Officer-H. Life--The Hartford Financial Services Group Inc., Hartford, CT; *U.S. Public*, pg. 794

Smith, Mark, Pres. & Chief Exec.Officer--Stewart Smith East, Inc., New York, NY; *Int'l*, pg. 1508

Smith, Mark C., Chm. Bd. & Chief Exec. Officer--ADTRAN, Inc., Huntsville, AL; *U.S. Public*, pg. 20

Smith, Michael J., Pres. & Chief Exec. Officer--Lands' End, Inc., Dodgeville, WI; *U.S. Public*, pg. 977

Smith, Mike, Chief Exec. Officer & V.P.--Reedspectrum, Holden, MA; *Int'l*, pg. 624

Smith, Mike E., Chief Exec. Officer, Betting & Gaming--Ladbroke Group Plc, London, United Kingdom; *Int'l*, pg. 787

Smith, Murray, Pres. & Chief Exec. Officer--CSS USA, New York, NY; *U.S. Public*, pg. 1642

Smith, Nate, Chief Exec. Officer--Sky Network Television Limited, Auckland, New Zealand; *U.S. Public*, pg. 204

Smith, O. Bruton, Chm. Bd. & Chief Exec. Officer--Sonic Automotive, Inc., Charlotte, NC; *U.S. Public*, pg. 1485

Smith, Orin R., Chm. Bd. & Chief Exec. Officer--Engelhard Corporation, Iselin, NJ; *U.S. Public*, pg. 582

Smith, Raymond W., Chm. Bd. & Chief Exec. Officer--Bell Atlantic Corporation, New York, NY; *U.S. Public*, pg. 201

Smith, Richard, Pres. & Chief Exec. Officer--Stern-Leach Company, Attleboro, MA; *Int'l*, pg. 329

Smith, Richard, Pres. & Chief Exec. Officer--Namanco LLC, Tulsa, OK; *U.S. Private*, pg. 773

Smith, Richard A., Chm., Pres. & Chief Exec. Officer-Real Estate Div.--HFS, Incorporated, Parsippany, NJ; *U.S. Public*, pg. 321

Smith, Richard A., Chm. Bd. & Chief Exec. Officer--GC Companies, Inc., Chestnut Hill, MA; *U.S. Public*, pg. 693

Smith, Richard A., Chm. Bd. & Chief Exec. Officer--Harcourt General, Inc., Chestnut Hill, MA; *U.S. Public*, pg. 782

Smith, Richard C., Chief Exec. Officer--Bellcore, Morristown, NJ; *U.S. Private*, pg. 976

Smith, Richard E., Chm. Bd. & Chief Exec. Officer--Integrated Brands Inc., Ronkonkoma, NY; *U.S. Public*, pg. 883

Smith, Richard P., Chief Exec. Officer--Dairylea Cooperative Inc., East Syracuse, NY; *U.S. Private*, pg. 307

Smith, Robert, Chief Exec. Officer--FTSB Broadcasting, Saint Petersburg, FL; *U.S. Private*, pg. 389

Smith, Robin B., Chm. & Chief Exec. Officer--Publishers Clearing House, Port Washington, NY; *U.S. Private*, pg. 893

Smith, Rodney, Chm. Bd., Pres. & Chief Exec. Officer--Altera Corporation, San Jose, CA; *U.S. Public*, pg. 59

Smith, S., Chief Exec. Officer--Zurich Insurance Company, Toronto, Canada; *Int'l*, pg. 1531

Smith, S., Chief Exec. Officer--Zurich Indemnity Company of Canada, Toronto, Canada; *Int'l*, pg. 1531

Smith, S.B., Pres. & Chief Exec. Officer--Ph. Orth Co., Oak Creek, WI; *Int'l*, pg. 244

Smith, Scott, Chief Exec. Officer--KBA-Motter Corp., York, PA; *Int'l*, pg. 742

Smith, Sheldon E., Chm. Bd., Pres. & Chief Exec. Officer--Old Fashion Foods, Inc., Austell, GA; *U.S. Private*, pg. 814

Smith, Steve, Pres. & Chief Exec. Officer--UPB of Central Arkansas NA, Clinton, AR; *U.S. Public*, pg. 1669

Smith, Steven B., Chm. Bd., Pres. & Chief Exec. Officer--SBS Enterprises Inc., Waco, TX; *U.S. Private*, pg. 955

Smith, Steven B., Chm. Bd., Pres. & Chief Exec. Officer--Spenco Medical Corporation, Waco, TX; *U.S. Private*, pg. 955

Smith, Terry, Chief Exec.--National Mutual Asia Ltd., Wan Chai, Hong Kong; *Int'l*, pg. 909

Smith, Theodore B., Jr., Chm. Bd. & Chief Exec. Officer--John Hassall, Inc., Westbury, NY; *U.S. Private*, pg. 509

Smith, Theodore J., Chm. Bd. & Chief Exec. Officer--FileNet Corporation, Costa Mesa, CA; *U.S. Public*, pg. 622

Smith, Thomas J., Pres. & Chief Exec. Officer--Coats North America, Charlotte, NC; *Int'l*, pg. 300

Smith, Thomas J., Pres. & Chief Exec. Officer--Norwesco, Inc., Saint Bonifacius, MN; *U.S. Private*, pg. 808
Smith, Tim, Chm. & Chief Exec. Officer--Red Sky Interactive, San Francisco, CA; *U.S. Public*, pg. 1224
Smith, Tim, Chief Exec. Officer--Red Sky Interactive, San Francisco, CA; *U.S. Public*, pg. 1224
Smith, Tom E., Chm. Bd., Pres. & Chief Exec. Officer--Food Lion, Inc., Salisbury, NC; *Int'l*, pg. 463
Smith, W. Keith, Chm. Bd. & Chief Exec. Officer--The Boston Company, Inc., Boston, MA; *U.S. Public*, pg. 1085
Smith, W. Keith, Chm. Bd. & Chief Exec. Officer--Boston Safe Deposit & Trust Co., Boston, MA; *U.S. Public*, pg. 1085
Smith, Wally, Pres. & Chief Exec. Officer--Recreational Equipment, Inc., Kent, WA; *U.S. Private*, pg. 914
Smith, Wayne, Chm. Bd., Pres. & Chief Exec./Fin. Officer--Bekins Distribution Services Co., Saint Louis, MO; *U.S. Public*, pg. 841
Smith, William B., Ph.D., Pres. & Chief Exec. Officer--Telco Systems, Inc., Norwood, MA; *U.S. Public*, pg. 1568
Smith, William D., Pres. & Chief Exec. Officer--Brown & Bigelow, Inc., Saint Paul, MN; *U.S. Private*, pg. 172
Smith, William J., Chm. Bd., Pres. & Chief Exec. Officer--U.S. Can Company, Oak Brook, IL; *U.S. Public*, pg. 1681
Smithson, John W., Pres. & Chief Exec. Officer--Pennsylvania Manufacturers Corp., Blue Bell, PA; *U.S. Public*, pg. 1272
Smithson, John W., Chm. Bd., Pres. & Chief Exec. Officer--PMA Reinsurance Corporation, Philadelphia, PA; *U.S. Public*, pg. 1272
Smitson, Robert M., Chief Exec. Officer--Maxon Corporation, Muncie, IN; *U.S. Private*, pg. 716
Smiy, P.R., Chief Exec. Officer--New Elliott Corporation, Jeannette, PA; *Int'l*, pg. 432
Smiy, Paul R., Chm. Bd. & Chief Exec. Officer--Elliott Company, Jeannette, PA; *U.S. Private*, pg. 373
Smrke, John R., Chief Exec. Officer--Highwood Resources Ltd., Calgary, Canada; *U.S. Public*, pg. 1411
Smurfit, M.W., Jr., Chief Exec. Officer--Smurfit Packaging Corporation, Saint Louis, MO; *Int'l*, pg. 1271
Smurfit, M.W.J., Chm. Bd. & Chief Exec. Officer--Jefferson Smurfit Group p.l.c., Dublin, Ireland; *Int'l*, pg. 1269
Snapp, James A., Pres. & Chief Exec. Officer--Certified Alloy Products, Inc., Long Beach, CA; *Int'l*, pg. 1467
Snavely, Wayne H., Chm. Bd., Pres. & Chief Exec. Officer--Imperial Credit Industries, Inc., Torrance, CA; *U.S. Public*, pg. 872
Snead, Michael J., Pres. & Chief Exec. Officer--Carolina Casualty Insurance Company, Jacksonville, FL; *U.S. Public*, pg. 216
Sneddon, Paul, Pres. & Chief Exec. Officer--H.J. Heinz Co. of Canada Ltd., North York, Canada; *U.S. Public*, pg. 806
Sneddon, Paul, Pres. & Chief Exec. Officer--Omstead Foods Limited, Wheatley, Canada; *U.S. Public*, pg. 806
Sneddon, Paul W., Chief Exec. Officer--Heinz Bakery Products, Mississauga, Canada; *U.S. Public*, pg. 806
Snediker, James M., Pres., Chief Exec. Officer & Chief Oper. Officer--Chicago Show Printing Co., Morton Grove, IL; *U.S. Private*, pg. 235
Sneep, Folkert, Chief Exec. Officer (Northern Europe)--McCain Foods Holland B.V. (The Netherlands), Hoofddorp, Netherlands; *Int'l*, pg. 850
Snell, Richard, Chm. Bd. & Chief Exec. Officer--Pinnacle West Capital Corporation, Phoenix, AZ; *U.S. Public*, pg. 1297
Snell, Richard A., Chm. Bd., Pres. & Chief Exec. Officer--Federal-Mogul Corporation, Southfield, MI; *U.S. Public*, pg. 615
Snider, Jeffrey A., Chm. Bd., Pres. & Chief Exec. Officer--PAULA Financial, Pasadena, CA; *U.S. Public*, pg. 1266
Snow, John J., Pres. & Chief Exec. Officer--First NH Investment Services Corporation, Manchester, NH; *Int'l*, pg. 153
Snow, John W., Chm. Bd., Pres. & Chief Exec. Officer--CSX Corporation, Richmond, VA; *U.S. Public*, pg. 284
Snowden, David, Pres. & Chief Exec. Officer--Tarco, North Little Rock, AR; *U.S. Private*, pg. 1068
Snowden, William F., Chm. Bd., Pres. & Chief Exec. Officer--Topline Imports, Inc., Bellevue, WA; *U.S. Private*, pg. 1091
Snyder, Bill, Chief Exec. Officer--Rinker Materials Corp., West Palm Beach, FL; *Int'l*, pg. 246
Snyder, Daniel M., Chm. Bd., Pres. & Chief Exec. Officer--Snyder Communications, Inc., Bethesda, MD; *U.S. Public*, pg. 1481
Snyder, Lynn E., Pres. & Chief Exec. Officer--Churubusco State Bank, Churubusco, IN; *U.S. Public*, pg. 674
Snyder, Richard E., Chm. Bd. & Chief Exec. Officer--Golden Books Family Entertainment Inc., New York, NY; *U.S. Public*, pg. 749
Snyder, Richard E., Chm. Bd. & Chief Exec. Officer--Golden Books Publishing, New York, NY; *U.S. Public*, pg. 749
Snyder, Richard G., Pres. & Chief Exec. Officer--Reflectone, Inc., Tampa, FL; *Int'l*, pg. 218
Snyder, Stephen G., Chm. Bd. & Chief Exec. Officer--General Electric Canada Inc., Mississauga, Canada; *U.S. Public*, pg. 713
Snyder, Stephen G., Pres. & Chief Exec. Officer--Transalta Corporation, Calgary, Canada; *Int'l*, pg. 1416
Soble, David S., Pres. & Chief Exec. Officer--Interstate Steel Co. Inc., Des Plaines, IL; *Int'l*, pg. 572
Sobol, Yehiel, Pres. & Chief Exec. Officer--Kao Infosystems Canada, Inc., Arnprior, Canada; *Int'l*, pg. 717
Socol, Howard, Chief Exec. Officer--J. Crew Group, Inc., New York, NY; *U.S. Private*, pg. 1078
Socol, Jerry M., Pres. & Chief Exec. Officer--Morse Shoe, Inc., Canton, MA; *U.S. Public*, pg. 168
Sodeberg, Per-Olaf, Pres. & Chief Exec. Officer--Dahl International AB, Stockholm, Sweden; *Int'l*, pg. 359
Soderstrom, Anders O., Chief Info. Officer--American Skandia Information Services & Tecnology Corp., Shelton, CT; *Int'l*, pg. 1257
Sodini, Peter J., Pres. & Chief Exec. Officer--The Pantry, Inc., Sanford, NC; *U.S. Private*, pg. 837
Soehnlen, Joseph A., Chief Exec. Officer--Superior Dairy, Inc., Canton, OH; *U.S. Private*, pg. 1054
Soenen, Don, Chm. Bd. & Chief Exec. Officer--Sensors, Inc., Saline, MI; *U.S. Private*, pg. 984
Soga, Yoshiki, Mng. Dir. & Chief Exec. Officer-Intl. Banking Grp., the Americas--The Long-Term Credit Bank of Japan, Limited, Tokyo, Japan; *Int'l*, pg. 815
Sokol, David L., Chm. Bd. & Chief Exec. Officer--CalEnergy Co., Omaha, NE; *U.S. Public*, pg. 292
Sokol, Si, Chm. Bd., Pres. & Chief Exec. Officer--Bancinsurance Corp., Columbus, OH; *U.S. Public*, pg. 175
Sola, Jure, Chm. Bd. & Chief Exec. Officer--Sanmina Corporation, San Jose, CA; *U.S. Public*, pg. 1431
Solari, Larry, Chief Exec. Officer--Sequentia Inc., Strongsville, OH; *U.S. Private*, pg. 985
Solberg, James L., Pres., Chief Exec. & Oper. Officer--AutoAlliance International Inc., Flat Rock, MI; *Int'l*, pg. 849
Solender, Stephen L., Esq., Pres. & Chief Exec. Officer--The Solender Group, Inc., Los Angeles, CA; *U.S. Private*, pg. 1012
Soliman, Anwar, Chm. Bd. & Chief Exec. Officer--American Restaurant Group, Inc., Newport Beach, CA; *U.S. Private*, pg. 61
Soliman, Anwar, Chm. Bd. & Chief Exec. Officer--Grandy's, Inc., Lewisville, TX; *U.S. Private*, pg. 61
Solley, Larry, Chm. Bd. & Chief Exec. Officer--Fisher Controls International, Inc., Marshalltown, IA; *U.S. Public*, *pg. 573*
Solombrino, Scott, Chm. Bd., Pres. & Chief Exec. Officer--Dav-El Worldwide, Chelsea, MA; *U.S. Private*, pg. 314
Solomon, Russell S., Pres. & Chief Exec. Officer--MTS, Inc., West Sacramento, CA; *U.S. Private*, pg. 688
Solomon, William T., Chm. Bd. & Chief Exec. Officer--Austin Industries, Inc., Dallas, TX; *U.S. Private*, pg. 99
Solomon, Zachary, Pres. & Chief Exec. Officer-Adrienne Vittadini Division--Marisa Christina Inc., New Hyde Park, NY; *U.S. Public*, pg. 1044
Solon, Richard A., Pres. & Chief Exec. Officer--Snorkel, Saint Joseph, MO; *U.S. Private*, pg. 500
Solsvig, Curtis G., Pres. & Chief Exec. Officer--Gilbert & Bennett Manufacturing Company, Georgetown, CT; *U.S. Private*, pg. 453
Somerville, Ervin W., Pres. & Chief Exec. Officer--M & I Central Bank & Trust, Marshfield, WI; *U.S. Public*, pg. 1050
Sommers, Patrick C., Chm. Bd., Pres. & Chief Exec. Officer--Medicus Systems Corporation, Evanston, IL; *U.S. Public*, pg. 1080
Sommers, William, Pres. & Chief Exec. Officer--SRI International, Menlo Park, CA; *U.S. Private*, pg. 958
Son, Masayoshi, Pres. & Chief Exec. Officer--Softbank Corporation, Tokyo, Japan; *Int'l*, pg. 1276
Sonaco, Mike, Chief Exec. Officer--C&L Communications, Inc., Boerne, TX; *U.S. Private*, pg. 191
Sondhi, Vir K., Pres. & Chief Exec. Officer--Overseas Capital Corporation, Medina, OH; *U.S. Private*, pg. 774
Sondker, Edward H., Pres. & Chief Exec. Officer--Bay View Capital Corporation, San Mateo, CA; *U.S. Public*, pg. 197
Song, Bo-Soon, Chm. Bd. & Chief Exec. Officer--Samsung Electronics North America Inc., Ridgefield Park, NJ; *Int'l*, *pg. 1183*
Sonnabend, Roger, Chm. Bd. & Chief Exec. Officer--Sonesta International Hotels Corporation, Boston, MA; *U.S. Public*, pg. 1485
Sonnenberg, Ralph, Pres. & Chief Exec. Officer--Hunter Douglas N.V., Rotterdam, Netherlands; *Int'l*, pg. 639
Sonstelie, R.R., Chm. Bd. & Chief Exec. Officer--Puget Sound Energy Co., Bellevue, WA; *U.S. Public*, pg. 1342
Sonstelie, Richard R., Chm. Bd. & Chief Exec. Officer--Puget Sound Energy, Inc., Bellevue, WA; *U.S. Public*, pg. 1342
Soo Hah, Alex Foong, Chief Exec. Officer--Great Eastern Life Assurance Company-Malaysia, Kuala Lumpur, Malaysia; *Int'l*, pg. 557
Soobuym, Young, Pres. & Chief Exec. Officer--Inkel USA Corporation, La Mirada, CA; *U.S. Private*, pg. 563
Soper, Willard B., II, Pres. & Chief Exec. Officer--MidCoast Mortgage Corporation, Lake Worth, FL; *U.S. Private*, pg. 744
Sopko, Michael D., Chm. Bd. & Chief Exec. Officer--Inco Limited, Toronto, Canada; *Int'l*, pg. 672
Sorba, Olivier, Pres. & Chief Exec. Officer--Lagardere Groupe North America, New York, NY; *Int'l*, pg. 794
Sorensen, Erik, Pres. & Chief Exec. Officer--Chr. Hansen Holding A/S, Horsholm, Denmark; *Int'l*, pg. 288
Soriano, Andres, III, Chm. Bd. & Chief Exec. Officer--San Miguel Corp., Manila, Philippines; *Int'l*, pg. 1183
Soro, Chris, Chm. Bd. & Chief Exec. Officer--Allen & Hoshall, Inc., Memphis, TN; *U.S. Private*, pg. 36
Sorokwasz, Michael, Pres. & Chief Exec. Officer--TST/Impreso, Inc., Coppell, TX; *U.S. Private*, pg. 1066
Sorrell, C.S., Pres. & Chief Exec. Officer--Calvert Group, Ltd., Bethesda, MD; *U.S. Private*, pg. 11
Sorrell, M.S., Chief. Exec. Officer--WPP Group plc, London, United Kingdom; *Int'l*, pg. 1482
Sorrent, M., Chief Oper. Officer--S.A. Entreprise de Travaux et de Constructions ENTRACON, Mont-Saint Guibert, Belgium; *Int'l*, pg. 301
Soto, Raymond M., Pres., Chief Exec. & Fin. Officer & Treas.--Bolt Technology Corporation, Norwalk, CT; *U.S. Public*, pg. 244
Sottile, John H., Pres. & Chief Exec. Officer--The Goldfield Corporation, Melbourne, FL; *U.S. Public*, pg. 750
Soukup, Mark A., Pres. & Chief Exec. Officer--The State Bank and Trust Company, Defiance, OH; *U.S. Public*, pg. 1413
Soule, Charles E., Pres. & Chief Exec. Officer--The Paul Revere Corporation, Worcester, MA; *U.S. Public*, pg. 1338
South, John R., Pres. & Chief Exec. Officer--Staodyn Inc., Longmont, CO; *U.S. Public*, pg. 1509
Southerland, S. Duane, Jr., Pres. & Chief Exec. Officer--Conso Products Company, Union, SC; *U.S. Public*, pg. 434
Southern, R.D., Chm. Bd. & Chief Exec. Officer--ATCO Group Co., Calgary, Canada; *Int'l*, pg. 95
Southwell, Leonard, Chief Exec. Officer & Exec. V.P.--Prairie Farms Dairy, Inc., Carlinville, IL; *U.S. Private*, pg. 878
Southworth, Richard A., Pres. & Chief Exec. Officer--Spectrum Control, Inc., Erie, PA; *U.S. Public*, pg. 1497
Sovey, William P., Vice Chm. & Chief Exec. Officer--Newell Co., Freeport, IL; *U.S. Public*, pg. 1176
Sovey, William P., Vice Chm. & Chief Exec. Officer--Mirro Company, Manitowoc, WI; *U.S. Public*, pg. 1177
Soyak, Necip, Pres. & Chief Exec. Officer--Chicago Pneumatic Tool Company, Rock Hill, SC; *Int'l*, pg. 96
Spadoni, Bruno, Deputy Chief Exec.--Cassa di Risparmio delle Provincie Lombarde SpA (CARIPLO), Milan, Italy; *Int'l*, pg. 274
Spain, W.J., Jr., Chief Exec. Officer--Birdsong Corporation, Suffolk, VA; *U.S. Private*, pg. 145
Spainhour, J. Patrick, Chm. Bd. & Chief Exec. Officer--AnnTaylor Stores Corporation, New York, NY; *U.S. Public*, pg. 116
Spangler, C. Gregory, Chm. Bd., Pres. & Chief Exec. Officer--Spangler Candy Company, Bryan, OH; *U.S. Private*, pg. 1020
Spangler, David B., Pres. & Chief Exec. Officer--Jefferson Mills, Inc., Pulaski, VA; *U.S. Private*, pg. 584
Spangler, David L., Chm. Bd., Pres. & Chief Exec. Officer--First National Bank of Huntington, Huntington, IN; *U.S. Public*, pg. 674
Spangler, Dean, Chief Exec. Officer--Fast Food Merchandisers Inc., Rocky Mount, NC; *U.S. Public*, pg. 278
Spangler, John, Pres. & Chief Exec. Officer--Milestone Contractors Inc., Indianapolis, IN; *U.S. Private*, pg. 745
Sparby, Neal R., Pres. & Chief Exec. Officer--Payco American Corporation, Brookfield, WI; *U.S. Public*, pg. 1267
Spatz, D. Dean, Chm. Bd., Pres. & Chief Exec. Officer--Osmonics, Inc., Minnetonka, MN; *U.S. Public*, pg. 1233
Spatz, D.D., Chm. Bd. & Chief Exec. Officer--Autotrol Corporation, Milwaukee, WI; *U.S. Public*, pg. 1234
Speakman, W.A. III, Pres. & Chief Exec. Officer--Speakman Company, Wilmington, DE; *U.S. Private*, pg. 1021
Spears, Alexander, Chm. Bd. & Chief Exec. Officer--Lorillard Tobacco Company, Greensboro, NC; *U.S. Public*, pg. 1011
Speers, Douglas E., Pres. & Chief Exec. & Oper. Officer--Emco Limited, London, Canada; *Int'l*, pg. 452
Speizer, Mark, Chm. Bd. & Chief Exec. Officer--National Insurance Group, South San Francisco, CA; *U.S. Public*, pg. 1157
Spelde, M.E., Chm. Bd., Pres. & Chief Exec. Officer--Empire Airlines, Coeur D'Alene, ID; *U.S. Private*, pg. 374
Spelling, Aaron, Chm. Bd. & Chief Exec. Officer--Spelling Television, Los Angeles, CA; *U.S. Private*, pg. 776
Spence, Robin, Chief Exec. Officer--Oakley Young/4th Dimension, Whetstone, United Kingdom; *Int'l*, pg. 1482
Spence, Will B., Pres. & Chief Exec. Officer--South Carolina National Corporation, Columbia, SC; *U.S. Public*, pg. 1730
Spence, Will B., Pres. & Chief Exec. Officer--Wachovia Bank of South Carolina, N.A., Columbia, SC; *U.S. Public*, *pg. 1730*
Spencer-Arscott, Robin, Chm. Bd. & Chief Exec. Officer--Rollins Burdick Hunter Co. (Bermuda) Ltd., Hamilton, Bermuda; *U.S. Public*, pg. 119
Spencer, Guy J., Jr., Chm. Bd., Pres. & Chief Exec. Officer--Spencer Companies Inc., Huntsville, AL; *U.S. Private*, pg. 1024
Spengler, James R., Jr., Pres. & Chief Exec. Officer--Osmose Wood Preserving, Inc., Buffalo, NY; *U.S. Private*, pg. 821
Sperber, Burton S., Chm. Bd., Pres. & Chief Exec. Officer--Environmental Industries, Inc., Calabasas, CA; *U.S. Private*, pg. 378
Sperber, Martin, Chm. Bd. & Chief Exec. Officer--Schein Pharmaceutical, Inc., Florham Park, NJ; *U.S. Private*, pg. 969
Sperling, John G., Ph.D., Chm. Bd. & Chief Exec. Officer--Apollo Group, Inc., Phoenix, AZ; *U.S. Public*, pg. 120
Spiegel, Jeffery, Pres. & Chief Exec. Officer--Randa Corp., Kinston, NC; *U.S. Private*, pg. 909
Spiegel, Nikolaus, Dr., Co-Chief Exec. Officer--Heidelberger Druckmaschinen A.G., Heidelberg, Germany; *Int'l*, pg. 604
Spier, Anthony, Chm. Bd. & Chief Exec. Officer--Wells-Gardner Electronics Corp., Chicago, IL; *U.S. Public*, pg. 1753
Spiewak, Michael, Chm. Bd. & Chief Exec. Officer--I. Spiewak & Sons, Inc., New York, NY; *U.S. Private*, pg. 1025
Spiewak, Michael, Chm. Bd. & Chief Exec. Officer--Golden Fleece Outerwear Co., New York, NY; *U.S. Private*, pg. 1025
Spitzer, T. Quinn, Pres. & Chief Exec. Officer--Kepner-Tregoe, Inc., Skillman, NJ; *U.S. Public*, pg. 1659
Spitznagel, John T., Pres. & Chief Exec. Officer--Roberts Pharmaceutical Corporation, Eatontown, NJ; *U.S. Public*, *pg. 1393*
Spitznagel, John T., Pres. & Chief Exec. Officer--VRG International, Inc., Eatontown, NJ; *U.S. Public*, pg. 1393
Spitznagel, John T., Pres. & Chief Exec. Officer--Monmouth Pharmaceutical, Ltd., Guildford, United Kingdom; *U.S. Public*, pg. 1394
Spitznagel, John T., Pres. & Chief Exec. Officer--Roberts Pharmaceutical of Canada, Oakville, Canada; *U.S. Public*, pg. 1394
Splude, John, Chm. Bd., Pres. & Chief Exec. Officer--HK Systems, Inc., New Berlin, WI; *U.S. Private*, pg. 491

Spoerry, Robert, Chief Exec. Officer--Mettler-Toledo AG, Greifensee, Switzerland; *U.S. Private*, pg. 4

Spolane, Ronald S., Chm. Bd., Pres. & Chief Exec. Officer--Sterling Electronics Corporation, Houston, TX; *U.S. Public*, pg. 1051

Spooner, Robert M., Chm. Bd. & Chief Exec. Officer--Georgia Tent & Awning Inc., Atlanta, GA; *U.S. Private*, pg. 448

Sport, Michael C., Chm. Bd., Pres. & Chief Exec. Officer--Production Management Companies, Inc., Harvey, LA; *U.S. Private*, pg. 888

Spradley, James W., Jr., Pres. & Chief Exec. Officer--Standard Candy Co., Inc., Nashville, TN; *U.S. Private*, pg. 1030

Spradlin, Robert, Pres. & Chief Exec. Officer--Contract Interiors Inc., Taylor, MI; *U.S. Private*, pg. 270

Sprague, Doug, Pres. & Chief Exec. Officer--Computerized Medical Systems, Inc., Saint Louis, MO; *U.S. Private*, pg. 260

Sprague, William W., III, Pres. & Chief Exec. Officer--Savannah Foods & Industries, Inc., Savannah, GA; *U.S. Public*, pg. 872

Spranger, Hanno W., Pres. & Chief Exec. Officer--Netzsch Incorporated, Exton, PA; *U.S. Private*, pg. 792

Spring, Ueli, Pres. & Chief Exec. Officer--Aetna Industries, Inc., Center Line, MI; *U.S. Private*, pg. 25

Springer, Andrew, Pres. & Chief Exec. Officer--Lee Grocery Company, Everett, WA; *U.S. Private*, pg. 657

Sprole, Robert R., II, Chm. Bd. & Chief Exec. Officer--Therm, Inc., Ithaca, NY; *U.S. Private*, pg. 1079

Sprott, H.B., Jr., Pres. & Chief Exec. Officer--Sprott Oil Co., Inc., Manning, SC; *U.S. Private*, pg. 1027

Spruell, J.R., Chief Exec. Officer--GKN Bound Brook Ltd., Lichfield, United Kingdom; *Int'l*, pg. 534

Spruell, J.R., Chief Exec.--GKN Powder Metallurgy Division, Lichfield, United Kingdom; *Int'l*, pg. 534

Spruijt, Herman P., Chm. Bd. & Chief Exec. Officer--Elsevier Science (International), Amsterdam, Netherlands; *Int'l*, pg. 1099

Spurck, Fredric C., Pres. & Chief Exec. Officer--Webster Industries Inc., Tiffin, OH; *U.S. Private*, pg. 1157

Spurrier, Martin, Chief Exec. Officer--Ludgate Communications, Hong Kong, Hong Kong; *U.S. Private*, pg. 1157

Squeri, Charles, Chm. Bd. & Chief Exec. Officer--Squeri Foodservice, Cincinnati, OH; *U.S. Public*, pg. 918

Squier, David L., Pres. & Chief Exec. Officer--Howmet Corporation, Greenwich, CT; *U.S. Private*, pg. 213

Squier, David L., Pres. & Chief Exec. Officer--Howmet Corporation, Greenwich, CT; *U.S. Public*, pg. 1597

Srednicki, Richard, Pres. & Chief Exec. Officer-Universal Card Services--AT&T Corporation, Basking Ridge, NJ; *U.S. Public*, pg. 10

Srere, Linda, Pres. & Chief Exec. Officer-Y&RNY--Young & Rubicam Inc., New York, NY; *U.S. Private*, pg. 1196

Srrickland, David M., Chief Exec. Officer--Barnett Investments Inc., Jacksonville, FL; *U.S. Public*, pg. 1162

St. George, Nicholas J., Chm. Bd., Pres. & Chief Exec. Officer--Oakwood Homes Corporation, Greensboro, NC; *U.S. Public*, pg. 1209

St. George, P. B., Chief Exec.--NatWest Markets Australia Limited, Sydney, Australia; *Int'l*, pg. 911

St. Jacques, R. J., Chief Exec. Officer--ING America Life, Chicago, IL; *Int'l*, pg. 647

St. Romain, Frank, Chief Exec. Officer--SCP Pool Corporation, Covington, LA; *U.S. Private*, pg. 249

Staats, Glen E., Pres. & Chief Exec. Officer--CCI/Triad Corporation, Austin, TX; *U.S. Private*, pg. 193

Stabile, Jeffrey, Pres. & Chief Exec. Officer--Aero Systems Aviation Corp., Miami, FL; *U.S. Private*, pg. 24

Stacey, Mike, Chief Exec. Officer--Meggitt plc, Wimborne Minster, United Kingdom; *Int'l*, pg. 853

Stacy, Parker, Chief Exec. Officer--NVW (USA) Inc., Scarsdale, NY; *Int'l*, pg. 754

Stadler, G., Chief Exec. Officer--Feldschlosschen Hurlimann Holding, Rhaeninfelden, Switzerland; *Int'l*, pg. 479

Staff, Joel, Chm. Bd., Pres. & Chief Exec. Officer--National-Oilwell Inc., Houston, TX; *U.S. Public*, pg. 1158

Stafford, Gerry S., Pres. & Chief Exec. Officer--Commercial Union of Canada Holdings Ltd, Toronto, Canada; *Int'l*, pg. 308

Stafford, Gerry S., Pres. & Chief Exec. Officer--Commercial Union Assurance Company of Canada, Toronto, Canada; *Int'l*, pg. 308

Stafford, James F., Pres. & Chief Exec. Officer--Chips and Technologies, Inc., San Jose, CA; *U.S. Public*, pg. 349

Stafford, John R., Chm. Bd., Pres. & Chief Exec. Officer--American Home Products Corporation, Madison, NJ; *U.S. Public*, pg. 79

Stafford, Randy, Pres. & Chief Exec. Officer--The Court Company, Memphis, TN; *U.S. Private*, pg. 279

Stalcup, Winston, Chief Exec. Officer--RS Electronics, Livonia, MI; *U.S. Private*, pg. 905

Stalkamp, William J., Chm. Bd. & Chief Exec. Officer--Mellon PSFS, Philadelphia, PA; *U.S. Public*, pg. 1085

Stallard, Hubert R., Pres. & Chief Exec. Officer--Bell Atlantic-VA, Richmond, VA; *U.S. Public*, pg. 203

Stancliffe, P.W., Mng. Dir. & Chief Exec. Officer--Australian National Industries Limited, Pyrmont, Australia; *Int'l*, pg. 100

Standberg, Robert C., Pres. & Chief Exec. Officer--PSC Inc., Webster, NY; *U.S. Public*, pg. 1245

Standbridge, Roger, Chief Exec. Steel Mills Div.-North America--Foseco Inc., Cleveland, OH; *Int'l*, pg. 234

Standen, Michael, Chm. Bd., Pres. & Chief Exec. Officer--Metallurg, Inc., New York, NY; *U.S. Private*, pg. 735

Standish, Victor J., Chm. Bd., Pres. & Chief Exec. Officer--York Barbell Co., Inc., York, PA; *U.S. Private*, pg. 1196

Stanford, Alan C., Chm. Bd. & Chief Exec. Officer--Broadway & Seymour, Inc., Charlotte, NC; *U.S. Public*, pg. 258

Stanford, James M., Pres. & Chief Exec. Officer--Petro-Canada, Calgary, Canada; *Int'l*, pg. 1041

Stanley, A. Jack, Chm. Bd. & Chief Exec. Officer--The M.W. Kellogg Company, Houston, TX; *U.S. Public*, pg. 528

Stanley, Clifford W., Pres. & Chief Exec. Officer--Guest Supply, Inc., Monmouth Junction, NJ; *U.S. Public*, pg. 768

Stanley, John C., IV, Chm. Bd. & Chief Exec. Officer--Outdoor Communications, Inc., Corinth, MS; *U.S. Private*, *pg. 822*

Stanley, John R., Chm. Bd., Pres. & Chief Exec. Officer--Transamerican Natural Gas Corporation, Houston, TX; *U.S. Private*, pg. 1096

Stanley, Larry, Dep. Chief Exec. Officer--Aer Lingus, Dublin, Ireland; *Int'l*, pg. 28

Stanton, Ronald, Chm. Bd. & Chief Exec. Officer--Transammonia Inc., New York, NY; *U.S. Private*, pg. 1096

Staples, Brian, Chief Exec. Officer--United Utilities plc, Warrington, United Kingdom; *Int'l*, pg. 1444

Star, Larry, Chief Exec. Officer-HS Group--Harrison & Star, Inc., New York, NY; *U.S. Private*, pg. 506

Stara, Friedrich, Pres. & Chief Exec. Officer--Henkel Austria Group, Vienna, Austria; *Int'l*, pg. 611

Starck, Henri, Chief Exec. Officer--Thomainfor, Velizy-Villacoublay, France; *Int'l*, pg. 1383

Stark, Robert, Chief Exec. Officer--San Gabriel Valley Medical Center, San Gabriel, CA; *U.S. Private*, pg. 1118

Starks, Daniel J., Chief Exec. Officer--Daig Corporation, Minnetonka, MN; *U.S. Public*, pg. 1428

Starkweather, Larry D., Pres. & Chief Exec. Officer--Fiberesin Industries Inc., Oconomowoc, WI; *U.S. Private*, *pg. 402*

Starnes, Michael S., Chm. Bd., Pres. & Chief Exec. Officer--M.S. Carriers, Inc., Memphis, TN; *U.S. Public*, pg. 1027

Starr, Michael D., Chief Exec. Officer & Sr. Exec. V.P.-Government Managed Care--PHP Healthcare Corporation, Reston, VA; *U.S. Public*, pg. 1241

Starrett, Douglas R., Chm. Bd. & Chief Exec. Officer--The L.S. Starrett Company, Athol, MA; *U.S. Public*, pg. 1511

Stasior, William F., Chm. Bd. & Chief Exec. Officer--Booz, Allen & Hamilton Inc., New York, NY; *U.S. Private*, pg. 157

Staton, B. Gene, Pres. & Chief Exec. Officer--Morrilton Security Bank, N.A., Morrilton, AR; *U.S. Public*, pg. 630

Stauber, Daniel A., Pres. & Chief Exec. Officer--Med/Waste, Inc., Hialeah, FL; *U.S. Public*, pg. 1077

Stauth, Robert E., Chm. Bd. & Chief Exec. Officer--Fleming Companies, Inc., Oklahoma City, OK; *U.S. Public*, pg. 652

Stavropoulos, William S., Pres. & Chief Exec. Officer--The Dow Chemical Company, Midland, MI; *U.S. Public*, pg. 522

Stavropoulos, William S., Pres. & Chief Exec. Officer--Essex Chemical Corporation, Clifton, NJ; *U.S. Public*, pg. 523

Stayer, Ralph C., Pres. & Chief Exec. Officer--Johnsonville Foods, Inc., Kohler, WI; *U.S. Private*, pg. 595

Stead, Jerre L., Chm. Bd. & Chief Exec. Officer--Ingram Micro Inc., Santa Ana, CA; *U.S. Public*, pg. 878

Steadman, Peter, Chief Exec.--ARC Advertising, London, United Kingdom; *Int'l*, pg. 17

Stearley, Doug, Chief Exec. Officer--Industrial Custom Products L.L.C., Minneapolis, MN; *U.S. Private*, pg. 352

Stearley, Doug, Chief Exec. Officer--We Vac Plastics, Elkhart, IN; *U.S. Private*, pg. 352

Stearns, Clive, Chief Exec. Officer--John Crane Polymer Division, Abingdon, United Kingdom; *Int'l*, pg. 1338

Stearns, Richard E., Pres. & Chief Exec. Officer--Lenox, Incorporated, Lawrenceville, NJ; *U.S. Public*, pg. 261

Steck, Brian J., Chm. Bd. & Chief Exec. Officer--The Nesbitt Thomson Corporation Limited, Toronto, Canada; *Int'l*, pg. 153

Stecko, Paul T., Pres. & Chief Exec. Officer--Tenneco Packaging, Evanston, IL; *U.S. Public*, pg. 1579

Steedman, Donald L., Pres. & Chief Exec. Officer--Littleford Day Inc., Florence, KY; *U.S. Private*, pg. 671

Steele, Harry R., Chm. Bd. & Chief Exec. Officer--Newfoundland Capital Corporation Limited, Dartmouth, Canada; *Int'l*, pg. 924

Steele, Loren, Vice Chm. & Chief Exec. Officer--The Rivet Group L.L.C., Aberdeen, SD; *U.S. Private*, pg. 934

Steele, William W., Pres. & Chief Exec. Officer--ABM Industries, San Francisco, CA; *U.S. Public*, pg. 2

Steen, Donald E., Pres. & Chief Exec. Officer--Columbia/H.C.A., Dallas, TX; *U.S. Public*, pg. 404

Steenbergen, James, Pres., Chief Exec. Officer & Chief Fin. Officer--AMATI Communications Corp., San Jose, CA; *U.S. Public*, pg. 1585

Steere, William C., Chm. Bd. & Chief Exec. Officer--Pfizer Inc., New York, NY; *U.S. Public*, pg. 1281

Stefanic, David, Chief Exec. Officer--TV Host Inc., Harrisburg, PA; *U.S. Private*, pg. 1066

Stefanutti, Oscar, Pres. & Chief Exec. Officer--AFM, Sterling Heights, MI; *U.S. Public*, pg. 1363

Steffensen, Dwight A., Chm. Bd. & Chief Exec. Officer--Merisel, Inc., El Segundo, CA; *U.S. Public*, pg. 1095

Steffey, Rex, Pres. & Chief Exec. Officer--Jay Jacobs, Inc., Seattle, WA; *U.S. Public*, pg. 922

Stegner, Edward J., Chm. Bd. & Chief Exec. Officer--Stegner Food Products Co., Cincinnati, OH; *U.S. Private*, *pg. 1039*

Steigerwaldt, Donna Wolf, Chm. Bd. & Chief Exec. Officer--Jockey International, Inc., Kenosha, WI; *U.S. Private*, pg. 588

Steigrad, Peter, Chm. & Chief Exec. Officer-Y&R Australia & Africa--Young & Rubicam Inc., New York, NY; *U.S. Private*, pg. 1196

Steil, Gordon E., Chm. & Chief Exec. Officer--Harrington & King, Chicago, IL; *U.S. Private*, pg. 504

Stein-Sapir, Leonard, Chm. Bd. & Chief Exec. Officer--Morgan's Foods, Inc., Beachwood, OH; *U.S. Public*, pg. 1133

Stein, Alfred J., Chm. Bd. & Chief Exec. Officer--VLSI Technology, Inc., San Jose, CA; *U.S. Public*, pg. 1703

Stein, Bill, Pres., Chief Exec. Officer & New Bus. Contact--McConnaughy Stein Schmidt Brown, Chicago, IL; *U.S. Private*, pg. 720

Stein, Howard, Chm. Bd. & Chief Exec. Officer--The Dreyfus Corporation, New York, NY; *U.S. Public*, pg. 1085

Stein, Jay, Pres. & Chief Exec. Officer--Butterick Company, Inc., New York, NY; *U.S. Private*, pg. 190

Stein, Jay, Chm. Bd. & Chief Exec. Officer--Stein Mart, Inc., Jacksonville, FL; *U.S. Public*, pg. 1514

Stein, John S., Pres. & Chief Exec. Officer--Golden Enterprises Inc., Birmingham, AL; *U.S. Public*, pg. 749

Stein, Martin, Pres. & Chief Exec. Officer--Dawn Joy Fashions, Inc., New York, NY; *U.S. Private*, pg. 316

Stein, Martin E., Jr., Chm. Bd. & Chief Exec. Officer--Regency Group Inc., Jacksonville, FL; *U.S. Private*, pg. 918

Stein, Robert, Pres. & Chief Exec. Officer--Dairy Mart Convenience Stores, Inc., Cuyahoga Falls, OH; *U.S. Public*, pg. 476

Stein, Robert, Pres. & Chief Exec. Officer--Tejon Ranch Company, Lebec, CA; *U.S. Public*, pg. 1566

Stein, Sidney J., Dr., Chm. Bd., Chief Exec. Officer--Electro-Science Laboratories, Inc., King of Prussia, PA; *U.S. Private*, pg. 369

Steinback, Kenneth, Chm. Bd. & Chief Exec. Officer--Computer Sales International Inc., Saint Louis, MO; *U.S. Private*, pg. 260

Steinbecker, Terry F., Pres. & Chief Exec. Officer--St. Joseph Light & Power Co., Saint Joseph, MO; *U.S. Public*, pg. 1427

Steinberg, Barry, Pres. & Chief Exec. Officer--Manchester Equipment Co., Hauppauge, NY; *U.S. Private*, pg. 699

Steinberg, Lawrence, Pres. & Chief Exec. Officer--Unisystems, Inc., New York, NY; *U.S. Private*, pg. 1120

Steinberg, Lawrence, Pres. & Chief Exec. Officer--Modern Publishing, New York, NY; *U.S. Private*, pg. 1120

Steinberg, Robert M., Chm. Bd. & Chief Exec. Officer--Reliance Insurance Company, Philadelphia, PA; *U.S. Public*, pg. 1374

Steinbrueck, Charles, Pres. & Chief Exec. Officer--Grease Monkey International Inc., Denver, CO; *U.S. Public*, pg. 759

Steinei, D., Chief Exec. Officer--Agrippina Ruckversicherung Aktiengesellschaft, Cologne, Germany; *Int'l*, pg. 1531

Steiner, Bob, IV, Pres. & Chief Exec. Officer--Regions Bank/Lee County, Auburn, AL; *U.S. Public*, pg. 1372

Steiner, Charles, Chm. Bd. & Chief Exec. Officer--Branch Group Inc., Upper Marlboro, MD; *U.S. Private*, pg. 165

Steiner, Jeffrey J., Chm. Bd. & Chief Exec. Officer--Banner Aerospace, Inc., Washington, DC; *U.S. Public*, pg. 187

Steiner, Jeffrey J., Chm. Bd., Pres. & Chief Exec. Officer--The Fairchild Corporation, Chantilly, VA; *U.S. Public*, pg. 610

Steiner, Lawrence G., Chief Exec. Officer--Ameripride Service Company, Minneapolis, MN; *U.S. Private*, pg. 65

Steiner, Richard R., Pres. & Chief Exec. Officer--Steiner Corporation, Salt Lake City, UT; *U.S. Private*, pg. 1039

Steinfeld, Paul N., Chm. Bd. & Chief Exec. Officer--Shelby Williams Industries, Inc., Morristown, TN; *U.S. Public*, pg. 1464

Steinhaus, A. E., Vice Chm., Pres. & Chief Exec. Officer--AFG, Inc., Westmont, IL; *U.S. Public*, pg. 955

Steinmetz, Arthur, Dr., Chief Exec. Officer--Nutrinova Nutrition Specialties & Food Ingredients GmbH, Frankfurt, Germany; *Int'l*, pg. 626

Steinwert, Kent A., Pres. & Chief Exec. Officer--Farmers & Merchants Bank of Central California, Lodi, CA; *U.S. Private*, pg. 394

Stell, Louis E., Pres. & Chief Exec. Officer--First National Bank of Conway, Conway, AR; *U.S. Public*, pg. 630

Stemberg, Thomas G., Chm. Bd. & Chief Exec. Officer--Staples, Inc., Westborough, MA; *U.S. Public*, pg. 1509

Stemmler, Robert M., Pres. & Chief Exec. Officer--AirSensors, Inc., Seattle, WA; *U.S. Public*, pg. 33

Stemmler, Robert M., Pres. & Chief Exec. Officer--IMPCO AirSensors Technologies, Cerritos, CA; *U.S. Public*, pg. 34

Stenberg, Jan, Pres., Chief Exec. Officer & Chief Oper. Officer--Scandinavian Airlines System (SAS), Solna, Sweden; *Int'l*, pg. 1201

Stendahl, Stig, Pres. & Chief Exec. Officer--Fiskars Oy AB, Helsinki, Finland; *Int'l*, pg. 492

Stenger, Ted, Chief Exec. Officer--Maidenform Worldwide, New York, NY; *U.S. Private*, pg. 697

Stensrud, Patricia, Pres. & Chief Exec. Officer--Victoria Creations, Inc., Warwick, RI; *U.S. Private*, pg. 1139

Stepan, F. Quinn, Chm. Bd., Pres. & Chief Exec. Officer--Stepan Company, Northfield, IL; *U.S. Public*, pg. 1514

Stepan, Walter, Pres. & Chief Exec. Officer--Bacou U.S.A., Inc., Smithfield, RI; *Int'l*, pg. 132

Stepan, Walter, Pres. & Chief Exec. Officer--Uvex Safety, Inc., Smithfield, RI; *Int'l*, pg. 132

Stephan, Joseph, Pres. & Chief Exec. Officer--Vertel, Woodland Hills, CA; *U.S. Public*, pg. 1717

Stephen, Philip, Chm. Bd., Pres., Chief Oper. & Chief Exec. Officer--Aid Auto Stores, Inc., Westbury, NY; *U.S. Public*, *pg. 29*

Stephens, Arthur, Chief Exec. Officer--Brown & Root Limited, London, United Kingdom; *U.S. Public*, pg. 775

Stephens, Gerald D., Pres. & Chief Exec. Officer--RLI Corp., Peoria, IL; *U.S. Public*, pg. 1356

Stephens, J.T., Pres. & Chief Exec. Officer--EBSCO Industries, Inc., Birmingham, AL; *U.S. Private*, pg. 358

Stephens, John J., Pres. & Chief Exec. Officer--U.S. Timberlands Company, L.P., Klamath Falls, OR; *U.S. Public*, pg. 1688

Stephens, W. Thomas, Pres. & Chief Exec. Officer--MacMillan Bloedel Limited, Vancouver, Canada; *Int'l*, pg. 828

Stephenson, Bryan, Pres. & Chief Exec. Officer--Independent Bankshares, Inc., Abilene, TX; *U.S. Public*, pg. 874

Stephenson, Bryan, Chief Exec. Officer--First State Bank N.A., Abilene, Abilene, TX; *U.S. Public*, pg. 874

Stephenson, E.W., Jr., Sr. Exec. V.P. & Chm. & Chief Exec. Officer-AmSouth Bank FL--AmSouth Bancorporation, Birmingham, AL; *U.S. Public*, pg. 105

Stephenson, William V., Chm. Bd., Pres. & Chief Exec. Officer--First Brands Corporation, Danbury, CT; *U.S. Public*, pg. 626

Stepien, Ronald W., Chm. Bd. & Chief Exec. Officer--MidAmerican Capital Company, Des Moines, IA; *U.S. Public*, pg. 1109

Sterling of Plaistow, Lord, Chm. Bd. & Chief Exec. Officer--The Peninsular and Oriental Steam Navigation Company, London, United Kingdom; *Int'l*, pg. 1032

Stern, Arlene H., Pres. & Chief Exec. Officer--Gantos Inc., Stamford, CT; *U.S. Public*, pg. 702

Stern, Marc, Chief Oper. Officer--Bermil Industries Corp., Inwood, NY; *U.S. Private*, pg. 136

Stern, Michael, Pres. & Chief Exec. Officer--HC Holdings, Columbus, OH; *U.S. Private*, pg. 489

Stern, Michael, Pres. & Chief Exec. Officer--Huntington Clothiers, Inc., Columbus, OH; *U.S. Private*, pg. 490

Sternbach, Stephen, Chm. Bd., Pres. & Chief Exec. Officer--Star Multi Care Services Inc., Hicksville, NY; *U.S. Public*, *pg. 1510*

Sternberg, Seymour, Chm. Bd., Pres., Chief Exec. Officer & Chief Oper. Officer--New York Life Insurance Company, New York, NY; *U.S. Private*, pg. 794

Sternberg, Sheldon, Chm. Bd. & Chief Exec. Officer--Bessin Corporation, Chicago, IL; *U.S. Public*, pg. 1433

Sterner, Al G., Chm. & Chief Exec. Officer--M & I Bank of Delavan, Delavan, WI; *U.S. Public*, pg. 1050

Sterner, Frank M., Dr., Pres. & Chief Exec. Officer--E.R. Wagner Manufacturing, Milwaukee, WI; *U.S. Private*, pg. 1146

Sternlicht, Barry, Pres. & Chief Exec. Officer--Starwood Capital Group LLC, Greenwich, CT; *U.S. Private*, pg. 1036

Sternlicht, Barry S., Chm. Bd. & Chief Exec. Officer-Trust--Starwood Hotels & Resorts, Phoenix, AZ; *U.S. Public*, pg. 1512

Steurer, Joe, Chm. Bd. & Chief Exec. Officer--Jofco Inc., Jasper, IN; *U.S. Private*, pg. 588

Stevens, Derek, Pres. & Chief Exec. Officer--Cold Heading Co., Warren, MI; *U.S. Private*, pg. 250

Stevens, Derek, Pres. & Chief Exec. Officer--Ajax Metal Processing, Detroit, MI; *U.S. Private*, pg. 250

Stevens, Gary, Chief Exec. Officer--American Glace, Ronkonkoma, NY; *U.S. Public*, pg. 883

Stevens, Paul I., Chm. Bd. & Chief Exec. Officer--Stevens International, Inc., Fort Worth, TX; *U.S. Public*, pg. 1517

Stevens, Rich, Chief Exec. Officer--Medical Advances Inc., Milwaukee, WI; *U.S. Public*, pg. 894

Stevenson, Bobby G., Chm. Bd., Chief Exec. Officer & Sec.--Ciber, Inc., Englewood, CO; *U.S. Public*, pg. 356

Stevenson, Charles E., Jr., Chm., Pres. & Chief Exec. Officer--CEBCOR (Consolidated Employment Benefits Corp.), Chicago, IL; *U.S. Private*, pg. 220

Stevenson, Craig H., Jr., Pres., Chief Exec. & Oper. Officer--OMI Corp., New York, NY; *U.S. Public*, pg. 1208

Stevenson, John R., Chm. Bd. & Chief Exec. Officer--McWhorter Technologies, Inc., Carpentersville, IL; *U.S. Public*, pg. 1074

Stevenson, Judy G., Pres., Chief Exec. Officer & Treas.--Magnetrol International, Downers Grove, IL; *U.S. Private*, *pg. 696*

Stevenson, Larry, Pres. & Chief Exec. Officer--Chapters Inc., Etobicoke, Canada; *Int'l*, pg. 280

Stevenson, Robert L., Pres. & Chief Exec. Officer--Eastman Worldwide, Buffalo, NY; *U.S. Private*, pg. 358

Steves, Edward Galt, Chief Exec. Officer--Steves & Sons, Inc., San Antonio, TX; *U.S. Private*, pg. 1042

Stewart, Andrew K., Chm. Bd., Pres. & Chief Exec. Officer--Computer Methods Corporation, Livonia, MI; *U.S. Private*, pg. 260

Stewart, Barry L., Pres., Chief Exec. Officer, Chief Fin. Officer & Treas.--Eneco Tech Group, Denver, CO; *U.S. Private*, pg. 376

Stewart, Brian J., Chief Exec.--Scottish & Newcastle plc, Edinburgh, United Kingdom; *Int'l*, pg. 1211

Stewart, Craig W., Pres. & Chief Exec. Officer--Poco Petroleums Ltd., Calgary, Canada; *Int'l*, pg. 1061

Stewart, David B., Pres. & Chief Exec. Officer--The UCS Group, Toronto, Canada; *Int'l*, pg. 792

Stewart, Doug, Pres. & Chief Exec. Officer--Sobey Inc., Stellarton, Canada; *Int'l*, pg. 454

Stewart, Hartley W., Publisher & Chief Exec. Officer--The Toronto Sun Publishing Corporation, Toronto, Canada; *Int'l*, pg. 1320

Stewart, J. Michael, Pres. & Chief Exec. Officer--Texas Micro, Inc., Houston, TX; *U.S. Public*, pg. 1586

Stewart, J.W., Chm. Bd., Pres. & Chief Exec. Officer--BJ Services Company, Houston, TX; *U.S. Public*, pg. 161

Stewart, John, Grp. Chief Exec.--Woolwich Plc, Bexley, United Kingdom; *Int'l*, pg. 1514

Stewart, M.J., Chief Exec. Officer-North America--Howden Group Plc, Renfrew, United Kingdom; *Int'l*, pg. 636

Stewart, Patricia, Chief Exec. Officer--MacNamara, Stewart & Saperstein, New York, NY; *U.S. Private*, pg. 692

Stewart, Richard, Chm. Bd. & Chief Exec. Officer--Computer Corporation of America, Framingham, MA; *U.S. Private*, pg. 260

Stewart, Richard, Pres. & Chief Exec. Officer--S&S Energy Products, Houston, TX; *U.S. Public*, pg. 711

Stewart, Robert A., Owner & Chief Exec. Officer--Advance Steel Co., Detroit, MI; *U.S. Private*, pg. 21

Stewart, S. Jay, Chm. Bd. & Chief Exec. Officer--Morton International Inc., Chicago, IL; *U.S. Public*, pg. 1134

Stewart, S. Jay, Chief Exec. Officer--Morton Automotive Coatings, Lansing, IL; *U.S. Public*, pg. 1135

Stewart, Thomas J., Chm. Bd. & Chief Exec. Officer--Services Group of America, Seattle, WA; *U.S. Private*, pg. 987

Steyn, C.G., Mng. Dir.--RMP Properties Ltd., Crown Mines, South Africa; *Int'l*, pg. 1081

Stibich, Ron, Pres. & Chief Exec. Officer--Fibre Glass-Evercoat Company, Cincinnati, OH; *U.S. Public*, pg. 866

Stich, Andrew C., Pres. & Chief Exec. Officer--Robert Scott/David Brooks, Dedham, MA; *U.S. Public*, pg. 948

Stiefel, W. K., Chm. Bd. & Chief Exec. Officer--Stiefel Laboratories, Inc., Coral Gables, FL; *U.S. Private*, pg. 1043

Stiff, P. Enoch, Pres. & Chief Exec. Officer--OmniQuip International, Inc., Port Washington, WI; *U.S. Private*, pg. 500

Stiffler, Carolyn S., Pres. & Chief Exec. Officer--Classic Markets Corp., Norcross, GA; *U.S. Private*, pg. 244

Stift, Robert C., Chm. Bd. & Chief Exec. Officer--Grove WorldWide, Shady Grove, PA; *Int'l*, pg. 593

Stiles, Terry W., Chm. Bd. & Chief Exec. Officer--Stiles Corporation, Fort Lauderdale, FL; *U.S. Private*, pg. 1043

Still, Willard J., Pres. & Chief Exec. Officer--Dealers Electrical Supply Co., Waco, TX; *U.S. Private*, pg. 318

Stillman, Larry, Pres. & Chief Exec. Officer--Ingram Paper Company, City of Industry, CA; *U.S. Public*, pg. 904

Stimpson, Fred T., Pres. & Chief Exec. Officer--Gulf Lumber Company, Inc., Mobile, AL; *U.S. Private*, pg. 487

Stingel, Russell E., Chm. Bd. & Chief Exec. Officer--IEC Electronics Corp., Newark, NY; *U.S. Public*, pg. 854

Stinnette, Joe L., Jr., Pres. & Chief Exec. Officer--Fireman's Fund Insurance Company, Novato, CA; *Int'l*, pg. 58

Stinson, Terry D., Pres. & Chief Exec. & Oper. Officer--Bell Helicopter Textron, Hurst, TX; *U.S. Public*, pg. 1588

Stipes, Frank C., Esq., Chm. Bd., Pres. & Chief Exec. Officer--Westernbank of Puerto Rico, Mayaguez, PR; *U.S. Public*, pg. 1760

Stipp, Scott L., Pres. & Chief Exec. Officer--District Petroleum Products, Inc., Sandusky, OH; *U.S. Private*, pg. 336

Stitt, William C., Chm. & Chief Exec. Officer--ICF Kaiser Engineers, Inc., Oakland, CA; *U.S. Public*, pg. 853

Stitzer, Todd, Pres. & Chief Exec. Officer--Dr Pepper/Seven Up No. America, Dallas, TX; *Int'l*, pg. 248

Stocchetti, Carlo, Chief Exec. Officer & Gen. Mgr.--Locazioni Finanziarie S.p.A., Brescia, Italy; *Int'l*, pg. 138

Stockdale, William, Chief Exec. Officer & Mng. Dir.--HSB Engineering Insurance Limited, London, United Kingdom; *U.S. Public*, pg. 795

Stocker, Michael A., Pres. & Chief Exec. Officer--Empire Blue Cross & Blue Shield, New York, NY; *U.S. Private*, pg. 374

Stockholm, G., Chief Exec. Officer--Zurich Livsforsikring, Copenhagen, Denmark; *Int'l*, pg. 1530

Stockley, Terry, Chief Exec.-UK & Ireland--NFC plc, London, United Kingdom; *Int'l*, pg. 901

Stockton, Frederic P., Pres. & Chief Exec. Officer--TRM Copy Centers Corporation, Portland, OR; *U.S. Public*, pg. 1558

Stoddard, Richard E., Chm. Bd. & Chief Exec. Officer--Kaiser Ventures, Inc., Ontario, CA; *U.S. Public*, pg. 941

Stoehr, James H., III, Pres. & Chief Exec. Officer--Robbins, Inc., Cincinnati, OH; *U.S. Private*, pg. 934

Stokely, John E., Pres. & Chief Exec. Officer--Richfood Holdings, Inc., Glen Allen, VA; *U.S. Public*, pg. 1388

Stokes, Gary, Pres. & Chief Exec. Officer--WVTM-TV, Inc., Birmingham, AL; *U.S. Public*, pg. 712

Stokes, Patrick T., Chm. Bd. & Chief Exec. Officer--Anheuser-Busch Investment Capital Corporation, Saint Louis, MO; *U.S. Public*, pg. 114

Stokholm, G., Chief Exec. Officer--Zurich Forsikring, Copenhagen, Denmark; *Int'l*, pg. 1531

Stolberg, Al, Chief Exec. Officer--Metrosonics Inc., Rochester, NY; *Int'l*, pg. 208

Stoll, Roger G., Ph.D., Chief Exec. Officer--Ohmeda, Inc., Liberty Corner, NJ; *Int'l*, pg. 121

Stollenwerk, John J., Pres. & Chief Exec. Officer--Allen-Edmonds Shoe Corp., Port Washington, WI; *U.S. Private*, *pg. 36*

Stollery, A. Gordon, Chm. Bd., Pres. & Chief Exec. Officer--Morrison Petroleums Ltd., Calgary, Canada; *Int'l*, pg. 895

Stolt-Nielsen, Jacob, Jr., Chm. Bd. & Chief Exec. Officer--Stolt-Nielsen S.A., London, United Kingdom; *Int'l*, pg. 1301

Stolte, Sandra L., Pres., Chief Exec. Officer & Sec.--Central Bank, Fairview Heights, IL; *U.S. Public*, pg. 643

Stolzenburg, Manfred, Dr., Chief Exec.--DOWC Ost-West-Consult GmbH, Frankfurt/Main, Germany; *Int'l*, pg. 418

Stone, Craig, Chm. Bd., Pres. & Chief Exec. Officer--K-D Lamp Company, Cincinnati, OH; *U.S. Private*, pg. 603

Stone, David J., Chm. Bd. & Chief Exec. Officer--Southwestern Financial Corporation, New York, NY; *U.S.* Private, pg. 1018

Stone, David J., Chm. Bd. & Chief Exec. Officer--PennCorp Financial Group, Inc., New York, NY; *U.S. Public*, pg. 1271

Stone, John McWilliams, Jr., Chm. Bd., Pres., Chief Exec. Officer & Chief Oper. Officer--Dukane Corporation, Saint Charles, IL; *U.S. Private*, pg. 345

Stone, Richard B., Chm. Bd. & Chief Exec. Officer--Dart Group Corporation, Landover, MD; *U.S. Public*, pg. 484

Stone, Richard B., Chm. Bd. & Chief Exec. Officer--Crown Books Corporation, Landover, MD; *U.S. Public*, pg. 484

Stone, Roger W., Chm. Bd., Pres. & Chief Exec. Officer--Stone Container Corporation, Chicago, IL; *U.S. Public*, pg. 1520

Stone, Roger W., Chm. Bd. & Chief Exec. Officer--Stone Forest Industries, Chicago, IL; *U.S. Public*, pg. 1521

Stone, Sherrill, Chm. Bd.,Pres. & Chief Exec. Officer--Peerless Mfg. Co., Dallas, TX; *U.S. Public*, pg. 1268

Stoneback, W. Keith, Pres. & Chief Exec. Officer--Surgical Laser Technologies, Inc., Montgomeryville, PA; *U.S. Public*, pg. 1542

Stonecipher, David A., Pres. & Chief Exec. Officer--Jefferson-Pilot Corporation, Greensboro, NC; *U.S. Public*, *pg. 925*

Stonecipher, Harland C., Chm. Bd. & Chief Exec. Officer--Pre-Paid Legal Services, Inc., Ada, OK; *U.S. Public*, pg. 1320

Stooksbury, Gary L., Chief Exec. Officer & Gen. Mgr.--Aiken Electric Cooperative Inc., Aiken, SC; *U.S. Private*, pg. 28

Stooksbury, Gary L., Chief Exec. Officer & Gen. Mgr.--Aiken Electric Satellite, Aiken, SC; *U.S. Private*, pg. 28

Stoppelmoor, Wayne H., Chm. Bd. & Chief Exec. Officer--Interstate Power Company, Dubuque, IA; *U.S. Public*, pg. 910

Storch, David P., Pres., Chief Exec. & Oper. Officer--AAR Corp., Wood Dale, IL; *U.S. Public*, pg. 1

Stork, Wayne A., Chm. & Chief Exec. Officer--Delaware Management Holdings, Inc., Philadelphia, PA; *U.S. Public*, pg. 997

Stormes, Ben F., II, Pres. & Chief Exec. Officer--The Wickman Corp., Oak Park, MI; *U.S. Private*, pg. 1175

Storms, Charles D., Pres. & Chief Exec. Officer--Red Spot Paint & Varnish Co., Evansville, IN; *U.S. Private*, pg. 915

Storr, Hans G., Chm. Bd. & Chief Exec. Officer--Philip Morris Capital Corporation, Rye Brook, NY; *U.S. Public*, pg. 1289

Storrie, Karl F., Pres. & Chief Exec. Officer--Dura Automotive Systems, Inc., Minneapolis, MN; *U.S. Public*, pg. 537

Story, Edward T., Pres. & Chief Exec. Officer--SOCO International, Inc., Houston, TX; *U.S. Public*, pg. 1482

Stott, Geoff, Chief Exec. Officer--Frontline, Peterborough, United Kingdom; *Int'l*, pg. 114

Stouffer, Ronald D., Pres. & Chief Exec. Officer--Bowles Fluidics Corporation, Columbia, MD; *U.S. Public*, pg. 248

Stout, Everett E., Pres., Chief Exec. Officer, Chief Fin. Officer & Controller--Metaltech, Inc., Kirkwood, MO; *U.S.* Private, pg. 735

Stout, Gary, Pres. & Chief Exec. Officer--Gannett Offset, Springfield, VA; *U.S. Public*, pg. 699

Stout, Lonnie J., II, Chm. Bd., Pres. & Chief Exec. Officer--J. Alexanders Corporation, Nashville, TN; *U.S. Public*, pg. 40

Stout, Raymond M., Pres. & Chief Exec. Officer--Fabwel Inc., Elkhart, IN; *U.S. Private*, pg. 390

Stout, Stephen, Chief Exec.--Butterworths British and Irish Legal, London, United Kingdom; *Int'l*, pg. 1095

Stover, Matthew J., Pres. & Chief Exec. Officer--Bell Atlantic Yellow Pages, Middleton, MA; *U.S. Public*, pg. 203

Stover, W. Robert, Chm. Bd. & Chief Exec. Officer--Western Staff Services, Walnut Creek, CA; *U.S. Public*, pg. 1760

Stover, W.G., Jr., Chief Exec. Officer--Micron Quantum Devices, Inc., Santa Clara, CA; *U.S. Public*, pg. 1105

Stowers, James, III, Chief Exec. Officer--American Century Companies, Inc., Kansas City, MO; *U.S. Private*, pg. 52

Strachan, Ian, Chief Exec. Officer--BTR plc, London, United Kingdom; *Int'l*, pg. 124

Stramaglia, M.P., Chief Exec. Officer--Zurich Life Insurance Co. of Canada, Willowdale, Canada; *Int'l*, pg. 1532

Strange, J. Leland, Pres. & Chief Exec. Officer--Intelligent Systems Corp., Norcross, GA; *U.S. Public*, pg. 888

Strange, Peter S., Pres. & Chief Exec. Officer--Frank Messer & Sons Construction Co., Cincinnati, OH; *U.S. Private*, pg. 734

Stratton, Frederick P., Jr., Chm. Bd. & Chief Exec. Officer--Briggs & Stratton Corporation, Wauwatosa, WI; *U.S. Public*, pg. 252

Stratton, Harold M., II, Pres. & Chief Exec. Officer--Strattec Securities Corporation, Milwaukee, WI; *U.S. Public*, pg. 1523

Stratton, Richard A., Pres. & Chief Exec. Officer--Litchfield Financial Corporation, Williamstown, MA; *U.S. Public*, pg. 1001

Straub, Walter W., Chm. Bd., Pres. & Chief Exec. Officer--Rainbow Technologies, Inc., Irvine, CA; *U.S. Public*, pg. 1359

Straube, Win, Chm. Bd.--Pegasus International Corporation, Pennington, NJ; *U.S. Private*, pg. 1046

Strauch, Charles S., Chm. Bd. & Chief Exec. Officer--PairGain Technologies Inc., Tustin, CA; *U.S. Public*, pg. 1253

Straus, David J., Chm. Bd. & Chief Exec. Officer--STRAFCO, Inc., San Antonio, TX; *U.S. Private*, pg. 1046

Straus, Roger W., Jr., Pres. & Chief Exec. Officer--Farrar, Straus & Giroux, Inc., New York, NY; *Int'l*, pg. 1479

Strausbaugh, Robert L., Vice Chm., Pres. & Chief Exec. Officer--Spring Grove National Bank, Spring Grove, PA; *U.S. Public*, pg. 1542

Strauss, Charles B., Pres. & Chief Exec. Officer--Lever Brothers Co., New York, NY; *Int'l*, pg. 1435

Strauss, David, Pres. & Chief Exec. Officer--Key Container Corporation, Pawtucket, RI; *U.S. Private*, pg. 617

Strauss, Richard H., Pres. & Chief Exec. Officer--Advance Packaging Corporation, Grand Rapids, MI; *U.S. Private*, pg. 18

Straw, Erwin T., Chm. Bd., Pres. & Chief Exec. Officer--Prime Bancorp, Inc., Fort Washington, PA; *U.S. Public*, pg. 1326

Street, Chriss W., Chm. Bd., Pres. & Chief Exec. & Oper. Officer--Comprehensive Care Corporation, Corona Del Mar, CA; *U.S. Public*, pg. 419

Street, Gordon P., Jr., Chm. Bd., Pres., Chief Exec. & Chief Oper. Officer--North American Royalties, Inc., Chattanooga, TN; *U.S. Private*, pg. 803

Street, William M., Pres. & Chief Exec. Officer--Brown-Forman Beverages Worldwide, Louisville, KY; *U.S. Public*, pg. 261

Stremme, Steffen, Dr., Chm. Bd., Pres. & Chief Exec. Officer--Quelle Group, Furth, Germany; *Int'l*, pg. 1078

Stretton, Jim, Chief Exec. Officer-U.K. Opers.--Standard Life Assurance, Edinburgh, United Kingdom; *Int'l*, pg. 1297

Strickland, D. Gordon, Pres. & Chief Exec. Officer--Kerr Group, Inc., Lancaster, PA; *U.S. Public*, pg. 952

Strickland, Ed, Pres. & Chief Exec. Officer--Valley Systems, Inc., Canal Fulton, OH; *U.S. Public*, pg. 1706

Strickland, Robert, Chm. Bd. & Chief Exec. Officer--Trust Company Of Georgia, Atlanta, GA; *U.S. Public*, pg. 1538

Strigl, Dennis F., Pres. & Chief Exec. Officer--Bell Atlantic Mobile, Bedminster, NJ; *U.S. Public*, pg. 202

Stringle, Stan, Chief Exec. Officer--Omega Environmental Inc., Bothell, WA; *U.S. Public*, pg. 1221

Stringle, Stan, Chief Exec. Officer--Omega Environmental Inc., Richmond, VA; *U.S. Public*, pg. 1222

Strite, L. Gerald, Pres. & Chief Exec. Officer--Shenandoah Mfg. Co. Inc., Harrisonburg, VA; *U.S. Private*, pg. 992

Stroburg, Jeff, Pres. & Chief Exec. Officer--Countrymark Cooperative, Inc., Indianapolis, IN; *U.S. Private*, pg. 279

Strohl, Bruce E., Chief Exec. Officer & Sr. V.P.-Fin.--The Cosmetic Center Inc., Columbia, MD; *U.S. Private*, pg. 689

Strome, Stephen, Pres. & Chief Exec. Officer--Handleman Company, Troy, MI; *U.S. Public*, pg. 779

Strong, Peter R., Pres. & Chief Exec. Officer--Buehler, Limited, Lake Bluff, IL; *U.S. Public*, pg. 574

Stroup, Paul A., III, Pres. & Chief Exec. Officer--Lance, Inc., Charlotte, NC; *U.S. Public*, pg. 977

Strudler, Robert J., Chm. Bd. & Co.-Chief Exec. Officer--U.S. Home Corporation, Houston, TX; *U.S. Public*, pg. 1682

Strum, Lonny, Chief Exec. Officer & New Bus. Contact--RBT/Strum, Cherry Hill, NJ; *U.S. Private*, pg. 902

Strumbos, George, Chief Exec. Officer--Alpha Bolt Company, Madison Heights, MI; *U.S. Private*, pg. 1152

Stuart, James, Jr., Chm. Bd. & Chief Exec. Officer--First Commerce Bancshares, Inc., Lincoln, NE; *U.S. Public*, pg. 629

Stuart, John E., Chm. Bd. & Chief Exec. Officer--Ikon Office Solutions, Inc., Malvern, PA; *U.S. Public*, pg. 862

Stuart, Thomas, Chm. Bd. & Chief Exec. Officer--Bureau of Engraving, Minneapolis, MN; *U.S. Private*, pg. 181

Stubblefield, David E., Pres. & Chief Exec. Officer--ABF Freight System, Inc., Fort Smith, AR; *U.S. Public*, pg. 130

Stubbs, Robert W., Chm. Bd. & Chief Exec. Officer--Bell Atlantic Properties, Inc., Philadelphia, PA; *U.S. Public*, pg. 203

Stubbs, Stoney M., Jr., Chm. Bd., Pres. & Chief Exec. Officer--Frozen Food Express Industries, Inc., Dallas, TX; *U.S. Public*, pg. 685

Stuckey, Charles R., Jr., Chm. Bd., Pres. & Chief Exec. Officer--Security Dynamics Technologies, Bedford, MA; *U.S. Public*, pg. 1453

Stuelpe, G. Walter, Jr., Pres. & Chief Exec. Officer--Apcoa, Inc., Cleveland, OH; *U.S. Private*, pg. 533

Stuenkel, Mark H., Pres. & Chief Exec. Officer--Southern California Bank, Newport Beach, CA; *U.S. Public*, pg. 1758

Stults, G. Ray, Chief Oper. Officer & Exec. V.P.--Shelter Components Corporation, Elkhart, IN; *U.S. Public*, pg. 952

Stump, Nick W., Mng. Dir. & Chief Exec.--M.I.M. Holdings Ltd., Brisbane, Australia; *Int'l*, pg. 827

Stumpo, James H., Pres. & Chief Exec. Officer--Athey Products Corporation, Wake Forest, NC; *U.S. Public*, pg. 142

Stunard, E. Arthur, Chief Oper. Officer--DeVRY Institute of Technology, Chicago, IL; *U.S. Public*, pg. 504

Stuntz, William, Pres.--Dranetz-BMI, Edison, NJ; *U.S. Private*, pg. 1144

Stupka, John T., Pres. & Chief Exec. Officer--Mobile Telecommunications Technologies Corp., Jackson, MS; *U.S. Public*, pg. 1120

Stupp, Robert P., Pres.--Stupp Bros Inc., Saint Louis, MO; *U.S. Private*, pg. 1048

Sturiale, Thomas, Pres. & Chief Exec. Officer--Neles-Jamesbury Corp., Worcester, MA; *Int'l*, pg. 1428

Sturken, Craig, Chm. Bd. & Chief Exec. Officer--Dominion Stores, Etobicoke, Canada; *Int'l*, pg. 1375

Sturken, Craig, Chm. & Chief Exec. Officer-Midwest Region--The Great Atlantic & Pacific Tea Company, Inc., Montvale, NJ; *Int'l*, pg. 1375

Stutz, Rolf, Chm. Bd. & Chief Exec. Officer--Zoll Medical Corporation, Burlington, MA; *U.S. Private*, pg. 1207

Stuzin, Charles B., Chm. Bd., Chief Exec. Officer & Pres.--NationsBank/Miami, Miami, FL; *U.S. Public*, pg. 1162

Styrlind, Kenneth A., Pres. & Chief Exec. Officer--Witcher Construction Company, Eden Prairie, MN; *U.S. Private*, pg. 347

Styrlund, Kenneth A., Pres.--Witcher Construction Co., Minneapolis, MN; *U.S. Private*, pg. 1185

Styslinger, Lee J., III, Pres. & Chief Exec. Officer--Altec Industries, Inc., Birmingham, AL; *U.S. Private*, pg. 47

Suarez, Amancio V., Chm. Bd., Pres., Chief Exec. & Chief Fin. Officer--Cosmo Communications Corporation, Miami, FL; *U.S. Public*, pg. 451

Subasi, Hasan, Vice Chm.--Arcelik A.S., Istanbul, Turkey; *Int'l*, pg. 741

Subia, Robert, Chm., Pres. & Chief Exec. Officer--Micron Custom Manufacturing Services, Inc., Nampa, ID; *U.S. Public*, pg. 1105

Subramaniam, Shivan S., Chm. Bd., Pres. & Chief Exec. Officer--Allendale Mutual Insurance Co., Johnston, RI; *U.S. Private*, pg. 37

Sudderth, Robert J., Jr., Chm. & Chief Exec. Officer--SunTrust Bank, Chattanooga, N.A., Chattanooga, TN; *U.S. Public*, pg. 1538

Suetsugu, Hiroshi, Pres. & Chief Exec. Officer--Nippon Steel U.S.A., Inc., New York, NY; *Int'l*, pg. 939

Suggs, Carroll W., Chm. Bd., Pres. & Chief Exec. Officer--Petroleum Helicopters, Inc., Metairie, LA; *U.S. Public*, pg. 1281

Suggs, Leo H., Chm. Bd. & Chief Exec. Officer--Overnite Transportation Co., Richmond, VA; *U.S. Public*, pg. 1668

Sugiura, Go, Chm. Bd. & Chief Exec. Officer--Miller Fluid Power Corp., Bensenville, IL; *U.S. Private*, pg. 747

Sugiyama, Mineo, Pres. & Chief Exec. Officer--NEC America, Inc., Melville, NY; *Int'l*, pg. 900

Suh, Chan, Pres. & Chief Exec. Officer--Agency.Com, New York, NY; *U.S. Public*, pg. 1223

Suhowatsky, Stephen J., Pres. & Chief Exec. Officer--Syracuse Supply Company, Syracuse, NY; *U.S. Private*, pg. 1060

Suila, Keijo, Pres. & Chief Exec. Officer--Leaf Group B.V., Espoo, Finland,; *Int'l*, pg. 638

Suitt, T. Howard, Chm. Bd. & Chief Exec. Officer--Suitt Construction Company, Inc., Greenville, SC; *U.S. Private*, pg. 106

Sukawaty, Andrew, Chief Exec. Officer--Sprint PCS, Kansas City, MO; *U.S. Public*, pg. 1501

Sullivan, Charles A., Chm. Bd. & Chief Exec. Officer--Interstate Bakeries Corporation, Kansas City, MO; *U.S. Public*, pg. 909

Sullivan, Chris T., Chm. Bd. & Chief Exec. Officer--Outback Steakhouse Inc., Tampa, FL; *U.S. Public*, pg. 1235

Sullivan, Daniel J., Chm. Bd., Pres. & Chief Exec. Officer--Caliber System, Inc., Akron, OH; *U.S. Public*, pg. 604

Sullivan, Don, Pres. & Chief Exec. Officer--Osicom Technologies Inc., Annapolis Junction, MD; *U.S. Public*, pg. 1233

Sullivan, Donald M., Chm. Bd., Pres. & Chief Exec. Officer--MTS Systems Corporation, Eden Prairie, MN; *U.S. Public*, pg. 1028

Sullivan, G. Craig, Chm. Bd., Pres. & Chief Exec. Officer--The Clorox Company, Oakland, CA; *U.S. Public*, pg. 386

Sullivan, John B., Pres. & Chief Exec. Officer--Willis Corroon Corp. of Illinois, Chicago, IL; *Int'l*, pg. 1506

Sullivan, John Fox, Chm., Pres., Chief Exec. Officer & Publr.--National Journal Group, Washington, DC; *U.S. Private*, pg. 785

Sullivan, Kenneth R., Pres. & Chief Exec. Officer--Sullivan Oil Company, Baton Rouge, LA; *U.S. Private*, pg. 1050

Sullivan, Michael P., Pres. & Chief Exec. Officer--International Dairy Queen, Inc., Minneapolis, MN; *U.S. Public*, pg. 220

Sullivan, Pat, Pres. & Chief Exec. Officer--Citizens Bank of Kentucky, Shively, KY; *U.S. Public*, pg. 280

Sullivan, Terrence T., Pres. & Chief Exec. Officer--American Paging, Inc., Minneapolis, MN; *U.S. Public*, pg. 1570

Sullivan, Thomas C., Chm. Bd. & Chief Exec. Officer--RPM, Inc., Medina, OH; *U.S. Public*, pg. 1356

Sullivan, William M., Pres. & Chief Exec. Officer--Oxford Health Plans Inc., Norwalk, CT; *U.S. Public*, pg. 1238

Sulzberger, Arthur Ochs, Chm. Bd. & Chief Exec. Officer--The New York Times Company, New York, NY; *U.S. Public*, pg. 1173

Sulzberger, Arthur Ochs, Chm. Bd. & Chief Exec. Officer--The New York Times, New York, NY; *U.S. Public*, pg. 1174

Suma, Charles M., Pres. & Chief Exec. Officer--The New Piper Aircraft, Inc., Vero Beach, FL; *U.S. Private*, pg. 794

Sumas, Perry, Pres. & Chief Exec. Officer--Village Super Market Inc., Springfield, NJ; *U.S. Public*, pg. 1721

Summa, Timo, Pres. & Chief Exec. Officer--Tamrock Corp., Tampere, Finland; *Int'l*, pg. 1352

Summerfield, David, Chief Exec. Officer--How Group Limited, West Bromwich, United Kingdom; *Int'l*, pg. 636

Summers, Cary, Pres. & Chief Exec. Officer--Silver Dollar City, Inc., Branson, MO; *U.S. Private*, pg. 1000

Summers, William B. Jr., Pres. & Chief Exec. Officer--McDonald & Company Investments, Inc., Cleveland, OH; *U.S. Public*, pg. 1068

Sumrall, Russ, V.P.-Opers.--Popeye's Chicken & Biscuits, Atlanta, GA; *U.S. Private*, pg. 5

Sundberg, Matti, Chm. Bd., Pres. & Chief Exec. Officer--Valmet Corporation, Helsinki, Finland; *Int'l*, pg. 1447

Sunderland, John, Chief Exec. Officer--Cadbury Schweppes p.l.c., London, United Kingdom; *Int'l*, pg. 247

Sunderland, Lee A., Pres. & Chief Exec. Officer--The Richman Brothers Co., Fall River, MA; *U.S. Public*, pg. 1777

Sundt, H. Wilson, Chm. Bd. & Chief Exec. Officer--Sundt Corp., Tucson, AZ; *U.S. Private*, pg. 1051

Sung On, Andrew Ng, Chm. Bd. & Chief Exec. Officer--GP Batteries International Ltd., Singapore, Singapore; *Int'l*, pg. 537

Surico, Richard, Chief Exec. Officer, Treas.--Feintool U.S. Operations Inc., White Plains, NY; *Int'l*, pg. 479

Suscavage, Michael G., Pres. & Chief Exec. Officer--Global Marketing Resources (GMR), New York, NY; *U.S. Private*, pg. 457

Sutherland, Michael, Pres. & Chief Exec. Officer--Spinnerin Inc., South Hackensack, NJ; *U.S. Private*, pg. 1025

Sutowski, Walter, Chm. Bd. & Chief Exec. Officer--Freeway Corporation, Cleveland, OH; *U.S. Private*, pg. 426

Sutter, Ruth A., Chief Exec. Officer--Fisheries Supply Company, Seattle, WA; *U.S. Private*, pg. 408

Sutton, Kelso F., Pres. & Chief Exec. Officer--The Time Inc. Book Company, New York, NY; *U.S. Public*, pg. 1613

Sutton, Nicholas J., Chm. Bd. & Chief Exec. Officer--HS Resources, San Francisco, CA; *U.S. Public*, pg. 772

Sutton, Thomas C., Chm. Bd. & Chief Exec. Officer--Pacific Life Insurance Company, Newport Beach, CA; *U.S. Private*, pg. 831

Suwyn, Mark A., Chm. Bd. & Chief Exec. Officer--Louisiana Pacific Corporation, Portland, OR; *U.S. Public*, pg. 1015

Suzuki, Osamu, Pres. & Chief Exec. Officer--Suzuki Motor Corporation, Shizuoka, Japan; *Int'l*, pg. 1322

Svanberg, Carl-Henric, Pres. & Chief Exec. Officer--Assa Abloy AB, Stockholm, Sweden; *Int'l*, pg. 17

Svendsen, Arthur, Chm. Bd. & Chief Exec. Officer--Standard Pacific Corp., Costa Mesa, CA; *U.S. Public*, pg. 1503

Svensson, H. Kjell, Pres. & Chief Exec. Officer--Cardo AB, Malmo, Sweden; *Int'l*, pg. 268

Svensson, Nils-Erik, Chief Exec.--Sulzer Metco (Norden) AB, Stockholm, Sweden; *Int'l*, pg. 1308

Swager, Richard E., Chm. Bd. & Chief Exec. Officer--Reinsurance Alternatives, Inc., Minneapolis, MN; *Int'l*, pg. 1503

Swahn, Hans, Chief Exec.--Esselte Meto, Heppenheim, Germany; *Int'l*, pg. 461

Swainston, Tony, Div. Chief Exec.-Fine Papers--Arjo Wiggins Appleton plc, Basingstoke, United Kingdom; *Int'l*, pg. 567

Swam, Robert L., Exec. V.P., Chm. Bd. & Chief Exec. Officer-Raytheon Appliances--Raytheon Company, Lexington, MA; *U.S. Public*, pg. 1364

Swaner, Keith, Chief Exec. Officer--Swaner Hardwood Company, Inc., Burbank, CA; *U.S. Private*, pg. 1057

Swanson, Armour F., Acting Pres. & Chief Exec. Officer--Carolina Steel Corporation, Greensboro, NC; *U.S. Private*, pg. 214

Swanson, Douglas E., Chm. Bd., Pres. & Chief Exec. Officer--Cliffs Drilling Company, Houston, TX; *U.S. Public*, pg. 386

Swanson, Robert, Pres. & Chief Exec. Officer--Fulton Industries Inc., Wauseon, OH; *U.S. Private*, pg. 431

Swanson, Robert H., Jr., Pres. & Chief Exec. Officer--Linear Technology Corp., Milpitas, CA; *U.S. Public*, pg. 1000

Swanson, William H., Chm. Bd. & Chief Exec. Officer--Raytheon Systems Company, Arlington, VA; *U.S. Public*, pg. 1364

Swanstrom, Kenneth A., Chm. Bd., Pres. & Chief Exec. Officer--Penn Engineering & Manufacturing Corp., Danboro, PA; *U.S. Public*, pg. 1269

Swanstrom, Steiner, Pres. & Chief Exec. Officer--Luxo A/S, Oslo, Norway; *Int'l*, pg. 821

Swartout, Hank B., Chm. Bd., Pres. & Chief Exec. Officer--Precision Drilling Corporation, Calgary, Canada; *Int'l*, pg. 1066

Swartwout, James R., Chm. Bd., Pres. & Chief Fin. Officer--Summa Industries, Torrance, CA; *U.S. Public*, pg. 1527

Swartz, Dr. Jerome, Chm. Bd. & Chief Exec. Officer--Symbol Technologies, Inc., Holtsville, NY; *U.S. Public*, pg. 1546

Swartz, Sidney W., Chm. Bd., Pres. & Chief Exec. Officer--The Timberland Company, Stratham, NH; *U.S. Public*, pg. 1609

Swartz, Thomas B., Chm. Bd. & Chief Exec. Officer--The Sierra Capital Companies, San Francisco, CA; *U.S. Private*, pg. 998

Swayne, Keith, Pres. & Chief Exec. Officer--Case-Swayne Co. Inc., Corona, CA; *U.S. Private*, pg. 218

Sweasy, William J., Chm. Bd.--Red Wing Shoe Co., Inc., Red Wing, MN; *U.S. Private*, pg. 915

Sween, Tom, Chm. Bd. & Chief Exec. Officer--E.A. Sween Company, Eden Prairie, MN; *U.S. Private*, pg. 1058

Sweet, Stedman G., Pres. & Chief Exec. Officer--The Eastern Company, Naugatuck, CT; *U.S. Public*, pg. 548

Sweetland, Mark R., Pres. & Chief Exec. Officer--SofTECH, Inc., Grand Rapids, MI; *U.S. Public*, pg. 1482

Sweig, Morton A, Vice Chm. & Chief Exec. Officer--ISS International Service System, Inc., Atlanta, GA; *Int'l*, pg. 656

Sweitzer, Brandon W., Pres. & Chief Exec. Officer--Guy Carpenter & Co., Inc, New York, NY; *U.S. Public*, pg. 1048

Swendrowski, John, Chm. Bd. & Chief Exec. Officer--Northland Cranberries, Inc., Wisconsin Rapids, WI; *U.S. Public*, pg. 1197

Swenson, Kurt M., Chm. Bd., Pres. & Chief Exec. Officer--Rock of Ages Corporation, Graniteville, VT; *U.S. Public*, pg. 1396

Swett, Ralph J., Chm. Bd., Pres. & Chief Exec. Officer--IXC Communications, Inc., Austin, TX; *U.S. Private*, pg. 556

Swift, George P., Jr., Chm. Bd. & Chief Exec. Officer--Columbus Mills, Inc., Columbus, GA; *U.S. Private*, pg. 256

Swift, Humphrey H., Pres., Chief Exec. Officer & Mgr.-Adv. & Sls. Promo.--Swift Instruments, Inc., Dorchester, MA; *U.S. Private*, pg. 1058

Swift, Richard J., Chm. Bd., Pres. & Chief Exec. Officer--Foster Wheeler Corporation, Clinton, NJ; *U.S. Public*, pg. 676

Swindell, Lloyd, Chief Exec. Officer--L & L Nursery Supply, Inc., Chino, CA; *U.S. Private*, pg. 638

Swinehart, Keith, Sr., Chm. Bd., Chief Exec. Officer & Chief Fin. Officer--Vanguard Plastics, Inc., Mc Pherson, KS; *U.S. Private*, pg. 1134

Swinimer, William A., Chm. Bd. & Chief Exec. Officer--Uniplast Industries, Inc., Orillia, Canada; *Int'l*, pg. 1424

Swink, James W., Pres., Chief Exec. Officer & Chief Oper. Officer--Young Pecan Company (A Partnership), Florence, SC; *U.S. Private*, pg. 1201

Swinsky, Morton, Pres. & Chief Exec. Officer--Fuji Securities Inc.-New York, New York, NY; *Int'l*, pg. 519

Swirsky, Benjamin, Pres. & Chief Exec. Officer--Slater Industries Inc., North York, Canada; *Int'l*, pg. 1262

Swisher, Bill, Chm. Bd. & Chief Exec. Officer--CMI Corporation, Oklahoma City, OK; *U.S. Public*, pg. 278

Swisher, John B., Pres. & Chief Exec. Officer--United Feeds, Inc., Sheridan, IN; *U.S. Private*, pg. 1122

Switzer, Mel, Jr., Pres. & Chief Exec. Officer--Sonoma Valley Bank, Sonoma, CA; *U.S. Public*, pg. 1487

Sydnor, Dale, Chm. Bd., Pres. & Chief Exec. Officer--Wireless Telecom Group, Inc., Paramus, NJ; *U.S. Public*, pg. 1772

Sykes, Greg, Pres. & Chief Exec. Officer--Hygrade Food Products Corporation, Southfield, MI; *U.S. Public*, pg. 1433

Sykes, Guy R., Vice Chm., Pres. & Chief Exec. Officer--Camellia Food Stores, Inc., Norfolk, VA; *U.S. Private*, pg. 203

Sylvester, Paul R., Pres. & Chief Exec. Officer--Manatron, Inc., Kalamazoo, MI; *U.S. Public*, pg. 1040

Symons, A.P., Chm. Bd. & Chief Exec. Officer--Canada Life Casualty Insurance Company, Etobicoke, Canada; *Int'l*, pg. 254

Synott, Lee, Chm. Bd., Pres. & Chief Exec. Officer--Ingram Book Company, La Vergne, TN; *U.S. Private*, pg. 563

Syron, M. Bernard, Chm. Bd. & Chief Exec. Officer--Cara Operations Limited, Toronto, Canada; *Int'l*, pg. 266

Syron, Richard F., Chm. Bd. & Chief Exec. Officer--The American Stock Exchange, New York, NY; *U.S. Private*, pg. 62

Syrota, Jean, Chm. & Chief Exec. Officer--COGEMA - Compagnie Generale des Matieres Nucleaires, Velizy-Villacoublay, France; *Int'l*, pg. 304

Syverson, David B., Chief Exec. Officer--Dave Syverson Truck Center, Inc., Rochester, MN; *U.S. Private*, pg. 1061

Syz, David W., Dr., Chief Exec. Officer & Member-Exec. Board--SIG Schweizersiche Industrie-Gesellschaft Holding AG, Neuhausen, Switzerland; *Int'l*, pg. 1156
Syz, Martin G., Dr., Chief Exec. Officer--Clariant International Ltd., Muttenz, Switzerland; *Int'l*, pg. 624
Szathmary, Sandor, Chief Exec. Officer--Malev Hungarian Airlines, Plc., Budapest, Hungary; *Int'l*, pg. 833
Sze, Andy, Pres. & Chief Exec. Officer--Clipper Exxpress, Lemont, IL; *U.S. Public*, pg. 130
Szetykiel, George W., Chm. Bd. & Chief Exec. Officer--Spartan Motors, Inc., Charlotte, MI; *U.S. Public*, pg. 1495
Szlasa, John P., Pres. & Chief Exec. Officer-Ferguson Consulting--CommonHealth USA, Parsippany, NJ; *Int'l*, pg. 1483
Szydlowski, T., Chief Exec. Officer--ISI Norgen, Inc., Fraser, MI; *Int'l*, pg. 646
Szymanczyk, Michael, Chief Exec. Officer--Philip Morris U.S.A., New York, NY; *U.S. Public*, pg. 1289
Taafe, Willie, Pres. & Chief Exec. Officer--Knapp Shoes Inc., Penn Yan, NY; *U.S. Private*, pg. 401
Tablak, Jeff, Pres., Chief Exec. Officer & Co-Founder--Nextron, San Jose, CA; *U.S. Public*, pg. 1424
Tabor, Jon K., Chm. Bd., Pres. & Chief Exec. Officer--Allied Mineral Products, Inc., Columbus, OH; *U.S. Private*, pg. 39
Tachikawa, Masami, Pres. & Chief Exec. Officer--The Yasuda Trust and Banking Co., Ltd., Tokyo, Japan; *Int'l*, pg. 1520
Tagawa, Craig K., Chief Exec. Officer--GK Financing, LLC, San Francisco, CA; *U.S. Public*, pg. 91
Taguchi, Tadao, Chm. & Chief Exec. Officer--Toshiba America Inc., New York, NY; *Int'l*, pg. 1405
Tague, John, Pres. & Chief Exec. Officer--American Trans Air, Inc., Indianapolis, IN; *U.S. Public*, pg. 106
Tague, John P., Pres. & Chief Exec. Officer--Amtran, Inc., Indianapolis, IN; *U.S. Public*, pg. 106
Taguinod, Teodorico C., Chm. Bd. & Chief Exec. Officer--EEI Corporation, Manila, Philippines; *Int'l*, pg. 425
Tahara, Masao, Chief Oper. Officer--Makita Power Tools (H.K.) LTD., Sha Tin, Hong Kong; *Int'l*, pg. 832
Taitz, Andrew, Chm. Bd.--Union City Body Company, L.P., Union City, IN; *U.S. Private*, pg. 1118
Takada, Hironaka, Pres. & Chief Exec. Officer--DBP - Daiwa Securities (Philippines), Inc., Manila, Philippines; *Int'l*, pg. 375
Takakura, Tom, Pres. & Chief Exec. Officer--Sanwa Bank California, Los Angeles, CA; *Int'l*, pg. 1189
Takehana, Hiroshi, Pres. & Chief Exec. Officer--G-Net Corporation, Osaka, Japan; *Int'l*, pg. 531
Takei, Toshifumi, Pres. & Chief Exec. Officer--Ishikawajima-Harima Heavy Industries Co., Ltd., Tokyo, Japan; *Int'l*, pg. 689
Takemoto, Yoshiyuki, Chm. & Chief Exec. Officer--Daiwa Europe Limited, London, United Kingdom; *Int'l*, pg. 375
Takenaka, Toichi, Pres. & Chief Exec. Officer--Takenaka Corporation, Osaka, Japan; *Int'l*, pg. 1351
Takeuchi, Masakazu, Pres. & Chief Exec. Officer--Gradco (Japan), Ltd., Tokyo, Japan; *U.S. Public*, pg. 757
Tal-Shir, Amos, Chief Exec. Officer--Ariely Advertising, Tel Aviv, Israel; *U.S. Private*, pg. 678
Talbert, J. Michael, Chm. Bd. & Chief Exec. Officer--Transocean Offshore, Inc., Houston, TX; *U.S. Public*, pg. 1631
Talbott, Cloyce A., Chm. Bd. & Chief Exec. Officer--Patterson Energy, Inc., Snyder, TX; *U.S. Public*, pg. 1265
Talbott, Cloyce A., Chm. Bd. & Chief Exec. Officer--Patterson Drilling Co., Snyder, TX; *U.S. Public*, pg. 1265
Talermo, Roger, Pres. & Chief Exec. Officer--Amer Group Ltd., Helsinki, Finland; *Int'l*, pg. 72
Tallec, Jean-Paul, Chief Exec. Officer & Dir.--Jimten, Alicante, Germany; *Int'l*, pg. 430
Tallichet, David C., Jr., Chm. Bd., Pres. & Chief Exec. Officer--Specialty Restaurants Corporation, Anaheim, CA; *U.S. Private*, pg. 1022
Tamahori, Tamehiko, Pres.--Tonen Corporation, Tokyo, Japan; *Int'l*, pg. 1398
Tamarites, John, Pres. & Chief Exec. Officer--Michigan Wheel Corporation, Grand Rapids, MI; *U.S. Private*, pg. 741
Tamke, George, Chief Exec. Officer--Astec America Inc., Carlsbad, CA; *Int'l*, pg. 93
Tamura, Norio, Pres. & Chief Exec. Officer--Teac Corporation, Tokyo, Japan; *Int'l*, pg. 1360
Tan, Lucio C., Chm. Bd. & Chief Exec. Officer--Philippine Airlines, Inc., Manila, Philippines; *Int'l*, pg. 1050
Tanabe, Kuninori, Pres. & Chief Exec. Officer--Fuji Bank Canada, Toronto, Canada; *Int'l*, pg. 521
Tanaka, Hiroshi, Chm. Bd. & Chief Exec. Officer--Kyotaru Co., Ltd., Tokyo, Japan; *Int'l*, pg. 777
Tanaka, Jun-Ichiro, Pres. & Chief Exec. Officer--Mitsui Fudosan Co., Ltd., Tokyo, Japan; *Int'l*, pg. 882
Tanaka, Shinichiro, Pres. & Chief Exec. Officer--Fuji Capital Markets Corporation, New York, NY; *Int'l*, pg. 519
Tananbaum, Stanley, Chm. Bd. & Chief Exec. Officer--Century Business Credit Corporation, New York, NY; *U.S. Private*, pg. 225
Tang, Sam, Chief Oper. Officer--The Shidler Group, Honolulu, HI; *U.S. Private*, pg. 994
Tang, V., Chief Exec. Officer--Sanshui Redland Building Materials Co. Ltd., Guangzhou, China; *Int'l*, pg. 1093
Tanguay, Louis, Chm. Bd. & Chief Exec. Officer--Telebec Ltee, Anjou, Canada; *Int'l*, pg. 116
Tank, V., Chief Exec. Officer--Shaoxing Redland Building Materials Co., Inc., Shaoxing, China; *Int'l*, pg. 1093
Tankersley, James I., Chm. Bd. & Chief Exec. Officer--United Foods, Inc., Bells, TN; *U.S. Public*, pg. 1677
Tanklage, Robert C., Chm. Bd., Chief Exec. & Chief Oper. Officer--La Victoria Foods, Inc., City of Industry, CA; *U.S. Private*, pg. 641
Tannenberg, Dieter E.A., Pres. & Chief Exec. Officer--Bell & Howell Document Management Products Company, Chicago, IL; *U.S. Public*, pg. 201
Tanner, Paul A., Chm. Bd., Pres. & Chief Exec. Officer--Polyphase Corporation, Dallas, TX; *U.S. Public*, pg. 1315
Tanner, Ray, Chm. Bd. & Chief Exec. Officer--Volunteer Bank, Jackson, TN; *U.S. Public*, pg. 176
Tanner, Travis, Pres.-Carlson Travel Grp.; Co-Pres. & Chief Exec. Officer CWT--Carlson Wagonlit Travel, Minneapolis, MN; *U.S. Private*, pg. 212
Tansky, Burton, Chm. Bd. & Chief Exec. Officer--Bergdorf Goodman, New York, NY; *U.S. Public*, pg. 785
Tansky, Burton, Chm. & Chief Exec. Officer--Neiman Marcus Co., Dallas, TX; *U.S. Public*, pg. 785
Tao, Harold L., Pres. & Chief Exec. Officer--International Commercial Bank of Cathay, Toronto, Canada; *Int'l*, pg. 684
Tarantino, Robert V., Pres. & Chief Exec. Officer--Dataram Corporation, Princeton, NJ; *U.S. Public*, pg. 487
Taranto, Joseph V., Chm. Bd. & Chief Exec. Officer--Everest Reinsurance Holdings, Liberty Corner, NJ; *U.S. Public*, pg. 597
Taranto, Joseph V., Chm. Bd. & Chief Exec. Officer--Everest Reinsurance Co., Liberty Corner, NJ; *U.S. Public*, pg. 597
Taratoot, Louis J., Chm. Bd. & Chief Exec. Officer--Taracorp, Inc., Atlanta, GA; *U.S. Private*, pg. 1068
Tarrant, R. Lane, Chm. Bd., Pres. & Chief Exec. Officer--Tarrant Service, Inc., Louisville, KY; *U.S. Private*, pg. 1069
Tarrant, Richard, Pres. & Chief Exec. Officer--IDX Systems Corporation, Burlington, VT; *U.S. Public*, pg. 854
Tarrant, Ronald W., Chm. Bd., Pres. & Chief Exec. Officer--Flow International Corporation, Kent, WA; *U.S. Public*, pg. 656
Tash, Martin E., Chm. Bd., Pres. & Chief Exec. Officer--Gradco Systems, Inc., Las Vegas, NV; *U.S. Public*, pg. 757
Tash, Martin E., Chm. Bd., Pres. & Chief Exec. Officer--Plenum Publishing Corporation, New York, NY; *U.S. Public*, pg. 1311
Tashiro, Madoka, Pres. & Chief Exec. Officer--Tosoh Corporation, Tokyo, Japan; *Int'l*, pg. 1407
Tashiro, Shunji, Pres. & Chief Exec. Officer--NEC Systems Laboratory, Inc., San Jose, CA; *Int'l*, pg. 900
Tassin, Ed, Pres. & Chief Exec. Officer--Capital Imaging, Summerville, SC; *U.S. Private*, pg. 206
Tatar, Jerome F., Chm. Bd., Pres. & Chief Exec. Officer--The Mead Corporation, Dayton, OH; *U.S. Public*, pg. 1074
Tatsch, Michael G., Pres. & Chief Exec. Officer--Chromium Corp., Dallas, TX; *U.S. Public*, pg. 568
Tattersall, Keith, Chm. Bd., Pres. & Chief Exec. Officer--Amperif Corporation, Chatsworth, CA; *U.S. Public*, pg. 1523
Tatum, Ronnie, Chief Exec. Officer--Morrison Restaurants, Inc., Atlanta, GA; *U.S. Public*, pg. 1134
Tauber, Orner J., Jr., Pres. & Chief Exec. Officer--Tauber Oil Company, Houston, TX; *U.S. Private*, pg. 1069
Taubman, Robert S., Pres. & Chief Exec. Officer--Taubman Centers, Inc., Bloomfield Hills, MI; *U.S. Public*, pg. 1561
Taunton-Rigby, Alison, Ph.D, Pres. & Chief Exec. Officer--Aquila Biopharmaceuticals, Inc., Worcester, MA; *U.S. Public*, pg. 126
Tauscher, William, Chm. Bd. & Chief Exec. Officer--Vanstar Corporation, Pleasanton, CA; *U.S. Public*, pg. 1708
Taxell, Christoffer, Pres. & Chief Exec. Officer--Partek Corporation, Helsinki, Finland; *Int'l*, pg. 1024
Taylor, Alexander, Pres. & Chief Exec. Officer--Agra Inc., Calgary, Canada; *Int'l*, pg. 30
Taylor, Andrew C., Pres. & Chief Exec. Officer--Enterprise Rent-A-Car Company, Saint Louis, MO; *U.S. Private*, pg. 377
Taylor, Ben, Asst. Chief Exec. Officer--Renishaw plc, Wotton-under-Edge, United Kingdom; *Int'l*, pg. 1103
Taylor, Bruce W., Pres. & Chief Exec. Officer--Cole Taylor Bank, Wheeling, IL; *U.S. Private*, pg. 1070
Taylor, Dale, Pres. & Chief Exec. Officer--Abelson-Taylor, Inc., Chicago, IL; *U.S. Private*, pg. 10
Taylor, David N., Chief Exec. Officer--Glynwed Metal Services Ltd., Kingston, United Kingdom; *Int'l*, pg. 554
Taylor, David P., Pres. & Chief Exec. Officer--ICI Explosives USA Inc., Dallas, TX; *Int'l*, pg. 663
Taylor, Dian C., Chm. Bd., Pres. & Chief Exec. Officer--Artesian Resources Corporation, Newark, DE; *U.S. Public*, pg. 135
Taylor, Ford, Pres. & Chief Exec. Officer--Brazos Sportswear Inc., Cincinnati, OH; *U.S. Public*, pg. 251
Taylor, Gerald H., Chief Exec. Officer--MCI Communications Corp., Atlanta, GA; *U.S. Public*, pg. 1023
Taylor, Glen A., Chm. Bd. & Chief Exec. Officer--Taylor Corporation, Mankato, MN; *U.S. Private*, pg. 1070
Taylor, Glenn, Chm. & Chief Exec. Officer--Bankhead Enterprises Inc., Atlanta, GA; *U.S. Private*, pg. 114
Taylor, Glenn D., Pres. & Chief Exec. Officer--Medical Graphics Corp., Saint Paul, MN; *U.S. Public*, pg. 1080
Taylor, Gregory F., Pres. & Chief Exec. Officer--Stifel Financial Corp., Saint Louis, MO; *U.S. Public*, pg. 1518
Taylor, H. Wayne, Pres. & Chief Exec. Officer--Pontiac Bancorp, Inc., Pontiac, IL; *U.S. Public*, pg. 1316
Taylor, Hollis, Pres. & Chief Exec. Officer--Pancho's Mexican Buffet, Inc., Fort Worth, TX; *U.S. Public*, pg. 1255
Taylor, J., Chief Exec. Officer--BNFL, Warrington, United Kingdom; *Int'l*, pg. 120
Taylor, James, Pres. & Chief Exec. Officer--Andros Incorporated, Berkeley, CA; *U.S. Private*, pg. 74
Taylor, James, Pres. & Chief Exec. Officer--Andros Service Inc., Hoenheim, France; *U.S. Private*, pg. 74
Taylor, James, Pres. & Chief Exec. Officer--Scitec Corporation, Kennewick, WA; *U.S. Private*, pg. 74
Taylor, James, Pres. & Chief Exec. & Fin. Officers--Reuter Manufacturing Inc., Hopkins, MN; *U.S. Public*, pg. 1383
Taylor, James I., Pres. & Chief Exec. Officer--Penn National Insurance, Harrisburg, PA; *U.S. Private*, pg. 850
Taylor, James W., Chm. Bd. & Chief Exec. Officer--Taylor Made Group, Inc., Gloversville, NY; *U.S. Private*, pg. 1070
Taylor, Jeffrey W., Chm. Bd. & Chief Exec. Officer--Taylor Capital Group, Wheeling, IL; *U.S. Private*, pg. 1070
Taylor, John, Pres. & Chief Exec. Officer--Ingram Entertainment Inc., La Vergne, TN; *U.S. Private*, pg. 563
Taylor, John A., Chm. Bd.--Taylor Oil Co. Inc., Winston Salem, NC; *U.S. Private*, pg. 1071
Taylor, John Martin, Chief Exec. Officer--Barclays Bank PLC, London, United Kingdom; *Int'l*, pg. 164
Taylor, John N., Jr., Chm. & Chief Exec. Officer--Kurz-Kasch, Inc., Wilmington, OH; *U.S. Private*, pg. 637
Taylor, Mark D., Pres. & Chief Exec. Officer--Tyndale House Publishers, Inc., Carol Stream, IL; *U.S. Private*, pg. 1112
Taylor, Maurice M., Jr., Pres. & Chief Exec. Officer--Titan International, Inc., Quincy, IL; *U.S. Public*, pg. 1618
Taylor, Maurice R., Chm. Bd. & Chief Exec. Officer--Chronimed Inc., Minnetonka, MN; *U.S. Public*, pg. 352
Taylor, T.H., Deputy Chief Exec. Officer--Toyota (Great Britain) Limited, Redhill, United Kingdom; *Int'l*, pg. 1414
Taylor, Thomas A., Pres. & Chief Exec. Officer--Amica Mutual Insurance Co., Lincoln, RI; *U.S. Private*, pg. 66
Taylor, Volney, Chm. Bd. & Chief Exec. Officer--The Dun & Bradstreet Corporation, Murray Hill, NJ; *U.S. Public*, pg. 535
Taylor, William, Pres. & Chief Exec. Officer--Fidelity Mutual Life Insurance Co., Radnor, PA; *U.S. Private*, pg. 403
Taylor, William, Chief Exec. Officer & Dir.-Fin.--Really Useful Holdings Limited, London, United Kingdom; *Int'l*, pg. 1089
Taylor, William W., Chm. Bd. & Chief Exec. Officer--D.C. Taylor Co., Cedar Rapids, IA; *U.S. Private*, pg. 1070
Tchuruk, Serge, Chm. Bd. & Chief Exec. Officer--Alcatel Alsthom Compagnie Generale D'Electricite, Paris, France; *Int'l*, pg. 52
Teague, Thomas L., Pres. & Chief Exec. Officer--Salem National Corporation, Winston Salem, NC; *U.S. Private*, pg. 962
Teare, Andrew, Chief Exec. Officer & Mng. Dir.--The Rank Group PLC, London, United Kingdom; *Int'l*, pg. 1086
Tearprasert, Tada, Chief Exec. Officer--CPAC Roof Tile Co., Limited, Bangkok, Thailand; *Int'l*, pg. 1092
Teasley, Larkin, Pres. & Chief Exec. Officer--Golden State Mutual Life Insurance Company, Los Angeles, CA; *U.S. Private*, pg. 461
Teck, Lim How, Deputy Chief Exec. Officer--Neptune Orient Lines Ltd., Singapore, Singapore; *Int'l*, pg. 912
Tee, Harry, Group Chief Exec.--The Roxboro Group PLC, Cambridge, United Kingdom; *Int'l*, pg. 1130
Teel, E. Gerald, Pres., Chief Exec. Officer & Chief Oper. Officer--Vitamilk Dairy, Inc., Seattle, WA; *U.S. Private*, pg. 1142
Tees, Jim, Pres. & Chief Exec. Officer--Pioneer Plastics Corporation, Auburn, ME; *U.S. Private*, pg. 867
Teeter, Finis F., Chm. Bd. & Co-Chief Exec. Officer--American Homestar Corporation, League City, TX; *U.S. Public*, pg. 83
Tegarden, William H., Chm. Bd., Pres. & Chief Exec. Officer--Citizens Bank of Central Indiana-Orleans Region, Orleans, IN; *U.S. Public*, pg. 280
Tellier, Paul, Pres. & Chief Exec. Officer--Canadian National Railway Company, Montreal, Canada; *Int'l*, pg. 258
Temiz, Leon, Chief Exec. Officer--Sixth Avenue Electronics City, Springfield, NJ; *U.S. Private*, pg. 1004
Temple, David J., Pres. & Chief Exec. Officer--Canplas Industries Ltd., Barrie, Canada; *Int'l*, pg. 430
Temple, John, Pres. & Chief Exec. Officer--Guideposts Associates, Inc., Carmel, NY; *U.S. Private*, pg. 487
Temple, Larry D., Chief Oper. Officer & Exec. V.P.--CMC Kalamazoo Inc., Kalamazoo, MI; *U.S. Private*, pg. 1030
Tendler, Stanley, Chm. Bd. & Chief Exec. Officer--Kennington Ltd., Inc., Van Nuys, CA; *U.S. Private*, pg. 615
Tenebeuso, Nick, Chief Exec. Officer--Strober Bros., Inc. Building Supply Centers, Brooklyn, NY; *U.S. Private*, pg. 403
Tennant, James R., Chm. Bd. & Chief Exec. Officer--Home Products International, Inc., Chicago, IL; *U.S. Public*, pg. 832
Tennant, James R., Chm. Bd. & Chief Exec. Officer--Selfix, Inc., Chicago, IL; *U.S. Public*, pg. 832
Tenneson, P., Chm. & Chief Exec. Officer--Herstal S.A., Herstal, Belgium; *Int'l*, pg. 617
Tenney, Arnold S., Pres. & Chief Exec. Officer--ARC International Corporation, Downsview, Canada; *Int'l*, pg. 17
Tenney, Robert N., Pres. & Chief Exec. Officer--Fremont Financial Corporation, Santa Monica, CA; *U.S. Public*, pg. 681
Tenny, Morton, Pres. & Chief Exec. Officer--Union Pen Company, Greenwich, CT; *U.S. Private*, pg. 1119
Tenoso, Harold J., Ph.D., Pres. & Chief Exec. Officer--Serologicals Corporation, Clarkston, GA; *U.S. Public*, pg. 1460
Teo, S., Chief Exec. Officer--Zurich Insurance (Singapore) Pte. Ltd., Singapore, Singapore; *Int'l*, pg. 1532
Tepas, Gary L., Pres. & Chief Exec. Officer--Emkay, Inc., Itasca, IL; *U.S. Private*, pg. 374
Tepper, Allen, Chm. Bd. & Chief Exec. Officer--PMR Corporation, San Diego, CA; *U.S. Public*, pg. 1242
Terborgh, Eliot, Pres. & Chief Exec. Officer--SmarTrunk Systems, Inc., Hayward, CA; *U.S. Private*, pg. 1006
Teresi, Robert G., Chm Bd., Chief Exec. Officer & Treas.--Caere Corporation, Los Gatos, CA; *U.S. Public*, pg. 291
Terlato, Anthony, Chm. Bd. & Chief Exec. Officer--Paterno Imports Limited, Lake Bluff, IL; *U.S. Private*, pg. 843
Terlizzi, N. Paul, Chief Exec. Officer--Capezio Ballet Makers Inc., Totowa, NJ; *U.S. Private*, pg. 205
Termeer, Henri A., Chm. Bd., Pres. & Chief Exec. Officer--Genzyme Corporation, Cambridge, MA; *U.S. Public*, pg. 733
Terral, Thomas F., Pres. & Chief Exec. Officer--Terral Seed Co., Inc., Lake Providence, LA; *U.S. Private*, pg. 1077
Terrell, Charles L., Pres., Chief Exec. Officer & Treas.--New Haven Savings Bank, New Haven, CT; *U.S. Private*, pg. 793

Terrien, Jean Francois, Pres. & Chief Exec. Officer--Neyrpic Framatome Mecanique (NFM), Paris, France; *Int'l*, pg. 503

Terrill, J.E., Pres. & Chief Exec. Officer--Jefferson Smurfit Corporation, Saint Louis, MO; *Int'l*, pg. 1271

Terry, Richard E., Chm. Bd. & Chief Exec. Officer--Peoples Energy Corporation, Chicago, IL; *U.S. Public*, pg. 1274

Terry, Richard E., Chm. Bd. & Chief Exec. Officer--Peoples District Energy Corporation, Chicago, IL; *U.S. Public*, pg. 1275

Terry, Richard E., Chm. Bd. & Chief Exec. Officer--Peoples Energy Services Corporation, Chicago, IL; *U.S. Public*, pg. 1275

Terry, Richard E., Chm. Bd. & Chief Exec. Officer--Peoples NGV Corp., Chicago, IL; *U.S. Public*, pg. 1275

Teruya, Raymond, Chm. Bd., Pres. & Chief Exec. Officer--Teruya Bros., Limited, Honolulu, HI; *U.S. Private*, pg. 1077

Terwilliger, Ron, Chief Exec. Officer--Trammell Crow Residential Services, Atlanta, GA; *U.S. Private*, pg. 1095

Terzic, Branco, Chm. Bd., Pres. & Chief Exec. Officer--Yankee Energy System, Inc., Meriden, CT; *U.S. Public*, pg. 1787

Terzic, Branko, Pres., Chief Exec./Oper. Officer--Yankee Energy Financial Services Company, Meriden, CT; *U.S. Public*, pg. 1787

Tessier, Edward J., Chm., Pres. & Chief Exec. Officer--Amerifoods Inc., Lancaster, PA; *U.S. Private*, pg. 65

Tessier, Edward J., Pres. & Chief Exec. Officer--Amerifoods Snacks, York, PA; *U.S. Private*, pg. 65

Tessier, Edward J., Pres. & Chief Exec. Officer--Bon Ton Foods, Inc., York, PA; *U.S. Private*, pg. 65

Tessier, Robert, Pres. & Chief Exec. Officer--Gaz Metropolitain & Company, Montreal, Canada; *Int'l*, pg. 541

Tessler, Allan R., Co-Chm. Bd. & Co-Chief Exec. Officer--Data Broadcasting Corporation, Jackson, WY; *U.S. Public*, pg. 484

Testa, Gianfranco, Deputy Chief Exec.--Cassa di Risparmio delle Provincie Lombarde SpA (CARIPLO), Milan, Italy; *Int'l*, pg. 274

Testa, Marco, Chm. Bd. & Chief Exec. Officer--Testa International, Milan, Italy; *Int'l*, pg. 1376

Testwuide, Thomas R., Pres. & Chief Exec. Officer--Schreier Malting Co., Sheboygan, WI; *U.S. Private*, pg. 972

Tetrault, Roger E., Chm. Bd. & Chief Exec. Officer--McDermott International, Inc., New Orleans, LA; *U.S. Public*, pg. 1067

Thacker, William L., Jr., Chm. Bd., Pres. & Chief Exec. Officer--TEPPCO Partners L.P., Houston, TX; *U.S. Public*, *pg. 534*

Thacker, William L., Jr., Pres. & Chief Exec. Officer--Texas Eastern Products Pipeline Company, L.P., Houston, TX; *U.S. Public*, pg. 535

Thalheimer, Louis B., Chm. Bd. & Chief Exec. Officer--American Trading and Production Corporation, Baltimore, MD; *U.S. Private*, pg. 63

Thalheimer, Richard, Chm. Bd. & Chief Exec. Officer--The Sharper Image, San Francisco, CA; *U.S. Public*, pg. 1464

Theisen, Claude I., Pres. & Chief Exec. Officer--T & S Brass & Bronze Works, Inc., Travelers Rest, SC; *U.S. Private*, pg. 1061

Thelin, Claus, Pres. & Chief Exec. Officer--Essex Industries, New Haven, CT; *Int'l*, pg. 18

Theobald, Stephen W., Pres. & Chief Exec. Officer--Stokely USA, Inc., Oconomowoc, WI; *U.S. Public*, pg. 1518

Theodosi, J.G., Chief Exec. Officer--Zurich Insurance Company, Athens, Greece; *Int'l*, pg. 1531

Theofilos, Steve P., Chm. Bd. & Chief Exec. Officer--Theochem Labs., Inc., Tampa, FL; *U.S. Private*, pg. 1079

Theriault, Roger, Pres. & Chief Exec. Officer--Brigham's, Inc., Arlington, MA; *U.S. Private*, pg. 483

Therien, Michel, Pres. & Chief Exec. Officer--Assurance vie Desjardins-Laurentienne, Levis, Canada; *Int'l*, pg. 396

Therrien, Michel, Chief Exec. Officer--Hydro-Quebec International, Montreal, Canada; *Int'l*, pg. 640

Thiel, Stephen, Chm. Bd., Pres. & Chief Exec. Officer--Thiel Cheese Co., Hilbert, WI; *U.S. Private*, pg. 1081

Thiele, P.A., Pres. & Chief Exec. Officer--St. Paul Fire and Marine Insurance Co., Saint Paul, MN; *U.S. Public*, pg. 1429

Thiele, Paul F., Chm. Bd. & Chief Exec. Officer--Thiele Kaolin Co., Sandersville, GA; *U.S. Private*, pg. 1081

Thielemans, Daniel, Chief Exec. Officer--Generale Bank, New York, NY; *Int'l*, pg. 547

Thielman, David, Chief Exec. Officer--E Z Loader Boat Trailers, Inc., Spokane, WA; *U.S. Private*, pg. 353

Thijs, Johnny, Chief Exec. Officer--Interbrew S.A., Leuven, Belgium; *Int'l*, pg. 679

Thiry, Kent J., Pres. & Chief Exec. Officer--Vivra Incorporated, San Mateo, CA; *U.S. Public*, pg. 1723

Thomann, Michael, Pres. & Chief Exec. Officer--Brad Ragan, Inc., Charlotte, NC; *U.S. Public*, pg. 753

Thomas, Andrew, Chm. Bd. & Chief Exec.--The Greenalls Group PLC, Warrington, United Kingdom; *Int'l*, pg. 558

Thomas, Berl M., Pres. & Chief Exec. Officer--Speedling Incorporated, Sun City, FL; *U.S. Private*, pg. 1024

Thomas, Charles C., Asst. to Chief Exec. Officer--LDB Corporation, Kerrville, TX; *U.S. Private*, pg. 639

Thomas, Frank L., Pres. & Chief Exec. Officer--Genstar Development Company, San Diego, CA; *Int'l*, pg. 112

Thomas, G. Andes, Chm. Bd., Pres. & Chief Exec. Officer--Magna Group, Inc., Saint Louis, MO; *U.S. Public*, pg. 1037

Thomas, G.N., Chm. Bd., Pres., & Chief Exec. Officer--A. Levy & J. Zentner Co., Sacramento, CA; *U.S. Private*, pg. 663

Thomas, Howard, Chief Exec. Officer--Hubert Company, Harrison, OH; *U.S. Private*, pg. 545

Thomas, J. Grover, Jr., Pres. & Chief Exec. Officer--United Family Life Insurance Co., Atlanta, GA; *Int'l*, pg. 499

Thomas, John E., Pres. & Chief Exec. Officer--Tippins Incorporated, Pittsburgh, PA; *U.S. Private*, pg. 1088

Thomas, John W., III, Pres. & Chief Exec. Officer--Thomas Built Buses, Inc., High Point, NC; *U.S. Private*, pg. 1082

Thomas, Johnny R., Chm. Bd. & Chief Exec. Officer--AgriBioTech, Inc., Las Vegas, NV; *U.S. Public*, pg. 28

Thomas, Joseph, Chief Exec. Officer-Thomas Medical Products, Inc.--Vital Signs, Inc., Totowa, NJ; *U.S. Public*, pg. 1723

Thomas, Mark, Pres. & Chief Exec. Officer--Standard Communications Corp., Torrance, CA; *Int'l*, pg. 841

Thomas, Michael E., Pres. & Chief Exec. Officer--Chromcraft Revington, Inc., Delphi, IN; *U.S. Public*, pg. 352

Thomas, Paul, Chief Exec. Officer--Ohmeda, Liberty Corner, NJ; *Int'l*, pg. 121

Thomas, Rick, Chm. Bd. & Chief Exec. Officer--Card Pak, Inc., Cleveland, OH; *U.S. Private*, pg. 208

Thomas, Steven C., Pres. & Chief Exec. Officer--MPS Corporation, Pittsburgh, PA; *U.S. Private*, pg. 687

Thomas, William O., Pres. & Chief Exec. Officer--DeVlieg-Bullard Inc., Westport, CT; *U.S. Public*, pg. 502

Thomason, Scott L., Pres. & Chief Exec. Officer--Thomason Auto Group, Gladstone, OR; *U.S. Private*, pg. 1083

Thomassen, P.W.M., Chief Exec. Officer--OCE Direct Export, Venlo, Netherlands; *Int'l*, pg. 994

Thomke, Ernst, Dr., Chief Exec. Officer--Bally Management AG, Schonenwerd, Switzerland; *Int'l*, pg. 996

Thomopoulos, Tony, Chief Exec. Officer--MTM Enterprises, Inc., Studio City, CA; *Int'l*, pg. 927

Thompson-Draper, Cheryl, Chm. Bd. & Chief Exec. Officer--Warren Electric Group, Houston, TX; *U.S. Private*, pg. 1151

Thompson, Cary H., Chief Exec. Officer--Aames Financial Corporation, Los Angeles, CA; *U.S. Public*, pg. 12

Thompson, Chris, Chief Exec. Officer--Austin Reed Limited, London, United Kingdom; *U.S. Public*, pg. 796

Thompson, D. Gary, Pres. & Chief Exec. Officer--Wachovia Bank of Georgia, N.A., Atlanta, GA; *U.S. Public*, pg. 1730

Thompson, Dan, Pres. & Chief Exec. Officer--ElectroCom Automation L.P., Arlington, TX; *Int'l*, pg. 1244

Thompson, David, Pres. & Chief Exec. Officer--Datamarine International, Inc., Mountlake Terrace, WA; *U.S. Public*, pg. 486

Thompson, David, Chm. Bd. & Chief Exec. Officer--Mikohn Gaming Corporation, Las Vegas, NV; *U.S. Public*, pg. 1111

Thompson, David A., Pres., Chief Exec. Officer, Chief Fin. Officer--Cominco, Ltd., Vancouver, Canada; *Int'l*, pg. 307

Thompson, David R., Pres. & Chief Exec. Officer--Kennedy Manufacturing Company, Van Wert, OH; *U.S. Private*, pg. 614

Thompson, David W., Chm. Bd., Pres. & Chief Exec. Officer--Orbital Sciences Corporation, Dulles, VA; *U.S. Public*, pg. 1229

Thompson, Donald L., Chm. Bd., Pres. & Chief Exec. Officer--Hunt Corporation, Philadelphia, PA; *U.S. Public*, pg. 848

Thompson, G.W., Pres. & Chief Exec. Officer--Getchell Gold Corp., Englewood, CO; *U.S. Public*, pg. 740

Thompson, H. Brian, Chm. Bd. & Chief Exec. Officer--LCI International, Inc., Dublin, OH; *U.S. Public*, pg. 969

Thompson, Jack E., Pres. & Chief Exec. Officer--Homestake Mining Company, San Francisco, CA; *U.S. Public*, pg. 832

Thompson, James W., Pres. & Chief Exec. Officer--Vallen Corporation, Houston, TX; *U.S. Public*, pg. 1705

Thompson, James W., Pres. & Chief Exec. Officer--Vallen Safety Supply Company, Ltd., Markham, Canada; *U.S. Public*, pg. 1705

Thompson, John, Pres. & Chief Exec. Officer--Montreal Trustco, Montreal, Canada; *Int'l*, pg. 155

Thompson, John S., Pres. & Chief Exec.--BTR, Inc., Stamford, CT; *Int'l*, pg. 127

Thompson, Keith M., Pres. & Chief Exec. Officer--Republic Automotive Parts, Inc., Brentwood, TN; *U.S. Public*, pg. 1377

Thompson, Kirk, Pres. & Chief Exec. Officer--J.B. Hunt Transport Services, Inc., Lowell, AR; *U.S. Public*, pg. 849

Thompson, L. Dan, Pres. & Chief Exec. Officer--Lou Ana Foods, Inc., Opelousas, LA; *Int'l*, pg. 879

Thompson, Leo G., Pres. & Chief Exec. Officer--Lindberg Corporation, Rosemont, IL; *U.S. Public*, pg. 999

Thompson, Michael D., Pres. & Chief Exec. Officer--Thompson Tractor Company, Birmingham, AL; *U.S. Private*, pg. 1083

Thompson, Norman J., Sr. V.P.--Air New Zealand Ltd. (U.S.A.), El Segundo, CA; *Int'l*, pg. 38

Thompson, Peter, Pres. & Chief Exec. Officer--Snack Ventures Europe, Zaventem, Belgium; *U.S. Public*, pg. 718

Thompson, Raymon F., Chm. Bd., Pres. & Chief Exec. Officer--Semitool, Inc., Kalispell, MT; *U.S. Public*, pg. 1456

Thompson, Richard, Pres. & Chief Exec. Officer--Microlog Corporation, Germantown, MD; *U.S. Public*, pg. 1105

Thompson, Robert M., Pres. & Chief Exec. Officer--Thompson-McCully Co., Belleville, MI; *U.S. Private*, pg. 1083

Thompson, Ted, Chm. Bd. & Chief Exec. Officer--X-Rite, Incorporated, Grandville, MI; *U.S. Public*, pg. 1783

Thompson, Terry W., Chm. Bd., Pres. & Chief Exec. Officer--State Bank of Standish, Standish, MI; *U.S. Public*, pg. 379

Thompson, Wade F.B., Chm. Bd., Pres. & Chief Exec. Officer--Thor Industries, Inc., Jackson Center, OH; *U.S. Public*, pg. 1602

Thompson, Wayne, Chief Exec. Officer--Interprovincial Cooperative Limited (IPCO), Saskatoon, Canada; *Int'l*, pg. 1195

Thompson, William R., Chm., Pres. & Chief Exec. Officer--SunTrust Bank, Augusta, N.A., Augusta, GA; *U.S. Public*, *pg. 1538*

Thomsen, Kurt, Chief Exec. Officer--Novo Nordisk Bioindustrial SA, Caracas, Venezuela; *Int'l*, pg. 989

Thomson, James A., Pres. & Chief Exec. Officer--RAND, Santa Monica, CA; *U.S. Private*, pg. 908

Thomson, Michael J., Pres. & Chief Exec. Officer--Community Energy Alternatives Incorporated, Ridgewood, NJ; *U.S. Public*, pg. 1340

Thorlakson, Al, Pres. & Chief Exec. Officer--Tolko Industries Ltd., Vernon, Canada; *Int'l*, pg. 1395

Thorne, Carl F., Chm. Bd., Pres. & Chief Exec. Officer--Ensco International Incorporated (ENSCO), Dallas, TX; *U.S. Public*, pg. 585

Thorner, Peter, Chm. Bd., Chief Exec. Officer & Chief Oper. Officer--Bradlees Inc., Braintree, MA; *U.S. Public*, pg. 249

Thornton, Laney, Chief Exec. Officer--Lanz, Inc., San Francisco, CA; *U.S. Private*, pg. 650

Thornton, Winfred L., Chm. Bd. & Chief Exec. Officer--St. Joe Corp., Jacksonville, FL; *U.S. Public*, pg. 1426

Thorrington, Peter, Joint Chief Exec. Officer--Union-Transport Corporation, Rancho Dominguez, CA; *U.S. Private*, pg. 1119

Thouvenet, Luc, Chief Exec. Officer--Auda S.A., Saint Germain-Lembron, France; *Int'l*, pg. 430

Thrall, J. Jeffrey, Chm. Bd. & Chief Exec. Officer--Naz-Dar Company, Chicago, IL; *U.S. Private*, pg. 1084

Throgmartin, William G., Chief Exec. Officer--Gregg Appliances Inc., Indianapolis, IN; *U.S. Private*, pg. 479

Throop, Robert S., Chm. Bd. & Chief Exec. Officer--Anthem Electronics Inc., San Jose, CA; *U.S. Public*, pg. 134

Thumon, Greg, Chief Exec. Officer--FISI Madison Financial Corporation, Nashville, TN; *U.S. Public*, pg. 320

Thunell, Lars, Pres. & Chief Exec. Officer--Trygg-Hansa, Stockholm, Sweden; *Int'l*, pg. 1425

Thunell, Lars H., Chief Exec. Officer--Skandinaviska Enskilda Banken, Stockholm, Sweden; *Int'l*, pg. 1258

Thurlow, Juan Gallardo, Chm. Bd. & Chief Exec. Officer--Grupo Embotelladoras Unidas SA de CV, Guadalajara, Mexico; *Int'l*, pg. 574

Thurnherr, Rolf, Joint Chief Exec. Officer--Eurodis Electron PLC, Reigate, United Kingdom; *Int'l*, pg. 1247

Thygesen, Clifford C., Pres. & Chief Exec. Officer--American Educational Products, Boulder, CO; *U.S. Public*, pg. 71

Tian, F., Chief Exec. Officer--Zurich Insurance Company, Beijing, China; *Int'l*, pg. 1531

Tidball, Robert N., Pres. & Chief Exec. Officer--PLM International, Inc., San Francisco, CA; *U.S. Public*, pg. 1241

Tierney, Brian P., Pres. & Chief Exec. Officer--Tierney & Partners, Philadelphia, PA; *U.S. Public*, pg. 1641

Tikkakoski, Matti, Pres. & Chief Exec. Officer--Polarcup Group Headquarters, Espoo, Finland; *Int'l*, pg. 638

Tilghman, Richard G., Chm. Bd. & Chief Exec. Officer--Crestar Financial Corporation, Richmond, VA; *U.S. Public*, pg. 458

Tilley, C.R., Chm. & Chief Exec. Officer--Columbia Gas Distribution Companies, Columbus, OH; *U.S. Public*, pg. 402

Tilley, Ralph W., Chm. Bd., Pres. & Chief Exec. Officer--Vevay Deposit Bank, Vevay, IN; *U.S. Public*, pg. 633

Tillman, Robert L., Chm. Bd., Pres. & Chief Exec. Officer--Lowe's Companies, Inc., North Wilkesboro, NC; *U.S. Public*, pg. 1015

Tilmant, Michel, Pres. & Chief Exec. Officer--Bank Brussels Lambert, Brussels, Belgium; *Int'l*, pg. 146

Timbers, Stephen B., Chm. & Chief Exec. Officer--Zurich Kemper Investments, Inc., Chicago, IL; *Int'l*, pg. 1530

Timbi, Sidney, Chief Exec. Officer--Covington Industries, Atlanta, GA; *U.S. Private*, pg. 280

Timble, James N., Pres. & Chief Exec. Officer--Bearing Headquarters Co., Broadview, IL; *U.S. Private*, pg. 127

Timken, W.R., Jr., Chm. Bd., Pres. & Chief Exec. Officer--The Timken Company, Canton, OH; *U.S. Public*, pg. 1617

Timmerman, William B., Chm. Bd., Pres., Chief Exec. & Oper. Officer--SCANA Corporation, Columbia, SC; *U.S. Public*, pg. 1436

Timpe, R.E., Pres. & Chief Exec. Officer--Standard Insurance Co., Portland, OR; *U.S. Private*, pg. 1031

Tinberg, Richard W., Pres. & Chief Exec. Officer--Bradford Exchange Ltd., Niles, IL; *U.S. Private*, pg. 163

Tinberg, Richard W., Chief Exec. Officer--Hammacher, Schlemmer & Co., Inc., Chicago, IL; *U.S. Private*, pg. 497

Ting, James H., Chm., Pres. & Chief Exec. Officer--Semi-Tech Corporation, Markham, Canada; *Int'l*, pg. 1220

Ting, Kenneth, Pres.--Bachmann Industries, Inc., Philadelphia, PA; *U.S. Private*, pg. 109

Tingley, Charles E., Pres. & Chief Exec. Officer--Transamerica Leasing Inc., Purchase, NY; *U.S. Public*, pg. 1630

Tino, J. Robert, Pres. & Chief Exec. Officer--Sandusky Plastics, Inc., Sandusky, OH; *U.S. Public*, pg. 586

Tinstman, Robert A., Pres. & Chief Exec. Officer--Morrison Knudsen Corporation, Boise, ID; *U.S. Public*, pg. 1133

Tisch, Jonathan M., Pres. & Chief Exec. Officer--Loews Hotels, New York, NY; *U.S. Public*, pg. 1011

Tisch, Laurence A., Co-Chm. Bd. & Co-Chief Exec. Officer--Loews Corporation, New York, NY; *U.S. Public*, pg. 1010

Tisch, Preston R., Co-Chm. Bd. & Co-Chief Exec. Officer--Loews Corporation, New York, NY; *U.S. Public*, pg. 1010

Tischler, Louis, Chief Exec. Officer, Chief Oper. Officer & Treas--Westwood Computer Corporation, Springfield, NJ; *U.S. Private*, pg. 1170

Tiun, Lau Chee, Chief Exec. Officer--CWT Distribution Limited, Singapore, Singapore; *Int'l*, pg. 246

Tkachuk, B., Chief Exec.--Viglen Technology PLC, Alperton, United Kingdom; *Int'l*, pg. 1468

Toan, Barrett A., Pres. & Chief Exec. Officer--Express Scripts, Inc., Maryland Heights, MO; *U.S. Public*, pg. 600

Tober, Donald G., Chm. & Chief Exec. Officer--Sugar Foods Corp, New York, NY; *U.S. Private*, pg. 1049

Tober, Lester V., Chm. Bd. & Chief Exec. Officer--Tober Industries, Inc., Saint Louis, MO; *U.S. Private*, pg. 1089

Tobey, Gary, Pres. & Chief Exec. Officer--Haworth Group Inc., Minneapolis, MN; *U.S. Private*, pg. 511
Tobey, Gary, Pres. & Chief Exec. Officer--The Haworth Group, Inc., Los Angeles, CA; *U.S. Private*, pg. 511
Tobias, Randall L., Chm. Bd. & Chief Exec. Officer--Eli Lilly and Company, Indianapolis, IN; *U.S. Public*, pg. 992
Tobin, James R., Pres. & Chief Exec. Officer--Biogen, Inc., Cambridge, MA; *U.S. Public*, pg. 230
Tobin, Robert G., Chm. Bd. & Chief Exec. Officer--The Stop & Shop Companies, Inc., Quincy, MA; *Int'l*, pg. 750
Tocci, Leaonard J., Chief Exec. Officer-Tamor--Home Products International, Inc., Chicago, IL; *U.S. Public*, pg. 832
Tockarshewsky, Joseph B., Chm. Bd., Pres. & Chief Exec. Officer--Poughkeepsie Financial Corp., Poughkeepsie, NY; *U.S. Public*, pg. 1319
Tockarshewsky, Joseph B., Chm. Bd., Pres. & Chief Exec. Officer--Bank of the Hudson, Poughkeepsie, NY; *U.S. Public*, pg. 1319
Tod, G. Robert, Pres. & Chief Exec. Officer--NordicTrack, Inc., Chaska, MN; *U.S. Public*, pg. 279
Todd, Charles J., Chm. Bd. & Chief Exec. Officer--SaniServ Manufacturing Corp., Indianapolis, IN; *U.S. Private*, pg. 965
Todd, Mark, Chief Oper. Officer & Mng. Dir.--Raleigh Industries Ltd., Nottingham, United Kingdom; *Int'l*, pg. 394
Tognietti, Terry, Co-Chief Exec. Officer--Dryper's Corp., Vancouver, WA; *U.S. Private*, pg. 344
Tolaney, Murli, Chm. Bd., Pres. & Chief Exec. Officer--Montgomery Watson, Pasadena, CA; *U.S. Private*, pg. 759
Toler, John, Pres. & Chief Exec. Officer--Little Switzerland, Inc., Charlotte Amalie, VI; *U.S. Public*, pg. 1001
Toliver, Bill, Chief Exec. Officer--Herring Newman, Seattle, WA; *U.S. Private*, pg. 524
Toll, Robert I., Chm. Bd. & Chief Exec. Officer--Toll Brothers, Inc., Huntingdon Valley, PA; *U.S. Public*, pg. 1620
Tollett, Leland, Chm. Bd. & Chief Exec. Officer--Tyson Foods, Inc., Springdale, AR; *U.S. Public*, pg. 1652
Tolliver, Ron, Pres. & Chief Exec. Officer--Interactive Telecard Services, Inc. (ITS), Miami, FL; *U.S. Private*, pg. 566
Tolson, Jay H., Chm. Bd. & Chief Exec. Officer--Bailey, Fischer & Porter Company, Warminster, PA; *Int'l*, pg. 449
Tolson, Ray H., Chm. Bd., Pres. & Chief Exec. Officer--Pride International, Inc., Houston, TX; *U.S. Public*, pg. 1324
Tom, Peter, Grp. Chief Exec.--Bardon Group PLC, Solihull, United Kingdom; *Int'l*, pg. 166
Tomasetta, Louis R., Pres. & Chief Exec. Officer--Vitesse Semiconductor Corporation, Camarillo, CA; *U.S. Public*, pg. 1723
Tomasetti, Thomas, Pres. & Chief Exec. Officer--Consilium, Inc., Mountain View, CA; *U.S. Public*, pg. 434
Tomasso, Donald C., Chm. Bd. & Chief Exec. Officer--Vitalink Pharmacy Services, Inc., Naperville, IL; *U.S. Public*, pg. 1041
Tombros, Peter, Pres. & Chief Exec. Officer--Enzon, Inc., Piscataway, NJ; *U.S. Public*, pg. 587
Tomeu, Enrique A., Pres. & Chief Exec. Officer--ECOS Group, Inc., West Palm Beach, FL; *U.S. Public*, pg. 563
Tominovich, A. Robert, Pres., Chief Exec. Officer & Compliance Officer--McGraw-Hill Securities Trading, Inc., New York, NY; *U.S. Public*, pg. 1071
Tomiyama, Tsuguo, Pres. & Chief Exec. Officer--DIC Trading (USA) Inc., Fort Lee, NJ; *Int'l*, pg. 369
Tomlin, Eugene B., Pres. & Chief Exec. Officer--I.H. French & Co. Inc., Champaign, IL; *U.S. Private*, pg. 427
Tomotake, Michisada, Chief Exec. & Sr. Mng. Dir-Intl. Div.--Wako Securities Co., Ltd., Tokyo, Japan; *Int'l*, pg. 1485
Tompkins, J. Richard, Chm. Bd. & Pres.--Middlesex Water Company, Iselin, NJ; *U.S. Public*, pg. 1110
Tompkins, Jon D., Chief Exec. Officer--KLA Tencor Corporation, San Jose, CA; *U.S. Public*, pg. 939
Toms, Nicholas R.H., Chm., Pres. & Chief Exec. Officer--Peak Technologies Group, Inc., New York, NY; *Int'l*, pg. 890
Tong Cuong, Eric, Co-Chief Exec. Officer--EURO RSCG Babinet, Erra, Tong Cuong, Levallois-Perret, France; *Int'l*, *pg. 600*
Toni, Sergio, Chief Exec. Officer--Schleicher & Schuell Italia SRL, Milan, Italy; *Int'l*, pg. 1206
Tonseth, Erik, Grp. Pres. & Chief Exec. Officer-Kvaerner a.s.--Kvaerner a.s.a., Lysaker, Norway; *Int'l*, pg. 766
Tonseth, Erik, Pres. & Chief Exec. Officer--Kvaerner a.s, Oslo, Norway; *Int'l*, pg. 766
Tooker, Carl, Pres., Chief Exec. Officer--Stage Stores, Inc., Houston, TX; *U.S. Private*, pg. 1028
Toole, David J., Pres. & Chief Exec. Officer--GaSonics International, San Jose, CA; *U.S. Public*, pg. 703
Toolson, Kay L., Chm. Bd., Pres. & Chief Exec. Officer--Monaco Coach Corporation, Coburg, OR; *U.S. Public*, pg. 1123
Torcasio, Anthony J., Pres. & Chief Exec. Officer & Vice Chm.-TMDSC--May Merchandising Company, Saint Louis, MO; *U.S. Public*, pg. 1064
Torchia, Armand, Co-Chief Exec. Officer-Canada--Edelman Houston Group, Montreal, Canada; *U.S. Private*, pg. 363
Torcivia, Benedict, Chm. Bd. & Chief Exec. Officer--Torcon, Inc., Westfield, NJ; *U.S. Private*, pg. 1092
Torrens, Frank J., Pres. & Chief Exec. Officer--Elopak, Inc., New Hudson, MI; *Int'l*, pg. 1390
Torres, Arturo G., Chm. Bd. & Chief Exec. Officer--Play by Play Toys & Novelties, Inc., San Antonio, TX; *U.S. Public*, pg. 1309
Tory, John H., Q.C., Pres. & Chief Exec. Officer--Maclean Hunter Publishing Ltd., Toronto, Canada; *Int'l*, pg. 1123
Toscano, Samuel, Chm. Bd. & Chief Exec. Officer--Neuman Distributors, Inc., Ridgefield, NJ; *U.S. Public*, pg. 1169
Touche, Ricardo Guardo, Chief Exec. Officer--Bancomer, S.A., Mexico, Mexico; *Int'l*, pg. 145
Touhy, Michael R., Chief Exec. Officer & Mng. Dir.--Tillinghast-Towers Penn, New York, NY; *U.S. Private*, pg. 1093
Toulouse, Christian, Vice Chm. & Chief Exec. Officer--Docks de France S.A., Tours, France; *Int'l*, pg. 98
Toulouse, Jean-Francois, Chief Exec. Officer--Docks de France S.A., Tours, France; *Int'l*, pg. 98
Toussaint, Philippe, Chm. & Chief Exec. Officer--Credit du Nord, Paris, France; *Int'l*, pg. 319
Tow, Leonard, Chm. Bd. & Chief Exec. Officer--Century Communications Corp., New Canaan, CT; *U.S. Public*, pg. 329
Tow, Leonard, Chm. Bd. & Chief Exec. & Fin. Officers--Citizens Utilities Company, Stamford, CT; *U.S. Public*, pg. 379
Tow, Leonard, Chm. Bd., Chief Exec. Officer & Chief Fin. Officer--Citizens Telecommunications, Stamford, CT; *U.S.* Public, pg. 380
Tower, H.L., III, Chm. Bd., Pres. & Chief Exec. Officer--Stanhome Inc., Westfield, MA; *U.S. Public*, pg. 1508
Townsend, D., Pres., Chief Exec. Officer & Gen. Mgr.--Simpson Dura-Vent Co., Inc., Vacaville, CA; *U.S. Public*, pg. 1474
Townsend, James M., Chm. Bd. & Chief Exec. Officer--First Coast Community Bank & Trust, Fernandina Beach, FL; *U.S. Public*, pg. 1549
Townsend, P. Coleman, Jr., Chm. Bd. & Chief Exec. Officer--Townsends, Inc., Wilmington, DE; *U.S. Private*, pg. 1094
Toyoda, Kuni, Pres. & Chief Exec. Officer--Seed Restaurant Group, Inc., Lexington, KY; *U.S. Private*, pg. 981
Toyomaru, Koichi, Pres. & Chief Exec. Officer--Nippon Life Insurance Company of America, New York, NY; *Int'l*, pg. 935
Trachtenberg, Joseph M., Chm. Bd. & Chief Exec. Officer--Victaulic Company of America, Easton, PA; *U.S. Private*, pg. 1138
Trad, Raja, Chief Exec. Officer--H&C, Leo Burnett, Beirut, Lebanon; *U.S. Private*, pg. 184
Traeger, Peter, Pres. & Chief Exec. Officer--Artistic Carton Company, Elgin, IL; *U.S. Private*, pg. 87
Traff, Anders, Chief Exec. Officer--Karlshamns AB, Karlshamn, Sweden; *Int'l*, pg. 718
Trafton, Stephen J., Chm. Bd., Pres., Chief Exec. Officer & Chief Oper. Officer--Glendale Federal Bank, F.S.B., Glendale, CA; *U.S. Public*, pg. 747
Tragos, Bill, Founder, Chm & Chief Exec. Officer-WW--TBWA Chiat/Day New York, New York, NY; *U.S. Private*, *pg. 1062*
Tragos, William G., Founder, Chm. Bd. & Chief Exec. Officer-WW--TBWA Chiat/Day, New York, NY; *U.S. Private*, pg. 1062
Trahan, Patrick J., Pres. & Chief Exec. Officer--Rapides Bank & Trust Company of Alexandria, Alexandria, LA; *U.S. Public*, pg. 630
Trainor, Edward J., Pres. & Chief Exec. Officer--Standex International Corporation, Salem, NH; *U.S. Public*, pg. 1505
Trallo, Ralph A., Pres. & Chief Exec. Officer--Canisco Resources, Inc., Wilmington, DE; *U.S. Public*, pg. 301
Tran, Thinh Q., Chm. Bd. & Chief Exec. Officer--Sigma Designs, Inc., Fremont, CA; *U.S. Public*, pg. 1472
Trani, John M., Pres. & Chief Exec. Officer--G.E. Medical Systems, Milwaukee, WI; *U.S. Public*, pg. 710
Trani, John M., Chm. Bd. & Chief Exec. Officer--The Stanley Works, New Britain, CT; *U.S. Public*, pg. 1508
Transou, Susan Busch, Chm. Bd. & Chief Exec. Officer--Busch Creative Services Corporation, Saint Louis, MO; *U.S. Public*, pg. 114
Trapani, Francesco, Chief Exec. Officer--Bulgari SPA, Rome, Italy; *Int'l*, pg. 232
Trapnell, David A., Chief Exec. Officer--Marley PLC, Sevenoaks, United Kingdom; *Int'l*, pg. 843
Traub, Reinhard, Chief Exec. Officer--Hostalen Polyethylen, Frankfurt, Germany; *Int'l*, pg. 626
Trauth, David E., Chm. Bd., Pres. & Chief Exec. Officer--Trauth Dairy Inc., Newport, KY; *U.S. Private*, pg. 1098
Travaglianti, Edward, Chm. Bd. & Chief Exec. Officer--European American Bank & Trust Co., Uniondale, NY; *Int'l*, pg. 9
Travis, Timothy J., Pres. & Chief Exec. Officer--Eaton Metal Products Company, Denver, CO; *U.S. Private*, pg. 358
Traylor, Steve, Pres. & Chief Exec. Officer--Regions Bank/ Santa Rosa County, Pensacola, FL; *U.S. Public*, pg. 1372
Treace, James T., Chm. Bd., Pres. & Cheif Exec. Officer--Xomed Surgical Products, Jacksonville, FL; *U.S. Public*, pg. 253
Treadwell, Mike, Chief Exec. Officer--Rural Electric Co-op, Lindsay, OK; *U.S. Private*, pg. 952
Trebel, John, Pres. & Chief Exec. Officer--Waterloo Industries, Inc., Waterloo, IA; *U.S. Public*, pg. 675
Tredennick, Curtis, Pres. & Chief Exec. Officer--Resco Products, Inc., Conshohocken, PA; *U.S. Private*, pg. 924
Tredinnick, Richard, Pres. & Chief Exec. Officer--Old America Stores, Howe, TX; *U.S. Public*, pg. 1215
Treen, William Raymond, Dir. & Chief Exec. Officer--Cornhill Insurance Plc, London, United Kingdom; *Int'l*, pg. 60
Treis, F. Edward, Chm. Bd. & Chief Exec. Officer--Arandell Corporation, Menomonee Falls, WI; *U.S. Private*, pg. 79
Treis, F. Edward, Chm. Bd. & Chief Exec. Officer--Arandell-Schmidt, Menomonee Falls, WI; *U.S. Private*, pg. 79
Tremblay, Marcel J., Pres. & Chief Exec. Officer--EnerMark Income Fund, Calgary, Canada; *Int'l*, pg. 454
Trenkamp, Robert, Pres. & Chief Exec. Officer--Prepress Solutions, Inc., Billerica, MA; *U.S. Private*, pg. 882
Trepat, Albert, Chief Exec. Officer-Barcelona--Grupo Barro Testa, Madrid, Spain; *Int'l*, pg. 1377
Trerice, Byron W., Jr., Chm. Bd. & Chief Exec. Officer--Trerice Tosto Colliers International, Bingham Farms, MI; *U.S. Private*, pg. 1099
Treschow, Michael, Chief Exec. Officer--Electrolux, AB, Stockholm, Sweden; *Int'l*, pg. 438
Trevino, Alex, Jr., Chm. Bd., Pres. & Chief Exec. Officer--ACR Group, Houston, TX; *U.S. Public*, pg. 3
Trevvett, Herbert E., Pres. & Chief Exec. Officer--Commercial Travelers Mutual Insurance Company, Utica, NY; *U.S. Private*, pg. 258
Trewhella, Stephen W., Chm. & Chief Exec. Officer--Glassmaster Company, Lexington, SC; *U.S. Public*, pg. 745
Trezies, David, Chief Exec. Officer--Sedgwick Limited, London, United Kingdom; *Int'l*, pg. 1218
Trezza, William R., Chief Exec. Officer--Bank of Agriculture & Commerce, Stockton, CA; *U.S. Private*, pg. 114
Triant, Deborah, Pres. & Chief Exec. Officer--Check Point Software Technologies Inc., Redwood City, CA; *U.S. Public*, pg. 342
Tribble, James L., Chm. Bd. & Chief Exec. Officer--Tribble & Stephens Co., Houston, TX; *U.S. Private*, pg. 1102
Tribull, Christoph, Chm. Bd., Pres., Chief Exec. Officer & Chief Oper. Officer--Sierracin Corporation, Sylmar, CA; *U.S. Private*, pg. 999
Trier, Clayton, Chief Exec. Officer--Corporate Express Delivery Systems, Houston, TX; *U.S. Public*, pg. 449
Triggs, Donald, Pres. & Chief Exec. Officer--Vincor International, Niagara Falls, Canada; *Int'l*, pg. 1468
Trimble, Charles R., Chm. Bd., Pres. & Chief Exec. Officer--Trimble Navigation Limited, Sunnyvale, CA; *U.S. Public*, pg. 1638
Trinchero, Louis, Chm. & Chief Exec. Officer--Sutter Home Winery, Inc., Saint Helena, CA; *U.S. Private*, pg. 1057
Triplett, William W., Chm. Bd. & Chief Exec. Officer--HDS Services, Farmington Hills, MI; *U.S. Private*, pg. 490
Trippitelli, Gerard J., Pres. & Chief Exec. Officer--Matlack Systems, Inc., Wilmington, DE; *U.S. Public*, pg. 1057
Trivisonno, Nicholas L., Chm. Bd., Chief Exec. Officer--A.C. Nielsen, Stamford, CT; *U.S. Public*, pg. 1183
Trofholz, LeRoy, Pres. & Chief Exec. Officer--Wagner Mills Inc., Schuyler, NE; *U.S. Private*, pg. 1146
Troger, Jay R., Pres. & Chief Exec. Officer--Transportation Technologies, Inc., Washington, NC; *U.S. Private*, pg. 1097
Troger, Jay R., Pres. & Chief Exec. Officer--Hackney and Sons, Inc., Washington, NC; *U.S. Private*, pg. 1097
Troike, Frank A., Chm. Bd., Chief Exec. Officer & Treas.--Central Steel & Wire Company, Chicago, IL; *U.S. Public*, pg. 327
Tronchetti Provera, Marco, Chm. & Chief Exec. Officer--Pirelli S.p.A., Milan, Italy; *Int'l*, pg. 1058
Tronction, Claude, Chief Exec. Officer--Air Liquide America Corporation, Houston, TX; *Int'l*, pg. 37
Troschow, Michael, Pres. & Chief Exec. Officer--White Consolidated Industries, Inc., Cleveland, OH; *Int'l*, pg. 439
Trotman, Alexander J., Chm. Bd., Pres. & Chief Exec. Officer--Ford Motor Company, Dearborn, MI; *U.S. Public*, *pg. 661*
Trott, Bob, Chief Exec.-The Cheese Company--Avonmore Waterford Group plc, Killkenny, Ireland; *Int'l*, pg. 102
Trott, Kenny A., Chm. Bd. & Chief Exec. Officer--Excel Communications, Inc., Dallas, TX; *U.S. Public*, pg. 598
Trott, Ralph, Pres. & Chief Exec. Officer--Beaver Lumber Company Limited, Markham, Canada; *Int'l*, pg. 887
Trotter, Lloyd G., Pres. & Chief Exec. Officer--G.E. Electric Distribution & Control Manufacturing, Plainville, CT; *U.S. Public*, pg. 710
Trotter, Thomas R., Pres. & Chief Exec. Officer--Orthologic Corporation, Tempe, AZ; *U.S. Public*, pg. 1232
Trotter, Tim, Chm. & Chief Exec. Officer--Ludgate Group Limited, London, United Kingdom; *U.S. Private*, pg. 1157
Troutman, F. Gil Jr., Pres. & Chief Exec. Officer--DSP Technology Inc., Fremont, CA; *U.S. Public*, pg. 475
Troutman, William M., Pres. & Chief Exec. Officer--Lone Star Industries, Inc., Stamford, CT; *U.S. Public*, pg. 1012
Trozzo, Samuel R., Chm. Bd. & Chief Exec. Officer--Rice, Hall, James & Associates, San Diego, CA; *U.S. Public*, pg. 1674
Truchard, James J., Chm. Bd., Pres. & Chief Exec. Officer--National Instruments Corp., Austin, TX; *U.S. Public*, pg. 1157
Truchi, David, Pres. & Chief Exec. Officer--Trucchis Markets, Raynham, MA; *U.S. Private*, pg. 1107
Truffelli, Graziano, Chief Exec. Officer & Gen. Mgr.--Caboto Holding S.p.A., Milan, Italy; *Int'l*, pg. 138
Trugman, Leonard A., Chm. Bd., Pres. & Chief Exec. Officer--Del Global Technologies, Valhalla, NY; *U.S. Public*, pg. 493
Trujillo, Sol, Pres. & Chief Exec. Officer--U S West Communications Group, Inc., Englewood, CO; *U.S. Public*, pg. 1689
Trumbull, George r., Chief Exec. Officer & Mng. Dir.--Australian Mutual Provident, Sydney, Australia; *Int'l*, pg. 100
Trump, Julius, Chm. Bd. & Chief Exec. Officer--The Trump Group, Miami, FL; *U.S. Private*, pg. 1107
Trupiano, James, Chief Exec. Officer & Treas.--Champion Aluminum Window Corporation, Syosset, NY; *U.S. Private*, pg. 227
Truslow, Henry, III, Chm. Bd. & Chief Exec. Officer--Sunbury Textiles, Sunbury, PA; *U.S. Private*, pg. 432
Tsang, Chung Ming, Chief Exec.--Banco Santander, Beijing, China; *Int'l*, pg. 144
Tsangarakis, Miltiadis, Chief Exec. Officer--Olympic Aviation, Athens, Greece; *Int'l*, pg. 1004
Tsuda, Shoji, Pres. & Chief Exec. Officer--Mitsukoshi, Ltd., Tokyo, Japan; *Int'l*, pg. 883
Tsui, Cyrus Y., Chm. Bd., Pres. & Chief Exec. Officer--Lattice Semiconductor Corporation, Hillsboro, OR; *U.S. Public*, pg. 979
Tsui, John K., Chm. Bd. & Chief Exec. Officer--First Hawaiian Leasing, Inc., Honolulu, HI; *U.S. Public*, pg. 635
Tsuji, Keiichi, Mng. Dir. & Chief Exec.--IBJ Australia Bank Limited, Sydney, Australia; *Int'l*, pg. 676
Tsuruta, Takuhiko, Pres. & Chief Exec. Officer--Nihon Keizai Shimbun, Inc., Tokyo, Japan; *Int'l*, pg. 929

Tu, Wen-Hu, Chm. Bd., Pres. & Chief Exec. Officer--Transico Incorporated, Santa Ana, CA; *U.S. Public*, pg. 1630

Tucci, Joseph M., Chm. Bd. & Chief Exec. Officer--Wang Laboratories, Inc., Billerica, MA; *U.S. Public*, pg. 1737

Tuchman, Martin, Chm. Bd. & Chief Exec. Officer--Interpool, Inc., Princeton, NJ; *U.S. Public*, pg. 908

Tucker, Garland, Pres. & Chief Exec. Officer--First Travelcorp Inc., Raleigh, NC; *U.S. Private*, pg. 408

Tucker, Gary F., Pres. & Chief Exec. Officer--Pope Resources, Poulsbo, WA; *U.S. Public*, pg. 1317

Tucker, Mark, Chief Exec.--Prudential Asia, Central, Hong Kong; *Int'l*, pg. 1073

Tuckman, Mitchell, Pres. & Chief Exec. Officer--General Microwave Corporation, Amityville, NY; *U.S. Public*, pg. 717

Tufts, W.E., Chief Exec. Officer--Plunkett-Webster, Inc., New Rochelle, NY; *U.S. Private*, pg. 872

Tuley, B.B., Pres. & Chief Exec. Officer--Pic'n Pay Stores, Inc., Matthews, NC; *U.S. Private*, pg. 864

Tulin, John, Pres. & Chief Exec. Officer--Swank, Inc., Attleboro, MA; *U.S. Public*, pg. 1543

Tullio, Douglas J., Pres. & Chief Exec. Officer--Alpha Microsystems, Santa Ana, CA; *U.S. Public*, pg. 57

Tullis, David A., Pres. & Chief Exec. Officer--Customer Service Center of F.N.B., L.L.C., Naples, FL; *U.S. Public*, *pg. 607*

Tunmire, Robert, Pres. & Chief Exec. Officer--The Dwyer Group, Inc., Waco, TX; *U.S. Public*, pg. 537

Tuozzolo, James A., Chief Exec. Officer--The Pyramid Companies, Syracuse, NY; *U.S. Private*, pg. 896

Turcan, William J., Chief Exec. Officer--Harrisons & Crosfield plc, London, United Kingdom; *Int'l*, pg. 598

Turcotte, G.J., Chm. & Chief Exec. Officer--Chauvco Resources Ltd., Calgary, Canada; *Int'l*, pg. 1424

Turcotte, Norman J., Pres. & Chief Exec. Officer--Associated Grocers of New England, Inc., Manchester, NH; *U.S. Private*, pg. 91

Turley, Robert, Pres. & Chief Oper. Officer--Perdue Farms Incorporated, Salisbury, MD; *U.S. Private*, pg. 852

Turner, Andrew, Chm. Bd., Pres. & Chief Exec. Officer--Sun Healthcare Group Inc., Albuquerque, NM; *U.S. Public*, pg. 1530

Turner, B.C., Chief Oper. Officer--Pillar Building Products ltd., London, United Kingdom; *Int'l*, pg. 267

Turner, Barry, Chm. Bd., Pres. & Chief Exec. Officer--KTI Fish, Houston, TX; *U.S. Private*, pg. 604

Turner, Cal, Jr., Chm. Bd. & Chief Exec. Officer--Dollar General Corporation, Nashville, TN; *U.S. Public*, pg. 515

Turner, Carlton E., Pres. & Chief Exec. Officer--Carrington Laboratories, Inc., Irving, TX; *U.S. Public*, pg. 309

Turner, Clyde T., Chm. Bd. & Chief Exec. Officer--Circus Circus - Las Vegas, Las Vegas, NV; *U.S. Public*, pg. 374

Turner, Clyde T., Chm. Bd. & Chief Exec. Officer--Circus Circus Hotel Casinos, Inc., Las Vegas, NV; *U.S. Public*, pg. 374

Turner, Dennis M.J., Chief Exec. Officer--Pharmaceutical Marketing Services Inc., Phoenix, AZ; *U.S. Public*, pg. 1284

Turner, Edward T., Jr., Chm. Bd. & Chief Exec. Officer--Weston Paper & Manufacturing Co., Terre Haute, IN; *U.S. Private*, pg. 1169

Turner, Jeffrey F., Pres. & Chief Exec. Officer--Peninsula Bank, Princess Anne, MD; *U.S. Public*, pg. 1089

Turner, Joe Ben, Chm. Bd., Pres. & Chief Exec. Officer--Willis Corroon Corp. of Knoxville, Knoxville, TN; *Int'l*, pg. 1506

Turner, John G., Chm. Bd. & Chief Exec. Officer--ReliaStar Financial Corp., Minneapolis, MN; *U.S. Public*, pg. 1375

Turner, R.E., Chief Exec. Officer--Turner Entertainment Company, Los Angeles, CA; *U.S. Public*, pg. 1615

Turner, Richard W., Pres. & Chief Exec. Officer--BEI Medical Systems Company, Hackensack, NJ; *U.S. Private*, pg. 106

Turtletaub, Marc, Pres. & Chief Exec. Officer--The Money Store, Sacramento, CA; *U.S. Public*, pg. 1124

Turturro, August B., Pres. & Chief Exec. Officer--Fischbach Corporation, Englewood, CO; *U.S. Public*, pg. 84

Tushman, J. Lawrence, Chief Exec. Officer & Sec.--Orleans International, Inc., Bloomfield Hills, MI; *U.S. Private*, pg. 820

Tutcher, Dan, Pres. & Chief Exec. Officer--Midcoast Energy Resources, Inc., Houston, TX; *U.S. Public*, pg. 1109

Tuten, Henderson G., Pres. & Chief Exec. Officer--Rothschild North America Inc., New York, NY; *U.S. Private*, pg. 947

Tuthill, James G., Jr., Pres. & Chief Exec. Officer--Tuthill Corporation, Hinsdale, IL; *U.S. Private*, pg. 1110

Tutor, Ronald N., Pres. & Chief Exec. Officer--Tutor-Saliba Corporation, Sylmar, CA; *U.S. Private*, pg. 1111

Tuttle, J.L., Pres. & Chief Exec. Officer--Ohio Gas Company, Bryan, OH; *U.S. Private*, pg. 812

Tuttle, Robert H., Chief Exec. Officer--Holmes Tuttle Ford, Inc., Tucson, AZ; *U.S. Private*, pg. 535

Tuttle, Robert H., Chief Exec. Officer & Partner--Tuttle-Click Automobile Group, Irvine, CA; *U.S. Private*, pg. 1111

Twigg-Smith, Thurston, Chm. Bd. & Chief Exec. Officer--Persis Corporation, Honolulu, HI; *U.S. Private*, pg. 855

Twomey, Christopher A., Pres. & Chief Exec. Officer--Arctic Cat Inc., Thief River Falls, MN; *U.S. Public*, pg. 128

Twomley, Dale E., Pres. & Chief Exec. Officer--Worthington Foods Inc., Worthington, OH; *U.S. Public*, pg. 1780

Tyabji, Hatim A., Chm. Bd., Pres. & Chief Exec. Officer--VeriFone, Inc., Redwood City, CA; *U.S. Public*, pg. 815

Tyda, William, Chm. Bd. & Chief Exec. Officer--LaSalle-Talman Bank, Chicago, IL; *Int'l*, pg. 11

Tyler, H.H., Pres. & Chief Exec. Officer--The Northern Trust Company, Lake Forest, IL; *U.S. Public*, pg. 1197

Tyler, H.H., Pres. & Chief Exec. Officer--The Northern Trust Company, Lake Bluff, IL; *U.S. Public*, pg. 1197

Tyree, James C., Chm. Bd. & Chief Exec. Officer--Mesirow Financial, Chicago, IL; *U.S. Private*, pg. 733

Tyson, Ted H., Pres., Chief Exec. Officer & Chief Oper. Officer--The Dickerson Group, Inc., Monroe, NC; *U.S. Private*, pg. 331

Tyson, Thomas J., Dr., Chm. Bd., Pres. & Chief Exec. Officer--Energy & Environmental Research Corp., Irvine, CA; *U.S. Private*, pg. 376

Uchida, Hisashi, Pres. & Chief Exec. Officer--Mitsubishi Silicon America, Palo Alto, CA; *Int'l*, pg. 875

Uchiyama, Etsuji, Chief Oper. Officer--Nittsu Kiko Unyu Co., Ltd., Sapporo, Japan; *Int'l*, pg. 934

Udvar-Hazy, Steven F., Pres. & Chief Exec. Officer--International Lease Finance Corporation, Los Angeles, CA; *U.S. Public*, pg. 85

Ueda, N., Office Chief--Man Nen Sha, Inc., Fukuoka, Japan; *Int'l*, pg. 834

Ueltschi, H.P., Chm. Bd., Pres. & Chief Exec. Officer--Bernina Holding AG, Steckborn, Switzerland; *Int'l*, pg. 189

Uematsu, Tomiji, Pres. & Chief Exec. Officer--Konica Corporation, Tokyo, Japan; *Int'l*, pg. 748

Ueno, Shinzo, Pres. & Chief Exec. Officer--Dentsu, Sudler & Hennessey Inc., Tokyo, Japan; *U.S. Private*, pg. 325

Ueno, Takashi, Pres. & Chief Exec. Officer--Sakura Global Capital, Inc., New York, NY; *Int'l*, pg. 1179

Ueshima, Shigeji, Pres. & Chief Exec. Officer--Mitsui & Co., Ltd., Tokyo, Japan; *Int'l*, pg. 877

Ughi, Pier, Chief Exec. Officer--The Dee Howard Company, San Antonio, TX; *U.S. Private*, pg. 542

Uhl, Richard J., Pres. & Chief Exec. Officer--Chicago Holdings, Inc., Pittsburgh, PA; *U.S. Private*, pg. 234

Uhlmann, Paul, III, Chm. Bd. & Chief Exec. Officer--The Uhlmann Co., Kansas City, MO; *U.S. Private*, pg. 1115

Uihlein, Walter R., Chm. & Chief Exec. Officer--Titleist & Foot-Joy Worldwide, Fairhaven, MA; *U.S. Public*, pg. 675

Uihlein, Walter R., Pres. & Chief Exec. Officer--Acushnet Company, Fairhaven, MA; *U.S. Public*, pg. 675

Ujiie, Junichi, Pres. & Chief Exec. Officer--The Nomura Securities Co., Ltd., Tokyo, Japan; *Int'l*, pg. 955

Ukrop, James E., Chm. Bd. & Chief Exec. Officer--Ukrop's Super Markets, Richmond, VA; *U.S. Private*, pg. 1115

Ulbrich, Frederick C., Jr., Chm. Bd., Pres. & Chief Exec. Officer--Ulbrich Stainless Steels & Special Metals, Inc., North Haven, CT; *U.S. Private*, pg. 1115

Ulery, Byron, Pres., Chief Exec. Officer & Gen. Mgr.--Farmway Co-Op Inc., Beloit, KS; *U.S. Private*, pg. 396

Ullman, S. Peter, Pres., Chief Exec. & Oper. Officer--Harris Calorific Co., Gainesville, GA; *U.S. Public*, pg. 996

Ullmark, Hans, Pres. & Chief Exec. Officer--Anderson & Lembke Inc., New York, NY; *U.S. Private*, pg. 72

Ullring, Sven, Pres. & Chief Exec. Officer--Det Norske Veritas, Hovik, Norway; *Int'l*, pg. 396

Ulrich, Robert J., Chm. Bd. & Chief Exec. Officer--Dayton Hudson Corporation, Minneapolis, MN; *U.S. Public*, pg. 489

Ulrich, Robert J., Chief Exec. Officer--Target Stores, Minneapolis, MN; *U.S. Public*, pg. 489

Ulsh, Gordon, Pres. & Chief Exec. Officer--Wagner Lighting Products, Chesterfield, MO; *U.S. Public*, pg. 442

Umans, A.R., Chm. Bd. & Chief Exec. Officer--RHC/Spacemaster Corporation, Melrose Park, IL; *U.S. Private*, *pg. 904*

Umon, Luis Garcia, Chief Exec. Officer--Grupo Simec, S.A. de C.V., Guadalajara, Mexico; *Int'l*, pg. 576

Umphenour, Russell, Jr., Chm. Bd., Pres. & Chief Exec. Officer--R.T.M. Winners, Atlanta, GA; *U.S. Private*, pg. 906

Underwood, Vernon, Chm. Bd., Pres. & Chief Exec. Officer--Young's Holdings Inc., Orange, CA; *U.S. Private*, pg. 1202

Ungar, William, Chief Exec. Officer--New York Envelope Corp, Long Island City, NY; *U.S. Private*, pg. 794

Unger, Les, Pres. & Chief Exec. Officer--Bufkor, Inc., Clearwater, FL; *U.S. Private*, pg. 179

Ungerer, S.B., Chief Exec. Officer--Atlantic Generation, Inc., Pleasantville, NJ; *U.S. Public*, pg. 430

Ungerer, S.B., Chief Exec. Officer--Atlantic Energy Technology, Inc., Pleasantville, NJ; *U.S. Public*, pg. 430

Ungerer, Scott B., Chief Exec. Officer--Atlantic Thermal Systems, Inc., Pleasantville, NJ; *U.S. Public*, pg. 430

Unschuld, Doran J., Pres. & Chief Exec. Officer--Binks Sames Corporation, Franklin Park, IL; *U.S. Public*, pg. 229

Upbin, Hal J., Pres. & Chief Exec. Officer--Kellwood Company, Chesterfield, MO; *U.S. Public*, pg. 948

Upfield, Bradley A., Chief Exec. Officer & Gen. Mgr.--Lea Lumber & Plywood LLC, Windsor, NC; *U.S. Private*, pg. 655

Upland, Ted, Pres. & Chief Exec. Officer--CPI Prints Plus, Inc., Concord, CA; *U.S. Public*, pg. 283

Urban, Phil, Pres. & Chief Exec. Officer--Guarantee National Insurance Company, Englewood, CO; *U.S. Public*, pg. 1231

Urdal, Alfredo Martinez, Chief Exec. Officer--Coca-Cola FEMSA, S.A. de CV, Mexico, Mexico; *Int'l*, pg. 496

Urek, Robert M., Pres. & Chief Exec. Officer--Heublein, Inc., Hartford, CT; *Int'l*, pg. 410

Urland, Robert S., Pres. & Chief Exec. Officer--Griffin Technology Incorporated, Farmington, NY; *U.S. Public*, pg. 506

Urstadt, Charles J., Chm. Bd. & Chief Exec. Officer--Urstadt Biddle Properties, Inc., Greenwich, CT; *U.S. Public*, pg. 1700

Usdan, James M., Pres. & Chief Exec. Officer--RehabCare Group, Inc., Saint Louis, MO; *U.S. Public*, pg. 1373

Usher, George, Pres. & Chief Exec. Officer--Polydex Pharmaceuticals Limited, Scarborough, Canada; *Int'l*, pg. 1062

Usher, Thomas J., Chm. Bd. & Chief Exec. Officer--USX Corporation, Pittsburgh, PA; *U.S. Public*, pg. 1661

Usher, Thomas J., Chm. Bd. & Chief Exec. Officer--U.S. Steel International, Inc., Pittsburgh, PA; *U.S. Public*, pg. 1661

Ushioda, Kenjiro, Pres. & Chief Exec. Officer--Tostem Corporation, Tokyo, Japan; *Int'l*, pg. 1408

Utick, David, Pres. & Chief Exec.. Officer--Hehr International Inc., Los Angeles, CA; *U.S. Private*, pg. 519

Utsumi, Jun, Pres. & Chief Exec. Officer--OMRON Systems, Inc., Schaumburg, IL; *Int'l*, pg. 1005

Vaajoki, Jorma, Pres. & Chief Exec. Officer--Metsa-Serla Corporation, Espoo, Finland; *Int'l*, pg. 863

Vague, Richard W., Chm. Bd. & Chief Exec. Officer--First USA, Inc., Dallas, TX; *U.S. Public*, pg. 174

Vague, Richard W., Chm. & Chief Exec. Officer--First USA Bank, Wilmington, DE; *U.S. Public*, pg. 174

Vaillaud, Pierre, Chm. Bd. & Chief Exec. Officer--Technip, Paris, France; *Int'l*, pg. 1360

Vainikka, Timo, Chief Exec. Officer--OAO Komsomolets, Kommunar, Russia; *Int'l*, pg. 864

Vainio, Vesa, Chm. Bd. & Chief Exec. Officer--Merita Ltd., Helsinki, Finland; *Int'l*, pg. 858

Vainio, Vesa, Chm. Bd. & Chief Exec. Officer--Merita Bank Ltd., Helsinki, Finland; *Int'l*, pg. 858

Vairo, Ricardo, Chief Exec. Officer--EURO RSCG Norton, Montevideo, Uruguay; *Int'l*, pg. 603

Vakoutis, John, Pres. & Chief Exec. Officer--Curative Health Services, East Setauket, NY; *U.S. Public*, pg. 469

Valade, Robert C., Chm. Bd. & Chief Exec. Officer--Carhartt, Inc., Dearborn, MI; *U.S. Private*, pg. 210

Valdiserri, Carl L., Chm. Bd. & Chief Exec. Officer--Rouge Steel Company, Dearborn, MI; *U.S. Public*, pg. 1406

Valente, Dan, Chm. Bd., Pres. & Chief Exec. Officer--Palomar Medical Technologies, Lexington, MA; *U.S. Public*, pg. 1255

Valenti, Nick, Pres. & Chief Exec. Officer--Restaurant Associates Corporation, New York, NY; *U.S. Private*, pg. 924

Valenti, Nick, Pres. & Chief Exec. Officer--Restaurant Associates Catering, New York, NY; *U.S. Private*, pg. 925

Valentine, Dean, Pres. & Chief Exec. Officer--UPN-United Paramount Network, Los Angeles, CA; *U.S. Public*, pg. 352

Valentine, Dean, Pres. & Chief Exec. Officer--UPN-United Paramount Network, Los Angeles, CA; *U.S. Private*, pg. 777

Valentine, Joseph C., Chm. Bd., Pres. & Chief Exec. Officer--Lubrication Engineers, Inc., Fort Worth, TX; *U.S. Private*, pg. 679

Valentini, Robert M., Pres. & Chief Exec. Officer-Bell Atlantic Pennsylvania, Inc.--Bell Atlantic Corporation, New York, NY; *U.S. Public*, pg. 201

Vallee, Louis-Eric, Pres. & Chief Exec. Officer--Saint Jacques Vallee Young & Rubicam, Inc., Montreal, Canada; *U.S. Private*, pg. 1200

Vallee, Roy, Chm. Bd., Pres. & Chief Exec. & Oper. Officer--Avnet, Inc., Great Neck, NY; *U.S. Public*, pg. 155

Valles, Jean-Paul, Chm. Bd. & Chief Exec. Officer--Minerals Technologies, Inc., New York, NY; *U.S. Public*, pg. 1115

Valley, R. Bruce, Chm. Bd., Pres. & Chief Exec. Officer--Piedmont Trust Bank, Martinsville, VA; *U.S. Public*, pg. 1039

Van Anken, Richard A., Pres. & Chief Exec. Officer--Jennings & Churella Construction Company, Wellington, OH; *U.S. Private*, pg. 586

van Apeloloum, H., Chief Exec. Officer--Hoogovens Staalverwerking en Handel BV, Bloemendaal, Netherlands; *Int'l*, pg. 754

van As, Eugene, Chm. Bd. & Chief Exec. Officer--Sappi Limited, Braamfontein, South Africa; *Int'l*, pg. 1193

van As, Eugene, Chm. Bd. & Chief Exec. Officer--S.D. Warren Co., Boston, MA; *Int'l*, pg. 1193

Van Bogan, R., Chm. Bd., Pres. & Chief Exec. Officer--SouthTrust Bank, Orlando, Orlando, FL; *U.S. Public*, pg. 1492

Van Brunt, John, Pres. & Chief Exec. Officer--Agrium Inc., Calgary, Canada; *Int'l*, pg. 31

Van Buren, David, Pres. & Chief Exec. Officer--Tecstar Inc., City of Industry, CA; *U.S. Private*, pg. 1072

Van Buren, Robert W., Pres. & Chief Exec. Officer--Domco Inc., Farnham, Canada; *Int'l*, pg. 415

van Dam, B., Pres. & Chief Exec. Officer--Van Leeuwen Pipe and Tube Group B.V., Zwijndrecht, Netherlands; *Int'l*, pg. 1449

Van Dawark, Tom, Pres. & Chief Exec. Officer--Foss Maritime Co., Seattle, WA; *U.S. Private*, pg. 1092

van de Geijn, P., Chm. Bd., Pres. & Chief Exec. Officer--AEGON Nederland N.V., Hague, Netherlands; *Int'l*, pg. 26

van de Meest, Henk, Chief Exec. Officer--Lawson Mardon Packaging Inc., Mississauga, Canada; *Int'l*, pg. 68

Van Degna, Robert M., Chm. & Chief Exec. Officer--Fleet Equity Partners, Providence, RI; *U.S. Public*, pg. 650

Van den Bergh, Jan, Chief Exec. Officer-Strategy & Creation--Quattro DMB&B, Brussels, Brussels, Belgium; *U.S. Private*, pg. 305

van den Bergh, R.F., Chariman & Chief Exec. Offier--NMU Marketing Information Services, New York, NY; *Int'l*, pg. 1446

Van Den Blink, N. Mooers, Chm. Bd., Chief Exec. Officer, & Treas.--Hilliard Corporation, Elmira, NY; *U.S. Private*, pg. 530

Van Der Kamp, Jerry, Chief Exec. Officer & Exec. V.P.--American Grain & Related Industries, West Des Moines, IA; *U.S. Private*, pg. 55

van Driel, A.A.J., Chief Exec. Officer--OCE Nederlandse Verkoopmaatschappij B.V., s Hertogenbosch, Netherlands; *Int'l*, pg. 994

Van Dyke, William G., Chm. Bd., Pres. & Chief Exec. Officer--Donaldson Company, Inc., Minneapolis, MN; *U.S. Public*, pg. 517

Van Eyck, Mike, Div. Chief Exec. Officer-Printing & Writing--Arjo Wiggins Appleton plc, Basingstoke, United Kingdom; *Int'l*, pg. 567

Van Faasen, William, Pres. & Chief Exec. Officer--Blue Cross and Blue Shield of Massachusetts, Boston, MA; *U.S. Private*, pg. 151

van Hecke, Jean-Francois, Chief Exec. Officer--Bernheim-Comofi, Brussels, Belgium; *Int'l*, pg. 562

Van Hefty, Claude L., Pres. & Chief Exec. Officer--Badger Paper Mills, Inc., Peshtigo, WI; *U.S. Public*, pg. 165
Van Hook, Jim, Chm. Bd. & Chief Exec. Officer--Provident Music Group, Brentwood, TN; *Int'l*, pg. 1529
Van Houten, James F., Pres. & Chief Exec. Officer--MSI Insurance Companies, Arden Hills, MN; *U.S. Private*, pg. 688
Van Kleeck, Peter, Pres. & Chief Exec. Officer--Progressive Bank, Inc., Fishkill, NY; *U.S. Public*, pg. 1334
Van Kleeck, Peter, Pres. & Chief Exec. Officer--Pawling Savings Bank, Pawling, NY; *U.S. Public*, pg. 1334
Van Lede, Cga, Pres. & Chief Exec. Officer--Akzo Nobel N.V., Arnhem, Netherlands; *Int'l*, pg. 42
Van Loan, Charles C., Pres. & Chief Exec. Officer--Independent Bank Corporation, Ionia, MI; *U.S. Public*, pg. 874
Van Loan, Dave, Pres. & Chief Exec. Officer--Everett Charles Technologies, Pomona, CA; *U.S. Private*, pg. 386
Van Mollenberg, H., Chm. Bd., Pres. & Chief Exec. Officer--Mollenberg-Betz Inc., Buffalo, NY; *U.S. Private*, pg. 756
van Osnabrugge, Jan, Pres. & Chief Exec. Officer--Peerless Industrial Group, Inc., Winona, MN; *U.S. Public*, pg. 1268
van Osnabrugge, Jan, Pres. & Chief Exec. Officer--Peerless Chain Company, Winona, MN; *U.S. Public*, pg. 1268
van Parys, Frederick, Pres. & Chief Exec. Officer--Pitney Bowes of Canada Ltd., Toronto, Canada; *U.S. Public*, pg. 1304
van Pelt, Bert, Chief Exec. Officer & Dir.-Mktg.--Elsevier Opleidingen BV, Zwijndrecht, Netherlands; *Int'l*, pg. 1094
Van Pelt, David B., Sr., Chm. Bd. & Chief Exec. Officer--Van Pelt Corporation, Detroit, MI; *U.S. Private*, pg. 1133
Van Pelt, David B., Sr., Chm. Bd. & Chief Exec. Officer--Service Steel Division, Detroit, MI; *U.S. Private*, pg. 1133
Van Pelt, Donald C., Jr., Pres. & Chief Exec. Officer--Plymouth Tube Company, Warrenville, IL; *U.S. Private*, pg. 873
Van Pelt, Wim, Pres. & Chief Exec. Officer--Banner Pharmacaps, Inc., High Point, NC; *Int'l*, pg. 1272
Van Sant, R. William, Chm. Bd. & Chief Exec. Officer--Lukens Inc., Coatesville, PA; *U.S. Public*, pg. 1019
Van Strydonck, John, Chm. Bd. & Chief Exec. Officer--NAPP Systems Inc, San Marcos, CA; *U.S. Public*, pg. 984
Van Tiflin, James, Pres. & Chief Exec. Officer--Second National Bank of Saginaw, Saginaw, MI; *U.S. Public*, pg. 379
Van Tuyl, Cecil L., Chm. Bd., Pres. & Chief Exec. Officer--V.T. Inc., Merriam, KS; *U.S. Private*, pg. 1131
Van Veen, M.C., Chm.-Bd. of Mngmt.--Koninklijke Hoogovens N.V., Ijmuiden, Netherlands; *Int'l*, pg. 753
Van Wagenen, Paul G., Chm. Bd., Pres. & Chief Exec. Officer--Pogo Producing Company, Houston, TX; *U.S. Public*, pg. 1312
Van Weelden, Thomas H., Pres. & Chief Exec. Officer--Allied Waste Industries, Scottsdale, AZ; *U.S. Public*, pg. 49
Van Winkle, John D., Pres. & Chief Exec. Officer--Beverly Bancorporation Inc., Chicago, IL; *U.S. Public*, pg. 227
Vana-Paxhia, Steven R., Pres & Chief Exec. Officer--INSO Corporation, Boston, MA; *U.S. Public*, pg. 882
VanBenthuysen, Walter G., Chm. Bd. & Chief Exec. Officer--Hazelwood Farms Bakeries, Inc., Hazelwood, MO; *U.S. Public*, pg. 1541
Vance, William C., Chm. Bd. & Chief Exec. Officer--Vance Publishing Corporation, Lincolnshire, IL; *U.S. Private*, pg. 1133
Vandenburgh, David S., Chm. Bd. & Chief Exec. Officer--American Fence & Security Company, Phoenix, AZ; *U.S.* Private, pg. 54
Vanderbilt, H.B., Jr., Pres. & Chief Exec. Officer--R.T. Vanderbilt Company, Inc., Norwalk, CT; *U.S. Private*, pg. 1133
Vanderboom, Steve, Pres. & Chief Exec. Officer--Pace Analytical Services, Minneapolis, MN; *U.S. Private*, pg. 829
Vanderminden, Robert D., Sr., Chief Exec. Officer--Telescope Casual Furniture, Inc., Granville, NY; *U.S. Private*, pg. 1074
Vanderstar, Cornelius C., Chm. Bd. & Chief Exec. Officer--International Aluminum Corporation, Monterey Park, CA; *U.S. Public*, pg. 894
Vandewalle, John, Chief Exec. Officer-Teva Marion Partners--Hoechst Marion Roussel North America, Kansas City, MO; *Int'l*, pg. 625
VanFaasen, William C., Chief Exec. Officer--Physician Partners of New England, Inc., Boston, MA; *U.S. Private*, *pg. 151*
VanLuvanee, Donald R., Pres. & Chief Exec. Officer--Electro Scientific Industries, Inc., Portland, OR; *U.S. Public*, pg. 568
Vann, James A., Jr., Pres. & Chief Exec. Officer--Alabama Electric Cooperative, Inc., Andalusia, AL; *U.S. Private*, pg. 30
Vannoy, Jack, Pres. & Chief Exec. Officer--Megas Beauty Care, Inc., Cleveland, OH; *U.S. Private*, pg. 729
Vanourek, Robert A., Pres. & Chief Exec. Officer--Sensormatic Electronics Corporation, Boca Raton, FL; *U.S. Public*, pg. 1457
Vardeman, J. Rex, Chm. Bd., Pres. & Chief Exec. Officer--Vertex Communications Corporation, Kilgore, TX; *U.S. Public*, pg. 1717
Varel, Daniel W., Chm. Bd., Pres., Chief Exec. Officer & Gen. Mgr.--Varel Manufacturing Co., Dallas, TX; *U.S. Private*, pg. 1134
Vargas, Eduardo, Exec. V.P. & Chm., Chief Exec. Officer-Latin America & Dir.--BBDO Worldwide Inc., New York, NY; *U.S. Public*, pg. 1223
Variati, Achille, Chief Exec. Officer & Gen. Mgr.--Itacard S.p.A., Milan, Italy; *Int'l*, pg. 138
Varlet, Didier, Pres. & Chief Exec. Officer--Carr Asset Management Inc., Chicago, IL; *Int'l*, pg. 313
Vassiliades, Thomas, Chm. Bd. & Chief Exec. Officer--Gandalf Technologies Inc., Nepean, Canada; *Int'l*, pg. 540
Vassiliadis, William, Pres. & Chief Exec. Officer--R&R Advertising, Las Vegas, NV; *U.S. Private*, pg. 902
Vaughan, Curtis T., III, Pres. & Chief Exec. Officer--Vaughan & Sons, Inc., San Antonio, TX; *U.S. Private*, pg. 1134
Vazquez, O., Chief Exec. Officer--Charles Atlas, Ltd., New York, NY; *U.S. Private*, pg. 229
Vecten, Philippe, Chm. & Chief Exec. Officer--MDPA, Wittelsheim, France; *Int'l*, pg. 459
Vega, Frank, Pres. & Chief Exec. Officer--Detroit Newspapers, Detroit, MI; *U.S. Public*, pg. 965
Veghte, Robert I., Pres. & Chief Exec. Officer--Wheaton Inc., Millville, NJ; *Int'l*, pg. 67
Veirto, Heikki, Chief Oper. Officer--Nokia Plant, Nokia, Finland; *Int'l*, pg. 863
Velasquez, Arthur R., Chm. Bd., Pres. & Chief Exec. Officer--Azteca Foods, Incorporated, Chicago, IL; *U.S. Private*, pg. 104
Venderbos, D. J., Chief Exec.--DSM Fine Chemicals, Sittard, Netherlands; *Int'l*, pg. 353
Vensel, John, Chm. Bd., Pres. & Chief Exec. Officer--Crucible Materials Corp., Solvay, NY; *U.S. Private*, pg. 293
Vento, Richard G., Co-Chm. Bd., Pres. & Chief Exec. Officer--Objective Systems Integrators, Inc., Folsom, CA; *U.S. Public*, pg. 1209
Ventre, John, Jr., Chm. Bd., Chief Exec. Officer & Treas.--Ventre Packing Company, Inc., Syracuse, NY; *U.S. Private*, pg. 1135
Ventre, Marc, Pres. & Chief Exec. Officer--Fan Blade Associates, Inc., Wilmington, DE; *Int'l*, pg. 1166
Venuti, Steve, Pres. & Chief Exec. Officer--LVL Interactive, Palo Alto, CA; *U.S. Private*, pg. 640
Veratti, Robert N., Pres. & Chief Exec. Officer--National Media Corporation, Philadelphia, PA; *U.S. Public*, pg. 1158
Verbicky, John W., Pres. & Chief Exec. Officer--Chemfab Corporation, Merrimack, NH; *U.S. Public*, pg. 344
Verble, C. Michael, Pres. & Chief Exec. Officer--North American Roofing Systems, Inc., Arden, NC; *U.S. Private*, pg. 803
Verdery, Edward H., Chief Exec. Officer--Environmental Elements Corporation, Baltimore, MD; *U.S. Public*, pg. 586
Verdonk, Juup, Chief Exec. Officer & Gen. Dir.--Opel Danmark, Soeborg, Denmark; *U.S. Public*, pg. 723
Verdoorn, Sid, Pres., Chief Exec. & Chief Oper. Officer--C.H. Robinson Co., Eden Prairie, MN; *U.S. Public*, pg. 1394
Vereen, W.J., Pres., Chief Exec. Officer & Treas.--Riverside Manufacturing Co., Moultrie, GA; *U.S. Private*, pg. 934
Verey, David, Chief Exec. Officer--Lazard Brothers & Co. Ltd., London, United Kingdom; *Int'l*, pg. 1026
Vergote, Hedwig, Chief Exec. Officer-Flat Prods. Div.--Sidmar N.V., Gent, Belgium; *Int'l*, pg. 79
Verhagen, J.K., Pres. & Chief Oper. Officer--Compaction America, Kewanee, IL; *U.S. Public*, pg. 1676
Verkamp, Gilbert, Pres. & Chief Exec. Officer--Aristokraft, Inc., Jasper, IN; *U.S. Public*, pg. 675
Vermeer, Robert, Chm. Bd. & Chief Exec. Officer--Vermeer Manufacturing Company, Pella, IA; *U.S. Private*, pg. 1137
VerMerris, R.C., Chm. Bd. & Pres. & Chief Exec. Officer--Radix Wire Company, Cleveland, OH; *U.S. Private*, pg. 907
Verner, George C., Jr., Chm. Bd. & Chief Exec. Officer--Acousti Engineering Co. of Florida, Orlando, FL; *U.S. Private*, pg. 14
Verni, Ralph F., Chm. Bd., Pres. & Chief Exec. Officer--State Street Research & Management Company, Boston, MA; *U.S. Private*, pg. 738
Vernick, Mitchell F., Pres. & Chief Exec. Officer--Transamerica Commercial Finance Corp., Inc., Chicago, IL; *U.S. Public*, pg. 1630
Vernon, Lillian, Chm. Bd. & Chief Exec. Officer--Lillian Vernon Corporation, New Rochelle, NY; *U.S. Public*, pg. 1716
Verschelde, Patrick, Pres. & Chief Exec. Officer--Air Liquide America Corporation, Houston, TX; *Int'l*, pg. 37
Verstegen, J.D.M., Chief Exec.--DSM Agro BV, Sittard, Netherlands; *Int'l*, pg. 353
Veru, Theodore D., Co-Chm. & Co-Chief Exec. Officer--Lois/USA Inc., New York, NY; *U.S. Public*, pg. 1011
Vest, Herb D., Chm. Bd., Pres. & Chief Exec. Officer--HD Vest Financial Services, Irving, TX; *U.S. Public*, pg. 770
Vesta, Rich, Pres.--Packerland Packing Co., Green Bay, WI; *U.S. Private*, pg. 833
Veyron, Pierre, Chief Exec. Officer & Dir.--Soparco, Conde-sur-Huisne, France; *Int'l*, pg. 430
Vichich, William M., Chief Oper. & Fin. Officer--CitFed Bancorp, Inc., Dayton, OH; *U.S. Public*, pg. 376
Vick, Edward H., Chm. & Chief Exec. Officer-Y&R/Wunderman Partnership--Young & Rubicam Inc., New York, NY; *U.S. Private*, pg. 1196
Vick, Edward H., Chm. & Chief Exec. Officer--Young & Rubicam Inc., New York, NY; *U.S. Private*, pg. 1196
Videon, Spence, Chief Exec. Officer--Snowshoe Resort, Inc., Snowshoe, WV; *Int'l*, pg. 685
Vie, Richard C., Pres. & Chief Exec. Officer--Unitrin, Inc., Chicago, IL; *U.S. Public*, pg. 1693
Vienot, Marc, Chm. Bd. & Chief Exec. Officer--Societe Generale, Paris, France; *Int'l*, pg. 1273
Vietor, Sandy, Pres. & Chief Exec. Officer--Willis Corroon Marine & Energy, New York, NY; *Int'l*, pg. 1508
Viets, Robert O., Pres. & Chief Exec. Officer--CILCORP Inc., Peoria, IL; *U.S. Public*, pg. 367
Viets, Robert O., Chm. & Chief Exec. Officer--QST Enterprises Inc., Peoria, IL; *U.S. Public*, pg. 367
Viggiano, Victor A., Chm. Bd. & Chief Exec. Officer--The Okonite Company, Ramsey, NJ; *U.S. Private*, pg. 813
Vilgrain, Jean-Louis, Chm. Bd. & Chief Exec. Officer--Cuisine Solutions, Inc., Alexandria, VA; *U.S. Public*, pg. 466
Villani, Edmond D., Pres. & Chief Exec. Officer--Scudder Kemper Investments, Inc., New York, NY; *Int'l*, pg. 1530
Villar, Salvador, Pres. & Chief Exec. Officer--California Commerce Bank, Los Angeles, CA; *Int'l*, pg. 574
Vincent, G., Chief Exec. Officer--P.T. Monier Indonesia, Jakarta, Indonesia; *Int'l*, pg. 1091
Vinciguerra, Salvatore J., Pres. & Chief Exec. Officer--Ferrofluidics Corporation, Nashua, NH; *U.S. Public*, pg. 620
Vinck, Karel, Chief Exec. Officer--Union Miniere, Brussels, Belgium; *Int'l*, pg. 1441
Vines, Roger A.G., Sir, Chm. Bd.--Alcoa of Australia Limited, Melbourne, Australia; *U.S. Public*, pg. 62
Vinsonneau, M., Chief Exec. Officer--OCE-France S.A., Noisy-le-Grand, France; *Int'l*, pg. 994
Vinum, Elvar, Deputy Chief Exec. Officer--Danisco A/S, Copenhagen, Denmark; *Int'l*, pg. 378
Vinyard, Lee E., Chief Oper. Officer--Intermatic Inc., Spring Grove, IL; *U.S. Private*, pg. 567
Viola, Ronald J., Pres. & Chief Exec. Officer--Rapid Power Technologies, Inc., Brookfield, CT; *U.S. Private*, pg. 910
Virolainen, Ossi, Vice Chm., Deputy Pres. & Deputy Chief Exec. Officer--Outokumpu Oyj, Espoo, Finland; *Int'l*, pg. 1015
Virtue, Robert A., Chm. Bd., Pres. & Chief Exec. Officer--Virco Mfg. Corporation, Torrance, CA; *U.S. Public*, pg. 1721
Vischer, Peter, Dr., Chief Exec. Officer--Heraeus Holding GmbH, Hanau, Germany; *Int'l*, pg. 615
Visentin, Maura, Chief Exec. Officer--Diadora America, Inc., Kent, WA; *U.S. Private*, pg. 330
Vitale, Alberto, Chm. Bd. & Chief Exec. Officer--Random House, Inc., New York, NY; *U.S. Private*, pg. 20
Vitito, Robert J., Pres. & Chief Exec. Officer--Citizens Banking Corporation, Flint, MI; *U.S. Public*, pg. 379
Vittorini, Carlo, Chm. Bd., Publisher, & Chief Exec. Officer--Parade Publications Inc., New York, NY; *U.S. Private*, pg. 20
Vittorini, Carlo, Chm. Bd., Publisher & Chief Exec. Officer--React Magazine, New York, NY; *U.S. Private*, pg. 20
Vituli, Alan, Chm. Bd. & Chief Exec. Officer--Carrols Corporation, Syracuse, NY; *U.S. Private*, pg. 216
Vitulli, Peter J., Chm. Bd. & Chief Exec. Officer--The O'Boise Corporation, Oak Brook, IL; *U.S. Private*, pg. 810
Viven, Paul, Chief Exec. Officer--Malaysian Tobacco Co./B.A.T. Indust., Kuala Lumpur, Malaysia; *Int'l*, pg. 111
Vives, Mauricio, Chief Exec. Officer--EURO RSCG Graffiti, Santiago, Chile; *Int'l*, pg. 603
Vodicka, Hermann, Chief Exec. Officer--Ciba Specialty Chemicals Holding Inc., Basel, Switzerland; *Int'l*, pg. 291
Voelker, Frank C., Chief Exec. Officer & Exec. V.P.--Celegec Automation Projects Inc., Macon, GA; *Int'l*, pg. 53
Voelker, Kenneth, Chief Exec. Officer--Mighty Distributing System, Norcross, GA; *U.S. Private*, pg. 745
Vogel, Michael J., Pres. & Chief Exec. Officer--Day-Timers of Canada, Limited, Niagara Falls, Canada; *U.S. Public*, pg. 674
Vogl, Alexander J., Chm. Bd. & Chief Exec. Officer--Wilton Corporation, Palatine, IL; *U.S. Private*, pg. 1181
Vogt, William, Pres. & Chief Exec. Officer--Springfield Precision Instruments, Inc., Wood Ridge, NJ; *U.S. Private*, pg. 1027
Vogtlander, Peter, Pres. & Chief Exec. Officer--Montell Polyolefins, Hoofddorp, Netherlands; *Int'l*, pg. 1136
Vohs, Dennis V., Chm. Bd. & Chief Exec. Officer--Ross Systems, Inc., Atlanta, GA; *U.S. Public*, pg. 1406
Voight, Randall L., Chief Exec. Officer--International Research & Evaluation, Eagan, MN; *U.S. Private*, pg. 571
Voigt, Gary, Pres. & Chief Exec. Officer--Arkansas Electric Cooperatives Inc., Little Rock, AR; *U.S. Private*, pg. 82
Vokos, T., Pres. & Chief Exec. Officer--Miller Freeman Asia Ltd, Wan Chai, Hong Kong; *Int'l*, pg. 1443
Volgenau, Ernst, Dr., Pres. & Chief Exec. Officer--SRA International Inc., Arlington, VA; *U.S. Private*, pg. 957
Volkema, Michael A., Chief Exec. Officer--Herman Miller, Inc., Zeeland, MI; *U.S. Public*, pg. 1111
Vollaro, John D., Pres. & Chief Exec. Officer--Signet Star Reinsurance Company, Florham Park, NJ; *U.S. Public*, pg. 216
Vollaro, John D., Pres. & Chief Exec. Officer--Signet Star Holdings, Inc., Stamford, CT; *U.S. Public*, pg. 216
Vollbracht, David E., Pres. & Chief Exec. Officer--Fleischer Manufacturing, Inc., Columbus, NE; *U.S. Private*, pg. 410
Vollrath, Walter III, Pres. & Chief Exec. Officer--Polar Ware Company, Sheboygan, WI; *U.S. Private*, pg. 873
Volny, Peter I., Pres., Chief Exec. Officer & New Bus. Contact--Griffin Bacal Volny, Toronto, Canada; *U.S. Private*, pg. 480
Volpara, Paolo, Chief Exec. Officer--Markom/Leo Burnett A.S., Istanbul, Turkey; *U.S. Private*, pg. 186
von Blomberg, Peter, Chief Exec. Officer--Allianz Versicherungs-AG, Cologne, Germany; *Int'l*, pg. 58
von Hornstein, Florian, Chief Exec. Officer--Serviceplan GmbH, Munich, Germany; *Int'l*, pg. 1225
von Matthiessen, Malte, Chm. Bd. & Chief Exec. Officer--YSI Incorporated, Yellow Springs, OH; *U.S. Private*, pg. 1195
von Minckwitz, Bernhard, Chm.-Exec. Committee--Bantam Doubleday Dell Publishing Group, Inc., New York, NY; *Int'l*, pg. 191
von Pierer, Heinrich, Dr., Pres. & Chief Exec. Officer--Siemens AG, Munich, Germany; *Int'l*, pg. 1244
von Rickenbach, Josef, Chm. Bd., Pres. & Chief Exec. Officer--PAREXEL International Corporation, Waltham, MA; *U.S. Public*, pg. 1257
von Rosenberg, Joseph L., Pres. & Chief Exec. Officer-Marine Gen. Corp--Zapata Corporation, Houston, TX; *U.S. Public*, pg. 1789
von Schack, Wesley W., Chm. Bd., Pres. & Chief Exec. Officer--New York State Electric & Gas Corporation, Binghamton, NY; *U.S. Public*, pg. 1173

von Schorlemer, Elmo Freiherr, Chief Exec. Officer--Aachener und Muenchener Versicherung Aktiengesellschaft, Aachen, Germany; *Int'l*, pg. 15

von Treskow, Hermann, Chief Exec. Officer--SCOR Deutschland, Hannover, Germany; *Int'l*, pg. 1153

von Wyss, Marc R., Pres. & Chief Exec. Officer--Holnam Inc. (West Division), Lakewood, CO; *Int'l*, pg. 628

Von Zuben, Fred G., Pres. & Chief Exec. Officer--The Newark Group, Inc., Cranford, NJ; *U.S. Private*, pg. 796

Vora, Ravi, Chief Exec. Officer--Bundy India Ltd., Baroda, India; *Int'l*, pg. 1341

Vortmann, R.H., Pres. & Chief Exec. Officer--National Steel & Shipbuilding Company, San Diego, CA; *U.S. Private*, pg. 787

Vosburg, N.E., Pres. & Chief Exec. Officer--Pacific Hide & Fur Depot, Great Falls, MT; *U.S. Private*, pg. 831

Voscherau, Eggert, Pres. & Chief Exec. Officer--BASF Corporation, Mount Olive, NJ; *Int'l*, pg. 105

Vosloo, M.H., Grp. Chief Exec.--Standard Bank Investment Corporation Limited, Johannesburg, South Africa; *Int'l*, pg. 1293

Voss, Dr. Gerd, Chief Exec. Officer & Mng. Dir.--Pfleiderer Industrie GmbH Wirus-Werke Guetersloh, Gutersloh, Germany; *Int'l*, pg. 1047

Voss, Michael, Pres. & Chief Exec. Officer--BVK/McDonald, Milwaukee, WI; *U.S. Private*, pg. 108

Voss, Michael, Chief Exec. Officer--BVK/McDonald, Cape Coral, FL; *U.S. Private*, pg. 108

Voss, Michael, Chief Exec. Officer--Mark Net World, Mequon, WI; *U.S. Private*, pg. 108

Voss, Peter S., Chief Exec. Officer--Hoare Govett Limited, London, United Kingdom; *U.S. Public*, pg. 183

Voss, Peter S., Pres. & Chief Exec. Officer--New England Investment Companies, Inc., Boston, MA; *U.S. Private*, pg. 737

Votel, Richard H., Pres. & Chief Exec. Officer--First American Insurance Agencies, Inc., Saint Paul, MN; *U.S.* Private, pg. 167

Vowell, J. Larry, Corp. V.P., Pres. & Chief Exec. Officer-Hussmann Corp.--Whitman Corporation, Rolling Meadows, IL; *U.S. Public*, pg. 1766

Vowell, J. Larry, Pres. & Chief Exec. Officer--Hussmann Corp., Bridgeton, MO; *U.S. Public*, pg. 1766

Vucins, Viesturs, Pres. & Chief Exec. Officer--Global One, Reston, VA; *U.S. Public*, pg. 1501

Vukadinovic, Borivoje, Pres. & Chief Exec. Officer--Retrospettiva, Inc., Beverly Hills, CA; *U.S. Public*, pg. 1383

Vukelich, Michael F., Chief Exec. Officer--Color Spot Nursery, Inc., Pleasant Hill, CA; *U.S. Private*, pg. 254

Vullings, Jaque T.H., Pres. & Chief Exec. Officer--TA Triumph-Adler Vertriebs GmbH, Nuremberg, Germany; *Int'l*, pg. 1004

Vuori, Kari, Chief Oper. Officer--Nummela Plant, Nummela, Finland; *Int'l*, pg. 863

Vyas, C.B., Pres. & Chief Exec. Officer--Zeigler Coal Holding Company, Fairview Heights, IL; *U.S. Public*, pg. 1790

Vyas, Meeta, Vice Chm. & Chief Exec. Officer--Signature Brands USA, Inc., Solon, OH; *U.S. Public*, pg. 1472

Wachi, Takashi, Pres. & Chief Exec. Officer--Terumo Corporation, Tokyo, Japan; *Int'l*, pg. 1375

Wachner, Linda J., Chm. Bd. & Chief Exec. Officer--Authentic Fitness Corp., Los Angeles, CA; *U.S. Public*, pg. 147

Wachner, Linda J., Chm. Bd., Pres. & Chief Exec. Officer--Warnaco Inc., New York, NY; *U.S. Public*, pg. 1738

Wachstein, Barbara, Pres. & Chief Exec. Officer--Great Lakes Realty Corp., Livonia, MI; *U.S. Private*, pg. 475

Wackenhut, George R., Chm. Bd. & Chief Exec. Officer--The Wackenhut Corporation, Palm Beach Gardens, FL; *U.S. Public*, pg. 1731

Waddell, Robert F., Chm. Bd. & Chief Exec. Officer--Standard Locknut, Inc., Westfield, IN; *U.S. Private*, pg. 1031

Wade, William S., Jr., Pres. & Chief Exec. Officer--FAG Bearings Corporation, Danbury, CT; *Int'l*, pg. 469

Wadsworth, Stanley, Pres. & Chief Exec. Officer--Golf Hosts, Inc., Palm Harbor, FL; *U.S. Private*, pg. 1036

Wagenhals, Fred W., Chm. Bd., Pres. & Chief Exec. Officer--Action Performance Companies, Inc., Phoenix, AZ; *U.S. Public*, pg. 17

Waggerman, Eugene S., Chief Exec. Officer--Perkins-Goodwin Co. Inc., Stamford, CT; *Int'l*, pg. 586

Wagner, Dan, Chief Exec.--The Dialog Corporation plc, London, United Kingdom; *Int'l*, pg. 412

Wagner, David J., Chm. Bd., Pres. & Chief Exec. Officer--Old Kent Financial Corporation, Grand Rapids, MI; *U.S. Public*, pg. 1216

Wagner, Harold A., Chm. Bd., Pres. & Chief Exec. Officer--Air Products and Chemicals, Inc., Allentown, PA; *U.S. Public*, pg. 30

Wagner, Matthew P., Pres. & Chief Exec. Officer--Western Bancorp, Newport Beach, CA; *U.S. Public*, pg. 1757

Wagner, Tom, Pres. & Chief Exec. Officer--Jones Blair Company, Dallas, TX; *U.S. Private*, pg. 596

Wagstaff, David, 111, 2res. & Chief Exec. Officer--Vectura Group, Inc., New Orleans, LA; *U.S. Private*, pg. 1135

Wahl, John F., Chief Exec. Officer--Wahl Clipper Corp., Sterling, IL; *U.S. Private*, pg. 1146

Wahl, Michael, Chm. Bd., & Chief Exec. Officer--H.M.G. Worldwide Corp., New York, NY; *U.S. Public*, pg. 771

Wahle, Elliott, Pres. & Chief Exec. Officer--Dylex Limited, Toronto, Canada; *Int'l*, pg. 425

Wahle, John L., Jr., Chm. Bd. & Chief Exec. Officer--The Genesee Brewing Company, Inc., Rochester, NY; *U.S. Public*, pg. 728

Waitt, Ted, Chm. Bd. & Chief Exec. Officer--Gateway 2000, North Sioux City, SD; *U.S. Public*, pg. 703

Wakahara, Yasuyuki, Chm. Bd. & Chief Exec. Officer--Asahi Mutual Life Insurance Company, Tokyo, Japan; *Int'l*, pg. 85

Wake, John, Pres. & Chief Exec. Officer--Western States Machine Company, Hamilton, OH; *U.S. Private*, pg. 1168

Wakeley, M.J., Chm. Bd. & Chief Exec. Officer--Jardine Insurance Brokers Ltd., London, United Kingdom; *Int'l*, pg. 705

Walburn, H. Fred, Pres. & Chief Exec. Officer--Regions Bank/Sumter County, Livingston, AL; *U.S. Public*, pg. 1373

Walcher, Jack, Chm. Bd. & Chief Exec. Officer--Eddins-Walcher Company, Midland, TX; *U.S. Private*, pg. 362

Waldenvik, A., Chief Exec. Officer--Zurich Forsakring, Stockholm, Sweden; *Int'l*, pg. 1531

Waldin, Thomas B., Pres. & Chief Exec. Officer--Essef Corporation, Chardon, OH; *U.S. Public*, pg. 592

Waldner, Stephen, Chm. Bd. & Chief Exec. Officer--D. Waldner Company, Inc., Farmingdale, NY; *U.S. Private*, pg. 1147

Waldron, William G., Chm. Bd. & Chief Exec. Officer--J.E. Goold & Company, Portland, ME; *U.S. Public*, pg. 229

Waldrop, Richard E., Pres., Chief Oper. Officer & V.P.-Sls.--Edwards Engineering Corporation, Pompton Plains, NJ; *U.S. Private*, pg. 365

Waldschurz, Gerhard, Chm. Bd., Pres. & Chief Exec. Officer--Optimaxx International, Rockleigh, NJ; *U.S. Private*, pg. 818

Walgenbach, Ewald, Deputy Chief Exec. Officer & Exec. V.P.-TV--CLT-UFA, Luxembourg, Luxembourg; *Int'l*, pg. 561

Walgreen, Charles R., III, Chm. Bd. & Chief Exec. Officer--Walgreen Co., Deerfield, IL; *U.S. Public*, pg. 1733

Walker, Andrew J., Chief Exec.--McKechnie PLC, Walsall, United Kingdom; *Int'l*, pg. 851

Walker, C. Denny, Pres. & Chief Exec. Officer--Draper Texmaco, Inc., Spartanburg, SC; *U.S. Private*, pg. 342

Walker, Cliff, Chief Exec. Officer--Brunel Holdings Plc, Chippenham, United Kingdom; *Int'l*, pg. 230

Walker, Donald, Pres.& Chief Exec. Officer--Magna International Inc., Markham, Canada; *Int'l*, pg. 829

Walker, Doug, Pres. & Chief Exec. Officer--WRQ, Inc., Seattle, WA; *U.S. Private*, pg. 1145

Walker, I., Chief Exec. Officer--Redland Stone Products Co., San Antonio, TX; *Int'l*, pg. 1091

Walker, Joseph P., Chm. Bd., Pres. & Chief Exec. Officer--CTS Corporation, Elkhart, IN; *U.S. Public*, pg. 285

Walker, K. Grahame, Chm. Bd. & Chief Exec. Officer--The Dexter Corporation, Windsor Locks, CT; *U.S. Public*, pg. 504

Walker, K.D., Pres. & Chief Exec. Officer--Meineke Discount Muffler Shops, Inc., Charlotte, NC; *Int'l*, pg. 535

Walker, M. Chris, Chief Exec. Officer--Walker & Associates, Inc., Welcome, NC; *U.S. Private*, pg. 1147

Walker, Malcolm C., Chm. Bd. & Chief Exec. Officer--Iceland Group plc, Deeside, United Kingdom; *Int'l*, pg. 658

Walker, Martin J., Chm. Bd & Chief Exec. Officer--Society Asset Mgmt., Inc., Cleveland, OH; *U.S. Public*, pg. 955

Walker, Michael R., Chm. Bd. & Chief Exec. Officer--Genesis Health Ventures, Inc., Kennett Square, PA; *U.S.* Public, pg. 728

Walker, Steven C., Pres. & Chief Exec. Officer--Cand Investments Inc., Shreveport, LA; *U.S. Public*, pg. 501

Wall, C.J., Chief Exec. Officer--Vittinge Tegel AB, Morgongava, Sweden; *Int'l*, pg. 1092

Wall, Jack, Pres.--Al Larson Boat Shop, Inc., Terminal Island, CA; *U.S. Private*, pg. 652

Wall, John R., Pres. & Chief Exec. Officer--Wall Data Incorporated, Kirkland, WA; *U.S. Public*, pg. 1734

Wall, Kay D., Chief Exec. Officer, Treas. & Sec.--Bryant Electric Company, Inc., High Point, NC; *U.S. Private*, pg. 176

Wall, Terrence D., Chm. Bd., Pres. & Chief Exec. Officer--Vital Signs, Inc., Totowa, NJ; *U.S. Public*, pg. 1723

Wallace, Carol P., Pres. & Chief Exec. Officer--Cooper Instrument Corp., Middlefield, CT; *U.S. Private*, pg. 274

Wallace, George, Chief Exec. Officer--Clark Boardman Company, Ltd., New York, NY; *U.S. Public*, pg. 1602

Wallace, Graham, Cheif Exec.--Cable & Wireless Communications plc, London, United Kingdom; *Int'l*, pg. 115

Wallace, Graham, Cheif Exec.--Cable & Wireless Communications plc, London, United Kingdom; *U.S. Public*, pg. 203

Wallace, Graham, Cheif Exec.--Cable & Wireless Communications plc, London, United Kingdom; *Int'l*, pg. 247

Wallace, J. Keith, Pres. & Chief Exec. Officer-Showboat Indiana, Inc.--Showboat, Incorporated, Las Vegas, NV; *U.S. Public*, pg. 1469

Wallace, James D., Pres. & Chief Exec. Officer--National Travelers Life Co., West Des Moines, IA; *U.S. Private*, pg. 787

Wallace, James E., Pres. & Chief Exec. Officer--Hamilton, Allen & Associates, Inc, Atlanta, GA; *U.S. Public*, pg. 1673

Wallace, John D., Chm. Bd. & Chief Exec. Officer--New Jersey National Bank, Pennington, NJ; *U.S. Public*, pg. 447

Wallace, Kevin, Pres. & Chief Exec. Officer--Thermo Separation Products, San Jose, CA; *U.S. Public*, pg. 1594

Wallace, Timothy, Chief Exec. Officer-XL Connect--Intelligent Electronics, Inc., Exton, PA; *U.S. Public*, pg. 887

Wallace, W. Ray, Chm. Bd., Pres. & Chief Exec. Officer--Trinity Industries Inc., Dallas, TX; *U.S. Public*, pg. 1638

Wallach, James, Pres. & Chief Exec. Officer--Central National-Gottesman Inc., Purchase, NY; *U.S. Private*, pg. 224

Wallack, Al, Pres. & Chief Exec. Officer--Royal Olympic Cruises, New York, NY; *U.S. Public*, pg. 1411

Wallbridge, Van, Chm. Bd., Pres. & Chief Exec. Officer--Mobil Tool International, Westminster, CO; *Int'l*, pg. 1486

Waller, Jim, Chm. Bd. & Chief Exec. Officer--Ithaca Industries, Inc., Wilkesboro, NC; *U.S. Private*, pg. 576

Waller, Joel N., Chm. Bd. & Chief Exec. Officer--Wilsons The Leather Experts Inc., Brooklyn Park, MN; *U.S. Private*, pg. 1181

Waller, Michael E., Chief Exec. Officer & Publisher--The Hartford Courant Company, Hartford, CT; *U.S. Public*, pg. 1616

Wallner, Edgar, Pres. & Chief Exec. Officer--Orthofix International N.V., Curacao, Netherlands Antilles; *Int'l*, pg. 1011

Wallner, M., Chief Exec. Officer--Schiedel Kaminwerke GmbH, Wartberg, Austria; *Int'l*, pg. 1092

Walsh, G., Pres. & Chief Exec. Officer--Pratt & Whitney, Grand Prairie, TX; *U.S. Public*, pg. 1690

Walsh, Joseph A., Pres., Chief Exec. Officer & Sls. Dir.--Multi-Local Media Corporation, Rockville Centre, NY; *U.S. Private*, pg. 767

Walsh, Michael, Chief Exec. Officer-O&M Europe--Ogilvy & Mather Worldwide, Inc., New York, NY; *Int'l*, pg. 1483

Walsh, Michael J., Pres. & Chief Exec. Officer--Tandycrafts, Inc., Fort Worth, TX; *U.S. Public*, pg. 1561

Walsh, Paul S., Chief Exec. Officer-Pillsbury--Grand Metropolitan Plc, London, United Kingdom; *Int'l*, pg. 408

Walsh, Steve, Chm. Bd. & Chief Exec. Officer--Signal Apparel Company, Inc., Chattanooga, TN; *U.S. Public*, pg. 1472

Walske, Steven C., Chm. Bd.--Parametric Technology Corporation, Waltham, MA; *U.S. Public*, pg. 1257

Walston, Robert, Chief Exec. Officer--Four Media Companies, Burbank, CA; *U.S. Private*, pg. 422

Walsworth, Don O., Pres. & Chief Exec. Officer--Walsworth Publishing Company, Inc., Marceline, MO; *U.S. Private*, pg. 1148

Walter, Frank, Pres. & Chief Exec. Officer--Bank One, Chicago, Chicago, IL; *U.S. Public*, pg. 173

Walter, John A., Pres. & Chief Exec. Officer--The Gorman-Rupp Company, Mansfield, OH; *U.S. Public*, pg. 754

Walter, Luta, Chief Exec. Officer--Mueller's Muehle GmbH, Gelsenkirchen, Germany; *Int'l*, pg. 896

Walter, Manfred, Chm. Bd. & Chief Exec. Officer--Traub-Hermle Corporation, Menomonee Falls, WI; *Int'l*, pg. 1419

Walter, Paul F., Chm. Bd., Pres. & Chief Exec. Officer--Thermo Electric Co., Inc., Saddle Brook, NJ; *U.S. Private*, pg. 1080

Walter, Richard A., Chm. Bd. & Chief Exec. Officer--Scicom Data Services, Ltd., Minnetonka, MN; *U.S. Private*, pg. 975

Walter, Robert D., Chm. Bd. & Chief Exec. Officer--Cardinal Health Inc., Dublin, OH; *U.S. Public*, pg. 304

Walters, Charles D., Chm. Bd. & Chief Exec. Officer--World Acceptance Corporation, Greenville, SC; *U.S. Public*, pg. 1778

Walters, Keith, Vice Chm. & Chief Exec. Officer--Ennis Business Forms, Inc., Ennis, TX; *U.S. Public*, pg. 583

Walters, Paul S., Chm. Bd. & Chief Exec. Officer--Sears Canada, Inc., Toronto, Canada; *U.S. Public*, pg. 1452

Walton, James H., Chm. Bd. & Chief Exec. Officer--ITC Learning Corp., Herndon, VA; *U.S. Public*, pg. 859

Walton, William, Chm. Bd. & Chief Exec. Officer--Allied Capital Corporation, Washington, DC; *U.S. Public*, pg. 47

Waltrip, Robert L., Chm. Bd. & Chief Exec. Officer--Service Corporation International, Houston, TX; *U.S. Public*, pg. 1460

Wamhoff, Richard H., Pres. & Chief Exec. Officer--Ore-Ida Foods, Inc., Boise, ID; *U.S. Public*, pg. 805

Wandel, Albrecht, Pres. & Chief Exec. Officer--Wandel & Goltermann GmbH & Co., Elektronische Messtechnik, Eningen, Germany; *Int'l*, pg. 1485

Wang, Ch. C.T., Chief Exec. Officer--Malayan Overseas Insurance Corporation, Taipei, Taiwan; *Int'l*, pg. 1532

Wang, Charles B., Chm. Bd. & Chief Exec. Officer--Computer Associates International, Inc., Islandia, NY; *U.S. Public*, pg. 420

Wang, Charles B., Chm. Bd. & Chief Exec. Officer--Cheyenne, Roslyn Heights, NY; *U.S. Public*, pg. 420

Wang, Charles B., Chm. Bd. & Chief Exec. Officer--ACCPAC International, Santa Clara, CA; *U.S. Public*, pg. 420

Wang, Charles B., Chm. Bd. & Chief Exec. Officer--Acacia Technologies, Lisle, IL; *U.S. Public*, pg. 420

Wang, Charles B., Chm. Bd. & Chief Exec. Officer--NetHaven, Islandia, NY; *U.S. Public*, pg. 420

Wang, Charles B., Chm. Bd. & Chief Exec. Officer--Computer Associates International, Inc., Islandia, NY; *U.S. Public*, pg. 420

Wang, Charles B., Chm. Bd. & Chief Exec. Officer--MK Group, Islandia, NY; *U.S. Public*, pg. 420

Wang, Charles B., Chm. Bd. & Chief Exec. Officer--Infresco Corporation, Sarasota, FL; *U.S. Public*, pg. 420

Wanglee, Vorawee, Chief Exec. Officer--Nakornthon Bank Public Company Limited, Bangkok, Thailand; *Int'l*, pg. 904

Wanless, D., Grp. Chief Exec. Officer--National Westminster Bank PLC, London, United Kingdom; *Int'l*, pg. 910

Ward, Brian P., Pres., Chief Exec. Officer & Treas.--Cortland Line Co., Inc., Cortland, NY; *U.S. Private*, pg. 277

Ward, D. Les, Pres. & Chief Exec. Officer--Source Services Corporation, Dallas, TX; *U.S. Public*, pg. 1488

Ward, David K., Pres.--Ward Trucking Corp., Altoona, PA; *U.S. Private*, pg. 1149

Ward, John, Chm. Bd. & Chief Exec. Officer--American Express Bank Ltd., New York, NY; *U.S. Public*, pg. 73

Ward, Michael, Chief Exec.--AAH plc, Runcorn, United Kingdom; *Int'l*, pg. 591

Ward, Milton H., Chm. Bd., Pres. & Chief Exec. Officer--Cyprus Amax Minerals Company, Englewood, CO; *U.S. Public*, pg. 470

Ward, Milton H., Chm. Bd. & Chief Exec. Officer--Amax Gold Inc., Englewood, CO; *U.S. Public*, pg. 470

Ward, Thomas S., Pres. & Oper. Exec. Officer--Russell Stover Candies, Inc., Kansas City, MO; *U.S. Private*, pg. 953

Wardeberg, George E., Chm. Bd. & Chief Exec. Officer--WICOR, Inc., Milwaukee, WI; *U.S. Public*, pg. 1767
Wardeberg, George E., Chm. Bd.--Hypro Corporation, New Brighton, MN; *U.S. Public*, pg. 1767
Wardrop, Richard, Chm. Bd., Pres. & Chief Exec. Officer--AK Steel Corporation, Middletown, OH; *U.S. Public*, pg. 7
Ware, Dennert O., Pres. & Chief Exec. Officer--Corange U.S. Holdings, Inc, Indianapolis, IN; *Int'l*, pg. 331
Warehime, John A., Chm. Bd., Pres. & Chief Exec. Officer--Hanover Foods Corporation, Hanover, PA; *U.S. Private*, pg. 499
Warehime, John A., Chief Exec. Officer--Hanover Foods Corp., Lancaster, PA; *U.S. Private*, pg. 499
Waring, Saul, Pres. & Co-Chief Exec. Officer--Waring & LaRosa, Inc., New York, NY; *U.S. Private*, pg. 1150
Warn, Michael T., Pres. & Chief Exec. Officer--Warn Industries, Inc., Clackamas, OR; *U.S. Private*, pg. 1150
Warner, Douglas A., III, Chm. Bd. & Chief Exec. Officer--J.P. Morgan Co. Incorporated, New York, NY; *U.S. Public*, pg. 1129
Warner, N.W., Chief Exec. Officer--Chloride Group PLC, London, United Kingdom; *Int'l*, pg. 287
Warnock, John E., Chm. & Chief Exec. Officer--Adobe Systems Incorporated, San Jose, CA; *U.S. Public*, pg. 20
Warren, James R., Pres. & Chief Exec. Officer--Cameron & Barkley Company, Charleston, SC; *U.S. Private*, pg. 203
Warren, John C., Chm. Bd., Pres. & Chief Exec. Officer--Washington Trust Bancorp, Inc., Westerly, RI; *U.S. Public*, pg. 1744
Warren, John C., Pres. & Chief Exec. Officer--The Washington Trust Company, Westerly, RI; *U.S. Public*, pg. 1744
Warren, Robert C., Jr., Pres. & Chief Exec. Officer--Cascade Corporation, Troutdale, OR; *U.S. Public*, pg. 310
Warren, Robert S., Jr., Chief Exec Officer--Warren Distributing Corp., Raleigh, NC; *U.S. Private*, pg. 1151
Warren, Terry W., Pres. & Chief Exec. Officer--MedTrac, Inc., Nashville, TN; *Int'l*, pg. 1504
Warren, Wm. Michael, Jr., Pres. & Chief Exec. Officer--Energen Corporation, Birmingham, AL; *U.S. Public*, pg. 581
Warren, Wm. Michael, Jr., Chief Exec. Officer--Taurus Exploration, Inc., Birmingham, AL; *U.S. Public*, pg. 581
Warrilow, Clive B., Pres. & Chief Exec. Officer--Volkswagen of America, Inc., Auburn Hills, MI; *Int'l*, pg. 1474
Warrington, Clayton L., Pres. & Chief Exec. Officer--Dugan/Farley Communications, Upper Saddle River, NJ; *U.S. Public*, pg. 1642
Washington, R. Peter, Chm. Bd. & Chief Exec. Officer--L & D Group, Aurora, IL; *U.S. Private*, pg. 638
Washington, R. Peter, Chm. Bd. & Chief Exec. Officer--Lyon Metal Products, Inc., Montgomery, IL; *U.S. Private*, pg. 638
Wass, Tom, Chm. & Chief Exec. Officer--Tequila UK Ltd., London, United Kingdom; *Int'l*, pg. 118
Wassarman, Elliot, Pres. & Chief Exec. Officer--Mitek Systems, Inc., San Diego, CA; *U.S. Public*, pg. 1117
Wassen, W. J., Chief Exec.--DSM Engineering Plastic Products, Zaventem, Belgium; *Int'l*, pg. 354
Wasserman, Martin, Dr., Chief Exec. Officer--Raschig GmbH, Ludwigshafen, Germany; *U.S. Private*, pg. 827
Wasserman, Stephen, Pres. & Chief Exec. Officer--National Bank of Hastings, Hastings, MI; *U.S. Public*, pg. 633
Wasserstrom, Rodney, Pres. & Chief Exec. Officer--Wasserstrom Company, Columbus, OH; *U.S. Private*, pg. 1152
Wassman, Ernie, Pres. & Chief Exec. Officer--Tecmar Technologies, Inc., Longmont, CO; *Int'l*, pg. 1361
Wassong, D.K., Chm. Bd., Pres. & Chief Exec. Officer--Sally Hansen, Farmingdale, NY; *U.S. Public*, pg. 494
Wassong, Dan K., Chm. Bd., Pres. & Chief Exec. Officer--Del Laboratories, Inc., Farmingdale, NY; *U.S. Public*, pg. 494
Watanabe, Haruro, Chm. Bd. & Chief Exec. Officer--Marubeni America Corporation, New York, NY; *Int'l*, pg. 844
Waterfield, Harry Lee II, Chm. Bd., Pres. & Chief Exec. Officer--Kentucky Investors, Inc., Frankfort, KY; *U.S. Public*, pg. 951
Waterfield, Patrick, Pres. & Chief Exec. Officer--Guerlain, Inc., New York, NY; *Int'l*, pg. 780
Waters, Warner S., Jr., Chm., Pres. & Chief Exec. Officer--Mellon Bank (DE) National Association, Wilmington, DE; *U.S. Public*, pg. 1085
Watkins, Alan, Chief Exec. Officer--Senior Engineering Group, plc., Rickmansworth, United Kingdom; *Int'l*, pg. 1220
Watkins, Edward G., Chm. Bd., Pres. & Chief Exec. Officer--Simplex Time Recorder Co., Gardner, MA; *U.S. Private*, pg. 1002
Watkins, Lee, Chm. Bd. & Chief Exec. Officer--SouthTrust Bank of Marion County, Hamilton, AL; *U.S. Public*, pg. 1492
Watsa, V. Prem, Chm. Bd. & Chief Exec. Officer--Fairfax Financial Holdings Limited, Toronto, Canada; *Int'l*, pg. 476
Watson, Chuck, Chm. Bd. & Chief Exec. Officer--NGC Corporation, Houston, TX; *U.S. Public*, pg. 1146
Watson, Colin D., Pres. & Chief Exec. Officer--Spar Aerospace Limited, Toronto, Canada; *Int'l*, pg. 1287
Watson, Donald K., Pres. & Chief Exec. Officer--Griffin Envelope, Inc., Seattle, WA; *U.S. Public*, pg. 1038
Watson, Donald K., Pres. & Chief Exec. Officer--Emerald Warehouse & Distribution Services, Seattle, WA; *U.S. Public*, pg. 1038
Watson, George W., Pres. & Chief Exec. Officer--Transcanada Pipelines Limited, Calgary, Canada; *Int'l*, pg. 1416
Watson, J.H., Chm., Pres. & Chief Exec. Officer--Confed Investment Counselling Limited, Toronto, Canada; *Int'l*, pg. 325
Watson, Jack O., Pres. & Chief Exec. Officer--Stanback Company, Salisbury, NC; *U.S. Private*, pg. 1030
Watson, John C., Chm. Bd., Pres. & Chief Exec. Officer--NACOLAH Holding Corp. Inc., Chicago, IL; *U.S. Private*, pg. 963
Watson, L., Chief Exec.-Protection--MLC Limited, Sydney, Australia; *Int'l*, pg. 806
Watson, Max P., Jr., Chm. Bd., Pres. & Chief Exec. Officer--BMC Software, Inc., Houston, TX; *U.S. Public*, pg. 162
Watson, Noel G., Pres. & Chief Exec. Officer--Jacobs Engineering Group Inc., Pasadena, CA; *U.S. Public*, pg. 921
Watson, Stephen, Pres. & Chief Exec. Officer--Gander Mountain Retail, Bloomington, MN; *U.S. Private*, pg. 534
Watson, William B., Pres. & Chief Exec. Officer--SouthTrust Bank, Hartselle, Decatur, AL; *U.S. Public*, pg. 1491
Watt, James W., Pres.--Watt Publishing Co., Mount Morris, IL; *U.S. Private*, pg. 1154
Wattelet, Paul L., Chm. Bd. & Chief Exec. Officer--Sargent & Lundy, Chicago, IL; *U.S. Private*, pg. 965
Watterson, Scott R., Chief Exec. Officer--Icon Health & Fitness, Inc., Logan, UT; *U.S. Private*, pg. 556
Wattles, Mark, Chief Exec. Officer--Hollywood Entertainment Corp., Wilsonville, OR; *U.S. Private*, pg. 535
Watts, Carl S., Pres. & Chief Exec. Officer--Tasty Baking Company, Philadelphia, PA; *U.S. Public*, pg. 1561
Watts, David H., Pres. & Chief Exec. Officer--Granite Construction Incorporated, Watsonville, CA; *U.S. Public*, pg. 759
Watts, William E., Pres. & Chief Exec. Officer--General Nutrition, Inc., Pittsburgh, PA; *U.S. Public*, pg. 725
Wattz, Carl S., Pres. & Chief Exec. Officer--TBC Financial Services, Philadelphia, PA; *U.S. Public*, pg. 1561
Waxman, Armond, Pres., Co-Chief Exec. Officer & Treas.--Waxman Industries, Inc., Bedford, OH; *U.S. Public*, pg. 1748
Waxman, Armond, Co-Chief Exec. Officer--TWI International, Inc., Cleveland, OH; *U.S. Public*, pg. 1749
Waxman, Melvin, Chm. Bd. & Co-Chief Exec. Officer--Waxman Industries, Inc., Bedford, OH; *U.S. Public*, pg. 1748
Waxman, Melvin, Chm. Bd. & Co-Chief Exec. Officer--WOC Inc., Bedford, OH; *U.S. Public*, pg. 1748
Way, Charles D., Chm. Bd., Pres. & Chief Exec. Officer--Ryan's Family Steak Houses, Inc., Greer, SC; *U.S. Public*, pg. 1413
Way, Kenneth L., Chm. Bd. & Chief Exec. Officer--Lear Corporation, Southfield, MI; *U.S. Public*, pg. 981
Weatherall, Percy, Chief Exec. Officer--Hongkong Land Holdings Limited, Hamilton, Bermuda; *Int'l*, pg. 704
Weatherup, Craig, Chm. Bd. & Chief Exec. Officer--Pepsi-Cola Company, Somers, NY; *U.S. Public*, pg. 1277
Weaver, Charles S., Pres. & Chief Exec. Officer--Peerless Pottery, Inc., Rockport, IN; *U.S. Private*, pg. 847
Weaver, John C., Exec. V.P. & Chm. Bd. & Chief Exec. Officer-Raytheon Intl., Inc.--Raytheon Company, Lexington, MA; *U.S. Public*, pg. 1364
Weaver, Michael E., Pres., Chief Exec. Officer & Chief Oper. Officer--Weaver Popcorn Company, Inc., Van Buren, IN; *U.S. Private*, pg. 1156
Weaver, Richard T., Chief Exec. & Fin. Officer, Treas. & Sec.--Hamburg Brothers, Pittsburgh, PA; *U.S. Private*, pg. 497
Weaver, Robert, Pres. & Chief Exec. Officer--P.A.M. Transport, Inc., Tontitown, AR; *U.S. Private*, pg. 825
Web, Tony A., Pres. & Chief Exec. Officer--Trust Corporation of Canada, Toronto, Canada; *Int'l*, pg. 1131
Webb, Barrie P., Chm. & Chief Exec. Officer--R.P. Scherer Holdings Pty. Ltd., Braeside, Australia; *U.S. Public*, pg. 1438
Webb, Dennis, Chief Exec. Officer--Beazer Group Plc, Bath, United Kingdom; *Int'l*, pg. 181
Webb, George H., Chm. Bd., Pres. & Chief Exec. Officer--Jervis B. Webb Company, Farmington Hills, MI; *U.S. Private*, pg. 1156
Webb, J.J., Pres. & Chief Exec. Officer--Atlantic Steel Industries, Inc., Atlanta, GA; *Int'l*, pg. 696
Webb, Jeffrey G., Pres. & Chief Exec. Officer--Varsity Spirit Corporation, Memphis, TN; *U.S. Public*, pg. 1389
Webb, R.M., Pres. & Chief Exec. Officer--Webb, Murray & Associates, Houston, TX; *U.S. Private*, pg. 1157
Webb, Timothy J., Chief Exec. Officer--Standard Register-Barrington, Barrington, IL; *U.S. Public*, pg. 1505
Webb, William H., Pres. & Chief Exec. Officer--Philip Morris International Inc., Rye Brook, NY; *U.S. Public*, pg. 1289
Webber, Randall M., Chm. Bd. & Chief Exec. Officer--Humphrey Products Company, Kalamazoo, MI; *U.S. Private*, pg. 547
Webber, Ruby, Pres. & Chief Exec. Officer--Contempo Colors, Kalamazoo, MI; *U.S. Private*, pg. 267
Weber, Alfred, Chm. Bd., Pres. & Chief Exec. Officer--C&D Charter Power Systems, Blue Bell, PA; *U.S. Public*, pg. 271
Weber, Alfred, Chm. Bd., Pres. & Chief Exec. Officer--C & D Technologies, Inc., Blue Bell, PA; *U.S. Public*, pg. 272
Weber, Joseph, Chief Exec. Officer--Caravan Products Company, Inc., Totowa, NJ; *U.S. Private*, pg. 208
Weber, Joseph A., Jr., Chm. Bd. Chief Exec. Officer--Weber Marking Systems, Inc., Arlington Heights, IL; *U.S. Private*, pg. 1157
Weber, Jurgen, Chm.-Exec. Bd. & Chief Exec. Officer--Deutsche Lufthansa AG, Cologne, Germany; *Int'l*, pg. 407
Weber, Larry, Chm. Bd. & Chief Exec. Officer--Drug Emporium of Arizona, Scottsdale, AZ; *U.S. Private*, pg. 343
Weber, Larry, Chm. & Chief Exec. Officer--Weber Public Relations Worldwide, Cambridge, MA; *U.S. Private*, pg. 1157
Webster, George K., Pres. & Chief Exec. Officer--Miltope Group, Inc., Hope Hull, AL; *U.S. Public*, pg. 1114
Webster, George K., Pres. & Chief Exec. Officer--Miltope Corporation, Montgomery, AL; *U.S. Public*, pg. 1114
Webster, Mark, Chief Exec. Officer, Chief Fin. Officer & Gen. Counsel--Heritage Co-op, Rushville, IN; *U.S. Private*, pg. 524
Webster, Steven A., Pres. & Chief Exec. Officer--R&B Falcon Corporation, Houston, TX; *U.S. Public*, pg. 1354
Webster, Timothy S., Pres. & Chief Exec. Officer--American Italian Pasta Company, Excelsior Springs, MO; *U.S. Public*, pg. 85
Wechsler, Bradley J., Chm. Bd. & Co-Chief Exec. Officer--Imax Corporation, Mississauga, Canada; *Int'l*, pg. 661
Wedel, Jan, Chief Exec. Officer--Stolper-Fabralloy Co. LLC, Brookfield, WI; *U.S. Public*, pg. 1640
Weed, Mark A., Pres. & Chief Exec. Officer--Fisher Properties Inc., Seattle, WA; *U.S. Public*, pg. 648
Weeder, Charles E., Chm. Bd., Pres. & Chief Exec. Officer--Homes of Merit Inc., Bartow, FL; *U.S. Private*, pg. 537
Weekley, David, Chief Exec. Officer--David Weekley Homes, Houston, TX; *U.S. Private*, pg. 1158
Weekly, John W., Vice Chm. & Chief Exec. Officer--Mutual of Omaha Insurance Company, Omaha, NE; *U.S. Private*, pg. 769
Weekly, John W., Vice Chm. & Chief Exec. Officer--United of Omaha Life Insurance Company, Omaha, NE; *U.S. Private*, pg. 770
Weeks, Ralph W., Pres. & Chief Exec. Officer--Quality Petroleum Corp., Lakeland, FL; *U.S. Private*, pg. 899
Wegner, Arthur E., Exec. V.P., Chm. Bd. & Chief Exec. Officer-Raytheon Aircraft Co.--Raytheon Company, Lexington, MA; *U.S. Public*, pg. 1364
Wegner, Hellmut, Pres. & Chief Exec. Officer--GIW Industries, Inc., Grovetown, GA; *Int'l*, pg. 721
Wehle, John L., Jr., Chm. Bd. & Chief Exec. Officer--Genesee Corporation, Rochester, NY; *U.S. Public*, pg. 728
Wehmeier, Heige H., Pres. & Chief Exec. Officer--Bayer Corporation, Pittsburgh, PA; *Int'l*, pg. 172
Wehmeier, Heige H., Pres. & Chief Exec. Officer--Bayer Corporation, Parsippany, NJ; *Int'l*, pg. 172
Wehmeier, Helge H., Pres. & Chief Exec. Officer--Bayer Corporation, Pittsburgh, PA; *Int'l*, pg. 172
Wehrle, Gary, Chm. Bd. & Chief Exec. Officer--Pacific Crest Capital, Inc., Agoura Hills, CA; *U.S. Public*, pg. 1248
Wehrle, Henry B., III, Pres. & Chief Exec. Officer--McJunkin Corporation, Charleston, WV; *U.S. Private*, pg. 722
Weibel, Fred E., Jr., Chm. Bd., Pres. & Chief Exec. Officer--Weibel Winery, Lodi, CA; *U.S. Private*, pg. 1159
Weil, A. Lorne, Chm. Bd. & Chief Exec. Officer--Autotote Corporation, Newark, DE; *U.S. Public*, pg. 150
Weil, David S., Pres., Chief Exec. Officer & Chief Oper. Officer--Ampacet Corporation, Tarrytown, NY; *U.S. Private*, pg. 67
Weil, Louis A., III, Pres. & Chief Exec. Officer--Central Newspapers, Inc., Indianapolis, IN; *U.S. Public*, pg. 326
Weil, Robert S., Sr., Chm. Bd. & Chief Exec. Officer--Weil Brothers Cotton Inc., Montgomery, AL; *U.S. Private*, pg. 1159
Weiler, Gerhard, Pres. & Chief Exec. Officer--Automatic Liquid Packaging, Inc., Woodstock, IL; *U.S. Private*, pg. 101
Weiler, Michael, Pres. & Chief Exec. Officer--Preferred Risk Life Insurance Co., West Des Moines, IA; *U.S. Private*, pg. 880
Weill, Sanford I., Chm. Bd. & Chief Exec. Officer--Travelers Group, New York, NY; *U.S. Public*, pg. 1632
Weimer, Garry, Pres. & Chief Exec. Officer--Westinghouse Canada Inc., Hamilton, Canada; *U.S. Public*, pg. 275
Wein, Bernard J., Chm. Bd., Pres. & Chief Exec. Officer--Catherines Stores Corporation, Memphis, TN; *U.S. Public*, pg. 317
Weinbach, Arthur F., Pres. & Chief Exec. Officer--Automatic Data Processing, Inc., Roseland, NJ; *U.S. Public*, pg. 150
Weinbach, Lawrence A., Chm. & Chief Exec. Officer--Unisys Corporation, Blue Bell, PA; *U.S. Public*, pg. 1671
Weinberg, David L., Chief Exec. Officer--Nippon Credit International Limited, London, United Kingdom; *Int'l*, pg. 933
Weiner, David L., Chm. & Chief Exec. Officer--Marketing Support, Incorporated, Chicago, IL; *U.S. Private*, pg. 705
Weiner, Louis, Pres. & Chief Exec. Officer--City Postal, Inc., New York, NY; *U.S. Private*, pg. 241
Weiner, Walter H., Chm. Bd. & Chief Exec. Officer--Republic New York Corporation, New York, NY; *U.S. Public*, pg. 1380
Weinhardt, J.W., Chm. Bd. & Chief Exec. Officer--SJW Corp., San Jose, CA; *U.S. Public*, pg. 1418
Weinhart, James J., Pres.--Master Molded Products Corporation, Elgin, IL; *U.S. Private*, pg. 714
Weinholtz, Mike, Chief Exec. Officer--CareerStaff Unlimited, Inc., Houston, TX; *U.S. Public*, pg. 1531
Weinstein, Alan I., Pres. & Chief Exec. Officer--J. Baker, Inc., Canton, MA; *U.S. Public*, pg. 167
Weinstein, Dr. Martin, Chm. & Chief Exec. Officer--Chromalloy Gas Turbine Corp., San Antonio, TX; *U.S. Public*, pg. 1458
Weinstein, Gary S., Chief Exec. Officer--ThermoTrex, San Diego, CA; *U.S. Public*, pg. 1595
Weinstein, Howard J., Chm. Bd., Pres. & Chief Exec. Officer--Adams Wine Co., Atlanta, GA; *U.S. Private*, pg. 17
Weinstein, Michael, Pres. & Chief Exec. Officer--Ark Restaurants Corp., New York, NY; *U.S. Public*, pg. 129
Weinstein, Michael F., Chief Exec. Officer--Triarc Beverage Group, White Plains, NY; *U.S. Public*, pg. 1635
Weintraub, Allen, Chm. Bd. & Chief Exec. Officer--The Advest Group, Inc., Hartford, CT; *U.S. Public*, pg. 23
Weintraub, Allen, Chm. Bd. & Chief Exec. Officer--Advest, Inc., Hartford, CT; *U.S. Public*, pg. 23
Weir, David, Pres., Chief Exec. Officer & Chief Fin. Officer--Denison Hydraulics, Inc., Marysville, OH; *U.S. Private*, pg. 324
Weis, Arthur M., Pres. & Chief Exec. Officer--Capintec Inc., Ramsey, NJ; *U.S. Private*, pg. 205

Weis, Dick, Pres. & Chief Exec. Officer--Food Services of America, Seattle, WA; *U.S. Private*, pg. 987

Weis, Jim, Pres. & Chief Exec. Officer--Publicker Industries Inc., Fairfield, CT; *U.S. Public*, pg. 1341

Weisbach, Lou, Chm. Bd., Pres. & Chief Exec. Officer--Ha-Lo Industries, Inc., Niles, IL; *U.S. Public*, pg. 773

Weisel, Tom, Chm. Bd. & Chief Exec. Officer--NationsBank Montgomery Securities LLC, San Francisco, CA; *U.S. Public*, pg. 1162

Weisend, C. Frederick, Chm. Bd., Pres. & Chief Exec. Officer--Fritz Industries Inc., Mesquite, TX; *U.S. Private*, pg. 429

Weiser, Irving, Chm. Bd., Pres. & Chief Exec. Officer--Dain Rauscher Corporation, Minneapolis, MN; *U.S. Public*, pg. 476

Weiser, Sherwood M., Chm. Bd. & Chief Exec. Officer--Carnival Hotels & Casinos, Miami, FL; *U.S. Public*, pg. 1265

Weisman, Ezra, Pres. & Chief Exec. Officer--New Brunswick Scientific Co., Inc., Edison, NJ; *U.S. Public*, pg. 1169

Weisman, Robert, Pres. & Chief Exec. Officer--Shofar Kosher Foods, Linden, NJ; *U.S. Public*, pg. 1433

Weisman, Steve, Chief Oper. Officer & Exec. V.P.--Gulf Coast Food Service Inc., Port Richey, FL; *U.S. Public*, pg. 1529

Weiss, Bernard, Co-Chm. Bd. & Chief Exec. Officer--Signature Eyewear, Inc., Inglewood, CA; *U.S. Public*, pg. 1473

Weiss, David E., Chm. Bd., Pres. & Chief Exec. Officer--Storage Technology Corporation, Louisville, CO; *U.S. Public*, pg. 1522

Weiss, Larry, Chm. Bd., Pres., Chief Exec. Officer & Sec.--Fresh Food, Inc., Hobart, IN; *U.S. Private*, pg. 427

Weiss, Michael, Chief Exec. Officer-Express--The Limited, Inc., Columbus, OH; *U.S. Public*, pg. 995

Weiss, Morry, Chm. Bd. & Chief Exec. Officer--American Greetings Corporation, Cleveland, OH; *U.S. Public*, pg. 77

Weiss, Sam, Chm. Bd., Pres. & Chief Exec. Officer--United Receptical, Inc., Pottsville, PA; *U.S. Private*, pg. 1123

Weiss, Stanley, Jr., Chief Exec. Officer & Treas.--Charles River Foods, Inc., Boston, MA; *U.S. Private*, pg. 230

Weiss, W.D., Co-Chief Exec. Officer--Medtech Inc., Jackson, WY; *U.S. Private*, pg. 728

Weissman, Jerrold, Pres. & Chief Exec. Officer--Carl Weissman & Sons, Inc., Great Falls, MT; *U.S. Private*, pg. 1160

Weissman, Morris, Chm. Bd. & Chief Exec. Officer--American Banknote Corp., New York, NY; *U.S. Public*, pg. 68

Weissman, Robert E., Chm. Bd. & Chief Exec. Officer--Cognizant Corporation, Westport, CT; *U.S. Public*, pg. 395

Weitz, Eric, Pres. & Chief Oper. Officer--Apparal America, Inc., New York, NY; *U.S. Public*, pg. 120

Weitz, Eric T., Pres. & Chief Exec. Officer--Robby Len Fashions, New York, NY; *U.S. Public*, pg. 121

Weitzel, Robert A., Chief Exec. Officer--International Total Services, Independence, OH; *U.S. Public*, pg. 908

Welch, Jerry R., Chm. Bd. & Chief Exec. Officer--Glacier Water Services Inc., Carlsbad, CA; *U.S. Public*, pg. 745

Welch, John F., Jr., Chm. Bd. & Chief Exec. Officer--General Electric Company, Fairfield, CT; *U.S. Public*, pg. 709

Welch, Joseph F., Chm. Bd., Pres. & Chief Exec. Officer--Bachman Company, Reading, PA; *U.S. Private*, pg. 109

Welch, Patrick, Chm. Bd. & Chief Exec. Officer--National Life Insurance Company, Montpelier, VT; *U.S. Private*, pg. 785

Welch, Patrick E., Chm. Bd., Pres. & Chief Exec. Officer--The Life Insurance Co. of Virginia, Richmond, VA; *U.S. Public*, pg. 712

Welk, Donald, Pres. & Chief Exec. Officer--Patch Communications, Titusville, FL; *U.S. Private*, pg. 842

Welka, Gene, Chm. Bd. & Chief Exec. Officer--Frozen Specialties, Inc., Archbold, OH; *U.S. Public*, pg. 378

Wellauer, Thomas, Dr., Pres.-Corp. Exec. Bd. & Chief Exec. Officer--Winterthur Schweizerische Versicherungs Gesellschaft, Winterthur, Switzerland; *Int'l*, pg. 345

Wellek, Richard L., Chm. Bd. & Chief Exec. Officer--Varlen Corporation, Naperville, IL; *U.S. Public*, pg. 1710

Wellens, Leroy, Chm. Bd., Pres., Chief Exec. & Chief Fin. Officer & Treas.--Wellens & Co., Inc., Minneapolis, MN; *U.S. Private*, pg. 1161

Welles, D.K., Jr., Chm. Bd. & Chief Exec. Officer--Therma-Tru Corp., Maumee, OH; *U.S. Private*, pg. 1079

Wells, Bradley H., Pres. & Chief Exec. Officer--Cohn & Wells, San Francisco, CA; *Int'l*, pg. 601

Wells, Calvin B., Chm. Bd., Pres. & Chief Exec. Officer--North Carolina Natural Gas Corporation, Fayetteville, NC; *U.S. Public*, pg. 1194

Wells, J.M., Jr., Chm. Bd. & Chief Exec. Officer--The Homer Laughlin China Company, Newell, WV; *U.S. Private*, pg. 653

Wells, John R., Pres. & Chief Exec. Officer--Interface Flooring Systems Inc., La Grange, GA; *U.S. Public*, pg. 889

Wells, John R., Pres. & Chief Exec. Officer--Pandel, Inc., Cartersville, GA; *U.S. Public*, pg. 889

Wells, Kenneth R., Pres. & Chief Exec. Officer--Briggs Industries, Inc., Tampa, FL; *U.S. Private*, pg. 168

Wells, Mike, Chief Exec. Officer-EMAP Exhibitions--EMAP Business Communications Division, London, United Kingdom; *Int'l*, pg. 451

Wells, Norman E., Jr., Pres. & Chief Exec. Officer--Easco Inc., Girard, OH; *U.S. Public*, pg. 548

Wells, Walter E., Chief Exec. Officer--Schult Homes Corporation, Middlebury, IN; *U.S. Public*, pg. 1442

Welsby, John, Chm. Bd. & Chief Exec. Officer--British Railways Board, London, United Kingdom; *Int'l*, pg. 220

Welsey, Norman H., Pres. & Chief Exec. Officer--ACCO Canada Inc., Willowdale, Canada; *U.S. Public*, pg. 674

Weltz, Skip, Pres. & Chief Exec. Officer--Lafayette Precast, Fremont, CA; *U.S. Private*, pg. 1149

Wen, Eric, Vice Chm. & Chief Exec. Officer--President Baking Company, Atlanta, GA; *Int'l*, pg. 1069

Wenaas, Eric P., Pres. & Chief Exec. Officer--Jacor, Inc., San Diego, CA; *U.S. Private*, pg. 584

Wenaas, Eric P., Ph.D., Chm. Bd., Pres. & Chief Exec. Officer--Jaymark, Inc., San Diego, CA; *U.S. Private*, pg. 584

Wendel, Thomas, Pres. & Chief Exec. Officer--Bridge, New York, NY; *U.S. Private*, pg. 1162

Wendel, Tom, Pres. & Chief Exec. Officer--Bridge, Saint Louis, MO; *U.S. Private*, pg. 1162

Wendel, W. Hall, Jr., Chm. Bd. & Chief Exec. Officer--Polaris Industries, Inc., Minneapolis, MN; *U.S. Public*, pg. 1313

Wendell, E.W., Pres. & Chief Exec. Officer--Gaylord Entertainment/Opryland USA, Nashville, TN; *U.S. Public*, *pg. 704*

Wender, Herbert, Chm. Bd. & Chief Exec. Officer--Commonwealth Land Title Insurance Company, Philadelphia, PA; *U.S. Public*, pg. 1374

Wendling, Erhard, Chief Exec. Officer--Knight Wendling AG, Zurich, Switzerland; *U.S. Private*, pg. 627

Wendt, Gary C., Chm., Pres. & Chief Exec. Officer--General Electric Capital Services, Inc., Stamford, CT; *U.S. Public*, *pg. 711*

Wenerowicz, Bill, Pres. & Chief Exec. Officer--Instrumentarium Imaging, Inc., Milwaukee, WI; *U.S. Private*, pg. 565

Wenick, Mark J., Chief Exec. Officer--MainStreet Trust Company, N.A., Martinsville, VA; *U.S. Public*, pg. 1039

Wenrich, Robert, Pres. & Chief Exec. Officer--Germantown (USA) Co., Broomall, PA; *Int'l*, pg. 555

Wenstrup, H.D., Pres. & Chief Exec. Officer--CHEMCENTRAL Corporation, Bedford Park, IL; *U.S. Private*, pg. 231

Went, D, Chief Exec.--Coutts & Co., London, United Kingdom; *Int'l*, pg. 910

Wentworth, Robert, Pres., Chief Exec. Officer, V.P.-Fin., Admin. & Treas.--Alden Electronics, Inc., Westborough, MA; *U.S. Private*, pg. 872

Werdelin, Hans, Pres. & Chief Exec. Officer--Sophus Berendsen A/S, Soeborg, Denmark; *Int'l*, pg. 1284

Werner, B.K., Chm. Bd. & Chief Exec. Officer--Safety National Casualty Corp., Saint Louis, MO; *U.S. Public*, pg. 496

Werner, Clarence L., Chm. Bd. & Chief Exec. Officer--Werner Enterprises, Inc., Omaha, NE; *U.S. Public*, pg. 1754

Werner, Helmut, Pres. & Chief Exec. Officer--Mercedes-Benz AG, Stuttgart, Germany; *Int'l*, pg. 368

Werner, Jack S., Chm., Pres. & Chief Exec. Officer--Second National Bank of Bay City, Bay City, MI; *U.S. Public*, pg. 379

Werra, Robert, Chm. Bd. & Chief Exec. Officer--Univesco Inc., Dallas, TX; *U.S. Private*, pg. 1128

Wert, Michael L., Chief Exec. Officer--DiMark, Inc., Langhorne, PA; *U.S. Public*, pg. 793

Wertman, Howard, Pres. & Chief Exec. Officer--Anthony and Sylvan Pools Corporation, Doylestown, PA; *U.S. Public*, pg. 593

Wesley, Norman H., Chm. Bd. & Chief Exec. Officer--ACCO World Corporation, Lincolnshire, IL; *U.S. Public*, pg. 674

Wesley, Norman H., Chm. Bd. & Chief Exec. Officer--MasterBrand Industries, Inc., Lincolnshire, IL; *U.S. Public*, pg. 675

Wessell, Dave, Pres. & Chief Exec. Officer--Towne Square Furniture, Inc., Hillsboro, TX; *U.S. Private*, pg. 1093

Wessels, Tiger, Joint Chief Exec. Officer--Union-Transport Corporation, Rancho Dominguez, CA; *U.S. Private*, pg. 1119

Wesson, Steve, Pres. & Chief Exec. Officer--Citadel Holdings Corp., Los Angeles, CA; *U.S. Public*, pg. 456

West, Alfred P., Jr., Chm. Bd. & Chief Exec. Officer--SEI Investments, Oaks, PA; *U.S. Public*, pg. 1417

West, Donald, Pres. & Chief Exec. Officer--Total Petroleum Canada Ltd., Calgary, Canada; *Int'l*, pg. 1409

West, Donald T., Pres. & Chief Exec. Officer--Rigel Energy Corporation, Calgary, Canada; *Int'l*, pg. 1117

West, Donald T., Pres. & Chief Exec. Officer--Rigel Oil & Gas Ltd., Calgary, Canada; *Int'l*, pg. 1117

West, Donald T., Pres. & Chief Exec. Officer--Rigel Petroleum, Inc., Calgary, Canada; *Int'l*, pg. 1117

West, Donald T., Pres. & Chief Exec. Officer--Rigel Petroleum (NI) Limited, Calgary, Canada; *Int'l*, pg. 1117

West, Donald T., Pres. & Chief Exec. Officer--Rigel Petroleum UK Limited, Calgary, Canada; *Int'l*, pg. 1117

West, Doyle D., Chm. Bd., Pres. & Chief Exec. Officer--Matrix Service Company, Tulsa, OK; *U.S. Public*, pg. 1057

West, Neil S., Chm. Bd. & Chief Exec. Officer--Tyler Bank & Trust, Tyler, TX; *U.S. Public*, pg. 630

West, Richard E., Chm. Bd. & Chief Exec. Officer--D & N Mortgage Corporation, Hancock, MI; *U.S. Public*, pg. 472

West, Robert H., Chm. Bd. & Chief Exec. Officer--Butler Manufacturing Company, Kansas City, MO; *U.S. Public*, pg. 271

West, Thomas L., Jr., Pres. & Chief Exec. Officer--The Variable Annuity Life Insurance Co., Houston, TX; *U.S. Public*, pg. 76

West, Thomas L., Jr., Chm. Bd. & Chief Exec. Officer--Western National Corporation, Houston, TX; *U.S. Public*, pg. 76

Westerberg, John R., Chm. Bd. & Chief Exec. Officer--Nelson Westerberg, Inc., Elk Grove Village, IL; *U.S. Private*, pg. 1163

Westerberg, John R., Chm. Bd. & Chief Exec. Officer--Nelson Westerberg International Inc., Elk Grove Village, IL; *U.S. Private*, pg. 1164

Westerberg, John R., Chm. Bd. & Chief Exec. Officer--Commercial Record Center, Elk Grove Village, IL; *U.S. Private*, pg. 1164

Westerberg, Lars, Pres. & Chief Exec. Officer--Granges AB, Stockholm, Sweden; *Int'l*, pg. 439

Westerfeld, William A., Chm. Bd., Pres., Chief Exec. Officer & Treas.--The Westerfelds, Inc., Pittsford, NY; *U.S. Private*, pg. 1164

Westfall, Don, Pres., Chief Exec. & Chief Fin. Officer--Newsprint South, Inc., Jackson, MS; *U.S. Private*, *pg. 797*

Westin, Richard S., Chm. Bd. & Chief Exec. Officer--Westin, Inc., Omaha, NE; *U.S. Private*, pg. 1169

Westlake, W. James, Pres. & Chief Exec. Officer--RBC Insurance Holdings Inc., Mississauga, Canada; *Int'l*, pg. 1131

Weston, Patrick H., Pres. & Chief Exec. Officer--Golden Eagle Group, Inc., Humble, TX; *U.S. Public*, pg. 749

Weston, Roger L., Chm. Bd., Pres. & Chief Exec. Officer--GreatBanc, Inc., Aurora, IL; *U.S. Public*, pg. 760

Westover, Tim, Pres.--Litton Systems Canada Ltd., Etobicoke, Canada; *U.S. Public*, pg. 1005

Westra, G.R., Chief Exec. Officer--Cleanaway Limited, Brentwood, United Kingdom; *Int'l*, pg. 212

Westrick, Thomas G., Pres. & Chief Exec. Officer--Sangamon Industries, Taylorville, IL; *U.S. Private*, pg. 965

Westring, Peter, Chief Officer.--Grona Konsum Stockholm AB, Stockholm, Sweden; *Int'l*, pg. 718

Wetsel, Gary, Chief Oper. Officer & Exec. V.P.--Wyse Technology Inc., San Jose, CA; *U.S. Private*, pg. 1194

Wevers, Pierre Albert, Pres. & Chief Exec. Officer--Bigg's Hyper Shoppes Ohio, Inc., Milford, OH; *U.S. Public*, pg. 1541

Wexler, Lewis P., Chm. Bd., Pres., Chief Exec. Officer & Chief Oper. Officer--Free Service Tire Company, Inc., Johnson City, TN; *U.S. Private*, pg. 425

Wexner, Leslie H., Pres. & Chief Exec. Officer--Intimate Brands, Inc., Columbus, OH; *U.S. Public*, pg. 995

Weyand, William, Pres. & Chief Exec. Officer--Structural Dynamics Research Corp., Milford, OH; *U.S. Public*, pg. 1525

Weyers, Larry L., Chm. Bd., Pres. & Chief Exec. Officer--WPS Resources Corp., Green Bay, WI; *U.S. Public*, pg. 1728

Weyers, Larry L., Chm. Bd. & Chief Exec. Officer--Wisconsin Public Service Corporation, Green Bay, WI; *U.S. Public*, pg. 1728

Weyers, Larry L., Pres. & Chief Exec. Officer--WPS Power Development, Inc., Green Bay, WI; *U.S. Public*, pg. 1728

Weyers, Larry L., Pres. & Chief Exec. Officer--WPS Leasing, Inc., Green Bay, WI; *U.S. Public*, pg. 1728

Weyforth, Frank G., Jr., Chm. Bd., Pres. & Chief Exec. Officer--MRA, An Integrated Marketing Communications Agency, Overland Park, KS; *U.S. Private*, pg. 687

Whalen, Michael J., Pres. & Chief Exec. Officer--Old Kent Bank-Illinois, Elmhurst, IL; *U.S. Public*, pg. 1216

Wheat, Allen D., Chm. Bd., Pres. & Chief Exec. Officer--Credit Suisse First Boston, Inc., New York, NY; *Int'l*, pg. 345

Wheatley, Charles N., Pres. & Chief Exec. Officer--Sahara Enterprises Inc., Chicago, IL; *U.S. Private*, pg. 960

Wheatley, John, Pres. & Chief Exec. Officer--Willis Corroon Corp. of Anchorage, Anchorage, AK; *Int'l*, pg. 1505

Wheaton, Robert E., Pres. & Chief Exec. Officer--Star Buffet, Inc., Salt Lake City, UT; *U.S. Public*, pg. 278

Wheeler, Dennis E., Chm., Pres. & Chief Exec. Officer--Coeur D'Alene Mines Corporation, Coeur D'Alene, ID; *U.S. Public*, pg. 394

Wheeler, Harry B., Chm. & Chief Exec. Officer--Cabre Exploration Ltd., Calgary, Canada; *Int'l*, pg. 247

Wheeler, Larry G., Pres. & Chief Exec. Officer--Mrs. Baird's Bakeries, Inc., Fort Worth, TX; *U.S. Private*, pg. 765

Wheeler, Robert C., Pres. & Chief Exec. Officer--Hill's Pet Nutrition, Topeka, KS; *U.S. Public*, pg. 397

Wheeler, Thomas B., Chm. Bd. & Chief Exec. Officer--Massachusetts Mutual Life Insurance Co., Springfield, MA; *U.S. Private*, pg. 712

Whent, Gerald A., Chief Exec. Officer--Vodafone Group PLC, Newbury, United Kingdom; *Int'l*, pg. 1469

Whitacre, Edward E., Jr., Chm. Bd. & Chief Exec. Officer--SBC Communications Inc., San Antonio, TX; *U.S. Public*, *pg. 1415*

Whitaker, C., Pres. & Chief Exec. Officer--Johnson Worldwide Associates, Inc., Sturtevant, WI; *U.S. Public*, pg. 932

Whitcome, Philip J., Pres. & Chief Exec. Officer--Neurogen Corporation, Branford, CT; *U.S. Public*, pg. 1169

White-Cooper, W.R., Chief Exec. Officer--Sedgwick Group plc, London, United Kingdom; *Int'l*, pg. 1217

White-Thomson, I. L., Pres.--U.S. Borax Inc., Valencia, CA; *Int'l*, pg. 1119

White, Charles R., Pres., Exec. V.P. & Chief Exec. Officer--Fastec Industrial, Elkhart, IN; *U.S. Private*, pg. 397

White, D.W., Chief Exec. Officer--Zurich Insurance Company, Portsmouth, United Kingdom; *Int'l*, pg. 1531

White, D.W., Chief Exec. Officer--Zurich International (UK) Limited, London, United Kingdom; *Int'l*, pg. 1532

White, George, Pres. & Chief Exec. Officer--Gymboree Corporation, Burlingame, CA; *U.S. Public*, pg. 770

White, John F., Chm. Bd., Pres. & Chief Exec. Officer--Haemonetics Corporation, Braintree, MA; *U.S. Public*, pg. 773

White, Lawrence D., Chm. Bd., Pres., & Chief Exec. Officer--Menley & James Laboratories, Inc., Horsham, PA; *U.S. Public*, pg. 1086

White, Michael H., Pres. & Chief Exec. Officer--Rite-Hite Corporation, Milwaukee, WI; *U.S. Private*, pg. 933

White, O.J.G., Chief Exec. Officer--Redland Tile & Brick, Crumlin, United Kingdom; *Int'l*, pg. 1091

White, Patrick, Chief Exec. Officer--Courtaulds European Fibres, Coventry, United Kingdom; *Int'l*, pg. 339

White, Peter, Grp. Chief Exec.--Alliance Leicester Building Society, London, United Kingdom; *Int'l*, pg. 57

White, Peter, Chief Exec. Officer--Alliance & Leicester Building Society, London, United Kingdom; *Int'l*, pg. 57

White, Randall W., Chm. Bd., Pres. & Treas.--Educational Development Corporation, Tulsa, OK; *U.S. Public*, pg. 564

White, Richard, Chief Exec. Officer--Premier Securities Corporation, Baton Rouge, LA; *U.S. Public*, pg. 173
White, Richard, Chief Exec. Officer--Healthsource Maine, Inc., Freeport, ME; *U.S. Public*, pg. 360
White, Richard C., Pres. & Chief Exec. Officer--Community Bancorp, Derby, VT; *U.S. Public*, pg. 416
White, Richard D., Pres. & Chief Exec. Officer--Regions Bank, Gainesville, GA; *U.S. Public*, pg. 1371
White, Robert E., Pres. & Chief Exec. Officer--Bankers Systems Incorporated, Saint Cloud, MN; *U.S. Private*, pg. 114
White, Robert P., Pres. & Chief Exec. Officer--Care America-Southern CA, Woodland Hills, CA; *U.S. Private*, pg. 153
White, Stephen E., Chief Exec. Officer--Metropolitan Life Holdings, Ltd., New York, NY; *U.S. Private*, pg. 737
White, Steven, Chief Exec. Officer--Healthsource Tennessee, Inc., Brentwood, TN; *U.S. Public*, pg. 360
White, Tony L., Chm. Bd., Pres. & Chief Exec. Officer--The Perkin-Elmer Corporation, Norwalk, CT; *U.S. Public*, pg. 1279
White, Tony L., Chm. Bd., Pres. & Chief Exec. Officer--Applied Biosystems, Foster City, CA; *U.S. Public*, pg. 1279
White, Victoria, Chm. Bd. & Co-Chief Exec. Officer--Tork, Inc., Mount Vernon, NY; *U.S. Private*, pg. 1092
Whiteford, Russell E., Pres. & Chief Exec. Officer--DHP Limited Partnership, Chicopee, MA; *U.S. Private*, pg. 302
Whitehead, Doug W.G., Pres. & Chief Exec. Officer-Canadian Opers.--Fletcher Challenge Canada Limited, Vancouver, Canada; *Int'l*, pg. 495
Whitehouse, Robert, Pres. & Chief Exec. Officer--AmTran Corporation, Conway, AR; *U.S. Public*, pg. 1167
Whitehouse, William L., Pres. & Chief Exec. Officer--Chelsea Moore Company, Loveland, OH; *U.S. Private*, pg. 1164
Whiteman, John O., Chm. Bd. & Chief Exec. Officer--Empire Southwest Co., Mesa, AZ; *U.S. Private*, pg. 374
Whitford, Peter D., Pres. & Chief Exec. Officer--Structure, Columbus, OH; *U.S. Public*, pg. 996
Whiting, A. Milton, Chm. Bd. & Chief Exec. Officer--Kaibab Industries, Phoenix, AZ; *U.S. Private*, pg. 605
Whiting, Richard T., Pres. & Chief Exec. Officer--Whiting Manufacturing Co., Inc., Cincinnati, OH; *U.S. Private*, pg. 1174
Whitley, Edward A., Pres. & Chief Exec. Officer--Centex-Rodgers Construction Company, Nashville, TN; *U.S. Public*, pg. 322
Whitley, Michael R., Chm. Bd., Pres. & Chief Exec. & Oper. Officer--KU Energy, Lexington, KY; *U.S. Public*, pg. 940
Whitlow, Maurice, Pres. & Chief Exec. Officer--General Processors, Inc., Oxford, NC; *U.S. Public*, pg. 1502
Whitman, Bob, Pres. & Chief Exec. Officer--Malibu Entertainment Worldwide, Dallas, TX; *U.S. Public*, pg. 1039
Whitman, Christine, Chm. Bd., Pres. & Chief Exec. Officer--CVC Products, Inc., Rochester, NY; *U.S. Private*, pg. 197
Whitman, Martin J., Chm. Bd. & Chief Exec. & Investment Officer--Danielson Holding Corporation, New York, NY; *U.S. Public*, pg. 483
Whitmarsh, Robert M., Pres. & Chief Exec. Officer--Willis Corroon Corp. of Portland, Portland, OR; *Int'l*, pg. 1507
Whitmer, Richard E., Pres. & Chief Exec. Officer--Blue Cross & Blue Shield of Michigan, Detroit, MI; *U.S. Private*, pg. 151
Whitmire, J.L., Chm. Bd. & Chief Exec. Officer--Union Texas Petroleum Holdings, Houston, TX; *U.S. Public*, pg. 1669
Whitmore, John R., Pres. & Chief Exec. Officer--Bessemer Group, Inc., New York, NY; *U.S. Private*, pg. 139
Whitney, Dickson L., Jr., Pres. & Chief Exec. Officer--McGean-Rohco, Inc., Cleveland, OH; *U.S. Private*, pg. 721
Whitney, Michael C., Jr., Chm. Bd., Pres. & Chief Exec. Officer--Fleet Bank NH, Manchester, NH; *U.S. Public*, pg. 649
Whitsell, Helen J., Chm. Bd., Chief Exec. Officer & Treas.--Copeland Lumber Yard, Inc., Portland, OR; *U.S. Private*, pg. 274
Whitson, Keith, Chief Exec. Officer--HSBC Holdings plc, London, United Kingdom; *Int'l*, pg. 579
Whittle, John J., Chm. Bd., Pres. & Chief Exec. Officer--Farmers and Traders Life Insurance Co., Syracuse, NY; *U.S. Private*, pg. 394
Whittle, Mack I., Jr., Pres. & Chief Exec. Officer--Carolina First Corporation, Greenville, SC; *U.S. Public*, pg. 306
Whitwam, David R., Chm. Bd., Chief Exec. Officer--Whirlpool Corporation, Benton Harbor, MI; *U.S. Public*, pg. 1764
Whyte, George C., Jr., Chm. Bd., Pres. & Chief Exec. Officer--Dakotah, Inc., Webster, SD; *U.S. Public*, pg. 477
Wichlenski, John J., Sr., Pres. & Chief Exec. Officer-Air Systems--Engineered Support Systems Inc., Saint Louis, MO; *U.S. Public*, pg. 583
Wick, Jeff, Pres. & Chief Exec. Officer--Wick Building Systems, Mazomanie, WI; *U.S. Private*, pg. 1174
Wicken, Michael J., Pres. & Chief Exec. Officer--Motch Corporation, Cleveland, OH; *Int'l*, pg. 1128
Wickersham, John, Pres. & Chief Exec. Officer--Bill Communications, Inc., New York, NY; *Int'l*, pg. 1446
Wickham, Michael W., Pres. & Chief Exec. Officer--Roadway Express, Inc., Akron, OH; *U.S. Public*, pg. 1392
Wickham, William A., Chief Exec. Officer--SBC Advertising, Columbus, OH; *U.S. Private*, pg. 955
Wickham, William A., Chief Exec. Officer--SBC Public Relations, Westerville, OH; *U.S. Private*, pg. 955
Wickland, John A., III, Chief Exec. Officer--Mock Resources, Inc., Irvine, CA; *U.S. Private*, pg. 1175
Wicks, Floyd E., Pres. & Chief Exec. Officer--Southern California Water Company, San Dimas, CA; *U.S. Public*, pg. 1489
Widmer, Hans, Dr., Chm. Bd., Pres., Chief Exec. & Oper. Officer--Oerlikon-Buhrle Holding AG, Zurich, Switzerland; *Int'l*, pg. 996
Wiedeking, Wendelin, Dr., Pres. & Chief Exec. Officer--Porsche AG, Stuttgart, Germany; *Int'l*, pg. 1063
Wiedemann, George S., Chm. & Chief Exec. Officer--Grey Direct, New York, NY; *U.S. Public*, pg. 764
Wiegand, Phillips, Pres. & Chief Exec. Officer--T.W. Phillips Gas and Oil Co., Butler, PA; *U.S. Private*, pg. 862
Wieger, Garth, Pres. & Chief Exec. Officer--UDC Homes, Inc., Scottsdale, AZ; *U.S. Private*, pg. 5
Wieland, John F., Chm. Bd., Pres. & Chief Exec. Officer--John Wieland Homes Inc., Atlanta, GA; *U.S. Private*, pg. 1175
Wiener, Daniel E., Pres. & Chief Exec. Officer--Lone Star Equities Inc., Lynbrook, NY; *U.S. Private*, pg. 674
Wienick, Mitch, Pres. & Chief Exec. Officer--CDI Corp., Philadelphia, PA; *U.S. Public*, pg. 276
Wiesner, John J., Chm. Bd. & Chief Exec. Officer--C.R. Anthony Company, Oklahoma City, OK; *U.S. Private*, pg. 1029
Wigand, Art F., Pres. & Chief Exec. Officer--Cubic Communications, San Diego, CA; *U.S. Public*, pg. 466
Wigdale, J.B., Chm. Bd. & Chief Exec. Officer--Marshall & Ilsley Corporation, Milwaukee, WI; *U.S. Public*, pg. 1049
Wigdale, J.B., Chm. Bd. & Chief Exec. Officer--M & I Marshall & Ilsley Bank, Milwaukee, WI; *U.S. Public*, pg. 1050
Wiggins, Robert S., Chm. Bd., Chief Exec. Officer & Sec.--Technology Research Corporation, Clearwater, FL; *U.S. Public*, pg. 1564
Wigley, Michael R., Pres., Chief Exec. Officer & Treas.--Great Plains Companies, Inc., Roseville, MN; *U.S. Private*, pg. 475
Wilansky, Heywood, Pres. & Chief Exec. Officer--The Bon Ton Stores, Inc., York, PA; *U.S. Public*, pg. 244
Wilbraham, David, Dr., Chief Exec. Officer--Hickson International Plc, Castleford, United Kingdom; *Int'l*, pg. 618
Wilbrett, Robert, Pres. & Chief Exec. Officer--Hilb, Rogal and Hamilton Company of Port Huron, Port Huron, MI; *U.S. Public*, pg. 827
Wilbur, Brayton, Jr., Pres. & Chief Exec. Officer--Wilbur-Ellis Company & Connell Brothers Company, San Francisco, CA; *U.S. Private*, pg. 1175
Wilburn, Robert, Pres. & Chief Exec. Officer--Colonial Williamsburg Foundation, Williamsburg, VA; *U.S. Private*, pg. 254
Wilcock, Michael, Chief Exec. Officer--Socanav Inc., Montreal, Canada; *Int'l*, pg. 1272
Wildeman, Karen, Chief Exec. Officer--Ruska Instrument Corporation, Houston, TX; *U.S. Private*, pg. 952
Wilder, Christopher, Chief Exec. Officer--Sealing Equipment Products Co., Inc., Pelham, AL; *U.S. Private*, pg. 978
Wilding, Ernest L., Chm. Bd., Pres. & Chief Exec. Officer--Spray-Tech, Inc., Longwood, FL; *U.S. Private*, pg. 1026
Wildrick, Robert N., Chm. Bd., Pres. & Chief Exec. Officer--Venture Stores, Inc., O Fallon, MO; *U.S. Public*, pg. 1716
Wiley, D. Linn, Pres. & Chief Exec. Officer--CVB Financial Corp., Ontario, CA; *U.S. Public*, pg. 286
Wilhelm, Marcus, Chm. Bd., Chief Exec. Officer & Chief Oper. Officer--Doubleday Direct, Garden City, NY; *Int'l*, pg. 191
Wilhelm, Markus, Chief Exec.--BCA, London, United Kingdom; *Int'l*, pg. 192
Wilke, Helmut, Chief Exec. Officer--Software AG, Darmstadt, Germany; *Int'l*, pg. 1276
Wilkens, Roy A., Pres. & Chief Exec. Officer--WilTel--WorldCom, Inc., Jackson, MS; *U.S. Public*, pg. 1779
Wilkens, Roy A., Pres. & Chief Exec. Officer--LDDS WorldCom, Tulsa, OK; *U.S. Public*, pg. 1779
Wilkes, John, Pres. & Chief Exec. Officer--John Dusenbery Co., Inc., Randolph, NJ; *U.S. Private*, pg. 349
Wilkie, Michael L., Chm. Bd., Pres., Chief Exec. & Chief Oper. Officer--DOALL Company, Des Plaines, IL; *U.S. Private*, pg. 337
Wilkinson, B. Andrew, Pres. & Chief Exec. Officer--Statex Petroleum, Inc., Dallas, TX; *U.S. Public*, pg. 1245
Wilkinson, Bruce W., Chm. Bd. & Chief Exec. Officer--CRSS Inc., Houston, TX; *Int'l*, pg. 1415
Wilkinson, Eugene R., Chm. Bd., Pres., & Chief Exec. Officer--Hanson Engineers Inc., Springfield, IL; *U.S. Private*, pg. 500
Wilkinson, Frank S., Jr., Chief Exec. Officer--Paragon Reinsurance Risk Management Services, Inc., Minneapolis, MN; *U.S. Public*, pg. 236
Wilkinson, Frank S., Jr., Chm. Bd. & Chief Exec. Officer--E.W. Blanch Capital Risk Solutions, Inc., Minneapolis, MN; *U.S. Public*, pg. 236
Wilkinson, Jon, Chief Exec. Officer--Research International, London, United Kingdom; *Int'l*, pg. 1482
Wilkinson, Louis Peter, Chief Exec. Officer--David Jones Limited, Sydney, Australia; *Int'l*, pg. 714
Will, James F., Chm. Bd., Pres. & Chief Exec. Officer--Armco Inc., Pittsburgh, PA; *U.S. Public*, pg. 131
Willard, Dean M., Chief Exec. Officer--Courtaulds Aerospace, Glendale, CA; *Int'l*, pg. 339
Willcox, James, Pres., Chief Exec. & Chief Oper. Officer--American Marketing Industries, Inc., Kansas City, MO; *U.S. Private*, pg. 58
Willes, Mark, Chm. Bd., Pres. & Chief Exec. Officer--The Times Mirror Company, Los Angeles, CA; *U.S. Public*, pg. 1615
Willet, Richard H., Chm. Bd., Pres. & Chief Exec. Officer--Consoltex Group Inc., Ville Saint Laurent, Canada; *Int'l*, pg. 326
Williams, Andrew W., Chm. Bd. & Chief Exec. Officer--Florafax International, Inc., Vero Beach, FL; *U.S. Public*, pg. 654
Williams, Chuck, Pres. & Chief Exec. Officer--Brightware, Inc., Novato, CA; *U.S. Private*, pg. 168
Williams, Clint O., Pres. & Chief Exec. Officer--Union Planters Bank of West Tennessee, Humboldt, TN; *U.S. Public*, pg. 1669
Williams, Colin V.K., Pres. & Chief Exec. Officer--MFS International, Inc., Vienna, VA; *U.S. Public*, pg. 1779
Williams, D. Wayne, Pres. & Chief Exec. Officer--Century Data Systems, Incorporated, Raleigh, NC; *U.S. Private*, pg. 226
Williams, D.K., Pres. & Chief Exec. Officer--Nuovo Pignone S.p.a., Florence, Italy; *Int'l*, pg. 990
Williams, Dave H., Chm. Bd. & Chief Exec. Officer--Alliance Capital Management Corp., New York, NY; *U.S. Public*, pg. 589
Williams, David D., Pres. & Chief Exec. Officer--Tribune Media Services, Inc., Chicago, IL; *U.S. Public*, pg. 1636
williams, Derek, Chief Oper. Officer & Exec. V.P.--Pall Ilfracombe Ltd., Ilfracombe, United Kingdom; *U.S. Public*, *pg. 1254*
Williams, Derek, Chief Oper. Officer & Exec. V.P.--Pall Process Filtration Ltd., Portsmouth, United Kingdom; *U.S. Public*, pg. 1254
Williams, Don E., Chm. Bd.--Don E. Williams Co., Rock Island, IL; *U.S. Private*, pg. 1177
Williams, Donald, Chm. Bd. & Chief Exec. Officer--First Banks, Inc., Sacramento, CA; *U.S. Public*, pg. 626
Williams, Ellen, Chief Exec. Officer & Chief Fin. Officer--Millennium Technology Services, Inc., White City, OR; *U.S. Private*, pg. 746
Williams, Francis M., Chm. Bd., Pres. & Chief Exec. Officer--Kimmins Corp., Tampa, FL; *U.S. Public*, pg. 960
Williams, Frank E., III, Chm. Bd., Pres. & Chief Exec. Officer--Williams Industries, Inc., Falls Church, VA; *U.S. Public*, pg. 1769
Williams, H. Edward, Pres. & Chief Exec. Officer--Security Bank & Trust Co., Vincennes, IN; *U.S. Public*, pg. 1217
Williams, J. Kelley, Chm. Bd. & Chief Exec. Officer--ChemFirst Inc., Jackson, MS; *U.S. Public*, pg. 344
Williams, James E., Chm. Bd. & Chief Exec. Officer--Golden State Foods, Irvine, CA; *U.S. Private*, pg. 460
Williams, James F., Chm. Bd. & Chief Exec. Officer--Integrated Waste Services, Inc., Buffalo, NY; *U.S. Public*, *pg. 886*
Williams, Jeffrey W., Pres. & Chief Exec. Officer--American Security Group, Atlanta, GA; *Int'l*, pg. 499
Williams, John, Pres. & Chief Exec. Officer--Gray Communications Systems, Inc., Albany, GA; *U.S. Public*, pg. 759
Williams, Kathleen, Chief Exec. Officer--Williams Worldwide, Santa Monica, CA; *U.S. Private*, pg. 1179
Williams, Kenneth, Chm. Bd. & Chief Exec. Officer--Sierra On-Line, Inc., Bellevue, WA; *U.S. Public*, pg. 321
Williams, Mark, Chief Exec. Officer--H.E. Williams, Inc., Carthage, MO; *U.S. Private*, pg. 1178
Williams, Mike, Pres. & Chief Exec. Officer--Texas Electric Cooperatives, Inc., Austin, TX; *U.S. Private*, pg. 1078
Williams, R.A., Vice Chm., Chief Exec. Officer & Sec.--Presstek, Inc., Hudson, NH; *U.S. Public*, pg. 1324
Williams, Richard F., Pres. & Chief Exec. Officer--Fidelity & Deposit Company of Maryland, Baltimore, MD; *Int'l*, pg. 1530
Williams, Robert M., Chm., Chief Exec. Officer & Treas.--Genova Products, Inc., Davison, MI; *U.S. Private*, pg. 447
Williams, Ronald, Pres. & Chief Exec. Officer--Gary-Williams Energy Corporation, Denver, CO; *U.S. Private*, pg. 440
Williams, Sam B., Dr., Chm. Bd. & Chief Exec. Officer--Williams International, Walled Lake, MI; *U.S. Private*, pg. 1178
Williams, Stephen, Pres. & Chief Exec. Officer--Carver Corporation, Lynnwood, WA; *U.S. Public*, pg. 310
Williams, Sterling L., Pres. & Chief Exec. Officer--Sterling Software, Inc., Dallas, TX; *U.S. Public*, pg. 1516
Williams, Steve, Chief Exec. Officer--Voyager Group, Inc., Jacksonville, FL; *U.S. Public*, pg. 68
Williams, Steve, Chief Exec. Officer--Voyager Service Warranties, Inc., Fort Worth, TX; *U.S. Public*, pg. 68
Williams, Steven, Chief Exec. Officer--American Reliable Insurance Company, Scottsdale, AZ; *U.S. Public*, pg. 67
Williams, Steven C., Chief Exec. Officer & Exec. V.P.--State Volunteer Mutual Insurance Co., Brentwood, TN; *U.S. Private*, pg. 1037
Williams, Thomas C., Pres. & Chief Exec. Officer--Rurban Financial Corp., Defiance, OH; *U.S. Public*, pg. 1412
Williams, Thomas C., Chm. Bd. & Chief Exec. Officer--The Peoples Banking Company, Findlay, OH; *U.S. Public*, pg. 1413
Williams, Thomas E., Pres. & Chief Exec. Officer--Applied Extrusion Technologies, Inc., Peabody, MA; *U.S. Public*, pg. 122
Williams, William S., Vice Chm., Chief Exec. Officer & Chief Fin. Officer--The W.W. Williams Company, Columbus, OH; *U.S. Private*, pg. 1178
Williams, Willis, Chm. Bd. & Chief Exec. Officer--Monticello Bank, Jacksonville, FL; *U.S. Private*, pg. 759
Williamson, George Malcolm, Chief Exec. Officer--Standard Chartered Bank PLC, London, United Kingdom; *Int'l*, pg. 1294
Williamson, Hugh H., III, Pres. & Chief Exec. Officer--KTM Holdings Corp., Denver, CO; *U.S. Private*, pg. 604
Williamson, Hugh H., III, Pres. & Chief Exec. Officer--Ketema, Inc., Denver, CO; *U.S. Private*, pg. 604
Williamson, Ian, Chief Exec. Officer--Carclo Engineering Group plc, Sheffield, United Kingdom; *Int'l*, pg. 268
Williamson, John B., III, Pres. & Chief Exec. Officer--Roanoke Gas Company, Roanoke, VA; *U.S. Public*, pg. 1392
Williamson, Peter H., Chief Exec. Officer--Foster's Brewing Group, Southbank, Australia; *Int'l*, pg. 501
Williamson, Philip C., Chm. Bd., Pres. & Chief Exec. Officer--Williamson-Dickie Mfg. Co., Fort Worth, TX; *U.S. Private*, pg. 1179
Williamson, Richard, Chief Exec. Officer--Berel Industries Inc., Cerritos, CA; *U.S. Private*, pg. 135
Williamson, Richard B., Chm. Bd., Pres. & Chief Exec. Officer--T.D. Williamson, Inc., Tulsa, OK; *U.S. Private*, pg. 1179
Williamson, Richard C., Pres. & Chief Exec. Officer--Pacific One Bank, Portland, OR; *U.S. Public*, pg. 635

Williome, Jack H., Pres. & Chief Exec. Officer--Kaufman and Broad of Texas, Ltd., San Antonio, TX; *U.S. Public*, pg. 945

Willis, Gary K., Pres. & Chief Exec. Officer--Zygo Corporation, Middlefield, CT; *U.S. Public*, pg. 1795

Willis, Robert E., Pres. & Chief Exec. Officer--EPX, Portland, ME; *U.S. Private*, pg. 354

Wills, J. Blacklock, Jr., Pres. & Chief Exec. Officer--Wills Group, Inc., La Plata, MD; *U.S. Private*, pg. 1180

Wills, Travers H., Pres. & Chief Exec. Officer--HealthWise of America, Nashville, TN; *U.S. Public*, pg. 1678

Willson, John M., Pres. & Chief Exec. Officer--Placer Dome Inc., Vancouver, Canada; *Int'l*, pg. 1060

Willson, Ricardo, Chief Exec. Officer--EURO RSCG Graffiti, Santiago, Chile; *Int'l*, pg. 603

Wilmers, John P., Pres. & Chief Exec. Officer--Ballantyne of Omaha, Inc., Omaha, NE; *Int'l*, pg. 17

Wilmers, Robert G., Chm. Bd. & Chief Exec. Officer--First Empire State Corporation, Buffalo, NY; *U.S. Public*, pg. 631

Wilmot, Thomas C., Pres. & Chief Exec. Officer--Wilmorite, Inc., Rochester, NY; *U.S. Private*, pg. 1180

Wilson, A.C., Chm. Bd. & Chief Exec. Officer--Ernest Paper Products, Inc., Los Angeles, CA; *U.S. Private*, pg. 381

Wilson, Anthony J., Chief Exec. Officer & Chief Fin. Officer--Glynwed International PLC, Birmingham, United Kingdom; *Int'l*, pg. 554

Wilson, Anthony J., Chief Exec. Officer & Mng. Dir.--Guilford Europe, Ltd., Derby, United Kingdom; *U.S. Public*, pg. 769

Wilson, Charles A., Pres. & Chief Exec. Officer--Connor Corporation, Fort Wayne, IN; *U.S. Private*, pg. 264

Wilson, Clifford D., Pres. & Chief Exec. Officer--Ritchie Industries, Inc., Conrad, IA; *U.S. Private*, pg. 933

Wilson, Diane M., Chm. Bd., Pres. & Chief Exec. Officer--Trend Laboratories Inc., Atlanta, GA; *U.S. Public*, pg. 1634

Wilson, Diane M., Chm. Bd. & Chief Exec. Officer--Trend Media, Atlanta, GA; *U.S. Public*, pg. 1634

Wilson, Faye, Chief Exec. Officer--Security Pacific Financial Services Inc., San Diego, CA; *U.S. Public*, pg. 181

Wilson, Fred, Chief Exec. Officer--The Ingersoll Milling Machine Co., Rockford, IL; *U.S. Private*, pg. 562

Wilson, Fred C., Chief Exec. Officer--Ingersoll International Inc., Rockford, IL; *U.S. Private*, pg. 562

Wilson, G. Larry, Chm. Bd., Pres. & Chief Exec. Officer--Policy Management Systems Corporation, Blythewood, SC; *U.S. Public*, pg. 1314

Wilson, George P., Pres. & Chief Exec. Officer--Equitrac Corporation, Coral Gables, FL; *U.S. Public*, pg. 590

Wilson, Glen W., Pres. & Chief Exec. Officer--AMCORE Trust Company, Rockford, IL; *U.S. Public*, pg. 65

Wilson, Gregory L., Chm. Bd., Pres. & Chief Exec. Officer--Mity-Lite, Inc., Orem, UT; *U.S. Public*, pg. 1118

Wilson, Hal, Chief Exec. Officer--Sico Incorporated, Edina, MN; *U.S. Private*, pg. 997

Wilson, Ian R., Chm. Bd., Pres., & Chief Exec. Officer--Dartford Partnership, San Francisco, CA; *U.S. Private*, pg. 312

Wilson, J. Lawrence, Chm. Bd. & Chief Exec. Officer--Rohm and Haas Company, Philadelphia, PA; *U.S. Public*, pg. 1403

Wilson, J. Steven, Chm. Bd., Pres. & Chief Exec. Officer--Riverside Group, Inc., Jacksonville, FL; *U.S. Public*, pg. 1391

Wilson, J. Steven, Chm. Bd. & Chief Exec. Officer--Wickes Inc., Vernon Hills, IL; *U.S. Public*, pg. 1391

Wilson, J.S., Jr., Pres. & Chief Exec. Officer--Conwood Company L.P., Memphis, TN; *U.S. Private*, pg. 272

Wilson, James D., Pres. & Chief Exec. Officer--Martin Industries, Inc. (AL), Florence, AL; *U.S. Private*, pg. 709

Wilson, James R., Chm. Bd., Pres. & Chief Exec. Officer--Thiokol Corporation, Ogden, UT; *U.S. Public*, pg. 1596

Wilson, John H., Pres. & Chief Exec. Officer--Hilb, Rogal and Hamilton Company of the District of Columbia, Rockville, MD; *U.S. Public*, pg. 827

Wilson, Lawrence, Chief Exec. Officer--Citadel Communications Corporation, Tempe, AZ; *U.S. Private*, pg. 241

Wilson, Lawrence, Chief Exec. Officer--Citadel Broadcasting Company, Greenbank, WA; *U.S. Private*, pg. 241

Wilson, Lawrence A., Pres. & Chief Exec. Officer--HCBeck, Dallas, TX; *U.S. Private*, pg. 490

Wilson, M. J., Chief Exec.--Ulster Investment Bank Limited, Dublin, Ireland; *Int'l*, pg. 912

Wilson, Marc, Pres. & Chief Exec. Officer--Safway Steel Products Inc., Waukesha, WI; *Int'l*, pg. 1389

Wilson, P.G., Grp. Chief Exec. Officer--Ransomes Plc, Ipswich, United Kingdom; *Int'l*, pg. 1087

Wilson, P.M., Chm. Bd. & Chief Exec. Officer--Gallaher Tobacco Ltd., Weybridge, United Kingdom; *Int'l*, pg. 539

Wilson, Peter, Chm. Bd. & Chief Exec.--Gallaher Limited, Weybridge, United Kingdom; *Int'l*, pg. 539

Wilson, Rich, Jr., Chm. Bd., Pres. & Chief Exec. Officer--Heavy Machines, Inc., Memphis, TN; *U.S. Private*, pg. 518

Wilson, Robert, Pres. & Chief Exec. Officer--Curtin & Pease/Peneco, Inc, Dunedin, FL; *U.S. Public*, pg. 1306

Wilson, Thomas A., Pres. & Chief Exec. Officer--Seer Technologies, Inc., Cary, NC; *U.S. Public*, pg. 1453

Wilson, Thomas D., Chm. Bd., Pres. & Chief Exec. Officer--Helian Health Group, Inc., Monterey, CA; *U.S. Public*, pg. 1715

Wilson, Tim, Pres. & Chief Exec. Officer--Marmac Corporation, Vienna, WV; *U.S. Private*, pg. 705

Wilson, Veronica, Pres. & Chief Exec. Officer--Aladdin Hotel & Casino, Las Vegas, NV; *U.S. Private*, pg. 30

Wilson, W. David, Chm. & Chief Exec. Officer--ScotiaMcLeod Inc., Toronto, Canada; *Int'l*, pg. 156

Wilson, W. David, Chm. & Chief Exec. Officer--Scotia Capital Markets, Toronto, Canada; *Int'l*, pg. 156

Wilson, Wallace S., Chm. Bd., Pres. & Chief Exec. Officer--Wilson Industries Inc., Houston, TX; *U.S. Private*, pg. 1181

Wilson, William J., Chief Exec. Officer--Roper Starch Worldwide, Mamaroneck, NY; *U.S. Private*, pg. 944

Wilton, E. Carlton, Chief Oper. Officer--Universal Wilton Inc., Richmond, VA; *U.S. Public*, pg. 1695

Wiltshire, R.W., Jr., Pres. & Chief Exec. Officer--Home Beneficial Corporation, Richmond, VA; *U.S. Public*, pg. 76

Wilzig, Siggi B., Chm. Bd. & Chief Exec. Officer--The Trustcompany Bancorporation, Jersey City, NJ; *U.S. Public*, pg. 1643

Winch, Harold, Chm. Bd. & Chief Exec. Officer--The Minster Machine Company, Minster, OH; *U.S. Private*, pg. 751

Winchell, W. Blake, Pres. & Chief Exec. Officer--Kleer-Vu Plastics, Inc., Compton, CA; *U.S. Public*, pg. 962

Winfield, Michael D., Pres. & Chief Exec. Officer--UOP, Des Plaines, IL; *U.S. Public*, pg. 52

Winfrey, Oprah, Chm. Bd. & Chief Exec. Officer--Harpo Entertainment Group, Chicago, IL; *U.S. Private*, pg. 504

Wing, John A., Chm. Bd. & Chief Exec. Officer--ABN AMRO Chicago Corporation, Chicago, IL; *Int'l*, pg. 10

Wingate, David A., Chm. Bd., Pres. & Chief Exec. Officer--Hi-Shear Industries Inc., New Hyde Park, NY; *U.S. Public*, pg. 824

Winger, Kenneth W., Pres. & Chief Exec. Officer--Laidlaw Environmental Services, Inc., Columbia, SC; *U.S. Public*, pg. 975

Winkhaus, Hans-Dietrich, Pres. & Chief Exec. Officer--Henkel KGaA, Dusseldorf, Germany; *Int'l*, pg. 609

Winkler, Agnieszka, Pres. & Chief Exec. Officer--Winkler Advertising, San Francisco, CA; *U.S. Private*, pg. 1183

Winn, Elwood, Pres. & Chief Exec. Officer--Certified Grocers Midwest, Inc., Hodgkins, IL; *U.S. Private*, pg. 226

Winn, Paul T., Pres. & Chief Exec. Officer--Genicom Corporation, Chantilly, VA; *U.S. Public*, pg. 729

Winn, Stephen T., Pres. & Chief Exec. Officer--Computer Language Research, Inc., Carrollton, TX; *U.S. Public*, pg. 421

Winship, Blanton C., Pres. & Chief Exec. Officer--Transus Intermodal L.L.C., Atlanta, GA; *U.S. Private*, pg. 1097

Wint, Dennis, Pres. & Chief Exec. Officer--The Franklin Institute, Philadelphia, PA; *U.S. Private*, pg. 424

Winter, Alison, Pres. & Chief Exec. Officer--Northern Trust Bank of California, N.A., San Francisco, CA; *U.S. Public*, pg. 1196

Winter, J. Burgess, Pres. & Chief Exec. Officer--BHP Copper North America, Tucson, AZ; *Int'l*, pg. 224

Winterbottom, Clare, Chm. & Chief Exec. Officer--Anchor Lamina Inc., Windsor, Canada; *Int'l*, pg. 75

Wintermans, Jos, Pres. & Chief Exec. Officer--Canadian Tire Acceptance Ltd., Welland, Canada; *Int'l*, pg. 259

Wintermute, Eric G., Pres. & Chief Exec. Officer--American Vanguard Corporation, Newport Beach, CA; *U.S. Public*, pg. 94

Wipfli, F., Chief Exec. Officer--Zurich Kosmos Versicherungen AG, Vienna, Austria; *Int'l*, pg. 1532

Wirth, Peter, Dr., Pres. & Chief Exec. Officer--Mikron Holding AG, Biel, Switzerland; *Int'l*, pg. 866

Wirtz, William W., Pres. & Chief Exec. Officer--Wirtz Corporation, Chicago, IL; *U.S. Private*, pg. 1184

Wirz, D., Chief Exec. Officer--Zurich Pension Fund Consultants & Investments Mngmt. Ltd., Zurich, Switzerland; *Int'l*, pg. 1530

Wise, Allen F., Pres. & Chief Exec. Officer--Coventry Corporation, Nashville, TN; *U.S. Public*, pg. 454

Wise, Brion G., Chm. Bd. & Chief Exec. Officer--Western Gas Resources, Inc., Denver, CO; *U.S. Public*, pg. 1758

Wise, William A., Chm. Bd., Pres. & Chief Exec. Officer--El Paso Natural Gas Co., Houston, TX; *U.S. Public*, pg. 567

Wishart, Steven W., Pres. & Chief Exec. Officer--ReliaStar Investment Research, Inc., Minneapolis, MN; *U.S. Public*, *pg. 1376*

Wishnack, Marshall B., Chm. Bd. & Chief Exec. Officer--Wheat First Butcher Singer, Inc., Richmond, VA; *U.S. Public*, pg. 640

Wisne, Lawrence A., Pres. & Chief Exec. Officer--Progressive Tool & Industries Co., Southfield, MI; *U.S. Private*, pg. 890

Wiss, Ronald A., Chm. Bd. & Chief Exec. Officer--Edwards and Kelcey, Inc., Boston, MA; *U.S. Private*, pg. 364

Witherow, James B., Pres. & Chief Exec. Officer--Sunbelt National Mortgage Corporation, Dallas, TX; *U.S. Public*, pg. 639

Withers, Joan, Chief Exec. Officer--The Radio Network, Auckland, New Zealand; *U.S. Public*, pg. 386

Withrow, David, Pres., Chief Exec. Officer & Dir.-Sls.--FATA Production Machinery, Cleveland, OH; *Int'l*, pg. 474

Withun, Frank, Pres. & Chief Exec. Officer--Acordia, Inc., Indianapolis, IN; *U.S. Private*, pg. 14

Witkin, Gary M., Pres. & Chief Exec. Officer--Service Merchandise Company, Inc., Brentwood, TN; *U.S. Public*, *pg. 1461*

Witmer, Thomas H., Pres. & Chief Exec. Officer--Medrad, Inc., Indianola, PA; *Int'l*, pg. 1204

Witt, Barry, Pres. & Chief Exec. Officer--Westgate Fabrics, Inc., Grand Prairie, TX; *U.S. Private*, pg. 1169

Witt, Howard B., Chm. Bd., Pres. & Chief Exec. Officer--Littelfuse, Inc., Des Plaines, IL; *U.S. Public*, pg. 1001

Witt, Richard A., Pres. & Chief Exec. Officer--Mutual of Omaha Investor Services, Inc., Omaha, NE; *U.S. Private*, *pg. 770*

Witte, Margaret K., Chm., Pres. & Chief Exec. Officer--Royal Oak Mines Inc., Kirkland, WA; *U.S. Public*, pg. 1410

Wittering, Peter E., Chief Oper. Officer & Mng. Dir.--Sturmey-Archer Limited, Nottingham, United Kingdom; *Int'l*, pg. 394

Witwer, Paul, Chief Exec. Officer--Kalas Manufacturing, Inc., Denver, PA; *U.S. Private*, pg. 606

Wlaker, Nancy, Pres. & Chief Exec. Officer--Krames Communications, San Bruno, CA; *U.S. Public*, pg. 1616

Wobst, Frank, Chm. Bd. & Chief Exec. Officer--Huntington Bancshares Inc., Columbus, OH; *U.S. Public*, pg. 849

Woessner, Mark, Dr., Pres. & Chief Exec. Officer--Bertelsmann AG, Gutersloh, Germany; *Int'l*, pg. 189

Woeste, Bill F., Jr., Pres.--Beechmont Investments Inc., Cincinnati, OH; *U.S. Private*, pg. 129

Woitas, Clayton H., Pres. & Chief Exec. Officer--Renaissance Energy Ltd., Calgary, Canada; *Int'l*, pg. 1102

Wojcik, Paul N., Pres. & Chief Exec. Officer--The Bureau of National Affairs, Inc., Washington, DC; *U.S. Private*, pg. 181

Wojcik, Paul N., Pres. & Chief Exec. Officer--BNA Books Div., Washington, DC; *U.S. Private*, pg. 181

Wojnowich, Saul, Pres. & Chief Exec. Officer--Highland Mills Inc., Charlotte, NC; *U.S. Private*, pg. 528

Wolf, Gregory H., Pres. & Chief Exec. Officer--Humana Inc., Louisville, KY; *U.S. Public*, pg. 847

Wolf, Melvin Lee, Chm. Bd. & Chief Exec. Officer--Star Furniture Company, Houston, TX; *U.S. Public*, pg. 221

Wolf, Norman, Chief Exec. Officer, Treas. & Sec.--Carole Wren, Inc., New York, NY; *U.S. Private*, pg. 1192

Wolf, Peter M., Chief Exec. Officer--Badische Tabakmanufaktur Roth-Handle GmbH, Lahr, Germany; *Int'l*, pg. 1101

Wolf, Robert D., Pres. & Chief Exec. Officer--Howard B. Wolf, Inc., Dallas, TX; *U.S. Public*, pg. 1774

Wolf, Stephen M., Chm. Bd. & Chief Exec. Officer--US Airways Group, Inc., Arlington, VA; *U.S. Public*, pg. 1680

Wolf, Tom, Chm. Bd., Pres. & Chief Exec. Officer--STS Consultants, Inc., Deerfield, IL; *U.S. Private*, pg. 959

Wolfe, F.C., Pres. & Chief Exec. Officer--NN Financial, Don Mills, Canada; *Int'l*, pg. 650

Wolfe, H.G., Pres. & Chief Exec. Officer--Ney Dental International, Bloomfield, CT; *Int'l*, pg. 388

Wolfe, Herb, Pres. & Chief Exec. Officer--Atlantic City Showboat, Atlantic City, NJ; *U.S. Public*, pg. 1469

Wolfe, John F., Pres., Chief Exec. Officer & Publisher--The Dispatch Printing Company, Columbus, OH; *U.S. Private*, *pg. 334*

Wolfe, Kenneth L., Chm. Bd. & Chief Exec. Officer--Hershey Foods Corporation, Hershey, PA; *U.S. Public*, pg. 811

Wolfe, Richard, Chief Exec. Officer--Travel U.K., London, United Kingdom,; *U.S. Private*, pg. 647

Wolfe, Ronald J., Pres. & Chief Exec. Officer--Restaurant Developers Corp., Independence, OH; *U.S. Private*, pg. 925

Wolfe, Thomas E., Chm. Bd, Pres. & Chief Exec. Officer--Ziebart International Corporation, Troy, MI; *U.S. Private*, pg. 1205

Wolfe, Tom, Pres. & Chief Exec. Officer--Persoft, Inc., Madison, WI; *U.S. Private*, pg. 856

Wolken, Cy, Chief Exec. Officer--A.W. Mendenhall Co., Inc., Elk Grove Village, IL; *U.S. Private*, pg. 731

Wolken, Hal, Pres. & Chief Exec. Officer--A.W. Mendenhall Co., Inc., Elk Grove Village, IL; *U.S. Private*, pg. 731

Wollenberg, Richard P., Chm. Bd., Pres. & Chief Exec. Officer--Longview Fibre Company, Longview, WA; *U.S. Public*, pg. 1013

Wolohan, James L., Chm. Bd., Pres. & Chief Exec. Officer--Wolohan Lumber Co., Saginaw, MI; *U.S. Public*, pg. 1774

Wolski, Lawrence G., Chief Exec. Officer--Joslyn Corporation, Chicago, IL; *U.S. Public*, pg. 481

Wolstein, Scott A., Chm. Bd., Pres. & Chief Exec. Officer--Developers Diversified Realty Corporation, Moreland Hills, OH; *U.S. Public*, pg. 502

Woltz, H.O., III, Pres. & Chief Exec. Officer--Insteel Industries, Inc., Mount Airy, NC; *U.S. Public*, pg. 882

Woltz, William, Jr., Pres. & Chief Exec. Officer--Page Holdings, Inc., Mount Airy, NC; *U.S. Private*, pg. 834

Woltz, William, Jr., Pres. & Chief Exec. Officer--Perry Mfg. Co., Mount Airy, NC; *U.S. Private*, pg. 834

Womack, Robert R., Chm. Bd. & Chief Exec. Officer--Zurn Industries, Inc., Erie, PA; *U.S. Public*, pg. 1794

Wong, Fred, Chief Exec. Officer--Ansco Photo-Optical Products Corp., Elk Grove Village, IL; *Int'l*, pg. 587

Wood, Alan, Chief Officer--Esselte Asia Pacific, Wan Chai, Hong Kong; *Int'l*, pg. 460

Wood, Andrew L., Chm. Bd. & Chief Exec. Officer--Burnham, Atlanta, GA; *Int'l*, pg. 686

Wood, Briggs, Chief Exec. Officer--Timec Company, Vallejo, CA; *U.S. Private*, pg. 1087

Wood, Bruce, Chm. Bd., Pres. & Chief Exec. Officer--Agromac International, Inc., Gering, NE; *U.S. Private*, pg. 27

Wood, David C., Chm. Bd. & Chief Exec. Officer--Norwest Financial, Inc., Des Moines, IA; *U.S. Public*, pg. 1202

Wood, James, Chm. Bd. & Co-Chief Exec. Officer--The Great Atlantic & Pacific Tea Company, Inc., Montvale, NJ; *Int'l*, pg. 1375

Wood, John B., Pres. & Chief Exec. Officer--Telos Corporation, Ashburn, VA; *U.S. Public*, pg. 1573

Wood, John W., Jr., Chm. Bd. & Chief Exec. Officer--Thermo Cardiosystems Inc., Woburn, MA; *U.S. Public*, pg. 1592

Wood, R. Ray, Chm. Bd., Pres., Chief Exec. & Oper. Officer--Rockford Products Corp., Rockford, IL; *U.S. Private*, pg. 938

Wood, Richard D., Jr., Pres. & Chief Exec. Officer--Wawa, Inc., Media, PA; *U.S. Private*, pg. 1155

Wood, Robert C., Pres. & Chief Exec. Officer--Winterthur Reinsurance Corporation of America, New York, NY; *Int'l*, pg. 346

Wood, Stephen F., Pres. & Chief Exec. Officer--Constellation Energy Projects & Services, Inc., Baltimore, MD; *U.S. Public*, pg. 172

Wood, Willis B., Jr., Chm. Bd. & Chief Exec. Officer--Pacific Enterprises, Los Angeles, CA; *U.S. Public*, pg. 1249

Woodard, James, Chief Exec. Officer--Tom James Company, Franklin, TN; *U.S. Private*, pg. 580

Woodfine, J. M., Dr., Chief Exec. Officer--WBB Technology Ltd., Newton Abbot, United Kingdom; *Int'l*, pg. 1487

Woodhall, J.A., Jr., Chm. Bd. Chief Exec. Officer--Central Allied Enterprises, Canton, OH; *U.S. Private*, pg. 222

Woodhouse, Charles F., Pres. & Chief Exec. Officer--MariFarms, Inc., Woodbridge, NJ; *Int'l*, pg. 593

Woodhouse, J. G., Chief Exec. Officer--Rover Finance Holding Limited, Solihull, United Kingdom; *Int'l*, pg. 911
Woodhull, John R., Pres. & Chief Exec. Officer--Logicon, Inc., Torrance, CA; *U.S. Public*, pg. 1198
Woodland, Fred, Pres. & Chief Exec. Officer--Hydroscience, Inc., Dallas, TX; *U.S. Private*, pg. 552
Woodring, Greig, Pres. & Chief Exec. Officer--Reinsurance Group Of America, Saint Louis, MO; *U.S. Private*, pg. 443
Woods, Douglas, Pres. & Chief Exec. Officer--Liberty Precision Industries, Rochester, NY; *U.S. Private*, pg. 666
Woods, Edward, Chief Exec. Officer--Westervelt Land Co., Tuscaloosa, AL; *U.S. Private*, pg. 488
Woods, Geoffrey D., Chief Exec. Officer--Bridport-Gundry p.l.c., Dorset, United Kingdom; *Int'l*, pg. 215
Woods, J. Edwards, Chief Exec. Officer--Gulf States Paper Corporation, Tuscaloosa, AL; *U.S. Private*, pg. 487
Woods, Joe E., Chm. Bd., Pres. & Chief Exec. Officer--Joe E. Woods, Inc., Mesa, AZ; *U.S. Private*, pg. 1187
Woods, John, Pres. & Chief Exec. Officer--Western Multiplex Corporation, Sunnyvale, CA; *U.S. Public*, pg. 747
Woodward, William C., V.P. & Chief Oper. Officer-Intl. Division--Wal-Mart Stores, Inc., Bentonville, AR; *U.S. Public*, pg. 1732
Wordeman, Mike, Chm. Bd. & Chief Exec. Officer--Sodak Gaming, Inc., Rapid City, SD; *U.S. Public*, pg. 1482
Worely, Floyd L., Chm. Bd. & Chief Exec. Officer--B-Line Systems, Inc., Highland, IL; *U.S. Public*, pg. 1471
Work, Harold K., Chm. Bd., Pres. & Chief Exec. Officer--Elcor Corporation, Dallas, TX; *U.S. Public*, pg. 567
Work, Harold K., Pres. & Chief Exec. Officer--Elk Corporation of Dallas, Dallas, TX; *U.S. Public*, pg. 568
Wornick, Ronald C., Pres. & Chief Exec. Officer--The Wornick Company, Burlingame, CA; *U.S. Private*, pg. 1191
Worrell, W. Alan, Chm. Bd. & Chief Exec. Officer--Sterling Bank, Montgomery, AL; *U.S. Public*, pg. 1549
Wosje, Walt, Chief Exec. Officer--Michigan Milk Producers Association, Novi, MI; *U.S. Private*, pg. 741
Wozniak, Edward F., Pres. & Chief Exec. Officer--Wozniak Industries, Inc., Oak Brook Terrace, IL; *U.S. Private*, pg. 1192
Wray, Tom, Pres. & Chief Exec. Officer--Farmers & Merchants Bank, Rogers, AR; *U.S. Public*, pg. 630
Wrede, Franz, Chief Exec. Officer--Vinnolit Kunststoff GmbH, Ismaning, Germany; *Int'l*, pg. 626
Wreede, Paul G., Pres. & Chief Exec. Officer--The Commercial Bank, Delphos, OH; *U.S. Public*, pg. 410
Wren, John, Pres. & Chief Exec. Officer--Omnicom Group Inc., New York, NY; *U.S. Public*, pg. 1223
Wren, John, Chm. Bd. & Chief Exec. Officer--Diversified Agency Services, New York, NY; *U.S. Public*, pg. 1223
Wright, D.J., Chief Exec. Officer--GKN Defence Ltd., Telford, United Kingdom; *Int'l*, pg. 534
Wright, David, Pres. & Chief Exec. Officer--Durakon Industries, Inc., Lapeer, MI; *U.S. Public*, pg. 537
Wright, David B., Pres. & Chief Exec. Officer--Amdahl Corporation, Sunnyvale, CA; *Int'l*, pg. 527
Wright, Donald F., Pres. & Chief Exec. Officer--Los Angeles Times, Los Angeles, CA; *U.S. Public*, pg. 1616
Wright, John P., Pres.--Ariel Corporation, Mount Vernon, OH; *U.S. Private*, pg. 81
Wright, Mark H., Acting Pres. & Chief Exec. Officer--USAA Federal Savings Bank, San Antonio, TX; *U.S. Private*, pg. 1114
Wright, Michael W., Chm. Bd., Pres. & Chief Exec. Officer--SuperValu, Inc., Eden Prairie, MN; *U.S. Public*, pg. 1540
Wright, Phillip E., Chm. Bd. & Chief Exec. Officer--SunTrust Bank, North Florida, N.A., Jacksonville, FL; *U.S. Public*, pg. 1537
Wright, Thomas C., Chm. Bd. & Chief Exec. Officer--Wright Group Publishing, Inc., Bothell, WA; *U.S. Public*, pg. 1636
Wright, W. Dan, Pres. & Chief Exec. Officer--Wright Brand Foods, Inc., Vernon, TX; *U.S. Private*, pg. 1192
Wrigley, James, Chief Exec. Officer--PAXAR Europe Ltd., Watford, United Kingdom; *U.S. Public*, pg. 1267
Wu, Peter, Vice Chm. & Chief Exec. Officer--Continental Carbon Company, Houston, TX; *Int'l*, pg. 286
Wu, Peter T.K., Chief Exec. Officer--China Synthetic Rubber Corporation, Taipei, Taiwan; *Int'l*, pg. 286
Wulf, Walter H., Jr., Pres., Chief Exec. Officer & Vice Chm.--Monarch Cement Co., Humboldt, KS; *U.S. Public*, pg. 1123
Wulfers, Claus, Deputy Chief Exec. Officer--Hapag-Lloyd AG, Hamburg, Germany; *Int'l*, pg. 596
Wurm, Robert J., Chm. Bd., Pres. & Chief Exec. Officer--Quest Technologies, Inc., Oconomowoc, WI; *U.S. Private*, pg. 900
Wurzel, Tom, Pres. & Chief Exec. Officer--AAI/ACL Technologies, Santa Ana, CA; *U.S. Public*, pg. 1679
Wyandt, Steven P., Pres. & Chief Exec. & Fin. Officer--Niches, Inc., San Diego, CA; *U.S. Public*, pg. 1181
Wyandt, Steven P., Chm., Pres. & Chief Exec. Officer--Body Drama, Inc., Culver City, CA; *U.S. Public*, pg. 1182
Wyatt, Jame A., Chm. Bd. & Chief Oper. officer--ICM Holdings Inc., New York, NY; *U.S. Private*, pg. 554
Wyatt, W. Whitlow, Chm. Bd., Pres. & Chief Exec. Officer--Altama Delta Corporation, Atlanta, GA; *U.S. Private*, pg. 47
Wyckaert, Luke, Chm. Bd., Pres. & Chief Exec. Officer--Intertrade Industries, Huntington Beach, CA; *U.S. Private*, pg. 573
Wydman, Marcy R., Chm. Bd. & Chief Exec. Officer--Witt Company, Cincinnati, OH; *U.S. Private*, pg. 1185
Wygod, Martin J., Chm. Bd.--MEDCO Containment Services, Inc., Montvale, NJ; *U.S. Public*, pg. 1091
Wyle, F. Stephen, Chm. Bd. & Chief Exec. Officer--Wyle Laboratories, Inc., El Segundo, CA; *U.S. Private*, pg. 1193
Wyne, Robert L., Pres. & Chief Exec. Officer--Citizens First State Bank, Hartford City, IN; *U.S. Public*, pg. 632
Wynn, Stephen A., Chm. Bd., Pres. & Chief Exec. Officer--Mirage Resorts Incorporated, Las Vegas, NV; *U.S. Public*, pg. 1116
Wynne, John O., Pres. & Chief Exec. Officer--Landmark Communications, Inc., Norfolk, VA; *U.S. Private*, pg. 647
Wyse, Marc A., Chm. & Chief Exec. Officer--Wyse Advertising, Cleveland, OH; *U.S. Private*, pg. 1193
Ximenes Alves Ferreira, Paulo Cesar, Chm. Bd. & Pres.--Banco do Brasil, Brasilia, Brazil; *Int'l*, pg. 141
Yaacob, Tan Sri Nik Mohamed, Grp. Chief Exec.--Sime Darby Berhad, Kuala Lumpur, Malaysia; *Int'l*, pg. 1249
Yaeger, David, Vice Chm. & Chief Exec. Officer--Hub Group, Inc., Lombard, IL; *U.S. Public*, pg. 844
Yaffe, Fred, Chm. Bd. & Chief Exec. Officer--Yaffe & Company, Southfield, MI; *U.S. Private*, pg. 1195
Yahn, Chuck, Pres. & Chief Exec. Officer--Ajay Leisure Products, Inc., Delavan, WI; *U.S. Public*, pg. 34
Yajima, Hisashi, Pres. & Chief Exec. Officer--Prap Japan, Inc., Tokyo, Japan; *U.S. Private*, pg. 617
Yamada, Yasuhiro, Chm. Bd. & Chief Exec. Officer--Mentholatum Company, Buffalo, NY; *Int'l*, pg. 1126
Yamada, Yasukuni, Pres. & Chief Exec. Officer--Rohto Pharmaceutical Co., Osaka, Japan; *Int'l*, pg. 1126
Yamada, Yoji, Pres. & Chief Exec. Officer--Nippon Shinpan Co., Ltd., Tokyo, Japan; *Int'l*, pg. 939
Yamagata, E., Pres. & Chief Exec. Officer--Yokohama Tire Corporation, Fullerton, CA; *Int'l*, pg. 1521
Yamaguchi, Masahiro, Chief Oper. Officer--Makita Manufacturing Europe LTD., Telford, United Kingdom; *Int'l*, pg. 832
Yamakoshi, Noby, Chm. Bd. & Chief Exec. Officer--Nobart, Inc., Chicago, IL; *U.S. Private*, pg. 800
Yamamoto, Kayunori, Pres. & Chief Exec. Officer--Pioneer Electronics (USA) Inc., Long Beach, CA; *Int'l*, pg. 1058
Yamamoto, Masayasu, Chief Exec. Officer--Nippon Credit International (HK) Limited, Hong Kong, Hong Kong; *Int'l*, pg. 933
Yamamoto, Yoshihide, Chm. Bd., Pres. & Chief Exec. Officer--Sumikin Bussan Corporation, Osaka, Japan; *Int'l*, pg. 1308
Yamamoto, Yoshiro, Pres. & Chief Exec. Officer--The Fuji Bank, Limited, Tokyo, Japan; *Int'l*, pg. 519
Yamamoto, Yukio, Pres. & Chief Exec. Officer--Aiwa America, Inc., Mahwah, NJ; *Int'l*, pg. 1280
Yamaoka, Takeo, Pres. & Chief Exec. Officer--Juki Corporation, Tokyo, Japan; *Int'l*, pg. 716
Yamazoe, Akiteru, Chief Oper. Officer--Makita France S.A., Noisy-le-Grand, France; *Int'l*, pg. 832
Yando, Gregory G., Chief Exec. Officer--Western Dairymen Cooperative, Inc., Thornton, CO; *U.S. Private*, pg. 1165
Yang, Huiqui, Co-Chief Exec. Officer--Bank of China, Beijing, China; *Int'l*, pg. 152
Yano, Makoto, Chief Exec. Officer--Konami Co. Ltd., Tokyo, Japan; *Int'l*, pg. 745
Yansouni, Cyril J., Chm. Bd. & Chief Exec. Officer--Read-Rite Corporation, Milpitas, CA; *U.S. Public*, pg. 1366
Yantis, Thomas G., Pres. & Chief Exec. Officer--Yantis Corporation, San Antonio, TX; *U.S. Private*, pg. 1195
Yarbrough, Jerry A., Chm. Bd. & Chief Exec. Officer--Integrated Distributions, Inc., Little Rock, AR; *U.S. Public*, pg. 131
Yasinsky, John B., Chm. Bd., Pres. & Chief Exec. Officer--GenCorp Inc., Fairlawn, OH; *U.S. Public*, pg. 705
Yau, Joseph, Chief Exec. Officer & Mng. Dir.--Metropolitan Life Insurance Company of Hong Kong, Ltd., Hong Kong, Hong Kong; *U.S. Private*, pg. 738
Yearley, Douglas C., Chm. Bd. & Chief Exec. Officer--Phelps Dodge Corporation, Phoenix, AZ; *U.S. Public*, pg. 1286
Yearsley, W.S., Chief Exec. Officer--Western Mobile Inc., Denver, CO; *Int'l*, pg. 1091
Yeates, Douglas T., Pres. & Chief Exec. Officer--Regions Bank/Habersham County, Cornelia, GA; *U.S. Public*, pg. 1372
Yeh, Ch., Chief Exec. Officer--OCE (Taiwan) Ltd., Taipei, Taiwan; *Int'l*, pg. 995
Yellowlees, Robert A., Chm. Bd. & Chief Exec. Officer--National Data Corporation, Atlanta, GA; *U.S. Public*, pg. 1155
Yelverton, William F., Chm. & Chief Exec. Officer--New York Life Worldwide Holding, Inc., New York, NY; *U.S. Private*, pg. 795
Yelverton, William F., Chief Exec. Officer-Individual Insurance Grp.--The Prudential Insurance Company of America, Newark, NJ; *U.S. Private*, pg. 892
Yerushalmi, Yaacov, Chief Exec. Officer & Gen. Mgr.--American Israeli Paper Mills Ltd., Hadera, Israel; *Int'l*, pg. 74
Yesawich, Peter C., Ph.D., Pres. & Chief Exec. Officer--Yesawich, Pepperdine & Brown, Orlando, FL; *U.S. Private*, pg. 1195
Yetman, William, Chief Exec. Officer--Dribeck Importers, Inc., Greenwich, CT; *U.S. Private*, pg. 343
Yetter, Wayne, Chief Exec. Officer--Novartis Pharmaceuticals, East Hanover, NJ; *Int'l*, pg. 973
Yocam, Delbert W., Chm. & Chief Exec. Officer--Borland International, Inc., Scotts Valley, CA; *U.S. Public*, pg. 246
Yocum, Dr. Ronald H., Pres. & Chief Exec. Officer--Millennium Petrochemicals, Inc., Cincinnati, OH; *Int'l*, pg. 594
Yoder, Edward L., Pres. & Chief Exec. Officer--Rurban Life Insurance Company, Defiance, OH; *U.S. Public*, pg. 1413
Yoder, Kent, Pres. & Chief Exec. Officer--Yoder Oil Company Inc., Elkhart, IN; *U.S. Private*, pg. 1196
Yoh, Harold L., Jr., Chm. Bd. & Chief Exec. Officer--Day & Zimmermann, Inc., Philadelphia, PA; *U.S. Private*, pg. 316
Yohman, Edward J., Chm. Bd. & Chief Exec. Officer--Cyberex, Inc., Mentor, OH; *U.S. Public*, pg. 481
Yokoi, Hiromasa, Vice Chm., Pres. & Chief Exec. Officer--Berlitz International, Inc., Princeton, NJ; *U.S. Public*, pg. 221
Yokokawa, Kiwamu, Vice Chm. & Chief Exec. Officer--Skylark Co., Ltd., Tokyo, Japan; *Int'l*, pg. 1262
Yokokawa, Norio, Chief Exec. Officer & V.P.--Skylark Co., Ltd., Tokyo, Japan; *Int'l*, pg. 1262
Yokomizo, Michio, Chief Exec. Officer--Novo Nordisk Biochemicals KK, Hokkaido, Japan; *Int'l*, pg. 989
Yokotani, Hiroshi, Chief Oper. Officer--Daiko Advertising, Inc., Fukuoka, Japan; *Int'l*, pg. 366
Yokoyama, Toshio, Co-Pres. & Co-Chief Exec. Officer--The Nikko Securities Co. International Inc., New York, NY; *Int'l*, pg. 930
Yomantas, Gary C., Pres. & Chief Exec. Officer--New Hampshire Ball Bearings, Inc., Peterborough, NH; *Int'l*, pg. 868
Yomazzo, Michael J., Pres. & Chief Exec. Officer--Photronics, Inc., Brookfield, CT; *U.S. Public*, pg. 1293
Yon, S., Chief Exec. Officer--Holaday Industries, Inc., Eden Prairie, MN; *Int'l*, pg. 208
Yonemoto, Hiroshi, Pres. & Chief Exec. Officer--Nissan Mutual Life Insurance Company, Tokyo, Japan; *Int'l*, pg. 945
Yong, Yun Jong, Pres. & Chief Exec. Officer--Samsung Group, Seoul, Korea; *Int'l*, pg. 1181
Yonker, Michael T., Pres. & Chief Exec. Officer--Portec, Inc., Lake Forest, IL; *U.S. Public*, pg. 1317
Yontz, Kenneth F., Chm. Bd., Pres., & Chief Exec. Officer--Sybron International Corporation, Milwaukee, WI; *U.S. Public*, pg. 1544
York, Roy B., Chm. Bd. & Chief Exec. Officer--Martin Electronics, Inc., Perry, FL; *U.S. Private*, pg. 709
Yoshida, Kanetaka, Pres. & Chief Exec. Officer--Union Bank of California, San Francisco, CA; *Int'l*, pg. 157
Yoshikawa, Atsushi, Co-Pres.--Nomura Securities International, Inc., New York, NY; *Int'l*, pg. 956
Yost, Larry D., Chm. Bd. & Chief Exec. Officer--Meritor Automotive, Inc., Troy, MI; *U.S. Public*, pg. 1096
Yost, R. David, Pres. & Chief Exec. Officer--AmeriSource Health Corp., Malvern, PA; *U.S. Public*, pg. 96
Yost, Wallace H., Chm. Bd. & Chief Exec. Officer--D.S.U.-Peterbilt & GMC, Inc., Portland, OR; *U.S. Private*, pg. 306
Youmans, Peter, Owner & Chief Exec. Officer--Connecticut Spring & Stamping Corporation, Farmington, CT; *U.S. Private*, pg. 263
Young, C. Steve, Pres. & Chief Exec. Officer--MicroBilt Corporation, Atlanta, GA; *U.S. Public*, pg. 631
Young, Daniel, Pres. & Chief Exec. Officer--Federal Data Corporation, Bethesda, MD; *U.S. Private*, pg. 398
Young, Donald A., Pres. & Chief Exec. Officer--Kapalua Land Co., Ltd., Lahaina, HI; *U.S. Public*, pg. 1060
Young, Gregg, Chief Exec. Officer--Bernard Johnson Young Inc., Austin, TX; *U.S. Private*, pg. 136
Young, Jack, Chief Exec. Officer--Pocono Knits, Inc., Hazleton, PA; *U.S. Private*, pg. 1201
Young, John, Chief Exec. Officer--Hewlett Packard Avondale, Wilmington, DE; *U.S. Public*, pg. 816
Young, John A., Jr., Chm. Bd. & Chief Exec. Officer--Burd & Fletcher Company, Kansas City, MO; *U.S. Private*, pg. 181
Young, John W.G., Dep. Chief Exec. Officer--Wolseley Plc., Droitwich, United Kingdom; *Int'l*, pg. 1511
Young, Mark W., Chief Exec. Officer--American Cometra, Inc., Fort Worth, TX; *Int'l*, pg. 562
Young, Maynard, Chief Exec. Officer--Canadian Erectors Ltd., North York, Canada; *Int'l*, pg. 256
Young, Neil, Chm. Bd. & Chief Exec. Officer--Grubb & Ellis Company, Northbrook, IL; *U.S. Public*, pg. 767
Young, P. L., Grp. Chief Exec.--RMC Group p.l.c., Egham, United Kingdom; *Int'l*, pg. 1078
Young, Richard F., Chm. Bd., Pres. & Chief Exec. Officer--Sues, Young & Brown Inc., Baldwin Park, CA; *U.S. Private*, pg. 1049
Young, Robert A., III, Pres. & Chief Exec. Officer--Arkansas Best Corporation, Fort Smith, AR; *U.S. Public*, pg. 130
Young, Robert H., Pres. & Chief Exec. Officer--Central Vermont Public Service Corporation, Rutland, VT; *U.S. Public*, pg. 327
Young, Robert H., Pres. & Chief Exec. Officer--Smart Energy Services, Inc., Rutland, VT; *U.S. Public*, pg. 328
Young, Roger A., Chm. Bd. & Chief Exec. Officer--Bay State Gas Company, Westborough, MA; *U.S. Public*, pg. 196
Young, Victor L., Chm. Bd. & Chief Exec. Officer--Fishery Products International Ltd., Saint Johns, Canada; *Int'l*, pg. 492
Young, Walter R., Jr., Chm. Bd., Pres. & Chief Exec. Officer--Champion Enterprises, Inc., Auburn Hills, MI; *U.S. Public*, pg. 332
Young, William B., Pres. & Chief Exec. Officer--The National Bank of Fredericksburg, Fredericksburg, VA; *U.S. Public*, pg. 1089
Young, William D., Sr., Pres. & Chief Exec. Officer--General Wholesale Company, Inc., Atlanta, GA; *U.S. Private*, pg. 445
Young, William J., Chm. Bd., Pres. & Chief Exec. Officer--Advanced Machine Vision Corp., Medford, OR; *U.S. Public*, pg. 20
Yount, Bradley A., Pres. & Chief Exec. Officer--Specialty Filaments Inc., Andover, MA; *U.S. Private*, pg. 77
Youssefzadeh, Emil, Pres., Chief Exec. Officer & Sec.--STM Wireless, Inc., Irvine, CA; *U.S. Public*, pg. 1421
Yu, Philip, Chm. Bd. & Chief Exec. Officer-Nortel China--Northern Telecom Limited, Brampton, Canada; *Int'l*, pg. 968
Yuasa, Hisao, Chm. & Chief Exec. Officer--Ricoh Corporation, West Caldwell, NJ; *Int'l*, pg. 1114
Yuasa, Teruhisa, Pres. & Chief Exec. Officer--Yuasa Corporation, Tokyo, Japan; *Int'l*, pg. 1522
Yuasa, Teruhisa, Chief Exec. Officer--Yuasa-Exide, Inc., Reading, PA; *Int'l*, pg. 1522
Yuchengco, Y.S., Chief Exec. Officer--First Nationwide Assurance Corporation, Manila, Philippines; *Int'l*, pg. 1532
Yuchengco, Y.S., Chief Exec. Officer--Malayan Insurance Company, Inc., Manila, Philippines; *Int'l*, pg. 1532

Yuchengco, Y.S., Chief Exec. Officer--Malayan Zurich Insurance Company, Inc., Makati, Philippines; *Int'l*, pg. 1532
Yull, Melbourne F., Chm. Bd. & Chief Exec. Officer--Intertape Polymer Group Inc., Saint-Laurent, Canada; *Int'l*, pg. 684
Yulo, J., Chief Oper. Officer--Batangas Bay Terminal, Inc., Rizal, Philippines; *Int'l*, pg. 947
Yun, Jong-Yong, Chm. Bd. & Chief Exec. Officer--Samsung Japan Corporation, Tokyo, Japan; *Int'l*, pg. 1183
Yung, Richard, Pres. & Chief Exec. Officer--MCRB Service Bureau, Inc., Chatsworth, CA; *U.S. Private*, pg. 686
Yunkun, Chris, Chief Exec. Officer--Pettibone Corporation, Lisle, IL; *U.S. Private*, pg. 859
Yurko, Allen, Chief Exec. Officer & Mng. Dir.--Siebe plc, Windsor, United Kingdom; *Int'l*, pg. 1240
Yurkovic, Leonard S., Pres. & Chief Exec. Officer--SI Handling Systems, Inc., Easton, PA; *U.S. Public*, pg. 1418
Zabel, Ron, Pres. & Chief Exec. Officer--Worldwide Sports & Recreation, Inc., Tulsa, OK; *U.S. Private*, pg. 1191
Zable, Walter J., Chm. Bd., Pres. & Chief Exec. Officer--Cubic Corporation, San Diego, CA; *U.S. Public*, pg. 466
Zabriskie, John L., Ph.D., Pres. & Chief Exec. Officer--Pharmacia & Upjohn, Kalamazoo, MI; *Int'l*, pg. 1048
Zacca, Christopher, Chief Exec. Officer--Air Jamaica Ltd., Miami, FL; *U.S. Private*, pg. 28
Zaccaglin, Victor, Chm. Bd. & Chief Exec. Officer--Calprop Corporation, Marina Del Rey, CA; *U.S. Public*, pg. 296
Zachry, H.B., Jr., Chm. Bd. & Chief Exec. Officer--H.B. Zachry, San Antonio, TX; *U.S. Private*, pg. 1203
Zacks, Gordon, Chm. Bd., Pres. & Chief Exec. Officer--R.G. Barry Corporation, Pickerington, OH; *U.S. Public*, pg. 192
Zadel, C. William, Chm. Bd., Pres. & Chief Exec. Officer--Millipore Corporation, Bedford, MA; *U.S. Public*, pg. 1112
Zades, Stephen H., Chm. & Chief Exec. Officer--Long Haymes Carr, Inc., Winston Salem, NC; *U.S. Public*, pg. 909
Zafiropoulo, Arthur W., Chm. Bd., Pres. & Chief Exec. Officer--Ultratech Stepper, Inc., San Jose, CA; *U.S. Public*, pg. 1663
Zaks, Rodnay, Pres. & Chief Exec. Officer--Sybex, Inc., Alameda, CA; *U.S. Private*, pg. 1059
Zalenski, Anthony F., Pres. & Chief Exec. Officer--Boca Research Inc., Boca Raton, FL; *U.S. Public*, pg. 239
Zaleschuk, Victor J., Pres., Chief Exec. & Fin. Officer--Canadian Occidental Petroleum Ltd., Calgary, Canada; *U.S. Public*, pg. 1210
Zambonini, Renato, Pres. & Chief Exec. Officer--Cognos Inc., Ottawa, Canada; *Int'l*, pg. 305
Zambrano, Lorenzo H., Chm. Bd. & Chief Exec. Officer--Cemex, S.A. de C.V., Monterrey, Mexico; *Int'l*, pg. 278
Zamora, M.B., Jr., Chief Oper. Officer--RIO-TUBA Nickel Mining Corp., Manila, Philippines; *Int'l*, pg. 949
Zanck, Charie A., Pres., Chief Exec. Officer & Dir.--AMCORE Bank N.A., Northwest, Woodstock, IL; *U.S. Public*, pg. 64
Zander, Glenn R., Pres. & Chief Exec. Officer--Aloha Airgroup, Inc., Honolulu, HI; *U.S. Private*, pg. 44
Zander, Glenn R., Vice Chm. & Chief Exec. Officer--Island Air, Honolulu, HI; *U.S. Private*, pg. 44
Zandman, Felix, Dr., Chm. Bd., Pres. & Chief Exec. Officer--Vishay Intertechnology, Inc., Malvern, PA; *U.S. Public*, pg. 1721
Zane, Ken, Pres. & Chief Exec. Officer--Idea Engineering & Fabricating, Detroit, MI; *U.S. Private*, pg. 557
Zantop, Duane A., Chm. Bd. & Chief Exec. Officer--Zantop International Airlines, Inc., Ypsilanti, MI; *U.S. Private*, pg. 1204
Zanzotto, Tommaso, Chief Exec. Officer-Hilton Intl.--Ladbroke Group Plc, London, United Kingdom; *Int'l*, pg. 787
Zapata, Dario Castano, Chief Exec. Officer--Central de Cervejas, S.A., Lisbon, Portugal; *Int'l*, pg. 279
Zaremba, Walter, Pres. & Chief Exec. Officer--Zaremba Group, Inc., Lakewood, OH; *U.S. Private*, pg. 1204
Zarges, Thomas H., Pres. & Chief Exec. Officer--Morrison Knudsen Corp.-Engineering & Construction, Cleveland, OH; *U.S. Public*, pg. 1134
Zarker, Gary, Superintendent--Seattle City Light, Seattle, WA; *U.S. Private*, pg. 979
Zarrow, Henry, Pres. & Chief Exec. Officer--Sooner Pipe & Supply Corp., Tulsa, OK; *U.S. Private*, pg. 1014
Zazulia, Irwin, Pres. & Chief Exec. Officer--Hecht's, Arlington, VA; *U.S. Public*, pg. 1063
Zech, Ronald H., Chm. Bd. & Chief Exec. Officer--GATX Corporation, Chicago, IL; *U.S. Public*, pg. 690
Zeien, Alfred M., Chm. Bd. & Chief Exec. Officer--The Gillette Company, Boston, MA; *U.S. Public*, pg. 743
Zeigler, Charles E., Jr., Chm. Bd., Pres. & Chief Exec. Officer--Public Service Company of North Carolina, Inc., Gastonia, NC; *U.S. Public*, pg. 1340
Zelazo, N.K., Chief Exec. Officer--Astronautics Corporation of America, Milwaukee, WI; *U.S. Private*, pg. 93
Zell, Samuel, Chm. Bd. & Chief Exec. Officer--Capsure Holdings Corp., Chicago, IL; *U.S. Public*, pg. 303
Zeller, M.C., Pres. & Chief Exec. Officer--Zeller Corp., Defiance, OH; *U.S. Private*, pg. 1204
Zelnak, Stephen P., Jr., Vice Chm., Pres. & Chief Exec. Officer--Martin Marietta Materials, Inc., Raleigh, NC; *U.S.* Public, pg. 1007
Zemanek, Bob, Pres. & Chief Exec. Officer--Public Service Company of Oklahoma, Tulsa, OK; *U.S. Public*, pg. 324
Zemenick, Carl A., Pres., Chief Exec. Officer & Chief Oper. Officer--GF Office Furniture Ltd., Gallatin, TN; *U.S. Private*, pg. 434
Zenk, Saul, Pres. & Treas.--Monico Alloys, Inc., Los Angeles, CA; *U.S. Private*, pg. 757
Zenner, Patrick J., Pres. & Chief Exec. Officer--Hoffmann-La Roche Inc., Nutley, NJ; *Int'l*, pg. 1120
Zensen, Dennis C., Chm. Bd., Pres. & Chief Exec. Officer--Sylvan Inc., Saxonburg, PA; *U.S. Public*, pg. 1545
Zetcher, Arnold B., Pres. & Chief Exec. Officer-The Talbots, Inc.--AEON Group, Chiba, Japan; *Int'l*, pg. 28
Zetcher, Arnold B., Pres. & Chief Exec. Officer--Talbots, Inc., Hingham, MA; *Int'l*, pg. 28
Zhubandykova, Leila A., Chief Exec.--Novo Nordisk A/S, Almaty, Kazakhstan; *Int'l*, pg. 987
Zicarelli, Jim, Chm. Bd., Chief Exec. Officer & Chief Oper. Officer--Cramer Inc., Kansas City, KS; *U.S. Private*, pg. 285
Zickler, Leo E., Chief Exec. Officer--Oxford Realty Financial Group, Bethesda, MD; *U.S. Private*, pg. 825
Ziegenbein, Klaus, Chm. Bd., Pres. & Chief Exec. Officer--Koh-I-Noor, Inc., Bloomsbury, NJ; *U.S. Private*, pg. 629
Zieger, Claus D., Chm. Bd., Pres., Chief Exec. Officer & Treas.--Interbath, Inc., City of Industry, CA; *U.S. Private*, pg. 566
Ziegler, John K., Chm. Bd. & Chief Exec. Officer--Willcox & Gibbs, Inc., Carteret, NJ; *U.S. Private*, pg. 1177
Ziegler, Klaus, Chief Oper. Officer--Siemens Matsushita Components GmbH & Co. KG, Munich, Germany; *Int'l*, pg. 1245
Ziegler, P.D., Pres. & Chief Exec. Officer--The Ziegler Companies, Inc., West Bend, WI; *U.S. Public*, pg. 1791
Ziegler, Willam, III, Chm. Bd. & Chief Exec. Officer--Swisher International Group, Inc., Darien, CT; *U.S. Public*, pg. 1543
Ziehm, Richard, Pres., Chief Exec. Officer & Treas.--Precision Extrusions, Bensenville, IL; *U.S. Private*, pg. 879
Zielman, H. H., Chief Exec. Officer--OCE-Deutschland Leasing GmbH, Mulheim, Germany; *Int'l*, pg. 994
Zielman, H.H., Chief Exec. Officer--OCE-Deutschland GmbH, Mulheim, Germany; *Int'l*, pg. 994
Zierdt, John V., Pres. & Chief Exec. Officer--Transcorp, Nashville, TN; *U.S. Public*, pg. 451
Ziering, Sigi, Ph.D., Chm. Bd. & Chief Exec. Officer--Diagnostic Products Corporation, Los Angeles, CA; *U.S. Public*, pg. 505
Zitterer, Morton F., Jr., Pres. & Chief Exec. Officer--New Standard Corporation, Mount Joy, PA; *U.S. Private*, pg. 794
Zilin, Yang, Vice Chm. & Chief Exec.-BOC Hong Kong/Macau--Bank of China, Beijing, China; *Int'l*, pg. 152
Zimdar, William L., Chm. Bd., Chief Exec. Officer, Chief Fin. Officer & V.P.--Zimdar Enterprises/Frames Unlimited, Wyoming, MI; *U.S. Private*, pg. 1206
Zimmer, Alan M., Pres. & Chief Exec. Officer--Reeds Jewelers, Inc., Wilmington, NC; *U.S. Public*, pg. 1370
Zimmer, Edward M., Jr., Chm. Bd. & Chief Exec. Officer--Telonic Berkeley, Inc., Laguna Beach, CA; *U.S. Private*, pg. 1074
Zimmer, George, Chm. Bd. & Chief Exec. Officer--Men's Wearhouse, Fremont, CA; *U.S. Public*, pg. 1086
Zimmerman, Adam H., Chm. Bd. & Chief Exec. Officer--Noranda Forest Inc., Toronto, Canada; *Int'l*, pg. 434
Zimmerman, Ann, Chief Exec. Officer--Fashion Shop of Kentucky Inc., Louisville, KY; *U.S. Private*, pg. 397
Zimmerman, Dennis A., Pres. & Chief Exec. Officer--ComSonics, Inc., Harrisonburg, VA; *U.S. Private*, pg. 260
Zimmerman, James M., Chm. Bd. & Chief Exec. Officer--Federated Department Stores, Inc., Cincinnati, OH; *U.S. Public*, pg. 617
Zimmerman, Martin E., Chm. Bd. & Chief Exec. Officer--LINC Capital Group, Chicago, IL; *U.S. Public*, pg. 996
Zimmerman, Ronald C., Pres. & Chief Exec. Officer--Hornor, Townsend & Kent, Philadelphia, PA; *U.S. Private*, pg. 849
Zinbarg, Benson, Pres., Chief Exec. Officer, Chief Fin. Officer & Treas.--Sun Hill Industries, Inc., Stamford, CT; *U.S. Private*, pg. 1051
Zingale, Anthony, Pres. & Chief Exec. Officer--Clarify Inc., San Jose, CA; *U.S. Public*, pg. 382
Zisman, Michael D., Chief Exec. Officer & Exec. V.P.--Lotus Business Products Div., Cambridge, MA; *U.S. Public*, pg. 896
Zissman, Lorin, Chm. Bd. & Chief Exec. Officer--Total Research Corporation, Princeton, NJ; *U.S. Public*, pg. 1625
Zito, Paul M., Pres. & Chief Exec. Officer--Bacharach Inc., Pittsburgh, PA; *U.S. Private*, pg. 109
Zitting, Gordon, Pres. & Chief Exec. Officer--Macrotech Plyseal, Inc., Salt Lake City, UT; *U.S. Private*, pg. 693
Zitz, Jay T., Pres. & Chief Exec. Officer--Fort Wayne Newspaper Agency, Fort Wayne, IN; *U.S. Public*, pg. 964
Zizza, Salvatore, Chm. Bd. & Chief Exec. Officer--The Bethlehem Corporation, Easton, PA; *U.S. Public*, pg. 225
Zizza, Salvatore J., Chm. Bd., Pres. & Chief Exec. Officer--First Medical Group Inc., Stamford, CT; *U.S. Public*, pg. 636
Zlatoper, Ronald J., Chief Exec. Officer--Sanchez Computer Associates, Malvern, PA; *U.S. Public*, pg. 1425
Zobl, Manfred, Pres. & Chief Exec. Officer--The Swiss Life/Rentenanstalt Group, Zurich, Switzerland; *Int'l*, pg. 1332
Zobrist, Phil, Pres. & Chief Exec. Officer--Valley Food Distributors of Nevada, Las Vegas, NV; *U.S. Public*, pg. 919
Zoley, George C., Vice Chm., Chief Exec. Officer & Sr. V.P.-Wackenhut Corrections--The Wackenhut Corporation, Palm Beach Gardens, FL; *U.S. Public*, pg. 1731
Zollars, Robert L., Pres.--Huitt-Zollars, Inc., Dallas, TX; *U.S. Private*, pg. 547
Zoota, Murray, Pres. & Chief Exec. Officer--Fremont Investment & Loan, Anaheim, CA; *U.S. Public*, pg. 681
Zoulkin, Jania, Chief Exec. Officer--Batterymarch Financial Management, Boston, MA; *U.S. Public*, pg. 985
Zriny, Bob, Chief Exec. Officer--Whitney Corr-Pak International, Inc., East Brunswick, NJ; *U.S. Private*, pg. 249
Zucaro, Aldo C., Chm. Bd., Pres. & Chief Exec. Officer--Old Republic International Corporation, Chicago, IL; *U.S. Public*, pg. 1218
Zuccotti, John E., Chm. Bd. & Chief Exec. Officer--World Financial Properties, Inc., New York, NY; *Int'l*, pg. 1004
Zucker, Fredrick, Pres. & Chief Exec. Officer--Advanced Input Devices, Inc., Coeur D'Alene, ID; *U.S. Private*, pg. 21
Zuckermaan, Ron, Chief Exec. Officer--Sapiens International Corporation N.V., Curacao, Netherlands Antilles; *Int'l*, pg. 1193
Zuckerman, Benjamin R., Pres.& Chief Exec. Officer--Zuckerman-Honickman Inc., King of Prussia, PA; *U.S. Private*, pg. 1207
Zuckerman, Ron, Chief Exec. Officer--Sapiens USA, Inc., Durham, NC; *Int'l*, pg. 1193
Zuckerwar, Richard J., Chm. Bd. & Chief Exec. Officer--The Grandoe Corp., Gloversville, NY; *U.S. Private*, pg. 469
Zuege, David A., Pres. & Chief Exec. Officer--The Oilgear Company, Milwaukee, WI; *U.S. Public*, pg. 1215
Zuidam, J., Chief Exec.--DSM Research B.V., Geleen, Netherlands; *Int'l*, pg. 353
Zumbach, Felix, Chief Exec. Officer & Exec. V.P.--Union Bank of Switzerland, Zurich, Switzerland; *Int'l*, pg. 1439
Zund, R., Dr., Chief Exec. Officer--Coutts & Co AG, Zurich, Switzerland; *Int'l*, pg. 911
Zurilla, Tom, Pres. & Chief Exec. Officer--G B Stores, Columbus, OH; *U.S. Private*, pg. 972
ZurSchmiede, W.T., Jr., Chm. Bd., Chief Exec. & Chief Fin. Officer--Federal Screw Works, Detroit, MI; *U.S. Public*, pg. 616
Zvolensky, John, Pres. & Chief Exec. Officer--Kuhlman Electric Corporation, Versailles, KY; *U.S. Public*, pg. 968
Zychick, Joel D., Pres. & Chief Exec. Officer--Getko Group Inc., Westbury, NY; *U.S. Public*, pg. 320
Zylstra, Russell, Pres. & Chief Exec. Officer--Rena-Ware Distributors Inc., Redmond, WA; *U.S. Private*, pg. 922
Zyss, Jacques, Special Asst. to the Chm. & Chief Exec. Officer--COGEMA - Compagnie Generale des Matieres Nucleaires, Velizy-Villacoublay, France; *Int'l*, pg. 304

CHIEF FINANCIAL OFFICER

Aaron, Morris C., Chief Fin. Officer--Employee Solutions, Inc., Phoenix, AZ; *U.S. Public*, pg. 579
Aaron, Robert, Chief Fin. Officer--American Trading Real Estate Properties, Inc., Baltimore, MD; *U.S. Private*, pg. 64
Abajian, Theodore, Chief Fin. Officer--Star Buffet, Inc., Salt Lake City, UT; *U.S. Public*, pg. 278
Abaunza, Carlos, Chief Fin. Officer--International Recovery Corp., Miami Springs, FL; *U.S. Public*, pg. 906
Abbatomarco, Frank, Chief Fin. Officer & Sr. V.P.--DHP Limited Partnership, Chicopee, MA; *U.S. Private*, pg. 302
Abbott, Don, Chief Fin. Officer--Millennium Inorganic Chemicals, Hunt Valley, MD; *Int'l*, pg. 593
Abbott, Michael E., Chm. Bd. & Chief Exec. Officer--American Republic Insurance Co., Des Moines, IA; *U.S. Private*, pg. 61
Abbott, R. William, Chief Fin. Officer & Exec. V.P.--WSFS Financial Corporation, Wilmington, DE; *U.S. Public*, pg. 1728
Abbrederis, Dale E., Chief Fin. Officer & Sr. V.P.--Unigard Insurance Co., Bellevue, WA; *Int'l*, pg. 345
Abbrederis, Dale E., Chief Fin. Officer & Sr. V.P.--Unigard Indemnity Co., Bellevue, WA; *Int'l*, pg. 345
Abdalian, Charles H., Chief Fin. Officer & V.P.--Del Laboratories, Inc., Farmingdale, NY; *U.S. Public*, pg. 494
Abdalla, A., Chief Fin. Officer--Waterville TG Inc., Waterville, Canada; *Int'l*, pg. 1487
Abe, S., Mgr.-Corp. Fin. Acctg.--Dainippon Ink & Chemicals, Inc., Tokyo, Japan; *Int'l*, pg. 369
Abel, James J., Chief Fin. Officer, Exec. V.P., Treas. & Sec.--The Lamson & Sessions Co., Cleveland, OH; *U.S. Public*, pg. 976
Abel, James J., Chief Fin. Officer--Carlon Chimes Co., Cleveland, OH; *U.S. Public*, pg. 976
Abely, Joseph F., Pres. & Chief Oper. Officer--LoJack Corporation, Dedham, MA; *U.S. Public*, pg. 1012
Aberasturi, Paul, Chief Fin. Officer--Amicale Industries, Inc., New York, NY; *U.S. Private*, pg. 66
Abernethy, John J., Chief Fin. Officer--CCH Incorporated, Riverwoods, IL; *Int'l*, pg. 1513
Abney, Mike, Chief Fin. Officer--AccuStaff Incorporated, Jacksonville, FL; *U.S. Public*, pg. 15
Abrahamsen, R.J.N., Chief Fin. Officer & Mng. Dir.--KLM Royal Dutch Airlines, Amstelveen, Netherlands; *Int'l*, pg. 719
Abrahamson, Mary Jo, Chief Fin. Officer--Kupper Parker Communications Inc., Saint Louis, MO; *U.S. Private*, pg. 637
Abrahamson, R.J.N., Mng. Dir. & Chief Fin. Officer--KLM Royal Dutch Airlines, Elmsford, NY; *Int'l*, pg. 719
Abramovic, A. Mark, Chief Fin. Officer & Sr. V.P.--NUI Corporation, Bedminster, NJ; *U.S. Public*, pg. 1147
Abrams, Archie, Chief Fin. Officer--Bermil Industries Corp., Inwood, NY; *U.S. Private*, pg. 136
Abrams, Gary N., Chief Fin. Officer, Sr. V.P. & Treas.--Somerset Savings Bank, Somerville, MA; *U.S. Public*, pg. 1484
Abrams, Jerry, Chief Fin. Officer & Treas.--Hoogovens Aluminium Corp., Secaucus, NJ; *Int'l*, pg. 755
Abrams, Sharlene, Chief Fin. Officer & V.P.-Fin.--Mercury Interactive Corp., Sunnyvale, CA; *U.S. Public*, pg. 1093
Abruzzio, P.A., Chief Fin. Officer--Union Camp Wood Products Div., Savannah, GA; *U.S. Public*, pg. 1666
Abshire, Richard B., V.P.-Fin. & Treas.--Adams Resources & Energy, Inc., Houston, TX; *U.S. Public*, pg. 18
Accardo, Jack, Chief Fin. Officer--Knurlet Tool Co., Warren, MI; *U.S. Private*, pg. 608
Accardo, Jack P., Chief Fin. Officer, V.P., Treas. & Sec.--Kasper Machine Company, Madison Heights, MI; *U.S. Private*, pg. 608
Acker, Heather, Chief Fin. Officer--Gentex Optics, Inc., Simpson, PA; *Int'l*, pg. 462
Ackerman, John, Chief Fin. Officer--Design Concepts Integration, Inc., Bloomington, MN; *U.S. Private*, pg. 572
Ackerman, Philip C., Chief Fin. Officer & Sr. V.P.--National Fuel Gas Company, Buffalo, NY; *U.S. Public*, pg. 1156

Ackerman, Sanford S., Chief Fin. Officer & Sr. V.P.--Blair Television, New York, NY; *U.S. Private*, pg. 148
Acord, Gary, Chief Fin. Officer & V.P.--Artisoft, Inc., Tucson, AZ; *U.S. Public*, pg. 136
Acosta, Jack, Chief Fin. Officer & Sr. V.P.--Sybase, Inc., Emeryville, CA; *U.S. Public*, pg. 1544
Adam, Jurgen, Dr., Chief Fin. Officer--Lista Holding AG, Erlen, Switzerland; *Int'l*, pg. 812
Adami, Gary, Chief Fin. Officer & Exec. V.P.--Ruppman Marketing Technologies, Inc., Peoria, IL; *U.S. Private*, pg. 951
Adams, Bonnie, Treas.--Dormeyer Industries, Chicago, IL; *U.S. Private*, pg. 340
Adams, Dale A., Chief Fin. Officer--Diversified Agency Services, New York, NY; *U.S. Public*, pg. 1223
Adams, James E., Chief Fin. Officer, Exec. V.P. & Treas.--MainStreet BankGroup Incorporated, Martinsville, VA; *U.S. Public*, pg. 1038
Adams, John B., Chief Fin. Officer, Exec. V.P.-Fin., Sec. & Treas.--Big O Tires Incorporated, Englewood, CO; *U.S. Public*, pg. 1553
Adams, Kenneth J., Chief Fin. Officer & Sr. V.P.--Movado Group, Inc., Lyndhurst, NJ; *U.S. Public*, pg. 1140
Adams, L. Ray, Chief Fin. Officer & V.P.-Fin.--Oregon Steel Mills Inc., Portland, OR; *U.S. Public*, pg. 1230
Adams, Paul D., Chief Fin. Officer, Sr. V.P. & Treas.--Old Republic International Corporation, Chicago, IL; *U.S. Public*, pg. 1218
Adams, Ron H., Chief Fin. Officer & V.P.-Fin. & Admin.--Cains Foods, L.P., Ayer, MA; *U.S. Private*, pg. 199
Adamson, Cameron, Chief Fin. Officer--B/E Aerospace, Inc./In Flight Entertainment Group, Irvine, CA; *U.S. Public*, pg. 159
Adamson, Randy, Chief Fin. Officer & V.P.--Golden Alaska Seafoods, Inc., Seattle, WA; *Int'l*, pg. 928
Addy, J.G., Div. Accountant--WBB Devon Clays Ltd., Newton Abbot, United Kingdom; *Int'l*, pg. 1487
Adelstein, Stanford M., Chm. Bd. & Treas.--Hills Materials Co., Rapid City, SD; *U.S. Private*, pg. 806
Adik, Stephen P., Chief Fin. Officer, Sr. V.P. & Treas.--NIPSCO Industries, Inc., Hammond, IN; *U.S. Public*, pg. 1185
Adik, Stephen P., Chief Fin. Officer & Exec. V.P.--Northern Indiana Public Service Company, Hammond, IN; *U.S. Public*, pg. 1185
Adler, Ira R., Chief Fin. Officer & Sr. V.P.--UniSource Energy Corporation, Tucson, AZ; *U.S. Public*, pg. 1670
Adler, Ira R., Chief Fin. Officer & Sr. V.P.--Tucson Electric Power Company, Tucson, AZ; *U.S. Public*, pg. 1670
Adrean, Lee, Chief Fin. Officer & Exec. V.P.--First Data Corporation, Hackensack, NJ; *U.S. Public*, pg. 630
Aebel, Charles F., Chief Fin. Officer & Exec. V.P.--Central States Diversified, Inc., Saint Louis, MO; *U.S. Private*, pg. 224
Aelen, Lucas O., Chief Fin. Officer--OPEL Nederland B.V., Sliedrecht, Netherlands; *U.S. Public*, pg. 723
Aelis, Gary, Chief Fin. Officer & Sr. V.P.--Consolidated Cigar Corporation, Fort Lauderdale, FL; *U.S. Private*, pg. 690
Aerni, Bernhard, Chief Fin. Officer & Sr. V.P.-Fin.--UMS Swiss Metalworks Holding Ltd, Dornach, Switzerland; *Int'l*, pg. 1427
Affleck, Robert A., Chief Fin. Officer--B of B (Europe) Limited, London, United Kingdom; *Int'l*, pg. 151
Agema, Gerald, Chief Fin. Officer & V.P.-Admin.--Tribune Broadcasting Company, Chicago, IL; *U.S. Public*, pg. 1636
Agius, Dan, Chief Fin. Officer--Skanska Fastigheter Riks AB, Danderyd, Sweden; *Int'l*, pg. 1260
Agostinelli, Richard, Chief Fin. Officer--Continental Graphics Holdings, Inc., Los Angeles, CA; *U.S. Private*, pg. 268
Agostinelli, Richard, Chief Fin. Officer & Exec. V.P.--Continental Graphics Corporation, Los Angeles, CA; *U.S. Private*, pg. 268
Aguirre, A., Chief Fin. Officer--Goodyear de Colombia S.A., Cali, Colombia; *U.S. Public*, pg. 753
Ahrens, Wilfred C., Chief Fin. Officer--HPM Corporation, Mount Gilead, OH; *U.S. Private*, pg. 492
Ahting, Frank, V.P.-Fin.--Athey Products Corporation, Wake Forest, NC; *U.S. Public*, pg. 142
Aiken, Richard, Chief Fin. Officer--Energy Systems Industries, Inc., Boston, MA; *U.S. Private*, pg. 376
Aiken, Robert M., Jr., Chief Fin. Officer & Sr. V.P.--Sun Company, Inc., Philadelphia, PA; *U.S. Public*, pg. 1530
Ailes, Walter, V.P., Treas. & Sec.--McGill Manufacturing Company, Inc., Valparaiso, IN; *U.S. Public*, pg. 573
Aimone, Michael V., Chief Fin. Officer & V.P.--Mississippi Lime Co., Alton, IL; *U.S. Private*, pg. 753
Ainsworth, E., Chief Fin. Officer--Hollandia Weathershields Limited, Birmingham, United Kingdom; *Int'l*, pg. 1463
Ainsworth, Kent P., Chief Fin. Officer, Exec. V.P. & Sec.--URS Corporation, San Francisco, CA; *U.S. Public*, pg. 1655
Aiquiuto, Tony, Chief Fin. Officer--O/E Automation, Inc., Troy, MI; *U.S. Private*, pg. 809
Aittola, Eero, Chief Fin. Officer--Neste Oy, Espoo, Finland; *Int'l*, pg. 912
Aizawa, Hiroshi, Chief Fin. Officer & Div. Mgr.--Sumitomo Bank of California, San Francisco, CA; *Int'l*, pg. 1309
Ajamian, Daniel, Chief Fin. Officer & V.P.--Southwest Marine, Inc., San Diego, CA; *U.S. Private*, pg. 213
Ajer, Randolph E., Chief Fin. Officer, Exec. V.P., Treas. & Sec.--Mercury Air Group Inc., Los Angeles, CA; *U.S. Public*, pg. 1092
Akbar, Javed, Chief Fin. Officer--Rotex Canada Inc., Scarborough, Canada; *Int'l*, pg. 462
AkhtarAdil, Humayun, Chief Fin. Officer--National Bank of Pakistan, Karachi, Pakistan; *Int'l*, pg. 907
Al Jassim, Yousef, Deputy Dir. Gen.--Kuwait Airways Corp., Safat, Kuwait; *Int'l*, pg. 764
Alabart, Jaime, Dir.-Fin.--Asland S.A., Madrid, Spain; *Int'l*, pg. 790
Alagna, Robert J., Chief Fin. Officer--Sea Containers Australia Ltd., Sydney, Australia; *Int'l*, pg. 1214
Alamaki, Tuomo, Chief Fin. Officer--Nokia Mobile Phones, Espoo, Finland; *Int'l*, pg. 951
Alberici, John S., Vice Chm., Chief Fin. Officer, Sr. V.P. & Sec.--J.S. Alberici Construction Co., Inc., Saint Louis, MO; *U.S. Private*, pg. 32
Alberini, Carlos, Chief Fin. Officer & Sr. V.P.--Footstar Inc., Mahwah, NJ; *U.S. Public*, pg. 661
Albers, Mike, Chief Fin. Officer--SAIC Engineering, Inc., Lakeville, MA; *U.S. Private*, pg. 976
Alberts, David C., Chief Fin. Officer--Pickering Inc., Tacoma, WA; *U.S. Private*, pg. 864
Albracht, K.L., Chief Fin. Officer & V.P.--International Systems & Controls Corp., Houston, TX; *U.S. Private*, pg. 572
Albreklsson, Kenneth, Chief Fin. Officer--Skanska Stalteknik AB, Kalmar, Sweden; *Int'l*, pg. 1261
Albright, Jerry, Chief Fin. Officer & V.P.--Armco Inc., Pittsburgh, PA; *U.S. Public*, pg. 131
Alcorn, Charles S., Pres., Chief Oper. Officer & Chief Fin. Officer--Donlee Technologies Inc., York, PA; *U.S. Private*, pg. 339
Alden, John R., Chief Fin. Officer, Sr. V.P.-Fin. & Sec.--Swift Energy Company, Houston, TX; *U.S. Public*, pg. 1543
Alderman, Ken, Chief Fin. Officer & Sr. V.P.--Gilbane Building Company, Providence, RI; *U.S. Private*, pg. 452
Aldinger, Philip C., Jr., V.P.-Fin. & Admin.--Carlisle Tire & Wheel Company, Aiken, SC; *U.S. Public*, pg. 305
Aldridge, David S., Chief Fin. Officer--The Alpine Group, Inc., New York, NY; *U.S. Public*, pg. 58
Aldridge, David S., Chief Fin. Officer--Superior Telecommunications, Atlanta, GA; *U.S. Public*, pg. 58
Alevizopoulas, G., Chief Fin. Officer--Karelia Tobacco Company Inc., Kalamata, Greece; *Int'l*, pg. 724
Alexander, Bill, Chief Fin. Officer, V.P. & Treas.--Purcell Co., Inc., Diamondhead, MS; *U.S. Private*, pg. 895
Alexander, Douglas S., Chief Fin. Officer & Sr. V.P.--London Life Insurance Group, London, Canada; *Int'l*, pg. 435
Alexander, I.R., Chief Fin. Officer & Exec. V.P.--Purina Mills, Inc., Saint Louis, MO; *U.S. Private*, pg. 895
Alexander, James C., Chief Fin. Officer & V.P.-Fin.--General Homes Corporation, Houston, TX; *U.S. Private*, pg. 444
Alexander, John, Chief Fin. Officer--Berendsen Fluid Power Pty. Ltd., Villawood, Australia; *Int'l*, pg. 1285
Alexander, John F., II, Chief Fin. Officer & Sr. V.P.--EG & G, Inc., Wellesley, MA; *U.S. Public*, pg. 542
Alexander, Michael D., Chief Fin. Officer--American Axle & Manufacturing, Detroit, MI; *U.S. Private*, pg. 51
Alexander, Neville, Chief Fin. Oficer--Harrington Industrial Plastics Inc., Chino, CA; *Int'l*, pg. 554
Alexander, R. Mark, Chief Fin. Officer--UFE Incorporated, Stillwater, MN; *U.S. Private*, pg. 1112
Alexander, Ronald, Chief Fin. Officer & Treas.--GRC International, Inc., Vienna, VA; *U.S. Public*, pg. 695
Alfaro, Rafael, Chief Fin. Officer--DMB&B S.A. de C.V., Mexico, Mexico; *U.S. Private*, pg. 304
Alford, M.L., Chief Fin. Officer & Treas.--Staple Cotton Cooperative Association, Greenwood, MS; *U.S. Private*, pg. 1033
Alfroid, Philippe, Chief Fin. Officer & Exec. V.P.-Admin. & Fin.--Essilor International Compagnie Generale d'Optique, Charenton-le-Pont, France; *Int'l*, pg. 462
Ali, A.J., V.P.-Fin.--Vista Gold Corp., Denver, CO; *U.S. Public*, pg. 1723
Ali, A.J., Chief Fin. Officer--Granges, Inc., Denver, CO; *U.S. Public*, pg. 1723
Allard, Hubert, Chief Fin. Officer--Esselte Meto SNC, Saint Quentin-en-Yvelines, France; *Int'l*, pg. 461
Allardyce, Fred A., Chief Fin. Officer & V.P.--American Standard Inc., Piscataway, NJ; *U.S. Public*, pg. 91
Alldredge, William T., Chief Fin. Officer & V.P.-Fin.--Newell Co., Freeport, IL; *U.S. Public*, pg. 1176
Allen, David, Chm. Bd., Pres., Chief Exec. Officer & Chief Fin. Officer--AMD Industries Inc., Cicero, IL; *U.S. Private*, pg. 6
Allen, David M., Chief Fin. Officer & V.P.-Fin. & Admin.--Objective Systems Integrators, Inc., Folsom, CA; *U.S. Public*, pg. 1209
Allen, James D., Chief Fin. Officer & Exec. V.P.--Tandycrafts, Inc., Fort Worth, TX; *U.S. Public*, pg. 1561
Allen, James P., Chief Fin. Officer & Exec. V.P.--CACI International Inc, Arlington, VA; *U.S. Public*, pg. 272
Allen, Jefferson F., Pres.--Tosco Corporation, Stamford, CT; *U.S. Public*, pg. 1624
Allen, John H., Chief Fin. Officer & V.P.-Fin.--Cohu, Inc., San Diego, CA; *U.S. Public*, pg. 396
Allen, Lindsey, Chief Fin. Officer & Sr. V.P.--Liquid Controls LLC, Lake Bluff, IL; *U.S. Private*, pg. 669
Allen, Patrick J., Chief Fin. Officer & Sr. V.P.--Hambrecht & Quist LLC., San Francisco, CA; *U.S. Public*, pg. 778
Allen, Richard, Chief Fin. Officer--J.D. Edwards & Company, Denver, CO; *U.S. Private*, pg. 365
Allen, Richard, Chief Fin. Officer--Triarc Beverage Group, White Plains, NY; *U.S. Public*, pg. 1635
Allen, Tim, V.P.-Fin.--Laidlaw Corporation, Scottsdale, AZ; *U.S. Private*, pg. 642
Allen, Tom R., Chief Fin. Officer--Harriet & Henderson Yarns, Inc., Henderson, NC; *U.S. Private*, pg. 504
Allender, Patrick W., Chief Fin. Officer, Sr. V.P. & Sec.--Danaher Corporation, Washington, DC; *U.S. Public*, pg. 480
Allerbrand, Tom, Chief Fin. Officer & Sr. V.P.--Vattenfall AB, Stockholm, Sweden; *Int'l*, pg. 1452
Alles, Timothy M., V.P. & Controller--PNC Bank, Philadelphia, PA; *U.S. Public*, pg. 1243
Allewaert, Jacques R., Chief Fin. Officer--Davidson & Associates, Inc., Torrance, CA; *U.S. Public*, pg. 320
Allgood, J. Michael, Chief Fin. Officer & V.P.-Fin.--PLM International, Inc., San Francisco, CA; *U.S. Public*, pg. 1241
Allgood, J. Michael, Chief Fin. Officer & V.P.--PLM Financial Services, Inc., San Francisco, CA; *U.S. Public*, pg. 1241
Allgood, J. Michael, Chief Fin. Officer--PLM Railcar Management Services, Inc., Chicago, IL; *U.S. Public*, pg. 1241
Allgood, J. Michael, Chief Fin. Officer & V.P.--PLM Trailer Leasing, San Francisco, CA; *U.S. Public*, pg. 1241
Allgrove, Jeffrey W., V.P.-Fin.--Unilever United States Inc., New York, NY; *Int'l*, pg. 1435
Allison, John R., Chief Fin. Officer & Exec. V.P.--Sun International Hotels Limited, Fort Lauderdale, FL; *U.S. Public*, pg. 1531
Allison, Mark J., Chief Fin. Officer & V.P.--Southern Pump & Tank Company, Charlotte, NC; *U.S. Private*, pg. 1017
Allmon, Diane, Controller--Gemtron Corporation, Sweetwater, TN; *Int'l*, pg. 1523
Allocati, Guillermo, Admin. & Fin. Dir.--Gowland Publicidad S.A., Buenos Aires, Argentina; *U.S. Public*, pg. 1642
Allott, Anthony J., Chief Fin. Officer & V.P.--Applied Extrusion Technologies, Inc., Peabody, MA; *U.S. Public*, pg. 122
Allschul, Alfred S., Chief Fin. Officer & V.P.-Fin. & Plng.--Amtrak-National Railroad Passenger Corp., Washington, DC; *U.S. Private*, pg. 68
Allsup, Jay, Chief Fin. Officer--Lund International Holdings, Inc., Anoka, MN; *U.S. Public*, pg. 1020
Allsup, Jay M., Chief Fin. Officer--Lund Industries Inc., Anoka, MN; *U.S. Public*, pg. 1020
Allvey, David Philip, Dir.-Fin.--B.A.T Industries P.L.C., London, United Kingdom; *Int'l*, pg. 110
Allwein, John, Chief Fin. Officer--Omnirel Corporation, Leominster, MA; *U.S. Public*, pg. 1792
Alm, John R., Chief Fin. Officer & Sr. V.P.--Coca-Cola Enterprises Inc., Atlanta, GA; *U.S. Public*, pg. 393
Almeida, Antonio Augusto, Chief Fin. Officer--Banco Totta & Acores, Lisbon, Portugal; *Int'l*, pg. 144
Almeida, Armand, Chief Fin. Officer--Avedis Zildjian Company, Norwell, MA; *U.S. Private*, pg. 1206
Almquist, Henry G., Chief Fin. Officer & V.P.--AMC, Inc., Atlanta, GA; *U.S. Private*, pg. 6
Aloe, Mark, Chief Fin. Officer--American Home Improvement, Monroeville, PA; *U.S. Private*, pg. 56
Alonso, V., Chief Fin. Officer--Compania Scholl S.A., Madrid, Spain; *Int'l*, pg. 1209
Alper, Merlin L., Exec. V.P. & Chief Fin. Officer--Madison Square Garden Corporation, New York, NY; *U.S. Public*, pg. 288
Alpers, Lynn, Chief Fin. Officer & V.P.--Hamilton Stores, Inc., Bozeman, MT; *U.S. Private*, pg. 497
Alstrin, J. Christopher, Chief Fin. Officer--Taylor Capital Group, Wheeling, IL; *U.S. Private*, pg. 1070
Alstrin, J. Christopher, Chief Fin. Officer--Cole Taylor Bank, Wheeling, IL; *U.S. Private*, pg. 1070
Altenbaumer, Larry F., Chief Fin. Officer, Controller & Treas.--Illinova Inc., Decatur, IL; *U.S. Public*, pg. 869
Altenbaumer, Larry F., Chief Fin. Officer & Sr. V.P.--Illinois Power Company, Decatur, IL; *U.S. Public*, pg. 869
Altherr, Jack R., Jr., Vice Chm. & Chief Fin. Officer--Avondale Incorporated, Monroe, GA; *U.S. Private*, pg. 102
Altieri, Donald R., Sr. V.P.-Fin.--Xerox Financial Services Inc., Stamford, CT; *U.S. Public*, pg. 1784
Altieri, Edward J., Chief Fin. Officer & Treas.--Construction Specialties, Inc., Cranford, NJ; *U.S. Private*, pg. 266
Altilio, David C., Chief Fin. Officer & Sr. V.P.--Federal Home Loan Bank of New York, New York, NY; *U.S. Private*, pg. 399
Altizer, Joseph W., II, Chief Fin. Officer--Jefferson Mills, Inc., Pulaski, VA; *U.S. Private*, pg. 584
Altman, Dan, Chief Fin. Officer & Sr. V.P.--Intertec Publishing, Overland Park, KS; *U.S. Public*, pg. 1327
Altman, Murray, Chief Fin. Officer--May Merchandising Company, Saint Louis, MO; *U.S. Public*, pg. 1064
Altstadt, Manfred, Chief Fin. Officer & Sr. Exec. V.P.--Mutual of America Life Insurance Company, New York, NY; *U.S. Private*, pg. 769
Altstadt, Manfred, Chief Fin. Officer & Sr. Exec. V.P.--American Life Insurance Company of New York, New York, NY; *U.S. Private*, pg. 769
Alvarez, Amparo, C.P.A., Chief Fin. Officer--American International Container, Inc., Miami, FL; *U.S. Private*, pg. 57
Alvarez, Charlie, Chief Fin. Officer & V.P.-Fin. & Admin.--Alliance Semiconductor Corp., San Jose, CA; *U.S. Public*, pg. 47
Alvarez, Jose Luis Palomo, Chief Fin. Officer--ENDESA - Empresa Nacional de Electricidad, S.A., Madrid, Spain; *Int'l*, pg. 1224
Alvey, Steven, Chief Fin. Officer & V.P.-Fin. & Opers.--Shugart Corporation, Mission Viejo, CA; *U.S. Private*, pg. 997
Alzua, Fernando, Chief Fin. Officer--Monsanto do Brasil Ltda. (Mobra S.A.), Sao Paulo, Brazil; *U.S. Public*, pg. 1125
Amari, Joseph, Chief Fin. Officer--Banner Pharmacaps Inc., High Point, NC; *Int'l*, pg. 1272
Amato, Ray, Chief Fin. Officer--Mactavish Machine Manufacturing Company, Richmond, VA; *U.S. Private*, pg. 693
Ambrose, Andy, Chief Fin. Officer, Exec. V.P. & Sec.--Miller Freeman Inc., San Francisco, CA; *Int'l*, pg. 1443
Ames, Robert A., CPA, Chief Fin. Officer--The Orioles, Inc., Baltimore, MD; *U.S. Private*, pg. 819
Amiry, Seyed, Chief Fin. Officer & Sr. V.P.--Heald Colleges, San Francisco, CA; *U.S. Private*, pg. 514
Amon, Walter, Vice Chm. & Chief Fin. Officer--Mang/DMB&B, Vienna, Vienna, Austria; *U.S. Private*, pg. 305
Amour, Mark, Chief Fin. Officer--Reed Elsevier plc, London, United Kingdom; *Int'l*, pg. 1093
Amstutz, Gary, Chief Fin. Officer--SAIC, Germantown, MD; *U.S. Private*, pg. 976
Amweg, James, Chief Fin. Officer--Champion Products Inc., Winston Salem, NC; *U.S. Public*, pg. 1433
Anand, Anil, Chief Fin. Officer--Andrew Sports Club Inc., Secaucus, NJ; *U.S. Private*, pg. 73
Ancira Elizondo, Jorge, Chief Fin. Officer--Grupo Acerero del Norte S.A. de C.V. (GAN), Mexico, Mexico; *Int'l*, pg. 572

Anders, Howard G., Chief Fin. Officer, Exec. V.P. & Sec.--Hospitality Worldwide Services, Inc., New York, NY; U.S. Public, pg. 841
Anders, Philip, Mng. Dir.-Fin.--EMAP Consumer Magazines, London, United Kingdom; Int'l, pg. 451
Andersen, John, Chief Fin. Officer--Coolidge Glass Co., Inc., Waukesha, WI; U.S. Private, pg. 273
Andersen, Jorgen Vendel, Chief Fin. Officer & Exec. V.P.--ISS-International Service System A/S, Holte, Denmark; Int'l, pg. 656
Andersen, Joseph G., V.P.-Fin., Treas. & Sec.--Continental Circuits Corp., Phoenix, AZ; U.S. Public, pg. 440
Andersen, Nevin N., Chief Fin. Officer & V.P.--Shaklee Corporation, San Francisco, CA; Int'l, pg. 1518
Andersen, Rick, Chief Fin. Officer--HATCO, Inc., Garland, TX; U.S. Private, pg. 510
Andersen, Ross, V.P. & Chief Fin. Officer--Berry Bearing Company, Lyons, IL; U.S. Public, pg. 732
Anderskow, David, Chief Fin. Officer, Controller & Treas.--Power Contracting & Engineering Corp., Schaumburg, IL; U.S. Private, pg. 877
Anderson, Al, V.P.-Fin.--Dreis & Krump Manufacturing Company, Chicago, IL; U.S. Private, pg. 342
Anderson, Andrew E., V.P.-Fin. & Treas.--Otter Tail Power Company, Fergus Falls, MN; U.S. Public, pg. 1234
Anderson, Basil L., Chief Fin. Officer, Exec. V.P. & Treas.--Campbell Soup Company, Camden, NJ; U.S. Public, pg. 298
Anderson, Bill, Chief Fin. Officer--Raley's & Bel Air, West Sacramento, CA; U.S. Private, pg. 907
Anderson, Carolyn J., Chief Fin. Officer & Corp. Sec.--Scott's Liquid Gold-Inc., Denver, CO; U.S. Public, pg. 1447
Anderson, Charlie, Mng. Partner & Chief Fin. Officer--Carmichael Lynch, Inc., Minneapolis, MN; U.S. Private, pg. 213
Anderson, Curt, Chief Fin. Officer--Automobile Club Insurance Company, Columbus, OH; U.S. Private, pg. 51
Anderson, D.J., Chief Fin. Officer & Sr. V.P.--Newport News Shipbuilding, Inc., Newport News, VA; U.S. Public, pg. 1179
Anderson, D.L., Chief Fin. Officer--Honeywell Defense Avionics Systems, Albuquerque, NM; U.S. Public, pg. 834
Anderson, Darl, Chief Fin. Officer--Bashas, Chandler, AZ; U.S. Private, pg. 120
Anderson, Don, Chief Fin. Officer & Sr. V.P.--Carr Gottstein Foods, Anchorage, AK; U.S. Public, pg. 308
Anderson, Donald W., Treas. & Chief Fin. Officer--J.E. Goold & Company, Portland, ME; U.S. Public, pg. 229
Anderson, Donald W., Chief Fin. Officer--Priority Healthcare Corporation, Altamonte Springs, FL; U.S. Public, pg. 229
Anderson, Erling J., Chief Fin. Officer & Dir.-Investor Rels.--Dotronix, Inc., New Brighton, MN; U.S. Public, pg. 520
Anderson, Fred D., Chief Fin. Officer & Exec. V.P.--Apple Computer, Inc., Cupertino, CA; U.S. Public, pg. 121
Anderson, Gary, Chief Fin. Officer & Exec. V.P.--Detroit Newspapers, Detroit, MI; U.S. Public, pg. 965
Anderson, George R., Chief Fin. Officer, V.P.-Fin. & Admin. & Treas.--Rock of Ages Corporation, Graniteville, VT; U.S. Public, pg. 1396
Anderson, Gerry, Chief Fin. Officer--Superior Coffee and Foods, Bensenville, IL; U.S. Public, pg. 1434
Anderson, Gregory, Chief Fin. Officer--Electrovert, Grand Prairie, TX; Int'l, pg. 328
Anderson, James R., Chief Fin. Officer & Sr. V.P.--HNTB Corporation, Kansas City, MO; U.S. Private, pg. 492
Anderson, James T., Acting Exec. V.P. & Chief Fin. Officer--U S West Inc., Englewood, CO; U.S. Public, pg. 1688
Anderson, John, Chief Fin. Officer--Pro-Log Corporation, Monterey, CA; U.S. Private, pg. 887
Anderson, John K., Chief Fin. Officer, Exec. V.P. & Treas.--American Heritage Life Insurance Co., Jacksonville, FL; U.S. Public, pg. 79
Anderson, John K., Jr., Chief Fin. Officer, Exec. V.P. & Treas.--American Heritage Life Investment Corp., Jacksonville, FL; U.S. Public, pg. 78
Anderson, John W., Vice Chm. & Chief Fin. Officer--Wilmorite, Inc., Rochester, NY; U.S. Private, pg. 1180
Anderson, Jon, Chief Fin. Officer--Gulf States Paper Corporation, Tuscaloosa, AL; U.S. Private, pg. 487
Anderson, Ken, Sr. V.P.-Fin. & Admin.--Freudenberg-NOK, Plymouth, MI; U.S. Private, pg. 427
Anderson, Lance, Chief Fin. Officer--New Century Media, Seattle, WA; U.S. Private, pg. 792
Anderson, Lane W., Chief Fin. Officer--Golden Sun Feeds, Inc., Estherville, IA; U.S. Private, pg. 895
Anderson, Larry, V.P.-Fin.--Star Markets Company, Inc., Cambridge, MA; U.S. Private, pg. 1035
Anderson, Loren W., Chief Fin. Officer--AMCORE Bank, Rock River Valley, Dixon, IL; U.S. Public, pg. 64
Anderson, M.D., Chief Fin. Officer--Copeland Lumber Yard, Inc., Portland, OR; U.S. Private, pg. 274
Anderson, Margaret A., Chief Fin. Officer, Sr. V.P.-Admin. & Treas.--Aerospace Corporation, El Segundo, CA; U.S. Private, pg. 24
Anderson, Mark, Chief Fin. Officer, V.P. & Dir.-Opers.--Anderson Wholesale Company, Muskogee, OK; U.S. Private, pg. 73
Anderson, Mark A., Chief Fin. Officer, Sec. & Treas.--Community First Bankshares, Inc., Fargo, ND; U.S. Public, pg. 416
Anderson, Per-Olof, Chief Fin. Officer--Fagersta Stainless AB, Fagersta, Sweden; Int'l, pg. 476
Anderson, Pete, Chief Fin. Officer--Totes/Isotoner, Inc., New York, NY; U.S. Public, pg. 1433
Anderson, Raymond C., Chief Fin. Officer--USA Floral Products, Inc., Washington, DC; U.S. Public, pg. 1685
Anderson, Richard, Chief Fin. Officer & V.P.--Instrument Specialties Company, Delaware Water Gap, PA; U.S. Private, pg. 565
Anderson, Robert, Chief Fin. Officer--Augat, Inc., Communications Division, Seattle, WA; U.S. Public, pg. 1598
Anderson, Roger, Chief Fin. Officer & Sec.--Pepsi-Cola General Bottlers, Inc., Rolling Meadows, IL; U.S. Public, pg. 1277
Anderson, Ronald G., Chief Fin. Officer & Sr. V.P.--Aid Association for Lutherans, Appleton, WI; U.S. Private, pg. 27
Anderson, Sandra M., Chief Fin. Officer & V.P.--RSR Corporation, Dallas, TX; U.S. Private, pg. 900
Anderson, T., Chief Fin. Officer--Elliott Group Limited, Peterborough, United Kingdom; Int'l, pg. 385
Andersson, Bo, Chief Fin. Officer--Icopal ab, Malmo, Sweden; Int'l, pg. 659
Andersson, Britt, Chief Fin. Officer--Esselte Meto AB, Solna, Sweden; Int'l, pg. 459
Andersson, Hans, Chief Fin. Officer--Skanska (U.S.A.) Inc., Greenwich, CT; Int'l, pg. 1261
Andersson, K., Chief Fin. Officer--Olivetti (Suomi) OY, Espoo, Finland; Int'l, pg. 1003
Ando, Tetsuo, Chief Fin. Officer, Exec. V.P. & Treas.--Bridgestone/Firestone, Inc., Nashville, TN; Int'l, pg. 213
Ando, Y., Exec. V.P.-Fin.--Konica Business Machines USA, Inc., Windsor, CT; Int'l, pg. 748
Andre, Charles M., Chief Fin. Officer & Controller--Lumber Group Inc., Dothan, AL; U.S. Private, pg. 680
Andreas, Ray A., Chief Fin. Officer & V.P.--The Lubrizol Corporation, Wickliffe, OH; U.S. Public, pg. 1016
Andrepont, Kevin, Chief Fin. Officer, V.P. & Treas.--Baton Rouge Water Works Company, Baton Rouge, LA; U.S. Private, pg. 122
Andrews, Robin, Chief Fin. Officer--George Philip Limited, London, United Kingdom; Int'l, pg. 1093
Andrews, Robin, Chief Fin. Officer--Osprey, London, United Kingdom; Int'l, pg. 1093
Andrews, Sue, Chief Fin. Officer & Sr. V.P.--Evans, Hardy & Young, Inc., Santa Barbara, CA; U.S. Private, pg. 384
Andrews, William E., Chief Fin. Officer & Sr. V.P.--Varco-Pruden Buildings, Memphis, TN; U.S. Public, pg. 1677
Andrus, Frederick, Chief Fin. Officer--Zoological Society of San Diego, San Diego, CA; U.S. Private, pg. 1207
Angart, Robert F., Chief Fin. Officer--Perlmuter Printing Company, Cleveland, OH; Int'l, pg. 1177
Angelella, John C., Chief Fin. Officer & V.P.--Gertrude Hawk Chocolates, Inc., Dunmore, PA; U.S. Private, pg. 449
Angelone, Fred, Chief Fin. Officer & V.P.--Circuit-Wise, Inc., North Haven, CT; U.S. Private, pg. 240
Angenent, W.C.J., Chief Fin. Officer--Vendex International N.V., Amsterdam, Netherlands; Int'l, pg. 1462
Angle, Martin D., Dir.-Grp. Fin.--TI Group plc, Abingdon, United Kingdom; Int'l, pg. 1337
Anglim, Don, Chief Fin. Officer--Berenfield Containers, Inc., Mason, OH; U.S. Private, pg. 135
Anglin, Richard J., Chief Fin. Officer--Florsheim Group Inc., Chicago, IL; U.S. Public, pg. 656
Ansari, Mr., Chief Fin. Officer & V.P.--Siemens Pakistan Engineering Co. Ltd., Karachi, Pakistan; Int'l, pg. 1247
Anshus, Gregg, Chief Fin. Officer & Controller--Waters Instruments, Inc., Rochester, MN; U.S. Public, pg. 1745
Ansted, James P., Chief Fin. Officer, Treas., & Sec.--Plastic Suppliers, Inc., Columbus, OH; U.S. Private, pg. 871
Anstett, Joseph L., Pres. & Chief Fin. Officer--Silver State Disposal Service, Inc., Las Vegas, NV; U.S. Public, pg. 1380
Antebi, Joseph, Chief Fin. Officer & Treas.--Simpson Gumpertz & Heger Inc., Arlington, MA; U.S. Private, pg. 1002
Antes, Richard, Chief Fin. Office & V.P.-Fin.--Tetko, Inc., Briarcliff Manor, NY; U.S. Private, pg. 1078
Antoniados, Paul, Chief Fin. Officer--Keeprite Inc, Brantford, Canada; U.S. Public, pg. 898
Antonini, Jack M., Vice Chm. & Chief Fin. Officer--First USA, Inc., Dallas, TX; U.S. Public, pg. 174
Antrasian, Robert B., Chief Fin. Officer & Sr. V.P.--Big Y Foods Inc., Springfield, MA; U.S. Private, pg. 143
Apgar, Phillip E., CPA, Chief Fin. Officer, V.P. & Treas.--American Indemnity Financial Corp., Galveston, TX; U.S. Public, pg. 83
Appel, Arthur S., Chief Fin. Officer & Exec. V.P.--Fire Controls Instruments, Waltham, MA; U.S. Public, pg. 1306
Appel, Egbert, Chief Fin. Officer--Hilti AG, Schaan, Liechtenstein; Int'l, pg. 619
Appel, John C., Vice Chm. & Chief Fin. Officer--Dain Rauscher Corporation, Minneapolis, MN; U.S. Public, pg. 476
Appel, Manfred, Chief Fin. Officer & V.P.-Fin.--Modcomp, Fort Lauderdale, FL; U.S. Public, pg. 283
Applegate, Henry, Chief Fin. Officer, Exec. V.P. & Sec.--Players International, Inc., Atlantic City, NJ; U.S. Public, pg. 1310
Appleyard, Geoffrey L., Chief Fin. Officer & V.P.-Fin.--Suncor Development Company, Phoenix, AZ; U.S. Public, pg. 1298
Aquila, Susan, Chief Fin. Officer & Controller--Edmund Scientific Company, Barrington, NJ; U.S. Private, pg. 364
Aranaho, Kauko, Vice Chm. & Chief Fin. Officer--Vanstar Corporation, Pleasanton, CA; U.S. Public, pg. 1708
Arango, C., Chief Fin. Officer--Gran Industria de Neumaticos Centroamericana, S.A., Guatemala, Guatemala; U.S. Public, pg. 753
Arbola, Gerald, Chief Fin. Officer--COGEMA - Compagnie Generale des Matieres Nucleaires, Velizy-Villacoublay, France; Int'l, pg. 304
Arbuckle, James E., Chief Fin. Officer, Exec. V.P. & Treas.--Besser Company, Alpena, MI; U.S. Private, pg. 139
Arcari, John J., Chief Fin. Officer--Robotic Vision Systems, Inc., Hauppauge, NY; U.S. Public, pg. 1395
Arceneaux, Darin, Chief Fin. Officer & Treas.--Associated Grocers, Inc., Baton Rouge, LA; U.S. Private, pg. 90
Archibald, Andrew M., Chief Fin. Officer, V.P.-Fin. & Sec.--Intertape Polymer Group Inc., Saint-Laurent, Canada; Int'l, pg. 684
Archibald, Rae W., Chief Fin. Officer & V.P.--RAND, Santa Monica, CA; U.S. Private, pg. 908
Ardiet, Francois, Chief Fin. Officer--Orangina France, Aix-en-Provence, France; Int'l, pg. 566
Ardizzone, Frank, Chief Fin. Officer--Allied Office Supplies, Hasbrouck Heights, NJ; U.S. Private, pg. 39
Arfmann, Bruce L., Chief Fin. Officer, Treas. & Sec.--Colorado MEDtech, Inc., Boulder, CO; U.S. Public, pg. 401
Argotte, Francisco Padilla, Chief Fin. Officer--Grupo Simec, S.A. de C.V., Guadalajara, Mexico; Int'l, pg. 576
Argudin, Bernard, Chief Fin. Officer & Treas.--Republic National Bank of Miami, Miami, FL; U.S. Private, pg. 924
Arieven, Yoram, Chief Fin. Officer--Ellen Tracy Inc., New York, NY; U.S. Private, pg. 372
Aris, Stanley J., Chief Fin. Officer & V.P.-Fin.--CTS Corporation, Elkhart, IN; U.S. Public, pg. 285
Arle, Henrik, Chief Fin. Officer & Exec. V.P.--FinnAir Oy, Helsinki, Finland; Int'l, pg. 485
Arlotta, Terry, Chief Fin. Officer--Peerless Importers, Inc., Brooklyn, NY; U.S. Private, pg. 847
Armbruster, William C., Chief Fin. Officer & Exec. V.P.--Peregrine Incorporated, Southfield, MI; U.S. Private, pg. 852
Armeren, Ole Christian, Chief Fin. Officer--Esmi A/S, Skare, Norway; Int'l, pg. 33
Armstrong, David, Chief Fin. Officer--Robinsons-May, North Hollywood, CA; U.S. Public, pg. 1064
Armstrong, J. N., V.P.-Fin. & Admin.--BTU Engineering Corporation, North Billerica, MA; U.S. Public, pg. 164
Armstrong, Peter C., Chief Fin. Officer--Tekgraf, Inc., Norcross, GA; U.S. Private, pg. 1073
Armstrong, Theodore M., Chief Fin. Officer & Sr. V.P.-Fin. & Admin.--Angelica Corporation, Chesterfield, MO; U.S. Public, pg. 113
Arndt, Larry, Chief Fin. Officer, V.P.-Fin. & Controller--WEN Products, Inc., Bensenville, IL; U.S. Private, pg. 1144
Arnholdt, Axel, Chief Fin. Officer--Mikron AG Diel, Nidau, Switzerland; Int'l, pg. 866
Arnold, Deon, Chief Fin. Officer--Adams Rite Manufacturing Co., City of Industry, CA; U.S. Private, pg. 17
Arnold, Desmond C., Dir.-Fin. & Admin.--Barlow Ltd., Sandton, South Africa; Int'l, pg. 167
Arnold, G. Jeff, Chief Fin. Officer & V.P.--Campbell Soup Company Ltd., Toronto, Canada; U.S. Public, pg. 299
Arnold, Gary M., Chief Fin. Officer & Sr. V.P.-Fin.--Mosby-Year Book, Inc., Saint Louis, MO; U.S. Public, pg. 1616
Arnold, H.G., Chm. Bd. & Chief Fin. Officer--Convenience Plus Partners Ltd., Denver, CO; U.S. Private, pg. 271
Arnold, James, Chief Fin. Officer--Turkey Hill Dairy, Inc., Conestoga, PA; U.S. Private, pg. 1109
Arnold, John Q., Chief Fin. Officer & Sr. Exec. V.P.--Mercantile Bancorporation Inc., Saint Louis, MO; U.S. Public, pg. 1087
Arnold, John Q., Sr. Exec. V.P. & Chief Fin. Officer--Mercantile Bank of St. Louis N.A., Saint Louis, MO; U.S. Public, pg. 1087
Arnold, Larry G., V.P.-Fin.--Bristol-Myers Squibb U.S. Pharmaceutical Group, Plainsboro, NJ; U.S. Public, pg. 255
Arnold, Neil, Chief Fin. Officer--Fifth Third Bancorp, Cincinnati, OH; U.S. Public, pg. 621
Arnold, Richard, Chief Fin. Officer & Controller--Conway Corporation, Conway, AR; U.S. Private, pg. 272
Arnold, William, Chief Fin. Officer & Treas.--McCoy Group Inc., Shullsburg, WI; U.S. Private, pg. 720
Aro, Jeanne, V.P.-Fin & Admin.--Mini Mart, Inc., Casper, WY; U.S. Public, pg. 967
Aronaho, Kauko O., Chief Fin. Officer & Sr. V.P.-Fin.--ComputerLand Canada, Brampton, Canada; Int'l, pg. 1154
Aronaho, Kauko O., Sr. V.P.-Fin. & Chief Fin. Officer--SHL Computer Innovations, Brampton, Canada; Int'l, pg. 1154
Arovas, Robert, Chief Fin. Officer--Fritz Companies, Inc., San Francisco, CA; U.S. Public, pg. 683
Arp, Earnest, Chief Fin. Officer--Sunbrand Div., Atlanta, GA; U.S. Private, pg. 1177
Arp, R.W., Chief Fin. Officer & Exec. V.P.-Fin.--Lone Star Steel Company, Dallas, TX; U.S. Public, pg. 1012
Arpey, Gerard J., Chief Fin. Officer & Sr. V.P.--AMR Corporation, Fort Worth, TX; U.S. Public, pg. 9
Arrigo, Joseph F., Chief Fin. Officer, Exec. V.P. & Treas.--UIS, Inc., Jersey City, NJ; U.S. Private, pg. 1113
Arrowsmith, Michael, Chief Fin. Officer--Astec International Limited, Wan Chai, Hong Kong; Int'l, pg. 92
Arth, Jerry, V.P.-Fin. & Admin., Controller & Treas.--Malco Products, Inc., Barberton, OH; U.S. Private, pg. 698
Arthur, Barry, Chief Fin. Officer & Exec. V.P.-Fin.--CPI Corp., Saint Louis, MO; U.S. Public, pg. 283
Arthurs, Ross, Chief Fin. Officer--Wicks 'n Sticks, Ltd, Houston, TX; U.S. Private, pg. 1175
Artmann, Susan E., Chief Fin. Officer--Beneficial National Bank USA, Wilmington, DE; U.S. Public, pg. 211
Artz, F.J., Treas.--Today's Kids, Booneville, AR; U.S. Private, pg. 1020
Arunwattanakul, Somchai, Deputy Mng. Dir.--Bangkok Athletic Co., Ltd., Bangkok, Thailand; Int'l, pg. 146
Arzbaecher, Robert, Chief Fin. Officer--Applied Power Inc., Butler, WI; U.S. Public, pg. 124
Asavavichienjinda, Surachai, Chief Fin. Officer--Janssen Pharmaceutical Ltd., Bangkok, Thailand; U.S. Public, pg. 930
Asch, Michael A., Pres., Chief Oper. Officer, Chief Fin. Officer & Treas.--Rexx Environmental Corp., New York, NY; U.S. Public, pg. 1384
Ash, Darron K., Chief Fin. Officer & V.P.--The Morning Star Group, Dallas, TX; U.S. Public, pg. 1527
Ashbrook, Brian W., Chief Fin. Officer--McCabe & Company, New York, NY; U.S. Private, pg. 719
Ashby, Michael, Chief Fin. Officer & Exec. V.P.--Ascend Communications, Inc., Alameda, CA; U.S. Public, pg. 138
Ashby, Michael, Chief Fin. Officer, V.P.-Fin./Admin. & Treas.--Bytex Corporation, Westborough, MA; U.S. Public, pg. 1522

Ashby, Michael F.G., Chief Oper. Officer & Chief Fin. Officer--Network Systems Corporation, Minneapolis, MN; *U.S. Public*, pg. 1522

Ashcraft, Charles F., V.P. & Loan Officer--Churubusco State Bank, Churubusco, IN; *U.S. Public*, pg. 674

Ashenberg, Wayne R., Chief Fin. Officer, Sr. V.P. & Treas.--Sentry Insurance, A Mutual Company, Stevens Point, WI; *U.S. Private*, pg. 985

Ashenbrenner, Tom, Chief Fin. Officer, V.P.-Fin. & Sec.--Outlook Group Corporation, Neenah, WI; *U.S. Public*, pg. 1235

Asher, W. Russell, Chief Fin. Officer--MB America, Inc., Westport, CT; *Int'l*, pg. 267

Ashken, Ian, Chief Fin. Officer & Exec. V.P.--BEC Group, Inc., Rye, NY; *U.S. Public*, pg. 160

Ashley, Kenneth, Chief Fin. Officer & Sec.--National R.V., Inc., Perris, CA; *U.S. Public*, pg. 1159

Ashton, M.G., Dir.-Fin.--BWI Plc, Altrincham, United Kingdom; *Int'l*, pg. 130

Ashwill, Terry M., Chief Fin. Officer & V.P.--Perot Systems Corporation, Dallas, TX; *U.S. Private*, pg. 854

Askey, Darrel F., Chief Fin. Officer, V.P.-Fin., Treas. & Sec.--Celestial Seasonings, Boulder, CO; *U.S. Public*, pg. 319

Asman, Don, Chief Fin. Officer & V.P.-Fin.--CanAmera Foods, Oakville, Canada; *Int'l*, pg. 1195

Aspergren, Anders, Chief Fin. Officer--Myresjo AB, Vetlanda, Sweden; *Int'l*, pg. 1260

Assennato, Vincent T., Chief Fin. Officer--Winterthur Reinsurance Corporation of America, New York, NY; *Int'l*, pg. 346

Assini, Vincent, Chief Fin. Officer--Leica A.G., Saint Gallen, Switzerland; *Int'l*, pg. 806

Asta, Richard A., Chief Fin. Officer & Exec. V.P.-Fin.--Dixon Ticonderoga Company, Heathrow, FL; *U.S. Public*, pg. 514

Astaburuaga, Javier, Chief Fin. Officer--Femsa Cerveza S.A. de CV, Monterrey, Mexico; *Int'l*, pg. 496

Aston, James A., Chief Fin. Officer--Insignia Financial Group, Inc., Greenville, SC; *U.S. Public*, pg. 881

Asunsola, A. Catena, Chief Fin. Officer--Eptisa SA, Madrid, Spain; *Int'l*, pg. 608

Athanasian, O., Chief Fin. Officer--Olivetti Hellas S.A., Athens, Greece; *Int'l*, pg. 1003

Athens, Zack G., Chief Fin. Officer, Sr. V.P. & Treas.--Columbia Universal Life Insurance Company, Austin, TX; *U.S. Public*, pg. 79

Atkin, William W., Chief Fin. Officer & Exec. V.P.--Security Mutual Life Insurance Co. of New York, Binghamton, NY; *U.S. Private*, pg. 981

Atkins, Howard I., Chief Fin. Officer & Exec. V.P.--New York Life Insurance Company, New York, NY; *U.S. Private*, pg. 794

Atkins, Susan, V.P.-Fin.--TST/Impreso, Inc., Coppell, TX; *U.S. Private*, pg. 1066

Atko, Karen, Controller--Braun-Brumfield, Inc., Ann Arbor, MI; *U.S. Private*, pg. 993

Attebury, Ronald L., Chief Fin. Officer & Treas.--Norbest, Inc., Midvale, UT; *U.S. Private*, pg. 801

Attias, Daniel, Chief Fin. Officer--Carmel Container Systems Ltd., Petah Tiqwa, Israel; *Int'l*, pg. 75

Attiyeh, Robert S., Chief Fin. Officer & Sr. V.P.-Fin. & Corp. Devel.--Amgen Inc., Thousand Oaks, CA; *U.S. Public*, pg. 100

Atwood, Bruce, Chief Fin. Officer--Hyer Industries Inc./Thayer Scale, Pembroke, MA; *U.S. Private*, pg. 552

Atwood, Robert T., Chief Fin. Officer & Exec. V.P.--First Union Corporation, Charlotte, NC; *U.S. Public*, pg. 639

Au Yeong, Hoh Koon, Chief Fin. Officer & Sr. V.P.--Club Med Sales, Inc., New York, NY; *Int'l*, pg. 298

Aubin, Tom, Chief Fin. Officer--Dacor Corporation, Northfield, IL; *U.S. Private*, pg. 306

Aucoin, Leonard A., Asst. V.P.--Swift Energy Company, Houston, TX; *U.S. Public*, pg. 1543

Audet, Paul, Chief Fin. Officer--PNC Bank, Philadelphia, PA; *U.S. Public*, pg. 1243

Auerbach, Mark, Chief Fin. Officer--Central Lewmar, Newark, NJ; *U.S. Private*, pg. 223

Augustine, Peter, Chief Oper. Officer & Chief Fin. Officer--New Era Cap. Co., Derby, NY; *U.S. Private*, pg. 793

Aujan, Fabrice, Chief Fin. Officer--Orlando Wyndham, Devon Park, Australia; *Int'l*, pg. 567

Auriemma, Sam, Chief Fin. Officer & V.P.-Fin.--Wonderware Corporation, Irvine, CA; *U.S. Public*, pg. 1775

Auriemma, Samuel, Chief Fin. Officer--Platinum Solutions, Inglewood, CA; *U.S. Public*, pg. 1309

Aurnou, Michael W., Chief Fin. Officer & Treas.--Yenkin-Majestic Paint Corporation, Columbus, OH; *U.S. Private*, pg. 1195

Ausburn, Kevin R., Chief Fin. Officer, Treas. & Sec.--Southern Missouri Containers Inc., Springfield, MO; *U.S. Private*, pg. 1017

Ausfahl, William R., Chief Fin. Officer & Grp. V.P.--The Clorox Company, Oakland, CA; *U.S. Public*, pg. 386

Austin, Dextral, Chief Fin. Officer--Grizzard, Atlanta, GA; *U.S. Private*, pg. 482

Austin, H. Brent, Chief Fin. Officer & Exec. V.P.--El Paso Natural Gas Co., Houston, TX; *U.S. Public*, pg. 567

Austin, Patrick, Sr. V.P.-Fin.--WPIX, Inc., New York, NY; *U.S. Public*, pg. 1636

Austin, Roxanne S., Chief Fin. Officer & Sr. V.P.--Hughes Electronics Corporation, Westchester, CA; *U.S. Public*, pg. 720

Austin, William, Chief Fin. Officer & Sr. V.P.--BMC Software, Inc., Houston, TX; *U.S. Public*, pg. 162

Ausura, John F., V.P. & Chief Fin. Officer--Sunshine Biscuits, Inc., Woodbridge, NJ; *U.S. Private*, pg. 434

Ausura, John F., V.P. & Chief Fin. Officer--Sunshine Biscuits, Inc., Woodbridge, NJ; *U.S. Public*, pg. 657

Auten, James C., Chief Fin. Officer & V.P.--MPSI Systems Inc., Tulsa, OK; *U.S. Public*, pg. 1027

Axelson, Michelle, Chief Fin. Officer & Mgr.-Investor Rels.--Scopus Technology, Inc., Emeryville, CA; *U.S. Public*, pg. 1444

Axelsson, Lars, Chief Fin. Officer--ACTIVE BioTech AB, Malmo, Sweden; *Int'l*, pg. 23

Ayers, Larry G., Chief Fin. Officer, V.P.-Fin., Treas. & Sec.--Southern Electronics Corporation, Tucker, GA; *U.S. Public*, pg. 1490

Ayers, Larry G., Chief Fin. Officer, V.P.-Fin., Sec. & Treas.--Southern Electronics Distributors International, Tucker, GA; *U.S. Public*, pg. 1490

Aylesworth, William A., Chief Fin. Officer, Sr. V.P. & Treas.--Texas Instruments Incorporated, Dallas, TX; *U.S. Public*, pg. 1585

Azar, Ken, Chief Fin. Officer--Carter-Jones Companies, Inc., Kent, OH; *U.S. Private*, pg. 217

Azzara, Cynthia O., Chief Fin. Officer, Sr. V.P. & Treas.--CRIIMI MAE, Rockville, MD; *U.S. Public*, pg. 459

Azzara, Cynthia O., Chief Fin. Officer--CRI Liquidating REIT, Inc., Rockville, MD; *U.S. Public*, pg. 459

Baab, Carlton, Chief Fin. Officer--CKS Group, Cupertino, CA; *U.S. Private*, pg. 195

Baba, Eizo, Mng. Dir.--Chiyoda Mutual Life Insurance Company, Tokyo, Japan; *Int'l*, pg. 286

Babb, Ralph, Chief Fin. Officer & Exec. V.P.-Comerica Inc. & Comerica Bank--Comerica Incorporated, Detroit, MI; *U.S. Public*, pg. 408

Babb, Ralph, Jr., Chief Fin. Officer--Comerica Bank Michigan, Detroit, MI; *U.S. Public*, pg. 409

Babcock, Ric, Chief Fin. Officer--The G&C Foundry Company, Sandusky, OH; *U.S. Public*, pg. 142

Babka, G., Chief Fin. Officer--Weldon, Inc., Columbus, OH; *Int'l*, pg. 449

Bach, Harold H., Jr., Chief Fin. Officer, Chief Acctg. Officer, Treas.& V.P.-Fin.--WMS Industries Inc., Chicago, IL; *U.S.* Public, pg. 1727

Bach, Peter, Chief Fin. Officer & Exec. V.P.--Campbell Mithun Esty, Minneapolis, MN; *U.S. Private*, pg. 204

Bachand, Charles J., Chief Fin. Officer & Sr. V.P.--Highlands Insurance Co., Houston, TX; *U.S. Public*, pg. 826

Bachman, Lee W., V.P.-Fin. & Treas.--Bachman's, Inc., Minneapolis, MN; *U.S. Private*, pg. 109

Bachman, Lesley A., Chief Fin. Officer--DiMark, Inc., Langhorne, PA; *U.S. Public*, pg. 793

Bachman, Vernon E., V.P.--Vulcan International Corporation, Wilmington, DE; *U.S. Public*, pg. 1725

Bachman, Vernon E., Chief Fin. Officer--Bowling Products Div., Cincinnati, OH; *U.S. Public*, pg. 1725

Bachman, Vernon E., Chief Fin. Officer--Rubber Products Div., Clarksville, TN; *U.S. Public*, pg. 1725

Bachman, Vernon E., Chief Fin. Officer--Shoe Last Div., Walnut Ridge, AR; *U.S. Public*, pg. 1725

Bachmeier, Ronald M., Chief Fin. Officer, V.P.-Fin. & Treas.--Xerxes Corporation, Minneapolis, MN; *U.S. Private*, pg. 1194

Backenson, Peter, Chief Fin. Officer & Controller--Phototype Color Graphics, Inc., Pennsauken, NJ; *U.S. Private*, pg. 864

Backes, Wilfried, Chief Fin. Officer, Exec. V.P. & Treas.--Osram Sylvania Inc., Malvern, PA; *Int'l*, pg. 1245

Backlund, Claus, V.P.-Fin.--Chicago Pneumatic Tool Company, Rock Hill, SC; *Int'l*, pg. 96

Bacon, Neil F., Chief Fin. Officer, Treas. & Controller--Homasote Company, Trenton, NJ; *U.S. Public*, pg. 831

Baddeley, Robert Gregory, Chief Fin. Officer & Sec.--Eurocamp Plc, Knutsford, United Kingdom; *Int'l*, pg. 464

Baehr, George E., V.P.-Fin. & Admin.--Lockheed Martin Information Display Systems, Atlanta, GA; *U.S. Public*, pg. 1008

Bagby, Kevin, Chief Fin. Officer--Stoneridge, Inc., Warren, OH; *U.S. Private*, pg. 1044

Baggett, W.T., Sr. V.P.-Fin.--NationsBank South, Atlanta, GA; *U.S. Public*, pg. 1163

Bagley, Patrick J., V.P.-Fin. & Treas.--Matlack Systems, Inc., Wilmington, DE; *U.S. Public*, pg. 1057

Bagley, Patrick J., Chief Fin. Officer, V.P.-Fin. & Treas.--Rollins Truck Leasing Corp., Wilmington, DE; *U.S. Public*, *pg. 1405*

Baham, Susan E., Chief Fin. Officer & Sr. V.P.--First Financial Holdings, Inc., Charleston, SC; *U.S. Public*, pg. 634

Baham, Susan E., Chief Fin. Officer & Sr. V.P.--First Federal Savings & Loan Association of Charleston, Charleston, SC; *U.S. Public*, pg. 634

Bahash, Robert J., Chief Fin. Officer & Exec. V.P.--The McGraw-Hill Companies, New York, NY; *U.S. Public*, pg. 1069

Bahlman, Robert, Chief Fin. Officer, V.P. & Treas.--Midwest Express Airlines, Inc., Oak Creek, WI; *U.S. Public*, pg. 1111

Bahlman, Robert S., Chief Fin. Officer, Sr. V.P. & Treas.--Midwest Express Holdings, Inc., Oak Creek, WI; *U.S. Public*, pg. 1111

Bahmueller, Steve, Chief Fin. Officer--Hull/Finmac, Inc., Warminster, PA; *U.S. Private*, pg. 547

Baiely, William, Chief Fin. Officer--Nobel Education Dynamics, Inc., Media, PA; *U.S. Public*, pg. 1185

Baier, Roger R., Chief Fin. Officer & V.P.-Fin.--Publishers Equipment Corporation, Dallas, TX; *U.S. Public*, pg. 1341

Bailey, John, Chm. Bd., Pres., Chief Exec. & Fin. Officer & Treas.--Cal Emblem Labels, Inc., Fresno, CA; *U.S. Private*, pg. 199

Bailey, Michael J., Chief Fin. Officer & Sr. V.P.-Admin. & Fin.--Standard Motor Products Inc., Long Island City, NY; *U.S. Public*, pg. 1503

Bailey, P., Chief Fin. Officer--Siemens Components Snd. Bhd., Melaka, Malaysia; *Int'l*, pg. 1247

Bailey, Richard W., Chief Fin. Officer & V.P.-Fin.--Tree Top, Inc., Selah, WA; *U.S. Private*, pg. 1098

Bailey, Roger, Chief Fin. Officer--Automatic Timing & Controls, Lancaster, PA; *U.S. Private*, pg. 327

Bailey, Roger, Chief Fin. Officer--Marsh Bellofram Corp., Newell, WV; *U.S. Private*, pg. 707

Bailey, Roger E., Chief Fin. Officer--Desco Corporation, Columbus, OH; *U.S. Private*, pg. 326

Bailey, Steven T., Chief Fin. Officer & Treas.--PIMCO Advisors, Stamford, CT; *U.S. Public*, pg. 1296

Bailey, Wayne R., Chief Fin. Officer & Exec. V.P.--Fremont General Corporation, Santa Monica, CA; *U.S. Public*, pg. 681

Bain, D.W., Treas. & Controller--Cyanamid Canada Inc., Markham, Canada; *U.S. Public*, pg. 80

Bain, Donald R., Chief Fin. Officer & Sr. V.P.--Diversco, Inc., Spartanburg, SC; *U.S. Private*, pg. 336

Bain, Howard, III, Chief Fin. Officer & Exec. V.P.-Worldwide Opers.--Symantec Corporation, Cupertino, CA; *U.S. Public*, pg. 1545

Baines, Don, Chief Fin. Officer--Chart Industries, Inc., Cleveland, OH; *U.S. Public*, pg. 336

Baird, Anna M., Chief Fin. Officer & V.P.--Black Box Corporation of PA, Lawrence, PA; *U.S. Public*, pg. 235

Baird, Anna M., Chief Fin. Officer & V.P.--Black Box Corporation of Pennsylvania, Lawrence, PA; *U.S. Public*, pg. 235

Baird, Donn, Treas.--Kalsec, Inc., Kalamazoo, MI; *U.S. Private*, pg. 606

Baird, Thomas P., Chief Fin. Officer, V.P. & Treas.--Comarco, Inc., Yorba Linda, CA; *U.S. Public*, pg. 406

Baireuther, James, Chief Fin. Officer & Sr. V.P.--The Bon Ton Stores, Inc., York, PA; *U.S. Public*, pg. 244

Bajalia, George A., Chief Fin. Officer & Treas.--Wickes Inc., Vernon Hills, IL; *U.S. Public*, pg. 1391

Baker, Alfred, Chief Fin. Officer & Exec. V.P.--Pro-Line Corporation, Dallas, TX; *U.S. Private*, pg. 887

Baker, Calvin A., Chief Fin. Officer & Teas.--Wisconsin Michigan Investment Corp., Milwaukee, WI; *U.S. Public*, pg. 1773

Baker, Calvin H., Chief Fin. Officer & V.P.-Fin.--Wisconsin Energy Corporation, Milwaukee, WI; *U.S. Public*, pg. 1773

Baker, Calvin H., Chief Fin. Officer & V.P.-Fin.--Wisconsin Electric Power Company, Milwaukee, WI; *U.S. Public*, pg. 1773

Baker, Calvin H., Chief Fin. Officer & Treas.--Wispark Corporation, Milwaukee, WI; *U.S. Public*, pg. 1773

Baker, Calvin H., Chief Fin. Officer & Treas.--Wisvest Corporation, Milwaukee, WI; *U.S. Public*, pg. 1773

Baker, Calvin H., Chief Fin. Officer & Treas.--Witech Corporation, Milwaukee, WI; *U.S. Public*, pg. 1773

Baker, Chantal, Chief Fin. Officer & Dir.-Opers.--Caristrap International Inc., Laval, Canada; *Int'l*, pg. 271

Baker, Davis, Chief Fin. Officer--American Trouser, Inc., Columbus, MS; *U.S. Private*, pg. 64

Baker, Diane Price, Chief Fin. Officer & Sr. V.P.--The New York Times Company, New York, NY; *U.S. Public*, pg. 1173

Baker, Eileen, Chief Fin. Officer--Spectra-Tech, Shelton, CT; *U.S. Public*, pg. 1593

Baker, G. Thomas, Pres., Chief Oper. Officer & Chief Fin. Officer--International Game Technology, Reno, NV; *U.S. Public*, pg. 900

Baker, Ian, Chief Fin. Officer--Union Camp Ireland, Ashbourne, Ireland; *U.S. Public*, pg. 1666

Baker, James E., Chief Fin. Officer, V.P.-Fin. & Treas.--Guy Gannett Communications, Portland, ME; *U.S. Private*, pg. 439

Baker, Jay, Chief Fin. Officer--Home Innovations, Inc., New York, NY; *U.S. Private*, pg. 536

Baker, Kent, Chief Fin. Officer--Insurance Brokers & Managers, Inc., New Orleans, LA; *U.S. Public*, pg. 1677

Baker, Kent, Chief Fin. Officer--Lafayette Insurance Company, New Orleans, LA; *U.S. Public*, pg. 1677

Baker, Kent G., Chief Fin. Officer & V.P.--United Fire & Casualty Company, Cedar Rapids, IA; *U.S. Public*, pg. 1677

Baker, Mark J., V.P.-Fin. & Treas.--Roppe Corp., Fostoria, OH; *U.S. Private*, pg. 944

Baker, Michael, Chief Fin. Officer--ECOS Group, Inc., West Palm Beach, FL; *U.S. Public*, pg. 563

Baker, Mike, Chief Fin. Officer--Cosmetic Group, U.S.A., Sun Valley, CA; *U.S. Private*, pg. 277

Baker, Phillips S., Jr., Chief Fin. Officer & Exec. V.P.--Pegasus Gold Corporation, Spokane, WA; *U.S. Public*, pg. 1269

Baker, Russell, Controller--Chattanooga Choo-Choo Holiday Inn, Chattanooga, TN; *U.S. Private*, pg. 231

Baker, T.F., Chief Fin. Officer, Grp. V.P.-Fin. & Treas.--Harvest States Cooperatives, Saint Paul, MN; *U.S. Private*, pg. 508

Baker, W. Randolph, Chief Fin. Officer & Exec. V.P.--Anheuser-Busch Companies, Inc., Saint Louis, MO; *U.S. Public*, pg. 113

Baker, William D., Chief Fin. Officer & V.P.--Trautman & Shreve, Inc., Denver, CO; *U.S. Public*, pg. 572

Baker, William D., Chief Fin. Officer & Treas.--The JPM Company, Lewisburg, PA; *U.S. Public*, pg. 919

Balardi, Patrick E., Chief Fin. Officer, V.P. & Treas.--The Lion Brewery, Inc., Wilkes-Barre, PA; *U.S. Public*, pg. 1000

Baldi, Phil, Chief Fin. Officer--The Flatley Company, Braintree, MA; *U.S. Private*, pg. 410

Baldwin, Jim, Chief Fin. Officer--Archway Cookies, Inc., Battle Creek, MI; *U.S. Private*, pg. 80

Baldwin, Pen, Chief Fin. Officer--Patton Management, Inc., Atlanta, GA; *U.S. Private*, pg. 843

Baldwin, Pen, Chief Fin. Officer--Wright & Lopez, Inc., Atlanta, GA; *U.S. Private*, pg. 843

Baldwin, Sandra Kaye, Pres. & Treas.--H & H Distributing Company, Inc., West Union, IA; *U.S. Private*, pg. 489

Baldwin, Sherry, Chief Fin. Officer & V.P.--Ameritech Cellular and Paging Services, Hoffman Estates, IL; *U.S. Public*, pg. 98

Baldwin, Thomas, Chief Fin. Officer--Morton's of Chicago, Inc., Chicago, IL; *U.S. Public*, pg. 1136

Baldwin, Thomas J., Chief Fin. Officer & Exec. V.P.--Morton's Restaurant Group, Inc., New Hyde Park, NY; *U.S. Public*, pg. 1136

Baleman, Robert, Pres. & Chief Fin. Officer--Griffon Corp., Jericho, NY; *U.S. Public*, pg. 766

Balgenorth, Richard V., Chief Fin. Officer & Treas.--Noble International Ltd., Bloomfield Hills, MI; *U.S. Public*, pg. 1187

Ball, Bruce, Chief Fin. Officer--Genesee Precision Fabricating, Grand Prairie, TX; *U.S. Private*, pg. 446

Ball, Bruce, Chief Fin. Officer--Genesee Stamping, Grand Prairie, TX; *U.S. Private*, pg. 446

Ball, Tracey C., Chief Fin. Officer & V.P.--Canadian Western Bank, Edmonton, Canada; *Int'l*, pg. 259

Ballard, John W., III, Chief Fin. Officer & Sec.--TCI International Inc., Sunnyvale, CA; *U.S. Public*, pg. 1555

Balle, Ole, Chief Fin. Officer & Exec. V.P.--Sophus Berendsen A/S, Soeborg, Denmark; *Int'l*, pg. 1284

Ballew, William, Chief Fin. Officer--Dallas Peterbilt, Inc., Irving, TX; *U.S. Private*, pg. 309

Balsama, J., V.P. & Chief Fin. Officer--Friden Alcatel, Hayward, CA; *Int'l*, pg. 55

Bamatter, Paul J., Chief Fin. Officer & V.P.-Fin.--Consoltex Group Inc., Ville Saint Laurent, Canada; *Int'l*, pg. 326

Bamberger, Ivor, Chief Fin. Officer & Sr. V.P.--Beber & Silverstein & Partners, Inc., Miami, FL; *U.S. Private*, pg. 128

Bane, Daniel T., Chief Fin. Officer & Sr. V.P.-Fin. & Admin.--Certified Grocers of California, Los Angeles, CA; *U.S. Private*, pg. 226

Bane, Daniel T., Chief Fin. Officer--Grocers Specialty Co., Los Angeles, CA; *U.S. Private*, pg. 227

Bane, Daniel T., Chief Fin. Officer--Grocers Development Co., Los Angeles, CA; *U.S. Private*, pg. 227

Bane, Daniel T., Pres. & Chief Fin. Officer--Crown Grocers, Inc., Los Angeles, CA; *U.S. Private*, pg. 227

Bane, Daniel T., Chief Fin. Officer & V.P.--Grocers General Merchandise Co., Los Angeles, CA; *U.S. Private*, pg. 227

Bane, Daniel T., Chief Fin. Officer & V.P.--Preferred Public Storage Co., Los Angeles, CA; *U.S. Private*, pg. 227

Banerjee, A., Dir.-Fin. & Information Systems--Tata Timken Limited, Jamshedpur, India; *U.S. Public*, pg. 1617

Bani, Richard, Chief Fin. Officer--Merrill Lynch International Bank, New York, NY; *U.S. Public*, pg. 1097

Banig, Linda, Chief Fin. Officer--Actron Manufacturing Company, Cleveland, OH; *U.S. Private*, pg. 16

Banks, R. Rendall, Chief Fin. Officer & V.P.-Fin.--Edwards Engineering Corporation, Pompton Plains, NJ; *U.S. Private*, pg. 365

Banta, Robert R., Chief Fin. Officer & Exec. V.P.--Moog Incorporated, East Aurora, NY; *U.S. Public*, pg. 1127

Bara, Jean-Marc, Chief Fin. Officer(New York)--Burson-Marsteller, New York, NY; *U.S. Private*, pg. 1197

Barakbah, Syed Fahkri, Grp. Dir.-Fin.--Sime Darby Berhad, Kuala Lumpur, Malaysia; *Int'l*, pg. 1249

Barber, Donald G., Chief Fin. Officer & Sr. V.P.--Santa Fe International Corporation, Dallas, TX; *Int'l*, pg. 765

Barber, John W., Chief Fin. Officer, V.P. & Controller--General American Life Insurance Co., Saint Louis, MO; *U.S. Private*, pg. 443

Barber, Kay A., Chief Fin. Officer, V.P. & Treas.--Merrill Corporation, Saint Paul, MN; *U.S. Public*, pg. 1097

Barbera, Henry, Chief Fin. Officer--Wire-Pro Inc., Salem, NJ; *U.S. Private*, pg. 1184

Barbera, Henry, Chief Fin. Officer--Viking Electronics, Inc., Chatsworth, CA; *U.S. Private*, pg. 1184

Barbieri, Robert G., Chief Fin. Officer & V.P.-Fin.--Apogee Enterprises, Inc., Minneapolis, MN; *U.S. Public*, pg. 120

Barbour, Rodney, Chief Fin. Officer & Gen. Counsel--Lawson Mechanical Contractors, Sacramento, CA; *U.S. Private*, pg. 654

Barclay, Fred, Chief Fin. Officer & V.P.--The Spencer Turbine Co., Windsor, CT; *U.S. Private*, pg. 1025

Barclay, R. Lee, Chief Fin. Officer & Exec. V.P.--Midas-International Corp., Chicago, IL; *U.S. Public*, pg. 1766

Bard, John F., Chief Fin. Officer--Wm. Wrigley Jr. Company, Chicago, IL; *U.S. Public*, pg. 1781

Bardach, Neil M., Chief Fin. Officer & V.P.--The Genlyte Group Incorporated, Union, NJ; *U.S. Public*, pg. 729

Bardina, Jaime, Controller--Mattel Espana, S.A., Barcelona, Spain; *U.S. Public*, pg. 1059

Bardo, Dennis, Mgr.-Fin.--U.S. Filter/Permutit, Warren, NJ; *U.S. Public*, pg. 1682

Bardusco, Alberto, Chief Fin. Officer--BGS DMB&B Milan, Milan, Italy; *U.S. Private*, pg. 303

Bare, James A., Chief Fin. Officer & Sr. V.P.--Consumer Finance Group, Tampa, FL; *U.S. Public*, pg. 1741

Bare, Richard, Chief Fin. Officer--BHC Securities, Inc., Philadelphia, PA; *U.S. Public*, pg. 647

Barefoot, D. Wayne, Chief Fin. Officer & V.P.-Fin.--Victaulic Company of America, Easton, PA; *U.S. Private*, pg. 1138

Bares, Roger, Controller & Dir.-Fin.--Northland Aluminum Products, Inc., Minneapolis, MN; *U.S. Private*, pg. 805

Barfield, Richard, Dir.-Grp. Fin.--MDIS Group plc, Hemel Hempstead, United Kingdom; *Int'l*, pg. 826

Barger, Donald G., Chief Fin. Officer, V.P. & Treas.--Worthington Industries, Inc., Columbus, OH; *U.S. Public*, pg. 1780

Bargull, Raymond C., Chief Fin. Officer & Exec. V.P.-Real Estate--Sundt Corp., Tucson, AZ; *U.S. Private*, pg. 1051

Barham, Diane, Chief Fin. Officer--Fields Stores, Richmond, Canada; *Int'l*, pg. 637

Barker, D.W., Chief Fin. Officer, Treas. & Sec.--Maescher Industries, Inc., Cincinnati, OH; *U.S. Private*, pg. 694

Barker, Edwin F., Chief Fin. Officer & V.P.--Winnebago Industries, Inc., Forest City, IA; *U.S. Public*, pg. 1772

Barker, Joseph F., Chief Fin. Officer & V.P.-Fin.--Haynes International, Inc., Kokomo, IN; *U.S. Public*, pg. 801

Barker, Roger, Chief Fin. Officer, V.P. & Treas.--Buffalo Rock Company, Birmingham, AL; *U.S. Private*, pg. 179

Barkley, Kenneth R., Chief Fin. Officer, Sr. V.P.-Fin. & Treas.--Cagle's Inc., Atlanta, GA; *U.S. Public*, pg. 291

Barkley, Kenneth R., Chief Fin. Officer, Sr. V.P.-Fin. & Treas.--Cagle's Farms Inc., Dalton, GA; *U.S. Public*, pg. 292

Barkofske, Francis L., Chief Fin. Officer & Sr. V.P.--Zeigler Coal Holding Company, Fairview Heights, IL; *U.S. Public*, pg. 1790

Barlett, Mauri, Chief Fin. Officer--Kruse International, Auburn, IN; *U.S. Private*, pg. 636

Barley, William B., Chief Fin. Officer & V.P.--Du Pont Canada Inc., Mississauga, Canada; *U.S. Public*, pg. 532

Barlow, Charles, Comptroller--Little America Refining, Inc., Evansville, WY; *U.S. Private*, pg. 1003

Barnes, James, Chief Fin. Officer, V.P. & Treas.--Wohlert Corp., Lansing, MI; *U.S. Private*, pg. 1185

Barnes, John L., Jr., Chief Fin. Officer & Sr. V.P.--Triarc Companies, Inc., New York, NY; *U.S. Public*, pg. 1634

Barnes, Michael H., Chief Fin. Officer, Sr. V.P. & Corp. Sec.--Intellicall, Inc., Carrollton, TX; *U.S. Public*, pg. 887

Barnes, R.A., Chief Fin. Officer--Waterford Wedgwood Plc, Dublin, Ireland; *Int'l*, pg. 1487

Barnes, W. Michael, Chief Fin. Officer & Sr. V.P.-Fin. & Plng.--Rockwell International Corporation, Costa Mesa, CA; *U.S. Public*, pg. 1397

Barnett, D.B., Chief Fin. Officer & V.P.--AirTouch Paging, Dallas, TX; *U.S. Public*, pg. 34

Barnett, Robert, Chief Fin. Officer & V.P.-Opers.--Interact Accessories, Inc., Hunt Valley, MD; *U.S. Public*, pg. 1369

Barnett, Steven B., Chief Fin. Officer, Sr. V.P. & Treas.--Rag Shops, Inc., Hawthorne, NJ; *U.S. Public*, pg. 1358

Barney, Joan M., CPA, Chief Fin. Officer--Omega World Travel, Inc., Fairfax, VA; *U.S. Private*, pg. 816

Barnhart, Jerry, Chief Fin. Officer--Goodby, Silverstein & Partners, San Francisco, CA; *U.S. Public*, pg. 1224

Barocas, Jeff, Chief Fin. Officer--Quipp Systems, Inc., Hialeah, FL; *U.S. Public*, pg. 1353

Barocas, Jeffrey S., Chief Fin. Officer--Quipp, Inc., Hialeah, FL; *U.S. Public*, pg. 1353

Barone, Anthony, Chief Fin. Officer, V.P. & Treas.--Tower Automotive, Inc., Grand Rapids, MI; *U.S. Public*, pg. 1625

Barr, David, Chief Fin. Officer--PacifiCare of California, Cypress, CA; *U.S. Public*, pg. 1251

Barravecchia, John R., Chief Fin. Officer & Exec. V.P.--Franchise Finance Corp. of America, Scottsdale, AZ; *U.S. Public*, pg. 679

Barret, Philippe, V.P.-Fin. & Opers.--Taylor Made Golf Co. Inc., Carlsbad, CA; *Int'l*, pg. 1181

Barrett, Deborah, Chief Fin. Officer & Sr. V.P.--Harrowston Corporation, Toronto, Canada; *Int'l*, pg. 599

Barrett, Emmett F., Chief Fin. Officer & V.P.--Fiske Brothers Refining Company, Newark, NJ; *U.S. Private*, pg. 408

Barrett, Gene, Chief Fin. Officer--Marshall Jaccoma Mitchell Advertising, New York, NY; *U.S. Private*, pg. 708

Barrett, Michael, Chief Fin. Officer--Mesirow Financial, Chicago, IL; *U.S. Private*, pg. 733

Barrett, Paul, Chief Fin. Officer, & Sr. V.P.-Fin.--Bill's Dollar Stores, Inc., Ridgeland, MS; *U.S. Private*, pg. 144

Barrett, Paula, Chief Fin. Officer--Kettler Brothers, Inc., Montgomery Village, MD; *U.S. Private*, pg. 617

Barrett, Walter B., Chief Fin. Officer--Devcon Crown Bay Corp., Saint Thomas, VI; *U.S. Public*, pg. 502

Barrette, Raymond, Exec. V.P., Chief Fin. Officer & Treas.--American Automobile Insurance Co., Creve Coeur, MO; *Int'l*, pg. 59

Barritt, James, Chief Fin. Officer--Coast Savings Financial, Inc., Los Angeles, CA; *U.S. Public*, pg. 388

Barrow, Robert G., Vice Chm. & Chief Fin. Officer--Wall Street Deli, Inc., Birmingham, AL; *U.S. Public*, pg. 1734

Barry, Daniel, Chief Fin. Officer--Orion Capital Companies, Inc., Farmington, CT; *U.S. Public*, pg. 1231

Barry, David, Chief Fin. Officer--Healthtex, Greensboro, NC; *U.S. Public*, pg. 1702

Barry, James A., Chief Fin. Officer, V.P. & Treas.--American Vanguard Corporation, Newport Beach, CA; *U.S. Public*, pg. 94

Barry, Ralph, Chief Fin. Officer, V.P., Treas. & Sec.--Imaging Technologies Corp., San Diego, CA; *U.S. Public*, pg. 870

Barsa, Karen, Chief Fin. Officer--Lost Arrow Corporation, Ventura, CA; *U.S. Private*, pg. 676

Bart, Todd, Chief Fin. Officer, Treas. & Sec.--Panaco, Inc., Kansas City, MO; *U.S. Public*, pg. 1255

Bartczak, Kevin, Chief Fin. Officer--Paravant Computer Systems, Inc., Melbourne, FL; *U.S. Public*, pg. 1257

Bartell, Gilbert G., Chief Fin. Officer & V.P.-Fin.--Conso Products Company, Union, SC; *U.S. Public*, pg. 434

Bartels, Mary J., Chief Fin. Officer & Controller--American Steamship Company, Williamsville, NY; *U.S. Public*, pg. 690

Bartholdson, John, Chief Fin. Officer & Sr. V.P.--Triumph Group, Inc., Wayne, PA; *U.S. Public*, pg. 1640

Bartis, Brian, Controller--Wolverine Packing Co., Detroit, MI; *U.S. Private*, pg. 1186

Bartlett, John B., Chief Fin. Officer & Sr. V.P.--UniFirst Corporation, Wilmington, MA; *U.S. Public*, pg. 1665

Bartman, Frank, Chief Fin. Officer & V.P.-Fin.--Richco Inc., Chicago, IL; *U.S. Private*, pg. 929

Barton, Francis, Chief Fin. Officer--Amdahl Corporation, Sunnyvale, CA; *Int'l*, pg. 527

Barton, Martin J., Chief Fin. Officer--Rapidforms, Inc., Thorofare, NJ; *U.S. Public*, pg. 1171

Barton, William E., Chief Fin. Officer & V.P.--Granite Construction Incorporated, Watsonville, CA; *U.S. Public*, pg. 759

Baruch, Yigal, Chief Fin. Officer--Sharplan Lasers, Inc., Allendale, NJ; *Int'l*, pg. 429

Barwick, John O., Chief Fin. Officer, V.P.-Fin. & Treas.--Carmike Cinemas, Inc., Columbus, GA; *U.S. Public*, pg. 305

Basar, John, Chief Fin. Officer & Controller--National Real Estate Services, Inc., Vancouver, Canada; *Int'l*, pg. 909

Basch, Saul, Chief Fin. Officer, Sr. V.P. & Treas.--The Hartford Steam Boiler Inspection & Insurance Co., Hartford, CT; *U.S. Public*, pg. 795

Basey, James L., Exec. V.P. & Chief Fin. Officer--Colorado National Bankshares, Inc., Denver, CO; *U.S. Public*, pg. 1680

Bash, Michael, Chief Fin. Officer--Anoka Electric Cooperative, Ramsey, MN; *U.S. Private*, pg. 75

Basile, Tony, Chief Fin. Officer--Charlie Thomas Dealerships, Houston, TX; *U.S. Private*, pg. 1082

Bassani, Becky, Chief Fin. Officer--Bassani Manufacturing, Anaheim, CA; *U.S. Private*, pg. 122

Bassini, Marco, Chief Fin. Officer--Skanska Oresund AB, Malmo, Sweden; *Int'l*, pg. 1261

Bastion, Bob, Chief Fin. Officer--Kirshenbaum, Bond & Partners, New York, NY; *U.S. Private*, pg. 624

Batelsson, Gunnar, Grp. Dir.-Fin.--Sandvik AB, Sandviken, Sweden; *Int'l*, pg. 1185

Bateman, Christopher H., Chief Fin. Officer & V.P.--HCC Industries, Rosemead, CA; *U.S. Private*, pg. 490

Bateman, Daniel, Chief Fin. Officer & Treas.--Bateman Brothers Lumber Co., Inc., New Britain, PA; *U.S. Private*, pg. 122

Bath, Doug, Chief Fin. Officer--Kruger Urban Forest Products, Inc., Bromptonville, Canada; *Int'l*, pg. 761

Batista, Jaime J., Chief Fin. Officer--Philippine Airlines, Inc., San Francisco, CA; *Int'l*, pg. 1051

Battaglia, Gregg, Chief Fin. Officer & V.P.-Fin.--Witt Company, Cincinnati, OH; *U.S. Private*, pg. 1185

Batten, James R., Chief Fin. Officer & V.P.-Fin.--O'Reilly Automotive Inc., Springfield, MO; *U.S. Public*, pg. 1230

Batten, James R., Chief Fin. Officer--Ozark Automotive Distributors, Inc., Springfield, MO; *U.S. Public*, pg. 1230

Batten, James R., Chief Fin. Officer--Greene County Realty Company, Springfield, MO; *U.S. Public*, pg. 1230

Baty, Rack, Chief Fin. Officer--NN Ball & Roller, Inc., Erwin, TN; *U.S. Public*, pg. 1146

Bauchman, M., Chief Fin. Officer--AHF-Ducommun Incorporated, Gardena, CA; *U.S. Public*, pg. 534

Baucom, Earl W., Sr. V.P. & Chief Fin. Officer--The Franklin Life Insurance Company, Springfield, IL; *U.S. Public*, pg. 76

Bauer, Gordon P., V.P.-Fin.--Osborn Manufacturing, Cleveland, OH; *U.S. Public*, pg. 924

Bauer, Hans-Peter, Partner & Chief Fin. Officer--Verin S.A., Berneck, Switzerland; *Int'l*, pg. 1322

Bauer, James P., V.P.-Fin. & Treas.--Small Parts, Inc., Logansport, IN; *U.S. Private*, pg. 1006

Bauerle, Robert, Chief Fin. Officer, Sr. V.P. & Treas.--American Bureau of Shipping, New York, NY; *U.S. Private*, pg. 51

Bauerlein, Dudley L., Jr., Chief Fin. Officer & Sr. V.P.--Fortune Brands, Inc., Old Greenwich, CT; *U.S. Public*, pg. 674

Baughman, Samuel L., Controller--First Gibraltar Bank, Irving, TX; *U.S. Public*, pg. 181

Baum, Kenneth, Chief Fin. Officer & V.P.-Fin.--Twin County Grocers, Inc., Edison, NJ; *U.S. Private*, pg. 1111

Baum, William A., Chief Fin. Officer & Exec. V.P.--Peoples Telephone Company, Inc., Miami, FL; *U.S. Public*, pg. 1275

Bauman, B. Kent, Pres. & Chief Fin. Officer--Condon Oil Company, Inc., Ripon, WI; *U.S. Private*, pg. 262

Baumann, Karl-Hermann, Chief Fin. Officer--Siemens AG, Munich, Germany; *Int'l*, pg. 1244

Baumgardner, David, Chief Fin. Officer--Smyth, Co., Saint Paul, MN; *U.S. Private*, pg. 1010

Baumgartner, Beat, Dr., Chief Fin. Officer--Oerlikon-Buhrle Holding AG, Zurich, Switzerland; *Int'l*, pg. 996

Baumhober, Roger, Chief Fin. Officer & V.P.--AmClyde Engineered Products Co., Inc., Saint Paul, MN; *U.S. Public*, pg. 778

Baumker, James, Chief Fin. Officer--Mycogen Corporation, San Diego, CA; *U.S. Public*, pg. 1142

Bautista, Jaimie J., Chief Fin. Officer & Sr. V.P.-Fin.--Philippine Airlines, Inc., Manila, Philippines; *Int'l*, pg. 1050

Bava, Michael, Chief Fin. Officer--John O. Butler Co., Chicago, IL; *Int'l*, pg. 1320

Bavely, Donald, Chief Fin. Officer & Exec. V.P.--Rosenthal Automotive Organization, Arlington, VA; *U.S. Private*, pg. 946

Baxter, James G., Chief Fin. Officer & Pres.-Consumer Prods. Grp.--CSS Industries, Inc., Philadelphia, PA; *U.S. Public*, pg. 283

Baxter, Philip, Chief Fin. Officer & Exec. V.P.--Mapco Inc., Tulsa, OK; *U.S. Public*, pg. 1042

Bayley, Nicholas, Chief Fin. Officer, V.P.-Fin. & Controller--Knapp Shoes Inc., Penn Yan, NY; *U.S. Private*, pg. 401

Beal, Mitch, Chief Fin. Officer--Fleischer Manufacturing, Inc., Columbus, NE; *U.S. Private*, pg. 410

Beames, Douglas K., Chief Fin. Officer & Controller--Reed Grain & Bean Company, Buhl, ID; *U.S. Private*, pg. 916

Beames, Douglas K., Chief Fin. Officer & Controller--Reed Brothers Inc., Buhl, ID; *U.S. Private*, pg. 916

Bean, Richard E., Chief Fin. Officer, Exec. V.P. & Sec.--Pearce Industries Inc., Houston, TX; *U.S. Private*, pg. 845

Beans, Patrick E., Chief Fin. Officer, V.P., Treas. & Sec.--National Research Corporation, Lincoln, NE; *U.S. Public*, pg. 1159

Bear, James W., Sr. V.P. & Treas.--Consolidated Products, Inc., Indianapolis, IN; *U.S. Public*, pg. 436

Bear, James W., Chief Fin. Officer, Sr. V.P. & Treas.--Steak 'n Shake, Inc., Indianapolis, IN; *U.S. Public*, pg. 437

Beard, Eugene P., Vice Chm., Chief Fin. Officer & Opers.--The Interpublic Group of Companies, Inc., New York, NY; *U.S. Public*, pg. 908

Beard, Peggy, Chief Fin. Officer, V.P.-Fin. & Treas.--Schwab Corp., Lafayette, IN; *U.S. Private*, pg. 974

Beard, Thomas, Chief Fin. Officer, Sr. V.P. & Treas.--Petroleum Inc., Wichita, KS; *U.S. Private*, pg. 858

Bearman, David, Chief Fin. Officer & Exec. V.P.--Cardinal Health Inc., Dublin, OH; *U.S. Public*, pg. 304

Beatty, Stephen E., Chief Fin. Officer & Treas.--The Dwyer Group, Inc., Waco, TX; *U.S. Public*, pg. 537

Beaudoin, Bernard, Chief Fin. Officer & Exec. V.P.--Kansas City Power & Light Company, Kansas City, MO; *U.S. Public*, pg. 943

Beauhall, Maelene, Chief Fin. Officer & V.P.-Fin.--InterBio Inc., Woodlands, TX; *U.S. Private*, pg. 566

Beaulieu, Brian P., Chief Fin. Officer--Capitol Construction Group, Inc., Wheeling, IL; *U.S. Private*, pg. 206
Beauregard, Ron, Chief Fin. Officer & V.P.-Fin.--Union Industries, Inc., Providence, RI; *U.S. Private*, pg. 1119
Beavais, Robert, Chief Fin. Officer--Austin Group, Flint, MI; *U.S. Private*, pg. 99
Bech, Louis Frank, Chief Fin. Officer--Janssen/Cilag (Pty) Limited, Sandton, South Africa; *U.S. Public*, pg. 929
Bechet, Paul R., Chief Fin. Officer & Sr. V.P.--Brookline Savings Bank, Brookline, MA; *U.S. Private*, pg. 171
Bechtel, Jim, Chief Fin. Officer & V.P.--Hausted, Medina, OH; *U.S. Private*, pg. 1001
Bechtold, Jesse, Chief Fin. Officer & V.P.--Havens Steel Co., Kansas City, MO; *U.S. Private*, pg. 510
Beck, Anthony J., Chief Fin. Officer--Intergen Company, Purchase, NY; *U.S. Private*, pg. 567
Beck, Frederick R., V.P.-Retail Acctg.--Riverside/Bi-Lo Division, Du Bois, PA; *U.S. Public*, pg. 1270
Beck, Michael, Sr. V.P.-Fin.--Westat Inc., Rockville, MD; *U.S. Private*, pg. 1163
Beck, Richard, Chief Fin. Officer & V.P.--Advanced Energy Industry, Fort Collins, CO; *U.S. Public*, pg. 20
Beck, S. Fred, Chief Fin. Officer--Icon Health & Fitness, Inc., Logan, UT; *U.S. Private*, pg. 556
Beck, Teresa, Chief Fin. Officer--American Stores Company, Salt Lake City, UT; *U.S. Public*, pg. 92
Beck, Timothy, Chief Fin. Officer--The Medical Protective Company, Fort Wayne, IN; *U.S. Private*, pg. 728
Becka, John, Chief Fin. Officer--PRC, Inc., Mc Lean, VA; *U.S. Public*, pg. 1003
Becker, Carolyn, Chief Fin. Officer--L.L. Olds Seed Company, Madison, WI; *U.S. Private*, pg. 814
Becker, Christian, Chief Fin. Officer, Sr. V.P. & Treas.--Comdial Corporation, Charlottesville, VA; *U.S. Public*, pg. 407
Becker, Heinz J., Mgr.-Fin.--Groschopp & Co. GmbH EMW Elektromotoren-Feinbauwerk, Viersen, Germany; *Int'l*, pg. 559
Becker, Jerome, Chief Fin. Officer, Controller & Treas.--Masters, Inc., Westbury, NY; *U.S. Private*, pg. 714
Becker, Larry K., Chief Fin. Officer & Exec. V.P.--Horace Mann Educators Corporation, Springfield, IL; *U.S. Public*, pg. 835
Becker, P., Joint Mng. Dir.--Funsoft Holding GmbH, Kaarst, Germany; *Int'l*, pg. 707
Becker, William C., Chief Fin. Officer & V.P.-Fin.--Shopsmith, Inc., Dayton, OH; *U.S. Public*, pg. 1467
Beckingham, Meryl K., Chief Fin. Officer--Epsilon, Burlington, MA; *U.S. Public*, pg. 74
Beckley, David, Chief Fin. Officer & Exec. V.P.--Century Aluminum Company, Monterey, CA; *U.S. Public*, pg. 328
Beckman, Richard, V.P.-Fin.--Yorktowne, Inc., Red Lion, PA; *U.S. Private*, pg. 1196
Beckstead, Roger, Chief Fin. Officer & V.P.--Fogarty Klein & Partners, Houston, TX; *U.S. Private*, pg. 415
Beckstead, Roger, Chief Fin. Officer & V.P.--Fogarty Klein & Partners, San Antonio, TX; *U.S. Private*, pg. 416
Beckwith, Shelley, Controller--Sensall, Div. of Rosemount, Inc., Hauppauge, NY; *U.S. Public*, pg. 574
Beckwith, Stephen R., Chief Fin. Officer--Scudder Kemper Investments, Inc., New York, NY; *Int'l*, pg. 1530
Bedard, Mark D., Chief Fin. Officer & Treas.--The Smithfield Companies, Inc., Portsmouth, VA; *U.S. Public*, pg. 1479
Beddoe, R.G., Chief Fin. Officer--Yale Security Products, Ltd., Wolverhampton, United Kingdom; *Int'l*, pg. 1499
Bedewi, Elizabeth M., Sr. V.P, Sec. & Treas.--New Mexico & Arizona Land Co., Phoenix, AZ; *U.S. Public*, pg. 1172
Bednorz, Nick, Chief Fin. Officer & Controller--Nichols-Homeshield, Davenport, IA; *U.S. Public*, pg. 1350
Bee, Dennis E., Treas.--United Refining Company, Warren, PA; *U.S. Private*, pg. 915
Beenham, Christopher G., Grp. Dir.-Fin.--Marley PLC, Sevenoaks, United Kingdom; *Int'l*, pg. 843
Begley, Kevin, Chief Fin. Officer--Village Super Market Inc., Springfield, NJ; *U.S. Public*, pg. 1721
Begnaud, James, Chief Acctg. Officer & Treas.--Allegiant Physician Services, Atlanta, GA; *U.S. Public*, pg. 45
Begnaud, James R., Chief Fin. Officer--Surgical Information Systems, Atlanta, GA; *U.S. Public*, pg. 45
Behar, Isaac M., Chief Fin. Officer & Sr. Deputy Mng. Dir.--Bank Hapoalim, Tel Aviv, Israel; *Int'l*, pg. 149
Behling, Jay, V.P.-Fin.--The Guber Peters Entertainment Company, Los Angeles, CA; *Int'l*, pg. 1283
Behling, Jay M., Sr. V.P. & Controller--MGM Entertainment Company, Culver City, CA; *U.S. Public*, pg. 1614
Behrens, Fred H., Chm. Bd., Chief Exec. Officer & Chief Fin. Officer--Amcor Capital Corporation, Coachella, CA; *U.S. Public*, pg. 64
Behrle, Keenan, Chief Fin. Officer & V.P.--Westminster Capital Inc., Beverly Hills, CA; *U.S. Public*, pg. 1761
Beier, Thomas E., Chief Fin. Officer & Sr. V.P.--IVAX Corporation, Miami, FL; *U.S. Public*, pg. 914
Beilstein, Frederick B., Chief Fin. Officer & Exec. V.P.--URS Logistics, Atlanta, GA; *U.S. Private*, pg. 1114
Beiriger, Terry, Chief Fin. Officer, Controller & Sec.--International FiberCom, Phoenix, AZ; *U.S. Public*, pg. 898
Beker, Johnny, Chief Fin. Officer--Conquest Europe S.A., Brussels, Belgium; *Int'l*, pg. 1484
Belanger, Paul, Chief Fin. Officer--General Tours Inc., Keene, NH; *U.S. Private*, pg. 445
Belden, Arthur B., Chief Fin. Officer & V.P.--Lord Corporation, Cary, NC; *U.S. Private*, pg. 675
Belinski, Tim, Chief Fin. Officer--Sport Obermeyer Ltd., USA, Aspen, CO; *U.S. Private*, pg. 1026
Belknap, John, Chief Fin. Officer & Sr. V.P.--Richfood Holdings, Inc., Glen Allen, VA; *U.S. Public*, pg. 1388
Belknap, John C., Chief Fin. Officer & Exec. V.P.--OfficeMax, Shaker Heights, OH; *U.S. Public*, pg. 1212
Bell, Bradley J., Chief Fin. Officer, V.P. & Treas.--Rohm and Haas Company, Philadelphia, PA; *U.S. Public*, pg. 1403
Bell, Forrest, Chief Fin. Officer & V.P.--Flair Corporation, Ocala, FL; *U.S. Public*, pg. 1676
Bell, M.J., Dir.-Fin.--Swire Pacific Limited, Central, Hong Kong; *Int'l*, pg. 1328
Bell, Marsha M., Chief Fin. Officer--Logicon Syscon Corporation, Falls Church, VA; *U.S. Public*, pg. 1199
Bell, S.A., Chief Fin. Officer--Confederation Trust Company, Toronto, Canada; *Int'l*, pg. 326
Bell, Sheldon, Chief Fin. Officer & Corp. V.P.--Scott Paper Limited, Mississauga, Canada; *Int'l*, pg. 762
Bellamy, Paul, Chief Fin. Officer & V.P.-Fin.--Graham-Field Health Products, Inc., Hauppauge, NY; *U.S. Public*, pg. 757
Bellary, Uday, Chief Fin. Officer, V.P. & Asst. Sec.--MMC Networks, Inc., Sunnyvale, CA; *U.S. Public*, pg. 1027
Belleau, Thomas F., Chief Fin. Officer & V.P.-Fin.--The Langer Biomechanics Group, Inc., Deer Park, NY; *U.S. Public*, pg. 978
Bellgraph, Tom, V.P.-Fin.--Hastings Manufacturing Company, Hastings, MI; *U.S. Public*, pg. 798
Bellino, Joseph P., Chief Fin. Officer & Treas.--Steel Technologies Inc., Louisville, KY; *U.S. Public*, pg. 1513
Bellis, William J., Chief Fin. Officer, V.P.-Fin., Controller & Treas.--AGR International, Inc., Butler, PA; *U.S. Private*, pg. 5
Bellisario, Earl J., Chief Fin. Officer & Sr. V.P.--Dravo Corporation, Pittsburgh, PA; *U.S. Public*, pg. 527
Bellora, Terry C., Chief Fin. Officer & V.P.-Fin.--Pace Industries, Inc., Fayetteville, AR; *U.S. Public*, pg. 986
Belmonte, Cassie, Chief Fin. Officer--Al Neyer, Inc., Cincinnati, OH; *U.S. Private*, pg. 797
Belrahmi, Amal, Chief Fin. Officer & Treas.--Hachette Filipacchi USA, New York, NY; *Int'l*, pg. 794
Belusic, Lori, Chief Fin. Officer & Chief Oper. Officer--KPR, New York, NY; *U.S. Public*, pg. 1224
Belzer, Burton E., Chm. Bd., Chief Exec. Officer, Cheif Fin. Officer & Treas.--E-Z Lok, Gardena, CA; *U.S. Private*, pg. 1063
Benacin, Philippe, Treas. & Sec.--Jordache Fragrances & Cosmetics, New York, NY; *U.S. Public*, pg. 924
Benapfl, William J., Chief Fin. Officer & Controller--California Custom Foods, Lodi, CA; *U.S. Private*, pg. 831
Benda, John, Chief Fin. Officer & V.P.-Fin.--Wagner Castings Company, Decatur, IL; *U.S. Public*, pg. 894
Bender, Brian W., Chief Fin. Officer, V.P. & Sec.--Egghead, Inc., Liberty Lake, WA; *U.S. Public*, pg. 566
Benecke, Mike, Chief Fin. Officer--Noble House Hotels and Resorts, Kirkland, WA; *U.S. Private*, pg. 800
Benedict, Robert, Chief Exec. Officer, Chief Fin. Officer & V.P.--Real World, Andover, MA; *U.S. Private*, pg. 913
Benedict, Shirley, V.P.-Fin.--Winona Knits, Winona, MN; *U.S. Private*, pg. 1183
Benefiel, R.I., Controller--Alumax Mill Products, Inc., Morris, IL; *U.S. Public*, pg. 59
Bengtson, Jan, Chief Fin. Officer--Elit Fonster AB, Vetlanda, Sweden; *Int'l*, pg. 1260
Bengtsson, Jan, Chief Fin. Officer--AB Gustaf Kahr, Nybro, Sweden; *Int'l*, pg. 1260
Benko, James A., Chief Fin. Officer--Corrpro Companies, Inc., Medina, OH; *U.S. Public*, pg. 451
Benne, Paul, Chief Fin. Officer--Prairie Farms Dairy, Inc., Carlinville, IL; *U.S. Private*, pg. 878
Bennerdt, Staffan, Sr. V.P.-Fin.--NCC AB, Solna, Sweden; *Int'l*, pg. 898
Bennett, Brad, Chief Acctg. Officer & Exec. V.P.--Integrated Health Services, Inc., Owings Mills, MD; *U.S. Public*, pg. 884
Bennett, Hugh, Chief Fin. Officer--Gulf States Steel, Inc., Gadsden, AL; *U.S. Private*, pg. 488
Bennett, J.D.S., Grp. Dir.-Fin.--John Menzies plc, Edinburgh, United Kingdom; *Int'l*, pg. 707
Bennett, Joel M., Chief Fin. Officer--JAKKS Pacific, Inc., Malibu, CA; *U.S. Public*, pg. 923
Bennett, Marcus C., Chief Fin. Officer & Exec. V.P.--Lockheed Martin Corporation, Bethesda, MD; *U.S. Public*, pg. 1006
Bennett, Mark, Chief Fin. Officer & V.P.--Egizii Electric, Inc., Springfield, IL; *U.S. Private*, pg. 366
Bennett, Martin, Chief Fin. Officer--Carnegie Holding AB, Stockholm, Sweden; *Int'l*, pg. 272
Bennett, Michael, Chief Fin. Officer & V.P.-Fin.--MFRI Inc., Niles, IL; *U.S. Public*, pg. 1026
Bennett, Phillip R., Chief Fin. Officer--Refco Group Ltd., Chicago, IL; *U.S. Private*, pg. 917
Bennett, R.F., Chief Fin. Officer--Northern Rock PLC, Newcastle upon Tyne, United Kingdom; *Int'l*, pg. 968
Bennett, Raymond T., V.P.-Taxes--MGM Entertainment Company, Culver City, CA; *U.S. Public*, pg. 1614
Bennett, Ronald L., Chief Fin. Officer--Kurdziel Industries, Inc., Muskegon, MI; *U.S. Private*, pg. 637
Bennett, Wycliff L., Chief Fin. Officer--Mormac Marine Transport, Inc., Stamford, CT; *U.S. Private*, pg. 762
Benoff, Michael, Chief Fin. Officer--The Money Store, Sacramento, CA; *U.S. Public*, pg. 1124
Benoit, David C., V.P.-Fin. & Treas.--Connecticut Water Service, Inc., Clinton, CT; *U.S. Public*, pg. 431
Bensen, Eric R., Chief Fin. Officer & V.P.--Cruise America, Inc., Mesa, AZ; *U.S. Private*, pg. 178
Bensimon, Raquel, Pres. & Chief Fin. Officer--Dearden's, Los Angeles, CA; *U.S. Private*, pg. 319
Benson, Andrew B., V.P.-Internal Audit--MGM Entertainment Company, Culver City, CA; *U.S. Public*, pg. 1614
Benson, Bill, Chief Fin. Officer & Exec. V.P.--Physicians Mutual Insurance Co., Omaha, NE; *U.S. Private*, pg. 864
Benson, D., Chief Fin. Officer & V.P.--The Budd Company, Troy, MI; *Int'l*, pg. 1388
Benson, Dave, Chief Fin. Officer--Bell Atlantic Mobile, Bedminster, NJ; *U.S. Public*, pg. 202
Benson, Donald E., Chief Fin. Officer & Exec. V.P.--Rieter Automotive North America Inc, Farmington Hills, MI; *Int'l*, pg. 1117
Benson, Gregory, Acting Chief Fin. Officer--American Pad and Paper Company, Dallas, TX; *U.S. Public*, pg. 88
Benson, John, Chief Fin. Officer & Chief Info. Officer--Dallas Gold & Silver Exchange, Inc., Dallas, TX; *U.S. Public*, pg. 478
Benson, Kevin E., Pres., Chief Exec. & Fin. Officer--Canadian Airlines Corporation, Calgary, Canada; *Int'l*, pg. 255
Benson, Nathan, Chief Fin. Officer--L.M. Sandler & Sons, Virginia Beach, VA; *U.S. Private*, pg. 964
Benson, Robert H., V.P.-Fin. & Admin.--NewTel Enterprises Limited, Saint Johns, Canada; *Int'l*, pg. 115
Benson, Tom, Chief Fin. Officer--SFX Broadcasting Incorporated, New York, NY; *U.S. Public*, pg. 1417
Bent, Brian, Chief Fin. Officer--Kenneth Gordon IAG, Inc., New Orleans, LA; *U.S. Private*, pg. 581
Bentata, I.S., Chief Fin. Officer--Turner Steiner International, New York, NY; *U.S. Public*, pg. 1646
Bentley, Steven, Chief Fin. Officer--Transport Development Group Plc, London, United Kingdom; *Int'l*, pg. 1418
Benton, Jane, Treas. & Sec.--Monroe Hardware Co., Monroe, NC; *U.S. Private*, pg. 335
Benton, William B., Chm. Bd., Chief Exec. Officer & Chief Fin. Officer--Mid South Sales, Helena, AR; *U.S. Private*, pg. 744
Berce, Daniel E., Vice Chm. & Chief Fin. Officer--AmeriCredit Corp., Fort Worth, TX; *U.S. Public*, pg. 96
Berenato, Joseph C., Pres., Chief Fin. Officer & Chief Oper. Officer--Ducommun Incorporated, Carson, CA; *U.S. Public*, pg. 533
Berey, Mark H., Chief Fin. Officer, Sr. V.P.-Fin. & Treas.--Giant Food Inc., Landover, MD; *U.S. Public*, pg. 741
Berg, Nancy, V.P. & Asst. Cashier--M & I Bank of Eagle River, Eagle River, WI; *U.S. Public*, pg. 1050
Berger, Morris W., Chief Fin. Officer--Careers USA Inc., Philadelphia, PA; *U.S. Private*, pg. 209
Berger, Richard N., Chief Fin. Officer, V.P. & Sec.--Richey Electronics, Inc., Garden Grove, CA; *U.S. Public*, pg. 1388
Berger, Robert J., Chief Fin. Officer, Sr. V.P. & Treas.--ONBANCorp, Inc., Syracuse, NY; *U.S. Public*, pg. 631
Berger, Stefan, Chief Fin. Officer--Sanitec Ltd. Oy, Ratingen, Germany; *Int'l*, pg. 863
Bergeron, Charles, Sr. V.P.-Fin.--Freightliner Corp., Portland, OR; *Int'l*, pg. 368
Bergeron, Dan, Chief Fin. Officer--Dorr-Oliver Incorporated, Milford, CT; *Int'l*, pg. 839
Berglund, Ulf, Chief Fin. Officer & Exec. V.P.--Granges AB, Stockholm, Sweden; *Int'l*, pg. 439
Bergman, Harry, Treas. & Sec.--The First Republic Corporation of America, New York, NY; *U.S. Public*, pg. 637
Bergonti, Carlo, Chief Fin. Officer--Procter & Gamble Health & Beauty Care So. Europe, Rome, Italy; *U.S. Public*, pg. 1332
Bergonzi, Frank, Chief Fin. Officer & Exec. V.P.--Rite Aid Corporation, Camp Hill, PA; *U.S. Public*, pg. 1390
Berkey, Dave, Chief Fin. Officer--Universal Studios Hollywood, Universal City, CA; *Int'l*, pg. 1216
Berkow, Miles, Chief Fin. Officer--Victaulic-Europe, Wetteren, Belgium; *U.S. Private*, pg. 1138
Berlin, Barry, Chief Fin. Officer--PMC Capital Inc., Dallas, TX; *U.S. Public*, pg. 1242
Berlin, Steven R., Chief Fin. Officer & Sr. V.P.-Fin.--Citgo Petroleum Corporation, Tulsa, OK; *Int'l*, pg. 1045
Berman, Ira W., Chm. Bd. & Chief Fin. Officer--CCA Industries, Inc., East Rutherford, NJ; *U.S. Public*, pg. 276
Bermani, Enzio, Chief Fin. Officer--Fila Sport S.p.A., Biella, Italy; *Int'l*, pg. 484
Bernard, James M., Chief Fin. Officer--Merrill Lynch Investment Partners, Inc., New York, NY; *U.S. Public*, pg. 1098
Bernat, Stan C., Chief Fin. Officer--Intool Rotor Company, Cleveland, OH; *U.S. Private*, pg. 574
Berner, Ch., Chief Fin. Officer--Kuehne & Nagel (AG & Co.), Bremen, Germany; *Int'l*, pg. 763
Berney, Linda, Chief Fin. Officer--Chief Industries, Inc., Grand Island, NE; *U.S. Private*, pg. 236
Bernica, Edward J., Chief Fin. Officer & V.P.--Energy West Inc., Great Falls, MT; *U.S. Public*, pg. 581
Bernstein, Emil S., Chief Fin. Officer, Exec. V.P. & Treas.--Chelsea Industries, Inc., Peabody, MA; *U.S. Private*, pg. 231
Bernstein, Richard, Chief Fin. Officer--Interactive Telecard Services, Inc. (ITS), Miami, FL; *U.S. Private*, pg. 566
Berry, Glenn A., Chief Fin. Officer & Exec. V.P.--The Dixie Group, Inc., Chattanooga, TN; *U.S. Public*, pg. 514
Berry, Phil, Chief Fin. Officer--Codar Technology Inc., Longmont, CO; *U.S. Public*, pg. 1144
Berry, Walter, Chief Fin. Officer & V.P.-Admin.--Bollinger Shipyards, Inc., Lockport, LA; *U.S. Private*, pg. 155
Berry, Walter, Chief Fin. Officer--Bollinger Algiers Inc., New Orleans, LA; *U.S. Private*, pg. 155
Berta, Vicent A., Treas.--PNC Bank, Louisville, KY; *U.S. Public*, pg. 1242
Bertelsen, Jeff, Chief Fin. Officer, V.P.-Fin. & Treas.--Computer Network Technology Corporation, Minneapolis, MN; *U.S. Public*, pg. 421
Berthezene, Michel, Gen. Mgr.-Fin.--Compagnie UAP, Paris, France; *Int'l*, pg. 323
Bertilsson, Tore, Chief Fin. Officer--AB SKF, Goteborg, Sweden; *Int'l*, pg. 1156
Berto, L. Rogerio, Chief Fin. Officer & Sr. V.P.--TVX Gold Inc., Toronto, Canada; *Int'l*, pg. 1345
Berto, L. Rogerio, V.P.-Fin.--Compania Nacional de Mineracao, Rio de Janeiro, Brazil; *Int'l*, pg. 1345
Bertolino, Margaret, Chief Fin. Officer--Agri-Mark, Inc., Lawrence, MA; *U.S. Private*, pg. 26
Bertrand, Richard L., Chief Fin. Officer & Sr. V.P.-Fin.--Extendicare (Canada) Inc., Markham, Canada; *Int'l*, pg. 468
Bertrand, Robert N., Chief Fin. Officer, V.P.-Fin. & Treas.--Industrial Acoustics Company, Inc., Bronx, NY; *U.S. Public*, pg. 875
Berube, Neal, Chief Fin. Officer & V.P.--Associated Food Stores Inc., Salt Lake City, UT; *U.S. Private*, pg. 90
Berube, Tom, V.P.-Fin. & Admin.--Schneider Automation, Inc., North Andover, MA; *Int'l*, pg. 1208

Besel, Daniel G., V.P.-Corp. Controller--BC Gas Inc., Vancouver, Canada; *Int'l*, pg. 114

Besing, Christopher S., Chief Fin. Officer, V.P. & Treas.--Action Performance Companies, Inc., Phoenix, AZ; *U.S. Public*, pg. 17

Besozzi, Massimo, Chief Fin. Officer--Home Products Italiana SpA, Milan, Italy; *U.S. Public*, pg. 81

Bessant, Thomas A., Jr., Chief Fin. Officer, Sr. V.P. & Treas.--Cash America International, Inc., Fort Worth, TX; *U.S. Public*, pg. 312

Best, Edgar, Chief Fin. Officer--Smith Hardware Company, Goldsboro, NC; *U.S. Private*, pg. 335

Best, Jerry, Chief Fin. Officer--Louis London Advertising & Sales Promotion, Saint Louis, MO; *U.S. Private*, pg. 674

Best, Larry, Chief Fin. Officer--Boston Scientific Corp., Natick, MA; *U.S. Public*, pg. 247

Bestsch, J.J., Chief Fin. Officer--Shieldalloy Metallurgical Corportation, Newfield, NJ; *U.S. Private*, pg. 735

Betlach, Douglas J., Chief Fin. Officer, V.P. & Treas.--Dycom Industries, Inc., Palm Beach Gardens, FL; *U.S. Public*, pg. 538

Betpera, Ed, Chief Fin. Officer--Trigon Adcotech, Fremont, CA; *U.S. Private*, pg. 1103

Betuker, Kenneth S., Chief Fin. Officer, V.P. & Sec.--Noodle Kidoodle Inc., Syosset, NY; *U.S. Public*, pg. 1188

Beudille, Reinhard, Chief Fin. Officer & V.P.--Siemens Automotive Corporation, Auburn Hills, MI; *Int'l*, pg. 1245

Beverage, Bill M., Chief Fin. Officer, Treas. & Sec.--Outdoor Systems, Inc., Phoenix, AZ; *U.S. Public*, pg. 1235

Bevevino, Daniel J., Chief Fin. Officer & V.P.--Respironics, Inc., Pittsburgh, PA; *U.S. Public*, pg. 1383

Bevins, William C., Jr., V.P. & Treas.--MGM Entertainment Company, Culver City, CA; *U.S. Public*, pg. 1614

Beyer, Richard P., Chief Fin. Officer, V.P.-Fin. & Treas.--Barrister Information Systems Corporation, Buffalo, NY; *U.S. Public*, pg. 192

Bhasin, Kris, Chief Fin. Officer--Picker International, Inc., Cleveland, OH; *Int'l*, pg. 545

Bhatt, Jay, Chief Fin. Officer--Spirit Cruises, Inc., Norfolk, VA; *Int'l*, pg. 1274

Bibler, Laurie, Chief Fin. Officer, Treas. & Sec.--Bibler Brothers, Inc., Russellville, AR; *U.S. Private*, pg. 142

Bickel, J.E., Chief Fin. Officer & V.P.--Raytheon Engineers & Constructors, Inc., Englewood, CO; *U.S. Public*, pg. 1366

Bickle, William D., Chief Fin. Officer--Teal Electronics, San Diego, CA; *U.S. Public*, pg. 1419

Biddle, R.M., Chief Fin. Officer & Dir.-Fin.--Eurotherm plc, Horsham, United Kingdom; *Int'l*, pg. 465

Bidelman, Jewell M., V.P. & Treas.--Northridge Industries, Inc., Chicago, IL; *U.S. Private*, pg. 551

Bieger, Michael, Chief Fin. Officer--Exolon-Esk Company, Tonawanda, NY; *U.S. Public*, pg. 600

Biegler, Jack, Chief Fin. Officer--Kaufman and Broad of Texas, Ltd., San Antonio, TX; *U.S. Public*, pg. 945

Biehl, George C., Chief Fin. Officer, Sr. V.P. & Sec.--Southwest Gas Corporation, Las Vegas, NV; *U.S. Public, pg. 1493*

Biehl, George C., Chief Fin. Officer & Sr. V.P.--Carson Water Co., Las Vegas, NV; *U.S. Public*, pg. 1493

Biehl, George C., Chief Fin. Officer--Utility Financial Corp., Las Vegas, NV; *U.S. Public*, pg. 1493

Biehl, George C., Chief Fin. Officer--Paiute Pipeline Co., Las Vegas, NV; *U.S. Public*, pg. 1493

Biehl, George C., Chief Fin. Officer--LNG Energy, Inc., Phoenix, AZ; *U.S. Public*, pg. 1493

Biehl, Joe, Chief Fin. Officer & V.P.--Sunstone Hotel Investors, Inc., San Clemente, CA; *U.S. Public*, pg. 1536

Biehn, Jergen, Chief Fin. Officer--Siliconix, Inc., Santa Clara, CA; *Int'l*, pg. 367

Biele, Anthony R., Chief Fin. Officer & Exec. V.P.--Talegen Corporation, Seattle, WA; *U.S. Public*, pg. 1784

Bielun, John A., Chief Fin. Officer, Sr. V.P. & Treas.--Alta Gold Co., Henderson, NV; *U.S. Public*, pg. 58

Biemeck, Bruce J., Chief Fin. Officer & Sr. V.P.--Great Lakes Dredge & Dock Co., Oak Brook, IL; *U.S. Private*, pg. 474

Bienvenu, Wayne, Treas. & Sec.--Turnbull Enterprises, Inc., Baltimore, MD; *U.S. Private*, pg. 1109

Bierer, Alice, Pres. & Chief Fin. Officer--Essex Grain Products, Inc., Frazer, PA; *U.S. Private*, pg. 383

Biggs, John, Sr. V.P.-Fin. Admin.--Hyatt Hotels Corporation, Chicago, IL; *U.S. Private*, pg. 551

Biggs, Tom, Chief Fin. Officer--Rose Acre Farms, Seymour, IN; *U.S. Private*, pg. 944

Bigham, James J., Vice Chm. & Chief Fin. Officer--Continental Grain Company, New York, NY; *U.S. Private, pg. 268*

Bigler, Robert J., Chief Fin. Officer & Sr. V.P.--Estee Lauder Companies Inc., New York, NY; *U.S. Public*, pg. 594

Bihan, L. M., Chief Fin. Officer--Pavailler Equipement S.A., Portes-les-Valence, France; *Int'l*, pg. 485

Billadeau, Jerry, Chief Fin. Officer--Riverside Millwork Company, Inc., Penacook, NH; *U.S. Private*, pg. 934

Billick, Steven M., Chief Fin. Officer, Sr. V.P. & Treas.--Signature Brands USA, Inc., Solon, OH; *U.S. Public*, pg. 1472

Billioud, Patrick, Sr. V.P.-Fin. Opers.--Compagnie de Suez, Paris, France; *Int'l*, pg. 313

Bilodeau, Normand, Chief Fin. Officer--BGS Systems, Inc., Waltham, MA; *U.S. Public*, pg. 161

Binder, Fredy, Chief Fin. Officer--Knurr AG, Fallanden, Switzerland; *Int'l*, pg. 739

Binder, Joe, Controller & Sec.--Acme Truck Line, Inc., Harvey, LA; *U.S. Private*, pg. 14

Binder, Kenneth, Chief Fin. Officer & Exec. V.P.-Fin.--Chromalloy Gas Turbine Corp., San Antonio, TX; *U.S. Public*, pg. 1458

Binder, U., Chief Fin. Officer--Molto Ges.m.b.H., Salzburg, Austria; *Int'l*, pg. 1501

Bineider, E., Chief Fin. Officer--ATCO Structures Inc., Calgary, Canada; *Int'l*, pg. 95

Bingham, H. Raymond, Chief Fin. Officer, Exec. V.P. & Sec.--Cadence Design Systems, Inc., San Jose, CA; *U.S. Public*, pg. 290

Bingham, Paul M., Sr. V.P.-Fin.--Fleetwood Enterprises, Inc., Riverside, CA; *U.S. Public*, pg. 650

Bingle, Jerry, Chief Fin. Officer & V.P.-Fin.--Da-Lite Screen Company, Inc., Warsaw, IN; *U.S. Private*, pg. 306

Binns, W. Gordon, Jr., V.P. & Chief Investment Funds Officer--General Motors Corporation, Detroit, MI; *U.S. Public*, pg. 718

Biorck, Hans, Chief Fin. Officer & Exec. V.P.--Esselte AB, Solna, Sweden; *Int'l*, pg. 459

Biquer, Gorge, Chief Fin. Officer--La Nacion S.A., Buenos Aires, Argentina; *Int'l*, pg. 785

Birch, John, Chief Fin. Officer--Jimmy Dean Foods, Cordova, TN; *U.S. Public*, pg. 1433

Birch, Paul, Chief Fin. Officer, Treas. & Exec. V.P.-Fin. & Admin.--PSDI, Bedford, MA; *U.S. Private*, pg. 828

Bird, Greg, Chief Fin. Officer--Horizon Investment Group, Taylor, MI; *U.S. Private*, pg. 539

Bird, R. Craig, Chief Fin. Officer, Exec. V.P.-Fin. & Devel. & Admin.--Showboat, Incorporated, Las Vegas, NV; *U.S. Public*, pg. 1469

Birdsong, Henry, Chief Fin. Officer--Intelligent Systems Corp., Norcross, GA; *U.S. Public*, pg. 888

Birks, Donna, Chief Fin. Officer--Comstream Corporation, San Diego, CA; *Int'l*, pg. 1288

Biroli, Amilcare, Dr., Chief Fin. Officer--Astra Veicoli Industriali S.p.A., Piacenza, Italy; *Int'l*, pg. 94

Bisaillon, R., V.P.-Fin. & Admin.--Grolier Interstate, Inc., Danbury, CT; *Int'l*, pg. 794

Bishop, Charles, Chief Fin. Officer--Willitts Design, Petaluma, CA; *U.S. Private*, pg. 1180

Bishop, J. Randall, Chief Fin. Officer, V.P. & Sec.--Cameron & Barkley Company, Charleston, SC; *U.S. Private*, pg. 203

Bishop, Laura M., Chief Fin. Officer & Sr. V.P.--Luby's Cafeterias, Inc., San Antonio, TX; *U.S. Public*, pg. 1017

Biskup, Zbig S., Chief Fin. Officer--Dynacare, Inc., Toronto, Canada; *Int'l*, pg. 425

Bisser, Ben, Chief Fin. Officer & V.P.-Fin.--Tomkins Industries Inc., Dayton, OH; *Int'l*, pg. 1397

Bisson, Eric, Chief Fin. Officer--Longlac Wood Industries Inc., Mississauga, Canada; *Int'l*, pg. 761

Bitar, Khalil, Chief Fin. Officer & Exec. V.P.--Intermarkets Advertising, Beirut, Lebanon; *Int'l*, pg. 680

Bittner, Daniel P., Chief Fin. Officer & V.P.--WPS Resources Corp., Green Bay, WI; *U.S. Public*, pg. 1728

Bittner, Daniel P., Sr. V.P.-Fin. & Corp. Svcs.--Wisconsin Public Service Corporation, Green Bay, WI; *U.S. Public*, pg. 1728

Bitzer, Brian, Chief Fin. Officer & V.P.--EFG Technologies Inc., Saint Paul, MN; *U.S. Public*, pg. 1679

Bivona, Frank J., Chief Fin. Officer, Sr. V.P. & Treas.--AMBAC Financial Group, Inc., New York, NY; *U.S. Public*, pg. 62

Black, Kenneth A., Chief Fin. Officer, Grp. V.P.-Corp. Fin., Controller & Treas.--First Citizens Banc Shares, Inc., Raleigh, NC; *U.S. Public*, pg. 628

Black, Paul, Chief Fin. Officer & V.P.--Elias Brothers Restaurants, Inc., Warren, MI; *U.S. Private*, pg. 371

Black, Paul R., Chief Fin. Officer--Calcor Space Facility, Inc., Whittier, CA; *U.S. Private*, pg. 200

Black, Sue, Chief Fin. Officer-NY--TBWA Chiat/Day New York, New York, NY; *U.S. Private*, pg. 1062

Black, William, V.P.-Fin. & Admin.--Farmland Dairies, Wallington, NJ; *U.S. Private*, pg. 395

Blackmon, Charles, Chief Fin. Officer & Exec. V.P.--American Buildings Co., Eufaula, AL; *U.S. Public*, pg. 69

Blackwell, C., Chief Fin. Officer--Integrated Photomatrix Ltd., Dorchester, United Kingdom; *Int'l*, pg. 448

Blackwell, Don W., Chief Fin. Officer, V.P. & Treas.--VASA Brougher, Inc., Indianapolis, IN; *Int'l*, pg. 464

Blades, B., Chief Fin. Officer--Barbados Dairy Industries Ltd., Saint Michael, Barbados; *Int'l*, pg. 923

Blaikie, John, Chief Fin. Officer--Wattyl, Canada Bay, Australia; *Int'l*, pg. 1488

Blain, Gerard, Chief Fin. Officer & V.P.--Meridian Diagnostics, Inc., Cincinnati, OH; *U.S. Public*, pg. 1094

Blair, Edward C., Jr., Chief Fin. Officer--Shakespeare Composites & Electronics, Newberry, SC; *U.S. Public*, pg. 940

Blake, Allen, Chief Fin. Officer, V.P. & Sec.--First Banks America, Inc., Clayton, MO; *U.S. Public*, pg. 626

Blake, Irvin N., Pres. & Treas.--NationsBank Insurance Agency, Inc., Norfolk, VA; *U.S. Public*, pg. 1163

Blakely, Robert T., Chief Fin. Officer & Exec. V.P.--Tenneco Inc., Greenwich, CT; *U.S. Public*, pg. 1577

Blakeman, Dan, Chief Fin. Officer--AirTouch Cellular - Western Region, Bellevue, WA; *U.S. Public*, pg. 34

Blakeslee, Eugene E., Exec. V.P. & Chief Fin. Officer--SJNB Financial Corp., San Jose, CA; *U.S. Public*, pg. 1418

Blanchard, Earl, Chief Fin. Officer, V.P. & Controller--Sturm, Ruger & Co., Inc., Southport, CT; *U.S. Public*, pg. 1526

Blaney, Dick, Chief Fin. Officer--Vinyl Plastics Incorporated, Sheboygan, WI; *U.S. Private*, pg. 1141

Blank, Dennis, Chief Fin. Officer--Wasserstrom Company, Columbus, OH; *U.S. Private*, pg. 1152

Blank, George, Chief Fin. Officer & Exec. V.P.--Univision Ltd. Partnership, New York, NY; *U.S. Private*, pg. 230

Blank, Randall, Chief Fin. Officer, Exec. V.P. & Sec.--Seacor Smit Inc., Houston, TX; *U.S. Public*, pg. 1449

Blankenship, C. Duane, Chief Fin. Officer & V.P.--Horizon Bancorp, Inc., Beckley, WV; *U.S. Public*, pg. 836

Blankley, John H., Chief Fin. Officer--Hvide Marine Incorporated, Fort Lauderdale, FL; *U.S. Public*, pg. 851

Blase, Paul, Controller--Schnuck Markets, Inc., Saint Louis, MO; *U.S. Private*, pg. 971

Blatterman, Todd, Chief Fin. Officer--Southern Container Corporation, Hauppauge, NY; *U.S. Private*, pg. 1016

Blattner, Simon J., III, Chief Fin. Officer--Rittenhouse Inc., Park Ridge, IL; *U.S. Private*, pg. 933

Blattner, Stephen C., Chief Fin. Officer, Treas. & Sec.--D.H. Blattner & Sons, Inc., Avon, MN; *U.S. Private*, pg. 148

Blazak, Bryan, Chief Fin. Officer--Chicago AutoWerks, Inc., Chicago, IL; *U.S. Private*, pg. 1030

Blazquez, Augustin, Chief Fin. Officer--Cartonajes Union, S.A., Gandia, Spain; *U.S. Public*, pg. 1666

Blevins, Ananetta, Chief Fin. Officer--Mason & Hanger Corporation, Inc., Lexington, KY; *U.S. Private*, pg. 711

Blickens, Robert, V.P.-Fin., Treas. & Controller--Komline-Sanderson Engineering Corp., Peapack, NJ; *U.S. Private, pg. 631*

Blickenstorfer, Hans Ulrich, Chief Fin. Officer & Member-Exec. Board--SIG Schweizersiche Industrie-Gesellschaft Holding AG, Neuhausen, Switzerland; *Int'l*, pg. 1156

Bloemer, J., Chief Fin. Officer--GESTRA GmbH, Bremen, Germany; *Int'l*, pg. 549

Blonder, Lloyd, Chief Fin. Officer, Sr. V.P. & Treas.--National Technical Systems, Inc., Calabasas, CA; *U.S. Public*, pg. 1161

Bloom, B.S., Chief Fin. Officer--Goodyear de Chile S.A.I.C., Santiago, Chile; *U.S. Public*, pg. 753

Bloom, David B., Chief Fin. Officer & Treas.--Bloom Electric Services, Inc., Oklahoma City, OK; *U.S. Private*, pg. 150

Bloom, Ken, Chief Fin. Officer--Pleasant Company, Middleton, WI; *U.S. Private*, pg. 872

Bloom, Larry L., Chief Fin. Officer & Treas.--Lee Enterprises, Incorporated, Davenport, IA; *U.S. Public*, pg. 983

Bloom, Robert S., Chief Fin. Officer & V.P.--Acxiom Corporation, Conway, AR; *U.S. Public*, pg. 18

Bloom, William J., Chief Fin. Officer--Exhibitgroup/Giltspur, Roselle, IL; *U.S. Public*, pg. 1718

Bloomer, Jonathan, Grp. Fin. Dir.--Prudential Corporation PLC, London, United Kingdom; *Int'l*, pg. 1073

Blose, Larry, Chief Fin. Officer--Blue Ridge Pressure Castings, Inc., Lehighton, PA; *U.S. Private*, pg. 153

Blouin, J. Scott, Chief Fin. Officer--Burr-Brown Corporation, Tucson, AZ; *U.S. Public*, pg. 270

Blount, Ben B., Jr., Chief Fin. Officer & Exec. V.P.-Plng., Admin. & Fin.--Oxford Industries, Inc., Atlanta, GA; *U.S. Public*, pg. 1239

Blount, Daniel J., Sr. V.P.-Fin.--Montgomery KONE Inc., Moline, IL; *Int'l*, pg. 746

Blount, David, Chief Fin. Officer--The Forum Corporation, Boston, MA; *U.S. Private*, pg. 420

Blount, Robert G., Sr. Exec. V.P.--American Home Products Corporation, Madison, NJ; *U.S. Public*, pg. 79

Blubaugh, Michael, Chief Fin. Officer--Bright National Bank, Flora, IN; *U.S. Public*, pg. 633

Bluhm, Leonard A., Chief Fin. Officer & Exec. V.P.--NRG Energy, Inc., Minneapolis, MN; *U.S. Public*, pg. 1195

Blume, Jon, Chief Fin. Officer & V.P.--Bel-Art Products, Pequannock, NJ; *U.S. Private*, pg. 130

Blumenthal, Reuben, Treas.--Lion Brand Yarn Co., New York, NY; *U.S. Private*, pg. 669

Board, Howard, Chief Fin. Officer & V.P.-Fin. & Admin.--Peoples Jewellers Corporation, Don Mills, Canada; *Int'l*, pg. 1036

Boase, Steve, Chief Fin. Officer & V.P.--McKinney & Silver, Raleigh, NC; *U.S. Private*, pg. 723

Bobel, Mary, Chief Fin. Officer--Genus Inc., Sunnyvale, CA; *U.S. Public*, pg. 732

Boberg, Kenneth G., Chief Fin. Officer--American Modern Home Insurance Group, Amelia, OH; *U.S. Public*, pg. 1110

Bocchini, David, Chief Fin. Officer--Cerdec Corporation, Washington, PA; *Int'l*, pg. 292

Bocklund, Scott R., Chief Fin. Officer--E.F. Johnson Radio Systems, Lincoln, NE; *U.S. Public*, pg. 1630

Bockstahler, Dana, Chief Fin. Officer--Bank of Agriculture & Commerce, Stockton, CA; *U.S. Private*, pg. 114

Bodane, Andrew S., Chief Fin. Officer--Nomaco, Inc., Zebulon, NC; *U.S. Private*, pg. 801

Bode, Jon A., Chief Fin. Officer--Active Software, Inc., Santa Clara, CA; *U.S. Private*, pg. 15

Bodine, William E., Chief Fin. Officer & Sr. V.P.--Bodine Assembly and Test Systems, Bridgeport, CT; *U.S. Private*, pg. 154

Boehlke, Robert J., Chief Fin. Officer & V.P.-Fin. & Admin.--KLA Tencor Corporation, San Jose, CA; *U.S. Public*, pg. 939

Boehm, Darnell, Chief Fin. Officer--Aetrium Inc., Saint Paul, MN; *U.S. Public*, pg. 27

Boehm, William J., Chm. Bd., Pres. & Chief Exec. Officer--Connector Manufacturing Company, Hamilton, OH; *U.S. Private*, pg. 264

Boelsen, Tom, Chief Fin. Officer & V.P.-Fin.--Olsten Health Services, Melville, NY; *U.S. Public*, pg. 1221

Boerlo, B., Chief Fin. Officer--Jaguar Cars Limited, Coventry, United Kingdom; *U.S. Public*, pg. 666

Boeve, Roger L., Chief Fin. Officer & Exec. V.P.--Performance Food Group Company, Richmond, VA; *U.S. Public*, pg. 1278

Bogan, Richard, Chief Fin. Officer--Miller Brewing Company, Milwaukee, WI; *U.S. Public*, pg. 1289

Bogan, Tom, Chief Fin. Officer--Brentwood Benson Publishing Group, Nashville, TN; *Int'l*, pg. 1529

Bogarde, Torgny, Corp. Treas.--Scancem AB, Malmo, Sweden; *Int'l*, pg. 1198

Bogdanovic, Darko, Chief Fin. Officer--MacGREGOR (HRV) d o o, Rijeka, Croatia; *Int'l*, pg. 671

Bogh, Niels, Chief Fin. Officer--Thrige-Titan A/S, Odense, Denmark; *Int'l*, pg. 1387

Bogins, Tom, Chief Fin. Officer & V.P.-Fin.--SQA, Inc., Burlington, MA; *U.S. Public*, pg. 1361

Bohlen, Richard E., Asst. Treas.--Global Marine Inc., Houston, TX; *U.S. Public*, pg. 748

Bohlin, Garen G., Chief Fin. Officer & Exec. V.P.--Genetics Institute, Inc., Cambridge, MA; *U.S. Public*, pg. 79

Bohlin, Torvald, Chief Fin. Officer--Aftonbladet AB, Stockholm, Sweden; *Int'l*, pg. 29

Bohling, J. Scott, Chief Fin. Officer, V.P. & Sec.--H.H. Brown Shoe Company, Inc., Greenwich, CT; *U.S. Public*, pg. 217

Bohm, H., Dir.-Fin.--Eli Lilly Italia, S.p.A., Sesto Fiorentino, Italy; *U.S. Public*, pg. 994

Bohn, Jim, Chief Fin. Officer, V.P.-Fin., Treas. & Sec.--Intermatic Inc., Spring Grove, IL; *U.S. Private*, pg. 567
Bohs, G. Lee, Chief Fin. Officer & Exec. V.P.--Right Management Consultants, Inc., Philadelphia, PA; *U.S. Public*, pg. 1390
Boisvert, Bill, Pres. & Chief Fin. Officer--Attachmate, Bellevue, WA; *U.S. Private*, pg. 98
Boisvert, Catherine M., V.P. & Controller--Farrel Corporation, Ansonia, CT; *U.S. Public*, pg. 614
Bolanos, Jorge Walter, Chief Fin. Officer, Sr. V.P. & Treas.--H.B. Fuller Company, Saint Paul, MN; *U.S. Public*, pg. 686
Boldon, Frank, Sr. V.P.-Fin.--Siecor Corporation, Hickory, NC; *U.S. Public*, pg. 449
Boldon, Frank, Sr. V.P.-Fin.--Siecor Corporation, Hickory, NC; *Int'l*, pg. 1245
Boldt, James R., Chief Fin. Officer & V.P.--Computer Task Group, Inc. (CTG), Buffalo, NY; *U.S. Public*, pg. 423
Boldt, Jim, Chief Fin. Officer, Treas. & Mgr.-Fin.--Austin Powder Co., Cleveland, OH; *U.S. Private*, pg. 100
Bolduc, James P., Chief Fin. Officer & Exec. V.P.--CTG Resources, Inc., Hartford, CT; *U.S. Public*, pg. 285
Bolduc, James P., Chief Fin. Officer & Exec. V.P.--Connecticut Natural Gas Corporation, Hartford, CT; *U.S. Public*, pg. 285
Bolduc, James P., Chief Fin. Officer & Exec. V.P.--Energy Networks, Inc. (ENI), Hartford, CT; *U.S. Public*, pg. 285
Bolger, Pat, Chief Fin. Officer & Sr. V.P.--The Bon Marche, Inc., Seattle, WA; *U.S. Public*, pg. 617
Bolin, Susan C., Chief Fin. Officer, Exec. V.P., Treas. & Sec.--The O'Boise Corporation, Oak Brook, IL; *U.S. Private*, pg. 810
Bollinger, Tom, Chief Fin. Officer--Sugar Creek Packing Co., Washington Court House, OH; *U.S. Private*, pg. 1049
Bollo, Robert J., Chief Fin. Officer & V.P.-Fin.--Photronics, Inc., Brookfield, CT; *U.S. Public*, pg. 1293
Bols, John, Chief Fin. Officer--Bromley, Aguilar & Associates, San Antonio, TX; *U.S. Private*, pg. 692
Bolt, J. Andrew, Chief Fin. Officer & V.P.--Arrow Shirt Company, New York, NY; *Int'l*, pg. 194
Bolten, Randall C., Chief Fin. Officer & V.P.-Opers.--BroadVision, Inc., Redwood City, CA; *U.S. Public*, pg. 258
Bolton, William J., Chief Fin. Officer & Corp. Sec.--Carolina Steel Corporation, Greensboro, NC; *U.S. Private*, pg. 214
Bolzan, Dennis, Chief Fin. Officer--Washington Specialty Metals, Buffalo Grove, IL; *U.S. Public*, pg. 1020
Bomberger, Glen R., Chief Fin. Officer & Exec. V.P.--A.O. Smith Corporation, Milwaukee, WI; *U.S. Public*, pg. 1476
Bomzer, Al, Chief Fin. Officer--Host Apparel, Inc., New York, NY; *U.S. Private*, pg. 540
Bonach, Edward J., Sr. V.P. & Chief Fin. Officer--Allianz Life Insurance Company of North America, Minneapolis, MN; *Int'l*, pg. 58
Bonahoom, Roger, V.P. & Treas.--Wolverine Packing Co., Detroit, MI; *U.S. Private*, pg. 1186
Bonaiuto, Paul, Chief Fin. Officer & Exec. V.P.-Fin.--Journal Communications Inc., Milwaukee, WI; *U.S. Private*, pg. 601
Bonalanze, L., Chief Fin. Officer--Caffaro S.p.A., Milan, Italy; *Int'l*, pg. 248
Bond, Ritchie L., Chief Fin. Officer & Sr. V.P.--Florimex Worldwide, Inc., Danville, VA; *U.S. Public*, pg. 510
Bond, Rodney S., Chief Fin. Officer, Treas. & Sec.--VTEL Corporation, Austin, TX; *U.S. Public*, pg. 1703
Bond, Thomas A., Chief Fin. Officer, Exec. V.P. & Sec.--Aluma Systems Corp., Toronto, Canada; *Int'l*, pg. 1423
Bonde, Preben, Chief Fin. Officer--Esselte A/S, Frederiksberg, Denmark; *Int'l*, pg. 460
Bondi, Mario, Chief Fin. Officer--Lati Industria Termoplastici S.p.A., Vedano Olona, Italy; *Int'l*, pg. 804
Bondus, Thom B., V.P. & Controller--The Somerset Group, Inc., Indianapolis, IN; *U.S. Public*, pg. 1484
Bondy, Timothy J., Chief Fin. Officer & V.P.--Northwestern Steel & Wire Co., Sterling, IL; *U.S. Public*, pg. 1201
Bone, Michael, Chief Fin. Officer--Esselte Australia Pty. Ltd., Wetherill Park, Australia; *Int'l*, pg. 461
Bonelli, Anthony, Pres. & Chief Oper. Officer--Neuman Distributors, Inc., Ridgefield, NJ; *U.S. Public*, pg. 1169
Bonelli, Ronald J., Chief Fin. Officer & V.P.--Berol Corporation, Brentwood, TN; *U.S. Public*, pg. 1178
Bonen, James J., Chief Fin. Officer--Sonic Couriers of Arizona, Inc., Scottsdale, AZ; *U.S. Private*, pg. 1123
Boness, Jerry, Chief Fin. Officer--United States Bakery, Portland, OR; *U.S. Private*, pg. 1124
Bonifaci, John A., Chief Fin. Officer--Old Home Foods, Inc., Saint Paul, MN; *U.S. Private*, pg. 814
Boning, Roger C., Chief Fin. Officer--Oxford University Press, Oxford, United Kingdom; *Int'l*, pg. 1018
Bonk, Jeanne, Chief Fin. Officer--San Diego Chargers, San Diego, CA; *U.S. Private*, pg. 964
Bonk, Robert, Chief Fin. Officer, V.P.-Fin. & Sec.--Northern Labs, Inc., Manitowoc, WI; *U.S. Private*, pg. 805
Bonney, Mark J., Chief Fin. Officer, V.P.-Fin. & Admin. & Treas.--Zygo Corporation, Middlefield, CT; *U.S. Public*, pg. 1795
Bonsall, Mark B., Chief Fin. Officer & Assoc. Gen. Mgr.--Salt River Project Agricultural Improvement and Power District, Tempe, AZ; *U.S. Private*, pg. 962
Booe, Robert G., Chief Fin. Officer & V.P.-Fin. & Admin.--Midwest Grain Products, Inc., Atchison, KS; *U.S. Public*, pg. 1111
Boomsma, Wouter, Pres.--NCT Holland B.V., Breda, Netherlands; *Int'l*, pg. 914
Booth, Erich J., Chief Fin. Officer & Treas.--Apple South, Inc., Madison, GA; *U.S. Public*, pg. 121
Booth, Larry, Chief Fin. Officer--Gleason/Calise/Associates, Inc., Dallas, TX; *U.S. Private*, pg. 455
Booth, Ralph H., II, Chm. Bd. & Chief Fin. Officer--Booth American, Detroit, MI; *U.S. Private*, pg. 156
Bopp, William C., Chief Fin. Officer & Exec. V.P.--C.R. Bard, Inc., Murray Hill, NJ; *U.S. Public*, pg. 189
Boppe, Larry, Chief Fin. Officer & V.P.-Opers.--Toter Incorporated, Statesville, NC; *U.S. Private*, pg. 1092
Bordeleau, Claude, Chief Fin. Officer--Cossette Communication Marketing, Quebec, Canada; *Int'l*, pg. 335
Borden, Lorraine, Chm. Bd., Chief Exec. Officer, Chief Fin. Officer, Pres.--Great Scott Advertising Co. Inc., New York, NY; *U.S. Private*, pg. 475
Bordignon, Agostino, Chief Fin. Officer--Gariboldi Parisi Verga/Interad, Milan, Italy; *U.S. Private*, pg. 678
Borelli, Frank J., Chief Fin. Officer & Sr. V.P.--Marsh & McLennan Companies, Inc., New York, NY; *U.S. Public*, pg. 1048
Boren, Robert P., C.P.A., Chief Fin. Officer & Sr. V.P.-Fin.--State Volunteer Mutual Insurance Co., Brentwood, TN; *U.S. Private*, pg. 1037
Born, Cheryl, Chief Fin. Officer--Quebecor Printing Arlington Heights, Arlington Heights, IL; *Int'l*, pg. 1076
Borocz, Michael S., Sr. V.P. & Controller--PNC Bank, Camp Hill, PA; *U.S. Public*, pg. 1243
Borok, Jonathan, Chief Fin. Officer--Paul Ecke Ranch, Encinitas, CA; *U.S. Private*, pg. 359
Borruso, Patrick, Chief Fin. Officer--Schroder & Co. Inc., New York, NY; *Int'l*, pg. 1210
Borsig, Clemens, Dr., Chief Fin. Officer--RWE AG, Essen, Germany; *Int'l*, pg. 1081
Borst, Stephen P., Chief Fin. Officer--Sampler Publications Inc., Saint Charles, IL; *U.S. Private*, pg. 963
Borsuk, Peter, Chief Fin. Officer & V.P.--Contempri Homes, Inc., Taylor, PA; *U.S. Public*, pg. 439
Bos, Gerald, Chief Fin. Officer--Mid-America Dairymen, Inc., Springfield, MO; *U.S. Private*, pg. 743
Bosch, Arie, Chief Fin. Officer--Power-Packer Europa B.V., Oldenzaal, Netherlands; *U.S. Public*, pg. 125
Boschma, Gerald A., Chief Fin. Officer, V.P. & Treas.--Michigan Sugar Company, Saginaw, MI; *U.S. Public*, pg. 873
Boschma, Gerald A., Chief Fin. Officer, V.P. & Treas.--Great Lakes Sugar Company, Fremont, OH; *U.S. Public*, pg. 873
Bose, D., Chief Fin. Officer--Esselte SA, Paris, France; *Int'l*, pg. 461
Bosowski, Ed, Chief Fin. Officer & V.P.-Ceilings--USG Interiors, Inc., Chicago, IL; *U.S. Public*, pg. 1660
Bospflug, Lance F., Chief Fin. Officer, Exec. V.P. & Treas.--T.L. James & Company, Ruston, LA; *U.S. Private*, pg. 580
Bosquet, Philippe, Chief Fin. Officer--Lowe Troost, Brussels, Belgium; *U.S. Private*, pg. 678
Bosser, Klaus, Chief Fin. Officer--Alno AG, Pfullendorf, Germany; *Int'l*, pg. 65
Bosserman, David N., Chief Fin. Officer, Exec. V.P. & Treas.--Best Software, Inc., Reston, VA; *U.S. Public*, pg. 223
Bosshard, Otto, Sr. V.P. & Treas.--Westfield Companies, Westfield Center, OH; *U.S. Private*, pg. 1169
Bost, Walter, Chief Fin. Officer--Ridgeview, Inc., Newton, NC; *U.S. Private*, pg. 930
Boston, Wallace E., Jr., V.P.-Fin.--Manor Healthcare Corp., Gaithersburg, MD; *U.S. Public*, pg. 1041
Bosworth, Robert, Chief Fin. Officer--Chattem (U.K.) Ltd., Basingstoke, United Kingdom; *U.S. Public*, pg. 342
Bosworth, Robert, Chief Fin. Officer--HBA Insurance Ltd., Hamilton, Bermuda; *U.S. Public*, pg. 342
Bosworth, Robert, Chief Fin. Officer--Signal Investment & Management Co., Wilmington, DE; *U.S. Public*, pg. 342
Botha, R.M., Chief Fin. Officer--Sasol Oil, Rosebank, South Africa; *Int'l*, pg. 1197
Botica, Luke F., Chief Fin. Officer & Exec. V.P.--Dames & Moore Inc., Los Angeles, CA; *Int'l*, pg. 624
Bottego, Douglas, Chief Fin. Officer & V.P.-Fin.--Pass & Seymour/Legrand, Syracuse, NY; *Int'l*, pg. 806
Bottini, Giancarlo, Chief Fin. Officer--Benetton Group S.p.A., Ponzano Veneto, Italy; *Int'l*, pg. 186
Bouchayer, Steve, Chief Fin. Officer--BC-USA, New Holland, PA; *Int'l*, pg. 201
Boucher, Daniel, Dir.-Admin. & Fin.--Kodak Pathe S.A., Paris, France; *U.S. Public*, pg. 554
Boudergard, John, Chief Fin. Officer--Lego System A/S, Billund, Denmark; *Int'l*, pg. 805
Boudreau, David, Chief Fin. Officer & Sr. V.P.--Jan Bell Marketing Inc., Sunrise, FL; *U.S. Public*, pg. 207
Boudreau, Ken, Chief Fin. Officer--M.C. Gill Corporation, El Monte, CA; *U.S. Private*, pg. 453
Bounds, Linda K., Chief Fin. Officer & Sr. V.P.--Bell Sports Corp., San Jose, CA; *U.S. Public*, pg. 207
Bounds, Robert, Chief Fin. Officer--Waverly International, Baltimore, MD; *U.S. Public*, pg. 1748
Bouquard, J.F., Chief Fin. Officer, Chief Info. Officer-Admin./Opers. & V.P.--Nestle Industrial e Commercial Ltda., Sao Paulo, Brazil; *Int'l*, pg. 921
Bourne, Richard, Acting Chief Fin. Officer, Exec. V.P. & Gen. Mgr.--ASICS Tiger Corporation, Fountain Valley, CA; *U.S. Private*, pg. 89
Bouthillette, Carole, V.P.-Fin.--The Jean Coutu Group (PJC) Inc., Longueuil, Canada; *Int'l*, pg. 340
Boutin, Bob, Chief Fin. Officer & Sr. V.P.--Computer City, Fort Worth, TX; *U.S. Public*, pg. 1560
Bouwmeester, A.G.M., Chief Fin. Officer--Whitehall Laboratoria B.V., Amsterdam, Netherlands; *U.S. Public*, pg. 82
Bovee, David R., Chief Fin. Officer, V.P. & Asst. Sec.--Dura Automotive Systems, Inc., Minneapolis, MN; *U.S. Public*, pg. 537
Bovird, Orlene, Chief Fin. Officer--Georgia Crown Distributing, Columbus, GA; *U.S. Private*, pg. 448
Bowden, James A., Chief Fin. Officer & Sr. V.P.--J.A. Jones, Inc., Charlotte, NC; *Int'l*, pg. 633
Bowen, Barry, Treas.--World Trade & Marketing, LTD., Chicago, IL; *U.S. Public*, pg. 1621
Bower, Curtis A., Chief Fin. Officer, Sr. V.P. & Treas.--Parsons Corporation, Pasadena, CA; *U.S. Private*, pg. 841
Bower, Kevin D., Chief Fin. Officer & Sr. V.P.--Alltrista Corporation, Muncie, IN; *U.S. Public*, pg. 56
Bower, Robert R., Sr. V.P.--S.T. Research, Newington, VA; *U.S. Private*, pg. 958
Bowers, R. Todd, Chief Fin. Officer & Sr. V.P.--SunTrust, Orlando, FL; *U.S. Public*, pg. 1537
Bowers, Robert E., V.P.-Fin.--Watt Publishing Co., Mount Morris, IL; *U.S. Private*, pg. 1154
Bowles, A. Eugene, Jr., General Auditor--SunTrust Banks of Georgia, Inc., Atlanta, GA; *U.S. Public*, pg. 1538
Bowman, Brian, Chm. Bd. & Chief Fin. Officer--Ryan Herco Products Corp., Burbank, CA; *U.S. Private*, pg. 953
Bowman, Elizabeth, Exec. V.P.-Fin. & Treas.--Universal Forest Products, Inc., Grand Rapids, MI; *U.S. Public*, pg. 1696
Bowman, Fred, Chief Fin. Officer & V.P.--Seessel Holdings, Inc., Memphis, TN; *U.S. Private*, pg. 981
Bowman, Richard F., Chief Fin. Officer, Sr. V.P. & Treas.--First Virginia Banks, Inc., Falls Church, VA; *U.S. Public*, pg. 641
Boyd, Dale, Chief Fin. Officer, Exec. V.P. & Sec.--MTI Technology Corporation, Anaheim, CA; *U.S. Public*, pg. 1028
Boyd, Ian, Grp. Dir.-Fin.--Weir Group PLC, Glasgow, United Kingdom; *Int'l*, pg. 1488
Boyd, James Y., Chief Fin. Officer--OPICOIL Houston, Inc., Houston, TX; *Int'l*, pg. 286
Boyd, Robert, Chief Fin. Officer & Exec. V.P.-Fin.--The Oshawa Group Limited, Etobicoke, Canada; *Int'l*, pg. 1012
Boyd, Thomas B., Sr. V.P.--Laserscope Surgical Systems, San Jose, CA; *U.S. Public*, pg. 979
Boyd, W. Glen, Chief Fin. Officer--Boral Concrete Products Inc., Rialto, CA; *Int'l*, pg. 203
Boyer, Norman L., Dir.-Fin. & Acct.--United McGill Corp., Groveport, OH; *U.S. Private*, pg. 1122
Boyes, Roger F., Dir.-Grp. Fin.--Halifax plc, Halifax, United Kingdom; *Int'l*, pg. 589
Boyle, Francis J., Chief Fin. Officer & V.P.-Fin./Admin.--Central Vermont Public Service Corporation, Rutland, VT; *U.S. Public*, pg. 327
Boyle, Francis J., Chief Fin. Officer--C.V. Realty, Inc., Rutland, VT; *U.S. Public*, pg. 328
Boyle, Francis J., Chief Fin. Officer--Connecticut Valley Electric Co., Inc., Rutland, VT; *U.S. Public*, pg. 328
Boyle, Francis J., Chief Fin. Officer--Catamount Energy Corporation, Rutland, VT; *U.S. Public*, pg. 328
Boyle, Francis J., Chief Fin. Officer--Catamount Investment Corporation, Rutland, VT; *U.S. Public*, pg. 328
Boyle, G.M., Dir.-Fin.--The Davis Service Group Plc., London, United Kingdom; *Int'l*, pg. 385
Boyle, James, Sr. V.P., Controller & Treas.--Broad National Bancorporation, Newark, NJ; *U.S. Public*, pg. 257
Boyle, Paul, Chief Fin. Officer--Cadbury Limited, Birmingham, United Kingdom; *Int'l*, pg. 248
Boyle, William, Chief Fin. Officer & V.P.-Fin.--Cubic Corporation, San Diego, CA; *U.S. Public*, pg. 466
Bozzelli, Rick, Chief Fin. Officer & V.P.--EBSCO Industries, Inc., Birmingham, AL; *U.S. Private*, pg. 358
Braam, James R., Chief Fin. Officer, V.P.-Fin., Treas. & Sec.--Virco Mfg. Corporation, Torrance, CA; *U.S. Public*, pg. 1721
Brace, James, Chief Fin. Officer, V.P. & Treas.--Littelfuse, Inc., Des Plaines, IL; *U.S. Public*, pg. 1001
Bradbury, R. Douglas, Chief Fin. Officer & Sr. V.P.--MFS WorldCom, Inc., Omaha, NE; *U.S. Public*, pg. 1779
Braddock, David A., Dir.-Corp. Acctg.--Inductotherm Industries, Inc., Rancocas, NJ; *U.S. Private*, pg. 560
Braden, Don, Chief Fin. Officer--Arctic Slope Regional Corporation, Barrow, AK; *U.S. Private*, pg. 80
Bradley, Ken, V.P.-Fin. & Admin. & Chief Fin. Officer--Garland Commercial Ranges, Ltd., Mississauga, Canada; *Int'l*, pg. 189
Bradley, Kevin, Chief Fin. Officer--Taylor & Francis, Washington, DC; *Int'l*, pg. 1358
Bradshaw, Jim, Chief Fin. Officer & Controller--Bruce Industries, Inc., Dayton, NV; *U.S. Private*, pg. 175
Bradshaw, Russ, Chief Fin. Officer & Treas.--Brown & Brown Venture Group, LLC, Mesa, AZ; *U.S. Private*, pg. 172
Bradshaw, Thomas, Chief Fin. Officer & Sr. Exec. V.P.--All American Communications, Inc., Santa Monica, CA; *U.S. Public*, pg. 41
Brady, David, Chief Fin. Officer & Controller--Deluxe Storage Systems, Inc., Warren, PA; *U.S. Private*, pg. 323
Brady, William, Treas.--Brady Enterprises, Inc., East Weymouth, MA; *U.S. Private*, pg. 165
Braemer, Dieter, Chief Fin. Officer--Siemens K.K., Tokyo, Japan; *Int'l*, pg. 1247
Brakken, William P., Chief Fin. Officer, Sr. V.P., Treas. & Sec.--Lanoga Corporation, Redmond, WA; *U.S. Private*, pg. 650
Braks, Edward J., Chief Fin. Officer--Paul Arpin Vanlines, Inc., West Warwick, RI; *U.S. Private*, pg. 85
Bram, Dana D., Chief Fin. Officer--The American Companies, Inc., Topeka, KS; *U.S. Private*, pg. 52
Brams, Leonard A., Chief Fin. Officer, Sr. V.P.-Fin. & Sec.--Handleman Company, Troy, MI; *U.S. Public*, pg. 779
Brams, Leonard A., V.P.-Fin.--United Technologies Automotive, Dearborn, MI; *U.S. Public*, pg. 1691
Branca, Michael, Chief Fin. Officer--Reptron Electronics, Inc., Tampa, FL; *U.S. Public*, pg. 1377
Branch, John D., Chief Fin. Officer & Sr. V.P.-Fin.--Earl Scheib, Inc., Beverly Hills, CA; *U.S. Public*, pg. 1437
Brandewie, Richard T., Chief Fin. Officer & Sr. V.P.--MTL Inc., Plant City, FL; *U.S. Public*, pg. 1028
Brandewie, Richard T., Chief Fin. Officer--Montgomery Tank Lines, Inc., Plant City, FL; *U.S. Public*, pg. 1028
Brandin, Seymour, Chief Fin. Officer & Treas.--Heyman Corporation, Niles, IL; *U.S. Private*, pg. 524
Brandon, Colleen, Chief Fin. Officer--Golin/Harris Technologies, San Francisco, CA; *Int'l*, pg. 1227
Brandon, Jim, Chief Fin. Officer--Riverside Manufacturing Co., Moultrie, GA; *U.S. Private*, pg. 934
Brandon, Joseph P., Chief Fin. Officer & Sr. V.P.--General Re Corporation, Stamford, CT; *U.S. Public*, pg. 725

Brandt, David N., Chief Fin. Officer & V.P.--Dutton-Lainson Co., Hastings, NE; *U.S. Private*, pg. 350

Brandt, Donald E., Sr. V.P.-Fin. & Corp. Services--AmerenUE, Saint Louis, MO; *U.S. Public*, pg. 66

Brandt, Paul E., Chief Fin. Officer & Exec. V.P.--California State Bank, West Covina, CA; *U.S. Public*, pg. 294

Brannon, Robert A., V.P.-Fin., Domestic home Video--Blockbuster Entertainment Group, Dallas, TX; *U.S. Private*, pg. 775

Brashaw, John, Chief Fin. Officer & V.P.--Danfoss Fluid Power, Racine, WI; *Int'l*, pg. 377

Braswell, R.L., V.P.-Fin. & Treas.--Dayton Superior Corporation, Miamisburg, OH; *U.S. Private*, pg. 931

Braswell, Steven C., Chief Fin. Officer & V.P.-Fin.--Meadowcraft, Inc., Birmingham, AL; *U.S. Private*, pg. 725

Bratton, Robert O., Chief Oper. Officer, Chief Fin. Officer & Exec. V.P.--First Charter Corporation, Concord, NC; *U.S. Public*, pg. 627

Brauer, Keith E., Chief Fin. Officer & V.P.-Fin.--Guidant Corporation, Indianapolis, IN; *U.S. Public*, pg. 768

Braun, Robert, Chief Fin. Officer & V.P.-Fin.--Zilber, Ltd., Milwaukee, WI; *U.S. Private*, pg. 1206

Braunegg, William T., Chief Fin. Officer & Treas.--Dwight Asset Management Company, Burlington, VT; *U.S. Public*, pg. 1673

Brausch, John J., Chief Fin. Officer--Umbro International, Inc., Greenville, SC; *U.S. Private*, pg. 1116

Bravard, Wyman, Chief Fin. Officer--Frost & Sullivan, Mountain View, CA; *U.S. Private*, pg. 430

Bray, Earl E., Chief Fin. Officer--National Health Enhancement Systems, Inc., Phoenix, AZ; *U.S. Public*, pg. 1157

Brayton, Roswell, Jr., Pres., Chief Exec. Officer & Chief Fin. Officer--Woolrich, Inc., Woolrich, PA; *U.S. Private*, pg. 1188

Brazener, Ronald D., V.P. & Chief Fin. Officer--General American Door Company, Montgomery, IL; *U.S. Private*, pg. 732

Brazzina, Paul, Chief Fin. Officer--National Media Corporation, Philadelphia, PA; *U.S. Public*, pg. 1158

Bready, Richard L., Chm. Bd. & Chief Exec. Officer--Nortek, Inc., Providence, RI; *U.S. Public*, pg. 1192

Brechtel, William J., Chief Fin. Officer & Sr. V.P.--ReliaStar Mortgage Company, West Des Moines, IA; *U.S. Public*, pg. 1376

Breckenridge, James, Controller--Rodefeld Co., Inc., Richmond, IN; *U.S. Private*, pg. 939

Brehm, John R., V.P. & Treas.--Ipalco Enterprises, Inc., Indianapolis, IN; *U.S. Public*, pg. 912

Brekke, Reidar, Chief Fin. Officer--Pronova Oleochemicals a.s., Sandefjord, Norway; *Int'l*, pg. 961

Bremer, Juergen, Chief Fin. Officer--Lowe & Partners, Frankfurt/Main, Germany; *U.S. Private*, pg. 678

Bremer, Keith, Chief Fin. Officer--DDB Needham Worldwide Inc., New York, NY; *Int'l*, pg. 357

Bremer, Keith, Chief Fin. Officer--DDB Needham Worldwide Inc., New York, NY; *U.S. Public*, pg. 1223

Brendan, Dwan, Chief Fin. Officer--Cantrell & Cochrane Group, Dublin, Ireland; *Int'l*, pg. 63

Brendzel, Ronald I., Chief Fin. Officer , Sr. V.P. & Sec.--Safeguard Health Enterprises, Inc., Anaheim, CA; *U.S. Public*, pg. 1424

Brennan, Chris, Chief Fin. Officer--UB Networks, Santa Clara, CA; *Int'l*, pg. 924

Brennan, James G., Chief Fin. Officer & Exec. V.P.--Taylor-Morley, Inc., Saint Louis, MO; *U.S. Private*, pg. 1071

Brennan, John D., Chief Fin. Officer--McAnally Enterprises, Inc., Yucaipa, CA; *U.S. Private*, pg. 718

Brennan, John V., Chief Fin. Officer, Exec. V.P. & Treas.--Webster Financial Corporation, Waterbury, CT; *U.S. Public*, pg. 1751

Brennan, Michael, Chief Fin. Officer--Trippe Mfg. Co., Chicago, IL; *U.S. Private*, pg. 1104

Brennan, Michael J., Chief Fin. Officer & V.P.--Binswanger, Philadelphia, PA; *U.S. Private*, pg. 144

Brennan, Niall, Chief Fin. Officer--Texaco (Ireland) Ltd., Dublin, Ireland; *U.S. Public*, pg. 1584

Brennan, Peter D., Chief Fin. Officer, V.P. & Treas.--Altron Incorporated, Wilmington, MA; *U.S. Public*, pg. 59

Brennan, Robert J., Chief Fin. Officer & V.P.--Superior Label Systems, Inc., Mason, OH; *U.S. Private*, pg. 1055

Brennan, Terry, Chief Fin. Officer & Sr. V.P.--Western Industries, Inc., Milwaukee, WI; *U.S. Private*, pg. 1165

Brennan, Tom, Chief Fin. Officer--Sandoz Agro, Inc., Des Plaines, IL; *Int'l*, pg. 974

Brenner, Hans, Chief Fin. Officer--Aesculap Aktiengesellschaft, Tuttlingen, Germany; *Int'l*, pg. 29

Brenner, Jeffrey, Chief Fin. Officer--Database America Companies, Montvale, NJ; *U.S. Private*, pg. 312

Brent, John, Chief Fin. Officer & V.P.--Mac Papers, Inc., Jacksonville, FL; *U.S. Private*, pg. 689

Brentnall, Terence D., Chief Fin. Officer--Sillcocks Plastics, Inc., Berkeley Heights, NJ; *U.S. Private*, pg. 63

Brepoels, Cor, Chief Fin. Officer--Esselte NV Produktion, Saint-Niklaas, Belgium; *Int'l*, pg. 461

Bressler, Richard J., Chief Fin. Officer--Time Warner Inc., New York, NY; *U.S. Public*, pg. 1610

Breu, Raymond, Chief Fin. Officer--Novartis AG, Basel, Switzerland; *Int'l*, pg. 971

Brewer, Barbara, Acctg. & Data Processing Mgr.--Harris Broadcast Division, Richmond, IN; *U.S. Public*, pg. 791

Brewer, R. Michael, Chief Fin. Officer & Sr. V.P.-Fin.--Boca Research Inc., Boca Raton, FL; *U.S. Public*, pg. 239

Brewer, Steven, Chief Fin. Officer & V.P.-Fin. & Admin.--Medical Meadow Gold Dairies, Inc., Ogden, UT; *U.S. Private*, pg. 1016

Brewer, Tom E., Chief Fin. Officer, Sr. V.P. & Treas.--Hillenbrand Industries, Inc., Batesville, IN; *U.S. Public*, pg. 828

Brewster, J. Chris, Chief Fin. Officer & V.P.--Sanifill, Inc., Houston, TX; *U.S. Public*, pg. 1686

Brian, J., Chief Fin. Officer & V.P.--Houston Lighting & Power Company, Houston, TX; *U.S. Public*, pg. 843

Brichant, Thierry, Chief Oper. Officer--Credit Mutuel, Paris, France; *Int'l*, pg. 344

Bridger, Cedric, Chief Fin. Officer & V.P.-Fin.--Y.P.F., S.A., Buenos Aires, Argentina; *Int'l*, pg. 1515

Briganti, Michael, Chief Fin. Officer & Sr. V.P.--SGS North America Inc., New York, NY; *Int'l*, pg. 1153

Brigden, Richard N., V.P.-Fin.--Ruddick Corporation, Charlotte, NC; *U.S. Public*, pg. 1412

Briggs, Steve, V.P.-Fin.--Star Lumber & Supply Company, Inc., Wichita, KS; *U.S. Private*, pg. 1034

Bright, Clifford J., Chief Fin. Officer & V.P.-Fin.--Interform Corporation, Bridgeville, PA; *U.S. Public*, pg. 333

Brillon, Dan, Chief Fin. Ofdficer--American Passage Media Corporation, Seattle, WA; *U.S. Private*, pg. 60

Brinegar, Dee A., Chief Fin. Officer--Gay Johnson's Inc., Grand Junction, CO; *U.S. Private*, pg. 595

Brininger, Thomas, Chief Fin. Officer--Lovejoy Inc., Downers Grove, IL; *U.S. Private*, pg. 677

Brink, Steven L., Chief Fin. Officer, Treas. & Sec.--Quiksilver, Inc., Costa Mesa, CA; *U.S. Public*, pg. 1353

Brinker, Nordried, Chief Fin. Officer--Neste Chemicals GmbH, Dusseldorf, Germany; *Int'l*, pg. 914

Brinkman, Anthony, Chief Fin. Officer--Accra Pac Group, Elkhart, IN; *U.S. Private*, pg. 11

Brino, E., V.P.-Fin.--Cornell Dubilier Electronics, Wayne, NJ; *U.S. Private*, pg. 607

Brinzo, J.S., Exec. V.P.-Fin.--The Cleveland-Cliffs Iron Company, Cleveland, OH; *U.S. Public*, pg. 386

Bristow, Donald A., Chief Fin. Officer & Exec. V.P.--Voith Hydro, Inc., York, PA; *Int'l*, pg. 1473

Brito, Luis, Chief Fin. Officer--Johnson & Johnson de Mexico SA de CV, Mexico, Mexico; *U.S. Public*, pg. 930

Britt, Robert D., Chief Fin. Officer, Treas. & Sec.--Green Mountain Coffee Roasters, Inc., Waterbury, VT; *U.S. Public*, pg. 761

Britt, Wayne, Chief Fin. Officer & Exec. V.P.-Fin.--Tyson Foods, Inc., Springdale, AR; *U.S. Public*, pg. 1652

Brittan, Kent, V.P.-Fin.--Otis Elevator Company, Farmington, CT; *U.S. Public*, pg. 1690

Brittelli, Brenda S., Chief Fin. Officer, Controller, Treas. & Sec.--Adams Wine Co., Atlanta, GA; *U.S. Private*, pg. 17

Britton, Robert A., Chief Fin. Officer & Exec. V.P.--Swisher International Group, Inc., Darien, CT; *U.S. Public*, pg. 1543

Brix, Berend, Chief Fin. Officer--CAP Volmac, Utrecht, Netherlands; *Int'l*, pg. 264

Broadbent, John H., Jr., V.P.-Fin. & Treas.--Arrow International, Inc., Reading, PA; *U.S. Public*, pg. 135

Broadbent, T., Chief Fin. Officer--Halifax Rack & Screw Cutting Co., Ltd., Brighouse, United Kingdom; *Int'l*, pg. 448

Broadley, David C., Chief Fin. Officer & Exec. V.P.--Sierra West Bancorp, Truckee, CA; *U.S. Public*, pg. 1470

Broatch, Robert E., Sr. V.P.-Fin.--Aetna Inc., Hartford, CT; *U.S. Public*, pg. 26

Broatch, Robert E., Chief Fin. Officer & Sr. V.P.-Fin.--UNUM Corporation, Portland, ME; *U.S. Public*, pg. 1699

Broatch, Robert E., Chief Fin. Officer & Sr. V.P.--UNUM Holding Company, Portland, ME; *U.S. Public*, pg. 1699

Brod, Frank, Controller--Essex Specialty Products, Inc., Clifton, NJ; *U.S. Public*, pg. 523

Broder, Stephen N., Chief Fin. Officer--J.G. Hook, Inc., New York, NY; *U.S. Private*, pg. 538

Brodie, Nancy S., Chief Fin. Officer & Exec. V.P.--The Penn Mutual Life Insurance Company, Philadelphia, PA; *U.S. Private*, pg. 849

Brodsky, Howard, Chief Fin. Officer & Exec. V.P.--Grey Direct, New York, NY; *U.S. Public*, pg. 764

Bronchetti, Robert J., Pres., Chief Exec. Officer & Chief Oper. Officer--National Auto Credit Inc., Solon, OH; *U.S. Public*, pg. 1152

Bronson, David, Chief Fin. Officer, Sr. V.P.-Fin. & Sec.--VWR Scientific Products, West Chester, PA; *U.S. Public*, pg. 1703

Brookner, Mark J., Chief Fin. Officer--First Gibraltar Bank, Irving, TX; *U.S. Public*, pg. 181

Brooks, D., Chief Fin. Officer--Copeland Corporation Ltd., Thatcham, United Kingdom; *U.S. Public*, pg. 576

Brooks, H. Edward, Jr., Chief Fin. Officer & V.P.--Morris Newspaper Corporation, Savannah, GA; *U.S. Private*, pg. 762

Brooks, Kenneth, Chief Fin. Officer & V.P.--Wells Mfg. Corp., Fond Du Lac, WI; *U.S. Private*, pg. 1113

Brooks, Robert J., Chief Fin. Officer--Westinghouse Air Brake Company, Wilmerding, PA; *U.S. Public*, pg. 1760

Brooks, Wallis, Chief Fin. Officer & Sr. V.P.--Authentic Fitness Corp., Los Angeles, CA; *U.S. Public*, pg. 147

Brooks, William R., Chief Fin. Officer, V.P. & Treas--Speedway Motorsports, Inc., Concord, NC; *U.S. Public*, pg. 1498

Brostoff, George, Chm. Bd. & Treas.--Symplex Communications Corp., Ann Arbor, MI; *U.S. Private*, pg. 1060

Brotherton, Ralph, Chief Fin. Officer--Pangburn Candy Company, Fort Worth, TX; *U.S. Private*, pg. 836

Brouillard, Jack, Chief Fin. Officer & Chief Admin. Officer--H.E. Butt Grocery Co., San Antonio, TX; *U.S. Private*, pg. 190

Brousseau, Gerald, Chief Oper. Officer & Chief Fin. Officer--Panneaux Malette-OSB Inc., Saint-Georges, Canada; *Int'l*, pg. 833

Brouwers, P.F., Sr. Dir.-Fin.--Hoogovens Groep B.V., Ijmuiden, Netherlands; *Int'l*, pg. 753

Brower, E., Chief Fin. Officer--Central/Shippee, Inc., Bloomingdale, NJ; *U.S. Private*, pg. 224

Brown, Adam, Chief Fin. Officer--Gelco Information Network, Inc., Eden Prairie, MN; *U.S. Private*, pg. 442

Brown, Allison, V.P. & Chief Fin. Officer--Krames Communications, San Bruno, CA; *U.S. Public*, pg. 1616

Brown, Carter, Chief Fin. Officer--Omega Performance Group, San Francisco, CA; *U.S. Private*, pg. 816

Brown, Charlie, Chief Fin. Officer--Denny's, Inc., Spartanburg, SC; *U.S. Public*, pg. 23

Brown, Craig, Chief Fin. Officer & Exec. V.P.-DMB&B Fin. & Opers.--DMB&B Communications, New York, NY; *U.S. Private*, pg. 302

Brown, Craig J., Chief Fin. Officer, Sr. V.P.-Admin. & Treas.--The Standard Register Company, Dayton, OH; *U.S. Public*, pg. 1505

Brown, D.A., Chief Fin. Officer--Courtaulds Aerospace, Littleborough, United Kingdom; *Int'l*, pg. 338

Brown, D.A., Chief Fin. Officer & Sr. V.P.-Admin.--Glaxo Wellcome Inc., Mississauga, Canada; *Int'l*, pg. 553

Brown, Dave, Controller--Douglas/Quikut, Walnut Ridge, AR; *U.S. Public*, pg. 217

Brown, David, Chief Fin. Officer--Louisville Scrap Material Co., Inc., Louisville, KY; *U.S. Private*, pg. 677

Brown, Dennis, Chief Fin. Officer, V.P. & Treas.--Sybron International Corporation, Milwaukee, WI; *U.S. Public*, pg. 1544

Brown, Don, Chief Fin. Officer--GHM Industries, Inc., Worcester, MA; *U.S. Private*, pg. 435

Brown, Frank, Chief Fin. Officer--Steering and Suspension Division, Saint Louis, MO; *U.S. Public*, pg. 443

Brown, Fred, V.P.-Fin.--Bush Boake Allen, Inc, Montvale, NJ; *U.S. Public*, pg. 1666

Brown, Gary, V.P.-Fin. & Admin.--Numetrix Ltd., Toronto, Canada; *Int'l*, pg. 990

Brown, Gehr W., Chief Fin. Officer & V.P.-Fin.--Mona Industries, Inc., Paterson, NJ; *U.S. Private*, pg. 756

Brown, Gerry, Chief Fin. Officer & Dir.-Fin.--John Mowlem & Company plc, Isleworth, United Kingdom; *Int'l*, pg. 896

Brown, Harold, Chief Fin. Officer & V.P.-Fin.--Aetna Industries, Inc., Center Line, MI; *U.S. Private*, pg. 25

Brown, Jack R., Chief Fin. Officer, Treas. & Sec.--Florida Public Utilities Company, West Palm Beach, FL; *U.S. Public*, pg. 655

Brown, James, Dir.-Fin.--British Printing Company Ltd., London, United Kingdom; *Int'l*, pg. 220

Brown, James B., Chief Fin. Officer--Capital-Gazette Communications, Inc., Annapolis, MD; *U.S. Private*, pg. 649

Brown, James C., Chief Fin. Officer, V.P.-Fin., Treas. & Sec.--Patterson Energy, Inc., Snyder, TX; *U.S. Public*, pg. 1265

Brown, John, Chief Fin. Officer--The Upper Room, Nashville, TN; *U.S. Private*, pg. 1129

Brown, Judd, Treas.--Spencer's Inc., Mount Airy, NC; *U.S. Private*, pg. 1025

Brown, Katrina, Chief Fin. Officer--C. Cakebread, Crayford, United Kingdom; *Int'l*, pg. 460

Brown, Keith C., Chief Fin. Officer--Lincoln Electric Systems, Lincoln, NE; *U.S. Private*, pg. 668

Brown, Leonard, Chief Fin. Officer--Dettra Flag Company, Oaks, PA; *U.S. Private*, pg. 328

Brown, Lonnie, V.P.-Fin.--Coleman Powermate Compressors, Springfield, MN; *U.S. Private*, pg. 691

Brown, Marc, Chief Fin. Officer--Gilrichco, Inc., Oxnard, CA; *U.S. Private*, pg. 454

Brown, Michael, Chief Fin. Officer & Controller--New Plan Realty Trust, New York, NY; *U.S. Public*, pg. 1172

Brown, Michael S., Pres. & Chief Oper. Officer--Wometco Enterprises, Inc., Coral Gables, FL; *U.S. Private*, pg. 1186

Brown, Paul M., Chief Fin. Officer & V.P.-Fin.--TRM Copy Centers Corporation, Portland, OR; *U.S. Public*, pg. 1558

Brown, Peter C., Pres. & Chief Fin. Officer--AMC Entertainment, Inc., Kansas City, MO; *U.S. Private*, pg. 6

Brown, Raymond, Chief Fin. Officer--All American Home Center, Downey, CA; *U.S. Private*, pg. 34

Brown, Raynard J., Chief Fin. Officer--Galamet, Inc., Kansas City, MO; *U.S. Private*, pg. 437

Brown, Raynard J., Chief Fin. Officer--Galamba Metals, Inc., Kansas City, KS; *U.S. Private*, pg. 437

Brown, Ronald C., Chief Fin. Officer & Sr. V.P.--Starwood Hotels & Resorts, Phoenix, AZ; *U.S. Public*, pg. 1512

Brown, Ronald D., Chief Fin. Officer & V.P.-Fin.--Cincinnati Milacron Inc., Cincinnati, OH; *U.S. Public*, pg. 368

Brown, Scott W., Chief Fin. Officer--Outdoor Technologies Group, Spirit Lake, IA; *U.S. Private*, pg. 822

Brown, Todd S., Chief Fin. Officer, V.P. & Treas.--DenAmerica Corp., Scottsdale, AZ; *U.S. Public*, pg. 498

Brown, William C., CPA, V.P.-Fin.--MGI PHARMA INC., Minneapolis, MN; *U.S. Public*, pg. 1026

Brown, William M., Chief Fin. Officer, Exec. V.P. & Controller--IMO Industries Inc., Lawrenceville, NJ; *U.S. Public*, pg. 856

Brownell, David A., Controller & Treas.--Electro Metrics, Inc., Johnstown, NY; *U.S. Private*, pg. 369

Brownell, Gary, Dr., Dir.-Fin. & Assoc. Exec. Dir.--American Mathematical Society, Inc., Providence, RI; *U.S. Private*, pg. 59

Brownfield, Debbie, Chief Fin. Officer, Sr. V.P. & Sec.--Lamonts Apparel, Inc., Kirkland, WA; *U.S. Public*, pg. 975

Browning, Keith D., Chief Fin. Officer & V.P.--Car Max, Glen Allen, VA; *U.S. Public*, pg. 374

Brownlow, I.P., V.P., Chief Fin. Officer & Treas.--Hondo Oil & Gas Company, Roswell, NM; *Int'l*, pg. 818

Brownson, John B., Chief Oper. Officer & Exec. V.P.--G.R. Herberger's, Inc., Saint Cloud, MN; *U.S. Public*, pg. 1333

Brownstein, Richard D., Chief Fin. Officer & V.P.--MedaSonics, Inc., Fremont, CA; *Int'l*, pg. 1225

Broyer, Paul, Chief Fin. Officer & V.P.--Candela Corporation, Wayland, MA; *U.S. Public*, pg. 300

Brozic, Edward F., Chief Fin. Officer & V.P.--Marie Brizard Wines & Spirits USA, North Miami, FL; *U.S. Private*, pg. 702

Brubaker, Jerry L., Chm. Bd. & Chief Fin. Officer--Schneller, Inc., Kent, OH; *U.S. Private*, pg. 971

Brumm, Gregg, Chief Fin. Officer & V.P.-Fin.--Acme Mills Co. Inc., Detroit, MI; *U.S. Private*, pg. 13

Brumm, P. Michael, Chief Fin. Officer & Sr. V.P.--The Fifth Third Bank, Cincinnati, OH; *U.S. Public*, pg. 621

Brummond, Brad, Chief Fin. Officer & Treas.--Super 8 Motels, Inc., Aberdeen, SD; *U.S. Public*, pg. 322

Brummond, Brad, Chief Fin. Officer--The Rivet Group L.L.C., Aberdeen, SD; *U.S. Private*, pg. 934
Brunais, Alain, Chief Fin. Officer--Air & Water Technologies Corporation, Branchburg, NJ; *U.S. Public*, pg. 29
Brune, David A., Chief Fin. Officer & V.P.-Fin. & Acctg.--Baltimore Gas and Electric Company, Baltimore, MD; *U.S. Public*, pg. 172
Brunell, Donald A. Jr., Chief Fin. Officer--Union Bank of California, San Diego, CA; *Int'l*, pg. 157
Brunelli, Massimo S., Chief Fin. Officer & Grp. V.P.--ELSAG Bailey Process Automation N.V., Schiphol, Netherlands; *Int'l*, pg. 449
Brunelli, Massino, Chief Fin. Officer-Fin. Grp.--Olivetti SpA, Turin, Italy; *Int'l*, pg. 1002
Bruner, Mike, V.P.-Fin--Atlanta Motor Speedway, Hampton, GA; *U.S. Public*, pg. 1498
Bruning, Bob, Chief Fin. Officer--Coastcast Corporation, Gardena, CA; *U.S. Public*, pg. 391
Bruning, Robert, Chief Fin. Officer--Lynx Golf, Inc., City of Industry, CA; *U.S. Private*, pg. 684
Brunken, Tessie L., Chief Fin. Officer--Stiefel Laboratories, Inc.; Coral Gables, FL; *U.S. Private*, pg. 1043
Brunner, York, Chief Fin. Officer--Insulating Materials, Inc., Schenectady, NY; *U.S. Private*, pg. 565
Brunswick, Paul L., Chief Fin. Officer, V.P. & Treas.--GoodMark Foods, Inc., Raleigh, NC; *U.S. Public*, pg. 751
Brunt, Phil, Chief Fin. Officer, V.P.--Alta-Dena Certified Dairy, City of Industry, CA; *Int'l*, pg. 201
Brust, Robert, Chief Fin. Officer, Sr. V.P. & Controller--Unisys Corporation Blue Bell, PA; *U.S. Public*, pg. 1671
Brustein, Lawrence, Chief Fin. Officer, Sec. & Treas.--Henry Modell & Company, Inc., New York, NY; *U.S. Private*, pg. 754
Bruthaupt, Greig, Chief Fin. Officer--Justiss Oil Co., Inc., Jena, LA; *U.S. Private*, pg. 602
Bruwelheide, Dale A., Chief Fin. Officer, V.P. & Treas.--Orange-Co., Inc., Bartow, FL; *U.S. Public*, pg. 1229
Bryant, Andy D., Chief Fin. Officer--Intel Corporation, Santa Clara, CA; *U.S. Public*, pg. 886
Bryant, Andy D., V.P. & Dir.-Fin.--Intel Systems Group, Santa Clara, CA; *U.S. Public*, pg. 887
Bryant, Michael L., Chief Fin. Officer & Exec. V.P.--Buehler, Limited, Lake Bluff, IL; *U.S. Public*, pg. 574
Bryars, Scott J., Chief Fin. Officer--Sechrist Industries, Inc., Anaheim, CA; *U.S. Private*, pg. 980
Bryson, R. Ray, Chief Fin. Officer--Shakespeare Monofilament, Columbia, SC; *U.S. Public*, pg. 940
Bubel, Mary, Chief Fin. Officer--Creative Publications, Mountain View, CA; *U.S. Private*, pg. 288
Buboltz, Walter, Chief Fin. Officer--Macbeth Div., New Windsor, NY; *U.S. Public*, pg. 965
Buchanan, James H., Chief Fin. Officer, Treas. & Sec.--Excalibur Technologies Corporation, Vienna, VA; *U.S. Public*, pg. 598
Buchanan, Jeffrey D., Chief Fin. Officer, V.P.-Fin./Admin., Treas. & Sec.--Three-Five Systems, Tempe, AZ; *U.S. Public*, pg. 1604
Buchanan, John G.S., Chief Fin. Officer--The British Petroleum Company P.L.C., London, United Kingdom; *Int'l*, pg. 219
Buchanan, Scott G., Chief Fin. Officer & V.P.--Watkins-Johnson Company, Palo Alto, CA; *U.S. Public*, pg. 1745
Buchel, Kevin S., Chief Fin. Officer & V.P.-Fin.--Napco Security Systems, Inc., Amityville, NY; *U.S. Public*, pg. 1151
Buchel, Per, Chief Fin. Officer--Skanska Bygg AB, Danderyd, Sweden; *Int'l*, pg. 1260
Buchholz, William E., Chief Fin. Officer & Sr. V.P.--Nalco Chemical Company, Naperville, IL; *U.S. Public*, pg. 1150
Buchler, George J., Chief Fin. Officer--Shamrock Holdings, Inc., Burbank, CA; *U.S. Private*, pg. 989
Bucholz, Dave, Chief Fin. Officer--Ritchie Corporation, Wichita, KS; *U.S. Private*, pg. 933
Buck, Robert, Chief Fin. Officer & Sr. V.P.--Bremer Financial Corporation, Saint Paul, MN; *U.S. Private*, pg. 167
Buckey, Alan, Chief Fin. Officer, Treas. & Legal Officer--Pease Industries, Inc., Fairfield, OH; *U.S. Private*, pg. 845
Buckley, Jan, V.P.-Fin.--Oak Grigsby, Sugar Grove, IL; *U.S. Public*, pg. 1209
Buckley, Raymond, Chief Fin. Officer--Jones Chemicals, Inc., Le Roy, NY; *U.S. Private*, pg. 596
Buckner, Steve, Chief Exec. & Chief Fin. Officer--Johnson County Farm Bureau Co-op, Franklin, IN; *U.S. Private*, pg. 591
Budde, Ken, Chief Fin. Officer, Chief Oper. Officer & V.P.--Arcade Inc., Chattanooga, TN; *U.S. Private*, pg. 79
Budnick, David, Treas. & Sec.--Hatfield Quality Meats, Hatfield, PA; *U.S. Private*, pg. 510
Budnick, Ronald V., V.P.-Fin.--Coats North America, Charlotte, NC; *Int'l*, pg. 300
Buehrle, John G., Chief Fin. Officer & V.P.-Fin.--National Cooperative Refinery Association, Mc Pherson, KS; *U.S. Private*, pg. 781
Buelck, Horst, Chief Fin. Officer--British-American Tobacco (Germany) GmbH, Hamburg, Germany; *Int'l*, pg. 111
Buenavista, Antonio, Chief Fin. Officer--BMC Forestry Corporation, Baguio, Philippines; *Int'l*, pg. 186
Bufalino, Salvatore, Chief Fin. Officer--Esselte S.P.A., Cascina, Italy; *Int'l*, pg. 461
Buffington, Douglas A., Pres., Chief Oper. & Fin. Officer & Treas.--Square Two Golf Incorporated, Fairfield, NJ; *U.S. Public*, pg. 1501
Buffone, Luigi, Chief Fin. Officer--Sokol & Company, Countryside, IL; *U.S. Private*, pg. 1012
Buhl, Tim, Chief Fin. Officer & Asst. Sec.--Aerco International Inc., Northvale, NJ; *U.S. Private*, pg. 23
Bull, Jeremy, Chief Fin. Officer--Arrington-Hillgate International, London, United Kingdom; *U.S. Private*, pg. 85
Bullig, Randall W., Chief Fin. Officer & Treas.--Midwest Employer's Casualty Company, Maryland Heights, MO; *U.S. Public*, pg. 215
Bundy, Dennis, Chief Exec. Officer & Chief Fin. Officer--Hood Lumber Co., Mill City, OR; *U.S. Private*, pg. 538
Bundy, P. David, Chief Fin. Officer & V.P.--OrCAD Inc., Beaverton, OR; *U.S. Public*, pg. 1230
Buniak, Al, Chief Fin. Officer--Brach & Brock Confections, Inc., Chicago, IL; *U.S. Private*, pg. 163
Bunker, Christopher J., Grp. Fin. Dir.--Tarmac plc, Wolverhampton, United Kingdom; *Int'l*, pg. 1355
Bunze, George J., Vice Chm. & Chief Fin. Officer--Kruger Inc., Montreal, Canada; *Int'l*, pg. 761
Buono, Jean-Claude, Dir.-Fin. & Admin.--Compagnie des Machines Bull, Louveciennes, France; *Int'l*, pg. 315
Burbage, Roger, Chief Fin. Officer, V.P.-Fin. & Sec.--Intrenet, Inc., Milford, OH; *U.S. Public*, pg. 910
Burch, Roger E., Controller--The Doe Run Company, Saint Louis, MO; *U.S. Private*, pg. 922
Burchill, Jill, Chief Fin. Officer--Imation Corporation, Oakdale, MN; *U.S. Public*, pg. 870
Burdett, Kathleen, Chief Fin. Officer & V.P.--The Dexter Corporation, Windsor Locks, CT; *U.S. Public*, pg. 504
Burdue, Rebecca, Chief Fin. Officer--Kellermeyer Co., Toledo, OH; *U.S. Private*, pg. 612
Burg, H. Peter, Pres., Chief Oper. & Fin. Officer--FirstEnergy Corp., Akron, OH; *U.S. Public*, pg. 644
Burgart, Richard H., Chief Fin. Officer, Treas. & Sec.--FSF Financial Corp., Hutchinson, MN; *U.S. Public*, pg. 608
Burgart, Richard H., Chief Fin. Officer--First Federal FSB, Hutchinson, MN; *U.S. Public*, pg. 608
Burgener, Ronald M., Chief Fin. Officer--Matthew Hall & Co., Houston, TX; *Int'l*, pg. 16
Burk, Kenneth, Chief Fin. Officer--Dick Corporation, Large, PA; *U.S. Private*, pg. 331
Burke, Brian T., Chief Acctg. Officer, Sr. V.P. & Controller--Symbol Technologies, Inc., Holtsville, NY; *U.S. Public*, pg. 1546
Burke, Eamonn, Chief Fin. Officer--Whitehall Laboratories Limited, Dublin, Ireland; *U.S. Public*, pg. 82
Burke, Ed, Chief Fin. Officer & V.P.--All Seasons Services, Inc., Braintree, MA; *U.S. Private*, pg. 35
Burke, Frank, Chief Fin. Officer--YAR Communications, New York, NY; *U.S. Private*, pg. 1195
Burke, Joseph J., Chief Fin. Officer & V.P.--Blockbuster Entertainment Group, Dallas, TX; *U.S. Private*, pg. 775
Burke, Judy, Chief Fin. Officer--East Coast Steel, Inc., Claremont, NH; *U.S. Private*, pg. 356
Burke, Kelly M., V.P.-Fin., Sec. & Admin.--Burke Engineering Company, South El Monte, CA; *U.S. Private*, *pg. 183*
Burke, Monica J., Chief. Fin. Officer, Treas. & Sec.--Valley Forge Corporation, San Rafael, CA; *U.S. Public*, pg. 1705
Burke, Raplh, V.P.-Fin.--LePage's Limited, Brampton, Canada; *Int'l*, pg. 613
Burke, Richard, Chief Fin. Officer--Elkay Products, Inc., Shrewsbury, MA; *U.S. Private*, pg. 372
Burke, Steve, Chief Fin. Officer--Butterick Company, Inc., New York, NY; *U.S. Private*, pg. 190
Burke, Steven C., Chief Fin. Officer, V.P.-Fin. & Admin. & Sec.--Quidel Corporation, San Diego, CA; *U.S. Public*, pg. 1352
Burke, William B., Chief Fin. Officer & Treas.--Wahl Clipper Corp., Sterling, IL; *U.S. Private*, pg. 1146
Burkett, Marvin D., Chief Fin. Officer, Sr. V.P. & Treas.--Advanced Micro Devices, Inc., Sunnyvale, CA; *U.S. Public*, pg. 21
Burkett, Thomas L., Chief Fin. Officer & V.P.--Golden Gem Growers Inc., Umatilla, FL; *U.S. Private*, pg. 460
Burkhart, Richard, Chief Fin. Officer & Controller--Mid-Continent Screw Products Co., Lincolnwood, IL; *U.S. Private*, pg. 743
Burks, Edward, Chief Fin. Officer, V.P. & Treas.--Fritz Industries Inc., Mesquite, TX; *U.S. Private*, pg. 429
Burmeister, James T., Chief Fin. Officer & Sr. V.P.--Tapemark, Saint Paul, MN; *U.S. Private*, pg. 1068
Burmeister, Tom, Chief Fin. Officer--ElectroCom Automation L.P., Arlington, TX; *Int'l*, pg. 1244
Burn, Bill, Chief Fin. Officer--C.M. Offray & Son Inc., Chester, NJ; *U.S. Private*, pg. 812
Burnard, Daniel, Chief Fin. Officer--Tri-Mark Metal Corp., Shelby, MI; *U.S. Private*, pg. 1100
Burne, Thomas C., Chief Fin. Officer & Sr. V.P.--Phillips Publishing International, Inc., Potomac, MD; *U.S. Private*, *pg. 862*
Burnett, Charles E., Chief Fin. Officer--Customer Development Corporation, Peoria, IL; *U.S. Private*, pg. 298
Burnett, J., Chief Fin. Officer--Jay-El Products, Inc., Carson, CA; *U.S. Public*, pg. 534
Burnett, Treavor, Chief Fin. Officer--Turtle & Hughes, Inc., Linden, NJ; *U.S. Private*, pg. 1110
Burnham, Jed J., Chief Fin. Officer & Treas.--ACX Technologies Inc., Golden, CO; *U.S. Public*, pg. 3
Burns, J., Chief Fin. Officer--John Menzies Wholesale, Edinburgh, United Kingdom; *Int'l*, pg. 707
Burns, John, V.P.-Fin.--The Felters Company, Roebuck, SC; *U.S. Private*, pg. 400
Burns, John E., Chief Fin. Officer & V.P.--First United Bancshares, Inc., El Dorado, AR; *U.S. Public*, pg. 641
Burns, John F., Chief Fin. Officer & Sr. V.P.--Arthur D. Little, Inc., Cambridge, MA; *U.S. Private*, pg. 670
Burns, Mary Ann, Chief Fin. Officer & V.P.--Aero Systems Aviation Corp., Miami, FL; *U.S. Private*, pg. 24
Burns, R.J., Chief Fin. Officer--Grede-Pryor, Inc., Pryor, OK; *U.S. Private*, pg. 476
Burns, Robert, Chief Fin. Officer--NutraMax Products, Inc., Gloucester, MA; *U.S. Public*, pg. 1206
Burns, Ron, Chief Fin. Officer, V.P. & Sec.--Grede Foundries, Inc., Milwaukee, WI; *U.S. Private*, pg. 476
Burns, Timothy J., Chief Fin. Officer--Number Nine Visual Technology, Lexington, MA; *U.S. Public*, pg. 1206
Burrell, Richard L., Sr. V.P.-Fin., Treas. & Sec.--R.G. Barry Corporation, Pickerington, OH; *U.S. Public*, pg. 192
Burris, Michael R., V.P.-Fin.--Benihana, Inc., Miami, FL; *U.S.* Public, pg. 211
Burris, Wayne C., Chief Fin. Officer--Corange U.S. Holdings, Inc, Indianapolis, IN; *Int'l*, pg. 331
Burrough, W.O., Asst. Treas.--Justin Industries, Inc., Fort Worth, TX; *U.S. Public*, pg. 936
Bursell, Gary, Chief Fin. Officer--American Nutrition, Inc., Ogden, UT; *U.S. Private*, pg. 60
Burslem, William, III, Chief Fin. Officer, V.P. & Sec.--Travel Ports of America Inc., Rochester, NY; *U.S. Public*, pg. 1632
Burtelow, John F., Chief Fin. Officer & Exec. V.P.--Ames Department Stores, Inc., Rocky Hill, CT; *U.S. Public*, pg. 99
Burton, C. Bruce, Chief Fin. Officer & V.P.--Rayrock Yellowknife Resources Inc., Toronto, Canada; *Int'l*, pg. 1089
Burton, Robert A., Chief Fin. Officer & Sr. V.P.--Krause's Furniture Inc., Brea, CA; *U.S. Public*, pg. 967
Bury, James, V.P.-Fin.--PremiumWear, Inc., Minneapolis, MN; *U.S. Public*, pg. 1323
Busby, Robert L., III, Chief Fin. & Admin. Officer, Sr. V.P. & Treas.--National Western Life Insurance Company, Austin, TX; *U.S. Public*, pg. 1161
Busch, Roger, Sr. V.P.-Fin.--IDV North America, Fort Lee, NJ; *Int'l*, pg. 411
Buschino, Guy, Chief Fin. Officer--Iveco France S.A., Trappes, France; *Int'l*, pg. 696
Buselmeier, Bernard J., Chief Fin. Officer & Exec. V.P.-Fin. & Admin.--Integon Corporation, Winston Salem, NC; *U.S.* Public, pg. 719
Buselmeier, Bernard J., Chief Fin. Officer & Exec. V.P.--Integon National Insurance Co., Winston Salem, NC; *U.S. Public*, pg. 720
Buselmeier, Bernard J., Chief Fin. Officer & Exec. V.P.--Integon Indemnity Corporation, Winston Salem, NC; *U.S.* Public, pg. 720
Buselmeier, Bernard J., Chief Fin. Officer & Exec. V.P.--Integon General Insurance Corporation, Winston Salem, NC; *U.S. Public*, pg. 720
Buselmeier, Bernard J., Chief Fin. Officer & Exec. V.P.--New South Insurance Company, Winston Salem, NC; *U.S. Public*, pg. 720
Buselmeier, Bernard J., Chief Fin. Officer & Exec. V.P.--Integon Specialty Insurance Company, Winston Salem, NC; *U.S. Public*, pg. 720
Buselmeier, Bernard J., Chief Fin. Officer & Exec. V.P.--Integon Preferred Insurance Company, Winston Salem, NC; *U.S. Public*, pg. 720
Buselmeier, Bernard J., Chief Fin. Officer & Exec. V.P.--Integon Casualty Insurance Company, Winston Salem, NC; *U.S. Public*, pg. 720
Bush, D., Chief Fin. Officer--Early Learning Centre, Swindon, United Kingdom; *Int'l*, pg. 707
Bush, Raymond T., Chief Fin. Officer & Sr. V.P.--Maguire Group Inc., Foxboro, MA; *U.S. Private*, pg. 696
Bushell, Dan, Chief Fin. Officer & Exec. V.P.--United Stationers Inc., Des Plaines, IL; *U.S. Public*, pg. 1689
Bushmann, Stephen J., Chief Fin. Officer, V.P. & Treas.--Stifel Financial Corp., Saint Louis, MO; *U.S. Public*, pg. 1518
Bushy, Kathleen, Chief Fin. Officer--Excell Manufacturing Company, Providence, RI; *U.S. Private*, pg. 387
Buske, J.L., Chief Fin. Officer--Union Camp Kraft Paper & Board Div., Savannah, GA; *U.S. Public*, pg. 1666
Busquet, J.R., Chief Fin. Officer--Credit Lyonnais Americas, New York, NY; *Int'l*, pg. 344
Buss, Ronald, V.P.-Fin.--Evcon Industries, Inc., Wichita, KS; *U.S. Public*, pg. 1788
Bussier, Bill, Chief Fin. Officer/Taren--Cole of California, Los Angeles, CA; *U.S. Public*, pg. 148
Bustamante, Jorge, Chief Fin. Officer--Onexa, S.A. de C.V., Garza Garcia, Mexico; *Int'l*, pg. 56
Butala, James, Chief Fin. Officer & Treas.--Lucht, Inc., Bloomington, MN; *U.S. Public*, pg. 1201
Butala, Raj, Chief Fin. Officer--Unity Sewing Supply Div., Carteret, NJ; *U.S. Private*, pg. 1177
Butcher, Robert M., Chief Fin. Officer & Sr. Exec. V.P.--HSBC Americas, Buffalo, NY; *Int'l*, pg. 580
Butcher, Robert M., Chief Fin. Officer & Exec. V.P.--Marine Midland Bank, Buffalo, NY; *Int'l*, pg. 581
Buti, Bob, V.P.-Fin.--National Van Lines, Inc., Broadview, IL; *U.S. Private*, pg. 788
Butler, Charl L., Chief Fin. Officer, V.P. & Sec.--NBSC Corporation, Columbia, SC; *U.S. Public*, pg. 1549
Butler, David, Chief Fin. Officer--HMO Texas, L.C., Houston, TX; *U.S. Public*, pg. 1470
Butler, James P., Chief Fin. Officer--Microtel International Inc., Ontario, CA; *U.S. Public*, pg. 1108
Butler, Keith, Chief Fin. Officer--Peoples Federal Savings & Loan Association, Conway, SC; *U.S. Public*, pg. 634
Butler, Mark, Chief Fin. Officer--Kaufman and Broad-Monterey Bay, Inc., Salinas, CA; *U.S. Public*, pg. 945
Butler, Michael, Chief Fin. Officer--Amtrade International Bank, Miami, FL; *U.S. Private*, pg. 68
Butler, R., Chief Fin. Officer--The Braidwater Spinning Company Ltd., Ballymena, United Kingdom; *Int'l*, pg. 797
Butler, R., Chief Fin. Officer--Hollybank Bleach & Dye Works Ltd., Ballyclare, United Kingdom; *Int'l*, pg. 798
Butler, William, Chief Fin. Officer--Giumarra Vineyards, Edison, CA; *U.S. Private*, pg. 455
Buttacavoli, Frank, Chief Fin. Officer & Exec. V.P.--Parlux Fragrances Inc., Fort Lauderdale, FL; *U.S. Public*, pg. 1264
Butterfield, Michael J., Chief Fin. Officer--Equis Financial Group, Boston, MA; *U.S. Private*, pg. 379
Butterfield, Michael J., Chief Fin. Officer--American Financial Group Securities Corp., Boston, MA; *U.S. Private*, pg. 380
Buttle, Leonard, Chief Fin. Officer--Gambro Ltd., Sidcup, United Kingdom; *Int'l*, pg. 668
By, Carl-Olof, Chief Fin. Officer & Exec.V.P.--AB Industrivarden, Stockholm, Sweden; *Int'l*, pg. 678
Byerly, Stanley W., Chief Fin. Officer--New England Confectionery Co., Cambridge, MA; *U.S. Private*, pg. 1113

Byers, R.A., Chief Fin. Officer, V.P.-Fin. & Treas.--Pitt-Des Moines, Inc., Pittsburgh, PA; *U.S. Public*, pg. 1304
Byington, Paul, Chief Fin. Officer--Idaho Supreme Company, Firth, ID; *U.S. Private*, pg. 557
Byler, David W., Chief Fin. Officer--Suncor Inc., Calgary, Canada; *Int'l*, pg. 1320
Bylin, Bob, Chief Fin. Officer & Sr. V.P.-Fin.--Storage Dimensions, Inc., Milpitas, CA; *U.S. Public*, pg. 1522
Byrd, Michael J., Chief Fin. Officer & V.P.--Maxim Integrated Products, Inc., Sunnyvale, CA; *U.S. Public*, pg. 1061
Byrne, Daniel G., Chief Fin. Officer & Sr. V.P.--Sterling Financial Corporation, Spokane, WA; *U.S. Public*, pg. 1516
Byrne, John J., Chief Fin. Officer & V.P.-Fin.--Mark IV Industries Inc., Amherst, NY; *U.S. Public*, pg. 1044
Byrne, Michael C., Chief Fin. Officer & Treas.--Gerald H. Phipps, Inc., Denver, CO; *U.S. Private*, pg. 862
Byrne, Mike, Chief Fin. Officer & Gen. Mgr.--Merkley Newman Harty, New York, NY; *U.S. Public*, pg. 1224
Byrne, Tim, Chief Fin. Officer & Sr. V.P.--Corson Lime Company, Plymouth Meeting, PA; *U.S. Public*, pg. 1685
Byrne, Timothy, Chief Fin. Officer & Sr. V.P.--Arkansas Lime Co., Batesville, AR; *U.S. Public*, pg. 1685
Byrne, Timothy, Chief Fin. Officer & Sr. V.P.--Texas Lime Co., Cleburne, TX; *U.S. Public*, pg. 1685
Byrne, Timothy W., Chief Fin. Officer, Sr. V.P. & Sec.--United States Lime & Minerals, Dallas, TX; *U.S. Public*, pg. 1684
Byrnes, Doug, Chief Fin. Officer--Manufacturers Consolidation Service, Inc., Memphis, TN; *U.S. Private*, pg. 700
Byrnes, John, Chief Fin. Officer--Norse Dairy Systems, Columbus, OH; *U.S. Private*, pg. 802
Caban, Robert, Chief Fin. Officer--Osram Societa Riunite Osram-Edison-Clerici S.p.A., Milan, Italy; *Int'l*, pg. 1244
Cabral, Milton C., Chief Fin. Officer--Souza Cruz, S.A., Rio de Janeiro, Brazil; *Int'l*, pg. 112
Caessa, J., Dir.-Fin.--Industrias Lever Portuguesa, Lda., Lisbon, Portugal; *Int'l*, pg. 1437
Cafarella, Ron, Chief Fin. Officer--Joan & David Helpern, Inc., New York, NY; *U.S. Private*, pg. 521
Caffarelli, Joseph J., Chief Fin. Officer & Exec. V.P.-Fin.--Physio-Control Corporation, Redmond, WA; *U.S. Public*, pg. 1294
Caffrey, Laura, Chief Fin. Officer & Exec. V.P.--FCB, New York, NY; *U.S. Private*, pg. 389
Cafiero, Paul J., Chief Fin. Officer--AM General Corporation, South Bend, IN; *U.S. Private*, pg. 922
Cagalj, Mike, Chief Fin. Officer, V.P. & Controller--Atlas Hotels, Inc., San Diego, CA; *U.S. Private*, pg. 96
Cahill, Gerald, Chief Fin. Officer & Sr. V.P.-Fin.--Carnival Corporation, Miami, FL; *U.S. Public*, pg. 306
Cahill, Greg, Chief Fin. Officer & V.P.--Sawyer Riley Compton Inc., Atlanta, GA; *U.S. Private*, pg. 969
Cahill, James, Chief Fin. Officer, Exec. V.P., Treas. & Sec.--Strattec Securities Corporation, Milwaukee, WI; *U.S. Public*, pg. 1523
Cahill, John, Sr. V.P.-Fin., Chief Fin. Officer & Treas.--Kentucky Fried Chicken Corporation (KFC), Louisville, KY; *U.S. Public*, pg. 1636
Cahill, Kirk, V.P.-Fin., Controller & Treas.--Chicago Extruded Metals Co., Cicero, IL; *U.S. Private*, pg. 234
Cahoon, Arthur, Chief Fin. Officer--Cain & Bultman, Jacksonville, FL; *U.S. Private*, pg. 199
Caine, Franklyn A., Chief Fin. Officer & Exec. V.P.--Wang Laboratories, Inc., Billerica, MA; *U.S. Public*, pg. 1737
Cakebread, Steve, Chief Fin. Officer--Autodesk, Inc., San Rafael, CA; *U.S. Public*, pg. 148
Cakebread, Steve, V.P.-Intl. Fin.--Silicon Graphics S.A. Intl., Geneva, Switzerland; *U.S. Public*, pg. 1474
Calabrese, Joseph J., Jr., Chief Fin. Officer, Exec. V.P. & Sec.--Harvey Electronics, Inc., Lyndhurst, NJ; *U.S. Public*, pg. 796
Calcagno, Karen, Chief Fin. Officer--William Bayley/Folger Adam Security, Inc., Springfield, OH; *U.S. Private*, pg. 125
Calcaterra, Tom, Chief Fin. Officer--Hydro Agri North America, Tampa, FL; *Int'l*, pg. 961
Calcott, Reid, Chief Fin. Officer--Educational Insights, Inc., Carson, CA; *U.S. Public*, pg. 565
Calderaui, Kuno, Chief Fin. Officer--Cereal Partners Worldwide, Morges, Switzerland; *U.S. Public*, pg. 718
Calderaui, Kuno, Chief Fin. Officer--Cereal Partners Worldwide, Morges, Switzerland; *Int'l*, pg. 916
Calderon, Ramon, Chief Fin. Officer & V.P.--Young & Rubicam, S.A. de C.V., Mexico, Mexico; *U.S. Private*, pg. 1200
Calderoni, Robert M., Chief Fin. Officer & Sr. V.P.-Fin.--Avery Dennison Corporation, Pasadena, CA; *U.S. Public*, *pg. 152*
Caldon, Daniel, Chief Fin. Officer & Sr. V.P.--Bissell Inc., Grand Rapids, MI; *U.S. Private*, pg. 145
Caldwell, A., Chief Fin. Officer & Controller--Puritan Maid Ltd., Aylesbury, United Kingdom; *Int'l*, pg. 210
Caldwell, Bruce, Chief Fin. Officer & Sr. V.P.--Great Western Consumer Finance Group, Tampa, FL; *U.S. Public*, pg. 1741
Caldwell, Eugene, Chief Fin. Officer, Sr. V.P. & Treas.--Venture Stores, Inc., O Fallon, MO; *U.S. Public*, pg. 1716
Caldwell, J. C., Exec. V.P.-Fin. & Admin.--Foster's Brewing Group, Toronto, Canada; *Int'l*, pg. 501
Caldwell, Robert F., Chief Fin. Officer & Exec. V.P.--Southeastern Michigan Gas Enterprises, Inc., Port Huron, MI; *U.S. Public*, pg. 1489
Calemard, Olivier, Chief Fin. Officer--Alcatel Cit (S.A.), Velizy-Villacoublay, France; *Int'l*, pg. 56
Calhoun, Lynn, Pres. & Chief Fin. Officer--Prime Technology, Inc., Grand Rapids, MI; *U.S. Private*, pg. 884
Calhoun, Patrick W., Chief Fin. Officer & V.P.--Datron Incorporated, Windsor, CT; *U.S. Private*, pg. 313
Calhoun, Patrick W., Dir.-Fin.--Intercontinental Mfg. Co., Garland, TX; *U.S. Private*, pg. 313
Call, Anita, Controller--Triangle Brass Manufacturing, Los Angeles, CA; *U.S. Private*, pg. 1101
Call, John, Chief Fin. Officer & Sr. V.P.--Ross Stores, Inc., Newark, CA; *U.S. Public*, pg. 1405
Call, Lawrence M., Chief Fin. Officer & Sr. V.P.--Amway Corporation, Ada, MI; *U.S. Private*, pg. 69
Callaghan, James H., Chief Fin. Officer--Matthew Warren Inc., Logansport, IN; *U.S. Private*, pg. 500
Callahan, J. Sean, Chief Fin. Officer & Sr. V.P.-Fin. & Admin.--Preston Trucking Company, Inc., Preston, MD; *U.S. Public*, pg. 1788
Callahan, Michael J., Chief Fin. Officer & Exec. V.P.--FMC Corporation, Chicago, IL; *U.S. Public*, pg. 604
Callahan, T.E., Chief Fin. Officer & Sr. V.P.-Fin.--Welch Foods Inc., A Cooperative, Concord, MA; *U.S. Private*, pg. 784
Callan, Richard T., Chief Fin. Officer, V.P. & Controller--Alliance Construction Solutions, Inc., Fort Collins, CO; *U.S. Private*, pg. 38
Callegari, John V., Jr., Chief Fin. Officer & V.P.-Admin.--Karts International Inc., Covington, LA; *U.S. Public*, pg. 944
Callender, DeLisle, Chief Fin. Officer & Sr. V.P.--The Chisholm-Mingo Group, New York, NY; *U.S. Private*, pg. 237
Callicutt, Thomas L., Jr., Exec. V.P., Controller & Principal Acctg. Officer--First Commerce Corporation, New Orleans, LA; *U.S. Public*, pg. 629
Calvache, William, Chief Fin. Officer--Metallurg do Brazil Ltda., Sao Paulo, Brazil; *U.S. Private*, pg. 735
Calvin, Boyd, Chief Fin. Officer--Clayton Industries Co., El Monte, CA; *U.S. Private*, pg. 245
Camell, Paul G., Chief Fin. Officer--Camp Dresser & McKee Inc., Cambridge, MA; *U.S. Private*, pg. 203
Cameron, Hugh, Dir.-Fin.--Meggitt Avionics, Fareham, United Kingdom; *Int'l*, pg. 853
Camiro Vazquez, Ruben, Chief Fin. Officer & Sr. V.P.--Grupo Casa Autrey, Mexico, Mexico; *Int'l*, pg. 573
Camon, Alain, Chief Fin. Officer--Havas Advertising, Levallois-Perret, France; *Int'l*, pg. 600
Camp, William C., Chief Fin. Officer, V.P. & Treas.--Science & Engineering Associates, Albuquerque, NM; *U.S. Private*, pg. 975
Campbell, Andrew, Chief Fin. Officer & Sr. V.P.--Safety-Kleen Corp., Elgin, IL; *U.S. Public*, pg. 1425
Campbell, C. Robert, Chief Fin. Officer & Exec. V.P.--Advantica Restaurant Group, Inc., Spartanburg, SC; *U.S.* Public, pg. 22
Campbell, Christopher, Chief Fin. Officer--Madison Graham Colorgraphics, Inc., Los Angeles, CA; *U.S. Private*, pg. 694
Campbell, David G., Chief Fin. Officer & V.P.-Fin.--Paradigm Technology, Inc., San Jose, CA; *U.S. Public*, pg. 1256
Campbell, Donald, Chief Fin. Officer & Exec. V.P.--The TJX Companies, Inc., Framingham, MA; *U.S. Public*, pg. 1556
Campbell, Frank, V.P.-Fin.--Wyeth-Ayerst Laboratories-Domestic, Radnor, PA; *U.S. Public*, pg. 80
Campbell, Gordon, Chief Fin. Officer--Courtaulds plc, London, United Kingdom; *Int'l*, pg. 338
Campbell, Greg, Chief Fin. Officer--Grand Holdings, Inc., Edina, MN; *U.S. Private*, pg. 468
Campbell, J.A., Chief Fin. Officer & Sr. V.P.-Fin.--ATCO Group Co., Calgary, Canada; *Int'l*, pg. 95
Campbell, J.A., Chief Fin. Officer--Canadian Utilities Limited, Calgary, Canada; *Int'l*, pg. 95
Campbell, John, Chief Fin. Officer & Dir.-Fin. Control--Costain Group PLC, London, United Kingdom; *Int'l*, pg. 336
Campbell, John, Chief Fin. Officer & Dir.-Fin.--Costain Engineering & Construction Limited, London, United Kingdom; *Int'l*, pg. 336
Campbell, Kenneth, Chief Fin. Officer--ICF Kaiser International Inc., Fairfax, VA; *U.S. Public*, pg. 852
Campbell, Terry, Chief Fin. Officer & Exec. V.P.--Farmland Industries, Inc., Kansas City, MO; *U.S. Private*, pg. 395
Campbell, William T., Chief Fin. Officer & V.P.-Fin.--Smith Environmental Technologies Corp., Plymouth Meeting, PA; *U.S. Public*, pg. 1477
Campi, W.P., Chief Fin. Officer--Therakos, Inc., Exton, PA; *U.S. Public*, pg. 929
Campion, Donald, Chief Fin. Officer & Sr. V.P.--Delco Electronics Corporation, Kokomo, IN; *U.S. Public*, pg. 720
Campion, Donald C., Chief Fin. Officer & Sr. V.P.--Oxford Automotive, Inc., Troy, MI; *U.S. Private*, pg. 825
Campoll, Bill, Chief Fin. Officer & V.P.--Coastal Lumber Company, Weldon, NC; *U.S. Private*, pg. 248
Campos-Filho, Ruy, Chief Fin. Officer--Brastemp S.A., Sao Bernardo do Campo, Brazil; *U.S. Public*, pg. 1765
Camps, Steven, Chief Oper. Officer & Chief Fin. Officer--Interplay Productions, Inc., Irvine, CA; *U.S. Private*, pg. 572
Camus, Daniel, Chief Fin. Officer--Hoechst Marion Roussel AG, Frankfurt/Main, Germany; *Int'l*, pg. 624
Camus, Daniel, Chief Fin. Officer & Exec. V.P.--Roussel UCLAF S.A., Romainville, France; *Int'l*, pg. 626
Canales Clariond, Marcelo, Vice Chm. & Chief Fin. Officer--Grupo IMSA S.A. de C.V., Garza Garcia, Mexico; *Int'l*, pg. 575
Canfield, Arthur, Chief Fin. Officer--Woodstuff Manufacturing, Inc., Phoenix, AZ; *U.S. Private*, pg. 1187
Cangemi, Michael, Chief Fin. Officer & Exec. V.P.--Etienne Aigner, New York, NY; *U.S. Private*, pg. 384
Cannata, David, Chief Fin. Officer & Dir.-Fin.--Plan International USA, Inc., Warwick, RI; *U.S. Private*, pg. 869
Cannon, Bruce A., Chief Fin. Officer, Sr. V.P., Treas. & Controller--SpecTran Corporation, Sturbridge, MA; *U.S. Public*, *pg. 1497*
Cannon, James, Vice Chm., Chief Fin. Officer & Dir.--BBDO Worldwide Inc., New York, NY; *U.S. Public*, pg. 1223
Cannon, Leonard, Jr., Chief Fin. Officer--Simplex Products, Adrian, MI; *U.S. Public*, pg. 940
Canosa, Albert A., Chief Fin. Officer & Corp. V.P.-Admin.--Raytech Corporation, Shelton, CT; *U.S. Public*, pg. 1363
Cantor, John, Chief Fin. Officer--Good Humor/Breyers Ice Cream, Green Bay, WI; *Int'l*, pg. 1435
Cantor, Sheldon G., Chief Fin. Officer--Couristan Inc., Fort Lee, NJ; *U.S. Private*, pg. 279
Cantos, Joel, Chief Fin. Officer--Pace Advertising, New York, NY; *Int'l*, pg. 1483
Cantu, Alfredo Livas, Chief Fin. Officer--Fomento Economico Mexicano, S.A. de CV, Monterrey, Mexico; *Int'l*, pg. 496
Caparros, Pedro, Exec. V.P.-Fin. Opers.--Credit Nationale, Paris, France; *Int'l*, pg. 344
Capellini, Joseph, Chief Fin. Officer--GCI Group Inc., New York, NY; *U.S. Public*, pg. 764
Capestro, David, Chief Fin. Officer--Cambro Manufacturing Company, Huntington Beach, CA; *U.S. Private*, pg. 203
Capo, Cris N., V.P.-Fin.--Rockefeller Group Telecommunications Services, Inc., New York, NY; *Int'l*, pg. 873
Caponigro, Ralph A., Chief Fin. Officer, Sr. V.P.-Fin. & Treas.--Compuware Corporation, Farmington Hills, MI; *U.S. Public*, pg. 423
Caporale, Charles, Chief Fin. Officer, Sr. V.P. & Treas.--Centris Group Inc., Costa Mesa, CA; *U.S. Public*, pg. 328
Caporella, Nick A., Chm. Bd., Pres., Chief Exec. Officer & Chief Fin. Officer--National Beverage Corp., Plantation, FL; *U.S. Public*, pg. 1153
Cappiello, Tony, Chief Fin. Officer--Waterford Crystal, Inc., Wall, NJ; *Int'l*, pg. 1487
Capps, Carl, Chief Fin. Officer--Cherokee Brick & Tile Co., Macon, GA; *U.S. Private*, pg. 233
Capps, Sherrill M., V.P., Sec. & Treas.--Washburn Graphics, Inc., Charlotte, NC; *U.S. Public*, pg. 291
Capps, Vickie L., Chief Fin. Officer--Wavetek Corporation, San Diego, CA; *U.S. Private*, pg. 1154
Caputa, Peter, Chief Fin. Officer & V.P.-Fin.--Stokely USA, Inc., Oconomowoc, WI; *U.S. Public*, pg. 1518
Caputo, Carmen M., Chief Fin. Officer, V.P.-Fin. & Treas.--Tork, Inc., Mount Vernon, NY; *U.S. Private*, pg. 1092
Carbone, Gene, Chief Fin. Officer, V.P.-Fin. & Sec.--Calavo Growers of California, Santa Ana, CA; *U.S. Private*, pg. 199
Carbone, Gene, Chief Fin. Officer--Calavo Foods, Inc., Santa Ana, CA; *U.S. Private*, pg. 199
Carbone, Gene, Chief Fin. Officer--Calavo Foods de Mexico, S.A. de C.V., Mexicali, Mexico; *U.S. Private*, pg. 200
Carbone, Richard, Chief Fin. Officer--The Prudential Insurance Company of America, Newark, NJ; *U.S. Private*, pg. 892
Carchedi, Frank A., Chief Fin. Officer & Treas.--ITC Learning Corp., Herndon, VA; *U.S. Public*, pg. 859
Card, Wesley, Chief Fin. Officer & Treas.--Jones Apparel Group, Inc., Bristol, PA; *U.S. Public*, pg. 933
Carden, Charles B., Chief Fin. Officer & Exec. V.P.--Paragon Health Network, Inc., Atlanta, GA; *U.S. Public*, pg. 1256
Cardiello, Sam, Chief Fin. Officer & Controller--Dan's Supreme Super Markets Inc., Hempstead, NY; *U.S. Private*, pg. 310
Cardillo, Art, Chief Fin. Officer--Survey Sampling, Inc., Fairfield, CT; *U.S. Private*, pg. 1056
Cardillo, Paul S., Chief Fin. Officer--Select Communications, L.P., New York, NY; *U.S. Private*, pg. 982
Cardinal, Robert, Chief Fin. Officer--Laurentian Bank of Canada, Montreal, Canada; *Int'l*, pg. 396
Carey, Bryan J., Chief Fin. Officer--Aearo Company, Boston, MA; *U.S. Private*, pg. 23
Carey, Richard N., V.P.-Fin. & Devel.--Manor Healthcare Corp., Gaithersburg, MD; *U.S. Public*, pg. 1041
Carey, Thomas J., V.P.-Fin.--Driver-Harris Company, Harrison, NJ; *U.S. Public*, pg. 530
Carey, William P., Treas.--Scanforms, Inc., Bristol, PA; *U.S. Public*, pg. 228
Cargotch, Paul, Chief Fin. Officer & Exec. V.P.--Russ Berrie and Company, Inc., Oakland, NJ; *U.S. Public*, pg. 222
Caridi, Tom, Chief Fin. Officer--Ullo International, Inc., Altamonte Springs, FL; *U.S. Private*, pg. 1116
Carl, John L., Chief Fin. Officer & Exec. V.P.--Amoco Corporation, Chicago, IL; *U.S. Public*, pg. 101
Carlin, Edward R., Chief Fin. Officer, Exec. V.P. & Sec.--Goody's Family Clothing, Inc., Knoxville, TN; *U.S. Public*, *pg. 753*
Carlino, David, Chief Fin. Officer--Cannon, Grand Island, NY; *U.S. Private*, pg. 205
Carlson, Carl M., V.P. & Chief Fin. Officer--Compass Investment Services, Mineola, NY; *U.S. Public*, pg. 1194
Carlson, H. Bill, Chief Fin. Officer--The Instant Web Companies, Chanhassen, MN; *U.S. Private*, pg. 565
Carlson, J.C., V.P. & Chief Fin. Officer--Carlson Marketing Group Japan Co. Ltd., Tokyo, Japan; *U.S. Private*, pg. 212
Carlson, Jane, Treas. & Sec.--D.C. Taylor Co., Cedar Rapids, IA; *U.S. Private*, pg. 1070
Carlson, Lawrence S., Chief Fin. Officer--Fleetwood Systems, Inc., Romeoville, IL; *U.S. Private*, pg. 410
Carlson, LeRoy, Chief Fin. Officer, Chief Acctg. Officer, Exec. V.P. & Sec.--BRE Properties, Inc., San Francisco, CA; *U.S. Public*, pg. 163
Carlson, Ronald A., V.P.-Fin.--Helwig Carbon Products, Inc., Milwaukee, WI; *U.S. Private*, pg. 521
Carlucci, Antonio, Chief Fin. Officer--Iveco-Unic S.A., Trappes, France; *Int'l*, pg. 484
Carman, Dhar, Chief Fin. Officer, Exec. V.P. & Sec.--Statex Petroleum, Inc., Dallas, TX; *U.S. Public*, pg. 1245
Carmany, David J., Chief Fin. Officer, V.P.-Fin., Treas. & Controller--Castleberry/Snow's Brands Inc., Augusta, GA; *U.S. Private*, pg. 219
Carnahan, John M., Treas. & Sec.--Woodfin Pontiac-Isuzu, Baton Rouge, LA; *U.S. Private*, pg. 1187
Carnar, Robert L., Chief Fin. Officer--Cornerstone Pipeline Co., Dallas, TX; *U.S. Public*, pg. 567

Carney, Dennis, Chief Fin. Officer, Treas. & Sec.--Midwest Mutual Insurance Co., West Des Moines, IA; *U.S. Private*, pg. 881
Carney, Michael, Chief Fin. Officer--Danielson Holding Corporation, New York, NY; *U.S. Public*, pg. 483
Carolus, Paul R., Chief Fin. Officer, Treas. & Sec.--Westwood Corporation, Tulsa, OK; *U.S. Public*, pg. 1763
Carpenter, Bill, Chief Fin. Officer--Midland Paper Co., Elk Grove Village, IL; *U.S. Private*, pg. 744
Carpenter, Clark, Chief Fin. Officer & V.P.--Elkay Manufacturing Company, Oak Brook, IL; *U.S. Private*, pg. 372
Carpenter, Farris E., Pres.-Disneyland Intl. & Chief Fin. Officer--Walt Disney Attractions Division, Anaheim, CA; *U.S. Public*, pg. 511
Carpenter, Marshall L., Chief Fin. Officer & V.P.--MTS Systems Corporation, Eden Prairie, MN; *U.S. Public*, pg. 1028
Carper, John T., Chief Fin. Officer--Sealright Company, Inc., De Soto, KS; *U.S. Public*, pg. 1451
Carr, Arthur, Chief Fin. Officer--Tape Products Div., Moorestown, NJ; *U.S. Public*, pg. 69
Carr, David, Chief Fin. Officer, Sr. V.P. & Sec.--Latshaw Enterprises, Inc., Wichita, KS; *U.S. Public*, pg. 979
Carr, Jerome H., Chief Fin. Officer & Sr. V.P.--Reliance Insurance Company, Philadelphia, PA; *U.S. Public*, pg. 1374
Carr, Mark, Chief Fin. Officer--Hugo Bosca Co., Inc., Springfield, OH; *U.S. Private*, pg. 160
Carr, Ron J., Chief Fin. Officer--Brad Ragan, Inc., Charlotte, NC; *U.S. Public*, pg. 753
Carr, Wayne, Chief Fin. Officer--Allied Foods, Inc., Atlanta, GA; *U.S. Private*, pg. 39
Carraziolo, Frank, Treas.--United Alliant Food Service, Albany, NY; *U.S. Private*, pg. 244
Carrey, Mark, Chief Fin. Officer & Sr. V.P.-Fin.--Signature Inns, Inc., Indianapolis, IN; *U.S. Public*, pg. 1473
Carrier, Jean-Jacques, Chief Fin. Officer & Sr. V.P.-Fin.--Mitel Corporation, Kanata, Canada; *Int'l*, pg. 870
Carrier, Jean-Jacques, Chief Fin. Officer--Mitel, Inc., Herndon, VA; *Int'l*, pg. 870
Carrillo, Martin, Chief Fin. Officer--Young & Rubicam Bogota, Bogota, Colombia; *U.S. Private*, pg. 1200
Carrington, H.G., Jr., Chief Fin. Officer & Exec. V.P.--Spaghetti Warehouse, Inc., Garland, TX; *U.S. Public*, pg. 1495
Carrock, Ray, Chief Fin. Officer--Syroco Inc., Peabody, MA; *Int'l*, pg. 844
Carroll, Anthony J., Chief Fin. Officer & Sr. V.P.--Au Bon Pain Co., Inc., Boston, MA; *U.S. Public*, pg. 146
Carroll, Charles, Chief Fin. Officer--W.L. Gore & Associates, Inc., Newark, DE; *U.S. Private*, pg. 465
Carroll, Dennis C., Chief Fin. Officer & Sr. V.P.-Fin. & Admin.--The Good Guys, Inc., Brisbane, CA; *U.S. Public*, pg. 750
Carroll, Edward, Chief Fin. Officer--DSC Logistics, Inc., Des Plaines, IL; *U.S. Private*, pg. 306
Carroll, J.L., Chief Fin. Officer--The Branigar Organization, Inc., Savannah, GA; *U.S. Public*, pg. 1666
Carroll, Patrick, Controller & Assoc. Dir.--Princeton University Press, Princeton, NJ; *U.S. Private*, pg. 885
Carroll, Paul, Chief Fin. Officer--Kaufman and Broad Multi-Housing Group, Long Beach, CA; *U.S. Public*, pg. 945
Carroll, Robert E., Chief Fin. Officer--Hughes-Peters, Inc., Columbus, OH; *U.S. Private*, pg. 547
Carruthers, George, Pres., Chief Exec. & Chief Fin. Officer--Polycoat Systems, Inc., Hudson Falls, NY; *U.S. Private*, pg. 875
Carsley, Paul, Chief Fin. Officer--Sonnenberg Murphy Leo Burnett, Sunninghill, South Africa; *U.S. Private*, pg. 186
Carson, Thomas, Chief Fin. Officer--Spelling Entertainment Group, Inc., Los Angeles, CA; *U.S. Private*, pg. 776
Carson, Tom, Chief Fin. Officer & Sr. V.P.--Spelling Television, Los Angeles, CA; *U.S. Private*, pg. 776
Carstensen, Susan J., Chief Fin. Officer--Power House Technologies, Inc., Bozeman, MT; *U.S. Public*, pg. 1319
Carter, Glen, Chief Fin. Officer & V.P.--U.S. Central Credit Union, Overland Park, KS; *U.S. Private*, pg. 288
Carter, James D., V.P.-Fin. & Treas.--Vertex Communications Corporation, Kilgore, TX; *U.S. Public*, pg. 1717
Carter, Larry R., Chief Fin. Officer, V.P.-Fin. & Admin. & Sec.--Cisco Systems, Inc., San Jose, CA; *U.S. Public*, pg. 375
Carter, Sam R., Chief Fin. Officer & Treas.--Farmers Co-op Market Inc., Frisco City, AL; *U.S. Private*, pg. 395
Carter, Stephen P., Chief Fin. Officer, V.P. & Treas.--Woodward Governor Company, Rockford, IL; *U.S. Public*, pg. 1776
Carter, William H., Chief Fin. Officer & Exec. V.P.--Borden, Inc., Columbus, OH; *U.S. Private*, pg. 157
Carteris, George, Chief Fin. Officer & Sr. V.P.--Lowe McAdams Healthcare, New York, NY; *U.S. Private*, pg. 678
Carton, Bernard, Chief Fin. Officer & Sr. V.P.--Sodexho S.A., Montigny-le-Bretonneux, France; *Int'l*, pg. 1274
Carty, Douglas A., Chief Fin. Officer & Sr. V.P.-Fin.--Canadian Airlines Corporation, Calgary, Canada; *Int'l*, pg. 255
Carty, Douglas A., Chief Fin. Officer & Sr. V.P.--Canadian Airlines International Ltd., Calgary, Canada; *Int'l*, pg. 256
Caruso, Dominic J., Chief Fin. Officer & Sr. V.P.--Centocor, Inc., Malvern, PA; *U.S. Public*, pg. 323
Caruso, Joseph P., Chief Fin. Officer--Palomar Medical Technologies, Lexington, MA; *U.S. Public*, pg. 1255
Caruso, Richard, Chief Fin. Officer & V.P.--Ormet Corporation, Wheeling, WV; *U.S. Private*, pg. 820
Carvin, Connie, Chief Fin. Officer--Crest Cadillac Company, Nashville, TN; *U.S. Private*, pg. 289
Casabona, George, Chief Fin. Officer & Exec. V.P.--Dugan Valva Contess Inc., Morristown, NJ; *U.S. Private*, pg. 345
Casciano, Ronald J., Chief Fin. Officer, V.P. & Treas.--PAR Technology Corporation, New Hartford, NY; *U.S. Public*, pg. 1256
Casey, Daniel P., Chief Fin. Officer & Exec. V.P.--Gaylord Container Corporation, Deerfield, IL; *U.S. Public*, pg. 704
Casey, James, Controller--H.B. Ives, Wallingford, CT; *U.S. Private*, pg. 506
Casey, Joe, Chief Fin. Officer & V.P.--Intertek Testing Services, Andover, MA; *Int'l*, pg. 672
Casey, John, Chief Fin. Officer & Exec. V.P.--BWAY Corp., Atlanta, GA; *U.S. Public*, pg. 164
Casey, John, Exec. V.P. & Chief Fin. Officer--Brierley & Partners, Dallas, TX; *U.S. Private*, pg. 168
Casey, Joseph F., Chief Fin. Officer & Treas.--Andover Bancorp, Inc., Andover, MA; *U.S. Public*, pg. 111
Casey, Joseph F., Chief Fin. Officer--Andover Bank NH, Salem, NH; *U.S. Public*, pg. 112
Casey, Michael, Chief Fin. Officer & Sr. V.P.--Starbucks Coffee Company, Seattle, WA; *U.S. Public*, pg. 1510
Casey, Mike, Chief Fin. Officer & Sr. V.P.--The William Carter Company, Morrow, GA; *U.S. Private*, pg. 217
Casey, P.H., Treas.--Carolina Builders Corporation, Raleigh, NC; *Int'l*, pg. 1512
Cashman, Maurice J., Chief Fin. Officer & V.P.--National Forge Company, Irvine, PA; *U.S. Private*, pg. 783
Cassar, Claude, Chief Fin. Officer & Sr. Exec. V.P.--Dentsu Young & Rubicam brand communications (Network Center), Singapore, Singapore; *U.S. Private*, pg. 325
Cassar, P.M., Chief Fin. Officer--Rolls-Royce Industries Canada Inc., Lachine, Canada; *Int'l*, pg. 1127
Cassel, Brian, Chief Fin. Officer--Farm & Home Oil Company, Telford, PA; *U.S. Private*, pg. 394
Cassella, Anthony, Chief Fin. Officer & V.P.-Fin.--Croscill, Inc., New York, NY; *U.S. Private*, pg. 290
Cassetta, Stephen K., Chief Fin. Officer--Sturgeon Electric Company, Henderson, CO; *U.S. Public*, pg. 1029
Cassidy, J., Chief Fin. Officer--Colgate-Palmolive Co., Institutional Products Div., Tenafly, NJ; *U.S. Public*, pg. 397
Cassidy, R. Brian, Chief Fin. Officer, Treas. & Sec.--Krasdale Foods Inc., White Plains, NY; *U.S. Private*, pg. 635
Castaigne, Robert, Chief Fin. Officer--Total S.A., Paris, France; *Int'l*, pg. 1408
Castalbi, Al, Chief Fin. Officer--Remington Products Company, L.L.C., Bridgeport, CT; *U.S. Private*, pg. 921
Castaldi, Alexander, Chief Fin. Officer & Sr. V.P.--Kendall Healthcare Products Company, Mansfield, MA; *U.S. Public*, pg. 1647
Castellano, Rosibel Rodriguez, Chief Fin. Officer--San Cristobal Mill & Plant, San Salvador, El Salvador; *U.S. Public*, pg. 410
Castellini, D.J., Sr. V.P.-Fin. & Admin.--The E.W. Scripps Company, Cincinnati, OH; *U.S. Public*, pg. 1447
Castellini, Daniel J., Chief Fin. Officer--Scripps Howard Broadcasting, Cincinnati, OH; *U.S. Public*, pg. 1447
Castiglione, Jorge, Chief Fin. Officer--Sudamtex de Uruguay, S.A., Montevideo, Uruguay; *Int'l*, pg. 1304
Castle, J., Chief Fin. Officer--Mosler Inc., Hamilton, OH; *U.S. Private*, pg. 763
Castonguay, Maurice L., Chief Fin. Officer & V.P.-Fin.--Stratus Computer, Inc., Marlborough, MA; *U.S. Public*, pg. 1524
Castro, Antionio, Dir.-Fin.--C.A. Cigarrera Bigott, Sucs., Caracas, Venezuela; *Int'l*, pg. 111
Catala, Angel Pascual, Chief Fin. Officer--Citroen Hispana S.A., Pontevedra, Spain; *Int'l*, pg. 1020
Catalano, Tony, Chief Fin. Officer & V.P.-Fin.--Transkrit Corporation, Roanoke, VA; *U.S. Private*, pg. 782
Cataldo, Wallace, Chief Fin. Officer & V.P.-Fin. & Admin.--Keane, Inc., Boston, MA; *U.S. Public*, pg. 946
Catanzaro, Steve, Chief Fin. Officer--Bisco Industries, Inc, Orange, CA; *U.S. Private*, pg. 145
Cate, Jim, Chief Fin. Officer--National City Processing, Inc., Louisville, KY; *U.S. Public*, pg. 1154
Cathcart, Joseph, Chief Fin. Officer & Treas.--F.A. Wilhelm Construction Co., Inc., Indianapolis, IN; *U.S. Private*, pg. 1176
Cato, Glenn P., Pres. & Chief Exec. Officer--Maxum Health Corp., Dallas, TX; *U.S. Public*, pg. 881
Catrambone, Gregory, Chief Fin. Officer & V.P.-Fin.--Sargent-Fletcher Inc., El Monte, CA; *Int'l*, pg. 301
Catsimatidis, John A., Pres. & Treas.--United Refining Inc., Warren, PA; *U.S. Private*, pg. 915
Catto, W. Martin, Chief Fin. Officer & Sr. V.P.-Fin.--Harlequin Enterprises Ltd., Don Mills, Canada; *Int'l*, pg. 1402
Cauley, Bob, Chief Fin. Officer--Houston Helm and Company, Los Angeles, CA; *U.S. Private*, pg. 542
Cavalle, Bill, Chief Fin. Officer & Sr. V.P.-Fin.--Chief Auto Parts, Dallas, TX; *U.S. Private*, pg. 236
Cave, Bill, Chief Fin. Officer--M.A. Hanna Engineered Materials, Bethlehem, PA; *U.S. Public*, pg. 781
Cavellier, Thomas E., Chief Fin. Officer--Gator Freightways, Inc., Wilmington, OH; *U.S. Private*, pg. 441
Cavnar, Robert L., Chief Fin. Officer, Sr. V.P. & Treas.--Cornerstone Natural Gas, Inc., Dallas, TX; *U.S. Public*, pg. 567
Cawley, Claude, Chief Fin. Officer & V.P.--Macrotech Plyseal, Inc., Salt Lake City, UT; *U.S. Private*, pg. 693
Cawley, Hugh, Chief Fin. Officer--Milk Products Holdings (Europe) Ltd., Reigate, United Kingdom; *Int'l*, pg. 923
Cawthon, Vernon, Chief Fin. Officer, Controller & Treas.--Strachan Shipping Co., Garden City, GA; *U.S. Private*, pg. 1045
Cearley, Ed, Chief Fin. Officer--Taylor Impression, Inc., Nashville, TN; *U.S. Private*, pg. 1070
Cecere, Domenico, Chief Fin. Officer & Sr. V.P.--Owens Corning, Toledo, OH; *U.S. Public*, pg. 1236
Celebrezze, Michael J., Chief Fin. Officer--Apcoa, Inc., Cleveland, OH; *U.S. Private*, pg. 533
Celli, Pat H., Chief Fin. Officer--The Care Group, Inc., New York, NY; *U.S. Public*, pg. 305
Celozzi, Anthony, Chief Fin. Officer--The Entwistle Company, Hudson, MA; *U.S. Private*, pg. 378
Centner, W., V.P.-Fin. & Chief Fin. Officer--Zero-Max, Inc., Minneapolis, MN; *Int'l*, pg. 866
Cervino, Paul, Dir.-Fin.--Sotheby's Europe, London, United Kingdom; *U.S. Public*, pg. 1487
Cervo, Michael, Chief Fin. Officer--Meritcare, Inc., Sewickley, PA; *U.S. Private*, pg. 733
Cespede, Francisco S.M., Chief Fin. & Admin. Officer--Sao Paulo Alpargatas S.A., Sao Paulo, Brazil; *Int'l*, pg. 1193
Chabot, Roland, Chief Fin. Officer--Stinson Seafood Company, Prospect Harbor, ME; *U.S. Private*, pg. 1043
Chadwick, Arthur D., Chief Fin. Officer & V.P.-Fin. & Admin.--Pinnacle Systems, Inc., Mountain View, CA; *U.S. Public*, pg. 1297
Chadwick, Marshall, Chief Fin. Officer & Controller--Monarch Avalon, Inc., Baltimore, MD; *U.S. Public*, pg. 1123
Chaiken, David, Chief Fin. Officer--MTI/The Image Group, Inc., New York, NY; *U.S. Private*, pg. 688
Chait, Jon F., Chief Fin. Officer, Exec. V.P. & Sec.--Manpower Inc., Milwaukee, WI; *U.S. Public*, pg. 1042
Chalifoux, Michael T., Chief Fin. Officer, Sr. V.P. & Sec.--Circuit City Stores, Inc., Richmond, VA; *U.S. Public*, pg. 374
Chalk, Bradford M., Chief Fin. Officer & Sr. V.P.--Betac International Corporation, Alexandria, VA; *U.S. Private*, pg. 140
Chalmers, Ron, Chief Fin. Officer--Jannock Imaging Companies Limited, Toronto, Canada; *Int'l*, pg. 698
Chamberlain, George A., III, Chief Fin. Officer--Marcam Solutions, Inc., Newton, MA; *U.S. Public*, pg. 1042
Chambers, Clayton, Chief Fin. Officer--Brazos Sportswear Inc., Cincinnati, OH; *U.S. Public*, pg. 251
Chambers, Ed, Chief Fin. Officer & Sr. V.P.--Wawa, Inc., Media, PA; *U.S. Private*, pg. 1155
Chambers, R.A., Chief Fin. Officer--The Glacier Metal Co. Ltd., Northwood, United Kingdom; *Int'l*, pg. 1334
Chambers, Sam, II, Chief Fin. Officer & Controller--Galaxy Food Company, Orlando, FL; *U.S. Public*, pg. 697
Chambers, T.L., Treas. & Sec.--Rumsey Electric Company, Conshohocken, PA; *U.S. Private*, pg. 951
Chambless, Ken, Chief Fin. Officer--Atkinson Construction, San Bruno, CA; *U.S. Public*, pg. 143
Champagne, George R., Chief Fin. Officer & Sr. V.P.--Service Corporation International, Houston, TX; *U.S. Public*, pg. 1460
Champion, Malcolm, Grp. Fin. Dir.--Brake Bros plc, Ashford, United Kingdom; *Int'l*, pg. 210
Champniss, Alex, Chief Fin. Officer--Head USA, Inc., Columbia, MD; *U.S. Private*, pg. 514
Chan, A., Chief Fin. Officer--Scholl (Asia) Limited, Wan Chai, Hong Kong; *Int'l*, pg. 1209
Chan, E., Controller--Kenner Parker (H.K.) Ltd., Kowloon, Hong Kong; *U.S. Public*, pg. 797
Chan, Raymond, Chief Fin. Officer--Bensons Metal Products Sdn Bhd, Shah Alam, Malaysia; *Int'l*, pg. 460
Chandler, William E., Chief Fin. Officer, Sr. V.P.-Fin. & Sec.--Hunt Corporation, Philadelphia, PA; *U.S. Public*, pg. 848
Chaney, Colleen, Chief Fin. Officer--National Card Control, Inc., Crozier, VA; *U.S. Public*, pg. 321
Chang, Ji-Soo, Chief Fin. Officer & Mng. Dir.--Jinbang Steel Co., Ltd., Pohang, Korea; *Int'l*, pg. 1291
Chapdelaine, J.C., Chief Fin. Officer--Lumec, Inc., Boisbriand, Canada; *U.S. Public*, pg. 1599
Chapko, Stephen J., Chief Fin. Officer, Exec. V.P., Treas. & Sec.--Kent Electronics Corp., Houston, TX; *U.S. Public*, pg. 951
Chapman, Brian, Chief Fin. Officer--Anchor Foods Limited, Swindon, United Kingdom; *Int'l*, pg. 923
Chapman, C. Phillip, Chief Fin. Officer, V.P. & Sec.--Microchip Technology, Inc., Chandler, AZ; *U.S. Public*, pg. 1105
Chapman, Carl L., Asst. Sec. & Asst. Treas.--Energy Realty, Inc., Indianapolis, IN; *U.S. Public*, pg. 875
Chapman, Donald R., Chief Fin. Officer & Exec. V.P.--Crawford & Company, Atlanta, GA; *U.S. Public*, pg. 458
Chapman, John, Chief Fin. Officer--Burns, Philp & Company Limited, Sydney, Australia; *Int'l*, pg. 236
Chapman, Laurence A., Chief Fin. Officer & Sr. V.P.--Rohr, Inc., Chula Vista, CA; *U.S. Public*, pg. 751
Chappel, Donald R., Chief Fin. Officer & Chief Info. Officer--Waste Management, Inc., Oak Brook, IL; *U.S. Public*, pg. 1744
Chappell, William, Chief Fin. Officer--Tecmar Technologies, Inc., Longmont, CO; *Int'l*, pg. 1361
Char, Sherman, Chief Fin. Officer--Engineering Technology Ltd. (E.T.), Troy, MI; *U.S. Private*, pg. 377
Charboneau, Darrell, Chief Fin. Officer--Faribault Foods Inc., Minneapolis, MN; *U.S. Private*, pg. 393
Chardovoyne, William, Chief Fin. Officer & Exec. V.P.--Columbia Tri-Star Home Video, Burbank, CA; *Int'l*, pg. 1282
Chareyre, Pierre, Chief Fin. Officer--Rexel, S.A., Paris, France; *Int'l*, pg. 1107
Charles, Debra, Controller--Clairson International Corp., Ocala, FL; *U.S. Public*, pg. 575
Charles, Dirkson, Chief Fin. Officer--K & F Industries Inc., New York, NY; *U.S. Private*, pg. 602
Charron, J. Paul, V.P.-Fin.--Morrison Petroleums Ltd., Calgary, Canada; *Int'l*, pg. 895
Charruau, Jerome, Chief Fin. Officer & V.P.-Fin.--American Eurocopter Corp., Grand Prairie, TX; *Int'l*, pg. 29
Chase, Lee, Chief Fin. Officer & V.P.-Corp. Svcs.--Blue Ridge Electric Membership Corp., Lenoir, NC; *U.S. Private*, pg. 153
Chastain, Paul R., Chief Fin. Officer & V.P.--Kinark Corporation, Tulsa, OK; *U.S. Public*, pg. 960
Chatt, Joseph R., Jr., Chief Fin. Officer & V.P.--Caribe Freight, Aguadilla, PR; *U.S. Private*, pg. 211
Chau, Al, Chief Fin. Officer--Adams Rite Sabre International, Glendale, CA; *U.S. Private*, pg. 1203
Chau, Emanuel, Chief Fin. Officer & Dir. Gen.-Fin.--SNCF, Paris, France; *Int'l*, pg. 1163
Chavez, Susan, Chief Fin. Officer & Sr. V.P.--Mendoza, Dillon & Asociados, Inc., Newport Beach, CA; *Int'l*, pg. 1483

Chawla, Ajit, Mgr.-Acctg.--Philips Speech Processing, Atlanta, GA; *Int'l*, pg. 1055

Chbosky, Frederick G., Chief Fin. Officer & Exec. V.P.--WHX Corporation, New York, NY; *U.S. Public*, pg. 1726

Cheema, Manjit S., Chief Fin. Officer & Sr. V.P.--TNP Enterprises, Inc., Fort Worth, TX; *U.S. Public*, pg. 1557

Cheesbrough, Peter H., Chief Fin. Officer & Sr. V.P.-Fin.--Echo Bay Mines Ltd., Englewood, CO; *U.S. Public*, pg. 561

Chelesnik, David F., Dir.-Fin.--Verbatim Tape Corporation, San Diego, CA; *Int'l*, pg. 872

Chellam, Kris, Chief Fin. Officer & V.P.-Fin. & Admin.--Atmel Corporation, San Jose, CA; *U.S. Public*, pg. 145

Chemerow, David I., Chief Fin. Officer, Exec. V.P.-Fin. & Opers.--Lifestyle Brands, Ltd., Chicago, IL; *U.S. Public*, pg. 1310

Chen, Elaine, Chief Fin. Officer--Quanta Systems Corporation, Gaithersburg, MD; *U.S. Public*, pg. 420

Chen, Lily C., Dr., Chief Fin. Officer, Exec. V.P. & Treas.--General Sciences Corp., Laurel, MD; *U.S. Private*, pg. 976

Chen, M.T., Chief Fin. Officer--China Ecotek Corporation, Kao-hsiung, Taiwan; *Int'l*, pg. 285

Chen, Terry, Chief Fin. Officer & Sr. V.P.--Allright Corporation, Houston, TX; *U.S. Private*, pg. 42

Chen, Vincent, Asst. Gen. Mgr. & Loan Mgr.--BFCE Singapore, Singapore, Singapore; *Int'l*, pg. 161

Chenu, R.L., Fin. Dir.--Australian National Industries Limited, Pyrmont, Australia; *Int'l*, pg. 100

Cheong, T.C., Chief Fin. Officer--PMC, Inc., Sun Valley, CA; *U.S. Private*, pg. 827

Cherigny, Jean-Pierre, Chief Fin. Officer--Square D Company, Palatine, IL; *Int'l*, pg. 1208

Cherkasly, Ronald L., Chief Fin. Officer & Treas.--J.C. Higgins Corp., Stoughton, MA; *U.S. Public*, pg. 572

Chesser, Leicle E., Chief Fin. Officer & Exec. V.P.--EMCOR Group, Inc., Norwalk, CT; *U.S. Public*, pg. 571

Chester, Maurice, Chief Fin. Officer--IGT-(Australia), Pty. Limited, Rosebery, Australia; *U.S. Public*, pg. 900

Chesterman, Tom, Chief Fin. Officer--Bio-Rad Laboratories, Inc., Hercules, CA; *U.S. Public*, pg. 230

Chestnut, Colette, Chief Fin. Officer-N.A.--TBWA Chiat/Day, New York, NY; *U.S. Private*, pg. 1062

Chestnut, Colette, Chief Fin. Officer-NA--TBWA Chiat/Day New York, New York, NY; *U.S. Private*, pg. 1062

Chestnut, James E., Chief Fin. Officer & Sr. V.P.--The Coca-Cola Company, Atlanta, GA; *U.S. Public*, pg. 392

Chiaro, Marty, Chief Fin. Officer--Persoft, Inc., Madison, WI; *U.S. Private*, pg. 856

Chichester, David, Chief Fin. Officer--Red Roof Inns, Inc., Hilliard, OH; *U.S. Public*, pg. 1369

Chicoine, Jerry, Chief Fin. Officer & Sr. V.P.--Pioneer Hi-Bred International, Inc., Des Moines, IA; *U.S. Public*, pg. 1298

Chicoine, Michelle L., Chief Fin. Officer, Sr. V.P. & Treas.--EnergyNorth, Inc., Manchester, NH; *U.S. Public*, pg. 581

Chien, Teddy, Chief Fin. Officer & V.P.--Slater Industries Inc., North York, Canada; *Int'l*, pg. 1262

Chihi, D.M., Chief Fin. Officer & V.P.-Fin.--Marigold Foods, Inc., Minneapolis, MN; *Int'l*, pg. 752

Childers, Richard D., Chief Fin. Officer & V.P.--L & L Oil Company, Inc., Metairie, LA; *U.S. Private*, pg. 638

Childers, Richard D., Chief Fin. Officer & V.P.--L & L Maintenance & Repair, Metairie, LA; *U.S. Private*, pg. 638

Chin, Henry W., Chief Fin. Officer, V.P.-Fin. & Sec.--Marshall Industries, El Monte, CA; *U.S. Public*, pg. 1051

Chin, Ray, Chief Fin. Officer & V.P.-Fin. & Admin.--Standun, Inc., Inglewood, CA; *U.S. Private*, pg. 1032

Chiodo, Michael J., Chief Fin. Officer--JB Oxford Holdings Inc., Beverly Hills, CA; *U.S. Public*, pg. 916

Chitwood, Jerry, Chief Fin. Officer--Covington Industries, Atlanta, GA; *U.S. Private*, pg. 280

Chitwood, Jerry, Chief Fin. Officer--Game Winner, Inc., Atlanta, GA; *U.S. Private*, pg. 280

Chiusolo, Eric, Chief Fin. Officer & V.P.--Medieval Times Dinner & Tournament, Inc., Buena Park, CA; *U.S. Private*, pg. 728

Cho, Jeong-Su, Chief Fin. Officer--Ssangyong Paper Co., Ltd., Seoul, Korea; *Int'l*, pg. 1292

Cho, Young-Han, Sr. V.P.-Fin., Acct. & Auditing--Korean Airlines Co., Ltd., Seoul, Korea; *Int'l*, pg. 758

Choi, Sang-Jun, Chief Fin. Officer--Ssangyong Engineering Co., Ltd., Seoul, Korea; *Int'l*, pg. 1292

Choi, Seung-Keun, Chief Fin. Officer--Ssangyong Finance Inc., Seoul, Korea; *Int'l*, pg. 1292

Chokel, Charles B., Chief Fin. Officer & Treas.--The Progressive Corporation, Cleveland, OH; *U.S. Public*, pg. 1334

Chomicki, Denise, Chief Fin. Officer--Computerized Medical Systems, Inc., Saint Louis, MO; *U.S. Private*, pg. 260

Chopra, Prem S., Chief Fin. Officer--Thermo-Mizer Environmental Corp., Rahway, NJ; *U.S. Public*, pg. 1596

Choug, Ken, Chief Fin. Officer & Mgr.-Cash Mngmt.--Televideo, Inc., San Jose, CA; *U.S. Public*, pg. 1572

Chouinard, John J., Chief Fin. Officer & Sr. V.P.--Geraghty & Miller, Inc., Denver, CO; *Int'l*, pg. 607

Chow, Hyston, Chief Fin. Officer--Sea Containers Asia Ltd., Hong Kong, Hong Kong; *Int'l*, pg. 1214

Chow, Hyston, Chief Fin. Officer--Sea Containers Hong Kong Ltd., Hong Kong, Hong Kong; *Int'l*, pg. 1214

Chow, Hyston, Chief Fin. Officer--Sea Containers Asia Pte. Ltd., Singapore, Singapore; *Int'l*, pg. 1214

Chow, Shirley, Sr. V.P.-Admin. & Fin. & Corp. Sec.--Bachmann Industries, Inc., Philadelphia, PA; *U.S. Private*, *pg. 109*

Choynake, Brian, Chief Fin. Officer--Shield Healthcare Centers, Valencia, CA; *Int'l*, pg. 740

Chrenc, Robert J., Chief Fin. Officer & Exec. V.P.--A.C. Nielsen, Stamford, CT; *U.S. Public*, pg. 1183

Chrintz-Gath, Lars-Bertil, Chief Fin. Officer--Stabilator AB, Danderyd, Sweden; *Int'l*, pg. 1261

Chrisco, Gerald, Chief Fin. Officer--Lofts Seed, Inc., Winston Salem, NC; *U.S. Public*, pg. 29

Christ, William F., Chief Fin. Officer & Sr. V.P.--Hershey Foods Corporation, Hershey, PA; *U.S. Public*, pg. 811

Christe, Michel, Chief Fin. Officer--Schweizerische Bundesbahnen - SBB AG, Bern, Switzerland; *Int'l*, pg. 1211

Christen, John Paul, Chief Fin. Officer--Valley Hospital Medical Center, Las Vegas, NV; *U.S. Public*, pg. 1697

Christensen, Carl E., Jr., Chief Oper. Officer & Chief Fin. Officer--Kreonite, Inc., Wichita, KS; *U.S. Private*, pg. 635

Christiansen, Dan, Chief Fin. Officer & Treas.--AVX Corporation, Myrtle Beach, SC; *Int'l*, pg. 775

Christie, Warren A., V.P.-Taxes--Warner Communications Inc., New York, NY; *U.S. Public*, pg. 1611

Christoffersen, Timothy R., Chief Fin. Officer & V.P.-Fin.--Chips and Technologies, Inc., San Jose, CA; *U.S. Public*, *pg. 349*

Christon, Anthony, Chief Fin. Officer--Jaclyn, Inc., West New York, NJ; *U.S. Public*, pg. 920

Chronis, John, Chief Fin. Officer & Sr. V.P.--Western Indemnity Insurance Company, Houston, TX; *U.S. Public*, *pg. 685*

Chronis, John C., V.P.-Fin. & Admin.--Textron Systems Corporation, Lowell, MA; *U.S. Public*, pg. 1589

Chu, Eric, Chief Fin. Officer--New Tai Milk Products Co. Ltd., Taipei, Taiwan; *Int'l*, pg. 923

Chua, Ler Ching, Chief Fin. Officer, Treas. & Sec.--GB Holdings, Jurong, Singapore; *Int'l*, pg. 531

Chua, Ler Ching, Chief Fin. Officer--American Marine Pte. Ltd., Jurong, Singapore; *Int'l*, pg. 531

Chua, Ler Ching, Chief Fin. Officer--Grand Banks Yachts, Ltd., Southport, CT; *Int'l*, pg. 531

Chuang, Lim, Chief Fin. Officer & Sec.--Haw Par Brothers International Limited, Singapore, Singapore; *Int'l*, pg. 603

Chujo, Kunihiro, Chief Fin. Officer & Mng. Dir.--Honda Motor Co., Ltd., Tokyo, Japan; *Int'l*, pg. 634

Chung, Jong-Moo, Chief Fin. Officer--Ssangyong Resources Development Co., Ltd., Tonghae, Korea; *Int'l*, pg. 1291

Chung, Ray, Chief Fin. Officer, Exec. V.P. & Treas.--Dartford Partnership, San Francisco, CA; *U.S. Private*, pg. 312

Church, Jeffrey W., Chief Fin. Officer & Exec. V.P.--Biospherics Incorporated, Beltsville, MD; *U.S. Public*, pg. 232

Church, Jerry, Chief Fin. Officer & V.P.-Fin.--Broyhill Furniture Industries, Inc., Saint Louis, MO; *U.S. Public*, pg. 688

Churchwell, Chuck, III, Chief Fin. Officer--McCoy's Building Supply Centers, San Marcos, TX; *U.S. Private*, pg. 720

Ciaccio, Don, Chief Fin. Officer--TTC Illinois Inc., Kankakee, IL; *U.S. Private*, pg. 1066

Ciccotelli, Tom, Chief Fin. Officer--Financial World Partners, New York, NY; *U.S. Private*, pg. 404

Ciepcielinski, Stanley, Chief Fin. Officer, Exec. V.P. & Sec.--Glenayre Technologies, Inc., Charlotte, NC; *U.S. Public*, pg. 746

Ciesluk, Ron, Chief Fin. Officer--Kao Infosystems Company (MA), Plymouth, MA; *Int'l*, pg. 717

Cifone, Michael P., Chief Fin. Officer & V.P.--ACMAT Corporation, New Britain, CT; *U.S. Public*, pg. 16

Cifor, Jerry S., Chief Fin. Officer, V.P. & Treas.--Casella Waste Systems, Inc., Rutland, VT; *U.S. Public*, pg. 312

Cimato, Giulio, Chief Fin. Officer--TBWA Italia S.p.A., Milan, Italy; *U.S. Private*, pg. 1063

Cimitile, Charles, Chief Fin. Officer & V.P.--GT Bicycles, Inc., Santa Ana, CA; *U.S. Public*, pg. 695

Cinquanta, I., Chief Fin. Officer--Dr. Scholl's SpA, Italy; *Int'l*, *pg. 1209*

Cinquin, Carl, Chief Fin. Officer & Controller--Cramer Company, Old Saybrook, CT; *U.S. Public*, pg. 1238

Ciotti, John, Chief Fin. Officer & Exec. V.P.--Eisner & Associates, Inc., Baltimore, MD; *U.S. Private*, pg. 366

Cipoletti, A.G., Chief Fin. Officer--Svedala Pumps & Process, Colorado Springs, CO; *Int'l*, pg. 1325

Cira, Chris T., Chief Fin. Officer--Tranzonic Industrial Textiles Division, Highland Heights, OH; *U.S. Public*, pg. 1632

Cistone, Dan, Chief Fin. Officer & V.P.-Fin.--M & C Specialties (Ireland) Limited, Athlone, Ireland; *U.S. Private*, pg. 684

Cistone, Daniel, V.P.-Fin. & Admin., Sec. & Dir.-Real Estate--M & C Specialties Company, Southampton, PA; *U.S. Private*, pg. 684

Citron, John, Chief Fin. Officer & Sr. V.P.--SFM Media Corporation, New York, NY; *U.S. Private*, pg. 956

Civiletto, Joseph, Chief Fin. Officer--Aviation Sales Company, Miami, FL; *U.S. Public*, pg. 154

Clancy, Paul G., Chief Fin. Officer, V.P. & Treas.--Diversified Communications, Portland, ME; *U.S. Private*, pg. 336

Clanin, Robert J., Chief Fin. Officer, Sr. V.P. & Treas.--United Parcel Service of America, Inc., Atlanta, GA; *U.S.* Private, pg. 1123

Clanton, Jim, Chief Fin. Officer--E Z Loader Corporate, Airway Heights, WA; *U.S. Private*, pg. 352

Clanton, Stephen L., Chief Fin. Officer, Sr. V.P. & Treas.--International Comfort Products, Franklin, TN; *U.S. Public*, *pg. 898*

Clanton, Stephen L., Chief Fin. Officer--International Comfort Products Corp., Lewisburg, TN; *U.S. Public*, pg. 898

Clapes, Jorge, Chief Fin. Officer--Johnson & Johnson de Argentina, S.A., Buenos Aires, Argentina; *U.S. Public*, pg. 930

Clapp, Norman, Chief Fin. Officer--Beaulieu United, Dalton, GA; *U.S. Private*, pg. 128

Clark, A. Bayard, Chief Fin. Officer, Exec. V.P. & Treas.--Commerce Bancshares, Inc., Kansas City, MO; *U.S. Public*, pg. 409

Clark, A. Bayard, Chief Fin. Officer--Commerce Bank, N.A., Clayton, MO; *U.S. Public*, pg. 409

Clark, Burt, V.P.-Fin.--Champion Ignition Products, Chesterfield, MO; *U.S. Public*, pg. 442

Clark, C.F., Chief Fin. Officer--Jardine (Lloyd's Underwriting Agents) Ltd., London, United Kingdom; *Int'l*, pg. 705

Clark, Dean, Chief Fin. Officer--Martin Door Mfg., Inc., Salt Lake City, UT; *U.S. Private*, pg. 708

Clark, Dennis, Chief Fin. Officer--B & P Manufacturing, Cadillac, MI; *U.S. Private*, pg. 105

Clark, Dennis, Chief Fin. Officer, V.P. & Sec.--Carus Corporation, Peru, IL; *U.S. Private*, pg. 217

Clark, Dennis, Chief Fin. Officer--Carus Chemical Company, Chemical Div., Peru, IL; *U.S. Private*, pg. 217

Clark, Dennis, Chief Fin. Officer--SIGAL CONSTRUCTION CORP., Washington, DC; *U.S. Private*, pg. 999

Clark, James A., Chief Fin. Officer & V.P.--Netopia, Inc., Alameda, CA; *U.S. Public*, pg. 1168

Clark, James T., Chief Fin. Officer & V.P.-Admin.--Osmose Wood Preserving, Inc., Buffalo, NY; *U.S. Private*, pg. 821

Clark, Janet F., Chief Fin. Officer & V.P.--Santa Fe Energy Resources, Inc., Houston, TX; *U.S. Public*, pg. 1431

Clark, Jeff C., Pres.--Covington Foods, Inc., Covington, IN; *U.S. Private*, pg. 280

Clark, John M., III, Sr. V.P., Gen. Counsel & Sec.--National Semiconductor Corporation, Santa Clara, CA; *U.S. Public*, pg. 1159

Clark, Pat, Chief Fin. Officer--Welbilt Corporation, Stamford, CT; *Int'l*, pg. 188

Clark, Peter, Chief Actuary--Sun Life and Provincial Holdings plc, London, United Kingdom; *Int'l*, pg. 1318

Clark, R., Chief Fin. Officer & V.P.--Knott's Berry Farm, Buena Park, CA; *U.S. Private*, pg. 627

Clark, Scott, Vice Chm. & Chief Fin. Officer--The Clark Group, Mission, Canada; *Int'l*, pg. 296

Clark, Steve, Chief Fin. Officer & V.P.-Fin.--Flanders Corp., Washington, NC; *U.S. Public*, pg. 648

Clark, Terry, Chief Fin. Officer--Milk Specialties Company, Dundee, IL; *U.S. Private*, pg. 746

Clark, William, Chief Fin. Officer & V.P.--Rex Lumber Company, Acton, MA; *U.S. Private*, pg. 926

Clarke, Colley, V.P. & Chief Fin. Officer--Canadian Satellite Communications Inc., Mississauga, Canada; *Int'l*, pg. 1481

Clarke, John U., Chief Fin. Officer & Sr. V.P.--NGC Corporation, Houston, TX; *U.S. Public*, pg. 1146

Clarke, Las, Chief Fin. Officer--The United Company, Bristol, VA; *U.S. Private*, pg. 1121

Clarke, Peter W., Chief Fin. Officer, Exec. V.P. & Sec.--Orthofix International N.V., Curacao, Netherlands Antilles; *Int'l*, pg. 1011

Clarke, R.A., Chief Fin. Officer & Treas.--British Mohair Spinners Limited, Bradford, United Kingdom; *Int'l*, pg. 219

Clausen, Dick, Chm. Bd., Pres. & Chief Exec. Officer--Verbatim Tape Corporation, San Diego, CA; *Int'l*, pg. 872

Clausen, Robert A., Chief Fin. Officer & Sr. V.P.--Solutia Inc., Saint Louis, MO; *U.S. Public*, pg. 1483

Clausing, Richard, Chief Fin. Officer--Famous-Barr, Saint Louis, MO; *U.S. Public*, pg. 1063

Clauson, M.L., Chief Fin. Officer--NIPA Hardwicke, Inc., Wilmington, DE; *U.S. Private*, pg. 771

Clay, David, Chief Fin. Officer & Controller--Universal Industrial Products Co., Pioneer, OH; *U.S. Public*, pg. 1677

Clayton, Charles, Chief Fin. Officer--The Gorton Group, Gloucester, MA; *Int'l*, pg. 1434

Clayton, Charles W., Chief Fin. Officer, V.P. & Treas.--Hampshire Group, Ltd., Anderson, SC; *U.S. Public*, pg. 778

Clayton, Tripp, Chief Fin. Officer, V.P. & Controller--Tanner Co., Rutherfordton, NC; *U.S. Private*, pg. 1068

Clear, Geoffrey P., Chief Fin. Officer--Microtouch Systems, Inc., Methuen, MA; *U.S. Public*, pg. 1108

Cleary, Paul, Chief Fin. Officer--Butler Automatic, Inc., Canton, MA; *U.S. Private*, pg. 189

Cleasby, Craig L., V.P., Controller & Chief Fin. Officer--ITT Cannon Sealectro, New Britain, CT; *U.S. Public*, pg. 859

Cleberg, Anthony S., Chief Fin. Officer & Exec. V.P.--Morrison Knudsen Corporation, Boise, ID; *U.S. Public*, pg. 1133

Cleeland, Kenneth K., Chief Fin. Officer & Treas.--Urban Outfitters, Inc., Philadelphia, PA; *U.S. Public*, pg. 1700

Clegg, Russ, Chief Fin. Officer--Food & Gas, Inc., Norcross, GA; *U.S. Private*, pg. 417

Clein, Mark P., Chief Fin. Officer & Exec. V.P.--PMR Corporation, San Diego, CA; *U.S. Public*, pg. 1242

Cleland, Mark, A., Chief Fin. Officer--Roney & Co., Detroit, MI; *U.S. Private*, pg. 943

Clement, Dale E., Sr. V.P.-Fin.--Black Hills Corporation, Rapid City, SD; *U.S. Public*, pg. 235

Clement, Debbie, Chief Fin. Officer--Quality Foods Inc., Little Rock, AR; *U.S. Private*, pg. 898

Clement, Patricia E., Treas. & Asst. Sec.--BNI Coal, Ltd., Bismarck, ND; *U.S. Public*, pg. 1116

Clements, James E., Chief Fin. Officer & Sec.--Dorsey Trailers, Inc., Atlanta, GA; *U.S. Public*, pg. 520

Clements, Richard H., Chm. Bd. & Chief Fin. Officer--Clements Foods Co., Oklahoma City, OK; *U.S. Private*, pg. 245

Clemmer, Richard L., Chief Fin. Officer & Exec. V.P.-Fin.--Quantum Corporation, Milpitas, CA; *U.S. Public*, pg. 1350

Clendenen, Robert B., V.P.-Audit & Business Ethics--Textron Inc., Providence, RI; *U.S. Public*, pg. 1588

Clerico, John A., Chief Fin. Officer & V.P.--Praxair Inc., Danbury, CT; *U.S. Public*, pg. 1319

Clifford, Elizabeth A., Chief Fin. Officer--Conseco Life of New York, Orangeburg, NY; *U.S. Public*, pg. 433

Clifford, Elizabeth A., Chief Fin. Officer--Charter National Life Insurance Co., Saint Louis, MO; *U.S. Public*, pg. 990

Clifford, Linda J., Chief Fin. Officer, Treas. & Dir.-Real Estate--C.C. Myers, Inc., Rancho Cordova, CA; *U.S. Private*, pg. 770

Clifton, Ellen, Chief Fin. Officer--Plains Electric Generation Transmission Co-Op, Inc., Albuquerque, NM; *U.S. Private*, pg. 868

Clifton, Jean B., Chief Fin. Officer, Exec. V.P., Treas. & Sec.--Journal Register Company, Trenton, NJ; *U.S. Public*, pg. 934

Climo, Ross, Chief Fin. Officer--Dean's Photo Service, San Diego, CA; *U.S. Private*, pg. 319
Clinebell, Kenneth M., Chief Fin. Officer, Treas. & Sec.--Precision Systems, Inc., Saint Petersburg, FL; *U.S. Public*, pg. 1321
Clock, Douglas G., Chief Fin. Officer & Exec. V.P.--Byerly's Inc., Edina, MN; *U.S. Private*, pg. 680
Cloherty, Michael J., Exec. V.P.--Arthur J. Gallagher & Co., Itasca, IL; *U.S. Public*, pg. 698
Cloniger, Kriss, III, Chief Fin. Officer & Exec. V.P.--AFLAC Incorporated, Columbus, GA; *U.S. Public*, pg. 28
Clonts, Richard, Chief Fin. Officer, V.P.-Fin & Sec.--Sewell Village Cadillac Co., Dallas, TX; *U.S. Private*, pg. 988
Clore, Harry, Chief Fin. Officer, Exec. V.P. & V.P.-Corp. Services--Service Supply Co. Inc. of Indiana, Indianapolis, IN; *U.S. Private*, pg. 987
Clothier, G.S., Sr. V.P.-Fin. & Plng.--The Phillies-A Limited Partnership, Philadelphia, PA; *U.S. Private*, pg. 861
Clow, Greg, Chief Fin. Officer--Valley Food Distributors of Nevada, Las Vegas, NV; *U.S. Public*, pg. 919
Clurczak, Richard, V.P.-Fin.--Nasco Modesto, Modesto, CA; *U.S. Private*, pg. 446
Cluss, Charles, Chief Fin. Officer--O.C. Cluss Lumber Co., Uniontown, PA; *U.S. Private*, pg. 248
Coates, Clive, Chief Fin. Officer--Eagle Star, London, United Kingdom; *Int'l*, pg. 110
Cobb, Alton H., Jr., Chief Fin. Officer & V.P.--Long MFG. NC, Inc., Tarboro, NC; *U.S. Private*, pg. 674
Cobuzzi, Robert J., Chief Fin. Officer, Sr. V.P. & Treas.--Kollmorgen Corporation, Waltham, MA; *U.S. Public*, pg. 965
Cochran, Sandy, Chief Fin. Officer--Books-A-Million, Inc., Birmingham, AL; *U.S. Public*, pg. 244
Cocke, James E., Sr. V.P.-Fin. & Admin.--Raytheon Systems Co., Kirkwood, NY; *U.S. Public*, pg. 1364
Cocke, Norman A., Chief Fin. Officer, Sr. V.P. & Sec.--Chronimed Inc., Minnetonka, MN; *U.S. Public*, pg. 352
Cockrell, D. Michael, Chief Fin. Officer & Treas.--Sanderson Farms, Inc., Laurel, MS; *U.S. Public*, pg. 1430
Cocquyt, Roger, Chief Fin. Officer--ASLK-CGER, Antwerp, Belgium; *Int'l*, pg. 17
Codd, Ronald E., Chief Fin. Officer--PeopleSoft, Inc., Pleasanton, CA; *U.S. Public*, pg. 1276
Coetzer, Trix, Dir.-Fin.--Foodcorp Limited, Bedfordview, South Africa; *Int'l*, pg. 496
Coffey, Robert, Chief Fin. Officer--Merchants Rent A Car, Inc., Hooksett, NH; *U.S. Private*, pg. 732
Coffman, Credit, V.P.-Credit Admin.--U.S. Operations Div., Hato Rey, PR; *U.S. Public*, pg. 176
Cogdill, Rick, Chief Fin. Officer & Exec. V.P.--Pilgrim's Pride Corporation, Pittsburg, TX; *U.S. Public*, pg. 1296
Cogg, Jurg, Chief Fin. Officer--Elektro-Apparatebau Olten AG, Olten, Switzerland; *Int'l*, pg. 444
Coggins, Richard C., Chief Fin. Officer & V.P.--Span-America Medical Systems Inc., Greenville, SC; *U.S. Public*, pg. 1495
Coghlan, Paul, Chief Fin. Officer & V.P.-Fin.--Linear Technology Corp., Milpitas, CA; *U.S. Public*, pg. 1000
Cohen, Al, V.P.-Fin. & Admin.--W. Braun Company, Chicago, IL; *U.S. Private*, pg. 166
Cohen, Alan, Chief Fin. Officer--NAPCO, Inc., Terryville, CT; *U.S. Public*, pg. 1592
Cohen, Albert J., Chief Fin. Officer & V.P.--Hollywood Casino Corp, Atlantic City, NJ; *U.S. Public*, pg. 830
Cohen, Amir, Treas.--Laser Industries Ltd., Tel Aviv, Israel; *Int'l*, pg. 429
Cohen, Benjamin, Exec. V.P.-Fin. & Investments--Accor S.A., Evry, France; *Int'l*, pg. 20
Cohen, Colin M., Chief Fin. Officer & Sr. V.P.--The Fairchild Corporation, Chantilly, VA; *U.S. Public*, pg. 610
Cohen, David, Chief Fin. Officer--McBee Systems, Inc., Parsippany, NJ; *U.S. Private*, pg. 718
Cohen, Donald, Chm. Bd., Pres., Chief Exec. Officer & Chief Fin. Officer--Tool King, Denver, CO; *U.S. Private*, pg. 1091
Cohen, Ira, Chief Fin. Officer & V.P.-Opers.--All-Luminum Products, Inc., Philadelphia, PA; *U.S. Private*, pg. 34
Cohen, Jeff, Chief Fin. Officer--Wavetek Corp., San Diego, CA; *U.S. Private*, pg. 1155
Cohen, Lawrence A., Vice Chm. & Chief Fin. Officer--Capital Senior Living, Inc., Dallas, TX; *U.S. Public*, pg. 302
Cohen, Marcia, Chief Fin. Officer--Coopers & Lybrand, New York, NY; *U.S. Private*, pg. 274
Cohen, Maryjo, Pres., Chief Exec. Officer & Chief Fin. Officer--National Presto Industries, Inc., Eau Claire, WI; *U.S. Public*, pg. 1159
Cohn, Th. M., Chief Fin. Officer--Siemens Nederland N.V., Hague, Netherlands; *Int'l*, pg. 1247
Colabraro, Tony, Chief Fin. Officer & Sr. V.P.--Worldvision Enterprises, New York, NY; *U.S. Private*, pg. 776
Colabuono, Scott, Chief Fin. Officer--Burger King Corporation, Miami, FL; *Int'l*, pg. 411
Colabuono, Scott, Chief Fin. Officer & V.P.--Norrell Corporation, Atlanta, GA; *U.S. Public*, pg. 1192
Colaiacovo, Mario, Chief Fin. Officer & Exec. V.P.--Societe d'Applications Generales d'Electricite et de Mechanique, Paris, France; *Int'l*, pg. 1273
Colaianne, John M., Chief Fin. Officer & Sec.--Cambridge Industries Inc., Madison Heights, MI; *U.S. Private*, pg. 202
Colalucci, Francis M., Chief Fin. Officer, Sr. V.P. & Treas.--Empire Insurance Group, New York, NY; *U.S. Public*, pg. 990
Colalucci, Francis M., Chief Fin. Officer, Sr. V.P. & Treas.--Allcity Insurance Co., New York, NY; *U.S. Public*, pg. 990
Colaou, Hadzini, Chief Exec. Officer & Chief Fin. Officer--CCF Athens, Athens, Greece; *Int'l*, pg. 342
Colavito, Michael, Chief Fin. Officer & Exec. V.P.--SCP Direct Inc., New York, NY; *U.S. Public*, pg. 1224
Colberg, Rick, Chief Fin. Officer, V.P. & Treas.--First Northern Capital Corp., Green Bay, WI; *U.S. Public*, pg. 636
Colby, David, Chief Fin. Officer & Treas.--Columbia/HCA Healthcare Corporation, Nashville, TN; *U.S. Public*, pg. 404
Cole, Bruce, Chief Fin. Officer & V.P.--Tandy Brands Accessories, Inc., Arlington, TX; *U.S. Public*, pg. 1560
Cole, David O., Chief Fin. Officer, V.P., Controller, Treas. & Sec.--Lincoln Foodservice Products, Inc., Fort Wayne, IN; *Int'l*, pg. 188
Cole, Denis C., Chief Fin. Offricer--SmithKline Beecham Pharmaceuticals, Tokyo, Japan; *Int'l*, pg. 1266
Cole, John, Chief Fin. Officer, Treas. & Controller--Square Industries, Inc., Jersey City, NJ; *U.S. Public*, pg. 326
Cole, Patricia, Chief Fin. Officer & Sr. V.P.--Fair, Isaac and Company, Inc., San Rafael, CA; *U.S. Public*, pg. 609
Cole, Tom, Chief Fin. Officer & Exec. V.P.--Maxum Health Corp., Dallas, TX; *U.S. Public*, pg. 881
Coleman, H.R., Chief Fin. Officer & Sr. V.P.--Turner Foods Corporation, Punta Gorda, FL; *U.S. Public*, pg. 608
Coleman, Ron, Chief Fin. Officer--Hitchcock Chair Company LTD, New Hartford, CT; *U.S. Private*, pg. 531
Coleman, Thomas W., Chief Fin. Officer--Midwest Products, Inc., Strafford, MO; *U.S. Public*, pg. 849
Coler, Robert, Chief Fin. Officer--Quantic Industries, Inc., San Carlos, CA; *U.S. Private*, pg. 899
Colin, Steve, Chief Fin. Officer--Schott Brothers, Inc., Perth Amboy, NJ; *U.S. Private*, pg. 972
Colleran, Dennis, Chief Fin. Officer--Agripac Inc., Salem, OR; *U.S. Private*, pg. 26
Collier, George, Chief Fin. Officer, V.P.-Fin. & Mgr.-Personnel--Streamlight Inc., Norristown, PA; *U.S. Private*, pg. 1047
Collier, Jackie, V.P. & Controller--Aviall, Inc., Dallas, TX; *U.S. Public*, pg. 154
Collin, Mark H., Chief Fin. Officer, Treas. & Sec.--Unitil Corporation, Hampton, NH; *U.S. Public*, pg. 1692
Collings, Glenn M., Chief Fin. Officer--Producto Machine Co. Ring Division, Jamestown, NY; *U.S. Private*, pg. 889
Collings, Glenn M., Chief Fin. Officer--The Producto Machine Co., Bridgeport, CT; *U.S. Private*, pg. 889
Collings, Glenn M., Chief Fin. Officer, V.P.-Fin. & Treas.--Moore Tool Company, Inc., Bridgeport, CT; *U.S. Private*, pg. 889
Collins, Craig B., Chief Fin. Officer & V.P.-Fin.--Optical Coating Laboratory, Inc., Santa Rosa, CA; *U.S. Public*, pg. 1227
Collins, Don, Controller--St. Louis Music, Inc., Saint Louis, MO; *U.S. Private*, pg. 960
Collins, Jack, Chief Fin. Officer--R.A. Jones & Co. Inc., Covington, KY; *U.S. Private*, pg. 597
Collins, John N., Chief Fin. Officer--The Homestead L.C., Hot Springs, VA; *U.S. Private*, pg. 247
Collins, Julie E., Chief Fin. Officer, Treas. & Sec.--Continental Homes Holding Corp., Scottsdale, AZ; *U.S. Public*, pg. 440
Collins, Julie E., Treas. & Sec.--Continental Homes, Inc., Scottsdale, AZ; *U.S. Public*, pg. 440
Collins, Kenneth J., Chief Fin. Officer & V.P.-Fin. & Admin.--Amgen Boulder, Inc., Boulder, CO; *U.S. Public*, pg. 101
Collins, Michael, Chief Fin. Officer--American Barmag Co., Charlotte, NC; *U.S. Private*, pg. 51
Collins, Roger, Chief Fin. Officer & Exec. V.P.--Harp's Food Stores, Inc., Springdale, AR; *U.S. Private*, pg. 504
Collins, Stephen, Chief Fin. Officer & Controller--Ocean Mist Farms Corp., Castroville, CA; *U.S. Private*, pg. 811
Collinson, J., Chief Fin. Officer--Britax-Excelsior Limited, Andover, United Kingdom; *Int'l*, pg. 216
Collinsworth, William J., Chief Fin. Officer, V.P.-Fin., Treas. & Asst. Sec.--Optek Technology, Inc., Carrollton, TX; *U.S. Public*, pg. 1227
Collova, J. James, Chief Fin. Officer & Sec.--Paper Calmenson & Co., Saint Paul, MN; *U.S. Private*, pg. 837
Collum, Hugh R., Chief Fin. Officer--SmithKline Beecham plc, Brentford, United Kingdom; *Int'l*, pg. 1264
Colonnetta, J.V., Chief Fin. Officer--Triangle Food Services Co., Dallas, TX; *U.S. Private*, pg. 1102
Colraine, Thomas, Chief Fin. Officer--Willis Corroon Group PLC, London, United Kingdom; *Int'l*, pg. 1501
Colraine, Tom, Chief Fin. Officer & Sr. V.P.--Willis Corroon Americas, Nashville, TN; *Int'l*, pg. 1505
Colsteter, John, Chief Fin. Officer--Crown International, Inc., Elkhart, IN; *U.S. Private*, pg. 293
Coltharp, Douglas E., Chief Fin. Officer & Exec. V.P.--Proffitt's, Inc., Alcoa, TN; *U.S. Public*, pg. 1333
Colton, Leonard H., Treas.--Domestic Uniform Rental Co., Farmington Hills, MI; *U.S. Private*, pg. 338
Colwell, Carrie, Chief Fin. Officer--The San Francisco Co., San Francisco, CA; *U.S. Public*, pg. 1430
Comoreia, Ann, Chief Fin. Officer, V.P. & Treas.--Syms Corporation, Secaucus, NJ; *U.S. Public*, pg. 1547
Compfelice, Joseph S., Chief Fin. Officer & V.P.--NL Industries, Inc., Houston, TX; *U.S. Private*, pg. 270
Compofelice, Joseph S., Chief Fin. Officer & V.P.--Tremont Corporation, Denver, CO; *U.S. Private*, pg. 270
Conaway, J. Michael, Chief Fin. Officer & Sr. V.P.--Fluor Corporation, Irvine, CA; *U.S. Public*, pg. 659
Condon, Gary, Chief Fin. Officer--Blue Streak-Hygrade Motor Products Ltd., Mississauga, Canada; *U.S. Public*, pg. 1503
Condon, Robert V., Chief Fin. Officer, V.P.-Fin., Treas. & Sec.--Merrimac Industries, Inc., West Caldwell, NJ; *U.S. Public*, pg. 1098
Condrin, J. Paul, III, Chief Fin. Officer & Sr. V.P.--Liberty Mutual Insurance Co., Boston, MA; *U.S. Private*, pg. 666
Condron, Mark, Chief Fin. Officer--Sunclipse, Inc., Buena Park, CA; *Int'l*, pg. 72
Cone, Stephen, Chief Fin. Officer--Southern Pilot Insurance Company, Greensboro, NC; *Int'l*, pg. 346
Congdon, Jeffrey, Chief Fin. Officer & Sec.--Budget Group, Inc., Daytona Beach, FL; *U.S. Private*, pg. 178
Congdon, Jeffrey, Chief Fin. Officer--Budget Rent A Car Corporation, Lisle, IL; *U.S. Private*, pg. 178
Congiliando, Ernie, Chief Fin. Officer & V.P.--Angelo Brothers Co., Philadelphia, PA; *U.S. Private*, pg. 74
Conklin, Jack, Chief Fin. Officer--Foresight Software, Inc., Atlanta, GA; *U.S. Private*, pg. 872
Conkol, Cliff, Chief Fin. Officer--Kitchen Investment Group, Madison, WI; *U.S. Private*, pg. 624
Conley, Olga L., Chief Fin. Officer--DM Management Company, Hingham, MA; *U.S. Public*, pg. 473
Conley, Paul, Chief Fin. Officer--Starving Students, Inc., Los Angeles, CA; *U.S. Private*, pg. 1035
Conlisk, John, Chief Fin. Officer--Supercuts, Inc., San Francisco, CA; *U.S. Public*, pg. 1373
Connally, John H., Pres., Chief Fin. Officer & Dir.--States, Inc., Breckenridge, TX; *U.S. Private*, pg. 1037
Connelly, Charles J., Chief Fin. Officer, Exec. V.P. & Controller--Dacon Electronics Plc., Hemel Hempstead, United Kingdom; *U.S. Public*, pg. 395
Conner, Frank, Chief Fin. Officer & Exec. V.P.-Acctg.--American Freightways Corporation, Harrison, AR; *U.S. Public*, pg. 75
Conner, Frank, Chief Fin. Officer--American Freightways, Inc., Harrison, AR; *U.S. Public*, pg. 76
Conner, Wayne, Chief Fin. Officer--Elgin National Industries, Inc., Downers Grove, IL; *U.S. Private*, pg. 370
Connolly, D., Chief Fin. Officer--Whittaker Electronic Systems, Simi Valley, CA; *U.S. Public*, pg. 1767
Connolly, John J., Chief Fin. Officer & V.P.--Davox Corp., Westford, MA; *U.S. Public*, pg. 488
Connolly, Paul, Chief Fin. Officer--Thermo Jarrell Ash Corporation, Franklin, MA; *U.S. Public*, pg. 1594
Connor, Robert M., Chief Oper. Officer & Chief Fin. Officer--Amcel Corp., Watertown, MA; *U.S. Private*, pg. 48
Connors, Chester L., Pres. & Chief Fin. Officer--Magneco/Metrel, Inc., Addison, IL; *U.S. Private*, pg. 695
Conrad, Conrad A., Vice Chm. & Chief Fin. Officer--Quaker State Corporation, Irving, TX; *U.S. Public*, pg. 1348
Conradt, Woody, Chief Fin. Officer, Treas. & Sec.--Telsco Industries, Garland, TX; *U.S. Private*, pg. 1074
Conroy, Tim, Chief Fin. Officer--Educational Management Group, Scottsdale, AZ; *U.S. Private*, pg. 778
Constancio, Gail, Chief Fin. Officer--Graphic Packaging Corporation, Wayne, PA; *U.S. Public*, pg. 3
Constantino, C.P. Enrique Vera, Chief Fin. Officer--Tablex, S.A. de C.V., Toluca, Mexico; *Int'l*, pg. 1346
Consul, H., Chief Fin. Officer & V.P.--Siemens S.A., Buenos Aires, Argentina; *Int'l*, pg. 1248
Controneo, Frank J., Chief Fin. Officer--Mastercard International, Inc., Purchase, NY; *U.S. Private*, pg. 714
Conway, Charles C., Chief Fin. Officer & Exec. V.P.--CVS Corp., Woonsocket, RI; *U.S. Public*, pg. 287
Conway, J.W., Sec. & Treas.--Atlas Tag & Label Inc., Neenah, WI; *U.S. Private*, pg. 145
Conway, Jeffrey A., Chief Fin. Officer & V.P.--Rent-Way, Inc., Erie, PA; *U.S. Public*, pg. 1377
Conway, Linda, Chief Fin. Officer--Velcon Filters, Inc., Colorado Springs, CO; *U.S. Private*, pg. 1135
Conwell, Duane, Controller--Carstens Inc., Chicago, IL; *U.S. Private*, pg. 216
Conzemius, Peter, Chief Fin. Officer & V.P.--M.A. Mortenson Company, Minneapolis, MN; *U.S. Private*, pg. 763
Cook, Cary, Chief Fin. Officer & Sr. V.P.--AMCORE Bank N.A., Northwest, Woodstock, IL; *U.S. Public*, pg. 64
Cook, Frederic L., Sr. V.P.-Admin.--Mark IV Industries Inc., Amherst, NY; *U.S. Public*, pg. 1044
Cook, George, Chief Fin. Officer--Maclean-Fogg Co., Mundelein, IL; *U.S. Private*, pg. 692
Cook, Jan, Chief Fin. Officer & Exec. V.P.--Polygram N.V., Baarn, Netherlands; *Int'l*, pg. 1051
Cook, Janet, Chief Fin. Officer--Aerostar International, Sioux Falls, SD; *U.S. Public*, pg. 1361
Cook, Jeffrey T., Chief Fin. Officer & V.P.-Fin.--Penford Corp., Bellevue, WA; *U.S. Public*, pg. 1269
Cook, John R., Chief Fin. Officer & Sr. V.P.--Harcourt General, Inc., Chestnut Hill, MA; *U.S. Public*, pg. 782
Cook, Paul R., Chief Fin. Officer, Exec. V.P. & Treas.--American Consumers, Inc., Fort Oglethorpe, GA; *U.S. Public*, pg. 70
Cook, Randy, Chief Fin. Officer--Nicklaus Golf Company, L.C., West Palm Beach, FL; *U.S. Private*, pg. 799
Cook, Richard, Chief Fin. Officer & Treasurer--Genfoot Inc., Montreal, Canada; *Int'l*, pg. 549
Cook, Richard A., Chief Fin. Officer, Treas. & Sec.--Johanna Foods Inc., Flemington, NJ; *U.S. Private*, pg. 589
Cook, Rosanne, Chief Fin. Officer & Exec. V.P.--Dominick & Dominick, Incorporated, New York, NY; *U.S. Private*, pg. 338
Cook, Troy D., Chief Fin. Officer, V.P.-Fin. & Treas.--NPC International, Inc., Pittsburg, KS; *U.S. Public*, pg. 1146
Cooke, Charles W., Chief Fin. Officer & V.P.--Jennings & Churella Construction Company, Wellington, OH; *U.S. Private*, pg. 586
Cooke, Edward F., Chief Fin. Officer & V.P.--Carlyle Industries, Inc., Carlstadt, NJ; *U.S. Public*, pg. 1187
Cooksey, David C., Chief Fin. Officer, V.P. & Sec.--Contico International, Inc., Saint Louis, MO; *U.S. Private*, pg. 267
Cookson, John S., Chief Fin. Officer, V.P.-Fin., Treas. & Sec.--Kingsbury Corporation, Keene, NH; *U.S. Private*, pg. 621
Cooler, Lamarr, Chief Fin. Officer--Norwegian Cruise Line, Miami, FL; *U.S. Private*, pg. 808
Coombe, John D., Dir.-Fin.--Glaxo Wellcome plc, London, United Kingdom; *Int'l*, pg. 552
Coomer, Ralph, Treas. & Sec.--Ziniz Inc., Louisville, KY; *U.S. Private*, pg. 1206
Cooney, Edward, Chief Fin. Officer, Sr. V.P. & Treas.--Amtrol Inc., West Warwick, RI; *U.S. Private*, pg. 300
Cooper, Bill, Chief Fin. Officer--DIC Entertainment, Burbank, CA; *U.S. Public*, pg. 513
Cooper, David B., Chief Fin. Officer & Exec. V.P.--Edison Brothers Stores, Inc., Saint Louis, MO; *U.S. Public*, pg. 563
Cooper, Geoffrey Ian, Chief Fin. Officer & Dir.-Fin.--Alliance UniChem PLC, Chessington, United Kingdom; *Int'l*, pg. 57

Cooper, J. Michael, Chief Fin. Officer--Noble & Associates, Springfield, MO; *U.S. Private*, pg. 800

Cooper, J. Michael, Chief Fin. Officer--Noble & Associates/ Chicago, Chicago, IL; *U.S. Private*, pg. 800

Cooper, Michael, Chief Fin. Officer--Noble & Associates Promotion Group, Springfield, MO; *U.S. Private*, pg. 800

Cooper, Michael, Chief Fin. Officer--Perdue Farms Incorporated, Salisbury, MD; *U.S. Private*, pg. 852

Cooper, P. Harry, Chief Fin. Officer--Whatman plc, Maidstone, United Kingdom; *Int'l*, pg. 1498

Cooper, Victoria, Fin. Dir.--BST-BDDP, London, United Kingdom; *Int'l*, pg. 117

Cooper, William B., Chief Fin. Officer--Communication Cable, Inc., Sanford, NC; *U.S. Public*, pg. 968

Cooperman, Michael, Chief Fin. Officer, V.P. & Treas.--ICM Holdings Inc., New York, NY; *U.S. Private*, pg. 554

Copeland, E.A., Jr., Dir.-Audits--The Mead Corporation, Dayton, OH; *U.S. Public*, pg. 1074

Coppens, Stu, Chief Fin. Officer--Matthew Bender & Company, Incorporated, New York, NY; *U.S. Public*, pg. 1616

Coppola, K.T., Chief Fin. Officer--Holman Enterprises, Pennsauken, NJ; *U.S. Private*, pg. 535

Copsey, Brian, Chief Fin. Officer--Alpha Omikron Limited, Monaco, Monaco; *Int'l*, pg. 65

Corbett, Michael, Chief Fin. Officer--Sholodge, Inc., Hendersonville, TN; *U.S. Public*, pg. 1467

Corbett, Mike, Exec. V.P.-Opers.--Crane Manufacturing, Cudahy, WI; *U.S. Private*, pg. 286

Corbin, D., Chief Fin. Officer--Eveready Battery Co., Saint Louis, MO; *U.S. Public*, pg. 1360

Corbin, Mac, Chief Fin. Officer--Amite Foundry and Machine, Inc., Amite, LA; *U.S. Public*, pg. 142

Corbin, Richard L., Chief Fin. Officer & Sr. V.P.--Thiokol Corporation, Ogden, UT; *U.S. Public*, pg. 1596

Corbitt, J. Larry, Chief Fin. Officer & Sr. V.P.--United Family Life Insurance Co., Atlanta, GA; *Int'l*, pg. 499

Corcoran, Francis J., Controller--Unisys Finance Corporation, Detroit, MI; *U.S. Public*, pg. 1671

Corcoran, J.F., Chief Fin. Officer & V.P.-Fin.--Grand Trunk Western Railroad, Inc., Detroit, MI; *Int'l*, pg. 258

Corcoran, Trevor, Chief Fin. Officer--Pacific Distribution, Hawthorn, Australia; *Int'l*, pg. 1021

Cordek, Lawrence D., Chief Fin. Officer & Corp. Sec.--G B Stores, Columbus, OH; *U.S. Private*, pg. 972

Corey, Bob L., Chief Fin. Officer & Exec. V.P.-Fin.--SyQuest Technology, Inc., Fremont, CA; *U.S. Public*, pg. 1550

Corigliano, Cosmo, Chief Fin. Officer & Sr. V.P.--Cendant Corporation, Stamford, CT; *U.S. Public*, pg. 320

Corigliano, Cosmo, Chief Fin. Officer & Sr. V.P.--CUC International, Inc., Stamford, CT; *U.S. Public*, pg. 320

Corliss, Dennis, Chief Fin. Officer--Encore Shoe Corporation, Rochester, NH; *U.S. Private*, pg. 375

Corn, Allan, Chief Fin. Officer & Sr. V.P.--Michael Anthony Jewelers, Inc., Mount Vernon, NY; *U.S. Public*, pg. 1103

Corn, Larry, Chief Fin. Officer & V.P.-Corp. Devel.--Manchester Tank & Equipment Company, Brentwood, TN; *U.S. Private*, pg. 699

Cornejo, H.T., Chief Fin. Officer--Osram Argentina S.A.C.I., Buenos Aires, Argentina; *Int'l*, pg. 1244

Cornell, John, Controller--Harris Corp. Broadcast Div., Quincy, IL; *U.S. Public*, pg. 791

Corner, David, Chief Fin. Officer, Treas.--Fleck Manufacturing Inc., Tillsonburg, Canada; *Int'l*, pg. 955

Cornez, Leonard A., Chief Fin. Officer & V.P.--Computalog Ltd., Calgary, Canada; *Int'l*, pg. 325

Cornish, Jeff, Chief Fin. Officer & V.P.--Pilot Corporation, Knoxville, TN; *U.S. Private*, pg. 865

Cornwall, Lyle E., Chief Fin. Officer & Exec. V.P.--Management Dynamics, New Providence, NJ; *U.S. Public*, pg. 1040

Corr, Jim, Controller & Gen. Mgr.--R.J. Corr Naturals, Inc., Posen, IL; *U.S. Private*, pg. 276

Corrado, Fred, Vice Chm. & Chief Fin. Officer--The Great Atlantic & Pacific Tea Company, Inc., Montvale, NJ; *Int'l, pg. 1375*

Correia, Armand, Chief Fin. Officer & Sr. V.P.--The Dress Barn, Inc., Suffern, NY; *U.S. Public*, pg. 528

Corrigan, Wilfred, Treas.--Silicon Power Cube Corporation, San Pedro, CA; *U.S. Private*, pg. 1000

Corsini, Roberto, Chief Fin. Officer--Eurocom Concato di Pace Srl, Milan, Italy; *Int'l*, pg. 603

Cortez, Jose, Chief Fin. Officer--Ebara-Benguet, Inc., Laguna, Philippines; *Int'l*, pg. 187

Corujo, Jose A., Chief Fin. Officer & Exec. V.P.--Puerto Rico Tourism Company, San Juan, PR; *U.S. Private*, pg. 894

Corwin, Daniel K., V.P., Treas. & Gen. Mgr.--Acme Electric Corporation, East Aurora, NY; *U.S. Public*, pg. 16

Corwin, Richard S., Chief Fin. Officer & Exec. V.P.--Adams Business Forms, Topeka, KS; *U.S. Private*, pg. 16

Cosaert, John P., Chief Fin. Officer, Exec. V.P.-Intl. Fin., Treas. & Controller--Heartland Express, Inc., Coralville, IA; *U.S. Public*, pg. 803

Cosh, Nicholas, Chief Fin. Officer--JIB Group plc, London, United Kingdom; *Int'l*, pg. 705

Cosky, Stanley W., Controller--YSD Industries, Youngstown, OH; *U.S. Private*, pg. 1194

Cosmez, Mark, II, Chief Fin. Officer--Giga-Tronics Incorporated, San Ramon, CA; *U.S. Public*, pg. 742

Cossuto, Tom, Chief Fin. Officer--Edwards Baking Co., Norcross, GA; *U.S. Private*, pg. 365

Costales, Thomas M., Chief Fin. Officer & Treas.--AirSensors, Inc., Seattle, WA; *U.S. Public*, pg. 33

Costantini, Lou, Jr., Chief Fin. Officer, V.P., Sec., & Treas.--Century Door U.S.A. Inc., Tampa, FL; *Int'l*, pg. 1067

Costello, Neil, Dir.-Fin.--Frontline, Peterborough, United Kingdom; *Int'l*, pg. 114

Costello, William F., Chief Fin. Officer & Exec. V.P.--QVC, Inc., West Chester, PA; *U.S. Public*, pg. 407

Costello, William F., Chief Fin. Officer & Exec. V.P.--QVC, Inc., West Chester, PA; *U.S. Private*, pg. 897

Costello, William F., Chief Fin. Officer & Exec. V.P.--QVC, Inc., West Chester, PA; *U.S. Public*, pg. 1555

Cote, Richard L., Chief Fin. Officer & Exec. V.P.--Transact Technologies Incorporated, Wallingford, CT; *U.S. Public*, pg. 1629

Cott, Burl G., Chief Fin. Officer & Sr. V.P.--Frozen Food Express Industries, Inc., Dallas, TX; *U.S. Public*, pg. 685

Cotter, Chris, Chief Fin. Officer--Tuttle-Click Automobile Group, Irvine, CA; *U.S. Private*, pg. 1111

Cotton, David L., Chief Fin. Officer--Flying Food Fare, Inc., Chicago, IL; *U.S. Private*, pg. 415

Cotton, Gary, Chief Fin. Officer, V.P.-Fin. & Treas.--Rexall Sundown Inc., Boca Raton, FL; *U.S. Public*, pg. 1384

Cottone, Sam A., Exec. V.P. & Chief Fin. Officer--Eagle Industries, Inc., Chicago, IL; *U.S. Private*, pg. 473

Cottrell, G. Walton, Chief Fin. Officer & Sr. V.P.-Fin.--Carpenter Technology Corporation, Reading, PA; *U.S. Public*, pg. 307

Cottrell, John, Chief Fin. Officer--Gene B. Glick Company, Inc., Indianapolis, IN; *U.S. Private*, pg. 457

Coughlan, Gary, Chief Fin. Officer & Sr. V.P.-Fin.--Abbott Laboratories, Abbott Park, IL; *U.S. Public*, pg. 12

Coughlin, Joseph, Chief Fin. Officer & V.P.--Bermo, Inc., Circle Pines, MN; *U.S. Private*, pg. 136

Coulombe, Paul G., Chief Exec. Officer & Chief Fin. Officer--White Rock Distilleries Inc., Lewiston, ME; *U.S. Private*, pg. 1173

Countryman, Peter J., Chief Fin. Officer & Treas.--Sabin Robbins Paper Co., Cincinnati, OH; *U.S. Private*, pg. 959

Counts, Vaughan, Chief Fin. Officer--Chemical Exchange Industries, Houston, TX; *U.S. Private*, pg. 232

Courtade, Auguste, Chief Fin. Officer--Societe de Transmissions Automatiques, Barlin, France; *Int'l*, pg. 1102

Cousino, Ron, Chief Fin. Officer--Freedom Textiles Chemicals Co., Charlotte, NC; *U.S. Private*, pg. 425

Couto, Terry, Chief Fin. Officer & Sr. V.P.--Citizens Mortgage Corporation, Atlanta, GA; *Int'l*, pg. 1132

Covert, Jim, Controller--Crescent Genlyte, Barrington, NJ; *U.S. Public*, pg. 730

Covey, Joy D., Chief Fin. Officer, V.P.-Fin., Treas. & Sec.--Amazon.com, Inc., Seattle, WA; *U.S. Public*, pg. 62

Covington, Michael, Chief Fin. Officer--Radio One Inc., Lanham, MD; *U.S. Private*, pg. 906

Cowan, Richard, Chief Fin. Officer, Treas., Controller & Sec.--Wheeler Brothers Grain Co., Watonga, OK; *U.S. Private*, pg. 1171

Cowell, Steven S., Chief Fin. Officer & Corp. V.P.--Agouron Pharmaceuticals, Inc., La Jolla, CA; *U.S. Public*, pg. 28

Cowen, Morrisson, Fin. Dir.--Riley Advertising (Scotland) Ltd., Glasgow, United Kingdom; *Int'l*, pg. 1117

Cowles, Alfred L., III, Chief Fin. Officer, Treas. & Controller--Bluff City Distributing Co., Inc., Memphis, TN; *U.S. Private*, pg. 153

Cox, Charles, Pres. & Chief Fin. Officer--Cox Furniture, Maxton, NC; *U.S. Private*, pg. 283

Cox, Dennis, Controller, Asst. Sec. & Treas.--McGill Manufacturing Company, Inc., Valparaiso, IN; *U.S. Public*, pg. 573

Cox, Douglas, Chief Fin. Officer & Sr. V.P.-Fin.--Elf Atochem North America, Inc., Philadelphia, PA; *Int'l*, pg. 445

Cox, F. Kim, Chief Fin. Officer & Exec. V.P.--Rentrak Corporation, Portland, OR; *U.S. Public*, pg. 1377

Cox, Jeff, Chief Fin. Officer--Ansell International, Glen Waverley, Australia; *Int'l*, pg. 1021

Cox, Jerry, Chief Fin. Officer--Advance Seed Co., Fulton, KY; *Int'l*, pg. 566

Cox, Kenneth A., Jr., Chief Fin. Officer & V.P.--Papa Gino's Inc., Dedham, MA; *U.S. Private*, pg. 837

Cox, Lamar, Chief Fin. Officer & Exec. V.P.--NationsBank of Tennessee, Nashville, TN; *U.S. Public*, pg. 1163

Cox, N. G., Grp. Dir.-Fin.--South African Breweries, Ltd., Johannesburg, South Africa; *Int'l*, pg. 1286

Cox, Peter G.M., Chief Fin. Officer--United Grain Growers Ltd., Winnipeg, Canada; *Int'l*, pg. 1442

Cox, R.J., Chief Fin. Officer--Kidde Thorn Fire Protection Limited, Oldham, United Kingdom; *Int'l*, pg. 1500

Cox, Thomas L., Chief Fin. Officer--Field Container Company, L.P., Elk Grove Village, IL; *U.S. Private*, pg. 403

Cox, Thomas P., Sr. V.P.-Fin., Sec. & Treas.--Timberline Software Corporation, Beaverton, OR; *U.S. Public*, pg. 1609

Coxson, Timothy C., Chief Fin. Officer, Treas. & Exec. V.P.-Fin.--American Waste Services, Inc., Warren, OH; *U.S. Public*, pg. 94

Coyle, Kevin P., Chief Fin. Officer & Grp. V.P.-Fin.--Jones Intercable, Inc., Englewood, CO; *U.S. Private*, pg. 597

Cozadd, Bruce, Chief Fin. Officer & Sr. V.P.--Alza Corporation, Palo Alto, CA; *U.S. Public*, pg. 62

Craft, Mike, Chief Fin. Officer & V.P.-Admin.--Provident Music Group, Brentwood, TN; *Int'l*, pg. 1529

Craft, Mike, Chief Fin. Officer & V.P.-Admin.--Provident Music Distribution, Nashville, TN; *Int'l*, pg. 1529

Cragg, Bernard, Chief Fin. Officer & Dir.-Strategy & Devel.--Carlton Communications Plc, London, United Kingdom; *Int'l*, pg. 272

Craig, David T., Chief Fin. Officer & Sec.--Australia & New Zealand Banking Group Limited, Melbourne, Australia; *Int'l*, pg. 98

Craig, David W., Chief Fin. Officer & V.P.--Convex Technology Center - Hewlett-Packard, Richardson, TX; *U.S. Public*, pg. 815

Craig, John J., Chief Fin. Officer--Midland National Life Insurance Co., Sioux Falls, SD; *U.S. Private*, pg. 963

Craig, Paul, Chief Fin. Officer, Exec. V.P. & Treas.--Pac Rim Holding Corporation, Woodland Hills, CA; *U.S. Public*, pg. 1246

Craig, Tom, Chief Fin. Officer--Wagner Spray Tech Corp., Plymouth, MN; *U.S. Private*, pg. 1146

Craigmile, Cindy, Chief Fin. Officer & V.P.--Downey Printing, Waukee, IA; *U.S. Private*, pg. 342

Cramb, Charles W., Chief Fin. Officer--The Gillette Company, Boston, MA; *U.S. Public*, pg. 743

Cramer, Carl, Chief Fin. Officer & V.P.-Fin.--Brush Wellman Inc., Cleveland, OH; *U.S. Public*, pg. 266

Cramm, C. Brian, Chief Fin. Officer & V.P.-Fin.--Dakota Mining Corporation, Denver, CO; *U.S. Public*, pg. 477

Crandall, L. Dale, Chief Fin. Officer, Exec. V.P. & Treas.--APL Limited, Oakland, CA; *Int'l*, pg. 912

Crane, David W., Chief Fin. Officer & V.P.--Crane & Co., Inc., Dalton, MA; *U.S. Private*, pg. 286

Craothers, Robert, Chief Fin. Officer--Quest Diagnostics, Inc., Teterboro, NJ; *U.S. Public*, pg. 1351

Crawford, John K., Chief Fin. Officer, V.P. & Treas.--Phycor, Inc., Nashville, TN; *U.S. Public*, pg. 1293

Creekmuir, William S., Chief Fin. Officer, Exec. V.P., Treas. & Sec.--Ladd Furniture, Inc., Greensboro, NC; *U.S. Public*, pg. 974

Creel, L. Anderson, Chief Fin. Officer, Sr. V.P., Treas. & Sec.--Prime Bancshares Inc., Houston, TX; *U.S. Public*, pg. 1326

Cregg, Roger, III, Chief Fin. Officer & Exec. V.P.--Zenith Electronics Corp., Glenview, IL; *U.S. Public*, pg. 1790

Cresenzi, L., V.P.-Fin. & Admin.--Fiatallis North America, Inc., Carol Stream, IL; *Int'l*, pg. 483

Cress, Sally, Treas. & Sec.--Bancinsurance Corp., Columbus, OH; *U.S. Public*, pg. 175

Crews, Hilliard, Chm. Bd., Pres., Chief Exec. & Chief Fin. Officer--Shelby Group International, Inc., Memphis, TN; *U.S. Private*, pg. 991

Crews, J. Russell, Chief Fin. Officer, Sr. V.P. & Treas.--Snelling Personnel Services, Dallas, TX; *U.S. Private*, pg. 1010

Crews, Roger, Chief Fin. Officer--Creative Alliance, Inc., Louisville, KY; *U.S. Private*, pg. 287

Crewse, Leonardo L., Dir.-Fin.--Varco-Pruden Buildings, Memphis, TN; *U.S. Public*, pg. 1677

Cribbs, Francis J., Exec. V.P., Chief Fin. Officer & Treas.--Lloyd Properties, Los Angeles, CA; *U.S. Private*, pg. 672

Crider, Steve, Chief Fin. Officer--Wood Equipment Company, Oregon, IL; *U.S. Private*, pg. 1186

Cripe, Richard L., Treas. & Controller--Gohmann Asphalt & Construction of KY., Inc., Louisville, KY; *U.S. Private*, pg. 459

Criscillis, Paul A., Jr., Chief Fin. Officer & V.P.-Fin.--Crown Crafts, Inc., Atlanta, GA; *U.S. Public*, pg. 465

Crisman, Craig D., Chm. Bd., Pres., Chief Exec. & Fin. Officer--Applied Magnetics Corporation, Goleta, CA; *U.S. Public*, pg. 123

Criste, Robert M., Chief Fin. Officer, V.P. & Treas.--Stephenson Equipment, Inc., Harrisburg, PA; *U.S. Private*, pg. 1040

Crneckiy, Martin, Jr., Chief Fin. Officer & Exec. V.P.--The Vollrath Company, L.L.C., Sheboygan, WI; *U.S. Private*, pg. 1143

Croal, Thomas V., Chief Fin. Officer, V.P. & Sec.--Insight Health Services Corp., Newport Beach, CA; *U.S. Public*, pg. 880

Crocker, Derwood, Chief Fin. Officer, V.P.-Fin. & Treas.--ScanTron Corporation, Tustin, CA; *U.S. Public*, pg. 786

Crocker, Frederick G., Jr., Chief Fin. Officer, V.P., Treas. & Sec.--Springborn Testing & Research, Inc., Enfield, CT; *U.S. Private*, pg. 1027

Crofton, James, Chief Fin. Officer--EA Industries, West Long Branch, NJ; *U.S. Public*, pg. 541

Crofton, James, Chief Fin. Officer--Tanon Manufacturing, Inc., West Long Branch, NJ; *U.S. Public*, pg. 541

Cromar, Michael, Chief Fin. Officer & V.P.--GATX Capital Corporation, San Francisco, CA; *U.S. Public*, pg. 690

Cromeek, Henry, Chief Fin. Officer & Exec. V.P.-Fin.--Artco-Bell Corporation, Temple, TX; *U.S. Private*, pg. 86

Cromer, Vicki, Chief Fin. Officer & Treas.--Bayou State Oil Corporation, Shreveport, LA; *U.S. Private*, pg. 125

Cronan, James E., Chief Fin. Officer & Sr. V.P.--Harvey Industries, Inc., Waltham, MA; *U.S. Private*, pg. 508

Cronin, Jack, Chief Fin. Officer--Industrial Ceramics, Inc., Lima, NY; *U.S. Private*, pg. 560

Cronin, James P., Chief Fin. Officer & Exec. V.P.--Cytec Industries Inc., West Paterson, NJ; *U.S. Public*, pg. 471

Cronin, John W., Chief Fin. Officer & V.P.-Fin.--Suitt Construction Company, Inc., Greenville, SC; *U.S. Private, pg. 106*

Cronin, Patrick, V.P.-Fin.--Delta Consolidated Industries, Inc. (Co. Headquarters), Jonesboro, AR; *U.S. Public*, pg. 481

Cronin, Richard J., III, Chief Fin. Officer & Sr. V.P.--Sithe Energies, Inc., New York, NY; *U.S. Private*, pg. 1004

Cronje, M., Sec. & Treas.--Timken South Africa Proprietary Ltd., Transvaal, South Africa; *U.S. Public*, pg. 1618

Crooks, Steve, Chief Fin. Officer--Metropolitan Mortgage & Securities Co., Inc., Spokane, WA; *U.S. Private*, pg. 738

Crookshank, George A., Chief Fin. Officer & V.P.-Fin.--Ocelot Energy Inc., Calgary, Canada; *Int'l*, pg. 996

Cropper, Karen, Chief Fin. Officer, V.P. & Controller--Theodore Barry & Associates, Los Angeles, CA; *U.S. Private*, pg. 118

Crosbie, Geoffrey L., Chief Fin. Officer--R & B Machine Tool Co., Saline, MI; *U.S. Private*, pg. 901

Cross, D., Chief Fin. Officer--Butler Newall Limited-Butler Machine Tool Div., Halifax, United Kingdom; *Int'l*, pg. 448

Cross, Eugene P., Chief Fin. Officer & Exec. V.P.-Fin.--Flowserve Corporation, Long Beach, CA; *U.S. Public*, pg. 658

Cross, John, Chief Fin. Officer & V.P.--Burris Foods, Inc., Milford, DE; *U.S. Private*, pg. 188

Crosson, Jeff, Chief Fin. Officer & V.P.-Fin.--Sterling Electric, Inc., Irvine, CA; *U.S. Private*, pg. 1041

Crosswhite, Randal, Chief Fin. Officer & Sr. V.P.--Independent Bankshares, Inc., Abilene, TX; *U.S. Public*, pg. 874

Crotty, Thomas, Chief Fin. Officer--Welsbach Electric Corp., College Point, NY; *U.S. Public*, pg. 572

Crouthamel, Michael R., Chief Fin. Officer & Treas.--John Solomon, Inc., Somerville, MA; *U.S. Private*, pg. 1013

Crowder, William L., Chief Fin. Officer & V.P.-Fin.--Hub Group, Inc., Lombard, IL; *U.S. Public*, pg. 844

Crowe, Kenneth, Chief Fin. Officer--Mann Theatres, Encino, CA; *U.S. Private*, pg. 239
Crowley, David, Chief Fin. Officer--Hedstrom Holding Co., Mount Prospect, IL; *U.S. Private*, pg. 526
Crowley, David, Chief Fin. Officer--ERO, Inc., Mount Prospect, IL; *U.S. Private*, pg. 526
Crowley, David, Chief Fin. Officer--ERO Industries, Inc., Mount Prospect, IL; *U.S. Private*, pg. 526
Crowley, Francis E., Chief Fin. Officer & Sr. V.P.--Cargill Salt Inc., Minneapolis, MN; *Int'l*, pg. 48
Crowley, James, Chief Fin. Officer--High Industries, Inc., Lancaster, PA; *U.S. Private*, pg. 528
Crowley, John J., Chief Fin. Officer & V.P.--Scope Industries, Santa Monica, CA; *U.S. Public*, pg. 1444
Crowley, Patrick, Chief Fin. Officer & Exec. V.P.--Abitibi-Consolidated Inc., Montreal, Canada; *Int'l*, pg. 19
Crowne, Joseph E., Chief Fin. Officer--Merrill Lynch Insurance Group, Inc., Plainsboro, NJ; *U.S. Public*, pg. 1098
Crownshaw, Stephen, Dir.-Fin.--Meristem plc, Wetherby, United Kingdom; *Int'l*, pg. 858
Crozier, Robert, V.P. & Chief Fin. Officer--Acousti Engineering Co. of Florida, Orlando, FL; *U.S. Private*, pg. 14
Crudele, Anthony, Chief Fin. Officer & Sr. V.P.--The Sports Authority Inc., Fort Lauderdale, FL; *U.S. Public*, pg. 1499
Cruickshank, D.J., Chief Fin. Officer & Sr. V.P.--Flexible Products Company, Marietta, GA; *U.S. Private*, pg. 412
Crum, David H., Pres., Chief Exec. & Chief Fin. Officer--Crum Electric Supply Co., Inc., Casper, WY; *U.S. Private, pg. 293*
Crumley, Ted, Chief Fin. Officer & V.P.--Boise Cascade Corporation, Boise, ID; *U.S. Public*, pg. 242
Crumlish, James P., Chief Fin. Officer & V.P.--Saab Automobile AB, Nykoping, Sweden; *Int'l*, pg. 687
Crumlish, James P., Chief Fin. Officer & V.P.--Saab Automobile AB, Nykoping, Sweden; *U.S. Public*, pg. 725
Crumlish, Jim, Dir.-Fin.--GM Powertrain Group, Pontiac, MI; *U.S. Public*, pg. 719
Crumlish, Jim, Chief Fin. Officer--White Rock Products Corp., Whitestone, NY; *U.S. Private*, pg. 1173
Crump, Terry, Chief Fin. Officer & V.P.-Fin.--O'Sullivan Industries Holdings, Lamar, MO; *U.S. Public*, pg. 1234
Crump, Tom, Chief Fin. Officer & Controller--Heilig Meyers Furniture Co., Richmond, VA; *U.S. Public*, pg. 804
Cruz, Lamberto, Mng. Partner, Chief Fin. Officer & Admin. Services--Fova, Inc., New York, NY; *U.S. Public*, pg. 764
Crvarich, Gene, Chief Fin. Officer, V.P., Treas. & Sec.--Al Larson Boat Shop, Inc., Terminal Island, CA; *U.S. Private*, pg. 652
Cryder, Jeffrey A., Chief Fin. Officer--Bliss-Salem, Inc., Salem, OH; *U.S. Private*, pg. 149
Cuddihy, Robert V., Jr., Chief Oper. Officer, & Chief Fin. Officer--H.M.G. Worldwide Corp., New York, NY; *U.S. Public*, pg. 771
Cudney, Cori, Chief Fin. Officer, V.P.-Fin. & Treas.--A. Levy & J. Zentner Co., Sacramento, CA; *U.S. Private*, pg. 663
Cudzewicz, Alexander J., Dir.-Fin.--Sargent & Lundy, Chicago, IL; *U.S. Private*, pg. 965
Cullinane, Michael P., Chief Fin. Officer, Exec. V.P. & Treas.--Platinum Technology, Inc., Oak Brook Terrace, IL; *U.S. Public*, pg. 1309
Culliton, Edward F., Chief Fin. Officer & V.P.--A.M. Castle & Co., Franklin Park, IL; *U.S. Public*, pg. 312
Culp, David G., Controller--Knoll Intl., Inc., East Greenville, PA; *U.S. Private*, pg. 627
Culver, Earl, Chief Fin. Officer--Chiron Vision, Irvine, CA; *U.S. Public*, pg. 350
Culver, Larry G., Chief Oper. & Fin. Officer & Exec. V.P.--CellPro, Incorporated, Bothell, WA; *U.S. Public*, pg. 320
Culver, Robert L., Chief Fin. Officer--Cabot Corporation, Boston, MA; *U.S. Public*, pg. 288
Cuming, David B., Sr. V.P.--Alleghany Corporation, New York, NY; *U.S. Public*, pg. 42
Cummings, Beverly A., Chief Fin. Officer & Treas.--PrimeEnergy Corporation, Stamford, CT; *U.S. Public*, pg. 1328
Cummings, Donald C., Chief Fin. Officer--Quality Bakers of America Cooperative, Inc., Greenwich, CT; *U.S. Private*, pg. 898
Cummings, Ian, Chief Fin. Officer-U.K.--Diversified Agency Services, New York, NY; *U.S. Public*, pg. 1223
Cummings, Marquis L., Chief Fin. Officer--Capital Pacific Holdings, Newport Beach, CA; *U.S. Public*, pg. 302
Cummings, Marquis L., Chief Fin. Officer--J.M. Peters Co., Newport Beach, CA; *U.S. Public*, pg. 302
Cunningham, J. Dawson, V.P.-Fin. & Admin. & Treas.--Roadway Express, Inc., Akron, OH; *U.S. Public*, pg. 1392
Cunningham, John P., Chief Fin. Officer & Exec. V.P.--Whirlpool Corporation, Benton Harbor, MI; *U.S. Public*, pg. 1764
Cunningham, Kathleen J., Chief Oper. Officer, Chief Fin. Officer & Sec.--NxTrend Technology, Inc., Colorado Springs, CO; *U.S. Private*, pg. 809
Cunningham, Timothy J., V.P.-Fin.--British Steel, Inc., Schaumburg, IL; *Int'l*, pg. 221
Cupp, Frank, Treas.--Smith Frozen Foods, Inc., Weston, OR; *U.S. Private*, pg. 1008
Curci, John, Chief Fin. Officer & Treas.--Arrowhead Holding Corporation, Brecksville, OH; *U.S. Private*, pg. 86
Curci, John, Chief Fin. Officer & Treas.--Vesper Corporation, Brecksville, OH; *U.S. Private*, pg. 86
Curci, Joseph E., Chief Fin. Officer--A. Finkl & Sons Co., Chicago, IL; *U.S. Private*, pg. 405
Curciarello, Gerry, Chief Fin. Officer--Landau & Heyman Inc., Chicago, IL; *U.S. Private*, pg. 646
Curley, Denis M., Chief Fin. Officer, Sr. V.P., Treas. & Sec.--The Ackerley Group, Seattle, WA; *U.S. Public*, pg. 15
Curran, Stephen H., Chief Fin. Officer & Exec. V.P.--Primark Corporation, Waltham, MA; *U.S. Public*, pg. 1325
Curran, William, Chief Fin. Officer & Exec. V.P.--Philips Electronics North America Corporation, New York, NY; *Int'l*, pg. 1053
Currie, John, Mgr.-Bus.--Seattle Post-Intelligencer, Seattle, WA; *U.S. Private*, pg. 517
Currie, Peter, Chief Fin. Officer, Chief Admin. Officer & Exec. V.P.--Netscape Communications Corp., Mountain View, CA; *U.S. Public*, pg. 1168
Currie, Peter L.S., Chief Fin. Officer & Sr. V.P.--AT&T Wireless Services, Kirkland, WA; *U.S. Public*, pg. 11
Currie, Peter W., Chief Fin. Officer & Sr. V.P.--Northern Telecom Limited, Brampton, Canada; *Int'l*, pg. 968
Currier, Jeffrey, Chief Fin. Officer & Exec. V.P.-Fin.--Empire of Carolina, Inc., Delray Beach, FL; *U.S. Public*, pg. 579
Currier, Jeffrey L., Sr. V.P.-Fin.--FKI Industries, Inc., Fairfield, CT; *Int'l*, pg. 472
Currier, Kevin E., Chief Fin. Officer--Dimeo Construction Company, Providence, RI; *U.S. Private*, pg. 333
Curry, Jeffrey, Chief Fin. Officer & Sec.--Kenworth of Indianapolis Inc., Indianapolis, IN; *U.S. Private*, pg. 615
Curry, John C., Chief Fin. Officer & V.P.--Continental General Tire, Inc., Charlotte, NC; *Int'l*, pg. 327
Curson, R. John, Chief Fin. Officer, Sr. V.P.-Fin. & Sec.--Truevision, Inc., Santa Clara, CA; *U.S. Public*, pg. 1642
Curtas, William W., Chief Exec., Chief Oper. & Chief Fin. Officer & Exec. V.P.--Steego Corporation, West Palm Beach, FL; *Int'l*, pg. 216
Curtin, Dennis J., Chief Fin. Officer & V.P.-Fin.--E-Z-Em, Inc., Westbury, NY; *U.S. Public*, pg. 540
Curtis, Daniel, Chief Fin. Officer & V.P.--Andover Controls, Andover, MA; *U.S. Private*, pg. 73
Curtis, Harold R., Chief Fin. Officer, Sr. V.P., Treas. & Sec.--The M/A/R/C Group, Irving, TX; *U.S. Public*, pg. 1022
Curtiss, Jeff, Chief Fin. Officer & Sr. V.P.--Browning-Ferris Industries, Inc., Houston, TX; *U.S. Public*, pg. 262
Curwen, Richard, Chief Fin. Officer & Exec. V.P.--Appleton Papers Inc., Appleton, WI; *Int'l*, pg. 567
Curwin, Ronald, Chief Fin. Officer & Treas.--Bed Bath & Beyond Inc., Union, NJ; *U.S. Public*, pg. 200
Cusano, Sam, Chief Fin. Officer & Exec.V.P.--Service Merchandise Company, Inc., Brentwood, TN; *U.S. Public, pg. 1461*
Cushing, Robert T., Chief Fin. Officer--TrustCo Bank Corp., NY, Schenectady, NY; *U.S. Public*, pg. 1643
Cushing, Robert T., Chief Fin. Officer & Sr. V.P.--Trustco Bank, N.A., Schenectady, NY; *U.S. Public*, pg. 1643
Cutillas, Eduardo, Chief Fin. Officer--Bacardi Limited, Pembroke, Bermuda; *Int'l*, pg. 131
Cutler, David, Chief Fin. Officer--Emess PLC, London, United Kingdom; *Int'l*, pg. 453
Cutrali, A., V.P.-Fin.--B/E Aerospace Seating Products Group, Litchfield, CT; *U.S. Public*, pg. 159
Cutwright, Brenda F., Chief Fin. Officer, Sr. V.P.-Fin. & Treas.--Aloha Airgroup, Inc., Honolulu, HI; *U.S. Private*, pg. 44
Cutwright, Brenda F., Chief Fin. Officer & Sr. V.P.-Fin. & Plng.--Island Air, Honolulu, HI; *U.S. Private*, pg. 44
Cuypers, Yves, Chief Fin. Officer--Herstal S.A., Herstal, Belgium; *Int'l*, pg. 617
Cybulski, James M., Controller & Treas.--American National Property & Casualty Co., Springfield, MO; *U.S. Public*, pg. 87
Cyranoski, David L., Sr. V.P., Controller & Sec.--NICOR Inc., Naperville, IL; *U.S. Public*, pg. 1182
Czaja, Kenneth A., Chief Fin. Officer, V.P.-Fin. & Sec.--Intellicorp Inc., Mountain View, CA; *U.S. Public*, pg. 887
Czarnuszewski, J.A., Chief Fin. Officer--Cuprinol Limited, Frome, United Kingdom; *Int'l*, pg. 1501
D'Aguiar, J.M., V.P.-Fin.--Ranger Oil Limited, Calgary, Canada; *Int'l*, pg. 1086
D'Alton, Paul, Grp. Chief Fin. Officer--Bank of Ireland, Dublin, Ireland; *Int'l*, pg. 152
D'Amelio, Yvonne, Principal & Chief Fin. Officer--Vox Medica Corporation, Philadelphia, PA; *U.S. Private*, pg. 1143
D'Angelo, Peter R., Chief Fin. Officer & Exec. V.P.--Raytheon Company, Lexington, MA; *U.S. Public*, pg. 1364
D'Onofrio, Joseph, Chief Fin. Officer & V.P.-Sls.--My Own Meals, Inc., Deerfield, IL; *U.S. Private*, pg. 770
Dabbs, Karl, V.P.-Fin.--B.A.S.S., Inc., Montgomery, AL; *U.S. Private*, pg. 105
Dabbs, Karl, Chief Fin. Officer--Fishing Tackle Retailer, Montgomery, AL; *U.S. Private*, pg. 105
Dabney, Thomas W., Chief Fin. Officer & V.P.--The Flexitallic Group, Inc., Houston, TX; *U.S. Private*, pg. 413
Daddario, Richard, Chief Fin. Officer & Exec. V.P.--The Mutual Life Insurance Company of New York, New York, NY; *U.S. Private*, pg. 769
Daddino, Anthony F., Chief Fin. Officer & Exec. V.P.--Donaldson, Lufkin, & Jenrette, Inc., New York, NY; *U.S. Public*, pg. 589
Daffin, Alton, Chief Fin. Officer--Cleo Inc., Memphis, TN; *U.S. Public*, pg. 284
Dagley, Larry J., Chief Fin. Officer & Exec. V.P.--Atmos Energy Corporation, Dallas, TX; *U.S. Public*, pg. 145
Daher, Thomas, Chief Fin. Officer & Exec. V.P.--Motch Corporation, Cleveland, OH; *Int'l*, pg. 1128
Dahl, Erik, V.P.-Fin.--Radiometer A/S, Bronshoj, Denmark; *Int'l*, pg. 1083
Dahlen, Keith, Chief Fin. Officer & V.P.-Fin.--Sico Incorporated, Edina, MN; *U.S. Private*, pg. 997
Dahlseid, Janet, Controller--American Natural Snacks, Saint Augustine, FL; *Int'l*, pg. 752
Dahly, John H., Chief Fin. Officer, Exec. V.P. & Sec.--Schultz Sav-O Stores, Inc., Sheboygan, WI; *U.S. Public*, pg. 1442
Daiker, John, Chief Fin. Officer--Simmons Company, Atlanta, GA; *Int'l*, pg. 686
Dailey, Bill, Chief Fin. Officer--Heckethorn Mfg. Company, Inc., Dyersburg, TN; *U.S. Private*, pg. 519
Dailey, Jan, Treas.--Seaman Timber Company, Inc., Montevallo, AL; *U.S. Private*, pg. 979
Dailey, Jeff, Chief Fin. Officer--Ransomes-Cushman-Ryan, Lincoln, NE; *Int'l*, pg. 1088
Dailey, Jeff, Chief Fin. Officer--Ransomes Inc., Johnson Creek, WI; *Int'l*, pg. 1088
Dailey, John, Chief Fin. Officer--Bear Creek Corporation, Medford, OR; *Int'l*, pg. 1518
Dakes, Robert, Chief Fin. Officer--Gould Instrument Systems, Inc., Valley View, OH; *U.S. Public*, pg. 1592
Dalbeck, Richard W., Exec. V.P., Chief Fin. Officer & Sec.--The Guber Peters Entertainment Company, Los Angeles, CA; *Int'l*, pg. 1283
Dale, J., Chief Fin. Officer--The Games, Eastleigh, United Kingdom; *Int'l*, pg. 707
Dales, Alstair, Chief Fin. Officer--Nationwide Building Society, Swindon, United Kingdom; *Int'l*, pg. 912
Daley, Michael R., Chief Fin. Officer & Exec. V.P.--ACC Corp., Rochester, NY; *U.S. Public*, pg. 2
Daley, Vincent, Chief Fin. Officer & V.P.--Guideposts Associates, Inc., Carmel, NY; *U.S. Private*, pg. 487
Dalinger, Trudy, Chief Fin. Officer & Sr. V.P.--TSC Shannock Corporation, Burnaby, Canada; *Int'l*, pg. 1343
Dalinger, Trudy, Chief Fin. Officer--TSC Shannock Corporation, Don Mills, Canada; *Int'l*, pg. 1343
Dalinger, Trudy, Chief Fin. Officer--TSC Shannock Corporation, Dartmouth, Canada; *Int'l*, pg. 1343
Dalinger, Trudy, Chief Fin. Officer--TSC Shannock Corporation, Saskatoon, Canada; *Int'l*, pg. 1343
Dalinger, Trudy, Chief Fin. Officer--TSC Shannock Corporation, Mississauga, Canada; *Int'l*, pg. 1343
Dalinger, Trudy, Chief Fin. Officer--TSC Shannock Corporation, Edmonton, Canada; *Int'l*, pg. 1343
Dalke, Gary, Chief Fin. Officer--Phoenix Fuel Company, Inc., Phoenix, AZ; *U.S. Private*, pg. 863
Dallacqua, John, Chief Fin. Officer, V.P.-Fin., Treas. & Sec.--Crowley, Milner & Company, Detroit, MI; *U.S. Public*, pg. 461
Dallacqua, John R., Chief Fin. Officer & V.P.--Steinbach Stores, Inc., Detroit, MI; *U.S. Public*, pg. 461
Dalrymple, Cheryl, V.P. & Chief Fin. Officer--LEXIS-NEXIS, Miamisburg, OH; *Int'l*, pg. 1096
Dalton, Richard J., Chief Fin. Officer & V.P.--Colorado Business Bankshares, Inc., Denver, CO; *U.S. Private*, pg. 255
Daly, Charles F., Chief Fin. Officer & V.P.--Millennium Petrochemicals, Inc., Cincinnati, OH; *Int'l*, pg. 594
Daly, Kathleen C., V.P.-Fin. & Admin.--Frank Messer & Sons Construction Co., Cincinnati, OH; *U.S. Private*, pg. 734
Dambach, Peter, V.P.-Fin.--Electro-Biology, Inc., Guaynabo, PR; *U.S. Public*, pg. 231
Dambrowski, Juergen, V.P.-Fin. & Admin.--Robert Bosch Fluid Power Corporation, Racine, WI; *Int'l*, pg. 204
Dammerman, Dennis D., Chief Fin. Officer--General Electric Company, Fairfield, CT; *U.S. Public*, pg. 709
Daneilson, Gilbert L., Chief Fin. Officer, V.P.-Fin. & Dir.-Investor Rels.--Aaron Rents, Inc., Atlanta, GA; *U.S. Public*, pg. 12
Daniel, James R., Chief Fin. Officer & Sr. V.P.--MicroAge, Inc., Tempe, AZ; *U.S. Public*, pg. 1104
Daniel, Richard, Chief Fin. Officer & Mng. Dir.--Bankers Trust Company, New York, NY; *U.S. Public*, pg. 185
Daniel, Richard H., Chief Fin. Officer & Exec. V.P.--Bankers Trust New York Corporation, New York, NY; *U.S. Public, pg. 185*
Daniels, George A., Chief Fin. Officer & V.P.--Zero Corporation, Los Angeles, CA; *U.S. Public*, pg. 1791
Danielson, Kenneth L., Chief Fin. Officer & Treas.--Sound Advice, Inc., Dania, FL; *U.S. Public*, pg. 1488
Danko, Douglas B., Chief Fin. Officer & Sec.--Stabler Companies, Inc., Harrisburg, PA; *U.S. Private*, pg. 1028
Dann, Diane, Chief Fin. Officer--Eastman Worldwide, Buffalo, NY; *U.S. Private*, pg. 358
Dannelly, Robert B., Sr., Chief Fin. Officer, V.P.-Fin. & Controller--Piedmont Mechanical, Inc., Spartanburg, SC; *U.S. Private*, pg. 865
Danner, Donald, Chief Fin. Officer & V.P.--Johnson & Quin, Inc., Niles, IL; *U.S. Private*, pg. 590
Danner, E.L., Chief Fin. Officer & Sr. V.P.--MidCon Corp., Lombard, IL; *U.S. Public*, pg. 1210
Danner, E.L., Chief Fin. Officer--Natural Gas Pipeline Co. America, Lombard, IL; *U.S. Public*, pg. 1210
Danner, E.L., Chief Fin. Officer & V.P.--MidCon Texas Pipeline Operator, Inc., Houston, TX; *U.S. Public*, pg. 1210
Danner, E.L., Chief Fin. Officer--MidCon Gas Services Corp., Houston, TX; *U.S. Public*, pg. 1210
Danner, E.L., Chief Fin. Officer & V.P.--MC2 Inc., Lombard, IL; *U.S. Public*, pg. 1210
Danner, E.L., Chief Fin. Officer & V.P.--MidCon Gas Products Corp., Houston, TX; *U.S. Public*, pg. 1210
Danowa, Paul, Sr. V.P. & Chief Fin. Officer--Del Monte Foods International Limited, Staines, United Kingdom; *Int'l*, pg. 388
Dantzler, Larry W., Chief Fin. Officer & Sr. V.P.--International Family Entertainment, Inc., Virginia Beach, VA; *Int'l*, pg. 927
Darak, Steven, Chief Fin. Officer--Ugly Duckling Corp., Phoenix, AZ; *U.S. Public*, pg. 1662
Darby, Geoffrey C., Chief Fin. Officer--Visioneer, Inc., Fremont, CA; *U.S. Public*, pg. 1722
Darden, J., Chief Fin. Officer & Sr. V.P.--GAB Robins North America, Inc., Parsippany, NJ; *Int'l*, pg. 1153
DaRin, Gabe, Chief Fin. Officer--Heidelberg Finishing Systems, Dayton, OH; *Int'l*, pg. 604
Darlington, Steven, Chief Fin. Officer--British Building & Engineering Appliances Plc, Sandy, United Kingdom; *Int'l*, pg. 219
Darretta, Robert J., V.P. & Treas.--Johnson & Johnson, New Brunswick, NJ; *U.S. Public*, pg. 927
Darrow, Chris, Chief Fin. Officer & Sr. V.P.--Western Beef, Inc., Ridgewood, NY; *U.S. Public*, pg. 1758
Dartis, Chuck, Chief Fin. Officer--CNB International, L.L.C., Charleston, SC; *U.S. Private*, pg. 196
Date, Y., Chief Fin. Officer--Tanabe U.S.A. Inc., Woodcliff Lake, NJ; *Int'l*, pg. 1354
Dathe, Robert F., Chief Fin. Officer, Sr. V.P.-Fin., & Corp. Sec.--Marotta Scientific Controls, Inc., Montville, NJ; *U.S.* Private, pg. 706

Davda, Paresh J., Chief Fin. Officer--Precision Dynamics Corporation, San Fernando, CA; *U.S. Private*, pg. 879
Davenport, A. Wayne, Exec. V.P. & Treas.--Hondo Oil & Gas Company, Roswell, NM; *Int'l*, pg. 818
Davenport, James, Chief Fin. Officer--Tupperware U.S., Inc., Orlando, FL; *U.S. Public*, pg. 1644
Davenport, Wayne, Chief Fin. Officer & V.P.--Giant Industries Inc., Scottsdale, AZ; *U.S. Public*, pg. 741
Davern, Alex, Chief Fin. Officer & Treas.--National Instruments Corp., Austin, TX; *U.S. Public*, pg. 1157
Davey, Robert G., Chief Fin. Officer & Exec. V.P.--McCormick & Company, Incorporated, Sparks, MD; *U.S. Public*, pg. 1066
David, George F., Chief Fin. Officer--Technic Incorporated, Cranston, RI; *U.S. Private*, pg. 1071
David, Jose S., Chief Fin. Officer--Active Voice Corporation, Seattle, WA; *U.S. Public*, pg. 17
David, Paul, Controller--Balanced Foods, Inc., North Bergen, NJ; *Int'l*, pg. 752
David, William W., Chief Fin. Officer & Exec. V.P.--Sunshine Mining And Refining Company, Boise, ID; *U.S. Public*, pg. 1536
Davidowski, Ronald J., Chief Fin. Officer--DPR Construction, Inc., Redwood City, CA; *U.S. Private*, pg. 305
Davidsen, Bjorn, V.P.-Fin. & Control--Frionor A/S, Lysaker, Norway; *Int'l*, pg. 516
Davidson, E.A.Q., Treas.--J. Sainsbury plc, London, United Kingdom; *Int'l*, pg. 1169
Davidson, Gary J., Chief Fin. Offcier & V.P.- Fin. & Admin.--Maxwell Technologies, Inc., San Diego, CA; *U.S. Public*, pg. 1061
Davidson, Gary J., Chief Fin. Officer--Maxwell Technologies-Information Systems Division, San Diego, CA; *U.S. Public*, pg. 1062
Davidson, Gary J., Chief Fin. Officer--Maxwell Technologies-Federal Division, San Diego, CA; *U.S. Public*, pg. 1062
Davidson, Lawrence J., Jr., Pres., Chief Exec.,Oper. & Fin. Officer--The Weathervane Retail Corp., New Britain, CT; *U.S. Private*, pg. 1156
Davies, Bill, Chief Fin. Officer--Weber Public Relations Worldwide, Cambridge, MA; *U.S. Private*, pg. 1157
Davies, Bob, Chief Fin. Officer & Sr. V.P.--Favorite Brands International, Inc., Lincolnshire, IL; *U.S. Private*, pg. 397
Davies, C.J. David, Chief Fin. Officer & Sr. V.P.-Fin.--Hawaiian Airlines, Inc., Honolulu, HI; *U.S. Public*, pg. 799
Davies, C.J. David, Chief Fin. Officer, Sr. V.P.-Fin.--Hawaiian Airlines, Inc., Honolulu, HI; *U.S. Public*, pg. 799
Davies, Richard J., Sr. V.P.-Fin., Treas. & Asst. Sec.--Time Warner Cable, Stamford, CT; *U.S. Public*, pg. 1610
Davis, A.F., Sr. V.P. & Chief Fin. Officer--Federal Industries Transport Group, Winnipeg, Canada; *Int'l*, pg. 1150
Davis, Alan, Chief Fin. Officer & Exec. V.P.--Shape Inc., Kennebunk, ME; *U.S. Private*, pg. 990
Davis, Bill, Chief Fin. Officer--Dexter Axle Div., Elkhart, IN; *Int'l*, pg. 1396
Davis, Bob, Chief Fin. Officer & V.P.--Paisano Publications, Inc., Agoura, CA; *U.S. Private*, pg. 834
Davis, Charles H., Chief Credit Officer--Harris & Bank, Chicago, IL; *Int'l*, pg. 154
Davis, Chris A., Chief Fin. Officer & Exec. V.P.--Gulfstream Aerospace Corporation, Savannah, GA; *U.S. Private*, pg. 419
Davis, Gary B., Chief Fin. Officer & Treas.--Polk Audio, Inc., Baltimore, MD; *U.S. Public*, pg. 1315
Davis, Glenn E., Chief Fin. Officer & V.P.-Fin.--CML Group, Inc., Acton, MA; *U.S. Public*, pg. 279
Davis, Gregg T., Chief Fin. Officer--Front Royal, Inc., Morrisville, NC; *U.S. Private*, pg. 430
Davis, James J., Chief Fin. Officer & V.P.-Fin.--Parker Drilling Company, Tulsa, OK; *U.S. Public*, pg. 1259
Davis, James R., Chief Fin. Officer & Controller--Rinker Materials Corp., West Palm Beach, FL; *Int'l*, pg. 246
Davis, Ken, Chief Fin. Officer--Preformed Line Products Canada, Cambridge, Canada; *U.S. Public*, pg. 1321
Davis, Ken, Chief Fin. Officer & V.P.--SL Waber, Inc., Mount Laurel, NJ; *U.S. Public*, pg. 1419
Davis, Ken, Chief Fin. Officer--SL Waber, Nogales, AZ; *U.S. Public*, pg. 1419
Davis, Lloyd G., Chief Fin. Officer, Exec. V.P.-Fin., Treas. & Sec.--Baldor Electric Company, Fort Smith, AR; *U.S. Public*, pg. 168
Davis, Michael C., Chief Fin. Officer--Nordberg-Read, Inc., Middleboro, MA; *Int'l*, pg. 1428
Davis, Michael L., Chief Fin. Officer, Treas. & Sec.--Crouch Supply Company, Inc., Fort Worth, TX; *U.S. Private*, pg. 291
Davis, Nancy, Natl. Chief Fin. Officer & Exec. V.P.--Lincoln Property Company, Dallas, TX; *U.S. Private*, pg. 668
Davis, Peter, Chief Fin. Officer--Winston Steel Products Co., Detroit, MI; *U.S. Private*, pg. 1183
Davis, Peter B., Chief Fin. Officer & V.P.-Fin.--XOMA Corporation, Berkeley, CA; *U.S. Public*, pg. 1786
Davis, Richard A., Chief Fin. Officer & Sr. V.P.-Fin.--PharmHouse, Inc., New York, NY; *U.S. Public*, pg. 1286
Davis, Solomon H., Chief Fin. Officer & Treas.--International Plastics Company, New York, NY; *U.S. Private*, pg. 571
Davis, Steve, Chief Fin. Officer--The Midland Grocery Company, Westville, IN; *U.S. Private*, pg. 948
Davis, Terry, Chief Fin. Officer--Jeff Wyler Dealer Group, Inc., Cincinnati, OH; *U.S. Private*, pg. 1193
Davis, William F., Chief Fin. Officer, V.P. & Treas.--Barnhill Contracting Company, Tarboro, NC; *U.S. Private*, pg. 117
Davis, William W., Chief Fin. Officer & Sr. V.P.--Sunshine Precious Metals, Inc., Kellogg, ID; *U.S. Public*, pg. 1536
Davis, William W., Chief Fin. Officer--Sunshine Argentina, Inc., Mendoza, Argentina; *U.S. Public*, pg. 1536
Davis, William W., Chief Fin. Officer--Minera Sunshine Del Peru, S.A., Lima, Peru; *U.S. Public*, pg. 1536
Davison, John M., Chief Fin. Officer & Exec. V.P.-Opers.--Imax Corporation, Mississauga, Canada; *Int'l*, pg. 661
Davit, Frank, Chief Fin. Officer & Partner--Bourton Group, Rockford, IL; *U.S. Private*, pg. 162
Dawe, Theodore G., V.P.-Fin.--NHD Hardware, Stoughton, MA; *U.S. Private*, pg. 3
Dawedeit, Volker, Chief Fin. Officer--Software AG, Darmstadt, Germany; *Int'l*, pg. 1276
Dawson, G. Steven, Chief Fin. Officer, Sr. V.P.-Fin. & Treas.--Camden Property Trust, Houston, TX; *U.S. Public*, pg. 298
Dawson, Timothy A., Chief Fin. Officer & V.P.-Fin.--Mississippi Chemical Corporation, Yazoo City, MS; *U.S. Public*, pg. 1117
Day, James, Chief Fin. Officer, V.P. & Controller--US 1 Industries Inc., Gary, IN; *U.S. Public*, pg. 1687
Day, Julian, Chief Fin. Officer & Exec. V.P.--Safeway Inc., Pleasanton, CA; *U.S. Public*, pg. 1426
Day, Marshall L., Chief Fin. Officer--The Home Depot, Inc., Atlanta, GA; *U.S. Public*, pg. 831
Day, William H., Chief Fin. Officer--Joseph Behr & Sons Inc., Rockford, IL; *U.S. Private*, pg. 130
Daya, Jackie, Chief Fin. Officer & Sr. V.P.--Reed Elsevier Business Information, Newton, MA; *Int'l*, pg. 1095
De Armas, Eloy R., Sr. V.P.--Business Mens Insurance Corporation, Coral Gables, FL; *U.S. Private*, pg. 189
de Barros, Viegas, Dr., Chief Fin. Officer--Portuguese Railways (CP), Lisbon, Portugal; *Int'l*, pg. 1063
De Blasio, Michael P., Chief Fin. Officer & Sr. V.P.--Loral Space & Communications, New York, NY; *U.S. Public*, pg. 1014
de Bruijn, Maartin, Chief Fin. Officer--Esselte BV, Woerden, Netherlands; *Int'l*, pg. 461
De Carbonell, Anne Astor, Chief Fin. Officer--First Federal Finance Corporation, Santurce, PR; *U.S. Public*, pg. 644
de Carbonell, Annie Astor, Chief Fin. Officer & Sr. Exec. V.P.--Firstbank Puerto Rico, Santurce, PR; *U.S. Public*, pg. 644
De Carbonell, Anne Astor, Chief Fin. Officer--First Leasing & Rental Corporation, Toa Baja, PR; *U.S. Public*, pg. 644
de Cima, Ernesto Zaragoza, Pres. & Chief Exec. & Chief Fin. Officer--Inversiones De Guaymas S.A. De C.V., Guaymas, Mexico; *Int'l*, pg. 685
De Clerk, H., Chief Fin. Officer--N.V. Polyfilla Products SA, Machelen, Belgium; *Int'l*, pg. 1501
de Cooman, Jean-Paul, Chief Fin. Officer--Esselte Meto NV, Ternat, Belgium; *Int'l*, pg. 461
de Goesbriand, Herve, Chief Fin. Officer--Peugeot-Citroen Moteurs (PCM), Nanterre, France; *Int'l*, pg. 1021
de Jong, Ben, Chief Fin. Officer--Bensons International Systems BV, Utrecht, Netherlands; *Int'l*, pg. 460
de la Martiniere, Garard, Chief Fin. Officer & Sr. Exec. V.P.-Holding Companies--AXA-UAP, Paris, France; *Int'l*, pg. 18
De Macedo Ficho, Agilio Leao, Chief Fin. Officer--Aracruz Celulose S.A., Rio de Janeiro, Brazil; *Int'l*, pg. 78
de Marcellus, Alain, Deputy Chief Fin. Officer--CAP Gemini S.A., Paris, France; *Int'l*, pg. 263
de Martin, M., Chief Fin. Officer--Pringle of Scotland, New York, NY; *Int'l*, pg. 386
de Menou, Jean-Regis, V.P.-Fin.--C.E.P. Communication Group, Paris, France; *Int'l*, pg. 239
de Monpalizet, Camille, Chief Fin. Officer--Bull S.A., Louveciennes, France; *Int'l*, pg. 315
de Noce, Vicente, Chief Fin. Officer & Exec. V.P.--LPC Industrias Alimenticias S.A., Vila Jaguara, Brazil; *Int'l*, pg. 380
de Pret, Arnoud, Chief Fin. Officer--Union Miniere, Brussels, Belgium; *Int'l*, pg. 1441
De Puppi, L., Chief Fin. Officer--Electrolux San Jose, Pordenone, Italy; *Int'l*, pg. 442
De Riemacker, Francois, V.P.- Fin. & Admin.--Maison Mathieu, S.A., Antwerp, Belgium; *Int'l*, pg. 846
de Rooij, Gerard, Chief Fin. Officer--Knurr NV Belgie, Kontich, Belgium; *Int'l*, pg. 739
de Sostoa, Vincent, Chief Fin. Officer, Sr. V.P.& Treas.--OMI Corp., New York, NY; *U.S. Public*, pg. 1208
de St. Paer, Jerry M., Exec. V.P., Treas. & Chief Fin. Officer--Equitable Investment Corporation, New York, NY; *U.S. Public*, pg. 589
de Toledo, Phil, Chief Fin. Officer--The Capital Group Companies Inc., Los Angeles, CA; *U.S. Private*, pg. 206
de Vries, Rob A., Chief Fin. Officer--Barenbrug Holland BV, Oosterhout, Netherlands; *Int'l*, pg. 166
De'Ath, A., Chief Fin. Officer--Rossing Uranium Ltd., Windhoek, Namibia; *Int'l*, pg. 1119
Deamer, Jane A., V.P.-Finance--Tighe Industries, Inc., York, PA; *U.S. Private*, pg. 1086
Dean, Gary, Chief Fin. Officer--LePage's, Inc., Pittsburgh, PA; *U.S. Private*, pg. 598
Dean, Jim, Chief Fin. Officer--Federal Data Corporation, Bethesda, MD; *U.S. Private*, pg. 398
Dean, Kevin, Chief Fin. Officer--Simplex Time Recorder Co., Gardner, MA; *U.S. Private*, pg. 1002
Dean, Tony, Dir.-Fin.--Betacom Plc, Brentwood, United Kingdom; *Int'l*, pg. 193
Deaner, Duane D., Chief Fin. Officer--Environmental Tectonics Corporation (ETC), Southampton, PA; *U.S. Public*, pg. 587
DeAngelis, Vincent, Chief Fin. Officer & V.P.--Walbridge Aldinger Company, Detroit, MI; *U.S. Private*, pg. 1146
DeAngelo, Thomas, Chief Fin. Officer--Skyland Scientific Services, Inc., Bozeman, MT; *U.S. Public*, pg. 1515
DeAngelo, Thomas, Chief Fin. Officer--Isomedix Operations Inc., Whippany, NJ; *U.S. Public*, pg. 1515
DeAngelo, Thomas, Chief Fin. Officer--Isomedix Management Inc., Whippany, NJ; *U.S. Public*, pg. 1515
DeAngelo, Thomas J., Chief Fin. Officer, Treas. & Sec.--Isomedix Inc., Whippany, NJ; *U.S. Public*, pg. 1515
Deas, Tom, Chief Fin. Officer--Airgas, Inc., Radnor, PA; *U.S. Public*, pg. 33
Deason, J.E., Chief Fin. Officer & Exec. V.P.--Wolverine Tube Inc., Huntsville, AL; *U.S. Public*, pg. 1774
DeBerge, John, Chief Fin. Officer--Continental Web Press, Inc., Itasca, IL; *U.S. Private*, pg. 269
DeBoer, Richard B., Chief Fin. Officer & Treas.--The Morgan Group, Inc., Elkhart, IN; *U.S. Public*, pg. 1022
DeBolt, Bruce R., Chief Fin. Officer & Sr. V.P.--Northwest Natural Gas Company, Portland, OR; *U.S. Public*, pg. 1200
DeBoni, Graziano, Exec. V.P. & Chief Fin. Officer--Hugo Boss USA, Inc., New York, NY; *Int'l*, pg. 637
Deboo, Tom, Chief Fin. Officer--Knurr USA East, Blythewood, SC; *Int'l*, pg. 739
DeBruyn, Barbara, Chief Fin. Officer & V.P.--Neway Anchorlok International Inc., Muskegon, MI; *U.S. Private*, pg. 796
DeCardenas, Gilbert L., Pres. & Chief Fin. Officer--Cacique, Inc., City of Industry, CA; *U.S. Private*, pg. 198
DeCecchis, Len, Chief Fin. Officer & Treas.--Prestone Products Corporation, Danbury, CT; *U.S. Public*, pg. 51
Dechnik, James, Chief Fin. Officer, V.P.-Fin. & Sec.--The Johnson Corporation, Three Rivers, MI; *U.S. Private*, pg. 591
DeCius, Dennis A., Chief Fin. Officer, Exec. V.P. & Asst. Sec.--Pacific Capital Bancorp, Salinas, CA; *U.S. Public*, pg. 1247
DeCius, Dennis A., Chief Fin. Officer & Sr. V.P.--First National Bank of Central California, Salinas, CA; *U.S. Public*, pg. 1248
Decker, Richard, Chief Fin. Officer, V.P.-Fin., Treas. & Sec.--CEM Corporation, Matthews, NC; *U.S. Public*, pg. 277
Decker, Robert, Chief Fin. Officer & Sr. V.P.-Fin. & Devel.--Churchill Downs, Inc., Louisville, KY; *U.S. Public*, pg. 356
Deckop, Joe, Exec. V.P. & Chief Fin. Officer--Victoria's Secret Stores, Reynoldsburg, OH; *U.S. Public*, pg. 995
DeCordova, Bryan, Chief Fin. Officer & Exec. V.P.--Michaels Stores, Inc., Irving, TX; *U.S. Public*, pg. 1104
DeCrona, Bruce, Chief Fin. Officer & Sr. V.P.--Exchange Bank, Santa Rosa, CA; *U.S. Public*, pg. 599
Deegan, Gail, Chief Fin. Officer, Exec. V.P. & Treas.--Houghton Mifflin Company, Boston, MA; *U.S. Public*, pg. 841
Deeney, Gerald, Chief Fin. Officer--KOB-TV, Inc., Albuquerque, NM; *U.S. Private*, pg. 544
Deeney, Gerald D., Chief Fin. Officer, V.P. & Treas.--Hubbard Broadcasting, Inc., Saint Paul, MN; *U.S. Private*, pg. 543
Deeney, Gerald D., Chief Fin. Officer--KSTP-TV, Saint Paul, MN; *U.S. Private*, pg. 544
DeFilippo, Paul M., V.P.-Fin.--Edwards Systems Tech, Cheshire, CT; *U.S. Public*, pg. 726
Defliese, Phil, Chief Fin. Officer & V.P.-Fin. & Information Res.--Darigold, Inc., Seattle, WA; *U.S. Private*, pg. 311
DeFoe, David F., Chief Fin. Officer--The News Corporation Limited, Sydney, Australia; *Int'l*, pg. 925
Deforrest, Daniel J., V.P.-Finance--General Electric Canada Inc., Mississauga, Canada; *U.S. Public*, pg. 713
Defrancesco, Camillo, Chief Fin. Officer & Sr. V.P.--Witco Corporation, Greenwich, CT; *U.S. Public*, pg. 1773
DeFrates, Earl E., Chief Fin. Officer--USA Waste Services, Inc., Houston, TX; *U.S. Public*, pg. 1686
Defty, David, Grp. Fin. Dir.--Sears plc, London, United Kingdom; *Int'l*, pg. 1217
DeGenring, Michael, Chief Fin. Officer--ARCO Coal Australia, Inc., Brisbane, Australia; *U.S. Public*, pg. 144
Degerman, A., Chief Fin. Officer--Scholl Danmark A/S, Copenhagen, Denmark; *Int'l*, pg. 1209
Degerman, A., Chief Fin. Officer--Scholl (Sverige) SA, Stockholm, Sweden; *Int'l*, pg. 1210
Degner, Don, Chief Fin. Officer & V.P.--Giorgio Beverly Hills, Santa Monica, CA; *U.S. Public*, pg. 1331
Degreve, R.H., V.P.-Fin.--Solvay America Inc., Houston, TX; *Int'l*, pg. 1278
DeGueldre, F., Controller--Kenner Parker Toys, Paris, France; *U.S. Public*, pg. 798
Dehne, Steve, V.P.-Fin.--Van Melle USA, Inc., Erlanger, KY; *Int'l*, pg. 1451
Deisinger, Robert, Chief Fin. Officer & Sr. V.P.--American Technical Publishers, Inc., Homewood, IL; *U.S. Private*, pg. 63
Deitchle, Gerald W., Chief Fin. Officer & Exec. V.P.--Cheesecake Factory Incorporated, Calabasas Hills, CA; *U.S. Public*, pg. 343
Deiter, Jon, Chief Fin. Officer & V.P.--Gerber Plumbing Fixtures Corporation, Chicago, IL; *U.S. Private*, pg. 449
DeJesus, David, Chief Fin. Officer & Sr. V.P.--Media General Cable of Fairfax County Inc., Chantilly, VA; *U.S. Public*, pg. 1078
del Fonso, Edgardo, Exec. V.P.-Fin.--Philippine Long Distance Telephone Company, Manila, Philippines; *Int'l*, pg. 1051
Del Gaudio, Anthony, Chief Fin. Officer--The Haband Co., Prospect Park, NJ; *U.S. Private*, pg. 492
Del Mastro, Robert, Chief Fin. Officer--K&M Associates, Providence, RI; *U.S. Public*, pg. 69
Del Mastro, Tom, Chief Fin. Officer--Foster Wheeler Environmental Corporation, Livingston, NJ; *U.S. Public*, pg. 677
Del Re, James, V.P.--Minerallac Co., Addison, IL; *U.S. Private*, pg. 750
Delabriere, Yann, Chief Fin. Officer--Peugeot S.A., Paris, France; *Int'l*, pg. 1020
DeLacey, Roger, Chief Fin. Officer--Kurt Manufacturing Co. Inc., Fridley, MN; *U.S. Private*, pg. 637
DeLak, Jerry, Chief Fin. Officer--Instructional Fair, Inc., Grand Rapids, MI; *U.S. Private*, pg. 288
Delark, Robert J., Chief Fin. Officer & V.P.--Henkels & McCoy, Inc., Blue Bell, PA; *U.S. Private*, pg. 522
DeLeon, Lawrence W., Chief Fin. Officer & V.P.-Fin.--Symix Systems, Inc., Columbus, OH; *U.S. Public*, pg. 1546
Delfs, James, Chief Fin. Officer & Sr. V.P.-Fin.--Stein Mart, Inc., Jacksonville, FL; *U.S. Public*, pg. 1514
Delisle, Andre, Chief Fin. Officer & Exec. V.P.-Corp. Plng.--Hydro-Quebec, Montreal, Canada; *Int'l*, pg. 640
Della Franco, Thomas, V.P.-Fin.--Zenith Products Corp., New Castle, DE; *U.S. Public*, pg. 1054
Della Torre, G., Chief Fin. Officer--Olivetti Australia Pty. Ltd., Silverwater, Australia; *Int'l*, pg. 1003

Dellamano, Patricia, Pres. & Chief Exec. & Chief Fin. Officer--Patson's Press, Sunnyvale, CA; *U.S. Private*, pg. 843
Dellasega, J. Philip, Chief Fin. Officer & Sr. V.P.-Fin. & Opers.--Lotus Development Corporation, Cambridge, MA; *U.S. Public*, pg. 896
Dellinger, Caroline K., Sr. V.P. & Chief Fin. Officer--Barclays American/Mortgage Corp., Charlotte, NC; *Int'l*, pg. 165
Delman, David, Chief Fin. Officer & Sr. V.P.--Key Risk Management Services, Inc., Greensboro, NC; *U.S. Public*, pg. 216
Delman, Richard, Chief Fin. Officer, Controller, Treas. & Sec.--New Age Intimates Inc., Long Island City, NY; *U.S.* Private, pg. 792
Delmar, Steven R., Chief Fin. Officer--Microlog Corporation, Germantown, MD; *U.S. Public*, pg. 1105
Delmore, Timothy C., Chief Fin. Officer & Sec.--Arctic Cat Inc., Thief River Falls, MN; *U.S. Public*, pg. 128
DeLoach, Thomas C., Jr., Chief Fin. Officer & Sr. V.P.--Mobil Oil Corporation, Fairfax, VA; *U.S. Public*, pg. 1118
DeLong, James, Chief Fin. Officer--Cummins Southwest Inc., Phoenix, AZ; *U.S. Private*, pg. 296
DelTufo, Anthony J., Chief Fin. Officer, Sr. V.P. & Treas.--W.R. Berkley Corporation, Greenwich, CT; *U.S. Public*, pg. 215
DeLuca, August F., Chief Fin. Officer & V.P.-Fin.--Elco Textron, Rockford, IL; *U.S. Public*, pg. 1590
DeLuca, David, Chief Fin. Officer--Catskill Savings Bank, Catskill, NY; *U.S. Public*, pg. 318
DeLuca, Filipo, Chief Fin. Officer--Gedy S.p.A., Senago, Italy; *Int'l*, pg. 542
DeLuca, Jon, Chief Fin. Officer--Allied Capital Corporation, Washington, DC; *U.S. Public*, pg. 47
DeLuca, Susan, Chief Fin. Officer, Exec. V.P. & Controller--Aero Data Metal Crafters, Ronkonkoma, NY; *U.S. Private*, pg. 23
DeMarco, Eric, Chief Fin. Officer & Sr. V.P.--The Titan Corporation, San Diego, CA; *U.S. Public*, pg. 1618
DeMarco, William, Chief Fin. Officer & V.P.--PrimeSource Corporation, Pennsauken, NJ; *U.S. Public*, pg. 1329
Dembro, Bob, Chief Fin. Officer--Fort Dearborn Company, Niles, IL; *U.S. Private*, pg. 419
Dembsky, Jay, Chief Fin. Officer--Vita Food Products, Inc., Chicago, IL; *U.S. Private*, pg. 1142
Dembsky, Maurice, Chief Fin. Officer & Sr. V.P.--Bergdorf Goodman, New York, NY; *U.S. Public*, pg. 785
DeMelle, Arthur W., Chief Fin. Officer & Sr. V.P.--Data General Corporation, Westborough, MA; *U.S. Public*, pg. 485
Demers, Norbert, Chief Fin. Officer & V.P.-Fin.--The Hilsinger Co. L.P., Plainville, MA; *U.S. Private*, pg. 530
Demetter, Richard, Chief Fin. Officer & V.P.-Fin.--Sifco Industries, Inc., Cleveland, OH; *U.S. Public*, pg. 1470
Dempsey, Don, Chief Fin. Officer & Sr. V.P.--Promus Hotel Corporation, Memphis, TN; *U.S. Public*, pg. 1335
Dempsey, Donald H., Chief Fin. Officer & Exec. V.P.--Choice Hotels International, Inc., Silver Spring, MD; *U.S. Public*, pg. 351
Dempsey, Donald H., V.P.-Admin. & Fin.--Hampton Inns, Inc., Memphis, TN; *U.S. Public*, pg. 1335
DeMuth, David P., Chief Fin. Officer & V.P.-Fin--Troy Corporation, Florham Park, NJ; *U.S. Private*, pg. 1105
Denaro, J., Chief Fin. Officer, V.P. & Treas.--R.T. Vanderbilt Company, Inc., Norwalk, CT; *U.S. Private*, pg. 1133
Denbo, Lawrence R., Chief Fin. Officer--Wabash Magnetics, Wabash, IN; *U.S. Private*, pg. 351
DeNicola, Mike, Chief Fin. Officer--Industrial Drives Div., Radford, VA; *U.S. Public*, pg. 965
Denis, Maurice, V.P.-Fin. & Admin.--Weyerhaeuser Canada Ltd., Vancouver, Canada; *U.S. Public*, pg. 1764
DeNisco, Thomas M., Chief Fin. Officer & V.P.--Knouse Foods Inc., Peach Glen, PA; *U.S. Private*, pg. 627
Denise, Robert, Chm. Bd., Pres., Chief Exec. Officer & Chief Fin. Officer--Bucilla Corporation, Hazleton, PA; *U.S.* Private, pg. 352
Denison, Floyd G., Exec. V.P.-Fin.--American Bankers Insurance Group, Inc., Miami, FL; *U.S. Public*, pg. 67
Dennee, Dons A., Intl. Chief Fin. Officer & V.P.--UNUM Corporation, Portland, ME; *U.S. Public*, pg. 1699
Dennen, Kurt, Chief Fin. Officer--Macmillan Publishing USA, Indianapolis, IN; *U.S. Private*, pg. 777
Dennen, Robert J., Chief Fin. Officer--Pacific Crest Capital, Inc., Agoura Hills, CA; *U.S. Public*, pg. 1248
Denney, Bob, Chief Fin. Officer--M.A. Hanna Color, Suwanee, GA; *U.S. Public*, pg. 781
Denny, Breck, R., Chief Fin. Officer, V.P.-Fin. & Treas.--Medusa Corporation, Cleveland, OH; *U.S. Public*, pg. 1084
Denny, R. Breck, Chief Fin. Officer, V.P. & Treas.--Cement Transit Co., Cleveland, OH; *U.S. Public*, pg. 1084
DeNoewer, Michael, Chief Fin. Officer--Columbus Pipe & Equipment Company, Columbus, OH; *U.S. Private*, pg. 257
DeNovellis, Donato A., Chief Fin. Officer & Exec. V.P.--Ekco Group, Inc., Nashua, NH; *U.S. Public*, pg. 566
DeNovellis, Donato A., Chief Fin. Officer & Sr. V.P.--Ekco Housewares, Inc., Franklin Park, IL; *U.S. Public*, pg. 566
DeNovellis, Donato A., Chief Fin. Officer, V.P. & Clerk--Ekco Cleaning, Inc., Franklin Park, IL; *U.S. Public*, pg. 566
DeNovellis, Donato A., Chief Fin. Officer & V.P.--Ekco International, Inc., Nashua, NH; *U.S. Public*, pg. 566
Denoyel, Gilles, Chief Fin. Officer & Exec. V.P.--Credit Commercial de France, Paris, France; *Int'l*, pg. 341
Denton, David, Chief Fin. Officer--Bale Of Kentucky, Inc., Horse Cave, KY; *U.S. Private*, pg. 112
Denton, Larry R., Chief Fin. Officer & V.P.-Fin.--Tension Envelope Corp., Kansas City, MO; *U.S. Private*, pg. 1077
Denton, Robert L., Acting Chief Fin. Officer--LIVE Entertainment Inc., Van Nuys, CA; *U.S. Private*, pg. 671
Denton, Robert L., Acting Chief Fin. Officer--LIVE Film & Mediaworks, Van Nuys, CA; *U.S. Private*, pg. 671
DeParis, Lawrence, Chief Fin. Officer & Sr. V.P.--Calvin Klein, Inc., New York, NY; *U.S. Private*, pg. 202
Deppen, Douglas D., Chief Fin. Officer & Sr. V.P.--First American Federal Savings Bank, Bristol, VA; *U.S. Public*, *pg. 624*
Derbyshire, J., Chief Fin. Officer--Air UK Ltd., Stansted, United Kingdom; *Int'l*, pg. 38
Derksen, Paul W., Chief Fin. Officer & Sr. V.P.--CT Financial Services, Inc., Toronto, Canada; *Int'l*, pg. 112
Dery, Ed G., Chief Fin. Officer & V.P.--Camellia Food Stores, Inc., Norfolk, VA; *U.S. Private*, pg. 203
Desai, K., Chief Fin. Officer--Tioxide Europe Limited, Billingham, United Kingdom; *Int'l*, pg. 663
DeSantis, Donald A., Chief Fin. Officer, Sr. V.P. & Treas.--First Brands Corporation, Danbury, CT; *U.S. Public*, pg. 626
DeSantis, Robert, Treas. & Fin. Admin. Officer--Citizens Resources Company, Stamford, CT; *U.S. Public*, pg. 380
DeSantis, Robert, Treas. & Fin. Admin. Officer--CU CapitalCorp, Stamford, CT; *U.S. Public*, pg. 380
DeSantis, Robert J., Chief Fin. Officer--Citizens Utilities Company, Stamford, CT; *U.S. Public*, pg. 379
Desautels, Robert O., Chief Fin. Officer, Sr. V.P. & Treas.--Domco Inc., Farnham, Canada; *Int'l*, pg. 415
Desheh, Eyal, Chief Fin. Officer & V.P.--Scitex Corporation Ltd., Holon, Israel; *Int'l*, pg. 644
Desideio, Ed, Chief Fin. Officer--Sansone Auto Mall, Avenel, NJ; *U.S. Private*, pg. 965
Desidevio, Nicholas J., Chief Fin. Officer & V.P.--First UNUM Life Insurance Company, Tarrytown, NY; *U.S. Public*, pg. 1699
Desloge, Stephen F., Chief Fin. Officer & Treas.--Watlow Electric Manufacturing Company, Saint Louis, MO; *U.S. Private*, pg. 1153
Desmond, Mark L., Chief Fin. Officer & Sr. V.P.--Nationwide Health Properties Inc., Newport Beach, CA; *U.S. Public*, pg. 1166
Desrosiers, Louis, V.P.-Admin. & Fin.--Groupe Morrow Inc., Montreal, Canada; *Int'l*, pg. 566
Dessing, Peter, Chief Fin. Officer--Waste Management International plc, London, United Kingdom; *U.S. Public*, pg. 1745
Deter, Robert, Chief Fin. Officer--Peerless Industrial Group, Inc., Winona, MN; *U.S. Public*, pg. 1268
Deter, Robert, Chief Fin. Officer--Peerless Chain Company, Winona, MN; *U.S. Public*, pg. 1268
Dettloff, Thierry, Chief Fin. Officer--Remy Cointreau, Paris, France; *Int'l*, pg. 1102
Deuschle, Mark J., Chief Fin. Officer, V.P.-Fin., Treas. & Sec.--Plasti-Line, Inc., Knoxville, TN; *U.S. Public*, pg. 1308
Deutcher, Klaus, Chief Fin. Officer--Bio-Tek Instruments, Inc., Winooski, VT; *U.S. Private*, pg. 144
Deutsch, John, Chief Fin. Officer & Controller--Teleflex (Canada) Ltd., Vancouver, Canada; *U.S. Public*, pg. 1570
Deutsch, Mark, Chief Fin. Officer & V.P.-Fin.--Diamedix Corporation, Miami, FL; *U.S. Public*, pg. 914
Deutsch, Robert V., Chief Fin. Officer & Exec. V.P.--Executive Risk, Inc., Simsbury, CT; *U.S. Public*, pg. 599
Devadason, M., Chief Fin. Officer--Burns, Philp Pacific Division, Brisbane, Australia; *Int'l*, pg. 237
DeVae, David, Jr., Chief Fin. Officer--TV Guide Magazine, Radnor, PA; *Int'l*, pg. 925
Devani, Yogesh, Chief Fin. Officer--Kelly Weedon Shute Partnership, London, United Kingdom; *Int'l*, pg. 727
Devantier, Andy, Chief Fin. Officer--SBC Advertising, Columbus, OH; *U.S. Private*, pg. 955
Devault, David V., Chief Fin. Officer, V.P. & Treas.--Washington Trust Bancorp, Inc., Westerly, RI; *U.S. Public*, pg. 1744
Devenney, Robert, V.P.-Fin.--Danaher Tool Group, Lancaster, PA; *U.S. Public*, pg. 480
Devereux, Robin W., Chief Fin. Officer & V.P.--Property Capital Trust, Boston, MA; *U.S. Public*, pg. 1335
Devine, Don, Chief Fin. Officer & V.P.-Fin.--The Dannon Co., Tarrytown, NY; *Int'l*, pg. 379
Devine, E. J., Controller--Varco Best Products, Houston, TX; *U.S. Public*, pg. 1709
Devine, John M., Chief Fin. Officer & Exec. V.P.--Ford Motor Company, Dearborn, MI; *U.S. Public*, pg. 661
Devine, Matthew E., Chief Fin. Officer, Exec. V.P. & Treas.--Chancellor Media Corporation, Irving, TX; *U.S. Public*, pg. 335
Devore, D., Chief Fin. Officer--Aerochem, Inc., Orange, CA; *U.S. Public*, pg. 534
Devos, Ron, Chief Fin. Officer, V.P.-Fin. & Sec.--Nathan's Famous Inc., Westbury, NY; *U.S. Public*, pg. 1152
DeVourzi, Michael, Chief Fin. Officer--Budget Marketing, Inc., Des Moines, IA; *U.S. Private*, pg. 178
DeWinter, A. Noel, Chief Fin. Officer & V.P.--Califia Company, San Diego, CA; *U.S. Public*, pg. 584
Dewispelaere, A., Chief Fin. Officer & Intl. Fin.--Sidmar N.V., Gent, Belgium; *Int'l*, pg. 79
DeWitt, Stephen P., Chief Fin. Officer & V.P.--The New York Times Company Regional Newspaper Group, Atlanta, GA; *U.S. Public*, pg. 1174
Dexmier, Jean-Yves, Chief Fin. Officer. & Exec. V.P.--Informix Software, Menlo Park, CA; *U.S. Public*, pg. 876
Dexter, S., Chief Fin. Officer--Aqualisa Products Limited, Westerham, United Kingdom; *Int'l*, pg. 925
Dharamshi, T., Chief Fin. Officer & V.P.-Fin.--OCE USA, Inc., Chicago, IL; *Int'l*, pg. 994
Dharamshi, Taj, Chief Fin. Officer--OCE-U.S.A., Itasca, IL; *Int'l*, pg. 994
Dhein, Peter D., 111, Chief Fin. Officer--Schoep's Ice Cream, Inc., Madison, WI; *U.S. Private*, pg. 972
Di Laurentiis, Giovanni, Chief Fin. Officer--Avions de Transport Regional - ATR, Blagnac, France; *Int'l*, pg. 654
Di Mauro, James, Controller--Paper Corporation of United States, New York, NY; *U.S. Public*, pg. 1671
Dial, Michael C., Chief Fin. Officer & Sr. V.P.--Cooper Communities, Inc., Bella Vista, AR; *U.S. Private*, pg. 273
Dial, Michael C., Chief Fin. Officer & V.P.--Cooper Ventures, Inc., Bella Vista, AR; *U.S. Private*, pg. 274
DiAngelo, Stephen, Chief Fin. Officer--Jewelmont Corporation, Minneapolis, MN; *U.S. Private*, pg. 587
Diaz, Bob, Chief Fin. Officer--Circle Freight International (U.S.A.), San Francisco, CA; *U.S. Public*, pg. 370
Diaz, Mario Anibal Rodas, Chief Fin. Officer--Central de Cervejas, S.A., Lisbon, Portugal; *Int'l*, pg. 279
Diaz, Robert, Chief Fin. Officer--Circle International Group, Inc., San Francisco, CA; *U.S. Public*, pg. 370
Dibble, Roy, Chief Fin. Officer--Buckman Laboratories Inc., Memphis, TN; *U.S. Private*, pg. 180
DiBenedetto, G.J., Chief Fin. Officer--Presstek, Inc., Hudson, NH; *U.S. Public*, pg. 1324
DiBiase, Filomena, Chief Fin. Officer--Bensons International Systems, Mississauga, Canada; *Int'l*, pg. 460
Dicapua, Nicholas, Chief Oper. Officer, Chief Fin. Officer, V.P., Treas. & Sec.--Liberty Fabrics, Inc., New York, NY; *Int'l*, pg. 340
DiCaro, Daniel P., Chief Fin. Officer, V.P. & Asst. Sec.--Medicus Systems Corporation, Evanston, IL; *U.S. Public*, *pg. 1080*
DiCataldo, Emilio, Chief Fin. Officer & V.P.-Res. & Devel.--CVC Products, Inc., Rochester, NY; *U.S. Private*, pg. 197
Dick, Rollin M., Chief Fin. Officer & Exec. V.P.--Conseco Inc., Carmel, IN; *U.S. Public*, pg. 432
Dick, Rollin M., Chief Fin. Officer--Bankers Life Holding Corp., Chicago, IL; *U.S. Public*, pg. 433
Dicke, Larry, Chief Fin. Officer, V.P.-Fin. & Treas.--Blue Diamond Growers, Sacramento, CA; *U.S. Private*, pg. 152
Dickerson, B.R., Chief Fin. Officer & V.P.--The Crispin Company, Houston, TX; *U.S. Private*, pg. 290
Dickerson, Frank M., Chief Fin. Officer, V.P., Gen. Counsel & Sec.--Harza Engineering Co., Chicago, IL; *U.S. Private*, *pg. 509*
Dickerson, James H., Jr., Chief Fin. Officer--U.S. Healthcare, Inc., Blue Bell, PA; *U.S. Public*, pg. 26
Dickerson, Larry, Chief Fin. Officer & Sr. V.P.--Diamond Offshore Drilling, Inc., Houston, TX; *U.S. Public*, pg. 1011
Dickey, Sam, Treas. & Sec.--O'Neil Data Systems, Inc., Los Angeles, CA; *U.S. Private*, pg. 817
Dickinson, S.M., Chief Fin. Officer--Polycell Products Limited, Welwyn Garden City, United Kingdom; *Int'l*, pg. 1501
Dickison, Hugh, Chief Fin. Officer--Lennox Industries Inc., Richardson, TX; *U.S. Private*, pg. 659
Dickson, Robin N., Chief Fin. Officer--Harmonic Lightwaves, Sunnyvale, CA; *U.S. Public*, pg. 788
Dickson, S., Chief Fin. Officer--Wyman-Gordon Limited, Livingston, United Kingdom; *U.S. Public*, pg. 1782
Diedrich, John C., Chief Fin. Officer--Glenview State Bank, Glenview, IL; *U.S. Private*, pg. 295
Diehl, Michelle, Chief Fin. Officer & Exec. V.P.--Kragie/Newell, Des Moines, IA; *U.S. Private*, pg. 634
Dienes, John R., Pres. & Chief Fin. Officer--Hercules Engine Company, Canton, OH; *U.S. Private*, pg. 523
Dieschbourg, Ed, Chief Fin. Officer--Replogle Globes, Inc., Broadview, IL; *U.S. Private*, pg. 923
Dietch, Horst, Chief Fin. Officer--Siemens Microelectronics Center GmbH & Co., Dresden, Germany; *Int'l*, pg. 1245
Dieter, Mary Q., Chief Oper. Officer, Chief Fin. Officer & Exec. V.P.--Sonoma Valley Bank, Sonoma, CA; *U.S. Public*, pg. 1487
Dietrich, Dennis, Chief Fin. Officer & V.P.--Primedia Inc., Peoria, IL; *U.S. Public*, pg. 1328
DiGiantommaso, Joe, Chief Fin. Officer & V.P.-Fin.--Proteon, Inc., Westborough, MA; *U.S. Public*, pg. 1336
Dignam, Arthur F., Chief Fin. Officer, Chief Acctg. Officer & Exec. V.P.--Caribiner International, Inc., New York, NY; *U.S. Public*, pg. 305
Dillard, Allen E., Chief Fin. Officer, V.P. & Treas.--Nichols Research Corporation, Huntsville, AL; *U.S. Public*, pg. 1182
Diller, Charles H., Jr., Chief Fin. Officer & Exec. V.P.--JLG Industries, Inc., McConnellsburg, PA; *U.S. Public*, pg. 918
Dillon, Adrian T., Chief Fin. Officer, Plng. Officer & Exec. V.P.--Eaton Corporation, Cleveland, OH; *U.S. Public*, pg. 555
Dillon, John, Group Dir.-Fin.--Kraft Jacobs Suchard, Cheltenham, United Kingdom; *U.S. Public*, pg. 1290
Dillon, William C., Chief Fin. Officer--Associated Merchandising Corp. (AMC), New York, NY; *U.S. Private*, *pg. 91*
Dimick, Neil F., Chief Fin. Officer & Exec. V.P.--Bergen Brunswig Corporation, Orange, CA; *U.S. Public*, pg. 213
Dimun, Anthony, Chief Fin. Officer, Exec. V.P., Treas. & Sec.--Vital Signs, Inc., Totowa, NJ; *U.S. Public*, pg. 1723
Dina, Charles, V.P.-Fin.--Telephonics Corp., Farmington, NY; *U.S. Public*, pg. 766
Dingler, Brian, V.P.-Fin. & Treas.--Mainship Corporation, Saint Augustine, FL; *U.S. Private*, pg. 697
DiNicola, Patrick, Chief Fin. Officer & Sr. V.P.-Fin. & Admin.--Trico Products Corporation, Buffalo, NY; *Int'l*, pg. 1397
Dinkelacker, Kurt E., Chief Fin. Officer & Exec. V.P.--Ikon Office Solutions, Inc., Malvern, PA; *U.S. Public*, pg. 862
Dinsmore, S., Chief Fin. Officer--Northern Ireland Carpets Ltd., Newtownards, United Kingdom; *Int'l*, pg. 797
Dion, Mike, Chief Fin. Officer--International Home Foods Inc., Parsippany, NJ; *U.S. Private*, pg. 526
Dionne, Gary, Treas.--Adams Industries, Inc., Suffield, CT; *U.S. Public*, pg. 187
DiOrio, Carolyn, V.P., Chief Fin. Officer & Treas.--DSL Service Co., Newport Beach, CA; *U.S. Public*, pg. 527
DiPaolo, Anthony M., Chief Fin. Officer & Sr. V.P.--Capital Associates, Inc., Lakewood, CO; *U.S. Public*, pg. 302
DiPietro, Frank, Chief Fin. Officer & Sr. V.P.-Fin.--Sipex Corporation, Billerica, MA; *Int'l*, pg. 1415
Dircks, John, Chief Fin. Officer--TNT Vacations, Boston, MA; *U.S. Private*, pg. 1065
Dirrim, Julie, Chief Fin. Officer & Sr. V.P.--Valley Bank & Trust, Brighton, CO; *U.S. Private*, pg. 1132

DiSante, Robert, Exec. V.P.-Fin.--FCA International Ltd., Westmount, Canada; *Int'l*, pg. 470

Dismuke, Charles, Chief Fin. Officer--Flexible Flyer Toys, West Point, MS; *U.S. Private*, pg. 412

DiStefano, James L., Chief Fin. Officer & Treas.--Healthcare Services Group, Inc., Huntingdon Valley, PA; *U.S. Public*, *pg. 803*

Diteresi, Emanuel, Chief Fin. Officer--North American Salt Company, Overland Park, KS; *U.S. Private*, pg. 505

DiTomaso, Gino, V.P.-Fin. & Treas.--FAG Bearings Corporation, Danbury, CT; *Int'l*, pg. 469

Dittmer, Robert G., Exec. V.P.-Fin./Admin. & Sec.--Agra Inc., Calgary, Canada; *Int'l*, pg. 30

Divine, David, Chief Fin. Officer--True Life, Dublin, Ireland; *Int'l*, pg. 1425

Dixon, Brian, V.P.-Fin.--Full House Sports & Entertainment, Seattle, WA; *U.S. Public*, pg. 16

Dixon, James D., Sr. Exec. V.P. & Chief Fin. Officer--NationsBank South, Atlanta, GA; *U.S. Public*, pg. 1163

Dixon, Mark, Chief Fin. Officer, V.P.-Fin. & Treas.--K-Tel International, Inc., Minneapolis, MN; *U.S. Public*, pg. 937

Dixon, Marsha, Chief Fin. Officer--Columbus Show Case Company, Columbus, OH; *U.S. Private*, pg. 257

Djergian, John, Mng. Dir. & Chief Fin. Officer--Kovel Kresser & Partners, Santa Monica, CA; *U.S. Private*, pg. 634

Dmiszewicki, Steven, Chief Fin. Officer & Sr. V.P.-Fin.--Seer Technologies, Inc., Cary, NC; *U.S. Public*, pg. 1453

Do Campo, Julius, Chief Fin. Officer--Royal Olympic Cruises, New York, NY; *U.S. Public*, pg. 1411

Do Carmo, Dr. Maria, Chief Fin. Officer--Vercoope-Uniao Das Adegas Cooperativas da Regiao Dos Vinhoa Verdes, U.C.R.L., Santo Tirso, Portugal; *Int'l*, pg. 1463

Dobbins, Judy, Chief Fin. Officer-USA--Radiometer A/S, Bronshoj, Denmark; *Int'l*, pg. 1083

Dobbins, Judy, Chief Fin. Officer--Radiometer America Inc., Westlake, OH; *Int'l*, pg. 1083

Dobot, Joseph A., Chief Fin. Officer & Treas.--Wall Colmonoy Corp., Madison Heights, MI; *U.S. Private*, pg. 1148

Dobral, Max, Chief Fin. Officer--Esselte Meto Ges mbH, Vienna, Austria; *Int'l*, pg. 461

Dobranowski, Anthony E., Chief Fin. Officer & Exec. V.P.--Tesma International Inc., Concord, Canada; *Int'l*, pg. 830

Dockendorf, Charles, Chief Fin. Officer & Sr. V.P.-Fin.--The Kendall Company, Mansfield, MA; *U.S. Public*, pg. 1647

Dodelin, F.J., Chief Fin. Officer & Exec. V.P.--The Hardaway Company, Columbus, GA; *U.S. Private*, pg. 501

Dodson, Larry S., Chief Fin. Officer & Sr. V.P.--Zimmerman Holdings, Inc., San Marino, CA; *U.S. Private*, pg. 1206

Dodson, William M., Chief Fin. Officer, V.P. & Treas.--Jefferson-Pilot Data Services, Inc., Memphis, TN; *U.S. Public*, pg. 925

Doe, Ernest, V.P.-Real Estate & Fin.--The Accor Group, Inc., Corona Del Mar, CA; *Int'l*, pg. 21

Doerfer, Rubens, Chief Fin. Officer--Siemens S.A., Madrid, Spain; *Int'l*, pg. 1248

Doerfler, Ronald J., Chief Fin. Officer & Sr. V.P.--ABC, Inc, New York, NY; *U.S. Public*, pg. 511

Doering, James D., Chief Fin. Officer, V.P. & Treas.--Artra Group Incorporated, Northfield, IL; *U.S. Public*, pg. 136

Doerr, Jack A., Pres., Chief Fin. Officer & Treas.--F.B. Wright Co., Dearborn, MI; *U.S. Private*, pg. 1192

Dogon, Gerald, Chief Fin. Officer & Sr. V.P.--DSP Communications Inc., Cupertino, CA; *U.S. Public*, pg. 475

Doherty, Hugh, Chief Fin. Officer--Conquest Europe S.A.R.L., Neuilly-sur-Seine, France; *Int'l*, pg. 1484

Doherty, John, Chief Fin. Officer--MeritCare Health System, Fargo, ND; *U.S. Private*, pg. 733

Doherty, John, Chief Fin. Officer--MeritCare Hospital, Fargo, ND; *U.S. Private*, pg. 733

Doherty, John, Chief Fin. Officer--HealthCare Accessories, Fargo, ND; *U.S. Private*, pg. 733

Doherty, John, Chief Fin. Officer--MeritCare Foundation, Fargo, ND; *U.S. Private*, pg. 733

Doherty, John, Chief Fin. Officer--Health Ventures, Fargo, ND; *U.S. Private*, pg. 733

Doherty, John, Chief Fin. Officer--MeritCare Medical Group, Fargo, ND; *U.S. Private*, pg. 733

Dolan, Dennis M., Chief Fin. Officer & V.P.--Air Express International Corporation, Darien, CT; *U.S. Public*, pg. 30

Dolan, Joseph, V.P.-Fin.--Landis & Staefa, Inc., Buffalo Grove, IL; *Int'l*, pg. 800

Dolan, Kevin E., Chief Fin. Officer & V.P.--Eatelcorp Inc., Gonzales, LA; *U.S. Private*, pg. 358

Dolan, Kevin E., Chief Fin. Officer & V.P.--East Ascension Telephone Company, Inc., Gonzales, LA; *U.S. Private*, pg. 358

Dolan, Maureen, Sec. & Treas.--Cargill Salt, Newark, CA; *U.S. Private*, pg. 210

Dolan, Michael, Vice Chm. & Chief Fin. Officer--Young & Rubicam Inc., New York, NY; *U.S. Private*, pg. 1196

Dolan, Regina, Chief Fin. Officer--PaineWebber Incorporated, New York, NY; *U.S. Public*, pg. 1252

Dolan, Robert E., Chief Fin. Officer--Lynch Corporation, Greenwich, CT; *U.S. Public*, pg. 1021

Dolan, Vincent T., Chief Fin. Officer--Superior Tube Company, Collegeville, PA; *U.S. Private*, pg. 1056

Doll, Thomas J., Chief Fin. Officer--Subaru of America, Inc., Cherry Hill, NJ; *Int'l*, pg. 523

Dolphin, James, Chief Fin. Officer--United Dominion Realty Trust, Inc., Richmond, VA; *U.S. Public*, pg. 1677

Dolson, Robert T., V.P.-Fin.--Featherlite Building Products Operation, Austin, TX; *U.S. Public*, pg. 936

Domanski, Robert, V.P.-Fin. & Admin.--Kysor/Warren, Conyers, GA; *U.S. Public*, pg. 1445

Dominguez, C.P. Irene, Chief Fin. Officer--Preformados De Mexico SA, Mexico, Mexico; *U.S. Public*, pg. 1321

Dominiak, Norman S., Chief Fin., V.P. & Treas.--Kimmins Corp., Tampa, FL; *U.S. Public*, pg. 960

Dominiak, Norman S., Chief Fin. Officer--TransCor Waste Service, Inc., Tampa, FL; *U.S. Public*, pg. 960

Dominic, Antoine, Chief Fin. Officer & Controller--Excel Technology, Inc., New York, NY; *U.S. Public*, pg. 599

Domis, Raymond C., Chief Fin. Officer & Exec. V.P.--GraphLine Inc., Tamarac, FL; *U.S. Private*, pg. 471

Donaghey, Eugene J., Chief Fin. Officer--Carl Buddig & Company, Homewood, IL; *U.S. Private*, pg. 178

Donahue, Ed, Chief Fin. Officer & V.P.--Transamerican Natural Gas Corporation, Houston, TX; *U.S. Private*, pg. 1096

Donahue, George, Chief Fin. Officer & V.P.--Siemens Transportation Systems, Inc., Iselin, NJ; *Int'l*, pg. 1246

Donahue, Jack, Chief Fin. Officer--Paul Stuart, Inc., New York, NY; *U.S. Private*, pg. 844

Donahue, Jeffrey H., Chief Fin. Officer & Sr. V.P.--The Rouse Company, Columbia, MD; *U.S. Public*, pg. 1407

Donahue, Robert, Chief Fin. Officer & Exec. V.P.--Manufacturers' Services Ltd., Concord, MA; *U.S. Private*, *pg. 701*

Donald, Ian, Chief Fin. Officer--Fletcher Challenge Limited, Auckland, New Zealand; *Int'l*, pg. 494

Donaldson, Darrell, Pres. & Chief Exec. Officer--Hot Shot Delivery Inc., Houston, TX; *U.S. Private*, pg. 541

Donaldson, George, Chief Fin. Officer--Henco, Inc., Selmer, TN; *U.S. Private*, pg. 521

Donaldson, John, Chief Fin. Officer & Sr. V.P.--Fremont Indemnity Corp., Santa Monica, CA; *U.S. Public*, pg. 681

Donaldson, Wm., Chief Fin. Officer--Goer Manufacturing Co., Charleston, SC; *U.S. Private*, pg. 904

Donatelli, Flavio Baras, Chief Fin. Officer--Acos Villares S.A., Sao Paulo, Brazil; *Int'l*, pg. 23

Donavan, Doug, Chief Fin. Officer, Chief Information Officer, & Treas. & Sec.--Campbell Oil Co., Massillon, OH; *U.S. Private*, pg. 204

Dondanville, Joseph E., Chief Fin. Officer & V.P.--RLI Corp., Peoria, IL; *U.S. Public*, pg. 1356

Dondanville, Joseph E., V.P. & Chief Fin. Officer--RLI Insurance Company, Peoria, IL; *U.S. Public*, pg. 1356

Donde, Ruben Martinez, Chief Fin. Officer--Empressa La Moderna SA de CV, Monterrey, Mexico; *Int'l*, pg. 454

Donehower, John W., Chief Fin. Officer & Sr. V.P.--Kimberly-Clark Corporation, Dallas, TX; *U.S. Public*, pg. 958

Doner, Dave, Chief Fin. Officer--Mexican Industries in Michigan, Detroit, MI; *U.S. Private*, pg. 739

Donmoyer, Tim, Chief Fin. Officer & Exec. V.P.--Eller Media Company, Phoenix, AZ; *U.S. Public*, pg. 383

Donnelly, Clifford W., Chief Fin. Officer & Sr. V.P.-Fin.--Physician Corporation of America, Miami, FL; *U.S. Public*, pg. 1293

Donnelly, John R., Chief Fin. Officer & V.P.-Fin.--General Automation, Inc., Irvine, CA; *U.S. Public*, pg. 706

Donnelly, Timothy J., Chief Fin. Officer & Sr. V.P.--District Petroleum Products, Inc., Sandusky, OH; *U.S. Private*, pg. 336

Donning, Richard, Chief Fin. Officer--APITECH, Butler, WI; *U.S. Public*, pg. 124

Donning, Richard, Chief Fin. Officer--Power-Packer U.S., Butler, WI; *U.S. Public*, pg. 124

Donohue, Jim, Chief Fin. Officer & Sr. V.P.--Vail Resorts, Inc., Vail, CO; *U.S. Public*, pg. 1704

Donohue, R.J., Chief Fin. Officer--Matson Intermodal System, Inc., San Francisco, CA; *U.S. Public*, pg. 40

Donohue, R.J., Chief Fin. Officer--Matson Terminals, Inc., San Francisco, CA; *U.S. Public*, pg. 40

Donohue, Raymond J., Chief Fin. Officer & Sr. V.P.--Matson Navigation Company, Inc., San Francisco, CA; *U.S. Public*, pg. 39

Donovan, Gordon S., Chief Fin. Officer & V.P.--Envirodyne Industries, Inc., Oak Brook, IL; *U.S. Public*, pg. 586

Donovan, James, Chief Fin. Officer--Azon Corporation, Johnson City, NY; *U.S. Private*, pg. 104

Donovan, Paul, Chief Fin. Officer & Exec. V.P.--Sundstrand Corporation, Rockford, IL; *U.S. Public*, pg. 1533

Donovan, Raymond J., Pres. & Chief Fin. Officer--Schiavone Construction Co., Secaucus, NJ; *U.S. Private*, *pg. 970*

Donovan, William T., Pres. & Chief Fin. Officer--Christiana Companies, Inc., Milwaukee, WI; *U.S. Public*, pg. 352

Dooher, Terry, Chief Fin. Officer & V.P.-Fin.--The Biltrite Corporation, Waltham, MA; *U.S. Private*, pg. 144

Doolen, Dennis G., Chief Fin. Officer--Granger Companies, Lansing, MI; *U.S. Private*, pg. 469

Doolittle, Charles, Chief Fin. Officer--Bank of Boston Connecticut, Hartford, CT; *U.S. Public*, pg. 184

Doolittle, John C., Chief Fin. Officer & Sr. V.P.--Shandwick Americas, New York, NY; *Int'l*, pg. 1226

Doomany, Charles G., Chief Fin. Officer & Sr. V.P.--Harrison & Star, Inc., New York, NY; *U.S. Private*, pg. 506

Doppelfeld, Volker, Dir.-Fin. & Controlling--Bayerische Motoren Werke Aktiengesellschaft, Munich, Germany; *Int'l*, pg. 177

Dor, Christian, Chief Fin. Officer & Sr. V.P.--Renault, Boulogne-Billancourt, France; *Int'l*, pg. 1102

Doran, J. C., Exec. V.P. & Chief Fin. Officer, Administrative Bank, CIBC--Canadian Imperial Bank of Commerce, Toronto, Canada; *Int'l*, pg. 256

Doran, Kevin, Chief Fin. Officer--Jomac, Inc., Warrington, PA; *U.S. Private*, pg. 595

Doria, Robert, Chief Fin. Officer & V.P.--Chipwich Inc., Ridgewood, NJ; *U.S. Private*, pg. 237

Dorier, Philippe, Chief Fin. Officer & Sr. V.P.--BGF Industries Inc., Greensboro, NC; *U.S. Private*, pg. 106

Dorme, Patrick J., Chief Fin. Officer & V.P.-Fin.--Dynamics Corporation of America, Greenwich, CT; *U.S. Public*, pg. 286

Dorn, Herb, Chief Fin. Officer--Tillamook County Creamery Assn., Tillamook, OR; *U.S. Private*, pg. 1086

Doroniuk, Roman, Chief Fin. Officer--Alliance Communications Corporation, Toronto, Canada; *Int'l*, pg. 57

Dorsch, Charles R., Chief Fin. Officer & V.P.-Fin.--Spang & Company, Butler, PA; *U.S. Private*, pg. 1020

Dorschel, Christoph, Acting Chief Fin. Officer--Swiss Reinsurance Company, Zurich, Switzerland; *Int'l*, pg. 1332

Dorsey, M., Chief Fin. Officer--Brown-Strauss Steel, Aurora, CO; *U.S. Private*, pg. 153

Dorst, Jim, Chief Fin. Officer--Western Micro Technology, Inc., Campbell, CA; *U.S. Public*, pg. 1759

Dos Santos, Geraldo Alfonso, Chief Fin. Officer--PLP Produtos Para Linhas Proformados Ltda., Sao Paulo, Brazil; *U.S. Public*, pg. 1321

Dosmann, Marc, Chief Fin. Officer & V.P.--Liberty Homes, Inc., Goshen, IN; *U.S. Public*, pg. 992

Dotson, J.D., Chief Fin. Officer, V.P. & Treas.--California & Hawaiian Sugar Company Inc., Crockett, CA; *U.S. Public*, *pg. 39*

Dotson, Richard, Chief Fin. Officer--Five Star Foods Incorporated, Dalton, GA; *U.S. Private*, pg. 409

Dotterer, Herbert T., Chief Fin. Officer, Sr. V.P.-Fin. & Admin. & Sec.--Eagle Food Centers, Inc., Milan, IL; *U.S. Public*, pg. 547

Doty, Michael, V.P.-Fin.--White Systems, Incorporated, Kenilworth, NJ; *U.S. Private*, pg. 866

Douard, Michel, Chief Fin. Officer--Mugler Triumvirat, Paris, France; *Int'l*, pg. 295

Douay, Philippe, Chief Fin. Officer & Exec. V.P.--Bertrand Faure, Boulogne, France; *Int'l*, pg. 192

Dougherty, B.D., Chief Fin. Officer--The Rawlplug Company Limited, Glasgow, United Kingdom; *Int'l*, pg. 925

Dougherty, Douglas, Chief Fin. Officer, V.P. Fin. & Treas.--Marsh Supermarkets, Inc., Indianapolis, IN; *U.S. Public*, pg. 1049

Dougherty, Jay, Chief Fin. Officer--Linpac Mouldings Limited, Birmingham, United Kingdom; *Int'l*, pg. 811

Dougherty, Joe, Chief Fin. Officer & Treas.--Prospect Foundry, Inc., Minneapolis, MN; *U.S. Public*, pg. 142

Dougherty, Thomas, Chief Fin. Officer & V.P.--Hoboken Wood Flooring Corporation, Wayne, NJ; *U.S. Private*, pg. 532

Douglas, G.A., Chief Fin. Officer & V.P.--Salem Asset Management Corp., Wilmington, DE; *U.S. Private*, pg. 961

Douglas, Gary, Chief Fin. Officer & V.P.--Kaufman and Broad Mortgage Co., Woodland Hills, CA; *U.S. Public*, pg. 945

Douglas, George A., Chief Fin. Officer, Controller & Treas.--Salem Group, Inc., Pittsburgh, PA; *U.S. Private*, pg. 961

Douglas, George A., Chief Fin. Officer, Controller & Treas.--Salem Corporation, Pittsburgh, PA; *U.S. Private*, pg. 961

Douglas, Jim, Chief Fin. Officer & Exec. V.P.--World Airways, Inc., Herndon, VA; *U.S. Public*, pg. 1780

Douglas, John, Chief Fin. Officer--Aerolyte Systems, Washington, MO; *U.S. Private*, pg. 24

Douglass, D.I., Chief Fin. Officer & V.P.--Jannock Vinyl Group, Pittsburgh, PA; *Int'l*, pg. 699

Dout, A. Jacqueline, Chief Fin. Officer & Exec. V.P.--Champion Enterprises, Inc., Auburn Hills, MI; *U.S. Public*, *pg. 332*

Douville, Richard A., Chief Fin. Officer & Sr. V.P.--U.S. Surgical Corp., Norwalk, CT; *U.S. Public*, pg. 1687

Dove, Barry, Controller--UnionTools, Inc., Columbus, OH; *U.S. Public*, pg. 17

Dow III, Howard L., Chief Fin. Officer & V.P.-Fin. & Reg. Affairs--MichCon, Detroit, MI; *U.S. Public*, pg. 1025

Dowd, R.D., V.P.-Fin. & Logistics--SK Hand Tool Corp., Chicago, IL; *Int'l*, pg. 570

Dowd, Tom, Chief Fin. Officer--Cushman & Wakefield, Inc., New York, NY; *Int'l*, pg. 873

Dowding, K.S., Chief Fin. Officer--Ferguson International Holdings, Banbury, United Kingdom; *Int'l*, pg. 479

Dowds, Allen, Chief Fin. Officer--J.W. Childs Associates, L.P., Boston, MA; *U.S. Private*, pg. 237

Dowell, Neville, Chief Fin. Officer--Union City Body Company, L.P., Union City, IN; *U.S. Private*, pg. 1118

Dowie, Wolfgang, Chief Fin. Officer--Bosch-Siemens Hausgeraete GmbH, Munich, Germany; *Int'l*, pg. 204

Dowlinis, Michael, Chief Fin. Officer--Micro Networks Corp., Worcester, MA; *U.S. Private*, pg. 969

Downes, David K., Chief Fin. Officer, Chief Admin. Officer, Sr. V.P. & Treas.--Delaware Management Holdings, Inc., Philadelphia, PA; *U.S. Public*, pg. 997

Downes, Laurence M., Chm. Bd. & Chief Fin. Officer--New Jersey Natural Gas Co., Wall, NJ; *U.S. Public*, pg. 1172

Downey, Chuck, Chief Fin. Officer--Warren Distribution, Inc., Omaha, NE; *U.S. Private*, pg. 1151

Downie, Robert, Chief Fin. Officer & V.P.--James Austin Co., Mars, PA; *U.S. Private*, pg. 99

Downing, Robin D., Chief Fin. Officer & Treas.--Boston Pacific, Inc., Anaheim, CA; *U.S. Public*, pg. 278

Downing, William E., Chief Fin. Officer, Exec. V.P. & Treas.--Pacific Telesis Group, San Francisco, CA; *U.S. Public*, pg. 1415

Downs, Benjamin T., Chief Fin. Officer, V.P.-Fin. & Admin. & Treas.--Molten Metal Technology, Inc., Fall River, MA; *U.S. Public*, pg. 1123

Dowsett, Connie, Chief Fin. Officer & Treas.--East Moline Metal Products Company, East Moline, IL; *U.S. Private*, pg. 357

Dox, James B., V.P.-Taxes--Transamerica Corporation, San Francisco, CA; *U.S. Public*, pg. 1629

Doyle, Cecil G., Chief Fin. Officer, Exec. V.P., Treas. & Sec.--Hayes, Seay, Mattern & Mattern, Inc., Roanoke, VA; *U.S. Private*, pg. 513

Doyle, Rick, Controller--Telescope Casual Furniture, Inc., Granville, NY; *U.S. Private*, pg. 1074

Drader, Kelly I., Chief Fin. Officer, Sr. V.P. & Corp. Sec.--EnerMark Income Fund, Calgary, Canada; *Int'l*, pg. 454

Draeger, Gary, Chief Fin. Officer--BVK/McDonald, Milwaukee, WI; *U.S. Private*, pg. 108

Draghi, Ronald L., Chief Fin. Officer & V.P.-MIS--Distribution America, Des Plaines, IL; *U.S. Private*, pg. 335

Drake, Don, Chief Fin. Officer--William O'Neil & Co., Inc., Los Angeles, CA; *U.S. Private*, pg. 817

Draper, Tim, Chief Fin. Officer--Radix Corporation, Salt Lake City, UT; *U.S. Private*, pg. 906

Draut, Erick J., Chief Fin. Officer & Treas.--Unitrin, Inc., Chicago, IL; *U.S. Public*, pg. 1693
Drayer, Nick, Chief Fin. Officer, V.P. & Treas.--Ambac International Corp., Columbia, SC; *U.S. Private*, pg. 48
Drayton, Patrick, Chief Fin. Officer--English China Clays Plc, Theale, United Kingdom; *Int'l*, pg. 455
Drechney, Daniel, Controller--World Trade & Marketing, LTD., Chicago, IL; *U.S. Public*, pg. 1621
Dreher, Gary R., Chief Fin. Officer & V.P.--Hach Company, Loveland, CO; *U.S. Public*, pg. 773
Drella, Dawn M., Chief Fin. Officer--Westmark Group Holdings Inc., Delray Beach, FL; *U.S. Public*, pg. 1761
Dreller, Michael J., Chief Fin. Officer & V.P.--Falcon Products, Inc., Saint Louis, MO; *U.S. Public*, pg. 611
Drew, James L., Chief Fin. Officer--Rehrig Pacific Company, Los Angeles, CA; *U.S. Private*, pg. 919
Drew, William Carl, Chief Fin. Officer--Pollo Tropical, Inc., Miami, FL; *U.S. Public*, pg. 1315
Drewry, George, Chief Fin. Officer--Karsten Manufacturing Corporation, Phoenix, AZ; *U.S. Private*, pg. 608
Dries, William J., Chief Fin. Officer--Guarantee Title & Trust Co., Cincinnati, OH; *U.S. Private*, pg. 485
Driessen, Christine F., Chief Fin. Officer & Sr. V.P.--ESPN, Inc., Bristol, CT; *U.S. Public*, pg. 512
Driggers, Michael, Chief Fin. Officer--Zebco, Tulsa, OK; *U.S. Public*, pg. 265
Driggers, Mike, Chief Fin. Officer--Brunswick Outdoor Recreation Group, Tulsa, OK; *U.S. Public*, pg. 265
Driver, Bob, Chief Fin. Officer--Sturgis Iron & Metal Company, Inc., Sturgis, MI; *U.S. Private*, pg. 1048
Driver, Doug, Chief Fin. Officer--Fortifiber Corporation, Incline Village, NV; *U.S. Private*, pg. 419
Drucker, Howard R., Chief Fin. Officer & V.P.--Monroe Systems For Business, Inc., Morris Plains, NJ; *U.S. Private*, pg. 757
Drucker, Nate, Chief Fin. Officer, Treas. & Sec.--Weber Marking Systems, Inc., Arlington Heights, IL; *U.S. Private*, pg. 1157
Drury, Anthony R., Chief Fin. Officer & V.P.--Quad Systems Corporation, Willow Grove, PA; *U.S. Private*, pg. 898
Drury, David, Chief Fin. Officer--Stolper-Fabralloy Co. LLC, Brookfield, WI; *U.S. Public*, pg. 1640
Drury, John, V.P.-Fin.--Amot Controls Corporation, Richmond, CA; *U.S. Public*, pg. 1405
Druten, Robert J., Chief Fin. Officer & Hallmark-V.P.-Admin.--Hallmark Cards, Inc., Kansas City, MO; *U.S. Private*, pg. 495
Drvostep, Bob, Chief Fin. Officer & V.P.--Dollar Rent A Car, Tulsa, OK; *U.S. Public*, pg. 354
Dryburgh, James T., Chief Fin. Officer & Sr. V.P.--Mackenzie Financial Corporation, Toronto, Canada; *Int'l*, pg. 828
Du Prey, Lefebvre, Chief Fin. Officer--Editions du Juris-Classeur, Paris, France; *Int'l*, pg. 1095
Duane, Dave, Chief Fin. Officer, Controller & Treas.--Heat Controller, Inc., Jackson, MI; *U.S. Private*, pg. 518
Dub, Susan, Chief Fin. Officer--Lawson Software, Minneapolis, MN; *U.S. Private*, pg. 654
Dubel, John, Chief Fin. Officer--Barneys Inc., New York, NY; *U.S. Private*, pg. 116
Dubois, Gunnar, Chief Fin. Officer--Siemens-Elema AB, Solna, Sweden; *Int'l*, pg. 1247
Duch, Gregory S., Chief Fin. Officer--Castle Convertible Fund, Inc., New York, NY; *U.S. Public*, pg. 313
Ducich, Dan, Chief Fin. Officer & Sr. V.P.--Recreational Equipment, Inc., Kent, WA; *U.S. Private*, pg. 914
DuCray, Dean T., Chief Fin. Officer & V.P.--York International Corporation, York, PA; *U.S. Public*, pg. 1788
Duda, Thomas, Chief Fin. Officer & Sec.--Westwood Computer Corporation, Springfield, NJ; *U.S. Private*, pg. 1170
Duddles, Charles W., Chief Fin. Officer & Exec. V.P.--Foodmaker, Inc., San Diego, CA; *U.S. Public*, pg. 661
Dudley, Duane, Chief Fin. Officer--Caltrol, Inc., Glendora, CA; *U.S. Private*, pg. 201
Dudley, Kenneth E., Treas.--The Gorman-Rupp Company, Mansfield, OH; *U.S. Public*, pg. 754
Duff, Philip, Chief Fin. Officer & Mng. Dir.--Morgan Stanley Group Inc., New York, NY; *U.S. Public*, pg. 1132
Duffey, Michael S., Chief Fin. Officer--M.A. Hanna Company, Cleveland, OH; *U.S. Public*, pg. 780
Duffy, James E., Chief Fin. Officer--HS Resources, San Francisco, CA; *U.S. Public*, pg. 772
Dufour, Paul V., Chief Fin. Officer & Exec. V.P.-Fin. & Admin.--IMCO Recycling Inc., Irving, TX; *U.S. Public*, pg. 870
Dufresne, D. Raymond, Chief Fin. Officer & Sr. V.P.--Mohawk Paper Mills, Inc., Cohoes, NY; *U.S. Private*, pg. 755
Dugan, Thomas A., Pres., Chief Exec. Officer & Chief Fin. Officer--Dugan Production Corp., Farmington, NM; *U.S. Private*, pg. 345
Duhamel, Pierre, Chief Fin. Officer & V.P.--Imperial Tobacco Limited, Montreal, Canada; *Int'l*, pg. 112
Duke, Jere R., V.P.--Lancaster Malleable Castings Company, Lancaster, PA; *U.S. Private*, pg. 645
Duke, Jim, Chief Fin. Officer--Century Bancshares, Inc., Washington, DC; *U.S. Public*, pg. 328
Duke, Ron, Sr. V.P. & Chief Fin. Officer--St. Clair Paint and Wallpaper Corporation, Toronto, Canada; *Int'l*, pg. 1170
Dukes, R.R., Chief Fin. Officer--O'Neil Industries Inc., Chicago, IL; *U.S. Private*, pg. 817
Dulik, Arthur, Jr., V.P.-Fin.--Altana, Inc., Melville, NY; *Int'l*, pg. 66
Dulin, Ann, Chief Fin. Officer & V.P.--Gerbig, Snell/Weisheimer & Assoc., Inc., Columbus, OH; *U.S. Private*, pg. 449
Dull, Karen, Chief Fin. Officer & Exec. V.P.--World's Finest Chocolate, Inc., Chicago, IL; *U.S. Private*, pg. 1191
Duman, Greg, Chief Fin. Officer & V.P.--Applied Communications, Inc., Omaha, NE; *U.S. Public*, pg. 1629
Duman, Gregory J., Chief Fin. Officer & Treas.--Transaction Systems Architects, Inc., Omaha, NE; *U.S. Public*, pg. 1629
Dumas, Jocelyn, Chief Fin. Officer & Sr. V.P.-Fin.--Fast Food Merchandisers Inc., Rocky Mount, NC; *U.S. Public*, *pg. 278*
Dumelin, Bruce C., Chief Fin. Officer--Fleet Capital Corporation, Glastonbury, CT; *U.S. Public*, pg. 649
Dumke, William E., Chief Fin. Officer & V.P.-Fin.--Henningsen Foods, Inc., White Plains, NY; *Int'l*, pg. 1074
Dumochel, Larry, Chief Fin. Officer--Comtech Communications Corp., Tempe, AZ; *U.S. Public*, pg. 425
Dumont, Jose J., Chief Fin. Officer & Exec. V.P.--PonceBank, F.S.B., Ponce, PR; *U.S. Public*, pg. 1316
Dumpis, Andy, Chief Fin. Officer--The Excellence Group, Stamford, CT; *U.S. Private*, pg. 387
Dunavant, Philip L., Chief Fin. Officer, V.P. & Treas.--Mark VII, Inc., Memphis, TN; *U.S. Public*, pg. 1046
Dunaway, Allen R., Chief Fin. Officer, V.P. & Sec.--Orthologic Corporation, Tempe, AZ; *U.S. Public*, pg. 1232
Dunaway, Harold, V.P.-Fin., Treas. & Sec.--Motion Industries, Inc., Irondale, AL; *U.S. Public*, pg. 732
Duncan, Art, Chief Fin. Officer--Rowe Furniture Corp., Mc Lean, VA; *U.S. Public*, pg. 1410
Duncan, K., Chief Fin. Officer--Rolls-Royce-Commercial Aero Engines Ltd., Derby, United Kingdom; *Int'l*, pg. 1127
Duncan, Terence W., Chief Fin. Officer & V.P.-Fin.--Methanex Corporation, Vancouver, Canada; *Int'l*, pg. 862
Dune, Daniel, Chief Fin. Officer, V.P.-Fin.& Treas.--Clark Foodservice, Inc., Elk Grove Village, IL; *U.S. Private*, pg. 242
Dunham, Joe, Chief Fin. Officer--DTC Communications, Inc., Nashua, NH; *U.S. Private*, pg. 306
Dunham, John L., Chief Fin. Officer & Exec. V.P.--The May Department Stores Company, Saint Louis, MO; *U.S. Public*, pg. 1063
Dunlap, Pamela L., Chief Fin. Officer & Sr. V.P.--ATL Ultrasound, Inc., Bothell, WA; *U.S. Public*, pg. 11
Dunleary, Charles, Chief Fin. Officer--Windy Hill Pet Food Co., Brentwood, TN; *U.S. Private*, pg. 1182
Dunleavy, Daniel S., Chief Fin. Officer & Admin. Officer & V.P.--Concurrent Computer Corporation, Fort Lauderdale, FL; *U.S. Public*, pg. 430
Dunleavy, Karen, Treas.--Georgetown Partners, Inc., Great Neck, NY; *U.S. Private*, pg. 466
Dunmead, Dave, Chief Fin. Officer & V.P.--Switchcraft, Inc., Chicago, IL; *U.S. Public*, pg. 1366
Dunn, Bill, Chief Fin. Officer--Howe Furniture Corporation, Trumbull, CT; *U.S. Private*, pg. 543
Dunn, Colin, Chief Fin. Officer--Bel Fuse Inc., Jersey City, NJ; *U.S. Public*, pg. 200
Dunn, Rex, Chief Fin. Officer--Peoples Security Insurance Company, Durham, NC; *Int'l*, pg. 27
Dunn, Richard, Chief Fin. Officer & V.P.-Fin.--Supreme International Corp., Miami, FL; *U.S. Public*, pg. 1542
Dunne, Frank, Chief Fin. Officer--Benthos, Inc., North Falmouth, MA; *U.S. Public*, pg. 212
Dunne, John, Chief Fin. Officer & V.P.--National Restaurant Management, Inc., New York, NY; *U.S. Private*, pg. 786
Dunt, Keith, Chief Fin. Officer--British-American Tobacco Co. Ltd., Staines, United Kingdom; *Int'l*, pg. 111
Duplain, Robert, Chief Fin. Officer & Sr. V.P.--The Buschman Co., Cincinnati, OH; *U.S. Private*, pg. 188
Dupont, Bertrand, Mng. Dir.-Fin.--Groupe SEB, Ecueille, France; *Int'l*, pg. 568
Dupont, Richard, Chief Fin. Officer & Sec.--Source Services Corporation, Dallas, TX; *U.S. Public*, pg. 1488
Dupuis, Frank J., Chm. Bd. & Chief Fin. Officer--Your Man Tours, Inc., Inglewood, CA; *U.S. Private*, pg. 1202
Durand, Patrice, Chief Fin. Officer--Groupe Air France, Roissy, France; *Int'l*, pg. 559
Durfee, J.Lang, V.P. & Sec.--Bethel Mills, Inc., Bethel, VT; *U.S. Private*, pg. 141
Durig, Greg, Chief Fin. Officer--Discovery Networks, Inc., Bethesda, MD; *U.S. Private*, pg. 334
Durig, Gregory, Chief Fin. Officer & Exec. V.P.--Discovery Communications, Inc., Bethesda, MD; *U.S. Private*, pg. 334
Duroscher, Robert, Chief Fin. Officer--U.S. Marine Division, Arlington, WA; *U.S. Public*, pg. 266
Dutro, Stephen L., Chief Fin. Officer & Treas.--KLLM Transport Services, Inc., Jackson, MS; *U.S. Public*, pg. 939
Dutta, P.S., Treas. & Chief Fin. Officer--Indian Aluminium Co. Ltd., Calcutta, India; *Int'l*, pg. 51
Dwyer, Daniel P., Chief Fin. Officer, Exec. V.P.-Fin. & Treas.--CommNet Cellular Inc., Englewood, CO; *U.S. Public*, pg. 414
Dwyer, Dean P., Chief Fin. Officer & V.P.-Fin.--The Copley Press, Inc., La Jolla, CA; *U.S. Private*, pg. 275
Dwyer, John, Chief Fin. Officer, Sr. V.P. & Treas.--Bally Total Fitness Holdings Corporation, Chicago, IL; *U.S. Public*, pg. 171
Dwyer, John, Chief Fin. Officer & Sr. V.P.--Bally Total Fitness Corporation, Chicago, IL; *U.S. Public*, pg. 171
Dwyer, Joseph, Chief Fin. Officer & Sr. V.P.--Winstar Global Products, Inc., Fairfield, NJ; *U.S. Public*, pg. 1772
Dyer, Daniel P., Chief Fin. Officer & Sr. V.P.--Advanta Business Services, Voorhees, NJ; *U.S. Public*, pg. 22
Dykema, Henry, Chief Fin. Officer & V.P.--Federal Signal Corporation, Oak Brook, IL; *U.S. Public*, pg. 616
Dykema, Scot, Chief Fin. Officer--The Richards Group, Inc., Dallas, TX; *U.S. Private*, pg. 929
Dykes, Ronald M., Chief Fin. Officer & Exec. V.P.--BellSouth Corporation, Atlanta, GA; *U.S. Public*, pg. 207
Dyson, Karen, V.P.-Fin.--NorAm Gas Transmission, Shreveport, LA; *U.S. Public*, pg. 843
Dzuricky, David J., Sr. V.P.-Fin.--Piedmont Natural Gas Co., Inc., Charlotte, NC; *U.S. Public*, pg. 1295
E., Robert, Ruhle, Chief Fin. Officer--Farrand Controls, Valhalla, NY; *U.S. Private*, pg. 951
Eadie, Graeme, Chief Fin. Officer & Exec. V.P.--Dylex Limited, Toronto, Canada; *Int'l*, pg. 425
Eagan, James, Chief Fin. Officer & Sr. V.P.--Riverwood International Corporation, Atlanta, GA; *U.S. Public*, pg. 1391
Eakin, David M., Chief Fin. Officer--Mellon Bank, N.A.-Northern Region, Erie, PA; *U.S. Public*, pg. 1085
Eakin, Thomas R., Chief Fin. Officer & V.P.-Fin.--Vacu-Dry Company, Sebastopol, CA; *U.S. Public*, pg. 1704
Eanes, Jasper R., Chief Fin. Officer, Exec. V.P. & Treas.--BankAtlantic Bancorp, Inc., Fort Lauderdale, FL; *U.S. Public*, pg. 183
Early, Creighton, Chief Fin. Officer & Exec. V.P.--Earth Technology Corp. USA, Long Beach, CA; *U.S. Public*, pg. 1648
Easley, Mike, Chief Fin. Officer--Tennsco Corporation, Dickson, TN; *U.S. Private*, pg. 1077
Easterman, Dave, Chief Fin. Officer & Controller--B&B Corporate Holdings, Inc., Tampa, FL; *U.S. Private*, pg. 104
Eaton, Dick, Chief Fin. Officer & Sr. V.P.--Highway One Communications, Integrated Marketing Services, San Francisco, CA; *U.S. Private*, pg. 303
Eaton, Mark R., V.P.-Fin.--Aramark Educational Resources Inc. Inc., Golden, CO; *U.S. Private*, pg. 79
Eaton, Rodney, Chief Fin. Officer & V.P.-Admin.--Wizards of the Coast, Renton, WA; *U.S. Private*, pg. 1185
Eaton, Rodney, Chief Fin. Officer & V.P.-Admin.--TSR, Inc., Renton, WA; *U.S. Private*, pg. 1185
Eberhardt, George J., Chief Fin. Officer & Exec. V.P.--Pinnacle Bank, Valparaiso, IN; *U.S. Public*, pg. 1297
Eberle, William, Chief Fin. Officer--Reichhold Chemicals, Inc., Durham, NC; *Int'l*, pg. 370
Ebersole, Richard W., Chief Fin. Officer & Treas.--Outdoor Communications, Inc., Corinth, MS; *U.S. Private*, pg. 822
Ebling, Timothy A., Chief Fin. Officer & Exec. V.P.--Greate Bay Casino Corporation, Atlantic City, NJ; *U.S. Public*, pg. 760
Ebrom, Charles, Exec. V.P.--H.B. Zachry, San Antonio, TX; *U.S. Private*, pg. 1203
Echarte Fernandez, Luis J., Chief Fin. Officer--Grupo Elektra S.A. de C.V., Mexico, Mexico; *Int'l*, pg. 573
Eckels, Paul, Chief Fin. Officer--H.E. Williams, Inc., Carthage, MO; *U.S. Private*, pg. 1178
Eckenrode, W.J., Chief Fin. Officer & Sr. V.P.--Berwind Corporation, Philadelphia, PA; *U.S. Private*, pg. 138
Eckert, Marty, Chief Fin. Officer--Rudolph and Sletten, Inc., Foster City, CA; *U.S. Private*, pg. 950
Eckhoff, Th., Chief Fin. Officer--Siemens A/S, Oslo, Norway; *Int'l*, pg. 1247
Eckstaedt, James R., Chief Fin. Officer & Sr. V.P.--The Cerplex Group, Inc., Tustin, CA; *U.S. Public*, pg. 332
Edby, Hakan, Chief Fin. Officer--Kvaerner Ships Equipment AB, Goteborg, Sweden; *Int'l*, pg. 771
Ede, Graham, Chief Fin. Officer--Lambert Smith Hampton, London, United Kingdom; *Int'l*, pg. 797
Edelman, Steven M., Chief Fin. & Investment Officer & Exec. V.P.--First Union Real Estate Investments, Cleveland, OH; *U.S. Public*, pg. 640
Edelmann, Klaus, Chief Fin. Officer & Exec. V.P.--Deutz AG, Cologne, Germany; *Int'l*, pg. 407
Eden, Jim, Chief Fin. Officer--ACS Industries, Inc., Woonsocket, RI; *U.S. Private*, pg. 3
Edge, John, Chief Fin. Officer--Burnham, Atlanta, GA; *Int'l*, pg. 686
Edlund, Jim, Chief Fin. Officer & V.P.--Le Peep's Grill Inc., Littleton, CO; *U.S. Private*, pg. 655
Edlund, Osoten, Chief Fin. Officer--Skanska Fastigheter Stockholm AB, Danderyd, Sweden; *Int'l*, pg. 1260
Edmond, Robert, Chief Fin. Officer & Controller--Big M, Inc., Totowa, NJ; *U.S. Private*, pg. 143
Edmonds, Rodney, Chief Fin. Officer--Rust Environment & Infrastructure, Inc., Greenville, SC; *U.S. Public*, pg. 1745
Edwards, W.F., Chief Fin. Officer & V.P.--Wexpro Company, Salt Lake City, UT; *U.S. Public*, pg. 1352
Edwards, David M., Chief Fin. Officer & V.P.-Fin.--GATX Corporation, Chicago, IL; *U.S. Public*, pg. 690
Edwards, Frank, Chief Fin. Officer--News Holdings Corp., Vienna, VA; *U.S. Private*, pg. 797
Edwards, G. Gail, Chief Fin. Officer--GC Companies, Inc., Chestnut Hill, MA; *U.S. Public*, pg. 693
Edwards, Ian, Chief Fin. Officer--Superdrug Stores PLC, Croydon, United Kingdom; *Int'l*, pg. 734
Edwards, Joe, Chief Fin. Officer & V.P.-Fin.--Aerovironment, Inc., Monrovia, CA; *U.S. Private*, pg. 25
Edwards, John J., Chief Oper. Officer & V.P.--Edwards Brothers, Inc., Ann Arbor, MI; *U.S. Private*, pg. 365
Edwards, Julie H., Chief Fin. Officer & Sr. V.P.-Fin.--Wainoco Oil Corporation, Houston, TX; *U.S. Public*, pg. 1732
Edwards, Linda M., Chief Fin. Officer & V.P.--Applied Science Associates, Inc., Mc Lean, VA; *U.S. Public*, pg. 109
Edwards, Mark J., Chief Fin. Officer--Newmond PLC, Tamworth, United Kingdom; *Int'l*, pg. 924
Edwards, Robert B., Jr., Chief Fin. Officer & V.P.--Axent Technologies, Rockville, MD; *U.S. Public*, pg. 157
Edwards, Simon P., Chief Fin. Officer--Petersburg Long Distance Inc., Toronto, Canada; *Int'l*, pg. 1040
Edwards, Tracy, Chief Fin. Officer & V.P.--Bell Industries, Inc., El Segundo, CA; *U.S. Public*, pg. 204
Edwards, William F., Chief Fin. Officer & Sr. V.P.--Niagara Mohawk Power Corporation, Syracuse, NY; *U.S. Public*, pg. 1181
Edwards, William F., Asst. V.P.-Investor Rels.--Questar Corporation, Salt Lake City, UT; *U.S. Public*, pg. 1352
Efklides, C., Chief Fin. Officer--Scholl International (ANZ) Pty. Ltd., Dingley, Australia; *Int'l*, pg. 1209
Egan, Daniel J., Chief Fin. Officer, Sr. V.P. & Treas.--ContiMortgage Corporation, Horsham, PA; *U.S. Public*, pg. 439
Egan, Gerald F., Chief Fin. Officer, V.P.-Fin., Treas. & Sec.--Duty Free International, Inc., Ridgefield, CT; *Int'l*, pg. 103

Egan, Michael J., Chief Fin. Officer--PECO Energy Company, Philadelphia, PA; *U.S. Public*, pg. 1268
Egan, Rosemarie C., Chief Fin. Officer--Wilton Corporation, Palatine, IL; *U.S. Private*, pg. 1181
Egan, Thomas, Chief Fin. Officer--The Clinipad Corporation, Rocky Hill, CT; *U.S. Private*, pg. 246
Egeland, John, Chief Fin. Officer & Exec. V.P.--Centex Corporation, Dallas, TX; *U.S. Public*, pg. 322
Eggleston, Michael, Chief Fin. Officer--Young Dental Manufacturing, Earth City, MO; *U.S. Private*, pg. 1201
Egley, Thomas, Chief Fin. Officer--Southland Industries, Long Beach, CA; *U.S. Private*, pg. 1018
Ehlers, Bernd, Chief Fin. Officer--Bosch Braking Systems-North America, South Bend, IN; *Int'l*, pg. 204
Ehrlich, Herbert, Chief Fin. Officer--W. Gamby & Co., New York, NY; *U.S. Private*, pg. 439
Eichel, Beverly, Chief Fin. Officer & Exec. V.P.--Danskin Inc., New York, NY; *U.S. Public*, pg. 483
Eichel, Beverly, Chief Fin. Officer--Pennaco Hosiery, New York, NY; *U.S. Public*, pg. 483
Eichenbaum, Samuel, Chief Fin. Officer & V.P.-Fin.--New Brunswick Scientific Co., Inc., Edison, NJ; *U.S. Public*, pg. 1169
Eickere, Heinz, Chief Fin. Officer--Kloeckner & Co. AG, Duisburg, Germany; *Int'l*, pg. 737
Eickhoff, John R., Chief Fin. Officer & Exec. V.P.--Ceridian Corporation, Bloomington, MN; *U.S. Public*, pg. 330
Eidam, Michael, Chief Fin. Officer--Siemens Osakeytioe, Helsinki, Finland; *Int'l*, pg. 1247
Eilert, Norman E., Chief Fin. Officer & Exec. V.P.--A. Teichert & Son, Inc., Sacramento, CA; *U.S. Private*, pg. 1072
Eiref, Zvi, Chief Fin. Officer & V.P.-Fin.--Church & Dwight Co., Inc., Princeton, NJ; *U.S. Public*, pg. 355
Eisele, Anne E., Chief Fin. Officer & Sr. V.P.--Geotek Communications, Montvale, NJ; *U.S. Public*, pg. 739
Eisenberg, Craig, Chief Fin. Officer & Treas.--American Strip Steel Inc., Kearny, NJ; *U.S. Private*, pg. 62
Eisenberg, Glenn A., Chief Fin. Officer & Sr. V.P.--United Dominion Industries, Ltd., Charlotte, NC; *U.S. Public*, pg. 1675
Eisenschenk, Mark, Exec. V.P.--Ringer Corporation, Bloomington, MN; *U.S. Public*, pg. 1390
Eisenschenk, Mark G., Chief Fin. Officer--Dexol, Torrance, CA; *U.S. Public*, pg. 1390
Ekholm, Thomas, Chief Fin. Officer--Swedish Rail System SRS, Ystad, Sweden; *Int'l*, pg. 1199
Ekle, Tom, Chief Fin. Officer & Treas.--AMI Industries, Inc., Colorado Springs, CO; *U.S. Public*, pg. 401
El-Hillow, Michael, Chief Fin. Officer & Sr. V.P.--Helix Technology Corp., Mansfield, MA; *U.S. Public*, pg. 808
Elam, Gene G., Chief Fin. Officer & V.P.-Fin.--Homestake Mining Company, San Francisco, CA; *U.S. Public*, pg. 832
Elbin, John C., Chief Fin. Officer--Lilly Industries, Inc., Indianapolis, IN; *U.S. Public*, pg. 994
Elchynski, Ted, Chief Fin. Officer & Sr. V.P.--Cincinnati Financial Corp., Fairfield, OH; *U.S. Public*, pg. 368
Elder, Jeffrey, Chief Fin. Officer--Foundation Health Systems, Inc., Pueblo, CO; *U.S. Public*, pg. 678
Eldridge, Robert H., Chief Fin. Officer & Exec. V.P.--Briggs & Stratton Corporation, Wauwatosa, WI; *U.S. Public*, pg. 252
Elets, Stan, Chief Fin. Officer--Oreck Corporation, New Orleans, LA; *U.S. Private*, pg. 819
Eliassen, Jon E., Chief Fin. Officer & V.P.-Fin.--The Washington Water Power Company, Spokane, WA; *U.S. Public*, pg. 1744
Elingburg, Wesley R., Chief Fin. Officer, Exec. V.P. & Treas.--Laboratory Corp. of America Holdings, Burlington, NC; *U.S. Public*, pg. 973
Elizondo, Jorge Ancira, Chief Fin. Officer--Altos Hornos de Mexico, S.A., Monclova, Mexico; *Int'l*, pg. 66
Elkes, Matthew O., Chief Fin. Officer & Treas.--Almo Corp., Philadelphia, PA; *U.S. Private*, pg. 44
Elkin, Michael, V.P., Chief Fin. Officer & Treas.--Med/Waste, Inc., Hialeah, FL; *U.S. Public*, pg. 1077
Ellberger, Larry, Chief Fin. Officer & Sr. V.P.-Strategic Plng. & Devel.--W.R. Grace & Co., Boca Raton, FL; *U.S. Public*, pg. 754
Ellerbrook, Niel C., V.P.-Fin.--IGC Energy, Inc., Indianapolis, IN; *U.S. Public*, pg. 875
Elletson, Jon D., Chief Fin. Officer--Foster & Gallagher, Inc., Peoria, IL; *U.S. Private*, pg. 420
Ellington, Donald E., Chief Fin. Officer--UniGroup, Inc., Fenton, MO; *U.S. Private*, pg. 1117
Ellington, Stanley E., Jr., Chief Fin. Officer, V.P.-Fin. & Treas.--Production Management Companies, Inc., Harvey, LA; *U.S. Private*, pg. 888
Elliott, H. Jay, Chief Fin. Officer, Sr. V.P. & Treas.--The Lincoln Electric Company, Cleveland, OH; *U.S. Public*, pg. 996
Elliott, Mike, Chief Fin. Officer & Controller--Anchor Industries Inc., Evansville, IN; *U.S. Private*, pg. 71
Elliott, Steven G., Vice Chm. & Chief Fin. Officer--Mellon Bank Corporation, Pittsburgh, PA; *U.S. Public*, pg. 1084
Elliott, Steven G., Chief Fin. Officer--Mellon Bank, N.A., Pittsburgh, PA; *U.S. Public*, pg. 1085
Ellis, Gary, Sr. V.P. & Chief Fin. Officer--Consolidated Cigar Corp., Fort Lauderdale, FL; *U.S. Private*, pg. 690
Ellis, Jack W., Comptroller--NorAm Energy Corp., Shreveport, LA; *U.S. Public*, pg. 843
Ellis, Rick, Chief Fin. Officer--Mary Maxim, Ltd., Paris, Canada; *U.S. Private*, pg. 716
Elliston, Michael, V.P.-Fin & Treas.--Holly's Inc., Grand Rapids, MI; *U.S. Private*, pg. 535
Ellwein, Leonard, Chief Fin. Officer & Controller--Randall Stores, Inc., Mitchell, SD; *U.S. Private*, pg. 909
Eloi, Fenel M., Chief Fin. Officer, V.P.-Fin. & Treas.--Genome Therapeutics Corporation, Waltham, MA; *U.S. Public*, pg. 730
Elsesser, James R., Chief Fin. Officer & V.P.--Ralston Purina Company, Saint Louis, MO; *U.S. Public*, pg. 1359
Elwood, John, Chief Fin. Officer & Exec. V.P.--Prime Hospitality Corp., Fairfield, NJ; *U.S. Public*, pg. 1326
Ember, G. Howard, Jr., V.P.-Fin. & Asst. Sec.--Tootsie Roll Industries, Inc., Chicago, IL; *U.S. Public*, pg. 1621
Ember, G. Howard, Jr., V.P.-Fin. & Admin.--World Trade & Marketing, LTD., Chicago, IL; *U.S. Public*, pg. 1621
Ember, H., V.P.-Fin.--Cella's Confections, Inc., New York, NY; *U.S. Public*, pg. 1621
Embleton, D., Chief Fin. Officer--The Sunlight Service Group Ltd., Basingstoke, United Kingdom; *Int'l*, pg. 385
Emde, Richard, V.P.-Fin.--Sun-Maid Growers of California, Kingsburg, CA; *U.S. Private*, pg. 1051
Emerman, Ronald P., Chief Fin. Officer--Macpherson Meistergram, Inc., Greensboro, NC; *U.S. Private*, pg. 1177
Emery, Rory M., Chief Fin. Officer & V.P.-Fin.--Bachman Company, Reading, PA; *U.S. Private*, pg. 109
Emmanuelli, Milton, Controller & Treas.--Crown Andersen Inc., Peachtree City, GA; *U.S. Public*, pg. 462
Emmanuelli, Milton, Chief Fin. Officer--Andersen 2000 Inc., Peachtree City, GA; *U.S. Public*, pg. 462
Emmert, John C., Jr., Chief Fin. Officer, Sr. V.P. & Treas.--American Arbitration Association, New York, NY; *U.S. Private*, pg. 50
Emson, Allan, Chief Fin. Officer--IMI Plc, Witton, United Kingdom; *Int'l*, pg. 646
Endres, John J., Chief Fin. Officer & V.P.-Fin.--Golub Corporation, Schenectady, NY; *U.S. Private*, pg. 463
Endres, Ronald J., Chief Fin. Officer & Exec. V.P.--Southern Union Company, Austin, TX; *U.S. Public*, pg. 1491
Engel, David, Chief Fin. Officer & Exec. V.P.--Del Global Technologies, Valhalla, NY; *U.S. Public*, pg. 493
Engel, Frank T., Chief Fin. Officer--ESAB Welding & Cutting Products, Hanover, PA; *Int'l*, pg. 281
Engelhardtsen, Jan, Chief Fin. Officer--Stolt-Nielsen S.A., London, United Kingdom; *Int'l*, pg. 1301
Engelman, Irwin, Chief Fin. Officer--MacAndrews & Forbes Holdings Inc., New York, NY; *U.S. Private*, pg. 689
Engelman, Irwin, Exec. V.P. & Chief Fin. Officer--Mafco Worldwide Corp., Camden, NJ; *U.S. Private*, pg. 690
Engelman, Wayne, Chief Fin. Officer & Sr. V.P.--Colle & McVoy Marketing Communications, Minneapolis, MN; *U.S. Private*, pg. 252
Engels, Lawrence A., Chief Fin. Officer, V.P., & Treas.--Commercial Metals Company, Dallas, TX; *U.S. Public*, pg. 411
Engelsma, Bruce W., Chief Fin. Officer--Kraus-Anderson Construction Company, Minneapolis, MN; *U.S. Private*, pg. 635
England, David, Chief Fin. Officer--Western International Media Corporation, Los Angeles, CA; *U.S. Private*, pg. 1165
Englefield, F.W., IV, Co-Pres., Chief Exec., Chief Fin. Officer & Sec.--Englefield, Inc., Newark, OH; *U.S. Private*, pg. 377
Englekirk, Robert E., Chm. Bd., Pres. & Chief Exec. Officer--Robert Englekirk, Inc., Los Angeles, CA; *U.S. Private*, pg. 377
English, Chris, Chief Fin. Officer & Treas.--Webster Industries Inc., Tiffin, OH; *U.S. Private*, pg. 1157
English, Robert, Chief Fin. Officer & Treas.--Value Property Trust, New Brunswick, NJ; *U.S. Public*, pg. 1707
Englund, James, Chief Fin. Officer--Milton Roy Company, Ivyland, PA; *U.S. Public*, pg. 1534
Ennest, John W., Vice Chm., Chief Fin. Officer & Treas.--Citizens Banking Corporation, Flint, MI; *U.S. Public*, pg. 379
Enochs, Jill, Chief Fin. Officer--Citizens First State Bank, Hartford City, IN; *U.S. Public*, pg. 632
Enright, James, Chief Fin. Officer--Miami Systems Corporation, Cincinnati, OH; *U.S. Private*, pg. 740
Enright, Vincent D., Chief Fin. Officer & Sr. V.P.--Brooklyn Union, Brooklyn, NY; *U.S. Public*, pg. 259
Enticknap, Joan, Chief Fin. Officer & Exec. V.P.--Seafirst Corporation, Seattle, WA; *U.S. Public*, pg. 181
Epp, Peter, Chief Fin. Officer--Dixie Union Verpackungen GmbH, Kempten, Germany; *U.S. Public*, pg. 440
Epperlein, Richard, Controller & Treas.--A. Zeregas Sons, Inc., Fair Lawn, NJ; *U.S. Private*, pg. 1204
Epperson, Robert J., Sec. & Treas.--Enterprise Electronics Corp., Enterprise, AL; *U.S. Public*, pg. 1563
Epskamp, Leo, Chief Fin. Officer--Reed Technology and Information Services Inc., Horsham, PA; *Int'l*, pg. 1096
Epstein, Glenn, Pres. & Chief Exec. Officer--Oxford Instruments-Nuclear Measurements Group, Oak Ridge, TN; *Int'l*, pg. 1018
Epstein, Steve, Chief Fin. Officer--Aquion, Elk Grove Village, IL; *U.S. Private*, pg. 78
Epstein, Steve, Chief Fin. Officer--RainSoft Water Treatment Systems, Elk Grove Village, IL; *U.S. Private*, pg. 78
Erath, David, Chief Fin. Officer--Schwegmann Giant Super Markets, New Orleans, LA; *U.S. Private*, pg. 629
Erazmus, Walter T., Chief Fin. Officer & Exec. V.P.--Gibraltar Steel Corp., Buffalo, NY; *U.S. Public*, pg. 742
Erb, Jeffrey L., Chief Fin. Officer--Owensboro Grain Co., Inc., Owensboro, KY; *U.S. Private*, pg. 824
Erbacher, John, Controller--H.M.G. Worldwide Corp., New York, NY; *U.S. Public*, pg. 771
Ercolino, George, Chief Fin. Officer--Trophy Holdings Inc., Elmwood Park, NJ; *U.S. Private*, pg. 1105
Ercolino, George, Chief Fin. Officer--Freeman Products, Elmwood Park, NJ; *U.S. Private*, pg. 1105
Erickson, Dennis D., Chief Fin. Officer, Treas. & Exec. V.P.--Norwest Bank Colorado N.A., Denver, CO; *U.S. Public*, pg. 1202
Erickson, Diane, Chief Fin. Officer & Sr. V.P.--Diversified Dynamics Corporation, Minneapolis, MN; *U.S. Private*, pg. 336
Erickson, Frederick J., Chief Fin. Officer, V.P., Treas. & Asst. Sec.--Bull Run Corporation, Atlanta, GA; *U.S. Public*, pg. 267
Erickson, Jerry L., Chief Fin. Officer--Padilla Speer Beardsley Inc., Minneapolis, MN; *U.S. Private*, pg. 833
Erickson, Robert M., Chief Fin. Officer & Treas.--Citation Insurance Group, San Jose, CA; *U.S. Public*, pg. 376
Erikson, Robert W., Pres., Chief Fin. Officer & Treas.--CERBCO, Inc., Landover, MD; *U.S. Public*, pg. 330
Eriksson, Bengt, Chief Fin. Officer--Esselte Chrono AB, Solna, Sweden; *Int'l*, pg. 459
Erl, Gerhard H., V.P.-Fin. & Plng.--NewTel Communications, Saint Johns, Canada; *Int'l*, pg. 115
Ernest, Ron, Chief Fin. Officer--Todd Pipe & Supply Hawthorne, Hawthorne, CA; *U.S. Private*, pg. 1090
Ervine, Brian R., Chief Fin. Officer & V.P.-Fin.--PC Service Source, Inc., Dallas, TX; *U.S. Public*, pg. 1240
Erwin, Tom, Chief Fin. Officer & Sr. V.P.-Fin.--Stant Corporation, Denver, CO; *Int'l*, pg. 1396
Esak, Mary, Chief Fin. Officer & Controller--Nexus Plastics, Inc., Hawthorne, NJ; *U.S. Private*, pg. 797
Escalante, Jaime, Chief Fin. Officer--Aero Peru Corporation, Coral Gables, FL; *U.S. Private*, pg. 24
Espensen, Niels Leth, Chief Fin. Officer--Royal Copenhagen A/S, Frederiksberg, Denmark; *Int'l*, pg. 1134
Esplin, Kimo, Chief Fin. Officer--Huntsman Corporation, Salt Lake City, UT; *U.S. Private*, pg. 549
Esposito, John, Chief Fin. Officer--Andin International Inc., New York, NY; *U.S. Private*, pg. 73
Essenburg, Sally, Pres.--CareerTrack Inc., Boulder, CO; *U.S. Public*, pg. 1555
Essex, David, Mng. Dir.-Fin.--Vickers PLC, London, United Kingdom; *Int'l*, pg. 1466
Estes, Larry, Chief Fin. Officer & First V.P.--Noel Canning Corporation, Yakima, WA; *U.S. Private*, pg. 800
Etheridge, Hugh, Chief Fin. Officer--Matthew Clark Taunton, Ltd., Bristol, United Kingdom; *Int'l*, pg. 848
Etherington, Glenn A., Chief Fin. Officer & Sec.--Brite Voice Systems, Inc., Heathrow, FL; *U.S. Public*, pg. 257
Etherington, Glenn A., Chief Fin. Officer & Exec. V.P.--Brite Voice Systems, Canton, MA; *U.S. Public*, pg. 257
Ethridge, Joseph A., Chief Fin. Officer & Sr. V.P.--Sammons Enterprises, Inc., Dallas, TX; *U.S. Private*, pg. 963
Ettl, Ali, Chief Fin. Officer, V.P.-Fin. & Controller--Putzmeister, Inc., Sturtevant, WI; *U.S. Private*, pg. 896
Ettwein, Falk, Chief Fin. Officer--Axel Springer Verlag AG, Berlin, Germany; *Int'l*, pg. 102
Euler, B., Chief Fin. Officer--Siemens plc, Sunbury, United Kingdom; *Int'l*, pg. 1247
Euliss, Dan, Chief Fin. Officer--Kyocera Industrial Ceramics Corp., Vancouver, WA; *Int'l*, pg. 776
Eustace, D.G., Chief Fin. Officer & Exec. V.P.--Philips Electronics N.V., Eindhoven, Netherlands; *Int'l*, pg. 1051
Eustace, Dudley G., Chief Fin. Officer & Exec. V.P.--Philips International B.V., Eindhoven, Netherlands; *Int'l*, pg. 1051
Evanger, Marc, Chief Fin. Officer & V.P.-Fin. & Admin.--Quality Food Centers, Inc., Bellevue, WA; *U.S. Public*, pg. 1349
Evanger, Marc, Chief Fin. Officer, V.P., Treas. & Sec.--QFC Holding Company, Stamford, CT; *U.S. Public*, pg. 1349
Evans, Andrew C., Chief Fin. Officer & Exec. V.P.--Simon & Schuster, New York, NY; *U.S. Private*, pg. 777
Evans, Andrew J., Chief Fin. Officer & Sr. V.P.--Harrison Paint Corp., Canton, OH; *U.S. Private*, pg. 506
Evans, Eric, Controller--FMC Corp., Agricultural Products Group, Philadelphia, PA; *U.S. Public*, pg. 605
Evans, Gregory M., Chief Fin. Officer--Robert Mondavi Winery, Inc., Oakville, CA; *U.S. Public*, pg. 1393
Evans, J.V., Chief Fin. Officer--Russell Castings Ltd., Leicester, United Kingdom; *Int'l*, pg. 449
Evans, Jerome W., Chief Fin. Officer & Exec. V.P.--First Maryland Bancorp, Baltimore, MD; *Int'l*, pg. 64
Evans, Jody, Treas. & Sec.--Ray Bell Construction Co. Inc., Brentwood, TN; *U.S. Private*, pg. 131
Evans, John E., Chief Fin. Officer--R.W. Beck, Inc., Seattle, WA; *U.S. Private*, pg. 128
Evans, Kenneth H., Jr., Chief Fin. Officer & Chief Acctg. Officer--Ameritruck Distribution Corporation, Fort Worth, TX; *U.S. Private*, pg. 65
Evans, Larry, Chief Fin. Officer--Banner Engineering Corp., Minneapolis, MN; *U.S. Private*, pg. 114
Evans, Ray G., Chief Fin. Officer & Controller--American Rug Craftsmen, Sugar Valley, GA; *U.S. Public*, pg. 1121
Evans, Richard L., Chief Oper. Officer, Chief Fin. Officer, Exec. V.P. & Treas.--Reunion Industries, Inc., Stamford, CT; *U.S. Public*, pg. 1383
Eveleigh, Robert J., Chief Fin. Officer, V.P-Fin. & Treas.--Metro Information Services, Virginia Beach, VA; *U.S. Public*, pg. 1102
Everett, Addison L., Chief Fin. Officer & V.P.--Syracuse Supply Company, Syracuse, NY; *U.S. Private*, pg. 1060
Everett, Ken, Chief Fin. Officer--Proto-Power Corporation, Groton, CT; *U.S. Public*, pg. 965
Evers, Susan K., Chief Fin. Officer--USAA Federal Savings Bank, San Antonio, TX; *U.S. Private*, pg. 1114
Evertsnn, Peter, Dr., Chief Fin. Officer--Migros, Zurich, Switzerland; *Int'l*, pg. 865
Ewersow, A., Chief Fin. Officer--Meyer Forest Products Ltd, London, United Kingdom; *Int'l*, pg. 864
Ewing, R. Stewart, Jr., Chief Fin. Officer & Sr. V.P.--Century Telephone Enterprises, Inc., Monroe, LA; *U.S. Public*, pg. 329
Ewing, Ron, Chief Fin. Officer, Chief Oper. Officer & Sec.--LVL Advertising, Palo Alto, CA; *U.S. Private*, pg. 640
Eyckens, Bayden, Chief Fin. Officer--Pacific Dunlop Cables Group, Tottenham, Australia; *Int'l*, pg. 1021
Eyster, Donald, Chief Fin. Officer & V.P.--Frog Switch & Manufacturing Company, Carlisle, PA; *U.S. Private*, pg. 429
Ezerski, Ronald E., Chief Fin. Officer, Exec. V.P., Treas. & Sec.--Patterson Dental Company, Saint Paul, MN; *U.S. Public*, pg. 1265
Fadden, Jerome T., Chief Fin. Officer, V.P. & Treas.--NAC Re Corp., Greenwich, CT; *U.S. Public*, pg. 1144
Fadden, Jerome T., Chief Fin. Officer, Exec. V.P. & Treas.--NAC Reinsurance Corporation, Greenwich, CT; *U.S. Public*, pg. 1144

Fadden, Jerome T., Chief Fin. Officer, Exec. V.P. & Treas.--Greenwich Insurance Company, Greenwich, CT; *U.S. Public*, pg. 1144

Fadden, Jerome T., Chief Fin. Officer, Exec. V.P. & Treas.--Indian Harbor Insurance Company, Greenwich, CT; *U.S. Public*, pg. 1144

Fagan, James F., Chief Fin. Officer, Exec. V.P. & Treas.--Arrow Automotive Industries, Inc., Framingham, MA; *U.S.* Public, pg. 133

Fagan, James S., Chief Fin. Officer & Sr. V.P.--Herbert Malarkey Roofing Company, Portland, OR; *U.S. Private*, pg. 698

Fagan, Mitchell, Chief Fin. Officer & V.P.--McMullen/Argus Publishers, Placentia, CA; *U.S. Public*, pg. 1328

Fagan, Richard J., Acting Chief Fin. Officer--Quaker Chemical Corporation, Conshohocken, PA; *U.S. Public*, pg. 1346

Fagerberg, Howard, Chief Fin. Officer & Exec. V.P.--Childrens Press Inc., Danbury, CT; *Int'l*, pg. 794

Fahrner, James, Chief Fin. Officer & V.P.--JPE, Inc., Ann Arbor, MI; *U.S. Public*, pg. 919

Fahy, A.E., Chief Fin. Officer--McPherson's Limited, Mulgrave, Australia; *Int'l*, pg. 852

Faibish, Mair, Chief Fin. Officer & Exec. V.P.--Krantor Corporation, Syosset, NY; *U.S. Public*, pg. 966

Fairbanks, John F., Chief Fin. Officer & V.P.--New England Business Service, Inc., Groton, MA; *U.S. Public*, pg. 1170

Faircloth, Phillip, Chief Fin. Officer, Sr. V.P., Treas.--Warehouse Home Furnishings Distributor, Dublin, GA; *U.S. Private*, pg. 1150

Faklaris, John R., Chief Fin. Officer--DMI, Inc., Goodfield, IL; *U.S. Private*, pg. 305

Falcone, Robert, Chief Fin. Officer & V.P.--Nike, Inc., Beaverton, OR; *U.S. Public*, pg. 1184

Falconi, Robert, Chief Fin. Officer, Treas. & Sec.--Planning Systems Inc., Mc Lean, VA; *U.S. Private*, pg. 869

Falero, Ralph, Chief Fin. Officer--Barnhardt Manufacturing Co., Charlotte, NC; *U.S. Private*, pg. 116

Falkenback, Claes, Chief Fin. Officer--Tretorn, Brockton, MA; *Int'l*, pg. 1072

Fancher, Jan T., Chief Fin. Officer, Treas. & Sec.--Cadet Manufacturing Company, Vancouver, WA; *U.S. Private*, pg. 198

Fancher, Robert B., Chief Fin. Officer & V.P.-Fin.--The Empire District Electric Company, Joplin, MO; *U.S. Public*, pg. 579

Fanchi, Joseph B., Chief Fin. Officer, V.P.-Fin. & Treas.--Skyline Corporation, Elkhart, IN; *U.S. Public*, pg. 1476

Fanelli, Bud, Chief Fin. Officer--Sinclair/Ameritone Paint Corp., Los Angeles, CA; *Int'l*, pg. 663

Fankhauser, James R., Chief Fin. Officer & Treas.--Fahlgren, Dublin, OH; *U.S. Private*, pg. 391

Fanska, Jerry W., Chief Fin. Officer--Layne Christenson Co., Mission Woods, KS; *U.S. Public*, pg. 981

Fanti, R. Timothy, Sr. V.P.-Fin. & Admin.--Beiersdorf, Inc., Norwalk, CT; *Int'l*, pg. 182

Faraone, Camillo, Chief Fin. Officer--Gitano Fashions Ltd., Bowling Green, KY; *U.S. Public*, pg. 686

Farber, Jack, Chm. Bd., Pres. & Chief Exec. Officer--CSS Industries, Inc., Philadelphia, PA; *U.S. Public*, pg. 283

Farer, Leon, Chief Fin. Officer--Meier & Frank, Portland, OR; *U.S. Public*, pg. 1064

Farish, Charles, Chief Fin. Officer & V.P.--Bird Machine Company, South Walpole, MA; *U.S. Public*, pg. 166

Farley, Walter, Chief Fin. Officer--Kohlberg & Company, LLC, Mount Kisco, NY; *U.S. Private*, pg. 629

Farlow, William S., Chief Fin. Officer--O.A. Newton & Son Co., Bridgeville, DE; *U.S. Private*, pg. 797

Farmer, Jim, Chief Fin. Officer--Frankel & Company, Chicago, IL; *U.S. Private*, pg. 424

Farquharson, Donald E., Chief Fin. Officer--Cambridge-Lee Industries, Inc., Boston, MA; *U.S. Private*, pg. 202

Farr, Joe H., Exec. V.P. & Chief Fin. Officer--Temple-Inland Mortgage Corporation, Austin, TX; *U.S. Public*, pg. 1575

Farr, Richard D., Sr. V.P. & Chief Fin. Officer--Tompkins County Trust Company, Ithaca, NY; *U.S. Public*, pg. 1621

Farrar, Fred, Chief Fin. Officer & Sec.--Hospital Affiliates Development Corporation, Nashville, TN; *U.S. Private*, pg. 540

Farrell, Christine, Controller--Northeast Environmental Services, Inc., Canastota, NY; *U.S. Public*, pg. 546

Farren, Owen, Pres. & Chief Exec. Officer--SL Industries, Inc., Mount Laurel, NJ; *U.S. Public*, pg. 1418

Farrenkopf, John, Chief Fin. Officer, Chief Acctg. Officer & V.P.--Provident Financial Group, Inc., Cincinnati, OH; *U.S. Public*, pg. 1338

Farrer, David, Chief Fin. Officer--GGK London Ltd., London, United Kingdom; *Int'l*, pg. 1335

Farstad, Atle, Chief Fin. Officer--Kvaerner a.s.a., Lysaker, Norway; *Int'l*, pg. 766

Fash, Victoria R., Chief Fin. Officer & Exec. V.P.--Cognizant Corporation, Westport, CT; *U.S. Public*, pg. 395

Fatkin, David, Chief Fin. Officer--Raleigh Industries Ltd., Nottingham, United Kingdom; *Int'l*, pg. 394

Faulders, C. Thomas, III, Chief Fin. Officer & Exec. V.P.--BDM International, Inc., Mc Lean, VA; *U.S. Public*, pg. 1558

Faulkner, Carolyn, Chief Fin. Officer & V.P.--Designs, Inc., Needham, MA; *U.S. Public*, pg. 501

Faulkner, David, Vice Chm. & Chief Fin. Officer--Memorex Telex Corp., Irving, TX; *Int'l*, pg. 857

Faulkner, David J., Vice Chm. & Chief Fin. Officer--Memorex Telex N.V., Amsterdam, Netherlands; *Int'l*, pg. 857

Fawer, Martin S., Chief Fin. Officer & Treas.--Zing Technologies, Inc., Valhalla, NY; *U.S. Public*, pg. 1792

Fealy, Robert S., Chief Fin. Officer--Duchossois Industries, Inc., Elmhurst, IL; *U.S. Private*, pg. 344

Fearon, J.A., Chief Fin. Officer--Waterford Crystal Ltd., Kilbarry, Ireland; *Int'l*, pg. 1487

Fears, Douglas, Chief Fin. Officer & V.P.-Fin.--Helmerich & Payne, Inc., Tulsa, OK; *U.S. Public*, pg. 808

Featherston, Charlie, Chief Fin. Officer--AGA Catalog Marketing & Design, New York, NY; *U.S. Private*, pg. 5

Featherstone, Bob, Chief Fin. Officer & Treas.--XATA Corporation, Burnsville, MN; *U.S. Public*, pg. 1783

Feely, Jim, Chief Fin. Officer--Transistor Devices, Inc., Cedar Knolls, NJ; *U.S. Private*, pg. 1097

Feeney, F. X., V.P.-Fin.--Sterling Davis Standard, South Plainfield, NJ; *Int'l*, pg. 1240

Feeney, Gerald F., Chief Fin. Officer, V.P. & Treas.--California Water Service Co., San Jose, CA; *U.S. Public*, pg. 294

Feeney, John R., Chief Fin. Officer--Summit Bank, Chatham, NJ; *U.S. Public*, pg. 1528

Feeney, Paul M., Chief Fin. Officer & Exec. V.P.--AEP Industries, Inc., South Hackensack, NJ; *U.S. Public*, pg. 4

Feher, Valorie, Chief Fin. Officer--Woodward-Clyde International, Denver, CO; *U.S. Public*, pg. 1657

Feher, Valorie, Chief Fin. Officer--Woodward-Clyde Consultants, Denver, CO; *U.S. Public*, pg. 1657

Fehr, Lawrence F., Chief Fin. Officer & V.P.-Fin.--Herff Jones Inc., Indianapolis, IN; *U.S. Private*, pg. 523

Fehsenfeld, Fred M., V.P. & Treas.--Crystal Flash Petroleum Corp., Indianapolis, IN; *U.S. Private*, pg. 294

Feist, Howard N., Sr. V.P.-Fin.--Congoleum Corporation, Mercerville, NJ; *U.S. Public*, pg. 69

Felderman, Douglas, Chief Fin. Officer--Strouds, Inc., City of Industry, CA; *U.S. Public*, pg. 1525

Feldkamp, Karen, Chief Fin. Officer--The Knight Publishing Co., Charlotte, NC; *U.S. Public*, pg. 964

Feldman, Mark, Chief Fin. Officer & Treas.--Fresh Juice Company, Great Neck, NY; *U.S. Private*, pg. 427

Feldman, Steve, Chief Fin. Officer--One Price Clothing Stores, Inc., Duncan, SC; *U.S. Public*, pg. 1225

Feldner, Ronald A., Chief Fin. Officer & Sec.--Bill Heard Enterprises, Inc., Columbus, GA; *U.S. Private*, pg. 515

Feldstein, Eric A., Chief Fin. Officer & Exec. V.P.--General Motors Acceptance Corporation (GMAC), Detroit, MI; *U.S. Public*, pg. 719

Feles, Aristedes, Chief Fin. Officer & V.P.-Fin.--Edelbrock Corp., Torrance, CA; *U.S. Public*, pg. 563

Felix, Robert F., Chief Fin. Officer, Exec. V.P. & Treas.--First Federal Savings, East Hartford, CT; *U.S. Public*, pg. 632

Feller, Alan, Chief Oper. Officer, Chief Fin. Officer, Treas. & Sec.--G-III Apparel Group, Ltd., New York, NY; *U.S. Public*, pg. 690

Fellerman, William, Chief Fin. Officer, Treas. & Sec.--Star Multi Care Services Inc., Hicksville, NY; *U.S. Public*, pg. 1510

Fenstermaker, Jerald, Chief Fin. Officer & V.P.--Citicorp Mortgage, Inc., Saint Louis, MO; *U.S. Public*, pg. 378

Ferandez, J.C., Chief Fin. Officer--CXR SA, Abondant, France; *U.S. Public*, pg. 1108

Ferguson, Bruce, Chief Fin. Officer & Treas.--Macro Computer Products Inc., Rochester Hills, MI; *U.S. Private*, pg. 693

Ferguson, Gary L., Chief Fin. Officer & V.P.--International Shipholding Corporation, New Orleans, LA; *U.S. Public*, pg. 907

Ferguson, Jack R., Chief Fin. Officer, V.P.-Fin. & Treas.--Ingles Markets, Incorporated, Black Mountain, NC; *U.S. Public*, pg. 878

Ferguson, John W., Chief Fin. Officer & V.P.--Poco Petroleums Ltd., Calgary, Canada; *Int'l*, pg. 1061

Fernandez, Chris, Chief Fin. Officer--McCormick Distilling Co., Weston, MO; *U.S. Private*, pg. 720

Fernandez, Claude, Chief Fin. Officer, Exec. V.P., Sr. V.P. & Mng. Dir.--W.P. Carey & Co., Inc., New York, NY; *U.S. Private*, pg. 209

Fernandez, Emanuel, Pres. & Chief Fin. Officer--Condal Distributors Inc., Bronx, NY; *U.S. Private*, pg. 262

Fernandez, James N., Chief Fin. Officer & Sr. V.P.-Fin.--Tiffany & Co., New York, NY; *U.S. Public*, pg. 1608

Fernandez, James N., Chief Fin. Officer--Tiffany & Co., London, United Kingdom; *U.S. Public*, pg. 1609

Fernandez, James N., Chief Fin. Officer--Tiffco Jewelery & Chain Crafts, Inc., New York, NY; *U.S. Public*, pg. 1609

Fernandez, James N., Chief Fin. Officer--Judel Products Corp., Elmsford, NY; *U.S. Public*, pg. 1609

Fernandez, James N., Chief Fin. Officer--Tiffany & Co. ICT, Inc., New York, NY; *U.S. Public*, pg. 1609

Fernandez, James N., Chief Fin. Officer--Tiffany & Co. Japan Inc., New York, NY; *U.S. Public*, pg. 1609

Fernandez, James N., Chief Fin. Officer--Tiffany & Co. International, New York, NY; *U.S. Public*, pg. 1609

Fernandez, James N., Chief Fin. Officer--Tiffany & Co. Japan Inc. - Japan Branch, New York, NY; *U.S. Public*, pg. 1609

Fernandez, Jorge A., Chief Fin. Offier--Greyhound Leisure Services, Inc., Miami, FL; *U.S. Public*, pg. 1718

Ferolie, Cathy, Dir.-Finance--Ferolie Group, Montvale, NJ; *U.S. Private*, pg. 401

Ferra, Dennis J., Chief Fin. Officer & Sr. V.P.--ALLTEL Corporation, Little Rock, AR; *U.S. Public*, pg. 55

Ferran, Rene J., Chief Fin. Officer & Exec. V.P.--The Martin Agency, Richmond, VA; *U.S. Private*, pg. 678

Ferran, Rene J., Chief Fin. Officer & Exec. V.P.--The Martin Agency, Richmond, VA; *U.S. Public*, pg. 909

Ferraro, Charles J., Chief Fin. Officer & Treas.--ANESCO, Kingston, PA; *U.S. Private*, pg. 74

Ferreira, Carlos, Chief Fin. Officer--Delco Remi-Componentes Electronicos, Lda., Seixal, Portugal; *U.S. Public*, pg. 721

Ferreira, Richard S., Chief Fin. Officer & Exec. V.P.--Golf Hosts, Inc., Palm Harbor, FL; *U.S. Private*, pg. 1036

Ferrell, Sam N., Chief Fin. Officer--Shelby Williams Industries, Inc., Morristown, TN; *U.S. Public*, pg. 1464

Ferretti, G., Chief Fin. Officer--Caleffi S.p.A., Viadana, Italy; *Int'l*, pg. 252

Ferretti, George S., Chief Fin. Officer--The Keyes Company Realtors, Miami, FL; *U.S. Private*, pg. 618

Ferrif, Adam, Chief Fin. Officer--Burns, Philp Inc., San Francisco, CA; *Int'l*, pg. 236

Ferriss, Joel G., Chief Fin. Officer & V.P.--Great River Insurance Company, Meridian, MS; *U.S. Public*, pg. 215

Fesler, John, Jr., Chief Fin. Officer & V.P. Fin.--Hillshire Farm & Kahn's, Cincinnati, OH; *U.S. Public*, pg. 1433

Fessenden, R., Chief Fin. Officer, V.P.-Fin. & Admin. Treas.--KDI Precision Products, Inc., Cincinnati, OH; *U.S. Private*, pg. 603

Fetter, Trevor, Chief Fin. Officer & Exec. V.P.--Tenet Healthcare Corporation, Santa Barbara, CA; *U.S. Public*, pg. 1576

Fevery, Patrick, Chief Fin. Officer & V.P.-Fin.--Rainbow Technologies, Inc., Irvine, CA; *U.S. Public*, pg. 1359

Feye, Lyle J., Chief Fin. Officer, V.P.-Fin. & Treas.--AXIA Incorporated, Lombard, IL; *U.S. Private*, pg. 103

Ficke, Michael, Chief Fin. Officer, V.P.-Fin. & Sec.--Alfin, Inc., New York, NY; *U.S. Public*, pg. 40

Fickes, Steven W., Pres. & Chief Fin. Officer--PennCorp Financial Group, Inc., New York, NY; *U.S. Public*, pg. 1271

Field, Benjamin R., III, Chief Fin. Officer, Sr. V.P. & Treas.--Bemis Company, Inc., Minneapolis, MN; *U.S. Public*, pg. 210

Field, David, Chief Fin. Officer--Entertainment Communications, Bala Cynwyd, PA; *U.S. Private*, pg. 378

Field, Norman M., Chief Fin. Officer, V.P.-Fin. & Treas.--First Capital Financial Corp., Troy, MI; *U.S. Private*, pg. 473

Fielder, Bill, V.P. & Chief Fin. Officer--Gray Communications Systems, Inc., Albany, GA; *U.S. Public*, pg. 759

Fielding, Thomas, Chief Fin. Officer--Glynwed Consumer & Construction Products Ltd., Royal Leamington Spa, United Kingdom; *Int'l*, pg. 554

Fields, Brian, Chief Fin. Officer, V.P. & Treas.--CarrAmerica Realty, Washington, DC; *U.S. Public*, pg. 308

Fievet, Denis, Chief Fin. Officer--SIAS - MPA, Paris, France; *Int'l*, pg. 566

Fight, Kevan A., Chief Fin. Officer & Exec. V.P.--Malrite Communications Group, Inc., Cleveland, OH; *U.S. Private*, pg. 698

Filcek, Rodney, Chief Fin. Officer--Dana Commercial Credit Corp. (Ohio), Toledo, OH; *U.S. Public*, pg. 479

Files, Karen, Chief Fin. Officer--Roush Industries Inc., Livonia, MI; *U.S. Private*, pg. 948

Filho, Orlando Galvao, Chief Fin. Officer--Petrobras - Petroleo Brasileiro S.A., Rio de Janeiro, Brazil; *Int'l*, pg. 1041

Filice, Pete, Chief Fin. Officer--KTXL Channel 40, Sacramento, CA; *U.S. Public*, pg. 1636

Filip, Jim, Chief Fin. Officer--L&J Technologies, Hillside, IL; *U.S. Private*, pg. 638

Fillingham, Robin A., Chief Fin. Officer & Sr. V.P.-Admin.--Baton Broadcasting Incorporated, Scarborough, Canada; *Int'l*, pg. 170

Filton, Steven G., V.P. & Controller--Universal Health Services, Inc., King of Prussia, PA; *U.S. Public*, pg. 1696

Finan, Dan, Chief Fin. Officer & Treas.--Peavey Electronics Corp., Meridian, MS; *U.S. Private*, pg. 845

Finch, D.J., Chief Fin. Officer--NFC plc, London, United Kingdom; *Int'l*, pg. 901

Fincher, Larry, Chief Fin. Officer & Exec. V.P.--Truman Arnold Companies, Texarkana, TX; *U.S. Private*, pg. 84

Finelli, Mary Lynn, Chief Fin. Officer & Exec. V.P.--Provident Mutual Life Insurance Co., Berwyn, PA; *U.S. Private*, pg. 891

Finely, Bill R., Chief Fin. Officer, V.P. & Sec.--Micronics Computers, Inc., Fremont, CA; *U.S. Public*, pg. 1106

Fineman, Evan, Chief Fin. Officer--Land O' Lakes, Carlisle, PA; *U.S. Private*, pg. 646

Finger, Larry E., Chief Fin. Officer & Sr. V.P.--Washington Real Estate Investment Trust, Kensington, MD; *U.S. Public*, pg. 1743

Finger, Manfred, Dir.-Fin.--Villeroy & Boch AG, Mettlach, Germany; *Int'l*, pg. 1468

Fink, Dennis L., Chief Fin. Officer & Exec. V.P.--Haverty Furniture Companies, Inc., Atlanta, GA; *U.S. Public*, pg. 799

Fink, John, Chief Fin. Officer & Treas.--C.J. Langenfelder & Son, Inc., Baltimore, MD; *U.S. Private*, pg. 650

Finkelstein, William S., Chief Fin. Officer & Sr. V.P.--Warnaco Inc., New York, NY; *U.S. Public*, pg. 1738

Finley, David, Chief Fin. Officer & Exec. V.P.--Broadway & Seymour, Inc., Charlotte, NC; *U.S. Public*, pg. 258

Finn, Brian, Chief Advisor--Clayton, Dubilier & Rice, Inc, New York, NY; *U.S. Private*, pg. 244

Finn, Edward L., Chief Fin. Officer & Exec. V.P.--Green Tree Financial Corporation, Saint Paul, MN; *U.S. Public*, pg. 761

Finn, Lawrence, Chief Fin. Officer--The Wiser Oil Company, Dallas, TX; *U.S. Public*, pg. 1773

Finn, Richard L., Sr. V.P.-Fin.--Kansas City Life Insurance Co., Kansas City, MO; *U.S. Public*, pg. 942

Finn, Richard L., Chief Fin. Officer, V.P. & Asst. Treas.--Old American Insurance Co., Kansas City, MO; *U.S. Public*, pg. 943

Finnegan, Laurence P. Jr., Chief Fin. Officer, Sr. V.P. & Treas.--Bailey, Fischer & Porter Company, Warminster, PA; *Int'l*, pg. 449

Finneran, Tom, Chief Fin. Officer & Exec. V.P.--Jordan, McGrath, Case & Taylor Inc., New York, NY; *U.S. Private*, pg. 598

Finnerty, Albert, Chief Fin. Officer--Hehr International Inc., Los Angeles, CA; *U.S. Private*, pg. 519

Finnerty, Robert, V.P.-Fin. & Opers.-NBC Television Stations--National Broadcasting Co., Inc., New York, NY; *U.S. Public*, pg. 712

Finnigan, G. Michael, Chief Fin. Officer, Exec. V.P., Treas. & Pres.-Gaming Div.--Hollywood Park, Inc., Inglewood, CA; *U.S. Public*, pg. 830

Finstad, James, Controller--LiphaTech, Inc., Milwaukee, WI; *Int'l*, pg. 812

Fiolet, Robert A.H., Fin. Dir.--Lowe Kuiper & Schouten, Amsterdam, Netherlands; *U.S. Private*, pg. 678

Fioravante, Raymond, Chief Fin. Officer & Controller--Fawn Industries, Inc., Hunt Valley, MD; *U.S. Private*, pg. 397

Fiorillo, Peter J., Chief Fin. Officer & Exec. V.P.-Fin. & Admin.--Find/SVP, Inc., New York, NY; *U.S. Public*, pg. 623
Firestone, Donald L., V.P. & Treas.--Tru-Weld Grating, Inc., Wexford, PA; *U.S. Private*, pg. 1107
Fische, Blake, Chief Fin. Officer--McLeodUSA Incorporated, Cedar Rapids, IA; *U.S. Public*, pg. 1073
Fischer, Andrew, Chief Fin. Officer--Vector Industries, Ltd., Doncaster, United Kingdom; *Int'l*, pg. 1461
Fischer, Bob, Chief Fin. Officer--Items International/Airwalk, Inc., Altoona, PA; *U.S. Private*, pg. 576
Fischer, John E., Chief Fin. Officer--Primex Technologies, Inc., Saint Petersburg, FL; *U.S. Public*, pg. 1329
Fischer, Pierre, Chief Fin. Officer--Osram S.A., Molsheim, France; *Int'l*, pg. 1244
Fischer, Tamara, Chief Fin. Officer--Chateau Communities, Inc., Englewood, CO; *U.S. Public*, pg. 341
Fiscus, Robert L., Pres. & Chief Fin. Officer--United Illuminating Company, New Haven, CT; *U.S. Public*, pg. 1678
Fish, Gary, Chief Fin. Officer--SEEQ Technology Inc., Fremont, CA; *U.S. Public*, pg. 1417
Fishberg, Bruce, Chief Fin. Officer & V.P.--Pincus Bros., Inc., Philadelphia, PA; *U.S. Private*, pg. 865
Fishbune, Robert, Chief Fin. Officer--Specialty Foods Corporation, Deerfield, IL; *U.S. Private*, pg. 1022
Fisher, Bruce A., Chief Fin. Officer, Sr. V.P. & Sec.--PCA International, Inc., Matthews, NC; *U.S. Public*, pg. 1240
Fisher, Henry, Chm. Bd. & Chief Fin. Officer--Pyramid Handbags Inc., New York, NY; *U.S. Private*, pg. 896
Fisher, James, Chief Fin. Officer--Benson International Systems Inc., Clifton, NJ; *Int'l*, pg. 460
Fisher, John R., Dir.-Fin.--Binney & Smith Ltd., Lindsay, Canada; *U.S. Private*, pg. 496
Fisher, Joseph F., Chief Fin. Officer & Sr. V.P.--Royal Insurance, Charlotte, NC; *Int'l*, pg. 1130
Fisher, Joseph F., Chief Fin. Officer--Royal Insurance Company of America, Charlotte, NC; *Int'l*, pg. 1131
Fisher, Kathleen, Chief Fin. Officer--Borland International, Inc., Scotts Valley, CA; *U.S. Public*, pg. 246
Fisher, Ken, Chief Fin. Officer--S&S Energy Products, Houston, TX; *U.S. Public*, pg. 711
Fisher, R.H., V.P.-Fin.--Standard Alloys & Manufacturing, Port Arthur, TX; *U.S. Private*, pg. 153
Fisher, Robert J., Chief Fin. Officer--Old Navy Stores, San Francisco, CA; *U.S. Public*, pg. 703
Fisher, William R., Chief Fin. Officer--Roche Constructors, Inc., Greeley, CO; *U.S. Private*, pg. 937
Fite, Andrew, Chief Fin. Officer--B/E Services, Orange, CA; *U.S. Public*, pg. 159
Fitton, J.S.H., Chief Fin. Officer & Exec. Gen. Mgr.--M.I.M. Holdings Ltd., Brisbane, Australia; *Int'l*, pg. 827
Fitz, David, Chief Fin. Officer--FTSB Broadcasting, Saint Petersburg, FL; *U.S. Private*, pg. 389
Fitzer, Theodore, Mgr.-Fin.--Hull Corporation, Hatboro, PA; *U.S. Private*, pg. 547
Fitzgerald, Daniel J., Chief Fin. Officer & Exec. V.P.--Massachusetts Mutual Life Insurance Co., Springfield, MA; *U.S. Private*, pg. 712
Fitzgerald, David, Chief Fin. Officer & Treas.--Carris Financial Group, Rutland, VT; *U.S. Private*, pg. 215
Fitzgerald, David, Chief Fin. Officer & Treas.--Carris Reels, Inc., Rutland, VT; *U.S. Private*, pg. 215
Fitzgerald, Ken, Chief Fin. Officer, Controller & Sec.--R.L. Zeigler Co. Inc., Tuscaloosa, AL; *U.S. Private*, pg. 1204
Fitzgerald, Michael, Chief Fin. Officer--Frozfruit Corporation, Gardena, CA; *U.S. Private*, pg. 430
Fitzgerald, W.T., Jr., Chief Fin. Officer--Empire National Bank, Traverse City, MI; *U.S. Private*, pg. 374
Fitzgerold, Robert M., Chief Fin. Officer--PIMCO Advisors L.P., Newport Beach, CA; *U.S. Private*, pg. 832
Fitzgibbon, Pierre, Chief Fin. Officer & Sr. V.P.-Fin.--Domtar Inc., Montreal, Canada; *Int'l*, pg. 416
Fitzhugh, A. Chad, Chief Fin. Officer, Treas. & Sec.--O'Charley's Inc., Nashville, TN; *U.S. Public*, pg. 1211
Fitzpatrick, Charles, Chief Fin. Officer--Commercial Union Corporation, Boston, MA; *Int'l*, pg. 308
Fitzpatrick, Charles R., Chief Fin. Officer & First Sr. V.P.--Commercial Union Insurance Company, Boston, MA; *Int'l*, pg. 308
Fitzpatrick, Mike, Chief Fin. Officer & V.P.--TD Industries Inc., Dallas, TX; *U.S. Private*, pg. 1063
FitzPatrick, Patrick C., Chief Fin. Officer, Sr. V.P. & Treas.--DynCorp, Reston, VA; *U.S. Private*, pg. 351
Fitzpatrick, Thomas P., Chief Fin. Officer & V.P.--Engelhard Corporation, Iselin, NJ; *U.S. Public*, pg. 582
Fitzpatrik, Brian J., Chief Fin. Officer & Sr. V.P.-Fin.--Jevic Transportation, Inc., Delanco, NJ; *U.S. Public*, pg. 927
Fiume, Orest J., Chief Fin. Officer & V.P.--The Wiremold Company, West Hartford, CT; *U.S. Private*, pg. 1184
Fjelstul, Dean M., Chief Fin. Officer & Sr. V.P.--Walter Industries, Inc., Tampa, FL; *U.S. Public*, pg. 1736
Fjelstul, Dean M., Chief Fin. Officer & V.P.--Mid-State Homes, Inc., Tampa, FL; *U.S. Public*, pg. 1736
Fjelstul, Dean M., Chief Fin. Officer--Cardem Insurance Co., Ltd., Tampa, FL; *U.S. Public*, pg. 1736
Flach, H.B., V.P.-Fin. & Admin.--Sunkist Growers, Inc., Sherman Oaks, CA; *U.S. Private*, pg. 1052
Flagezil, Jean-Pierre, Chief Fin. Officer--Rainbow Technologies, Neuilly-sur-Seine, France; *U.S. Public*, pg. 1359
Flaherty, Walter J., Chief Fin. Officer & Sr. V.P.--Eastern Enterprises, Weston, MA; *U.S. Public*, pg. 548
Flaherty, William, Chief Fin. Officer & Exec. V.P.--Kemper Reinsurance Co., Long Grove, IL; *U.S. Private*, pg. 614
Flaherty, William L., Chief Fin. Officer & V.P.-Fin.--Avid Technology, Inc., Tewksbury, MA; *U.S. Public*, pg. 154
Flanagan, Glenda, Chief Fin. Officer & V.P.--Whole Foods Market, Inc., Austin, TX; *U.S. Public*, pg. 1767
Flanagan, Martin L., Chief Fin. Officer & Sr. V.P.--Franklin Resources, Inc., San Mateo, CA; *U.S. Public*, pg. 679
Flanagan, Ray, Chief Fin. Officer--Utah Medical Products Ltd., Athlone, Ireland; *U.S. Public*, pg. 1700
Flanders, Howard L., Chief Fin. Officer & Exec. V.P.--All American Semiconductor, Inc., Miami, FL; *U.S. Public*, pg. 41
Flavin, Robert M., Chief Fin. Officer & Sr. V.P.--Basis Petroleum, Inc., Houston, TX; *U.S. Public*, pg. 1704
Flaws, James B., Chief Fin. Officer, Sr. V.P. & Treas.--Corning Incorporated, Corning, NY; *U.S. Public*, pg. 448
Fleischman, Donald, Chief Fin. Officer, V.P.-Fin. & Treas.--Ampacet Corporation, Tarrytown, NY; *U.S. Private*, pg. 67
Fleisher, David L., Chief Fin. Officer & Sr. Exec. V.P.--Maritz Inc., Fenton, MO; *U.S. Private*, pg. 703
Fleming, Brian, Chief Fin. Officer & Exec. V.P.--The Santa Anita Companies, Arcadia, CA; *U.S. Public*, pg. 1081
Fleming, Richard H., Chief Fin. Officer & Sr. V.P.--USG Corporation, Chicago, IL; *U.S. Public*, pg. 1660
Fleming, Robert T., Chief Fin. Officer & Exec. V.P.--Universal Studios TV, Universal City, CA; *Int'l*, pg. 1215
Fleming, William, Treas.--A.I. Root Company, Medina, OH; *U.S. Private*, pg. 944
Fletcher, Denise K., Chief Fin. Officer & V.P.-Fin.--Bowne & Co., Inc., New York, NY; *U.S. Public*, pg. 248
Flexer, Z., Chief Fin. Dir.--Elbit Computers Ltd., Haifa, Israel; *Int'l*, pg. 644
Flick, Rainer, Chief Fin. Officer--Esselte Meto International Produktions GmbH, Hirschhorn, Germany; *Int'l*, pg. 461
Flinders, Leon, Chief Fin. Officer--Bally's Grand Inc. (Las Vegas), Las Vegas, NV; *U.S. Public*, pg. 829
Flippin, Mike, Chief Fin. Officer--Process Systems Inc., Memphis, TN; *U.S. Private*, pg. 888
Floberg, Ron, Chief Fin. Officer--Electron Corp., Littleton, CO; *U.S. Private*, pg. 370
Floerchinger, Tom, Chief Fin. Officer & Sr. V.P.-Fin.--L. Luria & Son, Inc., Medley, FL; *U.S. Public*, pg. 1020
Flom, Douglas, Chief Fin. Officer--Burdines, Miami, FL; *U.S. Public*, pg. 618
Flood, Thomas, Chief Fin. Officer, V.P.-Admin. & Fin. & Treas.--Tractor Supply Co., Nashville, TN; *U.S. Public*, pg. 1627
Florek, Anita, Chief Fin. Officer & Treas.--Bank of Smithtown, Smithtown, NY; *U.S. Private*, pg. 114
Florek, Anita M., Chief Fin. Officer & Treas.--Smithtown Bancorp, Inc., Smithtown, NY; *U.S. Public*, pg. 1479
Flores, Rene, Chief Fin. Officer & Controller--Jones & Jones, Inc., McAllen, TX; *U.S. Private*, pg. 596
Flores, William, Chief Fin. Officer & Sr. V.P.--Western Atlas Inc., Houston, TX; *U.S. Public*, pg. 1757
Florness, Daniel L., Chief Fin. Officer, Chief Acctg. Officer & Treas.--Fastenal Company, Winona, MN; *U.S. Public*, pg. 614
Flory, Stephen, Chief Fin. Officer--Gatefield Corporation, Fremont, CA; *U.S. Public*, pg. 703
Flourney, Selwyn L., Jr., Chief Fin. Officer & Sr. V.P.--The Life Insurance Co. of Virginia, Richmond, VA; *U.S. Public*, pg. 712
Flower, Allen E., Chief Fin. Officer, V.P. & Acting Treas.--COMSAT Corporation, Bethesda, MD; *U.S. Public*, pg. 424
Flowers, Melvin, Chief Fin. Officer & V.P.-Fin. & Admin.--ACT Networks, Inc., Camarillo, CA; *U.S. Public*, pg. 3
Floyd, Chuck, Chief Fin. Officer & Controller--Inland Associates, Olathe, KS; *U.S. Private*, pg. 563
Floyd, Jeffrey W., Chief Fin. Officer--Central Allied Enterprises, Canton, OH; *U.S. Private*, pg. 222
Floyd, Robert K., Chief Fin. Officer & V.P.-Fin.--Tracor, Inc., Austin, TX; *U.S. Public*, pg. 1627
Floyd, Ted, Chief Fin. Officer--Adair Greene Advertising, Atlanta, GA; *U.S. Private*, pg. 16
Flucker, Robert, Chief Fin. Officer & V.P.-Fin.--Edward C. Levy Co., Dearborn, MI; *U.S. Private*, pg. 664
Fluegeman, Raymond W., Chief Fin. Officer, Treas., Controller & Dir.-D.P.--Robbins, Inc., Cincinnati, OH; *U.S. Private*, pg. 934
Fluke, Ken, Chief Fin. Officer--South Pacific Tyres, Somerton, Australia; *Int'l*, pg. 1021
Flyg, Bill, Chief Fin. Officer & Sr. V.P.--The Pantry, Inc., Sanford, NC; *U.S. Private*, pg. 837
Flynn, Carl, V.P.-Fin.& Technical Services--New Brunswick Power Corporation, Fredericton, Canada; *Int'l*, pg. 923
Flynn, Gerry, V.P.-Fin.--Vail Associates, Inc., Vail, CO; *U.S. Public*, pg. 1704
Flynn, Susan I., Chief Fin. Officer--Financial Life Assurance Co. of Canada, Etobicoke, Canada; *U.S. Public*, pg. 77
Fodale, Pat, Chief Fin. Officer--Color Tile, Inc., Fort Worth, TX; *Int'l*, pg. 686
Foege, Rich, Chief Fin. Officer& Controller--Dierbergs Markets Inc., Chesterfield, MO; *U.S. Private*, pg. 332
Fogarty, Andy, Chief Fin. Officer--Sea-Land Service, Inc., Charlotte, NC; *U.S. Public*, pg. 284
Fogarty, Patrick W., Chief Fin. Officer--RB&W Corporation, Cleveland, OH; *U.S. Public*, pg. 1259
Fogg, William, III, Chief Fin. Officer & Treas.--Southeastern Medequip, Inc., Jacksonville Beach, FL; *U.S. Private*, pg. 1015
Fohrer, Alan J., Chief Fin. Officer & Exec. V.P.--Edison International, Rosemead, CA; *U.S. Public*, pg. 564
Foley, Ann, Chief Fin. Officer--Foley Tractor Company, Inc., Wichita, KS; *U.S. Private*, pg. 416
Foley, Claire, Chief Fin. Officer & V.P.--Hardwoods Of Michigan, Inc., Clinton, MI; *U.S. Private*, pg. 502
Foley, Fred, Chief Fin. Officer--EIS International Inc., Herndon, VA; *U.S. Public*, pg. 544
Foley, John A., Chief Fin. Officer & V.P.--Uniblend Spinners, Inc., Conway, SC; *U.S. Private*, pg. 1117
Foley, Thomas, Chief Fin. Officer & V.P.--Print Northwest Company, L.P., Fife, WA; *Int'l*, pg. 1076
Foley, Thomas, Chief Fin. Officer--The Foxboro Company, Foxboro, MA; *Int'l*, pg. 1243
Follestad, Harald, Chief Fin. Officer--Longva Group, Alesund, Norway; *Int'l*, pg. 817
Follman, John P., Chief Fin. Officer & Sr. V.P.--Day & Zimmermann, Inc., Philadelphia, PA; *U.S. Private*, pg. 316
Folsoms, Graham, Chief Fin. Officer--Haney Seed Co., Twin Falls, ID; *U.S. Public*, pg. 428
Folson, Fred, V.P.-Fin.--Indian Head Industries Inc., Charlotte, NC; *U.S. Private*, pg. 559
Folwell, Ronald L., Sr., Chief Fin. Officer & V.P.-Fin., Leasing, Plng/Devel. & Real Est.--GSC Enterprises, Inc., Sulphur Springs, TX; *U.S. Private*, pg. 436
Fontaine, Michael, Chief Fin. Officer & V.P.--Nelson Photo Supplies, San Diego, CA; *U.S. Private*, pg. 791
Foong, S.S., Chief Fin. Officer--Olivetti Singapore Pte. Ltd., Singapore, Singapore; *Int'l*, pg. 1003
Forberg, Steiner, Sr. V.P.-Fin.--A/S Ivaran Rederi, Lysaker, Norway; *Int'l*, pg. 696
Forbes, Mike, Chief Fin. Officer--Eastern American Energy Corporation, Charleston, WV; *U.S. Private*, pg. 357
Ford, Bill, Chief Fin. Officer & Dir.-Investor Rels.--Ferrofluidics Corporation, Nashua, NH; *U.S. Public*, pg. 620
Ford, Edward D., Chief Fin. Officer & V.P.--Digital Courier International Inc., Burnaby, Canada; *Int'l*, pg. 413
Ford, Jess B., Chief Fin. Officer & V.P.--Franklin Electric Co., Inc., Bluffton, IN; *U.S. Public*, pg. 679
Ford, P.M., Chief Fin. Officer & Sr. V.P.--ESCO Electronics Corporation, Saint Louis, MO; *U.S. Public*, pg. 546
Ford, Patrick, Chief Fin. Officer--Southern Foods Group, Dallas, TX; *U.S. Private*, pg. 1016
Ford, Stephen, Chief Fin. Officer--Sleepeezee Limited, London, United Kingdom; *Int'l*, pg. 1263
Forde, Tim, Chief Fin. Officer--SL Montevideo Technology, Inc., Montevideo, MN; *U.S. Public*, pg. 1419
Fore, William, Chief Fin. Officer & V.P.-Fin.--The Long & Foster Companies, Inc., Fairfax, VA; *U.S. Private*, pg. 674
Forell, David C., Chief Fin. Officer & Exec. V.P.--Catherines Stores Corporation, Memphis, TN; *U.S. Public*, pg. 317
Forest, Carol A., Chief Fin. Officer, V.P.-Fin. & Treas.--Connecticut Energy Corporation, Bridgeport, CT; *U.S. Public*, pg. 431
Forest, Carol A., Chief Fin. Officer, V.P.-Fin. & Treas.--The Southern Connecticut Gas Company, Bridgeport, CT; *U.S. Public*, pg. 431
Forester, Scott, Chief Fin. Officer--Tiger Electronics, Inc., Vernon Hills, IL; *U.S. Private*, pg. 1086
Forget, Jean, Chief Fin. Officer--Wilcox Electric, Inc., Kansas City, MO; *Int'l*, pg. 1384
Fornella, Norman G., Chief Fin. Officer, Exec. V.P., Treas. & Sec.--Morse Diesel International, Inc., New York, NY; *U.S. Private*, pg. 762
Fornetti, Louis C., Chief Fin. Officer & Sr. V.P.--American Express Financial Advisor, Minneapolis, MN; *U.S. Public*, pg. 73
Forney, James L., Chief Fin. Officer & Treas.--Fone America, Inc., Portland, OR; *U.S. Public*, pg. 661
Forrest, Paul, Chief Fin. Officer--Heating Oil Partners L.P., Darien, CT; *U.S. Private*, pg. 518
Forsdick, D.L., Treas.--AT&T ISTEL Limited, Redditch, United Kingdom; *U.S. Public*, pg. 11
Forsgren, John H., Chief Fin. Officer & Exec. V.P.--Northeast Utilities, Berlin, CT; *U.S. Public*, pg. 1194
Forsguen, John H., Chief Fin. Officer & Exec. V.P.--Public Service Company of New Hampshire, Manchester, NH; *U.S. Public*, pg. 1195
Forster, David G., Chief Fin. Officer & V.P.-Fin.--FOTOBALL USA, Inc., San Diego, CA; *U.S. Public*, pg. 678
Fortener, Randy, V.P. & Chief Fin. Officer--Crane Plastics Company, Columbus, OH; *U.S. Private*, pg. 286
Fortmuller, George A., Chief Fin. Officer, V.P., Treas. & Sec.--Edwin B. Stimpson Company, Inc., Bayport, NY; *U.S. Private*, pg. 1043
Fortney, David J., Chief Fin. Officer, Controller & Treas.--York Barbell Co., Inc., York, PA; *U.S. Private*, pg. 1196
Forward, Frank D., Chief Fin. Officer & Exec. V.P.--BJ's Wholesale Club, Inc., Natick, MA; *U.S. Public*, pg. 162
Foss, John H., Chief Fin. Officer, V.P. & Treas.--Tecumseh Products Company, Tecumseh, MI; *U.S. Public*, pg. 1565
Foss, Robert E., Chief Fin. Officer & Exec. V.P.--Mid Atlantic Medical Services, Inc., Rockville, MD; *U.S. Public*, pg. 1109
Fossett, W. Curtis, Controller & Sec.--Educational Development Corporation, Tulsa, OK; *U.S. Public*, pg. 564
Fossett, W. Curtis, Chief Fin. Officer--Publishing Div., Tulsa, OK; *U.S. Public*, pg. 565
Fossett, W. Curtis, Chief Fin. Officer--Home Party Plan Div., Tulsa, OK; *U.S. Public*, pg. 565
Fossum, Jeff, Chief Fin. Officer--EMS Central Regional Office (Corporate), Milwaukee, WI; *U.S. Public*, pg. 565
Fossum, Jeffrey J., Chief Fin. Officer & V.P.--Effective Management Systems, Milwaukee, WI; *U.S. Public*, pg. 565
Foster, Betty F., Treas.--The Long & Foster Real Estate, Inc., Fairfax, VA; *U.S. Private*, pg. 674
Foster, Jim, Chief Fin. Officer & Exec. V.P.--JM Family Enterprises Inc., Deerfield Beach, FL; *U.S. Private*, pg. 577
Foster, Jonathan P., Chief Fin. Officer--Dryper's Corp., Vancouver, WA; *U.S. Private*, pg. 344
Foster, Kim, Chief Fin. Officer--Pacific Brands, Hawthorn, Australia; *Int'l*, pg. 1021
Foster, Martin L., V.P.-Fin.--Wine World Estates Company, Saint Helena, CA; *Int'l*, pg. 917
Foster, Mike, Chief Fin. Officer--Du Pont (Australia) Ltd., Sydney, Australia; *U.S. Public*, pg. 532
Foster, Norman P., Sr. V.P. & Chief Fin. Officer--American Family Life Assurance Co. of Columbus, Columbus, GA; *U.S. Public*, pg. 28
Foster, P.J., Dir.-Fin.--Commercial Union plc, London, United Kingdom; *Int'l*, pg. 308
Foster, Phillip W., Chief Fin. Officer & V.P.-Fin.--Remmele Engineering, Inc., New Brighton, MN; *U.S. Private*, pg. 921
Fought, Bonnie E., Chief Fin. Officer & V.P.-Fin. & Admin.--Connectix Corporation, San Mateo, CA; *U.S. Private*, pg. 264

Fowler, William, Chief Fin. Officer--Deloitte & Touche LLP, Wilton, CT; *U.S. Private*, pg. 322
Fowler, William J., V.P.-Fin.--Melody Foods, Inc., Farmington Hills, MI; *U.S. Private*, pg. 730
Fowles, William D., Chief Fin. Officer--Syndicate Systems, Inc., Middlebury, IN; *U.S. Private*, pg. 1060
Fox, Ian Russell, Grp. Fin. Dir.--Wagon Industrial Holdings PLC, Birmingham, United Kingdom; *Int'l*, pg. 1484
Fox, James L., Chief Fin. Officer & Sr. V.P.--Investors Services Group, Boston, MA; *U.S. Public*, pg. 631
Fox, Jim, Chief Fin. Officer--Bryant, Fulton & Shee, Vancouver, Canada; *U.S. Private*, pg. 678
Fox, Robert, Sr. V.P.-Fin. & Admin., Treas. & Sec.--Rocor Transportation Companies Inc., Oklahoma City, OK; *U.S. Private*, pg. 938
Fox, William J., Chief Fin. Officer & Sr. Exec. V.P.--Revlon, Inc., New York, NY; *U.S. Private*, pg. 689
Foxworth, Jack, Chief Fin. Officer--Foxworth-Galbraith Lumber Co., Dallas, TX; *U.S. Private*, pg. 423
Foy, John N., Chief Fin. Officer & Exec. V.P.--CBL & Associates Properties, Inc., Chattanooga, TN; *U.S. Public*, pg. 273
Foye, A., Chief Fin. Officer--Taylor & Francis Group Ltd., London, United Kingdom; *Int'l*, pg. 1357
Fraedrich, David S., Chief Fin. Officer, Exec. V.P. & Treas.--Rocky Shoes & Boots, Inc., Nelsonville, OH; *U.S. Public*, *pg. 1402*
Fraioli, Angelo, Chief Fin. Officer--Communications Supply Corporation, Stamford, CT; *U.S. Private*, pg. 259
Fraley, Steven, Chief Fin. Officer--Dyna Technology Incorporated, Le Center, MN; *U.S. Private*, pg. 350
Fraley, Steven, Chief Fin. Officer & V.P.-Fin.--WINCO, Le Center, MN; *U.S. Private*, pg. 350
Framer, Jeff M., Chief Fin. Officer--Image Entertainment, Inc., Chatsworth, CA; *U.S. Public*, pg. 870
Franciosa, John, Chief Fin. Officer--The Pastene Companies Ltd., Canton, MA; *U.S. Private*, pg. 842
Francis, George E., Chief Fin. Officer, Sr. V.P. & Sec.--First Commonwealth Corporation, Springfield, IL; *U.S. Private*, *pg. 406*
Francis, Reginald, Chief Fin. Officer--Spirol Ind. Ltd., Corby, United Kingdom; *U.S. Private*, pg. 1026
Francis, Spencer L., Chief Fin. Officer--NGL American Life, Menasha, WI; *U.S. Private*, pg. 784
Francis, William, Chief Fin. Officer, Treas. & Controller--Captive-Aire Systems, Inc., Youngsville, NC; *U.S. Private*, *pg. 207*
Francisco, Nilsa, V.P.-Acctg.--U.S. Operations Div., Hato Rey, PR; *U.S. Public*, pg. 176
Franco, Eloina, Chief Fin. Officer--Banco Santander International Miami, Miami, FL; *Int'l*, pg. 143
Franco, Joseph, Chief Fin. Officer & Treas.--Haydon Switch & Instrument, Inc., Waterbury, CT; *U.S. Private*, pg. 513
Franda, Chris, Chief Fin. Officer--Eclipse Manufacturing Company, Sheboygan, WI; *U.S. Private*, pg. 361
Frank, L.C., Chief Fin. Officer & V.P.-Fin.--Duraco Products, Inc., Streamwood, IL; *U.S. Private*, pg. 348
Frank, Peter, Chief Fin. Officer--Gramercy Pictures, Beverly Hills, CA; *U.S. Private*, pg. 468
Frank, Sandy, Chief Fin. Officer & Sr. V.P.--Berenter Greenhouse & Webster, Inc., New York, NY; *U.S. Private*, pg. 135
Frank, William H., V.P. & Treas.--D.V.F. Inc., New York, NY; *U.S. Private*, pg. 690
Frankel, Edward M., Chief Fin. Officer, V.P. & Gen. Counsel--Standard Textile Co., Inc., Cincinnati, OH; *U.S. Private*, pg. 1032
Frankel, Robert, Chief Fin. Officer--Titan Global Ltd., Montville, NJ; *U.S. Private*, pg. 266
Frankenhaeuser, Filip, Chief Fin. Officer--Cultor Ltd., Helsinki, Finland; *Int'l*, pg. 349
Frankland, G. Thomas, Vice Chm. & Chief Fin. Officer--Ideon Group, Inc., Jacksonville, FL; *U.S. Public*, pg. 320
Franklin, Beverly, Chief Fin. Officer--Wright Group Publishing, Inc., Bothell, WA; *U.S. Public*, pg. 1636
Franklin, Carol, Chief Fin. Officer & Sec.--Video Display Corporation, Tucker, GA; *U.S. Public*, pg. 1720
Franklin, Gary A., Pres. & Chief Fin. Officer--ServiceMaster of Canada Ltd., Mississauga, Canada; *U.S. Public*, pg. 1462
Franklin, James, Chief Fin. Officer & V.P.--Rice, Sangalis, Toole & Wilson, Houston, TX; *U.S. Private*, pg. 928
Franklin, Laura M., Chief Acctg. Officer & V.P.--Washington Real Estate Investment Trust, Kensington, MD; *U.S. Public*, pg. 1743
Franklin, Phil, Chief Fin. Officer & V.P.-Fin.--OmniQuip International, Inc., Port Washington, WI; *U.S. Private*, pg. 500
Franko, Robert M., Chief Fin. Officer & V.P.--Imperial Bancorp, Inglewood, CA; *U.S. Public*, pg. 871
Franze, Jose Edison, Chief Fin. Officer--AHP do Brasil, Sao Paulo, Brazil; *U.S. Public*, pg. 80
Franzel, Philip A., Chief Fin. Officer & Exec. V.P.--Salant Corporation, New York, NY; *U.S. Public*, pg. 1429
Franzky, Rudiger, Chief Fin. Officer--Bols Strothmann Brennereien GmbH & Co. KG, Nordrhein-Westfalen, Germany; *Int'l*, pg. 751
Fraser, Bruce D., Chief Fin. Officer & Sr. V.P.--Grease Monkey International Inc., Denver, CO; *U.S. Public*, pg. 759
Fraser, David, Chief Fin. Officer--Royal Consumer Business Products, Bridgewater, NJ; *Int'l*, pg. 1002
Fraser, David S., Chief Fin. Officer & Treas.--Graphic Industries, Inc., Atlanta, GA; *U.S. Public*, pg. 1735
Fraser, Gregory A., Ph.D., Chief Fin. Officer, Exec. V.P., Treas. & Sec.--FARO Technologies, Inc., Lake Mary, FL; *U.S. Public*, pg. 613
Fraser, M.F., Chief Fin. Officer--B.H. McCleery & Co. Ltd., Newtownards, United Kingdom; *Int'l*, pg. 797
Frazer, Lewis, III, Chief Fin. Officer, Exec. V.P. & Treas.--Regal Cinemas Inc., Knoxville, TN; *U.S. Public*, pg. 1371
Frazer, Miriam K., Chief Fin. Officer & V.P.--Software Publishing Corporation, Fairfield, NJ; *U.S. Public*, pg. 1483
Frazier, Terry L., Mgr.-Fin. & Comml.--CAP Gemini America (Minneapolis Branch), Edina, MN; *Int'l*, pg. 264
Freddo, M., Chief Fin. Officer & V.P.--SGS Control Services Inc., Edison, NJ; *Int'l*, pg. 1153
Frederick, Donald, Chief Fin. Officer & V.P.--ADFlex Solutions, Inc., Chandler, AZ; *U.S. Public*, pg. 20
Frederick, Thomas, Chief Fin. Officer & V.P.-Fin.--Huffy Corporation, Miamisburg, OH; *U.S. Public*, pg. 846
Fredholm, Jim, Chief Fin. Officer--Danzas Holding Ltd., Basel, Switzerland; *Int'l*, pg. 382
Fredianelli, Ronald E., Chief Fin. Officer & Sec.--ILC Technology, Inc., Sunnyvale, CA; *U.S. Public*, pg. 856
Fredianelli, Ronald E., Chief Fin. Officer--Q-ARC Limited, Cambridge, United Kingdom; *U.S. Public*, pg. 856
Fredianelli, Ronald E., Chief Fin. Officer--Precision Lamp, Inc., Cotati, CA; *U.S. Public*, pg. 856
Freed, Thomas J., Controller & Sec.--National City Bancorp, Minneapolis, MN; *U.S. Public*, pg. 1153
Freedman, Tom, Chief Fin. Officer & Sr. Exec. V.P.--Les Schwab Tire Centers, Prineville, OR; *U.S. Private*, pg. 974
Freeman, Dennis, Chief Fin. Officer--Imperial Die Casting, Easley, SC; *U.S. Private*, pg. 903
Freeman, James I., Chief Fin. Officer & Sr. V.P.--Dillard's, Inc., Little Rock, AR; *U.S. Public*, pg. 509
Freeman, John P., Chief Fin. Officer & V.P.--Spectrum Control, Inc., Erie, PA; *U.S. Public*, pg. 1497
Freeman, John P., Chief Fin. Officer--Spectrum Control, Filter Products Group, Fairview, PA; *U.S. Public*, pg. 1497
Freeman, Rick, Chief Fin. Officer--Hyre Electric Company of Indiana, Inc., Highland, IN; *U.S. Public*, pg. 572
Freeman, William, Chief Fin. Officer, V.P. & Treas.--Seymour of Sycamore, Inc., Sycamore, IL; *U.S. Private*, pg. 988
Freeze, Walter E., Chief Fin. Officer & Sr. V.P.--Doubleday Publishing Company, New York, NY; *Int'l*, pg. 191
Freibaum, Bernard, Chief Fin. Officer--General Growth Properties Inc., Chicago, IL; *U.S. Public*, pg. 715
Freiberg, Lowell C., Chief Fin. Officer & Sr. V.P.--Reliance Group Holdings, Inc., New York, NY; *U.S. Public*, pg. 1374
Freilich, Joan S., Chief Fin. Officer & Sr. V.P.--Consolidated Edison Company of New York, Inc., New York, NY; *U.S. Public*, pg. 434
Freimark, Jeffrey P., Chief Fin. Officer, Sr. V.P. & Sec.--The Grand Union Company, Wayne, NJ; *U.S. Public*, pg. 758
French, Morton R., Jr., Pres., Chief Exec. Officer, Chief Fin. Officer & Treas.--Commercial Plastics & Supplies Corp., Richmond Hill, NY; *U.S. Private*, pg. 258
French, Theodore R., Pres. & Chief Fin. Officer--Case Corporation, Racine, WI; *U.S. Public*, pg. 311
Frere, Louis, Chief Fin. Officer--GIB Group, Brussels, Belgium; *Int'l*, pg. 532
Freriks, Donald, Chief Fin. Officer & Exec. V.P.--O'Neal Steel Inc., Birmingham, AL; *U.S. Private*, pg. 817
Fresh, Barry, Chief Fin. Officer & V.P.-Fin.--J.W. Window Components, Inc., Elizabethton, TN; *U.S. Public*, pg. 1736
Frey, Keith G., Chief Fin. Officer, V.P.-Fin. & Admin. & Sec.--IL International Inc., Stratford, CT; *U.S. Public*, pg. 855
Freyberger, Larry, Chief Fin. Officer & Dir.-Fin.--BR Associates, Inc., Jasper, IN; *U.S. Private*, pg. 107
Friedl, Robert R., Chief Fin. Officer & Sr. V.P.--The Manitowoc Company, Inc., Manitowoc, WI; *U.S. Public*, pg. 1040
Friedman, Howard, Chief Fin. Officer & Treas.--Van Cleef & Arpels, Inc., New York, NY; *U.S. Private*, pg. 1132
Friedman, Jonathan M., Chief Fin. Officer & V.P.--Kids "R" Us, Paramus, NJ; *U.S. Public*, pg. 1626
Friedman, Jonathon M., Chief Fin. Officer & V.P.--Babies "R" Us, Paramus, NJ; *U.S. Public*, pg. 1626
Friedrichsen, B.T., Treas. & Sec.--Wagner Mills Inc., Schuyler, NE; *U.S. Private*, pg. 1146
Friesen, Eugene K., Chief Fin. Officer, Sr. V.P. & Treas.--Howard B. Wolf, Inc., Dallas, TX; *U.S. Public*, pg. 1774
Friman, Kaj, Chief Fin. Officer & Treas.--Kemira Oy, Helsinki, Finland; *Int'l*, pg. 727
Frinder, Landsdon, Chief Fin. Officer--Masterfoods Oy, Helsinki, Finland; *U.S. Private*, pg. 707
Frith, Michael, Dir.-Fin.--Thomson Tour Operations Ltd., London, United Kingdom; *U.S. Public*, pg. 1601
Fritsche, Richard, Chief Fin. Officer--L.G. Balfour Co., Inc., Austin, TX; *U.S. Private*, pg. 258
Fritz, Mike, Chief Fin. Officer & Treas.--Collegeville Flag & Mfg. Company, Collegeville, PA; *U.S. Private*, pg. 252
Fritz, Roy, Chief Fin. Officer & V.P.-Fin.--Anchor Lamina Inc., Windsor, Canada; *Int'l*, pg. 75
Fritzinger, Peter, Chief Fin. Officer & Treas.--Louis Dreyfus Natural Gas Corp., Oklahoma City, OK; *U.S. Private*, pg. 342
Frizzel, Johnny, Chief Fin. Officer--American Innovations, Ltd., Austin, TX; *U.S. Private*, pg. 491
Froelich, Eugene, Chief Fin. Officer & Exec. V.P.-Fin. & Admin.--Maxicare Health Plans, Inc., Los Angeles, CA; *U.S. Public*, pg. 1061
Froelich, John M., Chief Fin. Officer, V.P. & Treas.--Chatwins Group, Inc., Pittsburgh, PA; *U.S. Private*, pg. 231
Froesel, David W., Jr., Chief Fin. Officer & Sr. V.P.--Omnicare, Inc., Covington, KY; *U.S. Public*, pg. 1223
Frohauck, John, Chief Fin. Officer--Chivas Products Ltd., Sterling Heights, MI; *U.S. Private*, pg. 238
Fromi, Fred, Chief Fin. Officer & Controller--BeefAmerica Operating Co., Inc., Omaha, NE; *U.S. Private*, pg. 130
Frost, Andrew G., Chief Fin. Officer--Multi-Arc (U.K.) Ltd., Durham, United Kingdom; *Int'l*, pg. 1198
Fruitman, Harvey, Chief Fin. Officer, Exec. V.P. & Sec.--Tridel Enterprises Inc., Downsview, Canada; *Int'l*, pg. 1423
Frutko, David, Chief Fin. Officer & Exec. V.P.--Mezzina/Brown Inc., New York, NY; *U.S. Private*, pg. 739
Fry, Todd, Chief Fin. Officer--Broughton Foods Company, Marietta, OH; *U.S. Public*, pg. 259
Frye, John W., Chief Fin. Officer, Sr. V.P.-Fin. & Treas.--Old Dominion Freight Line, Inc., High Point, NC; *U.S. Public*, pg. 1216
Fu, Cary, Chief Fin. Officer & Exec. V.P.--Benchmark Electronics Inc., Angleton, TX; *U.S. Public*, pg. 210
Fuchs, Rita, Head Bookkeeper--Rosen Associates Management Corp., Jericho, NY; *U.S. Private*, pg. 945
Fuchs, William, Chief Fin. Officer & Controller--S. Rothchild & Co., Inc., New York, NY; *U.S. Private*, pg. 947
Fudale, Bill, Chief Fin. Officer--Carefree of Colorado, Broomfield, CO; *U.S. Public*, pg. 217
Fuette, Kenneth R., V.P. & Controller--Foamex, L.P., Linwood, PA; *U.S. Private*, pg. 1094
Fugate, J. Robert, Chief Fin. Officer, V.P.-Fin. & Treas.--Mobile Telecommunications Technologies Corp., Jackson, MS; *U.S. Public*, pg. 1120
Fuhrmann, Charles J., II, Pres., Chief Exec. Officer & Chief Fin. Officer--Lot$ Off Corporation, San Antonio, TX; *U.S. Public*, pg. 1014
Fujimura, Takuya, Mng. Dir.--Tonen Corporation, Tokyo, Japan; *Int'l*, pg. 1398
Fujinami, Iku, Chief Fin. Officer--Plaza Create, Tokyo, Japan; *Int'l*, pg. 1060
Fukuyama, Dave, Chief Fin. Officer & Treas.--Suntory International Corp., New York, NY; *Int'l*, pg. 1321
Fulle, Kurt, Chief Fin. Officer & V.P.-Fin--Andiamo, Inc., Fountain Valley, CA; *U.S. Private*, pg. 73
Fuller, H. Thomas, Chief Fin. Officer--WestWayne, Inc., Atlanta, GA; *U.S. Private*, pg. 1170
Fullmer, Brenda, Chief Fin. Officer--Huitt-Zollars, Inc., Dallas, TX; *U.S. Private*, pg. 547
Fulton, William R., Exec. V.P. & Chief Fin. Officer--Midland Walwyn Inc., Toronto, Canada; *Int'l*, pg. 865
Fulton, William R.J., Chief Fin. Officer--Midland Walwyn Capital Inc., Toronto, Canada; *Int'l*, pg. 865
Fumagalli, Maurizio, Chief Fin. Officer--Candy S.p.A., Brugherio, Italy; *Int'l*, pg. 259
Fundler, Jonathan, Dir.-Fin.--Berisford plc, London, United Kingdom; *Int'l*, pg. 188
Fung, Michael, Chief Fin. Officer & V.P.--Universal Foods Corporation, Milwaukee, WI; *U.S. Public*, pg. 1695
Funk, H. Benjamin, Auditor--Commerce Bancshares, Inc., Kansas City, MO; *U.S. Public*, pg. 409
Funk, John, Chief Fin. Officer--The GSI Group, Inc., Assumption, IL; *U.S. Private*, pg. 436
Funk, Ronald, Chief Fin. Officer--Columbian Mutual Life Insurance Co., Binghamton, NY; *U.S. Private*, pg. 256
Funk, S., Chief Fin. Officer--Vanner, Inc., Hilliard, OH; *Int'l*, pg. 449
Funke, J.R., Chief Fin. Officer& V.P.--Jefferson Smurfit Corporation, Saint Louis, MO; *Int'l*, pg. 1271
Funke, M., Chief Fin. Officer & V.P.--Comdial Enterprise Systems, Inc., Charlottesville, VA; *U.S. Public*, pg. 407
Funston, Mark, Chief Fin. Officer & V.P.-Fin.--Group 1 Software, Inc., Lanham, MD; *U.S. Public*, pg. 417
Funston, Mark D., Chief Fin. Officer, Exec. V.P. & Treas.--COMNET Corporation, Lanham, MD; *U.S. Public*, pg. 416
Fuoco, Dino, Chief Fin. Officer & Exec. V.P.--Alliance Forest Products Inc., Montreal, Canada; *Int'l*, pg. 57
Fuqua, Robert E., Chief Fin. Officer--Tenneco Packaging, Evanston, IL; *U.S. Public*, pg. 1579
Furr, Anthony L., Chief Fin. Officer & V.P.--Cone Mills Corporation, Greensboro, NC; *U.S. Public*, pg. 430
Furst, Rafael, Pres., Treas. & Sec.--The El-Bee Chargit Corp., Dayton, OH; *U.S. Private*, pg. 367
Furst, Thomas, Chief Fin. Officer & V.P.--SRI International, Menlo Park, CA; *U.S. Private*, pg. 958
Fuss, Michael D., Chief Fin. Officer & Exec. V.P.--Wm. E. Wright Limited Partnership, West Warren, MA; *U.S. Private*, pg. 1192
Fuss, Michael D., Chief Fin. Officer--EZ International, West Warren, MA; *U.S. Private*, pg. 1192
Fuster, Mark, Chief Fin. Officer--Long Island Bancorp, Inc., Melville, NY; *U.S. Public*, pg. 1013
Gable, Corey, Chief Fin. Officer & Treas.--Eateries, Inc., Oklahoma City, OK; *U.S. Public*, pg. 555
Gable, Corey, Chief Fin. Officer & Treas.--Pepperoni Grill, Oklahoma City, OK; *U.S. Public*, pg. 555
Gabrielsen, Robert, Chief Fin. Officer, Exec. V.P. & Treas.--Pawling Savings Bank, Pawling, NY; *U.S. Public*, pg. 1334
Gabrielsen, Robert A., Chief Fin. Officer & Treas.--Progressive Bank, Inc., Fishkill, NY; *U.S. Public*, pg. 1334
Gaehwiler, P., Chief Fin. Officer--Kuehne & Nagel GmbH, Vienna, Austria; *Int'l*, pg. 763
Gaertner, Suzie, Chief Fin. Officer--Shealy Electrical Wholesalers, Greenville, SC; *U.S. Private*, pg. 991
Gagalis, Robert J., Chief Fin. Officer, Treas. & V.P.--Wheelabrator Technologies Inc., Hampton, NH; *U.S. Public*, pg. 1745
Gagliardi, Joseph J., Chief Fin. Officer & V.P.-Fin.--Harvard Industries, Inc., Tampa, FL; *U.S. Public*, pg. 796
Gagnon, Benoit, Chief Fin. Officer & Treas.--Agropur, Granby, Canada; *Int'l*, pg. 31
Gagon, Natalie, Chief Fin. Officer--Canadian Steel Foundries, Ltd., Montreal, Canada; *U.S. Public*, pg. 142
Gahlon, Tom, Chief Fin. Officer, Chief Admin. Officer & V.P.--Sahara Enterprises Inc., Chicago, IL; *U.S. Private*, pg. 960
Gailius, Gilbert K., Chief Fin. Officer & V.P.-Fin.--American Biltrite Inc., Wellesley Hills, MA; *U.S. Public*, pg. 68
Galanti, Richard A., Chief Fin. Officer & Exec. V.P.--Costco Wholesale, Issaquah, WA; *U.S. Public*, pg. 451
Galbraith, John R., Sr. V.P. & Chief Fin. Officer--Liberty Northwest Insurance Corp., Portland, OR; *U.S. Private*, pg. 666
Galbraith, Leslie A., Chief Fin. Officer, Exec. V.P., Treas. & Sec.--First International Bancorp, Inc., Hartford, CT; *U.S. Public*, pg. 635
Gale, James C., Chief Fin. Officer & Sr. V.P.-Fin.--Genicom Corporation, Chantilly, VA; *U.S. Public*, pg. 729
Gale, William C., Chief Fin. Officer & V.P.-Fin.--Cintas Corporation, Mason, OH; *U.S. Public*, pg. 370

Galgano, Victor J., Chief Fin. Officer & V.P.--Hi-Shear Industries Inc., New Hyde Park, NY; *U.S. Public*, pg. 824
Gallagher, H. James, Chief Fin. Officer, Exec. V.P.-Fin. & Acting Treas.--CalMat Co., Los Angeles, CA; *U.S. Public, pg. 295*
Gallagher, H. James, Chief Fin. Officer--CalMat Co. of Arizona, Los Angeles, CA; *U.S. Public*, pg. 295
Gallagher, H. James, Chief Fin. Officer--Allied Concrete, Inc., Los Angeles, CA; *U.S. Public*, pg. 295
Gallagher, H. James, Chief Fin. Officer--CalMat Land Co., Los Angeles, CA; *U.S. Public*, pg. 295
Gallagher, H. James, Chief Fin. Officer--CalMat Leasing Co., Los Angeles, CA; *U.S. Public*, pg. 295
Gallagher, H. James, Chief Fin. Officer--Azusa Rock, Inc., Los Angeles, CA; *U.S. Public*, pg. 295
Gallagher, H. James, Chief Fin. Officer--Hidden Valley Coal Company, Los Angeles, CA; *U.S. Public*, pg. 296
Gallagher, H. James, Chief Fin. Officer--Kirst Construction Co., Inc., Los Angeles, CA; *U.S. Public*, pg. 296
Gallagher, H. James, Chief Fin. Officer--Reliance Land Co., Los Angeles, CA; *U.S. Public*, pg. 296
Gallagher, H. James, Chief Fin. Officer--Rio Norte Este Co., Los Angeles, CA; *U.S. Public*, pg. 296
Gallagher, H. James, Chief Fin. Officer--River Bend Corp., Los Angeles, CA; *U.S. Public*, pg. 296
Gallagher, Jack, Chief Fin. Officer--VKO, Inc., Taunton, MA; *U.S. Private*, pg. 1130
Gallagher, Tony, Chief Fin. Officer--GEC Plessey Semiconductors, Swindon, United Kingdom; *Int'l*, pg. 544
Gallaher, J. Kirk, Chief Fin. Officer & Exec. V.P--Uni-Marts, Inc., State College, PA; *U.S. Public*, pg. 1664
Gallant, Steve, Chief Fin. Officer--RI Holdings, Grand Rapids, MI; *U.S. Private*, pg. 904
Galligan, Edward, Chief Fin. Officer & Sr. Dir.--Port of Portland, Portland, OR; *U.S. Private*, pg. 876
Gallo, Kathleen, Chief Fin. Officer--Mellon Bank (DE) National Association, Wilmington, DE; *U.S. Public*, pg. 1085
Galon, Yoram, V.P.-Fin.--El Al Airlines Ltd., Lod, Israel; *Int'l, pg. 435*
Galvin, Robert, Chief Fin. Officer & Exec. V.P.--Nine West Group, Inc., Stamford, CT; *U.S. Public*, pg. 1185
Galvin, W.J., Chief Fin. Officer & Sr. V.P.-Fin.--Emerson Electric Co., Saint Louis, MO; *U.S. Public*, pg. 572
Gambill, Stephen T., Chief Fin. Officer--SPR, Inc., Oak Brook, IL; *U.S. Public*, pg. 1419
Ganasevici, Joan, Chief Fin. Officer--General Motors Venezolana, C.A., Caracas, Venezuela; *U.S. Public*, pg. 723
Gandy, Kartar, Pres. & Chief Fin. Officer--Signtech USA, Ltd., San Antonio, TX; *U.S. Private*, pg. 999
Gannon, Michael J., Chief Fin. Officer & Sr. V.P.--Flint Ink Corp., Detroit, MI; *U.S. Private*, pg. 413
Gannon, Tom, Chief Fin. Officer--Schneider National, Inc., Green Bay, WI; *U.S. Private*, pg. 971
Ganster, W., Chief Fin. Officer--Elektrowerk Weisweiler GmbH, Eschweiler, Germany; *U.S. Private*, pg. 735
Gant, Harry, Chief Fin. Officer, V.P., Treas. & Sec.--Young Radiator Company, Racine, WI; *U.S. Private*, pg. 1201
Ganzi, Victor F., Chief Fin. Officer, Exec. V.P. & Legal Officer--The Hearst Corporation, New York, NY; *U.S. Private*, pg. 515
Garbarding, Larry G., Chief Fin. Officer & Exec. V.P.--DTE Energy Company, Detroit, MI; *U.S. Public*, pg. 475
Garber, John, Chief Fin. Officer, V.P.-Fin. & Treas.--Newcor, Inc., Bloomfield Hills, MI; *U.S. Public*, pg. 1176
Garber, Murray L., Chief Fin. Officer--Young Pecan Company (A Partnership), Florence, SC; *U.S. Private*, pg. 1201
Garcia, Carlos M., Mng. Dir. & Chief Fin. Officer--Countrywide Funding Corporation, Pasadena, CA; *U.S. Public*, pg. 453
Garcia, Carlos M., Chief Fin. Officer--Countrywide Capital Markets, Inc., Pasadena, CA; *U.S. Public*, pg. 453
Garcia, Jose Luiz Jimenez, Chief Fin. Officer--Peugeot Talbot Espana, Madrid, Spain; *Int'l*, pg. 1021
Gardiner, Robert A., Chief Fin. Officer, V.P. & Controller--Zapata Corporation, Houston, TX; *U.S. Public*, pg. 1789
Gardiner, William J., Chief Fin. Officer, Sr. V.P. & Treas.--CRSS Inc., Houston, TX; *Int'l*, pg. 1415
Gardner, Donald R., Chief Fin. Officer, Sr. V.P. & Sec.--Rigel Energy Corporation, Calgary, Canada; *Int'l*, pg. 1117
Gardner, Donald R., Chief Fin. Officer--Rigel Oil & Gas Ltd., Calgary, Canada; *Int'l*, pg. 1117
Gardner, Donald R., Chief Fin. Officer--Rigel Petroleum, Inc., Calgary, Canada; *Int'l*, pg. 1117
Gardner, Donald R., Chief Fin. Officer--Rigel Petroleum (NI) Limited, Calgary, Canada; *Int'l*, pg. 1117
Gardner, Donald R., Chief Fin. Officer--Rigel Petroleum UK Limited, Calgary, Canada; *Int'l*, pg. 1117
Gardner, James, Chief Fin. Officer--Cherokee International LLC, Tustin, CA; *U.S. Private*, pg. 233
Gardner, John, Chief Fin. Officer & Exec. V.P.--New Balance Athletic Shoe, Inc., Boston, MA; *U.S. Private*, pg. 792
Gardner, John W., Chief Fin. Officer--Fabwel Inc., Elkhart, IN; *U.S. Private*, pg. 390
Gardner, R. Hartwell, Treas.--Mobil Oil Corporation, Fairfax, VA; *U.S. Public*, pg. 1118
Gardner, Tasia, V.P.-Fin.--Carpenter Industries, Inc., Richmond, IN; *U.S. Private*, pg. 215
Garefino, Anello C., Chief Fin. Officer, V.P.-Fin. & Treas.--Herley Industries, Inc., Lancaster, PA; *U.S. Public*, pg. 811
Garety, Andrew, Group Fin. Dir. & Sec.--Liberty PLC, London, United Kingdom; *Int'l*, pg. 807
Garitty, Joseph, Chief Fin. Officer--The Summit Media Group, New York, NY; *U.S. Private*, pg. 1050
Garland, Jerry, Chief Fin. Officer--Tessco Technologies, Inc., Sparks, MD; *U.S. Public*, pg. 1582
Garlington, John, Chief Fin. Officer--Warmington Homes, Costa Mesa, CA; *U.S. Private*, pg. 1150
Garneau, Robert M., Chief Fin. Officer & Exec. V.P.--Kaman Corporation, Bloomfield, CT; *U.S. Public*, pg. 941
Garnett, Gerald, Chief Fin. Officer & Exec. V.P.--Mississippi Farm Bureau Casualty Insurance Company, Jackson, MS; *U.S. Private*, pg. 1016
Garnett, Gerald, Chief Fin. Officer & Exec. V.P.--Louisiana Farm Bureau Casualty Insurance Company, Baton Rouge, LA; *U.S. Private*, pg. 1016
Garofolo, Gary, Chief Fin. Officer & V.P.-Fin.--Harkins Builders, Inc., Silver Spring, MD; *U.S. Private*, pg. 502
Garrard, William, Chief Fin. Officer--Mackie Designs, Inc., Woodinville, WA; *U.S. Public*, pg. 1030
Garreaud, Ann, Chief Fin. Officer--The Lord Group, New York, NY; *U.S. Private*, pg. 325
Garrett, C.L., Chief Fin. Officer & Sr. V.P.-Fin.--SENCORP, Newport, KY; *U.S. Private*, pg. 983
Garrett, Melinda S., Chief Fin. Officer--Abrams Industries, Inc., Atlanta, GA; *U.S. Public*, pg. 14
Garrett, Wayne P., Chief Fin. Officer & V.P.-Fin.--Cambridge Soundworks, Inc., Newton, MA; *U.S. Private*, pg. 202
Garrison, Gary G., Chief Fin. Officer, V.P.-Fin. & Treas.--Global Industrial Technologies, Dallas, TX; *U.S. Public*, pg. 747
Garrison, James W., Chief Fin. Officer, V.P.-Fin. & Treas.--InterDigital Communications Corp., King of Prussia, PA; *U.S. Public*, pg. 889
Garrity, Joe, Chief Fin. Officer--Digitron Tool Co., Inc., Miamisburg, OH; *U.S. Private*, pg. 332
Garrity, Thomas, Chief Fin. Officer--PCS Health Systems, Inc., Scottsdale, AZ; *U.S. Public*, pg. 993
Garry, William J., Chief Fin. Officer & V.P.--Richardson Electronics, Ltd., Lafox, IL; *U.S. Public*, pg. 1387
Garten, Wayne P., Chief Fin. Officer & Sr. V.P.--Micro Warehouse, Inc., Norwalk, CT; *U.S. Public*, pg. 1104
Gartenbach, V., Chief Fin. Officer--Molto GmbH, Lohnberg, Germany; *Int'l*, pg. 1501
Gartfinkel, Steven R., Chief Fin. Officer & Exec. V.P.--DVI, Inc., Doylestown, PA; *U.S. Public*, pg. 476
Gartin, Robert E., Chief Fin. Officer & Sr. V.P.--Manheim Auctions, Inc., Atlanta, GA; *U.S. Private*, pg. 282
Gartlan, Ronald B., Pres. & Chief Fin. Officer--Godfather's Pizza, Inc., Omaha, NE; *U.S. Private*, pg. 458
Gartland, Richard, Chief Fin. Officer--The JCM Group, Los Angeles, CA; *U.S. Private*, pg. 846
Gartzke, David G., Chief Fin. Officer & Sr. V.P.-Fin.--Minnesota Power, Duluth, MN; *U.S. Public*, pg. 1116
Garven, R. Lee, Chief Fin. Officer & Mgr.-Pur.--Directory Distributing Associates, Inc., Scarborough, Canada; *U.S. Private*, pg. 334
Garvey, H.T., Chief Fin. Officer--Precision Resource Inc., Shelton, CT; *U.S. Private*, pg. 880
Garvey, William P., Exec. V.P. & Chief Fin. Officer-U.S.--Grey Advertising Inc., New York, NY; *U.S. Public*, pg. 764
Garza Jimenez, Francisco, Chief Fin. Officer--Corporacion Industrial Sanluis, Mexico, Mexico; *Int'l*, pg. 332
Garza, Jose A. Elizondo, V.P.-Fin.--Corporacion E.G., S.A. de C.V., Monterrey, Mexico; *Int'l*, pg. 395
Gash, Jeffrey D., Chief Fin. Officer--Jaco Electronics, Inc., Hauppauge, NY; *U.S. Public*, pg. 920
Gasper, Ron, Chief Fin. Officer--American Tissue Corporation, Hauppauge, NY; *U.S. Private*, pg. 63
Gasper, Ron, Chief Fin. Officer--American Tissue, Inc., Mechanicville, NY; *U.S. Private*, pg. 63
Gasperlin, Bruce P., Chief Fin. Officer & V.P.--Haworth Group Inc., Minneapolis, MN; *U.S. Private*, pg. 511
Gassan, Marsha M., Chief Fin. Officer & Sr. Exec. V.P.--Hibernia Corporation, New Orleans, LA; *U.S. Public*, pg. 825
Gast, Brian, Chief Fin. Officer--Burlington Motor Holdings Inc., Daleville, IN; *U.S. Private*, pg. 183
Gaster, Pattie L., Chief Fin. Officer--Lee-Moore Oil Co., Inc., Sanford, NC; *U.S. Private*, pg. 657
Gaston, John, Chief Fin. Officer & Sr. V.P.-Corp. Svcs.--SF Services, North Little Rock, AR; *U.S. Private*, pg. 956
Gaston, Ron, Chief Fin. Officer & Exec. V.P.--Fabri-Centers of America, Inc., Hudson, OH; *U.S. Public*, pg. 609
Gaston, S. Albert, Chief Fin. Officer & Sr. V.P.--Tom's Foods, Inc., Columbus, GA; *U.S. Private*, pg. 1090
Gasztowtt, Guillaume, Chief Fin. Officer--Promodes SA, Mondeville, France; *Int'l*, pg. 1071
Gates, Joe, Chief Fin. Officer--MetalWest LLC, Brighton, CO; *U.S. Private*, pg. 817
Gates, Jordan, Chief Fin. Officer & Treas.--Expeditors International of Washington, Inc., Seattle, WA; *U.S. Public*, pg. 600
Gates, William S., Treas. & Sec.--Preferred Risk Life Insurance Co., West Des Moines, IA; *U.S. Private*, pg. 880
Gatsch, Mary E., Chief Fin. Officer & Sr. V.P.--Peterson's Guides, Inc., Princeton, NJ; *U.S. Private*, pg. 858
Gattuso, Dominic, Chief Fin. Officer--Kinro, Inc., Arlington, TX; *U.S. Public*, pg. 529
Gaubert, Daniel R., Chief Fin. Officer, Sr. V.P.-Fin. & Controller--McDermott International, Inc., New Orleans, LA; *U.S. Public*, pg. 1067
Gaubert, Harold, Chief Fin. Officer--Consolidated Graphics, Inc., Houston, TX; *U.S. Private*, pg. 265
Gaudefroy, Gilles, Deputy Chief Fin. Officer--LeGrand S.A., Limoges, France; *Int'l*, pg. 805
Gaul, Hans Michael, Dr., Chief Fin. Officer--Veba AG, Dusseldorf, Germany; *Int'l*, pg. 1454
Gauntt, Jim, Chief Fin. Officer--Totem Resources Corporation, Seattle, WA; *U.S. Private*, pg. 1092
Gaut, C. Christopher, Chief Fin. Officer & V.P.--Ensco International Incorporated (ENSCO), Dallas, TX; *U.S. Public*, pg. 585
Gauthier, Alan E., Chief Fin. Officer & Exec. V.P.-Fin.--Exide Corporation, Reading, PA; *U.S. Public*, pg. 600
Gauvreau, Paul R., V.P.-Fin. & Treas.--Pittway Corporation, Chicago, IL; *U.S. Public*, pg. 1305
Gauvreau, Pierre, Chief Fin. Officer & Treas.--Cooperative Federee de Quebec, Montreal, Canada; *Int'l*, pg. 330
Gavin, Jon D., Chief Fin. Officer, V.P., Sec. & Treas.--Frontier Oil Corporation, Englewood, CO; *U.S. Public*, pg. 1732
Gavin, Jon D., Chief Fin. Officer, V.P., Sec. & Treas.--Frontier Holdings Inc., Englewood, CO; *U.S. Public*, pg. 1732
Gavin, Pat, Chief Fin. Officer, Exec. V.P. & Treas.--General Media International Inc., New York, NY; *U.S. Private*, pg. 444
Gavlin, Jene G., Chief Fin. Officer & V.P.--Joseph Davis, Inc., Buffalo, NY; *U.S. Private*, pg. 315
Gawler, David, Chief Fin. Officer--Trafalgar House PLC, London, United Kingdom; *Int'l*, pg. 772
Gay, Phil, Exec. Gen. Mgr.-Fin.--Pacific Dunlop Limited, Melbourne, Australia; *Int'l*, pg. 1021
Gay, Philip, Chief Fin. Officer--California Pizza Kitchen Inc., Los Angeles, CA; *U.S. Public*, pg. 1277
Gayhart, Roy, Chief Fin. Officer--Photomatrix Corporation, San Diego, CA; *U.S. Public*, pg. 1292
Gaynor, John, Chief Fin. Officer--Boler Company, Itasca, IL; *U.S. Private*, pg. 155
Gaysunas, Clifford P., Chief Fin. Officer & V.P.--Robertson Factories, Inc., Taunton, MA; *U.S. Private*, pg. 936
Gazarek, Celeste, V.P.-Fin. & Treas.--National Frozen Foods Corp., Seattle, WA; *U.S. Private*, pg. 783
Gazmarian, Michael C., Chief Fin. Officer & Treas.--Insteel Industries, Inc., Mount Airy, NC; *U.S. Public*, pg. 882
Geater, Andy, Chief Fin. Officer--Univest Financial Services, LLC, Atlanta, GA; *U.S. Private*, pg. 1128
Gebhard, Jaachim, Chief Fin. Officer--Osram Ltd., Wembley, United Kingdom; *Int'l*, pg. 1244
Gebhardt, Chris, Chief Fin. Officer--Gold Medal Products Co., Cincinnati, OH; *U.S. Private*, pg. 459
Gebhardt, Patrick J., Chief Fin. Officer & V.P.--Enesco Corporation, Itasca, IL; *U.S. Public*, pg. 1508
Gehrig, Greg, Chief Fin. Officer, V.P. & Controller--Leslie Controls, Inc., Tampa, FL; *U.S. Public*, pg. 1746
Gehrig, James, Chief Fin. Officer--Keystone Brewers, Inc., Pittsburgh, PA; *U.S. Private*, pg. 618
Gehring, Pat, Controller--Northwest Dietetic Supply, Inc., Kent, WA; *Int'l*, pg. 752
Gehringer, Richard, Chief Fin. Officer--Oxford University Press, Inc., New York, NY; *Int'l*, pg. 1019
Geiger, Paul K., Chief Fin. Officer & Sr. V.P.--Kelly Services, Inc., Troy, MI; *U.S. Public*, pg. 949
Geilow, Ron, Chief Fin. Officer & V.P.--Landmark Systems Inc., Livonia, MI; *U.S. Private*, pg. 649
Geiser, James, Chief Fin. Officer, Controller & Treas.--Kokosing Construction Company, Inc., Fredericktown, OH; *U.S. Private*, pg. 631
Geiser, K., Chief Fin. Officer--Siemens Schieiz AG, Zurich, Switzerland; *Int'l*, pg. 1248
Geldmacher, Klaus, Chief Fin. Officer--Richardson G.m.b.H., Schwalbach, Germany; *U.S. Public*, pg. 1333
Gelfeld, Mark, Chief Fin. Officer & V.P.--Century America Corporation, Chicago, IL; *U.S. Private*, pg. 225
Geli, Gian Paolo, Chief Fin. Officer--Ideal Form Team S.r.L., Monsano, Italy; *Int'l*, pg. 659
Gelman, Howard, Chief Fin. Officer & Exec. V.P.--Adler Boschetto Peebles & Partners, Inc., New York, NY; *U.S. Private*, pg. 17
Gendreau, Ronald R., Chief Fin. Officer & V.P.--Colonial Companies, Inc., Columbia, SC; *U.S. Public*, pg. 1699
Gennrich, James N., V.P.-Fin.--Weasler Engineering Inc., West Bend, WI; *U.S. Private*, pg. 249
Genor, Andrew C., Chief Fin. Officer, V.P. & Treas.--Wyman-Gordon, North Grafton, MA; *U.S. Public*, pg. 1782
Genry, Christopher D., Chief Fin. Officer & V.P.--Centex Construction Group, Inc., Dallas, TX; *U.S. Public*, pg. 322
Gensinger, Donald, Chief Fin. Officer--Atlantic Hardware & Supply Co., New York, NY; *U.S. Public*, pg. 400
Gent, Jeffrey, V.P.-Fin.--Hallwood Realty Corporation, Dallas, TX; *U.S. Public*, pg. 778
Gent, Jeffrey, V.P.-Fin.--Hallwood Commercial Real Estate, Inc., Dallas, TX; *U.S. Public*, pg. 778
Gentilcore, James, V.P. & Controller-Distr. Acctg.--MGM Entertainment Company, Culver City, CA; *U.S. Public*, pg. 1614
Gentile, LouAnn, Chief Fin. Officer--Precision Extrusions, Bensenville, IL; *U.S. Private*, pg. 879
Gentner, Craig, Chief Fin. Officer, Sr. V.P.-Fin. & Admin. & Sec.--Network Equipment Technologies, Inc., Redwood City, CA; *U.S. Public*, pg. 1168
Gentz, Manfred, Chief Fin. Officer--Daimler-Benz Aktiengesellschaft, Stuttgart, Germany; *Int'l*, pg. 366
George, Michael, Controller--George E. Warren Corporation, Vero Beach, FL; *U.S. Private*, pg. 1151
George, Thomas A., Chief Fin. Officer & Sr. V.P.--Remec, Inc., San Diego, CA; *U.S. Public*, pg. 1376
Georgehead, Glen, Chief Fin. Officer--Gateway Press, Inc., Louisville, KY; *U.S. Private*, pg. 441
Geppner, Edward, Chief Fin. Officer--Shaer Shoe Corporation, Bedford, NH; *U.S. Private*, pg. 988
Geraghty, Michael, Chief Fin. Officer--Filene's, Boston, MA; *U.S. Public*, pg. 1063
Gerber, Laurie, Chief Fin. Officer--Meditrust Corporation, Needham, MA; *U.S. Public*, pg. 1081
Gerber, M., Chief Fin. Officer--Mikron AG Nidau, Nidau, Switzerland; *Int'l*, pg. 866
Gerbosi, Doug, Chief Fin. Officer & V.P.--Friendship Dairies, Inc., Jericho, NY; *U.S. Private*, pg. 429
Gerbosi, Douglas P., Chief Fin. Officer & Controller--Friendship Dairies, Inc., Friendship, NY; *U.S. Private*, pg. 429
Geremski, Terrence E., Chief Fin. Officer, V.P. & Treas.--Guilford Mills, Inc., Greensboro, NC; *U.S. Public*, pg. 768
Gerhard, Gilbert C., Chief Fin. Officer, Sr. V.P.-Fin. & Admin. & Treas.--Arbor Drugs, Inc., Troy, MI; *U.S. Public, pg. 126*
Gerhardt, Gary C., Chief Fin. Officer & Exec. V.P.--Engineered Support Systems Inc., Saint Louis, MO; *U.S. Public*, pg. 583

Gerhardt, Gary C., Chief Fin. Officer & Exec. V.P.--Engineered Specialty Plastics, Hot Springs National Park, AR; U.S. Public, pg. 583
Gerhart, Karl D., Chief Fin. Officer & Treas.--Sovereign Bancorp, Inc., Wyomissing, PA; U.S. Public, pg. 1494
Gerhartz, Scott, Chief Fin. Officer--DeVlieg-Bullard Services Group, Rockford, IL; U.S. Public, pg. 502
Gerhrad, Franz Kolarik, Chief Fin. Officer--Creditanstalt-Bankverein, Vienna, Austria; Int'l, pg. 346
Gerken, Robert C., Chief Fin. Officer--Norwalk Furniture Corporation, Norwalk, OH; U.S. Private, pg. 807
Gerkens, Henry H., Chief Fin. Officer & Exec. V.P.--Landstar Holding, Shelton, CT; U.S. Public, pg. 978
Gerlach, J.M., Chief Fin. Officer--American Life & Casualty Insurance Co., Des Moines, IA; U.S. Public, pg. 433
Gersie, Mike, Chief Fin. Officer, Chief Info. Officer & Sr. V.P.--The Principal Financial Group, Des Moines, IA; U.S. Private, pg. 885
Gersie, Mike, Chief Fin. Officer & Sr. V.P.--Principal Mutual Life Insurance Co., Des Moines, IA; U.S. Private, pg. 886
Gerstein, Harvey, V.P.--Miss Elaine Inc., Saint Louis, MO; U.S. Private, pg. 752
Gerstner, Kenneth W., Chief Fin. Officer & Sr. V.P.--Farr Company, El Segundo, CA; U.S. Public, pg. 613
Gersuk, D. Joseph, Chief Fin. Officer & Exec. V.P.--MapInfo Corp., Troy, NY; U.S. Public, pg. 1042
Gerth, David, Chief Fin. Officer--Allaire Corporation, Cambridge, MA; U.S. Private, pg. 36
Gervasio, Thomas, Controller--Zemco Industries, Inc., Buffalo, NY; U.S. Private, pg. 1204
Geschke, Charles M., Pres. & Chief Fin. Officer--Adobe Systems Incorporated, San Jose, CA; U.S. Public, pg. 20
Gesinski, Robert, Chief Fin. Officer & V.P.-Fin.--Andis Company, Sturtevant, WI; U.S. Private, pg. 73
Getchell, Julie, Chief Fin. Officer--IFG Asset Management Services, Inc., Minneapolis, MN; U.S. Public, pg. 476
Gettlefinger, Earl, Treas.--Superior Label Systems, Inc., Mason, OH; U.S. Private, pg. 1055
Gettlegfinger, Herman E., Chief Fin. Officer, Treas. & Sec.--Pride Oil Co., Inc., Knoxville, TN; U.S. Private, pg. 613
Gettler, Benjamin, Chm. Bd., Pres., Chief Exec. Officer & Chief Fin. Officer--Vulcan International Corporation, Wilmington, DE; U.S. Public, pg. 1725
Geurin, Lynn K., Chief Fin. Officer, Exec. V.P. & Sec.--Resource Mortgage Capital, Inc., Glen Allen, VA; U.S. Public, pg. 1382
Gfeller, Richard W., Chief Fin. Officer--Celegec Automation Projects Inc., Macon, GA; Int'l, pg. 53
Ghazey, Kenneth A., Chief Fin. Officer & Exec. V.P.-Fin. & Admin.--Entex Information Services, Rye Brook, NY; U.S. Private, pg. 378
Ghisoni, Daniele, Chief Fin. Officer--I.B.I.S.-S.p.A., Busseto, Italy; Int'l, pg. 642
Ghuzzi, John G., Chief Fin. Officer--Lyon's Restaurants, Inc., Foster City, CA; U.S. Private, pg. 684
Giacometti, Jacques, Chief Fin. Officer--Olivetti (Schweiz) AG, Wallisellen, Switzerland; Int'l, pg. 1003
Gianunzio, Gerald, Chief Fin. Officer--Letts Industries, Inc., Detroit, MI; U.S. Private, pg. 661
Gibbard, Mark, Dir.-Fin.--Cheltenham & Gloucester plc, Gloucester, United Kingdom; Int'l, pg. 283
Gibbons, Dale M., Exec. V.P.-Fin. & Sec.--Zions Bancorporation, Salt Lake City, UT; U.S. Public, pg. 1792
Gibbons, Danny, Chief Fin. Officer--Valero Energy Corporation, San Antonio, TX; U.S. Public, pg. 1704
Gibbons, John, Chief Fin. Officer--Federal Home Loan Mortgage Corporation, Mc Lean, VA; U.S. Public, pg. 615
Gibbons, Michael D., Acting Chief Fin. Officer--National Steel Corporation, Mishawaka, IN; Int'l, pg. 902
Gibbons, Peter, Chief Fin. Officer & V.P.--Gold Kist, Inc., Atlanta, GA; U.S. Private, pg. 459
Gibbs, David H., Treas.--Owen-Ames-Kimball Co., Grand Rapids, MI; U.S. Private, pg. 823
Gibney, Charles W., Chief Fin. Officer & Sr. V.P.--Macromedia Incorporated, Hackensack, NJ; U.S. Private, pg. 693
Gibney, Charles W., Chief Fin. Officer, Exec. V.P. & Treas.--Bergen Record Corp., Hackensack, NJ; U.S. Private, pg. 693
Gibney, Charles W., Chief Fin. Officer--Macromedia Leasing, Hackensack, NJ; U.S. Private, pg. 693
Gibney, Charles W., Chief Fin. Officer--Gremac Inc., Hackensack, NJ; U.S. Private, pg. 693
Gibney, Charles W., Chief Fin. Officer--Magna Media Inc., Hackensack, NJ; U.S. Private, pg. 693
Gibson, B. Baird, Sec. & Treas.--Patterson Pump Company, Toccoa, GA; U.S. Public, pg. 754
Gibson, David R., Chief Fin. Officer & Sr. V.P.-Fin.--Wilmington Trust Corporation, Wilmington, DE; U.S. Public, pg. 1770
Gibson, M.L., Chief Fin. Officer, Exec. V.P. & Treas.--Hardings, Inc., Elmira, NY; U.S. Private, pg. 502
Gibson, Neil, Chief Fin. Officer & V.P.--Synergistics Industries Limited, Mississauga, Canada; U.S. Public, pg. 734
Gibson, Neil, Chief Fin. Officer--Synergistics Industries (NJ) Inc., Farmingdale, NJ; U.S. Public, pg. 734
Gibson, Neil, Chief Fin. Officer--Synergistics Industries (TX) Inc., Conroe, TX; U.S. Public, pg. 734
Gibson, Neil, Chief Fin. Officer--Synergistics Industries Limited, Lindsay, Canada; U.S. Public, pg. 734
Gibson, Neil, Chief Fin. Officer--Synergistics Industries Limited, Orangeville, Canada; U.S. Public, pg. 734
Gibson, Neil, Chief Fin. Officer--Synergistics Industries Limited, Valleyfield, Canada; U.S. Public, pg. 734
Gibson, Neil, Chief Fin. Officer--Synergistics Industries Limited, Saint Remi-de-Napierville, Canada; U.S. Public, pg. 734
Gibson, Richard P., Asst. Treas. & Dir.-Taxes--Kennametal Inc., Latrobe, PA; U.S. Public, pg. 950
Gibson, Russell G., Chief Fin. Officer, Exec. V.P., Treas. & Asst. Sec.--Farah Incorporated, El Paso, TX; U.S. Public, pg. 612
Gibson, S.P., Chief Fin. Officer--Armstrong International, Inc., Three Rivers, MI; U.S. Private, pg. 83
Gibson, Terry, Chief Fin. Officer--GaSonics International, San Jose, CA; U.S. Public, pg. 703
Giegel, T.J., Chief Fin. Officer--Asko, Inc, Homestead, PA; U.S. Private, pg. 89
Gienapp, Dave, Chief Fin. Officer & Controller--Nematron Corp., Ann Arbor, MI; U.S. Private, pg. 791
Giering, John L., Chief Fin. Officer & Sr. V.P.-Fin. & Admin.--NCR Corporation, Dayton, OH; U.S. Public, pg. 1146
Giertz, James R., Chief Fin. Officer & Sr. V.P.--Donaldson Company, Inc., Minneapolis, MN; U.S. Public, pg. 517
Gies, L.W., V.P.-Fin.--Spartan Tool, Mendota, IL; U.S. Private, pg. 860
Gies, Larry W., Chief Fin. Officer & Exec. V.P.--Pettibone Corporation, Lisle, IL; U.S. Private, pg. 859
Giffen, Ian, V.P.-Fin., Treas. & Chief Fin. Officer--Alias Wavefront, Toronto, Canada; U.S. Public, pg. 1474
Gifford, Russell M., Chief Fin. Officer, V.P. & Treas.--Barnwell Industries, Inc., Honolulu, HI; U.S. Public, pg. 190
Gil, Bianco, Chief Fin. Officer & Sr. V.P.--Agis Industries Ltd., Bnei-Brak, Israel; Int'l, pg. 30
Gilbert, Paul W., Vice Chm.--Jacobson Stores Inc., Jackson, MI; U.S. Public, pg. 922
Gilbert, Richard D., Chief Fin. Officer, Treas. & Sec.--The Converse Professional Group, Inc., Monrovia, CA; U.S. Private, pg. 271
Gilbert, Suzanne H., Chief Fin. Officer, Chief Admin. Officer & Exec. V.P.--Campbell-Ewald Advertising, Warren, MI; U.S. Public, pg. 908
Gilbert, Walter F., Chm. Bd., Pres., Chief Exec. Officer & Treas.--Semco Industries Inc., Stoughton, MA; U.S. Private, pg. 983
Gilbertson, Jay, Pres., Co-Chief Oper. Officer, Chief Fin. Officer, Treas. & Sec.--HBOC, Atlanta, GA; U.S. Public, pg. 770
Gilbride, Joe, Chief Fin. Officer & Exec. V.P.--Lowe & Partners/SMS, New York, NY; U.S. Private, pg. 678
Gilbride, Joseph, Chief Fin. Officer & Exec. V.P.--The Lowe Group, New York, NY; U.S. Private, pg. 677
Gilcrest, Jerry, Chief Fin. Officer--Contempo Colors, Kalamazoo, MI; U.S. Private, pg. 267
Giles, Bill, Chief Fin. Officer--Linens 'n Things, Inc., Clifton, NJ; U.S. Private, pg. 668
Gill, David, Chief Fin. Officer--Proudfoot USA Company, West Palm Beach, FL; Int'l, pg. 1072
Gill, Nicholas P., Chief Fin. Officer, V.P., Treas. & Sec.--The Union Corporation, Greenwich, CT; U.S. Public, pg. 1667
Gill, Steve, Chief Fin. Officer--Sika Corporation, Lyndhurst, NJ; Int'l, pg. 1249
Gill, Thomas, Chief Oper. Officer & Chief Fin. Officer--FORE Systems, Inc., Warrendale, PA; U.S. Public, pg. 667
Gillette, James R., Chief Fin. Officer--Leonard Green & Partners, Los Angeles, CA; U.S. Private, pg. 477
Gillette, James R., Chief Fin. Officer--Green Equity Investors L.P., Los Angeles, CA; U.S. Private, pg. 477
Gillette, James R., Chief Fin. Officer--Green Equity Investors II, L.P., Los Angeles, CA; U.S. Private, pg. 477
Gilligan, Brendan, Chief Fin. Officer--Woodchester Investments plc, Dublin, Ireland; U.S. Public, pg. 712
Gillingham, Peter, Controller--Total Petroleum Canada Ltd., Calgary, Canada; Int'l, pg. 1409
Gillis, Edwin J., Chief Fin. Officer, Exec. V.P. & Treas.--Parametric Technology Corporation, Waltham, MA; U.S. Public, pg. 1257
Gillula, E. William, Chief Fin. Officer & Exec. V.P.--Computer Sales International Inc., Saint Louis, MO; U.S. Private, pg. 260
Gilmour, James H., Chief Fin. Officer, V.P. & Treas.--The Dispatch Printing Company, Columbus, OH; U.S. Private, pg. 334
Gilpin, John D., Sr. V.P. & Sec.--Lyman Lumber Company, Excelsior, MN; U.S. Private, pg. 683
Gilroy, Kelly, Chief Fin. Officer--Solar Communications, Inc., Naperville, IL; U.S. Private, pg. 1012
Gilstrap, James J., Chief Fin. Officer, V.P. & Treas.--Florida Rock Industries, Inc., Jacksonville, FL; U.S. Public, pg. 655
Giltner, Philip, Chief Fin. Officer--Shamrock Foods Company, Phoenix, AZ; U.S. Private, pg. 989
Gimlet, Geoffry, Chief Fin. Officer--RGA and East End Accessories, New York, NY; U.S. Private, pg. 903
Gingerich, James G., Chief Fin. Officer & Sr. V.P.--InterTAN Inc., Fort Worth, TX; U.S. Public, pg. 910
Gingras, Yvan, Corp. Controller--Donohue Inc., Quebec, Canada; Int'l, pg. 1075
Gingrich, William D., II, Chief Fin. Officer & Exec. V.P.--Hostmark Management Group, Rolling Meadows, IL; U.S. Private, pg. 541
Ginn, Alan, Div. Mgr.-Admin. Services--Union Camp Fine Paper Div., Franklin, VA; U.S. Public, pg. 1666
Ginocchio, Tom, Chief Fin. Officer--Via Tech Publishing Solutions, Bay Shore, NY; U.S. Private, pg. 1138
Ginolfi, Frank, Chief Fin. Officer--Williamhouse-Regency, Inc., New York, NY; U.S. Public, pg. 89
Ginsberg, Sheldon, Chief Fin. Officer & Exec. V.P.--Lazare Kaplan Intl., Inc., New York, NY; U.S. Public, pg. 981
Giordani, John E., Chief Fin. Officer, Exec. V.P. & Controller--ICN Pharmaceuticals, Inc., Costa Mesa, CA; U.S. Public, pg. 853
Giordano, Alejandro, Chief Fin. Officer--Grupo Synkro, S.A. de C.V., Mexico, Mexico; Int'l, pg. 576
Giordano, Alejandro, Chief Fin. Officer--Grupo Sidek, S.A. de C.V., Guadalajara, Mexico; Int'l, pg. 576
Giordano, Sebastian, Chief Fin. Officer--Sterling Vision, Inc., East Meadow, NY; U.S. Public, pg. 1516
Giorgio, Michael R., Chief Fin. Officer, Controller & Treas.--Suarez Corporation Industries, Canton, OH; U.S. Private, pg. 1048
Giraffa, Pietro, Chief Fin. Officer & Controller--Hanover Foods Corporation, Hanover, PA; U.S. Private, pg. 499
Girard, Don, Chief Fin. Officer--National Banner Company, Inc., Dallas, TX; U.S. Private, pg. 780
Girardi, Bob, Chief Fin. Officer--Gunver Manufacturing Co., Manchester, CT; U.S. Private, pg. 488
Gissleman, Dave, Chief Fin. Officer--Weinbrenner Shoe Company, Inc., Merrill, WI; U.S. Private, pg. 1160
Gitlin, Murray, Exec. V.P. & Treas.--Warner Bros. Records, Inc., Burbank, CA; U.S. Public, pg. 1611
Gittleman, Robert M., Chief Fin. Officer--Standard-Knapp, Inc., Portland, CT; U.S. Private, pg. 1031
Giuliano, James R., III, Chief Fin. Officer & Sr. V.P.--The Edward J. DeBartolo Corporation, Youngstown, OH; U.S. Private, pg. 319
Givan, Boyd E., Chief Fin. Officer & Sr. V.P.--The Boeing Company, Seattle, WA; U.S. Public, pg. 239
Givens, Mary S., Chief Fin. Officer & V.P.--ASI Market Research, Inc., Stamford, CT; U.S. Private, pg. 554
Giverholt, John, Chief Fin. Officer--Den norske Bank ASA, Oslo, Norway; Int'l, pg. 392
Gjertinsen, Einar, Chief Fin. Officer--Tine-Vestlandsmeieriet, Minde,, Norway; Int'l, pg. 1390
Gladstone, Debra, Chief Fin. Officer--Europa Cruises Corporation, Saint Petersburg, FL; U.S. Public, pg. 595
Glanvill, Shaun, Chief Fin. Officer--Ford Espana S.A., Madrid, Spain; U.S. Public, pg. 665
Glasberg, Larry, Chief Fin. Officer--MacDonald Communications, New York, NY; U.S. Private, pg. 691
Glasier, Richard J., Chief Fin. Officer & Sr. V.P.--Royal Caribbean Cruises Ltd., Miami, FL; U.S. Public, pg. 1410
Glass, Dennis R., Chief Fin. Officer, Sr. V.P. & Treas.--Jefferson-Pilot Corporation, Greensboro, NC; U.S. Public, pg. 925
Glass, Dennis R., Chief Fin. Officer, Exec. V.P. & Treas.--Jefferson-Pilot Life Insurance Co., Greensboro, NC; U.S. Public, pg. 926
Glass, Robert, Chief Fin. Officer & Sr. V.P.--Loehmann's, Inc., Bronx, NY; U.S. Public, pg. 1010
Glass, William, Chief Fin. Officer & Sr. V.P.--Quebecor Printing (USA) Corp., Boston, MA; Int'l, pg. 1076
Glasser, Brian, Chief Fin. Officer--Jacoby & Meyers Law Offices, New York, NY; U.S. Private, pg. 580
Glasser, David, Exec. V.P.-Fin. & Admin.--The Apparel Group, Ltd., Louisville, KY; U.S. Private, pg. 78
Glauber, Michael A., Sr. V.P.-Fin. & Admin.--Leggett & Platt, Incorporated, Carthage, MO; U.S. Public, pg. 985
Glazer, Edmund, Chief Fin. Officer--MRV Communications, Inc., Chatsworth, CA; U.S. Public, pg. 1027
Glazer, Mark, Chief Fin. Officer--Vicor Corporation, Andover, MA; U.S. Public, pg. 1719
Gleich, Peter A., Chief Fin. Officer & Treas.--Sigma-Aldrich Corporation, Saint Louis, MO; U.S. Public, pg. 1471
Glenn, Clyde A., Jr., Pres. & Treas.--Potter-Shackelford Construction Co., Greenville, SC; U.S. Private, pg. 877
Glessner, Dave, Chief Fin. Officer & Sec.--Agsco, Inc., Grand Forks, ND; U.S. Private, pg. 27
Glick, C.S., Chief Fin. Officer, Sr. V.P. & Sec.--Gulf Canada Resources Ltd., Calgary, Canada; Int'l, pg. 577
Glick, Norman, Chief Fin. Officer--Korn/Ferry International, Los Angeles, CA; U.S. Private, pg. 632
Glickman, Edward, Chief Fin. Officer & Exec. V.P.--Reuben Organization, Philadelphia, PA; U.S. Private, pg. 925
Glickman, Edward A., Chief Fin. Officer--Pennsylvania Real Estate Investment Trust, Fort Washington, PA; U.S. Public, pg. 1272
Glickman, Stuart, Chm. Bd., Pres., Chief Exec. Officer & Chief Fin. Officer--Safe Alarm, Inc., Davie, FL; U.S. Private, pg. 960
Glinsky, Michael P., Chief Fin. Officer & Exec. V.P.--U S West Inc., Englewood, CO; U.S. Public, pg. 1688
Glover, Keith E., Chief Fin. Officer, V.P.-Fin. & Admin.--Proxim, Inc., Mountain View, CA; U.S. Public, pg. 1338
Glynn, Brian, Chief Fin. Officer & V.P.--E.R. Wagner Manufacturing, Milwaukee, WI; U.S. Private, pg. 1146
Glynn, John J., Treas. & Sec.--Baird, Patrick & Co., Inc., New York, NY; U.S. Private, pg. 111
Goatcher, Gary A., Dir.-Fin. & Acctg.--Crown Crafts, Inc., Atlanta, GA; U.S. Public, pg. 465
Goddard, Douglas, Chief Fin. Officer & Exec. V.P.--FirstFed Financial Corp., Santa Monica, CA; U.S. Public, pg. 645
Goddard, Larry, Chief Fin. Officer, Treas. & Sec.--P.A.M. Transport, Inc., Tontitown, AR; U.S. Private, pg. 825
Godfrey, Bruce, Chief Fin. Officer--Commonwealth Telephone Co., Dallas, PA; U.S. Public, pg. 415
Godfrey, Bruce, Chief Fin. Officer--Commonwealth Communications, Princeton, NJ; U.S. Public, pg. 1354
Godfrey, Bruce, Chief Fin. Officer--RCN Long Distance, Princeton, NJ; U.S. Public, pg. 1354
Godfrey, Bruce C., Chief Fin. Officer--Commonwealth Telephone Enterprises, Inc., Dallas, PA; U.S. Public, pg. 415
Godfrey, Bruce C., Chief Fin. Officer--RCN Corporation, Princeton, NJ; U.S. Public, pg. 1354
Godin, Gilles C., Chief Fin. Officer & V.P.-Fin.--Tekelec, Calabasas, CA; U.S. Public, pg. 1566
Goebel, Andrew E., Chief Fin. Officer, Sr. V.P. & Sec.--SIGCORP, Inc., Evansville, IN; U.S. Public, pg. 1471
Goebel, Andrew E., Chief Fin. Officer, Sr. V.P. & Treas.--Southern Indiana Gas & Electric Co., Evansville, IN; U.S. Public, pg. 1471
Goedde, Ronald J., Chief Fin. Officer, Exec. V.P. & Sec.--Cornerstone Propane G.P. Inc., Watsonville, CA; U.S. Public, pg. 1201
Goedert, Philip H., Sec. & Treas.--Design-Build West, Denver, CO; U.S. Private, pg. 905
Goehring, Ralph J., Chief Fin. Officer & Sr. V.P.--Berry Petroleum Company, Taft, CA; U.S. Public, pg. 223
Goehring, Ralph J., Chief Fin. Officer & Tax Mngmt.--Berry Petroleum Company-Coastal Operations, Oxnard, CA; U.S. Public, pg. 223
Goeltz, R. K., Grp. Chief Fin. Officer--National Westminster Bank PLC, London, United Kingdom; Int'l, pg. 910
Goeltz, Richard, Vice Chm. & Chief Fin. Officer--American Express Company, New York, NY; U.S. Public, pg. 73

Goerg, Michael, V.P.-Fin. & Bus. Plng.--AgrEvo USA Company, Wilmington, DE; *Int'l*, pg. 1203

Goertz, Gary, Chief Fin. Officer & Exec. V.P.-Fin.--Telus Corporation, Edmonton, Canada; *Int'l*, pg. 1374

Goetting, Jerry, Chief Fin. Officer--General Trading Co., Carlstadt, NJ; *U.S. Private*, pg. 445

Goetz, Tim, Chief Fin. Officer, Treas. & Dir.-Mktg.--Robinson Helicopter Company, Torrance, CA; *U.S. Private*, pg. 936

Goff, Joe, Chief Fin. Officer--Granite Group Wholesale LLC, Manchester, NH; *U.S. Private*, pg. 469

Goforth, James, Treas.--Renosol Corp., Saline, MI; *U.S. Private*, pg. 922

Gogol, Gary J., Chief Fin. Officer--Annabelle Candy Company, Inc., Hayward, CA; *U.S. Private*, pg. 75

Goh, Jessie, Chief Fin. Officer--Scotts Holdings Limited, Singapore, Singapore; *Int'l*, pg. 1212

Goh, Lian Soh, Chief Fin. Officer--KONE Elevator Pte. Ltd., Singapore, Singapore; *Int'l*, pg. 747

Goheen, Michael B., Chief Fin. Officer & Treas.--Steuart Investment Company, Chevy Chase, MD; *U.S. Private*, pg. 1042

Goldberg, Leonard, Chief Fin. Officer--Yogen Fruz Worldwide Inc., Markham, Canada; *Int'l*, pg. 1520

Goldberg, Mike, Chief Fin. Officer & Exec. V.P.--Oil-Dri Corporation of America, Chicago, IL; *U.S. Public*, pg. 1214

Goldberg, Neil, Chief Fin. Officer & Controller--Harcrest International, Ltd., Clark, NJ; *U.S. Private*, pg. 500

Goldberg, Steven A., Chief Fin. Officer, V.P.-Fin. & Admin.--Prime Tanning Co., Inc., Rochester, NH; *U.S. Private*, pg. 884

Golden, Charles E., Chief Fin. Officer & Exec. V.P.--Eli Lilly and Company, Indianapolis, IN; *U.S. Public*, pg. 992

Golden, David, Chief Fin. Officer, Treas. & Sec.--Stephen Gould Paper Co., Inc., Whippany, NJ; *U.S. Private*, pg. 467

Golden, Jim, Chief Fin. Officer & Sr. V.P.--Lillie Rubin Fashions Inc., Miami, FL; *U.S. Private*, pg. 667

Golden, Robert B., Chief Fin. Officer--Anchor Tool & Die Company, Cleveland, OH; *U.S. Private*, pg. 71

Golden, Stephen D., Chief Fin. Officer & V.P.--The William Cook Agency, Inc., Jacksonville, FL; *U.S. Private*, pg. 273

Goldenberg, Rafael, Chief Fin. Officer--Industrias Gessy Lever Ltda., Sao Paulo, Brazil; *Int'l*, pg. 1437

Golder, Kenneth, Chief Fin. Officer & V.P.--Clariant Corporation, Charlotte, NC; *Int'l*, pg. 624

Goldfarb, Mark, Treas.--Grove's Dictionaries of Music Inc., New York, NY; *Int'l*, pg. 1479

Goldfarb, Mark, V.P. & Controller--St. Martins Press, Inc., New York, NY; *Int'l*, pg. 1479

Goldin, Martin, Chief Fin. Officer--Diners Club Inc., Chicago, IL; *U.S. Public*, pg. 377

Golding, Cornelius, Chief Fin. Officer, Sr. V.P. & Comptroller--Atlantic Mutual Companies, New York, NY; *U.S. Private*, pg. 95

Goldschein, Steven, Chief Exec. Officer, V.P.-Admin., Treas. & Sec.--Lambda Electronics Inc., Melville, NY; *Int'l*, pg. 1241

Goldstein, Alan, Chief Fin. Officer--Gordon Brothers Partners Inc., Boston, MA; *U.S. Private*, pg. 465

Goldstein, Barry J., Chief Fin. Officer, Exec. V.P.-Fin. & Sec.--Office Depot Inc., Delray Beach, FL; *U.S. Public*, pg. 1212

Goldstein, J. S., Chief Fin. Officer--Air Techniques, Inc., Hicksville, NY; *U.S. Private*, pg. 28

Goldstein, Melvyn C., V.P.-Fin. & Treas.--Sally Hansen, Farmingdale, NY; *U.S. Public*, pg. 494

Goldstein, Michael, Vice Chm. & Chief Exec. Officer--Toys "R" Us, Inc., Paramus, NJ; *U.S. Public*, pg. 1626

Goldstein, Steve, Chief Fin. Officer & Exec. V.P.--Ogilvy & Mather Worldwide, Inc., New York, NY; *Int'l*, pg. 1483

Goldstein, Steven J., Chief Fin. Officer--Centura Banks, Inc., Rocky Mount, NC; *U.S. Public*, pg. 328

Golik, Donald E., Chief Fin. Officer, Sr. V.P. & Sec.--Paul Mueller Company, Springfield, MO; *U.S. Public*, pg. 1141

Golmerg, Franz, Chief Fin. Officer--Harpen AG, Dortmund, Germany; *Int'l*, pg. 597

Gomez, Edward H., Chief Fin. Officer & Sr. V.P.--The Bank of Bermuda Limited, Hamilton, Bermuda; *Int'l*, pg. 150

Goncalves Caetano, Carlos Gilberto, Chief Fin. Officer & Dir.--Banco do Brasil, Brasilia, Brazil; *Int'l*, pg. 141

Gondek, Greg, Chief Fin. Officer--La Preferida, Inc., Chicago, IL; *U.S. Private*, pg. 640

Gonnelli, Patrick, Chief Fin. Officer--Towers Perrin, New York, NY; *U.S. Private*, pg. 1093

Gonopolsky, Allan, Chief Fin. Officer, V.P., Controller & Asst. Sec.--Rexel, Inc., Coral Gables, FL; *Int'l*, pg. 1107

Gonzales, Kenda, Chief Fin. Officer & Sr. Exec. V.P.--UDC Homes, Inc., Scottsdale, AZ; *U.S. Private*, pg. 5

Gonzalez Monroy, Jose, Chief Fin. Officer--Grupo Industrial Camesa S.A. de C.V., Mexico, Mexico; *Int'l*, pg. 575

Gonzalez, C., Treas., Sec. & Pur. Agent--Villazon Company Inc., Upper Saddle River, NJ; *U.S. Private*, pg. 1140

Gonzalez, Richard J., Chief Fin. Officer, V.P., Treas. & Sec.--Bayou Steel Corporation, La Place, LA; *U.S. Public*, pg. 197

Gonzalez, Vicente Garcia, Chief Fin. Officer--Union Naval de Levante, S.A., Madrid, Spain; *Int'l*, pg. 1442

Good, Charles E., V.P.--Snyder's of Hanover, Inc., Hanover, PA; *U.S. Private*, pg. 1011

Good, Jeff, Chief Fin. Officer--Esselte Pendaflex Canada, Inc., Mississauga, Canada; *Int'l*, pg. 460

Goodger, John V., V.P., Treas. & Asst. Sec.--Pioneer-Standard Electronics, Inc., Cleveland, OH; *U.S. Public*, pg. 1300

Goodlett, O.M., Chief Fin. Officer & Sr. V.P.-Fin. & Admin.--KU Energy, Lexington, KY; *U.S. Public*, pg. 940

Goodlett, O.M., Chief Fin. Officer & Sr. V.P.-Fin. & Admin.--Kentucky Utilities Company, Lexington, KY; *U.S. Public*, pg. 941

Goodlett, O.M., Sr. V.P.-Fin. & Admin. & Chief Fin. Officer--KU Capital Corporation, Lexington, KY; *U.S. Public*, pg. 941

Goodman, David, Chief Fin. Officer--Christy's Markets, Inc., Brockton, MA; *U.S. Private*, pg. 238

Goodman, Leonard, Chief Fin. Officer--GAF Premium Products, Inc., Wayne, NJ; *U.S. Private*, pg. 433

Goodman, Philip, Chief Fin. Officer--Dynabilt Products, Boston, MA; *U.S. Private*, pg. 188

Goodwin, Janice, Chief Fin. Officer--Patten-Beers Constructors, Nashville, TN; *Int'l*, pg. 1261

Goodwin, Paul R., Chief Fin. Officer & Exec. V.P.-Fin.--CSX Corporation, Richmond, VA; *U.S. Public*, pg. 284

Goodwin, Tevor J., Chief Fin. Officer, Company Sec. & Dir.--Norton Healthcare Limited, Harlow, United Kingdom; *U.S. Public*, pg. 915

Goodyear, Charles W., Chief Fin. Officer, Sr. V.P.-Fin. & Acctg.--Freeport-McMoRan Resource Partners, Ltd., New Orleans, LA; *U.S. Public*, pg. 681

Goodyear, Normand, Chief Fin. Officer--Sequentia Inc., Strongsville, OH; *U.S. Private*, pg. 985

Goold, David, Chief Fin. Officer Controller--AIM Safety Company Inc., Delta, Canada; *Int'l*, pg. 36

Goolsbee, Arthur L., Chief Fin. Officer & Dir.-Fin.--Utility Trailer Manufacturing Co., City of Industry, CA; *U.S. Private*, pg. 1130

Goransson, Kennet, Chief Fin. Officer--Bergman & Beving AB, Stockholm, Sweden; *Int'l*, pg. 188

Gordon, B. Diane, V.P.-Fin., Treas. & Sec.--Buckeye Corrugated Inc., Wooster, OH; *U.S. Private*, pg. 177

Gordon, Eric, Chief Fin. Officer & V.P.--Connaught Laboratories, Inc., Swiftwater, PA; *Int'l*, pg. 1109

Gordon, Leslie H., Chief Fin. Officer--C & J Clark America, Inc., Kennett Square, PA; *Int'l*, pg. 297

Gordon, William T., Chief Fin. Officer, Exec. V.P.-Fin. & Treas.--Black Entertainment Television Holdings Inc., Washington, DC; *U.S. Public*, pg. 235

Gore, Theresa, Chief Fin. Officer--Clayton, Dubilier & Rice, Inc, New York, NY; *U.S. Private*, pg. 244

Gorey, Daniel P., Chief Fin. Officer, V.P. & Treas.--Quixote Corporation, Chicago, IL; *U.S. Public*, pg. 1353

Gorin, Michael, Pres. & Chief Fin. Officer--Aeroflex Incorporated, Plainview, NY; *U.S. Public*, pg. 23

Gorkuscha, Mischa, Chief Fin. Officer & Sr. V.P.--Liberty Bancorp, Inc., Oklahoma City, OK; *U.S. Public*, pg. 174

Gorman, Barbara, Chief Fin. Officer--Ford Development Corporation, Cincinnati, OH; *U.S. Private*, pg. 418

Gorman, John T., Chief Fin. Officer & Exec. V.P.--American Banknote Corp., New York, NY; *U.S. Public*, pg. 68

Gorman, Kenneth, Chm. Bd., Pres., & Chief Exec. Officer--IDC Services, Inc., Chicago, IL; *U.S. Private*, pg. 554

Gorman, Kirk E., Chief Fin. Officer & Sr. V.P.--Universal Health Services, Inc., King of Prussia, PA; *U.S. Public*, pg. 1696

Gorman, Kirk E., Pres., Chief Oper. & Fin. Officer--Universal Health Realty Income Trust, King of Prussia, PA; *U.S. Public*, pg. 1697

Gormley, Charles, Controller & Treas.--Philadelphia Reserve Supply Company, Croydon, PA; *U.S. Private*, pg. 861

Goss, Michael, Chief Fin. Officer & Exec. V.P.--Playtex Products Inc., Westport, CT; *U.S. Public*, pg. 1310

Goss, Michael, Chief Fin. Officer--Playtex Beauty Care, Inc., Westport, CT; *U.S. Public*, pg. 1311

Goss, William, Chief Fin. Officer--Midwest Dental, Des Plaines, IL; *U.S. Public*, pg. 499

Gosselin, Mario, Chief Fin. Officer--Trois-Rivieres Mill, Trois-Rivieres, Canada; *Int'l*, pg. 761

Gothings, Robert, Chief Fin. Officer--Jackson Paper Company, Jackson, MS; *U.S. Private*, pg. 579

Gottfried, P. Gene, Chief Fin. Officer, Sr. V.P. & Treas.--Peoples Federal Savings Bank, Wooster, OH; *U.S. Public*, pg. 647

Gould, Anthony, Chief Fin. Officer--Bay Area Bancshares, Redwood City, CA; *U.S. Private*, pg. 124

Gould, Gregory A., Controller--RELA, Inc., Boulder, CO; *U.S. Public*, pg. 401

Gould, Maxine, Controller--Ventura Coastal Corporation, Ventura, CA; *U.S. Private*, pg. 1136

Gouveia, V., Chief Fin. Officer--Tintas Robbialac S.A., Sacavem, Portugal; *Int'l*, pg. 1501

Gover, Steve, Chief Fin. Officer--Parker Pen PLC, Newhaven, United Kingdom; *U.S. Public*, pg. 745

Gowan, Bruce, Chief Fin. Officer--Aeronca, Inc., Middletown, OH; *Int'l*, pg. 829

Gowan, Bruce W., Chief Fin. Officer & Sec.--Magellan Aerospace Corporation, Mississauga, Canada; *Int'l*, pg. 829

Gower, E.D., Chief Fin. Officer, V.P.-Fin. & Sec.--Farnam Companies, Inc., Phoenix, AZ; *U.S. Private*, pg. 396

Goyal, Prabhat, Chief Fin. Officer & V.P.-Fin.--Network Associates, Inc., Santa Clara, CA; *U.S. Public*, pg. 1168

Grab, John M. Jr., Chief Fin. Officer & Sr. V.P.--Equity Services, Inc., Montpelier, VT; *U.S. Private*, pg. 785

Grabel, William G., Chief Fin. Officer & Sr. V.P.-Fin., Human Resources & Admin.--TDS Telecommunications Corporation, Madison, WI; *U.S. Public*, pg. 1570

Graber, William R., Chief Fin. Officer & V.P.--The Mead Corporation, Dayton, OH; *U.S. Public*, pg. 1074

Grabowski, Jerry W., Pres., Chief Exec. Officer, Chief Fin. Officer & Treas.--Waters Instruments, Inc., Rochester, MN; *U.S. Public*, pg. 1745

Grace, Don, V.P.-Fin.--Ventura Coastal Corporation, Ventura, CA; *U.S. Private*, pg. 1136

Grady, Daniel A., Chief Fin. Officer--Bose Corporation, Framingham, MA; *U.S. Private*, pg. 160

Graeff, Rodney J., V.P.-Fin. & Treas.--Weaber, Inc, Lebanon, PA; *U.S. Private*, pg. 1155

Graf, Alan B., Jr., Chief Fin. Officer & Exec. V.P.--FDX Corporation, Memphis, TN; *U.S. Public*, pg. 603

Graf, Donald L., Chief Fin. Officer--A. Duda & Sons Inc., Oviedo, FL; *U.S. Private*, pg. 344

Grafer, William D., Chief Fin. Officer & V.P.-Fin.--National-Standard Co., Niles, MI; *U.S. Public*, pg. 1160

Graham, Barbara, Chief Fin. Officer & Sr. V.P.--Atlantic Electric Co., Pleasantville, NJ; *U.S. Public*, pg. 430

Graham, Barbara S., Chief Fin. Officer & Sr. V.P.--Conectiv, Wilmington, DE; *U.S. Public*, pg. 430

Graham, Barbara S., Chief Fin. Officer & Sr. V.P.--Delmarva Power & Light Company, Wilmington, DE; *U.S. Public*, pg. 430

Graham, Craig, Chm. Bd., Pres. & Chief Exec. Officer--Cashway Building Centres Ltd., Port Hope, Canada; *Int'l*, *pg. 274*

Graham, H. D., Jr., Treas. & Fin. Admin. Officer--Electric Energy Export Corp., Stamford, CT; *U.S. Public*, pg. 380

Graham, H. D., Jr., Treas. & Fin. Admin. Officer--Southwestern Investments, Inc., Stamford, CT; *U.S. Public*, pg. 380

Graham, J.G., Chief Fin. Officer & V.P.--Metropolitan Edison Co., Reading, PA; *U.S. Public*, pg. 695

Graham, Jim, Chief Fin. Officer--Manhattan Brass & Copper Co., Maspeth, NY; *U.S. Private*, pg. 699

Graham, John G., Chief Fin. Officer & Sr. V.P.--GPU, Inc., Morristown, NJ; *U.S. Public*, pg. 695

Graham, Joseph, Chief Fin. Officer--Netzsch Incorporated, Exton, PA; *U.S. Private*, pg. 792

Graham, Michael P., Chief Fin. Officer--Philadelphia Suburban Water Company, Bryn Mawr, PA; *U.S. Public*, pg. 1287

Graham, Rob-Roy, Chief Fin. Officer , Sec. & Controller--InterVoice, Inc., Dallas, TX; *U.S. Public*, pg. 910

Grahn, Gary, Chief Fin. Officer & Sr. V.P.-Fin. & Admin.--Mail Boxes Etc. USA, San Diego, CA; *U.S. Public*, pg. 1687

Grahn, Gary S., Chief Fin. Officer & V.P.-Fin. & Admin.--Mail Boxes Etc., San Diego, CA; *U.S. Public*, pg. 1687

Grainger, Mike, Chief Fin. Officer--Ingram Micro Inc., Santa Ana, CA; *U.S. Public*, pg. 878

Grainger, Tom, Chief Oper. Officer & Chief Fin. Officer--Weyerhaeuser Mortgage Company, Woodland Hills, CA; *U.S. Public*, pg. 1764

Grajeda, Mike, Chief Oper. Officer, Chief Fin. Officer & V.P.--Origin Systems, Inc., Austin, TX; *U.S. Public*, pg. 569

Grall, Wayne R., Chief Fin. Officer & Exec. V.P.--Serigraph, Inc., West Bend, WI; *U.S. Private*, pg. 985

Granander, June, Chief Fin. Officer & Sec.--Foster Products Corporation, Minneapolis, MN; *U.S. Public*, pg. 686

Grandin, Michael, Chief Fin. Officer & Exec. V.P.--Canadian Pacific Limited, Calgary, Canada; *Int'l*, pg. 258

Grandy, Jeff, Sr. Corp. Fin. Dir.--Citicorp Investment Bank Ltd., London, United Kingdom; *U.S. Public*, pg. 379

Graner, Dawn, Chief Fin. Officer--BIC Special Mkts. Div., Clearwater, FL; *Int'l*, pg. 1273

Granetz, Nancy, Chief Fin. Officer & Exec. V.P.--Jerry & Ketchum, New York, NY; *U.S. Private*, pg. 616

Granlund, Leland R., Chief Fin. Officer, Sr. V.P & Treas.--Western Petroleum Company, Eden Prairie, MN; *U.S. Private*, pg. 1168

Granquist, Torborn, Chief Fin. Officer--Cementa AB (Skovde), Skovde, Sweden; *Int'l*, pg. 1199

Grant, Clark C., Exec. V.P.-Fin. & Treas.--Buffets, Inc., Eden Prairie, MN; *U.S. Public*, pg. 267

Grant, Edward, Chief Fin. Officer, V.P. & Controller--Zoeller Co., Louisville, KY; *U.S. Private*, pg. 1207

Grant, Fred T., Chief Fin. Officer & V.P.-Fin.--Ryan's Family Steak Houses, Inc., Greer, SC; *U.S. Public*, pg. 1413

Grant, Joseph M., Chief Fin. Officer & Exec. V.P.--Electronic Data Systems Corporation, Plano, TX; *U.S. Public*, pg. 569

Grant, R., Chief Fin. Officer--Seven Seas Limited, Hull, United Kingdom; *Int'l*, pg. 593

Grathwohl, Joseph A., Treas.--Jake Sweeney Automotive Inc., Cincinnati, OH; *U.S. Private*, pg. 1058

Gratz, Jay M., Chief Fin. Officer & V.P.--Inland Steel Industries, Inc., Chicago, IL; *U.S. Public*, pg. 879

Gratzke, Carol, Chief Fin. Officer--Cherokee Inc., Van Nuys, CA; *U.S. Public*, pg. 345

Graven, D., V.P.-Fin.--Brillion Iron Works, Inc., Brillion, WI; *U.S. Public*, pg. 933

Graves, E.B., Chief Fin. Officer--International Chemical Company, Tulsa, OK; *U.S. Private*, pg. 568

Graves, Walter H., Sec. & Treas.--Tecom Industries, Inc., Chatsworth, CA; *U.S. Public*, pg. 1563

Gray, Catherine J., Chief Fin. Officer & V.P.-Fin.--Riverside Group, Inc., Jacksonville, FL; *U.S. Public*, pg. 1391

Gray, Colleen, Chief Fin. Officer & V.P.--Mylex Corporation, Fremont, CA; *U.S. Public*, pg. 1143

Gray, David L., Chief Fin. Officer, Sr. V.P.-Fin. Mngmt. Div. & Treas.--First Indiana Bank, A Federal Savings Bank, Indianapolis, IN; *U.S. Public*, pg. 1484

Gray, David L., Chief Fin. Officer, Sr. V.P. & Treas.--First Indiana Corporation, Indianapolis, IN; *U.S. Public*, pg. 1484

Gray, Gardner, Jr., Chief Fin. Officer & Sr. V.P.--CSE Insurance Group, San Francisco, CA; *U.S. Private*, pg. 197

Gray, George, Chief Fin. Officer--Furman Lumber Company, Inc., Billerica, MA; *U.S. Private*, pg. 431

Gray, J. Loren, Chief Fin. Officer & V.P.--Jones Dairy Farm, Fort Atkinson, WI; *U.S. Private*, pg. 596

Gray, James, Chief Fin. Officer & V.P.--Raytheon Aircraft Company, Wichita, KS; *U.S. Public*, pg. 1365

Gray, Jimmie L., Chief Fin. Officer, Sr. V.P. & Treas.--Universal Fidelity Life Insurance Company, Duncan, OK; *U.S. Private*, pg. 1127

Gray, John, Controller & Asst. Sec.-Treas.--Sugar Cane Growers Cooperative of Florida, Belle Glade, FL; *U.S. Private*, pg. 1049

Gray, Robert F., V.P. & Chief Fin. Officer-European Grp.--Coca-Cola Enterprises Inc., Atlanta, GA; *U.S. Public*, pg. 393

Gray, Timothy M., Chief Fin. Officer--Ryan Construction Company of Minnesota, Inc., Minneapolis, MN; *U.S. Private*, pg. 953

Greaves, John, Grp. Fin. Dir.--John Fairfax Holdings Limited, Sydney, Australia; *Int'l*, pg. 477

Greco, Louis A., Chief Fin. Officer & Sec.--The Macneal-Schwendler Corp., Los Angeles, CA; *U.S. Public,* pg. 1030
Green, Bruce, Chief Fin. Officer--WPT, Inc., Edison, NJ; *U.S. Private,* pg. 1144
Green, Bruce, Chief Fin. Officer--Dranetz-BMI, Edison, NJ; *U.S. Private,* pg. 1144
Green, C. C., Chief Fin. Officer--TNT Limited, Redfern, Australia; *Int'l,* pg. 1342
Green, Gary, Chief Fin. Officer--Compass Group-USA Division, Charlotte, NC; *Int'l,* pg. 324
Green, Gary K., Chief Fin. Officer--Canteen Corporation, Charlotte, NC; *Int'l,* pg. 324
Green, Guy F., Chief Fin. Officer--Southern Guaranty Insurance Companies, Montgomery, AL; *Int'l,* pg. 346
Green, James R., Chief Fin. & Oper. Officer & Exec. V.P.--Bearden Lumber Company, Inc., Bearden, AR; *U.S. Private,* pg. 127
Green, Jay M., Chief Fin. Officer, Exec. V.P. & Treas.--General Cigar Holdings Inc, New York, NY; *U.S. Public,* pg. 707
Green, John B., Chief Fin. Officer & V.P.--Genzyme Transgenics, Framingham, MA; *U.S. Public,* pg. 733
Green, Paul M., Chief Fin. Officer--Huntco Steel Co., Springfield, MO; *U.S. Public,* pg. 849
Green, Phillip D., Chief Fin. Officer & Exec. V.P.--Cullen/Frost Bankers, Inc., San Antonio, TX; *U.S. Public,* pg. 467
Green, Stanley D., Chief Fin. Officer & Exec. V.P.-Fin. & Corp. Devel.--Southwestern Energy Company, Fayetteville, AR; *U.S. Public,* pg. 1494
Greenberg, Russell, Chief Fin. Officer & Exec. V.P.--Jean Philippe Fragrances, Inc., New York, NY; *U.S. Public,* pg. 924
Greenberg, Scott N., Chief Fin. Officer & V.P.--GP Strategies Corporation, New York, NY; *U.S. Public,* pg. 694
Greene, David I., Chief Fin. Officer, V.P. & Treas.--Pearson, Inc., New York, NY; *Int'l,* pg. 1026
Greenlaw, Douglass C., Chief Fin. Officer & V.P.-Fin. & Admin.--ACT Manufacturing, Hudson, MA; *U.S. Public,* pg. 3
Greenlee, David W., Chief Fin. Officer--Circle Plastics Products, Inc., Circleville, OH; *U.S. Private,* pg. 240
Greenman, Jack F., Chief Fin. Officer--Sterling Healthcare Group, Inc., Miami, FL; *U.S. Public,* pg. 608
Greenwell, Daniel D., Chief Fin. Officer & Sec.--Zoltek Companies, Inc., Saint Louis, MO; *U.S. Public,* pg. 1794
Greenwood, Richard N., V.P. & Chief Fin. Officer--Certified Alloy Products, Inc., Long Beach, CA; *Int'l,* pg. 1467
Greer, Henry H., Pres., Chief Oper. Officer & Chief Fin. Officer--SEI Investments, Oaks, PA; *U.S. Public,* pg. 1417
Greffe, Pierre, Chief Fin. Officer--Harris Bankcorp, Inc., Chicago, IL; *Int'l,* pg. 154
Gregersen, Henrik, Chief Fin. Officer--GN Netcom A/S, Copenhagen, Denmark; *Int'l,* pg. 537
Gregg, Dennis, V.P.-Fin.--Lindal Cedar Homes, Inc., Seattle, WA; *U.S. Public,* pg. 998
Gregg, Jerry, Chief Fin. Officer & V.P.--Werthan Packaging, Inc., Nashville, TN; *U.S. Private,* pg. 1162
Gregg, Paul P., Chief Fin. Officer & Sr. V.P.-Fin.--CNG Producing Co., New Orleans, LA; *U.S. Public,* pg. 435
Gregg, Robert S., Chief Fin. Officer & Sr. V.P.-Fin. & Legal--Sequent Computer Systems, Inc., Beaverton, OR; *U.S. Public,* pg. 1459
Gregg, Walter E., Jr., Exec. V.P.-Fin. & Admin.--PNC Bank Corp., Pittsburgh, PA; *U.S. Public,* pg. 1242
Gregonowicz, Andrew, Chief Fin. Officer--International Correspondence Schools (New Zealand) Limited, Wellington, New Zealand; *U.S. Public,* pg. 784
Gregor, Andrew, Chief Fin. Officer & Sr. V.P.-Fin. & Admin.--GT Interactive Software Corp., New York, NY; *U.S. Public,* pg. 696
Gregorio, Richard S., Chief Fin. Officer & V.P.-Fin. & Admin.--Spire Corporation, Bedford, MA; *U.S. Public,* pg. 1499
Gregoris, Fred, Dir.-Taxation & Treas. Services--Domgroup Ltd., Toronto, Canada; *Int'l,* pg. 631
Gregory, Andrew, Exec. V.P. & Chief Fin. Officer--Maxwell Macmillan Professional & Business Reference Publishing, Englewood Cliffs, NJ; *U.S. Public,* pg. 1602
Gregory, Dennis, Chief Fin. Officer & V.P.-Fin.--Woodcraft Industries, Inc., Saint Cloud, MN; *U.S. Private,* pg. 1187
Gregory, Stephen, Chief Fin. Officer & V.P.-Fin.--The Interlake Corporation, Lisle, IL; *U.S. Public,* pg. 892
Grein, David E., Chief Fin. Officer & Sr. V.P.-Fin.--Thomas J. Lipton Company, Englewood Cliffs, NJ; *Int'l,* pg. 1435
Greishom, Jim, Chief Fin. Officer--Southern Foods, Inc., Greensboro, NC; *U.S. Private,* pg. 1016
Grelle, John K., Chief Fin. Officer & Sr. V.P.--ULLICO Inc., Washington, DC; *U.S. Private,* pg. 1115
Grenesko, Donald C., Sr. V.P.-Fin. & Admin.--Tribune Company, Chicago, IL; *U.S. Public,* pg. 1635
Grey, Scott, Chief Fin. Officer--CRC Industries, Inc., Warminster, PA; *U.S. Private,* pg. 138
Gricus, Michael J., Chief Fin. Officer & V.P.--Bearing Headquarters Co., Broadview, IL; *U.S. Private,* pg. 127
Griffin, Cornelius F., Chief Fin. Officer & V.P.-Fin.--Richton International Corporation, Madison, NJ; *U.S. Public,* pg. 1389
Griffin, Debra C., Chief Fin. Officer & Sr. V.P.--Tierney & Partners, Philadelphia, PA; *U.S. Public,* pg. 1641
Griffin, George G., III, Chief Fin. Officer--Sofamor Danek Group, Inc., Memphis, TN; *U.S. Public,* pg. 1482
Griffin, LaDeane, Chief Fin. Officer, Treas. Controller & Sec.--Jenkins & Associates, Shawnee Mission, KS; *U.S. Private,* pg. 585
Griffioen, C., Chief Fin. Officer--KPN Koninklyke PTT Nederland NV, Groningen, Netherlands; *Int'l,* pg. 720
Griffith, Ronald L., Sr., Chief Fin. Officer, Sr. V.P.-Fin., Treas. & Sec.--Burnham, Lancaster, PA; *U.S. Public,* pg. 270
Griffith, William C., Chief Fin. Officer & V.P.--Menasha Corporation, Neenah, WI; *U.S. Private,* pg. 731
Grigg, Roger, Chief Fin. Officer--Glynwed Metals Processing Ltd., Wednesbury, United Kingdom; *Int'l,* pg. 554
Griggs, David, Pres., Chief Exec. & Chief Fin. Officer & Treas.--Jack Griggs Inc., Exeter, CA; *U.S. Private,* pg. 482
Griggs, John W., Chief Fin. Officer & Exec. V.P.--The Alpha Corporation Of Tennessee, Collierville, TN; *U.S. Private,* pg. 44
Grigsby, Douglas C., Chief Fin. Officer & Exec. V.P.--Bank of the West, Walnut Creek, CA; *Int'l,* pg. 163
Grigson, David, Chief Fin. Officer--EMAP Plc, Peterborough, United Kingdom; *Int'l,* pg. 451
Grimball, Edward B., Chief Fin. Officer & Exec. V.P.--Whitney Holding Corporation, New Orleans, LA; *U.S. Public,* pg. 1766
Grimshaw, James Q., V.P.-Law for Corp. Fin. & Devel.--Joy Mining Machinery, Warrendale, PA; *U.S. Public,* pg. 789
Grise, Stan, Chief Fin. Officer & V.P.--Jumping Jacks, Monett, MO; *U.S. Private,* pg. 767
Grisetti, Mike, V.P. & Controller--Nationwide Homes, Inc., Martinsville, VA; *U.S. Private,* pg. 788
Grisold, Raymond E., Chief Fin. Officer & V.P.-Fin.--Atomic Energy of Canada Ltd., Mississauga, Canada; *Int'l,* pg. 97
Griswald, Scott, Chief Fin. Officer--Pacific Holding Corporation, Los Angeles, CA; *U.S. Private,* pg. 831
Gritton, Gregory C., Sr. V.P. & Chief Fin. Officer--Creswell, Munsell, Fultz & Zirbel, L.P., Cedar Rapids, IA; *U.S. Private,* pg. 1197
Grob, Timothy J., Chief Fin. Officer, Chief Admin. Officer & Sr. V.P.--Grant/Jacoby, Inc., Chicago, IL; *U.S. Private,* pg. 470
Groelinger, David, Chief Fin. Officer--Riddell Sports, Inc., New York, NY; *U.S. Public,* pg. 1389
Groelinger, David, Chief Fin. Officer--Riddell Sports, Inc., Chicago, IL; *U.S. Public,* pg. 1389
Groen, K., Chief Fin. Officer--Koninklijke PBNA BV, Arnhem, Netherlands; *Int'l,* pg. 1100
Groen, K., Chief Fin. Officer--CBBM BV, Zwijndrecht, Netherlands; *Int'l,* pg. 1100
Groen, K., Chief Fin. Officer--Nederlands Studiecentrum, Vlaardingen, Netherlands; *Int'l,* pg. 1100
Grogan, Dennis, Controller--Eastern Air Devices, Inc., Dover, NH; *U.S. Private,* pg. 357
Grogan, Richard B., Chief Fin. Officer & V.P.-Fin.--Emco Limited, London, Canada; *Int'l,* pg. 452
Grondahl, Lars K., Chief Fin. Officer--Cementa AB, Danderyd, Sweden; *Int'l,* pg. 1198
Gros, Brady, Chief Fin. Officer--The Fuller Brush Company, Great Bend, KS; *U.S. Public,* pg. 282
Gros, Brady A., Chief Fin. Officer & V.P.-Fin.--The Fuller Brush Company, Great Bend, KS; *U.S. Public,* pg. 282
Grose, J. David, Chief Fin. Officer & V.P.-Fin.--Basic Construction Company, Newport News, VA; *U.S. Private,* pg. 121
Gross, Edward H., Exec. V.P.-Fin. & Admin.--Baker & Taylor, Inc., Charlotte, NC; *U.S. Private,* pg. 111
Gross, James P., Chief Fin. Officer--INMC Mortgage Holdings, Inc., Pasadena, CA; *U.S. Public,* pg. 857
Gross, James P., Chief Fin. Officer--Indimac, Inc., Pasadena, CA; *U.S. Public,* pg. 857
Gross, Leonard D., Chief Fin. Officer--Familian Corp., Van Nuys, CA; *Int'l,* pg. 1512
Gross, Rebecca S., V.P. & Loan Officer--Churubusco State Bank, Churubusco, IN; *U.S. Public,* pg. 674
Gross, Timothy, Gen. Mgr.--Unity Manufacturing Co., Chicago, IL; *U.S. Private,* pg. 1126
Grossman, Bernard, V.P.-Sls., Mktg. & Fin.--M. Grossman & Son, Inc., Passaic, NJ; *U.S. Private,* pg. 483
Grossman, Morton, Chief Fin. Officer & Treas.--Waring & LaRosa, Inc., New York, NY; *U.S. Private,* pg. 1150
Grossman, Neal, Chief Fin. Officer-West--TBWA Chiat/Day Los Angeles, Venice, CA; *U.S. Private,* pg. 1062
Grossman, Paul, Chief Fin. Officer--Hi-Shear Corp., Torrance, CA; *U.S. Public,* pg. 825
Grove, Ware, Chief Fin. Officer & V.P.--Lesco, Inc., Rocky River, OH; *U.S. Public,* pg. 989
Grow, David R., Chief Oper. & Fin. Officer & Exec. V.P.--Daw Technologies, Inc., Salt Lake City, UT; *U.S. Public,* pg. 489
Grubb, Edgar H., Chief Fin. Officer & Exec. V.P.--Transamerica Corporation, San Francisco, CA; *U.S. Public,* pg. 1629
Grubb, Richard N., Chief Fin. Officer, V.P. & Treas.--Vishay Intertechnology, Inc., Malvern, PA; *U.S. Public,* pg. 1721
Grubbe, K.S., Chief Fin. Officer, Grp. V.P.-Fin. & Asst. Sec.--Ag Processing Inc., A Cooperative, Omaha, NE; *U.S. Private,* pg. 26
Grubbs, Dennis, Chief Fin. Officer--Asbury Worldwide, Miramar, FL; *U.S. Public,* pg. 1110
Gruber, Guenther, Exec. V.P. & Chief Fin. Officer--Siemens Nixdorf Information Systems Inc., Burlington, MA; *Int'l,* pg. 1245
Gruchacz, Craig, Chief Fin. Officer & V.P.--Philips Lighting, Somerset, NJ; *Int'l,* pg. 1055
Gruenstern, H., V.P.-Fin.--Meret Communications, San Diego, CA; *U.S. Public,* pg. 1233
Grueter, Frank J., Chief Fin. Officer & V.P.--George W. Prescott Publishing Co., Quincy, MA; *U.S. Private,* pg. 882
Grunander, Ulf, Chief Fin. Officer--Getinge Industrier AB, Getinge, Sweden; *Int'l,* pg. 551
Gruzewski, Frank, V.P.-Fin.--Ansco Photo-Optical Products Corp., Elk Grove Village, IL; *Int'l,* pg. 587
Grysinski, Robert, Chief Fin. Officer & V.P.--Howes Leather Corporation, Curwensville, PA; *U.S. Private,* pg. 543
Guarascio, Anthony, Chief Fin. Officer & V.P.-Fin.--Executone Information Systems, Inc., Milford, CT; *U.S. Public,* pg. 599
Guarino, Jose Carlos, Chief Fin. Officer--Esselte Meto Ind. e. Com. Ltda., Sao Paulo, Brazil; *Int'l,* pg. 461
Guber, Alfred M., V.P.-Fin. & Admin.--John Dusenbery Co., Inc., Randolph, NJ; *U.S. Private,* pg. 349
Guebert, D., Chief Fin. Officer & Treas.--Aircraft of Canada Ltd., Calgary, Canada; *U.S. Public,* pg. 1365
Guenthner, David, Chief Fin. Officer & Exec. V.P.--Inacom Corp., Omaha, NE; *U.S. Public,* pg. 873
Guercio, Thomas R., Chief Fin. Officer, Exec. V.P. & Treas.--Reliable Stores, Inc., Columbia, MD; *U.S. Private,* pg. 920
Guerrero, Vidal, Dir.-Fin.--Milupa S.A., Madrid, Spain; *Int'l,* pg. 991
Guest, T., Chief Fin. Officer--Autolease Fleets Limited, Birmingham, United Kingdom; *Int'l,* pg. 216
Guglielmi, Peter A., Chief Fin. Officer & Pres.-Tellabs Intl--Tellabs Operations, Inc., Lisle, IL; *U.S. Public,* pg. 1572
Guglier, Giovanni, Chief Fin. Officer--Ortho Clinical Diagnostic Systems S.p.A., Milan, Italy; *U.S. Public,* pg. 931
Gugliotta, R., V.P.-Fin. & Treas.--Uniflex, Inc., Hicksville, NY; *U.S. Public,* pg. 1665
Guichard, Kent B., Chief Fin. Officer & V.P.-Fin.--American Woodmark Corporation, Winchester, VA; *U.S. Public,* pg. 96
Guille, Danielle, Chief Fin. Officer--Tosoh Medics, Inc., Foster City, CA; *Int'l,* pg. 1407
Guire, Ronald W., Chief Fin. Officer, Exec. V.P. & Sec.--EXAR Corporation, Fremont, CA; *U.S. Public,* pg. 597
Guiu, Jean, Chief Fin. Officer & Dir.-Budgets & Accts.--AGF Assurances, Paris, France; *Int'l,* pg. 14
Gulis, Stephen L., Chief Fin. Officer & Exec. V.P.--Wolverine World Wide, Inc., Rockford, MI; *U.S. Public,* pg. 1775
Gulley, Mike, Chief Fin. Officer--Hale Brothers, Inc., Morristown, TN; *U.S. Public,* pg. 1278
Gulmi, James S., Chief Fin. Officer, Sr. V.P.-Fin. & Treas.--Genesco Inc., Nashville, TN; *U.S. Public,* pg. 728
Gummere, Jeff, Chief Fin. Officer & V.P.-Admin./Control--CPI Prints Plus, Inc., Concord, CA; *U.S. Public,* pg. 283
Guna, Edward F., V.P.-Acctg. & Fin.--U.S. Steel International, Inc., Pittsburgh, PA; *U.S. Public,* pg. 1661
Gundermann, Paul H., Chief Fin. Officer & Treas.--Apex Supply Co., Inc., Atlanta, GA; *U.S. Private,* pg. 77
Gundmundsson, Peter A., Chief Fin. Officer--Primedia Workplace Learning, Carrollton, TX; *U.S. Public,* pg. 1328
Gunn, G. Tom, Sr. V.P.-Capital Funds & Chief Fin. Officer--CT Financial Services, Inc., Toronto, Canada; *Int'l,* pg. 112
Gunn, Tom, Sr. V.P.-Capital Funds & Chief Fin. Officer--Canada Trustco Mortgage Company, London, Canada; *Int'l,* pg. 112
Gunterman, Gerhard, Chief Fin. Officer--Aachener und Muenchener Versicherung Aktiengesellschaft, Aachen, Germany; *Int'l,* pg. 15
Gurley, Paul G., Chief Fin. Officer--Performa Entertainment Real Estate, Inc., Memphis, TN; *U.S. Private,* pg. 853
Gurrieri, Marilyn, Chief Fin. Officer--Carco Electronics, Menlo Park, CA; *U.S. Private,* pg. 208
Guske, Lawrence A., Chief Fin. Officer & V.P.-Fin.--PS Group Holdings, San Diego, CA; *U.S. Public,* pg. 1245
Gustaferro, William R., Chief Fin. Officer & Exec. V.P.--Ameritech Phone Company, Cleveland, OH; *U.S. Public,* pg. 98
Gustafson, Bertill A., Chief Fin. Officer--Great Western Bank, Chatsworth, CA; *U.S. Public,* pg. 1741
Gustavsson, Jan, Chief Fin. Officer & V.P.--Gambro AB, Lund, Sweden; *Int'l,* pg. 666
Guterman, J., Chief Fin. Officer & V.P.--The Murray Ohio Mfg. Co., Brentwood, TN; *Int'l,* pg. 1397
Guthire, Jim, Chief Fin. Officer & Exec. V.P.--IXC Communications, Inc., Austin, TX; *U.S. Private,* pg. 556
Guthlein, William J., Chief Fin. Officer, V.P. & Treas.--Chancellor Corporation, Boston, MA; *U.S. Public,* pg. 335
Guthrie, Edward A., Chief Fin. Officer & V.P. Fin.--Cliffs Drilling Company, Houston, TX; *U.S. Public,* pg. 386
Guthrie, Roy A., Chief Fin. Officer & Exec. V.P.--Associates First Capital Corporation, Dallas, TX; *U.S. Public,* pg. 662
Guthrie, T.M., Chief Fin. Officer--Builders Transport, Inc., Camden, SC; *U.S. Public,* pg. 267
Gutierrez, Hector Trevino, Chief Fin. Officer--Coca-Cola FEMSA, S.A. de CV, Mexico, Mexico; *Int'l,* pg. 496
Gutmann, Clifford, Chief Fin. Officer--JG Industries, Inc., Chicago, IL; *U.S. Public,* pg. 917
Gutterman, Gerald S., Chief Fin. Officer & Exec. V.P.-Fin. & Admin.--Sequa Corporation, New York, NY; *U.S. Public,* pg. 1458
Guyatt, Raymond E., Chief Fin. Officer & Exec. V.P.--Imasco Limited, Montreal, Canada; *Int'l,* pg. 112
Guzik, William, Chief Fin. Officer & V.P.--Goldblatt's Department Stores, Chicago, IL; *U.S. Public,* pg. 917
Gweom, Ik-Nam, Chief Fin. Officer--Ssangyong Corporation, Seoul, Korea; *Int'l,* pg. 1291
Gwizdala, Lori A., Chief Fin. Officer, Sr. V.P. & Treas.--Chemical Financial Corporation, Midland, MI; *U.S. Public,* pg. 345
Gyani, Mohan S., Chief Fin. Officer & Exec. V.P.--AirTouch Communications, Inc., San Francisco, CA; *U.S. Public,* pg. 34
Gydell, Olof, Chief Fin. Officer--Skanska Bostader Stockholm AB, Solna, Sweden; *Int'l,* pg. 1260
Haapasaari, Toivo, Chief Fin. Officer--Valmet Automation Kajaani Ltd., Kajaani, Finland; *Int'l,* pg. 1449
Haberli, Ernst, Chief Fin. Officer & Exec. V.P.--Fort James Corporation, Richmond, VA; *U.S. Public,* pg. 670
Habrock, Thomas, V.P.-Fin.--The Wella Corporation, Montvale, NJ; *Int'l,* pg. 1489
Hack, Bruce L., Chief Fin. Officer & Exec. V.P.--Universal Studios, Inc., Universal City, CA; *Int'l,* pg. 1215
Hack, E.N., Chief Fin. Officer--Everbright Fasteners Ltd., Gloucester, United Kingdom; *Int'l,* pg. 585
Hackel, Ernst, Chief Fin. Officer--Henkel Austria Group, Vienna, Austria; *Int'l,* pg. 611
Hacker, Bill, Chief Fin. Officer--Block Industries, Inc., Wilmington, NC; *U.S. Private,* pg. 150

Hacker, Douglas A., Chief Fin. Officer & Sr. V.P.-Fin.--UAL Corporation, Elk Grove Village, IL; *U.S. Public*, pg. 1652
Hacker, Douglas A., Chief Fin. Officer--United Air Lines, Inc., Elk Grove Village, IL; *U.S. Public*, pg. 1653
Hacker, Ferdinand, Chief Fin. Officer & Mng. Dir.-Admin. & Support Services--Julius Meinl AG, Vienna, Austria; *Int'l*, pg. 856
Hackman, Earl, Chief Fin. Officer--Pressure Systems, Inc., City of Commerce, CA; *U.S. Private*, pg. 882
Hackner, Michael H., Chief Fin. Officer & V.P.-Fin. & Admin.--Deltak Inc., Plymouth, MN; *U.S. Public*, pg. 924
Haddock, Robert M., Chief Fin. Officer & Exec. V.P.--Aztar Corporation, Phoenix, AZ; *U.S. Public*, pg. 158
Hadfield, Neil, Chm. Bd., Chief Fin. Officer & Sec.--Western Pacific Data Systems, La Jolla, CA; *U.S. Private*, pg. 1168
Hadley, Gary L., Chief Fin. Officer & Treas.--World Aerospace Corporation, Maple Grove, MN; *U.S. Private*, pg. 1188
Haefner, James, Chief Fin. Officer & V.P.--Labelon Corporation, Canandaigua, NY; *U.S. Private*, pg. 641
Haensel, Douglas P., Chief Fin. Officer--SLJ Retail LLC, Smyrna, GA; *U.S. Private*, pg. 957
Hafstead, Christian R.C., Chief Fin. Officer & Sec.--M.F. Bank & Company, Inc., Minneapolis, MN; *U.S. Private*, pg. 113
Hafstead, Christian R.C., Chief Fin. Officer--M.F. Bank Restoration Co., Duluth, GA; *U.S. Private*, pg. 114
Haft, Linda G., V.P. & Treas.--Dart Group Financial Corp., Landover, MD; *U.S. Public*, pg. 484
Hagale, John E., Chief Fin. Officer & Exec. V.P.--Burlington Resources Inc., Houston, TX; *U.S. Public*, pg. 269
Hagan, James A., V.P. & Treas.--Roll Forming Corporation, Shelbyville, KY; *U.S. Private*, pg. 941
Hagan, James J., Chief Fin. Officer & Exec. V.P.-Fin.--Bruno's Inc., Birmingham, AL; *U.S. Public*, pg. 265
Hagedorn, Charles, Controller--Distrigas of Massachusetts Corporation, Boston, MA; *U.S. Public*, pg. 289
Hagemann, Doug, Grp. Dir.-Fin.--FTD, Inc./Florists Transworld Delivery, Inc., Downers Grove, IL; *U.S. Private*, pg. 389
Hagen, Doug, Chief Fin. Officer--American Foods Group, Inc., Green Bay, WI; *U.S. Private*, pg. 54
Hagen, Todd, Chief Fin. Officer & V.P.-Fin.--Hypermedia Communications, Inc., San Mateo, CA; *U.S. Public*, pg. 851
Hager, August, Dr., Chief Fin. Officer--CWS International A.G., Glattbrugg, Switzerland; *Int'l*, pg. 592
Hager, George V., Jr., Chief Fin. Officer & Sr. V.P.--Genesis Health Ventures, Inc., Kennett Square, PA; *U.S. Public*, pg. 728
Hager, George V., Jr., Chief Fin. Officer & Sr. V.P.--Genesis ElderCare, Philadelphia, PA; *U.S. Public*, pg. 728
Hager, Kenneth V., Chief Fin. Officer & V.P.--DST Systems, Inc., Kansas City, MO; *U.S. Public*, pg. 943
Hagge, Stephen, Chief Fin. Officer, Exec. V.P., Treas. & Sec.--AptarGroup, Inc., Crystal Lake, IL; *U.S. Public*, pg. 125
Haggerty, John R., Chief Fin. Officer & Sr. Exec. V.P.--Summit Bancorp, Princeton, NJ; *U.S. Public*, pg. 1527
Haggerty, Maria, Chief Fin. Officer--GoodTimes Entertainment Co., New York, NY; *U.S. Private*, pg. 464
Haggle, John E., Chief Fin. Officer & Exec. V.P.--Meridian Oil Holding Inc., Houston, TX; *U.S. Public*, pg. 269
Hagiwara, Y., Mng. Dir.--Thermometrics Japan Co. Ltd., Tokyo, Japan; *Int'l*, pg. 209
Hague, Samuel E., Chief Fin. Officer--United Life Insurance Company, Cedar Rapids, IA; *U.S. Public*, pg. 1677
Hahn, Arnold C., Chief Fin. Officer & Exec. V.P.--Western Bancorp, Newport Beach, CA; *U.S. Public*, pg. 1757
Hahn, Debra, Chief Fin. Officer--Sensors, Inc., Saline, MI; *U.S. Private*, pg. 984
Hahn, Douglas E., Chief Oper. Officer--Hahn Systems, Inc., Indianapolis, IN; *U.S. Private*, pg. 493
Hahn, E.L., V.P.-Fin. & Treas.--Chieftain Development Co. Ltd., Edmonton, Canada; *Int'l*, pg. 49
Hahn, Kenneth P., Chief Fin. Officer & V.P.--Gehl Company, West Bend, WI; *U.S. Public*, pg. 704
Hahn, Marc, Chief Fin. Officer & V.P.-Fin.--V-Band Corporation, Elmsford, NY; *U.S. Public*, pg. 1701
Hailey, V. Ann, Chief Fin. Officer & Exec. V.P.--The Limited, Inc., Columbus, OH; *U.S. Public*, pg. 995
Hain, Charles R., Chief Fin. Officer & Sr. V.P.-Fin.--Klein Tools Inc., Skokie, IL; *U.S. Private*, pg. 625
Haine, Richard, Chief Fin. Officer & V.P.--The B. Manischewitz Company, Jersey City, NJ; *U.S. Private*, pg. 699
Hake, W.E., Chief Fin. Officer--Frankel Metal Company, Detroit, MI; *U.S. Private*, pg. 735
Hakios, W., Chief Fin. Officer--Bernina Holding AG, Steckborn, Switzerland; *Int'l*, pg. 189
Hakler, Robert, Chief Fin. Officer & Exec. V.P.--Magna Group, Inc., Saint Louis, MO; *U.S. Public*, pg. 1037
Hale, Dan, Chief Fin. Officer & Exec. V.P.--USF&G Corporation, Baltimore, MD; *U.S. Public*, pg. 1659
Hale, Don, Chief Fin. Officer & Exec. V.P.-Fin.--United States Fidelity & Guaranty Company, Baltimore, MD; *U.S. Public*, pg. 1659
Hale, Jeffrey A., Chief Fin. Officer--Hickory Printing Group, Inc., Conover, NC; *U.S. Private*, pg. 525
Hale, Kenneth O., Chief Fin. Officer, V.P. & Sec.--Cable Design Technologies Corporation, Pittsburgh, PA; *U.S. Public*, pg. 287
Hale, Matthew, Chief Fin. Officer--CCI/Triad Corporation, Austin, TX; *U.S. Private*, pg. 193
Haley, C. James, Jr., Treas. & Sec.--Lufkin Industries, Inc., Lufkin, TX; *U.S. Public*, pg. 1019
Hall, Almon C., III, Chief Acctg. Officer, V.P. & Controller--Nortek, Inc., Providence, RI; *U.S. Public*, pg. 1192
Hall, David N., Sr. V.P.-Fin.--Eagle-Picher Industries, Inc., Cincinnati, OH; *U.S. Private*, pg. 355
Hall, Dennis R., V.P.-Fin. & Chief Fin. Officer--Electrolux Canada, Mississauga, Canada; *U.S. Private*, pg. 370
Hall, Dick, Chief Fin. Officer--Alimed, Inc., Dedham, MA; *U.S. Private*, pg. 34
Hall, Gary F., Chief Fin. Officer & Sr. V.P.--Cajun Electric Power Co-op, Baton Rouge, LA; *U.S. Private*, pg. 199
Hall, John F., V.P.-Fin., Sec. & Treas.--Delta Natural Gas Company, Inc., Winchester, KY; *U.S. Public*, pg. 497
Hall, Kenneth J., Chief Fin. Officer--Global Direct Mail Corp, Port Washington, NY; *U.S. Public*, pg. 747
Hall, Kurt C., Chief Fin. Officer & Exec. V.P.--United Artists Theatre Circuits Incorporated, Englewood, CO; *U.S. Private*, pg. 1120
Hall, Maxine, Chief Fin. Officer & V.P.--Allen Samuels Chevrolet GEO, Waco, TX; *U.S. Private*, pg. 964
Hall, Michael J., Chief Fin. Officer & V.P.-Fin.--Worldwide Sports & Recreation, Inc., Tulsa, OK; *U.S. Private*, pg. 1191
Hall, Michael R., Chief Fin. Officer--Mellon PSFS, Philadelphia, PA; *U.S. Public*, pg. 1085
Hall, Rick, Chief Fin. Officer--Century Data Systems, Incorporated, Raleigh, NC; *U.S. Private*, pg. 226
Hall, Rick, Chief Fin. Officer & Exec. V.P.--Hardee's Food Systems, Inc., Rocky Mount, NC; *U.S. Public*, pg. 278
Hall, Terry, Chief Fin. Officer & Sr. V.P.--US Airways Group, Inc., Arlington, VA; *U.S. Public*, pg. 1680
Hall, Wayne F., Chief Fin. Officer--Black & Veatch, Kansas City, MO; *U.S. Private*, pg. 146
Halle, Jean, Chief Fin. Officer--The Baltimore Sun Newspapers, Baltimore, MD; *U.S. Public*, pg. 1616
Halleen, David, V.P.-Fin.--TB Wood's Corporation, Chambersburg, PA; *U.S. Public*, pg. 1562
Halleen, Norman L., Chief Fin Officer & V.P.-Fin.--Collagen Corporation, Palo Alto, CA; *U.S. Public*, pg. 399
Haller, C.B., Treas.--General Electric Canada Inc., Mississauga, Canada; *U.S. Public*, pg. 713
Hallett, F.N., Chief Fin. Officer & Sr. V.P.--National Steel & Shipbuilding Company, San Diego, CA; *U.S. Private*, pg. 787
Halliday, James B., Chief Fin. Officer & Sr. V.P.--Argonaut Co., Menlo Park, CA; *U.S. Public*, pg. 129
Halliday, Robert J., Chief Fin. Officer & V.P.-Fin. & Acctg.--Ionics, Incorporated, Watertown, MA; *U.S. Public*, pg. 912
Halloran, Michael J., Chief Fin. Officer, V.P. & Asst. Sec.--Wallace Computer Services, Inc., Lisle, IL; *U.S. Public*, pg. 1735
Halvorsen, Andrew C., Chief Fin. Officer--Beneficial Corporation, Wilmington, DE; *U.S. Public*, pg. 211
Halvorsen, Tom, Chief Fin. Officer--The Chas. Levy Company, Chicago, IL; *U.S. Private*, pg. 664
Hamann, Dennis, Chief Fin. Officer & Sr. V.P.--Young's Holdings Inc., Orange, CA; *U.S. Private*, pg. 1202
Hamburg, Ed, Chief Fin. Officer & Sr. V.P.--SPSS Inc., Chicago, IL; *U.S. Public*, pg. 1420
Hamelin, Ray, Chief Fin. Officer, Comptroller & Treas.--Northwestel Inc., Whitehorse, Canada; *Int'l*, pg. 115
Hames, Ronald, Chief Fin. Officer & Sr. V.P.--Harbor Financial Mortgage Corp., Houston, TX; *U.S. Public*, pg. 644
Hamilton, Douglas, V.P.-Admin. & Chief Fin. Officer--USA Networks, New York, NY; *U.S. Public*, pg. 1686
Hamilton, Peter B., Chief Fin. Officer, Sr. V.P. & Sec.--Brunswick Corporation, Lake Forest, IL; *U.S. Public*, pg. 265
Hamlin, William, Chief Fin. Officer & Sr. V.P.--C & S Wholesale Grocery Inc., Brattleboro, VT; *U.S. Private*, pg. 192
Hammarberg, Torbjorn, Chief Fin. Officer--Fastighets AB Fundament/Real Estate Operations, Stockholm, Sweden; *Int'l*, pg. 678
Hammer, W., Chief Fin. Officer--Scholl AG, Reinach, Switzerland; *Int'l*, pg. 1209
Hammes, Lynn F., Chief Fin. Officer & Exec. V.P.--American Investors Life Insurance Company, Topeka, KS; *U.S. Private*, pg. 59
Hammett, Craig M., Chief Fin. Officer & Sr. V.P.--CalEnergy Co., Omaha, NE; *U.S. Public*, pg. 292
Hampel, Robert E., Chief Fin. Officer, Treas. & Sec.--Keller Crescent Co., Evansville, IN; *U.S. Private*, pg. 612
Hampore, Michael, Chief Fin. Officer--Getko Group Inc., Westbury, NY; *U.S. Public*, pg. 320
Hamrick, Grant L., Chief Fin. Officer, Sr. V.P. & Treas.--American City Business Journals, Inc., Charlotte, NC; *U.S. Private*, pg. 19
Hance, James H., Jr., Co-Vice Chm. & Chief Fin. Officer--NationsBank Corporation, Charlotte, NC; *U.S. Public*, pg. 1162
Hancock, John W., Sr. V.P. & Treas.--Atlantic American Corporation, Atlanta, GA; *U.S. Public*, pg. 143
Hancock, John W., Chief Fin. Officer--Atlantic American Life Insurance Company, Atlanta, GA; *U.S. Public*, pg. 143
Handeli, Larry, Chief Fin. Officer--Pamarco Technologies, Inc., New Providence, NJ; *U.S. Private*, pg. 835
Handler, Lawrence D., Chief Fin. Officer & Exec. V.P.--Dairy Mart, Inc., Enfield, CT; *U.S. Public*, pg. 476
Handler, Robert, Chief Fin. Officer--Sheldon Good & Co., Chicago, IL; *U.S. Private*, pg. 463
Handley, Patrick, Chief Fin. Officer & Grp. Exec.--Westpac Banking Corporation, Sydney, Australia; *Int'l*, pg. 1495
Handley, Phillip, Chief Fin. Officer--Packard Bell NEC, Sacramento, CA; *U.S. Private*, pg. 833
Haney, R.L., Chief Fin. Officer & Sr. V.P.--Orange and Rockland Utilities, Inc., Pearl River, NY; *U.S. Public*, pg. 1229
Haney, Wayne, Reg. Fin. Officer--Willis Corroon Corp. of Mobile, Mobile, AL; *Int'l*, pg. 1506
Hanifin, Kevin P., Chief Fin. Officer & Sr. V.P.--California State Bank-La Habra, La Habra, CA; *U.S. Public*, pg. 294
Hank, John L., Jr., Chief Fin. Officer--Apex Oil Company, Inc., Saint Louis, MO; *U.S. Private*, pg. 77
Hanka, Erina, Pres.--Suspa, Inc., Grand Rapids, MI; *Int'l*, pg. 1322
Hanley, Michael, Chief Fin. Officer & V.P.-Fin.--Gaz Metropolitain & Company, Montreal, Canada; *Int'l*, pg. 541
Hanley, Patrick D., Chief Fin. Officer & V.P.--Union Pacific Resources Company (UPRC), Fort Worth, TX; *U.S. Public*, pg. 1668
Hanley, Patrick D., Chief Fin. Officer & Sr. V.P.--Overnite Transportation Co., Richmond, VA; *U.S. Public*, pg. 1668
Hanley, Philip M., Sr. V.P. & Chief Fin. Officer--American General Finance, Inc., Evansville, IN; *U.S. Public*, pg. 76
Hanley, Philip M., Chief Fin. Officer--Yosemite Insurance Co., Evansville, IN; *U.S. Public*, pg. 77
Hanlon, E. Philip, Chief Fin. Officer & V.P.--Waverly, Inc., Baltimore, MD; *U.S. Public*, pg. 1748
Hanlon, John, Chief Fin. Officer & V.P.-Fin.--MDL Information Systems, Inc., San Leandro, CA; *Int'l*, pg. 1100
Hanna, John A., Chief Fin. Officer, Sr. V.P.-Fin. & Admin.--Westburne Inc., Montreal, Canada; *Int'l*, pg. 1491
Hanna, Kenneth G., Grp. Dir.-Fin.--Dalgety Plc, London, United Kingdom; *Int'l*, pg. 376
Hanna, William B., Chief Fin. Officer--Consorcio G. Grupo Dina, S.A. de C.V., Mexico, Mexico; *Int'l*, pg. 326
Hannah, David, Chief Fin. Officer & Treas.--Metalcenter, Inc., Santa Fe Springs, CA; *U.S. Public*, pg. 1375
Hannay, Roger A., Pres., Chief Exec. Officer & Chief Fin. Officer--Hannay Reels, Westerlo, NY; *U.S. Private*, pg. 499
Hanniford, Bruce, Chief Fin. Officer--Clayton, Williams & Sherwood, Inc., Newport Beach, CA; *U.S. Private*, pg. 245
Hansen-Damm, Peter, Chief Fin. Officer--Danfoss A/S, Nordborg, Denmark; *Int'l*, pg. 376
Hansen, Greg, Chief Fin. Officer--Firstcorp, Portland, OR; *U.S. Private*, pg. 408
Hansen, J. Ronald, Chief Fin. Officer & V.P.-Fin. & Admin.--Graham Corporation, Batavia, NY; *U.S. Public*, pg. 757
Hansen, J.R., Chief Fin. Officer & V.P.-Fin. & Admin.--Graham Manufacturing Co., Inc., Batavia, NY; *U.S. Public*, pg. 757
Hansen, Janet M., Chief Fin. Officer, Exec. V.P. & Treas.--Aquarion Company, Bridgeport, CT; *U.S. Public*, pg. 126
Hansen, Jeffrey, Chief Fin. Officer--Horizon Paper Co., Inc., New York, NY; *U.S. Private*, pg. 539
Hansen, Joe, Chief Fin. Officer--Zacky Farms, Inc., South El Monte, CA; *U.S. Private*, pg. 1203
Hansen, Larry, Chief Fin. Officer & Sr. V.P.--Signet Star Holdings, Inc., Stamford, CT; *U.S. Public*, pg. 216
Hansen, Paul G., Chief Fin. Officer & V.P.-Fin.--Adaptec, Inc., Milpitas, CA; *U.S. Public*, pg. 19
Hansen, Randal P., Chief Fin. Officer, Chief Acctg. Officer & V.P.-Fin.--Transcrypt International, Lincoln, NE; *U.S. Public*, pg. 1630
Hansen, Stein, Chief Fin. Officer--Luxo A/S, Oslo, Norway; *Int'l*, pg. 821
Hansen, Stephen, Chief Fin. Officer& Sr. V.P.--Universal Studios Recreation Services Group, Universal City, CA; *Int'l*, pg. 1216
Hanson, Dale S., Chief Fin. Officer, V.P.-Fin. & Treas.--C.H. Robinson Co., Eden Prairie, MN; *U.S. Public*, pg. 1394
Hanson, Dennis, Chief Fin. Officer--Steinway Musical Instruments, Inc., Waltham, MA; *U.S. Public*, pg. 1514
Hanson, Dennis, Chief Fin. Officer--Steinway & Sons, Long Island City, NY; *U.S. Public*, pg. 1514
Hanson, J. Brent, Chief Fin. Officer, V.P. & Controller--The Barbers, Hairstyling for Men & Women, Inc., Minneapolis, MN; *U.S. Private*, pg. 115
Hanson, Paul N., Chief Fin. Officer--Communications Systems, Inc., Hector, MN; *U.S. Public*, pg. 415
Hanson, Terry A., V.P.-Fin.--Madison Gas and Electric Company, Madison, WI; *U.S. Public*, pg. 1032
Harbert, David, Chief Fin. Officer & Exec. V.P.--Delco Remy International, Inc., Anderson, IN; *U.S. Public*, pg. 495
Harbert, David L., Chief Fin. Officer & Exec. V.P.--Delco Remy America, Inc., Anderson, IN; *U.S. Public*, pg. 495
Harbour, Ken, Chief Fin. Officer--Cleveland Electric Co., Atlanta, GA; *U.S. Private*, pg. 246
Harbour, Ken, Chief Fin. Officer--Cleveland Electric Company of Arkansas, Little Rock, AR; *U.S. Private*, pg. 246
Harczak, Harry J., Jr., Chief Fin. Officer--CDW Computer Centers, Inc., Vernon Hills, IL; *U.S. Public*, pg. 277
Harder, Glenn E., Chief Fin. Officer & Exec. V.P.-Fin. Svcs.--Carolina Power & Light Company, Raleigh, NC; *U.S. Public*, pg. 306
Hardey, Matthew W., V.P.-Fin.--Newpark Resources, Inc., Metairie, LA; *U.S. Public*, pg. 1179
Hardin, Donald M., Chief Fin. Officer & V.P.--CCI Corporation, Tulsa, OK; *U.S. Private*, pg. 193
Harding, Allan, V.P.-Fin.--Emcee Broadcast Products, Inc., White Haven, PA; *U.S. Public*, pg. 570
Harding, D.A., Dir.-Fin.--T & N Plc, Manchester, United Kingdom; *Int'l*, pg. 1334
Harding, Steve, Chief Fin. Officer & Sr. V.P.--Neiman Marcus Co., Dallas, TX; *U.S. Public*, pg. 785
Harding, Terry, Chief Fin. Officer--Mikron (Birmingham) Ltd., Birmingham, United Kingdom; *Int'l*, pg. 867
Hardman, William, Chief Fin. Officer--Delta Mills Marketing Company, New York, NY; *U.S. Public*, pg. 498
Hardwick, S., Chief Fin. Officer--Britax Wingard Limited, Chichester, United Kingdom; *Int'l*, pg. 216
Hardy, Karen, Chief Fin. Officer--Brown Evans Distributing Co., Mesa, AZ; *U.S. Private*, pg. 174
Hardy, Robert, Chief Fin. Officer--Printing House, Inc., Quincy, FL; *U.S. Private*, pg. 886
Hardy, William, Chief Fin. Officer--VF International, Wyomissing, PA; *U.S. Public*, pg. 1702
Hare, Steve, Chief Fin. Officer & Exec. V.P.--AMF Bowling Worldwide, Richmond, VA; *U.S. Private*, pg. 6
Harel, Roland, Chief Fin. Officer & Exec. V.P.--Provigo Inc., Montreal, Canada; *Int'l*, pg. 1072
Haren, H. Joseph, Chief Info. Officer & Sr. V.P.--FirstMerit Corporation, Akron, OH; *U.S. Public*, pg. 646
Hargadon, James J., Chief Fin. Officer & Sr. V.P.-Fin.--Okidata Group, Mount Laurel, NJ; *Int'l*, pg. 1000
Harger, Robert, Dir.-Fin.--Cliftex, New Bedford, MA; *U.S. Public*, pg. 1777

Harger, W., V.P.-Fin.--The Richman Brothers Co., Fall River, MA; *U.S. Public*, pg. 1777
Hargrave, Robert L., Chief Exec. & Fin. Officer & Treas.--Stewart & Stevenson Services, Inc., Houston, TX; *U.S. Public*, pg. 1517
Haring, Paul, Chief Fin. Officer--Feintool International Holding AG, Lyss, Switzerland; *Int'l*, pg. 479
Harker, Brian J., Chief Fin. Officer & Exec. V.P.--DIMON, Incorporated, Danville, VA; *U.S. Public*, pg. 509
Harker, Brian J., Chief Fin. Officer & Exec. V.P.--DIMON, International, Inc., Farmville, NC; *U.S. Public*, pg. 510
Harley, Ian, Chief Fin. Officer--CRC, Thame, United Kingdom; *Int'l*, pg. 241
Harmon, Barry L., Chief Fin. Officer & Sr. V.P.--Electro Scientific Industries, Inc., Portland, OR; *U.S. Public*, pg. 568
Harmon, Linda L., Chief Fin. Officer & Treas.--Progressive Driver Services, Inc., Jacksonville, FL; *U.S. Private*, pg. 890
Harmon, Michael E., Chief Fin. Officer--The Western Group, Saint Louis, MO; *U.S. Private*, pg. 1165
Harms, Daniel C., V.P.-Fin.--JII/Sales Promotion Associates, Inc., Coshocton, OH; *U.S. Private*, pg. 598
Harnass, R. Ray, Partner & Chief Fin. Officer--J.C. Bradford & Co., Nashville, TN; *U.S. Private*, pg. 163
Harner, Brent, Fin. Officer--Jofco Inc., Jasper, IN; *U.S. Private*, pg. 588
Harney, Dwayne, Chief Fin. Officer & Sec.--Allied Security, International, Spokane, WA; *U.S. Private*, pg. 41
Haroian, Gary, Chief Fin. Officer, V.P.-Fin. & Admin. & Treas.--Concord Communications, Inc., Marlborough, MA; *U.S. Public*, pg. 429
Harp, Randy, Chief Oper. Officer & Chief Fin. Officer--Pre-Paid Legal Services, Inc., Ada, OK; *U.S. Public*, pg. 1320
Harper, D., Chief Fin. Officer--Bristolipe Division, Bristol, IN; *Int'l*, pg. 618
Harper, David, Chief Fin. Officer--Montgomery Watson, Pasadena, CA; *U.S. Private*, pg. 759
Harper, John W., Chief Fin. Officer & Sr. V.P.-Fin.--US Airways, Inc., Arlington, VA; *U.S. Public*, pg. 1680
Harper, William, Chief Fin. Officer--The Newark Group, Inc., Cranford, NJ; *U.S. Private*, pg. 796
Harpin, Ellen, V.P.-Fin. & Admin. & Treas.--Media 100, Inc., Marlborough, MA; *U.S. Public*, pg. 1079
Harrah, Glen R., Chief Fin. Officer--Dewberry & Davis, Fairfax, VA; *U.S. Private*, pg. 329
Harral, William III, Chief Fin. Officer & V.P.-External Affairs--Bell Atlantic-PA, Philadelphia, PA; *U.S. Public*, pg. 203
Harrington, Bob, V.P.-Fin. & Plng.--Wisconsin Tissue Mills, Inc., Menasha, WI; *U.S. Public*, pg. 347
Harrington, Brian K., Chief Fin. Officer, Sr. V.P. & Treas.--Kirby Corporation, Houston, TX; *U.S. Public*, pg. 961
Harris, Bret J., Chief Fin. Officer & Treas.--Martin Color-Fi, Edgefield, SC; *U.S. Public*, pg. 1052
Harris, Brian, Chief Fin. Officer Worldwide--Sudler & Hennessey, New York, NY; *U.S. Private*, pg. 1197
Harris, David, Chief Fin. Officer, Sr. V.P. & Dir.-Human Resources--Whitin Roberts Co., Sanford, NC; *U.S. Private*, pg. 309
Harris, David S., Chief Fin. Officer & Exec. V.P.--Korey, Kay & Partners, New York, NY; *U.S. Private*, pg. 632
Harris, George, Pres. & Chief Fin. Officer--Harris, Baio & McCullough Inc., Philadelphia, PA; *U.S. Private*, pg. 504
Harris, H.L., Chief Fin. Officer--Invesco Group Asset Management Ltd., London, United Kingdom; *Int'l*, pg. 685
Harris, Isaiah, Jr., Chief Fin. Officer & V.P.--BellSouth Telecommunications, Inc., Atlanta, GA; *U.S. Public*, pg. 209
Harris, J., Chief Fin. Officer--E. & E. Kaye Limited, Enfield, United Kingdom; *Int'l*, pg. 727
Harris, Ken, Chief Fin. Officer--Allied Plywood Corp., Alexandria, VA; *U.S. Private*, pg. 40
Harris, Peter, Chief Fin. Officer--Lex Service PLC, Bourne, United Kingdom; *Int'l*, pg. 806
Harris, Ron, V.P.-Fin. & Admin.--Sunflower Mfg. Co., Inc., Beloit, KS; *U.S. Public*, pg. 1676
Harris, Sid, Chief Fin. Officer--MLT Vacations, Inc., Minnetonka, MN; *U.S. Public*, pg. 1200
Harris, Sue, Chief Fin. Officer--Woodward-Clyde Federal Services, Denver, CO; *U.S. Public*, pg. 1657
Harris, Titus H., III, Chief Fin. Officer & Sec.--The GNI Group, Inc., Deer Park, TX; *U.S. Public*, pg. 693
Harris, Tommy J., V.P.-Fin.--The Time Warner Cable Group, Stamford, CT; *U.S. Public*, pg. 1610
Harrison, Carl W., V.P.-Fin.--Owen Industries, Inc., Carter Lake, IA; *U.S. Private*, pg. 824
Harrison, Carl W., Chief Fin. Officer--Paxton & Vierling, Omaha, NE; *U.S. Private*, pg. 824
Harrison, David D., Chief Fin. Officer, Exec. V.P.-Fin & Treas.--Coltec Holdings Inc, Charlotte, NC; *U.S. Public*, pg. 401
Harrison, David H., Chief Fin. Officer & Exec. V.P.--Coltec Industries Inc., Charlotte, NC; *U.S. Public*, pg. 401
Harrison, Debbie, Controller--Giant Industries, Toledo, OH; *U.S. Private*, pg. 451
Harrison, Douglas, Chief Fin. Officer & V.P.--Lyon Metal Products, Inc., Montgomery, IL; *U.S. Private*, pg. 638
Harrison, Douglas M., Chief Fin. Officer, V.P.-Fin. & Treas.--L & D Group, Aurora, IL; *U.S. Private*, pg. 638
Harrison, James M., Chief Fin. Officer, Exec. V.P., Treas. & Sec.--C.R. Gibson Co., Norwalk, CT; *U.S. Public*, pg. 1168
Harrison, John A., Chief Fin. Officer--Financial Security Assurance Holdings Ltd., New York, NY; *U.S. Public*, pg. 622
Harrison, Mark, Chief Fin. Officer--Leach & Garner Company, North Attleboro, MA; *U.S. Private*, pg. 655
Harrison, N.C., Dir.-Fin.--Bernard Matthews PLC, Norwich, United Kingdom; *Int'l*, pg. 189
Harrison, Nigel R., Chief Fin. Officer & Exec. V.P.--The Thomson Corporation, Stamford, CT; *U.S. Public*, pg. 1599
Harrison, Robert E., Pres., Chief Exec. & Fin. Officer--Standard Commercial Corporation, Wilson, NC; *U.S. Public*, pg. 1501
Harrison, Robert E., Chief Fin. Officer & Sr. V.P.--Standard Commercial Tobacco Co., Inc., Wilson, NC; *U.S. Public*, pg. 1502
Harrison, Roger, Controller--Tradewind Technologies, Inc., Phoenix, AZ; *U.S. Public*, pg. 937
Harrison, Sandra, Treas. & Sec.--Bill Wink Chevrolet, Dearborn, MI; *U.S. Private*, pg. 144
Harrison, Sharon, Chief Fin. Officer--Risser Oil Corp., Clearwater, FL; *U.S. Private*, pg. 932
Harrison, Tammy, Chief Fin. Officer--Chicago West Pullman Corporation, Cincinnati, OH; *U.S. Private*, pg. 235
Harriss, Brian, Chief Fin. Officer--The Thompson-Minwax Company, Upper Saddle River, NJ; *U.S. Public*, pg. 1466
Harrod, Larry, Chief Fin. Officer & Controller--Charter Clinic Nightingale, London, United Kingdom; *U.S. Public*, pg. 1036
Harry, Gene, Sr. V.P. & Chief Fin. Officer--AmeriServe of Grand Rapids, Grand Rapids, MI; *U.S. Private*, pg. 533
Harry, Karen, Chief Fin. Officer--Mohawk Plastics, Inc., Riviera Beach, FL; *U.S. Private*, pg. 755
Hart, James W., Chm. Bd., Pres., Chief Exec. Officer & Chief Fin. Officer--Hart Holding Company, Inc., Norwalk, CT; *U.S. Private*, pg. 507
Hart, Matthew J., Chief Fin. Officer & Exec. V.P.--Hilton Hotels Corporation, Beverly Hills, CA; *U.S. Public*, pg. 828
Hart, Michael, Chief Fin. Officer--Nexstar Pharmaceuticals, Inc., Boulder, CO; *U.S. Public*, pg. 1180
Hart, Michael E., Chief Fin. Officer--Nexstar Pharmaceuticals, Inc., Boulder, CO; *U.S. Public*, pg. 1180
Hartig, John, Chief Fin. Officer--CAE Ransohoff Inc., Cincinnati, OH; *Int'l*, pg. 237
Hartis, Norman, Chief Fin. Officer--United Eco Systems, High Point, NC; *Int'l*, pg. 74
Hartl, Michael J., Exec. V.P., Chief Fin. Officer & Treas.--Norwich Financial Corp., Norwich, CT; *U.S. Public*, pg. 1203
Hartley, S.L., Chief Fin. Officer & Exec. V.P.--The Molson Companies Limited, Toronto, Canada; *Int'l*, pg. 887
Hartman, F., Chief Fin. Officer & V.P.--National Vendors, Bridgeton, MO; *U.S. Public*, pg. 457
Hartman, Gregory D., V.P.-Fin. & Treas.--Biomet, Inc., Warsaw, IN; *U.S. Public*, pg. 231
Hartman, Lawrence M., Chief Fin. Officer & Exec. V.P.--Velsicol Chemical Corporation, Rosemont, IL; *U.S. Private*, pg. 1135
Hartmann, Lothar, Chief Fin. Officer--Carl Zeiss, Oberkochen, Germany; *Int'l*, pg. 1522
Hartner, Craig, Chief Fin. Officer & Exec. V.P.--AEC, Inc., Wood Dale, IL; *U.S. Private*, pg. 500
Hartney, Terrence, Chief Fin. Officer--McDonald's Hamburgers Limited, London, United Kingdom; *U.S. Public*, pg. 1069
Hartsook, Larry D., V.P.-Fin.--Meredith Corporation, Des Moines, IA; *U.S. Public*, pg. 1094
Hartzell, Richard, Chief Fin. Officer--Southbend, Fuquay Varina, NC; *U.S. Public*, pg. 1110
Harvey, Curtis R., Chief Fin. Officer & Exec. V.P.--First Financial Bankshares, Inc., Abilene, TX; *U.S. Public*, pg. 633
Harvey, Kent M., Chief Fin. Officer, Sr. V.P. & Treas.--Pacific Gas & Electric Company, San Francisco, CA; *U.S. Public*, pg. 1241
Harvey, Richard J., Dir.-Grp. Fin.--Norwich Union Life Insurance, Norwich, United Kingdom; *Int'l*, pg. 970
Harwood, Charlie, Chief Fin. Officer & Exec. V.P.--Covance, Inc., Princeton, NJ; *U.S. Public*, pg. 453
Harwood, George L., Chief Fin. Officer, Sr. V.P-Information Systems & Sec.--Printronix, Inc., Irvine, CA; *U.S. Public*, pg. 1329
Hasch, J. Bruce, Pres. & Chief Oper. Officer--The Peoples Gas Light & Coke Co., Chicago, IL; *U.S. Public*, pg. 1275
Hasegawa, Sachiyuki, Chief Fin. Officer--Eurogenetics N.V., Tessenderlo, Belgium; *Int'l*, pg. 1408
Hashimoto, Kiyoshi, Chief Fin. Officer & Controller--Tosoh Corporation, Tokyo, Japan; *Int'l*, pg. 1407
Hashimoto, Noriyuki, Chief Fin. Officer--Delamine B.V., Amersfoort, Netherlands; *Int'l*, pg. 1408
Haskell, Eric, Chief Fin. Officer, Sr. V.P.-Fin. & Admin., & Treas.--Systems & Computer Technology Corporation, Malvern, PA; *U.S. Public*, pg. 1552
Haskins, Elizabeth, Chief Fin. Officer--Signature Flight Support, Orlando, FL; *Int'l*, pg. 114
Haslam, Douglas, Chief Fin. Officer & Exec. V.P.--Menu Foods, Inc., Pennsauken, NJ; *U.S. Private*, pg. 731
Hastings, James H., V.P. & Treas.--Essex County Gas Company, Amesbury, MA; *U.S. Public*, pg. 593
Hastings, John J., Chief Fin. Officer, Exec. V.P., Treas. & Sec.--The Middleby Corporation, Rolling Meadows, IL; *U.S. Public*, pg. 1109
Hata, Kemichiro, Chief Fin. Officer--Holland Sweetener Company V.O.F., Maastricht, Netherlands; *Int'l*, pg. 1408
Hatcher, Kenneth, Chief Fin. Officer & V.P.-Fin.--Maynard Oil Co., Dallas, TX; *U.S. Public*, pg. 1064
Hatcher, Stephen R., Chief Fin. Officer & Exec. V.P.--The Union Central Life Insurance Co., Cincinnati, OH; *U.S. Private*, pg. 1118
Hatfield, M.A., Sr. V.P. & Sec.--Marshall & Ilsley Corporation, Milwaukee, WI; *U.S. Public*, pg. 1049
Hatlen, Joel, Controller & Treas.--Data I/O Corporation, Redmond, WA; *U.S. Public*, pg. 486
Hatsopoulos, John, Chief Fin. Officer & V.P.--Thermolase, San Diego, CA; *U.S. Public*, pg. 1595
Hatsopoulos, John N., Pres. & Chief Fin. Officer--Thermo Electron Corporation, Waltham, MA; *U.S. Public*, pg. 1591
Hatsopoulos, John N., Chief Fin. Officer & V.P.--Trex Medical Corporation, Danbury, CT; *U.S. Public*, pg. 1595
Hattendorf, J. Mark, Chief Fin. Officer & V.P.--Broderbund Software, Inc., Novato, CA; *U.S. Public*, pg. 258
Hattendorf, J. Mark, Chief Fin. Officer & Sr. V.P.--Herbalife International of America, Inc., Century City, CA; *U.S. Public*, pg. 809
Hattox, Brock A., Chief Fin. Officer & Exec. V.P.--National Service Industries, Inc., Atlanta, GA; *U.S. Public*, pg. 1160
Hau, Emmanuel, Chief Fin. Officer--Electricite de France, Paris, France; *Int'l*, pg. 437
Haueisen, Margaret A., Chief Fin. Officer--Continental Forge Company, Compton, CA; *U.S. Private*, pg. 268
Haugen, Baard, Chief Fin. Officer & Sr. V.P.--Elkem ASA, Oslo, Norway; *Int'l*, pg. 446
Haugen, Bent M., Chief Fin. Officer--Nycomed Imaging AS, Oslo, Norway; *Int'l*, pg. 993
Haugen, Corky, Mgr.-Admin. & Fin.--North Dakota Mill & Elevator Association, Grand Forks, ND; *U.S. Private*, pg. 804
Haughey, Michael, Chief Fin. Officer & V.P.-Fin.--Sunnen Products Company, Saint Louis, MO; *U.S. Private*, pg. 1053
Hauk, Donald B., Chief Fin. Officer, Exec. V.P. & Sec.--Republic Automotive Parts, Inc., Brentwood, TN; *U.S. Public*, pg. 1377
Haunschild, Robert L., Chief Fin. Officer & Sr. V.P.--PNC Bank Corp., Pittsburgh, PA; *U.S. Public*, pg. 1242
Hausen, Larry A., Chief Fin. Officer & Exec. V.P.--Signet Star Reinsurance Company, Florham Park, NJ; *U.S. Public*, pg. 216
Hausman, Rita, Chief Fin. Officer--Warren Electric Group, Houston, TX; *U.S. Private*, pg. 1151
Hautamaki, Bob, Chief Fin. Officer--Martin Universal Design, Inc., Detroit, MI; *U.S. Private*, pg. 709
Havens, Theodore A., Chief Fin. Officer--Pac-Fab, Inc./East, Sanford, NC; *U.S. Public*, pg. 593
Haver, Kenneth W., Chief Fin. Officer & Sr. V.P.--Telxon Corporation, Akron, OH; *U.S. Public*, pg. 1573
Haverkamp, Werner, Chief Fin. Officer--Deutsche Unilever Gmbh, Hamburg, Germany; *Int'l*, pg. 1436
Haviland, Richard J., Chief Fin. Officer--Automatic Data Processing, Inc., Roseland, NJ; *U.S. Public*, pg. 150
Hawes, Steve, Chief Fin. Officer & Chief Info. Officer--Allfast Fastening Systems, Inc., City of Industry, CA; *U.S. Private*, pg. 37
Hawkins, Howard M., V.P. & Treas.--Hawkins Chemical, Inc., Minneapolis, MN; *U.S. Public*, pg. 800
Hawkins, Jonathan A., Chief Fin. Officer & Sr. V.P.--Southern States Cooperative, Inc., Richmond, VA; *U.S. Private*, pg. 1017
Hawkins, Richard, Chief Fin. Officer & V.P.--McKesson Corporation, San Francisco, CA; *U.S. Public*, pg. 1072
Hawkins, Steven B., Chief Fin. Officer, V.P.-Fin. & Admin., Treas. & Sec.--FFP Marketing Company, Inc., Fort Worth, TX; *U.S. Public*, pg. 604
Hawley, Gary, Chief Fin. Officer & V.P.-Fin.--Snyder's Drug Stores, Inc., Minnetonka, MN; *U.S. Private*, pg. 1011
Haworth, Leslie W., Chief Fin. Officer & Sr. V.P.--Laidlaw Inc., Burlington, Canada; *Int'l*, pg. 259
Hay, James F., Chief Fin. Officer & V.P.--Valk Manufacturing Company, New Kingstown, PA; *U.S. Private*, pg. 1131
Hay, Larry, Chief Fin. Officer--PolyVision Corp., New York, NY; *U.S. Public*, pg. 1315
Hay, Lewis, III, Chief Fin. Officer & Sr. V.P.--JP Foodservice, Inc., Columbia, MD; *U.S. Public*, pg. 918
Hay, Lewis, III, Chief Fin. Officer & Sr. V.P.--JP Foodservice Distributors, Inc., Columbia, MD; *U.S. Public*, pg. 918
Haydel, Agatha M., Treas.--Walk, Haydel & Associates, Inc., New Orleans, LA; *Int'l*, pg. 624
Hayden, Gerard M., Jr., Chief Fin. Officer, Sr. V.P. & Treas.--Allied Clinical Laboratories, Inc., Nashville, TN; *U.S. Public*, pg. 973
Hayes, Gregory, Chief Fin. Officer--Sullair Corporation, Michigan City, IN; *U.S. Public*, pg. 1534
Hayes, Jimmy W., Chief Fin. Officer & Sr. V.P.-Fin.--Cox Communications, Inc., Atlanta, GA; *U.S. Public*, pg. 454
Hayes, John, V.P.-Fin.--Black & Decker Canada Inc., Richmond Hill, Canada; *U.S. Public*, pg. 234
Hayes, Kevin J., Chief Fin. Officer, V.P., Treas. & Asst. Sec.--Methode Electronics Inc., Chicago, IL; *U.S. Public*, pg. 1101
Hayes, Michael, Chief Fin. Officer & V.P.--Davel Communications Group, Inc., Jacksonville, IL; *U.S. Public*, pg. 488
Hayes, Patsy, Chief Fin. Officer--Overholtzer Church Furniture, Inc., Modesto, CA; *U.S. Private*, pg. 823
Haynes, John E., Chief Fin. Officer & Exec. V.P.--Glendale Federal Bank, F.S.B., Glendale, CA; *U.S. Public*, pg. 747
Hays, Bill, Chief Fin. Officer & V.P.-Fin.--Varel Manufacturing Co., Dallas, TX; *U.S. Private*, pg. 1134
Hays, Don L., Chief Fin. Officer, V.P. & Treas.--Diemakers, Inc., Monroe City, MO; *U.S. Private*, pg. 332
Hays, Richard C., V.P.-Fin.--Southwestern Electric Service Co., Dallas, TX; *U.S. Public*, pg. 1588
Hayward-Surry, Jeremy, Pres., Chief Fin. Officer & Treas.--Pall Corporation, Greenvale, NY; *U.S. Public*, pg. 1253
Haywood, T., Chief Fin. Officer--Swish Products Ltd., Tamworth, United Kingdom; *Int'l*, pg. 925
Haywood, T.P., Chief Fin. Officer--Larch-Lap Limited, Hartlebury, United Kingdom; *Int'l*, pg. 925
Hazarian, Jeffrey R., Chief Fin. Officer & Exec. V.P.--Tenera, Inc., San Francisco, CA; *U.S. Public*, pg. 1576
Hazarian, Jeffrey R., Chief Fin. Officer--TENERA Rocky Flats, LLC, Louisville, CO; *U.S. Public*, pg. 1576
Hazelbaker, Steven R., Chief Fin. Officer, V.P. & Treas.--Meridian Insurance Group, Inc., Indianapolis, IN; *U.S. Public*, pg. 1095
Hazelbaker, Steven R., Chief Fin. Officer--Meridian Security Insurance Company, Indianapolis, IN; *U.S. Public*, pg. 1095
Heaberlin, David A., Chief Fin. Officer & Exec. V.P.--Bay View Capital Corporation, San Mateo, CA; *U.S. Public*, pg. 197
Headley, Martin S., Chief Fin. Officer--Roper Industries, Inc., Bogart, GA; *U.S. Public*, pg. 1405

Heagy, Thomas C., Vice Chm. & Chief Fin. Officer--LaSalle National Bank, Chicago, IL; *Int'l*, pg. 10
Heald, Malcolm, Grp. Dir.-Fin.--Hepworth Plc, London, United Kingdom; *Int'l*, pg. 614
Healey, Dennis, Chief Fin. Officer, Sr. V.P. & Treas.--Medicore Inc., Hialeah, FL; *U.S. Public*, pg. 1080
Healey, Jack P., Chief Fin. Officer, V.P. & Sec.--Industrial Distribution Group, Tucker, GA; *U.S. Public*, pg. 875
Healey, James E., Chief Fin. Officer & Exec. V.P.--Nabisco Inc., Parsippany, NJ; *U.S. Public*, pg. 1355
Healey, Karen, Chief Fin. Officer & Sec.--Connector Manufacturing Company, Hamilton, OH; *U.S. Private*, pg. 264
Healy, Daniel M., Chief Fin. Officer & Exec. V.P.--North Fork Bancorporation, Inc., Melville, NY; *U.S. Public*, pg. 1194
Healy, Daniel M., Chief Fin. Officer & Exec. V.P.--North Fork Bank, Mattituck, NY; *U.S. Public*, pg. 1194
Healy, E. Peter, Chief Fin. Officer, Exec. V.P. & Sec.--Barry's Jewelers, Inc., Monrovia, CA; *U.S. Public*, pg. 192
Healy, M. Brian, Chief Fin. Officer & Grp. V.P.-Fin. & Admin.--Computer Language Research, Inc., Carrollton, TX; *U.S. Public*, pg. 421
Healy, Robert E., Jr., Chief Fin. Officer & Sr. V.P.-Fin. & Admin.--NovaCare Inc., King of Prussia, PA; *U.S. Public*, pg. 1203
Hearn, John G. Kenneth, Dir.-Intl. Fin. Opers.--Ikon Office Solutions, Inc., Malvern, PA; *U.S. Public*, pg. 862
Heath, Patricia, Chief Fin. Officer--Wireless One Network LP, Fort Myers, FL; *U.S. Private*, pg. 1184
Hebble, David H., Chief Fin. Officer & V.P.-Fin.--ABM Industries, San Francisco, CA; *U.S. Public*, pg. 2
Hebert, Bruce, Chief Fin. Officer--Furmanite Worldwide, Inc., Richardson, TX; *U.S. Public*, pg. 942
Hebert, Edward, Chief Fin. Officer--Rymer Meat Inc., Chicago, IL; *U.S. Public*, pg. 1414
Hebert, Edward M., Chief Fin. Officer, Sr. V.P. & Treas.--Rymer Foods Inc., Chicago, IL; *U.S. Public*, pg. 1414
Hebert, William L., Chief Fin. Officer, Treas. & Dir.-Investor Rels.--Louisiana Pacific Corporation, Portland, OR; *U.S. Public*, pg. 1015
Hecht, John R., Chief Fin. Officer & Sr. V.P.--Amcore Financial, Inc., Rockford, IL; *U.S. Public*, pg. 64
Hecht, John R., Chief Fin. Officer & Sr. V.P.--AMCORE Bank N.A., Rockford, Rockford, IL; *U.S. Public*, pg. 64
Hecht, S.E. Melvin, Chief Fin. Officer & Treas.--Marisa Christina Inc., New Hyde Park, NY; *U.S. Public*, pg. 1044
Heck, Jeffrey M., Chief Fin. Officer & V.P.--Flexi-Van Leasing, Inc., Kenilworth, NJ; *U.S. Private*, pg. 413
Hedberg, Anders, Chief Fin. Officer--Stena Line AB, Goteborg, Sweden; *Int'l*, pg. 1300
Hedersen, Dave, Chief Fin. Officer & V.P.-Finance--Beaver Lumber Company Limited, Markham, Canada; *Int'l*, pg. 887
Hedges, Brian, Chief Fin. Officer & Sr. V.P.-Fin.--Russel Metals Inc., Mississauga, Canada; *Int'l*, pg. 1149
Hedlund, Peter, Chief Fin. Officer--Swedish Match do Brasil S/A, Rio de Janeiro, Brazil; *Int'l*, pg. 1328
Hedquist, John, Chief Fin. Officer--Park Construction Company, Minneapolis, MN; *U.S. Private*, pg. 839
Hedrick, Gary, Chief Fin. Officer, V.P. & Treas.--El Paso Electric Company, El Paso, TX; *U.S. Public*, pg. 567
Heeley, G.E., Exec. Gen. Mgr.-Fin.--The Broken Hill Proprietary Company Limited, Melbourne, Australia; *Int'l*, pg. 223
Heenan, John C., Chief Fin. Officer--Standard Chlorine Cloroben Chemical Corporation, Kearny, NJ; *U.S. Private*, pg. 1031
Heerey, Dan, Chief Fin. Officer--Quest Technologies, Inc., Oconomowoc, WI; *U.S. Private*, pg. 900
Heersink, Ewout R., Chief Fin. Officer & V.P.--Onex Corporation, Toronto, Canada; *Int'l*, pg. 1006
Heery, Joseph, V.P. & Chief Fin. Officer--Cyborg Systems, Inc., Chicago, IL; *U.S. Private*, pg. 299
Heffner, Donna, Chief Fin. Officer & V.P.--Citadel Communications Corporation, Tempe, AZ; *U.S. Private*, pg. 241
Hegel, Garrett, Chief Fin. Officer--Compass Bank, Plano, TX; *U.S. Public*, pg. 419
Hegel, Garrett R., Chief Fin. Officer--Compass Bancshares, Inc., Birmingham, AL; *U.S. Public*, pg. 418
Hehir, Joseph P., Chief Fin. Officer & Treas.--GZA GeoEnvironmental Technologies, Inc., Newton, MA; *U.S. Public*, pg. 697
Heidbreder, Warren W., Chief Fin. Officer, V.P. & Sec.--Bandag, Incorporated, Muscatine, IA; *U.S. Public*, pg. 177
Heidecorn, David, Chief Fin. Officer & Exec. V.P.--Alarmguard Holdings, Inc., Orange, CT; *U.S. Public*, pg. 35
Heidenthal, Tom, Chief Fin. Officer & Sr. V.P.--Doane Products Co., Joplin, MO; *U.S. Private*, pg. 337
Heidenthal, Tom, Chief Fin. Officer & Sr. V.P.--Doane Products Co., Branded Sales Div., Joplin, MO; *U.S. Private*, pg. 337
Heider, Gisela, Chief Fin. Officer--TBWA Germany, Frankfurt/Main, Germany; *U.S. Private*, pg. 1063
Heilferty, Michael, Chief Fin. Officer--Primepak Company, Teaneck, NJ; *U.S. Private*, pg. 884
Heinicka, Jeffrey R., Chief Fin. Officer & Sr. V.P.--Florida Progress Corporation, Saint Petersburg, FL; *U.S. Public*, pg. 655
Heinisto, Kari, Chief Fin. Officer--Partek Corporation, Helsinki, Finland; *Int'l*, pg. 1024
Heinrichs, Steve, Chm. Bd. & Chief Fin. Officer--Western Data Systems, Calabasas, CA; *U.S. Private*, pg. 1165
Heinsoo, Olav, Mgr.-Fin. & Admin.--Atlas Copco Berema AB, Nacka, Sweden; *Int'l*, pg. 96
Heintz, Joseph E., Chief Fin. Officer & Partner--KPMG LLP, New York, NY; *U.S. Private*, pg. 603
Heiser, James S., Chief Fin. Officer, V.P., Gen. Counsel, Sec. & Treas.--Ducommun Incorporated, Carson, CA; *U.S. Public*, pg. 533
Heit, Stephen A., Chief Fin. Officer & Treas.--AM Cosmetics Inc., Nyack, NY; *U.S. Private*, pg. 6
Heitland, Raymond P., Chief Fin. Officer--Boykin Lodging Co., Cleveland, OH; *U.S. Public*, pg. 249
Helcesen, Stein, Chief Fin. Officer--AS OSLO Sporveier, Oslo, Norway; *Int'l*, pg. 1012
Held, Bryan H., Chief Fin. Officer & Sr. V.P.--Derlan Industries Limited, Toronto, Canada; *Int'l*, pg. 395
Heldreth, Joseph B., Chief Fin. Officer--Mebane Packaging Group., Kearny, NJ; *U.S. Private*, pg. 726
Heldreth, Joseph B., III, Chief Fin. Officer--Mebane Packaging Group, Mebane, NC; *U.S. Private*, pg. 726
Heldt, Brian, Chief Fin. Officer--Acorn Window Systems Inc., Quincy, MI; *U.S. Private*, pg. 14
Heldt, Tod, Chief Fin. Officer--GFI America, Minneapolis, MN; *U.S. Private*, pg. 435
Helfand, Michael D., Chief Fin. Officer & Exec. V.P.--World Color Press, Inc., Greenwich, CT; *U.S. Public*, pg. 1778
Helgarman, Alan, Chief Fin. Officer--Kvaerner Davy, Pittsburgh, PA; *Int'l*, pg. 774
Helie, Claude, Chief Fin. Officer & V.P.--Donohue Inc., Quebec, Canada; *Int'l*, pg. 1075
Heller, Richard, Chief Fin. Officer--Albank Financial Corporation, Albany, NY; *U.S. Public*, pg. 36
Heller, Robert P., Chief Fin. Officer & V.P.-Fin.--National Home Health Care Corp., Scarsdale, NY; *U.S. Public*, pg. 1157
Hellman, Murray, Chief Fin. Officer, Controller, Sec. & Treas.--Pressman Toy Corp., New York, NY; *U.S. Private*, pg. 882
Hellriegel, Michael C., Chief Fin. Officer & Sr. V.P.-Fin.--Butler International, Inc., Montvale, NJ; *U.S. Public*, pg. 270
Helmbrecht, Glen V., Chief Fin. Officer, Controller & Sec.--Mayville Engineering Co., Inc., Mayville, WI; *U.S. Private*, pg. 718
Helser, Phil, Chief Fin. Officer & Treas.--Lord, Sullivan & Yoder Inc. Marketing Communications, Columbus, OH; *U.S. Private*, pg. 676
Helton, Elgin, Chief Fin. Officer--Bender Shipbuilding & Repair Company, Inc., Mobile, AL; *U.S. Private*, pg. 132
Helvey, J.L., Chief Fin. Officer, Exec. V.P. & Investor Rels. Officer--Golden West Financial Corporation, Oakland, CA; *U.S. Public*, pg. 750
Hembree, R. Michael, Chief Fin. Officer & V.P.--Printpack Inc., Atlanta, GA; *U.S. Private*, pg. 886
Hemmelgarn, Gerald A., Chief Fin. Officer--Steel Tank & Fabricating Corp., Columbia City, IN; *U.S. Private*, pg. 615
Hemmer, David G., Chief Fin. Officer, V.P. & Treas.--Stuart Hall Co., Inc., Kansas City, MO; *U.S. Public*, pg. 1178
Hemmingsen, Steen, Chief Fin. Officer--The East Asiatic Company Ltd. A/S, Copenhagen, Denmark; *Int'l*, pg. 430
Henderson, Alan C., Chief Fin. Officer, Exec. V.P. & Sec.--RehabCare Group, Inc., Saint Louis, MO; *U.S. Public*, pg. 1373
Henderson, Doug, Chief Fin. Officer & Sr. V.P.--Publicis/Bloom Inc., New York, NY; *Int'l*, pg. 470
Henderson, Grant W., Pres. & Chief Fin. Officer--Coda Energy, Inc., Dallas, TX; *U.S. Public*, pg. 584
Henderson, James R., Chief Fin. Officer, V.P. & Treas.--Aydin Corporation, Horsham, PA; *U.S. Public*, pg. 158
Henderson, Mike, Chief Exec. Officer & Chief Fin. Officer--Gibson's Discount Centers Inc., Dodge City, KS; *U.S. Private*, pg. 452
Henderson, Paul, Chief Fin. Officer & Exec. V.P.-Fin. & Admin.--Cott Corporation, Pointe-Claire, Canada; *Int'l*, pg. 337
Henderson, Ron A., Dir.-Fin.--BICC plc, London, United Kingdom; *Int'l*, pg. 120
Hendig, Klaus G., V.P.-Admin.--Xicor, Inc., Milpitas, CA; *U.S. Public*, pg. 1785
Hendrickson, Tom, Chief Fin. Officer--Sport Mart, Inc., Wheeling, IL; *U.S. Public*, pg. 1499
Hendrie, Neal, Chief Fin. Officer--E. Moss Limited, Feltham, United Kingdom; *Int'l*, pg. 58
Hendrix, Daniel T., Chief Fin. Officer, Sr. V.P. & Treas.--Interface Inc., Atlanta, GA; *U.S. Public*, pg. 889
Hendrix, John L., Chief Fin. Officer & Sr. V.P.--APS Holding Corporation, Houston, TX; *U.S. Public*, pg. 10
Hendrix, John L., Chief Fin. Officer--A.P.S., Inc., Houston, TX; *U.S. Public*, pg. 10
Hendry, William J., Chief Fin. Officer & Treas.--Citrus World Inc., Lake Wales, FL; *U.S. Private*, pg. 241
Henley, Jeffrey O., Chief Fin. Officer & Exec. V.P.--Oracle Corporation, Redwood City, CA; *U.S. Public*, pg. 1227
Henley, William Curtis, Chief Fin. Officer & Sr. V.P.--The Bionetics Corporation, Newport News, VA; *U.S. Private*, pg. 145
Henn, Michael, Chief Fin. Officer & Sr. V.P.--Kaufman and Broad Home Corporation, Los Angeles, CA; *U.S. Public*, pg. 944
Hennessey, Edward, Chief Fin. Officer--Littleton Coin Co., Inc., Littleton, NH; *U.S. Private*, pg. 671
Hennessey, F.M., Chief Fin. Officer & Controller--Wilbur Smith Associates, Columbia, SC; *U.S. Private*, pg. 1009
Hennessey, Tim, Chief Fin. Officer--Peter Piper, Inc., Phoenix, AZ; *Int'l*, pg. 157
Hennigan, Gerald J., Chief Fin. Officer--Galesi Group, Schenectady, NY; *U.S. Private*, pg. 437
Hennigan, Gerald J., Chief Fin. Officer--Rotterdam Ventures Inc., Guilderland Center, NY; *U.S. Private*, pg. 437
Henning, David, Chief Fin. Officer--Communications Instruments Inc., Fairview, NC; *U.S. Private*, pg. 259
Henry, Brian C., Chief Fin. Officer & Exec. V.P.--Cincinnati Bell Telephone, Cincinnati, OH; *U.S. Public*, pg. 367
Henry, Joseph C., Chief Fin. Officer, V.P. & Treas.--The Hanover Insurance Company, Worcester, MA; *U.S. Public*, pg. 54
Henry, Sam L., Chief Fin. Officer, Sr. V.P. & Sec.--Helen of Troy Corporation, El Paso, TX; *U.S. Public*, pg. 807
Henseler, Gerald A., Chief Fin. Officer & Exec. V.P.--Banta Corporation, Menasha, WI; *U.S. Public*, pg. 187
Hensey, Quintin, Chief Fin. Officer--GenCorp Printworld, New York, NY; *U.S. Public*, pg. 706
Henshaw, William, Chief Fin. Officer--Yellow Cab Co., Chicago, IL; *U.S. Private*, pg. 1030
Hensoey, Quintin, Chief Fin. Officer--GenCorp Printworld, Monroe, NC; *U.S. Public*, pg. 706
Heppard, Tammy, Chief Fin. Officer--Unitech Industries, Inc., Tempe, AZ; *U.S. Public*, pg. 1672
Heppard, Tammy, Chief Fin. Officer--Solidex, Scottsdale, AZ; *U.S. Public*, pg. 1672
Heppel, Scott, Chief Fin. Officer--nexAir, LLC, Memphis, TN; *U.S. Private*, pg. 797
Herail, Jacques, Chief Fin. Officer & Chief Oper. Officer--Havas Advertising, Levallois-Perret, France; *Int'l*, pg. 600
Herald, James E., Chief Fin. Officer--Mine Safety Appliances Co., Pittsburgh, PA; *U.S. Public*, pg. 1114
Herbert, Alestair, Chief Fin. Officer--Allied Domecq Spirits & Wine (UK) Ltd., Horsham, United Kingdom; *Int'l*, pg. 63
Herbert, Daniel S., Chief Fin. Officer & V.P.--Texaco Worldwide Exploration & Production, Scroggins, TX; *U.S. Public*, pg. 1583
Herda, John J., Chief Fin. Officer & V.P.-Fin.--Preformed Line Products, Cleveland, OH; *U.S. Public*, pg. 1321
Heredia, Raoul, Chief Fin. Officer & Sr. V.P.-Fin.--Peerless Carpet Corporation, Acton Vale, Canada; *Int'l*, pg. 1032
Hereford, Jay, Chief Fin. Officer--Continental Plastic Containers, Inc., Norwalk, CT; *U.S. Public*, pg. 440
Herkenhoff, John, Chief Fin. Officer--First American Real Estate Information Services, Inc., Saint Petersburg, FL; *U.S. Public*, pg. 625
Herlihy, Gerard A., Chief Fin. Officer & Sec.--Williams Controls, Inc., Portland, OR; *U.S. Public*, pg. 1769
Herlinger, Charles, Chief Fin. Officer & Exec. V.P.--Siemens Energy & Automation Inc., Alpharetta, GA; *Int'l*, pg. 1245
Herman, Michael P., Chief Fin. Officer, V.P. & Sec.--Vari-Lite International, Dallas, TX; *U.S. Public*, pg. 1709
Hermann, Robert J., V.P.-Tax--Enron Corp., Houston, TX; *U.S. Public*, pg. 584
Hernandez, Ben F., Chief Fin. Officer & V.P.-Fin.--UniCARE Financial Corp., Irvine, CA; *U.S. Private*, pg. 152
Hernandez, Claudio, Chief Fin. Officer--Banco Quilmes, Buenos Aires, Argentina; *Int'l*, pg. 142
Hernandez, Eduardo, Chief Fin. Officer--Bagley S.A., Buenos Aires, Argentina; *Int'l*, pg. 379
Hernandez, Gaudencio S., Jr., Chief Fin. Officer & V.P.--EEI Corporation, Manila, Philippines; *Int'l*, pg. 425
Hernandez, Luis, V.P.-Fin.--Glamourette Fashion Mills, Quebradillas, PR; *U.S. Public*, pg. 779
Hernandez, Manny, Chief Fin. Officer & V.P.-Fin. & Admin.--Cypress Semiconductor Corporation, San Jose, CA; *U.S. Public*, pg. 470
Hernandez, Robert M., Vice Chm. & Chief Fin. Officer--USX Corporation, Pittsburgh, PA; *U.S. Public*, pg. 1661
Hernandez, Robert M., Chief Fin. Officer--U.S. Steel International, Inc., Pittsburgh, PA; *U.S. Public*, pg. 1661
Hernandez, Robert M., Chm. Bd., Chief Fin. Officer & Exec. V.P.-Fin./USX Corp.--RMI Titanium Company, Niles, OH; *U.S. Public*, pg. 1662
Hernandez, William H., Sr. V.P.-Fin.--PPG Industries, Inc., Pittsburgh, PA; *U.S. Public*, pg. 1245
Herr, Henry D., Chief Fin. Officer & Exec. V.P.--American Healthcorp Inc., Nashville, TN; *U.S. Public*, pg. 78
Herreid, Mark, V.P.-Fin.--Carlson Real Estate Company, Minnetonka, MN; *U.S. Private*, pg. 212
Herrmann, Harold, Chief Fin. Officer & Controller--William B. Reily & Co., Inc., New Orleans, LA; *U.S. Private*, pg. 919
Herrmann, Henry, Chief Investment Officer--Waddell & Reed, Inc., Shawnee Mission, KS; *U.S. Public*, pg. 1623
Herron, Doug, Chief Fin. Officer--Safelite AutoGlass, Columbus, OH; *U.S. Private*, pg. 960
Hersh, Robert, Chief Fin. Officer & V.P.-Fin.--Network Peripherals Inc., Milpitas, CA; *U.S. Public*, pg. 1169
Hershberger, James M., Chief Fin. Officer--Continental Mills, Inc., Tukwila, WA; *U.S. Private*, pg. 269
Hershkowitz, Thomas, Chief Fin. Officer, V.P., Treas. & Sec.--American Journal of Nursing Company, New York, NY; *Int'l*, pg. 1513
Hertel, Geoffrey M., Chief Fin. Officer & Exec. V.P.-Fin. & Admin.--Tetra Technologies, Woodlands, TX; *U.S. Public*, pg. 1582
Hertel, Janie, Controller--West Central Cooperative, Ralston, IA; *U.S. Private*, pg. 1163
Hervey, George A., Chief Fin. Officer & Sr. V.P.-Fin.--S3 Incorporated, Santa Clara, CA; *U.S. Public*, pg. 1415
Hervieux, Phillippe, Chief Fin. Officer--Roulement Service S.A., Strasbourg, France; *Int'l*, pg. 212
Hess, Goltfried, Chief Fin. Officer--Deutsche Goodyear GmbH, Cologne, Germany; *U.S. Public*, pg. 753
Hess, Thomas W., Exec. V.P. & Cashier--M & I Bank of Eagle River, Eagle River, WI; *U.S. Public*, pg. 1050
Hessler, Kurt, Pres., Chief Exec. Officer & Chief Fin. Officer--Quarterdeck Corp., Marina Del Rey, CA; *U.S. Public*, pg. 1350
Hester, Stephen A.M., Chief Fin. Officer--Credit Suisse First Boston, Inc., New York, NY; *Int'l*, pg. 345
Heumann, Stephen M., Chief Fin. Officer, V.P. & Treas.--The West Company, Incorporated, Lionville, PA; *U.S. Public*, pg. 1755
Heusinkveld, Valerie, Chief Fin. Officer--Trus Joist MacMillan Limited, Surrey, Canada; *Int'l*, pg. 829
Heusinkveld, Valerie, Chief Fin. Officer--Trus Joist MacMillan Limited, Surrey, Canada; *U.S. Public*, pg. 1556
Heusinkveld, Valerie A., Chief Fin. Officer--Trus Joist MacMillan, Boise, ID; *Int'l*, pg. 829
Heusinkveld, Valerie A., Chief Fin. Officer & V.P.-Fin.--TJ International, Inc., Boise, ID; *U.S. Public*, pg. 1556
Heusinkveld, Valerie A., Chief Fin. Officer--Trus Joist (Western) Ltd., Surrey, Canada; *U.S. Public*, pg. 1556
Heusinkveld, Valerie A., Chief Fin. Officer--Norco Windows, Inc., Boise, ID; *U.S. Public*, pg. 1556
Heusinkveld, Valerie A., Chief Fin. Officer--Trus Joist MacMillan, Boise, ID; *U.S. Public*, pg. 1556

Hewett, Jack A., Sr. V.P.-Admin., Chief Fin. Officer & Treas.--VASA North Atlantic Insurance Company, Indianapolis, IN; *Int'l*, pg. 464
Hewett, Steve, Chief Fin. Officer, V.P. & Treas.--Quorum Health Group, Inc., Brentwood, TN; *U.S. Public*, pg. 1353
Hewitt, Paul, Grp. Fin. Dir.--Redland PLC, Reigate, United Kingdom; *Int'l*, pg. 1090
Hewitt, Robert C., Chief Fin. Officer, V.P.-Fin. & Sec.--Newport Corporation, Irvine, CA; *U.S. Public*, pg. 1179
Hewitt, Steven J., Chief Fin. Officer & Sr. V.P.--Commercial Intertech Corp., Youngstown, OH; *U.S. Public*, pg. 411
Hewitt, W.E., Exec. Dir.-Fin.--Sappi Limited, Braamfontein, South Africa; *Int'l*, pg. 1193
Hewlett, Spencer, Chief Fin. Officer--Maverik Country Stores, Inc., Salt Lake City, UT; *U.S. Private*, pg. 715
Heyn, Chuck, Chief Fin. Officer & V.P.--Amana Society, Inc., Amana, IA; *U.S. Private*, pg. 48
Hibner, Geoffrey J., Chief Fin. Officer & Sr. V.P.-Fin. & Admin.--Timberland GmbH c/o The Timberland Company, Stratham, NH; *U.S. Public*, pg. 1609
Hickey, Dennis, V.P.-Fin.--Colgate U.S.A., New York, NY; *U.S. Public*, pg. 397
Hickman, Brett M., Chief Fin. Officer & Sr. V.P.--National Infusion Services, Inc., Indianapolis, IN; *U.S. Public*, pg. 229
Hickman, Winston E., Chief Fin. Officer, Sr. V.P. & Sec.--Pacific Scientific Company, Newport Beach, CA; *U.S. Public*, pg. 1250
Hicks, Arthur W., Jr., Chief Fin. Officer & V.P.--U.M. Holding Limited, Haddonfield, NJ; *U.S. Private*, pg. 1113
Hicks, Coleman S., Chief Fin. Officer--Oak Industries Inc., Waltham, MA; *U.S. Public*, pg. 1209
Hidayatallah, Munawar H., Chief Fin. Officer & Exec. V.P.--IRI International Corporation, Houston, TX; *U.S. Public*, pg. 858
Hiemstra, Michael J., Chief Fin. Officer & V.P.-Fin. & Admin.--Parker Hannifin Corporation, Cleveland, OH; *U.S. Public*, pg. 1259
Hietpas, John, V.P.-Fin.--Revcor, Inc., Carpentersville, IL; *U.S. Private*, pg. 925
Higashio, Takeshi, Chief Fin. Officer--Haseko (USA) Corporation, Los Angeles, CA; *Int'l*, pg. 600
Higdon, John, Chief Fin. Officer--Capital Mercury Shirt, New York, NY; *U.S. Private*, pg. 206
Higgins, J.S., Chief Fin. Officer & Mng. Dir.--The Fremont Group, San Francisco, CA; *U.S. Private*, pg. 427
Higgins, Michael J., Chief Fin. Officer & Exec. V.P.--Service America Corporation, Stamford, CT; *U.S. Private*, pg. 986
High, Malcolm, Controller--TAD Resources International, Inc., Cambridge, MA; *U.S. Private*, pg. 1062
Hight, Thomas, Chief Fin. Officer & V.P.--Utilimaster Corp., Wakarusa, IN; *U.S. Private*, pg. 1130
Hignett, Kenneth L., Chief Fin. Officer, Sr. V.P. & Sec.--Morgan's Foods, Inc., Beachwood, OH; *U.S. Public*, pg. 1133
Hilberg, Steve, Chief Fin. Officer--Orchard Supply Hardware, San Jose, CA; *U.S. Public*, pg. 1452
Hilbert, Steve, V.P.-Fin. & Admin.--Telonic Berkeley, Inc., Laguna Beach, CA; *U.S. Private*, pg. 1074
Hildebrand, Steve, Chief Fin. Officer--Thrifty Rent-a-Car System, Inc., Tulsa, OK; *U.S. Public*, pg. 354
Hill, Alan, Chief Fin. Officer--Superior Federal Bank, Fort Smith, AR; *U.S. Private*, pg. 1054
Hill, David E., Chief Fin. Officer--Crop Growers Insurance, Overland Park, KS; *Int'l*, pg. 59
Hill, Dennis, Chief Fin. Officer--Universal International, Inc., New Hope, MN; *U.S. Public*, pg. 1697
Hill, F. Trent, Jr., Chief Fin. Officer & V.P.--Sonoco Products Company, Hartsville, SC; *U.S. Public*, pg. 1485
Hill, Gary M., Chief Fin. Officer & Exec. V.P.--Information Resources, Inc., Chicago, IL; *U.S. Public*, pg. 875
Hill, John P., Jr., Chief Fin. Officer & Sr. V.P.--Heery International, Inc., Atlanta, GA; *U.S. Private*, pg. 519
Hill, Joseph G., Chief Fin. Officer, V.P.-Fin., Treas. & Sec.--DMI Furniture Inc., Louisville, KY; *U.S. Public*, pg. 473
Hill, Justin, Jr., Sec. & Treas.--Lawrence Paper Company, Lawrence, KS; *U.S. Private*, pg. 654
Hill, Linda K., V.P. & Treas.--Tyler Corporation, Dallas, TX; *U.S. Public*, pg. 1651
Hill, Max E., Chief Fin. Officer, V.P.-Fin. & Sec.--I.C. System, Inc., Vadnais Heights, MN; *U.S. Private*, pg. 553
Hill, Timothy, Chief Fin. Officer--Sentinel Technologies Inc., Downers Grove, IL; *U.S. Private*, pg. 984
Hill, Wayne S., Chief Fin. Officer, V.P. & Sec.--Toromont Industries Ltd., Concord, Canada; *Int'l*, pg. 1400
Hillard, David D., Chief Fin. Officer & Sr. V.P.--Fisher Companies Inc., Seattle, WA; *U.S. Public*, pg. 647
Hillber, Jeffrey G., Chief Fin. Officer--UUNET Technologies, Inc., Fairfax, VA; *U.S. Public*, pg. 1779
Hillegeist, Willard, Chief Fin. Officer--SAIC Canada, Ottawa, Canada; *U.S. Private*, pg. 976
Hillier, David, Chief Fin. Officer--Tie Rack (Canada) Limited, Markham, Canada; *Int'l*, pg. 1389
Hillman, Kyle, Dir.-Fin.--Grocers Baking Co., Grand Rapids, MI; *U.S. Private*, pg. 482
Hilton, Thomas S., Chief Fin. Officer--Peabody Holding Company, Inc., Saint Louis, MO; *Int'l*, pg. 594
Hilty, Wayne, Chief Fin. Officer & Sr. V.P.--Copart, Inc., Benicia, CA; *U.S. Public*, pg. 446
Hilzinger, Kurt J., Chief Fin. Officer & Sr. V.P.--AmeriSource Health Corp., Malvern, PA; *U.S. Public*, pg. 96
Hinckley, Bruce, Chief Fin. Officer & Exec. V.P.--Iwerks Entertainment, Burbank, CA; *U.S. Public*, pg. 915
Hinckley, Greg, Chief Oper. Officer, Chief Fin. Officer & Sr. V.P.--Mentor Graphics Corporation, Wilsonville, OR; *U.S. Public*, pg. 1086
Hinderer, H. William III, Chief Fin. Officer & Exec. V.P.-Fin. & Admin.--Tacony Corporation, Fenton, MO; *U.S. Private*, pg. 1066
Hinds, Dan J., Chief Fin. Officer & V.P.--The Gilbert Companies, Inc., Muncie, IN; *U.S. Private*, pg. 453
Hinds, Ron, V.P.-Credits & Collections--Texas Refinery Corp., Fort Worth, TX; *U.S. Private*, pg. 1078
Hineman, Richard, Chief Fin. Officer & V.P.-Fin. & Legal Affairs--Consilium, Inc., Mountain View, CA; *U.S. Public*, pg. 434
Hines, Andy, Chief Fin. Officer--Wise Foods, Inc., Parsippany, NJ; *U.S. Private*, pg. 157
Hines, Edward J., Chief Fin. Officer & V.P.--Wolverine Massachusetts Corporation, Merrimac, MA; *U.S. Private*, pg. 1186
Hines, John, Chief Fin. Officer & Sr. V.P.-Admin.--HK Systems, Inc., New Berlin, WI; *U.S. Private*, pg. 491
Hines, Virginia, Chief Fin. Officer--Periscope Marketing Communications, Minneapolis, MN; *U.S. Private*, pg. 853
Hinkley, Gregory K., Chief Fin. Officer & V.P.-Fin.--VLSI Technology, Inc., San Jose, CA; *U.S. Public*, pg. 1703
Hinman, Kirk, Pres., Chief Exec. Officer, Chief Fin. Officer & Treas.--Rome Strip Steel Co., Inc., Rome, NY; *U.S. Private*, pg. 942
Hinson, Laura K., Chief Fin. Officer--Winterthur U.S. Holdings Inc., Wilmington, DE; *Int'l*, pg. 345
Hinson, Laura K., Chief Fin. Officer & Treas.--Republic Financial Services, Inc., Dallas, TX; *Int'l*, pg. 346
Hinson, Mel, Chief Fin. Officer--Master Graphic, Inc., Memphis, TN; *U.S. Private*, pg. 713
Hinton, John R., Chief Fin. Officer, Sr. V.P.-Admin.--Kellogg Company, Battle Creek, MI; *U.S. Public*, pg. 947
Hintz, Charles B., Chief Fin. Officer--Lehman Brothers Holdings Inc., New York, NY; *U.S. Public*, pg. 987
Hippe, N. Douglas, V.P.-Acctg. Services--Investors Heritage Life Insurance Co., Frankfort, KY; *U.S. Public*, pg. 952
Hipsley, R. Linda, V.P. & Treas.--Calvert Bank & Trust Co., Prince Frederick, MD; *U.S. Public*, pg. 1088
Hirai, Frank, Chief Fin. Officer & Treas.--Mutoh America Inc., Phoenix, AZ; *Int'l*, pg. 897
Hirano, T., Chief Fin. Officer--Royal Copenhagen Japan Ltd., Tokyo, Japan; *Int'l*, pg. 1135
Hirayama, Shinji, Pres. & Chief Exec. Officer--The Fuji Bank & Trust Co., New York, NY; *Int'l*, pg. 519
Hirgi, Murad, Chief Fin. Officer--Western Cooperative Fertilizers Limited (WCFL), Calgary, Canada; *Int'l*, pg. 1195
Hirjibehedin, Farokh, Chief Fin. Officer & Controller--West Mill Clothes, Inc., Woodside, NY; *U.S. Private*, pg. 1163
Hirko, Joseph M., Chief Fin. Officer, Sr. V.P. & Treas.--Portland General Electric Co., Portland, OR; *U.S. Public*, pg. 584
Hirooka, Yoshio, Chief Fin. Officer--OMRON Systems, Inc., Schaumburg, IL; *Int'l*, pg. 1005
Hirsch, Leonard, Chief Fin. Officer & V.P.-Fin.--General Tools Mfg., Co. Inc., New York, NY; *U.S. Private*, pg. 445
Hirsch, Stephen, Chief Fin. Officer--Pic'n Pay Stores, Inc., Matthews, NC; *U.S. Private*, pg. 864
Hirschfeld, Dennis C., Chief Fin. Officer & Exec. V.P.--Hirschfeld, Inc., San Angelo, TX; *U.S. Private*, pg. 530
Hirschfeld, Dennis C., Chief Fin. Officer--Hirschfeld Steel Company, Inc., San Angelo, TX; *U.S. Private*, pg. 531
Hirstreet, Joel, Chief Fin. Officer & V.P.--U.S. Clearing Corp., New York, NY; *U.S. Public*, pg. 650
Hislop, John, V.P. Chief Fin. Officer--Telex Communications, Inc., Minneapolis, MN; *U.S. Private*, pg. 1074
Hiss, Steve, Chief Fin. Officer--Greater Construction Corp., Altamonte Springs, FL; *U.S. Private*, pg. 476
Hitchcook, Pat, Chief Fin. Officer--Linn Products, Inc., Charlotte, MI; *U.S. Private*, pg. 669
Hitt, Steven M., Chief Fin. Officer & V.P.--Rexel, Inc., Coral Gables, FL; *Int'l*, pg. 1107
Hitter, J.I., Dir.-Taxes--The Mead Corporation, Dayton, OH; *U.S. Public*, pg. 1074
Hix, Thomas B., Jr., Chief Fin. Officer & V.P.--Western Atlas International, Inc., Houston, TX; *U.S. Public*, pg. 1757
Hixon, Maxine, V.P.-Fin.--Tri-State Wholesale Associated Grocers, Inc., El Paso, TX; *U.S. Private*, pg. 1101
Ho, Ivan, Chief Fin. Officer--Esselte Ltd., Wan Chai, Hong Kong; *Int'l*, pg. 461
Ho, Julie, Chief Fin. Officer--Asama Pte. Ltd., Asia, Singapore, Singapore; *U.S. Private*, pg. 1046
Hober, Calvin, Comptroller--Atlas Tag & Label Inc., Neenah, WI; *U.S. Private*, pg. 145
Hoberg, Michael C., Chief Fin. Officer & V.P.-Fin.--Faroudja, Inc., Sunnyvale, CA; *U.S. Public*, pg. 613
Hoblit, Tom, Chief Fin. Officer--Bridgeman's Restaurants Inc., Minnetonka, MN; *U.S. Private*, pg. 167
Hobratschk, M. Glenn, Chief Fin. Officer & Exec. V.P.--The Austin Company, Cleveland, OH; *U.S. Private*, pg. 99
Hobson, G. Brian, V.P. & Corp. Controller--Canfor Corporation, Vancouver, Canada; *Int'l*, pg. 260
Hochman, Seth, Chief Fin. Officer--Bally Management, New Rochelle, NY; *Int'l*, pg. 998
Hodapp, Don J., Chief Fin. Officer & Exec. V.P.--Hormel Foods Corp., Austin, MN; *U.S. Public*, pg. 840
Hodd, Donald A., V.P.-Fin.--Bayer Corporation/ Pharmaceutical Division, West Haven, CT; *Int'l*, pg. 173
Hodge, William W., Chief Fin. Officer & V.P.-Fin.--American Fast Print, Limited, Spartanburg, SC; *U.S. Private*, pg. 53
Hodgen, Paul J., V.P.-Fin.--Sandvik Coromant Company, Fair Lawn, NJ; *Int'l*, pg. 1185
Hodges, Jan H., Chief Fin. Officer--HealthAmerica Pennsylvania, Inc., Pittsburgh, PA; *U.S. Public*, pg. 454
Hodgins, Robert B., Chief Fin. Officer & Sr. V.P.--Transcanada Pipelines Limited, Calgary, Canada; *Int'l*, pg. 1416
Hodgkin, Phil, Chief Fin. Officer, Controller & Treas.--Minarik Corp, Glendale, CA; *U.S. Private*, pg. 749
Hodgson, Matthew P., Chief Fin. Officer & V.P.--Sea Island Company, Sea Island, GA; *U.S. Private*, pg. 977
Hodits, Steve, Chief Fin. Officer--Speedring Systems, Inc., Rochester Hills, MI; *U.S. Public*, pg. 158
Hodson, Thomas W., Chief Fin. Officer & Sr. V.P.--Caremark International Inc, Northbrook, IL; *U.S. Public*, pg. 1082
Hoefert, Tom, Chief Fin. Officer--InnoServ Technologies, Inc., Arlington, TX; *U.S. Public*, pg. 879
Hoesel, J.D., Chief Fin. Officer--The Gates Rubber Company, Denver, CO; *Int'l*, pg. 1396
Hoff, George H., Chief Fin. Officer & Exec. V.P.--Sargento Foods Inc., Plymouth, WI; *U.S. Private*, pg. 966
Hoffenberg, William, Chief Fin. Officer--Koll Co., Newport Beach, CA; *U.S. Private*, pg. 631
Hoffman, Ebba C., Chm. Bd., Pres., Chief Exec. Officer & Chief Fin. Officer--Smead Manufacturing Company, Hastings, MN; *U.S. Private*, pg. 1006
Hoffman, L.R., Corp. Sec. & Acting Chief Fin. Officer--Sybron Chemicals Inc., Birmingham, NJ; *U.S. Public*, pg. 1544
Hoffman, Lawrence R., Chief Fin. Officer--IGI, Inc., Buena, NJ; *U.S. Public*, pg. 855
Hoffman, Mark, Chief Fin. Officer--T.L. Smith Machine, Springville, NY; *U.S. Private*, pg. 1009
Hoffman, Martin, Pres., Chief Exec. & Fin. Officer, Treas.--Designatronics, Inc., New Hyde Park, NY; *U.S. Private*, pg. 327
Hoffman, N., Mgr.-Fin. Admin.--Rainbow Apparel Distribution Center, Brooklyn, NY; *U.S. Private*, pg. 907
Hoffman, Robert B., Chief Fin. Officer & Sr. V.P.--Monsanto Company, Saint Louis, MO; *U.S. Public*, pg. 1124
Hoffman, Ronald J., Chief Fin. Officer--Furnishings International, Inc., Thomasville, NC; *U.S. Private*, pg. 431
Hoffman, Ronald J., Chief Fin. Officer--LifeStyle Furnishings International, Ltd., Thomasville, NC; *U.S. Private*, pg. 431
Hoffman, Ronald S., Chief Fin. Officer & Sec.--Nantucket Industries, Inc., Melville, NY; *U.S. Public*, pg. 1151
Hoffmann, David R., Pres. & Chief Fin. Officer--ALZA Development Corporation, Palo Alto, CA; *U.S. Public*, pg. 62
Hoffmeyer, Mark, Chief Fin. Officer & Controller--United Laboratories, Inc., Saint Charles, IL; *U.S. Private*, pg. 1122
Hofland, C.M., Chief Fin. Officer--Meneba N.V., Hague, Netherlands; *Int'l*, pg. 555
Hofmann, William R., Chief Fin. Officer & V.P.--Commercial Credit Company, Baltimore, MD; *U.S. Public*, pg. 1633
Hogan, Joe, Chief Fin. Officer--Energy Products, San Diego, CA; *U.S. Public*, pg. 1061
Hogan, John, Chief Fin. Officer--Harrow Industries, Grand Rapids, MI; *U.S. Private*, pg. 506
Hogan, K.W., Chief Fin. Officer--Valley Gas Co., Cumberland, RI; *U.S. Public*, pg. 1706
Hogan, Kenneth W., Chief Fin. Officer, Sr. V.P. & Sec.--Valley Resources, Inc., Cumberland, RI; *U.S. Public*, pg. 1706
Hogan, Kenneth W., Chief Fin. Officer, Sr. V.P. & Sec.--Bristol & Warren Gas Company, Bristol, RI; *U.S. Public*, pg. 1706
Hoge, Charles, Chief Fin. Officer--Melroe Company, Fargo, ND; *U.S. Public*, pg. 877
Hogendijk, A.J., Chief Fin. Officer--Commonwealth Bank Group, Sydney, Australia; *Int'l*, pg. 312
Hoguet, Karen M., Chief Fin. Officer--Federated Department Stores, Inc., Cincinnati, OH; *U.S. Public*, pg. 617
Hoguet, R., Chief Fin. Officer & Sr. V.P.-Fin.--Horsehead Resource Development Company, Inc., Palmerton, PA; *U.S. Private*, pg. 540
Hohm, Dale J., V.P.-Fin. & Sec.--Numac Energy Inc., Calgary, Canada; *Int'l*, pg. 990
Hohman, Perry, Asst. Chief Fin. Officer--L.M. Sandler & Sons, Virginia Beach, VA; *U.S. Private*, pg. 964
Hoitink, Terry, Chief Fin. Officer--Dart Transit Company, Eagan, MN; *U.S. Private*, pg. 311
Hojnacki, Pat, Chief Fin. Officer--International Envelope Company, Exton, PA; *U.S. Public*, pg. 70
Holbery, Scott D., Chief Fin. Officer--The Generra Company, Seattle, WA; *U.S. Private*, pg. 446
Holcomb, Daryl K., Chief Fin. Officer, V.P. & Treas.--Ronson Corporation, Somerset, NJ; *U.S. Public*, pg. 1405
Holcomb, Phillip M., Chief Fin. Officer & V.P.-Fin.--Nalleys Fine Foods, Tacoma, WA; *U.S. Private*, pg. 887
Holcombe, Stephen L., Chief Fin. Officer & Exec. V.P.--Vanguard Cellular Systems, Inc., Greensboro, NC; *U.S. Public*, pg. 1707
Holdcraft, Phil, Chief Fin. Officer--Bon Ton Foods, Inc., York, PA; *U.S. Private*, pg. 65
Holden, Garry P., Chief Fin. Officer--Brown & Bigelow, Inc., Saint Paul, MN; *U.S. Private*, pg. 172
Holden, Mark R., Chief Fin. Officer & V.P.--Wabash National Corp., Lafayette, IN; *U.S. Public*, pg. 1730
Holden, Michael J., Chief Fin. Officer--The Pep Boys-Manny, Moe & Jack, Philadelphia, PA; *U.S. Public*, pg. 1276
Holden, Michael J., Chief Fin. Officer--The Pep Boys-Manny, Moe & Jack of California, Los Angeles, CA; *U.S. Public*, pg. 1276
Holden, Shirley, Treas. & Controller--Royal Oldsmobile Mazda, Inc., Metairie, LA; *U.S. Private*, pg. 948
Holdgate, Deborah, Chief Fin. Officer--Butterfield Day Devito Hockney Ltd., London, United Kingdom; *Int'l*, pg. 237
Holding, Carol, Treas.--Little America Refining, Inc., Evansville, WY; *U.S. Private*, pg. 1003
Holdren, Pamela, Chief Fin. Officer--Dimco-Gray Company, Centerville, OH; *U.S. Private*, pg. 333
Holihen, Jennifer A., Chief Fin. Officer, Treas. & Sec.--Crossmann Communities, Inc., Indianapolis, IN; *U.S. Public*, pg. 461
Holinski, Stephan A., Sr. V.P. & Chief Fin. Officer--Moore Document Solutions, Lake Forest, IL; *Int'l*, pg. 890
Holinski, Stephen A., Chief Fin. Officer & Sr. V.P.--Moore Corporation Limited, Toronto, Canada; *Int'l*, pg. 888
Holl, David, Chief Fin. Officer & Treas.--Mary Kay, Inc., Dallas, TX; *U.S. Private*, pg. 711
Holladay, Sue, Chief Fin. Officer & V.P.--San Jose Mercury News, San Jose, CA; *U.S. Public*, pg. 964
Holland, Al, Chief Fin. Officer & Sr. V.P.--Trinity Industries Inc., Dallas, TX; *U.S. Public*, pg. 1638
Holland, James M., Sr. V.P. & Sec.--Atwood Oceanics, Inc., Houston, TX; *U.S. Public*, pg. 146
Holland, Jim D., Chief Fin. Officer, Sr. V.P. & Treas.--CMI Corporation, Oklahoma City, OK; *U.S. Public*, pg. 278

Holland, Lewis E., Vice Chm., Chief Fin. Officer & Exec. V.P.--National Commerce Bancorporation, Memphis, TN; U.S. Public, pg. 1154

Holland, R. Van Ness, Jr., Chief Fin. Officer, Exec. V.P.-Fin. & Treas.--Wyle Electronics, Irvine, CA; Int'l, pg. 1457

Holland, Robert T., Chief Fin. Officer, V.P. & Sec.--Relm Wireless Corp., West Chester, PA; U.S. Public, pg. 1376

Holland, Thomas, Chief Fin. Officer & Exec. V.P.--Transcontinental Realty Investors, Inc., Dallas, TX; U.S. Public, pg. 1630

Holland, Thomas A., Chief Fin. Officer, Exec. V.P. & Sec.--Continental Mortgage and Equity Trust, Dallas, TX; U.S. Public, pg. 441

Hollerbach, Michael D., Chief Fin. Officer & Exec. V.P.--Pulte Corporation, Bloomfield Hills, MI; U.S. Public, pg. 1344

Hollerbach, Michael D., Exec. V.P. & Chief Fin. Officer--Pulte Home Corporation, Bloomfield Hills, MI; U.S. Public, pg. 1344

Hollingsworth, Linda, Treas. & Sec.--Sun Bulb Company, Inc., Arcadia, FL; U.S. Private, pg. 1050

Hollingworth, P., Grp. Fin. Dir.--Ransomes Plc, Ipswich, United Kingdom; Int'l, pg. 1087

Hollis, S., Chief Fin. Officer--ING Barings Southern Africa (Proprietary), Sandton, South Africa; Int'l, pg. 650

Holloway, Bob, Chief Fin. Officer--The Georgia Marble Company, Kennesaw, GA; U.S. Private, pg. 448

Holman, Bobby G., Chief Fin. Officer, Treas. & Asst. Sec.--WSMP, Inc., Claremont, NC; U.S. Public, pg. 1729

Holman, Sandra J., Chief Fin. Officer--Fidelity Federal Savings Bank, Marion, IN; U.S. Public, pg. 632

Holmboe, Carl F., Chief Fin. Officer--BBDO Oslo, Oslo, Norway; U.S. Public, pg. 1224

Holmes, Donald D., V.P.-Fin. & Sec.--Scotsman Industries, Inc., Vernon Hills, IL; U.S. Public, pg. 1444

Holmes, Douglas, Chief Fin. Officer & Exec. V.P.--MediaOne, Boston, MA; U.S. Public, pg. 1688

Holmes, Douglas D., V.P. & Chief Fin. Officer-Media Grp.--U S West Inc., Englewood, CO; U.S. Public, pg. 1688

Holmes, George B., Pres., Chief Exec. & Chief Fin. Officer--Dombrowski & Holmes, Inc., Hammond, IN; U.S. Private, pg. 338

Holmes, Richard H., Chief Fin. Officer--BellSouth Communication Systems, Inc., Roanoke, VA; U.S. Public, pg. 209

Holmes, William E., Chief Fin. Officer & Sec.--Compas Electronics, Inc., Kanata, Canada; Int'l, pg. 36

Holmstrom, Tim, V.P.-Fin. Admin.--Fort Dodge Animal Health, Overland Park, KS; U.S. Public, pg. 79

Holroyd, Charles T., Jr., Sr. V.P.-Fin. Modeling--Countrywide Funding Corporation, Pasadena, CA; U.S. Public, pg. 453

Holson, Philip L., Chief Fin. Officer & Sr. V.P.--Associated Industrial Supply, Inc., Columbia, SC; U.S. Private, pg. 91

Holt, Bill, Chief Fin. Officer--Eon Labs Manufacturing, Inc., Laurelton, NY; U.S. Private, pg. 379

Holter, Gary, Chief Fin. Officer--International Logistics Limited, Hillside, IL; U.S. Private, pg. 571

Holthaus, Dennis B., Chief Acctg. Officer & V.P.--NationsBank/Miami, Miami, FL; U.S. Public, pg. 1162

Holwell, R., Chief Fin. Officer--Air UK (Leisure) Ltd., Stansted, United Kingdom; Int'l, pg. 39

Hommel, Kenneth R., Controller--Tri-Continental Corporation, New York, NY; U.S. Private, pg. 982

Honaman, David G., Chief Fin. Officer, V.P.-Admin. & Sec.--Wolohan Lumber Co., Saginaw, MI; U.S. Public, pg. 1774

Honey, Joe, Chief Fin. Officer--Olan Mills, Inc., Chattanooga, TN; U.S. Private, pg. 749

Hong, K.H., Chief Fin. Officer & V.P.--Riverside Cement Co., Diamond Bar, CA; Int'l, pg. 1293

Hong, Kyung-Hum, Chief Fin. Officer--Ssangyong Pacific, Diamond Bar, CA; Int'l, pg. 1292

Hong, Sa-Seung, Chief Fin. Officer--Ssangyong Cement Industrial Co., Ltd., Seoul, Korea; Int'l, pg. 1291

Honig, Michael T., Chief Fin. Officer--Welsh Farms, Inc., Long Valley, NJ; U.S. Private, pg. 1162

Honrud, Arden, V.P. & Controller--Teledyne Ryan Aeronautical, San Diego, CA; U.S. Public, pg. 43

Honzl, John J., Chief Fin. Officer & V.P.--Scicom Data Services, Ltd., Minnetonka, MN; U.S. Private, pg. 975

Hood, Jack, V.P.-Fin. & Controller--Institutional Financing Services, Benicia, CA; U.S. Public, pg. 1652

Hood, Robert, Chief Fin. Officer & Chief Admin. Officer--Excite, Inc., Redwood City, CA; U.S. Public, pg. 599

Hoogerwerf, David J., Chief Fin. Officer-N. America & Sr. V.P.--Gerber Products Company, Fremont, MI; Int'l, pg. 973

Hooker, Bruce, Chief Fin. Officer & Sr. V.P.--Amperif Corporation, Chatsworth, CA; U.S. Public, pg. 1523

Hooker, Steven L., Chief Fin. Officer--Health Maintenance Oregon, Salem, OR; U.S. Private, pg. 918

Hooley, Peter, Grp. Dir.-Fin.--Smith & Nephew PLC, London, United Kingdom; Int'l, pg. 1263

Hooper, Gerald A., Chief Fin. Officer & V.P.--Schneider Corp., Kitchener, Canada; Int'l, pg. 1207

Hooper, Robert L., V.P.-Fin.--Rexair, Inc., Troy, MI; U.S. Public, pg. 1684

Hoover, Craig, Chief Fin. Officer--Supermarket Insurance Agency, Inc., Shawnee Mission, KS; U.S. Private, pg. 93

Hoover, Craig, Chief Fin. Officer--Benchmark Insurance Company, Shawnee Mission, KS; U.S. Private, pg. 93

Hope, David W., Chief Fin. Officer & V.P. Fin.--Red Ball Corporation, Seattle, WA; U.S. Private, pg. 97

Hopke, William J., V.P. & Treas.--Dominion Capital, Inc., Richmond, VA; U.S. Public, pg. 516

Hopkins, Bill, Chief Fin. Officer--Ouimet Corp., Nashville, TN; U.S. Private, pg. 821

Hopkins, Gary B., Sr. V.P.-Opers.--Business Week, New York, NY; U.S. Public, pg. 1069

Hopkins, James L., Chief Fin. Officer & V.P.-Strategic Mktg.--STB Systems, Inc., Richardson, TX; U.S. Public, pg. 1421

Hopkinson, Mark R., Chief Fin. Officer, Treas. & Asst. Sec.--Artistic Carton Company, Elgin, IL; U.S. Private, pg. 87

Hopkinson, Mark R., Chief Fin. Officer--White Pigeon Paper Company, White Pigeon, MI; U.S. Private, pg. 87

Hoppe, William S., Chief Fin. Officer & Exec. V.P.--Rock Bottom Restaurants, Louisville, CO; U.S. Public, pg. 1396

Hoppel, Thomas H., Chief Fin. Officer & V.P.--International Flavors & Fragrances, Inc., New York, NY; U.S. Public, pg. 898

Hopper, Mike, Chief Fin. Officer & Sr. V.P.--Ozark Motor Lines, Memphis, TN; U.S. Private, pg. 825

Horan, Dennis, Chief Fin. Officer, Treas. & Sec.--URM Stores, Inc., Spokane, WA; U.S. Private, pg. 1114

Horan, Thomas W., Chief Fin. Officer, Sr. V.P.-Fin. & Sec.--Great Dane Trailers, Inc., Savannah, GA; U.S. Private, pg. 1030

Horberg, Jane, Controller--Best Kosher Sausage Co., Chicago, IL; U.S. Public, pg. 1433

Horey, Thomas, Chief Fin. Officer & Exec. V.P.--Plaid Pantries, Inc., Beaverton, OR; U.S. Private, pg. 868

Horgan, Sam, Chief Fin. Officer & Sr. V.P.--OAO Technology Solutions, Inc., Greenbelt, MD; U.S. Public, pg. 1425

Horiuchi, Kentaro, Chief Fin. Officer--Meitsu Inc., Tokyo, Japan; Int'l, pg. 856

Horn, Alan D., Chief Fin. Officer--Rogers Communications, Inc., Toronto, Canada; Int'l, pg. 1122

Horn, Robert E., V.P. & Chief Fin. Officer--Pace Resources, Inc., York, PA; U.S. Private, pg. 829

Hornbaker, Renee, Chief Fin. Officer--BW/IP International, Inc., Long Beach, CA; U.S. Public, pg. 658

Hornbaker, Renee J., Chief Fin. Officer & V.P.--Flowserve Corporation, Dayton, OH; U.S. Public, pg. 658

Horning, J., Chief Fin. Officer--INCA Presswood Pallets, Ltd., Dover, OH; Int'l, pg. 678

Horowitz, Cindy, Chief Fin. Officer & V.P.--Primedia Informatin Group, New York, NY; U.S. Public, pg. 1328

Horowitz, Donald, Chief Fin. Officer, Treas. & Sec.--Aceto Corporation, Lake Success, NY; U.S. Public, pg. 15

Horsley, Jennifer, Chief Fin. Officer--CPS Chemical Company Inc., Woodbridge, NJ; U.S. Private, pg. 196

Horsley, Richard D., Vice Chm. & Exec. Fin. Officer--Regions Financial Corporation, Birmingham, AL; U.S. Public, pg. 1371

Horsley, Steve, Chief Fin. Officer--Thomas Built Buses, Inc., High Point, NC; U.S. Private, pg. 1082

Horton, Ann N., Chief Fin. Officer--Penn Virginia Coal Company, Duffield, VA; U.S. Public, pg. 1271

Horton, Gary B., Chief Fin. Officer & Treas.--Amerco, Reno, NV; U.S. Public, pg. 48

Horton, Ron, Controller--Rochester Gauges Inc. Of Texas, Dallas, TX; U.S. Private, pg. 440

Horvat, Peter D., Chief Fin. Officer, V.P., Treas. & Sec.--Lenape Forge, Inc., West Chester, PA; U.S. Private, pg. 659

Horvath, James J., Chief Fin. Officer--American Crystal Sugar Company, Moorhead, MN; U.S. Private, pg. 52

Horvath, Robert G., Chief Fin. Officer & Exec. V.P.--Rapp Collins Worldwide, New York, NY; U.S. Public, pg. 1224

Horwitz, Stewart, Chief Fin. Officer & Sec.--Elkay Plastics Company, Inc., Los Angeles, CA; U.S. Private, pg. 372

Hoshino, Hiroaki, Chief Oper. & Fin. Officer--Kajima U.S.A., Inc., New York, NY; Int'l, pg. 722

Hoshino, Shin, Chief Fin. Officer & Sr. V.P.--American Isuzu Motors Inc., Whittier, CA; Int'l, pg. 692

Host, Gerard R., Chief Fin. Officer & Exec. V.P.--Trustmark National Bank, Jackson, MS; U.S. Public, pg. 1643

Hotarek, Brian W., Chief Fin. Officer & Exec. V.P.--The Stop & Shop Companies, Inc., Quincy, MA; Int'l, pg. 750

Hotchkiss, Jeffrey R., Chief Fin. Officer--Teradyne, Inc., Boston, MA; U.S. Public, pg. 1580

Hotton, Vince, Chief Fin. Officer--Handschy Industries, Bellwood, IL; U.S. Private, pg. 403

Hottovy, Ronald J., Chief Fin. Officer, Exec. V.P., Treas. & Sec.--Scientific Software-Intercomp, Inc., Denver, CO; U.S. Public, pg. 1443

Houdeshell, Monty A., Chief Fin. Officer & V.P.--Furon Company, Laguna Niguel, CA; U.S. Public, pg. 688

Houel, Patrick, Chief Fin. Officer & Exec. V.P.--LVMH Moet Hennessy Louis Vuitton, Paris, France; Int'l, pg. 779

Hought, Derek E., Chief Fin. Officer--AFCO Credit Corp., New York, NY; U.S. Public, pg. 1085

Houghtby, Carol, Chief Fin. Officer--Fortis Financial Group, Woodbury, MN; Int'l, pg. 499

Houle, David A., Chief Fin. Officer, Exec. V.P. & Treas.--Pacific Century Financial Corporation, Honolulu, HI; U.S. Public, pg. 1248

Houle, David A., Chief Fin. Officer & Exec. V.P.-Treas. Admin.--Bank of Hawaii, Honolulu, HI; U.S. Public, pg. 1248

Houlihan, Lawrence M., Chm. Bd., Pres., Chief Exec. & Chief Fin. Officer, Treas. & Sec.--Frank B. Ross Co. Inc., Jersey City, NJ; U.S. Private, pg. 946

Houlton, J.C.B., Chief Fin. Officer--Redland Aggregates Ltd., Groby, United Kingdom; Int'l, pg. 1090

House, James T., Chief Fin. Officer & V.P.--Superior Consultant Holdings Corp., Southfield, MI; U.S. Public, pg. 1538

Houseman, Dave E., Chief Fin. Officer & Exec. V.P.--Signal Apparel Company, Inc., Chattanooga, TN; U.S. Public, pg. 1472

Housman, Peter J., II, Chief Fin. Officer & Treas.--Telemundo Group, Inc., Hialeah, FL; U.S. Public, pg. 1570

Houston, Alfred D., Chief Fin. Officer & Exec. V.P.--New England Electric System, Westborough, MA; U.S. Public, pg. 1171

Houston, B. Ord, Sec.--The Bethlehem Corporation, Easton, PA; U.S. Public, pg. 225

Houston, W. Tennent, Pres. & Chief Exec. Officer--Merry Land & Investment Company, Inc., Augusta, GA; U.S. Public, pg. 1098

Houston, William K., Chief Oper. Officer & Chief Fin. Officer--Georgia Tent & Awning Inc., Atlanta, GA; U.S. Private, pg. 448

Hov, Donald, Chief Fin. Officer--Anderson & Lembke Inc., New York, NY; U.S. Private, pg. 72

Hovanec, Eugene F., Chief Fin. Officer & Sec.--Vitesse Semiconductor Corporation, Camarillo, CA; U.S. Public, pg. 1723

Hovde, Robert A., Chief Fin. Officer--Rosens Diversified, Inc., Fairmont, MN; U.S. Private, pg. 945

Hoversen, Mike, Chief Fin. Officer & V.P.-Fin.--Bell-Carter Foods, Inc., Lafayette, CA; U.S. Private, pg. 131

Hovland, E. Keith, Exec. V.P.-Fin. & Admin.--Qual-Med, Inc., Pueblo, CO; U.S. Public, pg. 678

Howard, Connie, Controller--Camalloy, Incorporated, Washington, PA; U.S. Private, pg. 202

Howard, David P., Chief Fin. Officer, V.P. & Treas.--Furniture Brands International Inc., Saint Louis, MO; U.S. Public, pg. 688

Howard, James H., Chief Fin. Officer & Corp. Sec.--Stowe-Pharr Mills, Inc., Mc Adenville, NC; U.S. Private, pg. 1045

Howard, Michael T., Chief Fin. Officer. & Sr. V.P.--Medrad, Inc., Indianola, PA; Int'l, pg. 1204

Howard, Mike, Chief Fin. Officer--Mark Andy, Inc., Chesterfield, MO; U.S. Public, pg. 521

Howard, Rudy C., Chief Fin. Officer--PPD Pharmaco, Inc., Wilmington, NC; U.S. Public, pg. 1285

Howard, Rudy C., CPA, Chief Fin. Officer, V.P.-Fin., Treas. & Sec.--Pharmaceutical Product Development, Inc., Wilmington, NC; U.S. Public, pg. 1285

Howard, Timothy, Chief Fin. Officer & Exec. V.P.--Federal National Mortgage Association (Fannie Mae), Washington, DC; U.S. Public, pg. 615

Howard, W. Wesley, III, Chief Fin. Officer--Jergens Inc., Cleveland, OH; U.S. Private, pg. 586

Howe, Nick, Chief Fin. Officer--Zomba Recording Corp., London, United Kingdom; Int'l, pg. 1529

Howell-Saxton, Delight, Chief Fin. Officer, Sr. V.P. & Sec.--McGrath RentCorp, Livermore, CA; U.S. Public, pg. 1069

Howell, Danny, Loan Officer--Wieland Financial Services, Inc., Atlanta, GA; U.S. Private, pg. 1175

Howell, David, Chief Fin. Officer--Radica USA Limited, Dallas, TX; U.S. Private, pg. 906

Howell, Doug, Chief Fin. Officer, Sr. V.P. & Treas.--Preferred Risk Mutual Insurance, West Des Moines, IA; U.S. Private, pg. 880

Howell, Joseph, Chief Fin. Officer & Sr. V.P.--Merix Corporation, Forest Grove, OR; U.S. Public, pg. 1096

Howells, Jeffery P., Chief Fin. Officer & Sr. V.P.-Fin.--Tech Data Corporation, Clearwater, FL; U.S. Public, pg. 1562

Howells, Jeffrey P., Chief Fin. Officer--Tech Data Canada, Inc., Mississauga, Canada; U.S. Public, pg. 1562

Howells, Ted, Jr., Chief Fin. Officer & Exec. V.P.--Sony Pictures Entertainment, Culver City, CA; Int'l, pg. 1281

Howeth, Robert W., Chief Fin. Officer & Sr. V.P.--Fairfield Communities, Inc., Little Rock, AR; U.S. Public, pg. 610

Howie, Richard, Chief Fin. Officer & Chief Acctg. Officer--Sulcus Computer Corp., Greensburg, PA; U.S. Public, pg. 1527

Howlett, Richard, Chief Fin. Officer & V.P.--Army Times Publishing Co., Springfield, VA; U.S. Public, pg. 699

Hoy, Patrick, Chief Fin. Officer & V.P.--Pacesetter Corporation, Omaha, NE; U.S. Private, pg. 830

Hoyle, Eric, Chief Fin. Officer--Ithaca Industries, Inc., Wilkesboro, NC; U.S. Private, pg. 576

Hoyt, Jeffrey E., Chief Oper. Officer, Exec. V.P. & Sec.--Sun Bancorp, Inc., Selinsgrove, PA; U.S. Public, pg. 1529

Hsu, Weston, Fin. Controller--Jardine, Matheson & Co., Ltd., Taipei, Taiwan; Int'l, pg. 704

Hu, Evelyn, Chief Fin. Officer--Johnson & Johnson Taiwan Ltd., Taipei, Taiwan; U.S. Public, pg. 931

Huang, W.H., Chief Fin. Officer--Formosa Plastics Corporation, Kao-hsiung, Taiwan; Int'l, pg. 498

Huang, Yungyi, Chief Fin. Officer--Baldwin Asia Pacific Ltd., Hong Kong, Hong Kong; U.S. Public, pg. 170

Huat, Lee Chiang, V.P.-Fin. & Acctg.--Singapore Petroleum Company Ltd., Singapore, Singapore; U.S. Public, pg. 102

Hubbard, Sonja, Chief Fin. Officer--E-Z Mart Stores, Inc., Texarkana, TX; U.S. Private, pg. 353

Huber, Mark, Chief Fin. Officer--Southwest Chemical/ Services, Houston, TX; U.S. Public, pg. 781

Huber, Michael J., Chief Fin. Officer--BASES Worldwide, Covington, KY; U.S. Private, pg. 120

Huber, Romilda, Chief Fin. Officer--Peoples Bank & Trust Company, Sunman, IN; U.S. Public, pg. 633

Huber, Stephen, Chief Fin. Officer, Treas. & Sec.--Birdsong Corporation, Suffolk, VA; U.S. Private, pg. 145

Hubner, Klaus, Chief Fin. Officer--Fried. Krupp AG, Essen, Germany; Int'l, pg. 507

Huckvale, Robert W., Chief Fin. Officer--Landa, Inc., Portland, OR; U.S. Private, pg. 646

Hudak, Kristen M., Chief Fin. Officer & Sr. Exec. V.P.--AmSouth Bancorporation, Birmingham, AL; U.S. Public, pg. 105

Hudnall, David, Chief Fin. Officer--TLPartnership, Dallas, TX; U.S. Public, pg. 1224

Hudson, J.W., Chief Fin. Officer & V.P.-Fin.--B C Sugar Refinery, Ltd., Vancouver, Canada; Int'l, pg. 103

Huebner, Elizabeth J., Chief Fin. Officer & V.P.--Fluke Corporation, Everett, WA; U.S. Public, pg. 659

Huesgen, James H., Chief Fin. Officer & Exec. V.P.--Pacific Telecom Cellular, Inc., Vancouver, WA; U.S. Public, pg. 1252

Huesman, James L., Exec. V.P. & Treas.--Mission Viejo Company, Mission Viejo, CA; U.S. Public, pg. 1289

Huet, Bernard, Chief Fin. Officer--Thomson Multimedia SA, Paris, France; Int'l, pg. 1384

Huey, Gene K., Chief Fin. Officer & V.P.--Esco Corporation, Portland, OR; U.S. Private, pg. 382

Huff, Bruce N., Chief Fin. Officer & Sr. V.P.--Harken Energy Corporation, Irving, TX; U.S. Public, pg. 785

Huff, Craig D., Chief Fin. Officer, V.P.-Fin. & Treas.--Nature's Sunshine Products, Inc., Provo, UT; U.S. Public, pg. 1166

Huff, Ronald E., Pres. & Chief Fin. Officer--Belden & Blake Corporation, Canton, OH; *U.S. Private*, pg. 1078
Huff, Ronald E., Chief Fin. Officer--Arrow Oilfield Service Company, Canton, OH; *U.S. Private*, pg. 1078
Huff, Ronald E., Chief Fin. Officer--Ward Lake Drilling, Inc., Gaylord, MI; *U.S. Private*, pg. 1078
Huff, Ronald E., Chief Fin. Officer--Peake Energy, Inc., Ravenswood, WV; *U.S. Private*, pg. 1078
Huff, William, Chief Fin. Officer--The Boston Globe, Boston, MA; *U.S. Public*, pg. 1175
Huffaker, Craig, Chief Fin. Officer & Treas.--TIE/ Communications, Inc., Overland Park, KS; *U.S. Private*, pg. 1085
Huffman, Charles P., Chief Fin. Officer, V.P. & Treas.--Mobile Gas Service Corp., Mobile, AL; *U.S. Public*, pg. 1120
Huge, Art, Chief Fin. Officer & Sr. V.P.--The LTV Corporation, Cleveland, OH; *U.S. Public*, pg. 971
Huggins, Tommie, Chief Fin. Officer--SicolaMartin Inc., Austin, TX; *U.S. Private*, pg. 998
Hughes, Dwain H., Chief Fin. Officer & Sr. V.P.--Tandy Corporation, Fort Worth, TX; *U.S. Public*, pg. 1560
Hughes, J. Lowell, Chief Fin. Officer & Exec. V.P.-Fin.--Davis Electrical Constructors, Inc., Greenville, SC; *U.S. Private*, pg. 315
Hughes, Jack, Chief Fin. Officer & Sr. V.P.--BTG, Inc., Fairfax, VA; *U.S. Public*, pg. 164
Hughes, K.D., V.P. & Controller--The Scott Fetzer Company, Westlake, OH; *U.S. Public*, pg. 217
Hughes, Karen S., Chief Fin. Officer, V.P. & Sec.--Ridgewood Properties, Inc., Atlanta, GA; *U.S. Public*, pg. 1389
Hughes, Nick, Chief Fin. Officer & Treas.--TV Host Inc., Harrisburg, PA; *U.S. Private*, pg. 1066
Hughes, Robert J., Chief Fin. Officer & Exec. V.P.--Poughkeepsie Financial Corp., Poughkeepsie, NY; *U.S. Public*, pg. 1319
Hughes, Robert J., Chief Fin. Officer & Exec. V.P.--Bank of the Hudson, Poughkeepsie, NY; *U.S. Public*, pg. 1319
Hughes, Simon, Chief Fin. Officer--Mothercare World UK Ltd., Watford, United Kingdom; *Int'l*, pg. 1304
Hughes, Stephen C., Chief Fin. Officer & Sr. V.P.--SRA International Inc., Arlington, VA; *U.S. Private*, pg. 957
Hughes, T.D., Chief Exec. & Chief Fin. Officer--La Rosa's, Inc., Cincinnati, OH; *U.S. Private*, pg. 640
Hughes, Victor A., Sr., Chief Fin. Officer--Southeast Properties Holding Corporation, Inc., Jacksonville, FL; *U.S. Public*, pg. 965
Hughes, W. Alan, Treas.--Fleischli Oil Company, Inc., Cheyenne, WY; *U.S. Private*, pg. 410
Hughes, William J., Exec. V.P.-Admin. & Fin.--E.C.D., Inc., Hillside, NJ; *U.S. Private*, pg. 353
Hui Kian, Sally Lauw, Chief Fin. Officer--IPC Corporation Ltd., Singapore, Singapore; *Int'l*, pg. 651
Hui, Y.C., Chief Fin. Officer--ISC Systems Asia Pacific Ltd., Hong Kong, Hong Kong; *Int'l*, pg. 1003
Huisman, Bruce, Mgr.-Acctg.--Preferred Risk Life Insurance Co., West Des Moines, IA; *U.S. Private*, pg. 880
Hull, C.J., Mgr.-Fin.--Amic Industries Limited, Johanesburg, South Africa; *Int'l*, pg. 76
Hull, E. C., Controller--Landis, Waynesboro, PA; *U.S. Public*, *pg. 1699*
Hull, James C., Chief Fin. Officer & V.P.--EnviroSource, Inc., Horsham, PA; *U.S. Public*, pg. 587
Hull, Jeff, Chief Fin. Officer--Atrium Companies, Inc., Dallas, TX; *U.S. Private*, pg. 98
Hull, John, Chief Fin. Officer--CAE Electronics plc, Burgess Hill, United Kingdom; *Int'l*, pg. 238
Hull, John T., Chief Fin. Officer & Treas.--Modern American Life Insurance Company, Springfield, MO; *U.S. Public*, pg. 853
Hullibarger, Gail, Chief Fin. Officer & Asst. Gen. Mgr.--Sacramento Municipal Utility District, Sacramento, CA; *U.S. Private*, pg. 959
Hulliger, Sylvie, Chief Fin. Officer & Controller--La Metaire Clinic, Nyon, Switzerland; *U.S. Public*, pg. 1036
Hulsey, Joseph C., Sr. V.P.-Fin.--Old Fashion Foods, Inc., Austell, GA; *U.S. Private*, pg. 814
Huml, Donald S., Chief Fin. Officer & Sr. V.P.-Fin.--Snap-On Tools Corporation, Kenosha, WI; *U.S. Public*, pg. 1480
Hummell, Michael J., Chief Fin. Officer & V.P.-Fin.--BNI Coal, Ltd., Bismarck, ND; *U.S. Public*, pg. 1116
Hummers, William S., III, Chief Fin. Officer & Exec. V.P.--Carolina First Corporation, Greenville, SC; *U.S. Public*, pg. 306
Hummers, William S., III, Chief Fin. Officer--Carolina First Bank, Greenville, SC; *U.S. Public*, pg. 306
Humphreys, Paul R., Chief Fin. Officer & Sr. V.P.-Fin.--Laidlaw Environmental Services, Inc., Columbia, SC; *U.S. Public*, pg. 975
Humphreys, Robert K., Chief Fin. Officer, Treas. & Sec.--Valley Detroit Diesel Allison, City of Industry, CA; *U.S. Private*, pg. 1132
Hunceker, Jay, V.P.-Fin.--Cal Emblem Labels, Inc., Fresno, CA; *U.S. Private*, pg. 199
Huneke, Wayne R., Chief Fin. Officer, Sr. V.P. & Treas.--ReliaStar Financial Corp., Minneapolis, MN; *U.S. Public*, pg. 1375
Huneycutt, Ronald G., Chief Fin. Officer & V.P.-Fin.--Hospital Staffing Services, Inc., Fort Lauderdale, FL; *U.S. Public*, pg. 840
Hunger, John E., Chief Fin. Officer & Treas.--World Shipping, Inc., Rocky River, OH; *U.S. Private*, pg. 1190
Hunley, Jim, Chief Fin. Officer & Treas.--Plains Co-op Oil Mill, Lubbock, TX; *U.S. Private*, pg. 868
Hunt, James K., Chief Fin. Officer, Exec. V.P. & Treas.--UST Corporation, Boston, MA; *U.S. Public*, pg. 1660
Hunt, James K., Chief Fin. Officer & Exec. V.P.--USTrust, Boston, MA; *U.S. Public*, pg. 1660
Hunt, Judith, Chief Fin. Officer--Whitecable, Liverpool, United Kingdom; *Int'l*, pg. 462
Hunt, Raymond, Chief Fin. Officer--Connecticut Spring & Stamping Corporation, Farmington, CT; *U.S. Private*, pg. 263
Hunt, Robert J., Chief Fin. Officer & Exec. V.P.--AutoZone, Inc., Memphis, TN; *U.S. Public*, pg. 150
Hunt, W. Derald, Chief Fin. Officer--Jones, Day, Reavis & Pogue, Cleveland, OH; *U.S. Private*, pg. 596
Hunt, William, Chief Fin. Officer & V.P.-Fin.--Spirol International Corp., Danielson, CT; *U.S. Private*, pg. 1026
Hunte, Alan L., Chief Fin. Officer--Trenwick Group Inc., Stamford, CT; *U.S. Public*, pg. 1634
Hunte, Alan L., Chief Fin. Officer, Exec. V.P. & Treas.--Trenwick America Reinsurance Corporation, Stamford, CT; *U.S. Public*, pg. 1634
Hunter, John R., Chief Fin. Officer & V.P.--A.E. Staley Manufacturing Co., Decatur, IL; *Int'l*, pg. 1356
Hunter, Nelson C., Chief Fin. Officer & Sr. V.P.--Greenstone Roberts Advertising, Melville, NY; *U.S. Public*, pg. 763
Hunter, R.J., Chief Fin. Officer--Bradford-White Corporation, Ambler, PA; *U.S. Private*, pg. 164
Hunter, Timothy, Chief Fin. Officer & V.P.--McInnes Steel Company, Corry, PA; *U.S. Private*, pg. 722
Huntsman, Barry N., Chief Fin. Officer & Treas.--Ambar, Inc., Lafayette, LA; *U.S. Private*, pg. 126
Huppi, Rolf, Chm. Bd. & Chief Exec. Officer--Zurich Insurance Company, Zurich, Switzerland; *Int'l*, pg. 1529
Hurley, Bill, Chief Fin. Officer & V.P.--Cybex International, Inc., Medway, MA; *U.S. Private*, pg. 1114
Hurley, Charles T., Chief Fin. Officer & Exec. V.P.--Meldrum & Fewsmith Communications Inc., Cleveland, OH; *U.S. Private*, pg. 730
Hurley, Edward, Chief Fin. Officer--Edgewater Steel Company, Oakmont, PA; *U.S. Private*, pg. 364
Hurley, James, Chief Fin. Officer & Sr. V.P.-Fin./MIS--Quality Stores Inc., Muskegon, MI; *U.S. Private*, pg. 899
Hurt, Douglas, Chief Fin. Officer & Sr. V.P.--Glaxo Wellcome Inc., Research Triangle Park, NC; *Int'l*, pg. 552
Husband, W.D., Sec. & Treas.--Canadian Timken Ltd., Saint Thomas, Canada; *U.S. Public*, pg. 1617
Husby, Philip G., Chief Fin. Officer & Sr. V.P.--Ogden Corporation, New York, NY; *U.S. Public*, pg. 1213
Huskey, James, Chief Fin. Officer--National Print Group, Inc., Chattanooga, TN; *U.S. Private*, pg. 785
Hussey, Kent J., Chief Fin. Officer & V.P.--RAYOVAC Corporation, Madison, WI; *U.S. Private*, pg. 912
Huston, Edwin A., Chief Fin. Officer & Sr. Exec. V.P.-Fin.--Ryder System, Inc., Miami, FL; *U.S. Public*, pg. 1413
Hutchings, Peter L., Chief Fin. Officer & Exec. V.P.--The Guardian Life Insurance Company of America, New York, NY; *U.S. Private*, pg. 486
Hutchins, Bruce, Chief Fin. Officer & Exec. V.P.--Alabama Power Co., Birmingham, AL; *U.S. Public*, pg. 1489
Hutchinson, M.J., Chief Fin. Officer--Metallgesellschaft Ltd., London, United Kingdom; *Int'l*, pg. 948
Huth, Nancy, Chief Fin. Officer--Famous Restaurants Inc., Scottsdale, AZ; *U.S. Private*, pg. 393
Hutl, G., Chief Fin. Officer--Siemens Ltd., Mumbai, India; *Int'l*, pg. 1247
Huttner, Jay, Chief Fin. Officer--Marquette Coppersmithing Co., Inc., Philadelphia, PA; *U.S. Private*, pg. 706
Huydhe, Christian, Chief Exec. Officer & Chief Fin. Officer--Interbrew Italia S.p.A., Comun Nuovo, Italy; *Int'l*, pg. 679
Huyett, John, Chief Fin. Officer--Avanti, Fremont, CA; *U.S. Public*, pg. 151
Huzl, James F., Chief Fin. Officer & Exec. V.P.--Hendrick Automotive Group, Charlotte, NC; *U.S. Private*, pg. 522
Hyatt, Philip M., Chief Fin. Officer & V.P.--Sundowner Offshore Services, Inc., Houston, TX; *U.S. Public*, pg. 1149
Hyde, Donald, Chief Fin. Officer--Arch Aluminium & Glass L.C., Tamarac, FL; *U.S. Private*, pg. 79
Hyland, Robert J., Chief Fin. Officer, V.P. & Treas.--Barclay White Incorporated, Berwyn, PA; *U.S. Private*, pg. 115
Hyvonen, Gunnel, Chief Fin. Officer--Imatra Steel Oy Ab, Helsinki, Finland; *Int'l*, pg. 863
Iaco, James V., Jr., Chief Fin. Officer & Sr. V.P.--Edison Mission Energy, Irvine, CA; *U.S. Public*, pg. 564
Iacovetti, Benedict J., Chief Fin. Officer--American Travellers Life Insurance Company, Bensalem, PA; *U.S. Public*, pg. 433
Iacovetti, Benedict J., Chief Fin. Officer--United General Life Insurance, Bensalem, PA; *U.S. Public*, pg. 433
Ian, Macmillan, Chief Fin. Officer--Societe Mecanique Automobile de l'est, Hagondange, France; *Int'l*, pg. 1020
Iapalucci, Sam, Chief Fin. Officer & Exec. V.P.--CH2M Hill Companies, Ltd., Greenwood Village, CO; *U.S. Private*, pg. 195
Iapalucci, Samuel H., Chief Fin. Officer & Treas.--CH2M Hill, Inc., Greenwood Village, CO; *U.S. Private*, pg. 195
Ibarbia, Ezequiel P., Chief Fin. Officer & Sr. V.P.--P.L. Porter Co., Woodland Hills, CA; *U.S. Private*, pg. 876
Ibarbia, Zeke, V.P.-Fin.--HR Textron, Valencia, CA; *U.S. Public*, pg. 1589
Ibeling, John, Chief Fin. Officer--Alberto-Culver International, Inc., Melrose Park, IL; *U.S. Public*, pg. 38
Ide, Willy, Chief Fin. Officer--Bekaert International Trade, Zwevegem, Belgium; *Int'l*, pg. 183
Igarashi, Osamu, Sr. V.P. -Corp. Plng. & Sr. Mng. Dir.--Japan Airlines Company, Ltd., Tokyo, Japan; *Int'l*, pg. 699
Ihlenfeld, Brad, Chief Fin. Officer & Sr. V.P.--Meridian Technology Leasing Services, Deerfield, IL; *U.S. Private*, *pg. 732*
Iida, Yaoki, Chief Fin. Officer--Tokyu Agency Inc., Tokyo, Japan; *Int'l*, pg. 1394
Iida, Michio, Chief Fin. Officer & Sr. Mng. Dir.--Fujisawa Pharmaceutical Co. Ltd., Osaka, Japan; *Int'l*, pg. 525
Illson, James E., Chief Fin. Officer & Sr. V.P.-Fin.--Merisel, Inc., El Segundo, CA; *U.S. Public*, pg. 1095
Imbler, Stephen, Chief Fin. Officer & Sr. V.P.--Arbor Software Corporation, Sunnyvale, CA; *U.S. Public*, pg. 127
Imbs, Robert, Chief Fin. Officer & V.P.-Fin.--Louis P. Ciminelli Construction Co. Inc., Buffalo, NY; *U.S. Private*, *pg. 239*
Imel, Robert, Chief Fin. Officer & Sr. V.P.--National Energy Group, Inc., Dallas, TX; *U.S. Public*, pg. 1156
Imperiale, Mark F., Pres., Chief Oper. Officer & Chief Fin. Officer--Data Broadcasting Corporation, Jackson, WY; *U.S. Public*, pg. 484
Imura, Kiminobu, Chief Fin. Officer--Shimadzu Scientific Instruments, Inc., Columbia, MD; *Int'l*, pg. 1232
Imura, T., Chief Fin. Officer--AP Techno Glass Company, Bellefontaine, OH; *Int'l*, pg. 84
Inbar, Doron, Chief Fin. Officer & Sr. V.P.--ECI Telecom Ltd., Petah Tiqwa, Israel; *Int'l*, pg. 643
Inciarte, Matias R., Vice Chm., Chief Fin. Officer & Exec. V.P.--Banco Santander, Madrid, Spain; *Int'l*, pg. 143
Indiver, Peter, Chief Fin. Officer & V.P.-Fin.--Inverness Corp., Fair Lawn, NJ; *U.S. Private*, pg. 574
Indiveri, Peter, Chief Fin. Officer--ERI Laboratories, Fair Lawn, NJ; *U.S. Private*, pg. 574
Indiviri, Peter, Chief Fin. Officer--Inverness UK LTD., Slough, United Kingdom; *U.S. Private*, pg. 574
Inenstrues, Hanson, Chief Fin. Officer--Hanson PLC, London, United Kingdom; *Int'l*, pg. 592
Infram, Bruce G., V.P. & Chief Fin. Officer--LVMH Moet Hennessy Louis Vuitton, New York, NY; *Int'l*, pg. 781
Ing, Dennis R., Chief Fin. Officer & V.P.-Fin.--Trimble Navigation Limited, Sunnyvale, CA; *U.S. Public*, pg. 1638
Ing, Dennis R., Chief Fin. Officer & V.P.-Fin.--Trimble Navigation Ltd., Texas, Austin, TX; *U.S. Public*, pg. 1638
Ing, Dennis R., Chief Fin. Officer--Trimble Navigation International Limited, Sunnyvale, CA; *U.S. Public*, pg. 1638
Ing, Dennis R., Chief Fin. Officer--Trimble Navigation International Foreign Sales Corporation, Sunnyvale, CA; *U.S. Public*, pg. 1638
Ingalls, Harold, Chief Fin. Officer, V.P. & Treas.--Rust International Inc., Birmingham, AL; *U.S. Public*, pg. 1366
Ingalls, Harold W., Chief Fin. Officer & V.P.--LaRoche Industries Inc., Atlanta, GA; *U.S. Private*, pg. 651
Ingalls, Henry A., Chief Fin. Officer, V.P. & Treas.--AgriBioTech, Inc., Las Vegas, NV; *U.S. Public*, pg. 28
Ingberg, Donald D., Chief Fin. Officer & V.P.--Light Signatures, Inc., Los Angeles, CA; *U.S. Public*, pg. 588
Ingemarson, Bo, Exec. V.P.-Fin. & Economy--Skanska AB, Danderyd, Sweden; *Int'l*, pg. 1260
Ingham, James W., Chief Fin. Officer & V.P.--Mentholatum Company, Buffalo, NY; *Int'l*, pg. 1126
Ingleman, John A., Chief Fin. Officer & V.P.--Hutchinson Technology Inc., Hutchinson, MN; *U.S. Public*, pg. 850
Ingleman, John A., Chief Fin. Officer--Hutchinson Technology Inc., Hutchinson, MN; *U.S. Public*, pg. 851
Ingman, Richard W., Chief Fin. Officer & Exec. V.P.--Pentair, Inc., Saint Paul, MN; *U.S. Public*, pg. 1273
Ingraham, Beverly, Chief Fin. Officer--Foley's, Houston, TX; *U.S. Public*, pg. 1063
Ingram, Charles, Chief Fin. Officer--Ziebart International Corporation, Troy, MI; *U.S. Private*, pg. 1205
Ingram, Chuck, Chief Fin. Officer--Ziebart Corp., Troy, MI; *U.S. Private*, pg. 1205
Ingram, Chuck, Chief Fin. Officer--Tidy Car International, Inc., Troy, MI; *U.S. Private*, pg. 1205
Ingram, Chuck, Chief Fin. Officer--Ziebart Canada, Inc., Concord, Canada; *U.S. Private*, pg. 1205
Ingram, James G., Chief Fin. Officer & V.P.--Ingram Paper Company, City of Industry, CA; *U.S. Public*, pg. 904
Ingram, Richard S., Jr., Chief Fin. Officer, Treas. & Sec.--T.A. Loving Company, Goldsboro, NC; *U.S. Private*, pg. 677
Inskeep, Stephen, V.P.-Fin., Admin--Gold Lance, Inc., Houston, TX; *U.S. Public*, pg. 1625
Intino, Tony, Chief Fin. Officer & Treas.--Power Designs, Inc., Danbury, CT; *U.S. Private*, pg. 878
Ippolito, Robert S., Chief Fin. Officer, Treas. & Sec.--Penn National Gaming, Inc., Wyomissing, PA; *U.S. Public*, pg. 1270
Irace, Greg, Chief Fin. Officer & V.P.-Fin.--Sanofi Pharmaceuticals, Inc., New York, NY; *Int'l*, pg. 445
Irick, John E., Exec. V.P.--McBride and Associates, Inc., Albuquerque, NM; *U.S. Private*, pg. 719
Irvine, Bob, Chief Fin. Officer--Tarragon Realty Investors, Dallas, TX; *U.S. Public*, pg. 1561
Irvine, Diane M., Chief Fin. Officer & V.P.-Fin.--Plum Creek Timber Co., L.P., Seattle, WA; *U.S. Public*, pg. 1311
Irwin, Adam J., Chief Fin. Officer--Bensons International Systems Pty. Ltd., Yagoona, Australia; *Int'l*, pg. 460
Irwin, Thomas S., Chief Fin. Officer & Exec. V.P.--HEICO Corporation, Hollywood, FL; *U.S. Public*, pg. 804
Isaacs, Denise, Chief Fin. Officer--The Sherwood Group, Inc., Jersey City, NJ; *U.S. Public*, pg. 1466
Isaacs, Roger, Chief Fin. Officer--Sharpe Dry Goods Co., Inc., Checotah, OK; *U.S. Private*, pg. 990
Isacke, John F., Chief Fin. Officer & Sr. V.P.--Consumers Water Company, Portland, ME; *U.S. Public*, pg. 438
Isacsson, Lars, Chief Fin. Officer & Exec. V.P.--Skandinaviska Enskilda Banken, Stockholm, Sweden; *Int'l*, pg. 1258
Ishibashi, Yasuji, Chief Fin. Officer & Sr. Mng. Dir.--Ishihara Sangyo Kaisha, Ltd., Osaka, Japan; *Int'l*, pg. 689
Ishii, Seitaro, Chief Fin. Offier & V.P.--Applied Materials Japan, Inc., Chiba, Japan; *U.S. Public*, pg. 123
Iskra, Kathleen H., Chief Fin. Officer, V.P. & Treas.--Nextlink Communications Inc., Bellevue, WA; *U.S. Public*, *pg. 1181*
Israel, G.J., Chief Fin. Officer, V.P.-Fin. & Treas.--Detrex Corporation, Southfield, MI; *U.S. Public*, pg. 501
Itkin, Myles R., Chief Fin. Officer, Sr. V.P. & Treas.--Overseas Shipholding Group, Inc., New York, NY; *U.S. Public*, pg. 1236
Itoh, Yuji, Chief Fin. Officer & Mng. Dir.--Kyocera Corporation, Kyoto, Japan; *Int'l*, pg. 775
Iverson, Kitty, Chief Fin. Officer-Rosemount Measurement Div.--Rosemount Measurement Division, Eden Prairie, MN; *U.S. Public*, pg. 574
Iwasa, Yoshito, Sr. Mng. Dir--Sakata Seed Corporation, Yokohama, Japan; *Int'l*, pg. 1178

Jaakonaho, Mauri, Exec. V.P.-Fin.--Valmet Corporation, Helsinki, Finland; *Int'l*, pg. 1447

Jabbar, Masood A., Chief Fin. Officer & V.P.-Fin.--Sun Microsystems Computer Corporation, Mountain View, CA; *U.S. Public*, pg. 1531

Jabrialsson, Jan, Chief Fin. Officer--Swedish Match S.A., Stockholm, Sweden; *Int'l*, pg. 1328

Jack, James E., Chief Fin. Officer & Sr. Exec. V.P.--Associates Financial Services Corporation, Dallas, TX; *U.S. Public*, pg. 663

Jackels, Curtis R., Chief Fin. Officer--Photo Control Corporation, Minneapolis, MN; *U.S. Public*, pg. 1292

Jackland, Bob, Chief Fin. Officer--Teledyne Continental Motors, Mobile, AL; *U.S. Public*, pg. 43

Jackson, Bruce, Chief Fin. Officer--The Calgary Sun, Calgary, Canada; *Int'l*, pg. 1320

Jackson, Bruce A., Chief Fin. Officer & V.P.-Fin.--Cedar Fair, L.P., Sandusky, OH; *U.S. Public*, pg. 319

Jackson, C.T., Chief Fin. Officer & V.P.--Maguire Oil Co., Dallas, TX; *U.S. Private*, pg. 696

Jackson, D.C., Chief Fin. Officer--Janssen-Cilag Ltd., High Wycombe, United Kingdom; *U.S. Public*, pg. 929

Jackson, Darren, Chief Fin. Officer--Carson Pirie Scott & Co., Milwaukee, WI; *U.S. Public*, pg. 309

Jackson, Frederick H., Chief Fin. Officer & V.P.-Fin.--La-Z-Boy Incorporated, Monroe, MI; *U.S. Public*, pg. 972

Jackson, Kenneth G., Chief Fin. Officer & V.P.--Shaw Industries, Inc., Dalton, GA; *U.S. Public*, pg. 1464

Jackson, Mark A., Chief Fin. Officer & Sr. V.P.--Snyder Oil Corporation, Fort Worth, TX; *U.S. Public*, pg. 1481

Jackson, Richard, Chief Fin. Officer--J.B. Rodgers Mechanical Contractors, Phoenix, AZ; *U.S. Private*, pg. 939

Jackson, Robert, V.P.-Fin.--The World Almanac, Mahwah, NJ; *U.S. Public*, pg. 1328

Jackson, Robert C., V.P.-Fin.--Rockefeller Center Development Corporation, New York, NY; *Int'l*, pg. 873

Jackson, Robert R., Chief Fin. Officer--Zippo Manufacturing Company, Bradford, PA; *U.S. Private*, pg. 1207

Jackson, Robert T., Chief Fin. Officer--American Century Companies, Inc., Kansas City, MO; *U.S. Private*, pg. 52

Jackson, Robert T., Chief Fin. Officer & Sr. V.P.--American Century Investments, Kansas City, MO; *U.S. Private*, pg. 52

Jackson, W. Stephen, Chief Fin. Officer & Treas.--Mesa Air Group, Las Vegas, NV; *U.S. Public*, pg. 1098

Jacob, Ellis, Chief Fin. Officer & Exec. V.P.--Cineplex Odeon Corporation, Toronto, Canada; *Int'l*, pg. 292

Jacobi, Jorg, Treas.--M.L.&S. Werbeagentur GmbH, Dusseldorf, Germany; *Int'l*, pg. 827

Jacobs, David, Chief Fin. Officer--Rosewood Property Company, Dallas, TX; *U.S. Private*, pg. 946

Jacobs, Rodney L., Vice Chm. & Chief Fin. Officer--Wells Fargo Bank, National Assn., San Francisco, CA; *U.S. Public*, pg. 1753

Jacobsen, John, Chief Fin. Officer--Esselte Meto A/S, Oslo, Norway; *Int'l*, pg. 461

Jacobsen, Per G., Chief Fin. Officer--Scancem International ANS, Oslo, Norway; *Int'l*, pg. 1201

Jacobson, J.L., Chief Fin. Officer--Blue Chip Stamps, Los Angeles, CA; *U.S. Public*, pg. 217

Jacobson, Ken, Chief Fin. Officer, Treas. & Sec.--Idea Engineering & Fabricating, Detroit, MI; *U.S. Private*, pg. 557

Jacobson, Robert P., Chief Fin. Officer, Sr. V.P. & Treas.--Everest Reinsurance Holdings, Liberty Corner, NJ; *U.S. Public*, pg. 597

Jacobson, Robert P., Chief Fin. Officer--Everest National Insurance Co., Liberty Corner, NJ; *U.S. Public*, pg. 597

Jacobson, Robert P., Chief Fin. Officer--Everest Reinsurance Co., Liberty Corner, NJ; *U.S. Public*, pg. 597

Jacobsson, Bo, Chief Fin. Officer & Exec. V.P.--Trelleborg AB, Trelleborg, Sweden; *Int'l*, pg. 1419

Jacobstein, David M., V.P.-Admin. & Legal--Wilmorite, Inc., Rochester, NY; *U.S. Private*, pg. 1180

Jacoby, Andrea, Chief Fin. Officer--MBT Architecture, San Francisco, CA; *U.S. Private*, pg. 686

Jacowitz, Rob, Chief Fin. Officer--Harvest Partners Inc., New York, NY; *U.S. Private*, pg. 508

Jacques, Jerome C., Chief Fin. Officer, Sr. V.P. & Treas.--Guardsmark, Inc., Memphis, TN; *U.S. Private*, pg. 486

Jaeger, Stuart, Controller--Henry I. Siegel Company, Inc., New York, NY; *U.S. Private*, pg. 998

Jaeggi, Kenneth G., Chief Fin. Officer & Sr. V.P.--Symbol Technologies, Inc., Holtsville, NY; *U.S. Public*, pg. 1546

Jaehnest, Frank, Chief Fin. Officer--W.H. Brady Co., Milwaukee, WI; *U.S. Public*, pg. 250

Jahnke, Mark W., Chief Fin. Officer--Lifetime Doors Inc., Farmington, MI; *U.S. Private*, pg. 666

Jain, Karan, Controller--Interbath, Inc., City of Industry, CA; *U.S. Private*, pg. 566

James, Catherine B., Chief Fin. Officer--Strategic Distribution Inc., Bensalem, PA; *U.S. Public*, pg. 1523

James, David, Chief Fin. Officer & V.P.-Fin. & Treas.--Joe E. Woods, Inc., Mesa, AZ; *U.S. Private*, pg. 1187

James, George, Chief Fin. Officer & Sr. V.P.--Levi Strauss & Co., San Francisco, CA; *U.S. Private*, pg. 662

James, George L., III, Chief Fin. Officer--BetzDearborn Inc., Trevose, PA; *U.S. Public*, pg. 226

James, Henry D., Chief Fin. Officer & V.P.--Berlitz International, Inc., Princeton, NJ; *U.S. Public*, pg. 221

James, Stephen J., Chief Fin. Officer & Chief Acctg. Officer--Caprius, Inc., Wilmington, MA; *U.S. Public*, pg. 303

James, Tony, Chief Fin. Officer & Treas.--Eagle Iron Works, Des Moines, IA; *U.S. Private*, pg. 354

Jamet, Jane, Chief Oper. Officer & Treas.--Sexton Can Co., Inc., Cambridge, MA; *U.S. Private*, pg. 988

Jamieson, Brian W., Chief Fin. Officer & V.P.-Fin.--Jannock Limited, Toronto, Canada; *Int'l*, pg. 698

Jamieson, Christopher W., V.P. & Controller--Unicorp Canada Corporation, Toronto, Canada; *Int'l*, pg. 1433

Jamieson, Christopher W., Sr. V.P.-Fin. & Chief Fin. Officer--Union Energy Inc., Toronto, Canada; *Int'l*, pg. 1492

Jamieson, Patricia J., Chief Fin. Officer--McDonald & Company Investments, Inc., Cleveland, OH; *U.S. Public*, pg. 1068

Jamkus, Tom, Chief Fin. Officer--Purity Wholesale Grocers, Boca Raton, FL; *U.S. Private*, pg. 896

Janavey, Harry, Chief Fin. Officer & Sr. V.P.--The Chapman Agency, New York, NY; *U.S. Private*, pg. 1197

Jandernoa, Rex A., Chief Fin. Officer & V.P.--Peace Industries Inc., Rolling Meadows, IL; *U.S. Private*, pg. 845

Jandernoa, Rex A., Chief Fin. Officer--Spotnails, Rolling Meadows, IL; *U.S. Private*, pg. 845

Janey, T. Michael, Chief Fin. Officer, Sr. V.P. & Treas.--Datamax International Corporation, Orlando, FL; *U.S. Private*, pg. 313

Janochoski, Thomas A., V.P. & Sec.--Great Northern Iron Ore Properties, Saint Paul, MN; *U.S. Public*, pg. 760

Janofsky, William, Controller--Van Son Holland Ink Corp. of America, Mineola, NY; *U.S. Private*, pg. 1133

Jansen Kraemer, Harry M., Jr., Pres., Chief Fin. Officer & Sr. V.P.--Baxter International Inc., Deerfield, IL; *U.S. Public*, pg. 196

Jansen Kraemer, Harry M., Jr., Sr. V.P. & Chief Fin. Officer--Baxter Healthcare Corporation, Deerfield, IL; *U.S. Public*, pg. 196

Janson, Kenneth R., Chief Fin. Officer, Exec. V.P.-Fin. & Treas.--D & N Financial Corporation, Hancock, MI; *U.S. Public*, pg. 472

Janssen, Berndt, Chief Fin. Officer--Landesverlags und Druckgesellschaft mbH - Mecklenburg & Co. KG, Schwerin, Germany; *Int'l*, pg. 233

Janssen, Kathy, Chief Fin. Officer & Sr. V.P.--Contract Interiors Inc., Taylor, MI; *U.S. Private*, pg. 270

Jansson, G., Chief Fin. Officer--Assa Abloy AB, Stockholm, Sweden; *Int'l*, pg. 17

Jantz, Kenneth M., Chief Fin. Officer--Kiewit Construction Group, Inc., Omaha, NE; *U.S. Private*, pg. 619

Janutis, Ray, Chief Fin. Officer--Creative Publications, Mountain View, CA; *U.S. Private*, pg. 288

Janzaruk, Bill, V.P.-Fin. & Admin.--Hill-Rom Company, Inc., Batesville, IN; *U.S. Public*, pg. 828

Japha, Barbara, Chief Fin. Officer, V.P. & Treas.--U S West Inc., Englewood, CO; *U.S. Public*, pg. 1688

Jarc, Frank, Chief Fin. Officer & Exec. V.P.--Viking Office Products, Torrance, CA; *U.S. Public*, pg. 1720

Jarc, Frank R., Chief Fin. Officer & Exec. V.P.--R.R. Donnelley & Sons Company, Chicago, IL; *U.S. Public*, pg. 517

Jaros, Robert E., Chief Fin. Officer--Peterson American Corp., Southfield, MI; *U.S. Private*, pg. 857

Jarrick, Alan, Acting Chief Fin. Officer--Candle Corporation, Santa Monica, CA; *U.S. Private*, pg. 204

Jarvis, Daniel O., Chief Fin. Officer & Exec. V.P.--Intrawest Corporation, Vancouver, Canada; *Int'l*, pg. 685

Jarvis, Mark E., Chief Fin. Officer & Sr. V.P.--Tuesday Morning Corporation, Dallas, TX; *U.S. Public*, pg. 1644

Jarzebski, Jergen, Chief Fin. Officer--EURO RSCG, Dusseldorf, Germany; *Int'l*, pg. 602

Jasinkiewicz, Ken, Chief Fin. Officer--Wakefern Food Corporation, Elizabeth, NJ; *U.S. Private*, pg. 1146

Jasionowicz, J.J., Chief Fin. Officer--Bright Star Industries, Inc., Wilkes-Barre, PA; *U.S. Public*, pg. 1341

Jaska, James M., Chief Fin. Officer & Treas.--Tetra Tech, Inc., Pasadena, CA; *U.S. Public*, pg. 1582

Jaster, Kyle M., Chief Fin. Officer, Treas. & Sec.--Mooney Aircraft Corporation, Kerrville, TX; *U.S. Private*, pg. 759

Jastrow, Kenneth M., II, Chief Fin. Officer & Grp. V.P.--Temple-Inland Inc., Diboll, TX; *U.S. Public*, pg. 1574

Jatzen-Smith, Barbara, Chief Fin. Officer--Center Partners Management LLC, New York, NY; *U.S. Private*, pg. 222

Jay, Dan, Pres., Chief Exec. Officer & Chief Fin. Officer--Campmor Inc., Upper Saddle River, NJ; *U.S. Private*, pg. 204

Je, Man-Ho, Chief Fin. Officer--Ssangyong Information & Communication Corporation, Seoul, Korea; *Int'l*, pg. 1292

Jean-Pierre, Bertrand, Chief Fin. Officer--Salomon S.A., Annecy, France; *Int'l*, pg. 1181

Jean, J. Wayne, Chief Fin. Officer--HMT Inc., Houston, TX; *U.S. Public*, pg. 914

Jeanson, Daniel, Fin. Dir.--Crehalet Pouget Poussielgues, Paris, France; *U.S. Private*, pg. 1152

Jeens, Robert, Grp. Dir.-Fin.--Woolwich Plc, Bexley, United Kingdom; *Int'l*, pg. 1514

Jeffares, Robert T., Chief Fin. Officer & Exec. V.P.--Great Lakes Chemical Corporation, West Lafayette, IN; *U.S. Public*, pg. 760

Jeffrey, Richard, Chief Fin. Officer--Coach, New York, NY; *U.S. Public*, pg. 1433

Jeffrey, Thomas W., Chief Fin. Officer & Exec. V.P.--Atlantic Gulf Communities Corporation, Miami, FL; *U.S. Public*, pg. 144

Jehle, Kathryn A., Chief Fin. Officer & Sr. V.P.--Comshare, Incorporated, Ann Arbor, MI; *U.S. Public*, pg. 425

Jen, Enoch, Chief Fin. Officer, V.P.-Fin. & Treas.--Gentex Corporation, Zeeland, MI; *U.S. Public*, pg. 731

Jenkins, Bobby G., Chief Fin. Officer--Marvel Entertainment Group, New York, NY; *U.S. Public*, pg. 1052

Jenkins, Derek, Chief Fin. Officer--RMC Group p.l.c., Egham, United Kingdom; *Int'l*, pg. 1078

Jenkins, Joseph R., Chief Fin. Officer & Exec. V.P.--Heilig-Meyers Company, Richmond, VA; *U.S. Public*, pg. 804

Jenkins, Linda C., Chief Fin. Officer & V.P.--K-III Media Group, New York, NY; *U.S. Public*, pg. 1328

Jenkins, M., Treas.--Thruway Fasteners Inc., North Tonawanda, NY; *U.S. Private*, pg. 1084

Jenkins, Paul, Chief Fin. Officer--Brann Ltd., Cirencester, United Kingdom; *Int'l*, pg. 212

Jenkins, Richard N., Chief Fin. Officer--Aetna Bearing Company, Chicago, IL; *U.S. Private*, pg. 25

Jenkins, Robert M., Pres. & Chief Fin. Officer--Specialty Industries, Inc., Red Lion, PA; *U.S. Private*, pg. 1022

Jenkins, Thomas M., Chief Fin. Officer, Grp. V.P. & Treas-DPL, Inc.--DPL Inc., Dayton, OH; *U.S. Public*, pg. 473

Jenkins, Thomas M., Chief Fin. Officer & Grp. V.P.--Dayton Power & Light Co., Dayton, OH; *U.S. Public*, pg. 473

Jenner, Ray, Chief Fin. Officer & V.P.--Nord Resources Corporation, Albuquerque, NM; *U.S. Public*, pg. 1188

Jennings, Frank L., Chief Fin. Officer, Chief Acctg. Officer & V.P.--American Educational Products, Boulder, CO; *U.S. Public*, pg. 71

Jennings, James, Chief Fin. Officer--Loomis-Fargo & Co., Houston, TX; *U.S. Public*, pg. 245

Jennings, Monty, Chief Fin. Officer & V.P.-Fin.--Hubbard Scientific, Chippewa Falls, WI; *U.S. Public*, pg. 71

Jennings, Robert G., Chief Fin. Officer & V.P.-Fin.--Woodhead Industries, Inc., Buffalo Grove, IL; *U.S. Public*, pg. 1776

Jennings, William, V.P.-Fin.--Tanning Research Labs., Inc., Ormond Beach, FL; *U.S. Private*, pg. 1068

Jensen, Gary, Chief Fin. Officer--John B. Sanfilippo & Son, Inc., Elk Grove Village, IL; *U.S. Public*, pg. 1431

Jensen, Kenneth R., Chief Fin. Officer, Sr. Exec. V.P. & Treas.--Fiserv, Inc., Brookfield, WI; *U.S. Public*, pg. 647

Jensen, Mary F., Chief Fin. Officer & Treas.--Venturian Corp., Hopkins, MN; *U.S. Public*, pg. 1716

Jensen, Phillip, Chief Fin. Officer--Kaiser Permanente, California Division, Oakland, CA; *U.S. Private*, pg. 605

Jensen, Steen, Chief Fin. Officer--Siemens A/S, Ballerup, Denmark; *Int'l*, pg. 1247

Jenson, Warren, Chief Fin. Officer & Sr. V.P.--National Broadcasting Co., Inc., New York, NY; *U.S. Public*, pg. 712

Jeon, Woo-kyung, Chief Fin. Officer--Ssangyong Fire & Marine Insurance Co., Ltd., Seoul, Korea; *Int'l*, pg. 1292

Jepsen, Edward, Chief Fin. Officer & Exec. V.P.--Times Fiber Communications, Inc., Wallingford, CT; *U.S. Private*, pg. 629

Jepsen, Edward G., Chief Fin. Officer & Exec. V.P.--Amphenol Corporation, Wallingford, CT; *U.S. Private*, pg. 629

Jermin, Stewart, Chief Fin. Officer--Iggesund Paperboard (Workington) Ltd., Workington, United Kingdom; *Int'l*, pg. 886

Jerram, J.J., Vice Chm. & Chief Fin. Officer--British Railways Board, London, United Kingdom; *Int'l*, pg. 220

Jersenius, Tommy, Chief Fin. Officer--FFV Aerotech AB, Linkoping, Sweden; *Int'l*, pg. 276

Jeske, Steve, Chief Fin. Officer--PetCare Plus, Inc., Aurora, IL; *U.S. Private*, pg. 856

Jespersen, Jesper, Chief Fin. Officer--Sonofon, Horsholm, Denmark; *Int'l*, pg. 537

Jessick, Dave, Chief Fin. Officer--Fred Meyer Incorporated, Portland, OR; *U.S. Public*, pg. 1103

Jessick, Dave, Chief Fin. Officer & Sr. V.P.--Smith's Food & Drug Centers, Inc., Salt Lake City, UT; *U.S. Public*, pg. 1103

Jessick, David R., Chief Fin. Officer & Sr. V.P.-Fin.--Fred Meyer Stores, Portland, OR; *U.S. Public*, pg. 1103

Jessup, Catherine K., Chief Fin. Officer--The Topps Company, Inc., New York, NY; *U.S. Public*, pg. 1621

Jeub, Michael L., Chief Fin. Officer, Sr. V.P. & Treas.--Jenny Craig, Inc., La Jolla, CA; *U.S. Public*, pg. 926

Jewell, Stanley R., Chief Fin. Officer & V.P.-Fin.--RHC/Spacemaster Corporation, Melrose Park, IL; *U.S. Private*, pg. 904

Jewett, S., Chief Fin. Officer--Amplicon, Inc., Santa Ana, CA; *U.S. Public*, pg. 104

Jiropinyo, Pilik, Chief Fin. Officer & Exec. V.P.--JMP Newcor Holdings Inc., Northbrook, IL; *Int'l*, pg. 1025

Jirsa, James, Chief Fin. Officer & Exec. V.P.--A. Epstein and Sons, Intl., Inc., Chicago, IL; *U.S. Private*, pg. 379

Jobe, Warren Y., Chief Fin. Officer, Exec. V.P. & Treas.--Georgia Power Co., Atlanta, GA; *U.S. Public*, pg. 1490

Johannisson, Alf, Chief Fin. Officer--Janssen-Cilag AB, Sollentuna, Sweden; *U.S. Public*, pg. 929

Johansen, Erling, Chief Fin. Officer--Nordsten, Skive, Denmark; *Int'l*, pg. 1386

Johansson, Henry, Chief Fin. Officer--Holmen Paper AB, Norrkoping, Sweden; *Int'l*, pg. 885

Johansson, Lars-Eric, Chief Fin. Officer & Sr. V.P.--Falconbridge Limited, Toronto, Canada; *Int'l*, pg. 433

Johansson, Nils A., Chief Fin. Officer & Sr. V.P.--Bell & Howell Holdings, Skokie, IL; *U.S. Public*, pg. 201

John, Francis D., Pres., Chief Exec. Officer & Chief Fin. Officer--Key Energy Group Inc., East Brunswick, NJ; *U.S. Public*, pg. 953

John, Michael, Chief Fin. Officer & V.P.--Vulcan Iron Works, Inc., Detroit, MI; *U.S. Private*, pg. 1144

Johns, John D., Chief Fin. Officer & Exec. V.P.--Protective Life Insurance Co., Birmingham, AL; *U.S. Public*, pg. 1336

Johnsey, Walter F., Chief Fin. Officer, Sr. Exec. V.P. & Treas.--Drummond Company, Inc., Jasper, AL; *U.S. Private*, pg. 343

Johnson, Bradley K., Chief Fin. Officer, Chief Admin. Officer & Sr. V.P.--Lands' End, Inc., Dodgeville, WI; *U.S. Public*, pg. 977

Johnson, Bud, Exec. V.P. & Chief Fin. Officer--F.A.O. Schwarz, New York, NY; *Int'l*, pg. 750

Johnson, Charles, Chief Fin. Officer & V.P.-Fin.--TimeMed Labeling Systems, Inc., Burr Ridge, IL; *U.S. Private*, pg. 1087

Johnson, Claude, Pres, Chief Exec. Officer & Chief Fin. Officer--Research, Incorporated, Eden Prairie, MN; *U.S. Public*, pg. 1382

Johnson, D.A., Chief Fin. Officer & Mng. Dir.--Fine Art Developments plc, Bradford, United Kingdom; *Int'l*, pg. 485

Johnson, Dale H., Chief Fin. Officer--Medical Graphics Corp., Saint Paul, MN; *U.S. Public*, pg. 1080

Johnson, Dale M., Chief Fin. Officer--Medtech Inc., Jackson, WY; *U.S. Private*, pg. 728

Johnson, Daryl P., Chief Fin. Officer & Exec. V.P.--Response Oncology, Inc., Memphis, TN; *U.S. Public*, pg. 1449

Johnson, David, Chief Fin. Officer--Johnson & Towers, Inc., Mount Laurel, NJ; *U.S. Private*, pg. 590
Johnson, Donnie, Chief Fin. Officer--Brookshire Bros., Ltd., Lufkin, TX; *U.S. Private*, pg. 172
Johnson, Edwin D., Chief Fin. Officer & Sr. V.P.--MasTec, Inc., Miami, FL; *U.S. Public*, pg. 1055
Johnson, Frank, Chief Fin. Officer, Exec. V.P. & Treas.--Today's Man, Inc., Moorestown, NJ; *U.S. Public*, pg. 1619
Johnson, Gerard G., Chief Fin. Officer & V.P.-Fin.--VF Corporation, Wyomissing, PA; *U.S. Public*, pg. 1702
Johnson, Glenn, V.P., Controller & Treas.--Horizon Air Industries, Seattle, WA; *U.S. Public*, pg. 35
Johnson, Gordon, Asst. Treas.--The Stride Rite Corporation, Lexington, MA; *U.S. Public*, pg. 1524
Johnson, Grant W., Chief Fin. Officer & Sr. V.P.--Dep Corporation, Rancho Dominguez, CA; *U.S. Public*, pg. 500
Johnson, Greg A., Controller & Treas.--F.H. Stoltze Land & Lumber Company, Saint Paul, MN; *U.S. Private*, pg. 1044
Johnson, J. Fred, Chief Fin. Officer, Exec. V.P. & Treas.--Piccadilly Cafeterias, Inc., Baton Rouge, LA; *U.S. Public*, pg. 1294
Johnson, James R., Chief Fin. Officer--Premier Industries, Inc., Tacoma, WA; *U.S. Private*, pg. 881
Johnson, Jeff, Chief Fin. Officer, Treas. & Sec.--Evans Industries, Inc., Detroit, MI; *U.S. Private*, pg. 385
Johnson, Kent, Chief Fin. Officer & Asst. Treas.--Paddock Publications, Inc., Arlington Heights, IL; *U.S. Private*, pg. 833
Johnson, La Don, Chief Fin. Officer--Garst Seed Company, Slater, IA; *Int'l*, pg. 1524
Johnson, Les, Chief Fin. Officer--Rexdale Plant, Rexdale, Canada; *Int'l*, pg. 761
Johnson, M.O., Chief Fin. Officer, V.P. & Treas.--Andersen Corporation, Bayport, MN; *U.S. Private*, pg. 71
Johnson, Martin, Chief Fin. Officer & Sr. V.P.--Technology Solutions Company (TSC), Chicago, IL; *U.S. Public*, pg. 1564
Johnson, Mercedes, Chief Fin. Officer & V.P.-Fin.--Lam Research Corporation, Fremont, CA; *U.S. Public*, pg. 975
Johnson, P. Randy, Chief Fin. Officer & V.P.-Fin.--Jaymark, Inc., San Diego, CA; *U.S. Private*, pg. 584
Johnson, Patricia, Chief Fin. Officer & Gen. Mgr.--MGM Grand Australia Pty, Ltd., Darwin, Australia; *U.S. Public*, pg. 1027
Johnson, Peter, Chief Fin. Officer--Bestform Foundations, Inc., Long Island City, NY; *U.S. Private*, pg. 140
Johnson, Peter T., Mng. Dir.-Fin. & Secretariat Div.--Henderson Administration Group PLC, London, United Kingdom; *Int'l*, pg. 609
Johnson, Philip H., V.P.-Admin. & Fin.--Holt Hosiery Mills, Inc., Burlington, NC; *U.S. Private*, pg. 536
Johnson, Reid, Chief Fin. Officer & Exec. V.P.--Musicland Group Inc., Minnetonka, MN; *U.S. Public*, pg. 1142
Johnson, Reid, Chief Fin. Officer & Sr. V.P.--Woolworth Corporation, New York, NY; *U.S. Public*, pg. 1777
Johnson, Richard, Chief Fin. Officer--Bobit Publishing Company, Torrance, CA; *U.S. Private*, pg. 154
Johnson, Richard, Chief Fin. Officer & Treas.--WHG Resorts & Casinos, Carolina, PR; *U.S. Public*, pg. 1265
Johnson, Richard, Chief Fin. Officer--Williams Hospitality Group Inc., Carolina, PR; *U.S. Public*, pg. 1265
Johnson, Robert A., Dir.-Fin.--Ridg-U-Rak, Inc., North East, PA; *U.S. Private*, pg. 930
Johnson, Robert K., Chief Fin. Officer--Century Furniture Industries, Hickory, NC; *U.S. Private*, pg. 226
Johnson, S.A., Sec. & Treas.--WRR Environmental Services Co., Inc., Eau Claire, WI; *U.S. Public*, pg. 1792
Johnson, Stephen T., Chief Fin. Officer, V.P. & Treas.--Acuson Corporation, Mountain View, CA; *U.S. Public*, pg. 18
Johnson, Victor, Chief Fin. Officer, V.P.-Fin.--Reinke Manufacturing Co., Inc., Deshler, NE; *U.S. Private*, pg. 920
Johnson, William, Chief Fin. Officer & Exec. V.P.--Camping World, Inc., Bowling Green, KY; *U.S. Private*, pg. 204
Johnson, William, V.P.-Fin.--LNW Networks, New Providence, NJ; *U.S. Public*, pg. 276
Johnson, William A., Jr., Chief Fin. Officer & Treas.--Toymax International Inc., Plainview, NY; *U.S. Public*, pg. 1626
Johnsson, Christer, Chief Fin. Officer--Ikea Svenska AB, Almhult, Sweden; *Int'l*, pg. 660
Johnston, Fred B., II, Chm. Bd. & Chief Exec. Officer--Fred B. Johnston Company, Inc., Chapin, SC; *U.S. Private*, pg. 595
Johnston, Mark K., V.P.-Fin. & Admin.--Dale Carnegie Training, New York, NY; *U.S. Private*, pg. 308
Johnston, Mike D., Chief Fin. Officer & V.P.--Scott & Stringfellow Financial, Inc., Richmond, VA; *U.S. Public*, pg. 1445
Johnston, Mike D., Chief Fin. Officer & V.P.--Scott & Stringfellow, Inc., Richmond, VA; *U.S. Public*, pg. 1445
Johnston, R., Chief Fin. Officer--Alexander Drew & Sons Ltd., Rochdale, United Kingdom; *Int'l*, pg. 798
Johnston, Steven J., Chief Fin. Officer & V.P.--State Automobile Mutual Insurance Co., Columbus, OH; *U.S. Private*, pg. 1036
Johnstone, Aidan J., Chief Fin. Officer--Milk Products Holdings (Middle East) EC, Manama, Bahrain; *Int'l*, pg. 923
Joki, Vilho, Chief Fin. Officer--Comstock Canada Ltd., Burlington, Canada; *U.S. Public*, pg. 572
Jokiel, Peter, Chief Fin. Officer & Sr. V.P.--CNA Insurance Companies, Chicago, IL; *U.S. Public*, pg. 1010
Joncas, Gerard, Chief Fin. Officer--Cashway Building Centres Ltd., Port Hope, Canada; *Int'l*, pg. 274
Joneby, Robert, Chief Fin. Officer--Skanska Maskin AB, Danderyd, Sweden; *Int'l*, pg. 1261
Jones, Barry, Chief Fin. Officer--First Brands Africa (Pty) Ltd., Johannesburg, South Africa; *U.S. Public*, pg. 627
Jones, Bob, Chief Fin. Officer & Sr. V.P.-Opers.--Koh-I-Noor, Inc., Bloomsbury, NJ; *U.S. Private*, pg. 629
Jones, Carolyn, Chief Fin. Officer & Treas.--Hilb, Rogal and Hamilton Company, Glen Allen, VA; *U.S. Public*, pg. 826
Jones, Charles L., Chief Fin. Officer & Sr. V.P.--Country Life Insurance Company, Bloomington, IL; *U.S. Private*, pg. 278
Jones, Charles L., Chief Fin. Officer--Country Investors Life Assurance Company, Bloomington, IL; *U.S. Private*, pg. 279
Jones, Charles L., Chief Fin. Officer & Sr. V.P.--Country Mutual Insurance Company, Bloomington, IL; *U.S. Private*, pg. 279
Jones, Charles L., Chief Fin. Officer& Sr. V.P.--CC Services, Bloomington, IL; *U.S. Private*, pg. 279
Jones, Craig R., Chief Fin. Officer & V.P.--Electro Rent Corporation, Van Nuys, CA; *U.S. Public*, pg. 568
Jones, Eric, First V.P. & Treas.--BFCE New York, New York, NY; *Int'l*, pg. 161
Jones, Fred R., Chief Fin. Officer & Sr. V.P.--Joy Mining Machinery, Warrendale, PA; *U.S. Public*, pg. 789
Jones, Garry, Chief Fin. Officer, Exec. V.P. & Asst. Treas.--Espey Mfg. & Electronics Corp., Saratoga Springs, NY; *U.S. Public*, pg. 592
Jones, Glenn C., Chief Fin. Officer & Sr. V.P.--Sierra Semiconductor, San Jose, CA; *U.S. Public*, pg. 1470
Jones, James A., Chief Fin. Officer & V.P.-Fin.--Hayes Corporation, Norcross, GA; *U.S. Public*, pg. 800
Jones, James A., Chief Fin. Officer & V.P.--Hayes Microcomputer Products, Inc., Norcross, GA; *U.S. Public*, *pg. 801*
Jones, James E., Chief Fin. Officer, Treas. & Sec.--Modern Welding Co., Inc., Owensboro, KY; *U.S. Private*, pg. 755
Jones, James P., Chief Fin. Officer & V.P.--Edward Don & Company, North Riverside, IL; *U.S. Private*, pg. 339
Jones, Jay, Chief Fin. Officer--American Marketing Industries, Inc., Kansas City, MO; *U.S. Private*, pg. 58
Jones, Jeff, Chief Fin. Officer--ShopKo Stores, Inc., Green Bay, WI; *U.S. Public*, pg. 1467
Jones, Jerry, Chief Fin. Officer & Mgr.-Opers.--Jones Blair Company, Dallas, TX; *U.S. Private*, pg. 596
Jones, Jimmy R., Chief Fin. Officer, Sr. V.P. & Treas.--Attorneys' Title Insurance Fund, Orlando, FL; *U.S. Private*, pg. 98
Jones, Jo, Chief Fin. Officer & Mgr. Info. Systems--Nady Systems, Inc., Emeryville, CA; *U.S. Private*, pg. 773
Jones, Judith A., Chief Fin. Officer--Jones Medical Industries Inc., Saint Louis, MO; *U.S. Public*, pg. 933
Jones, Maureen A., Treas.--Petroleum & Resources Corp., Baltimore, MD; *U.S. Public*, pg. 1280
Jones, Maureen A., Chief Fin. Officer--Adams Express Co., Baltimore, MD; *U.S. Public*, pg. 1280
Jones, N.S., Chief Fin. Officer--Hepworth Minerals and Chemicals Limited, Sandbach, United Kingdom; *Int'l*, pg. 615
Jones, Patricia, Chief Fin. Officer--Stiles Corporation, Fort Lauderdale, FL; *U.S. Private*, pg. 1043
Jones, Paul, Sr. V.P.-Fin. & Admin.--Wyeth-Ayerst Laboratories-Research & Development, Radnor, PA; *U.S. Public*, pg. 80
Jones, R. W., V.P.--Parsons Infrastructure & Technology Group Inc., Pasadena, CA; *U.S. Private*, pg. 842
Jones, Reginald, Chief Fin. Officer & Sr. V.P.-Fin.--Hycor Biomedical, Inc., Irvine, CA; *U.S. Public*, pg. 851
Jones, Richard F., Chief Fin. Officer & V.P.-Fin.--Arinc Inc. (Consolidated), Annapolis, MD; *U.S. Private*, pg. 81
Jones, Robert H., Exec. V.P. & Chief Fin. Officer--LaSalle-Talman Bank, Chicago, IL; *Int'l*, pg. 11
Jones, Ross, Chief Fin. Officer--Knight-Ridder, Inc., Miami, FL; *U.S. Public*, pg. 963
Jones, Stanley H., V.P.-Fin. & Treas.--Keeneland Assoc., Inc., Lexington, KY; *U.S. Private*, pg. 611
Jones, Thomas E., Principal Fin. Officer & Exec. V.P.--Citicorp, New York, NY; *U.S. Public*, pg. 376
Jones, Thomas E., Jr., Chief Oper. & Chief Fin. Officer--Steadly Company, Carthage, MO; *U.S. Public*, pg. 986
Jones, William, Chief Fin. Officer--Schneider's Dairy, Inc., Pittsburgh, PA; *U.S. Private*, pg. 971
Jonson, Peter W., Chief Fin. Officer--Foster's Brewing Group Limited, Southbank, Australia; *Int'l*, pg. 500
Jonsson, Bo, Chief Fin. Officer--MacGREGOR (DNK) A/S, Herlev, Denmark; *Int'l*, pg. 670
Jordan, Henry, Chief Fin. Officer & Sr. V.P.--The Foothill Group, Inc., Los Angeles, CA; *U.S. Public*, pg. 1201
Jordan, Robert, Chief Fin. Officer--Cummins-Allison Corp., Mount Prospect, IL; *U.S. Private*, pg. 295
Joseph, Randy M., Chief Fin. Officer, V.P. & Treas.--Advance Ross Corporation, Chicago, IL; *U.S. Public*, pg. 320
Joseph, Randy M., Chief Fin. Officer--Precipitair Pollution Control, Longview, TX; *U.S. Public*, pg. 320
Joseph, Randy M., Chief Fin. Officer--Advance Ross Steel Co., Chicago, IL; *U.S. Public*, pg. 320
Joseph, Robert, Chief Fin. Officer--Gotham Incorporated, New York, NY; *U.S. Private*, pg. 677
Joslin, Mark W., Chief Fin. Officer & Treas.--Lawter International, Inc., Kenosha, WI; *U.S. Public*, pg. 980
Joy, Ray, Chief Fin. Officer--Grand Metropolitan Plc, London, United Kingdom; *Int'l*, pg. 408
Joyce, James R., Pres. & Chief Exec., Fin. & Acctg. Officer--Magellan Petroleum Corporation, Madison, CT; *U.S. Public*, pg. 1036
Joyce, Leon, Chief Fin. Officer, V.P. & Treas.--Carolina Biological Supply Co., Burlington, NC; *U.S. Private*, pg. 213
Joyce, Mike, Chief Fin. Officer--Titan Tool, Inc., Oakland, NJ; *U.S. Private*, pg. 500
Jubb, Tom, Chief Fin. Officer--Keller Ladders Inc., Fort Lauderdale, FL; *U.S. Public*, pg. 1684
Judson, Christopher M., Chief Fin. Officer--McKellar Companies, San Diego, CA; *U.S. Private*, pg. 723
Juetten, George H., Chief Fin. Officer & Sr. V.P.--Dresser Industries, Inc., Dallas, TX; *U.S. Public*, pg. 528
Juliano, Rich, Chief Fin. Officer--Hoffman Seeds, Inc., Landisville, PA; *U.S. Private*, pg. 532
Juliano, Richard, Chief Fin. Officer, Sec. & Treas.--A.H. Hoffman, Inc., Landisville, PA; *U.S. Private*, pg. 532
Julien, Jeffrey P., Chief Fin. Officer & V.P.-Fin.--Raymond James Financial, Inc., Saint Petersburg, FL; *U.S. Public*, pg. 923
Jungbauer, Franz, Chief Fin. Officer--Gartenhilfe Ges.m.b.H., Lienz, Austria; *Int'l*, pg. 356
Jungen, Dave, Chief Fin. Officer--Kramer International, Inc., Milwaukee, WI; *U.S. Public*, pg. 142
Junius, Daniel M., Chief Fin. Officer, V.P.-Fin. & Treas.--Nashua Corporation, Nashua, NH; *U.S. Public*, pg. 1152
Junkunc, Charles A., Chief Fin. Officer & V.P.--Brown & Sharpe Manufacturing Company, North Kingstown, RI; *U.S. Public*, pg. 260
Jurand, Henry A., Chief Fin. Officer--KCS Energy Marketing Inc., Edison, NJ; *U.S. Public*, pg. 938
Jurand, Henry A., Chief Fin. Officer--KCS Resources, Inc., Houston, TX; *U.S. Public*, pg. 939
Jurand, Henry A., Chief Fin. Officer--KCS Energy Marketing, Inc., Houston, TX; *U.S. Public*, pg. 939
Jurand, Henry A., Chief Fin. Officer--KCS Pipeline Systems, Inc., Houston, TX; *U.S. Public*, pg. 939
Jurand, Henry A., Chief Fin. Officer--KCS Power Marketing, Inc., Edison, NJ; *U.S. Public*, pg. 939
Jurand, Henry A., Chief Fin. Officer--KCS Michigan Resources, Inc., Houston, TX; *U.S. Public*, pg. 939
Jurand, Henry A., Chief Fin. Officer--National Enerdrill, Edison, NJ; *U.S. Public*, pg. 939
Jurasek, Kris, Chief Fin. Officer, V.P. & Treas.--Miner Enterprises Inc., Geneva, IL; *U.S. Private*, pg. 749
Jurek, Stephen, Chief Fin. Officer--JFC Inc., Saint Cloud, MN; *U.S. Private*, pg. 577
Jurek, Stephen, Chief Fin. Officer--Gold'n Plump Poultry, Saint Cloud, MN; *U.S. Private*, pg. 577
Juris, Eugene W., V.P.-Fin. & Sec.--Banner Aerospace, Inc., Washington, DC; *U.S. Public*, pg. 187
Juska, John E., Chief Fin. Officer--Chicago Mercantile Exchange, Chicago, IL; *U.S. Private*, pg. 235
Jusnek, Edward, Chief Fin. Officer--Nightingale-Conant Corp., Niles, IL; *U.S. Private*, pg. 799
Jutras, Ron, Chief Fin. Officer--ATS Automation Tooling Systems, Inc., Cambridge, Canada; *Int'l*, pg. 18
Jutte, P., Chief Fin. Officer & Controller--Holmatro Industrial & Rescue Equipment, Raamsdonksveer, Netherlands; *Int'l*, pg. 632
Kabacinski, Mary, Chief Fin. Officer--Marquette Medical Systems, Inc., Milwaukee, WI; *U.S. Public*, pg. 1047
Kachurak, Joseph J., Chief Fin. Officer--Ingersoll-Dresser Pump Company, Liberty Corner, NJ; *U.S. Public*, pg. 529
Kagan, Michael, Chief Fin. Officer & Exec. V.P.--Tropical Sportswear International, Tampa, FL; *U.S. Private*, pg. 1105
Kage, Robert B., V.P.-Fin.--Bell-Northern Research Ltd., Nepean, Canada; *Int'l*, pg. 116
Kahant, Elaine, V.P. & Treas.--CV Reit, Inc., West Palm Beach, FL; *U.S. Public*, pg. 286
Kahn, Douglas, Chief Fin. Officer--Health Professionals, Inc., Fort Lauderdale, FL; *U.S. Public*, pg. 802
Kahn, Steven A., Chief Fin. Officer & V.P.--ACI Telecentrics, Inc., Minneapolis, MN; *U.S. Public*, pg. 3
Kakimoto, Lane M., Chief Fin. Officer & V.P.--Calsonic International, Inc., Irvine, CA; *Int'l*, pg. 944
Kalafut, George W., Exec. V.P.-Fin. & Admin.--Genuine Parts Company, Atlanta, GA; *U.S. Public*, pg. 732
Kalajian, H., Chief Fin. Officer & Exec. V.P.--Ameritech, Detroit, MI; *U.S. Public*, pg. 97
Kalanges, Nick, Chief Fin. Officer--Pacific Coast Building Products Inc., Sacramento, CA; *U.S. Private*, pg. 830
Kalec, John J., Chief Fin. Officer, Sr. V.P. & Sec.--Clayton Homes, Inc., Knoxville, TN; *U.S. Public*, pg. 382
Kalish, David, Chief Fin. Officer--Georgetown Partners, Inc., Great Neck, NY; *U.S. Private*, pg. 466
Kalish, David W., Chief Fin. Officer--Gould Investors, L.P., Great Neck, NY; *U.S. Private*, pg. 466
Kallshian, Jan, Chief Fin. Officer--Datamarine International, Inc., Mountlake Terrace, WA; *U.S. Public*, pg. 486
Kamerich, Ken, Chief Fin. Officer--Enerpac U.S., Butler, WI; *U.S. Public*, pg. 124
Kamil, Harvey, Chief Fin. Officer & Exec. V.P.--Nature's Bounty Inc., Bohemia, NY; *U.S. Public*, pg. 1166
Kamins, Aaron J., Chief Fin. Officer--Accurate Perforating Co., Chicago, IL; *U.S. Private*, pg. 12
Kamm, C.P., Mgr.-Pension Admin. & Risk Mngmt.--Electric Furnace Co., Salem, OH; *U.S. Private*, pg. 367
Kamm, Jacob O., II, Chm. Bd., Pres. & Chief Exec. & Fin. Officer--Electric Furnace Co., Salem, OH; *U.S. Private*, pg. 367
Kamm, Rick, V.P., Treas. & Controller--The Blodgett Oven Co., Inc., Burlington, VT; *U.S. Public*, pg. 1064
Kamsler, J. Scott, Chief Fin. Officer, V.P.-Fin. & Sec.--SymmetriCom, Inc., San Jose, CA; *U.S. Public*, pg. 1547
Kamsler, J. Scott, Chief Fin. Officer-SymmetriCom--Telecom Solutions, San Jose, CA; *U.S. Public*, pg. 1547
Kanari, Yoshiaki, Chief Fin. Officer & Sr. V.P.--Gould Electronics Inc., Eastlake, OH; *U.S. Public*, pg. 1591
Kanbel, Robert L., Chief Fin. Officer, V.P. & Treas.--Robinson Nugent, Inc., New Albany, IN; *U.S. Public*, pg. 1394
Kane, Charles F., Chief Fin. Officer & V.P.-Fin.--Ardent Software, Inc., Westborough, MA; *U.S. Public*, pg. 129
Kane, Frank, Chief Fin. Officer--Chromcraft Corporation, Senatobia, MS; *U.S. Public*, pg. 352
Kane, Frank T., Chief Fin. Officer & V.P.-Fin.--Chromcraft Revington, Inc., Delphi, IN; *U.S. Public*, pg. 352
Kane, Frank T., Chief Fin. Officer--Peters-Revington Corp., Delphi, IN; *U.S. Public*, pg. 352
Kane, Frank T., Chief Fin. Officer, V.P. & Sec.--Cochrane Furniture Co., Inc., Lincolnton, NC; *U.S. Public*, pg. 352
Kane, John, Chief Fin. Officer, V.P. & Treas.--IDX Systems Corporation, Burlington, VT; *U.S. Public*, pg. 854
Kane, Phillip, Chief Fin. Officer--La Petite Academy Inc., Overland Park, KS; *U.S. Private*, pg. 640

Kangas, Ron, Chief Fin. Officer--Setzer Forest Products, Sacramento, CA; *U.S. Private*, pg. 987
Kanis, Alan, Chief Fin. Officer--Andover Togs, Inc., New York, NY; *U.S. Public*, pg. 112
Kanis, Spencer, Chief Oper. Officer & Chief Fin. Officer--Intercosmetics, Inc., New York, NY; *Int'l*, pg. 1489
Kankel, Keith V., V.P.-Fin., Treas. & Sec.--Patrick Industries Inc., Elkhart, IN; *U.S. Public*, pg. 1264
Kankowsky, Roland, Dr., Chm. & Chief Exec. Officer--Filterwerk Mann & Hummel GmbH, Ludwigsburg, Germany; *Int'l*, pg. 484
Kanner, Robert H., Chm. Bd., Pres., Chief Exec./Fin. Officer & Treas.--Pubco Corporation, Cleveland, OH; *U.S. Public*, pg. 1339
Kanvga, Sunvil, Chief Fin. Officer--Q3 Stamped Metal, Columbus, OH; *U.S. Private*, pg. 897
Kaplan, Andrew, Chief Fin. Officer & Chief Fin. Officer--Time-Life, Inc., Alexandria, VA; *U.S. Public*, pg. 1613
Kaplan, Andrew J., Sr. V.P.-Production, Fin. & Admin.--Columbia TriStar Television, Culver City, CA; *Int'l*, pg. 1282
Kaplan, Andrew P., Chief Fin. Officer & Sr. V.P.--Treasure Chest Advertising Co., Inc., Glendora, CA; *U.S. Public*, pg. 228
Kaplan, Ira, Chief Fin. Officer & Sr. V.P.--Claire's Boutiques, Inc., Pembroke Pines, FL; *U.S. Public*, pg. 381
Kaplan, Ira D., Chief Fin. Officer & Sr. V.P.--Claire's Stores Inc., Pembroke Pines, FL; *U.S. Public*, pg. 381
Kaplan, Jay M., Chief Fin. Officer--MEDIQ Incorporated, Pennsauken, NJ; *U.S. Public*, pg. 1081
Kaplan, Jay M., Chief Fin. Officer & Sr. V.P.--MEDIQ/PRN Life Support Services, Inc., Pennsauken, NJ; *U.S. Public*, *pg. 1081*
Kaplan, Sam D., Chief Fin. Officer, Controller, Treas. & Sec.--The He-Ro Group, Ltd., New York, NY; *U.S. Public*, pg. 801
Kappes, Hans-Peter, Chief Fin. Officer & Mng. Dir.--Bausparkasse Gemeinschaft der Freunde Wuestenrot gem.GmbH, Ludwigsburg, Germany; *Int'l*, pg. 1514
Kappler, David J., Grp. Dir.-Fin.--Cadbury Schweppes p.l.c., London, United Kingdom; *Int'l*, pg. 247
Kara, G.H., Chief Fin. Officer--Ensign-Bickford, Bromhof, South Africa; *Int'l*, pg. 1196
Karaty, George, Chief Fin. Officer--Lalique North America, Carlstadt, NJ; *Int'l*, pg. 797
Karlen, Gerald, Chief Fin. Officer, V.P. & Treas.--Automatic Equipment Mfg. Co., Pender, NE; *U.S. Private*, pg. 101
Karlsson, Lars, Chief Fin. Officer--Skanska International Civil Engineering AB, Danderyd, Sweden; *Int'l*, pg. 1260
Karlsson, Oskar, Chief Fin. Officer--Skanska Fastigheter Goteborg AB, Goteborg, Sweden; *Int'l*, pg. 1260
Karlsson, Ove, Chief Fin. Officer--Celsius Invest AB, Eskilstuna, Sweden; *Int'l*, pg. 276
Karn, Susan H., Chief Fin. Officer--The Arnold Agency, Richmond, VA; *U.S. Private*, pg. 84
Karnes, W. Michael, Chief Fin. Officer & Exec. V.P.--Prime Group Realty Trust, Chicago, IL; *U.S. Public*, pg. 1326
Karras, Peter W., Exec. V.P. & Treas.--First Colony Life Insurance Co., Lynchburg, VA; *U.S. Public*, pg. 711
Karrest, Jacques, Chief Fin. Officer--Chancellor Radio Broadcasting Co., Dallas, TX; *U.S. Public*, pg. 335
Karsh, Mark, Chief Fin. Officer & Sr. V.P.--Tseng Labs, Norristown, PA; *U.S. Public*, pg. 1643
Karsk, Bruce C., V.P.-Fin., Treas. & Sec.--Lindsay Manufacturing Company, Lindsay, NE; *U.S. Public*, pg. 999
Karsner, Michael S., Chief Fin. Officer & Sr. V.P.--Republic Industries, Inc., Fort Lauderdale, FL; *U.S. Public*, pg. 1378
Karst, Darren, Chief Fin. Officer & Sr. V.P.--Dominick's Finer Foods, Northlake, IL; *U.S. Private*, pg. 1202
Karvonen, Thomas D., Chief Fin. Officer & V.P.--Ambrake Corporation, Elizabethtown, KY; *U.S. Public*, pg. 721
Kaseff, Fred, Chief Fin. Officer--Blau Marketing Technologies, Inc., Wilton, CT; *U.S. Private*, pg. 148
Kasman, Joseph D., Chief Fin. Officer & Sr. V.P.--Tower Realty Trust, Inc., New York, NY; *U.S. Public*, pg. 1625
Kaspar, Hertha, Chief Fin. Officer--Feodor Burgmann Dichtungswerke GmbH, Wolfratshausen, Germany; *Int'l*, pg. 233
Kasper, Karen M., Chief Fin. Officer, Sr. V.P & Treas.--Fort Wayne National Corporation, Fort Wayne, IN; *U.S. Public*, pg. 673
Kasper, Karen M., Chief Fin. Officer & Sr. V.P.--Fort Wayne National Bank, Fort Wayne, IN; *U.S. Public*, pg. 674
Kasprisin, Stephen, Chief Fin. Officer--Acorn Products, Inc., Columbus, OH; *U.S. Public*, pg. 17
Kasprisin, Stephen M., Chief Fin. Officer & V.P.--UnionTools, Inc., Columbus, OH; *U.S. Public*, pg. 17
Kassab, Albert A., Chief Fin. Officer & Sr. V.P.--The Ivaco Group, Montreal, Canada; *Int'l*, pg. 695
Kassner, Mark S., Chief Fin. Officer, V.P. & Sec.--Sloan's Supermarkets, Inc., New York, NY; *U.S. Private*, pg. 915
Kassouf, James, Pres., Chief Exec. Officer & Treas.--Metropolitan Properties Systems, Cleveland, OH; *U.S. Private*, pg. 739
Kastenholz, Markus, Chief Fin. Officer--ElecSys Inc., Peoria, IL; *U.S. Private*, pg. 367
Kastner, Richard, Chief Fin. Officer--TEC Incorporated, Palatine, IL; *U.S. Public*, pg. 687
Kasvin, Thomas G., Chief Fin. Officer--American Safety Razor Company, Verona, VA; *U.S. Private*, pg. 597
Katchuk, Richard F., Chief Fin. Officer & Corp. Exec. V.P.--Crestar Financial Corporation, Richmond, VA; *U.S. Public*, pg. 458
Katchuk, Richard F., Chief Fin. Officer & Exec. V.P.--Crestar Bank, Richmond, VA; *U.S. Public*, pg. 458
Kathage, Hans, Chief Fin. Officer & Controller--Kloeckner Industrie-Anlagen Gmbh, Duisburg, Germany; *Int'l*, pg. 1081
Katko, Nicholas S., Chief Fin. Officer--E.D. Bullard Company, Cynthiana, KY; *U.S. Private*, pg. 180
Katsumata, Mark, Chief Fin. Officer & Sec.--Durum Energy Corp., Vancouver, Canada; *Int'l*, pg. 422
Katsumata, Mark, Chief Fin. Officer & Sec.--Durum Energy Corp., Sucursal Del Peru, Vancouver, Canada; *Int'l*, pg. 422
Katsumata, Mark, Chief Fin. Officer & Sec.--Durum (Australia) Pty. Ltd., Vancouver, Canada; *Int'l*, pg. 422
Katz, Barry, Chief Fin. Officer--Weir Floway Inc., Fresno, CA; *Int'l*, pg. 1489
Katz, Max E., Chief Fin. Officer--Brauerei AG, Zurich, Switzerland; *Int'l*, pg. 479
Katz, Robin J., V.P.-Consumer Prods.--Arrow Industries, Inc., Carrollton, TX; *U.S. Public*, pg. 426
Katzen, Brian L., Chief Fin. Officer--Octagon Process Inc., Edgewater, NJ; *U.S. Private*, pg. 811
Kaufman, Jack, Chief Fin. Officer--The Hain Food Group Inc., Uniondale, NY; *U.S. Public*, pg. 774
Kaufman, M. Scot, Sr. Vice Chm. & Chief Fin. Officer--MBNA Corporation, Wilmington, DE; *U.S. Public*, pg. 1023
Kaufman, M. Scot, Sr. Vice Chm. & Chief Fin. Officer--MBNA America Bank N.A., Wilmington, DE; *U.S. Public*, pg. 1023
Kaulman, John, Chief Fin. Officer--Cucina Classica Italiana Inc., Lakewood, NJ; *U.S. Public*, pg. 1435
Kauramaki, Kline, Chief Fin. Officer, V.P. & Controller--J.W. Messner, Inc., Grand Rapids, MI; *U.S. Private*, pg. 734
Kautz, Robert F., Pres. & Chief Fin. Officer--Koo Koo Roo, Inc., Los Angeles, CA; *U.S. Public*, pg. 966
Kautz, Walter J., Treas. & Sec.--Sugar Cane Growers Cooperative of Florida, Belle Glade, FL; *U.S. Private*, pg. 1049
Kautzman, Edward J., Treas.--Meyer Broadcasting Company, Bismarck, ND; *U.S. Private*, pg. 739
Kavetas, Harry L., Chief Fin. Officer & Exec. V.P.--Eastman Kodak Company, Rochester, NY; *U.S. Public*, pg. 550
Kavetas, Harry L., Exec. V.P. & Chief Fin. Officer--Scientific Imaging Systems, New Haven, CT; *U.S. Public*, pg. 550
Kawana, Atsushi, Chief Fin. Officer--Anritsu Corporation, Tokyo, Japan; *Int'l*, pg. 77
Kawayi, Nate, Chief Fin. Officer & V.P.-Fin.--Maxtor Corporation, Milpitas, CA; *Int'l*, pg. 641
Kay, George C., Chief Fin. Officer, V.P. & Treas.--A.T. Massey Coal Company, Inc., Richmond, VA; *U.S. Public*, *pg. 660*
Kay, Steven R., Chief Fin. Officer & Sr. V.P.--Amwest Insurance Group, Inc., Calabasas, CA; *U.S. Public*, pg. 106
Kayser, John P., Chief Fin. Officer--William Blair & Company L.L.C., Chicago, IL; *U.S. Private*, pg. 148
Kayser, Kraig H., Pres. & Chief Exec. Officer--Seneca Foods Corporation, Pittsford, NY; *U.S. Public*, pg. 1456
Kazmierczak, Stanley, Chief Fin. Officer, V.P.-Fin. & Admin. & Sec.--Digital Link Corporation, Sunnyvale, CA; *U.S. Public*, pg. 508
Keane, Kevin, Chief Fin. Officer--Renaissance Publishing Co., Inc., Auburn, IN; *Int'l*, pg. 185
Keane, Michael E., Chief Fin. Officer & Sr. V.P.--UNOVA, Inc., Beverly Hills, CA; *U.S. Public*, pg. 1698
Kearney, John, Chief Fin. Officer--Merial Ltd., London, United Kingdom; *U.S. Public*, pg. 1092
Kearney, John, Chief Fin. Officer--Merial Ltd., London, United Kingdom; *Int'l*, pg. 1110
Kearns, Dale, Chief Fin. Officer & Sr. V.P.-Fin.--O&Y Properties Corporation, Toronto, Canada; *Int'l*, pg. 993
Keay, Steven L., Chief Fin. Officer & Exec. V.P.--Textron Inc., Providence, RI; *U.S. Public*, pg. 1588
Kec, Janet, Treas. & Sec.--Western States Petroleum Inc., Phoenix, AZ; *U.S. Private*, pg. 1169
Keck, Elizabeth K., Chief Fin. Officer & Controller--Broadcast Electronics, Inc., Quincy, IL; *U.S. Private*, pg. 531
Keef, Jim W., Chief Fin. Officer & V.P.-Fin.--Applied Digital Access, San Diego, CA; *U.S. Public*, pg. 122
Keefe, Paul, Exec. V.P.-Fin. Opers. & Control Div.--Montreal Trustco, Montreal, Canada; *Int'l*, pg. 155
Keefe, Thomas G., Chief Fin. Officer & V.P.--Network Long Distance, Inc., Baton Rouge, LA; *U.S. Public*, pg. 1169
Keefer, R. Scott, Chief Fin. Officer & Sr. V.P.--Calgon Carbon Corporation, Pittsburgh, PA; *U.S. Public*, pg. 292
Keegan, James, Chief Fin. Officer--Trimark Holdings, Inc., Santa Monica, CA; *U.S. Public*, pg. 1638
Keegan, Judy, Chief Fin. Officer--Pacific Northern Inc., Seattle, WA; *U.S. Private*, pg. 832
Keegan, Peter, Chief Fin. Officer & Sr. V.P.--Loews Corporation, New York, NY; *U.S. Public*, pg. 1010
Keegan, Raymond, Chief Fin. Officer--Florida Pneumatic Mfg. Corp., Jupiter, FL; *U.S. Public*, pg. 1240
Keels, William A., Chief Fin. Officer--Page Holdings, Inc., Mount Airy, NC; *U.S. Private*, pg. 834
Keen, J. Lamont, Chief Fin. Officer, V.P. & Treas.--Idaho Power Company, Boise, ID; *U.S. Public*, pg. 861
Kees, Ray, Chief Fin. Officer, Corp. Sec. & Treas.--Gem-Dandy, Inc., Madison, NC; *U.S. Private*, pg. 442
Keesecker, Bob, Chief Fin. Officer--Coronado Paint Company, Edgewater, FL; *Int'l*, pg. 1488
Kegley, Don, Chief Fin. Officer & V.P.--Cunningham-Limp Development Co., Farmington Hills, MI; *U.S. Private*, pg. 297
Kehaya, Mark W., Dir.-Fin.--Standard Commercial Tobacco Co., Inc., Wilson, NC; *U.S. Public*, pg. 1502
Keiller, Eileen, Chief Fin. Officer & V.P.--Akzo Nobel Inc., Chicago, IL; *Int'l*, pg. 47
Keillor, Larry, Chief Fin. Officer--Foster Farms, Livingston, CA; *U.S. Private*, pg. 421
Keintz, Richard J., Chief Fin. Officer & Chief Info. Svcs. Officer--CUNA Mutual Insurance Society, Madison, WI; *U.S. Private*, pg. 296
Keirstead, Allan G., Vice Chm., Chief Fin. & Admin. Officer & Exec. V.P.--Stanhome Inc., Westfield, MA; *U.S. Public*, *pg. 1508*
Keitel, Chris, Chief Fin. Officer, V.P.-Fin., Treas. & Controller--Hobart Brothers Co., Troy, OH; *U.S. Public*, pg. 866
Keith, Alan, Chief Fin. Officer & Sr. V.P.--Hanna-Barbera Productions, Inc., Hollywood, CA; *U.S. Public*, pg. 1614
Kelecy, Richard T., Chief Fin. Officer--Perma-Fix Environmental Services, Inc., Gainesville, FL; *U.S. Public*, pg. 1279
Kelford, Chris, V.P.-Fin.--Elgar Corporation, San Diego, CA; *U.S. Public*, pg. 789
Kell, John F., Jr., V.P.-Fin.--Pennsylvania Enterprises Inc., Wilkes-Barre, PA; *U.S. Public*, pg. 1271
Kelleher, G.R., V.P.-Fin.--The Torrington Co., Torrington, CT; *U.S. Public*, pg. 877
Kelleher, Robert, Chief Fin. Officer--Wherehouse Entertainment, Inc., Torrance, CA; *U.S. Private*, pg. 1171
Kelleher, Robert S., Exec. V.P. & Chief Fin. Officer--Contempo Casuals, Los Angeles, CA; *U.S. Public*, pg. 1763
Kellen, Scott, Chief Fin. Officer--Micropure Medical, Inc., White Bear Lake, MN; *U.S. Private*, pg. 743
Keller, David J., Chief Fin. Officer & Treas.--D.R. Horton, Inc., Arlington, TX; *U.S. Public*, pg. 840
Keller, Douglas W., V.P.-Fin.--Innovex, Inc., Hopkins, MN; *U.S. Public*, pg. 880
Keller, J. Frank, Chief Fin. Officer, Exec. V.P. & Sec.--Barrett Resources Corporation, Denver, CO; *U.S. Public*, *pg. 191*
Keller, James E., Treas. & Controller--Rapid Mounting & Finishing Co., Chicago, IL; *U.S. Private*, pg. 910
Keller, Jeff, Chief Fin. Officer & Treas.--D.C.I., Inc., Saint Cloud, MN; *U.S. Private*, pg. 301
Keller, Jim, Chief Fin. Officer & Sec.--Ness Holding Co., Portland, OR; *U.S. Private*, pg. 791
Keller, R., Dr., Chief Fin. Officer--Buss AG, Pratteln, Switzerland; *Int'l*, pg. 490
Keller, Raymond H., Chief Fin. Officer & V.P.--AFC Cable Systems, Inc., Providence, RI; *U.S. Public*, pg. 6
Keller, Robert, Chief Fin. Officer & Exec. V.P.--Gateway Apparel, Inc., Saint Louis, MO; *U.S. Private*, pg. 441
Kelley, David H., Chief Fin. Officer--Trigen Energy Corporation, White Plains, NY; *U.S. Public*, pg. 1637
Kelley, Don K., Chief Fin. Officer & Treas.--Kappler Safety Group, Inc., Guntersville, AL; *U.S. Private*, pg. 607
Kellner, Lawrence W., Chief Fin. Officer & Exec. V.P.--Continental Airlines, Houston, TX; *U.S. Public*, pg. 439
Kellogg, Cynthia P., Chief Fin. Officer, V.P., Treas. & Sec.--Heartland Development Corporation, Madison, WI; *U.S. Public*, pg. 1728
Kelly, Carolyn, Chief Fin. Officer & V.P.--Seattle Times Company, Seattle, WA; *U.S. Private*, pg. 980
Kelly, Daniel, Chief Fin. Officer--Wickersham Hunt Schwantner, Boston, MA; *U.S. Private*, pg. 84
Kelly, David, Chief Fin. Officer--Warner-Chilcott Laboratories, Inc., Rockaway, NJ; *Int'l*, pg. 436
Kelly, Dennis P., Chief Fin. Officer & V.P.-Fin.--Oregon Metallurgical Corporation, Albany, OR; *U.S. Public*, pg. 43
Kelly, Don k., Chief Fin. Officer--Kappler USA, Guntersville, AL; *U.S. Private*, pg. 607
Kelly, Donald, Chief Fin. Officer, V.P.-Fin. & Sec.--Digital Solutions, Inc., Somerset, NJ; *U.S. Public*, pg. 508
Kelly, Edward W., Jr., Chief Fin. Officer & Exec. V.P.--Cottman Transmission Systems, Inc., Fort Washington, PA; *U.S. Private*, pg. 278
Kelly, Gary C., Chief Fin. Officer & V.P.-Fin.--Southwest Airlines Co., Dallas, TX; *U.S. Public*, pg. 1493
Kelly, J. Michael, Chief Fin. Officer & Sr. V.P.-Fin.--GTE Corporation, Stamford, CT; *U.S. Public*, pg. 696
Kelly, James, Chief Fin. Officer & Exec. V.P.--Midlantic Bank, N.A., Edison, NJ; *U.S. Public*, pg. 1242
Kelly, James J., Jr., Chief Fin. Officer & Sec.--Global Motor Sport Group, Inc., Morgan Hill, CA; *U.S. Public*, pg. 748
Kelly, Joe, Jr., Chief Fin. Officer, V.P. & Treas.--Jim Walter Homes, Inc., Tampa, FL; *U.S. Public*, pg. 1737
Kelly, Joseph T., Chief Fin. Officer, Treas. & Sec.--Ewing Cole Cherry Brott, Philadelphia, PA; *U.S. Private*, pg. 387
Kelly, Kathleen M., V.P.-Admin. & Sec.--American Technical Ceramics Corp., Huntington Station, NY; *U.S. Public*, pg. 93
Kelly, Marge, Chief Fin. Officer--Churny Company Inc., Northbrook, IL; *U.S. Public*, pg. 1288
Kelly, Michael, Chief Exec. Officer & Chief Fin. Officer--Regency Savings Bank, Naperville, IL; *U.S. Private*, pg. 406
Kelly, Patrick C., Chief Oper. Officer & Gen. Mgr.--Ozone Research & Equipment Corp., Phoenix, AZ; *U.S. Public*, pg. 1234
Kelly, Paul J., Chief Fin. Officer, V.P. & Sec.--Il Fornaio America Corporation, Corte Madera, CA; *U.S. Public*, pg. 864
Kelly, Richard, Chief Fin. Officer--Stone & Webster Engineering & Constructors Corp., Boston, MA; *U.S. Public*, pg. 1519
Kelly, Richard C., Chief Fin. Officer & Exec. V.P.--New Century Energies, Inc., Denver, CO; *U.S. Public*, pg. 1170
Kelly, Richard C., Chief Fin. Officer, Exec. V.P.-Fin. & Treas.--Public Service Company of Colorado, Denver, CO; *U.S. Public*, pg. 1170
Kelly, T. Patrick, Chief Fin. Officer--The SABRE Group Holdings, Inc., Fort Worth, TX; *U.S. Public*, pg. 10
Kelly, Vince, Chief Fin. Officer--Metrocall, Inc., Alexandria, VA; *U.S. Public*, pg. 1102
Kelly, William M., Chief Fin. Officer & Sr. V.P.-Corp. Opers.--Silicon Graphics, Inc., Mountain View, CA; *U.S. Public*, pg. 1473
Kelsey, Glenn B., Chief Fin. Officer & Exec. V.P.--Oneida Ltd., Oneida, NY; *U.S. Public*, pg. 1225
Kelsey, Marilee, Chief Fin. Officer--Arrington Travel Center Inc., Chicago, IL; *U.S. Private*, pg. 85
Kelsky, Richard B., V.P. & Gen. Counsel--Monroe Systems For Business, Inc., Morris Plains, NJ; *U.S. Private*, pg. 757
Kelso, David B., Chief Fin. Officer & Exec. V.P.--The Chubb Corporation, Warren, NJ; *U.S. Public*, pg. 354
Kelson, Richard B., Chief Fin. Officer & Exec. V.P.--Aluminum Company of America, Pittsburgh, PA; *U.S. Public*, pg. 60

Kemezys, K. Peter, V.P., Asst. Gen. Counsel & Asst. Sec.--Manor Care, Inc., Gaithersburg, MD; *U.S. Public*, pg. 1041
Kemmeren, Bram, Chief Fin. Officer--Wartsila Diesel International Ltd. Oy, Strasbourg, France; *Int'l*, pg. 863
Kemna, Ralf, Chief Fin. Officer--Scanvest Olivetti A/S, Oslo, Norway; *Int'l*, pg. 1004
Kemp, Alan L., Controller--Airtex Products, Fairfield, IL; *U.S. Private*, pg. 1113
Kemp, C.M.H., Grp. Chief Accountant--Tarmac plc, Wolverhampton, United Kingdom; *Int'l*, pg. 1355
Kemph, Fred, V.P & Chief Fin. Officer--Blue Circle America Inc., Marietta, GA; *Int'l*, pg. 197
Kendall, Cheryl L., Chief Fin. Officer, V.P., Treas. & Sec.--Acme United Corporation, Fairfield, CT; *U.S. Public*, pg. 17
Kendrick, Mike, Controller--Kern's Bakeries, Incorporated, Knoxville, TN; *U.S. Public*, pg. 547
Kendrick, Peter, Chief Fin. Officer--Precision Tune Autocare Inc., Leesburg, VA; *U.S. Public*, pg. 1321
Kenehan, Michael J., Chief Fin. Officer & V.P.-Fin.--Haddon Craftsmen, Inc., Scranton, PA; *U.S. Public*, pg. 518
Kenneally, Mary, Treas. & Sec.--Town Pump, Inc., Butte, MT; *U.S. Private*, pg. 1093
Kennedy, Charles G., Chief Fin. Officer & Exec. V.P.-Finance--Henley Paper Company, Greensboro, NC; *U.S. Private*, pg. 522
Kennedy, D., Chief Oper. Officer--Power Development, Taunton, United Kingdom; *Int'l*, pg. 207
Kennedy, Damien, Chief Fin. Officer--Arnold Bernhard & Co., New York, NY; *U.S. Private*, pg. 137
Kennedy, David, Chief Fin. Officer--Gallery Furniture, Houston, TX; *U.S. Private*, pg. 438
Kennedy, David J., Chief Fin. Officer & V.P.--Perfect Fit Industries, Inc., Monroe, NC; *U.S. Private*, pg. 852
Kennedy, Ed, Chief Fin. Officer--Peerless Lighting Corp., Berkeley, CA; *U.S. Private*, pg. 847
Kennedy, Glenn J., Chief Fin. Officer, Treas. & Sec.--Alba-Waldensian, Inc., Valdese, NC; *U.S. Public*, pg. 35
Kennedy, Glenn J., Chief Fin. Officer--Consumer Products Div., Valdese, NC; *U.S. Public*, pg. 36
Kennedy, J. Donald, Chief Fin. Officer & Exec. V.P.-Fin. & Admin.--King Kullen Grocery Co., Inc., Westbury, NY; *U.S. Private*, pg. 621
Kennedy, John, Chief Fin. Officer, Sr. V.P. & Treas.--Smith International, Inc., Houston, TX; *U.S. Public*, pg. 1478
Kennedy, Mark, Chief Fin. Officer & Sr. V.P.--Department 56 Inc., Eden Prairie, MN; *U.S. Public*, pg. 500
Kenney, R.J., Chief Fin. Officer & Sr. V.P.-Fin.--Consolidated Papers, Inc., Wisconsin Rapids, WI; *U.S. Public*, pg. 436
Kenney, Richard, Chief Fin. Officer--Daniels Printing Company, Everett, MA; *U.S. Private*, pg. 310
Kennison, Brad, Chief Fin. Officer--Koret of California, Inc., San Francisco, CA; *U.S. Private*, pg. 632
Kenny, John T., Exec. V.P.-Fin. & Oper.--Specialty Restaurants Corporation, Anaheim, CA; *U.S. Private*, pg. 1022
Kent, Matt, Chief Fin. Officer--Park Corp., Cleveland, OH; *U.S. Private*, pg. 839
Kentfield, I.P., Chief Fin. Officer--Bridport Aviation Products, Dorset, United Kingdom; *Int'l*, pg. 215
Kenyon, Ian, Chief Fin. Officer--The Music and Video Club Limited, Harrow, United Kingdom; *Int'l*, pg. 733
Keough, William H., Chief Fin. Officer, Sr. V.P. & Treas.--The Pioneer Group, Inc., Boston, MA; *U.S. Public*, pg. 1298
Keparaipis, Elizabeth, Chief Fin. Officer--F&B Manufacturing Co., Phoenix, AZ; *U.S. Private*, pg. 388
Kephart, Pam, Chief Fin. Officer--Connor Corporation, Fort Wayne, IN; *U.S. Private*, pg. 264
Kephart, R., V.P.-Treas. & Sec.--Furman Lumber Company Inc., Dallas, TX; *U.S. Private*, pg. 431
Ker, Alan S., Chief Fin. Officer, Treas. & Sec.--Universal Standard Healthcare, Inc., Southfield, MI; *U.S. Public*, pg. 1697
Ker, Alan S., Chief Fin. Officer & Treas.--Universal Standard HealthCare of Ohio Inc., Southfield, MI; *U.S. Public*, pg. 1698
Keresman, Michael, III, Chief Fin. Officer & Sr. V.P.--Steris Corporation, Mentor, OH; *U.S. Public*, pg. 1515
Kerkstra, Steven, Chief Fin. Officer, V.P. & Asst. Sec.--Three D Departments, Inc., Costa Mesa, CA; *U.S. Public*, *pg. 1604*
Kern, Peter M., Sr. V.P.-Strategic Devel. & Corp. Fin.--Home Shopping Network, Inc., Saint Petersburg, FL; *U.S. Public*, pg. 1685
Kerner, B., Chief Fin. Officer--Siemens S.A., Sao Paulo, Brazil; *Int'l*, pg. 1248
Kerns, Samuel, Chief Fin. Officer & V.P.--L. Robert Kimball & Associates, Ebensburg, PA; *U.S. Private*, pg. 619
Kerr, Stephen R., Chief Fin. Officer & V.P.--All American Bottling Corp., Oklahoma City, OK; *U.S. Private*, pg. 34
Kerrigan, James W., Chief Fin. Officer & V.P.-Fin. & Admin.--MacNeal-Schwendler Corp., Costa Mesa, CA; *U.S. Public*, pg. 1031
Kersh, Russell A., Chief Fin. Officer & Chief Oper. Officer--Adidas America, Spartanburg, SC; *Int'l*, pg. 24
Kerstein, Donald, Chief Fin. Officer--Hilton Active Apparel, Lincolnwood, IL; *U.S. Public*, pg. 940
Kertson, Richard A., Chief Fin. Officer & V.P.-Fin.--Varco International, Inc., Orange, CA; *U.S. Public*, pg. 1709
Kessel, Silvia, Chief Fin. Officer, Exec. V.P. & Treas.--Metromedia International Group, Inc., East Rutherford, NJ; *U.S. Public*, pg. 1102
Kesseler, H.D., Chief Fin. Officer--Kidde-Deugra GmbH, Ratingen, Germany; *Int'l*, pg. 1500
Kessler, Debra, Chief Fin. Officer--Chr. Hansen, Inc., Milwaukee, WI; *Int'l*, pg. 288
Kessler, Ernst, Chief Fin. Officer--Saurer AG, Arbon, Switzerland; *Int'l*, pg. 1198
Kessler, John F., Chief Fin. Officer--Mitek Systems, Inc., San Diego, CA; *U.S. Public*, pg. 1117
Kessler, Phyllis K., V.P.-Fin.--Kalin Enterprises, Inc., Sarasota, FL; *U.S. Private*, pg. 606
Kessler, Phyllis K., V.P.-Fin.--Kalin Financial Division, Sarasota, FL; *U.S. Private*, pg. 606
Kessler, Richard J., Chief Fin. Officer & V.P.-Fin. & Devel.--Oglebay Norton Company, Cleveland, OH; *U.S. Public*, pg. 1213
Kessock, Alan E., Chief Fin. Officer--Ultimate Electronics, Thornton, CO; *U.S. Public*, pg. 1662
Ketcham, Geoffrey C., Chief Fin. Officer, Exec. V.P. & Treas.--Energen Corporation, Birmingham, AL; *U.S. Public*, pg. 581
Ketelaar, Jacob, Chief Fin. Officer--Compaction America, Kewanee, IL; *U.S. Public*, pg. 1676
Ketteler, Thomas R., Chief Fin. Officer--Schottenstein Stores Corporation, Columbus, OH; *U.S. Private*, pg. 972
Keyes, James W., Chief Fin. Officer & Exec. V.P.--The Southland Corporation, Dallas, TX; *Int'l*, pg. 693
Keyes, Jim, Chief Fin. Officer--7-Eleven Stores, Dallas, TX; *Int'l*, pg. 693
Keys, David N., Chief Fin. Officer, Sr. V.P. & Treas.--American Pacific Corporation, Las Vegas, NV; *U.S. Public*, pg. 88
Keyser, Don, Chief Fin. Officer--Lau Div., Dayton, OH; *Int'l*, pg. 1398
Keyser, S.A., Chief Fin. Officer & Sr. V.P.--Burrows Paper Corporation, Little Falls, NY; *U.S. Private*, pg. 188
Keyte, David H., Chief Fin. Officer & Exec. V.P.--Forest Oil Corporation, Denver, CO; *U.S. Public*, pg. 670
Khalife, Robert, Chief Fin. Officer--Taylor Made Group, Inc., Gloversville, NY; *U.S. Private*, pg. 1070
Khan, Ejaz A., Controller--Vulcan Chemicals, Birmingham, AL; *U.S. Public*, pg. 1725
Khaneka, Bharat, Fin. Dir.--ARC Advertising, London, United Kingdom; *Int'l*, pg. 17
Khilnani, Vinod M., Chief Fin. Officer, V.P. & Treas.--Simpson Industries, Inc., Plymouth, MI; *U.S. Public*, pg. 1474
Kibbon, Larry J., Treas. & Sec.--Walsh Construction Co. of Illinois, Chicago, IL; *U.S. Private*, pg. 1148
Kiefe, Dan, Chief Fin. Officer--Griswold Industries, Inc., Costa Mesa, CA; *U.S. Private*, pg. 482
Kiefer, Carl, V.P.-Fin.--Dewco Chicago, Rolling Meadows, IL; *U.S. Private*, pg. 1178
Kiefer, Carl O., V.P.-Fin., Treas. & Sec.--Don E. Williams Co., Rock Island, IL; *U.S. Private*, pg. 1177
Kiefer, Charles F., III, Partner & Chief Fin. Officer--Arnold Communications, Inc., Boston, MA; *U.S. Private*, pg. 83
Kiehnle, Robert C., Chief Fin. Officer, Exec. V.P. & Asst. Sec.--Fresh America Corp., Dallas, TX; *U.S. Public*, pg. 681
Kiekel, Bill, Chief Fin. Officer--Ruskin Div., Grandview, MO; *Int'l*, pg. 1398
Kiel, Steven, Chief Fin. Officer & Treas.--Ground Round Inc., Braintree, MA; *U.S. Public*, pg. 766
Kienker, James W., Chief Fin. Officer & Exec. V.P.--NationsBank West, Saint Louis, MO; *U.S. Public*, pg. 1164
Kiernan, Donald E., Chief Fin. Officer, Sr. V.P. & Treas.--SBC Communications Inc., San Antonio, TX; *U.S. Public*, *pg. 1415*
Kiernan, Mike, Chief Fin. Officer--Grant Geophysical Inc., Houston, TX; *U.S. Private*, pg. 470
Kilbourne, C. Michael, Chief Fin. Officer & Exec. V.P.--Oakwood Homes Corporation, Greensboro, NC; *U.S. Public*, pg. 1209
Kilby, Andrew, Chief Fin. Officer & V.P.--Renfro Corp., Mount Airy, NC; *U.S. Private*, pg. 922
Kildal, Jan, Chief Fin. Officer & Exec. V.P.-Fin.--Norske Skogindustrier A.S, Skogn, Norway; *Int'l*, pg. 965
Kile, Cindy, Chief Fin. Officer & V.P.--California Hardware Company, Ontario, CA; *U.S. Private*, pg. 335
Kiley, James G., Chief Fin. Officer & V.P.--EVI, Inc., Houston, TX; *U.S. Public*, pg. 547
Kiley, Michael T., Partner, Chief Fin. Officer, & Exec. V.P.--Media That Works, Cincinnati, OH; *U.S. Private*, pg. 727
Killingsworth, Marti, Exec. V.P. & Treas.--Griffin Manufacturing Co., Muskogee, OK; *U.S. Private*, pg. 481
Killmer, Jonathon E., Chief Fin. Officer, Sr. V.P. & Treas.--Digi International Inc., Minnetonka, MN; *U.S. Public*, pg. 506
Killoran, Joseph F., Chief Fin. Officer & V.P.--Control Data Systems, Inc., Arden Hills, MN; *U.S. Public*, pg. 441
Kilmartin, Patrick J., V.P.-Corp. Fin.--Riverside/Bi-Lo Division, Du Bois, PA; *U.S. Public*, pg. 1270
Kilrea, Gregory J., Chief Fin. Officer--Ha-Lo Industries, Inc., Niles, IL; *U.S. Public*, pg. 773
Kim, Ann Cadier, Chief Fin. Officer & V.P.-Fin.--The Wet Seal, Inc., Irvine, CA; *U.S. Public*, pg. 1763
Kim, Hong-Sik, Chief Fin. Officer--Ssangyong Precision Industry Co., Ltd., Inchon, Korea; *Int'l*, pg. 1292
Kim, Man S., Chief Fin. Officer & Mng. Dir.--Crown Confectionery Co., Ltd., Seoul, Korea; *Int'l*, pg. 348
Kim, Seong-Ki, Chief Fin. Officer--Johnson & Johnson Korea, Ltd., Seoul, Korea; *U.S. Public*, pg. 930
Kimber, John, Grp. Fin. Dir.--Haden Maclellan Holdings plc, Egham, United Kingdom; *Int'l*, pg. 585
Kime, Roger, Chief Fin. Officer & Controller--Champion Boxed Beef, Denver, CO; *U.S. Private*, pg. 228
Kimmel, Gary D., V.P. & Chief Fin. Officer--ARGOSystems, Inc., Sunnyvale, CA; *U.S. Public*, pg. 240
Kinate, Paul, Chief Fin. Officer--Noel Olson Group, Stevens Point, WI; *U.S. Private*, pg. 800
Kinder, Terry, Chief Fin. Officer & V.P.--Giant Resource Recovery Company (Grr!), Harleyville, SC; *U.S. Public*, pg. 741
Kinder, Terry, Chief Fin. Officer--Keystone Cement Co., Bath, PA; *U.S. Public*, pg. 741
Kinder, Terry L., Chief Fin. Officer & V.P.--Giant Cement Holding Inc., Summerville, SC; *U.S. Public*, pg. 741
Kindl, Nancy A., Chief Fin. Officer, Treas., Controller & Sec.--Portec, Inc., Lake Forest, IL; *U.S. Public*, pg. 1317
Kindler, Wolfgang, Chief Fin. Officer--Spectris Messtechnik GmbH, Langen, Germany; *Int'l*, pg. 14
Kindlick, David A., V.P.-Fin. Opers.--South Jersey Industries, Inc., Folsom, NJ; *U.S. Public*, pg. 1488
Kindlick, David A., Chief Fin. Officer & V.P.-Rates & Budgeting--South Jersey Gas Co., Folsom, NJ; *U.S. Public*, pg. 1488
Kindlund, Joanne M., V.P.-Fin., Treas. & Sec.--Holiday RV Superstores, Inc., Orlando, FL; *U.S. Public*, pg. 829
Kindlund, Joanne M., Chief Fin. Officer--Holiday RV Superstores, Inc.-Orlando, Orlando, FL; *U.S. Public*, pg. 830
Kindlund, Newton C., Chief Fin. Officer--Holiday RV Superstores West, Inc., Bakersfield, CA; *U.S. Public*, pg. 830
Kinerk, Toby, V.P.-Fin.--Zemco Industries, Inc., Buffalo, NY; *U.S. Private*, pg. 1204
King, C. Eric, Chief Fin. Officer & Treas.--Warner Press, Inc., Anderson, IN; *U.S. Private*, pg. 1150
King, David, Chief Fin. Officer--Glynwed Metal Services Ltd., Kingston, United Kingdom; *Int'l*, pg. 554
King, Doug, Chief Fin. Officer & Controller--Wilson Products Co., Salt Lake City, UT; *U.S. Private*, pg. 1181
King, Fred, Chief Fin. Officer--Seitz Foods Inc., Saint Joseph, MO; *U.S. Public*, pg. 1434
King, James A., Chief Fin. Officer & V.P.--Valley Asphalt Corporation, Cincinnati, OH; *U.S. Private*, pg. 1131
King, John E., Chief Fin. Officer & V.P.--Total Renal Care Holdings, Inc., Torrance, CA; *U.S. Public*, pg. 1625
King, Mark A., Chief Fin. Officer & Exec. V.P.--Affiliated Computer Services, Inc., Dallas, TX; *U.S. Public*, pg. 27
King, Robert M., Chief Fin. Officer & Sr. V.P.--Nuevo Energy Company, Houston, TX; *U.S. Public*, pg. 1206
Kingman, Edward R., Jr., Chief Fin. Officer--Grupo Iusacell SA de CV, Mexico, Mexico; *U.S. Public*, pg. 204
Kingston, M. K., Chief Fin. Officer--T.H.E., Newcastle under Lyme, United Kingdom; *Int'l*, pg. 707
Kinnan, Doug, Chief Fin. Officer--Amerisure Companies, Farmington Hills, MI; *U.S. Private*, pg. 65
Kinnear, Timothy W., Chief Fin. Officer & V.P.--ODS Networks, Inc., Richardson, TX; *U.S. Public*, pg. 1206
Kinner, Ronald, Chief Fin. Officer--The Iowa Packing Co., Des Moines, IA; *U.S. Private*, pg. 575
Kinney, Jon C., Chief Fin. Officer & Sr. V.P.--Illinois Tool Works Inc., Glenview, IL; *U.S. Public*, pg. 865
Kinney, Larry, Chief Fin. Officer & Sr. V.P.--Chadwick's of Boston, West Bridgewater, MA; *U.S. Public*, pg. 996
Kinnier, Stephen K., Chief Fin. Officer--Virginia First Financial Corp., Petersburg, VA; *U.S. Public*, pg. 1721
Kinnier, Stephen R., Chief Fin. Officer & Sr. V.P.--Virginia First Savings Bank, F.S.B., Petersburg, VA; *U.S. Public*, pg. 1721
Kinsch, Russ, Chief Fin. Officer--SSE Telecom, Inc., Vienna, VA; *U.S. Public*, pg. 1421
Kinsch, Russ, Chief Fin. Officer--SEE Technologies Inc., Fremont, CA; *U.S. Public*, pg. 1421
Kinsella, Daniel, Chief Fin. Officer, V.P. & Treas.--Grist Mill Company, Lakeville, MN; *U.S. Public*, pg. 766
Kinsella, E.J., Reg. Treas.-Europe--Commonwealth Bank of Australia, London, United Kingdom; *Int'l*, pg. 313
Kinsella, Jim, Chief Fin. Officer--Irish Driver-Harris Co., Ltd., Walkinstown, Ireland; *U.S. Public*, pg. 530
Kiraly, Thomas, Chief Fin. Officer, V.P.-Fin. & Sec.--BRC Holdings, Dallas, TX; *U.S. Public*, pg. 163
Kirby, Alan, Chief Fin. Officer--Bestobell Service Co. Ltd., Maidenhead, United Kingdom; *Int'l*, pg. 853
Kirby, David, V.P.-Fin. & Treas.--The Arnold Palmer Golf Company, Ooltewah, TN; *U.S. Public*, pg. 132
Kirby, John, Chief Fin. Officer & Exec. V.P.--U.S. Trust Corporation, New York, NY; *U.S. Public*, pg. 1688
Kirby, Joseph A., Chief Fin. Officer & V.P.--Ansaldo Signal N.V., Amsterdam, Netherlands; *Int'l*, pg. 77
Kirby, Kerry J., Chief Fin. Officer & Exec. V.P.-Fin.--TruServ Corporation, Chicago, IL; *U.S. Private*, pg. 1108
Kirchoff, Phillip, Chief Fin. Officer & Controller--Farmway Co-Op Inc., Beloit, KS; *U.S. Private*, pg. 396
Kirk, Mark, Pres., Chief Oper. Officer & Chief Fin. Officer--HMI Industries, Cleveland, OH; *U.S. Public*, pg. 771
Kirk, T., Chief Fin. Officer--Rhone-Poulenc Inc., Princeton, NJ; *Int'l*, pg. 1112
Kirkwood, William T., Chief Fin. Officer & Exec. V.P.--Worthington Foods Inc., Worthington, OH; *U.S. Public*, pg. 1780
Kirkwood, William T., Chief Fin. Officer--Specialty Foods Investment Inl., Worthington, OH; *U.S. Public*, pg. 1780
Kirsner, James D., Chief Fin. Officer--Barra, Inc., Berkeley, CA; *U.S. Public*, pg. 191
Kirtley, Olivia F., V.P.-Fin. & Chief Financial Officer--Vermont American Tool Corp., Louisville, KY; *U.S. Public*, pg. 575
Kish, Timothy M., Chief Fin. Officer & V.P.-Fin.--Biogen, Inc., Cambridge, MA; *U.S. Public*, pg. 230
Kish, Tom, Chief Fin. Officer & V.P.-Fin.--Raynor Garage Doors, Dixon, IL; *U.S. Private*, pg. 912
Kishner, Gerald S., Chief Fin. Officer & Exec. V.P.-Fin. & Admin.--Canadian Tire Corporation Limited, Toronto, Canada; *Int'l*, pg. 259
Kitajima, Masahiro, Chief Fin. Officer & Dir.--Okuma Corporation, Niwa, Japan; *Int'l*, pg. 1000
Kitao, Yoshitaka, Chief Fin. Officer & Exec. V.P.--Softbank Corporation, Tokyo, Japan; *Int'l*, pg. 1276
Kitchen, Steven L., Chief Fin. Officer & Exec. V.P.--Western Resources, Inc., Topeka, KS; *U.S. Public*, pg. 1759
Kitchen, Thomas M., Chief Fin. Officer--Avondale Industries, Inc., Avondale, LA; *U.S. Public*, pg. 156
Kitson, John, Dir.-Fin.--Booker PLC, London, United Kingdom; *Int'l*, pg. 202
Kitter, Harry, Chief Fin. Officer--Financial Network Investment Corp, Torrance, CA; *U.S. Private*, pg. 404
Kjellander, Jim, Chief Fin. Officer--International Center for Entrepreneurial Development, Inc., Cypress, TX; *U.S. Private*, pg. 568
Klahn, Dennis D., Chief Fin. Officer--International Lottery & Totalizator Systems, Inc., Carlsbad, CA; *U.S. Public*, pg. 900

Klajbor, Jerry, Chief Fin. Officer, V.P. & Sec.--Stanford Telecommunications, Sunnyvale, CA; *U.S. Public*, pg. 1508

Klar, Hans-Juergen, Chief Fin. Officer--Letraset Deutschland GmbH, Frankfurt/Main, Germany; *Int'l*, pg. 461

Klar, Richard E., Chief Fin. Officer--Tremco, Inc., Beachwood, OH; *U.S. Public*, pg. 1358

Klatt, Gregg, Chief Fin. Officer--Midwest Coast Transport L.P., Sioux Falls, SD; *U.S. Private*, pg. 744

Klatt, Roger J., Chief Fin. Officer, Sr. V.P., Treas. & Asst. Sec.--Gundle/SLT Environmental, Inc., Houston, TX; *U.S. Public*, pg. 769

Klaus, Paul, Chief Fin. Officer--Norwesco, Inc., Saint Bonifacius, MN; *U.S. Private*, pg. 808

Klausen, Benny, Chief Fin. Officer--Berendsen Textil Service A/S, Soeborg, Denmark; *Int'l*, pg. 1284

Klaush, Greg, Chief Fin. Officer & V.P.-Fin.--Interphase Corporation, Dallas, TX; *U.S. Public*, pg. 908

Klawitter, Ronald F., Chief Fin. Officer, V.P.-Fin., Treas. & Sec.--Key Tronic Corporation, Spokane, WA; *U.S. Public*, pg. 953

Klei, Steven E., Chief Fin. Officer, Sr. V.P.-Fin. & Sec.--ProBusiness Services, Inc., Pleasanton, CA; *U.S. Public*, pg. 1330

Klein, Bruce, Chief Fin. Officer & V.P.-Fin.--CLARCOR, Inc., Rockford, IL; *U.S. Public*, pg. 381

Klein, Douglas P., Chief Fin. Officer, V.P., Sec. & Treas.--Go-Video, Inc., Scottsdale, AZ; *U.S. Public*, pg. 748

Klein, Larry, Chief Fin. Officer--ABS Global Inc., De Forest, WI; *U.S. Private*, pg. 3

Klein, Michael, Chief Fin. Officer--Murray's Discount Auto Stores, Belleville, MI; *U.S. Private*, pg. 768

Klein, Walter J., V.P.-Fin.--Stepan Company, Northfield, IL; *U.S. Public*, pg. 1514

Kleinhempel, M., Chief Fin. Officer--Siemens S.A., Caracas, Venezuela; *Int'l*, pg. 1248

Kleinhenz, Dennis, Chief Fin. Officer & Controller--Radix Wire Company, Cleveland, OH; *U.S. Private*, pg. 907

Kleinschmidt, J.C., Chief Fin. Officer--Companhia Goodyear do Brasil Produtos de Borracha, Sao Paulo, Brazil; *U.S. Public*, pg. 753

Kleiweg, Richel, Chief Fin. Officer--Esselte Meto BV, Nieuwegein, Netherlands; *Int'l*, pg. 461

Kleman, Charles, Chief Fin. Officer, Sec. & Treas.--Chico's Fas Inc, Fort Myers, FL; *U.S. Public*, pg. 349

Klemens, Thomas A., Chief Fin. Officer & Exec. V.P.--The First American Financial Corporation, Santa Ana, CA; *U.S. Public*, pg. 624

Klemens, Thomas A., Chief Fin. Officer & V.P.--First American Title Insurance Co., Santa Ana, CA; *U.S. Public*, pg. 625

Klepper, Bill, Chief Fin. Officer--Pizza Hut, Inc., Dallas, TX; *U.S. Public*, pg. 1636

Klettky, Bill, Chief Fin. Officer--Career Education Corporation, Hoffman Estates, IL; *U.S. Private*, pg. 209

Klima, David J., Chief Fin. Officer--UNR-Leavitt Div., Chicago, IL; *U.S. Public*, pg. 1404

Klima, Jim, Chief Fin. Officer & V.P.--Wood Group Pressure Control, Houston, TX; *U.S. Public*, pg. 1775

Klimara, Ronald, V.P. & Treas.--Wabash National Corp., Lafayette, IN; *U.S. Public*, pg. 1730

Kline, Allan M., Chief Fin. Officer & V.P.--Dynatech Corporation, Burlington, MA; *U.S. Public*, pg. 539

Kline, Barry L., Chief Fin. Officer & Sr. V.P.--Penn National Insurance, Harrisburg, PA; *U.S. Private*, pg. 850

Kline, Steven R., Chief Fin. Officer & Exec. V.P.--Gardner Publications, Inc., Cincinnati, OH; *U.S. Private*, pg. 440

Klinger, Ernest T., Chief Fin. Officer, V.P.-Fin. & Admin.--Arden Group, Inc., Los Angeles, CA; *U.S. Public*, pg. 128

Klinger, Ernest T., Chief Fin. Officer--Gelson's Markets, Encino, CA; *U.S. Public*, pg. 129

Klipper, Mitchell, Chief Fin. Officer & Exec. V.P.--B. Dalton Bookseller, Inc., New York, NY; *U.S. Public*, pg. 189

Klitten, Martin R., Chief Fin. Officer & V.P.--Chevron Corporation, San Francisco, CA; *U.S. Public*, pg. 347

Klosterman, Ronald, Chief Fin. Officer, V.P.-Fin. & Sec.--Flexsteel Industries, Inc., Dubuque, IA; *U.S. Public*, pg. 653

Klosterman, Scott, Chief Fin. Officer, V.P.-Fin. & Corp. Sec.--Chattanooga Group, Inc., Hixson, TN; *U.S. Private*, pg. 231

Klube, Leon, Chief Fin. Officer--Industra Inc., Seattle, WA; *Int'l*, pg. 74

Klube, Leon, Chief Fin. Officer--Industra Inc., Portland, OR; *Int'l*, pg. 74

Klube, Leon, Chief Fin. Officer--Industra Inc., Greenville, SC; *Int'l*, pg. 74

Kluesner, Terrence, Chief Fin. Officer--Reedrill Inc., Denison, TX; *Int'l*, pg. 1325

Kluting, Duane, Chief Fin. Officer & V.P.--X-Rite, Incorporated, Grandville, MI; *U.S. Public*, pg. 1783

Knapp, Arthur F., Jr., Chief Fin. Officer, Sr. V.P. & Sec.--Boole & Babbage, Inc., San Jose, CA; *U.S. Public*, pg. 244

Knapp, Janice, Chief Fin. Officer--Quark Inc., Denver, CO; *U.S. Private*, pg. 900

Knapp, Michael, Chief Fin. Officer & Sec.--Mission West Properties, Cupertino, CA; *U.S. Public*, pg. 1117

Knapp, Norbert, Chief Fin. Officer-Germany--DMB&B Frankfurt, Frankfurt/Main, Germany; *U.S. Private*, pg. 303

Knauf, Steve, Chief Fin. Officer--Industrial Towel & Uniform, New Berlin, WI; *U.S. Private*, pg. 561

Knedlik, Ronald, Chief Fin. Officer, Sr. V.P.-Fin., Treas. & Sec.--Alex Lee, Inc., Hickory, NC; *U.S. Private*, pg. 657

Knedlik, Ronald, Chief Fin. Officer & Treas.--Capital Resources, Inc., Hickory, NC; *U.S. Private*, pg. 657

Knedlik, Ronald, Chief Fin. Officer & Treas.--Merchants Transport of Hickory, Hickory, NC; *U.S. Private*, pg. 657

Knedlik, Ronald, Chief Fin. Officer & Treas.--Institution Food House, Inc., Hickory, NC; *U.S. Private*, pg. 657

Knedlik, Ronald, Chief Fin. Officer & Treas.--MDI Management Inc., Hickory, NC; *U.S. Private*, pg. 657

Knedlik, Ronald W., Chief Fin. Officer & Treas.--Lowe's Food Stores, Inc., Winston Salem, NC; *U.S. Private*, pg. 657

Knee, Kevin, Chief Oper. & Fin. Officer--Guthy-Renker Corp., Palm Desert, CA; *U.S. Private*, pg. 488

Kneip, Kurt R., Chief Fin. Officer, V.P. & Sec.--Inter-Tel, Incorporated, Phoenix, AZ; *U.S. Public*, pg. 888

Kneip, Kurt R., Chief Fin. Officer--Inter-Tel Leasing, Inc., Phoenix, AZ; *U.S. Public*, pg. 888

Kneip, Kurt R., Chief Fin. Officer--Inter-Tel Equipment UK, Ltd., Wellingborough, United Kingdom; *U.S. Public*, pg. 888

Kneip, Kurt R., Chief Fin. Officer--Inter-Tel Net Solutions, Phoenix, AZ; *U.S. Public*, pg. 888

Kneip, Kurt R., Chief Fin. Officer--Inter-Tel DataComm, Inc., Phoenix, AZ; *U.S. Public*, pg. 888

Kneip, Kurt R., Chief Fin. Officer--Inter-Tel Midwest, Inc., Phoenix, AZ; *U.S. Public*, pg. 888

Kneip, Kurt R., Chief Fin. Officer, V.P. & Sec.--Inter-Tel, Incorporated-New Jersey, Phoenix, AZ; *U.S. Public*, pg. 888

Kneip, Kurt R., Chief Fin. Officer, V.P., Sec. & Treas.--Southwest Telephone Systems, Inc., Phoenix, AZ; *U.S. Public*, pg. 888

Kneip, Kurt R., Chief Fin. Officer--Inter-Tel Japan, Inc., Tokyo, Japan; *U.S. Public*, pg. 888

Kneissler, Norman, Chief Fin. Officer & V.P.--Foster-Miller, Inc., Waltham, MA; *U.S. Private*, pg. 421

Knell, Sandra A., Chief Fin. Officer, Exec. V.P. & Sec.--The Coast Distribution System, San Jose, CA; *U.S. Public*, pg. 388

Knepp, Larry, Chief Fin. Officer--Rea Magnet Wire Company, Inc., Fort Wayne, IN; *U.S. Private*, pg. 913

Knepp, Lynn E., Chief Fin. Officer & Controller--Gannett Fleming Affiliates, Inc., Camp Hill, PA; *U.S. Private*, pg. 439

Knepper, Peter, Chief Fin. Officer, Sr. V.P. & Treas.--Ticketmaster Corporation, West Hollywood, CA; *U.S. Private*, pg. 1084

Kneubuhler, St., Chief Fin. Officer--Kuehne & Nagel International Ltd., Mississauga, Canada; *Int'l*, pg. 763

Knight, Gerald T., Chief Fin. Officer & Sr. V.P.--Fingerhut Corp., Minnetonka, MN; *U.S. Public*, pg. 623

Knight, Harold O., Jr., Chief Fin. Officer & Exec. V.P.--Medpartners Inc., Birmingham, AL; *U.S. Public*, pg. 1082

Knight, Ken, Chief Fin. Officer & Comptroller--Akers Packaging Service Inc., Middletown, OH; *U.S. Private*, pg. 29

Knight, Paul, Chief Fin. Officer--Ford Motor Company Limited, Brentwood, United Kingdom; *U.S. Public*, pg. 666

Knight, S., Chief Fin. Officer--Home and Building Control, Minneapolis, MN; *U.S. Public*, pg. 833

Knight, Warren, Chief Fin. Officer & V.P. Fin.--Servico, Inc., West Palm Beach, FL; *U.S. Public*, pg. 1462

Knight, William, Chief Fin. Officer & V.P.-Admin.--Zoll Medical Corporation, Burlington, MA; *U.S. Private*, pg. 1207

Knipe, Peter W., Treas. & Sec.--STV Group, Inc., Douglassville, PA; *U.S. Public*, pg. 1421

Knipp, Gregory T., Chief Fin. Officer & V.P.--Multigraphics Inc., Mount Prospect, IL; *U.S. Public*, pg. 1141

Kniskern, Pauline A., Chief Fin. Officer & Exec. V.P.--CD Products, Inc., New Providence, NJ; *U.S. Public*, pg. 276

Knoll, Patrick, Chief Fin. Officer & V.P.--Spectrulite Consortium, Inc., Madison, IL; *U.S. Private*, pg. 1024

Knoll, Timothy, Chief Fin. Officer--Atlapac Trading Company, Inc., Los Angeles, CA; *U.S. Private*, pg. 96

Knott, Wayne, Chief Fin. Officer--Philips Components, Jupiter, FL; *Int'l*, pg. 1054

Knous, Pamela K., Chief Fin. Officer & Exec. V.P.--SuperValu, Inc., Eden Prairie, MN; *U.S. Public*, pg. 1540

Knowles, A.S., Sec. & Mgr.-Fin.--Arnotts plc, Dublin, Ireland; *Int'l*, pg. 81

Knowles, Marie L., Chief Fin. Officer & Exec. V.P.--Atlantic Richfield Company, Los Angeles, CA; *U.S. Public*, pg. 144

Knowles, Robert E., Chief Fin. Officer & Exec. V.P.--S & K Famous Brands, Inc., Glen Allen, VA; *U.S. Public*, pg. 1414

Knox, John, Chief Fin. Officer & V.P.-Fin. & Admin.--The Franklin Institute, Philadelphia, PA; *U.S. Private*, pg. 424

Knox, Marion A., Jr., V.P., Treas. & Sec.--Terminix Service, Inc., Columbia, SC; *U.S. Private*, pg. 1077

Knuesel, Thomas W., Chief Fin. Officer & V.P.--Diamond Brands, Inc., Cloquet, MN; *U.S. Private*, pg. 330

Knueuen, Gerald R., Chief Fin. Officer, Exec. V.P. & Treas.--Harold M. Pitman Co., Inc., Totowa, NJ; *U.S. Private*, pg. 867

Knuuttila, Kari, Chief Fin. Officer--Esselte Meto, Helsinki, Finland; *Int'l*, pg. 461

Kobay, Seth, V.P.-Opers. & Controller--Georgetown Partners, Inc., Great Neck, NY; *U.S. Private*, pg. 466

Kobele, Robert S., Chief Fin. Officer & V.P.-Fin.--Sbarro, Inc., Commack, NY; *U.S. Public*, pg. 1435

Koch, Bernhard M., Chief Fin. Officer & Treas.--Desjardins Laurentian Life Assurance, Wayne, PA; *Int'l*, pg. 396

Koch, Bruce K., Chief Fin. Officer & Exec. V.P.-Opers. & Fin.--Devon Group, Inc., Stamford, CT; *U.S. Public*, pg. 503

Koch, David, V.P.-Fin.--Flambeau Corporation, Baraboo, WI; *U.S. Private*, pg. 409

Koch, Eckhart, Dr., Chief Fin. Officer--BHF-BANK (Switzerland) Ltd., Zurich, Switzerland; *Int'l*, pg. 119

Koch, Edward, Chief Fin. Officer--Universal Molding Company, Lynwood, CA; *U.S. Private*, pg. 1127

Koch, Joseph, Chief Fin. Officer--Fellowes Manufacturing Co., Itasca, IL; *U.S. Private*, pg. 400

Koch, Tim, Chief Fin. Officer, Exec. V.P. & Treas.--EBP Life Insurnace Co., Minneapolis, MN; *U.S. Public*, pg. 635

Kodde, David, Chief Fin. Officer--Snack Ventures Europe, Zaventem, Belgium; *U.S. Public*, pg. 718

Koebel, Wayne R., Chief Fin. Officer, Exec. V.P., Treas. & Sec.--Shoreline Financial Corp., Benton Harbor, MI; *U.S. Public*, pg. 1467

Koebel, Wayne R., Chief Fin. Officer & Exec. V.P.--Shoreline Bank, Benton Harbor, MI; *U.S. Public*, pg. 1468

Koechley, L. Thomas, Chief Fin. Officer, V.P.-Fin. & Treas.--Kirkwood Industries, Inc., Cleveland, OH; *U.S. Private*, pg. 623

Koehler, Craig, Chief Fin. Officer--Thrifty Oil Co., Santa Fe Springs, CA; *U.S. Private*, pg. 1084

Koehler, Jim, Chief Fin. Officer--Micro Electronics, Inc., Hilliard, OH; *U.S. Private*, pg. 742

Koehler, R.E., V.P.-Fin.--Wacker Silicones Corporation, Adrian, MI; *Int'l*, pg. 625

Koehler, Robert, Chief Fin. Officer & V.P.-Admin.--Sara Lee Knit Products, Winston Salem, NC; *U.S. Public*, pg. 1434

Koeleman, G.B.J., Chief Fin. Officer & V.P.--ABB Lummus Global Inc., Bloomfield, NJ; *Int'l*, pg. 4

Koenemann, Carl F., Chief Fin. Officer & Exec. V.P.--Motorola, Inc., Schaumburg, IL; *U.S. Public*, pg. 1136

Koersvelt, A., Chief Fin. Officer--Bayer B.V., Mijdrecht, Netherlands; *Int'l*, pg. 175

Koh, P.C., Chief Fin. Officer & Exec. V.P.--Husky Oil Ltd., Calgary, Canada; *Int'l*, pg. 640

Kohls, William R., Chief Fin. Officer & Exec. V.P.--Independent Bank Corporation, Ionia, MI; *U.S. Public*, pg. 874

Koikos, T., Chief Fin. Officer--Scholl Hellas SA, Athens, Greece; *Int'l*, pg. 1209

Kojima, Yasuyuki, Chief Fin. Officer--Haseko (California) Inc., Los Angeles, CA; *Int'l*, pg. 600

Kojima, Yasuyuki, Chief Fin. Officer--Haseko Realty (California), Inc., Los Angeles, CA; *Int'l*, pg. 600

Kojima, Yoshiharu, Sr. Mng. Dir.-Admin. & Treas.--Sogei Inc., Tokyo, Japan; *Int'l*, pg. 1277

Kolakawski, Stephen C., Chief Fin. Officer, Sr. V.P. & Treas.--Underwriters Reinsurance, Woodland Hills, CA; *U.S. Public*, pg. 42

Kolar, Susan, Sr. V.P. & Chief Fin. Officer--Viacom Entertainment, New York, NY; *U.S. Private*, pg. 779

Koler, Gerald, Chief Fin. Officer--Hill-Behan Lumber Company, Saint Louis, MO; *U.S. Private*, pg. 529

Kolk, Fritz D., Chief Fin. Officer & V.P.-Fin.--Meijer, Inc., Grand Rapids, MI; *U.S. Private*, pg. 729

Koller, Tim, Chief Fin. Officer--WPMT Channel 43, York, PA; *U.S. Public*, pg. 1636

Kolodziej, Raymond P., Chief Fin. Officer & V.P.--Turtle Wax, Inc., Chicago, IL; *U.S. Private*, pg. 1110

Kolodzieski, Edward, V.P.-Strategic Plng.--Ingles Markets, Incorporated, Black Mountain, NC; *U.S. Public*, pg. 878

Komorowski, Wayne T., Controller--Milwaukee Cylinder Division, Cudahy, WI; *U.S. Public*, pg. 124

Konings, Jan, Chief Fin. Officer--Sara Lee/DE, Utrecht, Netherlands; *U.S. Public*, pg. 1434

Konopacki, Thomas, Chief Fin. Officer & Exec. V.P.--Pulse Bancorp, Inc., South River, NJ; *U.S. Public*, pg. 1344

Konopacki, Thomas, Chief Fin. Officer & Exec. V.P.--Pulse Savings Bank, South River, NJ; *U.S. Public*, pg. 1344

Kontich, Michael J., Chief Fin. Officer & Treas.--Leupold & Stevens, Inc., Beaverton, OR; *U.S. Private*, pg. 662

Kontos, Mark W., Chief Fin. Officer, Sr. V.P. & Treas.--Battelle Memorial Institute, Columbus, OH; *U.S. Private*, pg. 123

Koonce, Joel, Chief Fin. Officer & Grp. V.P.-Fin.--CENEX, Inc., Inver Grove Heights, MN; *U.S. Private*, pg. 221

Kopala, Leonard M., Controller--Cole Hersee Company, Boston, MA; *U.S. Private*, pg. 251

Kopas, Robert A., V.P. & Treas.--Shenango Valley Water Co., Sharon, PA; *U.S. Public*, pg. 439

Kopec, Chet, Chief Fin. Officer, Sr. V.P. & Treas.--Michigan Wheel Corporation, Grand Rapids, MI; *U.S. Private*, pg. 741

Kopetzky, W., Chief Fin. Officer--Olivetti Austria G.m.b.H., Vienna, Austria; *Int'l*, pg. 1003

Kopfer, Frank J., Chief Fin. Officer & V.P.--Gaymar Industries, Inc., Orchard Park, NY; *U.S. Private*, pg. 442

Kopp, Brad, Chief Fin. Officer & V.P.--Computer Data Systems, Inc., Rockville, MD; *U.S. Public*, pg. 28

Kopp, Bradford B., Chief Fin. Officer--Citizens Trust Company, Providence, RI; *Int'l*, pg. 1132

Kopp, Melvin, Chief Fin. Officer & Controller--Block Drug Company, Inc., Jersey City, NJ; *U.S. Public*, pg. 236

Koppe, David P., Chief Fin. Officer--United HealthCare Corporation, Minnetonka, MN; *U.S. Public*, pg. 1677

Koppe, David P., Chief Fin. Officer--United HealthCare Services, Inc., Minnetonka, MN; *U.S. Public*, pg. 1678

Korby, Steve, Chief Fin. Officer & Exec. V.P.--Greyhound Lines, Inc., Dallas, TX; *U.S. Public*, pg. 765

Korby, Steven L., Chief Fin. Officer & Exec. V.P.--Greyhound Lines, Inc., Dallas, TX; *U.S. Public*, pg. 765

Kordik, Terry, Chief Fin. Officer--Delair Group, L.L.C., Delair, NJ; *U.S. Private*, pg. 47

Kordisch, Larry, Chief Fin. Officer & Exec. V.P.-Fin.--Homeland Stores, Inc., Oklahoma City, OK; *U.S. Public*, pg. 832

Kordisch, Larry W., Chief Fin. Officer, Exec. V.P.-Fin. & Sec.--Homeland Holding Corp., Oklahoma City, OK; *U.S. Public*, pg. 832

Korducki, Edward J., Chief Fin. Officer & Controller--California Drop Forge, Los Angeles, CA; *U.S. Public*, pg. 612

Korf, Robert, Chief Fin. Officer--Roll International Corporation, Los Angeles, CA; *U.S. Private*, pg. 941

Kornder, David J., Chief Fin. Officer & V.P.--Patina Oil & Gas Corp., Denver, CO; *U.S. Public*, pg. 1264

Kornfeld, Edward B., Chief Fin. Officer & V.P.--Porta Systems Corp., Syosset, NY; *U.S. Public*, pg. 1317

Korphage, George J., Chief Fin. Officer & V.P.--The Bureau of National Affairs, Inc., Washington, DC; *U.S. Private*, pg. 181

Korylak, John R., V.P. & Treas.--Unicorp Canada Corporation, Toronto, Canada; *Int'l*, pg. 1433

Koskela, Steven, Chief Fin. Officer & V.P.--Winkler Advertising, San Francisco, CA; *U.S. Private*, pg. 1183
Koskela, Thomo, Chief Fin. Officer--Lohja Abetoni Oy AB, Perttila, Finland; *Int'l*, pg. 1199
Kosky, Kent, Chief Fin. Officer--Thrustmaster, Inc., Hillsboro, OR; *U.S. Public*, pg. 1607
Kosowski, Barry, Chief Fin. Officer, Treas. & Sec.--Customedix Corporation, Wallingford, CT; *U.S. Private*, pg. 298
Koss, Michael J., Pres., Chief Exec., Oper. & Fin. Officer--Koss Corporation, Milwaukee, WI; *U.S. Public*, pg. 966
Koss, Michael J., Pres., Chief Exec. Officer & Chief Fin. Officer--Koss Classics Ltd., Milwaukee, WI; *U.S. Public*, pg. 966
Kost, Arvo, Chief Fin. Officer--AS Kandur, Tallinn, Estonia; *Int'l*, pg. 748
Kostelni, Jeffrey C., Chief Fin. Officer--Georgia-Bonded Fibers, Inc., Newark, NJ; *U.S. Public*, pg. 734
Koster, Michael, V.P. & Treas.--Williams Distributing Company, Grand Rapids, MI; *U.S. Private*, pg. 1177
Kosterich, Ron, Chief Fin. Officer--Lilyette Brassiere Co., New York, NY; *U.S. Private*, pg. 697
Kostick, Dale, Chief Fin. Officer & V.P.--Garland Commercial Industries, Inc., Freeland, PA; *Int'l*, pg. 188
Koth, Larry, Chief Fin. Officer--Wisconsin Insurance Management, Inc., Waukesha, WI; *U.S. Public*, pg. 141
Kotsonis, James N., Chief Fin. Officer, Sr. V.P. & Chief Actuary--Manhattan Life Insurance Company, Cincinnati, OH; *U.S. Private*, pg. 1118
Kottonen, Hannu, Sr. V.P.-Fin.--Huhtamaki Oy, Espoo, Finland; *Int'l*, pg. 638
Kouch, John, Chief Fin. Officer--Continental PIR Communications, Inc., Toronto, Canada; *Int'l*, pg. 1226
Koumantzelis, Arthur G., Chief Fin. Officer & Sr. V.P.--Cumberland Farms, Inc., Canton, MA; *U.S. Private*, pg. 295
Koupal, Raymond, Chief Fin. Officer--The Hartford Courant Company, Hartford, CT; *U.S. Public*, pg. 1616
Kovach, Charles, Chief Fin. Officer & V.P.-Admin.--Oki Telecom Group, Suwanee, GA; *Int'l*, pg. 1000
Kovach, Rick, Chief Fin. Officer--American Architectural Products, Inc., Youngstown, OH; *U.S. Public*, pg. 67
Kovalchuk, Brian, Chief Fin. Officer--Prince Sports Group Inc., Bordentown, NJ; *U.S. Private*, pg. 884
Kovalchuk, Brian, Chief Fin. Officer--Ektelon, Bordentown, NJ; *U.S. Private*, pg. 884
Kovalchuk, Brian, Chief Fin. Officer--Prince Golf International, Bordentown, NJ; *U.S. Private*, pg. 884
Kowal, Peter, Chief Fin. Officer & Controller--Premier Metal Products Company, Bronx, NY; *U.S. Private*, pg. 881
Kowalsky, Roger J., Chief Fin. Officer & Exec. V.P.-Fin.--Galoob Toys, Inc., South San Francisco, CA; *U.S. Public*, *pg. 698*
Kowalsky, William, Chief Fin. Officer & V.P.-Fin.--Advertising Checking Bureau Incorporated, New York, NY; *U.S. Private*, pg. 23
Kowarszyk, Stan, Chief Fin. Officer--Leo Burnett S.A. de C.V., Mexico, Mexico; *U.S. Private*, pg. 185
Koziel, William, Chief Fin. Officer & V.P.-Fin.--Evans, Inc., Chicago, IL; *U.S. Public*, pg. 596
Kozitza, William, Chief Fin. Officer & V.P.--Taylor Corporation, Mankato, MN; *U.S. Private*, pg. 1070
Kozlowski, Edwin J., Chief Fin. Officer & Exec. V.P.--General Nutrition, Inc., Pittsburgh, PA; *U.S. Public*, pg. 725
Kraber, Richard, Chief Fin. Officer & Sec.--Wind River Systems, Inc., Alameda, CA; *U.S. Public*, pg. 1770
Krablin, Steve, Chief Fin. Officer--National-Oilwell Inc., Houston, TX; *U.S. Public*, pg. 1158
Kraegel, Frederick, Chief Fin. Officer--Best Products Co., Inc., Richmond, VA; *U.S. Private*, pg. 990
Kraft, Brad, Chief Fin. Officer & V.P.-Fin.--Engineered Polymers Corporation, Mora, MN; *Int'l*, pg. 328
Kraft, Mark, Dir.-Fin.--Miracle Adhesives, Buffalo, NY; *U.S. Public*, pg. 1466
Krajewski, Janet A., V.P.-Taxes--General Cigar Holdings Inc, New York, NY; *U.S. Public*, pg. 707
Kramer, Kirby, Chief Fin. Officer--Emery Waterhouse Company, Portland, ME; *U.S. Private*, pg. 373
Kramer, Molly, Chief Fin. Officer--Films for the Humanities & Sciences, Inc., Monmouth Junction, NJ; *U.S. Public*, pg. 1327
Kramer, Phillip D., Chief Fin. Officer, Sr. V.P. & Treas.--Plains Resources Inc., Houston, TX; *U.S. Public*, pg. 1307
Kramer, Phillip D., Chief Fin. Officer--Plains Marketing & Transportation, Houston, TX; *U.S. Public*, pg. 1308
Kramer, Phillip D., Chief Fin. Officer--Stocker Resources, Inc., Los Angeles, CA; *U.S. Public*, pg. 1308
Kramer, Roger H., Chief Fin. Officer--Carroll's Foods, Inc., Warsaw, NC; *U.S. Private*, pg. 215
Krantz, James A., Chief Fin. Officer, V.P. & Treas.--Mission American Insurance Company, Rancho Dominguez, CA; *U.S. Public*, pg. 483
Krantz, Willy, Chief Fin. Officer--Proventus AB, Stockholm, Sweden; *Int'l*, pg. 1072
Kratochwil, John, Chief Fin. Officer--Clay-Park Labs, Inc., Bronx, NY; *Int'l*, pg. 30
Krausart, Gerald S., Chief Fin. Officer & Treas.--Dickten & Masch Manufacturing Co., Nashotah, WI; *U.S. Private*, pg. 331
Krause, Arthur B., Chief Fin. Officer & Exec. V.P.--Sprint Corporation, Westwood, KS; *U.S. Public*, pg. 1500
Krause, K.M., Chief Fin. Officer--Durr Industries, Inc., Plymouth, MI; *Int'l*, pg. 421
Krause, R., Chief Fin. Officer--Olivetti Germany, Frankfurt/Main, Germany; *Int'l*, pg. 1003
Krause, Roy, Chief Fin. Officer & Exec. V.P.--Interim Services Inc., Fort Lauderdale, FL; *U.S. Public*, pg. 892
Krauss, Martin, Chief Fin. Officer--Yellow Services, Inc., Overland Park, KS; *U.S. Public*, pg. 1788
Kreag, J.B., Chief Fin. Officer--Hawaiian Commercial & Sugar Co., Puunene, HI; *U.S. Public*, pg. 39
Krebs, Walter L., Chief Fin. Officer--Service America Systems, Inc., Deerfield Beach, FL; *U.S. Public*, pg. 344
Kreiger, Mark H., Chief Fin. Officer & V.P.--The Earthgrains Company, Clayton, MO; *U.S. Public*, pg. 547
Kreil, Walter N., Chief Fin. Officer--Multi-Arc Inc., Rockaway, NJ; *Int'l*, pg. 1198
Kreiter, Fredric J., Chief Fin. Officer & Legal Counsel--Castcraft Industries, Inc., Skokie, IL; *U.S. Private*, pg. 219
Krejca, Jack E., Chief Fin. Officer, Treas. & Controller--Curran Group, Inc., Crystal Lake, IL; *U.S. Private*, pg. 297
Kremer, Juergen, Chief Fin. Officer & Exec. V.P.--Metallgesellschaft Corp., New York, NY; *Int'l*, pg. 861
Krenek, Wilfred, Chief Fin. Officer, V.P., Treas. & Sec.--Bettis Corporation, Waller, TX; *U.S. Public*, pg. 482
Krepapas, P., Chief Fin. Officer & V.P.--Siemens A.E., Athens, Greece; *Int'l*, pg. 1247
Kressman, C., Chief Fin. Officer--N. Schlumberger & Cie, Guebwiller, France; *Int'l*, pg. 1206
Kretchman, Jerry, Controller--Hill-Rom Company, Inc., Batesville, IN; *U.S. Public*, pg. 828
Kreuze, Calvin, V.P.-Global Fin.--Haworth, Inc., Holland, MI; *U.S. Private*, pg. 511
Kriak, John M., Chief Fin. Officer & Exec. V.P.--Crown American Realty Trust, Johnstown, PA; *U.S. Public*, pg. 461
Kriebel, Robert I., Chief Fin. Officer & Exec. V.P.--U.S. Bioscience, Inc., Conshohocken, PA; *U.S. Public*, pg. 1681
Krieger, Walter L., V.P.-Fin. Opers.--Liz Claiborne, Inc., New York, NY; *U.S. Public*, pg. 1005
Kriegshauser, Patrick A., Chief Fin. Officer, Sr. V.P. & Treas.--Arch Coal, Inc., Saint Louis, MO; *U.S. Public*, pg. 139
Krishnan, Sankor, Chief Fin. Officer--Phar-Mor, Inc., Youngstown, OH; *U.S. Public*, pg. 1284
Krist, Sven Ljnng, Chief Fin. Officer--Abetong Prefab AB, Vaxjo, Sweden; *Int'l*, pg. 1199
Kroening, Ken, Controller--Cub Foods Stores, Stillwater, MN; *U.S. Public*, pg. 1541
Kroes, Leo, Chief Fin. Officer & V.P.--Chesebrough-Pond's USA Co., Greenwich, CT; *Int'l*, pg. 1435
Kroese, John S., III, Chief Fin. Officer, Treas. & Sec.--Gaffney-Kroese Electrical Supply Corp., Rahway, NJ; *U.S. Private*, pg. 437
Krohn, Don, Chief Fin. Officer--Mid-West Conveyor Co., Inc., Kansas City, KS; *Int'l*, pg. 1398
Kromer, Dennis R., Chief Fin. Officer & Treas.--Dunn-Edwards Corporation, Los Angeles, CA; *U.S. Private*, pg. 347
Krueger, Michael H., Chief Fin. Officer & V.P.-Fin. & Admin.--J.F. Ahern Co., Fond Du Lac, WI; *U.S. Private*, pg. 27
Krueger, Steve, V.P.-Fin.--Marine Travelift, Inc., Sturgeon Bay, WI; *U.S. Private*, pg. 703
Krueger, Steve, V.P.-Fin. & Chief Fin. Offcier--MTI Leasing, Ltd., Sturgeon Bay, WI; *U.S. Private*, pg. 703
Krueger, Steve, Chief Fin. Officer--Shuttlelift, Inc., Sturgeon Bay, WI; *U.S. Private*, pg. 703
Krueger, Terry, Chief Fin. Officer & Controller--Dairy Farmers of America, Inc., Arlington, TX; *U.S. Private*, pg. 307
Kruell, K., Chief Fin. Officer--Girmes GmbH, Grefrath, Germany; *Int'l*, pg. 552
Kruger, Milton, Chief Fin. Officer & V.P.--Amstore Corporation, Muskegon, MI; *U.S. Private*, pg. 68
Kruger, S.O., Asst. Treas. & Asst. Sec.--Tecumseh Products Company, Tecumseh, MI; *U.S. Public*, pg. 1565
Krugman, Mark, Chief Fin. Officer & Treas.--Lee National Corporation, New York, NY; *U.S. Private*, pg. 658
Krugman, Mark, Chief Fin. Officer & Treas.--Great Universal Capital Corp., New York, NY; *U.S. Private*, pg. 658
Krul, Joseph, Chief Fin. Officer & Sr. V.P.--Standard Federal Bank, Troy, MI; *Int'l*, pg. 10
Krumb, Phillip P., Chief Fin. Officer & V.P.--Datapoint Corporation, Paris, France; *Int'l*, pg. 384
Kruse, Stephen, Chief Fin. Officer & V.P.--Bradley Printing Company, Des Plaines, IL; *U.S. Public*, pg. 1778
Kruzel, Gerry, Chief Fin. Officer--Shelter Products Group, Elkhart, IN; *Int'l*, pg. 1396
Krysik, Helen, Chief Fin. Officer--Construction Counsellors, Inc., Montville, NJ; *U.S. Private*, pg. 266
Krzemien, Gregory M., Chief Fin. Officer & Treas.--Eastern Environmental Services, Inc., Drums, PA; *U.S. Public*, pg. 549
Krzyminski, Richard, Chief Fin. Officer, Treas. & Sec.--Baxter Hodell Donnelly Preston Inc., Cincinnati, OH; *U.S.* Private, pg. 124
Ksansnak, James, Chief Fin. Officer & Exec. V.P.-Fin.--Aramark Corporation, Philadelphia, PA; *U.S. Private*, pg. 79
Kubik, Ray, Chief Fin. Officer & V.P.--The Nielsen Company, Florence, KY; *U.S. Private*, pg. 799
Kubilus, John, Chief Fin. Officer & Treas.--Bovis Inc., New York, NY; *Int'l*, pg. 1033
Kuchinski, Thaddeus G., Chief Fin. Officer & Treas.--Holstein Association USA, Inc., Brattleboro, VT; *U.S. Private*, pg. 536
Kuck, Timothy W., Chief Fin. Officer, Treas. & Sec.--G&K Services, Inc., Minnetonka, MN; *U.S. Public*, pg. 690
Kuechler, Karl, V.P.-Fin.--Brimms Inc., Tonawanda, NY; *U.S.* Private, pg. 169
Kuefer, Yapie, Chief Fin. Officer--Olivetti Africa Pty. Ltd., Johannesburg, South Africa; *Int'l*, pg. 1003
Kuhn, Joseph W., Chief Fin. Officer & Exec. V.P.--ALARIS Medical, Inc., San Diego, CA; *U.S. Public*, pg. 35
Kuhn, Joseph W., Chief Fin. Officer & Exec. V.P.--ALARIS Medical Systems, Inc., San Diego, CA; *U.S. Public*, pg. 35
Kuhnemund, Robert F., Chief Fin. Officer & Exec. V.P.--First Data Corporation, Englewood, CO; *U.S. Public*, pg. 631
Kulkarni, P.M., Chief Fin. Officer--Geoffrey Manners and Co., Ltd., Mumbai, India; *U.S. Public*, pg. 81
Kullman, Tim, Chief Fin. Officer--Genuardi Family Markets Inc., Norristown, PA; *U.S. Private*, pg. 447
Kullmer, Hermann, Dr., Chief Fin. Officer--Altana AG, Bad Homburg, Germany; *Int'l*, pg. 65
Kulmala, Hannele, Chief Fin. Officer--Finnsementti Oy Ab, Pargas, Finland; *Int'l*, pg. 1198
Kulp, Jan-Henrik, Chief Fin. Officer--UPM-Kymmene Corporation, Helsinki, Finland; *Int'l*, pg. 1427
Kultner, Neil, Chief Fin. Officer--Sanford C. Bernstein & Co., Inc., New York, NY; *U.S. Private*, pg. 137
Kundert, Mick, Chief Fin. Officer--Quartet Manufacturing Co., Skokie, IL; *U.S. Public*, pg. 707
Kuneman, Thomas, Chief Fin. Officer & Sec.--Automation Software, Inc., Farmington, MI; *U.S. Public*, pg. 110
Kunkel, Taryn, Chief Fin. Officer, V.P. & Treas.--Pharmakinetics Laboratories, Inc., Baltimore, MD; *U.S. Public*, pg. 1285
Kuntz, Mike, Chief Info. Officer--R.A. Jones & Co. Inc., Covington, KY; *U.S. Private*, pg. 597
Kunz, Hansruedi, Chief Oper. Officer--Metallica SA, Crissier, Switzerland; *Int'l*, pg. 1427
Kunz, Heidi, Chief Fin. Officer & Sr. V.P.--ITT Industries, Inc., White Plains, NY; *U.S. Public*, pg. 859
Kunze, Wolfgang, Chief Fin. Officer--Schering Berlin Inc., Cedar Knolls, NJ; *Int'l*, pg. 1204
Kunzmann, Raymond F., Chief Fin. Officer, V.P.-Fin. & Controller--Axsys Technologies, Inc., New York, NY; *U.S. Public*, pg. 157
Kunzmann, Raymond F., Chief Fin. Officer--Vernitron Sensor Systems, Saint Petersburg, FL; *U.S. Public*, pg. 157
Kuoni, Charles, Chief Fin. Officer & Sr. V.P.--Coastal Physician Group, Inc., Durham, NC; *U.S. Public*, pg. 391
Kuriskin, Eileen, Chief Fin. Officer--Victory Refrigeration Co. LC, Cherry Hill, NJ; *U.S. Private*, pg. 1139
Kurland, Paul, Chief Fin. Officer--Handy Store Fixtures, Inc., Newark, NJ; *U.S. Private*, pg. 499
Kurpis, Louis, Chief Fin. Officer--Dial A Mattress USA, Long Island City, NY; *U.S. Private*, pg. 330
Kurry, Joseph, Chief Fin. Officer, V.P. & Treas.--Essex Corporation, Columbia, MD; *U.S. Public*, pg. 593
Kurty, Diana R., Chief Fin. Officer & V.P.-Fin.--IEC Electronics Corp., Newark, NY; *U.S. Public*, pg. 854
Kurtz, Geraldine A., V.P.-Cashier--M & I Bank, Ashland, WI; *U.S. Public*, pg. 1050
Kurtzweil, John T., Chief Fin. Officer & V.P.-Fin.--Read-Rite Corporation, Milpitas, CA; *U.S. Public*, pg. 1366
Kuruc, Andrew, Chief Fin. Officer & V.P.--Ark Restaurants Corp., New York, NY; *U.S. Public*, pg. 129
Kurz, Richard M., Chief Fin. Officer--American Eagle Group, Inc., Dallas, TX; *U.S. Public*, pg. 71
Kurzweg, Victor J., III, Chm. Bd., Chief Exec. Officer & Chief Fin. Officer--Consolidated Companies Inc. (CONCO), Metairie, LA; *U.S. Private*, pg. 265
Kusak, David, V.P.-Fin.--Mercury Marine, Fond Du Lac, WI; *U.S. Public*, pg. 265
Kuske, Kevin, Chief Fin. Officer--Abbott Electronics, Inc., Los Angeles, CA; *U.S. Private*, pg. 9
Kusunoki, Naotaka, Chm. & Chief Exec. Officer--NSK Corporation, Ann Arbor, MI; *Int'l*, pg. 903
Kutas, Tom, Chief Fin. Officer & V.P.-Admin.--The HOH Organizations, Chicago, IL; *U.S. Private*, pg. 492
Kutcher, Kenneth E., Chief Fin. Officer--Trevira, Charlotte, NC; *Int'l*, pg. 626
Kuykendall, David L., Chief Fin. Officer & Sr. V.P.--Freedom Communication Inc., Irvine, CA; *U.S. Private*, pg. 425
Kuzma, David R., Chief Fin. Officer, Sr. V.P. & Treas.--Enova Corp, San Diego, CA; *U.S. Public*, pg. 583
Kuzma, David R., Chief Fin. Officer, Sr. V.P. & Treas.--San Diego Gas & Electric Company, San Diego, CA; *U.S. Public*, pg. 584
Kuznetsov, Evgeni, Chief Oper. Officer--MacGREGOR (UKR) A/O, Ilyichevsk City, Russia; *Int'l*, pg. 671
Kvocha, John, Chief Fin. Officer--Garden Way, Inc., Troy, NY; *U.S. Private*, pg. 440
Kwak, Jae-dong, Auditor--Dong Bu Insurance Co., Seoul, Korea; *Int'l*, pg. 416
Kwasniewski, William, Chief Fin. Officer--Your Staff, Inc., Woodland, MI; *U.S. Public*, pg. 949
Kwiecien, Robert, V.P.-Rate Acct.--Amstore Corporation, Muskegon, MI; *U.S. Private*, pg. 68
Kyees, John, Chief Fin. Officer & Exec. V.P.--HC Holdings, Columbus, OH; *U.S. Private*, pg. 489
Kyees, John, Chief Fin. Officer & Exec. V.P.--Huntington Clothiers, Inc., Columbus, OH; *U.S. Private*, pg. 490
Kyle, Terrence W., Sr. V.P., Treas. & Asst. Sec.--Shared Medical Systems Corporation, Malvern, PA; *U.S. Public*, pg. 1463
La Greca, Salvatore, Exec. V.P. & Chief Fin. Officer-Intl.--McCann-Erickson Worldwide, New York, NY; *U.S. Public*, *pg. 909*
Laba, Richard, Chief Fin. Officer--Kelvinator Appliances, Dublin, OH; *Int'l*, pg. 440
Labbett, John, Chief Fin. Officer--House of Fabrics, Inc., Sherman Oaks, CA; *U.S. Public*, pg. 842
Laberge, Thomas W., Chief Fin. Officer & V.P.-Fin.--Tembec Inc., Montreal, Canada; *Int'l*, pg. 1374
Laborde, Clifford, Sr. V.P., Gen. Counsel & Sec.--Tidewater Inc., New Orleans, LA; *U.S. Public*, pg. 1608
LaBuda, Mark, Chief Fin. Officer--Tosoh SMD, Inc., Grove City, OH; *Int'l*, pg. 1407
Lacassagne, Laurent, Chief Fin. Officer--PR Europe, Paris, France; *Int'l*, pg. 566
Lacey, Daniel A., Chief Fin. Officer--The Bakersfield Californian, Bakersfield, CA; *U.S. Private*, pg. 112
Lacey, David E., Chief Fin. Officer & Exec. V.P.--Storage Technology Corporation, Louisville, CO; *U.S. Public*, pg. 1522
Lacy, Alan, Treas.--Ridg's Finer Foods, Garland, TX; *U.S. Public*, pg. 1288
Lacy, Alan J., Chief Fin. Officer & Exec. V.P.--Sears, Roebuck and Co., Hoffman Estates, IL; *U.S. Public*, pg. 1452

Lacy, Paul A., Chief Fin. Officer & V.P.-Fin.--Kronos Incorporated, Waltham, MA; *U.S. Public*, pg. 967

Lacy, Rose, Chief Fin. Officer--First Independence National Bank, Detroit, MI; *U.S. Public*, pg. 635

Ladd, T.F., Chief Fin. Officer--Compania Hulera Goodyear-Oxo Sociedad Anonima, Mexico, Mexico; *U.S. Public*, pg. 753

Ladecky, Robert, Chief Fin. Officer--Capsonic Group, Inc., Elgin, IL; *U.S. Private*, pg. 207

Ladecky, Robert, Chief Fin. Officer--American Antenna Corp, Elgin, IL; *U.S. Private*, pg. 207

Ladner, Charles L., Chief Fin. Officer, Sr. V.P.-Fin. & Treas.--UGI Corporation, King of Prussia, PA; *U.S. Public*, pg. 1653

LaDue, Jack W., Pres. & Treas.--Rochester Gauges Inc. Of Texas, Dallas, TX; *U.S. Private*, pg. 440

LaFauci, Peter, Chief Fin. Officer--Jay Advertising, Inc., Rochester, NY; *U.S. Private*, pg. 583

Lafollette, Matt, Chief Fin. Officer--EB5 Corporation, Portland, OR; *U.S. Private*, pg. 353

LaForte, Mario J., Chief Fin. Officer--Minyard Food Stores, Inc., Coppell, TX; *U.S. Private*, pg. 752

Lagana, John M., Chief Fin. Officer--Wenner Media, New York, NY; *U.S. Private*, pg. 1162

Lagana, John M., Chief Fin. Officer & V.P.--Rolling Stone Magazine, New York, NY; *U.S. Private*, pg. 1162

Lagana, John M., Chief Fin. Officer--Us Magazine, New York, NY; *U.S. Private*, pg. 1162

Lagowski, Lawrence A., Chief Fin. Officer & Sec.--Indeck Power Equipment Company, Wheeling, IL; *U.S. Private*, pg. 559

Lahr, Mitch, Chief Fin. Officer--Stella Foods, Inc., Green Bay, WI; *U.S. Private*, pg. 1040

Lahr, Mitch, Chief Fin. Officer, V.P. & Sec.--Morgan Products Ltd., Williamsburg, VA; *U.S. Public*, pg. 1132

Laidler, Stan F., Chief Fin. Officer--Laboratoire LaChartre S.A., Blois, France; *U.S. Public*, pg. 1331

Laiken, Lou, Controller--Rainbow Apparel Distribution Center, Brooklyn, NY; *U.S. Private*, pg. 907

Laing, Tim, Chief Fin. Officer--Young & Rubicam Australia/New Zealand, Sydney, Australia; *U.S. Private*, pg. 1198

Laino, Vince, Chief Fin. Officer & V.P.--Roy F. Weston, Inc., West Chester, PA; *U.S. Public*, pg. 1761

Laird, John E., III, Chief Fin. Officer & V.P.-Opers.--Laird & Company, Eatontown, NJ; *U.S. Private*, pg. 642

Lajoie, Keith B., Chief Fin. Officer--The Grandoe Corp., Gloversville, NY; *U.S. Private*, pg. 469

Lajoie, Richard J., Chief Fin. Officer--Belcan Corporation, Cincinnati, OH; *U.S. Private*, pg. 131

Lalor, Michael A., Chief Fin. Officer, V.P.-Fin. & Treas.--State Industries Inc., Ashland City, TN; *U.S. Private*, pg. 1036

Lam, Ron, Chief Fin. Officer & Sr. V.P.--Universal Studios Hollywood, Universal City, CA; *Int'l*, pg. 1216

Lam, Steven, Chief Fin. Officer & V.P.-Fin.--Star Video Entertainment, L.P., Jersey City, NJ; *U.S. Private*, pg. 1132

Lamadrid, Carlos, Chief Fin. Officer, Sr. V.P. & Sec.--Pope & Talbot, Inc., Portland, OR; *U.S. Public*, pg. 1316

Lamb, Ed, Chief Fin. Officer & Sr. V.P.--Fremont Financial Corporation, Santa Monica, CA; *U.S. Public*, pg. 681

Lambach, Tom, Chief Fin. Officer--Quaker Alloy, Inc., Myerstown, PA; *U.S. Public*, pg. 142

Lambert, Robert, Chm. Bd.--Aviall, Inc., Dallas, TX; *U.S. Public*, pg. 154

Lambert, Thomas W., Chief Fin. Officer & Exec. V.P.--First of America Bank Corporation, Kalamazoo, MI; *U.S. Public*, pg. 636

Lambesis, Vicki, Vice Chm., Chief Fin. Officer & Chief Oper. Officer--Lambesis, Del Mar, CA; *U.S. Private*, pg. 644

Lamers, Bradley K., Chief Fin. Officer, V.P., Treas. & Sec.--Alternative Resources Corporation, Lincolnshire, IL; *U.S. Public*, pg. 59

Lamorte, Tony, Chief Fin. Officer--Sentinel Consumer Products, Inc., Mentor, OH; *U.S. Private*, pg. 984

Lamp, Robert, Chief Fin. Officer & V.P.-Fin.--Hypro Corporation, New Brighton, MN; *U.S. Public*, pg. 1767

Lampe, Patricia, Chief Fin. Officer & Treas.--Chyron Corp., Melville, NY; *Int'l*, pg. 1372

Lampen, Richard, Dir.-Fin.--Spartan Stores Inc., Grand Rapids, MI; *U.S. Private*, pg. 1021

Lampro, Bob, Chief Fin. Officer--Empire Kosher Poultry, Inc., Mifflintown, PA; *U.S. Private*, pg. 374

Lampugnano, Phil, Chief Fin. Officer, V.P.-Fin. & Controller--Danka Business Systems, La Grange, IL; *Int'l*, pg. 379

Lamus, John, Chief Fin. Officer--Harveys of Bristol Limited, Bristol, United Kingdom; *Int'l*, pg. 63

Lanborg, Michael, Chief Fin. Officer--D. Anderson & Son Ltd., Stretford, United Kingdom; *Int'l*, pg. 659

Lancaster, Bruce, Chief Fin. Opers.--Acme Boot Co., Inc., El Paso, TX; *U.S. Private*, pg. 394

Lance, Lisa, Chief Fin. Officer, V.P. & Controller--Gateway Communications, Johnson City, NY; *U.S. Private*, pg. 693

Land, Thomas K., Chief Fin. Officer, Sr. V.P. & Asst. Sec.--Santa Fe Gaming Corporation, Las Vegas, NV; *U.S. Public*, pg. 1432

Land, Thomas K., Chief Fin. Officer--Casino Properties, Inc., Las Vegas, NV; *U.S. Public*, pg. 1432

Land, Thomas K., Chief Fin. Officer--Hacienda Hotel Inc., Las Vegas, NV; *U.S. Public*, pg. 1432

Land, Thomas K., Chief Fin. Officer--Hacienda Hawaiian Properties, Inc., Las Vegas, NV; *U.S. Public*, pg. 1432

Land, Thomas K., Chief Fin. Officer--Ever-Ski Properties, Inc., Las Vegas, NV; *U.S. Public*, pg. 1432

Land, Thomas K., Chief Fin. Officer--Sahara Resorts, Las Vegas, NV; *U.S. Public*, pg. 1432

Land, Thomas K., Chief Fin. Officer--Sahara Illinois Corp., Las Vegas, NV; *U.S. Public*, pg. 1432

Land, Thomas K., Chief Fin. Officer--Sahara Nevada Corp., Las Vegas, NV; *U.S. Public*, pg. 1432

Land, Thomas K., Chief Fin. Officer--Santa Fe Coffee Company, Las Vegas, NV; *U.S. Public*, pg. 1432

Land, Thomas K., Chief Fin. Officer--Santa Fe Hotel Inc., Las Vegas, NV; *U.S. Public*, pg. 1432

Land, Thomas K., Chief Fin. Officer--Pioneer Finance Corp., Las Vegas, NV; *U.S. Public*, pg. 1432

Land, Thomas K., Chief Fin. Officer--Sahara Mississippi Management Company, Inc., Las Vegas, NV; *U.S. Public*, pg. 1432

Land, Thomas K., Chief Fin. Officer--Sahara Parkville, Inc., Las Vegas, NV; *U.S. Public*, pg. 1432

Land, Thomas K., Chief Fin. Officer--Santa Fe Valley, Inc., Las Vegas, NV; *U.S. Public*, pg. 1432

Landa, Tom J., Chief Fin. Officer--AmeriSteel, Tampa, FL; *U.S. Private*, pg. 65

Landau, Ellis, Chief Fin. Officer, Exec. V.P. & Treas.--Boyd Gaming Corporation, Las Vegas, NV; *U.S. Public*, pg. 249

Landes, Barbara, Chief Fin. Officer--Watson Wyatt Worldwide, Bethesda, MD; *U.S. Private*, pg. 1154

Landgraf, Kurt M., Chief Fin. Officer--Du Pont (E.I. Du Pont De Nemours & Co.), Wilmington, DE; *U.S. Public*, pg. 530

Landis, Edgar D., Exec. V.P.-Fin.--CDI Corp., Philadelphia, PA; *U.S. Public*, pg. 276

Landry, Gregory G., Chief Fin. Officer & Exec. V.P.-Fin.--Dairy Mart Convenience Stores, Inc., Cuyahoga Falls, OH; *U.S. Public*, pg. 476

Landry, James E., Chief Fin. Officer & Exec. V.P.--United Piece Dye Works, LP, New York, NY; *U.S. Private*, pg. 1123

Landry, W.D., Chief Fin. Officer--Fischbach Corporation, Englewood, CO; *U.S. Public*, pg. 84

Landsberg, David, Chief Fin. Officer & V.P.-Fin.--The Miami Herald, Miami, FL; *U.S. Public*, pg. 964

Lane, Chris, Chief Fin. Officer--White Cap Industries, Inc., Costa Mesa, CA; *U.S. Public*, pg. 1765

Lane, J. Kirby, Chief Fin. Officer--Delta Pride Catfish, Inc., Indianola, MS; *U.S. Private*, pg. 322

Lane, Leman G., Controller--Stanley Roberts, Inc., Lodi, NJ; *U.S. Private*, pg. 936

Lane, Robert W., Chief Fin. Officer & Sr. V.P.-Fin./Tax/Acctg.--Deere & Company, Moline, IL; *U.S. Public*, pg. 491

Lane, Robert W., Chief Fin. Officer & V.P.--John Deere Capital Corporation, Reno, NV; *U.S. Public*, pg. 492

Lane, Stan, Chief Fin. Officer--Floral Glass & Mirror, Inc., Hauppauge, NY; *U.S. Private*, pg. 414

Lang, Carol, Chief Fin. Officer & V.P.--Ramsay Health Care, Inc., Coral Gables, FL; *U.S. Public*, pg. 1360

Lang, Jeffery R., Chief Fin. Officer & Treas.--Maxon Corporation, Muncie, IN; *U.S. Private*, pg. 716

Lang, Marty, Chief Fin. Officer--Famous Footwear, Madison, WI; *U.S. Public*, pg. 262

Lang, Rudolph, Chief Fin. Officer--Amecom Div., College Park, MD; *U.S. Public*, pg. 1002

Lang, Rudolph E., Jr., Chief Fin. Officer & Sr. V.P.--Litton Industries, Inc., Woodland Hills, CA; *U.S. Public*, pg. 1002

Lang, Sanda J., Chief Fin. Officer--Brutger Equities, Inc., Saint Cloud, MN; *U.S. Private*, pg. 176

Langdon, Richard S., Chief Fin. Officer & Exec. V.P.-Fin. & Admin.--EEX Corporation, Houston, TX; *U.S. Public*, pg. 542

Lange, Betsy, Chief Fin. Officer & V.P.-Fin.--Adept Technology, Inc., San Jose, CA; *U.S. Public*, pg. 19

Langer, Carol B., Chief Fin. Officer, Treas. & Sec.--Comverse Network Systems, Wakefield, MA; *U.S. Public*, pg. 425

Langer, Carol B., Chief Fin. Officer, V.P.-Investor Rels. & Treas.--LTX Corporation, Westwood, MA; *U.S. Public*, pg. 972

Langer, Ralph, Chief Fin. Officer--Interleaf, Inc., Waltham, MA; *U.S. Public*, pg. 893

Langer, Tom, V.P.-Fin.--Banta Direct Marketing Group, Elk Grove Village, IL; *U.S. Public*, pg. 188

Langert, Andy, V.P.-Fin. & Intl.--ConAgra Frozen Food Company, Omaha, NE; *U.S. Public*, pg. 427

Langford, Thomas L., Chief Fin. Officer & Exec. V.P.--Stone & Webster, Incorporated, Boston, MA; *U.S. Public*, pg. 1519

Langin, Robert H., Acting Chief Fin. Officer & Controller--Crestbrook Forest Industries Ltd., Cranbrook, Canada; *Int'l*, pg. 348

Langley, Max T., Chief Fin. Officer, Sr. V.P., Treas. & Sec.--Reliability Incorporated, Houston, TX; *U.S. Public*, pg. 1373

Langley, Richard L., Chief Fin. Officer & Treas.--Sparton Corporation, Jackson, MI; *U.S. Public*, pg. 1496

Langlois, Norman, Chief Fin. Officer & Exec. V.P.--Butterworth-Heinemann USA, Newton, MA; *Int'l*, pg. 1094

Langsdorf, William B., Chief Fin. Officer & Exec. V.P.--HomeBase, Inc., Irvine, CA; *U.S. Public*, pg. 832

Lanier, Thomas, Exec. V.P., Chief Fin. Officer & Sec.--Salem Carpet Mills, Inc., Winston Salem, NC; *U.S. Public*, pg. 1464

Lankenau, Bob, Chief Fin. Officer--Sasson Licensing Corp., New York, NY; *U.S. Private*, pg. 967

Lannert, Robert C., Chief Fin. Officer & Exec. V.P.--Navistar International Corporation, Chicago, IL; *U.S. Public*, pg. 1167

Lanyi, A.S., Exec. V.P. & Chief Fin. Officer--Canadian Pacific Railway, Calgary, Canada; *Int'l*, pg. 258

LaPalme, Robert, Chief Fin. Officer--Jen-Coat Inc., Westfield, MA; *U.S. Public*, pg. 70

LaPenta, Robert, Pres. & Chief Fin. Officer--L3 Communications, New York, NY; *U.S. Private*, pg. 638

Lapiejko, Kenneth J., Chief Fin. Officer & Sr. V.P.--R.J. Reynolds Tobacco Company, Winston Salem, NC; *U.S. Public*, pg. 1355

Lapina, John J., Chief Fin. Officer & V.P.-Fin.--Elliott Company, Jeannette, PA; *U.S. Private*, pg. 373

LaPlante, Larry E., V.P.-Fin. & Treas.--Maine Public Service Company, Presque Isle, ME; *U.S. Public*, pg. 1038

Lapointe, Jacques, Chief Fin. Officer--Bozell Retail, Toronto, Canada; *Int'l*, pg. 209

LaPrad, Guy, Chief Fin. Officer--The Detroit Medical Center, Detroit, MI; *U.S. Private*, pg. 328

Lara, Francisco, Chief Fin. Officer--Opel Espana, Zaragoza, Spain; *U.S. Public*, pg. 724

Laramy, William, Chief Fin. Officer, Treas. & Controller--The Purdy Corporation, Manchester, CT; *U.S. Private*, pg. 895

Laraya, Rogelio G., Sr. V.P.-Fin. & Treas.--Benguet Corporation, Manila, Philippines; *Int'l*, pg. 186

Largent, William H., Chief Fin. Officer & Sr. V.P.--Applied Innovation Inc., Dublin, OH; *U.S. Public*, pg. 123

Larini, Ernest, Chief Fin. Officer & Exec. V.P.--Warner-Lambert Consumer Healthcare, Morris Plains, NJ; *U.S. Public*, pg. 1739

Larini, Ernest J., Chief Fin. Officer & V.P.--Warner-Lambert Company, Morris Plains, NJ; *U.S. Public*, pg. 1738

Larkin, Paul, Chief Fin. Officer--Schott Corporation, Wayzata, MN; *U.S. Private*, pg. 972

Larkin, Peter, Chief Fin. Officer--Enthone-OMI, Inc., West Haven, CT; *U.S. Public*, pg. 138

Larkin, Richard, Chief Fin. Officer--Plaskolite Inc., Columbus, OH; *U.S. Private*, pg. 870

LaRosa, Pat, Chief Fin. Officer & V.P.-Admin.--The Penn Companies, Philadelphia, PA; *U.S. Private*, pg. 849

Larrivee, Bill, Chief Fin. Officer--Bradford Industries, Inc., Lowell, MA; *U.S. Private*, pg. 163

Larroucau, Enrique M., Chief Fin. Officer & Sr. V.P.--Destec Energy, Inc., Houston, TX; *U.S. Public*, pg. 1146

Larsen, Edwin, Chief Fin. Officer, V.P. & Treas.--Megapulse, Inc., Bedford, MA; *U.S. Private*, pg. 729

Larsen, Jack, Chief Fin. Officer--Blommer Chocolate Co., Chicago, IL; *U.S. Private*, pg. 150

Larsen, Russ, Chief Fin. Officer--BookCrafters U.S.A. Inc., Chelsea, MI; *U.S. Public*, pg. 70

Larsen, Winnie, Chief Fin. Officer--Letraset AS, Herlev, Denmark; *Int'l*, pg. 461

Larson, Brian L., Chief Fin. Officer, V.P., Treas. & Sec.--Data Transmission Network Corporation, Omaha, NE; *U.S. Public*, pg. 486

Larson, Clayton C., Pres. & Chief Fin. Officer--Pacific Capital Bancorp, Salinas, CA; *U.S. Public*, pg. 1247

Larson, Elliot J., Chief Fin. Officer--Marvin Lumber & Cedar Company, Warroad, MN; *U.S. Private*, pg. 710

Larson, Jack, Chief Fin. Officer--Hirsh Company, Skokie, IL; *U.S. Public*, pg. 963

Larsson, Annika, Chief Fin. Officer--Knurr-Norge AS, Oslo, Norway; *Int'l*, pg. 739

Larsson, Annika, Chief Fin. Officer--Knurr Sverige AB, Kista, Sweden; *Int'l*, pg. 739

Larsson, Mats, Chief Fin. Officer--Neste Kjemi A/S, Larvik, Norway; *Int'l*, pg. 915

Larsson, Stig-Arne, Chief Fin. Officer & Exec. V.P.--Telia AB, Farsta, Sweden; *Int'l*, pg. 1373

Larsson, William D., Chief Fin. Officer & V.P.--Precision Castparts Corp., Portland, OR; *U.S. Public*, pg. 1320

LaRusso, David, Chief Fin. Officer--UNR-Rohn Div., Peoria, IL; *U.S. Public*, pg. 1404

LaRusso, David V., Chief Fin. Officer, Sr. V.P.-Fin. & Treas.--ROHN Industries, Inc., Peoria, IL; *U.S. Public*, pg. 1404

Lasa, F.J., Chief Fin. Officer--Duperial S.A.I.C., Buenos Aires, Argentina; *Int'l*, pg. 664

Lash, Fred, Chief Fin. Officer, Sr. V.P. & Treas.--Hooper Holmes Corporation, Basking Ridge, NJ; *U.S. Public*, pg. 835

Lash, Steven M., Chief Fin. Officer, Exec. V.P. & Treas.--FPA Medical Management, Inc., San Diego, CA; *U.S. Public*, pg. 608

Laski, R.J., Chief Fin. Officer & V.P.--Clearing-Niagara, Buffalo, NY; *U.S. Private*, pg. 196

Lasko, John C., Chm. Bd., Pres. & Treas.--Republic Die & Tool Company, Belleville, MI; *U.S. Private*, pg. 923

Laster, Larry J., Chief Fin. Officer & Exec. V.P.--Intergraph Corporation, Huntsville, AL; *U.S. Public*, pg. 890

Lataille, Ronald, Chief Fin. Officer--UFP Technology, Georgetown, MA; *U.S. Private*, pg. 1112

Latendresse, Gary P., Chief Fin. Officer & V.P.--Rouge Steel Company, Dearborn, MI; *U.S. Public*, pg. 1406

Lattanzio, David, Chief Fin. Officer & V.P.-Fin. & Admin.--PharmChem Laboratories, Inc., Menlo Park, CA; *U.S. Public*, pg. 1285

Lau, Constance H., Chief Fin. Officer & Treas.--HEI Power Corp., Honolulu, HI; *U.S. Public*, pg. 800

Laubocher, Roger, Chief Fin. Officer--Action Instruments, Inc., San Diego, CA; *U.S. Private*, pg. 15

Lauer, J. Michael, Chief Fin. Officer & Exec. V.P.--MGIC Investment Corporation, Milwaukee, WI; *U.S. Public*, pg. 1026

Lauer, J. Michael, Chief Fin. Officer & Exec. V.P.--Mortgage Guaranty Insurance Corporation, Milwaukee, WI; *U.S. Public*, pg. 1026

Lauer, Steven, Chief Fin. Officer & Exec. V.P.--Topco Associates, Inc., Skokie, IL; *U.S. Private*, pg. 1091

Lauer, Steven K., Chief Fin. Officer--Shand, Morahan & Co., Inc., Evanston, IL; *U.S. Public*, pg. 1046

Lauer, Thomas H., Chief Fin. Officer & Sr. V.P.--Advent International, Boston, MA; *U.S. Private*, pg. 22

Laughlin, Jeff, Chief Fin. Officer--Lion Brothers Company, Inc., Owings Mills, MD; *U.S. Private*, pg. 669

Laughlin, William M., V.P.-Fin. Opers. Support--Ikon Office Solutions, Inc., Malvern, PA; *U.S. Public*, pg. 862

Laurence, Joseph A., Chief Fin. Officer & Exec. V.P.--LCI International, Inc., Dublin, OH; *U.S. Public*, pg. 969

Laurent, Jean Marie, Chief Fin. Officer & V.P.-Fin.--Poliet, Courbevoie, France; *Int'l*, pg. 1177

Laurent, Robert, Chief Fin. Officer--Fedders North America, Inc., Whitehouse, NJ; *U.S. Public*, pg. 614

Laurent, Robert Jr., Chief Fin. Officer & Exec. V.P.-Fin. & Admin.--Fedders Corporation, Liberty Corner, NJ; *U.S. Public*, pg. 614

Laures, Gerald M., V.P.-Fin., Sec. & Treas.--Cobra Electronics Corporation, Chicago, IL; *U.S. Public*, pg. 391

Lauricella, William J., Chief Fin. Officer, V.P. & Treas.--Baldwin Technology Company, Inc., Norwalk, CT; *U.S. Public*, pg. 169
Laut, M., Treas.--Intertec Presentations, Englewood, CO; *U.S. Public*, pg. 1328
Lautemann, George, Chief Fin. Officer & V.P.--Sara Lee Direct, Winston Salem, NC; *U.S. Public*, pg. 1434
LaValle, John W., Chief Fin. Officer, Sr. V.P. & Sec.--Trikon Technologies Inc., Chatsworth, CA; *U.S. Public*, pg. 1638
Lavelle, Joe, Chief Fin. Officer--Masterfoods Ltd., Dublin, Ireland; *U.S. Private*, pg. 707
Lavelle, John, Controller--Koch Engineering Company, Inc., Akron, OH; *U.S. Private*, pg. 628
Lavelle, Michael, Chief Fin. Officer--Damascus Bishop Tube Co., Greenville, PA; *Int'l*, pg. 842
LaVigne, Gregory P., Treas.--The Reliable Life Insurance Company, Webster Groves, MO; *U.S. Public*, pg. 1374
Lavigne, Leo R., Chief Fin. Officer & Sec.--Sanitary-Dash Manufacturing Co., Inc., North Grosvenordale, CT; *U.S. Public*, pg. 1795
Lavigne, Louis J., Jr., Chief Fin. Officer & V.P.--Genentech, Inc., South San Francisco, CA; *Int'l*, pg. 1120
Lavoie, Russell, Chief Fin. Officer--Computer Corporation of America, Framingham, MA; *U.S. Private*, pg. 260
LaVoy, Tom, Chief Fin. Officer--Supershuttle Inc., Phoenix, AZ; *U.S. Private*, pg. 1056
Law, Ben, Chief Fin. Officer--Sureco Inc., Fort Valley, GA; *U.S. Public*, pg. 1390
Lawlor, Lawrence, Chief Fin. Officer--Agromac International, Inc., Gering, NE; *U.S. Private*, pg. 27
Lawlor, Thomas J., Jr., Chief Fin. Officer & Sr. V.P.--Boeing Realty Corporation, Long Beach, CA; *U.S. Public*, pg. 241
Lawn, Gregory T., Chief Fin. Officer & V.P.-Fin. & Admin.--Red Devil Inc., Union, NJ; *U.S. Private*, pg. 915
Lawrence, H.G., V.P.-Fin.--UOP, Des Plaines, IL; *U.S. Public*, pg. 52
Lawrence, James A., Chief Fin. Officer & Exec. V.P.--Northwest Airlines Corp., Saint Paul, MN; *U.S. Public*, pg. 1199
Lawrence, Jim, Chief Fin. Officer & Exec. V.P.--Northwest Airlines, Inc., Saint Paul, MN; *U.S. Public*, pg. 1200
Lawrence, Randall L., Chief Fin. Officer & Sr. V.P.--Detroit Diesel Corp., Detroit, MI; *U.S. Private*, pg. 850
Lawrence, William, Chief Fin. Officer & Sr. V.P.--Jay Jacobs, Inc., Seattle, WA; *U.S. Public*, pg. 922
Lawrence, William S., Chief Fin. Officer & Sr. V.P.-Fin.--General Datacomm Industries, Inc., Middlebury, CT; *U.S. Public*, pg. 708
Lawry, Donald A., Exec. V.P.-Corp. Fin.--Southwest National Corporation, Greensburg, PA; *U.S. Public*, pg. 1493
Lawry, Donald A., Exec. V.P.--Southwest National Bank of Pennsylvania, Greensburg, PA; *U.S. Public*, pg. 1493
Lawson, James, Chief Fin. Officer--Barry-Wehmiller Company, Saint Louis, MO; *U.S. Private*, pg. 118
Laxton, David, Chief Fin. Officer--Thomas Pipe & Steel, Inc., Baton Rouge, LA; *U.S. Private*, pg. 508
Lay, F. Edwin, Jr., Chief Fin. Officer & Treas.--Lay's Fine Foods, Knoxville, TN; *U.S. Private*, pg. 655
Lay, Randall R., Chief Fin. Officer & V.P.--International Specialty Products, Inc., Wayne, NJ; *U.S. Public*, pg. 858
Laybourne, Linda, Chief Fin. Officer & Treas.--Sues, Young & Brown Inc., Baldwin Park, CA; *U.S. Private*, pg. 1049
Layer, Yvon, Chief Fin. Officer--Millipore S.A., Molsheim, France; *U.S. Public*, pg. 1113
Layman, Harold E., Chief Fin. Officer & Exec. V.P.--Blount, Inc., Montgomery, AL; *U.S. Public*, pg. 238
Layne, Audrey, Pres. & Chief Fin. Officer--The Great Atlantic Management Company, Hampton, VA; *U.S. Private*, pg. 473
Layton McCown, D., Chief Fin. Officer--Forest City Commercial Construction Company, Inc., Cleveland, OH; *U.S. Public*, pg. 668
Layton, Steve, Chief Fin. Officer--Alro Group, Jackson, MI; *U.S. Private*, pg. 45
Lazarcheck, Walter, Chief Fin. Officer & V.P.--Bridgeport Machines, Inc., Bridgeport, CT; *U.S. Public*, pg. 251
Le Fevre, Paul, Chief Fin. Officer & Exec. V.P.-Strategic Plng. & Mktg.--Keyport Life Insurance Company, Boston, MA; *U.S. Private*, pg. 666
Le Roux, Pierre, Chief Fin. Officer, V.P. & Dir. Mngmt. Control--Alcatel N.V., Amsterdam, Netherlands; *Int'l*, pg. 55
Lea, Anthony W., Grp. Fin. Dir.--Minorco, Luxembourg, Luxembourg; *Int'l*, pg. 77
Lea, Leiv, Chief Fin. Officer, V.P. & Sec.--Hill Phoenix, Colonial Heights, VA; *U.S. Public*, pg. 521
Leach, Anthony, Chief Fin. Officer & Exec. V.P.--Occidental Petroleum Corporation, Los Angeles, CA; *U.S. Public*, pg. 1210
Leach, Brock, Pres. & Chief Fin. Officer--Frito-Lay Company, Plano, TX; *U.S. Public*, pg. 1277
Leach, Chuck, Chief Fin. Officer--MFG Tray Co., Linesville, PA; *U.S. Private*, pg. 756
Leach, Wayne, Chief Fin. Officer--New Zealand Milk Products (CIS) AO, Moscow, Russia; *Int'l*, pg. 923
Leader, Lennert, Chief Fin. Officer, Sr. V.P. & Treas.--America Online Incorporated, Dulles, VA; *U.S. Public*, pg. 66
Leadle, Colin, Chief Fin. Officer--Ilco Unican Australia (Pty.) Ltd., Willoughby, Australia; *Int'l*, pg. 1432
Leary, Dennis, Chief Fin. Officer & Treas.--Creative Marketing International Corp., West Chicago, IL; *U.S. Private*, pg. 287
Leathe, Jeffrey C., Chief Fin. Officer--Erie Scientific Co., Portsmouth, NH; *U.S. Public*, pg. 1545
Leaver, Jack P., Chief Fin. Officer--Coast Business Credit, Los Angeles, CA; *U.S. Public*, pg. 872
Lebens, Jeffrey K., Chief Fin. Officer, V.P. & Treas.--Intermountain Industries, Inc., Boise, ID; *U.S. Private*, pg. 568
Lebens, Jeffrey K., Chief Fin. Officer--III Exploration Co., Boise, ID; *U.S. Private*, pg. 568
Leber, Mike, Chief Fin. Officer--Alcone Marketing Group, Irvine, CA; *U.S. Public*, pg. 1223
LeBlanc, Eddie M., Chief Fin. Officer & Sr. V.P.--Coho Energy, Inc., Dallas, TX; *U.S. Public*, pg. 396
LeBlanc, James, Jr., Chief Fin. Officer & Corp. Controller--Gaylord Chemical Corporation, Slidell, LA; *U.S. Public*, pg. 704
LeBlanc, Roger D., Chief Fin. Officer & Controller--Pollack Corporation, Scarborough, ME; *U.S. Private*, pg. 874
Lee, Byung-Uk, Chief Fin. Officer--Jaeneung Education Co., Ltd., Seoul, Korea; *Int'l*, pg. 697
Lee, C. William, Chief Fin. Officer & V.P.-Fin.--Matrix Service Company, Tulsa, OK; *U.S. Public*, pg. 1057
Lee, Charles P., Chief Fin. Officer--Muralo Co., Inc., Bayonne, NJ; *U.S. Private*, pg. 767
Lee, Clarence, III, Chief Fin. Officer--Icon International, Stamford, CT; *U.S. Private*, pg. 556
Lee, D., Chief Fin. Officer--Olivetti U.K. Ltd., London, United Kingdom; *Int'l*, pg. 1003
Lee, Daniel R., Chief Fin. Officer, Sr. V.P.-Fin. & Devel. & Treas.--Mirage Resorts Incorporated, Las Vegas, NV; *U.S. Public*, pg. 1116
Lee, Doo-Hwan, Pres.--Ssangyong Uni-Charm Co., Ltd., Kumi, Korea; *Int'l*, pg. 1291
Lee, Eric, Chief Fin. Officer--Electronica Condor De Mexico, S.A., Cuauhtemoc, Mexico; *U.S. Public*, pg. 1419
Lee, Eric, Chief Fin. Officer--Wedgestone Automotive Corp., Irwindale, CA; *U.S. Public*, pg. 1751
Lee, Eric, Chief Fin. Officer--Fey Mfg. Co., Inc., Irwindale, CA; *U.S. Public*, pg. 1751
Lee, Eric H., Chief Fin. Officer--Wedgestone Financial Inc., Irwindale, CA; *U.S. Public*, pg. 1751
Lee, Gary, Chief Fin. Officer--Great Plains Manufacturing, Inc., Salina, KS; *U.S. Private*, pg. 475
Lee, James, Chief Fin. Officer--La Victoria Foods, Inc., City of Industry, CA; *U.S. Private*, pg. 641
Lee, Jeong-Ho, Chief Fin. Officer--Namkwang Engineering & Construction Co., Ltd., Seoul, Korea; *Int'l*, pg. 1291
Lee, Jesse, Chief Fin. Officer, Sr. V.P. & Sec.--The IDI Group Companies, Arlington, VA; *U.S. Private*, pg. 554
Lee, Kwan-Sep, Chief Fin. Officer--Ssangyong Investment & Finance Co., Ltd., Inchon, Korea; *Int'l*, pg. 1292
Lee, Robert E., Chief Fin. Officer--Carver, Inc., Savannah, GA; *U.S. Private*, pg. 217
Lee, Robert E., Chief Fin. Officer & V.P.--Hanson North America, Woodbridge, NJ; *Int'l*, pg. 593
Lee, Sang-Rak, Chief Fin. Officer--Ssangyong Engineering & Construction Co., Ltd., Seoul, Korea; *Int'l*, pg. 1291
Lee, Shu-Shu, Chief Fin. Officer--China Hi-Ment Corp., Kaohsiung, Taiwan; *Int'l*, pg. 285
Leech, Ted A., Chief Fin. Officer--Van Waters & Rogers Inc., Kirkland, WA; *Int'l*, pg. 1147
Leeland, Craig, Chief Fin. Officer--Frank Russell Company, Tacoma, WA; *U.S. Private*, pg. 952
Lefebvre, Henri, Dir.-Controlling--Kali-Chemie Aktiengesellschaft, Hannover, Germany; *Int'l*, pg. 1278
Lefferts, E.A., Chief Fin. Officer--Golden Eagle Distributors, Inc., Tucson, AZ; *U.S. Private*, pg. 460
Legault, G.J., Chief. Fin. Officer & Sr. V.P.-Fin. & Admin.--AGRA Monenco, Oakville, Canada; *Int'l*, pg. 30
Legere, Ron, Chief Fin. Officer & V.P.-Fin.--Hackney and Sons, Inc., Washington, NC; *U.S. Private*, pg. 1097
Legere, Ronald J., Chief Fin. Officer--Transportation Technologies, Inc., Washington, NC; *U.S. Private*, pg. 1097
LeGrande, E. David, Mng. Dir.-Export Division & Treas.--Gudebrod, Inc., Pottstown, PA; *U.S. Private*, pg. 486
Lehman, Michael, Chief Fin. Officer & V.P.--Sun Microsystems, Inc., Palo Alto, CA; *U.S. Public*, pg. 1531
Lehmann, Thomas R., Chief. Fin. Officer & Controller--JSB Financial, Lynbrook, NY; *U.S. Public*, pg. 919
Lehnerer, Henry W., Chief Fin. Officer--Selkirk Metalbestos, Dallas, TX; *U.S. Public*, pg. 1794
Lehr, Harry, Sr. V.P.-Fin.--Alaska Air Group, Inc., Seattle, WA; *U.S. Public*, pg. 35
Lei, Zuhua, Chief Fin. Officer--Bank of China, Beijing, China; *Int'l*, pg. 152
Leidner, J.H., Chief Fin. Officer & Sr. V.P.--Fuller Company, Bethlehem, PA; *Int'l*, pg. 475
Leiferman, Ronald, Chief Fin. Officer & Sr. V.P.--Leo A. Daly Company, Omaha, NE; *U.S. Private*, pg. 309
Leinweber, M., Chief Fin. Officer--Howard Maschinenfabrik GmbH, Michelstadt, Germany; *Int'l*, pg. 1387
Leitner, George, V.P.-Natl. Accts.--The Disney Channel, Burbank, CA; *U.S. Public*, pg. 513
Leitner, Howard M., Chief Fin. Officer & Sr. V.P.--Chock Full O' Nuts Corporation, New York, NY; *U.S. Public*, pg. 351
Leke, Paulo, Chief Fin. Officer & Dir.-Fin.--Zivi S.A. Cutelaria, Porto Alegre, Brazil; *Int'l*, pg. 1529
Lemajeur, Jeffrey W., Chief Fin. Officer, V.P.-Fin. & Treas.--Binks Sames Corporation, Franklin Park, IL; *U.S. Public*, pg. 229
LeMarchand, Francois, V.P. & Treas.--Bombardier Inc., Montreal, Canada; *Int'l*, pg. 199
Lembeck, Larry, Chief Fin. Officer & Controller--Stadelman Fruit L.L.C., Yakima, WA; *U.S. Private*, pg. 1028
Lemice, Maurine, Chief Fin. Controller--Livingston S.A., Rungis, France; *Int'l*, pg. 212
Lemley, John T., Chief Fin. Officer & V.P.--Evans & Sutherland Computer Corporation, Salt Lake City, UT; *U.S. Public*, pg. 595
Lemon, John, Chief Fin. Officer & V.P.--Adams Extract Co., Inc., Austin, TX; *U.S. Private*, pg. 16
Lemos, Robert A., Chief Fin. Officer, V.P.-Fin. & Treas.--Varian Associates, Inc., Palo Alto, CA; *U.S. Public*, pg. 1710
Lenius, Robert L., Jr., Chief Fin. Officer & V.P.--First Team Sports Inc., Anoka, MN; *U.S. Public*, pg. 638
Lennox, Michael, Chief Fin. Officer--Weatherall Green & Smith, London, United Kingdom; *Int'l*, pg. 1488
Leno, Sam R., Chief Fin. Officer & Exec. V.P.--Corporate Express, Inc., Broomfield, CO; *U.S. Public*, pg. 449
Lensselink, P.J., Chief Fin. Officer--Boon Edam Inc., Salt Lake City, UT; *Int'l*, pg. 202
Lentych, Larry E., Chief Fin. Officer & Treas.--1st Source Corporation, South Bend, IN; *U.S. Public*, pg. 638
Lentz, Rudi, Chief Fin. Officer--Fairchild Aerospace Corporation, San Antonio, TX; *U.S. Private*, pg. 391
Lenz, Lawrence, Chief Fin. Officer & V.P.--Doak Dermatologics, Westbury, NY; *U.S. Public*, pg. 250
Lenz, Rudi, Chief Fin. Officer--Fairchild Dornier USA, San Antonio, TX; *U.S. Private*, pg. 391
Lenzmeier, Allen U., Chief Fin. Officer & Exec. V.P.--Best Buy Co., Inc., Eden Prairie, MN; *U.S. Public*, pg. 223
Leo, James J., Corp. Controller--Wegmans Food Markets, Inc., Rochester, NY; *U.S. Private*, pg. 1158
Leon, Luis, Chief Fin. Officer, Sr. V.P. & Treas.--GS Industries, Inc., Charlotte, NC; *U.S. Private*, pg. 435
Leonard, Charles H., Chief Fin. Officer & Sr. V.P.--TEPPCO Partners L.P., Houston, TX; *U.S. Public*, pg. 534
Leonard, Charles H., Sr. V.P. & Chief Fin. Officer--Texas Eastern Products Pipeline Company, L.P., Houston, TX; *U.S. Public*, pg. 535
Leonard, Don, Chief Fin. Officer--Mark Fabricks, Inc., Los Angeles, CA; *U.S. Private*, pg. 704
Leonard, Ed, Chief Fin. Officer--Doubleday Direct, Garden City, NY; *Int'l*, pg. 191
Leonard, J., Dir.-Fin.--Thilmany Division, Kaukauna, WI; *U.S. Public*, pg. 903
Leonard, Timothy M., Chief Fin. Officer, V.P.-Fin. & Treas.--DBT Online, Inc., Las Vegas, NV; *U.S. Public*, pg. 472
Leonardi, Al, Chief Fin. Officer--Esselte Meto, Morris Plains, NJ; *Int'l*, pg. 460
Leonardi, Harry, Chief Fin. Officer--Lykes Brothers Inc., Tampa, FL; *U.S. Private*, pg. 682
Lepri, Daniel B., Chief Fin. Officer & V.P.--Rheem Manufacturing Co., New York, NY; *Int'l*, pg. 1022
Lerch, Stephen E., Chief Fin. Officer & Exec. V.P.--Transmedia Network Inc., Miami, FL; *U.S. Public*, pg. 1631
Lerman, Robert, Chief Fin. Officer--Isfel Company, Inc., Rahway, NJ; *U.S. Private*, pg. 576
Lesh, Rodger L., Chief Fin. Officer, V.P. & Treas.--Lewis Brothers Bakeries, Inc., Evansville, IN; *U.S. Private*, pg. 665
Lesher, Steve, Chief Fin. Officer--Woodstream Corporation, Lititz, PA; *U.S. Public*, pg. 566
Leshin, Arthur, Chief Fin. Officer--Gucci America Inc., Secaucus, NJ; *Int'l*, pg. 686
Lesniak, Alicja, Chief Fin. Officer, Europe & Dir.--BBDO Worldwide Inc., New York, NY; *U.S. Public*, pg. 1223
Lessard, Pierre N., Chief Fin. Officer & V.P.-Fin.--BCE Mobile Communications Inc., Saint-Laurent, Canada; *Int'l*, pg. 115
Lesser, Seymour H., Chief Fin. & Chief Admin. Officer & Exec. V.P.--Arts & Entertainment Network/ABC/NBC, New York, NY; *U.S. Public*, pg. 512
Lesser, Seymour H., Chief Fin. & Chief Admin. Officer & Exec. V.P.--Arts & Entertainment Network/ABC/NBC, New York, NY; *U.S. Private*, pg. 516
Lester, Rick, Chief Fin. Officer, V.P. & Asst. Sec.--Domain Energy Corporation, Houston, TX; *U.S. Public*, pg. 515
Lester, Susan E., Chief Fin. Officer & Exec. V.P.--U.S. Bancorp, Minneapolis, MN; *U.S. Public*, pg. 1680
Lestochi, Robert, Treas. & Sec.--James Industries Inc., Hollidaysburg, PA; *U.S. Private*, pg. 580
Letham, Dennis J., Chief Fin. Officer & Sr. V.P.-Fin.--Anixter International, Chicago, IL; *U.S. Public*, pg. 115
Letham, G.L., Chief Fin. Officer--Armitage Shanks Limited, Rugeley, United Kingdom; *Int'l*, pg. 197
Letier, Scott, Chief Fin. Officer--Gorges/Quik-To-Fix Foods, Dallas, TX; *U.S. Private*, pg. 465
Leung, Elsie, Chief Oper. & Fin. Officer--Gemstar International Group Limited, Pasadena, CA; *U.S. Public*, pg. 705
Leung, Stephen, Chief Fin. Officer--Green Spot Packaging Inc., Claremont, CA; *U.S. Private*, pg. 477
Leunis, William G., III, Chief Fin. Officer, Sr. V.P.-Fin., Treas. & Sec.--Ultratech Stepper, Inc., San Jose, CA; *U.S. Public*, pg. 1663
Leutenegger, Aldo, Chief Oper. Officer--Swissmetal Italia s.r.l., Milan, Italy; *Int'l*, pg. 1427
LeVasseur, Gerald, Chief Fin. Officer--Pratt-Read Corporation, Bridgeport, CT; *U.S. Private*, pg. 879
Level, Leon J., Chief Fin. Officer, V.P. & Treas.--Computer Sciences Corporation, El Segundo, CA; *U.S. Public*, pg. 422
Lever, Ken, Chief Fin. Officer--Albright & Wilson plc, Oldbury, United Kingdom; *Int'l*, pg. 49
Levi, Mr., Chief Fin. Officer--P. Beretta S.P.A., Gardone Riviera, Italy; *Int'l*, pg. 187
Levin, Binnie J., Chief Fin. Officer & Exec. V.P.--Towne, Silverstein, Rotter Inc., New York, NY; *U.S. Private*, pg. 1093
Levin, Bruce, Chief Fin. Officer & Controller--ADWORKS, Inc., Washington, DC; *U.S. Private*, pg. 23
Levine, Arnold H., Chief Fin. Officer, V.P.-Fin., Treas. & Asst. Sec.--General Microwave Corporation, Amityville, NY; *U.S. Public*, pg. 717
Levine, Gary W., Chief Fin. Officer & V.P.-Fin.--CSP Inc., Billerica, MA; *U.S. Public*, pg. 283
Levine, Norman M., Chief Fin. Officer, V.P. & Controller--DeVry Institutes, Oak Brook Terrace, IL; *U.S. Public*, pg. 503
Levine, Paul, V.P.-Fin., Treas. & Sec.--Magnetic Analysis Corp., Mount Vernon, NY; *U.S. Private*, pg. 695
Levinson, Anthony, Chief Fin. Officer, V.P. & Treas.--Automobile Protection Corporation-APCO, Atlanta, GA; *U.S. Public*, pg. 150
Levinson, Anthony R., Chief Fin. Officer--The Aegis Group, Inc., Atlanta, GA; *U.S. Public*, pg. 150
Levinson, Lee, Chief Fin. Officer--Correctional Services Corporation, Sarasota, FL; *U.S. Public*, pg. 450
Levitt, Brian, Pres. & Chief Exec. Officer--Imasco Limited, Montreal, Canada; *Int'l*, pg. 112
Levy, David, Chief Fin. Officer & Exec. V.P.--Norman Levy Associates, Inc., Southfield, MI; *U.S. Private*, pg. 664

Levy, Lawrence B., Chief Fin. Officer & Exec. V.P.--Pixar Animation Studios, Richmond, CA; *U.S. Public*, pg. 1307
Levy, Philip R., Chief Fin. Officer & Exec. V.P.--American Reliable Insurance Company, Scottsdale, AZ; *U.S. Public*, pg. 67
Levy, Stuart, Chief Fin. Officer, V.P., Treas. & Sec.--Donnkenny, Inc., New York, NY; *U.S. Public*, pg. 519
Lewellen, Mitch, V.P.-Fin.--Shelby Group International, Inc., Memphis, TN; *U.S. Private*, pg. 991
Lewent, Judy C., Chief Fin. Officer & Sr. V.P.--Merck & Co., Inc., Whitehouse Station, NJ; *U.S. Public*, pg. 1090
Lewis, A.M., Treas.--The Thomson Corporation, Stamford, CT; *U.S. Public*, pg. 1599
Lewis, Chris, Chief Fin. Officer--Jabil Circuit, Inc., Saint Petersburg, FL; *U.S. Public*, pg. 919
Lewis, Dennis, Chief Fin. Officer--International Div., AM International, Mount Prospect, IL; *U.S. Public*, pg. 1141
Lewis, Jean M., Chief Fin. Officer--Aloette Cosmetics, Inc., West Chester, PA; *U.S. Public*, pg. 57
Lewis, Jeff, Chief Fin. Officer & Sr. V.P.--The Hunt Corporation, Indianapolis, IN; *U.S. Private*, pg. 548
Lewis, Jim, Chief Fin. Officer, V.P., Treas. & Sec.--Hale-Halsell Company, Tulsa, OK; *U.S. Private*, pg. 494
Lewis, Jim, Chief Fin. Officer--Ark-Mart, Tulsa, OK; *U.S. Private*, pg. 494
Lewis, Paul S., Dep. Chm. & Grp. Fin. Dir.--Tate & Lyle PLC, London, United Kingdom; *Int'l*, pg. 1356
Lewis, R. Gregory, Chief Fin. Officer & V.P.-Fin.--J. Alexanders Corporation, Nashville, TN; *U.S. Public*, pg. 40
Lewis, Richard H., Chm. Bd., Pres., Chief Exec. & Fin. Officer & Treas.--Prima Energy Corporation, Denver, CO; *U.S. Public*, pg. 1325
Lewis, Robert H., Chief Fin. Officer, V.P.-Fin. & Controller--John Boos & Company, Effingham, IL; *U.S. Private*, pg. 156
Lewitt, Charles, Chief Fin. Officer & Controller--Morrison Berkshire Inc., North Adams, MA; *U.S. Private*, pg. 762
Leybold, Timothy L., Chief Fin. Officer--RLC Industries Co., Dillard, OR; *U.S. Private*, pg. 905
Liebaers, Dirk, Chief Fin. Officer--SAIT-RadioHolland Group S.A., Brussels, Belgium; *Int'l*, pg. 1151
Liebaers, Dirk, Chief Fin. Officer & V.P.--Radio Holland Electronics, Almere, Netherlands; *Int'l*, pg. 1151
Lieberg, Eric N., Pres., Chief Fin. Officer & Exec. V.P.--Rundel Products, Inc., Portland, OR; *U.S. Private*, pg. 951
Lieberman, David, Chief Fin. Officer--Falcon Safety Products Inc., Somerville, NJ; *U.S. Private*, pg. 392
Lieberman, Gerald, Chief Fin. Officer--Fidelity Investments (FMR Corp.), Boston, MA; *U.S. Private*, pg. 402
Lieberora, Pamela Forbes, Chief Fin. Officer--Fel-Pro Incorporated, Skokie, IL; *U.S. Private*, pg. 399
Liebman, Howard M., Chief Fin. Officer & Exec. V.P.--Shorewood Packaging Corporation, New York, NY; *U.S. Public*, pg. 1468
Liebner, Mark, Chief Fin. Officer & Sr. V.P.--Rural Metro Corporation, Scottsdale, AZ; *U.S. Public*, pg. 1412
Liebowitz, Stu, Chief Fin. Officer--Sam Ash Music Corp., Hicksville, NY; *U.S. Private*, pg. 88
Liegel, Craig, Chief Fin. Officer & Asst. Sec.--Packerland Packing Co., Green Bay, WI; *U.S. Private*, pg. 833
Liem, James, Chief Fin. Officer & V.P.--Schuck & Sons Construction Co., Glendale, AZ; *U.S. Private*, pg. 973
Lies, James E., Chief Fin. Officer & Sr. V.P.--D.O.C. Optics Corporation, Southfield, MI; *U.S. Private*, pg. 305
Lifshatz, Stephen J., V.P.-Opers & Controller--Marcam Solutions, Inc., Newton, MA; *U.S. Public*, pg. 1042
Liggett, George, Chief Fin. Officer & Controller--Alliant Foodservice, Bensenville, IL; *U.S. Private*, pg. 244
Light, Kenneth B., Chief Fin. Officer, Chief Admin. Officer & Exec. V.P.--Allied Products Corporation, Chicago, IL; *U.S. Public*, pg. 48
Lightstone, Stephen, Chief Fin. Officer, Sr. V.P.-Fin. & Treas.--Payless Cashways, Inc., Kansas City, MO; *U.S. Public*, pg. 1267
Liang, T.Y., Chief Fin. Officer--Tainan Spinning Co., Ltd., Tai-nan, Taiwan; *Int'l*, pg. 1347
Lilienthal, Martin M., Chief Fin. Officer & Sr. V.P.--The Advest Group, Inc., Hartford, CT; *U.S. Public*, pg. 23
Lilienthal, Martin M., Chief Fin. Officer--Advest, Inc., Hartford, CT; *U.S. Public*, pg. 23
Liljebeck, Roy C., Chief Fin. Officer & Exec. V.P.--Airborne Freight Corporation, Seattle, WA; *U.S. Public*, pg. 32
Liljedahl, Arne, Sr. V.P. & Controller--Nordbanken AB, Stockholm, Sweden; *Int'l*, pg. 957
Lillis, Bernard, Chief Fin. Officer--Saratoga Brands, Inc., Lakewood, NJ; *U.S. Public*, pg. 1435
Lillis, Bernard F., Chief Fin. Officer--Cucina Classica Italiana, Inc., Lakewood, NJ; *U.S. Public*, pg. 1435
Lilly, Steven L., Chief Fin. Officer & Sr. V.P.--National Rural Utilities Cooperative Finance Corporation, Herndon, VA; *U.S. Private*, pg. 786
Limary, Remy, Chief Fin. Officer--Nielsen Sarl, Strasbourg, France; *Int'l*, pg. 462
Lin, Mei Chin, Chief Fin. Officer--China Steel Chemical Corp., Kao-hsiung, Taiwan; *Int'l*, pg. 286
Lincoln, Bill, V.P.-Fin.--Fox Television Stations Inc., Los Angeles, CA; *Int'l*, pg. 926
Lind, Ralph, Controller & Sec.--St. Croix Press, Inc., New Richmond, WI; *U.S. Private*, pg. 960
Lindahl, Dennis, Chief Fin. Officer--Holiday Companies, Bloomington, MN; *U.S. Private*, pg. 534
Lindborg, M., Chief Fin. Officer--AB Ferrolegeringar, Stockholm, Sweden; *U.S. Private*, pg. 735
Linden, David, Chief Fin. Officer & Sec.--Monrovia Nursery Co., Azusa, CA; *U.S. Private*, pg. 757
Linden, Mark, Chief Fin. Officer--Global Village Communication, Sunnyvale, CA; *U.S. Public*, pg. 748
Lindenauer, Arthur, Chief Fin. Officer & Exec. V.P.-Fin.--Schlumberger Limited, New York, NY; *U.S. Public*, pg. 1439
Lindgren, Alf, Chief Fin. Officer & Controller--Scancem AB, Malmo, Sweden; *Int'l*, pg. 1198
Lindholm, Rita, Chief Fin. Officer & Exec. V.P.--Ross Roy Communications, Inc., Bloomfield Hills, MI; *U.S. Private*, pg. 946
Lindley, William G., Treas. & Sec.--T.H. Rogers Lumber Co., Edmond, OK; *U.S. Private*, pg. 940
Lindner, Phil, Chief Fin. Officer & Sr. V.P.--MidAmerican Energy Holdings, Des Moines, IA; *U.S. Public*, pg. 1109
Lindner, Richard, Chief Fin. Officer--Acme Design Technology, Co., Crozet, VA; *U.S. Private*, pg. 13
Lindsay, Martha B., Chief Fin. Officer & V.P.-Fin.--AmeriGas Propane, Valley Forge, PA; *U.S. Public*, pg. 1653
Lindstrand, Kenneth, Chief Fin. Officer--Gyproc AB, Malmo, Sweden; *Int'l*, pg. 122
Lindstrom, Tom, Fin. Mgr.--DMB&B Helsinki, Helsinki, Finland; *U.S. Private*, pg. 303
Linehan, James B., Chief Fin. Officer--The Jewett Refrigerator Co., Inc., Buffalo, NY; *U.S. Private*, pg. 952
Linehan, James B., Chief Fin. Officer--Jewett International Corp., Buffalo, NY; *U.S. Private*, pg. 952
Linehan, John C., Chief Fin. Officer & Exec. V.P.--Kerr-McGee Corporation, Oklahoma City, OK; *U.S. Public*, pg. 952
Lines, Jim, Chief Fin. Officer, Gen. Counsel & Sec.--ITI Marketing Services, Inc., Omaha, NE; *U.S. Private*, pg. 555
Ling, Timothy H., Chief Fin. Officer--Unocal Corporation, El Segundo, CA; *U.S. Public*, pg. 1698
Lingen, Charles, Chief Fin. Officer & Sr. V.P.--The Sportsman's Guide, Inc., Saint Paul, MN; *U.S. Public*, pg. 1499
Lingen, Rick, Chief Fin. Officer--Lampert Yards, Inc., Saint Paul, MN; *U.S. Private*, pg. 645
Linger, Keith, Chief Fin. Officer--GN Rathdown, Ascot, United Kingdom; *Int'l*, pg. 537
Lingo, Irving E., Jr., Chief Fin. Officer--Bradley Real Estate, Inc., Northbrook, IL; *U.S. Public*, pg. 250
Link, Jim, Chief Fin. Officer--La Grange Foundry Inc., La Grange, MO; *U.S. Public*, pg. 142
Linley, Mike, Chief Fin. Officer--Milk Products Holdings (Latin America) Ltd., Fort Lauderdale, FL; *Int'l*, pg. 923
Linton, Bill, Chief Fin. Officer & Exec. V.P.--SHL Systemhouse, Ottawa, Canada; *Int'l*, pg. 1154
Lionel, Bouvier, Chief Fin. Officer--Societe de Distribution et d'Exportation Automobiles - SODEXA, Courbevoie, France; *Int'l*, pg. 1020
Lipczak, Dan, Chief Fin. Officer--ISS Darenas International A/S, Nivaa, Denmark; *Int'l*, pg. 656
Lipham, James B., Chief Fin. Officer & Sr. V.P.--Total System Services, Inc., Columbus, GA; *U.S. Public*, pg. 1550
Lipoff, Steven, Pres., Chief Fin. Officer & Treas.--Butler Foods, Inc., Philadelphia, PA; *U.S. Private*, pg. 190
Lipsas, Kathie, Chief Fin. Officer--Trident Financial Corporation, Raleigh, NC; *U.S. Private*, pg. 1103
Lipschitz, Henry, V.P.-Fin.--Dexter Magnetic Materials, Fremont, CA; *U.S. Public*, pg. 504
Lipschitz, Louis, Chief Fin. Officer & Exec. V.P.--Toys "R" Us, Inc., Paramus, NJ; *U.S. Public*, pg. 1626
Lipton, Steve, Chief Fin. Officer, V.P. & Controller--The Elder-Beerman Stores Corp., Dayton, OH; *U.S. Private*, pg. 367
Lis, Brad, Dir.-Investments--Carlson Real Estate Company, Minnetonka, MN; *U.S. Private*, pg. 212
Lisenby, J. Richard, Chief Fin. Officer & V.P.--Howell Corporation, Houston, TX; *U.S. Public*, pg. 843
Liska, P.J., Chief Fin. Officer & Exec. V.P.--The St. Paul Companies, Inc., Saint Paul, MN; *U.S. Public*, pg. 1429
List, Stephen T., Chief Fin. Officer--Colonial Penn Insurance Co., Norristown, PA; *U.S. Public*, pg. 712
Lista, Leslie, Controller--Scholastic Inc., New York, NY; *U.S. Public*, pg. 1440
Littauer, Robert, V.P. & Chief Fin. Officer--NeoRx Corporation, Seattle, WA; *U.S. Private*, pg. 791
Litten, C. Scott, Chief Fin. Officer & Exec. V.P.--Hills Stores Co., Canton, MA; *U.S. Public*, pg. 828
Little, Bradley A., Chief Fin. Officer, Sr. V.P.-Fin. & Treas.--Calton, Inc., Manalapan, NJ; *U.S. Public*, pg. 296
Little, William, V.P.-Treas.--Worzalla Publishing Co., Inc., Stevens Point, WI; *U.S. Private*, pg. 1191
Littlefield, George, Chief Fin. Officer & V.P.-Fin.--The Cardwell Machine Company, Richmond, VA; *U.S. Private*, pg. 209
Littlefield, Lawrence, Chief Fin. Officer & V.P.-Fin. & Admin.--Williams Telecommunications Systems, Inc., Houston, TX; *U.S. Public*, pg. 1769
Littmann, Jeffrey C., Chief Fin. Officer & V.P.--Ralph C. Wilson Enterprises, Detroit, MI; *U.S. Private*, pg. 1181
Liu, Joseph, Chief Fin. Officer & V.P.-Opers.--Diodes Incorporated, Westlake Village, CA; *U.S. Public*, pg. 510
Livingston, Philip B., Chief Fin. Officer & Sr. V.P.--Catalina Marketing Corporation, Saint Petersburg, FL; *U.S. Public*, *pg. 314*
Ljungberg, Robert, Chm. Bd., Pres., Chief Exec. & Chief Oper. Officer--Ultra Tool & Plastics, Inc., Amherst, NY; *U.S. Private*, pg. 1116
Lloyd, David G., Chief Fin. Officer & Sr. V.P.--Taco Cabana, San Antonio, TX; *U.S. Public*, pg. 1559
Lloyd, Rjay, Vice Chm. & Chief Fin. Officer--Forever Living Products International, Inc., Scottsdale, AZ; *U.S. Private*, *pg. 418*
Lloyd, Stuart, Chief Fin. Officer--Eisner, Petrou & Associates, Inc., Baltimore, MD; *U.S. Private*, pg. 366
Llusia, Jose Luis, Chief Fin. Officer--Esselte S.A., Terrassa, Spain; *Int'l*, pg. 461
Lo Coco, Anthony, Chief Fin. Officer--Chicago White Metal Casting, Inc., Bensenville, IL; *U.S. Private*, pg. 236
Lo, Dobbin, Pres. & Chief Fin. Officer--Robeson Appliance, Inc., Chino, CA; *U.S. Public*, pg. 1394
Loakso, Larry, Chief Fin. Officer--Jahn Foundry Corp., Springfield, MA; *U.S. Public*, pg. 142
LoCascio, Steven A., Interim Chief Fin. Officer, V.P. & Controller--King World Productions, Inc., New York, NY; *U.S. Public*, pg. 961
Lockany, Terry, Chief Fin. Officer--Champion Products, Winston Salem, NC; *U.S. Public*, pg. 1433
Lockwood, Glenn C., Chief Fin. Officer & Sr. V.P.--New Jersey Resources Corporation, Wall, NJ; *U.S. Public*, pg. 1172
Lockwood, Glenn C., Chief Fin. Officer, V.P. & Treas.--Commercial Realty & Resources Corp., Wall, NJ; *U.S. Public*, pg. 1172
Lockwood, Glenn C., Chief Fin. Officer, V.P. & Treas.--NJR Energy Services Corporation, Wall, NJ; *U.S. Public*, pg. 1172
Lockwood, Kent, Chief Fin. Officer & V.P.-Fin.--Producers Rice Mill Inc., Stuttgart, AR; *U.S. Private*, pg. 888
LoCurto, Thomas, Chief Fin. Officer & V.P.--P/A Industries, Inc., Bloomfield, CT; *U.S. Private*, pg. 825
Lodovic, Joseph, Chief Fin. Officer & Exec. V.P.--MediaNews Group Inc., Denver, CO; *U.S. Private*, pg. 727
Lodovic, Joseph J., IV, Chief Fin. Officer & Exec. V.P.--Garden State Newspapers, Inc., Denver, CO; *U.S. Private*, pg. 727
Lodwick, George, Chief Fin. Officer--Hydro-Mill Co., Chatsworth, CA; *U.S. Public*, pg. 1640
Loeffler, David E., Chief Fin. Officer, V.P. & Treas.--Arkansas Best Corporation, Fort Smith, AR; *U.S. Public*, pg. 130
Loesser, Roland, Chief Fin. Officer--Clariant International Ltd., Muttenz, Switzerland; *Int'l*, pg. 624
Loesser, Roland, Grp. V.P.-Fin. & Chief Fin. Officer--Sandoz Corporation, New York, NY; *Int'l*, pg. 974
Lofbom, W. Sonny, Chief Fin. Officer & V.P.--Robert F. Driver Co., Inc., San Diego, CA; *U.S. Private*, pg. 343
Loffa, Michael, Chief Fin. Officer & Exec. V. P.--Midland Life Insurance Co., Columbus, OH; *U.S. Private*, pg. 744
Lofgren, Frederick, Chief Fin. Officer & Exec. V.P.--Hitchiner Manufacturing Company, Inc., Milford, NH; *U.S. Private*, pg. 531
Loftis, Harry E., Chief Fin. Officer & V.P.--Riceland Foods, Inc., Stuttgart, AR; *U.S. Private*, pg. 928
Logan, Ann D., Chief Credit Officer & Exec. V.P.--Federal National Mortgage Association (Fannie Mae), Washington, DC; *U.S. Public*, pg. 615
Logan, John R., V.P.-Fin.--Sentrol Controls Group, Hickory, NC; *U.S. Private*, pg. 139
Loger, David E., Chief Fin. Officer--Lario Oil & Gas Company, Wichita, KS; *U.S. Private*, pg. 651
Lohne, Peter, V.P.--Tilcon, Inc., New Britain, CT; *U.S. Private*, pg. 1086
Lohr, William J., Chief Fin. Officer & Treas.--Citizens Insurance Company of America, Howell, MI; *U.S. Public*, pg. 54
Loiacono, Nicholas, Chief Fin. Officer & V.P.--Sulzermedica USA Inc., Angleton, TX; *Int'l*, pg. 1307
Lomax, Howard, Chief Fin. Officer & V.P.--Risdon Corporation, Naugatuck, CT; *U.S. Public*, pg. 463
Lomele, Mark R., Chief Fin. Officer--Norcal Waste Systems, San Francisco, CA; *U.S. Public*, pg. 1188
Londin, Gerald, Chief Fin. Officer--Roper Starch Worldwide, Mamaroneck, NY; *U.S. Private*, pg. 944
London, Terry, Chief Fin. Officer--Gaylord Entertainment/Opryland USA, Nashville, TN; *U.S. Public*, pg. 704
Long, Charles, Chief Fin. Officer, Sr. V.P. & Treas.--Highmark Inc., Pittsburgh, PA; *U.S. Private*, pg. 528
Long, Claranne R., Chief Fin. Officer--Synergism, Inc., Sunnyvale, CA; *U.S. Private*, pg. 1060
Long, Donald, Chief Fin. Officer & Exec. V.P.--Amerifoods Inc., Lancaster, PA; *U.S. Private*, pg. 65
Long, Jonathan R., Pres., Chief Exec. Officer & Chief Fin. Officer--J.E. Higgins Lumber Co., Concord, CA; *U.S. Private*, pg. 527
Long, Paul Tay Seo, Chief Fin. Officer--Lee Kim Tah Holdings Ltd., Singapore, Singapore; *Int'l*, pg. 1346
Long, Robert E., Chief Fin. Officer--Esselte Meto Canada, Mississauga, Canada; *Int'l*, pg. 461
Long, Robert L., Chief Fin. Officer & Sr. V.P.--Transocean Offshore, Inc., Houston, TX; *U.S. Public*, pg. 1631
Longbons, Jeffrey M., Chief Fin. Officer, V.P., Sec. & Treas.--Monitor Liability Managers, Inc., Rolling Meadows, IL; *U.S. Public*, pg. 215
Longbrake, William A., Chief Fin. Officer, Exec. V.P.-Corp. Finance--Washington Mutual Inc., Seattle, WA; *U.S. Public*, pg. 1741
Longo, Lawrence C., Jr., Chief Fin. Officer--Starter Corp., New Haven, CT; *U.S. Public*, pg. 1511
Loo, Jennifer, Asst. Treas.--HEI Investment Corp., Honolulu, HI; *U.S. Public*, pg. 800
Loomis, Randy, Chief Fin. Officer--FryeTech, Inc., Des Moines, IA; *U.S. Private*, pg. 430
Looney, Joe, Chief Fin. Officer--Manchester Equipment Co., Hauppauge, NY; *U.S. Private*, pg. 699
Looper, Tommy E., Chief Fin. Officer, Exec. V.P. & Sec.--Anchor Financial Corporation, Myrtle Beach, SC; *U.S. Public*, pg. 111
Lopes, Pedro Patrao, Chief Fin. Officer--Esselte Meto Portugal LDA, Oeiras, Portugal; *Int'l*, pg. 461
Lopez, Carmelo De Las Morenas, Dir.-Fin.--Repsol S.A., Madrid, Spain; *Int'l*, pg. 1104
Lopez, Miguel A., Chief Fin. Officer--Janssen-Cilag, Madrid, Spain; *U.S. Public*, pg. 929
Lops, Antonio, Chief Fin. Officer--Schiapparelli, Milan, Italy; *Int'l*, pg. 1204
Lords, Steven D., Chief Fin. Officer--Roy Anderson Corp., Gulfport, MS; *U.S. Private*, pg. 72
Lorentzian, Lisa, Chief Fin. Officer--Mercury Distributing Co., Inc., Chatsworth, CA; *U.S. Private*, pg. 732
Lorenz, Donald N., Chief Fin. Officer & V.P.-Fin.--Price Brothers Co., Dayton, OH; *U.S. Private*, pg. 883
Lorenz, Eric, Chief Fin. Officer--Plastic Engineered Components Inc., Waukesha, WI; *U.S. Private*, pg. 870
Lorenz, Richard B., Controller--U.S. Manufacturing Corp., Fraser, MI; *U.S. Private*, pg. 1125
Lorraine, Richard A., Chief Fin. Officer & Exec. V.P.--Occidental Chemical Corporation, Dallas, TX; *U.S. Public*, pg. 1210

Losh, J. Michael, Chief Fin. Officer & Exec. V.P.--General Motors Corporation, Detroit, MI; *U.S. Public*, pg. 718

Losik, Timothy P., Chief Fin. Officer, V.P. & Treas.--Hadco Corporation, Salem, NH; *U.S. Public*, pg. 773

Loski, R.J., Chief Fin. Officer--CNB International, Inc., Charleston, SC; *U.S. Private*, pg. 196

Loudon, James R.H., Dir.-Grp. Fin.--Blue Circle Industries PLC, London, United Kingdom; *Int'l*, pg. 197

Loughmiller, Eric M., Chief Fin. Officer & Exec. V.P.--May & Speh, Inc., Downers Grove, IL; *U.S. Public*, pg. 1063

Louly, J.F., Chief Fin. Officer--Van Melle-France S.A., Wasquehal, France; *Int'l*, pg. 1451

Loux, P. Ogden, Chief Fin. Officer & Sr. V.P.--W.W. Grainger, Inc., Lincolnshire, IL; *U.S. Public*, pg. 758

Love, Dan, Chief Fin. Officer--Rich's/Lazarus/Goldsmith's, Atlanta, GA; *U.S. Public*, pg. 618

LoVetere, Arthur J., Jr., Chief Fin. Officer--MacDermid Incorporated, Waterbury, CT; *U.S. Public*, pg. 1029

Lovett, Darryl A., Chief Fin. Officer--Evenflo Company, Inc., Piqua, OH; *U.S. Private*, pg. 629

Lovett, M.F., Chief Fin. Officer & Sr. V.P.--Ingram Book Company, La Vergne, TN; *U.S. Private*, pg. 563

Lovett, R., Chief Fin. Officer--VNU USA, Inc., New York, NY; *Int'l*, pg. 1447

Lovett, Rosalee, Chief Fin. Officer & Sr. V.P.--BPI Communications Inc., New York, NY; *Int'l*, pg. 1446

Lowber, John M., Chief Fin. Officer, Sr. V.P., Treas. & Sec.--General Communication, Inc., Anchorage, AK; *U.S. Public*, pg. 708

Lowder, Warren, Chief Fin. Officer & V.P.--The Lane Company, Inc., Altavista, VA; *U.S. Public*, pg. 688

Lowell, J. Drennan, Chief Fin. Officer--National Surface Cleaning, Inc., Methuen, MA; *U.S. Public*, pg. 1208

Lowery, William, Chief Fin. Officer--Constitution Reinsurance Corporation, New York, NY; *Int'l*, pg. 467

Lowes, Robert C., Chief Fin. Officer--Tricon Global Restaurants, Inc., Louisville, KY; *U.S. Public*, pg. 1636

Lowry, Steve, Chief Fin. Officer--Intisys, Inc., Pleasanton, CA; *U.S. Private*, pg. 93

Lozano, Joe J., Controller--H.B. Zachry Company, San Antonio, TX; *U.S. Private*, pg. 1203

Lozano, Juanita E., Chief Fin. Officer & Treas.--Play by Play Toys & Novelties, Inc., San Antonio, TX; *U.S. Public*, pg. 1309

Lozyniak, Andrew, Chief Fin. Officer & Exec. V.P.--Semiconductor Packaging Materials Co., Inc., Armonk, NY; *U.S. Public*, pg. 1456

Lozyniak, Andrew, Chief Fin. Officer--American Silicon Products, Inc., Providence, RI; *U.S. Public*, pg. 1456

Lubliner, William, Treas.--Helmsley-Spear Inc., New York, NY; *U.S. Private*, pg. 521

Lubrano, Vincent, Chief Fin. Officer & Exec. V.P.--Ammirati Puris Lintas Worldwide, New York, NY; *U.S. Public*, pg. 908

Luca, William, Chief Fin. Officer, V.P.-Fin. & Treas.--Cannondale Corporation, Bethel, CT; *U.S. Public*, pg. 301

Lucarelli, Brian M., Chief Fin. Officer, Controller, Asst Treas. & Asst. Sec.--Alaskan Copper Companies, Seattle, WA; *U.S. Private*, pg. 31

Lucas, Peter, Chief Fin. Officer & Sr. V.P.--Westower Corporation, Vancouver, WA; *U.S. Public*, pg. 1762

Lucas, Scott, Chief Fin. Officer--K & R Express Systems Inc., Hinsdale, IL; *U.S. Private*, pg. 602

Lucey, Richard E., Chief Fin. Officer & Sr. V.P.-Edison Capital--Edison Capital, Irvine, CA; *U.S. Public*, pg. 564

Luciana, Eugene, Chief Fin. Officer--Sunbelt Beverages, Lutherville, MD; *U.S. Private*, pg. 1051

Luciano, William J., Chief Fin. Officer--Zellers Inc., Toronto, Canada; *Int'l*, pg. 637

Luciano, William J., Chief Fin. Officer--The Bay, Toronto, Canada; *Int'l*, pg. 637

Lucien, Kent T., Chief Fin. Officer, Exec. V.P. & Treas.--Buyco, Inc., Honolulu, HI; *U.S. Private*, pg. 190

Lucien, Kent T., Chief Fin. Officer, Exec. V.P. & Treas.--C. Brewer & Company, Limited, Honolulu, HI; *U.S. Private*, pg. 190

Luckey, Dennis N., V.P. & Controller--Baker Commodities, Inc., Los Angeles, CA; *U.S. Private*, pg. 111

Ludlow, Madeleine, Chief Fin. Officer & V.P.--Cinergy Corp., Cincinnati, OH; *U.S. Public*, pg. 368

Ludwick, Arthur, Chief Fin. Officer--Rain Bird Sprinklers Manufacturing Corp., Glendora, CA; *U.S. Private*, pg. 907

Ludwig, Douglas L., Chief Fin. Officer, Sr. V.P. & Treas.--Four Seasons Hotels Inc., Don Mills, Canada; *Int'l*, pg. 502

Ludwig, Edward J., Chief Fin. Officer & Sr. V.P.-Fin.--Becton Dickinson & Company, Franklin Lakes, NJ; *U.S. Public*, pg. 199

Ludwigsen, Scott J., Chief Fin. Officer & V.P.--Woodward & Dickerson, Portland, OR; *U.S. Private*, pg. 1188

Lueken, Ted, Chief Fin. Officer--The Thermos Company, Schaumburg, IL; *Int'l*, pg. 938

Lugar, Todd, V.P.-Opers., Treas. & Sec.--Thomas L. Green & Co., Inc., Indianapolis, IN; *U.S. Private*, pg. 477

Lugo, Orestes L., Chief Fin. Officer & V.P.-Fin.--Renex Corp., Coral Gables, FL; *U.S. Public*, pg. 1377

Luhrs, Randy, Chief Fin. Officer & Treas.--Muska Electric Company, Roseville, MN; *U.S. Private*, pg. 768

Luiga, Andrea, Chief Fin. Officer--Barnett Inc., Jacksonville, FL; *U.S. Public*, pg. 1749

Lukassen, Gary J., Chief Fin. Officer & Exec. V.P.--Hudson's Bay Company, Toronto, Canada; *Int'l*, pg. 637

Luke, Paul B., Chief Fin. Officer, Sr. V.P., Treas. & Sec.--T&W Financial Corporation, Tacoma, WA; *U.S. Public*, pg. 1552

Luker, Robert C., Chief Fin. Officer & V.P.--Kokomo Sanitary Pottery Corp., Kokomo, IN; *U.S. Private*, pg. 449

Lumpkins, Robert L., Chief Fin. Officer & V.P.--Cargill, Wayzata, MN; *U.S. Private*, pg. 210

Lumsden, Iain, Grp. Fin. Dir.--Standard Life Assurance, Edinburgh, United Kingdom; *Int'l*, pg. 1297

Lund, Alan H., Chief Fin. Officer, Sr. V.P., Treas.--International Lease Finance Corporation, Los Angeles, CA; *U.S. Public*, pg. 85

Lund, Helge, Chief Fin. Officer--Nycomed Pharma AS, Oslo, Norway; *Int'l*, pg. 993

Lund, Vic, V.P.-Fin. & Acctg.--Sioux Honey Association, Sioux City, IA; *U.S. Private*, pg. 1003

Lundgren, Rob, Chief Fin. Officer, V.P. & Treas.--New Valley Corporation, Miami, FL; *U.S. Public*, pg. 1173

Lundkvist, Sverker, Chief Fin. Officer, Sr. V.P.-Fin. & Admin.--Incentive AB, Stockholm, Sweden; *Int'l*, pg. 666

Lundmark, Anders, Chief Fin. Officer--Iggesund Paperboard AB, Iggesund, Sweden; *Int'l*, pg. 886

Lungo, Robert, Chief Fin. Officer--Howtek, Inc., Hudson, NH; *U.S. Public*, pg. 844

Lunsford, Tim, Chief Fin. Officer--MUDD Jeans, Inc., New York, NY; *U.S. Private*, pg. 766

Luntz, Gregory W., Chief Fin. Officer & Treas.--Luntz Corporation, Canton, OH; *U.S. Private*, pg. 681

Lupinski, Thomas, Chief Fin. Officer--R.H. Forschner Division, Shelton, CT; *U.S. Public*, pg. 1544

Lupinski, Thomas, Chief Fin. Officer--Swiss Army Brands Ltd., Shelton, CT; *U.S. Public*, pg. 1544

Lupinski, Thomas M., Chief Fin. Officer & Sr. V.P.--Swiss Army Brands, Inc., Shelton, CT; *U.S. Public*, pg. 1544

Lupo, Michael A., Chief Fin. Officer, Exec. V.P. & Sec.--ABT Building Products Corporation, Neenah, WI; *Int'l*, pg. 20

Luscinski, Steven, Chm. Bd., Chief Fin. Officer & V.P.-Fin./Admin.--Accu-Sort Systems, Inc., Telford, PA; *U.S. Private*, pg. 11

Lusdall, Lotte, Chief Fin. Officer--DAB-Silkeborg a/s, Silkeborg, Denmark; *Int'l*, pg. 350

Lusenhop, Paul, Chief Fin. Officer--Keymark Corporation, Fonda, NY; *U.S. Private*, pg. 618

Lushefski, John E., Chief Fin. Officer & Sr. V.P.--Millennium Chemicals Inc., Iselin, NJ; *U.S. Public*, pg. 1111

Lusso, Gian Franco, Chief FIn. Officer & Dir.-Fin.--Davide Campari, Milan, Italy; *Int'l*, pg. 385

Luterman, Gerald, Chief Fin. Officer & Sr. V.P.--Arrow Electronics, Inc., Melville, NY; *U.S. Public*, pg. 133

Lutes, Bill, Chief Fin. Officer & Sr. V.P.--Pyramid Mouldings, Jacksonville, FL; *Int'l*, pg. 1335

Luther, Siegfried, Dr., Chief Fin. Officer--Bertelsmann AG, Gutersloh, Germany; *Int'l*, pg. 189

Lutz, Bruce, Chief Fin. Officer--Lockhart Cadillac Inc., Indianapolis, IN; *U.S. Private*, pg. 672

Lux, Harald, Chief Fin. Officer--OBI Bau-und Heimwerkermaerkte GmbH & Co. KG, Wermelskirchen, Germany; *Int'l*, pg. 993

Luxenberg, Irwin, Controller--Jacques Moret, Inc., New York, NY; *U.S. Private*, pg. 580

Luzum, James A., Chief Fin. Officer, Controller & Treas.--Villaume Industries, Inc., Saint Paul, MN; *U.S. Private*, pg. 1140

Luzum, James A., Chief Fin. Officer--Valley Forest Resources Co., Marcell, MN; *U.S. Private*, pg. 1140

Luzum, William J., V.P. & Treas.--Tyler Industries, Benson, MN; *U.S. Private*, pg. 1112

Lydic, John R., Chief Fin. Officer--Harley Ellington Design, Southfield, MI; *U.S. Private*, pg. 503

Lyke, Audrey R., Chief Fin. Officer & Treas.--Lyke Corporation, Ripon, WI; *U.S. Private*, pg. 682

Lyle, Freeman, Chief Oper. Officer & Chief Fin. Officer--Kennedy-Wilson, Inc., Santa Monica, CA; *U.S. Public*, pg. 951

Lynch, Chuck, Chief Fin. Officer & Sr. V.P.--Mervyn's California, Hayward, CA; *U.S. Public*, pg. 489

Lynch, D.G., Chief Fin. Officer--Bonded Fibre Fabric Ltd., Bridgwater, United Kingdom; *Int'l*, pg. 798

Lynch, John, Acting Chief Fin. Officer, Controller & Treas.--Sun TV & Appliances, Inc., Groveport, OH; *U.S. Public*, pg. 1532

Lynch, Martin A., Chief Fin. Officer & Exec. V.P.--Smart & Final, Vernon, CA; *Int'l*, pg. 563

Lynch, Michael, Chief Fin. Officer--Oldcastle, Inc., Los Angeles, CA; *Int'l*, pg. 242

Lynch, Patrick J., Chief Fin. Officer & Sr. V.P.--Texaco Inc., White Plains, NY; *U.S. Public*, pg. 1582

Lynch, Thomas G., Chief Fin. Officer & Exec. V.P.--Elan Corporation Plc, Dublin, Ireland; *Int'l*, pg. 435

Lynch, Tim, Chief Fin. Officer & Exec. V.P.--The Crown Group, Inc., Warren, MI; *U.S. Private*, pg. 292

Lynkowski, Garry, Pres. & Chief Fin. Officer--Highwood Resources Ltd., Calgary, Canada; *U.S. Public*, pg. 1411

Lyons, Lewis, Chief Fin. Officer & V.P.-Fin.--Deb Shops, Inc., Philadelphia, PA; *U.S. Public*, pg. 491

Ma, Kin Wung, Treas. & Asst. Mgr.--The Sincere Co. Ltd., Hong Kong, Hong Kong; *Int'l*, pg. 1252

Ma, Patrick, Chief Fin. Officer--Galco International Toys, N.V., Kowloon, Hong Kong; *U.S. Public*, pg. 698

Maas, C., Chief Fin. Officer--ING Groep N.V., Amsterdam, Netherlands; *Int'l*, pg. 647

MacAndrew, Nicholas R., Chief Fin. Officer--Schroders PLC, London, United Kingdom; *Int'l*, pg. 1210

Macartney, J.W., Chief Fin. Officer--Ballievey Ltd., Banbridge, United Kingdom; *Int'l*, pg. 797

Macartney, J.W., Chief Fin. Officer--Moygashel Ltd., Dungannon, United Kingdom; *Int'l*, pg. 798

Macau, Carlos, Chief Fin. Officer--Fairmont Homes, Inc., Nappanee, IN; *U.S. Private*, pg. 391

MacConnell, George, Chief Fin. Officer--Indian River Transport Co., Winter Haven, FL; *U.S. Private*, pg. 560

MacDonald, Bob, Chief Fin. Officer--Societe BIC S.A., Clichy, France; *Int'l*, pg. 1272

MacDonald, D., Chief Fin. Officer--ABC Rail Cogifer Industries, Cincinnati, OH; *U.S. Public*, pg. 2

MacDonald, D., Chief Fin. Officer--Cogifer SA, Croissy-sur-Seine, France; *Int'l*, pg. 386

MacDonald, H., Chief Fin. Officer & V.P.-Fin.--Versa Services Ltd., Etobicoke, Canada; *U.S. Private*, pg. 79

MacDonald, John R., Chief Fin. Officer & V.P.--Investment Technology Group, Inc., New York, NY; *U.S. Public*, pg. 924

Macdonald, Neal, Chief Fin. Officer--Firth-Rixson Forgings, Matlock, United Kingdom; *Int'l*, pg. 487

MacDonald, Peter J., Chief Fin. Officer & V.P.--Bestop, Inc., Broomfield, CO; *Int'l*, pg. 830

MacDonald, Thomas E., Chief Fin. Officer--Ernst W. Dorn Co., Inc., Gardena, CA; *U.S. Private*, pg. 340

MacDonald, Walter, Chief Fin. Officer--Gandalf Canada Ltd., Nepean, Canada; *Int'l*, pg. 540

MacDowell, Larry, V.P.-Fin.--Hampshire Hosiery, Inc., Spruce Pine, NC; *U.S. Public*, pg. 778

MacGillivray, Thomas K., Chief Fin. Officer & V.P.--Central Newspapers, Inc., Indianapolis, IN; *U.S. Public*, pg. 326

MacGinnitie, W. James, Chief Fin. Officer & Sr. V.P.--Continental Assurance Company, Chicago, IL; *U.S. Private*, pg. 267

MacGinnitie, W. James, Chief Fin. Officer--Valley Forge Life Insurance Company, Chicago, IL; *U.S. Private*, pg. 267

Machado, Edward J., Chief Fin. Officer & Sr. V.P.--Shenandoah Life Insurance Company, Roanoke, VA; *U.S. Private*, pg. 992

Machado, Edward J., Chief Fin. Officer & V.P.--Old Dominion Life Insurance Co., Roanoke, VA; *U.S. Private*, pg. 992

MacInnes, Dennis, Asst. Chief Fin. Officer--Ed Morse Automotive Group, Fort Lauderdale, FL; *U.S. Private*, pg. 763

MacInnes, Donald A., Chief Fin. Officer & V.P.--Ed Morse Automotive Group, Fort Lauderdale, FL; *U.S. Private*, pg. 763

MacIntyre, Susan, Chief Fin. Officer--California Cedar Products, Inc., Stockton, CA; *U.S. Private*, pg. 200

MacIver, Dana, Chief Fin. Officer--MIC Technology Corporation, North Andover, MA; *U.S. Public*, pg. 24

MacKenzie, David, Dir.-Fin.--Comshare Ltd., London, United Kingdom; *U.S. Public*, pg. 425

MacKenzie, George, Chief Fin. Officer & Sr. V.P.--Hercules Incorporated, Wilmington, DE; *U.S. Public*, pg. 809

MacKenzie, Ken, V.P.-Fin.--Bayco Industries, Winnipeg, Canada; *Int'l*, pg. 395

MacKenzie, Ken, Chief Fin. Officer--Norstan, Inc., Plymouth, MN; *U.S. Public*, pg. 1192

Mackey, Craig, Chief Fin. Officer--Williamson-Dickie Mfg. Co., Fort Worth, TX; *U.S. Private*, pg. 1179

Mackie, Ray, Chief Fin. Officer--Hillsdown Holdings Plc, London, United Kingdom; *Int'l*, pg. 619

Maclean, Donald W., Chief Fin. Officer & V.P.-Admin. & Treas.--Truelove & Maclean Inc., Waterbury, CT; *U.S. Private*, pg. 1107

Macleod, Donald, Chief Fin. Officer & Sr. V.P.-Fin.--National Semiconductor Corporation, Santa Clara, CA; *U.S. Public*, pg. 1159

Macleod, Jack, Controller--Inner Secrets, Inc., Harrison, NJ; *U.S. Private*, pg. 564

MacLeod, Rory, Chief Fin. Officer--Vanguard Plastics, Inc., Mc Pherson, KS; *U.S. Private*, pg. 1134

MacMillan, Douglas, Chief Fin. Officer & V.P.--Cambrex Corporation, East Rutherford, NJ; *U.S. Public*, pg. 297

MacMillian, Frederick W., Chief Fin. Officer & Treas.--Troy Mills, Inc., Troy, NH; *U.S. Private*, pg. 1106

Macnow, Joseph, Chief Fin. Officer & V.P.--Vornado Realty Trust, Saddle Brook, NJ; *U.S. Public*, pg. 1725

Macomber, Scott, Chief Fin. Officer, Sr. V.P. & Treas.--Vitalink Pharmacy Services, Inc., Atlanta, GA; *U.S. Public*, pg. 1042

MacPhee, Donald J., V.P. & Controller--IGI, Inc., Buena, NJ; *U.S. Public*, pg. 855

Macpherson, Donald D., Chief Fin. Officer--Industrial Equipment News, New York, NY; *U.S. Private*, pg. 1082

Macrini, Edward L., Sr. V.P.-Finance & Admin.--BPA International, New York, NY; *U.S. Private*, pg. 107

MacSporran, Graham, Sec. & Dir.-Fin.--Bridport-Gundry p.l.c., Dorset, United Kingdom; *Int'l*, pg. 215

Madden, Keith, Chief Fin. Officer--Artistcare Pty. Ltd., Brookvale, Australia; *Int'l*, pg. 460

Madden, Keith, Chief Fin. Officer--Letraset Australia Pty. Ltd., Brookvale, Australia; *Int'l*, pg. 461

Madden, Richard O., Chief Fin. Officer, Exec. V.P., Treas. & Sec.--Vermont Financial Services Corp., Brattleboro, VT; *U.S. Public*, pg. 1716

Madden, Ted, Chief Fin. Officer--Bomford Turner Limited, Evesham, United Kingdom; *U.S. Public*, pg. 35

Madden, Thomas J., Chief Fin. & Acctg. Officer, V.P.-Fin. & Treas.--Daisytek Incorporated, Plano, TX; *U.S. Public*, pg. 477

Madden, Thomas J., Chief Fin. & Acctg. Officer, V.P.-Fin. & Treas.--Daisytek (Canada) Inc., Toronto, Canada; *U.S. Public*, pg. 477

Madden, Thomas J., Chief Fin. & Acctg. Officer, V.P.-Fin. & Treas.--Daisytek Latin America, Miami, FL; *U.S. Public*, pg. 477

Madden, Thomas J., Chief Fin. & Acctg. Officer, V.P.-Fin. & Treas.--Daisytek De Mexico S.A. de C.V., Mexico, Mexico; *U.S. Public*, pg. 477

Madden, Thomas J., Chief Fin. & Acctg. Officer, V.P.-Fin. & Treas.--Priority Fulfillment Services, Inc., Plano, TX; *U.S. Public*, pg. 477

Madden, Thomas J., Chief Fin. & Acctg. Officer, V.P.-Fin. & Treas.--Daisytek Australia Pty. Ltd., Alexandria, Australia; *U.S. Public*, pg. 477

Madison, T. Jerome, Chief Fin. Officer & V.P.-Fin.--Cytogen Corporation, Princeton, NJ; *U.S. Public*, pg. 471

Madlinger, Steven R., Chief Fin. Officer, V.P., Treas. & Sec.--GreatBanc, Inc., Aurora, IL; *U.S. Public*, pg. 760

Maduri, John D., Chief Fin. Officer & Sr. V.P.-Fin.--Rogers Cantel Mobile Communications Inc., Saint-Laurent, Canada; *Int'l*, pg. 1122

Maeillot, Matthew, Chief Fin. Officer--Lever S.A., Levallois-Perret, France; *Int'l*, pg. 1438

Maerki, Max H., Chief Fin. Officer & Sr. V.P.--Public Service Company of New Mexico, Albuquerque, NM; *U.S. Public*, pg. 1339

Maffei, Greg, Chief Fin. Officer & V.P.-Fin.--Microsoft Corporation, Redmond, WA; *U.S. Public*, pg. 1107

Maffucci, David G., Chief Fin. Officer & Sr. V.P.--Bowater Incorporated, Greenville, SC; *U.S. Public*, pg. 247

Maga, Bruno, V.P.-Fin. & Chief Fin. Officer--Olsy North America Inc., Liberty Lake, WA; *Int'l*, pg. 1002

Magana, Alfredo, Chief Fin. Officer--Esselte de Mexico, S.A. de C.V., Mexico, Mexico; *Int'l*, pg. 461

Magasko, John C., Chief Fin. Officer & Controller--Interstate Steel Supply Company, Philadelphia, PA; *U.S. Public*, pg. 1100

Magdol, Michael O., Vice Chm., Chief Fin. Officer & Exec. V.P.--Fiduciary Trust Company International, New York, NY; *U.S. Public*, pg. 621

Magee, Bruce J., Chief Fin. Officer & Sr. V.P.--Harleysville Group, Harleysville, PA; *U.S. Public*, pg. 786

Magelitz, Larry L., V.P.-Fin.--Dillingham Construction Corporation, Pleasanton, CA; *U.S. Private*, pg. 333

Mager, Mark, Chief Fin. Officer--Atchison/St. Joe Division, Atchison, KS; *U.S. Public*, pg. 142

Maggi, Joe, Chief Fin. Officer--F.L. Roberts & Co. Inc., Springfield, MA; *U.S. Private*, pg. 935

MaGill, Mike, Chief Fin. Officer & Sr. V.P.--Safeguard Business Systems, Inc., Fort Washington, PA; *U.S. Private*, pg. 960

Maginniss, Christopher M., Chief Fin. Officer & Exec. V.P.--Microdyne Corporation, Alexandria, VA; *U.S. Public*, pg. 1105

Magnani, Joseph, Chief Fin. Officer & Sr. V.P.--New York City Off-Track Betting Corp., New York, NY; *U.S. Private*, *pg. 794*

Magnani, Thomas, Chief Fin. Officer--CDM Federal Programs Corporation, Fairfax, VA; *U.S. Private*, pg. 204

Magnohi, Gary, Chief Fin. Officer--Ney Dental International, Bloomfield, CT; *Int'l*, pg. 388

Maharry, Anne, Pres. & Chief Fin. Officer--Bull, Inc., San Diego, CA; *U.S. Private*, pg. 976

Mahoney, John, Chief Fin. Officer & Exec. V.P.--Staples, Inc., Westborough, MA; *U.S. Public*, pg. 1509

Mahoney, Kevin, Chief Fin. Officer--Winona Knitting Mills, Inc., Winona, MN; *U.S. Public*, pg. 779

Mahoney, Mike, Chief Fin. Officer--Windpoint Partners, Southfield, MI; *U.S. Private*, pg. 1182

Mahoney, Richard, Chief Fin. Officer--Westin Hotels & Resorts, Seattle, WA; *U.S. Public*, pg. 1512

Mahoney, Robert B., Chief Fin. Officer, V.P. & Treas.--Molex Incorporated, Lisle, IL; *U.S. Public*, pg. 1121

Maier, Richard, Sr. V.P.-Fin.--LaSalle National Bank, Chicago, IL; *Int'l*, pg. 10

Maimonis, Tom, Chief Fin. Officer--Gibson Electric Co., Oak Brook, IL; *U.S. Public*, pg. 572

Main, Bill, Grp. Dir.-Fin.--Scottish Widows' Fund & Life Assurance Society, Edinburgh, United Kingdom; *Int'l*, pg. 1212

Maine, Douglas, Chief Fin. Officer & Exec. V.P.--MCI Communications Corp., Atlanta, GA; *U.S. Public*, pg. 1023

Mak, F.O., Mgr.-Fin. & Admin.--MSA Nederland B.V., Hoorn, Netherlands; *U.S. Public*, pg. 1115

Makela, Wayne, Chief Fin. Officer & Treas.--Cable Constructors, Inc., Iron Mountain, MI; *U.S. Private*, pg. 197

Makenas, Bob, Chief Fin. Officer & V.P.-Fin.--Spectra-Physics Laserplane Inc., Dayton, OH; *U.S. Public*, pg. 1594

Makes, Brigid, Chief Fin. Officer--Haemonetics Corporation, Braintree, MA; *U.S. Public*, pg. 773

Makhani, Madan P., Chm. Bd., Pres., Chief Oper. & Chief Fin. Officer--American Foundry Group, Inc., Bixby, OK; *U.S. Private*, pg. 54

Makinson, John, Chief Fin. Officer--Pearson plc, London, United Kingdom; *Int'l*, pg. 1025

Makinson, T., Dir.-Fin.--The Simba Group, Isando, South Africa; *Int'l*, pg. 496

Makonoff, Lon, Chief Fin. Officer--Sherwood Foods, Maple Heights, OH; *U.S. Private*, pg. 994

Maland, Timothy, Chief Fin. Officer & Sr. V.P.--Caesars Palace, Las Vegas, NV; *U.S. Public*, pg. 1512

Maldonado, Freddy, Chief Fin. Officer & V.P.-Fin. & Investment--Westernbank of Puerto Rico, Mayaguez, PR; *U.S. Public*, pg. 1760

Malgerud, Carl, Mgr.-Fin. & Admin.--Atlas Copco ACT, Wilrijk, Belgium; *Int'l*, pg. 96

Mallaina, Krikov, Fin. Dir.--EURO RSCG, Vienna, Austria; *Int'l*, pg. 602

Malmqvist, Torbjorn, Fin. Controller--Skandia UK Insurance plc, London, United Kingdom; *Int'l*, pg. 1258

Malone, Archie, V.P.-Fin.--SGS-Thomson Microelectronics, Inc., Carrollton, TX; *Int'l*, pg. 1153

Malone, Michael, Chief Fin. Officer & Exec. V.P.--Polaris Industries, Inc., Minneapolis, MN; *U.S. Public*, pg. 1313

Maloney, Robert, Chief Fin. Officer--Tingley Rubber Corporation, South Plainfield, NJ; *U.S. Private*, pg. 1088

Maloney, W., V.P.-Fin.--EnviroSource-International Mill Service, Inc., Horsham, PA; *U.S. Public*, pg. 587

Maloy, Sean, Chief Fin. Officer--Pure Pulse Technologies, Inc., San Diego, CA; *U.S. Public*, pg. 1062

Maltzman, Michael, Chief Fin. Officer--Stratus Services Group, Inc., Manalapan, NJ; *U.S. Private*, pg. 1046

Malwitz, Donald W., Chief Fin. Officer & Exec. V.P.--United National Bancorp, Bridgewater, NJ; *U.S. Public*, pg. 1679

Malys, Gerald J., Chief Fin. Officer & Sr. V.P.--Cyprus Amax Minerals Company, Englewood, CO; *U.S. Public*, pg. 470

Manberg, Ed, Chief Fin. Officer & V.P.--Byer California, San Francisco, CA; *U.S. Private*, pg. 191

Mancuso, Michael J., Chief Fin. Officer & Sr. V.P.--General Dynamics Corporation, Falls Church, VA; *U.S. Public*, pg. 708

Mancuso, Vince, Chief Fin. Officer & Sr. V.P.--Rubin Postaer & Associates, Santa Monica, CA; *U.S. Private*, pg. 949

Mandell, Andrew, Chief Fin. Officer & Sr. V.P.--ITT Sheraton Corporation, Boston, MA; *U.S. Public*, pg. 1512

Mandeville, Robert, Chief Fin. Officer, Treas. & Sec.--Cranston Print Works Company, Cranston, RI; *U.S. Private*, pg. 286

Mandia, Albert W., Chief Fin. Officer & Exec. V.P.--CoreStates Financial Corp., Philadelphia, PA; *U.S. Public*, pg. 446

Maney, William J., Chief Fin. Officer, Sr. V.P. & Treas.--American Annuity Group, Cincinnati, OH; *U.S. Public*, pg. 74

Mangam, Thomas, Chief Fin. Officer--Land N Sea, Inc., New York, NY; *U.S. Private*, pg. 645

Mangan, James, Chief Fin. Officer & Controller--Bixby International Corp., Newburyport, MA; *U.S. Private*, pg. 146

Mangan, Michael D., Chief Fin. Officer & Exec. V.P.--The Ryland Group, Inc., Columbia, MD; *U.S. Public*, pg. 1414

Mangan, Pete, Chief Fin. Officer, V.P.-Fin. & Sec.--Trident Microsystems, Inc., Mountain View, CA; *U.S. Public*, pg. 1637

Mangano, Frank, Chief Fin. Officer--Aid Auto Stores, Inc., Westbury, NY; *U.S. Public*, pg. 29

Manginelli, John, Chief Fin. Officer--Colivita USA, Inc., Linden, NJ; *U.S. Private*, pg. 252

Mangion, George, Chief Fin. Officer--Sunstrand Fluid Handling, Arvada, CO; *U.S. Public*, pg. 1534

Mangum, Harleigh J., V.P.-Fin.--Standard Plywoods, Inc., Clinton, SC; *U.S. Private*, pg. 1032

Mangum, Stephen F., Chief Fin. Officer & Sr. V.P.--Pier 1 Imports, Inc., Fort Worth, TX; *U.S. Public*, pg. 1295

Manion, Kevin, Chief Fin. Officer--Applied Industrial Materials Corporation, Stamford, CT; *U.S. Public*, pg. 1736

Maniscalco, Diane, Chief Fin. Officer-Admin./Opers.-Sec. & Treas.--Colonna Bros., Inc., North Bergen, NJ; *U.S. Private*, pg. 254

Maniyar, Prabhav V., Chief Fin. Officer, Sr. V.P. & Sec.--Startec Global Communications Corporation, Bethesda, MD; *U.S. Public*, pg. 1511

Mann, Ed, Chief Fin. Officer--Transamerica Leasing Inc., Purchase, NY; *U.S. Public*, pg. 1630

Mann, Michael F., Chief Fin. Officer & Exec. V.P.--Florasynth Inc., Teterboro, NJ; *Int'l*, pg. 173

Mann, Robert A., Chief Fin. Officer & Exec. V.P.-Fin. & Admin.--Park Foods L.P., Barrington, IL; *U.S. Private*, pg. 839

Mann, Roger, Chief Exec. Officer & Dir.-Fin.--Siebe plc, Windsor, United Kingdom; *Int'l*, pg. 1240

Mannerjarvi, Kauko, Chief Fin. Officer--Raisio Group, Raisio, Finland; *Int'l*, pg. 1085

Manning, Claude, Chief Fin. Officer & V.P.--Texas Petro Chemicals, Houston, TX; *U.S. Private*, pg. 1078

Manning, James V., Chief Fin. Officer & Sr. Exec. V.P.--MEDCO Containment Services, Inc., Montvale, NJ; *U.S. Public*, pg. 1091

Manning, Phil, Chief Fin. Officer--Willcox & Gibbs, Ltd., Braintree, United Kingdom; *U.S. Private*, pg. 1177

Manoff, Thomas G., V.P.-Fin.--The Saturn Corporation, Troy, MI; *U.S. Public*, pg. 721

Manoni, Doug, Chief Fin. Officer--Cowles Business Media, Inc., Stamford, CT; *U.S. Private*, pg. 281

Mansfield, Dick, Chief Fin. Officer & V.P.--Duckwall-Alco Stores, Inc., Abilene, KS; *U.S. Public*, pg. 533

Manso, Antonio Luiz, Chief Fin. Officer & Exec. V.P.-Fin.--Embraer-Empresa Brasileira de Aeronautica S.A., Sao Jose dos Campos, Brazil; *Int'l*, pg. 452

Manson, Clair S., V.P. & Chief Actuary--Investors Heritage Life Insurance Co., Frankfort, KY; *U.S. Public*, pg. 952

Manz, Kenneth, Chief Fin. Officer--Journal of Commerce, Inc., New York, NY; *Int'l*, pg. 1026

Marach, Roger K., Chief Fin. Officer & Treas.--SpeedFan International, Inc., Chandler, AZ; *U.S. Public*, pg. 1497

Marandola, Albert M., Chief Fin. Officer & Gen. Mgr.-Opers.--Atlantic Metals Corporation, Philadelphia, PA; *U.S. Private*, pg. 95

Maraone, Michael, Chief Fin. Officer--American International Airways, Ypsilanti, MI; *U.S. Private*, pg. 57

March, Don, Chief Fin. Officer--Cosco, Inc., Columbus, IN; *U.S. Private*, pg. 277

March, Jose, Chief Fin. Officer--Motion Control Systems Division, San Diego, CA; *U.S. Public*, pg. 157

Marchand, Albert, Chief Fin. Officer--S.A. Cimenteries CBR, Brussels, Belgium; *Int'l*, pg. 605

Marchese, Frank, Chief Fin. Officer, V.P.-Fin. & Treas.--Pharmaceutical Formulations, Inc., Edison, NJ; *U.S. Public*, pg. 1284

Marchese, Richard B., Chief Fin. Officer, V.P.-Fin. & Treas.--Georgia Gulf Corporation, Atlanta, GA; *U.S. Public*, pg. 734

Marchetti, C., Chief Fin. Officer--Scholl Plc, Newton, United Kingdom; *Int'l*, pg. 1209

Marchio, Braulio, V.P.-Fin.--CPC Latin American Consumer Foods Division, Englewood Cliffs, NJ; *U.S. Public*, pg. 447

Marchuk, Raymond, V.P.-Fin. Opers.--Scholastic Inc., New York, NY; *U.S. Public*, pg. 1440

Marcic, Irene S., Chief Fin. Officer, Exec. V.P., Treas. & Sec.--Astrex, Inc., Plainview, NY; *U.S. Public*, pg. 141

Marcic, Irene S., Chief Fin. Officer--T.F. Cushing, Inc., West Springfield, MA; *U.S. Public*, pg. 141

Marcic, Irene S., Chief Fin. Officer--Progress International Limited, Plainview, NY; *U.S. Public*, pg. 141

Marcucci, George, Chief Fin. Officer & Treas.--Gonnella Baking Co., Chicago, IL; *U.S. Private*, pg. 463

Marcus, Stephen, Chm. Bd., Pres. & Chief Exec. Officer--The Marcus Corporation, Milwaukee, WI; *U.S. Public*, pg. 1044

Marczak, David J., Chief Fin. Officer, Treas. & Sec.--Secom General Corporation, Novi, MI; *U.S. Public*, pg. 1453

Marden, Jim, Chief Fin. Officer--RDM Sports Group, Atlanta, GA; *U.S. Public*, pg. 1354

Mardy, Mike, Chief Fin. Officer--Keystone Foods Corporation, Bala Cynwyd, PA; *U.S. Private*, pg. 619

Marek, Alan J., Chief Fin. Officer & Exec. V.P.--DG Foods, LLC, Chicago, IL; *U.S. Private*, pg. 301

Maresca, Anthony R., Chief Fin. Officer, Sr. V.P., Treas. & Sec.--ACR Group, Houston, TX; *U.S. Public*, pg. 3

Margolis, A.E., Chief Fin. Officer--Mallet & Co., Carnegie, PA; *U.S. Private*, pg. 698

Margolis, Lawrence A., Chief Fin. Officer, Exec. V.P. & Sec.--The Antec Corporation, Rolling Meadows, IL; *U.S. Public*, pg. 116

Marhoefer, Kurt E., V.P.-Fin.--Dresher, Inc., Carthage, MO; *U.S. Public*, pg. 986

Mariangeli, Dan, Sr. V.P.-Fin. Div.--The Toronto Dominion Bank, Toronto, Canada; *Int'l*, pg. 1401

Marina Cortes, Jacinto, Chief Fin. Officer--Transportacion Maritima Mexicana S.A. de C.V., Mexico, Mexico; *Int'l*, pg. 1418

Marinelli, Gene, Chief Fin. Officer & V.P.--Intelligent Electronics, Inc., Exton, PA; *U.S. Public*, pg. 887

Marino, Eduardo, Chief Fin. Officer--Jugos del Valle, S.A. de C.V., Mexico, Mexico; *Int'l*, pg. 716

Marischen, Robert J., Vice Chm. & Chief Fin. Officer--Huntco Inc., Town and Country, MO; *U.S. Public*, pg. 849

Markel, Lynn, Chief Fin. Officer--Koch Industries, Incorporated, Wichita, KS; *U.S. Private*, pg. 628

Markert, Stephen E., Jr., Chief Fin. Officer & V.P.-Fin.--C & D Technologies, Inc., Blue Bell, PA; *U.S. Public*, pg. 272

Markey, Arthur, Chief Fin. Officer, Sr. V.P. & Treas.--Carpenter Co., Richmond, VA; *U.S. Private*, pg. 214

Markowski, Glen, Chief Fin. Officer--SRDS, Des Plaines, IL; *U.S. Private*, pg. 958

Marks, Bill, Chief Fin. Officer--Fleer-Skybox International Inc., Mount Laurel, NJ; *U.S. Public*, pg. 1052

Marks, Jim, Chief Fin. Officer & V.P.--Providian Agency Group, Louisville, KY; *Int'l*, pg. 27

Markum, James A., Chief Fin. Officer & Exec. V.P.--Stage Stores, Inc., Houston, TX; *U.S. Private*, pg. 1028

Markusse, A.J., Chief Fin. Officer--CSM Suiker BV, Diemen, Netherlands; *Int'l*, pg. 243

Marlott, Chuck, Chief Fin. Officer--Claire Manufacturing Co., Addison, IL; *U.S. Private*, pg. 462

Marquardt, Timothy A., Chief Fin. Officer & Sr. V.P.--NationsBank Sunwest, Inc., Albuquerque, NM; *U.S. Public*, pg. 1165

Marquardt, Walter, Chief Fin. Officer & Treas.--Louis Allis Company, Milwaukee, WI; *U.S. Private*, pg. 677

Marquis, Thomas W., Chief Fin. Officer, Chief Acctg. Officer & Treas.--VSI Holdings, Inc., Bloomfield Hills, MI; *U.S. Public*, pg. 1703

Marra, Ralph V., Sr. V.P. & Treas.--Unicorp American Corporation, New York, NY; *Int'l*, pg. 1433

Marrama, Ken, Chief Fin. Officer--The Score Board, Inc., Cherry Hill, NJ; *U.S. Public*, pg. 1444

Marrero, Grace E., Chief Fin. Officer & Treas.--J.E. Baker Co., York, PA; *U.S. Private*, pg. 112

Marrero, Manuel, Chief Fin. Officer, Sr. V.P.-Admin., Treas. & Sec.--Autologic Information International, Inc., Thousand Oaks, CA; *U.S. Public*, pg. 1724

Marriner, William L., Chief Fin. Officer, Sr. V.P.-Fin. & Admin., & Sec.--Exabyte Corporation, Boulder, CO; *U.S. Public*, pg. 597

Marrone, Michael J., Chief Fin. Officer, Treas. & V.P.--The Berkshire Gas Company, Pittsfield, MA; *U.S. Public*, pg. 216

Marrs, Pamela, Chief Fin. Officer--Dey Laboratories Inc., Napa, CA; *Int'l*, pg. 812

Marsalili, John, Chief Fin. Officer--National Airmotive Corporation, Oakland, CA; *U.S. Private*, pg. 775

Marschalk, William J., Chief Fin. Officer--California Reconveyance Co., Chatsworth, CA; *U.S. Public*, pg. 1741

Marsden, Charles J., Chief Fin. Officer & V.P.-Fin.--Crompton & Knowles Corporation, Stamford, CT; *U.S. Public*, pg. 459

Marsh, David E., Chief Fin. Officer & V.P.-Corp. Services--Central Maine Power Company, Augusta, ME; *U.S. Public*, pg. 325

Marsh, Donald L., Chief Fin. Officer--Commonwealth Aluminum-Lewisport, Lewisport, KY; *U.S. Public*, pg. 415

Marsh, Donald L., Chief Fin. Officer, Exec. V.P. & Corp. Sec.--Alflex, Long Beach, CA; *U.S. Public*, pg. 415

Marsh, Donald L., Jr., Chief Fin. Officer, Exec. V.P. & Sec.--Commonwealth Industries, Inc., Louisville, KY; *U.S. Public*, pg. 415

Marsh, Kevin B., Chief Fin. Officer, V.P.-Fin. & Controller--SCANA Corporation, Columbia, SC; *U.S. Public*, pg. 1436

Marsh, Stephen P., Chief Fin. Officer, Sr V.P. & Cashier--Community National Bank, Derby, VT; *U.S. Public*, pg. 416

Marshak, Lewis J., V.P.-Fin. & Treas.--M & I First National Leasing Corp., Milwaukee, WI; *U.S. Public*, pg. 1051

Marshall, Allen, Chief Fin. Officer--Heller Seasonings & Ingredients, Inc., Bedford Park, IL; *U.S. Private*, pg. 520

Marshall, Brad, Chief Fin. Officer--Democratic National Committee, Washington, DC; *U.S. Private*, pg. 324

Marshall, Jeff, Chief Fin. Officer--Maurin-Ogden Management Corporation, New Orleans, LA; *U.S. Private*, pg. 715

Marshall, John, Chief Fin. Officer--Duro-Test Canada, Rexdale, Canada; *U.S. Private*, pg. 349

Marshall, Robert, Chief Fin. Officer & V.P.-Fin. & Credit--COP Communications, Glendale, CA; *U.S. Private*, pg. 196

Marshall, Robert, Chief Fin. Officer & V.P.-Fin. & Credit--California Offset Printers, Inc., Glendale, CA; *U.S. Private*, pg. 196

Marshall, Robin L., Pres. & Chief Exec. Officer--Great Lakes Technologies Corp., Kalamazoo, MI; *U.S. Private*, pg. 475

Marshall, Ron, Chief Fin. Officer & Exec. V.P.--Pathmark Stores Incorporated, Woodbridge, NJ; *U.S. Private*, pg. 843

Marshall, Steven, Chief Fin. Officer--Thorn plc, Chertsey, United Kingdom; *Int'l*, pg. 1385

Marsicano, John, Chief Fin. Officer--D. Waldner Company, Inc., Farmingdale, NY; *U.S. Private*, pg. 1147

Marszowski, Bruno A., Chief Fin. Officer & Controller--The FINOVA Group Inc., Phoenix, AZ; *U.S. Public*, pg. 624
Marszowski, Bruno A., Chief Fin. Officer--FINOVA Capital Corporation, Phoenix, AZ; *U.S. Public*, pg. 624
Martel, Bob, Pres. & Chief Exec. Officer--Cerdec Corporation, Washington, PA; *Int'l*, pg. 292
Martignoni, C., Chief Fin. Officer--Kuehne & Nagel SpA, Milan, Italy; *Int'l*, pg. 763
Martin, A.K., Mgr.-Credit--True Companies, Casper, WY; *U.S. Private*, pg. 1107
Martin, Charles, Chief Fin. Officer & V.P.--Interlaken Capital, Inc., Greenwich, CT; *U.S. Private*, pg. 567
Martin, Christopher, Dir.-Grp. Fin.--Storehouse PLC, London, United Kingdom; *Int'l*, pg. 1304
Martin, Clarence, Chief Exec. Officer & Chief Fin. Officer--State Electric Supply Co., Huntington, WV; *U.S. Private*, pg. 1036
Martin, Dale, Chief Fin. Officer--Davis Industries Inc., Plymouth, MI; *U.S. Private*, pg. 315
Martin, Darrel D., Chief Fin. Officer & Exec. V.P.--Markel Corporation, Glen Allen, VA; *U.S. Public*, pg. 1046
Martin, Daryl, Chief Fin. Officer & Exec. V.P.--Elwell-Parker Limited, Cleveland, OH; *U.S. Private*, pg. 373
Martin, David W., Chief Fin. Officer & Dir.--Jardine Insurance Brokers Ltd., Hong Kong, Hong Kong; *Int'l*, pg. 705
Martin, Gladys, Chief Fin. Officer, Treas. & Sec.--Welsco Inc., North Little Rock, AR; *U.S. Private*, pg. 1161
Martin, Jerry C., Chief Fin. Officer & Sr. V.P.--Global Marine Inc., Houston, TX; *U.S. Public*, pg. 748
Martin, Jerry H., Chief Fin. Officer--H.O. Penn Machinery Co. Inc., Poughkeepsie, NY; *U.S. Private*, pg. 849
Martin, Jesus, Chief Fin. Officer--Ricardo Perez Asociados, Madrid, Spain; *Int'l*, pg. 1036
Martin, JoAnn M., Chief Fin. Officer, Sr. V.P. & Controller--Ameritas Life Insurance Corp., Lincoln, NE; *U.S. Private*, pg. 65
Martin, John, Chief Fin. Officer--Trend Offset Printing Services, Los Alamitos, CA; *U.S. Private*, pg. 1099
Martin, John C., III, Chief Fin. Officer, V.P., Treas. & Sec.--TransPro, Inc., New Haven, CT; *U.S. Public*, pg. 1631
Martin, Joseph A., Chief Fin. Officer--United Farm Family Life Insurance Co., Indianapolis, IN; *U.S. Private*, pg. 1122
Martin, K. Stanley, Chief Fin. Officer & V.P.-Fin.--WTD Industries, Inc., Portland, OR; *U.S. Public*, pg. 1729
Martin, Lauralee E., Chief Fin. Officer & Exec. V.P.--Heller International Corporation, Chicago, IL; *Int'l*, pg. 519
Martin, Lauralee E., Chief Fin. Officer & Exec. V.P.--Heller Financial, Inc., Chicago, IL; *Int'l*, pg. 519
Martin, Lauralee E., Chief Fin. Officer--Heller International, Chicago, IL; *U.S. Private*, pg. 520
Martin, M. Lamar, Chief Fin. Officer, Sr. V.P. & Treas.--Centex Construction Company, Dallas, TX; *U.S. Public*, pg. 322
Martin, Matthew G., Chief Oper. & Fin. Officer--Cattleman's, Inc., Detroit, MI; *U.S. Public*, pg. 318
Martin, Michael D., Chief Fin. Officer, Exec. V.P. & Treas.--Healthsouth Corporation, Birmingham, AL; *U.S. Public*, pg. 803
Martin, Mike, Chief Fin. Officer--Healthsouth Corporation, Sunnyvale, CA; *U.S. Public*, pg. 803
Martin, Paul F., Chief Fin. Officer--Rawlings Sporting Goods Company, Fenton, MO; *U.S. Public*, pg. 1361
Martin, Randy C., Chief Fin. Officer & V.P.-Fin.--Spartech Corporation, Clayton, MO; *U.S. Public*, pg. 1495
Martin, Richard J., Chief Fin. Officer & Exec. V.P.--Rykoff-Sexton, Inc., Wilkes-Barre, PA; *U.S. Public*, pg. 918
Martin, Robert, V.P.-Fin. & Sec.--UAP, Inc., Montreal, Canada; *Int'l*, pg. 1426
Martin, Steven, Chief Fin. Officer--PNC Bank, Scranton, PA; *U.S. Public*, pg. 1243
Martin, Terence D., Chief Fin. Officer & Exec. V.P.--General Signal Corporation, Stamford, CT; *U.S. Public*, pg. 726
Martin, Thomas E., III, Chief Fin. Officer & Exec. V.P.--Taracorp, Inc., Atlanta, GA; *U.S. Private*, pg. 1068
Martin, Timothy I., Chief Fin. Officer & V.P.--Land O'Lakes Fluid Dairy Division, Arden Hills, MN; *U.S. Private*, pg. 646
Martin, Von, Chief Fin. Officer--Lund's Inc., Edina, MN; *U.S. Private*, pg. 680
Martin, William A., Chief Fin. Officer, Sr. V.P. & Asst. Sec.--Insituform Technologies, Inc., Chesterfield, MO; *U.S. Public*, pg. 881
Martindale, Patty, Chief Fin. Officer--Brunner Engineering & Manufacturing, Inc., Bedford, IN; *U.S. Private*, pg. 176
Martinelli, James, Chief Fin. Officer & Treas.--II-VI Incorporated, Saxonburg, PA; *U.S. Public*, pg. 1647
Martinez de la Vega, Francisco, Chief Fin. Officer--Controladora Comercial Mexicana, S.A. de C.V., Mexico, Mexico; *Int'l*, pg. 328
Martinez, Faustino, Chief Fin. Officer--Sol Melia America, Miami, FL; *Int'l*, pg. 1277
Martinez, Fred, Chief Fin. Officer--Goldbergs Marine Distributors, Edison, NJ; *U.S. Public*, pg. 1756
Martinez, Len A., V.P. & Chief Fin. Officer--ICF Kaiser Engineers, Inc., Oakland, CA; *U.S. Public*, pg. 853
Martinez, Walfred A., Chief Fin. Officer & V.P.--Sea Ranger Products, Edison, NJ; *U.S. Public*, pg. 1756
Martinez, Walfrido A., Chief Fin. Officer, Sr. V.P. & Controller--E & B Marine Incorporated, Edison, NJ; *U.S. Public*, pg. 1756
Martinez, Walfrios A., Chief Fin. Officer & V.P.--James Bliss & Co., Inc., Edison, NJ; *U.S. Public*, pg. 1756
Martino, Anthony J., Chief Fin. Officer & Sr. V.P.-Fin.--Nestle Holdings, Inc., Stamford, CT; *Int'l*, pg. 916
Martonen, Ari, Chief Fin. Officer & Sr. V.P.--Metsa-Serla Corporation, Espoo, Finland; *Int'l*, pg. 863
Marvelley, Brian, V.P.-Fin.--Battenfeld Gloucester Engineering Co. Inc., Gloucester, MA; *U.S. Private*, pg. 123
Marz, Brian D., Chief Fin. Officer--Putman Publishing Co., Itasca, IL; *U.S. Private*, pg. 896
Marzano, Vincent M., Treas.--Scholastic Inc., New York, NY; *U.S. Public*, pg. 1440
Masenthin, Gregg, Chief Exec. Officer & Chief Fin. Officer--Jami, Inc., Shawnee Mission, KS; *U.S. Private*, pg. 581
Maslick, Joseph R., Chief Fin. Officer, Exec. V.P. & Sec.--Griffith Laboratories Worldwide, Inc., Alsip, IL; *U.S. Private*, pg. 481
Maslowe, Philip L., Chief Fin. Officer--The Wackenhut Corporation, Palm Beach Gardens, FL; *U.S. Public*, pg. 1731
Maslowski, Clem, Chief Fin. Officer--Rite-Hite Corporation, Milwaukee, WI; *U.S. Private*, pg. 933
Maslowski, Clem, Chief Fin. Officer--Rite-Hite Corporation (WI), Milwaukee, WI; *U.S. Private*, pg. 933
Mason, Chip, Chief Fin. Officer & V.P.-Fin.--Gulf States Toyota, Inc., Houston, TX; *U.S. Private*, pg. 488
Mason, Dave, Chief Fin. Officer--Brian Unlimited Distribution Company, Inc., Detroit, MI; *U.S. Private*, pg. 167
Mason, David A., Chief Fin. Officer, Exec. V.P. & Treas.--Moto Photo, Inc., Dayton, OH; *U.S. Public*, pg. 1136
Mason, Earl, Chief Fin. Officer & Sr. V.P.-Fin.--COMPAQ Computer Corporation, Houston, TX; *U.S. Public*, pg. 417
Mason, Geoffrey, Chief Fin. Officer--Preformed Line Products(Great Britain) Ltd., Andover, United Kingdom; *U.S. Public*, pg. 1321
Mason, Michael, Chief Fin. Officer--New Hermes Incorporated, Duluth, GA; *U.S. Private*, pg. 793
Mason, Steve, Chief Fin. Officer--McCoy Electronics Co., Mount Holly Springs, PA; *U.S. Public*, pg. 1209
Mason, Wallace, Chief Fin. Officer, V.P., Sec. & Acct. Exec.--Temkin & Temkin, Northbrook, IL; *U.S. Private*, pg. 1074
Massaro, Louis L., Chief Fin. Officer, Chief Admin. Officer & Exec. V.P.--Frontier Corporation, Rochester, NY; *U.S. Public*, pg. 683
Massengale, Darrell K., Chief Fin. Officer, V.P.-Fin., Treas. & Sec.--Corrections Corporation of America, Nashville, TN; *U.S. Public*, pg. 450
Massicotte, Norm, Chief Fin. Officer & V.P.--Heath Consultants Incorporated, Houston, TX; *U.S. Private*, pg. 518
Massie, William C., Exec. V.P.--B.B. Walker Company, Asheboro, NC; *U.S. Public*, pg. 1734
Massman, Edward L., Chief Fin. Officer & V.P.--Avatex Corporation, Dallas, TX; *U.S. Public*, pg. 151
Masson, Florence, Chief Fin. Officer--EURO RSCG Partnership, Singapore, Singapore; *Int'l*, pg. 602
Mastellon, Bill, Chief Fin. Officer & Exec. V.P.--DeWitt Media, Inc., New York, NY; *U.S. Private*, pg. 329
Masters, Charles, Chief Fin. Officer--Cardinal Scale Manufacturing Company, Webb City, MO; *U.S. Private*, pg. 209
Masters, Charles, Chief Fin. Officer--Detecto Scale Company, Webb City, MO; *U.S. Private*, pg. 209
Mather, Jonathan R., Chief Fin. Officer--Applause Inc., Woodland Hills, CA; *U.S. Private*, pg. 78
Mathiesem, Jeffrey, Chief Fin. Officer & V.P.-Fin. & Admin.--Micro Component Technology Inc., Saint Paul, MN; *U.S. Public*, pg. 1104
Mathiesen, G., Chief Fin. Officer--C.D. Smith Drug Company, Saint Joseph, MO; *U.S. Private*, pg. 1007
Mathieu, Raymond M., Chief Fin. Officer & Treas.--Narragansett Capital Inc., Providence, RI; *U.S. Private*, pg. 774
Mathis, Robert, Chief Fin. Officer--Pendleton Woolen Mills, Inc., Portland, OR; *U.S. Private*, pg. 848
Matschullat, Robert W., Vice Chm. & Chief Fin. Officer--The Seagram Company Ltd., Montreal, Canada; *Int'l*, pg. 1214
Matsuda, Matt, Chief Fin. Officer & Sr. V.P.--Clarion Corporation of America, Gardena, CA; *Int'l*, pg. 296
Matteodo, Maurice, Chief Fin. Officer--JPS Elastomerics Corp., Holyoke, MA; *U.S. Private*, pg. 578
Mattey, David, Chief Fin. Officer--The Dialog Corporation plc, London, United Kingdom; *Int'l*, pg. 412
Matthes, Lesa, Controller--Champion Laboratories, Inc., Albion, IL; *U.S. Private*, pg. 1113
Matthews, Edward, Chief Fin. Officer--Trans Financial, Inc., Bowling Green, KY; *U.S. Public*, pg. 1628
Matthews, James E., Chief Fin. Officer, V.P.-Fin. & Sec.--Miltope Group, Inc., Hope Hull, AL; *U.S. Public*, pg. 1114
Matthews, James E., Chief Fin. Officer & V.P.-Fin.--Miltope Corporation, Montgomery, AL; *U.S. Public*, pg. 1114
Matthews, Jay, Chief Fin. Officer--Marglen Industries, Rome, GA; *U.S. Private*, pg. 702
Matthews, Jerry, Chief Fin. Officer & Sr. V.P.--D & W Food Centers, Inc., Grand Rapids, MI; *U.S. Private*, pg. 300
Matthews, Ken, Chief Fin. Officer--Byers Industries, Inc., Portland, OR; *U.S. Private*, pg. 191
Matthews, Ken, Chief Fin. Officer--Byers Portland Willamette, Portland, OR; *U.S. Private*, pg. 191
Mattingly, David F., Chief Fin. Officer & Exec. V.P.--Metro Foods, Inc., Olive Branch, MS; *U.S. Private*, pg. 736
Mattke, Georgianna, Chief Fin. Officer & Bus. Mgr.--SJL of Kansas Corp., Wichita, KS; *U.S. Public*, pg. 984
Mattson, Eric L., Chief Fin. Officer & Sr. V.P.--Baker Hughes Incorporated, Houston, TX; *U.S. Public*, pg. 165
Maturo, J. Michael, Chief Fin. Officer--Reckson Associates Realty Corp., Melville, NY; *U.S. Public*, pg. 1368
Matushi, Jim, Chief Fin. Officer--American Products, Inc., Moorpark, CA; *U.S. Public*, pg. 593
Matza, Robert, Chief Fin. Officer--Lehman Brothers, New York, NY; *U.S. Public*, pg. 987
Mauer, Otto-Erich, Chief Fin. Officer--Esselte Meto GmbH, Hirschhorn, Germany; *Int'l*, pg. 461
Maun, Thomas P., Chief Fin. Officer & V.P.--INCSTAR Corporation, Stillwater, MN; *Int'l*, pg. 483
Maurer, James R., V.P. & Treas.--Consumers Illinois Water Co., Kankakee, IL; *U.S. Public*, pg. 438
Maurer, Kurt, Chief Fin. Officer--Knurr AG, Munich, Germany; *Int'l*, pg. 739
Mauro, Steve, Chief Fin. Officer & Controller--Powell Electronics Inc., Philadelphia, PA; *U.S. Private*, pg. 877
Maver, Bob, Chief Fin. Officer, V.P. & Sec.--Standard Insurance Co., Portland, OR; *U.S. Private*, pg. 1031
Mawhorter, Robert L., Sr. V.P.-Fin., Admin. & Sec--Millers Mutual Insurance Assn., Alton, IL; *U.S. Private*, pg. 748
Maxim, Mark A., Chief Fin. Officer--Nalge Company, Rochester, NY; *U.S. Public*, pg. 1545
May, Alison, Chief Oper. Officer & Chief Fin. Officer--Esprit de Corp., San Francisco, CA; *U.S. Private*, pg. 383
May, Kerry H., Chief Fin. Officer--McGean-Rohco, Inc., Cleveland, OH; *U.S. Private*, pg. 721
May, Linda, Chief Fin. Officer--Bam Media, Pleasant Hill, CA; *U.S. Private*, pg. 113
Mayberry, Steve, Chief Fin. Officer--USA Casualty Company, Chino, CA; *U.S. Private*, pg. 1116
Mayer, Jeffrey P., Chief Fin. Officer--Bristol Hotels & Resorts, Dallas, TX; *U.S. Public*, pg. 253
Mayer, John A., Chief Fin. Officer--J.P. Morgan Co. Incorporated, New York, NY; *U.S. Public*, pg. 1129
Mayer, Myra L., Treas.--First Gibraltar Bank, Irving, TX; *U.S. Public*, pg. 181
Mayer, Stan, Chief Fin. Officer--Kenneth Cole Productions, New York, NY; *U.S. Public*, pg. 951
Mayo, Al F., Chief Fin. Officer--Cornucopia, Inc., Irvine, CA; *U.S. Private*, pg. 276
Mayotte, Clifford, Chief Fin. Officer--Bromar Inc., Newport Beach, CA; *U.S. Private*, pg. 171
Mays, Randall T., Chief Fin. Officer & V.P.--Clear Channel Communications, Inc., San Antonio, TX; *U.S. Public*, pg. 383
Mayuex, Jay, Chief Fin. Officer--Hydril Company, Houston, TX; *U.S. Private*, pg. 551
Maziejka, Edward M. Jr., Chief Fin. Officer--The Troy Savings Bank, Troy, NY; *U.S. Private*, pg. 1106
Mazurek, Cathy, Chief Fin. Officer & Sr. V.P.--RBT/Strum, Cherry Hill, NJ; *U.S. Private*, pg. 902
Mazza, Thomas J., Exec. V.P. & Chief Fin. Officer--Simmons Juvenile Products, Rutherford, NJ; *U.S. Private*, pg. 1001
Mazzaferro, Thomas M., Chief Fin. Officer--American Skandia Investment Services, Inc., Shelton, CT; *Int'l*, pg. 1257
McAfee, Lawrence W., Chief Fin. Officer & Exec. V.P.--ITEQ, Inc., Houston, TX; *U.S. Public*, pg. 914
McAleenan, Patrick, Chief Fin. Officer & Dir.-Fin.--EMAP Business Communications Division, London, United Kingdom; *Int'l*, pg. 451
McAlexander, Wallace R., Jr., Chief Fin. Officer--Building Plastics, Inc., Memphis, TN; *U.S. Private*, pg. 180
McAlhaney, W. Hardee, Chief Fin. Officer & V.P.--Holiday RV Superstores, Inc., Orlando, FL; *U.S. Public*, pg. 829
McAlhaney, W. Hardee, Chief Fin. Officer--Holiday RV Superstores West, Inc., Sacramento, CA; *U.S. Public*, pg. 830
McAlhaney, W. Hardee, Chief Fin. Officer--Holiday RV Superstores of New Mexico Inc., Las Cruces, NM; *U.S. Public*, pg. 830
McAndrew, Kevin J., Chief Oper. & Fin. Officer & Exec. V.P.--Canterbury Corporate Services, Inc., Medford, NJ; *U.S. Public*, pg. 301
McAnulty, Richard, Chief Fin. Officer--Super D Drugs Acquisition Co., Pine Bluff, AR; *U.S. Private*, pg. 642
McArthur, Rawdon W., Chief Fin. Officer & Treas.--BellSouth International, Inc., Atlanta, GA; *U.S. Public*, pg. 208
McAulay, Jeffrey J., Chief Fin. Officer & V.P.--Moran Transporation Company, Greenwich, CT; *U.S. Private*, pg. 760
McAulay, Jeffrey J., Chief Fin. Officer & V.P.-Fin.--Moran Towing Corporation, Greenwich, CT; *U.S. Private*, pg. 760
McAuliffe, Joan, Chief Fin. Officer & Gen. Counsel--Compendium Systems Corporation, Greenwich, CT; *U.S. Private*, pg. 259
McAuliffe, Lawrence, Controller--Whitney Blake Company of Vermont, Inc., Bellows Falls, VT; *U.S. Private*, pg. 148
McAvoy, K.J., Chief Fin. Officer--KF Industries, Oklahoma City, OK; *U.S. Public*, pg. 1746
McAvoy, Kenneth J., Chief Fin. Officer--Watts Industries, Inc., North Andover, MA; *U.S. Public*, pg. 1746
McBrayer, Charles W., Chief Fin. Officer--PairGain Technologies Inc., Tustin, CA; *U.S. Public*, pg. 1253
McBride, Dorothy Z., Sec./Treas.--Doubleday Canada Ltd., Toronto, Canada; *Int'l*, pg. 192
McBride, Gary, Chief Fin. Officer & V.P.--Cain's Coffee Co., Oklahoma City, OK; *U.S. Public*, pg. 351
McBride, Tom, Chief Fin. Officer--McWilliams Forge Co., Rockaway, NJ; *U.S. Private*, pg. 725
McCabe, James B., Chief Fin. Officer & V.P.-Fin.--Chick-fil-A, Inc., Atlanta, GA; *U.S. Private*, pg. 236
McCaffrey, Bill, Chief Fin. Officer--Grandy's, Inc., Lewisville, TX; *U.S. Private*, pg. 61
McCaffrey, Thomas, Chief Fin. Officer & Corp. Sr. V.P.-Admin.--B/E Aerospace, Inc., Wellington, FL; *U.S. Public*, pg. 159
McCaffrey, William, Jr., Chief Fin. Officer--American Restaurant Group, Inc., Newport Beach, CA; *U.S. Private*, pg. 61
McCall, Ronald L., Vice Chm., Chief Exec. Officer, Chief Fin. Officer & Treas.--M.B. Kahn Construction Co., Inc., Columbia, SC; *U.S. Private*, pg. 604
McCallon, Anne D., Sr. V.P.-Corp. Fin. & Investor Rels.--Countrywide Funding Corporation, Pasadena, CA; *U.S. Public*, pg. 453
McCalmont, William S., Chief Fin. Officer--La Quinta Inns, Inc., San Antonio, TX; *U.S. Public*, pg. 972
McCann, Jeff, Chief Fin. Officer--Nashville Wire Product Co., Nashville, TN; *U.S. Private*, pg. 775
McCann, Michael, Controller--Genzyme Diagnostics, Medix Biotech, San Carlos, CA; *U.S. Public*, pg. 733
McCann, Richard L., Chief Oper. Officer, Chief Fin. Officer & Exec. V.P.--Union Pump Company, Battle Creek, MI; *U.S. Private*, pg. 1119
McCann, Vince, Chief Fin. Officer--Sussex Publishers, Inc., New York, NY; *U.S. Private*, pg. 1056

McCann, Vince, Chief Fin. Officer--Mother Earth News, New York, NY; *U.S. Private*, pg. 1056
McCann, Vince, Chief Fin. Officer--Psychology Today, New York, NY; *U.S. Private*, pg. 1056
McCarey, J., Chief Fin. Officer--Lockheed Information Management Services Co., Teaneck, NJ; *U.S. Public*, pg. 1009
McCarthy, Arthur, Chief Fin. Officer & Sr. V.P.--New York Islanders Hockey Club, Uniondale, NY; *U.S. Private*, pg. 794
McCarthy, Colin M., Dir.-Fin.--Bowthorpe plc, Crawley, United Kingdom; *Int'l*, pg. 207
McCarthy, David, Chief Fin. Officer--Columbia Farms Inc., Leesville, SC; *U.S. Private*, pg. 255
McCarthy, Jack D., Chief Fin. Officer & V.P.--Apco Argentina Inc., Tulsa, OK; *U.S. Public*, pg. 119
McCarthy, Jack D., Chief Fin. Officer & Sr. V.P.-Fin.--The Williams Companies, Inc., Tulsa, OK; *U.S. Public*, pg. 1769
McCarthy, Joe, Chief Fin. Officer--Case-Swayne Co. Inc., Corona, CA; *U.S. Private*, pg. 218
McCarthy, Kevin, Chief Fin. Officer--Sloan Valve Company, Franklin Park, IL; *U.S. Private*, pg. 1006
McCarthy, Raymond, Chief Fin. Officer--Nashua Photo Limited, Newton Abbot, United Kingdom; *U.S. Public*, pg. 1152
McCay, Darrel, Chief Fin. Officer--Collins & Aikman Floorcoverings, Inc., Dalton, GA; *U.S. Private*, pg. 192
McClain, Terry J., Chief Fin. Officer & Sr. V.P.--Valmont Industries, Inc., Valley, NE; *U.S. Public*, pg. 1706
McClain, W. Scott, Chief Fin. Officer & V.P.-Fin.--Sonic Corporation, Oklahoma City, OK; *U.S. Public*, pg. 1485
McClanahan, Patricia N., Chief Fin. Officer & Controller--First Farmers & Merchants National Bank, Columbia, TN; *U.S. Private*, pg. 407
McClary, Dan, Chief Fin. Officer--American Rehability Services, Inc., Brentwood, TN; *U.S. Public*, pg. 1257
McClary, Dennie L., Chief Fin. Officer--The Cloister, Sea Island, GA; *U.S. Private*, pg. 978
McClellan, Steven R., Chief Fin. Officer & Exec. V.P.--Perkins Family Restaurants, Memphis, TN; *U.S. Private*, pg. 925
McClelland, George R., Chief Fin. Officer & V.P.-Admin.--Independent Can Company, Belcamp, MD; *U.S. Private*, pg. 559
McClelland, Kerwin T., Treas.--Old Republic International Corporation, Chicago, IL; *U.S. Public*, pg. 1218
McClennan, Howard, Chief Fin. Officer, Treas. & Sec.--Uncle B's Bakery, Inc., Ellsworth, IA; *U.S. Public*, pg. 1664
McCloskey, Brenda, Chief Fin. Officer & Controller--Marketing Displays International, Farmington Hills, MI; *U.S. Private*, pg. 705
McCloskey, James, Chief Fin. Officer & Exec. V.P.--Pinkerton's Inc., Encino, CA; *U.S. Public*, pg. 1296
McCloskey, Thomas, Chief Fin. Officer--American Paper Group, Inc., Youngstown, OH; *U.S. Private*, pg. 60
McClure, Kevin, Controller--API Harowe, West Chester, PA; *U.S. Public*, pg. 90
McCluski, Steven, Chief Fin. Officer--Bausch & Lomb Incorporated, Rochester, NY; *U.S. Public*, pg. 194
McCoach, J., Chief Fin. Officer--John Menzies Retail, Edinburgh, United Kingdom; *Int'l*, pg. 707
McCoach, William P., Chief Fin. Officer & Treas.--The Fabri-Form Company, Byesville, OH; *U.S. Private*, pg. 390
McCobb, James E., Treas.--American Radio Relay League, Newington, CT; *U.S. Private*, pg. 60
McCollum, W. Lee, Chief Fin. Officer & Sr. V.P.--S.C. Johnson & Son, Inc., Racine, WI; *U.S. Private*, pg. 592
McCombs, Donald E., Chief Fin. Officer & Sr. V.P.--ADVO, Inc., Windsor, CT; *U.S. Public*, pg. 23
McCombs, R.N., Chief Fin. Officer, V.P. & Sec.--Erly Industries, Inc., Los Angeles, CA; *U.S. Public*, pg. 591
McCombs, R.N., Chief Fin. Officer--Comet American Marketing, Houston, TX; *U.S. Public*, pg. 591
McComish, B., Chief Fin. Officer--National Australia Bank Limited, Melbourne, Australia; *Int'l*, pg. 906
McConathy, J. Thompson, Chief Fin. Officer & V.P.-Fin.--OEA, Inc., Aurora, CO; *U.S. Public*, pg. 1206
McConnell, Mac, Chief Fin. Officer & V.P.--Sterling Electronics Corporation, Houston, TX; *U.S. Public*, pg. 1051
McConnell, Thomas J., Chief Fin. Officer & V.P.-Fin.--Discount Drug Mart Inc., Medina, OH; *U.S. Private*, pg. 334
McConnell, Tom, Chief Fin. Officer--Imediate Pharmaceutical Services Inc., Medina, OH; *U.S. Private*, pg. 334
McConville, Rita J., Chief Fin. Officer, Treas. & Sec.--Akorn, Inc., Lincolnshire, IL; *U.S. Public*, pg. 34
McConville, Rita J., Chief Fin. Officer--Akorn Manufacturing, Inc., Decatur, IL; *U.S. Public*, pg. 34
McCook, R.P., Chief Fin. Officer & V.P.-Fin.--Winn-Dixie Stores, Inc., Jacksonville, FL; *U.S. Public*, pg. 1771
McCool, Michael, Chief Fin. Officer--AP North American Aftermarket Division, Goldsboro, NC; *U.S. Private*, pg. 230
McCord, Timothy S., Chief Fin. Officer & Treas.--Drug Emporium, Inc., Powell, OH; *U.S. Public*, pg. 530
McCord, William F., Chief Fin. Officer--Dubin-Clark & Company, Greenwich, CT; *U.S. Private*, pg. 344
McCormick, James, Chief Fin. Officer--Hollister Incorporated, Libertyville, IL; *U.S. Private*, pg. 535
McCormick, Steven, Chief Fin. Officer--J.H. McCormick, Inc., Burbank, CA; *U.S. Private*, pg. 720
McCoy, James P., Jr., Chief Fin. Officer--Club Corporation International, Dallas, TX; *U.S. Private*, pg. 247
McCoy, Robert S., Jr., Chief Fin. Officer & Exec. V.P.--Wachovia Corporation, Winston Salem, NC; *U.S. Public*, pg. 1730
McCracken, Alan L., Chief Fin. Officer & Exec. V.P.-Fin.--Baltimore Stationery Co./Total Office, Baltimore, MD; *U.S. Private*, pg. 113
McCrackin, William K., Vice Chm. & Chief Fin. Officer--MCN Energy Group, Inc., Detroit, MI; *U.S. Public*, pg. 1024
McCrackin, William K., Vice Chm. & Chief Fin. Officer--MCN Investment, Detroit, MI; *U.S. Public*, pg. 1025
McCraken, Eric, Chief Fin. Officer--Aerosonic Corporation, Clearwater, FL; *U.S. Public*, pg. 25
McCready, Patrick, Chief Fin. Officer--Pulse Engineering, Inc., San Diego, CA; *U.S. Public*, pg. 1564
McCreedy, Matt, Chief Fin. Officer, Sr. V.P.-Fin. & Treas.--Jackson Hole Ski Resort, Teton Village, WY; *U.S. Private*, pg. 579
McCreery, Harry, Chief Fin. Officer & Treas.--Software AG Americas, Inc., Reston, VA; *U.S. Public*, pg. 1482
McCreery, Thomas A., Jr., V.P.-Fin. & Admin.--Wickland Properties, Sacramento, CA; *U.S. Private*, pg. 1175
McCubbin, Donald K., Chief Fin. Officer & Controller--Nadel Architects, Inc., Los Angeles, CA; *U.S. Private*, pg. 773
McCullars, Denise, Chief Fin. Officer, Treas. & Sec.--Dawson Construction Co., Inc., Gadsden, AL; *U.S. Private*, pg. 316
McCullough, Robert F., Chief Fin. Officer--Invesco Group Asset Management Ltd., London, United Kingdom; *Int'l*, pg. 685
McCully, E. Nichol, Chief Fin. Officer & Sr. V.P.-Fin.--Keebler Company, Elmhurst, IL; *U.S. Public*, pg. 657
McCurdy, Donna, Chief Fin. Officer--Rocco Inc., Harrisonburg, VA; *U.S. Private*, pg. 937
McCusker, Francis C., Chief Fin. Officer--Marmac Corporation, Vienna, WV; *U.S. Private*, pg. 705
McCusty, Paul R., Chief Fin. Officer & V.P.-Fin.--The Ohio Art Company, Inc., Bryan, OH; *U.S. Public*, pg. 1214
McCutcheon, Jim, V.P.-Fin.--Choice Hotels International, Inc., Silver Spring, MD; *U.S. Public*, pg. 351
McDaniel, Felix, Chief Fin. Officer--Americal Corporation, Henderson, NC; *U.S. Private*, pg. 49
McDaniel, T.W., Chief Fin. Officer--Solar Turbines Incorporated, San Diego, CA; *U.S. Public*, pg. 316
McDermed, Kevin T., Chief Fin. Officer, V.P., Treas. & Sec.--Atchison Casting Corporation, Atchison, KS; *U.S. Public*, pg. 142
McDermott, Robert J., Chief Fin. Officer & V.P.--Charan Industries, Inc., Garden City, NY; *U.S. Private*, pg. 229
McDermott, William J., Chief Fin. Officer, V.P. & Sec.--Sevenson Environmental Services, Inc., Niagara Falls, NY; *U.S. Public*, pg. 1462
McDevitt, Larry, V.P. & Controller--Levitz Furniture Corporation, Boca Raton, FL; *U.S. Public*, pg. 990
McDevitt, Richard H., Chief Fin. Officer, V.P.-Fin. & Treas.--AmeriData Technologies, Inc., Stamford, CT; *U.S. Public*, pg. 711
McDevitt, Thomas F., Chief Fin. Officer & V.P.-Fin.--Morton International Inc., Chicago, IL; *U.S. Public*, pg. 1134
McDonald, Arlen L., Chief Fin. Officer--Deposit Guaranty Corp., Jackson, MS; *U.S. Public*, pg. 500
McDonald, D.G., Chief Fin. Officer & V.P.-Fin.--Pioneer Plastics Corporation, Auburn, ME; *U.S. Private*, pg. 867
McDonald, Jerry, Exec. V.P., Chief Fin. Officer & Treas.--Resistance Technology Inc., Arden Hills, MN; *U.S. Public*, pg. 1455
McDonald, John, Chief Fin. Officer--Bessemer Group, Inc., New York, NY; *U.S. Private*, pg. 139
Mcdonald, Michael, Chief Fin. Officer--Carpentry & Hardware Services, Columbia, MD; *U.S. Private*, pg. 503
McDonald, Michael, Chief Fin. Officer--Ikea North America, Inc., Plymouth Meeting, PA; *Int'l*, pg. 660
McDonald, Paul, Chief Acctg. Officer & Sr. Exec. V.P.--Friendly Ice Cream Corp., Wilbraham, MA; *U.S. Public*, pg. 682
McDonald, Thomas, Chief Fin. Officer & Treas.--Jernberg Industries, Inc., Chicago, IL; *U.S. Private*, pg. 586
McDonald, Thomas J., Chief Fin. Officer & V.P.--National Education Training Group, Naperville, IL; *U.S. Public*, pg. 784
McDonald, Thomas J., Chief Fin. Officer & V.P.--NETG Holding, Inc., Irvine, CA; *U.S. Public*, pg. 784
McDonald, Walter, Chief Fin. Officer & V.P.-Fin.--Gandalf Technologies Inc., Nepean, Canada; *Int'l*, pg. 540
McDonnell, Francis W., Chief Fin. Officer & Exec. V.P.--Pennsylvania Manufacturers Corp., Blue Bell, PA; *U.S. Public*, pg. 1272
McDonnell, Francis W., Chief Fin. Officer & Sr. V.P.--PMA Reinsurance Corporation, Philadelphia, PA; *U.S. Public*, pg. 1272
McDonnell, Joe, Chief Fin. Officer--American Security Distribution, Anaheim, CA; *U.S. Private*, pg. 61
McDonnell, John, Chief Fin. Officer--American Express Travel Related Services Co., Inc., New York, NY; *U.S. Public*, pg. 73
McDonough, Joseph E., Chief Fin. Officer & V.P.-Fin.--Analog Devices, Inc., Norwood, MA; *U.S. Public*, pg. 107
McDonough, Thomas F., V.P. & Sec.--Montgomery St. Income Securities, Inc., San Francisco, CA; *U.S. Public*, pg. 1127
McDougall, Bill, Chief Fin. Officer & V.P.--Cegelec AEG Automation Systems Corp., Canonsburg, PA; *Int'l*, pg. 52
McDowell, Robbyn, Chief Fin. Officer--Earnhardt's Motor Companies, Gilbert, AZ; *U.S. Private*, pg. 356
McElderry, C.J., Chief Fin. Officer & V.P.-Fin.--Rosauers Supermarkets, Inc., Spokane, WA; *U.S. Private*, pg. 944
McElwee, Dixon, Chief Fin. Officer--Cameron Ashley Building Products, Inc., Dallas, TX; *U.S. Public*, pg. 298
McEnery, Kevin J., Chief Fin. Officer & Exec. V.P.--Scholastic Corporation, New York, NY; *U.S. Public*, pg. 1440
McEnroe, Joseph J., V.P. & Dir.-Fin. & Admin.--SmithKline Beecham Consumer Healthcare, U.S., Pittsburgh, PA; *Int'l*, pg. 1264
McEntee, R. Michael, Chief Fin. Officer & V.P.--Fansteel, Inc., North Chicago, IL; *U.S. Public*, pg. 612
McEwan, Ray, Treas.--Jack Daniels Distillery, Lynchburg, TN; *U.S. Public*, pg. 261
McFadden, Edward H., Chief Fin. Officer & Exec. V.P.--Breed Technologies, Inc., Lakeland, FL; *U.S. Public*, pg. 251
McFadden, Harry W., M.D., Treas.--Physicians Mutual Insurance Co., Omaha, NE; *U.S. Private*, pg. 864
McFadden, J. C., Exec. Dir.-Fin.--James Hardie Industries Ltd., Sydney, Australia; *Int'l*, pg. 596
McFadden, Michael, Chief Fin. Officer--Astro Dairy Products Ltd., Etobicoke, Canada; *Int'l*, pg. 95
McFarland, Charles, Chief Fin. Officer--Tri-City Electrical Contractors Inc., Altamonte Springs, FL; *U.S. Private*, pg. 1100
McFarland, Joseph M., Chief Fin. Officer--First National Mortgage Corporation, Glen Burnie, MD; *Int'l*, pg. 64
McFarlane, Jason, Chief Fin. Officer--Farmington Hills Holding Company, Farmington, MI; *U.S. Private*, pg. 395
McGarvey, Jim, Chief Fin. Officer--Green Seed Co., Baltimore, MD; *U.S. Private*, pg. 477
McGarvie, Blythe J., Chief Fin. Officer & Sr. V.P.--Hannaford Bros. Co., Scarborough, ME; *U.S. Public*, pg. 781
McGee, Lee, Chief Fin. Officer--Sylvan Learning Systems Inc., Baltimore, MD; *U.S. Public*, pg. 1545
McGee, Michael P., Chief Fin. Officer & V.P.--International Rectifier Corporation, El Segundo, CA; *U.S. Public*, pg. 906
McGeough, Peter, Chief Fin. & Admin. Officer & Exec. V.P.--Seaman Furniture Company, Inc., Woodbury, NY; *U.S. Public*, pg. 1452
McGhee, James E., Chief Fin. Officer & Treas.--Weil Brothers Cotton Inc., Montgomery, AL; *U.S. Private*, pg. 1159
McGill, Chuck, Chief Fin. Officer--Teledyne Electronic Technologies, Los Angeles, CA; *U.S. Public*, pg. 43
McGill, Dan, Chief Fin. Officer--Universal Studios Music Entertainment Group, Universal City, CA; *Int'l*, pg. 1215
McGill, Edmund R., Chief Fin. Officer & V.P.--Marketing Corp. of America, Westport, CT; *U.S. Private*, pg. 704
McGill, Paul, Chief Fin. Officer--Advanced Manufacturing & Development, Willits, CA; *U.S. Private*, pg. 22
McGinnis, Vern, Chief Fin. Officer & V.P.--Growmark, Inc., Bloomington, IL; *U.S. Private*, pg. 484
McGlogan, J., Chief Fin. Officer--Procter & Gamble Inc., North York, Canada; *U.S. Public*, pg. 1332
McGlone, John F., Chief Fin. Officer & V.P.--Chicago Tube & Iron Co., Chicago, IL; *U.S. Private*, pg. 235
McGlone, Roy, Chief Fin. Officer--BBA Group plc, London, United Kingdom; *Int'l*, pg. 112
McGorry, Fran, Chief Fin. Officer & V.P.--Philadelphia Coca-Cola Bottling Co., Philadelphia, PA; *U.S. Private*, pg. 861
McGovern, John F., Chief Fin. Officer & Exec. V.P.-Fin.--Georgia-Pacific Corporation, Atlanta, GA; *U.S. Public*, pg. 735
McGraime, Douglas, Chief Fin. Officer, Exec. V.P. & Treas.--Combe Incorporated, White Plains, NY; *U.S. Private*, pg. 257
McGranaghan, M.R., Chief Fin. Officer--Johnson & Johnson/Merck Consumer Pharmaceuticals Co., Whitehouse Station, NJ; *U.S. Public*, pg. 929
McGrath, Brent P., Chief Fin. Officer, Treas. & Sec.--Mico Inc., North Mankato, MN; *U.S. Private*, pg. 741
McGrath, George, V.P.-Fin.--Lane Limited, Tucker, GA; *Int'l*, pg. 1129
McGrath, Gerald M., Chief Fin. Officer, V.P. & Treas.--Analysts International Corporation, Minneapolis, MN; *U.S. Public*, pg. 110
McGrath, Richard, Chief Fin. Officer & Controller--Budapest Marriott Hotel, Budapest, Hungary; *Int'l*, pg. 232
McGrath, William, Chief Fin. Officer & Grp. Fin. Dir.--Bardon Group PLC, Solihull, United Kingdom; *Int'l*, pg. 166
McGrattan, Leo, Chief Fin. Officer--Ithaco Inc., Ithaca, NY; *U.S. Private*, pg. 576
McGraw, Robert J., V.P. & Treas.--AUSA Holding Company, Baltimore, MD; *Int'l*, pg. 27
McGregor, Ian, Chief Fin. Officer--OzEmail Limited, Sydney, Australia; *Int'l*, pg. 1019
McGregor, W.H., Dir.-Fin.--Bruntons Areo Product, Musselburgh, United Kingdom; *Int'l*, pg. 268
McGuinness, Matthew, Chief Fin. Officer--El Pollo Loco, Irvine, CA; *U.S. Public*, pg. 23
McGurk, Nancy J., Chief Fin. Officer & V.P.-Fin. & Treas.--Resource America, Inc., Philadelphia, PA; *U.S. Public*, pg. 1382
McHome, Randy, Chief Fin. Officer--Weber Aircraft, Inc., Fullerton, CA; *Int'l*, pg. 572
McHugh, Jerry, Chief Fin. Officer--North American Products Corp., Jasper, IN; *U.S. Private*, pg. 803
McHugh, Joseph W., Jr., Chief Fin. Officer & V.P.-Fin.--High Voltage Engineering Corporation, Wakefield, MA; *U.S. Private*, pg. 528
McHugh, Michael P., Chief Fin. Officer & V.P.--J. Crew Group, Inc., New York, NY; *U.S. Private*, pg. 1078
McIllroy, Jim, Chief Fin. Officer--Esselte Meto International GmbH, Heppenheim, Germany; *Int'l*, pg. 461
McInnes, Ross, Dir.-Fin.--Eridania Beghin-Say Group, Neuilly-sur-Seine, France; *Int'l*, pg. 324
McIntosh, James, Chief Fin. Officer--FMC-Crosby Valve, Inc., Wrentham, MA; *U.S. Public*, pg. 605
McIntosh, L. William, Chief Fin. Officer & Sr. V.P.-Bus. Devel. & Fin.--VIMRx Pharmaceuticals, Inc., Wilmington, DE; *U.S. Public*, pg. 1702
McIntyre, Edward J., Chief Fin. Officer & V.P.--Northern States Power Company, Minneapolis, MN; *U.S. Public*, pg. 1195
McIntyre, G. William, Chief Fin. Officer & Dir.-Fin.--ComSonics, Inc., Harrisonburg, VA; *U.S. Private*, pg. 260
McIntyre, Jerry, Chief Fin. Officer--David Joseph Co., Cincinnati, OH; *U.S. Private*, pg. 601
McIntyre, Tom, Sr. V.P. & Chief Fin. Officer--Bertelsmann Music Group, Wilmington, DE; *Int'l*, pg. 191
McInvale, Gerald D., Chief Fin. Officer & Exec. V.P.--Entergy Corporation, New Orleans, LA; *U.S. Public*, pg. 585
McInvale, Gerald D., Chief Fin. Officer--Entergy Arkansas, Inc., Little Rock, AR; *U.S. Public*, pg. 586
McIsaac, Donald, Controller--Canadian Kenworth Co., Mississauga, Canada; *U.S. Public*, pg. 1247

McIver, Jimmy R., Treas.--Kentucky Investors, Inc., Frankfort, KY; *U.S. Public*, pg. 951
McKaba, Bob, Chief Fin. Officer & V.P.-Fin.--Burdick, Inc., Milton, WI; *U.S. Private*, pg. 181
McKay, Donald A., Chief Fin. Officer & Exec. V.P.--JC Penney Company, Inc., Plano, TX; *U.S. Public*, pg. 916
McKay, Donald K., Chief Fin. Officer, Exec. V.P., Treas. & Sec.--Specialty Equipment Companies Inc., Aurora, IL; *U.S. Public*, pg. 1496
McKee, E. Stanton, Jr., Chief Fin. & Chief Admin. Officer & Exec. V.P.--Electronic Arts, San Mateo, CA; *U.S. Public*, pg. 569
McKee, Kenneth A., Chief Fin. Officer, Treas. & Gen. Counsel--Johnson Storage Moving Co, Denver, CO; *U.S.* Private, pg. 594
McKee, Kenneth A., Chief Fin. Officer--Johnson Storage & Moving, San Diego, Poway, CA; *U.S. Private*, pg. 594
McKee, Kenneth A., Chief Fin. Officer--Johnson Storage & Moving, Santa Fe, Santa Fe, NM; *U.S. Private*, pg. 594
McKee, Michael, Vice Chm. & Chief Fin. Officer--The Irvine Company, Newport Beach, CA; *U.S. Private*, pg. 575
McKee, Peter B., Chief Fin. Officer & Sr. V.P.--Allegiance Healthcare Corp., McGaw Park, IL; *U.S. Public*, pg. 44
McKee, William T., Chief Fin. Officer & Treas.--Barr Laboratories Inc., Pomona, NY; *U.S. Public*, pg. 191
Mckeibier, Michael, Chief Fin. Officer--Superior Die Tool And Machine Company, Columbus, OH; *U.S. Private*, pg. 1054
McKelvey, Patrick M., Treas.--RNL/Interplan, Los Angeles, CA; *U.S. Private*, pg. 905
McKenna, James M., V.P.-Fin. & Admin.--CBS News, New York, NY; *U.S. Public*, pg. 274
McKenna, Steve, Chief Fin. Officer & Sr. Exec. V.P.-Singapore--Dentsu Young & Rubicam Partnerships, New York, NY; *U.S. Private*, pg. 325
McKenna, William P., V.P.-Fin. & Treas.--Bourns, Inc., Riverside, CA; *U.S. Private*, pg. 161
McKenzie, Clyde E., Chief Fin. Officer & V.P.--K N Energy, Inc., Lakewood, CO; *U.S. Public*, pg. 937
McKeon, Kevin J., Chief Fin. Officer & Exec. V.P.--Home Shopping Network, Inc., Saint Petersburg, FL; *U.S. Public*, pg. 1685
McKeon, Ross W., Chief Fin. Officer & Exec. V.P.-Field Opers.--News America Marketing, Norwalk, CT; *Int'l*, pg. 925
McKeown, Bill, Chief Fin. Officer--Meherrin Agriculture & Chemical Co., Severn, NC; *U.S. Private*, pg. 729
McKeown, Sean, Chief Fin. Officer--McMaster Carr Supply Co. Inc., Elmhurst, IL; *U.S. Private*, pg. 724
McKibben, Craig, Chief Fin. Officer & V.P.--Ampex Corporation, Redwood City, CA; *U.S. Public*, pg. 104
McKibbin, Chris, Chief Fin. Officer--Electronic Arts (Canada) Inc., Burnaby, Canada; *U.S. Public*, pg. 569
McKinley, Ellis, Jr., Chief Fin. Officer, V.P. & Treas.--Kevco, Inc., Fort Worth, TX; *U.S. Public*, pg. 952
McKinney, Don, Chief Fin. Officer--Precision Parts Corp., Morristown, TN; *U.S. Private*, pg. 879
McKinnis, Archie, Chief Fin. Officer--Gulf States Manufacturers, Inc., Starkville, MS; *Int'l*, pg. 699
McKittrick, David J., Chief Fin. Officer, Sr. V.P. & Treas.--Gateway 2000, North Sioux City, SD; *U.S. Public*, pg. 703
McKnight, Craig, Chief Fin. Officer & Exec. V.P.--Magellan Health Services, Inc., Atlanta, GA; *U.S. Public*, pg. 1033
McKnight, Craig, Chief Fin. Officer--Merit Behavioral Care Corp., Park Ridge, NJ; *U.S. Public*, pg. 1036
McLachlan, David, Audit Dir.--Midland Bank PLC, London, United Kingdom; *Int'l*, pg. 580
McLachlan, David J., Chief Fin. Officer & Sr. V.P.--Genzyme Corporation, Cambridge, MA; *U.S. Public*, pg. 733
McLamb, George T., Chief Fin. Officer, Exec. V.P. & Treas.--Kingsdown, Inc., Mebane, NC; *U.S. Private*, pg. 622
McLanghan, James, Chief Fin. Officer--Rollins Leasing Corp., Wilmington, DE; *U.S. Public*, pg. 1405
McLaughlin, James, Sr. V.P. & Chief Fin. Officer--John Hancock Advisers, Inc., Boston, MA; *U.S. Private*, pg. 589
McLaughlin, Joe, V.P.-Fin.--Videojet Systems International, Inc., Wood Dale, IL; *Int'l*, pg. 545
McLaughlin, Michael, Chief Fin. Officer--A.T. Clayton & Company, Inc., Greenwich, CT; *U.S. Private*, pg. 244
McLaughlin, Paul V., Chief Fin. Officer & V.P.--The Time Inc. Book Company, New York, NY; *U.S. Public*, pg. 1613
McLaughlin, Richard, Chief Fin. Officer--Dallas Stars, Irving, TX; *U.S. Private*, pg. 309
McLaughlin, Thomas K., Chief Fin. Officer & Mng. Dir.--Countrywide Home Loans Inc., Pasadena, CA; *U.S. Public*, pg. 452
McLaughlin, Thomas N., Chief Fin. Officer & Controller--Insulate LLC, Auburn, WA; *Int'l*, pg. 1171
McLean, A. Alexander, Chief Fin. Officer--Paradata Financial Systems, Chesterfield, MO; *U.S. Public*, pg. 1778
McLean, A. Alexander, III, Chief Fin. Officer & Exec. V.P.--World Acceptance Corporation, Greenville, SC; *U.S. Public*, pg. 1778
McLean, Gordon, Chief Fin. Officer--Boston Digital Corp., Milford, MA; *U.S. Private*, pg. 161
McLeish, Gordon, Comptroller--Semblex Corporation, Elmhurst, IL; *U.S. Private*, pg. 983
McLellan, Michael, Chief Fin. Officer & Sr. V.P.-Svcs. Grp.--Whataburger, Inc., Corpus Christi, TX; *U.S. Private*, pg. 1170
McLennan, Rex J., Chief Fin. Officer & Sr. V.P.--Placer Dome Inc., Vancouver, Canada; *Int'l*, pg. 1060
McLeod, D., Treas. & Controller--Tranter, Inc., Augusta, GA; *U.S. Public*, pg. 521
McLeod, John, Jr., Chief Fin. Officer & V.P.--Lone Star Corrugated Container Corporation, Irving, TX; *U.S. Private*, pg. 674
McLoughlin, Malcolm, Chief Fin. Officer--Pilkington Barnes Hind (PBH), San Diego, CA; *U.S. Private*, pg. 111
McMahan, Rick, Chief Fin. Officer--Miller Fluid Power Corp., Bensenville, IL; *U.S. Private*, pg. 747
McMahon, Chris, Chief Fin. Officer--Veeder-Root Company, Simsbury, CT; *U.S. Public*, pg. 482
McMahon, Mary, Chief Fin. Officer & V.P.--Colorado Business Bank of Littleton, N.A., Littleton, CO; *U.S. Private*, pg. 255
McMahon, Mary, Chief Fin. Officer & V.P.--Colorado Business Bank, Denver, CO; *U.S. Private*, pg. 255
McMakin, Kelly, Chief Fin. Officer & Treas.--Florafax International, Inc., Vero Beach, FL; *U.S. Public*, pg. 654
McManaman, William R., Chief Fin. Officer & V.P.-Fin.--Dean Foods Company, Franklin Park, IL; *U.S. Public*, pg. 489
McManmon, Thomas, Chief Fin. Officer & Sr. V.P.--Global Petroleum Corp., Waltham, MA; *U.S. Private*, pg. 457
McManus, Edward, Chief Fin. Officer--Diemolding Corp., Canastota, NY; *U.S. Private*, pg. 332
McManus, John V., V.P.-Fin. & Asst. Sec.--Sheldahl, Inc., Northfield, MN; *U.S. Public*, pg. 1465
McMartin, Kam, Chief Fin. Officer--DataCard Corporation, Minnetonka, MN; *U.S. Private*, pg. 312
McMasters, Michael P., Chief Fin. Officer, V.P. & Treas--Chesapeake Utilities Corporation, Dover, DE; *U.S. Public*, pg. 347
McMennamin, Michael J., Chief Fin. Officer & Exec. V.P.--Banc One Corporation, Columbus, OH; *U.S. Public*, pg. 172
McMillin, Tom, Chief Fin. Officer & Sr. V.P.-Fin.--Marcus Cable Company, L.P., Dallas, TX; *U.S. Private*, pg. 702
McMullen, W. Rodney, Chief Fin. Officer & Sr. V.P.--The Kroger Co., Cincinnati, OH; *U.S. Public*, pg. 967
McNabb, Christopher R., Dir.-Fin.--GTE Supply, Irving, TX; *U.S. Public*, pg. 697
McNairy, Charles, Chief Fin. Officer, Exec. V.P. & Treas.--Avatar Holdings Inc., Coral Gables, FL; *U.S. Public*, pg. 151
McNairy, Richard, Chief Fin. Officer & V.P.--Veritas DGC Inc, Houston, TX; *U.S. Private*, pg. 1136
McNallen, Kathy, Chief Fin. Officer--UniHealth, Burbank, CA; *U.S. Private*, pg. 1117
McNally, Michael J., Chief Fin. Officer--Texas Utilities Company, Dallas, TX; *U.S. Public*, pg. 1586
McNamara, Kevin, Chief Fin. Officer--Envoy Corporation, Nashville, TN; *U.S. Public*, pg. 587
McNea, R.D., Chief Fin. Officer--Hiniker Company, Mankato, MN; *U.S. Private*, pg. 530
McNeive, Gerald T., Jr., Chief Fin. Officer & Sr. V.P.--Laclede Gas Company, Saint Louis, MO; *U.S. Public*, pg. 973
McNiel, Earl W., Chief Fin. Officer & V.P.--Pride International, Inc., Houston, TX; *U.S. Public*, pg. 1324
McNiff, John, Chief Fin. Officer--Dover Corporation, New York, NY; *U.S. Public*, pg. 520
McNulty, Edward J., Chief Fin. Officer & V.P.--General Binding Corporation, Northbrook, IL; *U.S. Public*, pg. 707
McPartlin, Paul A., Chief Fin. Officer & V.P.--Tech/Ops Sevcon, Inc., Boston, MA; *U.S. Public*, pg. 1563
McPhail, Douglas J., Pres., Chief Exec. & Fin. Officer & Treas.--Indiana Records Managers, Fishers, IN; *U.S. Private*, pg. 560
McQuade, Eugene M., Vice Chm., Chief Fin. Officer & Exec. V.P.--Fleet Financial Group, Inc., Boston, MA; *U.S.* Public, pg. 648
McQuade, Robert C., Chief Fin. Officer, Sec. & Controller--Legacy Storage Systems Corp., Markham, Canada; *Int'l*, pg. 805
McQuaide, Lawrence F., Exec. V.P.-Fin.--Western Waste Industries, Torrance, CA; *U.S. Public*, pg. 1686
McShane, Michael, Chief Fin. Officer & Sr. V.P.-Fin.--BJ Services Company, Houston, TX; *U.S. Public*, pg. 161
McSweeney, Declan, Chief Fin. Officer--Allied Irish Banks, p.l.c., Dublin, Ireland; *Int'l*, pg. 64
McTear, Paul, Chief Fin. Officer--Raycom Media, Inc., Montgomery, AL; *U.S. Private*, pg. 911
McVicker, James M., Chief Fin. Officer & Sr. V.P.--Mercantile Stores Company, Inc., Fairfield, OH; *U.S. Public*, pg. 1089
McWilliams, D. Bradley, Chief Fin. Officer & Sr. V.P.-Fin.--Cooper Industries, Inc., Houston, TX; *U.S. Public*, pg. 442
Mead, Robert R., Chief Fin. Officer--Forest City Auto Parts, Beachwood, OH; *U.S. Public*, pg. 1652
Meade, Walter, Chief Fin. Officer--Pioneer Flour Mills, San Antonio, TX; *U.S. Private*, pg. 866
Meades, Derek, Chief Fin. Officer--Hoskyns Group Plc, London, United Kingdom; *Int'l*, pg. 264
Meadows, Allen D., Chief Fin. Officer, Exec. V.P. & Treas.--Fidelity National Financial, Inc., Irvine, CA; *U.S. Public*, pg. 620
Meadows, Allen D., Chief Fin. Officer, Exec. V.P. & Treas.--Fidelity National Title Insurance Company, Irvine, CA; *U.S. Public*, pg. 620
Mecaughey, William, Chief Fin. Officer, V.P. & Treas.--Roy F. Weston, Inc., West Chester, PA; *U.S. Public*, pg. 1761
Meckley, Scott, Chief Fin. Officer--Reeves Southeastern Corporation, Tampa, FL; *U.S. Private*, pg. 916
Medding, David, Chief Fin. Officer & Controller--Quadrangle Development Corporation, Washington, DC; *U.S. Private*, pg. 898
Medford, Dale L., Chief Fin. Officer & V.P.-Fin.--The Reynolds and Reynolds Company, Dayton, OH; *U.S. Public*, pg. 1384
Medlock, Robert J., Chief Fin. Officer & V.P.--NCI Building Systems, Inc., Houston, TX; *U.S. Public*, pg. 1145
Mednick, Robert, Chief Fin. Officer & V.P.--Lillian Vernon Corporation, New Rochelle, NY; *U.S. Public*, pg. 1716
Medvin, Harvey N., Chief Fin. Officer, Exec. V.P. & Treas.--AON Corporation, Chicago, IL; *U.S. Public*, pg. 117
Medvin, Harvey N., Chief Fin. Officer & Exec. V.P.--Combined Insurance Company of America, Chicago, IL; *U.S. Public*, pg. 118
Mee, Michael F., Chief Fin. Officer & Sr. V.P.--Bristol-Myers Squibb Company, New York, NY; *U.S. Public*, pg. 253
Mee, Susan Ho Siew, Chief Fin. Officer--Singapore Factory Development Ltd., Singapore, Singapore; *Int'l*, pg. 351
Meechan, George, Chief Fin. Officer & V.P.--Exel Logistics North America, Westerville, OH; *Int'l*, pg. 901
Meehan, Gregory W.A., Chief Fin. Officer, V.P. & Treas.--High Point Financial Corp., Branchville, NJ; *U.S. Public*, pg. 826
Meehan, M.R., Chief Fin.Officer--Vi-Spring Limited, Plymouth, United Kingdom; *Int'l*, pg. 925
Meehan, William P., Chief Fin. Officer, V.P.-Fin. & Treas.--Hexcel Corporation, Pleasanton, CA; *U.S. Public*, pg. 824
Meertens, H.J.A.F., Chief Fin. Officer & Dir.-MIS--Oce-van der Grinten N.V., Venlo, Netherlands; *Int'l*, pg. 993
Meeusen, Richard A., Chief Fin. Officer, V.P.-Fin. & Treas.--Badger Meter, Inc., Milwaukee, WI; *U.S. Public*, pg. 164
Meglaughlin, William T., Jr., Chief Fin. Officer & Treas.--Asbury Carbons, Inc., Asbury, NJ; *U.S. Private*, pg. 87
Mehra, Ajay, Chief Fin. Officer--UDT Sensors, Inc., Hawthorne, CA; *U.S. Private*, pg. 1112
Mehra, Ajay, Chief Fin. Officer, V.P. & Sec.--OSI Systems, Inc., Hawthorne, CA; *U.S. Public*, pg. 1208
Meier, Arlene, Chief Fin. Officer & Exec. V.P.--Kohl's Corporation, Menomonee Falls, WI; *U.S. Public*, pg. 965
Meier, Frank, Chief Fin. Officer--Rominger Reisebuero GmbH, Stuttgart, Germany; *Int'l*, pg. 1127
Meier, Henri B., Chief Fin. Officer--Roche Holding Ltd., Basel, Switzerland; *Int'l*, pg. 1119
Meier, Michael J., Chief Fin. Officer, V.P.-Fin., Treas. & Sec.--Defiance, Inc., Cleveland, OH; *U.S. Public*, pg. 493
Meikle, Mark G., Chief Fin. Officer, V.P. & Treas.--Steel of West Virginia, Inc., Huntington, WV; *U.S. Public*, pg. 1513
Meilland, Arnold, Chief Fin. Officer--Banque Piguet & Cie S.A., Yverdon, Switzerland; *Int'l*, pg. 160
Meininger, C., Chief Fin. Officer--Dosimeter Corporation of America, Cincinnati, OH; *Int'l*, pg. 892
Meisner, Gary B., Chief Fin. Officer--Ceco Door Products, Brentwood, TN; *U.S. Public*, pg. 1676
Meister, Paul M., Vice Chm., Chief Fin. Officer & Sr. V.P.--Fisher Scientific International, Hampton, NH; *U.S. Private*, pg. 658
Meister, Stefan, Dir.-Grp. Fin.--AAH plc, Runcorn, United Kingdom; *Int'l*, pg. 591
Mejrup, Find, Chief Fin. Officer--Thrige Agro A/S, Odense, Denmark; *Int'l*, pg. 1386
Melchiori, William, Chief Fin. Officer--Fetzer Vineyards California Wines, Hopland, CA; *U.S. Public*, pg. 261
Melle, Melvin J., Chief Fin. Officer, V.P. & Sec.--The Hallwood Group Incorporated, Dallas, TX; *U.S. Public*, pg. 777
Mellett, John R., Chief Fin. Officer & Sr. V.P.--Zurn Industries, Inc., Erie, PA; *U.S. Public*, pg. 1794
Mellinger, David, Chief Fin. Officer--Quantum Plus, New York, NY; *U.S. Public*, pg. 1224
Melnyk, Dennis, Chief Fin. Officer--Kalas Manufacturing, Inc., Denver, PA; *U.S. Private*, pg. 606
Melone, John, Chief Fin. Officer--Air Cruisers Co., Belmar, NJ; *Int'l*, pg. 572
Melton, Gary, Chief Fin. Officer--Lake Region Manufacturing, Inc., Chaska, MN; *U.S. Private*, pg. 643
Melton, Gary, Chief Fin. Officer--Lake Region Medical, Inc., Pittsburgh, PA; *U.S. Private*, pg. 643
Meltz, Edward E., Chm. Bd., Chief Exec. Officer & Chief Fin. Officer--Carsen Group Inc., Markham, Canada; *U.S. Public*, pg. 301
Melzer, Michael R., Chief Fin. Officer, V.P.-Fin. & Treas.--Wisconsin Machine and Tool Corporation, Milwaukee, WI; *U.S. Private*, pg. 1185
Memory, David W., Dir.-Fin.--Tie Rack plc, Brentford, United Kingdom; *Int'l*, pg. 1389
Menac, Ed, Chief Fin. Officer--Walker Wire & Steel Company, Ferndale, MI; *U.S. Private*, pg. 1147
Menchinger, Steven R., Chief. Fin. Officer, Treas. & Sec.--Glassmaster Company, Lexington, SC; *U.S. Public*, pg. 745
Mendez, Meredith, Chief Fin. Officer--Medline Industries, Inc., Mundelein, IL; *U.S. Private*, pg. 728
Mendoza, Jorje, Chief Fin. Officer--Kodak America, Ltda., Lima, Peru; *U.S. Public*, pg. 554
Mendoza, Sergio, Chief Fin. Officer--CIBA-GEIGY S.A., Barcelona, Spain; *Int'l*, pg. 979
Mendoza, V., Chief Fin. Officer, Chief Information Officer & Treas.--Gator Industries Inc., Hialeah, FL; *U.S. Private*, pg. 441
Meninger, Ken, Chief Fin. Officer--Bernards Brothers, Inc., San Fernando, CA; *U.S. Private*, pg. 136
Menke, Gerald T., Treas. & Sec.--The F.D. Lawrence Electric Co., Cincinnati, OH; *U.S. Private*, pg. 654
Mente, Richard C., Chief Fin. Officer & V.P.--Empire Southwest Co., Mesa, AZ; *U.S. Private*, pg. 374
Menten, Jurgen, Chief Oper. Officer & Chief Fin. Officer--Boehringer Mannheim GmbH, Mannheim, Germany; *Int'l*, pg. 331
Menz, Walter, Chief Fin. Officer--Aachener und Muenchener Lebensversicherung, Aachen, Germany; *Int'l*, pg. 15
Menzer, John, Chief Fin. Officer & Exec. V.P.--Wal-Mart Stores, Inc., Bentonville, AR; *U.S. Public*, pg. 1732
Mercado, Asuncion V., Chief Fin. Officer, V.P. & Treas.--Benguet Management Corporation, Manila, Philippines; *Int'l*, pg. 186
Mercer, Harold B., Chief Fin. Officer,Exec. V.P. & Treas.--Swift Instruments, Inc., Dorchester, MA; *U.S. Private*, pg. 1058
Merclean, David B., Chief Fin. Officer & Sr. V.P.--Selective Insurance Group, Inc, Branchville, NJ; *U.S. Public*, pg. 1455
Mercurio, John, Chief Fin. Officer & Sr. V.P.--Lowe Direct, New York, NY; *U.S. Private*, pg. 678
Meredith, Frank, Chief Fin. Officer, Gen. Counsel & Sec.--Harman International Industries, Inc., Woodbury, NY; *U.S. Public*, pg. 787
Meredith, Thomas J., Chief Fin. Officer & Sr. V.P.-Fin. & MIS--Dell Computer Corporation, Round Rock, TX; *U.S. Public*, pg. 495

Mereschuk, Jeffrey A., Chief Fin. Officer, V.P. & Treas.--Essex Industries, New Haven, CT; *Int'l*, pg. 18
Mergy, Thomas J., Chief Fin. Officer--U.S. Turbine Corporation, Maineville, OH; *Int'l*, pg. 1127
Merker, Steven, Chm. Bd., Chief Fin. Officer & Treas.--Standard Automotive Corporation, Hillsborough, NJ; *U.S.* Private, pg. 1030
Merlet, Jean-Francois, Chief Fin. Officer--Dim S.A., Lavallois Perret, France; *U.S. Public*, pg. 1434
Merriam, Russell, Chief Fin. Officer-N.E. Region--Willis Corroon Corp. of New Hampshire, Rochester, NH; *Int'l*, pg. 1506
Merrick, Nicholas A., Chief Fin. Officer & Exec. V.P.--Excel Communications, Inc., Dallas, TX; *U.S. Public*, pg. 598
Merrill, F. Robert, III, Chief Fin. Officer, V.P.-Fin., Treas. & Sec.--Quest Medical, Inc., Allen, TX; *U.S. Public*, pg. 1352
Merritt, Robert S., Chief Fin. Officer, Sr. V.P.-Fin. & Treas.--Outback Steakhouse Inc., Tampa, FL; *U.S. Public*, pg. 1235
Merryman, George, Chief Fin. Officer--Jordan Motors, Inc., Mishawaka, IN; *U.S. Private*, pg. 599
Merson, Barbara, Chief Fin. Officer & Sr. V.P.--Castle Oil Corporation, Harrison, NY; *U.S. Private*, pg. 219
Mertzlufft, Douglas, Chief Fin. Officer & Treas.--Guarantee Electrical Company, Saint Louis, MO; *U.S. Private*, pg. 485
Merz, J. Frederick, Jr., Chm. Bd. & Treas.--Scott Specialty Gases, Plumsteadville, PA; *U.S. Private*, pg. 977
Mesker, David W., Sr. V.P. & Dir.-Staff--A.G. Edwards & Sons, Inc., Saint Louis, MO; *U.S. Public*, pg. 565
Meslard, Christophe, Chief Fin. Officer--CSR Pampryl, La Courneuve, France; *Int'l*, pg. 566
Messerli, Peter, Chief Fin. Officer--Kuehne & Nagel Inc., Jersey City, NJ; *Int'l*, pg. 763
Messey, R.J., Chief Fin. Officer & Sr. V.P.--Sverdrup Corporation, Maryland Heights, MO; *U.S. Private*, pg. 1057
Messier, Robert A., Chief Fin. Officer & V.P.-Fin. & Admin.--Beloit Corporation, Beloit, WI; *U.S. Public*, pg. 789
Messina, Daniel S., Chief Fin. Oficer--Aetna Inc., Hartford, CT; *U.S. Public*, pg. 26
Metcalf, John, Chief Fin. Officer & Sr. V.P.-Fin.--Mitsubishi Silicon America, Salem, OR; *Int'l*, pg. 875
Meth, Joseph, Chief Fin. Officer & Treas.--F. Schumacher & Co., New York, NY; *U.S. Private*, pg. 973
Metz, Adam, Chief Fin. Officer--Urban Shopping Centers, Inc., Chicago, IL; *U.S. Public*, pg. 1700
Metzger, Don, Chief Fin. Officer--Miracle Recreation Equipment Company, Monett, MO; *U.S. Private*, pg. 752
Meyer, Francis G., Sr., Chief Fin. Officer & V.P.--Terra Industries, Inc., Sioux City, IA; *U.S. Public*, pg. 1581
Meyer, Fred J., Chief Fin. Officer--Omnicom Group Inc., New York, NY; *U.S. Public*, pg. 1223
Meyer, Gary, Chief Fin. Officer--Erickson's Diversified Corp., Hudson, WI; *U.S. Private*, pg. 381
Meyer, Hans Ola, Sr. V.P.-Fin.--Atlas Copco AB, Stockholm, Sweden; *Int'l*, pg. 95
Meyer, James B., Pres. & Chief Fin. Officer--Spartan Stores Inc., Grand Rapids, MI; *U.S. Private*, pg. 1021
Meyer, John F., Chief Fin. Officer & Exec. V.P.--Fireman's Fund Insurance Company, Novato, CA; *Int'l*, pg. 58
Meyer, Klaus, Chief Fin. Officer--Vacuumschmelze GmbH, Hanau, Germany; *Int'l*, pg. 1245
Meyer, Lawrence H., Chief Fin. Officer (Intl.) & V.P.--Toys "R" Us, Inc., Paramus, NJ; *U.S. Public*, pg. 1626
Meyer, Lawrence H., Chief Fin. Officer & V.P.--Toys "R" Us International, Paramus, NJ; *U.S. Public*, pg. 1626
Meyer, M.J., Chief Fin. Officer--Haltermann Ltd., Houston, TX; *Int'l*, pg. 590
Meyer, Robert, V.P.-Fin.--U.S. Filter/Arrowhead Inc., Rockford, IL; *U.S. Public*, pg. 1682
Meyer, Ron, Chief Fin. Officer--The John C. Groub Company Inc., Seymour, IN; *U.S. Private*, pg. 484
Meyer, William S., Chief Fin. Officer, Sr. V.P. & Controller--American Greetings Corporation, Cleveland, OH; *U.S. Public*, pg. 77
Meyers, Charles E., Chief Fin. Officer & Sr. V.P.--Chartwell Re Corporation, Stamford, CT; *U.S. Public*, pg. 336
Meyers, Charles E., Chief Fin. Officer & Sr. V.P.--The Insurance Corp. of New York, New York, NY; *U.S. Public*, pg. 336
Meyers, David L., Chief Fin. Officer & Exec. V.P.--Del Monte Foods, San Francisco, CA; *U.S. Private*, pg. 321
Meyers, Geoffrey G., Chief Fin. Officer, Exec. V.P. & Treas.--Health Care & Retirement Corporation, Toledo, OH; *U.S. Public*, pg. 801
Meyers, J.A., Chief Fin. Officer--Wyman-Gordon Investment Castings, Inc., Groton, CT; *U.S. Public*, pg. 1782
Meyers, Kenneth R., Chief Fin. Officer & V.P.-Fin.--United States Cellular Corporation, Chicago, IL; *U.S. Public*, pg. 1572
Meyers, Kevin, Chief Fin. Officer & Sr. V.P.-Loan Admin.--Countrywide Funding Corporation, Pasadena, CA; *U.S. Public*, pg. 453
Meyers, Pierre, Chief Fin. Officer & Dir.-Fin.--Cockerill Sambre, Brussels, Belgium; *Int'l*, pg. 301
Meyers, Suzanne M., Chief Fin. Officer--Baker & McKenzie, Attorneys At Law, Chicago, IL; *U.S. Private*, pg. 111
Meynard, John, Chief Fin. Officer & Sr. V.P.--Royal LePage Limited, Don Mills, Canada; *Int'l*, pg. 1143
Mhundwa, Walter, Chief Fin. Officer--Johnson & Johnson Central/East Africa, Harare, Zimbabwe; *U.S. Public*, pg. 930
Micali, Jim, Chief Fin. Officer & Exec. V.P.--Michelin Americas Small Tires (MAST), Greenville, SC; *Int'l*, pg. 322
Miceli, Anthony J., Chief Fin. Officer & V.P.--United Capital Corp., Great Neck, NY; *U.S. Public*, pg. 1674
Miceli, Jim, Chief Fin. Officer--Bridge, New York, NY; *U.S. Private*, pg. 1162
Miceli, Jim, Chief Fin. Officer--Bridge, Saint Louis, MO; *U.S.* Private, pg. 1162
Micelli, Tony, V.P.-Fin., Treas. & Sec.--Metex Corporation, Edison, NJ; *U.S. Public*, pg. 1674
Michaeleski, R.B., V.P.-Fin.--Pembina Pipeline Corporation, Calgary, Canada; *Int'l*, pg. 1032
Michalek, John S., Chief Fin. Officer & V.P.-Fin.--Plaid Enterprises Inc., Norcross, GA; *U.S. Private*, pg. 352
Michalossky, Michael, Chief Fin. Officer & Exec. V.P.--Kinney System, Inc., New York, NY; *U.S. Private*, pg. 622
Michaud, Paul J., Chief Fin. Officer & Treas.--AAI Corporation, Hunt Valley, MD; *U.S. Public*, pg. 1679
Michel, Charles, Chief Fin. Officer & V.P.--Dave & Buster's, Dallas, TX; *U.S. Public*, pg. 488
Michelmore, Tom, Controller--Vacudyne Inc., Chicago Heights, IL; *U.S. Private*, pg. 46
Michielsen, Jan, Chief Fin. Officer--Banque Nationale de Belgique, Brussels, Belgium; *Int'l*, pg. 162
Micke, Dave, Chief Fin. Officer--Beta Raven Inc., Bridgeton, MO; *U.S. Public*, pg. 1361
Middleton, Bernie, Chief Fin. Officer & Controller--Cassano's Inc., Dayton, OH; *U.S. Private*, pg. 218
Midgette, Stephen, Controller--NewAge Industries Inc., Willow Grove, PA; *U.S. Private*, pg. 796
Midgette, Steven, Controller--Newage Industries Inc., Plastics Technology Group, Willow Grove, PA; *U.S. Private*, pg. 796
Midtun, Lee, Chief Fin. Officer--Pointe Group Ltd., Phoenix, AZ; *U.S. Private*, pg. 873
Midtun, Lee, Chief Fin. Officer--Gosnell Builders, Phoenix, AZ; *U.S. Private*, pg. 873
Mies, Bob, Chief Fin. Officer & V.P.--Philadelphia Daily News, Philadelphia, PA; *U.S. Public*, pg. 964
Mieth, William S., Chief Fin. Officer & Sr. V.P.-Fin.--Dataproducts Corporation, Simi Valley, CA; *Int'l*, pg. 620
Migoya, Alfonso Gonzalez, Chief Fin. Officer--Alfa, S.A. de C.V., Garza Garcia, Mexico; *Int'l*, pg. 56
Migura, Marvin J., Chief Fin. Officer & Sr. V.P.--Oceaneering International, Inc., Houston, TX; *U.S. Public*, pg. 1211
Migura, Marvin J., Chief Fin. Officer & Sr. V.P.--Oceaneering International, Inc., Morgan City, LA; *U.S. Public*, pg. 1211
Mihalko, George R., Jr., Chief Fin. Officer, Sr. V.P., Treas. & Asst. Sec.--Pamida Holdings Corporation, Omaha, NE; *U.S. Public*, pg. 1255
Mihalovics, Betty, Chief Fin. Officer--Trace Mountain Products, San Jose, CA; *U.S. Private*, pg. 1095
Miike, Patrick T., V.P.-Fin. & Treas.--Amelco Corporation, Gardena, CA; *U.S. Public*, pg. 65
Mikel, Steve H., Chief Exec., Oper. & Fin. Officers--Southern Mineral Corporation, Houston, TX; *U.S. Public*, pg. 1490
Mikita, Martha, V.P. & Controller-Corp. Acctg.--MGM Entertainment Company, Culver City, CA; *U.S. Public*, pg. 1614
Mikity, Michael E., Chief Fin. Officer & V.P.--Syncor International Corporation, Woodland Hills, CA; *U.S. Public*, pg. 1548
Miklich, Thomas R., Chief Fin. Officer, Treas., Gen. Counsel & Sec.--Invacare Corporation, Elyria, OH; *U.S. Public*, pg. 911
Mikolajczyk, Michael E., Chief Fin. Officer & Chief Admin. Officer--Diamond Technology Partners, Chicago, IL; *U.S.* Public, pg. 1424
Mikulits, Karl, Chief Fin. Officer--Semikron International, GmbH & Co. KG, Nuremberg, Germany; *Int'l*, pg. 1220
Milack, Joseph, V.P.-Fin., Treas. & Sec.--Brinkmann Instruments, Inc., Westbury, NY; *U.S. Private*, pg. 169
Milack, Joseph, Chief Fin. Officer--Brinkmann Instruments (Canada) Ltd., Mississauga, Canada; *U.S. Private*, pg. 169
Milan, Edgar J., Chief Fin. Officer & V.P.--Cabot Oil & Gas Corporation, Houston, TX; *U.S. Public*, pg. 289
Milano, Joseph, Chief Fin. Officer--American Color Graphics, Brentwood, TN; *U.S. Public*, pg. 1132
Miles, Edwin, Chief Fin. Officer--Young & Rubicam (Zambia) Ltd., Lusaka, Zambia; *U.S. Private*, pg. 1198
Miles, Kenneth, Chief Fin. Officer & Treas.--Care Matrix Corp., Needham, MA; *U.S. Public*, pg. 305
Miles, Michael W., Chief Fin. Officer & Sr. V.P.--Safeguard Scientifics, Inc., Wayne, PA; *U.S. Public*, pg. 1424
Milet, Pierre, Chief Fin. Officer, V.P. & Sec.--Clarins, Neuilly-sur-Seine, France; *Int'l*, pg. 295
Mileusnic, George, Chief Fin. Officer & Sr. V.P.--The Coleman Company, Inc., Golden, CO; *U.S. Private*, pg. 690
Milewski, Ronald L., V.P.-Fin.--North American Van Lines, Inc., Fort Wayne, IN; *U.S. Public*, pg. 1191
Miley, Pat, Chief Fin. Officer--C & C (Wholesale) Ltd.., Tipperary, Ireland; *Int'l*, pg. 64
Milke, Drury A., Chief Fin. Officer--Offshore Logistics, Inc., Lafayette, LA; *U.S. Public*, pg. 1212
Millandra, Jim, Asst. Chief Fin. Officer--Surgical Specialties, Reading, PA; *U.S. Private*, pg. 1056
Millard, Donald R., Pres., Chief Exec. Officer & Chief Fin. Officer--Matria Healthcare, Inc., Marietta, GA; *U.S. Public*, pg. 1057
Millares, Joe M., Chief Fin. Officer, V.P.-Fin. & Sec.--DSP Technology Inc., Fremont, CA; *U.S. Public*, pg. 475
Millenbruch, Gary L., Chief Fin. Officer, Exec. V.P. & Treas.--Bethlehem Steel Corporation, Bethlehem, PA; *U.S. Public*, pg. 226
Miller, Allen, Chief Fin. Officer--Frequency Electronics, Inc., Uniondale, NY; *U.S. Public*, pg. 681
Miller, Anita, V.P.-Fin, Treas. & Sec.--Wholesale Electronic Supply, Dallas, TX; *U.S. Private*, pg. 1174
Miller, Carl G., Chief Fin. Officer & V.P.--TRW Inc., Cleveland, OH; *U.S. Public*, pg. 1558
Miller, Chris A., V.P.-Fin., Treas. & Sec.--C-COR Electronics, Inc., State College, PA; *U.S. Public*, pg. 272
Miller, Cory J., Chief Fin. Officer & V.P.-Fin.--Ciprico, Inc., Plymouth, MN; *U.S. Public*, pg. 370
Miller, D.W., Chief Fin. Officer & Sr. V.P.--Russell-Stanley Corporation, Red Bank, NJ; *U.S. Private*, pg. 953
Miller, Darren B., Chief Fin. Officer & Sr. V.P.--Group Maintenance America Corp., Houston, TX; *U.S. Public*, pg. 766
Miller, David, Chief Fin. Officer & Treas.--Fab Industries, Inc., New York, NY; *U.S. Public*, pg. 603
Miller, David, Chief Fin. Officer, Controller, Treas. & Sec.--Monterey Mechanical Company, Oakland, CA; *U.S. Private*, pg. 758
Miller, Diane M., Chief Fin. Officer--American Dental Technologies, Southfield, MI; *U.S. Public*, pg. 70
Miller, Don, Chief Fin. Officer--Palmer Jarvis Communications, Vancouver, Canada; *Int'l*, pg. 1022
Miller, Donald, Chief Fin. Officer--Schwan's Sales Enterprises, Marshall, MN; *U.S. Private*, pg. 974
Miller, Doug, Chief Fin. Officer & V.P.--Bassett Furniture Industries, Incorporated, Bassett, VA; *U.S. Public*, pg. 193
Miller, Douglas C., Chief Fin. Officer & V.P.--Meridian Industries, Inc., Milwaukee, WI; *U.S. Private*, pg. 732
Miller, Fred, Chief Fin. Officer & V.P.--Millstein Industries, Youngwood, PA; *U.S. Private*, pg. 749
Miller, G.G., Chief Fin. Officer, V.P.-Fin. & Treas.--AFG Industries, Inc., Kingsport, TN; *Int'l*, pg. 84
Miller, Gary H., Chief Fin. Officer & Sr. V.P.--FirstCity Financial Corporation, Waco, TX; *U.S. Public*, pg. 644
Miller, Gary L., Chief Fin. Officer--Enterprise Products Company, Houston, TX; *U.S. Private*, pg. 377
Miller, Heidi G., Chief Fin. Officer & Sr. V.P.--Travelers Group, New York, NY; *U.S. Public*, pg. 1632
Miller, James P., Exec. V.P.-Fin.--Cascade Corporation, Troutdale, OR; *U.S. Public*, pg. 310
Miller, Jane, Chief Fin. Officer--Union Trust Bank, Union City, IN; *U.S. Public*, pg. 633
Miller, Jeanne M., Chief Fin. Officer, V.P. & Sec.--Gish Biomedical, Inc., Irvine, CA; *U.S. Public*, pg. 745
Miller, Joel, Chief Fin. Officer--Honeywell's Micro Switch Division, Freeport, IL; *U.S. Public*, pg. 834
Miller, John T., Chief Fin. Officer & Sr. V.P.-Fin.--E-Z Serve Corp., Houston, TX; *U.S. Public*, pg. 540
Miller, John T., Chief Fin. Officer--E-Z Serve Convenience Stores, Inc., Houston, TX; *U.S. Public*, pg. 540
Miller, Kathleen A., Chief Fin. Officer & Mgr.-Sys.--The Commercial Bank, Delphos, OH; *U.S. Public*, pg. 410
Miller, Kenneth I., Chief Fin. Officer, Treas., Sr. V.P. & Sec.--Johnston, Lemon & Co. Inc., Washington, DC; *U.S. Private*, pg. 595
Miller, Kevin, Chief Fin. Officer--Stock Yards Packing Co., Inc., Chicago, IL; *U.S. Private*, pg. 1043
Miller, Larry F., Chief Fin. Officer & Exec. V.P.--Gannett Company, Inc., Arlington, VA; *U.S. Public*, pg. 698
Miller, Lester, Controller--Times Printing Company, Inc., Random Lake, WI; *U.S. Private*, pg. 1087
Miller, M., Chief Fin. Officer & V.P.-Fin.--BFC Construction Corporation, Scarborough, Canada; *Int'l*, pg. 118
Miller, Michael, Chief Fin. Officer & Sr. V.P.-Fin.--Fender Musical Instruments, Scottsdale, AZ; *U.S. Private*, pg. 400
Miller, Michael, V.P.-Fin.--Silver Dollar City, Inc., Branson, MO; *U.S. Private*, pg. 1000
Miller, Mike, V.P.-Fin.--Blaw-Knox Construction Equipment Corporation, Mattoon, IL; *U.S. Public*, pg. 877
Miller, Mike J., Chief Fin. Officer--Miller Oil Co., Inc., Norfolk, VA; *U.S. Private*, pg. 747
Miller, Neil, Chief Fin. Officer, Chief Oper. Officer & Exec. V.P.--Partners & Shevack, Inc., New York, NY; *U.S. Private*, pg. 842
Miller, Neil, Chief Fin. Officer--Syntellect, Inc., Phoenix, AZ; *U.S. Public*, pg. 1550
Miller, Paul, Chief Fin. Officer--Leather Center, Inc., Carrollton, TX; *U.S. Private*, pg. 656
Miller, Paul, Chief Fin. Officer--E Wood Limited, Northallerton, United Kingdom; *Int'l*, pg. 858
Miller, Randall, Controller--Georg Fischer Disa Inc., Oswego, IL; *Int'l*, pg. 382
Miller, Raymond, Chief Fin. Officer, V.P. & Corp. Sec.--Weiners Stores, Inc., Houston, TX; *U.S. Private*, pg. 1160
Miller, Richard, Chief Fin. Officer & Sr. V.P.--Sterling Inc., Akron, OH; *Int'l*, pg. 1248
Miller, Richard J., Chief Fin. Officer & V.P.--Precision Products Corporation, Rockford, IL; *U.S. Private*, pg. 879
Miller, Robert, Chief Fin. Officer--D&H Distributing Company, Harrisburg, PA; *U.S. Private*, pg. 300
Miller, Robert, Controller--Baldwin Hardware Corporation, Reading, PA; *U.S. Public*, pg. 1053
Miller, Ron, Chief Fin. Officer--Cytec Fiberite Inc., Tempe, AZ; *U.S. Public*, pg. 471
Miller, Samuel M., Chief Fin. Officer & Sr. V.P.-Fin.--Liz Claiborne, Inc., New York, NY; *U.S. Public*, pg. 1005
Miller, Wayne, Chief Fin. Officer, Exec. V.P.-Fin. & Admin. & Sec.--Bernard Chaus, Inc., Secaucus, NJ; *U.S. Public*, pg. 342
Millerick, John J., Chief Fin. Officer & Sr. V.P.--CalComp Technology, Inc., Anaheim, CA; *U.S. Public*, pg. 1007
Milliken, Minot, Chief Fin. Officer--Milliken & Company, Spartanburg, SC; *U.S. Private*, pg. 748
Millington, Herbert, V.P. & Treas.--Philip Morris Management Corp., New York, NY; *U.S. Public*, pg. 1289
Mills, Daniel J., Chief Fin. Officer & V.P.--Lebhar-Friedman, Inc., New York, NY; *U.S. Private*, pg. 656
Mills, John, Chief Fin. Officer & Controller--Affiliated Foods Southwest, Little Rock, AR; *U.S. Private*, pg. 26
Mills, John F., Chief Fin. Officer--Hill, Holliday, Connors, Cosmopulos, Inc., Boston, MA; *U.S. Private*, pg. 529
Mills, John M., Jr., Chief Fin. Officer--Dryden & Palmer Company, Branford, CT; *U.S. Private*, pg. 471
Mills, John T., V.P.-Taxes--USX Corporation, Pittsburgh, PA; *U.S. Public*, pg. 1661
Mills, Peter G., Sr. V.P.-Admin. & Chief Fin. Officer--Franklin Bank, San Mateo, CA; *U.S. Public*, pg. 680
Mills, Thomas E., CPA, Chief Fin. Officer--Metrologic Instruments, Inc., Blackwood, NJ; *U.S. Public*, pg. 1102
Mills, William R., Chief Fin. Officer & V.P.-Fin.--Weis Markets, Inc., Sunbury, PA; *U.S. Public*, pg. 1751

Millstein, Steve, Chief Fin. Officer--Flexible Circuit Products Division, Methuen, MA; *U.S. Public*, pg. 1264
Millstein, Steven M., Chief Fin. Officer & V.P.--Parlex Corporation, Methuen, MA; *U.S. Public*, pg. 1264
Milner, David, Chief Fin. Officer--Voit Sports, Inc., Carlsbad, CA; *U.S. Private*, pg. 1143
Milone, Michael D., Chief Revenue Officer-Heinz Pet Prods.--Star-Kist Foods, Inc., Newport, KY; *U.S. Public*, pg. 806
Miltner, Bill, Chief Fin. Officer--E Z Loader Boat Trailers, Inc., Spokane, WA; *U.S. Private*, pg. 353
Miluka, Ida, Chief Fin. Officer & V.P.-Fin.--Conklin Instrument Corporation, Pleasant Valley, NY; *U.S. Private*, pg. 263
Minard, David L., V.P. & Comptroller--M & I Thunderbird Bank, Phoenix, AZ; *U.S. Public*, pg. 1050
Minard, John D., Chief Fin. Officer V.P. & Controller--Manna Pro Corporation, Saint Louis, MO; *U.S. Private*, pg. 700
Mineart, Carol J., Chief Fin. Officer & Treas.--Avis Industrial Corporation, Upland, IN; *U.S. Private*, pg. 102
Miner, Greg, Chief Fin. Officer & V.P.--Odetics Inc., Anaheim, CA; *U.S. Public*, pg. 1212
Miner, Greg, Chief Fin. Officer--ATL Products, Inc., Anaheim, CA; *U.S. Public*, pg. 1212
Minnich, Thomas M., Sr., Chief Fin. Officer--Kuhlman Electric Corporation, Versailles, KY; *U.S. Public*, pg. 968
Minor, Joe C., Chief Fin. Officer, Sr. V.P. & Treas.--NBT Bancorp Inc., Norwich, NY; *U.S. Public*, pg. 1144
Minsky, Robert, V.P. & Chief Fin. Officer--Berlitz Publishing Company Inc., New York, NY; *U.S. Public*, pg. 221
Minter, Gordon, Chief Fin. Officer & V.P.--Auburn Hosiery Mills, Inc., Auburn, KY; *U.S. Private*, pg. 98
Mintern, Fred, Chief Fin. Officer & Exec. V.P.--APX International, Auburn Hills, MI; *U.S. Private*, pg. 7
Mintz, Murray, Chief Fin. Officer--Tropar Mfg. Co., Inc., Florham Park, NJ; *U.S. Private*, pg. 1105
Miressi, Joseph V., Chief Fin. Officer--Powers Fastening, Inc., New Rochelle, NY; *U.S. Private*, pg. 878
Miret, Luis, Chief Fin. Officer--Purity Wholesale Grocers, Boca Raton, FL; *U.S. Private*, pg. 896
Mischler, Harland L., Chief Fin. Officer & Exec. V.P.--Gradco Systems, Inc., Las Vegas, NV; *U.S. Public*, pg. 757
Miserendino, James, V.P. & Controller--Seal Group, Irvine, CA; *U.S. Public*, pg. 1262
Mishler, Mark, Chief Fin. Officer--Medical Professional Liability Agency, Ltd., Bedford Hills, NY; *U.S. Public*, pg. 685
Mishler, Mark H., Chief Fin. Officer & V.P.--Frontier Insurance Group, Inc., Rock Hill, NY; *U.S. Public*, pg. 684
Mishler, Mark H., Chief Fin. Officer--Frontier Insurance Company, Rock Hill, NY; *U.S. Public*, pg. 685
Mishler, Mark H., Chief Fin. Officer--Frontier Pacific Insurance Company, La Jolla, CA; *U.S. Public*, pg. 685
Mishoe, Thomas M., Chief Fin. Officer, V.P., Treas. & Sec.--Eskimo Pie Corporation, Richmond, VA; *U.S. Public*, pg. 592
Misialek, Kurt A., Chief Fin. Officer & V.P.--Eggland's Best, Inc., King of Prussia, PA; *U.S. Private*, pg. 366
Missorten, L., Exec. V.P. & Chief Fin. Officer--Labatt Breweries of Canada, Toronto, Canada; *Int'l*, pg. 679
Mistlin, Gary E., V.P.-Fin. & Treas.--Mentor Corporation, Santa Barbara, CA; *U.S. Public*, pg. 1086
Mitchell, Gerald R., V.P.-Fin.--KV Pharmaceutical Company, Saint Louis, MO; *U.S. Public*, pg. 941
Mitchell, James E., Chief Fin. Officer & V.P.--Sunset Publishing Corporation, Menlo Park, CA; *U.S. Public*, pg. 1613
Mitchell, Jim, Chief Fin. Officer--Becker Milk Co. Ltd., Scarborough, Canada; *Int'l*, pg. 182
Mitchell, John M., Pres., Chief Exec. & Chief Oper. Officer--Pluess-Staufer Industries, Inc., Proctor, VT; *Int'l*, pg. 1061
Mitchell, L.D., V.P.--Parsons Process Group Inc., Houston, TX; *U.S. Private*, pg. 842
Mitchell, Linda, Chief Fin. Officer--Star Tribune, Minneapolis-St. Paul, Minneapolis, MN; *U.S. Private*, pg. 281
Mitchell, Paul, Chief Fin. Officer & Exec. V.P.--Edelman Public Relations Worldwide, Chicago, IL; *U.S. Private*, pg. 362
Mitchell, Randy, Treas. & Sec.--The Hotsy Corporation, Englewood, CO; *U.S. Private*, pg. 500
Mitchell, Robert, Chief Fin. Officer--Glynwed Pipe Systems, Coleshill, United Kingdom; *Int'l*, pg. 554
Mitchell, Scott, Sr. V.P. & Natl. Audit Mgr.--Fremont Financial Corporation, Santa Monica, CA; *U.S. Public*, pg. 681
Mitchell, Stuart, Grp. Fin. Dir.--Alvis plc, London, United Kingdom; *Int'l*, pg. 69
Mite, Dale, Chief Fin. Officer--Vinings Industries Inc., Atlanta, GA; *U.S. Private*, pg. 1141
Mixtacki, Steven B., Chief Fin. Officer & V.P.--American TV & Appliance of Madison, Inc., Madison, WI; *U.S. Private*, pg. 64
Miyatake, Motoo, Chief Fin. Officer & Exec. Dir.--Duskin Co., Ltd., Osaka, Japan; *Int'l*, pg. 422
Miyoshi, Koichiro, Mng. Dir.--Hosokawa Micron Corporation, Osaka, Japan; *Int'l*, pg. 635
Mize, E.J., Jr., Chief Fin. Officer, Chief Acctg. Officer, V.P.-Fin. & Treas.--United States Pipe & Foundry Company, Inc., Birmingham, AL; *U.S. Public*, pg. 1736
Mizell, Donna, Chief Fin. Officer--Bellamy Brothers, Inc., Ellenwood, GA; *U.S. Private*, pg. 132
Mizerek, Tom, V.P.-Fin. & Controller--Richard Young Office Products, Inc., Deerfield Beach, FL; *U.S. Public*, pg. 450
Moberley, Stuart Greville, Grp. Fin. Dir.--McKechnie PLC, Walsall, United Kingdom; *Int'l*, pg. 851
Mock, C.A., Chief Fin. Officer, Sr. V.P. & Sec.--Consolidated Pipe & Supply Company, Birmingham, AL; *U.S. Private*, pg. 266
Modist, Scott J., Chief Fin. Officer, V.P.-Fin. & Treas.--Equitrac Corporation, Coral Gables, FL; *U.S. Public*, pg. 590
Moeller, Paul R., V.P.-Fin.--Health-Chem Corporation, New York, NY; *U.S. Public*, pg. 802
Moerbeek, Peter J., Chief Fin. Officer, V.P.-Fin. & Sec.--Southwest Water Company, West Covina, CA; *U.S. Public*, pg. 1494
Moerdyk, Carol B., Chief Fin. Officer & Sr. V.P.--Boise Cascade Office Products Corporation, Itasca, IL; *U.S. Public*, pg. 243
Moffatt, Doug, Chief Fin. Officer & V.P.--The UCS Group, Toronto, Canada; *Int'l*, pg. 792
Moffett, David J., Chief Fin. Officer & Information Officer, Exec. V.P.--Starbanc Corporation, Cincinnati, OH; *U.S. Public*, pg. 1510
Moffett, David M., Chief Fin. Officer--Star Bank, N.A., Cincinnati, OH; *U.S. Public*, pg. 1510
Mogas, V. Louis, Pres. & Chief Exec. Officer--Mogas Industries, Inc., Houston, TX; *U.S. Private*, pg. 755
Mogensen, Dennis, Chief Fin. Officer & Sr. V.P.--J.R. Simplot Company, Boise, ID; *U.S. Private*, pg. 1002
Mogul, Charles G., Chief Fin. Officer--Richter & Ratner Contracting Corporation, Maspeth, NY; *U.S. Private*, pg. 930
Mohning, Raymond, Chief Fin. Officer--Clarks Cos. N.A., Newton, MA; *Int'l*, pg. 297
Mohr, Heinz-Peter, Chief Fin. Officer--Osram GmbH, Munich, Germany; *Int'l*, pg. 1244
Molinaro, Samuel L., Jr., Chief Fin. Officer & Sr. Mng. Dir.--The Bear Stearns Companies Inc., New York, NY; *U.S. Public*, pg. 197
Molinaro, Samuel L., Jr., Chief Fin. Officer--Bear, Stearns & Co. Inc., New York, New York, NY; *U.S. Public*, pg. 198
Molinelli, John J., Chief Fin. Officer & Sr. V.P.--AMETEK, Inc., Paoli, PA; *U.S. Public*, pg. 99
Molino, Joseph A., Jr., Chief Fin. Officer & V.P.--P & F Industries, Inc., Farmingdale, NY; *U.S. Public*, pg. 1239
Molloy, Richard, Chief Fin. Officer & Treas.--Davenport Insulation, Inc, Upper Marlboro, MD; *U.S. Private*, pg. 314
Moloney, Thomas E., Chief Fin. Officer--John Hancock Mutual Life Insurance Company, Boston, MA; *U.S. Private*, pg. 589
Moloney, Thomas E., Chief Fin. Officer--John Hancock Subsidiaries, Inc., Boston, MA; *U.S. Private*, pg. 589
Molony, John, Chief Fin. Officer--Augat, Inc., Wiring Systems, Montgomery, AL; *U.S. Public*, pg. 1598
Molta, Donald A., Chief Fin. Officer & V.P.--Spec's Music, Inc., Miami, FL; *U.S. Public*, pg. 1497
Molteni, Renzo, Chief Fin. Officer--Olivetti Corporation of Japan, Tokyo, Japan; *Int'l*, pg. 1003
Momboisse, R. Michael, Chief Fin. Officer, V.P.-Legal & Sec.--EMCON, San Mateo, CA; *U.S. Public*, pg. 571
Monaco, Dominick J., V.P.-Fin.--American Electronics, Inc., Fullerton, CA; *U.S. Private*, pg. 5
Monaco, Michael P., Vice Chm. & Chief Fin. Officer--HFS, Incorporated, Parsippany, NJ; *U.S. Public*, pg. 321
Monea, Patrick D., Chief Fin. Officer & V.P.--Granger Construction Co., Lansing, MI; *U.S. Private*, pg. 469
Monello, Joseph D., Chief Fin. Officer & V.P.--Kansas City Southern Industries, Inc., Kansas City, MO; *U.S. Public*, pg. 943
Moneypenny, Edward W., Chief Fin. Officer & Exec. V.P.-Fin.--Oryx Energy, Dallas, TX; *U.S. Public*, pg. 1232
Monk, Robert D., Chief Fin. Officer--Triple S Plastics, Inc., Vicksburg, MI; *U.S. Public*, pg. 1639
Monnoyeur, Denis, Dir.-Fin.--Monnoyeur SCA, Saint Denis, France; *Int'l*, pg. 888
Monroe, Tom, Chief Fin. Officer--National Seating Co., Vonore, TN; *U.S. Private*, pg. 786
Monsma, Calvin J., Chief Fin. Officer, V.P. & Sec.--Trion, Inc., Sanford, NC; *U.S. Public*, pg. 1639
Mont, Stuart, Chief Oper. Officer, Chief Fin. Officer, Exec. V.P. & Sec.--Recoton Corporation, Lake Mary, FL; *U.S. Public*, pg. 1369
Montague, Carlos S., Chief Fin. Officer, V.P., Treas. & Asst. Sec.--Ault Incorporated, Minneapolis, MN; *U.S. Public*, pg. 147
Montgomery, David, Chief Fin. Officer, V.P.-Fin. & Sec.--Advanstar Communications, Cleveland, OH; *U.S. Private*, *pg. 22*
Montgomery, Gary B., Chief Fin. Officer--Amsted Industries Incorporated, Chicago, IL; *U.S. Private*, pg. 68
Montgomery, Herbert D., Chief Fin. Officer & V.P.--Atkinson, San Bruno, CA; *U.S. Public*, pg. 143
Montgomery, P.E., Chief Fin. Officer--Kelley Advertising Inc., Toronto, Canada; *U.S. Public*, pg. 765
Montgomery, R.L., Chief Fin. Officer, Exec. V.P. & Treas.--Columbus McKinnon Corp., Amherst, NY; *U.S. Public*, pg. 405
Montoni, Richard A., Chief Fin. Officer & Exec. V.P.--Ciber, Inc., Englewood, CO; *U.S. Public*, pg. 356
Montry, Gerald F., Chief Fin. Officer & Sr. V.P.--DSC Communications Corporation, Plano, TX; *U.S. Public*, pg. 475
Mooney, Michael W., Chief Fin. Officer & Exec. V.P.--Gibraltar Savings, Simi Valley, CA; *U.S. Public*, pg. 181
Mooney, Robert J., Chief Fin. Officer & Sr. V.P.--Ethyl Corporation, Richmond, VA; *U.S. Public*, pg. 595
Mooney, William P., Chief Fin. Officer--Sylvan Inc., Saxonburg, PA; *U.S. Public*, pg. 1545
Moore, Bruce, Chief Fin. Officer & V.P.--FiberMark Inc., Brattleboro, VT; *U.S. Public*, pg. 620
Moore, Bruce E., Chief Fin. Officer & V.P.--Dunn Industries Inc., Kansas City, MO; *U.S. Private*, pg. 347
Moore, Bruce E., Chief Fin. Officer & Sr. V.P.--J.E. Dunn Construction Co., Kansas City, MO; *U.S. Private*, pg. 347
Moore, C. Michael, Chief Fin. Officer--Discount Auto Parts, Inc., Lakeland, FL; *U.S. Public*, pg. 510
Moore, Cindy A., Chief Fin. Officer, Sr. V.P. & Controller--ACCEL International Corporation, Dublin, OH; *U.S. Public*, pg. 14
Moore, Daniel D., Chief Fin. Officer & Sr. V.P.--GATX Logistics, Inc., Jacksonville, FL; *U.S. Public*, pg. 691
Moore, David R., Chief Fin. Officer & V.P.--Tarlton Corporation, Saint Louis, MO; *U.S. Private*, pg. 1069
Moore, Dennis G., Chief Fin. Officer, Sr. V.P., Treas. & Sec.--J & J Snack Foods Corporation, Pennsauken, NJ; *U.S. Public*, pg. 916
Moore, Donald, Chief Fin. Officer--Container Graphics Corporation, Cary, NC; *U.S. Private*, pg. 267
Moore, Donald, Chief Fin. Officer & Sr. V.P.--Unique Casual Restaurants, inc., Danvers, MA; *Int'l*, pg. 324
Moore, Donnie, Chief Fin. Officer--Cognos Corp., Burlington, MA; *Int'l*, pg. 306
Moore, Donnie M., Chief Fin. Officer & Sr. V.P.-Fin. & Admin.--Cognos Inc., Ottawa, Canada; *Int'l*, pg. 305
Moore, James R., Chief Fin. Officer, Exec. V.P. & Sec.--Urstadt Biddle Properties, Inc., Greenwich, CT; *U.S. Public*, pg. 1700
Moore, Kent, Chief Fin. Officer--United Supermarkets Inc., Lubbock, TX; *U.S. Private*, pg. 1126
Moore, Kevin, Chief Fin. Officer--Softride, Inc., Bellingham, WA; *U.S. Private*, pg. 44
Moore, Rod A., Chief Fin. Officer & V.P.--Southern Farm Bureau Casualty Insurance Company, Ridgeland, MS; *U.S. Private*, pg. 1016
Moore, Scott, Chief Fin. Officer & Exec. V.P.--PartnerRe Ltd., Pembroke, Bermuda; *Int'l*, pg. 1024
Moosa, Moosa E., Chief Fin. Officer, V.P.-Fin. & Treas.--Chemfab Corporation, Merrimack, NH; *U.S. Public*, pg. 344
Moothart, Gary, Chief Fin. Officer & Controller--Indigo Group Ltd., Daytona Beach, FL; *U.S. Public*, pg. 437
Mooty, Charles W., Chief Fin. Officer, V.P. & Treas.--International Dairy Queen, Inc., Minneapolis, MN; *U.S. Public*, pg. 220
Mora, Richard, Chief Fin. Officer--Mattson Technology, Inc., Fremont, CA; *U.S. Public*, pg. 1060
Morak, Ferdinand, Chief Fin. Officer--Mazda Austria GmbH, Klagenfurt, Austria; *Int'l*, pg. 849
Moran, Richard, Chief Fin. Officer--Ortho Biotech Inc., Raritan, NJ; *U.S. Public*, pg. 929
Moran, Richard E., Jr., Chief Fin. Officer & Exec. V.P.--Irvine Apartment Communities Incorporated, Newport Beach, CA; *U.S. Private*, pg. 575
Morano, Kevin R., Chief Fin. Officer & V.P.-Fin.--Asarco Incorporated, New York, NY; *U.S. Public*, pg. 137
Morash, David L., Chief Fin. Officer & Exec. V.P.--Safeskin Corporation, San Diego, CA; *U.S. Public*, pg. 1425
Morcomb, Roger, Chief Fin. Officer--Competitive Media Reporting, New York, NY; *Int'l*, pg. 1447
Mordini, Joseph J., Chief Fin. Officer--E.R. Moore Co., Chicago, IL; *U.S. Private*, pg. 759
Mordo, Jean H., Chief Fin. Officer & Exec. V.P.--The Scotts Company, Marysville, OH; *U.S. Public*, pg. 1446
Moreau, Don, Controller--Kingston-Warren Corporation, Newfields, NH; *U.S. Public*, pg. 796
Morecroft, Bruce, Chief Fin. Officer--Purity Products Inc., Miami, FL; *U.S. Private*, pg. 896
Morefield, M.T., Chief Fin. Officer & V.P.-Fin.--White Cap, Inc., Downers Grove, IL; *Int'l*, pg. 1207
Morelli, Frank, Chief Oper. Officer & Chief Fin. Officer--MarketSource Corporation, Cranbury, NJ; *U.S. Private*, pg. 705
Morelli, Frank, Chief Fin. Officer--The Texwipe Co., Inc., Upper Saddle River, NJ; *U.S. Private*, pg. 1079
Morello, James J., Chief Fin. Officer & Treas.--Medical Assurance, Inc., Birmingham, AL; *U.S. Public*, pg. 1079
Moret, Fernand, Chief Fin. Officer--Lemo SA, Ecublens, Switzerland; *Int'l*, pg. 806
Morford, John A., Chief Fin. Officer & V.P.--V.T. Inc., Merriam, KS; *U.S. Private*, pg. 1131
Morgan, Gary J., Chief Fin. Officer, V.P.-Fin. & Treas.--Met-Pro Corporation, Harleysville, PA; *U.S. Public*, pg. 1100
Morgan, Glenn R., Chief Fin. Officer & Exec. V.P.--Hartmarx Corporation, Chicago, IL; *U.S. Public*, pg. 795
Morgan, Larkin C., Chief Fin. Officer, Treas. & Sec.--Arrow Gear Company, Downers Grove, IL; *U.S. Private*, pg. 85
Morgan, Leroy, Chief Fin. Officer--The Bergquist Company, Minneapolis, MN; *U.S. Private*, pg. 135
Morgan, Michael J., Chief Fin. Officer & V.P.--U.S. Timberlands Company, L.P., Klamath Falls, OR; *U.S. Public*, pg. 1688
Morgan, Paul, Chief Fin. Officer--Park Place Motorcars, Ltd., Dallas, TX; *U.S. Private*, pg. 840
Morgan, Stephen W., Chief Fin. Officer & V.P.--Aquapore Moisture Systems, Inc., Phoenix, AZ; *Int'l*, pg. 1066
Mori, Tsukasa, V.P., Controller & Sec.--Descente Ltd., Osaka, Japan; *Int'l*, pg. 395
Mori, Yasuto, Chief Fin. Officer--Haseko Development Inc., Osaka, Japan; *Int'l*, pg. 600
Moriarity, S.L., Chief Fin. Officer--Fletcher Challenge Canada Limited, Vancouver, Canada; *Int'l*, pg. 495
Moriguchi, Takahiro, Vice Chm. & Chief Fin. Officer--Union Bank of California, San Francisco, CA; *Int'l*, pg. 157
Morin, C. H., Chief Fin. Officer--P.R. Newswire Association Inc., New York, NY; *Int'l*, pg. 1443
Morin, Curtis L., Pres., Treas. & Sec.--Bennington Iron Works, Inc., Bennington, VT; *U.S. Private*, pg. 133
Morin, Gary, Chief Fin. Officer--Lexmark International Group, Inc., Lexington, KY; *U.S. Public*, pg. 991
Morin, Gary, Chief Fin. Officer--Lexmark International, Inc., Lexington, KY; *U.S. Public*, pg. 991
Morin, Rudolph, Sr. V.P.-Fin. & Admin.--Memorex Telex Corp., Irving, TX; *Int'l*, pg. 857
Morin, Rudolph G., Chief Fin. Officer & Exec. V.P.-Opers. & Fin.--Network Computing Devices, Inc., Mountain View, CA; *U.S. Public*, pg. 1168
Moriya, Kazuhiko, Sr. Mng. Dir.--Dentsu Young & Rubicam Inc. (Tokyo), Tokyo, Japan; *U.S. Private*, pg. 325
Mork, Stuart R., Chief Fin. Officer & Sr. V.P.--The Newhall Land And Farming Company, Valencia, CA; *U.S. Public*, pg. 1178

Morley, Donald M., Chief Fin. Officer--Western Mining Corporation Holdings Limited, Southbank, Australia; *Int'l*, pg. 1494
Morley, Walter J., Chief Fin. Officer & Treas.--John Hassall, Inc., Westbury, NY; *U.S. Private*, pg. 509
Morley, Walter J., Chief Fin. Officer--HITCO, Westbury, NY; *U.S. Private*, pg. 509
Morneault, Henry D., Chief Fin. Officer--Allbritton Communications Company, Washington, DC; *U.S. Private*, pg. 854
Morphis, Gene, Chief Fin. Officer & Sr. V.P.-Fin.--Stream International Holdings Inc., Canton, MA; *U.S. Public*, pg. 518
Morrell, Michael P., Chief Fin. Officer & Sr. V.P.--Allegheny Power System, Inc., Hagerstown, MD; *U.S. Public*, pg. 42
Morris, Craig, Chief Fin. Officer--Integral Systems, Inc., Walnut Creek, CA; *Int'l*, pg. 242
Morris, Craig, V.P. & Chief Fin. Officer.--InPower Inc., San Francisco, CA; *Int'l*, pg. 242
Morris, Cynthia R., Chief Fin. Officer, Exec. V.P, Treas. & Sec.--Sun Coast Industries, Inc, Dallas, TX; *U.S. Public*, pg. 1529
Morris, D.E.A., Chief Fin. Officer--The Peninsular and Oriental Steam Navigation Company, London, United Kingdom; *Int'l*, pg. 1032
Morris, Donna R., Dir.-Investor Rels., Asst. Sec. & Treas.--Walk, Haydel & Associates, Inc., New Orleans, LA; *Int'l*, pg. 624
Morris, Gary, Chief Fin. Officer & Exec. V.P.--Halliburton Company, Dallas, TX; *U.S. Public*, pg. 775
Morris, George, Chief Fin. Officer--Iams Company, Dayton, OH; *U.S. Private*, pg. 556
Morris, Gerald F., Chief Fin. Officer & Exec. V.P.--Diebold, Incorporated, Canton, OH; *U.S. Public*, pg. 506
Morris, Michelle, Chief Fin. Officer--Philip Morris/Cash & Carry Ltd., London, United Kingdom; *U.S. Public*, pg. 1290
Morris, P., Chief Fin. Officer--Procter & Gamble Ltd., Newcastle upon Tyne, United Kingdom; *U.S. Public*, pg. 1332
Morris, R. Don, Chief Fin. Officer& Exec. V.P.--Michaels Stores, Inc., Irving, TX; *U.S. Public*, pg. 1104
Morris, Reg, Chief Fin. Officer--Petroferm Inc., Fernandina Beach, FL; *U.S. Private*, pg. 858
Morris, T.C., Chief Fin. Officer & Sr. V.P.--Phillips Petroleum Company, Bartlesville, OK; *U.S. Public*, pg. 1290
Morrison, Burton J., Exec. V.P.-Fin. & Admin.--MGM Entertainment Company, Culver City, CA; *U.S. Public*, pg. 1614
Morrison, Daniel R., Chief Fin. Officer & Treas.--First Signature Bank & Trust Co., Portsmouth, NH; *U.S. Private*, pg. 589
Morrison, David F., Chief Fin. Officer, Exec. V.P. & Treas.--Consolidated Freightways Corp., Menlo Park, CA; *U.S. Public*, pg. 435
Morrison, James E., Chief Fin. Officer & V.P.-Fin.--ANGUS Chemical Company, Buffalo Grove, IL; *U.S. Private*, pg. 75
Morriss, George W., Chief Fin. Officer & Exec. V.P.--People's Bank, Bridgeport, CT; *U.S. Public*, pg. 1274
Morrow, Georgette, Controller--CBS Entertainment, Los Angeles, CA; *U.S. Public*, pg. 274
Morrow, Mary Jane, Chief Fin. Officer--Federal Realty Investment Trust, Rockville, MD; *U.S. Public*, pg. 616
Morse, John B. Jr., Chief Fin. Officer & V.P.-Fin.--The Washington Post Company, Washington, DC; *U.S. Public*, pg. 1742
Morse, Robert, Controller--McDowell Mfg. Co. Inc., Du Bois, PA; *U.S. Private*, pg. 300
Morse, Roger, Chief Fin. Officer--TLC Group, Inc., Zeeland, MI; *U.S. Public*, pg. 352
Mortenson, Jerald H., Chief Fin. Officer, V.P-Fin. & Administration, Treas. & Sec.--HEI, Inc., Victoria, MN; *U.S. Public*, pg. 770
Morthorst, Tom, Chief Fin. Officer--Altair Corporation, Lincolnshire, IL; *U.S. Private*, pg. 46
Morton, Marshall N., Chief Fin. Officer & Sr. V.P.--Media General, Inc., Richmond, VA; *U.S. Public*, pg. 1077
Morton, Mike, Chief Fin. Officer, V.P. & Treas.--The H.T. Hackney Co., Knoxville, TN; *U.S. Private*, pg. 493
Morton, P. Michael, Chief Fin. Officer & V.P.--Borden Foods Corporation, Columbus, OH; *U.S. Private*, pg. 157
Mos, Martin, Chief Fin. Officer--Elsevier Bedrijfinformatie B.V., Doetinchem, Netherlands; *Int'l*, pg. 1099
Moschonas, Panos, Chief Fin. Officer--EURO RSCG, Maroussi, Greece; *Int'l*, pg. 602
Moscioni, Frank, Chief Fin. Officer & V.P.--J.H. Routh Packing Co., Sandusky, OH; *U.S. Private*, pg. 948
Moser, Jack, Chief Fin. Officer--Euclid Hitachi, Cleveland, OH; *Int'l*, pg. 622
Moser, Kurt, Chief Fin. Officer--Meto, Reinach, Switzerland; *Int'l*, pg. 462
Moser, Ron, Chief Fin. Officer--Crane Construction Co., Northbrook, IL; *U.S. Private*, pg. 286
Moser, Wayne D., Chief Fin. Officer--Kennametal Hertel AG, Furth, Germany; *U.S. Public*, pg. 951
Moses, Neil, Chief Fin. Officer & Sr. V.P.--Bradlees Inc., Braintree, MA; *U.S. Public*, pg. 249
Mosher, Stephen, Chief Fin. Officer & V.P.-Fin. & Admin.--Kayem Foods, Inc., Chelsea, MA; *U.S. Private*, pg. 610
Mosier, Terry, Chief Fin. Officer--Contractors Supply Company, Inc., Kansas City, MO; *U.S. Private*, pg. 270
Moskowitz, Erwin, Chief Fin. Officer--Queens Group, Inc., Long Island City, NY; *U.S. Private*, pg. 900
Mosley, John, Chief Fin. Officer & Exec. V.P.--Sheplers, Inc., Wichita, KS; *U.S. Private*, pg. 993
Mosley, Lyndell G., Chief Fin. Officer, Treas. & Asst. Sec.--Monarch Cement Co., Humboldt, KS; *U.S. Public*, pg. 1123
Moss, Duane, Chief Fin. Officer--Mining Services International, Inc., Sandy, UT; *U.S. Public*, pg. 1115
Mossberg, Alan I., Pres., Chief Exec. & Chief Oper. Officer & Treas.--O.F. Mossberg & Sons, Inc., North Haven, CT; *U.S. Private*, pg. 764
Mosteller, Richard G., Chief Fin. Officer & Sr. V.P.--Masco Corporation, Taylor, MI; *U.S. Public*, pg. 1052
Mothershed, J. Russell, Chief Fin. Officer & Sr. V.P.-Fin.--Ruby Tuesday, Inc., Mobile, AL; *U.S. Public*, pg. 1411
Motherway, Thomas J., Pres. & Chief Fin. Officer--Boeing Realty Corporation, Long Beach, CA; *U.S. Public*, pg. 241
Moto, Fernando, Dr., Chief Fin. Officer--Nestle Portugal, S.A., Carnaxide, Portugal; *Int'l*, pg. 921
Mottino, Piergiacomo, Chief Fin. Officer--Olivetti Malaysia Sdn Bhd, Kuala Lumpur, Malaysia; *Int'l*, pg. 1003
Motzer, William R., V.P., Chief Fin. Officer & Sec.--Berwind Pharmaceutical Services, Inc., West Point, PA; *U.S. Private*, pg. 139
Mougeot, Robert F., Chief Fin. Officer & V.P.-Fin.--Hawaiian Electric Industries, Inc., Honolulu, HI; *U.S. Public*, pg. 799
Moulding, Linton, Chief Fin. Officer--Instron Corporation, Canton, MA; *U.S. Public*, pg. 882
Moulding, Linton, Chief Fin. Officer--Wilson/Shore Instruments, Canton, MA; *U.S. Public*, pg. 883
Moulton, Gregory T., Chief Fin. Officer & V.P.--Spencer Gifts, Inc., Egg Harbor Township, NJ; *Int'l*, pg. 1216
Mowrer, Jack F., V.P. & Controller--Philip Morris Management Corp., New York, NY; *U.S. Public*, pg. 1289
Moyer, A.J., Chief Fin. Officer & Corp. V.P.-Fin.--Allergan, Inc., Irvine, CA; *U.S. Public*, pg. 46
Moylan, James E., Jr., Chief Fin. Officer & Sr. V.P. & Pres.-Sonat Services Inc.--Sonat Inc., Birmingham, AL; *U.S. Public*, pg. 1484
Moyle, James, Chief Fin. Officer--CSR America Inc., Atlanta, GA; *Int'l*, pg. 245
Moynihan, Peter J., Sr. V.P.-Investments--UNUM Life Insurance Company of America, Portland, ME; *U.S. Public*, pg. 1699
Mraz, Joseph B., Chief Fin. Officer & Controller--Beacon Container Corporation, Birdsboro, PA; *U.S. Private*, pg. 125
Mrkonic, George, Vice Chm.--Borders Group, Inc., Ann Arbor, MI; *U.S. Public*, pg. 245
Mucciolo, Michael R., Chief Fin. Officer & Sr. V.P.--Beverage America, Inc., Holland, MI; *U.S. Private*, pg. 141
Muegge, Lyn, Chief Fin. Officer & Exec. V.P.--Hal Riney & Partners, Inc., San Francisco, CA; *U.S. Private*, pg. 931
Mueller, Bill, Chief Fin. Officer--French Fragrances Inc., Miami, FL; *U.S. Public*, pg. 681
Mueller, Gerd D., Chief Fin. Officer, Chief Admin. Officer & Exec. V.P.--Bayer Corporation, Pittsburgh, PA; *Int'l*, pg. 172
Mueller, Gerd D., Chief Admin. & Fin. Officer & Exec. V.P.--Bayer Corporation, Pittsburgh, PA; *Int'l*, pg. 172
Mueller, Gerd D., Chief Fin. Officer, Chief Admin. Officer & Exec. V.P.--Bayer Corporation, Parsippany, NJ; *Int'l*, pg. 172
Mugan, Michael J., Chief Fin. Officer & V.P.-Fin.--Weston Resources, Toronto, Canada; *Int'l*, pg. 1495
Muir, Donald M., Chief Fin. Officer--American Power Conversion Corporation, West Kingston, RI; *U.S. Public*, pg. 89
Muir, Glenn P., V.P.-Fin. & Treas.--Hologic, Inc., Waltham, MA; *U.S. Public*, pg. 831
Muir, Tom, Chief Fin. Officer & Exec. V.P.--Maple Leaf Foods Inc., Toronto, Canada; *Int'l*, pg. 841
Mulkey, John, Chief Fin. Officer & Treas.--The Zamoiski Co., Baltimore, MD; *U.S. Private*, pg. 1203
Mullady, Agnes N., Sr. V.P. & Chief Fin. Officer--Northstar Investment Management Corporation, Greenwich, CT; *U.S. Public*, pg. 1375
Mullaney, Joseph P., Chief Fin. Officer, V.P. & Treas.--SofTECH, Inc., Grand Rapids, MI; *U.S. Public*, pg. 1482
Mullarkey, Vincent J., Chief Fin. Officer & V.P.-Fin.--Digital Equipment Corporation, Maynard, MA; *U.S. Public*, pg. 507
Mullen, Daniel R., V.P. & Treas.--Talley Industries, Inc., Phoenix, AZ; *U.S. Public*, pg. 307
Mullen, Larry M., Chief Fin. Officer--Columbia/H.C.A., Dallas, TX; *U.S. Public*, pg. 404
Muller, Eric, Exec. V.P.-Fin. & Admin.--Sulzer Ltd., Winterthur, Switzerland; *Int'l*, pg. 1305
Muller, S. A., Chief Fin. Officer--Ferrolegeringar AG, Dubendorf, Switzerland; *U.S. Private*, pg. 735
Mullin, David, Chief Fin. Officer--Smart Modular Technologies, Fremont, CA; *U.S. Public*, pg. 1476
Mullins, Brian C., V.P.-Fin. & Treas.--Tuscarora Incorporated, New Brighton, PA; *U.S. Public*, pg. 1646
Mullins, William, Chief Fin. Officer--Handex Environment Inc., Morganville, NJ; *U.S. Private*, pg. 498
Mullis, Elbert N., Jr., Chief Fin. & Admin. Officer, Exec. V.P. & Treas.--Coca-Cola Bottling Co. United, Inc., Birmingham, AL; *U.S. Private*, pg. 248
Mulrain, Mike, Chief Fin. Officer--Polar Beverages, Worcester, MA; *U.S. Private*, pg. 873
Mulvihill, John W., Chief Fin. Officer--National Marine, Inc., New Orleans, LA; *U.S. Private*, pg. 1135
Mumm, Michael, Chief Fin. Officer, Sr. V.P. & Treas.--Petty Company, Inc., Effingham, IL; *U.S. Private*, pg. 860
Muncy, Darlene, Chief Fin. Officer, V.P. & Treas.--Caldwell VanRiper, Inc., Indianapolis, IN; *U.S. Private*, pg. 200
Munday, Anthony E., Chief Fin. Officer & Exec. V.P.--Inco Limited, Toronto, Canada; *Int'l*, pg. 672
Munday, Warren, Chief Fin. Officer & Exec. V.P.--CHF Industries, Inc., New York, NY; *U.S. Private*, pg. 1094
Mundy, Peter J., Chief Fin. Officer, V.P.-Fin., Treas. & Sec.--Sentry Technology Corp., Hauppauge, NY; *U.S. Public*, pg. 1458
Mungcal, Edward, Controller--Wells/Bloomfield, Verdi, NV; *U.S. Public*, pg. 1497
Munyan, Christopher, Chief Fin. Officer--Berwick Industries, Inc., Berwick, PA; *U.S. Public*, pg. 284
Munzenrider, Robert E., Chief Fin. Officer & V.P.-Fin.--St. Jude Medical, Inc., Saint Paul, MN; *U.S. Public*, pg. 1427
Murakami, Hitoshi, Chief Fin. Officer--Showpla Asia Limited, Singapore, Singapore; *Int'l*, pg. 1237
Murakami, Makoto, Chief Fin. Officer--Haseko (Hawaii) Inc., Honolulu, HI; *Int'l*, pg. 600
Murata, Akiya, Chief Fin. Officer & Gen. Mgr.-Sls. & Mktg.--Okazaki Golf Club KK, Okazaki, Japan; *Int'l*, pg. 1362
Murata, Hitoshi, Chief Fin. Officer--Siemens Matsushita Components GmbH & Co. KG, Munich, Germany; *Int'l*, pg. 1245
Muratore, Michael, Chief Fin. Officer--SunGard Financial Systems, Voorhees, NJ; *U.S. Public*, pg. 1535
Murdy, James L., Chief Fin. Officer & Exec. V.P.-Fin. & Admin.--Allegheny Teledyne Incorporated, Pittsburgh, PA; *U.S. Public*, pg. 43
Murdy, Wayne W., Chief Fin. Officer & Exec. V.P.--Newmont Mining Corporation, Denver, CO; *U.S. Public*, pg. 1178
Murdy, Wayne W., Chief Fin. Officer & Exec. V.P.--Newmont Gold Company, Denver, CO; *U.S. Public*, pg. 1179
Muretta, Bruce, Chief Fin. Officer & Controller--West Chemical Products, Inc., Princeton, NJ; *U.S. Private*, pg. 1158
Murff, Ronald D., Chief Fin. Officer--Guaranty F.S.B., Dallas, TX; *U.S. Public*, pg. 1575
Murnane, George, III, Chief Fin. Officer & Exec. V.P.--International Airline Support Group, Inc., Atlanta, GA; *U.S. Public*, pg. 894
Murnane, Stephen, Chief Fin. Officer--U.S. Divers Co., Inc., Santa Ana, CA; *U.S. Private*, pg. 1125
Murphy, C.I., Chief Fin. Officer & V.P.-Fin.--SouthCo. Inc., Concordville, PA; *U.S. Private*, pg. 1014
Murphy, Daniel T., Chief Fin. Officer--Helm Resources Inc., Greenwich, CT; *U.S. Public*, pg. 808
Murphy, Daniel T., Chief Fin. Officer & V.P.--Unapix Entertainment Inc., New York, NY; *U.S. Public*, pg. 1664
Murphy, Donna, Chief Fin. Officer & V.P.--Lally, McFarland & Pantello Inc., New York, NY; *Int'l*, pg. 601
Murphy, Gregory E., Chief Fin. Officer & Treas.--Selective Insurance Company of South Carolina, Charlotte, NC; *U.S. Public*, pg. 1455
Murphy, Gregory E., Chief Fin. Officer & Sr. V.P.-Fin.--Selective Insurance Company of America, Branchville, NJ; *U.S. Public*, pg. 1455
Murphy, Gregory E., Chief Fin. Officer & V.P.--Exchange Insurance Company, Buffalo, NY; *U.S. Public*, pg. 1455
Murphy, Jeremiah T., V.P.-Fin.--The Spanos Companies, Stockton, CA; *U.S. Private*, pg. 1020
Murphy, John J., Chief Fin. Officer, Exec. V.P. & Treas.--Arrow Financial Corporation, Glens Falls, NY; *U.S. Public*, pg. 135
Murphy, John P., Chief Fin. Officer & Sr. V.P.--Johns Manville Corporation, Denver, CO; *U.S. Public*, pg. 927
Murphy, Judith C., V.P. & Treas.--M & I Investment Management Corp., Milwaukee, WI; *U.S. Public*, pg. 1051
Murphy, Kathleen A., Chief Fin. Officer & V.P.--Connell Limited Partnership, Boston, MA; *U.S. Private*, pg. 264
Murphy, Michael R., Chief Fin. Officer--Cavalier Homes, Inc., Wichita Falls, TX; *U.S. Public*, pg. 318
Murphy, N.E., Chief Fin. Officer & V.P.--PQ Corporation, Berwyn, PA; *U.S. Private*, pg. 827
Murphy, Norman, Chief Fin. Officer--Oasis Corp., Columbus, OH; *U.S. Private*, pg. 810
Murphy, Pat, Chief Fin. Officer--Paradyne, Largo, FL; *U.S. Private*, pg. 838
Murphy, Peter E., Chief Fin. Officer & Sr. V.P.--ABC Inc., Los Angeles, CA; *U.S. Public*, pg. 511
Murphy, Robert, Chief Fin. Officer--International Creative Management, Inc., Los Angeles, CA; *U.S. Private*, pg. 554
Murphy, Susan, Chief Fin. Officer--Cohn & Wells, San Francisco, CA; *Int'l*, pg. 601
Murphy, Tim, Chief Fin. Officer--Charles Pankow Builders, Ltd., Altadena, CA; *U.S. Private*, pg. 836
Murphy, William, Chief Fin. Officer, Exec. V.P. & Sec.--Computer Horizons Corp., Mountain Lakes, NJ; *U.S. Public*, pg. 421
Murphy, William, V.P.-Fin.--Crompton & Knowles Ingredient Technology Corp., Mahwah, NJ; *U.S. Public*, pg. 459
Murray, James E., Chief Fin. Officer--Humana Inc., Louisville, KY; *U.S. Public*, pg. 847
Murray, James E., Chief Fin. Officer--Humana Health Insurance of Nevada, Inc., Las Vegas, NV; *U.S. Public*, pg. 847
Murray, James E., Chief Fin. Officer--Humana Health Chicago, Inc., Chicago, IL; *U.S. Public*, pg. 847
Murray, James E., Chief Fin. Officer--Employers Health Insurance Company, Green Bay, WI; *U.S. Public*, pg. 847
Murray, James E., Chief Fin. Officer--Humana Health Plan of Texas, Inc., San Antonio, TX; *U.S. Public*, pg. 848
Murray, James E., Chief Fin. Officer--Humana Medical Plan Inc.-Miami, Miramar, FL; *U.S. Public*, pg. 848
Murray, James E., Chief Fin. Officer--Humana Health Plan of Georgia, Inc., Louisville, KY; *U.S. Public*, pg. 848
Murray, James E., Chief Fin. Officer--Humana Health Plan of Louisiana, Inc., Louisville, KY; *U.S. Public*, pg. 848
Murray, James E., Chief Fin. Officer--Humana Insurance Company, Kansas City, MO; *U.S. Public*, pg. 848
Murray, James E., Chief Fin. Officer--Humana Health Plan of Ohio, Inc., Cincinnati, OH; *U.S. Public*, pg. 848
Murray, James E., Chief Fin. Officer--Humana Health Plan of Utah, Inc., Salt Lake City, UT; *U.S. Public*, pg. 848
Murray, James E., Chief Fin. Officer--Humana Health Plan, Inc., Louisville, KY; *U.S. Public*, pg. 848
Murray, James E., Chief Fin. Officer--Humana Medical Plan Inc.-Jacksonville, Jacksonville, FL; *U.S. Public*, pg. 848
Murray, James E., Chief Fin. Officer--Humana Health Plan of Alabama, Inc., Montgomery, AL; *U.S. Public*, pg. 848
Murray, James E., Chief Fin. Officer--Humana Wisconsin Health Organization Insurance Corporation, Milwaukee, WI; *U.S. Public*, pg. 848

Murray, James E., Chief Fin. Officer--Network EPO, Inc., Milwaukee, WI; *U.S. Public*, pg. 848
Murray, James E., Chief Fin. Officer--Humana Wisconsin Health Organization Insurance Corporation, Milwaukee, WI; *U.S. Public*, pg. 848
Murray, James J., Chief Fin. Officer & V.P.--Johnston Industries, Inc., Columbus, GA; *U.S. Public*, pg. 933
Murray, John A., Chief Fin. Officer, V.P. & Treas.--Moore Medical Corp., New Britain, CT; *U.S. Public*, pg. 1128
Murray, John J., V.P.-Fin., Sec. & Treas.--Alcoa Fujikura, Troy, MI; *U.S. Public*, pg. 61
Murray, Kevin J., Chief Fin. Officer--Milk Products Holdings (SEA), Singapore, Singapore; *Int'l*, pg. 923
Murray, Lawrence M., Chief Fin. Officer, V.P. & Sec.--DeVlieg-Bullard Inc., Westport, CT; *U.S. Public*, pg. 502
Murray, Mark, Chief Fin. Officer & V.P.--Guidant Corporation-Vascular Intervention Group, Santa Clara, CA; *U.S. Public*, pg. 768
Murray, R. Scott, Chief Fin. Officer--The Learning Co., Inc., Cambridge, MA; *U.S. Public*, pg. 982
Murray, R.W., Chief Fin. Officer, Sr. V.P., Treas., Controller & Sec.--Webb, Murray & Associates, Houston, TX; *U.S. Private*, pg. 1157
Murray, Richard, Chief Fin. Officer--Allard Industries, Manchester, NH; *U.S. Private*, pg. 36
Murray, Richard, Chief Fin. Officer--Granite State Manufacturing Co., Manchester, NH; *U.S. Private*, pg. 36
Murray, Robert C., Chief Fin. Officer & Exec. V.P.--Public Service Enterprise Group Incorporated, Newark, NJ; *U.S.* Public, pg. 1340
Murray, Robert W., Pres., Chief Exec. Officer & Chief Fin. Officer--Mercantile Bank of Iowa, Des Moines, IA; *U.S. Public*, pg. 1087
Murren, James J., Chief Fin. Officer & Exec. V.P.--MGM Grand, Inc., Las Vegas, NV; *U.S. Public*, pg. 1026
Murtaugh, J.R., Chief Fin. Officer--ANSER (Analytic Services Inc.), Arlington, VA; *U.S. Private*, pg. 75
Musachia, Sandy, V.P.-Fin.--Clear Shield National, Inc., Wheeling, IL; *U.S. Public*, pg. 586
Muschalek, John, Chief Fin. Officer & Controller--First Southwest Company, Dallas, TX; *U.S. Private*, pg. 407
Muse, Charles H., Jr., Chief Fin. Officer & Treas.--Crown Coal & Coke Co. Inc., Pittsburgh, PA; *U.S. Private*, pg. 292
Muse, John O., Chief Fin. Officer--Darling International, Inc, Irving, TX; *U.S. Public*, pg. 484
Muselman, Marilyn, Treas. & Sec.--House of White Birches, Inc., Berne, IN; *U.S. Private*, pg. 542
Musser, Robert C., Controller--Mobil Oil Corporation, Fairfax, VA; *U.S. Public*, pg. 1118
Mustad, Hans, Chief Fin. Officer--Emil Moestue as, Oslo, Norway; *Int'l*, pg. 460
Mustilli, Joseph M., Chief Fin. Officer, Sr. V.P. & Opers. Dir.--The McClure Group, Wayne, PA; *U.S. Private*, pg. 719
Mutch, Carl F., Chief Fin. Officer & Treas.--Cox Wood Preserving Co., Orangeburg, SC; *U.S. Private*, pg. 283
Mutch, Scott, Chief Fin. Officer--Royal Rubber & Manufacturing Co., South Gate, CA; *U.S. Private*, pg. 949
Myers, Arthur R., Jr., V.P.-Fin. & Admin.--Cadmus Journal Services, Richmond, VA; *U.S. Public*, pg. 291
Myers, Bruce, Chief Fin. Officer & V.P.-Fin.--GTI Corporation, San Diego, CA; *U.S. Public*, pg. 767
Myers, H.J., Chief Fin. Officer--LubeCon Systems, Inc., White Cloud, MI; *U.S. Private*, pg. 679
Myers, Larry F., Chief Fin. Officer, Sr. V.P., Treas. & Sec.--Mitre Corporation, Bedford, MA; *U.S. Private*, pg. 753
Myers, Leland, Controller--Double-Cola Co.-USA, Chattanooga, TN; *U.S. Private*, pg. 341
Myers, Norman S., Pres., Chief Exec. & Fin. Officers & Treas.--IDM Controls, Houston, TX; *U.S. Private*, pg. 554
Myers, Robert, Chief Fin. Officer--Capitol Chevrolet Cadillac GEO Subaru Inc., Salem, OR; *U.S. Private*, pg. 206
Myers, Robert M., Chief Fin. Officer, Treas. & Sec.--Tri-State Mack Inc, Memphis, TN; *U.S. Private*, pg. 1101
Myers, Ronald W., Chief Fin. Officer & V.P.-Fin. & Admin.--GF Office Furniture Ltd., Gallatin, TN; *U.S. Private*, pg. 434
Myers, Ronald W., Chief Fin. Officer & V.P.-Fin. & Admin.--GF Office Furniture, Canfield, OH; *U.S. Private*, pg. 435
Myers, Russell R., Chief Fin. Officer--Geneva Corporation, Greensboro, NC; *U.S. Private*, pg. 446
Myntti, Diane, Chief Fin. Officer--S. Bent & Brothers, Inc., Gardner, MA; *U.S. Private*, pg. 134
Myskowski, Stephen, Chief Fin. Officer & Sr. V.P.--Recon/Optical, Inc., Barrington, IL; *U.S. Private*, pg. 914
Na Ranong, Vachira, Chief Fin. Officer--Finance One Public Company Limited, Bangkok, Thailand; *Int'l*, pg. 484
Nabors, James D., Chief Fin. Officer & Exec. V.P.--Russell Corporation, Alexander City, AL; *U.S. Public*, pg. 1413
Nadalin, JoAnn, Chief Fin. Officer--Coors Ceramics Company, Golden, CO; *U.S. Public*, pg. 3
Nadel, George, Chief Fin. Officer, Exec. V.P. & Treas.--Jennifer Convertibles Inc., Woodbury, NY; *U.S. Public*, pg. 926
Naess, Bjorn Erik, Chief Fin. Officer--Orkla A.S.A., Oslo, Norway; *Int'l*, pg. 1010
Naeve, Stephen W., Chief Fin. Officer & Exec. V.P.--Houston Industries Incorporated, Houston, TX; *U.S. Public*, pg. 842
Naftaly, Robert H., Chief Fin. Officer & Exec. V.P.--Blue Cross & Blue Shield of Michigan, Detroit, MI; *U.S. Private*, pg. 151
Nagel, Vernon J., Chief Fin. Officer, Exec. V.P.-Fin. & Treas.--Kuhlman Corporation, Savannah, GA; *U.S. Public*, pg. 968
Nagelberg, Howard, Chief Fin. Officer-GHG & Sr. V.P.--Grey Healthcare Group, New York, NY; *U.S. Public*, pg. 765
Nagle, T.W., Exec. V.P.-Fin. & Admin.--Reading & Bates Corporation, Houston, TX; *U.S. Public*, pg. 1354
Nagler, Stewart G., Chief Fin. Officer & Sr. Exec. V.P.--Metropolitan Life Insurance Co., New York, NY; *U.S. Private*, pg. 737
Nagumo, S., Chief Fin. Officer--Freios Varga S/A, Limeira, Brazil; *Int'l*, pg. 820
Nahirny, Michael, Chief Fin. Officer & Exec. V.P.-Fin. & Admin.--Cara Operations Limited, Toronto, Canada; *Int'l*, pg. 266
Nahl, M.C., Chief Fin. Officer & Sr. V.P.--Albany International Corp., Albany, NY; *U.S. Public*, pg. 36
Nahmens, Daniel J., Chief Fin. Officer, V.P.-Fin., Treas. & Sec.--Track 'n Trail, El Dorado Hills, CA; *U.S. Public*, pg. 1626
Naim, Bernard, Chief Fin. Officer & Treas.--Forasol S.A., Velizy-Villacoublay, France; *Int'l*, pg. 496
Nakagawa, Ken, Chief Fin. Officer, Sr. V.P.-Treasury--Alpha Therapeutic Corp., Los Angeles, CA; *Int'l*, pg. 558
Nakahara, Asuka, Chief Fin. Officer & Exec. V.P.--Trammell Crow Company, Dallas, TX; *U.S. Public*, pg. 1628
Nakajima, Hidenobu, Chief Fin. Officer & V.P.--Kawasho International (U.S.A.) Inc., Fort Lee, NJ; *Int'l*, pg. 726
Nakamura, Masaharu, Chief Fin. Officer--Houston General Insurance Co., Fort Worth, TX; *Int'l*, pg. 1392
Nam, Kee-Il, Chief Fin. Officer--Ssangyong Heavy Industries Co., Ltd., Seoul, Korea; *Int'l*, pg. 1292
Nance, Blair T., Chief Fin. Officer, Controller & Treas.--AFG, Inc., Westmont, IL; *U.S. Public*, pg. 955
Nance, Tom, Grp. Controller--Borden Italian Foods, Columbus, OH; *U.S. Private*, pg. 158
Nanula, Richard D., Chief Fin. Officer & Sr. Exec. V.P.--The Walt Disney Company, Burbank, CA; *U.S. Public*, pg. 511
Napa, Tom, V.P.-Fin.--Precor, Inc., Bothell, WA; *U.S. Public*, *pg. 1322*
Napiecek, Barry, Chief Fin. Officer--CR LLC, Evanston, IL; *U.S. Private*, pg. 196
Napoli, Michael G., Chief Fin. Officer--R.J. Reynolds Tobacco Intl., Inc., Geneva, Switzerland; *U.S. Public*, pg. 1355
Napoli, Thomas A., Chief Fin. Officer & V.P.-Fin.--U.S. Home Corporation, Houston, TX; *U.S. Public*, pg. 1682
Naporano, Joseph A., Chief Fin. Officer, Chief Oper. Officer & Exec. V.P.--Long Haymes Carr, Inc., Winston Salem, NC; *U.S. Public*, pg. 909
Nash, Jack, Chief Fin. Officer--Windsor Quality Food Co., Ltd., Houston, TX; *U.S. Private*, pg. 1182
Nash, James S., Chief Fin. Officer, Treas. & Controller--E.P. Henry Corporation, Woodbury, NJ; *U.S. Private*, pg. 522
Natole, Tim, Chief Fin. Officer--Tuscan/Lehigh Dairies LP, Union, NJ; *U.S. Private*, pg. 1110
Nattier, Robert, Chief Oper. Officer, Chief Fin. Officer & Gen. Mgr.--Mid-Kansas Co-op Association, Moundridge, KS; *U.S. Private*, pg. 743
Nattier, Robert, Chief Oper. Officer, Chief Fin. Officer & Gen. Mgr.--Lubrication Consultants, L.L.C., Moundridge, KS; *U.S. Private*, pg. 743
Naughton, J.J., Chief Fin. Officer & Treas.--The Camden Fire Insurance Assn., Philadelphia, PA; *Int'l*, pg. 543
Naughton, John J., Chief Fin. Officer--General Assurance Company, Melville, NY; *Int'l*, pg. 543
Naughton, Marc G., Chief Fin. Officer & V.P.--Cerner Corporation, Kansas City, MO; *U.S. Public*, pg. 331
Navarro, Bernabe L. Jr., Chief Oper. & Fin. Officer & Exec. V.P.--La Tondena Distillers, Inc., Manila, Philippines; *Int'l*, *pg. 785*
Nay, Donald A., Chief Fin. Officer, V.P. & Treas.--CGAS, Inc., Columbus, OH; *U.S. Public*, pg. 585
Nazarian, Robert H., Chief Fin. Officer--Air New Zealand Ltd., Auckland, New Zealand; *Int'l*, pg. 38
Neal, Jerry D., Chief Fin. Officer, V.P., & Treas.--ONEOK Inc., Tulsa, OK; *U.S. Public*, pg. 1226
Neary, Kevin, Chief Fin. Officer--Channel One Communications, New York, NY; *U.S. Public*, pg. 1328
Nease, Jim, Dir.-Fin. & Acctg.--Hollingsworth Saco Lowell Corporation, Inc., Easley, SC; *U.S. Private*, pg. 535
Nebbf, Louise, Chief Fin. Officer--Ensis Corporation Inc., Winnipeg, Canada; *Int'l*, pg. 455
Nebulori, Angelo, Chief Fin. Officer--Allen Foods, Inc., Saint Louis, MO; *U.S. Private*, pg. 37
Necarsulmar, Robert, Chief Fin. Officer--Townsends, Inc., Wilmington, DE; *U.S. Private*, pg. 1094
Neff, Richard, Chief Fin. Officer--Di Giorgio Corporation, Carteret, NJ; *U.S. Private*, pg. 330
Neidus, Stuart D., Chief Fin. Officer & Exec. V.P.--Essef Corporation, Chardon, OH; *U.S. Public*, pg. 592
Neil, Steve M., Chief Fin. Officer, V.P.-Fin. & Treas.--L. Perrigo Company, Allegan, MI; *U.S. Public*, pg. 1280
Neill, S. Collin, Chief Fin. Officer & V.P.--Continental Health Affiliates, Inc., Englewood Cliffs, NJ; *U.S. Public*, pg. 440
Neilsen, Mark, Chief Fin. Officer--AGEMA Infrared Systems, Inc., Secaucus, NJ; *Int'l*, pg. 1289
Neio, Eran, Chief Fin. Officer--Bogen Communications, Inc., Ramsey, NJ; *U.S. Public*, pg. 739
Neis, Douglas A., Chief Fin. Officer & Treas.--The Marcus Corporation, Milwaukee, WI; *U.S. Public*, pg. 1044
Neithercut, D.J., Chief Fin. Officer & Exec. V.P.--Equity Residential Properties Trust, Chicago, IL; *U.S. Public*, pg. 590
Nejes, Robert F., Chief Fin. Officer, Sr. V.P.-Fin. & Admin.--L.B. Foster Company, Pittsburgh, PA; *U.S. Public*, pg. 675
Nekman, Donald, Chm., Partner & Chief Fin. Officer--EURO RSCG, Copenhagen, Copenhagen, Denmark; *Int'l*, pg. 602
Nelli, John, Chief Fin. Officer--Tangram Enterprise Solutions, Inc., Cary, NC; *U.S. Public*, pg. 1424
Nelson, Bill, Chief Fin. Officer & Sr. V.P.--Home Box Office, Inc., New York, NY; *U.S. Public*, pg. 1612
Nelson, David, Chief Fin. Officer--Gantos Inc., Stamford, CT; *U.S. Public*, pg. 702
Nelson, David P., Chief Fin. Officer & V.P.--Logicon Geodynamic, Torrance, CA; *U.S. Public*, pg. 1199
Nelson, David R., Chief Fin. Officer & Asst. Sec.--RisComp Industries, Inc., Minneapolis, MN; *U.S. Private*, pg. 932
Nelson, Erik G., Chief Fin. Officer & Sr. V.P.--The Procter & Gamble Company, Cincinnati, OH; *U.S. Public*, pg. 1330
Nelson, Grant, Chief Fin. Officer, V.P. & Sec.--West Information Publishing Group, Saint Paul, MN; *U.S. Public*, pg. 1602
Nelson, Howard, Chief Fin. Officer & V.P.-Opers.--Erie Plastics, Corry, PA; *U.S. Private*, pg. 381
Nelson, Ian, Chief Fin. Officer--British Film Institute, London, United Kingdom; *Int'l*, pg. 219
Nelson, Jeff, Chief Fin. Officer--Columbine JDS Systems, Inc., Denver, CO; *U.S. Public*, pg. 228
Nelson, Jeff, Chief Fin. Officer--Cousins Submarines, Menomonee Falls, WI; *U.S. Private*, pg. 280
Nelson, Julane, Sec. & Treas.--Qualheim, Inc., New Hartford, CT; *U.S. Public*, pg. 286
Nelson, K.L., Chief Fin. Officer & V.P.-Corp. Svcs.--National Sea Products Limited, Lunenburg, Canada; *Int'l*, pg. 909
Nelson, Robert, Chief Fin. Officer--McNeil & NRM., Inc., Akron, OH; *U.S. Private*, pg. 725
Nelson, Robert, Chief Fin. Officer & Chief Oper. Officer--Trace International Holdings, Inc., New York, NY; *U.S. Private*, pg. 1094
Nelson, Tom S., Chief Fin. Officer--E.W. Blanch Holdings, Inc., Minneapolis, MN; *U.S. Public*, pg. 236
Nelson, Wayne, Chief Fin. Officer--Gast Mfg. Corp., Benton Harbor, MI; *U.S. Private*, pg. 440
Nemmers, David A., Controller--Advance Packaging Corporation, Grand Rapids, MI; *U.S. Private*, pg. 18
Nen, Richard W., Chief Fin. Officer & Exec. V.P.--Charter One Bank, Cleveland, OH; *U.S. Public*, pg. 336
Neptune, John, Chief Fin. Officer--Monaco Coach Corporation, Coburg, OR; *U.S. Public*, pg. 1123
Nepute, John, Chief Fin. Officer & V.P.-Fin.--Monaco Coach Corporation, Coburg, OR; *U.S. Public*, pg. 1123
Nergaard, Leiv L., Chief Fin. Officer & Exec. V.P.--Norsk Hydro a.s, Oslo, Norway; *Int'l*, pg. 959
Nesbit, Don, Chief Fin. Officer--Westec Security Inc., Irvine, CA; *Int'l*, pg. 1217
Neskey, David A., Chief Fin. Officer & Exec. V.P.--Spaulding & Slye, Boston, MA; *U.S. Private*, pg. 1021
Nesler, Dennis J., V.P. & Treas.--General DataComm, Inc., Middlebury, CT; *U.S. Public*, pg. 708
Ness, Paul D., Chief Fin. Officer, Chief Information Officer, Sec. & Treas.--Polymer Composites Inc., Winona, MN; *Int'l*, pg. 624
Neubauer, Alfred, Dr., Chief Fin. Officer--DSM Chemie Linz GmbH, Lienz, Austria; *Int'l*, pg. 356
Neubauer, Gabriele, Chief Fin. Officer--Esselte GmbH, Hannover, Germany; *Int'l*, pg. 461
Neuman, Ronald W., Chief Fin. Officer, Treas. & Controller--Allen-Edmonds Shoe Corp., Port Washington, WI; *U.S. Private*, pg. 36
Neuman, Ronald W., Chief Fin. Officer--Woodlore, Port Washington, WI; *U.S. Private*, pg. 37
Neun, Carl W., Chief Fin. Officer & Sr. V.P.--Tektronix, Inc., Wilsonville, OR; *U.S. Public*, pg. 1567
Neuschaefer, Thomas H., Chief Fin. Officer, V.P. & Treas.--First Financial Corporation, Stevens Point, WI; *U.S. Public*, pg. 140
Neuschaefer, Thomas H., Chief Fin. Officer & Exec. V.P.--First Financial Bank, FSB, Stevens Point, WI; *U.S. Public*, pg. 140
Neuweiler, Walter, Chief Fin. Officer--Haws Drinking Faucet Co., Berkeley, CA; *U.S. Private*, pg. 512
Neve, Ken, Chief Fin. Officer--Letraset Export, Ashford, United Kingdom; *Int'l*, pg. 461
Nevius, Bruce, Chief Fin. Officer--Nebraska Book Co., Inc., Lincoln, NE; *U.S. Private*, pg. 789
Newby, Brian, Acting Chief Fin. Officer--Bradley Pharmaceuticals, Fairfield, NJ; *U.S. Public*, pg. 249
Newcomb, Nancy S., Sr. Corp. Officer-Fin. & Funding--Citicorp, New York, NY; *U.S. Public*, pg. 376
Newcomer, R.P., Chief Fin. Officer & Sr. V.P.--P.H. Glatfelter Company, Spring Grove, PA; *U.S. Public*, pg. 746
Newell, Daniel K., V.P.-Fin.--Northwestern Public Service, Huron, SD; *U.S. Public*, pg. 1200
Newell, William, Pres. & Chief Fin. Officer--Noll Printing Corporation, Huntington, IN; *U.S. Private*, pg. 821
Newman, Charles W., Chief Fin. Officer--Barnett Banks, Inc., Jacksonville, FL; *U.S. Public*, pg. 1162
Newman, Gerald, Sr. Exec. V.P. & Chief Acctg. Officer--McDonald's Corporation, Oak Brook, IL; *U.S. Public*, pg. 1068
Newman, James H., Chief Fin. Officer--Bridon PLC, Doncaster, United Kingdom; *Int'l*, pg. 215
Newman, Michael J., Chief Fin. Officer & V.P.-Fin.--Staodyn Inc., Longmont, CO; *U.S. Public*, pg. 1509
Newman, Paul, Chief Fin. Officer--The New Piper Aircraft, Inc., Vero Beach, FL; *U.S. Private*, pg. 794
Newman, Ronald P., Chief Fin. Officer, V.P.-Fin., Treas. & Sec.--Watsco, Inc., Coconut Grove, FL; *U.S. Public*, pg. 1745
Newsome, Larry J., Chief Fin. Officer, Sr. V.P., Treas. & Sec.--Echelon International Corporation, Saint Petersburg, FL; *U.S. Public*, pg. 560
Newton, Clay, Chief Fin. Officer & Treas.--Equity Oil Company, Salt Lake City, UT; *U.S. Public*, pg. 590
Newton, James T., Chief Fin. Officer--Victor Corporation, West Warwick, RI; *U.S. Private*, pg. 1138
Newton, Scott, V.P.-Fin.--American Tourister, Inc., Warren, RI; *U.S. Public*, pg. 1430
Ng, Emma, Chief Fin. Officer--Orbotech Pacific Ltd., Wan Chai, Hong Kong; *Int'l*, pg. 1007
Nicholas, Charles R., Chief Fin. Officer & Exec. V.P.-Fin./Admin.--Andrew Corporation, Orland Park, IL; *U.S. Public*, pg. 112
Nicholls, Sidney O., Sr. V.P. & Chief Fin. Officer--Playfield Industries Inc., Chatsworth, GA; *Int'l*, pg. 1362
Nichols, Alan, Chief Fin. Officer--Chronicle Publishing Co. Inc., San Francisco, CA; *U.S. Private*, pg. 239
Nichols, Gregory L., CPA, Chief Fin. Officer, V.P. & Treas.--Giffels Associates, Inc., Southfield, MI; *U.S. Private*, pg. 452
Nichols, Gregory L., CPA, Chief Fin. Officer--Giffels Hoyem Basso, Inc., Troy, MI; *U.S. Private*, pg. 452

Nichols, Gregory L., CPA, Chief Fin. Officer & Treas.--Giffels Technologies, Inc., Southfield, MI; *U.S. Private,* pg. 452
Nichols, Gregory L., CPA, Chief Fin. Officer--Giffels Associates Inc., Phoenix, AZ; *U.S. Private,* pg. 452
Nichols, Gregory L., CPA, Chief Fin. Officer--Giffels Strategic Consultants, L.L.C., Southfield, MI; *U.S. Private,* pg. 452
Nichols, John M., Chief Fin. Officer--Varsity Spirit Corporation, Memphis, TN; *U.S. Public,* pg. 1389
Nichols, Otto J., Chief Fin. Officer & Admin. V.P.--Harcourt Brace & Company - Elementary Div., Orlando, FL; *U.S. Public,* pg. 783
Nicholson, David C., Chief Fin. Officer & Sr. V.P.--Rock-Tenn Company, Norcross, GA; *U.S. Public,* pg. 1396
Nicholson, James A., Chief Fin. Officer & Sr. V.P.--PAULA Financial, Pasadena, CA; *U.S. Public,* pg. 1266
Nicholson, Robert C., Chief Fin. Officer & Controller--IMI Cornelius Inc. (MN), Anoka, MN; *Int'l,* pg. 646
Nicholson, Robert C., Chief Fin. Officer--IMI Cornelius, Inc. (IA), Mason City, IA; *Int'l,* pg. 646
Nicholson, Steve, Chief Fin. Officer--Katy Industries, Inc., Englewood, CO; *U.S. Public,* pg. 944
Nicholson, Stuart C., Chief Fin. Officer & Sr. V.P.--D.A. Davidson & Co., Great Falls, MT; *U.S. Private,* pg. 314
Nickel, Paul, Chief Fin. Officer--Dover Elevator Systems, Inc., Horn Lake, MS; *U.S. Public,* pg. 521
Nicks, Duane, Chief Fin. Officer--Hecht's, Arlington, VA; *U.S. Public,* pg. 1063
Nicol, David J., Chief Fin. Officer--Berli Jucker Public Co. Ltd., Bangkok, Thailand; *Int'l,* pg. 487
Nicola, Raul, Chief Fin. Officer--Juan Minetti S.A., Cordoba, Argentina; *Int'l,* pg. 869
Nicolai, Frank A., Chief Fin. Officer & Exec. V.P.--American Management Systems, Inc., Fairfax, VA; *U.S. Public,* pg. 86
Niedergang, Claude, Chief Fin. Officer--Entreprise Miniere et Chimique, Paris, France; *Int'l,* pg. 458
Niedermaier, John, Chief Fin. Officer & V.P.-Fin.--SCM Microsystems, Inc., Los Gatos, CA; *U.S. Public,* pg. 1417
Niegsch, W.C., Jr., Chief Fin. Officer, Exec. V.P., Treas. & Sec.--Max & Erma's Restaurants, Columbus, OH; *U.S. Public,* pg. 1060
Nielsen, Kurt Anker, Chief Fin. Officer--Novo Nordisk A/S, Bagsvaerd, Denmark; *Int'l,* pg. 987
Nielsen, Poul, Chief Fin. Officer--Ferrosan International A/S, Soeborg, Denmark; *Int'l,* pg. 987
Nielsen, Soren Bjerre, Chief Fin. Officer & Exec. V.P.--Danisco A/S, Copenhagen, Denmark; *Int'l,* pg. 378
Nielson, Bob, Chief Fin. Officer--Fisher Gauge Limited, Peterborough, Canada; *Int'l,* pg. 491
Nielson, Brad, Chief Fin. Officer--Mity-Lite, Inc., Orem, UT; *U.S. Public,* pg. 1118
Nielson, Gary W., Chief Fin. Officer & Exec. V.P.--Price Enterprises, Inc., San Diego, CA; *U.S. Public,* pg. 1324
Niemayer, W. Phil, Chief Fin. Officer & Exec. V.P.-Sls.--Nasco International, Inc., Fort Atkinson, WI; *U.S. Private,* pg. 446
Niermeyer, Eric P., Chief Fin. Officer--Stakmore Inc., Owego, NY; *U.S. Private,* pg. 1029
Niessner, B., Chief Fin. Officer--Scholl Oesterreisch GmbH, Vienna, Austria; *Int'l,* pg. 1210
Nightingale, R.B., V.P.-Fin.--North American Refractories Company, Cleveland, OH; *U.S. Private,* pg. 803
Nigl, Jeffrey M., Chief Fin. Officer, V.P. & Treas.--Electronic Tele-Communications, Inc., Waukesha, WI; *U.S. Public,* pg. 570
Nihoul, Michelle, Chief Fin. Officer--MECAR S.A., Petit-Roeulz-Lez-Nivelles, Belgium; *U.S. Public,* pg. 49
Niklasson, Sten, Mng. Dir.--Neste Sverige AB, Stockholm, Sweden; *Int'l,* pg. 915
Nill, Stephen J., Chief Fin. Officer & V.P.-Fin.--VideoServer, Inc., Burlington, MA; *U.S. Public,* pg. 1720
Nilsen, Bjorn, Chief Fin. Officer--ISS Norge a.s., Oslo, Norway; *Int'l,* pg. 656
Nilsen, Terje, Chief Fin. Officer, Treas. & Controller--AGA Ges.m.b.H., Vienna, Austria; *Int'l,* pg. 13
Nilsson, Bernth, Chief Fin. Officer--Korsnas AB, Gavle, Sweden; *Int'l,* pg. 759
Nilsson, Karl-Axel, Chief Fin. Officer--Skanska International Building AB, Malmo, Sweden; *Int'l,* pg. 1260
Nilsson, Mats, Chief Fin. Officer--Karlshamns AB, Karlshamn, Sweden; *Int'l,* pg. 718
Ninemire, Stanley, Chief Fin. Officer & Sr. V.P.--Tandy Brands Accessories, Inc., Arlington, TX; *U.S. Public,* pg. 1560
Nisbett, Janet S., Chief Fin. Officer & Sr. V.P.--Old Kent Bank, Grand Rapids, MI; *U.S. Public,* pg. 1216
Nishimura, Jumichi, Chief Fin. Officer & V.P.--Aisin World Corp. of America, Torrance, CA; *Int'l,* pg. 39
Nishimura, S., Sec./Treas.--Kansai Paint (America), Inc., Fort Lee, NJ; *Int'l,* pg. 723
Nissen, Elise, Chief Fin. Officer--AFP Imaging Corporation, Elmsford, NY; *U.S. Public,* pg. 6
Nissim, Igal, Chief Fin. Officer--Comverse Technology, Inc., Woodbury, NY; *U.S. Public,* pg. 425
Nistendirk, Jack, Chief Fin. Officer & Exec. V.P.--J.H. Fletcher & Co., Huntington, WV; *U.S. Private,* pg. 412
Nitani, Akinori, Chief Fin. Officer--Murata Machinery, Ltd., Kyoto, Japan; *Int'l,* pg. 897
Nithart, Jean, Chief Fin. Officer--Librairie Artheme Fayard, Paris, France; *Int'l,* pg. 792
Nitsche, John, Chief Fin. Officer, V.P. & Treas.--United Hardware Distributing Co., Plymouth, MN; *U.S. Private,* pg. 335
Nixon, Larry, V.P. & Chief Fin. Officer--Grey Advertising Inc., Western Div., Los Angeles, CA; *U.S. Public,* pg. 764
Nizam, Jamil, Vice Chm. & Chief Fin. Officer--Master International Corp., Santa Monica, CA; *U.S. Private,* pg. 713
Noble, Steven P., Chief Fin. Officer & Sec.--Lustine Oldsmobile & Buick, Inc., Hyattsville, MD; *U.S. Private,* pg. 681
Nobles, Herbert, Treas.--Upstate Milk Cooperatives Inc., Le Roy, NY; *U.S. Private,* pg. 1129
Nocella, Frank P., V.P.-Admin. & Fin.--Resource Net International, New York, NY; *U.S. Public,* pg. 903
Nocl, Nicholas A., Chief Fin. Officer & Controller--Western Regional Off Track Betting, Batavia, NY; *U.S. Private,* pg. 1168
Nodorft, Donald A., Chief Fin. Officer & V.P.-Fin.--Golden Eagle Group, Inc., Humble, TX; *U.S. Public,* pg. 749
Noe, Lewis G., Jr., Chief Fin. Officer & V.P.-Admin.--APAC Holdings, Inc., Atlanta, GA; *U.S. Public,* pg. 139
Noel, Michael, Chief Fin. Officer & Sr. V.P.--The Mission Group, Irvine, CA; *U.S. Public,* pg. 564
Nofziger, Hope, Mgr.-Credit--Toledo Blade Co., Toledo, OH; *U.S. Private,* pg. 147
Nogawa, K., Chief Fin. Officer--Fujitsu Computer Products of America, Inc., San Jose, CA; *Int'l,* pg. 526
Noguchi, Sadayoshi, Chief Fin. Officer--Japan Airlines American Region, New York, NY; *Int'l,* pg. 700
Nohren, Roger, Chief Fin. Officer & Treas.--Tucson Realty & Trust Co., Tucson, AZ; *U.S. Private,* pg. 1109
Nolan, Michael J., Chief Fin. Officer--United Waste Systems, Inc., Houston, TX; *U.S. Public,* pg. 1691
Nolan, Miriam, Chief Fin. Officer--Vibration Mountings & Controls, Inc., Bloomingdale, NJ; *U.S. Public,* pg. 24
Nolan, Patrick J., Chief Fin. Officer & Sr. V.P.-Fin.--Levitz Furniture Incorporated, Boca Raton, FL; *U.S. Public,* pg. 990
Nolan, Patrick J., Chief Fin. Officer--John M. Smyth Co., Downers Grove, IL; *U.S. Public,* pg. 990
Nolan, Paul, Chief Fin. Officer--Nanometrics Incorporated, Sunnyvale, CA; *U.S. Public,* pg. 1151
Nolan, Steve, Chief Fin. Officer & Sec.--Grey Eagle Distributors Inc., Maryland Heights, MO; *U.S. Private,* pg. 480
Nolan, Thomas J., Chief Fin Officer, V.P.-Fin, Treas. & Sec.--Minuteman International, Inc., Addison, IL; *Int'l,* pg. 587
Nole, Robert J., Treas. & Mgr.-MIS--Doron Precision Systems, Inc., Binghamton, NY; *U.S. Private,* pg. 341
Nolen, I.R., Chief Fin. Officer--Sivalls, Inc., Odessa, TX; *U.S. Private,* pg. 1004
Nolen, Norman W., Chief Fin. Officer, Sr. V.P. & Treas.--Weatherford Enterra Incorporated, Houston, TX; *U.S. Public,* pg. 1749
Nolen, Sean, Chief Fin. Officer--Simula, Inc., Phoenix, AZ; *U.S. Public,* pg. 1475
Nolf, David M., Chief Fin. Officer, Exec. V.P.-Admin. & Sec.--Analysis & Technology, Inc., North Stonington, CT; *U.S. Public,* pg. 109
Noll, Tracy, Chief Fin. Officer & V.P.--Suiza Foods Corporation, Dallas, TX; *U.S. Public,* pg. 1526
Noll, William B., Chief Fin. Officer & Exec. V.P.--GMAC Insurance Holdings, Detroit, MI; *U.S. Public,* pg. 719
Noma, Suichi, Chief Fin. Officer--Haseko Community Inc., Tokyo, Japan; *Int'l,* pg. 600
Noman, Dennis, Chief Fin. Officer--Honda East, Cincinnati, OH; *U.S. Private,* pg. 129
Noonan, Robert, Chief Fin. Officer--Noonan Machine Co., Franklin Park, IL; *U.S. Private,* pg. 801
Norberg, Paul, Chief Fin. Officer--Western Light Industrial Services, Walnut Creek, CA; *U.S. Public,* pg. 1760
Norberg, Paul A., Chief Fin. Officer & Exec. V.P.--Western Staff Services, Walnut Creek, CA; *U.S. Public,* pg. 1760
Nordgren, Bradley J., Chief Fin. Officer, Sr. V.P. & Dir.--EvansGroup, Salt Lake City, UT; *U.S. Private,* pg. 385
Nordling, Lars, Chief Fin. Officer--Euroc Beton AB, Vaxjo, Sweden; *Int'l,* pg. 1199
Nordmeyer, Andreas, Dr., Chief Fin. Officer, Member-Exec. Bd.--Thyssen Stahl AG, Duisburg, Germany; *Int'l,* pg. 1388
Norelid, Jan A., Chief Fin. Officer, V.P.-Fin. & Treas.--Devcon International Corp., Deerfield Beach, FL; *U.S. Public,* pg. 502
Norkiewicz, Larry, Chief Fin. Officer--Economy Mechanical Industries, Inc., Wheeling, IL; *U.S. Private,* pg. 602
Norman, Frederick S., Chief Fin. Officer & V.P.-Fin.--Alpha/Owens Corning LLC, Collierville, TN; *U.S. Private,* pg. 45
Norrell, Paul, Chief Fin. Officer--Johnston Industries Composite Reinforcements, Phenix City, AL; *U.S. Public,* pg. 933
Norris, Alan, Chief Fin. Officer, Sr. V.P. & Sec.--Consolidated Carma Corporation, Calgary, Canada; *Int'l,* pg. 229
Norris, Charles A., Chief Fin. Officer & V.P.-Fin.--Corel Corporation, Ottawa, Canada; *Int'l,* pg. 331
Norris, David G., Exec. V.P.-Fin. & Bus. Devel.--Fishery Products International Ltd., Saint Johns, Canada; *Int'l,* pg. 492
Norris, David L., Chief Fin. Officer & Sr. V.P.--American Eco Corporation, Toronto, Canada; *Int'l,* pg. 73
Norris, Peter S., Chief Fin. Officer, V.P.-Fin. & Treas.--HMT Technology Corporation, Fremont, CA; *U.S. Public,* pg. 771
North, Richard, Chief Fin. Officer, Treas. & Dir.-Tax & Property--Bass PLC, London, United Kingdom; *Int'l,* pg. 169
Northenscold, Thomas R., Chief Fin. Officer--PPT Vision, Inc., Eden Prairie, MN; *U.S. Public,* pg. 1245
Notas, Bernie, Chief Fin. Officer--NationsBank Montgomery Securities LLC, San Francisco, CA; *U.S. Public,* pg. 1162
Noto, Lucio A., V.P.-Fin.--Mobil Oil Corporation, Fairfax, VA; *U.S. Public,* pg. 1118
Noury, Richard, Chief Fin. Officer--St. Lawrence Brick Division, La Prairie, Canada; *Int'l,* pg. 698
Novak, Peter J., Chief Fin. Officer--University Mechanical & Engineering Contractors, Inc., San Diego, CA; *U.S. Public,* pg. 572
Novak, Ron, Chief Fin. Officer--Weider Publications, Inc., Woodland Hills, CA; *U.S. Private,* pg. 1159
Novak, William T., Exec. V.P.-Admin.--Riverdale Chemical Co., Glenwood, IL; *U.S. Private,* pg. 934
Novasic, Nicholas J., Chief Fin. Officer--Charleston Containers Shops Inc., Charleston, SC; *Int'l,* pg. 1214
Novik, Steve, Principal & Chief Fin. Officer--Edward Jones, Saint Louis, MO; *U.S. Private,* pg. 597
Novotny, Paul, V.P.-Fin. Services--Coachmen Industries, Inc., Elkhart, IN; *U.S. Public,* pg. 387
Nowakowski, Eugene T., Chief Fin. Officer--Hickok Incorporated, Cleveland, OH; *U.S. Public,* pg. 825
Nowaycyk, Nora, Chief Fin. Officer--Krone Casting Corp., North Chicago, IL; *U.S. Private,* pg. 636
Nowlin, Robert, Chief Fin. Officer--Restaurants Unlimited, Seattle, WA; *U.S. Private,* pg. 925
Nowling, Eric, Acting Chief Fin. Officer, V.P. & Controller--Standard Microsystems Corp., Hauppauge, NY; *U.S. Public,* pg. 1502
Nowosad, Alfred, Chief Fin. Officer--Siemens-Nixdorf Informationssysteme AG, Paderborn, Germany; *Int'l,* pg. 1245
Nozzolillo, Anthony, Chief Fin. Officer & Sr. V.P.-Fin.--Long Island Lighting Company, Hicksville, NY; *U.S. Public,* pg. 1013
Nuesa, Leslie, Chief Fin. Officer--Z. Cavaricci Inc., Los Angeles, CA; *U.S. Private,* pg. 1203
Nugent, Charles J., Chief Fin. Officer & Exec. V.P.--Fulton Financial Corp., Lancaster, PA; *U.S. Public,* pg. 687
Numata, Mae, Chief Fin. Officer & V.P.--Seattle Times Company, Seattle, WA; *U.S. Private,* pg. 980
Nunemaker, Richard A., Chief Fin. Officer & V.P.-Fin.--Varlen Corporation, Naperville, IL; *U.S. Public,* pg. 1710
Nunes, J.C., Dir.-Fin.--RMP Properties Ltd., Crown Mines, South Africa; *Int'l,* pg. 1081
Nunez, Alejandro, Chief Fin. Officer--Banco Espanol de Credito SA, Madrid, Spain; *Int'l,* pg. 143
Nunez, Elsa, Chief Fin. Officer--Johnson & Johnson Medical Caribbean, Caguas, PR; *U.S. Public,* pg. 928
Nuss, Albert, Controller--Agrolinz Melamin GmbH, Lienz, Austria; *Int'l,* pg. 356
Nussbaumer, Gerhard, V.P.-Fin., Treas.--Voest-Alpine International Corporation, New York, NY; *Int'l,* pg. 1470
Nussler, Joachim, Chief Fin. Officer--BHW Bausparkasse AG, Hameln, Germany; *Int'l,* pg. 120
Nyberg, Lenard, Chief Fin. Officer--Eureko B.V., Amsterdam, Netherlands; *Int'l,* pg. 464
Nyguard, Robert L., V.P. & Cashier--M & I Mid-State Bank, Stevens Point, WI; *U.S. Public,* pg. 1050
Nyman, Steve, V.P.-Fin.--Bulova Watch Company Limited, Toronto, Canada; *U.S. Public,* pg. 1011
Nystrom, Lowell D., Chief Fin. Officer & V.P.--TSI Incorporated, Shoreview, MN; *U.S. Public,* pg. 1559
Nystrom, Ulf, Chief Fin. Officer--ICA Handlarnas AB, Solna, Sweden; *Int'l,* pg. 642
Nyvold, Ole, Chief Fin. Officer--GN Danavox A/S, Taastrup, Denmark; *Int'l,* pg. 537
O'Bannion, Margaret, Chief Fin. Officer & V.P.--Gamma Biologicals Inc., Houston, TX; *U.S. Public,* pg. 698
O'Boyle, Kevin, Chief Fin. Officer--ChromaVision Medical Systems, Inc., San Juan Capistrano, CA; *U.S. Public,* pg. 1424
O'Brien, Alice, Asst. Chief Fin. Officer--Pharmaceutical Resources, Spring Valley, NY; *U.S. Public,* pg. 1285
O'Brien, D., Chief Fin. Officer--Dreamland Appliances Limited, Oldham, United Kingdom; *Int'l,* pg. 925
O'Brien, Gary, Dir.-Grp. Fin.--Signet Group plc, London, United Kingdom; *Int'l,* pg. 1248
O'Brien, George A., V.P., Chief Fin. Officer & Sec.--GenRad Electronic Manufacturing Tests Systems, Westford, MA; *U.S. Public,* pg. 731
O'Brien, John, Chief Fin. Officer--Jac Pac Foods, Ltd., Manchester, NH; *U.S. Private,* pg. 579
O'Brien, Kevin, V.P.-Fin.--Periphonics Corp., Bohemia, NY; *U.S. Public,* pg. 1278
O'Brien, Mark, Chief Fin. Officer & Sr. V.P.--Griffin Bacal Inc., New York, NY; *U.S. Private,* pg. 480
O'Brien, Patrick, Chief Fin. Officer, V.P. & Dir.-Bus. Fin.--The Associated Press, New York, NY; *U.S. Private,* pg. 92
O'Brien, R., Controller--Kenner Parker (N.Z.) Ltd., Auckland, New Zealand; *U.S. Public,* pg. 798
O'Brien, Richard T., Chief Fin. Officer & Sr. V.P.--PacifiCorp, Portland, OR; *U.S. Public,* pg. 1251
O'Brien, Robert, V.P.-Fin.--Forest City Enterprises, Inc., Cleveland, OH; *U.S. Public,* pg. 667
O'Brien, Timothy, Chief Fin. Officer--Ziff-Davis Publishing Company, New York, NY; *Int'l,* pg. 1276
O'Brien, Tony, Chief Fin. Officer & Sr. V.P.--Atlantic Recording Corporation, New York, NY; *U.S. Public,* pg. 1611
O'Byrne, Kevin, Chief Fin. Officer--Quaker Oats Limited, Southall, United Kingdom; *U.S. Public,* pg. 1348
O'Connell, Francis M., Chief Fin. Officer--Innovir Laboratories, Inc., New York, NY; *U.S. Public,* pg. 1702
O'Connell, James M., Chief Fin. Officer, V.P., Treas. & Sec.--Landauer, Inc., Glenwood, IL; *U.S. Public,* pg. 977
O'Connell, John T., Chief Fin. Officer--Enterprise Rent-A-Car Company, Saint Louis, MO; *U.S. Private,* pg. 377
O'Connell, Joseph, Chief Fin. Officer--Astro-Med, Inc., West Warwick, RI; *U.S. Public,* pg. 141
O'Connell, Michael, Chief Fin. Officer, Chief Admin. Officer & Exec. V.P.--Advanced Polymer Systems, Redwood City, CA; *U.S. Public,* pg. 22
O'Connor, A. Bruce, V.P. & Controller--Middlesex Water Company, Iselin, NJ; *U.S. Public,* pg. 1110
O'Connor, Bill, Chief Fin. Officer--Logistix, Fremont, CA; *U.S. Private,* pg. 673
O'Connor, Dennis, Chief Fin. Officer, V.P.-Fin. & Sec.--Pharmaceutical Resources, Spring Valley, NY; *U.S. Public,* pg. 1285
O'Connor, John, Chief Fin. Officer & V.P.--Hachette Filipacchi Magazines Inc., New York, NY; *Int'l,* pg. 794
O'Connor, John, Chief Fin. Officer, Sr. V.P. & Treas.--Woman's Day, New York, NY; *Int'l,* pg. 795
O'Dea, Fred, Chief Fin. Officer & V.P.--Hubbard Construction Co., Winter Park, FL; *U.S. Private,* pg. 544
O'Dell, Jane, Pres. & Treas.--Westfall GMC Truck Inc., Kansas City, MO; *U.S. Private,* pg. 1169

O'Dell, Kenneth, Chief Fin. Officer & Sr. V.P.-Fin.--Kolmar Laboratories, Inc., Port Jervis, NY; *Int'l*, pg. 239
O'Dell, Michael R., Chief Fin. Officer, Sr. V.P. & Sec.--First Financial Bancorp, Hamilton, OH; *U.S. Public*, pg. 632
O'Dell, Michael R., Chief Fin. Officer & Sr. V.P.--First National Bank of Southwestern Ohio, Hamilton, OH; *U.S. Public*, pg. 633
O'Donnell, James P., Chief Fin. Officer & Sr. V.P.--ConAgra, Inc., Omaha, NE; *U.S. Public*, pg. 425
O'Donnell, Michael, Chief Fin. Officer & Sr. V.P.--ChemDesign Corporation, Fitchburg, MA; *Int'l*, pg. 173
O'Donnell, Michael W., Chief Fin. Officer & Sr. V.P.--Columbia Energy Group, Reston, VA; *U.S. Public*, pg. 402
O'Donnell, Michael W., Chief Fin. Officer & Sr. V.P.--Columbia Gas System Service Corp., Wilmington, DE; *U.S. Public*, pg. 403
O'Donnell, Patrick, Controller--Rock of Ages Corporation, Graniteville, VT; *U.S. Public*, pg. 1396
O'Drobinak, James, Chief Fin. Officer, Sr. V.P. & Controller--ABR Information Services, Inc., Palm Harbor, FL; *U.S. Public*, pg. 2
O'Halloran, David, Chief Fin. Officer & V.P.--Carolina Builders Corporation, Raleigh, NC; *Int'l*, pg. 1512
O'Hern, Thomas E., Chief Fin. Officer, Chief Acctg. Officer & Sr. V.P.--The Macerich Company, Santa Monica, CA; *U.S. Public*, pg. 1030
O'Keefe, Michael, Chief Fin. Officer & V.P.--Melitta U.S.A., Inc., Clearwater, FL; *Int'l*, pg. 857
O'Keefe, Scott, Chief Fin. Officer & Sr. V.P.--Grey Wolf, Inc., Houston, TX; *U.S. Public*, pg. 765
O'Keefe, T. Scott, Chief Fin. & Info. Officer & Exec. V.P.--Marine Drilling Companies, Inc., Sugar Land, TX; *U.S. Public*, pg. 1044
O'Kelley, Ronald L., Chief Fin. Officer--State Street Corporation, Boston, MA; *U.S. Public*, pg. 1513
O'Kelley, Ronald L., Chief Fin. Officer--State Street Bank & Trust Co., Boston, MA; *U.S. Public*, pg. 1513
O'Leary, Bob, Chief Fin. Officer & Sr. V.P.--Cox Enterprises, Inc., Atlanta, GA; *U.S. Private*, pg. 281
O'Leary, Brendan, Chief Fin. Officer--Janssen Pharmaceutical Limited, Little Island, Ireland; *U.S. Public*, pg. 930
O'leary, Dan, Chief Fin. Officer & Exec. V.P.--Pueblo Xtra International, Inc., Pompano Beach, FL; *U.S. Private*, pg. 894
O'leary, Dan, Chief Fin. Officer--Pueblo International, Inc., Pompano Beach, FL; *U.S. Private*, pg. 894
O'Leary, Patrick J., Chief Fin. Officer, V.P. & Treas.--SPX Corporation, Muskegon, MI; *U.S. Public*, pg. 1420
O'Leary, Thomas M., Chief Fin. Officer & Gen. Counsel--The Pepper Companies, Inc., Chicago, IL; *U.S. Private*, pg. 851
O'Malley, Charles, Chief Fin. Officer--Nurre Caxton, Sunrise, FL; *Int'l*, pg. 460
O'Malley, John P., III, Chief Fin. Officer--Medical Resources Inc., Hackensack, NJ; *U.S. Public*, pg. 1080
O'Malley, Michael, Chief Oper. & Fin. Officer & V.P.-Fin.--TelCom Semiconductor, Inc., Mountain View, CA; *U.S. Public*, pg. 1569
O'Mohoney, Charlie, Chief Fin. Officer--JPS Converter & Industrial Corp., Greenville, SC; *U.S. Private*, pg. 578
O'Neal, Michael H., V.P. & Controller--CBS Radio Div., New York, NY; *U.S. Public*, pg. 274
O'Neil, Paul A., Chief Fin. Officer & Treas.--Boykin Management Co., Cleveland, OH; *U.S. Private*, pg. 162
O'Neill, Jack, Chief Fin. Officer--Town Pump, Inc., Butte, MT; *U.S. Private*, pg. 1093
O'Neill, John, Chief Fin. Officer--Beverly National Bank, Wilmington, IL; *U.S. Public*, pg. 227
O'Neill, John T., Chief Fin. Officer & Exec. V.P.--Hasbro, Inc., Pawtucket, RI; *U.S. Public*, pg. 797
O'Neill, John T., Chief Fin. Officer--Tonka Corporation, Pawtucket, RI; *U.S. Public*, pg. 797
O'Neill, Michael E., Vice Chm. & Chief Fin. Officer--Bank of America NT&SA, San Francisco, CA; *U.S. Public*, pg. 180
O'Neill, Thomas P., Chief Fin. Officer & Sr. V.P.--Tupperware Corporation, Orlando, FL; *U.S. Public*, pg. 1644
O'Reilly, John J., Chief Fin. Officer & Sr. V.P.--Esselte Corporation, Garden City, NY; *Int'l*, pg. 459
O'Rourke, Dennis, Chief Fin. Officer & Sr. V.P.--Goldberg Moser O'Neill, San Francisco, CA; *U.S. Private*, pg. 459
O'Rourke, Jerry, Chief Fin. Officer, Sr. V.P. & Treas.--Wackenhut Corrections Corporation, Palm Beach Gardens, FL; *U.S. Public*, pg. 1731
O'Shea, Andrew, Chief Fin. Officer--The J.M. Ney Company, Bloomfield, CT; *U.S. Public*, pg. 111
O'Shea, Daniel, Chief Oper. Officer--Bill Communications, Inc., New York, NY; *Int'l*, pg. 1446
O'Sullivan, D. J., Chief Fin. Officer--Sea Containers America Inc., New York, NY; *Int'l*, pg. 1213
O'Sullivan, D. J., Chief Fin. Officer--Windsor Court Hotel L.P., New Orleans, LA; *Int'l*, pg. 1214
O'Sullivan, Daniel J., Chief Fin. Officer--Sea Containers Ltd., Hamilton, Bermuda; *Int'l*, pg. 1213
O'Sullivan, Eugene, Chief Fin. Officer--The Conair Group, Inc., Pittsburgh, PA; *U.S. Private*, pg. 261
O'Wourk, Morty, Chief Fin. Officer--Elizabeth Arden Company, New York, NY; *Int'l*, pg. 1435
Oaas, T. Erik, Chief Fin. Officer--Micron Custom Manufacturing Services, Inc., Nampa, ID; *U.S. Public*, pg. 1105
Oaas, T. Erik, Chief Fin. Officer & V.P.-Fin.--Micron Electronics, Inc., Nampa, ID; *U.S. Public*, pg. 1105
Oak, Alan D., Chief Fin. Officer, Sr. V.P.-Fin. & Treas.--TECO Energy, Inc., Tampa, FL; *U.S. Public*, pg. 1565
Oak, Alan D., Chief Fin. Officer, V.P. & Treas.--Tampa Electric Co., Tampa, FL; *U.S. Public*, pg. 1565
Oakey, A.L., Chief Fin. Officer--Butterley Engineering Ltd., Ripley, United Kingdom; *Int'l*, pg. 585
Oakley, Robert, Chief Fin. Officer--Nationwide Mutual Insurance Co., Columbus, OH; *U.S. Private*, pg. 789
Oakley, Robert A., Chief Fin. Officer & Sr. V.P.--Nationwide Insurance Enterprise, Columbus, OH; *U.S. Private*, pg. 788
Oakley, W. Flake, Chief Fin. Officer--Colonial Bank, Montgomery, AL; *U.S. Public*, pg. 400
Oakley, W. Flake, IV, Chief Fin. Officer, Exec. V.P., Treas. & Sec.--The Colonial BancGroup, Inc., Montgomery, AL; *U.S. Public*, pg. 400
Obenauf, Brad A., Chief Fin. Officer & V.P.--ASC Incorporated, Southgate, MI; *U.S. Private*, pg. 8
Obereder, Erich, Chief Fin. Officer--Agrolinz Melamin GmbH, Lienz, Austria; *Int'l*, pg. 356
Oberg, Catherine, Chief Fin. Officer & Controller--Hudson County News Company, North Bergen, NJ; *U.S. Private*, pg. 545
Oberg, George, Chief Fin. Officer & V.P.--Costain Coal Inc., Lexington, KY; *Int'l*, pg. 337
Oberhauser, Roland, Chief Fin. Officer--GGK Zurich, Zurich, Switzerland; *Int'l*, pg. 1335
Oberhelman, Douglas R., Chief Fin. Officer & V.P.--Caterpillar Inc., Peoria, IL; *U.S. Public*, pg. 315
Oberli, Hans-Jurg, Chief Fin. Officer--Transammonia AG, Lachen, Switzerland; *U.S. Private*, pg. 1096
Obsbaum, Frederic, Chief Oper. Officer & Chief Fin. Officer--Midland Walwyn Capital Corporation, New York, NY; *Int'l*, pg. 865
Obscherning, William E., V.P.-Fin.--Metal Lubricants Co., Harvey, IL; *Int'l*, pg. 518
Obst, J.C., Treas.--Schenectady International, Inc., Schenectady, NY; *U.S. Private*, pg. 969
Ocasek, Ronald W., Chief Fin. Officer, Sr. V.P. & Treas.--Riser Foods, Inc., Bedford, OH; *U.S. Private*, pg. 450
Ocasek, Ronald W., Chief Fin. Officer & Treas.--Rini-Rego Supermarkets, Inc., Cleveland, OH; *U.S. Private*, pg. 451
Ock, Kee, Chief Fin. Officer--Asiana Airlines, Los Angeles, CA; *U.S. Private*, pg. 89
Ockels, Theodore S., Pres., Chief Exec. Officer, Chief Fin. Officer & Treas.--Up-Right Work Platforms Division, Selma, CA; *U.S. Private*, pg. 1128
Odajima, M., Chief Fin. Officer--Scholl Japan Limited, Tokyo, Japan; *Int'l*, pg. 1210
Odeman, K., Dr., Chief Fin. Officer--Richard Hirschmann GmbH & Co., Neckartenzlingen, Germany; *Int'l*, pg. 1108
Odlund, Lars-Olof, Chief Fin. Officer--Swedbank, Stockholm, Sweden; *Int'l*, pg. 1328
Odowd, Patrick, Chief Fin. Officer--Adams Business Media, Cathedral City, CA; *U.S. Private*, pg. 16
Oertling, Lawrence P., Chief Fin. Officer--The Laitram Corporation, Harahan, LA; *U.S. Private*, pg. 643
Oetsch, A., Chief Fin. Officer--Siemens AG Oesterreich, Vienna, Austria; *Int'l*, pg. 1247
Offerdahl, James R., Chief Fin. Officer, V.P.-Fin. & Admin. & Sec.--Pervasive Software Inc., Austin, TX; *U.S. Public*, pg. 1280
Offermann, Peter, Chief Fin. Officer & Exec. V.P.--TLC Beatrice International Holdings Inc., New York, NY; *U.S. Private*, pg. 1064
Ofstad, Cort, Chief Oper. Officer & Chief Fin. Officer--GKN Westland Aerospace North America Inc., Compton, CA; *Int'l*, pg. 535
Ogan, Roby, Chief Fin. Officer & Sr. Exec. V.P.--TeleCheck Services, Inc., Houston, TX; *U.S. Public*, pg. 631
Ogata, Keith K., Chief Fin. Officer--International Correspondence Schools Canadian Ltd., Montreal, Canada; *U.S. Public*, pg. 784
Ogden, Jeff, Chief Fin. Officer & V.P.-Admin.--Despatch Industries, Minneapolis, MN; *U.S. Private*, pg. 327
Oggioni, Giuseppe, Chief Fin. Officer--Esselte S.P.A., Cusago, Italy; *Int'l*, pg. 461
Ogram, Jay, Chief Fin. Officer & Sec.--Hudson, RCI, Temecula, CA; *U.S. Private*, pg. 546
Oguri, Hisaki, Chief Fin. Officer--Yamamoto Mfg. (USA) Inc., San Jose, CA; *Int'l*, pg. 295
Oguro, Kiyo, Sec. & Treas.--Nozaki America, Inc., New York, NY; *Int'l*, pg. 990
Oh, Dong-Hwee, Pres.--Ssangyong Research Institute, Seoul, Korea; *Int'l*, pg. 1292
Ohba, S., Chief Fin. Officer--Miyata Industry Co., Ltd., Chigasaki, Japan; *Int'l*, pg. 884
Ohlsson, Clas G., Chief Fin. Officer--Drott AB, Goteborg, Sweden; *Int'l*, pg. 1260
Okada, Lon K., Asst. Treas.--HEI Investment Corp., Honolulu, HI; *U.S. Public*, pg. 800
Okahashi, Osamu, Pres. & Chief Exec. Officer--The Sumitomo Bank of Canada, Toronto, Canada; *Int'l*, pg. 1310
Okonow, Dale, Chief Fin. Officer & Sr. V.P.--H M K Enterprises, Inc., Waltham, MA; *U.S. Private*, pg. 489
Oksendahl, Douglas C., Chief Fin. Officer, Exec. V.P.-Fin. & Treas.--Pioneer Mutual Life Insurance Company, Fargo, ND; *U.S. Private*, pg. 866
Okumoto, Richard, Controller--Novell Inc., San Jose, CA; *U.S. Public*, pg. 1203
Olausson, Anders, Chief Fin. Officer--Skanska Installation AB, Sundbyberg, Sweden; *Int'l*, pg. 1260
Olbrych, John S., Chief Fin. Officer & Treas.--Mac-Gray Corporation, Cambridge, MA; *U.S. Public*, pg. 1029
Oldfather, Grayson W., Pres. & Chief Fin. Officer--Tristate Electrical Supply Co., Inc., Hagerstown, MD; *U.S. Private*, pg. 1104
Oldham, Dennis M., Chief Fin. Officer & Exec. V.P.--Willis Corroon Melling Inc., Montreal, Canada; *Int'l*, pg. 1509
Oldham, Ginny, Chief Fin. Officer & V.P.-Fin.--Klipsch, Inc., Hope, AR; *U.S. Private*, pg. 626
Olegen, Robert W., Chief Fin. Officer & Exec.V.P.--Renaissance Hotel Group N.V., Central, Hong Kong; *U.S. Public*, pg. 1048
Olen, Gary, Pres., Chief Exec. Officer--The Sportsman's Guide, Inc., Saint Paul, MN; *U.S. Public*, pg. 1499
Olin, Per, Chief Fin. Officer & Dir.-Admin.--Gunnebo Industrier AB, Gunnebo, Sweden; *Int'l*, pg. 578
Oliphant, Randall, Chief Fin. Officer & Exec. V.P.--Barrick Gold Corporation, Toronto, Canada; *Int'l*, pg. 168
Oller, Lynn, V.P.--Quality Chekd Dairies, Inc., Naperville, IL; *U.S. Private*, pg. 898
Olsen, Greg, Dir.-Fin.--Preservative Paint Company, Seattle, WA; *U.S. Private*, pg. 613
Olsen, Richard B., Chief Fin. Officer & Sr. V.P.--ISP Chemicals Inc., Calvert City, KY; *U.S. Public*, pg. 858
Olsen, Richard B., Sr. V.P. & Chief Fin. Officer--ISP Technologies Inc., Texas City, TX; *U.S. Public*, pg. 859
Olson, A. Craig, Chief Fin. Officer & Sr. V.P.-Fin.--Albertson's, Inc., Boise, ID; *U.S. Public*, pg. 38
Olson, E.J., Chief Fin. Officer--Germantown (USA) Co., Broomall, PA; *Int'l*, pg. 555
Olson, Gene L., Chief Fin. Officer & Exec. V.P.--Golden State Foods, Irvine, CA; *U.S. Private*, pg. 460
Olson, Jim, Chief Fin. Officer--C&L Communications, Inc., Boerne, TX; *U.S. Private*, pg. 191
Olson, John R., Chief Fin. Officer & Exec. V.P.--Farmers & Merchants Bank of Central California, Lodi, CA; *U.S. Private*, pg. 394
Olson, Michael J., Chief Fin. Officer & V.P.--Canisco Resources, Inc., Wilmington, DE; *U.S. Public*, pg. 301
Olson, Rich, Chief Fin. Officer--Morse Hardware Company, Bellingham, WA; *U.S. Private*, pg. 763
Olson, Rodney E., Chief Fin. Officer & Sr. V.P.-Fin. & Corp. Devel.--Sabreliner Corporation, Saint Louis, MO; *U.S. Private*, pg. 959
Oltmans, Joseph O., II, Pres. & Chief Fin. Officer--Oltmans Construction Company, Whittier, CA; *U.S. Private*, pg. 815
Omachinski, D.L., Chief Fin. Officer, V.P.-Fin. & Treas.--OshKosh B'Gosh, Inc., Oshkosh, WI; *U.S. Public*, pg. 1232
Omreng, Knut, Chief Fin. Officer--Norcem a.s., Oslo, Norway; *Int'l*, pg. 1199
Onorato, Joseph A., Chief Fin. Officer & V.P.--Echlin Inc., Branford, CT; *U.S. Public*, pg. 560
Ooms, Ronald, Chief Fin. Officer--Monti NV, Lier, Belgium; *Int'l*, pg. 462
Oporto, Michael, Chief Fin. Officer & Treas.--Presidential Life Corporation, Nyack, NY; *U.S. Public*, pg. 1323
Ord, Kenneth S., Chief Fin. Officer & Sr. V.P.--Pacificare Health Systems, Santa Ana, CA; *U.S. Public*, pg. 1251
Ordway, Robert, Chief Fin. Officer--Horrigan American Inc., Reading, PA; *Int'l*, pg. 9
Orenstein, Robert A., Chief Fin. Officer, Treas. & V.P.--BKM Enterprises, Inc., East Hartford, CT; *U.S. Private*, pg. 107
Orenstein, Steven, Chief Fin. Officer & Exec. V.P.--DavisElen Advertising, Inc., Los Angeles, CA; *U.S. Private*, pg. 316
Oringer, Kenneth W., Chief Fin. Officer, Exec. V.P. & Treas.--U.S. Security Associates, Inc., Roswell, GA; *U.S. Private*, pg. 1126
Orlando, Joseph A., Chief Fin. Officer & V.P.--Leucadia National Corporation, New York, NY; *U.S. Public*, pg. 989
Ornstein, R. Jeffrey, Chief Fin. Officer, V.P.-Fin. & Treas.--Superior Industries International, Inc., Van Nuys, CA; *U.S. Public*, pg. 1539
Orr, Hal, Chief Fin. Officer--Dentsply New Image, Carlsbad, CA; *U.S. Public*, pg. 499
Orre, Odd, Chief Fin. Officer--Toyota Norge A/S, Drammen, Norway; *Int'l*, pg. 1414
Orrow, Roy, Chief Fin. Officer--Pandrol Jackson, Inc., Ludington, MI; *Int'l*, pg. 280
Ortega, Rafael, Chief Fin. Officer--Banco Chase Manhattan S.A., Rio de Janeiro, Brazil; *U.S. Public*, pg. 339
Ortega, Randy, Chief Fin. Officer--Robinson Lumber & Export Company, New Orleans, LA; *U.S. Private*, pg. 936
Ortiz, Ernesto, Chief Fin. Officer--Hylsamex, S.A. de C.V., San Nicolas, Mexico; *Int'l*, pg. 56
Orvell, Hakan, Chief Fin. Officer--Geotronics of North America, Inc., Itasca, IL; *Int'l*, pg. 1289
Orwig, Richard J., Chief Fin. & Chief Admin. Officer--Kennametal Inc., Latrobe, PA; *U.S. Public*, pg. 950
Orwin, Jeffrey, Chief Fin. Officer & Sr. V.P.--Gilmore Bros., Inc., Kalamazoo, MI; *U.S. Private*, pg. 454
Orzech, Paul M., Chief Fin. Officer & Exec. V.P.--MMI Companies, Inc., Deerfield, IL; *U.S. Public*, pg. 1027
Osada, M., Chief Fin. Officer--Ikegami Electronics (U.S.A.), Inc., Maywood, NJ; *Int'l*, pg. 660
Osborn, Richard J., Chief Fin. Officer & Sr. V.P.--Duke Energy Corporation, Charlotte, NC; *U.S. Public*, pg. 534
Oscherwitz, Jerry, V.P., Asst. Treas. & Sec.--Best Kosher Sausage Co., Chicago, IL; *U.S. Public*, pg. 1433
Osdoba, David J., Jr., Chief Fin. Officer & V.P.-Fin.--Grow Biz International, Inc., Minneapolis, MN; *U.S. Public*, pg. 767
Osenga, Marvin, Chief Fin. Officer--BAT Office Products, Zion, IL; *U.S. Public*, pg. 1686
Oshiro, Don, Chief Fin. Officer--International Rotex, Inc., Reno, NV; *Int'l*, pg. 460
Ossenberger, Eric, Chief Fin. Officer--Smith Pipe & Steel Co., Phoenix, AZ; *U.S. Private*, pg. 1009
Ostberg, A. Peter, Chief Fin. Officer--Holberg Industries, Inc., Greenwich, CT; *U.S. Private*, pg. 533
Ostby, Ron, Chief Fin. Officer & Grp. V.P.--Land O'Lakes, Inc., Arden Hills, MN; *U.S. Private*, pg. 645
Oster, Richard, Chief Fin. Officer & Sr. V.P.-Fin.--Crowley Maritime Corporation, Oakland, CA; *U.S. Private*, pg. 292
Osterer, Mark J., V.P.-Fin.--Columbia House Music Club, New York, NY; *Int'l*, pg. 1281
Osterman, John C., Pres., Chief Oper. Officer & Treas.--Chicago Rivet & Machine Company, Naperville, IL; *U.S. Public*, pg. 348
Ostrowski, James, Chief Fin. Officer, Treas. & Sec.--Awrey Bakeries, Inc., Livonia, MI; *U.S. Private*, pg. 103
Osusky, Frank, Chief Fin. Officer & V.P.-Fin.--Wechsler Coffee Corp., Moonachie, NJ; *U.S. Private*, pg. 1158
Otremba, Edward, Chief Fin. Officer & Treas.--Bituminous Roadways, Inc., Inver Grove Heights, MN; *U.S. Private*, pg. 146
Ott, John, Chief Fin. Officer & Sr. V.P.--The Fairmont Hotels, San Francisco, CA; *U.S. Private*, pg. 391

Otto, Albert J., Chief Fin. Officer & Sr. V.P.--Branford Savings Bank, Branford, CT; *U.S. Public*, pg. 250
Otto, William, Chief Fin. Officer & Asst. Sec.--Ripon Foods, Inc., Ripon, WI; *U.S. Private*, pg. 931
Otts, O.M., III, Chief Fin. Officer & V.P.--Autry Greer & Sons, Inc., Prichard, AL; *U.S. Private*, pg. 479
Ovenden, James A., Chief Fin. Officer--CMI Industries, Inc., Columbia, SC; *U.S. Private*, pg. 195
Overend, Mark G., Chief Fin. Officer & Sr. V.P.--SLM Holding Corp., Washington, DC; *U.S. Public*, pg. 1419
Overholtzer, Greg, Chief Fin. Officer & V.P.--Telesensory Corporation, Sunnyvale, CA; *U.S. Private*, pg. 1074
Owen, David, Chief Fin. Officer & Exec. V.P.--Essex International, Inc., Fort Wayne, IN; *U.S. Public*, pg. 593
Owen, Terry J., Chief Fin. Officer & V.P.--Trimac Corporation, Calgary, Canada; *Int'l*, pg. 1423
Owens, Bobby, Chief Fin. Officer--Professional Putters Association, Fayetteville, NC; *U.S. Private*, pg. 896
Owens, Dennis J., Chief Fin. Officer & V.P.-Admin.--The Pollock Corp., Pottstown, PA; *U.S. Private*, pg. 874
Owens, Dennis J., Chief Fin. Officer--Mayer Pollack Steel Corporation, Pottstown, PA; *U.S. Private*, pg. 874
Owens, Diane, Chief Fin. Officer & V.P.-Fin.--Weight Watchers International, Inc., Woodbury, NY; *U.S. Public*, pg. 806
Owens, Michael L., V.P., Treas. & Chief Fin. Officer--Monumental General Insurance Group, Inc., Baltimore, MD; *Int'l*, pg. 27
Oxendine, Anthony, Chief Fin. Officer--House of Raeford Farms, Inc., Raeford, NC; *U.S. Private*, pg. 542
Oyer, Paul A., V.P.-Fin. & Treas.--Hawaii Electric Light Co., Inc., Hilo, HI; *U.S. Public*, pg. 800
Ozmun, Robert, Chief Fin. Officer & Controller--Grocers Supply Co. Inc., Houston, TX; *U.S. Private*, pg. 483
Paalanne, Pekka, Chief Fin. Officer & Sr. V.P.--Amer Group Ltd., Helsinki, Finland; *Int'l*, pg. 72
Pacchini, Carlo, Chief Fin. Officer, Exec. V.P., Controller & Real Estate--Nyltech North America Inc., Manchester, NH; *Int'l*, pg. 482
Pace, Wayne, Chief Fin. Officer--CNN Headline News, Atlanta, GA; *U.S. Public*, pg. 1614
Pace, Wayne, Chief Fin. Officer--CNN (Cable News Network), Atlanta, GA; *U.S. Public*, pg. 1614
Pace, Wayne H., Chief Fin. Officer & Exec. V.P.--Turner Broadcasting System Inc., Atlanta, GA; *U.S. Public*, pg. 1614
Pacholder, Asher O., Chm. Bd. & Chief Fin. Officer--ICO, Inc., Houston, TX; *U.S. Public*, pg. 853
Packard, Ralph K., Chief Fin. Officer & Sr. V.P.--The Vanguard Group, Inc., Valley Forge, PA; *U.S. Private*, pg. 1133
Packer, Kurt R., Chief Fin. Officer--Wayne Dalton Corporation, Mount Hope, OH; *U.S. Private*, pg. 1155
Packman, Michael, Chief Fin. Officer & Exec. V.P.--Active International, Pearl River, NY; *U.S. Private*, pg. 15
Pacsay, Zsolt, Chief Fin. Officer--EURO RSCG, Budapest, Hungary; *Int'l*, pg. 602
Pagano, James, Chief Fin. Officer & Sr. V.P.--Cogentrix Incorporated, Charlotte, NC; *U.S. Private*, pg. 249
Page, Cary, Chief Fin. Officer--Teca Corporation, Pleasantville, NY; *Int'l*, pg. 1468
Page, Larry, Chief Fin. Officer, Exec. V.P. & Treas.--ShowBiz Pizza Time, Inc., Irving, TX; *U.S. Public*, pg. 1468
Page, Roger B., Chm. Bd., Pres., Chief Exec. Officer & Fin. Officer--Pace Oil Co., Inc., Winston Salem, NC; *U.S. Private*, pg. 829
Page, Stephan F., Chief Fin. Officer & Exec. V.P.--United Technologies Corporation, Hartford, CT; *U.S. Public*, pg. 1689
Paille, Daniel, Chief Fin. Officer & V.P.--Societe Generale de Financement du Quebec, Montreal, Canada; *Int'l*, pg. 1274
Pais, Pedro, Chief Fin. Officer--Whitehall Laboratorios S.A., Buenos Aires, Argentina; *U.S. Public*, pg. 82
Paisley, Christopher B., Chief Fin. Officer & Sr. V.P.-Fin.--3Com Corporation, Santa Clara, CA; *U.S. Public*, pg. 1603
Pakenham, Jerome J., Sr. V.P.-Fin. & Admin.--Shieffelin Somerset Co., New York, NY; *Int'l*, pg. 412
Paladino, Kenneth A., V.P.-Fin. & Treas.--EDO Corporation, New York, NY; *U.S. Public*, pg. 541
Paladino, Steven, Chief Fin. Officer & Sr. V.P.--Henry Schein, Inc., Melville, NY; *U.S. Public*, pg. 1437
Palardy, Robert, V.P.-Fin.--Smith & Nephew Endoscopy, Andover, MA; *Int'l*, pg. 1263
Palasota, Peter, Chief Fin. Officer--Plantation Foods Inc., Waco, TX; *U.S. Private*, pg. 869
Palazzo, Phil, Exec. V.P., Gen. Mgr. & Chief Fin. Officer--Ammirati, Puris & Lintas, Inc., New York, NY; *U.S. Private*, pg. 66
Palladino, Wayne, Chief Fin. Officer & Sr. V.P.--Transworld Home Healthcare, Inc., New York, NY; *U.S. Public*, pg. 1632
Pallat, Daniel J., Chief Fin. Officer, V.P., Treas. & Sec.--Home Juice Co., Melrose Park, IL; *U.S. Private*, pg. 537
Palles, Allen P., Chief Fin. Officer & Exec. V.P.--LINC Capital Group, Chicago, IL; *U.S. Public*, pg. 996
Palma-Fernandez, Olga, Chief Fin. Officer--del Rivero Messianu Advertising, Ltd., Coral Gables, FL; *U.S. Private*, pg. 321
Palmer, Ben M., Chief Fin. Officer--RPC Incorporated, Atlanta, GA; *U.S. Public*, pg. 1356
Palmer, David, Chief Fin. Officer--Stevcoknit Fabrics Company, Greer, SC; *U.S. Public*, pg. 498
Palmer, Douglas E., Pres. & Chief Fin. Officer--Terminal Grain Corp., Sioux City, IA; *U.S. Private*, pg. 1077
Palmer, John M., Chief Fin. Officer & V.P.-Fin.--Tab Products Co., Palo Alto, CA; *U.S. Public*, pg. 1559
Palmer, Keri, Chief Fin. Officer & Sr. V.P.--Austin Kelley Advertising, Inc., Atlanta, GA; *U.S. Private*, pg. 100
Palmer, Paul V., Chief Fin. Officer & Mng. Dir.--Capital Markets Assurance Corporation, New York, NY; *U.S. Public*, pg. 1023
Palmer, Richard, Chief Fin. Officer & Sr. V.P.--Western Financial Bank, Irvine, CA; *U.S. Public*, pg. 1757
Palmer, Ronald A., Chief Fin. Officer, Exec. V.P. & Treas.--TCF Financial Corp., Minneapolis, MN; *U.S. Public*, pg. 1554
Palmer, Ronald J., V.P.-Corp. Acctg.--Citicorp Mortgage, Inc., Saint Louis, MO; *U.S. Public*, pg. 378
Palmer, Ronald J., Chief Fin. Officer, Exec. V.P. & Treas.--TCF Bank Minnesota FSB, Minneapolis, MN; *U.S. Public*, *pg. 1554*
Palmiere, Allen J., Chief Fin. Officer & V.P.--Zemex Corporation, Toronto, Canada; *Int'l*, pg. 1523
Palomo, Joaquin, V.P.-Fin. & Admin.--Taca International Airlines, S. A., San Salvador, El Salvador; *Int'l*, pg. 1346
Palovik, John, Chief Fin. Officer--Berendsen Fluid Power, Inc., Tulsa, OK; *Int'l*, pg. 1284
Palumbo, Mike, Chief Fin. Officer--Trans World Airlines, Inc., Saint Louis, MO; *U.S. Public*, pg. 1629
Palumbo, Robert A., Chief Fin. Officer & V.P.-Fin. & Admin.--Fragrance Resources, Inc., Clifton, NJ; *U.S. Private*, pg. 423
Palvisak, Karl, Chief Fin. Officer--GAI Consultants-NC, Inc., Raleigh, NC; *U.S. Private*, pg. 434
Pannek, Matt, Chief Fin. Officer--Aaron Brothers, Inc., City of Commerce, CA; *U.S. Public*, pg. 1104
Pannier, Loren, Sr. V.P.-Fin.--Carl's Jr., Anaheim, CA; *U.S. Public*, pg. 278
Pannier, Loren C., Chief Fin. Officer & Sr. V.P.--Carl Karcher Enterprises, Inc., Anaheim, CA; *U.S. Public*, pg. 278
Pannus, Darrius, Chief Fin. Officer, V.P.-Fin. & Controller--Good Companies, Carson, CA; *U.S. Private*, pg. 463
Paola, J., Chief Fin. Officer & Sec.--CIBA-GEIGY (Pty.) Ltd., Isando, South Africa; *Int'l*, pg. 978
Papadakis, Joan, Chief Fin. Officer--ServiCenter USA, Deerfield Beach, FL; *U.S. Public*, pg. 1201
Papadatos-Gigantes, Stavros, Chief Fin. Officer--Janssen/Cilag S.A.C.I., Athens, Greece; *U.S. Public*, pg. 929
Pape, Eldon C., Chief Fin. & Plng. Officer & Exec. V.P.--Omaha Public Power District, Omaha, NE; *U.S. Private*, pg. 815
Pappagallo, Michael V., Chief Fin. Officer--Kimco Realty Corporation, New Hyde Park, NY; *U.S. Public*, pg. 960
Paquelet, Clare, Chief Fin. Officer & Exec. V.P.- Fin. & Admin.--FINAST, Maple Heights, OH; *Int'l*, pg. 750
Paquin, William, V.P.-Fin. & Treas.--MCI International Inc., Rye Brook, NY; *U.S. Public*, pg. 1024
Para, Gregory, Chief Fin. Officer & Controller--Dimensional Merchandising, Inc., Wharton, NJ; *U.S. Private*, pg. 333
Paradis, Robert D., Chief Fin. Officer, V.P. & Sec.--Yale/Chase Materials Handling, Inc., City of Industry, CA; *U.S. Private*, pg. 1195
Parent, Kenneth R., Chief Fin. Officer & Sr. V.P.--The Mills Corporation, Arlington, VA; *U.S. Public*, pg. 1113
Parfitt, Elaine, Chief Fin. Officer, V.P. & Controller--Integral Systems, Inc., Lanham, MD; *U.S. Public*, pg. 883
Paris, Chuck, Controller--LubeCon Systems, Inc., White Cloud, MI; *U.S. Private*, pg. 679
Paris, Jr., Stanley A., V.P.-Fin.--Sage Energy Company, San Antonio, TX; *U.S. Public*, pg. 1426
Parizeau, Jean, Chief Fin. Officer, V.P. & Treas.--Publicis BCP Montreal Inc., Montreal, Canada; *Int'l*, pg. 116
Park, Charles, Chief Fin. Officer, Exec. V.P.-Fin. & Sec.--Briggs Industries, Inc., Tampa, FL; *U.S. Private*, pg. 168
Park, Chung-Il, Pres.--Bum-A Petroleum Co., Ltd., Seoul, Korea; *Int'l*, pg. 1292
Park, Dong-won, Auditor--Dong Bu Insurance Co., Seoul, Korea; *Int'l*, pg. 416
Park, Moo-In, Chief Fin. Officer--Ssangyong Shipping Co. Ltd., Seoul, Korea; *Int'l*, pg. 1292
Park, Seung-Ki, Pres.--Dongseong Express Tourists Co., Ltd., Busan, Korea; *Int'l*, pg. 1292
Park, William H., Chief Fin. Officer & Exec. V.P.--United Asset Management Corporation, Boston, MA; *U.S. Public*, pg. 1672
Parke, James A., Sr. V.P.-Fin.--G.E. Capital Commercial Real Estate Financing, Stamford, CT; *U.S. Public*, pg. 712
Parke, Robert N., Chief Fin. Officer & Sr. V.P.-Fin.--St. Paul Bancorp, Inc., Chicago, IL; *U.S. Public*, pg. 1428
Parker, Brian, Chief Fin. Officer & Sr. V.P.--Grubb & Ellis Company, Northbrook, IL; *U.S. Public*, pg. 767
Parker, Brian, Chief Fin. Officer & Sr. V.P.--Grubb & Ellis Management Services, Inc., Northbrook, IL; *U.S. Public*, pg. 767
Parker, D. Michael, Chief Fin. Officer, V.P.-Fin., Sec. & Treas.--Kewaunee Scientific Corporation, Statesville, NC; *U.S. Public*, pg. 953
Parker, Dave, Chief Fin. Officer--Molded Fiber Glass Co., Ashtabula, OH; *U.S. Private*, pg. 756
Parker, Gerard, Chief Fin. Officer--Haas Publishing Companies, Inc., Norcross, GA; *U.S. Public*, pg. 1327
Parker, Howard E., Chief Fin. Officer & Sr. V.P.-Fin. & Admin.--Atlas World Group, Inc., Evansville, IN; *U.S. Private*, pg. 97
Parker, Howard E., Chief Fin. Officer & Sr. V.P.-Fin./Admin.--Atlas Van Lines, Inc., Evansville, IN; *U.S. Private*, pg. 97
Parker, Jack, Chief Fin. Officer & Exec. V.P.--Union Planters Corporation, Cordova, TN; *U.S. Public*, pg. 1668
Parker, John J., Controller & Treas.--Bell Atlantic-DE, Wilmington, DE; *U.S. Public*, pg. 202
Parker, John R., Chief Fin. Officer, V.P. & Treas.--NS Group, Inc., Newport, KY; *U.S. Public*, pg. 1147
Parker, John W., Chief Fin. Officer & Exec. V.P.--Union Planters Bank, Memphis, TN; *U.S. Public*, pg. 1669
Parker, Melvin C., Chm. Bd., Pres., Chief Exec. Officer, Chief Fin. Officer & Treas.--Investors Insurance Group, Inc., Boca Raton, FL; *U.S. Public*, pg. 911
Parker, Steve H., Chief Fin. Officer & Sr. V.P.--Old National Bancorp, Evansville, IN; *U.S. Public*, pg. 1217
Parker, Thomas, Chief Fin. Officer--General Casualty Company of Wisconsin, Sun Prairie, WI; *Int'l*, pg. 345
Parker, Thomas, Chief Fin. Officer--General Casualty Company of Illinois, Freeport, IL; *Int'l*, pg. 346
Parker, Thomas, Chief Fin. Officer--Hoosier Insurance Company, Indianapolis, IN; *Int'l*, pg. 346
Parker, W. Douglas, Chief Fin. Officer & Sr. V.P.--America West Holdings Corporation, Phoenix, AZ; *U.S. Public*, pg. 66
Parker, W. Douglas, Chief Fin. Officer & Sr. V.P.--America West Airlines, Inc., Phoenix, AZ; *U.S. Public*, pg. 67
Parkinson, Nick, Chief Fin. Dir.--EURO RSCG Healthcare, London, United Kingdom; *Int'l*, pg. 603
Parkinson, Terry, Chief Fin. Officer--Corn States Hybrid Service, Inc., Des Moines, IA; *U.S. Public*, pg. 1124
Parks, Stephen E., Chief Fin. Officer, V.P. & Treas.--Questar Corporation, Salt Lake City, UT; *U.S. Public*, pg. 1352
Parks, Walter J., Chief Fin. Officer & Sr. V.P.--AnnTaylor Stores Corporation, New York, NY; *U.S. Public*, pg. 116
Parks, Walter J., Chief Fin. Officer, Sr. V.P. & Treas.--AnnTaylor, Inc., New York, NY; *U.S. Public*, pg. 116
Parnes, Andrew H., Chief Fin. Officer--Standard Pacific Corp., Costa Mesa, CA; *U.S. Public*, pg. 1503
Parra, Mike, Chief Fin. Officer, Controller & Treas.--F.P.A., Inc., Irving, TX; *U.S. Private*, pg. 389
Parrett, Michael S., Chief Fin. Officer & V.P.--Rio Algom Limited, Toronto, Canada; *Int'l*, pg. 1118
Parretta, Marina, Chief Fin. Officer--Craftwell Containers & Packaging Limited, Rexdale, Canada; *Int'l*, pg. 761
Parrette, William, Pres. & Chief Exec. Officer--Solitec Wafer Processing, Inc., San Jose, CA; *U.S. Private*, pg. 1013
Parris, Gail, Chief Fin. Officer & Sr. V.P.--Yellow Freight System, Inc., Overland Park, KS; *U.S. Public*, pg. 1788
Parrish, James O., V.P.-Fin. & Treas.--Twin Disc, Incorporated, Racine, WI; *U.S. Public*, pg. 1646
Parrott, Anita N., Chief Fin. Officer & Sr. V.P.--St. Michaels Bank, Saint Michaels, MD; *U.S. Public*, pg. 1089
Parrs, Marianne M., Chief Fin. Officer & Sr. V.P.--International Paper Company, Purchase, NY; *U.S. Public*, *pg. 901*
Parry, Edward J., III, Chief Fin. Officer--Allmerica Securities Trust, Worcester, MA; *U.S. Public*, pg. 54
Parry, Edward J., III, Chief Fin. Officer, V.P. & Treas.--Allmerica Financial Corporation, Worcester, MA; *U.S. Public*, pg. 54
Parsons, J.A., Chief Fin. Officer, Exec. V.P., Treas. & Sec.--Willamette Industries, Inc., Portland, OR; *U.S. Public*, pg. 1768
Parsons, Jeff, Chief Fin. Officer & Sr. V.P.--Redgate Communications Corp., Vero Beach, FL; *U.S. Public*, pg. 66
Parsons, Joe, Chief Fin. Officer--Donna Karan, New York, NY; *U.S. Public*, pg. 517
Parsons, John, Chief Fin. Officer & V.P.--Cimlinc Incorporated, Itasca, IL; *U.S. Private*, pg. 239
Parsons, Robert E., Jr., Chief Fin. Officer & Exec. V.P.--Host Marriott Corporation, Bethesda, MD; *U.S. Public*, pg. 841
Partington, John, Chief Fin. Officer--AJC International, Inc., Atlanta, GA; *U.S. Private*, pg. 6
Parton, M.J., Chief Fin. Officer--GPT Holdings Ltd., London, United Kingdom; *Int'l*, pg. 1248
Paruta, Alberto, Chief Fin. Officer--Unil-It S.p.A., Milan, Italy; *Int'l*, pg. 1438
Pasco, Robert, Chief Fin. Officer--Coburn Optical Industries Inc., Tulsa, OK; *U.S. Private*, pg. 248
Pascolini, Mario, Chief Fin. Officer & Treas.--The Will-Burt Company, Orrville, OH; *U.S. Private*, pg. 1177
Pascolini, Mario, Chief Fin. Officer--Enviromental Products Inc., Orrville, OH; *U.S. Private*, pg. 1177
Pascuzzi, Bob, Chief Fin. Officer & Sec.--The Dorris Lumber & Moulding Co., Sacramento, CA; *U.S. Private*, pg. 341
Passino, Ralph, V.P. & Chief Fin. Officer-General Chemical Corp.--The General Chemical Group, Inc., Hampton, NH; *U.S. Public*, pg. 707
Passino, Ralph M., Chief Fin. Officer & V.P.--General Chemical Corporation, Parsippany, NJ; *U.S. Public*, pg. 707
Passman, S. David, III, Chief Fin. Officer & Sr. V.P.--John H. Harland Company, Decatur, GA; *U.S. Public*, pg. 785
Passman, S. David, III, Chief Fin. Officer & Sr. V.P.--The Check Store, Lakewood, CO; *U.S. Public*, pg. 785
Pasteris, Marco, Chief Fin. Officer--Henry Birks & Sons (1993) Inc., Montreal, Canada; *Int'l*, pg. 196
Pasto, Juan, Chief Fin. Officer--Sony Corporation of Panama, Panama, Panama; *Int'l*, pg. 1284
Pastorek, Pat, Chief Fin. Officer--Therma-Tru Corp., Maumee, OH; *U.S. Private*, pg. 1079
Patane, Anthony, Chief Fin. Officer--The Spencer Group Inc., Princeton, NJ; *U.S. Private*, pg. 1025
Patel, Bharat, Chief Fin. Officer--Woolworths plc, London, United Kingdom; *Int'l*, pg. 734
Patel, Ghanshyam A., Chief Fin. Officer & Treas.--Plenum Publishing Corporation, New York, NY; *U.S. Public*, pg. 1311
Patel, Kiran M., Chief Fin. Officer--Cummins Engine Company, Inc., Columbus, IN; *U.S. Public*, pg. 467
Patino, Rudy, Chief Fin. Officer--Video City Inc., Bakersfield, CA; *U.S. Public*, pg. 1719
Patnoad, Lynda, Chief Fin. Officer--Ship Analytics, Inc., North Stonington, CT; *U.S. Private*, pg. 994
Paton, H.G., Controller--Sundor Brands Inc., Mount Dora, FL; *U.S. Public*, pg. 1331
Patout, William S., III, Pres. & Chief Fin. Officer--M.A. Patout & Son, Jeanerette, LA; *U.S. Private*, pg. 843
Patrick, Stephen C., Chief Fin. Officer--Colgate-Palmolive Company, New York, NY; *U.S. Public*, pg. 397
Patridge, George, Dir.-Fin. & Treas.--National Bank of Malawi, Blantyre, Malawi; *Int'l*, pg. 1296
Patron, Ronald H., Chief Fin. Officer, Pres.-Corp. Div. & Exec. V.P.--Stewart Enterprises, Inc., Metairie, LA; *U.S. Public*, pg. 1518
Patterson, Brian, Chief Exec. Officer-Wedgwood Grp.--Waterford Wedgwood Plc, Dublin, Ireland; *Int'l*, pg. 1487
Patterson, Dana L., V.P.-Fin. & Treas.--Freedom Forge Corporation, Burnham, PA; *U.S. Private*, pg. 425

Patterson, James J., Chief Fin. Officer & V.P.--The Vigoro Corporation, Chicago, IL; *U.S. Public*, pg. 856
Patterson, K., Chief Fin. Officer--Rolls-Royce Inc., Reston, VA; *Int'l*, pg. 1127
Patterson, Mary Lou, Controller--Sherwood, Lockport, NY; *U.S. Public*, pg. 793
Patterson, Pat, Chief Fin. Officer--Catellus Residential Group, Irvine, CA; *U.S. Public*, pg. 315
Patterson, Roger, Chief Fin. Officer & V.P.-Fin.--Diagraph Corporation, Earth City, MO; *U.S. Private*, pg. 330
Patterson, William, Chief Fin. Officer--Schawk, Inc., Des Plaines, IL; *U.S. Public*, pg. 1437
Pattison, Doug, Chief Fin. Officer--Harpo Entertainment Group, Chicago, IL; *U.S. Private*, pg. 504
Pattison, K., V.P.-Fin. & Controller--Hydro-Aire, Burbank, CA; *U.S. Public*, pg. 457
Patty, David A., Chief Fin. Officer, Treas. & Sec.--Donahue Schriber, Newport Beach, CA; *Int'l*, pg. 253
Paulk, Terry, Chief Fin. Officer--H. Kessler & Company, Atlanta, GA; *U.S. Private*, pg. 616
Paulus, S., Chief Fin. Officer--S.A. Olivetti Belgium N.V., Brussels, Belgium; *Int'l*, pg. 1003
Paup, Thomas, Chief Fin. Officer--Montgomery Ward & Co., Inc., Chicago, IL; *U.S. Private*, pg. 758
Paup, Thomas, Chief Fin. Officer--Lord & Taylor, New York, NY; *U.S. Public*, pg. 1064
Paupe, Christian M., Chief Fin. Officer & Sr. V.P.--Southam Inc., Don Mills, Canada; *Int'l*, pg. 631
Pavey, Michael A., Chief Fin. Officer & Sr. V.P.--Transalta Corporation, Calgary, Canada; *Int'l*, pg. 1416
Pavey, Michael A., Chief Fin. Officer--TransAlta Enterprises Corporation, Calgary, Canada; *Int'l*, pg. 1416
Pavey, Michael A., Chief Fin. Officer--TransAlta Utilities, Calgary, Canada; *Int'l*, pg. 1416
Pawelko, Ronald G., Chief Fin. Officer--Superior Graphite Europe, Ltd., Sundsvall, Sweden; *U.S. Private*, pg. 1055
Payne, D. W., Controller & Asst. Sec.--Kerr-McGee Chemical Corp., Oklahoma City, OK; *U.S. Public*, pg. 952
Payne, Douglas, Sr. V.P.-Fin. & Admin.--Stanley Furniture Co. Inc., Stanleytown, VA; *U.S. Public*, pg. 1508
Payne, George N., Exec. V.P. & Chief Fin. Officer--Interstate Distributor Company, Tacoma, WA; *U.S. Private*, pg. 573
Payne, Lisa, Chief Fin. Officer & Exec. V.P.--Taubman Centers, Inc., Bloomfield Hills, MI; *U.S. Public*, pg. 1561
Payton, Earl E., Chief Fin. Officer--Great American Oak, Inc., Chino, CA; *U.S. Private*, pg. 280
Payton, Earl E., Pres., Chief Exec. Officer & Chief Fin. Officer--Cowden Metal-San Jose, San Jose, CA; *U.S. Private*, pg. 280
Paz, George, Chief Fin. Officer--Express Scripts, Inc., Maryland Heights, MO; *U.S. Public*, pg. 600
Pazurek, John, V.P.-Fin., Treas. & Controller--Northland Cranberries, Inc., Wisconsin Rapids, WI; *U.S. Public*, pg. 1197
Pazurek, John, Chief Fin. Officer & Controller--WildHawk, Inc., Wisconsin Rapids, WI; *U.S. Public*, pg. 1197
Peabody, Richard A., Chief Fin. Officer--Checkers Drive-In Restaurants, Inc., Clearwater, FL; *U.S. Public*, pg. 342
Peacock, Bob, Chief Fin. Officer--Letraset Ashford, Ashford, United Kingdom; *Int'l*, pg. 461
Pearce, Andrew J., Dir.-Fin.--Yorkshire Building Society, Bradford, United Kingdom; *Int'l*, pg. 1522
Pearce, C.T., Dir.-Fin.--Rentokil Ltd., East Grinstead, United Kingdom; *Int'l*, pg. 1285
Pearce, Harry J., Chief Fin. Officer--Mattel, Inc., El Segundo, CA; *U.S. Public*, pg. 1057
Pearce, Walter, Pres. & Chief Fin. Officer--KCI Communications, Inc, Mc Lean, VA; *U.S. Private*, pg. 784
Pease, Steven, Chief Fin. Officer & Dir.-Fin.--Ceras Johnson Ltda., Rio de Janeiro, Brazil; *U.S. Private*, pg. 593
Peason, R.A., Gen. Mgr.-Fin.--Feltrax International, Inc., Auckland, New Zealand; *Int'l*, pg. 130
Pecciha, Michael, Chief Fin. Officer--Rainbow Rentals, Inc., Canfield, OH; *U.S. Private*, pg. 907
Pechota, A., Dr., Chief Fin. Officer--Luwa AG, Zurich, Switzerland; *Int'l*, pg. 617
Peck, Gary S., Chief Fin. Officer, V.P.-Fin. & Sec.--HarCor Energy, Inc., Houston, TX; *U.S. Public*, pg. 782
Pedersen, Andrew, Chief Fin. Officer--Frank Ix & Sons, Inc., New York, NY; *U.S. Private*, pg. 423
Pedersen, Zaid, Chief Fin. Officer & Sr. V.P.--Trygg-Hansa, Stockholm, Sweden; *Int'l*, pg. 1425
Pederson, J.P., Chief Fin. Officer & V.P.--Entech, Inc., Butte, MT; *U.S. Public*, pg. 1127
Pederson, Jerrold P., Chief Fin. Officer, Chief Information Officer & V.P.--Montana Power Company, Butte, MT; *U.S. Public*, pg. 1126
Pedrazzoli, F., Chief Fin Officer--Credit Suisse, Zurich, Switzerland; *Int'l*, pg. 345
Peister, Richard, Chief Fin. Officer--The Howden Fan Co., Buffalo, NY; *U.S. Private*, pg. 543
Pekar, James, Chief Fin. Officer & V.P.--Color Arts, Inc., Racine, WI; *U.S. Private*, pg. 254
Pekny, Frank P., Vice Chm. & Chief Fin. Officer--City National Corporation, Beverly Hills, CA; *U.S. Public*, pg. 380
Pekny, Frank P., Vice Chm. & Chief Fin. Officer--City National Bank, Beverly Hills, CA; *U.S. Public*, pg. 381
Peles, John, Chief Fin. Officer & V.P.--Peugeot Motors of America Inc., Little Falls, NJ; *Int'l*, pg. 1020
Pelka, Wilfried, Mgr.-Finances & Acctg.--Gebr. Eickhoff Maschinenfabrik und Eisengiesserei mbH, Bochum, Germany; *Int'l*, pg. 542
Pellegrino, Louis, Controller & Sec.--Northway Motorcar Corporation, Latham, NY; *U.S. Private*, pg. 806
Peloso, J.R., V.P. & Chief Fin. Officer--Kaman Aerospace Corp., Bloomfield, CT; *U.S. Public*, pg. 942
Pelsenius, Tommy, Chief. Fin. Officer--ISS Sverige AB, Stockholm, Sweden; *Int'l*, pg. 656
Pena, Armando A., Chief Fin. Officer, Sr. V.P.-Fin. & Treas.--American Electric Power Service Corp., Columbus, OH; *U.S. Public*, pg. 72
Pena, Luis X., Pres., Chief Exec. Officer & Chief Fin. Officer--Gulf States Asphalt Company, Inc., South Houston, TX; *U.S. Private*, pg. 487
Pendergast, John M., Chief Fin. Officer--AR Accessories Group, Inc., Milwaukee, WI; *U.S. Private*, pg. 7
Pendergrass, J., Chief Fin. Officer--Lucas NovaSensor Inc., Fremont, CA; *Int'l*, pg. 820
Pendrey, J.C., Jr., Chief Fin. Officer, Sr. V.P., Treas. & Sec.--Holder Corporation, Atlanta, GA; *U.S. Private*, pg. 533
Peninger, Michael J., Chief Fin. Officer & Sr. V.P.--Fortis Benefits Insurance Company, Kansas City, MO; *Int'l*, pg. 499
Penley, Stephen S., Chief Fin. Officer--Lindberg Corporation, Rosemont, IL; *U.S. Public*, pg. 999
Penney, Patrick, Chief Fin. Officer & V.P.--The Austad Company, San Diego, CA; *U.S. Public*, pg. 782
Penney, Patrick D., V.P.-Fin.--Henry Birks & Sons (1993) Inc., Montreal, Canada; *Int'l*, pg. 196
Penney, S.C., Chief Fin. Officer--The Hongkong and Shanghai Banking Corporation Limited (HongkongBank), Central, Hong Kong; *Int'l*, pg. 583
Pennington, Donald, Chief Fin. Officer--Nautica Enterprises, Inc., New York, NY; *U.S. Public*, pg. 1167
Pennington, Robert L., V.P. & Controller--Union Boiler Co., Nitro, WV; *U.S. Private*, pg. 262
Pennington, W.A., Chief Fin. Officer & Controller--Tech-Tran Corporation, Rancocas, NJ; *U.S. Private*, pg. 560
Penno, D. Bruce, Chief Fin. Officer & Treas.--Pridgeon & Clay, Inc., Grand Rapids, MI; *U.S. Private*, pg. 883
Penny, Brian W., Chief Fin. Officer & V.P.-Fin.--Kinross Gold Corporation, Toronto, Canada; *Int'l*, pg. 734
Penz, William F., Exec. V.P. & Treas.--Ludington News Co. Inc., Detroit, MI; *U.S. Private*, pg. 679
Penzes, Josefina, Chief Fin. Officer--Uniworld Group, Inc., New York, NY; *U.S. Private*, pg. 1128
Penzes, Josie, Chief Fin. Officer--UniWorld Hispanic, New York, NY; *U.S. Private*, pg. 1128
Pepe, Barbara, Chief Fin. Officer & Treas.--Capital Resources of Virginia, Inc., Richmond, VA; *U.S. Private*, pg. 657
Pepe, Francis, Chief Fin. Officer & Sr. V.P.--JWK International Corp., Annandale, VA; *U.S. Private*, pg. 579
Pepin, Alain, Chief Fin. Officer--Banque Hydro-Energie, Paris, France; *Int'l*, pg. 822
Pepin, Phil, Chief Fin. Officer--G.I. Joe's Inc., Wilsonville, OR; *U.S. Private*, pg. 435
Peppin, Paul, Controller--Taystee Bakeries, Marquette, MI; *U.S. Private*, pg. 1022
Perego, Sergi, Chief Dealer & Treas.--BFCE Milan, Milan, Italy; *Int'l*, pg. 161
Pereira, Douglas L., Chief Fin. Officer & Sr. V.P.--Clothestime Stores, Inc., Anaheim, CA; *U.S. Public*, pg. 387
Pereira, Ken, Chief Fin. Officer--American Industrial Partners, New York, NY; *U.S. Private*, pg. 56
Perelman, Alan S., Chief Fin. Officer--Whitbread PLC, London, United Kingdom; *Int'l*, pg. 1498
Perelson, Jerome M., Chief Fin. Officer & Sr. V.P.--ContiFinancial Corporation, New York, NY; *U.S. Public*, pg. 439
Perera, Geff, Chief Fin. Officer & Exec. V.P.--Rexene Corporation, Dallas, TX; *U.S. Private*, pg. 549
Perez, Aciscli, Chief Fin. Officer--Editorial Planeta - DeAgostini, S.A., Barcelona, Spain; *Int'l*, pg. 433
Perez, Bernardino, Chief Fin. Officer--Banca March S.A., Palma de Mallorca, Spain; *Int'l*, pg. 136
Perez, Carl A., Chief Fin. Officer & Sr. V.P.--Perez Trading Co. Inc., Miami, FL; *U.S. Private*, pg. 852
Perez, Ernesto, Chief Fin. Officer--Home Products Inc., Guayaquil, Ecuador; *U.S. Public*, pg. 81
Perez, Jose A., Chief Fin. Officer--OFC/DMB&B Bucharest, Bucharest, Romania; *U.S. Private*, pg. 305
Perez, Luis Eduardo, Chief Fin. Officer--Home Products Inc., Cali, Colombia; *U.S. Public*, pg. 81
Perfall, A. Clayton, Chief Fin. Officer--Snyder Communications, Inc., Bethesda, MD; *U.S. Public*, pg. 1481
Perkins, Chris E., Chief Fin. Officer & V.P.--AGCO Corporation, Duluth, GA; *U.S. Public*, pg. 28
Perkins, Daniel, Chief Fin. Officer--Masland, Carlisle, PA; *U.S. Public*, pg. 981
Perkins, I.T., Chief Exec. Officer-Corp. Fin.--ACI International Ltd., Melbourne, Australia; *Int'l*, pg. 128
Perkins, M.W., Chief Fin. Officer--Valor Ltd., Birmingham, United Kingdom; *Int'l*, pg. 925
Perkins, Mark, Chief Fin. Officer & Controller--Handgards Inc., Northbrook, IL; *U.S. Private*, pg. 499
Perkins, P. Thomas, Treas. & Sec.--Thomas & Howard Co., Columbia, SC; *U.S. Private*, pg. 1081
Perkins, Patrick, Chief Fin. Officer--Clinton Machinery and Supply, Miami, FL; *U.S. Private*, pg. 1177
Pero, Perry R., Chief Fin. Officer, Sr. Exec. V.P. & Cashier--Northern Trust Corporation, Chicago, IL; *U.S. Public*, pg. 1195
Perocchi, William, Chief Fin. Officer, Exec. V.P. & Treas.--Doubletree Corporation, Memphis, TN; *U.S. Public*, pg. 1335
Perrin, Jean Claude, Chief Fin. Officer--Schneider S.A., Boulogne-Billancourt, France; *Int'l*, pg. 1207
Perron, Allen A., Pres. & Treas.--Tellus, Inc., Bellevue, WA; *U.S. Public*, pg. 1342
Perrotti, John, Chief Fin. Officer, V.P.-Fin. & Treas.--Gleason Corporation, Rochester, NY; *U.S. Public*, pg. 746
Perry, Brian M., Chief Fin. Officer & Treas.--Interface Electronics Corporation, Hopkinton, MA; *U.S. Private*, pg. 567
Perry, Carmen, Chief Fin. Officer, Treas., Controller & Sec.--Outdoor Venture Corp., Stearns, KY; *U.S. Private*, pg. 822
Perry, Dana, Chief Fin. Officer & Asst. Sec.--Aztec Manufacturing Co., Crowley, TX; *U.S. Public*, pg. 159
Perry, James H., Chief Fin. Officer & Treas.--United Industrial Corporation, New York, NY; *U.S. Public*, pg. 1679
Perry, Michael D., Chief Fin. Officer & Sr. Corp. V.P.--A.H. Belo Corporation, Dallas, TX; *U.S. Public*, pg. 209
Perry, Stephen B., Chief Fin. Officer--CFA Holding Company, Charlotte, MI; *U.S. Private*, pg. 194
Perry, Verdun, Chief Fin. Officer--The Peterson Group, New York, NY; *U.S. Public*, pg. 1642
Persavich, Warren D., Chief Fin. Officer & Sr. V.P.--Banner Aerospace, Inc., Washington, DC; *U.S. Public*, pg. 187
Persichini, M., Chief Fin. Officer--Crown Lance Italia Srl, Rome, Italy; *U.S. Private*, pg. 155
Pertl, David, Chief Fin. Officer & V.P.--Fresh Choice, Inc., Santa Clara, CA; *U.S. Public*, pg. 682
Perugini, Tom, Chief Fin. Officer--Gores Technology Group, Sherman Oaks, CA; *U.S. Private*, pg. 465
Pescosolido, Vin, V.P.-Fin.--J.A. Sexauer, Inc., Scarsdale, NY; *U.S. Private*, pg. 352
Pesek, Tom, Chief Fin. Officer--Plastech Corporation, Forest Lake, MN; *U.S. Private*, pg. 870
Pessolano, Joseph, Jr., Partner & Chief Fin. Officer--Houston Herstek Favat, Boston, MA; *U.S. Private*, pg. 542
Peterman, T., Chief Fin. Officer--Lift Tech International, Muskegon, MI; *U.S. Public*, pg. 406
Peters, B.G., Chief Fin. Officer, V.P.-Fin. & Controller--ICI Americas, Inc., Wilmington, DE; *Int'l*, pg. 663
Peters, Charles E., Jr., Chief Fin. Officer & Sr. V.P.--Burlington Industries, Inc., Greensboro, NC; *U.S. Public*, pg. 268
Peters, Fred, V.P.-Fin. & Treas.--Teleglobe Insurance Systems, Richmond Hill, Canada; *Int'l*, pg. 1373
Peters, Gary, V.P.-Fin.--Trinidad/Benham Corp., Denver, CO; *U.S. Private*, pg. 1103
Peters, Jeanette, Chief Fin. Officer & Sr. V.P.--Rose's Stores, Inc., Henderson, NC; *U.S. Public*, pg. 1405
Peters, Joe, Controller--Recaro North America, Inc., Clawson, MI; *U.S. Private*, pg. 914
Peters, Joey, Chief Fin. Officer & Controller--Specialty Textile Products, Talladega, AL; *U.S. Private*, pg. 1023
Peterson, Brian, Chief Fin. Officer--Richmond Homes, Inc. I, Denver, CO; *U.S. Public*, pg. 1025
Peterson, Charles, Chief Fin. Officer & Mng. Dir.--Cowen & Company, New York, NY; *U.S. Private*, pg. 280
Peterson, Clarence O., III, Chief Fin. Officer--Wagner Stott Clearing Corp., New York, NY; *U.S. Public*, pg. 1097
Peterson, Don, Chief Fin. Officer & Exec. V.P.--Lucent Technologies Inc., Murray Hill, NJ; *U.S. Public*, pg. 1017
Peterson, Gary P., Chief Fin. Officer--Wausau-Mosinee Paper Corporation, Mosinee, WI; *U.S. Public*, pg. 1747
Peterson, J. Craig, Chief Fin. & Admin. Officer & Exec. V.P.--Unitog Company, Kansas City, MO; *U.S. Public*, pg. 1693
Peterson, Jack, Exec. V.P. & Chief Fin. Officer--Alliant Foodservice, Inc., Deerfield, IL; *U.S. Private*, pg. 244
Peterson, Kathleen, Chief Fin. Officer--Crescive Die & Tool, Inc., Saline, MI; *U.S. Private*, pg. 289
Peterson, Larry, Chief Fin. Officer & Sr. V.P.-Fin.--Sunglass Hut International, Coral Gables, FL; *U.S. Public*, pg. 1535
Peterson, M. Robert, Chief Fin. Officer & Sr. V.P.-Fin.--Air Canada, Saint-Laurent, Canada; *Int'l*, pg. 36
Peterson, Michael A., Exec. V.P.-Fin. & Legal--Geupel DeMars, Inc., Indianapolis, IN; *U.S. Private*, pg. 449
Peterson, Ralph, Exec. V.P. & Treas.--Warner Bros. Studios, Inc., Burbank, CA; *U.S. Public*, pg. 1611
Peterson, Raymond A., Chief Fin. Officer & V.P.-Fin.--Media Arts Group, Inc., San Jose, CA; *U.S. Public*, pg. 1077
Peterson, Richard, Chief Fin. Officer--American Louver Co., Skokie, IL; *U.S. Private*, pg. 58
Peterson, Stephen, Chief Fin. Officer--The Times Leader, Wilkes-Barre, PA; *U.S. Public*, pg. 964
Peterson, Steven W., Chief Fin. Officer, V.P.-Fin. & Sec.--Mesa Laboratories, Inc., Wheat Ridge, CO; *U.S. Public*, pg. 1099
Peterson, Wayne S., Chief Fin. Officer, Sr. V.P. & Sec.--Buttrey Food & Drug Company, Great Falls, MT; *U.S. Public*, pg. 271
Petersson, Hakan, Chief Fin. Officer & Treas.--Fastighetsaktiebolaget Hufvudstaden, Stockholm, Sweden; *Int'l*, pg. 478
Petersson, Ingvar, Chief Fin. Officer & Exec. V.P.--Stora Kopparbergs Bergslags AB, Falun, Sweden; *Int'l*, pg. 1302
Petersson, Jan, Mgr.-Fin.--Atlas Copco Airpower N.V., Wilrijk, Belgium; *Int'l*, pg. 96
Petit, Geoffrey, Chief Fin. Officer, V.P. & Treas.--Fina, Inc., Dallas, TX; *Int'l*, pg. 1044
Petkus, Jim, Chief Fin. Officer--Kendall Regional Medical Center, Miami, FL; *U.S. Public*, pg. 405
Petrini, David J., Chief Fin. Officer & Sr. V.P.--Providian Financial Corporation, San Francisco, CA; *U.S. Public*, pg. 1338
Petrovs, Diana, Chief Fin. Officer--F.W. Myers & Co., Inc., Rouses Point, NY; *U.S. Private*, pg. 770
Petrucci, Dominic J., Jr., Chief Fin. Officer & V.P.--Kitchell Corporation, Phoenix, AZ; *U.S. Private*, pg. 624
Petry, Michael, Controller--Peace River Electric Cooperative, Inc., Wauchula, FL; *U.S. Private*, pg. 845
Pettersson, Inge, Chief Fin. Officer--Neste Oxo AB, Stenungsund, Sweden; *Int'l*, pg. 915
Pettersson, Lars, Chief Fin. Officer--D. Carnegie AB, Stockholm, Sweden; *Int'l*, pg. 272
Petteway, Dave A., Chief Fin. Officer--UHP Healthcare, Inglewood, CA; *U.S. Private*, pg. 1113
Pettey, John, Chief Fin. Officer & Treas.--Kemmons Wilson, Inc., Memphis, TN; *U.S. Private*, pg. 613
Pettinella, Nicholas A., Chief Fin. Officer, Sr. V.P., Treas. & Asst. Sec.--Intermetrics, Inc., Burlington, MA; *U.S. Private*, pg. 567
Pettinella, Nicholas A., Chief Fin. Officer--Intermetrics Securities, Inc., Burlington, MA; *U.S. Private*, pg. 568

Pettit, Dan, Chief Fin. Officer & V.P.-Fin.--Uniphase Corporation, San Jose, CA; *U.S. Public*, pg. 1670
Pezet, Philippe, Chief Fin. Officer--C.M.C. SA, Saint Quentin-en-Yvelines, France; *Int'l*, pg. 792
Pfautsch, George E., Chief Fin. Officer & Sr. V.P.--Potlatch Corporation, Spokane, WA; *U.S. Public*, pg. 1318
Pfeifer, Greg, Chief Fin. Officer & Treas.--Rochester-Midland ICL, Omaha, NE; *U.S. Private*, pg. 937
Pfeil, Thomas B., Chief Fin. Officer, V.P. & Sec.--Vectra Technologies, Inc., San Ramon, CA; *U.S. Public*, pg. 1711
Pfeil, U., Chief Fin. Officer & V.P.-Fin.--RFL Electronics, Inc., Boonton, NJ; *U.S. Private*, pg. 903
Pfinsgraff, Marty, Chief Fin. Officer--Prudential Securities Inc., New York, NY; *U.S. Private*, pg. 892
Pfister, Peter, Chief Fin. Officer--Adecco S.A., Lausanne, Switzerland; *Int'l*, pg. 23
Pfister, Terry W., Chief Fin. Officer, V.P.-Fin., Treas. & Sec.--Enerfab Inc., Cincinnati, OH; *U.S. Private*, pg. 376
Phagans, T.M., Treas. & Sec.--Addison Steel Inc., Albany, GA; *U.S. Private*, pg. 17
Pheffer, P.B., Chief Fin. Officer--Standard Management Corporation, Indianapolis, IN; *U.S. Public*, pg. 1502
Phelan, Jerry, Chief Fin. Officer--Kenco, Middlebury, IN; *U.S. Public*, pg. 1769
Phelps, Mike, Controller--J-Star Industries, Inc., Fort Atkinson, WI; *U.S. Private*, pg. 576
Philby, Richard A., Chief Fin. Officer & V.P.-Fin.--Topline Imports, Inc., Bellevue, WA; *U.S. Private*, pg. 1091
Philen, Terrell, Chief Fin. Officer & Treas.--TRT Holdings Inc., Irving, TX; *U.S. Private*, pg. 1065
Philips, Mark, Chief Fin. Officer--Furst-McNess Company, Freeport, IL; *U.S. Private*, pg. 432
Phillips, Dale W., Chief Fin. Officer & V.P.--Illinois Central Corporation, Chicago, IL; *U.S. Public*, pg. 864
Phillips, Douglas M., Chief Fin. Officer & Sr. V.P.-Fin.--MDS Inc., Etobicoke, Canada; *Int'l*, pg. 826
Phillips, Gary, Chief Fin. Officer & Exec V.P.--Associated Wholesale Grocers, Inc., Kansas City, KS; *U.S. Private*, pg. 93
Phillips, Keith, Chief Fin. Officer, V.P. & Treas.--Wellman, Inc., Shrewsbury, NJ; *U.S. Public*, pg. 1752
Phillips, Kurt A., Chief Fin. Officer & Exec. V.P.--Lebanon Valley Farmers Bank, Lebanon, PA; *U.S. Public*, pg. 688
Phillips, N. LaRon, CPA, Chief Fin. Officer, Treas. & Sec.--The Newtron Group Inc., Baton Rouge, LA; *U.S. Private*, *pg. 797*
Phillips, Regina S., Chief Fin. Officer & Treas.--George & Lynch, Inc., New Castle, DE; *U.S. Private*, pg. 448
Phillips, Ronald, V.P. & Chief Fin. Officer--J.J. Keller & Associates, Inc., Neenah, WI; *U.S. Private*, pg. 612
Phippen, Ron, Chief Fin. Officer--Jim Lupient Enterprises, Golden Valley, MN; *U.S. Private*, pg. 681
Phippen, Ron, Chief Fin. Officer--Lupient Automotive Group, Minneapolis, MN; *U.S. Private*, pg. 681
Phua, Amelia, Chief Fin. Officer--Bensons Metal Products Pte. Ltd., Singapore, Singapore; *Int'l*, pg. 460
Pi, Pedro, V.P. & Treas.--Vallehermoso, S.A., Madrid, Spain; *Int'l*, pg. 1447
Piani, Brian, Chief Fin. Officer--Yankee Publishing Incorporated, Dublin, NH; *U.S. Private*, pg. 1195
Piasecki, Andrew, Chief Fin. Officer & V.P.--Cornell Forge Company, Chicago, IL; *U.S. Private*, pg. 276
Picard, K.J., Chief Fin. Officer & Mgr.-Grp. Fin.--Australian Oil & Gas Corporation Limited, Sydney, Australia; *Int'l*, pg. 101
Picard, K.J., Chief Fin. Officer--Oil Drilling & Exploration Limited, Sydney, Australia; *Int'l*, pg. 101
Picardi, John, Chief Fin. Officer-Sulcus Hospitality Group--Lodgistix, Inc., Phoenix, AZ; *U.S. Public*, pg. 1527
Picini, Anthony M., Chief Fin. Officer & Exec. V.P.--PHP Healthcare Corporation, Reston, VA; *U.S. Public*, pg. 1241
Pickerd, Richard W., Chief Fin. Officer--Star Editorial, Inc., Lantana, FL; *U.S. Public*, pg. 87
Pickering, J., Chief Fin. Officer--Garryson-Insley Ltd., Ibstock, United Kingdom; *Int'l*, pg. 448
Pickert, Richard W., Chief Fin. Officer & Sr. V.P.--American Media, Inc., Lake Worth, FL; *U.S. Public*, pg. 87
Pickert, Richard W., Chief Fin. Officer--The National Enquirer, New York, NY; *U.S. Public*, pg. 87
Pickert, Richard W., Chief Fin. Officer--NDSI, Inc., Lantana, FL; *U.S. Public*, pg. 87
Pickert, Richard W., Chief Fin. Officer--Soap Opera Magazine, Lantana, FL; *U.S. Public*, pg. 87
Pickert, Richard W., Chief Fin. Officer--Weekly World News, Inc., Lantana, FL; *U.S. Public*, pg. 87
Pickert, Richard W., Chief Fin. Officer--Country Weekly, Inc., Lantana, FL; *U.S. Public*, pg. 87
Pickert, Richard W., Chief Fin. Officer--Fairview Printing, Lantana, FL; *U.S. Public*, pg. 87
Pickett, Edwin G., Chief Fin. Officer & Exec. V.P.--TIG Holdings, Inc., New York, NY; *U.S. Public*, pg. 1555
Piech, Peter, Chief Fin. Officer--Black Millwork Co., Inc., Allendale, NJ; *U.S. Private*, pg. 147
Pierce, A. Kenneth, Jr., V.P.--The Dispatch Printing Company, Columbus, OH; *U.S. Private*, pg. 334
Pierce, Daniel, V.P. & Asst. Treas.--Montgomery St. Income Securities, Inc., San Francisco, CA; *U.S. Public*, pg. 1127
Pierce, Frank R., Chief Fin. Officer, Exec. V.P., Treas. & Sec.--Gulfmark Offshore Inc., Houston, TX; *U.S. Public*, pg. 769
Pierce, Garrett E., Sr. V.P. & Chief Fin. Officer--Sensormatic Electronics Corporation, Boca Raton, FL; *U.S. Public*, pg. 1457
Pierce, James, Chief Fin. Officer & Treas.--Academy Corporation, Katy, TX; *U.S. Private*, pg. 11
Pierce, L. Tim, Chief Fin. Officer--Mrs. Fields' Original Cookies, Inc., Salt Lake City, UT; *U.S. Private*, pg. 688
Pierce, Robert W., Chief Fin. Officer--Carson Products Company, Savannah, GA; *U.S. Public*, pg. 309
Pierce, Teri L., Chief Fin. Officer--First American Trust Co., Santa Ana, CA; *U.S. Public*, pg. 626
Pierce, William M., Chief Fin. Officer & Sr. V.P.--Florida Panthers Holdings, Inc., Fort Lauderdale, FL; *U.S. Public*, *pg. 654*
Pierpont, Grant, Chief Fin. Officer--Universal Security Instruments Inc., Owings Mills, MD; *U.S. Public*, pg. 1697
Pierson, Rodney, Chief Fin. Officer, Sr. V.P. & Sec.--SAFECO Corporation, Seattle, WA; *U.S. Public*, pg. 1423
Pietruszewski, Craig, V.P. & Chief Fin. Officer--American West Insurance Company, Grand Forks, ND; *U.S. Public*, *pg. 216*
Pietrzak, Leonard W., Chief Fin. Officer & V.P.-Fin.--Jetronic Industries, Inc., Philadelphia, PA; *U.S. Public*, pg. 926
Pifer, Glenn A., Chief Fin. Officer, Treas. & Sec.--Allied Security, Inc., Pittsburgh, PA; *U.S. Private*, pg. 40
Pigeonniere, J. Lerebourg, Chief Fin. Officer & Treas.--Jeumont-Schneider Trenformeteurs, Lyon, France; *Int'l*, pg. 706
Pihl, Larry D., Chief Fin. Officer, V.P.-Fin., Treas. & Controller--UTILX Corporation, Kent, WA; *U.S. Public*, pg. 1701
Pijor, Dennis, Chief Fin. Officer--Merck Medco Managed Care, Independence, OH; *U.S. Public*, pg. 1091
Pike, Carla, Chief Fin. Officer--Siouxland Galvanizing Corp., Sioux City, IA; *U.S. Private*, pg. 656
Pikert, Richard W., Chief Fin. Officer--Distribution Services, Inc., Lantana, FL; *U.S. Public*, pg. 87
Piland, Robert, Chief Fin. Officer--Lapham-Hickey Steel Corp., Chicago, IL; *U.S. Private*, pg. 651
Pilcher, Thomas E., V.P. & Cashier--M & I Central Bank & Trust, Marshfield, WI; *U.S. Public*, pg. 1050
Pillmore, Eric, Chief Fin. Officer & V.P.--General Instrument Corporation, Horsham, PA; *U.S. Public*, pg. 716
Pinedo, Edwin, Chief Fin. Officer--United Advertising Publications, Inc., Dallas, TX; *Int'l*, pg. 1443
Pinkerton, Betty, Chief Fin. Officer--Winters Welding Works, Inc., Winters, TX; *U.S. Private*, pg. 1183
Pinkerton, Jane E., Chief Fin. Officer, V.P.-Admin. & Sec.--Irex Corporation, Lancaster, PA; *U.S. Public*, pg. 913
Pinkston, Larry D., Chief Fin. Officer, V.P. & Treas.--Unit Corporation, Tulsa, OK; *U.S. Public*, pg. 1672
Pinteaux, P., Chief Fin. Officer--Saunier Duval Eau Chaude Chauffage SA, Fontenay-sous-Bois, France; *Int'l*, pg. 615
Pinto, I., Dir.-Fin. Admin.--Duracell do Brasil Industria & Comercio Ltda., Sao Paulo, Brazil; *U.S. Public*, pg. 743
Pinto, Michael, Chief Fin. Officer & Exec. V.P.--First Empire State Corporation, Buffalo, NY; *U.S. Public*, pg. 631
Pionke, Edward J., Chief Fin. Officer & Sr. V.P.-Fin., Admin. & Intl. Fin.--Nelson Westerberg, Inc., Elk Grove Village, IL; *U.S. Private*, pg. 1163
Pionke, Edward J., Chief Fin. Officer & V.P.-Fin.--Nelson Westerberg Atlas, Mableton, GA; *U.S. Private*, pg. 1164
Pionke, Edward J., Chief Fin. Officer & Sr. V.P.-Fin.--Nelson Westerberg of Illinois, Elk Grove Village, IL; *U.S. Private*, *pg. 1164*
Pionke, Edward J., Chief Fin. Officer & Sr. V.P.-Fin.--Nelson Westerberg Atlas, Carrollton, TX; *U.S. Private*, pg. 1164
Pionke, Edward J., Chief Fin. Officer & Sr. V.P.-Fin.--Nelson Westerberg International Inc., Elk Grove Village, IL; *U.S. Private*, pg. 1164
Piontkowski, John, Chief Fin. Officer & Exec. V.P.--Smith Corona Corp., Cortland, NY; *U.S. Private*, pg. 1007
Pipes, Keith, Chief Fin. Officer--Sierra Capital Management Corporation, Los Angeles, CA; *U.S. Public*, pg. 1742
Pipes, Keith B., Chief Fin. Officer & Sr. V.P.--Sierra Capital Management, Northridge, CA; *U.S. Public*, pg. 1742
Pipitone, Tony, V.P. & Treas.--Warner Special Products, Burbank, CA; *U.S. Public*, pg. 1612
Pipp, Patrick J., Chief Fin. Officer--Roman, Inc., Roselle, IL; *U.S. Private*, pg. 942
Pirone, Jeffrey V., Chief Fin. Officer & Exec. V.P.--Orbital Sciences Corporation, Dulles, VA; *U.S. Public*, pg. 1229
Pironti, Louis, Chief Fin. Officer--MacGREGOR (FRA) S.A., Marseilles, France; *Int'l*, pg. 670
Pirus, Janet, Chief Fin. Officer--Winchell's Donut Houses, L.P., Santa Ana, CA; *Int'l*, pg. 1230
Pisano, Anthony, Chief Fin. Officer--Amerex USA, Inc., New York, NY; *U.S. Private*, pg. 49
Piscopo, Phillip, Chief Fin. Officer & Exec. V.P.--Neuman Distributors, Inc., Ridgefield, NJ; *U.S. Public*, pg. 1169
Pistorius, S.J.A., Chief Fin. Officer--DSM N.V., Heerlen, Netherlands; *Int'l*, pg. 352
Pitkowsky, Murray, Chief Fin. Officer, Sr. V.P. & Treas.--Datascope Corp., Montvale, NJ; *U.S. Public*, pg. 487
Pitorak, Larry J., Chief Fin. Officer, Sr. V.P.-Fin. & Treas.--The Sherwin-Williams Company, Cleveland, OH; *U.S. Public*, pg. 1465
Pitsellos, Nick, Controller--Autocon Technologies, Inc., Farmington, MI; *U.S. Public*, pg. 850
Pittman, Gary, Chm. Bd., Pres., Chief Exec., Chief Oper. & Chief Fin. Officer--PCI, Austin, TX; *U.S. Private*, pg. 826
Pittsman, Santo J., Chief Fin. Officer & Sr. V.P.--MobileComm, Ridgefield Park, NJ; *U.S. Public*, pg. 1120
Pivinski, Joseph, Chief Fin. Officer, V.P. & Treas.--Oriole Homes Corp., Delray Beach, FL; *U.S. Public*, pg. 1230
Pizel, Ken, Chief Fin. Officer, V.P.-Fin. & Treas.--Wenger Corporation, Owatonna, MN; *U.S. Private*, pg. 1162
Pizzo, Jim, Chief Fin. Officer--Young Stuff Apparel Group, Inc., New York, NY; *U.S. Private*, pg. 1202
Plake, Jim, Chief Fin. Officer--Pittsburgh Associates, Pittsburgh, PA; *U.S. Private*, pg. 867
Plamer, D., Chief Fin. Officer--Econolite Control Products, Inc., Anaheim, CA; *U.S. Private*, pg. 361
Plank, Roger B., Chief Fin. Officer & V.P.--Apache Corporation, Houston, TX; *U.S. Public*, pg. 119
Plaster, E. Dwain, Chief Fin. Officer, V.P. & Treas.--Triangle Pacific Corporation, Dallas, TX; *U.S. Public*, pg. 1634
Platt, Donald H., Chief Fin. Officer & Sr. V.P.--U.S. Office Products Company, Washington, DC; *U.S. Public*, pg. 1686
Platt, Roger, Chief Fin. Officer & Exec. V.P.--Brooks Brothers, New York, NY; *Int'l*, pg. 843
Plattner, Jim, Chief Fin. Officer & Sr. V.P.--J. Brown/LMC Group, Stamford, CT; *U.S. Public*, pg. 764
Plavko, Edward R., Chief Fin. Officer--Xtek, Inc., Cincinnati, OH; *U.S. Private*, pg. 1194
Plaxe, Jack R., Chief Fin. Officer & Sr. V.P.--PAXAR Corporation, White Plains, NY; *U.S. Public*, pg. 1266
Pleasant, Richard, Chief Fin. Officer & Exec. V.P.--Industrial Electronic Engineers, Inc., Van Nuys, CA; *U.S. Private*, pg. 561
Plomgren, Ronald A., Chief Fin. Officer & Sr. V.P.--Longs Drug Stores Corporation, Walnut Creek, CA; *U.S. Public*, *pg. 1013*
Plongren, Ronald A., Chief Fin. Officer--Longs Drug Stores California, Inc., Walnut Creek, CA; *U.S. Public*, pg. 1013
Plumb, Russell H., Chief Fin. Officer, & V.P.-Fin. & Admin.--Serologicals Corporation, Clarkston, GA; *U.S. Public*, pg. 1460
Podber, Gilda, Controller & Treas.--Lone Star Equities Inc., Lynbrook, NY; *U.S. Private*, pg. 674
Podczerwinski, John L., Chief Fin. Officer & V.P.-Fin.--Schnadig Corporation, Des Plaines, IL; *U.S. Private*, pg. 971
Poddighe, Giovanni, Chief Fin. Officer--Mikron SpA Zingonia, Ciserano-Zingonia, Italy; *Int'l*, pg. 867
Podehl, Edward J., Chief Fin. Officer--Mellon Bank, N.A.-Northeastern Region, Wilkes-Barre, PA; *U.S. Public*, pg. 1085
Poff, John, Chief Fin. Officer & V.P.--Mutual Service Corporation, North Palm Beach, FL; *U.S. Private*, pg. 831
Pohmer, Tom, Chief Fin. Officer--P.C. Richard & Son, Farmingdale, NY; *U.S. Private*, pg. 928
Polak, Kenneth S., Chief Fin. Officer--Datametrics Corporation, Calabasas, CA; *U.S. Public*, pg. 487
Polark, Roger L., Chief Fin. Officer & Sr. V.P.--Walgreen Co., Deerfield, IL; *U.S. Public*, pg. 1733
Polishook, David, Chief Fin. Officer, Treas. & Sec.--The Strober Organization, Inc., Brooklyn, NY; *U.S. Private*, pg. 403
Pollack, Carol, Chief Fin. Officer, V.P., Treas. & Sec.--Comprehensive Care Corporation, Corona Del Mar, CA; *U.S. Public*, pg. 419
Pollack, Gerald D., Chief Fin. Officer & Sr. V.P.--Rayonier Inc., Stamford, CT; *U.S. Public*, pg. 1363
Pollack, Larry, Pres. & Chief Fin. Officer--Heublein Inc., Hartford, CT; *Int'l*, pg. 410
Pollard, Don, Chief Fin. Officer, Treas. & Sec.--Allied Sporting Goods Inc., Louisville, KY; *U.S. Private*, pg. 41
Polley, Dale W., Vice Chm. & Pres.-First American Natl. Bank--First American Corporation, Nashville, TN; *U.S. Public*, pg. 624
Pollnow, C., Chief Fin. Officer & Sr. V.P.--Simpson Investment Co., Seattle, WA; *U.S. Private*, pg. 1003
Pollock, Michael J., Chief Fin. Officer & V.P.--Global Industries, Ltd., Lafayette, LA; *U.S. Public*, pg. 748
Polomeros, Dean, Chief Fin. Officer--Bloch/New England, Inc., Worcester, MA; *U.S. Private*, pg. 149
Polson, Cathy, Chief Fin. Officer--CKE Restaurants Inc., Anaheim, CA; *U.S. Public*, pg. 278
Pomerantz, Saul, Chief Fin. Officer, Sr. V.P. & Sec.--Movie Star, Inc., New York, NY; *U.S. Public*, pg. 1140
Pomeroy, Stephen E., Chief Fin. Officer--Pomeroy Computer Resources, Hebron, KY; *U.S. Public*, pg. 1315
Pompeo, Tony, Treas. & Dir.-Fin.--Du Pont Canada Inc., Mississauga, Canada; *U.S. Public*, pg. 532
Pomponi, Bill, Chief Fin. Officer & V.P.--Boat America Corp., Alexandria, VA; *U.S. Private*, pg. 153
Ponce de Leon, Jorge, Chief Fin. Officer--Jeronimo Martins, Lisbon, Portugal; *Int'l*, pg. 705
Pond, Richard G., Chief Fin. Officer, Chief Oper. Officer & Exec. V.P.--Boston Celtics Limited Partnership, Boston, MA; *U.S. Public*, pg. 246
Ponthus, Michel, Chief Fin. Officer--Compagnie Generale de Geophysique, Massy, France; *Int'l*, pg. 241
Ponzetti, Bill, Chief Fin. Officer, Controller & Treas.--Active Electrical Supply Company, Chicago, IL; *U.S. Private*, pg. 15
Ponzi, Guido, Dir.-Personnel & Admin.--Metropolitana Milanese S.P.A., Milan, Italy; *Int'l*, pg. 863
Poole, A. Terry, Chief Fin. Officer & Sr. V.P.--Nova Corporation, Calgary, Canada; *Int'l*, pg. 971
Pope, James Arthur, Chief Fin. Officer, Exec. V.P. & Gen. Counsel--Variety Wholesalers, Incorporated, Raleigh, NC; *U.S. Private*, pg. 1134
Pope, James W., Chief Fin. Officer & V.P.-Fin.--Raytheon E-Systems, Greenville, TX; *U.S. Public*, pg. 1365
Pope, Michael, Chief Fin. Officer & V.P.--Dionex Corporation, Sunnyvale, CA; *U.S. Public*, pg. 510
Popma, Tom, Chief Fin. Officer--Paulstra CRC Corporation, Grand Rapids, MI; *Int'l*, pg. 1410
Popowycz, Mike, Chief Fin. Officer--Case Foods, Inc., Salisbury, MD; *U.S. Private*, pg. 217
Porper, Hank, Chief Fin. Officer--Italia/Gal Advertising, Los Angeles, CA; *U.S. Private*, pg. 576
Porta, Christian, Chief Fin. Officer--Pernod, Creteil, France; *Int'l*, pg. 566
Porter, Barry S., Chief Fin. Officer & Treas.--Ohio Casualty Corporation, Hamilton, OH; *U.S. Public*, pg. 1214
Porter, Marc A., Chief Fin. Officer, V.P., Treas. & Sec.--The Law Company, Inc., Wichita, KS; *U.S. Private*, pg. 653
Porter, Michael A., Pres. & Chief Oper. Officer--Belcan Corporation, Cincinnati, OH; *U.S. Private*, pg. 131
Porter, Robert C., V.P., Treas., Sec. & Asst. Controller--CIPSCO Investment Company, Springfield, IL; *U.S. Public*, pg. 66
Porth, Susan E., Chief Fin. Officer & Sr. V.P.-Corp. Svcs.--Kaiser Permanente, Oakland, CA; *U.S. Private*, pg. 605
Porzio, Patrick F., Chief Fin. Officer & V.P.--H.J. Baker & Bro., Inc., Stamford, CT; *U.S. Private*, pg. 112
Posada, Jaime, Chief Fin. Officer--Capital Bank, N.A., Rockville, MD; *U.S. Private*, pg. 205
Posner, Bruce, Chief Fin. Officer--CAP Gemini America, New York, NY; *Int'l*, pg. 263
Posner, Lawrence E., MD, Sr. V.P.-Fin.--Bayer Corporation/Pharmaceutical Division, West Haven, CT; *Int'l*, pg. 173

Post, D.A., Chief Fin. Officer & V.P.--Equifax Inc., Atlanta, GA; *U.S. Public*, pg. 588

Potier, Michel, Chief Fin. Officer & Chief Info. Officer--Dickson Elberton Mills Inc., Elberton, GA; *U.S. Private*, pg. 331

Potter, Douglas R., Chief Fin. Officer & V.P.-Fin.--Dynamics Research Corporation, Andover, MA; *U.S. Public*, pg. 539

Potter, Linda, Chief Fin. Officer & Exec. V.P.--SunTrust Banks of Tennessee, Inc., Nashville, TN; *U.S. Public*, pg. 1538

Potter, Martin J., Chief Fin. Officer & V.P.--Courtaulds Coatings Inc., Louisville, KY; *Int'l*, pg. 338

Potter, Michael J., Chief Fin. Officer & Sr. V.P.--Consolidated Stores Corp., Columbus, OH; *U.S. Public*, pg. 437

Potts, M. William, Chief Fin. Officer & Exec. V.P.--Johnny Appleseed's, Inc., Beverly, MA; *U.S. Private*, pg. 590

Potts, William L., Jr., Chief Fin. Officer, V.P.-Fin. & Sec.--Komag, Incorporated, San Jose, CA; *U.S. Public*, pg. 966

Poulter, A.D., Chief Fin. Officer--Potterton Myson, Warwick, United Kingdom; *Int'l*, pg. 197

Pounds, L. Fred, Chief Fin. Officer, V.P.-Fin. & Treas.--American Oncology Resources, Inc., Houston, TX; *U.S. Public*, pg. 88

Poupart-Lafarge, Olivier, Grp. Dir.-Economics & Fin.--Bouygues, Saint Quentin-en-Yvelines, France; *Int'l*, pg. 206

Pouttu, Ernest, Chief Fin. Officer--Harwick Standard Distribution Corporation, Akron, OH; *U.S. Private*, pg. 509

Powell, G.W., Chief Fin. Officer--Qualitas Bathrooms Ltd., Burton on Trent, United Kingdom; *Int'l*, pg. 197

Powell, Gary, Chief Fin. Officer--AMF Reece Incorporated, Mechanicsville, VA; *U.S. Private*, pg. 7

Powell, William, Chief Fin. Officer & V.P.-Fin.--Components Corporation Of America, Dallas, TX; *U.S. Private*, pg. 259

Power, Bill, Chief Fin. Officer--Convair Cooler Corp., Phoenix, AZ; *U.S. Private*, pg. 271

Power, Thomas F., Jr., Chief Fin. Officer & Exec. V.P.--Wisconsin Central Transportation Corporation, Rosemont, IL; *U.S. Public*, pg. 1772

Powers, Donald A., Chief Fin. Officer--United HealthCare Plans of New England, Inc., Warwick, RI; *U.S. Public*, pg. 1678

Powers, Earl, Chief Fin. Officer & V.P.--Curtice Burns Foods, Rochester, NY; *U.S. Private*, pg. 887

Powers, Earl, Chief Fin. Officer & V.P.-Fin.--Agrilink Foods, Inc., Rochester, NY; *U.S. Private*, pg. 887

Powers, Edward, Chief Fin. Officer--BSMG Worldwide, New York, NY; *U.S. Public*, pg. 1642

Powers, Raymond, Chief Fin. Officer & Exec. V.P.-Fin.--Barton Incorporated, Chicago, IL; *U.S. Public*, pg. 300

Powers, Richard P., Chief Fin. Officer & Sr. V.P.--Syntex, Palo Alto, CA; *Int'l*, pg. 1120

Powers, Timothy L., Chief Fin. Officer--Quest Staffing, Atlanta, GA; *U.S. Public*, pg. 45

Powlick, George, Chief Fin. Officer, V.P.-Fin. & Sec.--K-Swiss Inc., Chatsworth, CA; *U.S. Public*, pg. 937

Pozzo, Jim Dal, Pres. & Chief Fin. Officer--Jacmar Companies, Inc., Alhambra, CA; *U.S. Private*, pg. 580

Prabhat, Shivakumar, Chief Fin. Officer & Exec. V.P.-Admin-DCA Advertising, Inc., New York, NY; *Int'l*, pg. 393

Prairie, Greg, Chief Fin. Officer & V.P.--Inland Printing Co., Inc., La Crosse, WI; *U.S. Private*, pg. 564

Prange, Richard, Chief Fin. Officer--Schwitzer, Inc., Indianapolis, IN; *U.S. Public*, pg. 968

Prather, Robert L., Chief Fin. Officer, Exec. V.P., Treas. & Sec.--Kocolene Oil Corp., Seymour, IN; *U.S. Private*, pg. 629

Prati, Pieranna, Chief Fin. Officer--Italiana Luce S.r.l., Settimo Milanese, Italy; *U.S. Public*, pg. 856

Pratt, Edward, Jr., Chief Fin. & Acctg. Officer--Pratt Casino Corporation, Dallas, TX; *U.S. Public*, pg. 761

Pratte, Gary D., Chief Fin. Officer--E.J. Bartells Co., Renton, WA; *U.S. Private*, pg. 118

Pratten, Robert A., Chief Fin. Officer--Regency Associates Limited Partnership, Champaign, IL; *U.S. Private*, pg. 918

Pratzel, Robert M., Chief Fin. Officer--Hellmuth, Obata & Kassabaum, Inc., Saint Louis, MO; *U.S. Private*, pg. 520

Prentice, Christopher, Chief Fin. Officer--Greenbull Inc., Louisville, KY; *U.S. Private*, pg. 477

Prescott, Gerald J., V.P., Chief Fin. Officer & Treas.--Vital Signs MN, Inc., Burnsville, MN; *U.S. Public*, pg. 1723

Prescott, Thomas J., Chief Fin. Officer & Exec. V.P.--Synovus Financial Corp., Columbus, GA; *U.S. Public*, pg. 1548

Preslar, B. Clyde, Chief Fin. Officer & Treas.--Lance, Inc., Charlotte, NC; *U.S. Public*, pg. 977

Press, Michael, V.P.-Fin.--PC Quote, Inc., Chicago, IL; *U.S. Public*, pg. 1240

Pressley, James Z., Jr., V.P.-Fin. & Admin. & Treas.--Transus Intermodal L.L.C., Atlanta, GA; *U.S. Private*, pg. 1097

Pressman, Robert, Gen. Counsel--InterDigital Patents Corporation, King of Prussia, PA; *U.S. Public*, pg. 889

Preston, James, Chief Fin. Officer--ATAPCO Office Products Group, Saint Louis, MO; *U.S. Private*, pg. 64

Preston, Steven, Chief Fin. Officer. & Sr. V.P.--The ServiceMaster Company, Downers Grove, IL; *U.S. Public*, pg. 1461

Previty, Roxane, Corp. Fin. Officer--TMP Worldwide, Inc., New York, NY; *U.S. Private*, pg. 1064

Pribanic, Gerald J., Chief Fin. Officer & Exec. V.P.--Maytag Corporation, Newton, IA; *U.S. Public*, pg. 1064

Price, A., Dir.-Fin.--Addison Tube Forming Limited, Preston, United Kingdom; *Int'l*, pg. 448

Price, Fredric D., Pres., Chief Exec. Officer & Acting Chief Fin. Officer--AMBI Inc., Tarrytown, NY; *U.S. Public*, pg. 7

Price, Michael D., Chief Fin. Officer, V.P., Treas. & Sec.--Bentley Pharmaceuticals, Inc., Tampa, FL; *U.S. Public*, pg. 212

Price, Robert J., Chief Fin. Officer, V.P. & Treas.--The Suddath Companies, Jacksonville, FL; *U.S. Private*, pg. 1049

Price, Ronald D., Chief Fin. Officer, Sr. V.P. & Sec.--Slocan Forest Products Ltd., Richmond, Canada; *Int'l*, pg. 1263

Price, T. Derek, Chief Fin. Officer & V.P.-Fin.--Wheaton River Minerals Ltd., Toronto, Canada; *Int'l*, pg. 1498

Price, Thomas A., Chief Fin. Officer--Family Smacks, Inc., Liberty, MO; *U.S. Private*, pg. 393

Price, William, Chief Fin. Officer--RCM Capital Management, San Francisco, CA; *Int'l*, pg. 418

Priddle, Donald F., Chief Fin. Officer & Exec. V.P.--Cambridge Shopping Centres Limited, Toronto, Canada; *Int'l*, pg. 253

Pride, R.J., Chief Fin. Officer--Jewson Ltd., London, United Kingdom; *Int'l*, pg. 864

Priest, Gregory M., Chief Fin. Officer & V.P.-Fin.--CBT Systems USA Ltd., Menlo Park, CA; *U.S. Public*, pg. 275

Priester, Lonnie, Pres. & Chief Fin. Officer--Fosters Freeze International, Inc., San Luis Obispo, CA; *U.S. Public*, pg. 677

Primrose, Nigel, Chief Fin. Officer--Virgin Hotel, Crathorne, United Kingdom; *Int'l*, pg. 1468

Prince, David N., Chief Fin. Officer--Hong Kong Telecommunications Limited, Quarry Bay, Hong Kong; *Int'l*, pg. 247

Prince, Michael, Chief Fin. Officer--Signature Eyewear, Inc., Inglewood, CA; *U.S. Public*, pg. 1473

Prince, Thomas E., Chief Fin. Officer & Exec. V.P.--Downey Financial Corp., Newport Beach, CA; *U.S. Public*, pg. 525

Prince, Thomas E., Chief Fin. Officer & Exec. V.P.--Downey Savings & Loan Association, F.A., Newport Beach, CA; *U.S. Public*, pg. 526

Prior, John C., Chief Fin. Officer, Sr. V.P.-Fin. & Sec.--Curative Health Services, East Setauket, NY; *U.S. Public*, pg. 469

Pritchard, Marianne, Chief Fin. Officer & Sr. V.P.--Berkshire Realty Company, Inc., Boston, MA; *U.S. Public*, pg. 221

Pritchett, Dusty, Chief Fin. Officer--Barber Dairies, Inc., Birmingham, AL; *U.S. Private*, pg. 115

Pritticer, Mike, Chief Fin. Officer.--Thermo Industries Inc., Charlotte, NC; *U.S. Private*, pg. 1080

Pritzker, Alan, Chief Fin. Officer & Exec. V.P.--Commodore Holdings, Hollywood, FL; *U.S. Public*, pg. 414

Proctor, Georganne C., Chief Fin. Officer--Bechtel Group, Inc., San Francisco, CA; *U.S. Private*, pg. 128

Proctor, Ted L., Controller & Asst. Treas.--Maui Land & Pineapple Co., Inc., Kahului, HI; *U.S. Public*, pg. 1060

Prokes, James A., Chief Fin. Officer & Exec. V.P.--Ferrous Processing & Trading Co., Detroit, MI; *U.S. Private*, pg. 402

Pronsky, Paul, Jr., Chief Fin. Officer & V.P.--GenRad, Inc., Westford, MA; *U.S. Public*, pg. 731

Proost, Robert L., Corp. V.P. & Treas.--A.G. Edwards, Inc., Saint Louis, MO; *U.S. Public*, pg. 565

Proske, Robert, Chief Fin. Officer--Craftex Mills Inc. of Pennsylvania, Blue Bell, PA; *U.S. Private*, pg. 284

Protze, Gerhard, Chm. Bd., Chief Exec. Officer, Chief Fin. Officer & Mng. Dir.--Traub AG, Reichenbach, Germany; *Int'l*, pg. 1419

Pruitt, Gary, Chief Fin. Officer & V.P.--Van Waters & Rogers, Kirkland, WA; *Int'l*, pg. 1147

Pruitt, Thomas J., Chief Fin. Officer & Exec. V.P.--Banknorth Group Inc., Burlington, VT; *U.S. Public*, pg. 186

Prunk, Tim M., Chief Oper. Officer--Customer Development Corporation, Peoria, IL; *U.S. Private*, pg. 298

Prvger, Robert J., Chief Fin. Officer--Rudolph/Libbe, Inc., Walbridge, OH; *U.S. Private*, pg. 950

Prygocki, Mark, Chief Fin. Officer--Medicis Pharmaceutical Corp., Phoenix, AZ; *U.S. Public*, pg. 1080

Psotta, Joachim, Chief Fin. Officer--Philip Morris Gmbh, Munich, Germany; *U.S. Public*, pg. 1290

Pszenny, Lawrence J., V.P.-Fin.--Bickford's Family Restaurants, Brighton, MA; *U.S. Public*, pg. 545

Puccio, Peter, Chief Fin. Officer--Delta Resins & Refractories, Inc., Milwaukee, WI; *U.S. Private*, pg. 323

Pudim, D.R., Controller--The Kerite Company, Seymour, CT; *U.S. Public*, pg. 844

Puerari, Giovanni, Chief Fin. Officer, Sec. & Treas.--Arnoldo Mondadori Editore S.p.A., Segrate, Italy; *Int'l*, pg. 887

Pugiello, Peter, Chief Fin. Officer, Sr. V.P., Treas. & Asst. Sec.--Blonder-Tongue Laboratories, Inc., Old Bridge, NJ; *U.S. Public*, pg. 237

Puglisi, Anthony J., Chief Fin. Officer, Sr. V.P. & Treas.--Olsten Corporation, Melville, NY; *U.S. Public*, pg. 1220

Puglisi, Michael A., Chief Fin. & Admin. Officer--The Blackstone Group, New York, NY; *U.S. Private*, pg. 147

Pulaski, Mark L., Chief Fin. Officer, Exec. V.P. & Treas.--Keystone Financial Inc., Harrisburg, PA; *U.S. Public*, pg. 956

Pulito, Vito, Chief Fin. Officer--Nycomed Amersham, Princeton, NJ; *Int'l*, pg. 993

Pullen, Jeff, Chief Fin. Officer--Baker Petrolite Corporation, Houston, TX; *U.S. Public*, pg. 166

Pulley, Frank, Chief Fin. Officer--Interstate Van Lines, Inc., Springfield, VA; *U.S. Private*, pg. 573

Purcell, Patrick B., Exec. V.P. & Chief Fin. & Admin. Officer-Paramount Pictures Corporation, Los Angeles, CA; *U.S. Private*, pg. 776

Purcell, Steve, Chief Fin. Officer--American Business Advertising, Omaha, NE; *U.S. Private*, pg. 51

Purcell, Steven, Chief Fin. Officer & Corp. Sec.--American Business Information, Inc., Omaha, NE; *U.S. Public*, pg. 69

Purcell, Tom, Chief Fin. Officer & V.P.-Fin.--The Advocate, Newark, OH; *U.S. Private*, pg. 23

Purdom, Douglas J., Chief Fin. Officer & V.P.--BHP Copper North America, Tucson, AZ; *Int'l*, pg. 224

Purdy, Alan M., Chief Fin. Officer & Sr. V.P.--RemedyTemp, Inc., San Juan Capistrano, CA; *U.S. Public*, pg. 1376

Puricelli, Dick, Chief Fin. Officer--Scangas Brothers Holdings, Inc., Lynn, MA; *U.S. Private*, pg. 969

Purkis, Len, Chief Fin. Officer--G.E. Capital Fleet Services, Eden Prairie, MN; *U.S. Public*, pg. 710

Purkis, Len, Chief Fin. Officer, Sr. V.P.-Fin. & Treas.--Iomega Corporation, Roy, UT; *U.S. Public*, pg. 912

Purpura, Salvatore, Chief Fin. Officer & Exec. V.P.--Asoma Corporation, White Plains, NY; *U.S. Private*, pg. 89

Pustay, Fred, Chief Fin. Officer--Weiss, Whitten, Stagliano Inc., New York, NY; *U.S. Private*, pg. 1160

Pustelak, Chris, Chief Fin. Officer--Ricart Ford Inc., Groveport, OH; *U.S. Private*, pg. 927

Quah, Albert, Country Fin. Officer--Standard Chartered Bank Malaysia Berhad, Kuala Lumpur, Malaysia; *Int'l*, pg. 1295

Quam, D.L., Controller--Convenience Plus Partners Ltd., Denver, CO; *U.S. Private*, pg. 271

Quarles, W. Greyson, Chief Fin. Officer & V.P.--SAS Institute Inc., Cary, NC; *U.S. Private*, pg. 966

Quattro, L., Chief Fin. Officer & Exec. V.P.--BBDO Canada, Toronto, Canada; *U.S. Private*, pg. 104

Queen, Andy, Chief Fin. Officer--The Botsford Group, Atlanta, GA; *U.S. Private*, pg. 409

Queen, Michael, Chief Fin. Officer--3i Group plc, London, United Kingdom; *Int'l*, pg. 1386

Quicksall, D.E., Chief Fin. Officer, Sr. V.P. & Treas.--Central Freight Lines, Inc., Waco, TX; *U.S. Private*, pg. 223

Quigley, Keith, Chief Fin. Officer, V.P. & Treas.--Clear Springs Foods, Inc., Buhl, ID; *U.S. Private*, pg. 245

Quigley, Trish, Chief Fin. Officer--Executive Software, Glendale, CA; *U.S. Private*, pg. 388

Quillinan, Robert J., Chief Fin. Officer & Exec. V.P.--Coherent, Inc., Santa Clara, CA; *U.S. Public*, pg. 395

Quiloz, Louis, Chief Fin. Officer--EPG/TBWA, Lisbon, Portugal; *U.S. Private*, pg. 1062

Quin, J. Marvin, Chief Fin. Officer & Sr. V.P.--Ashland, Inc., Russell, KY; *U.S. Public*, pg. 138

Quinn, David W., Vice Chm. & Chief Fin. Officer--Centex Corporation, Dallas, TX; *U.S. Public*, pg. 322

Quinn, Tracy, Chief Fin. Officer--Weight Watchers Gourmet Food Company, Pittsburgh, PA; *U.S. Public*, pg. 806

Quist, S.J., Chief Fin. Officer & Dir.-Fin. & Admin.--Royal Gist-Brocades N.V., Delft, Netherlands; *Int'l*, pg. 1142

Raat, Jan, Chief Fin. Officer--ARA/BDDP, Rotterdam, Netherlands; *Int'l*, pg. 117

Rabidou, Ronald E., Chief Fin. Officer--Litchfield Financial Corporation, Williamstown, MA; *U.S. Public*, pg. 1001

Rabinoff, Robert, Chief Fin. Officer--The Quick & Reilly Group Inc., Palm Beach, FL; *U.S. Public*, pg. 650

Race, Kevin D., Chief Fin. Officer, Exec. V.P. & Treas.--Fleet Mortgage Group, Inc., Columbia, SC; *U.S. Public*, pg. 650

Rachmiel, George J., Sr. V.P. & Treas.--Talegen Corporation, Seattle, WA; *U.S. Public*, pg. 1784

Rackoff, Lester, Chief Fin. Officer--Grolier Inc., Danbury, CT; *Int'l*, pg. 794

Radcliffe, Ronald J., Chief Fin. Officer, V.P. & Treas.--Rio Hotel & Casino Inc., Las Vegas, NV; *U.S. Public*, pg. 1390

Rademacher, Randy D., Chief Fin. Officer & Sr. V.P.--Comair Holdings, Inc., Erlanger, KY; *U.S. Public*, pg. 406

Radigan, Tom, Chief Fin. Officer--Symplex Communications Corp., Ann Arbor, MI; *U.S. Private*, pg. 1060

Radkoski, Donald J., Chief Fin. Officer, Grp. V.P.-Fin. & Treas.--Bob Evans Farms, Inc., Columbus, OH; *U.S. Public*, pg. 596

Radler, Jeffrey, Pres. & Chief Fin. Officer--Chessco Industries, Inc., Westport, CT; *U.S. Private*, pg. 234

Radwill, Scott, Pres., Chief Exec., Oper. & Fin. Officer--Master Appliance Corp., Racine, WI; *U.S. Private*, pg. 713

Radzinski, Paul, V.P.-Fin.--The Crown Divisions, Wooster, OH; *U.S. Public*, pg. 1631

Rae, J., Chief Fin.Officer--Comtech Antenna Systems, Inc., Saint Cloud, FL; *U.S. Public*, pg. 425

Rae, Rick, Chief Fin. Officer & V.P.-Corp. Fin.--Nob Hill General Store, Inc., Gilroy, CA; *U.S. Private*, pg. 799

Rafferty, Sherwood J., Chief Fin. Officer & Sr. V.P.--New York State Electric & Gas Corporation, Binghamton, NY; *U.S. Public*, pg. 1173

Rafferty, William, Chief Fin. Officer & Treas.--Kelley Dock Systems, Milwaukee, WI; *U.S. Private*, pg. 612

Ragaller, Steve, Chief Fin. Officer--Schroff, Straubenhardt, Germany; *U.S. Public*, pg. 1274

Ragin, Luther M., Jr., Chief Fin. Officer--Earl G. Graves Publishing Co., Inc., New York, NY; *U.S. Private*, pg. 471

Ragneback, Jan, Chief Fin. Officer--Skanska Vast, Goteborg, Sweden; *Int'l*, pg. 1261

Ragsdale, John E., Chief Fin. Officer & V.P.--Century Products Co., Macedonia, OH; *U.S. Private*, pg. 226

Rahausen, Susan B., Chief Fin. Officer & V.P.--Gianettino & Meredith Advertising, Short Hills, NJ; *U.S. Private*, pg. 450

Rahr, Stewart, Pres., Chief Exec. Officer & Chief Fin. Officer--Kinray Inc., Whitestone, NY; *U.S. Private*, pg. 622

Raines, Rosser R., Chief Fin. Officer & Treas.--Thomaston Mills, Inc., Thomaston, GA; *U.S. Public*, pg. 1599

Rainey, J. Walker, Chief Fin. Officer--X.L. Europe Insurance, Dublin, Ireland; *Int'l*, pg. 467

Rains, Kevin, Chief Fin. Officer & V.P.-Bus. Devel.--Multigen Inc., San Jose, CA; *U.S. Public*, pg. 1425

Rainsford, B.C., Chief Fin. Officer, Exec. V.P. & Treas.--Delta Woodside Industries, Inc., Greenville, SC; *U.S. Public*, pg. 497

Rainwater, Tom, Chief Fin. Officer, Treas. & Sec.--E.C. Barton & Company, Jonesboro, AR; *U.S. Private*, pg. 119

Raivio, Richard, V.P.-Fin. & Controller--Pac Paper Inc., Vancouver, WA; *U.S. Private*, pg. 828

Rajahalme, Aimo, Sr. V.P.-Fin. & Treas.--Kone Corporation, Helsinki, Finland; *Int'l*, pg. 746

Rajaji, Raj, Chief Fin. Officer & Sr. V.P.--BancTec, Inc., Dallas, TX; *U.S. Public*, pg. 176

Rajan, Ramesh, Exec. V.P. & Chief Fin. Officer--Bozell Worldwide, Inc., New York, NY; *U.S. Public*, pg. 1642

Raju, Augustine S., Chief Fin. Officer--First American Title Co. of Los Angeles, Glendale, CA; *U.S. Public*, pg. 625
Rakauskas, Mike, Sr. V.P.-Fin. & Admin. & Treas.--The Spring Air Company, Des Plaines, IL; *U.S. Private*, pg. 1027
Raleigh, John, Chief Fin. Officer & V.P.-Fin.--C.H. Heist Corp., Clearwater, FL; *U.S. Public*, pg. 807
Rallo, Thomas, Sr. V.P.-Fin. & Admin.--American White Cross, Dayville, CT; *U.S. Public*, pg. 694
Rambach, Ralph, Chief Fin. Officer--Blue Cross and Blue Shield Association, Chicago, IL; *U.S. Private*, pg. 151
Ramig, James, Chief Fin. Officer--Strombecker Corporation, Chicago, IL; *U.S. Private*, pg. 1047
Ramos, Ann Marie, Chief Fin. Officer--Georgia Stone Industries, Inc., Elberton, GA; *U.S. Private*, pg. 793
Ramos, Anne Marie, Chief Fin. Officer--New England Stone Industries, Inc., Esmond, RI; *U.S. Private*, pg. 793
Ramsay, Scott, Chief Fin. Officer, Sr. V.P., Treas. & Sec.-Admin.--Shaw's Supermarkets, Inc., East Bridgewater, MA; *Int'l*, pg. 1170
Ramsey, Doyle R., Chief Fin. Officer & V.P.-Fin.--Republic Group Incorporated, Hutchinson, KS; *U.S. Public*, pg. 1378
Ramsey, Steven C., Chief Fin. Officer & Sr. V.P.--Buckeye Partners, L.P., Allentown, PA; *U.S. Public*, pg. 266
Ramsey, Steven C., Chief Fin. Officer & Sr. V.P.-Fin.--Buckeye Pipe Line Company, L.P., Allentown, PA; *U.S. Public*, pg. 266
Ramsey, Steven C., Chief Fin. Officer--International Murex Technologies Corporation, Guelph, Canada; *Int'l*, pg. 684
Ramsey, William, Chief Fin. Officer & V.P.--WIC Western International Communications Ltd., Vancouver, Canada; *Int'l*, pg. 1481
Rance, Brent, Chief Fin. Officer, V.P. & Sec.--Universal Folding Box Company, Inc., Hoboken, NJ; *U.S. Private*, pg. 1127
Rancourt, Cathy, Controller--Diversey Water Technologies, Inc., Chagrin Falls, OH; *U.S. Public*, pg. 1150
Randall, John, Chief Fin. Officer--Capral Aluminium Limited, Granville, Australia; *Int'l*, pg. 266
Randall, Steve, Chief Fin. Officer--Elmer's Products, Inc., Columbus, OH; *U.S. Private*, pg. 158
Randazzo, John S., Chief Fin. Officer--Microphase Corporation, Norwalk, CT; *U.S. Private*, pg. 742
Randolph, E. Merle, V.P. & Chief Fin. Officer--Wallace International Silversmiths, Inc., East Boston, MA; *U.S. Private*, pg. 1061
Randolph, Merle, Chief Fin. Officer-Syratech--Carvel Hall, Crisfield, MD; *U.S. Private*, pg. 1061
Rands, L. William, Chief Fin. Officer, V.P., Treas. & Sec.--Monroc, Inc., Salt Lake City, UT; *U.S. Public*, pg. 1124
Rane, David, Chief Fin. Officer & V.P.--Callaway Golf Company, Carlsbad, CA; *U.S. Public*, pg. 294
Raney, Dennis R., Chief Fin. Officer & Sr. V.P.-Fin. & Admin.--QAD Inc, Carpinteria, CA; *U.S. Public*, pg. 1345
Ranford, P., Chief Fin. Officer--Osprey Park Ltd., London, United Kingdom; *Int'l*, pg. 1012
Rangel, John J., Sr. V.P.-Fin.--K2 Inc., Los Angeles, CA; *U.S. Public*, pg. 940
Rankin, Harley, Jr., Chief Fin. Officer & Exec. V.P.--Silgan Corporation, Stamford, CT; *U.S. Public*, pg. 1473
Rankin, W.J., Chief Fin. Officer--Blue Bell Creameries, L.P., Brenham, TX; *U.S. Private*, pg. 150
Ranus, Robert D., Chief Fin. Officer & V.P.--Roundy's, Inc., Pewaukee, WI; *U.S. Private*, pg. 948
Rapaport, Jonathan, Chief Fin. Officer, V.P. & Treas.--Pacesetter Steel Service, Inc., Kennesaw, GA; *U.S. Private*, pg. 830
Raphael, Donald S., Chief Fin. Officer--Descente America Inc., Englewood, CO; *Int'l*, pg. 395
Rapp, Charles, Chief Fin. Officer & Exec. V.P.-Opers.--Stimson Lane Ltd., Woodinville, WA; *U.S. Public*, pg. 1661
Rapp, Nemmart, Chief Fin. Officer & Sr. V.P.--Spectra-Physics AB, Stockholm, Sweden; *Int'l*, pg. 1288
Rappaport, Dean S., Chief Oper. Officer & Exec. V.P.--Catalina Lighting, Inc., Miami, FL; *U.S. Public*, pg. 314
Rarnes, Lee, Chief Fin. Officer & V.P.--Wellcraft Marine Corp., Sarasota, FL; *U.S. Private*, pg. 447
Rascon, Roger, Chief Fin. Officer & Controller--Interstate Electronics Corp., Anaheim, CA; *U.S. Public*, pg. 622
Rash, James T., Chm. Bd., Chief Exec. Officer & Chief Fin. Officer--Tidel Technologies, Inc., Houston, TX; *U.S. Public*, pg. 1608
Rashid, Zafar, Chief Fin. Officer--American General Life Insurance Company, Houston, TX; *U.S. Public*, pg. 76
Rashidn, Zafar Kerry, Chief Fin. Officer & Sr. V.P.--Fortis, Inc., New York, NY; *Int'l*, pg. 499
Rasmussen, Gary D., Chief Fin. Officer & V.P.--City Meats & Provisions Co., Phoenix, AZ; *U.S. Private*, pg. 244
Rasmussen, Robert, Chief Fin. Officer & V.P.-Fin.--TransLogic Corp., Denver, CO; *Int'l*, pg. 1387
Raspino, Louis A., Jr., Chief Fin. Officer & Sr. V.P.--The Louisiana Land and Exploration Company, New Orleans, LA; *U.S. Public*, pg. 269
Raspino, Louis A., Jr., Chief Fin. Officer & V.P.--LL&E (UK) Inc., London, United Kingdom; *U.S. Public*, pg. 269
Raspino, Louis A., Jr., Chief Fin. Officer--Inexco Oil Company, New Orleans, LA; *U.S. Public*, pg. 269
Rassman, Joel H., Chief Fin. Officer, Sr. V.P., Treas. & Asst. Sec.--Toll Brothers, Inc., Huntingdon Valley, PA; *U.S. Public*, pg. 1620
Ratcliff, Karen J., Chief Fin. Officer & Exec. V.P.--PriceSmart Inc., San Diego, CA; *U.S. Public*, pg. 1324
Ratcliffe, T., Chief Fin. Officer--Litton Systems Canada Ltd., Etobicoke, Canada; *U.S. Public*, pg. 1005
Ratcliffe, William, Chief Fin. Officer--S. Freedman & Sons, Inc., Landover, MD; *U.S. Private*, pg. 425
Rathgeber, Christopher, Chief Fin. Officer--Globelle Corporation, Mississauga, Canada; *Int'l*, pg. 554
Rathke, Francis, Chief Fin. Officer, Treas. & Sec.--Ben & Jerry's Homemade Inc., South Burlington, VT; *U.S. Public*, pg. 210
Ratnathicam, Chutta, Chief Fin. Officer & Sr. V.P.--CNF Transportation Inc., Palo Alto, CA; *U.S. Public*, pg. 281
Ratoff, Steven B., Chief Fin. Officer & Exec. V.P.--Brown-Forman Corporation, Louisville, KY; *U.S. Public*, pg. 261
Rauman, Thomas R., Chief Fin. Officer & V.P.-Fin.--Dekalb Genetics Corporation, De Kalb, IL; *U.S. Public*, pg. 493
Rauscher, Helmut, Chief Fin. Officer--Pfleiderer AG, Neumarkt, Germany; *Int'l*, pg. 1046
Rauwerdink, William J., Chief Fin. Officer, Exec. V.P., Treas. & Sec.--Lason, Inc., Troy, MI; *U.S. Public*, pg. 979
Ravilly, Claude, Chief Fin. Officer & Sr. Exec. V.P.--Club Mediterranee SA, Paris, France; *Int'l*, pg. 298
Rawley, Don, Chief Fin. Officer--Edwardstone & Company, Inc., New York, NY; *U.S. Private*, pg. 365
Rawlinson, D.J., Chief Fin. Officer--Reunert Ltd., Sandton, South Africa; *Int'l*, pg. 1105
Rawls, Warren L., Chief Fin. Officer & Sec.--Littlefield, Adams & Company, Huber Heights, OH; *U.S. Public*, pg. 1001
Raxter, Alan, Chief Fin. Officer, Exec. V.P. & Treas.--Younkers, Inc., Des Moines, IA; *U.S. Public*, pg. 1334
Ray, E. Wayne, Jr., Chief Fin. Officer, V.P. & Treas.--Riviana Foods Inc., Houston, TX; *U.S. Public*, pg. 1392
Ray, Jeff, Chief Fin. Officer--Comtech Systems, Inc., Saint Cloud, FL; *U.S. Public*, pg. 425
Ray, R. F., Chief Fin. Officer--Marley Roof Tiles Holdings (U.S.A.) Inc., Johnson City, TN; *Int'l*, pg. 844
Ray, Richard F., Chief Fin. Officer, V.P. & Dir.-Fin.--General Shale Products Corp., Johnson City, TN; *Int'l*, pg. 843
Ray, Stephen M., Chief Fin. Officer & Sr. V.P.--Health Management Associates, Inc., Naples, FL; *U.S. Public*, pg. 802
Ray, William H, Jr., Exec. V.P. & Treas.--Torchmark Investment Advisory Company, Inc., Birmingham, AL; *U.S. Public*, pg. 1623
Raybuck, Roger, Chief Fin. Officer & Exec. V.P.--Boyer Candy Company Inc., Altoona, PA; *U.S. Private*, pg. 162
Rayner, Keith, Chief Fin. Officer--Esselte Meto Ltd., Bracknell, United Kingdom; *Int'l*, pg. 461
Read, Michael J., Chief Fin. Officer, Treas. & Mng. Dir.--Barr Brothers & Co., Inc., New York, NY; *U.S. Private*, pg. 117
Read, Randolph C., Chief Fin. Officer-Fin. & Plng. & Sr. V.P.--Stone Container Corporation, Chicago, IL; *U.S. Public*, pg. 1520
Ready, George W., Treas. & Corp. Sec.--Watkins Associated Industries Inc., Atlanta, GA; *U.S. Private*, pg. 1153
Reagan, Larry, Chief Fin. Officer & Exec. V.P.--Pascoe Building Systems, Inc., Columbus, GA; *U.S. Private*, pg. 842
Reardon, Joseph M., Chief Fin. Officer, Exec. V.P. & Treas.--B.M.J. Financial Corp., Bordentown, NJ; *U.S. Public*, pg. 1528
Reardon, Michael, Exec. V.P. & Gen. Mgr.--U.S. Filter, Palm Desert, CA; *U.S. Public*, pg. 61
Reatgegey, Randy, Chief Fin. Officer--Al & Ed's Auto Sound Center, Monterey Park, CA; *U.S. Private*, pg. 30
Rebello, Algusto Indraide, Chief Fin. Officer--EURO RSCG, Oeiras, Portugal; *Int'l*, pg. 602
Rebmann, Emil, Exec. V.P.-Fin. & Controller--Sika Finanz AG, Baar, Switzerland; *Int'l*, pg. 1248
Rebmann, R. Robert, Jr., Chief Fin. Officer & Treas.--Box Hill Systems Corporation, New York, NY; *U.S. Public*, pg. 249
Rebner, Ronald, Chief Fin. Officer & V.P.--Keithley Instruments, Inc., Cleveland, OH; *U.S. Public*, pg. 946
Recchia, Robert L., Chief Fin. Officer & V.P.--Valassis Communications, Inc., Livonia, MI; *U.S. Public*, pg. 1704
Recco, Jerry, Chief Fin. Officer--Members Only By Europe Craft, New York, NY; *U.S. Public*, pg. 129
Rector, Ann Greer, Chief Fin. Officer & Sr. V.P.-Opers.--Owens & Minor Inc., Glen Allen, VA; *U.S. Public*, pg. 1236
Redard, Michael, Chief Fin. Officer--Medical Analysis Systems Inc., Camarillo, CA; *U.S. Private*, pg. 727
Reddekopp, Suzi, Chief Fin. Officer--Kline Iron & Steel Co., Inc., Columbia, SC; *U.S. Private*, pg. 626
Redding, Virginia M., Chief Fin. Officer--W & D Securities, Inc., Jersey City, NJ; *U.S. Public*, pg. 925
Redgrave, Martyn R., Chief Fin. Officer--Carlson Companies, Inc., Minnetonka, MN; *U.S. Private*, pg. 211
Rediehs, Richard L., Dir.-Fin.--Griffith Micro Science International Inc., Oak Brook, IL; *U.S. Private*, pg. 481
Redman, Dale E., Chief Fin. Officer & Exec. V.P.--United Companies Financial Corporation, Baton Rouge, LA; *U.S. Public*, pg. 1675
Redman, Monte N., Chief Fin. Officer, Sr. V.P. & Treas.--Astoria Financial Corporation, Lake Success, NY; *U.S. Public*, pg. 141
Redmond, Richard V., Chief Fin. Officer--Structron Corporation, San Marcos, CA; *U.S. Private*, pg. 988
Reece, Paris G., III, Chief Fin. Officer & Sr. V.P.--M.D.C. Holdings, Inc., Denver, CO; *U.S. Public*, pg. 1025
Reece, Richard K., Chief Fin. Officer, V.P.-Fin. & Treas.--Belden Inc., Saint Louis, MO; *U.S. Public*, pg. 200
Reed, Colin, Chief Fin. Officer & Exec. V.P.--Harrah's Entertainment, Inc., Memphis, TN; *U.S. Public*, pg. 790
Reed, Darrell L., Chief Fin. Officer--AIL Systems Inc., Deer Park, NY; *U.S. Public*, pg. 556
Reed, Frederick, Chief Fin. Officer, Exec. V.P. & Gen. Counsel--Wendy's International Inc., Dublin, OH; *U.S. Public*, pg. 1754
Reed, J.M., Vice Chm. & Chief Fin. Officer--Union Camp Corporation, Wayne, NJ; *U.S. Public*, pg. 1665
Reed, Jim, Chief Fin. Officer--Sommer Metalcraft Corporation, Crawfordsville, IN; *U.S. Private*, pg. 1013
Reed, M. Scott, Chief Fin. Officer & Dir.-Fin. & Admin.--Grant Thornton LLP, Chicago, IL; *U.S. Private*, pg. 470
Reed, Robert, Chief Fin. Officer--Sutter Health, Sacramento, CA; *U.S. Private*, pg. 1057
Reed, Scott, Chief Fin. Officer--Branch Banking & Trust, Winston Salem, NC; *U.S. Public*, pg. 160
Reed, Scott E., Chief Fin. Officer & Sr. Exec. V.P.--BB&T Corporation, Winston Salem, NC; *U.S. Public*, pg. 159
Reed, W. Earl, III, Chief Fin. Officer & Exec. V.P.--Vencor, Inc., Louisville, KY; *U.S. Public*, pg. 1711
Reed, Ward, Chief Fin. Officer--Campus Point Realty Corporation, San Diego, CA; *U.S. Private*, pg. 976
Reed, Ward, Chief Fin. Officer & V.P.--Bellcore, Morristown, NJ; *U.S. Private*, pg. 976
Reeder, Glen, Chief Fin. Officer & V.P.--Maaco Enterprises Inc., King of Prussia, PA; *U.S. Private*, pg. 689
Reeder, Jeff, Chief Fin. Officer, V.P. & Treas.--Gerland Corp., Houston, TX; *U.S. Private*, pg. 449
Reedy, John D., Chief Fin. Officer & Treas.--Michael Foods, Inc., Minneapolis, MN; *U.S. Public*, pg. 1103
Reen, John G., Chief Fin. Officer & Exec. V.P.-Fin.--Caldor, Inc., Norwalk, CT; *U.S. Public*, pg. 292
Rees, Burton S., Chief Fin. Officer & V.P.--Salz Leathers, Inc., Santa Cruz, CA; *U.S. Private*, pg. 963
Reese, Ann N., Chief Fin. Officer & Exec. V.P.--ITT Corporation, New York, NY; *U.S. Public*, pg. 1512
Reese, Larry, Chief Fin. Officer & Sr. V.P.--ADT Automotive, Inc., Nashville, TN; *U.S. Public*, pg. 1648
Reese, Mark E., Chief Fin. Officer--EMC Insurance Group, Inc., Des Moines, IA; *U.S. Public*, pg. 545
Reeves, Philip, Chief Fin. Officer--American Grain & Related Industries, West Des Moines, IA; *U.S. Private*, pg. 55
Reeves, Philip, Chief Fin. Officer--Agri Financial Services Inc., West Des Moines, IA; *U.S. Private*, pg. 55
Reeves, Philip, Chief Fin. Officer--Agri Terminal Corporation, West Des Moines, IA; *U.S. Private*, pg. 55
Rega, David J., Chief Fin. Officer--Ensoniq, Malvern, PA; *U.S. Private*, pg. 377
Regan, Dennis, Chief Fin. Officer--Leo Burnett Limited, London, United Kingdom; *U.S. Private*, pg. 185
Regan, Timothy J., V.P. & Treas.--The Scoular Company, Omaha, NE; *U.S. Private*, pg. 977
Reger, Thomas G., Chief Fin. Officer & V.P.--Schwarz Paper Company, Morton Grove, IL; *U.S. Private*, pg. 974
Regli, Werner, Chief Fin. Officer--Panalpina Welttransport (Holding) AG, Binningen, Switzerland; *Int'l*, pg. 1022
Regnier, Claude, Sr. V.P.-Legal & Tax--Compagnie de Suez, Paris, France; *Int'l*, pg. 313
Rehkatch, A.F., Chief Fin. Officer & Sr. V.P.--A&W Food Services of Canada Inc., North Vancouver, Canada; *Int'l*, pg. 1
Reho, John W., Chief Fin. Officer--Wickland Oil Company, Inc., Sacramento, CA; *U.S. Private*, pg. 1175
Reho, John W., Chief Fin. Officer--Mock Resources, Inc., Irvine, CA; *U.S. Private*, pg. 1175
Reichenbach, Stephen D., Chief Fin. Officer & V.P.--Flow International Corporation, Kent, WA; *U.S. Public*, pg. 656
Reichenstein, Murray, Chief Fin. Officer & V.P.--Pitney Bowes Inc., Stamford, CT; *U.S. Public*, pg. 1303
Reichwein, John H., Chm. Bd.--Revcor, Inc., Carpentersville, IL; *U.S. Private*, pg. 925
Reid-Anderson, James, Chief Fin. Officer--The Haagen-Dazs Company Inc., Minneapolis, MN; *Int'l*, pg. 411
Reid, A.D., Chief Fin. Officer & V.P.-Fin.--Modine Manufacturing Company, Racine, WI; *U.S. Public*, pg. 1121
Reid, A.M., Chief Fin. Officer--Britax Vega Limited, Droitwich, United Kingdom; *Int'l*, pg. 216
Reid, Dal C., Chief Fin. Officer, V.P. & Treas.--Friona Industries, L.P., Amarillo, TX; *U.S. Private*, pg. 429
Reid, Donald G., Chief Fin. Officer & Sr. V.P.--George Weston Limited, Toronto, Canada; *Int'l*, pg. 1494
Reid, J. F., Chief Fin. Officer--WBB Pacific Clays Ltd., Singapore, Singapore; *Int'l*, pg. 1488
Reid, John, Chief Fin. Officer & Exec. V.P.-Fin.--BC Gas Inc., Vancouver, Canada; *Int'l*, pg. 114
Reid, John W., Exec. V.P. & Chief Fin. Officer--Ranco North America, Plain City, OH; *Int'l*, pg. 1243
Reidy, P.G., Sec. & Treas.--Australian Timken Proprietary Ltd., Ballarat, Australia; *U.S. Public*, pg. 1617
Reiland, David P., Chief Fin. Officer & Sr. V.P.--MagneTek, Inc., Nashville, TN; *U.S. Public*, pg. 1037
Reilly, Edward G., Chief Fin. Officer & V.P.--Co-Steel Inc., Toronto, Canada; *Int'l*, pg. 298
Reilly, Frank R., Chief Fin. Officer & Sr. V.P.--U.S. Industries, Inc., Iselin, NJ; *U.S. Public*, pg. 1683
Reilly, Jim, Chief Fin. Officer & V.P.-Fin.--B/E Aerospace Seating Products, Winston Salem, NC; *U.S. Public*, pg. 159
Reilly, Kevin W., Chief Fin. Officer--Mechanical Technology Inc.-Technology Grp.(Latham), Latham, NY; *U.S. Public*, pg. 1077
Reilly, Paul V., Pres. & Chief Oper. & Fin. Officer--Mail-Well Inc., Englewood, CO; *U.S. Public*, pg. 1037
Rein, Jack, Chief Fin. Officer--Veeco Instruments, Inc., Plainview, NY; *U.S. Public*, pg. 1711
Reinckens, Thomas E., Chief Fin. Officer & V.P.--Cache, Inc., New York, NY; *U.S. Public*, pg. 289
Reinebach, Thomas J., Chief Info. Officer & Sr. V.P.--Toys "R" Us, Inc., Paramus, NJ; *U.S. Public*, pg. 1626
Reiner, John, Controller--Parmalat New Atlanta Dairies, Atlanta, GA; *Int'l*, pg. 1023
Reinhard, J. Pedro, Chief Fin. Officer & Exec. V.P.-Fin.--The Dow Chemical Company, Midland, MI; *U.S. Public*, pg. 522
Reinhardt, J. Alec, Chief Fin. Officer & Exec. V.P.--Cooper Tire & Rubber Company, Findlay, OH; *U.S. Public*, pg. 445
Reinhold, Jeffrey A., Chief Fin. Officer, V.P. & Treas.--Checkpoint Systems Inc., Thorofare, NJ; *U.S. Public*, pg. 343
Reis, Morgan, Chief Fin. Officer--Omega Performance Group, Sausalito, CA; *U.S. Private*, pg. 816
Reisler, Barry, Chief Fin. Officer--Hunter Fan Company, Memphis, TN; *U.S. Private*, pg. 549
Reiss, Clifford E. II, Sec. & Asst. To Pres.--R.C.A. Rubber Company, Akron, OH; *U.S. Private*, pg. 902

Reitan, Gunnar, Chief Fin. Officer & Corp. Controller--Scandinavian Airlines System (SAS), Solna, Sweden; *Int'l*, pg. 1201
Reitano, Stevephen, Chief Fin. Officer--Metropolitan Transportation Authority, New York, NY; *U.S. Private*, pg. 739
Reitzoff, Cheryl, Chief Fin. Officer--Vesco Oil Corp., Southfield, MI; *U.S. Private*, pg. 1138
Rejzer, Eugene, Chief Fin. Officer--Snap-Tite, Inc., Erie, PA; *U.S. Private*, pg. 1010
Remar, Frank, Chief Fin. Officer--Dillon Companies, Inc., Hutchinson, KS; *U.S. Public*, pg. 967
Remedios, Robert T., Sr. V.P. & Cashier--SJNB Financial Corp., San Jose, CA; *U.S. Public*, pg. 1418
Remedios, Robert T., Sr. V.P. & Cashier--San Jose National Bank, San Jose, CA; *U.S. Public*, pg. 1418
Remes, Audrey, Chief Fin. Officer & Treas.--Initio, Inc., Carson City, NV; *U.S. Public*, pg. 879
Remeta, George R., Vice Chm., Chief Fin. Officer & Sec.--United Retail Group, Inc., Rochelle Park, NJ; *U.S. Public*, *pg. 1679*
Remillard, R.P., Chief Fin. Officer--Ottawa River Steel Co., Toledo, OH; *U.S. Public*, pg. 1095
Remington, David G., Chief Fin. Officer--Itron Inc., Spokane, WA; *U.S. Public*, pg. 914
Renaud, Paul G., Chief Fin. Officer, V.P.-Fin. & Sec.--CAE Inc., Toronto, Canada; *Int'l*, pg. 237
Renihan, Diane, Chief Fin Officer--Dolan Northwest LLC, Seattle, WA; *U.S. Private*, pg. 338
Renne, Paul F., Chief Fin. Officer & Exec. V.P.--H.J. Heinz Company, Pittsburgh, PA; *U.S. Public*, pg. 805
Rennocks, J.L., Chief Fin. Officer--British Steel Plc, London, United Kingdom; *Int'l*, pg. 220
Renz, Charles, Mgr.-Credit--Journal of Commerce, Inc., New York, NY; *Int'l*, pg. 1026
Renzow, R., Chief Fin. Officer--Kuehne & Nagel N.V., Rotterdam, Netherlands; *Int'l*, pg. 763
Repetti, Peter Q., Chief Fin. Officer & V.P.-Fin. & Admin.--Manugistics Group, Inc., Rockville, MD; *U.S. Public*, pg. 1042
Repp, Timothy J., Chief Fin. Officer & V.P.-Fin.--SBE, Inc., San Ramon, CA; *U.S. Public*, pg. 1416
Rescoe, Michael E., Chief Fin. Officer, Sr. V.P. & Treas.--PG&E Corporation, San Francisco, CA; *U.S. Public*, pg. 1240
Resnick, Donald W., Chief Fin. Officer--Ameriquest Technologies, Santa Ana, CA; *U.S. Public*, pg. 96
Respler, Bruce, Chief Fin. Officer--Rockbottom Stores, Inc., Lake Success, NY; *U.S. Private*, pg. 938
Restivo, Joe, Chief Fin. Officer--CASI-RUSCO Inc., Boca Raton, FL; *U.S. Private*, pg. 218
Retcher, M.F., Chief Fin. Officer & Treas.--Art Iron, Inc., Toledo, OH; *U.S. Private*, pg. 86
Retherford, John C., Chief Fin. Officer & Sr. V.P.-Fin.--Ag-Chem Equipment Co., Inc., Minnetonka, MN; *U.S. Public*, *pg. 6*
Retterath, William, Chief Fin. & Oper. Officer--Dakotah, Inc., Webster, SD; *U.S. Public*, pg. 477
Rettinger, Dale G., Chief Fin. Officer & Exec. V.P.--Petroleum Development Corporation, Bridgeport, WV; *U.S. Public*, pg. 1280
Retzlaff, Robert Z., Pres. & Chief Fin. Officer--Retzlaff Incorporated, San Rafael, CA; *U.S. Private*, pg. 925
Reuter, Wolsgang, Chief Fin. Officer--Deutsche Bahn, Frankfurt/Main, Germany; *Int'l*, pg. 401
Reuther, John W., Chief Fin. Officer & Sr. Exec. V.P.--Pioneer American Holding Company, Carbondale, PA; *U.S. Public*, pg. 1298
Rewolinski, Thomas, Chief Fin. Officer, Treas. & Sec.--Western States Envelope Co., Milwaukee, WI; *U.S. Private*, pg. 1168
Reybet-Degat, Hubert, Chief Fin. Officer--Editions Grasset-Fasquelle, Paris, France; *Int'l*, pg. 792
Reyelts, Paul C., V.P.-Fin.--The Valspar Corporation, Minneapolis, MN; *U.S. Public*, pg. 1707
Reyes, George, Chief Fin. Officer--Nestle Del Uruguay S.A., Montevideo, Uruguay; *Int'l*, pg. 921
Reyes, John, Chief Fin. Officer & V.P.--Public Storage, Inc., Glendale, CA; *U.S. Public*, pg. 1340
Reymann, Mary C., V.P.-Fin., Controller & Sec.--Flanigan's Enterprises, Inc., Fort Lauderdale, FL; *U.S. Public*, pg. 648
Reymann, T., Chief Fin. Officer--Siemens S.A., Bogota, Colombia; *Int'l*, pg. 1248
Reymond, Kevin L., Chief Fin. Officer & Sr. V.P.--Viacom Broadcasting Inc., New York, NY; *U.S. Private*, pg. 778
Reynolds, Craig A., Chief Fin. Officer, Exec. V.P. & Sec.--American Homestar Corporation, League City, TX; *U.S. Public*, pg. 83
Reynolds, Damien, Chief Fin. Officer--Banner Pharmacaps, Inc., High Point, NC; *Int'l*, pg. 1272
Reynolds, Fred, Chief Fin. Officer & Exec. V.P.--CBS, New York, NY; *U.S. Public*, pg. 273
Reynolds, Fredric G., Chief Fin. Officer & Exec. V.P.--CBS Corporation, Pittsburgh, PA; *U.S. Public*, pg. 273
Reynolds, James G., Chief Fin. Officer & Exec. V.P.--Health Care Property Investors, Inc., Newport Beach, CA; *U.S. Public*, pg. 801
Reynolds, James K., Chief Fin. Officer & V.P.-Fin.--Baker Commodities, Inc., Los Angeles, CA; *U.S. Private*, pg. 111
Reynolds, Joe, Chief Fin. Officer & Sr. V.P.--RE/MAX International, Inc., Englewood, CO; *U.S. Private*, pg. 912
Reynolds, Kenneth, Chief Fin. Officer--Ariel Corporation, Mount Vernon, OH; *U.S. Private*, pg. 81
Reynolds, Tom, Chief Fin. Officer--Mrs. Alison's Cookie Company, Saint Louis, MO; *U.S. Private*, pg. 765
Rhoads, Karen B., Chief Fin. Officer, V.P.-Fin. & Treas.--The Buckle, Inc., Kearney, NE; *U.S. Public*, pg. 267
Rhoads, Michael A., Chief Fin. Officer & Exec. V.P.--Blue Cross and Blue Shield of Oklahoma, Tulsa, OK; *U.S. Private*, pg. 151
Rhodes, Michael G., Chief Oper. Officer & Chief Fin. Officer--Modtech, Inc., Perris, CA; *U.S. Public*, pg. 1121
Rhodes,Robin, V.P.-Fin.--Decibel Products, Inc., Dallas, TX; *U.S. Public*, pg. 46
Rhude, Howard L., V.P.-Fin.--Sanders, A Lockheed Martin Company, Nashua, NH; *U.S. Public*, pg. 1008
Rhudy, Huey J., Treas. & Sec.--STRAFCO, Inc., San Antonio, TX; *U.S. Private*, pg. 1046
Ribbing, Christoffer, Chief Fin. Officer--Hagglunds Drives AB, Mellansel, Sweden; *Int'l*, pg. 670
Ribera, Rosendo Camats, Chief Fin. Officer--Agropecuaria de Guissona, S. Coop. Ltda., Guisona, Spain; *Int'l*, pg. 31
Ricciardi, Lucy, Chief Fin. Officer--Hyperion Software, Stamford, CT; *U.S. Public*, pg. 851
Rice, Andrew J., Chief Fin. Officer & Treas.--Nicholas Paper, Inc., Fitchburg, MA; *U.S. Private*, pg. 798
Rice, Craig, Chief Fin. Officer, V.P. & Treas.--First Central Financial Corporation, Lynbrook, NY; *U.S. Private*, pg. 406
Rice, David, Chief Fin. Officer--Universal Builders Supply, Inc., Mount Vernon, NY; *U.S. Private*, pg. 1126
Rice, Peter J., Chief Fin. Officer, V.P.-Fin. & Treas.--Media 100, Inc., Marlborough, MA; *U.S. Public*, pg. 1079
Rice, Philip, Chief Fin. Officer--Gallagher-Kaiser Corp., Detroit, MI; *U.S. Private*, pg. 438
Rice, Tom, Chief Fin. Officer--Steiner Turf Equipment Inc., Orrville, OH; *Int'l*, pg. 1088
Rich, Bradford R., Chief Fin. Officer, Exec. V.P. & Treas.--SkyWest Inc., Saint George, UT; *U.S. Public*, pg. 1476
Rich, Harry E., Chief Fin. Officer & Exec. V.P.--Brown Group, Inc., Saint Louis, MO; *U.S. Public*, pg. 262
Rich, Marvin P., Exec. V.P.-Strategic Plng., Fin. & Admin.--Kmart Corporation, Troy, MI; *U.S. Public*, pg. 963
Richardon, Brian, Chief Fin. Officer--American Color, Phoenix, AZ; *U.S. Public*, pg. 1133
Richards, George G., V.P.-Devel. & Fin.--Ragazzis, Inc., Raleigh, NC; *U.S. Private*, pg. 575
Richards, Martin, Chief Fin. Officer--Esselte Meto Pty. Ltd., Wantirna, Australia; *Int'l*, pg. 461
Richards, Philip W., Chief Fin. Officer, V.P. & Treas.--Dollar General Corporation, Nashville, TN; *U.S. Public*, pg. 515
Richards, Roger T., Chief Fin. Officer & Sec.--Granite Furniture Co., Salt Lake City, UT; *U.S. Private*, pg. 469
Richards, Ron, Controller--Sargento Foods Inc., Plymouth, WI; *U.S. Private*, pg. 966
Richardson, Dave M., Chief Fin. Officer & V.P.-Castings--Schlosser Forge Company, Rancho Cucamonga, CA; *U.S. Private*, pg. 970
Richardson, F. Shelton, Jr., Chief Fin. Officer & V.P.--Curtis Mathes Holding Corp., Dallas, TX; *U.S. Public*, pg. 1057
Richardson, John, Chief Fin. Officer--Ridley Canada Limited, Winnipeg, Canada; *Int'l*, pg. 1116
Richardson, John G., Pres., Chief Exec. & Chief Fin. Officer--Sugar Creek Packing Co., Washington Court House, OH; *U.S. Private*, pg. 1049
Richardson, Melanie, Chief Fin. Officer, Treas. & V.P.--Central Power and Light Company, Corpus Christi, TX; *U.S. Public*, pg. 324
Richardson, Paul, Grp. Fin. Dir.--WPP Group plc, London, United Kingdom; *Int'l*, pg. 1482
Richardson, Shelton, Chief Fin. Officer--Curtis Mathes Corporation, Dallas, TX; *U.S. Public*, pg. 1057
Richey, Ron, Chief Fin. Officer--Precision Plastics Inc., Columbia City, IN; *U.S. Private*, pg. 879
Richmon, Wayne M., Chief Fin. Officer, Exec. V.P. & Treas.--The Flight International Group, Inc., Newport News, VA; *U.S. Public*, pg. 654
Richmond-Watson, A.E., Deputy Chm. & Chief Fin. Officer--Morgan Grenfell Group PLC, London, United Kingdom; *Int'l*, pg. 405
Richmond, Barbara, Chief Fin. Officer--Whessoe Plc, Newton Aycliffe, United Kingdom; *Int'l*, pg. 1498
Richstone, Ellen B., Chief Fin. Officer & V.P.--Augat, Inc., Mansfield, MA; *U.S. Public*, pg. 1597
Richter, Hans, Treas.--Ervaco Gruppen AB, Stockholm, Sweden; *Int'l*, pg. 459
Richter, Joseph M., Chief Fin. Officer, Exec. V.P. & Treas.--The Somerset Group, Inc., Indianapolis, IN; *U.S. Public*, pg. 1484
Richter, Lyle H., Chief Fin. Officer, V.P., Treas. & Sec.--Fox Valley Corporation, Appleton, WI; *U.S. Private*, pg. 422
Rickard, David B., Chief Fin. Officer & Sr. V.P.--RJR Nabisco Holdings Corp., New York, NY; *U.S. Public*, pg. 1354
Ricker-Rosato, Debra A., V.P.-Fin.--Boston Acoustics, Inc., Peabody, MA; *U.S. Public*, pg. 246
Ricketts, Barrie, Chief Fin. Officer & Sr. V.P.--Ball Horticultural Company, West Chicago, IL; *U.S. Private*, pg. 112
Ricklin, Larry, Chief Fin. Officer--The Kaempfer Company, Investment Builders, Washington, DC; *U.S. Private*, pg. 604
Rickling, Penny, Chief Fin. Officer & V.P.--Howden Fluid Systems, Santa Barbara, CA; *U.S. Public*, pg. 1045
Riddell, J.H., Chief Fin. Officer--Hagemeyer N.V., Naarden, Netherlands; *Int'l*, pg. 487
Riddick, Frank A., III, Chief Fin. Officer & Sr. V.P.--Armstrong World Industries, Inc., Lancaster, PA; *U.S. Public*, pg. 131
Riddle, Larry D., Treas. & Controller--Continental Western Insurance Company, Urbandale, IA; *U.S. Public*, pg. 215
Rideout, Stanton K., Chief Fin. Officer & V.P.--Phelps Dodge Intl. Corp., Coral Gables, FL; *U.S. Public*, pg. 1286
Ridgway, Ronald, Sr. V.P.-Fin.--St. Louis Post-Dispatch, Saint Louis, MO; *U.S. Public*, pg. 1343
Ridgway, Ronald H., Sr. V.P.-Fin.--Pulitzer Publishing Company, Saint Louis, MO; *U.S. Public*, pg. 1343
Ridsdale, M.R., Chief Fin. Officer--Email Limited, Waterloo, Australia; *Int'l*, pg. 450
Riecke, Robert, Chief Fin. Officer, Treas. & Sec.--Walle Corporation, Harahan, LA; *U.S. Private*, pg. 1148
Riedel, Gregory, Chief Fin. Officer & V.P.-Fin.--Galileo Corp., Sturbridge, MA; *U.S. Public*, pg. 698
Rieger, James, Chief Fin. Officer & Sr. V.P.--Ponderosa Steakhouse, Dallas, TX; *U.S. Private*, pg. 736
Riegler, William J., Chief Fin. Officer & V.P.--Linbeck Construction Corp, Houston, TX; *U.S. Private*, pg. 667
Riegler, William J., Chief Fin. Officer--LTB, Houston, TX; *U.S. Private*, pg. 668
Riesenbeck, Ronald, Chief Fin. Officer & V.P.-Fin.--Save Mart Supermarkets, Modesto, CA; *U.S. Private*, pg. 968
Rieske, Gordon, Exec. V.P. & Chief Fin. Officer--Ventura Foods LLC, City of Industry, CA; *Int'l*, pg. 879
Rietz, Ake, Chief Fin. Officer & Exec. V.P.--Svenska Cellulosa Aktiebolaget (SCA), Stockholm, Sweden; *Int'l*, pg. 1326
Rife, Teri, Treas. & Controller--Casa Bonita, Inc., Carrollton, TX; *U.S. Public*, pg. 278
Rigazio, Steven W., Chief Fin. Officer, V.P.-Fin. & Treas.--Nevada Power Company, Las Vegas, NV; *U.S. Public*, pg. 1169
Riggs, Sidney W., Chm. Bd., Sec. & Treas.--Somerset Welding & Steel, Inc., Somerset, PA; *U.S. Private*, pg. 930
Rigsbee, Mike, Chief Fin. Officer--Fournier Furniture, Saint Paul, VA; *U.S. Private*, pg. 422
Riiser, Fan, Dir.-Fin.--Union Bank of Norway, Oslo, Norway; *Int'l*, pg. 1439
Riley, Charles R., Sr. V.P.-Fin. & Mngmt.--Lockheed Martin Electronic Defense Systems, Yonkers, NY; *U.S. Public*, pg. 1008
Riley, J. Michael, Chief Fin. Officer & V.P.--AGL Resources, Atlanta, GA; *U.S. Public*, pg. 6
Riley, James B., Chief Fin. Officer & Exec. V.P.--Republic Engineered Steels, Inc., Massillon, OH; *U.S. Public*, pg. 1378
Riley, Kevin, Chief Fin. Officer--Information Systems Division, San Diego, CA; *U.S. Public*, pg. 1062
Riley, Michael, Chief Fin. Officer & Controller--Wellman Dynamics Corp., Creston, IA; *U.S. Public*, pg. 612
Riley, P.T., Chief Fin. Officer--King Press Corporation, Joplin, MO; *U.S. Public*, pg. 1341
Riley, Robin, Chief Fin. Officer--The Faxon Company, Inc., Westwood, MA; *Int'l*, pg. 385
Riley, William F., III, Chief Fin. Officer & Exec V.P.--Swift Transportation Co., Sparks, NV; *U.S. Public*, pg. 1543
Ringo, Thomas M., Chief Fin. Officer & V.P.-Fin.--Pope Resources, Poulsbo, WA; *U.S. Public*, pg. 1317
Ringsberg, Marten, Chief Fin. Officer & V.P.-Fin.--Trelleborg YSH, Inc., South Haven, MI; *Int'l*, pg. 1422
Ringstead, Bent, Chief Fin. Officer--Scan Globe A/S, Havdrup, Denmark; *U.S. Private*, pg. 923
Rinhart, Boje, Chief Fin. Officer--Olicom A/S, Lyngby, Denmark; *Int'l*, pg. 1001
Rinker, Corey, Chief Fin. Officer--Intellisource, Fairfield, CT; *U.S. Public*, pg. 1425
Riopel, Robert J., Chief Fin. Officer, V.P.-Fin. & Treas.--Phoenix Technologies Ltd., San Jose, CA; *U.S. Public*, pg. 1292
Riordan, David, Chief Fin. Officer & V.P.--Senco Products, Inc., Cincinnati, OH; *U.S. Private*, pg. 984
Riordan, S., Chief Fin. Officer--ABG Allgemeine Baumaschinen-Gesellschaft mbH, Hameln, Germany; *U.S. Public*, pg. 877
Ripley, James W., Chief Fin. Officer & V.P.-Fin.--Corn Products International, Inc., Bedford Park, IL; *U.S. Public*, pg. 447
Ripp, Peter, Chief Fin. Officer & Sr. V.P.--Northville Industries Corp., Melville, NY; *U.S. Private*, pg. 806
Risberg, Gun, Chief Fin. Officer--Nielsen Design AB, Sollentuna, Sweden; *Int'l*, pg. 459
Risley, David M., Chief Fin. Officer & V.P.-Fin.--Aeroquip-Vickers, Inc., Maumee, OH; *U.S. Public*, pg. 24
Rissman, Dennis, Chief Fin. Officer & Controller--Bresler's Industries, Inc., Des Plaines, IL; *Int'l*, pg. 1520
Ritch, David, Chief Fin. Officer & Exec. V.P.--Republic Beverage Company, Houston, TX; *U.S. Private*, pg. 149
Ritch, David, Chief Fin. Officer & Exec. V.P.--Republic Beverage Co., Dallas, TX; *U.S. Private*, pg. 150
Ritch, Jim, Deputy Superintendent-Fin. & Admin.--Seattle City Light, Seattle, WA; *U.S. Private*, pg. 979
Ritchason, Marvin, Chief Exec. Officer--Ray-Carroll County Grain Co-op, Richmond, MO; *U.S. Private*, pg. 911
Ritchie, Lewis, Chief Fin. Officer & Exec. V.P.-Fin. & Admin.--Cinram Ltd., Scarborough, Canada; *Int'l*, pg. 293
Ritondaro, Gary H., Chief Fin. Officer & V.P.--Ferro Corporation, Cleveland, OH; *U.S. Public*, pg. 618
Ritschdorff, Michael W., Chief Fin. Officer & V.P.-Fin.--Dukane Corporation, Saint Charles, IL; *U.S. Private*, pg. 345
Ritter, Alan J., Chief Fin. Officer--Audits & Surveys Worldwide, New York, NY; *U.S. Public*, pg. 147
Ritter, Alfred F., Jr., Chief Fin. Officer & Exec. V.P.--Landmark Communications, Inc., Norfolk, VA; *U.S. Private*, pg. 647
Ritter, Robert T., Chief Fin. Officer--WLR Foods, Inc., Timberville, VA; *U.S. Public*, pg. 1727
Rittmann, Ron, V.P.-Fin. & Admin.--Kathabar Incorporated, Somerset, NJ; *U.S. Private*, pg. 609
Riveri, Leo, Chief Fin. Officer--Banca Agricola Mantovana SARL, Mantova, Italy; *Int'l*, pg. 135
Roach, Ed, Chief Fin. Officer, Exec. V.P. & Treas.--Dominion Resources, Inc., Richmond, VA; *U.S. Public*, pg. 516
Robards, Thomas F., Chief Fin. Officer & Treas.--Republic New York Corporation, New York, NY; *U.S. Public*, pg. 1380
Robataille, Pierre, Chief Fin. Officer & Exec. V.P.--SNC-Lavalin Group Inc., Montreal, Canada; *Int'l*, pg. 1161
Robbins, Charlie, Treas.--Robbins Manufacturing Company, Tampa, FL; *U.S. Private*, pg. 935
Robbins, Elliott C., Chief Fin. Officer, Sr. V.P. & Treas.--MYR Group Inc., Rolling Meadows, IL; *U.S. Public*, pg. 1029
Robbins, Elliott C., Chief Fin. Officer--Hawkeye Construction, Inc., Troutdale, OR; *U.S. Public*, pg. 1029

Robbins, Jim, Chief Fin. Officer--South Trust Bank of Georgia, Atlanta, GA; *U.S. Public*, pg. 1492

Robbins, Lee A., Chief Fin. Officer & V.P.--Medical Manager Corporation, Tampa, FL; *U.S. Public*, pg. 1080

Robbinson, R. Courtney, Chief Fin. Officer & Sec.--Robinson Lumber Company, New Orleans, LA; *U.S. Private*, pg. 936

Roberson, E.S., Chief Fin. Officer--Conwood Company L.P., Memphis, TN; *U.S. Private*, pg. 272

Robert, Elizabeth, Chief Fin. Officer & Treas.--The Vermont Teddy Bear Company, Inc., Shelburne, VT; *U.S. Public*, pg. 1716

Robert, Richard, Chief Fin. Officer--Midcoast Energy Resources, Inc., Houston, TX; *U.S. Public*, pg. 1109

Roberto, Vinscenti, Chief Fin. Officer--D. Lazzaroni & C. S.p.A., Saronno, Italy; *Int'l*, pg. 804

Roberts, B.K., Chief Fin. Officer--Siemens Ltd., Richmond, Australia; *Int'l*, pg. 1247

Roberts, David J., Vice Chm. & Chief Fin. Officer--Foster Wheeler Corporation, Clinton, NJ; *U.S. Public*, pg. 676

Roberts, Gary, Chief Fin. Officer, Sr. V.P.-Admin. & Sec.--Sierracin Corporation, Sylmar, CA; *U.S. Private*, pg. 999

Roberts, Gary L., Chief Fin. Officer, V.P. & Treas.--A.P. Green Industries, Inc., Mexico, MO; *U.S. Public*, pg. 761

Roberts, I.R., Treas.--Monticello Drug Co., Jacksonville, FL; *U.S. Private*, pg. 759

Roberts, John, Chief Fin. Officer--Neste Chemicals UK Ltd., Stockport, United Kingdom; *Int'l*, pg. 914

Roberts, Linda, Exec. Sec.--Keystone Consolidated Industries, Inc., Dallas, TX; *U.S. Public*, pg. 955

Roberts, P., Chief Fin. Officer--Smythson of Bond Street, London, United Kingdom; *Int'l*, pg. 707

Roberts, W.K., Chief Gen. Mgr.-Fin. & Chief Actuary--Australian Mutual Provident, Sydney, Australia; *Int'l*, pg. 100

Roberts, William E., Chief Fin. Officer, V.P., Controller & Treas.--Lone Star Industries, Inc., Stamford, CT; *U.S. Public*, pg. 1012

Roberts, William G., Chief Fin. Officer--Dexter Shoe Company, Dexter, ME; *U.S. Public*, pg. 217

Robertson, Alastair J., Chief Fin. Officer, V.P. & Treas.--Nowsco Well Service Ltd., Calgary, Canada; *Int'l*, pg. 989

Robertson, Gordon M., Chief Fin. Officer & V.P.--Fair Grounds Corporation, New Orleans, LA; *U.S. Public*, pg. 609

Robertson, I. Howard, Jr., Chief Fin. Officer & Treas.--Robertson's Auto Salvage, Wareham, MA; *U.S. Private*, pg. 936

Robertson, Joseph W., Chief Fin. Officer & Exec. V.P.--Weingarten Realty Investors, Houston, TX; *U.S. Public*, pg. 1751

Robertson, Mary Jane, Chief Fin. Officer & Sr. V.P.--Capsure Holdings Corp., Chicago, IL; *U.S. Public*, pg. 303

Robey, Randall, Chief Fin. Officer & Sr. V.P.--The Annapolis Banking & Trust Co., Annapolis, MD; *U.S. Public*, pg. 1088

Robins, Cheryl, Chief Fin. Officer--Cohn & Wells, New York, NY; *Int'l*, pg. 601

Robins, R. Steven, Chief Fin. Officer, Treas. & Sec--Builder Marts of America, Inc., Greenville, SC; *U.S. Private*, pg. 179

Robinson, Charles K., Jr., Pres. & Treas.--Swayne Robinson & Company, Richmond, IN; *U.S. Private*, pg. 936

Robinson, E. Montgomery, Pres. & Treas.--Top Flight, Inc., Chattanooga, TN; *U.S. Private*, pg. 1091

Robinson, Gary, Chief Fin. Officer--Sally Beauty Company, Inc., Denton, TX; *U.S. Public*, pg. 38

Robinson, H. Ivens, Pres. & Chief Fin. Officer--Robinson Lumber & Export Company, New Orleans, LA; *U.S. Private*, pg. 936

Robinson, Jack, Chief Fin. Officer--Sara Lee Bakery, Chicago, IL; *U.S. Public*, pg. 1433

Robinson, Jerry D., Chief Fin. Officer, V.P. & Treas.--SFA, Inc., Hyattsville, MD; *U.S. Private*, pg. 956

Robinson, Joseph A., Chief Fin. Officer, Sr. V.P., Treas. & Sec.--Excel Industries, Inc., Elkhart, IN; *U.S. Public*, pg. 598

Robinson, Warren L., Chief Fin. Officer, V.P. & Treas.--MDU Resources Group, Inc., Bismarck, ND; *U.S. Public*, pg. 1025

Robinson, Wilburn, Chief Fin. Officer & Exec. V.P.--Omniflight, Inc., Dallas, TX; *U.S. Private*, pg. 816

Robinson, Wilburn, Chief Fin. Officer & Exec. V.P.--Omniflight Helicopters, Inc., Dallas, TX; *U.S. Private*, pg. 817

Robinson, William S., Jr., Chief Fin. Officer--Production Operators, Inc., Houston, TX; *U.S. Public*, pg. 298

Robles, Josue, Jr., Chief Fin. Officer, Sr. V.P. & Treas.--USAA (United Services Automobile Association), San Antonio, TX; *U.S. Private*, pg. 1114

Robles, Ricardo, Pres. & Chief Fin. Officer--La Reina, Inc., Los Angeles, CA; *U.S. Private*, pg. 640

Robson, Donald, Chief Fin. Officer, Treas. & Sec.--Coldwater Creek, Sandpoint, ID; *U.S. Public*, pg. 396

Robson, Donald S., Chief Fin. Officer & V.P.--Getchell Gold Corp., Englewood, CO; *U.S. Public*, pg. 740

Rocca, Michael, Chief Fin. Officer--Mallinckrodt Inc., Saint Louis, MO; *U.S. Public*, pg. 1039

Rocca, Michael A., Chief Fin. Officer & Sr. V.P.--Mallinckrodt Inc., Saint Louis, MO; *U.S. Public*, pg. 1039

Roche, Arthur D., Chief Fin. Officer & Exec. V.P.--Vicon Industries, Inc., Hauppauge, NY; *U.S. Public*, pg. 1719

Roche, Kevin, Chief Fin. Officer--Barron's The Dow Jones Business & Financial Weekly, New York, NY; *U.S. Public*, pg. 524

Roche, Kevin, V.P. & Chief Fin. Officer-Dow Jones--The Wall Street Journal, New York, NY; *U.S. Public*, pg. 524

Roche, Kevin J., Chief Fin. Officer & V.P.--Dow Jones & Company, Inc., New York, NY; *U.S. Public*, pg. 524

Rocheleau, Michael, Chief Fin. Officer & Exec. V.P.--PTA Corporation, Oxford, CT; *U.S. Private*, pg. 828

Rock, W.C., Chief Fin. Officer--Quanta SecurSystems, Inc., Hanover, MD; *U.S. Public*, pg. 420

Rock, William C., Chief Fin. Officer--CompuDyne Corporation, Willimantic, CT; *U.S. Public*, pg. 419

Rockefeller, Herman, Chief Fin. Officer--Brierley Investments Limited, Wellington, New Zealand; *Int'l*, pg. 215

Rockenbach, Michael J., Acting Chief Fin. Officer, V.P.-Fin. & Sec.--Emulex Corporation, Costa Mesa, CA; *U.S. Public*, pg. 579

Rockom, Joseph W., Chief Fin. Officer & V.P.-Fin. & Admin.--IKOS Systems, Inc., Cupertino, CA; *U.S. Public*, pg. 864

Roczera, Rudolph R., Chief Fin. Officer--Pacer Infotec Inc., Billerica, MA; *U.S. Private*, pg. 830

Roddy, Bob, Chief Fin. Officer & V.P.--Sun Data Inc., Norcross, GA; *U.S. Private*, pg. 1050

Roderick, Richard, Chief Fin. Officer & V.P.-Real Estate--Dead River Company, Portland, ME; *U.S. Private*, pg. 318

Rodert, Per, Chief Fin. Officer--Munksjo AB, Jonkoping, Sweden; *Int'l*, pg. 1423

Rodler, John, Chief Fin. Officer, Sr. V.P., Treas. & Sec.--Folger Nolan Fleming Douglas, Washington, DC; *U.S. Private*, pg. 416

Rodnar, M., Chief Fin. Officer--Duraloy Technologies, Scottdale, PA; *U.S. Private*, pg. 839

Rodrigo Trevino, Medina, Chief Fin. Officer--Cemex, S.A. de C.V., Monterrey, Mexico; *Int'l*, pg. 278

Rodrigues, Joseph, Chief Fin. Officer, Exec. V.P. & Treas.--Seaboard Corporation, Shawnee Mission, KS; *U.S. Public*, pg. 1448

Rodriguez, Juana D., Treas.--Mason Distributors, Inc., Hialeah, FL; *U.S. Private*, pg. 712

Roe, Christian, Chief Fin. Officer--Discount Tire, Scottsdale, AZ; *U.S. Private*, pg. 334

Roeck, Thomas J., Jr., Chief Fin. Officer & Sr. V.P.-Fin.--Delta Air Lines, Inc., Atlanta, GA; *U.S. Public*, pg. 497

Roedl, Suzanne, V.P.-Fin.--Condor D.C. Power Supplies Inc., Oxnard, CA; *U.S. Public*, pg. 1419

Roell, Stephen A., Chief Fin. Officer & V.P.--Johnson Controls, Inc., Milwaukee, WI; *U.S. Public*, pg. 932

Roell, Stephen A., Chief Fin. Officer & V.P.--Johnson Controls, Inc., Controls Group, Milwaukee, WI; *U.S. Public*, pg. 932

Roesler, Deborah, Chief Fin. Officer--Piper Jaffray Companies, Inc., Minneapolis, MN; *U.S. Public*, pg. 1300

Roesslein, Charles, V.P., Chief Fin. Officer & Treas.--Southwestern Bell Telephone Co., Saint Louis, MO; *U.S.* Public, pg. 1416

Rogalin, Peter, Chief Fin. Officer, V.P. & Treas.--Roberts Pharmaceutical Corporation, Eatontown, NJ; *U.S. Public*, *pg. 1393*

Rogalin, Peter, Chief Fin. Officer, V.P. & Treas.--VRG International, Inc., Eatontown, NJ; *U.S. Public*, pg. 1393

Rogalin, Peter, Chief Fin. Officer, V.P. & Treas.--Roberts Laboratories, Inc., Eatontown, NJ; *U.S. Public*, pg. 1393

Rogalin, Peter, Chief Fin. Officer, V.P. & Treas.--Monmouth Pharmaceutical, Ltd., Guildford, United Kingdom; *U.S. Public*, pg. 1394

Rogalin, Peter, Chief Fin. Officer, V.P. & Treas.--Roberts Pharmaceutical of Canada, Oakville, Canada; *U.S. Public*, pg. 1394

Rogan, R. Eric, Chief Fin. Officer & Exec. V.P.--Stelco Inc., Hamilton, Canada; *Int'l*, pg. 1299

Rogers, C.C.B., Chief Fin. Officer--Comet, Rickmansworth, United Kingdom; *Int'l*, pg. 733

Rogers, Deborah R., V.P. & Cashier--M & I Bank of Menomonee Falls, Menomonee Falls, WI; *U.S. Public*, pg. 1050

Rogers, Dorothy M., Sr. V.P.-Fin. Prod. Group--The Russell National Bank, Lewistown, PA; *U.S. Public*, pg. 1222

Rogers, Edward F., Chief Fin. Officer--IBM Personal Computer Company, Somers, NY; *U.S. Public*, pg. 896

Rogers, Floyd D., Chief Fin. Officer & V.P.-Fin.--Steck-Vaughn Publishing Corporation, Austin, TX; *U.S. Public*, pg. 784

Rogers, G.R., Chief Fin. Officer, Exec. V.P. & Treas.--Alexander & Baldwin, Inc., Honolulu, HI; *U.S. Public*, pg. 39

Rogers, Jack, Chief Fin. Officer--Camelot Music, Inc., Canton, OH; *U.S. Private*, pg. 203

Rogers, James P., Chief Fin. Officer & Sr. V.P.--GAF Corporation, Wayne, NJ; *U.S. Private*, pg. 433

Rogers, James P., Chief Fin. Officer & Sr. V.P.--G Industries Corporation, Wilmington, DE; *U.S. Private*, pg. 433

Rogers, James P., Chief Fin. Officer & Sr. V.P.--GAF Materials Corporation, Wayne, NJ; *U.S. Private*, pg. 433

Rogers, James P., Chief Fin. Officer & Sr. V.P.--Building Materials Corporation of America, Wayne, NJ; *U.S. Private*, pg. 433

Rogers, James P., Chief Fin. Officer & Sr. V.P.--ISP Holdings, Inc., Wayne, NJ; *U.S. Public*, pg. 858

Rogers, John J., Jr., Chief Fin. Officer & V.P.-Fin. & Admin.--Cognex Corporation, Natick, MA; *U.S. Public*, pg. 394

Rogers, Margie E., Chief Fin. Officer, V.P., Treas. & Sec.--Team, Inc., Alvin, TX; *U.S. Public*, pg. 1562

Rogers, Nigel, Chief Fin. Officer & Sec.--Stadium Limited, Hartlepool, United Kingdom; *Int'l*, pg. 1293

Rogers, Ray, Chief Fin. Officer & V.P.-Fin.--BMC Industries, Inc., Minneapolis, MN; *U.S. Public*, pg. 162

Rogers, Reba, Chief Fin. Officer--Guarantee National Insurance Company, Englewood, CO; *U.S. Public*, pg. 1231

Rogliano, Gary R., Chief Fin. Officer & Sr. V.P.--The Pittston Company, Glen Allen, VA; *U.S. Public*, pg. 1305

Rogliano, Gary R., Chief Fin. Officer--BAX Global, Irvine, CA; *U.S. Public*, pg. 1305

Rohde, Stephen L., Chief Fin. Officer & V.P.-Fin. & Admin.--MSI Insurance Companies, Arden Hills, MN; *U.S. Private*, *pg. 688*

Roher, Charles, Pres. Chief Exec. & Fin. Officer--C. Roher Inc., Fleetwood, PA; *U.S. Private*, pg. 940

Rohloff, William M., Chief Fin. Officer, Treas. & Sec.--Stebbins Engineering & Mfg. Co., Watertown, NY; *U.S. Private*, pg. 1037

Rohr-Dralle, Randi, Chief Fin. Officer--GB Electrical, Inc., Milwaukee, WI; *U.S. Public*, pg. 124

Rohr, Raymond C., Treas.--Russell Harrington Cutlery Inc., Southbridge, MA; *U.S. Private*, pg. 551

Rohr, Robert E., Chief Fin. Officer--Chempower, Inc., Akron, OH; *Int'l*, pg. 74

Rohrbacker, Raymond B., Chief Fin. Officer--Nooter Corporation, Saint Louis, MO; *U.S. Private*, pg. 801

Rohrer, Philip L., Jr., Chief Fin. Officer & V.P.--BioWhittaker, Inc., Walkersville, MD; *U.S. Public*, pg. 297

Roldan, Simeon Y., Chief Fin. Officer & Controller--King Wire Inc., North Chicago, IL; *U.S. Private*, pg. 621

Rollins, O.R., Chief Fin. Officer & V.P.--Logo 7, Inc., Indianapolis, IN; *U.S. Public*, pg. 1644

Rollins, O.R., Chief Fin. Officer--Loga Athletic/Headwear Inc., Mattapoisett, MA; *U.S. Public*, pg. 1644

Rollins, Royce L., Chief Fin. Officer & Exec. V.P.--Fleishman-Hillard Inc., Saint Louis, MO; *U.S. Private*, pg. 411

Rollins, Royce L., Chief Fin. Officer--Fleishman-Hillard, Saint Louis, MO; *U.S. Private*, pg. 411

Roloff, Kirk D., Chief Fin. Officer & Sr. V.P.--Monticello Management Co., San Diego, CA; *U.S. Private*, pg. 759

Roman, Peter J., Chief Fin. Officer & V.P.--Unifab International Inc., New Iberia, LA; *U.S. Public*, pg. 1665

Romanczuk, Wayne, Chief Fin. Officer & Treas.--Perfecseal Company, Philadelphia, PA; *U.S. Public*, pg. 210

Romaneiro, Jorge M., Chief Fin. Officer--Janssen Cilag Brazil, Sao Paulo, Brazil; *U.S. Public*, pg. 929

Romanowski, Thomas S., Chief Fin. Officer & V.P.--Central Illinois Light Company, Peoria, IL; *U.S. Public*, pg. 367

Romenesko, Timothy J., Chief Fin. Officer, V.P. & Treas.--AAR Corp., Wood Dale, IL; *U.S. Public*, pg. 1

Romeril, Barry D., Chief Fin. Officer & Exec. V.P.--Xerox Corporation, Stamford, CT; *U.S. Public*, pg. 1783

Romig, Michael V., Chief Fin. Officer & V.P.--Marine Construction & Design Co., Seattle, WA; *U.S. Private*, pg. 703

Rone, Charles C., Jr., Chief Fin. Officer, V.P.-Fin. & Treas.--Loxcreen Company, West Columbia, SC; *U.S. Private*, pg. 679

Roof, Donald L., Chief Fin. Officer & Sr. V.P.-Finance--J.H. Heafner Co. Inc., Lincolnton, NC; *U.S. Private*, pg. 514

Roohan, Edward C., Chief Fin. Officer--Castle & Cooke Inc., Los Angeles, CA; *U.S. Public*, pg. 313

Rooks, Charles, Chief Fin. Officer--Aero Systems Engineering Inc., Saint Paul, MN; *Int'l*, pg. 276

Roome, L.B., Chief Fin. Officer--Sasolchem, Rosebank, South Africa; *Int'l*, pg. 1196

Roos, Arthur W., V.P. & Treas.--Niagara Mohawk Power Corporation, Syracuse, NY; *U.S. Public*, pg. 1181

Root, Timothy L., Chief Fin. Officer & V.P.-Fin.--Maclean Hunter Publishing Ltd., Toronto, Canada; *Int'l*, pg. 1123

Roper, Hartwell H., Chief Fin. Officer & V.P.--Universal Corporation, Richmond, VA; *U.S. Public*, pg. 1694

Roper, Hartwell H., Chief Fin. Officer & Exec. V.P.--Universal Leaf Tobacco Company, Inc., Richmond, VA; *U.S. Public*, pg. 1694

Roper, W.A., Jr., Chief Fin. Officer--Science Applications International Corp., San Diego, CA; *U.S. Private*, pg. 975

Ros, Carl Wilhelm, Chief Fin. Officer & Exec. V.P.--Telefonaktiebolaget LM Ericsson, Stockholm, Sweden; *Int'l*, pg. 1363

Rosa, Tony, Chief Fin. Officer--Penguin Air Conditioning Corp., Brooklyn, NY; *U.S. Public*, pg. 572

Rose, David, Chief Fin. Officer & Exec. V.P.--Environmental Industries, Inc., Calabasas, CA; *U.S. Private*, pg. 378

Rose, David, Chief Fin. Officer--Letraset UK, London, United Kingdom; *Int'l*, pg. 462

Rose, Estelle, Chief Fin. Officer--Kobra International Ltd, New York, NY; *U.S. Private*, pg. 628

Rose, Howard E., Chief Fin. Officer--Blyth Industries, Greenwich, CT; *U.S. Public*, pg. 239

Rose, Michael E., Chief Fin. Officer & Sr. V.P.-Fin.--Anadarko Petroleum Corporation, Houston, TX; *U.S. Public*, pg. 107

Rose, Richard, Chief Fin. Officer--Netrix, Corp., Herndon, VA; *U.S. Private*, pg. 791

Rose, Thomas F., Chief Fin. Officer & V.P.--A.M. Todd Company, Kalamazoo, MI; *U.S. Private*, pg. 1089

Rose, Wayne M., Chief Fin. Officer & V.P.-Fin. & Corp. Devel.--Quanex Corporation, Houston, TX; *U.S. Public*, pg. 1349

Rosebery, Richard J., Vice Chm., Chief Fin. & Admin. Officer & Treas.--Elcor Corporation, Dallas, TX; *U.S. Public*, pg. 567

Rosemann, Harold, Chief Fin. Officer--Cookie Tree Inc., Salt Lake City, UT; *U.S. Private*, pg. 273

Rosen, Aaron, Chief Fin. Officer & V.P.--McKinney & McKinney Advertising, Redondo Beach, CA; *U.S. Private*, *pg. 723*

Rosen, Barry A., Chief Fin. Officer, V.P. & Treas.--Schnitzer Steel Industries, Inc., Portland, OR; *U.S. Public*, pg. 1439

Rosen, Florence, Exec. V.P.--Rosen Associates Management Corp., Jericho, NY; *U.S. Private*, pg. 945

Rosen, Martin, Chief Fin. Officer--BLH Electronics, Inc., Canton, MA; *Int'l*, pg. 1289

Rosenbaum, Stanley, Chief Fin. Officer--Nice-Pak Products, Inc., Orangeburg, NY; *U.S. Private*, pg. 798

Rosenberg, Philip G., Chief Fin. Officer--J. Baker, Inc., Canton, MA; *U.S. Public*, pg. 167

Rosenberg, Philip G., Chief Fin. Officer, Exec. V.P. & Asst. Sec.--Casual Male, Inc., Hyde Park, MA; *U.S. Public*, pg. 168

Rosenberg, Steven, Chief Fin. Officer--Forest Electric Corp., New York, NY; *U.S. Public*, pg. 571

Rosenberger, Fred R., V.P.-Fin.--Hutchens Industries Inc., Springfield, MO; *U.S. Private*, pg. 550

Rosenblatt, Robert J., Chief Fin. Officer & Exec. V.P.--USA Networks, Inc., Saint Petersburg, FL; *U.S. Public*, pg. 1685

Rosenfeld, Richard S., Chief Fin. Officer, V.P. & Treas.--Barringer Technologies Inc., New Providence, NJ; *U.S. Public*, pg. 191
Rosenfeld, Robert, Chief Fin. Officer & V.P.--Barton Press, Inc., West Orange, NJ; *U.S. Private*, pg. 120
Rosenfield, Mark, Chief Fin. Officer--Craftmatic Industries, Inc., Trevose, PA; *U.S. Private*, pg. 284
Rosengarten, Felix J., Chief Fin. Officer--Information Storage Devices, San Jose, CA; *U.S. Public*, pg. 876
Rosenkranz, Bob, Chief Fin. Officer & V.P.-Fin.--Alloy Products Corp, Waukesha, WI; *U.S. Private*, pg. 42
Rosenstein, Earl, Chief Fin. Officer--Ronco, Inventions. LLC, Chatsworth, CA; *U.S. Private*, pg. 943
Rosenstein, Stuart B., Chief Fin. Officer, Sr. V.P. & Treas.--Pricellular Corporation, White Plains, NY; *U.S. Public*, pg. 1324
Rosenthal, David, Chief Fin. Officer, V.P.-Fin. & Treas.--LeaRonal, Inc., Freeport, NY; *U.S. Public*, pg. 982
Rosenthal, Paul, Chief Fin. Officer--Lindenmeyr Munroe, Purchase, NY; *U.S. Private*, pg. 224
Rosenthal, Paul S., Chief Fin. Officer--Lindenmeyr Munroe, North Reading, MA; *U.S. Private*, pg. 224
Rosenthal, Robert, Chief Fin. Officer--Union Pen Company, Greenwich, CT; *U.S. Private*, pg. 1119
Rosholt, Robert A., Chief Fin. Officer & Exec. V.P.--First Chicago NBD Corporation, Chicago, IL; *U.S. Public*, pg. 627
Rosilier, Glenn D., Chief Fin. Officer & Sr. V.P.--Central and South West Corporation, Dallas, TX; *U.S. Public*, pg. 324
Rosilier, Glenn D., Chief Fin. Officer & Sr. V.P.--Central and South West Services, Inc., Dallas, TX; *U.S. Public*, pg. 324
Rosino, James, Chief Fin. Officer & V.P.--Meridian National Corporation, Toledo, OH; *U.S. Public*, pg. 1095
Rosler, Joachim, Chief Oper. & Chief Fin. Officer--Gruner + Jahr USA Publishing, Inc., New York, NY; *Int'l*, pg. 190
Ross, Cam, Chief Fin. Officer--Miles Kimball Company, Oshkosh, WI; *U.S. Private*, pg. 745
Ross, Gerald, Pres., Chief Exec. & Chief Fin. Officer--MGR Equipment Corp., Inwood, NY; *U.S. Private*, pg. 687
Ross, Hamish, Chief Fin. Officer--NETG Applied Learning GmbH, Dusseldorf, Germany; *U.S. Public*, pg. 784
Ross, Janice, Treas.--T & R Electric Supply Company, Inc., Colman, SD; *U.S. Private*, pg. 1061
Ross, Richard A., Chief Fin. Officer & V.P.-Fin.--Inmet Mining Corporation, Toronto, Canada; *Int'l*, pg. 678
Ross, Robert W., Chief Fin. Officer, V.P., Treas. & Sec.--Selas Corporation of America, Dresher, PA; *U.S. Public*, pg. 1454
Ross, Stuart R., Chief Fin. Officer--Clearly Canadian Beverage Corp., Vancouver, Canada; *Int'l*, pg. 297
Ross, Tammy, Pres.-Opers. & Chief Fin. Officer--Hampton Print Works, Inc., Johnson City, TN; *U.S. Private*, pg. 498
Rossel, Cary, Chief Fin. Officer & V.P.-Admin.--Glazer's Wholesale Drug Co. Inc., Dallas, TX; *U.S. Private*, pg. 455
Rosselet, Thomas, Chief Oper. Officer--Milprint Inc., Oshkosh, WI; *U.S. Public*, pg. 210
Rossetti, Pamela A., Exec. V.P. & Chief Fin. Officer-Ferguson Communications Grp.--CommonHealth USA, Parsippany, NJ; *Int'l*, pg. 1483
Rossew, N., Chief Fin. Officer--Tosas (Pty) Ltd., Wadeville, South Africa; *Int'l*, pg. 1197
Rossi, Piergiorgio, Chief Fin. Officer--Olivetti Hong Kong Ltd., Causeway Bay, Hong Kong; *Int'l*, pg. 1003
Roth, George R., Chief Fin. Officer, V.P. & Treas.--Xerox Credit Corporation, Stamford, CT; *U.S. Public*, pg. 1785
Roth, Hal, Chief Fin. Officer & Sr. V.P.--NW Transport Service, Inc., Denver, CO; *U.S. Private*, pg. 772
Roth, Ivan, Treas.--National Income Realty Trust, New York, NY; *U.S. Public*, pg. 1157
Roth, Philip, Chief Fin. Officer & V.P.-Fin.--Gardner Denver Machinery Inc., Quincy, IL; *U.S. Public*, pg. 703
Roth, Richard J., Chief Fin. Officer--RMS Information Systems, Inc., Lanham, MD; *U.S. Public*, pg. 1425
Rothenberg, Joseph, Chief Fin. Officer & V.P.--Aamco Transmissions, Inc., Bala Cynwyd, PA; *U.S. Private*, pg. 9
Rothwell, Alan, Grp. Fin. Dir.--The Greenalls Group PLC, Warrington, United Kingdom; *Int'l*, pg. 558
Rothwell, Allan, Chief Fin. Officer & Sr. V.P.--Eastman Chemical Company, Kingsport, TN; *U.S. Public*, pg. 550
Roub, Bryan R., Chief Fin. Officer & Sr. V.P.--Harris Corporation, Melbourne, FL; *U.S. Public*, pg. 791
Rougier-Chapman, Alwyn, Chief Fin. Officer--Steelcase Inc., Grand Rapids, MI; *U.S. Private*, pg. 1038
Rouse, Bob, Chief Fin. Officer--Timec Company, Vallejo, CA; *U.S. Private*, pg. 1087
Rouse, James, Chief Fin. Officer--Reeds Financial Services, Inc., Wilmington, NC; *U.S. Public*, pg. 1370
Rouse, James R., Chief Fin. Officer & Treas.--Reeds Jewelers, Inc., Wilmington, NC; *U.S. Public*, pg. 1370
Roush, Margaret, Chief Fin. Officer--Todco, Marion, OH; *U.S. Private*, pg. 823
Routledge, Monty, Chief Fin. Officer--Interstate Payco Seed Company, West Fargo, ND; *U.S. Private*, pg. 573
Roux, Jean-Luc, Chief Fin. Officer--EURO RSCG Babinet, Erra, Tong Cuong, Levallois-Perret, France; *Int'l*, pg. 600
Rovner, Michael, Controller--GreatBanc, Inc., Aurora, IL; *U.S. Public*, pg. 760
Rowe, Allan D., Chief Fin. Officer & Sr. V.P.-Fin.--Empire Company Limited, Stellarton, Canada; *Int'l*, pg. 453
Rowell, Harry B., Jr., Exec. V.P.--Hubbell Incorporated, Orange, CT; *U.S. Public*, pg. 844
Rowley, Cheryl, Chief Fin. Officer--Kurz-Kasch, Inc., Dayton, OH; *U.S. Private*, pg. 637
Rowley, Philip, Chief Fin. Officer & Exec. V.P.--Golden Books Family Entertainment Inc., New York, NY; *U.S. Public*, pg. 749
Roy, Carol, Chief Fin. Officer & Sr. V.P.--Biggs Gilmore Communications, Kalamazoo, MI; *U.S. Private*, pg. 143
Roy, Francois R., Chief Fin. Officer & Exec. V.P.--Avenor, Inc., Montreal, Canada; *Int'l*, pg. 101
Roy, G., Controller--Place Turcot Mill, Montreal, Canada; *Int'l*, pg. 761
Roy, Henry A., Chief Fin. Officer & Sr. V.P.-Admin. & Fin.--Cambior Inc., Montreal, Canada; *Int'l*, pg. 253
Royan, Patrick M., Chief Fin. Officer & V.P.-Fin.--Alantec Corp., San Jose, CA; *U.S. Public*, pg. 667
Royzin, Philip W., Chief Fin. Officer, Treas. & Dir.-Admin.--Brookstone Company, Inc., Nashua, NH; *U.S. Public*, pg. 259
Rozanski, Raymond, Chief Fin. Officer--Niagara Corporation, New York, NY; *U.S. Public*, pg. 1181
Rozea, John M., Chief Fin. Officer--SAIC, Mc Lean, VA; *U.S. Private*, pg. 976
Ruane, Michael J., Chief Fin. Officer & V.P.-Fin.--SunGard Data Systems Inc., Wayne, PA; *U.S. Public*, pg. 1534
Ruane, Thomas G., Chief Fin. Officer & Sr. V.P.--PerSeptive Biosystems, Inc., Framingham, MA; *U.S. Public*, pg. 1279
Rubach, Ron, Chief Fin. Officer--Oregon Automobile Insurance Company, Portland, OR; *Int'l*, pg. 543
Rubel, Darrell D., Chief Fin. Officer, Exec. V.P., Treas. & Asst. Sec.--Marten Transport, Ltd., Mondovi, WI; *U.S. Public*, pg. 1052
Rubin, Dan, Dir.-Fin.--Time Inc., New York, NY; *U.S. Public*, pg. 1612
Rubin, Gary, Chief Fin. Officer & V.P.-Fin.--Cramer Inc., Kansas City, KS; *U.S. Private*, pg. 285
Rubin, Michael, Pres. & Chief Fin. Officer--Hudson General Corporation, Great Neck, NY; *U.S. Public*, pg. 845
Rubzin, Todd, Chief Fin. Officer--Power Plastics Inc., Paterson, NJ; *U.S. Private*, pg. 1086
Ruch, Mike, Chief Fin. Officer& Exec. V.P.--Feld Productions, Vienna, VA; *U.S. Private*, pg. 399
Rudd, John, Chief Fin. Officer--Paramount Petroleum Corp., Paramount, CA; *U.S. Private*, pg. 838
Rudolph, Fred, Chief Fin. Officer--Gramex Corporation, Bridgeton, MO; *U.S. Private*, pg. 468
Rudolph, Scott, Chm. Bd., Pres., Chief Exec. Officer & Chief Oper. Officer--Nature's Bounty Inc., Bohemia, NY; *U.S. Public*, pg. 1166
Rudovsky, Paul, Chief Fin. Officer & Exec. V.P.-Fin. & Plng.--Atlantis Plastic, Inc., Atlanta, GA; *U.S. Public*, pg. 145
Rudzik, John A., Chief Fin. Officer, Sr. V.P.-Fin. & Treas.--Centimark Corporation, Canonsburg, PA; *U.S. Private*, pg. 222
Rue, Richard, Chief Fin. Officer & Sr. V.P.--ITA Group Inc., West Des Moines, IA; *U.S. Private*, pg. 555
Rue, William B., Chief Oper. Officer & Sr. V.P.--Salton/Maxim Housewares, Inc., Mount Prospect, IL; *U.S. Public*, pg. 1430
Rued, Scott D., Chief Fin. Officer & V.P.--Lear Corporation, Rochester Hills, MI; *U.S. Public*, pg. 982
Ruegger, Richard, Chief Fin. Officer--Swing-N-Slide Corp., Janesville, WI; *U.S. Public*, pg. 1543
Ruff, Edward C., Chief Fin. Officer & Sr. Mng. Dir.--Interstate/Johnson Lane Corporation, Charlotte, NC; *U.S. Public*, pg. 910
Rugg, Peter, Chief Fin. Officer & Sr. V.P.--Triton Energy Limited, Dallas, TX; *U.S. Public*, pg. 1640
Ruggieri, John T., Chief Fin. Officer, V.P.-Fin., Treas & Dir.-Investor Rels.--A.T. Cross Co., Lincoln, RI; *U.S. Public*, pg. 460
Ruggiero, Anthony W., Chief Fin. Officer & Sr. V.P.--Olin Corporation, Norwalk, CT; *U.S. Public*, pg. 1218
Ruhkala, Peter D., Chief Fin. Officer, Treas. & Sec.--Nor-Cal Beverage Co., Inc., West Sacramento, CA; *U.S. Private*, pg. 801
Ruhle, Robert E., Chief Fin. Officer, Exec. V.P., Treas. & Sec.--Ruhle Companies, Inc., Valhalla, NY; *U.S. Private*, pg. 950
Rundquist, Lorne, V.P.-Finance--Rosendin Electric, Inc., San Jose, CA; *U.S. Private*, pg. 945
Runk, Fred J., Chief Fin. Officer, V.P. & Treas.--Spelling Entertainment Group, Inc., Los Angeles, CA; *U.S. Private*, pg. 776
Runyen, Dennis R., Chief Fin. Officer--Giles & Ransome, Inc., Bensalem, PA; *U.S. Private*, pg. 453
Runzheimer, L. Lee, Chief Fin. Officer--Osmonics, Inc., Minnetonka, MN; *U.S. Public*, pg. 1233
Rupert, Timothy G., Chief Fin. Officer & Exec. V.P.--RMI Titanium Company, Niles, OH; *U.S. Public*, pg. 1662
Rupp, Robert R., Chief Fin. Officer--Chase Manhattan Mortgage Corporation, Worthington, OH; *U.S. Public*, pg. 338
Rusch, Jack C., Chief Fin. Officer--First Federal Savings Bank La Crosse-Madison, La Crosse, WI; *U.S. Public*, pg. 632
Ruscher, Stephen, Chief Fin. Officer & V.P.-Fin.--Columbia National Group, Inc., Cleveland, OH; *U.S. Private*, pg. 255
Ruscher, Stephen, Chief Fin. Officer--Atlas Lederer Co., Cleveland, OH; *U.S. Private*, pg. 256
Ruscher, Stephen, Chief Fin. Officer--Columbia Iron & Metal Co., Cleveland, OH; *U.S. Private*, pg. 256
Ruscher, Stephen, Chief Fin. Officer--Grant Steel Corp., Pittsburgh, PA; *U.S. Private*, pg. 256
Rush, Dave, Chief Fin. Officer & V.P.--Bojangles' Restaraunts, Inc., Charlotte, NC; *U.S. Private*, pg. 154
Rush, Howard, Chief Fin. Officer--Murphy Family Farms, Rose Hill, NC; *U.S. Private*, pg. 768
Russ, Chester, Chief Fin. Officer & V.P.-Fin.--The Ertl Company, Inc, Dyersville, IA; *U.S. Public*, pg. 1684
Russeau, Michael, Chief Fin. Officer--Silcorp Limited, Scarborough, Canada; *Int'l*, pg. 1249
Russel, Joyce, Chief Fin. Officer, Sr. V.P. & Controller--Jostens Learning Corporation, San Diego, CA; *U.S. Private*, pg. 601
Russell, Douglas W., Chief Fin. Officer, Treas. & Asst. Sec.--Rotonics Manufacturing Inc., Gardena, CA; *U.S. Public*, pg. 1406
Russian, David H., Chief Fin. Officer, V.P.-Fin., Sec. & Treas.--Brooktree Rockwell Semiconductor Systems Div., San Diego, CA; *U.S. Public*, pg. 1398
Russin, Frank, Controller--Selecto-Flash, Inc., West Orange, NJ; *U.S. Private*, pg. 982
Russler, Dave, Chief Fin. Dir. & V.P.--McConnaughy Stein Schmidt Brown, Chicago, IL; *U.S. Private*, pg. 720
Rutherford, Alan, Chief Fin. Officer & Exec. V.P.--Crown Cork & Seal Company, Inc., Philadelphia, PA; *U.S. Public*, pg. 462
Rutherford, J. Kenneth, Chief Fin. Officer & Corp. Sec.--NBS Technologies, Inc., Mississauga, Canada; *Int'l*, pg. 898
Ruttenberg, Harold J., Chief Fin. Officer--Canadian Locker Co., Ltd., Scarborough, Canada; *U.S. Public*, pg. 86
Ruzbacki, Timothy J., Chief Fin. Officer--Wayne Wire Cloth Products, Inc., Kalkaska, MI; *U.S. Private*, pg. 1155
Rwelle, Mark, Chief Fin. Officer & Sr. V.P.--Sierra Pacific Resources, Reno, NV; *U.S. Public*, pg. 1470
Ryan, Anthony, Chief Fin. Officer--Travelers Express Company, Inc., Saint Louis Park, MN; *U.S. Public*, pg. 1718
Ryan, Christopher J., Chief Fin. Officer, Exec. V.P.-Fin. & Sec.--Lakeland Industries, Inc., Ronkonkoma, NY; *U.S. Public*, pg. 975
Ryan, Dwight P., Chief Fin. Officer, V.P., Treas. & Sec.--IntegraMed America, Purchase, NY; *U.S. Public*, pg. 883
Ryan, Frank J., Chief Fin. Officer & Sec.--Detection Systems, Inc., Fairport, NY; *U.S. Public*, pg. 501
Ryan, Mark, Chief Fin. Officer--WDZL Channel 39, Hollywood, FL; *U.S. Public*, pg. 1636
Ryan, Mary L., Chief Fin. Officer & Sr. V.P.--Thompson Steel Co., Inc., Canton, MA; *U.S. Private*, pg. 1083
Ryan, Robert, Chief Fin. Officer & V.P.--Carlisle Companies Incorporated, Syracuse, NY; *U.S. Public*, pg. 305
Ryan, Robert, Chief Fin. Officer & Treas.--Rogers, Lunt & Bowlen Co., Greenfield, MA; *U.S. Private*, pg. 939
Ryan, Robert L., Chief Fin. Officer & Sr. V.P.--Medtronic, Inc., Minneapolis, MN; *U.S. Public*, pg. 1082
Ryan, Ron, Chief Fin. Officer, Treas. & Sec.--Punch Press Products, Inc., Los Angeles, CA; *U.S. Private*, pg. 895
Ryan, Ronald J., Sr. V.P.-Fin. & Admin.--Converse Inc., North Reading, MA; *U.S. Public*, pg. 441
Ryan, Thomas W., Chief Fin. Officer & Sr. V.P.--Federal-Mogul Corporation, Southfield, MI; *U.S. Public*, pg. 615
Rydin, Wes, Chief Fin. Officer & V.P.--Malden Mills Industries, Inc., Lawrence, MA; *U.S. Private*, pg. 698
Rydzinski, David, Chief Fin. Officer, V.P. & Asst. Sec.--William A. Randolph, Inc., Morton Grove, IL; *U.S. Private*, pg. 909
Ryland, G. Neal, Chief Fin. Officer--New England Investment Companies, Inc., Boston, MA; *U.S. Private*, pg. 737
Rynn, John A., V.P. & Treas.--Berol Corporation, Brentwood, TN; *U.S. Public*, pg. 1178
Rynne, David, Chief Fin. Officer & Exec. V.P.--Bay Networks, Inc., Santa Clara, CA; *U.S. Public*, pg. 196
Ryou, J. R., Chief Fin. Officer & V.P.--Samsung Electronics America, Inc., Ridgefield Park, NJ; *Int'l*, pg. 1183
Rzad, Jim, Chief Fin. Officer--Reyco Industries, Inc., Springfield, MO; *U.S. Private*, pg. 926
Rzicznek, Frank, Chief Fin. Officer & V.P.-Fin.--NESCO, Inc., Cleveland, OH; *U.S. Private*, pg. 791
Sabala, James A., Chief Fin. Officer & Sr. V.P.-Fin.--Coeur D'Alene Mines Corporation, Coeur D'Alene, ID; *U.S. Public*, pg. 394
Sabatini, Ralph, Chief Fin. Officer & V.P.--Publishers Clearing House, Port Washington, NY; *U.S. Private*, pg. 893
Sabia, Michael, Chief Fin. Officer & Sr. V.P.--Canadian National Railway Company, Montreal, Canada; *Int'l*, pg. 258
Sabina, Frank, Controller & Treas.--Case Paper Co., Inc., Long Island City, NY; *U.S. Private*, pg. 218
Sabisky, E.V., Chief Fin. Officer--Vauxhall Motors Limited, Luton, United Kingdom; *U.S. Public*, pg. 724
Sable, Robert M., Jr., Chief Fin. Officer & Sr. V.P.--CNG Energy Services Corporation, Pittsburgh, PA; *U.S. Public, pg. 435*
Sabol, Albert T., Chief Fin. Officer & Exec. V.P.-Fin. & Admin.--Central Sprinkler Corporation, Lansdale, PA; *U.S. Public*, pg. 327
Sabourin, Richard, Chief Fin. Officer & Exec. V.P.--Vicorp Restaurants, Inc., Denver, CO; *U.S. Public*, pg. 1719
Sackman, D., Chief Fin. Officer--Printed Motors Ltd., Borden, United Kingdom; *Int'l*, pg. 448
Saculla, William F., Chief Fin. Officer--Arthur Treacher's, Inc., Jacksonville, FL; *U.S. Public*, pg. 136
Sadek, John A., V.P. & Comptroller--The Southern New England Telephone Company, New Haven, CT; *U.S. Public*, pg. 1491
Sadowski, Raymond, Chief Fin. Officer, Sr. V.P. & Asst. Sec.--Avnet, Inc., Great Neck, NY; *U.S. Public*, pg. 155
Saeckl, Ken, Chief Fin. Officer--Gunther Mele Limited, Brantford, Canada; *Int'l*, pg. 578
Saeckl, Ken, Chief Fin. Officer--Gunther Mele Packaging, Inc., Buffalo, NY; *Int'l*, pg. 578
Saeki, George, Chief Fin. Officer--Sakata Seed do Brasil Ltda., Sao Paulo, Brazil; *Int'l*, pg. 1178
Saenger, Eugene L., Jr., Chief Fin. Officer & Exec. V.P.--Avon Workshop Ficks Reed, Cincinnati, OH; *U.S. Private*, pg. 102
Saevitzon, Brett, Chief Fin. Officer--Freeman Cosmetic Corp., Los Angeles, CA; *U.S. Private*, pg. 426
Saewert, Pete, Chief Fin. Officer--Holoubek Inc., Waukesha, WI; *U.S. Private*, pg. 536
Saffert, Paul, Chief Fin. Officer--Allianz of America, Inc., Westport, CT; *Int'l*, pg. 58
Sagues, Francisco, Chief Fin. Officer--Esselte S.A., Barcelona, Spain; *Int'l*, pg. 461
Sahlman, Seppo, Chief Fin. Officer & Exec. V.P.-Treas.--Rautaruukki Oy, Helsinki, Finland; *Int'l*, pg. 1088
Saia, Ron, Chief Fin. Officer--Eight O'Clock Coffee, Hyattsville, MD; *Int'l*, pg. 1375
Saint-Denis, A., Chief Fin. Officer--Royal Packaging Industries Van Leer B.V., Amstelveen, Netherlands; *Int'l*, pg. 1145
Sais, Joe, Chief Fin. Officer--Consolidated Paper Co., Bronx, NY; *U.S. Private*, pg. 838

Saji, Mark, Chief Fin. Officer & V.P.--Linzer Products Corp., Flushing, NY; *U.S. Private*, pg. 669

Sakamato, Kazuhiko, Chief Fin. & Admin. Officer & Sr. V.P.--Marubeni America Corporation, New York, NY; *Int'l*, pg. 844

Sakamoto, Alvin N., Chief Fin. Officer & Sr. V.P.--American Savings Bank, F.S.B., Honolulu, HI; *U.S. Public*, pg. 800

Sakamoto, Lisa M.K., V.P.-Fin. & Govt. Rels.--Hawaiian Tug & Barge Corp., Honolulu, HI; *U.S. Public*, pg. 800

Sakamoto, Shuzo, Exec. V.P.--OYO Corporation, Tokyo, Japan; *Int'l*, pg. 1019

Salbaing, Michel P., Chief Fin. Officer & V.P.--Quebecor Printing, Inc., Montreal, Canada; *Int'l*, pg. 1076

Salbaing, Michel P., Chief Fin. Officer & V.P.--Imprimerie Quebecor Inc., Montreal, Canada; *Int'l*, pg. 1077

Salentine, Thomas J., Chief Fin. Officer & Exec. V.P.--Bindley Western Industries, Inc., Indianapolis, IN; *U.S. Public*, pg. 228

Salerno, Frederic V., Chief Fin. Officer & Sr. Exec. V.P.--Bell Atlantic Corporation, New York, NY; *U.S. Public*, pg. 201

Sales, Arthur J., Chief Fin. Officer--Hilb, Rogal and Hamilton Company of Pittsburgh, Inc., Pittsburgh, PA; *U.S. Public*, pg. 827

Salford, Carlo, Chief Fin. Officer--Letraset Italia Srl, Milan, Italy; *Int'l*, pg. 462

Salice, Thomas, Chief Fin. Officer & Mng. Dir.--AEA Investors Inc., New York, NY; *U.S. Private*, pg. 4

Salierno, Thomas, Chief Fin. Officer--Savin Corporation, Stamford, CT; *Int'l*, pg. 1114

Saling, Robert, Controller--IBT, Inc., Merriam, KS; *U.S. Private*, pg. 553

Salipante, Robert C., Chief Fin. Officer & Sr. V.P.--Northwestern National Life Insurance Co., Minneapolis, MN; *U.S. Public*, pg. 1375

Salisbury, George, Chief Fin. Officer, Treas. & Sec.--Symons Corporation, Pasadena, CA; *U.S. Private*, pg. 932

Salisbury, Robert C., Chief Fin. Officer & Exec. V.P.-Fin. & Admin.--Pharmacia & Upjohn, Inc., Windsor, United Kingdom; *Int'l*, pg. 1047

Salisbury, Ronald C., Chief Fin. Officer & Exec. V.P.--Pharmacia & Upjohn Kalamazoo, MI; *Int'l*, pg. 1048

Sallak, Dean, Chief Fin. Officer--Niagara Frontier Transportation Authority, Buffalo, NY; *U.S. Private*, pg. 798

Sallak, Dean, Chief Fin. Officer--Niagara Frontier Transit & Metro System, Buffalo, NY; *U.S. Private*, pg. 798

Salmons, Stan, Chief Fin. Officer--Tri Tech Laboratories, Inc., Lynchburg, VA; *U.S. Private*, pg. 1101

Salmoon, Gary, Chief Fin. Officer--Acorn Computers Ltd., Cambridge, United Kingdom; *Int'l*, pg. 1002

Salo, Ralph, Chief Fin. Officer & Sr. V.P.--Target Stores, Minneapolis, MN; *U.S. Public*, pg. 489

Saltzman, Bill, Chief Fin. Officer--Milk Products Holdings (North America) Inc., Santa Rosa, CA; *Int'l*, pg. 923

Salvaria, Robert J., Chief Fin. Officer--Central Plants, Inc., Los Angeles, CA; *U.S. Public*, pg. 1249

Salvati, Michael E., Chief Fin. Officer & V.P.-Fin.--Culligan International Company, Northbrook, IL; *U.S. Public*, pg. 467

Salvati, Vincent W., Chief Fin. Officer & Grp. V.P.--Bell Canada, Montreal, Canada; *Int'l*, pg. 115

Salvia, Joseph, Chief Fin. Officer--Plastek Group, Erie, PA; *U.S. Private*, pg. 870

Salwasser, Margaret, Treas. & Sec.--Salwasser Manufacturing Company, Inc., Reedley, CA; *U.S. Private*, *pg. 963*

Salzano, Jim, Chief Fin. Officer--Bostonian Shoe Co., Newton, MA; *Int'l*, pg. 297

Salzmann, B., Chief Fin. Officer--Kuehne & Nagel International AG, Schindellegi, Switzerland; *Int'l*, pg. 763

Samorano, Hector, Chief Fin. Officer--Grupo Industrial Saltillo, Saltillo, Mexico; *Int'l*, pg. 1469

Sampson, Jim, Treas.--Western Grain, Inc., Wichita, KS; *U.S. Private*, pg. 1165

Samuelson, Marjorie, Chief Fin. Officer & Partner--J.D. Power and Associates, Agoura Hills, CA; *U.S. Private*, pg. 878

San Jose, Juan Luis, Chief Fin. Officer--Alpek, S.A. de C.V., Garza Garcia, Mexico; *Int'l*, pg. 56

San Pedro, Jose Luis, Controller, Treas. & Mng. Dir.-Economy & Fin.--Iberdrola, S.A., Bilbao, Spain; *Int'l*, pg. 657

Sanchez, Raul de Jesus, Chief Fin. Officer--Laboratories Griffith de Mexico, S.A. de C.V., Monterrey, Mexico; *U.S. Private*, pg. 482

Sanchez, Ricardo, Chief Fin. Officer--Xerox Argentina I.C.S.A., Buenos Aires, Argentina; *U.S. Public*, pg. 1785

Sandal, G., Chief Fin. Officer--Siemens Ltd., Dublin, Ireland; *Int'l*, pg. 1247

Sander, William C., Exec. V.P., Treas. & Sec.--Hunt Building Corporation, El Paso, TX; *U.S. Private*, pg. 548

Sanders, John, Chief Fin. Officer--Spartan Mills, Spartanburg, SC; *U.S. Private*, pg. 1020

Sanders, Kenneth W., Chief Fin. Officer, Sr. V.P.-Fin., Treas. & Asst. Sec.--Paging Network, Inc., Plano, TX; *U.S. Public*, pg. 1252

Sanderson, Martin R., Chief Fin. Officer--Carbo Plc, Manchester, United Kingdom; *Int'l*, pg. 268

Sanderson, Michael, Chief Fin. Officer--Sam Swope Auto Group, Inc., Louisville, KY; *U.S. Private*, pg. 1059

Sandler, Patrik, Chief Fin. Officer--Skanska Prefab AB, Malmo, Sweden; *Int'l*, pg. 1261

Sandler, Richard, CPA, Chief Fin. Officer & Corp. Clerk--M.S. Walker, Inc., Somerville, MA; *U.S. Private*, pg. 1147

Sandlow, Richard, Chief Fin. Officer--Dudek & Bock Spring Manufacturing Company, Chicago, IL; *U.S. Private*, pg. 344

Sandnes, Ludvik, Chief Fin. Officer & Grp. Exec. V.P.--Christiania Bank og Kreditkasse ASA, Oslo, Norway; *Int'l*, pg. 289

Sandstrom, Christina, Chief Fin. Officer--Skanska Data AB, Danderyd, Sweden; *Int'l*, pg. 1260

Sandstrom, Krister, Chief Fin. Officer--Skanska Teknik AB, Malmo, Sweden; *Int'l*, pg. 1261

Sandstrom, Roy, Chief Fin. Officer & V.P.--Grant Marketing Communications, Ardmore, PA; *U.S. Private*, pg. 470

Sandstrom, Roy, Chief Fin. Officer & V.P.--Kingswood Advertising, Inc., Ardmore, PA; *U.S. Private*, pg. 622

Sanjana, Espi, Chief Fin. Officer--The Vendo Company, Fresno, CA; *Int'l*, pg. 1184

Santa, Richard A., Chief Fin. Officer--Dynamic Materials Corporation, Lafayette, CO; *U.S. Public*, pg. 539

Santamaria, Jose Domingo, Chief Fin. Officer--CIBA-GEIGY Colombiana S.A., Bogota, Colombia; *Int'l*, pg. 976

Santangelo, Joseph A., Chief Fin. Officer, Treas. & Sec.--FPA Corporation, Bensalem, PA; *U.S. Public*, pg. 608

Santi, G., Chief Fin. Officer--Olivetti A/B, Upplands Vasby, Sweden; *Int'l*, pg. 1003

Santina, John, Chief Fin. Officer & Exec. V.P.--Milton Industries, Inc., Chicago, IL; *U.S. Private*, pg. 749

Santora, Greg J., Chief Fin. Officer, Chief Acctg. Officer & V.P.--Intuit, Inc., Mountain View, CA; *U.S. Public*, pg. 911

Saper, Ronald L., Chief Fin. Officer & Exec. V.P.--Washington Federal Savings, Seattle, WA; *U.S. Public*, pg. 1740

Sapp, Ronald V., Chief Fin. Officer, V.P.-Fin. & Treas.--Atlantic Southeast Airlines Inc., Atlanta, GA; *U.S. Public*, pg. 144

Sargent, Michael, Chief Fin. Officer--Ampco Metal Incorporated, Milwaukee, WI; *U.S. Private*, pg. 67

Sarid, Karen, Chief Fin. Officer & V.P.--ESC Medical Systems Ltd., Yokneam, Israel; *Int'l*, pg. 429

Sarkisian, Nathan, Chief Fin. Officer & V.P.-Fin.--Altera Corporation, San Jose, CA; *U.S. Public*, pg. 59

Sarmiento, Galiermo, Chief Fin. Officer--General Motors Chile S.A., Industria Automotriz, Santiago, Chile; *U.S. Public*, pg. 721

Sarno, Charles, Chief Fin. Officer--Knight Equipment International Inc., Costa Mesa, CA; *U.S. Public*, pg. 862

Saruwatari, Steven T., Chief Fin. Officer & Treas.--Pacific American Income Shares, Inc., Pasadena, CA; *U.S. Public*, pg. 1247

Sasnett, David, Chief Fin. Officer & V.P.--Catalina Lighting, Inc., Miami, FL; *U.S. Public*, pg. 314

Sass, Gordon, Chief Fin. Officer--Prime Cast, Inc., South Beloit, IL; *U.S. Public*, pg. 142

Satter, D.M., Chief Fin. Officer--Dow Hickam Pharmaceuticals Inc., Sugar Land, TX; *U.S. Public*, pg. 1143

Sauder, Clair, Chief Fin. Officer & Exec. V.P.--Huffman Koos, River Edge, NJ; *U.S. Private*, pg. 546

Sauer, Julian, Chief Fin. Officer--Atlas Supply Company, Atlanta, GA; *U.S. Private*, pg. 96

Sauerberg, Robert A., Jr., Chief Fin. Officer & V.P.--Women's Magazines Group, New York, NY; *Int'l*, pg. 190

Saul, Stephen R., Chief Fin. Officer & Exec. V.P.--Glenborough Realty Trust Incorporated, San Mateo, CA; *U.S. Public*, pg. 747

Saunders, Brenda, Chief Fin. Officer--Fleck Controls, Milwaukee, WI; *U.S. Public*, pg. 1273

Saunders, Gary, Chief Fin. Officer & Exec. V.P.--Robert Bosch Corporation, Broadview, IL; *Int'l*, pg. 204

Saunders, Gregory S., Chief Fin. Officer, Exec. V.P. & Treas.--National Insurance Group, South San Francisco, CA; *U.S. Public*, pg. 1157

Saunders, Gregory S., Chief Fin. Officer & Exec. V.P.--Great Pacific Insurance Company, San Bruno, CA; *U.S. Public*, pg. 1158

Saunders, Gregory S., Chief Fin. Officer & Exec. V.P.--FASTRAC Systems, Inc., San Bruno, CA; *U.S. Public*, pg. 1158

Saunders, Gregory S., Chief Fin. Officer & Exec. V.P.--Pinnacle Data Corporation, San Bruno, CA; *U.S. Public*, pg. 1158

Saunders, Gregory S., Chief Fin. Officer & Exec. V.P.--FASTRAC Systems, Inc.-Insurance Agent & Broker, South San Francisco, CA; *U.S. Public*, pg. 1158

Saunders, Keith C., Chief Fin. Officer, Exec. V.P. & Sec.--Zions Co-operative Mercantile Institution, Salt Lake City, UT; *U.S. Public*, pg. 1793

Sauser, Thomas, Chief Fin. Officer--GTECH Corporation, West Greenwich, RI; *U.S. Public*, pg. 767

Savage, Betty J., V.P., Chief Fin. Officer & Treas.--INSO Corporation, Boston, MA; *U.S. Public*, pg. 882

Savedge, Henry S., Jr., Chief Fin. Officer & Exec. V.P.--Reynolds Metals Company, Richmond, VA; *U.S. Public*, pg. 1385

Saville, Paul, Chief Fin. Officer & Sr. V.P.--NVR, Inc., Mc Lean, VA; *U.S. Public*, pg. 1148

Savinel, Philippe, Chief Fin. Officer--Ricard, Marseilles, France; *Int'l*, pg. 566

Sawamura, Akira, Chief Fin. Officer--Toray Industries, Inc., Tokyo, Japan; *Int'l*, pg. 1399

Sawin, David, Chief Fin. Officer--Delta Rubber Company, Danielson, CT; *U.S. Private*, pg. 323

Saxon, Franklin N., Chief Fin. Officer, Sr. V.P., Treas. & Sec.--Culp, Inc., High Point, NC; *U.S. Public*, pg. 467

Sayatovic, Wayne P., Chief Fin. Officer & Sr. V.P.-Fin.--IDEX Corporation, Northbrook, IL; *U.S. Public*, pg. 862

Sayre, Larry, Chief Fin. Officer, V.P.-Fin., Controller & Treas.--Collins Industries, Inc., Hutchinson, KS; *U.S. Public*, pg. 399

Scales, Mark S., Chief Fin. Officer, V.P. & Treas.--General Housewares Corp., Terre Haute, IN; *U.S. Public*, pg. 715

Scalfaro, Frank, Chief Fin. Officer, V.P. & Treas.--NavCom Defense Electronics, Inc., El Monte, CA; *U.S. Private*, pg. 789

Scangamor, Joseph A., Chief Fin. Officer & Exec. V.P.--Carat MBS, New York, NY; *U.S. Private*, pg. 208

Scanlon, Ian, Chief Fin. Officer--W.A. Flick & Co. Pty. Limited, Lane Cove, Australia; *Int'l*, pg. 495

Scanlon, Kathy, Chief Fin. Officer--Southwest Recreational Industries Inc., Leander, TX; *U.S. Private*, pg. 1018

Scanlon, Raymond, Chief Fin. Officer & V.P.--Al Paul Lefton Co., Inc., Philadelphia, PA; *U.S. Private*, pg. 658

Scardaci, Leslie, Controller--AVA Leasing Service Company, Atlanta, GA; *U.S. Private*, pg. 8

Scarson, Dee, Chief Fin. Officer & V.P.-Fin.--MTS, Inc., West Sacramento, CA; *U.S. Private*, pg. 688

Schaapveld, Larry, Chief Fin. Officer, V.P., Controller & Treas.--Varied Investments, Inc., Muscatine, IA; *U.S. Private*, pg. 1134

Schaefer, John L., Chief Fin. Officer, V.P.-Fin. & Sec.--The Wm. Powell Company, Cincinnati, OH; *U.S. Private*, pg. 877

Schaefer, Scott, Chief Fin. Officer & V.P.-Fin.--Megas Beauty Care, Inc., Cleveland, OH; *U.S. Private*, pg. 729

Schaefer, Thomas C., Chief Fin. Officer & Exec. V.P.--United Planners' Financial Services of America, Scottsdale, AZ; *U.S. Private*, pg. 831

Schaeffer, Glenn, Pres. & Chief Fin. Officer--Circus Circus - Las Vegas, Las Vegas, NV; *U.S. Public*, pg. 374

Schafer, William H., Chief Fin. Officer & V.P.--Developers Diversified Realty Corporation, Moreland Hills, OH; *U.S. Public*, pg. 502

Schaffer, Donald J., Chief Fin. Officer & Sr. V.P.-Fin.--General American Transportation Corporation, Chicago, IL; *U.S. Public*, pg. 692

Schaffer, John G., Chief Fin. Officer & V.P.--American Automobile Association, Heathrow, FL; *U.S. Private*, pg. 50

Schaffer, John G., Chief Fin. Officer--AAA Investment Company, Wilmington, DE; *U.S. Private*, pg. 51

Schalter, Rich, Chief Fin. Officer, Treas. & Sec.--Spartan Motors, Inc., Charlotte, MI; *U.S. Public*, pg. 1495

Schanll, Carol, Chief Fin. Officer & V.P.--United States Luggage Company, Hauppauge, NY; *U.S. Private*, pg. 1125

Scharf, Charles, Chief Fin. Officer & Exec. V.P.--Salomon Smith Barney Holdings, Inc., New York, NY; *U.S. Public*, pg. 1633

Scharf, H. Douglas, Chief Fin. Officer & V.P.-Fin.--Metall Mining Corporation, Toronto, Canada; *Int'l*, pg. 862

Scharm, Henry B., Sr. V.P. & Chief Acctg. Officer--Chubb & Son, Inc., Warren, NJ; *U.S. Public*, pg. 355

Schauder, Frederick, Chief Fin. Officer--Lonza Inc., Fair Lawn, NJ; *Int'l*, pg. 67

Schaumann, Robert, Dir.-Fin. Reporting--The Marmon Group, Inc., Chicago, IL; *U.S. Private*, pg. 706

Scheckner, Barry D., Chief Fin. Officer & Sr. V.P.--Finlay Enterprises, Inc., New York, NY; *U.S. Public*, pg. 623

Scheckner, Barry D., Chief Fin. Officer--Finlay Fine Jewelry Corporation, New York, NY; *U.S. Public*, pg. 624

Scheick, David, Credit Mgr.--Neapco, Inc., Pottstown, PA; *U.S. Private*, pg. 1113

Scheid, Steven L., Chief Fin. Officer & Exec. V.P.--The Charles Schwab Corporation, San Francisco, CA; *U.S. Public*, pg. 1442

Schein, Steven M., Treas. & Asst. Sec.--IGC Energy, Inc., Indianapolis, IN; *U.S. Public*, pg. 875

Scheinford, Scott, Chief Fin. Officer--Alliance Gaming Corporation, Las Vegas, NV; *U.S. Public*, pg. 46

Scheinkman, Steven W., Pres., Chief Fin. Officer & Mng. Dir.--Samsteel, Inc., Torrance, CA; *U.S. Private*, pg. 402

Scheiwiller, Regina, Chief Fin. Officer--Impuls Advertising AG, Kusnacht, Switzerland; *Int'l*, pg. 666

Scheller, Jim, V.P. & Gen. Mgr.--Roller Derby Skate Corp., Litchfield, IL; *U.S. Private*, pg. 941

Schemeuauer, Joseph, Chief Fin. Officer--Fountain Powerboat Industries, Inc., Washington, NC; *U.S. Public*, pg. 678

Schenk, James M., Chief Fin. Officer & V.P.--BBS Holdings, Inc., Atlanta, GA; *U.S. Public*, pg. 209

Schenk, Joseph A., Chief Fin. Officer, Treas. & Dir.-Investor Rels.--Tel-Save Holdings, Inc., New Hope, PA; *U.S. Public*, pg. 1568

Scher, Norman A., Chief Fin. Officer & Exec. V.P.--Tredegar Industries Inc., Richmond, VA; *U.S. Public*, pg. 1633

Schere, Ken, Chief Fin. Officer--Walden Book Company, Ann Arbor, MI; *U.S. Public*, pg. 245

Scherer, Barbara V., Chief Fin. Officer & V.P.-Fin. & Admin.--Plantronics Inc., Santa Cruz, CA; *U.S. Public*, pg. 1308

Scherer, Gary M., V.P.-Fin.--Scherer Bros. Lumber Company, Minneapolis, MN; *U.S. Private*, pg. 970

Scherer, George F., Chief Fin. Officer, Exec. V.P. & Treas.--McCarthy Building Companies, Saint Louis, MO; *U.S. Private*, pg. 719

Scherer, John R., Chief Fin. Officer & V.P.--Nash Finch Company, Edina, MN; *U.S. Public*, pg. 1151

Scherer, Kirk, Chief Fin. Officer & Treas.--Paul-Son Gaming Corporation, Las Vegas, NV; *U.S. Public*, pg. 1265

Scherer, Thomas W., Chief Fin. Officer & Sr. V.P.--ServiceMaster Consumer Services Company, Memphis, TN; *U.S. Public*, pg. 1461

Scherich, Robert, Chief Fin. Officer--Valley National Gasses Inc., Wheeling, WV; *U.S. Private*, pg. 1132

Schermerhorn, G.F., Asst. Treas.--Stone & Webster, Incorporated, Boston, MA; *U.S. Public*, pg. 1519

Scheuer, Cynthia A., Chief Fin. Officer, V.P. & Treas.--Mechanical Technology Inc., Latham, NY; *U.S. Public*, pg. 1077

Schiavone, Caesar J., Chief Fin. Officer & V.P.--Blue Ridge Insurance Co., Simsbury, CT; *Int'l*, pg. 345

Schiavone, Caesar J., Chief Fin. Officer & V.P.--Blue Ridge Indemnity Co., Simsbury, CT; *Int'l*, pg. 345

Schiavone, Caesar J., Chief Fin. Officer & V.P.--MassWest Insurance Company, West Springfield, MA; *Int'l*, pg. 345

Schick, Kevin C., Chief Fin. Officer, V.P., Controller & Treas.--Con-Way Transportation Services, Palo Alto, CA; *U.S. Public*, pg. 281

Schieber, Phil, Chief Fin. Officer & V.P.--Berry-Brown Advertising, Inc., Dallas, TX; *U.S. Private*, pg. 137

Schierholz, John, Chief Fin. Officer--BCS Wireless, New Glarus, WI; *U.S. Public*, pg. 609

Schiess, John, Chief Fin. Officer & V.P.--Pabst Brewing Co./Tumwater, Tumwater, WA; *U.S. Private*, pg. 954

Schievelbein, Karen, Chief Fin. Officer & Sr. V.P.--Blue Shield of California, San Francisco, CA; *U.S. Private*, pg. 153

Schimmoller, John M., Chief Fin. Officer--Bemrose USA, Inc., Fort Wayne, IN; *Int'l*, pg. 185
Schirrmacher, Axel, Chief Fin. Officer--MacGREGOR Conver GmbH, Bremen, Germany; *Int'l*, pg. 670
Schkade, Craig, Chief Fin. Officer & Treas.--Hitox Corporation of America, Corpus Christi, TX; *U.S. Public*, pg. 829
Schlapbach, Jakob, Chief Fin. Officer--Ascom Holding AG, Bern, Switzerland; *Int'l*, pg. 86
Schlede, Klaus G., Dr., Deputy Chm. & Chief Fin. Officer--Deutsche Lufthansa AG, Cologne, Germany; *Int'l*, pg. 407
Schlegel, Charles, Chief Fin. Officer & Treas.--Arizona Cardinals, Phoenix, AZ; *U.S. Private*, pg. 81
Schlenoff, Larry B., Chief Fin. Officer & V.P.-Fin.--Zitel Corporation, Fremont, CA; *U.S. Public*, pg. 1793
Schlobohm, Jon, Treas. & Sec.--National Corset Supply House, Los Angeles, CA; *U.S. Private*, pg. 781
Schlomann, James M., Chief Fin. Officer & Sr. Exec. V.P.--USLIFE Corporation, New York, NY; *U.S. Public*, pg. 77
Schloss, Marcel, Sr. V.P.-Fin. & Admin.--Parade Publications Inc., New York, NY; *U.S. Private*, pg. 20
Schlosser, P., Treas. & Sec.--Krupp Robins, Inc., Englewood, CO; *Int'l*, pg. 511
Schlosser, Rod, Chief Fin. Officer, V.P. & Treas.--Martin Industries, Inc. (AL), Florence, AL; *U.S. Private*, pg. 709
Schlosser, Seymour A., Chief Fin. Officer & V.P.-Fin.--Wynn's International, Inc., Orange, CA; *U.S. Public*, pg. 1782
Schlueter, Mr., Chief Fin. Officer--Eckes AG, Nieder-Olm, Germany; *Int'l*, pg. 432
Schlveter, William, Chief Fin. Officer--Flavor House Products, Inc., Dothan, AL; *U.S. Private*, pg. 410
Schmale, Neal E., Chief Fin. Officer & Exec. V.P.--Pacific Enterprises, Los Angeles, CA; *U.S. Public*, pg. 1249
Schmale, Neal E., Chief Fin. Officer & Exec. V.P.--Southern California Gas Co., Los Angeles, CA; *U.S. Public*, pg. 1249
Schmalz, Douglas J., Chief Fin. Officer & V.P.--Archer Daniels Midland Company (ADM), Decatur, IL; *U.S. Public*, pg. 127
Schmehl, Don C., Chief Fin. Officer & Treas.--Centrex Corporation, Findlay, OH; *U.S. Private*, pg. 225
Schmid, P., Chief Fin. Officer--SAIA AG, Murten, Switzerland; *Int'l*, pg. 1500
Schmid, Rolf, Chief Fin. Officer--Wandel & Goltermann GmbH & Co., Elektronische Messtechnik, Eningen, Germany; *Int'l*, pg. 1485
Schmid, Werner, Chief Fin. Officer--InterAmerican-Star Group, Los Angeles, CA; *Int'l*, pg. 1529
Schmider, Susan D., Sec. & Asst. Treas.--Vornado Realty Trust, Saddle Brook, NJ; *U.S. Public*, pg. 1725
Schmidt, Carl G., Chief Fin. Officer, Sr. V.P., Treas. & Sec.--Johnson Worldwide Associates, Inc., Sturtevant, WI; *U.S. Public*, pg. 932
Schmidt, Charles R., Chief Fin. Officer--Quadion Corporation, Minneapolis, MN; *U.S. Private*, pg. 898
Schmidt, Dennis, Chief Fin. Officer--Kitchen Fair, Jacksonville, AR; *U.S. Private*, pg. 917
Schmidt, Duane, Chief Fin. Officer--Brookwood Companies Inc., New York, NY; *U.S. Public*, pg. 777
Schmidt, Herbert L., V.P. & Treas.--The Pyramid Life Insurance Co., Mission, KS; *U.S. Public*, pg. 1694
Schmidt, Karl Josef, Chief Fin. Officer & V.P.-Fin.--Degussa Corporation, Ridgefield Park, NJ; *Int'l*, pg. 388
Schmidt, Leslie, Treas. & Sec.--Warrens Waller Press, Inc., South San Francisco, CA; *U.S. Private*, pg. 1151
Schmieder, Klaus-Jurgen, Chief Fin. Officer--Hoechst Aktiengesellschaft, Frankfurt/Main, Germany; *Int'l*, pg. 624
Schmitt, Mark, Chief Fin. Officer--General Motors do Brasil Ltda., Sao Caetano do Sul, Brazil; *U.S. Public*, pg. 722
Schmitt, Peter A., Chief Fin. Officer & V.P.-Fin.--Isolyser Company, Inc., Norcross, GA; *U.S. Public*, pg. 914
Schmitt, Thomas E., Chief Fin. Officer--Young Automotive Group, Indianapolis, IN; *U.S. Private*, pg. 1095
Schmitz, Clarence T., Chief Fin. Officer & Exec. V.P.--Jefferies Group, Inc., Los Angeles, CA; *U.S. Public*, pg. 924
Schmoll, P., Chief Fin. Officer--Ethicon G.m.b.H. & Co. KG, Norderstedt, Germany; *U.S. Public*, pg. 929
Schnabel, Susan, Fin. Officer--PETsMART, Inc., Phoenix, AZ; *U.S. Public*, pg. 1281
Schneeberger, R. Louis, Chief Fin. Officer--Olympic Steel Inc., Cleveland, OH; *U.S. Public*, pg. 1221
Schneider, D., Chief Oper. Officer--Busch-Jaeger Ludenscheider Metallwerk GmbH, Ludenscheid, Germany; *Int'l*, pg. 1427
Schneider, David M., Treas.--Progressive Max Insurance Co., Cleveland, OH; *U.S. Public*, pg. 1335
Schneider, Debra, Chief Fin. Officer--Wolf Mansfield Bolling Advertising Inc., Buffalo, NY; *U.S. Private*, pg. 1185
Schneider, Dieter, Chief Fin. Officer & Mng. Dir.--O&K Orenstein & Koppel Aktiengesellschaft, Dortmund, Germany; *Int'l*, pg. 516
Schneider, Elaine, Chief Fin. Officer--Media First International, Inc., New York, NY; *U.S. Private*, pg. 726
Schneider, Erich, Chief Oper. Officer--Oerlikon-Contraves AG, Zurich, Switzerland; *Int'l*, pg. 998
Schneider, Forrest M., Chief Fin. Officer & Sr. V.P.--Lane Industries, Inc., Northbrook, IL; *U.S. Private*, pg. 649
Schneider, Joe, Chief Fin. Officer--Weaver Popcorn Company, Inc., Van Buren, IN; *U.S. Private*, pg. 1156
Schneider, Paul L., Chief Fin. Officer & Sr. V.P.--The Acacia Group - Acacia Life Insurance Co., Bethesda, MD; *U.S. Private*, pg. 10
Schneider, Paul L., Chief Fin. Officer & Sr. V.P.--Acacia Financial Corporation, Bethesda, MD; *U.S. Private*, pg. 11
Schneider, Richard A., Chief Fin. Officer--NAI Technologies, Inc., Huntington, NY; *U.S. Public*, pg. 1144
Schneider, Robert E., Chief Fin. Officer & Exec. V.P.--The New England, Boston, MA; *U.S. Private*, pg. 737
Schneider, Robert F., Chief Fin. Officer, Exec. V.P. & Asst. Treas.--Kimball International, Inc., Jasper, IN; *U.S. Public*, pg. 956
Schneider, Scott, Chief Fin. Officer--Centennial Cellular Corp., New Canaan, CT; *U.S. Public*, pg. 329
Schneider, Scott N., Chief Fin. Officer, Sr. V.P. & Treas.--Century Communications Corp., New Canaan, CT; *U.S. Public*, pg. 329
Schneider, Scott V., Chief Fin. Officer, V.P., Treas. & Sec.--Saul Centers Inc., Chevy Chase, MD; *U.S. Public*, pg. 1435
Schneider, Steven J., Chief Fin. Officer & V.P.-Fin.--Finish Line, Inc., Indianapolis, IN; *U.S. Public*, pg. 623
Schneider, Thomas C., Chief Fin. Officer & Exec. V.P.--Dean Witter, Discover & Co., New York, NY; *U.S. Public*, pg. 1132
Schneidewind, Bruce, Chief Fin. Officer--Euromarket Designs, Inc., Northbrook, IL; *U.S. Private*, pg. 384
Schnell, Lonnie D., Chief Fin. Officer--Haskel International, Inc., Burbank, CA; *U.S. Public*, pg. 798
Schnepf, George, Chief Fin. Officer--Cold Spring Granite Company, Cold Spring, MN; *U.S. Private*, pg. 250
Schnepp, Gilles, Chief Fin. Officer--LeGrand S.A., Limoges, France; *Int'l*, pg. 805
Schnitzius, Robert W., Chief Fin. Officer & Treas.--Carrington Laboratories, Inc., Irving, TX; *U.S. Public*, pg. 309
Schnuck, Todd R., Chief Fin. Officer & V.P.--Schnuck Markets, Inc., Saint Louis, MO; *U.S. Private*, pg. 971
Schober, G. Stephen, Chief Fin. Officer--Glentel Inc., Burnaby, Canada; *Int'l*, pg. 1336
Schocke, Robert P., Chief Fin. Officer, Treas., Controller & Sec.--Greenhorne & O'Mara, Inc., Greenbelt, MD; *U.S. Private*, pg. 477
Schoenbachler, C.L., Chief Fin. Officer & Exec. V.P.--Brown & Williamson Tobacco Corp., Louisville, KY; *Int'l*, pg. 111
Schoenholz, David A., Chief Fin. Officer & Sr. V.P.--Household International, Inc., Prospect Heights, IL; *U.S. Public*, pg. 842
Schoewe, Thomas M., Chief Fin. Officer & Sr. V.P.--The Black & Decker Corporation, Towson, MD; *U.S. Public*, pg. 233
Schofield, Ernest A., Chief Fin. Officer & Sr. V.P.--Horizon/CMS Healthcare Corporation, Albuquerque, NM; *U.S. Public*, pg. 836
Scholler, Bernice, Treas. & Sec.--Times Printing Company, Inc., Random Lake, WI; *U.S. Private*, pg. 1087
Schomer, Fred K., Chief Fin. Officer & Exec. V.P.--Gerber Products Company, Fremont, MI; *Int'l*, pg. 973
Schonau, Mark R., Chief Fin. Officer, Sec., Treas., & Investor Rels.--HBO & Company/Cycare Business Group, Scottsdale, AZ; *U.S. Public*, pg. 770
Schonau, Mark R., Chief Fin. Officer--CyData, Inc., Scottsdale, AZ; *U.S. Public*, pg. 770
Schonberg, I., Chief Fin. Officer--JM Byggnads och Fastighets AB, Stockholm, Sweden; *Int'l*, pg. 1260
Schopp, Alryn A., Chief Fin. Officer & Exec. V.P.--T-NETIX, Inc., Englewood, CO; *U.S. Public*, pg. 1553
Schorderet, Georges, Exec. V.P.-Corp. Fin. & Devel.--The Swissair Group, Zurich, Switzerland; *Int'l*, pg. 1333
Schorr, Stephen I., V.P.-Fin., Treas. & Sec.--Westbrae Natural, Inc., Carson, CA; *U.S. Public*, pg. 774
Schram, C.R., Chief Oper. Officer & Chief Fin. Officer--RAM Golf Corporation, Melrose Park, IL; *U.S. Private*, pg. 908
Schram, W.T., V.P.-Fin. & Admin.--Morton International Inc., Chicago, IL; *U.S. Public*, pg. 1135
Schreiber, David R., Chief Fin. Officer, Treas. & Sec.--Dianon Systems, Inc., Stratford, CT; *U.S. Public*, pg. 506
Schreiber, G.C., V.P.-Fin.--Emerson Power Transmission Corporation, Ithaca, NY; *U.S. Public*, pg. 573
Schreiber, George A., Jr., Chief Fin. Officer & Exec. V.P.--Pinnacle West Capital Corporation, Phoenix, AZ; *U.S. Public*, pg. 1297
Schreiber, George A., Jr., Chief Fin. Officer & Exec. V.P.--APS, Phoenix, AZ; *U.S. Public*, pg. 1297
Schreyer, John Y., Chief Fin. Officer & Exec. V.P.--Amerada Hess Corporation, New York, NY; *U.S. Public*, pg. 65
Schriber, Allan, Chief Fin. Officer--Sentry Technology Group, Westborough, MA; *U.S. Public*, pg. 1425
Schrocke, Len, Chief Fin. Officer--InfoVest, Inc., Chicago, IL; *U.S. Private*, pg. 562
Schrodeder, Karsten, Fin. Exec.--Hermal Kurt Herrmann & Co., Reinbek, Germany; *Int'l*, pg. 616
Schroeck, Albert F., V.P.-Fin. & Asst. Sec.--PSA Airlines, Inc., Vandalia, OH; *U.S. Public*, pg. 1680
Schroeck, Raymond, Chief Fin. Officer--Lawrence Metal Products, Inc., Bay Shore, NY; *U.S. Private*, pg. 654
Schroeder, Bradley A., Chief. Fin. Officer--Houston Foods Company, Franklin Park, IL; *U.S. Private*, pg. 542
Schroeder, Jeff, Chief Fin. Officer--Farley, Inc., Chicago, IL; *U.S. Private*, pg. 394
Schroeder, Paul, Chief Fin. Officer & Sr. V.P.--DataCard Corporation, Minnetonka, MN; *U.S. Private*, pg. 312
Schroeder, Wayne, V.P. & Chief Fin. Officer--Arrhythmia Research Technology, Inc., Austin, TX; *U.S. Public*, pg. 133
Schubert, Thomas D., Chief Fin. & Acctg. Officer & Sr. V.P.--NovaCare Employee Services, Inc., Norristown, PA; *U.S. Public*, pg. 1203
Schudy, George, V.P.-Fin.--Kearney Company, Tucker, GA; *U.S. Public*, pg. 444
Schuele, Alban W., Chief Fin. Officer & V.P.--Hoechst Marion Roussel North America, Kansas City, MO; *Int'l*, pg. 625
Schueler, Kirk, Chief Fin. Officer & Treas.--Brooks Resources Corporation, Bend, OR; *U.S. Private*, pg. 172
Schueler, Tammy, Chief Fin. Officer--Evans Adhesive Corp., Columbus, OH; *U.S. Private*, pg. 384
Schueppert, George L., Chief Fin. Officer & Exec. V.P.--Outboard Marine Corporation, Waukegan, IL; *U.S. Private*, pg. 478
Schuering, Jim, Controller & Treas.--J.D. Streett & Co., Inc., Maryland Heights, MO; *U.S. Private*, pg. 1047
Schuessler, Morgan M., Chief Fin. Officer--WestPoint Stevens Inc., West Point, GA; *U.S. Public*, pg. 1762
Schuette, Marvin, Chm. Bd., Pres., Chief Exec. Officer & Chief Oper. Officer--Wausau Homes, Inc., Rothschild, WI; *U.S. Private*, pg. 1154
Schuette, Marvin, Chm. Bd., Pres., Chief Exec. Officer & Chief Oper. Officer--Sterling Building Systems, Inc., Rothschild, WI; *U.S. Private*, pg. 1154
Schugart, Charles F., Chief Fin. Officer & Sr. V.P.--Innovative Valve Technology, Inc., Houston, TX; *U.S. Public*, pg. 880
Schuler, Mark, Chief Fin. Officer & Sr. V.P.--IIT Research Institute, Chicago, IL; *U.S. Private*, pg. 555
Schuler, Steven T., Chief Fin. Officer, Corp. Sr. V.P., Treas. & Sec.--Brenton Banks, Inc., Des Moines, IA; *U.S. Public*, pg. 251
Schulman, Harry D., Chief Fin. Officer & Exec. V.P.-Fin. & Admin--Windmere-Durable Holdings, Hialeah, FL; *U.S. Public*, pg. 1771
Schulte, Edward A., Chief Fin. Officer--Emtec Products Corporation, Coldwater, MI; *U.S. Public*, pg. 968
Schulte, Fred, Chief Fin. Officer--Thermon Manufacturing Company, San Marcos, TX; *U.S. Private*, pg. 1080
Schulte, Gail, Chief Fin. Officer--Andy's Restaurants Inc., Little Rock, AR; *U.S. Private*, pg. 74
Schulte, Joseph W., Chief Fin. Officer & V.P.-Fin.--Transtar Holdings, L.P., Monroeville, PA; *U.S. Private*, pg. 1097
Schultz, Dan, Chief Fin. Officer & Sr. V.P.--Grey Entertainment Inc., New York, NY; *U.S. Public*, pg. 764
Schultz, Dennis, Chief Fin. Officer & V.P.--Cranford Johnson Robinson Woods, Little Rock, AR; *U.S. Private*, pg. 286
Schultz, Douglas R., Chief Fin. Officer--Sanwa Business Credit Corporation, Chicago, IL; *Int'l*, pg. 1189
Schultz, Gary, Chief Fin. Officer, Treas. & Sec.--Arrowhead Mills, Inc., Hereford, TX; *U.S. Private*, pg. 86
Schultz, James D., Chief Fin. Officer, Sr. V.P., Treas. & Sec.--Old America Stores, Howe, TX; *U.S. Public*, pg. 1215
Schultz, Robert J., Chief Fin. Officer, Treas. & Sec.--Great Lakes Lithograph Co., Cleveland, OH; *U.S. Private*, pg. 474
Schultz, Theodore E., Chief Fin. Officer--Midco International Inc., Chicago, IL; *U.S. Private*, pg. 744
Schultz, Tom, Chief Fin. Officer--Barry Controls Aerospace, Burbank, CA; *U.S. Public*, pg. 124
Schulz, Jack, Chief Fin. Officer--New Hampshire Ball Bearings, Inc., Peterborough, NH; *Int'l*, pg. 868
Schulz, Paul J., V.P.-Fin. & Controller--Wrought Washer Mfg., Inc., Milwaukee, WI; *U.S. Private*, pg. 1192
Schulze, Max H., V.P., Treas., Gen. Counsel & Sec.--MCRB Service Bureau, Inc., Chatsworth, CA; *U.S. Private*, pg. 686
Schumacher, Bill, Chief Fin. Officer & Sr. V.P.--Select Beverages, Inc., Darien, IL; *U.S. Private*, pg. 982
Schumacher, D.A., Chief Fin. Officer & Treas.--The Cretex Companies, Elk River, MN; *U.S. Private*, pg. 289
Schumacher, Frank, Chief Fin. Officer--Heritage Air Systems, Inc., Deer Park, NY; *U.S. Public*, pg. 572
Schumacher, Norbert, Chief Fin. Officer, Sr. V.P. & Controller--Marathon Cheese Corp., Marathon, WI; *U.S. Private*, pg. 701
Schumert, Robert, Controller--Warner-Jenkinson Co., Saint Louis, MO; *U.S. Public*, pg. 1696
Schurheck, Robert J., Chief Fin. Officer & Exec. V.P.--CVB Financial Corp., Ontario, CA; *U.S. Public*, pg. 286
Schuster, Loes, Pres., Treas. & Production Dir.--Schuster & Partner, Neuss, Germany; *Int'l*, pg. 1210
Schute, E. Alan, Exec. V.P., Chief Fin. Officer-HLS Corp.--CommonHealth USA, Parsippany, NJ; *Int'l*, pg. 1483
Schwab, Mary Lou, Chief Fin. Officer, Controller & Treas.--Auto-trol Technology Corporation, Denver, CO; *U.S. Public*, pg. 148
Schwab, Patrick, Chief Fin. Officer--Clarins SA, Les Plans, Switzerland; *Int'l*, pg. 295
Schwach, Barry, Chief Fin. Officer & Exec. V.P.--Sunrise Leasing Corporation, Golden Valley, MN; *U.S. Public*, pg. 1535
Schwartz, Alan, Chief Fin. Officer & V.P.--Valleyfair, Shakopee, MN; *U.S. Public*, pg. 319
Schwartz, Alan L., V.P.-Fin., Valley Fair--Cedar Fair, L.P., Sandusky, OH; *U.S. Public*, pg. 319
Schwartz, Alan V., Chief Oper. & Fin. Officer & Exec. V.P.--Bernard Hodes Group, New York, NY; *U.S. Public*, pg. 1224
Schwartz, Chuck, Chief Fin. Officer & Sr. V.P.--People's Choice TV Corp., Shelton, CT; *U.S. Public*, pg. 1274
Schwartz, Edmund, Chief Fin. Officer--Electrolux Corporation, Atlanta, GA; *U.S. Private*, pg. 369
Schwartz, Hagi, Chief Fin. Officer & V.P.--Check Point Software Technologies Ltd., Redwood City, CA; *U.S. Public*, pg. 342
Schwartz, John P., Chief Fin. Officer--European American Bank & Trust Co., Uniondale, NY; *Int'l*, pg. 9
Schwartz, Larry, V.P.-Fin. & Admin.--RTG Furniture Corp., Seffner, FL; *U.S. Private*, pg. 905
Schwartz, M., Controller--Crest-Foam Corporation, Moonachie, NJ; *U.S. Public*, pg. 986
Schwartz, Marvin, Chief Fin. Officer & Controller--Eagle Button Co., Inc., Carlstadt, NJ; *U.S. Private*, pg. 354
Schwartz, Paul N., Pres. & Chief Oper. & Fin. Officer--Maxxam Inc., Houston, TX; *U.S. Public*, pg. 1062
Schwartz, Paul N., Chief Fin. Officer & V.P.--The Pacific Lumber Company, Scotia, CA; *U.S. Public*, pg. 1062
Schwartz, Perry, Chief Fin. Officer & Exec. V.P.--Baldwin Piano & Organ Company, Loveland, OH; *U.S. Public*, pg. 169
Schwartz, Peter A., Chief Fin. Officer & Sr. V.P.--Computer Associates International, Inc., Islandia, NY; *U.S. Public*, pg. 420
Schwartzkopf, Juanita, V.P. & Cashier--M & I First American Bank, Wausau, WI; *U.S. Public*, pg. 1050
Schwarzenbach, Robert, Chief Fin. Officer--Baltec Maschinenbau AG, Pfaffikon, Switzerland; *Int'l*, pg. 479

Schwarzer, Bernard, Chief Fin. Officer--Huber & Suhner AG, Pfaffikon, Switzerland; *Int'l*, pg. 637

Schwass, Gary, Chief Fin. Officer & Exec. V.P.--DQE Inc., Coraopolis, PA; *U.S. Public*, pg. 474

Schwass, Gary, Chief Fin. Officer & V.P.-Fin.--Duquesne Light Company, Pittsburgh, PA; *U.S. Public*, pg. 474

Schwei, James P., Controller--Columbia House Music Club, New York, NY; *Int'l*, pg. 1281

Schweitzer, Mark W., Chief Fin. Officer & V.P.--Norcen Energy Resources Limited, Calgary, Canada; *Int'l*, pg. 434

Schwella, Norbert, Chief Fin. Officer--Apollinaris & Schweppes Gmbh & Co., Hamburg, Germany; *Int'l*, pg. 78

Schwenk, Guenter, Chief Fin. Officer--ZF Friedrichshafen A.G., Friedrichshafen, Germany; *Int'l*, pg. 1522

Schwentor, Larry, Chief Fin. Officer--CMI International Inc., Southfield, MI; *U.S. Private*, pg. 195

Schweppe, Richard J., Chief Fin. Officer--CorVel Corporation, Irvine, CA; *U.S. Public*, pg. 451

Schwertly, Gary, Chief Fin. Officer & Exec. V.P.--The Woodfin Suite Hotels, San Diego, CA; *U.S. Private*, pg. 1187

Sciame, Frank, Pres., Treas., Chief Exec. & Chief Fin. Officer--F.J. Sciame Construction Co. Inc., New York, NY; *U.S. Private*, pg. 975

Sciberras, Mario, Chief Fin. Officer & V.P.--Dearborn Gage Company, Garden City, MI; *U.S. Private*, pg. 319

Scimone, George S., Chief Fin. Officer--The Reader's Digest Association, Inc., Pleasantville, NY; *U.S. Public*, pg. 1367

Sciuk, Kevin, Mgr.-Fin. & Controller--KSB Inc., Richmond, VA; *Int'l*, pg. 721

Scoggins, Rex R., Chief Fin. Officer, Controller & Sec.--C & K Market, Inc., Brookings, OR; *U.S. Private*, pg. 191

Scordo, Christopher, Chief Fin. Officer & Treas.--The Hite Company, Altoona, PA; *U.S. Private*, pg. 531

Scott, Daniel H., Chief Fin. Officer & Sr. V.P.--MGM Grand Hotel, Inc., Las Vegas, NV; *U.S. Public*, pg. 1027

Scott, J.E., Chief Fin. Officer--John Brown E & C Corporate Offices (U.S.), Houston, TX; *Int'l*, pg. 774

Scott, John, Chief Fin. Officer--Standard Communications Corp., Torrance, CA; *Int'l*, pg. 841

Scott, Malcolm, Chief Fin. Officer--The Citadel Assurance Companies, Toronto, Canada; *Int'l*, pg. 346

Scott, Peter F., Chief Fin. Officer & Sr. V.P.-Fin. & Opers.--Beringer Wine Estates Holdings, Inc., Saint Helena, CA; *U.S. Private*, pg. 1078

Scott, Robert, Chief Fin. Officer & Exec. V.P.--Morgan Stanley Dean Witter & Co., New York, NY; *U.S. Public*, pg. 1132

Scott, Ronald S., Chief Fin. Officer--Fischer Imaging Corporation, RMS Manufacturing Division, Addison, IL; *U.S. Public*, pg. 647

Scott, Sidney A., Chief Fin. Officer & Sr. V.P.-Fin. & Admin.--Daubert Industries, Inc., Westchester, IL; *U.S. Private*, pg. 313

Scotto, John A., Chief Fin. Officer, V.P. & Treas.--Iron Road Railways Inc., Washington, DC; *U.S. Private*, pg. 575

Scovanner, Doug, Chief Fin. Officer & Sr. V.P.--Dayton Hudson Corporation, Minneapolis, MN; *U.S. Public*, pg. 489

Scoville, Randy, Chief Fin. Officer--Grocers and Merchants Insurance, Inc., Covina, CA; *U.S. Private*, pg. 227

Scoville, Randy, Chief Fin. Officer& V.P.--Grocers & Merchants Management Co., Covina, CA; *U.S. Private*, pg. 227

Scoville, Randy, Chief Fin. Officer--Springfield Insurance Company, Covina, CA; *U.S. Private*, pg. 227

Scribner, John, Chief Fin. Officer & V.P.--Paterno Imports Limited, Lake Bluff, IL; *U.S. Private*, pg. 843

Scribner, Julie, Chief Fin. Officer--L.F. Driscoll Co., Bala Cynwyd, PA; *U.S. Private*, pg. 343

Scritsmier, Lyle K., Chief Fin. Officer--Pharmaceutical Marketing Services Inc., Phoenix, AZ; *U.S. Public*, pg. 1284

Scro, Jerome, Chief Fin. Officer & Sr. V.P.--Showtime Networks Inc., New York, NY; *U.S. Private*, pg. 779

Scruggs, Walter L., Chief Fin. Officer--Electrocatalytic, Inc., Union, NJ; *U.S. Private*, pg. 369

Sculley, Jay R., Chief Fin. Officer--Allied Research Corporation, Vienna, VA; *U.S. Public*, pg. 48

Sealy-Fisher, Richard, Chief Fin. Officer--Letraset New Zealand Ltd., Auckland, New Zealand; *Int'l*, pg. 462

Searfoss, David W., Chief Fin. Officer & Exec. V.P.--Phoenix Home Life Mutual Insurance Company, Hartford, CT; *U.S. Private*, pg. 863

Searfoss, David W., Chief Fin. Officer & Exec. V.P.--Phoenix Home Life Mutual Insurance Co., Hartford, CT; *U.S. Private*, pg. 863

Searls, Barbara, Chief Fin. Officer--Sealaska Corporation, Juneau, AK; *U.S. Private*, pg. 978

Seawell, Larry, Chief Fin. Officer--The Hercules Tire & Rubber Company, Findlay, OH; *U.S. Private*, pg. 523

Sebastian, Jack, Chief Fin. Officer--Norpac Foods, Inc., Stayton, OR; *U.S. Private*, pg. 802

Sebban, Armand, Chief Fin. Officer--Motel 6 Operating L.P., Dallas, TX; *Int'l*, pg. 21

Sebetic, Paul G., Chief Fin. Officer & V.P.-Fin.--TII Industries, Inc., Copiague, NY; *U.S. Public*, pg. 1556

Seblatnigg, Gerhard H., Chief Fin. Officer-Zanders--International Paper Company, Purchase, NY; *U.S. Public*, pg. 901

Seckel, Douglas, Chief Fin. Officer, Treas. & Sec.--Eagle USA Airfreight, Houston, TX; *U.S. Public*, pg. 547

Seckinger, Jacques, Chief Fin. Officer--Swissmetal Plant Dornach, Dornach, Switzerland; *Int'l*, pg. 1427

Sedgwick, Bill, Chief Fin. Officer--Dusenbery Europe Ltd., Bedford, United Kingdom; *U.S. Private*, pg. 350

Sedwick, Lindsay M., Chief Fin. Officer & Sr. V.P.--Standex International Corporation, Salem, NH; *U.S. Public*, pg. 1505

Seeley, Donald L., Chief Fin. Officer & Exec. V.P.-True North Communications Inc.--True North Communications Inc., Chicago, IL; *U.S. Public*, pg. 1641

Seery, Patrick, Chief Fin. Officer, Controller & Treas.--James McHugh Construction Co., Chicago, IL; *U.S. Private*, pg. 721

Seery, Robert P., Chief Fin. Officer & Sr. V.P.--Sumitomo Bank Securities, Inc., New York, NY; *Int'l*, pg. 1309

Segersin, Daniel T., Chief Fin. Officer & V.P.--Norwest Mortgage, Inc., Des Moines, IA; *U.S. Public*, pg. 1202

Segretto, Jim, Chief Fin. Officer--Spar Marketing Force, Inc., Rochester Hills, MI; *U.S. Public*, pg. 23

Seguin, Claude, Exec. V.P.-Fin. & Chief Fin. Officer--Teleglobe, Inc., Montreal, Canada; *Int'l*, pg. 1373

Seiffert, Robert, Chief Fin. Officer & Sr. V.P.--The Levy Organization, Chicago, IL; *U.S. Private*, pg. 664

Seikel, Terrance, Chief Fin. Officer & V.P.-Fin.--Advanced Accessories Systems, LLC., Sterling Heights, MI; *U.S. Private*, pg. 21

Selawski, Mark, Chief Fin. Officer & Sec.--Medstone International, Inc., Aliso Viejo, CA; *U.S. Public*, pg. 1082

Selfridge, Steven G., Chief Oper. Officer & Exec. V.P.--Checkpoint Systems Inc., Thorofare, NJ; *U.S. Public*, pg. 343

Seligson, Stan, Chief Fin. Officer & V.P.--Bernstein-Rein Advertising, Inc., Kansas City, MO; *U.S. Private*, pg. 137

Sellar, N.A., Chief Fin. Officer--Rolls-Royce Power Engineering plc, Newcastle upon Tyne, United Kingdom; *Int'l*, pg. 1127

Sellars, Robert M., Chief Fin. Officer--First Marathon Inc., Toronto, Canada; *Int'l*, pg. 486

Sellars, Robert M., Chief Fin. Officer--First Marathon Securities Limited, Toronto, Canada; *Int'l*, pg. 486

Sellberg, Steven, Chief Fin. Officer--Blue Bird Coach Lines Inc., Olean, NY; *U.S. Private*, pg. 150

Sellyn, Laurence G., Chief Fin. Officer & Sr. V.P.-Fin. & Corp. Devel.--Wajax Limited, Delta, Canada; *Int'l*, pg. 1484

Selman, Roger, Grp. Fin. Dir.--Shandwick International Plc, London, United Kingdom; *Int'l*, pg. 1226

Selner, Joseph B., Chief Fin. Officer & Sr. V.P.--Associated Banc-Corp, Green Bay, WI; *U.S. Public*, pg. 140

Selzer, Jim, Chief Fin. Officer, Sr. V.P.-Fin. & Asst. Corp. Sec.--Pico Products, Inc., Lake View Terrace, CA; *U.S. Public*, pg. 1294

Semones, Lewis F., Chief Fin. Officer--Interstate/Johnson Lane, Inc., Charlotte, NC; *U.S. Public*, pg. 909

Senechal, Ellen M., V.P. & Treas.--Entech, Inc., Butte, MT; *U.S. Public*, pg. 1127

Seneta, Eugene, Chief Fin. Officer, V.P., Treas. & Sec.--Xyvision, Inc., Wakefield, MA; *U.S. Public*, pg. 1787

Seng, Chew Choon, Chief Fin. Officer--Singapore Airlines, Los Angeles, CA; *Int'l*, pg. 1374

Seng, Tan Kai, Chief Fin. Officer--Parkway Holdings Limited, Singapore, Singapore; *Int'l*, pg. 1023

Senhoff, Gary, Chief Fin. Officer--Williams Worldwide, Santa Monica, CA; *U.S. Private*, pg. 1179

Senkowski, Walt, Chief Fin. Officer--New York Wire Co., Mount Wolf, PA; *U.S. Private*, pg. 795

Senseman, David S., Chief Fin. Officer & Treas--Van Dyne-Crotty, Inc., Dayton, OH; *U.S. Private*, pg. 1132

Sentillo, Carl, Chief Fin. Officer & Sr. V.P.--American General Corporation, Houston, TX; *U.S. Public*, pg. 76

Sentman, David K., Chief Fin. Officer, Sr. V.P. & Treas.--American Telecasting, Inc., Colorado Springs, CO; *U.S. Public*, pg. 93

Sents, Bruce, V.P.-Fin.--Searle & Co., Skokie, IL; *U.S. Public*, pg. 1125

Sents, Bruce R., V.P.-Fin.--Searle Laboratories, Skokie, IL; *U.S. Public*, pg. 1125

Sepanski, James M., Chief Fin. Officer & V.P.--Yankee Energy System, Inc., Meriden, CT; *U.S. Public*, pg. 1787

Seppala, Paul A., Chief Fin. Officer, V.P. & Treas.--Paul A. Schmitt Music Company, Minneapolis, MN; *U.S. Private*, pg. 971

Serafini, Claudio, Chief Exec. Officer & Mng. Dir.--Heinz Plasmon Dietetci Alimentari S.p.A., Milan, Italy; *U.S. Public*, pg. 806

Serenci, Bill, Chief Fin. Officer--The Hibbert Company, Trenton, NJ; *U.S. Private*, pg. 525

Sergesketter, Michael K., Chief Fin. Officer--Kimball Electronics Group, Jasper, IN; *U.S. Public*, pg. 957

Sergi, Martin, Vice Chm., Pres. & Chief Fin. Officer--KTI, Inc., Guttenberg, NJ; *U.S. Public*, pg. 939

Sergio, George, Chief Fin. Officer & Exec. V.P.--WWF Paper Corporation, Bala Cynwyd, PA; *U.S. Private*, pg. 1145

Serre, Yves De La, Chief Fin. Officer & Sec.--Cegelec, Levallois-Perret, France; *Int'l*, pg. 52

Serrone, H. James, Gen. Mgr.--Torotel, Inc., Grandview, MO; *U.S. Public*, pg. 1624

Serrone, H. James, Chief Fin. Officer--OPT Industries, Inc., Phillipsburg, NJ; *U.S. Public*, pg. 1624

Servoise, E., Chief Fin. Officer--Scholl Belgique SA, Brussels, Belgium; *Int'l*, pg. 1209

Sesetyan, Sevin, Chief Fin. Officer--Sixth Avenue Electronics City, Springfield, NJ; *U.S. Private*, pg. 1004

Sessions, Glen, Exec. V.P. & Chief Fin. Officer--International Women's Apparel Group, Easton, PA; *U.S. Public*, pg. 796

Sessoms, R.D., Chief Fin. Officer & Sec.--Carolina Builders Corporation, Raleigh, NC; *Int'l*, pg. 1512

Setterberg, Per, Chief Fin. Officer--Europe Tax-Free Shopping Ltd., Chicago, IL; *U.S. Public*, pg. 320

Seuthe, Brenda, Chief Fin. Officer--Topa Equities Ltd, Inc., Los Angeles, CA; *U.S. Private*, pg. 1091

Seutin, Guy, Chief Exec. Officer & Mng. Dir.--SAIT-RadioHolland Group S.A., Brussels, Belgium; *Int'l*, pg. 1151

Seutin, Guy, Chief Exec. Officer--Radio Holland Electronics, Almere, Netherlands; *Int'l*, pg. 1151

Severson, Sid, Chief Fin. Officer & Sr. V.P.--Sunflower Electric Power Corporation, Hays, KS; *U.S. Private*, pg. 1052

Sevick, Daniel M., Chief Fin. Officer & Treas.--Environmental Resources Management, Exton, PA; *U.S. Private*, pg. 378

Sevig, David, Chief Fin. Officer & Chief Information Officer--Cooker Restaurant Corporation, West Palm Beach, FL; *U.S. Public*, pg. 442

Sevillano, Jorge R., Chief Fin. Officer--Whitehall Laboratories, Guaynabo, PR; *U.S. Public*, pg. 81

Seward, James R., CFA, Chief Fin. Officer & Exec. V.P.--Seafield Capital Corporation, Kansas City, MO; *U.S. Public*, pg. 1449

Seward, Martin, Vice Chm. & Chief Fin. Officer--Kenwal Products Corp., Dearborn, MI; *U.S. Private*, pg. 615

Sewitch, Sandy B., Chief Fin. Officer--General Kinetics Incorporated, Chantilly, VA; *U.S. Public*, pg. 716

Sexton, Michael J., Chief Fin. Officer & Treas.--Prime Bancorp, Inc., Fort Washington, PA; *U.S. Public*, pg. 1326

Sexton, Roger, Chief Fin. Officer--Blazer Plc, London, United Kingdom; *Int'l*, pg. 896

Seyhun, Michael, Chief Fin. Officer--Bugle Boy Industries, Inc., Simi Valley, CA; *U.S. Private*, pg. 179

Sgambellone, James J., Asst. Sec. & Corp. Dir.-Taxes--The Sherwin-Williams Company, Cleveland, OH; *U.S. Public*, pg. 1465

Sganga, John B., Chief Fin. Officer & Exec. V.P.--Consolidated Furniture Corporation, Wilmington, DE; *U.S. Private*, pg. 265

Shackford, Paul, Chief Fin. Officer, V.P., Treas. & Sec.--Park Electrochemical Corporation, Lake Success, NY; *U.S. Public*, pg. 1258

Shackford, Paul R., Chief Fin. Officer--The American Stock Exchange, New York, NY; *U.S. Private*, pg. 62

Shadid, George D., Chief Fin. Officer & Exec. V.P.--Applebee's International, Inc., Overland Park, KS; *U.S. Public*, pg. 122

Shaffer, Oren G., Chief Fin. Officer & Exec. V.P.--Ameritech Corporation, Chicago, IL; *U.S. Public*, pg. 97

Shaffer, Oren G., Chief Fin. Officer & Exec. V.P.--Ameritech Corp., Chicago, IL; *U.S. Public*, pg. 98

Shaffet, Michael, Chief Fin. Officer--M. Fabrikant & Sons, Inc., New York, NY; *U.S. Private*, pg. 390

Shaffner, Bob, Chief Fin. Officer & Sec.--Klaussner Corporation, Asheboro, NC; *U.S. Private*, pg. 625

Shager, Philip A., Chief Fin. & Acctg. Officer & Treas.--Marietta Corporation, Cortland, NY; *U.S. Private*, pg. 702

Shah, Dipak, Treas. & Sec.--Village Ford Inc., Dearborn, MI; *U.S. Private*, pg. 1140

Shahan, Kevin, Chief Fin. Officer--Smith & Hawken, Mill Valley, CA; *U.S. Public*, pg. 279

Shaked, Yonni, Chief Fin. Officer--Egged Israel Transport Cooperative Society Ltd., Tel Aviv, Israel; *Int'l*, pg. 435

Shamilzadeh, David, Chief Fin. Officer & Sr. V.P.-Fin.--Allou Health & Beauty Care, Inc., Brentwood, NY; *U.S. Public*, pg. 55

Shamilzadeh, David, Chief Fin. Officer--Allou Distributors Inc., Brentwood, NY; *U.S. Public*, pg. 55

Shamsaei, Marcus, Chief Fin. Officer--Rainbow Technologies, GmbH, Unterschleissheim, Germany; *U.S. Public*, pg. 1359

Shamsi, A., Mgr.-Fin.--Pakistan International Airlines Corporation, New York, NY; *Int'l*, pg. 1022

Shandro, Wayne, Chief Fin. Officer--TELUS Mobility, Calgary, Canada; *Int'l*, pg. 1374

Shane, William R., Chief Fin. Officer-Cemetery & Combination Div. & Sr. V.P.--The Loewen Group, Inc., Burnaby, Canada; *Int'l*, pg. 814

Shannon, Dennis, Chief Fin. Officer--Cadaco, Chicago, IL; *U.S. Private*, pg. 910

Shannon, Michael E., Chm. Bd. & Chief Fin. Officer--Ecolab Inc., Saint Paul, MN; *U.S. Public*, pg. 562

Shannon, William, Chief Fin. Officer--Ingersoll International Inc., Rockford, IL; *U.S. Private*, pg. 562

Shao, Michael, Chief Fin. Officer--China Synthetic Rubber Corporation, Taipei, Taiwan; *Int'l*, pg. 286

Shao, Shiu, Chief Fin. Officer & Sr. V.P.--Oroamerica, Inc., Burbank, CA; *U.S. Public*, pg. 1232

Shapiro, David, Chief Fin. Officer & V.P.-Fin.--Engle Homes, Inc., Boca Raton, FL; *U.S. Public*, pg. 583

Shapiro, Lawrence B., Chief Fin. Officer--The Rottlund Company, Inc., Roseville, MN; *U.S. Public*, pg. 1406

Shapland, Dave, Chief Fin. Officer & V.P.-Plng.--Bryan Foods, West Point, MS; *U.S. Public*, pg. 1433

Sharapp, Shelton, Chief Fin. Officer--Branch Group Inc., Upper Marlboro, MD; *U.S. Private*, pg. 165

Sharkey, Daniel P., Chief Fin. Officer, V.P. & Treas.--ATMI, Inc., Danbury, CT; *U.S. Public*, pg. 12

Sharkey, Dennis M., V.P.-Fin.--Southwestern Electric Power Co., Shreveport, LA; *U.S. Public*, pg. 324

Sharland, John, Chief Fin. Officer--Lawrence Savings Bank, North Andover, MA; *U.S. Public*, pg. 980

Sharma, Anil, Chief Fin. Officer & Exec. V.P.--Raleigh Enterprises, Inc., Santa Monica, CA; *U.S. Private*, pg. 907

Sharp, Barry J., Chief Fin. Officer & V.P.--AES Corporation, Arlington, VA; *U.S. Public*, pg. 5

Sharp, Jack, Chief Fin. Officer & Sr. V.P.--Aladdin Mills, Dalton, GA; *U.S. Public*, pg. 1121

Sharp, Jim, Chief Fin. Officer--Pinnacle Automation Inc., Saint Louis, MO; *U.S. Private*, pg. 866

Sharp, Robert R., Chief Fin. Officer & V.P.--Gussco Manufacturing, Inc., Brooklyn, NY; *U.S. Private*, pg. 488

Sharpe, C.L., Grp. Fin. Controller--Q.U.F. Industries Ltd., Brisbane, Australia; *Int'l*, pg. 1074

Shassian, D.R., Chief Fin. Officer & Sr. V.P.--The Southern New England Telephone Company, New Haven, CT; *U.S. Public*, pg. 1491

Shassian, Donald R., Chief Fin. Officer & Sr. V.P.--Southern New England Telecommunications Corporation, New Haven, CT; *U.S. Public*, pg. 1490

Shatley, William, Chief Fin. Officer, Sr. V.P. & Treas.--Polyphase Corporation, Dallas, TX; *U.S. Public*, pg. 1315

Shatz, Arthur M., Chief Fin. Officer & V.P.--Alexander Doll Company, Inc., New York, NY; *U.S. Private*, pg. 33

Shauer, Gina, Chief Fin. Officer--Right Start, Inc., Westlake Village, CA; *U.S. Private*, pg. 930
Shaver, Jon, Chief Fin. Officer & Dir.-Opers.--Product Information Network, Englewood, CO; *U.S. Private*, pg. 597
Shaw, Andrew, Chief Fin. Officer--Arjo Wiggins Appleton plc, Basingstoke, United Kingdom; *Int'l*, pg. 567
Shaw, James, Chief Fin. Officer & Sr. V.P.--Newsday, Melville, NY; *U.S. Public*, pg. 1616
Shaw, Robert C., Chief Fin. Officer & Exec. V.P.-Opers.--ELXSI Corporation, Orlando, FL; *U.S. Public*, pg. 545
Shawhan, Jerry, Chief Fin. Officer & Treas.--Cincom Systems, Inc., Cincinnati, OH; *U.S. Private*, pg. 240
Shay, James C., Chief Fin. Officer & Treas.--BHA Group Holdings Inc., Kansas City, MO; *U.S. Public*, pg. 161
Shaykin, Robert H., Chief Fin. Officer--Shaykin & Company, New York, NY; *U.S. Private*, pg. 990
Shea, B.F., Chief Fin. Officer & V.P.-Fin.--Dan River Inc., Danville, VA; *U.S. Public*, pg. 478
Shea, Dave, Chief Fin. Officer--Warren Gorham Lamont, New York, NY; *U.S. Public*, pg. 1602
Shea, John, Chief Fin. Officer--Newbridge Communications, Inc., New York, NY; *Int'l*, pg. 191
Shea, Michael J., Chief Fin. Officer, Exec V.P. & Treas.--Grossman's, Inc., Stoughton, MA; *U.S. Private*, pg. 585
Shea, Stephen M., Chief Fin. Officer--Mestek, Inc., Westfield, MA; *U.S. Public*, pg. 1099
Shea, Willaim J., Chief Fin. Officer--BayBank, N.A., Boston, MA; *U.S. Public*, pg. 184
Shearer, William L., III, Chm. Bd. & Treas.--Paine Furniture Co., Natick, MA; *U.S. Private*, pg. 834
Shearing, John, Chief Fin. Officer WH & Sr. V.P.--Hilti Inc., Tulsa, OK; *Int'l*, pg. 620
Shechtman, Stephen, V.P.-Corp. Fin. Plng.--Joseph E. Seagram & Sons, Inc., New York, NY; *Int'l*, pg. 1215
Shedd, Steven T., Chief Fin. Officer & V.P.-Fin.--Proteon, Inc., Westborough, MA; *U.S. Public*, pg. 1336
Shedlarz, David L., Chief Fin. Officer & Sr. V.P.--Pfizer Inc., New York, NY; *U.S. Public*, pg. 1281
Sheehan, Edward, Chief Fin. Officer--Lake Business Products, Inc., Willoughby, OH; *U.S. Private*, pg. 643
Sheehan, Kevin, Chief Fin. Officer & Exec. V.P.--Avis Rent A Car System, Inc., Garden City, NY; *U.S. Public*, pg. 321
Sheets, Dennis D., Chief Fin. Officer, Treas. & Sec.--Valley Systems, Inc., Canal Fulton, OH; *U.S. Public*, pg. 1706
Shelby, Tony M., Chief Fin. Officer & Sr. V.P.--LSB Industries, Inc., Oklahoma City, OK; *U.S. Public*, pg. 970
Shelby, Tony M., V.P.-Fin.--L & S Bearing Co., Oklahoma City, OK; *U.S. Public*, pg. 970
Sheley, Donald R., Jr., Chief Fin. Officer & V.P.-Fin.--The Standard Products Company, Dearborn, MI; *U.S. Public*, pg. 1504
Shelley, Barry J., Chief Fin. Officer--American Radio Relay League, Newington, CT; *U.S. Private*, pg. 60
Shelton, James D., Chief Fin. Officer, Exec. V.P. & Sec.--PharMerica, Inc., Tampa, FL; *U.S. Public*, pg. 1286
Shelton, Jeff W., Chief Fin. Officer & V.P.-Fin.--Skyline Chili, Inc., Fairfield, OH; *U.S. Public*, pg. 1475
Shelton, Michael, Chief Fin. Officer, V.P. & Treas.--Directory Distributing Associates, Inc., Saint Louis, MO; *U.S. Private*, pg. 334
Shelton, Paul G., Chief Fin. Officer, Sr. V.P. & Pres.-Americo Carriers--AMCOL International Corp., Arlington Heights, IL; *U.S. Public*, pg. 63
Shelton, Rick, Chief Fin. Officer--TSI Holdings, Inc., Kansas City, KS; *U.S. Private*, pg. 1066
Shen, H.W., Chief Fin. Officer--China Steel Structure Co., Ltd., Kao-hsiung, Taiwan; *Int'l*, pg. 286
Shepard, Barry, Chief Fin. Officer, Treas. & Asst. Sec.--Scott's Liquid Gold-Inc., Denver, CO; *U.S. Public*, pg. 1447
Shepard, Barry, Treas.--SLG Plastics, Inc., Denver, CO; *U.S. Public*, pg. 1447
Shepard, John, Chief Fin. Officer--Dupey Management Corp., Coppell, TX; *U.S. Private*, pg. 348
Shephard, M.A., Chief Fin. Officer & V.P.-Fin.--Marley Mouldings Inc., Marion, VA; *Int'l*, pg. 843
Shepherd, Dale, Chief Fin. Officer--Rogers Corporation, Rogers, CT; *U.S. Public*, pg. 1402
Shepley, Lewis B., Chief Fin. Officer & Exec. V.P.--The Reliable Life Insurance Company, Webster Groves, MO; *U.S. Public*, pg. 1374
Shereck, Barry M., Chief Fin. Officer & V.P.--Concord Camera Corporation, Avenel, NJ; *U.S. Public*, pg. 429
Sheridan, Harry, Dir.-Fin.--CRH, plc, Dublin, Ireland; *Int'l*, pg. 242
Sheridan, Patrick M., Chief Fin. Officer & Exec. V.P.--Anthem, Inc., Indianapolis, IN; *U.S. Private*, pg. 76
Sheridan, Ralph S., Pres. & Chief Exec. Officer--American Science & Engineering, Inc., Billerica, MA; *U.S. Public*, pg. 90
Sheridan, William S., Chief Fin. Officer & Sr. V.P.--Sotheby's Holdings Inc., New York, NY; *U.S. Public*, pg. 1487
Sherlock, John P., Chief Fin. Officer, V.P. & Treas.--Iveco Trucks Of North America Inc., Bensalem, PA; *Int'l*, pg. 484
Sherlock, Timothy, Chief Fin. Officer & Sec.--Advantage Learning Systems, Inc., Wisconsin Rapids, WI; *U.S. Public*, pg. 22
Sherman, Brooks, Chief Fin. Officer & V.P.--National Propane Corp., Cedar Rapids, IA; *U.S. Public*, pg. 1635
Sherman, Thomas W., Chief Fin. Officer, Exec. V.P. & Treas.--Bay State Gas Company, Westborough, MA; *U.S. Public*, pg. 196
Sherman, Vernon F., Jr., Chief Fin. Officer--Lily Transportation Corp., Needham, MA; *U.S. Private*, pg. 667
Sherrick, Ed, Chief Fin. Officer--Brant Allen Industries, Inc., Greenwich, CT; *U.S. Private*, pg. 165
Sherrill, Robert, Chief Fin. Officer--Tubular Services, Inc., Houston, TX; *U.S. Private*, pg. 1108
Sherwin, J.T., Chief Fin. Officer & Exec. V.P.--Hunter Douglas N.V., Rotterdam, Netherlands; *Int'l*, pg. 639
Sherwood, David, Chief Fin. Officer--The Great Atlantic Management Company, Hampton, VA; *U.S. Private*, pg. 473
Sherwood, R.C., Chief Fin. Officer & Exec. V.P.--L.B. Smith, Inc., Camp Hill, PA; *U.S. Private*, pg. 1009
Shevchik, Daniel R., Chief Fin. Officer, V.P., Treas. & Sec.--Malcolm Pirnie, Inc., White Plains, NY; *U.S. Private*, pg. 867
Shields, Douglas G., Chief Fin. Officer, V.P. & Sec.--Noma Industries Limited, North York, Canada; *Int'l*, pg. 954
Shields, Jeffrey, Dir.-Fin.--Dreyer's Grand Ice Cream, Inc., Oakland, CA; *U.S. Public*, pg. 529
Shields, Wayne L., Chief Fin. Officer & Treas.--IBT, Inc., Merriam, KS; *U.S. Private*, pg. 553
Shiflet, Steven P., Chief Fin. Officer & Sr. V.P.--Sterling Commerce, Inc., Dublin, OH; *U.S. Public*, pg. 1515
Shifrin, Kenneth, Chief Fin. Officer & V.P.-Fin.--Hirsch International Corp., Hauppauge, NY; *U.S. Public*, pg. 829
Shillam, Paul L., Chief Fin. Officer--Diadora America, Inc., Kent, WA; *U.S. Private*, pg. 330
Shinal, Frank A., Chief Fin. Officer--J.J. Kenny Co., Inc., New York, NY; *U.S. Public*, pg. 1070
Shindler, Steven M., Chief Fin. Officer & Sr. V.P.--Nextel Communications, Mc Lean, VA; *U.S. Public*, pg. 1180
Shinomiya, Akira, Chief Fin. Officer & Dir.--Gradco (Japan), Ltd., Tokyo, Japan; *U.S. Public*, pg. 757
Shipley, Zachary, Chief Fin. Officer--Oxbow Corporation, West Palm Beach, FL; *U.S. Private*, pg. 825
Shirley, Ronald, Chief Fin. Officer, V.P. & Treas.--Golden West Baseball Club, Anaheim, CA; *U.S. Private*, pg. 461
Shively, Art., Chief Fin. Officer & Sr. V.P.--Glencoe/McGraw Hill, Westerville, OH; *U.S. Public*, pg. 1070
Shively, Arthur C., Chief Fin. Officer & Sr. V.P.--SRA McGraw Hill, Worthington, OH; *U.S. Public*, pg. 1070
Shiver, Todd, Chief Fin. Officer--Mountain Valley Spring Company, Hot Springs National Park, AR; *U.S. Private*, pg. 963
Shleinberg, A., Chief Fin. Officer--Orbotech Inc., Billerica, MA; *Int'l*, pg. 1007
Shneider, Jerry, Chief Fin. Officer & Sr. V.P.--Kelly, Scott And Madison, Inc., Chicago, IL; *U.S. Private*, pg. 613
Shockley, William M., Chief Fin. Officer, V.P. & Controller--SPS Technologies, Inc., Jenkintown, PA; *U.S. Public*, pg. 1419
Shoemaker, Kevin, Chief Fin. Officer & V.P.--Seneca Wire & Manufacturing Co., Fostoria, OH; *U.S. Private*, pg. 984
Shomaker, Thomas M., Chief Fin. Officer, V.P. & Treas.--T.D. Williamson, Inc., Tulsa, OK; *U.S. Private*, pg. 1179
Shomper, Michael L., Chief Fin. Officer & Sr. VP.--Fairfax Savings Bank, Baltimore, MD; *U.S. Public*, pg. 1543
Shong, Bruce, Chief Fin. Officer & Controller--Burnstad Brothers, Inc., Tomah, WI; *U.S. Private*, pg. 187
Shope, Michael A., Chief Fin. Officer & Treas.--Walbro Corporation, Cass City, MI; *U.S. Public*, pg. 1733
Shore, Jerry, Chief Fin. Officer--Wang's International, Inc., Memphis, TN; *U.S. Private*, pg. 1149
Short, Brian J., Chief Fin. Officer & V.P.-Fin. & Admin.--Dover Industries Limited, Burlington, Canada; *Int'l*, pg. 417
Short, Daniel L., Chief Fin. Officer & Treas.--Mid-America Energy Resources, Indianapolis, IN; *U.S. Public*, pg. 913
Short, Daniel L., Chief Fin. Officer & Treas.--Cleveland Thermal Energy Corporation, Cleveland, OH; *U.S. Public*, pg. 913
Shorten, Michael, Chief Fin. Officer--Sifco Turbine Components, Ltd., Cork, Ireland; *U.S. Public*, pg. 1471
Shovers, William, Chief Fin. Officer & V.P.-Fin.--Hayes Wheels International, Inc., Romulus, MI; *U.S. Private*, pg. 513
Showers, Mark, Chief Fin. Officer, Treas. & Sec.--Spartech Plastics, Portage, WI; *U.S. Public*, pg. 1496
Shozawa, Arata, Chief Fin. Officer & V.P.--DIC Trading (USA) Inc., Fort Lee, NJ; *Int'l*, pg. 369
Shrager, Robert, Dir.-Fin.--Dixons Group plc, Hemel Hempstead, United Kingdom,; *Int'l*, pg. 413
Shropshire, William S., Jr., Chief Fin. Officer, Exec. V.P., Treas. & Sec.--Dyersburg Corporation, Dyersburg, TN; *U.S. Public*, pg. 538
Shroyer, Will, Chief Fin. Officer--Valley American Bank, South Bend, IN; *U.S. Public*, pg. 674
Shuford, Hunt, Chief Fin. Officer & Treas.--Shuford Mills, Inc., Hickory, NC; *U.S. Private*, pg. 996
Shull, Douglas K., Chief Fin. Officer & Treas.--Casey's General Stores, Inc., Ankeny, IA; *U.S. Public*, pg. 312
Shurtleff, Douglas, Chief Fin. Officer & Sr. V.P.-Fin.--USCS International, Inc., Rancho Cordova, CA; *U.S. Public*, pg. 1659
Sibol, Mike, V.P.-Finance--The Pfaltzgraff Co., York, PA; *U.S. Private*, pg. 860
Sibold, Stephen P., Sr. V.P., Gen. Counsel & Corp. Sec.--Canadian Airlines Corporation, Calgary, Canada; *Int'l*, pg. 255
Sichler, Joseph E., Chief Fin. Officer & V.P.--CMP Media, Inc., Manhasset, NY; *U.S. Public*, pg. 279
Sider, Thomas M., Chief Fin. Officer & Exec. V.P.--Erie Family Life Insurance Company, Erie, PA; *U.S. Public*, pg. 590
Sider, Thomas M., Chief Fin. Officer--Erie Insurance Group, Erie, PA; *U.S. Public*, pg. 591
Sider, Thomas M., Chief Fin. Officer--Erie Indemnity Company, Erie, PA; *U.S. Public*, pg. 591
Sider, Thomas M., Chief Fin. Officer--Erie Insurance Exchange, Erie, PA; *U.S. Public*, pg. 591
Sider, Thomas M., Chief Fin. Officer--Flagship City Insurance Company, Erie, PA; *U.S. Public*, pg. 591
Sider, William, Chief Fin. Officer--Hertz Equipment Rental Corp., Park Ridge, NJ; *U.S. Public*, pg. 664
Sidman, Alan M., Chief Fin. Officer & Controller--Instrumentarium Imaging, Inc., Milwaukee, WI; *U.S. Private*, pg. 565
Siebert, Thomas R., Chief Fin. Officer & Exec. V.P.--Hoxan America Incorporated, Piscataway, NJ; *Int'l*, pg. 363
Siebeu, Horst, Chief Fin. Officer--Freedom Chemical Company, Radnor, PA; *U.S. Private*, pg. 425
Siefers, Robert G., Vice Chm. & Chief Fin. Officer--National City Corporation, Cleveland, OH; *U.S. Public*, pg. 1154
Siefkes, Joe, Chief Fin. Officer--Trek Corporation, Waterloo, WI; *U.S. Private*, pg. 1099
Siegel, Leonard, V.P. & Treas.--Anglo Fabrics Company, Inc., New York, NY; *U.S. Private*, pg. 74
Siegel, Mel, Chief Fin. Officer--Morgan Marshall Industries, Inc., Chicago Heights, IL; *U.S. Private*, pg. 904
Siegel, Philip, Chief Fin. Officer & V.P.--Health Management Systems, Inc., New York, NY; *U.S. Public*, pg. 802
Siegel, Samuel, Co-Vice Chm., Chief Fin. Officer, Treas. & Sec.--Nucor Corporation, Charlotte, NC; *U.S. Public*, pg. 1205
Siegel, Sheldon M., Chief Fin. Officer--OppenheimerFunds Distributor, Inc., New York, NY; *U.S. Private*, pg. 818
Siegel, Steven, Chief Fin. Officer & Gen. Counsel--Filene's Basement, Inc., Wellesley, MA; *U.S. Public*, pg. 622
Siegfried, Edward R., Chief Fin. Officer, V.P.-Fin. & Opers. & Treas.--NewsEdge Corporation, Burlington, MA; *U.S. Public*, pg. 1180
Siegfried, Robert D., V.P.-Corp. Fin. & Admin.--Medtronic, Inc., Minneapolis, MN; *U.S. Public*, pg. 1082
Siemborski, Steven L., Chief Fin. Officer & Sr. V.P.--Figgie International Inc., Cleveland, OH; *U.S. Public*, pg. 622
Sieracki, Eric P., Exec. V.P.-Corp. Fin. & Investor Rels.--Countrywide Funding Corporation, Pasadena, CA; *U.S. Public*, pg. 453
Sievers, James W., Chief Fin. Officer & Exec. V.P.--Spiegel, Inc., Downers Grove, IL; *U.S. Public*, pg. 1498
Sigman, Richard, Chief Fin. Officer--IWI Holding Limited, Westmont, IL; *U.S. Public*, pg. 861
Sigman, Richard, Chief Fin. Officer--World Pacific Ullenberg Corp., Chattanooga, TN; *U.S. Public*, pg. 861
Signorini, John E., Chief Fin. Officer, Exec. V.P. & Treas.--The F.A. Bartlett Tree Expert Co., Stamford, CT; *U.S. Private*, pg. 119
Sikora, W.A., Chief Fin. Officer--Transmontaigne, Fayetteville, AR; *U.S. Public*, pg. 1631
Silberman, Larry, V.P.-Fin. & Chief Fin. Officer--The Pilot Pen Corp. of America, Trumbull, CT; *Int'l*, pg. 1057
Silberman, Mark, Chief Fin. Officer--Refrigiwear, Inc., Dahlonega, GA; *U.S. Private*, pg. 917
Silberman, Michael D., Chief Fin. Officer & Sec.--Retrospettiva, Inc., Beverly Hills, CA; *U.S. Public*, pg. 1383
Silhacek, Robert J., Chief Fin. Officer--Acrometal Companies, Inc., Plymouth, MN; *U.S. Private*, pg. 14
Silles, Victor, Chief Fin. Officer & Treas.--Thetford Corporation, Ann Arbor, MI; *U.S. Private*, pg. 352
Silny, Frederick G., Chief Fin. Officer & V.P.--IHOP Corp., Glendale, CA; *U.S. Public*, pg. 862
Silver, Joel, Chm. Bd., Chief Fin. Officer & Chief Exec. Officer--International Cutlery, LTD, New York, NY; *U.S. Private*, pg. 569
Silver, Richard L., Chm. Bd. & Chief Fin. Officer--Akrochem Corporation, Akron, OH; *U.S. Private*, pg. 30
Silverman, Harry, Chief Fin. Officer & V.P.-Fin.--Domino's Pizza Inc., Ann Arbor, MI; *U.S. Private*, pg. 339
Silverman, John L., Chief Fin. Officer--Chi Systems Division, Ann Arbor, MI; *U.S. Public*, pg. 1539
Silverman, Mark, V.P.-Fin.--FDP Corp., Miami, FL; *U.S. Public*, pg. 603
Silzer, Frank S., Chief Fin. Officer & V.P.--MTI Vacations, Inc., Downers Grove, IL; *U.S. Private*, pg. 688
Simard, Maurice, Chief Fin. Officer--Lista International Corporation, Holliston, MA; *Int'l*, pg. 812
Simkins, Richard C., Chief Fin. Officer, Exec. V.P., Treas. & Sec.--Knape & Vogt Mfg. Co., Grand Rapids, MI; *U.S. Public*, pg. 963
Simmons, John E., Treas.--Farmer Brothers Company, Torrance, CA; *U.S. Public*, pg. 613
Simmons, John E., V.P.-Credit Life--Investors Heritage Life Insurance Co., Frankfort, KY; *U.S. Public*, pg. 952
Simmons, L. Craig, Chief Fin. Officer, V.P. & Treas.--Alico, Inc., La Belle, FL; *U.S. Public*, pg. 41
Simmons, P.R., Chief Actuary & Fin. Officer--Pearl Group Plc, Peterborough, United Kingdom; *Int'l*, pg. 100
Simmons, Tom, Chief Fin. Officer--Haviland Enterprises, Grand Rapids, MI; *U.S. Private*, pg. 511
Simon, Jacques, Chief Fin. Officer--Tefal S.A., Rumilly, France; *Int'l*, pg. 569
Simon, Jean-Marie, Dir.-Fin.--EMAP France, Paris, France; *Int'l*, pg. 451
Simon, Mark W., V.P.-Fin. & Corp. Sec.--Penn Engineering & Manufacturing Corp., Danboro, PA; *U.S. Public*, pg. 1269
Simon, William A., Chief Fin. Officer & Sr. V.P.-Admin.--Advantage Companies, Inc., Wichita, KS; *U.S. Private*, pg. 22
Simone, Andre, Chief Fin. Officer & V.P.-Fin.--ADAC Laboratories Inc., Milpitas, CA; *U.S. Public*, pg. 3
Simonis, Dennis J., Chief Fin. Officer & Sr. V.P.--Mauna Loa Macadamia Nut Corporation, Hilo, HI; *U.S. Private*, pg. 190
Simons, Michael, Chief Fin. Officer--Blauer Manufacturing Co., Inc., Boston, MA; *U.S. Private*, pg. 149
Simonsen, Eric A., Chief Fin. Officer & Sr. V.P.--First Allmerica Financial Life Insurance Company, Worcester, MA; *U.S. Public*, pg. 54
Simpkins, Art, Chief Fin. Officer--Zack Electronics, San Jose, CA; *U.S. Private*, pg. 1203
Simpson, David J., Chief Fin. Officer, V.P. & Sec.--Stryker Corporation, Kalamazoo, MI; *U.S. Public*, pg. 1525
Simpson, J. Kirk, Chief Fin. Officer--Call Interactive, Omaha, NE; *U.S. Public*, pg. 631
Simpson, James, Chief Fin. Officer--General Host Corporation, Stamford, CT; *U.S. Public*, pg. 715
Simpson, John S., Chief Fin. Officer, V.P. & Treas.--Dana Corporation, Toledo, OH; *U.S. Public*, pg. 479
Simpson, Kevin, Chief Fin. Officer & Partner--Friedman, Eisenstein, Raemer and Schwartz, LLP, Chicago, IL; *U.S. Private*, pg. 428

Simpson, Randy, Chief Fin. Officer & V.P.--Florida Crushed Stone Company, Leesburg, FL; *U.S. Private*, pg. 414
Simpson, Reid, Chief Fin. Officer & V.P.--DonTech, Chicago, IL; *U.S. Public*, pg. 98
Simpson, Wendy L., Chief Fin. Officer--Coram Healthcare Corporation, Denver, CO; *U.S. Public*, pg. 446
Sims, Barry D., Chief Fin. Officer & Sr. V.P.--Taco John's International, Inc., Cheyenne, WY; *U.S. Private*, pg. 1066
Sims, Linda, Chief Fin. Officer--The Sunflower Group, Overland Park, KS; *U.S. Private*, pg. 1052
Sims, Raymond J., Chief Fin. Officer & Sr. V.P.--Raychem Corporation, Menlo Park, CA; *U.S. Public*, pg. 1362
Simson, Jim, Chief Fin. Officer & V.P.--CS Brooks Canada Inc., Greenwich, CT; *U.S. Private*, pg. 197
Sinclair, Coral, V.P.--DEECO Industries, Hillside, NJ; *U.S. Private*, pg. 320
Sinclair, David, Pres. & Chief Fin. Officer--Pasotex Corporation, El Paso, TX; *U.S. Private*, pg. 842
Sinclair, Robert P., Chief Fin. Officer--Aaron's Rental Purchase, Atlanta, GA; *U.S. Public*, pg. 12
Sinclair, W. Ted, Chief Fin. Officer & V.P.--HD Vest Financial Services, Irving, TX; *U.S. Public*, pg. 770
Sindelar, David, Chief Fin. Officer--Mills & Partners, Saint Louis, MO; *U.S. Private*, pg. 526
Sindelar, David M., Chief Fin. Officer & Sr. V.P.--Berg Electronics, Saint Louis, MO; *U.S. Public*, pg. 212
Singer, David, Chief Fin. Officer & V.P.--Coca-Cola Consolidated, Charlotte, NC; *U.S. Public*, pg. 392
Singer, David V., Chief Fin. Officer & V.P.--Coca-Cola Bottling Co. Consolidated, Charlotte, NC; *U.S. Public*, pg. 391
Singer, Gary, Chief Fin. Officer & Controller--Habisat Globe Inc., Buffalo, NY; *Int'l*, pg. 585
Singer, Howard S., Exec. V.P.-Corp. Fin. & Investor Rels.--Centris Group Inc., Costa Mesa, CA; *U.S. Public*, pg. 328
Singer, Steven, Chief Fin. Officer--Weatherly Private Capital, Inc., New York, NY; *U.S. Private*, pg. 1156
Singholaka, Nipaporn, Chief Fin. Officer--Bangkok Bank Public Company Limited, Bangkok, Thailand; *Int'l*, pg. 146
Singleton, Raun V., Chief Fin. Officer & Sr. V.P.--Four-S Baking Company, Los Angeles, CA; *U.S. Private*, pg. 422
Sinha, Awadhesh, Chief Oper. Officer & Chief Fin. Officer--Perry Ellis, New York, NY; *U.S. Public*, pg. 1429
Sinkheiner, Rick, Chief Fin. Officer--Creative Computers, Inc., Torrance, CA; *U.S. Public*, pg. 458
Sinnott, Lawrence W., Chief Fin. Officer, V.P. & Treas.--Versar Inc., Springfield, VA; *U.S. Public*, pg. 1717
Sipkovich, Ronald J., Chief Fin. Officer, V.P.-Fin. & Admin. & Sec.--Advanced Logic Research, Inc., Irvine, CA; *U.S. Public*, pg. 703
Siracusa, Paul J., Chief Fin. Officer & Exec. V.P.--The Hertz Corporation, Park Ridge, NJ; *U.S. Public*, pg. 664
Sjoquist, Ingemar, Chief Fin. Officer--Spintab, Stockholm, Sweden; *Int'l*, pg. 1328
Sjostrom, Tomas, Chief Fin. Officer--BTL AB, Goteborg, Sweden; *Int'l*, pg. 123
Skadra, Joseph J., Chief Fin. Officer & V.P.--System Software Associates, Inc., Chicago, IL; *U.S. Public*, pg. 1552
Skaff, Larry, Chief Fin. Officer & V.P.-Fin.--Peterson Builders, Inc., Sturgeon Bay, WI; *U.S. Private*, pg. 857
Skaggs, Rick, Chief Fin. Officer & Sr. V.P.--MRA, An Integrated Marketing Communications Agency, Overland Park, KS; *U.S. Private*, pg. 687
Skaggs, Stephen, Chief Fin. Officer & Sr. V.P.--Lattice Semiconductor Corporation, Hillsboro, OR; *U.S. Public*, pg. 979
Skalicky, Steven, V.P. & Comptroller--National Union Fire Ins. Co. of Pittsburgh, Pa., New York, NY; *U.S. Public*, pg. 84
Skarupa, Tony, Chief Fin. Officer & V.P.--National Journal Group, Washington, DC; *U.S. Private*, pg. 785
Skatoff, Lawrence B., Chief Fin. Officer & Sr. V.P.--Premark International, Inc., Deerfield, IL; *U.S. Public*, pg. 1321
Skelton, Reggy, Controller--General Slicing/Red Goat Disposers, Murfreesboro, TN; *U.S. Public*, pg. 1506
Skelton, Rick, Chief Fin. Officer--T & S Brass & Bronze Works, Inc., Travelers Rest, SC; *U.S. Private*, pg. 1061
Skero, Kathleen, Chief Fin. Officer--Merrill Lynch Bank & Trust Co., Plainsboro, NJ; *U.S. Public*, pg. 1097
Skiba, Ted, Chief Fin. Officer--Fort Lock Corporation, River Grove, IL; *U.S. Private*, pg. 419
Skillen, Lynn, Chief Fin. Officer & V.P.--Snappy Car Rental, Inc., Tulsa, OK; *U.S. Private*, pg. 1010
Skinner, David J., Chief Fin. Officer-Intl.--Liberty Mutual Insurance Co., Boston, MA; *U.S. Private*, pg. 666
Skinner, Gary, Chief Fin. Officer--Mil Systems Engineering, Ottawa, Canada; *Int'l*, pg. 385
Skinner, James E., Chief Fin. Officer, Exec. V.P., Treas. & Asst. Sec.--CompUSA, Dallas, TX; *U.S. Public*, pg. 420
Sklar, David A., Chief Fin. Officer & Exec. V.P.--Imperial Bank, Inglewood, CA; *U.S. Public*, pg. 871
Skoglund, Bjorn, Mng. Dir. & Chief Fin. Officer--W.R. Grace AB, Helsingborg, Sweden; *U.S. Public*, pg. 755
Skokan, Ralph, Chief Fin. Officer--Pawling Corporation, Pawling, NY; *U.S. Private*, pg. 844
Skold, Carl, Chief Fin. Officer--CAP Programmator, Bromma, Sweden; *Int'l*, pg. 264
Skolout, William G., Chief Fin. Officer--Heska Corporation, Fort Collins, CO; *U.S. Public*, pg. 812
Skophammer, Robin W., Chief Fin. Officer, Treas. & Sec.--Craig Corporation, Los Angeles, CA; *U.S. Public*, pg. 456
Skrippak, Steve, Chief Fin. Officer--Hygrade Food Products Corporation, Southfield, MI; *U.S. Public*, pg. 1433
Skrzpczak, J. D., Chief Fin. Officer--Dictaphone Corp., Stratford, CT; *U.S. Private*, pg. 1045
Skrzypczak, Joseph, Chief Fin. Officer--Stonington Partners Inc., New York, NY; *U.S. Private*, pg. 1045
Skubas, Charles E., Chief Fin. Officer & Sec.--Herlin Press Inc., West Haven, CT; *U.S. Private*, pg. 524
Skup, David A., Chief Fin. Officer--Legacy Marketing Group, Petaluma, CA; *U.S. Private*, pg. 658
Skyum, Peder, Chief Fin. Officer--Dansk Industri Syndikat A/S, Herlev, Denmark; *Int'l*, pg. 381
Slabas, Stanley F., Chief Fin. Officer & Sr. V.P.--S & C Electric Company, Chicago, IL; *U.S. Private*, pg. 954
Slack, Paul, Sr. V.P. & Controller--Mullen Advertising, Inc., Wenham, MA; *U.S. Private*, pg. 766
Slaght, Whitney, Chief Fin. Officer--Dreison International, Inc., Cleveland, OH; *U.S. Private*, pg. 342
Slaght, Whitney, Chief Fin. Officer--Eagle Engineering & Manufacturing, Inc., Cleveland, OH; *U.S. Private*, pg. 342
Slaght, Whitney, Chief Fin. Officer--Turbo Industries, Cleveland, OH; *U.S. Private*, pg. 342
Slamad, Donald G., Chief Fin. Officer & Sr. V.P.--Turner Construction Company, New York, NY; *U.S. Public*, pg. 1645
Slamon, James, Chief Fin. Officer & V.P.-Fin.--United States Cold Storage, Inc., Cherry Hill, NJ; *U.S. Private*, pg. 1124
Slattery, James S., Chief Fin. Officer--DAP Inc., Tipp City, OH; *Int'l*, pg. 1486
Slaughter, Ken, V.P. & Treas.--The Gazette Company, Cedar Rapids, IA; *U.S. Private*, pg. 442
Sleeman, Donald G., Chief Fin. Officer, Sr. V.P., Controller & Treas.--The Turner Corporation, New York, NY; *U.S. Public*, pg. 1645
Sleeman, Donald G., Chief Fin. Officer--Turner Development Corporation, New York, NY; *U.S. Public*, pg. 1646
Slesinski, Douglas G., Chief Fin. Officer & V.P.--NVF Company, Yorklyn, DE; *U.S. Private*, pg. 772
Slevin, Paul C., Chief Fin. Officer & Treas.--Tipperary Corporation, Denver, CO; *U.S. Public*, pg. 1618
Slevin, Paul C., Chief Fin. Officer--Burro Pipeline Corp., Denver, CO; *U.S. Public*, pg. 1618
Slevin, Paul C., Chief Fin. Office--Tipperary Oil & Gas Corp., Denver, CO; *U.S. Public*, pg. 1618
Slezak, Dominic, Controller--Harford Systems, Inc., Aberdeen, MD; *U.S. Private*, pg. 641
Slivka, Ralph, Chief Fin. Officer--Kenny Rogers Roasters, Fort Lauderdale, FL; *U.S. Private*, pg. 939
Sloan, Dale R., Chief Fin. Officer & Sr. V.P.--Rochester Midland Corporation, Rochester, NY; *U.S. Private*, pg. 937
Sloan, Kenneth H., Chief Exec. Officer & Sr. Exec. V.P.-Fin., Plng.--Shoppers Drug Mart, Ltd., Toronto, Canada; *Int'l*, pg. 112
Sloan, Kerry, Chief Fin. Officer, V.P.-Fin. & Treas.--Hardaway Construction Corp. of Tennessee, Inc., Nashville, TN; *U.S. Private*, pg. 501
Slockers, Erik L., V.P. & Controller--Terra Nitrogen Company, L.P., Tulsa, OK; *U.S. Public*, pg. 1581
Slocum, Jack, Chief Fin. Officer--Molded Fiber Glass Co., Union City, PA; *U.S. Private*, pg. 756
Slutz, Larry, Chief Fin. Officer & North American Controller--Zenith Data Systems, Deerfield, IL; *Int'l*, pg. 317
Smalara, Jerome S., Chief Fin. Officer--Tressa, Inc., Erlanger, KY; *U.S. Private*, pg. 1100
Small, Mark, Chief Fin. Officer--Charles Jacquin et Cie, Inc., Philadelphia, PA; *U.S. Private*, pg. 580
Small, Michael J., Chief Fin. Officer & Exec. V.P.--360 Degrees Communications Company, Chicago, IL; *U.S. Public*, pg. 1607
Small, Scott, Chief Fin. Officer--Titan Information Systems, San Diego, CA; *U.S. Public*, pg. 1618
Smallen, Lawrence H., Chief Fin. Officer, Sr. V.P.-Fin. & Treas.--Apria Healthcare Group Inc., Costa Mesa, CA; *U.S. Public*, pg. 125
Smalley, Randall S., Chief Fin. Officer & V.P.--American Land Cruisers, Mesa, AZ; *U.S. Private*, pg. 178
Smarto, Michael G., Chief Fin. Officer & Exec. V.P.-Fin.--Tippins Incorporated, Pittsburgh, PA; *U.S. Private*, pg. 1088
Smartt, Bill, Chief Fin. Officer & Sr. V.P.-Fin.--DHL Worldwide Express, Redwood City, CA; *U.S. Private*, pg. 301
Smartt, Bill, Chief Fin. Officer--DHL Airways, Inc., Redwood City, CA; *U.S. Private*, pg. 302
Smead, H.J., Chm. Bd., Chief Exec. & Chief Fin. Officer & Sec.--Kaiser Aerospace & Electronics Corp., Foster City, CA; *U.S. Private*, pg. 605
Smernoff, Richard Louis, Chief Fin. Officer--LASMO plc, London, United Kingdom; *Int'l*, pg. 803
Smetana, Mark, Chief Fin. Officer--Eby-Brown Co., Naperville, IL; *U.S. Private*, pg. 359
Smith, Andrew, Chief Fin. Officer--Robert Fleming, Inc., New York, NY; *Int'l*, pg. 493
Smith, Brian J., Chief Fin. Officer & Exec. V.P.--IMC Global, Bannockburn, IL; *U.S. Public*, pg. 856
Smith, Bruce D., Chief Fin. Officer & Sr. V.P.--Hancock Fabrics, Inc., Tupelo, MS; *U.S. Public*, pg. 779
Smith, Caroline, Chief Fin. Officer & V.P.--Presto Food Stores, Inc., Plant City, FL; *U.S. Private*, pg. 882
Smith, Clyde M., Chief Fin. Officer & V.P.--BE & K, Inc., Birmingham, AL; *U.S. Private*, pg. 106
Smith, Curen, Chief Fin. Officer--Kaufmann's, Pittsburgh, PA; *U.S. Public*, pg. 1063
Smith, D. Todd, Treas.--Torstar Corporation, Toronto, Canada; *Int'l*, pg. 1402
Smith, David, Chief Fin. Officer--Colin Stewart Minchem Limited, Winsford, United Kingdom; *Int'l*, pg. 858
Smith, David, Chief Fin. Officer--Seed Restaurant Group, Inc., Lexington, KY; *U.S. Private*, pg. 981
Smith, David, Chief Fin. Officer--Physician Sales and Services Inc., Jacksonville, FL; *U.S. Public*, pg. 1293
Smith, David N., Chief Fin. Officer--Tennessee Valley Authority, Knoxville, TN; *U.S. Public*, pg. 1580
Smith, David S., Chief Fin. Officer & V.P.-Fin.--Crane Co., Stamford, CT; *U.S. Public*, pg. 456
Smith, Donald L., Chief Fin. Officer--The Stellar Group Inc., Jacksonville, FL; *U.S. Private*, pg. 1040
Smith, Douglas, Chief Fin. Officer--Massachusetts Envelope Co., Somerville, MA; *U.S. Private*, pg. 712
Smith, Ellen M., Chief Fin. Officer, V.P. & Comptroller--Transco Inc., Chicago, IL; *U.S. Private*, pg. 1096
Smith, Frank E., Chief Fin. Officer, Sr. V.P. & Sec.--West Coast Bancorp, Newport Beach, CA; *U.S. Public*, pg. 1755
Smith, Frank E., Chief Fin. Officer & Sr. V. P.--Sunwest Bank, Tustin, CA; *U.S. Public*, pg. 1755
Smith, G. Neil, V.P.-Fin.--Cosmos Broadcasting Corp., Greenville, SC; *U.S. Public*, pg. 992
Smith, Gene, Chief Fin. Officer, Treas. & Sec.--Rollins, Inc., Atlanta, GA; *U.S. Public*, pg. 1404
Smith, George S., Sr. V.P. & Chief Fin. Officer--Viacom International Inc., New York, NY; *U.S. Private*, pg. 778
Smith, H. Pete, Chief Fin. Officer & Exec. V.P.--Ultramar Diamond Shamrock Corporation, San Antonio, TX; *U.S. Public*, pg. 1663
Smith, Heather, Chief Fin. Officer--Derst Baking Company, Inc., Savannah, GA; *U.S. Private*, pg. 326
Smith, Howard I., Chief Fin. Officer, Exec. V.P. & Comptroller--American International Group, Inc., New York, NY; *U.S. Public*, pg. 83
Smith, James P., V.P.-Fin. & Treas.--McClatchy Newspapers Inc., Sacramento, CA; *U.S. Public*, pg. 1065
Smith, Jeffrey E., Chief Fin. Officer & V.P.--Alpharma Inc., Fort Lee, NJ; *U.S. Public*, pg. 57
Smith, Jim A., Chief Fin. Officer--Alamo Group, Inc., Seguin, TX; *U.S. Public*, pg. 34
Smith, John, Chief Fin. Officer & Dir.-Fin.--Caparo Group Ltd., London, United Kingdom; *Int'l*, pg. 264
Smith, John B., Chief Fin. Officer--Duncan Equipment Company, Oklahoma City, OK; *U.S. Private*, pg. 346
Smith, Kathleen, Controller & Asst. Sec.--Algood Food Company, Louisville, KY; *U.S. Private*, pg. 34
Smith, Kelly, Chief Fin. Officer--Replacements, Ltd., Mc Leansville, NC; *U.S. Private*, pg. 923
Smith, Kraig, Chief Fin. Officer--Rice Lake Weighing Systems, Rice Lake, WI; *U.S. Private*, pg. 927
Smith, L. Craig, Chief Fin. Officer & Sr. V.P.--Wyle Laboratories, Inc., El Segundo, CA; *U.S. Private*, pg. 1193
Smith, Lachlan M., Chief Fin. Officer, Sr. V.P. & Treas.--National City Bank, Kentucky, Louisville, KY; *U.S. Public, pg. 1154*
Smith, Larry G., Controller--Pepsi-Cola General Bottlers, Inc., Rolling Meadows, IL; *U.S. Public*, pg. 1277
Smith, M. Garrett, Chief Fin. Officer, Sr. V.P. & Treas.--Pioneer Natural Resources Co., Irving, TX; *U.S. Public*, pg. 1299
Smith, M. Lazane, Chief Fin. Officer & Sr. V.P.-Fin.--CompuCom Systems, Inc., Dallas, TX; *U.S. Public*, pg. 1424
Smith, Margaret E., Chief Fin. Officer & V.P.--Celeritek, Inc., Santa Clara, CA; *U.S. Public*, pg. 319
Smith, Marlan R., Chief Fin. Officer & Treas.--C.R.A. Holdings Inc., Kalamazoo, MI; *U.S. Private*, pg. 1029
Smith, Michael J., Gen. Counsel & Sec.--Royal Caribbean Cruises Ltd., Miami, FL; *U.S. Public*, pg. 1410
Smith, Milo A., Chief Fin. Officer & Sr. V.P.--Dominion Textile Inc., Montreal, Canada; *Int'l*, pg. 415
Smith, Molly T., Chief Fin. Officer--Weiss Scientific Glass Blowing Co., Inc., Portland, OR; *Int'l*, pg. 1408
Smith, Monica, Chief Fin. Officer--Namanco LLC, Tulsa, OK; *U.S. Private*, pg. 773
Smith, P. Jeremy, Jr., V.P.-Fin.--Gate Petroleum Company, Jacksonville, FL; *U.S. Private*, pg. 441
Smith, Paul, Chief Fin. Officer--J. Richard Industries, L.P., Toledo, OH; *U.S. Private*, pg. 249
Smith, Paul, Chief Fin. Officer--Sturmey-Archer Limited, Nottingham, United Kingdom; *Int'l*, pg. 394
Smith, Peter Sydney, Chief Fin. Officer--BPB Industries PLC, Slough, United Kingdom; *Int'l*, pg. 122
Smith, Philip S., Chief Fin. Officer, Sr. V.P. & Pres.-Admin.--Mitchell Energy & Development Corp., Spring, TX; *U.S. Public*, pg. 1117
Smith, R.P., Chief Fin. Officer--Ancon CLC, Sheffield, United Kingdom; *Int'l*, pg. 925
Smith, Ray C., Dir.-Information Sys.--BP Oil Co., Cleveland, OH; *Int'l*, pg. 220
Smith, Richard, Chief Fin. Officer & Exec. V.P.--Long John Silver's, Inc., Lexington, KY; *U.S. Private*, pg. 674
Smith, Richard A., Chief Fin. Officer & V.P.-Fin.--Arvin Industries, Inc., Columbus, IN; *U.S. Public*, pg. 136
Smith, Richard G., Chief Fin. Officer & V.P.-Fin.--American Business Products, Inc., Atlanta, GA; *U.S. Public*, pg. 70
Smith, Richard H., Sr. V.P. & Chief Fin. Officer--National Liberty Corporation, Frazer, PA; *Int'l*, pg. 26
Smith, Richard M., Pres. & Chief Fin. Officer--Coram Healthcare Corporation, Denver, CO; *U.S. Public*, pg. 446
Smith, Robert, Chief Fin. Officer & V.P.-Finance--International Correspondence Schools, Inc., Scranton, PA; *U.S. Public*, pg. 783
Smith, Robert, Chief Fin. Officer--Merrill Lynch Specialists Inc., New York, NY; *U.S. Public*, pg. 1098
Smith, Robert H., Exec. V.P. & Gen. Auditor--Nationsbank/Tennessee, Nashville, TN; *U.S. Public*, pg. 1163
Smith, Robert H., Chief Fin. Officer & Exec. V.P.-Fin. & Admin.--Novellus Systems, Inc., San Jose, CA; *U.S. Public*, pg. 1204
Smith, Robert J., Chief Fin. Officer--ICS Learning Systems, Inc., Scranton, PA; *U.S. Public*, pg. 783
Smith, Robert J., Chief Fin. Officer--NETG Applied Learning GmbH, Vienna, Austria; *U.S. Public*, pg. 784
Smith, Ronald L., V.P. & Loan Officer--Churubusco State Bank, Churubusco, IN; *U.S. Public*, pg. 674
Smith, S.A., Exec. V.P.-Worldwide Finance & Admin.--Occidental Oil & Gas Corporation, Bakersfield, CA; *U.S. Public*, pg. 1210
Smith, Terry D., Chief Fin. Officer, Exec. V.P. & Sec.--Easco Inc., Girard, OH; *U.S. Public*, pg. 548
Smith, Theresa, Chief Fin. Officer--Highway Equipment Company, Cedar Rapids, IA; *U.S. Private*, pg. 529
Smith, Thomas G., Chief Fin. Officer, Sr. V.P. & Sec.--Forest City Enterprises, Inc., Cleveland, OH; *U.S. Public, pg. 667*

Smith, Tom, Chief Fin. Officer--GNB Technologies, Atlanta, GA; *Int'l*, pg. 1021

Smith, Wayne, Chief Fin. Officer--Gebo Distributing Co., Inc., Plainview, TX; *U.S. Private*, pg. 442

Smith, Wayne, Chm. Bd., Pres. & Chief Exec./Fin. Officer--Bekins Distribution Services Co., Saint Louis, MO; *U.S. Public*, pg. 841

Smith, Wayne A., Chief Fin. Officer--Affiliated Foods, Inc., Amarillo, TX; *U.S. Private*, pg. 25

Smith, Wayne A., Chief Fin. Officer--Affiliated Finance Inc., Amarillo, TX; *U.S. Private*, pg. 25

Smith, Wayne A., Chief Fin. Officer--Affiliated Funding Inc., Amarillo, TX; *U.S. Private*, pg. 25

Smith, William, Chief Fin. Officer--Integrated Systems, Inc., Sunnyvale, CA; *U.S. Public*, pg. 885

Smith, William C., Chief Fin. Officer--Wadsworth Publishing co., Belmont, CA; *U.S. Public*, pg. 1600

Smithart, Debra L., Chief Fin. Officer & Exec. V.P.--Brinker International, Inc., Dallas, TX; *U.S. Public*, pg. 253

Smithen, Robert M., Chief Fin. Officer & Exec. V.P.--The Canada Life Assurance Company, Toronto, Canada; *Int'l, pg. 254*

Smithers, John, Chief Fin. Officer & Controller--B & R Foods, Dover, FL; *U.S. Public*, pg. 1278

Smithers, Nick, V.P.-Fin.--GEC Precision Corp., Wellington, KS; *Int'l*, pg. 545

Smoke, Daniel J., Chief Fin. Officer & V.P.--Bucyrus International, South Milwaukee, WI; *U.S. Private*, pg. 177

Smolak, John W., Chief Fin. Officer & V.P.--Lechters, Inc., Harrison, NJ; *U.S. Public*, pg. 983

Smorada, Joseph F., Chief Fin. Officer & Sr. V.P.--Axel Johnson Inc., Stamford, CT; *Int'l*, pg. 709

Smyre, Dane, Sec. & Treas.--Diamond Hill Plywood Company, Darlington, SC; *U.S. Private*, pg. 311

Smyth, C.A.G., Chief Fin. Officer--AMI, Crawley, United Kingdom; *Int'l*, pg. 707

Smyth, C.A.G., Chief Fin. Officer--Concorde Express, Bedford, United Kingdom; *Int'l*, pg. 707

Smyth, Jeff A., Chief Fin. Officer & V.P.--Bovaird Supply Co., Tulsa, OK; *U.S. Private*, pg. 162

Snead, Paul, Chief Fin. Officer--Vertex Computer Cable Products, Farmingdale, NY; *U.S. Public*, pg. 1718

Snider, Terry L., V.P. & Comptroller--Atlas Foundry & Machine Co., Tacoma, WA; *U.S. Private*, pg. 1063

Snover, Karl, Sr. V.P.-Fin.--West Coast Life Insurance Co., San Francisco, CA; *U.S. Public*, pg. 1336

Snowden, Robert, Chief Fin. Officer--Peters & Brownes Foods Ltd., Balcatta, Australia; *Int'l*, pg. 1040

Snyder, Barbara S., V.P.-Finance--Rudolph Foods Company, Lima, OH; *U.S. Private*, pg. 950

Snyder, Colby H., V.P.-Fin. & Sec.--Namico, Inc., Philadelphia, PA; *U.S. Private*, pg. 773

Snyder, Paul, Chief Fin. Officer & V.P.--The Dreyfus Corporation, New York, NY; *U.S. Public*, pg. 1085

Snyder, Paul H., Chief Fin. Officer & Sr. V.P.--Salient 3 Communications, Inc., Reading, PA; *U.S. Public*, pg. 1429

Snyder, Richard A., Chief Fin. Officer, V.P. & Treas.--Tennant Company, Minneapolis, MN; *U.S. Public*, pg. 1577

Snyder, S.I., Chief Fin. Officer, Sr. V.P.-Fin., Treas. & Sec.--Kaufman Footwear, Kitchener, Canada; *Int'l*, pg. 725

Snyder, Tom, Chief Fin. Officer--The Hammerblow Corp., Wausau, WI; *U.S. Private*, pg. 498

Snyder, Wayne, Sr. V.P. & Chief Fin. Officer--Anthem Electronics Inc., San Jose, CA; *U.S. Public*, pg. 134

Snyder, William D., Chief Fin. Officer & V.P.-Fin.--Integrated Device Technology, Inc., Santa Clara, CA; *U.S. Public*, pg. 884

Sobczyk, John S., Chief Fin. Officer & V.P.-Fin.--Jervis B. Webb Company, Farmington Hills, MI; *U.S. Private*, pg. 1156

Sobo, William T., Jr., Chief Fin. Officer, Sr. V.P. & Treas.--PAREXEL International Corporation, Waltham, MA; *U.S. Public*, pg. 1257

Sobotik, Mark, Chief Fin. Officer & V.P.-Fin.--Alamo Industrial Group, San Antonio, TX; *U.S. Private*, pg. 31

Sobotko, Ira J., Dir.-Fin.--GP Strategies Corporation, New York, NY; *U.S. Public*, pg. 694

Soderstig, Johnny, Chief Fin. Officer--Cementa AB (Degerhamn), Degerhamn, Sweden; *Int'l*, pg. 1199

Sofira, David J., Chief Fin. Officer--The Okonite Company, Ramsey, NJ; *U.S. Private*, pg. 813

Sohm, Woo-Heon, Pres.--Ssangyong Investment Management Co., Ltd., Seoul, Korea; *Int'l*, pg. 1292

Sohm, Woo-Heun, Chief Fin. Officer--Ssangyong Investment & Securities Co., Ltd., Seoul, Korea; *Int'l*, pg. 1292

Sohns, Chris, Dir.-Fin.--Smith & Nephew Rehabilitation Inc., Germantown, WI; *Int'l*, pg. 1263

Soja, Michael J., Chief Fin. Officer & V.P.--Xtra Corporation, Boston, MA; *U.S. Public*, pg. 1786

Solato, Tom, Chief Fin. Officer & Controller--Roosevelt Paper Co., Philadelphia, PA; *U.S. Private*, pg. 943

Soldano, Antonio Ricardo, Chief Fin. Officer--Johnson & Johnson Ltda., Sao Paulo, Brazil; *U.S. Public*, pg. 931

Sole, Ian, Chief Fin. Officer--Kellogg Company of Great Britain Ltd., Manchester, United Kingdom; *U.S. Public*, pg. 947

Solender, Elsie, Chief Fin. Officer--The Solender Group, Inc., Los Angeles, CA; *U.S. Private*, pg. 1012

Sollenberger, Mark L., Exec. V.P., Treas. & Asst. Sec.--BT Financial Corporation, Johnstown, PA; *U.S. Public*, pg. 163

Sollinger, Erich, Chief Fin. Officer--Asea Brown Boveri AG, Vienna, Austria; *Int'l*, pg. 2

Solomon, Steven L., Chief Fin. Officer & V.P.-Fin.--Elixir Industries, Gardena, CA; *U.S. Private*, pg. 371

Solomon, William W., V.P. & Controller--American Pad and Paper Company, Dallas, TX; *U.S. Public*, pg. 88

Solt, Russell E., Chief Fin. Officer, Sr. V.P.-Fin. & Sec.--Williams-Sonoma, Inc., San Francisco, CA; *U.S. Public*, pg. 1770

Somers, Daniel E., Chief Fin. Officer & Sr. Exec. V.P.--AT&T Corporation, Basking Ridge, NJ; *U.S. Public*, pg. 10

Somers, K. Brent, Chief Fin. Officer & Sr. Exec. V.P.--Keycorp, Cleveland, OH; *U.S. Public*, pg. 954

Sommer, James, Pres., Chief Oper. & Fin. Officer & Treas.--Service Motor Company, Dale, WI; *U.S. Private*, pg. 986

Sommer, Regina, Chief Fin. Officer & Sr. V.P.--Open Market, Inc., Burlington, MA; *U.S. Public*, pg. 1226

Sommerkamp, David, Chief Fin. Officer--The United States Playing Card Company, Cincinnati, OH; *U.S. Private*, pg. 1125

Sonderegger, Paul, Chief Oper. Officer--Swissmetal Deutschland Handelsgesellschaft mbH, Schwenningen, Germany; *Int'l*, pg. 1427

Sonksen, David R., Chief Fin Officer, V.P.-Fin., Treas. & Sec.--Microsemi Corporation, Santa Ana, CA; *U.S. Public*, pg. 1107

Sonksen, John, Chief Fin. Officer & Sr. V.P.--J.H. Baxter & Company, San Mateo, CA; *U.S. Private*, pg. 124

Sonnabend, Paul, Chief Fin. Officer--Sonesta International Hotels Corporation, Boston, MA; *U.S. Public*, pg. 1485

Soo-Doon, Loi, Chief Fin. Officer--CAM International Holdings Ltd., Singapore, Singapore; *Int'l*, pg. 238

Sooper, Bruce N., Chief Fin. Officer--Brice Building Co., Inc., Birmingham, AL; *U.S. Private*, pg. 167

Sorenson, James A., Chief Fin. Officer & V.P.--Alpha Microsystems, Santa Ana, CA; *U.S. Public*, pg. 57

Sorenson, Kenneth R., Chief Fin. Officer & Treas.--Ballard Medical Products, Draper, UT; *U.S. Public*, pg. 171

Sorheim, Dennis R., Chief Fin. Officer--System One Control, Saint Paul, MN; *U.S. Private*, pg. 851

Sorsby, J. Larry, Chief Fin. Officer, Sr. V.P. & Treas.--Hovnanian Enterprises, Inc., Red Bank, NJ; *U.S. Public*, pg. 843

Sortwell, Christopher, Chief Fin. Officer & Exec. V.P.-Intl.--The Stroh Brewery Company, Detroit, MI; *U.S. Private*, pg. 1047

Sorzano, Carl L., Chief Fin. Officer & Treas.--DeVault Foods, Devault, PA; *U.S. Private*, pg. 329

Sosne, Marshall A., Chief Fin. Officer & V.P.--Dunham's Athleisure Corporation, Waterford, MI; *U.S. Private*, pg. 346

Sosnoski, Donald S., Chief Fin. Officer, V.P. & Treas.--PVS Chemicals, Inc., Detroit, MI; *U.S. Private*, pg. 828

Soto, Raul, Chief Fin. Officer & Exec. V.P.--Carrafiello, Diehl & Associates, Inc., Irvington, NY; *U.S. Private*, pg. 215

Soto, Raymond M., Pres., Chief Exec. & Fin. Officer & Treas.--Bolt Technology Corporation, Norwalk, CT; *U.S. Public*, pg. 244

Souders, Thomas L., Chief Fin. Officer--Wheat First Butcher Singer, Inc., Richmond, VA; *U.S. Public*, pg. 640

Soukup, Larry, Controller--J.H. Larson Electrical Company, Golden Valley, MN; *U.S. Private*, pg. 652

Sourdiff, Gerald, Chief Fin. Officer & Sr. V.P.--Lutheran Brotherhood, Minneapolis, MN; *U.S. Private*, pg. 681

Southern, Douglas G., Chief Fin. Officer & Sr. V.P.--Immunex Corporation, Seattle, WA; *U.S. Public*, pg. 871

Southern, Michael W., Chief Fin. Officer & V.P.--Mississippi Power Co., Gulfport, MS; *U.S. Public*, pg. 1490

Southwood, Bill, Chief Fin. Officer--Comtext International, London, United Kingdom; *Int'l*, pg. 537

Souza, Ralph, Chief Fin. Officer, V.P. & Treas.--BIW Cable Systems, Inc., Franklin, MA; *Int'l*, pg. 417

Sowell, L. Dale, Chief Fin. Officer & Asst. Sec.--Winchester Homes, Inc., Calverton, MD; *U.S. Public*, pg. 1764

Sowerby, Ronald E., Chief Fin. Officer, Exec. V.P.-Fin., & Sec.--TCG International Inc., Burnaby, Canada; *Int'l*, pg. 1336

Sowinski, Frank, Chief Fin. Officer & Sr. V.P.--The Dun & Bradstreet Corporation, Murray Hill, NJ; *U.S. Public*, pg. 535

Spacht, Brian B., Chief Fin. Officer--The Southwood Company, Newark, DE; *U.S. Public*, pg. 136

Spacht, David B., Chief Fin. Officer, V.P. & Treas.--Artesian Resources Corporation, Newark, DE; *U.S. Public*, pg. 135

Spagliardi, Giorgio, Chief Fin. Officer--Fila USA, Sparks, MD; *Int'l*, pg. 484

Spain, Jeri, Chief Fin. & Admin. Officer--Willis Corroon Advanced Risk Management Services, Nashville, TN; *Int'l*, pg. 1505

Spallina, George, Chief Fin. Officer & V.P.--Potamkin Manhattan, New York, NY; *U.S. Private*, pg. 876

Spang, Ulf, Chief Fin. Officer & V.P.--Skandia Insurance Company Limited, Stockholm, Sweden; *Int'l*, pg. 1256

Spanier, Joseph, Chief Fin. Officer, V.P. & Treas.--TransTechnology Corporation, Liberty Corner, NJ; *U.S. Public*, pg. 1632

Sparks, Christopher, Chief Fin. Officer--John Burnham & Co., San Diego, CA; *U.S. Private*, pg. 186

Sparks, David, Chief Fin. Officer--The Dime Savings Bank of New York, New York, NY; *U.S. Public*, pg. 509

Sparks, Gary, Chief Fin. Officer & Controller--Trauth Dairy Inc., Newport, KY; *U.S. Private*, pg. 1098

Sparks, Richard T., Chief Fin. Officer--HLW International LLP, New York, NY; *U.S. Private*, pg. 491

Sparks, W. Alvon, Jr., Chief Fin. Officer & Exec. V.P.--GEICO Corporation, Washington, DC; *U.S. Public*, pg. 219

Sparks, William, Chief Fin. Officer, V.P. & Sec.--Tutor-Saliba Corporation, Sylmar, CA; *U.S. Private*, pg. 1111

Speas, John D., Chief Fin. Officer & V.P.-Fin.--Cummings Inc., Nashville, TN; *U.S. Private*, pg. 295

Specht, Dennis, Chief Oper. Officer & Chief Fin. Officer--Services Group of America, Seattle, WA; *U.S. Private*, pg. 987

Specht, Gerhard, Chief Fin. Officer--Schleicher & Schuell GmbH, Einbeck, Germany; *Int'l*, pg. 1206

Speck, Brian, Chief Fin. Officer--TargetCom, Inc., Chicago, IL; *U.S. Private*, pg. 1069

Specter, Eric M., Chief Fin. Officer & Exec. V.P.--Charming Shoppes, Inc., Bensalem, PA; *U.S. Public*, pg. 335

Spector, Paul, Chief Fin. Officer, Sr. V.P., Treas. & Sec.--Aris Industries, Inc., New York, NY; *U.S. Public*, pg. 129

Speed, Ian, Chief Fin. Officer--Courier International, Ltd., East Kilbride, United Kingdom; *U.S. Public*, pg. 453

Speers, S., Chief Fin. Officer--Chemtronics Inc., Kennesaw, GA; *Int'l*, pg. 892

Spence, J., Chief Fin. Officer--Bristol Street Motors Limited, Birmingham, United Kingdom; *Int'l*, pg. 216

Spence, Jeffrey E., Chm. Bd., Pres., Controller & Chief Exec. & Fin. Officer--Controlled Systems of Wisconsin, Inc., Nashotah, WI; *U.S. Private*, pg. 271

Spence, Kevin L., Chief Fin. Officer & V.P.--United States Filter Corporation, Palm Desert, CA; *U.S. Public*, pg. 1681

Spencer, John A., Chief Fin. Officer & Sr. V.P.-Fin.--Del Webb Corporation, Phoenix, AZ; *U.S. Public*, pg. 494

Spencer, Leroy, Chief Fin. Officer & Sr. V.P.--Jerell, Inc., Dallas, TX; *U.S. Private*, pg. 586

Spencer, Lyle, Chief Fin. Officer--Saskatchewan Wheat Pool, Regina, Canada; *Int'l*, pg. 1195

Spencer, R.W., Chief Fin. Officer & V.P.--W.A. Roosevelt Co., La Crosse, WI; *U.S. Private*, pg. 943

Spencer, Stewart, Chief Fin. Officer--National Information Corporation, Mc Lean, VA; *U.S. Private*, pg. 784

Spendley, Christopher, Chief Fin. Officer & Sr. V.P.--Washington Homes, Inc., Landover, MD; *U.S. Public*, pg. 1741

Spengler, William F., Chief Fin. Officer--Sweetheart Cup Company Inc., Owings Mills, MD; *U.S. Private*, pg. 1058

Spenia, Sam, Chief Fin. Officer--Downey Designs International, Indianapolis, IN; *U.S. Private*, pg. 342

Sperling, H., Chief Fin. Officer--Burgess GmbH, Oldenburg, Germany; *Int'l*, pg. 1500

Spett, Steven, Chief Fin. Officer--The Pace Collection, Long Island City, NY; *U.S. Private*, pg. 829

Spicer, Roberta, Chief Fin. Officer--Shillcraft, Inc., Baltimore, MD; *U.S. Private*, pg. 994

Spiegel, David A., Chief Fin. Officer--The Stephan Company, Fort Lauderdale, FL; *U.S. Public*, pg. 1514

Spiegel, John, Sec. & Treas.--Bucyrus Blades Inc., Bucyrus, OH; *U.S. Private*, pg. 383

Spiegel, John W., Chief Fin. Officer & Exec. V.P.--SunTrust Banks, Inc., Atlanta, GA; *U.S. Public*, pg. 1537

Spiewak, Roy, Pres., Chief Oper. Officer & Chief Fin. Officer--I. Spiewak & Sons, Inc., New York, NY; *U.S. Private*, pg. 1025

Spiezio, James M., V.P.-Fin.--Starmet Corporation, Concord, MA; *U.S. Public*, pg. 1511

Spilker, Frank, Chief Fin. Officer & Treas.--Cummins Intermountain Diesel, Salt Lake City, UT; *U.S. Private*, pg. 295

Spillane, George L., Chief Fin. Officer, V.P. & Sec.--California Microwave, Inc., Sunnyvale, CA; *U.S. Public*, pg. 293

Spillard, Ernest J., Sr. V.P.-Fin.--Pool Energy Services Co., Houston, TX; *U.S. Public*, pg. 1316

Spiro, Mark F., Chief Fin. Officer, V.P.-Fin., Treas. & Sec.--Calprop Corporation, Marina Del Rey, CA; *U.S. Public*, pg. 296

Spitz, Gary M., Chief Fin. Officer & V.P.--Sterling Chemicals Holdings, Inc., Houston, TX; *U.S. Public*, pg. 1515

Spitzer, Louis, Chief Fin. Officer--WTIC, Hartford, CT; *U.S. Public*, pg. 1636

Spivak, Stuart, Chief Fin. Officer--Red Apple Companies, New York, NY; *U.S. Private*, pg. 914

Spivey, Richard V., Jr., V.P.-Fin.--Sunnyland Refining Co., Inc., Birmingham, AL; *U.S. Private*, pg. 607

Spooner, Charles, Mgr.-Acctg.--Spectrum Control Technology Inc., New Orleans, LA; *U.S. Public*, pg. 1497

Spowart, Jay R., V.P.-Fin. & Corp. Sec.--Casio Phone-Mate, Inc., Torrance, CA; *Int'l*, pg. 274

Sprague, Clifford G., Chief Fin. Officer & Sr. V.P.--Kulicke & Soffa Industries, Inc., Willow Grove, PA; *U.S. Public*, pg. 968

Sprecher, Greg, Chief Fin. Officer & Sr. V.P.--Mauna Loa Resources Inc., Honolulu, HI; *U.S. Private*, pg. 191

Sprecher, Gregory A., Chief Fin. Officer & Sr. V.P.--Mauna Loa Macadamia Partners, L.P., Honolulu, HI; *U.S. Public, pg. 1060*

Spriesen, John R., Chief Fin. Officer, Sr. V.P. & Sec.--IDC Services, Inc., Chicago, IL; *U.S. Private*, pg. 554

Spriesen, Judith A., Chief Fin. Officer & Sr. V.P.--Sara Lee Corporation, Chicago, IL; *U.S. Public*, pg. 1432

Sprik, Harlan, Chief Fin. Officer & V.P.-Fin.--Trendway Corporation, Holland, MI; *U.S. Private*, pg. 1099

Springer, Branch J., Chief Fin. Officer, V.P. & Treas.--Abbey Etna Machine Company, Perrysburg, OH; *U.S. Private*, pg. 9

Springer, David, Chief Fin. Officer & Controller--Snyder Industries, Inc., Lincoln, NE; *U.S. Private*, pg. 1011

Springer, Denis E., Chief Fin. Officer & Sr. V.P.--Burlington Northern Santa Fe Corporation, Fort Worth, TX; *U.S. Public*, pg. 268

Springer, Jerry M., Chief Fin. Officer & V.P.--Shore Line Shops, Inc., Hammond, IN; *U.S. Public*, pg. 1185

Springer, Ray, Chief Fin. Officer--Jumbo Sports Inc., Tampa, FL; *U.S. Public*, pg. 935

Sproule, Michael Edward, Chief Fin. Officer & Exec. V.P.--American Mutual Life Holding Co., Des Moines, IA; *U.S. Private*, pg. 59

Sprowls, Robert J., Chief Fin. Officer & Sr. V.P.--QST Enterprises Inc., Peoria, IL; *U.S. Public*, pg. 367

Spruill, John R., Chief Fin. Officer & Exec. V.P.--CNB Bancshares, Inc., Evansville, IN; *U.S. Public*, pg. 280

Sprung, Joseph, Chief Fin. Officer--Museum Boutique Intercontinental, Ltd., New York, NY; *U.S. Private*, pg. 768

Spruyt, Michael, Chief Fin. Officer, V.P. & Treas.--Bloomsburg Mills Inc., New York, NY; *U.S. Private*, pg. 150

Spry-Bailey, Philip, Chief Fin. Officer--Alcoa of Australia Limited, Melbourne, Australia; *U.S. Public*, pg. 62

Squindo, Fritz, Chief Fin. Officer--Recordati Industria Chimica e Farmaceutica S.p.A., Milan, Italy; *Int'l,* pg. 1090

Squirra, Jose, Chief Fin. Officer--Johnson & Johnson S.A. Consumer, Madrid, Spain; *U.S. Public,* pg. 931

St. Clair, Frances, Chief Fin. Officer & V.P.--Argo-Tech Corporation, Cleveland, OH; *U.S. Private,* pg. 81

St. Clair, Thomas M., Chief Fin. Officer & Sr. V.P.--Phelps Dodge Corporation, Phoenix, AZ; *U.S. Public,* pg. 1286

St. Clare, Mark S., Chief Fin. Officer, Sr. V.P.-Fin. & Sec.--FileNet Corporation, Costa Mesa, CA; *U.S. Public,* pg. 622

St. Germain, Thomas A., Chief Fin. Officer & Sr. V.P.--Summa Four, Inc., Manchester, NH; *U.S. Public,* pg. 1527

St. Hilaire, Gary, Chief Fin. Officer--Blue Cross and Blue Shield of Massachusetts, Boston, MA; *U.S. Private,* pg. 151

St. Martin, William C., Chief Fin. Officer & V.P.--Morgan Construction Co., Worcester, MA; *U.S. Private,* pg. 761

Staab, Thomas R., Chief Fin. Officer--Fieldcrest Cannon, Inc., Kannapolis, NC; *U.S. Public,* pg. 1296

Stachtiaus, Alex, Chief Fin. Officer--M.A. Hanna Resin Distribution, Kent, WA; *U.S. Public,* pg. 781

Stack, John, Chief Fin. Officer--Minerals Technologies, Inc., New York, NY; *U.S. Public,* pg. 1115

Stackhouse, Bill, Chief Fin. Officer--Adesa Inc., Indianapolis, IN; *U.S. Public,* pg. 1116

Staedtler, Richard, Chief Fin. Officer--Castle Energy Corporation, Radnor, PA; *U.S. Public,* pg. 313

Staelens, Peter, Chief Fin. Officer, Treas. & Asst. Sec.--Dawn Food Products, Inc., Jackson, MI; *U.S. Private,* pg. 316

Staffieri, Victor A., Chief Fin. Officer--LG & E Energy Corp., Louisville, KY; *U.S. Public,* pg. 970

Staheli, Austin, Chief Fin. Officer & V.P.--The Athlete's Foot Group, Inc., Kennesaw, GA; *U.S. Private,* pg. 94

Stahlin, Kurt, Chief Fin. Officer--Knight Wendling AG, Zurich, Switzerland; *U.S. Private,* pg. 627

Staley, Graham, Chief Fin. Officer--Holiday Inn Worldwide, Atlanta, GA; *Int'l,* pg. 170

Stalkfleet, Rick, Chief Fin. Officer, V.P. & Controller--Rauland-Borg Corporation, Skokie, IL; *U.S. Private,* pg. 911

Stallard Gerald L., Chief Fin. Officer & V.P.--The Dunlap Company, Fort Worth, TX; *U.S. Private,* pg. 346

Stallings, Wayne, Chief Fin. Officer--Wellington Industries Inc., Madison, GA; *U.S. Private,* pg. 1161

Stamm, Eltriede, Chief Fin. Officer--Young & Rubicam GmbH, Vienna, Austria; *U.S. Private,* pg. 1199

Standley, John, Chief Fin. Officer & Sr. V.P.--Ralphs Grocery Company, Compton, CA; *U.S. Private,* pg. 1202

Stanek, John G., Chief Fin. Officer & Sr. V.P.--Burrell Communications Group Inc., Chicago, IL; *U.S. Private,* pg. 188

Stanger, Kent W., Chief Fin. Officer, Treas. & Sec.--Merit Medical Systems, Inc., South Jordan, UT; *U.S. Public,* pg. 1096

Stanger, Yamna M., Chief Fin. Officer--McCormick Paint Works Company, Rockville, MD; *U.S. Private,* pg. 720

Stangler, Kevin J., Chief Fin. Officer & Exec. V.P.--Security American Financial Enterprises, Inc., Minnetonka, MN; *U.S. Private,* pg. 980

Stangler, Kevin J., Chief Fin. Officer--Security Life Insurance Company of America, Minnetonka, MN; *U.S. Private,* pg. 980

Stangler, Kevin J., Chief Fin. Officer--Congress Life Insurance Company, Minnetonka, MN; *U.S. Private,* pg. 980

Stanhaus, John D., Chief Fin. Officer & V.P.--Shurfine International, Inc., Northlake, IL; *U.S. Private,* pg. 997

Stanislaw, Richard, Chief Fin. Officer--Farm Journal Inc., Philadelphia, PA; *U.S. Private,* pg. 394

Stanton, David T., Chief Fin. Officer--RAV Construction Company, Akron, OH; *U.S. Private,* pg. 586

Stanton, Kathryn, Chief Fin. Officer & V.P.-Fin.--Follett Corporation, River Grove, IL; *U.S. Private,* pg. 416

Stanton, Lee, Chief Fin. Officer--Hills Precision Components Ltd., Stoke on Trent, United Kingdom; *Int'l,* pg. 1021

Stanziale, Ronald C., Chief Fin. Officer & Sr. V.P.--Willis Faber North America, Inc.-New York, New York, NY; *Int'l,* pg. 1503

Stark, Tom, Chief Fin. Officer--IMI Cash Valve, Inc., Cullman, AL; *Int'l,* pg. 646

Starkweather, Ken, Chief Fin. Officer & Exec. V.P.-Fin.--Copley Pharmaceuticals, Inc., Canton, MA; *U.S. Public,* pg. 446

Starman, Wayne, Chief Fin. Officer--Aircraft Products Company, Delray Beach, FL; *U.S. Public,* pg. 159

Starr, James L., Chief Fin. Officer, Sr. V.P. & Treas.--Sierra Health Services, Inc., Las Vegas, NV; *U.S. Public,* pg. 1469

Startin, Richard, Chief Fin. Officer--Esselte Chrono AB, Solna, Sweden; *Int'l,* pg. 459

Stastny, John Shelby, Chief Fin. Officer--Nana Regional Corporation, Inc., Anchorage, AK; *U.S. Private,* pg. 774

Stastny, John Shelby, Chief Fin. Officer--Nana Development Corporation, Kotzebue, AK; *U.S. Private,* pg. 774

Statz, J.J., V.P. & Treas.--The Shaler Company, Waupun, WI; *U.S. Private,* pg. 786

Stavling, Ake, Exec. V.P. & Chief Fin. Officer--Astra AB, Sodertalje, Sweden; *Int'l,* pg. 93

Stavropoulos, Nickolas, Chief Fin. Officer & Exec. V.P.-Fin. & Mktg.--Colonial Gas Company, Lowell, MA; *U.S. Public,* pg. 400

Steadman, G., Chief Fin. Officer--Robertson Tooling Ltd., Kempston, United Kingdom; *Int'l,* pg. 449

Stech, Jim, Chief Fin. Officer--Gowan, Inc., Houston, TX; *U.S. Public,* pg. 572

Stedman, Jeff, Chief Fin. Officer--Cinemark USA, Inc., Dallas, TX; *U.S. Private,* pg. 240

Steel, Gordon M., Chief Fin. Officer & Sr. V.P.-Fin.--Xilinx, Inc., San Jose, CA; *U.S. Public,* pg. 1786

Steele, Alan, Chief Fin. Officer, V.P.-Fin. & Sec.--Advanced Machine Vision Corp., Medford, OR; *U.S. Public,* pg. 20

Steele, John J., Chief Fin. Officer, V.P. & Treas.--Werner Enterprises, Inc., Omaha, NE; *U.S. Public,* pg. 1754

Steele, Lee C., Chief Fin. Officer, V.P.-Fin. & Treas.--American Science & Engineering, Inc., Billerica, MA; *U.S. Public,* pg. 90

Steele, Oscar W., V.P. & Controller--M & I First National Bank, West Bend, WI; *U.S. Public,* pg. 1050

Steenbeke, Joseph J., Chief Fin. Officer, Treas., Sec. & Controller--Spray-Tech, Inc., Longwood, FL; *U.S. Private, pg. 1026*

Steenbergen, James, Pres., Chief Exec. Officer & Chief Fin. Officer--AMATI Communications Corp., San Jose, CA; *U.S. Public,* pg. 1585

Steenbergen, Leo, Chief Fin. Officer & Corp V.P.-Fin. & Admin.--N.V. Bekaert S.A., Kortrijk, Belgium; *Int'l,* pg. 183

Steeves, William H., Chief Fin. Officer & V.P.-Corp. Services--Bruncor, Inc., Saint John, Canada; *Int'l,* pg. 230

Stefanko, Robert A., Chm. Bd. & Chief Fin. Officer--A. Schulman, Inc., Akron, OH; *U.S. Public,* pg. 1441

Stefano, Brian R., Chief Fin. Officer & Controller--Peter Pan Bus Lines, Inc., Springfield, MA; *U.S. Private,* pg. 856

Stefanski, Stan, Exec. V.P. & Chief Fin. Officer--Young & Rubicam Inc., New York, NY; *U.S. Private,* pg. 1196

Stegall, Armand, Chief Fin. Officer--Electroglas, Inc., Santa Clara, CA; *U.S. Public,* pg. 727

Stegall, Douglas C., Chief Fin. Officer, V.P. & Controller--Global Marine Drilling Co., Houston, TX; *U.S. Public,* pg. 748

Stegrat, Jau-Ake, Chief Fin. Officer--Cementa AB (Slite), Slite, Sweden; *Int'l,* pg. 1199

Steichem, Charles, Chief Fin. Officer & V.P.--Penhall International, Anaheim, CA; *U.S. Private,* pg. 849

Stein, Dr., Chief Fin. Officer--Thyssen AG, Dusseldorf, Germany; *Int'l,* pg. 1387

Stein, Edward, Chief Fin. Officer--Perry H. Koplik & Sons, New York, NY; *U.S. Private,* pg. 632

Stein, Michael A., Chief Fin. Officer & Exec. V.P.--Marriott International, Inc., Washington, DC; *U.S. Public,* pg. 1047

Stein, Michael A., Chief Fin. Officer & Exec. V.P.--Fairfield Inn, Washington, DC; *U.S. Public,* pg. 1048

Steinbacher, Don, Chief Fin. Officer--Mannington Resilient Floors, Salem, NJ; *U.S. Private,* pg. 700

Steinbrun, John, Chief Fin. Officer--Ancra International LLC, Hawthorne, CA; *U.S. Private,* pg. 71

Steiner, Kevin K., Chief Fin. Officer & V.P.-Fin.--Steiner Corporation, Salt Lake City, UT; *U.S. Private,* pg. 1039

Steinhilber, Don, Chief Fin. Officer, V.P. & Treas.--CTB International Corp., Milford, IN; *U.S. Public,* pg. 284

Steinman, Mark C., Chief Fin Officer & Sr. V.P.--Spar Aerospace Limited, Toronto, Canada; *Int'l,* pg. 1287

Stejskal, Rick, Chief Fin. Officer--DCV Inc., Wilmington, DE; *U.S. Private,* pg. 301

Stelben, John, Chief Fin. Officer--HealthCare USA, Jacksonville, FL; *U.S. Public,* pg. 454

Steltmann, Harry F., Chief Fin. Officer, V.P., Treas & Sec.--Eclipse Inc., Rockford, IL; *U.S. Private,* pg. 360

Stelzel, Walter T., Chief Fin. Officer & Sr. Exec. V.P.--American National Can Company, Chicago, IL; *Int'l,* pg. 1029

Stengel, Jerome, Chief Fin. Officer, V.P. & Treas.--Genovese Drug Stores, Inc., Melville, NY; *U.S. Public,* pg. 730

Stenger, James W., Chief Fin. Officer, V.P. & Treas.--The Ailing & Cory Company, Rochester, NY; *U.S. Public,* pg. 1666

Stepanek, Mark, Chief Fin. Officer--Moroch & Assoc., Inc., Dallas, TX; *U.S. Private,* pg. 762

Stepenson, Todd R., Chief Fin. Officer, Sr. V.P. & Treas.--American States Insurance Companies, Indianapolis, IN; *U.S. Public,* pg. 997

Stephens, Barry L., Chief Fin. Officer, V.P. & Sec.--Extendicare Inc., Markham, Canada; *Int'l,* pg. 468

Stephens, Edward B., Chief Fin. Officer, V.P. & Treas.--Cade Industries, Inc., Lansing, MI; *U.S. Public,* pg. 289

Stephens, Joseph M., Chief Fin. Officer, Sr. V.P. & Treas.--Centex-Rodgers Construction Company, Nashville, TN; *U.S. Public,* pg. 322

Stephens, Mark, Vice Chm. & Chief Fin. Officer--Boston Chicken, Inc., Golden, CO; *U.S. Public,* pg. 247

Stephenson, Kirk, Dir.-Fin.--Coats Viyella plc, Manchester, United Kingdom; *Int'l,* pg. 299

Stepp, J. Michael, Chief Fin. Officer & Exec. V.P.--Collins & Aikman Corporation, Charlotte, NC; *U.S. Public,* pg. 399

Stern, Charles R., Dir.-Fin.--United News & Media plc, London, United Kingdom; *Int'l,* pg. 1443

Sternheimer, Ross, Chief Fin. Officer & Sr. V.P.--Sternheimer Brothers Inc., Sandston, VA; *U.S. Private,* pg. 1042

Sterns, Kevin, Chief Fin. Officer--Waterhouse Investor Services, New York, NY; *Int'l,* pg. 1401

Stetter, Bill, Chief Fin. Officer--Holland Mark Martin, Boston, MA; *U.S. Private,* pg. 534

Stetzenbach, John, Chief Fin. Officer--Payco American Corporation, Brookfield, WI; *U.S. Public,* pg. 1267

Steuart, John, Reg. Dir.-Fin.--DHL International (Singapore) Pte. Ltd., Singapore, Singapore; *U.S. Private,* pg. 302

Steuber, Thomas, Chief Fin. Officer--National Electric Coil, Columbus, OH; *U.S. Private,* pg. 782

Steuert, D. Michael, Chief Fin. Officer & Sr. V.P.--GenCorp Inc., Fairlawn, OH; *U.S. Public,* pg. 705

Steul, William M., Chief Fin. Officer & Treas.--Eaton Vance Corp., Boston, MA; *U.S. Public,* pg. 559

Stevens, Dave, Chief Fin. Officer, Treas. & Sec.--Scott Sports Group, Ketchum, ID; *U.S. Private,* pg. 977

Stevens, Derek, Chief Fin. Officer--British Airways PLC, London, United Kingdom; *Int'l,* pg. 218

Stevens, Donald W., Chief Fin. Officer, Exec. V.P. & Treas.--Mikohn Gaming Corporation, Las Vegas, NV; *U.S. Public,* pg. 1111

Stevens, Edward A., Chief Fin. Officer, Exec. V.P. & Sec.--Peak Technologies Group, Inc., New York, NY; *Int'l,* pg. 890

Stevens, James, Chief Fin. Officer--Nielsen, Gainesboro, TN; *Int'l,* pg. 460

Stevens, R., Chief Fin. Officer & Exec. V.P.--Robertson-Ceco Corporation, San Ramon, CA; *U.S. Public,* pg. 1394

Stevens, Richard, Chief Fin. Officer--W.B. Johnson Properties, LLC, Atlanta, GA; *U.S. Private,* pg. 594

Stevenson, Allan J., Chief Fin. Officer, Sr. V.P. & Controller--Parsons Brinckerhoff Inc., New York, NY; *U.S. Private,* pg. 841

Stevenson, Judy, Chief Fin. Officer--Introtek International, Edgewood, NY; *U.S. Private,* pg. 696

Stevenson, Marion P., Interim Chief Fin. Officer--National Data Corporation, Atlanta, GA; *U.S. Public,* pg. 1155

Stevenson, Robert W., Chief Fin. Officer, Exec. V.P. & Sec.--Esterline Technologies Corporation, Bellevue, WA; *U.S. Public,* pg. 594

Stevenson, T. A., Chief Fin. Officer--Kennecott Holdings Corporation, Magna, UT; *Int'l,* pg. 1119

Stewart, James G., Chief Fin. Officer & Exec. V.P.--Cigna Corp., Philadelphia, PA; *U.S. Public,* pg. 356

Stewart, James W., Exec. V.P. & Treas.--Colonial Commercial Corp., Levittown, NY; *U.S. Public,* pg. 400

Stewart, John, Chief Fin. Officer--ADD, Inc., Waupaca, WI; *U.S. Private,* pg. 601

Stewart, Mark, Chief Fin. Officer--Hurd Locks, Greeneville, TN; *U.S. Private,* pg. 102

Stewart, Michael R., Chief Fin. Officer, V.P., Treas. & Controller--Surgical Laser Technologies, Inc., Montgomeryville, PA; *U.S. Public,* pg. 1542

Stewart, Mike, Chief Fin. Officer--Schlegel North American Automotive Operations, Madison Heights, MI; *Int'l,* pg. 128

Stewart, Richard A.B., Chief Fin. Officer--SkyePharma PLC, London, United Kingdom; *Int'l,* pg. 1262

Stewart, Robert, Chief Fin. Officer & Exec. V.P.--Lois/EJL New York, New York, NY; *U.S. Public,* pg. 1011

Stewart, Robert K., Chief Fin. Officer & Exec. V.P.--Lois/USA Inc., New York, NY; *U.S. Public,* pg. 1011

Stewart, Ronald G., Chief Fin. Officer & V.P.--North Coast Electric Company, Bellevue, WA; *U.S. Private,* pg. 804

Stewart, William, Controller--Hunter Marine Corporation, Alachua, FL; *U.S. Private,* pg. 549

Stickley, Arthur, Chief Fin. Officer--International Dessert Partners, Miami, FL; *U.S. Public,* pg. 447

Stieber, Jay, V.P.-Fin.--Lettuce Entertain You Enterprises, Inc., Chicago, IL; *U.S. Private,* pg. 661

Stiehl, Robert J., Jr., Chief Fin. Officer, Exec. V.P.-Opers. & Treas.--Hampton Industries, Inc., Kinston, NC; *U.S. Public,* pg. 779

Still, James S., Sr. V.P., Chief Fin. Officer & Treas.--Bell Atlantic Properties, Inc., Philadelphia, PA; *U.S. Public,* pg. 203

Stillwagon, Greg, Chief Fin. Officer--Emson, Inc., Bridgeport, CT; *U.S. Private,* pg. 375

Stilwell, John P., V.P.-Fin. & Treas.--Hecla Mining Company, Coeur D'Alene, ID; *U.S. Public,* pg. 803

Stimpson, William Sandy, Chief Fin. Officer & Sr. V.P.--Gulf Lumber Company, Inc., Mobile, AL; *U.S. Private,* pg. 487

Stinchcomb, G.M., V.P. & Treas.--The Daily & Sunday Oklahoman, Oklahoma City, OK; *U.S. Private,* pg. 813

Stinnett, Wayne D., Jr., Chief Fin. Officer & Sr. V.P.--Entex, Houston, TX; *U.S. Public,* pg. 843

Stinson, Max L., Chief Fin. Officer--Reilly Industries, Inc., Indianapolis, IN; *U.S. Private,* pg. 919

Stinson, Ruth Ann, Treas. & Dir.-Personnel--Young Supply Company, Detroit, MI; *U.S. Private,* pg. 1202

Stitcher, Brian, Chief Fin. Officer--AMI Group, Inc., Lanham, MD; *U.S. Private,* pg. 7

Stivers, R.N., Chief Fin. Officer, V.P.-Fin., Treas. & Sec.--Temtex Industries Inc., Dallas, TX; *U.S. Public,* pg. 1575

Stivers, William C., Chief Fin. Officer & Sr. V.P.--Weyerhaeuser Company, Federal Way, WA; *U.S. Public,* pg. 1764

Stockett, C. Andrew, Chief Fin. Officer--Big River Grille & Brewery Works, Chattanooga, TN; *U.S. Public,* pg. 1396

Stockhausen, John, Chief Fin. Officer--Snavely Forest Products, Inc., Pittsburgh, PA; *U.S. Private,* pg. 1010

Stockinger, Richard, Chief Fin. Officer--Restaurant Associates Corporation, New York, NY; *U.S. Private,* pg. 924

Stockman, John, Chief Fin. Officer--Ellicott Machine Corporation International, Baltimore, MD; *U.S. Private,* pg. 372

Stockton, O.H.J., Chief Fin. Officer--Barclays Bank PLC, London, United Kingdom; *Int'l,* pg. 164

Stodnick, Gregory J., Chief Fin. Officer--Myers Industries, Inc., Akron, OH; *U.S. Public,* pg. 1143

Stoefen, Gary E., Treas. & Mgr.-Investments--Modern Woodmen of America, Rock Island, IL; *U.S. Private,* pg. 755

Stoehr, Charles M., Chief Fin. Officer & Sr. V.P.--Audiovox Corporation, Hauppauge, NY; *U.S. Public,* pg. 147

Stoelk, Thomas W., Chief Fin. Officer & Sr. V.P.-Fin. & Admin.--Lomak Petroleum Inc., Fort Worth, TX; *U.S. Public,* pg. 1012

Stoelk, Thomas W., Chief Fin. Officer--Lomak Operating Company, Hartville, OH; *U.S. Public,* pg. 1012

Stoga, Len, V.P.-Fin.--Hyatt International Corporation, Chicago, IL; *U.S. Private,* pg. 551

Stokes, Burt, Chief Fin. Officer & Sr. V.P.-Corp. Services--Rochester Gas And Electric Corporation, Rochester, NY; *U.S. Public,* pg. 1395

Stokes, Joseph C., Jr., Chief Fin. Officer & Sr. V.P.--Life Technologies, Inc., Rockville, MD; *U.S. Public,* pg. 504

Stokes, Terry, Chief Fin. Officer--National Cattlemen's Beef Association, Greenwood Village, CO; *U.S. Private,* pg. 780

Stoklosa, Timothy, Chief Fin. Officer--Cable Michigan, Inc., Princeton, NJ; *U.S. Public,* pg. 287

Stoll, Larry J., V.P.-Fin., Treas. & Asst. Sec.--St. Joseph Light & Power Co., Saint Joseph, MO; *U.S. Public*, pg. 1427
Stoll, Linda A., Controller--Richter-Schroeder Company, Inc., Milwaukee, WI; *U.S. Public*, pg. 1051
Stoll, Michael E., Chief Fin. Officer--Halstead Industries, Inc., Greensboro, NC; *U.S. Private*, pg. 496
Stolz, Steve, Chief Fin. Officer--PYA/Monarch, Inc., Greenville, SC; *U.S. Public*, pg. 1433
Stone, Archie, Chief Fin. Officer & Controller--Fletcher Jones Management Group, Las Vegas, NV; *U.S. Private*, *pg. 597*
Stone, David, Chief Fin. Officer & Treas.--Millipore Tylan Products, San Diego, CA; *U.S. Public*, pg. 1112
Stone, Rick, Sr. V.P. & Chief Fin. Officer--Sea Ray, Knoxville, TN; *U.S. Public*, pg. 266
Stoneburg, William K., Chief Fin. Officer & Sr. V.P.--Metz Baking Company, Deerfield, IL; *U.S. Private*, pg. 1022
Stones, Douglas G., V.P.-Fin.--Canadian Shipbuilding & Engineering Ltd., Saint Catharines, Canada; *Int'l*, pg. 259
Stonich, Timothy W., Chief Fin. Officer & Exec. V.P.--U.S. Can Company, Oak Brook, IL; *U.S. Public*, pg. 1681
Storch, P.M., Chief Fin. Officer--Scaled Composites, Inc., Mojave, CA; *U.S. Public*, pg. 1782
Storey, David, Chief Fin. Officer & Sec.--Poulter Communications PLC, Leeds, United Kingdom; *Int'l*, pg. 1065
Storin, Phillip J., Chief Fin. Officer & Sr. V.P.--USLD Communications Corp., San Antonio, TX; *U.S. Public*, pg. 969
Stork, Jake, Chief Fin. Officer--Kimball Systems BV, Terborg, Netherlands; *Int'l*, pg. 461
Storm, W.L., Chief Fin. Officer--Bee Line Company, Bettendorf, IA; *U.S. Private*, pg. 129
Story, Kendra A., Chief Fin. Officer--ABC Supply Company, Inc., Beloit, WI; *U.S. Private*, pg. 3
Story, Robert P., Jr., Chief Fin. Officer & Sr. V.P.--Courier Corporation, North Chelmsford, MA; *U.S. Public*, pg. 453
Stoudenmire, Stan, Chief Fin. Officer, V.P.-Fin. & Admin. & Sec.--Ross Systems, Inc., Atlanta, GA; *U.S. Public*, pg. 1406
Stout, Everett E., Pres., Chief Exec. Officer, Chief Fin. Officer & Controller--Metaltech, Inc., Kirkwood, MO; *U.S.* Private, pg. 735
Stoveken, James E., Jr., Chief Fin. Officer & Sr. V.P.--Westvaco Corporation, New York, NY; *U.S. Public*, pg. 1762
Stoven, Wolfgang, Chief Fin. Officer--MacGREGOR (BEL) N.V., Antwerp, Belgium; *Int'l*, pg. 670
Stoven, Wolfgang, Chief Fin. Officer--MacGREGOR (DEU) GmbH, Hamburg, Germany; *Int'l*, pg. 670
Stover, Roy, Chief Fin. Officer--Cerberus Pyrotronics Inc., Cedar Knolls, NJ; *Int'l*, pg. 1246
Stover, Wilbur G., Jr., Chief Fin. Officer & V.P.-Fin.--Micron Technology Inc., Boise, ID; *U.S. Public*, pg. 1105
Stowell, Ronald, Chief Fin. Officer--LSI Industries, Inc., Cincinnati, OH; *U.S. Public*, pg. 971
Stowell, Ronald S., Chief Fin. Officer & Treas.--LSI Industries, Inc., Cincinnati, OH; *U.S. Public*, pg. 971
Strahman, Peggy A., V.P. & Treas.--Strahman Valves, Inc., Florham Park, NJ; *U.S. Private*, pg. 1046
Strande, Steve, Chief Fin. Officer--Miller Meester Advertising Inc., Minneapolis, MN; *U.S. Private*, pg. 747
Strange, Todd W., Chief Fin. Officer--Draper Texmaco, Inc., Spartanburg, SC; *U.S. Private*, pg. 342
Stranghoener, Larry W., Chief Fin. Officer & V.P.--Honeywell Inc., Minneapolis, MN; *U.S. Public*, pg. 833
Stranghoener, Lawrence W., Chief Fin. Officer--Honeywell Europe S.A., Brussels, Belgium; *U.S. Public*, pg. 834
Strasma, Edward J., Chief Fin. Officer, Exec. V.P. & Controller--Interstate Producers Livestock Association, Peoria, IL; *U.S. Private*, pg. 573
Stratton, Andrew, Chief Fin. Officer--Reed Publishing (NZ) Ltd., Birkenhead, New Zealand; *Int'l*, pg. 1094
Stratz, Sheri, Chief Fin. Officer--Friedland Jacobs Communications, Burbank, CA; *U.S. Private*, pg. 428
Straub, Gerard, Chief Fin. Officer & Exec. V.P.--Viking Yacht Co., New Gretna, NJ; *U.S. Private*, pg. 1140
Straube, D.R., Chief Fin. Officer--Raytheon Systems Mississippi, Forest, MS; *U.S. Public*, pg. 1365
Strawbridge, Philip O., Chief Fin. Officer, Chief Admin. Officer & V.P.--OHM Corporation, Findlay, OH; *U.S. Public*, pg. 1207
Strawbridge, Philip O., Chief Fin. Officer, Chief Admin. Officer & Sr. V.P.--OHM Remediation Services Corp., Findlay, OH; *U.S. Public*, pg. 1208
Streck, Ludwig A., Chief Fin. Officer & V.P.--J.W. Allen & Company, Wheeling, IL; *U.S. Private*, pg. 37
Strecker, Al M., Sr. V.P.-Fin. & Admin.--OGE Energy Corp., Oklahoma City, OK; *U.S. Public*, pg. 1207
Stredni, Salomon, Chief Fin. Officer, V.P.-Opers. & Treas.--Omega Research Inc., Miami, FL; *U.S. Public*, pg. 1222
Street, Eileen, Chief Fin. Officer--Davis Selected Advisors, L.P., Santa Fe, NM; *U.S. Private*, pg. 315
Streich, Gordon, Chief Fin. Officer & V.P.--RK Mechanical, Inc., Denver, CO; *U.S. Private*, pg. 904
Strickland, Jeffery, Chief Fin. Officer & V.P.--Atrion Corporation, Arab, AL; *U.S. Public*, pg. 146
Strickland, Mike, Chief Fin. Officer--Nalle Plastics Inc., Austin, TX; *U.S. Private*, pg. 773
Strickley, Randy, Chief Fin. Officer--The Todd-AO Corporation, Hollywood, CA; *U.S. Public*, pg. 1619
Stringer, C.E., Chief Fin. Officer--Hansberger Precision Golf Inc., Pontotoc, MS; *U.S. Private*, pg. 499
Strodel, H.D., Chief Fin. Officer--Oerlikon-Contraves AG, Zurich, Switzerland; *Int'l*, pg. 998
Strohl, Bruce E., Chief Exec. Officer & Sr. V.P.-Fin.--The Cosmetic Center Inc., Columbia, MD; *U.S. Private*, pg. 689
Strong, Richard, Exec. V. P.-Fin. & Admin.--Lockheed Martin Electro-Optical Systems, Pasadena, CA; *U.S. Public*, pg. 1008
Stroud, Debra, Chief Fin. Officer & V.P.--Fibrebond Corporation, Minden, LA; *U.S. Private*, pg. 402
Stroud, Marie, Mgr.-Acctg.--Alamo Group, Inc., La Grange, IL; *U.S. Public*, pg. 35
Strub, Peter, Co-Owner & Chief Fin. Officer--Eurad RSCG, Zurich, Switzerland; *Int'l*, pg. 602
Struckhoff, Charles O., Chief Fin. Officer, V.P.-Fin. & Admin., Treas. & Sec.--Maverick Tube Corporation, Chesterfield, MO; *U.S. Public*, pg. 1060
Strutt, David, Chief Fin. Officer, Gen. Counsel & Sec.--The Weitz Company, Inc., Des Moines, IA; *U.S. Private*, pg. 1160
Strzelec, M.E., Chief Fin. Officer--Pressed Steel Tank Co., Inc., Milwaukee, WI; *U.S. Private*, pg. 882
Stuart, Ian R., Chief Fin. Officer--The Travelers Life & Annuity Co., Hartford, CT; *U.S. Public*, pg. 1633
Stuart, John J., Jr., Chief Fin. Officer & Treas.--Irvine Sensors Corporation, Costa Mesa, CA; *U.S. Public*, pg. 913
Stuart, R. Neil, Chief Fin. Officer--Crown Vantage Inc., Oakland, CA; *U.S. Public*, pg. 465
Stuart, William, Chief Fin. Officer & V.P.--Telco Systems, Inc., Norwood, MA; *U.S. Public*, pg. 1568
Stubblefield, Jerry W., Chief Fin. Officer, Exec. V.P. & Treas.--nVIEW Corporation, Newport News, VA; *U.S. Public*, pg. 1206
Stubblefield, John K., Jr., Chief Fin. Officer & Sr. V.P.--Sysco Corporation, Houston, TX; *U.S. Public*, pg. 1550
Stucki, Wayne, Pres. & Chief Fin. Officer--Rocky Mountain Company, Saint George, UT; *U.S. Private*, pg. 938
Stuckwisch, Vicki, Chief Fin. Officer--Barkley & Evergreen Advertising, Inc., Kansas City, MO; *U.S. Private*, pg. 116
Stuebe, David C., Chief Fin. Officer & V.P.--HON Industries Inc., Muscatine, IA; *U.S. Public*, pg. 772
Stuecker, Phillip J., Chief Fin. Officer, V.P.-Fin. & Sec.--Thomas Industries Inc., Louisville, KY; *U.S. Public*, pg. 1598
Stuehmeier, Joern, Chief Fin. Officer--Huls America Inc., Somerset, NJ; *Int'l*, pg. 1455
Stuenkel, Wayne E., Sr. V.P. & Chief Actuary--Protective Life Corporation, Birmingham, AL; *U.S. Public*, pg. 1336
Stull, Frank B., Chief Fin. Officer & Sr. V.P.--Kayser-Roth Corporation, Inc., Greensboro, NC; *Int'l*, pg. 576
Stumpo, Frank D., Chief Fin. Officer & V.P.-Finance--Resco Products, Inc., Conshohocken, PA; *U.S. Private*, pg. 924
Sturges, H.G., Dir.-Fin.--Modo Merchants Ltd., Byfleet, United Kingdom; *Int'l*, pg. 886
Sturgis, Sam, Chief Fin. Officer--Sans, S.A., Barcelona, Spain; *U.S. Public*, pg. 1434
Suarez, Amancio V., Chm. Bd., Pres., Chief Exec. & Chief Fin. Officer--Cosmo Communications Corporation, Miami, FL; *U.S. Public*, pg. 451
Suarez, J. Luis, Chief Fin. Officer--The Harodite Finishing Company Inc., North Dighton, MA; *U.S. Private*, pg. 503
Suarez, Luis Daniel Sanz, Chief Fin. Officer--Sepi, Madrid, Spain; *Int'l*, pg. 1224
Subranni, Robert, P., Chief Fin. Officer & V.P.--Peirce-Phelps, Inc., Philadelphia, PA; *U.S. Private*, pg. 847
Sudhoff, Robert, Chief Fin. Officer, V.P.-Fin. & Sec.--The Minster Machine Company, Minster, OH; *U.S. Private*, pg. 751
Sue, Christopher E., Chief Fin. Officer & Sec.--Osicom Technologies Inc., Santa Monica, CA; *U.S. Public*, pg. 1233
Suesskind, Dan S., Chief Fin. Officer--Teva Pharmaceutical Industries Ltd., Petah Tiqwa, Israel; *Int'l*, pg. 1380
Sugaya, K., Treas.--Otto Sumisho Inc., Tokyo, Japan; *Int'l*, pg. 1015
Sugishita, David M., Chief Fin. Officer & Sr. V.P.-Fin.--Synopsys, Inc., Mountain View, CA; *U.S. Public*, pg. 1548
Suh, B. Robert, Chief Fin. Officer--Digital Sound Corporation, Carpinteria, CA; *U.S. Public*, pg. 508
Suleman, Farid, Chief Fin. Officer & V.P.-Fin.--CBS Radio, New York, NY; *U.S. Public*, pg. 274
Suleman, Farid, Chief Fin. Officer & Sec.--Westwood One, Inc., New York, NY; *U.S. Public*, pg. 1763
Sullivan, Charles J., V.P.-Fin.--Wehr Constructors Inc., Louisville, KY; *U.S. Private*, pg. 1159
Sullivan, Dennis J., V.P.-Fin.--King & Prince Seafood Corporation, Brunswick, GA; *U.S. Private*, pg. 620
Sullivan, Eugene, Chief Fin. Officer--Spencer Press, Inc., Wells, ME; *U.S. Private*, pg. 1025
Sullivan, Frank C., Chief Fin. Officer & V.P.--RPM, Inc., Medina, OH; *U.S. Public*, pg. 1356
Sullivan, Garrett, Chief Fin. Officer & Treas.--Cognitronics Corporation, Danbury, CT; *U.S. Public*, pg. 394
Sullivan, Gregory W., Chief Fin. Officer & Exec. V.P.--TrizecHahn Corporation, Toronto, Canada; *Int'l*, pg. 1424
Sullivan, John, Chief Fin. Officer--Harrison & Star, New York, NY; *U.S. Private*, pg. 506
Sullivan, John, Chief Fin. Officer , Sr. V.P.-Fin. & Treas.--Trans World Entertainment Corporation, Albany, NY; *U.S. Public*, pg. 1629
Sullivan, John W., Chief Fin. Officer--Semitool, Inc., Kalispell, MT; *U.S. Public*, pg. 1456
Sullivan, Mark W., Treas.--Creative Productions, Pittsburgh, PA; *U.S. Private*, pg. 288
Sullivan, Pat, Chief Fin. Officer--Ogden Entertainment, Inc., New York, NY; *U.S. Public*, pg. 1213
Sullivan, Scott D., Chief Fin. Officer & Sec.--WorldCom, Inc., Jackson, MS; *U.S. Public*, pg. 1779
Sullivan, Scott D., Chief Fin. Officer--LDDS WorldCom Inc., East Rutherford, NJ; *U.S. Public*, pg. 1779
Sullivan, Scott D., Chief Fin. Officer--LDDS/WorldCom Communications, Revere, MA; *U.S. Public*, pg. 1779
Sullivan, Sylvia, Chief Fin. Officer & Sec.--McDonald Equipment Co., Willoughby, OH; *U.S. Private*, pg. 721
Sullivan, Terrence, Chief Fin. Officer & V.P.--DMB&B Los Angeles, Los Angeles, CA; *U.S. Private*, pg. 303
Sullivan, Thomas C., Pres. & Chief Fin. Officer--Sullivan Paper Company, West Springfield, MA; *U.S. Private*, pg. 1050
Sullivan, Timothy J., Chief Fin. Officer, Chief Admin. Officer, Sr. V.P., Treas. & Sec.--Market Facts, Inc., Arlington Heights, IL; *U.S. Public*, pg. 1046
Sulzbach, D.J., Chief Fin. Officer, V.P. & Controller--Wyman-Gordon Forgings, North Grafton, MA; *U.S. Public*, pg. 1782
Sulzbach, D.J., Chief Fin. Officer--Wyman-Gordon Forgings, Inc., Houston, TX; *U.S. Public*, pg. 1782
Sum, Joseph J., Chief Fin. Officer, V.P. & Treas.--Continental Materials Corporation, Chicago, IL; *U.S. Public*, pg. 441
Summer, Thomas, Chief Fin. Officer & Sr. V.P.--Canandaigua Wine Company, Inc., Canandaigua, NY; *U.S. Public*, pg. 300
Summerford, R. Michael, Chief Fin. Officer & V.P.--ChemFirst Inc., Jackson, MS; *U.S. Public*, pg. 344
Summers, Curtis D., Chief Fin. Officer--D.A. Stuart Company, Warrenville, IL; *U.S. Private*, pg. 1048
Summers, William E., V.P. & Controller--Plant City Steel Co., Plant City, FL; *U.S. Public*, pg. 793
Sumner, Ronald H., Exec. V.P.-Fin.--Miramichi Pulp & Paper Inc., Newcastle, Canada; *Int'l*, pg. 1104
Sumner, Sharon, Chief Fin. Officer & Controller--Craddock-Terry Inc., Lynchburg, VA; *U.S. Private*, pg. 284
Sumrall, K.R., Acting Chief Fin. Officer & Sec.--Texas Micro, Inc., Houston, TX; *U.S. Public*, pg. 1586
Sumrall, K.R., Chief Fin. Officer--Texas Microsystems Inc., Houston, TX; *U.S. Public*, pg. 1586
Sumrall, O. Malcolm, Chief Fin. Officer, Treas. & Sec.--Associated Equipment Company of Delaware, Mobile, AL; *U.S. Private*, pg. 90
Sundberg, Nils-Erik, Chief Fin. Officer--Opel Oy, Espoo, Finland; *U.S. Public*, pg. 723
Sundblad, Erik, Mng. Dir.--Neste Cellplast AB, Norrtalje, Sweden; *Int'l*, pg. 914
Sundell, Susan, Chief Fin. Officer--Stocker & Yale, Inc., Salem, NH; *U.S. Public*, pg. 1518
Sunderhaft, Eugene R., Chief Fin. Officer, Sr. V.P.-Fin. & Sec.--The Penn Traffic Company, Syracuse, NY; *U.S. Public*, pg. 1270
Sundquist, Jan, Chief Fin. Officer--Nobel Biocare, Goteborg, Sweden; *Int'l*, pg. 951
Sundstrom, David A., V.P.-Fin. & Admin.--Barbour Thread, Inc., Blue Mountain, AL; *Int'l*, pg. 618
Sunnermalm, Leif, Exec. V.P. & Chief Fin. Officer--Sandvik AB, Sandviken, Sweden; *Int'l*, pg. 1185
Suokko, Ronald, Chief Fin. Officer--SAIC Commercial Enterprises, Inc., San Diego, CA; *U.S. Private*, pg. 976
Surico, Richard, Chief Exec. Officer, Treas.--Feintool U.S. Operations Inc., White Plains, NY; *Int'l*, pg. 479
Surma, Ronald F., Chief Fin. Officer & Controller--Processed Plastic Company, Montgomery, IL; *U.S. Private*, pg. 888
Susani, Franca, Chief Fin. Officer--EURO RSCG Mezzano Costantini Mignani, Milan, Italy; *Int'l*, pg. 603
Sussman, Greta, Sec. & Treas.--Pretty Neat Products, Kearny, NJ; *U.S. Public*, pg. 1177
Sussman, I. Harvey, Chief Fin. Officer--Jabel, Inc., Irvington, NJ; *U.S. Private*, pg. 579
Sussman, Stuart, Chief Fin. Officer & V.P.--Leslie - Locke, Inc., Atlanta, GA; *U.S. Public*, pg. 989
Sutherland, Fred, Chief Fin. Officer & Exec. V.P.--Aramark Corp., Philadelphia, PA; *U.S. Private*, pg. 78
Sutherland, Gary L., V.P.-Fin.--The Kelly-Springfield Tire Company, Cumberland, MD; *U.S. Public*, pg. 753
Sutherland, Robert, Chief Fin. Officer--Teknor Apex Company, Pawtucket, RI; *U.S. Private*, pg. 1073
Sutten, Doug, V.P.-Fin.--Westin Hotels & Resorts, Seattle, WA; *U.S. Public*, pg. 1512
Sutter, Blanche M., Chief Fin. Officer, Exec. V.P. & Sec.--Caere Corporation, Los Gatos, CA; *U.S. Public*, pg. 291
Sutterfield, Howard, Chief Fin. Officer--Brink Electric Construction Company, Rapid City, SD; *U.S. Private*, pg. 169
Sutton, Terrye, Chief Fin. Officer--Letraset Canada Ltd., Markham, Canada; *Int'l*, pg. 461
Suwald, Stephan, Chief Fin. Officer--Sonotron Holding AG, Zug, Switzerland; *Int'l*, pg. 644
Suzuki, Teiji, Chief Fin. Officer, Sec. & Mng. Dir.--Achilles Corporation, Tokyo, Japan; *Int'l*, pg. 22
Suzumura, Koichi, Sr. Mng. Dir.--Nippon Yusen K.K., Tokyo, Japan; *Int'l*, pg. 941
Svendsen, Steve, Chief Fin. Officer & Sr. V.P.--Edward Hines Lumber Co., Itasca, IL; *U.S. Private*, pg. 530
Svensson, Lennart, Chief Fin. Officer--Mo och Domsjo AB, Stockholm, Sweden; *Int'l*, pg. 885
Svoboda, Larry J., Chief Fin. Officer & Sr. V.P.--Hanover Direct, Inc., Weehawken, NJ; *U.S. Public*, pg. 782
Swain, Don, V.P.-Fin. & Corp. Treas.--Parthenon Insurance Co., Nashville, TN; *U.S. Public*, pg. 405
Swallow, Adrian, Chief Fin. Officer--Brimax Books Limited, Newmarket, United Kingdom; *Int'l*, pg. 1093
Swanson, Craig M., Chief Fin. Officer, V.P.-Fin. & Sec.--Protocol Systems, Inc., Beaverton, OR; *U.S. Public*, pg. 1336
Swanson, Dennis, V.P.-Fin.--Gits Manufacturing Company, Inc., Creston, IA; *U.S. Public*, pg. 1705
Swanson, Larry, Chief Fin. Officer--Beaulieu Group, Dalton, GA; *U.S. Private*, pg. 127
Swart, Dave, Chief Fin. Officer--DARCOM Technologies, Inc., Nashua, NH; *U.S. Private*, pg. 311
Swartwout, James R., Chm. Bd., Pres. & Chief Fin. Officer--Summa Industries, Torrance, CA; *U.S. Public*, pg. 1527
Swartz, G. I., Chief Fin. Officer, Treas. & Controller--U.S. Borax Inc., Valencia, CA; *Int'l*, pg. 1119
Swartz, Jesse, Chief Fin. Officer--B. Green & Co., Owings Mills, MD; *U.S. Private*, pg. 476
Swartz, Mark, Chief Fin. Officer--Keystone International, Inc., Exeter, NH; *U.S. Public*, pg. 1650
Swartz, Mark H., Chief Fin. Officer & Exec. V.P.--Tyco International Ltd., Exeter, NH; *U.S. Public*, pg. 1647
Swartz, Robert A., Chief Fin. Officer & V.P.--International Total Services, Independence, OH; *U.S. Public*, pg. 908
Sweeney, Robert, Chief Fin. Officer & V.P.-Fin.--American Felt & Filter, Newburgh, NY; *U.S. Private*, pg. 54
Swent, Jay, Chief Fin. Officer--Cyrix Corporation, Richardson, TX; *U.S. Public*, pg. 1160

Swergert, Charles, Chief Fin. Officer--Taylor Oil Co. Inc., Winston Salem, NC; *U.S. Private*, pg. 1071
Swift, John D., V.P.-Fin. & Chief Fin. Officer--Mohawk Industries, Inc., Calhoun, GA; *U.S. Public*, pg. 1121
Swihart, Susannah M., Chief Fin. Officer--BankBoston Corporation, Boston, MA; *U.S. Public*, pg. 183
Swinehart, Keith, Sr., Chm. Bd., Chief Exec. Officer & Chief Fin. Officer--Vanguard Plastics, Inc., Mc Pherson, KS; *U.S. Private*, pg. 1134
Swistowicz, Donald J., Chief Fin. & Acctg. Officer & Exec. V.P.--First Midwest Bancorp, Inc., Itasca, IL; *U.S. Public*, pg. 636
Switz, Robert E., Chief Fin. Officer & Sr. V.P.--ADC Telecommunications, Inc., Minnetonka, MN; *U.S. Public*, pg. 4
Swope, P.F., Chief Fin. Officer--IDenticard Systems, Inc., Lancaster, PA; *U.S. Private*, pg. 557
Swycher, Ian, Chief Fin. Officer--Esselte Europe, London, United Kingdom; *Int'l*, pg. 460
Sylvia, Joseph, Chief Fin. Officer & Exec. V.P.--Simonds Industries Inc., Fitchburg, MA; *U.S. Private*, pg. 1001
Symington, A.E., V.P.-Investments--Simpson Investment Co., Seattle, WA; *U.S. Private*, pg. 1003
Symons, Larry L., Chief Fin. Officer & V.P.--Ellwood City Forge, Ellwood City, PA; *U.S. Private*, pg. 373
Syrjamaki, Maxine, Chief Fin. Officer & Exec. V.P.--Jefferies & Company, Inc., Los Angeles, CA; *U.S. Public*, pg. 925
Szablowski, David, Chief Fin. Officer--Pennsylvania Steel Foundry & Machine Company, Hamburg, PA; *U.S. Public*, pg. 142
Szabo, J. Gregory, Chief Fin. Officer & V.P.--Accuride Corp., Henderson, KY; *U.S. Public*, pg. 1286
Szews, Charles, Chief Fin. Officer & Exec. V.P.--Oshkosh Truck Corporation, Oshkosh, WI; *U.S. Public*, pg. 1233
Szidik, Judy, V.P.-Fin. & Admin.--Allied Digital Technologies, Elk Grove Village, IL; *U.S. Public*, pg. 48
Szklany, Al, Chief Fin. Officer--Leica Inc., Deerfield, IL; *Int'l*, pg. 806
Szostak, David, Chief Fin. Officer--XL Vision Inc., Sebastian, FL; *U.S. Public*, pg. 1424
Taanila, Antti, Chief Fin. Officer--Leiras Oy, Turku, Finland; *Int'l*, pg. 639
Tabakin, Scott M., Chief Fin. Officer & Exec. V.P.--Beverly Enterprises, Inc., Fort Smith, AR; *U.S. Public*, pg. 227
Taber, Michael, V.P.-Fin.--RFI Corp., Bay Shore, NY; *U.S. Public*, pg. 494
Taber, Michael, V.P.-Fin--Bertan High Voltage, Hicksville, NY; *U.S. Public*, pg. 494
Tabor, Ed, Chief Fin. Officer & Treas.--Acorn Structures, Acton, MA; *U.S. Private*, pg. 320
Tabor, Edward, Treas.--Deck House Inc., Acton, MA; *U.S. Private*, pg. 320
Tabs, Leonard, Chief Fin. Officer & Sr. V.P.-Fin.--Fortunoff, Uniondale, NY; *U.S. Private*, pg. 420
Tacke, Kelly, Chief Fin. Officer, V.P.-Fin. & Sec.--Palm Harbor Homes, Inc., Dallas, TX; *U.S. Public*, pg. 1254
Tadano, Hiroshi, Gen. Mgr.--S.B. Merchant Bank (Singapore) Limited, Singapore, Singapore; *Int'l*, pg. 1309
Tagawa, Craig K., Chief Fin. Officer & Sr. V.P.--American Shared Hospital Services, San Francisco, CA; *U.S. Public*, pg. 91
Taggart, John M., Chief Fin. Officer--American Investment Bank, NA, Salt Lake City, UT; *U.S. Public*, pg. 990
Taglianetti, Richard, Controller--Helmsley-Spear Inc., New York, NY; *U.S. Private*, pg. 521
Takada, J., Sec. & Treas.--Yamaha Motor Canada Ltd., North York, Canada; *Int'l*, pg. 1516
Takagi, Yogi, Chief Fin. Officer--Sumitomo Sitix Silicon, Inc., Fremont, CA; *Int'l*, pg. 1317
Takahashi, Hidemitsu, Chief Fin. Officer & Dir.-Investor Rels.--Pentel of America, Ltd., Torrance, CA; *Int'l*, pg. 1035
Takahashi, Masaki, Chief Fin. Officer & Exec. V.P.--Mitsubishi Motor Sales of America, Inc., Cypress, CA; *Int'l*, pg. 875
Takashima, A., Chief Fin. Officer--Fujitsu Ten Corp. of America, Torrance, CA; *Int'l*, pg. 526
Talaba, Sam, Chief Fin. Officer--PAR Microsystems Corporation, New Hartford, NY; *U.S. Public*, pg. 1256
Talamo, Felix, Chief Fin. Officer--Media Incorporated, New York, NY; *U.S. Private*, pg. 726
Tally, Joe, Chief Fin. Officer--Ruiz Food Products, Inc., Dinuba, CA; *U.S. Private*, pg. 951
Talma, John, Chief Fin. Officer--Kraft Jacobs Suchard, Velizy-Villacoublay, France; *U.S. Public*, pg. 1290
Talmidge, Joe, Chief Fin. Officer--Country Home Bakery, Inc., Bridgeport, CT; *U.S. Private*, pg. 278
Tam, Chuck C.H., Exec. V.P. & Chief Fin. Officer--Semi-Tech Corporation, Markham, Canada; *Int'l*, pg. 1220
Tamblyn, Ken C., Chief Fin. Officer & Exec. V.P.--Tidewater Inc., New Orleans, LA; *U.S. Public*, pg. 1608
Tamblyn, Ken C., Chief Fin. Officer--Pental Insurance Co., Ltd., New Orleans, LA; *U.S. Public*, pg. 1608
Tamblyn, Ken C., Chief Fin. Officer--Tidewater Marine Service, Inc., New Orleans, LA; *U.S. Public*, pg. 1608
Tamblyn, Ken C., Chief Fin. Officer--Pan-Marine International, Inc., New Orleans, LA; *U.S. Public*, pg. 1608
Tamblyn, Ken C., Chief Fin. Officer--Tidewater Marine, Inc., Amelia, LA; *U.S. Public*, pg. 1608
Tamblyn, Ken C., Chief Fin. Officer--Tidewater Marine International, Inc., New Orleans, LA; *U.S. Public*, pg. 1608
Tamblyn, Ken C., Chief Fin. Officer--Tidewater Marine Western, Inc., New Orleans, LA; *U.S. Public*, pg. 1608
Tamblyn, Ken C., Chief Fin. Officer--Point Marine, Inc., New Orleans, LA; *U.S. Public*, pg. 1608
Tamblyn, Ken C., Chief Fin. Officer--Tidewater Offshore Services, Inc., New Orleans, LA; *U.S. Public*, pg. 1608
Tamblyn, Ken C., Chief Fin. Officer--Twenty Grand Offshore, New Orleans, LA; *U.S. Public*, pg. 1608
Tamblyn, Ken C., Chief Fin. Officer--Seafarer Boat Corporation, New Orleans, LA; *U.S. Public*, pg. 1608
Tamburro, Louis, Chief Fin. Officer--Patient Care, Inc., West Orange, NJ; *U.S. Public*, pg. 344
Tamir, Oded, Chief Fin. Officer--Diasonics Ultra Sound, Inc., Santa Clara, CA; *Int'l*, pg. 644
Tananantnarapool, Adisorn, Mgr.-Fin.--Benetone Land & Houses Co., Ltd., Bangkok, Thailand; *Int'l*, pg. 186
Tananbaum, Andrew, Pres. & Chief Fin. Officer--Century Business Credit Corporation, New York, NY; *U.S. Private*, pg. 225
Tanenberg, Marc T., Chief Fin. Officer, V.P.-Fin. & Sec.--Recoton Auto Corporation, Lincolnshire, IL; *U.S. Public*, pg. 1369
Taniguchi, Sadao, Chief Fin Officer, Legal Officer & Dir.-Personnel & Inv. Rels.--Kosugi Sangyo Co., Ltd., Tokyo, Japan; *Int'l*, pg. 759
Tanner, Scott, Chief Fin. Officer--Clover Club Foods, Inc., Kaysville, UT; *U.S. Private*, pg. 469
Tannura, Frank V., Chief Fin. Officer & V.P.--Ivex Packaging Corporation, Lincolnshire, IL; *U.S. Public*, pg. 915
Tansey, James R., Chief Fin. Officer & Sr. V.P.--Jaydon Incorporated, Rock Island, IL; *U.S. Private*, pg. 584
Tapino, Randall J., Chief Fin. Officer--Rose Art Industries, Livingston, NJ; *U.S. Private*, pg. 945
Tapscott, James T., Chief Fin. Officer, Treas. & Sec.--Columbus Mills, Inc., Columbus, GA; *U.S. Private*, pg. 256
Tarbet, Ted N., Chief Fin. Officer & Sr. V.P.--Sunrise Medical, Inc., Carlsbad, CA; *U.S. Public*, pg. 1535
Tardio, Thomas, V.P.-Fin. Admin. & Controls--Columbia TriStar Television, Culver City, CA; *Int'l*, pg. 1282
Tarello, John A., Sr. V.P. & Treas.--Analogic Corporation, Peabody, MA; *U.S. Public*, pg. 109
Tarnay, Dennis, Chief Fin. Officer & Treas.--Lake Erie Electric, Inc., Westlake, OH; *U.S. Private*, pg. 643
Tarrant, S.S., Grp. Fin. Dir.--Sedgwick Group plc, London, United Kingdom; *Int'l*, pg. 1217
Tartikoff, Peter A., Chief Fin. Officer & Sr. V.P.--Cousins Properties Incorporated, Atlanta, GA; *U.S. Public*, pg. 453
Tassi, Michael J., Chief Fin. Officer & Treas.--Torco Oil Co., Chicago, IL; *U.S. Private*, pg. 1092
Tate, John, Chief Fin. Officer & V.P.--Dole Food Company, Inc., Westlake Village, CA; *U.S. Public*, pg. 515
Tatum, Robert, Chief Fin. Officer--R.L. Polk & Co., Southfield, MI; *U.S. Private*, pg. 874
Taubitz, Fredricka, Chief Fin. Officer & Exec. V.P.--Zenith National Insurance Corp., Woodland Hills, CA; *U.S. Public*, pg. 1790
Tavel, Mark K., Pres. & Chief Investment Officer--Rothchild Asset Management Inc., New York, NY; *U.S. Private*, pg. 947
Tawil, Theodore, Treas.--Tawil Associates Inc., Carteret, NJ; *U.S. Private*, pg. 1070
Taylor, A.C., Dir.-Fin.--Dobson Park Industries Plc, Wigan, United Kingdom; *U.S. Public*, pg. 789
Taylor, Carrol, Chief Fin. Officer--The Virtual Group, Allen Park, MI; *U.S. Private*, pg. 1141
Taylor, David H., Chief Fin. Officer, Exec. V.P.-Fin. & Sec.--JPS Textile Group, Inc., Greenville, SC; *U.S. Private*, pg. 578
Taylor, Dennis, Chief Fin. Officer--United Presidential Life Insurance Co., Carmel, IN; *U.S. Public*, pg. 434
Taylor, Diana, Chief Fin. Officer & Controller--Horizon Bancorp, Michigan City, IN; *U.S. Private*, pg. 538
Taylor, Don, Chief Fin. Officer--Andros Incorporated, Berkeley, CA; *U.S. Private*, pg. 74
Taylor, Gerald F., Chief Fin. Officer & Sr. V.P.--Applied Materials, Inc., Santa Clara, CA; *U.S. Public*, pg. 123
Taylor, Harold, Chief Fin. Officer & Controller--RNL Facilities Corporation, Denver, CO; *U.S. Private*, pg. 905
Taylor, Harper, V.P.-Fin. & Admin.--Western Geophysical, Houston, TX; *U.S. Public*, pg. 1757
Taylor, James, Pres. & Chief Exec. & Fin. Officers--Reuter Manufacturing Inc., Hopkins, MN; *U.S. Public*, pg. 1383
Taylor, Jeffrey W., Chief Fin. Officer--National Computer Systems, Eden Prairie, MN; *U.S. Public*, pg. 1155
Taylor, Jimmie F., Chief Fin. Officer, V.P. & Treas.--TCA Cable TV, Inc., Tyler, TX; *U.S. Public*, pg. 1553
Taylor, Jimmie F., Chief Fin. Officer, Sr. V.P. & Treas.--TCA Management Company, Tyler, TX; *U.S. Public*, pg. 1553
Taylor, John, Chief Fin. Officer--Mikron Corp. Monroe, Monroe, CT; *Int'l*, pg. 866
Taylor, Louis, Chief Fin. Officer & Controller--Caro Produce & Institutional Foods, Houma, LA; *U.S. Public*, pg. 1278
Taylor, Mark, Chief Fin. Officer--Burns & McDonnell Engineers-Architects-Consultants, Kansas City, MO; *U.S. Private*, pg. 187
Taylor, Mark, Chief Fin. Officer--Burns & McDonnell Waste Consultants, Inc., Kansas City, MO; *U.S. Private*, pg. 187
Taylor, Paul W., Chief Fin. Officer--Key Bank of Colorado, Fort Collins, CO; *U.S. Public*, pg. 954
Taylor, William, Chief Exec. Officer & Dir.-Fin.--Really Useful Holdings Limited, London, United Kingdom; *Int'l*, pg. 1089
Taymore, Philip, Chief Fin. Officer--Waters Corporation, Milford, MA; *U.S. Public*, pg. 1745
Tebbe, Horst, Chief Fin. Officer & V.P.--Sealed Air Corporation, Saddle Brook, NJ; *U.S. Public*, pg. 1450
Teele, Gerald A., Chief Fin. Officer, Sr. V.P. & Treas.--North Carolina Natural Gas Corporation, Fayetteville, NC; *U.S. Public*, pg. 1194
Teeple, William W., Chief Fin. Officer, V.P. & Treas.--Stackpole Ltd., Newton, MA; *U.S. Private*, pg. 1028
Teeter, Lynne, Chief Fin. Officer--American Demographics, Inc., Ithaca, NY; *U.S. Private*, pg. 281
Teeters, Bruce W., Sr. V.P.-Fin. & Treas.--Consolidated-Tomoka Land Co., Daytona Beach, FL; *U.S. Public*, pg. 437
Teeters, Bruce W., Chief Fin. Officer--Lake Placid Groves, Lake Placid, FL; *U.S. Public*, pg. 437
Teeters, Bruce W., Chief Fin. Officer & V.P.--Indigo Development Inc., Daytona Beach, FL; *U.S. Public*, pg. 437
Tehle, Dave, Chief Fin. Officer--Haggar Corporation, Dallas, TX; *U.S. Public*, pg. 774
Tehrami, Julliette S., Chief Fin. Officer & Exec. V.P.--MBIA Inc., Armonk, NY; *U.S. Public*, pg. 1023
Tell, Martin T., Chief Fin. Officer & V.P. & Treas.--JJI Lighting Group Inc., Greenwich, CT; *Int'l*, pg. 821
Tellez, Lorenzo, Chief Fin. Officer & Treas.--Telos Corporation, Ashburn, VA; *U.S. Public*, pg. 1573
Tello, A., Chief Fin. Officer--Hispano Olivetti Office, Barcelona, Spain; *Int'l*, pg. 1003
Temling, Peter, Chief Fin. Officer & Exec. V.P.--Carnival Hotels & Casinos, Miami, FL; *U.S. Public*, pg. 1265
Templer, Jeffrey A., Chief Fin. Officer & Sr. V.P.--Aerovox Inc., New Bedford, MA; *U.S. Public*, pg. 25
Templin, Dan, V.P.-Fin.--Christian Dior Perfumes Inc., New York, NY; *Int'l*, pg. 781
Tenczar, Bob, Chief Fin. Officer & V.P.--MMI Products, Inc., Houston, TX; *U.S. Private*, pg. 687
Tendler, Lance, Pres., Chief Exec. Officer& Treas.--Kennington Ltd., Inc., Van Nuys, CA; *U.S. Private*, pg. 615
Teo, Steven, Mgr.-Fin.--Champion Motors (1975) Pte. Ltd., Singapore, Singapore; *Int'l*, pg. 672
Tepperman, Fred L., Sr. Exec. V.P. & Chief Fin. Officer--Andrews Group, Incorporated, New York, NY; *U.S. Private*, pg. 689
Terada, Kozo, Chief Fin. Officer, V.P.-Fin. & Treas.--Asahi/America, Inc., Malden, MA; *U.S. Public*, pg. 137
Teradore, Gabriel, Chief Fin. Officer--Mercury General Corporation, Los Angeles, CA; *U.S. Public*, pg. 1093
Terhune, David N., Chief Oper. Officer & Exec. V.P.--Applied Extrusion Technologies, Inc., Peabody, MA; *U.S. Public*, pg. 122
Termotto, Robert, Chief Fin. Officer & Sr. V.P.--Newspapers First, New York, NY; *U.S. Public*, pg. 964
Ternes, John R., Chief Fin. Officer & V.P.--Interface Systems, Inc., Ann Arbor, MI; *U.S. Public*, pg. 889
Terrano, Bob, Chief Fin. Officer & Exec. V.P.--Del Taco, Inc., Laguna Hills, CA; *U.S. Private*, pg. 321
Terras, J., Chief Fin. Officer--Continental Europe, West Drayton, United Kingdom; *Int'l*, pg. 1442
Terry, Charles P., Sr. V.P.-Fin. & Treas.--Reed & Barton Corporation, Taunton, MA; *U.S. Private*, pg. 916
Terry, J. Bruce, Chief Fin. Officer & V.P.--McCain Foods Limited, Florenceville, Canada; *Int'l*, pg. 850
Terzian, Richard, Chief Fin. Officer--California Federal Bank, San Francisco, CA; *U.S. Private*, pg. 690
Tessensohn, Joseph, Chief Fin. Officer & Sr. Exec. V.P.--F. J. Benjamin Holdings Ltd., Singapore, Singapore; *Int'l*, pg. 187
Tessmer, James, Chief Estimator--Walbridge Aldinger Company, Detroit, MI; *U.S. Private*, pg. 1146
Tetens, Arnold, V.P.-Fin.--Buehler, Limited, Lake Bluff, IL; *U.S. Public*, pg. 574
Tetsuyama, Yutaka, Chief Fin. Officer--Mitsukoshi (U.S.A.) Inc., New York, NY; *Int'l*, pg. 883
Tetzlaff, David L., Chief Fin. Officer & Treas.--Premium Budget Plan, Inc., Winston Salem, NC; *U.S. Public*, pg. 1453
Tetzlaff, David L., Chief Fin. Officer & Treas.--The Innovative Company, Winston Salem, NC; *U.S. Public*, pg. 1454
Tetzlaff, David L., Chief Fin. Officer & Treas.--Universal Insurance Co., Winston Salem, NC; *U.S. Public*, pg. 1454
Tewksbury, Gregg R., CPA, Chief Fin. Officer & Controller--CFX Bank, Keene, NH; *U.S. Public*, pg. 277
Thackston, Steve, Controller & Treas.--Dugan & Meyers Interests, Inc., Cincinnati, OH; *U.S. Private*, pg. 345
Thadhani, Suresh, Chief Fin. Officer & V.P.--Alcan Aluminium Limited, Montreal, Canada; *Int'l*, pg. 50
Thatcher, G.D., Sr. V.P. & Treas.--All America Insurance Company, Van Wert, OH; *U.S. Private*, pg. 224
Thatcher, Gerald D., Chief Fin. Officer, Sr. V.P. & Treas.--Central Mutual Insurance Co., Van Wert, OH; *U.S. Private*, pg. 223
Theisen, Thomas G., Chief Fin. Officer & V.P.-Fin.--Omega Environmental Inc., Richmond, VA; *U.S. Public*, pg. 1222
Thelen, James, Chief Fin. Officer & V.P.-Fin.--Rogerson Aircraft Corporation, Irvine, CA; *U.S. Private*, pg. 940
Theler, John L., Chief Fin. Officer, Exec. V.P. & Treas.--Franklin Covey, Salt Lake City, UT; *U.S. Public*, pg. 679
Theurillat, Jacques, Chief Fin. Officer--Ares-Serono S.A., Geneva, Switzerland; *Int'l*, pg. 80
Thews, Michael V., Chief Fin. Officer, & V.P.--John Roberts Company, Minneapolis, MN; *U.S. Private*, pg. 935
Thiara, Sultan, Chief Fin. Officer--Shato Holdings Ltd., Vancouver, Canada; *Int'l*, pg. 1230
Thieme, Paul, Chief Fin. Officer--Keeners, Inc., Renton, WA; *U.S. Private*, pg. 611
Thieme, Paul, Chief Fin. Officer--Beef Distributors, Inc., Renton, WA; *U.S. Private*, pg. 611
Thies, Doug, Chief Fin. Officer, Treas. & Sec.--Field Packing Company, Owensboro, KY; *U.S. Private*, pg. 403
Thill, Robert, V.P.-Fin.--Maynard Steel Casting Company, Milwaukee, WI; *U.S. Private*, pg. 718
Thiman, Lennart, Chief Fin. Officer--Esselte Sverige AB, Solna, Sweden; *Int'l*, pg. 459
Thimjon, Steve, Chief Fin. Officer & V.P.--Apertus Technologies Incorporated, Eden Prairie, MN; *U.S. Public*, pg. 119
Thimont, Paul, Chief Fin. Officer--Chartwell Land Plc., London, United Kingdom; *Int'l*, pg. 733
Thirion, Anne-Daniele, Chief Fin. Officer--Neste Chimie France S.N.C., Silic, France; *Int'l*, pg. 914
Thiry, Claude R., Chief Fin. Officer--Whitehall Benelux S.A., Gembloux, Belgium; *U.S. Public*, pg. 82
Tholen, Steven W., Chief Fin. Officer, V.P. & Treas.--Penn Virginia Corporation, Radnor, PA; *U.S. Public*, pg. 1271
Thoman, G. Richard, Chief Fin. Officer & Sr. V.P.--International Business Machines Corporation, Armonk, NY; *U.S. Public*, pg. 895
Thomas, Alan R., Chief Fin. Officer, Sr. V.P. & Treas.--Noranda Inc., Toronto, Canada; *Int'l*, pg. 433

Thomas, Bruce V., Chief Fin. Officer, Sr. V.P. & Gen. Counsel--Cadmus Communications Corporation, Richmond, VA; *U.S. Public*, pg. 290
Thomas, Elbert L., Jr., Chief Fin. Officer & Exec. V.P.--First Tennessee National Corporation, Memphis, TN; *U.S. Public*, pg. 638
Thomas, Jeffrey L., Chief Fin. Officer & V.P.--This End Up Furniture, Richmond, VA; *U.S. Private*, pg. 1081
Thomas, John W., V.P.-Internal Auditing--Warner Communications Inc., New York, NY; *U.S. Public*, pg. 1611
Thomas, Kenneth A., Chief Fin. Officer & Sr. V.P.--Triarc Restaurant Group, Fort Lauderdale, FL; *U.S. Public*, pg. 1635
Thomas, Louis, Chief Fin. Officer & Sr. V.P.-Fin.--Associated Grocers of Florida, Inc., Miami, FL; *U.S. Private*, pg. 91
Thomas, Mary M., Chief Fin. Officer & Exec. V.P.--IRT Property Company, Atlanta, GA; *U.S. Public*, pg. 858
Thomas, P.N., Grp. Fin. Dir.--HSS Hire Service Group PLC, Mitcham, United Kingdom; *Int'l*, pg. 385
Thomas, Paul, Chief Fin. Officer--Bass Brewers Ltd., Burton on Trent, United Kingdom; *Int'l*, pg. 170
Thomas, Phil, Chief Fin. Officer--Milk Products Holdings (Australia) Pty Ltd, Rowville, Australia; *Int'l*, pg. 923
Thomas, Richard, Treas.--The New York Times, New York, NY; *U.S. Public*, pg. 1174
Thomasch, James, Chief Fin. Officer--XRE Corporation, Littleton, MA; *U.S. Public*, pg. 1595
Thomason, Robert S., Chief Fin. Officer & Sr. V.P.-Fin.--The Quaker Oats Company, Chicago, IL; *U.S. Public*, pg. 1347
Thompson, Bruce, Exec. V.P. & Chief Fin. Officer--Circon Video Div., Santa Barbara, CA; *U.S. Public*, pg. 373
Thompson, Curtis A., V.P. & Controller--Primedia Inc., New York, NY; *U.S. Public*, pg. 1327
Thompson, David, Treas. & Sec.--Vulcan Inc., Foley, AL; *U.S. Private*, pg. 1144
Thompson, David A., Pres., Chief Exec. Officer, Chief Fin. Officer--Cominco, Ltd., Vancouver, Canada; *Int'l*, pg. 307
Thompson, Gary L., Chief Fin. Officer, V.P.-Fin. & Asst. Sec.--Legato Systems, Inc., Palo Alto, CA; *U.S. Public*, pg. 984
Thompson, James G., Treas.--General Felt Industries, Inc., Linwood, PA; *U.S. Private*, pg. 1094
Thompson, Jim, Chief Fin. Officer--Titan Linkabit, San Diego, CA; *U.S. Public*, pg. 1618
Thompson, John, Exec. V.P. & Treas.--Toastmaster, Inc., Columbia, MO; *U.S. Public*, pg. 1619
Thompson, Kevin J., Grp. Fin. Dir.--Halma p.l.c., Amersham, United Kingdom; *Int'l*, pg. 589
Thompson, Mark D., Chief Fin. Officer & Exec. V.P.--Lexford Residential Trust, Columbus, OH; *U.S. Public*, pg. 991
Thompson, Michael, Dir.-Fin.--Central Coca-Cola Bottling Company, Inc., Richmond, VA; *U.S. Private*, pg. 222
Thompson, Mike, Chief Fin. Officer--Bass Leisure, Burton on Trent, United Kingdom; *Int'l*, pg. 170
Thompson, P., Chief Fin. Officer--DeLeuw, Cather & Company, Washington, DC; *U.S. Private*, pg. 841
Thompson, Patrick, V.P.-Fin.--Modern Drop Forge Co., Blue Island, IL; *U.S. Private*, pg. 754
Thompson, R. Bruce, Chief Fin. Officer & Exec. V.P.--Circon Corporation, Santa Barbara, CA; *U.S. Public*, pg. 373
Thompson, Randy, Chief Fin. Officer--St. John Knits, Irvine, CA; *U.S. Private*, pg. 960
Thompson, Richard, Treas.--Office Connection, Inc., Fort Lauderdale, FL; *U.S. Public*, pg. 1687
Thompson, Richard J., Chief Fin. Officer, V.P.-Fin., Treas. & Sec.--Computer Products, Inc., Boca Raton, FL; *U.S. Public*, pg. 422
Thompson, Robert D., Chief Fin. Officer & Exec. V.P.--Lab One, Lenexa, KS; *U.S. Public*, pg. 1449
Thompson, Scott L., Chief Fin. Officer, Sr. V.P. & Treas.--Group 1 Automotive, Inc., Houston, TX; *U.S. Public*, pg. 767
Thompson, Terry W., Chief Fin. Officer, V.P. & Treas.--Jack Henry & Associates, Inc., Monett, MO; *U.S. Public*, pg. 808
Thompson, Wayne, Pres. & Treas.--Tank Service, Inc., Knoxville, TN; *U.S. Public*, pg. 521
Thomsen, Carl, Chief Fin. Officer, V.P. & Sec.--Digital Microwave Corporation, San Jose, CA; *U.S. Public*, pg. 508
Thomsen, Mikael, Chief Fin. Officer--C.G. Jensen A/S, Ballerup, Denmark; *Int'l*, pg. 1261
Thomson, John A., Chief Fin. Officer, Sr. V.P. & Sec.--Renaissance Energy Ltd., Calgary, Canada; *Int'l*, pg. 1102
Thorell, G., Chief Fin. Officer--Scholl Deutschland GmbH, Maintal, Germany; *Int'l*, pg. 1209
Thornburgh, Richard E., Chief Fin. Officer--Credit Suisse Group, Zurich, Switzerland; *Int'l*, pg. 345
Thorne, Chris, Chief Fin. Officer--Johnson & Johnson Limited, Maidenhead, United Kingdom; *U.S. Public*, pg. 930
Thorne, Mark, Chief Fin. Officer & Chief Oper. Officer--Hill and Knowlton, Inc., New York, NY; *Int'l*, pg. 1483
Thornley, Anthony S., Chief Fin. Officer & Exec. V.P.--QUALCOMM, San Diego, CA; *U.S. Public*, pg. 1348
Thornton, Greg, Chief Fin. Officer, V.P. & Treas.--Harding Lawson Associates Group, Inc., Novato, CA; *U.S. Public*, *pg. 785*
Thornton, John T., Chief Fin. Officer & Exec. V.P.--Norwest Corporation, Minneapolis, MN; *U.S. Public*, pg. 1201
Thornton, Robert M., Jr., Pres.--Krug International Corp., Houston, TX; *U.S. Public*, pg. 967
Thorp, Albert, III, Chief Fin. Officer & V.P.-Fin.--Technitrol, Inc., Trevose, PA; *U.S. Public*, pg. 1564
Thostrup, Peter, Exec. V.P.-Fin.--Bang & Olufsen A/S, Struer, Denmark; *Int'l*, pg. 145
Thrapp, Richard, Chief Fin. Officer & Controller--Salant Childrens Apparel Group, New York, NY; *U.S. Public*, pg. 1429
Thrash, H. Lee, III, Chief Fin. Officer & V.P.-Planning & Devel.--Caraustar Industries, Inc., Austell, GA; *U.S. Public*, pg. 303
Throckmorton, John C., Chief Fin. Officer--Lotus Word Processing Division, Atlanta, GA; *U.S. Public*, pg. 896
Thue, Arnold J., Chief Fin. Officer--Raven Industries, Inc., Sioux Falls, SD; *U.S. Public*, pg. 1361
Thung, Roy T.K., Chief Fin. Officer, Exec. V.P. & Treas.--Independence Holding Company, Stamford, CT; *U.S. Private*, pg. 446
Thurston, George R., Exec. V.P.-Fin., Intl.--North Pacific Lumber Company, Portland, OR; *U.S. Private*, pg. 805
Thurston, K.P., Chief Fin. Officer & V.P.-Fin.--Atlantic Steel Industries, Inc., Atlanta, GA; *Int'l*, pg. 696
Tiang, Koh Chay, Chief Fin. Officer, V.P.-Acctg. & Sec.--Hong Fok Corporation Ltd., Singapore, Singapore; *Int'l*, pg. 635
Tibbets, Robert, Chief Fin. Officer--Branson Ultrasonics, Danbury, CT; *U.S. Public*, pg. 574
Tiberii, Tony, Sr. V.P.-Fin.--The Rockport Company, Marlborough, MA; *U.S. Public*, pg. 1370
Tidwell, James M., Chief Fin. Officer & Exec. V.P.--Daniel Industries, Inc., Houston, TX; *U.S. Public*, pg. 482
Tieken, Robert W., Chief Fin. Officer & Exec. V.P.--The Goodyear Tire & Rubber Company, Akron, OH; *U.S. Public*, pg. 752
Tierney, John F., Chief Fin. Officer--Brother International Corporation, Somerset, NJ; *Int'l*, pg. 229
Tiger, Peter E., V.P.-Fin.--Superba, Inc., Los Angeles, CA; *U.S. Private*, pg. 1054
Tighe, Gary, Chief Fin. Officer & Sr. V.P.--Staff Builders Inc., Lake Success, NY; *U.S. Public*, pg. 1501
Tilson, Stephen, Chief Fin. Officer--American Television Time, Inc., Austin, TX; *U.S. Private*, pg. 63
Timbie, Thomas E., Chief Fin. Officer, V.P. & Sec.--Xomed Surgical Products, Jacksonville, FL; *U.S. Public*, pg. 253
Timmer, M., Chief Fin. Officer--PURAC Group, Gorcum, Netherlands; *Int'l*, pg. 244
Timmermann, Dieter, Chief Fin. Officer--Braun AG, Kronberg, Germany; *U.S. Public*, pg. 744
Tippitt, Coma L., Sec. & Treas.--Snyder-Crown, Inc., Marked Tree, AR; *U.S. Private*, pg. 1011
Tirouflet, Jean-Pierre, Chief Fin. Officer & Exec. V.P.-Fin.--Rhone-Poulenc S.A., Courbevoie, France; *Int'l*, pg. 1108
Tisdell, Stephen, Chief Fin. Officer--Central Parking Corp., Nashville, TN; *U.S. Public*, pg. 326
Tiusanen, Bertil, Chief Fin. Officer--Pharmacia & Upjohn Biosystems AB, Uppsala, Sweden; *Int'l*, pg. 1047
To, Paul Tong Hon, Chief Fin. Officer--Johnson Electric Holdings Limited, Tai No, Hong Kong; *Int'l*, pg. 712
Toberman, David, Treas. & Sec.--Toberman, Clayton, MO; *U.S. Private*, pg. 1089
Tobin, Ronald M., Chief Fin. Officer, Chief Acctg. Officer & V.P.-Fin.--Elcotel, Inc., Sarasota, FL; *U.S. Public*, pg. 568
Tobler, D. Lee, Chief Fin. Officer & Exec. V.P.--The B.F. Goodrich Company, Richfield, OH; *U.S. Public*, pg. 751
Todd, Curt, Chief Fin. Officer--Omaha Steaks, Omaha, NE; *U.S. Private*, pg. 815
Todd, Doris, Treas.--J.L. Todd Auction Co., Rome, GA; *U.S.* Private, pg. 1090
Toffolon, John E., Jr., Co-Chief Fin. Officer--Nomura Securities International, Inc., New York, NY; *Int'l*, pg. 956
Tofte, Poul Erik, Chief Fin. Officer--GN Great Nordic Ltd., Copenhagen, Denmark; *Int'l*, pg. 536
Tokatlian, Matthew, Chief Fin. Officer & V.P.--Biederman, Kelly & Shaffer, Inc., New York, NY; *U.S. Private*, pg. 142
Toledo, Crescenciavo D., Chief Fin. Officer--Johnson & Johnson (Philippines) Inc., Manila, Philippines; *U.S. Public*, pg. 931
Tolhurst, Harland, Chief Fin. Officer & V.P.--PHB Machining Division, Fairview, PA; *U.S. Private*, pg. 826
Tolhurst, Harland, Chief Fin. Officer & V.P.--PHB Tool & Die, Girard, PA; *U.S. Private*, pg. 826
Tolhurst, Harland, Chief Fin. Officer & V.P.--PHB Plastic & Rubber Molding Division, Fairview, PA; *U.S. Private*, pg. 826
Tolhurst, Pete, Chief Fin. Officer & V.P.--PHB Die Casting, Fairview, PA; *U.S. Private*, pg. 826
Tolis, Gust, Chief Fin. Officer & Sr. V.P.--Chicago Title & Trust Co., Chicago, IL; *U.S. Public*, pg. 42
Tolis, Gust J., Chief Fin. Officer & Sr. V.P.--Chicago Title Insurance Co., Chicago, IL; *U.S. Public*, pg. 42
Tolley, William T., Chief Fin. Officer--Chesapeake Corporation, Richmond, VA; *U.S. Public*, pg. 346
Tolonen, Jim, Chief Fin. Officer & Exec. V.P.--Novell, Inc., Orem, UT; *U.S. Public*, pg. 1203
Tolonen, Jim, Chief Fin. Officer & Sr. V.P.--Novell Inc., San Jose, CA; *U.S. Public*, pg. 1203
Tolot, Jerome, Chief Oper. Officer--Groupe GTM, Nanterre, France; *Int'l*, pg. 823
Tolton, C., Chief Fin. Officer--Muratech America, Inc., Plano, TX; *Int'l*, pg. 897
Toma, George, Chief Fin. Officer, Treas. & Sec.--Wells-Gardner Electronics Corp., Chicago, IL; *U.S. Public*, pg. 1753
Tomas, Gary, Chief Fin. Officer--Richmond Screw Anchor Company, Fort Worth, TX; *U.S. Private*, pg. 932
Tomaszewski, Gerald E., Chief Fin. Officer--Epstein Civil Engineering, Inc., Chicago, IL; *U.S. Private*, pg. 379
Tomcheck, Jay, Chief Fin. Officer, V.P. & Treas.--Wisconsin Label Corporation, Algoma, WI; *U.S. Private*, pg. 1184
Tomlinson, R., Dir.-Fin.--Rolls-Royce Military Aero Engines Ltd., Bristol, United Kingdom; *Int'l*, pg. 1127
Tomlinson, Robert E., Chief Fin. Officer & Treas.--Outsource International, Deerfield Beach, FL; *U.S. Public*, pg. 1236
Tomm, Charles, Chief Fin. Officer--Coggin Automotive Group, Jacksonville, FL; *U.S. Private*, pg. 250
Tomney, Douglas, Chief Fin. Officer--Chelsea Milling Co., Chelsea, MI; *U.S. Private*, pg. 231
Tondro, Ryan, Chief Fin. Officer & V.P.--Sizzler International, Inc., Los Angeles, CA; *U.S. Public*, pg. 1475
Tonkko, Maija, Sr. V.P.-Fin. & Control--Oy Nokia Ab/Nokia Group, Helsinki, Finland; *Int'l*, pg. 951
Tonozzi-Frederick, Louise, Chief Fin. Officer & V.P.--McWhorter Technologies, Inc., Carpentersville, IL; *U.S. Public*, pg. 1074
Toombs, Eugene M., Pres. & Chief Exec. Officer--MiTek, Inc., Chesterfield, MO; *Int'l*, pg. 1106
Toomey, Gary K., Dir.-Fin.--Qantas Airways Ltd., Mascot, Australia; *Int'l*, pg. 1074
Toopes, James A., Exec. V.P.-Fin. & Admin.--BI-LO Inc., Greenville, SC; *Int'l*, pg. 749
Tootle, John, Chief Fin. Officer & V.P.-Fin.--Dominguez Water Company, Long Beach, CA; *U.S. Public*, pg. 516
Tootle, John S., Chief Fin. Officer, V.P. & Sec.--Dominguez Services Corporation, Long Beach, CA; *U.S. Public*, pg. 516
Topham, Neil, Chief Fin. Officer & V.P.--HarperCollins Publishers, New York, NY; *Int'l*, pg. 926
Toppenberg, Hroar, Chief Fin. Officer & V.P.-Opers.--Advance Machine Company, Plymouth, MN; *Int'l*, pg. 932
Toppi, Angela, Chief Fin. Officer, Sr. V.P., Treas. & Sec.--Trans-Lux Corporation, Norwalk, CT; *U.S. Public*, pg. 1628
Torda, Jay, Chief Fin. Officer--David McDavid Auto Dealership, Irving, TX; *U.S. Private*, pg. 721
Torey, Donald W., Chief Fin. Officer & Exec. V.P.-Fin. & Admin.--General Electric Investment Corp., Stamford, CT; *U.S. Public*, pg. 712
Torgerson, James, Chief Fin. Officer & V.P.--Puget Sound Energy, Inc., Bellevue, WA; *U.S. Public*, pg. 1342
Torkar, Bob, Sr. V.P.-Fin., Treas. & Chief Acctg. Officer--Jackpot Enterprises, Inc., Las Vegas, NV; *U.S. Public*, pg. 920
Torno, Tim, Chief Fin. Officer--Ultrak Inc., Lewisville, TX; *U.S. Public*, pg. 1663
Torno, Tim, Chief Fin. Officer--Diamond Electronics, Inc., Carroll, OH; *U.S. Public*, pg. 1663
Torrance, David, Chief Fin. Officer--PPP hc, Tunbridge Wells, United Kingdom; *Int'l*, pg. 1020
Torre, Nelson, Chief Fin. Officer--Industrias Pacocha S.A. (Unilever), Lima, Peru; *Int'l*, pg. 1437
Torres, Heliodoro Ramirez, Dir.-Fin.--Vitromex, S.A., Saltillo, Mexico; *Int'l*, pg. 1469
Torres, Hiram, V.P. & Mgr.-Credit--The Times-Picayune Publishing Corp., New Orleans, LA; *U.S. Private*, pg. 1087
Torres, Jose O., V.P.-Fin., Treas. & Sec.--Puerto Rican Cement Co., Inc., Guaynabo, PR; *U.S. Public*, pg. 1341
Torres, William, Exec. V.P. & Chief Fin. Officer--Gibbs Wire & Steel Company, Inc., Southington, CT; *U.S. Private*, pg. 451
Tortorici, John, Chief Fin. Officer, V.P. & Treas.--Milgray Electronics, Inc., Farmingdale, NY; *U.S. Public*, pg. 205
Tortorici, John, Chief Fin. Officer--Milgray/Western Canada, Burnaby, Canada; *U.S. Public*, pg. 207
Toscanini, Arthur M., Chief Fin. Officer, Exec. V.P.-Fin. & Treas.--Cambridge Technology Partners, Cambridge, MA; *U.S. Public*, pg. 1424
Toter, Benjamin, V.P.-Fin., Sec. & Treas.--Quality Markets, Inc., Jamestown, NY; *U.S. Public*, pg. 1270
Tousignant, Normand, Chief Fin. Officer--Harris Drury Cohen, Fort Lauderdale, FL; *U.S. Private*, pg. 505
Toussaint, Ignacio, Chief Fin. Officer--Grupo Gigante S.A. de C.V., Mexico, Mexico; *Int'l*, pg. 574
Toustou, Rene, Fin. Dir.--Ecom et Partenaire, Neuilly-sur-Seine, France; *Int'l*, pg. 433
Tow, Leonard, Chm. Bd. & Chief Exec. & Fin. Officers--Citizens Utilities Company, Stamford, CT; *U.S. Public*, pg. 379
Tow, Leonard, Chm. Bd., Chief Exec. Officer & Chief Fin. Officer--Citizens Telecommunications, Stamford, CT; *U.S.* Public, pg. 380
Towne, William, Chief Fin. Officer & Exec. V.P.-Fin.--Leiner Health Products, Inc., Carson, CA; *U.S. Private*, pg. 659
Townsend, Arthur T., Chief Oper. Officer & Chief Fin. Officer--Lat Purser & Associates, Charlotte, NC; *U.S. Private*, pg. 896
Townsend, Michael, Chief Fin. Officer & Dir.-Fin.--Rolls-Royce plc, London, United Kingdom; *Int'l*, pg. 1126
Toyne, William, Chief Fin. Officer & V.P.-Fin.--Package Service Company, LLC., Kansas City, MO; *U.S. Private*, pg. 833
Toyoda, Shinobu, Chief Fin. Officer, Exec. V.P. & Sec.--Sega of America Inc., Redwood City, CA; *Int'l*, pg. 1218
Trabucco, Robert, Chief Fin. Officer--NordicTrack, Inc., Chaska, MN; *U.S. Public*, pg. 279
Trachtenberg, Michael, Chief Fin. Officer, Chief Acctg. Officer, Exec. V.P. & Sec.--York Research Corporation, New York, NY; *U.S. Public*, pg. 1789
Tracy, Enos, Chief Fin. Officer--Quanterra Environmental Services, Englewood, CO; *U.S. Private*, pg. 899
Trad, Louis, Chief Fin. Officer--H&C, Leo Burnett, Beirut, Lebanon; *U.S. Private*, pg. 184
Tralies, Philip J., Sr. V.P.-Fin. & Admin.--E-Z-GO Textron, Augusta, GA; *U.S. Public*, pg. 1589
Trametzki, Thomas, Chief Fin. Officer, V.P., Treas. & Sec.--Orval Kent Food Co., Wheeling, IL; *U.S. Private*, pg. 820
Tran, Khanh T., Chief Fin. Officer & Sr. V.P.--Pacific Life Insurance Company, Newport Beach, CA; *U.S. Private*, pg. 831
Trane, Niels Erik, Controller--BancTec Danmark A/S, Herlev, Denmark; *U.S. Public*, pg. 177
Transier, William L., Chief Fin. Officer & Sr. V.P.--Seagull Energy Corporation, Houston, TX; *U.S. Public*, pg. 1450
Trapani, Cosmo S., Chief Fin. Officer, Exec. V.P. & Treas.--Unitrode Corporation, Merrimack, NH; *U.S. Public*, pg. 1694
Trauber, A., Chief Fin. Officer--Syratech Corporation, East Boston, MA; *U.S. Private*, pg. 1060
Traverso, Daniel, Chief Fin. Officer--Laboratorios Americanos S.A., Montevideo, Uruguay; *U.S. Public*, pg. 81

Traynor, Pat, Chief Fin. Officer--QT Optoelectronics, Sunnyvale, CA; *U.S. Private*, pg. 897

Trebing, Robert T., Chief Fin. Officer & Exec. V.P.--Family Restaurants, Inc., Irvine, CA; *U.S. Private*, pg. 393

Treff, Douglas J., Chief Fin. Officer & V.P.--Wilsons The Leather Experts Inc., Brooklyn Park, MN; *U.S. Private*, pg. 1181

Trego, Charles, Jr., Chief Fin. Officer & Exec. V.P.--Rich Products Corp., Buffalo, NY; *U.S. Private*, pg. 928

Treinen, David C., Sr. V.P.-Fin. & Sec.--International Aluminum Corporation, Monterey Park, CA; *U.S. Public*, pg. 894

Tremayne, John C., Chief Fin. Officer & Sr. V.P.--EdperBrascan Corporation, Toronto, Canada; *Int'l*, pg. 433

Tremblay, Dale E., Chief Fin. Officer & Sr. V.P.--Precision Drilling Corporation, Calgary, Canada; *Int'l*, pg. 1066

Trencher, Lewis J., Chief Oper. Officer & Chief Fin. Officer--J. Walter Thompson Company, New York, NY; *Int'l*, pg. 1483

Tressel, Mark G., Chief Fin. Officer--Amspec Chemical Corporation, Gloucester City, NJ; *U.S. Private*, pg. 67

Trexler, Tom, Chief Fin. Officer & Exec. V.P.--Nobility Homes, Inc., Ocala, FL; *U.S. Public*, pg. 1186

Tricot, H., Chief Fin. Officer & Corp. Sec.--Dumez-GTM, Nanterre, France; *Int'l*, pg. 823

Trigeiro, Frank, Chief Fin. Officer & V.P.-Fin.--Patriot American Hospitality Operating Company, San Mateo, CA; *U.S. Public*, pg. 1265

Trigg, Greg, Chief Fin. Officer & Co-Mng. Dir.--International Correspondence Schools (Australasia) Limited, Lane Cove, Australia; *U.S. Public*, pg. 784

Trigwell, Jim, Chief Fin. Officer--Colgate-Palmolive Ltd., Guildford, United Kingdom; *U.S. Public*, pg. 398

Tripodo, Anthony, Chief Fin. Officer--Veritas DGC Inc., Houston, TX; *U.S. Private*, pg. 1136

Tripp, David, Grp. Fin. Controller--APV U.K. Plc, Coaley, United Kingdom; *Int'l*, pg. 1240

Trippel, Joe, Chief Fin. Officer, Treas. & Sec.--Creation Windows of Indiana, Inc., Elkhart, IN; *U.S. Private*, pg. 287

Trippetti, Vic, Chief Fin. Officer & Controller--L.A. Gear, Inc., Santa Monica, CA; *U.S. Public*, pg. 969

Trobaugh, John, Chief Fin. Officer, Treas. & Sec.--Delta Foremost Chemical Corp., Memphis, TN; *U.S. Private*, pg. 322

Trochemenco, Shelly, Chief Fin. Officer--G.I. Plastek, Elyria, OH; *U.S. Private*, pg. 435

Troester, Dean, Chief Fin. Officer & V.P.--Crete Carrier Corp., Lincoln, NE; *U.S. Private*, pg. 289

Troffa, Paolo, Chief Fin. Officer--Fiat Auto Ireland Ltd., Dublin, Ireland; *Int'l*, pg. 481

Troilo, Louis G., Chief Fin. Officer & V.P.-Fin.--The Children's Hospital of Philadelphia, Philadelphia, PA; *U.S. Private*, pg. 236

Trojan, Dean N., Chief Fin. Officer & V.P.--Colorbus Inc., Irvine, CA; *U.S. Private*, pg. 255

Tronson, Keith, Chief Fin. Officer--Bel Air Markets, West Sacramento, CA; *U.S. Private*, pg. 908

Tropeano, A., Chief Fin. Officer & Exec. V.P.--Italimpianti of America, Incorporated, Coraopolis, PA; *Int'l*, pg. 655

Tropp, Jim, Chief Fin. Officer--Metcal, Inc., Menlo Park, CA; *U.S. Private*, pg. 735

Trott, Thelma, Chief Fin. Officer--KMIC Investment Company, Louisville, KY; *U.S. Private*, pg. 741

Trotter, L.R., Chief Fin. Officer--Knoxville Utilities Board, Knoxville, TN; *U.S. Private*, pg. 627

Troupe, Terry L., Chief Fin. Officer & Treas.--Mercantile Bankshares Corporation, Baltimore, MD; *U.S. Public*, pg. 1088

Trubeck, William L., Chief Fin. Officer & Sr. V.P.--International Multifoods Corporation, Minneapolis, MN; *U.S. Public*, pg. 900

Truchi, James, Chief Fin. Officer, Controller & Treas.--Trucchis Markets, Raynham, MA; *U.S. Private*, pg. 1107

Trucksess, H.A., III, Chief Fin. Officer & Sr. V.P.-Fin.--Yellow Corporation, Overland Park, KS; *U.S. Public*, pg. 1788

Truetzel, David W., Chief Fin. Officer--First USA Paymentech, Inc., Salem, NH; *U.S. Public*, pg. 174

Truswell, Derek P., Chief Fin. Officer & Sr. V.P.--IPL Energy Inc., Calgary, Canada; *Int'l*, pg. 651

Truswell, Derek P., Chief Fin. Officer & Sr. V.P.--Interprovincial Pipe Line Inc., Edmonton, Canada; *Int'l*, pg. 652

Tsai, Martin, Chief Fin. Officer, Chief Info. Officer & V.P.-Fin.--Liuski International, Inc., Norcross, GA; *U.S. Public*, pg. 1005

Tsang, Carl, Chief Fin. Officer--Slim-Fast Foods Company, West Palm Beach, FL; *U.S. Private*, pg. 1006

Tsang, K.S., Chief Fin. Officer--Review Publishing Company Ltd., Hong Kong, Hong Kong; *U.S. Public*, pg. 525

Tsangaraki, Ekaterini, Chief Fin. Officer--Olympic Airways, New York, NY; *Int'l*, pg. 1004

Tsuei, Dan, Chief Fin. Officer--DTK Computer Inc., City of Industry, CA; *U.S. Private*, pg. 306

Tsui, Kit, Chief Fin. Officer--Sigma Designs, Inc., Fremont, CA; *U.S. Public*, pg. 1472

Tsujino, Iwao, Treas.--Ricoh Electronics, Inc., Tustin, CA; *Int'l*, pg. 1114

Tsutsumi, Shingo, Chief Fin. Officer--P.T. Standard Toyo Polymer, Jakarta, Indonesia; *Int'l*, pg. 1408

Tubbesing, Robert, Chief Fin. Officer & Treas.--Premdor Inc., Mississauga, Canada; *Int'l*, pg. 1066

Tucker, M. Douglas, Chief Fin. & Acctg. Officer, Sr. V.P.-Fin. & Sec.--BeautiControl Cosmetics, Inc., Carrollton, TX; *U.S. Public*, pg. 198

Tueber, William, Chief Fin. Officer & Controller--EMC Corporation, Hopkinton, MA; *U.S. Public*, pg. 545

Tulin, Stanley B., Chief Fin. Officer--The Equitable Companies Incorporated, New York, NY; *U.S. Public*, pg. 588

Tumbas, Dave, Chief Fin. Officer--Hy-Tek Material Handling, Inc., Columbus, OH; *U.S. Private*, pg. 550

Tuner, Mats, Exec. V.P.-Fin.--Perstorp AB, Perstorp, Sweden; *Int'l*, pg. 1036

Tunink, Paul C., Chief Fin. Officer, V.P.-Fin. & Treas.--Stuart Entertainment Inc., Council Bluffs, IA; *U.S. Public*, pg. 1526

Turgeon, Guy, Chief Fin. Officer & Sr. V.P.--St. Lawrence Cement Inc., Montreal, Canada; *Int'l*, pg. 628

Turk, Stan, Chief Fin. Officer--National Safety Associates, Memphis, TN; *U.S. Private*, pg. 786

Turnbull, A.M. Gordon, Chief Fin. Officer & Sr. V.P.-Fin.--Hawker Siddeley Canada Inc., Mississauga, Canada; *Int'l*, pg. 604

Turnbull, Alexander W., Chief Fin. Officer & Sr. V.P.--Ocean Spray Cranberries, Inc., Middleboro, MA; *U.S. Private*, pg. 811

Turnbull, Laurie, Chief Fin. Officer--Texas Holdings Ltd., Manchester, United Kingdom; *Int'l*, pg. 1381

Turnbull, Nigel V., Chief Fin. Officer & Dir.-Pub. Rels.--The Rank Group PLC, London, United Kingdom; *Int'l*, pg. 1086

Turner, Dave, Chief Fin. Officer & V.P.--RJO Enterprises, Inc., Lanham, MD; *U.S. Private*, pg. 904

Turner, David J., Dir.-Fin.--GKN plc, Redditch, United Kingdom; *Int'l*, pg. 534

Turner, John J., Chief Fin. Officer--United Water New York, West Nyack, NY; *U.S. Public*, pg. 1692

Turner, John J., Chief Fin. Officer--United Metering Inc., Long Island City, NY; *U.S. Public*, pg. 1692

Turner, John J., Chief Fin. Officer--United Water Mid-Atlantic, Succasunna, NJ; *U.S. Public*, pg. 1692

Turner, John J., Chief Fin. Officer--United Water New Jersey, Inc., Harrington Park, NJ; *U.S. Public*, pg. 1692

Turner, John L., Exec. V.P. & Chief Oper. Officer--Allied Mineral Products, Inc., Columbus, OH; *U.S. Private*, pg. 39

Turner, John T., Chief Fin. Officer--United Water Works, Harrington Park, NJ; *U.S. Public*, pg. 1692

Turner, Michael E., Chief Fin. Officer--Sealing Equipment Products Co., Inc., Pelham, AL; *U.S. Private*, pg. 978

Turner, Roger, Chief Fin. Officer--Davidson Printing Company, Duluth, MN; *U.S. Private*, pg. 314

Turner, Rose, Chief Fin. Officer--Bollinger Industries Inc., Grand Prairie, TX; *U.S. Public*, pg. 243

Turtora, Lenard, V.P.-Fin.--Six Flags Great Adventure Theme Park & Wild Safari Animal Park, Jackson, NJ; *U.S. Public*, pg. 1611

Tusa, David P., Chief Fin. Officer & Sr. V.P.--Tyler Corporation, Dallas, TX; *U.S. Public*, pg. 1651

Tweedie, Harry, Chief Fin. Officer--TosoHaas Company, Montgomeryville, PA; *U.S. Public*, pg. 1403

Tweedie, Harry, Chief Fin. Officer--TosoHaas Company, Montgomeryville, PA; *Int'l*, pg. 1408

Tweetie, Mark, Chief Fin. Officer & Asst. Treas.--United Grocers Inc., Portland, OR; *U.S. Private*, pg. 1122

Twetle, Steve, Chief Fin. Officer--Nesco Ameican Harvest Inc., Chaska, MN; *U.S. Private*, pg. 735

Twigg-Smith, Oona, Chief Fin. Officer & Treas.--Persis Corporation, Honolulu, HI; *U.S. Private*, pg. 855

Twigg, T. J., Chief Fin. Officer--Rolls-Royce Industrial & Marine Gas Turbines Ltd., Coventry, United Kingdom; *Int'l*, pg. 1127

Twigger, T., Dir.-Fin.--Meggitt plc, Wimborne Minster, United Kingdom; *Int'l*, pg. 853

Twist, Bill, Chief Fin. Officer--Danish Creamery Association, Fresno, CA; *U.S. Private*, pg. 310

Twomey, Kevin M., Vice Chm., Chief Fin. Officer & Sr. Exec. V.P.--H.F. Ahmanson & Co., Irwindale, CA; *U.S. Public*, pg. 29

Twonig, Steve, Chief Fin. Officer & Sr. V.P.--The Donohoe Companies, Inc., Washington, DC; *U.S. Private*, pg. 340

Twyman, P.J., Grp. Dir.-Fin.--General Accident Fire and Life Assurance Corporation p.l.c., Perth, United Kingdom; *Int'l*, pg. 542

Tychsen, Ulf C., Pres. & Chief Fin. Officer--The West Company Deutschland, Eschweiler, Germany; *U.S. Public*, pg. 1756

Tyler, David, Fin. Dir.--The Great Universal Stores P.L.C., London, United Kingdom; *Int'l*, pg. 557

Tyler, Robert L., Chief Fin. Officer & Sr. V.P.--Aliant Communications Inc., Lincoln, NE; *U.S. Public*, pg. 40

Tzomg, Mei, Chief Fin. Officer, Treas. & Controller--Pantech Construction Co., Lanham, MD; *U.S. Private*, pg. 837

Udasin, Seth, Chief Fin. Officer--The Children's Place Retail Stores, Inc., West Caldwell, NJ; *U.S. Private*, pg. 237

Uhlenhut, Ilse, Chief Fin. Officer--Australian Guarantee Corporation Limited, Sydney, Australia; *Int'l*, pg. 1496

Ulbrich, Scott C., Chief Fin. Officer & Exec. V.P.--First Security Corporation, Salt Lake City, UT; *U.S. Public*, pg. 637

Ulezalka, Jesse, Chief Fin. Officer--Winston Resources, Inc., New York, NY; *U.S. Public*, pg. 1772

Umphlette, Ed, Chief Fin. Officer--Charter House Incorporated, Holland, MI; *U.S. Private*, pg. 1029

Underhill, Stephen M., Chief Fin. Officer, Controller & Dir.-Personnel--R.O. Whitesell & Associates, Inc, Indianapolis, IN; *U.S. Private*, pg. 1173

Underwood, David, Chief Fin. Officer--AGI Inc., Melrose Park, IL; *U.S. Private*, pg. 5

Underwood, David, Chief Fin. Officer & Treas.--Curries Company, Mason City, IA; *Int'l*, pg. 18

Underwood, Leslie, Treas.--Weiss Group., Palm Beach Gardens, FL; *U.S. Private*, pg. 1160

Undreiter, Netgar, Chief Fin. Officer--Temca Chemische Union GmbH, Nuremberg, Germany; *U.S. Public*, pg. 1333

Unruh, Dave, Chief Fin. Officer--BTR Aerspace Group, Winnipeg, Canada; *Int'l*, pg. 127

Untereker, John, Chief Fin. Officer, V.P. & Treas.--Petroleum Helicopters, Inc., Metairie, LA; *U.S. Public*, pg. 1281

Unterman, Thomas, Chief Fin. Officer & Sr. V.P.--The Times Mirror Company, Los Angeles, CA; *U.S. Public*, pg. 1615

Unterreiner, Ronald J., Chief Fin. Officer--HBE Corporation/Design Build Divisions, Saint Louis, MO; *U.S. Private*, pg. 489

Unverzagt, Philip, Chief Fin. Officer & Sr. V.P.--Oregon Freeze Dry, Inc., Albany, OR; *U.S. Private*, pg. 819

Upstone, Velora, Chief Fin. Officer--National Group Life Insurance Company, Rockford, IL; *U.S. Public*, pg. 433

Uraomanskis, Fran, Chief Fin. Officer--Prudential Real Estate Affiliates Inc., Costa Mesa, CA; *U.S. Private*, pg. 892

Urban, C., Chief Fin. Officer--Simko Ticaret ve Sanayi A.S., Karakoy, Turkey; *Int'l*, pg. 1248

Urie, John, Chief Fin. Officer--Nielsen & Bainbridge, Cranbury, NJ; *Int'l*, pg. 460

Urkiel, William S., Chief Fin. Officer--AMP Incorporated, Harrisburg, PA; *U.S. Public*, pg. 7

Urquhart, Richard A., III, V.P.-Fin.--Investors Management Corp., Raleigh, NC; *U.S. Private*, pg. 574

Ursettie, Howard, Chief Fin. Officer--bd Systems, Inc, Torrance, CA; *U.S. Private*, pg. 106

Usher, George, Chief Exec. Officer--Dextran Products Limited, Scarborough, Canada; *Int'l*, pg. 1063

Uveges, George, Chief Fin. Officer & V.P.-Admin.--Gelman Sciences, Inc., Ann Arbor, MI; *U.S. Public*, pg. 1253

Uzokwe, John, Chief Fin. Officer--Peugeot Automobile Nigeria Ltd., Kaduna, Nigeria; *Int'l*, pg. 1021

Uzolins, Uldis, Chief Fin. Officer, Exec. V.P. & Treas.--Fred V. Fowler Company, Inc., Newton, MA; *U.S. Private*, pg. 422

Uzupis, Steven, Chief Fin. Officer & V.P.-Fin.--Brodart Company, Williamsport, PA; *U.S. Private*, pg. 170

Vaccaro, Thomas S., Chief Fin. Officer & Sec.--The Orvis Company, Inc., Manchester, VT; *U.S. Private*, pg. 820

Vacek, Richard, Chief Fin. Officer & Sr. V.P.--Horace Small Apparel Company, Nashville, TN; *Int'l*, pg. 635

Vachani, Mohan, Chief Fin. Officer & Sr. V.P.--AMREP Corporation, New York, NY; *U.S. Public*, pg. 104

Vadala, Nicholas A., Chief Fin. Officer & Exec. V.P.-Opers.--CPS Direct, Inc., Woburn, MA; *U.S. Private*, pg. 196

Vainstein, Israel, Chief Fin. Officer--Security Plastics, Inc., Hialeah, FL; *U.S. Private*, pg. 981

Valade, Gary C., Chief Fin. Officer & Exec. V.P.-Fin.--Chrysler Corporation, Auburn Hills, MI; *U.S. Public*, pg. 352

Valanti, Chuck, Chief Fin. Officer & Controller--Eberline Instrument Corporation, Santa Fe, NM; *U.S. Public*, pg. 1593

Valdes, David, Chief Oper. Officer & Chief Fin. Officer--Zimmerman & Partners Advertising, Inc., Fort Lauderdale, FL; *U.S. Private*, pg. 1206

Valenti, Richard J., Chief Fin. Officer--Dexter Aerospace Materials Division, Pittsburg, CA; *U.S. Public*, pg. 504

Valentin, Christian, Chief Fin. Officer--Posso S.A., Paris, France; *Int'l*, pg. 1064

Valento, Jim, Chief Fin. Officer, V.P. & Treas.--Washington Scientific Industries, Inc., Long Lake, MN; *U.S. Public*, pg. 1744

Valenza, Mike, Chief Fin. Officer--WinCup, Phoenix, AZ; *U.S. Private*, pg. 1182

Valenzuela, Gary, Chief Fin. Officer & Sr. V.P.-Fin. & Admin.--Yahoo!, Inc., Santa Clara, CA; *U.S. Public*, pg. 1787

Valerio, Louis J., Chief Fin. Officer & V.P.-Fin.--Caliber System, Inc., Akron, OH; *U.S. Public*, pg. 604

Valiando, Peter, Chief Fin. Officer--Marine Transport Lines, Inc., Weehawken, NJ; *U.S. Private*, pg. 703

Valice, Debra D., Chief Fin. Officer, Treas. & Corp. Sec.--Seitel, Inc., Houston, TX; *U.S. Public*, pg. 1454

Valla, Pierre, Chief Fin. Officer & V.P.--Rhone-Poulenc Inc., Princeton, NJ; *Int'l*, pg. 1112

Valunas, Thomas, Chief Fin. Officer & V.P.-Fin.--Computational Systems Inc., Knoxville, TN; *U.S. Public*, pg. 572

Vamos, Julie, Chief Fin. Officer--Riker Products, Inc., Toledo, OH; *U.S. Private*, pg. 300

van Andel, A., Chief Fin. Officer--DSM Resins B.V., Zwolle, Netherlands; *Int'l*, pg. 353

Van Biesbroeck, Jo, Chief Fin. Officer--Interbrew S.A., Leuven, Belgium; *Int'l*, pg. 679

Van Biljon, A.F., Sr. Gen. Mgr.-Grp. Fin. Services--Standard Bank Investment Corporation Limited, Johannesburg, South Africa; *Int'l*, pg. 1293

Van Bueren, Boudewyn Lammerts, Controller--BancTec Benelux B.V., Amsterdam, Netherlands; *U.S. Public*, pg. 177

Van Caeneghem, L., Chief Fin. Officer--Lilly France S.A., Saint Cloud, France; *U.S. Public*, pg. 994

van de Wiel, Frans, Chief Fin. Officer--Hansa Industrial Insurance N.V., Rotterdam, Netherlands; *Int'l*, pg. 1425

van dem Ochtemd, Jan J., Chief Fin. Officer--Heidemij N.V., Arnhem, Netherlands; *Int'l*, pg. 606

van den Berg, R., Chief Fin. Officer--Siemens S.A., Saint-Gilles, Belgium; *Int'l*, pg. 1248

van der Rest, J.J., Dir.-Fin. & Economic Affairs--VNU Verenigde Nederlandse Uitgeversbedrijven B.V., Haarlem, Netherlands; *Int'l*, pg. 1445

Van Der Sijpe, Johan, Chief Fin. Officer--Barry Callebaut, Saint Albans, VT; *Int'l*, pg. 252

Van Devender, James, Chief Fin. Officer & Exec. V.P.--Champion HealthCare Corporation, Houston, TX; *U.S. Public*, pg. 333

van Dinter, J.E.M., Chief Fin. Officer--Wolters Kluwer N.V., Amsterdam, Netherlands; *Int'l*, pg. 1512

Van Dusseldorp, Steve, Chief Fin. Officer--Vermeer Manufacturing Company, Pella, IA; *U.S. Private*, pg. 1137

van Dyk, T., Pres. & Treas.--Gist-Brocades, Inc., Wilmington, DE; *Int'l*, pg. 1143

Van Dyke, John, Chief Fin. Officer & Sr. V.P.--American Optical Corporation, Greenwich, CT; *U.S. Private*, pg. 60

Van Erp, Albert J., Chief Fin. Officer--Professional Auto Warehouse, Rochester, NY; *U.S. Public*, pg. 774

Van Himbergen, Thomas W., Chief Fin. Officer & Sr. V.P.--Deluxe Corporation, Shoreview, MN; *U.S. Public*, pg. 498

Van Hoesen, Richard H., Chief Fin. Officer & V.P.-Fin.--Wall Data Incorporated, Kirkland, WA; *U.S. Public*, pg. 1734
Van Hoof, Herman, Chief Fin. Officer--Janssen/Cilag B.V., Tilburg, Netherlands; *U.S. Public*, pg. 929
Van Hoof, Herman, Chief Fin. Officer--Taxandria Pharmaceutica B.V., Tilburg, Netherlands; *U.S. Public*, pg. 932
Van Hoofstat, Robert, Head-Internal Fin. Mgmnt.--Bank Brussels Lambert, Brussels, Belgium; *Int'l*, pg. 146
Van Houten, Jeff, Chief Fin. Officer--Graham Group, Inc., Des Moines, IA; *U.S. Private*, pg. 468
Van Houten, Kent J., Chief Fin. Officer, Treas. & Sec.--Peerless Mfg. Co., Dallas, TX; *U.S. Public*, pg. 1268
van Kesteren, Loes, Chief Fin. Officer--Letraset Nederland BV, Capelle aan den Ijssel, Netherlands; *Int'l*, pg. 462
Van Kleef, William T., Exec. V.P.-Opers.--Tesoro Petroleum Corporation, San Antonio, TX; *U.S. Public*, pg. 1581
Van Leeuwen, Holly, Chief Fin. Officer--Clifford Paper Inc., Upper Saddle River, NJ; *U.S. Private*, pg. 246
Van Loo, Jan, Chief Fin. Officer--Structural Europe, Herentals, Belgium; *U.S. Public*, pg. 593
Van Luven, G.A., Chief Fin. Officer, V.P. Treas. & Sec.--The Gage Company, Pittsburgh, PA; *U.S. Private*, pg. 437
Van Maanen, J.H., Chief Fin. Officer--Olivetti Nederland B.V., Leiden, Netherlands; *Int'l*, pg. 1003
van Meurs, R.E., Chief Fin. Officer--Nedlloyd Lines B.V., Rotterdam, Netherlands; *Int'l*, pg. 1145
van Moorleghem, William, Chief Oper. Officer--Advanced Materials and Technologies N.V., Herk-de-Stad, Belgium; *Int'l*, pg. 1427
Van Ness, Ray, Chief Fin. Officer--Waldes Truarc/Industrial Retaining Ring, Somerset, NJ; *U.S. Public*, pg. 1632
Van Noord, C.C.M., Chief Fin. Officer--N.V. Interturbine, Hilversum, Netherlands; *Int'l*, pg. 673
van Oostrum, P., Chief Fin. Officer--Schering Nederland B.V., Weesp, Netherlands; *Int'l*, pg. 1204
van Roden, John C., Jr., Chief Fin. Officer, Sr. V.P. & Treas.--Lukens Inc., Coatesville, PA; *U.S. Public*, pg. 1019
van Saun, Bruce, Chief Fin. Officer--The Bank of New York, New York, NY; *U.S. Public*, pg. 178
van Saur, Bruce, Chief Fin. Officer & Exec. V.P.--The Bank of New York Company, Inc., New York, NY; *U.S. Public*, pg. 178
Van Schaick, Anthony G., Chief Fin. Officer & Sr. V.P.--John Wieland Homes Inc., Atlanta, GA; *U.S. Private*, pg. 1175
Van Schoor, Franz, Dir.-Fin.--Bacardi-Martini Belgium, Brussels, Belgium; *U.S. Private*, pg. 109
Van Siclen, Jo, Chief Fin. Officer, V.P. & Treas.--Brooke Group Ltd., Miami, FL; *U.S. Public*, pg. 259
Van Siclen, Joselynn D., Chief Fin. Officer, V.P. & Treas.--BGLS Inc., Miami, FL; *U.S. Public*, pg. 259
Van Slooten, Matt, Dir.-Investments--Carlson Real Estate Company, Minnetonka, MN; *U.S. Private*, pg. 212
Van Stippen, Marty, Chief Fin. Officer & Controller--Creative Group Inc., Appleton, WI; *U.S. Private*, pg. 287
Van Vliet, G., Chief Fin. Officer--Black & Decker (Nederland) B.V., Etten-Leur, Netherlands; *U.S. Public*, pg. 234
Vanaria, Robert, Chief Fin. Officer & Sr. V.P.-Admin.--Greenwich Air Services, Miami, FL; *U.S. Public*, pg. 710
Vance, Walter R., Chief Fin. Officer--Royster-Clark, Inc., Tarboro, NC; *U.S. Private*, pg. 949
Vandenberg, Peter, Jr., Pres. & Chief Fin. Officer--Biscayne Apparel Inc., Clifton, NJ; *U.S. Public*, pg. 232
Vandenberghe, James, Chief Fin. Officer & Exec. V.P.-Fin.--Lear Corporation, Southfield, MI; *U.S. Public*, pg. 981
Vander Pol, Daryl L., Chief Fin. Officer, Exec. V.P., Treas. & Sec.--Vitamilk Dairy, Inc., Seattle, WA; *U.S. Private*, pg. 1142
Vander Pool, Jack, Chief Fin. Officer--The Shoe Show of Rocky Mt., Inc., Concord, NC; *U.S. Private*, pg. 996
Vanderwal, Richard B., Chief Fin. Officer & Sr. V.P.-Fin.--Gingiss International, Addison, IL; *U.S. Private*, pg. 455
VanDycke, Maurice, Chief Fin. Officer--SCP Pool Corporation, Covington, LA; *U.S. Private*, pg. 249
VanErp, Albert J., Chief Fin. Officer & V.P.-Fin.--Hahn Automotive Warehouse, Inc., Rochester, NY; *U.S. Public*, *pg. 774*
VanHall, Tom, Chief Fin. Officer--Bil Mar Foods, Inc., Zeeland, MI; *U.S. Public*, pg. 1433
VanHarten, Kenton, Chief Fin.Officer--Brown Jordan Company, El Monte, CA; *U.S. Private*, pg. 174
VanLuvanee, Donald R., Pres. & Chief Exec. Officer--Electro Scientific Industries, Inc., Portland, OR; *U.S. Public*, pg. 568
VanMarren, Herman, Chief Fin. Officer, V.P.-Fin. & Treas.--Kamax-G.B. DuPont L.P., Troy, MI; *U.S. Private*, pg. 606
VanMetre, Robert E., Chief Fin. Officer--US SerVis, West Orange, NJ; *U.S. Public*, pg. 1687
Vanneman, Thomas E., Chief Fin. Officer & V.P.-Fin.--Trivoli Systems, Indianapolis, IN; *U.S. Public*, pg. 896
Vannice, Thaddeus P., Chief Fin. Officer--Top Air Manufacturing, Inc., Cedar Falls, IA; *U.S. Public*, pg. 1621
Vantz, Ronald, Chief Fin. Officer--J.R. Wood Inc., Atwater, CA; *U.S. Private*, pg. 1186
Varblow, Carl R., Chief Fin. Officer--Veda Systems, Incorporated, California, MD; *U.S. Private*, pg. 1136
Varela, Gerardo, Chief Fin. Officer--Tubos de Acero de Mexico, S.A., Mexico, Mexico; *Int'l*, pg. 1426
Vargo, Ed, Chief Fin. Officer--Moltrup Steel Products Company, Beaver Falls, PA; *U.S. Private*, pg. 756
Varnell, John C., Chief Fin. Officer & V.P.--Fairfax Financial Holdings Limited, Toronto, Canada; *Int'l*, pg. 476
Varpen, Hy, Chief Fin. Officer--Naturalle Springs, Inc., Greeneville, TN; *U.S. Private*, pg. 106
Vasily, Michael W., Vice Chm. & Chief Exec. Officer--BayBanks, Inc., Boston, MA; *U.S. Public*, pg. 184
Vass, M. L., Chief Fin. Officer--Chloride Group PLC, London, United Kingdom; *Int'l*, pg. 287
Vasto, Salvatore J., Chief Fin. Officer, Sr. V.P. & Treas.--American Security Group, Atlanta, GA; *Int'l*, pg. 499
Vaswani, Richard N., Chief Fin. Officer & Sr. V.P.--Clark Construction Group, Inc., Bethesda, MD; *U.S. Private*, pg. 242
Vaudano, Gualtiero, Chief Fin. Officer--Bozzalla & Lesna S.p.A., Coggiola, Italy; *Int'l*, pg. 209
Vaughan, Lee, Chief Fin. Officer & V.P.--Overseas Service Corporation, West Palm Beach, FL; *U.S. Private*, pg. 823
Vaughan, Richard, Chief Fin. Officer & Exec. V.P.--Lincoln National Corporation, Fort Wayne, IN; *U.S. Public*, pg. 997
Vaughan, Robert L., Chief Fin. Officer & Exec. V.P.--Vaughan & Sons, Inc., San Antonio, TX; *U.S. Private*, pg. 1134
Vaupen, Hy, Chief Fin. Officer, Exec. V.P. & Sec.--BCI Holding Corporation, Miami, FL; *U.S. Private*, pg. 106
Vaupen, Hy, Chief Fin. Officer, Exec. V.P. & Sec.--Beverage Canners International Corp., Miami, FL; *U.S. Private*, pg. 106
Veasey, Samuel, Chief Fin. Officer & Sr. V.P.--Liggett Group Inc., Durham, NC; *U.S. Public*, pg. 259
Veazey, Doug, Sr. V.P. & Treas.--Deposit Guaranty Mortgage Co., Jackson, MS; *U.S. Public*, pg. 501
Vedoprvoec, Alexander, Fin. Dir.--GGK Wien Werbeagentur GmbH, Vienna, Austria; *Int'l*, pg. 1336
Veen, Steven C., Chief Fin. Officer & Sr. V.P.--Aura Systems, Inc., El Segundo, CA; *U.S. Public*, pg. 147
Veen, Steven C., Chief Fin. Officer--Newcom, Inc., Westlake Village, CA; *U.S. Public*, pg. 147
Vegter, Bill, Chief Fin. Officer & V.P.-Fin.--All-Phase Electric Supply Co., Benton Harbor, MI; *U.S. Private*, pg. 35
Veilleux, Jacques, Chief Fin. Officer--Bromptonville Mill, Bromptonville, Canada; *Int'l*, pg. 761
Veilleux, Martin J., Chief Fin. Officer, Exec. V.P.-Fin., Treas. & Sec.--Boron LePore Group, Fair Lawn, NJ; *U.S. Public*, *pg. 246*
Velasco, Ernesto Vega, Chief Oper. Officer, Chief Fin. Officer & Sec.--Desc, S.A. de C.V., Mexico, Mexico; *Int'l*, *pg. 395*
Velasco, Mayela R., Chief Fin. Officer--Grupo Industrial Durango S.A. de C.V., Durango, Mexico; *Int'l*, pg. 575
Vella, Alain, Chief Fin. Officer--Fanner-PLP, Northmead, Australia; *U.S. Public*, pg. 1321
Veltman, Warren A., Chief Fin. Officer--Autocam Corporation, Grand Rapids, MI; *U.S. Public*, pg. 148
Vendig, Richard, Chief Fin. Officer--Katz Media Group, Inc., New York, NY; *U.S. Public*, pg. 335
Venechanos, Steven, Chief Fin. Officer & Sec.--Suprema Specialties, Inc., Paterson, NJ; *U.S. Public*, pg. 1541
Venechanos, Steven, Chief Fin. Officer & Sec.--Suprema Specialties Northeast, Inc., Ogdensburg, NY; *U.S. Public*, *pg. 1541*
Venkat, S., Reg. Mgr.-Fin. & Accts.-U.S.A. & Can.--Air-India, New York, NY; *Int'l*, pg. 37
Verbeke, G., Chief Fin. Officer--Gist-Brocades France S.A., Seclin, France; *Int'l*, pg. 1143
Verhoef, Hans P.M., Chief Fin. Officer--Euroconsult BV, Arnhem, Netherlands; *Int'l*, pg. 606
Vermeulen, John, Exec. Dir.-Fin.--Volkswagen of America, Inc., Auburn Hills, MI; *Int'l*, pg. 1474
Verrey, Raymond T., Chief Fin. Officer--Insituform East, Inc., Hyattsville, MD; *U.S. Public*, pg. 330
Verrill, Peter J., Chief Oper. Officer, Exec. V.P. & Treas.--Peoples Heritage Financial Group, Inc., Portland, ME; *U.S. Public*, pg. 1275
Versteeg, Sjaak, Chief Fin. Officer--Kadee Delft BV, Delft, Netherlands; *Int'l*, pg. 461
Veteri, Paul A., Chief Fin. Officer & V.P.-Fin.--Carter-Wallace, Inc., New York, NY; *U.S. Public*, pg. 309
Vezzani, Pablo, Mgr.-Fin.--3M Chile S.A., Santiago, Chile; *U.S. Public*, pg. 1606
Vichich, William M., Chief Oper. & Fin. Officer--CitFed Bancorp, Inc., Dayton, OH; *U.S. Public*, pg. 376
Vickers, John, Chief Fin. Officer & Chief Information Officer--Pharmavite Corp., Mission Hills, CA; *U.S. Private*, pg. 860
Vickery, Steven, Chief Fin. Officer--GAC Color Graphics, Atlanta, GA; *U.S. Public*, pg. 1038
Vickrey, Michael, Chief Fin. Officer--The Selmer Co., Inc., Elkhart, IN; *U.S. Public*, pg. 1514
Viefhues, Ludger, V.P.-Fin.--MEMC Electronic Materials, Inc., Saint Peters, MO; *Int'l*, pg. 1455
Viera, James J., Chief Fin. Officer & V.P.--Cowles Media Company, Minneapolis, MN; *U.S. Private*, pg. 280
Vierima, Scott W., V.P. & Chief Fin. Officer--Heater Utilities, Incorporated, Cary, NC; *U.S. Public*, pg. 1116
Viertel, Thomas, Chief Fin. Officer & Exec. V.P.--Presidential Realty Corporation, White Plains, NY; *U.S. Public*, pg. 1323
Viertel, Thomas, Chief Fin. Officer & Exec. V.P.--PDL, Inc., White Plains, NY; *U.S. Public*, pg. 1323
Viertel, Thomas, Chief Fin. Officer & Exec. V.P.--Presidential Realty of Iowa, Inc., White Plains, NY; *U.S. Public*, pg. 1324
Viezens, Hans, Chief Fin. Officer--Fire Control Instruments, Inc., Waltham, MA; *U.S. Private*, pg. 406
Vignola, Frank, Chief Fin. Officer & V.P.--Jimlar Corporation, Great Neck, NY; *U.S. Private*, pg. 587
Vigor, David A., Chief Fin. Officer & V.P.-Fin.--Ohmeda, Inc., Liberty Corner, NJ; *Int'l*, pg. 121
Viles, Donald L., Chief Fin. Officer & Exec. V.P.--Anacomp, Inc., Indianapolis, IN; *U.S. Public*, pg. 106
Vilhjalmsson, Halldor, Sr. V.P.-Fin.--IceLandAir, Columbia, MD; *Int'l*, pg. 658
Villani, Kevin E., Chief Fin. Officer & Exec. V.P.--Imperial Credit Industries, Inc., Torrance, CA; *U.S. Public*, pg. 872
Villano, Michael J., Chief Fin. Officer, V.P., Treas. & Asst. Sec.--Scan-Optics, Inc., Manchester, CT; *U.S. Public*, pg. 1436
Villarreal, Luis Gerardo, Chief Fin. Officer--Sigma Alimentos, S.A. de C.V., Garza Garcia, Mexico; *Int'l*, pg. 56
Villrroya, Santiago, Chief Fin. Officer--Pepsico de Mexico, S.A. de C.V., Mexico, Mexico; *U.S. Public*, pg. 1277
Vilmos, Andras, Dir.-Controlling, Ventures & Investments--Malev Hungarian Airlines, Plc., Budapest, Hungary; *Int'l*, pg. 833
Vincent, Dane L., Chief Fin. Officer & Treas.--Texfi Industries, Inc., Raleigh, NC; *U.S. Public*, pg. 1588
Vincent, Joseph A., Chief Oper. & Fin. Officer & V.P.-Fin.--Novametrix Medical Systems Inc., Wallingford, CT; *U.S. Public*, pg. 1203
Vincent, Paul, Chief Fin. Officer--Alpha Industries, Inc., Woburn, MA; *U.S. Public*, pg. 57
Vincent, Robert M., Chief Fin. Officer & Sr. V.P.-Fin. & Treas.--Uno Restaurant Corporation, West Roxbury, MA; *U.S. Public*, pg. 1698
Vining, Lon, Chief Fin. Officer & V.P.--McGraw-Hill Ryerson, Ltd., Whitby, Canada; *U.S. Public*, pg. 1072
Vinke, John T., Chief Fin. Officer & V.P.-Fin.--Special Devices, Incorporated, Newhall, CA; *U.S. Public*, pg. 1496
Viola, Robert, Chief Fin. Officer--Tristar Corp., San Antonio, TX; *U.S. Public*, pg. 1640
Virgulak, Christopher, Chief Fin. Officer & Exec. V.P.--General Cable Corporation, Highland Heights, KY; *Int'l*, pg. 1486
Visentin, Robert, Chief Fin. Officer & Sr. V.P.--Brookfield Homes, Del Mar, CA; *Int'l*, pg. 228
Visentine, Robert, Chief Fin. Officer & Sr. V.P.--Brookfield Homes Ltd., Toronto, Canada; *Int'l*, pg. 228
Visgar, Dale, Chief Fin. Officer--Dorner Manufacturing Corp., Hartland, WI; *U.S. Private*, pg. 340
Visintini Freschi, Sergio, Chief Fin. Officer & V.P.--Industrias Penoles S.A. de C.V., Cuauhtemoc, Mexico; *Int'l*, pg. 677
Visone, William, Chief Fin. Officer--Pentech International, Inc., Edison, NJ; *U.S. Public*, pg. 1274
Visosky, Leonard M., Chief Fin. Officer & Exec. V.P. & Sec.--Tapco International Corporation, Plymouth, MI; *U.S. Private*, pg. 1068
Vitelle, Richard K., Chief Fin. Officer, V.P.-Fin.--DDL Electronics, Inc., Newbury Park, CA; *U.S. Public*, pg. 473
Vivinetto, Jack, Chief Fin. Officer--Sugar Foods Corp, New York, NY; *U.S. Private*, pg. 1049
Voegele, Ron, Chief Fin. Officer--North American Capacitor Co., Indianapolis, IN; *U.S. Private*, pg. 803
Voelkel, Harold G., Jr., Chief Fin. Officer & Treas.--Southland Oil Company, Jackson, MS; *U.S. Private*, pg. 1018
Voet, Doug, Chief Fin. Officer--Fire King International, Inc., New Albany, IN; *U.S. Private*, pg. 406
Vogel, Gerhard, Dr., Chief Fin. Officer, V.P.-Fin. & Controller--Fuchs Petrolub AG Oel + Chemie, Mannheim, Germany; *Int'l*, pg. 517
Vogt, Andy, Chief Fin. Officer & Sr. V.P.--Galles Chevrolet, Albuquerque, NM; *U.S. Private*, pg. 438
Vohra, Naresh, Chief Fin. Officer--Canada Alloy Castings, Ltd., Kitchener, Canada; *U.S. Public*, pg. 142
Voight, Valantia, Chief Fin. Officer--International Research & Evaluation, Eagan, MN; *U.S. Private*, pg. 571
Voigt, Richard, Controller--Wick Bldg. Systems Inc. Manufactured Homes Div., Marshfield, WI; *U.S. Private*, pg. 1174
Volinsky, Steve, Chief Fin. Officer--Raymour and Flanigan Furniture Co., Liverpool, NY; *U.S. Private*, pg. 912
Vollkommer, Michael T., Chief Fin. Officer & V.P.--Alumax Inc., Atlanta, GA; *U.S. Public*, pg. 59
Vollmer, John E., III, V.P. & Chief Fin. Officer, Music Div.--Blockbuster Entertainment Group, Dallas, TX; *U.S. Private*, pg. 775
Vollmer, John E., III, Chief Fin. Officer, V.P. & Treas.--Blockbuster Music, Dallas, TX; *U.S. Private*, pg. 776
Vollmuth, George, Chief Fin. Officer & Sr. V.P.--Time Inc., New York, NY; *U.S. Public*, pg. 1612
Volz, Larry H., Chief Fin. Officer--Carver Boat Corp., Pulaski, WI; *U.S. Private*, pg. 447
von der Heyden, Karl M., Vice Chm. & Chief Fin. Officer--PepsiCo, Inc., Purchase, NY; *U.S. Public*, pg. 1276
von Dirsztay, Oliver, Chief Fin. Officer--Clarins GmbH, Starnberg, Germany; *Int'l*, pg. 295
Von Lehman, John I., Chief Fin. Officer, V.P. & Treas.--The Midland Company, Cincinnati, OH; *U.S. Public*, pg. 1110
Von Memerty, Sandy, Chief Fin. Officer & Controller--Charter Medical of England Ltd., London, United Kingdom; *U.S. Public*, pg. 1036
von Stange, Fredric E., Chief Fin. Officer--Winstar Communications, New York, NY; *U.S. Public*, pg. 1772
VonderSchmidt, Margaret, V.P.-Fin.--Vital Signs, Englewood, CO; *U.S. Public*, pg. 1723
Vorgity, Eric, Chief Fin. Officer & Controller--Dietrich's Milk Products, Inc., Reading, PA; *U.S. Private*, pg. 332
Vosicky, John J., Chief Fin. Officer & Exec. V.P.--Comdisco, Inc., Rosemont, IL; *U.S. Public*, pg. 407
Voss, Jeffrey, Chief Fin. Officer, Exec. V.P. & Treas.--Beverly Bancorporation Inc., Chicago, IL; *U.S. Public*, pg. 227
Voth, Clarence, Chief Fin. Officer--Medicalodges, Inc., Coffeyville, KS; *U.S. Private*, pg. 728
Vranek, William, Chief Fin. Officer--Coleman Cable Systems, Inc., North Chicago, IL; *U.S. Public*, pg. 968
Vroman, Ralph, Chief Fin. Officer--Success Development International, Jacksonville, FL; *U.S. Private*, pg. 1048
Vuolo, Anthony, Chief Fin. Officer--Synetic, Inc., Elmwood Park, NJ; *U.S. Public*, pg. 1548
Wabler, Robert C., Chief Fin. Officer & Exec. V.P.--Just For Feet, Inc., Pelham, AL; *U.S. Public*, pg. 935
Wachter, Karl, Treas.--Michael Weinig, Inc., Statesville, NC; *Int'l*, pg. 1488
Waclawik, James J., Chief Fin. Officer, Sr. V.P. & Sec.--Material Sciences Corporation, Elk Grove Village, IL; *U.S. Public*, pg. 1056
Waddell, M. Keith, Chief Fin. Officer, Sr. V.P. & Treas.--Robert Half International Inc., Menlo Park, CA; *U.S. Public*, pg. 774
Wadsworth, Howard, V.P.-Fin. & Admin., Treas. & Sec.--Kaneb Services, Inc., Richardson, TX; *U.S. Public*, pg. 942

Wagler, Paul, Chief Fin. Officer & Sr. V.P.-Fin.--The Loewen Group, Inc., Burnaby, Canada; *Int'l*, pg. 814
Wagner, Gary, Chief Fin. Officer, Sr. V.P. & Treas.--Ameron International Corporation, Pasadena, CA; *U.S. Public*, pg. 98
Wagner, H.L., Comptroller--Ohio Edison Co.-Akron Div., Akron, OH; *U.S. Public*, pg. 645
Wagner, Harvey A., Chief Fin. Officer, Sr. V.P.-Fin. & Treas.--Scientific-Atlanta, Inc., Norcross, GA; *U.S. Public*, *pg. 1443*
Wagner, Heinz-Joachim, Chief Fin. Officer--Degussa AG, Frankfurt/Main, Germany; *Int'l*, pg. 388
Wagner, James, Controller--Jacuzzi Bros., Jacuzzi, Inc., Little Rock, AR; *U.S. Public*, pg. 1684
Wagner, James J., Exec. V.P., Chief Fin. Officer--Sani-Dairy Div., Johnstown, PA; *U.S. Public*, pg. 1271
Wagner, Jerry, V.P.-Acctg.--Thermotron Industries, Holland, MI; *U.S. Private*, pg. 1136
Wagner, Juergen, Chief Fin. Officer--Boehringer Ingelheim Animal Health Inc., Saint Joseph, MO; *Int'l*, pg. 199
Wagner, Karen, Chief Fin. Officer, V.P. & Treas.--American Recreation Centers, Inc., Sacramento, CA; *U.S. Public*, pg. 90
Wagner, Kenneth A., V.P. & Controller-Prod. Acctg.--MGM Entertainment Company, Culver City, CA; *U.S. Public*, pg. 1614
Wagner, Mary Jane, Chief Fin. Officer, Treas. & Sec.--American Inks & Coatings Corp., Phoenixville, PA; *U.S. Private*, pg. 56
Wagner, Robert, Chief Fin. Officer--CC-Bank, A.G., Monchengladbach, Germany; *Int'l*, pg. 144
Wagner, Robert, Chief Fin. Officer, V.P.-Fin., Treas. & Sec.--XETA Corporation, Tulsa, OK; *U.S. Public*, pg. 1783
Wagner, Robert V., Chief Fin. Officer, V.P.-Fin., Sec. & Treas.--Code-Alarm, Inc., Madison Heights, MI; *U.S. Public*, pg. 393
Wahlgren, Leif, Chief Fin. Officer--Cederroth International AB, Upplands Vasby, Sweden; *U.S. Public*, pg. 38
Wahlman, Mark M., Chief Fin. Officer, V.P.-Fin. & Treas.--Pacific Coast Producers, Lodi, CA; *U.S. Private*, pg. 830
Wain, A., Chief Fin. Officer--Hepworth Home Products Limited, Belper, United Kingdom; *Int'l*, pg. 615
Waisanen, Larry, Chief Fin. Officer & Sr. V.P.--Lafarge Canada Inc., Montreal, Canada; *Int'l*, pg. 789
Waisanen, Larry J., Chief Fin. Officer & Sr. V.P.--Lafarge Corporation, Reston, VA; *Int'l*, pg. 788
Waite, Donald L., Chief Fin. Officer, Exec. V.P.-Fin. & Sec.--Seagate Technology Inc., Scotts Valley, CA; *U.S. Public*, *pg. 1449*
Walborn, Ronald E., C.P.A., Chief Fin. Officer & Treas.--Arnold Industries, Inc., Lebanon, PA; *U.S. Public*, pg. 132
Wald, Gary, Chief Fin. Officer--Health Products Corporation, Yonkers, NY; *U.S. Private*, pg. 514
Waldbillig, Ron, Asst. V.P.-MIS--Hy-Vee Food Stores Incorporated, West Des Moines, IA; *U.S. Private*, pg. 550
Waleryszak, Michael, Chief Fin. Officer--Crescent Manufacturing Company, Fremont, OH; *U.S. Private*, pg. 289
Walford, Brian G., Exec. V.P., Chief Fin. Officer & Sec.--Exel Insurance Co. Ltd., Hamilton, Bermuda; *Int'l*, pg. 467
Waligurski, Raymond, Controller--Noma-International, Inc., Itasca, IL; *Int'l*, pg. 955
Walkel, Vicki, Chief Fin. Officer--Heil Environmental Industries, Chattanooga, TN; *U.S. Public*, pg. 520
Walker, Baker, Chief Fin. Officer, Controller, Treas. & Sec.--C.B. Ragland Company, Nashville, TN; *U.S. Private*, pg. 907
Walker, Brian, Chief Fin. Officer--Herman Miller, Inc., Zeeland, MI; *U.S. Public*, pg. 1111
Walker, Charles B., Vice Chm., Chief Fin. Officer & Treas.--Albemarle Corporation, Richmond, VA; *U.S. Public*, pg. 37
Walker, Charles S., Chief Fin. Officer & V.P.-Fin.--Federal Compress & Warehouse Company, Inc., Memphis, TN; *U.S. Private*, pg. 398
Walker, Dave, Sr. V.P.-Admin. & Fin.--Cover Girl Cosmetics, Hunt Valley, MD; *U.S. Public*, pg. 1330
Walker, Donald H., Chief Fin. Officer, V.P.-Fin.--Frisch's Restaurants, Inc., Cincinnati, OH; *U.S. Public*, pg. 682
Walker, George M., Chief Fin. Officer & V.P.--Robbins & Myers, Inc., Dayton, OH; *U.S. Public*, pg. 1393
Walker, H. Glen, Chief Fin. Officer--Whirlpool Europe B.V., Comerio, Italy; *U.S. Public*, pg. 1765
Walker, Heike, Chief Fin. Officer--TosoHaas GmbH, Stuttgart, Germany; *Int'l*, pg. 1408
Walker, James M., Chief Fin. Officer & Sr. V.P.--Diamond Multimedia Systems, Inc., San Jose, CA; *U.S. Public*, pg. 505
Walker, James S., Chief Fin. Officer & V.P.--Park-Ohio Industries, Inc., Cleveland, OH; *U.S. Public*, pg. 1258
Walker, Jim, Chief Fin. Officer--Geffen Records, Los Angeles, CA; *Int'l*, pg. 1215
Walker, John, Chief Fin. Officer & Exec. V.P.--Emerson Radio Corp., Parsippany, NJ; *U.S. Public*, pg. 578
Walker, John P., Chief Fin. Officer & Exec. V.P.--Sport Supply Group, Inc., Dallas, TX; *U.S. Public*, pg. 1499
Walker, Kevin P., Chief Fin. Officer, Treas. & Sec.--Duncanson & Holt, New York, NY; *U.S. Public*, pg. 1699
Walker, Robert L., Chief Fin. Officer & Sr. V.P.-Fin.--AEGON USA, Inc., Louisville, KY; *Int'l*, pg. 26
Walker, Thomas, Chief Fin. Officer--IES Utilities Inc., Cedar Rapids, IA; *U.S. Public*, pg. 855
Walker, Thomas M., Chief Fin. Officer & Exec. V.P.--IES Industries Inc., Cedar Rapids, IA; *U.S. Public*, pg. 855
Walker, Vernon W., Chief Fin. Officer & Treas.--Blue Cross & Blue Shield of Texas, Inc., Richardson, TX; *U.S. Private*, pg. 152
Walkins, Patrick M., Chief Fin. Officer--Janssen-Cilag Pharmaceutica AG, Baar, Switzerland; *U.S. Public*, pg. 929
Wall, Chris, Chief Fin. Officer & Mng. Dir.--Vicon Industries (U.K.) Ltd., Fareham, United Kingdom; *U.S. Public*, pg. 1719
Wall, Dave, Mgr.-Acctg.--Graymills Corp., Chicago, IL; *U.S. Private*, pg. 473
Wall, David A., Chief Fin. Officer, V.P.-Fin. & Treas.--DOALL Company, Des Plaines, IL; *U.S. Private*, pg. 337
Wall, Don, Chief Fin. Officer--A.P. Wyott, Dallas, TX; *U.S. Private*, pg. 1193
Wall, Mark, Chief Fin. Officer--The Milnot Company, Saint Louis, MO; *U.S. Private*, pg. 749
Wallace, B., Chief Fin. Officer--Hilton International Co., Coral Gables, FL; *Int'l*, pg. 787
Wallace, Bob, V.P.-Fin. & Admin.--Blue Bird Corporation, Macon, GA; *U.S. Private*, pg. 151
Wallace, David G., Chief Fin. Officer--Community Bank N.A., De Witt, NY; *U.S. Public*, pg. 416
Wallace, Joe, Chief Fin. Officer & V.P.-Fin.--STM Wireless, Inc., Irvine, CA; *U.S. Public*, pg. 1421
Wallace, Larry, Chief Fin. Officer--The United Methodist Publishing House, Nashville, TN; *U.S. Private*, pg. 1122
Wallace, Mark A., Chief Fin. Officer & V.P.--Titanium Metals Corporation, Denver, CO; *U.S. Private*, pg. 270
Wallace, Stephen P., Chief Fin. Officer & Sr. V.P.--Catellus Development Corporation, San Francisco, CA; *U.S. Public*, pg. 314
Wallant, Jean-Claude Coppieters 't, Chief Fin. Officer & Sec.--Etablissements Delhaize Freres Et Cie "Le Lion" S.A., Brussels, Belgium; *Int'l*, pg. 462
Waller, Matthew S., Chief Fin. Officer--ATC Communications Group, Inc., Dallas, TX; *U.S. Public*, pg. 11
Walles, Gregory D., Chief Fin. Officer--Sybron Dental Specialties, Inc., Glendora, CA; *U.S. Public*, pg. 1545
Walles, John R., Chief Fin. Officer & V.P.--GLS Corporation, Arlington Heights, IL; *U.S. Private*, pg. 435
Wallman, Richaard F., Chief Fin. Officer & V.P.--AlliedSignal Inc., Morristown, NJ; *U.S. Public*, pg. 49
Walloner, Carol, Treas.--Sunflower Electric Power Corporation, Hays, KS; *U.S. Private*, pg. 1052
Walsh, Chuck, Mng. Partner & Chief Fin. Officer--Earle Palmer Brown, New York, NY; *U.S. Private*, pg. 173
Walsh, Jerry, Controller--Ply-Gem Manufacturing, Haddon Heights, NJ; *U.S. Public*, pg. 1193
Walsh, Terry J., Chief Fin. Officer & Sr. V.P.--Scott's Restaurants Inc., Markham, Canada; *Int'l*, pg. 1213
Walter, Bernhard, Chief Exec. Officer--Dresdner Bank AG, Frankfurt/Main, Germany; *Int'l*, pg. 417
Walter, Frank, Chief Fin. Officer--SSB Advertising Sydney, Sydney, Australia; *Int'l*, pg. 394
Walter, Malcolm S., Chief Fin. Officer--R&B, Inc., Colmar, PA; *U.S. Public*, pg. 1354
Walter, Richard C., Chief Fin. Officer--Airlease Ltd., San Francisco, CA; *U.S. Public*, pg. 33
Walters, Eric G., Chief Fin. Officer & Treas.--PolyMedica Industries, Inc., Woburn, MA; *U.S. Public*, pg. 1315
Walters, Kirk, Chief Fin. Officer, Sr. V.P. & Treas.--Chittenden Corporation, Burlington, VT; *U.S. Public*, pg. 350
Walton, Jerry W., Chief Fin. Officer & Exec. V.P.-Fin.--J.B. Hunt Transport Services, Inc., Lowell, AR; *U.S. Public*, pg. 849
Wan, David, Chief Fin. Officer--Excelsior Inc., City of Industry, CA; *U.S. Private*, pg. 387
Wan, Tracy, Chief Fin. Officer, Sr. V.P. & Sec.--The Sharper Image, San Francisco, CA; *U.S. Public*, pg. 1464
Wang, Susan S., Chief Fin. Officer, Sr. V.P. & Sec.--Solectron Corporation, Milpitas, CA; *U.S. Public*, pg. 1483
Wanlass, Dennis L., Chief Fin. Officer, V.P. & Treas.--Geneva Steel, Vineyard, UT; *U.S. Public*, pg. 729
Ward-Burns, J. Robert, Chief Oper. Officer & Exec. V.P.--BeautiControl Cosmetics, Inc., Carrollton, TX; *U.S. Public*, pg. 198
Ward, Charles C., Jr., Treas.--Sunniland Corporation, Sanford, FL; *U.S. Private*, pg. 1053
Ward, Gerald L., V.P.-Admin.--Seats Incorporated, Reedsburg, WI; *U.S. Private*, pg. 410
Ward, Larry M., Chief Fin. Officer--Johnstown Corporation, Johnstown, PA; *U.S. Private*, pg. 595
Ward, Robert, Chief Fin. Officer, Chief Acctg. Officer & V.P.--Cavco Industries, Inc., Phoenix, AZ; *U.S. Public*, pg. 323
Ward, Ronald G., Chief Fin. Officer--Dairyland Greyhound Park, Inc., Kenosha, WI; *U.S. Private*, pg. 307
Ward, Scott H., Pres. & Chief Fin. Officer--Russell Stover Candies, Inc., Kansas City, MO; *U.S. Private*, pg. 953
Ward, Scott H., Pres. & Chief Fin. Officer--Whitman's Candies, Inc., Kansas City, MO; *U.S. Private*, pg. 953
Wardenaar, David "DJ", Chief Fin. Officer--L.M. Scofield Company, Los Angeles, CA; *U.S. Private*, pg. 976
Wardlaw, Sharon, Chief Fin. Officer, Treas. & Sec.--Polydex Pharmaceuticals Limited, Scarborough, Canada; *Int'l*, pg. 1062
Ware, Todd P., Chief Fin. Officer & V.P.--National Gas & Oil Company, Newark, OH; *U.S. Public*, pg. 1156
Warfel, Daniel L., Chief Fin. Officer & Exec. V.P.--Omega Financial Corporation, State College, PA; *U.S. Public*, pg. 1222
Warfel, Willis W., Jr., Gen. Auditor--UGI Corporation, King of Prussia, PA; *U.S. Public*, pg. 1653
Warga, John E., Chief Fin. Officer & Exec. V.P.--Dynalectric Company, Mc Lean, VA; *U.S. Public*, pg. 571
Wargolet, Thomas S., Chief Fin. Officer & V.P.-Fin.--ENStar, Inc., Eden Prairie, MN; *U.S. Public*, pg. 585
Wark, Dale A., Chief Fin. Officer, Exec. V.P., Treas. & Sec.--R.M. Shoemaker Co., West Conshohocken, PA; *U.S. Private*, pg. 996
Warnock, John J., Jr., Chief Fin. Officer & Sr. V.P.--FTP Software Inc., Andover, MA; *U.S. Public*, pg. 609
Warren, J.A., Grp. Dir.-Fin.--United Biscuits (Holdings) Plc, West Drayton, United Kingdom; *Int'l*, pg. 1442
Warren, James L., Chief Fin. Officer, V.P. & Treas.--Aquila Biopharmaceuticals, Inc., Worcester, MA; *U.S. Public*, pg. 126
Warren, Jeffrey R., Chief Fin. Officer--Bristol & West Building Society, Bristol, United Kingdom; *Int'l*, pg. 216
Warren, Joe G., Chief Fin. Officer--White Microelectronics, Phoenix, AZ; *U.S. Public*, pg. 248
Warren, Joseph G., Chief Fin. Officer, V.P.-Fin., Treas. & Sec.--Bowmar Instrument Corporation, Phoenix, AZ; *U.S. Public*, pg. 248
Warren, R. Conner, Chief Fin. Officer, & Exec. V.P.-Fin. & Admin.--Citation Corporation, Birmingham, AL; *U.S. Public*, pg. 376
Warren, Tom, Chief Fin. Officer--Mednet, MPC Corporation, Las Vegas, NV; *U.S. Public*, pg. 1082
Warrener, Richard C., Chief Fin. Officer & Sr. V.P.--Rurban Financial Corp., Defiance, OH; *U.S. Public*, pg. 1412
Warshaw, Steven G., Pres., Chief Oper. & Fin. Officer--Chiquita Brands International, Inc., Cincinnati, OH; *U.S. Public*, pg. 349
Warsinske, Steven W., Treas. & Sec.--Southeastern Michigan Gas Company, Port Huron, MI; *U.S. Public*, pg. 1489
Wascher, William J., Chief Fin. Officer--U.S.S. Seko Worldwide, Elk Grove Village, IL; *U.S. Private*, pg. 1115
Waslaski, Douglas, Chief Fin. Officer--American Fence & Security Company, Phoenix, AZ; *U.S. Private*, pg. 54
Wassenaar, Craig G., Chief Fin. Officer, V.P. & Sec.--Ameriwood Industries International Inc., Grand Rapids, MI; *U.S. Public*, pg. 98
Wasserspring, Arthur J., V.P.-Fin.--Eastco Industrial Safety Corp., Huntington Station, NY; *U.S. Public*, pg. 548
Wasson, Robert, Chief Fin. Officer--Messier-Dowty, Abingdon, United Kingdom; *Int'l*, pg. 1340
Watanbe, Neil, Chief Fin. Officer--Mac Frugal's Bargains Close-Outs Inc., Rancho Dominguez, CA; *U.S. Public*, pg. 437
Waterman, B.G., Chief Fin. Officer & V.P.-Fin.--Talisman Energy Inc., Calgary, Canada; *Int'l*, pg. 1352
Waterman, Joseph F., Chief Fin. Officer & Sr. V.P.--Sanchez Computer Associates, Malvern, PA; *U.S. Public*, *pg. 1425*
Waters, Bob, Chief Fin. Officer--Avanti Press Inc., Miami, FL; *U.S. Private*, pg. 101
Waters, John D., Chief Fin. Officer & V.P.--F.N.B. Corporation, Hermitage, PA; *U.S. Public*, pg. 607
Waters, John D., Sr. V.P. & Chief Fin. Officer--First National Bank of Pennsylvania, Hermitage, PA; *U.S. Public*, pg. 607
Waters, Robert, Chief Fin. Officer--Inktel Marketing, Miami, FL; *U.S. Private*, pg. 101
Waters, Tricia, Chief Fin. Officer & Dir.-Fin.--Rice Growers Association of California, West Sacramento, CA; *U.S. Private*, pg. 927
Waters, Tricia, Chief Fin. Officer--RGA Products Inc., Sacramento, CA; *U.S. Private*, pg. 927
Waterston, Michael, Chief Fin. Officer--Blumberg Communications Inc., Minneapolis, MN; *U.S. Public*, pg. 305
Watjen, Thomas R., Chief Fin. Officer & Exec. V.P.--Provident Companies, Inc., Chattanooga, TN; *U.S. Public*, pg. 1337
Watkins, Aurmond A., Jr., V.P.-Taxes--Occidental Petroleum Corporation, Los Angeles, CA; *U.S. Public*, pg. 1210
Watson, David, Dir.-Fin. Europe--Leasing Solutions International, Ltd., Woking, United Kingdom; *U.S. Public*, pg. 983
Watson, David E., Chief Fin. Officer & Exec. V.P.--American Italian Pasta Company, Excelsior Springs, MO; *U.S. Public*, pg. 85
Watson, Emma, Chief Fin. Officer--Conran Octopus Limited, London, United Kingdom; *Int'l*, pg. 1093
Watson, John, V.P.-Fin.--Reily Foods Company, New Orleans, LA; *U.S. Private*, pg. 919
Watson, John, Chief Fin. Officer & Exec. V.P.--Rank America, Inc., Atlanta, GA; *Int'l*, pg. 1087
Watson, John D., Chief Fin. Officer & V.P.-Fin.--Alberta Energy Company, Ltd., Calgary, Canada; *Int'l*, pg. 48
Watson, Kenneth, Chief Fin. Officer & Exec. V.P.--MBL Life Assurance Corporation, Newark, NJ; *U.S. Private*, pg. 685
Watson, Robbie, Chief Fin. Officer--Binning's Building Products, Inc., Lexington, NC; *U.S. Public*, pg. 67
Watson, Susan B., Chief Fin. Officer & Sr. V.P.--Equitable Life Insurance Company of Iowa, Des Moines, IA; *Int'l*, pg. 647
Watson, Tom, Chief Fin. Officer--Rainbow Technologies, Ltd., Chertsey, United Kingdom; *U.S. Public*, pg. 1359
Watts, Douglas D., V.P.-Fin.--Amcast Industrial Corporation, Dayton, OH; *U.S. Public*, pg. 63
Watts, Garry, Dir.-Fin--Medeva PLC, London, United Kingdom; *Int'l*, pg. 852
Watts, Robert, Chief Fin. Officer--Electrical Insulation Suppliers, Atlanta, GA; *U.S. Private*, pg. 368
Waugh, Richard B., Jr., Chief Fin. Officer & V.P.--Northrop Grumman Corporation, Los Angeles, CA; *U.S. Public*, pg. 1197
Way, Michael G., Chief Fin. Officer, Legal, Treas. & Sec.--Bristile Clay Tiles, Ltd., Caversham, Australia; *Int'l*, pg. 216
Way, T.L., V.P.-Fin.--Miller Chemical & Fertilizer Corp., Hanover, PA; *U.S. Private*, pg. 33
Wayman, Robert P., Chief Fin. Officer & Exec. V.P.-Fin. & Admin.--Hewlett-Packard Company, Palo Alto, CA; *U.S. Public*, pg. 813
Weatherford, Bobby J., Chief Fin. Officer--Quincy Corp., Quincy, FL; *U.S. Public*, pg. 1545
Weatherly, John S., Chief Fin. Officer, V.P. & Treas.--Callon Petroleum Company, Natchez, MS; *U.S. Public*, pg. 295
Weathers, Earl, Chief Fin. Officer--Houchens Industries Inc., Bowling Green, KY; *U.S. Private*, pg. 541
Weaver, Bill, Chief Fin. Officer--All Nation Insurance Company, Southfield, MI; *U.S. Private*, pg. 35
Weaver, Paul, Chief Fin. Officer--Ogden Aviation Services, New York, NY; *U.S. Public*, pg. 1213
Weaver, Richard T., Chief Exec. & Fin. Officer, Treas. & Sec.--Hamburg Brothers, Pittsburgh, PA; *U.S. Private*, pg. 497

Weaver, Stephen D., Chief Fin. Officer & V.P.-Fin.--The Carbide/Graphite Group, Inc., Pittsburgh, PA; *U.S. Public*, pg. 304
Weaver, Thomas C., Chief Fin. Officer--Polyfibron Technologies Corp., Billerica, MA; *U.S. Private*, pg. 875
Webb, A. Grant, III, Chief Fin. Officer & V.P.-Fin.--Prym-Dritz Corporation, Spartanburg, SC; *Int'l*, pg. 1499
Webb, Paul, Chief Fin. Officer--Mikron U.K. Ltd., Huddersfield, United Kingdom; *Int'l*, pg. 867
Webb, T. E., Mrs., Chief Fin. Officer & V.P.-Fin.--Crowley Foods, Inc., Binghamton, NY; *Int'l*, pg. 752
Weber, C.R., Chief Fin. Officer & Sr. V.P.--OMNI Superstores, Northlake, IL; *U.S. Private*, pg. 1202
Weber, Donald, Chief Fin. Officer--Rosco Manufacturing Co., Madison, SD; *U.S. Private*, pg. 944
Weber, Douglas, Chief Fin. Officer & Treas.--Edwards Brothers, Inc., Ann Arbor, MI; *U.S. Private*, pg. 365
Weber, John, Chief Fin. Officer--Fuji Medical Systems USA, Inc., Stamford, CT; *Int'l*, pg. 524
Weber, John R., Chief Fin. Officer , V.P.-Fin. & Treas.--The Chardon Rubber Co., Chardon, OH; *U.S. Private*, pg. 229
Weber, R. Christopher, Chief Fin. Officer & Sr. V.P.--Jacor Communications, Inc., Covington, KY; *U.S. Public*, pg. 922
Weber, Stanley G., Chief Fin. Officer, Sr. V.P.-Fin. & Sec.--Sceptre Resources Limited, Calgary, Canada; *Int'l*, pg. 1203
Webster, J., Dir.-Fin.--Janesville Products, Norwalk, OH; *U.S. Public*, pg. 924
Webster, Jonathan, Fin. Controller & Commercial Mgr.--The Lancet Limited, London, United Kingdom; *Int'l*, pg. 1100
Webster, Mark, Chief Exec. Officer, Chief Fin. Officer & Gen. Counsel--Heritage Co-op, Rushville, IN; *U.S. Private*, pg. 524
Webster, Ralph L., Chief Fin. Officer & V.P.--Logicon, Inc., Torrance, CA; *U.S. Public*, pg. 1198
Webster, Stepehn W., Chief Fin. Officer--Wolseley Plc., Droitwich, United Kingdom; *Int'l*, pg. 1511
Wedel, H. Charles, Chief Fin. Officer & Treas.--NJ Transit, Newark, NJ; *U.S. Private*, pg. 794
Wee, Larry, Foreign Exchange & Money Market Mgr.--BFCE Singapore, Singapore, Singapore; *Int'l*, pg. 161
Wegman, Robert B., Chm. Bd., Chief Exec. Officer & Treas.--Wegmans Food Markets, Inc., Rochester, NY; *U.S. Private*, pg. 1158
Wehrle, Michael H., Chief Fin. Officer & Sr. V.P.--McJunkin Corporation, Charleston, WV; *U.S. Private*, pg. 722
Weiden, Jeff, Chief Fin. Officer--Flexfab Horizons International, Inc., Hastings, MI; *U.S. Private*, pg. 412
Weiden, Jeff, Sr. V.P.-Fin. & Treas.--Firstar Corporation, Milwaukee, WI; *U.S. Public*, pg. 642
Weidler, Allen, V.P.-Fin. & Sec.--Fred Usinger, Inc., Milwaukee, WI; *U.S. Private*, pg. 1129
Weigand, George W., Chief Fin. Officer & Sr. V.P.--Rubbermaid Incorporated, Wooster, OH; *U.S. Public*, pg. 1411
Weilminster, Robert, V.P.-Fin.--Poly-Seal Corporation, Baltimore, MD; *U.S. Private*, pg. 875
Weinand, Paul, Chief Fin. Officer & V.P.-Fin.--Daktronics, Inc., Brookings, SD; *U.S. Public*, pg. 478
Weinberg, Brian, Chief Fin. Officer & V.P.--Argus Publishers, Placentia, CA; *U.S. Public*, pg. 1328
Weinberg, David L., Chief Fin. Officer, V.P.-Fin. & Admin., Treas. & Sec.--Columbia Laboratories, Inc., Miami, FL; *U.S. Public*, pg. 405
Weinberg, Robert W., Chief Fin. Officer, Sr. Exec. V.P. & Treas.--K-Tron International, Inc., Pitman, NJ; *U.S. Public*, pg. 938
Weiner, Edward G., Chief Fin. Officer--Transammonia Inc., New York, NY; *U.S. Private*, pg. 1096
Weiner, Eugene L., Exec. V.P., Sec. & Treas.--Paradise, Inc., Plant City, FL; *U.S. Public*, pg. 1256
Weiner, Paul, Chief Fin. Officer, Sr. V.P. & Treas.--McCrory Corporation, New York, NY; *U.S. Private*, pg. 720
Weinfeld, Lewis, Chief Fin. Officer & Sr. V.P.--HRH Construction Corp., New York, NY; *U.S. Private*, pg. 1035
Weinfeld, Lewis A., Chief Fin. Officer & Exec. V.P.--Starrett HRH, New York, NY; *U.S. Private*, pg. 1035
Weinhold, Kevin, Chief Fin. Officer--Empire Steel Castings, Inc., Laureldale, PA; *U.S. Public*, pg. 142
Weinhuff, Jeffry K., Exec. V.P. & Dir.-Corp. Fin.--Jefferies & Company, Inc., Los Angeles, CA; *U.S. Public*, pg. 925
Weinstein, Alan A., Chief Fin. Officer & Sr. V.P.--Gottschalks Inc., Fresno, CA; *U.S. Public*, pg. 754
Weinstein, Alan I., Chief Fin. & Admin. Officer, Sr. Exec. V.P. & Sec.--Morse Shoe, Inc., Canton, MA; *U.S. Public*, pg. 168
Weinstock, Russell G., Chief Fin. Officer & V.P.-Fin.--Silicon Valley Group, Inc., San Jose, CA; *U.S. Public*, pg. 1474
Weir, David, Pres., Chief Exec. Officer & Chief Fin. Officer--Denison Hydraulics, Inc., Marysville, OH; *U.S. Private*, pg. 324
Weir, Stephen J., Chief Fin. Officer & Exec. V.P.--Telemedia Inc., Montreal, Canada; *Int'l*, pg. 1373
Weis, Steven S., Chief Fin. Officer--Reliance Steel & Aluminum Co., Los Angeles, CA; *U.S. Public*, pg. 1375
Weisberg, Arie, Chief Fin. Officer & V.P.-Fin.--Orbotech Ltd., Yavne, Israel; *Int'l*, pg. 1007
Weisel, Trudy, Chief Fin. Officer--Service Web Offset Corporation, Chicago, IL; *U.S. Private*, pg. 987
Weisman, Rich, Chief Fin. Officer--Whitney Corr-Pak International, Inc., East Brunswick, NJ; *U.S. Private*, pg. 249
Weiss, Howard, Chief Fin. Officer--Castle-Harlan, Inc., New York, NY; *U.S. Private*, pg. 219
Weiss, Neil, Chief Fin. Officer--Butler Capital Corp., New York, NY; *U.S. Private*, pg. 190
Weiss, Robert S., Chief Fin. Officer & Exec. V.P.--The Cooper Companies, Inc., Irvine, CA; *U.S. Public*, pg. 442
Weissberg, Ron, Chief Fin. Officer & Dir.--The Israel Land Development Co., Ltd., Tel Aviv, Israel; *Int'l*, pg. 691
Weissman, Steve, Chief Fin. Officer--United States Realty & Investment Co., New York, NY; *U.S. Private*, pg. 1125
Weitz, Randy, Chief Fin. Officer--International Typeface Corporation (ITC), New York, NY; *Int'l*, pg. 460
Weitzel, John A., Chief Fin. Officer--The Seibels Bruce Group, Inc., Columbia, SC; *U.S. Public*, pg. 1453
Weitzel, John A., Chief Fin. Officer & V.P.--South Carolina Insurance Company, Columbia, SC; *U.S. Public*, pg. 1453
Weitzel, John A., Chief Fin. Officer & V.P.--Consolidated American Insurance Co., Columbia, SC; *U.S. Public*, pg. 1454
Weitzel, John A., Chief Fin. Officer--Catawba Insurance Co., Columbia, SC; *U.S. Public*, pg. 1454
Weitzel, John A., Chief Fin. Officer & V.P.--Investors National Life Insurance Co., Columbia, SC; *U.S. Public*, pg. 1454
Weitzel, John A., Chief Fin. Officer & V.P.--Kentucky Insurance Co., Louisville, KY; *U.S. Public*, pg. 1454
Weitzel, John A., Chief Fin. Officer & V.P.--Seibels, Bruce & Co., Columbia, SC; *U.S. Public*, pg. 1454
Weitzel, John A., Chief Fin. Officer & V.P.--Agency Specialty Inc., Columbia, SC; *U.S. Public*, pg. 1454
Weitzel, John A., Chief Fin. Officer & V.P.--Forest Lake Travel Service, Inc., Columbia, SC; *U.S. Public*, pg. 1454
Weitzenfeld, Marvin, Chief Fin. Officer, Sec. & Treas.--Globe-Amerada Glass Company, Elk Grove Village, IL; *U.S. Private*, pg. 458
Weitzenfeld, Marvin, Chief Fin. Officer, Treas. & Sec.--Assurance Glass Co. of Alabama, Selma, AL; *U.S. Private*, pg. 458
Weitzman, William, Pres. & Chief Oper. Officer--Electro Rent Corporation, Van Nuys, CA; *U.S. Public*, pg. 568
Weix, Mark A., V.P. & Cashier--M & I Citizens American Bank, Merrill, WI; *U.S. Public*, pg. 1050
Welch, John, Chief Fin. Officer--Liberty Precision Industries, Rochester, NY; *U.S. Private*, pg. 666
Welch, Mark V., Chief Fin. Officer--The L & B Group, Dallas, TX; *U.S. Public*, pg. 1673
Welch, Martin E., III, Chief Fin. Officer & Sr. V.P.--Kmart Corporation, Troy, MI; *U.S. Public*, pg. 963
Welch, Michael, Chm.-Credit Policy Committee--Citicorp, New York, NY; *U.S. Public*, pg. 376
Welch, Stephen, Chief Fin. Officer & Treas.--Todd Pacific Shipyards Corp., Seattle, WA; *U.S. Public*, pg. 1619
Welchko, Donald C., Chief Fin. Officer & V.P.--Anicom, Inc., Rosemont, IL; *U.S. Public*, pg. 115
Welder, Paul, Chief Fin. Officer--Greenwood Mills, Inc., Greenwood, SC; *U.S. Private*, pg. 479
Weldgen, Thomas J., Chief Fin. Officer--CPAC, Inc., Leicester, NY; *U.S. Public*, pg. 282
Weldgen, Tom, Chief Fin. Officer--CPAC Equipment Division, Leicester, NY; *U.S. Public*, pg. 282
Welhouse, Dennis J., Chief Fin. Officer--Lexington Precision Corporation, New York, NY; *U.S. Public*, pg. 991
Wellborn, Chris, Chief Fin. Officer--Dal-Tile International, Dallas, TX; *U.S. Private*, pg. 308
Wellborn, William C., Chief Fin. Officer & Sr. V.P.--Lenox, Incorporated, Lawrenceville, NJ; *U.S. Public*, pg. 261
Wellens, Leroy, Chm. Bd., Pres., Chief Exec. & Chief Fin. Officer & Treas.--Wellens & Co., Inc., Minneapolis, MN; *U.S. Private*, pg. 1161
Weller, Andrew, Chief Fin. Officer--Truck Components Inc., Rockford, IL; *U.S. Public*, pg. 933
Weller, Andrew M., Chief Fin. Officer, Exec. V.P., Dir. & Sec--Johnstown America Industries, Chicago, IL; *U.S. Public*, pg. 933
Weller, Joseph C., Chief Fin. Officer, Treas. & Sec.--Morgan Keegan, Inc., Memphis, TN; *U.S. Public*, pg. 1131
Wellman, Thomas A., Chief Fin. Officer--A & B Development Co. (California), Honolulu, HI; *U.S. Public*, pg. 39
Wellman, Thomas A., Chief Fin. Officer--A & B Properties, Inc., Honolulu, HI; *U.S. Public*, pg. 39
Wellman, Thomas A., Chief Fin. Officer--Kahului Trucking & Storage, Inc., Kahului, HI; *U.S. Public*, pg. 39
Wells, Barbara, Chief Fin. Officer--Gray Kirk/VanSant Advertising, Inc., Baltimore, MD; *U.S. Private*, pg. 472
Wells, Doug, Chief Fin. Officer--Rockford Products Corp., Rockford, IL; *U.S. Private*, pg. 938
Wells, Gary H., Chief Fin. Officer,Treas & Sec.--Chittenden & Eastman Co., Burlington, IA; *U.S. Private*, pg. 237
Wells, Gary H., Chief Fin. Officer, Treas. & Sec--Eastman House Of California, Inc., Burlington, IA; *U.S. Private*, pg. 238
Wells, Gary H., Chief Fin. Officer, Treas. & Sec.--Eastman House Of Alabama, Inc., Burlington, IA; *U.S. Private*, pg. 238
Wells, Robert B., Chief Fin. Officer & Exec. V.P.--Bank of Montreal, Toronto, Canada; *Int'l*, pg. 153
Wells, Roddy, Chief Fin. Officer & V.P.--Snapper Power Equipment, Mc Donough, GA; *U.S. Public*, pg. 1103
Welsh, Richard, Chief Fin. Officer--First Omni Bank, N.A., Millsboro, DE; *Int'l*, pg. 65
Welsh, Stephen, Chief Fin. Officer & V.P.--Nissan Motor Corporation in U.S.A., Gardena, CA; *Int'l*, pg. 945
Welsh, Steven A., CPA, Chief Fin. Officer--Ace Tank & Equipment Co., Seattle, WA; *U.S. Private*, pg. 12
Welshhans, Richard W., Chief Fin. Officer, V.P. & Treas.--Reflectone, Inc., Tampa, FL; *Int'l*, pg. 218
Welton, Robert, Chief Fin. Officer & V.P.-Bus.--Beech Holdings, Inc., Wichita, KS; *U.S. Public*, pg. 1365
Wendel, Peter, Chief Fin. Officer & V.P.-Opers.--Karakas, VanSickle, Ouellette Advertising & Public Relations, Portland, OR; *U.S. Private*, pg. 607
Wendell, Daniel, Chief Fin. Officer--Teledyne Portland Forge, Portland, IN; *U.S. Public*, pg. 43
Wendt, Lee, Chief Fin. Officer--Fremont Premium Finance Corp., Santa Monica, CA; *U.S. Public*, pg. 681
Wenger, Jurg E., Chief Fin. Officer & Exec. V.P.--Mikron Holding AG, Biel, Switzerland; *Int'l*, pg. 866
Wenich, Ozzie, Chief Fin. Officer, Sr. V.P. & Treas.--H & R Block, Inc., Kansas City, MO; *U.S. Public*, pg. 770
Wentworth, Bob, Chief Fin. Officer & Sr. V.P.--Pilot Software, Cambridge, MA; *U.S. Private*, pg. 872
Wentworth, Robert, Chief Fin. Officer--Platinum Equity Holdings, LLC, Los Angeles, CA; *U.S. Private*, pg. 872
Wenz, Richard E., Pres. & Chief Oper. Officer--Safety 1st, Inc., Chestnut Hill, MA; *U.S. Public*, pg. 1425
Wenzler, Joseph P., Chief Fin. Officer, Sr. V.P. & Treas.--WICOR, Inc., Milwaukee, WI; *U.S. Public*, pg. 1767
Wenzler, Matthew, Controller--Orlane, Inc., New York, NY; *Int'l*, pg. 1011
Werle, Udo, Chief Fin. Officer--Fresenius AG, Bad Hamburg, Germany; *Int'l*, pg. 505
Werlinger, Mark, Chief Fin. Officer--Cole Papers Inc., Fargo, ND; *U.S. Private*, pg. 251
Werner, David, Chief Fin. Officer & Exec. V.P.--KTI, Orange, CA; *U.S. Public*, pg. 939
Werner, Nina, Chief Fin. Officer & Exec. V.P.--Zenith Media Services, Inc., New York, NY; *U.S. Private*, pg. 1204
Wernett, Karl, Chief Fin. Officer--Princess Cruise Lines, Los Angeles, CA; *Int'l*, pg. 1035
Wert, John H., Jr., Chief Fin. Officer & Sr. V.P.-Fin.--Owosso Corporation, King of Prussia, PA; *U.S. Public*, pg. 1238
Wertz, Larry J., Exec. V.P. & Chief Fin. Officer-First Union Nat'l Bank of FL--First Union Corporation, Charlotte, NC; *U.S. Public*, pg. 639
Wertz, Larry J., Chief Fin. Officer & Exec. V.P.--First Union National Bank of Florida, Jacksonville, FL; *U.S. Public*, pg. 640
Wesolowski, Gerald, Chief Fin. Officer--Burns & Wilcox Ltd., Farmington, MI; *U.S. Private*, pg. 609
Wesolowski, Gerald F., Chief Fin. Officer--H.W. Kaufman Financial Group, Inc., Farmington, MI; *U.S. Private*, pg. 609
Wesorick, L., Chief Fin. Officer & Controller--Rapid Engineering Inc., Comstock Park, MI; *U.S. Private*, pg. 910
Wessel, Rick L., Chief Fin. Officer, Treas. & Sec.--First Cash, Inc., Arlington, TX; *U.S. Public*, pg. 627
Wesselink, David, Chief Fin. Officer & Sr. V.P.--Advanta Corp., Spring House, PA; *U.S. Public*, pg. 22
Wesselmann, Lee A., Chief Fin. Officer & Sr. V.P.--Owens-Illinois, Inc., Toledo, OH; *U.S. Public*, pg. 1238
Wessling, J.D., Chief Fin. Officer & V.P.-Fin.--Cascade Natural Gas Corporation, Seattle, WA; *U.S. Public*, pg. 311
West, David, Chief Fin. Officer--The Kendall Co. (UK) Ltd., Basingstoke, United Kingdom; *U.S. Public*, pg. 1647
West, Paul, Chief Fin. Officer--Landry's Seafood Restaurants Inc., Houston, TX; *U.S. Public*, pg. 977
West, Todd K., Chief Fin. Officer, V.P.-Fin. & Sec.--Noel Group, Inc., New York, NY; *U.S. Public*, pg. 1187
Westaway, Peter W., Chief Fin. Officer--Commercial Union of Canada Holdings Ltd, Toronto, Canada; *Int'l*, pg. 308
Westaway, Peter W., Chief Fin. Officer--Commercial Union Assurance Company of Canada, Toronto, Canada; *Int'l*, pg. 308
Westaway, Peter W., Chief Fin. Officer--Commercial Union Life Assurance Company of Canada, Scarborough, Canada; *Int'l*, pg. 308
Westberg, Anders, Chief Fin. Officer--Morgardshammar AB, Smedjebacken, Sweden; *Int'l*, pg. 378
Westbrook, W.L., Chief Fin. Officer & Exec. V.P.--Southern Company Services, Inc., Atlanta, GA; *U.S. Public*, pg. 1490
Wester, Mark, Chief Fin. Officer & V.P.-Fin.--Waxman Industries, Inc., Bedford, OH; *U.S. Public*, pg. 1748
Wester, Mark, Chief Fin. Officer & V.P.-Fin.--WOC Inc., Bedford, OH; *U.S. Public*, pg. 1748
Wester, Mark, Chief Fin. Officer & V.P.-Fin.--Waxman USA Inc., Bedford, OH; *U.S. Public*, pg. 1749
Westergaard, Carsten, Chief Fin. Officer--Esselte Meto A-S, Herlev, Denmark; *Int'l*, pg. 461
Westermann, John L., III, Chief Fin. Officer, V.P., Treas. & Sec.--CSC Financial Services Group, Austin, TX; *U.S. Public*, pg. 422
Westfall, David M., Chief Fin. Officer & Sr. V.P.--Consolidated Natural Gas Company, Pittsburgh, PA; *U.S. Public*, pg. 435
Westfall, Don, Pres., Chief Exec. & Chief Fin. Officer--Newsprint South, Inc., Jackson, MS; *U.S. Private*, pg. 797
Westinghouse, T.A., Chief Fin. Officer--Dairy Farm International Holdings Limited, Hamilton, Bermuda; *Int'l*, pg. 703
Westman, Larry, Chief Fin. Officer--James Crean PLC, Dublin, Ireland; *Int'l*, pg. 340
Westmeyer, E.A., Chief Fin. Officer, V.P., Treas. & Sec.--Zeller Corp., Defiance, OH; *U.S. Private*, pg. 1204
Wettlaufer, Keith, Chief Fin. Officer & Exec. V.P.--A.G. Simpson Co. Limited, Scarborough, Canada; *Int'l*, pg. 1252
Weymuller, Bruno, Chief Fin. Officer& Sr. V.P.--Elf Aquitane, Paris, France; *Int'l*, pg. 444
Whalen, James W., Chief Fin. Officer, Sr. Exec. V.P. & Treas.--Tejas Gas Corporation, Houston, TX; *Int'l*, pg. 1136
Whalen, John, Chief Fin. Officer--Flambeau Corporation, Baraboo, WI; *U.S. Private*, pg. 409
Whalen, John A., Comptroller--COM/Energy Services Co., Cambridge, MA; *U.S. Public*, pg. 414
Whalen, John A., Comptroller--Hopkinton LNG Corp., Cambridge, MA; *U.S. Public*, pg. 415
Whaley, J. D., Treas.--Mail Well Services Inc., Memphis, TN; *U.S. Public*, pg. 1328
Whatcott, Lee A., Chief Fin. Officer & Sr. V.P.--Westcorp, Irvine, CA; *U.S. Public*, pg. 1756
Whatcott, Lee A., Chief Fin. Officer--WFS Financial, Inc., Irvine, CA; *U.S. Public*, pg. 1757
Wheeler, C., Asst. Treas., Asst. Sec. & Controller--American Welding & Manufacturing Co., Warren, OH; *U.S. Private*, pg. 425
Wheeler, Eric, Chief Fin. Officer--DeKalb Concrete Products, Inc., Eastonollee, GA; *U.S. Private*, pg. 417

Wheeler, John E., Chief Fin. Officer, Exec. V.P. & Treas.--Crown Central Petroleum Corporation, Baltimore, MD; *U.S. Public*, pg. 462

Wheeler, Mike, Chief Fin. Officer, V.P. & Treas.--Hy-Vee Food Stores Incorporated, West Des Moines, IA; *U.S. Private*, pg. 550

Wheeler, Mike, Chief Fin. Officer--TBWA Payne Stracey, London, United Kingdom; *Int'l*, pg. 1336

Wheeler, Patrick O., Chief Fin. Officer--CyberGuard Corporation, Fort Lauderdale, FL; *U.S. Public*, pg. 470

Whelan, Michael, Chief Fin. Officer--BIC Corporation, Milford, CT; *Int'l*, pg. 1273

Whelpley, William J., Chief Fin. Officer, V.P. & Gen. Mgr.--BEI Defense Systems Company, Euless, TX; *U.S. Public*, *pg. 160*

Wherry, Stephen R., Chief Fin. Officer, V.P. & Treas.--The Goldfield Corporation, Melbourne, FL; *U.S. Public*, pg. 750

Whiddon, Thomas E., Chief Fin. Officer & Exec. V.P.--Lowe's Companies, Inc., North Wilkesboro, NC; *U.S. Public*, pg. 1015

Whipkey, James M., Chief Fin. Officer & Sr. V.P.--Benton Oil & Gas Company, Carpinteria, CA; *U.S. Public*, pg. 212

Whipps, George, Pres. & Chief Fin. Officer--Whipps, Athol, MA; *U.S. Private*, pg. 1171

Whisenhunt, Gene, Chief Fin. Officer, Sr. V.P.-Fin. & Treas.--TCBY Enterprises Inc., Little Rock, AR; *U.S. Public*, pg. 1553

Whisnant, John R., Chief Fin. Officer & V.P.-Fin.--Insignia Systems, Inc., Minnetonka, MN; *U.S. Public*, pg. 881

Whitaker, David, V.P.-Fin.--ECO Resources, Inc., Sugar Land, TX; *U.S. Public*, pg. 1494

Whitaker, Mark, Chief Fin. Officer--Ke-Master, Dover, DE; *U.S. Private*, pg. 1053

Whitaker, Mark C., Chief Fin. Officer--Sunroc Corporation, Dover, DE; *U.S. Private*, pg. 1053

Whitby, S., Chief Fin. Officer--Air UK Engineering, Norfolk, United Kingdom; *Int'l*, pg. 39

Whitby, S., Chief Fin. Officer--Air UK Engineering Ltd., Stansted, United Kingdom; *Int'l*, pg. 39

Whitchurch, Charles R., Chief Fin. Officer & Treas.--Zebra Technologies Corporation, Vernon Hills, IL; *U.S. Public*, pg. 1790

White, Bernard J., Chief Fin. Officer & Treas.--Warrantech Corporation, Stamford, CT; *U.S. Public*, pg. 1740

White, Betty, Chief Fin. Officer--Mason & Hanger Engineering Inc., Lexington, KY; *U.S. Private*, pg. 711

White, Bob, Chief Fin. Officer & V.P.--MPD, Inc., Owensboro, KY; *U.S. Private*, pg. 687

White, Cliff, Chief Fin. Officer, Chief Information Officer & Treas.--National Electronics Warranty Corporation, Sterling, VA; *U.S. Private*, pg. 782

White, Harry J., Jr., Chief Fin. Officer, Chief Acct. Officer & V.P.--U.S. Trails, Dallas, TX; *U.S. Public*, pg. 1688

White, J. Robert, Chief Fin. Officer, Exec. V.P. & Treas.--Michael Baker Corporation, Pittsburgh, PA; *U.S. Public*, pg. 168

White, James A., Chief Fin. Officer & Exec. V.P.--BOK Financial Corp., Tulsa, OK; *U.S. Public*, pg. 163

White, James A., Chief Fin. Officer & Exec. V.P.--Bank of Oklahoma, N.A., Tulsa, OK; *U.S. Public*, pg. 163

White, James A., Chief Fin. Officer--Citizens Bank of Northwest Arkansas, Fayetteville, AR; *U.S. Public*, pg. 163

White, James L., Chief Fin. Officer & V.P.-Fin.--Four Queens Inc., Las Vegas, NV; *U.S. Public*, pg. 570

White, Lawrence E., Chief Fin. Officer & Exec. V.P.--El Chico Restaurants, Inc., Dallas, TX; *U.S. Private*, pg. 283

White, Loren, Chief Fin. Officer & V.P.--Land-O-Sun Dairies, Inc., Johnson City, TN; *U.S. Private*, pg. 646

White, Michael J., Sr. V.P.-Corporate & Chief Investment Officer--Confederation Life Insurance Company, Toronto, Canada; *Int'l*, pg. 325

White, Paul, Chief Fin. Officer--Orient-Express Hotels Inc., New York, NY; *Int'l*, pg. 1213

White, Stan, Chief Fin. Officer, V.P.-Fin., Sec. & Treas.--U.S. Filter/Davis Water & Waste Industries, Inc., Thomasville, GA; *U.S. Public*, pg. 1682

White, Walter, Chief Fin. Officer & Exec. V.P.--Lumbermen's Mutual Casualty Company, Long Grove, IL; *U.S. Private*, pg. 614

White, Walter, Chief Fin. Officer & Exec. V.P.--American Manufacturers Mutual Insurance Company, Long Grove, IL; *U.S. Private*, pg. 614

White, Walter, Chief Fin. Officer--American Motorists Insurance Co., Long Grove, IL; *U.S. Private*, pg. 614

White, Walter L., Chief Fin. Officer & Exec. V.P.--Kemper Insurance Companies, Long Grove, IL; *U.S. Private*, pg. 614

Whitehead, Gary W., Chief Fin. Officer & V.P.--New Hampshire Insurance Group, New York, NY; *U.S. Public*, *pg. 84*

Whiteway, Grant, Controller--Litton Solid State, Santa Clara, CA; *U.S. Public*, pg. 1003

Whiting, Mark, Chief Fin. Officer--Lifetime Products Inc., Clearfield, UT; *U.S. Private*, pg. 667

Whitley, Marc L., Chief Fin. Officer--Walker & Associates, Inc., Welcome, NC; *U.S. Private*, pg. 1147

Whitman, William E., Chief Fin. Officer, Exec. V.P. & Treas.--Ogden Energy Group, Inc., Fairfield, NJ; *U.S. Public*, pg. 1213

Whitmore, Donald E., Jr., Chief Fin. Officer & Exec. V.P.--The Eastern Company, Naugatuck, CT; *U.S. Public*, pg. 548

Whitney, Bernard J., Chief Fin. Officer & V.P.--Sanmina Corporation, San Jose, CA; *U.S. Public*, pg. 1431

Whitten, Earl, Chief Fin. Officer, Treas. & Controller--Sherley Grain Company, Bovina, TX; *U.S. Private*, pg. 993

Whitters, Joseph E., Chief Fin. Officer--First Health Group Corp., Downers Grove, IL; *U.S. Public*, pg. 635

Whittingham, L.N., Chief Fin. Officer--Jardine Insurance Brokers Ltd., London, United Kingdom; *Int'l*, pg. 705

Whittler, Dennis A., Chief Fin. Officer & V.P.-Fin.--Proxima Corporation, San Diego, CA; *U.S. Public*, pg. 1339

Whynot, Geoff, Chief Fin. Officer & V.P.--Kerr Group, Inc., Lancaster, PA; *U.S. Public*, pg. 952

Wickett, Richard A., Chief Fin. Officer & Exec. V.P.--The PBS&J Corporation, Miami, FL; *U.S. Private*, pg. 825

Wickland, Don, III, Chief Fin Officer--Wickland Corporation, Sacramento, CA; *U.S. Private*, pg. 1174

Wickman, Paul P., Jr., Chief Fin. Officer & V.P.--Laser Power Corporation, San Diego, CA; *U.S. Private*, pg. 652

Widen, Anders, Chief Fin. Officer & Controller--H.A. Schlatter AG, Schlieren, Switzerland; *Int'l*, pg. 1205

Widman, Philip, Chief Fin. Officer & Sr. V.P.--ABB Inc., Norwalk, CT; *Int'l*, pg. 3

Wiegers, Charles, Chief Fin. Officer--LaBarge Pipe & Steel Company, Saint Louis, MO; *U.S. Private*, pg. 641

Wieland, Rich, Chief Fin. Officer & Sr. V.P.--Fujisawa U.S.A., Deerfield, IL; *Int'l*, pg. 525

Wiemels, William P., Chief Fin. Officer, V.P. & Treas.--UCAR International Inc., Danbury, CT; *U.S. Public*, pg. 1662

Wiers, Marc, Chief Fin. Officer--UCB, S.A., Brussels, Belgium; *Int'l*, pg. 1427

Wiest, Joel, Chief Fin. Officer & V.P.--The Department Store Division of Dayton Hudson Corporation, Minneapolis, MN; *U.S. Public*, pg. 489

Wigglesworth, Kenneth B., Chief Fin. Officer & V.P.--Newbridge Networks Corporation, Kanata, Canada; *Int'l*, pg. 923

Wilcock, Ray, Chief Fin. Officer--Armtec, Guelph, Canada; *Int'l*, pg. 698

Wilcox, Jann Ozzello, Chief Fin. Officer & Sr. V.P.--Marquette Bancshares Inc., Minneapolis, MN; *U.S. Private*, pg. 706

Wild, J., Chief Fin. Officer--Fischer Packing Co., Louisville, KY; *Int'l*, pg. 201

Wilde, Paul K., Chief Fin. Officer & V.P.--Synon Corporation, Larkspur, CA; *U.S. Private*, pg. 1060

Wilder, Pelham, Chief Fin. Officer--Mighty Distributing System, Norcross, GA; *U.S. Private*, pg. 745

Wilder, Robert D., Chief Fin. Officer & Exec. V.P.--John Wiley & Sons, Inc., New York, NY; *U.S. Public*, pg. 1768

Wildman, R. Joseph, Chief Fin. Officer & V.P.--Amarillo Hardware Company, Amarillo, TX; *U.S. Private*, pg. 335

Wiley, Alan E., Chief Fin. & Admin. Officer, Sr. Exec. V.P. & Sec.--The Cato Corporation, Charlotte, NC; *U.S. Public*, pg. 318

Wilfert, Gary, Chief Fin. Officer--Tropitone Furniture Co. Inc., Irvine, CA; *U.S. Private*, pg. 1105

Wilfred, William, Chief Fin. Officer--The Great Eastern Life Assurance Company Limited, Singapore, Singapore; *Int'l*, *pg. 557*

Wilhelm, Ed, Chief Fin. Officer--Borders, Inc., Ann Arbor, MI; *U.S. Public*, pg. 245

Wilk, Ernest J., Treas.--Mid-Valley Oil Company, Inc., New Windsor, NY; *U.S. Private*, pg. 1151

Wilkes, Doug, Chief Fin. Officer--Tolko Industries Ltd., Vernon, Canada; *Int'l*, pg. 1395

Wilkie, Kirk, Chief Fin. Officer--Durham Transportation, Inc., Austin, TX; *U.S. Private*, pg. 348

Wilkins, Anne Marie, Chief Fin. Officer--Clarins (UK) Ltd., London, United Kingdom; *Int'l*, pg. 295

Wilkins, Gerald, Chief Fin. Officer--AFC Enterprises, Atlanta, GA; *U.S. Private*, pg. 5

Wilkins, Kent M., Chief Fin. Officer--CXR Telcom Corporation, Fremont, CA; *U.S. Public*, pg. 1108

Wilkinson, George S., Chief Fin. Officer & Exec. V.P.--Modern Group Ltd., Bristol, PA; *U.S. Private*, pg. 754

Wilkinson, J. Robert, V.P.-Fin. & Treas.--Bairnco Corporation, Maitland, FL; *U.S. Public*, pg. 165

Willbrant, Rick, Chief Fin. Officer--Alliance Automated, Rochester, NY; *U.S. Private*, pg. 38

Willcox, Riley R., Chief Fin. Officer, Sr. V.P.-Fin. & Admin.--Premisys Communications, Inc., Fremont, CA; *U.S. Public*, pg. 1323

Willeinson, Neil, Chief Fin. Officer--SLD Holdings Ltd., Stevenage, United Kingdom; *Int'l*, pg. 1160

Willert, William D., Pres.--Willert Home Products, Inc., Saint Louis, MO; *U.S. Private*, pg. 1177

Willett, Joseph, Chief Fin. Officer--Merrill Lynch & Co., Inc., New York, NY; *U.S. Public*, pg. 1097

Williams, Anthony R., Chief Fin. & Acctg. Officer & Exec. V.P.--Acclaim Entertainment, Inc., Glen Cove, NY; *U.S. Public*, pg. 15

Williams, Bruce E., Pres. & Treas.--Williams Company Of Orlando, Inc., Orlando, FL; *U.S. Private*, pg. 1177

Williams, Cheryl, Chief Fin. Officer & Sec.--Prime Medical Services, Inc., Austin, TX; *U.S. Public*, pg. 1327

Williams, Chris, Chief Fin. Officer--Beers Construction Company, Atlanta, GA; *Int'l*, pg. 1261

Williams, D. Richard, Chief Fin. Officer & Exec. V.P.--Primerica Financial Services, Duluth, GA; *U.S. Public*, pg. 1633

Williams, Daniel, Chief Fin. Officer--EVEREN Securities, Inc., Chicago, IL; *U.S. Public*, pg. 597

Williams, Duston, Chief Fin. Officer & Sr. V.P.--Western Digital Corporation, Irvine, CA; *U.S. Public*, pg. 1758

Williams, Eric, Chief Fin. Officer & Sr. V.P.-Fin.--MG Products, San Antonio, TX; *U.S. Public*, pg. 1026

Williams, Gerald, Chief Fin. Officer & Exec. V.P.--Huntington Bancshares Inc., Columbus, OH; *U.S. Public*, pg. 849

Williams, Glen E., Jr., Chief Fin. Officer & Exec. V.P.--Dodson Group, Kansas City, MO; *U.S. Private*, pg. 338

Williams, Gordon, Chief Fin. Officer--Wards Cove Packing Company, Seattle, WA; *U.S. Private*, pg. 1149

Williams, J. Don, Chief Fin. Officer & Sr. V.P.-Corp. Support Grp.--Altec Industries, Inc., Birmingham, AL; *U.S. Private*, *pg. 47*

Williams, Jacquelyn C., Chief Fin. Officer & Sr. V.P.--Nevada State Bank, Las Vegas, NV; *U.S. Public*, pg. 1793

Williams, James, Chief Fin. Officer--Clayton Group, Inc., Tampa, FL; *U.S. Private*, pg. 244

Williams, Jay, Chief Fin. Officer & Treas.--Pacific Lumber & Shipping Co., Seattle, WA; *U.S. Private*, pg. 832

Williams, Jeffrey, Chief Fin. Officer--Amrion Inc., Boulder, CO; *U.S. Public*, pg. 1767

Williams, Jerry F., Chief Fin. Officer, V.P.-Fin. & Admin. & Treas.--Acme Metals Incorporated, Riverdale, IL; *U.S. Public*, pg. 16

Williams, Jimmie D., Chief Fin. Officer, Exec. V.P., Treas. & Sec.--Belz Enterprises, Memphis, TN; *U.S. Private*, pg. 132

Williams, John, Chief Fin. Officer & V.P.-Fin--Iceland Seafood Corporation, Newport, VA; *U.S. Private*, pg. 556

Williams, Joseph M., Treas. & Sec.--Kimmins Corp., Tampa, FL; *U.S. Public*, pg. 960

Williams, Mark, Chief Fin. Officer--Derby Cycle Corporation, Kent, WA; *Int'l*, pg. 394

Williams, Michael, Chief Fin. Officer & V.P.--Aeroglide Corporation, Cary, NC; *U.S. Private*, pg. 24

Williams, Michael, Controller--Young Supply Company, Detroit, MI; *U.S. Private*, pg. 1202

Williams, Nicole S., Chief Fin. Officer, Exec. V.P.-Fin. & Sec.--R.P. Scherer Corporation, Troy, MI; *U.S. Public*, pg. 1437

Williams, Peter E., Chief Fin. Officer, V.P.-Fin. & Asst. Sec.--WD-40 Company, San Diego, CA; *U.S. Public*, pg. 1726

Williams, Robert, Chief Fin. Officer--EDO Acoustic Products, Salt Lake City, UT; *U.S. Public*, pg. 542

Williams, Robert, Chief Fin. Officer & Exec. V.P.--Keyes Martin, East Hanover, NJ; *U.S. Private*, pg. 618

Williams, Robin, Chief Fin. Officer--Pacifico Auto Group, Philadelphia, PA; *U.S. Private*, pg. 832

Williams, Thomas A., Chief Fin. Officer, V.P., Treas. & Sec.--Houghton International Inc., Valley Forge, PA; *U.S. Private*, pg. 541

Williams, Timothy V., Chief Fin. Officer & Exec. V.P.--Policy Management Systems Corporation, Blythewood, SC; *U.S. Public*, pg. 1314

Williams, Tracy, Chief Fin. Officer--Sam Kane Beef Processors, Inc., Corpus Christi, TX; *U.S. Private*, pg. 607

Williams, William S., Vice Chm., Chief Exec. Officer & Chief Fin. Officer--The W.W. Williams Company, Columbus, OH; *U.S. Private*, pg. 1178

Williams, Willis F., Chief Fin. Officer--The Boston Company, Inc., Boston, MA; *U.S. Public*, pg. 1085

Williams, Willis F., Chief Fin. Officer--Boston Safe Deposit & Trust Co., Boston, MA; *U.S. Public*, pg. 1085

Williamson, Richard A., Chief Fin. Officer & Treas.--Brunschwig & Fils, Inc., White Plains, NY; *U.S. Private*, pg. 176

Williamson, Scott, Chief Fin. Officer & Exec. V.P.--Plasti-Kote Company Inc., Medina, OH; *U.S. Private*, pg. 870

Williamson, Scott, Chief Fin. Officer--Tempo Products Company, Solon, OH; *U.S. Private*, pg. 870

Willinger, Louis A., Chief Fin. Officer & Treas.--Cummins Cumberland Inc., Louisville, KY; *U.S. Private*, pg. 295

Willis, Charlotte Y., Chief Fin. Officer & V.P.--Harrison Construction Corp., Miami, FL; *U.S. Private*, pg. 506

Willis, Cliff, Chief Fin. Officer--Esprit Systems, Inc., San Jose, CA; *U.S. Private*, pg. 383

Willis, Kirby R., Chief Fin. Officer, V.P. & Treas.--Savannah Electric & Power Co., Savannah, GA; *U.S. Public*, pg. 1490

Willis, Richard, Chief Fin. Officer & Exec. V.P.--Petersen Publishing Company, L.L.C., Los Angeles, CA; *U.S. Private*, pg. 856

Willis, Scott, Chief Fin. Officer--Tetra Tech NUS, Inc., Gaithersburg, MD; *U.S. Public*, pg. 1582

Willmschen, Robert W., Chief Fin. Officer, Sr. V.P. & Sec.--ABC Rail Products Corp., Chicago, IL; *U.S. Public*, pg. 2

Willoboughy, Jack, Chief Fin. Officer--Pennsylvania House Casegoods, Lewisburg, PA; *U.S. Public*, pg. 975

Wilmoth, Mark C., Chief Fin. Officer & V.P.-Fin.--Lowrance Electronics, Inc., Tulsa, OK; *U.S. Public*, pg. 1015

Wilmoth, Mark C., Chief Fin. Officer--Eagle Electronics, Catoosa, OK; *U.S. Public*, pg. 1016

Wilson, Anthony J., Chief Exec. Officer & Chief Fin. Officer--Glynwed International PLC, Birmingham, United Kingdom; *Int'l*, pg. 554

Wilson, B.E., Chief Fin. Officer & Sr. V.P.--National Trustco Inc., Toronto, Canada; *Int'l*, pg. 909

Wilson, Dan, Chief Fin. Officer & V.P.-Fin.--Parkdale Mills, Gastonia, NC; *U.S. Private*, pg. 840

Wilson, David A., Chief Fin. Officer--The Geon Company, Avon Lake, OH; *U.S. Public*, pg. 733

Wilson, Dennis K., Chief Fin. Officer & V.P.-Fin.--Beckman Instruments, Inc., Fullerton, CA; *U.S. Public*, pg. 199

Wilson, Diana, Chief Fin. Officer--Deckers Outdoor Corporation, Goleta, CA; *U.S. Public*, pg. 491

Wilson, Graham M., Chief Fin. Officer & Exec. V.P.--Westcoast Energy Inc., Vancouver, Canada; *Int'l*, pg. 1492

Wilson, Gregory L., Chief Fin. Officer--Lasersight Inc., Saint Louis, MO; *U.S. Public*, pg. 979

Wilson, Hamline C., Chief Fin. Officer & V.P.--Massmutual Corporate Investors, Springfield, MA; *U.S. Public*, pg. 1055

Wilson, J. Lynn, Chief Fin. Officer, Treas. & Sec.--Nashville Machine Co. Inc., Nashville, TN; *U.S. Private*, pg. 774

Wilson, Jack, Chief Fin. Officer--RELTEC Corporation, Cleveland, OH; *U.S. Private*, pg. 921

Wilson, James T., Chief Fin. Officer & Exec. V.P.-Opers. & Fin.--Gibson Greetings, Inc., Cincinnati, OH; *U.S. Public*, pg. 742

Wilson, Jimmy, Chief Fin. Officer, Treas. & Controller--J.M. Smith Corp., Spartanburg, SC; *U.S. Private*, pg. 1008

Wilson, John R., Chief Fin. Officer & V.P.--Escalade Sports, Evansville, IN; *U.S. Public*, pg. 591

Wilson, Lawrence, Controller--Southern Container Corporation, Hauppauge, NY; *U.S. Private*, pg. 1016

Wilson, Malcolm John, Chief Fin. Officer--Yorkshire Chemicals Plc, Leeds, United Kingdom; *Int'l*, pg. 1522

Wilson, Michael, Chief Fin. Officer & V.P.-Fin.--Advanced Input Devices, Inc., Coeur D'Alene, ID; *U.S. Private*, pg. 21
Wilson, Mike, Chief Fin. Officer--North Specialty Products, Brea, CA; *Int'l*, pg. 1243
Wilson, Riley C., Chief Fin. Officer & V.P.--Rapid Power Technologies, Inc., Brookfield, CT; *U.S. Private*, pg. 910
Wilson, Robert, Chief Fin. Officer & Pub. Rels.--Supreme Corporation, Goshen, IN; *U.S. Public*, pg. 1542
Wilson, Robert, Chief Fin. Officer & V.P.--Supreme Corporation of Texas, Cleburne, TX; *U.S. Public*, pg. 1542
Wilson, Robert, Chief Fin. Officer--Supreme MidAtlantic Corporation, Jonestown, PA; *U.S. Public*, pg. 1542
Wilson, Robert, Chief Fin. Officer--Supreme Murphy Corp., Wilson, NC; *U.S. Public*, pg. 1542
Wilson, Robert K., Chief Fin. Officer & Exec. V.P.--Woodward-Clyde Group, Inc., Denver, CO; *U.S. Public*, pg. 1655
Wilson, Robert M., Chief Fin. Officer, Exec. V.P., Gen. Counsel & Sec.--Roberds, Inc., Carrollton, OH; *U.S. Public*, pg. 1393
Wilson, Robert W., Chief Fin. Officer, Exec. V.P., Controller, Treas. & Asst. Sec.--Supreme Industries, Inc., Goshen, IN; *U.S. Public*, pg. 1541
Wilson, Stephen R., Chief Fin. Officer & Sr. V.P.--CF Industries, Inc., Long Grove, IL; *U.S. Private*, pg. 193
Wilson, Steven E., Chief Fin. Officer, Exec. V.P., Treas. & Sec.--United Bankshares, Inc., Parkersburg, WV; *U.S. Public*, pg. 1674
Wilson, Thomas J., Chief Fin. Officer & Sr. V.P.--The Allstate Corporation, Northbrook, IL; *U.S. Public*, pg. 55
Wilson, Wayne, Chief Fin. Officer--PC Connection, Inc., Milford, MA; *U.S. Private*, pg. 826
Windus, J. Preston, Chief Fin. Officer & V.P.--Comtech Telecommunications Corp., Melville, NY; *U.S. Public*, pg. 425
Windus, J. Preston, Pres. & Chief Fin. Officer--Comtech PST Corp., Melville, NY; *U.S. Public*, pg. 425
Winer, Leo, Chief Fin. Officer & V.P.--Penda Corporation, Portage, WI; *U.S. Private*, pg. 848
Wines, Leland E., Chief Fin. Officer & Exec. V.P.--BWC Financial Corp., Walnut Creek, CA; *U.S. Private*, pg. 108
Winger, Dennis L., Chief Fin. Officer & Sr. V.P.-Fin. & Admin.--Chiron Corporation, Emeryville, CA; *U.S. Public*, pg. 349
Winger, Dennis L., Chief Fin. Officer, Sr. V.P. & Treas.--The Perkin-Elmer Corporation, Norwalk, CT; *U.S. Public*, pg. 1279
Winget, Bob, Chief Fin. Officer & Controller--Richards Industries, Inc., Cincinnati, OH; *U.S. Private*, pg. 929
Winiarz, Ed, Chief Fin. Officer--Triangle Services, Inc., Valley Stream, NY; *U.S. Private*, pg. 1102
Winiewicz, Nicholas, Chief Fin. Officer & V.P.-Fin.--Aladdin Industries, Incorporated, Nashville, TN; *U.S. Private*, pg. 30
Winkleblack, Art, Chief Fin. Officer & V.P.--Six Flags Theme Parks Inc., Parsippany, NJ; *U.S. Public*, pg. 1611
Winkler, David, Chief Fin. Officer--IA Corporation, Emeryville, CA; *U.S. Private*, pg. 553
Winkler, Joe, Chief Fin. Officer, Exec. V.P. & Treas.--Tuboscope Incorporated, Houston, TX; *U.S. Public*, pg. 1643
Winn, Harry L., Chief Fin. Officer & Exec. V.P.--Fleming Companies, Inc., Oklahoma City, OK; *U.S. Public*, pg. 652
Winn, Mark W., Chief Fin. Officer--Research Industries Corporation, Midvale, UT; *U.S. Public*, pg. 196
Winslow, James E., Chief Fin. Officer, Exec. V.P. & Sec.--Home Products International, Inc., Chicago, IL; *U.S. Public*, pg. 832
Winslow, Jim, Chief Fin. Officer & Exec. V.P.--Selfix, Inc., Chicago, IL; *U.S. Public*, pg. 832
Winslow, Richard H., Chief Fin. Officer, V.P.-Fin., Controller & Treas.--Norfolk Shipbuilding & Drydock Corporation, Norfolk, VA; *U.S. Private*, pg. 802
Winter, Carl, Chief Fin. Officer--United Auto Group, Inc., New York, NY; *U.S. Private*, pg. 1095
Winter, Irwin W., Chief Fin. Officer & Exec. V.P.--Phillips-Van Heusen Corporation, New York, NY; *U.S. Public*, pg. 1291
Winter, Mitchel R., Chief Fin. Officer & V.P.--Laughlin/Constable, Inc., Milwaukee, WI; *U.S. Private*, pg. 653
Winton, R., Chief Fin. Officer--United Clays, Inc., Brentwood, TN; *Int'l*, pg. 1487
Wintroub, Steve, Chief Fin. Officer & V.P.--Carpeteria, Inc., Valencia, CA; *U.S. Private*, pg. 215
Wintzer, Heinrich S., Chief Fin. Officer--BHF-BANK International S.A., Luxembourg, Luxembourg; *Int'l*, pg. 119
Wirackara, Anil, Chief Fin. Officer & Sec.--MacDonald Dettwiler & Associates Ltd., Richmond, Canada; *U.S. Public*, pg. 1229
Wirtz, Norman, Chief Fin. Officer & V.P.-Fin.--TAD Resources International, Inc., Cambridge, MA; *U.S. Private*, pg. 1062
Wise, B., Chief Fin. Officer--Pratt & Whitney, Grand Prairie, TX; *U.S. Public*, pg. 1690
Wise, Chris, V.P.-Fin., Treas. & Sec.--Southco Distributing Company, Goldsboro, NC; *U.S. Private*, pg. 1014
Wise, Jim P., Chief Fin. Officer & V.P.-Fin.--Sterling Chemicals, Inc., Houston, TX; *U.S. Public*, pg. 1515
Wise, Richard, Chief Fin. Officer--Leadtec Systems, Inc., Canoga Park, CA; *U.S. Private*, pg. 1177
Wiseman, Michael L., Chief Fin. Officer & Treas.--Motorists Mutual Insurance Co., Columbus, OH; *U.S. Private*, pg. 764
Wiseman, Michael L., Chief Fin. Officer & Treas.--American Hardware Mutual Insurance Co., Columbus, OH; *U.S. Private*, pg. 764
Wiseman, Michael L., Chief Fin. Officer--American Merchants Casualty Co., Columbus, OH; *U.S. Private*, pg. 764
Wishart, Warren T., Chief Fin. Officer & Sr. V.P.--The Leslie Fay Companies, Inc., New York, NY; *U.S. Public*, pg. 989
Wissinger, Randy, Chief Fin. Officer & V.P.-Fin.--Beltone Electronics Corporation, Chicago, IL; *U.S. Private*, pg. 132
Witaszak, Richard B., Chief Fin. Officer & Exec. V.P.--Fred's Inc., Memphis, TN; *U.S. Public*, pg. 680
Withers, F. Wayne, Chief Fin. Officer & Sr. V.P.--Aurora Electronics, Inc., Irvine, CA; *U.S. Public*, pg. 147
Witherspoon, Gregory J., Chief Fin. Officer & Exec. V.P.-Fin.--Aames Financial Corporation, Los Angeles, CA; *U.S. Public*, pg. 12
Witmer, James, Chief Fin. Officer & Gen. Mgr.--Avis Ford Inc., Southfield, MI; *U.S. Private*, pg. 101
Wittenauer, Steve, Chief Fin. Officer--Fleischmann's Yeast, Fenton, MO; *Int'l*, pg. 237
Witteveen, Jaap, Chief Fin. Officer--MoDo Van Gelder, Amsterdam, Netherlands; *Int'l*, pg. 886
Witteveen, Raoul J., Pres., Chief Oper. Officer & Chief Fin. Officer--Interpool, Inc., Princeton, NJ; *U.S. Public*, pg. 908
Wittig, Philip M., Chief Fin. Officer & Treas.--Isco, Inc., Lincoln, NE; *U.S. Public*, pg. 913
Wittman, Alois, Dr., Chief Fin. Officer--KSB Aktiengesellschaft, Frankenthal, Germany; *Int'l*, pg. 721
Witworth, Clark L., Chief Fin. Officer--Larry H. Miller Group, Murray, UT; *U.S. Private*, pg. 747
Woda, Jerry W., Chief Fin. Officer, Sr. V.P. & Treas.--Miami Subs Corporation, Fort Lauderdale, FL; *U.S. Public*, pg. 1103
Wohleber, David, Chief Fin. Officer--Eat N Park Restaurants, Pittsburgh, PA; *U.S. Private*, pg. 358
Wohleber, Robert M., Chief Fin. Officer & Sr. V.P.--Freeport-McMoRan Inc., New Orleans, LA; *U.S. Public*, pg. 680
Wojtila, James, Chief Fin. Officer--Hunt Valve, Salem, OH; *U.S. Private*, pg. 549
Wolf, Christopher F., Chief Fin. Officer, Sr. V.P., Treas. & Sec.--Swank, Inc., Attleboro, MA; *U.S. Public*, pg. 1543
Wolf, Claudia, Chief Fin. Officer--Strobelgasse 2, Vienna, Austria; *Int'l*, pg. 1377
Wolf, Dale B., Chief Fin. Officer, Sr. V.P. & Treas.--Coventry Corporation, Nashville, TN; *U.S. Public*, pg. 454
Wolf, Dennis, Chief Fin. Officer & Sr. V.P.-Opers. & Admin.--Centigram Communications Corporation, San Jose, CA; *U.S. Public*, pg. 323
Wolf, John, Chief Fin. Officer--Business Equipment Center, Washington, DC; *U.S. Private*, pg. 189
Wolf, Lawrence, Pres., Chief Exec. Officer, Treas. & Sec.--Leonard Wholesale, Inc., Springfield, NJ; *U.S. Private*, pg. 660
Wolf, Roger J., Chief Fin. Officer, Sr. V.P., Sec. & Treas.--Hurco Companies, Inc., Indianapolis, IN; *U.S. Public*, pg. 850
Wolf, Steven A., Chief Fin. Officer & Sec.--Ryka Incorporated, King of Prussia, PA; *U.S. Public*, pg. 1414
Wolff, Timothy V., Chief Fin. Officer & Sr. V.P.--Adolph Coors Company, Golden, CO; *U.S. Public*, pg. 445
Wolff, Timothy V., Chief Fin. Officer, Sr. V.P. & Treas.--Coors Brewing Company, Golden, CO; *U.S. Public*, pg. 445
Wolfe, Jane, Exec. V.P. & Chief Lending Officer--Downey Savings & Loan Association, F.A., Newport Beach, CA; *U.S. Public*, pg. 526
Wolfe, John, Chief Fin. Officer--The York Bank and Trust Company, York, PA; *Int'l*, pg. 65
Wolfe, Stephen P., Chief Fin. Officer, V.P. & Treas.--The Toro Company, Bloomington, MN; *U.S. Public*, pg. 1623
Wolfe, Steve, Chief Fin. Officer & Treas.--David Manufacturing Company (DMC), Mason City, IA; *U.S. Private*, pg. 436
Wolff, Diane, Chief Fin. Officer--Organizational Dynamics Inc., Burlington, MA; *U.S. Private*, pg. 819
Wolff, Gary, Chief Fin. Officer & Exec. V.P.--Fenn Manufacturing Co., Newington, CT; *U.S. Public*, pg. 1676
Wolff, Kenneth K., Chief Fin. Officer & Exec. V.P.--Amtran, Inc., Indianapolis, IN; *U.S. Public*, pg. 106
Wolfson, Alan, Chief Fin. Officer--Benderson Development Co., Inc., Buffalo, NY; *U.S. Private*, pg. 132
Wolfson, Martin, Chief Fin. Officer & Sr. V.P.--Concord Fabrics Inc., New York, NY; *U.S. Public*, pg. 429
Wolle, Rainer, Chief Fin. Officer--EMS Kurierpost GmbH, Bonn, Germany; *Int'l*, pg. 407
Wolski, Larry, Chief Fin. Officer--Pettibone Corporation, Lisle, IL; *U.S. Private*, pg. 859
Wolthausen, Reed, Chief Fin. Officer & Sr. V.P.--Burke Industries, Inc., San Jose, CA; *U.S. Private*, pg. 183
Woltil, Robert D., Chief Fin. Officer & Sr. V.P.-Fin.--Sun Healthcare Group Inc., Albuquerque, NM; *U.S. Public*, pg. 1530
Wong, Calvin, Chief Fin. Officer & V.P.--Pacific Steel Casting Co., Berkeley, CA; *U.S. Private*, pg. 832
Wong, Clifton, Chief Fin. Officer--Consilium, Inc., Mountain View, CA; *U.S. Public*, pg. 434
Wong, David, Chief Fin. Officer--First Pacific Davies Limited, Central, Hong Kong; *Int'l*, pg. 487
Wong, William, Chief Fin. Officer--Bel Fuse Ltd., Kowloon, Hong Kong; *U.S. Public*, pg. 200
Wong, Winnie, Chief Fin. Officer--MacGREGOR (HKG), Ltd., Kowloon, Hong Kong; *Int'l*, pg. 671
Wonowich, Simon, Chief Fin. Officer & V.P.--Admiration Hosiery Mills, Inc., Charlotte, NC; *U.S. Private*, pg. 528
Wood, C. Martin, III, Chief Fin. Officer & Sr. V.P.--Flowers Industries, Inc., Thomasville, GA; *U.S. Public*, pg. 656
Wood, Carol S., Chief Fin. Officer, Controller, Treas. & Sec.--Higginbotham-Bartlett Co., Lubbock, TX; *U.S. Private*, pg. 527
Wood, David R., Chief Fin. Officer, Exec. V.P.-Admin. & Treas.--The Sands Regent, Reno, NV; *U.S. Public*, pg. 1431
Wood, Donald, Chief Fin. Officer & Sr. V.P.--Caesars World, Inc., Las Vegas, NV; *U.S. Public*, pg. 1512
Wood, J. Tom, V.P.-Fin.--MW Manufacturers Inc., Rocky Mount, VA; *Int'l*, pg. 593
Wood, James H., Chief Fin. Officer--Royal Oak Mines Inc., Kirkland, WA; *U.S. Public*, pg. 1410
Wood, N. D., Dir.-Fin.--The Guthrie Corporation, PLC, London, United Kingdom; *Int'l*, pg. 113
Wood, Rene M., V.P.-Fin. & Sec.--McNeel International Corp., Tampa, FL; *U.S. Private*, pg. 724
Wood, Rick, Chief Fin. Officer & Sr. V.P.-Opers.--Quintus Corporation, Fremont, CA; *U.S. Private*, pg. 901
Wood, Susanne, Chief Fin. Officer & V.P.--Tultex Corporation, Martinsville, VA; *U.S. Public*, pg. 1644
Wood, Timothy M., Chief Fin. Officer, V.P. & Controller--Borg-Warner Security Corporation, Chicago, IL; *U.S. Public*, pg. 245
Woodbeck, Milford E., Chm. Bd. & Chief Exec. Officer--Overhead Conveyor Co., Ferndale, MI; *U.S. Private*, pg. 822
Woodbury, C. Troy, Jr., Chief Fin. Officer & Treas.--Wegener Corporation, Duluth, GA; *U.S. Public*, pg. 1751
Woodbury, Edwina, Chief Fin. & Chief Admin. Officer--Avon Products, Inc., New York, NY; *U.S. Public*, pg. 155
Woodfill, John F., Chief Fin. Officer & V.P.-Fin.--Ash Grove Cement Company, Shawnee Mission, KS; *U.S. Private*, pg. 87
Woodhouse, Michael, Chief Fin. Officer & Exec. V.P.--Metromedia Steakhouses, Inc., Vandalia, OH; *U.S. Private*, pg. 736
Woodhouse, Michael A., Chief Fin. Officer--Fuddruckers, Inc., Danvers, MA; *Int'l*, pg. 325
Woodhouse, Michael A., Chief Fin. Officer & Sr. V.P.--Cracker Barrel Old Country Store, Inc., Lebanon, TN; *U.S. Public*, pg. 455
Woodland, Paul R., Chief Fin. Officer, V.P.-Fin. & Admin. & Asst. Sec.--Dreyer's Grand Ice Cream, Inc., Oakland, CA; *U.S. Public*, pg. 529
Woodmansee, Richard, Controller--CorryHiebert Corporation, Corry, PA; *U.S. Public*, pg. 772
Woodruff, Jack, Chief Fin. Officer & V.P.--Continental/Midland, Inc., Park Forest, IL; *U.S. Private*, pg. 268
Woods, C., Chief Fin. Officer--J & B Products, Inc., South Bend, IN; *U.S. Private*, pg. 399
Woods, James J., Exec. V.P. & Chief Fin. Officer--Holnam Inc. (West Division), Lakewood, CO; *Int'l*, pg. 628
Woods, V. Lehman, Chief Fin. Officer & Exec. V.P.--Analysis & Technology International Corporation, North Stonington, CT; *U.S. Public*, pg. 109
Woodson, Kenneth, Pres. & Chief Exec. Officer--Louis Vuitton North America, Inc., New York, NY; *Int'l*, pg. 781
Woodward, William J., Chief Fin. Officer--PSC Inc., Webster, NY; *U.S. Public*, pg. 1245
Woodworth, Rodney, Chief Fin. Officer--Merchants Publishing Co., Kalamazoo, MI; *U.S. Private*, pg. 732
Wooten, R. Edward, Jr., Chief Fin. Officer & Treas.--Brown Wooten Mills, Inc., Burlington, NC; *U.S. Private*, pg. 174
Worboys, Andrew, Chief Fin. Officer--Hospital Management & Supplies Limited, Northampton, United Kingdom; *Int'l*, pg. 58
Worby, J.G., Chief Fin. Officer--Unigate PLC, London, United Kingdom; *Int'l*, pg. 1433
Worden, John, Chief Fin. Officer--WestEx, Inc., Phoenix, AZ; *U.S. Public*, pg. 1788
Workman, David, Chief Fin. Officer--Escort, Inc., West Chester, OH; *U.S. Private*, pg. 383
Workman, Stephan, Chief Fin. Officer, V.P.-Fin. & Treas.--Ortel Corporation, Alhambra, CA; *U.S. Public*, pg. 1232
Worley, Dana, Chief Fin. Officer & Sr. V.P.--Black Rogers Sullivan Goodnight, Inc., Houston, TX; *U.S. Private*, pg. 147
Worrell, Douglas C., Chief Fin. Officer, Sr. V.P. & Cashier--Texas National Bank, Southlake, TX; *U.S. Public*, pg. 633
Worth, John, Chief Fin. Officer--Pinnacle Brands, Inc., Dallas, TX; *U.S. Private*, pg. 866
Worth, Joseph C., III, Chief Fin. Officer & V.P.--Champion Industries, Huntington, WV; *U.S. Public*, pg. 333
Worthy, W. Craig, Chief Fin. Officer & Sr. V.P.--Boddie-Noell Enterprises Inc., Rocky Mount, NC; *U.S. Private*, pg. 154
Woudstra, F. Robert, Exec. V.P. & Treas.--Foremost Corporation of America, Caledonia, MI; *U.S. Public*, pg. 667
Woudstra, F. Robert, Exec. V.P. & Treas.--Foremost Insurance Co., Caledonia, MI; *U.S. Public*, pg. 667
Wraase, Dennis R., Chief Fin. Officer & Sr. V.P.--Potomac Electric Power Company, Washington, DC; *U.S. Public*, pg. 1318
Wraback, Thomas F., Chief Fin. Officer & Sr. V.P.--Physician Computer Network, Inc., Morris Plains, NJ; *U.S. Public*, pg. 1293
Wray, R. Logan, Chief Fin. Officer & Sr. V.P.--Sterling Software, Inc., Dallas, TX; *U.S. Public*, pg. 1516
Wrench, Gary D., Chief Fin. Officer & Sr. V.P.--BEI Technologies, Inc., San Francisco, CA; *U.S. Public*, pg. 160
Wride, Ann, Chief Fin. Officer--Coco's & Carrows Restaurants, Irvine, CA; *U.S. Public*, pg. 23
Wright, Alan M., Chief Fin. Officer, Sr. V.P. & Treas.--CMS Energy Corporation, Dearborn, MI; *U.S. Public*, pg. 279
Wright, B., Dir.-Fin.--Meyer International PLC, London, United Kingdom; *Int'l*, pg. 864
Wright, Beverly L., Chief Fin. Officer & Treas.--BT Alex. Brown Inc., Baltimore, MD; *U.S. Public*, pg. 185
Wright, Cheryl, Chief Fin. Officer--Olympia & York Developments Ltd., Toronto, Canada; *Int'l*, pg. 1004
Wright, Daniel P., Chief Fin. Officer & Sr. V.P.--Electrohome Ltd., Kitchener, Canada; *Int'l*, pg. 438
Wright, David A., Chief Fin. Officer & V.P.--Laurentian Financial Services, Toronto, Canada; *Int'l*, pg. 396
Wright, Ike, Chief Fin. Officer--Mobil Tool International, Westminster, CO; *Int'l*, pg. 1486
Wright, Jeff, Chief Fin. Officer--Gerry Sportswear Company, Mercer Island, WA; *U.S. Private*, pg. 449
Wright, John, Sec. & Treas.--American National Insurance Service Co., Springfield, MO; *U.S. Public*, pg. 88

Wright, John, Chief Fin. Officer--Cal-Air Inc., Whittier, CA; *U.S. Private*, pg. 199
Wright, John R., Jr., V.P.-Fin.--United Power Association, Elk River, MN; *U.S. Private*, pg. 1123
Wright, Lisa, Chief Fin. Officer--Optic Graphics, Inc., Glen Burnie, MD; *U.S. Private*, pg. 818
Wright, Samuel G., Chief Fin. Officer & Exec. V.P.--Eckerd Corporation, Largo, FL; *U.S. Public*, pg. 917
Wright, Theodore M., Chief Fin. Officer, V.P.-Fin., Treas. & Sec.--Sonic Automotive, Inc., Charlotte, NC; *U.S. Public*, pg. 1485
Wrightman, Ken, Chief Fin. Officer--Speedy Muffler King, Inc., Toronto, Canada; *U.S. Public*, pg. 1578
Wroten, Richad W., Chief Fin. Officer & Exec. V.P.--Old Kent Financial Corporation, Grand Rapids, MI; *U.S. Public*, pg. 1216
Wuffli, P.A., Chief Fin. Officer--Schweizerischer Bankverein, Basel, Switzerland; *Int'l*, pg. 1329
Wuffli, Peter A., Chief Fin. Officer--Swiss Bank Corporation, Basel, Switzerland; *Int'l*, pg. 1329
Wulff, Dirk, Chief Fin. Officer--Siemens S.p.A., Milan, Italy; *Int'l*, pg. 1248
Wulff, John K., Chief Fin. Officer, V.P. & Controller--Union Carbide Corporation, Danbury, CT; *U.S. Public*, pg. 1666
Wulz, Jack, V.P.-Fin. & Admin.--Hollytex Carpet Mills, Inc., Ontario, CA; *U.S. Private*, pg. 535
Wunderle, James A., Chief Fin. Officer--Reading Entertainment Inc., Philadelphia, PA; *U.S. Public*, pg. 456
Wunderle, Richard, Chief Fin. Officer--Revenue Collection Group, San Diego, CA; *U.S. Public*, pg. 466
Wunderlich, John D., Chief Fin. Officer & Exec. V.P.--Fred Weber, Inc., Maryland Heights, MO; *U.S. Private*, pg. 424
Wurtzler, Stephen D., Chief Fin. Officer & Treas.--Wire Rope Corporation of America, Inc., Saint Joseph, MO; *U.S. Private*, pg. 1184
Wust, Pierre, Treas., Controller & Chief Fin. Officer--Sandoz Pharma Ltd., Eden Terrace, New Zealand; *Int'l*, pg. 985
Wyandt, Steven P., Pres. & Chief Exec. & Fin. Officer--Niches, Inc., San Diego, CA; *U.S. Public*, pg. 1181
Wyant, Clyde, Chief Fin. Officer & Exec. V.P.--Lennox International Inc., Richardson, TX; *U.S. Private*, pg. 659
Wyatt, Gordon, Chief Fin. Officer--Dun & Bradstreet Software Services, Atlanta, GA; *Int'l*, pg. 532
Wyckaert, Veronica M., Chief Fin. Officer, V.P. & Treas.--Intertrade Industries, Huntington Beach, CA; *U.S. Private*, pg. 573
Wyman, Mead, Chief Fin. Officer & Treas.--Mercury Computer Systems, Inc., Chelmsford, MA; *U.S. Private*, pg. 732
Wyman, Mike, Chief Fin. Officer--Work/Family Directions, Boston, MA; *U.S. Private*, pg. 1188
Wynn, Robert P., Chief Fin. Officer, Exec. V.P. & Sec.--AmeriPath, Inc., Riviera Beach, FL; *U.S. Public*, pg. 96
Wynstra, Bruce G., Controller--Mox-Med, Inc., Portage, WI; *U.S. Public*, pg. 124
Wyrofsky, Randy, Chief Fin. Officer & V.P.--The Jean Coutu (PJC) USA Inc., Warwick, RI; *Int'l*, pg. 340
Wysinski, Robert, Chief Fin. Officer, V.P., Treas. & Sec.--Value City Department Stores, Inc., Columbus, OH; *U.S. Private*, pg. 972
Wysong, Phil, Chief Fin. Officer, Treas & Sec.--Jones Company, Inc., Waycross, GA; *U.S. Private*, pg. 596
Wyszomierski, Jack L., Chief Fin. Officer & Exec. V.P.--Schering-Plough Corporation, Madison, NJ; *U.S. Public*, pg. 1438
Yablon, Leonard H., Chief Fin. Officer & Exec. V.P.--Forbes, Inc., New York, NY; *U.S. Private*, pg. 417
Yackira, Michael, Chief Fin. Officer & V.P.--FPL Group, Inc., North Palm Beach, FL; *U.S. Public*, pg. 608
Yager, Earl L., Chief Fin. Officer, Sr. V.P. & Sec.--Chad Therapeutics, Chatsworth, CA; *U.S. Public*, pg. 332
Yager, Keith, Chief Fin. Officer & V.P.-Fin.--HM International, Tulsa, OK; *U.S. Private*, pg. 491
Yakira, Michael, Chief Fin. Officer & Sr. V.P.-Fin.--Florida Power & Light Company, North Palm Beach, FL; *U.S. Public*, pg. 608
Yam, Colin, Chief Fin. Officer & Exec. V.P.--Times Publishing Limited, Singapore, Singapore; *Int'l*, pg. 1390
Yamada, Albert M., Chief Fin. Officer & Exec. V.P.--First Hawaiian Bank, Honolulu, HI; *U.S. Public*, pg. 634
Yamamura, Takehiko, Chief Fin. Officer, Exec. V.P. & Dir.-Inv. Rels.--Haseko Corporation, Tokyo, Japan; *Int'l*, pg. 599
Yaman, F.M., Jr., V.P.-Fin. & Admin.--Airport Group International, Inc., Glendale, CA; *U.S. Public*, pg. 1009
Yamashita, Tadashi, Chief Fin. Officer--American Drug Corporation, Tokyo, Japan; *U.S. Public*, pg. 80
Yanagawa, Masao, Chief Fin. Officer--Sakata Seed America, Inc., Morgan Hill, CA; *Int'l*, pg. 1178
Yanai, Yuval, Chief Fin. Officer & V.P.-Fin.--Elscint Ltd., Haifa, Israel; *Int'l*, pg. 450
Yancey, Robert, V.P.-Fin.--Halliburton Energy Services, Carrollton, TX; *U.S. Public*, pg. 776
Yang, Won S., Acting Chief Fin. Officer & Sr. V.P.--AST Research Inc., Irvine, CA; *Int'l*, pg. 1181
Yann, D., Chief Fin. Officer--Banque PSA Finance Holding, Paris, France; *Int'l*, pg. 1021
Yartz, Deanne, Chief Fin. Officer & Sr. V.P.--Wallpapers-To-Go, Houston, TX; *U.S. Private*, pg. 1175
Yates, David, Chief Fin. Officer & V.P.--Kasle Steel Corporation, Dearborn, MI; *U.S. Private*, pg. 608
Yates, Edward D., Chief Fin. Officer & Sr. V.P.--Dentsply International Inc., York, PA; *U.S. Public*, pg. 498
Yates, Herbert S., Chief Fin. Officer & Sr. V.P.--Camco International Inc., Houston, TX; *U.S. Public*, pg. 297
Yates, Herbert S., Chief Fin. Officer & Sr. V.P.-Fin.--Camco International Inc., Houston, TX; *U.S. Public*, pg. 298
Yauch, Edward, Chief Fin. Officer & V.P.--Commercial Testing & Engineering Co., Lombard, IL; *Int'l*, pg. 1153
Yauch, Kent M., Chief Fin. Officer & Treas.--General Employment Enterprises, Inc., Oak Brook Terrace, IL; *U.S. Public*, pg. 714
Yea, Philip, Grp. Fin. Dir.--Diageo Plc, London, United Kingdom; *Int'l*, pg. 408
Yea, Philip, Dir.-Fin. & Admin.--Guinness Plc, London, United Kingdom; *Int'l*, pg. 412
Yeager, Paul, Chief Fin. Officer--Hyponex Corporation, Marysville, OH; *U.S. Public*, pg. 1447
Yeager, Paul D., Chief Fin. Officer--Color Spot Nursery, Inc., Pleasant Hill, CA; *U.S. Private*, pg. 254
Yeager, Waldo E., Chief Fin. Officer & Treas.--Seaway Food Town, Inc., Maumee, OH; *U.S. Public*, pg. 1452
Yeager, William, Chief Fin. Officer--Menley & James Laboratories, Inc., Horsham, PA; *U.S. Public*, pg. 1086
Yeager, William, Chief Fin. Officer--Pollenex, Kansas City, MO; *U.S. Public*, pg. 1391
Yeakey, John, Chief Fin. Officer--Bomarko, Inc., Plymouth, IN; *U.S. Private*, pg. 156
Yeffa, Steven L., Chief Fin. Officer & V.P.-Fin.--Leasing Solutions, Inc., San Jose, CA; *U.S. Public*, pg. 982
Yemenidjian, Alex, Pres. & Chief Oper. & Fin. Officer--MGM Grand, Inc., Las Vegas, NV; *U.S. Public*, pg. 1026
Yessa, John M., Chief Fin. Officer, V.P.-Fin. & Treas.--Astronics Corporation, Buffalo, NY; *U.S. Public*, pg. 142
Yeung, Donald, Chief Fin. Officer & V.P.--The Apparel Group, Ltd., Louisville, KY; *U.S. Private*, pg. 78
Yincenz, Pierin, Chief Fin. Officer--Schweizer Verband der Raiffeisenbanken, Saint Gallen, Switzerland; *Int'l*, pg. 1211
Yip, Angela, Chief Fin. Officer & Treas--SJW Corp., San Jose, CA; *U.S. Public*, pg. 1418
Yip, Angela, Chief Fin. Officer--San Jose Water Company, San Jose, CA; *U.S. Public*, pg. 1418
Yocoubieu, Mark, Chief Fin. Officer--Johnson & Johnson Panama S.A., Panama, Panama; *U.S. Public*, pg. 931
Yoder, Elvin D., Chief Fin. Officer--Sauder Woodworking Co., Archbold, OH; *U.S. Private*, pg. 967
Yoder, John, Chief Fin. Officer--Pfaff-Pegasus of U.S.A., Suwanee, GA; *Int'l*, pg. 1046
Yoder, Kent A., Chief Fin. Officer--Jayco Inc., Middlebury, IN; *U.S. Private*, pg. 583
Yokota, Sywichi, V.P. & Treas.--TYK Refractories Co., Clairton, PA; *Int'l*, pg. 1345
Yoldi, E., Chief Fin. Officer--Lucas Girling S.A., Pamplona, Spain; *Int'l*, pg. 820
Yonker, Michael D., Chief Fin. Officer, V.P.-Fin. & Admin. & Treas.--In Focus Systems, Inc., Wilsonville, OR; *U.S. Public*, pg. 873
Yoo, Ho-ki, Chief Fin. Officer--Ssangyong Oil Refining Co. Ltd., Seoul, Korea; *Int'l*, pg. 1292
Yoo, Paul J., Chief Fin. Officer, Exec. V.P. & Sec.--Jockey International, Inc., Kenosha, WI; *U.S. Private*, pg. 588
Yopp, Bradley C., Chief Fin. Officer--Ultra Pac, Inc., Rogers, MN; *U.S. Public*, pg. 1662
Yorga, Carlos, Chief Fin. Officer--L'Oreal Prodesca S.A., Buenos Aires, Argentina; *Int'l*, pg. 819
York, E. Malcolm, Chief Fin. Officer & Exec. V.P.--Paul Inman Associates Inc., Farmington, MI; *U.S. Private*, pg. 564
York, Steve M., Chief Fin. Officer, Sr. V.P. & Treas.--Amtech Corporation, Dallas, TX; *U.S. Public*, pg. 105
Yoshida, M., Chief Fin. Officer--Tamura Corporation of America, Temecula, CA; *U.S. Private*, pg. 1067
Yosowitz, Sanford, V.P., Gen. Counsel & Sec.--Alcan Aluminum Corporation, Cleveland, OH; *Int'l*, pg. 50
Yostrum, James, Chief Fin. Officer--Ward Manufacturing, Inc., Blossburg, PA; *U.S. Private*, pg. 1149
Youdelman, Robert A., Chief Fin. Officer & Exec. V.P.--Allen Telecom, Inc., Beachwood, OH; *U.S. Public*, pg. 45
Youmans, Tammy, Chief Fin. Officer--Richard Hirschmann of America, Inc., Riverdale, NJ; *Int'l*, pg. 1108
Youmans, Thomas, Chief Fin. Officer--S.B. Foot Tanning Co., Red Wing, MN; *U.S. Private*, pg. 915
Youner, Lester W., Chief Fin. Officer, V.P. & Treas.--Trans Resources, Inc., New York, NY; *U.S. Private*, pg. 1096
Young, Beulah, Controller--Remco Toys, New York, NY; *U.S. Public*, pg. 923
Young, D.T.M., Chief Fin. Officer--Bradstock Group plc, London, United Kingdom; *Int'l*, pg. 210
Young, Dale, Chief Fin. Officer & Treas.--Kansas City Chiefs Football Club, Inc., Kansas City, MO; *U.S. Private*, pg. 607
Young, David A., Chief Fin. Officer & V.P.--Datum Inc., Irvine, CA; *U.S. Public*, pg. 488
Young, Douglas E., Chief Fin. Officer & Sr. V.P.--Copperweld Fayetteville Division, Fayetteville, TN; *Int'l*, pg. 662
Young, Jack, Chm. Bd., Pres., Chief Exec. & Chief Fin. Officer--Jack Young Associates, Hazleton, PA; *U.S. Private*, pg. 1201
Young, James G., Jr., Chief Fin. Officer & Treas.--Schurz Communications, Inc., South Bend, IN; *U.S. Private*, pg. 973
Young, Jeffrey, Chief Fin. Officer & Exec. V.P.--Courtaulds Aerospace, Glendale, CA; *Int'l*, pg. 339
Young, Jim, V.P.-Fin. & Admin.--Mark IV Automotive Canada Inc., Weston, Canada; *U.S. Public*, pg. 1045
Young, John E., Chief Fin. Officer & V.P.-Fin.--Alco Industries, Inc., Valley Forge, PA; *U.S. Private*, pg. 32
Young, M.R., Dr., Chief Fin. Officer--Watts Blake Bearne & Co. Plc, Newton Abbot, United Kingdom; *Int'l*, pg. 1487
Young, Michael, Chief Fin. Officer--Arburg, Inc., Newington, CT; *U.S. Private*, pg. 79
Young, Michael R., Chief Fin. Officer & V.P.-Intl. Div.--Allen & Hoshall, Inc., Memphis, TN; *U.S. Private*, pg. 36
Young, Richard, Chief Fin. Officer--Banca March S.A., London, United Kingdom; *Int'l*, pg. 136
Young, Robert H., Chief Fin. Officer, Exec. V.P., Treas. & Corp. Sec.--First Western Bancorp, Inc., New Castle, PA; *U.S. Public*, pg. 642
Young, Trudy, Chief Fin. Officer--R.S. Young Excavating, Inc., Flint, MI; *U.S. Private*, pg. 1202
Younger, Alvin M., Jr., Chief Fin. Officer, Mng. Dir., Treas. & Sec.--T. Rowe Price Associates, Inc., Baltimore, MD; *U.S. Public*, pg. 1324
Youngman, Carl, Chief Fin. Officer & Treas.--Cuisine Solutions, Inc., Alexandria, VA; *U.S. Public*, pg. 466
Younk, James L., V.P.-Fin.--David White, L.L.C., Germantown, WI; *U.S. Public*, pg. 1765
Younk, James L., V.P.-Fin.--David White, L.L.C., Germantown, WI; *U.S. Private*, pg. 1765
Yount, G. Stuart, Chm. Bd. & Chief Exec. Officer--Fortifiber Corporation, Incline Village, NV; *U.S. Private*, pg. 419
Yu, Lillian, Treas.--Keng Hua Paper Products Co., Inc., Manila, Philippines; *Int'l*, pg. 729
Yule, Peter, Chief Fin. Officer--NewBold Corporation, Rocky Mount, VA; *U.S. Private*, pg. 796
Yuska, John R., Chief Fin. Officer & Sr. V.P.--Avemco Corporation, Frederick, MD; *U.S. Public*, pg. 151
Yusko, Dave, Chief Fin. Officer--Potamkin Company, Miami, FL; *U.S. Private*, pg. 876
Zabinski, A.F., Jr., Chief Fin. Officer, Controller & Treas.--George Sollitt Construction, Wood Dale, IL; *U.S. Private*, pg. 1013
Zaegel, C., Chief Fin. Officer--Bank Building, Manchester, MO; *U.S. Private*, pg. 407
Zaegel, Charles, Chief Fin. Officer & Dir.-Cash Mngmt.--First Financial Building Corporation, Manchester, MO; *U.S. Private*, pg. 407
Zaelit, Joseph M., Chief Fin. Officer & V.P.-Fin./Admin.--VeriFone, Inc., Redwood City, CA; *U.S. Public*, pg. 815
Zahrn, James F., Chief Fin. Officer & Sr. V.P.--Springs Industries, Inc., Fort Mill, SC; *U.S. Public*, pg. 1499
Zajac, Dan, Chief Fin. Officer--Smith System Manufacturing Company, Plano, TX; *U.S. Private*, pg. 1009
Zalak, Timothy F., Chief Fin. Officer, Treas. & Sec.--Multi-Local Media Corporation, Rockville Centre, NY; *U.S. Private*, pg. 767
Zaleschuk, Victor J., Pres., Chief Exec. & Fin. Officer--Canadian Occidental Petroleum Ltd., Calgary, Canada; *U.S. Public*, pg. 1210
Zambelli, Thomas, Chief Fin. Officer & Sr. V.P.--Tops Appliance City, Edison, NJ; *U.S. Public*, pg. 1622
Zamprogna, Adriano, Chief Fin. Officer--Mikron SA Agno, Lugano, Switzerland; *Int'l*, pg. 866
Zannino, Richard, Chief Fin. Officer & Exec. V.P.--Saks Fifth Avenue, New York, NY; *U.S. Public*, pg. 1429
Zapisek, John R., Chief Fin. Officer, Sr. V.P. & Treas.--Utica Mutual Insurance Company, New Hartford, NY; *U.S. Private*, pg. 1129
Zarcone, Donna F., Chief Fin. Officer & V.P.--Eaglemark Financial Services, Inc., Chicago, IL; *U.S. Public*, pg. 786
Zarrilli, David, Chief Fin. Officer--Surgical Specialties, Reading, PA; *U.S. Private*, pg. 1056
Zator, Todd, Chief Fin. Officer--GN Nettest, Datacom Division, Markham, Canada; *Int'l*, pg. 537
Zaun, Darek, Chief Fin. Officer--Westlie Motor Company, Minot, ND; *U.S. Private*, pg. 1169
Zaunders, Per, Chief Fin. Officer & Exec. V.P.--BT Industries AB, Mjolby, Sweden; *Int'l*, pg. 123
Zausner, Meryl, Dir.-Fin. & Admin.--Sandoz Pharmaceuticals Corp., East Hanover, NJ; *Int'l*, pg. 974
Zbiegien, Thomas J., Chief Fin. Officer--Structural North America, Chardon, OH; *U.S. Public*, pg. 593
Zeck, William J., Chief Fin. Officer & V.P.--The David J. Joseph Company, Cincinnati, OH; *Int'l*, pg. 1155
Zeigert, G., Chief Fin. Officer--BPC Division, Bristol, IN; *Int'l*, pg. 618
Zeigler, Charles E., Jr., Chm. Bd., Pres. & Chief Exec. Officer--Public Service Company of North Carolina, Inc., Gastonia, NC; *U.S. Public*, pg. 1340
Zeigler, Michael C., Chief Fin. Officer & Sr. V.P.-Fin.--Intermagnetics General Corporation, Latham, NY; *U.S. Public*, pg. 893
Zeihn, Christine, Chief Fin. Officer & V.P.-Fin.--W.M. Grace Development, Phoenix, AZ; *U.S. Private*, pg. 468
Zeitler, Albert, Chief Fin. Officer--Amerford International Corporation, Atlanta, GA; *Int'l*, pg. 1388
Zeleniak, David A., Chief Fin. Officer--Ross Technology, Inc., Austin, TX; *Int'l*, pg. 526
Zeller, Walter, Chief Fin. Officer--Corange Limited, Hamilton, Bermuda; *Int'l*, pg. 330
Zelnick, Moshe, Chief Fin. Officer--Mennen Medical Ltd., Rehovot, Israel; *Int'l*, pg. 858
Zenger, Gerold, Chief Fin. Officer & Investor Rels.--Forbo Holding SA, Eglisau, Switzerland; *Int'l*, pg. 496
Zenk, Saul, Pres. & Treas.--Monico Alloys, Inc., Los Angeles, CA; *U.S. Private*, pg. 757
Zepf, Edward C., Sr. V.P.-Fin. & Treas.--Clopay Corporation, Cincinnati, OH; *U.S. Public*, pg. 766
Zepf, Stephen J., Chief Fin. Officer & Treas.--Hughes Supply, Inc., Orlando, FL; *U.S. Public*, pg. 846
Zern, Allen W., Chief Fin. Officer--Morgan Stanley & Co. Incorporated, New York, NY; *U.S. Public*, pg. 1132
Zettek, Chris R., Chief Fin. Officer & Exec. V.P.--Firstbank of Illinois Co., Springfield, IL; *U.S. Public*, pg. 643
Ziegler, Donald E., Chief Fin. Officer & Sr. V.P.--Hadron, Inc., Alexandria, VA; *U.S. Public*, pg. 773
Ziegler, John K., Jr., Chief Fin. Officer & Controller--Willcox & Gibbs, Inc., Carteret, NJ; *U.S. Private*, pg. 1177
Ziegler, O., Chief Fin. Officer & V.P.--Siemens AB, Stockholm, Sweden; *Int'l*, pg. 1247
Ziegler, Scott F., V.P.-Fin., Controller & Sec.--Emons Transportation Group, Inc., York, PA; *U.S. Public*, pg. 578
Ziegler, Scott F., Chief Fin. Officer--St. Lawrence & Atlantic Railroad, York, PA; *U.S. Public*, pg. 578
Ziegler, Scott F., Chief Fin. Officer--Emons Railroad Group, Inc., York, PA; *U.S. Public*, pg. 578
Ziegler, Scott F., Chief Fin. Officer--Emons Industries, Inc., York, PA; *U.S. Public*, pg. 578
Ziegler, Scott F., Chief Fin. Officer--Emons Logistics Services Inc., York, PA; *U.S. Public*, pg. 578
Ziegler, Scott F., Chief Fin. Officer--Yorkrail Inc., York, PA; *U.S. Public*, pg. 579
Ziehl, Karen L., V.P. & Controller--M & I Northern Bank, Brookfield, WI; *U.S. Public*, pg. 1050
Ziemer, James L., Chief Fin. Officer, V.P. & Asst. Treasurer--Harley-Davidson, Inc., Milwaukee, WI; *U.S. Public*, pg. 786

Ziemke, Duane G., V.P.- Fin.--Ausco Products, Inc., Benton Harbor, MI; *U.S. Private*, pg. 299
Ziemniak, Frances Ann, Chief Fin. Officer, V.P.-Fin. & Asst. Sec.--CORT Business Services Corporation, Fairfax, VA; *U.S. Public*, pg. 451
Zikias, Robert, Chief Fin. Officer--The Advocate, Stamford, CT; *U.S. Public*, pg. 1616
Zilcias, Robert, Chief Fin. Officer--Greenwich Times, Greenwich, CT; *U.S. Public*, pg. 1616
Zildjian, Armand, Chm. Bd. & Pres.--Avedis Zildjian Company, Norwell, MA; *U.S. Private*, pg. 1206
Zilinskas, M.J., Chief Fin. Officer & Sr. V.P.--The Dyson-Kissner-Moran Corporation, New York, NY; *U.S. Private*, pg. 351
Zils, Joseph C., Pres. & Chief Fin. Officer--Flex Products, Inc., Santa Rosa, CA; *U.S. Public*, pg. 1227
Zimdar, William L., Chm. Bd., Chief Exec. Officer, Chief Fin. Officer & V.P.--Zimdar Enterprises/Frames Unlimited, Wyoming, MI; *U.S. Private*, pg. 1206
Zimk, Robbie, Chief Fin. Officer, Treas. & Sec.--Schmieding Enterprises Inc., Springdale, AR; *U.S. Private*, pg. 971
Zimmer, Richard, Chief Fin. Officer, Treas., Sec. & Dir.-Acctg.--Active Tool & Manufacturing Co., Inc., Roseville, MI; *U.S. Private*, pg. 16
Zimmer, Robert J., Chief Fin. Officer, V.P.-Fin. & Sec.--Acheson Industries, Inc., Port Huron, MI; *U.S. Private*, pg. 12
Zimmer, William A., Chief Fin. Officer, V.P. & Treas.--Poe & Brown, Inc., Daytona Beach, FL; *U.S. Public*, pg. 1312
Zimmerman, Alan, V.P.-Fin. & Treas.--Hasselblad USA, Inc., Fairfield, NJ; *Int'l*, pg. 1468
Zimmerman, Andy, Chief Fin. Officer--Mission Industries, Las Vegas, NV; *U.S. Private*, pg. 752
Zimmerman, Gail, Chief Fin. Officer--R.S. Hughes Co., Inc., Sunnyvale, CA; *U.S. Private*, pg. 547
Zimmerman, Lee D., Gen. Mgr.-Acctg.--Steelox Systems Inc., Mason, OH; *U.S. Private*, pg. 1038
Zimmerman, R.E., Chief Fin. Officer & V.P.--TTX Co., Chicago, IL; *U.S. Private*, pg. 1066
Zimmerman, Roger, Chief Fin. Officer--Tony Lama Co., Inc., El Paso, TX; *U.S. Public*, pg. 937
Zimmermann, James D., Chief Fin. Officer--Independent Metals, Germantown, WI; *U.S. Private*, pg. 559
Zinbarg, Benson, Pres., Chief Exec. Officer, Chief Fin. Officer & Treas.--Sun Hill Industries, Inc., Stamford, CT; *U.S. Private*, pg. 1051
Zink, Darell E., Jr., Chief Fin. Officer, Exec. V.P. & Asst. Sec.--Duke Realty Investments, Inc., Indianapolis, IN; *U.S. Public*, pg. 535
Zinn, Fredric M., Chief Fin. Officer--Drew Industries Incorporated, White Plains, NY; *U.S. Public*, pg. 529
Zinn, Fredric M., Chief Fin. Officer--Leslie Building Products, Inc., White Plains, NY; *U.S. Public*, pg. 989
Zinn, James M., Chief Fin. Officer & Sr. V.P.--Capital One Financial Corporation, Falls Church, VA; *U.S. Public*, pg. 302
Zinter, Erv, Chief Fin. Officer & Exec. V.P.--National Car Rental System, Inc., Minneapolis, MN; *U.S. Public*, pg. 1379
Ziplow, Howard, Chief Fin. Officer--West Mill Clothes, Tuxedo Accessories Div., Bristol, PA; *U.S. Private*, pg. 1163
Zirnkilton, Frank C., Jr., Chief Fin. Officer & Sr. V.P.--Atlantic Aviation Corp., New Castle, DE; *U.S. Private*, pg. 94
Zissman, Eric, Chief Fin. Officer--Total Research Corporation, Princeton, NJ; *U.S. Public*, pg. 1625
Zitko, Jeff, Chief Fin. Officer--Smith-Emery Company, Los Angeles, CA; *U.S. Private*, pg. 1007
Zlobeck, Roland, Chief Fin. Officer--Skanska Anlaggning AB, Malmo, Sweden; *Int'l*, pg. 1260
Zoller, Jeffrey, Chief Fin. Officer--National Fruit Product Company, Winchester, VA; *U.S. Private*, pg. 783
Zolot, Stu, Chief Fin. Officer-Marc & Co.--MARC Promotion, Indianapolis, IN; *U.S. Private*, pg. 701
Zolot, Stuart M., Chief Fin. Officer & Sr. V.P.--MARC, Pittsburgh, PA; *U.S. Private*, pg. 701
Zore, Edward J., Chief Fin. Officer & Exec. V.P.--Northwestern Mutual Life Insurance Co., Milwaukee, WI; *U.S. Private*, pg. 807
Zorko, Mark, Chief Fin. & Info. Officer--Network Services Company, Mount Prospect, IL; *U.S. Private*, pg. 791
Zorn, Tilman, Chief Fin. Officer--Haarmann & Reimer Corp., Springfield, NJ; *Int'l*, pg. 173
Zott, John C., Chief Fin. Officer & Sr. V.P.-Fin.--West Marine, Inc., Watsonville, CA; *U.S. Public*, pg. 1756
Zsolcsak, Veronica, Chief Fin. Officer & V.P.--Town & Country Fine Jewelry Group, Inc., Chelsea, MA; *U.S. Public*, pg. 1625
Zsolcsak, Veronica M., Chief Fin. Officer--DRI/McGraw-Hill, Lexington, MA; *U.S. Public*, pg. 1071
Zubek, Wayne, Chief Fin. Officer & V.P.-Fin.--Metroland Printing & Distributing, Mississauga, Canada; *Int'l*, pg. 1402
Zuber, Harold L., Jr., Chief Fin. Officer & V.P.--Teleflex Incorporated, Plymouth Meeting, PA; *U.S. Public*, pg. 1569
Zucker, Gary, Chief Fin. Officer--American Technology Corporation, Hudson, MA; *U.S. Private*, pg. 63
Zuckerman, Howard F., Chief Fin. Officer, V.P. & Treas.--Bell Atlantic Investment Development Corporation, Philadelphia, PA; *U.S. Public*, pg. 202
Zuerblis, Ken, V.P.-Fin.--Enzon, Inc., Piscataway, NJ; *U.S. Public*, pg. 587
Zulanas, George J., Jr., Chief Fin. Officer, V.P. & Treas.--Uniroyal Technology Corporation, Sarasota, FL; *U.S. Public*, pg. 1670
Zullinger, R. Fredric, Chief Fin. Officer, V.P.-Acctg. & Treas.--Consumers Financial Corporation, Camp Hill, PA; *U.S. Public*, pg. 437
Zullinger, R. Fredric, V.P.-Acctg. & Chief Fin. Officer--Consumers Life Insurance Company, Camp Hill, PA; *U.S. Public*, pg. 438
Zumwalt, LeAnne M., Chief Fin. Officer, Treas. & Sec.--Vivra Incorporated, San Mateo, CA; *U.S. Public*, pg. 1723
Zundel, Randy, Chief Fin. Officer & V.P.--OEC Medical Systems, Inc., Salt Lake City, UT; *U.S. Public*, pg. 1207
Zunker, Arthur R., Chief Fin. Officer, Sr. V.P.-Fin. & Treas.--Centex Construction Products, Inc., Dallas, TX; *U.S. Public*, pg. 322
Zutty, Mark, Chief Fin. Officer--JJC Specialist Corp., New York, NY; *U.S. Public*, pg. 650
Zvesper, Joseph P., Chief Fin. Officer, Exec. V.P., Treas. & Sec.--American Appraisal Associates, Inc., Milwaukee, WI; *U.S. Private*, pg. 49
Zwarych, Brian P., Chief Fin. Officer--White River Corporation, White Plains, NY; *U.S. Public*, pg. 1765
Zweifel, James A., Chief Fin. Officer & Exec. V.P.--President Casinos, Inc., Saint Louis, MO; *U.S. Public*, pg. 1323
Zylstra, Ken, Chief Fin. Officer--Schuff Steel Co., Phoenix, AZ; *U.S. Private*, pg. 973

CHIEF OFFICER OF SUBSIDIARY

Aaberg, Erik R., Mng. Dir.--Jotun Saudia Co. Ltd., Yanbu, Saudi Arabia; *Int'l*, pg. 716
Aagaard, A. Kim, Pres. & Chief Exec. Officer--Synergistics Industries Limited, Mississauga, Canada; *U.S. Public*, pg. 734
Aagaard, A. Kim, Pres.--Synergistics Industries (NJ) Inc., Farmingdale, NJ; *U.S. Public*, pg. 734
Aagaard, A. Kim, Pres.--Synergistics Industries (TX) Inc., Conroe, TX; *U.S. Public*, pg. 734
Aagaard, A. Kim, Pres.--Synergistics Industries Limited, Lindsay, Canada; *U.S. Public*, pg. 734
Aagaard, A. Kim, Pres.--Synergistics Industries Limited, Orangeville, Canada; *U.S. Public*, pg. 734
Aagaard, A. Kim, Pres.--Synergistics Industries Limited, Valleyfield, Canada; *U.S. Public*, pg. 734
Aagaard, A. Kim, Pres.--Synergistics Industries Limited, Saint Remi-de-Napierville, Canada; *U.S. Public*, pg. 734
Aagaard, A.K., Pres.--Synergistics Chemicals, Inc., Mississauga, Canada; *U.S. Public*, pg. 734
Aagaard, Lone, Pres.--Astra Pharmaceuticals Kft., Budapest, Hungary; *Int'l*, pg. 94
Aalders, G. Ch., Mng. Dir.--Interpharm bv, s Hertogenbosch, Netherlands; *Int'l*, pg. 681
Aalen, Gary, Pres.--Mountain Operations Land Division, Englewood, CO; *U.S. Public*, pg. 1683
Aalto, Rainer, Chief Oper. Officer--MacGREGOR (DNK) A/S, Herlev, Denmark; *Int'l*, pg. 670
Aam, Knut, Pres. & Mng. Dir.--Phillips Petroleum Co. Norway, Tananger, Norway; *U.S. Public*, pg. 1291
Aamodt, Arne, Plant Mgr.--Elkem Saudefaldine, Sauda, Norway; *Int'l*, pg. 447
Aamodt, O., Chief Oper. Officer--Den norske Bank (Luxembourg) S.A., Senningerberg, Luxembourg; *Int'l*, pg. 392
Aamodt, Tor Arne, Pres.--Kvaerner Rosenberg a.s., Stavanger, Norway; *Int'l*, pg. 769
Aamot, Haldor, Mng. Dir.--Sud Electra GmbH, Schwieberdingen, Germany; *Int'l*, pg. 712
Aanstoot, Hein, Mng. Dir.--ELVIA Levenverzekeringen N.V., Amsterdam, Netherlands; *Int'l*, pg. 60
Aanstoot, Hein, Mng. Dir.--ELVIA Schadeverzekeringen N.V., Amsterdam, Netherlands; *Int'l*, pg. 60
Aarnes, Roar, Gen. Mgr.--Tektronix A/S, Skovlunde, Denmark; *U.S. Public*, pg. 1567
Aaron, C.H., Pres. & Mgr.--Videk, Rochester, NY; *U.S. Public*, pg. 551
Aaron, James, Gen. Mgr.--Martin Marietta International, Inc., Seoul, Korea; *U.S. Public*, pg. 1010
Aaron, Marcus, II, Pres. & Treas.--The Newell Company, Newell, WV; *U.S. Private*, pg. 653
Aaron, Marcus, II, Pres. & Treas.--Newell Bridge & Railway Company, Newell, WV; *U.S. Private*, pg. 653
Aas, Svein Arne, Mng. Dir.--TiMar Seafood A/S, Trondheim, Norway; *Int'l*, pg. 1390
Aaser, Svein, Deputy Chief Exec. Officer--Nycomed Amersham, Oslo, Norway; *Int'l*, pg. 993
Abad, Jose, Controller & Gen. Mgr.--AEP Industries Packaging Espana, S.A., Alicante, Spain; *U.S. Public*, pg. 5
Abad, Ron, Mng. Dir.--Beebe Rubber Company, Nashua, NH; *U.S. Private*, pg. 229
Abajo, Mario, Mng. Dir.--Zardoya Otis SA, Madrid, Spain; *U.S. Public*, pg. 1691
Abascal, Manual, Gen. Mgr.--Editorial Caribe Inc., Miami, FL; *U.S. Public*, pg. 1168
Abastar, Fernando, Pres.--Banco Central Hispano-U.S.A., New York, NY; *Int'l*, pg. 139
Abbasie, Javaid, Chief Oper. Officer--National Bank of Pakistan, Washington, DC; *Int'l*, pg. 908
Abbate, Phil, Reg. V.P.-Mid Atlantic Reg.--Circle Freight International USA, Lawrence, NY; *U.S. Public*, pg. 371
Abbes, Gerhard, Mng. Dir.--Oberrheinische Mineraloelwerke GmbH, Karlsruhe, Germany; *U.S. Public*, pg. 533
Abbink, Peter, Unit Mgr.--Weatherford Oil Tool Nederland B.V., Beverwijk, Netherlands; *U.S. Public*, pg. 1750
Abbis, John, Pres.--Applied Research Labs, Valencia, CA; *Int'l*, pg. 1111
Abbott, Catherine Good, Pres. & Chief Exec. Officer--Columbia Gas Transmission Corp., Charleston, WV; *U.S. Public*, pg. 403
Abbott, Frank, Gen. Mgr.--Comprint, Inc., Gaithersburg, MD; *U.S. Public*, pg. 1743
Abbott, James A., Pres. & Chief Exec. Officer--First Union Mortgage Corporation, Charlotte, NC; *U.S. Public*, pg. 640
Abbott, John T., Pres.--Magazine Services Inc., New York, NY; *U.S. Private*, pg. 623
Abbott, Steven R., Pres.--Wire & Cable Sector, Fort Wayne, IN; *U.S. Public*, pg. 593
Abdalla, Herbert A., Pres.--Brothers, Lafayette, LA; *U.S. Private*, pg. 10
Abdalla, Herbert A., Pres.--Naturalizer Women's Shoe Salon, Lafayette, LA; *U.S. Private*, pg. 10
Abdalla, Herbert A., Pres.--Abform Company, Lafayette, LA; *U.S. Private*, pg. 10
Abdelmalak, George, Chief Exec. Officer--GAM/DMB&B Beirut, Beirut, Lebanon; *U.S. Private*, pg. 304
Abdelrahman, Chahira, Gen. Mgr.--DMB&B Egypt Ltd., Giza, Egypt; *U.S. Private*, pg. 303
Abdine, A.S., Chm. Bd. & Mng. Dir.--Gulf of Suez Petroleum Company, Cairo, Egypt; *U.S. Public*, pg. 102
Abdoo, Richard A., Pres. & Chief Exec. Officer--Wisconsin Michigan Investment Corp., Milwaukee, WI; *U.S. Public*, pg. 1773
Abdouch, Don, Admin.--Clayton House Healthcare, Manchester, MO; *U.S. Public*, pg. 1712
Abdul Hak, Mohd Amin, Gen. Mgr.--Det Norske Veritas, Kuala Lumpur, Malaysia; *Int'l*, pg. 397
Abe, Anna, Dir.--New York Language Center, Milan, Italy; *U.S. Public*, pg. 222
Abe, Hideo, Pres.--Chiyoda Life Asset Management of America Inc., New York, NY; *Int'l*, pg. 287
Abe, Hideo, Pres.--Chiyoda Life Realty of America, Inc., New York, NY; *Int'l*, pg. 287
Abe, Hirohisa, Gen. Mgr.--The Sumitomo Trust & Banking Co., Ltd., Georgetown, Cayman Islands; *Int'l*, pg. 1317
Abe, Isao, Gen. Mgr.--Kincheng-Tokyo Finance Co., Ltd., Hong Kong, Hong Kong; *Int'l*, pg. 158
Abe, Katsuhiko, Mng. Dir.--Yamaichi Advisory Services (Malaysia) Sdn. Bhd., Kuala Lumpur, Malaysia; *Int'l*, pg. 1517
Abe, Kenji, Dir.--Takenaka Europe GmbH, Berlin, Berlin, Germany; *Int'l*, pg. 1351
Abe, Shunichi, Pres.--Hakuhodo Bangkok Co., Ltd., Bangkok, Thailand; *Int'l*, pg. 588
Abe, T., Dir.--Hankuk Safety Glass Limited, Seoul, Korea; *Int'l*, pg. 1057
Abe, Tomohide, Chief Oper. Officer--Makita Benelux B.V., Son, Netherlands; *Int'l*, pg. 832
Abecassis, Michel, Mng. Dir.--ISS France S.A., Arcueil, France; *Int'l*, pg. 656
Abehsera, Daniel, Pres. & Dir. Gen.--Rohr Europe, Toulouse, France; *U.S. Public*, pg. 752
Abel, James, Mgr.--Uddeholm Corporation, Dallas, TX; *Int'l*, pg. 1472
Abel, Larry F., Gen. Mgr.--Securair Ltd., Hong Kong, Hong Kong; *Int'l*, pg. 705
Abend, Arie, Joint Mng. Dir. & Reg. Mgr.-Western Hemisphere--Bank Hapoalim B.M., New York, NY; *Int'l*, pg. 149
Aberg, B., Gen. Mgr.--Parker Hannifin Oy (Finland), Vantaa, Finland; *U.S. Public*, pg. 1263
Abernathy, Dorothy, Publisher--The Oldham Era, La Grange, KY; *U.S. Private*, pg. 648
Abernathy, Jerry, Pres. & Chief Oper. Officer--Coty Inc., New York, NY; *Int'l*, pg. 185
Abernathy, Michael, Publr.--Style Weekly, Richmond, VA; *U.S. Private*, pg. 649
Abersek, Iztok, Mng. Dir.--Vision Factory Productions, Ljubljana, Slovenia; *U.S. Private*, pg. 305
Abildtrup, Henrik, Mng. Dir.--Ericsson Radio Systems A/S, Tastrup, Denmark; *Int'l*, pg. 1367
Able, A.R., Branch Mgr.--Zellerbach Division, Richmond, VA; *U.S. Public*, pg. 1075
Ablon, R. Richard, Pres.--Ogden Entertainment, Inc., New York, NY; *U.S. Public*, pg. 1213
Ablon, R. Richard, Pres.--Ogden Aviation Services, New York, NY; *U.S. Public*, pg. 1213
Abodeely, John, V.P. & Gen. Mgr.--Packaging Operations, Montvale, NJ; *U.S. Public*, pg. 903
Abou Taleb, Amira, Media Dir.--AMA Leo Burnett, Giza, Egypt; *U.S. Private*, pg. 184
Abouchar, Ernest, Mng. Dir.--McCormick S.A., Regensdorf, Switzerland; *U.S. Public*, pg. 1067
Abouhamad, Emilio, Pres.--Maraven, S.A., Caracas, Venezuela; *Int'l*, pg. 1045
Abraham, Seth G., Pres. & Chief Exec. Officer--Time Warner Sports, New York, NY; *U.S. Public*, pg. 1611
Abrahams, B., Chm. Bd. & Chief Exec. Officer--Greenham Trading Limited, Isleworth, United Kingdom; *Int'l*, pg. 1358
Abrahams, Kenneth, Pres.--Holyoke Food Mart, Inc., Holyoke, MA; *Int'l*, pg. 1375
Abrahams, Mark, Gen. Mgr.--AET Specialty Nets & Profiles, Middletown, DE; *U.S. Public*, pg. 122
Abrahams, Robert, Pres.--Health-Mor Acceptance Pty Ltd., Sydney, Australia; *U.S. Public*, pg. 771
Abrahams, Robert J., Pres.--Health-Mor Acceptance Corp., Cleveland, OH; *U.S. Public*, pg. 771
Abrahamson, David A., Pres. & Chief Exec. Officer--Medicine Shoppe International, Inc., Saint Louis, MO; *U.S. Public*, pg. 304
Abrahamson, Robert J., Pres.--HMI Acceptance Corp., Toronto, Canada; *U.S. Public*, pg. 771
Abrahamsson, Anders, Gen. Mgr.--Merita Bank Ltd. - Stockholm Branch, Stockholm, Sweden; *Int'l*, pg. 859
Abrahamsson, Lars, Mgr.--Ahlsell VVS AB, Stockholm, Sweden; *Int'l*, pg. 1422
Abrahamsson, Roland, Pres.--Elitfonster AB, Vetlanda, Sweden; *Int'l*, pg. 678
Abrahamsson, Roland, Pres.--Elit Fonster AB, Vetlanda, Sweden; *Int'l*, pg. 1260
Abrahman, Sajan, V.P.--Rediffusion-Dentsu, Young & Rubicam (Madras), Madras, India; *U.S. Private*, pg. 326
Abraira, Phillip, Pres.--DSI Transports, Inc., Houston, TX; *Int'l*, pg. 1285
Abram, John, Pres.--In-Stat Incorporated, Scottsdale, AZ; *Int'l*, pg. 1096
Abram, Michael F., Pres.--Erskine House Group Plc, Sevenoaks, United Kingdom; *U.S. Public*, pg. 864
Abram, Ronald A., Pres. & Chief Oper. Officer--Markel Insurance Co., Glen Allen, VA; *U.S. Public*, pg. 1046
Abramowicz, Daniel A., Sr. V.P.--Crown Cork & Seal Company, Inc.-Corporate Technologies, Alsip, IL; *U.S. Public*, pg. 463

Abrams, Ellen J., Pres. & Chief Exec. Officer--National City Trust Company, West Palm Beach, FL; *U.S. Public*, pg. 1154
Abrams, Gerald W., Chm. Bd.--Hearst Entertainment Productions, Inc., Los Angeles, CA; *U.S. Private*, pg. 516
Abrams, Glen, Mng. Dir.--Triumph Releasing Corporation - Central Territory, Des Plaines, IL; *Int'l*, pg. 1282
Abrams, Jerry, Gen. Mgr.--Southwire Specialty Products, Osceola, AR; *U.S. Private*, pg. 1019
Abrams, Ralph D., Pres.--Lea & Perrins, Inc., Fair Lawn, NJ; *Int'l*, pg. 380
Abrams, Richard, Pres.--New Dimensions in Education, Waterbury, CT; *U.S. Private*, pg. 10
Abramson, Larry, Pres.--Camerican International, Paramus, NJ; *U.S. Public*, pg. 426
Abril, Mario, Gen. Mgr.--Colonnade Enterprise Corporation, Coral Gables, FL; *Int'l*, pg. 132
Abrisz, James, Chief Fin. Officer--Forged Products, Houston, TX; *U.S. Private*, pg. 299
Abromovic, A. Mark, Pres.--ERI Realty, Inc., Pittsburgh, PA; *U.S. Public*, pg. 589
Abruzzio, P.A., Chief Fin. Officer--Union Camp Wood Products Div., Savannah, GA; *U.S. Public*, pg. 1666
Abu, Amiruddin B., Dir.--Tourism Malaysia - Sydney Office, Sydney, Australia; *Int'l*, pg. 833
Abubshait, Waleed A., Gen. Mgr.--Saudi Electro-Mechanical Construction Co. (Petcon), Dammam, Saudi Arabia; *Int'l*, pg. 502
Accardi, Larry J., Pres.--Sysco Food Services of Atlanta, Inc., College Park, GA; *U.S. Public*, pg. 1551
Acciaro, Adamo, Chm. Bd.--Fiscambi Leasing Sud S.p.A., Bari, Italy; *Int'l*, pg. 138
Acencio, Francisco, Pres.--Indi Servicios C. Ltda., Quito, Ecuador; *U.S. Public*, pg. 363
Acerbi, Giuliano, Pres.--Ferrero U.S.A., Inc., Somerset, NJ; *Int'l*, pg. 480
Aceval, Heber, Gen. Mgr.--Circle Freight International Argentina S.A., Buenos Aires, Argentina; *U.S. Public*, pg. 372
Acevedo, Jose Ignacio, Pres.--C.V.G. Aluminio del Caroni, S.A., Ciudad Guayana, Venezuela; *U.S. Public*, pg. 1386
Achour, Samy, Mgr.--Gensym S.A., Rungis, France; *U.S. Public*, pg. 731
Achs, Stephan, Gen. Mgr.--Kabelschlepp America Inc., Milwaukee, WI; *Int'l*, pg. 721
Acker, David, Pres.--Kleinsleep, Port Washington, NY; *U.S. Private*, pg. 1006
Acker, Fred, Exec. V.P.-Sls. & Mktg.--Kleer-Vu Plastics Corp., Compton, CA; *U.S. Public*, pg. 962
Acker, Joseph G., Pres. & Gen. Mgr.--SpecialtyChem Products Corporation, Marinette, WI; *Int'l*, pg. 173
Ackerman, A., Dr., Chief Exec. Officer--Ascom Immobilien AG, Bern, Switzerland; *Int'l*, pg. 86
Ackerman, G.T., Gen. Mgr.--CHEMCENTRAL/Oklahoma City, Oklahoma City, OK; *U.S. Private*, pg. 232
Ackerman, Philip C., Pres.--Highland Land Minerals, Inc., Buffalo, NY; *U.S. Public*, pg. 1156
Ackerman, Robert, Plant Mgr.--Hershey Chocolate U.S.A.-Western Plant, Oakdale, CA; *U.S. Public*, pg. 812
Ackerman, S. Jeffrey, Pres.--Cigna Dental Health of Pennsylvania, Inc., Plantation, FL; *U.S. Public*, pg. 358
Ackerman, Simon J., Pres.--Cigna Dental Health, Inc., Plantation, FL; *U.S. Public*, pg. 358
Ackerman, Thomas, Gen. Mgr.--Cutler-Hammer Products, Watertown, WI; *U.S. Public*, pg. 556
Ackerstaff, Gerd, Mng. Dir.--L-TEC Deutschland GmbH, Wissen, Germany; *Int'l*, pg. 283
Ackley, Robert W., Pres.--Davis Standard Corporation, Pawcatuck, CT; *U.S. Public*, pg. 459
Ackmann, Steven C., Pres.--Laurel Community Development Corporation, Johnstown, PA; *U.S. Public*, pg. 164
Acolas, G., Reg. Mgr.--Air France (North Central), Chicago, IL; *Int'l*, pg. 560
Acosta, Alex, Gen. Mgr.--Talleres Rancagua Division, Rancagua, Chile; *Int'l*, pg. 302
Acosta, J.P., V.P.--Chrysler Credit Canada Ltd., Burlington, Canada; *U.S. Public*, pg. 354
Acosta, R.E., V.P.-Car & Truck Assembly Oper.--Chrysler Advance Manufacturing Operations, Detroit, MI; *U.S. Public*, pg. 353
Acquaviva, Jean-Mark, Mng. Dir.--Autologic Information International, Inc., Ivry-sur-Seine, France; *U.S. Public*, pg. 1724
Acridge, James E., Chm. Bd.--Giant Exploration & Production Co., Farmington, NM; *U.S. Public*, pg. 742
Acridge, James E., Chm., Pres. & Chief Exec. Officer--Giant Industries Arizona, Inc., Scottsdale, AZ; *U.S. Public*, pg. 742
Acton, Peter L., Gen. Mgr.-Chemical Prods. Div.--Union Camp Chemical Products Div., Wayne, NJ; *U.S. Public*, pg. 1666
Acton, William C., Pres.--Axel Johnson Metals, Inc., Lionville, PA; *Int'l*, pg. 709
Adachi, Hiroshi, Mng. Dir.--Nanometrics Japan Ltd., Tokyo, Japan; *U.S. Public*, pg. 1151
Adachi, Masakazu, Pres.--Japan Immunoresearch Laboratories Co., Ltd., Gunma, Japan; *Int'l*, pg. 1013
Adachi, Misako, Reservations Mgr.--Utell International-Japan, Osaka, Japan; *Int'l*, pg. 1098
Adachi, Yusuke, Gen. Mgr.--NSK-RHP Canada Inc., Mississauga, Canada; *Int'l*, pg. 904
Adair, Roy, Mgr.--Irlandus Circuits Limited, Craigavon, United Kingdom; *U.S. Public*, pg. 473
Adair, Roy, Mng. Dir.--DDL Europe Ltd., Armagh, United Kingdom; *U.S. Public*, pg. 473
Adair, Roy, Mng. Dir.--DDL Electronics Ltd., Armagh, United Kingdom; *U.S. Public*, pg. 473
Adair, W.D., Div. Mng. Dir.--Phosphates Division, Albright & Wilson Limited, Oldbury, United Kingdom; *Int'l*, pg. 49
Adair, W.D., Div. Mng. Dir.--Resins & Organics Division, Albright & Wilson Limited, Bristol, United Kingdom; *Int'l*, pg. 49
Adair, Wes, Pres.--Flanders Air Seal Filters Housings Inc., Stafford, TX; *U.S. Public*, pg. 648
Adalid, Antonio Gonzalez, Pres.--Repsol Quimica, Madrid, Spain; *Int'l*, pg. 1104
Adam, Alberto, Chief Oper. Officer--Langford Inc., Guelph, Canada; *U.S. Public*, pg. 81
Adam, Brian, Pres.--Passenger Railroad Insurance Ltd., Hamilton, Bermuda; *U.S. Private*, pg. 69
Adam, I., Dir.--BT Telecomunicaciones S.A., Madrid, Spain; *Int'l*, pg. 223
Adam, William, Mgr.--CCF Mellon Partners, Pittsburgh, PA; *Int'l*, pg. 342
Adamec, Jiri, Resident Mgr.--ESAB s.r.o., Prague, Czech Republic; *Int'l*, pg. 282
Adamek, Marek, Chm.--Ekokonrem Spolka z o.o., Wroclaw, Poland; *Int'l*, pg. 608
Adames, Neftali, Gen. Agent--CUNA Mutual Group-Puerto Rico, San Juan, PR; *U.S. Private*, pg. 296
Adamic, Edmund, Plant Mgr.--Waterloo Malting Co., Inc., Waterloo, WI; *U.S. Public*, pg. 1289
Adamission, Paul, Plant Mgr.--Orleans Food Co., Beaufort, SC; *U.S. Private*, pg. 158
Adamopoulos, William, Mng. Dir.--Asian Wall Street Journal, Hong Kong, Hong Kong; *U.S. Public*, pg. 525
Adamowski, Andre, Chief Oper. Officer--AGEMA Infrared Systems S.A.R.L., Issy-les-Moulineaux, France; *Int'l*, pg. 1289
Adams, Alain, Mgr.--A. Schulman, Inc., Birmingham, MI; *U.S. Public*, pg. 1441
Adams, Alan, Pres.--Prime Cast, Inc., South Beloit, IL; *U.S. Public*, pg. 142
Adams, Bill, Mgr.--Plastic Suppliers Inc., Dallas, TX; *U.S. Private*, pg. 871
Adams, Bryon, Pres.--Force 10 Marine Ltd., Richmond, Canada; *U.S. Public*, pg. 1705
Adams, Craig G., Pres.--Woodmark Originals Inc., Archdale, NC; *U.S. Private*, pg. 747
Adams, Daryll, Gen. Mgr.--Ogallala Electronics, Ogallala, NE; *U.S. Public*, pg. 1420
Adams, Derek F.C., Pres.--Financial Management, Los Angeles, CA; *U.S. Public*, pg. 181
Adams, Don, V.P.--Kemet De Mexico De S.A. De C.V., Matamoros, Mexico; *U.S. Public*, pg. 949
Adams, Donald, Chief Oper. Officer--Augat, Inc., Interconnection Products-Mashpee, Mashpee, MA; *U.S. Public*, pg. 1598
Adams, Donald E., Pres. & Chief Exec. Officer--SouthTrust Mobile Services, Birmingham, AL; *U.S. Public*, pg. 1492
Adams, Dorothy, Pres.--Gump's By Mail, Inc., San Francisco, CA; *U.S. Public*, pg. 782
Adams, Douglas W., Pres. & Gen. Mgr.--KXAS-TV, Fort Worth, TX; *U.S. Public*, pg. 11
Adams, Ed., Gen. Mgr.--WNCT-TV, Greenville, NC; *U.S. Public*, pg. 1078
Adams, Edwin, Pres.--First American Title Guaranty Agency of Sublette County, Pinedale, WY; *U.S. Public*, pg. 625
Adams, F.H., Chm. Bd.--Adams Products Company, Morrisville, NC; *Int'l*, pg. 242
Adams, G.D.J., Gen. Mgr.--Simago, S.A., Madrid, Spain; *Int'l*, pg. 704
Adams, Gerald, Pres.--Box USA Inc., Compton, CA; *U.S. Private*, pg. 421
Adams, J., Mng. Dir.--Ascom Timeplex GmbH, Frankfurt, Germany; *Int'l*, pg. 87
Adams, J.E., Pres.--Tapoco, Inc., Alcoa, TN; *U.S. Public*, pg. 61
Adams, Jimmy, Mng. Dir.--Barratt Newcastle, Newcastle upon Tyne, United Kingdom; *Int'l*, pg. 168
Adams, John, Mgr.--DWF of Omaha, Omaha, NE; *U.S. Private*, pg. 326
Adams, John W., Plant Mgr.-Alternators & Starters--Delco Remy Division, Sarreguemines, France; *U.S. Public*, pg. 725
Adams, K.L., Pres.--Phillips Communications, Inc., Bartlesville, OK; *U.S. Public*, pg. 1291
Adams, Ken, Chief Oper. Officer--Saab-Scania Financial Services Corp, Orange, CT; *Int'l*, pg. 687
Adams, Lawrence, Gen. Mgr.--Memphis Title Company, Memphis, TN; *U.S. Public*, pg. 626
Adams, Mark, Pres.--Adams Business Media, Arlington Heights, IL; *U.S. Private*, pg. 16
Adams, Michael A., Pres.--Commonwealth Communications, Princeton, NJ; *U.S. Public*, pg. 1354
Adams, Murray, Gen. Mgr.--Smorgon Cyclone Rural, Footscray, Australia; *Int'l*, pg. 1269
Adams, P.J., Chief Oper. Officer--Stelrad Components Ltd., Listowel, Ireland; *Int'l*, pg. 268
Adams, Paul, Gen. Mgr.--Circle International, Tullamarine, Australia; *U.S. Public*, pg. 373
Adams, Peter, Mng. Dir.--Costain Building Products Limited, Rickmansworth, United Kingdom; *Int'l*, pg. 336
Adams, Peter S., Pres. & Treas.--UNUM Sales Corp., Portland, ME; *U.S. Public*, pg. 1700
Adams, R.J., V.P.--J.M. Huber, Wood Products Div., Charlotte, NC; *U.S. Private*, pg. 545
Adams, R.L., Pres.--CNG Transmission Corporation, Clarksburg, WV; *U.S. Public*, pg. 435
Adams, Rick, Pres.--Parts Company of America, Northbrook, IL; *U.S. Public*, pg. 758
Adams, Rob, Pres.--United HealthCare of Oregon, Inc., Minnetonka, MN; *U.S. Public*, pg. 1678
Adams, Robert, Gen. Mgr.--Simrad Optronics Ltd., Crawley, United Kingdom; *Int'l*, pg. 770
Adams, Robert E., Pres. & Chief Exec. Officer--MidSouth Ice Co., Huntsville, AL; *U.S. Private*, pg. 1025
Adams, Robert L., Gen. Mgr.--Ford Transmission and Chassis Div., Dearborn, MI; *U.S. Public*, pg. 662
Adams, Rocky, Mgr.--Commercial Metals Co. Liberty Div., Dallas, TX; *U.S. Public*, pg. 413
Adams, Rodney K., Pres.--Beneficial Canada Inc., Thornhill, Canada; *U.S. Public*, pg. 211
Adams, Ronald D., Pres. & Chief Exec. Officer--Peoples Security Finance Company, Inc., Madisonville, KY; *U.S. Public*, pg. 280
Adams, Steve, Mng. Dir.--Outdoor Services, Dallas, TX; *U.S. Private*, pg. 1166
Adams, Steve, Gen. Mgr.--Stanfast, Inc., Pleasanton, CA; *U.S. Public*, pg. 1505
Adams, W Randolph, Chief Exec. Officer--Mississippi Valley Advisors Inc., Saint Louis, MO; *U.S. Public*, pg. 1087
Adams, W. Randolph, Chief Exec. Officer--Mercantile Investment Services, Inc., Saint Louis, MO; *U.S. Public*, pg. 1087
Adams, W. Randolph, Pres. & Chief Exec. Officer--Mercantile Trust Company N.A., Saint Louis, MO; *U.S. Public*, pg. 1088
Adams, William, Mng. Dir.--Formica Limited, North Shields, United Kingdom; *Int'l*, pg. 129
Adams, William A., Pres. & Chief Oper. Officer--Bliss Manufacturing Company, Youngstown, OH; *U.S. Public*, pg. 771
Adamson, Tom, Chief Exec. Officer--Commercial Construction Div., Bloomington, MN; *U.S. Public*, pg. 120
Adans, Steve, Gen. Mgr.--S.C. Johnson New Zealand Ltd., Auckland, New Zealand; *U.S. Private*, pg. 594
Adarraga, Luis, Mng. Dir.--Accesorios de Tuberia de Cobre S.A., Cordoba, Spain; *Int'l*, pg. 391
Adasiak, Robert J., V.P. & Gen. Mgr.--All American Homes of Tennessee, Inc., Springfield, TN; *U.S. Public*, pg. 388
Adcock, Bob, Mng. Dir.--Nationwide Trust Ltd., Saint Albans, United Kingdom; *Int'l*, pg. 912
Adcock, D.W., Gen. Mgr.--Crane Resistoflex/Defense, Jacksonville, FL; *U.S. Public*, pg. 457
Addington, Raymond J., Pres.--Kelly Douglas & Company Limited, Vancouver, Canada; *Int'l*, pg. 1495
Addler, Wallace E., V.P. & Gen. Mgr.--Boeing Computer Support Services, Inc., Bellevue, WA; *U.S. Public*, pg. 240
Addy, William W., Pres. & Chief Exec. Officer--Bank of Homewood, Homewood, IL; *U.S. Private*, pg. 474
Adegbite, L., Company Head--SKF Nigeria Limited, Ikeja, Nigeria; *Int'l*, pg. 1159
Adelekan, Dr., Mng. Dir.--Macmillan Nigeria Publishers Ltd., Yaba, Nigeria; *Int'l*, pg. 1480
Adelman, Vince, Gen. Mgr.--Solar Communications, Perryville, MO; *U.S. Private*, pg. 1012
Adelmann, Fred, Mng. Dir.--Esselte Meto GmbH, Hirschhorn, Germany; *Int'l*, pg. 461
Aden, Mohamed, Chm.--BCI Mer Rouge, Djibouti, Djibouti; *Int'l*, pg. 163
Ader, Jeff, Store Mgr.--Maxco Inc.-Painters Supply Division, Lansing, MI; *U.S. Public*, pg. 1061
Adessa, Phil, Plant Mgr.--Albany International Appleton Wire Div., Menasha, WI; *U.S. Public*, pg. 36
Adhikari, S., Mgr.--Tefal India Household Appliances Pvt. Ltd., New Delhi, India; *Int'l*, pg. 568
Adik, Steven P., Pres.--NIPSCO Capital Markets, Inc., Hammond, IN; *U.S. Public*, pg. 1185
Adiletta, Dr. Joseph G., Sr. V.P.--Pallflex, Inc., Putnam, CT; *U.S. Public*, pg. 1254
Adkins, Dale, V.P.--Eckerd Drug Co., Conroe, TX; *U.S. Public*, pg. 917
Adkins, Paul, Plant Mgr.--Interlake Material Handling, Lodi, CA; *U.S. Public*, pg. 893
Adkins, Ralph J., Chief Exec. Officer--Chesapeake Investment Co., Dover, DE; *U.S. Public*, pg. 347
Adkins, Ralph J., Chief Exec. Officer--Skipjack, Inc., Dover, DE; *U.S. Public*, pg. 347
Adkins, William E., Chief Oper. Officer & Exec. V.P.--Hickory Hill Furniture Corporation, Valdese, NC; *U.S. Private*, pg. 808
Adkins, William J., Pres.--Torrance Nissan, Inc., Torrance, CA; *U.S. Public*, pg. 1380
Adkinson, C. Wayne, Pres. & Chief Exec. Officer--Regions Investments, Inc., Birmingham, AL; *U.S. Public*, pg. 1371
Adler, Bill, Gen. Mgr.--Metz Baking Company (WI), La Crosse, WI; *U.S. Private*, pg. 1022
Adler, David B., Mng. Partner--Coscan Adler Limited Partnership, Columbia, MD; *Int'l*, pg. 228
Adler, Dr. E., Gen. Mgr.--Laboratorios Wyeth Inc., Bogota, Colombia; *U.S. Public*, pg. 81
Adler, Frederick R., Mng. Partner--Athena Venture Partners L.P., New York, NY; *Int'l*, pg. 644
Adler, Gideon, Chief Oper. Officer--Onyx Technologies Ltd., Fair Lawn, NJ; *Int'l*, pg. 1007
Adler, Marc, Branch Mgr.--Burns & Wilcox - Phoenix Office, Phoenix, AZ; *U.S. Private*, pg. 610
Adler, Norman, V.P.--Norman Levy Associates, Inc., Northbrook, IL; *U.S. Private*, pg. 664
Adler, Robert, Pres.--DeCorp, Carrollton, TX; *U.S. Public*, pg. 948
Adler, Robert, Pres. & Chief Exec. Officer--Vintage Blue, Arleta, CA; *U.S. Public*, pg. 948
Adler, Robert W., Pres. & Chief Exec. Officer--Halmode Apparel, Inc., New York, NY; *U.S. Public*, pg. 948
Adloms, Ralph J., Pres. & Chief Exec. Officer--Sharp Energy, Inc., Pocomoke City, MD; *U.S. Public*, pg. 347
Adlung, Klaus, Mng. Dir.--RHEINHYP Rheinische Hypothekenbank, Frankfurt/Main, Germany; *Int'l*, pg. 310
Admon, David, Mng. Dir.--Admon Advertising, Tel Aviv, Israel; *Int'l*, pg. 117
Admon, Eran, Mng. Dir.--Admon Advertising, Tel Aviv, Israel; *Int'l*, pg. 117
Adolff, Peter, Dr., Chief Exec. Officer--Allianz Versicherungs-AG, Stuttgart, Germany; *Int'l*, pg. 58
Adrean, Lee, Chief Exec. Officer--Capital Liberty, L.P., Louisville, KY; *Int'l*, pg. 26
Adrean, Lee, Pres. & Chief Exec. Officer--Peoples Security Insurance Company, Durham, NC; *Int'l*, pg. 27
Adrian, R., Gen. Mgr.--Central, East Central, West Central Divs., Niles, IL; *U.S. Private*, pg. 809
Adriance, Brenda, Pres. & Gen. Mgr.--KHKS-FM, Dallas, TX; *U.S. Public*, pg. 335
Adriano, R.A., Pres.--Borden Intl. Philippines, Inc., Manila, Philippines; *U.S. Private*, pg. 159
Adrick, J., Dir.-Prod.--Harris Allied Systems, Highland Heights, KY; *U.S. Public*, pg. 791

Adrion, Robert, Ph.D., Pres.--Becton Dickinson Infusion Therapy, Inc., Sandy, UT; *U.S. Public*, pg. 199

Adt., Henning, Dr., Sr. Mng. Dir.--Deutsche Bank-Kreditbank AG (Berlin), Berlin, Germany; *Int'l*, pg. 402

Aebi, Geri, Mng. Dir.--GGK Vienna, Vienna, Austria; *Int'l*, pg. 1336

Aebli, Robert J., Pres.--Heurikon Corporation, Madison, WI; *U.S. Public*, pg. 422

Aelick, Ron, Pres.--Inco Limited, Manitoba Division, Thompson, Canada; *Int'l*, pg. 672

Aelker, Erich, Gen. Mgr.--Landesverlags und Druckgesellschaft mbH - Mecklenburg & Co. KG, Schwerin, Germany; *Int'l*, pg. 233

Aerne, Bruno, Chief Exec.--Morning Star Cement Ltd., Ho Chi Minh City, Vietnam; *Int'l*, pg. 629

Aernouts, P.C.J., Gen. Mgr.--Eij Imtech N.V., Antwerp, Belgium; *Int'l*, pg. 682

Aert, R. Stey, Mgr.--Amersham Belgium NV/SA, Gent, Belgium; *Int'l*, pg. 992

Afander, Stefan, Mng. Dir.--Wrigley Poland, Sp. z.o.o., Poznan, Poland; *U.S. Public*, pg. 1781

Affeldt, Dawn, Branch Mgr.--TMP Worldwide/Recruitment Division, Troy, MI; *U.S. Private*, pg. 1065

Affleck, John A., Pres.--Stratton Growth Fund, Inc., Plymouth Meeting, PA; *U.S. Private*, pg. 1046

Affolter, Max, Mng. Dir.--Uto Albis AG, Zurich, Switzerland; *Int'l*, pg. 998

Affonso, Janice, Project Leader-Indus. Mkt.--SKF USA Inc., King of Prussia, PA; *Int'l*, pg. 1157

Agallano, Angel, Chief Oper. Officer--Banco Santander Argentina, Buenos Aires, Argentina; *Int'l*, pg. 143

Agarwal, D.D., Dir.--Howe (India) Private Ltd., New Delhi, India; *Int'l*, pg. 31

Agarwal, P.K., Gen. Mgr.--Eastern Region, Calcutta, India; *Int'l*, pg. 673

Agathos, Louis, Chm. Bd., Pres. & Chief Exec. Officer--Belshaw Brothers, Inc., Seattle, WA; *Int'l*, pg. 188

Agee, H. Mike, Pres.--South Charleston Sewage Treatment Co., South Charleston, WV; *U.S. Public*, pg. 1667

Agerbeek, B.P., Chief Oper. Officer--P.T. Rabo Finance Indonesia, Jakarta, Indonesia; *Int'l*, pg. 1082

Agerup, Kurt, Chief Oper. Officer--Husqvarna Svenska Forsaljnings AB, Huskvarna, Sweden; *Int'l*, pg. 439

Aggeback, Sigurd, Representative--Svenska Handelsbanken Marbella, Marbella, Spain; *Int'l*, pg. 1327

Aggrawall, Vijay, Gen. Mgr.--SmithKline Beecham Clinical Laboratories of Northern California, Dublin, CA; *Int'l*, pg. 1265

Aghion, Philippe, Pres.--Papeteries de Maudit S.A., Quimper, France; *U.S. Public*, pg. 959

Aghion, Philippe, Pres.--Papeteries de Malaucene S.A., Malaucene, France; *U.S. Public*, pg. 959

Agier, Bernard, Gen. Mgr.--CCF Randburg, Randburg, South Africa; *Int'l*, pg. 342

Agnello, Alexis, Chief Oper. Officer--Club Mediterranee K.K., Tokyo, Japan; *Int'l*, pg. 298

Agnevall, Jan, Mng. Dir.--Sodra Cell (UK) Ltd., Teddington, United Kingdom; *Int'l*, pg. 1276

Agnew, D.J., Gen. Mgr.--Ameron (Hong Kong) Ltd., Hong Kong, Hong Kong; *U.S. Public*, pg. 99

Agnew, Mike, Mng. Dir.--Quebecor Printing Semline Inc., Westwood, MA; *Int'l*, pg. 1077

Agnew, Rudolph, Chm.--Stena Line Limited, Ashford, United Kingdom; *Int'l*, pg. 1300

Agnihotri, Krish, V.P. & Gen. Mgr.--National Beryllia Div., Haskell, NJ; *Int'l*, pg. 1394

Agnvall, Hugo, Mng. Dir.--Telefonaktiebolaget LM Ericsson Bureaux Techniques d'Algerie, Hydra, Algeria; *Int'l*, pg. 1370

Agostini, A., Gen. Mgr.--Kodak S.p.A., Milan, Italy; *U.S. Public*, pg. 554

Agostini, B., Gen. Mgr.--Cariplo Bank International S.A., Luxembourg, Luxembourg; *Int'l*, pg. 275

Agrawal, Raj, Pres.--LICOM, Inc., Herndon, VA; *U.S. Public*, pg. 1702

Agsten, Carl F., Pres.--Carlton, Inc., Charleston, WV; *U.S. Private*, pg. 694

Agterberg, L.C., Mng. Dir.--Bristol-Myers B.V., Weesp, Netherlands; *U.S. Public*, pg. 255

Agudelo, J., Gen. Mgr.--A.C. Nielsen de Colombia, S.A., Bogota, Colombia; *U.S. Public*, pg. 1183

Aguiar, Geraldo de, Mng. Dir.--Alcan Finances B.V., Amsterdam, Netherlands; *Int'l*, pg. 51

Aguilar, Julia S., Gen. Mgr.--San Luis Obispo Telegram-Tribune, San Luis Obispo, CA; *U.S. Public*, pg. 964

Aguilar, Pedro, Pres. & Chief Exec. Officer-DMB&B/Spain--D'Arcy Masius Benton & Bowles, S.A., Madrid, Spain; *U.S. Private*, pg. 304

Aguinaga, Gerardo, Gen. Mgr.--Stanhome de Mexico, S.A. de C.V., Mexico, Mexico; *U.S. Public*, pg. 1508

Aguire, Hector, Mng. Dir.--Sensormatic S.A. de C.V., Mexico, Mexico; *U.S. Public*, pg. 1458

Aguirre-Rojas, Ventura, Chief Oper. Officer--Novo Nordisk A/S, Mexico, Mexico; *Int'l*, pg. 988

Aguirre-Rojas, Ventura Lind, Chief Oper. Officer--Novo Nordisk de Mexico S.A. de C.V., Mexico, Mexico; *Int'l*, pg. 989

Aguirre, A., Chief Exec. Officer--Zurich Insurance (Guam), Inc., Agana, GU; *Int'l*, pg. 1532

Aguirre, Carlos E., Chm. Bd., Pres. & Chief Exec. Officer--Oregon Metallurgical Corporation, Albany, OR; *U.S. Public*, pg. 43

Aguirre, G., Chief Exec. Officer--Compania de Seguros La Chilena Consolidada, Santiago, Chile; *Int'l*, pg. 1531

Agullo, Javier Garcia, Gen. Mgr.--DELTA - Desgasificacion y Limpieza de Tangues, S.A., Madrid, Spain; *Int'l*, pg. 1223

Agung, A.A. Gde., Gen. Mgr.--P.T. S.C. Johnson & Son (Indonesia) Ltd., Jakarta, Indonesia; *U.S. Private*, pg. 593

Aguren, Matts, Chief Oper. Officer--Zig-Zag Fabriks AB, Malmkoping, Sweden; *Int'l*, pg. 439

Ah Soo, Sim, Mgr.-Tubular Svcs.--Weatherford Inc., Hong Kong, Hong Kong; *U.S. Public*, pg. 1750

Aharonian, Steve, M.D., Chief Exec. Officer--Facey Medical Foundation, Mission Hills, CA; *U.S. Private*, pg. 1118

Ahearn, Lance W., Chm. Bd. & Chief Exec. Officer--RMT, Inc., Madison, WI; *U.S. Public*, pg. 1728

Ahearn, Lance W., Pres. & Chief Exec. Officer--ENSERV, Inc., Madison, WI; *U.S. Public*, pg. 1728

Ahearn, Lance W., Pres. & Chief Exec. Officer--Heartland Development Corporation, Madison, WI; *U.S. Public*, pg. 1728

Ahern, James, Pres.--Puritan Oil Company, Inc., Belmar, NJ; *U.S. Private*, pg. 1151

Ahern, James F., Pres.--Drake Petroleum Company, Inc., Providence, RI; *U.S. Private*, pg. 1151

Ahern, Joseph J., Pres. & Gen. Mgr.--WLS Television, Inc., Chicago, IL; *U.S. Public*, pg. 512

Ahern, Joseph M., Pres. & Chief Exec. Officer--Colorforms, Ramsey, NJ; *U.S. Public*, pg. 1625

Ahlback, Folke, Chief Rep.--Nokia Representative Office, Beijing, China; *Int'l*, pg. 953

Ahlback, Folke, Chief Rep.--Nokia Shanghai Representative Office, Shanghai, China; *Int'l*, pg. 953

Ahlberg, Per Axel, Chief Oper. Officer--Electrolux S.A., Lima, Peru; *Int'l*, pg. 443

Ahlberg, Tedd, Plant Mgr.--Rhone-Poulenc Basic Chemicals Co., Portland, OR; *Int'l*, pg. 1110

Ahlbin, Frank, V.P. & Sec.--Atlantic Guest, Inc., Meriden, CT; *U.S. Public*, pg. 1705

Ahlbrecht, Bill, Plant Mgr.--Donaldson Co., Inc., Chillicothe, MO; *U.S. Public*, pg. 517

Ahlgren, Peter, Mng. Dir.--Gambro China Ltd, Hong Kong; *Int'l*, pg. 667

Ahlgren, Peter, Mng. Dir.--Gambro Jr. China Ltd., Tianjin, China; *Int'l*, pg. 667

Ahlinder, Hans, Chief Oper. Officer--Saab Missiles AB, Linkoping, Sweden; *Int'l*, pg. 686

Ahlmann, Kaj, Chm., Pres. & Chief Exec. Officer--Employers Reinsurance Corp., Overland Park, KS; *U.S. Public*, pg. 711

Ahlstrand, William, Plant Mgr.--Advance Transformer Co., Chicago, IL; *Int'l*, pg. 1054

Ahlstrom, Morten, Chief Oper. Officer--Ahlstromforetagen Svenska AB, Stockholm, Sweden; *Int'l*, pg. 33

Ahm, B.H., Pres.--Hyundai Steel Industries Inc., Long Beach, CA; *Int'l*, pg. 642

Ahm, Jong-Won, Pres.--Ssangyong Corporation, Seoul, Korea; *Int'l*, pg. 1291

Ahmad, Edward, Mng. Dir.-European N.V.H.--Simpson International (UK) Ltd., Huddersfield, United Kingdom; *U.S. Public*, pg. 1475

Ahmad, Edward, Mng. Dir.-European N.V.H.--Simpson International (UK) Ltd., West Yorkshire, United Kingdom; *U.S. Public*, pg. 1475

Ahmad, Mohd Zuhri, Dir.--Tourism Malaysia - London Office, London, United Kingdom; *Int'l*, pg. 833

Ahman, Ulf, Pres.--ABB Motors AB, Vasteras, Sweden; *Int'l*, pg. 7

Ahmed, Farkad, Supvr.-Opers.--Weatherford Bin Hamodah, Abu Dhabi, United Arab Emirates; *U.S. Public*, pg. 1750

Ahmed, Iftikhar, Pres. & Chief Oper. Officer--The Singer Company, Hong Kong, Hong Kong; *Int'l*, pg. 1220

Ahmed, Raja Aman, Exec. Dir.--Perwira Habib Bank Malaysia Berhad, Kuala Lumpur, Malaysia; *Int'l*, pg. 585

Ahmed, Sadig, Chief-Resident Mission--The World Bank, Islamabad, Pakistan; *U.S. Private*, pg. 1189

Ahn, J., Opers. Mgr.--ITW Korea Incorporated, Seoul, Korea; *U.S. Public*, pg. 868

Ahn, Seung-Sool, Mng. Dir.--Dong Bang Communications, Seoul, Korea; *Int'l*, pg. 117

Ahonen, Markku, Chief Rep. Officer--Merita Bank Ltd., Frankfurt Representative Office, Frankfurt, Germany; *Int'l*, pg. 859

Ahopelto, Olli, Mng. Dir.--Schauman Iberica S.A., Las Rozas, Spain; *Int'l*, pg. 1429

Ahrela, Jouni, Mng. Dir.--Metsa-Serla Tissue Ltd., Cheam, United Kingdom; *Int'l*, pg. 864

Ahrendt, Dieter, Dr., Pres.--NEUMAG-Neumunstersche Maschinen-und Anlagenbau GmbH, Neumunster, Germany; *Int'l*, pg. 399

Ahrens, Ronald A., Pres.--Bristol-Myers Squibb Consumer Products Group, New York, NY; *U.S. Public*, pg. 254

Ahrens, Ronald A., Pres.--Merck Consumer Healthcare Group, Iselin, NJ; *U.S. Public*, pg. 1090

Ahrens, Stephen C., V.P. & Gen. Mgr.--Harris Semiconductor, Somerville, NJ; *U.S. Public*, pg. 792

Ahrens, Terry, Gen. Mgr.--Harte Hanks Shopper Dallas Fort Worth, Grand Prairie, TX; *U.S. Public*, pg. 794

Ahrens, William H., Pres.--Fleming Foods West, Portland, OR; *U.S. Public*, pg. 653

Ahs, Bjorn, Pres. & Chief Exec. Officer--Kvaerner Pulping Technologies AB, Goteborg, Sweden; *Int'l*, pg. 768

Ahs, Bjorn, Exec. V.P.--Kvaerner Pulping Technologies, Karlstad, Sweden; *Int'l*, pg. 772

Ahtiainen, Ari, Gen. Mgr.--Nordson Finland Oy, Helsinki, Finland; *U.S. Public*, pg. 1189

Ahtiainen, Samppa, Chief Oper. Officer--Ahlstrom Machinery Pump Industry, Karhula, Finland; *Int'l*, pg. 34

Ahuja, Sanjiv, Pres.--Bellcore, Morristown, NJ; *U.S. Private*, pg. 976

Ahumada, Oscar, Mgr.--EMPIRE Power Systems - Tucson, Tucson, AZ; *U.S. Private*, pg. 375

Ai, Sumio, Chief Rep.--Bank of Yokohama Beijing, Beijing, China; *Int'l*, pg. 159

Aiba, Noboru, Pres.--Yamaichi International (America) Inc., New York, NY; *Int'l*, pg. 1517

Aida, Joji, Pres.--Nippon Quaker Chemical, Ltd., Osaka, Japan; *U.S. Public*, pg. 1346

Aielli, Roberto, Mgr.--Sandvik Process Systems S.p.A., Milan, Italy; *Int'l*, pg. 1187

Aihara, Katsuhide, Chief Oper. Officer--Nesco Ltd., Tokyo, Japan; *Int'l*, pg. 443

Aiken, Robert V., Pres. & Chief Exec. Officer--PNC Bank, Hershey, PA; *U.S. Public*, pg. 1243

Aines, Jean-Claude, Site Mgr.--Target Technology France SARL, Couhe, France; *Int'l*, pg. 854

Ainscough, S.B., Pres.--Chemical Specialties, Inc., Charlotte, NC; *Int'l*, pg. 802

Ainsley, P. Steve, Publisher--Santa Barbara News-Press, Santa Barbara, CA; *U.S. Public*, pg. 1175

Ainsworth, James C., Chm. Bd., Pres. & Chief Exec. Officer--United Missouri Bank of Carthage, Carthage, MO; *U.S. Public*, pg. 1654

Ainsworth, Jim, Gen. Mgr.-U.K. North--Nordson U.K., Ltd., Stockport, United Kingdom; *U.S. Public*, pg. 1189

Ainsworth, Larry, District Mgr.--Houston District Office, Houston, TX; *U.S. Private*, pg. 150

Airey, Roy, Gen. Mgr.--Wilson Supply International (U.K.) Ltd., Seven Oaks, United Kingdom; *U.S. Private*, pg. 1181

Airington, H.L., Pres.--Brunswick Pulp & Paper Company, Brunswick, GA; *U.S. Public*, pg. 736

Airola, Dominique, Chief Oper. Officer--Societe Civile Immobiliere de Vergeze, Paris, France; *Int'l*, pg. 919

Aitken, James R., Chm. Bd.--Reynolds Aluminium France, Merxheim, France; *U.S. Public*, pg. 1387

Aitkens, Donald, Mgr.--Intra-Acoustics Company, Ltd., Montreal, Canada; *U.S. Public*, pg. 875

Aiu, Tim, Gen. Mgr.--Transchem Div., Corona, CA; *U.S. Public*, pg. 926

Aiu, Tim, Gen. Mgr.--Power Systems Group, Corona, CA; *U.S. Public*, pg. 927

Aixeira Vinhoza, Jose Alberto, Gen. Mgr.--Banco do Brasil S.A.-Cayman Islands, Georgetown, Cayman Islands; *Int'l*, pg. 141

Aizlewood, Ian Geoffrey, Chief Oper. Officer--Continental Microwave Ltd., Luton, United Kingdom; *Int'l*, pg. 1289

Ajello, James, Sr. V.P. & Branch Mgr.--Union Bank of Switzerland, Chicago, IL; *Int'l*, pg. 1440

Ajouri, B., Gen. Mgr.--Assurex, Sin El-Fil, Lebanon; *Int'l*, pg. 564

Akabane, Yoshitaka, Chief Oper. Officer--Brain Forum Co., Ltd., Tokyo, Japan; *Int'l*, pg. 1262

Akabayashi, H., Pres.--Nissan Ferro Organic Chemical Co. Ltd., Tokyo, Japan; *U.S. Public*, pg. 620

Akabayashi, H., Pres.--NFE Co., Ltd., Tokyo, Japan; *U.S. Public*, pg. 620

Akabori, Kazuo, Pres.--Dentsu Holdings B.V., Amsterdam, Netherlands; *Int'l*, pg. 393

Akahodani, S., Mng. Dir.--Sharp-Roxy Corporation (M) Sdn. Bhd., Sungai Petani, Malaysia; *Int'l*, pg. 1230

Akai, J., Gen. Mgr.--Bobst Japan Ltd., Tokyo, Japan; *Int'l*, pg. 199

Akamatsu, Akira, Chief Rep.--Dai-Ichi Kangyo Bank, Ltd.-Dalian, Dalian, China; *Int'l*, pg. 361

Akamatsu, Koyoshige, Gen. Mgr.--The Industrial Bank of Japan, Limited (Shanghai), Shanghai, China; *Int'l*, pg. 675

Akamatsu, Yasuo, Chief Rep.--Daiwa Bank-Mexico, Mexico, Mexico; *Int'l*, pg. 374

Akasaka, Kazuo, Pres.--Isuzu Motors America Inc., Plymouth, MI; *Int'l*, pg. 692

Akashi, Katsumi, Pres.--Cordis-Japan, Ltd., Tokyo, Japan; *U.S. Public*, pg. 928

Akatsuka, Tamotsu, Mng. Dir.--Cosmo (Switzerland) Ltd., Zurich, Switzerland; *Int'l*, pg. 335

Akbar, Masood, Dir.--Jardine Fleming Pakistan Limited, Lahore, Pakistan; *Int'l*, pg. 494

Akbulut, Dursun, Gen. Mgr.--BNP-AK Dresdner Finansal Kiralama A.S., Istanbul, Turkey; *Int'l*, pg. 421

Akcakoca, Engin, Mng. Dir.--Kocbank A.S., Istanbul, Turkey; *Int'l*, pg. 741

Akerman, Ivar, Mng. Dir.--ESAB Treasury AB, Goteborg, Sweden; *Int'l*, pg. 281

Akermark, Henrik, Mng. Dir.--Neste Oxo AB, Stenungsund, Sweden; *Int'l*, pg. 915

Akers-Jones, David, Sir, Chm.--National Mutual Asia Ltd., Wan Chai, Hong Kong; *Int'l*, pg. 909

Akers, Mike, V.P.--Steel Wheels, Ltd., Cookley, United Kingdom; *U.S. Public*, pg. 1619

Akesson, Bo, Pres.--Betongindustri AB, Stockholm, Sweden; *Int'l*, pg. 1199

Akhoury, Ravi, Chm. & Chief Exec. Officer--MacKay-Shields Financial Corp., New York, NY; *U.S. Private*, pg. 795

Akiba, Junjiro, Chief Oper. Officer--Chek Lap Kok Project Office, Tsim Tsa Tsui, Hong Kong; *Int'l*, pg. 942

Akiksa, Fumiyuki, Gen. Mgr.--The Bank of Tokyo-Mitsubishi, Ltd. (Dusseldorf Branch), Dusseldorf, Germany; *Int'l*, pg. 158

Akimoto, Hidekazu, Gen. Mgr.--The Sakura Bank - Barcelona Branch, Barcelona, Spain; *Int'l*, pg. 1179

Akimoto, Hidekazu, Gen. Mgr.--The Sakura Bank - Madrid Branch, Madrid, Spain; *Int'l*, pg. 1179

Akimoto, Minoru, Sr. V.P. & Mgr.--The Bank of Tokyo-Mitsubishi, Ltd. (Columbus Corporate Banking), Columbus, OH; *Int'l*, pg. 157

Akins, Bruce, Pres.--Catellus Residential Group, Irvine, CA; *U.S. Public*, pg. 315

Akins, Jerry, Gen. Mgr.-Coated Prods. Div.--Technical Products Division, Conover, NC; *U.S. Public*, pg. 1451

Akioka, Hiroshi, Pres.--Kintetsu World Express (Benelux) B.V., Schiphol, Netherlands; *Int'l*, pg. 735

Akisadu, Yasuo, Pres.--Kawasaki Motors (UK) Ltd., Buckingham, United Kingdom; *Int'l*, pg. 726

Akisato, T., Pres.--Sharp Electronics GmbH, Vienna, Austria; *Int'l*, pg. 1230

Akiyama, Satoru, Pres.--BioKyowa Inc., Cape Girardeau, MO; *Int'l*, pg. 778

Akiyama, Toshiyuki, Sr. Rep.--Nippon Credit Bank Ltd.-Sao Paulo, Sao Paulo, Brazil; *Int'l*, pg. 933

Akizawa, Sachio, Gen. Mgr.--OMRON Business Sistemas Eletronicos Da America Latina Ltda., Sao Paulo, Brazil; *Int'l*, pg. 1005

Akizuki, Teiken, Pres.--NS Finance, Inc., New York, NY; *Int'l*, pg. 940

Akkerman, Rey, Dir.-Mktg.--Capital Equipment Div., Raleigh, NC; *U.S. Public*, pg. 143

Akkoyunlu, Salim, Mng. Dir.--Noksel A.S., Ankara, Turkey; *Int'l*, pg. 954

Akoglu, Tuncay, Fin. Dir.--Markom/Leo Burnett A.S., Istanbul, Turkey; *U.S. Private*, pg. 186
Akrami, Ahmad, Pres.--NexStar Automation, Inc., Longmont, CO; *U.S. Public*, pg. 1795
Aks, Lars, Pres.--Nokia General Communications Ltd., Swindon, United Kingdom; *Int'l*, pg. 954
Aksaranuwat, Pin, Mgr.--Tomco Co. Ltd., Bangkok, Thailand; *U.S. Private*, pg. 361
Aksoy, Atilla, Chm.--Young & Rubicam Turkey, Istanbul, Turkey; *U.S. Private*, pg. 1200
Aksoy, Tuncer, Gen. Mgr.--Turk Philips Aydinlatma Sanayi Ve Ticaret A.S., Istanbul, Turkey; *Int'l*, pg. 1055
Akton, Richard A., Pres. & Chief Exec. Officer--Bell Atlantic TeleProducts Corp., Exton, PA; *U.S. Public*, pg. 203
Al Bader, Abdul Fattah S., Chief Oper. Officer--Kuwait Oil Tanker Company K.S.C., Kuwait; *Int'l*, pg. 765
Al Duwaisan, Khaled, Mng. Dir.--Kuwait Aviation Services Co., Safat, Kuwait; *Int'l*, pg. 764
Al Ibrahim, A., Chief Oper. Officer--Technip Saudi Arabia Ltd., Al-Khobar, Saudi Arabia; *Int'l*, pg. 1361
Al Soufi, Zakaria, Gen. Dir.--Marcam U.A.E., Abu Dhabi, United Arab Emirates; *U.S. Public*, pg. 1043
Al Sultan, Nader, Chief Oper. Officer--Kuwait Petroleum International (KPI), London, United Kingdom; *Int'l*, pg. 766
Al Zufairi, Naef, Chief Oper. Officer--Kuwait Shipbuilding & Repair Yard Company K.S.C., Safat, Kuwait; *Int'l*, pg. 765
Al-Gharabally, Abdul Malik Mohammad, Chief Oper. Officer--Kuwait Oil Company K.S.C., Ahmadi, Kuwait; *Int'l*, pg. 765
Al-Heureithi, Ramzi, Mng. Dir.--Weatherford/Espana, S.A., Madrid, Spain; *U.S. Public*, pg. 1750
Al-Jarbou, A.S., Chm.--Al-Jubail Petrochemical Company, Tareet, Saudi Arabia; *U.S. Public*, pg. 601
Al-Kaff, Omar, Gen. Mgr.--Fouad Travel & Cargo Agency, Dammam, Saudi Arabia; *Int'l*, pg. 502
Al-Magaleh, Abdul Kareem, New Bus. Contact--Vidcom DMB&B, Sania, Yemen; *U.S. Private*, pg. 305
Al-Muaid, Tgufig A., Dr., Chief Oper. Officer--Gulf Petrochemical Industries Co., Manama, Bahrain; *Int'l*, pg. 766
Al-Mutair, Ahmed Abdul Muhsin, Chief Oper. Officer--Kuwait National Petroleum Company K.S.C., Safat, Kuwait; *Int'l*, pg. 765
Al-Nouri, Abdul Baoi Abdullah, Chief Oper. Officer--Petrochemical Industries Company K.S.C., Safat, Kuwait; *Int'l*, pg. 765
Al-Slamy, Mohammed M., Chief Oper. Officer--Industrien Chimiques Maghrebines Company, Tunis, Tunisia; *Int'l*, pg. 766
Ala-Jaaski, Eero, Mng. Dir.--Enso-Eurocan Far East Co. Ltd., Osaka, Japan; *Int'l*, pg. 457
Ala-Pietila, Pekka, Pres.--Nokia Mobile Phones, Espoo, Finland; *Int'l*, pg. 951
Alabiso, Vincent, Exec. Photo Editor--Wide World Photos, Inc., New York, NY; *U.S. Private*, pg. 92
Alagh, S., Gen. Mgr.--Britannia Industries Ltd., Vimanapura, India; *Int'l*, pg. 380
Alaimo, Al A., Pres.--Banc One Financial Services, Inc., Marion, IN; *U.S. Public*, pg. 173
Alajarvi, Jorma, Pres.--Tampella Power Inc. Manufacturing Facility, Tampere, Finland; *Int'l*, pg. 1353
Alam, Masood, V.P. & Chief Mgr.--Habib Bank Ltd., Beirut, Lebanon; *Int'l*, pg. 584
Alamo, Tony, Pres.--Luxor Hotel, Las Vegas, NV; *U.S. Public*, pg. 375
Alarie, Pierre, Mng. Dir.--Grupo inmobiliario Caisse, Mexico, Mexico; *Int'l*, pg. 249
Alario, G., Branch Supervisor--Kodak S.p.A., Naples, Italy; *U.S. Public*, pg. 554
Alba, Jose Martin, Pres.--Bemis Craftil, S.A., Matehuala, Mexico; *U.S. Public*, pg. 210
Alba, Jose Martin, Pres.--Bemis Maral, S.A. de C.V., San Luis Potosi, Mexico; *U.S. Public*, pg. 210
Alba, Jose Martin, Pres.--MACtac Mexico, S.A., San Luis Potosi, Mexico; *U.S. Public*, pg. 210
Alba, K., Pres.--NI Steel Products Co., Ltd., Tokyo, Japan; *Int'l*, pg. 946
Albano, Jack, Plant Mgr.--Glass Plant, Millbury, OH; *U.S. Private*, pg. 486
Albans, Graham, Chief Oper. Officer--Electrolux Jordan Trading Company Ltd., Amman, Jordan; *Int'l*, pg. 443
Alber, Kim, V.P., Branch Mgr.--Phoenix Branch Office, Tempe, AZ; *U.S. Public*, pg. 1683
Alberghina, Thomas, Mgr.--Commerzbank AG-Milan Representative Office, Milan, Italy; *Int'l*, pg. 311
Alberini, G.C., Chm. Bd.--Monsanto Italiana S.p.A., Milan, Italy; *U.S. Public*, pg. 1125
Albero, Carl M., Pres.--American Systems Engineering Corporation, Virginia Beach, VA; *U.S. Private*, pg. 976
Albero, F., Mng. Dir.--Bondioli & Pavesi GmbH Deutschland, Gross-Gerau, Germany; *Int'l*, pg. 201
Albers, Blair, Reg. Mgr.--Nowsco Well Service Ltd., Calgary, Canada; *U.S. Public*, pg. 161
Albers, Dan, Gen. Mgr.--Santa Fe Shaft Drilling Co., Alhambra, CA; *Int'l*, pg. 765
Albers, Walter, Chief Oper. Officer--Thompson-Siegel GmbH, Dusseldorf, Germany; *Int'l*, pg. 610
Albert, Steven P., Chief Oper. Officer--Forest City Grand Terrace, Inc., Cleveland, OH; *U.S. Public*, pg. 668
Albert, Steven P., Chief Oper. Officer--F.C. Properties Co., Los Angeles, CA; *U.S. Public*, pg. 668
Albert, Steven P., Chief Oper. Officer--Forest City Southpark Two, Inc., Cleveland, OH; *U.S. Public*, pg. 669
Alberthal, Lester M., Jr., Chm. Bd. & Chief Exec. Officer--Electronic Data Systems Corporation, Plano, TX; *U.S. Public*, pg. 569
Alberti, Joseph A., Pres.--Elan Insurance Services, Inc., Milwaukee, WI; *U.S. Public*, pg. 643
Alberti, Joseph A., Pres.--Elan Life Insurance Company, Milwaukee, WI; *U.S. Public*, pg. 643
Albertini, William O., Pres. & Chief Exec. Officer--Bell Atlantic Enterprises Corporation, Philadelphia, PA; *U.S. Public*, pg. 202
Alberto, Pedinelli, Chief Oper. Officer--Candy Domestic Appliances Limited, Bromborough, United Kingdom; *Int'l*, pg. 260
Alberts, Karl-Armin, Dir.--Bayerische Kapitalanlagegesellschaft mbH, Munich, Germany; *Int'l*, pg. 179
Alberts, R. Michaels, V.P. & Gen. Mgr.--Hercules Inc., Resins Group, Wilmington, DE; *U.S. Public*, pg. 810
Albertson, Gary, Pres.--Sunds Defibrator Woodhandling, Inc., Birmingham, AL; *Int'l*, pg. 1428
Albertson, Gerry L., Pres.--FMP-Rauma Company, Birmingham, AL; *Int'l*, pg. 1428
Albini, A., Chief Exec. Officer--MCG Graficarbo Division, Milan, Italy; *Int'l*, pg. 891
Albino, John, Pres.--MacGREGOR (USA) Inc., Pine Brook, NJ; *Int'l*, pg. 670
Albino, John R., V.P. & Gen. Mgr.--Dorney Park & Wildwater Kingdom, Allentown, PA; *U.S. Public*, pg. 319
Albinsson, Sune, Mng. Dir.--Uddcomb Sweden AB, Karlskrona, Sweden; *Int'l*, pg. 1421
Alborelli, Rodolfo, Sr. V.P. & Country Mgr.--Bank of America NT&SA, Buenos Aires, Argentina; *U.S. Public*, pg. 182
Albornoz Bonet, Carlos Martinez de, Pres.--AESA Astilleros Espanoles, S.A., Madrid, Spain; *Int'l*, pg. 1223
Albornoz Bonet, Carlos Martinez de, Pres.--ASTANO - Astilleros y Talleres del Noroeste, S.A., Madrid, Spain; *Int'l*, pg. 1223
Albrecht, Bill, Gen. Mgr.--The Gazette Marketing, Cedar Rapids, IA; *U.S. Private*, pg. 442
Albrecht, G., Mng. Dir.--Nutricia Nahrungsmittel GmbH, Vienna, Austria; *Int'l*, pg. 992
Albrecht, Gert, Chief Oper. Officer--Babcock Sempell Armaturen-Service GmbH, Oberhausen, Germany; *Int'l*, pg. 400
Albrecht, Ivan, Pres.--Gilcrest Storage, Akron, OH; *U.S. Private*, pg. 32
Albrecht, Jay, Region Opers. Mgr.--BJ Coil Tech, Houston, TX; *U.S. Public*, pg. 161
Albrecht, K.D., Dir.-Central Region--Monsanto (Deutschland) GmbH, Dusseldorf, Germany; *U.S. Public*, pg. 1125
Albrecht, Karlheinz, Exec. Dir.--Deutsche Bank AG (Singapore), Singapore, Singapore; *Int'l*, pg. 404
Albrecht, Klaus-Dieter, Mng. Dir.--Knurr-Ercotec GmbH, Nettetal, Germany; *Int'l*, pg. 739
Albrecht, Klaus, Dr., Mng. Dir.--DB U.K. Finance p.l.c., London, United Kingdom; *Int'l*, pg. 404
Albrecht, Ronald, V.P.-Fin.--Smiths Industries Aerospace & Defense Systems Inc.-Washington D.C., Arlington, VA; *Int'l*, pg. 1268
Albrecht, William, Pres.--Barry Controls, Brighton, MA; *U.S. Public*, pg. 124
Albrecht, William, Gen. Mgr.--JMS Specialty Foods, Inc., Ripon, WI; *U.S. Public*, pg. 1480
Albrecht, William, Mng. Dir.--Henry Jones Foods Pty. Ltd., Kyabram, Australia; *U.S. Public*, pg. 1480
Albrecht, William J., Gen. Mgr.--APITECH, Butler, WI; *U.S. Public*, pg. 124
Albregts, Paul, Mng. Dir.--Foot Locker Europe B.V., Vianen, Netherlands; *U.S. Public*, pg. 1778
Albright, David, Chm. Bd.--Pepperidge Farm, Incorporated, Norwalk, CT; *U.S. Public*, pg. 299
Albright, T. Rosie, Pres.--Carter Products Div., Cranbury, NJ; *U.S. Public*, pg. 310
Albuquerque, A.L., Mng. Dir.--BCN-Barclays Banco de Investimento S.A., Sao Paulo, Brazil; *Int'l*, pg. 165
Alcantara, Orlando, Chief Oper. Officer--KONE Ascensores C.A., Caracas, Venezuela; *Int'l*, pg. 747
Alcock, John M., Chief Oper. Officer--BHF-BANK (Jersey) Ltd., Saint Helier, United Kingdom; *Int'l*, pg. 119
Alcordo, Jesus N., Pres. & Chief Oper. Officer--Reynolds Philippine Corporation, Manila, Philippines; *U.S. Public*, pg. 1387
Alcott, Charles, III, Pres.--Compass Bank of the South, N.A., Pensacola, FL; *U.S. Public*, pg. 419
Aldahondo, Pedro, Gen. Mgr.--Center Laboratories, Inc., Port Washington, NY; *U.S. Public*, pg. 813
Alday, Ray C., Mng. Dir.--IBP Ltd., Dunstable, United Kingdom; *Int'l*, pg. 391
Aldeheim, Ian, Chief Oper. Officer--Medical Data Intelligence AB, Lund, Sweden; *Int'l*, pg. 667
Alden, Blair, V.P.--Harza-Hidrobrasileira Engenharia e Projetos Ltda, Sao Paulo, Brazil; *U.S. Private*, pg. 509
Alden, I., Gen. Mgr.--Merck Sharp & Dohme (Sweden) AB, Sollentuna, Sweden; *U.S. Public*, pg. 1092
Alden, M., Mng. Dir.--Bristol Street Motors Limited, Birmingham, United Kingdom; *Int'l*, pg. 216
Alderson, Loren, Plant Mgr.--Hydraulics Div., Hutchinson, KS; *U.S. Public*, pg. 557
Aldington, John T., Chief Oper. Officer--A.F.N. Ltd., Reading, United Kingdom; *Int'l*, pg. 1063
Aldred, P.J., Pres. & Chief Exec. Officer--Enerflex Systems Ltd., Calgary, Canada; *Int'l*, pg. 1400
Aldrete, Enrique Martinez, Country Mgr. & Gen. Mgr.-Consumer Opers.--Productos de Maiz S.A., Mexico, Mexico; *U.S. Public*, pg. 447
Aldrich, Charles R., Treas. & Sec.--LGS Concord Corp., Harvey, LA; *U.S. Public*, pg. 380
Aldrich, David, Pres.--SAIC, Germantown, MD; *U.S. Private*, pg. 976
Aldrich, Larry, Pres.--Tucson Newspapers, Inc., Tucson, AZ; *U.S. Public*, pg. 701
Aldrich, Winthrop W., Pres.--Georgetown Jet Center, Inc., Georgetown, TX; *U.S. Public*, pg. 187
Aldrick, P., Mgr.--Kodak Limited, Nottingham, United Kingdom; *U.S. Public*, pg. 553
Aldridge, J. Mac, Div. Mgr.--Stationers, Inc., Huntington, WV; *U.S. Public*, pg. 333
Aldridge, Ron, V.P. & Publisher--Electronic Media, Chicago, IL; *U.S. Private*, pg. 285
Aldunate, Pedr Pablo, Gen. Mgr.--Circle Freight International Agencia Chilena, Santiago, Chile; *U.S. Public*, pg. 372
Aldunate, Pedro Pablo, Gen. Mgr.--Max Gruenhut Chile, Santiago, Chile; *U.S. Public*, pg. 373
Aleff, Gary A., Mgr.-Branch--Piper Jaffray Inc., Two Harbors, MN; *U.S. Public*, pg. 1301
Aleixo, Fernando J., Mng. Dir.--D & B Zimbabwe (Pvt) Ltd., Harare, Zimbabwe; *U.S. Public*, pg. 536
Alejandro, Gerardo F., Chief Exec. Officer--Avia EURO RSCG, Manila, Philippines; *Int'l*, pg. 602
Alejos, Joe, Gen. Mgr.--Sterling Electronics, Lenexa, KS; *U.S. Public*, pg. 1052
Alem, Fernando P., Pres.--Compar, New York, NY; *Int'l*, pg. 1073
Aleman, Ralph, Chief Exec. Officer--Cedars Medical Center Victoria Pavillion, Miami, FL; *U.S. Public*, pg. 404
Alemo, M.J.G., Dir.--Cirex BV, Almelo, Netherlands; *Int'l*, pg. 753
Alepian, Taro, Pres.--SNC - Aker Offshore Inc. (AE), Montreal, Canada; *Int'l*, pg. 42
Aleshire, Arthur A., Pres.--Plain Street Properties, Inc., Scarborough, ME; *U.S. Public*, pg. 782
Alesi, Pierre, Pres.--Corse Composites Aeronautiques, Ajaccio, France; *Int'l*, pg. 1166
Alessandrello, Rosario, Pres.--Tecnimont Spa, Milan, Italy; *Int'l*, pg. 324
Alessandria, Roberto, Mgr.--Sanpaolo-Singapore Branch, Singapore, Singapore; *Int'l*, pg. 692
Alessi, Alessandro, Chm. Bd.--La Centrale Fondi S.p.A., Milan, Italy; *Int'l*, pg. 138
Alexander, Bruce, Gen. Mgr.--Westpac - Western Australia, Perth, Australia; *Int'l*, pg. 1496
Alexander, Charles, Dr., Mng. Dir.--Sasol Minchem, Johannesburg, South Africa; *Int'l*, pg. 1196
Alexander, D., Gen. Mgr.--Texaco Overseas Tankship Ltd., London, United Kingdom; *U.S. Public*, pg. 1584
Alexander, Donna, Admin.--Meadowview Care Center, Seville, OH; *U.S. Public*, pg. 838
Alexander, Gordon, Mgr.-Opers.--Gillette (Australia) Pty., Limited, Scoresby, Australia; *U.S. Public*, pg. 744
Alexander, Herbert, Pres.--UPB of Jackson, Jackson, TN; *U.S. Public*, pg. 1669
Alexander, J., Editor-in-Chief--The Sydney Morning Herald, Sydney, Australia; *Int'l*, pg. 477
Alexander, J.D., Publisher & Editor--Seattle Post-Intelligencer, Seattle, WA; *U.S. Private*, pg. 517
Alexander, James, V.P. & Gen Mgr.--Recordati Corporation, Allendale, NJ; *Int'l*, pg. 1090
Alexander, John, Chief Fin. Officer--Berendsen Fluid Power Pty. Ltd., Villawood, Australia; *Int'l*, pg. 1285
Alexander, John G., Pres.--Bank One, Ohio Trust Company, N.A., Columbus, OH; *U.S. Public*, pg. 173
Alexander, Mary, Gen. Mgr.--Fremont County Title Company, Lander, WY; *U.S. Public*, pg. 626
Alexander, Michael, Mng. Dir.--British Gas Trading Ltd., Staines, United Kingdom; *Int'l*, pg. 279
Alexander, Michael B., Chief Oper. Officer--L & L/Jiroch Distributing Co., Wyoming, MI; *U.S. Private*, pg. 1021
Alexander, Nick, Chief Oper. Officer--Pearson New Entertainment Europe, London, United Kingdom; *Int'l*, pg. 1026
Alexander, Robert, Mng. Dir.--Eberhard Hardware Manufacturing Ltd., Tillsonburg, Canada; *U.S. Public*, pg. 548
Alexandnesson, Leif, Pres.--Geotronics of North America, Inc., Itasca, IL; *Int'l*, pg. 1289
Alfano, Joseph, Mgr.-Branch--Piper Jaffray Inc., Hoboken, NJ; *U.S. Public*, pg. 1301
Alfaro, Rodrigo, Fin. Dir.--Leo Burnett-Costa Rica, Barrio Francisco Peralta, Costa Rica; *U.S. Private*, pg. 185
Alfheim, Roar L., Grp. Exec. V.P.--Jotun Polymer A/S, Sandefjord, Norway; *Int'l*, pg. 714
Alfi, Moataz Al, Chm. & Chief Exec. Officer--Cairo Foods Industries SAE, Cairo, Egypt; *U.S. Public*, pg. 806
Alford, Bill, Pres.--Covington Specialty Print, Covington, GA; *U.S. Public*, pg. 786
Alford, Brad, Pres.--Food Services Division, Glendale, CA; *Int'l*, pg. 917
Alford, Doug, Pres.--First Commerce Mortgage Company, Lincoln, NE; *U.S. Public*, pg. 629
Alford, LaVerne, Admin.--Columbia Training Center, Columbia, SC; *U.S. Public*, pg. 450
Alfredsen, Hermod, Pres.--Kvaerner Kleven a.s., Ulsteinvik, Norway; *Int'l*, pg. 769
Alfson, Donald, Pres.--Dale Electronics, Inc., Columbus, NE; *U.S. Public*, pg. 1722
Alfson, Donald, Pres.--Dale Electronics, Columbus Div., Columbus, NE; *U.S. Public*, pg. 1722
Alfstrom, Rainer, Chief Oper. Officer--AB Volta, Stockholm, Sweden; *Int'l*, pg. 439
Alfter, Willi, Pres.--Volksfursorge Krankenversicherung AG, Hamburg, Germany; *Int'l*, pg. 16
Alger, R. Kennedy, Pres.--LaSalle Bank Madison, Calumet City, IL; *Int'l*, pg. 10
Algie, Robert, V.P.--Trans-Lux Pty. Ltd., Newcastle, Australia; *U.S. Public*, pg. 1629
Algotsson, Alf, Pres.--NCC Civil Engineering, Solna, Sweden; *Int'l*, pg. 899
Ali, M. Ghazanfar, V.P. & Mgr.--Habib Bank Ltd., Brussels, Belgium; *Int'l*, pg. 584
Ali, Malik, Mgr.--America, Mc Lean, VA; *U.S. Public*, pg. 130
Ali, Rashid, Mng. Dir.--CPC Rufhan Limited, Faisalabad, Pakistan; *U.S. Public*, pg. 225
Ali, Reza, Mng. Dir.--Bitopi Advertising Ltd., Dhaka, Bangladesh; *U.S. Private*, pg. 184
Ali, Sadiq, Fin. Controller--Manhattan Pakistan (Private) Limited, Karachi, Pakistan; *U.S. Private*, pg. 186
Ali, Syed Zahid, Mgr.--National Bank of Pakistan, New York, NY; *Int'l*, pg. 908
Alibau, Maite, Sls. & Mktg. Mgr.--Whitehall Spain, Barcelona, Spain; *U.S. Public*, pg. 82
Alicea, Margarita, Mgr.-Opers.--First Leasing & Rental Corporation, Toa Baja, PR; *U.S. Public*, pg. 644

Alich, John A., Jr., Pres.--Baker Hughes Mining Tools, Inc., Grand Prairie, TX; *U.S. Public*, pg. 166
Aliphas, Avi, Gen. Mgr.--Caristrap de Mexico S.A. de C.V., Mexico, Mexico; *Int'l*, pg. 272
Aliprando, Paul, Gen. Mgr.--Krafcor Unlimited, Baltimore, MD; *U.S. Private*, pg. 1022
Alisop, R., Mgr.--ING Barings India Private Equity, Mumbai, India; *Int'l*, pg. 650
Alkins, V., Pres.--Lips Propellers, Inc., Chesapeake, VA; *Int'l*, pg. 812
Allan, Adam, Mng. Dir.--DYWIDAG Systems International, USA, Inc., Concord, Canada; *Int'l*, pg. 424
Allan, Dave, Mng. Dir.--ESAB Group Canada, Inc., Mississauga, Canada; *Int'l*, pg. 282
Allan, Gregor, Chief Exec. Officer--Robert Fleming Management (Jersey) Limited, Saint Helier, United Kingdom; *Int'l*, pg. 493
Allan, Gregor, Gen. Mgr.--Flemings (Jersey) Limited, Saint Helier, United Kingdom; *Int'l*, pg. 493
Allan, W., Mng. Dir.--Barclays Bank Finance Co. (Guernsey) Ltd., Saint Peter Port, United Kingdom; *Int'l*, pg. 165
Allansson, Lennart, Mng. Dir.--Korn/Ferry International, Goteborg, Sweden; *U.S. Private*, pg. 634
Allard, Ron, Gen. Mgr.--Alro Group, Flint, Flint, MI; *U.S. Private*, pg. 46
Allatt, Dennis, Sr. V.P.--Willis Corroon Melling Ltd., Vancouver, Canada; *Int'l*, pg. 1509
Allbritton, Joe L., Chm. Bd. & Chief Exec. Officer--Allbritton Communications Company, Washington, DC; *U.S. Private*, pg. 854
Allbritton, Joe L., Chm. Bd.--Allbritton Group, Inc., Washington, DC; *U.S. Private*, pg. 854
Allbritton, Joe L., Chm. Bd.--Allfinco, Inc., Wilmington, DE; *U.S. Private*, pg. 854
Allbritton, Robert L., Pres.--KTUL, LLC, Tulsa, OK; *U.S. Private*, pg. 854
Allbritton, Robert L., Pres.--Allbritton Group, Inc., Washington, DC; *U.S. Private*, pg. 854
Allbritton, Robert L., Pres.--Harrisburg Television, Inc, Harrisburg, PA; *U.S. Private*, pg. 854
Allcock, Charles, Pres.--World Trade Center Northwest Corporation, Portland, OR; *U.S. Public*, pg. 585
Allcock, Harry, V.P.--IFI/Plenum Data Corporation, Wilmington, NC; *U.S. Public*, pg. 1311
Alleger, Robert B., V.P.--Martin Marietta Range Services, Colorado Springs, CO; *U.S. Public*, pg. 1007
Allegra, Robert T., Pres.--Sarasota/Manatee Regional Div., Sarasota, FL; *U.S. Public*, pg. 1683
Allegretti, Cosimo, Mng. Dir.--Gestetner Italia SpA, Milan, Italy; *Int'l*, pg. 1115
Allegretti, Cosimo, Mng. Dir.--NRG Italia S.p.A., Milan, Italy; *Int'l*, pg. 1116
Allegretti, Victor, Pres.--Bayside Fuel Oil Corp., Brooklyn, NY; *U.S. Private*, pg. 125
Allegretti, Victor, Pres.--Rose Fuel Corporation, Brooklyn, NY; *U.S. Private*, pg. 125
Allegue, J., Mng. Dir.--Saduc, Riyadh, Saudi Arabia; *Int'l*, pg. 823
Allein, Gilles, Mng. Dir.--Credit Lyonnais Japan, Tokyo, Japan; *Int'l*, pg. 344
Alleman, Jay, Pres.--Universal Fleet, San Jose, CA; *U.S. Private*, pg. 939
Allemand, Jacques, Chm. Bd. & Chief Exec. Officer--GTM Construction, Nanterre, France; *Int'l*, pg. 823
Allen, Anthony C., Pres.--Scotia Realty Bahamas Limited, Nassau, Bahamas; *Int'l*, pg. 156
Allen, Arly, Pres.--Sheridan Electronic Systems, Baltimore, MD; *U.S. Private*, pg. 993
Allen, Barry D., Pres.--AmSouth Bank of Walker County, Jasper, AL; *U.S. Public*, pg. 105
Allen, Bart, Mgr.--Stewart Smith East, Inc., Philadelphia, PA; *Int'l*, pg. 1508
Allen, Ben, Mgr.--State Electric Supply Company, Chillicothe, OH; *U.S. Private*, pg. 1036
Allen, Bill, Gen. Mgr.--Oletex, Inc., South Holland, IL; *U.S. Private*, pg. 56
Allen, Bill, Pres.--Triad Systems Financial Corp., Livermore, CA; *U.S. Private*, pg. 193
Allen, Bob, Gen. Mgr.--KCRG Radio & TV Stations, Cedar Rapids, IA; *U.S. Private*, pg. 442
Allen, Bob D., Chm. Bd.--Indigo Group Inc., Daytona Beach, FL; *U.S. Public*, pg. 437
Allen, Bruce, Gen. Mgr.--Owens-Corning Canada, North York, Canada; *U.S. Public*, pg. 1237
Allen, C.H., Gen. Mgr.--Indiana Harbor Belt Railroad Co., Hammond, IN; *U.S. Public*, pg. 432
Allen, C.J., V.P.--The Bank of Nova Scotia, Chicago, IL; *Int'l*, pg. 156
Allen, D., Chief Oper. Officer--Dreamland Appliances Limited, Oldham, United Kingdom; *Int'l*, pg. 925
Allen, David, Mng. Dir.--Bankgesellschaft Berlin (Ireland) plc, Dublin, Ireland; *Int'l*, pg. 160
Allen, David, Mng. Dir.--BGB Finance (Ireland) plc, IRL-I.F.S.C., Ireland; *Int'l*, pg. 160
Allen, David, Chief Exec.--Sampson Tyrrell Enterprise, London, United Kingdom; *Int'l*, pg. 1482
Allen, Davis, Chief Exec. Officer--Zapata Haynie Corp., Hammond, LA; *U.S. Public*, pg. 1789
Allen, Dean, Mng. Dir.--Parsons Group International Limited, Brentford, United Kingdom; *U.S. Private*, pg. 842
Allen, Frank, Pres.--National-Arnold Magnetics Company, Adelanto, CA; *U.S. Public*, pg. 1420
Allen, Franklin P., III, Dir.--Fixed Income Div., Memphis, TN; *U.S. Public*, pg. 1131
Allen, Gail E., Pres.--Sysco Food Services-Albany, Albany, NY; *U.S. Public*, pg. 1551
Allen, Gary, Administrator--Greenery Neurological Rehabilitation, Slidell, LA; *U.S. Public*, pg. 837
Allen, Gary, Pres.--International Petroleum Corporation, Plant City, FL; *U.S. Public*, pg. 906
Allen, Geoff, Gen. Mgr.--ANI Mineral Processing, Karrabin, Australia; *Int'l*, pg. 100
Allen, George, Chief Oper. Officer--Stride Rite Footwear, Inc., Hamilton, MO; *U.S. Public*, pg. 1525
Allen, Gerald, Pres.--Avatar Utilities, Inc., Coral Gables, FL; *U.S. Public*, pg. 151
Allen, Gerald, Pres.--Consolidated Water Co., Miami, FL; *U.S. Public*, pg. 151
Allen, Gerald, Pres.--Florida Cities Water Co., Sarasota, FL; *U.S. Public*, pg. 151
Allen, J. Lamar, Pres. & Chief Oper. Officer--Kaman Sciences Corp., Colorado Springs, CO; *U.S. Public*, pg. 942
Allen, J.M., Chm. Bd.--Laing Management Ltd., London, United Kingdom; *Int'l*, pg. 796
Allen, James, Pres. & Chief Oper. Officer--European Bakers, LTD, Tucker, GA; *U.S. Public*, pg. 657
Allen, James, Pres.--LPS Laboratories Inc., Tucker, GA; *Int'l*, pg. 892
Allen, Jerry, Pres.--Ferguson Lyon Conklin & Company Inc., Baltimore, MD; *Int'l*, pg. 1512
Allen, Jim, Plant Mgr.--Plastic Suppliers, Inc, Columbus, OH; *U.S. Private*, pg. 871
Allen, Jim, Gen. Mgr.--Mid-America Auto Auction, Louisville, KY; *U.S. Public*, pg. 1649
Allen, John E., Pres.--LincAm Properties, Inc., Chicago, IL; *U.S. Public*, pg. 997
Allen, John M., District Mgr.-Life & Health Sls.--Willis Corroon Corporation of Owensboro, Owensboro, KY; *Int'l*, pg. 1505
Allen, Kenneth, Pres.--Atlantic Homes Corp., Hampton, VA; *U.S. Private*, pg. 473
Allen, Kerry B., Mng. Dir.--DYWIDAG Systems International, USA, Inc., Grand Prairie, TX; *Int'l*, pg. 424
Allen, Marty, Gen. Mgr. & V.P.--California Closet Company, Inc., San Francisco, CA; *U.S. Public*, pg. 1770
Allen, Patricia, Pres. & Chief Oper. Officer--Monticello Bank, Jacksonville, FL; *U.S. Private*, pg. 759
Allen, R. Lee, Dir.--Optus Communications, Sydney, Australia; *U.S. Public*, pg. 209
Allen, Ralph, Gen. Mgr.--Union Bank of California, San Diego, CA; *Int'l*, pg. 157
Allen, Randy, Pres.--Lilli Ann Corporation, San Francisco, CA; *U.S. Private*, pg. 582
Allen, Rex, Pres.--Allen Communication, Salt Lake City, UT; *U.S. Public*, pg. 1616
Allen, Ricky, Mgr.--Truck Center South, Jackson, MS; *U.S. Private*, pg. 1101
Allen, Robert F., Pres.--Campbell Industries, Inc., San Diego, CA; *U.S. Private*, pg. 703
Allen, Roy, Mgr.-Sls.--Nichifu America, Inc., Pottstown, PA; *Int'l*, pg. 927
Allen, Thomas W., Chm. Bd. & Chief Exec. Officer--First Midwest Trust Company, N.A., Joliet, IL; *U.S. Public*, pg. 636
Allen, Todd, Pres.--The Harry Alter Company, Lansing, IL; *U.S. Private*, pg. 1075
Allen, Tom, Station Mgr.--WRAL-TV, Raleigh, NC; *U.S. Private*, pg. 206
Allen, W.W., Chm. Bd.--Phillips Gas Company, Bartlesville, OK; *U.S. Public*, pg. 1291
Allen, Wayne S., Fac. Mgr.--AlliedSignal Turbocharging & Truck Brake Systems Aftermarket Distribution Center, Louisville, KY; *U.S. Public*, pg. 51
Allen, William A., Pres.--Wells Mfg. Corp., Fond Du Lac, WI; *U.S. Private*, pg. 1113
Allen, William A., Chief Oper. Officer--Wells Manufacturera de Mexico S.A. de C.V., Reynosa, Mexico; *U.S. Private*, pg. 1113
Allen, William H., Pres.--Whitehall-Robins Laboratories Ltd., Mississauga, Canada; *U.S. Public*, pg. 82
Allender, Richard C., Pres. & Chief Exec. Officer--Farah Sales Corp., El Paso, TX; *U.S. Public*, pg. 613
Allender, Richard C., Pres. & Chief Exec. Officer--Farah Clothing, Inc., El Paso, TX; *U.S. Public*, pg. 613
Allender, Richard C., Pres. & Chief Exec. Officer--Farah Manufacturing Services, Inc., El Paso, TX; *U.S. Public*, pg. 613
Allenspach, Mike, Mgr.-Office--Woodward-Clyde, Houston, TX; *U.S. Public*, pg. 1656
Allenspach, W., Chief Exec. Officer--Zurich International de Venezuela C.A. de Corretaje de Reaseguros, Caracas, Venezuela; *Int'l*, pg. 1532
Aller, Thomas L., V.P.--IES Investments Inc., Cedar Rapids, IA; *U.S. Public*, pg. 855
Allerbring, Benny, Pres.--Kalmar Inc., Newark, NJ; *Int'l*, pg. 1421
Allerd, Greg, Pres.--Smith Hardware Company, Goldsboro, NC; *U.S. Private*, pg. 335
Allers, Tyark, Chm. Bd.--Krupp Polysius AG, Beckum, Germany; *Int'l*, pg. 512
Alles, J.A., Pres.--ICI Films, Wilmington, DE; *Int'l*, pg. 664
Allesandri, Daniela, Dir.--Europe Language Center SrL, Rome, Italy; *U.S. Public*, pg. 222
Allessandra, Jack, V.P. & Gen. Mgr.--Interplastic Molding Products Div., South Bend, IN; *U.S. Private*, pg. 572
Alley, Michael J., Pres.--Fifth Third Bank of Central Indiana, Greensburg, IN; *U.S. Public*, pg. 621
Allick, Christopher W., Exec. V.P. & Dir.-Fin.--Jefferies & Company, Inc., Los Angeles, CA; *U.S. Public*, pg. 925
Alliman, Mike, Chief Oper. Officer--River Ranch - Orlando, Orlando, FL; *Int'l*, pg. 491
Allinen, Risto, Mng. Dir.--Malvaux S.A., Loulay, France; *Int'l*, pg. 1429
Allingham, Richard, Mng. Dir.--Ericsson Components Europe GmbH, Engen, Germany; *Int'l*, pg. 1366
Allington, Robert W., Gen. Mgr.--Isco Separation Instruments Division, Lincoln, NE; *U.S. Public*, pg. 914
Allington, Robert W., Chief Oper. Officer--Isco Instruments (Europe) AG, Herrliberg, Switzerland; *U.S. Public*, pg. 914
Allione, Miro, Chief Exec. Officer--Stream, Rome, Italy; *Int'l*, pg. 1363
Allis, John E., Asst V.P.--IBP-Louisa County, Columbus Junction, IA; *U.S. Public*, pg. 852
Allison Bob, Reg. V.P.--Arrow/Schweber Electronics, Chatsworth, CA; *U.S. Public*, pg. 134
Allison, Steve, Pres.--Mercantile Bank of Cedar Rapids, Cedar Rapids, IA; *U.S. Public*, pg. 1088
Allison, William V., Pres.--Florida Gas Transmission Co., Houston, TX; *U.S. Public*, pg. 585
Allitt, M., Mng. Dir.--Babcock Materials Handling Ltd., Reading, United Kingdom; *Int'l*, pg. 131
Allmendinger, Rolf, Chief Oper. Officer--Boehme Fettchemie GmbH, Hamburg, Germany; *Int'l*, pg. 609
Allnatt, C., Branch Mgr.--Senior Wellington Limited, Wellington, New Zealand; *Int'l*, pg. 1223
Allocca, Michael A., Pres.--Ascom Hasler Mailing Systems, Inc., Shelton, CT; *Int'l*, pg. 86
Allred, C. Stephen, Pres.--Environmental/Government Group, Boise, ID; *U.S. Public*, pg. 1134
Allred, Donald E., Pres.--Premier Investment Advisors, L.C., New Orleans, LA; *U.S. Public*, pg. 173
Allred, Rick, Plant Mgr.--Butterball Turkey Company, Huntsville, AR; *U.S. Public*, pg. 426
Allsop, Graham, Mng. Dir.--Esselte Meto Pty. Ltd., Wantirna, Australia; *Int'l*, pg. 461
Allsop, M.V.F., Chm. Bd.--NatWest Corporate Investments Limited, London, United Kingdom; *Int'l*, pg. 910
Allsopp, R.W., Mng. Dir.--GKN Technology Ltd., Wolverhampton, United Kingdom; *Int'l*, pg. 535
Allstaff, Kenneth R., Mng. Dir.--TRAK Microwave Co. Ltd., Dundee, United Kingdom; *U.S. Public*, pg. 1563
Allwin, James M., Pres.--Morgan Stanley Realty, Inc., New York, NY; *U.S. Public*, pg. 1132
Alm, Jarmo, Mgr.--Kotka Mills, Kotka, Finland; *Int'l*, pg. 457
Alm, Lars, Chief Oper. Officer--Geotronics Scandinavia AB, Danderyd, Sweden; *Int'l*, pg. 1289
Alm, Ted, Chief Oper. Officer--Flo-Pac Pacific, Fontana, CA; *U.S. Private*, pg. 414
Alm, Thomas, Mgr.-Sweden--SCEM Reinsurance S.A., Luxembourg, Luxembourg; *Int'l*, pg. 1261
Almada, E.L. Sutcliffe, Pres.-Dir. Gen.--Parker Seal de Mexico SA, Tlalnepantla, Mexico; *U.S. Public*, pg. 1262
Almashy, Don, Mgr.-Opers.--Titan Wheel Corporation of Virginia, Saltville, VA; *U.S. Public*, pg. 1619
Almeida, Julien, Vice Chm.--Chaitra Leo Burnett Private Ltd., Mumbai, India; *U.S. Private*, pg. 184
Almeida, R. Ponce, Representative--Morgan Grenfell (Ecuador), Quito, Ecuador; *Int'l*, pg. 405
Almeida, Richard J., Chm. Bd., Pres. & Chief Exec. Officer--Heller International Corporation, Chicago, IL; *Int'l*, pg. 519
Almeida, Richard J., Chm. & Chief Exec. Officer--Heller International Group, Inc., Chicago, IL; *Int'l*, pg. 519
Almenara, Manuel, Mng. Dir.--Willis Faber North America, Inc.-Florida, Miami, FL; *Int'l*, pg. 1503
Almenteros, Pedro, Gen. Mgr.--Sein Mendez Laboratories, Inc., Rio Piedras, PR; *U.S. Public*, pg. 670
Almerfors, Arne, Pres.--Agema Infrared Systems AB, Danderyd, Sweden; *Int'l*, pg. 1289
Almerfors, Arne, Chief Oper. Officer--C E Johansson AB, Eskilstuna, Sweden; *Int'l*, pg. 1289
Almgren, Sven, Mng. Dir.--Vera Klippan AB, Klippan, Sweden; *Int'l*, pg. 715
Almond, John, Gen. Mgr.--Allen & Hoshall, Jackson, MS; *U.S. Private*, pg. 36
Almquist, Anders, Chief Oper. Officer--Electrolux Gjuteriprodukter AB, Hallefors, Sweden; *Int'l*, pg. 438
Almquist, Hans, Mng. Dir.--Interspiro Inc., Branford, CT; *Int'l*, pg. 1289
Aloe, Joao, Territory Mgr.--Grace Especialidades Quimicos e Plasticas, Sao Paulo, Brazil; *U.S. Public*, pg. 755
Alonso, A.E., Dir.--Hormel Deli Division, Austin, MN; *U.S. Public*, pg. 840
Alonso, Adolfo Castanon, Pres.--Minas de Figaredo, S.A., Oviedo, Spain; *Int'l*, pg. 1224
Alonso, Francisco, Mgr. Dir.--Cilag de Mexico, S.A. de C.V., Mexico, Mexico; *U.S. Public*, pg. 929
Alonso, J., Gen. Mgr.--Minas De Gador S.A., Madrid, Spain; *Int'l*, pg. 803
Alonso, Julio, Chief Exec. Officer--Flowmax S.A., Madrid, Spain; *Int'l*, pg. 710
Alonso, Miguel, Mgr.-Office--Woodward-Clyde/Limnos, S.A. Barcelona, Barcelona, Spain; *U.S. Public*, pg. 1658
Alonso, Miguel Aguilo, Pres.--Iberia Lineas Aereas de Espana, S.A., Madrid, Spain; *Int'l*, pg. 1224
Aloschi, Vince, Chief Oper. Officer--A.I. Ocean (New Zealand) Ltd., Auckland, New Zealand; *Int'l*, pg. 14
Alossi, Mike, Pres.--Butler (Shanghai), Inc., Shanghai, China; *U.S. Public*, pg. 271
Aloukos, Alexandrou, Dir. Gen.--Olympic Airtours, Athens, Greece; *Int'l*, pg. 1004
Alpaerts, J., Chief Oper. Officer--De Lage Landen Leasing N.V., Zaventem, Belgium; *Int'l*, pg. 1082
Alper, Martin, Pres. & Chief Exec. Officer--Virgin Interactive Entertainment Inc., Irvine, CA; *U.S. Private*, pg. 776
Alperstein, L., Dir.--Washington Analysis Corporation, Washington, DC; *Int'l*, pg. 911
Alpert, Seth, Publr.--Data Sources, Cherry Hill, NJ; *U.S. Public*, pg. 1600
Alpher, David, Publr.--Suburban Publications, Inc., Wayne, PA; *U.S. Public*, pg. 935
Alpher, David, Publr.--The King of Prussia Courier, King of Prussia, PA; *U.S. Public*, pg. 935
Alpher, David, Publr.--The Suburban Advertiser, Exton, PA; *U.S. Public*, pg. 935
Alran, Andre, Plant Mgr.--Raisio France S.A., Toulouse, France; *Int'l*, pg. 1086
Alred, Michael W., Chm. Bd. & Chief Exec. Officer--SouthTrust Bank of Marshall County, Boaz, AL; *U.S. Public*, pg. 1492
Als, Heinzpeter, Gen. Mgr.--Crones Co. GmbH, Ansbach, Germany; *U.S. Public*, pg. 867
Alsi, Heinzpeter, Gen. Mgr.--ITW Befestigungssysteme (Ansbach) GmbH, Ansbach, Germany; *U.S. Public*, pg. 868
Alstad, Ray, Pres.--QMS Circuits, Inc., Fort Walton Beach, FL; *U.S. Public*, pg. 1346
Alston, Willie E. Jr., Admin.--Medicenter, Virginia Beach, Virginia Beach, VA; *U.S. Public*, pg. 1714

Alt, Dan, V.P. & Gen. Mgr.--Ventline Div., Bristol, IN; *Int'l*, pg. 1398
Alt, Willis E., Jr., Pres. & Chief Exec. Officer--First National Bank of Warsaw, Warsaw, IN; *U.S. Public*, pg. 674
Alten, Helge, Pres.--Volvo Cars Intercontinental AB, Goteborg, Sweden; *Int'l*, pg. 1476
Althardt, Ronald L., V.P.-Quality Assurance--Abbott Diagnostic Products, North Chicago, IL; *U.S. Public*, pg. 13
Althen, Wilhem, Mng. Dir.--Lufthansa Cargo AG, Frankfurt, Germany; *Int'l*, pg. 407
Altieri, Jerry, Pres.--Merck Medco Managed Care, Independence, OH; *U.S. Public*, pg. 1091
Altman, David, V.P.--Cherry Hill Center, Inc., Cherry Hill, NJ; *U.S. Public*, pg. 1408
Altman, Dennis R., Mng. Dir.--Coastal Petroleum (Far East) Pte Ltd., Singapore, Singapore; *U.S. Public*, pg. 390
Altman, Dennis R., Mng. Dir.--Coastal Belcher Petroleum Pte. Ltd., Singapore, Singapore; *U.S. Public*, pg. 390
Altman, Gregory, Pres.--Bristol Babcock, Inc., Watertown, CT; *Int'l*, pg. 472
Altman, Lyle, Chief Exec. Officer--Network Systems Credit Corp., Minneapolis, MN; *U.S. Public*, pg. 1522
Altman, Murray, Pres.--May Department Stores International, Inc., Saint Louis, MO; *U.S. Public*, pg. 1064
Altmann, Alain, Mng. Dir.--R.P. Scherer S.A., Beinheim, France; *U.S. Public*, pg. 1438
Altmann, Lauro, Dir.--Deutsche Bank AG (Porto Alegre), Porto Alegre, Brazil; *Int'l*, pg. 404
Altmeyer, John W., Pres.--Carlisle SynTec Inc., Carlisle, PA; *U.S. Public*, pg. 305
Altorfer, Rolf, Pres. & Chief Exec. officer--Panalpina, Inc., Jersey City, NJ; *Int'l*, pg. 1022
Alvarado, Candida, Branch Mgr.--First Leasing & Rental Corporation, Toa Baja, PR; *U.S. Public*, pg. 644
Alvarado, D., Pres.--Kaufel International Inc., Orocovis, PR; *Int'l*, pg. 725
Alvarenga, Carlos Alberto, Gen. Mgr.--Banco do Brasil S.A.-London, London, United Kingdom; *Int'l*, pg. 141
Alvarez de Toledo, Manuel, Gen. Mgr.--Banco Santander Switzerland, Central, Hong Kong; *Int'l*, pg. 144
Alvarez, Eduardo R., Pres. & Chief Exec. Officer--Consolidated ORIX Leasing and Finance Corporation, Manila, Philippines; *Int'l*, pg. 1009
Alvarez, Enrique E., Gen. Mgr.--Abbott Laboratories C.A., Caracas, Venezuela; *U.S. Public*, pg. 13
Alvarez, Ernesto, Gen. Mgr.--John Crane Chile, Santiago, Chile; *Int'l*, pg. 1340
Alvarez, Francisco, Mng. Dir.--SKF Colombia S.A., Bogota, Colombia; *Int'l*, pg. 1158
Alvarez, Generoso, Dir.--FCA!BMZ CID/Valencia, Valencia, Spain; *Int'l*, pg. 469
Alvarez, Helios, V.P. & Gen. Mgr.-Latin America--Columbia Tri-Star Films of Brazil, Inc., Sao Paulo, Brazil; *Int'l*, pg. 1282
Alvarez, Javier, Pres.--Iberia Air Lines of Spain, Miami, FL; *Int'l*, pg. 575
Alvarez, Javier, Gen. Mgr.--Bombas Goulds de Mexico, S.A. de C.V., Mexico, Mexico; *U.S. Public*, pg. 861
Alvarez, Jorge, Gen. Mgr.--Grupo ECA S.A. de C.V., Mexico, Mexico; *U.S. Private*, pg. 361
Alvarez, Jose, Gen. Dir.--Clevite de Mexico, Mexico, Mexico; *U.S. Public*, pg. 1577
Alvarez, Louis, Pres.--Hennessy/Coats Division, La Vergne, TN; *U.S. Public*, pg. 481
Alvarez, Mary M., Branch Mgr.--Valley National Bank, Branchville, NJ; *U.S. Public*, pg. 1706
Alvarez, Miguel, Gen. Mgr.--Grupo Financiero Santander Mexico, Mexico, Mexico; *Int'l*, pg. 144
Alvarino, Jose, V.P.--Berlitz de Mexico, S.A. de C.V., Mexico, Mexico; *U.S. Public*, pg. 221
Alves, A. Clovis, Gen. Mgr.--Loctite Brasil Ltda., Sao Paulo, Brazil; *Int'l*, pg. 611
Alves, J., Gen. Mgr.--A.C. Nielsen Company of Portugal, Lisbon, Portugal; *U.S. Public*, pg. 1183
Alvesalo, Tapio, Chief Oper. Officer--NAPS International, Espoo, Finland; *Int'l*, pg. 913
Alway, E.J., Mng. Dir.--Kiwi Brands Pty. Ltd., Clayton, Australia; *U.S. Public*, pg. 1434
Amacker, Jefferson Z., Div. Pres.--HTL/Kin-Tech Division, Duarte, CA; *U.S. Public*, pg. 1250
Amador, Eugenio, Pres.--Herramientas Snap-on de Mexico, S.A., Mexico, Mexico; *U.S. Public*, pg. 1481
Amagai, Koji, Mng. Dir.--Stange (Japan) K.K., Tokyo, Japan; *U.S. Public*, pg. 1067
Amagliani, Paolo, Dir. Gen.--Fiat Auto Belgio SA, Brussels, Belgium; *Int'l*, pg. 481
Amann, James J., Chm. Bd.--The FACS Group, Mason, OH; *U.S. Public*, pg. 618
Amann, James J., Chm.--Federated Systems Group, Norcross, GA; *U.S. Public*, pg. 618
Amann, Steve, N.W. Reg. Mgr.--Air Conditioning Co., Inc., Kent, WA; *U.S. Private*, pg. 28
Amano, Hideki, Mng. Dir.--NEC Electronics Hong Kong Limited, Hong Kong, Hong Kong; *Int'l*, pg. 901
Amano, Ken, Pres.--Denso Sales California, Long Beach, CA; *Int'l*, pg. 1412
Amano, Y., Chm.--Morgan Grenfell Japan Limited, Tokyo, Japan; *Int'l*, pg. 406
Amano, Yadoru, Chief Rep.--Asahi Bank Beijing Representative Office, Beijing, China; *Int'l*, pg. 83
Amaro, Francisco J., V.P.-Latin America--Comunicaciones Mtel, S.A. de C.V., Mexico, Mexico; *U.S. Public*, pg. 1120
Amaro, Y., Mgr.--Ballast Nedam Construction Inc., Miami, FL; *Int'l*, pg. 134
Amase, Takao, Mng. Dir.--Bridgestone/Firestone Europe, S.A., Brussels, Belgium; *Int'l*, pg. 214
Amato, G.N., V.P. & Gen. Mgr.--Hubbell Industrial Controls, Inc., Madison, OH; *U.S. Public*, pg. 844
Amatyakul, Damrongsuk, Pres.--The Mutual Fund Co., Ltd., Bangkok, Thailand; *Int'l*, pg. 677
Amaya, Toshio, Chief Oper. Officer--Asia Cable Engineering Co., Pte. Ltd. (ACECO), Singapore, Singapore; *Int'l*, pg. 530
Ambler, Bruce M., Pres. & Chief Exec. Officer--Constellation Holdings, Inc., Baltimore, MD; *U.S. Public*, pg. 172
Ambler, T.F.J., Mng. Dir.--Gilbey Canada Inc., Etobicoke, Canada; *Int'l*, pg. 409
Ambros, Dieter H., Dr., Pres.--Matthes & Weber GmbH, Duisburg, Germany; *Int'l*, pg. 610
Ambrose, Daniel, Publisher--Child Magazine, New York, NY; *Int'l*, pg. 190
Ambrose, William, Mgr.--SmithKline Beecham Clinical Laboratories, Syosset, NY; *Int'l*, pg. 1265
Ambroseo, John, Dr., Exec. V.P.--Coherent, Inc.-Laser Group, Santa Clara, CA; *U.S. Public*, pg. 395
Ambrosi, Nicholas, Pres.--ABD Group Inc., Chicago, IL; *U.S. Public*, pg. 503
Ambrosi, Nicholas, Pres.--Ambrosi & Associates, Inc., Chicago, IL; *U.S. Public*, pg. 503
Ambrosino, Allan, Pres.--Database America Companies, Montvale, NJ; *U.S. Public*, pg. 70
Ambur, Jon, Mgr.--Sandvik Norge A/S, Oslo, Norway; *Int'l*, pg. 1186
Ambwani, Narendra K., Pres. & Mng. Dir.--Johnson & Johnson Limited, Mumbai, India; *U.S. Public*, pg. 930
Amedia, Frank, Chief Oper. Officer--Taylor Building Products Company, West Branch, MI; *U.S. Public*, pg. 67
Amelang, Mark B., Pres.--Symtronix Corporation, Houston, TX; *U.S. Public*, pg. 1563
Amelang, Mark B., Pres.--Symtronix Corporation, Moscow, Russia; *U.S. Public*, pg. 1563
Amellal, Ramdane, Chief Oper. Officer--Novo Nordisk A/S, Hydra, Algeria; *Int'l*, pg. 987
Amemiya, Hideo, V.P.--Disneyland Hotel, Anaheim, CA; *U.S. Public*, pg. 513
Amemiya, Koichi, Pres.--American Honda Motor Co., Inc. Automobile Sales Division, Torrance, CA; *Int'l*, pg. 634
Amemiya, Masaaki, Gen. Mgr.--Nittobo Norplex Oak Co., Ltd. (NNO), Taipei, Taiwan; *U.S. Public*, pg. 53
Amendola, Richard D., Branch Mgr.--Zellerbach Division, Kalamazoo, MI; *U.S. Public*, pg. 1075
Amendola, Richard D., Branch Mgr.--Zellerbach Division, Grand Rapids, MI; *U.S. Public*, pg. 1076
Amerace, William, Pres. & Gen. Mgr.--Transportation Services Division, Cleveland, OH; *U.S. Public*, pg. 1466
Amerin, Zeno J., Mng. Dir.--Audatex Holding AG, Zurich, Switzerland; *U.S. Public*, pg. 150
Amerman, John M., Chm.--Mattel Overseas, Inc., El Segundo, CA; *U.S. Public*, pg. 1058
Amerson, Robert, Pres.--Flanders Filters, Inc., Washington, NC; *U.S. Public*, pg. 648
Ames, Charles, Pres. & Chief Exec. Officer--Packaging Division, Atlanta, GA; *U.S. Public*, pg. 1391
Ames, Hermes, Pres.--Chase Manhattan Bank of Connecticut, Bridgeport, CT; *U.S. Public*, pg. 338
Ames, Hermes L., Pres.--Fleet Bank, Albany, NY; *U.S. Public*, pg. 649
Ames, Tim, Pres.--The Toy Factory, Elizabeth, NJ; *U.S. Private*, pg. 883
Amezawa, Hitoshi, Chief Representative--Bangkok Representative Office, Bangkok, Thailand; *Int'l*, pg. 1517
Amgwerd, S.E., Gen. Mgr.--Mees & Hope Management AG, Zug, Switzerland; *Int'l*, pg. 12
Amich, Simon, Pres.--First Chicago Trading Co., Chicago, IL; *U.S. Public*, pg. 628
Amick, W. Michael, Pres.--International Paper (Europe) S.A., Brussels, Belgium; *U.S. Public*, pg. 905
Amin, Shaheen, Mng. Dir.--Oman ORIX Leasing Saog, Muscat, Oman; *Int'l*, pg. 1009
Amin, Tariq, Chief Oper. Officer--Rhone-Poulenc Pakistan (Pvt.) Ltd., Karachi, Pakistan; *Int'l*, pg. 1113
Amiot, Alain, Pres.--Etablissements Vallaroche (SA), Paris, France; *Int'l*, pg. 1165
Amiot, Alain, Pres.--Societe de Reassurance Vallaroche SA (SOREVAL), Senningerberg, Luxembourg; *Int'l*, pg. 1165
Amis, Stephane, Mng. Dir.--Media PA, Paris, France; *Int'l*, pg. 116
Amman, F., Gen. Rep.--Gan S.A. Vietnam, Hanoi, Vietnam; *Int'l*, pg. 565
Amman, Robert S., Pres.--Western Union Financial Services, Inc., Paramus, NJ; *U.S. Public*, pg. 631
Ammer, Bonnie, Pres. & Publisher-Travel--Fodor's Travel Publications, Inc., New York, NY; *U.S. Private*, pg. 21
Ammerman, Kent, Plant Mgr.--Eaton Corp., Fluid Power Div., Fletcher, NC; *U.S. Public*, pg. 556
Amonett, Thomas N., Pres.--Reunion Energy Company, Houston, TX; *U.S. Public*, pg. 1383
Amore, Paul, Gen. Mgr.--Tenney Environmental, Parsippany, NJ; *U.S. Private*, pg. 1077
Amorin, Antonio, Pres.--Merck Sharp & Dohme de Venezuela C.A., Caracas, Venezuela; *U.S. Public*, pg. 1092
Amory, Gregorie, V.P.-European Opers.--N.V. Owens-Corning S.A., Brussels, Belgium; *U.S. Public*, pg. 1237
Amos, Daniel P., Pres.--American Family Life Assurance Co. of Columbus, Columbus, GA; *U.S. Public*, pg. 28
Amos, Gordon, Chief Oper. Officer--Sierra Pacific Industries-Arcata Division, Arcata, CA; *U.S. Private*, pg. 998
Amos, James H., Pres. & Chief Oper. Officer--Mail Boxes Etc., San Diego, CA; *U.S. Public*, pg. 1687
Amos, P.V., Mng. Dir.--Quaker Chemical (Australasia) Pty. Ltd., Seven Hills, Australia; *U.S. Public*, pg. 1346
Amos, S.R., Chief Oper. Officer--ENI Power Systems, Rochester, NY; *U.S. Public*, pg. 574
Amos, Stephen, Pres.--Cleveland Range, Cleveland, OH; *Int'l*, pg. 188
Ampthill, Hon. Lord, The Rt., Vice Chm.--Express Newspapers plc, London, United Kingdom; *Int'l*, pg. 1443
Ampula, Bob, Pres.--Total Beverage Corporation, Landover, MD; *U.S. Public*, pg. 484
Amsterdam, Michael, Pres.--Steelworks, Inc. Dover Division, Dover, DE; *U.S. Private*, pg. 1039
Amtage, Wilhelm, Gen. Mgr.--Dresdner Bank AG, New York, NY; *Int'l*, pg. 418
Amundsen, Jim, Pres.--LASCO Panel Products, Florence, KY; *Int'l*, pg. 1398
Amundsen, Oddvar, Mgr.--Frionor Fabrikker A/S, Trondheim, Norway; *Int'l*, pg. 516
Amundsen, Tore, Gen. Mgr.--Kvaerner Energy a.s., Oslo, Norway; *Int'l*, pg. 767
Anagnostopolous, Georgios, Chief Exec. Officer & Dir. Gen.--Olympic Catering, Athens, Greece; *Int'l*, pg. 1004
Anagnostopoulos, Haris, Plant Mgr.--Athens Mill, Athens, Greece; *U.S. Public*, pg. 672
Anaka, Wayne, Chief Oper. Officer--Hudson General Aviation Services Inc., Toronto, Canada; *U.S. Public*, pg. 846
Anand, Jaggy, Pres.--Firestone Fibers & Textiles Co., Kings Mountain, NC; *Int'l*, pg. 214
Anasis, Emanuel, Mng. Dir.--Roehlen Industries Pty. Ltd. (Sidney Division), Kirrawee, Australia; *U.S. Public*, pg. 1507
Anastasiadis, Paul, Chief Oper. Officer--Cartonpack S.A., Corinth, Greece; *Int'l*, pg. 864
Anastassiou, Philip, Chief Oper. Officer--Alfa-Laval AB Athens, Athens, Greece; *Int'l*, pg. 1380
Anat, Juan Dolins, Chief Exec. Officer--Promsa, Barcelona, Spain; *Int'l*, pg. 292
Anaya, Raul, Exec. V.P.--Banco Nacional de Mexico, S.A., New York, NY; *Int'l*, pg. 574
Anchisi, Emilio, Pres.--Ferrari North America, Hasbrouck Heights, NJ; *Int'l*, pg. 483
Anchustegui, Pedro C., Pres.--GATX Logistics de Mexico, S.A. de C.V., Mexico, Mexico; *U.S. Public*, pg. 692
Andal, B.J., Pres.--Interactive Market Systems, Inc., New York, NY; *Int'l*, pg. 1447
Andal, B.J., Gen. Mgr.--Marketing Resources Plus, Redwood City, CA; *Int'l*, pg. 1447
Anders, Bob, Creative Dir.--Black Bag Communications, Inc., New York, NY; *U.S. Private*, pg. 1152
Anders, Mike, Publisher--News-Enterprise, Elizabethtown, KY; *U.S. Private*, pg. 648
Anders, Robert, Plant Mgr.--Axle and Brake Div., Henderson, KY; *U.S. Public*, pg. 556
Andersch, H. Torsten, V.P.--BHA International GmbH, Ahlen, Germany; *U.S. Public*, pg. 161
Andersen, Bent, Pres.--Astra Japan, Osaka, Japan; *Int'l*, pg. 94
Andersen, Bjarne, Mng. Dir.--DanTransport Holding A/S, Glostrup, Denmark; *Int'l*, pg. 476
Andersen, Bruce, V.P. & Gen. Mgr.--Northland Publishing Co., Flagstaff, AZ; *U.S. Public*, pg. 937
Andersen, Charles P., Pres.--Aero-Motive Company, Kalamazoo, MI; *U.S. Public*, pg. 1776
Andersen, Hakon Chr., Managing Dir.--Nidar AS, Trondheim, Norway; *Int'l*, pg. 1011
Andersen, Heiner, Gen. Mgr.--Liebert G.m.b.H., Kirchheim, Germany; *U.S. Public*, pg. 577
Andersen, Henning, Pres.--All Plast A-S, Havndal, Denmark; *Int'l*, pg. 460
Andersen, James N., Jr., Pres.--Banta Information Services Group, Eden Prairie, MN; *U.S. Public*, pg. 188
Andersen, Kaare, Chief Oper. Officer--Novo Nordisk A/S, Wan Chai, Hong Kong; *Int'l*, pg. 989
Andersen, Kalle Braa, Pres.--Danapak A.m.b.a., Holte, Denmark; *Int'l*, pg. 826
Andersen, Kenneth, Chief Oper. Officer--Prosess-Styring A/S, Drammen, Norway; *Int'l*, pg. 1040
Andersen, Kurt, Exec. V.P.--Republic National Bank of New York (Singapore) Ltd., Singapore, Singapore; *U.S. Public*, *pg. 1381*
Andersen, Kurt, Exec. V.P.--RNBNY Branch Office-Singapore, Singapore, Singapore; *U.S. Public*, pg. 1381
Andersen, L.A., Pres.--Texaco Arabia Inc., Dhahran, Saudi Arabia; *U.S. Public*, pg. 1584
Andersen, Mogens, Mgr.--Distribution Division, Roedovre, Denmark; *Int'l*, pg. 1083
Andersen, Morgens, Chief Oper. Officer--Rhone-Poulenc-Textile, Courbevoie, France; *Int'l*, pg. 1109
Andersen, Niels Otto, Pres.--C.G. Jensen A/S, Ballerup, Denmark; *Int'l*, pg. 1261
Andersen, Ole B. L., Pres.--Tri-Clover Inc., Kenosha, WI; *Int'l*, pg. 1379
Andersen, Per, Chief Oper. Officer--Novo Nordisk Engineering A/S, Bagsvaerd, Denmark; *Int'l*, pg. 987
Andersen, Per, Chief Oper. Officer--Novo Nordisk A/S, Bagsvaerd, Denmark; *Int'l*, pg. 989
Andersen, Torben Steen, Gen. Mgr.--Axel Johnson Teknik A/S, Skovlunde, Denmark; *Int'l*, pg. 712
Anderson, A.S., Branch Mgr.--Barclays Bank PLC, Manila, Philippines; *Int'l*, pg. 165
Anderson, Alistair, Mng. Dir.--Personal Performance Consultants UK Limited (PPC), London, United Kingdom; *Int'l*, pg. 1502
Anderson, Arthur A., Mgr.-Branch--Piper Jaffray Inc., Minneapolis, MN; *U.S. Public*, pg. 1303
Anderson, Basil, Pres.--Campbell Finance Corp., Newark, DE; *U.S. Public*, pg. 299
Anderson, Benny, Pres.--Machinery Stockholm, Jarfalla, Sweden; *Int'l*, pg. 899
Anderson, Bent, Pres.--Astra Japan Ltd., Osaka, Japan; *Int'l*, pg. 94
Anderson, Bill, Pres. & Gen. Mgr.--WTWC-TV, Tallahassee, FL; *U.S. Private*, pg. 439
Anderson, Bill, Chief Oper. Officer--Custom Servo Motors, New Ulm, MN; *U.S. Public*, pg. 1029
Anderson, Bob, Plant Mgr.--Quanex Heat Treating Div., Huntington, IN; *U.S. Public*, pg. 1349
Anderson, C. William, Chief Oper. Officer--Fibreweb International, Ltd., Norwalk, CT; *U.S. Private*, pg. 467
Anderson, Carl H., Pres. & Chief Exec. Officer--Paragon Life Insurance Co., Saint Louis, MO; *U.S. Private*, pg. 443
Anderson, Carol, Dir.--Columbia Behavioral Center, El Paso, TX; *U.S. Public*, pg. 404
Anderson, Charles, Exec. Editor--Wilmington Morning Star, Wilmington, NC; *U.S. Public*, pg. 1175

Anderson, Charles M., Pres. & Chief Oper. Officer--Stamler Corporation, Millersburg, KY; *U.S. Private*, pg. 814
Anderson, Colin, Dir. & Gen. Mgr.--Alcan Specialty Extrusions, Warrington, United Kingdom; *Int'l*, pg. 51
Anderson, Craig, Gen. Mgr.--Fisher Controls International, Inc., North Stonington, CT; *U.S. Public*, pg. 573
Anderson, Craig, Pres.--Norenco Corp., Minneapolis, MN; *U.S. Public*, pg. 1195
Anderson, Curtis I., Mgr.-Branch--Piper Jaffray Inc., Austin, MN; *U.S. Public*, pg. 1302
Anderson, D., Chief Exec. Officer--THORN Europe, Reading, United Kingdom; *Int'l*, pg. 1385
Anderson, D.J., Pres.--International Nickel, Inc., Saddle Brook, NJ; *Int'l*, pg. 672
Anderson, D.W., Asst. Mng. Dir.--P&O Australia Ltd., Sydney, Australia; *Int'l*, pg. 1035
Anderson, Dan, Gen. Mgr.--Elco SDD, Rockford, IL; *U.S. Public*, pg. 1590
Anderson, Dave, Exec. Dir.--QualMed Plans for Health-Spokane, Spokane, WA; *U.S. Public*, pg. 678
Anderson, David, Pres.--Canatom Inc., Montreal, Canada; *Int'l*, pg. 31
Anderson, Donald C., Pres. & Chief Exec. Officer--Norwest Agricultural Credit, Inc., Sioux Falls, SD; *U.S. Public*, pg. 1201
Anderson, Donald V., Jr., Pres.--EF Data Corp., Tempe, AZ; *U.S. Public*, pg. 293
Anderson, Doug, Gen. Mgr.--BHP Steel Building Products (Shanghai) Ltd., Shanghai, China; *Int'l*, pg. 226
Anderson, Doug, Pres. & Chief Exec. Officer--Remco America, Inc., Wichita, KS; *Int'l*, pg. 1385
Anderson, Douglas E., Pres.--BNE Land & Development Co., Rocky Mount, NC; *U.S. Private*, pg. 154
Anderson, E. Van, V.P.--Ogden Publishing, Topeka, KS; *U.S. Private*, pg. 812
Anderson, Ed, Gen. Mgr.--Bunnell Plastics Division, Mickleton, NJ; *U.S. Public*, pg. 689
Anderson, Ed, Gen. Mgr.--Bunnell Plastics Division, Anaheim, CA; *U.S. Public*, pg. 689
Anderson, Eric B., Mgr.-Reg. Sls.--AlliedSignal (Australia) Sales Ltd. Fibers & Chemicals, Melbourne, Australia; *U.S. Public*, pg. 52
Anderson, Frank O., Pres. & Chief Exec. Officer--Hobart Brothers Co., Troy, OH; *U.S. Public*, pg. 866
Anderson, Frank R., Dir.--Uni-Dan A/S, Copenhagen, Denmark; *Int'l*, pg. 1438
Anderson, Fred, Pres. & Chief Exec. Officer--Stewart Smith West, Inc., Los Angeles, CA; *Int'l*, pg. 1508
Anderson, G.K., Chief Oper. Officer--Harmon Contract Glazing, Inc., Minneapolis, MN; *U.S. Public*, pg. 120
Anderson, Gavin, Chm. Bd. & Chief Exec. Officer--Gavin Anderson & Company, New York, NY; *U.S. Public*, pg. 1223
Anderson, Gloria, Exec. Editor--The New York Times Syndicate, New York, NY; *U.S. Public*, pg. 1174
Anderson, Gordon M., Chm. Bd. & Chief Exec. Officer--Santa Fe International Corporation, Dallas, TX; *Int'l*, pg. 765
Anderson, Gordon M., Pres.--Santa Fe Drilling Co., Alhambra, CA; *Int'l*, pg. 765
Anderson, Gregg A., Pres.--Monogram Aerospace Fasteners, Inc., Los Angeles, CA; *U.S. Public*, pg. 1054
Anderson, Grieg L., Pres.--Portland General Holdings, Inc., Portland, OR; *U.S. Public*, pg. 585
Anderson, Herbert W., V.P.--Data Systems and Services Division, Herndon, VA; *U.S. Public*, pg. 1198
Anderson, Ian, State Mgr.--National Mutual Tasmania, Hobart, Australia; *Int'l*, pg. 908
Anderson, J.A., Chief Exec. Officer--National Bank of New Zealand Ltd., Wellington, New Zealand; *Int'l*, pg. 814
Anderson, J.H.F., Mng. Dir.--Bovis Construction Limited, Harrow, United Kingdom; *Int'l*, pg. 1033
Anderson, J.H.F., Mng. Dir.--P&O Property Developments Ltd., London, United Kingdom; *Int'l*, pg. 1034
Anderson, James, Pres.--Fremont Life Insurance Co., Orange, CA; *U.S. Public*, pg. 681
Anderson, James, V.P. & Controller--American Furniture Company, Incorporated, Martinsville, VA; *U.S. Public*, pg. 974
Anderson, James, Mng. Dir.--Batchelors Foods, Ltd., Sheffield, United Kingdom; *Int'l*, pg. 1434
Anderson, James E., Pres.--Applied Intelligence Systems, Inc., Ann Arbor, MI; *U.S. Public*, pg. 569
Anderson, James M., Sr. V.P.-Labor Rels. & Corp. Admin.--Hilton Hotels Div., Beverly Hills, CA; *U.S. Public*, pg. 829
Anderson, James N., Pres.--Builders Supply and Lumber Co., Inc., Frederick, MD; *U.S. Public*, pg. 1344
Anderson, Jeff, Pres.--Mambosock, Mercer Island, WA; *U.S. Private*, pg. 449
Anderson, Jeff, Pres. & Gen. Mgr.--First American Title Insurance Agency of Yuma, Inc., Yuma, AZ; *U.S. Public*, pg. 626
Anderson, Jeff, Pres. & Gen. Mgr.--Williams Technologies, Inc., Summerville, SC; *U.S. Private*, pg. 1179
Anderson, Jeffries D., Reg. Dir.--Piper Jaffray Inc., Kansas City, MO; *U.S. Public*, pg. 1301
Anderson, Jim, Gen. Mgr.--Welch/Thomas Vacuum, Skokie, IL; *U.S. Public*, pg. 1599
Anderson, John H., Chm. & Chief Exec. Officer--Laurel Bank, Johnstown, PA; *U.S. Public*, pg. 164
Anderson, K.A., Mgr.-Opers.--Diamonite Plant, Shreve, OH; *U.S. Public*, pg. 618
Anderson, Keith, V.P. & Gen. Mgr.--ITW Heartland Components, Alexandria, MN; *U.S. Public*, pg. 866
Anderson, Keith, Mgr.--INX Incorporated/Midland Color Company, Seattle, WA; *Int'l*, pg. 1311
Anderson, Kenneth C., Pres.--Reed Minerals, Highland, IN; *U.S. Public*, pg. 793
Anderson, Kent T., Gen. Mgr.--American Stores Properties, Inc., Salt Lake City, UT; *U.S. Public*, pg. 93
Anderson, Kjeld, Pres.--ALK Sverge AB, Kungsbacka, Sweden; *Int'l*, pg. 288
Anderson, Lance, V.P. & Gen. Mgr.--KJR-AM, Seattle, WA; *U.S. Private*, pg. 792
Anderson, Larry C., Chief Oper. Officer--Harmon Glass Company, Minneapolis, MN; *U.S. Public*, pg. 120
Anderson, Lars Erik, Mng. Dir.--ESAB Welding Equipment AB, Laxa, Sweden; *Int'l*, pg. 281
Anderson, Lavon N., Dr., Pres. & Chief Oper. Officer--Rexene Corporation, Dallas, TX; *U.S. Private*, pg. 549
Anderson, Lee, Pres.--Pentax Vision Inc., Minnetonka, MN; *Int'l*, pg. 85
Anderson, Leonard C., Mgr.--CAP Gemini America (Richmond Branch), Richmond, VA; *Int'l*, pg. 264
Anderson, Lynn A., Chm. Bd.--Willis Corroon Corp. of Utah, Salt Lake City, UT; *Int'l*, pg. 1507
Anderson, N.J., Gen. Mgr.--Grindlays Bahrain Bank B.S.C. (c), Manama, Bahrain; *Int'l*, pg. 100
Anderson, Neill, Pres.--Anderson-Barrows Metals Corp., Palmdale, CA; *U.S. Public*, pg. 1746
Anderson, Noble, Reg. Mgr.--Southern Region, Arlington, TX; *U.S. Private*, pg. 307
Anderson, Ole, Pres.--Tetra-Pak Processing Systems, Pleasant Prairie, WI; *Int'l*, pg. 1379
Anderson, P.F., Dir. & Gen. Mgr.--Britax Vega Limited, Droitwich, United Kingdom; *Int'l*, pg. 216
Anderson, Paul, Admin.--Physicians Hospital for Extended Care, Reno, NV; *U.S. Public*, pg. 837
Anderson, Paul M., Pres. & Chief Oper. Officer--Duke Energy International, L.L.C., Houston, TX; *U.S. Public*, pg. 534
Anderson, Pete, Mgr.--Dallas Flower Market, Inc., Dallas, TX; *U.S. Private*, pg. 326
Anderson, Peter John, Pres.--Banco Chase Manhattan S.A., Rio de Janeiro, Brazil; *U.S. Public*, pg. 339
Anderson, R. Richard, Pres.--Mills & Lupton Supply Co., Chattanooga, TN; *U.S. Public*, pg. 847
Anderson, R.C., Chief Oper. Officer--Kidde International Protection Systems Pre. Ltd., Singapore, Singapore; *Int'l, pg. 1500*
Anderson, Richard, Pres.--Control Transformer Corp., Cortland, OH; *Int'l*, pg. 113
Anderson, Richard, Gen. Mgr.--The New Home Sewing Machine Co., Elk Grove Village, IL; *Int'l*, pg. 699
Anderson, Richard, Pres.-Pacific Northwest Publishing Grp.--Albany Democrat-Herald, Albany, OR; *U.S. Public*, pg. 983
Anderson, Richard, Pres.-Pacific Northwest Publishing Grp.--The Daily Tidings, Ashland, OR; *U.S. Public*, pg. 983
Anderson, Richard A., Pres.--BBS Holdings, Inc., Atlanta, GA; *U.S. Public*, pg. 209
Anderson, Richard F., Pres.-Pacific Northwest Publishing Grp.--Cottage Grove Sentinel, Cottage Grove, OR; *U.S. Public*, pg. 983
Anderson, Richard F., Pres.-Pacific Northwest Publishing Grp.--Lebanon Express, Lebanon, OR; *U.S. Public*, pg. 983
Anderson, Richard L., Chm. Bd.--Crusader Insurance Company of Australia Limited, Sydney, Australia; *U.S. Public*, pg. 364
Anderson, Richard L., Chief Exec. Officer--Cigna Life Insurance Australia Limited, Sydney, Australia; *U.S. Public*, pg. 364
Anderson, Richard T., Pres.--Design-Build West, Denver, CO; *U.S. Private*, pg. 905
Anderson, Robb K., Pres.--Pierce Chemical Company, Rockford, IL; *Int'l*, pg. 1037
Anderson, Robert, Pres.--Brambles USA Inc., Chicago, IL; *Int'l*, pg. 211
Anderson, Robert D., Pres.--Helvetia Coal Co., Indiana, PA; *U.S. Public*, pg. 1395
Anderson, Robert D., Pres.--Keystone Coal Mining Corp., Indiana, PA; *U.S. Public*, pg. 1395
Anderson, Robert L., Mng. Dir.--ITT Flygt Limited, Silverwater, Australia; *U.S. Public*, pg. 860
Anderson, Rodger N., Gen. Mgr.--Columbia Grain, Inc., Portland, OR; *Int'l*, pg. 845
Anderson, Roland, Pres.--Lyndon Property Insurance Company, Saint Louis, MO; *U.S. Public*, pg. 685
Anderson, Ronald G., Pres.--AAL Capital Management Corp., Appleton, WI; *U.S. Private*, pg. 28
Anderson, Ross, Pres.--Lamson and Goodnow Mfg. Co., Shelburne Falls, MA; *U.S. Private*, pg. 940
Anderson, Ross, V.P. & Gen. Mgr.--Application Specific Products Group, Sunnyvale, CA; *Int'l*, pg. 1053
Anderson, S.W., Pres.--Norton Canada Inc., Hamilton, Canada; *Int'l*, pg. 1175
Anderson, Stanley, Chief Oper. Officer--Dyer-Lauderdale Farmers Co-op, Dyersburg, TN; *U.S. Private*, pg. 1076
Anderson, Steve, V.P. & Plant Mgr.--Electro Corporation, Sarasota, FL; *Int'l*, pg. 127
Anderson, Stuart, Gen. Mgr.--Commercial Simulation--Simulation Division, Salt Lake City, UT; *U.S. Public*, pg. 596
Anderson, Susan, Station Mgr.--KSAX-TV, Alexandria, MN; *U.S. Private*, pg. 544
Anderson, T.A., Mng. Dir.--Presspart Manufacturing Ltd., Blackburn, United Kingdom; *Int'l*, pg. 124
Anderson, Thomas, Chief Oper. Officer--Axel Johnson Ore & Metals Ltd., London, United Kingdom; *Int'l*, pg. 712
Anderson, Thomas L., Pres.--U.S. Pharmaceuticals, Baltimore, MD; *U.S. Public*, pg. 58
Anderson, Thomas, Jr., Admin.--Ambulatory Services, Inc., Richmond, VA; *U.S. Public*, pg. 403
Anderson, Thore, Pres.--AB Nobel Plast, Hisings Backa, Sweden; *Int'l*, pg. 48
Anderson, Tim, Lab Mgr.--Quest Diagnostic-Hilton, Hilton, NY; *U.S. Public*, pg. 1351
Anderson, Tom, Pres.--Schwing America Inc., Saint Paul, MN; *Int'l*, pg. 1211
Anderson, Victor L., Mgr.--Piper Jaffray Inc., Wayzata, MN; *U.S. Public*, pg. 1302
Anderson, William C., Pres.--Guyot-Hicks-Anderson & Associates, Traverse City, MI; *U.S. Public*, pg. 1217
Anderson, William D., Pres. & Gen. Mgr.--Clark Distribution Services Company, Chicago, IL; *U.S. Public*, pg. 876
Anderssen, Bjorn, Mng. Dir.--Berendsen Components A/S, Oslo, Norway; *Int'l*, pg. 1284
Anderssen, Runar, Mgr.--Ventilizationunion AB, Kista, Sweden; *Int'l*, pg. 1422
Andersson, Alf, Chief Officer--Juvelbagerierna AB, Stockholm, Sweden; *Int'l*, pg. 718
Andersson, Arne H., Chief Oper. Officer--Amdent AB, Nynashamn, Sweden; *Int'l*, pg. 708
Andersson, Bjorn, Mgr.--Stockholms Byggplat, Stockholm, Sweden; *Int'l*, pg. 1422
Andersson, Borje, Mng. Dir.--SKF Nova AB, Goteborg, Sweden; *Int'l*, pg. 1157
Andersson, Christer, Mgr.--Edmeston AB, Goteborg, Sweden; *Int'l*, pg. 1185
Andersson, Goran, Pres.--Chr. Hansen AB, Goteborg, Sweden; *Int'l*, pg. 288
Andersson, Hans, Pres.--ABB ASEA Skandia AB, Sollentuna, Sweden; *Int'l*, pg. 7
Andersson, Hans-Jaguar, Chief Oper. Officer--S.A. Electrolux, Buenos Aires, Argentina; *Int'l*, pg. 440
Andersson, Jan Erik, Mng. Dir.--Fios e Cabos Plasticos do Brasil S.A., Manaus, Brazil; *Int'l*, pg. 1368
Andersson, K., Chief Fin. Officer--Olivetti (Suomi) OY, Espoo, Finland; *Int'l*, pg. 1003
Andersson, Kaj, Pres.--Alvesta Gjuteri AB, Alvesta, Sweden; *Int'l*, pg. 1323
Andersson, Karl Henrik, Chief Oper. Officer--Electrolux Constructor AB, Saffle, Sweden; *Int'l*, pg. 438
Andersson, Kennert, Pres.--Precon VA System AB, Vanersborg, Sweden; *Int'l*, pg. 1199
Andersson, Kjell S., Mng. Dir.--Radiosystem Sweden AB, Kista, Sweden; *Int'l*, pg. 1364
Andersson, Krister, Pres.--Ballast Ost AB, Linkoping, Sweden; *Int'l*, pg. 899
Andersson, Lennart, Mng. Dir.--Gisebo Vagnindustri AB, Jonkoping, Sweden; *Int'l*, pg. 436
Andersson, Lennart, Mng. Dir.--Eldon Rental Trailer, Nassjo, Sweden; *Int'l*, pg. 436
Andersson, Mats, Mgr.--Sandvik Russia A/O, Moscow, Russia; *Int'l*, pg. 1187
Andersson, Robert, Mng. Dir.--Telefonaktiebolaget LM Ericsson Technical Office UAE, Abu Dhabi, United Arab Emirates; *Int'l*, pg. 1371
Andersson, Rolf, Chief Oper. Officer--Johnson Metall AB, Orebro, Sweden; *Int'l*, pg. 439
Andersson, Sten, Mng. Dir.--Svenska Foder AB, Lidkoping, Sweden; *Int'l*, pg. 350
Andersson, Sten, Chief Oper. Officer--KONE Hissar AB, Kista, Sweden; *Int'l*, pg. 747
Andersson, Stig, Pres.--Volvo International Development Corp., Goteborg, Sweden; *Int'l*, pg. 1476
Andersson, Sven-Ake, Chief Oper. Officer--Electrolux S.A., Bogota, Colombia; *Int'l*, pg. 441
Andjus, Dan D., Resident V.P.--Northeastern Regional Office, Waltham, MA; *U.S. Private*, pg. 224
Ando, June, Exec. V.P.--Kawai America Corporation, Compton, CA; *Int'l*, pg. 725
Ando, Noriaki, Pres.--Rohm Fukuoka Co., Ltd., Fukuoka, Japan; *Int'l*, pg. 1125
Ando, Takatoshi, Pres.--Kanto Auto Works, Ltd., Yokosuka, Japan; *Int'l*, pg. 1412
Ando, Yashitaka, Sr. V.P. & Gen. Mgr.--Sumitomo Corporation of America, Houston, TX; *Int'l*, pg. 1312
Andoh, Hiroshi, Reg. Mgr.--Rammer Oy Japan Office, Yokohama, Japan; *Int'l*, pg. 1352
Andrade, Armando, Exec. Pres.--Pragma/DMB&B, Lima, Peru; *U.S. Private*, pg. 305
Andre, Joao Costa, Gen. Mgr.--Banco Financial Portugues-Brazil, Sao Paulo, Brazil; *Int'l*, pg. 251
Andreae, Jan, Pres.--Albert Heijn B.V., Zaandam, Netherlands; *Int'l*, pg. 749
Andreen, Gunnar, Chief Oper. Officer--Bergis Produktions AB, Svenljunga, Sweden; *Int'l*, pg. 438
Andren, Anders, Reg. Dir.-South Europe--ESAB France S.A., Cergy-Pontoise, France; *Int'l*, pg. 282
Andren, Anders, Chief Oper. Officer--Electrolux S.A., Senlis, France; *Int'l*, pg. 441
Andren, Johann, Rep.--Svenska Handelsbanken Taipei, Taipei, Taiwan; *Int'l*, pg. 1327
Andren, Lars, Mng. Dir.--SKF Venezolana S.A., Caracas, Venezuela; *Int'l*, pg. 1159
Andreoli, James M., Pres.--One More Time Inc., Los Angeles, CA; *U.S. Private*, pg. 111
Andreozzi, Lou, Chief Oper. Officer--National Register Publishing, New Providence, NJ; *Int'l*, pg. 1096
Andreozzi, Lou, Chief Oper. Officer--Marquis Who's Who, New Providence, NJ; *Int'l*, pg. 1096
Andres, Ron, Gen. Mgr.--Sunprene Co., Bellevue, OH; *U.S. Public*, pg. 1441
Andres, Ron, Mgr.--A. Schulman, Inc., Bellevue, OH; *U.S. Public*, pg. 1441
Andres, Wernfried, Mng. Dir.--Sulzer-Escher Wyss AG, Zurich, Switzerland; *Int'l*, pg. 1305
Andresen, C., Mng. Dir.--Haden Drysys GmbH, Frankfurt, Germany; *Int'l*, pg. 586
Andrew, E.J., Pres.--Andrew International Corp., Orland Park, IL; *U.S. Public*, pg. 112
Andrew, J., Mng. Dir.--Alhambra Longman S.A., Madrid, Spain; *Int'l*, pg. 1025
Andrew, R.A., Chm.--Wimpey Homes Holdings Ltd., London, United Kingdom; *Int'l*, pg. 1510
Andrews, Bob, Dir.--Anaren Microwave, Ltd., Waterlooville, United Kingdom; *U.S. Public*, pg. 111
Andrews, Bruce I., Pres.--Animal Health, Fort Lee, NJ; *U.S. Public*, pg. 58
Andrews, Chrisopher, Dr., Mng. Dir.--Rhone-Poulenc Chemicals Ltd., Watford, United Kingdom; *Int'l*, pg. 1112
Andrews, Clive, Bus. Mgr.--Chemical Construction Products, Whetstone, United Kingdom; *U.S. Public*, pg. 867
Andrews, J.R., Pres.--Connecticut General Realty Resources, Inc., Bloomfield, CT; *U.S. Public*, pg. 359
Andrews, John, Pres.--CSX Technology, Inc., Jacksonville, FL; *U.S. Public*, pg. 284
Andrews, John V., Pres.--Allvac, Monroe, NC; *U.S. Public*, pg. 43

Andrews, Ken, Gen. Mgr.--Antenna & Cable Division, Amesbury, MA; *U.S. Public*, pg. 8
Andrews, Nigel D.T., V.P. & Gen. Mgr.--G.E. Plastics-America, Pittsfield, MA; *U.S. Public*, pg. 711
Andrews, Paul, Gen. Mgr.--McCain Foods (NZ) Ltd., Timaru, New Zealand; *Int'l*, pg. 850
Andrews, Richard S., Pres.--Firemen's Insurance Company of Washington, D.C., Bethesda, MD; *U.S. Public*, pg. 215
Andrews, Richard S., Mng. Dir.--Cutting Edges Pty. Ltd., Revesby, Australia; *Int'l*, pg. 391
Andrews, S.J., V.P. & Gen. Mgr.--The Ohio Brass Co., Wadsworth, OH; *U.S. Public*, pg. 845
Andrews, Stephen W., Pres.--W.E. Andrews Co., Inc., of Connecticut, Hartford, CT; *U.S. Public*, pg. 1735
Andrews, Steven A., Plant Mgr.--The Lamson & Sessions Co., Oklahoma City, OK; *U.S. Public*, pg. 976
Andrews, Tom, Pres.--Lubriquip, Inc., Cleveland, OH; *U.S. Public*, pg. 862
Andrino, Victorio, Chief Exec.--Banco Santander, Brussels, Belgium; *Int'l*, pg. 144
Androlla, Brian, Mng. Dir.--Apricot Computers, Birmingham, United Kingdom; *Int'l*, pg. 873
Andrusko, F.G., Pres.--Amoco Fabrics & Fibers Company, Atlanta, GA; *U.S. Public*, pg. 102
Andrusko, F.G., Chief Exec. Officer--Amoco Nisseki Claf Inc. (ANCI), Atlanta, GA; *U.S. Public*, pg. 102
Andrzejewski, John R., Pres.--Anning-Johnson Company, Melrose Park, IL; *U.S. Private*, pg. 76
Anell, Gunnar, Mgr.--Sandvik Rock Tools Svenska Forsaljnings AB, Sandviken, Sweden; *Int'l*, pg. 1185
Anezaki, H., Branch Mgr.--Mitrans Corporation, Elk Grove Village, IL; *Int'l*, pg. 874
Ang, Richard, Gen. Mgr.--Cognos Far East Pte. Limited, Singapore, Singapore; *Int'l*, pg. 306
Angeby, Lennart, Chief Oper. Officer--ASAB Serviceforetaget AB, Stockholm, Sweden; *Int'l*, pg. 438
Angel, Eugene, Pres.--U.S. Ring Binder Corp., New Bedford, MA; *U.S. Public*, pg. 707
Angel, Mike, Distr. Mgr.--Milchem Western Hemisphere Inc., Quito, Ecuador; *U.S. Public*, pg. 167
Angel, Victor Manuel, Mgr.--Sandvik Colombia S.A., Bogota, Colombia; *Int'l*, pg. 1188
Angelastri, Sandro, Gen. Mgr.--Robert Fleming (Switzerland) A.G., Zurich, Switzerland; *Int'l*, pg. 494
Angeli, C., Pres.--Pacific Motor Transport Co., Burlingame, CA; *U.S. Public*, pg. 1668
Angelich, Mark S., Pres.--Amelco Industries, Gardena, CA; *U.S. Public*, pg. 65
Angell, Bradley D., Mgr.--Piper Jaffray Inc., Duluth, MN; *U.S. Public*, pg. 1301
Angelo, Jean-Carlos, Mgr.--Companhia Nacional de Cimento Portland (C.N.C.P.), Rio de Janeiro, Brazil; *Int'l*, pg. 789
Angelo, Vince, Pres.--Lehigh Asphalt, Paving & Construction, Tamaqua, PA; *U.S. Private*, pg. 116
Angeloff, Paul, V.P. & Gen. Mgr.--Chattahoochee Industrial Railroad, Cedar Springs, GA; *U.S. Public*, pg. 736
Anger, Staffan, Chief Oper. Officer--Evert Larsson Industri AB, Kungalv, Sweden; *Int'l*, pg. 439
Angermann, Bernd, Chief Oper. Officer--WABAG Leipzig GmbH Wassertechnische Anlagen, Markkleeberg, Germany; *Int'l*, pg. 399
Angi, Joseph A., Div. Mgr.--Amcast Automotive-Cedarburg Plant, Cedarburg, WI; *U.S. Public*, pg. 63
Angle, Harold, Sr. V.P.-Domestic Mfg.--Isabela Shoe Corp., Isabela, PR; *U.S. Public*, pg. 217
Anglin, Dave, Div. Gen. Mgr.--United Cities Gas Co., GA/SC Div., Columbus, GA; *U.S. Public*, pg. 146
Anglin, Jerry, Gen. Mgr.--Elixir Industries, Tuscumbia, AL; *U.S. Private*, pg. 371
Angove, Dave, V.P. & Gen. Mgr.--Spartan Plastics Canada, London, Canada; *U.S. Private*, pg. 1020
Angus, Christopher, Pres.--Astro-Valcour Inc., Glens Falls, NY; *Int'l*, pg. 756
Angwald, Stefan, Chief Oper. Officer--Molnlycke AB Incontinence Care Products, Goteborg, Sweden; *Int'l*, pg. 1326
Angwerd, S.E., Chief Oper. Officer--Mees & Hope Finanzgesellschaft AG, Zug, Switzerland; *Int'l*, pg. 12
Anichini, Frank, Mgr.--General Employment Enterprises, Inc., Schaumburg, IL; *U.S. Public*, pg. 714
Ankarstig, Gunnar, Mng. Dir.--Munters Nederland B.V., Alphen aan den Rijn, Netherlands; *Int'l*, pg. 669
Anker, Robert A., Chm. Bd.--American States Insurance Companies, Indianapolis, IN; *U.S. Public*, pg. 997
Annable, C.D., Pres. & Chief Oper. Officer--Canuck Engineering Inc., Calgary, Canada; *Int'l*, pg. 31
Annandsingh, Clive, Dir.-Fin.--Johnson & Johnson Hemisferica, Caguas, PR; *U.S. Public*, pg. 928
Annee, Frans L.J., Gen. Mgr.--Celtona B.V., Cuyk, Netherlands; *U.S. Public*, pg. 672
Ansbro, Peter M., Gen. Mgr.--Electronic Controls Division, Carthage, IL; *U.S. Public*, pg. 1101
Ansell, Robin, Mgr.--EG & G Ireland, Instruments Division, Dublin, Ireland; *U.S. Public*, pg. 544
Ansell, Tom, Plant Mgr.--Lamson & Sessions Ltd., Saint-Laurent, Canada; *U.S. Public*, pg. 976
Anselmo, Peter, Pres.--Baldwin Graphic Systems, Inc., Shelton, CT; *U.S. Public*, pg. 170
Ansley, William S., Pres.--W.G. Carroll, Inc., Atlanta, GA; *U.S. Public*, pg. 1071
Anspack, C., Mng. Dir.--Metalair Limited, Spalding, United Kingdom; *Int'l*, pg. 1065
Anspack, C.J., Mng. Dir.--Metalair-Filliat Limited, Spalding, United Kingdom; *Int'l*, pg. 1065
Anstaett, Douglas J., Publr.--The Newton Kansan, Newton, KS; *U.S. Private*, pg. 995
Ansteeg, H.P., Pres.--Intochem B.V., Woerden, Netherlands; *Int'l*, pg. 682
Anstett, Joseph L., Pres. & Chief Fin. Officer--Silver State Disposal Service, Inc., Las Vegas, NV; *U.S. Public*, pg. 1380
Anstett, Joseph L., Pres.--Disposal Urban Maintenance Procession Co., Inc., Las Vegas, NV; *U.S. Public*, pg. 1380
Anstice, David W., Pres.--Merck Human Health Division, Rahway, NJ; *U.S. Public*, pg. 1090
Antal, Joe, Plant Mgr.--Clinton Plant, Clinton, AR; *U.S. Public*, pg. 201
Antczack, Joachim, Mng. Dir.--LBB Betriebsservice GmbH, Berlin, Germany; *Int'l*, pg. 160
Antekeiev, Steve, Gen. Mgr.--The Access Works, Inc., Muskegon, MI; *U.S. Private*, pg. 410
Antes, Ernie, Pres.--Casting Materials Division, Chattanooga, TN; *U.S. Private*, pg. 525
Anthony, A.J., Mng. Dir.--Lucas Aftermarket Operations, Solihull, United Kingdom; *Int'l*, pg. 819
Anthony, Brian, Gen. Mgr.--Bowen Tools, Ltd., Edmonton, Canada; *U.S. Public*, pg. 858
Anthony, Carl, V.P.--Burnup & Sims Communications Services, Norcross, GA; *U.S. Public*, pg. 1056
Anthony, Clary, Jr., V.P. & Gen. Mgr.--Anthony Forest Div., Atlanta, TX; *U.S. Private*, pg. 76
Anthony, John, V.P.--Engineered Wood Div., El Dorado, AR; *U.S. Private*, pg. 76
Anthony, Robert T., Gen. Mgr.--Stacey Moving & Storage, Cincinnati, OH; *U.S. Private*, pg. 869
Anthony, Russ, V.P. & Gen. Mgr.--Anthony Forest Div., Urbana, AR; *U.S. Private*, pg. 76
Anthony, William H., Pres.--Daden-Anthony Associates, Inc., San Clemente, CA; *U.S. Public*, pg. 1563
Antila, Timo, Mng. Dir.--Tako Carton Plant Ltd., Tampere, Finland; *Int'l*, pg. 863
Antin, Roger, Publisher--Bride's, New York, NY; *U.S. Private*, pg. 20
Antinucci, Joseph D., Pres.--Martin Marietta Electronics & Missiles, Orlando, FL; *U.S. Public*, pg. 1007
Antioco, John, Chief Exec. Officer--Blockbuster Entertainment Group, Dallas, TX; *U.S. Private*, pg. 775
Antle, Jerry, V.P.--B. Elliott Inc., Hilliard, OH; *Int'l*, pg. 449
Antollini, Massimo, Rep.--Cariplo (Beijing), Beijing, China; *Int'l*, pg. 275
Antolock, Rod, V.P.--San Antonio Division, San Antonio, TX; *U.S. Public*, pg. 38
Anton, Jose, V.P.-Info.--Publicitas C.A., Guayaquil, Ecuador; *U.S. Public*, pg. 1422
Antonacci, Sandra, Mgr.--Utell International-Venezuela, Caracas, Venezuela; *Int'l*, pg. 1099
Antonellis, Domenic M., Pres. & Chief Oper. Officer--New England Confectionery Co., Cambridge, MA; *U.S. Private*, pg. 1113
Antonellis, Dominic, Pres.--Haviland Candy Inc., Cambridge, MA; *U.S. Private*, pg. 1113
Antoni, Manfred, Mng. Dir.--Wiley-VCH, Weinheim, Germany; *U.S. Public*, pg. 1768
Antoni, Manfred, Dr., Mng. Dir.--Schaffer-Poeschel Verlag, Stuttgart, Germany; *Int'l*, pg. 1478
Antonietti, Alfredo, Mng. Dir.--ESAB Saldatura S.p.A., Milan, Italy; *Int'l*, pg. 282
Antonino, Dell'Orto ing., Chm. & Mng. Dir.--Acquedotto Monferrato S.p.A., Turin, Italy; *Int'l*, pg. 428
Antonio, Helio Aparecido, Mgr.--Grand Cayman Branch, Grand Cayman, Cayman Islands; *Int'l*, pg. 139
Antonoff, David, Gen. Mgr.--Nordson de Mexico, S.A. de C.V., Mexico, Mexico; *U.S. Public*, pg. 1189
Antonsen, Peter, Mng. Dir.--Carl Munters ApS, Farum, Denmark; *Int'l*, pg. 669
Antonsson, Bengt, Gen. Mgr.--Tele Facilities, Vaxjo, Sweden; *Int'l*, pg. 277
Antoun, Jane, Pres.--Prentice Hall School, Upper Saddle River, NJ; *U.S. Private*, pg. 778
Antoun, Jane, Pres.--Secondary Division, Upper Saddle River, NJ; *U.S. Private*, pg. 778
Antoun, S.D., Pres.-Worldwide Sls.--Dresser-Rand Sales, Houston, TX; *U.S. Public*, pg. 529
Antsalo, Ari, Mng. Dir.--MD Papier GmbH, Dachau, Germany; *Int'l*, pg. 864
Antsalo, Ari, Mng. Dir.--MD Papier GmbH - Plattling Mill, Plattling, Germany; *Int'l*, pg. 864
Anttila, Jaakko, Mng. Dir.--Schauman S.A., Bihorel, France; *Int'l*, pg. 1429
Anttila, Mikko, Chief Oper. Officer--Perstorp Form Oy, Heinola, Finland; *Int'l*, pg. 1038
Anttomer, Risto, Chief Oper. Officer--Ahlstrom Alcore Ltd., Karhula, Finland; *Int'l*, pg. 33
Anttonen, Risto, Pres.--Ahlstrom Alcore Ltd, Karhula, Finland; *Int'l*, pg. 32
Anundi, Sven, Pres.--NCC Building, Lulea, Sweden; *Int'l*, pg. 898
Anzai, K., Gen. Mgr.--Mitsui & Co. (Canada), Calgary, Canada; *Int'l*, pg. 880
Anzilotti, Michael G., Pres. & Chief Exec. Officer--First Virginia Bank, Falls Church, VA; *U.S. Public*, pg. 641
Anzola, Francisco, Pres.--Bariven, S.A., Caracas, Venezuela; *Int'l*, pg. 1045
Anzola, H., Pres.--Etoxyl, C.A., Caracas, Venezuela; *U.S. Public*, pg. 1219
Anzuini, Henry G., Pres.--Metal Forge, Columbus, OH; *U.S. Public*, pg. 727
Aoki, E., V.P. & Gen. Mgr.--Ishihara Corporation (U.S.A.), San Francisco, CA; *Int'l*, pg. 689
Aoki, Harriet M., Pres. & Chief Exec. Officer--First Hawaiian Creditcorp, Inc., Honolulu, HI; *U.S. Public*, pg. 635
Aoki, Hatsuo, Chm. Bd.--Fujisawa U.S.A., Deerfield, IL; *Int'l*, pg. 525
Aoki, Hirohisa, Pres.--Tokai Bank of California, Los Angeles, CA; *Int'l*, pg. 1391
Aoki, Kazuyoshi, Gen. Mgr.--Nikko Bank (Switzerland) Ltd., Lugano, Switzerland; *Int'l*, pg. 930
Aoki, Marcia, V.P.--United Media Japan, Tokyo, Japan; *U.S. Public*, pg. 1448
Aoki, Rocky H., Chm. Bd.--Big Splash Kendall Corp., Miami, FL; *U.S. Public*, pg. 212
Aoki, Rocky H., Chm. Bd.--Teppan Restaurants, Beaverton, OR; *U.S. Public*, pg. 212
Aoki, Rocky H., Chm. Bd.--Benihana Sunrise Corp., Citrus Heights, CA; *U.S. Public*, pg. 212
Aoki, Rocky H., Chm. Bd.--Benihana National Corp., Miami, FL; *U.S. Public*, pg. 212
Aoki, Setsuo, Pres.--Matsushita Refrigeration Company, Osaka, Japan; *Int'l*, pg. 846
Aoki, Tatsuo, Pres.--The Meijiseimei Insurance Services of California, Inc., Los Angeles, CA; *Int'l*, pg. 854
Aoki, Tsuneo, Chief Representative--Ashikaga Bank-Hong Kong Representative Office, Hong Kong, Hong Kong; *Int'l*, pg. 88
Aoki, Tsuneo, Mng. Dir. & Gen. Mgr.--Ashikaga Finance (H.K.) Limited, Hong Kong, Hong Kong; *Int'l*, pg. 88
Aoki, Yashimitsu, Pres.--Diamond Lease U.S.A. Inc., Greenwich, CT; *Int'l*, pg. 413
Aonuma, Hiroji, Pres.--Kyushu Matsushita Electric Co. Ltd., Fukuoka, Japan; *Int'l*, pg. 846
Aota, N., Gen. Mgr.--Marubeni America Corporation, Indianapolis Office, Indianapolis, IN; *Int'l*, pg. 844
Aoya, Tomoo, Rep.--The Kyoei Mutual Fire & Marine Insurance Company, London Representative Office, London, United Kingdom; *Int'l*, pg. 777
Aoyagi, Kazuhiro, Pres.--Komatsu Europe International N.V., Vilvoorde, Belgium; *Int'l*, pg. 744
Aoyagi, Susumu, Pres.--Quick Nikkei News, Inc., New York, NY; *Int'l*, pg. 929
Aoyama, Yukio, Chief Rep.--The Sumitomo Trust & Banking Co., Ltd., Bellevue, WA; *Int'l*, pg. 1317
Aparecido dos Santos, Manoel, Gen. Mgr.--Banco do Brasil S.A.-Singapore, Singapore, Singapore; *Int'l*, pg. 141
Apenor, Jose, Gen. Mgr.--BancTec (Puerto Rico), Inc., Juana Diaz, PR; *U.S. Public*, pg. 177
Apichit, Boonchai, Mgr.--B.A. Resources Co., Ltd., Bangkok, Thailand; *U.S. Public*, pg. 414
Appel, Ing. H., Chief Oper. Officer--IAV Ingenieurgesellschaft fur Aggregatetechnik und Verkehrsfahrzeuge mbH, Berlin, Germany; *Int'l*, pg. 1473
Appel, John, Pres.--General Business Services, Inc., Waco, TX; *U.S. Public*, pg. 538
Appel, John, Pres.--E.K. Williams, Waco, TX; *U.S. Public*, pg. 538
Appel, John C., Pres. & Exec. V.P.-Network Opers.--GTE North Incorporated, Irving, TX; *U.S. Public*, pg. 696
Appel, John C., Pres.--GTE South Incorporated, Irving, TX; *U.S. Public*, pg. 697
Appel, Marcia, Chief Oper. Officer--Request, Minnetonka, MN; *U.S. Public*, pg. 1142
Appel, Michael, Country Mgr.--Autodesk AG, Pratteln, Switzerland; *U.S. Public*, pg. 149
Appel, Norman, Plant Mgr.--Bell Flavors & Fragrances, Middletown, NY; *U.S. Private*, pg. 131
Appelgren, James, Pres.--Danaher Corporation, Gurnee, IL; *U.S. Public*, pg. 480
Appelgren, James W., Pres.--Danaher Controls, Morristown, NJ; *U.S. Public*, pg. 480
Appelgren, Jim, Pres.--Automatic Signal/Eagle Signal, Austin, TX; *Int'l*, pg. 1245
Appell, L.J., Jr., Chm. Bd.--The Pfaltzgraff Co., York, PA; *U.S. Private*, pg. 860
Appleby, Charles L., Pres.--Sumbank Life Insurance Co., Sumter, SC; *U.S. Public*, pg. 1549
Appleby, Trevor H., Pres.--Manufacturers Life Mortgage Securities Corporation, Richmond, VA; *Int'l*, pg. 840
Applegate, Malcolm W., Pres. & Gen. Mgr.--Indianapolis Newspapers, Inc., Indianapolis, IN; *U.S. Public*, pg. 326
Appleton, Neil, Mng. Dir.--John Wyeth & Brother Ltd., Maidenhead, United Kingdom; *U.S. Public*, pg. 82
Appleton, Stuart, Chief Exec. Officer--Metro Group, London, United Kingdom; *Int'l*, pg. 1482
Applewhite, Marvin, Pres.--Applications International Division, Sunbury-on-Thames, United Kingdom; *U.S. Public*, pg. 1516
Applewhite, Marvin, V.P.-Information Technology--Texas Instruments Information Technology Group, Austin, TX; *U.S. Public*, pg. 1586
Appoloni, Peter, Chief Exec. Officer--Ascom Zelcom AG, Hombrechtikon, Switzerland; *Int'l*, pg. 86
Apraxine, Elisabeth, Rep.--Generale Bank, Moscow, Russia; *Int'l*, pg. 547
April, Rand S., Partner--Skadden, Arps, Slate, Meagher & Flom LLP, Los Angeles, CA; *U.S. Private*, pg. 1004
Aprilae, Umberto, Pres.--Industrias Gessy Lever Ltda., Sao Paulo, Brazil; *Int'l*, pg. 1437
Aprile, Joe, Pres.--Canteen Corporation, Charlotte, NC; *Int'l*, pg. 324
Aque, Charles A., Pres.--Nevco Housewares, Inc., Garfield, NJ; *U.S. Public*, pg. 1341
Aquin, Richard, Gen. Mgr.--DEMIX Construction, Longueuil, Canada; *Int'l*, pg. 629
Aragon, Ivan, Gen. Mgr.--Viacom Video-Audio Comunicacoes, Ltda., Sao Paulo, Brazil; *U.S. Private*, pg. 780
Arai, Atsumi, Chief Oper. Officer--Tesco Co., Ltd., Yamanashi, Japan; *Int'l*, pg. 1262
Arai, Hiroshi, Pres.--Kyokuyo America Corp., Seattle, WA; *Int'l*, pg. 777
Arai, Hyoma, Pres.--PT Hanken Indonesia, Bekasi, Indonesia; *Int'l*, pg. 745
Arai, Kentaro, Pres. & Chief Exec. Officer--Calsonic International, Inc., Irvine, CA; *Int'l*, pg. 944
Arai, Masanori, Chief Oper. Officer--P.T. Tembaga Mulia Semanan (TMS), Jakarta, Indonesia; *Int'l*, pg. 531
Arai, Michio, Chief Oper. Officer--Furukawa Industrial S.A. Produtos Eletricos (FISA), Curitiba, Brazil; *Int'l*, pg. 531
Arai, Moasami, Sr. V.P.--Ryobi North America, Inc., Chicago, IL; *Int'l*, pg. 1151
Arai, Satoshi, Pres.--Kawasho International Canada Ltd., Vancouver, Canada; *Int'l*, pg. 727
Arai, Shuzo, Chief Exec.--Sanwa International plc, London, United Kingdom; *Int'l*, pg. 1190
Arai, Takao, Pres. & Chief Exec. Officer--Nippon Life Insurance Company of the Philippines, Inc., Makati, Philippines; *Int'l*, pg. 936

Arai, Takashi, Pres.--Daiko HWG Advertising Corp., Taipei, Taiwan; *Int'l*, pg. 366
Arakawa, Carolyn, Gen. Mgr.--Loewe Hawaii Inc., Honolulu, HI; *Int'l*, pg. 781
Arakawa, Kenichiro, Mng. Dir.--Nippon Express (Australia) Pty., Ltd., Mascot, Australia; *Int'l*, pg. 934
Arakawa, Masao, V.P. & Gen. Mgr.--Matsushita Electric Works Research & Development Laboratory Inc., San Jose, CA; *Int'l*, pg. 848
Arakawa, Minoru, Pres.--Nintendo of America, Redmond, WA; *Int'l*, pg. 932
Arakawa, Shipei, Chief Oper. Officer--Honda Automobili Italia S.p.A., Verona, Italy; *Int'l*, pg. 635
Arakawa, Sinpei, Chief Oper. Officer--Honda Nederland B.V., Ridderkerk, Netherlands; *Int'l*, pg. 635
Araki, Keisuke, Pres. & Chief Exec. Officer--Oki America Inc., Hackensack, NJ; *Int'l*, pg. 1000
Araki, Kimio, Chief Rep.--Jakarta Representative Office, Jakarta, Indonesia; *Int'l*, pg. 520
Araki, Ryoichi, Pres.--Igaku-Shoin MYW Ltd., Tokyo, Japan; *U.S. Public*, pg. 1748
Arako, Toshihiko, Pres.--Chugai Boyeki Co., Ltd., Torrance, CA; *Int'l*, pg. 290
Aramani, Ronald A., Pres. & Chief Exec. Officer--Allegheny Airlines, Inc., Middletown, PA; *U.S. Public*, pg. 1680
Arana, Jose Manuel Jimendez, Pres.--ENCASUR - E.N. Carbonifera del Sur, S.A., Madrid, Spain; *Int'l*, pg. 1224
Arancibia, Carlos, Mng. Dir.--Alfonzo Rivas Co., C.A., Caracas, Venezuela; *U.S. Public*, pg. 447
Arands, Peter, Mng. Dir.--Hamilton/Livingston, Veenendaal, Netherlands; *Int'l*, pg. 212
Arango Correa, Alvaro, Pres.--Sancho S.A., Bogota, Colombia; *U.S. Public*, pg. 1422
Aranguren, Ignacio, Pres.--Productos de Maiz S.A., Guadalajara, Mexico; *U.S. Public*, pg. 448
Arashida, Masao, U.S. Dir.--AG Industries, Inc., Redmond, WA; *Int'l*, pg. 40
Arata, Frank N., Jr, Pres.--Keyes Asset Managemet, Miami, FL; *U.S. Private*, pg. 618
Aratani, Masao, Chief Rep.--The Meiji Life Insurance Company Toronto Office, Toronto, Canada; *Int'l*, pg. 854
Aratani, Seiichi, Chief Oper. Officer--Oki Electric Europe GmbH, Neuss, Germany; *Int'l*, pg. 1000
Aratani, Sho, Pres.--Charmilles Technologies (Japan) Ltd., Yokohama, Japan; *Int'l*, pg. 489
Aratani, Sho, Gen. Mgr.--Georg Fischer Japan Ltd., Tokyo, Japan; *Int'l*, pg. 490
Araujo, Jose Almeida, Mgr.--Recife Branch, Recife, Brazil; *Int'l*, pg. 139
Aravind, Indira, Mng. Dir.--MDK Consultants (Malaysia), Kuala Lumpur, Malaysia; *Int'l*, pg. 117
Aravind, Indira, Mng. Dir.--Daniel J. Edelman Sdn. Bhd., Kuala Lumpur, Malaysia; *U.S. Private*, pg. 363
Arayama, Mitsu, Pres.--Nissin Foods (U.S.A.) Co. Ltd., Gardena, CA; *Int'l*, pg. 949
Arazi, Igal, Mgr.--Bank Leumi le-Israel B.M., Encino, CA; *Int'l*, pg. 150
Arazi, Z., Gen. Mgr.--Engineering Division/Commercial Aircraft Group, Israel; *Int'l*, pg. 690
Arbman, Jan, Creative Dir.--Jan Arbman EURO RSCG, Stockholm, Sweden; *Int'l*, pg. 602
Arbo, Lester H., Sr. V.P. & Gen. Mgr.--Santa Fe Offshore Construction Co., Houston, TX; *Int'l*, pg. 765
Arbuthnot, P.A., Mng. Dir.--Christie's Scotland Ltd., Glasgow, United Kingdom; *Int'l*, pg. 290
Arcara, James A., Pres. & Chief Oper. Officer--KRXY Holding Corporation, New York, NY; *U.S. Public*, pg. 512
Arcara, James P., Pres.--Capital Cities/ABC Radio, New York, NY; *U.S. Public*, pg. 512
Arce, Francisco, Chm. Bd.--Derly, S.A., Madrid, Spain; *U.S. Public*, pg. 993
Arce, Jose, Chm. Bd.--Dista, S.A., Madrid, Spain; *U.S. Public*, pg. 993
Arcella, Frank, Pres.--AeroMet Corporation, Eden Prairie, MN; *U.S. Public*, pg. 1029
Archambault, David, Gen. Mgr.--Whale Scientific Inc., Commerce City, CO; *U.S. Public*, pg. 1595
Archer, B.F., Plant Superintendant--General Shale Products Corp., Johnson City, TN; *Int'l*, pg. 843
Archer, Charles L., Pres.--Associated Business Products, Inc., Las Vegas, NV; *U.S. Public*, pg. 863
Archer, Chris, Mgr.--Amano Cincinnati - Los Angeles Branch Office, Anaheim, CA; *Int'l*, pg. 70
Archer, David, Pres.--Cello Bag Company, Inc., Renton, WA; *Int'l*, pg. 72
Archer, Doris, Dir.--Columbia LifeCare Center, El Paso, TX; *U.S. Public*, pg. 404
Archer, Frank, Pres.--LaSalle Steel Company, Hammond, IN; *U.S. Public*, pg. 1181
Archer, Ian, Chief Oper. Officer--CTS U.K., Ltd., Glasgow, United Kingdom; *U.S. Public*, pg. 286
Archer, James P., Pres.--Newell Paper Co. of Hattiesburg, Hattiesburg, MS; *U.S. Private*, pg. 579
Archer, Ken, Acting Pres.--European Business Development, Farnborough, United Kingdom; *U.S. Public*, pg. 423
Archer, P., Chief Oper. Officer--Britax-Excelsior Limited, Andover, United Kingdom; *Int'l*, pg. 216
Archer, Paul D., Pres.--Ikon Office Solutions-Colorado, Denver, CO; *U.S. Public*, pg. 863
Archer, R. H., Mng. Dir.--WBB Pacific Clays Ltd., Singapore, Singapore; *Int'l*, pg. 1488
Archer, Ricardo A., Mng. Dir.--Publicidad Diaz, S.A. de C.V., San Salvador, El Salvador; *U.S. Private*, pg. 186
Archer, Tracy, Dir.--GGT Direct Manchester, Manchester, United Kingdom; *Int'l*, pg. 532
Archibald, Art, Div. Mgr.--Champion Homes Div., Ridgeville, IN; *U.S. Public*, pg. 332
Archibald, W. A., Mgr.--De La Rue Systems Ltd., Havant, United Kingdom; *Int'l*, pg. 387
Archibeque, Charlie, Plant Mgr.--McKee Complex, Sunray, TX; *U.S. Public*, pg. 1663
Archila, Guillermo A., Pres.--Corpoven, S.A., Caracas, Venezuela; *Int'l*, pg. 1045
Archiszewski, Kasimar, Chief Oper. Officer--Speech Design, Munich, Germany; *U.S. Public*, pg. 740
Architas, Pauline, Acting Pres.--Europe Division, Paris, France; *U.S. Public*, pg. 1516
Archuleta, Al, Base Mgr.--Mercury Air Center, Dallas, TX; *U.S. Public*, pg. 1093
Ardrinard, J.B., Gen. Mgr.--Analog Devices, Greensboro, NC; *U.S. Public*, pg. 108
Areheim, Gunnar, Mng. Dir.--Acuson AB, Arlandastad, Sweden; *U.S. Public*, pg. 18
Arellano, Alfonso Rodriguez, Mng. Dir.--Woolworth Mexicana, S.A. de C.V., Mexico, Mexico; *U.S. Public*, pg. 1778
Arellano, Frank, Plant Mgr.--Hydro Conduit Corp., Fresno, CA; *Int'l*, pg. 245
Arellano, Jose Lopez, Mgr.--Grupo Termoindustrial ECA, S.A. de C.V., Puebla, Mexico; *U.S. Public*, pg. 361
Arena, George, Pres.--Microwave Data Systems, Inc., Rochester, NY; *U.S. Public*, pg. 293
Arena, Pier Carlo, Rep.--Sanpaolo-Athens Representative Office, Athens, Greece; *Int'l*, pg. 691
Arends, Mike, Gen. Mgr.--Arrow/Schweber Electronics, Eden Prairie, MN; *U.S. Public*, pg. 134
Arendse, Albert, Mng. Dir.--Shakespeare Hengelsport B.V., Nederhorst den Berg, Netherlands; *U.S. Public*, pg. 940
Arentowicz, Frank, V.P.--SMS Physician Services Division, Malvern, PA; *U.S. Public*, pg. 1463
Argabright, Steve, Pres.--Nalco Fuel Tech, Naperville, IL; *U.S. Public*, pg. 1150
Arganbright, David M., Pres.--Grolier Electronic Publishing, Inc., Danbury, CT; *Int'l*, pg. 794
Argente, Faustino de Andres, Pres.--SODIEX - Sociedad Para el Desarrollo Industrial de Extremadura, S.A., Caceres, Spain; *Int'l*, pg. 1225
Argente, Juan Vicente, Mgr.--Valencia Terminal, Valencia, Spain; *U.S. Public*, pg. 693
Arguedas, Alejandro Munoz, Gen. Mgr.--Investigaciones Pioneer S de R.L. de C.V., Guadalajara, Mexico; *U.S. Public*, pg. 1299
Arguedas, Alejandro Munoz, Gen. Mgr.--Hibridos Pioneer De Mexico S.A. DE C.V., Guadalajara, Mexico; *U.S. Public*, pg. 1299
Aricci, Don, Gen. Mgr.--Bryant Park Grill, New York, NY; *U.S. Public*, pg. 130
Arici, D., Dir.--Bols-Cynar, AG, Zurich, Switzerland; *Int'l*, pg. 751
Arikawa, Hiroyuki, Mgr.--Noritake Service Center, Arlington Heights, IL; *Int'l*, pg. 959
Arikoglu, Dr. Osman, Gen. Mgr.--Pioneer Tohumculuk A.S., Istanbul, Turkey; *U.S. Public*, pg. 1299
Arima, Jun, Country Mgr.--BMC Software Japan Ltd., Tokyo, Japan; *U.S. Public*, pg. 163
Arima, K., Pres.--Nippon Crown House Co., Ltd., Sasima, Japan; *Int'l*, pg. 946
Arima, Yukinori, Gen. Mgr.--Dai-ichi Kangyo Bank, Ltd.-Kaohsiung Branch, Kao-hsiung, Taiwan; *Int'l*, pg. 360
Arimura, R., Chief Oper. Officer--N.V. Nissho Iwai (Benelux) S.A., Brussels, Belgium; *Int'l*, pg. 948
Arise, Bill, Mgr.--Merit Steel Company, Inc., Kouts, IN; *U.S. Public*, pg. 986
Arismendi, Miguel Francisco, Gen. Mgr.--Amway Colombia, Bogota, Colombia; *U.S. Private*, pg. 69
Arita, Tomojiro, Pres.--Sumitrans Corporation, Lake Success, NY; *Int'l*, pg. 1312
Aritake, Masami, Chief Oper. Officer--Haseko Corp.-Kansai Office, Osaka, Japan; *Int'l*, pg. 600
Ariura, Hiroshi, Pres.--Nissan Motor del Peru S.A., Lima, Peru; *Int'l*, pg. 945
Arkayin, Sukru, Gen. Mgr.--Philsa Philip Morris Sabanci Sigara Ve Tutunculuk A.S., Istanbul, Turkey; *Int'l*, pg. 1168
Arkayin, Sukru, Gen. Mgr.--Philsa Philip Morris Sabanci Sigara Ve Tutunculuk A.S., Istanbul, Turkey; *U.S. Public*, pg. 1290
Arkenberg, Pedro, Chief Oper. Officer--Henkel Argentina S.A., Buenos Aires, Argentina; *Int'l*, pg. 611
Arkin, Annette, Gen. Mgr.--MTI Systems Div., New York, NY; *U.S. Public*, pg. 135
Arld, P.G., Chief Oper. Officer--Haden Technical Services Corporation, Madison Heights, MI; *Int'l*, pg. 586
Arledge, David A., Mng. Dir.--ANR Finance N.V., Curacao, Netherlands Antilles; *U.S. Public*, pg. 391
Arledge, Roone, Pres. & Chief Oper. Officer--ABC News Holding Company, Inc., New York, NY; *U.S. Public*, pg. 511
Arlint, Tom, Opers. Mgr.--Willamette Industries, Inc., Eugene, OR; *U.S. Public*, pg. 1769
Arlot, Bernard, Mgr.--SAS, Saint Laurent-de-Mure, France; *Int'l*, pg. 430
Armbrust, Rick, V.P.--Square D Automation Products, Milwaukee, WI; *Int'l*, pg. 1208
Armbruster, David, Laboratory Dir.--PharmChem Laboratories, Inc.-Texas Division, Fort Worth, TX; *U.S. Public*, pg. 1285
Armendariz, Ramos Gaztelu, Chm. Bd.--Arteaga, Sociedad Anomima, "Arteaga, S.A.", Logrono, Spain; *U.S. Public*, pg. 1386
Armiger, Jeff, Mng. Dir.--Eagle-Picher Fluid Systems Limited, Market Harborough, United Kingdom; *U.S. Private*, pg. 355
Armit, C., Mng. Dir.--Glaxo Wellcome Australia Ltd., Boronia, Australia; *Int'l*, pg. 553
Armitage, Alan, Mgr.--Simpson Industries, Inc. (Germany), Gross-Gerau, Germany; *U.S. Public*, pg. 1475
Armour, Bruce, Site Leader--AlliedSignal Aerospatiale Canada Inc., Montreal, Canada; *U.S. Public*, pg. 53
Armour, James A., Pres. & Chief Exec. Officer--AM General Corporation, South Bend, IN; *U.S. Private*, pg. 922
Arms, Bradley C., Pres.--Cigna Healthcare of Florida, Inc., Tampa, FL; *U.S. Public*, pg. 359
Armstrong, Anthony N., Mng. Dir.--Skandia UK Insurance plc, London, United Kingdom; *Int'l*, pg. 1258
Armstrong, Beverly W., Pres.--AMF Bowling Centers Inc., Richmond, VA; *U.S. Private*, pg. 7
Armstrong, Bill, Sr. V.P.--Americana Foods, Inc., Dallas, TX; *U.S. Public*, pg. 1554
Armstrong, Bruce, Sr. V.P. & Gen. Mgr.--ICL, Inc., Irvine, CA; *Int'l*, pg. 529
Armstrong, C. Michael, Pres.--IBM World Trade Europe/Middle East/Africa Corp., Rye Brook, NY; *U.S. Public*, pg. 896
Armstrong, D.F., Plant Mgr.--Longview Fibre Co. Western Container Div., Oakland, CA; *U.S. Public*, pg. 1014
Armstrong, David M., Pres.--Armstrong-Yoshitake, Inc., Three Rivers, MI; *U.S. Private*, pg. 83
Armstrong, F. Scott, Mgr.-Sls.--PENCO-Arizona, Phoenix, AZ; *Int'l*, pg. 1508
Armstrong, Gary, Pres.--Brown Machine Div., Beaverton, MI; *Int'l*, pg. 773
Armstrong, Gary, V.P. & Gen. Mgr.--Newcor Bay City Division, Bay City, MI; *U.S. Public*, pg. 1176
Armstrong, Gerard M., Pres.--Coscan Washington, Inc., Vienna, VA; *Int'l*, pg. 228
Armstrong, Greg L., Pres.--Calumet Florida, Inc., Immokalee, FL; *U.S. Public*, pg. 1308
Armstrong, Greg L., Pres. & Chief Exec. Officer--Plains Illinois, Inc., Bridgeport, IL; *U.S. Public*, pg. 1308
Armstrong, Ian, Dir.-Admin. & Systems--Willis Corroon Midlands Limited, Birmingham, United Kingdom; *Int'l*, pg. 1502
Armstrong, Ian, Dir.-Admin.--Willis Corroon Scotland Limited, Glasgow, United Kingdom; *Int'l*, pg. 1503
Armstrong, Jeff, Pres.--ASI Landmark, Inc., Cary, NC; *U.S. Public*, pg. 110
Armstrong, John A., V.P.-Science & Technology--IBM Research Div., Yorktown Heights, NY; *U.S. Public*, pg. 896
Armstrong, M. Reid, Pres.--Overland Energy, Inc., Overland Park, KS; *U.S. Public*, pg. 1788
Armstrong, M.E., V.P. & Gen. Mgr.--Flowserve Corporation, Foundry Div., Dayton, OH; *U.S. Public*, pg. 658
Armstrong, Peter, Mng. Dir.--Young & Rubicam (Zambia) Ltd., Lusaka, Zambia; *U.S. Private*, pg. 1198
Armstrong, R.K., Pres.--Canada West Indies Molasses Co. Ltd., Mississauga, Canada; *Int'l*, pg. 1357
Armstrong, Roberta, Lab Mgr.--Quest Diagnostic-Lewistown, Lewistown, PA; *U.S. Public*, pg. 1351
Armstrong, W. Charles, Chm. & Pres.--Bank of America Oregon, Portland, OR; *U.S. Public*, pg. 180
Armstrong, Wayne, Pres.--Lockheed Martin Tactical Defense Systems, Archbald, PA; *U.S. Public*, pg. 1009
Arnaboldi, F., Mgr.--Societa di Banca Svizzera, Lugano, Switzerland; *Int'l*, pg. 1329
Arnaiz, Ramon B., Gen. Mgr.--Raco Trading Phils., Inc., Manila, Philippines; *Int'l*, pg. 303
Arnaldo, Jose A., Mng. Dir.--Heinz Iberica, S.A., Madrid, Spain; *U.S. Public*, pg. 806
Arner, Howard, Gen. Mgr. & Controller--SMI Miscellaneous, Cayce, SC; *U.S. Public*, pg. 412
Arneth, Gerhard, Gen. Mgr.--Select Communications, GmbH, Hamburg, Hamburg, Germany; *U.S. Private*, pg. 982
Arnett, Greg, Plant Mgr.--Dayton Superior Corp., Birmingham, AL; *U.S. Private*, pg. 931
Arnette, F. Davis, Pres. & Chief Exec. Officer--Regions Bank/Elbert County, Elberton, GA; *U.S. Public*, pg. 1372
Arno, Raymond, Pres.--Airtex, Lancaster, NY; *U.S. Private*, pg. 1113
Arnold, Barbara, Pres.--Optical Products Group, Brooklyn Park, MN; *U.S. Public*, pg. 162
Arnold, Barbara, Pres.--Vision-Ease Lens Inc., Brooklyn Park, MN; *U.S. Public*, pg. 162
Arnold, Bernd, Chief Oper. Officer--GSG Siedlungsgesellschaft fuer Wohnungs-und Staedtebau mbH, Frankfurt/Main, Germany; *Int'l*, pg. 799
Arnold, Bob, Gen. Mgr.--Allied Advertising Agency, Public Relations, Philadelphia, PA; *U.S. Private*, pg. 38
Arnold, Cissy, V.P. & Gen. Mgr.--Fogarty Klein & Partners Yellow Pages, Inc., Austin, TX; *U.S. Private*, pg. 416
Arnold, D., Dir.--Telford Foods Ltd., Telford, United Kingdom; *Int'l*, pg. 753
Arnold, Dale P., Pres.--Hickory Point Bank & Trust, Decatur, IL; *U.S. Public*, pg. 128
Arnold, Edward, Pres.--Lockheed Martin Librascope, Glendale, CA; *U.S. Public*, pg. 1008
Arnold, Eric S., Mgr.-Terminal--Richmond Terminal, Richmond, CA; *U.S. Public*, pg. 692
Arnold, Franz, Mng. Dir.--Bayerische Vereinsbank AG, Madrid, Spain; *Int'l*, pg. 180
Arnold, G. Steven, Gen. Mgr.--EG & G Automotive Research, San Antonio, TX; *U.S. Public*, pg. 544
Arnold, Glen, Pres.--Ameritech Applied Technologies, Inc., Chicago, IL; *U.S. Public*, pg. 90
Arnold, Gray, Pres.--Consultec, Inc., Atlanta, GA; *U.S. Private*, pg. 443
Arnold, Hans, Dr., Mng. Dir.--Dresdner Bank Kreditbank AG, Dresden, Germany; *Int'l*, pg. 418
Arnold, Harry, Sr. V.P.-Airplane Devel. & Definition--Engineering Division, Renton, WA; *U.S. Public*, pg. 240
Arnold, J., Rep.--Swiss Bank Corporation, Bangkok, Thailand; *Int'l*, pg. 1330
Arnold, Jack, V.P.--Moore's Quality Snack Foods, Inc., Bristol, VA; *U.S. Private*, pg. 158
Arnold, James, Gen. Mgr.--AlliedSignal Turbochargers, Inc., Kyoei, Japan; *U.S. Public*, pg. 53
Arnold, Jeffrey R., V.P. & Mgr.--The Bank of Tokyo-Mitsubishi, Ltd. (Minnesota Corporate Banking), Minneapolis, MN; *Int'l*, pg. 157
Arnold, John B., Pres.--The Fifth Third Bank of Western Ohio, National Association, Piqua, OH; *U.S. Public*, pg. 622
Arnold, Junius H., Jr., Pres. & Gen. Mgr.--Technical Products Division, Sterling, VA; *U.S. Public*, pg. 424
Arnold, Karl, Chief Oper. Officer--Lintapharm AG, Zurich, Switzerland; *Int'l*, pg. 356
Arnold, Karl-Goutz, Mng. Dir.--SKF Textilmaschinen-Komponenten GmbH, Stuttgart, Germany; *Int'l*, pg. 1159

Arnold, N.D., Chm.--Lucas France SA, Paris, France; *Int'l*, pg. 820
Arnold, Rich, Dir.--The Merten Company, Cincinnati, OH; *U.S. Public*, pg. 333
Arnold, Sharon, Admin.--Bozeman Care Center, Bozeman, MT; *U.S. Public*, pg. 1712
Arnold, Stuart, Publisher--PC Week, Medford, MA; *Int'l*, pg. 1276
Arnold, Walter, Chief Oper. Officer--Banque Generale du Luxembourg (Suisse) SA, Zurich, Switzerland; *Int'l*, pg. 162
Arnold, Wayne H., V.P. & Gen. Mgr.--Miramichi Pulp & Paper Inc., Newcastle, Canada; *Int'l*, pg. 1104
Arnold, William V., III, Pres.--M & I Central State Bank, Ripon, WI; *U.S. Public*, pg. 1050
Arnoldi, Geoff, Pres. & Gen. Mgr.--Publicis BCP Toronto Inc., Toronto, Canada; *Int'l*, pg. 116
Arnott, Harvey, Branch Mgr.--Bergen Brunswig Medical Corporation, Renton, WA; *U.S. Public*, pg. 214
Arnstein, John, Representative--Generale Bank, Sao Paulo, Brazil; *Int'l*, pg. 547
Arnstrup, Knud, Chief Oper. Officer--Novo Nordisk A/S, Beijing, China; *Int'l*, pg. 987
Arntz, M., Mng. Dir.--GKN Walterscheid GmbH, Lohmar, Germany; *Int'l*, pg. 535
Arntzen, Jay, Chief Oper. Officer--FHE Services, Inc., Long Island City, NY; *Int'l*, pg. 746
Arnus, G., Mng. Dir.--De La Rue Systems SA, Madrid, Spain; *Int'l*, pg. 387
Aro, Pentti, Gen. Mgr.--Koneportaat Oy, Vantaa, Finland; *Int'l*, pg. 746
Aronen, Ilmo, Mng. Dir.--Raisio Feed Ltd., Raisio, Finland; *Int'l*, pg. 1085
Aronsson, Hans, Gen. Mgr.--Communications Systems, Vaxjo, Sweden; *Int'l*, pg. 277
Aronstam, Peter, Pres.--Downhole Seismic Services, Houston, TX; *U.S. Public*, pg. 1003
Arotsky, Steven, Mgr.--Kvaerner Energy a.s. Business Area Hydropower, London, United Kingdom; *Int'l*, pg. 767
Arp, Fredrik, Deputy Grp. Mng. Dir.--Trelleborg Rubber & Plastics Div., Trelleborg, Sweden; *Int'l*, pg. 1422
Arpel, Adrien, Chief Exec. Officer--Adrien Arpel, New York, NY; *U.S. Public*, pg. 40
Arppe, Martti, Mng. Dir.--Papierfabrik Albbruck GmbH, Albbruck, Germany; *Int'l*, pg. 864
Arque, Arnaldo, Mng. Dir.--Union Carbide Comercial C.A., Caracas, Venezuela; *U.S. Public*, pg. 1667
Arranz, Enrique Gil, Gen. Mgr.--Bailey-Fischer & Porter Espana S.A., Madrid, Spain; *Int'l*, pg. 449
Arranz, Gonzalo, Chief Exec.--Banco Santander, Shanghai, China; *Int'l*, pg. 144
Arreghini, Luciano, Mng. Dir.--Battenfeld Italia S.r.l., Saronno, Italy; *Int'l*, pg. 826
Arrendale, Thomas A., Pres.--Best Aviation, Baldwin, GA; *U.S. Private*, pg. 403
Arribas, D. Antonio Mayor, Dir.--Banco de Extremadura, S.A., Caceres, Spain; *Int'l*, pg. 251
Arrieta, C., Sr. V.P.-Gulf Coast Region--Daher Golden Eagle, Humble, TX; *U.S. Public*, pg. 749
Arrieta, Edgar, Pres.--Consultores Occidentales, S.A. (COSA), Maracaibo, Venezuela; *Int'l*, pg. 31
Arrieta, Jose Valentin, Gen. Mgr.--Rorer de Centro America (Guatemala) S.A., Guatemala, Guatemala; *Int'l*, pg. 1111
Arrigoni, Enrico, Mgr.--Sanpaolo-Frankfurt am Main Branch, Frankfurt, Germany; *Int'l*, pg. 692
Arrington, Charles M., Pres.--Supplemental Insurance Division, Inc., Little Rock, AR; *Int'l*, pg. 27
Arrington, Michael B., Chief Oper. Officer--Arrington-Hillgate International, London, United Kingdom; *U.S. Private*, pg. 85
Arrison, Craig, Pres.--Smith Metal Arts Company, Inc., Buffalo, NY; *U.S. Private*, pg. 1009
Arrowsmith, Peter D., Pres. & Chief Oper. Officer--Tetra Tech NUS, Inc., Gaithersburg, MD; *U.S. Public*, pg. 1582
Arroyo, Eduardo, Pres.--Orion Research Puerto Rico, Inc., Carolina, PR; *U.S. Public*, pg. 1592
Arruebarrena, Dennis, Mgr.--Commercial Metals Co., Chattanooga, TN; *U.S. Public*, pg. 413
Arsenault, Michael, Pres.--Florasynth Canada, Inc., Mont Royal, Canada; *Int'l*, pg. 173
Arslan, Muzaffer, Gen. Mgr.--Oysa Iskenderun Cimento Sanayi Ve Ticaret A.S., Iskenderun, Turkey; *Int'l*, pg. 1168
Arsuffi, Paolo, Pres.--Luxo Italiana S.p.a., Bergamo, Italy; *Int'l*, pg. 821
Arterbury, B.A., Pres.--Howard Smith Screen Co., Houston, TX; *U.S. Public*, pg. 776
Arthofer, Frank, Pres.--Nestle Chocolate & Confection, Glendale, CA; *Int'l*, pg. 917
Arthur, Erik, Mng. Dir.--Dun & Bradstreet Sverige AB, Solna, Sweden; *U.S. Public*, pg. 537
Arthur, Erik, Mng. Dir.--Dun & Bradstreet Soliditet AB, Stockholm, Sweden; *U.S. Public*, pg. 537
Arthur, Michael, Sr., Pres.--The Paper House/Southern Paper, Miami, FL; *U.S. Private*, pg. 467
Arthur, Rob, Gen. Mgr.-Emerging Markets--Dun & Bradstreet Hungaria Kft., Budapest, Hungary; *U.S. Public*, pg. 536
Arthur, Rob, Gen. Mgr.-Emerging Markets--Dun & Bradstreet spol s.r.o., Prague, Czech Republic; *U.S. Public*, pg. 537
Arthur, Ronald, Gen. Mgr.--Charleston Food Div., Charleston, WV; *U.S. Public*, pg. 260
Artigas de Pont, Montserrat, Chief Oper. Officer--Hospal S.A., Barcelona, Spain; *Int'l*, pg. 668
Artin, A.Y., Gen. Mgr.--Kodak (Near East) Inc., Beirut, Lebanon; *U.S. Public*, pg. 554
Artinger, Frank, Chief Oper. Officer--Williamhouse of Texas, Dallas, TX; *U.S. Public*, pg. 89
Artinian, Garo, Pres.--Draka U.S.A., Franklin, MA; *Int'l*, pg. 417
Artinian, Garo G., Pres.--Delta Suprenant Wire & Cable Inc., Clinton, MA; *Int'l*, pg. 391
Arts, H.J.J., Dir.--Ballast Nedam Funderingstechnieken B.V., Dordrecht, Netherlands; *Int'l*, pg. 133
Arts, Umberto, Gen. Mgr.--Kredietbank Hong Kong Branch, Wan Chai, Hong Kong; *Int'l*, pg. 760
Artz, Robert D., Branch Mgr.--Zellerbach Division, Columbus, OH; *U.S. Public*, pg. 1075
Artzt, Edwin L., Pres.--Procter & Gamble Commercial Co., Cincinnati, OH; *U.S. Public*, pg. 1331
Aruda, Ron, Branch Mgr.--Burns & Wilcox - Boston Office, Boston, MA; *U.S. Private*, pg. 609
Arunanondchai, Suvit, Pres.--Thai Orix Leasing Co., Ltd., Bangkok, Thailand; *Int'l*, pg. 677
Arundell, Terry, State Mgr.--National Mutual Victoria, Melbourne, Australia; *Int'l*, pg. 908
Arvanites, Hank, Pres.--Rexam Graphics, South Hadley, MA; *Int'l*, pg. 1107
Arzac, J. Pepe, Mng. Dir.--Simpson Industries S.A. de C.V. (Mexico), Mexico, Mexico; *U.S. Public*, pg. 1475
Arzac, J. Pepe, Mng. Dir.--Simpson Industries S.A. de C.V. (Mexico), San Luis Potosi, Mexico; *U.S. Public*, pg. 1475
Arzi, D., V.P. & Gen. Mgr.--BEDEK Aviation Group (IAI), Israel; *Int'l*, pg. 690
Asaba, Michiro, Exec. V.P. & Gen. Mgr.--Bank of Yokohama New York, New York, NY; *Int'l*, pg. 159
Asaba, Minoru, Pres.--Asahi America Inc., New York, NY; *Int'l*, pg. 85
Asaba, Minoru, Pres.--Asahi International Ltd., New York, NY; *Int'l*, pg. 85
Asad, Mohammed Khalid, Prod. Devel. Mgr.--Utell International-United Arab Emirates, Dubai, United Arab Emirates; *Int'l*, pg. 1099
Asada, Hiroshi, Pres.--Tigerpoly Manufacturing, Inc., Grove City, OH; *Int'l*, pg. 1390
Asada, Hiroshi, Pres.--Tigerflex Corporation, Elk Grove Village, IL; *Int'l*, pg. 1390
Asada, Junzo, Choef Oper. Officer--Dolmar GmbH, Hamburg, Germany; *Int'l*, pg. 831
Asada, Kentaro, Pres.--Meiji Seika (U.S.A.) Inc., New York, NY; *Int'l*, pg. 855
Asada, Toshihiro, Chief Representative--The Sumitomo Bank, Ltd.-Jakarta Representative Office, Jakarta, Indonesia; *Int'l*, pg. 1310
Asaji, Soichi, Pres.--Wackenhut Keibi K.K., Tokyo, Japan; *U.S. Public*, pg. 1731
Asaka, Eiji, Mng. Dir.--Daihatsu-Phranakorn Motor Co., Ltd., Bangkok, Thailand; *Int'l*, pg. 365
Asakura, Hideo, Mng. Dir.--Brother Industries (U.K.) Ltd.-Ruabon Factory, Wrexham, United Kingdom; *Int'l*, pg. 229
Asakura, Masa, Pres.--JAE Oregon, Inc., Tualatin, OR; *Int'l*, pg. 701
Asano, Kiyoshi, V.P. & Branch Mgr.--Noritake Co., Inc.-Table Top Div., New York, Secaucus, NJ; *Int'l*, pg. 959
Asano, Masayoshi, Mng. Dir.--Daiwa Europe (Italia) SIM p.A., Milan, Italy; *Int'l*, pg. 375
Asano, Tadanao, Pres.--Toray Textiles Europe Ltd., Nottingham, United Kingdom; *Int'l*, pg. 1400
Asano, Toshiyuki, Gen. Mgr.--Kyodo Advertising Co., Ltd., Sendai, Japan; *Int'l*, pg. 776
Asanshiwed, Pier, Pres.--Bull Electronics, Lowell, MA; *Int'l*, pg. 316
Asanuma, Motohiko, Gen. Mgr.--The Sakura Bank - Labuan Branch, Labuan, Malaysia; *Int'l*, pg. 1179
Asanuma, Tadaaki, Dir. & Gen. Mgr.--Okayama Branch Office, Okayama, Japan; *Int'l*, pg. 1491
Asao, Takeshi, Mng. Dir.--Siam Asahi Technoglass Co., Ltd., Ban Si Racha, Thailand; *Int'l*, pg. 1238
Asaro, Vincent J., Pres.--SunAmerica Securities, Inc., Phoenix, AZ; *U.S. Public*, pg. 1533
Asaumi, Naoaki, Pres. & Chief Exec. Officer--The Sakura Bank (Canada), Toronto, Canada; *Int'l*, pg. 1180
Asberg, Thomas, Pres.--Kvaerner Turbin AB, Kristinehamn, Sweden; *Int'l*, pg. 770
Asbill, Steve, Plant Mgr.--Pike Div., Zebulon, GA; *U.S. Public*, pg. 1599
Asbury, Neal, Pres.--Asbury Worldwide, Miramar, FL; *U.S. Public*, pg. 1110
Ascher, Michael C., Pres.--Triborough Bridge & Tunnel Authority, New York, NY; *U.S. Private*, pg. 739
Aschinger, Carl J., Jr., Chm. Bd. & Pres.--Columbus Showcase, Ashland Division, Ashland, KY; *U.S. Private*, pg. 257
Ash, Chuck, Plant Mgr.--Donaldson Co., Inc., Baldwin, WI; *U.S. Public*, pg. 517
Ash, Phyllis, Mgr.--Club Med Boutique, San Francisco, CA; *Int'l*, pg. 298
Ash, Rick, Gen. Mgr.--MTI Systems Div., Huntsville, AL; *U.S. Public*, pg. 135
Ashar, Mike, Exec. V.P.-Oil Sands Group--Suncor Oil Sands Group, Fort McMurray, Canada; *Int'l*, pg. 1320
Ashberry, Bill, Pres.--Enco-Georgia, Albany, GA; *U.S. Private*, pg. 375
Ashburn, Blaine, Mgr.-Property & Casualty Claims--Willis Corroon Administrative Services Corporation, Atlanta, GA; *Int'l*, pg. 1504
Ashby, Allan J., Mng. Dir.--Velsicol Chemical Limited, Basingstoke, United Kingdom; *U.S. Private*, pg. 1135
Ashby, C. Edward, Jr., Pres.--Envirosafe Services, Inc., King of Prussia, PA; *U.S. Public*, pg. 587
Ashby, Thomas W., Pres.--Brake Supply Co., Evansville, IN; *U.S. Private*, pg. 628
Ashcraft, David L., Grp. V.P.--Temple-Inland Forest Products Corp.-Bleached Paperboard Group, Evadale, TX; *U.S. Public*, pg. 1575
Ashcraft, Steven P., Pres.--Global Special Risks, Inc. of Texas, Dallas, TX; *Int'l*, pg. 1503
Ashcroft, James, Pres.--Inco Limited, Ontario Division, Copper Cliff, Canada; *Int'l*, pg. 672
Ashcroft, Richard P., Mng. Dir.--Cambridge Vacuum Engineering Ltd., Waterbeach, United Kingdom; *Int'l*, pg. 1337
Asheim, Steinar, Div. Mgr.--Munksjoe Hygien AB, Jonkoping, Sweden; *Int'l*, pg. 1423
Ashenberg, Wayne R., Chief Fin. Officer, Sr. V.P. & Treas.--Sentry Insurance, A Mutual Company, Stevens Point, WI; *U.S. Private*, pg. 985
Asher, E., Mgr.-Mktg.--Science Fiction Book Club, Garden City, NY; *Int'l*, pg. 191
Asher, Glenn, Mgr.--Wyle Electronics-Research Div., Santa Clara, CA; *Int'l*, pg. 1457
Asher, Offir, Pres.--Mul-T-Lock Ltd., Lodi, NJ; *Int'l*, pg. 644
Asher, Russell, Pres.--Master Craft Corp., Kalamazoo, MI; *Int'l*, pg. 267
Ashford, Rodney, Mng. Dir.--Iggesund Board Sales Ltd. (Waltham Abbey), Milton Keynes, United Kingdom; *Int'l*, pg. 886
Ashida, K., Gen. Mgr.--The Hi-Daiei Trading Co., Ltd., Manila, Philippines; *Int'l*, pg. 364
Ashida, Masahiro, Gen. Mgr.--P.T. Bank Sumitomo Niaga-Surabaya Branch, Surabaya, Indonesia; *Int'l*, pg. 1309
Ashida, Mitsumasa, Pres.--Fujitsu Microelectronics, Inc., San Jose, CA; *Int'l*, pg. 527
Ashida, Nobuhiro, Chief Rep.--Mexico City Representative Office, Mexico, Mexico; *Int'l*, pg. 816
Ashkettle, Phillip D., Pres. & Chief Exec. Officer--Reichhold Chemicals, Inc., Durham, NC; *Int'l*, pg. 370
Ashkettle, Phillip D., Pres.--Reichhold Chemie AG, Hausen, Switzerland; *Int'l*, pg. 370
Ashley, Larry, Pres.--Lockheed Canada, Ottawa, Canada; *U.S. Public*, pg. 1009
Ashley, Pamela J., Editor/Gen. Mgr.--Coldwater Reporter, Inc., Coldwater, MI; *U.S. Public*, pg. 1077
Ashman, Colin, Dir.--IE Management Consultant Pty. Ltd., Chatswood, Australia; *U.S. Private*, pg. 162
Ashman, R.A., Chief Opr. Officer--The General Electric Co. of Singapore Private Ltd., Singapore, Singapore; *Int'l*, pg. 546
Ashour, Mamdouh, Pres.--Scubapro France S.A., Antibes, France; *U.S. Public*, pg. 933
Ashton, Judy A., Dir.-Canada--Baskin-Robbins Canada, Etobicoke, Canada; *Int'l*, pg. 63
Ashworth, Noel, Pres.--Lister-Petter Inc., Olathe, KS; *Int'l*, pg. 127
Asiaanen, Alan, Pres.--Maguire Group Architects, Inc., New Britain, CT; *U.S. Private*, pg. 696
Asinari, Matthew, Pres. & Chief Exec. Officer--Dentsu Young & Rubicam brand communications (Network Center), Singapore, Singapore; *U.S. Private*, pg. 325
Askerlund, F., Mng. Dir.--Haniel Reederei Holding GmbH, Duisburg, Germany; *Int'l*, pg. 592
Askew, Ellen, Mgr.--Villa South Inc., Sandersville, GA; *U.S. Private*, pg. 1081
Askey, Dan, Pres.--Balkamp, Inc., Indianapolis, IN; *U.S. Public*, pg. 732
Asklund, Fredrik, Gen. Mgr.--Skandia AFS Southeast Asia (L) Ltd., Labuan, Malaysia; *Int'l*, pg. 1258
Aslanian, Michael E., Sr. V.P. & Chief Oper. Officer--Hillsdale Tool & Mfg. Co., Hillsdale, MI; *U.S. Private*, pg. 355
Aslin, Malcolm M., Pres.--UMB Properties, Inc., Kansas City, MO; *U.S. Public*, pg. 1655
Aslin, Malcolm M., Pres.--United Missouri Insurance Co., Kansas City, MO; *U.S. Public*, pg. 1655
Asman, Don, Chief Fin. Officer & V.P.-Fin.--CanAmera Foods, Oakville, Canada; *Int'l*, pg. 1195
Asmus, Wilhelm, Gen. Mgr.--A.C. Nielsen Co., GmbH, Vienna, Austria; *U.S. Public*, pg. 1183
Aso, Tetsuo, Gen. Mgr.--The Sakura Bank - Ayudhya Branch, Pailing, Thailand; *Int'l*, pg. 1179
Asp, Arvid, Mng. Dir.--Inter-Scan Airfreight A/S, Copenhagen, Denmark; *U.S. Private*, pg. 1120
Asp, Lennart, Mgr.--Viskafors AB, Viskafors, Sweden; *Int'l*, pg. 1423
Aspaas, Ulf A., Mng. Dir.--Jotun Cathodic Protection A/S, Langesund, Norway; *Int'l*, pg. 714
Aspden, Jane, Publr. & Mng. Dir.--Mitchell Beazley, London, United Kingdom; *Int'l*, pg. 1093
Asplund, Mark, Branch Mgr.--Downey Savings & Loan Association, F.A., Los Altos, CA; *U.S. Public*, pg. 526
Assadpour, Mohammad, Chief Rep.--The Sumitomo Bank, Ltd.-Vienna Representative Office, Vienna, Austria; *Int'l*, pg. 1310
Assam, Peter, Mng. Dir.--Unicon Beton Holding A/S, Roskilde, Denmark; *Int'l*, pg. 475
Assard, David G., Pres.--Textron Lycoming, Williamsport, PA; *U.S. Public*, pg. 1589
Asscher, Jane, Mng. Dir.--Tequila UK Ltd., London, United Kingdom; *Int'l*, pg. 118
Asselin, Michel, Mgr.--L.N.G. Plant, Montreal, Canada; *Int'l*, pg. 541
Asselineau, Michel, Mgr.--EURO RSCG Quartet, Dijon, France; *Int'l*, pg. 601
Asso, Giorgio, Mng. Dir.--AS. Co S.p.A., Milan, Italy; *Int'l*, pg. 170
Assouad, Georges, Mgr.--Willis Faber (Middle East) S.A.L., Beirut, Lebanon; *Int'l*, pg. 1510
Assouad, Georges, Mgr.--Willis Faber (Malaysia) Sdn Bhd, Johor Baharu, Malaysia; *Int'l*, pg. 1510
Astafan, C., Chief Oper. Officer--CM Shredder Div., Sarasota, FL; *U.S. Public*, pg. 405
Aston, B.A., G.M.--Unbrako Pty. Ltd., Nunawading, Australia; *U.S. Public*, pg. 1420
Aston, Edward, V.P.-Intl. Opers.--Encore Computer (UK) Ltd., Leatherhead, United Kingdom; *U.S. Public*, pg. 580
Aston, J., Plant Mgr.--Peterbilt Motors Co., Madison, TN; *U.S. Public*, pg. 1247
Aston, Peter, Mgr.-Sls. & Mktg.--Rolls-Royce Motor Cars Limited, Specialist Engines, Crewe, United Kingdom; *Int'l*, pg. 1467
Astrom, Torgny, Mgr.--Goodall Rubber Company, Ewing, NJ; *Int'l*, pg. 1423
Astrup, Ebbe C., Mgr.--Ebbe C Astrup AS, Oslo, Norway; *Int'l*, pg. 731
Astur, Cliff, Branch Dir.--N.G. Bailey & Co. Ltd.-Southampton Branch, Southampton, United Kingdom; *Int'l*, pg. 132

Asuka, H., Pres.--The Chuo Woollen Mills, Ltd., Nagoya, Japan; *Int'l*, pg. 946

Atad, Effi, Pres.--New Media Communication, Tel Aviv, Israel; *U.S. Public*, pg. 788

Ataham, Bala, Media Dir.--Markom/Leo Burnett A.S., Istanbul, Turkey; *U.S. Private*, pg. 186

Atamian, Mitch, Mng. Dir.--A. Schulman, Inc., Schaumburg, IL; *U.S. Public*, pg. 1441

Atarashi, Yoshiyuki, Chief Representative--Seoul Representative Office, Seoul, Korea; *Int'l*, pg. 1517

Atchison, Robert, Pres.--Ampex Data Systems, Redwood City, CA; *U.S. Public*, pg. 104

Ates, Luther A., Pres. & Chief Exec. Officer--Regions Bank/ Walton/Holmes County, De Funiak Springs, FL; *U.S. Public*, pg. 1373

Atfield, R.J., Mng. Dir.--Mercantile Mutual Holdings Limited, Sydney, Australia; *Int'l*, pg. 650

Athanasian, O., Chief Fin. Officer--Olivetti Hellas S.A., Athens, Greece; *Int'l*, pg. 1003

Atkin, D.J., Mng. Dir.--Fortress Security Pty Limited, Mordialloc, Australia; *Int'l*, pg. 590

Atkin, Edward, Mng. Dir.--Avent America Inc., Addison, IL; *Int'l*, pg. 261

Atkin, Elizabeth, Branch Mgr.--Downey Savings & Loan Association, F.A., Costa Mesa, CA; *U.S. Public*, pg. 526

Atkins, A., Plant Mgr.-Dyeing--National Spinning Co., Washington, NC; *U.S. Private*, pg. 787

Atkins, David, Chief Oper. Officer--Bran & Luebbe (G.B.) Ltd., Brixworth, United Kingdom; *Int'l*, pg. 1380

Atkins, Robert, Gen. Mgr.--Robertshaw Controls (Canada) Inc., Mississauga, Canada; *Int'l*, pg. 1244

Atkinson, A. Kelley, Pres., Chief Exec. Officer & Treas.--United HealthCare of Georgia, Inc., Atlanta, GA; *U.S. Public*, pg. 1678

Atkinson, Duane E., Pres. & Gen. Mgr.--Atkinson Dynamics Company, South San Francisco, CA; *U.S. Public*, pg. 143

Atkinson, Kathleen, V.P. & Mgr.--City National Bank - Sherman Oaks Office, Sherman Oaks, CA; *U.S. Public*, pg. 381

Atkinson, Paul, Mgr.--Sydney Steel Mill, Rooty Hill, Australia; *Int'l*, pg. 227

Atkinson, R.J., Chm. & Pres.--Ferrum Inc., Brampton, Canada; *Int'l*, pg. 414

Atkinson, Richard, Dr., Pres.--Shandon Lipshaw Inc., Pittsburgh, PA; *U.S. Public*, pg. 1595

Atkinson, Robert, V.P. & Gen. Mgr.--Angelica International, Ltd., Weston, Canada; *U.S. Public*, pg. 113

Atkinson, William, Chief Exec. Officer--Aurora Regional Medical Center, Aurora, CO; *U.S. Public*, pg. 403

Atman, Robert, Pres. & Chief Exec. Officer--General Media Automotive Group Inc., New York, NY; *U.S. Private*, pg. 444

Atria, Jaime, V.P. & Creative Dir.--Leo Burnett Chile, Santiago, Chile; *U.S. Private*, pg. 185

Atsushi, Ida, Mng. Dir.--Hitachi Television (Taiwan) Ltd., Kao-hsiung, Taiwan; *Int'l*, pg. 622

Attansio, Fulvio, Chief Oper. Officer--SCA Packaging Italia S.p.A., Porcari, Italy; *Int'l*, pg. 1326

Attard, P.M., Mng. Dir.--De La Rue Systems Imports Pty Limited, Sydney, Australia; *Int'l*, pg. 387

Attaway, J. Paul, Gen. Mgr.--M M Systems Corporation, Phoenix, AZ; *U.S. Private*, pg. 685

Atte, Sidney Anuar, Chief Oper. Officer--BB-Tur-Viagens e Turismo, Brasilia, Brazil; *Int'l*, pg. 141

Atterton, David, Chm. Bd.--Guinness Mahon Holdings Plc, London, United Kingdom; *Int'l*, pg. 159

Attolini, Gianfranco, Dr., Mng. Dir.--Ortho Clinical Diagnostic Systems S.p.A., Milan, Italy; *U.S. Public*, pg. 931

Attorre-Marzetti, Mrs. L.M., Gen. Mgr.--Algemene Bank Nederland, Rome, Italy; *Int'l*, pg. 11

Attwell, W. R., Pres.--Battlefield Equipment Rentals, Stoney Creek, Canada; *Int'l*, pg. 1400

Atwater, A.G., Jr., Pres. & Chief Exec. Officer--Amurol Confections Co., Yorkville, IL; *U.S. Public*, pg. 1781

Atwater, N. William, Chm. Bd., Pres. & Chief Exec. Officer--Foster Wheeler International Corporation, New York, NY; *U.S. Public*, pg. 677

Atwater, N. William, Pres. & Chief Exec. Officer--Foster Wheeler World Services Corp., Clinton, NJ; *U.S. Public*, pg. 677

Atwood, Dan, Gen. Mgr.--Pro-Line Boats, Crystal River, FL; *U.S. Private*, pg. 58

Atwood, Jim, Mgr.--Sargent Metal Fabricating, Ames, IA; *U.S. Private*, pg. 1089

Atwood, Robert G., Pres.--United Sugars Corp., Bloomington, MN; *U.S. Private*, pg. 52

Atwood, Rossie, Plant Mgr.--Block Plant, Lubbock, TX; *U.S.* Public, pg. 936

Au-Yueng, D., Gen. Mgr.--Hunter Douglas Canada Inc., Mississauga, Canada; *Int'l*, pg. 639

Au, Y.T., Chief Rep.--Commonwealth Bank-Beijing, Beijing, China; *Int'l*, pg. 313

Au, Y.T., Chief Rep.--Commomnwealth Bank-Shanghai, Shanghai, China; *Int'l*, pg. 313

Aube, Greg, Pres.--First Consumers National Bank, Beaverton, OR; *U.S. Public*, pg. 1499

Auberry, Horace, Pres.--Ro-Search, Inc., Hazelwood, NC; *U.S. Public*, pg. 1752

Aubert, J.P., Pres.--Union Europeenne de Cic, Paris, France; *Int'l*, pg. 565

Aubin, P.A., Gen. Mgr.--Banque Morgan Grenfell en Suisse S. A. (Switzerland), Geneva, Switzerland; *Int'l*, pg. 406

Aubry, E., Station Mgr.--Limagrain Genetics Corp., Champaign, IL; *Int'l*, pg. 566

Auch, Fred J., Jr., Pres.--GenCon Services, Inc., Pontiac, MI; *U.S. Private*, pg. 98

Auch, Mel, Pres.--Chief Industries - Housing Div., Aurora, NE; *U.S. Private*, pg. 236

Aucoin, Camille, Pres.--Sunbrand Div., Atlanta, GA; *U.S. Private*, pg. 1177

Aucoin, Charles, Mng. Dir.--SBC Warburg Dillon Read Inc., Boston, MA; *Int'l*, pg. 1329

Aucoin, Kenny, Mgr.-Sls.--PENCO-Louisiana, Baton Rouge, LA; *Int'l*, pg. 1508

Audiseshu, G.K., Sr. Tech. Rep--Dowty Aerospace, New Delhi, India; *Int'l*, pg. 1337

Audouard, O., Mng. Dir.--Ascom SA, Antony, France; *Int'l*, pg. 87

Audouze, Francois, Pres. & Dir. Gen.--Arus Group, Aubervilliers, France; *Int'l*, pg. 79

Audrain, Cathie, Chief Oper. Officer--Octel Messaging Div., Sarasota, FL; *U.S. Public*, pg. 1018

Auer, Glenn D., Pres.--Powell ESCO Company, Greenville, TX; *U.S. Public*, pg. 1319

Augsburger, Stan, V.P. & Gen. Mgr.--The New Bakery Company of Ohio, Inc., Zanesville, OH; *U.S. Public*, pg. 1754

Augsdorfer, Jules, V.P. & General Mgr.--Silmar Resins, Fort Wright, KY; *U.S. Private*, pg. 572

August, Arthur, V.P.-Professional Division--Helen of Troy, Professional Salon Div., El Paso, TX; *U.S. Public*, pg. 807

August, Monty S., Chief Exec. Officer--U.K. Paper Plc, Sittingbourne, United Kingdom; *Int'l*, pg. 495

Augustensen, Barry, City Mgr.--The DIALOG Corporation, New York, NY; *Int'l*, pg. 412

Augustine, Mark, Div. Mgr.--Wyle Electronics-San Diego, San Diego, CA; *Int'l*, pg. 1458

Augustssen, Kurth, Pres.--Molnlycke AB, Goteborg, Sweden; *Int'l*, pg. 1326

Auld, Douglas G., Pres.--Atlas Van Lines (Canada) Ltd., Oakville, Canada; *U.S. Private*, pg. 97

Ault III, Lee A., Pres. & Chief Exec. Officer--Light Signatures, Inc., Los Angeles, CA; *U.S. Public*, pg. 588

Aultman, Buddy, Gen. Mgr.--The News and Reporter, Chester, SC; *U.S. Private*, pg. 648

Aulund, Knut, Mng. Dir.--Semafor A/S, Kolbjoernsvki, Norway; *Int'l*, pg. 1369

Aumont, Brigitte, Mgr.--EURO RSCG Est, Strasbourg, France; *Int'l*, pg. 600

Aunallo, Dick, Gen. Mgr.--BancTec, Inc.-Atlanta, Duluth, GA; *U.S. Public*, pg. 177

Aurenche, Pascal, Mng. Dir.--International Marketing & Promotions, Asnieres-sur-Seine, France; *U.S. Private*, pg. 304

Aurichio, Joseph L., Pres. & Chief Exec. Officer--Kearney-National, Inc., White Plains, NY; *U.S. Private*, pg. 351

Ausburn, Lawrence J., Sr. V.P.--Western Loan Administration, Sherman Oaks, CA; *U.S. Public*, pg. 650

Auslander, Stephen E., Editor--The Arizona Daily Star, Tucson, AZ; *U.S. Public*, pg. 1343

Ausmus, Mike, Gen. Mgr.--Industrial Packaging Div. (Columbus), Columbus, OH; *Int'l*, pg. 1270

Ausner, R., Mng. Dir.--Albright & Wilson AB, Vastra Frolunda, Sweden; *Int'l*, pg. 49

Aussant, Jean M., Mgr.-Location--Vickers Systems Div., Saint Ouen-l'Aumone, France; *U.S. Public*, pg. 25

Austen, P.G., Dir.--The Oxford Collection Ltd., Oxford, United Kingdom; *Int'l*, pg. 807

Austgen, Donald R., V.P. & Mgr.--California State Bank-Lake Forest Irvine, Irvine, CA; *U.S. Public*, pg. 294

Austin, Aubrey L., Chm. Bd., Pres. & Chief Exec. Officer--Santa Monica Bank, Santa Monica, CA; *U.S. Public*, pg. 1757

Austin, Bill, Mng. Dir.--Derby Cycle Corporation, Kent, WA; *Int'l*, pg. 394

Austin, Brett, Gen. Mgr.--Williams Furnace Co., Colton, CA; *U.S. Public*, pg. 441

Austin, C.T., Pres.--Photo Mechanical Services Inc., Minneapolis, MN; *U.S. Private*, pg. 891

Austin, Ed, Plant Mgr.--Silgan Containers, Vancouver, WA; *U.S. Public*, pg. 1473

Austin, Floyd, Plant Mgr.--AFG Industries, Inc., Cinnaminson, NJ; *Int'l*, pg. 84

Austin, L.J., Dr., Mng. Dir.--Shell Refining (F.O.M.) Bhd., Kuala Lumpur, Malaysia; *Int'l*, pg. 1140

Austin, M.J., Mng. Dir.--Crane Limited U.K., Ipswich, United Kingdom; *U.S. Public*, pg. 458

Austin, Peter, Mgr.-Prod.--Kingsbury Assembly Machine Div., Keene, NH; *U.S. Private*, pg. 622

Austin, T.G., Pres.--Gustafson, Inc., Plano, TX; *U.S. Public*, pg. 460

Autio, J., Mng. Dir.--Ascom Energy Systems OY, Espoo, Finland; *Int'l*, pg. 87

Autterson, Matthew, Pres.--Resources Trust Company, Englewood, CO; *U.S. Public*, pg. 1533

Auty, J. Donald, Pres.--The Pantene Co., Wilton, CT; *U.S. Public*, pg. 1330

Auvinen, Thomas, Pres.--The Pyramid Life Insurance Co., Mission, KS; *U.S. Public*, pg. 1694

Auxenfans, B.P., V.P.-Intl.--The Agricultural Group, Monsanto Company, Saint Louis, MO; *U.S. Public*, pg. 1125

Auyanet, Antonio Castellano, Pres.--UNELCO - Union Electrica de Canarias, S.A., Las Palmas, Spain; *Int'l*, pg. 1224

Auyeung, Rex, V.P.-Reg. & Mng. Dir.--Principal International Asia Limited, Wan Chai, Hong Kong; *U.S. Private*, pg. 886

Auzenberga, Laila, Mng. Dir.--Norvista, Riga, Latvia; *Int'l*, pg. 486

Avache, Joe, Mgr.--Intermarkets Bahrain, Manama, Bahrain; *Int'l*, pg. 680

Avedisian, Guy, Pres.--Citizens National Bank of Lake Geneva, Lake Geneva, WI; *U.S. Public*, pg. 643

Avellone, Joseph C., Chief Oper. Officer--Physician Partners of New England, Inc., Boston, MA; *U.S. Private*, pg. 151

Avento, Joseph, Pres.--Bristol Metals, L.P., Bristol, TN; *U.S.* Public, pg. 1548

Averett, J.N., Jr., Chm. Bd. & Chief Exec. Officer--Crystal Eurasia Oil Co., Shreveport, LA; *U.S. Public*, pg. 466

Averett, Joe N., Jr., Pres.--Crystal Program Ltd., Inc., Shreveport, LA; *U.S. Public*, pg. 466

Averett, Joe N., Jr., Pres.--Crystal Exploration & Production Co., Shreveport, LA; *U.S. Public*, pg. 466

Averitt, David H., Pres.--Sea Island Bank, Statesboro, GA; *U.S. Public*, pg. 1549

Averlant, Michel, Chief Oper. Officer--Librairie des Champs-Elysees, Paris, France; *Int'l*, pg. 792

Avery, Bruce C., Chm. Bd.--MFS Service Center Inc., Boston, MA; *Int'l*, pg. 1319

Avery, David, Pres.--Novellus Systems, Ltd., Horsham, United Kingdom; *U.S. Public*, pg. 1204

Avery, David, Pres.--Novellus Systems, B.V., Eindhoven, Netherlands; *U.S. Public*, pg. 1204

Avery, David, Pres.--Novellus Systems, Ltd., Lorgues, France; *U.S. Public*, pg. 1204

Avery, David, Pres.--Novellus Systems, Ltd., Falkirk, United Kingdom; *U.S. Public*, pg. 1204

Avery, Frederick F., Pres.--Ridg's Finer Foods, Garland, TX; *U.S. Public*, pg. 1288

Avery, James P., Sr. V.P.--Louisiana Gas Service Co., Harvey, LA; *U.S. Public*, pg. 380

Avery, John M., Pres.--International Insurance Underwriters, Inc., Denver, CO; *U.S. Public*, pg. 220

Avery, John M., Pres. & Chief Exec. Officer--Government Employees Financial Corporation, Washington, DC; *U.S. Public*, pg. 220

Avery, R., Mgr.-Factory--Thomas De La Rue Ltd., Gateshead, United Kingdom; *Int'l*, pg. 386

Avery, V. Keith, Gen. Mgr.--Fletcher Merchants Limited, Auckland, New Zealand; *Int'l*, pg. 495

Avignone, Peter, Gen. Mgr.--Golden State Foods-Hawaii Div., Waipahu, HI; *U.S. Private*, pg. 460

Avila, Arturo, Mgr.--Grupo Termoindustrial ECA, S.A. de C.V., San Luis Potosi, Mexico; *U.S. Private*, pg. 361

Avila, G., Branch Mgr.--A.M. Castle & Co., Phoenix, AZ; *U.S. Public*, pg. 313

Avila, Max, Gen. Mgr.--Banco Nacional de Mexico, Madrid, Spain; *Int'l*, pg. 574

Avila, S., Chief Oper. Officer--Ciquine-Companhia Petroquimica, Camacari, Brazil; *Int'l*, pg. 947

Aviles, C., Pres.--Safeguard Business Systems Limited, Mississauga, Canada; *U.S. Private*, pg. 960

Aviles, Jose Fernandez, Gen. Mgr.--Iberia Tecnologia, S.A., Madrid, Spain; *Int'l*, pg. 1225

Avis, James C., Exec. V.P., Gen. Counsel & Sec.--Newbridge Networks Corporation, Kanata, Canada; *Int'l*, pg. 924

Avis, John, Pres.--Kvaerner Masa Marine Inc., Annapolis, MD; *Int'l*, pg. 770

Avis, Robert G., Chm. Bd.--A.G. Edwards Trust Company, Saint Louis, MO; *U.S. Public*, pg. 565

Avison, Patrick D., Dir.--Bank of Montreal - Los Angeles, Los Angeles, CA; *Int'l*, pg. 154

Avratoglou, Philip, Mng. Dir.--SKF Hellas S.A., Athens, Greece; *Int'l*, pg. 1158

Awad, Ali, Mgr.-Zone--Santa Fe International (Egypt) Inc., Cairo, Egypt; *Int'l*, pg. 765

Awalt, Terry, Gen. Mgr.--McLane Food Service, Temple, TX; *U.S. Public*, pg. 1733

Awan, A. Rashid, V.P. & Chief Mgr.--Habib Bank Ltd., Rotterdam, Netherlands; *Int'l*, pg. 585

Axberg, Peter, Mng. Dir.--Oy Getinge AB, Helsinki, Finland; *Int'l*, pg. 551

Axelsen, Ken, Mgr.--Woodward Governor India Pvt. Ltd., Ballabgarh, India; *U.S. Public*, pg. 1777

Axelson, Ake, Mgr.--Gusab Stainless AB, Mjolby, Sweden; *Int'l*, pg. 1185

Axelson, Karl Axel, Pres.--Gambro AB Oy, Sahaajankatu, Finland; *Int'l*, pg. 667

Axelsson, Bygg Larry, Pres.--Byggs Sprutbetong AB, Malung, Sweden; *Int'l*, pg. 899

Axelsson, Fredrik, Chief Oper. Officer--Electrolux Kalte-und Warmetechnik GmbH, Hamburg, Germany; *Int'l*, pg. 442

Ayao, Shinji, Pres.--Solectron Japan, Inc., Tokyo, Japan; *U.S. Public*, pg. 1483

Aycock, Kenneth, Gen. Mgr.--Aycock Auto Auction, Kenly, NC; *U.S. Public*, pg. 1648

Aydiner, Selahattin, Mng. Dir.--Turk Maadin Sirketi A.S., Istanbul, Turkey; *U.S. Private*, pg. 735

Aydogdu, M, Dir. & Gen. Mgr.--Gunes Sigorta, Istanbul, Turkey; *Int'l*, pg. 565

Ayed, Adbessalem Ben, Chm.--UBCI (Tunisia), Tunis, Tunisia; *Int'l*, pg. 163

Ayer, Ramani, Pres. & Chief Oper. Officer--Hartford Fire Insurance Co., Hartford, CT; *U.S. Public*, pg. 794

Ayers, J., Process Engnr.--Carbone of America, Chemical Equipment Div., Salem, VA; *Int'l*, pg. 1028

Ayers, James C., Pres.--CTL Steel Co., Columbus, OH; *U.S.* Private, pg. 243

Ayers, Jeremiah J., Pres.--Equitech Division, Pittsburgh, PA; *U.S. Public*, pg. 590

Ayers, Robert, Gen. Mgr.--Michelin Aircraft Tire Corporation, Charlotte, NC; *Int'l*, pg. 322

Ayers, Robert L., Pres. & Chief Exec. Officer--Sulzer Bingham Pumps Inc., Portland, OR; *Int'l*, pg. 1305

Ayers, Robert L., Mng. Dir.--Sulzer Bingham Pumps Inc., Burnaby, Canada; *Int'l*, pg. 1305

Ayers, Terry, V.P. & Gen. Mgr.--Agrotec, Williams Inc., Pendleton, NC; *U.S. Public*, pg. 1769

Aykroyd, Nicholas C., Mng. Dir.--Crown Cork Company S.A. (Pty.) Ltd., Wadeville, South Africa; *U.S. Public*, pg. 464

Aylward, Joe, V.P.-Sls.--Fairfield Branson, Branson, MO; *U.S. Public*, pg. 610

Aymar, Mary M., Asst. Treas. & Branch Mgr.--Valley National Bank, Dover, NJ; *U.S. Public*, pg. 1706

Aynsley, Eric, Exec. V.P.--Scott Environmental Technology, Plumsteadville, PA; *U.S. Public*, pg. 546

Ayora, Martin, Mng. Dir.--Esselte S.A., Barcelona, Spain; *Int'l*, pg. 461

Ayoub, Sam, V.P. & Gen. Mgr.--B/E Services, Orange, CA; *U.S. Public*, pg. 159

Ayre, James, Pres.--Tab Products of Canada, Ltd., Willowdale, Canada; *U.S. Public*, pg. 1559

Ayre, Miller, Chief Exec. Officer & Grp. Publisher--The Evening Telegram, Saint Johns, Canada; *Int'l*, pg. 631

Ayres, R.W., Jr., Sr. V.P.-Opers.--Service Parts Supply Div., Racine, WI; *U.S. Public*, pg. 311

Ayrton, H.S., Dir.--Chaitra Leo Burnett Private Ltd., Mumbai, India; *U.S. Private,* pg. 184
Ayton, Vernon, Chm. Bd.--Ayton Young & Rubicam Ltd., Nairobi, Kenya; *U.S. Private,* pg. 1198
Aza, Lee, Gen. Mgr.--Flagship, Norfolk, VA; *U.S. Private,* pg. 649
Azefor, Michael N., Resident Rep.--The World Bank, Cotonou, Benin; *U.S. Private,* pg. 1189
Azevedo, C.G., Gen. Mgr.--Brother International (Portugal) Distribuidores de Equipamentos Electricos LDA., Carnaxide, Portugal; *Int'l,* pg. 230
Aziz, Azizah, V.P.--Tourism Malaysia - N.Y. Office, New York, NY; *Int'l,* pg. 833
Azizzadeh, R., Chief Oper. Officer--BHP-Bank Representative Office, Tehran, Iran; *Int'l,* pg. 120
Azizzadeh, Rasoul, Rep.--Kredietbank Inter-Alpha Representative Office, Tehran, Iran; *Int'l,* pg. 760
Aznarez, Nicolas Martin, Dir.--Nivel Publicidad, Asuncion, Paraguay; *U.S. Private,* pg. 389
Azoff, Irving, Pres.--Universal Studios Distributing Corp., New York, NY; *Int'l,* pg. 1216
Azubel, Amos, Chm. Bd.--Elscint NV/SA, Zaventem, Belgium; *Int'l,* pg. 450
Azuma, Minrou, Pres.--Canadian Autoparts Toyota, Inc., Delta, Canada; *Int'l,* pg. 1413
Azzam, R.H., Gen. Mgr.--Kodak (Near East), Inc., Istanbul, Turkey; *U.S. Public,* pg. 554
Ba, L.D., Dir.--Ebara Hai Duong Company Ltd., Hai Duong, Vietnam; *Int'l,* pg. 432
Baader, K., Mgr.--Schweizerischer Bankverein, Schaffhausen, Switzerland; *Int'l,* pg. 1329
Baaijens, P.M.A., Mng. Dir.--Ballast Nedam IGB B.V., Amstelveen, Netherlands; *Int'l,* pg. 133
Baarle, A.J., Gen. Mgr.--Kathabar Systems Europe, Zoetermeer, Zoetermeer, Netherlands; *Int'l,* pg. 681
Baars, Dirk M., Div. Mgr.--Molding Materials Div., Manchester, CT; *U.S. Public,* pg. 1403
Baas, M.M., Mng. Dir.--Berson Milieutechniek B.V., Nuenen, Netherlands; *Int'l,* pg. 590
Baasen, J. Daniel, Mgr.--Piper Jaffray Inc., Saint Paul, MN; *U.S. Public,* pg. 1302
Baba, Eizo, Pres.--Chiyoda Life Investment Luxemburg S.A., Luxembourg, Luxembourg; *Int'l,* pg. 287
Baba, Eizo, Pres.--Chiyoda Investment Cayman Limited, Georgetown, Cayman Islands; *Int'l,* pg. 287
Baba, Hisao, Pres. & Chief Exec. Officer--Oki Semiconductor Group, Sunnyvale, CA; *Int'l,* pg. 1000
Baba, Kuniyuki, Pres.--Hakuhodo Capco, Inc., Tokyo, Japan; *Int'l,* pg. 587
Baba, Masaki, Gen. Mgr.--Kyodo Advertising Co., Ltd., Shizuoka, Japan; *Int'l,* pg. 776
Baba, Masako, Gen. Mgr.-Sls./Japan--Utell International-Japan, Tokyo, Japan; *Int'l,* pg. 1098
Baba, Ryutaro, Pres.--Ricoh Development of California, Inc., Tustin, CA; *Int'l,* pg. 1114
Baba, Tetsuo, Pres.--DKB Securities Corporation, New York, NY; *Int'l,* pg. 360
Baba, Y., Pres.--Foster Electric (U.S.A.) Inc., Schaumburg, IL; *Int'l,* pg. 500
Babacan, Hasan, Mng. Dir.--Burgmann Endustriyel Sizdirmalik San Ve Tic Ltd Sti, Istanbul, Turkey; *Int'l,* pg. 233
Babarovic, Nicolas, Gen. Mgr.--Comercio Exterior de Chile Ltda., Belgrade, Serbia; *Int'l,* pg. 303
Babb, Donald, Pres.--Hickham Industries Inc., La Porte, TX; *Int'l,* pg. 1305
Babb, Jim, Mgr.--Eclipse Combustion, Inc., Dublin, NH; *U.S.* Private, pg. 360
Babcock, Doug, Mgr.--Harley Valve & Instrument, Chesterton, IN; *U.S. Public,* pg. 880
Babcock, J.A., Pres.--Amoco Ras Al Khaimah Oil Co., Sharjah, United Arab Emirates; *U.S. Public,* pg. 102
Babcock, Richard, Editor--Chicago Magazine, Chicago, IL; *U.S. Public,* pg. 1328
Babel, Bernard, Pres.--Charmilles Technologies Manufacturing Corp., Owosso, MI; *Int'l,* pg. 489
Babensee, David F., Chm. & Chief Exec. Officer--Scotiabank de Puerto Rico, Hato Rey, PR; *Int'l,* pg. 156
Babick, Don, Pres.--Southam Inc., Don Mills, Canada; *Int'l,* pg. 631
Babick, Don, Pres. & Publisher--The Province, Vancouver, Canada; *Int'l,* pg. 631
Babick, Donald, Pres. & Publshr.--Pacific Press Ltd., Vancouver, Canada; *Int'l,* pg. 631
Babin, W.E., Pres.--Great Southern Paper, Cedar Springs, GA; *U.S. Public,* pg. 736
Babin, W.E., Pres.--J & J Corrugated Box, Fall River, MA; *U.S Public,* pg. 736
Babineau, Jay, Pres.-Creative & Admin.--Simon Marketing, Inc., Oak Brook Terrace, IL; *U.S. Private,* pg. 1001
Babineau, R., Div. Mgr.--Curtis 1000, Inc., Fontana, CA; *U.S. Public,* pg. 70
Babineaux, D.J., Pres.--American Valve & Hydrant Co., Beaumont, TX; *U.S. Private,* pg. 52
Babinski, Hugh, Worldwide Dir.--Minet, Inc., New York, NY; *U.S. Public,* pg. 118
Babits, Gerd, Mng. Dir., Creative Dir. & New Bus. Contact--Strobelgasse 2, Vienna, Austria; *Int'l,* pg. 1377
Babler, William, Gen. Mgr.--Dowty O Rings North America, San Diego, CA; *Int'l,* pg. 1338
Babler, William, Gen. Mgr.--Dowty O Rings North America, Tijuana, Mexico; *Int'l,* pg. 1338
Baboulis, Steve, Gen. Mgr.--WNYT-TV, Albany, NY; *U.S. Private,* pg. 544
Babriele, Del Torchio, Pres.--FKI FAI Komatsu Industries, S.p.A., Este, Italy; *Int'l,* pg. 474
Baca, Eduardo, Pres.--Graffiti/DMB&B, Buenos Aires, Argentina; *U.S. Private,* pg. 304
Baca, Ricardo, Regional Bus. Mgr.--Especialidades Quimicias Grace de Mexico S.A. de C.V., Tecamachalco, Mexico; *U.S. Public,* pg. 755
Bacardats, Jacques, Exec. V.P.-N. & S. American Opers.--Essilor of America, Glen Head, NY; *Int'l,* pg. 462
Bacchiega, Carlo, Dir.--Instant S.R.L., Pavia, Italy; *U.S. Private,* pg. 1128
Baccich, C.T., Pres.--Mineral Research & Development Corp., Charlotte, NC; *Int'l,* pg. 802
Bach, Bjorn, Pres.--Hydro Agri North America, Tampa, FL; *Int'l,* pg. 961
Bach, Carlos Guillem, Chief Oper. Officer--Electronica Basica, S.A. (ELBASA), Barcelona, Spain; *U.S. Public,* pg. 1199
Bach, Jose Maria, Mng. Dir.--BASF Espanola S.A., Barcelona, Spain; *Int'l,* pg. 106
Bach, W., Mng. Dir.--Georg Fischer Automobilguss Ges.m.b.H,, Herzogenburg, Austria; *Int'l,* pg. 488
Bachar, Tobi, Chm. Bd.--Elscint MR Inc., Fort Collins, CO; *Int'l,* pg. 450
Bachar, Tobi, Chm. Bd.--Elscint Cryomagnetics Ltd., Wallington, United Kingdom; *Int'l,* pg. 450
Bacharach, Dov, Pres.--Wyle-Ginsbury Electronics, Oradell, NJ; *Int'l,* pg. 1458
Bachaud, Jean-Paul, Exec. V.P.--Montreal Trustco Investment Management Services, Montreal, Canada; *Int'l,* pg. 155
Bachiddu, Gianni, Mng. Dir.--Foster Wheeler Asia, Singapore, Singapore; *U.S. Public,* pg. 677
Bachle, Tony C., Mng. Dir.--Meto, Reinach, Switzerland; *Int'l,* pg. 462
Bachler, Kurt, Mng. Dir.--Nissen Trampoline AG, Gumligen, Sweden; *Int'l,* pg. 595
Bachman, Brian, V.P. & Gen. Mgr.--Standard Products Group, Sunnyvale, CA; *Int'l,* pg. 1054
Bachman, Gilbert L., V.P.-Far East--Hartmarx Corporation, Chicago, IL; *U.S. Public,* pg. 795
Bachman, Vernon E., Chief Fin. Officer--Bowling Products Div., Cincinnati, OH; *U.S. Public,* pg. 1725
Bachman, Vernon E., Chief Fin. Officer--Rubber Products Div., Clarksville, TN; *U.S. Public,* pg. 1725
Bachman, Vernon E., Chief Fin. Officer--Shoe Last Div., Walnut Ridge, AR; *U.S. Public,* pg. 1725
Bachmann, H., Mgr.-Opers.--Nordiskafilt GmbH, Ahlen, Germany; *U.S. Public,* pg. 37
Bacich, John, Pres.--Baxter-Hyland, Glendale, CA; *U.S. Public,* pg. 196
Bacik, Brian, Pres.--GSW Thermoplastics Company, Barrie, Canada; *Int'l,* pg. 538
Backman, Frank, Pres.--Dahl Sverige, Spangenas, Sweden; *Int'l,* pg. 359
Backman, Hans, Chief Oper. Officer--Flymo GmbH, Hamburg, Germany; *Int'l,* pg. 442
Backman, Hans G., Chief Oper. Officer--Electrolux Motor AB, Huskvarna, Sweden; *Int'l,* pg. 438
Backstrom, Rolf, Mng. Dir.--Ericsson Communications (Thailand) Ltd., Bangkok, Thailand; *Int'l,* pg. 1366
Backus, John C., Jr., Pres. & Chief Oper. Officer--InteliData, Herndon, VA; *U.S. Public,* pg. 1780
Bacon, Donald G., Chm. Bd., Pres. & Chief Exec. Officer--West Kootenay Power, Trail, Canada; *U.S. Public,* pg. 1701
Bacon, Eric V., Chief Oper. Officer--Care Free Aluminum Products, Inc., Charlotte, MI; *U.S. Private,* pg. 194
Bacus, Jim, Pres.--Diversitech, Inc., Gainesville, FL; *Int'l,* pg. 288
Baczwaski, Lee, Asst. V.P.--IBP-Pasco, Pasco, WA; *U.S. Public,* pg. 852
Badagliacco, John A., V.P.--North Star Mall, Inc., San Antonio, TX; *U.S. Public,* pg. 1409
Badal, Herb S., Gen. Mgr.--Package Products Specialty-Paperboard Div., Charlotte, NC; *U.S. Public,* pg. 1486
Badault, Jean Luc, Pres.--Thomson Software Products, Norwalk, CT; *Int'l,* pg. 1384
Baden, John, Chm. Bd.--Girobank, London, United Kingdom; *Int'l,* pg. 57
Badenoch, J.A., Chief Oper. Officer--Babcock Mexico SA de CV, Polanco, Mexico; *Int'l,* pg. 474
Badetti, Luigi, Mng. Dir.--Circle Freight International Italia-Eurolevant SRL, Milan, Italy; *U.S. Public,* pg. 372
Badger, Susan, Pres. & Chief Exec. Officer--Wadsworth Publishing co., Belmont, CA; *U.S. Public,* pg. 1600
Badgerow, D.B., V.P. & Gen. Mgr.--Skinner Valve Division, New Britain, CT; *U.S. Public,* pg. 1260
Badgett, Guy M., III, Pres.--Vulcan Materials Company-Southeast Div., Atlanta, GA; *U.S. Public,* pg. 1726
Badgley, Dave, Div. Mgr.--Transilwrap Co. of Philadelphia, Bensalem, PA; *U.S. Private,* pg. 1097
Badju, Jon, Mng. Dir.--SKF Specialty Products, Bethlehem, PA; *Int'l,* pg. 1157
Badosa, Juan, Pres.--Repsol Butano S.A., Madrid, Spain; *Int'l,* pg. 1104
Badoux, Jean-Claude, Chm.--Coop Vaud Chablais Valaisan, Renens, Switzerland; *Int'l,* pg. 329
Badran, Ibrahim, Chm. Bd.--Egypt Otsuka Pharmaceutical Co., S.A.E., Cairo, Egypt; *Int'l,* pg. 1014
Badran, Serge, Mng. Dir.--STECD, Tunis, Tunisia; *Int'l,* pg. 823
Baduy, Miguel, Pres.--Creacional/DMB&B, Guayaquil, Ecuador; *U.S. Private,* pg. 303
Badyna, Edward, Pres. & Gen. Mgr.--Chesapeake Packaging Co./Binghamton, Binghamton, NY; *U.S. Public,* pg. 346
Badyna, Edward R., Pres.--Chesapeake Packaging Co./Scranton, Scranton, PA; *U.S. Public,* pg. 347
Bae, H. M., Pres.-SAMI--Saniserv-Korea, Seoul, Korea; *U.S.* Private, pg. 965
Bae, Jung Kyun, Pres.--Newmax Co., Ltd., Cheongju, Korea; *Int'l,* pg. 1347
Bae, T.W., Gen. Mgr.--Grace Korea, Inc., Inchon, Korea; *U.S. Public,* pg. 756
Baebler, Siegfried, Dr., Chief Oper. Officer--Rhone-Poulenc Viscosuisse, Emmen, Switzerland; *Int'l,* pg. 1114
Baelz, M., Chief Oper. Officer--Rossignol Ski Deutschland GmbH, Maisach, Germany; *Int'l,* pg. 1127
Baena, Richard, Chief Exec. Officer--Olaer Group, Colombes, France; *Int'l,* pg. 467
Baer, Art, Pres.--Zyan, Inc., King of Prussia, PA; *U.S. Private,* pg. 421
Baer, Colleen J., Mgr.--Commerzbank Futures Corporation, Chicago, IL; *Int'l,* pg. 310
Baert, Elmar, Mng. Dir.--Credit Europeen, Luxembourg, Luxembourg; *Int'l,* pg. 148
Baertz, Wolfgang A., Joint Acting Pres.--Dresdner Bank Luxembourg S.A., Luxembourg, Luxembourg; *Int'l,* pg. 419
Baez, Fidel, Gen. Mgr.--Salvador Division, El Salvador, Chile; *Int'l,* pg. 302
Baeza, Eduardo, Gen. Mgr.-Laundry & Cleaning--Procter & Gamble Espana S.A., Madrid, Spain; *U.S. Public,* pg. 1332
Baeza, Eduardo, V.P. & Gen. Dir.--Procter & Gamble Greece, Athens, Greece; *U.S. Public,* pg. 1332
Baeza, Sergio, Chm. Bd.--Aetna International Chile S.A., Santiago, Chile; *U.S. Public,* pg. 27
Baffico, Paul A., Pres.--National Tire & Battery, Hoffman Estates, IL; *U.S. Public,* pg. 1452
Baffico, Paul A., Pres.--Sears Tire Group, Hoffman Estates, IL; *U.S. Public,* pg. 1452
Baffico, Paul A., Pres.--Sears Auto Centers, Hoffman Estates, IL; *U.S. Public,* pg. 1452
Bagby, Steven, Pres.--Salomon-North America Inc., Georgetown, MA; *Int'l,* pg. 1181
Bagetta, Don, Pur. Dir.--Doodle Art Div., Los Angeles, CA; *Int'l,* pg. 1215
Baggett, Toby, Chief Oper. Officer--Sanco Inc., Taos, NM; *U.S. Public,* pg. 49
Bagley, George D., Pres. & Chief Exec. Officer--Horizon Air Industries, Seattle, WA; *U.S. Public,* pg. 35
Bagnall, R.K., Plant Mgr.--AlliedSignal Controls & Accessories, Burbank, CA; *U.S. Public,* pg. 50
Bago, Ernest G., Pres.--TSR Consulting Services, Inc., New York, NY; *U.S. Public,* pg. 1559
Bagot, Pierre, Gen. Mng. Dir.--Livingston S.A., Rungis, France; *Int'l,* pg. 212
Bagshawe, James, Dir.--Robert Fleming (France) S.A., Paris, France; *Int'l,* pg. 494
Baguley, P.J., Mng. Dir.--Boots Properties, Nottingham, United Kingdom; *Int'l,* pg. 203
Bahat, Baruch, Gen. Mgr.--Iscar Blades Ltd., Nahariyya, Israel; *Int'l,* pg. 644
Bahia-Guimaraes, Paulo F., Dir.-Pres.--Mineracao Marex Ltda., Rio de Janeiro, Brazil; *Int'l,* pg. 224
Bahlmann, Jerome R., Pres.--Scientific Advances Inc., Columbus, OH; *U.S. Private,* pg. 123
Bahniuk, Frank T., Sr. V.P.--Elizabethtown Gas Co., Union, NJ; *U.S. Public,* pg. 1147
Bahr, John, Reg. Mgr.-Relays--Aromat Northwestern Sales Office, San Jose, CA; *Int'l,* pg. 848
Bahrami, Massoud, Mng. Dir.--Sulzer Iran, Tehran, Iran; *Int'l, pg. 1306*
Bahre, Everett, Pres. & Chief Exec. Officer--Lambda Advanced Analog, Santa Clara, CA; *Int'l,* pg. 1241
Bahri, Mehnarz, Branch Mgr.--Downey Savings & Loan Association, F.A., Encino, CA; *U.S. Public,* pg. 526
Baich, Kevin, Pres.--Crown Shoe Company, L.L.C., Saint Louis, MO; *U.S. Private,* pg. 1089
Baik, Joung-Young, Pres.--Goldstar Instrument & Electric Co. Ltd., Seoul, Korea; *Int'l,* pg. 779
Bailer, Monika, Chief Oper. Officer--BLH SR-4 Sensoren GmbH, Heilbronn, Germany; *Int'l,* pg. 1289
Bailes, George, Mng. Dir.--C.G. Hibbert Ltd., Dover, United Kingdom; *Int'l,* pg. 63
Bailey, Arvel, Gen. Mgr.--Duro Paper Bag Mfg. Co., Tampa, FL; *U.S. Private,* pg. 349
Bailey, Bill, Div. Mgr.--AAR Advanced Structures Div., Livonia, MI; *U.S. Public,* pg. 1
Bailey, Bob, Gen. Mgr.--The Southland Corporation, Englewood, CO; *Int'l,* pg. 694
Bailey, C.A. Bud, Pres.--Bud Bailey Construction Inc., Salt Lake City, UT; *U.S. Private,* pg. 1059
Bailey, D., Plant Mgr.--Crowley Galvanizing Div., Crowley, TX; *U.S. Public,* pg. 159
Bailey, Don, Plant Mgr.--Hydro Conduit Corp., Albuquerque, NM; *Int'l,* pg. 245
Bailey, Don, Pres.--Talley Metals Technology, Inc., Hartsville, SC; *U.S. Public,* pg. 308
Bailey, Doyle, Pres.--First National Bank of Jenks, Jenks, OK; *U.S. Public,* pg. 174
Bailey, Edward T., Sr. V.P. & Gen. Mgr.--Independent Cement Corporation, Albany, NY; *Int'l,* pg. 629
Bailey, Gary S., Pres.--Miami Elevator, Miami, FL; *U.S. Public,* pg. 521
Bailey, George, Mng. Dir.-Sotheby's Europe--Sotheby's Europe, London, United Kingdom; *U.S. Public,* pg. 1487
Bailey, James E., Pres.--Centex Materials, Inc., Austin, TX; *U.S. Public,* pg. 322
Bailey, James E., Pres.--Brazos Point, Inc., Fort Worth, TX; *U.S. Public,* pg. 322
Bailey, James R., Plant Mgr.--Industrial Bag Division - Des Moines Plant, Des Moines, IA; *U.S. Public,* pg. 1521
Bailey, Joe, Gen. Mgr.--Elixir Industries, Elkhart, IN; *U.S. Private,* pg. 371
Bailey, Kathy, Gen. Acctg. Mgr.--Falcon-Belding, Belding, MI; *U.S. Public,* pg. 611
Bailey, L. Douglas, Pres.--Home Shopping Club, Inc., Clearwater, FL; *U.S. Public,* pg. 1685
Bailey, Milton, Mgr.--IBP-Madison, Madison, NE; *U.S. Public, pg. 852*
Bailey, P. L., Dr., Mng. Dir.--Memco Limited, Maidenhead, United Kingdom; *Int'l,* pg. 589
Bailey, Randall E., Gen. Mgr.--Mead Packaging (Canada) Ltd., Ajax, Canada; *U.S. Public,* pg. 1076
Bailey, Randy, Branch Mgr.--Roosevelt Rice Lake Branch, Rice Lake, WI; *U.S. Private,* pg. 943
Bailey, Robert, Reg. Mgr.--Green Tree Acceptance, Inc., Woodbridge, VA; *U.S. Public,* pg. 762
Bailey, Robert, Mng. Dir.--FlowMole Limited, Corby, United Kingdom; *U.S. Public,* pg. 1701
Bailey, Robert L., Chief Exec. Officer--State Auto P & C, Columbus, OH; *U.S. Private,* pg. 1036
Bailey, Robert L., Pres. & Chief Exec. Officer--PMC Sierra, Inc., Burnaby, Canada; *U.S. Public,* pg. 1470

Bailey, Roger, Mng. Dir.--Banque Belge (Guernsey) Ltd., Saint Peter Port, United Kingdom; *Int'l*, pg. 547
Bailey, S., Dir.--Fortress Interlocks Limited, Wolverhampton, United Kingdom; *Int'l*, pg. 589
Bailey, Steven M., Chm. Bd.--Miami Elevator, Miami, FL; *U.S. Public*, pg. 521
Bailey, T.H., Chm. Bd. & Pres.--Janus Capital Corporation, Denver, CO; *U.S. Public*, pg. 944
Bailey, Tom A., Div. Mgr.--Citizens Utilities Company, Newport, VT; *U.S. Public*, pg. 380
Bailin, Mark, Pres.--Rymer International Seafood Inc., Chicago, IL; *U.S. Public*, pg. 1414
Baillargeon, Claude, V.P. & Gen. Mgr.--Bombardier Inc.-Industrial Division, Granby, Canada; *Int'l*, pg. 200
Bailleres, Alberto, Pres.--Quimica del Rey S.A. de C.V., Mexico, Mexico; *Int'l*, pg. 677
Bailliart, Christian, Pres.-Dir. Gen.--Selas S.A., Gennevilliers, France; *U.S. Public*, pg. 1455
Baillie, Brian, Mng. Dir.--Cascade (Africa) Pty. Ltd., Johannesburg, South Africa; *U.S. Public*, pg. 311
Baillie, Robert, Gen. Mgr.--Australasian HMT Pty. Ltd., Edgecliff, Australia; *U.S. Public*, pg. 914
Baillie, Ross, Mng. Dir.--Transworld Publishers (Nz) Ltd., Albany, New Zealand; *Int'l*, pg. 191
Baily, Lawrence, Pres.--New England Power Co., Westborough, MA; *U.S. Public*, pg. 1171
Bain, Lowell, Div. Mgr.--Lexington Div., Lexington, KY; *U.S. Public*, pg. 1504
Bain, Mike, Div. Pres.--Grocery Supply Company Division, Sulphur Springs, TX; *U.S. Private*, pg. 436
Bain, N.C., Mng. Dir.--J. & P. Coats Limited, Glasgow, United Kingdom; *Int'l*, pg. 299
Bain, Steve, Chm.--First Chicago Leasing Corp., Chicago, IL; *U.S. Public*, pg. 628
Baines, Alan, Mng. Dir.--BioWhittaker UK Ltd., Wokingham, United Kingdom; *U.S. Public*, pg. 297
Baines, Mary, Administrator--Pecos Valley Care Center, Fort Sumner, NM; *U.S. Public*, pg. 838
Bair, Neil S., Asst. V.P. & Branch Mgr.--The Commercial Bank-Elida, Elida, OH; *U.S. Public*, pg. 410
Baird, Gordon, Publisher--Musician Magazine, Gloucester, MA; *Int'l*, pg. 1446
Baird, Ian, Gen. Mgr. & Publisher--The Western Star, Corner Brook, Canada; *Int'l*, pg. 632
Baird, William J., Jr., Pres. & Chief Exec. Officer--Willis Corroon Corp. of Maryland, Hunt Valley, MD; *Int'l*, pg. 1506
Bairstow, Paul, Publisher--Hendersonville Newspaper Corporation, Hendersonville, NC; *U.S. Public*, pg. 1175
Bak, Moon, Pres.--Lucky Goldstar International Corp., Seoul, Korea; *Int'l*, pg. 779
Bak, Per, Pres.--De danske Mejeriers Faellesindkeb amba, Kolding, Denmark; *Int'l*, pg. 826
Bakane, John L., Pres.--Cone Apparel Products, Greensboro, NC; *U.S. Public*, pg. 430
Bakeeff, Pierre, Rep.--Generale de Banque - Generale Bank, Brussels, Belgium; *Int'l*, pg. 546
Baker, Bruce R., V.P. & Gen. Mgr.--WSOC Television, Inc., Charlotte, NC; *U.S. Private*, pg. 282
Baker, Charles E., Gen. Mgr.--Barber-Colman Indev, Providence, RI; *Int'l*, pg. 1242
Baker, Clive A., Pres.--Grancol, Asesoramiento Y Servicios Ltda., Bogota, Colombia; *U.S. Public*, pg. 364
Baker, Craig, Mgr.--Anixter Edmonton, Edmonton, Canada; *U.S. Public*, pg. 115
Baker, Dan R., Pres.--Energy West Mining Company, Portland, OR; *U.S. Public*, pg. 1251
Baker, David, Chief Exec. Officer--Advertising Investment Services Pty. Ltd., Surrey Hills, Australia; *Int'l*, pg. 394
Baker, Dick, Pres.--Esprit Sport, San Francisco, CA; *U.S. Private*, pg. 383
Baker, Ed, Publr.--American Cities Business Journals, Inc., Atlanta, GA; *U.S. Private*, pg. 19
Baker, Ed, Mgr.-Opers.--Woodward-Clyde, Atlanta, GA; *U.S. Public*, pg. 1657
Baker, F. Gregory, Pres.--Westward Seafoods, Inc., Seattle, WA; *Int'l*, pg. 845
Baker, F.C. "Buzz", Pres. & Chief Exec. Officer--Creswell, Munsell, Fultz & Zirbel, L.P., Cedar Rapids, IA; *U.S. Private*, pg. 1197
Baker, G., Gen. Mgr.--Germantown International, Gladesville, Australia; *Int'l*, pg. 555
Baker, Gary, Chief Oper. Officer--Porsche-Delta Engineering Co., Troy, MI; *Int'l*, pg. 1063
Baker, J.A., Pres.--Equifax Credit Marketing Services, Inc., Atlanta, GA; *U.S. Public*, pg. 588
Baker, J.D., Rep.--Barclays Bank PLC, Jakarta, Indonesia; *Int'l*, pg. 166
Baker, Jack, V.P. & Mgr.--California State Bank-Placentia, Placentia, CA; *U.S. Public*, pg. 294
Baker, James, Pres.--Delavan Gas Turbine Products Division, West Des Moines, IA; *U.S. Public*, pg. 401
Baker, James, Mgr.--Sandvik Coromant Company, Fair Lawn, NJ; *Int'l*, pg. 1185
Baker, James T., Mgr.--Sandvik, Inc., Fair Lawn, NJ; *Int'l*, pg. 1185
Baker, Jim, Branch Dir.--N.G. Bailey & Co. Ltd.-Birmingham Branch, Birmingham, United Kingdom; *Int'l*, pg. 132
Baker, Joseph L., Pres.--Illinois Cement Co., La Salle, IL; *U.S. Public*, pg. 322
Baker, Kenneth D., Chief Exec. Officer--Newage Industries Inc., Testing Instruments Group, Willow Grove, PA; *U.S. Private*, pg. 796
Baker, L.M. Jr., Chm. Bd.--Wachovia Bank of North Carolina, N.A., Winston Salem, NC; *U.S. Public*, pg. 1730
Baker, Larry, Gen. Mgr.--Jeep/Eagle Division, Detroit, MI; *U.S. Public*, pg. 353
Baker, Lester, Gen. Mgr.--StorageTek Peripherals, Longmont, CO; *U.S. Public*, pg. 1523
Baker, M.J., Mng. Dir.--Devlin Electronics Limited, Basingstoke, United Kingdom; *Int'l*, pg. 207
Baker, Merrill, Plant Mgr.--CTS Corporation-Connector Division, Cokato, MN; *U.S. Public*, pg. 285
Baker, Michael, Pres.--Moduline International, Inc., Lacey, WA; *U.S. Public*, pg. 333
Baker, Paul T., Pres.--IGC Energy, Inc., Indianapolis, IN; *U.S. Public*, pg. 875
Baker, R. Daniel, Pres.--TIE Systems Colorado, Denver, CO; *U.S. Private*, pg. 1085
Baker, R.A., Mng. Dir.--Tube Products, Oldbury, United Kingdom; *Int'l*, pg. 1222
Baker, Ralph, Mgr.-Terminal--South State Terminal, Tampa, FL; *U.S. Public*, pg. 692
Baker, Richard, Pres.--Waterway Communications Inc., Jeffersonville, IN; *U.S. Public*, pg. 284
Baker, Rick, Gen. Mgr.--McCoy/Cove Mines, Battle Mountain, NV; *U.S. Public*, pg. 562
Baker, Robert, Chief Exec. Officer--The Chamberlain Group, Inc., Elmhurst, IL; *U.S. Private*, pg. 344
Baker, Robert J., Pres.--Bowne of New York City, Inc., New York, NY; *U.S. Public*, pg. 249
Baker, Roland C., Pres.--First Penn-Pacific Life Insurance Co., Oak Brook Terrace, IL; *U.S. Public*, pg. 998
Baker, Russell, Mng. Dir.--Hallmark Cards New Zealand Ltd., Mangere, New Zealand; *U.S. Private*, pg. 496
Baker, Sandra, Pres. & Publr.--Southland Publishing Co., Gainesville, GA; *U.S. Public*, pg. 701
Baker, Sherman N., Chm. Bd.--Morse Shoe, Inc., Canton, MA; *U.S. Public*, pg. 168
Baker, Sherman N., Chm. Bd.--Casual Male, Inc., Hyde Park, MA; *U.S. Public*, pg. 168
Baker, Stephen, Gen. Mgr.--Westpac Banking Corp. - Kiribati, Tarawa, Kiribati; *Int'l*, pg. 1497
Baker, Thomas J., Pres.--American President Real Estate Co., Ltd., Oakland, CA; *Int'l*, pg. 912
Baker, Thomas, II, Chief Oper. Officer--Aggregates Division, Jacksonville, FL; *U.S. Public*, pg. 656
Baker, Timothy J., Chief Exec. Officer-Australia--Moore Paragon Australia Limited, Wagga Wagga, Australia; *Int'l*, pg. 889
Baker, Tommy, Div. Mgr.--Century Telephone of North LA, Inc., Plain Dealing, LA; *U.S. Public*, pg. 329
Baker, Vernon, Gen. Mgr.--Homestake Mine, Lead, SD; *U.S. Public*, pg. 833
Baker, William, Pres.--Penn Machine Company, Johnstown, PA; *Int'l*, pg. 281
Baker, William C., Chm. Bd., Pres. & Chief Exec. Officer--The Santa Anita Companies, Arcadia, CA; *U.S. Public*, pg. 1081
Baker, William K., V.P.--UTP (United Technical Publications) Division, Garden City, NY; *U.S. Private*, pg. 516
Bakerink, Jack, Gen. Mgr.--Wellman Dynamics Corp., Creston, IA; *U.S. Public*, pg. 612
Bakey, Ray, Reg. Mgr.--Jaco Electronics, Inc., Richardson, TX; *U.S. Public*, pg. 921
Bakke, Jorund, Gen. Mgr.--Kvaerner Moss Technology a.s., Moss Division, Moss, Norway; *Int'l*, pg. 769
Bakke, Kjell, Chief Oper Officer--Ferrosan A/S, Soeborg, Denmark; *Int'l*, pg. 987
Bakken, Steven, Admin.--Greenery Health Care Center at Clarkston, Clarkston, MI; *U.S. Public*, pg. 837
Bakker, Gerard T., Mng. Dir.--Industar B.V., Utrecht, Netherlands; *Int'l*, pg. 283
Bakker, L.O., Chief Oper. Officer--Rabobank France, Paris, France; *Int'l*, pg. 1082
Bakowski, Marie, Medical Dir.--Duphar Laboratories Ltd., Southampton, United Kingdom; *Int'l*, pg. 1278
Baksha, Joseph, Pres.--Outlook Label Systems, Inc., Neenah, WI; *U.S. Public*, pg. 1235
Baksha, Joseph, Pres.--Outlook Packaging, Inc., Oak Creek, WI; *U.S. Public*, pg. 1236
Balaban, Octavian, Mgr.--AB Sandvik International, Bucharest, Romania; *Int'l*, pg. 1186
Balachowski, T.J., Chief Exec. Officer--ING Investment Management Inc., Atlanta, GA; *Int'l*, pg. 648
Balaguer, James J., Chm. Bd.--Willis Corroon Corp. of Northern Ohio, Cleveland, OH; *Int'l*, pg. 1506
Balaguer, John P., Pres.--Pratt & Whitney Government Engine & Space Propulsion, West Palm Beach, FL; *U.S. Public*, pg. 1690
Balaji, T.K., Chief Oper. Officer--Lucas-TVS Ltd., Padi, India; *Int'l*, pg. 820
Balakrishnan, Ajit, Mng. Dir.--Rediffusion-DY&R Pvt. Ltd., Mumbai, India; *U.S. Private*, pg. 326
Balarin, L. A., Mng. Dir.--Macmillan Boleswa Publishing (Pty) Ltd., Manzini, Swaziland; *Int'l*, pg. 1479
Balber, Michael B., Exec. V.P.--Sports Imprints/Fun Wear, Huber Heights, OH; *U.S. Public*, pg. 1002
Balboni, John N., Gen. Mgr.--Veratec Division, Walpole, MA; *U.S. Public*, pg. 904
Balch, Alan, Chm. Bd. & Chief Exec. Officer--Lane Limited, Tucker, GA; *Int'l*, pg. 1129
Baldasare, Rick, Mng. Dir.--Cartwright Communications Co., Cincinnati, OH; *U.S. Public*, pg. 1582
Baldassari, Dennis, Pres. & Chief Oper. Officer--Jersey Central Power & Light Co., Morristown, NJ; *U.S. Public*, pg. 695
Baldassari, Dennis, Pres.--Pennsylvania Electric Company, Reading, PA; *U.S. Public*, pg. 695
Baldauf, Sari, Pres.--Nokia Cellular Systems, Espoo, Finland; *Int'l*, pg. 953
Balderson, Clark, Pres.--Balderson Inc., Wamego, KS; *U.S. Public*, pg. 315
Baldetti, Paul, Pres.--AMW Industries Inc., Conway, AR; *U.S. Public*, pg. 457
Baldi, Anthony, Pres.--Aceto Agricultural Chemicals Corp., Lake Success, NY; *U.S. Public*, pg. 15
Baldini, David, Pres.--Avionics Specialities, Inc., Charlottesville, VA; *U.S. Public*, pg. 25
Baldini, Ricardo, Pres.--Agusta Aerospace Services A.A.S., S.A.-Belgio, Hollogne-sur-Geer, Belgium; *Int'l*, pg. 32
Baldock, David, Mgr.--Gould Midwest, Inc., Ellisville, MO; *U.S. Private*, pg. 467
Baldwin, D.W., Pres.--Campus Point Realty Corporation, San Diego, CA; *U.S. Private*, pg. 976
Baldwin, J.W., Chm. Bd.--Caterpillar Logistics Services, Inc., Peoria, IL; *U.S. Public*, pg. 316
Baldwin, John L., Pres.--Pittsburgh Corning Corporation, Pittsburgh, PA; *U.S. Public*, pg. 449
Baldwin, Mark, Div. Mgr.--Wyle Electronics-Sacramento, Rancho Cordova, CA; *Int'l*, pg. 1457
Baldwin, Mike, Pres.--Market Data Retrieval, Shelton, CT; *U.S. Public*, pg. 536
Baldwin, Peter, Assoc. Dir.--WF Corroon-Cardiff, Cardiff, United Kingdom; *Int'l*, pg. 1501
Baldwin, R.K., Mng. Dir.--APV Baker Plc, Peterborough, United Kingdom; *Int'l*, pg. 1240
Baldwin, Ralph L., Pres.--Community Credit Corporation, New Castle, DE; *U.S. Public*, pg. 1729
Baldwin, Robert H., Pres. & Chief Exec. Officer--The Mirage Casino/Hotel, Las Vegas, NV; *U.S. Public*, pg. 1117
Baldwin, Rod, Mng. Dir.--Comalco-CHH Aluminum, Auckland, New Zealand; *U.S. Public*, pg. 905
Baldwin, William, Pres.--Speedring, Inc., Cullman, AL; *U.S. Public*, pg. 158
Balentine, P.H., Pres.--Mount Vernon Mills, Smith & Waters, Inc., Ware Shoals, SC; *U.S. Private*, pg. 835
Bales, Robert, Pres.--Huron Manufacturing Div., Lexington, MI; *U.S. Public*, pg. 1684
Balika, Arthur, Gen. Mgr.--Alden Press, Oberlin, OH; *U.S. Public*, pg. 1778
Balkenende, R.C., Pres.--Van Leeuwen Pipe & Tube Corp., Houston, TX; *Int'l*, pg. 1449
Ball, C. Jordan, Mgr.--Scott & Stringfellow, Inc., Richmond, VA; *U.S. Public*, pg. 1445
Ball, Daniel H., Mgr.-Branch--Piper Jaffray Inc., Great Falls, MT; *U.S. Public*, pg. 1301
Ball, Dexter, Pres. & Gen. Mgr.--First American Title Co. of Idaho, Boise, ID; *U.S. Public*, pg. 625
Ball, F., Dr., Pres.--S.A. USA, North Stonington, CT; *U.S. Private*, pg. 994
Ball, James, Admin.--Tall Trees, Memphis, TN; *U.S. Public*, pg. 451
Ball, James H., Admin.--Shelby County Training Center, Memphis, TN; *U.S. Public*, pg. 451
Ball, John E., V.P. & Gen. Mgr.--Coltec Automotive Division, Troy, MI; *U.S. Public*, pg. 401
Ball, Kenneth L., Pres. & Gen. Mgr.--Borden Decorative Products, Saint Louis, MO; *U.S. Private*, pg. 158
Ball, Larry, County Mgr.--First American Title Co. of Clark County, Vancouver, WA; *U.S. Public*, pg. 625
Ball, Larry, Pres.--Litton Poly-Scientific, Blacksburg, VA; *U.S. Public*, pg. 1003
Ball, Michael D., Mgr.--Scott & Stringfellow, Inc., Manassas, VA; *U.S. Public*, pg. 1446
Ball, Robert L., Pres.--Alcan Rolled Products Division, Cleveland, OH; *Int'l*, pg. 50
Ball, Robert W., V.P. & Gen. Mgr.--Supreme/Mirro, Pickering, Canada; *U.S. Public*, pg. 1178
Ball, Tim, V.P.-Sls.--Tredit Tire & Wheel Co., Elkhart, IN; *U.S. Private*, pg. 300
Ballard, Bob, Sr. V.P. & Branch Mgr.--California State Bank-Ontario, Ontario, CA; *U.S. Public*, pg. 294
Ballard, Jerry, Pres.--Valley Manufacturing Corporation, Wilkes-Barre, PA; *Int'l*, pg. 1338
Ballard, John H., Pres.--Loss Management Services, Inc., Frederick, MD; *U.S. Public*, pg. 152
Ballard, John W., III, Chief Oper. Officer--Technology for Communications International, Sunnyvale, CA; *U.S. Public*, pg. 1555
Ballard, Tim, Publr.--The Lebanon Enterprise, Lebanon, KY; *U.S. Private*, pg. 648
Ballard, Tim, Gen. Mgr. & Editor--The Springfield Sun, Springfield, KY; *U.S. Private*, pg. 648
Ballard, Tony, Mng. Dir.--SSB Advertising Melbourne, Melbourne, Australia; *Int'l*, pg. 394
Ballard, William C., Jr., Pres.--Galen Hospital of Baytown, Inc., Louisville, KY; *U.S. Public*, pg. 404
Ballay, Joseph, Admin.--Bay Breeze Center, Gulf Breeze, FL; *U.S. Public*, pg. 836
Balle, Hellmut, Sr. Mng. Dir.--Deutsche Bank AG (Stuttgart), Stuttgart, Germany; *Int'l*, pg. 402
Ballentine, James M., Pres. & Chief Exec. Officer--Detroit Stoker Co., Monroe, MI; *U.S. Public*, pg. 1679
Ballesteros, Mimi, Billing Mgr.--TMP Worldwide Ltd., Toronto, Canada; *U.S. Private*, pg. 1065
Balletti, Robert, Pres.--Kvaerner Venture Inc., Stamford, CT; *Int'l*, pg. 770
Ballew, Glenn, Pres.--Equity Fire & Casualty Insurance Company, West Des Moines, IA; *U.S. Private*, pg. 881
Ballhaus, William F., Jr., Dr., Pres.--Lockheed Martin Aerostructure, Baltimore, MD; *U.S. Public*, pg. 1006
Ballin, Robert, Pres. & Chief Exec. Officer--Willis Corroon Corp. of Eugene, Eugene, OR; *Int'l*, pg. 1505
Ballion, Marc, Dir.-Admin.--Banque Belgolaise, Brussels, Belgium; *Int'l*, pg. 546
Ballman, Karlheinz, Gen. Mgr.--Air Products GmbH, Hattingen, Germany; *U.S. Public*, pg. 31
Ballou, Roger H., Pres. & Chief Oper. Officer--Alamo Rent-A-Car Inc., Fort Lauderdale, FL; *U.S. Public*, pg. 1379
Ballowe, Jeff, Div. Head--Ziff-Davis Marketing & Development, New York, NY; *Int'l*, pg. 1276
Bally, Michel, Pres.--Sulzer, Inc., New York, NY; *Int'l*, pg. 1306
Balmas, Bruce B., Pres. & Chief Exec. Officer--D & N Mortgage Corporation, Hancock, MI; *U.S. Public*, pg. 472
Balmuth, Marc, Chm. Bd. & Chief Exec. Officer--Bob's Stores, Inc., Meriden, CT; *U.S. Public*, pg. 287
Balocco, Marco, Fin. Dir.--Matter Leo Burnett, Zurich, Switzerland; *U.S. Private*, pg. 186
Baloun, Terry, Pres.--Norwest Bank Minnesota West, N.A., Moorhead, MN; *U.S. Public*, pg. 1202
Baloun, Terry, Pres.--Norwest Bank North Dakota, N.A., Fargo, ND; *U.S. Public*, pg. 1202
Balsara, Sam, Chief Exec. Officer--Madison DMB&B Advertising, PVT Ltd., Mumbai, India; *U.S. Private*, pg. 304
Balta, Steven P., Gen. Mgr.--Danfoss Fluid Power, Easley, SC; *Int'l*, pg. 377

Balthrop, Judy, Rep.-Sls. Promo.--Dillard, A ResourceNet International Company, Morrisville, NC; *U.S. Public*, pg. 902

Baltimore, G., Mgr.-Sls.--Augat, Inc., Interconnection Products-Carol Stream, Glen Ellyn, IL; *U.S. Public*, pg. 1598

Baltz, Timothy, Warden--Silverdale Facilities, Chattanooga, TN; *U.S. Public*, pg. 451

Baltzell, Michael, Pres.--Alumax Primary Aluminum Corporation, Norcross, GA; *U.S. Public*, pg. 60

Baltzelle, Jim, Exec. Editor--Palatka Daily News, Palatka, FL; *U.S. Public*, pg. 1175

Balucci, Dave, Chief Oper. Officer--MacDermid Taiwan Ltd., Hsin-chu, Taiwan; *U.S. Public*, pg. 1030

Balwa, Uman A.K., Mng. Dir.--Burgmann India Pvt. Ltd, Mumbai, India; *Int'l*, pg. 234

Baly, Dominique, Pres.--Millipore Intertech, Milford, MA; *U.S. Public*, pg. 1113

Balzer, Glen, V.P.-Sls. & Mktg., Asia-Pacific Opers.--AMD Far East, Ltd., Sunnyvale, CA; *U.S. Public*, pg. 21

Balzer, W. Bernd, Chief Oper. Officer--Advanced Micro Devices GmbH, Munich, Germany; *U.S. Public*, pg. 21

Bamford, Laura, Publr. & Mng. Dir.--Hamlyn/Octopus, London, United Kingdom; *Int'l*, pg. 1093

Bamford, Laura, Publr. & Mng. Dir.--Bounty Books, London, United Kingdom; *Int'l*, pg. 1093

Ban, Shoji, Pres.--Toyoda Gosei Co. Ltd., Kasugai, Japan; *Int'l*, pg. 1412

Banakis, Jimmy, V.P.-Opers.--R.J. Grunts/Chicago, Chicago, IL; *U.S. Private*, pg. 661

Bancet, Jean Jacques, Promo. Dir.--Simon Marketing International, Paris, France; *U.S. Private*, pg. 1001

Banchini, Saverio A., Chief Exec.--HISALBA - Hornos Ibericos Alba S.A., Madrid, Spain; *Int'l*, pg. 629

Banchong-Silpa, Methei, Mng. Dir.--Siam Lemmerz Co., Ltd., Sara Buri, Thailand; *Int'l*, pg. 1238

Bancroft, David, V.P.-European Opers.--Cilag AG, Schaffhausen, Switzerland; *U.S. Public*, pg. 929

Bancroft, Jon, Chief Admin. Officer--The Care Group of New York, Inc., New York, NY; *U.S. Public*, pg. 305

Bancroft, Robert, Pres.--Aydin Electro-Fab Div., Croydon, PA; *U.S. Public*, pg. 158

Band, M. H. W., Chief Oper. Officer--Babcock Hydro-Pneumatics Ltd., London, United Kingdom; *Int'l*, pg. 471

Band, Ray B., Dr., District Mgr.--Falconbridge Explorations, Winnipeg, Canada; *Int'l*, pg. 433

Band, Raymond B., Reg. Mgr.--Falconbridge Explorations, Timmins, Canada; *Int'l*, pg. 434

Band, Robert, Pres.--Perini Management Services, Inc., Framingham, MA; *U.S. Public*, pg. 1278

Bande, Andres B., Pres.--Ameritech International Inc., Chicago, IL; *U.S. Public*, pg. 98

Bandera, Richard, Chief Exec. Officer--Schoeller-Beckmann Nooter Apparatetechnik GMBH, Ternitz, Austria; *U.S. Private*, pg. 801

Bandfield, Peter, Gen. Mgr.--FlightSafety Academy, Vero Beach, FL; *U.S. Public*, pg. 218

Bandier, M., Pres. & Chief Exec. Officer--EMI Music Publishing, New York, NY; *Int'l*, pg. 427

Bandreaux, Philip, Chief Oper. Officer--Ahlstrom Process Equipment Inc., Baton Rouge, LA; *Int'l*, pg. 34

Bandrowski, Jeff, Gen. Mgr.--MAST Microwave Division, Wilmington, MA; *U.S. Public*, pg. 953

Bandstigen, Bengt, Mng. Dir.--Sweden Table Tennis AB, Eskilstuna, Sweden; *U.S. Public*, pg. 591

Bandy, C.M., Mng. Dir.--Texaco Hong Kong Ltd., Hong Kong, Hong Kong; *U.S. Public*, pg. 1584

Bandy, James, Gen. Mgr.--Supreme Corporation of Texas, Cleburne, TX; *U.S. Public*, pg. 1542

Bane, Daniel T., Pres.--Grocers Equipment Co., Los Angeles, CA; *U.S. Private*, pg. 227

Bane, Daniel T., Pres. & Chief Fin. Officer--Crown Grocers, Inc., Los Angeles, CA; *U.S. Private*, pg. 227

Banfield, David, Gen. Mgr.--Specialty Ceramics Division, East Liverpool, OH; *U.S. Public*, pg. 618

Bang, Bjarne A., Mgr.-Station--Det Norske Veritas, Godthab, Greenland; *Int'l*, pg. 396

Bang, Chul, Pres.--Keystone Valve (Korea) Ltd., Kyonggi-do, Korea; *U.S. Public*, pg. 1650

Bang, Han-Woo, Pres.--Ssangyong Pacific, Diamond Bar, CA; *Int'l*, pg. 1292

Bang, N.W., Pres. & Gen. Mgr.--Pamco Division, Calgary, Canada; *Int'l*, pg. 1400

Bang, William H., Pres.--CCB/NILS, Inc., Chatsworth, CA; *U.S. Public*, pg. 512

Bang, William H., Pres.--NILS Publishing Company, Chatsworth, CA; *Int'l*, pg. 1513

Bangert, Bruce A., Mng. Dir.--RHM Technology Ltd., High Wycombe, United Kingdom; *Int'l*, pg. 1396

Banghart, John F., Pres. & Chief Oper. Officer--The Worcester Insurance Co., Worcester, MA; *U.S. Public*, pg. 787

Banhardt, Hans, V.P.--Automotive Electronic Control Systems, Inc., Anderson, SC; *Int'l*, pg. 205

Bania, Beth, Pres.--PVS Transportation, Detroit, MI; *U.S. Private*, pg. 828

Baninet, Guy, Exec. V.P. & Chief Oper. Officer--Marine Division, Montreal, Canada; *Int'l*, pg. 1272

Bank, David, Pres.--M.F. Bank Restoration Co., Duluth, GA; *U.S. Private*, pg. 114

Banks, Alastair, Gen. Mgr.--Viacom Canada Ltd., Toronto, Canada; *U.S. Private*, pg. 779

Banks, Alastair, Gen. Mgr.--Viacom Enterprises Canada Ltd., Toronto, Canada; *U.S. Private*, pg. 779

Banks, Allen, Pres.--The Program Exchange, New York, NY; *U.S. Public*, pg. 1422

Banks, Charles A., Pres. & Chief Exec. Officer--Ferguson Enterprises, Inc., Newport News, VA; *Int'l*, pg. 1512

Banks, Hamish, Mng. Partner--Noordervliet & Winninghoff/Leo Burnett B.V., Amsterdam, Netherlands; *U.S. Private*, pg. 186

Banks, J.D., Gen. Mgr.--Industrial Packaging Div. (Monroe), Monroe, MI; *Int'l*, pg. 1270

Banks, James, Pres.--International Rotex, Inc., Reno, NV; *Int'l*, pg. 460

Banks, James B., Publr.--Multimedia Publishing of North Carolina, Inc., Asheville, NC; *U.S. Public*, pg. 699

Banks, Larry, Pres.--Household Life Insurance Co., Farmington, MI; *U.S. Public*, pg. 842

Banks, W., Plant Mgr.--Foamex, Fort Wayne, IN; *U.S. Private*, pg. 1094

Bankston, James G., Chm. Bd., Pres. & Chief Exec. Officer--W.O. Bankston Enterprises Inc., Dallas, TX; *U.S. Public*, pg. 1379

Bankston, James G., Chm. Bd. & Pres.--W.O. Bankston Lincoln Mercury, Dallas, TX; *U.S. Public*, pg. 1379

Banner, Mack, Dir.--Subang Jaya Medical Centre Sdn. Bhd., Kuala Lumpur, Malaysia; *Int'l*, pg. 1250

Banner, Warren, Gen. Mgr.--Ball FloraPlant, West Chicago, IL; *U.S. Private*, pg. 112

Banner, William C., Pres.--American Commercial Security & Investigative Services, San Francisco, CA; *U.S. Public*, pg. 2

Banning, L., Mng. Dir.--Glaenzer-Seurre NV/SA, Drogenbos, Belgium; *Int'l*, pg. 536

Bannister, Denise, Pres. & Publr.--Pensacola News-Journal, Inc., Pensacola, FL; *U.S. Public*, pg. 701

Bannister, Peter, Gen. Mgr.--KTNV-TV, Las Vegas, NV; *U.S. Private*, pg. 601

Bannon, Eugene, Reg. Sls. Mgr.-Eastern Region--GATX Logistics (LWD), Inc., Winston Salem, NC; *U.S. Public*, pg. 691

Bannon, R.N., Pres.--Sterling Pulp Chemicals, Ltd., Etobicoke, Canada; *U.S. Public*, pg. 1580

Bannon, Robert G., Pres. & Chief Exec. Officer--First American Title Insurance Co. of N.Y., New York, NY; *U.S. Public*, pg. 626

Bannon, Timothy, Actg. Gen. Mgr.--Domtech Holdings, Inc., Trenton, Canada; *U.S. Public*, pg. 990

Banoli, Carlo, Pres.--Sorin Biomedica, Irvine, CA; *Int'l*, pg. 483

Bansholt, Soren, Pres.--Scandinavian Division, Copenhagen, Denmark; *U.S. Public*, pg. 423

Bansholt, Soren, Mng. Dir.--Olivetti A/S, Copenhagen, Denmark; *Int'l*, pg. 1003

Bantoft, Chris, Pres.--ACC Long Distance U.K. Ltd., London, United Kingdom; *U.S. Public*, pg. 3

Banton, Julian W., Chm., Pres. & Chief Exec. Officer--SouthTrust Bank of Alabama, Birmingham, AL; *U.S. Public*, pg. 1491

Banyackski, Stephen, Pres.--Spence Engineering Co., Walden, NY; *U.S. Public*, pg. 1747

Banzet, Serge, Pres. & Chief Oper. Officer--Peugeot Motors of America Inc., Little Falls, NJ; *Int'l*, pg. 1020

Bapes, Peter C., Pres. & Chief Exec. Officer--Associated Leasing, Inc., Menomonee Falls, WI; *U.S. Public*, pg. 140

Baptista, Carlos J.F., Mng. Dir.--Crown Cork & Seal (Portugal) S.A., Lisbon, Portugal; *U.S. Public*, pg. 464

Baptista, Jose, Dr., Chief Mgr.--Willis Faber Limitada, Lisbon, Portugal; *Int'l*, pg. 1510

Baqir, Asshad, V.P. & Chief Mgr.--Habib Bank Ltd., Dubai, United Arab Emirates; *Int'l*, pg. 585

Barabino, C., Chief Oper. Officer--Saiwa, Genoa, Italy; *Int'l*, pg. 381

Baracos, Leon, Pres.--Weilwood Industries, Inc., New York, NY; *U.S. Private*, pg. 965

Baradarien, Diane, Pres.--Allegria Inc., Harrison, NJ; *U.S. Private*, pg. 565

Barakett, E.J., Pres.--Junors, Toronto, Canada; *Int'l*, pg. 1150

Baranski, Dennis, Pres.--Northern Cross, Ltd., Lecompton, KS; *U.S. Private*, pg. 115

Barash, C., Pres.--OMI Bulk Management Co., New York, NY; *U.S. Public*, pg. 1208

Barata, A., Mng. Dir.--Chaussures Bally Moulins SA, Moulins, France; *Int'l*, pg. 997

Barazer, Pierre, Pres.--Compagnie IBM France, S.A, Paris, France; *U.S. Public*, pg. 897

Barazer, Pierre, Pres.--IBM France Diffusion, S.A, Paris, France; *U.S. Public*, pg. 897

Barb, James, Gen. Mgr.--Unitog Company, Fort Smith, AR; *U.S. Public*, pg. 1693

Barba, Guillermo, Chief Exec. Officer--Betancourt Barba EURO RSCG, Mexico, Mexico; *Int'l*, pg. 603

Barba, L. Douglas, Sr. V.P. & Gen. Mgr.--Catamount Energy Corporation, Rutland, VT; *U.S. Public*, pg. 328

Barbara, P., Plant Mgr.--Dampers Iberica, S.A., Gava, Spain; *U.S. Public*, pg. 469

Barbara, Pedro, Mng. Dir.--R.J. Simpson International, SL (Spain), Barcelona, Spain; *U.S. Public*, pg. 1475

Barbarich, Antony M., Gen. Mgr.--Dimond Industries, Auckland, New Zealand; *Int'l*, pg. 495

Barbarossa, Franco, Chief Exec. Officer--Redi, Bologna, Italy; *Int'l*, pg. 430

Barbarossa, Franco, Chief Exec. Officer--Europlast, Treviso, Italy; *Int'l*, pg. 430

Barbato, Gianfranco, Chm. Bd.--C.S.O. Centrale Supporti Operativi S.p.A., Torri di Quartesolo, Italy; *Int'l*, pg. 138

Barbato, Gianfranco, Chm. Bd.--Itaservice S.p.A., Milan, Italy; *Int'l*, pg. 138

Barbaum, Bernd, Chm. Bd.--CC-Bank, A.G., Monchengladbach, Germany; *Int'l*, pg. 144

Barbe, Yves, Chief Oper. Officer--Automobiles Peugeot S.A., Paris, France; *Int'l*, pg. 1020

Barbeau, Faye, Mgr.--Centre Court Travel, Denver, CO; *U.S. Public*, pg. 1758

Barbeau, James, Pres.--Managistics Incorporated, Woodside, NY; *U.S. Public*, pg. 181

Barbee, Erwin, Pres.--Bancroft-Whitney Co., San Francisco, CA; *U.S. Public*, pg. 1602

Barbee, Michael L., V.P.--Southern Div., Norcross, GA; *U.S. Public*, pg. 732

Barber, Betty, Admin.--Medicenter, Louisville, Louisville, KY; *U.S. Public*, pg. 1714

Barber, Bruce, Pres. & Chief Oper. Officer--First National Bank, Palestine, Palestine, TX; *U.S. Public*, pg. 630

Barber, C., Chief Oper. Officer--Laing Technology Group Ltd., London, United Kingdom; *Int'l*, pg. 796

Barber, Dona L., Pres.--GenMark, Inc., Saint Louis, MO; *U.S. Private*, pg. 443

Barber, James W., V.P.--Lufkin Industries, Trailer Div., Lufkin, TX; *U.S. Public*, pg. 1019

Barber, Mack, V.P. & Gen. Mgr.--Mississippi Phosphates Corp., Pascagoula, MS; *U.S. Public*, pg. 1117

Barber, Philip F., Pres.--Shenandoah Valley Land Development Div., Silver Spring, MD; *U.S. Public*, pg. 1683

Barber, Rick, Mng. Dir.--Lake Placid Granite Co., Au Sable Forks, NY; *U.S. Private*, pg. 251

Barber, W. Freeman, Chief Oper. Officer--ISC Futures Corporation, Charlotte, NC; *U.S. Public*, pg. 910

Barber, Walter, Pres. & Chief Exec. Officer--Fluor Daniel GTI, Inc., Norwood, MA; *U.S. Public*, pg. 660

Barbera, John, Pres.--Turner Broadcasting Sales, Inc., Atlanta, GA; *U.S. Public*, pg. 1615

Barbera, Joseph A., Pres.--Intracorp, Inc., Wilmington, DE; *U.S. Public*, pg. 362

Barbera, M., Chief Oper. Officer--Rossignol SC S.p.A., Vercelli, Italy; *Int'l*, pg. 1127

Barbereau, Daniel, Pres.--John Deere, Saint-Jean-de-la-Ruelle, France; *U.S. Public*, pg. 492

Barberena, Juan Garcia, Chm. Bd.--Grafiba Sociedad Anonima, Rubi, Spain; *U.S. Public*, pg. 1387

Barbero, Bruno, Mng. Dir.--Barbero S.p.A., Canale, Italy; *Int'l*, pg. 64

Barbi, Alessio, Mng. Dir.--SASIB Bakery Italia S.p.A., Verona, Italy; *Int'l*, pg. 1194

Barbieux, Y., Gen. Mgr.--Nestle (Thailand) Ltd., Bangkok, Thailand; *Int'l*, pg. 921

Barbieux, Yves, Pres. & Mng. Dir.--Nestle France, Courbevoie, France; *Int'l*, pg. 921

Barbosa, Mario Leite, Gen. Mgr.--R.J. Reynolds (Portugal) Limitada, Lisbon, Portugal; *U.S. Public*, pg. 1355

Barbosa, Marise, V.P.-Fin. & Admin.--Transbrasil Airlines, Inc., Miami, FL; *Int'l*, pg. 1416

Barbosa, Tulio, Acting Head-Field Office--Banco Mundial, Recife, Brazil; *U.S. Private*, pg. 1189

Barbosa, Victor Manuel Goncalves, Gen. Mgr.--Novo Nordisk Bioindustrial do Brasil Ltda., Parana, Brazil; *Int'l*, pg. 988

Barbosa, Wagner, Chief Oper. Officer--KONE Elevadores Ltda., Sao Jose dos Campos, Brazil; *Int'l*, pg. 747

Barbour, Dwayne, Branch Mgr.--National Mine Service Company, Mt. Vernon Div., Mount Vernon, IL; *Int'l*, pg. 281

Barbour, John, Pres.--OddzOn Products, Inc., Campbell, CA; *U.S. Public*, pg. 797

Barbovitch, Igor, Mng. Dir.--Costain Developments SA, Cadiz, Spain; *Int'l*, pg. 337

Barbovitch, Igor, Mng. Dir.--Alcaidesa Costain Developments S.A., Cadiz, Spain; *Int'l*, pg. 337

Barcam, Michael, Pres.--Old World Automotive Products, Northbrook, IL; *U.S. Private*, pg. 814

Barcellini, Jean, Dir.--Motorola Semi Conducteurs (Societe), Toulouse, France; *U.S. Public*, pg. 1140

Barch, Robert, Pres.--Dynalco Controls Corporation, Fort Lauderdale, FL; *U.S. Public*, pg. 457

Barcham, Terry, Mng. Dir.--Snap-on Tools Limited, Sale, United Kingdom; *U.S. Public*, pg. 1481

Barcik, Stephen J., Pres.--Interpak Terminals, Inc., Houston, TX; *Int'l*, pg. 724

Barclay, Nick, Reg. Dir.-Asia--Royal Skandia Life Assurance Ltd., Hong Kong, Hong Kong; *Int'l*, pg. 1257

Barclay, Richard D., Pres. & Chief Exec. Officer--First National Bank of Central Illinois, Springfield, IL; *U.S. Public*, pg. 644

Barcroft, A. Paul, Mng. Dir.--The Langer Biomechanics Group (UK) Ltd., Stoke on Trent, United Kingdom; *U.S. Public*, pg. 978

Bardaji, Angela, Gen. Mgr.--EURO RSCG Barcelona, Barcelona, Spain; *Int'l*, pg. 603

Barden, William, Mgr.--Stephen Gould of Indiana, Inc., Warsaw, IN; *U.S. Private*, pg. 467

Barder, D. Richard, Pres.--M & I Bank of Beloit, Beloit, WI; *U.S. Public*, pg. 1050

Bardini, Robert, Dir.--Martin Merkel France-Sarl, Marne la Vallee, France; *Int'l*, pg. 860

Bardo, Charles, Pres.--Ceramic Cooling Tower Co., Fort Worth, TX; *U.S. Private*, pg. 68

Bardon, P., Gen. Mgr.--Belin/LU, Evry, France; *Int'l*, pg. 380

Bardsley, Michael, Sec.--AMEC Process & Energy, London, United Kingdom; *Int'l*, pg. 16

Bardsley, Stephen, Mng. Dir.--Battenfeld Australia Pty. Ltd., Braeside, Australia; *Int'l*, pg. 825

Bare, Jean, Admin.--Davidson Nursing Center, Inc., Thomasville, NC; *U.S. Public*, pg. 1712

Bared, Luis, Pres.--Bared Jewelers, Saint Thomas, VI; *Int'l*, pg. 103

Barefoot, G.D., Div. Mgr.--Matthews Intl. Corp.-Graphic Systems Div., Pittsburgh, PA; *U.S. Public*, pg. 1060

Bareiss, Bernard, Gen. Mgr.-Lotus--Kaysersberg S.A., Courbevoie, France; *U.S. Public*, pg. 673

Bareiss, Ernst, Sr. Mng. Dir.--Deutsche Bank AG (Freiburg), Freiburg, Germany; *Int'l*, pg. 402

Barela, George, Plant Mgr.--Advanced Polymers Division, Anaheim, CA; *U.S. Public*, pg. 689

Barenbuem, Carlos, Mng. Dir.--Sulzer Argentina S.A., Buenos Aires, Argentina; *Int'l*, pg. 1306

Barenco, Sergio, Gen. Mgr.--Monte Generoso Railway AG, Capolago, Switzerland; *Int'l*, pg. 866

Barendrecht, J.F.M., Chief Oper. Officer--Banco Surinvest S.A., Montevideo, Uruguay; *Int'l*, pg. 1082

Barendse, Thurso, V.P.-Fin.--Union-Transport Corporation-Melville Office, Melville, NY; *U.S. Private*, pg. 1119

Bares, Jim, Mgr.-Fin. & Admin.--W.R. Grace (N.Z.) Ltd., Elsdon, New Zealand; *U.S. Public*, pg. 756

Barger, Bill, Mgr.-Mfg.--J.R. Simplot Company Lathrop Plant, Lathrop, CA; *U.S. Private*, pg. 1002

Bargeron, Walter N., Pres.--Bethlehem Steel-Burns Harbor Division, Chesterton, IN; *U.S. Public*, pg. 226

Bargery, Alan, Warden--Hardeman Co. Correctional Facility, Whiteville, TN; *U.S. Public*, pg. 450
Barillas, Haroldo, Consumer Marketing Mgr.--Productos de Maiz y Alimentos, S.A., Guatemala, Guatemala; *U.S. Public*, pg. 447
Barington, Rene, Mng. Dir.--B&K Ultrasound A/S, Gentofte, Denmark; *U.S. Public*, pg. 109
Bario, Bob, Mgr.--Lincoln Holdings, Inc., Englewood, CO; *U.S. Public*, pg. 647
Barish, Michael S., Pres.--Cambiar Investors, Inc., Englewood, CO; *U.S. Public*, pg. 1672
Bark, Gunnar, Chief Oper. Officer--Electrolux Autoliv, Stockholm, Sweden; *Int'l*, pg. 439
Bark, Th. J., Gen. Mgr.--ABN (Head Office), Amsterdam, Netherlands; *Int'l*, pg. 11
Bark, Tom, Gen. Mgr.--Allen & Hoshall, Nashville, TN; *U.S. Private*, pg. 36
Barkalow, Walter, Gen. Mgr.--Triple S Plastics, Texas Central, Georgetown, TX; *U.S. Public*, pg. 1640
Barkaszi, Stephen F., Mgr.-Opers.--Fincor Electronics, York, PA; *U.S. Public*, pg. 857
Barke, Bill, Pres.--Allyn & Bacon, Needham, MA; *U.S. Private*, pg. 778
Barkell, Dave, Mgr.--Davco Service, Inc., Meridian, ID; *U.S. Private*, pg. 673
Barkell, William, Pres.--Ackerley Communications of Florida, Inc., Miami, FL; *U.S. Public*, pg. 16
Barker, David R., Pres.--Penn Virginia Oil & Gas Company, Kingsport, TN; *U.S. Public*, pg. 1271
Barker, G. Carlton, Chm. Bd., Pres. & Chief Exec. Officer--Regions Bank/Montgomery/Alexander City, Montgomery, AL; *U.S. Public*, pg. 1372
Barker, H. Paul, Gen. Mgr.--Chemical Division (U.S.), Mill Hall, PA; *U.S. Public*, pg. 153
Barker, Mary, Admin. Sec.--Mid-State Wire Company, Crawfordsville, IN; *U.S. Private*, pg. 686
Barker, Michael, Gen. Mgr.--Schult Homes Corporation, Navasota, TX; *U.S. Public*, pg. 1442
Barker, Peter, Mng. Dir.--Rank Hovis Limited, High Wycombe, United Kingdom; *Int'l*, pg. 1396
Barker, Richard, Gen. Mgr.--G.E. Canada, Peterborough, Peterborough, Canada; *U.S. Public*, pg. 713
Barker, W.R., Pres.--Ravarino & Freschi, Inc., Saint Louis, MO; *U.S. Private*, pg. 158
Barkhurst, Ross, Pres. & Chief Exec. Officer--Vermont Yankee Nuclear Power Corp., Brattleboro, VT; *U.S. Public*, pg. 328
Barkley, Andy, Pres.--Six Flags Fiesta Texas, San Antonio, TX; *U.S. Public*, pg. 1611
Barkley, Drew S., Pres.--Permanent General Companies, Nashville, TN; *U.S. Private*, pg. 563
Barkley, Drew S., Pres.--Tennessee Insurance Co., Nashville, TN; *U.S. Private*, pg. 563
Barksdale, Darrell, Gen. Mgr.--Sackner-Southeast Div., Statesville, NC; *U.S. Public*, pg. 924
Barksdale, Gordon T., Pres. & Chief Exec. Officer--Regions Bank/Decatur/Hartselle, Decatur, AL; *U.S. Public*, pg. 1372
Barkus, Bruce, V.P.--Eckerd Drug Co., Clearwater, FL; *U.S. Public*, pg. 917
Barlett, David, Pres. & Chief Exec. Officer--NationsBank of Hot Springs, Hot Springs National Park, AR; *U.S. Public*, pg. 1164
Barlett, Gordon, Gen. Mgr.--Isomedix Operations Inc., Sandy, UT; *U.S. Public*, pg. 1515
Barlocher, Ph., Mgr.--Societa di Banca Svizzera, Lugano, Switzerland; *Int'l*, pg. 1329
Barlocher, Urs, Dr., Chief Exec. Officer--Sandoz Nutrition Ltd., Bern, Switzerland; *Int'l*, pg. 972
Barlow, Bruce, Mr., Pres.--Conida Farms, Hazelton, ID; *U.S.* Private, pg. 693
Barlow, Hal, V.P. & Gen. Mgr.--REAL Applications, Ltd., Woodland Hills, CA; *U.S. Private*, pg. 366
Barlow, Philip, Pres.--Carriage Industries, Inc., Calhoun, GA; *U.S. Public*, pg. 514
Barlow, Tony, Mng. Dir.--Pharmaco Intl. Ltd., Cambridge, United Kingdom; *U.S. Public*, pg. 1285
Barlup, Lou, Pres.--Crane Pumps & Systems Inc., Piqua, OH; *U.S. Public*, pg. 457
Barlup, Lou, Pres.--Sellers Cleaning Systems, Piqua, OH; *U.S. Public*, pg. 457
Barlup, Louis M., III, Pres.--ChemPump, Warrington, PA; *U.S. Public*, pg. 456
Barnaby, Richard G., Pres.--Kaiser Permanente, California Division, Oakland, CA; *U.S. Private*, pg. 605
Barnard, Bill, Chief Exec. Officer--Alfa-Laval Agri Ltd, Cwmbran, United Kingdom; *Int'l*, pg. 1380
Barnard, D.R., Pres.--Facility Works Inc., Fort Worth, TX; *U.S. Public*, pg. 1557
Barnard, D.R., Pres.--TNP Operating Company, Fort Worth, TX; *U.S. Public*, pg. 1557
Barnard, Edward K., Mng. Dir.--Commercial Intertech Corp., Hicksville, OH; *U.S. Public*, pg. 411
Barnard, Glen, Pres.--Kaufman and Broad Colorado Division, Denver, CO; *U.S. Public*, pg. 945
Barnard, Glen, Pres.--Kaufman and Broad Utah Division, Midvale, UT; *U.S. Public*, pg. 945
Barnard, Ron, V.P.-Northeast Regional Mgr.--Sterling Electronics, Woburn, MA; *U.S. Public*, pg. 1051
Barnes, A., Chief Oper. Officer--Lloyds Equipment Leasing Ltd., London, United Kingdom; *Int'l*, pg. 813
Barnes, C., Mng. Dir.--Lancer USA Inc., Longwood, FL; *Int'l*, *pg. 551*
Barnes, Christopher A., Mng. Dir.--The Bank of Nova Scotia International Limited, Nassau, Bahamas; *Int'l*, pg. 156
Barnes, Craig, Pres.--Invista Capital Management Inc., Des Moines, IA; *U.S. Private*, pg. 885
Barnes, Cristopher A., Mng. Dir.--The Bank of Nova Scotia Trust Company (Bahamas) Limited, Nassau, Bahamas; *Int'l*, pg. 156
Barnes, D.M., V.P. & Gen. Mgr.--Power and Compression Group, Calgary, Canada; *Int'l*, pg. 1400
Barnes, David, Mgr.--C.M. Offray & Son, Danville, VA; *U.S. Private*, pg. 812
Barnes, Donald F., Pres.--ALLTEL Georgia, Inc., Commerce, GA; *U.S. Public*, pg. 56
Barnes, Geoffrey, Chief Oper. Officer--Novo Nordisk Entotech, Inc., Davis, CA; *Int'l*, pg. 987
Barnes, George, Pres.--Chesapeake Display and Packaging Co., Winston Salem, NC; *U.S. Public*, pg. 346
Barnes, John M., Sr. V.P.--Group Department, Chattanooga, TN; *U.S. Public*, pg. 1338
Barnes, Joseph, Dir.-Lufkin Opers.--Lufkin, Apex, NC; *U.S. Public*, pg. 444
Barnes, L.L., Pres.--Cyantek Corporation, Fremont, CA; *Int'l*, *pg. 802*
Barnes, Mike, Gen. Mgr.--Marcam Europe, Middle East & Afica S.R.L., Paris, France; *U.S. Public*, pg. 1043
Barnes, Phil, Gen. Mgr.--Inn On The Park, Houston, TX; *Int'l*, pg. 502
Barnes, Philip, Dir.-Collectibles--Collectibles Plant, Toronto, Canada; *U.S. Public*, pg. 672
Barnes, Richard F., Pres.--Enstar Natural Gas Co., Anchorage, AK; *U.S. Public*, pg. 1450
Barnes, Richard F., Pres.--Alaska Pipeline Co., Anchorage, AK; *U.S. Public*, pg. 1450
Barnes, Romaine, Admin.--Hillhaven Rehabilitation & Convalescent Center, Marietta, GA; *U.S. Public*, pg. 1713
Barnes, S., Chief Mgr.--Barclays Bank PLC, Mumbai, India; *Int'l*, pg. 165
Barnes, Steve, Gen. Mgr.--O-Seal Div., San Diego, CA; *U.S.* Public, pg. 1262
Barnes, William, Pres.--Kansa Corporation, Emporia, KS; *U.S. Public*, pg. 170
Barnes, William, Chief Oper. Officer--MacDermid Asia, Ltd., Sha Tin, Hong Kong; *U.S. Public*, pg. 1030
Barnet, Bruce, Pres. & Chief Exec. Officer--Reed Elsevier Business Information, Newton, MA; *Int'l*, pg. 1095
Barnett, Bill M., Sr. V.P.--Holt, Rinehart and Winston College Division, Fort Worth, TX; *U.S. Public*, pg. 783
Barnett, Daniel, Pres.-Wine Div.--Canandaigua Wine Company Div., Canandaigua, NY; *U.S. Public*, pg. 300
Barnett, Daniel C., Pres.--Canandaigua Wine Co., Canandaigua, NY; *U.S. Public*, pg. 300
Barnett, Earnest H., Pres.--Tulon Co., Gardena, CA; *U.S. Public*, pg. 594
Barnett, Glen, Area Mgr.--Gensym Corporation, South Central Regional Office, Spring, TX; *U.S. Public*, pg. 731
Barnett, Glen, Plant Mgr.--American Natl. Can Co., Saint Paul, MN; *Int'l*, pg. 1029
Barnett, James, Mng. Dir.--Dun & Bradstreet (HK) Ltd., North Point, Hong Kong; *U.S. Public*, pg. 536
Barnett, John, Pres. & Chief Exec. Officer--Molson Breweries, Toronto, Canada; *Int'l*, pg. 500
Barnett, John, Pres. & Chief Exec. Officer--Molson Breweries, Toronto, Canada; *U.S. Public*, pg. 1289
Barnett, Mike, Plant Mgr.--Dayton Superior Corp., Parsons, KS; *U.S. Private*, pg. 932
Barnett, P., V.P.-Acct. Services, Europe--Merrell/Chisholm, London, United Kingdom; *U.S. Private*, pg. 543
Barnett, Steve, Mng. Dir.--Check Point Software Technologies (UK) Ltd., Cambridge, United Kingdom; *U.S. Public*, pg. 342
Barnett, Wayne, V.P. & Gen. Mgr.--WDSU Television, Inc., New Orleans, LA; *U.S. Public*, pg. 1344
Barnette, Joseph D. Jr., Pres. & Chief Exec. Officer--Bank One, Indiana, N.A., Indianapolis, IN; *U.S. Public*, pg. 173
Barneveld, Jan William, Dir.-Log & Info. Mngmt.--Johnson & Johnson Medical B.V., Amersfoort, Netherlands; *U.S. Public*, pg. 931
Barnewitz, Jochen O., Mng. Dir.--SABM, Societe Africaine de Beton Manufacture S.A., Lyon, France; *Int'l*, pg. 425
Barnhardt, J.C., Jr., Pres.--North Carolina Foam Industries, Inc., Mount Airy, NC; *U.S. Private*, pg. 117
Barnhardt, T.M., III, Pres. & Chief Exec. Officer--Richmond Dental, Charlotte, NC; *U.S. Private*, pg. 117
Barnhill, Keith, Admin.--Medical Center Nursing Facility, San Antonio, TX; *U.S. Public*, pg. 839
Barnhill, Richard, Plant Mgr.--Tara Foods, Albany, GA; *U.S. Public*, pg. 967
Barnhill, Tim, Pres.--Central State Bank, Lexington, TN; *U.S. Public*, pg. 1669
Barni, Fabio, Gen. Mgr.--Lee Sri, Milan, Italy; *U.S. Private*, pg. 657
Barnicoat, Carol, Admin.--Henderson Convalescent Hospital, Henderson, NV; *U.S. Public*, pg. 837
Barnwell, Allan, Mgr.--Asbury Wilkinson Graphite & Foundry Supply Co., Mississauga, Canada; *U.S. Private*, pg. 87
Baron, Andre, Mgr.--Sandvik S.A., Orleans, France; *Int'l*, pg. 1187
Baron, Bengt, Chief Oper. Officer--AB Frionor, Stockholm, Sweden; *Int'l*, pg. 516
Baron, Carole, Pres.--Dell Publishing, New York, NY; *Int'l*, pg. 191
Baron, Denis, Dir.--Banque Regionale du Nord, Roubaix, France; *Int'l*, pg. 548
Baron, Donald, Pres.-Goodman Grp. E.--Goodman Knitting Company, Brockton, MA; *U.S. Public*, pg. 948
Baron, Peter P., Dr., Gen. Mgr.--Bayerische Vereinsbank AG, Tokyo, Japan; *Int'l*, pg. 180
Barone, Gregory J., V.P. & Gen. Mgr.--L.D. Caulk Division, Milford, DE; *U.S. Public*, pg. 499
Barone, Tim, Gen. Mgr.--Barone Foods, Tucson, AZ; *U.S. Private*, pg. 244
Baroudi, Roudi E., Gen. Mgr.-Middle East Sls.--Santa Fe Braun Inc., Dhahran, Saudi Arabia; *Int'l*, pg. 765
Barr, J. James, Pres.--Occoquan Land Corporation, Voorhees, NJ; *U.S. Public*, pg. 95
Barr, J. James, Pres.--American Commonwealth Company, Voorhees, NJ; *U.S. Public*, pg. 95
Barr, J. James, Pres.--American Water Works Service Company, Inc., Voorhees, NJ; *U.S. Public*, pg. 95
Barr, J. James, Pres.--Greenwich Water System, Inc., Voorhees, NJ; *U.S. Public*, pg. 95
Barr, J. James, Pres.--American International Water Services Company, Voorhees, NJ; *U.S. Public*, pg. 95
Barr, James, III, Pres. & Chief Exec. Officer--TDS Telecommunications Corporation, Madison, WI; *U.S. Public*, pg. 1570
Barr, John, Gen. Mgr.--Sunbeam Corporation Ltd., Palmerston, New Zealand; *Int'l*, pg. 539
Barr, Tom, Gen. Mgr. & Editor--Pioneer News, Shepherdsville, KY; *U.S. Private*, pg. 648
Barr, Wallace, Pres. & Chief Oper. Officer-AC Hilton & Bally's Park Place--Atlantic City Hilton, Atlantic City, NJ; *U.S. Public*, pg. 829
Barraclough, Richard, Chief Oper. Officer--Holiday RV Superstores of South Atlanta, Inc., Forest Park, GA; *U.S.* Public, pg. 830
Barral, Gervasio, Pres. & Chief Exec. Officer--Unitros, Madrid, Spain; *Int'l*, pg. 603
Barral, Vincent, Mgr.--Ateliers Sucre Liquide et Depot de Toulouse/Colomiers, Toulouse, France; *Int'l*, pg. 549
Barralis, Jean-Paul, Gen. Mgr.--Elkem s.a.r.l., Paris, France; *Int'l*, pg. 447
Barrans, Terry, Pres. & Chief Exec. Officer--Fisher Mills, Inc., Seattle, WA; *U.S. Public*, pg. 648
Barrat, Sherry S., V.P. & Mng. Exec.--Northern Trust Bank of Florida, N.A., North Palm Beach, FL; *U.S. Public*, pg. 1196
Barraza, Nelson, Gen. Mgr.--Union Publicitaria, DMB&B, San Jose, Costa Rica; *U.S. Private*, pg. 305
Barrelli, Joseph, V.P. & Gen. Mgr.--NationsBank International, New York, NY; *U.S. Public*, pg. 1165
Barretau, Jean-Pierre, Plant Mgr.--Rochefort Plant, Rochefort, France; *U.S. Public*, pg. 673
Barreteau, Jean-Pierre, Plant Mgr.--Neuilly Plant, Neuilly-en-Thelle, France; *U.S. Public*, pg. 673
Barrett, Bob, Gen. Mgr.--EG & G Wright Components, Phelps, NY; *U.S. Public*, pg. 542
Barrett, Craig, Sr. V.P. & Gen. Mgr.--Intel Components Technology & Manufacturing Group, Santa Clara, CA; *U.S. Public*, pg. 886
Barrett, Douglas M., V.P. & Gen. Mgr.--Information Systems Div., Merrimack, NH; *U.S. Public*, pg. 1008
Barrett, Earl, Chief Oper. Officer--Allright Parking of Indianapolis, Inc., Indianapolis, IN; *U.S. Private*, pg. 43
Barrett, Edward J., V.P. & Gen. Mgr.--The School Division, Menlo Park, CA; *Int'l*, pg. 1026
Barrett, James H., Pres. & Chief Exec. Officer--Duchesne Bank, Saint Peters, MO; *U.S. Public*, pg. 643
Barrett, James W., V.P. & Gen. Mgr.--Lindenmeyr Munroe, King of Prussia, PA; *U.S. Private*, pg. 224
Barrett, Jerry, Branch Mgr.--Continental/Murray, Harlingen, TX; *U.S. Private*, pg. 268
Barrett, John F., Pres. & Chief Exec. Officer--Western-Southern Life Assurance Co., Cincinnati, OH; *U.S. Private*, pg. 1164
Barrett, L.C., Pres.--Emerson Electric Canada Ltd., Markham, Canada; *U.S. Public*, pg. 576
Barrett, Lea, Sls. Mgr.-Southern Region--Utell International-Australia, Melbourne, Australia; *Int'l*, pg. 1098
Barrett, Marilyn, V.P. & Grp. Creative Dir.--Frankel & Company, San Francisco, CA; *U.S. Private*, pg. 424
Barrett, Marty, Pres.--Global Processing & Recycling Group, Shied-Tech Cambridge, Cambridge, Canada; *U.S. Public*, *pg. 749*
Barrett, Richard, Gen. Mgr.--Tempil Inc., South Plainfield, NJ; *U.S. Private*, pg. 90
Barrett, Robert, Pres. & Chm. Bd.--Banc One Services Corporation, Columbus, OH; *U.S. Public*, pg. 175
Barrett, Robert A., V.P. & Gen. Mgr.--EG & G Aerospace & Engineered Products, Beltsville, MD; *U.S. Public*, pg. 542
Barrett, Robert A., Gen. Mgr.--EG & G KT Aerofab, El Cajon, CA; *U.S. Public*, pg. 542
Barrett, Roy, Mng. Dir.--Goodbody Stockbrokers, Dublin, Ireland; *Int'l*, pg. 64
Barrett, Walter B., Chief Fin. Officer--Devcon Crown Bay Corp., Saint Thomas, VI; *U.S. Public*, pg. 502
Barriga, Mauricio, Mng. Dir.--Leo Burnett Columbiana, S.A., Bogota, Colombia; *U.S. Private*, pg. 185
Barrington, William J., Pres. & Chief Exec. Officer--Sea Ray, Knoxville, TN; *U.S. Public*, pg. 266
Barron, Christopher, Dir.--Nicolet Test & Measurement Division, Madison, WI; *U.S. Public*, pg. 1593
Barron, Millard E., Pres.--Zellers Inc., Toronto, Canada; *Int'l*, *pg. 637*
Barron, Patricia, Pres.--Xerox Engineering Systems Division, Rochester, NY; *U.S. Public*, pg. 1784
Barron, R. C., Gen. Mgr.--AR Division of Telenex, Springfield, VA; *U.S. Public*, pg. 727
Barros, L., Dir. Gen.--ING Insurance Mexico, Mexico, Mexico; *Int'l*, pg. 650
Barros, Valentin, Gen. Mgr.--Nueva Vision, Santiago, Chile; *U.S. Public*, pg. 553
Barrow, Deborah Jones, Publr.--Traditional Home, Des Moines, IA; *U.S. Public*, pg. 1094
Barrow, Kay, V.P. & Gen. Mgr.--Mart Corporation, Sanford, NC; *U.S. Private*, pg. 309
Barrs, Andrew F., Pres.--Bird-Johnson Company-Seattle Operations, Seattle, WA; *Int'l*, pg. 709
Barry, Alan H., Chief Oper. Officer--Brass-Craft Manufacturing Company, Southfield, MI; *U.S. Public*, pg. 1053
Barry, Alan H., Chief Oper. Officer--Brass-Craft Holding Co., Lancaster, TX; *U.S. Public*, pg. 1053
Barry, Alan H., Chief Oper. Officer--Brass-Craft Western Company, Lancaster, TX; *U.S. Public*, pg. 1053
Barry, David, Pres.--Vivra Renal Care, Aliso Viejo, CA; *U.S. Public*, pg. 1724
Barry, Edward W., Pres.--Oxford University Press, Inc., New York, NY; *Int'l*, pg. 1019
Barry, Joseph A., Pres.--Cast-Matic Corporation, Stevensville, MI; *U.S. Public*, pg. 894
Barry, Kevin J., Publisher--San Angelo Standard, Inc., San Angelo, TX; *U.S. Public*, pg. 794
Barry, Robert, Mng. Dir.-Capital Mkts.--Samuel Montagu & Co. Limited, London, United Kingdom; *Int'l*, pg. 580
Barry, Thomas A., V.P. & Gen. Mgr.--McCormick Ingredients, Hunt Valley, MD; *U.S. Public*, pg. 1066

Barry, Tony, Exec. V.P.-Sls.--Sheaffer Pen Crownmark, Lincoln, RI; *Int'l*, pg. 542
Barry, W. Russell, Chm. Bd.--Turner Program Services, Inc., Atlanta, GA; *U.S. Public*, pg. 1615
Bars, Joe, Pres.--Horizon Properties, Taylor, MI; *U.S. Private*, pg. 539
Barsalou, Frank, Mgr.--Century Telephone of Idaho, Inc., Salmon, ID; *U.S. Public*, pg. 329
Barsema, James A., Pres. & County Mgr.--First American Title Insurance Agency, Inc., Pinetop, AZ; *U.S. Public*, pg. 626
Barsema, James A., Pres. & Gen. Mgr.--First American Title Insurance Agency of Gila, Inc., Payson, AZ; *U.S. Public*, pg. 626
Barsoum, Khalil, Pres. & Chief Exec. Officer--IBM Canada Limited, Markham, Canada; *U.S. Public*, pg. 897
Barss, E.G., Pres.--BIW Cable Systems-Connector Systems Div., Santa Rosa, CA; *Int'l*, pg. 417
Barstad, Einar, Pres.--Kvaerner Floro Consult a.s., Floro, Norway; *Int'l*, pg. 769
Barstead, Gregory, Pres.--Colonial Penn Group, Inc., Wilmington, DE; *U.S. Public*, pg. 990
Bartczak, Andre, Gen. Mgr.--Precision Resource Canadian Div., Kitchener, Canada; *U.S. Private*, pg. 880
Bartel, Mark H., Pres.--Delavan Commercial Products Division, Lexington, TN; *U.S. Public*, pg. 401
Bartel, Wolfgang, Gen. Mgr.--Weyburn-Bartel GmbH, Rellingen, Germany; *Int'l*, pg. 1334
Bartels, A., Gen. Mgr.--Polaroid (Belgium) NV, Brussels, Belgium; *U.S. Public*, pg. 1314
Bartels, Bill, Pres. & Chief Exec. Officer--Spar Marketing Force, Inc., Rochester Hills, MI; *U.S. Public*, pg. 23
Bartels, Franz, Chief Oper. Officer--Bergemann GmbH Maschinen-und Apparatebau, Wesel, Germany; *Int'l*, pg. 398
Bartels, Juergen, Pres.--Radisson Hotels International Inc., Minneapolis, MN; *U.S. Private*, pg. 212
Bartels, Juergen, Pres. & Chief Oper. Officer--Carlson Hospitality Group, Inc., Minneapolis, MN; *U.S. Private*, pg. 212
Bartels, Peter, Chief Exec. Officer--Foster's Brewing Group, Toronto, Canada; *Int'l*, pg. 501
Bartels, Robert P., Mgr.--International Paper-Bleached Board Div., Memphis, TN; *U.S. Public*, pg. 902
Bartels, William P., Pres.--Timco, Inc., Center Barnstead, NH; *U.S. Public*, pg. 126
Bartelt, Kenneth H., Pres. & Chief Oper. Officer--PowderTech Corporation, Valparaiso, IN; *Int'l*, pg. 878
Bartenbach, Klaus G., Pres. & Chief Exec. Officer--Ford, Bacon & Davis Companies Inc., Duluth, GA; *Int'l*, pg. 401
Bartenbach, Klaus G., Pres. & Chief Exec. Officer--Ford, Bacon & Davis Companies, Inc., Duluth, GA; *Int'l*, pg. 401
Bartges, Hans, Pres. & Chief Exec. Officer--Auto Lenders Acceptance Corp., Atlanta, GA; *Int'l*, pg. 499
Barth, Edgar, Chief Oper. Officer--Himmelwerk GmbH & Co., Tubingen, Germany; *Int'l*, pg. 400
Barth, Hans J., Dr., Mng. Dir.--Prognos AG, Basel, Switzerland; *Int'l*, pg. 1480
Barth, Jean Paul, Pres.--Hutchinson S.A., Paris, France; *Int'l*, pg. 1409
Barth, John M., V.P. & Gen. Mgr.--Johnson Controls, Inc., Plastics Technology Group, Manchester, MI; *U.S. Public*, *pg. 932*
Barth, John M., V.P. & Gen. Mgr.--Johnson Controls, Inc. (Engineered Plastics Div.), Manchester, MI; *U.S. Public*, pg. 932
Barth, Joseph, V.P.--Harris Technical Services Corporation, Alexandria, VA; *U.S. Public*, pg. 792
Barth, Manfred, Mng. Dir.--Dresdner (S.E. Asia) Ltd., Singapore, Singapore; *Int'l*, pg. 420
Barth, Richard, Pres.--COREQ, Inc., New York, NY; *U.S. Public*, pg. 338
Barth, Steve, Pres. & Chief Exec. Officer--Challenger Electrical Equipment Corp., Pittsburgh, PA; *U.S. Public*, pg. 558
Barth, William, Pres. & Chief Exec. Officer--Packaged Products Division, McAllen, TX; *U.S. Private*, pg. 1191
Barthaud, Paul, Mng. Dir.--Christie's South Kensington Limited, London, United Kingdom; *Int'l*, pg. 290
Barthe, Marcel, Mng. Dir.--Optimum Inc., Montreal, Canada; *Int'l*, pg. 336
Barthe, Patrick, Dir.--Cogesal S.A., Nanterre, France; *Int'l*, pg. 1436
Barthelet, Luc, Gen. Mgr.--Maxis, Walnut Creek, CA; *U.S. Public*, pg. 569
Barthmus, Hans, Mgr.-Plant--Nestle Beverage Company, Freehold, NJ; *Int'l*, pg. 918
Barthold, Charles, Editor--Yachting, Greenwich, CT; *U.S. Public*, pg. 1617
Bartholin, Christian, Sr. V.P.--Bank of America NT&SA, Paris, France; *U.S. Public*, pg. 182
Bartholomae, Raymond E., Exec. V.P. & Gen. Mgr.--Symons Corporation, Des Plaines, IL; *U.S. Private*, pg. 932
Bartholomew, Dave, Pres. & Chief Exec. Officer--MSR, Seattle, WA; *U.S. Private*, pg. 914
Bartholomew, George, Mng. Dir.--LK Limited, Derby, United Kingdom; *Int'l*, pg. 1418
Bartholomew, Martin F., Mng. Dir.--Periphonics Voice Processing Systems Ltd., Camberley, United Kingdom; *U.S. Public*, pg. 1279
Bartic, Juarez, Gen. Mgr.--Simpson Industries, Ltda. (Brazil), Sao Paulo, Brazil; *U.S. Public*, pg. 1475
Bartlam, P., Chief Oper. Officer--Integrated Photomatrix Ltd., Dorchester, United Kingdom; *Int'l*, pg. 448
Bartles, Dean L., Pres.--G.D. International, Ltd., Charlotte Amalie, VI; *U.S. Public*, pg. 1219
Bartles, H., Mng. Dir.--Schiess Moweg GmbH, Monchengladbach, Germany; *Int'l*, pg. 860
Bartlett, Dan, Gen. Mgr.--AAR Engine Component Services, Frankfort, NY; *U.S. Public*, pg. 1
Bartlett, Dennis M., Pres.--Chino Mines Company, Hurley, NM; *U.S. Public*, pg. 1287
Bartlett, Joe L., Mgr.-Kaliper Services--Global Pipeline Surveys, Tulsa, OK; *U.S. Private*, pg. 1180
Bartlett, John, Pres.--Stamford Superior Drug Co., Inc., Stamford, CT; *U.S. Public*, pg. 229
Bartlett, William P., Pres.--Callidus Technologies Inc., Tulsa, OK; *U.S. Public*, pg. 344
Bartley, John, Chief Exec. Officer--Inchcape Middle East, Manama, Bahrain; *Int'l*, pg. 672
Bartliff, Charles E., Sr. V.P.-Global Non-Bank Financial Institutions--Corporate & Institutional Financial Services - Montreal, Toronto, Canada; *Int'l*, pg. 153
Bartmess, Donna, Admin.--Horizon Healthcare Nursing Center, Santa Fe, NM; *U.S. Public*, pg. 838
Bartnett, Thomas, Gen. Mgr.--Ecological Chemical Products Co., Adell, WI; *U.S. Public*, pg. 531
Barto, Ken, Mgr.-Fin.--Russell Div., Brea, CA; *U.S. Private*, pg. 80
Bartolini, Masimo, Country Mgr.--Autodesk S.p.A., Assago, Italy; *U.S. Public*, pg. 150
Bartolome, Higinio, Pres.--PAMCO Espana Sociedad Anonima de Seguros, Barcelona, Spain; *U.S. Private*, pg. 893
Bartolotti, J.H., Branch Mgr.--Zellerbach Division, Fort Myers, FL; *U.S. Public*, pg. 1075
Barton, Francis J., Chm. & Chief Exec. Officer--Wahlstrom & Company, Stamford, CT; *U.S. Public*, pg. 1641
Barton, Glen A., Chm. Bd.--Caterpillar Paving Products Inc., Minneapolis, MN; *U.S. Public*, pg. 316
Barton, Peter, Chief Exec. Officer--Inchcape Timuran Bhd, Shah Alam, Malaysia; *Int'l*, pg. 672
Barton, Richard D., Pres. & Chief Exec. Officer--The Paper Magic Group, Inc., Scranton, PA; *U.S. Public*, pg. 284
Bartos, Jerzy, Mng. Dir.--Getinge Poland Sp.zo.o., Warsaw, Poland; *Int'l*, pg. 551
Bartosh, Bob, Mgr.-Coal Line, Real Estate & Opers.--Basin Co-Operative Services, Bismarck, ND; *U.S. Private*, pg. 121
Bartosh, Bob, Mgr.-Coal Line, Real Estate & Opers.--Dakota Coal Company, Bismarck, ND; *U.S. Private*, pg. 121
Bartz, James W., Pres.--Colwood Co., Inc., Columbia, SC; *U.S. Private*, pg. 255
Barusch, Ronald C., Partner--Skadden, Arps, Slate, Meagher & Flom, Sydney, Australia; *U.S. Private*, pg. 1005
Barutel, Vincente Tardio, Dir Gen.--Allianz-RAS Seguros y Reaseguros, S.A., Barcelona, Spain; *Int'l*, pg. 60
Barwig, U., Dr., Chief Oper. Officer--Rhenania Umschlag und Lagerei GmbH, Mannheim, Germany; *Int'l*, pg. 1034
Basabe, Tom, Pres.--J.R. Simplot Company-Agriculture Group, Grand View, ID; *U.S. Private*, pg. 1002
Basara, Stanley, Pres. & Chief Oper. Officer--Panasonic Broadcast Systems Co., Secaucus, NJ; *Int'l*, pg. 847
Baseley, C., Mng. Dir.--EIP Metals Limited, Birmingham, United Kingdom; *Int'l*, pg. 426
Basil, Neal, Exec. V.P. & Acting Gen. Mgr.--SMC Environmental Services Group Inc., King of Prussia, PA; *U.S. Public*, pg. 1717
Basil, Steven E., Mng. Dir.--Brown Brothers Harriman (Luxembourg) S.A., Luxembourg, Luxembourg; *U.S. Private*, pg. 173
Basile, Peter A., Pres.--Metropolitan Asphalt, Inc., Livonia, MI; *U.S. Private*, pg. 121
Basing, M.P., Pres.--Swiss Bank Corporation (Canada), Toronto, Canada; *Int'l*, pg. 1331
Baskin, Michael, Pres.--Mark Shale Direct, Burr Ridge, IL; *U.S. Private*, pg. 989
Basler, Melvin, Gen. Mgr.--Container Div. (Murfreesboro), Murfreesboro, TN; *Int'l*, pg. 1269
Basmadgeuv, A., Pres.--Essilor Canada Ltee., Montreal, Canada; *Int'l*, pg. 462
Bass, Brian, Gen. Mgr.--Jannock Steel Fabricating, Inc., Little Rock, AR; *Int'l*, pg. 699
Bass, Melton L., Mng. Dir.--DYWIDAG Systems International, USA, Inc., Saint Petersburg, FL; *Int'l*, pg. 424
Basserman, Michael, Chm. Bd. & Chief Exec. Officer--Mercedes-Benz of North America, Inc., Montvale, NJ; *Int'l*, pg. 368
Basserman, Peter P., Pres.--SNET Mobility, Inc., Rocky Hill, CT; *U.S. Public*, pg. 1491
Basset, Christian, Pres. & Chief Exec. Officer--Coronado Paint Company, Edgewater, FL; *Int'l*, pg. 1488
Basset, Geoff, Sec.--Hastings Deering (PNG) Pty Ltd, Boroko, Papua New Guinea; *Int'l*, pg. 1250
Bassett, B., Gen. Mgr.--Boyne Smelters Limited, Boyne, Australia; *Int'l*, pg. 307
Bassett, Glenn, Chief Oper. Officer--Hudson General Corp., Jamaica, NY; *U.S. Public*, pg. 845
Bassett, I. Jay, Pres.--Crown Coat, Inc., Grand Rapids, MI; *U.S. Private*, pg. 1024
Bassett, M. Glen, Pres.--Baker Petrolite Corporation, Houston, TX; *U.S. Public*, pg. 166
Bassetti, Aldo, Chm.--Publifactoring S.p.A., Milan, Italy; *Int'l*, *pg. 138*
Bassetti, Aldo, Chm. Bd.--Publicfactoring S.p.A., Milan, Italy; *Int'l*, pg. 138
Bassi, Peter A., Pres.--Tricon Restaurants International, Dallas, TX; *U.S. Public*, pg. 1637
Bassil, Clive, Mng. Dir.--Costain Urban Enterprises Limited, Manchester, United Kingdom; *Int'l*, pg. 337
Bassingthwaite, J., Pres.--Simon-Telelect Inc., Watertown, SD; *Int'l*, pg. 1252
Bassoul, Selim, Pres.--Southbend, Fuquay Varina, NC; *U.S. Public*, pg. 1110
Bassoun, Hassan, Gen. Mgr.--Saudi Building Systems, Ltd., Jeddah, Saudi Arabia; *U.S. Public*, pg. 271
Bast, Thomas R., Pres.--M & I First National Bank, West Bend, WI; *U.S. Public*, pg. 1050
Bastable, Colum P., Exec. V.P.-Comml. Real Estate Services--Royal LePage Real Estate Services Ltd., Toronto, Canada; *Int'l*, pg. 1143
Bastable, John, Sr. V.P.--Aer Lingus, Melville, NY; *Int'l*, pg. 28
Bastam, Ina, Dr., Mng. Dir.--Wuestenrot Immobilien GmbH, Ludwigsburg, Germany; *Int'l*, pg. 1514
Bastenier, Enrique, Chief Oper. Officer--MacDermid Espanola S.A., Barcelona, Spain; *U.S. Public*, pg. 1030
Bastien, Dennis, Owner--Hardware City Rock Cats, New Britain, CT; *U.S. Private*, pg. 751
Bastien, Jean-Marie, Mng. Dir.--SMR (Societe Metallurgique de Revigny), Revigny, France; *Int'l*, pg. 571
Bastien, Michael, Chief Oper. Officer--Favorite Products Co., Chomedey, Canada; *U.S. Public*, pg. 1215
Basting, Dirk, Dr., Reg. Gen. Mgr.--Lambda Physik GmbH, Gottingen, Germany; *U.S. Public*, pg. 396
Bastis, T.E., Grp. Pres.--HC&D Div., Honolulu, HI; *U.S. Public*, pg. 99
Bastlein, Roger, Mgr.--Commerzbank AG Representative Office-Kiev, Kiev, Ukraine; *Int'l*, pg. 311
Bastow, David, Pres.--F.R. Gross Company, Stow, OH; *U.S.* Public, pg. 103
Batalha, Nuno, Mgr.--Sandvik Portuguesa Lda., Lisbon, Portugal; *Int'l*, pg. 1186
Batchelder, E.L., Pres.--Phillips Driscopipe, Inc., Dallas, TX; *U.S. Public*, pg. 1291
Batchelor, David, Pres.--Lifestyle Brands, Ltd., Chicago, IL; *U.S. Public*, pg. 1310
Batchelor, P.R., Chm.--Lever Brothers (Malawi) Ltd., Limbe, Malawi; *Int'l*, pg. 1437
Batdorf, Michael C., Mgr.--Piper Jaffray Inc., Wenatchee, WA; *U.S. Public*, pg. 1302
Batdorf, Michael C., Mgr.-Branch--Piper Jaffray Inc., Chelan, WA; *U.S. Public*, pg. 1302
Bate, Michael, Mng. Dir.--Totes U.K. Limited, Billericay, United Kingdom; *U.S. Private*, pg. 111
Bateman, Chris, Mng. Dir.--Jones Environmental (Ireland) Ltd., Dublin, Ireland; *Int'l*, pg. 1444
Bateman, Colin P., V.P.--Harris Trust & Savings Bank, London, United Kingdom; *Int'l*, pg. 154
Bateman, Kevin, V.P.--Bateman Lumber Co., Inc., Doylestown, PA; *U.S. Private*, pg. 122
Bateman, Walter R., Chm. Bd. & Chief Exec. Officer--Great Oaks Insurance Company, Dublin, OH; *U.S. Public*, pg. 786
Bateman, Walter R., Chm. Bd. & Pres.--Harleysville Services Inc, Harleysville, PA; *U.S. Public*, pg. 787
Bateman, Walter R., Chm., Pres. & Chief Oper. Officer--Mainland Insurance Co., Harleysville, PA; *U.S. Public*, pg. 787
Bateman, Walter R., Pres. & Chief Exec. Officer--Minnesota Fire & Casualty Company, Minnetonka, MN; *U.S. Public*, pg. 787
Batenic, Mark K., Pres.--Fleming Foods of Pennsylvania, Inc., Oaks, PA; *U.S. Public*, pg. 653
Bates, Anthony R., Mng. Dir.--Cyanamid Australia, Pty., Ltd., Baulkham Hills, Australia; *U.S. Public*, pg. 80
Bates, Dave, Gen. Mgr.--Elkay Plastics Co., Inc., Stock Service Center, Aurora, CO; *U.S. Private*, pg. 372
Bates, Edward W., Mng. Dir.--Dayton Progress Intl., Foots Cray, United Kingdom; *U.S. Public*, pg. 617
Bates, Ernest A., M.D., Chief Exec. Officer--American Shared-CuraCare, San Francisco, CA; *U.S. Public*, pg. 91
Bates, Ernest A., M.D., Pres.--CuraCare, Inc., Modesto, CA; *U.S. Public*, pg. 91
Bates, Garth C., Jr., Pres.--Stewart & Stevenson de las Americas, Inc., Houston, TX; *U.S. Public*, pg. 1517
Bates, Garth C., Jr., Pres.--Stewart & Stevenson de Venezuela, S.A., Maracaibo, Venezuela; *U.S. Public*, pg. 1518
Bates, Gavin, Reg. Business Mgr.--Manville Canada Inc. (Innisfail), Innisfail, Canada; *U.S. Public*, pg. 927
Bates, George E., Pres.--Enerco, Inc., Honolulu, HI; *Int'l*, pg. 225
Bates, Jim, Div. Mgr.--Titan Homes Div., Lillington, NC; *U.S.* Public, pg. 332
Bates, Mary K., Pres. & Gen. Mgr.--First American Title Co. of Spokane, Spokane, WA; *U.S. Public*, pg. 625
Bates, Richard B., Pres.--Sonat Energy Services Company, Birmingham, AL; *U.S. Public*, pg. 1485
Bates, Robert R., Chief Oper. Officer--Armstrong Patents Co., Ltd., York, United Kingdom; *Int'l*, pg. 265
Bates, Thomas R., Pres.--Weatherford U.S., Inc., Houston, TX; *U.S. Public*, pg. 1749
Bates, Thomas R., Pres.--Weatherford Canada Limited, Calgary, Canada; *U.S. Public*, pg. 1750
Bates, Thomas R., Jr., Pres.--Weatherford US Inc., Santa Paula, CA; *U.S. Public*, pg. 1749
Bates, Timothy, V.P.--Washington Homes, Inc. of Virginia, Hyattsville, MD; *U.S. Public*, pg. 1741
Bates, Tom, Gen. Mgr.--Marlette Homes, Inc., Hermiston, OR; *U.S. Public*, pg. 1442
Batey, Gary, Gen. Mgr.--Hagerstown Cement Plant Independent Cement Corp., Hagerstown, MD; *Int'l*, pg. 629
Batisse, Jean-Paul, Pres.--Serpo France S.A., Nimes, France; *Int'l*, pg. 1200
Batlnlurst, Chris, Plant Mgr.--North Tucson Business Center, Tucson, AZ; *U.S. Public*, pg. 1250
Batoz, Jean-Francois, Industrial Mgr.--Meaux, Villenoiy-Meaux, France; *U.S. Public*, pg. 673
Batrouney, C.M., Mng. Dir.--ANZ McCaughan Securities Limited, Melbourne, Australia; *Int'l*, pg. 98
Batruno, G., Chief Oper. Officer--Refradige, Mezzocorona, Italy; *Int'l*, pg. 1176
Batsche, George M., Pres. & Chief Oper. Officer--Electra Communications, Austin, TX; *U.S. Private*, pg. 556
Batsche, George M., Pres. & Chief Oper. Officer--Mutual Signal Corporation of Michigan, Austin, TX; *U.S. Private*, pg. 556
Batstone, Ross, Gen. Mgr.--Boral Australian Gypsum Ltd., Melbourne, Australia; *Int'l*, pg. 203
Battaglia, Joseph, Pres.--Telephonics Corp., Farmington, NY; *U.S. Public*, pg. 766
Battapaglia, Jack, Jr., V.P.-Sls.--Eastern Division, New York, NY; *Int'l*, pg. 412

Batteaux, Armand, Pres.--Valeo Distribution, Saint Ouen, France; *Int'l*, pg. 240
Batten, Chip, Gen. Mgr.--Batten Converter Services, Mississauga, Canada; *Int'l*, pg. 698
Batten, Gary, Branch Mgr.--Burns & Wilcox - Metairie Office, Metairie, LA; *U.S. Private*, pg. 610
Battenberg, J.T., III, V.P. & Grp. Exec.--General Motors Corporation-Automotive Components Grp. Worldwide, Detroit, MI; *U.S. Public*, pg. 719
Batterberg, J.T., Pres.--Delphi Packard Electric Systems, Beachwood, OH; *U.S. Public*, pg. 719
Batterham, R., V.P.--Comalco Research & Technology, Melbourne, Australia; *Int'l*, pg. 307
Battersby, John J., Pres.--Summit Food Service Distributors, London, Canada; *Int'l*, pg. 266
Batterton, John C., Pres. & Chief Exec. Officer--CalComp Technology, Inc., Anaheim, CA; *U.S. Public*, pg. 1007
Batti, Gerald V., Gen. Mgr.--UMEX Company, Greenwich, CT; *Int'l*, pg. 1435
Battin, Jim, Mng. Dir.--Partners & Shevack Direct, New York, NY; *U.S. Private*, pg. 842
Battista, G.A., Chief Exec. Officer--Network Solutions, Inc., Herndon, VA; *U.S. Private*, pg. 976
Battjer, Bruce, Chief Exec. Officer--Sungard Computer Services Group, Voorhees, NJ; *U.S. Public*, pg. 1534
Battner, Gary, V.P.--Genicom Corporation, Waynesboro, VA; *U.S. Public*, pg. 729
Batty, Mark J., Pres.--International Typeface Corporation (ITC), New York, NY; *Int'l*, pg. 460
Batusic, Greg, Pres.--Westwood One Entertainment, New York, NY; *U.S. Public*, pg. 1763
Batz, H. D., Pres.--Shimadzu Europa GmbH, Duisburg, Germany; *Int'l*, pg. 1232
Bauchiero, Pierluigi, Gen. Mgr.--Sanpaolo-Sao Paulo Representative Office, Sao Paulo, Brazil; *Int'l*, pg. 692
Bauchman, Robert W., V.P. & Mng. Exec.--Northern Trust Bank of Florida, N.A., Coral Gables, FL; *U.S. Public*, pg. 1196
Baucum, Michael, Pres.--Splitfire, Inc., Northbrook, IL; *U.S. Private*, pg. 814
Baudet, Michel, Pres.--SEPIC, Paris, France; *Int'l*, pg. 239
Bauduin, M. Claude, Chief Oper. Officer--Societe Financiere et de Developpement Alimentaire, Paris, France; *Int'l*, pg. 557
Bauer, Charles, Chief Exec. Officer--Aim Equity Funds, Inc., Houston, TX; *Int'l*, pg. 685
Bauer, Chris M., Chm. Bd. & Chief Exec. Officer--Firstar Milwaukee Bank, N.A., Milwaukee, WI; *U.S. Public*, pg. 643
Bauer, Dan, Mgr.-Plant--Akzo Salt of Utah, Tooele, UT; *Int'l*, pg. 48
Bauer, David J., Pres.--Mountain States Airgas, Charleston, WV; *U.S. Public*, pg. 33
Bauer, G.K., Pres.--CU Power International Ltd., Calgary, Canada; *Int'l*, pg. 95
Bauer, Gary, Mgr.-Zone--Santa Fe Intl. Services Inc., Ruwi, Oman; *Int'l*, pg. 765
Bauer, Georg, Pres.--Mercedes-Benz Credit Corp., Norwalk, CT; *Int'l*, pg. 368
Bauer, Gunther, Pres.--Reading Tube Corp., Reading, PA; *U.S. Private*, pg. 202
Bauer, Hans-Peter, Partner & Chief Fin. Officer--Verin S.A., Berneck, Switzerland; *Int'l*, pg. 1322
Bauer, J.W., Pres.--M.A. Hanna Color, Suwanee, GA; *U.S. Public*, pg. 781
Bauer, John, Publr.--Boca Raton News, Inc., Boca Raton, FL; *U.S. Private*, pg. 259
Bauer, John, Mng. Dir.--Brockhouse Modernfold Limited, Llanelli, United Kingdom; *Int'l*, pg. 426
Bauer, John P., Pres.--Global Food Corporation, Fort Lauderdale, FL; *U.S. Private*, pg. 121
Bauer, Joseph W., Pres.--M.A. Hanna Color, Somerset, NJ; *U.S. Public*, pg. 781
Bauer, K., Dr., Chief Oper. Officer--Agrolinz Agrarchemikalien GesellschaftmbH Berlin, Berlin, Germany; *Int'l*, pg. 356
Bauer, Manuel, Branch Mgr.--Allainz Versicherungs-AG (Dubai Branch), Dubai, United Arab Emirates; *Int'l*, pg. 60
Bauer, Robert, Pres.--Real Brick Products, Inc., Owosso, MI; *Int'l*, pg. 699
Bauer, Stan, V.P. & Gen. Mgr.--Fuji Magnetic Products Div., Elmsford, NY; *Int'l*, pg. 524
Bauer, Stephen, Pres.--Prudential Real Estate Affiliates Inc., Costa Mesa, CA; *U.S. Private*, pg. 892
Bauer, Theodore J., Pres. & Chief Oper. Officer--Medite Corporation, Medford, OR; *U.S. Private*, pg. 999
Bauer, Tim, Reg. Mgr.--Green Tree Acceptance, Inc., Earth City, MO; *U.S. Public*, pg. 762
Bauermeister, Hanns, Dr., Chief Exec. Officer--Central Krankenversicherung AG, Cologne, Germany; *Int'l*, pg. 15
Bauerschmidt, Reinhard, Chm. Bd.--Gerlach-Werke GmbH, Hamburg, Germany; *Int'l*, pg. 508
Baugh, Bill, Gen. Mgr.--Snavely Forest Products, Inc., Denver, CO; *U.S. Private*, pg. 1010
Baugh, Michael A., Pres. & Gen. Mgr.--BHP Petroleum Pty Ltd., Melbourne, Australia; *Int'l*, pg. 225
Baugh, Ralph L., Pres.--PNC Realty Mortgage Co., Cincinnati, OH; *U.S. Public*, pg. 1243
Baughman, Charles, Gen. Mgr.--Watlow Columbia, Inc., Columbia, MO; *U.S. Private*, pg. 1153
Baughman, Chuck, Gen. Mgr.--Watlow Aov, Inc., Anaheim, CA; *U.S. Private*, pg. 1153
Baughman, Gary, Pres. & Chief Exec. Officer--Fisher-Price, Inc., East Aurora, NY; *U.S. Public*, pg. 1058
Baughman, Terry, Plant Mgr.--Hydraulics Div., Shawnee, OK; *U.S. Public*, pg. 557
Bauhs, David J., V.P. & Gen. Mgr.--Schindler Elevator Company, Morristown, NJ; *Int'l*, pg. 1205
Bauler, Kevin, Site Mgr.--Hi-Temp Materials, Inc., Schaumburg, IL; *U.S. Public*, pg. 344
Baum, Christopher, Branch Mgr.--Zellerbach Division, Saint Paul, MN; *U.S. Public*, pg. 1075
Bauman, James J., Co-President & Co-Chief Exec. Officer--Eastbridge Capital Inc., New York, NY; *Int'l*, pg. 933
Bauman, James R., Pres.--M & I Bank of Burlington, Burlington, WI; *U.S. Public*, pg. 1050
Bauman, William P., V.P. & Gen. Mgr.--WESH Television, Inc., Winter Park, FL; *U.S. Public*, pg. 1344
Baumann, Andreas, Mng. Dir.--W.C. Heraeus GmbH, Hanau, Germany; *Int'l*, pg. 616
Baumann, E., Gen. Mgr.--Semilab AG, Fruthwilen, Switzerland; *Int'l*, pg. 803
Baumann, N., Dr., Dir.--Nyffeler Corti AG, Kirchberg, Switzerland; *Int'l*, pg. 755
Baumann, Peter, Pres.--Transammonia AG, Lachen, Switzerland; *U.S. Private*, pg. 1096
Baumann, Thomas, Mng. Dir.--Schroedel Schulbuchverlag GmbH, Hannover, Germany; *Int'l*, pg. 1478
Baumann, Thomas, Mng. Dir.--Verlag Dr. Max Gehlen GmbH & Co. KG, Bad Homburg, Germany; *Int'l*, pg. 1479
Baume, Georges, Gen. Mgr.--Unicom, Rennes, France; *Int'l*, pg. 601
Baument, Detlef R., Dir.-Admin.--DG Bank-Luxembourg, Luxembourg, Luxembourg; *Int'l*, pg. 352
Baumgardner, Robert M., Pres.--Unisource, Gahanna, OH; *U.S. Public*, pg. 1671
Baumgardt, James, Branch Mgr.--Zellerbach Division, Seattle, WA; *U.S. Public*, pg. 1075
Baumgart, D.W., Gen. Mgr.--CHEMCENTRAL/Detroit, Romulus, MI; *U.S. Private*, pg. 232
Baumgarten, David A., Pres. & Chief Exec. Officer--First Bank N.A., Milwaukee, WI; *U.S. Public*, pg. 1680
Baumgarten, J.C., Chief Oper. Officer--Frequence Plus, Villepinte, France; *Int'l*, pg. 560
Baumgartner, A.R., Dr., Pres.--Ayerst, McKenna & Harrison Inc., Saint-Laurent, Canada; *U.S. Public*, pg. 80
Baumgartner, J., Pres.--Van Leeuven Pipe & Tube (Canada) Inc., Edmonton, Canada; *Int'l*, pg. 1450
Baumgartner, James D., Pres.--Standard Property Corporation, Pittsburgh, PA; *U.S. Private*, pg. 529
Baumgartner, James W., Pres.--First USA Financial Services, Inc., Murray, UT; *U.S. Public*, pg. 174
Baumgartner, V.H., Pres.--Caterpillar Materiels Routiers, Rantigny, France; *U.S. Public*, pg. 316
Baumgartner, Werner, Pres.--Behr Systems, Inc., Auburn Hills, MI; *Int'l*, pg. 421
Baun, N.C., Mng. Dir.--Tootal Group plc, Manchester, United Kingdom; *Int'l*, pg. 300
Baunton, Michael J., Grp. Chief Exec.--Varity Perkins, Peterborough, United Kingdom; *Int'l*, pg. 820
Baur, Victor W., Pres.--Transgas Inc., Lowell, MA; *U.S. Public*, pg. 401
Bausch, Donald, Gen. Mgr.--Wehle Electric Co., Inc., Buffalo, NY; *Int'l*, pg. 1492
Bausman, Joseph N., Pres.--Reynolds and Reynolds-Automotive Systems Division, Dayton, OH; *U.S. Public*, pg. 1385
Baustert, Alain, Sr. V.P.--Landesbank Rheinland Pfalz International S.A., Luxembourg, Luxembourg; *Int'l*, pg. 799
Bavage, C. J., Chief Oper. Officer--Boart Longyear Inc., North Bay, Canada; *Int'l*, pg. 76
Bavier, John, Gen. Mgr.--Banta Information Services Group, Eden Prairie, MN; *U.S. Public*, pg. 188
Bawden, Murry G., Pres.--Fletcher Pacific Construction Company Limited, Honolulu, HI; *Int'l*, pg. 495
Baxter, Brian, Dir.-Mktg. & Sls.--EECO, Switch, Cambridge, United Kingdom; *U.S. Public*, pg. 1631
Baxter, D., Pres.--Swiss Bank Corporation, Saint Helier, United Kingdom; *Int'l*, pg. 1330
Baxter, Daniel R., Reg. Mgr.--Green Tree Acceptance, Inc., Pittsburgh, PA; *U.S. Public*, pg. 762
Baxter, Davette, Gen. Mgr. & Editor--The News-Democrat, Carrollton, KY; *U.S. Private*, pg. 648
Baxter, Donald R., Gen. Mgr.--Elco International/Synergy Division, Rockford, IL; *U.S. Public*, pg. 1590
Baxter, Harold J., Chm. Bd. & Chief Exec. Officer--Newbold's Asset Management Inc., Bryn Mawr, PA; *U.S.* Public, pg. 1673
Baxter, Harold J., Chm. Bd. & Chief Exec. Officer--Pilgram Baxter & Associates, Wayne, PA; *U.S. Public*, pg. 1673
Baxter, John, Pres.--Metroland Printing & Distributing, Mississauga, Canada; *Int'l*, pg. 1402
Baxter, Lionel F., Jr., Chm. Bd., Pres. & Chief Exec. Officer--SouthTrust Bank, Jasper, Jasper, AL; *U.S. Public*, pg. 1491
Baxter, Raymond A., Pres. & Chief Oper. Officer--Interbake Foods Inc., Richmond, VA; *Int'l*, pg. 1495
Baxter, Roger, Chief Oper. Officer--Electrolux Ltd., Luton, United Kingdom; *Int'l*, pg. 444
Baxter, Stephen Paul, V.P.-Corp. Mktg.--Data General Sales & Marketing Division, Westborough, MA; *U.S. Public*, pg. 485
Baxter, Thomas, Pres.--Comcast Cable Communications, Inc., Philadelphia, PA; *U.S. Public*, pg. 407
Baxter, Travis, Mng. Dir.--Atlantic 252, Meath, Ireland; *Int'l*, pg. 561
Bay, Lynn, Pres.--Randell, Weidman, MI; *U.S. Public*, pg. 520
Bay, Steve, Mgr.-Oper.--Edon Machine Div., Edon, OH; *U.S.* Public, pg. 1475
Bayard, Roland, Mng. Dir.--Sulzer (Mexico) S.A. de C.V., Cuautitlan, Mexico; *Int'l*, pg. 1306
Bayard, T., Mgr.-Sls.--International Paint Gulf Div., New Orleans, LA; *Int'l*, pg. 339
Bayer, Jack C., Pres.--AlliedSignal Airline Services, Torrance, CA; *U.S. Public*, pg. 50
Bayers, William G., Pres.--President Baking-Louisville, Louisville, KY; *Int'l*, pg. 1069
Bayless, Charles E., Chm. Bd., Pres. & Chief Exec. Officer--Tucson Electric Power Company, Tucson, AZ; *U.S. Public*, pg. 1670
Baylor, Tim, Admin.--Horizon Specialty Hospital - Dallas, Dallas, TX; *U.S. Public*, pg. 839
Baynard, Charles M., Pres. & Chief Exec. Officer--NationsBank/Delaware, Dover, DE; *U.S. Public*, pg. 1162
Bayuk, F., Mgr.-Reg.--MacMillan Bloedel Building Materials - Western Region, Vancouver, Canada; *Int'l*, pg. 828
Bazelmans, J.C.J.M., Dir.--Dailycer BV, Tilburg, Netherlands; *Int'l*, pg. 751
Bazemore, William, V.P.--Wellman Bonded Fibers Div., Charlotte, NC; *U.S. Public*, pg. 1753
Bazen, M., Pres.--Algemene Friese Onderlinge Schadeverzekeringmaatschappij 'Zevenwouden' U.A., Heerenveen, Netherlands; *Int'l*, pg. 26
Bazie, Tracey A., Pres. & Mng. Dir.--Johnson & Johnson Hemisferica, Caguas, PR; *U.S. Public*, pg. 928
Bazie, Tracie A., Mng. Dir.--Johnson & Johnson (Jamaica) Limited, Kingston, Jamaica; *U.S. Public*, pg. 930
Bazlen, James, Pres.--C S K Auto Inc., Phoenix, AZ; *U.S. Private*, pg. 1108
Bazzi, Augusto D., Mng. Dir.--Compania Ericsson S.A., Montevideo, Uruguay; *Int'l*, pg. 1365
Bazzi, Carlo, Gen. Mgr.--Analog Devices SRL, Milan, Italy; *U.S. Public*, pg. 108
Beach, Berton, Gen. Mgr.--Miami Learning Center, Miami, FL; *U.S. Public*, pg. 219
Beach, Dwight E., Pres.--Houston Engineers, Houston, TX; *U.S. Private*, pg. 1181
Beach, Kenneth W., V.P.--ALLTEL Publishing Corporation, Hudson, OH; *U.S. Public*, pg. 56
Beacock, T.W., Mng. Dir.--Senior Foster Wheeler Construction Division, Snaith, United Kingdom; *Int'l*, pg. 1221
Beadle, G., Mng. Dir.--Kenwood (S.A.) (Pty.) Ltd., Industria, South Africa; *Int'l*, pg. 730
Beadle, J.M., Mng. Dir.-Convenience Div.--Campbell's (U.K.) Limited, Kings Lynn, United Kingdom; *U.S. Public*, pg. 299
Beadles, Gary W., V.P.--Delta International Machinery Corp. (Tupelo), Tupelo, MS; *U.S. Public*, pg. 1273
Beadling, Glenn, Asst. V.P.--Willis Corroon Aerospace-Southwest Region, Houston, TX; *Int'l*, pg. 1505
Beadon, Perry R., Mgr.--Remington Products (Canada) Inc., Markham, Canada; *U.S. Private*, pg. 921
Beagle, Scott, V.P. & Gen. Mgr.--Subaru Financial Services, Inc., Cherry Hill, NJ; *Int'l*, pg. 523
Beahm, Michael B., Mgr.--Scott & Stringfellow, Inc., Harrisonburg, VA; *U.S. Public*, pg. 1445
Beal, David L., Mgr.-Opers.--Lake Superior Paper Industries, Duluth, MN; *U.S. Public*, pg. 436
Beal, Franklyn H., Exec. V.P.--Inland International, Inc., Chicago, IL; *U.S. Public*, pg. 879
Beal, Gary, Gen. Mgr.--Universal Polymer & Rubber Co., Middlefield, OH; *U.S. Private*, pg. 56
Beal, Karen, Sec. & Treas.--Cedartone Specialties, Kent, WA; *Int'l*, pg. 1071
Beal, Karen, Sec. & Treas.--Crane Creek Cedar, Kent, WA; *Int'l*, pg. 1071
Beale, Robert B., Pres.--Artist Graphics, Saint Paul, MN; *U.S. Private*, pg. 271
Beales, Norma, Admin.--Reno Convalescent Center, Reno, NV; *U.S. Public*, pg. 1714
Beall, Pamela K.M., Pres.--Environmental Treatment & Technologies Corp., Findlay, OH; *U.S. Public*, pg. 1208
Beall, Wilbur W., Jr., Pres.--NBD Bank (Ohio), Columbus, OH; *U.S. Public*, pg. 628
Bealmear, Keith, V.P.--Southwest Div., Dallas, TX; *U.S. Public*, pg. 732
Beam, Alan M., Pres. & Chief Exec. Officer--F.W. Woolworth Co. Limited, Canada, Weston, Canada; *U.S. Public*, pg. 1778
Beam, James D., Pres.--Silgan Container Corp., Woodland Hills, CA; *U.S. Public*, pg. 1473
Beaman, Scott, V.P. & Gen. Mgr.--Circus Circus-Reno Hotel & Casino, Reno, NV; *U.S. Public*, pg. 375
Beaman, Terry, Pres.--NBD Brokerage Services, Inc., Indianapolis, IN; *U.S. Public*, pg. 628
Beamish, Robert, Mng. Dir.--WBF Technologies, Mississauga, Canada; *Int'l*, pg. 193
Bean, Delcie D., Pres.--W.W. Cross, Inc., Jaffrey, NH; *U.S. Private*, pg. 127
Bean, Paul A., V.P. & Gen. Mgr.--Walker National, Inc., Columbus, OH; *U.S. Private*, pg. 1147
Bean, W. D., Pres.--CIBC Wood Gundy Inc., Toronto, Canada; *Int'l*, pg. 256
Bear, Jon H., Pres.--Kibo Compressor Corp., Wichita Falls, TX; *U.S. Private*, pg. 183
Bear, Stephen E., Pres.--Bristol-Myers Products, New York, NY; *U.S. Public*, pg. 254
Beard, Bob, Foundry Mgr.--Sloan Valve, Foundry Div., Augusta, AR; *U.S. Private*, pg. 1006
Beard, Frederick K., Chm. Bd., Pres. & Chief Exec. Officer--Mellon Bank (MD), Rockville, MD; *U.S. Public*, pg. 1085
Beard, James S., Pres.--Caterpillar Financial Services Corporation, Nashville, TN; *U.S. Public*, pg. 315
Beard, James S., Chm. Bd.--Caterpillar Finance France S.A., Saint Denis, France; *U.S. Public*, pg. 315
Beard, James S., Pres.--Caterpillar Financial Services Holding GmbH, Ismaning, Germany; *U.S. Public*, pg. 315
Beard, Tom, Gen. Mgr.--Supreme Murphy Corp., Wilson, NC; *U.S. Public*, pg. 1542
Beardall, Dennis, Exec. V.P.--Crawford Industries, Crawfordsville, IN; *U.S. Private*, pg. 64
Beardi, James, Pres.--M&T Mortgage Corp., Buffalo, NY; *U.S. Public*, pg. 631
Beardi, James, Pres.--M&T Credit Corporation, Buffalo, NY; *U.S. Public*, pg. 631
Beardmore, Ron, Mng. Dir.--Australian Guarantee Corporation (NZ) Limited, Auckland, New Zealand; *Int'l*, pg. 1497
Beards, David M., Mng. Dir.--Rust Craft Greeting Cards (U.K.) Limited, Dewsbury, United Kingdom; *U.S. Public*, pg. 78
Beardsell, K., Mng. Dir.--Hepworth Industrial Plastics Ltd., Burnley, United Kingdom; *Int'l*, pg. 615
Beardwood, Bruce A., V.P.--Du Pont Fabricated Products, Wilmington, DE; *U.S. Public*, pg. 531

Bearn, Alan E., Gen. Mgr.--Delta Encon Ltd., Enfield, United Kingdom; *Int'l*, pg. 391

Beasley, Christopher E., Mng. Dir.--Cinema International Corp., N.V., Amsterdam, Netherlands; *Int'l*, pg. 1216

Beasley, D., Mgr.-Opers.--Long Automotive, Inc.-Dallas Aftermarket Div., Carrollton, TX; *Int'l*, pg. 815

Beasley, J.F., Pres.--Poco Graphite, Incorporated, Decatur, TX; *U.S. Public*, pg. 1698

Beasley, Kathy, Mgr.--DWF of Cincinnati, Inc., Cincinnati, OH; *U.S. Private*, pg. 326

Beasley, Larry, Publr.--Lake Wales Daily Highlander, Lake Wales, FL; *U.S. Private*, pg. 995

Beasley, Larry, Publr.--Winter Haven News Chief, Winter Haven, FL; *U.S. Private*, pg. 995

Beasley, Larry, Publr.--Auburndale Star, Auburndale, FL; *U.S. Private*, pg. 995

Beasley, Larry, Publr.--Haines City Herald & Ridge Shopper, Haines City, FL; *U.S. Private*, pg. 995

Beasley, Larry, Publr.--Shopper Publishing Group, Lakeland, FL; *U.S. Private*, pg. 995

Beasley, M.A., Mgr.-Apparel Finishing Div.--Dan River Inc.-Finishing Div., Danville, VA; *U.S. Public*, pg. 479

Beasley, Marvin E., Pres.--Keystone Valvtron, Inc., Houston, TX; *U.S. Public*, pg. 1650

Beatson, David I., Pres. & Chief Exec. Officer--Emery Worldwide, Redwood City, CA; *U.S. Public*, pg. 281

Beattie, George, Gen. Mgr.--Eastside Lincoln Mercury, Cincinnati, OH; *U.S. Private*, pg. 129

Beattie, Graham, Mng. Dir.--Ashton/Scholastic Ltd., Greenmont, New Zealand; *U.S. Public*, pg. 1440

Beattie, R., Branch Mgr.--RHG New Orleans, Harahan, LA; *Int'l*, pg. 1151

Beattie, Rory W., Mng. Dir.--Kgalagadi Soap Industries(Pty) Ltd., Gaborone, Botswana; *U.S. Public*, pg. 806

Beatty, Chadwick M., Publr.--The Middletown Press, Middletown, CT; *U.S. Public*, pg. 935

Beatty, Craig, Plant Mgr.--Hydro Conduit Corp., Corona, CA; *Int'l*, pg. 245

Beatty, Fred F., Pres.--IKG Industries, Clark, NJ; *U.S. Public*, pg. 793

Beaucamps, Jacques, Dir.--Novotel UK Ltd., London, United Kingdom; *Int'l*, pg. 21

Beauchamp, C., Branch Mgr.--Van Leeuwen Pipe & Tube Corp., Port Allen, LA; *Int'l*, pg. 1449

Beauchamp, C., Branch Mgr.--Van Leeuwen Pipe & Tube Corp., Harvey, LA; *Int'l*, pg. 1449

Beauchamp, David, Gen. Mgr.--Whitehall Laboratories Ltd., London, United Kingdom; *U.S. Public*, pg. 82

Beauchamp, Rick, V.P.-Southeast Asia--Nordson S.E. Asia (Pte.), Ltd., Singapore, Singapore; *U.S. Public*, pg. 1189

Beaudet, Andre, Pres.--Hano Document Printers, Inc., Springfield, MA; *U.S. Public*, pg. 1686

Beaudin, Kirk, Pres. & Chief Oper. Officer--Sara Lee Knit Products, Winston Salem, NC; *U.S. Public*, pg. 1434

Beaudoin, Jean-Pierre, Exec. V.P.-Paper & Board Machines--Valmet Inc., Charlotte Division, Charlotte, NC; *Int'l*, pg. 1448

Beaudoin, Pierre, Pres. & Chief Exec. Officer--Bombardier Motorized Consumer Products Group, Montreal, Canada; *Int'l*, pg. 200

Beaudoin, Pierre, Pres. & Chief Oper. Officer--Bombardier Recreational Products, Montreal, Canada; *Int'l*, pg. 200

Beaudry, Chantal, Controller--Kulicke & Soffa, AG, Zug, Switzerland; *U.S. Public*, pg. 969

Beauford, W., Dr., Mng. Dir.--Bio-Kil Laboratories Limited, Gillingham, United Kingdom; *Int'l*, pg. 802

Beaulieu, David, Supvr.--Millinocket Division, Millinocket, ME; *U.S. Public*, pg. 438

Beaulieu, Ronald R., Pres.--Improved Blow Molding Equipment Company, Inc., Bedford Park, IL; *U.S. Private*, *pg. 464*

Beaumont, Donald F., V.P. & Gen. Mgr.--Valmet Inc.-Honeycomb Division, Biddeford, ME; *Int'l*, pg. 1448

Beaumont, Mark, Chief Oper. Officer--Delta Apparel, Duluth, GA; *U.S. Public*, pg. 498

Beaumont, Michel, Mgr.--Huguenot-Fenal, Pargny-sur-Saulx, France; *Int'l*, pg. 661

Beaumont, Neal, Pres.--Stainless Ice-Tainer Co. (SITCO), Roswell, GA; *Int'l*, pg. 646

Beaumont, Peter, Gen. Mgr.--Amway Indonesia, Jakarta, Indonesia; *U.S. Private*, pg. 70

Beaumont, Ron, Mgr.--Cascade Diamond, Thorndike, MA; *Int'l*, pg. 274

Beaumont, Ronald R., Pres. & Chief Exec. Officer--MFS Telecom Companies, Oak Brook, IL; *U.S. Public*, pg. 1779

Beausejour, D.F., Assoc. Gen. Mgr.--Procter & Gamble Australia, Villawood, Australia; *U.S. Public*, pg. 1332

Beauvais, Greg, Gen. Mgr.--Arrow/Schweber Electronics, Brookfield, WI; *U.S. Public*, pg. 134

Beauvais, Kenny, Pres.--HDW, Incorporated, Shreveport, LA; *U.S. Private*, pg. 335

Beaux, George, Mng. Dir.--Hallmark Group France, S.A., Compiegne, France; *U.S. Private*, pg. 496

Beaven, Richard, Media Dir.--Leo Burnett Limited, London, United Kingdom; *U.S. Private*, pg. 185

Beaver, Don, V.P. & Gen. Mgr.--Walker Systems, Inc., Williamstown, WV; *U.S. Private*, pg. 1184

Beaver, Jerry, Co-Chm. Bd.--Beaver Free Corp., Santa Barbara, CA; *U.S. Private*, pg. 832

Beaver, Paul, Publisher--Jane's Information Group, Coulsdon, United Kingdom; *U.S. Public*, pg. 1601

Beavers, George, Sr. V.P.--Stanley Smith Security, Inc., San Antonio, TX; *Int'l*, pg. 1286

Beavers, Shirley, Pres. & Chief Exec. Officer--First Virginia Life Insurance Company, Falls Church, VA; *U.S. Public*, pg. 642

Beazley, John, V.P.-Opers.--Pacifica Hotel Company, Santa Barbara, CA; *U.S. Private*, pg. 832

Beben, Henry, Pres. & Chief Exec. Officer--Principal Marques Inc., Toronto, Canada; *Int'l*, pg. 599

Beben, Henry, Pres. & Chief Exec. Officer--Principal Marques Meat Co., Etobicoke, Canada; *Int'l*, pg. 841

Becchi, Carlo, Pres.--Tecnord @ Delta Power Co., Daggiovada, Italy; *U.S. Private*, pg. 322

Becco, Nello, Gen. Mgr.--Cordis Italia SpA, Milan, Italy; *U.S. Public*, pg. 928

Bech, Tore, Pres.--Aker ExClay a.s., Oslo, Norway; *Int'l*, pg. 42

Becher, Hans, V.P.-Sls.--Stark Candy Company, Cambridge, MA; *U.S. Private*, pg. 1113

Becherer, Hans W., Pres.--Deere Marketing Services, Inc., Moline, IL; *U.S. Public*, pg. 492

Becherer, Joseph L., V.P. & Gen. Mgr.--Cutler-Hammer, Inc., Pittsburgh, PA; *U.S. Public*, pg. 558

Bechivar, Stephen P., Mng. Dir.--Lands' End GmbH, Mettlach, Germany; *U.S. Public*, pg. 978

Bechman, Steve, Reg. Pres.--Citizens Bank of Central Indiana-Central Region, Greenwood, IN; *U.S. Public*, pg. 280

Bechmann, H., Chief Oper. Officer--Buss-SMS GmbH Verfahrenstechnik, Butzbach, Germany; *Int'l*, pg. 490

Becht, Bernard, Mng. Dir.--Korf-Transport-France S.A.R.L, Montereau, France; *Int'l*, pg. 759

Bechtler, Thomas W., Chm.--Zellweger Uster AG, Uster, Switzerland; *Int'l*, pg. 618

Bechtler, Thomas W., Dr., Pres.--Schiesser Eminence Holding AG, Stein, Switzerland; *Int'l*, pg. 618

Becicka, Christine, Ctr. Dir.--Keller Graduate School of Management, Kansas City, MO; *U.S. Public*, pg. 504

Beck, Al, Gen. Mgr.--PEC El Paso, El Paso, TX; *U.S. Private*, pg. 871

Beck, Arthur R., Pres. & Chief Oper. Officer--Precision Twist Drill Co., Crystal Lake, IL; *Int'l*, pg. 1185

Beck, Arthur R., Pres.--Triumph Twist Drill Co., Crystal Lake, IL; *Int'l*, pg. 1185

Beck, Barbara, Reg. Mgr.--SMS-Oakland, Oakland, CA; *U.S. Public*, pg. 1463

Beck, Connie, Office Mgr.--North Mining Inc., Denver, CO; *Int'l*, pg. 967

Beck, Dan, Pres.--Sir Speedy, Inc., Mission Viejo, CA; *U.S. Private*, pg. 423

Beck, Dennis, Gen. Mgr.--MacSteel Div., Jackson, MI; *U.S. Public*, pg. 1349

Beck, Hans-Jurgen, Dr., Mng. Dir.--Deutsche Bank Australia Ltd., Melbourne, Australia; *Int'l*, pg. 405

Beck, James A., Pres.--Seneca Resources Corp., Houston, TX; *U.S. Public*, pg. 1156

Beck, James A., Chm. Bd., Pres. & Chief Exec. Officer--SouthTrust Bank of North Carolina, Raleigh, NC; *U.S. Public*, pg. 1492

Beck, Kenneth, Plant Mgr.--Nacogdoches Plant, Nacogdoches, TX; *U.S. Public*, pg. 443

Beck, Martin, Chm.--Young & Rubicam Prague, Prague, Czech Republic; *U.S. Private*, pg. 1199

Beck, Philip D., Pres.--First Valley Life Insurance Company, Bethlehem, PA; *U.S. Public*, pg. 1528

Beck, R.J., Mgr.--Ballast Nedam Groep N.V., Riyadh, Saudi Arabia; *Int'l*, pg. 134

Beck, Randy, Gen. Mgr.--Gilt Edge Mine, Deadwood, SD; *U.S. Public*, pg. 477

Beck, Richard, V.P.-Surety--Willis Corroon Corp. of Pittsburgh, Pittsburgh, PA; *Int'l*, pg. 1507

Beck, Stephen, Pres.--Beck Manufacturing, Inc., Waynesboro, PA; *U.S. Private*, pg. 146

Beck, William F., V.P. & Gen. Mgr.--Chemical Products Group, Philadelphia, PA; *U.S. Public*, pg. 605

Becker, Al, Sr. V.P.-Opers.--Oscar Mayer Foods Corp., Madison, WI; *U.S. Public*, pg. 1288

Becker, Alan, Pres.--Woodard Inc., Owosso, MI; *U.S. Private*, pg. 192

Becker, Bernard, Pres.--Reed Exhibition Companies-Europe, Paris, France; *Int'l*, pg. 1096

Becker, Bernard, Pres.--Reed Expositions-France, Paris, France; *Int'l*, pg. 1097

Becker, Christopher, Pres. & Chief Exec. Officer--GeneTrace Systems, Inc., Menlo Park, CA; *U.S. Private*, pg. 958

Becker, Cindy, Laboratory Mgr.--Quest Diagnostic, Rochester, NY; *U.S. Public*, pg. 1351

Becker, Dan, Pres.--Aegis, Inc., New Bedford, MA; *U.S. Public*, pg. 1219

Becker, David M., Pres. & Chief Oper. Officer--Ward Lake Drilling, Inc., Gaylord, MI; *U.S. Private*, pg. 1078

Becker, Dipl.-Ing. Egon A., Mng. Dir.--GESTRA Espanola S.A., Madrid, Spain; *Int'l*, pg. 550

Becker, Don C., Pres. and Publr.--Journal of Commerce, Inc., New York, NY; *Int'l*, pg. 1026

Becker, Edmund F., Jr., V.P.--Medical Imaging Products Group, Peabody, MA; *U.S. Public*, pg. 109

Becker, Fred, Dir.-Architecture & Construction--National Associated Design Co., Indianapolis, IN; *Int'l*, pg. 215

Becker, Fred, Sr. V.P.--Chancellor Financial Sales & Services, Inc., Boston, MA; *U.S. Public*, pg. 335

Becker, Gregory W., Acting Gen. Mgr.--Dun & Bradstreet Business Education Services, New York, NY; *U.S. Public*, pg. 536

Becker, Heribert, Chm. Bd.--Lehnkering Montan Transport AG, Duisburg, Germany; *Int'l*, pg. 862

Becker, John, Plant Mgr.--Sweetheart Cup Company Inc., Springfield, MO; *U.S. Private*, pg. 1058

Becker, Manfred, Co-Chief Oper. Officer--BHF & IKB Immobilien-Leasing GmbH, Dusseldorf, Germany; *Int'l*, pg. 645

Becker, Norbert, Pres. & Chief Exec. Officer--Dana Perfumes Corp., New York, NY; *U.S. Private*, pg. 922

Becker, Norman, Mgr.--Allied Construction Specialities, Omaha, NE; *U.S. Private*, pg. 39

Becker, P., Chief Oper. Officer--GEC Composants S.A., Asnieres-sur-Seine, France; *Int'l*, pg. 546

Becker, Pascal, Gen. Mgr.--BFCE Thailand, Bangkok, Thailand; *Int'l*, pg. 161

Becker, Phillip E., Pres. & Chief Exec. Officer--First National Bank in Massillon, Massillon, OH; *U.S. Public*, pg. 646

Becker, Richard, Pres. & Chief Exec. Officer--M & I Bank of Menomonee Falls, Menomonee Falls, WI; *U.S. Public*, pg. 1050

Becker, Richard, Gen. Mgr.--Hano Document Printers, Inc., Conyers, GA; *U.S. Public*, pg. 1686

Becker, Robert, Chief Exec. Officer--Thomson & Thomson, Quincy, MA; *U.S. Public*, pg. 1601

Becker, Robert C., Pres.--James Steel & Tube Company, Madison Heights, MI; *U.S. Private*, pg. 102

Becker, Sharon, Pur. Agent--Eagle Zinc Co., Hillsboro, IL; *U.S. Private*, pg. 331

Becker, Thomas J., Pres.--Chase Manhattan Mortgage Corporation, Worthington, OH; *U.S. Public*, pg. 338

Becker, W. Marston, Pres.--J&H Marsh & McLennan Management Services (Guernsey) Ltd., Saint Peter Port, United Kingdom; *U.S. Public*, pg. 1049

Beckerman, Rick, Mgr.--Gould Paper Inc/Midhudson Div., Fishkill, NY; *U.S. Private*, pg. 467

Beckers, M., Mgr.--Max Gruenhut International, Inc., Bensenville, IL; *U.S. Public*, pg. 372

Beckert, John F., Reg. Pres.-Middletown--Citizens Bank Of Connecticut, New London, CT; *Int'l*, pg. 1132

Beckett, Tom, Chief Fin. Officer--Leo Burnett Company Ltd., Toronto, Canada; *U.S. Private*, pg. 185

Beckfield, Brad, Pres.--ConAgra Frozen Foods, Council Bluffs, IA; *U.S. Public*, pg. 427

Beckman, Bill, V.P.-Fin.--Prince Corporation, Holland, MI; *U.S. Public*, pg. 932

Beckman, J. Stephen, Pres.--United Investors Equity Services, Inc., Birmingham, AL; *U.S. Public*, pg. 1623

Beckman, Jeffrey, Reg. Mgr.--The C.P. Hall Company, Memphis, TN; *U.S. Private*, pg. 495

Beckman, Jerry, Pres. & Mng. Dir.-Intl.--Simon Marketing International GmbH - Munich, Unterhaching, Germany; *U.S. Private*, pg. 1001

Beckman, Ken, Gen. Mgr.--Sterling Electronics, Eden Prairie, MN; *U.S. Public*, pg. 1051

Beckman, Richard, Publisher--Conde Nast Traveler, New York, NY; *U.S. Private*, pg. 20

Beckman, Richard, Publisher--Gentlemen's Quarterly, New York, NY; *U.S. Private*, pg. 20

Beckord, Michael, Chief Exec. Officer--Allianz Versicherungs-AG, Berlin, Germany; *Int'l*, pg. 58

Beckwith, C. William, Chm. & Chief Exec. Officer--Wellman International Ltd., Kells, Ireland; *U.S. Public*, pg. 1753

Becraft, J., Pres.--Armco Inc.-Butler Opers., Butler, PA; *U.S. Public*, pg. 131

Becraft, Joe, Pres.--Aquila Gas Pipeline Corporation, San Antonio, TX; *U.S. Public*, pg. 1701

Bedard, P., Div. Mgr.--Port Alfred Div., La Baie, Canada; *Int'l*, pg. 20

Bedard, Paul, Mgr.--Barrick Gold, Malartic, Canada; *Int'l*, pg. 169

Bedard, Wanda, Pres.--Bedarco Nooter, Inc., Montreal, Canada; *U.S. Private*, pg. 801

Beddow, John, Publr.--Business Journal Publications, Inc., Tampa, FL; *U.S. Private*, pg. 19

Bedell, Thomas, Pres.--Berkley, Inc., Spirit Lake, IA; *U.S. Private*, pg. 822

Bedenbaugh, Tommyr, Regional Gen. Mgr.--Saw & Wood Chip Mills, Orangeburg, SC; *U.S. Public*, pg. 1521

Bedford, Steve, Chm. Bd.--Blazer Plc, London, United Kingdom; *Int'l*, pg. 896

Bednar, Barbara A., Chief Oper. Officer & V.P.--Total Renal Care, Berwyn, PA; *U.S. Public*, pg. 1625

Bednar, Pete, Plant Mgr.-Plant V--Tread Rubber Plant, Muscatine, IA; *U.S. Public*, pg. 177

Bednar, Steve, V.P.-Sls.--MB Manufacturing, Valparaiso, IN; *U.S. Private*, pg. 300

Bednarzyk, Klaus, Mng. Dir.--LBB Kartenservice GmbH, Berlin, Germany; *Int'l*, pg. 160

Bednorz, John, Exec. V.P.--Saw Drilling, Inc., Victoria, TX; *U.S. Public*, pg. 1519

Bedogni, K.G., Gen. Mgr.--Senior New Zealand Limited, Auckland, New Zealand; *Int'l*, pg. 1223

Bedoni, Maury, Gen. Mgr.--Lowara S.p.A, Montecchio Maggiore, Italy; *U.S. Public*, pg. 861

Bedorey, Tom, Gen. Mgr.--Rogers CFGP-AM, Grande Prairie, Canada; *Int'l*, pg. 1123

Bedorf, Hans-Wolf, Mng. Dir.--Deutsche Hypothekenbank FrankfurtAG, Frankfurt/Main, Germany; *Int'l*, pg. 418

Beebe, Brett, Gen. Mgr.--SMC South, Auburn, AL; *U.S. Private*, pg. 1014

Beech, Paul, Gen. Mgr.--EG & G Optoelectronics-Salem, Salem, MA; *U.S. Public*, pg. 543

Beech, Paul, Gen. Mgr.--EG & G Optoelectronics-Covina, Covina, CA; *U.S. Public*, pg. 543

Beecroft, John, Mng. Dir.--SASIB Bakery UK Ltd., Newton-le-Willows, United Kingdom; *Int'l*, pg. 1194

Beel, Ken, Pres.--Derlan Aerospace Canada Limited, Milton, Canada; *Int'l*, pg. 395

Beel, N. C., Chief Oper. Officer--Babcock Robey Limited, Lincoln, United Kingdom; *Int'l*, pg. 472

Beeler, Hermann, Gen. Mgr.--Forbo Teppichwerke SA, Ennenda, Switzerland; *Int'l*, pg. 497

Beelien, P., Chief Oper. Officer--Gevetex Textilglas GmbH, Aachen, Germany; *Int'l*, pg. 1177

Beene, John, Mng. Dir.--Thermon Far East, Ltd., Yokohama, Japan; *U.S. Private*, pg. 1081

Beer, David, Chief Oper. Officer--Panduit Aust. Pty. Ltd., Dandenong, Australia; *U.S. Private*, pg. 836

Beers, Ed, Plant Mgr.--Miller Brewing Company, Irwindale, CA; *U.S. Public*, pg. 1289

Beers, Jim, Chief Oper. Officer--Frank Paxton Lumber Company, Tulsa, OK; *U.S. Private*, pg. 585

Beesley, Cliff, Gen. Mgr.--Frontier Communications of Thorntown, Inc., Thorntown, IN; *U.S. Public*, pg. 684

Beesley, K., Mng. Dir.--Simon-Diasol, Hadnall, United Kingdom; *Int'l*, pg. 1251

Beetz, Bernd E., Reg. V.P.-Health & Beauty Prods., So. Eur.--Procter & Gamble Health & Beauty Care So. Europe, Rome, Italy; *U.S. Public*, pg. 1332

Befani, P., Mng. Dir.--Pignone Espanola S.A., Madrid, Spain; *Int'l*, pg. 991

Beg, Mirza Mohammed Taiyab, Dir.--Tourism Malaysia - Tokyo Office, Tokyo, Japan; *Int'l*, pg. 833

Begel, Thomas, Pres.--Truck Components Inc., Rockford, IL; *U.S. Public*, pg. 933
Begg, James, Pres.--BLD Europe S.A., Brussels, Belgium; *Int'l*, pg. 394
Beggington, Andrew, Chief Exec. Officer--NESLAB Instruments, Inc., Newington, NH; *U.S. Public*, pg. 1595
Beggs, Lyman, Pres.--Norelco Consumer Products Company, Stamford, CT; *Int'l*, pg. 1054
Beghini, Victor G., Pres.--Marathon Oil Company, Houston, TX; *U.S. Public*, pg. 1661
Begin, Brad, Pres.--MetalWest LLC, Brighton, CO; *U.S. Private*, pg. 817
Begin, Richard, Pres.--Charcuterie la Tour Eiffel Inc., Ville Vanier, Canada; *Int'l*, pg. 850
Begler, James C., Pres.--SuperValu, Inc.-Spokane Div., Spokane, WA; *U.S. Public*, pg. 1541
Begoun, Alan, Gen. Mgr.--Corrugated Container Div.-Bedford Park Plant, Bedford Park, IL; *U.S. Public*, pg. 1520
Beh, Paul, Pres.--Reed Exhibition Companies-South Asia/Pacific, Singapore, Singapore; *Int'l*, pg. 1097
Beh, S.P., Mng. Dir.--EMI (Malaysia) Sdn Bhd, Kuala Lumpur, Malaysia; *Int'l*, pg. 427
Behar, Elazar, Rep. for Chile--Bank Hapoalim (Santiago), Santiago, Chile; *Int'l*, pg. 149
Beharrell, B., Chm. Bd.--Amercard, Moscow, Russia; *Int'l*, pg. 993
Behets, John, Gen. Mgr.--Elscint NV/SA, Zaventem, Belgium; *Int'l*, pg. 450
Behlav, Hartmut, Pres.--Georg Fischer Plastik A.G., Landquart, Switzerland; *Int'l*, pg. 489
Behling, Al, Gen. Mgr.--Schult Homes Corporation, Middlebury, IN; *U.S. Public*, pg. 1442
Behm, Brian, Pres.--Power Team Division, Owatonna, MN; *U.S. Public*, pg. 1421
Behnke, Bruce I., Pres. & Gen. Mgr.--Stanley Fastening Systems, East Greenwich, RI; *U.S. Public*, pg. 1509
Behnke, James, V.P. & Gen. Mgr.--The Benjamin/Cummings Publishing Company, Menlo Park, CA; *Int'l*, pg. 1026
Behnke, Robert, Mgr.--Tekra Corp., East Coast Div., Westborough, MA; *U.S. Private*, pg. 1073
Behr, Giselbert, Gen. Mgr.--Dresdner Bank AG, New York, NY; *Int'l*, pg. 418
Behrends, Frank, Chief Oper. Officer--BHF-Bank, Singapore, Singapore; *Int'l*, pg. 119
Behrendt, Hans, Gen. Mgr.--Elscint GmbH, Wiesbaden, Germany; *Int'l*, pg. 450
Behrens, Fredrik H., Dir.--Kvaerner Rosenberg a.s. International Developments, Stavanger, Norway; *Int'l*, pg. 770
Behrens, Robert, Pres.--Tetra-Pak Processing Systems, Indianapolis, IN; *Int'l*, pg. 1379
Behrenwaldt, Udo, Mng. Dir.--International Investment Management Gesellschaft S.A., Luxembourg, Luxembourg; *Int'l*, pg. 405
Behrouzi, Massued, Pres.--Solectron Technology, Inc., Charlotte, NC; *U.S. Public*, pg. 1483
Beien, Chuck, Gen. Mgr.--Alro Specialty Metals, Tonawanda, Tonawanda, NY; *U.S. Private*, pg. 46
Beiles, Herbert N., Mng. Dir.--Crown Financial Management Limited, Woking, United Kingdom; *Int'l*, pg. 468
Beilfuss, William H., Admin.--Winston-Salem Convalescent Center, Winston Salem, NC; *U.S. Public*, pg. 1715
Beiling, Bill, Opers. Mgr.--Schrader Bellows Division, Cuyahoga Falls, OH; *U.S. Public*, pg. 1261
Beindner, Helmut, Dir.--Franken WKV Bank GmbH, Nuremberg, Germany; *Int'l*, pg. 179
Beirne, Patrick, Pres.--Pulte Illinois Division, Hoffman Estates, IL; *U.S. Public*, pg. 1344
Beisenherz, Robert, Pres.--Union Banker Insurance Co., Dallas, TX; *U.S. Private*, pg. 1018
Beissinger, Frederick W., Chm. Bd., Pres. & Chief Exec. Officer--American General Finance, Inc., Evansville, IN; *U.S. Public*, pg. 76
Beissner, Hans Peter, Chief Oper. Officer--Quimica Schering Colombiana S. A., Bogota, Colombia; *Int'l*, pg. 1204
Beitter, John, Principal--Jackhammer, Dallas, TX; *U.S. Private*, pg. 929
Bek, Ole, Mng. Dir.--Bang & Olufsen Espana S.A., Madrid, Spain; *Int'l*, pg. 146
Bekaert, Eugene, V.P. & Dir.-Creative Services--Greenwood Mills, Inc., New York, NY; *U.S. Private*, pg. 479
Beker, Bill, Mgr.-Plant--Akzo Coatings Inc., Baxley, GA; *Int'l*, pg. 47
Beketic, Ralph, Pres.--Roundy's, Milwaukee Division, Milwaukee, WI; *U.S. Private*, pg. 948
Bekins, Michael, Office Mgr.--Korn/Ferry International, Kuala Lumpur, Malaysia; *U.S. Private*, pg. 633
Belair, A.C., Pres.--ALLTEL Answering Service, Inc., Export, PA; *U.S. Public*, pg. 55
Belan, Robert D., Pres.--Badger Meter Utility Div., Milwaukee, WI; *U.S. Public*, pg. 165
Belanger, Jean, Pres.--Premier Tech Ltee, Riviere-du-Loup, Canada; *Int'l*, pg. 1068
Belanger, Leo, Pres.--SunGard Financial Systems, Inc., Canoga Park, CA; *U.S. Public*, pg. 1534
Belanger, Leo, Pres.--Warrington Financial Systems Inc., Hopkins, MN; *U.S. Public*, pg. 1535
Belcastro, John V., Gen. Mgr.--Frit Division, Cleveland, OH; *U.S. Public*, pg. 619
Belcher, Donald D., Grp. V.P.--Avery Converted Products Group, Covina, CA; *U.S. Public*, pg. 152
Belcher, Joe J., V.P.-Textiles--Sybron Chemicals Inc., Wellford, SC; *U.S. Public*, pg. 1544
Belcher, Joe J., V.P.-Textiles--Sybron Chemicals, Inc., Norwich, CT; *U.S. Public*, pg. 1544
Belda, Alain, Pres.--Alcoa Aluminio S.A., Pocos de Caldas, Brazil; *U.S. Public*, pg. 61
Belda, Ricardo E., Pres.--Alcoa Nederland Holding B. V., Drunen, Netherlands; *U.S. Public*, pg. 62
Belding, Tom, Gen. Mgr.--Republic Automotive Parts Sales, Inc., Anchorage, AK; *U.S. Public*, pg. 1378
Belec, Bob, Mng. Dir.--Kelly Services (Ltd.), Sydney, Australia; *U.S. Public*, pg. 949
Belec, Jean, Pres.--Wajax Industries Limited, Montreal, Canada; *Int'l*, pg. 1485
Belenguier, B., Chm. Bd.--Gan UK plc, London, United Kingdom; *Int'l*, pg. 565
Belfield, E.A., Gen. Mgr.--Morgan Matroc Limited Advanced Materials Engineering Division, Stourport, United Kingdom; *Int'l*, pg. 893
Belford, Ray, Chief Fin. Officer & Controller--Hayes Axle, Inc., Seminole, OK; *U.S. Private*, pg. 299
Belfus, Linda, Pres.--Hanley & Belfus, Inc., Philadelphia, PA; *Int'l*, pg. 1479
Belhassan, Said Alauoi, Mng. Partner--Wackenhut Morocco, Inc., Rabat, Morocco; *U.S. Public*, pg. 1731
Belinguier, B., Chm. Bd.--Gan North America Inc., New York, NY; *Int'l*, pg. 564
Belisle, Syl, Publisher--The Northern Daily News, Kirkland Lake, Canada; *Int'l*, pg. 631
Bell-Jones, Derek, Mng. Dir.--Deeko Plc, London, United Kingdom; *U.S. Public*, pg. 672
Bell, A.J., Chm. & Chief Exec.--Senior Control Engineering Limited, Derby, United Kingdom; *Int'l*, pg. 1220
Bell, Alonzo, V.P.--Great Atlantic Hospitality Co. Inc., Hampton, VA; *U.S. Private*, pg. 473
Bell, C., Dir.--Ladbroke & Co. Ltd., Harrow, United Kingdom; *Int'l*, pg. 787
Bell, Charles H., Chm. & Chief Exec. Officer--Triad International Maintenance Corporation, Greensboro, NC; *U.S. Public*, pg. 1325
Bell, Christopher, Mgr.--Keppel (UK) Ltd., London, United Kingdom; *Int'l*, pg. 731
Bell, Clark, Assoc. Publ./Editor--Modern Healthcare, Chicago, IL; *U.S. Private*, pg. 285
Bell, Dan, Mng. Dir.--J.W. Messner, Inc., Cincinnati, OH; *U.S. Private*, pg. 734
Bell, David R., Publr.--Vandalia Leader-Union, Vandalia, IL; *U.S. Private*, pg. 648
Bell, David R., Pres.--Nuevo Camino Constructors Co., Upland, CA; *U.S. Public*, pg. 1795
Bell, Derek, V.P.--Linear Div., Sunnyvale, CA; *Int'l*, pg. 1054
Bell, Donal, Gen. Mgr.--Micromotors Groschopp Ireland Ltd., Galway, Ireland; *Int'l*, pg. 559
Bell, Duff, Mgr.--Vickers Truck Equipment, Salt Lake City, UT; *U.S. Private*, pg. 84
Bell, Graham S., Chm. & Mng. Dir.--The Crown Company (Singapore) Ltd., Jurong, Singapore; *U.S. Public*, pg. 464
Bell, Gus, Gen. Mgr.--Bettis Electric Actuator Company, Cincinnati, OH; *U.S. Public*, pg. 483
Bell, James, Pres.--U.S. Central Credit Union, Overland Park, KS; *U.S. Private*, pg. 288
Bell, James D., Pres.--Thomson-CSF, Inc., Arlington, VA; *Int'l*, pg. 1384
Bell, Janet, Lab Mgr.--Quest Diagnostic-Moorestown, Moorestown, NJ; *U.S. Public*, pg. 1351
Bell, Janet, Lab Mgr.--Quest Diagnostic-Vineland, Vineland, NJ; *U.S. Public*, pg. 1352
Bell, Jerry, Admin.--Medicenter, Corpus Christi, Corpus Christi, TX; *U.S. Public*, pg. 1714
Bell, Jim, Publisher--The Missoulian, Missoula, MT; *U.S. Public*, pg. 984
Bell, John, Pres.--Nabob Foods Limited, Burnaby, Canada; *U.S. Public*, pg. 1289
Bell, John Hickman, Reg. Dir.--Sime Darby Hong Kong Limited, Causeway Bay, Hong Kong; *Int'l*, pg. 1251
Bell, Joseph, Exec. V.P. & Gen. Mgr.--WPTF, Raleigh, NC; *U.S. Private*, pg. 298
Bell, Joseph G., Mng. Dir.--Richards (Shipbuilders) Ltd., Lowestoft, United Kingdom; *Int'l*, pg. 1356
Bell, Martin, Mgr.--American Appraisal (AAR), Inc., Saint Petersburg, Russia; *U.S. Private*, pg. 50
Bell, Robert W., Plant Mgr.--AC Rochester Products Austria Ges.m.b.H, Vienna, Austria; *U.S. Public*, pg. 723
Bell, Ronald, Mng. Dir.--Terry's Group, Cheltenham, United Kingdom; *U.S. Public*, pg. 1290
Bell, Sheryl, Gen. Mgr.--Legi-Tech, Sacramento, CA; *U.S. Public*, pg. 1066
Bell, Stephen, Pres.--Bruce Hardwood Floors, Ltd., Abingdon, United Kingdom; *U.S. Public*, pg. 1634
Bell, Stuart, Gen. Mgr.--BHP Steel Building Products South Pacific Ltd., Samabula, Fiji; *Int'l*, pg. 226
Bell, T., Mng. Dir.--Senior Colman Limited, Sale, United Kingdom; *Int'l*, pg. 1220
Bell, Vicki, Admin.--Hillhaven-LaSalle Nursing Center, Durham, NC; *U.S. Public*, pg. 1713
Bella, John L., Gen. Mgr.--Nielsen, Gainesboro, TN; *Int'l*, pg. 460
Bellah, Kris, Chief Oper. Officer--Dixie Royal Homes, Inc., Cookeville, TN; *U.S. Private*, pg. 392
Bellamy, W.F., Gen. Mgr.--CHEMCENTRAL/Salt Lake City, Woods Cross, UT; *U.S. Private*, pg. 232
Bellanger, Daniel, Pres.--Etablissement Robert Bellanger S.A., Saint Berthevin, France; *U.S. Public*, pg. 1579
Bellas, Jean, Pres.--Interior Space International, Chicago, IL; *U.S. Private*, pg. 379
Belle, Adamu, Mng. Dir.--Habib Nigeria Bank Ltd., Lagos, Nigeria; *Int'l*, pg. 585
Belle, Eugene, Admin.--Greenery Extended Care Center of Beverly, Beverly, MA; *U.S. Public*, pg. 836
Belle, Thomas V., Pres. & Chief Exec. Officer--Carlson Learning Company, Minneapolis, MN; *U.S. Private*, pg. 212
Bellego, H., Gen. Mgr.--Carstab Products, Cincinnati, OH; *U.S. Public*, pg. 1135
Belleveau, Michael, V.P. & Gen. Mgr.--Swiss Army Brands Ltd., Shelton, CT; *U.S. Public*, pg. 1544
Bellew, George, Pres.--Dayton Progress of Canada, Toronto, Canada; *U.S. Public*, pg. 617
Bellezza, Dominick, Gen. Mgr.--Barry Controls Aerospace, Burbank, CA; *U.S. Public*, pg. 124
Belli, Luca, Chief Oper. Officer--Glo SpA, Poggio Rusco, Italy; *U.S. Public*, pg. 1055
Belli, Thomas, Pres.--QSP, Inc., Ridgefield, CT; *U.S. Public*, pg. 1367
Bellini, Giampiero, Dr., Chief Oper. Officer--Schering S.p.A., Mailand, Italy; *Int'l*, pg. 1204
Bellini, Marco, V.P. & Gen. Mgr.--Dentsply Italia, Rome, Italy; *U.S. Public*, pg. 499
Bellini, Marco, Chief Oper. Officer--DeTrey/Dentsply S.r.l., Rome, Italy; *U.S. Public*, pg. 500
Bellinkx, Jos, Chief Oper. Officer--S.A. Alfa-Laval N.V., Brussels, Belgium; *Int'l*, pg. 1379
Bellis, Marc, Chief Exec. Officer--Generale Bank - London, London, United Kingdom; *Int'l*, pg. 547
Bellis, Robert, Pres.--Cerplex Ltd., Enfield, United Kingdom; *U.S. Public*, pg. 332
Belliveau, Norman, Pres.--Summit Plastic Co., Tallmadge, OH; *Int'l*, pg. 974
Bello, Regis, Chm. & Chief Exec. Officer--Cogifer SA, Croissy-sur-Seine, France; *Int'l*, pg. 386
Bellomo, Anthony, Pres.--Erisco, Inc., New York, NY; *U.S. Public*, pg. 395
Belloni, Giorgio, Mng. Dir.--Janssen-Cilag Farmaceutici S.p.A., Cologno Monzese, Italy; *U.S. Public*, pg. 929
Belloni, Giorgio, Dr., Mng. Dir.--Janssen-Cilag S.p.A., Milan, Italy; *U.S. Public*, pg. 929
Bellorin, E., Mng. Dir.--Gran Industria de Neumaticos Centroamericana, S.A., Guatemala, Guatemala; *U.S. Public*, pg. 753
Bellow, H. Arthur, Chief Oper. Officer--Triangle Special Products, Livonia, MI; *U.S. Public*, pg. 147
Bellowe, Arnold, Co-Chief Exec. Officer--Forest City Auto Parts, Beachwood, OH; *U.S. Public*, pg. 1652
Bellowe, Stanley, Co-Chief Exec. Officer--Forest City Auto Parts, Beachwood, OH; *U.S. Public*, pg. 1652
Bellringer, Stephen T., Pres.--Union Gas Limited, Chatham, Canada; *Int'l*, pg. 1492
Bellstedt, Roland, Dr., Sr. Mng. Dir.--Deutsche Bank AG (Bremen), Bremen, Germany; *Int'l*, pg. 402
Bellucci, Louis V., Sr., Exec. V.P. & Mgr.-Natl. Equities Sls.--Jefferies & Company, Inc., Los Angeles, CA; *U.S. Public*, pg. 925
Bellucci, Louis V., Sr., Mgr.-Natl. Equity Sls.--Jefferies & Company, Inc., Short Hills, NJ; *U.S. Public*, pg. 925
Belluche, Robert, Admin.--Greenery Rehabilitation Center, Brighton, MA; *U.S. Public*, pg. 837
Bellut, Jacques, Chief Exec. Officer--Credit Agricole Asset Management - Southeast Asia, Central, Hong Kong; *Int'l*, pg. 341
Belman, Henry M., Dir.-Engrng.--Vickers Tedeco Div., Glenolden, PA; *U.S. Public*, pg. 25
Belmans, Eddy, Mng. Dir.--BBL Asset Management (Singapore) Pte. Ltd., Singapore, Singapore; *Int'l*, pg. 148
Belmont, R., Pres.--Hunt-Wesson Refrigerated Foods Div., Fullerton, CA; *U.S. Public*, pg. 426
Belmonte, Dennis R., Chm. & Pres.--Benguet Management Corporation, Manila, Philippines; *Int'l*, pg. 186
Beloubad, Abdelaziz, Gen. Mgr.--Crown Cork Company (Morocco) S.A., Casablanca, Morocco; *U.S. Public*, pg. 464
Belschner, Ronald R., Div. V.P.--Industrial Tape & Specialties Division, Saint Paul, MN; *U.S. Public*, pg. 1605
Belsham, Philip, Chief Oper. Officer--Nobel Systems Ltd., Bedford, United Kingdom; *Int'l*, pg. 1290
Belsky, Stanley, Pres. & Chief Oper. Officer--Assembly Component Systems, Inc., Burr Ridge, IL; *U.S. Public*, pg. 980
Belsky, Stanley, Pres. & Chief Oper. Officer--Automatic Screw Machines Products Company, Decatur, AL; *U.S. Public*, pg. 980
Belson, Harvey, Pres.--Ben Arnold Co., Inc., Columbia, SC; *U.S. Private*, pg. 83
Belson, Ross A., Pres. & Chief Oper. Officer--General DataComm, Inc., Middlebury, CT; *U.S. Public*, pg. 708
Belton, Colin, Gen. Mgr.--Aracruz Celulose (USA) Inc., Raleigh, NC; *Int'l*, pg. 78
Beltrame, B., Gen. Dir.--Volkswagen IFA Pkw. GmbH., Wolfsburg, Germany; *Int'l*, pg. 1476
Beltz, John F., Mgr.-Mktg. Svcs.--Wellhead Equipment Division, Houston, TX; *U.S. Public*, pg. 605
Belz, Helmut, Mng. Dir--Ingersoll Maschinen und Werkzeuge GmbH, Burbach, Germany; *U.S. Private*, pg. 562
Belzer, Burton E., Chm. Bd., Chief Exec. Officer, Cheif Fin. Officer & Treas.--E-Z Lok, Gardena, CA; *U.S. Private*, pg. 1063
Belzer, Richard, V.P.--Stacey's/J. K. Gill Retail Stores, Solana Beach, CA; *U.S. Private*, pg. 170
Belzung, Geary, Gen. Mgr.--Peterson Spring-Maumee Plant, Holland, OH; *U.S. Private*, pg. 857
Bemelmans, Berry H., Pres.--Alcoa Chemie Nederland B.V., Rotterdam, Netherlands; *U.S. Public*, pg. 61
Bement, John, Pres. & Gen. Mgr.--Six Flags Over Georgia, Austell, GA; *U.S. Public*, pg. 1612
Bemis, Scott, Publr.--ACBJ Business Publications, Inc., Cincinnati, OH; *U.S. Private*, pg. 19
Bemme, Gunter, Chief Oper. Officer--KONE Garant Aufzug GmbH, Chemnitz, Germany; *Int'l*, pg. 748
Ben Nasr, Mahmoud, Chief Oper. Officer--TECI, Tunis, Tunisia; *Int'l*, pg. 1361
Ben-Ami, Rafi, Rep.-Toronto--Bank Hapoalim B.M., Downsview, Canada; *Int'l*, pg. 149
Ben-Gera, BC, Dir. & Gen. Mgr.--Hadar Insurance Company Ltd., Tel Aviv, Israel; *Int'l*, pg. 565
Ben-Porath, M., Gen. Mgr.--MHT Division, Israel; *Int'l*, pg. 690
Benachi, Nicholas M., Mng. Dir.--Bear Stearns Finance S.A., Paris, France; *U.S. Public*, pg. 198
Benadiba, Mark, Exec. V.P.--Cott Corporation - Central Division, Toronto, Canada; *Int'l*, pg. 337
Benadof, David, Mng. Dir.--J.I. Case do Brasil & Cia (a Partnership), Sao Paulo, Brazil; *U.S. Public*, pg. 1579
Benadof, David B., Pres.--Poclain do Brasil S.A., Sorocaba, Brazil; *U.S. Public*, pg. 1580
Benanar, Gary G., Pres.--Aetna Life Insurance and Annuity Co., Hartford, CT; *U.S. Public*, pg. 26

Benante, Martin R., Pres. & Gen. Mgr.--Target Rock Corp., Farmingdale, NY; *U.S. Public*, pg. 470

Benarroch, Carlos, Gen. Mgr.--Nordson International de Venezuela, C.A., Caracas, Venezuela; *U.S. Public*, pg. 1189

Benassini, George, Dir.-Sls.--Griffith Laboratories Worldwide, Cuautitlan, Mexico; *U.S. Private*, pg. 481

Benazeraf, Claude, Gen. Mgr.--Florasynth S.A., Le Plan-de-Grasse, France; *Int'l*, pg. 174

Bencivenni, P., Gen. Mgr.--Ferro (Italia) S.r.L., Casinalbo, Italy; *U.S. Public*, pg. 619

Bencomo, J., Mng. Dir.--Ayra Servicio SA, Barcelona, Spain; *Int'l*, pg. 535

Bencsik, Doris D., Pres. & Chief Oper. Officer--Datapoint Corporation, San Antonio, TX; *Int'l*, pg. 384

Bendall, D.V., Chm.--Morgan Grenfell Italia S.p.A., Milan, Italy; *Int'l*, pg. 406

Bende, Andrea B., Pres.--Sprint International, Westwood, KS; *U.S. Public*, pg. 1500

Bendele, Gerald E., Pres.--Knoll Pharmaceutical Company, Whippany, NJ; *Int'l*, pg. 105

Bendell, D.V., Pres.--Banque Morgan Grenfell en Suisse S. A. (Switzerland), Geneva, Switzerland; *Int'l*, pg. 406

Bender, A. Thomas, Chief Oper. Officer--CooperVision, Inc., Irvine, CA; *U.S. Public*, pg. 442

Bender, G.I., Gen. Mgr.--Powell River Division, Powell River, Canada; *Int'l*, pg. 828

Bender, James J., Asst. Gen. Counsel--NRG Energy, Inc., Minneapolis, MN; *U.S. Public*, pg. 1195

Bender, James T., Pres.--Ziebart Corp., Troy, MI; *U.S. Private*, pg. 1205

Bender, James T., Pres.--Ziebart Canada, Inc., Concord, Canada; *U.S. Private*, pg. 1205

Bender, James T., Pres.--TKD, N.A., Troy, MI; *U.S. Private*, pg. 1205

Bender, Jim, Pres.--Tidy Car International, Inc., Troy, MI; *U.S. Private*, pg. 1205

Bender, Keith, Gen. Mgr.--Folding Carton (Kansas City), North Kansas City, MO; *Int'l*, pg. 1270

Bender, Robert, Pres.--Pentax Technologies Corp., Broomfield, CO; *Int'l*, pg. 85

Bender, T., Mng. Dir.--Timken de Mexico, S.A. de C.V., Tlalnepantla, Mexico; *U.S. Public*, pg. 1617

Bendheim, Ralf E., Chief Exec.--A.M.A. Asset Management Advisors of Dresdner Bank, Frankfurt/Main, Germany; *Int'l*, pg. 418

Bendix, Selina, Pres.--Bendix Environmental Research, Berkeley, CA; *U.S. Public*, pg. 51

Benecki, Walter, Pres.--The Arnold Engineering Company, Marengo, IL; *U.S. Public*, pg. 1420

Benedict, Kim M., Publr.--The Arkansas City Daily Traveler, Arkansas City, KS; *U.S. Private*, pg. 995

Benedict, Lori, Lab Mgr.--Quest Diagnostic-Chambersburg, Chambersburg, PA; *U.S. Public*, pg. 1351

Benedini, Flavio, Mgr.--Sandvik-Villares Wire Industria e Comerico Ltda., Sao Paulo, Brazil; *Int'l*, pg. 1188

Benefield, J. Dewey, Exec. V.P.--Sea Island Properties, Inc., Sea Island, GA; *U.S. Private*, pg. 978

Benefield, Jerry L., Pres. & Chief Exec. Officer--Nissan Motor Mfg. Corp., U.S.A., Smyrna, TN; *Int'l*, pg. 945

Benefield, Roby, Gen. Mgr.--Dothan Auto Auction, Dothan, AL; *U.S. Public*, pg. 1649

Beneke, Brad, V.P.-Sls.--All Star Gas Co.-Region XIII, Lebanon, MO; *U.S. Private*, pg. 35

Benemar, Per, Gen. Mgr.--Gillette Europe, Isleworth, United Kingdom; *U.S. Public*, pg. 744

Benemar, Per, Gen. Mgr.--Gillette Products Division-Europe AMEE, Isleworth, United Kingdom; *U.S. Public*, pg. 745

Benestad, Dag C., Mng. Dir.--Sodra Cell A/S, Oslo, Norway; *Int'l*, pg. 1276

Beng, O H., Gen. Mgr.--BHP Steel Building Products Taiwan Ltd., Taipei, Taiwan; *Int'l*, pg. 226

Bengelsdorff, Carl-Henrik, Mng. Dir.--Valmet Skandinavien AB, Karlstad, Sweden; *Int'l*, pg. 1448

Benglsson, Lars, Pres.--Stora Papyrus AB, Molndal, Sweden; *Int'l*, pg. 1303

Bengs, Robert, Gen. Mgr.--Wisapak Oy Ab, Pietarsaari Factory, Pietarsaari, Finland; *Int'l*, pg. 1429

Bengtson, Bengt, Mng. Dir.--Bang & Olufsen Svenska AB, Goteborg, Sweden; *Int'l*, pg. 146

Bengtson, Bengt O., Chief Opr. Officer--Pharmacia & Upjohn S.A., Guyancourt, France; *Int'l*, pg. 1050

Bengtsson, Anders, Gen. Mgr.--Tektronix AB, Bromma, Sweden; *U.S. Public*, pg. 1567

Benham, Ronald C., Pres.--Dexter Electronic Materials Division, City of Industry, CA; *U.S. Public*, pg. 504

Benhanou, Frank, Gen. Mgr.--S.C. Johnson Kiev Corp., Kiev, Ukraine,; *U.S. Private*, pg. 593

Benincasa, Anthony, Pres.--Benco Pet Foods, Inc., Zanesville, OH; *U.S. Public*, pg. 1360

Beningson, Robert M., Pres.--Cogeneration Technologies Inc., New York, NY; *U.S. Public*, pg. 1789

Benites, Ramon Arosemena, Chief Oper. Officer--Bolivar, Compania de Seguros del Ecuador, Guayaquil, Ecuador; *U.S. Public*, pg. 355

Benito, Bucay, Chm. Bd. & Gen. Dir.--Industrias Resistol, S.A., Mexico, Mexico; *U.S. Public*, pg. 1125

Benjamens, Rob, Chm.--Benjamens, Van Doorn EURO RSCG, Amstelveen, Netherlands; *Int'l*, pg. 602

Benjamin, C. J., Mgr.--Sheet & Coil Products Victoria, Hastings, Australia; *Int'l*, pg. 227

Benjamin, Douglas, Chief Exec. Officer--F.J. Benjamin Fashions (Singapore) Pte. Ltd., Singapore, Singapore; *Int'l*, pg. 187

Benjamin, Floyd, Pres.--Akorn Manufacturing, Inc., Decatur, IL; *U.S. Public*, pg. 34

Benjamin, John, Mgr.--Woodward Governor de Mexico S.A. de C.V., Mexico, Mexico; *U.S. Public*, pg. 1776

Benjaminsen, P., Chief Exec. Officer--Zurich Forsikring, Oslo, Norway; *Int'l*, pg. 1531

Benk, Tosun, Mng. Dir.--SKF Turk Sanayi ve Ticaret, Istanbul, Turkey; *Int'l*, pg. 1159

Benkavska, Jana, Branch Mgr.--Allianz poistovna a.s., Bratislava, Slovakia; *Int'l*, pg. 60

Benko, Leo, Mng. Dir.--Addey Milner Limited, Salford, United Kingdom; *Int'l*, pg. 1462

Benn, David, Mng. Dir.--Korn/Ferry International, Sydney, Australia; *U.S. Private*, pg. 633

Bennack, Frank, Pres. & Chief Exec. Officer-Hearst Corp.--Cosmopolitan, New York, NY; *U.S. Private*, pg. 517

Bennack, Frank A., Jr., Pres. & Chief Exec. Officer--Hearst Realty Development Co., Inc., New York, NY; *U.S. Private*, pg. 515

Bennerdt, Staffan, Pres.--NCC Finans, Solna, Sweden; *Int'l*, pg. 899

Bennet, Carl, Chief Oper. Officer--Electrolux Storkok AB, Alingsas, Sweden; *Int'l*, pg. 438

Bennet, Carl, Mng. Dir.--Getinge AB, Getinge, Sweden; *Int'l*, pg. 551

Bennet, Melvynn, Mng. Dir.--Asia Computerworld, Quarry Bay, Hong Kong; *U.S. Private*, pg. 569

Bennet, P., Gen. Mgr.--ING Bank London, London, United Kingdom; *Int'l*, pg. 650

Bennet, Richard W., III, Pres. & Chief Exec. Officer--Kaufmann's, Pittsburgh, PA; *U.S. Public*, pg. 1063

Bennet, T.R., Sr. Mgr.--Australian Guarantee Corporation Limited - Western Australia, Perth, Australia; *Int'l*, pg. 1496

Bennet, Ulf, Mng. Dir.--AB Bahco Ventilation, Enkoping, Sweden; *Int'l*, pg. 7

Bennett, Bill, Pres.-Geffen & DGC Records--Geffen Records, Los Angeles, CA; *Int'l*, pg. 1215

Bennett, D.A., Chm. Bd.--Texaco Limited, London, United Kingdom; *U.S. Public*, pg. 1584

Bennett, D.A., Chm. Bd.--Texaco North Sea U.K. Co., Aberdeen, United Kingdom; *U.S. Public*, pg. 1584

Bennett, Ed, V.P & Gen. Mgr.--Bayerische Vereinsbank AG, Chicago, IL; *Int'l*, pg. 180

Bennett, Edward A., Pres.--VH-1/Video Hits One, New York, NY; *U.S. Private*, pg. 779

Bennett, Eugene F., Pres.--Rollins Hudig Hall of Hawaii, Inc., Honolulu, HI; *U.S. Public*, pg. 117

Bennett, Gary, V.P.--Hitachi Home Electronics, Eastern Region, Norcross, GA; *Int'l*, pg. 622

Bennett, Geoffrey, Mng. Dir.--Loctite (UK) Ltd., Welwyn Garden City, United Kingdom; *Int'l*, pg. 611

Bennett, J.G., Sr. Dir.--Barclays Bank PLC, Caribbean, Christchurch, Barbados; *Int'l*, pg. 166

Bennett, Jeff, Mgr.--Pyramid Electric Supply Co., Inc., Oklahoma City, OK; *Int'l*, pg. 1108

Bennett, Keith R., Mng. Dir.--Lapmaster International Ltd., Morton Grove, IL; *Int'l*, pg. 1338

Bennett, Michael F., Pres.--Emtex Leasing Corp., Roswell, GA; *U.S. Private*, pg. 1177

Bennett, Nicholas J M, Exec. Dir.--WF Corroon-London, London, United Kingdom; *Int'l*, pg. 1502

Bennett, Richard W., Pres.--Market Facts of Canada, Ltd., Toronto, Canada; *U.S. Public*, pg. 1047

Bennett, Robert, Sr. V.P.--Willis Corroon Administrative Services Corporation, Nashville, TN; *Int'l*, pg. 1505

Bennett, Robert J., Chm. Bd., Pres. & Chief Exec. Officer--ONBANCorp, Inc., Syracuse, NY; *U.S. Public*, pg. 631

Bennett, Thomas Bert, Pres. & Chief Oper. Officer--Wayne Dalton Corporation, Mount Hope, OH; *U.S. Private*, pg. 1155

Bennett, W., Gen. Mgr.--Hunter Douglas do Brazil Ltda., Sao Paulo, Brazil; *Int'l*, pg. 640

Bennett, William M., Pres.--Banc One Ohio Corporation, Columbus, OH; *U.S. Public*, pg. 173

Bennett, William W., Gen. Mgr.--Electric Boat, Quonset Facility, Groton, CT; *U.S. Public*, pg. 709

Bennewitz, M., Mng. Dir.--Robert Bosch SpA, Milan, Italy; *Int'l*, pg. 206

Bennie, Mal, Mng. Dir.--Cadillac Plastic, Silverwater, Australia; *U.S. Public*, pg. 781

Bennigsen, J., Mng. Dir.--Toshiba (U.K.) Ltd., Camberley, United Kingdom; *Int'l*, pg. 1407

Bennington, Jack, Chief Oper. Officer--Halex Div., Bedford, OH; *U.S. Public*, pg. 217

Benoit, Roy, Div. Mgr.--Century Telephone of Evangeline, Inc., Welsh, LA; *U.S. Public*, pg. 329

Bensabat, Paul, Pres. & Chief Exec. Officer--Sorrento Cheese Company, Inc., Buffalo, NY; *Int'l*, pg. 323

Bensabat, Paul, Mgr.--Besnier USA, New York, NY; *Int'l*, pg. 323

Bense, Hans, Pres.--D.W.M Copeland G.m.b.H., Berlin, Germany; *U.S. Public*, pg. 576

Bensimon, Jack, Pres. & Chief Exec. Officer--Bensimon Byrne DMB&B Toronto, Toronto, Canada; *U.S. Private*, pg. 303

Bension, Marc, V.P. & Gen. Mgr.--Universal Amphitheatre, Universal City, CA; *Int'l*, pg. 1216

Bensmail, Ibrahim, Mng. Dir.--SITEL-Societe Industrielle Algerienne de Telecommunications, Tlemcen, Algeria; *Int'l*, pg. 1370

Benso, William E., Chm.--Martin Marietta Canada Ltd., Ottawa, Canada; *U.S. Public*, pg. 1009

Benson, A.L., Pres.--Amoco Colombia Petroleum Company, Bogota, Colombia; *U.S. Public*, pg. 102

Benson, Jack D., Pres.--Old Kent Bank of Cadillac, Cadillac, MI; *U.S. Public*, pg. 1216

Benson, Keith, Pres.--Suncoast Motion Picture Co., Minnetonka, MN; *U.S. Public*, pg. 1142

Benson, Larry, Pres.--Benson's Old Home Kitchens, Bogart, GA; *U.S. Private*, pg. 134

Benson, P.J., Dep. Mng. Dir.--AEGON Insurance Company (UK) Limited, London, United Kingdom; *Int'l*, pg. 28

Benson, Paul, Chief Oper. Officer--Alpine Industries, Inc., Bothell, WA; *U.S. Private*, pg. 194

Benson, Robert L., Pres.--The Coteau Properties Co., Beulah, ND; *U.S. Public*, pg. 1149

Benson, Thomas, Pres.--Atlanta Gas Light Company, Atlanta, GA; *U.S. Public*, pg. 7

Benson, Thomas, Publ.--Midwest Living Magazine, Des Moines, IA; *U.S. Public*, pg. 1094

Benson, W. Arthur, Pres.--MG Electric Power, Inc., New York, NY; *Int'l*, pg. 862

Benson, Wayne, Sr. Mktg. Officer--Southeast Marketing Div., Duluth, GA; *U.S. Private*, pg. 296

Bensoussan-Torres, Robert, Mng. Dir.--Christian Lacroix U.K., London, United Kingdom; *Int'l*, pg. 782

Bensussan, R., Chm.--European Vacuum Interrupters S.A., Lattes, France; *Int'l*, pg. 1405

Bentjerodt, J. Roberto, Resident Rep.--The World Bank, Colombo, Sri Lanka; *U.S. Private*, pg. 1190

Bentley, A., Dir. & Gen. Mgr.--Hamworthy Industramar Limited, Poole, United Kingdom; *Int'l*, pg. 1065

Bentley, John, Gen. Mgr.--Letraset Australia Pty. Ltd., Brookvale, Australia; *Int'l*, pg. 461

Bentley, P.J., Dir.--Marshalls Finance Limited, London, United Kingdom; *Int'l*, pg. 222

Bentley, Sara, Publr.--Statesman-Journal Co., Inc., Salem, OR; *U.S. Public*, pg. 701

Benton, Bert, Gen. Mgr.--Valmont Northwest, Pasco, WA; *U.S. Public*, pg. 1707

Benton, John, V.P.--J.L. Clark Tube Div., Downers Grove, IL; *U.S. Public*, pg. 382

Benton, Richard, Pres.--Harris Systems Ltd., Don Mills, Canada; *U.S. Public*, pg. 791

Benton, Rick, Mgr.-Distr.--Weatherford US Inc., Rio Vista, CA; *U.S. Public*, pg. 1749

Bentson, Steve, Pres.--Century Manufacturing, Bloomington, MN; *U.S. Public*, pg. 1273

Bentz, J., Pres.--Enceratec, Inc., Columbus, IN; *Int'l*, pg. 1405

Bentz, J.C., Gen. Mgr.--Engineering Ceramic Technologies, Inc., Columbus, IN; *U.S. Public*, pg. 469

Bentz, Werner F., Pres.--Dresdner Bank (Switzerland) Ltd., Geneva, Switzerland; *Int'l*, pg. 419

Benvenuto, Joe, Gen. Mgr.--Hardware & Components Operation, Beacon Falls, CT; *U.S. Public*, pg. 1177

Benzing, William L., Pres.--SuperValu, Inc.-JM Jones Div., Champaign, IL; *U.S. Public*, pg. 1540

Beppu, Masakatsu, Chief Oper. Officer--Nittsu Real Estate Co., Ltd., Tokyo, Japan; *Int'l*, pg. 934

Beranek, Ivan, Gen. Mgr.--Jotun Spolchemie a.s., Usti nad Labem, Czech Republic; *Int'l*, pg. 715

Berard, Guy D., Gen. Mgr.--Forbo Industries Inc., Montreal, Canada; *Int'l*, pg. 497

Berard, Jean-Jacques, Mng. Dir.--Ordo, Montaigu, France; *U.S. Private*, pg. 512

Berberian, Paul, Pres.--Link-VTC, Inc., Boulder, CO; *U.S. Public*, pg. 684

Berdell, Jonathan, Admin.--Hillside Manor Convalescent Hospital, San Rafael, CA; *U.S. Public*, pg. 1714

Berdoz, Denis, Dir.--Tiffany & Co. Watch Center S.A., Morges, Switzerland; *U.S. Public*, pg. 1609

Bere, David, Pres. & Chief Exec. Officer--McCain Foods Inc., Oak Brook, IL; *Int'l*, pg. 850

Berenpas, E.J., Mng. Dir.--Verosol Fabrics B.V., Eibergen, Netherlands; *Int'l*, pg. 198

Berenpas, E.J., Mng. Dir.--De Haes Holland B.V., Eibergen, Netherlands; *Int'l*, pg. 198

Berens, Ron J., Exec. V.P.-Retail Divs.--Foot Locker, New York, NY; *U.S. Public*, pg. 1777

Beresky-White, Julie, Branch Mgr.--BSA Advertising, Inc., Houston, TX; *U.S. Private*, pg. 108

Berg, Carl, Mgr.-Chicago--Metro-Puck Comics Network, New York, NY; *U.S. Private*, pg. 739

Berg, Christopher B., Pres.--The McGuire Furniture Company, San Francisco, CA; *U.S. Private*, pg. 630

Berg, D., Gen. Mgr.--Standard Marine A/S, Oslo, Norway; *Int'l*, pg. 1152

Berg, G., Dir.--EC Erdolchemie GmbH, Cologne, Germany; *Int'l*, pg. 172

Berg, Ian J., Pres.--Copelco Financial Services Group Inc., Pennsauken, NJ; *Int'l*, pg. 694

Berg, Jack H., Pres.--A.S.M. Industries, Lancaster, PA; *U.S. Private*, pg. 985

Berg, Jeffrey K., Pres.--Suttle Apparatus Corporation, Hector, MN; *U.S. Public*, pg. 416

Berg, John, Pres.--Norwest Bank Minnesota South, N.A., Rochester, MN; *U.S. Public*, pg. 1202

Berg, John A., Pres. & Chief Exec. Officer--Norwest Bank Minnesota North, N.A., Duluth, MN; *U.S. Public*, pg. 1202

Berg, John A., Pres.--Norwest Bank Red Wing, N.A., Red Wing, MN; *U.S. Public*, pg. 1202

Berg, Julie, Pres.--AirTouch Cellular - Western Region, Bellevue, WA; *U.S. Public*, pg. 34

Berg, Kory L., Pres.--Arrosto Coffee Company, Los Angeles, CA; *U.S. Public*, pg. 966

Berg, Lai, Chm. Bd.--Parker Hannifin A/S, Stavanger, Norway; *U.S. Public*, pg. 1263

Berg, Lars, Sr. V.P. & Mng. Dir.--Ericsson Cables AB, Sundbyberg, Sweden; *Int'l*, pg. 1363

Berg, N.A., Pres.--American Steel Foundries, Chicago, IL; *U.S. Private*, pg. 68

Berg, P. Eric, V.P. & Gen. Mgr.--Precision Tools Div., North Kingstown, RI; *U.S. Public*, pg. 260

Berg, Richard M., Pres.--A.J. Oster Company, Warwick, RI; *U.S. Public*, pg. 1219

Berg, Rick, Pres.--Dowty Aerospace, Los Angeles, Duarte, CA; *Int'l*, pg. 1337

Berg, Tom, Div. Mgr.--Samedan Oil of Canada, Inc., Calgary, Canada; *U.S. Public*, pg. 1186

Bergamaschi, Gino, Dir.-Admin.--ORVAC Spa, Carpi, Italy; *U.S. Public*, pg. 1266

Bergamini, Franco, Mng. Dir.--KONE Elevators, BU 1, Milan, Italy; *Int'l*, pg. 747

Bergan, Cole, Pres.--McDonald Products Company, Buffalo, NY; *U.S. Private*, pg. 1009

Berge, Knut, Mgr.--Kvaerner Energy, Damsgard, Solheimsvik, Norway; *Int'l*, pg. 767

Bergeman, Carl T., Pres.--Computer Knowledge, Mountain Lakes, NJ; *U.S. Public*, pg. 421

Bergen, Larry, Chief Oper. Officer--Allright Carpark, Inc., Kansas City, MO; *U.S. Private*, pg. 42

Bergen, Roger, Pres.--The Nature Company, Berkeley, CA; *U.S. Private*, pg. 334

Bergenudd, Ulf, Pres.--Axel Johnson Servicehandelsgruppen AB, Stockholm, Sweden; *Int'l*, pg. 709
Berger, Allen, Mgr.--Fargo Glass & Paint Co, Bismarck, ND; *U.S. Private*, pg. 393
Berger, Chris, Mng. Dir.--Nira Nederland B.V., Utrecht, Netherlands; *Int'l*, pg. 1369
Berger, Chris, Pres. & Gen. Mgr.--Hazelwood Farms Bakeries, Inc., McMinnville, OR; *U.S. Public*, pg. 1541
Berger, David, Chief Oper. Officer--Datapoint (U.K.) Ltd., London, United Kingdom; *Int'l*, pg. 384
Berger, Donald, Pres.--Pony Express Delivery Services, Inc, Atlanta, GA; *U.S. Public*, pg. 245
Berger, Gerry, Terminal Mgr.--Kintetsu World Express Inc., Cleveland, OH; *Int'l*, pg. 735
Berger, H.U., Mgr.--Swiss Bank Corporation, Nicosia, Cyprus; *Int'l*, pg. 1330
Berger, Hans, Mng. Dir.--Butler Building Systems Ltd., Kirkcaldy, United Kingdom; *U.S. Public*, pg. 271
Berger, J., Mgr.--Schweizerischer Bankverein, Vienna, Austria; *Int'l*, pg. 1330
Berger, Jeffrey, Pres.-Food Service Division--Heinz U.S.A. Div., Pittsburgh, PA; *U.S. Public*, pg. 805
Berger, Jim, Plant Mgr.--Household Products, Aberdeen, MD; *U.S. Public*, pg. 387
Berger, John, Pres.--Eagle Engineering & Manufacturing, Inc., Cleveland, OH; *U.S. Private*, pg. 342
Berger, John, Pres.--DCM Manufacturing, Inc., Cleveland, OH; *U.S. Private*, pg. 342
Berger, John, Pres.--SuperTrapp Industries, Cleveland, OH; *U.S. Private*, pg. 342
Berger, John, Pres.--Maradyne Corporation, Cleveland, OH; *U.S. Private*, pg. 342
Berger, John, Pres.--Marion Manufacturing, Cleveland, OH; *U.S. Private*, pg. 342
Berger, John, Pres.--Turbo Industries, Cleveland, OH; *U.S. Private*, pg. 342
Berger, John R., Pres.--F&G Re, Inc., Morristown, NJ; *U.S. Public*, pg. 1659
Berger, Knut, Exec. V.P.--BTE Brauerel-Technik Essen GmbH, Essen, Germany; *Int'l*, pg. 400
Berger, Mark, Gen. Mgr.--Elkay Plastics Co., Inc., Stock Service Center, Plymouth Meeting, PA; *U.S. Private*, pg. 372
Berger, Pal, Mgr.--Frionor Tiefkuhl-Produkte GmbH, Bremen, Germany; *Int'l*, pg. 516
Berger, Paul, Dir.--Takenaka Netherlands B.V., Amsterdam, Netherlands; *Int'l*, pg. 1351
Berger, Primus, Dir. V.P.-Gen.European Opers.--Data General Europe, Inc., Paris, France; *U.S. Public*, pg. 486
Berger, Randy, Head of Fin.--Henry Pratt Co., Aurora, IL; *U.S. Public*, pg. 1651
Berger, S.J., Exec. Chm.--Amalgamated Retail Ltd., Braamfontein, South Africa; *Int'l*, pg. 1286
Berger, Steve, Pres.--Promotional Broadcast Services, Los Angeles, CA; *U.S. Private*, pg. 1166
Berger, Steve, Pres.--Western Product Placement, Los Angeles, CA; *U.S. Private*, pg. 1167
Berger, Steven, Pres.--Nationwide Communications, Inc., Columbus, OH; *U.S. Private*, pg. 789
Berger, Stuart, Owner & Pres.--IMG International, Harrison, NY; *U.S. Private*, pg. 566
Berger, Walter Z., Pres.--LG & E Energy Systems Inc., Louisville, KY; *U.S. Public*, pg. 970
Bergeron, Albert A., Pres.--PartyLite Gifts, Inc., Plymouth, MA; *U.S. Public*, pg. 239
Bergeron, Edmond, Pres.--Carnrick Laboratories, Inc., Cedar Knolls, NJ; *U.S. Private*, pg. 436
Bergeron, N.W., Exec. V.P. & Gen. Mgr.--Plymkraft Inc., Newport News, VA; *U.S. Private*, pg. 256
Bergeron, Robert, Chief Oper. Officer--Canadian Steel Foundries, Ltd., Montreal, Canada; *U.S. Public*, pg. 142
Bergers, Diethard, Dr., Mng. Dir.--Krupp Entwicklungszentrum GmbH, Essen, Germany; *Int'l*, pg. 512
Bergersen, Tore, Pres.--Aker Oil and Gas Technology, Oslo, Norway; *Int'l*, pg. 41
Bergeson, Rolly, Pres.--Westair Commuter Airlines, Inc., Fresno, CA; *U.S. Public*, pg. 1099
Bergevin, Paul, Exec. V.P., Gen. Mgr. & Global Tech. Dir.--Edelman Worldwide, Inc., Palo Alto, CA; *U.S. Private*, pg. 362
Bergez, Philippe, Gen. Mgr.--Bank Brussels Lambert, Breda, Breda, Netherlands; *Int'l*, pg. 148
Berghs, Steven J., Mgr.--Piper Jaffray Inc., Minneapolis, MN; *U.S. Public*, pg. 1302
Bergin, John R., Dir.--Textron Pacific Limited, Gordon, Australia; *U.S. Public*, pg. 1590
Berglie, Sven-Ake, Chief Oper. Officer--Perstorp Components, Vastra Frolunda, Sweden; *Int'l*, pg. 1040
Berglin, Vern, Pres.--Alumacraft Boat Co., Saint Peter, MN; *U.S. Private*, pg. 1088
Berglund, A., Mng. Dir.--De La Rue Systems Ltd., Singapore, Singapore; *Int'l*, pg. 387
Berglund, Hans Fredrik, Gen. Mgr.--Jotun Nederland B.V., Le Spijkenisse, Netherlands; *Int'l*, pg. 715
Berglund, Steven W., Mgr.-Branch--Piper Jaffray Inc., Everett, WA; *U.S. Public*, pg. 1301
Berglund, Steven W., Mgr.-Branch--Piper Jaffray Inc., Bellingham, WA; *U.S. Public*, pg. 1302
Berglund, Steven W., Mgr.-Branch--Piper Jaffray Inc., Poulsbo, WA; *U.S. Public*, pg. 1303
Bergman, Ake, Chief Officer--City Stormarknad, Stockholm, Sweden; *Int'l*, pg. 718
Bergman, Bertil, Pres.--Draco Lakemedel AB/Tika Lakemedel AB, Lund, Sweden; *Int'l*, pg. 93
Bergman, Bjorn, Chief Oper. Officer--Axel Johnson Instrument AB, Solna, Sweden; *Int'l*, pg. 709
Bergman, Christer, Chief Oper. Officer--Avesta Information Systems AB, Vasteras, Sweden; *Int'l*, pg. 221
Bergman, Donald A., Pres.--Bulldog Co., Memphis, TN; *U.S. Public*, pg. 1176
Bergman, Klaus, Pres. & Chief Exec. Officer--Allegheny Generating Co., New York, NY; *U.S. Public*, pg. 42
Bergman, Klaus, Pres.--Allegheny Pittsburgh Coal Co., Greensburg, PA; *U.S. Public*, pg. 42
Bergman, Rustan, Chm. Bd.--Hispano Sueca de Soldadura S.A. (Hissol), Alcobendas, Spain; *Int'l*, pg. 283
Bergman, Tommie, Pres.--ABB Flexible Automation, New Berlin, WI; *Int'l*, pg. 4
Bergman, Tor, Mng. Dir.--Raisio Chemicals Ltd., Raisio, Finland; *Int'l*, pg. 1085
Bergmann, E.Y.M. van Zinnicq, Chief Oper. Officer--Lloyds Eurofinance NV, Amsterdam, Netherlands; *Int'l*, pg. 813
Bergmann, Horst A., Chm. Bd., Pres. & Chief Exec. Officer--Jeppesen Sanderson, Englewood, CO; *U.S. Public*, pg. 1616
Bergmann, Horst A., Chm. Bd., Pres. & Chief Exec. Officer--Jeppesen and Co. GmbH, Frankfurt/Main, Germany; *U.S. Public*, pg. 1617
Bergmann, Horst A., Chm., Pres. & Chief Exec. Officer--Achieve Global, Tampa, FL; *U.S. Public*, pg. 1617
Bergmann, Johann, Mgr.--Munich Branch, Munich, Germany; *Int'l*, pg. 401
Bergmann, Preben, Gen. Mgr.--Forbo A/S, Lyngby, Denmark; *Int'l*, pg. 497
Bergmark, J.E., Pres.--Avesta Sandvik Tube AB, Fagersta, Sweden; *Int'l*, pg. 221
Bergren, Paul, Pres.--Air Compressor Group, Davidson, NC; *U.S. Public*, pg. 876
Bergsjo, Mats, Pres.--Albin Komponenter AB, Kristinehamn, Sweden; *Int'l*, pg. 1323
Bergsma, Daniel E., V.P. & Gen. Mgr.--Appleton Wire Div., Albany International, Appleton, WI; *U.S. Public*, pg. 36
Bergstein, Anthonies J.H., Chief Oper. Officer--MassGlas B.V., Tiel, Netherlands; *Int'l*, pg. 85
Bergstein, Jeff, Gen. Mgr.--Arrow/Schweber Electronics, Hauppauge, NY; *U.S. Public*, pg. 133
Bergstein, Melvyn E., Chm. Bd. & Chief Exec. Officer--Diamond Technology Partners, Chicago, IL; *U.S. Public*, pg. 1424
Bergsten, Gunnar, Pres.--Husdjurforsakrings AB Sleipner, Stockholm, Sweden; *Int'l*, pg. 1256
Bergstrom, Gary L., Ph.D., Dr., Pres.--Acadian Asset Management, Boston, MA; *U.S. Public*, pg. 1672
Bergstrom, James D., Pres.--Ragnar Benson, Inc., Park Ridge, IL; *U.S. Private*, pg. 99
Bergstrom, Jan-Eric, Pres.--Perstorp Surface Materials, Perstorp, Sweden; *Int'l*, pg. 1038
Bergstrom, Lars, Pres.--Dynapac Light Equipment AB, Ljungby, Sweden; *Int'l*, pg. 1420
Bergstrom, Robert, Pres.--Real Decisions Corp., Stamford, CT; *U.S. Public*, pg. 395
Bergstrom, Rolf, Chief Oper. Officer--Perstorp Flooring AB, Trelleborg, Sweden; *Int'l*, pg. 1039
Bergstrom, Ulf, Pres.--NCC Linkoping, Linkoping, Sweden; *Int'l*, pg. 899
Berk, James G., Pres.--Hard Rock Cafe International Inc., Wilmington, DE; *Int'l*, pg. 1087
Berkedal, Thomas R., Mgr.--Piper Jaffray Inc., La Crosse, WI; *U.S. Public*, pg. 1302
Berkeley, D.J., Chm. Bd. & Mng. Dir.--Standard Bank (Jersey) Limited, Saint Helier, United Kingdom; *Int'l*, pg. 1294
Berkenbosch, J., Mng. Dir.--Koninklijke De Ruyter BV, Baarn, Netherlands; *Int'l*, pg. 244
Berkley, Gary, Pres. & Publr.--Belleville News-Democrat, Belleville, IL; *U.S. Public*, pg. 964
Berkley, William R., Chm. Bd.--Midwest Employer's Casualty Company, Maryland Heights, MO; *U.S. Public*, pg. 215
Berkoben, Russell C., V.P. & Gen. Mgr.--Owens-Brockway Plastic Containers, Toledo, OH; *U.S. Public*, pg. 1238
Berkow, Miles, Chief Fin. Officer--Victaulic International, Easton, PA; *U.S. Private*, pg. 1138
Berkson, E.J., Pres.--Locust Street Securities, Inc., Des Moines, IA; *Int'l*, pg. 647
Berkstresser, David M., Gen. Mgr.--Arizona Auto Auction Services, Phoenix, AZ; *U.S. Private*, pg. 282
Berlam, Steve, V.P. & Gen. Mgr.--Elmwood Sensors, Inc., Pawtucket, RI; *Int'l*, pg. 125
Berlek, G., Mng. Dir.--Bondioli & Pavesi GS.M.B.H, Vienna, Austria; *Int'l*, pg. 201
Berlekamp, Elwyn R., Pres.--Kodak Berkeley Research, Berkeley, CA; *U.S. Public*, pg. 555
Berlin, Charles L., Pres.--Old Kent Bank of Gaylord, Gaylord, MI; *U.S. Public*, pg. 1217
Berlin, Gunter, Pres.--Signode Europa, Dinslaken, Germany; *U.S. Public*, pg. 869
Berlin, Marvin, Pres.--New York Carpet World, Dalton, GA; *U.S. Public*, pg. 1464
Berlind, Jeffrey P., Publr.--Restaurant Business, New York, NY; *Int'l*, pg. 1446
Berlis, Douglas A., Chm. Bd.--Philips Canada Ltd., Scarborough, Canada; *Int'l*, pg. 1055
Berman, Eileen, V.P. & Mng. Exec.--Northern Trust Bank of Florida, N.A., Palm Beach, FL; *U.S. Public*, pg. 1196
Berman, Knight, Exec. V.P.--Willis Corroon Corp. of Birmingham, Montgomery, AL; *Int'l*, pg. 1505
Berman, Walter S., Chm. Bd.--American Express Credit Corporation, Wilmington, DE; *U.S. Public*, pg. 74
Bermosk, Greg, V.P.-Sls.--SOCO-Lynch Corp., Los Angeles, CA; *Int'l*, pg. 1458
Bernadet, Hubert, Fin. Dir.--Michael Conrad & Leo Burnett GmbH, Frankfurt/Main, Germany; *U.S. Private*, pg. 184
Bernadi, Raymond, Gen. Mgr.--Hallmark Cards Iberica, S.A., Barcelona, Spain; *U.S. Private*, pg. 496
Bernal, Alejandro, Mgr.-Northern Reg.--Medtronic, S. de R.L. de C.V., Mexico, Mexico; *U.S. Public*, pg. 1084
Bernal, Ronald, Pres.--MIPS Technologies, Inc., Mountain View, CA; *U.S. Public*, pg. 1473
Bernard, Alain, Chief Oper. Officer--Ted Cook Tours Islands in the Sun, Costa Mesa, CA; *Int'l*, pg. 21
Bernard, Jon, Sr. V.P.--Air Conditioning Co., Inc., San Carlos, CA; *U.S. Private*, pg. 28
Bernard, Rob, Pres.--Limited Stores, Columbus, OH; *U.S. Public*, pg. 996
Bernardi, Richard, Mgr.--Bernardi Italian Foods, Toluca, IL; *U.S. Private*, pg. 1182
Bernasconi, Leo, Pres.--Tufira S.r.l., Milan, Italy; *Int'l*, pg. 490
Bernatz, Gerald, Mng. Dir.--World Import Co., Saint Louis, MO; *U.S. Private*, pg. 1089
Berndt, Wolfgang C., Pres.--Millstone Coffee, Inc., Everett, WA; *U.S. Public*, pg. 1331
Berneiser, L., Chief Exec. Officer--THORN-Europe, Bad Homburg, Germany; *Int'l*, pg. 1386
Bernhard, Barney, Pres.--Reed MIDEM Organisation Inc., New York, NY; *Int'l*, pg. 1096
Bernhard, David C., V.P. & Gen. Mgr.--Filter Products Division, Richmond, VA; *U.S. Public*, pg. 620
Bernhardt, A.H., Gen. Mgr.--CHEMCENTRAL/Buffalo, Tonawanda, NY; *U.S. Private*, pg. 232
Bernhardt, Andrew B., Pres.--Harris Bank Frankfort, Frankfort, IL; *Int'l*, pg. 154
Bernhed, Ingemar, Mgr.--Network Systems AB, Vasby, Sweden; *U.S. Public*, pg. 1522
Bernicke, Thomas, Plant Mgr.--Presto Products Manufacturing Co., Alamogordo, NM; *U.S. Public*, pg. 1159
Bernier, Pierre, V.P. & Gen. Mgr.--Farinon Canada Ltd., Dorval, Canada; *U.S. Public*, pg. 791
Bernique, Michael, Pres.--Satellite Data Networks, San Diego, CA; *U.S. Public*, pg. 716
Bernmo, Curt, Pres.--Componenta Vagstal AB, Hagfors, Sweden; *Int'l*, pg. 1421
Bernois, Jean-Luc, Mng. Dir.--Johnson & Johnson Morocco S.A., Casablanca, Morocco; *U.S. Public*, pg. 931
Bernon, Alan J., Pres.--Garelick Farms, Inc., Franklin, MA; *U.S. Public*, pg. 1527
Berns, Ed, Branch Mgr.--Lindenmeyr Munroe, Manchester, NH; *U.S. Private*, pg. 224
Berns, P., Mng. Dir.--Dr. Renger GmbH, Strullendorf, Germany; *U.S. Public*, pg. 1135
Bernstein, Armyan, Chm. Bd.--Beacon Communications, Los Angeles, CA; *U.S. Public*, pg. 138
Bernstein, Ronald, Publisher--Popular Science, New York, NY; *U.S. Public*, pg. 1617
Bernstein, Stephen, Chief Exec. Officer--Miami Heart Institute-South, Miami Beach, FL; *U.S. Public*, pg. 405
Berntson, Bernard R., V.P. & Gen. Mgr.--Thomas Industries Inc., Sheboygan, WI; *U.S. Public*, pg. 1599
Berntssom, Leif, Mng. Dir.--Eldon Elmateriel AB, Nassjo, Sweden; *Int'l*, pg. 436
Berntsson, Sven-Olof, Mng. Dir.--Ancra ABT AB, Vargarda, Sweden; *U.S. Private*, pg. 71
Berntzen, Jan, Mng. Dir.--Eldon A/S, Skare, Norway; *Int'l*, pg. 436
Bero, Ronald A., Pres.--F.W.S.F. Corporation, Milwaukee, WI; *U.S. Public*, pg. 643
Bero, Ronald A., Pres.--Firstar Corporation Illinois, Milwaukee, WI; *U.S. Public*, pg. 643
Bero, Ronald A., Pres.--Firstar Corporation Arizona, Milwaukee, WI; *U.S. Public*, pg. 643
Berouard, Gilles, Chief Exec. Officer--EURO RSCG, Praha, Prague, Czech Republic; *Int'l*, pg. 602
Berray, William J., Mgr.--Condon TV Systems, Inc., Condon, OR; *U.S. Public*, pg. 1571
Berray, William J., Mgr.--Home Telephone Co., Condon, OR; *U.S. Public*, pg. 1571
Berrill, Kathy, Mgr.--A.O. Smith-Enterprises Ltd., Stratford, Canada; *U.S. Public*, pg. 1477
Berrio, H., Gen. Mgr.--A.H. Robins International, S.A., Bogota, Colombia; *U.S. Public*, pg. 82
Berrio, Hugo Enrique, Gen. Mgr.--Home Products Inc., Cali, Colombia; *U.S. Public*, pg. 81
Berrirer, Alain, Dir.-Radio & TV Programming--RTL Radio Letzebuerg, Luxembourg, Luxembourg; *Int'l*, pg. 561
Berrisford, R., V.P. & Gen. Mgr.--EFI Corporation, Fremont, CA; *Int'l*, pg. 1082
Berrit, Bob, Mgr.-Plant--Golden Sun Feeds, Inc., Sioux Falls, SD; *U.S. Private*, pg. 895
Berroll, Jean, Mng. Dir.--Beau Marais S.A. (France), Bethune, France; *Int'l*, pg. 850
Berry, Allen D., Gen. Mgr.--Anderson Products, Worcester, MA; *U.S. Private*, pg. 1181
Berry, Ambrose, Gen. Mgr.--H.A. Stiles Co., Westbrook, ME; *U.S. Private*, pg. 968
Berry, Burl, Gen. Mgr.-Container Div.--Mid-Western Nursery Division, Tahlequah, OK; *U.S. Private*, pg. 60
Berry, Charles, Plant Mgr.--Retail Bag Division - Yulee Plant, Yulee, FL; *U.S. Public*, pg. 1521
Berry, David J., Pres.--Bank of America Texas, Dallas, TX; *U.S. Public*, pg. 180
Berry, Dennis, Pres. & Chief Exec. Officer--Manheim Auctions, Inc., Atlanta, GA; *U.S. Private*, pg. 282
Berry, Eugene, Pres.--Chase Bank of Florida, N.A., Tampa, FL; *U.S. Public*, pg. 338
Berry, Glenn, Mng. Dir.--AlliedSignal Laminate Systems GmbH, Wipperfurth, Germany; *U.S. Public*, pg. 53
Berry, Gordon, Mgr.--Midland Seaboard Printing Ink, Inc., Warminster, PA; *Int'l*, pg. 1311
Berry, J., Chief Oper. Officer--Hill Samuel International Banking Corp., New York, NY; *Int'l*, pg. 813
Berry, K., Chm. & Chief Exec. Officer--Virgin Music Group, London, United Kingdom; *Int'l*, pg. 427
Berry, L. Wilson, Jr., V.P.--TRMI Holdings Inc., Wilmington, CA; *U.S. Public*, pg. 1583
Berry, L.W., Jr., Pres.--Texaco Refining & Marketing, Inc., Tulsa, OK; *U.S. Public*, pg. 1583
Berry, Lester, Exec. V.P.--Microtek Medical, Inc., Columbus, MS; *U.S. Public*, pg. 914
Berry, Michael J., Pres.--Firetrol Protection Systems, Inc., Salt Lake City, UT; *U.S. Public*, pg. 1795
Berry, Nancy, Vice Chm.--Virgin Records America Inc., Beverly Hills, CA; *Int'l*, pg. 427
Berry, Robert, Pres.--Space Systems/Loral, Inc., Palo Alto, CA; *U.S. Public*, pg. 1014
Berry, Steve, Pres.--Mastercraft Corporation, Winnsboro, IA; *U.S. Private*, pg. 447
Berry, William K., Pres.--Goody Products, Inc., Peachtree City, GA; *U.S. Public*, pg. 1177

Berry, William K., Pres.--Duray, Inc., Kearny, NJ; *U.S. Public*, pg. 1177
Berry, William K., Pres.--Ace Comb Company Inc., Booneville, AR; *U.S. Public*, pg. 1177
Berry, William S., Pres.--Rayonier New Zealand Limited, Auckland, New Zealand; *U.S. Public*, pg. 1363
Berryhill, Douglas, Mgr.--Cap Gemini America (Jacksonville Branch), Jacksonville, FL; *Int'l*, pg. 264
Bersett, Gerald W., Pres.--Metals Segment, East Alton, IL; *U.S. Public*, pg. 1219
Berta, Michael A., Ph.D., Pres. & Chief Exec. Officer--RMS Information Systems, Inc., Lanham, MD; *U.S. Public*, pg. 1425
Berta, Robert W., Jr., Pres. & Chief Oper. Officer--Countrywide Securities Corporation, Pasadena, CA; *U.S. Public*, pg. 453
Bertacchi, Larry, Chm. Bd.--Casa Di Bertacchi, Vineland, NJ; *U.S. Private*, pg. 928
Bertani, A., Chief Exec. Officer--Zurigo Compagnia di Assicurazioni Sulla Vita, Milan, Italy; *Int'l*, pg. 1530
Bertani, A., Chief Exec. Officer--Zurigo Compagnia di Assicurazioni, Milan, Italy; *Int'l*, pg. 1531
Bertelli, Giuliano, Mng. Dir.--Donaldson Italia s.r.l., Ostiglia, Italy; *U.S. Public*, pg. 517
Bertges, Jack, V.P. & Office Mgr.--Creditanstaldt-Bankverein, San Francisco Representative Office, San Francisco, CA; *Int'l*, pg. 347
Berthelet, Lawrence, Mgr.--Saskatchewan Mineral Div., Chaplin, Canada; *Int'l*, pg. 243
Berthelot, Pershing, Mgr.--Stewart Smith Southwest, Inc, Dallas, TX; *Int'l*, pg. 1508
Berthelsen, Bruce, Pres. & Chief Exec. Officer--Willis Corroon Corp. of Georgia, Atlanta, GA; *Int'l*, pg. 1506
Berthelsen, John R., Pres.--Suttle Press, Inc, Waunakee, WI; *U.S. Public*, pg. 1570
Berthelsen, Lee, Pres.--Marc Plaza Corp., Milwaukee, WI; *U.S. Public*, pg. 1044
Berthiaume, J., Gen. Mgr.--Picker International Canada Inc., Brampton, Canada; *Int'l*, pg. 545
Berti, Mario, Dir.--Banca d'America e d'Italia S.p.A. (Milano), Milan, Italy; *Int'l*, pg. 403
Bertilsson, Goran, Gen. Mgr.--Nordic Baumaschinenhandel GmbH, Stralsund, Germany; *Int'l*, pg. 712
Bertin, Pierre, Chief Oper. Officer--Perstorp S.A.-Div. Components France, Bezons, France; *Int'l*, pg. 1040
Bertini, Carlo, Mng. Dir.--RFT S.p.A., Villanova d'Asti, Italy; *Int'l*, pg. 1158
Bertola, Giovanni, Mng. Dir.--Reeves S.p.A., Milan, Italy; *U.S. Private*, pg. 507
Bertolaccini, Francisco Edmir, Chm. & Pres.--Equipamentos Clark Ltda., Valinhos, Brazil; *U.S. Public*, pg. 559
Bertolani, I., Gen. Mgr.--Starlux, Barcelona, Spain; *U.S. Public*, pg. 225
Bertolasi, R., Chief Oper. Officer--TD Electronics, Inc., Loves Park, IL; *U.S. Public*, pg. 1646
Bertolini, Enzo, Pres.--Chr. Hansen Biosystems S.p.A., Vedano al Lambro, Italy; *Int'l*, pg. 289
Bertolucci, Michael D., Pres.--Interface Research Corporation, Kennesaw, GA; *U.S. Public*, pg. 889
Bertoni, Giovanni, Chm.--Berco S.p.A., Copparo, Italy; *Int'l*, pg. 511
Bertram, Dennis A., Div. Mgr.--Amcast Automotive-Fremont Plant, Fremont, IN; *U.S. Public*, pg. 63
Bertrand, Bruno, Gen. Mgr.--Harman France, Paris, France; *U.S. Public*, pg. 787
Bertrand, Didier, Mng. Dir.--Esselte SA, Paris, France; *Int'l*, pg. 461
Bertrand, J., Chief Oper. Officer--Polyfilla SA, La Courneuve, France; *Int'l*, pg. 1501
Bertrand, J.A., Pres.--A.O. Smith Electrical Products Company, Tipp City, OH; *U.S. Public*, pg. 1477
Bertrand, Leo, Gen. Mgr.--Uniboard Division Sayabec, Sayabec, Canada; *Int'l*, pg. 1431
Bertrand, M., Chief Oper. Officer--Foratex Inc., Houston, TX; *Int'l*, pg. 496
Bertrand, Victor, Mng. Dir.--Ancra New Zealand, Auckland, New Zealand; *U.S. Private*, pg. 71
Bertsch, Don, Chief Oper. Officer--Intairdril Ltd., Quito, Ecuador; *U.S. Public*, pg. 1316
Bertsch, K., Mng. Dir.--Butler Newall GmbH, Hattersheim, Germany; *Int'l*, pg. 449
Bertsch, Paul, Exec. V.P.--Primex Plastics Corp., Garfield, NJ; *U.S. Private*, pg. 553
Bertsch, Paul, Chief Opr. Officer--Primex Plastics Corp., Richmond, IN; *U.S. Private*, pg. 553
Bertsch, Paul, Chief Opr. Officer--Primex Plastics Corp., Oakwood, GA; *U.S. Private*, pg. 553
Bertuccioli, Giorgio, Pres.--Bristol Italiana (Sud), S.p.A., Rome, Italy; *U.S. Public*, pg. 255
Berwerger, R., Rep.--Swiss Bank Corporation, Beijing, China; *Int'l*, pg. 1330
Berylston, John G., Pres.--GCC Investments, Inc., Chestnut Hill, MA; *U.S. Public*, pg. 693
Besant, Craig, V.P. & Gen. Mgr.--TMP Worldwide, Inc., Chicago, IL; *U.S. Private*, pg. 1065
Besch, Helmut, Co-Chief Oper. Officer--Saarberg-Fernwaerme GmbH, Saarbruecken, Germany; *Int'l*, pg. 1166
Besch, Helmut, Co-Chief Oper. Officer--GVT Gesellschaft fuer Versorgungstechnik mbH, Saarbruecken, Germany; *Int'l*, pg. 1167
Besenyei, M., Pres.--Repeelacki Sajtyre, Budapest, Hungary; *Int'l*, pg. 201
Beshears, Kim, Mgr.-Opers.--Weatherford Enterra U.S., L.P., Oklahoma City, OK; *U.S. Public*, pg. 1749
Besler, James, Branch Mgr.--Zellerbach Division, Tampa, FL; *U.S. Public*, pg. 1075
Besse, Stephen A., Pres. & Chief Oper. Officer--Dryden & Palmer Company, Branford, CT; *U.S. Private*, pg. 471
Besserud, Roland A., Pres.--Economy Mechanical Industries, Inc., Wheeling, IL; *U.S. Private*, pg. 602
Bessette, Peter A., Mgr.-Branch--Piper Jaffray Inc., Sacramento, CA; *U.S. Public*, pg. 1303
Bessinger, Dan, Pres. & Gen. Mgr.--Black Clawson Converting Machinery Company, Fulton, NY; *U.S. Private*, pg. 147
Besson, Michel L., Pres.--CertainTeed Corporation Foundation, Valley Forge, PA; *Int'l*, pg. 1171
Best, Alan E., Mng. Dir.-Truck Components, Europe--Eaton Limited, Hounslow, United Kingdom; *U.S. Public*, pg. 558
Best, Arthur, Jr., Div. Pres.--Malone & Hyde, Inc.-Goodlettsville, Goodlettsville, TN; *U.S. Public*, pg. 653
Best, David, Dr., Pres.--BESTMED, Inc., New York, NY; *U.S. Public*, pg. 1422
Best, James W, Pres. & Gen. Mgr.--CAE Machinery Ltd., Vancouver, Canada; *Int'l*, pg. 237
Best, Lucius P., Pres. & Treas.--Carftique, Inc., Pulaski, VA; *U.S. Public*, pg. 1342
Best, Raymond M., Pres.--Buchart Horn Inc., York, PA; *U.S. Private*, pg. 830
Bester, Peter, Mng. Dir.--Cadbury Schweppes South Africa Ltd., Johannesburg, South Africa; *Int'l*, pg. 248
Bestgen, Guenter, Chief Exec. Officer & Gen. Mgr.--Lowe & Partners, Frankfurt/Main, Germany; *U.S. Private*, pg. 678
Besting, J., Mng. Dir.--GKN Service GmbH, Rosrath, Germany; *Int'l*, pg. 536
Beswick, Melinda, Chief Exec. Officer--California Hospital Medical Center, Los Angeles, CA; *U.S. Private*, pg. 1118
Beswick, William F., Mng. Dir.--Graham Precision Pumps Ltd., Congleton, United Kingdom; *U.S. Public*, pg. 757
Beswick, William F., Pres.--Graham Vacuum & Heat Transfer Ltd., Congleton,, United Kingdom; *U.S. Public*, pg. 757
Betancourt, Jose Luis, Chief Exec. Officer--Betancourt Barba EURO RSCG, Mexico, Mexico; *Int'l*, pg. 603
Betchaver, Mark, V.P. & Gen. Mgr.--Sethco Division, Hauppauge, NY; *U.S. Public*, pg. 1100
Betcher, Rich, Pres.--Inland Die Casting, Wheeling, IL; *U.S. Private*, pg. 903
Beteo, Dante, Mng. Editor--La Prensa Asociada, Inc., San Mateo, CA; *U.S. Private*, pg. 92
Bethards, Brandon, Pres. & Chief Oper. Officer--Kvaerner Pulping Inc., Charlotte, NC; *Int'l*, pg. 770
Bethea, David, Chief Oper. Officer--General Business Services, Inc., Waco, TX; *U.S. Public*, pg. 538
Bethel, Nancy, V.P. & Gen. Mgr.--Customer Services Division, Seattle, WA; *U.S. Public*, pg. 240
Bethman, Pam, Branch Mgr.--Union-Transport Corporation-Seattle Office, Seattle, WA; *U.S. Private*, pg. 1120
Betke, Bill, Pres.--Revco Scientific, Asheville, NC; *U.S. Public*, pg. 727
Betsch, Harald, Mng. Dir.--SKF Linearsysteme GmbH, Schweinfurt, Germany; *Int'l*, pg. 1159
Betschart, Johann, V.P.-Opers.--Focke & Co., Inc., Whitsett, NC; *Int'l*, pg. 496
Bett, M., Dir.--Telecom Securicor Cellular Radio Limited, Slough, United Kingdom; *Int'l*, pg. 222
Bettacchi, Robert J., Pres.--Grace Construction Products, Cambridge, MA; *U.S. Public*, pg. 755
Bettencourt, Mary, Branch Mgr.--Downey Savings & Loan Association, F.A., Santa Clara, CA; *U.S. Public*, pg. 526
Bettini, Mario, Pres.--Georg Fischer Sloane Inc., Little Rock, AR; *Int'l*, pg. 490
Bettis, F., Mgr.--Lyman, Lyman, SC; *Int'l*, pg. 1222
Betts, Bill, Gen. Mgr.--Citadel Broadcasting Co., Wilkes-Barre, PA; *U.S. Private*, pg. 241
Betts, Derek W., V.P. & Controller--Tolko Manitoba, Inc., The Pas, Canada; *Int'l*, pg. 1395
Betts, John, Gen. Mgr.--Turner Caribe, Inc., Guaynabo, PR; *U.S. Public*, pg. 1646
Betts, Keith S., Trust Mgr.--Canadian Imperial Bank of Commerce Trust Co. (Channel Islands) Ltd., Saint Peter Port, United Kingdom; *Int'l*, pg. 257
Bettwy, Teo, Pres.--Mykotronx, Torrance, CA; *U.S. Public*, pg. 1359
Betz, M., Chief Oper. Officer--Lagera S.a.r.l., Sarreguemines, France; *Int'l*, pg. 1034
Betz, Wes, Mgr.-Sls./Regina--SGI Canada Insurance Services Ltd., Regina, Canada; *Int'l*, pg. 1195
Beuchat, Gerard, Chief Oper. Officer--P. Roch, Ltd., Rolle, Switzerland; *U.S. Public*, pg. 260
Beuchler, Bruce, Pres. & Gen. Mgr.--Richtex Corporation, Columbia, SC; *Int'l*, pg. 699
Beugelsdyk, L.J., Chm. Bd.--AMEV Nederland N.V., Utrecht, Netherlands; *Int'l*, pg. 498
Beumer, Louis A., Mgr.--Vicker Medical Nederlands, Nieuwkoop, Netherlands; *Int'l*, pg. 1467
Beusebroek, Niko, Reg. Pres.--Melitta Nederland B.V., Veenendaal, Netherlands; *Int'l*, pg. 857
Beute, Roger, Pres.--Liberty Dairy, Evart, MI; *U.S. Public*, pg. 490
Beuthin, William E., Gen. Mgr.--Circle Freight International LLC, Muscat, Oman; *U.S. Public*, pg. 372
Bevan, R.L., Mng. Dir.--Black Horse Financial Services Ltd., Chatham, United Kingdom; *Int'l*, pg. 813
Bevec, Theodore, Gen. Mgr.--Ameron Saudi Arabia, Ltd., Dammam, Saudi Arabia; *U.S. Public*, pg. 99
Bever, Charles, Publr.--Suburban Newspaper Group, Cherry Hill, NJ; *U.S. Public*, pg. 700
Beveridge, David, V.P.-Engrng.--Brite Voice Systems, Inc., Wichita, KS; *U.S. Public*, pg. 257
Beverwijk, Joop, Gen. Mgr.--ITT Flygt S.V., Dordrecht, Netherlands; *U.S. Public*, pg. 860
Bevilacqua, Corrado, Mng. Dir.--Mondialcine S.p.A., Milan, Italy; *Int'l*, pg. 170
Bevilacqua, Michael, Pres.--CPC Foodservice Group, Franklin Park, IL; *U.S. Public*, pg. 224
Beville, James J., Pres.--Dielectric Communications, Raymond, ME; *U.S. Public*, pg. 727
Bevins, Thomas P., Mgr.-Opers.--BYRON Valve Facility, Siloam Springs, AR; *U.S. Public*, pg. 1260
Bew, R.E., Chief Exec. Officer--ICI Chemicals & Polymers Ltd., Runcorn, United Kingdom; *Int'l*, pg. 663
Beyer, C., Pres.--C.A. Cigarrera Bigott, Sucs., Caracas, Venezuela; *Int'l*, pg. 111
Beyer, Claus, Mng. Dir.--SMM Spindel AG, Uster, Switzerland; *Int'l*, pg. 1160
Beyer, Trond, Chief Oper. Officer--NIFE A/S, Oslo, Norway; *Int'l*, pg. 54
Beynel, Roland, Mgr.-Area--Ficomet S.A.R.L., Fontenay-sous-Bois, France; *U.S. Private*, pg. 103
Beytout, Jacqueline, Publisher--Les Echos SA, Paris, France; *Int'l*, pg. 1027
Bezecny, Miroslav, Mng. Dir.--Lecotex, Tabor, Czech Republic; *Int'l*, pg. 193
Bezemer, A.W., Chief Exec. Officer--OCE-Nederland B.V., Venlo, Netherlands; *Int'l*, pg. 994
Bezilla, Cindy, Lab Mgr.--Quest Diagnostic-Williamsport, Williamsport, PA; *U.S. Public*, pg. 1352
Bgashira, Ty, Pres.--Belletech Corp., Bellefontaine, OH; *Int'l*, pg. 84
Bhagat, Jai, Pres.--SkyTel Corp., Washington, DC; *U.S. Public*, pg. 1120
Bhah, Prakash, Pres.--VF Factory Outlet Stores, Hempstead, TX; *U.S. Public*, pg. 1702
Bhargava, P., Pres.--Kalyani Sharp India Limited, Sirur, India; *Int'l*, pg. 1229
Bhargava, Vinay K., Country Dir.--The World Bank, Manila, Philippines; *U.S. Private*, pg. 1189
Bhatnagar, A.K., Dr., Gen. Mgr.--R&D Centre, Faridabad, India; *Int'l*, pg. 673
Bhatt, Santosh, Gen. Mgr.--International Polymer Corp., Mojave, CA; *Int'l*, pg. 339
Bhattacharya, Shankar, Mng. Dir.--ITW Signode India Limited, Hyderabad, India; *U.S. Public*, pg. 869
Bhattacharyya, Sanat, Mng. Dir.--ESAB India Ltd., Mumbai, India; *Int'l*, pg. 282
Bhide, Roopa, Dir.-Pub. Rels.--IRI Software, Waltham, MA; *U.S. Public*, pg. 876
Biaggi, Jorge L., Sr. V.P.- Comml. Banking Centers--Commercial Banking Div., Hato Rey, PR; *U.S. Public*, pg. 175
Bial, Leo, Pres.--Solair, Inc., Fort Lauderdale, FL; *U.S. Public*, pg. 187
Bialis, David A., V.P. & Gen. Mgr.--Cox Communications-Oklahoma City, Oklahoma City, OK; *U.S. Public*, pg. 455
Bialon, Dan, Reg. Mgr.--Green Tree Acceptance, Inc., Tampa, FL; *U.S. Public*, pg. 762
Bianchi, Arduino, Mng. Dir.--McCormick de Centro America, S.A., San Salvador, El Salvador; *U.S. Public*, pg. 1067
Bianchi, M., Mng. Dir.--Oldelft Electronic Instruments Srl, Rome, Italy; *Int'l*, pg. 389
Bianchin, Ed, Area Sls. Mgr.-East Canada--Gensym Canada Ltd., Mississauga, Canada; *U.S. Public*, pg. 731
Bianquis, R., Fin. Controller & Mgr.--AEP France S.A.S., Fecamp, France; *U.S. Public*, pg. 5
Biblowitz, Joshua, Pres.--Lady Rose Div., Westbury, NY; *U.S. Private*, pg. 714
Biblowitz, Joshua, Pres.--Lord Bibb Div., Westbury, NY; *U.S. Private*, pg. 714
Biblowitz, Joshua, Pres.--Susan Terry Div., Westbury, NY; *U.S. Private*, pg. 714
Bice, Don C., Pres.--Norstan Communications, Inc., Plymouth, MN; *U.S. Public*, pg. 1192
Bice, Jess, V.P.--Union Seed Co., Nampa, ID; *U.S. Private*, pg. 646
Bich, Bruno, Chm. Bd. & Chief Exec. Officer--BIC Corporation, Milford, CT; *Int'l*, pg. 1273
Bichet, J.J., Mgr.--Antennes Andrew S.A.R.L., Buc, France; *U.S. Public*, pg. 113
Bickford, Tom, Mgr.--Rexam Graphics, Portland, OR; *Int'l*, pg. 1107
Biddinger, John W., Chm. Bd.--ADT Security Systems, Inc., Carmel, IN; *U.S. Public*, pg. 1649
Biddle, Ross, Country Mgr.--Standard Chartered Bank (Taiwan), Taipei, Taiwan; *Int'l*, pg. 1296
Bideau, Michel, Chief Oper. Officer--Chateauneuf-les-Bains S.A., Saint Gervais-d'Auvergne, France; *Int'l*, pg. 918
Bider, Giuliano, Dr., Gen. Mgr.--R.P. Scherer S.p.A., Aprilia, Italy; *U.S. Public*, pg. 1438
Bider, Leslie E., Pres. & Chief Exec. Officer--Warner/Chappell Music Inc., Los Angeles, CA; *U.S. Public*, pg. 1612
Bidiwala, Ashraf, Exec. V.P. & Gen. Mgr.--Habib Bank Ltd., Singapore, Singapore; *Int'l*, pg. 584
Bidlack, Robin, Mgr.-Branch--Atlantic Lumber Company, Waverly, NY; *U.S. Private*, pg. 959
Bidrawn, Sam, Gen. Mgr.--Northwestern Flavors Inc., West Chicago, IL; *U.S. Public*, pg. 1781
Bidstrup, T. A., Mng. Dir.--MSA (Australia) Pty. Ltd., Sydney, Australia; *U.S. Public*, pg. 1114
Bidwell, Mike, Pres.--Rainbow International Carpet Dyeing & Cleaning Co., Waco, TX; *U.S. Public*, pg. 538
Biebuyck, Albert, Gen. Mgr.--Bank Brussels Lambert, Sede di Milano, Milan, Italy; *Int'l*, pg. 147
Biedermann, Pierre, Chief Oper. Officer--Novo Nordisk Ferment AG, Athens, Greece; *Int'l*, pg. 989
Biedron, Ted, V.P.-Adv. & Promotion--Pioneer Press Newspapers Inc., Glenview, IL; *Int'l*, pg. 632
Bielenberg, Peter, Gen. Mgr.--Bayerische Vereinsbank AG, Athens, Greece; *Int'l*, pg. 180
Bieler, Reinhart, Pres--Sukab Intertrade GesmbH, Vienna, Austria; *Int'l*, pg. 712
Bielke, Dennis, Pres. & Chief Exec. Officer--NationsBank of Belleville, Belleville, IL; *U.S. Public*, pg. 1164
Bieller, U., Dir.--Laporte ESD-Germany, Ladenburg, Germany; *Int'l*, pg. 803
Bielou, Anders, Mgr.--Bentone-Electro Oil AB, Ljungby, Sweden; *Int'l*, pg. 1422
Bielou, Anders, Mgr.--CTC Parca AB, Ljungby, Sweden; *Int'l*, pg. 1422
Bienek, David, Pres.--LASCO Bathware, Anaheim, CA; *Int'l*, pg. 1398
Bienkowski, Detlef, Mng. Dir.--BB-Privat Finanz-Service GmbH, Berlin, Germany; *Int'l*, pg. 159
Bier, Horst H., V.P.-Opers.--Gould Instrument Systems GmbH, Seligenstadt, Germany; *U.S. Public*, pg. 1592
Bierhoff, T., Gen. Mgr.--Kalkzandsteenfabriek Hoogdonk B.V., Liessel, Netherlands; *Int'l*, pg. 1199
Bieri, Robert K., Chief Exec. Officer--Barnett Recovery Corporation, Jacksonville, FL; *U.S. Public*, pg. 1162

Biermann, Frank J., Pres.--Dynecol, Inc., Detroit, MI; *U.S. Private*, pg. 828

Biermann, Syl, Gen. Mgr.--RS Electronics, Maryland Heights, MO; *U.S. Private*, pg. 905

Bierre, Francois, Mng. Dir.--Sodra France SA, Rueil-Malmaison, France; *Int'l*, pg. 1276

Bierschenck, Burkhard, Mng. Dir.--Werk-Verlag, Grafelfing, Germany; *Int'l*, pg. 1099

Bieschuval, Sherry, Mgr.--Turner Bit Services, Odessa, TX; *U.S. Private*, pg. 1134

Biesmans, Stephanie, Dir.--Generale Bank - Breda, Breda, Netherlands; *Int'l*, pg. 547

Biffignani, Glenn, Pres.--United Leasing, Inc., Fenton, MO; *U.S. Private*, pg. 1117

Bifulk, Phillip J., Pres.--Merrill/Seattle, Seattle, WA; *U.S. Public*, pg. 1097

Bigay, Jean-Francois, Dir.--Eurocopter Holding S.A., Paris, France; *Int'l*, pg. 29

Biget, J.P., Chief Exec. Officer--Hellermann France SA, Trappes, France; *Int'l*, pg. 209

Bigford, Andrew, Editor--SKI, New York, NY; *U.S. Public*, pg. 1617

Biggar, James M., Pres. & Chief Exec. Officer--Nestle Holdings, Inc., Stamford, CT; *Int'l*, pg. 916

Biggemann, Rainer, Exec. V.P.--Associated Fuel Pump Systems Corp., Anderson, SC; *Int'l*, pg. 205

Bigger, Daniele, Chm.--Coop Graubunden-Sarganserland, Chur, Switzerland; *Int'l*, pg. 329

Bigger, Danielle, Chm.--Coop Ticino, Saint Antonino, Switzerland; *Int'l*, pg. 329

Biggerstaff, Bobby G., Chm. Bd.--Key Risk Management Services, Inc., Greensboro, NC; *U.S. Public*, pg. 216

Biggerstaff, Theresa, V.P.--Vision-Ease Lens, Brooklyn Center, MN; *U.S. Public*, pg. 162

Biggins, K. W., Mng. Dir.--Rank Film Laboratories Limited, Uxbridge, United Kingdom; *Int'l*, pg. 1087

Biggins, William, Pres.--The Family Insurance Agency, Inc., Watervliet, NY; *U.S. Private*, pg. 1106

Biggott, Don, Supervisor-Property & Casualty--Willis Corroon Administrative Services Corporation, Lake Geneva, WI; *Int'l*, pg. 1505

Biggs, John E., III, Mgr.--Scott & Stringfellow, Inc., Bluefield, WV; *U.S. Public*, pg. 1446

Bigler, Gary W., Pres.--First American Bank, International Falls, MN; *U.S. Private*, pg. 167

Bigwood, Peter, Gen. Mgr.--Atlas Copco Berema, Inc., Holyoke, MA; *Int'l*, pg. 96

Bihler, Jurgen, Mng. Dir.--Iggesund Verkaufsgesellschaft G.m.b.H, Hamburg, Germany; *Int'l*, pg. 886

Bijou, Thomas, Pres.--Advanced Telemarketing Corp., Irving, TX; *U.S. Public*, pg. 11

Bijvoets, V.L., Mng. Dir.--Nedlloyd Lines B.V., Rotterdam, Netherlands; *Int'l*, pg. 1145

Bik, A.Y., Dir.--Intervam B.V., Rijswijk, Netherlands; *Int'l*, pg. 630

Bilde, Jesper, Gen. Mgr.--AMETEK Denmark, Allerod, Denmark; *U.S. Public*, pg. 100

Bilger, Pierre, Chm. & Chief Oper. Officer--GEC Alsthom, Paris, France; *Int'l*, pg. 52

Bilicke, Dan, Pres.--Crossfield Chemical, Joliet, IL; *Int'l*, pg. 1435

Biliotti, Maurizio, Gen. Mgr.--Gestione Fondi Investimento Milano SpA, Milan, Italy; *Int'l*, pg. 137

Bill, W. J., Area Mgr.--Hawks Nest Mine, Tea Gardens, Australia; *Int'l*, pg. 224

Billarreal, Carlos, Gen. Mgr.--Duro Paper Bag Mfg. Co., Brownsville, TX; *U.S. Private*, pg. 349

Billeter, Ernst, Mng. Dir.--Sulzer Electronics Ltd., Winterthur, Switzerland; *Int'l*, pg. 1305

Billeter, H.A., Pres. & Chief Exec. Officer--Johnny Appleseed's, Inc., Beverly, MA; *U.S. Private*, pg. 590

Billiard, Phillipe, Dir.--Van Leer France S.A.R.L., Le Grand-Quevilly, France; *Int'l*, pg. 1147

Billing, Grant D., Pres. & Chief Exec. Officer--Norcen Energy Resources Limited, Calgary, Canada; *Int'l*, pg. 434

Billing, Jan, Mgr.--Duni AB-Finess Forsaljning, Klippan, Sweden; *Int'l*, pg. 421

Billing, Thomas, Mgr.--J.D. Stenquist AB, Kuidinge, Sweden; *Int'l*, pg. 421

Billingsley, R.W., Chm. Bd.--Olin Canada Inc., Mississauga, Canada; *U.S. Public*, pg. 1220

Billman, Raphael, Mgr.--Grand Prairie Co-op, Inc., Savoy, IL; *U.S. Private*, pg. 469

Billman, Thomas E., Mgr.--Grand Prairie Co-op, Inc., Saint Joseph, IL; *U.S. Private*, pg. 469

Billoni, Michael, V.P. & Gen. Mgr.--Bison Baseball Inc., Buffalo, NY; *U.S. Private*, pg. 928

Billot, Thierry, Chief Oper. Officer--Pernod, Creteil, France; *Int'l*, pg. 566

Bilodeau, Marc, Chief Oper. Officer--Aeroservices J.T. Inc., Mirabel, Canada; *U.S. Public*, pg. 845

Bilodeau, Paul, Pres. & Gen. Mgr.--Wyeth Ltd., North York, Canada; *U.S. Public*, pg. 82

bin Abdul Kadir, Kamaludin, Mng. Dir.--Perwira Ericsson Sdn. Bhd., Shah Alam, Malaysia; *Int'l*, pg. 1369

Bin Ahmad, Haji Yahaya, Pres.--Automotive Manufacturers (Malaysia) Sdn. Bhd., Pekan, Malaysia; *Int'l*, pg. 692

bin Dato Mokhtar, Mohd Haneed, Dr., Mng. Dir.--Electroscon Network Engineering Sdn. Bhd., Petaling Jaya, Malaysia; *Int'l*, pg. 1366

bin Kosnan, Ahmad, Dir.--MTPB - Southern Region, Johor Baharu, Malaysia; *Int'l*, pg. 833

Bin Mohd Ali, Mohd Yusoff, Chief Oper. Officer--Ke-Zan Securities Sdn Bhd, Penang, Malaysia; *Int'l*, pg. 733

bin Osman, Idris, Dir.--MTPB - Sarawak Region, Kuching, Malaysia; *Int'l*, pg. 833

bin Yusof, Taha, Dir.--Tourism Malaysia - Bangkok Office, Bangkok, Thailand; *Int'l*, pg. 833

bin Zainal, Mohd Razaleigh, Dir.--Tourism Malaysia - Osaka Office, Osaka, Japan; *Int'l*, pg. 833

Binau, Tori, Mngmt. Supvr.--Fahlgren, Charlotte, NC; *U.S. Private*, pg. 391

Binch, Stuart, Mng. Dir.--Syntron Europe Limited, Alfreton, United Kingdom; *U.S. Public*, pg. 1563

Bindel, Edward, Pres.--MiniData Services, Inc., Pine Brook, NJ; *U.S. Public*, pg. 331

Binder, Christian, Chief Oper. Officer--Steno Diabetes Center, Gentofte, Denmark; *Int'l*, pg. 987

Binder, Hans-Peter, Dr., Sr. Mng. Dir.--Deutsche Bank AG (Munich), Munich, Germany; *Int'l*, pg. 402

Binder, Heinrich, Dr., Chm. Bd.--Pieburg AG, Neckarsulm, Germany; *Int'l*, pg. 1108

Binderup, Torben, Pres.--Astra Danmark A/S, Albertslund, Denmark; *Int'l*, pg. 93

Bineider, E., Chief Fin. Officer--ATCO Structures Inc., Calgary, Canada; *Int'l*, pg. 95

Bingel, James W., Pres.--Delevan Div., East Aurora, NY; *U.S. Public*, pg. 90

Bingel, James W., Pres.--Surface Mounted Devices Division, Arcade, NY; *U.S. Public*, pg. 90

Bingham, J. Peter, Dr., Pres.--Philips Laboratories, Briarcliff Manor, NY; *Int'l*, pg. 1054

Bingham, Nicholas, Pres.--Columbia Tri-Star International Television, Culver City, CA; *Int'l*, pg. 1281

Bingham, Ray, Mng. Dir.--Mather & Platt (Ireland) Limited, Dublin, Ireland; *U.S. Public*, pg. 1650

Bingham, Rodney, Mng. Dir.--Thermon Heat Tracing Services, Inc. I, Houston, TX; *U.S. Private*, pg. 1080

Bingler, Doug, Gen. Mgr.--Water Technologies Group, Seneca Falls, NY; *U.S. Public*, pg. 861

Binkley, Bruce, Mgr.-WHR Opers.--Tulsa Manufacturing Plant, Tulsa, OK; *U.S. Private*, pg. 1180

Binkley, Chris, Sr. V.P.--Kaiser Permanente, Southeast Division, Atlanta, GA; *U.S. Private*, pg. 605

Binks, Simon, Chief Oper. Officer--Neste Exploration Ltd., London, United Kingdom; *Int'l*, pg. 915

Binmore, A.C., Chief Oper. Officer--Russell Castings Ltd., Leicester, United Kingdom; *Int'l*, pg. 449

Binnie, G., Pres.--Baycoat, Hamilton, Canada; *Int'l*, pg. 414

Binnix, Steve M., Gen. Mgr.--RTI Electronics Inc., Anaheim, CA; *U.S. Public*, pg. 1455

Binns, M., Mng. Dir.--The Fletcher Construction Company Limited, Penrose, New Zealand; *Int'l*, pg. 495

Binswanger, David R., Pres.--Binswanger Advisory Group, Philadelphia, PA; *U.S. Private*, pg. 144

Biondi, Frank J., Jr., Chm. Bd. & Chief Exec. Officer--Universal Studios, Inc., Universal City, CA; *Int'l*, pg. 1215

Biosca, Fernando Vela, Pres.--INITEC - E.N. de Ingenieria y Tecnologia, S.A., Madrid, Spain; *Int'l*, pg. 1225

Birch, Kjeld, Chief Oper. Officer--Novo Nordisk Farmaka Danmark A/S, Bagsvaerd, Denmark; *Int'l*, pg. 987

Birch, N.J., Chief Oper. Officer--National-Standard Co. Ltd., Kidderminster, United Kingdom; *U.S. Public*, pg. 1161

Birch, Viggo L., Chief Oper. Officer--Novo Nordisk Pharma S.A., Madrid, Spain; *Int'l*, pg. 988

Birchenough, A.J., Vice Chm.--AGRA Monenco, Oakville, Canada; *Int'l*, pg. 30

Birchfield, John, Reg. Mgr.--Green Tree Acceptance, Inc., Topeka, KS; *U.S. Public*, pg. 762

Bird, Anita, Editor--Illinois Star-Courier, Kewanee, IL; *U.S. Public*, pg. 983

Bird, James E., Pres.--Unisource, Omaha, NE; *U.S. Public*, pg. 1671

Bird, R.A., Mng. Dir.--Barclays Bank of Kenya Ltd., Nairobi, Kenya; *Int'l*, pg. 165

Bird, Robert H., Pres.--Blue Chip Stamps, Los Angeles, CA; *U.S. Public*, pg. 217

Bird, Tim, Pres.--Integrated Information Services Inc., Carmel, IN; *U.S. Private*, pg. 860

Birdwell, Donald W., Pres.--SunGard Asset Management Systems, Birmingham, AL; *U.S. Public*, pg. 1535

Bires, Beverly, Mgr.-Export--Courtaulds Aerospace, Glendale, CA; *Int'l*, pg. 339

Birigt, Holger U., Dir.-Continental European Opers.--Kellogg's Produits Alimentaires, S.A., Rosny-sous-Bois, France; *U.S. Public*, pg. 948

Biringer, Robert, Sr. V.P.--Creditanstalt-Bankverein, Atlanta Representative Office, Atlanta, GA; *Int'l*, pg. 347

Birk, Tim, Pres.--Electronic Transaction Corporation, Seattle, WA; *U.S. Public*, pg. 498

Birkenbeck, Heinz, Chief Oper. Officer--Akerlund & Rausing Verpackung GmbH, Hochheim, Germany; *Int'l*, pg. 33

Birkett, J.N., Dir. & Gen. Mgr.--Lloyds Bank Trust Company (Channel Islands) Limited, Saint Helier, United Kingdom; *Int'l*, pg. 813

Biro-Belane, Gabrielle, Mng. Dir.--ISS Servisystem Kft., Budapest, Hungary; *Int'l*, pg. 657

Biron, Francois, Mgr.--Barrick Gold, Rouyn-Noranda, Canada; *Int'l*, pg. 169

Birrell, Kenneth Raymond, Reg. Dir.--Sime Darby Australia Limited, Perth, Australia; *Int'l*, pg. 1251

Birrell, N., Dr., Chief Exec.--County NatWest Australia Investment, Melbourne, Australia; *Int'l*, pg. 911

Birsa, Rick, Gen. Mgr.--Tru-Space, Bowling Green, OH; *U.S. Private*, pg. 1080

Birtwistle, D., Dir.--LucasVarity plc, Solihull, United Kingdom; *Int'l*, pg. 819

Bisang, Frank, Pres. & Chief Exec. Officer--Garnac Grain Co., Inc., Overland Park, KS; *U.S. Private*, pg. 802

Bisasky, Louis W., Pres. & Chief Oper. Officer--Schlumberger Malco Inc., Owings Mills, MD; *Int'l*, pg. 1206

Bischaf, Heinz, Mktg. Mgr.--AlliedSignal Truck Brake Systems, Stuttgart, Germany; *U.S. Public*, pg. 54

Bischoff, E.A., Export Mgr.--Coe Manufacturing Co, Painesville, OH; *U.S. Private*, pg. 249

Bischoff, E.A., Gen. Mgr.--United States Wallboard Machinery, Painesville, OH; *U.S. Private*, pg. 249

Bischoff, Manfred, Chief Exec.--Daimler-Benz Aerospace AG, Bremen, Germany; *Int'l*, pg. 367

Bischoff, Manfred, Dr., Chm. Bd.--Daimler-Benz Aerospace AG, Munich, Germany; *Int'l*, pg. 367

Bischoff, William, Mgr.-Office--Woodward-Clyde, San Jose, CA; *U.S. Public*, pg. 1657

Bischwiller, Francis, Gen. Mgr.--Forbo Participations SA, Surbourg, France; *Int'l*, pg. 498

Biscotti, Robert V., Gen. Mgr.--Willing B Wire Corporation, Willingboro, NJ; *U.S. Public*, pg. 780

Bishko, Roy Colin, Pres.--Tie Rack (Canada) Limited, Markham, Canada; *Int'l*, pg. 1389

Bishoff, Mark, Pres.--Farmers Union Co-Operative Insurance Company of Nebraska, Omaha, NE; *U.S. Private*, pg. 395

Bishog, John H., Pres.--IBM Korea, Inc., Seoul, Korea; *U.S. Public*, pg. 897

Bishop, Cam, Sr. V.P.--Intertec Publishing, Overland Park, KS; *U.S. Public*, pg. 1327

Bishop, Darrel, Mgr.--Furman Wholesale Lumber Branch, Dallas, TX; *U.S. Private*, pg. 431

Bishop, Dave, Plant Mgr.--Sealy Mattress Company - Portland, Portland, OR; *U.S. Private*, pg. 979

Bishop, Del, Pres.--SDL Construction, Bellevue, WA; *U.S. Private*, pg. 719

Bishop, Del A., Pres.--R.R. Donnelley Far East Limited, Singapore, Singapore; *U.S. Public*, pg. 519

Bishop, Dennis, Pres. & Gen. Mgr.--Stanley Hydraulic Tools Div., Milwaukie, OR; *U.S. Public*, pg. 1509

Bishop, Dennis, Mgr.-Opers.--Woodward-Clyde International, North Point, Hong Kong; *U.S. Public*, pg. 1658

Bishop, Eugene D., II, V.P.--Citrus State Development Corp., West Covina, CA; *U.S. Public*, pg. 294

Bishop, Eugene D., II, V.P.--Granada Realty Services, Inc., West Covina, CA; *U.S. Public*, pg. 294

Bishop, Jamie, V.P.--Bader Rutter & Assoc. Inc., Lincoln, NE; *U.S. Private*, pg. 110

Bishop, Ken, Pres.--Matec Instruments, Inc., Northborough, MA; *U.S. Public*, pg. 1056

Bishop, Ken, Pres.--Matec Applied Sciences, Inc., Hopkinton, MA; *U.S. Public*, pg. 1056

Bishop, Larry, Mgr.--Farm Store No. 1, Meridian, ID; *U.S. Private*, pg. 1039

Bishop, Leland B., II, Pres.--American Overseas Marine Corp., Quincy, MA; *U.S. Public*, pg. 709

Bishop, Mark, Gen. Mgr.--Tennant Maintenance Systems, Limited, East Molesey, United Kingdom; *U.S. Public*, pg. 1577

Bishop, R. Gary, Pres.--CB & T Bank of Middle Georgia, Warner Robins, GA; *U.S. Public*, pg. 1549

Bishop, Robert, Pres.-SGI Intl.--Silicon Graphics S.A. Intl., Geneva, Switzerland; *U.S. Public*, pg. 1474

Bishop, Robert D., Chm. & Pres.--SunTrust Bank, Northeast Georgia, N.A., Athens, GA; *U.S. Public*, pg. 1538

Bishop, Roger F., Mng. Dir.--John Crane Asia Pacific, Singapore, Singapore; *Int'l*, pg. 1339

Bishop, Ros, Gen. Mgr.--Polaroid (UK) Ltd., Saint Albans, United Kingdom; *U.S. Public*, pg. 1314

Bishop, Thomas A., Gen. Mgr.--Arizona Auction Services, Inc., Chandler, AZ; *U.S. Private*, pg. 282

Bishop, William S., Pres.--Chrysler Capital Corp., Stamford, CT; *U.S. Public*, pg. 354

Bishovsky, Robert, Pres.--Diosynth, Inc., Chicago, IL; *Int'l*, pg. 48

Biskner, Charles, V.P. & Gen. Mgr.--U.S. Filter Co., Ames, Ames, IA; *U.S. Public*, pg. 61

Bisogni, Adriano, Sr. V.P. & Mgr.--Banca Commerciale Italiana, New York, NY; *Int'l*, pg. 652

Bissara, Giovanni Biego di Costa, Pres.--Cinestella S.p.A., Milan, Italy; *Int'l*, pg. 170

Bissara, Giovanni Biego di Costa, Mng. Dir.--Titanus Distribuzione S.p.A., Milan, Italy; *Int'l*, pg. 170

Bissell, J.R., Pres.--Venturi Inc., Traverse City, MI; *U.S. Private*, pg. 1136

Bissell, John M., Pres.--Atlas Tag & Label Inc., Neenah, WI; *U.S. Private*, pg. 145

Bissell, Robin, Pres. & Chief Oper. Officer--Esskay, Riderwood, MD; *U.S. Public*, pg. 1479

Bisser, Ben, Chief Fin. Officer & V.P.-Fin.--Tomkins Industries Inc., Dayton, OH; *Int'l*, pg. 1397

Bissett, Ian, Dir.--Bissett & Rogers, Nairobi, Kenya; *Int'l*, pg. 1502

Bissinger, Peter, V.P. & Gen. Mgr.--ASF Thomas, Puchheim, Germany; *U.S. Public*, pg. 1599

Bisson, William T., V.P. & Publisher--Pensions & Investments, Chicago, IL; *U.S. Private*, pg. 285

Biswell, Stephen, Pres.--Nash DeCamp Company, Visalia, CA; *U.S. Public*, pg. 1152

Bitensky, Samson, Chm. Bd.--Fab Recreational Division, New York, NY; *U.S. Public*, pg. 603

Bither, Richard A., PE, Pres.--Giffels Technologies, Inc., Southfield, MI; *U.S. Private*, pg. 452

Bither, Richard A., PE, Chief Exec. Officer--Giffels Strategic Consultants, L.L.C., Southfield, MI; *U.S. Private*, pg. 452

Bitler, Harold P., Pres.--Preferred Surety Corporation, Madison, GA; *U.S. Public*, pg. 1538

Bitner, Georges, Chief Rep.--ORIX Europe Limited-Paris Liaison Office, Paris, France; *Int'l*, pg. 1009

Bito, Saburo, Pres.--Toyota Auto Body Co., Ltd., Kariya City, Japan; *Int'l*, pg. 1412

Bitou, Mineo, Mng. Dir.--The Nikko Securities (Australia) Ltd., Sydney, Australia; *Int'l*, pg. 931

Bitterman, Robert, Pres.--Dermik Laboratories, Inc., Collegeville, PA; *Int'l*, pg. 1110

Bittman, Bob, Pres.--IGT North America, Reno, NV; *U.S. Public*, pg. 900

Bittner, Gary W., Pres. & Chief Oper. Officer--Richfood, Inc., Mechanicsville, VA; *U.S. Public*, pg. 1389

Bittner, Thomas, Pres. & Chief Exec. Officer--Polychrome Corp. Div., Fort Lee, NJ; *Int'l*, pg. 370

Bitton, A., Gen. Mgr.--Bank Leumi Le-Israel B.M., Panama, Panama; *Int'l*, pg. 150

Bitzer, Rainer, Chief Oper. Officer--Berlimed-Productos Quimicos Farmaceulicos e Biologicos Ltda., Sao Paulo, Brazil; *Int'l*, pg. 1204

Biver, Jean-Claude, Mng. Dir.--Blancpain S.A., Le Brassus, Switzerland; *Int'l*, pg. 1160

Bivins, Lem, Gen. Mgr.--Barton's of Manila, Manila, AR; *U.S. Private*, pg. 119

Bixby, Edward K., Pres.--General Mills, Consumer Foods Sales Div., Minneapolis, MN; *U.S. Public*, pg. 718

Bixby, Edward K., Pres.--General Mills Sales, Inc., Minneapolis, MN; *U.S. Public*, pg. 718

Bixby, Walter E., Chm. Bd.--Sunset Life Insurance Co. of America, Olympia, WA; *U.S. Public*, pg. 943

Bixby, Walter E., Chm. Bd. & Chief Exec. Officer--Old American Insurance Co., Kansas City, MO; *U.S. Public*, pg. 943

Bjareholt, Sture, Div. Mgr.--Munskjoe Paper AB, Jonkoping, Sweden; *Int'l*, pg. 1423

Bjars, Ake, Mgr.--Fasson Tarra Oy, Helsinki, Finland; *U.S. Public*, pg. 154

Bjelica, Milos, Company Head--SKF Maktrade d.o.o., Kavadarci, Macedonia; *Int'l*, pg. 1159

Bjelkelov, Sten, Chief Oper. Officer--AxTrade East Asia Ltd., Stockholm, Sweden; *Int'l*, pg. 708

Bjelland, Ludolf, Chief Oper. Officer--Alfa-Laval Agri Scandinavia A/S, Ski, Norway; *Int'l*, pg. 1377

Bjerkestan, Leif, Gen. Mgr.--S.C. Johnson, Skytta, Norway; *U.S. Private*, pg. 593

Bjernfalk, Bengt, Chm.--ITT Flygt Corporation, Trumbull, CT; *U.S. Public*, pg. 860

Bjerrum, C. A., Chief Exec. Officer--Sea Containers Asia Ltd., Hong Kong, Hong Kong; *Int'l*, pg. 1214

Bjertnes, Henning, Pres.--Interconsult Norge A/S, Skarnes, Norway; *Int'l*, pg. 1420

Bjokdahl, Per, Chief Oper. Officer--TAC Control Pte. Ltd., Singapore, Singapore; *Int'l*, pg. 670

Bjorck, Erik, Pres.--ABB Hafo AB, Jarfalla, Sweden; *Int'l*, pg. 7

Bjorgan, Jon Erling, Chief Oper. Officer--Kvaerner Prosjekt a.s., Oslo, Norway; *Int'l*, pg. 769

Bjork, Claes, Pres.--Skanska (U.S.A.) Inc., Greenwich, CT; *Int'l*, pg. 1261

Bjork, Kjell, Mng. Dir.--Compania Anonima Ericsson, Caracas, Venezuela; *Int'l*, pg. 1365

Bjorklund, Elisabet Salander, Mng. Dir.--Stora Timber AB, Falun, Sweden; *Int'l*, pg. 1303

Bjorklund, Hakan, Pres.--Astra Lakemedal AB, Sodertalje, Sweden; *Int'l*, pg. 93

Bjorklund, Hakan, Mng. Dlr.--Sodra Timber AB, Roskilde, Denmark; *Int'l*, pg. 1276

Bjorklund, Willy, Mgr.--Ampex Europa GMBH, Sulzbach, Germany; *U.S. Public*, pg. 104

Bjorkman, Nils, Pres.--Tetra Laval Food, Lund, Sweden; *Int'l*, pg. 1378

Bjorkman, P., Mng. Dir.--Balzers Sandvik Coating AB, Stockholm, Sweden; *Int'l*, pg. 997

Bjorkmann, Inge, Mgr.--BSD Teknik, Malmo, Sweden; *U.S. Private*, pg. 361

Bjorkstrand, Randy, Plant Mgr.--Advance Circuits, Commercial Div. Plant, Hopkins, MN; *Int'l*, pg. 713

Bjorn, Anne, Gen. Mgr.--Kvaernerkonsernets Pensjonskasse, Oslo, Norway; *Int'l*, pg. 770

Bjorn, Lundgren, Exec. V.P.--Ericsson Business Communications, Inc., Anaheim, CA; *Int'l*, pg. 1364

Bjorn, Marjatta, Mng. Dir.--Seppala, Vantaa, Finland; *Int'l*, pg. 1301

Bjorn, Per, Mgr.--Stifab, Jonkoping, Sweden; *Int'l*, pg. 1422

Bjurstroem, Bjoern-Maarten, Gen. Mgr.--Oy Forbo AB, Helsinki, Finland; *Int'l*, pg. 497

Bjurstrom, Dag, Chief Oper. Officer--Axel Johnson Resources AB, Stockholm, Sweden; *Int'l*, pg. 709

Bjurstrom, Olle, Chief Oper. Officer--Advanced Micro Devices AB, Sundbyberg, Sweden; *U.S. Public*, pg. 21

Blabac, Gerald, Administrator--Canterbury Villa of Alliance, Alliance, OH; *U.S. Public*, pg. 838

Blachere, Francois, Pres.--EURO RSCG Gregoire, Blachere, Huard & Roussel, Levallois-Perret, France; *Int'l*, pg. 601

Black, Andrew, Mng. Dir.--Marine Underwriting Agencies (NZ) Ltd. (Cornhill), Wellington, New Zealand; *Int'l*, pg. 60

Black, C. Robert, Chm. & Pres.--Texaco Overseas Holdings Inc., White Plains, NY; *U.S. Public*, pg. 1583

Black, C. Robert, Pres.--Texaco Worldwide Exploration & Production, Scroggins, TX; *U.S. Public*, pg. 1583

Black, Cathleen, Pres.--Hearst Magazines Division, New York, NY; *U.S. Private*, pg. 516

Black, David, V.P.-Synchronous Transport Networks--Newbridge Networks Corporation, Kanata, Canada; *Int'l*, pg. 924

Black, David, Pres.--Silicon Graphics Canada Inc., Mississauga, Canada; *U.S. Public*, pg. 1474

Black, Graham, Mgr.-Mktg. Communications--Case United Kingdom Limited, Doncaster, United Kingdom; *U.S. Public*, pg. 1579

Black, Greg, Gen. Mgr.--Fleming-Potter Webkote, Peoria, IL; *U.S. Private*, pg. 411

Black, J. A., Reg. Mgr.--Thomas De La Rue Ltd., Manama, Bahrain; *Int'l*, pg. 386

Black, Jim, Chief Oper. Officer--Allright Sierra Parking, Inc., Reno, NV; *U.S. Private*, pg. 43

Black, Lloyd, Div. Mgr.--Atlantic Homes Div., Claysburg, PA; *U.S. Public*, pg. 332

Black, R.A., Gen. Mgr.--CHEMCENTRAL/Seattle, Kent, WA; *U.S. Private*, pg. 232

Black, R.B., V.P. & Gen. Mgr.--J.M. Huber, Calcium Carbonate Division, Quincy, IL; *U.S. Private*, pg. 545

Black, Robert C., Pres.--ICI Pharmaceuticals Group, Wilmington, DE; *Int'l*, pg. 664

Black, Stephen F., V.P.--Kimberly-Clark Durafab, Inc., Cleburne, TX; *U.S. Public*, pg. 959

Black, Thomas B., Reg. Chm., Pres. & Chief Exec. Officer--Mellon Bank, N.A.-Northern Region, Erie, PA; *U.S. Public*, pg. 1085

Blackadder, T. S., Chief Oper. Officer--Diamond Power Specialty Ltd., Dumbarton, United Kingdom; *Int'l*, pg. 472

Blackall, Gary, Pres.--BLD Products, Ltd., Holland, MI; *U.S. Public*, pg. 1055

Blackburn, Roland, Mng. Dir.-Europe--Champion Spark Plug Division, Upton, United Kingdom; *U.S. Public*, pg. 445

Blackburn, Stephan P., Pres. & Chief Oper. Officer--United Missouri Bank of St. Louis, Saint Louis, MO; *U.S. Public*, pg. 1655

Blackburn, T., Mng. Dir.--Northern Dairies Ltd., Wakefield, United Kingdom; *Int'l*, pg. 968

Blackburn, Wilson, Pres.--PWA Rolland Decor Inc., Fitchburg, MA; *Int'l*, pg. 274

Blackburn, Wilson, Pres.--Cross Pointe Paper Corporation, Saint Paul, MN; *Int'l*, pg. 434

Blackenhorn, Gunter, Dr., Mng. Dir.--R.P. Scherer GmbH, Baden Baden, Germany; *U.S. Public*, pg. 1438

Blackenhorn, Gunter, Dr., Mng. Dir.--R.P. Scherer GmbH-Werk Strehla, Strehla, Germany; *U.S. Public*, pg. 1438

Blackenhorn, Gunter, Dr., Mng. Dir.--Allcaps Weichgelatinekapseln GmbH, Backnang, Germany; *U.S. Public*, pg. 1438

Blackerby, Larry, V.P. & Gen. Mgr.--WJTV, Jackson, MS; *U.S. Public*, pg. 1078

Blackmon, Philip, Pres.--Quanta Systems Corporation, Gaithersburg, MD; *U.S. Public*, pg. 420

Blackmore, Pattijean, Branch Mgr.--Downey Savings & Loan Association, F.A., San Jose, CA; *U.S. Public*, pg. 527

Blackmore, Ross, Mng. Dir.--Velsicol Australia Limited, Turramurra, Australia; *U.S. Private*, pg. 1135

Blackwell, E. Scott, Pres. & Chief Exec. Officer--eMerge Vision Systems, Sebastian, FL; *U.S. Public*, pg. 1425

Blackwell, Geoffrey, Gen. Mgr.--IMC/A.K. Fans Ltd., London, United Kingdom; *Int'l*, pg. 868

Blackwell, James A., Pres.--Lockheed Aeronautical Systems Company, Marietta, GA; *U.S. Public*, pg. 1007

Blackwell, Larry L., V.P. & Gen. Mgr.--Tesoro Bolivia Petroleum Company, Santa Cruz, Bolivia; *U.S. Public*, pg. 1582

Blackwell, William E., Pres.--Jefferson-Pilot Communications Company, Greensboro, NC; *U.S. Public*, pg. 925

Blackwell, William E., Pres.--Jefferson-Pilot Communications, Charlotte, NC; *U.S. Public*, pg. 925

Blackwell, William E., Pres.--Jefferson-Pilot Communications Co. of Virginia, Richmond, VA; *U.S. Public*, pg. 926

Blackwood, Jason T., Pres.--Physiotherapy Associates, Inc., Kalamazoo, MI; *U.S. Public*, pg. 1526

Blaesing, Janice M., Gen. Mgr.--Neradt Tool & Stamping Company, Elk Grove Village, IL; *U.S. Private*, pg. 269

Blagg, John, Branch Dir.--N.G. Bailey & Co. Ltd.-Bristol Branch, Bristol, United Kingdom; *Int'l*, pg. 132

Blaine, John L., Mng. Dir.--Falconbridge Explorations (Zimbabwe), Bulawayo, Zimbabwe; *Int'l*, pg. 434

Blair, Douglas K., Pres.--Canadian Thermos Products Ltd., Scarborough, Canada; *Int'l*, pg. 938

Blair, Ed A., Pres. & Gen. Mgr.--BHP Petroleum (Americas) Inc., Houston, TX; *Int'l*, pg. 225

Blair, Jack, Pres.--Smith & Nephew North America, Memphis, TN; *Int'l*, pg. 1263

Blair, Jason, Gen. Mgr.--Mebane Plant, Mebane, NC; *U.S. Private*, pg. 1044

Blais, Al, V.P. & Gen. Mgr.--Fuji Industrial Photo Products Div., Elmsford, NY; *Int'l*, pg. 524

Blajfeder, Delcio, Exec. Dir.--BB Securities Ltd., London, United Kingdom; *Int'l*, pg. 142

Blake, D.R., Mgr.--MacMillan Bloedel Limited - Alberni Pacific Div., Port Alberni, Canada; *Int'l*, pg. 828

Blake, David, Mgr.--IBP-Luverne, Luverne, MN; *U.S. Public*, pg. 852

Blake, David T., V.P. & Gen. Mgr.--Hercules Inc., Absorbent & Textile Products Group, Wilmington, DE; *U.S. Public*, pg. 810

Blake, Harry, Pres.--ZD Press, Emeryville, CA; *Int'l*, pg. 1276

Blake, Irvin N., Pres. & Treas.--NationsBank Life Insurance Co., Norfolk, VA; *U.S. Public*, pg. 1164

Blake, Jeffrey, Pres.-Domestic Distr.--Sony Pictures Studios, Culver City, CA; *Int'l*, pg. 1283

Blake, John E., Gen. Mgr.--Xerox Installment Sales Div., Rochester, NY; *U.S. Public*, pg. 1785

Blake, Mike, Gen. Mgr.--Metallic Gasket Division, Houston, TX; *U.S. Public*, pg. 689

Blake, Phil, Publisher--Wisconsin State Journal, Madison, WI; *U.S. Public*, pg. 984

Blake, Ron, Regional Sls. Mgr.--Prime Technology, Inc., Indianapolis, IN; *U.S. Private*, pg. 884

Blake, Ronald L., Pres.--Ameritech Enhanced Business Services, Chicago, IL; *U.S. Public*, pg. 98

Blake, Thomas H., V.P. & Gen. Mgr.--Equitable Resources Exploration Division, Kingsport, TN; *U.S. Public*, pg. 589

Blake, William A., V.P. & Gen. Mgr.--White Castle Distributing, Inc., Columbus, OH; *U.S. Private*, pg. 1172

Blakeley, Steve, Plant Mgr.--Carolina Steel-Hickory Plant, Hickory, NC; *U.S. Private*, pg. 214

Blakely, Sylvia, Chief Oper. Officer--Akerlund & Rausing Ltd., Bury, United Kingdom; *Int'l*, pg. 33

Blakemore, David, Mng. Dir.--Link-Miles Limited, Lancing, United Kingdom; *Int'l*, pg. 1385

Blakeney, Steve, Chief Oper. Officer--Allright Missouri, Inc., Saint Louis, MO; *U.S. Private*, pg. 42

Blakesley, Bob, Sr. Mktg. Officer--North Central Marketing Div., Bloomington, MN; *U.S. Private*, pg. 296

Blakey, Colin, Deputy Chm.--Northern Rock Homes Limited, Newcastle upon Tyne, United Kingdom; *Int'l*, pg. 968

Blakney, Matthew A., Pres.--Ikon Office Solutions-North Ohio, Canton, OH; *U.S. Public*, pg. 864

Blalock, Wendy, Admin.--Hillhaven Convalescent Hospital Burlingame, Burlingame, CA; *U.S. Public*, pg. 1713

Blampied, Geoffrey, Mng. Dir.--Willis Corroon Limited, Wellington, New Zealand; *Int'l*, pg. 1509

Blanc, Arturo, Gen. Mgr. & Mgr.-Sls.--APLI Combustion, S.A., Barcelona, Spain; *U.S. Private*, pg. 361

Blanc, Lucien, Chief Oper. Officer--Rhone-Poulenc Chemicals Ltd., Seoul, Korea; *Int'l*, pg. 1109

Blanc, Lucien, Mng. Dir.--Bureau Rhone-Poulenc SA, Moscow, Russia; *Int'l*, pg. 1112

Blanch, E.W., Jr., Chief Exec. Officer--E.W. Blanch International, Inc., Minneapolis, MN; *U.S. Public*, pg. 236

Blanch, E.W., Jr., Chm. Bd. & Chief Exec. Officer--E.W. Blanch Wholesale Insurance Services Inc., Minneapolis, MN; *U.S. Public*, pg. 236

Blanchard, Charles H., Pres. & Chief Exec. Officer--First National Bank of Russellville, Russellville, AR; *U.S. Public*, pg. 630

Blanchard, Earl, Gen. Mgr.--Sturm, Ruger-Newport Plant, Newport, NH; *U.S. Public*, pg. 1526

Blanchard, Paul, Mgr.-Opers.--Forge Division, Marion, OH; *U.S. Public*, pg. 557

Blanchard, Robert T., Pres.--Procter & Gamble Beauty Care Div., Cincinnati, OH; *U.S. Public*, pg. 1330

Blanchard, Robert T., V.P.-Beauty Products--Richardson-Vicks, Inc., Cincinnati, OH; *U.S. Public*, pg. 1331

Blanchard, William, Dr., Pres.--Lockheed Martin Space & Range Systems, Sunnyvale, CA; *U.S. Public*, pg. 1009

Blanco, Jose, Gen. Mgr.--Banco Santander, Sydney, Australia; *Int'l*, pg. 144

Blanco, Phillip, Pres.--Bloomingdale's By Mail, Ltd., Cheshire, CT; *U.S. Public*, pg. 618

Bland, Des, Mgr.--Boart Longyear Pty. Ltd., Mitchell Park, Australia; *Int'l*, pg. 76

Bland, Dorothy, Pres. & Publr.--Fort Collins Newspapers, Inc., Fort Collins, CO; *U.S. Public*, pg. 700

Bland, Douglas J., Pres.--Alcan Cable Division, Atlanta, GA; *Int'l*, pg. 50

Bland, Peter G., Chm. Bd.--Fleet Capital Corporation, Glastonbury, CT; *U.S. Public*, pg. 649

Bland, W. Greg, Pres. & Chief Exec. Officer--Tasco Sales Inc., Miramar, FL; *U.S. Private*, pg. 928

Blaney, T.W.D., Mng. Dir.--Colorcon Ltd., Orpington, United Kingdom; *U.S. Private*, pg. 139

Blanford, Geoffrey G., Mng. Dir.--Bettis UK Limited, Fareham, United Kingdom; *U.S. Public*, pg. 483

Blank, Dale E., Mgr.--Sanin Learning, Minneapolis, MN; *U.S. Private*, pg. 210

Blank, Martin J., Chief Oper. Officer--The Aegis Group, Inc., Atlanta, GA; *U.S. Public*, pg. 150

Blank, Martin J., Chief Oper. Officer--W.I.N. Systems, Inc., Atlanta, GA; *U.S. Public*, pg. 150

Blank, Ulrich, Dr., Mng. Dir.--Heinrich Industrie-und Handels-Aktiengesellschaft, Essen, Germany; *Int'l*, pg. 597

Blankemeyer, Franklin, Plant Superintendent--Valleydale Foods, Inc., Salem, VA; *U.S. Public*, pg. 1479

Blankemeyer, Robert H., Pres.--Storz Instrument Co., Saint Louis, MO; *U.S. Public*, pg. 79

Blanken, J., Dir.--Star-Kist Europe, Inc., Douarnenez, France; *U.S. Public*, pg. 807

Blankenship, Al, Pres.--Trans-Tech, Inc., Adamstown, MD; *U.S. Public*, pg. 57

Blankenship, Don L., Chm. Bd., Pres. & Chief Exec. Officer--A.T. Massey Coal Company, Inc., Richmond, VA; *U.S. Public*, pg. 660

Blankinship, Scott F., Pres.--PM Properties Inc., Roanoke, VA; *U.S. Private*, pg. 859

Blanks, Terry, Pres.--Alfa-Laval Agri, Inc., Kansas City, MO; *Int'l*, pg. 1378

Blaser, Marlies E., Mgr.-Mktg.--Singapore Tourist Promotion Board - Zurich, Zurich, Switzerland; *Int'l*, pg. 1254

Blaser, Susan, Pres.--FBS Life Insurance Company, Hopkins, MN; *U.S. Public*, pg. 1681

Blasi, Michael T., Pres.--Pennypower Shopping News, Inc., Wichita, KS; *U.S. Public*, pg. 794

Blasich, Bruno, Plant Mgr.--Calenzano Plant, Calenzano, Italy; *U.S. Public*, pg. 673

Blasius, Donald, Pres.--National Union Electric Corp., Cleveland, OH; *Int'l*, pg. 440

Blasius, Larry, Sr. V.P. & Dir.-NBU--National Broadcast Unit, New York, NY; *U.S. Public*, pg. 1641

Blass, John, V.P. & Gen. Mgr.--Old Town Canoe, Old Town, ME; *U.S. Public*, pg. 933

Blass, Walter P., Chm. & Chief Exec. Officer--G.E. Capital Mortgage Services, Irvine, CA; *U.S. Public*, pg. 712

Blatt, Sid, Pres.--Columbus Steel Drum, Inc., Blacklick, OH; *U.S. Private*, pg. 385

Blattmachr, Doug, Sr. V.P. & Trust Officer--TrustCorp., Great Falls, MT; *U.S. Private*, pg. 314

Blattner, Robert, Pres.-MCA Home Video, Inc. & V.P.--Universal Studios, Inc., Universal City, CA; *Int'l*, pg. 1215

Blauvelt, Henry, Div. Mgr.--Instrument Specialties - Western Division, Placentia, CA; *U.S. Private*, pg. 565

Blazeby, James, Mng. Dir.--ICIS LOR-Europe, Sutton, United Kingdom; *Int'l*, pg. 1094

Blazek, Jarolav, Mng. Dir.--ESAB Vamberk a.s., Vamberk, Czech Republic; *Int'l*, pg. 282

Blazquez, Pedro, Area Mgr.--Milchem Drilling Fluids Ltd., London, United Kingdom; *U.S. Public*, pg. 167

Bleackley, Frank, Mng. Dir.--Chubb Hong Kong Ltd., Kowloon, Hong Kong; *Int'l*, pg. 705

Blecher, Leo, V.P.-Intl. Bus. Devel. & Mgr.-Engrng.--Intermagnetics General Corporation, Latham, NY; *U.S. Public*, pg. 894

Blechman, Michael S., Pres.--PAMCO Printed Tape & Label Company, Inc., Des Plaines, IL; *U.S. Private*, pg. 598

Bleier, Ed, Exec. V.P.-TV Div.--Warner Bros. Inc., New York, NY; *U.S. Public*, pg. 1611

Bleil, James S., Pres. & Gen. Mgr.--Williams Detroit Diesel-Allison S.W., Inc., Phoenix, AZ; *U.S. Private*, pg. 1179

Blennow, Rutger, Chm. Bd.--Skandinaviska Enskilda Banken South East Asia Limited, Singapore, Singapore; *Int'l*, pg. 1260

Blessios, Nicholaos, Chm.--Olympic Airways, New York, NY; *Int'l*, pg. 1004

Blessmann, Heinz, Dipl.-Ing.--Kali-Chemie Aktiengesellschaft, Hannover, Germany; *Int'l*, pg. 1278

Bletas, James D., Pres.--California Microwave-TeleCom Transmission Systems, Inc., Fremont, CA; *U.S. Public*, pg. 293

Bleusteen, Jeffrey L., Pres.--H-D Michigan, Inc., Ann Arbor, MI; *U.S. Public*, pg. 786

Blevi, Dirk L., Gen. Mgr.-Europe--Cabot Plastics International, Brussels, Belgium; *U.S. Public*, pg. 289

Blevins, J. William, Pres.--The Marble Company, Nashville, TN; *U.S. Private*, pg. 149

Blevins, Kenneth W., Pres.--Alcoa Electronic Packaging, Inc., San Diego, CA; *U.S. Public*, pg. 60

Blevins, Tony C., Pres.--Texaco Brasil S. A.-Produtos de Petroleo, Rio de Janeiro, Brazil; *U.S. Public*, pg. 1584
Bleyendaal, Pete, Pres.--Pharmaceutical Basics, Inc., Chicago, IL; *Int'l*, pg. 48
Blichfeldt, Jens, Adm. Dir.--Bausch & Lomb Danmark A/S, Copenhagen, Denmark; *U.S. Public*, pg. 195
Bliesze, Helmut, Mng. Dir.--Acuson GmbH, Erlangen, Germany; *U.S. Public*, pg. 18
Blight, K., Gen. Mgr.--The Royal Bank of Scotland (Gibraltar) Limited, Gibraltar, Gibraltar; *Int'l*, pg. 1133
Blind, Francis, Mng. Dir.--Ethnor S.A., Neuilly-sur-Seine, France; *U.S. Public*, pg. 929
Blinn, Richard, Admin.--Dover House Healthcare, Dover, NH; *U.S. Public*, pg. 1712
Bliss, John, Gen. Mgr.--Swisher County Cattle Co., Tulia, TX; *U.S. Private*, pg. 429
Bliss, Mike, Mgr.--Longmont Foods, Longmont, CO; *U.S. Public*, pg. 426
Bliss, William, Pres.--Wollard Airport Equipment Co., Miami, FL; *U.S. Public*, pg. 866
Blissenbach, Henry, Pres.--Diversified Pharmaceutical Services, Inc., Edina, MN; *Int'l*, pg. 1265
Blitz, Bonnie, Mng. Dir. & Media Dir.--Western International Media Corporation, Denver, CO; *U.S. Private*, pg. 1167
Blitzer, Michael, Pres.--Gant Retail, Bridgewater, NJ; *U.S. Public*, pg. 1292
Blitzer, Mike, Pres.--Van Heusen Retail Division, Bridgewater, NJ; *U.S. Public*, pg. 1291
Blizenec, M., Mng. Dir.--Kenwood Manufacturing GmbH, Vienna, Austria; *Int'l*, pg. 730
Blobel, Peter, Chief Oper. Officer & Exec. V.P.--Bertelsmann Inc., New York, NY; *Int'l*, pg. 191
Bloch, Maurice, Pres.--SECA (Societe d'Exploitation et de Construction Aeronautiques), Le Bourget, France; *Int'l*, pg. 29
Bloch, Thomas, Pres.--The CIT Group/Business Credit, New York, NY; *Int'l*, pg. 360
Blocha, John, Pres. & Chief Oper. Officer--Coburn Optical Industries Inc., Tulsa, OK; *U.S. Private*, pg. 248
Blocher, Terry, Gen. Mgr.--Southland Corporation, Brea, CA; *Int'l*, pg. 694
Blochman, F.O., Country Pres.--TNT Holding GmbH, Troisdorf, Germany; *Int'l*, pg. 1343
Block, Carl, Gen. Mgr.--Sunoco Sarnia Refinery, Sarnia, Canada; *Int'l*, pg. 1320
Block, James, Dir.--Stafford-Miller (Ireland) Limited, Waterford, Ireland; *U.S. Public*, pg. 237
Block, John, Mng. Dir.--MGR Performance Media, Wilton, CT; *U.S. Public*, pg. 1641
Block, Kean, Mng. Dir.--Highland Park Financial Center, Highland Park, IL; *U.S. Public*, pg. 1196
Block, Leonard, Chm. Bd.--Dentco, Inc., Humacao, PR; *U.S. Public*, pg. 237
Block, Leonard, Chm. Bd.--Reedco, Inc., Humacao, PR; *U.S. Public*, pg. 237
Block, Leonard, Pres.--Block Drug Corporation Dental Products Co., Jersey City, NJ; *U.S. Public*, pg. 237
Block, Thomas R., Pres.--Block Drug Company, International Division, Jersey City, NJ; *U.S. Public*, pg. 237
Block, William, Jr., Pres. & Co-Publr.--Toledo Blade Co., Toledo, OH; *U.S. Private*, pg. 147
Blockus, G., Chief Exec. Office--Zurich Ubezpieczenie Service Sp. z o.o., Warsaw, Poland; *Int'l*, pg. 1532
Bloebaum, W.D., Jr., Chief Oper. Officer--Mead Export, Inc., Saint Thomas, VI; *U.S. Public*, pg. 1076
Bloebaum, William D., Jr., Pres.--Mead Pulp Sales, Inc., Dayton, OH; *U.S. Public*, pg. 1074
Bloem, Anthero, Pres. & Gen. Mgr.--Valvulas Keystone de Mexico, S.A. de C.V., Guadalajara, Mexico; *U.S. Public*, pg. 1650
Bloemendaal, Curtis W., Pres.--Tri-State Insurance Company of Minnesota, Luverne, MN; *U.S. Public*, pg. 215
Blok, J., Works Dir.--Breda Sugar Factory, Breda, Netherlands; *Int'l*, pg. 244
Blok, Thorleif, Chief Oper. Officer--Ahlstrom Paper AG, Meggen, Switzerland; *Int'l*, pg. 35
Blom, Inger Eriksson, Mng. Dir.--Berendsen PMC Oy AB, Vantaa, Finland; *Int'l*, pg. 1285
Blomquist, Thomas E., Pres.--Fichtel & Sachs Industries, Inc., Colmar, PA; *Int'l*, pg. 835
Blomqvist, Kaj, Chief Exec. Officer--DMB&B Helsinki, Helsinki, Finland; *U.S. Private*, pg. 303
Blomstrom, Bruce, Chief Exec. Officer--Clinishare, Chatsworth, CA; *U.S. Private*, pg. 1118
Blomstrom, John W., Gen. Mgr.--General Latex & Chemical Corporation, North Billerica, MA; *U.S. Private*, pg. 444
Blondeau, Andre, Chief Oper. Officer--S.A. Mineracao de Amianto, Sao Paulo, Brazil; *Int'l*, pg. 1171
Blondeau, Jacques, Chm.--SCOR U.S. Corporation, New York, NY; *Int'l*, pg. 1152
Blondeau, Jean, Chm. Bd.--Banque PSA Finance Holding, Paris, France; *Int'l*, pg. 1021
Blondel, Jean-Francois, Chief Exec. Officer--C.M.C. SA, Saint Quentin-en-Yvelines, France; *Int'l*, pg. 792
Blonder, Lloyd, V.P.--NTS Engineering, Los Angeles, CA; *U.S. Public*, pg. 1161
Bloom, Darrel, Mgr.--Raynor Distribution Center, Denver, CO; *U.S. Private*, pg. 912
Bloom, David R., Chm. Bd. & Chief Exec. Officer--Shoppers Drug Mart, Ltd., Toronto, Canada; *Int'l*, pg. 112
Bloom, Lawrence B., Pres. & Sr. Lending Officer--LaSalle Bank Northbrook, Northbrook, IL; *Int'l*, pg. 10
Bloom, Marshall, Chief Oper. Officer--Bio-Lab, Inc., Decatur, GA; *U.S. Public*, pg. 760
Bloom, Marvin, Sr. V.P.--URS Greiner, New York, NY; *U.S. Public*, pg. 1659
Bloom, Robert H., Chm. Bd. & Chief Exec. Officer--Publicis/Bloom Inc., New York, NY; *Int'l*, pg. 470
Bloomfield, Coleman, Pres.--Ministers Life Insurance Co, Saint Paul, MN; *U.S. Private*, pg. 750
Bloomfield, Robert M., Pres.--Enteric Products, Inc., Westbury, NY; *U.S. Public*, pg. 540
Blose, Thomas R., Jr., Pres.--United Cities Gas Company, Brentwood, TN; *U.S. Public*, pg. 146
Bloss, Bradley H., Exec. V.P.--Instant Web, Inc., Chanhassen, MN; *U.S. Private*, pg. 565
Blossom, Donald M., Pres. & Chief Exec. Officer--The First National Bank of Ottawa, Ottawa, OH; *U.S. Public*, pg. 1413
Blossom, John, Pres.--Small, Parker & Blossom, Peoria, IL; *U.S. Public*, pg. 280
Blossom, Rick L., Pres. & Chief Oper. Officer--First National Bank of Southwestern Ohio, Hamilton, OH; *U.S. Public*, pg. 633
Blouin, Dale, Gen. Mgr.--Ulbrich of Illinois, Inc., Alsip, IL; *U.S. Private*, pg. 1115
Blue, Dale, Pres. & Chief Exec. Officer--The Chase Manhattan Bank of Canada, Toronto, Canada; *U.S. Public*, pg. 340
Blue, J. Charles, Pres. & Chief Oper. Officer--United Agri Products Co., Greeley, CO; *U.S. Public*, pg. 426
Bluestein, David G., Pres.--Chesebrough-Pond's Household Products Div., Jacksonville, FL; *Int'l*, pg. 1435
Bluestone, Stanton, Chm. Bd. & Pres.--Boston Store, Milwaukee, WI; *U.S. Public*, pg. 309
Bluhm, Leland, Mgr.-Dist. Sls.-S.E.--Singapore Airlines Ltd., Atlanta, GA; *Int'l*, pg. 1374
Blum, Brad, Pres.--Olive Garden Italian Restaurants, Orlando, FL; *U.S. Public*, pg. 484
Blum, Erich, Dr., Mng. Dir.--Berag GmbH, Dusseldorf, Germany; *Int'l*, pg. 1502
Blum, G., Grp. Chief Exec. Officer--Schweizerischer Bankverein, Basel, Switzerland; *Int'l*, pg. 1329
Blum, Gerald S., Pres.--WQXI-WSTR, Atlanta, GA; *U.S. Public*, pg. 926
Blum, Malloy Pohrer, Mgr.--Amano Cincinnati - Chicago Branch Office, Mount Prospect, IL; *Int'l*, pg. 70
Blum, Peter A.C., Gen. Mgr.--Microsoft AG, Spreitenbach, Switzerland; *U.S. Public*, pg. 1108
Blumbach, Gotz-Peter, Chm. Bd.--Hoesch Federn GmbH, Hagen, Germany; *Int'l*, pg. 508
Blumberg, David, Pres. & Chief Exec. Officer--Blumberg Communications Inc., Minneapolis, MN; *U.S. Public*, pg. 305
Blumberg, David, Chief Oper. Officer--Blumberg Communications of Florida Inc., Fort Lauderdale, FL; *U.S. Public*, pg. 305
Blumenberg, Fritz, Pres.--Burda Publications, Inc., New York, NY; *Int'l*, pg. 233
Blumenfeld, Seth D., Pres.--Western Union International, Inc., Piscataway, NJ; *U.S. Public*, pg. 1024
Blumenfeld, Seth D., Pres. & Grp. Exec.--MCI International Inc., Rye Brook, NY; *U.S. Public*, pg. 1024
Blumenthal, Arthur H., Pres.--SL Waber, Inc., Mount Laurel, NJ; *U.S. Public*, pg. 1419
Blumenthal, Arthur H., Pres.--SL Waber, Nogales, AZ; *U.S. Public*, pg. 1419
Blumer, Christof, Pres.--Georg Fischer Rohrleitungssystems GmbH, Herzogenburg, Austria; *Int'l*, pg. 490
Blumkin, Louie, Chm.--Nebraska Furniture Mart, Inc., Omaha, NE; *U.S. Public*, pg. 221
Blundell, A.M, Mng. Dir.-European Print Opers.--Thomas De La Rue and Company Limited, Dunstable, United Kingdom; *Int'l*, pg. 386
Blutstein, Morton, Exec. V.P. & Mgr.-Pur.--Halper Bros., Milwaukee, WI; *U.S. Private*, pg. 920
Bly, Steven, V.P. & Gen. Mgr.--Rochester Gear, Inc., Rochester, MI; *U.S. Public*, pg. 1176
Blyth, Alan, Mgr.--ITW Nexus UK, Basingstoke, United Kingdom; *U.S. Public*, pg. 868
Blyth, Terry E., Mng. Dir.--John Heath & Co. Limited, Birmingham, United Kingdom; *U.S. Private*, pg. 64
Blythe, John C., Chm.--FW Management Operations Ltd., Reading, United Kingdom; *U.S. Public*, pg. 677
Blythe, Jr., Richard N., Pres.--The Huntington Investment Company, Columbus, OH; *U.S. Public*, pg. 850
Blythe, Patty, Mgr.--General Employment Enterprises, Inc., Memphis, TN; *U.S. Public*, pg. 715
Blythe, R.A., Reg. Mng. Dir.--Ballast Wiltshier Plc - South East Region, Canterbury, United Kingdom; *Int'l*, pg. 135
Bo, Arild, Chief Oper. Officer--Nortec Electronics A/S, Hvalstad, Norway; *Int'l*, pg. 712
Boache, John, V.P.-Opers.--Snyder Southeast Div., Roanoke, AL; *U.S. Private*, pg. 1011
Boal, Brenda, Mng. Dir.--Shandwick Northern Ireland Ltd., Belfast, United Kingdom; *Int'l*, pg. 1226
Boan, Edward, V.P. & Gen. Mgr.--Thorn Apple Valley-Frederick Division, Detroit, MI; *U.S. Public*, pg. 1603
Board, W.G., Resident Dir.--Balfour Timber Ltd., Sevenoaks, United Kingdom; *Int'l*, pg. 260
Boardman, Harry, Mgr.--Southern Electric Supply Co., Inc., Kissimmee, FL; *Int'l*, pg. 1107
Boas, J.V., Chief Oper. Officer--Polialden-Petroquimica S.A., Camacari, Brazil; *Int'l*, pg. 949
Boas, Tim, Mgr.-Branch--Ferro Union, Inc., Northern California, Stockton, CA; *U.S. Private*, pg. 402
Bobbins, Chuck, Pres.--R.F. Technology, Inc., Norwalk, CT; *Int'l*, pg. 1289
Bober, David, Pres. & Chief Exec. Officer--American Beverage Corp. Inc., Akron, OH; *Int'l*, pg. 752
Bober, Stephen, Gen. Mgr.--Arrow/Schweber Electronics, Houston, TX; *U.S. Public*, pg. 134
Bobins, Norman, Pres. & Chief Exec. Officer--LaSalle National Bank, Chicago, IL; *Int'l*, pg. 10
Bobis, C., Mng. Dir.--General Motors Marketing Services Hellas AEE, Russelsheim, Germany; *U.S. Public*, pg. 722
Boccards, Louis D., Pres. & Chief Exec. Officer--Wide World Photos, Inc., New York, NY; *U.S. Private*, pg. 92
Bocchino, Robert M., Pres.--DeVRY Technical Institute, North Brunswick, NJ; *U.S. Public*, pg. 504
Bocek, J., Chief Exec. Officer--Zurich Pojistovna, Prague, Czech Republic; *Int'l*, pg. 1531
Bochette, Don, Reg. Mgr.--Green Tree Acceptance of Mississippi, Inc., Jackson, MS; *U.S. Public*, pg. 762
Bock, James D., V.P.-Opers.--Bock Industries Inc., Elkhart, IN; *Int'l*, pg. 265
Bock, Michael, Gen. Mgr.--Fleck Manufacturing Inc., Hyde Park, Canada; *Int'l*, pg. 955
Bock, Warren, Pres.--International Relocation Insurance Services Inc., Vienna, VA; *Int'l*, pg. 1503
Bodager, Brian R., Pres. & Chief Exec. Officer--Banc Life Insurance Corporation, Phoenix, AZ; *U.S. Public*, pg. 140
Boddye, Tim, Pres.--Structron Corporation, San Marcos, CA; *U.S. Private*, pg. 988
Bode, Henry J., Pres.--Videojet Systems International, Inc., Wood Dale, IL; *Int'l*, pg. 545
Bode, U., Dr., Gen. Mgr.--Glaxo Wellcome Pharma GmbH, Vienna, Austria; *Int'l*, pg. 553
Bodel, Didier, Pres.--Tyco Toys (France) S.A., Paris, France; *U.S. Public*, pg. 1059
Boden, John C., Pres.--Temple Insurance Company Limited, Hamilton, Bermuda; *U.S. Public*, pg. 360
Boden, John C., Pres.--Cigna International Reinsurance Company Ltd., Hamilton, Bermuda; *U.S. Public*, pg. 364
Bodensteiner, Carol A., Pres.--CMF&Z Public Relations, Des Moines, IA; *U.S. Private*, pg. 1197
Boderck, Steve S., V.P. & Gen. Mgr.--Huck International Installation Systems Division, Kingston, NY; *U.S. Public*, pg. 1597
Bodman, James, Pres.--Chipico Pickles, Chicago, IL; *U.S. Private*, pg. 1140
Bodnar, Peter, Chief Oper. Officer--TSP Inc., Chatham, NJ; *Int'l*, pg. 457
Bodor, Paul W., Sr. V.P. & Dir.-Compliance & Risk Mngmt.--Jefferies & Company, Inc., Los Angeles, CA; *U.S. Public*, pg. 925
Bodow, Warren G., Pres.--WQXR/FM, WQEW/AM, New York, NY; *U.S. Public*, pg. 1174
Bodziony, Dennis, Pres.--Tempo Products Company, Solon, OH; *U.S. Private*, pg. 870
Boe, Nils G., Mgr.-Station--Det Norske Veritas, Durban, South Africa; *Int'l*, pg. 397
Boeckman, Steven L., Pres.--Northern Tree Service, Inc., Sault Sainte Marie, MI; *U.S. Public*, pg. 592
Boeglin, John, Div. Mgr.--Wyle Electronics-Atlanta, Norcross, GA; *Int'l*, pg. 1457
Boehl, Guus, Mng. Dir.--Power-Packer Europa B.V., Oldenzaal, Netherlands; *U.S. Public*, pg. 125
Boehm, David W., Pres.--Normandeau Engineers Inc., Concord, NH; *U.S. Public*, pg. 1593
Boehm, David W., Pres.--Thermo Consulting Engineers Inc., Middleboro, MA; *U.S. Public*, pg. 1594
Boehm, David W., Chief Oper. Officer--Thermo Consulting Engineers, Williston, VT; *U.S. Public*, pg. 1594
Boehm, Gilles, Gen. Mgr.--ITW Deltar-Special Products, Frankfort, IL; *U.S. Public*, pg. 866
Boehm, Josef F., Pres.--General Hardware Distributors, Anchorage, AK; *U.S. Private*, pg. 31
Boehning, T.D., Pres.--Colorcon, West Point, PA; *U.S. Private*, pg. 139
Boel, Guus, Pres.--Enerpac U.S., Butler, WI; *U.S. Public*, pg. 124
Boemio, Setgio, Gen. Mgr.--Merloni Hausgerate GMBH, Frankfurt/Main, Germany; *Int'l*, pg. 860
Boender, Rene, Mng. Partner--Bercum Boender Cardozo & Werkendam B.V., Amsterdam, Netherlands; *U.S. Private*, pg. 1198
Boer, G.J., Dir.--N.V. Immobilien en Grindexploitatlemaatschappij, Dilsen, Belgium; *Int'l*, pg. 135
Boer, W., Chief Exec. Officer--Kuehne & Nagel N.V., Rotterdam, Netherlands; *Int'l*, pg. 763
Boerma, Michael J., Pres.--M.A.R.C.O., Ann Arbor, MI; *U.S. Private*, pg. 355
Boermons, Huib, Chm. of the Mng. Bd.--RTL4, Luxembourg, Luxembourg; *Int'l*, pg. 561
Boesch, Fritz F., Chm. Bd.--Feintool AG Lyss, Lyss, Switzerland; *Int'l*, pg. 479
Boeshaar, Karl, Co-Chief Oper. Officer--Saarlaendische Kraftwerksgesellschaft mbH, Saarbruecken, Germany; *Int'l*, pg. 1167
Boesken, Dietrich H., Gen. Mgr.--Lawson Mardon Singen GmbH, Singen, Germany; *Int'l*, pg. 69
Boeskov, Jens, Mng. Dir. & Mgr.-Network--Willis Corroon A/S, Copenhagen, Denmark; *Int'l*, pg. 1509
Boetius, Jan, Dr., Chm.-Bd. of Mgmnt.--Deutsche Krankenversicherung AG, Cologne, Germany; *Int'l*, pg. 58
Boeuf, Michel, Chief Oper. Officer--Club Mediterranee U.K. Ltd., London, United Kingdom; *Int'l*, pg. 298
Boffetta, Giancarlo, Chief Oper. Officer--Turbomotori Internazionale S.p.A., Rome, Italy; *Int'l*, pg. 481
Bogaard, W.J., Gen. Mgr.--Senior TIFT B.V., Rotterdam, Netherlands; *Int'l*, pg. 1223
Bogaerts, Ronald, Chief Oper. Officer--Tefal Belgium, Fleurus, Belgium; *Int'l*, pg. 568
Bogart, Tom, V.P.-Mktg.--Utell International-Oak Brook, Oak Brook, IL; *Int'l*, pg. 1098
Bogdanov, O., Mng. Dir.--Bestrom, Moscow, Russia; *Int'l*, pg. 1134
Boger, Paul, Publisher--Schirmer Books, New York, NY; *U.S. Private*, pg. 777
Boggan, Joseph, V.P.-Opers. & Customer Support--Engineered Prods. Div., Seneca Falls, NY; *U.S. Public*, pg. 860
Boggs, Dave, Mgr.--Ferguson Lyon Conklin & Company Inc., Baltimore, MD; *Int'l*, pg. 1512
Boggs, Marcus L., Pres.--Academic Press, Inc., San Diego, CA; *U.S. Public*, pg. 783
Boglione, Enrico, Mng. Dir.--UTA, Turin, Italy; *Int'l*, pg. 1502
Bognanno, P. F., Pres. & Chief Exec. Officer--Principal Residential Mortgage, Inc., Des Moines, IA; *U.S. Private*, pg. 886
Bogner, Herbert, Mgr.-Austria--Medtronic GmbH, Vienna, Austria; *U.S. Public*, pg. 1083
Bogorad, Maria, Gen. Mgr.--Credit Commercial de France, Moscow, Russia; *Int'l*, pg. 343
Bogyo, Josef, Chief Oper. Officer--Skanska Hungaria Ltd., Budapest, Hungary; *Int'l*, pg. 1261

Bohannan, Robert, Pres.--Marine Midland Mortgage Corporation, Buffalo, NY; *Int'l*, pg. 581

Bohannon, Robert H., Chm. Bd.--Dobbs International Services, Inc., Memphis, TN; *U.S. Public*, pg. 1718

Bohannon, Terri, R.N., Admin.--The Care Group of Texas, Inc., Houston, TX; *U.S. Public*, pg. 305

Bohanon, James D., Dir.--Sociede Anonyme de l'Exploitation de L'Hopital de la Tour, Louisville, KY; *U.S. Public*, pg. 405

Bohart, John R., Mng. Dir.--Framatome Cogema Fuels, Lynchburg, VA; *Int'l*, pg. 503

Bohart, John R., Mng. Dir.--Framatome Technologies, Inc., Lynchburg, VA; *Int'l*, pg. 503

Bohjort, Thomas, Dir.-Sweden--Raychem Aktiebolag, Skarholmen, Sweden; *U.S. Public*, pg. 1362

Bohla, Ulf, Chm. Bd.--o.tel.o Communications GmbH Co., Dusseldorf, Germany; *Int'l*, pg. 1082

Bohlander, Frans A.C.M., Mng. Dir.--Sulzer Caliqua B.V., Tilburg, Netherlands; *Int'l*, pg. 1306

Bohlander, Frans A.C.M., Chief Exec.--Sulzer Infra Nederland B.V., Tilburg, Netherlands; *Int'l*, pg. 1306

Bohle, Heinz, Mng. Dir.--Sulzer Triebwerke AG, Winterthur, Switzerland; *Int'l*, pg. 1307

Bohlen, Richard, Pres.--BTR-Measurement & Flow Control Division, Pittsburgh, PA; *Int'l*, pg. 125

Bohlen, Urs, Chief Exec.--Holderbank Cement & Beton, Eclepens, Switzerland; *Int'l*, pg. 628

Bohlender, Thomas, Pres.--Dean Dairy Products Co., Sharpsville, PA; *U.S. Public*, pg. 490

Bohler, Alan, V.P. & Dir.-Sls.--Bassett Upholstery Division, Newton, NC; *U.S. Public*, pg. 193

Bohlmeyer, Eugene M., Pres.--Baraboo-Sysco Food Services, Inc., Baraboo, WI; *U.S. Public*, pg. 1550

Bohlund, Kjell, Chief Officer--Raben & Sjogren AB, Stockholm, Sweden; *Int'l*, pg. 718

Bohm, Georg, Dr., Mgr.-Res.--Bridgestone/Firestone Research Laboratories, Akron, OH; *Int'l*, pg. 213

Bohm, Michael, Mng. Dir.--Deutsche Bank Saar AG, Saarbruecken, Germany; *Int'l*, pg. 402

Bohman, Staffan, Pres.--Alfa Laval Agri AB, Lund, Sweden; *Int'l*, pg. 1378

Bohman, Tommy, Pres.--Donnelley Information Publishing, Inc., Orange, CA; *U.S. Public*, pg. 535

Bohn, Nathan, V.P. & Gen. Mgr.--Dillard, A ResourceNet International Company, Orlando, FL; *U.S. Public*, pg. 902

Bohner, Richard, Sr. V.P.-Tech. Opers.--Sandoz Pharmaceuticals Corp., East Hanover, NJ; *Int'l*, pg. 974

Bohon, Roger L., Pres.--ENCAP Systems, Inc., Roanoke, VA; *U.S. Private*, pg. 513

Bohorques, Juan Cristobal Ferrer, Chief Exec. Officer--Publicidad Ferrer y Asociados, S.A. de C.V., Mexico, Mexico; *Int'l*, pg. 1073

Bohringer, Werner, Pres.--Terrot Strickmaschinen GmbH, Stuttgart, Germany; *Int'l*, pg. 1307

Boidin, Michel, Mng. Dir.--ATEA, Carquefou, France; *Int'l*, pg. 503

Boies, Jeffery E., Pres.--VSA, Inc., Denver, CO; *U.S. Public*, *pg. 901*

Boiko, Alexander, Chief Oper. Officer--Novo Nordisk A/S, Kiev, Ukraine; *Int'l*, pg. 987

Boileau, Oliver C., Pres. & Gen. Mgr.--B-2 Division, Pico Rivera, CA; *U.S. Public*, pg. 1198

Boire, John L., Pres.--Byers Portland Willamette, Portland, OR; *U.S. Private*, pg. 191

Bois, M. Pascal, Gen. Mgr.--GECI (Groupe d'Etudes et Conseils en Ingenierie), Paris, France; *U.S. Public*, pg. 1032

Boisset, Alain, Chm.--JANIN, Montreal, Canada; *Int'l*, pg. 823

Boissinot, Tim, Pres. & Gen. Mgr.--Quebecor Printing Edmonton, Edmonton, Canada; *Int'l*, pg. 1077

Boissonneault, Roger M., Pres. & Chief Oper. Officer--Warner-Chilcott Laboratories, Inc., Rockaway, NJ; *Int'l*, pg. 436

Boisvert, Kenneth, Controller--Teleflex Fluid Systems Inc., Suffield, CT; *U.S. Public*, pg. 1569

Boisvert, Norman, V.P.-Admin.--Cascades, Inc., Kingsey Falls, Canada; *Int'l*, pg. 273

Boivie, Jan-Erik, Mng. Dir.--Skega Mexicana SA de CV, Irapuato, Mexico; *Int'l*, pg. 1324

Boivin, Daniel W., Pres.--Nova Chemicals Ltd., Calgary, Canada; *Int'l*, pg. 971

Boixeda, Jorge, Mng. Dir.--Korn/Ferry International, Barcelona, Spain; *U.S. Private*, pg. 634

Bojack, S.D., Pres.--Amoco Gas Company, Houston, TX; *Int'l*, pg. 1136

Boker, Karl, Chm. Bd.--Wiemer und Trachte, Dortmund, Germany; *Int'l*, pg. 824

Bokser, Stephen R., Pres. & Chief Oper. Officer--White Rose Food, Carteret, NJ; *U.S. Private*, pg. 330

Bol, G., Mng. Dir.--Crowcon Instruments B.V., Rotterdam, Netherlands; *Int'l*, pg. 590

Bol, Gerrit J., Pres.--Verily Enterprises, Inc., Orlando, FL; *U.S. Public*, pg. 783

Bolafanti, Matthew, Pres.--Marine Midland Business Loans, Inc., Norwalk, CT; *Int'l*, pg. 581

Bolam, B., Mng. Dir.--TNT Logistics Europe, Amsterdam, Netherlands; *Int'l*, pg. 1343

Bolam, Brian, Mng. Dir.--TNT Logistics UK, Tewkesbury, United Kingdom; *Int'l*, pg. 1343

Boland, Michael, Pres.--Maritz Travel Co., Fenton, MO; *U.S. Private*, pg. 704

Boland, Nick, Exec. Fin. Dir. & Controller--MTI Ireland, Dublin, Ireland; *U.S. Public*, pg. 1028

Bolconi, Emilio, Mng. Dir.--Thermon Italia S.P.A., Milan, Italy; *U.S. Private*, pg. 1081

Bold, Jean, V.P. & Gen. Mgr.--Oneida Rostone Corporation, Oneida, NY; *U.S. Public*, pg. 1383

Bole, Mark, Mng. Dir.--Nokia Telecommunications (H.K.) Ltd., Taikoo Shing, Hong Kong; *Int'l*, pg. 953

Bolger, David P., Pres.--American National Bank & Trust Co. of Chicago, Chicago, IL; *U.S. Public*, pg. 628

Bolinger, Robert S., Chm. Bd. & Chief Exec. Officer--Farmers First Bank, Lititz, PA; *U.S. Public*, pg. 1542

Bolivar, Liliana, Fin. Dir.--Comunica Leo Burnett Panama, S.A., Panama, Panama; *U.S. Private*, pg. 184

Bolle, M.B., Chm. Bd. & Gen. Mgr.--Westland/Utrecht Hypotheekbank, Amsterdam, Netherlands; *Int'l*, pg. 647

Boller, Claude, Pres.--Genetic Design Inc., Greensboro, NC; *U.S. Public*, pg. 733

Bolleter, Ulrich, Mng. Dir.--Sulzer Innotec Ltd., Winterthur, Switzerland; *Int'l*, pg. 1306

Bolliger, Heinz, Gen. Mgr.--Bischofszell Canning Factory AG, Bischofszell, Switzerland; *Int'l*, pg. 865

Bolliger, Peter, Office Mgr.--Korn/Ferry International, Zurich, Switzerland; *U.S. Private*, pg. 633

Bolling, Klaus, Mng. Dir.--Krupp Bruninghaus GmbH, Werdohl, Germany; *Int'l*, pg. 508

Bologna, Thomas A., Pres. & Chief Exec. Officer--Gen-Probe Inc., San Diego, CA; *Int'l*, pg. 291

Bolsover, J.D., Chm.--Baring Asset Management, London, United Kingdom; *Int'l*, pg. 648

Bolster, H. D., Mgr.-Opers.--Qatar Drilling Co., Doha, Qatar; *Int'l*, pg. 765

Bolster, William, Pres. & Gen. Mgr.-WNBC-TV--National Broadcasting Co., Inc., New York, NY; *U.S. Public*, pg. 712

Bolster, William, Pres.--CNBC, Fort Lee, NJ; *U.S. Public*, pg. 712

Bolt, J.W., Mng. Dir.--Ballast Nedam Services B.V., Amstelveen, Netherlands; *Int'l*, pg. 134

Bolt, Paul, Gen. Mgr.-Pharmaceutical Div.--CIBA-GEIGY Australia Ltd., Pendle Hill, Australia; *Int'l*, pg. 976

Bolt, R.A., Gen. Mgr.--Rocol (Hong Kong) Limited, Tsuen Wan, Hong Kong; *Int'l*, pg. 892

Bolton, Harvey, V.P. & Reg. Mgr.--Bergen Brunswig Medical Corporation, Spokane, WA; *U.S. Public*, pg. 214

Bolton, Matthew, Mgr.-Prop.--Skandia Property (UK) Ltd., London, United Kingdom; *Int'l*, pg. 1258

Bolton, Rod, Pres.--Electronic Solutions, San Diego, CA; *U.S. Public*, pg. 1791

Bolton, William J., Chm.--Graham Miller Group Limited, London, United Kingdom; *U.S. Public*, pg. 458

Bolz, H.R., Branch Mgr.--Swiss Bank Corporation (Canada), Vancouver, Canada; *Int'l*, pg. 1332

Bolza-Schunemann, Albrecht, Chief Oper. Officer--KBA-Planeta AG, Radebeul, Germany; *Int'l*, pg. 742

Boman, Per, Mng. Dir.--Sodra Italia Srl, Milan, Italy; *Int'l*, pg. 1276

Bombardi, Enzo, Mgr.-Argentina--Raychem S.A. Industrial Y Commercial, Ampang, Malaysia; *U.S. Public*, pg. 1363

Bomeisel, Pery, Chief Oper. Officer--Weldotron do Brasil, Sao Paulo, Brazil; *U.S. Public*, pg. 1752

Bommakanti, A.K., Chief Exec. Officer-South Asia--ANZ Grindlays Bank plc South Asia Headquarters, Mumbai, India; *Int'l*, pg. 99

Bommer, J., Mng. Dir.--Wolters Kluwer Business Publishing, Deventer, Netherlands; *Int'l*, pg. 1513

Bonafe, Pierre, Chief Oper. Officer--Sogelerg, Rungis, France; *Int'l*, pg. 54

Bonamico, Cesar, Chief Oper. Officer--Brastemp S.A., Sao Bernardo do Campo, Brazil; *U.S. Public*, pg. 1765

Bonander, John, V.P. & Reg. Mgr.--Leslie-Michigan, Troy, MI; *U.S. Public*, pg. 903

Bonanni, Sandra, Dir.--Ufficio Affari Quebec Italia, Milan, Italy; *Int'l*, pg. 249

Bonanno, Salvatore J., Pres.--Foamex, L.P., Linwood, PA; *U.S. Private*, pg. 1094

Bonato, Bob, Administrator--Colonial Manor of Deer Lodge, Deer Lodge, MT; *U.S. Public*, pg. 837

Bonaventura, Frank, Plant Mgr.--Ruger Investment Castings, Prescott, AZ; *U.S. Public*, pg. 1526

Bonazzi, Vittorio, Pres.--Astra Farmaceutici S.p.A., Milan, Italy; *Int'l*, pg. 93

Bonczyk, Robert, Pres. & Chief Exec. Officer--U.S. Can Company, Newnan, GA; *U.S. Public*, pg. 1681

Bond, Charles, Gen. Mgr.--Sterling Electronics, Houston, TX; *U.S. Public*, pg. 1052

Bond, Christopher, Publisher--The Daily Comet, Thibodaux, LA; *U.S. Public*, pg. 1175

Bond, Christopher, Publisher--Comet-Press Newspapers, Inc., Thibodaux, LA; *U.S. Public*, pg. 1175

Bond, David, Mgr.--General Employment Enterprises, Inc., Walnut Creek, CA; *U.S. Public*, pg. 715

Bond, Henry M., Pres.--Ikon Office Solutions-Baltimore, Baltimore, MD; *U.S. Public*, pg. 863

Bond, Kevin, Gen. Mgr.--Radisson Suite Hotel, Tucson, AZ; *U.S. Public*, pg. 1250

Bond, P.D., Chief Oper. Officer--The Linc Corp., Pittsburgh, PA; *Int'l*, pg. 322

Bond, Richard J., Chm. Bd.--Security Bank & Trust Co., Vincennes, IN; *U.S. Public*, pg. 1217

Bond, Robert, Gen. Mgr.--Parker Hannifin Corp., Quick Coupling Div., Minneapolis, MN; *U.S. Public*, pg. 1260

Bond, Ronald, Exec. V.P.-Corp. Srvcs. Div.--Montreal Trustco-Corporate Services Div., Montreal, Canada; *Int'l*, pg. 155

Bond, Steve, Gen. Mgr.--Esselte New Zealand, Auckland, New Zealand; *Int'l*, pg. 461

Bond, Tom, Chief Oper. Officer--Mac Cosmetics, Toronto, Canada; *U.S. Public*, pg. 594

Bondi, David, Gen. Mgr.--Dun & Bradstreet (Israel) Ltd., Tel Aviv, Israel; *U.S. Public*, pg. 536

Bondi, Enrico, Pres.--Edison S.p.A., Milan, Italy; *Int'l*, pg. 324

Bondi, W.C., V.P. & Mng. Dir.--AlliedSignal Canada Inc.-Filters & Spark Plugs Canada, Stratford, Canada; *U.S. Public*, pg. 54

Bondueli, Alain, Mgr.--ITW Espana S.A. SPIT, Barcelona, Spain; *U.S. Public*, pg. 868

Bondurant, Jay, Gen. Mgr.--Bedford Bulletin, Bedford, VA; *U.S. Private*, pg. 648

Bondurant, Sharon, Mgr.--General Employment Enterprises, Inc., Tempe, AZ; *U.S. Public*, pg. 715

Bone, Barry, Pres.--Brookhollow Corp., Dallas, TX; *U.S. Public*, pg. 1585

Bone, George, Pres.-Psychiatric Grp.--HCA Psychiatric Co., Nashville, TN; *U.S. Public*, pg. 405

Bone, John, Dir. & Mgr.--The Crown Cork Company (East Africa) Ltd., Nairobi, Kenya; *U.S. Public*, pg. 464

Bone, Lindsay, Chief Chemist--BHP Australia Coal Ltd., Mackay Laboratory, Mackay, Australia; *Int'l*, pg. 227

Bonel, Guy, Chief Oper. Officer--Bois et Sciages de Sougy S.A., Decize, France; *Int'l*, pg. 1429

Bonemeyer, Arthur, Mng. Dir.--Loctite Belgium N.V., Kontich, Belgium; *Int'l*, pg. 611

Boness, M., V.P. & Gen. Mgr.--Commercial Aircraft Group, Israel; *Int'l*, pg. 690

Bonet, Roger, Gen. Dir.--Eniac C.A., Caracas, Venezuela; *U.S. Public*, pg. 1043

Boneto, Mariano, Rep.--Banco Di Napoli-Seoul, Seoul, Korea; *Int'l*, pg. 140

Bonetti, Alessandro, Pres.--Antibioticos S.A., Madrid, Spain; *Int'l*, pg. 324

Boney, Gordon C., V.P.--CDI Telecommunications, Inc., Scottsdale, AZ; *U.S. Public*, pg. 277

Bonfield, B.M., Chm.--Fasco Controls Corporation, Shelby, NC; *Int'l*, pg. 125

Bonfield, P.L., Deputy Chief Exec.--ICL PLC, Putney, United Kingdom; *Int'l*, pg. 528

Bonfiglio, Frank J., Pres.--Vanguard Financial Services, Lombard, IL; *U.S. Public*, pg. 1216

Bong-jin, Ko, Exec. Dir.--Hankook Ilbo Time-Life Ltd., Seoul, Korea; *U.S. Public*, pg. 1615

Bongartz, Edmond, Mng. Dir.--Walker Deutschland GmbH, Viernheim, Germany; *U.S. Public*, pg. 1580

Bongers, Manfred, Mng. Dir.--Diehl & Eagle-Picher GmbH, Nuremberg, Germany; *U.S. Private*, pg. 355

Bongiorno, John J., Pres.--Navistar Financial Corporation, Rolling Meadows, IL; *U.S. Public*, pg. 1167

Bongrand, Laurent, Mng. Dir.--Watts Eurotherm, Fressenneville, France; *U.S. Public*, pg. 1747

Bonham, Ben, Gen. Mgr.--Industrial Packaging Div. (Cedartown), Cedartown, GA; *Int'l*, pg. 1270

Bonham, John, Div. Mgr.--Bindley Western, Austell Division, Austell, GA; *U.S. Public*, pg. 228

Bonham, Steve, Chief Oper. Officer--DentiCare of California, Inc., Rancho Cordova, CA; *U.S. Public*, pg. 678

Bonhomme, J.C., Chief Exec. Officer--Ciap S.A., Argenteuil, France; *Int'l*, pg. 994

Boni, Belinda A., Pres.--The Family Investment Services Co., Inc., Troy, NY; *U.S. Private*, pg. 1106

Bonica, Steven, Pres.--Panasonic Broadcast & Television Systems Company, Secaucus, NJ; *Int'l*, pg. 847

Bonica, Vincent, Pres.--L.A. Dreyfus Co., South Plainfield, NJ; *U.S. Public*, pg. 1781

Bonicelli, Jerry, Gen. Mgr.--M&H Retail Food Group, Memphis, TN; *U.S. Public*, pg. 653

Boniface, Rudolph H., Chm. Bd.--Credit Ford S.A., Rueil-Malmaison, France; *U.S. Public*, pg. 666

Boniface, Rudolph H., Pres.--Ford France S.A., Rueil-Malmaison, France; *U.S. Public*, pg. 666

Bonifacio, R., Dir.--Fiat Auto S.p.A., Milan, Italy; *Int'l*, pg. 481

Bonifacio, Renato, Pres.--Alenia, Naples, Italy; *Int'l*, pg. 653

Bonig, Klaus, Mng. Dir.--Bonig & Yamaoka International Public Relations, Hamburg, Germany; *Int'l*, pg. 1210

Bonilla, Pedro, Pres.--Allied Diagnostic Imaging Resources, Inc., Irwindale, CA; *U.S. Public*, pg. 282

Bonilla, Pedro P., Pres.--Allied Diagnostic Imaging Resources, Inc., Norcross, GA; *U.S. Public*, pg. 282

Bonilla, Predo P., Pres.--Trebla Chemical Company, Saint Louis, MO; *U.S. Public*, pg. 282

Bonnal, J., Mng. Dir.--Ferro France S.a.r.l., Saint Dizier, France; *U.S. Public*, pg. 619

Bonnaud, J.J., Pres.--Gan Sa, Paris, France; *Int'l*, pg. 565

Bonne, Jack, Pres.--Icon International, Inc., Irvine, CA; *Int'l*, pg. 1191

Bonne, Marco, Pres.--Prince Foods Div., Lowell, MA; *U.S. Private*, pg. 158

Bonnefin, Annie, Mgr.--Etoile Bleue, Tours, France; *Int'l*, pg. 600

Bonnefoi, Jean Claude, Pres.--Parbel Inc., Miami, FL; *Int'l*, pg. 818

Bonnelyche, Christina, Chief Oper. Officer--Georg Jensen Silver AB, Stockholm, Sweden; *Int'l*, pg. 1134

Bonnema, Ronald, Mgr.-Plant--APG Lime Corp., Ripplemead, VA; *U.S. Public*, pg. 761

Bonner, Joel, Pres. & Chief Exec. Officer--Hydrotex Inc., Dallas, TX; *Int'l*, pg. 892

Bonner, Stephen B., Pres.--McGraw-Hill Construction Information Group, New York, NY; *U.S. Public*, pg. 1070

Bonner, Stephen B., Pres.--F.W. Dodge Group, New York, NY; *U.S. Public*, pg. 1070

Bonnet-Bidaud, M., Chm. Bd.--Wattohm, Paris, France; *Int'l*, *pg. 662*

Bonnet, Christian, Dir.-Fin.--Ferembal S.A., Clichy, France; *U.S. Public*, pg. 440

Bonnet, Thierry, Mng. Dir.--UPM-Kymmene France S.A., Paris, France; *Int'l*, pg. 1430

Bonnet, William A., Pres.--Maui Electric Co., Ltd., Kahului, HI; *U.S. Public*, pg. 800

Bonnett, J. P., Gen. Mgr.--Eurand France S.A., Nogent-sur-Oise, France; *U.S. Public*, pg. 81

Bonnetti, Alessandro, Pres.--Antibioticos S.p.A., Milan, Italy; *Int'l*, pg. 324

Bonnevie, J.C., Mng. Dir.--Caterpillar France S.A., Grenoble, France; *U.S. Public*, pg. 317

Bonnevier, Rainer, Chief Exec. Officer--Oy Qtronic AB, Helsinki, Finland; *Int'l*, pg. 712

Bonnier, Kaj, Representative--Svenska Handelsbanken Zurich, Zurich, Switzerland; *Int'l*, pg. 1327

Bonnin, Gilles, Chief Oper. Officer--CIEMI, Pantin, France; *Int'l*, pg. 260

Bonnington, Mark, Mgr.-Opers.--Woodward-Clyde International, Honiara, Solomon Islands,; *U.S. Public*, pg. 1658

Bonnotte, Franck, Mng. Dir.--Bertrand Faure Components Ltd. - Norfinch Plant, North York, Canada; *Int'l*, pg. 193

Bonopera, Georges, Gen. Mgr.--Voyage, Issy-les-Moulineaux, France; *U.S. Private*, pg. 647

Bonse-Geisking, Wilhelm, Chief Exec. Officer--VEBA OEL AG, Gelsenkirchen, Germany; *Int'l*, pg. 1460
Bonta, Patricio, Exec. V.P., Pres. & CEO JWT/Argentina--J. Walter Thompson Company, New York, NY; *Int'l*, pg. 1483
Bontell, James, Mgr.--Shepler's College Station, College Station, TX; *U.S. Public*, pg. 413
Bontempo, Joseph, Admin.--Hamilton Pavilion Healthcare, Norwich, CT; *U.S. Public*, pg. 1713
Bontems, Pierre, Chm.--Millipore S.A., Molsheim, France; *U.S. Public*, pg. 1113
Bonus, Bob, Pres.--Corporate Foods Ltd., Etobicoke, Canada; *Int'l*, pg. 841
Bonyhady, Bruce, Mng. Dir.--NM Funds Management (Europe) Ltd. United Kingdom, Bournemouth, United Kingdom; *Int'l*, pg. 908
Bonzom, C., Mng. Dir.--Chaussures Bally Villeurbanne SA, Villeurbanne, France; *Int'l*, pg. 997
Book, Jay, Plant Mgr.--Coldwater Seafood Corp., Cambridge, MD; *U.S. Private*, pg. 251
Booker, Noel, Pres. & Chief Exec. Officer--K.C.I. Coatings, Inc., Louisville, KY; *U.S. Private*, pg. 890
Booker, W. Wayne, Pres.--Ford Asia-Pacific, Inc., Dearborn, MI; *U.S. Public*, pg. 664
Bookman, Lee, Pres.--Heads & Threads, Northbrook, IL; *U.S. Public*, pg. 42
Bookmyer, Bruce, Pres.--Hess & Clark Company, Ashland, OH; *U.S. Public*, pg. 426
Bookstaver, Thomas, Publr.--The Advertiser Co., Montgomery, AL; *U.S. Public*, pg. 699
Bookstaver, Thomas, Pres. & Publr.--The Herald-Dispatch, Huntington, WV; *U.S. Public*, pg. 701
Boomsma, Wouter, Pres.--NCT Holland B.V., Breda, Netherlands; *Int'l*, pg. 914
Boon, Lim Yaw, Gen. Mgr.--Superior Metal Printing (Huiyang) Co. Ltd., Huizhou, China; *Int'l*, pg. 1322
Boon, Roy, V.P.--Birtcher, El Monte, CA; *U.S. Public*, pg. 1791
Boon, S., Rep.--Ballast Nedam Dredging, Rio de Janeiro, Brazil; *Int'l*, pg. 134
Boon, Y.C., Chm. Bd.--Jardine Matheson (Singapore) Ltd, Singapore, Singapore; *Int'l*, pg. 705
Boondej, Aran, Gen. Mgr.--ITW (Thailand) Co. Ltd., Bangkok, Thailand; *U.S. Public*, pg. 869
Boone, Charles E., Pres.--Con-Way Western Express, Inc., Buena Park, CA; *U.S. Public*, pg. 281
Boone, Florence, Chm. Bd.--Pace, Arlington Heights, IL; *U.S. Private*, pg. 919
Boone, J. Christopher, Chief Oper. Officer--ISC Realty Corporation, Charlotte, NC; *U.S. Public*, pg. 910
Boone, Micahel, Pres.--Gasboy International, Inc., Lansdale, PA; *U.S. Public*, pg. 1620
Boone, Sam, Chief Exec. Officer--United Self Insured Services, Orlando, FL; *U.S. Public*, pg. 1312
Boone, Thomas H., Chm. Bd. & Chief Exec. Officer--Countrywide Agency, Inc., Pasadena, CA; *U.S. Public*, pg. 452
Boone, Thomas H., Chm. Bd. & Chief Oper. Officer--Countrywide Title Corporation, Pasadena, CA; *U.S. Public*, pg. 453
Boonen, Tjeert, Chief Oper. Officer--SCA Packaging Benelux, Eerbeek, Netherlands; *Int'l*, pg. 1326
Boonstra, C., Chm. Bd. & Pres.--Philips Electronics N.V., Eindhoven, Netherlands; *Int'l*, pg. 1051
Boonstra, Cor, Pres.--Philips International B.V., Eindhoven, Netherlands; *Int'l*, pg. 1051
Boonstra, John, Pres.--Dempster Equipment, Toccoa, GA; *U.S. Private*, pg. 1089
Boonyavanich, Vivat, Area Mgr.--Thai Airways Intl. Ltd.-Dallas, Dallas, TX; *Int'l*, pg. 1381
Boos, Frederich, Dir.-Opers.--The Toro Co., Tomah, WI; *U.S. Public*, pg. 1624
Boosey, Harry, Chief Oper. Officer--Aqua Glass Corp., Adamsville, TN; *U.S. Public*, pg. 1053
Boot, P.A.J.A., Rep.--Netherlands Caribbean Bank Cuba, Havana, Cuba; *Int'l*, pg. 651
Booth, A., Gen. Mgr.--Holset Engineering Company Ltd., Madison, IN; *U.S. Public*, pg. 468
Booth, C.G.R., Mng. Dir.--Colin Booth Ltd., Barton-upon-Humber, United Kingdom; *Int'l*, pg. 1251
Booth, George N., Gen. Mgr.--Ford Casting Division, Dearborn, MI; *U.S. Public*, pg. 662
Booth, John P., Waltham Plant Mgr.--Raytheon Electronics Systems, Waltham, MA; *U.S. Public*, pg. 1364
Booth, Judith A., Pres.--Courier Connection, Inc., Westford, MA; *U.S. Public*, pg. 453
Booth, Robert W., Gen. Mgr.--Wackenhut of Canada Ltd., Don Mills, Canada; *U.S. Public*, pg. 1731
Boots, James, Gen. Mgr.--Wichita Raytheon Learning Center, Wichita, KS; *U.S. Public*, pg. 219
Booty, S., Mng. Dir.--Chep UK Limited, Addlestone, United Kingdom; *Int'l*, pg. 212
Bootzin, Jerry, Admin.--Elms Haven Care Center, Thornton, CO; *U.S. Public*, pg. 836
Boozer, G.R., V.P.-Mfg.--Dan River Danville Mfg. Div., Danville, VA; *U.S. Public*, pg. 479
Bopst, Wolf-Dieter, Chief Oper. Officer--Osram GmbH, Munich, Germany; *Int'l*, pg. 1244
Borbolla, Gustavo, Res. Dir.--Leo Burnett S.A. de C.V., Mexico, Mexico; *U.S. Private*, pg. 185
Borchardt, Robert L., Pres.--DiscWasher, Lake Mary, FL; *U.S. Public*, pg. 1369
Borchardt, Robert L., Chm. Bd. & Chief Exec. Officer--Interact Accessories, Inc., Hunt Valley, MD; *U.S. Public*, pg. 1369
Borchers, R.L., Pres.--Texaco Guatemala Inc., Guatemala, Guatemala; *U.S. Public*, pg. 1584
Borchert, Ernst-August, Gen. Mgr.--Deutsche Bank AG (Taipei), Taipei, Taiwan; *Int'l*, pg. 405
Borchsenius, Jette, Fin. Dir.--Leo Burnett Denmark, Copenhagen, Denmark; *U.S. Private*, pg. 185
Borda, Paul, Gen. Mgr.--Lawry's The Prime Rib, Dallas, TX; *U.S. Private*, pg. 654
Bordage, Real, Pres.--H.B. Fuller, Canada Inc., Mississauga, Canada; *U.S. Public*, pg. 687
Bordas, G., Chm. & Gen. Mgr.--Nationale-Nederlanden, Budapest, Hungary; *Int'l*, pg. 650
Bordau, Roland, Mng. Dir.--S.A. Bergiers N.V., Brussels, Belgium; *Int'l*, pg. 281
Bordelon, Wayne, Mgr.-Sls.--Klockner-Moeller, Itasca, IL; *Int'l*, pg. 736
Borden, D., Pres.--Luxfer USA Ltd., Riverside, CA; *Int'l*, pg. 50
Borden, Lester, V.P. & Gen. Mgr.--Columbia Pictures Merchandising, New York, NY; *Int'l*, pg. 1281
Bordenape, Philippe, Pres.--BNP Finance, Paris, France; *Int'l*, pg. 163
Borders, Elzie Z., Pres.--Noranda Aluminium, Brentwood, TN; *Int'l*, pg. 434
Bordetas, Javier, Mgr.--Allergan S.A.E., Madrid, Spain; *U.S. Public*, pg. 46
Bordier, Laurent, Mgr.-Opers.--Titan France SA, Gennevilliers Cedex, France; *U.S. Public*, pg. 1619
Bordoni, Nuccio, Pres.--Leo Burnett Co., S.r.l., Milan, Italy; *U.S. Private*, pg. 185
Borer, Mel, Pres.--Share Technologies - Fairchild, South Hackensack, NJ; *U.S. Public*, pg. 1568
Borer, Melvin D., Pres.--Share Technologies - Fairchild, Chantilly, VA; *U.S. Public*, pg. 1568
Boresjo, Hans, Chief Oper. Officer--Perstorp Form Ltd., Abingdon, United Kingdom; *Int'l*, pg. 1038
Borg, Malcom A., Chief Oper. Officer--Macromedia Leasing, Hackensack, NJ; *U.S. Private*, pg. 693
Borgar, P., Gen. Mgr.--Boonville Mining Services, Inc., Boonville, IN; *U.S. Private*, pg. 177
Borge, Richard, Mgr.--RealCold Storage, Miami, FL; *U.S. Private*, pg. 1025
Borgen, Bjorgn, Fin. Dir.--Leo Burnett A/S, Oslo, Norway; *U.S. Private*, pg. 184
Borgen, Knut, Pres.--Aker Engineering plc (AE), London, United Kingdom; *Int'l*, pg. 42
Borgersen, Kari, Controller--Sensormatic A/S, Oslo, Norway; *U.S. Public*, pg. 1457
Borgfeld, Roland, Opers. Dir.--Vickers Systems GmbH (Aerospace-Marine-Defense Trinova GmbH), Bad Homburg, Germany; *U.S. Public*, pg. 25
Borghese, Francesco, Chm. Bd. & Pres.--Orlane, Inc., New York, NY; *Int'l*, pg. 1011
Borgkrantz, Anders, Pres.--Sparbanken Finans, Stockholm, Sweden; *Int'l*, pg. 1328
Borgman, Dean C., Sr. V.P. & Gen. Mgr.--Boeing Helicopter Division, Mesa, AZ; *U.S. Public*, pg. 241
Borgstrom, Bo, Mgr.--Tolkkinen Sawmill, Porvoo, Finland; *Int'l*, pg. 456
Boright, Ken, Gen. Mgr.--RTS Packaging, Orange, CA; *U.S. Public*, pg. 1397
Borin, A., Dr., Mgr.--Morgan Matroc Srl, Milan, Italy; *Int'l*, pg. 893
Boris, James R., Chm. & Chief Exec. Officer--EVEREN Securities, Inc., Chicago, IL; *U.S. Public*, pg. 597
Borke, George, Gen. Mgr.--Sterling Electronics, Columbia, MD; *U.S. Public*, pg. 1051
Borkenhagen, Hansi, Mgr.--GGK Oslo, Oslo, Norway; *Int'l*, pg. 1335
Borkovee, Mark T., V.P.--Willis Corroon Financial Services Corp., Denver, CO; *Int'l*, pg. 1507
Borkowski, Bill, Gen. Mgr.--Cit-Con Oil Corporation, Lake Charles, LA; *Int'l*, pg. 1045
Borlet, Robert A., Pres.--Jay-El Products, Inc., Carson, CA; *U.S. Public*, pg. 534
Borm, Gunter, Gen. Mgr.--Chemische Fabrik Kalk GmbH, Cologne, Germany; *Int'l*, pg. 104
Borm, Udo, Mgr.--Hapag-Lloyd Reiseburo GmbH, Bremen, Germany; *Int'l*, pg. 596
Borman, Laurie, Dir. & Editor In Chief--Endless Vacation, Indianapolis, IN; *U.S. Public*, pg. 322
Bormaster, Lisa, Publr.--American City Business Journals, Inc., Austin, TX; *U.S. Private*, pg. 19
Born, Cheryl, Chief Fin. Officer--Quebecor Printing Arlington Heights, Arlington Heights, IL; *Int'l*, pg. 1076
Born, George W., Mgr.--Voest-Alpine Services and Technologies Corp.-Material Handling Equipment, Pittsburgh, PA; *Int'l*, pg. 1471
Born, Jurgen L., Mng. Dir.--Banco de Montevideo, Montevideo, Uruguay; *Int'l*, pg. 403
Born, Rik, Pres.--Installation Products Div., Lancaster, PA; *U.S. Public*, pg. 132
Borne, Mike, Pres.--Phillips & Jacobs/North, Lititz, PA; *U.S. Public*, pg. 1329
Bornemann, Burkhard, Mng. Dir.--Dresdner Bank AG, Seoul, Korea; *Int'l*, pg. 419
Bornemeiza, Paul, Gen. Mgr.--S.C. Johnson de Centroamerica S.A., San Jose, Costa Rica; *U.S. Private*, pg. 593
Borneson, Hans, Mgr.--Cardo Pump AB, Molndal, Sweden; *Int'l*, pg. 270
Borney, Gian Mario, Mng. Dir.--PAXAR Italia S.r.l., Milan, Italy; *U.S. Public*, pg. 1267
Bornhuetter, Ronald L., Chm. Bd.--Greenwich Insurance Company, Greenwich, CT; *U.S. Public*, pg. 1144
Bornichen, Gunter, Dir.--Meeraner Dampfkeeselbau GmbH, Meerane, Germany; *Int'l*, pg. 398
Bornschein, Karl, V.P.-Central Reg. & Gen. Mgr.-Germany--Medtronic GmbH, Dusseldorf, Germany; *U.S. Public*, pg. 1083
Boron, Paul, Mgr.--Calgon Carbon Canada, Inc., Mississauga, Canada; *U.S. Public*, pg. 293
Borone, Robert P., Chief Exec. Officer--InterBold, Canton, OH; *U.S. Public*, pg. 506
Boronow, Gordon C., Chief Oper. Officer--American Skandia Life Assurance Corporation, Shelton, CT; *Int'l*, pg. 1257
Borow, Len, Pres.--Comstron Division, Plainview, NY; *U.S. Public*, pg. 24
Borowitz, Judith A., Pres. & Chief Exec. Officer--Chemical Bank South, Marshall, MI; *U.S. Public*, pg. 345
Borregales, Carlos, Pres.--Bitumenes Orinoco, S.A. (BITOR), Caracas, Venezuela; *Int'l*, pg. 1045
Borrello, Dina, Mgr.--Broad National Bank-North Arlington, North Arlington, NJ; *U.S. Public*, pg. 258
Borren, Lars, Chief Oper. Officer--AB Hoors Plat, Hoor, Sweden; *Int'l*, pg. 439
Borroni, Giorgia, Dir.--Hyster Italia S.r.L., Milan, Italy; *U.S. Public*, pg. 1149
Borsch, Hans, Div. Pres.--Klockner-Borsch Tooling Technologies, Clearwater, FL; *Int'l*, pg. 737
Borserini, Riccardo, Sr. Mng. Dir.--Dr. Scholl's SpA, Italy; *Int'l*, pg. 1209
Borst, Frank, Pres.--Gyyr, Inc., Anaheim, CA; *U.S. Public*, pg. 1212
Borst, Robert, Resident V.P.--Fireman's Fund Insurance Co. of Wisconsin, Wauwatosa, WI; *Int'l*, pg. 59
Bortak, John, Pres.--Franklin Oil Corp., Bedford, OH; *Int'l*, pg. 892
Bortnak, John T., V.P.--Commonwealth Indonesia, Jakarta, Indonesia; *U.S. Public*, pg. 143
Bortolleto, Hamilton, Gen. Mgr.--Global Trading Ltd., Miami, FL; *Int'l*, pg. 688
Borunda, Claudia, Admin.--Horizon Healthcare Nursing Center, Albuquerque, NM; *U.S. Public*, pg. 838
Borwege, Brenda, V.P.--Faribo Woolens, Inc., Faribault, MN; *U.S. Private*, pg. 394
Borzino, Leo, Pres. & Chief Exec. Officer--Petite Sophisticate Outlet, Enfield, CT; *U.S. Private*, pg. 219
Bos, Gerrit, Mng. Dir.--Krips Repro B.V., Meppel, Netherlands; *Int'l*, pg. 1100
Bos, Henk, Chief Oper. Officer--SCA De Hoop, Eerbeek, Netherlands; *Int'l*, pg. 1326
Bosau, Robert D., Pres.--Tribune Education, Chicago, IL; *U.S. Public*, pg. 1636
Boscamp, Jim, Pres.--Nautica Footwear, Nashville, TN; *U.S. Public*, pg. 728
Bosch, Fred, Pres.--Barenbrug Northeast, Ogdensburg, NJ; *Int'l*, pg. 167
Bosch, Frederick J.L., Mgr.--Barenbrug USA, Tangent, OR; *Int'l*, pg. 166
Bosch, H.J., Pres.--Swiss Bank Corporation (Overseas) S.A., Panama, Panama; *Int'l*, pg. 1332
Bosch, Manfred, Liaison Officer--DAMM Agentur Fur Marketing und Werbung, Frankfurt/Main, Germany; *U.S. Private*, pg. 1152
Bosch, Walter, Creative Dir. & Member of the Bd.--Bosch & Butz, Zollikon, Switzerland; *U.S. Private*, pg. 678
Boscheinen, Hans, Gen. Mgr.--Avon Cosmetics GmbH, Neufahrn, Germany; *U.S. Public*, pg. 156
Boschetto, Andrew, Pres.--Quebecor Printing Modern Inc., Brookfield, CT; *Int'l*, pg. 1078
Boschian, Sante, Chief Oper. Officer--AGEMA Infrared Systems SRL, Cascina, Italy; *Int'l*, pg. 1289
Boschsler, Karl, Chief Exec.--Sulzer Infra Deutschland GmbH., Stuttgart, Germany; *Int'l*, pg. 1306
Boscia, Jon A., Pres.--Lincoln Financial Group, Inc., Fort Wayne, IN; *U.S. Public*, pg. 997
Bosco, Carmine F., Grp. V.P.--Giddings & Lewis Sheffield Measurement Systems, Dayton, OH; *Int'l*, pg. 1389
Bosco, Frank A., Gen. Mgr.--Tech Systems Corp., Thomaston, CT; *U.S. Private*, pg. 313
Bosco, Lorenzo, Mng. Dir.--SI Sealing Parts SpA, Carpi, Italy; *Int'l*, pg. 1338
Bose, U., Chm. Bd.--Creditcapital Finance Corp., Ltd., Mumbai, India; *Int'l*, pg. 1440
Bosha, Jim, Creative Dir.--Campbell Mithun Esty, New York, NY; *U.S. Private*, pg. 204
Boshell, J., Mgr.--Angus Fire Armour (S.A.) Limited, Primrose, South Africa; *Int'l*, pg. 1500
Boshi, Edward, Pres.--Legal & General Holdings (France) S.A., Paris, France; *Int'l*, pg. 805
Bosin, Seth, Mkt. Mgr.--Outdoor Systems, Inc.-Connecticut, New Haven, CT; *U.S. Public*, pg. 1235
Bosio, Giovanni, Mng. Dir.--Stanhome S.p.A., Rome, Italy; *U.S. Public*, pg. 1508
Bosma, Tiemen, V.P.-Y&R Europe--PMSVW/Young & Rubicam B.V., Amsterdam, Netherlands; *U.S. Private*, pg. 1199
Bosmans, Luc, Chief Oper. Officer--S.A. Novo Nordisk Pharma NV, Brussels, Belgium; *Int'l*, pg. 988
Bosnik, Douglas, Gen. Mgr.--SFZ Transportation Inc., Cleveland, OH; *U.S. Public*, pg. 218
Bosquez, Ramon, Pres.--UETA, Inc., Laredo, TX; *Int'l*, pg. 103
Boss, Russell A., Pres.--A.T. Cross Export Co., Lincoln, RI; *U.S. Public*, pg. 461
Bossard, Alexander, Mng. Dir.--De Pretto-Escher Wyss s.r.l., Schio, Italy; *Int'l*, pg. 1305
Bossard, Franz, Mng. Dir.--Neste Chemicals Handelsgesellschaft mbH, Vienna, Austria; *Int'l*, pg. 914
Bossard, Franz, Mng. Dir.--Borealis S.A., Geneva, Switzerland; *Int'l*, pg. 914
Bosschart, Edmund A., Chief Oper. Officer--Electrolux-Servicos Soc. Commercial Ltda., Sao Paulo, Brazil; *Int'l*, pg. 441
Bosser, Gottfried J.K., Rep.--Bayerische Landesbank Girozentrale, Johannesburg, South Africa; *Int'l*, pg. 177
Bossidy, Bruce, Pres.--EGA, Seymour, CT; *Int'l*, pg. 436
Bossidy, Lawrence A., Chief Exec. Officer--AlliedSignal Aerospace, Stratford, CT; *U.S. Public*, pg. 50
Bossini, G.I., Mng. Dir.--Marchon Italiana S.P.A., Castiglione delle Stiviere, Italy; *U.S. Public*, pg. 1580
Bostic, Sid, Pres.--Norwest Bank Indiana, N.A., Fort Wayne, IN; *U.S. Public*, pg. 1202
Bostic, Steve, Pres.--American Photo Group, Atlanta, GA; *U.S. Public*, pg. 551
Boston, Larry D., Pres.--UMB First State Bank of Morrisonville, Morrisonville, IL; *U.S. Public*, pg. 1654
Boston, Michael L., Pres.--Fuel Systems Textron Inc., Zeeland, MI; *U.S. Public*, pg. 1589
Boston, Ward, Pres.--Fawcett Memorial Hospital, Inc., Port Charlotte, FL; *U.S. Public*, pg. 404
Boswell, E.F., Pres. & Chief Oper. Officer--Eddy Paper Company Limited, Ottawa, Canada; *Int'l*, pg. 1495

Boswell, Jim, V.P.--Lou Ana Foods, Inc., Opelousas, LA; *Int'l*, pg. 879

Boswell, Roy, Pres.--Flanders Airpure Products Co., LLC, Selma, NC; *U.S. Public*, pg. 648

Bosworth, Robert, Chief Fin. Officer--HBA Insurance Ltd., Hamilton, Bermuda; *U.S. Public*, pg. 342

Bosworth, Robert, Chief Fin. Officer--Signal Investment & Management Co., Wilmington, DE; *U.S. Public*, pg. 342

Botar, Bela, Pres.--Omnibus BB Transportes, S.A., Quito, Ecuador; *U.S. Public*, pg. 723

Botelho, Eduardo, Gen. Mgr.--Parker Hannifin Industria e Comercio Ltda., Sao Paulo, Brazil; *U.S. Public*, pg. 1260

Botha, Hannes, Mng. Dir.--Sasol Synthetic Fuels (Pty.) Ltd., Secunda, South Africa; *Int'l*, pg. 1197

Botha, Kobus, Mgr.-Sls. & Admin.--Sasol Ammonia, Johannesburg, South Africa; *Int'l*, pg. 1196

Botha, R.M., Chief Fin. Officer--Sasol Oil, Rosebank, South Africa; *Int'l*, pg. 1197

Bothe, Klau, Co-Chief Oper. Officer--Daarberg-Oekotechnik GmbH, Saarbruecken, Germany; *Int'l*, pg. 1167

Bothe, Siegfried, Chief Oper. Officer--BORSIG Kugelhahn GmbH, Berlin, Germany; *Int'l*, pg. 400

Bothmer, Wolf-Dieter, Sr. Mng. Dir.--Deutsche Bank-Kreditbank AG (Dresden), Dresden, Germany; *Int'l*, pg. 402

Botkin, Steve T., Plant Mgr.--Kohler Co. (TX), Brownwood, TX; *U.S. Private*, pg. 630

Botnar, Octave, Chm. Bd. & Chief Exec. Officer--Nissan Motor Manufacturing (UK) Ltd., Sunderland, United Kingdom; *Int'l*, pg. 945

Bottani, G. F., Dir.--Marchon Hellas Limited, Athens, Greece; *U.S. Public*, pg. 1580

Bottcher, Eric, Chm.--Suez Nederland Securities N.V., Amsterdam, Netherlands; *Int'l*, pg. 314

Botterbusch, Reiner, Mng. Dir.--Preussag International Steel Corp., Atlanta, GA; *Int'l*, pg. 1070

Bottger, Christian, Mgr.--Hurth Branch, Hurth, Germany; *Int'l*, pg. 401

Bottiglieri, Denise, Pres.--Health Science Communications, New York, NY; *U.S. Private*, pg. 506

Botting, Harvey, Reg. V.P.--Quebecor Printing Atlantic Saint John, Saint John, Canada; *Int'l*, pg. 1077

Bottom, J.D., Chief Oper. Officer--Laing Homes Ltd., Milton Keynes, United Kingdom; *Int'l*, pg. 796

Bottoms, Jack, Pres.--FOCAS, Alpharetta, GA; *Int'l*, pg. 329

Botton, John M., V.P. & Gen. Mgr.--Selkirk (HVAC) Europe, Barnstaple, United Kingdom; *U.S. Public*, pg. 1795

Bottorf, Richard, Publisher--The Bulletin Company, Norwich, CT; *U.S. Public*, pg. 700

Botts, V.V., Gen. Mgr.--Porgera Joint Venture, Port Moresby, Papua New Guinea; *Int'l*, pg. 1060

Botvin, Peter, Gen. Mgr.--ACS Internacional S.A. de C.V., Monterrey, Mexico; *U.S. Private*, pg. 4

Botwick, William S., Pres.--General Motors Taiwan, Inc., Taipei, Taiwan; *U.S. Public*, pg. 723

Boucard, A., Chief Oper. Officer--Renault Bisquit, Rouillac, France; *Int'l*, pg. 566

Bouchard, J., Chief Oper. Officer--Elf Petroleum U.K., London, United Kingdom; *Int'l*, pg. 446

Bouchard, Michel, Sr. V.P. & Gen. Mgr.--Allergan France S.A., Lingolsheim, France; *U.S. Public*, pg. 46

Bouchard, Michel, Pres.--Beauticontrol Cosmetics Canada Ltd., Burlington, Canada; *U.S. Public*, pg. 199

Bouchard, Roger, Chief Exec. Officer--Green Mountain Steel Erectors Inc., Bennington, VT; *U.S. Private*, pg. 133

Bouchat, Andrew, V.P. & Gen. Mgr.--Sudler & Hennessey/Gall Inc., Montreal, Canada; *U.S. Private*, pg. 1200

Boucher, George, Pres.--Marine Exhibition Corporation, Miami, FL; *U.S. Private*, pg. 1186

Boucher, Greg, Gen. Mgr.--Ulbrich of California, Inc., Fresno, CA; *U.S. Private*, pg. 1115

Boucher, Michel, V.P.--RX Information Centre Ltd., Longueuil, Canada; *Int'l*, pg. 340

Bouchet, Philippe, Dr., Mng. Dir.--Barringer Europe, SARL, Roissy, France; *U.S. Public*, pg. 192

Bouchie, L. Kirk, Reg. Pres.--Citizens Bank, Vincennes Region, Vincennes, IN; *U.S. Public*, pg. 281

Bouchier, Michael W., Chief Oper. Officer & Mng. Dir.--Sasol Fibres, Reunion, South Africa; *Int'l*, pg. 1196

Bouchoms, Jacques, Mgr.--MMRA Metallurgique et Miniere de Rodange-Athus S.A., Rodange, Luxembourg; *Int'l*, pg. 80

Bouck, J. Steven, Pres.--Superior Blends, Inc., Seattle, WA; *U.S. Public*, pg. 1652

Boucquey, Philippe, Gen. Mgr.--N.V. Crown-Baele S. A., Brussels, Belgium; *U.S. Public*, pg. 464

Boudewijns, A.A., Gen. Mgr.--Peco Suikerwerken B.V., Breda, Netherlands; *Int'l*, pg. 1451

Boudieau, Edward J., Jr., Chm. & Chief Exec. Officer--Berkeley Financial Group, Boston, MA; *U.S. Private*, pg. 589

Boudreaux, Gerald P., Pres.--LGS Securities, Inc., Harvey, LA; *U.S. Public*, pg. 380

Bouey, Jacques, Mng. Dir.--Messages & Tequila, Paris, France; *Int'l*, pg. 116

Bouftas, Haj Abderrahman, Pres.--Algemene Bank Marokko S.A., Casablanca, Morocco; *Int'l*, pg. 11

Boughtwood, A.J., Chief Exec. Officer--Protimeter plc, Marlow, United Kingdom; *Int'l*, pg. 207

Bouhelier, Jacques, Chm. Bd. & Chief Exec. Officer--Messier-Dowty SAS, Velizy-Villacoublay, France; *Int'l*, pg. 1340

Bouis, H., Chief Oper. Officer--Vetrotex France, Chambery, France; *Int'l*, pg. 1177

Boujo, Patrick, Pres.--IPC Peripherals Pte Ltd., Singapore, Singapore; *Int'l*, pg. 651

Boulaire, Michael, Gen. Mgr.--Gie Moet Hennessy Distribution, Epernay, France; *Int'l*, pg. 781

Boulan, Thierry, Pres. & Dir. General--Societe de Banque de l'Orleanais, Orleans, France; *Int'l*, pg. 548

Bouland, Harold, Gen. Mgr.--Barton's of Jonesboro, Jonesboro, AR; *U.S. Private*, pg. 119

Boulet, Oliver, Gen. Mgr.--Kenner Parker Toys, Paris, France; *U.S. Public*, pg. 798

Bouley, Bruno, Chm. Bd. & Chief Exec. Officer--Dumez Construction, Malakoff, France; *Int'l*, pg. 823

Boulonois, Bram, Chief Oper. Officer--Villares Steel International BV, Dordrecht, Netherlands; *Int'l*, pg. 23

Bouloukos, Don P., Pres.--WABC-AM Radio, Inc., New York, NY; *U.S. Public*, pg. 512

Bouloukos, Don P., Pres.-Group I--Capital Cities/ABC Owned Radio Stations, New York, NY; *U.S. Public*, pg. 512

Boultbee, John, Pres.--Saturday Night Magazine Limited, Toronto, Canada; *Int'l*, pg. 631

Boultinghouse, Marlan, Pres.--ARCO Aluminum, Russellville, KY; *U.S. Public*, pg. 144

Boulton, Bruce, Gen. Mgr.--Richmond Mill, Richmond, VA; *U.S. Public*, pg. 466

Boulton, S., Mng. Dir.--Penny & Giles Aerospace Ltd., Christchurch, United Kingdom; *Int'l*, pg. 207

Boulware, Thomas M. III, Pres.--Brown-Service Funeral Homes Co., Inc., Birmingham, AL; *U.S. Public*, pg. 1622

Boumal, Philippe, Gen. Mgr.--Notifier (Benelux) S.A., Alleur, Belgium; *U.S. Public*, pg. 1307

Bouniol, Bruno, Chief Oper. Officer--Diabolo-Manus S.A., Les Clayes-sous-Bois, France; *Int'l*, pg. 1379

Bourbeau, Jean-Louis, Chm.--William M. Mercer Limited, Toronto, Canada; *U.S. Public*, pg. 1049

Bourbon, Bruce R., Pres.--Advanced Information Technology Center, San Jose, CA; *Int'l*, pg. 1405

Bourda, Michael, Mng. Dir.--Rust Craft International, S.A., Monaco, Monaco; *U.S. Public*, pg. 78

Bouree, Denis, Mgr.-Plant--Raffinerie de Marseille, Marseilles, France; *Int'l*, pg. 549

Bourg, Bob, Pres.--Southcorp Packaging USA, Inc., Peotone, IL; *Int'l*, pg. 1287

Bourgeaux, Eric, Mng. Dir.--Nokia Finance International B.V., Geneva Branch, Carouge, Switzerland; *Int'l*, pg. 954

Bourgeois, Herve, Reg. Mgr.--Check Point Software Technologies SARL, Paris, France; *U.S. Public*, pg. 342

Bourgois, Jean-Manuel, Pres.--Editions Bordas, Paris, France; *Int'l*, pg. 239

Bourgue, Mary-Elle M., Dir.--Cognos Barbados Ltd., Bridgetown, Barbados; *Int'l*, pg. 306

Bourguignon, Patrick, Pres.-Novotel--Accor North America, Scarsdale, NY; *Int'l*, pg. 21

Bourhill, John, Mgr.-Order Dept.--Aeroclo Metal Products, Yonkers, NY; *U.S. Private*, pg. 880

Bourke, Paul G., Chm. & Mng. Dir.--Campbell's Soups (Aust.) Pty. Ltd., Melbourne, Australia; *U.S. Public*, pg. 299

Bourke, Roger, Mgr.--International Public Relations, Pty Ltd., Perth, Australia; *Int'l*, pg. 1227

Bourland, Curtis F., Pres. & Chief Exec. Officer--Continental Graphics Corporation, Los Angeles, CA; *U.S. Private*, pg. 268

Bourlet, Jean Francois, Chm.--CAP Sesa Informatique Hospitaliere, Paris, France; *Int'l*, pg. 263

Bourne, J.P., Pres.--Warner-Lambert K.K., Tokyo, Japan; *U.S. Public*, pg. 1739

Bourne, N., Mng. Dir.--Staeng Limited, Cornwall, United Kingdom; *Int'l*, pg. 207

Bourque, Dennis, Pres.--Western Enterprises Div., Westlake, OH; *U.S. Public*, pg. 218

Bourque, M. Phyllis, Pres.--Sunterra Gas Gathering Company, Albuquerque, NM; *U.S. Public*, pg. 1340

Bourque, M. Phyllis, Pres.--Sunterra Gas Processing Company, Albuquerque, NM; *U.S. Public*, pg. 1340

Boursoit, Jean, Rep.--Banque Indosuez Generale Euro Turk AS, Istanbul, Turkey; *Int'l*, pg. 548

Boury, Patrick, Mng. Dir.--Compagnie Hobart, S.A., Croissy-Beaubourg, France; *U.S. Public*, pg. 1322

Bousfield, David, Dir.--Elsevier Advanced Technology, Kidlington, United Kingdom; *Int'l*, pg. 1100

Bousfield, David, Dir.--Elsevier Trends Journals, Cambridge, United Kingdom; *Int'l*, pg. 1100

Bousman, Jim, Dir.--Sight and Sound, Milwaukee, WI; *U.S. Public*, pg. 749

Bout, J.A.J., Mgr.--ABN Trustcompany (Luxembourg) S.A., Luxembourg, Luxembourg; *Int'l*, pg. 11

Bouteille, Francois, Deputy Mng. Dir.--NPI, Paris, France; *Int'l*, pg. 503

Boutin, Andre J., V.P.-Cable--NORDX/CDT, Lachine, Canada; *U.S. Public*, pg. 287

Bouton, Tom, Plant Mgr.--Firestone Synthetic Rubber & Latex Company-Lake Charles, Sulphur, LA; *Int'l*, pg. 214

Boutte, Boyd, Mgr.--Trappey's Fine Foods, Inc., New Iberia, LA; *U.S. Private*, pg. 105

Bouvette, Bill, Pres.--Media Duplication International, Calgary, Canada; *Int'l*, pg. 853

Bouvia, Robert, Gen. Mgr.--Ilco Unican Corp., Plattsburgh, NY; *Int'l*, pg. 1432

Bouvier, Roy L., Pres.--Crystal Biotech, Inc., Northborough, MA; *U.S. Public*, pg. 1056

Bouvier, Yves, V.P. & Gen. Mgr.--Gould Instrument Systems, S.A., Longjumeau, France; *U.S. Public*, pg. 1592

Bouw, Pieter, Pres.--KLM Royal Dutch Airlines, Elmsford, NY; *Int'l*, pg. 719

Bouwman, T.G.G., Chm. Bd.--VNU Tijdschriftengroep Nederland Bv, Amstelveen, Netherlands; *Int'l*, pg. 1445

Bouwman, T.G.G., Gen. Mgr.--Tableau Fine Arts Magazine bv, Haastrecht, Netherlands; *Int'l*, pg. 1445

Bouwman, T.G.G., Gen. Mgr.--Uitgeverij Veldhuis bv, Raalte, Netherlands; *Int'l*, pg. 1445

Bouwman, T.G.G., Gen. Mgr.--Accres Uitgevers bv, Naarden, Netherlands; *Int'l*, pg. 1445

Bouwman, T.G.G., Gen. Mgr.--Uitgeverij Veldhuis bv, Hoofddorp, Netherlands; *Int'l*, pg. 1445

Bouwman, T.G.G., Gen. Dir.--Uitgeverij Woudestein bv, Naarden, Netherlands; *Int'l*, pg. 1445

Bouysset, A., Pres.--Laboratoires Merck Sharp & Dohme S.A., Paris, France; *U.S. Public*, pg. 1092

Bova, Alfred T., V.P. & Gen. Mgr.-Radio--KYW TV, Philadelphia, PA; *U.S. Public*, pg. 275

Bovie, D. Fred, Reg. Dir.-North America--The Esab Group, Inc., Hanover, PA; *Int'l*, pg. 281

Bovington, Nigel, Mng. Dir.--Credit Insurance Association, London, United Kingdom; *Int'l*, pg. 671

Bovis, Claude, Pres.--Les Cables de Lyon, Clichy, France; *Int'l*, pg. 56

Bovy, Edouard, Dir. Gen.--Banque de Kigali, Kigali, Rwanda; *Int'l*, pg. 548

Bovy, M., Chief Oper. Officer--S.A. P.A.G.E. Municipal, Liege, Belgium; *Int'l*, pg. 301

Bovy, M., Chief Oper. Officer--S.A. Legrain, Blehories, Belgium; *Int'l*, pg. 301

Bovy, Michel, Mgr.--Credit Agricole (CNCA) Representative Office-Tokyo, Tokyo, Japan; *Int'l*, pg. 341

Bowcutt, A.J., V.P. & Gen. Mgr.--Nucor Steel-Utah, Plymouth, UT; *U.S. Public*, pg. 1205

Bowden, Anthony, Mng. Dir.--Liebert Corporation Australia Pty. Ltd., Regents Park, Australia; *U.S. Public*, pg. 577

Bowden, Ashley E., Pres. & Chief Oper. Officer--QST Communications, Inc., Peoria, IL; *U.S. Public*, pg. 367

Bowden, Benjamin J., Pres.--BancBoston Financial Co., Boston, MA; *U.S. Public*, pg. 184

Bowden, Bill R., Pres.--Hardin's-Sysco Food Services, Inc., Memphis, TN; *U.S. Public*, pg. 1551

Bowden, Del, Pres.--First Mortgage Corporation, Omaha, NE; *U.S. Public*, pg. 501

Bowden, Earl, Gen. Mgr.--Boeing Aerospace & Electronics, Oak Ridge, Oak Ridge, TN; *U.S. Public*, pg. 240

Bowden, G.E., Gen. Mgr.--PACCAR Winch Division, Broken Arrow, OK; *U.S. Public*, pg. 1246

Bowden, J. W., Exec. V.P.--Canadian Imperial Holdings, Inc., Wilmington, DE; *Int'l*, pg. 257

Bowden, John, Mgr.--Commerzbank Europe (Ireland), Dublin, Ireland; *Int'l*, pg. 312

Bowden, Travis J., Pres. & Chief Exec. Officer--Gulf Power Company, Pensacola, FL; *U.S. Public*, pg. 1490

Bowen, C. J., V.P. & Gen. Mgr.--Meals Div., White Plains, NY; *U.S. Public*, pg. 1287

Bowen, Howard, Gen. Mgr.-Production--Juver Industrial S.A. de C.V., Juarez, Mexico; *U.S. Public*, pg. 1065

Bowen, Jim C., V.P.--Sonoco Paper Division, Hartsville, SC; *U.S. Public*, pg. 1486

Bowen, Kevin C., Pres. & Chief Exec. Officer--K-Tron America, Inc., Pitman, NJ; *U.S. Public*, pg. 938

Bowen, Kris, V.P.--Piping Resources, Houston, TX; *U.S. Private*, pg. 162

Bowen, Michael, V.P. & Gen. Mgr.--Environmental Services of America-IN, Inc., South Bend, IN; *U.S. Public*, pg. 546

Bowen, Mike, Gen. Mgr.--Azzura-International Marketing & Promotions, Milan, Italy; *U.S. Private*, pg. 303

Bowen, Norman W., Pres.--Century Credit Life Insurance Company, Tupelo, MS; *U.S. Public*, pg. 176

Bowen, Peter L., Pres.-Retail Prods. Grp.--Heinz U.S.A. Div., Pittsburgh, PA; *U.S. Public*, pg. 805

Bowen, Robert, Pres.--Hueller Hille Corporation, Troy, MI; *Int'l*, pg. 1387

Bowen, Robert M., Pres.--First American Title Co. of Nevada, Reno, NV; *U.S. Public*, pg. 625

Bowen, Stephen T., Pres. & Chief Exec. Officer--Polymer Composites Inc., Winona, MN; *Int'l*, pg. 624

Bowen, William, Regional Pres.--First Tennessee Bank - Gallatin, Gallatin, TN; *U.S. Public*, pg. 639

Bower, Hayward W., Chm. Bd.--Rowe Industries, Toledo, OH; *U.S. Public*, pg. 308

Bower, Haywood, Pres.--Porcelain Products, Carey, OH; *U.S. Public*, pg. 308

Bower, Haywood, Div. V.P.--Olean Advanced Products Division, Olean, NY; *Int'l*, pg. 775

Bower, John, Pres. & Gen. Mgr.--Hanover Wire Cloth, Hanover, PA; *U.S. Private*, pg. 193

Bower, Marvin D., Chm. Bd.--State Farm Life Insurance Co., Bloomington, IL; *U.S. Private*, pg. 1036

Bower, Mike, V.P. & Gen. Mgr.--Dillard, A ResourceNet International Company, Macon, GA; *U.S. Public*, pg. 902

Bower, Norm, Mgr.-Plant--Nestle Beich Inc., Bloomington, IL; *Int'l*, pg. 917

Bowers, Christopher D., Pres.--United GHS Inc., Elk Grove Village, IL; *U.S. Public*, pg. 1653

Bowers, D.G., Branch Mgr.--Zellerbach Division, Jacksonville, FL; *U.S. Public*, pg. 1075

Bowers, David A., Pres.--National Cabinet Lock, Inc., Mauldin, SC; *U.S. Private*, pg. 270

Bowers, Franklin R., V.P. & Gen. Mgr.--Cox Cable Hampton Roads, Inc., Virginia Beach, VA; *U.S. Public*, pg. 455

Bowers, J., Facility Mgr.--Square D Co., Dallas, TX; *Int'l*, pg. 1208

Bowers, John, Pres. & Chief Exec. Officer--Southwestern Financial Services Corp., Dallas, TX; *U.S. Private*, pg. 1018

Bowers, John, Chief Oper. Officer--Marquette National Life Insurance Co., Dallas, TX; *U.S. Private*, pg. 1018

Bowers, William S., Chief Engineer--European Technical Center, Bascharage, Luxembourg; *U.S. Public*, pg. 721

Bowersock, James N., Pres. & Chief Oper. Officer--Miramichi Pulp & Paper Inc., Newcastle, Canada; *Int'l*, pg. 1104

Bowes, William E., Pres.--Sentinel Self-Storage Corporation, Calgary, Canada; *Int'l*, pg. 253

Bowie, Robert A., II, Pres.--First USA Capital Markets, Inc., Dallas, TX; *U.S. Public*, pg. 174

Bowker, Ray, Mng. Dir.--Westpac Insurance Services (Brokers) Limited, Sydney, Australia; *Int'l*, pg. 1496

Bowkett, Alan, Chm. Bd.--Magnet Ltd., Keighley, United Kingdom; *Int'l*, pg. 188

Bowler, G.J., Chief Exec. Officer--Kwik Save Group plc, Prestatyn, United Kingdom; *Int'l*, pg. 704

Bowles, Debra, Mgr.--California Physicians Insurance Corp., San Francisco, CA; *U.S. Private*, pg. 153

Bowles, Ian, Founder--Pronexus, Inc., Carp, Canada; *U.S. Public*, pg. 17

Bowles, Robert L., Pres. & Chief Exec. Officer--D.C. Chartered Health Plan, Washington, DC; *U.S. Public*, pg. 1241
Bowles, Timothy, Chief Exec. Officer--MRB Group, Inc., New York, NY; *Int'l*, pg. 1483
Bowlin, Jerry, Pres. & Sec.--Yellow Redevelopment Corp., Overland Park, KS; *U.S. Public*, pg. 1788
Bowlin, John, Pres.--Lender's Bagel Bakery, White Plains, NY; *U.S. Public*, pg. 1288
Bowlin, John D., Pres. & Chief Exec. Officer--Kraft Foods International, Rye Brook, NY; *U.S. Public*, pg. 1288
Bowling, H.T., Pres.--Lockheed Martin Skunk Works, Palmdale, CA; *U.S. Public*, pg. 1007
Bowling, Tom, Gen. Mgr.--Hollywood Park Casino, Inglewood, CA; *U.S. Public*, pg. 831
Bowlus, Brad, Pres.--PacifiCare of Washington, Seattle, WA; *U.S. Public*, pg. 1251
Bowlus, Brad A., Pres. & Chief Exec. Officer--PacifiCare of California, Cypress, CA; *U.S. Public*, pg. 1251
Bowman, Bob, Pres.--MGM Grand Merchandising, Inc., Las Vegas, NV; *U.S. Public*, pg. 1027
Bowman, C. Don, Pres.--Hilb, Rogal & Hamilton Company of McAllen, McAllen, TX; *U.S. Public*, pg. 827
Bowman, C.H., Chm. Bd.--BP Oil Co., Cleveland, OH; *Int'l*, pg. 220
Bowman, Donald E., Pres.--Redland Genstar Stone Products Company, Hunt Valley, MD; *Int'l*, pg. 1091
Bowman, Harry W., Chm. Bd., Pres. & Chief Exec. Officer--Outboard Marine Corporation, Waukegan, IL; *U.S. Private*, pg. 478
Bowman, John, Mng. Dir.--E-Z-EM Ltd., London, United Kingdom; *U.S. Public*, pg. 540
Bowman, Rick, Pres.--U.S. Bancorp Insurance Agency, Inc., Portland, OR; *U.S. Public*, pg. 1681
Bowmar, Mark, Mgr.--W.C. Caye & Co., Macon, GA; *U.S. Private*, pg. 220
Bowser, Lee H., Chief Oper. Officer--Insurer Physician Services Organization, Camp Hill, PA; *U.S. Private*, pg. 529
Bowtic, Bill, Gen. Mgr.--Payson Georgia, Inc., Atlanta, GA; *U.S. Private*, pg. 844
Bowyer, Robert, Mgr.--Esco Ltd., Port Coquitlam, Canada; *U.S. Private*, pg. 383
Box, L. Richard, Pres.--Bourns Sensors & Controls Division, Ogden, UT; *U.S. Private*, pg. 161
Box, Ray, Mng. Dir.-European--Autologic Information International Ltd., Saint Albans, United Kingdom; *U.S. Public*, pg. 1724
Box, Sam W., Chm. Bd., Pres. & Chief Exec. Officer--Foster Wheeler Environmental Corporation, Livingston, NJ; *U.S.* Public, pg. 677
Boyajian, Ned, Mgr.-Plant--Nestle Beverage Company, Casa Grande, AZ; *Int'l*, pg. 917
Boyan, William L., Pres.--John Hancock Subsidiaries, Inc., Boston, MA; *U.S. Private*, pg. 589
Boyar, Paul, Administrator--Desert Lane Care Center, Las Vegas, NV; *U.S. Public*, pg. 837
Boyce, G. H., Pres. & Chief Exec. Officer--Kennecott Energy and Coal Company, Salt Lake City, UT; *Int'l*, pg. 1119
Boyce, Michael, Chief Oper. Officer--North American Salt Company, Overland Park, KS; *U.S. Private*, pg. 505
Boyce, Wayne, Chief Oper. Officer--Allright Parking System, Inc., Dallas, TX; *U.S. Private*, pg. 43
Boyd, Bill, Mgr.--Heil Trailer International, Athens, TN; *U.S. Public*, pg. 520
Boyd, Bill, Chief Oper. Officer--Forest City Pierrepont, Inc., New York, NY; *U.S. Public*, pg. 669
Boyd, Bo, Pres.--Walt Disney Consumer Products, Burbank, CA; *U.S. Public*, pg. 511
Boyd, Cathy, Office Admin.--ENVIRON Corporation, Irvine, CA; *U.S. Public*, pg. 1285
Boyd, Charles, Mng. Dir.--Doctors Hospital of Shreveport, Shreveport, LA; *U.S. Public*, pg. 1697
Boyd, Dennis, Pres.--Accent Furniture, Inc., Maryland Heights, MO; *U.S. Private*, pg. 949
Boyd, Dennis, Pres. & Chief Exec. Officer--Boyd Flotation, Inc, Maryland Heights, MO; *U.S. Private*, pg. 949
Boyd, Ed, Pres.--Harman Speaker Manufacturing, Northridge, CA; *U.S. Public*, pg. 787
Boyd, J. Blake, Jr., Pres.--Paper Stock Dealers, Inc., Statesville, NC; *U.S. Public*, pg. 1486
Boyd, L., Chm.--Amic Industries Limited, Johanesburg, South Africa; *Int'l*, pg. 76
Boyd, Margaret, Admin.--Hillhaven Convalescent Hospital Oakland, Oakland, CA; *U.S. Public*, pg. 1713
Boyd, Michael L., Pres. & Chief Exec. Officer--San Angelo National Bank, San Angelo, TX; *U.S. Public*, pg. 633
Boyd, Mike, Branch Mgr.--Continental/Murray, Lubbock, TX; *U.S. Private*, pg. 267
Boyd, Steve, Pres. & Chief Exec. Officer--U S West DEX, Denver, CO; *U.S. Public*, pg. 1689
Boyd, Walter, Pres.--International Data Corp., Framingham, MA; *U.S. Private*, pg. 570
Boyd, William W., Chm. Bd.--Sterling Plumbing Group, Inc., Rolling Meadows, IL; *U.S. Private*, pg. 630
Boyda, K.L., Pres.--SLC Technologies, Portland, OR; *U.S. Private*, pg. 138
Boyden, J.W., Pres. & Chief Exec. Officer--Bush Boake Allen Ltd., London, United Kingdom; *U.S. Public*, pg. 1666
Boyden, Julian W., Pres.--Bush Boake Allen, Inc, Montvale, NJ; *U.S. Public*, pg. 1666
Boyen, Richard, V.P.--Puerto Rico Safety Equipment Corporation, Aguadilla, PR; *U.S. Public*, pg. 548
Boyen, Richard, V.P.--Puerto Rico Safety Corporation, Aguadilla, PR; *U.S. Public*, pg. 548
Boyer, Dan, Plant Mgr.--ElJay Division, Eugene, OR; *U.S. Public*, pg. 1365
Boyett, Otto, V.P. & Gen. Mgr.--Pyramid Southern Mouldings, Green Cove Springs, FL; *Int'l*, pg. 1335
Boyett, Otto, Pres.--Pyramid Mouldings, Jacksonville, FL; *Int'l*, pg. 1335
Boyette, John V., Pres. & Mng. Dir.--Geraghty & Miller, Inc., Denver, CO; *Int'l*, pg. 607
Boyette, Mary, V.P.-Mktg.--Stendhal, New York, NY; *Int'l*, pg. 445
Boykin, Edward P., Pres.--CSC Pinnacle Alliance, New York, NY; *U.S. Public*, pg. 423
Boylan, John F., Pres.--J.I. Case International Sales, Racine, WI; *U.S. Public*, pg. 312
Boylan, Michael J., Pres.--The National Enquirer, New York, NY; *U.S. Public*, pg. 87
Boylan, Michael J., Pres.--NDSI, Inc., Lantana, FL; *U.S. Public*, pg. 87
Boylan, Michael J., Pres.--Weekly World News, Inc., Lantana, FL; *U.S. Public*, pg. 87
Boylan, Michael J., Pres.--Country Weekly, Inc., Lantana, FL; *U.S. Public*, pg. 87
Boylan, Wayne, Plant Mgr.--Ardell Industries Inc., Union, NJ; *U.S. Private*, pg. 597
Boyle, Allan, Div. Mng. Dir.--Godwins Limited, Manchester, United Kingdom; *U.S. Public*, pg. 119
Boyle, Bob, Mgr.--West Penetone Corporation, Downey, CA; *U.S. Private*, pg. 1158
Boyle, Edward J., Jr., V.P.-Sls.-Eastern Div.--Crown Cork & Seal, Eastern Div., Philadelphia, PA; *U.S. Public*, pg. 463
Boyle, G., Mng. Dir.--Isovel International Ltd., Andover, United Kingdom; *Int'l*, pg. 585
Boyle, James H., V.P.-Canadian Opers.--Barnwell of Canada Ltd., Calgary, Canada; *U.S. Public*, pg. 191
Boyle, Lester J., Exec. V.P.--JL Media, Inc., Tulsa, OK; *U.S.* Private, pg. 577
Boyle, Patrick G., Chm. Bd.--Monitor Capital Advisors Inc., Princeton, NJ; *U.S. Private*, pg. 795
Boyle, Peter, Pres.--American Camper, Tulsa, OK; *U.S. Public*, pg. 265
Boyle, Richard, Chm. Bd. & Chief Exec. Officer--Spinnaker Industries, Inc., Dallas, TX; *U.S. Public*, pg. 1022
Boyle, Richard A., Pres.--Wright & Lopez, Inc., Atlanta, GA; *U.S. Private*, pg. 843
Boyle, Richard A., Pres.--Wright & Lopez of Alabama, Inc., Birmingham, AL; *U.S. Private*, pg. 844
Boyle, William, Pres.--Cardio Data Services, Haddonfield, NJ; *U.S. Private*, pg. 1114
Boyles, David L., Pres.--BA ATM, Inc., San Francisco, CA; *U.S. Public*, pg. 181
Boyles, William B., Gen. Mgr.--Wyoming Land Title Company, Green River, WY; *U.S. Public*, pg. 626
Boyoli, J., Gen. Mgr.--Whitehall-Robins de Mexico, S.A. de C.V., Cuautitlan, Mexico; *U.S. Public*, pg. 82
Boys, B.L., Chief Oper. Officer--John Laing International Ltd., Hemel Hempstead, United Kingdom; *Int'l*, pg. 796
Boze, Jimmy R., Chm. Bd., Pres. & Chief Exec. Officer--The Security Bank, Harrison, Harrison, AR; *U.S. Public*, pg. 630
Bozic, Michael, Chm. Bd. & Chief Exec. Officer--John M. Smyth Co., Downers Grove, IL; *U.S. Public*, pg. 990
Bozniak, Murray, Pres.--Home Depot Canada, Scarborough, Canada; *U.S. Public*, pg. 832
Bozym, Charles P., Pres.--Somat Corporation, Coatesville, PA; *U.S. Public*, pg. 1322
Bozzini, A., Mgr.--Amersham Italia Srl, Milan, Italy; *Int'l*, pg. 993
Bozzini, Gianfranco, Mng. Dir.--Unikay S.r.l., Genoa, Italy; *U.S. Public*, pg. 673
Bozzuto, Adam J., Pres.--AB-Small Business Investment Company, Inc., Cheshire, CT; *U.S. Public*, pg. 249
Braam, Ronald, Pres.--Manufacturers Soap & Chemical Co., Cleveland, TN; *U.S. Public*, pg. 1548
Braasch, John M., Pres. & Chief Exec. Officer--United HealthCare of the Midlands, Inc., Omaha, NE; *U.S. Public*, pg. 1678
Braatz, Dan, V.P.-Flatbed Div.--Builders Transport, Incorporated, Camden, SC; *U.S. Public*, pg. 267
Brabandt, Rodger, Mgr.--Fargo Glass & Paint Co., Minot, ND; *U.S. Private*, pg. 393
Brabant, Marc, Dir.--Thibeau, Tourcoing, France; *Int'l*, pg. 1206
Brace, R., Dir.--BT Property Ltd., London, United Kingdom; *Int'l*, pg. 222
Bracero, Diego, Reg. Mgr.--Det Norske Veritas, Madrid, Spain; *Int'l*, pg. 397
Brach, Robert W., Pres.--Central Florida Press L.C., Orlando, FL; *U.S. Public*, pg. 291
Brack, Reginald K. Jr., Chm. Bd., Pres. & Chief Exec. Officer--Time Warner Publishing Inc., New York, NY; *U.S. Public*, pg. 1614
Bracke, Luc, Pres.--Volvo Italia SpA, Bologna, Italy; *Int'l*, pg. 1476
Bracken, James, Pres.--Billcom Exposition & Conference, Sterling, VA; *Int'l*, pg. 1446
Bracken, Peter A., Pres. & Chief Exec. Officer--Computer Data Systems, Inc., Rockville, MD; *U.S. Public*, pg. 28
Bracken, Peter A., Pres.--Martin Marietta Information Group, Bethesda, MD; *U.S. Public*, pg. 1007
Bracken, Thomas A., Pres.--New Jersey National Bank, Pennington, NJ; *U.S. Public*, pg. 447
Bradburn, Gareth G., Mng. Dir.--International Risk Management Group Ltd., Hamilton, Bermuda; *Int'l*, pg. 1333
Bradburn, S.E., Mng. Dir.--P&O Roadtanks Limited, Altrincham, United Kingdom; *Int'l*, pg. 1034
Bradbury, Christopher, Pres.--Contaminant Recovery Systems, Centredale, RI; *U.S. Public*, pg. 592
Bradbury, Richard F., Pres.--Ceco Door Products, Oklahoma City, OK; *U.S. Public*, pg. 1676
Braden, J.M., Pres-PDM Water--Engineered Construction-Pittsburgh, Pittsburgh, PA; *U.S. Public*, pg. 1304
Brader, J.H.M., Mng. Dir.--Uitgeversmaatschappij De Stem bv, Breda, Netherlands; *Int'l*, pg. 1445
Bradfield, William, Pres.--Bell Atlantic Systems Integration Corp., Arlington, VA; *U.S. Public*, pg. 203
Bradfield, William S., Pres. & Sr. V.P.--Sathers Inc., Round Lake, MN; *U.S. Private*, pg. 397
Bradford, Brian, Mng. Dir.--Reed Exhibition Companies (UK) Ltd., Richmond, United Kingdom; *Int'l*, pg. 1097
Bradford, Chuck, Plant Mgr.--Electrocomponents, Bentonville, AR; *U.S. Public*, pg. 285
Bradford, Greg, Pres.--Aerospatiale Inc., Washington, DC; *Int'l*, pg. 29
Bradley, Bruce, Pres. & Publr.--The Virginian-Pilot, Norfolk, VA; *U.S. Private*, pg. 649
Bradley, C.C., Pres.--Sharp Laboratories of Europe, Ltd., Oxford, United Kingdom; *Int'l*, pg. 1230
Bradley, Charles, Gen. Mgr.--Esquire Canada, Inc., Port Robinson, Canada; *U.S. Private*, pg. 1047
Bradley, D. I., Chief Oper. Officer--Husqvarna Chainsaws Ltd., Auckland, New Zealand; *Int'l*, pg. 443
Bradley, Ed, V.P. & Gen. Mgr.--KSLA-TV, Shreveport, LA; *U.S. Private*, pg. 912
Bradley, Floyd, Country Mgr.--Lotus Development (U.K.) Limited, Windsor, United Kingdom; *U.S. Public*, pg. 896
Bradley, George, Gen. Mgr.--Teleflex Marine, Limerick, PA; *U.S. Public*, pg. 1569
Bradley, George, Gen. Mgr.--TFX Marine, Hagerstown, MD; *U.S. Public*, pg. 1570
Bradley, George R., Chief Opr. Officer--Penn Engineering & Manufacturing Corp. North Carolina Div., Winston Salem, NC; *U.S. Public*, pg. 1270
Bradley, J., Mng. Dir.--Scholl Consumer Products Ltd., Luton, United Kingdom; *Int'l*, pg. 1209
Bradley, Jeff, Mgr.--Leo Burnett (China) Advertising Co., Ltd.-Guangzhou, Guangzhou, China; *U.S. Private*, pg. 184
Bradley, John, Pool Mgr.--Kvaerner Havtor (UK) Limited, London, United Kingdom; *Int'l*, pg. 771
Bradley, Martin, Mng. Dir.--Racal Radar Defence, Crawley, United Kingdom; *Int'l*, pg. 1082
Bradley, Merrill, Plant Mgr.--Baldor Electric Company, Clarksville, AR; *U.S. Public*, pg. 169
Bradley, Richard, Chief Exec. Officer--Asia Equity Holding Limited, Hong Kong, Hong Kong; *Int'l*, pg. 485
Bradley, Richard, Pres.--Missouri Medical Insurance Company, Saint Louis, MO; *U.S. Public*, pg. 1080
Bradley, Steve, Plant Mgr.--Cylinder Div., Portland, OR; *U.S.* Public, pg. 1261
Bradley, Wade, Jr., Gen. Mgr.--Industrial Environmental Products, Inc., Alpharetta, GA; *U.S. Public*, pg. 1215
Bradly, Glen, Dr., Pres. & Chief Exec. Officer--CIBA Vision AG, Niederwangen, Switzerland; *Int'l*, pg. 972
Bradly, Miles, Mgr.-Sls.--Hartley Courseware, San Diego, CA; *U.S. Private*, pg. 601
Bradshaw, Delmer G., V.P.-Prod. Devel.--Electronic Systems Division, Kent, WA; *U.S. Public*, pg. 241
Bradshaw, H.A., Grp. V.P.-Bldg. Prods. Opers.--ISO Holding, AG, Schwyz, Switzerland; *U.S. Public*, pg. 132
Bradshaw, J., Gen. Mgr.--ANZ Grindlays Bank plc Jordan, Amman, Jordan; *Int'l*, pg. 99
Bradshaw, J. K., Mng. Dir.--Natal Thread Co. (Pty) Ltd., Durban, South Africa; *Int'l*, pg. 299
Bradshaw, Robert, Pres.--Boon Edam Inc., Salt Lake City, UT; *Int'l*, pg. 202
Bradway, Jeff, Plant Mgr.--Liqui-Box Corp., Auburn, MA; *U.S. Public*, pg. 1001
Brady, C. Edwin, Pres.--Precision Specialty Metals, Inc., Los Angeles, CA; *U.S. Private*, pg. 344
Brady, Caroline C., Plant Mgr.--Dayton Thermal Products Div., Dayton, OH; *U.S. Public*, pg. 353
Brady, Dermot P., Plant Mgr.--Olin Chemicals, B.V., Swords, Ireland; *U.S. Public*, pg. 1220
Brady, Gerald J.P., Mng. Dir.--Management International (Dublin) Limited, Dublin, Ireland; *Int'l*, pg. 151
Brady, Joseph F., Pres.--Centrilift, Claremore, OK; *U.S. Public*, pg. 167
Brady, Milton, Mng. Dir.--Skandinaviska Enskilda Banking, New York & Cayman Island Branch, New York, NY; *Int'l, pg. 1259*
Brady, Patrick J., Pres. & Chief Exec. Officer--Semiconductor Equipment Group, Scotts Valley, CA; *U.S. Public*, pg. 1745
Brady, Richard N., Mgr.--Kearsarge Telephone Co., New London, NH; *U.S. Public*, pg. 1571
Brady, Robert, Pres. & Chief Exec. Officer--First NH Mortgage Corp., Hooksett, NH; *Int'l*, pg. 153
Brady, Robert, Pres. & Chief Oper. Officer--Parfums Givenchy Inc., New York, NY; *Int'l*, pg. 781
Braekeveldt, Steven, Head-BBL/Singapore Branch--Bank Brussels Lambert, Singapore Branch, Singapore, Singapore; *Int'l*, pg. 148
Braendli, Max, Mng. Dir.--Robinson-Nugent S.A., Delemont, Switzerland; *U.S. Public*, pg. 1395
Braenig, J., V.P. & Gen. Mgr.--Hedstrom Corp., Ashland, OH; *U.S. Private*, pg. 526
Braet, Jerry, Gen. Mgr.--KUTP Television, Inc., Phoenix, AZ; *U.S. Public*, pg. 352
Brafford, H. Wayne, Gen. Mgr.--Label Division, Memphis, TN; *U.S. Public*, pg. 903
Braga, Daniel Olaso, Country Mgr.--Berlitz Escola de Idiomas Ltda., Sao Paulo, Brazil; *U.S. Public*, pg. 221
Braganza, Len, Chief Oper. Officer--COBE Canada Ltd., Scarborough, Canada; *Int'l*, pg. 667
Bragg, Jeffery S., Pres.--Policy Management Systems Information and Administration Services, Inc., Blythewood, SC; *U.S. Public*, pg. 1314
Bragg, Russ, Pres.--ConAgra Poultry Co., Duluth, GA; *U.S. Public*, pg. 427
Braggiotti, Enrico, Mng. Dir.--Banca Commerciale Italiana S.p.A., Milan, Italy; *Int'l*, pg. 652
Braghieri, Luigi, Gen. Mgr.--Banca Popolare di Milano, London, United Kingdom; *Int'l*, pg. 137
Bragman, Barbro, Chief Officer--Fakta, Stockholm, Sweden; *Int'l*, pg. 718
Braid, John, Plant Mgr.--Interox America, Deer Park, TX; *Int'l*, pg. 1278
Brainard, R.C., Pres.--Kentucky Berwind Land Company, Charleston, WV; *U.S. Private*, pg. 138
Brainin, Gary, Chm. Bd. & Pres.--Harvest Industries, Inc., Lincolnshire, IL; *U.S. Private*, pg. 46
Brait, Wolfgang, Chief Oper. Officer--Novo Nordisk A/S, Sofia, Bulgaria; *Int'l*, pg. 987

Braithwaite, Keith, Zone Sls. Mgr.--IRD Mechanalysis Limited, Stoney Creek, Canada; *U.S. Public*, pg. 790

Brak, P., Dir.-Sls.--Spectra-Physics Belgium BVBA, Antwerp, Belgium; *Int'l*, pg. 1290

Brakefield, W.H., V.P. & Plant Mgr.--The JPM Company of South Carolina, Inc., Winnsboro, SC; *U.S. Public*, pg. 919

Bramble, Frank P., Pres. & Chief Exec. Officer--First Maryland Bancorp, Baltimore, MD; *Int'l*, pg. 64

Bramble, Jeff, Gen. Mgr.--Herschel Adams, Indianola, IA; *U.S. Public*, pg. 35

Brame, Cyrus W., Jr., Mgr.--Scott & Stringfellow, Inc., North Wilkesboro, NC; *U.S. Public*, pg. 1446

Brame, Helen, Admin.--Guardian Care of Henderson, Henderson, NC; *U.S. Public*, pg. 1712

Brame, Warren, Mng. Dir.--Hosokawa Micron Australia Pty. Ltd., Wetherill Park, Australia; *Int'l*, pg. 636

Bramer, Kurt R., Pres.--Kinney Vacuum Company, Canton, MA; *U.S. Private*, pg. 1110

Bramlage, S.A., Branch Mgr.--Zellerbach Division, Nashville, TN; *U.S. Public*, pg. 1075

Bramley, B.G., Pres. & Gen. Mgr.--Amoco Sharjah Oil Co., Sharjah, United Arab Emirates; *U.S. Public*, pg. 102

Bramley, B.G., Pres. & Gen. Mgr.--Amoco Sharjah LPG Co., Sharjah, United Arab Emirates; *U.S. Public*, pg. 102

Bramm, Soren, Mng. Dir.--Soren Berggreen & Co. A/S, Vejle, Denmark; *Int'l*, pg. 864

Bramson, Robert, Pres. & Chief Exec. Officer--InterDigital Patents Corporation, King of Prussia, PA; *U.S. Public*, pg. 889

Bramwell, Mike, V.P. & Gen. Mgr.--Tellabs Communications CDA, Mississauga, Canada; *U.S. Public*, pg. 1573

Branaugh, James, Gen. Mgr.--Star Expansion Shields Ltd., Mississauga, Canada; *U.S. Private*, pg. 1034

Branca, Prof. G., Dir.--Fiat Auto S.p.A., Milan, Italy; *Int'l*, pg. 481

Branch, Clair, Plant Mgr.--Hydro Conduit Corp., Houston, TX; *Int'l*, pg. 245

Branch, Linda, Branch Mgr.--Circle Freight International USA, Charlotte, NC; *U.S. Public*, pg. 370

Branchaude, Michel, Pres.--Infradev International, Montreal, Canada; *Int'l*, pg. 249

Branche, Francois, Pres. & Chief Exec. Officer--Calberson, Paris, France; *Int'l*, pg. 549

Branchflower, Norman, Pres.--Western States Assoc., Los Angeles, CA; *U.S. Private*, pg. 739

Branchi, S., Mng. Dir.--Intochimica Marketing S.r.l., Milan, Italy; *Int'l*, pg. 682

Branco, Isabel, Mgr.--Broad National Bank-Ironbound, Newark, NJ; *U.S. Public*, pg. 257

Branco, Joao Paulo Castel, Pres. & Creative Dir.--Cineponto/Leo Burnett Publicidade Lda., Lisbon, Portugal; *U.S. Private*, pg. 184

Brand, Dave, Chief Oper. Officer--Advanced Micro Devices, (UK), Ltd., Woking, United Kingdom; *U.S. Public*, pg. 21

Brand, Gwynn, Chief Oper. Officer & Dir.-Admin.--La Metaire Clinic, Nyon, Switzerland; *U.S. Public*, pg. 1036

Brand, Michel, Mgr.--Sandvik S.A. Bureau de Liasion, Algiers, Algeria; *Int'l*, pg. 1187

Brand, Stan, V.P. & Reg. Mgr.--Riedel-Smith Environmental Services, Chesterfield, MO; *U.S. Public*, pg. 1478

Brandenberg, Ernest A., Chief Oper. Officer--KONE Elevator GmbH, Baar, Switzerland; *Int'l*, pg. 748

Brandenberg, Frank, Pres.--Tanon Manufacturing, Inc., West Long Branch, NJ; *U.S. Public*, pg. 541

Brandenburg, David, Pres.--Continental Wood Preservers, Inc., Detroit, MI; *U.S. Public*, pg. 1193

Brander, Don, Gen. Mgr. & Publisher--The Guardian, Charlottetown, Canada; *Int'l*, pg. 631

Brandfon, Bruce L., Pres.--SuperValu, Inc.-Quincy Div., Quincy, FL; *U.S. Public*, pg. 1540

Brandhorst, W.L., Dir.--Ivacon B.V., Badhoevedorp, Netherlands; *Int'l*, pg. 134

Brandi, Erik, Mgr.--Vectur Aluminumstallningar, Ishoj, Denmark; *U.S. Private*, pg. 1128

Brandis, Ken, Mgr.--Marble Products Div., Wichita, KS; *Int'l*, pg. 1349

Brandjord, Gregory A., Pres.--Joslins, Denver, CO; *U.S. Public*, pg. 1090

Brandjord, Gregory A., Pres.--Glass Block, Duluth, MN; *U.S. Public*, pg. 1090

Brandner, Anton, Chief Oper. Officer--Tricosal GmbH, Illertissen, Germany; *Int'l*, pg. 610

Brandon, Raymond D., Mng. Dir.--DYWIDAG Systems International, USA, Inc., Grand Junction, CO; *Int'l*, pg. 424

Brands, Peter, Mng. Dir.--Kreymborg, Hilversum, Netherlands; *Int'l*, pg. 1462

Brandt, Dana, Mgr.--Pella Window & Door Company, Livermore, CA; *U.S. Private*, pg. 528

Brandt, David N., Pres. & Chief Exec. Officer--Dresdner Bank Canada, Toronto, Canada; *Int'l*, pg. 419

Brandt, Douglas, Pres. & Gen. Mgr.--C-Tech Systems, Plymouth, MN; *U.S. Public*, pg. 865

Brandt, Ed, Gen. Mgr.--Ulbrich of Georgia, Inc., Norcross, GA; *U.S. Private*, pg. 1115

Brandt, Steve, Pres. & Publr.--Democrat & Chronicle, Rochester, NY; *U.S. Public*, pg. 699

Brandt, Tom, Pres.--Bivona Inc., Gary, IN; *Int'l*, pg. 818

Brandtzaeg, Bernt, Pres.--Volvo Trucks (Great Britain) Ltd., Warwick, United Kingdom; *Int'l*, pg. 1478

Brang, Joe, Mgr.--Greeneville Plant, Greeneville, TN; *Int'l*, pg. 1055

Braniff, Thomas M, Pres.--Texas Instruments Consulting, Houston, TX; *U.S. Public*, pg. 1586

Branigan, Gerard P., Mng. Dir.--Vehicle Spares Ltd., Dublin, Ireland; *Int'l*, pg. 861

Branjord, Gregory A., Pres.--The Jones Store Co., Kansas City, MO; *U.S. Public*, pg. 1090

Branknoff, G., Export Mgr.--Elron Electronic Industries Ltd., Haifa, Israel; *Int'l*, pg. 644

Brann, Alton J., Pres.--Guidance & Control Systems Div., Woodland Hills, CA; *U.S. Public*, pg. 1002

Brannan, Stanley G., Chm. Bd.--Brite Voice Systems, Canton, MA; *U.S. Public*, pg. 257

Brannstiom, Ake, Chief Oper. Officer--Scania do Brasil Ltda, Sao Bernardo do Campo, Brazil; *Int'l*, pg. 687

Branson, Philip, Chm.--First American Home Buyers Protection Corp., Van Nuys, CA; *U.S. Public*, pg. 625

Branson, W.C., Pres.--The Quincy State Bank, Quincy, FL; *U.S. Public*, pg. 1549

Brant, James, Pres.--Ampco Auto System Parking, Los Angeles, CA; *U.S. Public*, pg. 2

Brant, Nancy K., V.P. & Branch Mgr.--California State Bank-La Palma, La Palma, CA; *U.S. Public*, pg. 294

Brant, W. D., Dir.-Information Services--Grand Metropolitan Information Services Ltd., London, United Kingdom; *Int'l, pg. 408*

Brantjes, Jan, Pres.--Aritech Europe & Central Life Safety Europe, Zaventem, Belgium; *U.S. Private*, pg. 139

Brantley, Kevin, Mgr.-Plant--Servitex, Inc., Kinston, NC; *U.S.* Private, pg. 781

Brantley, L. Wayne, Pres.--Lanier Clothes, Atlanta, GA; *U.S.* Public, pg. 1239

Brantner, Richard, Mng. Dir.--Esselte Meto Ges mbH, Vienna, Austria; *Int'l*, pg. 461

Branyan, Bruce H., Pres.--Business Markets Organization, Overland Park, KS; *U.S. Public*, pg. 1500

Brasell, D.F., Gen. Mgr.--Dulmison Inc., Lawrenceville, GA; *Int'l*, pg. 894

Brasen, Ulf, Chief Oper. Officer--Alfa-Laval Co. Ltd., Brentford, United Kingdom; *Int'l*, pg. 1380

Brashaw, Gerald L., V.P., Controller & Treas.--Paragon Electric Co., Inc., Two Rivers, WI; *Int'l*, pg. 1243

Brashear, Richard, Pres.--ALLTEL Florida, Inc., Live Oak, FL; *U.S. Public*, pg. 56

Brashears, Melvin R., Pres. & Chief Oper. Officer-Space & Strategic Missiles--Lockheed Martin Corporation, Bethesda, MD; *U.S. Public*, pg. 1006

Brassell, Pres.--Kokosing Materials, Inc., Fredericktown, OH; *U.S. Private*, pg. 631

Brasser, Wayne E., Pres. & Chief Exec. Officer--Chemtech Products Inc., Saint Louis, MO; *U.S. Private*, pg. 39

Braswell, Gerald, V.P. & Gen. Mgr.--Systron Donner-Inertial Division, Concord, CA; *U.S. Public*, pg. 160

Bratcher, S.V., Dir. & Gen. Mgr.--Hamworthy Heating Limited, Poole, United Kingdom; *Int'l*, pg. 1065

Braten, Arvid, Gen. Mgr.--NUS Italia, s.r.l., Milan, Italy; *U.S. Private*, pg. 787

Bratsburg, Jeffrey A., Pres. & Chief Exec. Officer--Independent Bank-West Michigan, Rockford, MI; *U.S. Public*, pg. 874

Bratt, Frederic, Gen. Mgr.--Falconbridge International Russia, Moscow, Russia; *Int'l*, pg. 434

Bratter, Robert, Pres.--SVG Track Systems, San Jose, CA; *U.S. Public*, pg. 1474

Brattoen, Dunn, Plant Mgr.--Salem Carpet Mills, South Pittsburg, TN; *U.S. Public*, pg. 1464

Bratton, Joseph A., Chm., Pres. & Chief Exec. Officer--First Alabama Bank/Covington/Conecuh/Monroe Counties, Andalusia, AL; *U.S. Public*, pg. 1371

Brauch, Karl, Chief Oper. Officer--Suddeutsche Brennstoffhandelsgesellschaft mbH, Mannheim, Germany; *Int'l*, pg. 1167

Brauckman, Dennis, V.P.-Fin.--Boston Scientific Symbiosis, Miami, FL; *U.S. Public*, pg. 247

Brauer, Bernie, Pres.--Unocal Canada Limited, Calgary, Canada; *U.S. Public*, pg. 1698

Brauer, Dieter, Pres.--Philips Broadband Networks, Manlius, NY; *Int'l*, pg. 1054

Brauer, Kevin E., Pres.--National Integrated Services, Overland Park, KS; *U.S. Public*, pg. 1500

Brault, Lionel, Pres.--Kendo, Puteaux, France; *Int'l*, pg. 601

Braun, Al, Chief Oper. Officer--Regency Thermographers of Texas, Inc., Dallas, TX; *U.S. Public*, pg. 89

Braun, B.E., Mgr.--Bar Soap & Household Cleaning Products Div., Cincinnati, OH; *U.S. Public*, pg. 1330

Braun, Bernhard, Dr., Mng. Dir.--Wuestenrot stavebni sporitelna a.s., Prague, Czech Republic; *Int'l*, pg. 1514

Braun, Gary A., Gen. Mgr.--Transelco Div., Penn Yan, NY; *U.S. Public*, pg. 619

Braun, Hartmut, Chief Oper. Officer--Skandia Lebensversicherung AG, Berlin, Germany; *Int'l*, pg. 1258

Braun, J., Pres.--Safeguard Financial Corp., Fort Washington, PA; *U.S. Private*, pg. 960

Braun, Jaime A., Mng. Dir.--Astra S.A. Productos Farmaceuticos y Quimicos, Haedo, Argentina; *Int'l*, pg. 94

Braun, Mike, Sr. Mktg. Officer--Northeast Marketing Div., Albany, NY; *U.S. Private*, pg. 296

Braun, Richard, Gen. Mgr.--Corrugated Container Div.-Philadelphia (East) Plant, Philadelphia, PA; *U.S. Public*, pg. 1520

Braun, Ron, Pres.--PsyCare, Atlanta, GA; *U.S. Public*, pg. 888

Braun, Thomas, Chief Oper. Officer--Corporate Finance Magazine, New York, NY; *U.S. Private*, pg. 405

Braun, Tom, Gen. Mgr.--American Dynamics, Orangeburg, NY; *U.S. Public*, pg. 1457

Braune, Gerson Nogueira, Chief Exec. Officer--New York Representative Office (ESNOR), New York, NY; *Int'l*, pg. 1042

Braunlich, Bill, V.P.--Voltelcon, West Palm Beach, FL; *U.S. Public*, pg. 1724

Braunlich, Heiko, Pres.--Kvaerner Ships Equipment GmbH, Bremen, Germany; *Int'l*, pg. 768

Braunlich, Heiko, Pres.--Kvaerner Brug (Deutschland) GmbH, Bremen, Germany; *Int'l*, pg. 771

Brauns, Jurgen, Pres.--Babcock Textilmaschinen GmbH, Seevetal, Germany; *Int'l*, pg. 399

Brauns, Jurgen, Dir.--H. Krantz Textilmaschinen GmbH, Aachen, Germany; *Int'l*, pg. 399

Braunwalder, Peter F., Pres. & Chief Exec. Officer--UBS Phillips & Drew Intl. Ltd., Tokyo, Japan; *Int'l*, pg. 1440

Brautigam, Margit, Gen. Mgr.--Nairn Bodenbelag GmbH, Paderborn, Germany; *Int'l*, pg. 498

Braverman, Leonard, Gen. Mgr.--Hipotronics, Inc., Brewster, NY; *U.S. Public*, pg. 844

Braves, Christopher, Gen. Mgr.--Nikko Bank (Switzerland) Ltd., Geneva, Switzerland; *Int'l*, pg. 930

Bravo, Jaime, Chief Oper. Officer--Industrias Universales Unions de Mexico SA, Tijuana, Mexico; *U.S. Public*, pg. 1539

Bravo, Juan, Pres.--Harbison-Walker Refractories, Pittsburgh, PA; *U.S. Public*, pg. 748

Brawner, E.L., Pres.--ICI Canada Inc., North York, Canada; *Int'l*, pg. 664

Brawner, Pat, V.P. & Gen. Mgr.--SMI Steel Florida, Whitehouse, FL; *U.S. Public*, pg. 412

Bray, Jack, Pres.--R.A. Briggs & Co., Lake Zurich, IL; *U.S. Private*, pg. 536

Bray, K.A., Mng. Dir.--GEC Alsthom N.V., Amsterdam, Netherlands; *Int'l*, pg. 56

Bray, Michael E., Pres.--Deutsche Babcock-Riley International Inc., Worcester, MA; *Int'l*, pg. 401

Bray, Michael E., H., Pres. & Chief Oper. Officer--Riley Consolidated, Inc., Worcester, MA; *Int'l*, pg. 401

Bray, Ralph, Mng. Dir.--The West Company Australia Pty. Ltd., Brookvale, Australia; *U.S. Public*, pg. 1755

Brayshaw, David J., Chief Rep.--The Sumitomo Bank, Ltd.-Birmingham Representative Office, Birmingham, United Kingdom; *Int'l*, pg. 1309

Braz, Antonio, Chief Oper. Officer--Anacomp do Brasil Ltda., Sao Paulo, Brazil; *U.S. Public*, pg. 107

Brazao, Anne, Gen. Mgr.--Bytex DataCom Ltd., Toronto, Canada; *U.S. Public*, pg. 1522

Brazeal, Chuck, V.P.-Mfg.--Steel Processors Div., Seymour, MO; *U.S. Private*, pg. 550

Brazeal, Chuck, V.P.-Mfg.--Mans-Steel Div., Mansfield, MO; *U.S. Private*, pg. 550

Brazeal, Chuck, V.P.-Mfg.--Mans-Steel Foundry, Mansfield, MO; *U.S. Private*, pg. 550

Brazell, Carl, Co-Pres.--Metromedia International Telecommunications, Inc., Stamford, CT; *U.S. Public*, pg. 1103

Braznell, Dick, Mgr.--Midland Color Company, Saint Louis, MO; *Int'l*, pg. 1311

Brea, Joe, Gen. Mgr.--Jane's Information Group, Alexandria, VA; *U.S. Public*, pg. 1601

Breach, Harold, Gen. Mgr.--M1 KIT Mfg. Co., Caldwell, ID; *U.S. Public*, pg. 962

Breach, P.E., Mng. Dir.--Seagram Europe and Africa, London, United Kingdom; *Int'l*, pg. 1217

Brear, S., Mng. Dir.--Bailey Telecom LTD, Leeds, United Kingdom; *Int'l*, pg. 133

Brearley, Charles T., Pres.--John O. Butler Co., Chicago, IL; *Int'l*, pg. 1320

Breathwick, C.J., Chm.--Ford Personal Import Export Ltd., London, United Kingdom; *U.S. Public*, pg. 666

Breazeale, Joyce, Sr. V.P. & Div. Dir.--Underwriters Management Associates, Inc., Nashville, TN; *Int'l*, pg. 1508

Brechbuehler, Alfred, Representative--UBS Representative Office, Caracas, Venezuela; *Int'l*, pg. 1441

Brecht, Edwin, Co-Chief Oper. Officer--International Finance Division, Dusseldorf, Germany; *Int'l*, pg. 645

Brecht, Robert P., Pres. & Chief Exec. Officer--Peoples Savings Bank of Ashtabula, Ashtabula, OH; *U.S. Public*, pg. 647

Bredahl, Svein, Pres.--Aker Eiendom, Oslo, Norway; *Int'l*, pg. 41

Brede, Oddvar, Mgr.--Trelleborg Atlas A/S, Oslo, Norway; *Int'l*, pg. 1423

Bredel, John, Chief Oper. Officer--General Ionics, Cuyahoga Falls, OH; *U.S. Public*, pg. 912

Breden, P.J., Mgr.-Milling, Australia--Goodman Fielder Mills Ltd., Eastwood, Australia; *Int'l*, pg. 555

Bredfeld, S., Mng. Dir.--Consilium Claudius Peters Babcock (HK) LTD, Central, Hong Kong; *Int'l*, pg. 131

Bredthauer, Patrick, Chief Exec.--La Cemento Nacional C.A., Guayaquil, Ecuador; *Int'l*, pg. 630

Breed, J.F., V.P. & Gen. Mgr.--Thermal Ceramics, Burlington, Canada; *Int'l*, pg. 894

Breeding, Rebecca B., V.P. & Gen. Mgr.--Outdoor Systems, Inc. of Texas, Houston, TX; *U.S. Public*, pg. 1235

Breekweg, C., Mng. Dir.--Wolters Kluwer Belgium, Diegem, Belgium; *Int'l*, pg. 1513

Breen, Daniel A., Chm.--Daniel Breen and Co., Houston, TX; *Int'l*, pg. 313

Breen, Edward, Pres.--Broadband Networks Group, Hatboro, PA; *U.S. Public*, pg. 716

Breen, J. G., Pres. & Chief Exec. Officer--Contract Transportation Systems Co., Cleveland, OH; *U.S. Public, pg. 1466*

Breen, J. Richard, Pres.--Tenneco Automotive Europe, Inc., Amstelveen, Netherlands; *U.S. Public*, pg. 1580

Breen, J.G., Pres.--Sherwin-Williams Company Resources Limited, Kingston, Jamaica; *U.S. Public*, pg. 1466

Breen, James, Pres.--Everett/Charles Automation Systems, Inc., Pomona, CA; *U.S. Private*, pg. 386

Breen, K., Mng. Dir.--Toshiba Medical Systems Ltd., Crawley, United Kingdom; *Int'l*, pg. 1407

Breen, Neil, Pres. & Chief Oper. Officer--Callaghan & Company, Deerfield, IL; *U.S. Public*, pg. 1601

Breen, Terry, Mng. Dir.--Remsdaq Limited, Deeside, United Kingdom; *U.S. Private*, pg. 300

Breesch, R.J., Gen. Mgr.--Quality Bakers Nederland B.V., Gouda, Netherlands; *Int'l*, pg. 555

Breffort, Jean Claade, Chief Oper. Officer--Brasilit S.A., Sao Paulo, Brazil; *Int'l*, pg. 1171

Breffort, Jean Claude, Chief Oper. Officer--Sao Lourenco, Sao Paulo, Brazil; *Int'l*, pg. 1177

Bregman, Marlene, V.P.-Plng.--Leo Burnett Publicidade, Ltda., Sao Paulo, Brazil; *U.S. Private*, pg. 185

Bregolato, J.L., Mng. Dir.--Quaker Chemical Industrial Comercio Ltda., Sao Paulo, Brazil; *U.S. Public*, pg. 1346

Bregolato, Jose Luiz, V.P.-South America--Quaker Chemical Participacoes Ltda., Sao Paulo, Brazil; *U.S. Public*, pg. 1347

Bregolato, Jose Luiz, V.P.-South America--Quaker Chemical S.A., Buenos Aires, Argentina; *U.S. Public*, pg. 1347

Bregou, Christian, Chm. & Mng. Dir.--Librairie Larousse, Paris, France; *Int'l*, pg. 239
Breguet, Gilles, Pres.--ASEA S.A., Persan, France; *Int'l*, pg. 8
Breguet, Gilles, Mng. Dir.--Ansul S.A., Brussels, Belgium; *U.S. Public*, pg. 1651
Breiger, Bernd, Chief Oper. Officer--Pharos Holdings GmbH, Weiterstadt, Germany; *Int'l*, pg. 1290
Breiner, James, Pres.--Baltimore Business Publications, Inc., Baltimore, MD; *U.S. Private*, pg. 19
Breisinger, James R., Chief Oper. Officer--Greenfield Industries Inc., Evans, GA; *U.S. Public*, pg. 950
Breitenstein, Heinz, Dr., Chief Oper. Officer--DVO-Datenverabeitungs-Service Oberhausen GmbH, Oberhausen, Germany; *Int'l*, pg. 401
Breithaupt, John D., V.P. & Gen. Mgr.--Communications & CableVision, Inc., Monroe, MI; *U.S. Public*, pg. 287
Breithaupt, John D., V.P. & Gen. Mgr.--Coldwater Cablevision Inc., Coldwater, MI; *U.S. Public*, pg. 287
Breithaupt, John D., V.P. & Gen. Mgr.--River Raisin Cablevision Inc., Monroe, MI; *U.S. Public*, pg. 287
Breitzka, Steve, Pres.--Fisher Pierce Division, Weymouth, MA; *U.S. Public*, pg. 1250
Brejot, Charles, Chief Oper. Officer--Three States Supply Co., Inc., Memphis, TN; *U.S. Private*, pg. 1113
Brejtfus, Vincent, Mgr.--General Employment Enterprises, Inc., Oak Brook, IL; *U.S. Public*, pg. 714
Breker, Frank, Mng. Dir.--Eberhard Manufacturing, Strongsville, OH; *U.S. Public*, pg. 548
Brekke, Ed, Plant Mgr.--Square D Company-Pacifico, San Ysidro, CA; *Int'l*, pg. 1208
Brem, Michael M., Pres.--Gilroy Foods, Inc., Gilroy, CA; *U.S. Public*, pg. 428
Breme, Herald, Pres.--Schumag AG, Aachen, Germany; *Int'l*, pg. 399
Bremer, Andreas, Mgr.--Commerzbank Aktiengesellschaft Atlanta Agency, Atlanta, GA; *Int'l*, pg. 310
Bremer, Richard H., Pres. & Chief Exec. Officer--Southwestern Electric Power Co., Shreveport, LA; *U.S. Public*, pg. 324
Bremgartner, F., Rep.--Swiss Bank Corporation, Caracas, Venezuela; *Int'l*, pg. 1330
Bremond, John H., Pres.--Kaufman and Broad-Monterey Bay, Inc., Salinas, CA; *U.S. Public*, pg. 945
Brendan, Dwan, Chief Fin. Officer--Cantrell & Cochrane Group, Dublin, Ireland; *Int'l*, pg. 63
Brendecke, Hermann, Dr., Mng. Dir.--Heraeus Instruments GmbH, Hanau, Germany; *Int'l*, pg. 616
Brendt, Horst, Gen. Mgr.--Fasson Handelsgesellshaft GmbH, Dortmund, Germany; *U.S. Public*, pg. 154
Brenez, Alain, Gen. Mgr.--Bepac SC (Ropac Products), Brussels, Belgium,; *Int'l*, pg. 1339
Brennan-Jesson, Gordon, Sec.--C.I. Property & Investments Limited, London, United Kingdom; *Int'l*, pg. 290
Brennan, Chris, Gen. Mgr.--E.C. Ernst South East, Orlando, FL; *U.S. Private*, pg. 861
Brennan, Donald D., Pres.--Elgood-Mayo Corp., Lancaster, PA; *U.S. Private*, pg. 439
Brennan, Dr. Patrick, Mng. Dir.--PRC (UK) Ltd., Newcastle upon Tyne, United Kingdom; *Int'l*, pg. 339
Brennan, Edward, District Mgr.--A.M. Castle & Co., Worcester, MA; *U.S. Public*, pg. 313
Brennan, Michael J., Pres.--Micromatic Textron, Holland, MI; *U.S. Public*, pg. 1589
Brennan, Michael P., Pres. & Chief Exec. Officer--Deer Park Federal Savings and Loan Association, Cincinnati, OH; *U.S. Public*, pg. 66
Brennan, Pat, Mng. Dir. & Gen. Mgr.-Opers.--Tygaflor Ltd., Littleborough, United Kingdom; *U.S. Public*, pg. 344
Brennan, Robert, V.P.--Stewart Connector Systems, Inc., Glen Rock, PA; *U.S. Public*, pg. 881
Brennan, Robert J., Exec. V.P.--College Division, Greenwich, CT; *U.S. Private*, pg. 57
Brennan, Terrence, Pres.--Research Data Corp, Haddonfield, NJ; *U.S. Private*, pg. 1114
Brennan, Tom, Pres.--Hendrix Wire & Cable, Milford, NH; *U.S. Public*, pg. 1598
Brennand, T.P., Mng. Dir.--Shell Company of Hong Kong Ltd., Hong Kong, Hong Kong; *Int'l*, pg. 1139
Brenneman, R.A., Pres.--Esso Nederland B.V., Hague, Netherlands; *U.S. Public*, pg. 602
Brenner, Beth Fuchs, Publisher--Self, New York, NY; *U.S. Private*, pg. 20
Brenner, Karen, Chm. Bd., Pres. & Chief Exec. Officer--Carlyle Industries, Inc., Carlstadt, NJ; *U.S. Public*, pg. 1187
Brenner, Leon J., Chm. Bd.--Burbank Aircraft Supply Inc., Sun Valley, CA; *U.S. Public*, pg. 187
Brenner, S., Pres.--Beck Electric Manufacturing Company, Concord, Canada; *Int'l*, pg. 955
Brent, A. Mason, Pres.--Commonwealth Propane, Inc., Richmond, VA; *U.S. Public*, pg. 403
Brent, A. Mason, Pres.--Columbia Propane Corp., Richmond, VA; *U.S. Public*, pg. 403
Brent, Douglas, Pres.--BT Capital Partners, New York, NY; *U.S. Public*, pg. 185
Brent, Howard, Pres.--Brent Transportation Co., Greenville, MS; *U.S. Public*, pg. 961
Brent, Jack, Chm. Bd.--PCL-Braun-Simons Ltd., Calgary, Canada; *Int'l*, pg. 765
Brent, Mark, Plant Mgr.--Cambridge Industries, Inc., Newton, NC; *U.S. Private*, pg. 202
Brentnall, N., Mng. Dir.--Barclays Bank of Zambia Ltd., Lusaka, Zambia; *Int'l*, pg. 165
Brenton, Tom, Gen. Mgr.--Electra-Gear Div., Anaheim, CA; *U.S. Public*, pg. 1370
Bresciani, Ivo, Region Mgr.--Mediterranean--Weatherford Mediterranea S.p.A., Ravenna, Italy; *U.S. Public*, pg. 1750
Bresge, Les, Pres.--Kamro Lighting Products Ltd., Rexdale, Canada; *Int'l*, pg. 725
Bresky, Harry, Pres.--Seaboard Flour Corporation, Newton, MA; *U.S. Public*, pg. 1449
Bresnahan, Thomas J., Pres. & Gen. Mgr.-WMAL-AM--WMAL, Inc., Washington, DC; *U.S. Public*, pg. 512
Breton, Mike, Gen. Mgr.--Bontex S.A., Stembert, Belgium; *U.S. Public*, pg. 734
Breton, Mike, Pres.--Mapa Pioneer Corporation, Willard, OH; *Int'l*, pg. 1409
Brett, Paul, Mng. Dir. & Chief Exec. Officer--Thomson Tour Operations Ltd., London, United Kingdom; *U.S. Public*, pg. 1601
Breuer, Manfred, Mgr.--Commerzbank (Nederland) N.V., Amsterdam, Netherlands; *Int'l*, pg. 311
Breuninger, Joyce, V.P. & Mgr.--California State Bank-Anaheim, Anaheim, CA; *U.S. Public*, pg. 294
Brevard, J. Rolan, Pres.--Professional Food Systems, El Dorado, AR; *U.S. Public*, pg. 427
Brevard, J. Roland, Pres.--Professional Food Systems, El Dorado, AR; *U.S. Public*, pg. 427
Brew, R., Bus. Devel. Mgr.--M.I.M. Technology Marketing Limited, Northfleet, United Kingdom; *Int'l*, pg. 827
Brewer, Bill, Gen. Mgr.--Westpac - Queensland, Brisbane, Australia; *Int'l*, pg. 1496
Brewer, C. James, Pres.--Burgess-Norton Mfg. Co., Geneva, IL; *U.S. Private*, pg. 68
Brewer, D.T., Gen. Mgr.--New Zealand Aluminium Smelters Ltd., Invercargill, New Zealand; *Int'l*, pg. 307
Brewer, Darrell, Pres.--Sunset P&A Services, Inc., Houma, LA; *U.S. Public*, pg. 1149
Brewer, Fayte, Dr., Gen. Mgr.--Semillas Pioneer, S.A., Spain; *U.S. Public*, pg. 1299
Brewer, Gary, Chief Exec. Officer--Galen Hospital-Alaska, Anchorage, AK; *U.S. Public*, pg. 404
Brewer, John C., Pres.--The New York Times Syndication Sales Corporation, New York, NY; *U.S. Public*, pg. 1174
Brewer, Larry, Mgr.--Southern Electric Supply Co., Inc., Columbus, MS; *Int'l*, pg. 1108
Brewer, Marian, Dir.--Willis Corroon Credit Limited, Reading, United Kingdom; *Int'l*, pg. 1502
Brewer, Mark, Pres.--Falley's Inc., Topeka, KS; *U.S. Private*, pg. 1202
Brewer, Matt, Gen. Mgr.--Poe & Brown of Florida, West Palm Beach, FL; *U.S. Public*, pg. 1312
Brewster, Dan, Pres.-Amex Publ.--American Express Publishing Corporation, New York, NY; *U.S. Public*, pg. 74
Brewster, John, Chief Rep.--Westpac Banking - Indonesia, Jakarta, Indonesia; *Int'l*, pg. 1497
Brewster, Joseph F., V.P. & Gen. Mgr.--Cox Cable University City, Inc., Gainesville, FL; *U.S. Public*, pg. 455
Brewton, Kenneth, Jr., Pres. & Chief Exec. Officer--Clariant Corporation, Charlotte, NC; *Int'l*, pg. 624
Breyer, Gabor, Mgr.-Sls.--Sensormatic kfi, Budapest, Hungary; *U.S. Public*, pg. 1458
Breyvogel, Gilbert, Mng. Dir.--Nestle-Lyons Maid, Telford, United Kingdom; *Int'l*, pg. 922
Bria, Frank, Gen. Mgr.--Rhone-Poulenc Inc., Films Division, Holcomb, NY; *Int'l*, pg. 1110
Brian, Joseph M., Chief Oper. Officer--Axel Johnson, Inc., Montreal, Canada; *Int'l*, pg. 711
Brian, Rick, Mgr.--Big A Auto Parts, Davenport, IA; *U.S. Public*, pg. 10
Brian, Steven R., Mgr.--Seymour Housewares, Seymour, IN; *U.S. Public*, pg. 832
Briand, Jean-Claude, Gen. Mgr.--Aztronic, Chateau-Gontier, France; *U.S. Public*, pg. 1722
Briand, Michael, V.P. & Gen. Mgr.--BancTec Canada Inc., Markham, Canada; *U.S. Public*, pg. 177
Briceno, Jose, Mng. Dir.--Trimble Navigation Japan, Tokyo, Japan; *U.S. Public*, pg. 1638
Brickel, Jack W., Pres. & Treas.--Brencal Contractors Inc., Detroit, MI; *U.S. Private*, pg. 106
Brickwood, David J., Dr., Mng. Dir.--Janssen-Cilag Ltd., High Wycombe, United Kingdom; *U.S. Public*, pg. 929
Bricot, Michele, Chief Oper. Officer--G. Leblanc S.A., Boossey, France; *U.S. Private*, pg. 657
Bridenbecker, R.H., Pres. & Chief Exec. Officer--Mono Power Company, Rosemead, CA; *U.S. Public*, pg. 564
Bridge, A., Mng. Dir.--Bypy Hydraulics & Transmissions Ltd., Ludlow, United Kingdom; *Int'l*, pg. 201
Bridge, Larry, Pres.--Pacificare of Utah, Salt Lake City, UT; *U.S. Public*, pg. 1251
Bridgen, John, Ph.D., Pres.--Wampole Laboratories, Cranbury, NJ; *U.S. Public*, pg. 310
Bridger, Cedric, Chm. Bd.--Maxus Energy Corporation, Dallas, TX; *Int'l*, pg. 1515
Bridger, Mac, Pres.--Collins & Aikman Floorcoverings, Inc., Dalton, GA; *U.S. Private*, pg. 192
Bridges, Barton, Chief Exec. Officer--Diamond Products Company, Seffner, FL; *U.S. Private*, pg. 510
Bridges, Charles, Resident Mgr.--Newark Mill, Newark, DE; *U.S. Public*, pg. 465
Bridges, Ed, Plant Superintendant--General Shale Products Corp., Knoxville, TN; *Int'l*, pg. 843
Bridges, Herschel, Mgr.--Rhone-Poulenc Rorer, Tucker, GA; *Int'l*, pg. 1111
Bridges, L. Michael, Pres.--Columbia Atlantic Trading Corporation, Wilmington, DE; *U.S. Public*, pg. 402
Bridges, L. Michael, Pres. & Chief Exec. Officer--Columbia LNG Corp., Wilmington, DE; *U.S. Public*, pg. 403
Bridges, Lamar, Mgr.--Commercial Metals Co., Tampa, FL; *U.S. Public*, pg. 413
Bridges, Roy, Gen. Mgr.--Poe & Brown of Florida, Fort Myers, FL; *U.S. Public*, pg. 1312
Bridges, Terrell R., Pres.--Chandeleur Homes, Inc., Boaz, AL; *U.S. Public*, pg. 333
Bridges, Thomas, Gen. Mgr.--Staflex/Harotex, Taylors, SC; *U.S. Private*, pg. 504
Bridgford, Allan L., Jr., Pres.--Bridgford Foods of Illinois, Chicago, IL; *U.S. Public*, pg. 252
Bridgford, Bill, Plant Mgr.--Bridgford Distributing Co., Anaheim, CA; *U.S. Public*, pg. 252
Bridgford, Bill, Plant Mgr.--Bridgford Food Corporation, Anaheim, CA; *U.S. Public*, pg. 252
Bridgford, William L., Mgr.-Plant--Bridgford Distributing Co., Modesto, CA; *U.S. Public*, pg. 252
Bridgman, Larry W., Pres.--Simmons Outdoor Corporation, Tallahassee, FL; *U.S. Public*, pg. 238
Bridtmia, John, Pres.--ABB Control Inc., Wichita Falls, TX; *Int'l*, pg. 4
Briece, David, Plant Mgr.--Kalamazoo Recycled Mill, Kalamazoo, MI; *U.S. Public*, pg. 671
Brieger, M. L., Chief Exec. Officer--OCE-Brasil Comercio e Industria Ltda., Sao Paulo, Brazil; *Int'l*, pg. 994
Brien, Nick, Chief Exec. Officer--Leo Burnett Limited, London, United Kingdom; *U.S. Private*, pg. 185
Briengar, Daniel, V.P.--Gerber Garment Technology, Inc., Richardson, TX; *U.S. Public*, pg. 740
Brier, Jack, Chm. Bd. & Chief Exec. Officer--Scott Mills, Gastonia, NC; *U.S. Private*, pg. 625
Briere, Denis, Pres.--Scierie Parent Inc., Trois Rivieres, Canada; *Int'l*, pg. 761
Brierley, Kenneth C., Mng. Dir.--The Bank of Nova Scotia Channel Islands Limited, Saint Helier, United Kingdom; *Int'l*, pg. 156
Brierley, Kenneth C., Mng. Dir.--The Bank of Nova Scotia Trust Company Channel Islands Limited, Saint Helier, United Kingdom; *Int'l*, pg. 157
Bries, Jules, Gen. Mgr.--Nairn Floors Benelux S.A., Braine-l'Alleud, Belgium; *Int'l*, pg. 498
Briesch, John, Pres.--Consumer Sales Products Co., Paramus, NJ; *Int'l*, pg. 1281
Briganti, Joseph, V.P.-Lithography--Beta Squared, Inc., Brookfield, CT; *U.S. Public*, pg. 1293
Brigatti, Aldo, Rep.--Sanpaolo-Beijing Representative Office, Beijing, China; *Int'l*, pg. 691
Briggs, Douglas S., Pres.--QVC, Inc., West Chester, PA; *U.S. Public*, pg. 407
Briggs, Dr. Randy, Pres.--Sunsoft Corporation, Albuquerque, NM; *Int'l*, pg. 462
Briggs, Earl, Pres.--First American Title Insurance Agency of Coconino, Inc., Flagstaff, AZ; *U.S. Public*, pg. 626
Briggs, Paul, Gen. Mgr.--ITW Adhesives, Danvers, MA; *U.S. Public*, pg. 866
Briggs, R. Stephen, Pres.--Empire General Life Assurance Corporation, Birmingham, AL; *U.S. Public*, pg. 1336
Briggs, Steve, Branch Dir.--N.G. Bailey & Co. Ltd.-Reading Branch, Reading, United Kingdom; *Int'l*, pg. 132
Briggs, Steve, V.P.--Color Corp. of America, Rockford, IL; *U.S. Public*, pg. 1707
Briggs, Thomas, Pres.--B-Line Systems, Inc., Highland, IL; *U.S. Public*, pg. 1471
Brigham, Troy, Admin.--Hacienda de Salud - Espanola, Espanola, NM; *U.S. Public*, pg. 838
Brighigna, Mario, Pres. & Mng. Dir.--VM Motori S.p.A., Cento, Italy; *Int'l*, pg. 654
Bright, Al, Plant Mgr.--Silgan Containers, Pevely, MO; *U.S. Public*, pg. 1473
Bright, Harvey W., Pres. & Chief Exec. Officer--Engineered Specialty Plastics, Hot Springs National Park, AR; *U.S. Public*, pg. 583
Brightbill, William R., Pres.--NORCAM Construction Company, Harrisburg, PA; *U.S. Private*, pg. 934
Brigish, Ronald B., ResidentRep.--The World Bank, Dar es Salaam, Tanzania; *U.S. Private*, pg. 1190
Briley, Martha Clark, Dir.--Prudential Overseas Funding Corp. N.V., Curacao, Netherlands Antilles; *U.S. Private*, pg. 893
Brill, Edward T., Pres.--GS Electric, Carlisle, PA; *U.S. Public*, pg. 726
Brill, Martin, Pres.--Tweeds, Inc., Weehawken, NJ; *U.S. Public*, pg. 782
Brillhart, Jerry, V.P.--Cleveland Division, Cleveland, OH; *Int'l*, pg. 518
Brimble, A.J., Mng. Dir.--Babcock King - Wilkinson Limited, Crawley, United Kingdom; *Int'l*, pg. 131
Brinck, William C., V.P.--Yosuba Farms, Robbins, CA; *U.S. Public*, pg. 1062
Brinckmann, Karl-Dietrich, Chief Oper. Officer--Kossack Chemie GmbH, Dusseldorf, Germany; *Int'l*, pg. 610
Brind, Peter, Gen. Mgr.-European Div.--Westpac Banking Corporation-European Div., London, United Kingdom; *Int'l*, pg. 1497
Brindle, Robert, Gen. Mgr.--James Burn Binders, Eynsham, United Kingdom; *U.S. Public*, pg. 1507
Bring, Gosta, Mng. Dir.--Neste Kemi Forsaljnings AB, Stenungsund, Sweden; *Int'l*, pg. 915
Bring, Luiz, Pres.--Asea Brown Boveri Ltda., Bogota, Colombia; *Int'l*, pg. 8
Bringewald, Wolf-Roderich, Dr., Sr. Mng. Dir.--Deutsche Bank AG (Cologne), Cologne, Germany; *Int'l*, pg. 402
Bringhurst, Brent, V.P.--Midwest Division, Tulsa, OK; *U.S. Public*, pg. 38
Brings, Baxter, Chief Oper. Officer--T.S. Denison & Company, Minneapolis, MN; *U.S. Private*, pg. 288
Brink, William A., Chm. Bd.--The Burton Company, North Haven, CT; *U.S. Public*, pg. 826
Brinker, D.O., Gen. Mgr.--Explo-Midwest, Inc., Joplin, MO; *Int'l*, pg. 663
Brinkhuysen, J., Gen. Mgr.--Kiekens B.V., Amsterdam, Amsterdam, Netherlands; *Int'l*, pg. 681
Brinkley, D.R., Pres. & Chief Exec. Officer--Colonial Pipeline Co., Atlanta, GA; *U.S. Public*, pg. 1584
Brinkley, Jesse A., Pres.--Lea Industries, Greensboro, NC; *U.S. Public*, pg. 974
Brinkley, Nicholas B., Chm. Bd. & Chief Exec. Officer--BankAmerica Financial Services System, Inc., San Diego, CA; *U.S. Public*, pg. 181
Brinkman, B.P., Gen. Mgr.--Industrial Packaging Div. (Lafayette), Lafayette, IN; *Int'l*, pg. 1270
Brinkman, Craig, Mng. Dir.--West Bend of Canada Ltd., Barrie, Canada; *U.S. Public*, pg. 1323
Brinkman, J., Mgr.--Snap-on Tools, GmbH, Obersulm, Germany; *U.S. Public*, pg. 1481
Brinkman, L.D., Chief Oper. Officer--LDB Food Services, Inc., Kerrville, TX; *U.S. Private*, pg. 639
Brinkman, R.J., V.P. & Gen Mgr.--Lighting Div., Anaheim, CA; *U.S. Public*, pg. 844
Brinkman, Robert, Gen. Mgr.--Hubbell Premise Wiring, Inc., Stonington, CT; *U.S. Public*, pg. 844

Brinkmann, Bernd, Dr., Gen. Mgr.--Witco GmbH, Bergkamen, Germany; U.S. Public, pg. 1774
Brinly, Jack H., Pres.--Ecova Corporation, Golden, CO; U.S. Public, pg. 103
Brinson, Danny, Pres.--Bunny Bread Co., Inc., New Orleans, LA; U.S. Public, pg. 657
Brisbane, Arthur S., Publr.--The Kansas City Star Company, Kansas City, MO; U.S. Public, pg. 964
Brisbin, Thomas, Pres.--PRC Environmental Management, Inc., Chicago, IL; U.S. Public, pg. 1582
Briscoe, Don, Pres.--Tarmac California, Inc., Palm Desert, CA; Int'l, pg. 1355
Brisebois, Mark F., Pres.--Excelis, Inc., Dallas, TX; U.S. Public, pg. 625
Brisighella, D.G., Jr., Gen. Mgr.--OEA Automotive Safety Products Division, Aurora, CO; U.S. Public, pg. 1207
Bristow, A., Dir.-Sls. & Mktg.--Andres Wines (Atlantic) Ltd., Dartmouth, Canada; Int'l, pg. 76
Brito, Julio L., Reg. Chief Exec. Officer--Formularios y Procedimientos Moore S.A., Maracay, Venezuela; Int'l, pg. 890
Brito, Pedro, Mng. Dir.--Publinter/BDDP, Lisbon, Portugal; Int'l, pg. 118
Britt, Glen A., Exec. V.P. & Treas.--State Farm Life and Accident Assurance Co., Bloomington, IL; U.S. Private, pg. 1036
Britt, William R., Chm. Bd., Pres. & Chief Exec. Officer--Palmer-American National Bank, Danville, IL; U.S. Public, pg. 1717
Brittain, Jack R., Mng. Dir.--Rank Cintel Ltd., Ware, United Kingdom; Int'l, pg. 1087
Brittelle, Douglas J., Pres.--Compool Corporation, Mountain View, CA; U.S. Public, pg. 592
Britton, Bob, Mgr.--Martin Band Instrument Co., Kenosha, WI; U.S. Private, pg. 657
Britton, Rhonda, Acct. Supvr.--TMP Worldwide/Recruitment Division, Raleigh, NC; U.S. Private, pg. 1065
Brix, Berend, Chief Fin. Officer--CAP Volmac, Utrecht, Netherlands; Int'l, pg. 264
Brizzolara, A.J., Pres.--Jet Electronics & Technology, Inc., Grand Rapids, MI; U.S. Public, pg. 751
Brletich, Frank, Pres.--LinkUSA Corporation, Cedar Rapids, IA; U.S. Public, pg. 684
Bro, Jack, V.P. & Mng. Dir.--Herman Miller, Ltd., Bath, United Kingdom; U.S. Public, pg. 1112
Broad, Robert C., Pres.--CCL Label, Burlington, Canada; Int'l, pg. 238
Broad, Robert C., Pres.--CCL Label, Winnipeg, Canada; Int'l, pg. 238
Broadbent, J.S.L., Chm. Bd.--Marley Floors (USA) Inc., Tuscumbia, AL; Int'l, pg. 843
Broadbent, Les, Gen. Mgr.--Ohse Foods Inc., Topeka, KS; U.S. Private, pg. 396
Broadhead, R., Chm. Bd.--Taylor Woodrow Construction (Southern) Ltd., Southall, United Kingdom; Int'l, pg. 1358
Broadhurst, Joseph D., Pres.--Integrated Material Handling Company, Oshkosh, WI; Int'l, pg. 1397
Broadwater, C. C., Pres.--Republic Hose Manufacturing Co., Youngstown, OH; Int'l, pg. 1423
Broas, Matthew, Pres.--Harbour Island, Inc., Tampa, FL; U.S. Public, pg. 211
Broberg, Gunnar, Chief Oper. Officer--Electrolux Malaysia Sdn. Bhd., Petaling Jaya, Malaysia; Int'l, pg. 443
Broc, Pierre, Mng. Dir.--Kenzo, Paris, France; Int'l, pg. 781
Brocata, R. J., Div. Pres.--Winn-Dixie Louisiana, Inc., Harahan, LA; U.S. Public, pg. 1771
Broccato, Danilo, Gen. Mgr.--Wang Italia S.p.A, Milan, Italy; U.S. Public, pg. 1738
Brochart, J., Pres.--Van Leer Singapore Pte. Ltd., Jurong, Singapore; Int'l, pg. 1147
Brochu, Michael A., Pres. & Chief Oper. Officer--Sierra On-Line, Inc., Bellevue, WA; U.S. Public, pg. 321
Brock, Gunnar, Pres.--Tetra Pak, Lund, Sweden; Int'l, pg. 1378
Brock, Jerry, Pres.--Jacobs Applied Technology, Inc., Orangeburg, SC; U.S. Public, pg. 921
Brock, John, Office Mgr.--Korn/Ferry International, Houston, TX; U.S. Private, pg. 633
Brock, Lee, V.P.-Sls.--Fairfield Bay, Fairfield Bay, AR; U.S. Public, pg. 610
Brock, Mark, Pres.--Shea Homes San Diego, San Diego, CA; U.S. Private, pg. 991
Brock, Paul K., Chm. Bd.--Brach & Brock Confections Inc., Chattanooga, TN; U.S. Private, pg. 163
Brock, Steve G., Pres. & Gen. Mgr--WCIV, LLC, Mount Pleasant, SC; U.S. Private, pg. 854
Brocke, John, Plant Mgr.--Contadina/Libby/Trenton Div., Trenton, MO; Int'l, pg. 916
Brockel, Detlef, Dr., Co-Chief Oper. Officer--IKB Consult GmbH, Dusseldorf, Germany; Int'l, pg. 645
Brockhuijsen, P.L., Gen. Mgr.--BS-Service B.V., Zoetermeer, Zoetermeer, Netherlands; Int'l, pg. 682
Brockhum, Wayne, Branch Mgr.--Tampa Bay Steel, Clearwater, FL; U.S. Private, pg. 1067
Brockman, Dan, Gen. Mgr.--Independent Metals, Broadview, IL; U.S. Private, pg. 559
Brockmann, Rolf, Dr., Chief Oper. Officer--Siegert & Cie GmbH, Neuwied, Germany; Int'l, pg. 610
Broda, J., Mgr.--Wiltshier Interiors (Brunei) Sdn. Bhd., Bandar Seri Begawan, Brunei Darussalam; Int'l, pg. 134
Brodbeck, Rolf, Dr., Mng. Dir.--AUTARKA GmbH, Vermittlung von Versicherungen aller Art, Munich, Germany; Int'l, pg. 423
Brodd, Lars, Reg. Dir.-Nordic Region--ESAB Sverige AB, Goteborg, Sweden; Int'l, pg. 281
Brodd, Ulf K., Pres--Bensons, Gloucester, United Kingdom; Int'l, pg. 460
Broderick, John J., Pres.--Judd's Incorporated, Washington, DC; U.S. Private, pg. 855
Broderick, Robert D., Pres.--Dakota Energy Alternatives, Inc., Farmington, MN; U.S. Private, pg. 308
Brodersen, Norbert, Chief Oper. Officer--KME Rohstoff GmbH, Osnabruck, Germany; Int'l, pg. 719
Brodetsky, David, Mng. Dir.--Sourdillon SA, Esvres, France; Int'l, pg. 391
Brodeur, G., Mgr.-Winery--Les Vins Andres du Quebec Ltee., Saint-Hyacinthe, Canada; Int'l, pg. 76
Brodeur, Pauline N., Chief Oper. Officer--Les Publications CCH/FM Ltee, Farnham, Canada; Int'l, pg. 1513
Brodie, Michael, Mng. Dir.--Universal Studios Artists (England) Ltd., London, United Kingdom; Int'l, pg. 1216
Brodkin, A. Keith, Chm. Bd. & Pres.--Massachusetts Financial Services Company (MFS), Boston, MA; Int'l, pg. 1319
Brodkorb, Rudi, Mng. Dir.--IBP, West Bromwich, United Kingdom; Int'l, pg. 391
Brodtkorb, Arnt, Pres.--A/S Jotul Industrier, Oslo, Norway; Int'l, pg. 42
Brodtkorb, E.M., Mng. Dir.--Norsk Texaco A/S, Oslo, Norway; U.S. Public, pg. 1584
Brody, D., Mgr.--Nalco Australia, Botany, Australia; U.S. Public, pg. 1150
Brody, Martin, Chief Exec. Officer--Sag Harbor, New York, NY; U.S. Public, pg. 948
Broekema, A.R., Chief Oper. Officer--Gist-Brocades Benelux B.V., Dordrecht, Netherlands; Int'l, pg. 1143
Broekema, Dirk, Jr., Pres.--Centennial Federal Savings Bank F.S.B., Durango, CO; U.S. Public, pg. 1793
Broeker, Michael, Gen. Mgr.--Kubota Tractor Corp., Farmers Branch, TX; Int'l, pg. 762
Broekhuijsen, P.L., Gen. Mgr.--Hapam-Goldbach b.v., Amersfoort, Netherlands; Int'l, pg. 681
Broese van Groenou, Leonard, Mng. Dir.--Air Products S.A., Brussels, Belgium; U.S. Public, pg. 32
Brog, J. Eugene, Mng. Dir.--Neho Versand G.m.b.H., Seeheim, Germany; Int'l, pg. 1216
Brogan, Thomas M., Gen. Mgr.--Argo Terminal, Argo, IL; U.S. Public, pg. 692
Brokdorff, Peter, Media Dir.--Leo Burnett Denmark, Copenhagen, Denmark; U.S. Private, pg. 185
Brolin, Anders, Pres.--Stora Project, Solna, Sweden; Int'l, pg. 899
Brolin, Anders, Pres.--NCC Stora Projelet, Solna, Sweden; Int'l, pg. 899
Brolsma, John, Div. Mgr.--Transilwrap Company, Inc., Nazareth, PA; U.S. Private, pg. 1097
Brolund, Theodore F., Pres.--W.A. Whitney Co., Rockford, IL; U.S. Public, pg. 594
Bromley, Peter, Pres.-Agrichemicals--Elf Atochem North America, Agrichemicals Div., Philadelphia, PA; Int'l, pg. 446
Bromley, Peter T., Exec. V.P.--Pharmosol Corporation, South Easton, MA; Int'l, pg. 446
Bromley, Stan, V.P. & Gen. Mgr.--Four Seasons Washington, Washington, DC; Int'l, pg. 502
Broms, Edward, Pres.--AGA Gas C.A., Caracas, Venezuela; Int'l, pg. 13
Brondum, L., Chief Exec. Officer--B&C Danmark A/S, Moldrup, Denmark; Int'l, pg. 1091
Bronfman, Samuel II, Pres.--The Seagram Classics Wine Company, San Mateo, CA; Int'l, pg. 1215
Bronoff, Georges, Mng. Dir.--PDA International France, Saint Quentin-en-Yvelines, France; U.S. Public, pg. 1031
Brons, Jan, Mng. Dir.--SKF Condition Monitoring Inc., San Diego, CA; Int'l, pg. 1157
Bronson, Thomas E., Chief Oper. Officer--Kevaland Corp., Denver, CO; Int'l, pg. 628
Brook, Ben, Gen. Mgr.--CEI Enterprises, Albuquerque, NM; U.S. Public, pg. 141
Brooke, G., Div. Mgr.--Aerospace & Power Controls Div., Loves Park, IL; Int'l, pg. 1242
Brooke, George W., Mgr.--Tech Development Inc., Dayton, OH; Int'l, pg. 1242
Brooker, Graeme, Mgr.--Geelong Rod Mill, North Shore, Australia; Int'l, pg. 227
Brooker, Marvin, Reg. Mgr.--Green Tree Acceptance, Inc., West Palm Beach, FL; U.S. Public, pg. 762
Brooker, T., Mgr.-Sls..--A.M. Castle & Co., Clarence, NY; U.S. Public, pg. 313
Brookes, A. Stafford, Mktg. Mgr.--AlliedSignal Aerospace Service Corporation, Munich, Germany; U.S. Public, pg. 52
Brookes, Nickolas K., Pres.--Texas Instruments Materials & Controls Group, Attleboro, MA; U.S. Public, pg. 1586
Brookfield, W. L., Pres.--Reliance Realty, Inc., Daytona Beach, FL; U.S. Public, pg. 355
Brookman, Amber M., Pres. & Chief Exec. Officer--Brookwood Companies Inc., New York, NY; U.S. Public, pg. 777
Brookman, Ben J., Pres.--Allied Indus., Inc., Houston, TX; U.S. Public, pg. 775
Brookman, Carol Ann, Mgr.--Piper Jaffray Inc., Stillwater, MN; U.S. Public, pg. 1302
Brooks, Benjamin, Admin.--Windsor Manor, Starke, FL; U.S. Public, pg. 837
Brooks, C. Benjamin, Jr., Pres.--Clairol's Consumer Products Division, New York, NY; U.S. Public, pg. 254
Brooks, C. Benjamin, Jr., Pres.--The Professional Products Division, New York, NY; U.S. Public, pg. 254
Brooks, David R., Pres.--American Airlines Cargo, Fort Worth, TX; U.S. Public, pg. 9
Brooks, Del, Gen. Mgr.--Paperboard Mill (Alton), Alton, IL; Int'l, pg. 1270
Brooks, Diana D., Pres. & Chief Exec. Officer--Sotheby's Inc., New York, NY; U.S. Public, pg. 1487
Brooks, Don, Gen. Mgr.--Houston Marketing Office, Houston, TX; U.S. Public, pg. 1759
Brooks, Donald M., V.P. & Gen. Mgr.--Crafco, Inc., Chandler, AZ; U.S. Private, pg. 381
Brooks, Edward, Mng. Dir.--Linread Northbridge, Redditch, United Kingdom; Int'l, pg. 852
Brooks, J., Mng. Dir.--Thai Shell Exploration & Production, Co. Ltd., Bangkok, Thailand; Int'l, pg. 1140
Brooks, James R., Pres. & Chief Exec. Officer--Global Special Risks, Inc. Holdings, Metairie, LA; Int'l, pg. 1503
Brooks, James R., Pres. & Chief Exec. Officer--Global Special Risks, Inc. of Houston, Houston, TX; Int'l, pg. 1503
Brooks, Jamie, Acct. Exec.--Zimmerman & Partners Advertising, Inc., Chicago, IL; U.S. Private, pg. 1206
Brooks, Jay W., Pres.--Brooks, Montague & Associates, Inc., Chattanooga, TN; U.S. Public, pg. 1155
Brooks, Jim, Gen. Mgr.--Golden State Foods-North Carolina Div., Greensboro, NC; U.S. Private, pg. 460
Brooks, Kevin P., Pres.--General Star Management Company, Stamford, CT; U.S. Public, pg. 725
Brooks, Kim, Pres.--Kaufman and Broad New Mexico Division, Albuquerque, NM; U.S. Public, pg. 945
Brooks, Landon E., Pres.--Gits Manufacturing Company, Inc., Creston, IA; U.S. Public, pg. 1705
Brooks, M., Sr. V.P.--Jelrus International, Hicksville, NY; U.S. Private, pg. 28
Brooks, R.J., Pres.--Freeman Energy Corporation, Springfield, IL; U.S. Public, pg. 709
Brooks, Robert W., Chief Oper. Officer--P.H.I. Engineering Ltd., London, United Kingdom; Int'l, pg. 398
Brooks, Roger E., Pres.--Dynisco, Inc., Sharon, MA; U.S. Private, pg. 138
Brooks, Thomas F., Gen. Mgr.--Ketema Division, El Cajon, CA; Int'l, pg. 1222
Brooks, Tim, Mng. Dir.--EMAP Architecture Ltd., London, United Kingdom; Int'l, pg. 451
Brooks, Tim, Mng. Dir.--NCE Group, London, United Kingdom; Int'l, pg. 451
Brooks, Tom, Gen. Mgr.--Tampa Soap Div., Tampa, FL; U.S. Private, pg. 481
Brooks, William J., V.P. & Gen. Mgr.--WPTV, West Palm Beach, FL; U.S. Public, pg. 1448
Broome, Hoyle S., V.P. & Gen. Mgr.--WBMG-TV, Birmingham, AL; U.S. Public, pg. 1078
Broomer, Anthony, Pres.--Chessco Process Research Products Div., Trenton, NJ; U.S. Private, pg. 234
Broomfield, Robert A., V.P. & Gen. Mgr.-Asia Pacific Region--Newbridge Networks Corporation, Kanata, Canada; Int'l, pg. 924
Broos, Frank, Mng. Dir.--Sanderson Computers Pty. Ltd., Sydney, Australia; Int'l, pg. 1185
Brophy, Bill, Gen. Plant Mgr.--CSP Industries B.V., Kildare, Ireland; U.S. Public, pg. 445
Brophy, George T., Chm. Bd., Pres. & Chief Exec. Officer--ABT Building Products Corporation, Neenah, WI; Int'l, pg. 20
Brophy, John M., Pres. & Chief Oper. Officer--Lockheed Information Management Services Co., Teaneck, NJ; U.S. Public, pg. 1009
Brose, Rolf, Mng. Dir.--Henkel Genthin GmbH, Genthin, Germany; Int'l, pg. 610
Brosig, K., V.P.--Klockner INA Industrial Installations, Inc., Huntington, NY; Int'l, pg. 1081
Brostrom, Ingemar, Mgr.--Dormer Tools B.V., Veenendaal, Netherlands; Int'l, pg. 1186
Brostrom, J.A.F., Representative--Morgan Grenfell (Sweden), Stockholm, Sweden; Int'l, pg. 406
Brotherhood, P., Pres.--Alcon Canada, Inc., Mississauga, Canada; Int'l, pg. 918
Brothers, Clive, V.P.--Weight Watchers Foods Central Europe B.V., Maidenhead, United Kingdom; U.S. Public, pg. 807
Brothers, John A., Grp. Oper. Officer--Valvoline, Inc., Hernando, MS; U.S. Public, pg. 139
Brotons, Jose, Chief Oper. Officer--Club Med S.R.L., Caracas, Venezuela; Int'l, pg. 298
Brotzman, Rich, Pres. & Dir. Gen.--Hallmark Mexicana, S. de R.I. de C.V., Mexico, Mexico; U.S. Private, pg. 496
Brough, Ray, Mng. Dir.--Skega Canada Ltd., North Bay, Canada; Int'l, pg. 1323
Brougham, J.H., Dir.--BT Communications Management Limited, London, United Kingdom; Int'l, pg. 222
Broughman, Stephen, V.P. & Gen. Mgr.--Dillard, A ResourceNet International Company, Chattanooga, TN; U.S. Public, pg. 902
Brouilette, Alan, Chief Oper. Officer--Tootsietoy Preschool Products Div., Chicago, IL; U.S. Private, pg. 1047
Brouillard, Thom, Reg. Mgr.--Liebert International B.V., Cork, Ireland; U.S. Public, pg. 577
Brouillette, Romeo, Chief Oper. Officer--Boart Longyear Ltda., Santiago, Chile; Int'l, pg. 76
Broussard, Sidney, Div. Mgr.--Coastal Telephone & Electronics, Breaux Bridge, LA; U.S. Public, pg. 329
Brousse, Bernard, Dir.--Banco International de Credito SA (Portugal), Lisbon, Portugal; Int'l, pg. 341
Brousseau, S. B., Div. Mgr.--Chicoutimi Div., Chicoutimi, Canada; Int'l, pg. 19
Broussy, Claude, Chief Oper. Officer--Pall France S.A., Saint Germain-en-Laye, France; U.S. Public, pg. 1254
Broutin, Patrick, Mgr.--Duni SARL, Epone, France; Int'l, pg. 421
Brouwer, Frank, Dir.--Fleming Canada Partners Inc., Vancouver, Canada; Int'l, pg. 493
Brouwer, Hans, Mgr.-Country--Colgate-Palmolive Nederland, Weesp, Netherlands; U.S. Public, pg. 398
Brouwer, J., Pres.--Paktank International B.V., Rotterdam, Netherlands; Int'l, pg. 1147
Brouzos, Andreas, Gen. Mgr.--Colgate-Palmolive S.p.A., Rome, Italy; U.S. Public, pg. 399
Brow, Wayne, Admin.--Hartford Care Center, Hartford, WI; U.S. Public, pg. 840
Browaldth, Tore, Vice Chm.--IBM Svenska Aktiebolag, Stockholm, Sweden; U.S. Public, pg. 897
Browall, Torbjorn, Company Head--SKF Trgovina d.o.o., Ljubljana, Slovenia; Int'l, pg. 1159
Browell, Torbjorn, Mng. Dir.--SKF Services d.o.o., Zagreb, Croatia; Int'l, pg. 1159
Brown, A.E., Chm. Bd.--Barclays Trust & Banking Company (Japan) Ltd., Tokyo, Japan; Int'l, pg. 166
Brown, Alistair, Div. Mgr.--Duni Ltd., Runcorn, United Kingdom; Int'l, pg. 421
Brown, Andy, Pres. & Chief Oper. Officer--El Paso Baking Co., Inc., El Paso, TX; U.S. Public, pg. 657

Brown, Archie, Gen. Mgr.-Door Division--Elixir Industries, Douglas, GA; *U.S. Private*, pg. 371
Brown, Arthur V., V.P.-Opers. & Tech. Services--The Jim Dandy Co., Inc., Atlanta, GA; *Int'l*, pg. 918
Brown, Barry, Sr. V.P.--CB Commercial Real Estate Group Eastern Division, Stamford, CT; *U.S. Public*, pg. 272
Brown, Betty L., Pres.--Meldrum & Fewsmith Directory Marketing, Cleveland, OH; *U.S. Private*, pg. 730
Brown, Beverly, Branch Mgr.--Zellerbach Division, Portland, OR; *U.S. Public*, pg. 1075
Brown, Bob, Gen. Mgr.--Tri-Manufacturing, Terre Haute, IN; *U.S. Public*, pg. 710
Brown, Bob, Mng. Dir.--Thermon Heat Tracing Services, Inc., Calgary, Canada,; *U.S. Private*, pg. 1081
Brown, Bob, Div. Head--Computer Intelligence InfoCorp, New York, NY; *Int'l*, pg. 1276
Brown, Bruce, Pres.--Vertel, Woodland Hills, CA; *U.S. Public*, pg. 1717
Brown, Charles G., V.P. & Gen. Mgr.--Klockner-Bartelt, Inc., Sarasota, FL; *Int'l*, pg. 737
Brown, Clarke R. Jr., Pres.-Radio Div. & Gen. Mgr.-WQXI-AM & WSTR-FM--Jefferson-Pilot Communications Company, Greensboro, NC; *U.S. Public*, pg. 925
Brown, Clarke R., Jr., Pres.-Radio Div.--Jefferson-Pilot Communications Co. of Virginia, Richmond, VA; *U.S. Public*, pg. 926
Brown, Clarke R., Jr., V.P. & Gen. Mgr.--KSON AM & FM, San Diego, CA; *U.S. Public*, pg. 926
Brown, Colleen, Pres. & Gen. Mgr.--WFMY-TV, Greensboro, NC; *U.S. Public*, pg. 702
Brown, D., Pres.--Tempo Instrument Inc., Commack, NY; *Int'l*, pg. 208
Brown, D.L., Chief Opr. Officer--O.C. Summers Ltd., Borehamwood, United Kingdom; *Int'l*, pg. 796
Brown, D.N.D., Joint Mng. Dir.--P&O (New Zealand) Ltd., Wellington, New Zealand; *Int'l*, pg. 1035
Brown, Dale, Pres. & Chief Exec. Officer--Sive/Young & Rubicam L.P., Cincinnati, OH; *U.S. Private*, pg. 1197
Brown, Dave, Mgr.-Opers.--R.J. Simpson Mfg. Co. (Canada) Ltd., Thamesville, Canada; *U.S. Public*, pg. 1475
Brown, David, Gen. Mgr.--Commonwealth Steel Co. Ltd., Waratah, Australia; *Int'l*, pg. 101
Brown, David, Pres.--Bowne of Cleveland, Inc., Cleveland, OH; *U.S. Public*, pg. 249
Brown, David, Pres.--ManuLife (International) Limited, Hamilton, Bermuda; *Int'l*, pg. 841
Brown, David, V.P.--La-Z-Boy Tennessee, Dayton, TN; *U.S. Public*, pg. 973
Brown, David C., Plant Mgr.--Sterling Faucet Co., Sheridan, AR; *U.S. Private*, pg. 630
Brown, David J., Pres.--Morgan Distribution, Mechanicsburg, PA; *U.S. Public*, pg. 1132
Brown, Dennis, Mine Mgr.--Red Lake Mine, Balmertown, Canada; *Int'l*, pg. 243
Brown, Dick, Pres.--Quality Stamp, Memphis, TN; *U.S. Public*, pg. 653
Brown, Don, Plant Mgr.--McCowan Mobile Mix, Agincourt, Canada; *Int'l*, pg. 629
Brown, Donald, Gen. Mgr.--Esselte Pendaflex, Kankakee, IL; *Int'l*, pg. 460
Brown, Donald, Mgr.--Sanpaolo-Los Angeles Branch, Los Angeles, CA; *Int'l*, pg. 691
Brown, Donald, Pres.--Lista International Corporation, Holliston, MA; *Int'l*, pg. 812
Brown, Donald, Pres.--Hoffmann-La Roche Ltd., Mississauga, Canada; *Int'l*, pg. 1121
Brown, Doug, Gen. Mgr.--Stanfast, Inc., Dallas, TX; *U.S. Public*, pg. 1505
Brown, Duncan, Pres.--Epitronics, Inc., Mesa, AZ; *U.S. Public*, pg. 12
Brown, Earl, Mgr.-Branch--GAI Consultants, Inc., Charleston, WV; *U.S. Private*, pg. 434
Brown, Eddie R., Pres.--Landstar Ranger, Inc., Jacksonville, FL; *U.S. Public*, pg. 978
Brown, Edgar Jr., Pres.--Bell Atlantic International, Inc., Arlington, VA; *U.S. Public*, pg. 202
Brown, Edgar L., Pres. & Chief Exec. Officer--Bell Atlanticom Systems, Inc., Princeton, NJ; *U.S. Public*, pg. 203
Brown, Edward K., Resident Rep.--Banque Mondiale, Namey, Niger; *U.S. Private*, pg. 1189
Brown, Eric, Grp. V.P.-Grocery Prods.--Hormel Grocery Prods. Div., Austin, MN; *U.S. Public*, pg. 840
Brown, Fiona, Mgr.--Kelly Temporary Services, Ltd.-Ireland, Dublin, Ireland; *U.S. Public*, pg. 949
Brown, Frank, Plant Mgr.--Monticello Plant, Monticello, KY; *U.S. Public*, pg. 201
Brown, Franklin, Pres.--BHP Trading Inc., Long Beach, CA; *Int'l*, pg. 226
Brown, Franklin D., Pres. & Chief Exec. Officer--Pharmacia & Upjohn Deltec, Inc., Arden Hills, MN; *Int'l*, pg. 1049
Brown, George A., Pres.--Brown & Company Securities Corporation, Boston, MA; *U.S. Public*, pg. 337
Brown, Gerry, Pres.--Coleman Powermate, Inc., Omaha, NE; *U.S. Private*, pg. 691
Brown, Greg, Pres.--Ameritech Custom Business Services, Chicago, IL; *U.S. Public*, pg. 98
Brown, Gregory C., Gen. Mgr.--Corrugated Container Div.-Mansfield Plant, Mansfield, OH; *U.S. Public*, pg. 1520
Brown, J., Mng. Dir.--Addison Tube Forming Limited, Preston, United Kingdom; *Int'l*, pg. 448
Brown, J. Hyatt, Pres.--Tampa Retail Division, Tampa, FL; *U.S. Public*, pg. 1312
Brown, J.F., Gen. Mgr.--GF International Limited, Alexandria, Australia; *Int'l*, pg. 555
Brown, J.M., Pres. & Gen. Mgr.--Electronics Div., San Diego, CA; *U.S. Public*, pg. 396
Brown, Jack, Gen. Mgr.--NVF Industries of Canada Ltd., Rexdale, Canada; *U.S. Private*, pg. 772
Brown, Jack D., Pres. & Gen. Mgr.--Mid Valley Title & Escrow Co., Chico, CA; *U.S. Public*, pg. 626
Brown, Jack H., Chm. Bd., Pres. & Chief Exec. Officer--Stater Bros. Inc., Colton, CA; *U.S. Public*, pg. 456
Brown, Jack W., Pres.--Gish International, Inc., Irvine, CA; *U.S. Public*, pg. 745
Brown, James, Mng. Dir.--ESAB (Malaysia) Sdn, Bhd, Petaling Jaya, Malaysia; *Int'l*, pg. 282
Brown, James, Dir.-Mktg.--Microsoft Press, Bellevue, WA; *U.S. Public*, pg. 1107
Brown, James, Pres. & Chief Exec. Officer--Union Planters Bank of Mississippi, Grenada, MS; *U.S. Public*, pg. 1669
Brown, James L., Chief Oper. Officer--Casino Aztar, Evansville, IN; *U.S. Public*, pg. 158
Brown, Jay W., Pres. & Chief Exec. Officer--Du Pont Protein Technologies International, Saint Louis, MO; *U.S. Public*, *pg. 531*
Brown, Jerry B., V.P.--Georgia Region, Atlanta, GA; *U.S. Public*, pg. 7
Brown, Jim A., Jr., Area Sls. Rep.--Production Operators, Inc. (Midland-Odessa Office), Midland, TX; *U.S. Public*, pg. 298
Brown, Joe, Mgr.--Harley Valve & Instrument, Cartersville, GA; *U.S. Public*, pg. 880
Brown, Joe, Mgr.-Opers.--Parker Technology, Inc., Odessa, TX; *U.S. Public*, pg. 1259
Brown, John, Sr. V.P. & Mng. Dir.--State Street Australia Ltd., Sydney, Australia; *U.S. Public*, pg. 1513
Brown, K. N., Mng. Dir.--Portals (Bathford) Ltd., Bath, United Kingdom; *Int'l*, pg. 386
Brown, Kevin, Chief Oper. Officer--Blue Crab Lounge, Chicago, IL; *U.S. Private*, pg. 661
Brown, L.T., Administrator--Hernando County Jail, Brooksville, FL; *U.S. Public*, pg. 450
Brown, Larry, Region Mgr.--Pacific Hardwoods-South Bend Co., Raymond, WA; *U.S. Public*, pg. 1730
Brown, Lloyd, Mng. Dir.--SKF Uruguay S.A., Montevideo, Uruguay; *Int'l*, pg. 1159
Brown, Marvin R., M.D., Pres.--Alanex Corporation, San Diego, CA; *U.S. Public*, pg. 28
Brown, Max, Dir.--Crusteel Ltd., Sheffield, United Kingdom; *U.S. Private*, pg. 293
Brown, Michael, V.P.--The Bank of Nova Scotia, Portland, OR; *Int'l*, pg. 156
Brown, Michael, Opers. Mgr.--TWD Baltimore, Baltimore, MD; *U.S. Public*, pg. 229
Brown, Michael C., Pres.--Ryland Mortgage Co., Columbia, MD; *U.S. Public*, pg. 1414
Brown, Mike, Pres. & Chief Oper. Officer--City Meats & Provisions Co., Phoenix, AZ; *U.S. Private*, pg. 244
Brown, Montie, Admin.--Silverado Convalescent Hospital, Napa, CA; *U.S. Public*, pg. 1714
Brown, Nancy M., Asst. Treas. & Branch Mgr.--Valley National Bank, Hackettstown, NJ; *U.S. Public*, pg. 1706
Brown, P.G., Dir.--Lloyds Private Banking & Financial Services, Haywards Heath, United Kingdom; *Int'l*, pg. 813
Brown, P.M., Mgr.--Kingcome Navigation Company Ltd., Vancouver, Canada; *Int'l*, pg. 828
Brown, Patrick, Branch Mgr.--Zellerbach Division, Pittsburgh, PA; *U.S. Public*, pg. 1075
Brown, Paul, Pres.--Liquid Molding Systems, Inc., Midland, MI; *U.S. Public*, pg. 125
Brown, Philip H., Pres.--National Posters, Inc., Chattanooga, TN; *U.S. Private*, pg. 786
Brown, R. Donald, Chm. Bd., Pres. & Chief Exec. Officer--Imperial Tobacco Limited, Montreal, Canada; *Int'l*, pg. 112
Brown, R.J., Chm. Bd.--R.J. Brown and Associates Corporation AG, Zug, Switzerland; *Int'l*, pg. 766
Brown, R.W., Pres.--Baymont Technologies Inc., Clearwater, FL; *Int'l*, pg. 31
Brown, R.W., Dir.--First State Computing Pty Ltd, Sydney, Australia; *Int'l*, pg. 222
Brown, Richard J., Pres.--HGC Bank, Chicago, IL; *Int'l*, pg. 154
Brown, Richard L., Pres.--Rockford Mercantile Agency, Rockford, IL; *U.S. Public*, pg. 65
Brown, Richard L., Pres. & Chief Exec. Officer--Houston General Insurance Co., Fort Worth, TX; *Int'l*, pg. 1392
Brown, Richard M., Pres. & Chief Exec. Officer--Golden West Baseball Club, Anaheim, CA; *U.S. Private*, pg. 461
Brown, Robert, Mgr.--Boeing Agri-Industrial Co., Boardman, OR; *U.S. Public*, pg. 242
Brown, Robert, West Coast Nursery Mgr.--Speedling Incorporated Nipomo Nursery, Nipomo, CA; *U.S. Private*, *pg. 1024*
Brown, Robert, West Coast Nursery Mgr.--Speedling Incorporated San Juan Bautista Nursery, San Juan Bautista, CA; *U.S. Private*, pg. 1024
Brown, Robert, Mgr.--Speedling Incorporated, Santa Cruz, CA; *U.S. Private*, pg. 1024
Brown, Robert, Mng. Dir.--Benford Limited, Warwick, United Kingdom; *Int'l*, pg. 1066
Brown, Robert, Gen. Mgr.--Tektronix Canada Inc., Weston, Canada; *U.S. Public*, pg. 1567
Brown, Robert E., Pres. & Chief Oper. Officer--Bombardier Aerospace, Dorval, Canada; *Int'l*, pg. 200
Brown, Robert E., Chm. Bd., Pres. & Chief Exec. Officer--Laurentian Financial Services, Toronto, Canada; *Int'l*, pg. 396
Brown, Robin, Gen. Mgr.--Four Seasons Hotel, Boston, MA; *Int'l*, pg. 502
Brown, Roger, Pres.--Informatica, Negocios y Tecnologia, S.A., Chacaito, Venezuela; *U.S. Private*, pg. 976
Brown, Roger, Pres.--Informatica, Negocios y Tecnologia, S.A., Chacaito, Venezuela; *Int'l*, pg. 1045
Brown, Ronald D., Pres. & Chief Exec. Officer--Sales Technologies, Atlanta, GA; *U.S. Public*, pg. 395
Brown, Stephen, Admin.--Horizon Specialty & Rehabilitation Center of Kissimmee, Kissimmee, FL; *U.S. Public*, pg. 836
Brown, Stephen J., V.P. & Gen. Mgr.--Champ/Pik-A-Nut Service Line, Edwardsville, KS; *U.S. Public*, pg. 1503
Brown, Steve, Midwest Region Dir.--Miller Advertising Agency Inc.-Chicago, Northfield, IL; *U.S. Private*, pg. 746
Brown, Terri, Gen. Mgr.--Design USA, Alhambra, CA; *U.S. Private*, pg. 580
Brown, Terry, Mgr.-Opers. & Production--Devon Energy Canada Corporation, Calgary, Canada; *U.S. Public*, pg. 503
Brown, Thomas D., Jr., Gen. Mgr.--P.T. Kimsari Paper-Indonesia, Medan, Indonesia; *U.S. Public*, pg. 959
Brown, Tim, Mng. Dir.--Fedders North America, Inc., Effingham, IL; *U.S. Public*, pg. 615
Brown, Tim K., Pres.--Sysco Food Services of South Florida, Inc., Miami, FL; *U.S. Public*, pg. 1552
Brown, Todd, V.P. & Mill Mgr.--Republic Paperboard Co.-Commerce City Mill, Commerce City, CO; *U.S. Public*, pg. 1378
Brown, Tom, V.P.--International Paint Western Div., Brisbane, CA; *Int'l*, pg. 339
Brown, V.G., Exec. V.P.--ING North America Insurance Company, Atlanta, GA; *Int'l*, pg. 648
Brown, W.M., V.P. & Gen. Mgr.--Wiring Device Div., Bridgeport, CT; *U.S. Public*, pg. 844
Brown, W.M., Pres.--Thomson U.S. Inc., Stamford, CT; *U.S. Public*, pg. 1601
Brown, William, V.P.--The Bank of Nova Scotia, Atlanta, GA; *Int'l*, pg. 156
Brown, William, Plant Mgr.--Bridgestone/Firestone Tire Manufacturing Operations-Decatur, Decatur, IL; *Int'l*, pg. 213
Brown, William, Chief Exec. Officer--Columbia Health Care, Inc., Toronto, Canada; *U.S. Public*, pg. 1531
Brown, William K., V.P.--Minerals and Mining Group, Pittsburgh, PA; *U.S. Public*, pg. 748
Brown, William W., Gen. Mgr.--Mining and Construction Division, Latrobe, PA; *U.S. Public*, pg. 950
Browne, B. W., Pres.--Diameter Paper Co., Atlanta, GA; *U.S. Private*, pg. 165
Browne, Donald T., Chief Oper. Officer--Financial Life Insurance Co. of Georgia, Atlanta, GA; *U.S. Public*, pg. 1730
Browne, Gregg, Gen. Mgr.--Capitol Consolidated, Indianapolis, IN; *Int'l*, pg. 233
Browne, Gregg, Pres. & Gen. Mgr.--Loga Athletic/Headwear Inc., Mattapoisett, MA; *U.S. Public*, pg. 1644
Browne, Leo, Mng. Dir.-Australia/New Zealand Reg.--Tyco International Pty Ltd., Chatswood, Australia; *U.S. Public*, pg. 1651
Browne, M., Gen. Mgr.--Aer Lingus, Milan, Italy; *Int'l*, pg. 28
Browne, Nick, Mng. Dir.--Costain Oil, Gas & Process Limited Process Contracting Division, Manchester, United Kingdom; *Int'l*, pg. 336
Browne, Ronald, Pres.--Pacific Forge, Inc., Fontana, CA; *U.S. Private*, pg. 102
Browne, Stephen B., Pres. & Chief Exec. Officer--All-American Bottling Financial Corp., Oklahoma City, OK; *U.S. Private*, pg. 34
Browne, W. P., Mng. Dir.--GEC Distributors (Ireland) Ltd., Dublin, Ireland; *Int'l*, pg. 546
Brownell, Patricia, Exec. Dir.--Credit Union Foundation, Madison, WI; *U.S. Private*, pg. 288
Brownfield, Ray, Pres.--Capital Agricultural Property Services, Inc., Lisle, IL; *U.S. Private*, pg. 892
Browning, Charlie, Gen. Mgr.--Omega Environmental Services, Dallas, TX; *U.S. Public*, pg. 1222
Browning, Gary, Mng. Dir.--BDG/McColl, London, United Kingdom; *Int'l*, pg. 1482
Browning, J.M., Mng. Dir.--Reifenhauser Ltd., Tewkesbury, United Kingdom; *Int'l*, pg. 1101
Browning, James R., V.P. & Gen. Mgr.--WHIO, Inc., Dayton, OH; *U.S. Private*, pg. 282
Browning, John H., Pres.--DYWIDAG Systems International, USA, Inc., Bolingbrook, IL; *Int'l*, pg. 424
Browning, William K., Pres.--The Huntington National Life Insurance Company, Columbus, OH; *U.S. Public*, pg. 850
Brownlee, John R., Exec. Dir.--WF Corroon-Kingston, Kingston upon Thames, United Kingdom; *Int'l*, pg. 1502
Brownlee, Kevin, Mng. Dir.--Expamet Fencing, Hartlepool, United Kingdom; *Int'l*, pg. 467
Brownlee, Neil, Copywriter--Lois/EJL Direct, New York, NY; *U.S. Public*, pg. 1011
Brownley, Carolyn, Reg. Mgr.--Green Tree Acceptance, Inc., Grand Rapids, MI; *U.S. Public*, pg. 762
Brownlie, I.T., V.P. & Gen. Mgr.--Celanese Canada Chemicals & Industrial Products Group, Etobicoke, Canada; *Int'l*, pg. 625
Brownrigg, James A., Gen. Mgr.--Acme Ruler Co. Ltd., Mount Forest, Canada; *U.S. Public*, pg. 17
Brownstein, Michael, Publr.--Ladies' Home Journal, New York, NY; *U.S. Public*, pg. 1094
Browsky, Dick, Pres.--Bando America, Inc., Itasca, IL; *Int'l*, pg. 145
Broyles, Joseph R., Pres. & Chief Oper. Officer--Indianapolis Water Company, Indianapolis, IN; *U.S. Public*, pg. 1185
Brozna, Anthony S., V.P. & Gen. Mgr.--Chesapeake Packaging Co./Richmond, Richmond, VA; *U.S. Public*, pg. 347
Brualdi, Ulysses J., Jr., Pres. & Chief Exec. Officer--ADT Security Services, Inc., Aurora, CO; *U.S. Public*, pg. 1649
Bruan, Rufo, Pres.--Seafirst Insurance Corporation, Seattle, WA; *U.S. Public*, pg. 181
Brubaker, Bob, Pres.--Clark Filter, Lancaster, PA; *U.S. Public*, pg. 381
Brubaker, Dean, Gen. Mgr.--Woolrich Store Div., Woolrich, PA; *U.S. Private*, pg. 1188
Brubaker, H., Mgr.--Morton Salt Division, Newark, CA; *U.S. Public*, pg. 1135
Bruce, Bernard, Mgr.--Credit Agricole (CNCA) Representative Office-Rio de Janeiro, Rio de Janeiro, Brazil; *Int'l*, pg. 341
Bruce, Bill, Mng. Dir.--Quorum Graphic Design Consultants Ltd., Glasgow, United Kingdom; *Int'l*, pg. 1226
Bruce, Bill, Country Mgr.--Standard Chartered Bank (Negara Brunei Darussalam), Bandar Seri Begawan, Brunei Darussalam; *Int'l*, pg. 1295
Bruce, Christine, Branch Mgr.--Bergen Brunswig Medical Corporation, Modesto, CA; *U.S. Public*, pg. 214

Bruce, Douglas, Mng. Dir.--Bensons International Systems Pty. Ltd., Yagoona, Australia; *Int'l*, pg. 460
Bruce, Jim, Pres. & Publisher--The Windsor Star, Windsor, Canada; *Int'l*, pg. 632
Bruce, Johan, Mng. Dir.--Ericsson Telekomunikasyon A.S., Istanbul, Turkey; *Int'l*, pg. 1368
Bruce, P.J., Mng. Dir.--Glover Webb Ltd., Southampton, United Kingdom; *Int'l*, pg. 535
Bruce, Randy, Acting Dir.--Taylor Bros., Winston Salem, NC; *U.S. Private*, pg. 272
Bruce, Robert, Pres.--International Correspondence Schools (Australasia) Limited, Lane Cove, Australia; *U.S. Public*, pg. 784
Bruce, William B., Pres.--BB&T Savings Bank, Elkin, NC; *U.S. Public*, pg. 160
Bruch, Chris, Gen. Mgr.--Garretson Equipment Co., Inc., Mount Pleasant, IA; *U.S. Public*, pg. 1300
Bruch, Karl F., III, Pres.--Sherwood, Lockport, NY; *U.S. Public*, pg. 793
Bruck, Wolfgang, Chief Oper. Officer--Saarberg-Hoelter-Lurgi GmbH, Saarbruecken, Germany; *Int'l*, pg. 1167
Bruck, Wolfgang, Chief Oper. Officer--Saarberg-Hoelter Umwelttechnik GmbH, Saarbruecken, Germany; *Int'l*, pg. 1167
Brucker, Gerald, Pres.--AlliedSignal Controls & Accessories, South Bend, IN; *U.S. Public*, pg. 50
Bruckmayer, Peter, Chief Oper. Officer--Flottweg GmbH, Vilsbiburg, Germany; *Int'l*, pg. 836
Bruder, Otto, Mng. Dir.--A. Schulman Plastics S.A., Givet, France; *U.S. Public*, pg. 1442
Bruder, Thomas A., Pres.--M.A.B. Paints, Terre Haute, IN; *U.S. Private*, pg. 175
Brudnick, Richard, Pres.--James Brudnick Company, Malden, MA; *U.S. Private*, pg. 1007
Brueck, Wolfgang, Co-Chief Oper. Officer--Saarberg-Interplan Gesellschaft fuer Rohstoff-, Energie-und Ingenieurtechnik mbH, Saarbruecken, Germany; *Int'l*, pg. 1167
Brueggemann, Alois, Mgr.--Commerzbank AG-Barcelona, Barcelona, Spain; *Int'l*, pg. 311
Bruel, William D., Dir.--Multi Finans A/S, Copenhagen, Denmark; *Int'l*, pg. 1257
Bruer, Rory, V.P. & Western Div. Mgr.--TriStar Pictures Western Division, Burbank, CA; *Int'l*, pg. 1283
Bruewer, Klaus W., Sr. V.P. & Mgr.--Deutsche Bank AG (Los Angeles Branch), Los Angeles, CA; *Int'l*, pg. 403
Brufan, Joaquin Coello, Gen. Mgr.--NAVINTEC - Naval de Investigacion y Tecnologia, S.A., Madrid, Spain; *Int'l*, pg. 1223
Bruggeman, Frans, Mgr.--Elsevier Editorial Services, Oxford, United Kingdom; *Int'l*, pg. 1100
Bruggeting, Johannes S., Pres.--Boole & Babbage Europe, Foxrock, Ireland; *U.S. Public*, pg. 245
Bruggink, Herman, Chm.-Exec. Bd.--Elsevier NV, Amsterdam, Netherlands; *Int'l*, pg. 1093
Bruggink, Herman, Chm.--Reed Elsevier Nederland BV, Amsterdam, Netherlands; *Int'l*, pg. 1100
Bruggisser, Philippe, Pres. & Chief Exec. Officer--The Swissair Group, Zurich, Switzerland; *Int'l*, pg. 1333
Brugier, S., Chief Oper. Officer--Tanabe Pharma S.A., Paris, France; *Int'l*, pg. 1354
Brugman, H., Chief Oper. Officer--Van Rietschoten & Houwens Noord-West bv, Zaandam, Netherlands; *Int'l*, pg. 681
Brugman, Russell, Chief Oper. Officer--Vigorena Feeds, Inc., Storm Lake, IA; *Int'l*, pg. 1116
Bruhl, Hans-Hubert, Chief Exec. Officer--Harpen Transport AG, Duisburg, Germany; *Int'l*, pg. 597
Bruijn, F.J.A.N., Pres.--Spaarbeleg N.V., Nieuwegein, Netherlands; *Int'l*, pg. 26
Bruins, Koert, Mng. Dir.--Iggesund Benelux B.V., Haren, Netherlands; *Int'l*, pg. 886
Bruk, Manuel, Pres. & Gen. Mgr.--Cyanamid Mexico, Mexico, Mexico; *U.S. Public*, pg. 81
Brum, Roger, Pres.--Southwest Aerospace, Tustin, CA; *Int'l*, pg. 853
Brumback, Emerson L., Pres. & Chief Exec. Officer--Bank One, Cincinnati, Cincinnati, OH; *U.S. Public*, pg. 173
Brumbaugh, J., Mgr.--Morton Salt Division, Rittman, OH; *U.S. Public*, pg. 1135
Brumbaugh, Kevin, V.P. & Gen. Mgr.--Nelco Technology, Inc., Tempe, AZ; *U.S. Public*, pg. 1258
Brumbaugh, Virgil, Gen. Mgr.--South Haven Coil Inc., South Haven, MI; *U.S. Private*, pg. 548
Brumfield, Geoff, Dir.--AlliedSignal Laminate Systems, Hollingworth Hyde, United Kingdom; *U.S. Public*, pg. 53
Brumm, Dan, Mktg. Mgr.--Triad Retail Hardlines & Lumber Div., Livermore, CA; *U.S. Private*, pg. 193
Brumm, Jaqualine S., V.P. & Gen. Mgr.--WEBN-FM, Cincinnati, OH; *U.S. Public*, pg. 922
Brummell, Charles, Pres.--Continental Community Development Corp., Chicago, IL; *U.S. Public*, pg. 181
Brummer, Barbara, Ph.D., Mng. Dir.--Johnson & Johnson Inc., Montreal, Canada; *U.S. Public*, pg. 930
Brummett, M. David, Pres.--Deluxe Specialties Mfg. Co., Hutchinson, KS; *U.S. Public*, pg. 1640
Brummett, W.L., Pres.--Computer Power Div., Santa Ana, CA; *U.S. Public*, pg. 573
Brun, Patrick, Mng. Dir.--Grace S.A, Epernon, France; *U.S. Public*, pg. 756
Brunberg, Raul, Chief Oper. Officer--SAB Nife OY, Espoo, Finland; *Int'l*, pg. 54
Brundel, E.J. Ten, Gen. Mgr.--Datastream International Limited, Rotterdam, Netherlands; *U.S. Public*, pg. 1326
Brundige, Winston N., Ph.D., V.P. & Gen. Mgr.--Defense & Launch Vehicles Division, Brigham City, UT; *U.S. Public*, pg. 1597
Brundler, O., Chief Oper. Officer--CIBA-Pilatus Aerial Spraying Co. Ltd., Stans, Switzerland; *Int'l*, pg. 998
Bruneau, Gilles, Gen. Mgr.--Sun Microsystems of Canada-Eastern Canada, Saint-Laurent, Canada; *U.S. Public*, pg. 1532
Bruneau, Herve, Chief Oper. Officer--Rhovyl, Neuilly-sur-Seine, France; *Int'l*, pg. 1109
Brunel, Jerome, Chief Exec. Officer-Credit Lyonnais-Americas--Credit Lyonnais Americas, New York, NY; *Int'l*, pg. 344
Brunell, Val E., Pres.--Janssen/Ortho Inc., North York, Canada; *U.S. Public*, pg. 930
Brunelli, Antonio, Dir.--Banca d'America e d'Italia S.p.A. (Sorrento), Sorrento, Italy; *Int'l*, pg. 403
Bruner, Phyllis, Mgr.-Office--Woodward-Clyde, Seattle, WA; *U.S. Public*, pg. 1657
Brunet, Allain, Pres.--Tembec Forest Products Inc., Rouyn-Noranda, Canada; *Int'l*, pg. 1375
Brunet, Didier, Mng. Dir.--EURO RSCG Audience, Levallois-Perret, France; *Int'l*, pg. 600
Brunet, Pierre, Pres.--Bourgey Montreuil, Mery-sur-Seine, France; *Int'l*, pg. 549
Brunetti, Wayne H., Pres.--1480 Welton, Inc., Denver, CO; *U.S. Public*, pg. 1170
Brunetti, Wayne H., Pres.--P.S.R. Investments, Inc., Denver, CO; *U.S. Public*, pg. 1170
Brunetti, Wayne H., Pres.--P.S. Colorado Credit Corp., Denver, CO; *U.S. Public*, pg. 1170
Bruni, G., Mng. Dir.--Ascom TCS SpA, Modena, Italy; *Int'l*, pg. 87
Bruning, Hans, Gen. Mgr.--Analog Devices Nederland B.V., Oosterhout, Netherlands; *U.S. Public*, pg. 108
Brunkel, Peter, Chief Exec. Officer & Mng. Dir.--DMB&B Reklamebureau A/S, Frederiksberg, Denmark; *U.S. Private*, pg. 304
Brunkel, Peter, Mng. Dir.--International Marketing & Promotions, Frederiksberg, Denmark; *U.S. Private*, pg. 304
Brunnberg, Goran, Pres.--Saba Fastighets AB, Stockholm, Sweden; *Int'l*, pg. 272
Brunnenmiller, Siegfried K., Representative--Deutsche Bank AG (Johannesburg), Johannesburg, South Africa; *Int'l*, pg. 404
Brunner, D.G., Chm. Bd.--Waupaca Foundry Inc., Waupaca, WI; *Int'l*, pg. 1389
Brunner, Daniel, Pres.--The Affordable Medical Networks, West Sacramento, CA; *U.S. Public*, pg. 635
Brunner, Donald R., Pres.--J.P. Morgan Delaware, Wilmington, DE; *U.S. Public*, pg. 1129
Brunner, Horst, Mng. Dir.--Bayerische Vereinsbank AG, Johannesburg, South Africa; *Int'l*, pg. 180
Brunner, L. Douglas, Pres. & Chief Exec. Officer--ACI Holding Inc., Baltimore, MD; *Int'l*, pg. 464
Brunner, L. Douglas, Pres.--American Credit Indemnity, Baltimore, MD; *Int'l*, pg. 464
Brunner, L. Douglas, Pres. & Chief Exec. Officer--ACI Holding Inc., Baltimore, MD; *Int'l*, pg. 1332
Brunner, Walter, Gen. Mgr.--Metallurg Mexico, S.A. de CV, Mexico, Mexico; *U.S. Private*, pg. 735
Bruno, C.J., Pres.--American Lenders Facilities, Inc., Irvine, CA; *U.S. Public*, pg. 366
Bruno, J.A., Gen. Mgr.--Senior Engineering Co.-Berlin, Berlin, WI; *Int'l*, pg. 1222
Brunon, Jean-Rene, Mng. Dir.--BNP BAIL, Puteaux, France; *Int'l*, pg. 163
Bruns, G., Mng. Dir.--Ascom Infrasys GmbH, Aachen, Germany; *Int'l*, pg. 87
Bruns, Juergen, Chm. Bd. of Mngmt.--Europa Carton AG, Hamburg, Germany; *Int'l*, pg. 20
Bruns, Robert, Plant Mgr.--MWS, Ellaville, GA; *U.S. Public*, pg. 443
Brunsbold, Susan, Gen. Mgr.--Vital Signs MN, Inc., Burnsville, MN; *U.S. Public*, pg. 1723
Brunson, D. Bruce, Pres.--Merrill Lynch, Hubbard, Inc., New York, NY; *U.S. Public*, pg. 1098
Brunton, Ann, Chief Exec. Officer--Welbeck Golin/Harris Communications Ltd., London, United Kingdom; *Int'l*, pg. 1226
Brunton, Tim, Pres.--Chr. Hansen Limited (Canada), Mississauga, Canada; *Int'l*, pg. 288
Brusberg, Gregory J., V.P. & Reg. Representative--NationsBank (Singapore) Branch, Singapore, Singapore; *U.S. Public*, pg. 1166
Brush, Anthony S., Gen. Mgr.--Ikon Office Solutions-Carolinas, Greensboro, NC; *U.S. Public*, pg. 863
Brush, John, Warden--Delta Correctional Facility, Greenwood, MS; *U.S. Public*, pg. 450
Brush, Vincent, Mgr.-Property & Casualty Claims--Willis Corroon Administrative Services Corporation, Indianapolis, IN; *Int'l*, pg. 1504
Brusman, Andrew I., Mgr.--Scott & Stringfellow, Inc., Alexandria, VA; *U.S. Public*, pg. 1446
Brutsche, Peter, Exec. V.P.-Japan Reg. Mngmt.--UBS Securities Limited, Tokyo Branch, Tokyo, Japan; *Int'l*, pg. 1440
Bruvik, Trygve, Dir.-Fin.--Vesta Forsikring A/S, Bergen, Norway; *Int'l*, pg. 1257
Bryan, Anthony, Chief Oper. Officer--Novo Nordisk Bioindustrial Pty Ltd., North Rocks, Australia; *Int'l*, pg. 989
Bryan, Earl, V.P.--La-Z-Boy South, Newton, MS; *U.S. Public*, pg. 973
Bryan, G.R., Pres. & Chief Oper. Officer--Enserch Gas Co., Dallas, TX; *U.S. Public*, pg. 1587
Bryan, J. P., Jr., Pres. & Chief Exec. Officer--Torch Energy Corp., Houston, TX; *U.S. Public*, pg. 1623
Bryan, J. Stewart III, Chm. & Publr.--Richmond Newspapers, Inc., Richmond, VA; *U.S. Public*, pg. 1079
Bryan, J.P., Pres. & Chief Exec. Officer--Gulf Canada Resources Ltd., Calgary, Canada; *Int'l*, pg. 577
Bryan, J.P., Pres.--Blackhawk Holding Company, Houston, TX; *U.S. Public*, pg. 1623
Bryan, J.P., Pres.--Dry Hole Oil & Gas Corporation, Houston, TX; *U.S. Public*, pg. 1623
Bryan, J.P., Pres.--Torch Operating Co., Houston, TX; *U.S. Public*, pg. 1623
Bryan, John H., III, Pres. & Chief Exec. Officer--Bryan Foods, West Point, MS; *U.S. Public*, pg. 1433
Bryans, Antony, Mng. Dir.--Banque Bruxelles Lambert Trust Company Ltd., Saint Helier, United Kingdom; *Int'l*, pg. 148
Bryant, Barbara, Branch Mgr.--Downey Savings & Loan Association, F.A., Cupertino, CA; *U.S. Public*, pg. 526
Bryant, Bill, Mgr.-Mktg.--Sasol Solvents, Rosebank, South Africa; *Int'l*, pg. 1196
Bryant, C. Edward, Jr., Pres.--Continental Conveyor & Equipment Company, Winfield, AL; *U.S. Private*, pg. 791
Bryant, Chuck, Pres.--UPB of East Tennessee, Knoxville, TN; *U.S. Public*, pg. 1669
Bryant, Darryl, Pres.--Stow Davis Furniture Co., Kentwood, MI; *U.S. Private*, pg. 1038
Bryant, Douglas E., Dr., Pres.--Foseco Holding Inc., Cleveland, OH; *Int'l*, pg. 234
Bryant, George, V.P. & Gen. Mgr.--Dillard, A ResourceNet International Company, Doraville, GA; *U.S. Public*, pg. 902
Bryant, Lawrence, Chm.--International Public Relations (NZ) Ltd., Wellington, New Zealand; *Int'l*, pg. 1227
Bryant, Paul, Gen. Mgr.--Lilly Industries, Inc., Montebello, CA; *U.S. Public*, pg. 994
Bryant, Richard, Chief Oper. Officer--Datalink Systems, LLC, South Bend, IN; *U.S. Public*, pg. 647
Bryant, Robert, Pres.--Bryant, Fulton & Shee, Vancouver, Canada; *U.S. Private*, pg. 678
Bryant, Warren, Pres.--Dillon Companies, Inc., Hutchinson, KS; *U.S. Public*, pg. 967
Bryce, Bill, Gen. Dir.--Marcam Australia Pty., Ltd., Box Hill, Australia; *U.S. Public*, pg. 1043
Bryce, Doug, V.P. & Gen. Mgr.--Allders International (Canada) Limited, Mississauga, Canada; *Int'l*, pg. 30
Bryd, David, Mgr.--Wholesale Electric Division, Kingsport, TN; *Int'l*, pg. 1108
Bryden, D.W., Gen. Mgr.--Albright & Wilson Asia (HK) Ltd., Kowloon, Hong Kong; *Int'l*, pg. 49
Brydon, David J., Chief Exec. Officer--ACI International Ltd., Melbourne, Australia; *Int'l*, pg. 128
Bryne, Tom, V.P.--Willis Corroon Management (Cayman) Ltd., Grand Cayman, Cayman Islands; *Int'l*, pg. 1505
Bryngelson, Hakan, Chief Oper. Officer--AxTrade Care AB, Solna, Sweden; *Int'l*, pg. 708
Brynildsen, Jon Chr, Exec. V.P.--Kvaerner Shipping a.s., Oslo, Norway; *Int'l*, pg. 770
Bryson, George M., Pres.--Addison-Wesley Publishers Ltd., Don Mills, Canada; *Int'l*, pg. 1027
Bryson, Michael A., Pres. & Chief Exec. Officer--Mellon Europe-London, London, United Kingdom; *U.S. Public*, pg. 1086
Brzezinski, Francis, Pres. & Chief Oper. Officer--Wispark Corporation, Milwaukee, WI; *U.S. Public*, pg. 1773
Brzezinski, Francis, Pres. & Chief Oper. Officer--Wisvest Corporation, Milwaukee, WI; *U.S. Public*, pg. 1773
Brzezinski, Francis, Pres. & Chief Oper. Officer--Witech Corporation, Milwaukee, WI; *U.S. Public*, pg. 1773
Brzuska, Wolfgang, Co-Chief Oper. Officer--IKB Leasing Berlin GmbH, Berlin, Germany; *Int'l*, pg. 645
Brzuska, Wolfgang, Co-Chief Oper. Officer--IKB Leasing GmbH, Hamburg, Germany; *Int'l*, pg. 645
Bublath, Hans-Jurgen, Mng. Dir.--Werner & Pfleiderer Lebensmitteltechnik GmbH, Stuttgart, Germany; *Int'l*, pg. 511
Bublitz, Maxwell, Pres.--Conseco Capital Management, Inc., Carmel, IN; *U.S. Public*, pg. 433
Bubshait, A.R., Gen. Mgr.--Abdulla Fouad Auctioneers, Dammam, Saudi Arabia; *Int'l*, pg. 502
Buce, Doug, Plant Mgr.--Mount Vernon Textile Group, Alto, GA; *U.S. Private*, pg. 836
Buch, Allan, Gen. Mgr.--KSNW-TV, Wichita, KS; *U.S. Public*, pg. 983
Buchan, Andrew J., Dir.-Opers.--Trinova Limited Aeroquip Automotive Operations, Brierley Hill, United Kingdom; *U.S. Public*, pg. 25
Buchan, Brian J., V.P. & Gen. Mgr.-Laundry, Cleaning & Paper Prods.-Germany--Procter & Gamble GmbH, Schwalbach, Germany; *U.S. Public*, pg. 1332
Buchan, William S., Pres.--Terex Trucks, Tulsa, OK; *U.S. Public*, pg. 1581
Buchanan, Bruce, Plant Mgr.--PAXAR Woven Labels, Hillsville, VA; *U.S. Public*, pg. 1266
Buchanan, Danne L., Pres.--Zions Data Service Co., Salt Lake City, UT; *U.S. Public*, pg. 1793
Buchanan, Florence, Gen. Mgr.--Monroe Cablevision Inc., Monroe, MI; *U.S. Private*, pg. 147
Buchanan, James, Pres.--Concord Specialty Corp., Batesville, AR; *U.S. Private*, pg. 177
Buchanan, James K., Pres.--Super Food Services, Inc., Miamisburg, OH; *U.S. Public*, pg. 1152
Buchanan, John, V.P.-Opers.--Hat Dance, Chicago, IL; *U.S. Private*, pg. 661
Buchanan, L., Plant Mgr.--Thomaston Div., Thomaston, GA; *U.S. Public*, pg. 1599
Buchanan, Pat, Mng. Dir.--Applied Magnetics Ireland, Ltd., Dublin, Ireland; *U.S. Public*, pg. 123
Buchanan, R.M., Pres.--Beckman-IPD/Doric, San Diego, CA; *U.S. Public*, pg. 574
Buchanan, Richard, Gen. Mgr.--Telemation Productions Inc., Greenwood Village, CO; *U.S. Public*, pg. 1685
Buchanan, Robert C., Chm. Bd. & Pres.--Fox River Paper Company, Appleton, WI; *U.S. Private*, pg. 422
Buchanan, Robert D., Pres.--Permea, Inc., Saint Louis, MO; *U.S. Public*, pg. 31
Buchanan, W.F., Pres.--MHI Lithograph Printing, Lincolnshire, IL; *Int'l*, pg. 874
Buchanan, William J., Pres.--NBD Bank, Canada, Toronto, Canada; *U.S. Public*, pg. 628
Buchanon, A.J., Chm. Bd.--Mees & Hope Investment Management Ltd., London, United Kingdom; *Int'l*, pg. 12
Buche, W. Brad, Mgr.--Piper Jaffray Inc., Mitchell, SD; *U.S. Public*, pg. 1302
Buchi, Claus, Sr. Mgr.--UBS Representative Office Ltd., Manama, Bahrain; *Int'l*, pg. 1441
Buchi, Rudolph, Mng. Dir.--Sulzer Bulachguss AG, Bulach, Switzerland; *Int'l*, pg. 1307
Buchle, R., Chief Oper. Officer--Galenus Mannheim GmbH, Mannheim, Germany; *Int'l*, pg. 331

Buchloh, A., Mng. Dir.--Gesellschaft fur Elektrometallurgie m.b.H., Nuremberg, Germany; *U.S. Private*, pg. 735
Buchsenschutz, Y., Chief Oper. Officer--Diepal-N.S.A., Villefranche-sur-Saone, France; *Int'l*, pg. 380
Buchwald, Per, Pres.--Granzow A/S, Glostrup, Denmark; *Int'l*, pg. 678
Buck, Bruce D., Dir.-Intl. Mktg. & Sls.--Precision Technology, Harrison, NJ; *Int'l*, pg. 17
Buck, Bruce M., Partner--Skadden, Arps, Slate, Meagher & Flom, London, United Kingdom; *U.S. Private*, pg. 1004
Buck, Charles B., Pres.--County Tool & Abrasive, Santee, CA; *U.S. Private*, pg. 177
Buck, Dawson, Pres.-Intl. Div.--Sensormatic Limited, Hemel Hempstead, United Kingdom; *U.S. Public*, pg. 1458
Buck, John, Mng. Dir.--Sowester Limited, Poole, United Kingdom; *U.S. Public*, pg. 968
Buck, M.J., Gen. Mgr.--LASMO Grand Maghreb Limited, Tripoli, Libya; *Int'l*, pg. 804
Buck, Merle K., Pres.--U.S. Bancorp Leasing & Financial, Portland, OR; *U.S. Public*, pg. 1681
Buck, Ron, Pres.--Balance Engineering Corp., Troy, MI; *U.S. Public*, pg. 865
Buck, Stephen, Pres.--Dayton Progress Corporation, Dayton, OH; *U.S. Public*, pg. 617
Buck, Stephen, Chief Oper. Officer--Container Tooling Corporation, Neptune, NJ; *U.S. Public*, pg. 617
Buck, Werner, V.P.--Bell-Escher Wyss Ltd., Kriens, Switzerland; *Int'l*, pg. 1305
Buckholz, N.L., Plant Mgr.--Longview Fibre Co. Western Div., Seattle, WA; *U.S. Public*, pg. 1014
Buckhout, Craig, Pres.--Agri-Service Agencies, Inc., Syracuse, NY; *U.S. Private*, pg. 308
Buckingham, Colin, Mng. Dir.--DPSA Deutsche Personensuch-Anlagen GmbH, Frankfurt/Main, Germany; *Int'l*, pg. 1365
Buckingham, James, V.P.-Mexico & Latin American Devel.--Lawson Products de Mexico, S.A., Guadalajara, Mexico; *U.S. Public*, pg. 980
Buckle, Peter, Mng. Dir.--R.A.R.E. (Pty) Ltd., Edenvale, South Africa; *Int'l*, pg. 1306
Buckle, T.J., Mng. Dir.--Edgcumbe Instruments Ltd., Glasgow, United Kingdom; *Int'l*, pg. 207
Buckleigh, P., Resident Dir.--EMI Music International Services Ltd., Tokyo, Japan; *Int'l*, pg. 427
Buckler, Steven N., Pres.--ACS Industries, Inc., Fiber Operation, Woonsocket, RI; *U.S. Private*, pg. 4
Buckles, Brian, V.P.-Operational Plng.--Manulife Financial, Toronto, Canada; *Int'l*, pg. 840
Buckley, A. J., Pres.--Le Nickel Inc., Pittsburgh, PA; *Int'l*, pg. 661
Buckley, Brady, V.P.--LDDS/WorldCom Communications, Revere, MA; *U.S. Public*, pg. 1779
Buckley, C.E., V.P. & Treas.--Trafalgar House Holdings Inc., West Warwick, RI; *Int'l*, pg. 774
Buckley, Charles, Pres. & Chief Exec. Officer--John Brown Plastics Machinery, Attleboro, MA; *Int'l*, pg. 773
Buckley, D.C., Mng. Dir.--SEAC Limited, Leicester, United Kingdom; *Int'l*, pg. 590
Buckley, Eugene, Pres. & Chief Exec. Officer--Sikorsky Aircraft, Stratford, CT; *U.S. Public*, pg. 1691
Buckley, George, Pres.--U.S. Electrical Motor Division, Saint Louis, MO; *U.S. Public*, pg. 573
Buckley, J.C., Mng. Dir.--Wormald Ansul U.K. Ltd., Manchester, United Kingdom; *U.S. Public*, pg. 1651
Buckley, J.C., Mng. Dir.--Wormald Holdings U.K. Limited, Manchester, United Kingdom; *U.S. Public*, pg. 1651
Buckley, Joseph W., Jr., Pres. & Chief Exec. Officer--Profesco Corporation, Boston, MA; *U.S. Private*, pg. 590
Buckley, Joseph W., Jr., Pres. & Chief Exec. Officer--Professional Economic Services, Inc., Boston, MA; *U.S. Private*, pg. 590
Buckley, Michael D., Mng. Dir.--AIB Capital Markets plc, Dublin, Ireland; *Int'l*, pg. 64
Buckley, R., Dr., Mng. Dir.--Balzers Process Systems, Inc., Hudson, NH; *Int'l*, pg. 997
Buckley, S.W., Chm. Bd.--Barclays Mercantile Business Finance Limited, Basingstoke, United Kingdom; *Int'l*, pg. 165
Buckley, T.A., Chief Oper. Officer--Industrial Tires Incorporated, Mississauga, Canada; *U.S. Public*, pg. 311
Buckman, Leonard C., Pres.--Meritor Wabco Vehicle Control Systems, Troy, MI; *U.S. Public*, pg. 1096
Buckner, C. Dennis, Chm., Pres. & Chief Exec. Officer--Regions Bank/Anniston, Anniston, AL; *U.S. Public*, pg. 1371
Buckner, Nancy, Admin.--Hillhaven West, Portland, OR; *U.S. Public*, pg. 1714
Buckner, Steve, V.P. & Gen. Mgr.--Mayfield Swain Rockwall, Fate, TX; *U.S. Private*, pg. 686
Bucks, Charles, Pres.--Airvision, Valencia, CA; *Int'l*, pg. 1053
Bucksbaum, Dr. F., Pres.--Stock Drive Products Div., New Hyde Park, NY; *U.S. Private*, pg. 327
Buday, Ron, Div. Pres.--Winn-Dixie Stores, Inc.-Orlando Div., Orlando, FL; *U.S. Public*, pg. 1771
Budd, Allen T., V.P.--Miller Publishing Co., Minnetonka, MN; *U.S. Public*, pg. 513
Budd, B.L, Chm. Bd.--Monsanto Export Limited, Basingstoke, United Kingdom; *U.S. Public*, pg. 1125
Budd, Kenneth R., Pres.--Lofts Seed, Inc., Winston Salem, NC; *U.S. Public*, pg. 29
Budd, Mike, Pres.--Harman Electronics, Inc., Northridge, CA; *U.S. Public*, pg. 787
Budde, Peter, Gen. Mgr.--Weatherford France, S.A., Billere., France; *U.S. Public*, pg. 1750
Buddle, Richard, New Bus. Contact--Hakuhodo Lintas, Tokyo, Japan; *Int'l*, pg. 587
Budialim, Rahardjo, Chief Exec.--PT. KONE Indo Elevator, Java, Indonesia; *Int'l*, pg. 747
Budig, Otto M., Jr., Pres.--Life Equipment Rebuilders, Cincinnati, OH; *U.S. Private*, pg. 178
Budnick, Alfred S., Pres.--Cherry Semiconductor Corp., East Greenwich, RI; *U.S. Public*, pg. 346
Budolfsen, Elsebeth, Pres.--ALK A/S, Horsholm, Denmark; *Int'l*, pg. 288
Buduson, Nick, Mgr.-Watertown Opers.--Fisher Gauge Inc./ Fishercast Div., Watertown, NY; *Int'l*, pg. 492
Budweg, Rick, Gen. Mgr.--ITW Philadelphia Resins, Montgomeryville, PA; *U.S. Public*, pg. 867
Budz, Robert, Dir.--CNB International, Troy, MI; *U.S. Private*, pg. 196
Bue, Robert L., Pres.--Norwest Bank La Crosse, N.A., La Crosse, WI; *U.S. Public*, pg. 1202
Buell, Dick, Pres. & Chief Exec. Officer--The Griffith Laboratories Ltd., Scarborough, Canada; *U.S. Private*, pg. 481
Buell, Erik, Pres.--Buell Motorcycle Company, East Troy, WI; *U.S. Public*, pg. 786
Buell, Thomas A., Pres. & Chief Exec. Officer--Weldwood of Canada Limited, Vancouver, Canada; *U.S. Public*, pg. 334
Buelna, Nick, Gen. Mgr.--North American Enclosures, Inc., Fullerton, CA; *U.S. Private*, pg. 803
Buenaventura, C.A., Mng. Dir.--Pilipinas Shell Petroleum Corporation, Manila, Philippines; *Int'l*, pg. 1140
Buenconsejo, V.B., Mng. Dir.--P.T. Ferro Mas Dinamika, Cibarusah-Bekosi, Indonesia; *U.S. Public*, pg. 619
Buennagel, David, Pres.--Rolock of California, Cucamonga, CA; *U.S. Private*, pg. 942
Bueno, Manuel Anquela, Chief Oper. Officer--Frigoscandia Food Process Systems S.A., Madrid, Spain; *U.S. Public*, pg. 607
Buentello, Armando, Gen. Mgr.--Manufacturera Thermon de Mexico, S.A., Monterrey, Mexico; *U.S. Private*, pg. 1081
Buerger, Hermann, Mgr.--Commerzbank Aktiengesellschaft New York Branch, New York, NY; *Int'l*, pg. 310
Buerkle, Howard, Pres.--Melru Corporation, Ramsey, NJ; *U.S. Public*, pg. 933
Buerkner, Alexander, Dr., Gen. Mgr.--DG Securities-Tokyo Branch, Tokyo, Japan; *Int'l*, pg. 352
Buesebroek, Niko, Reg. Pres.--Melitta-Nederland B.V., Naarden, Netherlands; *Int'l*, pg. 857
Buettner, Mark, Reg. V.P.-Sls.--All Star Gas Co.-Region II, Lebanon, MO; *U.S. Private*, pg. 35
Buff, Richard, Gen. Mgr.--Portage Tool Company, Elk Grove Village, IL; *U.S. Private*, pg. 1075
Buffa, Gasper, Chief Oper. Officer--Augat, Inc., Automotive Division, Mount Clemens, MI; *U.S. Public*, pg. 1598
Buffart, Roland, Head-BBL Waloon Region--BBL Walloon Region, Wavre, Belgium; *Int'l*, pg. 147
Buffington, Larry, Chief Oper. Officer--Augat, LRC., Communications Division-Horseheads Plant, Horseheads, NY; *U.S. Public*, pg. 1598
Buffington, Larry, Chief Oper. Officer--Augat, Inc., Communications Division, Seattle, WA; *U.S. Public*, pg. 1598
Bugada, Dr. Ing. Franco, Chief Oper. Officer--Selas Italiana, S.r.L., Milan, Italy; *U.S. Public*, pg. 1455
Bugelli, Don, Mgr.--Howard's Electronics, Chicago, IL; *U.S. Public*, pg. 1720
Bugmann, A., Gen. Mgr.--Wellcome AG, Reinach, Switzerland; *Int'l*, pg. 553
Buhler, Alfred P., Chm., Pres. & Chief Exec. Officer--Bank of America Canada, Toronto, Canada; *U.S. Public*, pg. 182
Buhlmann, G., Chief Exec. Officer--Schiedel GmbH & Co., Munich, Germany; *Int'l*, pg. 1091
Buhr, Dale R., Pres.--Industrial Powder Coatings, Inc., Norwalk, OH; *U.S. Public*, pg. 894
Buhrer, Gerold, Pres.--Georg Fischer AG & Co., Singen, Germany; *Int'l*, pg. 491
Buhring, Rolf, Mng. Dir.--Dyckerhoff & Widmann Berlin GmbH, Berlin, Germany; *Int'l*, pg. 423
Buirski, David, Founder Chm.-Cape Town--Young & Rubicam South Africa, Johannesburg, South Africa; *U.S. Private*, pg. 1198
Buirski, David, Founder Chm.--Young & Rubicam Tholet, Cape Town, South Africa; *U.S. Private*, pg. 1198
Buis, Mike, Pres.--Wabash Magnetics, Wabash, IN; *U.S. Private*, pg. 351
Buiten, Roger, Gen. Mgr.--Ann Arbor Computer, Ann Arbor, MI; *U.S. Private*, pg. 1156
Buitendijk, Theo, Mng. Dir.--ISS Servisystem B.V., Amersfoort, Netherlands; *Int'l*, pg. 657
Buitta, Ariberto, Gen. Mgr.--Banco di Sicilia, Frankfurt/Main, Germany; *Int'l*, pg. 140
Bukaty, Mike, Pres.--Wescon Products Company, Wichita, KS; *U.S. Public*, pg. 979
Bukeleca, Michael C., Gen. Mgr.--Reclamation Div. (Fresno), Fresno, CA; *Int'l*, pg. 1270
Buker, J., Gen. Mgr.--Interturbine Holland B.V., Lomm, Netherlands; *Int'l*, pg. 673
Bukowick, P.A., Pres.--Alliant Techsystems (Aerospace Division), Wilmington, DE; *U.S. Public*, pg. 47
Bulcao, Gilberto, Pres.--Becton Dickinson Ind. Cirurgicas, S.A., Sao Paulo, Brazil; *U.S. Public*, pg. 200
Bulgin, Ed, Factory Supt.--Amalgamated Sugar Co., Nampa, ID; *U.S. Private*, pg. 48
Bull, E.M., Gen. Mgr.--Fortis Benefits Insurance Company, Kansas City, MO; *Int'l*, pg. 499
Bull, Larry M., Jr., Mgr.--Piper Jaffray Inc., Pocatello, ID; *U.S. Public*, pg. 1302
Bull, Marshall R., Pres.--Fundamental Management, Inc., Pomona, CA; *U.S. Private*, pg. 561
Bull, Marshall R., Pres.--Industrial Alloys, Inc., Pomona, CA; *U.S. Private*, pg. 561
Bull, Matthew, Creative Partner--Bull Calvert Pace, Cape Town, South Africa; *U.S. Private*, pg. 678
Bull, R.P.A., Dir.--NatWest Specialist Finance Limited, London, United Kingdom; *Int'l*, pg. 910
Bull, Richard S., III, Pres.--Rotary Paper Manifold Co., Schiller Park, IL; *U.S. Private*, pg. 165
Bull, Scott, J., Pres.--Pace Industries, Inc., Fayetteville, AR; *U.S. Public*, pg. 986
Bull, Steve, Area Mgr.--Brooktree Ltd., Fleet, United Kingdom; *U.S. Public*, pg. 1398
Bullert, Rick, V.P.-Sls.--MedTrac, Inc., Minneapolis, MN; *Int'l*, pg. 1504
Bullis, William G., Gen. Mgr.--Jamaica Flour Mills, Ltd., Kingston, Jamaica; *Int'l*, pg. 411
Bullock, Gary, Pres.--Pioneer Concrete Of Texas, Inc., Houston, TX; *Int'l*, pg. 1058
Bullock, George, Gen. Mgr.--Alro Specialty Metals, Tallmadge, Tallmadge, OH; *U.S. Private*, pg. 46
Bullock, Jerry, V.P. & Div. Mgr.--East Div., Springfield, OH; *U.S. Private*, pg. 180
Bullock, John M., V.P. & Gen. Mgr.--Mead Johnson Laboratories, Evansville, IN; *U.S. Public*, pg. 255
Bullock, M., Mng. Dir.--Morgan Grenfell Asset Management Limited, London, United Kingdom; *Int'l*, pg. 405
Bullock, Neal, Mgr.--Orem Plant, Orem, UT; *Int'l*, pg. 1054
Bullos, Carlos, Representative--First RepublicBank Dallas, N.A. Representative Office, Caracas, Venezuela; *U.S. Public*, pg. 1165
Bullough, Mark, Mng. Dir.--Jardine Fleming India Securities Private Limited, Mumbai, India; *Int'l*, pg. 494
Bulman, Dan, Plant Mgr.--Brown Wooten/Ballston Plant, Mount Airy, NC; *U.S. Private*, pg. 175
Bulmer, Edward E., Pres. & Chief Exec. Officer--Sprague Energy Corp. Northeast Operation, Portsmouth, NH; *Int'l*, pg. 710
Bulmer, Edward E., Pres.--Sprague Energy Corp., Portsmouth, NH; *Int'l*, pg. 710
Bulow, Klaus, Chief Oper. Officer--Schering S.A., Gif-sur-Yvette, France; *Int'l*, pg. 1204
Bultel, Michel, Gen. Mgr.--Martin S.A., Villeurbanne, France; *Int'l*, pg. 199
Bulthaup, Gerd, Pres.--Bulthaup GmbH & Co., Aich, Germany; *Int'l*, pg. 1410
Bulwer, John, Mng. Dir.--Trucast Ltd., Ryde, United Kingdom; *Int'l*, pg. 1467
Bulych, Sam, Pres.--Torchinsky Engineering Ltd, Calgary, Canada; *Int'l*, pg. 31
Bulzacchelli, John, Pres.--Revlon Service, Inc., New York, NY; *U.S. Private*, pg. 690
Bumenauer, Leo, Pres.--Advanced Distribution System, Inc., Columbus, OH; *U.S. Public*, pg. 911
Bumharter, F.G., Gen. Mgr.--ING Bank Hamburg, Hamburg, Germany; *Int'l*, pg. 649
Bump, Milo, Pres.--Texas Copy Systems, Inc., Austin, TX; *U.S. Public*, pg. 864
Bunce, James A., Plant Mgr.--Gordonsville Plant, Gordonsville, TN; *U.S. Public*, pg. 671
Bunce, John, Pres.--CaliTek Corporation, Grove City, PA; *U.S. Private*, pg. 967
Bunch, Clint, Plant Mgr.--Acme Brick Co., Kanopolis, KS; *U.S. Public*, pg. 936
Bunch, Ellen, Branch Mgr.--Downey Savings & Loan Association, F.A., Victorville, CA; *U.S. Public*, pg. 527
Bundschuh, Erwin, Dr., Mng. Dir.--Osterreichische Unilever Ges. m.b.H., Vienna, Austria; *Int'l*, pg. 1438
Bungner, Paulo, Country Mgr.--Det Norske Veritas, Valparaiso, Chile; *Int'l*, pg. 397
Buning, Willem DeCock, Mng. Dir.--Loctite Espana, S.A., Madrid, Spain; *Int'l*, pg. 611
Bunker, William A., Pres.--International Transducer Corporation, Santa Barbara, CA; *U.S. Private*, pg. 228
Bunn, Richard C., Pres. & Chief Exec. Officr--UGI Utilities, Inc., Reading, PA; *U.S. Public*, pg. 1653
Bunnell, H. Dean, Pres.--Maxtech, Inc., State College, PA; *U.S. Public*, pg. 1718
Bunney, M., Mng. Dir.--Laporte Electronics, Riddings, United Kingdom; *Int'l*, pg. 802
Bunnik, Marteen, Chief Oper. Officer--Tefal Nederland B.V., Veenendaal, Netherlands; *Int'l*, pg. 568
Bunshaw, H.R., V.P. & Gen. Mgr.--Turner Construction Company, Nashville, TN; *U.S. Public*, pg. 1645
Bunting, Christopher, Chm. & Chief Exec. Officer--Continental PIR Communications, Inc., Toronto, Canada; *Int'l*, pg. 1226
Bunting, George L., Jr., Chm.--Noxell Corporation, New York, NY; *U.S. Public*, pg. 1330
Bunting, Robert, Pres.--Everlasting Valve Co., South Plainfield, NJ; *U.S. Private*, pg. 83
Bunton, Randolph L., V.P. & Gen. Mgr.--Dillard, A ResourceNet International Company, Charleston, SC; *U.S. Public*, pg. 902
Buonaiuto, Val, Pres.--Hitachi Instruments, Inc., San Jose, CA; *Int'l*, pg. 622
Buono, Bernard, Gen. Mgr.--Unicom, Rennes, France; *Int'l*, pg. 601
Buono, Frank, V.P.--Ajax Metal Processing, Detroit, MI; *U.S. Private*, pg. 250
Buonomo, Sergio, Dir.--Banca d'America e d'Italia S.P.A. (Taranto), Taranto, Italy; *Int'l*, pg. 403
Buousoit, Jean, Head Rep.--Generale Bank, Istanbul, Turkey; *Int'l*, pg. 547
Burbach, Jeffrey J., Pres.--EZ Paintr Corp., Saint Francis, WI; *U.S. Public*, pg. 1177
Burbach, Stuart P., V.P. & Offshore Div. Mgr.--Pogo Producing Company, Offshore Division, Houston, TX; *U.S. Public*, pg. 1313
Burbach, Stuart P., V.P. & Offshore Div. Mgr.--Pogo Producing Company, Onshore Division, Houston, TX; *U.S. Public*, pg. 1313
Burbach, Stuart P., V.P. & Offshore Div. Mgr.--Pogo Producing Company, International Division, Houston, TX; *U.S. Public*, pg. 1313
Burbage, Roger T., Pres.--Landstar Poole, Inc., Evergreen, AL; *U.S. Public*, pg. 978
Burberry, Craig, Mgr.-Property & Casualty Claims--Willis Corroon Administrative Services Corporation, Orlando, FL; *Int'l*, pg. 1504
Burbidge, Fred, Gen. Mgr.--Northern Plains Steel Co., Fargo, ND; *U.S. Private*, pg. 824
Burbrink, David, Gen. Mgr.--Bunzl Packaging, Lombard, IL; *Int'l*, pg. 233
Burch, A. Leroy, Pres.--Gifford-Hill-American, Inc., Dallas, TX; *U.S. Public*, pg. 99

Burch, Jeffrey I., Publisher--House Beautiful, New York, NY; *U.S. Private*, pg. 517
Burch, Stephen P., Pres.--NationsBank of Cassville, Cassville, MO; *U.S. Public*, pg. 1164
Burchfield, Jay D., Chm. Bd. & Pres.--NationsBank of Southern Missouri, Springfield, MO; *U.S. Public*, pg. 1164
Burcin, Robert, Pres. & Chief Exec. Officer--Foster Wheeler Constructors, Inc., Clinton, NJ; *U.S. Public*, pg. 677
Burden, Rob, Oper. Group Leader--Woodward-Clyde International, Windsor, United Kingdom; *U.S. Public*, pg. 1658
Burdett, A. F., Gen. Mgr.--Dominion Insurance Ltd., London, United Kingdom; *Int'l*, pg. 784
Burdick, Howard, Gen. Mgr.--Newport Learning Center, Middletown, RI; *U.S. Public*, pg. 219
Burdick, Jon, Chief Oper. Officer--Lynden Logistics, Inc., Seattle, WA; *U.S. Private*, pg. 684
Burdick, Mark, Pres.--Cellex Manufacturing, Inc., San Marcos, TX; *U.S. Private*, pg. 1080
Burdick, Norman H., Pres.--Agronaut Great Central Insurance Co., Peoria, IL; *U.S. Public*, pg. 129
Burdon, Bob, Publr.--Washington Business Journal, Inc., Arlington, VA; *U.S. Private*, pg. 20
Burdon, S., Dir.--BT Australasia Pty Limited, Sydney, Australia; *Int'l*, pg. 223
Burdsall, John, Pres.--Heraeus Inc., New York, NY; *Int'l*, pg. 616
Burellis, Leo W., Pres.--Ultra Building Systems, Inc., South Hackensack, NJ; *U.S. Private*, pg. 194
Burello, A., Chm.--Zeltron S.p.A., Campoformido, Italy; *Int'l*, pg. 443
Burenga, Kenneth, Chief Exec. Officer--Dow Jones Markets, Jersey City, NJ; *U.S. Public*, pg. 525
Burg, H. Peter, Pres.--Ohio Edison Company, Akron, OH; *U.S. Public*, pg. 645
Burg, Jean-Marie, Chief Oper. Officer--Matra Aerospace Inc., Arlington, VA; *Int'l*, pg. 795
Burg, Stanley, Plant Mgr.--AVX Filters Div., Sun Valley, CA; *Int'l*, pg. 775
Burgdorf, Dale, Div. Mgr.--Higgins Riverside Operations, Corona, CA; *U.S. Private*, pg. 527
Burgdorff, Peter, Pres. & Chief Exec. Officer--ERA Real Estate, Parsippany, NJ; *U.S. Public*, pg. 321
Burge, Christopher, Chm.--Christie's Inc., New York, NY; *Int'l*, pg. 290
Burge, Larry, Mng. Dir.--Turning Point Care Center, Moultrie, GA; *U.S. Public*, pg. 1697
Burgener, Peter, Mng. Dir.--Commercial Intertech do Brasil Ltda., Sao Paulo, Brazil; *U.S. Public*, pg. 411
Burger, A., Chief Exec. Officer--Biwag-Getranke AG, Uster, Switzerland; *Int'l*, pg. 479
Burger, J.A., Chief Oper. Officer--Rhenus Transport International Corp., Bensenville, IL; *Int'l*, pg. 1460
Burger, Willem, Mng. Dir.--Time-Life International B.V., Amsterdam, Netherlands; *U.S. Public*, pg. 1615
Burgersdijk, C.G., Pres.--Radio Holland Group-Defense Staff Div., Amsterdam, Netherlands; *Int'l*, pg. 1151
Burgertt, Michael J., Gen. Mgr.--Calnev Pipeline Company, San Bernardino, CA; *U.S. Public*, pg. 692
Burges, R.J., Gen. Mgr.--Cummins Engine Company, Ltd., Daventry, United Kingdom; *U.S. Public*, pg. 469
Burgess, Bob, Chief Oper. Officer--Ghafari Associates, Inc., Sterling Heights, MI; *U.S. Private*, pg. 450
Burgess, Derek, V.P.--Svenska Handelsbanken Manchester, Manchester, United Kingdom; *Int'l*, pg. 1327
Burgess, John K., Pres. & Chief Exec. Officer--BAT Office Products, Zion, IL; *U.S. Public*, pg. 1686
Burgess, John M., Gen. Mgr.--Research, Melbourne, Australia; *Int'l*, pg. 227
Burgess, Michael, Pres.--The Hamilton Collection, Jacksonville, FL; *U.S. Private*, pg. 163
Burgess, Michael, Pres.--Hamilton Worldwide Direct Response Group, Jacksonville, FL; *U.S. Private*, pg. 163
Burgess, R., Mng. Dir.--UK Petroleum Products Ltd., Kidderminster, United Kingdom; *Int'l*, pg. 1065
Burgess, R. J., Pres.--Nomeco Exploration Canada, Inc., Calgary, Canada; *U.S. Public*, pg. 280
Burgess, Robert, V.P. & Gen. Mgr.--Snow's/Doxee Inc., Cape May, NJ; *U.S. Private*, pg. 219
Burgess, Robert K., Pres.--Pulte Diversified Companies, Inc., Bloomfield Hills, MI; *U.S. Public*, pg. 1344
Burgess, Robert K., Pres.--Alias Wavefront, New York, NY; *U.S. Public*, pg. 1474
Burgess, Tim, Plant Mgr.--Ethone OMI-West Haven, West Haven, CT; *U.S. Public*, pg. 138
Burgge, Trygve, Mng. Dir.--Jotun Midex AB, Goteborg, Sweden; *Int'l*, pg. 715
Burghardt, F., Chief Oper. Officer--Siemens Nederland N.V., Hague, Netherlands; *Int'l*, pg. 1247
Burghi, A., Jr., Chief Oper. Officer--Makro Atacadista S.A., Sao Paulo, Brazil; *Int'l*, pg. 1155
Burghouts, Toon, Gen. Mgr.--Forbo Genderen B.V., Genderen, Netherlands; *Int'l*, pg. 497
Burgin, Alfred, Mng. Dir.--Moore Special Tool AG, Zurich, Switzerland; *U.S. Private*, pg. 889
Burgin, Patrick, Pres.--Total Oil Great Britain Ltd., London, United Kingdom; *Int'l*, pg. 1409
Burgin, Urs, Chief Exec. Officer--Kunz & Dietfurt, Windisch, Switzerland; *Int'l*, pg. 998
Burgio, A., Gen. Mgr.--Australia & New Zealand Banking Group Limited Japan, Tokyo, Japan; *Int'l*, pg. 99
Burgoyne, Alistair, Dir.--Ord Minnett Group Limited, Tokyo, Japan; *Int'l*, pg. 1497
Burkard, Randy, Gen. Mgr.--Levy United News, Philadelphia, PA; *U.S. Private*, pg. 664
Burkart, Clemens, Chief Oper. Officer--BHF-Bank Representative Office, Ho Chi Minh City, Vietnam; *Int'l*, pg. 120
Burkart, T.D., V.P. & Gen. Mgr.--Flexsteel Division, Riverside, CA; *U.S. Public*, pg. 654
Burke, Al, Pres.--Phoenix Learning Resources, New York, NY; *U.S. Private*, pg. 863
Burke, D.R., V.P.--Mead Coated Board Intl., Inc., Dayton, OH; *U.S. Public*, pg. 1076
Burke, Dan, V.P. & Gen. Mgr.--PAXAR Printed Labels, Lenoir, NC; *U.S. Public*, pg. 1266
Burke, Gary, Mng. Dir.--Le Concorde, Quebec, Canada; *U.S. Public*, pg. 1011
Burke, Gerry, Pres.--Astra Pharmaceuticals (Ireland) Ltd., Dublin, Ireland; *Int'l*, pg. 94
Burke, I.M., Chief Exec. Officer--Gala Leisure Ltd., Nottingham, United Kingdom; *Int'l*, pg. 170
Burke, Jack, Mgr.--California Farm Products, Watsonville, CA; *U.S. Public*, pg. 1480
Burke, Jack, Mgr.--Smucker Oxnard Plant, Watsonville, CA; *U.S. Public*, pg. 1480
Burke, James R., Pres.--Enterra Petroleum Equipment Group, Inc., Houston, TX; *U.S. Public*, pg. 1749
Burke, Joe, Gen. Mgr.--Arrow Commercial Systems Div., Tustin, CA; *U.S. Public*, pg. 133
Burke, Joe W., Plant Mgr.--Cresive Milan Division, Milan, MI; *U.S. Private*, pg. 289
Burke, Lawrence E., Chm. Bd.--Alexander & Alexander Inc., New York, NY; *U.S. Public*, pg. 117
Burke, Mark, Pres.--ACI Kimtruss Corp., Chino, CA; *Int'l*, pg. 129
Burke, Michael K., Mng. Dir.--Syntron Asia Pte. Ltd., Singapore, Singapore; *U.S. Public*, pg. 1563
Burke, Richard, Pres.--Moffet, Larson, & Johnson, Arlington, VA; *U.S. Public*, pg. 1743
Burke, Robert, Pres.--Burke, Bales & Mills/HEPY, Inc., Maitland, FL; *U.S. Private*, pg. 503
Burke, Simon, Gen. Dir.--INTERMEC Group, Dun Laoghaire, Ireland; *U.S. Public*, pg. 1043
Burke, Stephen J., Acting Mng. Dir.--Moore Products Co. (Australia) Pty. Ltd., Waterloo, Australia; *U.S. Public*, pg. 1128
Burke, Stephen R., Reg. Chm., Pres. & Chief Exec. Officer--Mellon Bank, N.A.-Commonwealth Region, Harrisburg, PA; *U.S. Public*, pg. 1085
Burke, Steven F., Pres. & Chief Exec. Officer--North American Outdoor Group, Inc., Minnetonka, MN; *U.S. Public*, pg. 321
Burke, Terrence C., Pres.--First Equicor Life Insurance Company, Bloomfield, CT; *U.S. Public*, pg. 361
Burke, Tony, Div. Mgr.--Higgins Ventura, Oxnard, CA; *U.S. Private*, pg. 527
Burkemper, Richard J., Pres.--Forbo Industries Inc., Hazleton, PA; *Int'l*, pg. 497
Burken, Roger, Gen. Mgr.--Chief Ethanol Fuels, Inc., Hastings, NE; *U.S. Private*, pg. 236
Burkenpas, Tom, Plant Mgr.--The Kingsford Products Co., Burnside, KY; *U.S. Public*, pg. 387
Burkett, James, Pres.--Trinity Universal Insurance Co., Dallas, TX; *U.S. Public*, pg. 1694
Burkett, Tom, Dir.-Central Div.--Sunkist Growers, Inc.-Central Division, Cincinnati, OH; *U.S. Private*, pg. 1052
Burkhardt, Edward A., Pres.--Wisconsin Central International, Inc., Rosemont, IL; *U.S. Public*, pg. 1773
Burkhardt, Joachim, Mng. Dir.--Bundy G.m.b.H., Heidelberg, Germany; *Int'l*, pg. 1341
Burkhardt, Martin E., Pres.--W.E. Andrews Co., Inc., Bedford, MA; *U.S. Public*, pg. 1735
Burkhardt, Martin E., Pres.--A.C. Scanning, Inc., Bedford, MA; *U.S. Public*, pg. 1735
Burkhardt, W., Chief Oper. Officer--BHF-Bank Representative Office, Paris, France; *Int'l*, pg. 120
Burkhead, R., Chief Oper. Officer--Marks Transfer & Storage, Cambridge, OH; *U.S. Private*, pg. 390
Burkholder, Harold, Gen. Mgr.--Rohr Aero Services, Inc., Fairhope, AL; *U.S. Public*, pg. 751
Burkle, Joseph, Chm. Bd.--Falley's Inc., Topeka, KS; *U.S. Private*, pg. 1202
Burks, Keith W., Pres.--Bindley Western Drug Company, Indianapolis, IN; *U.S. Public*, pg. 228
Burks, Sam, Gen. Mgr.-Field Div.--Mid-Western Nursery Division, Tahlequah, OK; *U.S. Private*, pg. 60
Burleigh, Dennis, Gen. Mgr.--The Pilot Corporation of America, Jacksonville, FL; *Int'l*, pg. 1057
Burleson, Robert K., Pres.--Noble Gas Marketing, Inc., Houston, TX; *U.S. Public*, pg. 1186
Burlet, R.J.H., Mgr.--Vredestein Rubber Recycling B.V., Maastricht, Netherlands; *Int'l*, pg. 1481
Burlington, Peter, Mng. Dir.--Harman Motive Ltd, Bridgend, United Kingdom; *U.S. Public*, pg. 787
Burlot, Sylvie, Mng. Dir.--Bertrand Faure Equipements SA, Nogent-sur-Seine, France; *Int'l*, pg. 192
Burmeier, Harald, Mgr.-Office--Woodward-Clyde, Wennigsen, Germany; *U.S. Public*, pg. 1657
Burn, Marion, Gen. Mgr.--Containerboard & Paper Div.-Hodge Mill, Hodge, LA; *U.S. Public*, pg. 1520
Burnay, Luis, Chief Exec.--Sulzer Infra Portugal, Ltda., Lisbon, Portugal; *Int'l*, pg. 1306
Burnell, Roger, Mng. Dir.--Britannia Airways Ltd., Luton, United Kingdom; *U.S. Public*, pg. 1601
Burnell, Thomas, Sr. V.P. & Gen. Mgr.--Animal Nutrition Div., Chicago, IL; *U.S. Private*, pg. 268
Burnet, Thomas, Pres.-Advancing Mkts. Grp.--Brown-Forman Beverages Worldwide, Louisville, KY; *U.S. Public*, pg. 261
Burnett, Dale, Gen. Mgr.--Packing Div., Salt Lake City, UT; *U.S. Public*, pg. 1262
Burnett, G. Kent, Chm. Bd.--Phoenix Division, Tempe, AZ; *U.S. Public*, pg. 509
Burnett, Hugh, Mng. Dir.--OMRON Terminals (U.K.) Ltd., New Malden, United Kingdom; *Int'l*, pg. 1006
Burnett, Hugh T., Pres.--Cash Bases Incorporated, Westport, CT; *U.S. Public*, pg. 1637
Burnett, Peter, Controller--Messier-Dowty Customer Support Center- Americas, Sterling, VA; *Int'l*, pg. 1340
Burnett, Steven, Chief Exec. Officer--Healthsource Connecticut, Farmington, CT; *U.S. Public*, pg. 360
Burnett, T., Pres.--Unibus, Inc., Strongsville, OH; *U.S. Public*, pg. 1319
Burnett, W., Pres.--Boral Bricks Inc., Augusta, GA; *Int'l*, pg. 203
Burnett, Weldon, Gen. Mgr.--Lakeland Flight Academy, Lakeland, FL; *U.S. Public*, pg. 218
Burnett, William O., Pres.--Shaw Data Services, New York, NY; *U.S. Public*, pg. 1534
Burney, Derek H., Chm., Pres. & Chief Exec. Officer--Bell Canada International, Inc., Montreal, Canada; *Int'l*, pg. 115
Burnham, Daniel P., Pres.--AlliedSignal Aerospace, Torrance, CA; *U.S. Public*, pg. 50
Burnham, Dave, Admin.--Horizon Meadows, Alliance, OH; *U.S. Public*, pg. 838
Burnham, H.B., Mng. Dir.--Thyssen Haniel Logistics, Brentwood, United Kingdom; *Int'l*, pg. 1388
Burnham, John M., Pres.--Weeks Dairy Foods, Inc., Concord, NH; *Int'l*, pg. 752
Burns, Andrea, Branch Mgr.--Downey Savings & Loan Association, F.A., Huntington Beach, CA; *U.S. Public*, pg. 526
Burns, C. Robert, Jr., Pres. & Mng. Dir.--Fencourt Reinsurance Co. Ltd., Hamilton, Bermuda; *U.S. Public*, pg. 795
Burns, Cathie, Mng. Dir.--Riley Advertising (Leeds) Ltd., Leeds, United Kingdom; *Int'l*, pg. 1117
Burns, Colleen, Mgr.--Miller Brands of Phoenix, Glendale, AZ; *U.S. Public*, pg. 1289
Burns, D., Plant Mgr.--Ruetgers-Nease Corporation, Gracewood, GA; *Int'l*, pg. 1148
Burns, Dave, Gen. Mgr.--Retailer Development, Memphis, TN; *U.S. Public*, pg. 653
Burns, George D., Mng. Dir.--Motorola Limited, Glasgow, United Kingdom; *U.S. Public*, pg. 1139
Burns, Harry A., Pres. & Chief Exec. Officer--Cargill Salt Inc., Minneapolis, MN; *Int'l*, pg. 48
Burns, J. Dennis, V.P. & Gen. Mgr.--Tape Products Div., Moorestown, NJ; *U.S. Public*, pg. 69
Burns, J. Dennis, Gen. Mgr.--Ideal Tape Company, Lowell, MA; *U.S. Public*, pg. 69
Burns, J. F., Gen. Mgr.--Saval B.V., Prinsenbeek, Prinsenbeek, Netherlands; *Int'l*, pg. 681
Burns, James, Pres.--ATMI Ecosys Corp., San Jose, CA; *U.S. Public*, pg. 12
Burns, Jerry A., Chief Exec. Officer--Cramerton Automotive Products, L.P., Cramerton, NC; *U.S. Private*, pg. 1095
Burns, Jerry N., Sls. Mgr.--American Ductile Iron Pipe Div., Birmingham, AL; *U.S. Private*, pg. 52
Burns, Jordan, Pres.--Tussenderlo Kerley Inc., Phoenix, AZ; *Int'l*, pg. 619
Burns, Lewis E., Pres. & Chief Exec. Officer--Dover Industries, Inc., Elgin, IL; *U.S. Public*, pg. 520
Burns, Malcolm J., Mng. Dir.--BHP New Zealand Steel Ltd., Glenbrook, New Zealand; *Int'l*, pg. 226
Burns, Merrill, Pres.--BankAmerica International, New York, NY; *U.S. Public*, pg. 181
Burns, Michael, Pres.--Sea Watch International, Ltd., Easton, MD; *Int'l*, pg. 928
Burns, Michael J., Pres. & Chief Exec. Officer--Key Bank of Alaska, Anchorage, AK; *U.S. Public*, pg. 954
Burns, R. Howard, Pres.--Windsor Door, Little Rock, AR; *U.S. Public*, pg. 69
Burns, R. J., Pres.--Enron Operations Corp., Houston, TX; *U.S. Public*, pg. 584
Burns, Robert, Gen. Mgr.--Lewis & Saunders Inc., Laconia, NH; *Int'l*, pg. 1337
Burns, Robert C., Div. Mgr.--HMT Inspection & Engineering Services, Houston, TX; *U.S. Public*, pg. 914
Burns, Robert L., Pres.--Heatilator Inc., Mount Pleasant, IA; *U.S. Public*, pg. 772
Burns, Robert T., Pres. & Gen. Mgr.--Gannett Telemarketing Inc., Springfield, VA; *U.S. Public*, pg. 699
Burns, Ronald S., Exec V.P., Pres. Global Bus. & Global Bus Dir.-Kraft--J. Walter Thompson Company, New York, NY; *Int'l*, pg. 1483
Burns, Russ, Pres.--Universal Construction Co., Huntsville, AL; *U.S. Public*, pg. 1646
Burns, Steve, Div. Mgr.--Champion Home Builders Co., Lindsay, CA; *U.S. Public*, pg. 332
Burns, Tom, Gen. Mgr.--Dale Electronics, Norfolk Div., Norfolk, NE; *U.S. Public*, pg. 1722
Burns, Tom, Gen. Mgr.--Bradford Electronic Inc., Bradford, PA; *U.S. Public*, pg. 1722
Burns, Warwick Every, Chief Oper. Officer--First Brands Australia, Padstow, Australia; *U.S. Public*, pg. 627
Burns, William J.D., Mng. Dir.--Ortho Clinical Diagnostic N.V., Beersel, Belgium; *U.S. Public*, pg. 931
Burnside, Don, Reg. V.P.--The Southland Corporation, San Diego, CA; *Int'l*, pg. 694
Burpo, James O., Chm. Bd.--Willis Corroon Corp. of Sacramento, Sacramento, CA; *Int'l*, pg. 1582
Burr, Christopher D., Pres. & Gen. Mgr.--Johnson & Johnson K.K., Tokyo, Japan; *U.S. Public*, pg. 930
Burr, Christopher D., Pres. & Mng. Dir.--Johnson & Johnson Medical K.K., Tokyo, Japan; *U.S. Public*, pg. 931
Burr, David F., Chm. Bd.--Rollins Leasing Corp., Wilmington, DE; *U.S. Public*, pg. 1405
Burr, George S., Trustee--Instron Realty Trust, Canton, MA; *U.S. Public*, pg. 883
Burr, Les, Chm.--Galleon Ltd., Woking, United Kingdom; *Int'l*, pg. 114
Burr, Rick, V.P. & Gen. Mgr.--Safety Railway Service, Victoria, TX; *U.S. Public*, pg. 412
Burr, Rick, V.P. & Gen. Mgr.--Safety Railway Service-Tulsa, Tulsa, OK; *U.S. Public*, pg. 412
Burrage, Anthony R., Mgr.--Foster Wheeler Australia Pty. Ltd., Mount Waverley, Australia; *U.S. Public*, pg. 677
Burrell, M.W., Chm. Bd.--Lakeside Trading Estate Ltd., Essex, United Kingdom; *Int'l*, pg. 1025
Burress, Chuck, Publr.--The Gazette, Galax, VA; *U.S. Private*, pg. 648
Burri, Ernst A., Pres. & Gen. Mgr.--Compania Dominicana de Telefonos, C. por A., Santo Domingo, Dominican Republic; *U.S. Public*, pg. 697
Burrill, David, Chief Mgr.--Westpac Banking Corp. - Singapore, Singapore, Singapore; *Int'l*, pg. 1497
Burris, O. Dale, Pres.--TRAK Microwave Corp., Tampa, FL; *U.S. Public*, pg. 1563

Burris, Watt, Exec. V.P. & Gen. Mgr.--Paramount Carowinds, Charlotte, NC; *U.S. Private*, pg. 776
Burroughs, Ken, Pres.--Skeeter Products, Inc., Kilgore, TX; *U.S. Private*, pg. 689
Burroughs, Mary, Admin.--Savannah Convalescent Center, Savannah, GA; *U.S. Public*, pg. 1714
Burrows, John, Dir.-Mfg.--Astec Europe Limited, Stourbridge, United Kingdom; *Int'l*, pg. 93
Burrows, John, Pres. & Chief Exec. Officer--SPI Polyols, Inc., New Castle, DE; *Int'l*, pg. 599
Burrows, K.F., Pres.--Bristol Aerospace Ltd., Winnipeg, Canada; *Int'l*, pg. 1127
Burrows, P.J., Dr., Chief Exec.--GKN Westland Technologies Limited, Yeovil, United Kingdom; *Int'l*, pg. 535
Burrows, Penny, Pres.--Sunwest Bank of Sandoval County, N.A., Rio Rancho, NM; *U.S. Public*, pg. 1165
Burrus, Clark, Chm. Bd.--Chicago Transit Authority, Chicago, IL; *U.S. Private*, pg. 919
Burrus, Y., Mng. Dir.--Banque Cantrade, Ormond Burrus SA, Geneva, Switzerland; *Int'l*, pg. 1439
Bursma, Albert, Jr., Pres.--Great Source Education Group, Wilmington, MA; *U.S. Public*, pg. 841
Burson, Bill, Pres.--Halstead Industrial Prods. Div., Wynne, AR; *U.S. Private*, pg. 497
Burstein, David, Pres.--Harland Bartholomew & Associates Inc., Memphis, TN; *U.S. Private*, pg. 841
Burstein, David, Pres.--Parsons Engineering Science, Inc., Pasadena, CA; *U.S. Private*, pg. 842
Burt, John, Mgr.--W.C. Caye & Co., Mobile, AL; *U.S. Private*, pg. 220
Burt, Richard L., Pres.--Comtech Systems, Inc., Saint Cloud, FL; *U.S. Public*, pg. 425
Burtman, Charles, Pres.--Dynabilt Products, Boston, MA; *U.S. Private*, pg. 188
Burton, Anthony, Acct. Exec.--TIE Systems-Athens, Bogart, GA; *U.S. Private*, pg. 1085
Burton, Bill, Gen. Mgr.--McGraw Glass Div., Detroit, MI; *U.S. Public*, pg. 353
Burton, Charles, Chief Oper. Officer--Allright Dayton Parking, Inc., Dayton, OH; *U.S. Private*, pg. 42
Burton, J.L., Pres.--Nacan Products Ltd., Brampton, Canada; *Int'l*, pg. 1436
Burton, Ken, Mng. Dir.--Reed Business Information-East Grinstead, East Grinstead, United Kingdom; *Int'l*, pg. 1094
Burton, Phil, Mgr.-Shop Opers.--HMI Electric, Memphis, TN; *U.S. Private*, pg. 518
Burton, W. Blaine, Mgr.-Branch--Piper Jaffray Inc., Idaho Falls, ID; *U.S. Public*, pg. 1301
Burtraw, Roger, Pres.--Kingston-Warren Corporation, Newfields, NH; *U.S. Public*, pg. 796
Burtraw, Roger L., Pres.--Kingston Warren, Farmington Hills, MI; *U.S. Public*, pg. 796
Burwell, Bruce, Dir.--Joslyn Research & Development Corporation, Woodstock, IL; *U.S. Public*, pg. 482
Bury, Christian, Chief Oper. Officer--Ahlstrom-Hanssen S.A., Moder, France; *Int'l*, pg. 34
Burzin, Klaus, Pres. & Chief Oper. Officer--Huls America Inc., Somerset, NJ; *Int'l*, pg. 1455
Burzycki, Thomas, Pres. & Chief Exec. Officer--The Selmer Co., Inc., Elkhart, IN; *U.S. Public*, pg. 1514
Burzycki, Thomas, Pres.--Vincent Bach Co., Elkhart, IN; *U.S. Public*, pg. 1514
Busby, Don C., Pres.--Huck International Industrial Fastener Division, Waco, TX; *U.S. Public*, pg. 1597
Busby, H.T., Gen. Mgr.--Virgo Optics, Inc., Port Richey, FL; *U.S. Public*, pg. 1647
Busby, R.A., Plant Mgr.--Aerospace & Commercial Controls Div., Selma, NC; *U.S. Public*, pg. 557
Busby, Robert L., Pres.--NWL Investments, Inc., Austin, TX; *U.S. Public*, pg. 1161
Busby, Robert L., III, Pres.--NWL 806 Main, Inc., Austin, TX; *U.S. Public*, pg. 1161
Busby, Robert L., III, Pres.--NWL Properties, Inc., Austin, TX; *U.S. Public*, pg. 1161
Busby, Robert L., III, Pres.--NWL Financial, Inc., Austin, TX; *U.S. Public*, pg. 1161
Buscaglia, A., Gen. Mgr.--A.C. Nielsen, Ltda., Sao Paulo, Brazil; *U.S. Public*, pg. 1183
Busch, Clarence, Plant Mgr.--Block Plant, Converse, TX; *U.S. Public*, pg. 936
Busch, Greg, V.P.--Richardson Wood Preserving, Sheboygan Falls, WI; *U.S. Private*, pg. 929
Busch, Greg, V.P.--Richardson Lumber Co., Sheboygan Falls, WI; *U.S. Private*, pg. 929
Busch, Johannes, Gen. Mgr.--Robert Fleming (Deutschland) GmbH, Frankfurt/Main, Germany; *Int'l*, pg. 493
Busch, Walter, Plant Mgr.--CIMCO, Dayton, NV; *U.S. Private*, pg. 574
Busche, Jurgen, Mng. Dir.--Bayerische-Bulgarische Handelsbank GmbH, Munich, Germany; *Int'l*, pg. 179
Buschling, Randy, Gen. Mgr.--Watlow Infrared Company, Decorah, IA; *U.S. Private*, pg. 1153
Buschmeier, Wolfgang, Dir.--Berag GmbH, Bremen, Germany; *Int'l*, pg. 1502
Buser, Ed, Div. Mgr.--Rubber Products Division, Belcamp, MD; *U.S. Private*, pg. 195
Buser, Werner, Gen. Mgr.--Knorr-Nahrmittel Aktiengesellschaft, Thayngen, Switzerland; *U.S. Public*, pg. 225
Busey, George, Chm.--Liberty National Bank of Shelbyville, Shelbyville, KY; *U.S. Public*, pg. 173
Buseyne, Valere, Mng. Dir.--ISS Food Hygiene S.A.-N.V., Brussels, Belgium; *Int'l*, pg. 657
Bush, David C., Plant Mgr.--Crown Cork & Seal, Northeast Div., Lawrence, MA; *U.S. Public*, pg. 463
Bush, Geoffrey, Dir.--Grand Metropolitan Community Relations, Brighton, United Kingdom; *Int'l*, pg. 408
Bush, George, Pres.--Phoenix Concrete Cutting, Phoenix, AZ; *U.S. Private*, pg. 849
Bush, John, Chief Exec. Officer--International Dessert Partners, Miami, FL; *U.S. Public*, pg. 447
Bush, Robert, Pres.--First Ameritas Life Insurance Corp. of New York, Suffern, NY; *U.S. Private*, pg. 65
Bush, Ronald, Pres.--DeVry Institute of Technology, Decatur, GA; *U.S. Public*, pg. 504
Bush, Steve, Plant Mgr.--Block Plant, Roswell, NM; *U.S. Public*, pg. 936
Bush, Suzanne, Pres. & Publr.--The Reporter Equitable Publishing Co., Lansdale, PA; *U.S. Public*, pg. 701
Bushar, T.A., V.P. & Gen. Mgr.--Kaydon Corporation, Filtration Division, La Grange, GA; *U.S. Public*, pg. 946
Bushell, C.J., Chm. & Mng. Dir.--BPB Paper & Packaging Ltd., Northwich, United Kingdom; *Int'l*, pg. 122
Bushen, David A., Pres.--Old Kent Brokerage Services, Inc., Grand Rapids, MI; *U.S. Public*, pg. 1216
Bushman, Steven, Chm. Bd.--Banta Information Services Group, Spanish Fork, UT; *U.S. Public*, pg. 188
Bushong, Gerald, Reg. Mgr.-Western--Weatherford, Odessa, TX; *U.S. Public*, pg. 1749
Busin, Marco, Chief Oper. Officer--Biosol S.p.A., Sondalo, Italy; *Int'l*, pg. 667
Buske, John M., Pres.--UNR Home Products Div., Ruston, LA; *U.S. Public*, pg. 1404
Buss, Richard M., Pres.--First of America Community Development Corporation, Detroit, MI; *U.S. Public*, pg. 637
Buss, W., Gen. Mgr.--Durco GmbH Atomac Division, Ahaus, Germany; *U.S. Public*, pg. 659
Busse, Dieter, Co-Chief Oper. Officer--Winschermann Sued GmbH, Karlsruhe, Germany; *Int'l*, pg. 1167
Busse, Richard Balthasar von, Mng. Dir.--Dresdner Bank AG, Rome, Italy; *Int'l*, pg. 419
Busselberg, Wolfgang, Sr. Mng. Dir.--Deutsche Bank AG (Hannover), Hannover, Germany; *Int'l*, pg. 402
Bustamante, Alejandro, Client Services Dir.--Leo Burnett Comunica S.A., Guatemala, Guatemala; *U.S. Private*, pg. 185
Bustamante, Amalia, Mgr.--Circle Freight International de Panama S.A., Colon, Panama; *U.S. Public*, pg. 372
Bustamante, Victor, Gen. Dir.--Ford Motor Credit S.A., Valencia, Venezuela; *U.S. Public*, pg. 666
Busteed, R.T., V.P. & Div. Mgr.--Matthews International Marking Systems Div., Pittsburgh, PA; *U.S. Public*, pg. 1059
Busti, Dennis, Pres. & Chief Exec. Officer--Reliance National Insurance Company, New York, NY; *U.S. Public*, pg. 1374
Bustos, Luis, Pres.--Allied Domecq Brasil Industria e Comercio Ltda., Rio de Janeiro, Brazil; *Int'l*, pg. 63
Busweiler, E., Mng. Dir.--VNU Business Publications bv, Amsterdam, Netherlands; *Int'l*, pg. 1445
Butcher, Brian, Mng. Dir.--PDA International/United Kingdom, Basingstoke, United Kingdom; *U.S. Public*, pg. 1031
Butcher, Bruce, V.P & Gen. Mgr.--Parish Div., Reading, PA; *U.S. Public*, pg. 479
Butcher, C. Preston, Pres. & Chief Exec. Officer--Lincoln Property Co., Northern California, Foster City, CA; *U.S. Private*, pg. 668
Butcher, J., Chm. Bd.--The Tampa Tribune, Tampa, FL; *U.S. Public*, pg. 1079
Butcher, Jerry, Administrator--Butte Convalescent Center, Butte, MT; *U.S. Public*, pg. 837
Butcher, Jonathan, Pres.--Butcher Energy, Philadelphia, PA; *U.S. Private*, pg. 189
Butel, Jean-Luc, Pres.--Nippon Becton Dickinson Company Ltd., Tokyo, Japan; *U.S. Public*, pg. 200
Buten, Max, V.P.-Fin. & Treas.--Buten, Division of Duron, King of Prussia, PA; *U.S. Private*, pg. 349
Butensky, Irwin S., V.P.-Family Prods., Res. & Devel.--Playtex Products Corp., Westport, CT; *U.S. Public*, pg. 1311
Buterbaugh, Noel L., Pres. & Chief Exec. Officer--BioWhittaker, Inc., Walkersville, MD; *U.S. Public*, pg. 297
Buterbaugh, Noel L., Pres.--Clonetics, Inc., Walkersville, MD; *U.S. Public*, pg. 297
Buthker, K., Deputy Mng. Dir.--Lowe & Jaegers GmbH, Duisburg, Germany; *Int'l*, pg. 1450
Butler, Allan T., V.P. & Gen. Mgr.--Howell Packaging, Burlington, Canada; *Int'l*, pg. 417
Butler, B.R., Mng. Dir.--De La Rue Systems (UK), Newbury, United Kingdom; *Int'l*, pg. 387
Butler, Basil, Chm. Bd.--Brown & Root Limited, London, United Kingdom; *U.S. Public*, pg. 775
Butler, Bill, V.P. & Gen. Mgr.--Eclipse Combustion, Mississauga, Canada; *U.S. Private*, pg. 361
Butler, Bruce, Pres. & Gen. Mgr.--EMC Test System, L.P., Austin, TX; *U.S. Public*, pg. 546
Butler, Charles, Exec. V.P.--Simon Marketing, Inc., Lawrenceville, GA; *U.S. Private*, pg. 1001
Butler, Craig M., Admin.--Hillhaven-Rose Manor Convalescent Center, Durham, NC; *U.S. Public*, pg. 1714
Butler, Debby, Gen. Mgr./Editor--Park Newspapers of Clinton, Inc., Clinton, NC; *U.S. Public*, pg. 1078
Butler, Debby, Gen. Mgr./Editor--Samson Independent, Inc., Clinton, NC; *U.S. Public*, pg. 1078
Butler, Edmund R., Chief Oper. Officer--Mississippi Energies, Inc., Jackson, MS; *U.S. Private*, pg. 753
Butler, Edward F., Chm. Bd., Pres. & Chief Exec. Officer--Regions Bank/Southern Louisiana, New Orleans, LA; *U.S. Public*, pg. 1373
Butler, Eugene W., Pres.--Harris Bank St. Charles, Saint Charles, IL; *Int'l*, pg. 154
Butler, Frank E., Pres. & Gen. Mgr.--Sherwin-Williams Coatings Division, Cleveland, OH; *U.S. Public*, pg. 1466
Butler, G. E., Mng. Dir.--Hunter Douglas Ltd., Walton-on-Thames, United Kingdom; *Int'l*, pg. 640
Butler, J.B., Distr. Mgr.--Milchem International Limited, Dubai, United Arab Emirates; *U.S. Public*, pg. 167
Butler, Jim, Pres.--ALZA International, Palo Alto, CA; *U.S. Public*, pg. 62
Butler, John, Pres.--Heating and Cooling Supply Inc., San Diego, CA; *U.S. Public*, pg. 1746
Butler, John M., Pres. & Treas.--John Hancock Leasing Corporation, Boston, MA; *U.S. Private*, pg. 590
Butler, John Scott, Gen. Mgr.--City Meat Alliant, Tucson, AZ; *U.S. Private*, pg. 244
Butler, K.H., V.P. & Gen. Mgr.--Turner Construction Co., Cincinnati, OH; *U.S. Public*, pg. 1645
Butler, Lester, Chm. Bd., Pres. & Chief Exec. Officer--SouthTrust Bank of Charleston, Charleston, SC; *U.S. Public*, pg. 1492
Butler, Matthew, Mgr.-Office--Woodward-Clyde, Lake Charles, LA; *U.S. Public*, pg. 1656
Butler, Mike, Area Mgr.--Dexter Electronic Materials, Slough, United Kingdom; *U.S. Public*, pg. 505
Butler, Paul D., Chief Oper. Officer--Pool Company, Harvey, LA; *U.S. Public*, pg. 1316
Butler, Philip, Mng. Dir.--Blount U.K. Limited, Tewkesbury, United Kingdom; *U.S. Public*, pg. 239
Butler, R., Chief Fin. Officer--The Braidwater Spinning Company Ltd., Ballymena, United Kingdom; *Int'l*, pg. 797
Butler, R.W., Pres.--Sverdrup Technology, Inc., Tullahoma, TN; *U.S. Private*, pg. 1057
Butler, Robert, Chm. Bd.--Subaru Distributor Corp., Orangeburg, NY; *Int'l*, pg. 523
Butler, Robert C., V.P.--Southern California Division, Brea, CA; *U.S. Public*, pg. 38
Butler, Robert L., Pres.--Pioneer Funds Distributor, Inc., Boston, MA; *U.S. Public*, pg. 1298
Butler, Ron, Pres.--Eastland National Bank, Eastland, TX; *U.S. Public*, pg. 633
Butler, Ronald, Gen. Mgr.--Teradyne Assembly Test/West Division, Walnut Creek, CA; *U.S. Public*, pg. 1581
Butler, Sir Richard, The Hon., Chm. Bd.--NatWest Investment Management Limited, London, United Kingdom; *Int'l*, pg. 910
Butler, Thomas R., Pres. & Chief Oper. Officer-Novus Services, Inc.--Dean Witter, Discover & Co., New York, NY; *U.S. Public*, pg. 1132
Butler, Viggo, Pres.--Airport Group International, Inc., Glendale, CA; *U.S. Public*, pg. 1009
Butler, Walter J., V.P. & Gen. Mgr.--Microwave Electronics Div., Nashua, NH; *U.S. Public*, pg. 1008
Butler, Wayne, Complex Mgr.--Tyson Foods, Inc., Magee, MS; *U.S. Public*, pg. 1652
Butler, William K., Pres.--Aaron's Rental Purchase, Atlanta, GA; *U.S. Public*, pg. 12
Buto, Rudolpho Maza, Pres.--Asea Reguladores S.A. de C.V., Mexico, Mexico; *Int'l*, pg. 8
Butrum, Carl, Pres.--Eastman Radio, Inc., New York, NY; *U.S. Public*, pg. 335
Butryn, G.L., Pres.--Escanaba Paper Co., Escanaba, MI; *U.S. Public*, pg. 1076
Butryn, Gary L., Pres. & Gen. Mgr.--Mead Publishing Paper, Escanaba, MI; *U.S. Public*, pg. 1074
Butta, Tom, Chief Exec. Officer--FGI New York, New York, NY; *U.S. Private*, pg. 389
Butterfield, Brian, Mng. Dir.--Bi-Tech Engineering, Dunleer, Ireland; *Int'l*, pg. 554
Butterfield, Bruce, Pres.--Prentice Hall Regents/ESL, Upper Saddle River, NJ; *U.S. Private*, pg. 778
Butterfield, J.R., Chief Oper. Officer--GEC (New Zealand) Ltd., Elsdon, New Zealand; *Int'l*, pg. 546
Butterfield, Michael J., Chief Fin. Officer--American Financial Group Securities Corp., Boston, MA; *U.S. Private*, pg. 380
Butters, Brian, Pres. & Publisher--The Kamloops Daily News, Kamloops, Canada; *Int'l*, pg. 631
Butterwick, A.J., Mng. Dir.--P&O Bulk Carriers Ltd. (Bermuda), London, United Kingdom; *Int'l*, pg. 1033
Butterworth, John, Mng. Dir.--RoyScot Factors Limited, Croydon, United Kingdom; *Int'l*, pg. 1132
Butterworth, Rob, Branch Mgr.--Burns & Wilcox - Charlotte Office, Charlotte, NC; *U.S. Private*, pg. 609
Buttery, Christopher, Dir.--Ord Minnett Group, New York, NY; *Int'l*, pg. 1496
Buttler, Heinz, Chief Oper. Officer--MBA-KONE AG, Bassersdorf, Switzerland; *Int'l*, pg. 748
Buttner, Jean Bernhard, Chm. Bd., Pres. & Chief Exec. Officer--Value Line, Inc., New York, NY; *U.S. Private*, pg. 137
Button, David, Gen. Mgr.--Parker & Amchem, Etobicoke, Canada; *Int'l*, pg. 612
Buttrill, W. Shelly, Pres.--Lockheed Martin Aeronutronic, Santa Margarita, CA; *U.S. Public*, pg. 1008
Butts, Mervin, Exec. V.P.-Engrng.--ZEXEL Inc., Decatur, IL; *Int'l*, pg. 1528
Butwin, R., Gen. Mgr.--Ghafari Associates, Inc., Indianapolis, IN; *U.S. Private*, pg. 450
Butyniec, J.S., V.P. & Gen. Mgr.--Bristol Aerospace Limited, Winnipeg, Canada; *Int'l*, pg. 829
Butynski, Donald L., Pres.--National Energy Production Corporation, Redmond, WA; *U.S. Public*, pg. 1795
Butynski, Donald L., Pres.--ZURN/NEPCO, Redmond, WA; *U.S. Public*, pg. 1795
Butz, Gordon, Gen. Mgr.--Lloydminster Pool, Lloydminster, Canada; *Int'l*, pg. 1195
Butz, John, Pres.--Allomatic Products Company, Sullivan, IN; *U.S. Public*, pg. 1363
Butz, Theophil, Chm. & Creative Dir.--Bosch & Butz, Zollikon, Switzerland; *U.S. Private*, pg. 678
Butzberger, Paul T., Pres.--Dresser Oil Tools, Dallas, TX; *U.S. Public*, pg. 528
Butzer, Bart, Pres.--Mervyn's California, Hayward, CA; *U.S. Public*, pg. 489
Butzlaff, Steve, V.P. & Mng. Dir.--The Northern Trust Company, Lake Bluff, IL; *U.S. Public*, pg. 1197
Buuck, Charles T., V.P. & Gen. Mgr.--Turner Construction Co., Boston, MA; *U.S. Public*, pg. 1645
Buxados, Carlos E., Mng. Dir.--Tyco Toys Espana, Barcelona, Spain; *U.S. Public*, pg. 1059
Buxbaum, Matthew, Chief Exec. Officer--GGP/Homart, Inc., Chicago, IL; *U.S. Public*, pg. 715
Buxton, W.H., Chm. Bd. & Chief Exec. Officer--McNeil (Ohio) Corporation, Saint Paul, MN; *U.S. Public*, pg. 1273
Buyer, Rick, Gen. Mgr. & Winemaker--Jekel Vineyards, Monterey, CA; *U.S. Public*, pg. 261

Buysse, Paul, Gen. Mgr.--S.A. Tenneco Belgium (Poclain-Monroe-Petro-Tex) N.V., Aartselaar, Belgium; *U.S. Public*, pg. 1580

Buzas, Joe, Chief Exec. Officer--Salt Lake City Buzz, Salt Lake City, UT; *U.S. Private*, pg. 751

Buziak, Robert, Pres. of RCA Label--BMG/Music, New York, NY; *Int'l*, pg. 191

Buzogany, R.J. "Buzz", Exec. V.P.--Wyse-Landau Public Relations, Cleveland, OH; *U.S. Private*, pg. 1194

Buzzard, James A., V.P. & Div. Mgr.--Westvaco Corporation-Envelope Div., Springfield, MA; *U.S. Public*, pg. 1762

Buzzi, Giampaolo, Mng. Dir.--Neste Chemicals Italia S.r.l., Milan, Italy; *Int'l*, pg. 914

Byanski, Richard J., Mgr.-Service Parts--Fremont Plant, Fremont, IN; *U.S. Public*, pg. 1620

Byer, Trevor A., Resident Rep.--The World Bank, Lagos, Nigeria; *U.S. Private*, pg. 1189

Byer, Wane, Gen. Mgr.--Circle Freight International USA, Sterling, VA; *U.S. Public*, pg. 370

Byers, Norman P., Pres.--Telos International Corp., Ashburn, VA; *U.S. Public*, pg. 1573

Byers, Peter, Mng. Dir.--ORIX New Zealand (NZ) Limited, Auckland, New Zealand; *Int'l*, pg. 1010

Byers, Ronald, Admin.--Heritage Oaks, Arlington, TX; *U.S. Public*, pg. 839

Bynum, David, Gen. Mgr.--Southern States Vehicle Auction of Atlanta Inc., Newnan, GA; *U.S. Public*, pg. 1649

Bynum, W. David, Gen. Mgr.--Lincolnton Mfg. Div., Lincolnton, NC; *U.S. Public*, pg. 575

Byrd, David, Mgr.--Southern Electric Supply Co., Inc., Morristown, TN; *Int'l*, pg. 1108

Byrd, Jeff, Pres.--Bristol Motor Speedway, Bristol, TN; *U.S. Public*, pg. 1498

Byrd, John, Exec. V.P.--Mister Twister, Minden, LA; *U.S. Private*, pg. 992

Byrd, R. Bryant, V.P.-Human Resources--GTE Information Services Incorporated, Dallas-Fort Worth Airport, TX; *U.S. Public*, pg. 696

Byrd, Robert, Mgr.--Tri-State Mack Inc., Tupelo, MS; *U.S. Private*, pg. 1101

Byrkit, Larry, Pres.--UPB of the Tennessee Valley, Harriman, TN; *U.S. Public*, pg. 1669

Byrn, Becky, Media Planner & Media Buyer--J.W. Messner, Inc., Vista, CA; *U.S. Private*, pg. 734

Byrne, Chris, Gen. Mgr.--Now Hear This (NHT), Benicia, CA; *U.S. Public*, pg. 1369

Byrne, David, Representative & Asst. V.P.--First RepublicBank Dallas, N.A. Representative Office, Seoul, Korea; *U.S. Public*, pg. 1165

Byrne, Derek F., Gen. Mgr.--Forbo Ireland Ltd., Dublin, Ireland; *Int'l*, pg. 497

Byrne, Donald, Mng. Dir.--Cadbury Ireland p.l.c., Dublin, Ireland; *Int'l*, pg. 248

Byrne, J.J., Jr., Pres.--Berwind Pharmaceutical Services, Inc., West Point, PA; *U.S. Private*, pg. 139

Byrne, Joseph, Pres.--Property Development Associates, Oakland, CA; *U.S. Public*, pg. 1426

Byrne, Michael K., Dir. & Gen. Mgr.--The Irish Crown Cork Co., Ltd., Cork, Ireland; *U.S. Public*, pg. 465

Byrne, Patrick P., Vice Chm. & Mng. Dir.--Ford Credit S.A., Madrid, Spain; *U.S. Public*, pg. 665

Byrne, Phyllis, Dir.--IBM United Kingdom Laboratories Limited, Winchester, United Kingdom; *U.S. Public*, pg. 897

Byrne, Robert P., Chief Oper. Officer--CT&I Corp. of Wisconsin, Milwaukee, WI; *U.S. Private*, pg. 235

Byrne, Roger, Pres.--Trim Division, Kalkaska, MI; *U.S. Private*, pg. 355

Byrne, Tom, V.P. & Gen. Mgr.--Robertshaw Tennessee, Knoxville, TN; *Int'l*, pg. 1243

Byrnes, Bruce L., Pres.--Procter & Gamble Cleaning & Paper Products Div., Cincinnati, OH; *U.S. Public*, pg. 1330

Byrnes, John T., Pres.--M & I Brokerage Services, Inc., Milwaukee, WI; *U.S. Public*, pg. 1050

Byrnes, John T., Pres & Treas.--M & I Capital Markets Group, Inc., Milwaukee, WI; *U.S. Public*, pg. 1051

Byrnes, Peter, Pres.--Winchester Homes, Inc., Calverton, MD; *U.S. Public*, pg. 1764

Byron, Steven J., Gen. Mgr.--Franklin-Burlington Plastics, Kearny, NJ; *U.S. Public*, pg. 1496

Bysiek, Edward J., Pres.--ABB Air Preheater Inc., Wellsville, NY; *Int'l*, pg. 3

Bystedt, Barry, Chief Oper. Officer--NIFE Argentina S.A., Buenos Aires, Argentina; *Int'l*, pg. 54

Bystrom, Dale, V.P.-Managed Care--Integrated Health Concepts, Walnut Creek, CA; *U.S. Public*, pg. 1013

Bystrom, Ulf, Rep.--Svenska Handelsbanken Moscow, Moscow, Russia; *Int'l*, pg. 1327

Bytnar, Michael W., Pres.--Nooter Fabricators, Inc., Saint Louis, MO; *U.S. Private*, pg. 801

Byun, D.S., Pres.--Simpson Industries, Inc., Seoul, Korea; *U.S. Public*, pg. 1475

Caballeiro, M., Gen. Mgr.--Axson Espana, Barcelona, Spain; *Int'l*, pg. 103

Caballero, John, Gen. Mgr.--Poe & Brown of Florida, Naples, FL; *U.S. Public*, pg. 1312

Caban, R., Chief Oper. Officer--Osram Ltd., Wembley, United Kingdom; *Int'l*, pg. 1244

Cabaret, J.C., Pres.--Crane Canada Inc., Montreal, Canada; *U.S. Public*, pg. 457

Cabeke, Gui, Pres. & Chief Exec. Officer--Porcelanite, Inc., Lexington, NC; *Int'l*, pg. 573

Caboni, Giorgio M., Mng. Dir.--John Crane Iberica S.A., Madrid, Spain; *Int'l*, pg. 1339

Cabral, Peter, Farm Mgr.--Maui Fresh Eggs, Makawao, HI; *U.S. Private*, pg. 1132

Cabrera, Carlos, Mng. Dir.--Skandia Portugal Propriedades S.A., Lisbon, Portugal; *Int'l*, pg. 1258

Cabrero, Daniel, Dir.--Aceros Nacionales, Tlanepantla, Mexico; *Int'l*, pg. 66

Cabrey, John, Pres. & Gen. Mgr.--Sequa Chemicals, Inc., Chester, SC; *U.S. Public*, pg. 1459

Cabrol, Yves, Mgr.--Ateliers Sucre Liquide et Conditionnement de Lyon, Lyon, France; *Int'l*, pg. 549

Cacciatore, G., Mng. Dir.--OMRON Electronics N.V./S.A., Groot-Bijgaarden, Belgium; *Int'l*, pg. 1006

Caccini, Gian Paolo, Vice Chm., Pres., Chief Exec. & Chief Oper. Officer--CertainTeed Corporation, Valley Forge, PA; *Int'l*, pg. 1170

Caccini, Gian Paolo, Chm. Bd. & Chief Exec. Officer--Vetrotex CertainTeed Corporation, Wichita Falls, TX; *Int'l*, pg. 1171

Caceres, Oscar, Distr. Mgr.--Colgate-Palmolive (Central America, Inc.), San Salvador, El Salvador; *U.S. Public*, pg. 398

Caceres, Ramon, Pres.--Ideal Dominicana, S.A., Santo Domingo, Dominican Republic; *Int'l*, pg. 628

Cachet, Joel, Rep.--Kredietbank Representative Office (Moscow), Moscow, Russia; *Int'l*, pg. 760

Cadbury, Dominic, Chm. Bd.--The Economist Group Limited., London, United Kingdom; *Int'l*, pg. 1026

Cadden, Thomas W., Sr. V.P. & Gen. Mgr.--Industrial & Retail Packaging Div., Chicago, IL; *U.S. Public*, pg. 1521

Cadden, William P., Pres.--Progressive Northern Insurance Co., Cleveland, OH; *U.S. Public*, pg. 1335

Caddock, James C., Mng. Dir.--Caddock Electronics Europe B.V., Kerkrade, Netherlands; *U.S. Private*, pg. 198

Caddock, John B., Dir.--Applied Sciences Division, Roseburg, OR; *U.S. Private*, pg. 198

Cadelli, Diego, Mgr.--Anixter London, London, Canada; *U.S.* Public, pg. 115

Cadena, Alvaro, Pres. & Chief Oper. Officer--Graham Manufacturing Co., Inc., Batavia, NY; *U.S. Public*, pg. 757

Cadigan, Joseph J., Gen. Mgr.--Skyline Auto Exchange, Fairfield, NJ; *U.S. Public*, pg. 1649

Cadis, Harmon, Pres.--Microsource Corp., Tempe, AZ; *U.S. Public*, pg. 1105

Cado, Lou, Gen. Mgr.--Triangle Machine Product Co., Valley View, OH; *U.S. Private*, pg. 426

Cadonna, M., Chief Oper. Officer--Ritasa Freight Services Pty. Ltd., Jet Park, South Africa; *Int'l*, pg. 14

Cady, Al, Grp. V.P.--TMP Worldwide, Inc., Minneapolis, MN; *U.S. Private*, pg. 1064

Cady, Lyle E., Jr., Pres.--Precision Scientific Inc., Winchester, VA; *U.S. Private*, pg. 601

Caeiro, Leonardo, Mng. Dir.--IDAL(Industrias de Alimentacao, Lda.), Lisbon, Portugal; *U.S. Public*, pg. 807

Caeiro, Leonardo, Mng. Dir.--IDAL-Benavente, Lisbon, Portugal; *U.S. Public*, pg. 807

Caetano. Salvador F., Chm.--Salvador Caetano I.M.V.T., S.A.R.L., Vila Nova de Gaia, Portugal; *Int'l*, pg. 1413

Cafaro, Al, Pres.--A&M Records, Hollywood, CA; *Int'l*, pg. 1052

Cafferata, Patricia A., Pres. & Chief Exec. Officer--Young & Rubicam Chicago, Chicago, IL; *U.S. Private*, pg. 1198

Caffrey, Hugh R., Pres. & Chief Exec. Officer--Hilb, Rogal and Hamilton Company of Atlanta, Inc., Atlanta, GA; *U.S. Public*, pg. 827

Caffrey, Matthew, Pres.--James Howden America Inc., Bloomfield, CT; *Int'l*, pg. 636

Caffyn, Andrew D., Gen. Mgr.--John Crane UK Ltd., Slough, United Kingdom; *Int'l*, pg. 1338

Caflik, Dave, Gen. Mgr.--Denver Auto Auction, Aurora, CO; *U.S. Private*, pg. 282

Cagey, Barbara, V.P.--Dreyfus Retirement Services, New York, NY; *U.S. Public*, pg. 1085

Caggiano, Feliciano, Dir.--Banca d'America e d'Italia S.p.A. (Biella), Biella, Italy; *Int'l*, pg. 403

Caggiano, Michael V., Chm. Bd.--Bank of America-The Sequor Group, New York, NY; *U.S. Public*, pg. 181

Caglieris, Mario, Pres.--Olivetti Synthesis, Massa, Italy; *Int'l*, pg. 1002

Cagnol Hveem, Yvonne, Dir.--Berlitz A/S, Oslo, Norway; *U.S. Public*, pg. 221

Cahill, Ian, Mng. Dir.--LM Ericsson Ltd., Dublin, Ireland; *Int'l*, *pg. 1369*

Cahill, J.A., Dir. & Gen. Mgr.--Hamworthy Compressor Systems Limited, Gloucester, United Kingdom; *Int'l*, pg. 1065

Cahill, Mark, Plant Mgr.--Hershey Pasta Group Winchester, Inc., Winchester, VA; *U.S. Public*, pg. 812

Cailliet, Sue, Sls. Broker--Brooks Resources Sales Corp., Bend, OR; *U.S. Private*, pg. 172

Cain, Ernie, Gen. Mgr.--Surplus Warehouse-Tyler, Tyler, TX; *U.S. Private*, pg. 120

Cain, Keith, Mng. Dir.--Viking Direct Holding Co., Leicester, United Kingdom; *U.S. Public*, pg. 1721

Cain, Paul E., Dr., Pres.-CBI Laboratories, Inc.--Thermolase, San Diego, CA; *U.S. Public*, pg. 1595

Cain, Paul W., Pres.--Mesa Environmental, Fort Worth, TX; *U.S. Public*, pg. 1300

Cain, Richard, Corp. V.P. & Chm. Bd.-West Hudson--Allegiance Healthcare Corp., McGaw Park, IL; *U.S. Public*, pg. 44

Cain, Richard, Chm. Bd. & Corp. V.P.--West Hudson, Inc. (Healthcare Consulting Services), Dallas, TX; *U.S. Public*, *pg. 45*

Cain, Roger C., Pres.--Banner Aircraft International, Inc., South San Francisco, CA; *U.S. Public*, pg. 187

Caine, Cathy, Mng. Dir.--Triumph Releasing Corporation - New York Territory, New York, NY; *Int'l*, pg. 1282

Cainer, Edoardo, Chm.--AGIP (Overseas) Ltd., Saint Helier, United Kingdom; *Int'l*, pg. 428

Cainer, Edoardo, Chm.--AGIP (North Africa & Middle East) Ltd., Saint Helier, United Kingdom; *Int'l*, pg. 428

Caio, Severino, Chief Oper. Officer--Commerciale Finanziaria S.p.A., Milan, Italy; *Int'l*, pg. 481

Caird, Fiona, Gen. Mgr.--Young & Rubicam Mattingly, Retail Group, Auckland, New Zealand; *U.S. Private*, pg. 325

Cairns, Lord, Chm. Bd.--British-American Tobacco (Germany) GmbH, Hamburg, Germany; *Int'l*, pg. 111

Cairns, T.C., Mng. Dir.--P&O Properties International, London, United Kingdom; *Int'l*, pg. 1034

Caithard, Daniel, Chief Oper. Officer--Go Sport, Fresnes, France; *Int'l*, pg. 734

Cakiroglu, Ender, Mng. Dir.--Turk Elektrik Endustrisi A.S., Istanbul, Turkey; *Int'l*, pg. 741

Calamani, Carlo, Chm. Bd.--Crown Cork Company (Italy) S.p.A., Voghera, Italy; *U.S. Public*, pg. 464

Calamati, Mario, Chm. Bd.--Itafinco S.p.A., Milan, Italy; *Int'l*, pg. 138

Calamati, Mario, Chm. Bd.--Finanziaria BTB S.p.A., Trento, Italy; *Int'l*, pg. 138

Calandra, T.M., Pres.--Signatures, Perris, CA; *U.S. Private*, pg. 1035

Calandra, T.M., Pres.--Starcrest of California, Perris, CA; *U.S. Private*, pg. 1035

Calandra, T.M., Pres.--Handsome Rewards, Perris, CA; *U.S.* Private, pg. 1035

Calarco, Vincent A., Pres. & Chief Exec. Officer--Uniroyal Chemical Company, Inc., Middlebury, CT; *U.S. Public*, pg. 460

Calcagni, Robert, Mng. Dir. & Group V.P.--Astron S.A.R.L., Vincennes, France; *U.S. Public*, pg. 411

Calcagni, Robert A., Mng. Dir.--Commercial Intertech S.A., Diekirch, Luxembourg; *U.S. Public*, pg. 411

Calcagno, Carlo, Mng. Dir.--Bobst Italiana SpA, Milan, Italy; *Int'l*, pg. 199

Calcutt, John, Gen. Mgr.--Gene Reed Chevrolet, Charleston, SC; *U.S. Private*, pg. 1095

Caldeira, David, Mgr.--Madeira Offshore, Funchal, Portugal; *Int'l*, pg. 250

Calder, Alex, Mgr.--Anixter Glasgow U.K., Bellshill, United Kingdom; *U.S. Public*, pg. 116

Calder, Clive, Chm. Bd. & Pres.--Zomba Group of Companies, New York, NY; *Int'l*, pg. 1529

Calder, Richard D., Pres.--Banta Digital Group, Menasha, WI; *U.S. Public*, pg. 188

Calderon-Velasquez, Carlos, Chief Oper. Officer--Electrolux S.A., Guatemala, Guatemala; *Int'l*, pg. 442

Calderon, Ramon, Mng. Dir.--Publispana/BDDP, Mexico, Mexico; *Int'l*, pg. 118

Caldwell, Allen, Chief Oper. Officer--Dutch Parking Inc., Elmira, NY; *U.S. Private*, pg. 43

Caldwell, Bruce, Area Dir.--Rorer Pharmaceutical (Singapore) Pte. Ltd., Singapore, Singapore; *Int'l*, pg. 1112

Caldwell, Don, Publisher--Lake City Reporter, Inc., Lake City, FL; *U.S. Public*, pg. 1175

Caldwell, E.C., Pres.--Xerox Custom Systems Division, Mc Lean, VA; *U.S. Public*, pg. 1784

Caldwell, J.W., Pres.--Instrument Division, Stratford, CT; *U.S. Public*, pg. 528

Caldwell, John, Pres.--Swing-N-Slide Corp., Janesville, WI; *U.S. Public*, pg. 1543

Caldwell, Kenneth A., Pres.--Aker Omega Inc. (AE), Houston, TX; *Int'l*, pg. 42

Caldwell, Kim A., V.P. & Gen. Mgr.--Fasson Roll Materials Div., Quakertown, PA; *U.S. Public*, pg. 153

Caldwell, Max, Pres.--NAPCO, Inc., Terryville, CT; *U.S. Public*, pg. 1592

Caldwell, R.W., Chief Oper. Officer--Masterchem Industries, Antonia, MO; *Int'l*, pg. 1501

Caldwell, Roger, Gen. Mgr.--Valmont/ALS, Brenham, TX; *U.S. Public*, pg. 1707

Caldwell, Steven J., Pres.--Ziff Technologies, Medford, MA; *Int'l*, pg. 1276

Calegari, Pier Angelo, Div. Mgr.--SASIB Packaging Italia S.r.l.-Wrapper Division, Vicenza, Italy; *Int'l*, pg. 1194

Caleras, Mats, Mgr.--Sandvik Coromant, Dusseldorf, Germany; *Int'l*, pg. 1186

Calhoun, David, Pres. & Chief Exec. Officer--G.E. Lighting Division, Cleveland, OH; *U.S. Public*, pg. 710

Calhoun, David L., Pres. & Chief Exec. Officer--GE Transportation Systems, Erie, PA; *U.S. Public*, pg. 711

Calhoun, Don, Exec. V.P.--Aloe-Vera of America, Dallas, TX; *U.S. Private*, pg. 418

Calhoun, John W., Pres. & Chief Exec. Officer--NationsBank Tri-Lakes, Forsyth, MO; *U.S. Public*, pg. 1165

Calhoun, Scott, Plant Mgr.--L.B. Foster Company-Niles Plant, Niles, OH; *U.S. Public*, pg. 676

Calhy, Ronald B., Chm., Pres. & Chief Exec. Officer--United HealthCare Insurance Company, Hartford, CT; *U.S. Public*, pg. 1678

Caliari, Roberto, Pres.-Reinforcement Div.--Vetrotex France, Chambery, France; *Int'l*, pg. 1177

Caliari, Roberto, Pres.--Vetrotex International, Chambery, France; *Int'l*, pg. 1177

Caligari, Pietro, Mgr.--Sandvik Coromant, Milan, Italy; *Int'l*, pg. 1186

Calimbahin, Ramon C., Mng. Dir.--First Brands Philippines, Manila, Philippines; *U.S. Public*, pg. 627

Calisina, William A., V.P. & Gen. Mgr.--Bissell Ltd., Niagara Falls, Canada; *U.S. Private*, pg. 145

Calkins, Craig, Div. Mgr.--Titan Homes Div., Berthoud, CO; *U.S. Public*, pg. 332

Calkins, Kim, Pres.--Animal Fair, Minneapolis, MN; *U.S. Private*, pg. 885

Calkins, W. C., Div. Pres.--Winn-Dixie, Inc.-Jacksonville Div., Jacksonville, FL; *U.S. Public*, pg. 1771

Call, Bill, Reg. Mgr.--Air Conditioning Co, Inc, Concord, CA; *U.S. Private*, pg. 28

Call, Harry M., Pres. & Chief Oper. Officer--Goody's Family Clothing, Inc., Knoxville, TN; *U.S. Public*, pg. 753

Call, Ralph, Pres. & Chief Exec. Officer--WINCO, Le Center, MN; *U.S. Private*, pg. 350

Call, Robert V., Jr., Chm. Bd.--Curtice Burns Foods, Rochester, NY; *U.S. Private*, pg. 887

Call, Scott, Plant Mgr.--Sentinel Consumer Products, Inc., Clearfield, UT; *U.S. Private*, pg. 984

Calladine, David G., Mng. Dir.--ITT Flygt Ltd., Colwich, United Kingdom; *U.S. Public*, pg. 860

Callaghan, Iain M., Mng. Dir.--John Menzies Wholesale, Edinburgh, United Kingdom; *Int'l*, pg. 707

Callaghan, James, Country Mgr.--Network Systems Nederland B.V., Weesp, Netherlands; *U.S. Public*, pg. 1523

Callahan-Guion, Kathleen, Pres. & Chief Oper. Officer--E-Z Serve Convenience Stores, Inc., Houston, TX; *U.S. Public*, pg. 540
Callahan-Guion, Kathleen, Gen. Mgr.--Ito-Yokado Capitol Division, Alexandria, VA; *Int'l*, pg. 694
Callahan, Cecil, Gen. Mgr.--SMI Rebar North Carolina, Gastonia, NC; *U.S. Public*, pg. 412
Callahan, Charles E., Pres.--Policy Management Systems Life, Inc., Waco, TX; *U.S. Public*, pg. 1314
Callahan, Dennis, Pres. & Chief Exec. Officer--Steinbach Stores, Inc., Detroit, MI; *U.S. Public*, pg. 461
Callahan, James, Pres.--CIBA-Vision Corporation, Duluth, GA; *Int'l*, pg. 973
Callahan, James E., Gen. Mgr.--Bank of Boston, Santiago, Chile; *U.S. Public*, pg. 184
Callahan, James M., Pres.--Vistakon Johnson & Johnson Vision Products, Inc., Jacksonville, FL; *U.S. Public*, pg. 929
Callahan, Michael, Mng. Dir.--Sparks Family Hospital, Sparks, NV; *U.S. Public*, pg. 1697
Callahan, Robert F., Pres.--ABC/Watermark, Inc., Los Angeles, CA; *U.S. Public*, pg. 511
Callan, Ron, V.P. & Gen. Mgr.--Baldwin Web Controls, Lombard, IL; *U.S. Public*, pg. 170
Callander, Robert, Pres.--United Leasing Company, Louisville, KY; *U.S. Private*, pg. 741
Callaway, Edward C., Pres.--Crested Butte Marriott Resort, Crested Butte, CO; *U.S. Private*, pg. 289
Callaway, Roy, Publr.--The Garden Island, Lihue, HI; *U.S. Public*, pg. 1343
Callejo, Luis Miguel Jarillo, Mng. Dir.--Swiss Life (Espana), Madrid, Spain; *Int'l*, pg. 1332
Callen, Christopher J., Pres.--Elan Title Services, Inc., Milwaukee, WI; *U.S. Public*, pg. 643
Callen, Christopher J., Pres.--Firstar Real Estate Services, Inc., Milwaukee, WI; *U.S. Public*, pg. 643
Callen, Dawn, Admin.--Hacienda de Salud - Bloomfield, Bloomfield, NM; *U.S. Public*, pg. 838
Callens, Philippe, Mng. Dir.--FCB Brussels, Brussels, Belgium; *U.S. Private*, pg. 389
Calleri, Giampiero, Chm. Bd.--Fiscambi Factoring S.p.A., Milan, Italy; *Int'l*, pg. 138
Callert, Karl-Ake, Chief Oper. Officer--Pharmacia & Upjohn AS, Copenhagen, Denmark; *Int'l*, pg. 1049
Calley, John, Pres. & Chief Oper. Officer--Sony Pictures Entertainment, Culver City, CA; *Int'l*, pg. 1281
Callicott, James, Mgr.-Property & Casualty Claims--Willis Corroon Administrative Services Corporation, Jackson, MS; *Int'l*, pg. 1504
Callihan, William, Pres.--PNC Realty Co., Ohio, Cincinnati, OH; *U.S. Public*, pg. 1243
Callin, Bjoern M., Mng. Dir.--Grindex AB, Handen, Sweden; *U.S. Public*, pg. 860
Callis, Brian L., Mng. Dir.--Pacific Scientific, Ltd., Maidenhead, United Kingdom; *U.S. Public*, pg. 1250
Calliss, Brian L., Mng. Dir.--Pacific Scientific Ltd., Bourne, United Kingdom; *U.S. Public*, pg. 1250
Callon, John S., Pres.--Wilcox Energy Company, Natchez, MS; *U.S. Public*, pg. 295
Calloway, Craig J., Pres.--Mathews Readymix, Inc., Gridley, CA; *U.S. Public*, pg. 323
Calloway, Steve, Pres.--Six Flags Over Texas, Arlington, TX; *U.S. Public*, pg. 1612
Calmeyer, Roger, Gen. Mgr.--Colgate-Palmolive (E. Africa) Ltd., Nairobi, Kenya; *U.S. Public*, pg. 398
Calo, L. Franco, Mng. Dir.--Bose S.P.A., Rome, Italy; *U.S. Private*, pg. 161
Calton, Richard, Reg. Mng. Dir.--Willis Corroon South Limited, Reading, United Kingdom; *Int'l*, pg. 1503
Caluwaerts, Marc, Mng. Dir.--Bekaert-Stanwick N.V., Kortrijk, Belgium; *Int'l*, pg. 183
Calvani, Margaret, Asst. Treas. & Branch Mgr.--Valley National Bank, Landing, NJ; *U.S. Public*, pg. 1706
Calverley, D.M., Deputy Chm. & Mng. Dir.--Trafalgar House Property Ltd., London, United Kingdom; *Int'l*, pg. 773
Calverley, D.M., Chm. Bd.--Ideal Homes Holdings Plc, Woking, United Kingdom; *Int'l*, pg. 773
Calvert, Dave, V.P.-Glass Opers.--Hehr Glass Company Inc., Pomona, CA; *U.S. Private*, pg. 519
Calvert, Horace A., Pres.--Exsol, Inc., Houston, TX; *U.S. Public*, pg. 1454
Calvert, Michael, Pres.--Brown-Strauss Steel, Aurora, CO; *U.S. Private*, pg. 153
Calvet, Gerard, Chief Oper. Officer--Hospal S.A., Lyon, France; *Int'l*, pg. 668
Calvetti, Alfred, V.P. & Gen. Mgr.--Parlex Laminated Cable, Salem, NH; *U.S. Public*, pg. 1264
Calvo, Luis, Gen. Mgr.--Tektronix Espanola S.A.-Madrid, Madrid, Spain; *U.S. Public*, pg. 1567
Calzado, Eric, Div. Mgr.--Taca International Airlines, S.A., Miami, FL; *Int'l*, pg. 1346
Calzolari, Attilio, Dir.--Recordati Pharmaceutical Chemicals Division:, Milan, Italy; *Int'l*, pg. 1090
Camacho, Hector, Gen. Mgr.--Wichita Raytheon Maintenance Learning Center, Wichita, KS; *U.S. Public*, pg. 219
Camara, Sergio Ribas, Mgr.--Banco do Brasil S.A.-Austria, Vienna, Austria; *Int'l*, pg. 142
Camarco, Kenneth, Gen. Mgr.-Apex Opers.--Apex Operation, Dayton, OH; *U.S. Public*, pg. 444
Camardo, Michael F., Pres.--Martin Marietta Services Group, Cherry Hill, NJ; *U.S. Public*, pg. 1007
Camargo, A.N., Mng. Dir.--Morganite Isolantes Termicos Limitada, Rio de Janeiro, Brazil; *Int'l*, pg. 895
Camargo, Amador, Chm.-Y&R Group--Young & Rubicam Brazil, Sao Paulo, Brazil; *U.S. Private*, pg. 1200
Cambier, Patrick, Gen. Mgr.--Mold-Tech S.a.r.L., Pringy, France; *U.S. Public*, pg. 1507
Camera, F.P., Chief Oper. Officer--Simkins New Haven Board, New Haven, CT; *U.S. Private*, pg. 1000
Camerer, R. A., Chief Oper. Officer--BHF-Bank Representative Office, Rosebank, South Africa; *Int'l*, pg. 120
Cameron, Alan, Pres.--Epic Technical Group, Auburn Hills, MI; *U.S. Public*, pg. 560
Cameron, Chris, Gen. Mgr.--Young & Rubicam, Auckland, New Zealand; *U.S. Private*, pg. 1198
Cameron, Craig, Pres.--N.C. Cameron & Sons, Ltd., Mississauga, Canada; *U.S. Public*, pg. 1508
Cameron, D., Pres.--Capitol Records-EMI of Canada Ltd., Mississauga, Canada; *Int'l*, pg. 427
Cameron, Danny H., Pres.--National City Community Development Corp., Cleveland, OH; *U.S. Public*, pg. 1154
Cameron, Donald, Pres.--Lawtons Drug Stores Limited, Dartmouth, Canada; *Int'l*, pg. 454
Cameron, John, Chief Oper. Officer--Jahn Foundry Corp., Springfield, MA; *U.S. Public*, pg. 142
Cameron, John, Gen. Mgr.--Octel Messaging Division, Willowdale, Canada; *U.S. Public*, pg. 1018
Caminarata, Tom, Creative Dir.--J.W. Messner, Inc., Oakland, CA; *U.S. Private*, pg. 734
Cammins, James J., V.P. & Gen. Mgr.--Data Industrial Corporation, Pocasset, MA; *U.S. Public*, pg. 487
Camora, Mark, Pres.--Commercial Union Capital Corporation, New York, NY; *Int'l*, pg. 308
Camp, Glen B., Pres.--Mono Pumps Ltd., Manchester, United Kingdom; *U.S. Public*, pg. 529
Camp, H.D., Mng. Dir.--Deminex Egypt, Cairo, Egypt; *Int'l*, pg. 1461
Camp, J., Pres.--Penny & Giles Drives Technology Inc., Arcadia, CA; *Int'l*, pg. 208
Camp, Rodney E., Mgr.--Cleveland County Telephone Company, Inc., Rison, AR; *U.S. Public*, pg. 1571
Camp, William T., Pres.--CFC Investment Corp., Fairfield, OH; *U.S. Public*, pg. 368
Campbell, Ava, Mgr.--Downey Savings & Loan Association, F.A., Lancaster, CA; *U.S. Public*, pg. 527
Campbell, Bill, Mgr.-Opers.--Titan Tire Corporation, Des Moines, IA; *U.S. Public*, pg. 1618
Campbell, Dave, Gen. Mgr.--Whitmire Micro-Gen Research Laboratories Incorporated, San Antonio, TX; *U.S. Private*, pg. 592
Campbell, David, Pres. & Chief Exec. Officer--Master Lock Company, Milwaukee, WI; *U.S. Public*, pg. 675
Campbell, David D., Pres.--Milwaukee Lock Company, Milwaukee, WI; *U.S. Public*, pg. 675
Campbell, David G., Pres.--Dawn Distributors, Scarborough, Canada; *U.S. Public*, pg. 1168
Campbell, Donald W., V.P.--Food Service & Lodging Products Div., Cincinnati, OH; *U.S. Public*, pg. 1330
Campbell, Edward, Div. Mgr.--Connecticut Driveshaft, West Springfield, MA; *U.S. Private*, pg. 263
Campbell, Edward J., Pres.--Asheville Industries, Inc., Arden, NC; *U.S. Public*, pg. 1180
Campbell, Edward J., Chm. Bd.--Newport News Industrial Corp., Newport News, VA; *U.S. Public*, pg. 1180
Campbell, Edward J., Pres.--Newport News Reactor Services, Inc., Springfield, PA; *U.S. Public*, pg. 1180
Campbell, Edward J., Pres.--Newport News Technical Services, Inc. (Wisconsin), Brookfield, WI; *U.S. Public*, pg. 1180
Campbell, Edward P., Pres. & Chief Oper. Officer--Nordson Corporation, Amherst, OH; *U.S. Public*, pg. 1188
Campbell, Gary, Div. Pres.--Coz Plastics Inc., Northbridge, MA; *U.S. Private*, pg. 827
Campbell, George M., Pres. & Chief Exec. Officer--Regions Bank/North Louisiana, Monroe, LA; *U.S. Public*, pg. 1372
Campbell, Gerry, Branch Dir.--N.G. Bailey & Co. Ltd.-Glasgow Branch, Glasgow, United Kingdom; *Int'l*, pg. 132
Campbell, Gordon W., Pres.--R.P. Scherer K.K., Tokyo, Japan; *U.S. Public*, pg. 1438
Campbell, Harold L., Chm., Pres. & Chief Exec. Officer--Florence Deposit Bank, Florence, KY; *U.S. Public*, pg. 173
Campbell, Howard F., Pres.--Emco Distribution, Mississauga, Canada; *Int'l*, pg. 453
Campbell, Hugh, Gen. Mgr.--New Zealand Milk Products (Pacific) Ltd., Auckland, New Zealand; *Int'l*, pg. 923
Campbell, Ian, Fin. Controller--AEP Industries (NZ) Ltd., Panmure, New Zealand; *U.S. Public*, pg. 5
Campbell, Ian, Chief Exec. Officer--Lambert Smith Hampton, London, United Kingdom; *Int'l*, pg. 797
Campbell, J.H.S., Pres. & Chief Exec. Officer--First Brands (Canada) Corp., Scarborough, Canada; *U.S. Public*, pg. 627
Campbell, J.S., Pres.--IPC Resistors Inc., Mississauga, Canada; *Int'l*, pg. 590
Campbell, Jack, Chief Exec. Officer--Automated Label Systems, Inc., Twinsburg, OH; *U.S. Public*, pg. 865
Campbell, Jack, Pres.--Minigrip Zip-Pak, Orangeburg, NY; *U.S. Public*, pg. 867
Campbell, James, Chm. Bd., Pres. & Chief Exec. Officer--First Community Bank of Saltville, Saltville, VA; *U.S. Public*, pg. 1039
Campbell, James, Pres.--Trans Financial Bank, N.A., Bowling Green, KY; *U.S. Public*, pg. 1628
Campbell, James E., V.P. & Gen. Mgr.--Vulcraft Div., Fort Payne, AL; *U.S. Public*, pg. 1206
Campbell, James P., Sr. V.P.--Chancellor Fleet Corporation, Boston, MA; *U.S. Public*, pg. 335
Campbell, James R., Pres. & Chief Exec. Officer--Norwest Bank Minnesota N.A., Minneapolis, MN; *U.S. Public*, pg. 1202
Campbell, James R., Pres.--Norwest Bank Faribault, N.A., Faribault, MN; *U.S. Public*, pg. 1202
Campbell, Joel, Pres.--Cooper Automotive Division, Chesterfield, MO; *U.S. Public*, pg. 443
Campbell, Joel M., V.P.-Opers.--Wagner Lighting Products, Chesterfield, MO; *U.S. Public*, pg. 442
Campbell, John, Pres.--Car Brite, Inc., Indianapolis, IN; *U.S. Private*, pg. 352
Campbell, John A., Pres. & Chief Exec. Officer--The Pacific Lumber Company, Scotia, CA; *U.S. Public*, pg. 1062
Campbell, Jon R., Pres. & Chief Exec. Officer--Norwest Bank Arizona, N.A., Phoenix, AZ; *U.S. Public*, pg. 1202
Campbell, Karen, Mng. Dir.--NYT Event/Sports Marketing, Trumbull, CT; *U.S. Public*, pg. 1174
Campbell, Ken, Pres.--Sunwest Bank of Santa Fe, Santa Fe, NM; *U.S. Public*, pg. 1165
Campbell, M. Ralph, Chm. Bd.--Montour Bank, Danville, PA; *U.S. Public*, pg. 1222
Campbell, Michael, Pres.--Wolf-Campbell Public Relations, Toronto, Canada; *U.S. Private*, pg. 1186
Campbell, Neil, Pres.--Bio Medic Data Systems, Seaford, DE; *U.S. Private*, pg. 641
Campbell, P.L., Mng. Dir.--Metal Box South Africa Limited, Johannesburg, South Africa; *Int'l*, pg. 267
Campbell, Paul, V.P. & Gen. Mgr.--Alumax of South Carolina Mt. Holly, Mount Holly, SC; *U.S. Public*, pg. 60
Campbell, Peter J., Pres. & Chief Oper. Officer--Connaught Laboratories Limited, Willowdale, Canada; *Int'l*, pg. 1109
Campbell, Phyllis, Chm. & Chief Exec. Officer--U.S. Bank of Washington N.A., Seattle, WA; *U.S. Public*, pg. 1681
Campbell, R. Bruce, Mgr.--Scott & Stringfellow, Inc., Lexington, VA; *U.S. Public*, pg. 1446
Campbell, R. Bruce, Mgr.--Scott & Stringfellow, Inc., Staunton, VA; *U.S. Public*, pg. 1446
Campbell, R.H., Chief Oper. Officer--Babcock Plant Leasing Ltd., London, United Kingdom; *Int'l*, pg. 472
Campbell, Richard, Chief Oper. Officer--Tennessee Packaging, Sweetwater, TN; *U.S. Private*, pg. 177
Campbell, Richard, Pres.--BP Exploration (Alaska) Inc., Anchorage, AK; *Int'l*, pg. 220
Campbell, Richard A., Pres.--Norwalk Furniture Corporation of Tennessee, Cookeville, TN; *U.S. Private*, pg. 808
Campbell, Robyn, Sr. V.P. & Mng. Dir.--Western International Media Corporation, Minneapolis, MN; *U.S. Private*, pg. 1167
Campbell, Roland J., Chief Exec. Officer--BASO Precision Optics, Tai-chung, Taiwan; *U.S. Public*, pg. 551
Campbell, T., Plant Mgr.--Square D Company, Columbia, SC; *Int'l*, pg. 1208
Campbell, Thomas R., Pres.--Roadtec, Inc., Chattanooga, TN; *U.S. Public*, pg. 141
Campbell, Thomas R., Pres.--AC Products, Inc., Placentia, CA; *U.S. Public*, pg. 1346
Campbell, W. Patrick, Pres.--Columbia Tri-Star Home Video, Burbank, CA; *Int'l*, pg. 1282
Campbell, William I., Chm. Bd.--Philip Morris U.S.A., New York, NY; *U.S. Public*, pg. 1289
Camper, David, Plant Superintendant--General Shale Products Corp., Atlanta, GA; *Int'l*, pg. 844
Campino, Pedro B., Pres.--Compania Minera Cerro Colorado Limitada, Santiago, Chile; *Int'l*, pg. 1118
Campion, Annelies, Reg. Dir.--Excerpta Medica Asia Limited-Hong Kong, Chai Wan, Hong Kong; *Int'l*, pg. 1099
Campo, Joseph, Gen. Mgr.--All-American Co., San Antonio, TX; *U.S. Public*, pg. 1389
Campolong, Joseph, Pres.--Pall Aero Power, Pinellas Park, FL; *U.S. Public*, pg. 1253
Campolong, Joseph, Pres.--Pall Safety Atmospheres, Inc., Pinellas Park, FL; *U.S. Public*, pg. 1254
Campos, Andrade, Gen. Mgr.--Caixa Geral de Depositos (France), Paris, France; *Int'l*, pg. 251
Campos, Antonio, Pres.--Banco Central Canada, Toronto, Canada; *Int'l*, pg. 140
Campos, Luis, Pres.--House of Fuller, S.A. de C.V., Mexico, Mexico; *U.S. Public*, pg. 1434
Campos, Rafael del Riego, Pres.--SODICAMAN - Sociedad Para el Desarrollo Industrial de Castilla-La Mancha, S.A., Guadalajara, Spain; *Int'l*, pg. 1225
Camps, Joan, Mgr.--Autologic Information International, Inc., Barcelona, Spain; *U.S. Public*, pg. 1724
Camstra, William A., Area Dir.-Kellogg Latin America--Kellogg Company Argentina S.A.C.I.F., Buenos Aires, Argentina; *U.S. Public*, pg. 947
Camstra, William A., Gen. Mgr.-Latin America Opers.--Kellogg de Colombia S.A., Bogota, Colombia; *U.S. Public*, pg. 947
Camunas, D. Julio, Pres.--Compania Gestora de Servicio Mensatel, S.A., Madrid, Spain; *Int'l*, pg. 1372
Camus, Maria Isabel, Mng. Dir.--Codelco-France S.A.R.L., Paris, France; *Int'l*, pg. 303
Canada, Richard, V.P. & Gen. Mgr.--Webb Forging, Carlisle, SC; *U.S. Private*, pg. 1156
Canada, Ronald G., Chief Oper. Officer--CSI Services, Knoxville, TN; *U.S. Public*, pg. 573
Canadas, Francisco Vano, Gen. Mgr.--Banco Santander, Milan, Italy; *Int'l*, pg. 144
Canario, Louis, V.P.--Dunavant Commodity Corp., New York, NY; *U.S. Private*, pg. 346
Canas, R.G., Gen. Mgr.--Marquinarias Ingersoll-Rand de Colombia S.A., Bogota, Colombia; *U.S. Public*, pg. 877
Canastra, Joseph, Gen. Mgr.--Edgcomb Metals of New England, Nashua, NH; *Int'l*, pg. 572
Canatella, Charles, Opers. Superintendent--Koppel Steel-Baytown, Baytown, TX; *U.S. Public*, pg. 1147
Canavesi, Maurizio, Mgr.--Tonka Italia S.p.A., Milan, Italy; *U.S. Public*, pg. 798
Canback, Goran, Chief Oper. Officer--Molnlycke AB Research, Goteborg, Sweden; *Int'l*, pg. 1326
Cancarini, Giovanni, Chief Oper. Officer--Flymo S.r.l., Brescia, Italy; *Int'l*, pg. 442
Cancellieri, Jorge J., Gen. Mgr.--SylvaPen Distribuidora S.A.C.I.Y.F., Buenos Aires, Argentina; *U.S. Public*, pg. 745
Candela, John A., Pres. & Chief Exec. Officer--The First National Bank of St. Mary's, Leonardtown, MD; *U.S. Public*, pg. 1089
Candell, John, Gen. Mgr.--S.C. Johnson, Camberley, United Kingdom; *U.S. Private*, pg. 593
Candell, Peter, Gen. Mgr.-Opers.--Leaf Sweden, Gavle, Sweden; *Int'l*, pg. 638
Canfield, Mark, Gen. Mgr.--Contractor Equipment Supply Company (CESCO), Boise, ID; *U.S. Private*, pg. 673

Cankes, Robert M., V.P. & Gen. Mgr.--D.V.F. Inc., New York, NY; *U.S. Private*, pg. 690
Cannan, Robert W., Gen. Mgr.--Schlegel Building Products Div., Rochester, NY; *Int'l*, pg. 128
Cannan, William, Pres.--Casco-Northern Corporation, Portland, ME; *U.S. Public*, pg. 184
Cannata, Mike, Sr. V.P.--ADI Mexico, Colonia, Mexico; *U.S. Public*, pg. 1307
Cannata, Mike, Sr. V.P.--ADI Puerto Rico, San Juan, PR; *U.S. Public*, pg. 1307
Cannava, Donald J., Pres.--Bowne of Boston, Inc., Boston, MA; *U.S. Public*, pg. 248
Canning, John, Pres.--First Capital Corp. of Chicago, Chicago, IL; *U.S. Public*, pg. 628
Canning, John, Pres.--First Chicago Investment Corp., Chicago, IL; *U.S. Public*, pg. 628
Canning, Kathy, Mgr.--Kvaerner Fish Process, Seattle, Seattle, WA; *Int'l*, pg. 770
Canning, Simon, Pres. & Chief Oper. Officer--SBC Warburg Dillon Read, Stamford, CT; *Int'l*, pg. 1329
Canning, Simon, Pres. & Chief Exec. Officer--SBC Warburg Dillon Read Inc., Boston, MA; *Int'l*, pg. 1329
Canning, Simon, Pres. & Chief Exec. Officer--SBC Warburg Dillon Read Inc., New York, NY; *Int'l*, pg. 1329
Cannizzo, Michael, Sr. V.P.-Admin.--NVR Homes, Inc., Gaithersburg, MD; *U.S. Public*, pg. 1148
Cannon, Douglas, Pres.--ITT Controls & Instruments Division, Midland Park, NJ; *U.S. Public*, pg. 860
Cannon, Francis, Pres.--DeVRY Institute of Technology, Irving, TX; *U.S. Public*, pg. 504
Cannon, John R., Exec. V.P.--DataMate Products Group, Chicago, IL; *U.S. Public*, pg. 1101
Cannon, Kent, Pres.--Beneficial Life Insurance, Salt Lake City, UT; *U.S. Private*, pg. 327
Cannon, Michael C., V.P.--Sulzer (UK) Holdings Limited, Farnborough, United Kingdom; *Int'l*, pg. 1307
Cannon, Michael J., V.P.-Grocery--Grocery Division, Lakeville, MN; *U.S. Public*, pg. 766
Cannon, R.E., Pres.--Buckeye Cellulose Corp., Memphis, TN; *U.S. Public*, pg. 1331
Cannon, R.E., Pres.--The Buckeye Oilseed Products Co., Cincinnati, OH; *U.S. Public*, pg. 1331
Cannon, Russell, Publr.--The Daily Journal, Park Hills, MO; *U.S. Public*, pg. 1343
Cannova, Carl S., Pres.--Sysco Food Services of West Coast Florida, Inc., Palmetto, FL; *U.S. Public*, pg. 1552
Canny, Brent, Mgr.-Opers.--Titan Wheel, Greenwood, SC; *U.S. Public*, pg. 1618
Cano, Francisco, Pres.--Charmilles Technologies Iberica S.A., Madrid, Spain; *Int'l*, pg. 489
Cantalupo, James R., Pres.--McDonald's Intl., Oak Brook, IL; *U.S. Public*, pg. 1069
Cantile, Jack, Pres.--Duplex Envelope Co., Richmond, VA; *U.S. Public*, pg. 903
Canto, Ataide Medeiros, Mgr.--Porto Alegre Branch, Porto Alegre, Brazil; *Int'l*, pg. 139
Cantone, Tom, Service Mgr.--Philips Consumer Electronics, Cornwells Heights, PA; *Int'l*, pg. 1055
Cantor, Paul, Chm. & Chief Exec. Officer--National Trust Company, Stratford, Canada; *Int'l*, pg. 910
Cantrall, Edward, Ph.D., V.P. & Gen. Mgr.--PE Molecular Informatics, Santa Fe, NM; *U.S. Public*, pg. 1279
Cantrell, Jerry, Plant Superintendant--General Shale Products Corp.-Smithville Concrete Div., Smithville, TN; *Int'l*, pg. 844
Cantrell, Wesley, Pres. & Chief Exec. Officer--Lanier Worldwide Inc., Atlanta, GA; *U.S. Public*, pg. 791
Cantrell, William, Pres.--Peoples Gas System, Inc., Tampa, FL; *U.S. Public*, pg. 1565
Cantu, Carlos, Chief Exec. Officer--American Home Shield Corporation, Memphis, TN; *U.S. Public*, pg. 1461
Cantwell, Jim N., Pres.--SCANA Petroleum Resources, Inc., Houston, TX; *U.S. Public*, pg. 1436
Canull, William R., V.P. & Oper. Mgr.--First Finance Mortgage Company, Fairfield, OH; *U.S. Public*, pg. 633
Canuto, Jose Leonardo, Tech. Dir.--BB Corretora de Seguros e Administradora de Bens S.A., Brasilia, Brazil; *Int'l*, pg. 141
Canzone, Pete, Chm. Bd.--Brylane L.P., New York, NY; *U.S. Public*, pg. 996
Cao, Cuoi V., V.P.--Jefferies & Company, Inc., Los Angeles, CA; *U.S. Public*, pg. 925
Cao, S., Chm.--Saipem International A.G., Zurich, Switzerland; *Int'l*, pg. 429
Caouette, John B., Chm. Bd. & Chief Exec. Officer--Capital Markets Assurance Corporation, New York, NY; *U.S. Public*, pg. 1023
Capaldini, Mark, Pres. & Chief Exec. Officer--Congressional Information Service (CIS), Bethesda, MD; *Int'l*, pg. 1096
Capallupo, Frank, V.P. & Gen. Mgr.--Lawson Products, Inc., Reno, NV; *U.S. Public*, pg. 980
Capell, Harry, V.P.-Opers.--Johnson & Johnson Worldwide Absorbent Products & Materials Research, Skillman, NJ; *U.S. Public*, pg. 928
Capell, Peter, Pres.--Snacks Unlimited Division, Minneapolis, MN; *U.S. Public*, pg. 718
Capelmann, James J., V.P.-Opers.--International Power Machines Corporation, Garland, TX; *Int'l*, pg. 126
Capeloto, Robert, Office Mgr.--Korn/Ferry International, Seattle, WA; *U.S. Private*, pg. 633
Capitanno, Tommaso, Chief Exec. Officer--Crediop Overseas Bank Ltd., Georgetown, Cayman Islands; *Int'l*, pg. 341
Caplan, Joe, Chief Oper. Officer--Hampco Apparel, Inc., Kinston, NC; *U.S. Public*, pg. 779
Caplan, Jon, Pres.--Laredo Boot Co., Nashville, TN; *U.S. Public*, pg. 728
Caplan, Jon, Pres.--Stride Rite Children's Group-Wholesale Div., Lexington, MA; *U.S. Public*, pg. 1525
Caplea, George C., Pres. & Chief Exec. Officer--Trelleborg YSH, Inc., South Haven, MI; *Int'l*, pg. 1422
Capone, John T., Gen. Mgr.--Martin Marietta Stategic Systems, Blue Bell, PA; *U.S. Public*, pg. 1007
Caponecchi, August J., Pres.--Tactair Fluid Controls Corp., Liverpool, NY; *U.S. Private*, pg. 1196
Caporella, R. N., Pres.--Burnup & Sims TelCom, Inc., West Palm Beach, FL; *U.S. Public*, pg. 1056
Caporella, Robert N., Pres.--Fitton & Pittman, Inc., Columbia, SC; *U.S. Public*, pg. 1056
Capp, Ray, Pres.--Ingram Merchandising Service Inc., La Vergne, TN; *U.S. Private*, pg. 563
Capp, W.F., V.P. & Gen. Mgr.--Centrifugal Air Compressor Division, Mayfield, KY; *U.S. Public*, pg. 876
Cappelletti, A., Gen. Mgr.--MSA Italiana S.p.A., Rozzano, Italy; *U.S. Public*, pg. 1115
Cappiello, Tony, Chief Fin. Officer--Waterford Crystal, Inc., Wall, NJ; *Int'l*, pg. 1487
Capps, Colin, Chief Exec. Officer--MPL Pumps Ltd, Feltham, United Kingdom; *Int'l*, pg. 1380
Capps, E. L., V.P.--Tenneco Norge, Inc., Houston, TX; *U.S. Public*, pg. 1578
Capps, E.L., Pres.--Eastern Insurance Company Ltd., Hamilton, Bermuda; *U.S. Public*, pg. 1579
Cappy, Joseph E., Chm.--Pentastar Transportation Corp., Tulsa, OK; *U.S. Public*, pg. 354
Capra, N.J., Gen. Mgr.--Senior Engineering Co.-Joplin, Joplin, MO; *Int'l*, pg. 1222
Caprio, A. Arthur, Pres.--Sigma Diagnostics Div., Saint Louis, MO; *U.S. Public*, pg. 1472
Caprioli, G., Gen. Mgr.--La Previdente S.p.A., Milan, Italy; *Int'l*, pg. 784
Capron, Hal, V.P. & Gen. Mgr.--KOKI-TV, Tulsa, OK; *U.S. Public*, pg. 384
Capron, John, Distr. Mgr.--Browning-Ferris Industries of New York, Inc., Latham, NY; *U.S. Public*, pg. 264
Capron, Wendy, Gen. Mgr.--Coluson Technologies, Billings, MT; *U.S. Public*, pg. 1523
Capuano, Ken, Chief Officer--Novo Nordisk Pharmaceuticals, Inc., Princeton, NJ; *Int'l*, pg. 987
Caputo, Anthony, Pres.--Spar Aviation Services, Mississauga, Canada; *Int'l*, pg. 1288
Caraballo, Malcolm J., Pres.--Wireless Products Group, Palo Alto, CA; *U.S. Public*, pg. 1745
Caravaggi, Roberto, Pres.--Ansaldo Componenti srl, Genoa, Italy; *Int'l*, pg. 653
Caravia, Manuel, Pres.--Komfort Corporation, Milwaukie, OR; *U.S. Public*, pg. 1602
Carbonari, Bruce A., Chm. & Chief Exec. Officer--Moen Incorporated, North Olmsted, OH; *U.S. Public*, pg. 675
Carbonell, Robert J., Pres. & Chief Exec. Officer--Tetley USA Inc., Shelton, CT; *Int'l*, pg. 1377
Carboni, Daniel, Gen. Mgr.--EIS Brake Parts Div., Berlin, CT; *U.S. Public*, pg. 1503
Carboni, Gianmario, Gen. Mgr.--Gillette France, S.A., Levallois-Perret, France; *U.S. Public*, pg. 744
Carbonnier, Jean Claude, Pres.--Zimmer S.A., Vitry-sur-Seine, France; *U.S. Public*, pg. 257
Carbonnieres, Gerard, Co-Mgr.--Unicom, Nantes, France; *Int'l*, pg. 601
Carcelle, Yves, Mng. Dir.--Louis Vuitton Malletier, Paris, France; *Int'l*, pg. 781
Carcieri, Donald, Pres.--Cookson America Inc., Providence, RI; *Int'l*, pg. 328
Card, Wesley R., Pres.--Jones Investment Co., Inc., Wilmington, DE; *U.S. Public*, pg. 933
Card, Wesley R., Pres.--Jones Holding Corporation, Wilmington, DE; *U.S. Public*, pg. 933
Cardenas, Francisco, Pres.--Leo Burnett S.A. de C.V., Mexico, Mexico; *U.S. Private*, pg. 185
Cardenas, S., Mgr.--Daher Golden Eagle - Laredo, Laredo, TX; *U.S. Public*, pg. 749
Carderas, Rafael, Pres.--Carvel Print Grupo Serigraph, Queretaro, Mexico; *U.S. Private*, pg. 985
Cardillo, Harry M., Pres.--Habisat Globe Inc., Buffalo, NY; *Int'l*, pg. 585
Cardillo, Michael J., Pres.--U.S. Healthcare (New York), Uniondale, NY; *U.S. Public*, pg. 26
Cardillo, Michael J., Pres.--U.S. Healthcare, Inc. (Connecticut), Middletown, CT; *U.S. Public*, pg. 26
Cardillo, Michael J., Pres.--U.S. Healthcare, Inc. (Massachusetts), Burlington, MA; *U.S. Public*, pg. 26
Cardillo, Michael J., Pres.--U.S. Health Insurance Company, Blue Bell, PA; *U.S. Public*, pg. 26
Cardillo, Michael J., Pres. & Sec.--United States Physicians Care Systems, Inc., Blue Bell, PA; *U.S. Public*, pg. 27
Cardillo, Michael J., Pres.--U.S. Mental Health Systems, Inc., Blue Bell, PA; *U.S. Public*, pg. 27
Cardillo, Michael J., Pres.--U.S. Healthcare of New Hampshire, Inc., Burlington, MA; *U.S. Public*, pg. 27
Cardin, R. Larry, Pres. & Chief Exec. Officer--Regions Bank/Columbus, Columbus, GA; *U.S. Public*, pg. 1372
Cardin, R. Larry, Jr., Pres. & Chief Exec. Officer--Regions Bank/Phenix City, Phenix City, AL; *U.S. Public*, pg. 1372
Cardinal, Claus, Pres. & Chief Exec. Officer--Jefferson Insurance Company of New York, Jersey City, NJ; *Int'l*, pg. 59
Cardinal, F.A., Gen. Mgr.--Turner Construction Company, Orlando, FL; *U.S. Public*, pg. 1645
Cardo, G., Mng. Dir.--NRG France S.A., Creteil, France; *Int'l*, pg. 1116
Cardo, Gerard, Mng. Dir.--Gestetner S.A., Creteil, France; *Int'l*, pg. 1115
Cardon, William, Pres.--Kaufman and Broad of San Diego, Inc., San Diego, CA; *U.S. Public*, pg. 945
Cardon, William R., Pres.--Kaufman and Broad Coastal, Newport Beach, CA; *U.S. Public*, pg. 945
Cardoro, John J., Pres.--Entergy Louisiana, Inc., New Orleans, LA; *U.S. Public*, pg. 586
Cardos, Sid Lopes, Gen. Dir.--Marcam Do Brasil, Sao Paulo, Brazil; *U.S. Public*, pg. 1043
Cardoso Salgado, Jose Manuel Pereira, Dr., Chm.--EIVAL, S.A., Lisbon, Portugal; *Int'l*, pg. 1045
Cardoso, Jorge, Mng. Dir.--CABLESA-Industria de Componentes Electricos Sociedade Anonima, Sintra, Portugal; *U.S. Public*, pg. 721
Cardoso, Jose Tomas, Mgr.-Credit--Caixa Geral de Depositos, Porto, Portugal; *Int'l*, pg. 250
Cardoso, Mauro, Mgr.--Sao Paulo Branch, Sao Paulo, Brazil; *Int'l*, pg. 139
Cardwell, Harvey, Pres.--Robin's Foods Inc., Thunder Bay, Canada; *Int'l*, pg. 1195
Carell, Lars, Mng. Dir.--Janssen-Cilag AB, Sollentuna, Sweden; *U.S. Public*, pg. 929
Carell, Lars, Mng. Dir.--Janssen-Cilag A/S, Birkerod, Denmark; *U.S. Public*, pg. 929
Carendi, Jan R., First Exec. V.P.--Assurance & Financial Services, Stockholm, Sweden; *Int'l*, pg. 1256
Carendi, Jan R., Chief Exec. Officer--American Skandia Investment Holding Corporation, Shelton, CT; *Int'l*, pg. 1257
Carendi, Jan R., Chief Oper. Officer--Skandia Leben Holding GmbH, Berlin, Germany; *Int'l*, pg. 1258
Carestio, Ralph M., Jr., Pres.--Comfortable Mortgages, Inc., Charlotte, NC; *U.S. Public*, pg. 1163
Carestio, Ralph M., Jr., Pres.--TIM, Inc., Charlotte, NC; *U.S. Public*, pg. 1165
Carette, Bruno, Chief Exec. Officer--LG Seeds Inc., Peoria, IL; *Int'l*, pg. 566
Carey, Chase, Chief Oper. Officer--Fox, Inc., Los Angeles, CA; *Int'l*, pg. 926
Carey, Dale, Mgr.-Reg. Sls.--Pennsylvania Cellular Telephone Corp., Bethlehem, PA; *U.S. Public*, pg. 1708
Carey, Dale, V.P. & Gen. Mgr.-Northern Pennsylvania Opers.--Pennsylvania Cellular Telephone Corp., Stroudsburg, PA; *U.S. Public*, pg. 1708
Carey, Earl T., Div. Mgr.--Ohio Edison Co.-Youngstown Div., Youngstown, OH; *U.S. Public*, pg. 645
Carey, George, Gen. Mgr.--Just Kid, Inc., Stamford, CT; *U.S. Private*, pg. 804
Carey, H.N., Pres.--Master Shield Building Products, Mississauga, Canada; *Int'l*, pg. 698
Carey, James, Pres. & Publr.--Burlington Free Press, Burlington, VT; *U.S. Public*, pg. 700
Carey, Peter, Chief Oper. Officer & Exec. V.P.--SGI Integrated Graphic Systems, Houston, TX; *U.S. Public*, pg. 971
Carey, T.W., Mng. Dir.--Vivitar (Europe) Ltd. Hanimex-Vivitar, Swindon, United Kingdom; *Int'l*, pg. 1061
Carey, Tom, Mgr.--Safety Steel Service, Inc., Corpus Christi, TX; *U.S. Public*, pg. 412
Carey, Tom, Mgr.--Safety Steel Service, Inc., Victoria, TX; *U.S. Public*, pg. 412
Cargiulo, Ralph J., Pres. & Chief Exec. Officer--The United States Life Ins. Co. In the City of New York, New York, NY; *U.S. Public*, pg. 77
Cargol, Pat, Reg. Mgr.-Sls.--Weatherford Enterra U.S., L.P., New Orleans, LA; *U.S. Public*, pg. 1749
Caribe, Rachel, Pres.--Caribe Express Latin American Div., Miami, FL; *U.S. Private*, pg. 211
Carideo, Frank H., Pres.--Fire Controls Instruments, Waltham, MA; *U.S. Public*, pg. 1306
Carifa, John D., Pres., Chief Oper. Officer & Chief Fin. Officer--Alliance Capital Management Corp., New York, NY; *U.S. Public*, pg. 589
Carinci, Gabriele, Pres.--AGIE U.S.A. Ltd., Wood Dale, IL; *Int'l*, pg. 490
Carington, Robert, Mgr.--Jefferies & Company, Inc., Houston, TX; *U.S. Public*, pg. 925
Carini, Robert, Pres.--Electronics Division-Materials, Bear, DE; *U.S. Public*, pg. 165
Carini, Robert, Pres.--Silicone Technologies, Bear, DE; *U.S. Public*, pg. 165
Carion, William A., V.P. & Mng. Dir.--General Dynamics Services Co., Troy, MI; *U.S. Public*, pg. 709
Carl, D.E., Chief Oper. Officer--AEG Sorting Systems Inc., Ajax, Canada; *Int'l*, pg. 1244
Carland, Robert, Pres.--Kentucky-Tennessee Clay Co., Mayfield, KY; *U.S. Public*, pg. 804
Carlberg, Anders G., Pres.--Axel Johnson International AB, Kista, Sweden; *Int'l*, pg. 709
Carlen, Hilean, Pres.--NCC Eskilstuna, Eskilstuna, Sweden; *Int'l*, pg. 899
Carleson, Jack, V.P.-Opers.--Prebound Periodicals, Inc., Topeka, KS; *U.S. Private*, pg. 52
Carleson, Sven, Pres.--ABB Generation AB, Vasteras, Sweden; *Int'l*, pg. 7
Carleton, Gary, Gen. Mgr.--Vivitar Canada Limited, Mississauga, Canada; *Int'l*, pg. 1116
Carleton, Larry, Chief Oper. Officer & Exec. V.P.--TCI West, Bellevue, WA; *U.S. Public*, pg. 1555
Carletti, A., Branch Mgr.--Kodak S.p.A., Rome, Italy; *U.S. Public*, pg. 554
Carley, Stephen, Pres. & Chief Oper. Officer--Universal Studios Hollywood, Universal City, CA; *Int'l*, pg. 1216
Carlile, Rex, Pres.--Trim Trends, Farmington Hills, MI; *U.S. Public*, pg. 796
Carlin, Carlo, Exec. V.P.--Adriatica de Seguros C.A., Caracas, Venezuela; *Int'l*, pg. 61
Carlin, Carlo Graf, Pres.--Allianz RAS Argentina, Buenos Aires, Argentina; *Int'l*, pg. 60
Carlin, F. Taylor, Chm.--AMCORE Capital Management, Inc., Rockford, IL; *U.S. Public*, pg. 64
Carlin, Steve, Mgr.--Stephen Gould of Maryland, Inc., Lutherville, MD; *U.S. Private*, pg. 467
Carline, C.G., Gen. Mgr.--Hong Kong Air Cargo Terminals Ltd., Kowloon, Hong Kong; *Int'l*, pg. 705
Carling, Christian, Sls. Officer--Martin Merkel Svenska AB, Solna, Sweden; *Int'l*, pg. 860
Carlino, Steve, Admin.--Silvercrest Manor, Crestview, FL; *U.S. Public*, pg. 837
Carlisle, John H., Assoc. Dir.--WF Corroon-Ipswich, Ipswich, United Kingdom; *Int'l*, pg. 1501
Carlisle, Tom, Mgr.--Triad Personnel Services, Atlanta, GA; *U.S. Public*, pg. 715
Carlisle, W.N., Chief Exec. Officer--GA Ltd., Glasgow, United Kingdom; *Int'l*, pg. 630
Carlisle, Wayne, Pres.--Carlisle Equipment Co, Indianapolis, IN; *U.S. Private*, pg. 211
Carlisle, Wayne, Pres.--Carlisle Crane Co, Orlando, FL; *U.S. Private*, pg. 211

Carlo, Petrin, Gen. Mgr.--SASIB Beverage UK Ltd., London, United Kingdom; *Int'l*, pg. 1195
Carlos, Simoes, Mng. Dir.--Nokia Telecomunicacones Portugal S.A., Lisbon, Portugal; *Int'l*, pg. 954
Carlsom, Clayton E., V.P. & Publr.--HarperCollins San Francisco, San Francisco, CA; *Int'l*, pg. 927
Carlson, Bruce D., Resident Rep.--Banco Mundial, Caracas, Venezuela; *U.S. Private*, pg. 1189
Carlson, C., Branch Mgr.--A.M. Castle & Co., Roseville, MN; *U.S. Public*, pg. 313
Carlson, Cynthia, Pres. & Chief Exec. Officer--American Enterprise Investment Services, Inc., Minneapolis, MN; *U.S. Public*, pg. 73
Carlson, Cynthia, Mng. Dir.--Electronic Tele-Communications, Inc., Pleasanton, CA; *U.S. Public*, pg. 570
Carlson, D.A., Mgr.-Mktg.--The Uncle Toby's Company Ltd., Richmond, Australia; *Int'l*, pg. 555
Carlson, Gary E., Pres.--PCS Nitrogen, Memphis, TN; *Int'l*, pg. 1064
Carlson, Gerald K., Gen. Mgr.--Ecolab Institutional Group, Saint Paul, MN; *U.S. Public*, pg. 562
Carlson, Gerald K., Sr. V.P.--Ecolab International Div., Saint Paul, MN; *U.S. Public*, pg. 562
Carlson, Greg, Pres.--Marco Sales Co., Saint Louis, MO; *U.S. Private*, pg. 628
Carlson, Jack, V.P.-Opers.--American Bindry-Midwest, Topeka, KS; *U.S. Private*, pg. 52
Carlson, Lars, Mgr.--Kativo Chemical Industries, S.A., San Jose, Costa Rica; *U.S. Public*, pg. 687
Carlson, Lisa, Principal--The PowerBase Marketing Group, Dallas, TX; *U.S. Private*, pg. 651
Carlson, Marilyn B., V.P.--GTE Information Services Incorporated, Dallas-Fort Worth Airport, TX; *U.S. Public*, pg. 696
Carlson, Neal M., Chm. Bd.--First National Bank of Warsaw, Warsaw, IN; *U.S. Public*, pg. 674
Carlson, Robert, Gen. Mgr.--International California Glass Corp., South Gate, CA; *U.S. Public*, pg. 895
Carlson, Robert F., Jr., Pres.--Seabeam Instruments, Inc., Walpole, MA; *U.S. Private*, pg. 228
Carlson, Robert N., Pres.--Transicoil, Inc., Valley Forge, PA; *U.S. Private*, pg. 538
Carlson, Robert S., Chief Oper. Officer--HRH/Atlas Construction Inc., Stamford, CT; *U.S. Private*, pg. 1035
Carlson, W. Pierce, Chief Exec. Officer--Nord Pacific Limited, Albuquerque, NM; *U.S. Public*, pg. 1188
Carlson, William J., Pres. & Gen. Mgr.--Atkinson Construction, San Bruno, CA; *U.S. Public*, pg. 143
Carlsson, Anders, Chief Exec. Officer--Ericsson Utvecklings AB, Alvsjo, Sweden; *Int'l*, pg. 1364
Carlsson, Arne, Chief Oper. Officer--Scania Nederland B.V., Zwolle, Netherlands; *Int'l*, pg. 687
Carlsson, Billy, Mng. Dir.--Norvista Travel AB, Stockholm, Sweden; *Int'l*, pg. 486
Carlsson, Bjorn, Mgr.--Sandvik Saws and Tools U.K., Birmingham, United Kingdom; *Int'l*, pg. 1187
Carlsson, Kjell, Pres.--Uniroc AB, Fagersta, Sweden; *Int'l*, pg. 96
Carlsson, Milton, Mng. Dir.--Fraktarna AB, Helsingborg, Sweden; *Int'l*, pg. 476
Carlston, Steve, Pres.--SF Broadcasting Companies, Santa Monica, CA; *U.S. Public*, pg. 1685
Carlstrom, Ed, Gen. Mgr.--Wisconsin Tissue, Flagstaff, AZ; *U.S. Public*, pg. 347
Carlton, Donald M., Pres. & Chief Exec. Officer--Radian International LLC, Austin, TX; *U.S. Public*, pg. 522
Carlucci, Frank, Chm.--The Carlyle Group, Washington, DC; *U.S. Private*, pg. 213
Carmaine, William, Gen. Mgr.--Elkay Plastics Co., Inc., Stock Service Center, Atlanta, GA; *U.S. Private*, pg. 372
Carmel, Yves, V.P. & Gen. Mgr.--Roll-It, Lachine, Canada; *U.S. Public*, pg. 963
Carmer, Charles E., Pres.--Merrill/Washington, Washington, DC; *U.S. Public*, pg. 1097
Carmer, Charles E., Pres.--Merrill/Boston, Boston, MA; *U.S. Public*, pg. 1097
Carmichael, Arthur C., Jr., Chm. Bd.--Willis Corroon Corp. of San Jose, San Jose, CA; *Int'l*, pg. 1507
Carmichael, Ian B., Exec. V.P.--Crown Cork & Seal Company, Inc.-Corporate Technologies, Wantage, United Kingdom; *U.S. Public*, pg. 464
Carmichael, J. B., Div. Mgr.--MB General Packaging Div., Reading, United Kingdom; *Int'l*, pg. 266
Carmichael, Jr., Robert L., Pres.--Commercial Bank and Trust Company of Troup County, La Grange, GA; *U.S. Public*, pg. 1549
Carmichael, Laird, V.P. & Gen. Mgr.--Saft America, Portable Battery Div., Valdosta, GA; *Int'l*, pg. 55
Carmichael, Robert F., Pres.--Canefco Limited, Scarborough, Canada; *U.S. Private*, pg. 368
Carmody, Don, Pres.--Mercantile Bank of Mount Pleasant, Mount Pleasant, IA; *U.S. Public*, pg. 1088
Carmody, James M., Pres.--Operations & Maintenance Division, Cleveland, OH; *U.S. Public*, pg. 1134
Carmon, Jack, Mgr.--Century Telephone Company, Hardy, AR; *U.S. Public*, pg. 329
Carn, Nicholas D.P., Pres. & Chief Exec. Officer--Draycott Partners, Ltd., London, United Kingdom; *U.S. Private*, pg. 738
Carnegie, Ronda, Mgr.-Los Angeles/Asia/Pacific--The New Yorker - California, Santa Monica, CA; *U.S. Private*, pg. 796
Carneiro, J. Lamy, Chief Exec. Officer--Lusoceram-Empreendimentos Ceramicos, S.A., Lisbon, Portugal; *Int'l*, pg. 1092
Carnes, James E., Pres. & Chief Oper. Officer--Sarnoff Corporation, Princeton, NJ; *U.S. Private*, pg. 958
Carney, Donald G., Pres.--Value Slacks, Inc., El Paso, TX; *U.S. Public*, pg. 613
Carney, Donald G., Pres.--Value Clothing Company, Inc., El Paso, TX; *U.S. Public*, pg. 613
Carney, Edward O., Pres.--Superior Graphite Europe, Ltd., Sundsvall, Sweden; *U.S. Private*, pg. 1055
Carney, John D., Pres.--Blackstone Valley Electric Co., Lincoln, RI; *U.S. Public*, pg. 549
Carney, John D., Pres.--Eastern Edison Company, Brockton, MA; *U.S. Public*, pg. 550
Carney, John D., Pres.--Newport Electric Corporation, Middletown, RI; *U.S. Public*, pg. 550
Carney, John F., Pres.--Ohio State Life Insurance Co., Columbus, OH; *Int'l*, pg. 110
Carney, John J., Pres.--Spectra-Physics USA, Inc., Blue Bell, PA; *Int'l*, pg. 1289
Carney, Roger, Admin.--Auburn Manor, Washington Court House, OH; *U.S. Public*, pg. 838
Carney, Steve, Gen. Mgr.--San Francisco French Bread Company, Oakland, CA; *U.S. Public*, pg. 909
Carni, Giora, Pres. & Chief Exec. Officer--Clay-Park Labs, Inc., Bronx, NY; *Int'l*, pg. 30
Carns, Neil, Pres.--Wolf Creek Nuclear Operating Corp., Burlington, KS; *U.S. Public*, pg. 943
Carnuccio, Nick, Plant Mgr.--H.S. Crocker Co., Inc., Norristown, PA; *U.S. Private*, pg. 290
Caro, Liz, Gen. Mgr.--Metropolitan Cafe, New York, NY; *U.S. Public*, pg. 130
Carol, Lewis, Gen. Mgr.--Aakronite New Zealand, Glenfield, New Zealand; *U.S. Public*, pg. 904
Carolan, J.F., Mng. Dir.--Black Horse Relocation Services Limited, Windsor, United Kingdom; *Int'l*, pg. 813
Carollo, Jerome, Pres.--Kaiser Electro Optics, Carlsbad, CA; *U.S. Private*, pg. 605
Carollo, Joe, Gen. Mgr.--St. Pete Auto Auction, Clearwater, FL; *U.S. Private*, pg. 283
Caron, J.R., Pres.--Cigna Information Services, Inc., Voorhees, NJ; *U.S. Public*, pg. 357
Caron, Michael A., Sr. V.P. & Pres.-Armor All Intl.--Armor All Products Group, Oakland, CA; *U.S. Public*, pg. 387
Carothers, Dave, V.P.-Contract Field Teams--UNC Lear Siegler, Oklahoma City, OK; *U.S. Public*, pg. 710
Carovano, Ron G., Plant Mgr.--Abtco, Inc., Alpena, MI; *Int'l*, pg. 20
Carow, Dr. Bernd, Chief Oper. Officer--Schering A/S, Roedovre, Denmark; *Int'l*, pg. 1204
Carozza, E.J., Pres.--Certech International Ltd., Corby, United Kingdom; *U.S. Public*, pg. 308
Carp, D.A., Mgr.-Factory--Eastman Kodak Company-European Region, London, United Kingdom; *U.S. Public*, pg. 551
Carpenter, Alvin R., Pres. & Chief Exec. Officer--CSX Transportation, Inc., Jacksonville, FL; *U.S. Public*, pg. 284
Carpenter, Candice, Pres.-Time-Life Video & Television--Time-Life, Inc., Alexandria, VA; *U.S. Public*, pg. 1613
Carpenter, Chris, Pres.--David Corporation, San Francisco, CA; *U.S. Private*, pg. 872
Carpenter, David, V.P.-Cultures & Enzymes Div.--Sanofi Bio Industries, Waukesha, WI; *Int'l*, pg. 445
Carpenter, George E., Pres.--Artwood Products, Millersburg, OH; *U.S. Private*, pg. 983
Carpenter, J.P., Gen. Dir.--BIAO Niger, Namey, Niger; *Int'l*, pg. 547
Carpenter, John, Mng. Dir.--Jardine Fleming New Zealand Limited, Wellington, New Zealand; *Int'l*, pg. 494
Carpenter, L.E., Jr., Plant Mgr.--Longview Fibre Co. Eastern Container Div., Springfield, MA; *U.S. Public*, pg. 1014
Carpenter, Michael A., Chm. & Chief Exec. Officer--The Travelers Life & Annuity Co., Hartford, CT; *U.S. Public*, pg. 1633
Carpenter, Philip, Mng. Dir.--Bose U.K., Ltd., Sittingbourne, United Kingdom; *U.S. Private*, pg. 161
Carpenter, Ron L., Dir.-Technology Programs--Science and Engineering Huntsville Office, Huntsville, AL; *U.S. Public*, pg. 1597
Carpenter, Vic, V.P.-Opers.--Pemko Manufacturing, Memphis, TN; *U.S. Private*, pg. 848
Carpenter, W.R., V.P. & Gen. Mgr.--Killark Electric Manufacturing Co., Saint Louis, MO; *U.S. Public*, pg. 844
Carpenter, William D., Pres.--Teal Electronics, San Diego, CA; *U.S. Public*, pg. 1419
Carpentier, Dirk, Deputy Reg. Mgr.--Det Norske Veritas, Rotterdam, Netherlands; *Int'l*, pg. 397
Carr, A.L., Chm.--Unilever New Zealand Ltd., Petone, New Zealand; *Int'l*, pg. 1439
Carr, Andrew D., Pres.--J&H Marsh & McLennan Management Services (Bermuda) Ltd., Hamilton, Bermuda; *U.S. Public*, pg. 1049
Carr, Brian, V.P. & Gen. Mgr.--Consolidated Communications Public Services, Inc., Mattoon, IL; *U.S. Public*, pg. 1073
Carr, Chris, Pres.--Euclid Hitachi, Cleveland, OH; *Int'l*, pg. 622
Carr, Dennis M., Pres.--Ameritech Credit Corporation, Rolling Meadows, IL; *U.S. Public*, pg. 98
Carr, Emerson F., Plant Mgr.--AC Rochester Corporation, Southampton, United Kingdom; *U.S. Public*, pg. 721
Carr, George, Pres.--Follett Campus Resources, River Grove, IL; *U.S. Private*, pg. 417
Carr, Harry J., V.P.--Lucent Technologies, Silver Spring, MD; *U.S. Public*, pg. 1017
Carr, Jay F., Pres.--Hershey International, Hershey, PA; *U.S. Public*, pg. 812
Carr, Jeremiah, Chief Exec. Officer--Rochester Telephone Corp., Rochester, NY; *U.S. Public*, pg. 684
Carr, Jim, Gen. Mgr.--RESCO Steel Products Corp., Salem, VA; *U.S. Public*, pg. 1392
Carr, Kevinel S., V.P. & Publisher--Motor Publications, Garden City, NY; *U.S. Private*, pg. 516
Carr, Mark, V.P. & Gen. Mgr.--Hasper Equipment Co., Muskegon, MI; *U.S. Private*, pg. 247
Carr, Michael, Branch Mgr.--Union-Transport Corporation-Dallas Office, Grapevine, TX; *U.S. Private*, pg. 1119
Carr, Phillip J., Pres.--Town & Country Tours, Phoenix, AZ; *U.S. Private*, pg. 23
Carr, R.C., Pres.--Amoco Credit Corporation, Chicago, IL; *U.S. Public*, pg. 103
Carr, Robert O., Chm. Bd. & Pres.--Carr Real Estate Services, Washington, DC; *U.S. Public*, pg. 309
Carrara, G., Pres.--Italimpianti of America, Incorporated, Coraopolis, PA; *Int'l*, pg. 655
Carrasco, Andres, Mng. Dir.--American Appraisal Espana, S.A., Madrid, Spain; *U.S. Private*, pg. 50
Carrasco, Arturo, Mng. Dir.--Danomex, S.A. de C.V., Tlalnepantla, Mexico; *U.S. Public*, pg. 505
Carrasco, M., Chief Exec. Officer--TNT Logistics, Redfern, Australia; *Int'l*, pg. 1343
Carrasquillo, Maruici, Mng. Dir.--The West Company de Colombia, S.A., Bogota, Colombia; *U.S. Public*, pg. 1756
Carre, Bruno, Gen. Mgr.--Thilmany Division, Kaukauna, WI; *U.S. Public*, pg. 903
Carrejo, Gene, V.P.-Sls. & Mktg.--Price's Creameries, El Paso, TX; *U.S. Public*, pg. 491
Carrera-Justiz, Francisco, Pres.--Bacardi-Martini Product Development Inc., Jacksonville, FL; *Int'l*, pg. 131
Carrera-Justiz, Francisco, Pres.--Bacardi-Martini Product Quality Americas Inc., Jacksonville, FL; *Int'l*, pg. 131
Carrera, Luis, Country Mgr.--Compaq Computer S.A., Madrid, Spain; *U.S. Public*, pg. 418
Carrier, John, Mng. Dir.--NIG Skandia PLC, London, United Kingdom; *Int'l*, pg. 1258
Carrigan, Michael, V.P. & Gen. Mgr.--Boston Weatherhead Div., Brentwood, TN; *U.S. Public*, pg. 479
Carriker, Dr. Roy C., Pres. & Chief Oper. Officer--Sermatech International, Inc., Limerick, PA; *U.S. Public*, pg. 1569
Carrim, Jafar, Mng. Dir.--Sime Darby Berhad Tyre Manufacturing Division, Petaling Jaya, Malaysia; *Int'l*, pg. 1250
Carriminana, Fernando, Mng. Dir.--Ericsson Terminales Moviles S.A., Madrid, Spain; *Int'l*, pg. 1368
Carrington, Beth R., Pres.--Acutex Division, Whitehall, MI; *U.S. Public*, pg. 1421
Carrington, John, Mgr.-Employee Rels.--Brunswick Plant, Brunswick, ME; *U.S. Public*, pg. 444
Carrington, Nick, Gen. Mgr.--Park Newspapers of Mooresville, Inc., Mooresville, NC; *U.S. Public*, pg. 1079
Carrington, Nick, Gen. Mgr.--Mooresville Tribune Inc., Mooresville, NC; *U.S. Public*, pg. 1079
Carrio, Juan Llorens, Chm. Bd.--SEAT, S.A., Barcelona, Spain; *Int'l*, pg. 1475
Carris, William, Pres.--Vermont Tubbs, Inc., Brandon, VT; *U.S. Private*, pg. 215
Carris, William, Pres.--Carris Reels, Inc., Rutland, VT; *U.S. Private*, pg. 215
Carrizosa, Fernando, Pres.--Wackenhut Intl., Inc., Coral Gables, FL; *U.S. Public*, pg. 1731
Carrol, Charlie, Chief Oper. Officer--The G&C Foundry Company, Sandusky, OH; *U.S. Public*, pg. 142
Carroll, Bill J., Pres.--Saginaw Overseas Corporation, Detroit, MI; *U.S. Public*, pg. 723
Carroll, Chester, Gen. Mgr.--Manheim's Greater Orlando Auto Auction, Orlando, FL; *U.S. Private*, pg. 282
Carroll, Chuck, Mgr.--Eclipse Combustion, Inc., Shreveport, LA; *U.S. Private*, pg. 360
Carroll, David M., Pres.--First Union National Bank of Florida, Jacksonville, FL; *U.S. Public*, pg. 640
Carroll, Henry, Distr. Mgr.--Browning-Ferris Industries of Mississippi, Inc., Ocean Springs, MS; *U.S. Public*, pg. 263
Carroll, Jane, Cheif Exec. Officer-Forum Europe--Forum Europe Ltd., London, United Kingdom; *U.S. Private*, pg. 420
Carroll, Loren, Pres. & Chief Exec. Officer--M-I L.L.C., Houston, TX; *U.S. Public*, pg. 776
Carroll, Mary Alice, Mng. Dir.--Grapheme Inc., Toronto, Canada; *Int'l*, pg. 336
Carroll, Michael P., Pres.--Millipore Asia Limited, Kowloon, Hong Kong; *U.S. Public*, pg. 1113
Carroll, Richard, Pres.--Sommer & Maca Industries, Inc.-Industrial Machinery Division, Cicero, IL; *U.S. Private*, pg. 1013
Carroll, Robert B., Chief Oper. Officer--Greenway Corporation, Jessup, MD; *U.S. Public*, pg. 1770
Carroll, Robert C., Contact--Libmar Four, Inc., Monrovia, Liberia; *U.S. Public*, pg. 341
Carroll, Tom, Pres. & Gen. Mgr.--Outdoor Systems, Inc.-Michigan, Detroit, MI; *U.S. Public*, pg. 1235
Carroll, W., Office Mgr.--Kodak New Zealand Ltd., Christchurch, New Zealand; *U.S. Public*, pg. 554
Carruthers, J.L., Rep.--Barclays Bank PLC, Kuala Lumpur, Malaysia; *Int'l*, pg. 166
Carsky, James B., Pres.--California School Book Fairs, Inc., Anaheim, CA; *U.S. Public*, pg. 1440
Carson, Don, Branch Mgr.--Burns & Wilcox - Arlington Office, Arlington, TX; *U.S. Private*, pg. 609
Carson, Don, Mng. Partner--Don and Charlie's, Scottsdale, AZ; *U.S. Private*, pg. 661
Carson, John, Pres.--Webcraft Games, Inc., North Brunswick, NJ; *U.S. Public*, pg. 228
Carson, Lee, Gen. Mgr.--Speedling Incorporated Alamo Transplants Division, Alamo, TX; *U.S. Private*, pg. 1024
Carson, Randy, Exec. V.P.--Reliance Electric Company, Cleveland, OH; *U.S. Public*, pg. 1398
Carson, Robin, Exec. V.P. & Gen. Mgr.--Sea World of Texas, San Antonio, TX; *U.S. Public*, pg. 114
Carson, Russell A., Pres.--Cavenham Forest Industries Inc., Portland, OR; *Int'l*, pg. 593
Carson, S.A., Pres.--Control Components, Inc., Rancho Santa Margarita, CA; *Int'l*, pg. 646
Carson, Susan, Pres.--Herman Miller, Ltd., Toronto, Canada; *U.S. Public*, pg. 1112
Carson, Terry, Pres.--Arkansas State Bank, Clarksville, AR; *U.S. Public*, pg. 630
Carson, W. Howard, Pres.--Peabody Western Coal Company, Flagstaff, AZ; *Int'l*, pg. 594
Carson, W.H., V.P.-Scientific Affairs, OTC--Sandoz Pharmaceuticals Corp., East Hanover, NJ; *Int'l*, pg. 974
Carstensen, Teri, Pres.--Fiserv Fresno, Inc., Fresno, CA; *U.S. Public*, pg. 647
Carte, B. A., Chm. Bd.--Lombard Bank Limited, Enfield, United Kingdom; *Int'l*, pg. 910
Carteaux, Bill, Pres.--Auto Jectors, Inc., Avilla, IN; *U.S. Private*, pg. 484

Carter, A., Gen. Mgr.--Moore Business Systems Pty. Ltd., Boroko, Papua New Guinea; *Int'l*, pg. 889

Carter, Arthur L., Pres.--Utilities & Industries Management Corp., New York, NY; *U.S. Private*, pg. 993

Carter, David L., Sr. V.P.--Roberts & Schaefer Company-Salt Lake City, Salt Lake City, UT; *U.S. Private*, pg. 371

Carter, Derek, Mng. Dir.--EMAP Maclaren, Croydon, United Kingdom; *Int'l*, pg. 451

Carter, Donald, Pres.--DC Company, Fresno, CA; *Int'l*, pg. 736

Carter, Doug O., V.P. & Gen. Mgr.--Pacific Westeel, Burlington, Canada; *Int'l*, pg. 698

Carter, G.K., Pres.--Chevron Oil Finance Company, San Francisco, CA; *U.S. Public*, pg. 348

Carter, Gary, Plant Mgr.--Uniland Mfg. Co., Inc., Saint Joseph, MO; *U.S. Public*, pg. 975

Carter, Harry, Pres.--HDW, Incorporated, Greenwood, MS; *U.S. Private*, pg. 335

Carter, J., Pres.--Keystone Thermometrics Corporation, Saint Marys, PA; *Int'l*, pg. 208

Carter, J.D., Chief Exec.--Hepworth Heating Ltd., Belper, United Kingdom; *Int'l*, pg. 615

Carter, Jack, V.P.-Mfg.--KMW Systems Corporation, Austin, TX; *U.S. Public*, pg. 112

Carter, James J., V.P. & Gen. Mgr.--WTAE-AM, Pittsburgh, PA; *U.S. Public*, pg. 1418

Carter, James J., V.P. & Gen. Mgr.--WVTY-FM, Pittsburgh, PA; *U.S. Public*, pg. 1418

Carter, Jerry, Pres.--Marta Technologies, Inc., Nashville, TN; *U.S. Public*, pg. 46

Carter, Joan, Acting Pres.--Life Extension Institute, New York, NY; *U.S. Private*, pg. 1114

Carter, John, Country Mgr.--Centro de Idiomas Berlitz de Venezuela, Caracas, Venezuela; *U.S. Public*, pg. 222

Carter, John, Div. Mgr.--The Southland Corporation, Virginia Beach, VA; *Int'l*, pg. 694

Carter, Jon, Pres.--Ward Leonard Electric Company, Inc., Mount Vernon, NY; *U.S. Private*, pg. 1118

Carter, Mary, Admin.--Guardian Care of Monroe, Monroe, NC; *U.S. Public*, pg. 1712

Carter, Michael, Pres.--Pierre Fabre, Azusa, CA; *Int'l*, pg. 1056

Carter, Michael J., Country Dir.--The World Bank, Moscow, Russia; *U.S. Private*, pg. 1190

Carter, Patricia, Dir.--Columbia Reg. Oncology, El Paso, TX; *U.S. Public*, pg. 404

Carter, Philip L., Pres. & Chief Exec. Officer--Mac Frugal's Bargains Close-Outs Inc., Rancho Dominguez, CA; *U.S. Public*, pg. 437

Carter, R., Dir.--Ladbroke Racecourse Management Ltd., Harrow, United Kingdom; *Int'l*, pg. 787

Carter, R. J., Grp. Gen. Mgr.--BHP Iron Ore, Perth, Australia; *Int'l*, pg. 224

Carter, Reginald, Exec. V.P.--Americold Compressor Co., Cullman, AL; *Int'l*, pg. 439

Carter, Richard, Gen. Mgr.--SMI Specialties, Columbia, SC; *U.S. Public*, pg. 413

Carter, Robert L., Plant Mgr.--Wisconsin Preparatory Center, Neenah, WI; *U.S. Public*, pg. 672

Carter, Stephen K., M.D., Pres.--Bristol-Myers Pharmaceutical Research & Development Division, Princeton, NJ; *U.S. Public*, pg. 254

Carter, Van, Chief Oper. Officer--Allright System Parking, Inc., Memphis, TN; *U.S. Private*, pg. 43

Carter, Wayne S., Pres.--Chesapeake Insurance Division, Richmond, VA; *U.S. Public*, pg. 215

Cartledge, Barbara, Dir.--Au Pair in America, Greenwich, CT; *U.S. Private*, pg. 56

Cartone, Tommaso, Chm. Bd.--Ambro Italia Societa di Intermediazione Mobiliare S.p.A., Milan, Italy; *Int'l*, pg. 138

Cartwright, Dennis H., Pres. & Chief Exec. Officer--Media General Financial Services, Inc., Richmond, VA; *U.S. Public*, pg. 1078

Cartwright, J. David, Pres.--Cooper Hand Tools, Raleigh, NC; *U.S. Public*, pg. 444

Cartwright, James M., Pres.--Banta Direct Marketing Group, Elk Grove Village, IL; *U.S. Public*, pg. 188

Cartwright, John, Mgr.--Westco Products/Seattle, Seattle, WA; *Int'l*, pg. 244

Cartwright, Terry, Gen. Mgr.--Beijing Crown Can Company Ltd., Beijing, China; *U.S. Public*, pg. 465

Carty, Donald J., Pres.--American Airlines, Inc., Fort Worth, TX; *U.S. Public*, pg. 9

Carty, William P.M., Gen. Mgr.--Abbott Ireland Ltd., Ballytivnan, Ireland; *U.S. Public*, pg. 13

Carusillo, Tina, Publr.--American City Business Journals, Inc., Houston, TX; *U.S. Private*, pg. 19

Caruso, Antoine, Gen. Mgr.--Formica Switzerland AG, Rumlang, Switzerland; *Int'l*, pg. 129

Caruso, Bob, Exec. V.P. & Gen. Mgr.--Sesame Place, Langhorne, PA; *U.S. Public*, pg. 114

Caruso, Francisco, Mng. Dir.--SHL Systemhouse Argentina S.A., Buenos Aires, Argentina; *Int'l*, pg. 1154

Caruso, Giacomo, Mng. Dir.--SIELTE Engineering S.p.A., Milan, Italy; *Int'l*, pg. 1370

Carvajal, Cecilia, V.P. & Media Dir.--Leo Burnett Inc., Hato Rey, PR; *U.S. Private*, pg. 185

Carval, Jamie, Pres.--Ford Espana S.A., Madrid, Spain; *U.S. Public*, pg. 665

Carvalho, Antonio Cesar, Mgr.--Belem Branch, Belem, Brazil; *Int'l*, pg. 139

Carvallio, Jose, Chief Oper. Officer--Continental Mabor Industria de Aneus S.A., Vila Nova de Famalicao, Portugal; *Int'l*, pg. 328

Carvallo, Sergio, Chief Oper. Officer--Fermentaciones Mexicanas, S.A. de C.V. (FERMEX), Mexico, Mexico; *Int'l*, pg. 778

Carver, Carl E., Pres.--Great River Insurance Company, Meridian, MS; *U.S. Public*, pg. 215

Carver, Charles, III, Plant Mgr.--Hydro Aluminum Bohn, Inc., Rockledge, FL; *Int'l*, pg. 961

Carver, Steve, V.P. & Gen. Mgr.-WBBM-AM--CBS Radio Div., New York, NY; *U.S. Public*, pg. 274

Cary, Peter, V.P.-Intl.--Paramount Television Ltd., London, United Kingdom; *U.S. Private*, pg. 777

Casado, J.L., Gen. Mgr.--Fleetguard Mexico S.A. de C.V., Zaragoza, Mexico; *U.S. Public*, pg. 469

Casala, G., Chief Oper. Officer--Danone, Levallois-Perret, France; *Int'l*, pg. 379

Casale, Michael J., Dir.--Voyager American Insurance Company, Ltd., Fort Worth, TX; *U.S. Public*, pg. 68

Casals, Patrick, Chief Oper. Officer--General Tire & Rubber Co. of Morocco, Casablanca, Morocco; *Int'l*, pg. 327

Casanova, David, Gen. Mgr.--Amway de Mexico, S.A. de C.V., Monterrey, Mexico; *U.S. Private*, pg. 69

Casanova, Vincent, Pres.--Chicago Tribune Direct, Northlake, IL; *U.S. Public*, pg. 1635

Casanueva, C.A., Gen. Mgr.--MSA de Chile Ltda., Santiago, Chile; *U.S. Public*, pg. 1114

Casarez, Teresa, Admin.--Sunset Villa Nursing Home, Roswell, NM; *U.S. Public*, pg. 838

Casarin, Mario, Chm. Bd.--Itacard S.p.A., Milan, Italy; *Int'l*, pg. 138

Casas, Lorenzo, Gen. Mgr.--Security Plastics de Mexico, Chihuahua, Mexico; *U.S. Private*, pg. 981

Casas, Manuel, Gen. Mgr.--Banco Santander, Paris, France; *Int'l*, pg. 144

Cascarano, Francesco, Gen. Mgr.--Bujias Champion de Venezuela, C.A., Velencia, Venezuela; *U.S. Public*, pg. 444

Casciani, Thomas A., Mgr.-Opers.--Expansion Valve Division, Longwood, FL; *U.S. Public*, pg. 1260

Case, Daniel H., Sr. V.P. & Gen. Mgr.-Voice Messaging Div.--Glenayre Electronics, Inc., Quincy, IL; *U.S. Public*, pg. 747

Case, R.I., Chief Exec.--GKN Westland Helicopters Limited, Yeovil, United Kingdom; *Int'l*, pg. 535

Casele, Ralph P., Chm. Bd.--New York Life Insurance Worldwide Ltd., Hamilton, Bermuda; *U.S. Private*, pg. 795

Casey, Edward F., Pres. & Chief Exec. Officer--Stewart Smith Group, Inc., Nashville, TN; *Int'l*, pg. 1508

Casey, Edward J. Jr., Pres.--Roanoke Valley Plant, Irvine, CA; *U.S. Public*, pg. 970

Casey, Jim, Gen. Mgr.--Data General (Canada) Ltd., Mississauga, Canada; *U.S. Public*, pg. 485

Casey, John, V.P.--Teradyne Telecommunications Division, Deerfield, IL; *U.S. Public*, pg. 1581

Casey, Richard T., Pres.--F.W. Myers & Co., Rouses Point, NY; *U.S. Private*, pg. 771

Cash, R.D., Chm. Bd.--Questar Development Corporation, Salt Lake City, UT; *U.S. Public*, pg. 1352

Cash, R.D., Chm. Bd.--Questar InfoComm, Salt Lake City, UT; *U.S. Public*, pg. 1352

Cashin, W.A., V.P.--Control Systems Div., Richmond, VA; *Int'l*, pg. 1243

Cashman, Martha, V.P.-International--Land O'Lakes International Division, Minneapolis, MN; *U.S. Private*, pg. 646

Cashman, Martha, V.P.--Ventures Group, Minneapolis, MN; *U.S. Private*, pg. 646

Casier, Dominique, Chief Rep.--Generale Bank, Beijing, China; *Int'l*, pg. 547

Casimir, Bill, Acting Mng. Dir.--ANZ Funds Management, Sydney, Australia; *Int'l*, pg. 98

Casl, Robert, Publisher--Golf Shop Operations, Trumbull, CT; *U.S. Public*, pg. 1174

Casner, Paul G., Jr., Pres.--Electronic Systems Group, Gaithersburg, MD; *U.S. Public*, pg. 474

Caspers, Warner, Sr. V.P.--THP United Enterprises, Waukesha, WI; *Int'l*, pg. 1061

Cass, Peter, Pres.--Transax Data, Bridgewater, NJ; *Int'l*, pg. 1026

Cass, Shirley, District Mgr.--Enthone OMI-Long Beach, Long Beach, CA; *U.S. Public*, pg. 138

Cassaday, Fred, Plant Mgr.--American Natl. Can Co., Piscataway, NJ; *Int'l*, pg. 1029

Cassady, Kenneth, Pres.--Monarch Marking Systems, Miamisburg, OH; *U.S. Public*, pg. 1266

Cassan, Jean-Pierre, Mng. Dir.--Laboratories Astra France, Nanterre, France; *Int'l*, pg. 94

Cassard, Gary E., V.P. & Gen. Mgr.--Cox Cable Greater Ocala, Inc., Ocala, FL; *U.S. Public*, pg. 455

Cassel, William M., Exec. V.P.--Petroleum Division, Phoenix, AZ; *U.S. Private*, pg. 605

Casselman, Hubert, V.P. & Mng. Dir.--GATX National Leasing, Ltd., Toronto, Canada; *U.S. Public*, pg. 691

Cassen, Michael, Admin. Mgr.--Reinshagen Italia Srl., Turin, Italy; *U.S. Public*, pg. 723

Cassese, John J., Pres.--Computer Horizons Corp., Mountain Lakes, NJ; *U.S. Public*, pg. 421

Cassetta, Stephen K., Chief Fin. Officer--Sturgeon Electric Company, Henderson, CO; *U.S. Public*, pg. 1029

Cassey, Rick, V.P. & Gen. Mgr.--WVEE-FM, Atlanta, GA; *U.S. Private*, pg. 470

Cassiano Bastos Filho , Arthur, Chief Exec. Officer--London Representative Office (ESLON), London, United Kingdom; *Int'l*, pg. 1042

Cassidy, Charles T., Sr. V.P. & Mng. Dir.--State Street Bank & Trust Co., London, London, United Kingdom; *U.S. Public*, pg. 1513

Cassidy, Frank, Pres. & Chief Exec. Officer--Energis Resources Incorporated, Edison, NJ; *U.S. Public*, pg. 1340

Cassidy, John F., Jr., Dir.-Res.--United Technologies Research Center, East Hartford, CT; *U.S. Public*, pg. 1690

Cassidy, W.A., Reg. Mgr.--Ames Taping Tools Co. of Canada Limited, Burnaby, Canada; *U.S. Private*, pg. 103

Cassie, Neal, New Bus. Dir.--Leo Burnett Limited, London, United Kingdom; *U.S. Private*, pg. 185

Cassignol, Etienne-Jean, Chief Oper. Officer--Nouvelles Messageries de la Presse Parisienne, Paris, France; *Int'l*, pg. 793

Cassin, B., Gen. Mgr.--Baring Brothers International, New York, NY; *Int'l*, pg. 647

Cassina, Franco, Pres.--Cassina, Milan, Italy; *Int'l*, pg. 570

Cassina, Umberto, V.P.-Contracts--Cassina, Milan, Italy; *Int'l*, pg. 570

Cassis, Jorge, Mng. Dir.--Leo Burnett Chile, Santiago, Chile; *U.S. Private*, pg. 185

Castaing, Bernard, V.P. & Gen. Mgr.-Laundry, Cleaning & Paper Prods.-France--Procter & Gamble France, Neuilly-sur-Seine, France; *U.S. Public*, pg. 1332

Castan, Leopoldo Garcia, Gen. Dir.--Lever Iberica S.A., Madrid, Spain; *Int'l*, pg. 1437

Castaneda, Gus, Branch Mgr.--Union-Transport Corporation-Miami Office, Miami, FL; *U.S. Private*, pg. 1119

Castaneda, Juan Miguel, Gen. Dir.--Fundacion GCN S.A., Mexico, Mexico; *U.S. Public*, pg. 1043

Castberg, Anders Stang, Branch Mgr.--Christiania Bank-Stockholm Branch, Stockholm, Sweden; *Int'l*, pg. 289

Casteel, Ritchie, Div. Mgr.--Utah Division, Salt Lake City, UT; *U.S. Public*, pg. 39

Castel-Branco, Pedro, Media Dir.--Cineponto/Leo Burnett Publicidade Lda., Lisbon, Portugal; *U.S. Private*, pg. 184

Casteline, John R., Mgr.-Prod.--Aquamine, LLC, Bristol, TN; *U.S. Private*, pg. 1138

Castellani, F., Pres.--Compagnie Francaise des Petroles (Algerie) CFP (A), Paris, France; *Int'l*, pg. 1409

Castellano, Robert J., Pres.--Cucina Classica Italiana, Inc., Lakewood, NJ; *U.S. Public*, pg. 1435

Castellano, Steve, Pres.--Todd-AO Studios/East, New York, NY; *U.S. Public*, pg. 1619

Castellanos, Jaime, Chm. Bd.--S&C Willis Corroon Correduria de Seguros y Reaseguros S.A., Madrid, Spain; *Int'l*, pg. 1509

Castelli, Giulio, Chm. Bd.--Ambrofid Gestioni Fiduciarie S.p.A., Milan, Italy; *Int'l*, pg. 138

Castellon, Diego, Pres.--MacGregor Golf France S.A., Paris, France; *Int'l*, pg. 73

Caster, Douglas, Mng. Dir.--Ultra Electronics Sonar & Communications Systems, Greenford, United Kingdom; *Int'l*, pg. 1431

Caster, Robert, Pres. & Chief Exec. Officer--Lennox Industries (Canada) Ltd., Calgary, Canada; *U.S. Private*, pg. 660

Casterlin, Carl, Mgr.--Selective Insurance Company-Northern New Jersey Branch, Branchville, NJ; *U.S. Public*, pg. 1455

Castillo, J., Gen. Mgr.--Sun Electric de Mexico S.A. de C.V., Mexico, Mexico; *U.S. Public*, pg. 1481

Castillo, Rigoberto, Ing., Chief Oper. Officer--Cydsa S.A. Packaging Div., Garza Garcia, Mexico; *Int'l*, pg. 246

Castillo, Vicente T., Gen. Mgr.--Banco Santander Philippines Ltd., Manila, Philippines; *Int'l*, pg. 144

Castillon, Enrique, Director General--Seguros Monterrey, S.A., Mexico, Mexico; *U.S. Public*, pg. 27

Castle, A.M., Pres.--Astro Homes, Shippenville, PA; *U.S. Public*, pg. 318

Castle, A.M., Pres.--Brigadier Homes of North Carolina, Nashville, NC; *U.S. Public*, pg. 318

Castle, A.M., Pres.--Mansion Homes, Robbins, NC; *U.S. Public*, pg. 318

Castle, Richard C., Plant Mgr.--Vicksburg Plant, Vicksburg, MS; *U.S. Public*, pg. 1348

Castle, Ron, Pres.--SICO South Pacific, Berkeley Vale, Australia; *U.S. Private*, pg. 998

Castleberry, W. Thomas, Chief Exec. Officer--RezSolutions, Inc., Phoenix, AZ; *Int'l*, pg. 1098

Caston, R.W., Mng. Dir.--Trusthoase Forte plc, London, United Kingdom; *Int'l*, pg. 170

Castorena Sanchez-Gavito, Dario, Ing., Gen. Mgr.--Morton Thiokol S.A. de C.V., Mexico, Mexico; *U.S. Public*, pg. 1136

Castoriano, M., Mgr.--Parker Hannifin do Brazil Industria Comercio Ltda., Sao Paulo, Brazil; *U.S. Public*, pg. 1263

Castorina, Orlando, V.P.-Opers.--Monroe Forgings Inc., Rochester, NY; *Int'l*, pg. 488

Castro Herrera, Roberto, Pres. & Gen. Mgr.--Elevadores Otis, S.A. de C.V., Mexico, Mexico; *U.S. Public*, pg. 1691

Castro, Adolfo, Chief Exec. Officer--Lowe MBAC, Barcelona, Spain; *U.S. Private*, pg. 678

Castro, Antonio, Pres.--Aceromex Atlas, S.A. de C.V., Tlalnepantla, Mexico; *U.S. Public*, pg. 308

Castro, Carlos, Ind. Rels. Dir.--Gillette de Mexico S.A. de C.V., Mexico, Mexico; *U.S. Public*, pg. 744

Castro, J.H., Pres. & Gen. Mgr.--R.P. Scherer Argentina S.A.I.C., Buenos Aires, Argentina; *U.S. Public*, pg. 1438

Castro, J.L., Sr. Representative-Tech. Sls.--Ceramicas Termicas de Guatemala S.A., Guatemala, Guatemala; *Int'l*, pg. 894

Castro, John W., Pres.--K.F. Merrill Company, Saint Paul, MN; *U.S. Public*, pg. 1097

Castro, W.A., Gen. Mgr.--Wellcome Philippines Inc, Manila, Philippines; *Int'l*, pg. 553

Castroviejo, Jordi J., Reg. Sls. Mgr.--Square D Company Espana S.A., Barcelona, Spain; *Int'l*, pg. 1209

Castrucci, George E., Pres.--GACC Holding Company, Cincinnati, OH; *U.S. Public*, pg. 75

Casty, Ronald, Pres.--Webster Industries Div., Peabody, MA; *U.S. Private*, pg. 231

Caswell, Dan, Gen. Mgr.--Wadkin USA, Greensboro, NC; *Int'l*, pg. 231

Caswell, Graham, Gen. Mgr.--Kelly (UK) Services Ltd., Kingston upon Thames, United Kingdom; *U.S. Public*, pg. 949

Caswell, William B., Pres.--Saratoga Processing Company Ltd., Vancouver, Canada; *Int'l*, pg. 1492

Catalani, John, Gen. Mgr.--Surplus Warehouse-Greenville, Greenville, MS; *U.S. Private*, pg. 119

Catalani, Riccardo, V.P. & Gen. Mgr.-Laundry, Cleaning & Paper Prods.-Italy--Procter & Gamble Italia S.p.A., Rome, Italy; *U.S. Public*, pg. 1332

Catalano, Joseph P., V.P.--Fortis Long Term Care, Milwaukee, WI; *Int'l*, pg. 499

Catan, Ruben, Pres.--Industrias Sola Basic, Mexico, Mexico; *U.S. Public*, pg. 727

Catapole, Steven, Mgr.--Laporte Fluorides, Rotherham, United Kingdom; *Int'l*, pg. 802

Catchpole, Barrie, Gen. Mgr.--Quilter & Co. Ltd., London, United Kingdom; *Int'l*, pg. 343
Cate, Rufus, Jr., Branch Mgr.--Bergen Brunswig Medical Corporation, Mobile, AL; *U.S. Public*, pg. 214
Catena, N., Chief Oper. Officer--FATA-New Hunter Engineering S.p.A, Turin, Italy; *Int'l*, pg. 474
Cater, John T., Pres.--Compass Bank Houston, Houston, TX; *U.S. Public*, pg. 419
Cates, Winfred R., V.P. & Gen. Mgr.--Cabot Canada Ltd., Sarnia, Canada; *U.S. Public*, pg. 289
Catesby, Peter, Chm.--Vaux Inns Ltd., Sunderland, United Kingdom; *Int'l*, pg. 1454
Catey, Stan, Plant Mgr.--Essex Plant, Belden Wire & Cable, Essex Junction, VT; *U.S. Public*, pg. 201
Cather, Brian, Gen. Mgr.--The Original Chili Bowl, Inc., Tulsa, OK; *U.S. Private*, pg. 1182
Catheral, Peter, Mgr.-Opers.--Dexter Packaging Products Div., Deeside, United Kingdom; *U.S. Public*, pg. 505
Cathey, Peter, Pres. & Chief Exec. Officer--DFI/Inflight, Inc., Ridgefield, CT; *Int'l*, pg. 103
Catindig, Sydney, Gen. Dir.--Right Computer Systems, Manila, Philippines; *U.S. Public*, pg. 1043
Cation, Kenneth L., Grp. Pres.--Atlas/Soundolier, Fenton, MO; *U.S. Private*, pg. 64
Catling, Alan, Pres.--Inchcape Dodwell K.K., Tokyo, Japan; *Int'l*, pg. 672
Cato, Albert, Mgr.--General Employment Enterprises, Inc., San Jose, CA; *U.S. Public*, pg. 714
Cato, Kenneth, Pres.--Osby Armatur AB, Osby, Sweden; *Int'l*, pg. 1323
Catonnet, M., Chief Oper. Officer--Societe des Bouchages, Emballages et Conditionnement Modernes, Lavardac, France; *Int'l*, pg. 919
Catrambone, John, Pres.--Omnirel Corporation, Leominster, MA; *U.S. Public*, pg. 1792
Catsicas, Costas, Sls. & Mktg. Mgr.--Whitehall Greece, Athens, Greece; *U.S. Public*, pg. 82
Catsimatidis, John A., Pres. & Treas.--United Refining Inc., Warren, PA; *U.S. Private*, pg. 915
Catt, Charles J., Mng. Dir.--NAC Reinsurance International Limited, London, United Kingdom; *U.S. Public*, pg. 1144
Cattaneo, Carlo, Gen. Mgr.--Banca Agricola Milanese S.p.A., Milan, Italy; *Int'l*, pg. 137
Cattaneo, Stelio, Plant Mgr.--Avigliano Mill, Potenza, Italy; *U.S. Public*, pg. 673
Cattaneo, Stelio, Plant Mgr.--Castelnuovo Mill, Castelnuovo di Garfagnana, Italy; *U.S. Public*, pg. 673
Cattani, G., Chief Oper. Officer--FATA European Group S.p.A, Parma, Italy; *Int'l*, pg. 474
Cattapan, Domenico, Chief Oper. Officer--Kyowa Italiana Farmaceutici s.r.l., Milan, Italy; *Int'l*, pg. 778
Caterall, F. A., Dr., Mng. Dir.--Glaxo Far East Pte. Ltd., Singapore, Singapore; *Int'l*, pg. 553
Caterall, F.A., Dr., Mng. Dir.--Glaxochem Pte. Ltd., Singapore, Singapore; *Int'l*, pg. 553
Cattivera, Joseph, Pres. & Chief Exec. Officer--Angeles Funding Corporation, Los Angeles, CA; *U.S. Private*, pg. 74
Cattoi, Ed, Plant Mgr.--Trus Joist (Western) Ltd., Surrey, Canada; *U.S. Public*, pg. 1556
Catton, P., Chm. & Mng. Dir.--Butler Newall Limited-Butler Machine Tool Div., Halifax, United Kingdom; *Int'l*, pg. 448
Caudell, J. Keith, Pres.--National Bank of Walton County, Monroe, GA; *U.S. Public*, pg. 1549
Caudill, E.B., Gen. Mgr.--PACCAR Parts, Renton, WA; *U.S. Public*, pg. 1246
Caughey, Dick, Gen. Mgr.--Quality Incentive & Travel, Memphis, TN; *U.S. Public*, pg. 653
Caughman, Gerald W., Pres.--Power Sources, Inc., Charlotte, NC; *U.S. Public*, pg. 344
Caulo, Ralph, Pres.--Simon & Schuster Education Group, Upper Saddle River, NJ; *U.S. Private*, pg. 778
Caurette, J.R., Mgr.--Sepam, Courbevoie, France; *Int'l*, pg. 1501
Causey, C.R., Pres.--Puget Western, Inc., Bellevue, WA; *U.S. Public*, pg. 1342
Causey, James D., Pres. & Chief Exec. Officer--Tuff Stuff Publications, Inc., Richmond, VA; *U.S. Public*, pg. 291
Causey, James D., Chief Exec. Officer--Cadmus Custom Publishing, Boston, MA; *U.S. Public*, pg. 291
Causey, Jerry L., Pres.--Virginia Natural Gas, Inc., Norfolk, VA; *U.S. Public*, pg. 436
Cauthen, Michael, Gen. Mgr.--Maryland Ribbon Company, Hagerstown, MD; *U.S. Private*, pg. 812
Cauthen, Robert S., Jr., Pres.--American General Life Insurance Company, Houston, TX; *U.S. Public*, pg. 76
Cavaliere, Phyllis, Pres. & Chief Exec. Officer--Sunday Magazine Network, New York, NY; *U.S. Private*, pg. 739
Cavalli-Bjorkman, Magnus, Mng. Dir.--Skandinaviska Enskilda Banken Hong Kong, Hong Kong, Hong Kong; *Int'l*, pg. 1259
Cavalli, Alberto, Rep.--Sanpaolo-Moscow Representative Office, Moscow, Russia; *Int'l*, pg. 692
Cavallo, Barbara J., Div. Controller--Pipeline & Surface Facilities Division, Houston, TX; *U.S. Public*, pg. 1443
Cavallo, Ernest J., Pres. & Chief Oper. Officer--Triarc Beverage Group, White Plains, NY; *U.S. Public*, pg. 1635
Cavanagh, Daniel J., Pres. & Chief Exec. Officer--Metropolitan Property & Casualty Insurance Co. (Met P&C), Warwick, RI; *U.S. Private*, pg. 737
Cavanagh, Patrick W., V.P. & Gen. Mgr.--Synchro-Start Products, Inc., Niles, IL; *U.S. Private*, pg. 627
Cavanagh, W., Mng. Dir.--EMI Records (Ireland) Ltd., Dublin, Ireland; *Int'l*, pg. 427
cavanash, Mike, Mgr.-Office--Edwards & Kelcey Engineers, Inc., New York, NY; *U.S. Private*, pg. 364
Cavanaugh, James, Gen. Mgr.--Poly-Craft Systems, Cottage Grove, OR; *U.S. Public*, pg. 229
Cavanaugh, Mike, Exec. Editor--BNA Business Information Division, Washington, DC; *U.S. Private*, pg. 181
Cavazos, Joel, Gen. Mgr.--C&C Bakery Inc., Kingsville, TX; *Int'l*, pg. 575
Cavazos, Ricardo A., Chief Oper. Officer--Griffith Panama S.A., Panama, Panama; *U.S. Private*, pg. 481
Cavell, Charles G., Pres.--Quebecor Printing Hazleton Inc., Hazleton, PA; *Int'l*, pg. 1076
Cavendish, William A., Gen. Mgr.--Home Products Italiana SpA, Milan, Italy; *U.S. Public*, pg. 81
Cavers, Timothy, Branch Mgr.--Zellerbach Division, Novi, MI; *U.S. Public*, pg. 1075
Cavitt, Jerry, Pres. & Chief Oper. Officer--President Baking-Augusta, Augusta, GA; *Int'l*, pg. 1069
Cavoorees, John, Chm.--Chubb Insurance Company of Europe, Brussels, Belgium; *U.S. Public*, pg. 355
Cawley, Charles M., Chm. Bd., Pres. & Chief Exec. Officer--MBNA America Bank N.A., Wilmington, DE; *U.S. Public*, pg. 1023
Cawley, Thomas J., Pres.--Mount Holly Water Co., Mount Holly, NJ; *U.S. Public*, pg. 540
Cawley, Timothy J., Pres.--Ameritech Small Business Services, Hoffman Estates, IL; *U.S. Public*, pg. 98
Cawly, Robert H., Pres. & Chief Exec. Officer--Sentry Technology Group, Westborough, MA; *U.S. Public*, pg. 1425
Cawte, Dennis, Mng. Dir.--Keystone Valve (U.K.) Ltd., Glasgow, United Kingdom; *U.S. Public*, pg. 1650
Cawthorn, Robert E., Chief Oper. Officer--Rorer-Inter-American Corp., Collegeville, PA; *Int'l*, pg. 1111
Caycedo, Mauricio, Gen. Mgr.--Pintacasa, Valencia, Venezuela; *Int'l*, pg. 332
Cazzolla, Peter, Pres.--California Capital Insurance Company, Monterey, CA; *U.S. Private*, pg. 613
Cebrian Sanchez, Juan Jose, Pres.--Proyeparsons, C.A., Caracas, Venezuela; *U.S. Private*, pg. 842
Cecan, Ayhan, Chm.--Markom/Leo Burnett A.S., Istanbul, Turkey; *U.S. Private*, pg. 186
Ceccarelli, Massimo, Gen. Mgr.--Biotec International S.R.L., Bologna, Italy; *U.S. Public*, pg. 1083
Ceccaroli, Bruno, Plant Mgr.--Elkem Fiskaa Silicon, Kristiansand, Norway; *Int'l*, pg. 448
Ceccatelli, Ercole, Mng. Dir.--Banco di Roma, Rome, Italy; *Int'l*, pg. 652
Cecchettini, R.A., Pres.--Title Insurance Company of Minnesota, Minneapolis, MN; *U.S. Public*, pg. 1218
Cecchi, Bill, Mgr.--BlueLine Software Inc., Saint Paul, MN; *U.S. Public*, pg. 120
Cecil, Reed H., Sec.--Tenneco United Kingdom Holdings Limited, London, United Kingdom; *U.S. Public*, pg. 1580
Cecil, Robert S., Pres.--LIN Cellular Group, Kirkland, WA; *U.S. Public*, pg. 11
Cecil, Roy, V.P.-Mfg.--Monroe City Division, Monroe City, MO; *U.S. Public*, pg. 986
Cecil, Wink, Base Mgr.--Mercury Air Center, Bakersfield, CA; *U.S. Public*, pg. 1093
Cecilia, Diane, Lab Mgr.--Quest Diagnostic-Fulton, Fulton, NY; *U.S. Public*, pg. 1351
Cecilia, Diane, Lab. Mgr.--Quest Diagnostic-Syracuse, Syracuse, NY; *U.S. Public*, pg. 1352
Cedeno, Mario, Gen. Mgr.--Wackenhut, S.A., San Jose, Costa Rica; *U.S. Public*, pg. 1732
Cederborg, Thomas, Mgr.--NAF AB, Linkoping, Sweden; *Int'l*, pg. 1422
Cederborgh, Claes, Gen. Mgr.--Nielsen Design AB, Sollentuna, Sweden; *Int'l*, pg. 459
Cederstrom, Clas, Mng. Dir.--Ericsson Mobilfunk GmbH, Dusseldorf, Germany; *Int'l*, pg. 1367
Cedwall, Jan, Pres.--Thorsman & Co. AB, Nykoping, Sweden; *Int'l*, pg. 678
Cefalo, Romeo R., Sr. V.P. & Gen. Mgr.--Lucky Stores Southern California Division, Buena Park, CA; *U.S. Public*, pg. 93
Cekela, V. W., Chief Oper. Officer--Krupp Wilputte Corp., Bridgeville, PA; *Int'l*, pg. 512
Cela, J., Chief Exec. Officer--Zurich Compania de Seguros sobre la Vida, Barcelona, Spain; *Int'l*, pg. 1529
Cela, J., Chief Exec. Officer--Zurich Compania de Seguros, Barcelona, Spain; *Int'l*, pg. 1531
Cela, J., Chief Exec. Officer--Caudal S.A. de Seguros y Reaseguros, Madrid, Spain; *Int'l*, pg. 1531
Celentano, E., Pres.--Getty Oil (Guatemala), Inc., Coral Gables, FL; *U.S. Public*, pg. 1583
Celentano, E., Pres.--Lubricantes y Tambores del Ecuador, C.A., Guayaquil, Ecuador; *U.S. Public*, pg. 1584
Celentano, E., Pres.--Texaco Chile S.A.C., Santiago, Chile; *U.S. Public*, pg. 1584
Celentano, E., Pres.--Texaco Cote d'Ivorie, Abidjan, Cote d'Ivoire; *U.S. Public*, pg. 1584
Celentano, E., Chm. Bd.--Texaco Interamerican Exploration Co., Bridgetown, Barbados; *U.S. Public*, pg. 1584
Celentano, E., Chm.--Texaco Panama Inc., Panama, Panama; *U.S. Public*, pg. 1584
Celentano, E., Chm. Bd.--Texaco Petroleum Co., Quito, Ecuador; *U.S. Public*, pg. 1584
Celentano, E., Chm.--Texaco Trinidad, Inc., Port of Spain, Trinidad & Tobago; *U.S. Public*, pg. 1584
Celentano, E., Pres.--Texaco Uruguay Sociedad Anonima, Montevideo, Uruguay; *U.S. Public*, pg. 1584
Celinder, S., Gen. Mgr.--Wellcome Danmark A/S, Naerum, Denmark; *Int'l*, pg. 553
Celis, Frank E., Sales Mgr.--Aqualon Belgium N.V., Doel, Belgium; *U.S. Public*, pg. 810
Cella, S., Mng. Dir.--Simon-Cella S.r.l., Castegnato, Italy; *Int'l*, pg. 1252
Celler, Nicolas, V.P.--Sulzer Infra S.A., Courbevoie, France; *Int'l*, pg. 1306
Cellerino, J., Opers. Dir.--EMI-Odeon SAIC, Buenos Aires, Argentina; *Int'l*, pg. 427
Celli, Oscar, Base Mgr.--Weatherford Services S.A., Pointe Noire, Congo; *U.S. Public*, pg. 1750
Cellini, Melvin, Pres.-Production--Bisceglia Brothers Wine Co., Madera, CA; *U.S. Public*, pg. 300
Cels, Roger, Mng. Dir.--Triumph Releasing Corporation - Pacific Territory, Los Angeles, CA; *Int'l*, pg. 1282
Cenal, J., Mng. Dir.--GKN Ayra Cardan SA, Deba, Spain; *Int'l*, pg. 535
Ceniga, Alberto, Mng. Dir.--Formica Espanola S.A., Bilbao, Spain; *Int'l*, pg. 129
Cenker, Ismail, Gen. Mgr.--Bundy SpA, Istanbul, Turkey; *Int'l*, pg. 1341
Centaures, Marc, Chief Oper. Officer--Huhtamaki Finance B.V., Lausanne, Switzerland; *Int'l*, pg. 639
Centella, Larry, Mng. Dir.--Gambro Healthcare, Lakewood, CO; *Int'l*, pg. 667
Center, Carl N., Pres.--Utility Tree Service, Eureka, CA; *U.S. Private*, pg. 119
Center, Robert, Pres.--STI Optronics, Bellevue, WA; *Int'l*, pg. 1289
Centerman, Jorgen, Pres.--Asea Brown Boveri Pte. Ltd., Jurong, Singapore; *Int'l*, pg. 8
Centrello, Gina, Pres. & Publisher--Pocket Books, New York, NY; *U.S. Private*, pg. 777
Cerana, Nicoletta, Mng. Dir.--Ketchum Public Relations, SRL, Milan, Italy; *U.S. Private*, pg. 617
Ceravolo, Thomas, Gen. Mgr.--Lockport Union Sun & Journal, Lockport, NY; *U.S. Public*, pg. 1078
Cereda, Gianni, Pres.--GenCorp Printworld, New York, NY; *U.S. Public*, pg. 706
Cereda, Gianni, Pres.--GenCorp Printworld, Monroe, NC; *U.S. Public*, pg. 706
Ceresa, Attilio, Pres.-Italy Opers. & Gen. Mgr.--Biffi Italia S.r.l., Piacenza, Italy; *U.S. Public*, pg. 1650
Cereti, Fausto, Chm.--Alenia, Naples, Italy; *Int'l*, pg. 653
Cerini, Elio, V.P. & Gen. Mgr.--Unisys Italia S.p.A., Milan, Italy; *U.S. Public*, pg. 1671
Cerini, F. Brian, Pres. & Chief Exec. Officer--Sierra Capital Management, Northridge, CA; *U.S. Public*, pg. 1742
Cerini, F. Brian, Pres.--Sierra Capital Management Corporation, Los Angeles, CA; *U.S. Public*, pg. 1742
Cernak, Werner F., Mng. Dir.--Janssen Cilag GmbH, Neuss, Germany; *U.S. Public*, pg. 929
Cernibori, Livio, Pres.--Neo Abello S.p.A., Ospiate di Bollate, Italy; *Int'l*, pg. 289
Cerny, Bohumil, Mgr.--Westvaco Svitavy, SPOL, S.R.O., Svitavy, Czech Republic; *U.S. Public*, pg. 1763
Cerny, Dennis, Mgr.--Plastic Suppliers, Inc., Marietta, GA; *U.S. Private*, pg. 871
Cerny, Ronald, Pres.--The J.M. Ney Company, Bloomfield, CT; *U.S. Public*, pg. 111
Ceron, Marcelino, Media Dir.--Causa Publicidad, Lima, Peru; *U.S. Private*, pg. 184
Cerqueira Lopes, J., Chief Exec. Officer--AXIMS Acos Especiais Lda, Linda-a-Velha, Portugal; *Int'l*, pg. 710
Cerri, Fabrizio, Dir.--Banca d'America e d'Italia S.p.A. (Firenze), Florence, Italy; *Int'l*, pg. 403
Ceruzzi, Louis, V.P. & Sec.--Massachusetts Container Corporation, Marlborough, MA; *U.S. Private*, pg. 263
Cervantes, Mauro, Gen. Mgr.--BHP Steel Building Products (Sarawak) Sdn Bhd, Kuching, Malaysia; *Int'l*, pg. 226
Cervantos, Alfredo, Exploration Mgr.--Mexicoro S.A. de C.V., Hermosillo, Mexico; *Int'l*, pg. 169
Cesar, L.F., Pres.--Plantations Lever au Zaire s.a.r.l., Kinshasa, Congo; *Int'l*, pg. 1438
Cespedes, Maria, Mgr.--Circle International, Miami, FL; *U.S. Public*, pg. 372
Cetti, J., Mng. Dir.--Videojet Ltd., Hatfield, United Kingdom; *Int'l*, pg. 546
Ch'ng, A.L. (Anne), Rep.--Westpac Banking Corp.-Malaysia, Kuala Lumpur, Malaysia; *Int'l*, pg. 1497
Cha, Kevin, Asst. Mgr.--International Aero-Sea Forwarders, Inc., Inglewood, CA; *Int'l*, pg. 683
Chabannes, Jean-Antoine, Mng. Dir.--Societe suisse (France), Paris, France; *Int'l*, pg. 1332
Chabot, G., Dist. Mgr.--A.M. Castle & Co. (Canada), Inc., Pointe-Claire, Canada; *U.S. Public*, pg. 313
Chabot, Jacques, V.P.--Guay, Blouin, & Associates, Inc., Sainte-Foy, Canada; *Int'l*, pg. 1509
Chabot, Martial, V.P.--Imprimerie Quebecor Magog, Magog, Canada; *Int'l*, pg. 1077
Chabot, Martial, V.P.--Imprimerie Quebecor Montreal, Montreal, Canada; *Int'l*, pg. 1077
Chabot, Martial, V.P.--Quebecor Photolitho, Pointe-Claire, Canada; *Int'l*, pg. 1077
Chacas Lessa, Wiz Fernando, Gen. Mgr.--Banco do Brasil S.A.-Japan, Tokyo, Japan; *Int'l*, pg. 141
Chace, Eugene, Gen. Mgr.--Forbo America Inc., Wilmington, DE; *Int'l*, pg. 497
Chachawal, Somboon, Mng. Dir.--Siam Cellulose Co., Ltd., Bangkok, Thailand; *Int'l*, pg. 1238
Chacm, Juan Pena, Plant Mgr.--AlliedSignal Automotive Ltda., Sao Paulo, Brazil; *U.S. Public*, pg. 52
Chacon, Juan Pena, Plant Mgr.--AlliedSignal Automotive Ltda., Guarulhos, Brazil; *U.S. Public*, pg. 52
Chadronnier, J. M., Pres. & Dir. Gen.--Grands Terroirs Associes BV, Nieuw-Vennep, Netherlands; *Int'l*, pg. 751
Chadronnier, J.M., Pres. & Gen. Dir.--C.V.B.G. (Consortium Vinicole de Bordeaux et de la Gironde), Blanquefort, France; *Int'l*, pg. 751
Chadwick, Bruce A., Chief Exec. Officer--Kelley Advertising Inc., Toronto, Canada; *U.S. Public*, pg. 765
Chadwick, Fred, Pres.-Los Angeles Div.--Rollins Hudig Hall of Southern California, Universal City, CA; *U.S. Public*, pg. 117
Chadwick, Martin, Mgr.-Opers.--General Magnaplate California, Ventura, CA; *U.S. Public*, pg. 717
Chadwick, Simon, Chief Exec. Officer--Winona Research, Phoenix, AZ; *Int'l*, pg. 1483
Chae, Hong-shik, Chief Rep.--Kexim Asia Limited, Central, Hong Kong; *Int'l*, pg. 468
Chae, Yoon-Byung, Pres.--Ssangyong Developments Pte. Ltd., Singapore, Singapore; *Int'l*, pg. 1292
Chaffe, George A., Mng. Dir.--Skandia International Risk Management (Vermont), Inc., Burlington, VT; *Int'l*, pg. 1257
Chaffe, Mike, Dir.--McCarthy Bailey Limited, Birmingham, United Kingdom; *Int'l*, pg. 133
Chaffin, R.C., Pres.--Capital Assurance Company, Inc., Coral Gables, FL; *Int'l*, pg. 1257
Chaffin, Richard, Pres.--Gillette Dairy of the Black Hills, Inc., Rapid City, SD; *U.S. Public*, pg. 1152

Chaffin, Richard, Pres.--Nebraska Dairies, Inc., Norfolk, NE; *U.S. Public*, pg. 1152

Chaffringeon, Andre, Chief Exec. Officer--Banque Nationale de Paris (Canada), Montreal, Canada; *Int'l*, pg. 164

Chai, C.F., Chief Oper. Officer & Mng. Dir.--Littelfuse Fareast, PTE Ltd., Singapore, Singapore; *U.S. Public*, pg. 1001

Chainet, Martial, Gen. Mgr.--Fleming Finance S.A., Paris, France; *Int'l*, pg. 493

Chainey, David E., Mgr.-Sls. & Mktg.--Amicon Canada Ltd., Oakville, Canada; *U.S. Public*, pg. 1113

Chais, Khom, Pres.--JMP Newcor International Inc., Northbrook, IL; *Int'l*, pg. 1025

Chakrubarty, Tapan, Country Rep.--CPC/AJI (Singapore) Pte. Ltd., Singapore, Singapore; *U.S. Public*, pg. 225

Chalhoub, Joseph, Pres.--Breslube Division of Safety-Kleen Canada Inc., Breslau, Canada; *U.S. Public*, pg. 1426

Chali, Riad, V.P. & Mng. Dir.--MISR-America International Bank S.A.E., Cairo, Egypt; *U.S. Public*, pg. 183

Chalin, William, Pres. & Chief Oper. Officer--Bertelsmann Printing & Manufacturing Corp., Berryville, VA; *Int'l*, pg. 191

Chalker, John, Grp. Chm.--Maritz Europa Limited, Marlow, United Kingdom; *U.S. Private*, pg. 704

Chalklin, Dave, Gen. Mgr.--Astronautics U.K., Camberley, United Kingdom; *U.S. Private*, pg. 93

Challacombe, Nick, Gen. Mgr.--Keithley Instruments Ltd., Reading, United Kingdom; *U.S. Public*, pg. 947

Challe, Bruno, Gen. Mgr.--Paris Learning Center, Le Bourget, France; *U.S. Public*, pg. 219

Challender, Jerry, Gen. Mgr.--Ademco de Juarez, Chihuahua, Mexico; *U.S. Public*, pg. 1307

Challioris, A.N., Gen. Mgr.--Wyeth Hellas EPE, Athens, Greece; *U.S. Public*, pg. 82

Challis, C.E., Dir.--Yellow Pages Sales Limited, London, United Kingdom; *Int'l*, pg. 222

Chalmers, Bernie, Pres.--NBS Imprinter, Kitchener, Canada; *Int'l*, pg. 898

Chalmers, Brian, Opers. Mgr.--Amway of Canada, Ltd., London, Canada; *U.S. Private*, pg. 70

Chalmers, Peter S., Pres.--NationsBank Lease Investments, Inc., Charlotte, NC; *U.S. Public*, pg. 1165

Chalmers, W. R., Mng. Dir.--Avery Label Systems Ltd., Maidenhead, United Kingdom; *U.S. Public*, pg. 153

Chaloupek, Kenneth W., Gen. Plant Mgr.--UTA Iowa City Plant, Iowa City, IA; *U.S. Public*, pg. 1691

Chaloux, Leonard, Pres.--Taylor Hobson Pneumo, Rolling Meadows, IL; *Int'l*, pg. 1087

Chalsty, John S., Pres. & Chief Exec. Officer--Donaldson, Lufkin & Jenrette Securities Corp., New York, NY; *U.S. Public*, pg. 589

Chambat, A., Gen. Mgr.--Kilometrage S.A., Neuilly-sur-Seine, France; *Int'l*, pg. 650

Chamberlain, Everett, Plant Mgr.--Ringier America, Phoenix Division, Phoenix, AZ; *U.S. Public*, pg. 1778

Chamberlain, G. S., Gen. Mgr.--Abdulla Fouad Impalloy Ltd. Co., Dammam, Saudi Arabia; *Int'l*, pg. 502

Chamberlain, Mark, Mgr.-Plant Opers.--Red Wing Company, San Jose, CA; *Int'l*, pg. 1398

Chamberlain, Phillip, V.P. & Controller--BarcaLounger Company, Rocky Mount, NC; *U.S. Private*, pg. 265

Chamberlain, Robin, Pres.--Snapper Power Equipment, Mc Donough, GA; *U.S. Public*, pg. 1103

Chamberland, Claude, Pres.--Alcan Smelters & Chemicals Ltd., Montreal, Canada; *Int'l*, pg. 50

Chambers, Chris, Pres.--Continental Homes of California, San Diego, CA; *U.S. Public*, pg. 441

Chambers, Chuck, Chief Oper. Officer--Sara Lee Direct, Winston Salem, NC; *U.S. Public*, pg. 1434

Chambers, Dale, Gen. Mgr.--Empire Livestock Marketing Inc., Syracuse, NY; *U.S. Private*, pg. 308

Chambers, David, Chm. Bd.--Merrill Lynch Fiduciary Services, Inc., New York, NY; *U.S. Public*, pg. 1098

Chambers, Glenn, Pres.--Heil Environmental Industries, Chattanooga, TN; *U.S. Public*, pg. 520

Chambers, Harry, Chief Oper. Officer--Armstrong Fastenings Ltd., Kingston-upon-Hull, United Kingdom; *Int'l*, pg. 265

Chambers, James, Controller--Wyle Laboratories-Eastern Operations, Huntsville, AL; *U.S. Private*, pg. 1193

Chambers, R.A., Chief Fin. Officer--The Glacier Metal Co. Ltd., Northwood, United Kingdom; *Int'l*, pg. 1334

Chambers, Roland, Gen. Mgr.--Louis Kemp Seafood Company, Duluth, MN; *U.S. Public*, pg. 1652

Chambraud, Eric, Mng. Dir.--Dumez Moscou, Moscow, Russia; *Int'l*, pg. 823

Chamides, Ronald H., Pres.--Fleet Credit Corporation, Providence, RI; *U.S. Public*, pg. 650

Chamides, Ronald H., Pres.--Fleet Capital Leasing, Providence, RI; *U.S. Public*, pg. 650

Chaminadour, Bernard, Mng. Dir.--Allo Pro France Sarl, Paris, France; *Int'l*, pg. 1307

Chamla, Alain, Chief Oper. Officer--CSR Pampryl, La Courneuve, France; *Int'l*, pg. 566

Champel, Louis, Pres.--Rhodia-Merieux Chile, Santiago, Chile; *Int'l*, pg. 1112

Champion, Mike, Plant Mgr.--Fleming-Potter Fast Printing, Peoria, IL; *U.S. Private*, pg. 411

Champlin, Kathleen, Admin.--Washington Square Nursing Center, Warren, OH; *U.S. Public*, pg. 838

Champness, G., Pres. & Chief Exec. Officer--Svedala Industries Inc., York, PA; *Int'l*, pg. 1325

Chamroendararussamee, Surachat, Mng. Dir.--The Siam Fiberglass Co., Ltd., Bangkok, Thailand; *Int'l*, pg. 1238

Chan, Alex, Gen. Mgr.--Hewlett-Packard Singapore Pte. Ltd., Singapore, Singapore; *U.S. Public*, pg. 822

Chan, Andrew, Chief Oper. Officer--A & A Intl. (YICHI-HK) Ltd., Kowloon, Hong Kong; *U.S. Public*, pg. 1561

Chan, C., Mng. Dir.--Ascom Timeplex Far East Ltd., Hong Kong, Hong Kong; *Int'l*, pg. 87

Chan, Dawen, Rep.--Generale Belgian Bank, Taipei, Taiwan; *Int'l*, pg. 547

Chan, Eric C.W., Mng. Dir.--Esselte Ltd., Wan Chai, Hong Kong; *Int'l*, pg. 461

Chan, Francis, Admin. Mgr.--Ecolab Pte. Ltd., Jurong, Singapore; *U.S. Public*, pg. 562

Chan, Gordon, Gen. Mgr.--BHP Steel Building Products (Guangzhou) Ltd., Guangzhou, China; *Int'l*, pg. 226

Chan, Howard, Gen. Mgr.--Cherasia Limited, North Point, Hong Kong; *U.S. Public*, pg. 346

Chan, K.K., Gen. Mgr.--Cobra Electronics International (Hong Kong) Ltd., Kowloon, Hong Kong; *U.S. Public*, pg. 391

Chan, Kwok C., Chief Exec. Officer--LaFehr Chan Technologies, Houston, TX; *U.S. Private*, pg. 642

Chan, Mark, Chief Exec. Officer--Axel Johnson Corp. (Taiwan) Ltd, Neihu, Taiwan; *Int'l*, pg. 711

Chan, Matthew, Pres.--Novellus Singapore Pte Ltd., Singapore, Singapore; *U.S. Public*, pg. 1204

Chan, Matthew, Pres.--Intraco Asia Singapore, Singapore, Singapore; *U.S. Public*, pg. 1205

Chan, Matthew, Pres.--Novellus Systems Taiwan, Hsin-chu, Taiwan; *U.S. Public*, pg. 1205

Chan, Matthew, Pres.--Novellus Systems Shanghai, Shanghai, China; *U.S. Public*, pg. 1205

Chan, Matthew, Gen. Mgr.--Tektronix China Ltd., Wan Chai, Hong Kong; *U.S. Public*, pg. 1567

Chan, Michael, Gen. Mgr.--Silk Air, Singapore, Singapore; *Int'l*, pg. 1374

Chan, P.K., Pres. & Chief Oper. Officer--Hayes Microcomputer Products, Inc., Norcross, GA; *U.S. Public*, *pg. 801*

Chan, Raymond, Chief Fin. Officer--Bensons Metal Products Sdn Bhd, Shah Alam, Malaysia; *Int'l*, pg. 460

Chan, Ronald A., Mng. Dir.--The Bank of Nova Scotia Trinidad and Tobago Limited, Port of Spain, Trinidad & Tobago; *Int'l*, pg. 157

Chan, Ronald A., Mng. Dir.--The Bank of Nova Scotia Trust Company of Trinidad and Tobago Limited, Port of Spain, Trinidad & Tobago; *Int'l*, pg. 157

Chan, Rosalind, Gen. Mgr.--Dentsu Young & Rubicam/ Singapore, Singapore, Singapore; *U.S. Private*, pg. 325

Chan, Simon, Contact--Chemical Asia Ltd., Central, Hong Kong; *U.S. Public*, pg. 341

Chan, Tom, Gen. Mgr.--Enesco International (Hong Kong) Ltd., Kowloon, Hong Kong; *U.S. Public*, pg. 1508

Chan, Trevor, Gen. Mgr.--National Mutual Macao, Macau, Macau; *Int'l*, pg. 908

Chan, W., Controller--Avex Electronics Pte. Ltd., Singapore, Singapore; *U.S. Private*, pg. 545

Chan, Y.P., Gen. Mgr.--Pacific Film Laboratories, Coburg, Australia; *U.S. Public*, pg. 552

Chance, Larry, Dir.--Beloit Corporation-Blackhawk Plant, Rockton, IL; *U.S. Public*, pg. 789

Chancellor, Glenn A., Grp. V.P.--Temple-Inland Forest Products Corp.-Forests Division, Diboll, TX; *U.S. Public*, pg. 1575

Chandak, Ramesh, Mgr.-India--Raychem RPG Limited, Mumbai, India; *U.S. Public*, pg. 1363

Chandler, Al, Mgr.--Helena Sportswear Co., West Helena, AR; *U.S. Public*, pg. 795

Chandler, David L., Pres.--Greater Washington Investments, Inc., Columbus, GA; *U.S. Public*, pg. 933

Chandler, Jeanne, Pres.--Benchmark Appraisal Group, Columbia, MD; *U.S. Public*, pg. 1089

Chandler, Jim, Dir.-Opers.--Intercraft Industries of Canada, Ltd., Mississauga, Canada; *U.S. Public*, pg. 1178

Chandler, Mike, Gen. Mgr.--Crosby-National Swage Co., Jacksonville, AR; *Int'l*, pg. 473

Chandler, T.F., Pres. & Chief Exec. Officer--The Western Sugar Company, Denver, CO; *Int'l*, pg. 1357

Chandler, Tom, Gen. Mgr.--Cadillac Plastic (New Zealand) Ltd., Auckland, New Zealand; *U.S. Public*, pg. 781

Chandler, William F., Jr., Chm.-Management Committee, Principal & Mng. Dir.--National Asset Management Corporation, Louisville, KY; *U.S. Public*, pg. 1154

Chandonnet, Peter, Pres.--SPS Aerospace Products Div., Jenkintown, PA; *U.S. Public*, pg. 1420

Chanecka, Steve, Pres. & Publr.--Senior Spectrum, Sacramento, CA; *U.S. Public*, pg. 1066

Chaney, Andrew, Chm. Bd. & Chief Exec. Officer--Barnett Bank N.A., Jacksonville, FL; *U.S. Public*, pg. 1162

Chaney, E. Thomas, Pres. & Chief Exec. Officer--Community Health Systems, Inc., Brentwood, TN; *U.S. Private*, pg. 419

Chaney, John D., Pres. & Chief Exec. Officer--TeleCheck Services, Inc., Houston, TX; *U.S. Public*, pg. 631

Chaney, John W., Pres.-Cleveland Div.--Rollins Hudig Hall of Ohio, Inc., Cleveland, OH; *U.S. Public*, pg. 117

Chaney, Robert J., V.P. & Gen. Mgr.--Gas Utility Div., Reading, PA; *U.S. Public*, pg. 1653

Chaney, William R., Pres.--Tiffany & Co. International, New York, NY; *U.S. Public*, pg. 1609

Chang, C.C., Mng. Dir.--Singapore Petroleum Co (Japan) Ltd., Tokyo, Japan; *U.S. Public*, pg. 102

Chang, Frederick K.Y., V.P. & Chief Admin. Officer--Fireman's Fund Insurance Co. of Hawaii, Inc., Honolulu, HI; *Int'l*, pg. 59

Chang, Hector, Gen. Dir.--BCTS, Lima, Peru; *U.S. Public*, pg. 1043

Chang, Jack, Chief Exec. Officer--TWI International Taiwan, Inc., Tai-chung, Taiwan; *U.S. Public*, pg. 1749

Chang, Jack, Pres.--CWI International China, Ltd., Fujian, China; *U.S. Public*, pg. 1749

Chang, Jack, Pres.--TWI International, Inc., Cleveland, OH; *U.S. Public*, pg. 1749

Chang, Jay J.H., V.P.-Intl.--Janssen Korea, Ltd., Seoul, Korea; *U.S. Public*, pg. 929

Chang, Jeannette, Publisher--Harper's Bazaar, New York, NY; *U.S. Private*, pg. 517

Chang, Paul, Chief Oper. Officer--Hagglunds Drives Ltd, Tsuen Wan, Hong Kong; *Int'l*, pg. 670

Chang, Roger, Mng. Dir.--World Lock Co. Ltd., Taipei, Taiwan; *U.S. Public*, pg. 548

Chang, Stella, Mng. Dir.--MDK Consultants, Taipei, Taiwan; *Int'l*, pg. 117

Chang, Sung In, Gen. Mgr.--ITW Korea, Inc., Seoul, Korea; *U.S. Public*, pg. 868

Chang, Wu-Hsiung, V.P. & Gen. Mgr.--The International Commercial Bank of China, Osaka, Japan; *Int'l*, pg. 683

Chang, Yeong-Ho, Sr. V.P. & Country Mgr.--Bank of America NT&SA, Seoul, Korea; *U.S. Public*, pg. 182

Channell, Jeff, Area Sls. Mgr.--Analog Devices Ltd. - Eastern Sales Office, Harlow, United Kingdom; *U.S. Public*, pg. 108

Chanprapavut, S., Mng. Dir.--Monsanto Thailand Ltd., Bangkok, Thailand; *U.S. Public*, pg. 1126

Chantres, Gerald R., Gen. Mgr.--Commonwealth Industries, Detroit, MI; *U.S. Public*, pg. 1054

Chao, Allen Y., Ph.D., Pres.--Watson Laboratories, Inc., Corona, CA; *U.S. Public*, pg. 1746

Chao, C.H., Chm.--Hsin-feng Chemical Corp., Taipei, Taiwan; *U.S. Public*, pg. 924

Chao, Claire, Mng. Dir.--Tiffany & Co. of New York Limited, Hong Kong, Hong Kong; *U.S. Public*, pg. 1609

Chao, Donald K.L., Pres.--China Steel Express Corporation, Kao-hsiung, Taiwan; *Int'l*, pg. 285

Chao, Kenneth, Chief Rep.--MetLife Shanghai Representative Office, Shanghai, China; *U.S. Private*, pg. 738

Chapa, Maria Estella, Admin.--Horizon Specialty Hospital - Corpus Christi, Corpus Christi, TX; *U.S. Public*, pg. 839

Chapell, Robert, V.P. & Gen. Mgr.--Prairie Malt Limited, Biggar, Canada; *Int'l*, pg. 1195

Chapin, Jere D., Chm. & Chief Exec. Officer--M & I Central State Bank, Ripon, WI; *U.S. Public*, pg. 1050

Chapius, H.F., Pres.--Industrial Material Distributors, Cincinnati, OH; *U.S. Public*, pg. 903

Chaplin, P., Mgr.--Van Leeuwen Pipe and Tube Eastern Australia Pty. Ltd., Greenfields, Australia; *Int'l*, pg. 1450

Chaplin, Wayne, Pres. & Chief Oper. Officer--Southern Wine & Spirits of America Inc., Miami, FL; *U.S. Private*, pg. 1017

Chapman, A. John, Mng. Dir.--Joy Manufacturing Company (Pty) Ltd., Sydney Plant, Moss Vale, Australia; *U.S. Public*, pg. 789

Chapman, A.J., Mng. Dir.--Thames Side-Maywood Limited, Reading, United Kingdom; *Int'l*, pg. 590

Chapman, Allan, Co-Gen. Mgr.--WWF Paper Corporation - International, Greenwich, CT; *U.S. Private*, pg. 1145

Chapman, Andrew, Pres.--Elizabethtown Water Company, Westfield, NJ; *U.S. Public*, pg. 540

Chapman, Charles, Pres.--Saint Marys Railroad Co., Saint Marys, GA; *U.S. Private*, pg. 454

Chapman, D.J., Gen. Mgr.--S.C. Johnson, Ltd., Kowloon, Hong Kong; *U.S. Private*, pg. 593

Chapman, Daniel H., Pres. & Chief Exec. Officer--Northern Trust Bank of Texas, N.A., Dallas, TX; *U.S. Public*, pg. 1197

Chapman, Frank, Exec. Dir.--BG Plc Exploration & Production Ltd., Reading, United Kingdom; *Int'l*, pg. 119

Chapman, Gary, Pres. & Chief Exec. Officer--LIN Central Broadcasting Corporation (WOTV), Providence, RI; *U.S. Public*, pg. 11

Chapman, Gordon R., Pres.--Wellstream Company, Panama City, FL; *U.S. Public*, pg. 528

Chapman, Harry S., Jr., Pres.--Cigna Health Network, Inc., Dallas, TX; *U.S. Public*, pg. 359

Chapman, Howard G., Mgr.-Opers.--Planes Moving & Storage Of Dayton, Inc., Centerville, OH; *U.S. Private*, pg. 869

Chapman, Hugh M., Chm. Bd.--NationsBank of Florida Corporation, Fort Lauderdale, FL; *U.S. Public*, pg. 1162

Chapman, I.E., Chief Oper. Officer--Northern Rock Unit Trust Limited, Newcastle upon Tyne, United Kingdom; *Int'l*, pg. 968

Chapman, Jack, Gen. Mgr.--Barton's of Sikeston, Sikeston, MO; *U.S. Private*, pg. 119

Chapman, James K., Pres.--M.A. Hanna Engineered Materials, Bethlehem, PA; *U.S. Public*, pg. 781

Chapman, Jim, Pres.--M.A. Hanna Engineered Materials, Corona, CA; *U.S. Public*, pg. 781

Chapman, John S., Mng. Dir.--Baldwin (UK) Ltd., Dunstable, United Kingdom; *U.S. Public*, pg. 170

Chapman, Ken, Gen. Mgr.--Kenner Parker (Australia) Ltd., Alexandria, Australia; *U.S. Public*, pg. 797

Chapman, L.A., Pres.--Rohr Credit Corporation, Chula Vista, CA; *U.S. Public*, pg. 751

Chapman, Mike, Gen. Mgr.--GATX Logistics (JmH), Inc., Dacula, GA; *U.S. Public*, pg. 691

Chapman, Norman L., Chm. Bd. & Pres.--BankAmerica, San Francisco, CA; *U.S. Public*, pg. 181

Chapman, R.P., Pres.--Rose Bearings Ltd., Lincoln, United Kingdom; *Int'l*, pg. 869

Chapman, Richard, Pres. & Chief Exec. Officer--Vermont Electric Power Co., Inc., Rutland, VT; *U.S. Public*, pg. 328

Chapman, T.F., Pres.--The Credit Bureau, Inc. of Georgia, Atlanta, GA; *U.S. Public*, pg. 588

Chapman, Thomas Neal, Chm.--The Southern Life Association Limited, Cape Town, South Africa; *Int'l*, pg. 77

Chapman, Tim, Field Mgr.-Sls.--Briggs & Stratton U.K. Limited, Brentwood, United Kingdom; *U.S. Public*, pg. 252

Chapman, Tracy, Mng. Dir.--Marcam U.K., Northern Region, Manchester, United Kingdom; *U.S. Public*, pg. 1043

Chapman, William D., Pres.--International Division, Kansas City, MO; *U.S. Public*, pg. 271

Chapon, Jean-Luc Oizan, Pres. & Chief Exec. Officer--Club Med, Inc., Georgetown, Cayman Islands; *Int'l*, pg. 298

Chappell, Richard, Pres.--Chappell Agency Inc., Richmond, VA; *Int'l*, pg. 736

Chappell, Robert E., Chm. Bd. & Chief Exec. Officer--PNC Bank, Philadelphia, PA; *U.S. Public*, pg. 1243

Chappell, Sarah, Mgr.--Ceramic Tile International, Marietta, GA; *U.S. Private*, pg. 564

Chapplow, D., Gen. Mgr.--Thomas De La Rue (Hong Kong) Limited, Tai No, Hong Kong; *Int'l*, pg. 1187

Charbonneau, G.A., Chief Exec. Officer--World Council of Credit Unions, Madison, WI; *U.S. Private*, pg. 288

Charbonneau, Y., V.P.--Doucet, Inc., Montreal, Canada; *Int'l, pg. 197*

Chardavoyne, David E., Pres.--United Water New York, West Nyack, NY; *U.S. Public*, pg. 1692

Chardavoyne, David E., Pres.--United Water Works, Harrington Park, NJ; *U.S. Public*, pg. 1692

Chardome, P., Gen. Mgr.--ABN International Diamond Division, Antwerp, Belgium; *Int'l*, pg. 11

Chareyre, P., Chief Exec. Officer--Sogem, Brussels, Belgium; *Int'l*, pg. 1442

Charez, Alejandro, Gen. Mgr.--Warner-Jenkinson S.A. de C.V., Mexico, Mexico; *U.S. Public*, pg. 1696

Charlebois, Brian J., Chief Oper. Officer--First National Bank of New England, Hartford, CT; *U.S. Public*, pg. 636

Charlebois, Dennis, Pres.--Xetron, West Chicago, IL; *U.S. Public*, pg. 1306

Charles, Barry, Joint Chief Exec. Officer--Eurodis Electron Group, Reigate, United Kingdom; *Int'l*, pg. 1247

Charles, Claude, Gen. Mgr.--Equinox Capital (HK) Ltd., Central, Hong Kong; *Int'l*, pg. 343

Charles, Ed, Mng. Dir.--Cold Spring Granite (Canada) Ltd., Cold Spring, MN; *U.S. Private*, pg. 251

Charles, Lyle, Gen. Mgr.--Miller Brands, Inc., Kent, WA; *U.S. Public*, pg. 1289

Charles, M., Chief Oper. Officer--Elf Serepca, Douala, Cameroon; *Int'l*, pg. 446

Charles, M., Mng. Dir.--Northern Ireland Trailers, Ardrossan, United Kingdom; *Int'l*, pg. 1033

Charles, Martyn, Mng. Dir.--Avery Flight International Limited, Isleworth, United Kingdom; *Int'l*, pg. 215

Charlety, Paul, Chief Oper. Officer--Autoliv et Cie, Paris, France; *Int'l*, pg. 441

Charls, Ph.W., Mng. Dir.--RVS Verzekeringen NV, Brussels, Belgium; *Int'l*, pg. 651

Charlton, Edward, Mng. Dir.--Banque Internationale a Luxembourg S.A., London Branch, London, United Kingdom; *Int'l*, pg. 162

Charlton, Russell T., Pres. & Chief Exec. Officer--Transamerica Real Estate Information Companies, Dallas, TX; *U.S. Public*, pg. 1630

Charlton, S.A., Mgr.--Morgan Matroc, Troisdorf, Germany; *Int'l*, pg. 893

Charlton, Samuel H., III, Sr. V.P.--American Oil & Gas Corporation, Houston, TX; *U.S. Public*, pg. 937

Charmorro, Luis, Pres.--AGA-FANO S.A., Bogota, Colombia; *Int'l*, pg. 13

Charnay, Jean-Pierre, Pres. & Dir.-Gen.--Witco S.A., Paris, France; *U.S. Public*, pg. 1774

Charney, William, V.P.--BCL Magnetics, Burlington, Canada; *U.S. Private*, pg. 1075

Charnkolrawee, Santi, Mng. Dir.--The Siam Iron and Steel Co., Ltd., Bangkok, Thailand; *Int'l*, pg. 1238

Charnogursky, Michael, Exec. V.P.--National Book Company Inc., Scranton, PA; *U.S. Private*, pg. 807

Charrier, John P., Jr., Pres. & Chief Exec. Officer--Atlantic Bank, Ocean City, MD; *U.S. Public*, pg. 642

Charrlin, Jerry, Pres.--Fleming Foods of Missouri, Inc., Joplin, MO; *U.S. Public*, pg. 653

Charro, Jose Ignacio Encinas, Pres.--Defex, S.A., Madrid, Spain; *Int'l*, pg. 1224

Charron, Celine, Pres.--Touch Infopublicite Inc. (Infomercials), Montreal, Canada; *Int'l*, pg. 116

Charter, A.C., Mng. Dir.--Hong Kong Air Cargo Terminals Ltd., Kowloon, Hong Kong; *Int'l*, pg. 705

Chartier, Guy, Pres. & Dir. General--Banque Parisienne de Credit, Paris, France; *Int'l*, pg. 548

Chartrand, J.C., Vice Chm. & Mng. Dir.--Equifax Canada, Anjou, Canada; *U.S. Public*, pg. 588

Chartrand, Sandra, Office Mgr.--Kintetsu World Express Inc., Mirabel, Canada; *Int'l*, pg. 735

Chartrau, Ron, Div. Mgr.--OMC Parts & Accessories, Beloit, WI; *U.S. Private*, pg. 478

Chase, Don, Gen. Mgr.--Stihl Parts, Inc., Virginia Beach, VA; *Int'l*, pg. 1301

Chase, J.B., V.P. & Gen. Mgr.--WCPO-TV, Cincinnati, OH; *U.S. Public*, pg. 1448

Chase, M.R., Chief Oper. Officer--IPC Development Co., Dubuque, IA; *U.S. Public*, pg. 910

Chase, Matt, Gen. Mgr.--WWBB, Providence, RI; *U.S. Public*, pg. 385

Chase, Matt, Gen. Mgr.--WWRX, Providence, RI; *U.S. Public*, pg. 385

Chase, Peter, Pres.--Humiseal Div., Woodside, NY; *U.S. Public*, pg. 337

Chassagne, Gerard, Company Head--Ovako Acier S.A., Rosny-sous-Bois, France; *Int'l*, pg. 1157

Chasse, Carl, V.P. & Gen. Mgr.--Nielsen/Sessions, Hartford, CT; *U.S. Public*, pg. 1791

Chassen, Shari, Chief Oper. Officer--MTI Systems Div., New York, NY; *U.S. Public*, pg. 135

Chastain, C.L., Plant Mgr.--Marglen Yarn Plant, White, GA; *U.S. Private*, pg. 702

Chastain, Roger, Pres.--Mount Vernon Mills, Inc., Riegel Textile Div., Greenville, SC; *U.S. Private*, pg. 835

Chastain, Terry, Mng. Dir.--ABB Vetco U.K. Ltd., Aberdeen, United Kingdom; *Int'l*, pg. 5

Chateau, Guy, Dir.-European Bus. Devel.--Ortho Clinical Diagnostic S.A., Roissy, France; *U.S. Public*, pg. 931

Chatelin, N.T., Distr. Mgr.--Milchem International Limited, Hague, Netherlands; *U.S. Public*, pg. 167

Chatellier, Robert, Gen. Mgr.--S.W. Airfreight, Roissy Charles de Gaulle, France; *U.S. Public*, pg. 373

Chatfield, D.A., Dr., V.P. & Gen. Mgr.--National Steel Corp., Midwest Division, Portage, IN; *Int'l*, pg. 903

Chatikavanij, Korn, Mng. Dir.--Jardine Fleming Thanakom Securities Limited, Bangkok, Thailand; *Int'l*, pg. 494

Chatillon, Jean-Pierre, Dir.-Mill--Chapelle Darblay Saint Etienne S.A., Saint Etienne-du-Rouvray, France; *Int'l*, pg. 1430

Chatt, Joseph R., Pres.--Island Express, Catano, PR; *U.S. Private*, pg. 211

Chatterjee, Rames C., Mng. Dir.--Black & Decker Housewares (Pte.) Ltd., Jurong, Singapore; *U.S. Public*, pg. 234

Chattman, Martin E., Pres.--NorVal, Inc., Lafayette, NJ; *Int'l, pg. 1201*

Chattwell, R., Gen. Mgr.--B.E. International Foods Ltd., Enfield, United Kingdom; *Int'l*, pg. 380

Chaturedi, Anupam, Rep.--DG Bank-Mumbai, Mumbai, India; *Int'l*, pg. 352

Chaufty, William L., Pres.--Hilb, Rogal and Hamilton Company of Oklahoma, Oklahoma City, OK; *U.S. Public*, pg. 827

Chaus, Josephine, Chm. Bd.--Bernard Chaus, Inc., Secaucus, NJ; *U.S. Public*, pg. 342

Chausse, Linda, Dir.--Services Securivol Inc., Longueuil, Canada; *Int'l*, pg. 340

Chauvel, Bernard, Sr. V.P. & Gen. Mgr.-USA--Credit Agricole (CNCA) U.S.A. (New York), New York, NY; *Int'l, pg. 341*

Chauvet, Pierre, Chief Oper. Officer--Sabliere du Ventoux, Paris, France; *Int'l*, pg. 919

Chaves, Denis, V.P. & Gen. Mgr.--Advanced Products Division, Latham, NY; *U.S. Public*, pg. 1077

Chaves, Ruy A., V.P.-Sls.--Sensormatic Do Brazil Electronica Ltda., Santo Andre, Brazil; *U.S. Public*, pg. 1457

Chavez, Roberto, Resident Rep.--World Bank, Maputo, Mozambique; *U.S. Private*, pg. 1189

Chavis, Veronica, Mgr.--Copamex Paper, El Paso, TX; *Int'l*, pg. 330

Chavoya, Rene Castro, Chm. Bd.--Compania Siderurgia de Guadalajara, Guadalajara, Mexico; *Int'l*, pg. 576

Chawki, A., Gen. Mgr.--Laboratoires Polymedic, S.A., Casablanca, Morocco; *U.S. Public*, pg. 1092

Cheah, Annie, Mgr.-Admin.--Swensen's of Singapore Pte. Ltd., Singapore, Singapore; *U.S. Public*, pg. 884

Cheatham, Thomas K., Gen. Mgr.--Kansas City Royals Radio Network, Kansas City, MO; *U.S. Private*, pg. 995

Cheatley, H.W., Pres.--Bunn-O-Matic Corp. of Canada Ltd., Aurora, Canada; *U.S. Private*, pg. 181

Cheatwood, Steve, Plant Mgr.--Sentinel Consumer Products, Inc., Anniston, AL; *U.S. Private*, pg. 984

Check, John, Gen. Mgr. & Publisher--The Chatham Daily News, Chatham, Canada; *Int'l*, pg. 631

Checketts, David W., Pres. & Chief Exec. Officer--Madison Square Garden Corporation, New York, NY; *U.S. Public*, pg. 288

Chedraui Obeso, Antonio, Pres.--Tiendas Chedraui S.A. de C.V., Veracruz, Mexico; *Int'l*, pg. 573

Chee Siong, Robert Ng, Chm. Bd.--Yeo Hiap Seng Limited, Singapore, Singapore; *Int'l*, pg. 1008

Cheeseman, Edward, Mng. Dir.--Raychem (Australia) Pty. Limited, Auburn, Australia; *U.S. Public*, pg. 1362

Cheeseman, Edward, Mng. Dir.--Raychem New Zealand Limited, Auckland, New Zealand; *U.S. Public*, pg. 1362

Cheing, Kuar Hock, Dir.--Superior Metal Printing Philippines, Inc., Manila, Philippines; *Int'l*, pg. 1322

Chelf, W.E., Gen. Mgr.--CHEMCENTRAL/Portland, Portland, OR; *U.S. Private*, pg. 232

Chelin, Jeffrey D., V.P.--Canrad Inc., Newark, NJ; *Int'l*, pg. 17

Chellgren, Paul, Pres.--Nokia Mobile Phones Inc., Tampa, FL; *Int'l*, pg. 952

Chellis, David A., Mgr.--Meriden Telephone Co., Inc., Meriden, NH; *U.S. Public*, pg. 1571

Chelminski, Andrew, Pres.--Agnew Group, London, Canada; *Int'l*, pg. 187

Chelton, John, Corp. Mfg.--Estee Lauder, Melville, NY; *U.S. Public*, pg. 594

Cheminard-Serre, Jean-Claude, Gen. Mgr.--Nordson France, S.A., Lagny, France; *U.S. Public*, pg. 1189

Chemke, Esteban, Gen. Mgr.--Unimet Pty Ltd, Melbourne, Australia; *Int'l*, pg. 303

Chen, Alfred, Gen. Mgr.--Mentholatum Taiwan Ltd., Taipei, Taiwan; *Int'l*, pg. 1126

Chen, Bryon, Pres.--Astra Pharmaceuticals (Taiwan) Ltd., Taipei, Taiwan; *Int'l*, pg. 94

Chen, Dr. Rocky, Gen. Mgr.--Sino-American Great Wall Food Industries Co., Ltd., Taipei, Taiwan; *Int'l*, pg. 411

Chen, Glen K.L., Chm.--Ford Enterprise Company Taiwan, Ltd., Taipei, Taiwan; *U.S. Public*, pg. 665

Chen, H.H., Pres.--China Ecotek Corporation, Kao-hsiung, Taiwan; *Int'l*, pg. 285

Chen, Herman Chuh, V.P. & Gen. Mgr.--The International Commercial Bank of China, Makati, Philippines; *Int'l*, pg. 683

Chen, J.H., Gen. Mgr.--Taiwan Petroleum Exploration Division, Miao-li, Taiwan; *Int'l*, pg. 286

Chen, James, Mng. Dir.--CTS Components Taiwan, Ltd., Kao-hsiung, Taiwan; *U.S. Public*, pg. 286

Chen, James, Gen. Mgr.--Tatung Co. of America, Marietta, GA; *Int'l*, pg. 1357

Chen, John T., Chief Oper. Officer--Neste Shipping Canada Ltd., Toronto, Canada; *Int'l*, pg. 915

Chen, M.P., Mng. Dir.--Sony Video Taiwan Co. Ltd., Chung Li, Taiwan; *Int'l*, pg. 1284

Chen, May, Media--Leo Burnett Company, Ltd.-Taiwan Branch, Taipei, Taiwan; *U.S. Private*, pg. 185

Chen, Pao Yuan, Pres.--China Steel Chemical Corp., Kao-hsiung, Taiwan; *Int'l*, pg. 286

Chen, Paul, Mgr.-Sls.--Liebert Malaysia Sdn. Bhd., Sulang Jaya, Malaysia; *U.S. Public*, pg. 577

Chen, Peter C.S., Gen. Mgr.--RTE Far East Corporation, Tao-yuan, Taiwan,; *U.S. Public*, pg. 445

Chen, Roger, Gen. Mgr.--Liebert Hong Kong, Aberdeen, Hong Kong; *U.S. Public*, pg. 577

Chen, Shin Hsiung, Gen. Mgr.--A.H. Robins International Company, Taipei, Taiwan; *U.S. Public*, pg. 82

Chen, Y.T., Chm.--Sharp Electronic Components (Taiwan) Corporation, Taipei, Taiwan; *Int'l*, pg. 1229

Chenard, Pierre, Interim Pres.--Cambinex Exploration, Montreal, Canada; *Int'l*, pg. 253

Chenault, Randy, Mgr.--Southern Electric Supply Co., Inc., Gulfport, MS; *Int'l*, pg. 1108

Chene, Jean-Francois, Dir. Gen.--Saunier Duval Eau Chaude Chauffage SA, Fontenay-sous-Bois, France; *Int'l, pg. 615*

Chenery, R.J., Chief Exec. Officer--Redland Properties Ltd., Reigate, United Kingdom; *Int'l*, pg. 1091

Chenevert, Louis, Exec. V.P.-Opers.--Pratt & Whitney Operations, East Hartford, CT; *U.S. Public*, pg. 1690

Cheney, Jeff, Sr. V.P., & Gen. Counsel--Atari Games Corporation, Milpitas, CA; *U.S. Public*, pg. 1727

Cheney, Peter, Pres.--Kal Kan Foods, Inc., Vernon, CA; *U.S. Private*, pg. 707

Cheney, Philip W., Acting Gen. Mgr.--Research Div., Lexington, MA; *U.S. Public*, pg. 1365

Cheney, Richard B., Chm. Bd., Pres. & Chief Exec. Officer--Halliburton Energy Services, Inc., Dallas, TX; *U.S. Public, pg. 776*

Cheney, William J., Chm. Bd., Pres. & Chief Exec. Officer--Steadly Company, Carthage, MO; *U.S. Public*, pg. 986

Cheng, Chih-Wen, Mng. Dir.--Cathay Finance International (Holdings) Limited, Sydney, Australia; *Int'l*, pg. 684

Cheng, Eva, Chief Exec.--Amway Asia Pacific Ltd-Hong Kong Branch, Causeway Bay, Hong Kong; *U.S. Private*, pg. 69

Cheng, L.W., Chief Exec. Officer--Zurich International (Bermuda) Ltd., Hamilton, Bermuda; *Int'l*, pg. 1532

Cheng, Robin, Mng. Dir.--AGRA (Hong Kong) Limited, Kowloon, Hong Kong; *Int'l*, pg. 31

Cheng, Y. C., Chm. Bd.--Chiaphua Shinko Copper Alloy Co., Ltd., Kowloon, Hong Kong; *Int'l*, pg. 741

Chenhall, R.H., Mng. Dir.--Penny & Giles Drives Technology Ltd., Dorset, United Kingdom; *Int'l*, pg. 207

Chenoweth, Joe, Mgr.-Personnel--Flambeau Plastics Co., Baraboo, WI; *U.S. Private*, pg. 409

Chenu, J.P., Gen. Mgr.--ITW Belgium S.A./N.V., Brussels, Belgium; *U.S. Public*, pg. 868

Chenu, J.P., Gen. Mgr.--Impex Walchar B.V., Tolbert, Netherlands; *U.S. Public*, pg. 869

Chenuet, Jean-Claude, Gen. Mgr.--Keithley Instruments S.A.R.L., Palaiseau, France; *U.S. Public*, pg. 947

Cheong, Dato Tan Guan, Mng. Dir.--United ORIX Leasing Berhad, Kuala Lumpur, Malaysia; *Int'l*, pg. 1010

Cheong, Dato Tan Guan, Dir.--ORIX Rentec (Malaysia) Sdn. Bhd., Petaling Jaya, Malaysia; *Int'l*, pg. 1010

Cheong, Gerry, Pres.--KE-Burgmann Singapore Pte. Ltd., Singapore, Singapore; *Int'l*, pg. 234

Cheong, Heon-mo, Chief Rep.--The Export-Import Bank of Korea, Central, Hong Kong; *Int'l*, pg. 467

Cheong, K.P., Chief Oper. Officer--Hong Fok Land Pte. Ltd., Singapore, Singapore; *Int'l*, pg. 635

Cheong, K.P., Chief Oper. Officer--Yat Yuen Hong Company Limited, Singapore, Singapore; *Int'l*, pg. 635

Cheow, Michael, Mng. Dir.--Hoover Stainless Pte Ltd., Singapore, Singapore; *Int'l*, pg. 1322

Cher, Charles, Mng. Dir.--Reed International (Singapore) PTE Limited, Singapore, Singapore; *Int'l*, pg. 1095

Chereau, Jean Luc, Chief Exec. Officer-Taiwan--Presicarre Corp., Taipei, Taiwan; *Int'l*, pg. 273

Cheret, Ivan, Sr. V.P.-Water Div.--Eau et Force, Nanterre, France; *Int'l*, pg. 822

Cherim, J.G., Gen. Mgr.--ING Bank Bangkok, Bangkok, Thailand; *Int'l*, pg. 648

Cherkaoui, A., Chm.--L'Alliance Africaine, Casablanca, Morocco; *Int'l*, pg. 565

Chernago, Michael, V.P.-Opers.--Smith Corona Financial Division, Cortland, NY; *U.S. Private*, pg. 1007

Cherney, Edward, Pres.--CMI Holding Co., Bloomfield Hills, MI; *U.S. Public*, pg. 1623

Chernick, Vic, Mng. Dir.--Vivitar Corporation, Newbury Park, CA; *Int'l*, pg. 1060

Chernin, Peter, Pres.--The News Corporation Limited, Sydney, Australia; *Int'l*, pg. 925

Chernow, Rocky, V.P.--Construction & Mining Division, Salt Lake City, UT; *U.S. Private*, pg. 84

Chernoyarov, V., Mng. Dir.--RECON, Moscow, Russia; *Int'l*, pg. 608

Cherrier, J.P., Chief Exec. Officer--Redland Granulats SA, Rungis, France; *Int'l*, pg. 1093

Cherruau, F., Chief Oper. Officer--Intercontrole S.A., Rungis, France; *Int'l*, pg. 1361

Cherry, A., Mng. Dir.--Ballast Wlitshier plc - Airport Services Div., Slough, United Kingdom; *Int'l*, pg. 135

Cherry, Allen, Plant Mgr.--Dixie Packers, Madison, FL; *U.S. Public*, pg. 1772

Cherry, John, Pres.--Flanders CSC Corp., Bath, NC; *U.S. Public*, pg. 648

cherry, Tom, V.P. & Gen. Mgr.--Chase Manhattan Financial Center, Inc., Bloomington, MN; *U.S. Public*, pg. 338

Chertow, Brent, Co-Pres.--Kidd Creek Division, Timmins, Canada; *Int'l*, pg. 433

Chervenak, Timothy R., Mgr.-Branch--Piper Jaffray Inc., Spokane, WA; *U.S. Public*, pg. 1302

Cheskaty, Rex, Gen. Mgr.--Armstrong International, Three Rivers, MI; *U.S. Private*, pg. 83

Cheskin, Greg, Pres.--Coats & Clark Inc. (Sales Office), Stamford, CT; *Int'l*, pg. 300

Chesner, Donald, V.P. & Gen. Mgr.--Acme Power Distribution Products, Lumberton, NC; *U.S. Public*, pg. 16

Chesney, David H., Pres. & Gen. Mgr.--Nestaway, Cleveland, OH; *U.S. Private*, pg. 103

Chess, David, Pres.--Superior Pool Products, Inc., Anaheim, CA; *U.S. Public*, pg. 1219

Chessin, James L., Pres.--Bondo/Mar-Hyde Corporation, Cleveland, OH; *U.S. Public*, pg. 1357

Chessin, James L., Pres.--Paramount Technical Products, Inc., Spearfish, SD; *U.S. Public*, pg. 1357

Chester, Arthur, V.P. & Dir.--Hughes Research Laboratories, Malibu, CA; *U.S. Public*, pg. 721

Chester, J. S., Mng. Dir.--NatWest Stockbrokers Limited, London, United Kingdom; *Int'l*, pg. 910

Chester, Perry, Pres.--WQAD-TV, Moline, IL; *U.S. Public*, pg. 1174

Chester, Reed, Pres.--Advertising Promotions, Inc., Denver, CO; *U.S. Public*, pg. 1447

Chesterman, I.A., Gen. Mgr.--Commonwealth Bank of Australia-South Australia, Adelaide, Australia; *Int'l*, pg. 313

Chesterman, Kenneth W., Pres.--Omnicare Pharmacy Services, Cincinnati, OH; *U.S. Public*, pg. 1223
Cheung, B.C.S., Mng. Dir.--Wyeth (HK) Limited, Wan Chai, Hong Kong; *U.S. Public*, pg. 82
Cheung, B.C.S., Mng. Dir.--Wyeth-Ayerst (Asia) Ltd., Taipei, Taiwan; *U.S. Public*, pg. 82
Cheung, Caroline, Chief Exec. Officer--F.J. Benjamin Fashions (HK) Ltd., Causeway Bay, Hong Kong; *Int'l*, pg. 187
Cheung, Jason W.K., V.P.-Intl.--Johnson & Johnson International (Hong Kong), Kowloon, Hong Kong; *U.S. Public*, pg. 930
Cheung, K.L., Plant Mgr.--Digital Equipment Hong Kong Limited, Taikoo Shing, Hong Kong; *U.S. Public*, pg. 508
Cheung, L., Chief Rep.--Barclays Bank PLC, Beijing, China; *Int'l*, pg. 165
Cheung, Randy, Mng. Dir.--Wormald Engineering Systems Taiwan Limited, Taipei, Taiwan; *U.S. Public*, pg. 1651
Cheung, Randy, Mng. Dir.--Tyco Laboratories Asia Pacific (S) Pte Ltd., Singapore, Singapore; *U.S. Public*, pg. 1651
Cheung, Shirley S., Pres.--Heinz-UFE Ltd., Guangzhou, China; *U.S. Public*, pg. 807
Cheung, Steve, Pres.--Georg Fischer Disa Inc., Oswego, IL; *Int'l*, pg. 382
Cheung, Tony, Mng. Dir.--THORN Hong Kong Ltd., North Point, Hong Kong; *Int'l*, pg. 1386
Cheval, F., Mng. Dir.--Howard S.A., Loudun, France; *Int'l*, pg. 1387
Chevalier, Gilles, Pres.--The Roberval & Saguenay Railway Co., Jonquiere, Canada; *Int'l*, pg. 50
Chevalier, Roger, Pres.--Serat, Paris, France; *Int'l*, pg. 29
Chevallier, Alain, Chm. Bd., Stepan Europe--Stepan Europe, Voreppe, France; *U.S. Public*, pg. 1514
Chevrier, Christophe, Mng. Dir.--RTL9, Metz, France; *Int'l*, pg. 561
Chevrier, Robert, Chm. Bd., Pres. & Chief Exec. Officer--Westburne Industrial Enterprises, Ltd., Ville Saint Laurent, Canada; *Int'l*, pg. 1492
Chew, Arthur, Chief Oper. Officer--Motorola Singapore Pte., Ltd., Singapore, Singapore; *U.S. Public*, pg. 1140
Chew, David, Dir.-Malaysia--North West Water (Malaysia) Ltd., Kuala Lumpur, Malaysia; *Int'l*, pg. 1444
Chew, Mike, Mng. Dir.--Oceaneering International Services, Ltd., Aberdeen, United Kingdom; *U.S. Public*, pg. 1211
Chewning, Thomas, Pres. & Chief Exec. Officer--Dominion Energy, Inc., Richmond, VA; *U.S. Public*, pg. 516
Chi, Steven Y., Pres.--Mining Group, San Antonio, TX; *U.S. Public*, pg. 1134
Chi, Y.K., Pres.--C.S. Aluminium Corporation, Kao-hsiung, Taiwan; *Int'l*, pg. 285
Chia-Ozaku, Elsie, Reg. Dir.-Japan--Singapore Tourist Promotion Board - Tokyo, Tokyo, Japan; *Int'l*, pg. 1254
Chiam, Charles, Mgr.--Keppel Prince Engineering Engineering Pty Ltd., Melbourne, Australia; *Int'l*, pg. 731
Chiappetta, Albert C., Gen. Mgr.--Methode Development Company, Chicago, IL; *U.S. Public*, pg. 1101
Chiappetta, Richard J., V.P.-Central Region--Analysts International, Central Region, Indianapolis, IN; *U.S. Public*, pg. 110
Chiaraluce, Marshall T., Pres.--The Connecticut Water Company, Clinton, CT; *U.S. Public*, pg. 431
Chiarchiaro, Nick, Sr., Mgr.--AFA Protective Systems, Inc., New York, NY; *U.S. Public*, pg. 5
Chiasson, Tim, Plant Mgr.--L.B. Foster Company-Birmingham Plant, Birmingham, AL; *U.S. Public*, pg. 676
Chiba, M., Chm. & Chief Exec. Officer--ING Life Insurance Company, Tokyo, Japan; *Int'l*, pg. 650
Chiba, Minoru, Pres.--DKB Financial Products, Inc., New York, NY; *Int'l*, pg. 360
Chichester, Allen, Chm.-Greater China--Leo Burnett Worldwide Asia/Pacific Hdqtrs., Hong Kong, Hong Kong; *U.S. Private*, pg. 186
Chichester, Allen C., Chm.-Greater China--Leo Burnett Greater China, Quarry Bay, Hong Kong; *U.S. Private*, pg. 185
Chickering, George, Plant Mgr.--Farr Company, Conover, NC; *U.S. Public*, pg. 614
Chickering, Kenton, III, Pres.--Daniel Valve Company, Houston, TX; *U.S. Public*, pg. 483
Chidester, Chuck, Administrator--Greenery Rehab - Waterbury, Waterbury, CT; *U.S. Public*, pg. 836
Chiellini, Augusto, Pres.--Dynapac S.p.A., Arluno, Italy; *Int'l*, pg. 1420
Chien, Mateo, Mng. Dir.--Lowe & Partners/Live, Causeway Bay, Hong Kong; *U.S. Private*, pg. 678
Chiew, Choong Chee, Gen. Mgr.--Nippon Paint (Vietnam) Co., Ltd., Bien Hoa, Vietnam; *Int'l*, pg. 1322
Chiew, Richard, Dir.--Takenaka (Malaysia) Sdn. Bhd., Kuala Lumpur, Kuala Lumpur, Malaysia; *Int'l*, pg. 1351
Chiga, Shigeharu, Chief Rep.--Sao Paulo Representative Office, Sao Paulo, Brazil; *Int'l*, pg. 816
Chigi, Yoshitara, Pres.--Yumex/ILC, Himeji, Japan; *U.S. Public*, pg. 856
Chihak, Michael, Pres. & Publr.--Salinas Californian, Salinas, CA; *U.S. Public*, pg. 701
Chikasaka, Tatsuo, Gen. Mgr.-Intl. Opers. Center--Daiwa Bank International Business Division-Head Office, Osaka, Japan; *Int'l*, pg. 373
Child, Denis, Chm. Bd.--Orbital Park Limited, London, United Kingdom; *Int'l*, pg. 466
Child, Kent, Pres.--Kwal-Howells, Inc.(Denver), Denver, CO; *Int'l*, pg. 1501
Child, R.E., Mng. Dir.--Systematic Drill Head Co. Ltd., Coventry, United Kingdom; *Int'l*, pg. 585
Childers, R.D., Pres.--CDA Distributors, Erie, PA; *U.S. Public*, pg. 903
Childers, Steve, Pres. & Gen. Mgr.--Consolidated Market Response, Charleston, IL; *U.S. Public*, pg. 1073
Childress, Brad, Pres.--Plastomer Products Div., Newtown, PA; *U.S. Public*, pg. 402
Childress, Doug, Plant Mgr.--A. Schulman, Inc.-Dispersion Plant, Orange, TX; *U.S. Public*, pg. 1441
Childress, Gary, Pres.--MWCA, Rexburg, ID; *U.S. Public*, pg. 804
Childs, E.A.T., Chief Oper. Officer--Holloway White Allom Ltd., London, United Kingdom; *Int'l*, pg. 796
Chiles, James, Sr.-V.P.-Prod.--Early Times Distillers Co., Louisville, KY; *U.S. Public*, pg. 261
Chiles, James B., Pres.--Canadian Mist Distillers Ltd., Collingwood, Canada; *U.S. Public*, pg. 262
Chiles, John G., Mng. Dir.--Jefferies & Company, Inc., Los Angeles, CA; *U.S. Public*, pg. 925
Chillingsworth, Gordon, Chief Oper. Officer--MacDermid Korea Ltd., Seoul, Korea; *U.S. Public*, pg. 1030
Chilton, H.G., Pres.--Kuss Corporation, Findlay, OH; *U.S. Public*, pg. 468
Chilton, Jeff, Gen. Mgr.--Sunnyland Inc., Thomasville, GA; *U.S. Public*, pg. 1479
Chilton, Peter M., Mng. Dir.--Bristol-Myers Company Pty. Limited, Rydalmere, Australia; *U.S. Public*, pg. 255
Chilton, Peter M., Mng. Dir.--Bristol-Myers Marketing Services Pty. Ltd., Rydalmere, Australia; *U.S. Public*, pg. 255
Chilvers, Anthony, Sec.--The West Company (UK) Ltd., Saint Austell, United Kingdom; *U.S. Public*, pg. 1756
Chilvers, Anthony, Chief Oper. Officer--The West Company Group Limited, Saint Austell, United Kingdom; *U.S. Public*, pg. 1756
Chilvers, Derek, Chm.--John Hancock Intl. Services S.A., Brussels, Belgium; *U.S. Private*, pg. 590
Chilvers, Derek, Mng. Dir.-Quota Holder--John Hancock Servicos Internacionais S/C, Ltda., Sao Paulo, Brazil; *U.S. Private*, pg. 590
Chin Tuan, Quek, Gen. Mgr.-Korea--Singapore Tourist Promotion Board - Seoul, Seoul, Korea; *Int'l*, pg. 1254
Chin, Daniel J., Pres.--Dress Division, New York, NY; *U.S. Public*, pg. 1239
Chin, Eddy, Deputy Gen Mgr.--Dentsu Young & Rubicam Sdn. Bhd. (Kuala Lumpur), Kuala Lumpur, Malaysia; *U.S. Private*, pg. 325
Chin, Lee, V.P. & Gen. Mgr.--CBM America Corp., Torrance, CA; *U.S. Private*, pg. 192
Chin, Sik Ping, Mng. Dir.--ITW Meritex SDN BHD, Penang, Malaysia; *U.S. Public*, pg. 868
Chinchilla, Ernie, Gen. Mgr.--LFE Traffic Control, Clinton, MA; *U.S. Public*, pg. 1045
Ching, Eddie, Gen. Mgr.--Pak Pacific (South East Asia) Pte. Ltd., Singapore, Singapore; *Int'l*, pg. 129
Chipman, Jeff, Pres.--Bowne of Canada Inc., Toronto, Canada; *U.S. Public*, pg. 249
Chiranakhon, Cheer, Dir.--Tonka Far East Limited, Kowloon, Hong Kong; *U.S. Public*, pg. 798
Chirichigno, Francesco, Chief Exec. Officer--TELECOM ITALIA S.p.A., Rome, Italy; *Int'l*, pg. 1363
Chisholm, A., Pres.--Merrell/Chisholm, Raleigh, NC; *U.S. Private*, pg. 543
Chisholm, David, Gen. Mgr.--Westpac - Tasmania, Hobart, Australia; *Int'l*, pg. 1496
Chisholm, Gerald M., Mgr.-Division--Gould Paper Corporation-New England, Stoughton, MA; *U.S. Private*, pg. 467
Chisholm, Ian, Mng. Dir.--Western Staff Services Pty. Ltd., Melbourne, Australia; *U.S. Public*, pg. 1760
Chisholm, Ian, Mng. Dir.--Western Staff Services (N.Z.) Ltd., Auckland, New Zealand; *U.S. Public*, pg. 1760
Chisholm, J.R., Pres.--Hamilton Precision Metals, Lancaster, PA; *U.S. Public*, pg. 944
Chit, Quah Seng, Gen. Mgr.--Leo Burnett Advertising SDN.BHD., Kuala Lumpur, Malaysia; *U.S. Private*, pg. 184
Chiti, Ing. Carlo, Chief Oper. Officer--Autodelta S.p.A., Settimo Milanese, Italy; *Int'l*, pg. 481
Chittom, Pat, Branch Mgr.--Union-Transport Corporation-Denver Office, Denver, CO; *U.S. Private*, pg. 1119
Chiu, Bennett, V.P.-Asia Pacific--EURO RSCG Partnership, Quarry Bay, Hong Kong; *Int'l*, pg. 602
Chiu, J., Mng. Dir.--The General Electric Company of Hong Kong Ltd., Wan Chai, Hong Kong; *Int'l*, pg. 546
Chiummo, Piero, Gen. Mgr.--Gillette Group Italy S.r.l., Milan, Italy; *U.S. Public*, pg. 745
Chlapowski, Roland, Mng. Dir.--La Suisse - Assurances-vie (France), Lyon, France; *Int'l*, pg. 1332
Chlouverakis, Manolis, Mng. Dir.--Johnson & Johnson Hellas S.A., Athens, Greece; *U.S. Public*, pg. 930
Chludil, Ron, Mgr.--DWF of Flint, Inc., Flint, MI; *U.S. Private*, pg. 326
Chmelka, Donald F., Pres.--L&S Machine Company, Inc., Wichita, KS; *U.S. Public*, pg. 157
Chng, Bee Kek, Mng. Dir.--SKF China Ltd., Hong Kong, Hong Kong; *Int'l*, pg. 1158
Cho, Hyonju, Media Dir.--Leo Burnett Sonyon Inc., Seoul, Korea; *U.S. Private*, pg. 185
Cho, Kook-pil, Pres.--Ssangyong Resources Pty., Ltd., Sydney, Australia; *Int'l*, pg. 1293
Cho, Kuk-Pil, Pres.--Jinbang Steel Co., Ltd., Pohang, Korea; *Int'l*, pg. 1291
Cho, Seon H., Dr., Gen. Mgr.--Wang Computer Korea, Ltd., Seoul, Korea; *U.S. Public*, pg. 1737
Cho, Soo-Young, Reg. Mgr.--Cho Hung Bank, New York, NY; *Int'l*, pg. 287
Cho, Y.S., Chm. Bd.--Korag Company, Ltd., Inchon, Korea; *U.S. Public*, pg. 1126
Choate, Donald, Pres.--Wall Trends, Inc., Avenel, NJ; *Int'l*, pg. 1278
Choate, Eugene, Pres.--Atlantic American Life Insurance Company, Atlanta, GA; *U.S. Public*, pg. 143
Choate, Eugene, Pres.--Bankers Fidelity Life Insurance Company, Atlanta, GA; *U.S. Public*, pg. 143
Choate, Harold, Gen. Mgr.--M.O.V. of Louisiana, Inc., Baton Rouge, LA; *U.S. Private*, pg. 162
Chocholous, I., Gen. Mgr.--Mona spol. sr.o., Prague, Czech Republic; *Int'l*, pg. 1445
Choel, Patrick J., Pres. & Chief Exec. Officer--Chesebrough-Pond's USA Co., Greenwich, CT; *Int'l*, pg. 1435
Choi, Alan, Partner--Korn/Ferry International, Central, Hong Kong; *U.S. Private*, pg. 633
Choi, Alan C.L., Mng. Dir.--Korn/Ferry International, Beijing, China; *U.S. Private*, pg. 634
Choi, Dong-Soo, Chief Mgr.--Westpac Banking Corp. - Korea, Seoul, Korea; *Int'l*, pg. 1497
Choi, Eun-Soon, Pres.--Daewoo Electric Motor Industries, Ltd., Kwangju, Korea; *Int'l*, pg. 357
Choi, H. M., Gen. Mgr.--Lord Korea Ltd., Seoul, Korea; *U.S. Private*, pg. 676
Choi, J.L., Mng. Dir.--Nanometrics Korea Ltd., Seoul, Korea; *U.S. Public*, pg. 1151
Choi, Jang Kyu, Chief Oper. Officer--Daewoo Securities (Europe) Ltd., London, United Kingdom; *Int'l*, pg. 359
Choi, Keun-sun, Pres.--Goldstar Co. Ltd., Seoul, Korea; *Int'l*, pg. 778
Choi, Sung-Rai, Chm. Bd. & Chief Exec. Officer--Samsung Europe Headquarters, Brentford, United Kingdom; *Int'l*, pg. 1183
Choi, Tan, Pres.--Ssangyong Engineering Co., Ltd., Seoul, Korea; *Int'l*, pg. 1292
Choi, Yoon-Sung, Pres.--Hyosung Metal Products Co., Ltd., Seoul, Korea; *Int'l*, pg. 641
Chojnacki, Jack S., Co-Pres.--Those Characters From Cleveland, Inc., Cleveland, OH; *U.S. Public*, pg. 78
Chokwatana, Boon-ek, Chm. Bd.--Sahapathanapibul Public Company Limited, Bangkok, Thailand; *Int'l*, pg. 1169
Chokwatana, Boonsithi, Pres.--Thai Sports Garment Co., Ltd., Bangkok, Thailand; *Int'l*, pg. 885
Chomeau, James W., Pres.--Capitol County Mutual Fire Insurance Co., Houston, TX; *U.S. Public*, pg. 1374
Chon, Tan Chwee, Pres.--Astra Pharmaceuticals (Singapore) Pte. Ltd., Singapore, Singapore; *Int'l*, pg. 94
Chong, Angie, Deputy Mng. Dir.--F.J. Benjamin Fashions (M) Sdn. Bhd., Kuala Lumpur, Malaysia; *Int'l*, pg. 187
Chong, Howe Yoon, Exec. Chm.--Great Eastern Life Assurance Company-Malaysia, Kuala Lumpur, Malaysia; *Int'l*, pg. 557
Chong, Khor Chin, Mng. Dir.--Soss of Singapore Pte. Ltd., Jurong, Singapore; *U.S. Public*, pg. 1677
Choo, J.S., Pres.--Hyosung-Ebara Environment Engineering Co., Ltd., Seoul, Korea; *Int'l*, pg. 432
Choo, Michael W.S., Gen. Mgr.--ORIX Car Rentals Pte Ltd., Singapore, Singapore; *Int'l*, pg. 1009
Choo, Yoon H., Dr., Chm. Bd., Pres. & Chief Exec. Officer--National Micronetics, Inc., Kingston, NY; *Int'l*, pg. 1347
Chooligorn, Dacha, Rep.--Kredietbank Representative Office (Bangkok), Bangkok, Thailand; *Int'l*, pg. 760
Choong, Kwok Kai, Mgr.--Keppel FELS Energy Incorporated, Manila, Philippines; *Int'l*, pg. 731
Choong, L.H., Mng. Dir.--Amway (Malaysia) Sdn. Bhd., Petaling Jaya, Malaysia; *U.S. Private*, pg. 70
Chorbajian, Herbert G., Chief Exec. Officer--Albany Savings Bank, Albany, NY; *U.S. Public*, pg. 36
Chorengel, Bernd, Pres.--Hyatt International Corporation, Chicago, IL; *U.S. Private*, pg. 551
Chou, Rachel, Mgr.--Commerzbank AG Representative Office-Taipei, Taipei, Taiwan; *Int'l*, pg. 312
Choudhry, Anwar Ali, V.P. & Mgr.--Habib Bank Limited, Manama, Bahrain; *Int'l*, pg. 584
Choudhury, S., Branch Mgr.--India Photographic Company Limited, Calcutta, India; *U.S. Public*, pg. 552
Choufoer, F. R., Mng. Dir.--DSM Energie B.V., Heerlen, Netherlands; *Int'l*, pg. 353
Chouinard, Richard J., Pres. & Chief Exec. Officer--USLIFE Advisers, Inc., New York, NY; *U.S. Public*, pg. 77
Chouinard, Robert, Mng. Dir.--SmithKline Beecham Pharmaceuticals Inc., Oakville, Canada; *Int'l*, pg. 1266
Chouinard, Yvon, Pres.--Patagonia, Ventura, CA; *U.S. Private*, pg. 677
Choulet, Robert, Pres.--AlliedSignal Engines, Phoenix, AZ; *U.S. Public*, pg. 50
Choupin, G., Mgr.--Van Leeuwen Tubes SA, Meyzieu, France; *Int'l*, pg. 1450
Chouraqui, R., Pres.--Hydrochim, S.A., Amboise, France; *U.S. Public*, pg. 1219
Chow Yeow, Tony Soh, V.P.-Eastern U.S.A.--Singapore Tourist Promotion Board - New York, New York, NY; *Int'l*, pg. 1254
Chow, G.T., Mng. Dir.--Associated Engineers Ltd., Kowloon, Hong Kong; *Int'l*, pg. 705
Chow, Kyle, V.P. & Gen. Mgr.--Frigidaire Home Products-Laundry Products, Webster City, IA; *Int'l*, pg. 440
Chow, Sidney H., V.P.-Far East Sls.--Santa Fe Braun Intl. Ltd., Beijing, China; *Int'l*, pg. 765
Chowaniec, Adam, V.P. & Gen. Mgr.-Microsystems Division--Newbridge Networks Corporation, Kanata, Canada; *Int'l*, pg. 924
Chowdhury, K.B., Mng. Dir.--Gestetner Bangladesh Ltd., Dhaka, Bangladesh; *Int'l*, pg. 1115
Chowdhury, Mujibur, Chief Oper. Officer--Rhone-Poulenc Bangladesh Ltd., Dhaka, Bangladesh; *Int'l*, pg. 1112
Chown, Kyle, Gen. Mgr.--Frigidaire Home Products-Freezer Products, Saint Cloud, MN; *Int'l*, pg. 440
Chraibi, A., Chm. & Chief Exec. Officer--Al Wataniya, Casablanca, Morocco; *Int'l*, pg. 564
Chretin, Alberto, V.P.--Alphabet de Mexico, Chihuahua, Mexico; *U.S. Private*, pg. 1045
Christakas, Sparky, Pres.--Gladding Braided Products LLC, South Otselic, NY; *U.S. Private*, pg. 291
Christen, Peter, Chm. Bd. & Chief Exec. Officer--MassWest Insurance Company, West Springfield, MA; *Int'l*, pg. 345
Christen, W.E., Gen. Dir.--Auergesellschaft GmbH, Berlin, Germany; *U.S. Public*, pg. 1114
Christensen, Ejner, Mng. Dir.--Brenderup Trailers A/S, Aaby, Denmark; *Int'l*, pg. 436
Christensen, James, V.P. & Mng. Dir.--AlliedSignal Aerospace Service Corporation, Drancy, France; *U.S. Public*, pg. 52
Christensen, James, Dir.-Natl. Sls. & Mktg.--Decora', Jasper, IN; *U.S. Public*, pg. 675
Christensen, Jerry, Plant Mgr.--Ringier America, Jonesboro Division, Jonesboro, AR; *U.S. Public*, pg. 1778
Christensen, Johs Bogh, Chief Oper. Officer--Alfa-Laval Venezolana S.A., Caracas, Venezuela; *Int'l*, pg. 1380
Christensen, Jorgen, Chief Oper. Officer--Novo Nordisk A/S, Kalundborg, Denmark; *Int'l*, pg. 987

Christensen, Jos, Chief Oper. Officer--Ibex Engineering Co. Ltd., Hastings, United Kingdom; *Int'l*, pg. 1380
Christensen, Kaj, Mng. Dir.--Nitodan A/S, Haderslev, Denmark; *Int'l*, pg. 932
Christensen, Knut O., Mng. Dir.--Bang & Olufsen A/S, Drammen, Norway; *Int'l*, pg. 146
Christensen, Leon, Chief Oper. Officer--Hudson General Corp., Salt Lake City, UT; *U.S. Public*, pg. 845
Christensen, Lief, Pres.--Manistique Papers, Inc., Manistique, MI; *Int'l*, pg. 762
Christensen, Soren K., Sr. V.P. & Branch Mgr.--Bank of Montreal - England, London, United Kingdom; *Int'l*, pg. 155
Christensen, Thorkil K., Chief Oper. Officer--Novo Nordisk A/S, Singapore, Singapore; *Int'l*, pg. 987
Christenson, Mats, Mgr.--Prototyp-Werke GmbH, Zell, Germany; *Int'l*, pg. 1186
Christiaens, Jean-Marie, Gen. Mgr.--Aki Bricolage, Barcelona, Spain; *Int'l*, pg. 534
Christian, Adelbert, Pres.--FAG Interamericana AG, Miami, FL; *Int'l*, pg. 469
Christian, Cristine, Acting Gen. Mgr.--Dun & Bradstreet (Australia) Pty. Ltd., Melbourne, Australia; *U.S. Public*, pg. 536
Christian, Dennis W., Pres.--Callon Offshore Production, Natchez, MS; *U.S. Public*, pg. 295
Christian, Dennis W., Pres.--Mississippi Marketing, Inc., Natchez, MS; *U.S. Public*, pg. 295
Christian, Gary, Mgr.-Division--Allied Oil & Supply, Omaha, NE; *U.S. Private*, pg. 39
Christian, George, Gen. Mgr.--BancTec Financial Systems, Dallas, TX; *U.S. Public*, pg. 177
Christian, Jon, Mgr.--Downey Savings & Loan Association, F.A., Indio, CA; *U.S. Public*, pg. 527
Christian, Nathan, Pres. & Chief Exec. Officer--Norwest Bank El Paso, N.A., El Paso, TX; *U.S. Public*, pg. 1201
Christian, W. L., V.P.--Bleu Water Company, Richmond, VA; *U.S. Private*, pg. 223
Christians, James, Gen. Mgr.--Kysor/Michigan Fleet, Grand Rapids, MI; *U.S. Public*, pg. 968
Christiansen, Allan, Gen. Mgr.--CPC Foods A/S, Skovlunde, Denmark; *U.S. Public*, pg. 225
Christiansen, Berndt, Mng. Dir.--Ericsson Radio Systemer A/S, Nesbru, Norway; *Int'l*, pg. 1367
Christiansen, Finn, District Mgr.--Det Norske Veritas, Torshavn, Faroe Islands; *Int'l*, pg. 397
Christiansen, Jeff, Pres. & Gen. Mgr.--Algona Food Equipment Co., Algona, IA; *U.S. Public*, pg. 840
Christiansen, Olav K., Pres.--Aker Oil & Gas Technology, Inc., Houston, TX; *Int'l*, pg. 42
Christianson, Finn Normann, Pres.--Burmeister & Wain Energi A/S, Virum, Denmark; *Int'l*, pg. 398
Christianson, Harry, Pres.--Tool & Engineering Co., Chicago, IL; *U.S. Private*, pg. 394
Christianson, Karl, V.P.--Parchment Mill, Parchment, MI; *U.S. Public*, pg. 465
Christianson, Robert D., Pres.--Burton Medical Products Corporation, Chatsworth, CA; *Int'l*, pg. 821
Christie, Beth, Gen. Mgr.--Avent America Inc., Addison, IL; *Int'l*, pg. 261
Christie, Guy, Pres.--Descente Canada Inc., Vancouver, Canada; *Int'l*, pg. 396
Christie, Jeffrey S., Partner--Skadden, Arps, Slate, Meagher & Flom International, Singapore, Singapore; *U.S. Private*, pg. 1004
Christie, P.J., Mgr.--Rockware Glass Ltd.-Bagleys Factory, Knottingley, United Kingdom; *Int'l*, pg. 124
Christie, Robert S., Pres.--McGraw-Hill College Division, New York, NY; *U.S. Public*, pg. 1070
Christie, Ron, Chief Exec. Officer--Novo Nordisk (Pty) Ltd., Woodmead, South Africa; *Int'l*, pg. 988
Christine, Bob, Gen. Mgr.--SMI Rebar Virginia, Fredericksburg, VA; *U.S. Public*, pg. 412
Christison, D., Mng. Dir.--Pacific Fire Hose Pty Ltd., Boronia, Australia; *Int'l*, pg. 1500
Christison, D., Mng. Dir.--Angus Fire Armour (Australia) Pty Ltd., Boronia, Australia; *Int'l*, pg. 1500
Christmas, James W., Pres.--Proliq, Inc., Edison, NJ; *U.S. Public*, pg. 939
Christmas, James W., Pres.--National Enerdrill, Edison, NJ; *U.S. Public*, pg. 939
Christner, Tom, Mgr.-Plant--Akzo Salt Inc., Manistee, MI; *Int'l*, pg. 48
Christofferson, Lars H., Mng. Dir.--LM Ericsson (Nigeria) Ltd., Lagos, Nigeria; *Int'l*, pg. 1369
Christofferson, Randy L., Pres.--First USA Bank, Wilmington, DE; *U.S. Public*, pg. 174
Christoffersson, John, Gen. Mgr.--Healthcare Management Group, New York, NY; *U.S. Public*, pg. 1071
Christofori, James, Admin.--Greenery Extended Care Center of North Andover, North Andover, MA; *U.S. Public*, pg. 837
Christopher, David, Pres.--A & A International, Inc., Fort Worth, TX; *U.S. Public*, pg. 1560
Christopher, R., Pres.--UGL, Inc., Chicago Heights, IL; *Int'l*, pg. 1117
Christopher, S.M., Pres.--Security Life of Denver Insurance Company, Denver, CO; *Int'l*, pg. 648
Christopher, Socrates, Chief Oper. Officer--Jacobs Sirrine Engineers, Inc., Greenville, SC; *U.S. Public*, pg. 921
Christopher, Thomas, Pres.--Bookstop, Inc., New York, NY; *U.S. Public*, pg. 189
Christopher, Todd, Pres. & Chief Exec. Officer--Physician Sales & Services Inc., Beaumont, TX; *U.S. Public*, pg. 1294
Christopher, William F., Pres.--Alcoa Forged Products, Cleveland, OH; *U.S. Public*, pg. 60
Christophersen, Bjorn, V.P. & Gen. Mgr.--Health & Beauty Prods.-Scandanavia--Procter & Gamble Health & Beauty Care Scandinavia, Amersfoort, Netherlands; *U.S. Public*, pg. 1332
Christou, Marios, Auditor--Wackenhut Security Cyprus, Nicosia, Cyprus; *U.S. Public*, pg. 1732
Christy, Michael, Pres.--Lima Division, Lima, OH; *U.S. Private*, pg. 948
Chrobok, Werner, Dir.--Bankhaus Gebruder Bethmann, Frankfurt/Main, Germany; *Int'l*, pg. 179
Chrosch, Peter, Co-Chief Oper. Officer--Winschermann Berlin GmbH, Berlin, Germany; *Int'l*, pg. 1167
Chrysler, Robert T., Pres.--Sachs Automotive Corp.-North American OEM Operations, Troy, MI; *Int'l*, pg. 835
Chrystal, Colin, Plant Mgr.--Acme Brick Co., Sealy, TX; *U.S. Public*, pg. 936
Chu, Bennett, Grp. Representative--Nicoll Asia Ltd., Wan Chai, Hong Kong; *Int'l*, pg. 430
Chu, Leo, Gen. Mgr.--Crystal Park Casino, Compton, CA; *U.S. Public*, pg. 831
Chu, Liu Ji, Gen. Mgr.--Beijing Huade Metal Packaging Container Co. Ltd., Beijing, China; *Int'l*, pg. 1322
Chu, Paul, Mng. Dir.--PAXAR Far East Limited, Kowloon, Hong Kong; *U.S. Public*, pg. 1267
Chu, T.Z., Pres.--Finnigan MAT, San Jose, CA; *U.S. Public*, pg. 1591
Chua, Y.H., Mng. Dir.--Hunter Douglas Singapore Pte. Ltd., Singapore, Singapore; *Int'l*, pg. 640
Chuamnsu, James, Mng. Dir.--McCormick-Philippines, Inc., Quezon City, Philippines; *U.S. Public*, pg. 1067
Chuang, Nang-Tan, Pres.--Prince Housing Development Corp., Taipei, Taiwan; *Int'l*, pg. 1347
Chubb, Percy, III, Pres.--Chubb Custom Insurance Company, Dover, DE; *U.S. Public*, pg. 355
Chuderewicz, Leonard H., Pres.--USS-POSCO Industries, Pittsburg, CA; *Int'l*, pg. 1062
Chuderewicz, Leonard H., Pres.--USS-POSCO Industries, Pittsburg, CA; *U.S. Public*, pg. 1662
Chui, Louis, Gen. Mgr.--Foshan Crown Can Company Ltd., Foshan, China; *U.S. Public*, pg. 465
Chui, Louis, Gen. Mgr.--Foshan Easy-Opening End Company Ltd., Foshan, China; *U.S. Public*, pg. 465
Chul-Ho, Park, Gen. Mgr.--Perak Hanjung Sinien Sdn. Bhd., Perak, Malaysia; *Int'l*, pg. 758
Chumbley, Avery B., Pres.--Wailuku Agribusiness Co., Inc., Wailuku, HI; *U.S. Private*, pg. 191
Chun, Gao Hai, Pres.--China Otsuka Pharmaceutical Co., Ltd., Tianjin, China; *Int'l*, pg. 1014
Chun, Yang Xiao, Pres.--Shanghai Bao Tai Long Concrete Products Co., Ltd., Shanghai, China; *Int'l*, pg. 1293
Chunbai, Zhu, Pres. & Dir.--China Kang Fu International Leasing Co., Ltd., Beijing, China; *Int'l*, pg. 521
Chung-Kon, Lee, Pres.--Dong-Myung Industrial Co., Ltd., Kyonggi-do, Korea; *Int'l*, pg. 856
Chung-Kong, Lee, Pres.--Sung San Company, Ltd., Taegu, Korea; *U.S. Public*, pg. 724
Chung, B.M., Chief Oper. Officer--Ahlstrom Korea Co., Ltd., Seoul, Korea; *Int'l*, pg. 35
Chung, Dong-ho, Chief Rep.--The Export-Import Bank of Korea, London, United Kingdom; *Int'l*, pg. 468
Chung, Doo-Young, Chief Officer--Ssangyong Singapore PTE., Ltd., Singapore, Singapore; *Int'l*, pg. 1291
Chung, I. Young, Pres.--Shinsung Packard Company, Ltd., Kyonggi-Do, Korea; *U.S. Public*, pg. 724
Chung, In Yung, Pres.--Saehan Merchant Banking Corporation, Seoul, Korea; *Int'l*, pg. 676
Chung, Jeff, Mgr.--EURO RSCG Korea, Seoul, Korea; *Int'l*, pg. 602
Chung, Jesse, V.P.--Degussa Corp., Dental Dept., South Plainfield, NJ; *Int'l*, pg. 388
Chung, Kun-Il, Mgr.--Deutsche Bank AG (Pusan), Pusan, Korea; *Int'l*, pg. 404
Chung, Mong Hun, Pres.--Hyundai Electronics Industries Co., Ltd., Kyonggi-do, Korea; *Int'l*, pg. 641
Chung, Mong Joon, Pres.--Hyundai Heavy Industries Co., Ltd., Ulsan, Korea; *Int'l*, pg. 641
Chung, Nak-Kyung, Pres.--Novellus Systems Korea, Seoul, Korea; *U.S. Public*, pg. 1204
Chung, S.O., Dir.--Sunkyong America, Inc.-Los Angeles Branch, Carson, CA; *Int'l*, pg. 1320
Chung, Soo-Jin, Country Mgr.--Raychem Korea Limited, Seoul, Korea; *U.S. Public*, pg. 1362
Chung, W.S., Pres.--Hyosung-Ebara Company Ltd., Seoul, Korea; *Int'l*, pg. 432
Chung, Yong, Chm. Bd. & Chief Exec. Officer--Samsung China Headquarters, Beijing, China; *Int'l*, pg. 1183
Chura-Donovan, Lois, Branch Mgr.--Troy Savings Bank-Main Office, Troy, NY; *U.S. Private*, pg. 1106
Church, D.A., Pres.--Seibert-Oxidermo, Inc., Romulus, MI; *U.S. Public*, pg. 502
Church, Gordon L., Pres.--Cigna Healthcare of Ohio, Inc., Columbus, OH; *U.S. Public*, pg. 360
Church, John, Gen. Mgr.--Poe & Brown of Florida, Brooksville, FL; *U.S. Public*, pg. 1312
Church, Kenneth E., Pres.--Clayton-Marcus Company, Inc., Hickory, NC; *U.S. Public*, pg. 975
Church, Steven, Pres.--Hamilton Hallmark, Culver City, CA; *U.S. Public*, pg. 155
Church, Tom, Chief Oper. Officer--Fresh Western International, Salinas, CA; *Int'l*, pg. 491
Church, Walter G., Sr., Pres. & Chief Exec. Officer--BB&T Savings Bank, SSB, Valdese, NC; *U.S. Public*, pg. 160
Churchill, Tony, V.P. & Gen. Mgr.--NIKE International Ltd., Weiterstadt, Germany; *U.S. Public*, pg. 1184
Churchill, Winston J., Mng. Gen. Partner--SCP Private Equity Partners, Wayne, PA; *U.S. Public*, pg. 1424
Churchwell, Gary, Mng. Dir.--Florasynth Singapore Pte Ltd., Singapore, Singapore; *Int'l*, pg. 174
Chuter, C.D., Gen. Mgr.--Wellcome Ilac Urunleri Ltd Sirketi, Istanbul, Turkey; *Int'l*, pg. 553
Chutinaw, Alongkot, Mng. Dir.--The Siam Nawaloha Foundry Co., Ltd., Bangkok, Thailand; *Int'l*, pg. 1238
Chwo, H., Rep.--Cariplo (Taipei), Taipei, Taiwan; *Int'l*, pg. 275
Cia, Richard, Field Service Engnrg.--AlliedSignal Engines, Geneva, Switzerland; *U.S. Public*, pg. 52
Ciabotti, Doug, Pres.--Milwaukee Cylinder Division, Cudahy, WI; *U.S. Public*, pg. 124
Ciamarro, Roberto, Pres. & Gen. Mgr.--Canagex Investments Limited, Montreal, Canada; *Int'l*, pg. 396
Ciampa, A.J., Business Mgr.--Lord Corp., Elastomer Products, Erie, PA; *U.S. Private*, pg. 676
Cianci, Giovanni, Pres.--Quaker-Chiari & Forti S.P.A., Silea, Italy; *U.S. Public*, pg. 1348
Ciardella, Robert L., Pres.--Asymtek, Carlsbad, CA; *U.S. Public*, pg. 1188
Ciborowski, J., Gen. Mgr.--Soderec International, Evry, France; *Int'l*, pg. 803
Cicatko, Joe G., Jr., Admin.--Lakeview Manor, Chapel Hill, NC; *U.S. Public*, pg. 1714
Ciccarelli, John A., Pres. & Chief Exec. Officer--Dayton Superior Corporation, Miamisburg, OH; *U.S. Private*, pg. 931
Ciccateri, Jim, Mgr.-Opers.--Shanghai Donnelly Fu Hua Window Systems Company, Ltd., Shanghai, China; *U.S. Public*, pg. 519
Ciccolella, Francesco, Mng. Dir.--Dodi S.p.A., Milan, Italy; *Int'l*, pg. 146
Cichon, Thomas, Mgr.--Arrow Sintered Products, Forest Park, IL; *U.S. Private*, pg. 85
Cichowlaz, Clifford, Gen. Mgr.--Day & Zimmermann Hawthorne Corporation, Hawthorne, NV; *U.S. Private*, pg. 317
Cichy, J.S., Pres.--White-Rodgers Div., Emerson Electric Co., Saint Louis, MO; *U.S. Public*, pg. 573
Cicurel, Michel, Gen. Mgr.--Banque Dumenil-Leble, Paris, France; *Int'l*, pg. 240
Cid, Chuck, Chief Oper. Officer--Allright San Francisco Parking, Inc., San Francisco, CA; *U.S. Private*, pg. 43
Cieglak, Lee, Branch Mgr.--First of America Bank Florida, Tampa, FL; *U.S. Public*, pg. 636
Cieremans, Jan, Gen. Mgr.--Turkkablo A.O., Izmit, Turkey; *Int'l*, pg. 954
Cifuentes, Alvaro, Mng. Dir.--Sistemas Ericsson S.A., Caracas, Venezuela; *Int'l*, pg. 1370
Ciklik, Jose, Pres.--Envases Multipac S.A. De C.V., Tlalnepantla, Mexico; *U.S. Public*, pg. 868
Cillo, Larry J., Pres.--Harris Investors Direct, Inc., Chicago, IL; *Int'l*, pg. 154
Cimmarusti, John A., Pres.--Butler Design Services, Inc., Montvale, NJ; *U.S. Public*, pg. 271
Cimmins, John, V.P.--Customer Development Corporation, Downers Grove, IL; *U.S. Private*, pg. 298
Ciofalo, Tony, Chief Oper. Officer--W.J. Flyte Corporation, Apache Junction, AZ; *U.S. Public*, pg. 49
Ciolino, Paul, Pres.--Unit Rail Anchor Company, Atchison, KS; *U.S. Public*, pg. 1711
Ciotti, Daniel B., Pres.--Boston Trade Bank, Boston, MA; *U.S. Public*, pg. 184
Cip, Ing. Ernst, Chief Oper. Officer--Gartenhilfe Ges.m.b.H., Lienz, Austria; *Int'l*, pg. 356
Cipollaro, Michael A., Pres.--Gerber Finance Co., Fremont, MI; *Int'l*, pg. 973
Cipollaro, Michael A., Pres.--Gerber Products Overseas, Fremont, MI; *Int'l*, pg. 973
Cipriani, Giorgio, Dir.--Banca d'America e d'Italia S.p.a. (Prato), Prato, Italy; *Int'l*, pg. 403
Cipriani, Robert, Chm.--Cipriani Kremer Design, Boston, MA; *U.S. Private*, pg. 84
Ciprietti, B.J., Pres.--DNN Galvanizing Corporation, Windsor, Canada; *Int'l*, pg. 414
Ciprut, Aydin Toni, Pres.--Peyma Chr. Hansen's A.S., Istanbul, Turkey; *Int'l*, pg. 289
Cirelli, Elio, Chief Oper. Officer--COBE Lab. Italia s.r.l., Felino, Italy; *Int'l*, pg. 667
Cirelli, Elio, Chief Oper. Officer--Hospal Dasco S.p.A., Medolla, Italy; *Int'l*, pg. 668
Cirilli, Dante, Pres. & Dir.-Mktg. Div.--Grolier Inc., Danbury, CT; *Int'l*, pg. 794
Cirina, Lawrence J., Pres.--Schlegel Lining Technology, Inc., Spring, TX; *Int'l*, pg. 128
Cirone, Alejandro, Mng. Dir.--Korn/Ferry International, Buenos Aires, Argentina; *U.S. Private*, pg. 633
Cirone, Alejandro, Mng. Dir.--Korn/Ferry International, Santiago, Chile; *U.S. Private*, pg. 634
Cirone, Ray, Gen. Mgr.--Cadillac Plastic (Canada) Ltd., Rexdale, Canada; *U.S. Public*, pg. 781
Cissell, Mary, Publr.--Democrat News, Fredericktown, MO; *U.S. Public*, pg. 1343
Citro, Carmine, V.P. & Gen. Mgr.--Berger Instruments, Braintree, MA; *U.S. Private*, pg. 235
Citterio, R., Reg. Mng. Dir.--EMI Italiana SpA, Milan, Italy; *Int'l*, pg. 427
Ciundziewicki, T., Mng. Dir. Mktg.--Dataproducts Handelsgesellschaft M.b.H., Vienna, Austria; *Int'l*, pg. 621
Ciuret, Javier Llussa, Mng. Dir.--GGK Sao Paulo, Sao Paulo, Brazil; *Int'l*, pg. 1335
Ciuro, Juan, Mgr.--Compania General de Esencias Grupo Florasynth S.A., Barcelona, Spain; *Int'l*, pg. 173
Civile, Alfonso, Retail Food Distributor--D'Jesco, Inc., Old San Juan, PR; *U.S. Private*, pg. 6
Claar, Donald K., Pres.--UtilCo Group, Overland, MO; *U.S. Public*, pg. 1701
Claassen, Gregg, Pres.--The Midland Grocery Company, Westville, IN; *U.S. Private*, pg. 948
Clabaugh, Michael, V.P.-Advanced Systems--Cincinnati Milacron-Canada Ltd, Toronto, Canada; *U.S. Public*, pg. 368
Clabby, Joseph S., Sr. V.P.-Insurance Co. Services--Willis Corroon Financial Services Corp., New York, NY; *Int'l*, pg. 1507
Clack, Edwin, Dir.-Coating Services-West--Sermatech West, Airfoil Management Co., Compton, CA; *U.S. Public*, pg. 1570
Clack, Ronald D., Sr. V.P.--Southeast Marketing-Atlanta Business Center, Atlanta, GA; *U.S. Public*, pg. 649
Cladianos, P. Jr., Pres.--Zante, Inc., Reno, NV; *U.S. Public*, pg. 1431
Claes, Marcel, V.P. & Country Mgr.--Bank of America NT&SA, Antwerp, Belgium; *U.S. Public*, pg. 182
Claessens, Maaike, Dir.--Inamed B.V.B.A., Turnhout, Belgium; *U.S. Public*, pg. 874

Claessens, Thierry, Admin.--Banque Commerciale Zairoise, Kinshasa, Congo; *Int'l*, pg. 547
Claesson, Anders, Chief Fin. Officer--SAS Financial Services, Stockholm, Sweden; *Int'l*, pg. 1201
Claesson, H., Mng. Dir.--De La Rue Inter Innovation AB, Flen, Sweden; *Int'l*, pg. 387
Claesson, Rolf, Chief Oper. Officer--V.A.G. Stockholm AB, Stockholm, Sweden; *Int'l*, pg. 1476
Claesson, Tore, Pres.--Perstorp Components Europe, Vastra Frolunda, Sweden; *Int'l*, pg. 1040
Claeys, T., Chief Oper. Officer--Monsanto (Suisse) S.A., Zurich, Switzerland; *U.S. Public*, pg. 1126
Claflin, David, Gen. Mgr.--Harvey Electronics, Greenwich, CT; *U.S. Public*, pg. 797
Clain, G., Pres. & Chief Exec. Officer--J. Gerber & Co. Inc., New York, NY; *U.S. Private*, pg. 449
Clairet, Michel, Mill Mgr.--St. Just Mill, Saint-Just-le-Martel, France; *U.S. Public*, pg. 673
Clancy, Michael, Mng. Dir.--Topps Ireland Ltd., Ireland; *U.S.* Public, pg. 1622
Clancy, Michael J., Mng. Dir.--SSI Medical Systems, Inc., Solihull, United Kingdom; *U.S. Public*, pg. 828
Clanton, Ray, Sr., Gen. Mgr.--Clanton's Auto Auction, Darlington, SC; *U.S. Private*, pg. 282
Clapes, Jorge, Chief Fin. Officer--Johnson & Johnson de Argentina, S.A., Buenos Aires, Argentina; *U.S. Public*, pg. 930
Clapp, William A., Pres.--Mayville Metal Products Division, Mayville, WI; *U.S. Private*, pg. 264
Clapprood, Robert A., Pres.--Tyco Printed Circuit Group, Stafford, CT; *U.S. Public*, pg. 1648
Claprood, Pierre, Pres. & Chief Exec. Officer--Natrel Inc., Longueuil, Canada; *Int'l*, pg. 32
Claramunt, Dennis D., Pres.--Jacobs Chuck Manufacturing, Clemson, SC; *U.S. Public*, pg. 481
Clare, B., Mng. Dir.--Boots Healthcare International, Nottingham, United Kingdom; *Int'l*, pg. 202
Claret, Philippe, Mgr.--EURO RSCG Quartet, Ecueille, France; *Int'l*, pg. 601
Clarice, David, Pres.--Lambert Smith Hampton, Atlanta, GA; *Int'l*, pg. 797
Clarizio, Mike, Mgr.--INX Incorporated/Midland Color Company, Portland, OR; *Int'l*, pg. 1311
Clark-Jackson, Sue, Pres. & Publr.--Reno Gazette Journal, Reno, NV; *U.S. Public*, pg. 701
Clark, A., Editor--The Sun-Herald, Sydney, Australia; *Int'l*, pg. 477
Clark, Allason N., Pres. & Chief Exec. Officer--Franklin Bank, San Mateo, CA; *U.S. Public*, pg. 680
Clark, Barry, Mng. Dir. & Sec.--Sime Darby Commodities Limited, London, United Kingdom; *Int'l*, pg. 1250
Clark, Barry W., Pres. & Chief Exec. Officer--Steel Parts Corp., Tipton, IN; *U.S. Public*, pg. 881
Clark, Beth, Publisher--Corvallis Gazette-Times, Corvallis, OR; *U.S. Public*, pg. 983
Clark, Brian, Reg. V.P.--Arrow/Schweber Electronics, Sunnyvale, CA; *U.S. Public*, pg. 134
Clark, Bruce, Pres. & Chief Exec. Officer--COMMCORP Financial Services Inc., Burlington, Canada; *Int'l*, pg. 256
Clark, C.R.N., Chm.--Cookson Matthey Ceramics PLC, Stoke on Trent, United Kingdom; *Int'l*, pg. 713
Clark, Charles, V.P. & G.M.--Subsystems Div., Santa Clara, CA; *U.S. Public*, pg. 884
Clark, Coley, Sr. V.P.--EDS, Business Operations Group, Southfield, MI; *U.S. Public*, pg. 570
Clark, D.L., Pres.--Smiths Industries Aerospace & Defense Systems Inc.-Clearwater, Clearwater, FL; *Int'l*, pg. 1268
Clark, David, Mng. Dir.--Bankgesellschaft Berlin (UK) plc, London, United Kingdom; *Int'l*, pg. 160
Clark, David, Pres. & Chief Exec. Officer--Homeland Stores, Inc., Oklahoma City, OK; *U.S. Public*, pg. 832
Clark, Dick, Pres.--Dick Clark Corporate Productions, Inc., Burbank, CA; *U.S. Public*, pg. 382
Clark, Douglas, Pres.--Smiths Industries Aerospace & Defense Systems Inc.-Malvern, Malvern, PA; *Int'l*, pg. 1268
Clark, E. Roger, Pres.--The Kanthal Corporation, Bethel, CT; *Int'l*, pg. 723
Clark, Frank, Chief Oper. Officer--Electrolux (Commercial Equipment) Ltd., Luton, United Kingdom; *Int'l*, pg. 444
Clark, G. Denton, Chm. Bd., Pres. & Chief Exec. Officer--BMG Music Canada, Toronto, Canada; *Int'l*, pg. 192
Clark, G.J., Pres. & Gen. Mgr.--John Deere Ltd., Grimsby, Canada; *U.S. Public*, pg. 493
Clark, Garet B., Mng. Dir.--Northern Trust Bank of California, N.A., San Diego, CA; *U.S. Public*, pg. 1196
Clark, Gary, Pres. & Chief Exec. Officer--Indimac Third Party Construction Lending Division, Pasadena, CA; *U.S.* Public, pg. 857
Clark, Gary M., Exec. V.P.--Westinghouse Industries & Technologies Group, Pittsburgh, PA; *U.S. Public*, pg. 273
Clark, Gary O., Pres. & Chief Exec. Officer--Commercial National Bank of Berwyn, Berwyn, IL; *U.S. Public*, pg. 379
Clark, Gerald, Chm. Bd--MetLife Capital Holdings, Inc., Bellevue, WA; *U.S. Private*, pg. 737
Clark, Glenn, Mgr.-Mfg.--Plastic Products Division, Tillsonburg, Canada; *U.S. Private*, pg. 428
Clark, H., Pres.--Trade Dimensions, Stamford, CT; *Int'l*, pg. 1447
Clark, Howard L., Chm. Bd.--Skandinaviska Enskilda Banken Corporation, New York, NY; *Int'l*, pg. 1259
Clark, J., Mng. Dir.--ANZ Grindlays Bank plc Sri Lanka, Colombo, Sri Lanka; *Int'l*, pg. 99
Clark, J. Roderick, Pres.--Sperry-Sun Drilling Services Division, Houston, TX; *U.S. Public*, pg. 528
Clark, Jack L., Mgr.-Opers.--Jacobs Engineering Group Inc., Albuquerque, NM; *U.S. Public*, pg. 921
Clark, James, Mng. Dir.--AAR Allen Airmotive, Inc., Hoofddorp, Netherlands; *U.S. Public*, pg. 1
Clark, Jeffrey, Chief Oper. Officer--TAC (UK) Ltd., Harpenden, United Kingdom; *Int'l*, pg. 670
Clark, Jerome, Pres.--Shade Foods, Inc., Union City, CA; *U.S. Private*, pg. 802
Clark, Jim, V.P.-Medium Voltage & Switchgear Opers.--Square D Company, Smyrna, TN; *Int'l*, pg. 1208
Clark, Jimmie D., Pres.--Sysco/Louisville Food Services Co., Louisville, KY; *U.S. Public*, pg. 1552
Clark, John, Plant Mgr.--Sealy Mattress Company - Orlando, Orlando, FL; *U.S. Private*, pg. 979
Clark, John N., Pres.--Smith & Nephew Rehabilitation Inc., Germantown, WI; *Int'l*, pg. 1263
Clark, Ken, Office Mgr.--Korn/Ferry International, Princeton, NJ; *U.S. Private*, pg. 633
Clark, Kenneth J., Pres.--Lincoln National Intermediaries, Inc., Fort Wayne, IN; *U.S. Public*, pg. 998
Clark, Kenneth P., Mgr.-Branch--Piper Jaffray Inc., New York, NY; *U.S. Public*, pg. 1302
Clark, Kevin, Chief Fin. Officer--Prior Gaskets Inc., Dallas, TX; *U.S. Private*, pg. 300
Clark, Lionel, Gen. Mgr.--Schult Homes Corporation, Buckeye, AZ; *U.S. Public*, pg. 1442
Clark, Neil, Gen. Mgr.--Frost Wire Products, Ltd., Hamilton, Canada; *Int'l*, pg. 1299
Clark, P.J., Chief Exec. Officer--The Mount Cook Group Limited, Christchurch, New Zealand; *Int'l*, pg. 38
Clark, Paul N., V.P.-Pharmaceutical Opers.--Abbott Pharmaceutical Products Division, Abbott Park, IL; *U.S. Public*, pg. 13
Clark, Peter, V.P.--Huber, Hunt & Nichols, Inc., Branchburg, NJ; *U.S. Private*, pg. 548
Clark, R. Kerry, Pres.--Procter & Gamble Laundry Products Division, Cincinnati, OH; *U.S. Public*, pg. 1331
Clark, R.J., Jr., V.P.-Specialties--National Electrical Carbon Corporation, Fostoria, OH; *Int'l*, pg. 891
Clark, R.M., Chief Exec. Officer--Zurich Compagnie d'assurances sur la vie, Brussels, Belgium; *Int'l*, pg. 1529
Clark, R.M., Chief Exec. Officer--Zurich International (Belgique) S.A., Brussels, Belgium; *Int'l*, pg. 1532
Clark, Randall T., Mng. Dir.--Emery Global Logistics, Redwood City, CA; *U.S. Public*, pg. 281
Clark, Randy, Gen. Mgr.--Logistics Worldwide, Palo Alto, CA; *U.S. Public*, pg. 281
Clark, Richard, V.P.-Opers.--Presto Food Products, Inc., City of Industry, CA; *U.S. Public*, pg. 1527
Clark, Richard, Pres.--Enterra Compressions Co., Corpus Christi, TX; *U.S. Public*, pg. 1749
Clark, Richard H., Pres. & Chief Exec. Officer--Bank of America Public Finance, Los Angeles, CA; *U.S. Public*, pg. 181
Clark, Richard P., Pres.--M/A-COM Inc., Lowell, MA; *U.S. Public*, pg. 8
Clark, Robert, Pres.--Great Salt Lake Minerals Corp., Overland Park, KS; *U.S. Private*, pg. 505
Clark, Robert G., Chm., Pres. & Chief Exec. Officer--I.C.E. International Capital Equipment, Inc., Larchmont, NY; *Int'l*, pg. 683
Clark, Robert W., Pres.--Old Dominion Life Insurance Co., Roanoke, VA; *U.S. Private*, pg. 992
Clark, Rush S., Pres.--Amoco Fabrics & Fibers, Ltd., Hawkesbury, Canada; *U.S. Public*, pg. 102
Clark, Rusty, Mgr.-Opers.--American Paper Products, Youngstown, OH; *U.S. Private*, pg. 60
Clark, Samuel A., Pres. & Chief Exec. Officer--Security Pacific International Finance, Inc., San Diego, CA; *U.S. Public*, pg. 182
Clark, Scott, Plant Mgr.--Cambridge Industries, Inc., Centralia, IL; *U.S. Private*, pg. 202
Clark, Stephen R., Pres.--SOCO Chemical, Inc., Reading, PA; *Int'l*, pg. 1458
Clark, Stephen S., Pres.--Love Controls Corporation, Michigan City, IN; *U.S. Private*, pg. 350
Clark, Stephen W., Pres.--Galderma Laboratories, Inc., Fort Worth, TX; *Int'l*, pg. 819
Clark, Steve, Pres.--Precisionaire, Inc., Saint Petersburg, FL; *U.S. Public*, pg. 648
Clark, Steve, V.P. & Gen. Mgr.-Forest Prods. & Resources--Wood Products/Forest Resources/Energy Resource Div., West Monroe, LA; *U.S. Public*, pg. 1311
Clark, Stuart, Pres.--Interactive Data Corporation, Lexington, MA; *Int'l*, pg. 1025
Clark, T. Daniel, Sr. Div. Pres.--Dexter Packaging Products, Waukegan, IL; *U.S. Public*, pg. 504
Clark, T.A., Div. Mgr.--Ohio Edison Co.-Springfield Div., Springfield, OH; *U.S. Public*, pg. 645
Clark, Thomas H., Pres.--Guaranty Income Life Insurance Co., Baton Rouge, LA; *U.S. Private*, pg. 485
Clark, W. Richard, Sr. V.P.--Bausch & Lomb Pharmaceutical Division, Tampa, FL; *U.S. Public*, pg. 194
Clark, W. Roger, Pres.--United Companies Lending Corporation, Baton Rouge, LA; *U.S. Public*, pg. 1675
Clark, Wayne, Pres.--Pure Pulse Technologies, Inc., San Diego, CA; *U.S. Public*, pg. 1062
Clark, William S., Pres. & Chief Exec. Officer--First Bank of Stuart, Stuart, VA; *U.S. Public*, pg. 1039
Clarke, C.D., Chief Exec. Officer--Lloyds Bank NZA Limited, Sydney, Australia; *Int'l*, pg. 813
Clarke, Charles, Chief Oper. Officer--Clarke Electronics, Milwaukie, OR; *U.S. Public*, pg. 1720
Clarke, D.F., Pres.--Nova Chemicals, Inc., Monaca, PA; *Int'l*, pg. 971
Clarke, David, Pres.--CSR America Inc., Atlanta, GA; *Int'l*, pg. 245
Clarke, Gareth, Pres.--London International, U.S. Holdings Inc., Norcross, GA; *Int'l*, pg. 815
Clarke, Garry, Sls. Rep.--Toro Australia Pty. Ltd., Waitara, Australia; *U.S. Public*, pg. 1624
Clarke, George, Exec. V.P.--Stewart Smith Specialty Risks, Inc., Southfield, MI; *Int'l*, pg. 1508
Clarke, Glenn, Gen. Mgr.--Freudenberg NOK, Tillsonburg, Canada; *Int'l*, pg. 505
Clarke, J.W., Chief Exec. Officer--Monier Inc., Orange, CA; *Int'l*, pg. 1091
Clarke, Jeffrey, Mng. Dir.--TAC (UK) Ltd., Harpenden, United Kingdom; *Int'l*, pg. 670
Clarke, John M., Pres.--SmithKline Beecham Canada, Inc., Oakville, Canada; *Int'l*, pg. 1265
Clarke, John P., Publr.--The State Journal-Register, Springfield, IL; *U.S. Private*, pg. 275
Clarke, Kenneth R., Pres. & Chief Exec. Officer--Trilon Financial Corp., Toronto, Canada; *Int'l*, pg. 434
Clarke, M. Key, Pres.--Great River Oil & Gas Corp., New Orleans, LA; *U.S. Public*, pg. 735
Clarke, M.B., Pres.--Glens Falls Cement Co., Glens Falls, NY; *Int'l*, pg. 423
Clarke, Maureen, Branch Mgr.--Troy Savings Bank-Colonie, Albany, NY; *U.S. Private*, pg. 1106
Clarke, Nathan, Pres.--Trademark Research Corporation, New York, NY; *Int'l*, pg. 1513
Clarke, Phillip M., Mng. Dir.--Klark-Teknik Plc, Kidderminster, United Kingdom; *U.S. Public*, pg. 1045
Clarke, Pierce, Gen. Mgr.--S.C. Johnson & Son of South Africa (Pty.) Ltd., Fairland, South Africa; *U.S. Private*, pg. 593
Clarke, R. Curtis, V.P. & Gen. Mgr.--MACtac Scranton Facility, Scranton, PA; *U.S. Public*, pg. 210
Clarke, R. Michael, Gen. Mgr.--Minera Cominco Resources Chile Ltda., Santiago, Chile; *Int'l*, pg. 308
Clarke, R.A., Dir.-Sls. & Mktg.--International Factors Limited, Brighton, United Kingdom; *Int'l*, pg. 813
Clarke, Rob, Mng. Dir.--Leo Burnett/Connaghan & May Pty. Ltd., Sydney, Australia; *U.S. Private*, pg. 185
Clarke, Robert, Gen. Mgr.--Felton Worldwide Ltd., Bletchley, United Kingdom; *U.S. Public*, pg. 1696
Clarke, Robert F., Chm. Bd. & Pres.--Pacific Energy Conservation Services, Inc., Honolulu, HI; *U.S. Public*, pg. 800
Clarke, Robert F., Pres.--SunGard Trust Systems Inc., Charlotte, NC; *U.S. Public*, pg. 1535
Clarke, Robert H., Gen. Mgr.--WDEF AM/FM, Chattanooga, TN; *U.S. Public*, pg. 1078
Clarke, Sir Rupert, Chm. Bd.--P&O Australia Ltd., Sydney, Australia; *Int'l*, pg. 1035
Clarke, William, Gen. Mgr.--Gillette Espanola, S.A., Madrid, Spain; *U.S. Public*, pg. 744
Clarke, William A., Pres.--Johnson & Johnson Medical, Inc., Arlington, TX; *U.S. Public*, pg. 928
Clarkin, J., Gen. Mgr.--Australia & New Zealand Banking Group Limited Korea, Seoul, Korea; *Int'l*, pg. 99
Clarkson, Colin, Chief Exec. Officer & V.P.-Mktg.--Lotus Cars USA, Inc., Lawrenceville, GA; *Int'l*, pg. 1071
Clarkson, Malcolm, Pres.--Falmer Press Ltd., London, United Kingdom; *Int'l*, pg. 1358
Clarkson, Michael, Mng. Dir.--Kvaerner Boving, Doncaster, United Kingdom; *Int'l*, pg. 772
Clarkson, S.J., Reg. Mng. Dir.--Ballast Wiltshier Plc - Northern Region, Leeds, United Kingdom; *Int'l*, pg. 135
Clarkson, S.J., Reg. Mng. Dir.--Ballast Wiltshier Plc - East Midland Area, Nottingham, United Kingdom; *Int'l*, pg. 135
Clarno, K.K., Pres.--Cablecraft Inc., Tacoma, WA; *U.S. Private*, pg. 1110
Claro, Milton, Intl. Dir.--Salles/DMB&B Publicidade S.A., Sao Paulo, Brazil; *U.S. Private*, pg. 305
Clary, John P., Pres. & Chief Exec. Officer--Modcomp, Fort Lauderdale, FL; *U.S. Public*, pg. 283
Claslin, John, V.P.-Opers. & Site Mgr.--Academy Insurance Group, Inc., Alpharetta, GA; *Int'l*, pg. 27
Class, Richard, Dir.-Pur.--SuperValu, Inc.-Keene Div., Keene, NH; *U.S. Public*, pg. 1540
Class, Richard H., Mng. Dir.--Hobart GmbH, Offenburg, Germany; *U.S. Public*, pg. 1322
Classen, Daniel, Gen. Mgr.--Howmet Turbine Component Corporation, Branford, CT; *U.S. Private*, pg. 213
Claster, John, Pres.--Claster Television, Timonium, MD; *U.S.* Public, pg. 797
Claster, John H., Pres.--Romper Room Enterprises, Inc., Timonium, MD; *U.S. Public*, pg. 797
Claude, Aycoberry, Chief Oper. Officer--Societe Generale pour les Techniques Nouvelles S.A. (SGN), Saint Quentin, France; *Int'l*, pg. 1361
Claude, Brad, Mgr.-Sls.--Jaco Electronics, Inc., Tustin, CA; *U.S. Public*, pg. 921
Claudel, Jacques, Gen. Mgr.--National Utility Service, S.A., Paris, France; *U.S. Private*, pg. 787
Claudel, Jacques, Gen. Mgr.--National Utility Service, S.A., Brussels, Belgium; *U.S. Private*, pg. 788
Claudo, Franchi, V.P. & Mgr.--Banca Nazionale Del Lavoro (Miami), Miami, FL; *Int'l*, pg. 136
Claudon, Jean Gerard, Chm.-Supvr. Bd.--Poliet, Courbevoie, France; *Int'l*, pg. 1177
Claudon, Jean-Louis, Dir.--Arianespace Tokyo, Tokyo, Japan; *Int'l*, pg. 81
Clausen, Oluf, Mng. Dir.--SASIB Bakery Nordic A/S, Skovlunde, Denmark; *Int'l*, pg. 1194
Claussen, John H., Pres.--TRC Environmental Corporation, Windsor, CT; *U.S. Public*, pg. 1558
Clausson, Burt, Pres.--Asea Brown Boveri Ltd., Bangkok, Thailand; *Int'l*, pg. 8
Clauster, Brendan R., Pres.--Liberty Programming Corporation, Englewood, CO; *U.S. Public*, pg. 1555
Claverie, Roy E., Pres.--Ingram Coal Company, Nashville, TN; *U.S. Private*, pg. 563
Claverie, Roy E., Pres.--Ingram Production Company, Nashville, TN; *U.S. Private*, pg. 563
Clawson, Mike, V.P.--Western Washington Division, Bellevue, WA; *U.S. Public*, pg. 39
Clawson, Terry, Plant Mgr.--Sevierville Facility, Wagner Lighting Division, Sevierville, TN; *U.S. Public*, pg. 442
Clay, Bill, V.P.-Opers.--Padnos-Summit, Lansing, MI; *U.S. Private*, pg. 834
Clay, John, Pres.--Practitioners Publishing Co., Fort Worth, TX; *U.S. Public*, pg. 1601
Clay, John W., Jr., Chm. & Chief Exec. Officer--SunTrust Bank, Nashville, N.A., Nashville, TN; *U.S. Public*, pg. 1538
Clay, Kermit, V.P.-Sls.--All Star Gas Co.-Region V, Lebanon, MO; *U.S. Private*, pg. 35
Clayden, Richard, Dir.-Commercial Prods.--Target Rock Corp., Farmingdale, NY; *U.S. Public*, pg. 470
Claypoole, R.E., Chm. Bd.--GATX Terminals Corporation, Chicago, IL; *U.S. Public*, pg. 692

Clayton, David, Gen. Mgr.--DigiCourse, Inc., Houston, TX; *U.S. Private*, pg. 643
Clayton, F.O., Pres. & Chief Exec. Officer--Shand Mining Inc., Indianapolis, IN; *Int'l*, pg. 281
Clayton, James M., Pres.--Paper Recycling International, Norcross, GA; *U.S. Public*, pg. 1522
Clayton, Larry, Editor--Better Homes and Gardens Wood Magazine, Des Moines, IA; *U.S. Public*, pg. 1094
Clayton, Mike, Chief Exec. Officer--CMT Steels & Supplies, Audenshaw, United Kingdom; *Int'l*, pg. 265
Clayton, Pamela, Admin.--Care Line, Inc., Dallas, TX; *U.S. Public*, pg. 305
Clayton, Rick, V.P. & Gen. Mgr.--Spicer Heavy Axle & Brake Div., Fort Wayne, IN; *U.S. Public*, pg. 479
Clayton, Ronald W., Mgr.--The Rosebud Mining Company, L.L.C., Winnemucca, NV; *U.S. Public*, pg. 804
Cleary, Gerald V., Pres.--Tonka Products Division, Minnetonka, MN; *U.S. Public*, pg. 797
Cleary, J. Michael, V.P. & Gen. Mgr.-Health & Beauty Care Prods.-Belgium--Procter & Gamble Health & Beauty Care Belgium, Brussels, Belgium; *U.S. Public*, pg. 1332
Cleary, J.V., Chief Oper. Officer--GMP Real Estate Corp., South Burlington, VT; *U.S. Public*, pg. 761
Cleary, Pal R., Mng. Dir.--Universal Studios Australia Pty. Ltd., Sydney, Australia; *Int'l*, pg. 1216
Cleary, Thomas, Pres.--Alumax Foils, Inc., Saint Louis, MO; *U.S. Public*, pg. 60
Cleaton, Chuck, Chief Oper. Officer--Auto-Graph Computer Designing Systems, Inc., Lexington, NC; *U.S. Public*, pg. 1053
Cleave, James H., Pres. & Chief Exec. Officer--HSBC Americas, Buffalo, NY; *Int'l*, pg. 580
Cleave, James H., Pres. & Chief Exec. Officer--Marine Midland Bank, Buffalo, NY; *Int'l*, pg. 581
Cleaver, A. B., Chief Exec. Officer--IBM United Kingdom Holdings Limited, Portsmouth, United Kingdom; *U.S. Public*, pg. 897
Cleaver, A.B., Chm.--IBM United Kingdom Limited, Portsmouth, United Kingdom; *U.S. Public*, pg. 898
Clegg, Jack, Chm. & Pres.--Merryhill Country Schools, Inc., Sacramento, CA; *U.S. Public*, pg. 1186
Clegg, Jack, Chm. & Pres.--Rocking Horse Development Corporation, Media, PA; *U.S. Public*, pg. 1186
Clegg, Jack, Chm. & Pres.--Imagine Educational Products, Inc., Media, PA; *U.S. Public*, pg. 1186
Cleife, Peter J., Mng. Dir.--Commercial Hydraulics Keelavite, Ltd., Warwick, United Kingdom; *U.S. Public*, pg. 411
Clelland, Ian, Gen. Mgr.--ITW Paktron, Lynchburg, VA; *U.S. Public*, pg. 866
Clem, Roy J., Pres. & Gen. Mgr.--WSET Incorporatd, Lynchburg, VA; *U.S. Private*, pg. 854
Clem, W.H., Chief Oper. Officer--Allright Nashville Parking, Inc., Nashville, TN; *U.S. Private*, pg. 42
Clemence, Richard, Pres.--Wilson Machine Knife Co., Inc., Dayville, CT; *U.S. Private*, pg. 551
Clement-Jones, C.O.G., Chief Exec. Officer--Alcan Siam Limited, Bangkok, Thailand; *Int'l*, pg. 51
Clement, Candace, Publr.--The Business Journal of Portland, Inc., Portland, OR; *U.S. Private*, pg. 19
Clement, J. A., Reg. Mgr.--De La Rue Security Printing, Miami, FL; *Int'l*, pg. 386
Clement, James B., Chief Oper. Officer--Air Logistics Div., New Iberia, LA; *U.S. Public*, pg. 1213
Clement, James B., Pres.--Offshore Logistics Services, Inc., Lafayette, LA; *U.S. Public*, pg. 1213
Clement, James W., Pres. & Chief Exec. Officer--Bank of Carroll, Hillsville, VA; *U.S. Public*, pg. 1038
Clement, Jean Michel, Mng. Dir.--Elsevier Thomas Fachverlag GmbH, Mainz, Germany; *Int'l*, pg. 1100
Clement, Jean Pierre, Gen. Mgr.--Formica Canada, Inc., Saint Jean-sur-Richelieu, Canada; *Int'l*, pg. 129
Clement, T.T.J.P., Gen. Mgr.--ABN Capital Markets Far East Ltd., Central, Hong Kong; *Int'l*, pg. 11
Clements, Edward B., V.P.--Clements Nut Co., Lewisville, TX; *U.S. Private*, pg. 245
Clements, Edward B., Pres.--American Nut Co., Lewisville, TX; *U.S. Private*, pg. 245
Clements, Norbert, Chm. Bd.--Willis Corroon Corp. of Orange County, Santa Ana, CA; *Int'l*, pg. 1506
Clements, Robert, Pres.--K. Hovnanian Investment Properties, Inc., Red Bank, NJ; *U.S. Public*, pg. 843
Clemons, Philip J., Pres.--CorryHiebert Corporation, Corry, PA; *U.S. Public*, pg. 772
Clemons, Robert, Exec. V.P.--Herrmidifier Co., Inc., Lancaster, PA; *U.S. Public*, pg. 1639
Clerc, Jacques, Mng. Dir.--Swiss Life (Luxembourg), Luxembourg, Luxembourg; *Int'l*, pg. 1332
Clerici, Enrico, Pres.--Dresdner Asset Management (Schweiz) AG, Zurich, Switzerland; *Int'l*, pg. 419
Clerici, Giacomo, Pres.--Somocar S.p.A., Genoa, Italy; *Int'l*, pg. 303
Clermont, Olivier, Plant Mgr.--Grenoble Mill, Grenoble, France; *U.S. Public*, pg. 673
Clerval, Pierre, Pres. & Chief Exec. Officer--Stillman Seal, Carlsbad, CA; *U.S. Private*, pg. 550
Clerx, J., Div. Mgr.--Campina Melkunie, Butter Division, Breda, Netherlands; *Int'l*, pg. 254
Cleveland, C. Peyton, Jr., Pres.--International Chempack Inc., Clifton, NJ; *U.S. Public*, pg. 523
Cleveland, David, Pres.--Hilti Latin America, Tulsa, OK; *Int'l, pg. 620*
Cleveland, James R., Jr., Pres.--Cleveland Electric Co., Atlanta, GA; *U.S. Private*, pg. 246
Clevenger, J.G., Pres.--Cyprus Bagdad Copper Corporation, Bagdad, AZ; *U.S. Public*, pg. 471
Clevenger, J.G., Pres.--Cyprus Sierrita, Green Valley, AZ; *U.S. Public*, pg. 471
Clevenger, J.G., Pres.--Cyprus Tohono Corporation, Casa Grande, AZ; *U.S. Public*, pg. 471
Clevenger, J.G., Pres.--Cyprus Miami Mining Corporation, Claypool, AZ; *U.S. Public*, pg. 471
Clevenger, J.G., Pres.--Cyprus Rod Chicago Corporation, Chicago, IL; *U.S. Public*, pg. 471
Cleverly, A. Bruce, Pres.--Oral-B Laboratories, Belmont, CA; *U.S. Public*, pg. 743
Clewett, Merle, Pres.--Ingersoll Cutting Tool Co., Rockford, IL; *U.S. Private*, pg. 562
Cliff, David, Chief Oper. Officer--Spline Gauges Ltd., Tamworth, United Kingdom; *U.S. Public*, pg. 482
Cliff, R.L., Chm.--Alpac Construction & Surveys Limited, Vancouver, Canada; *Int'l*, pg. 114
Clifford, Christine, Gen. Mgr.--Jupiter Beach Resort, Jupiter, FL; *U.S. Private*, pg. 800
Clifford, John, Chief Oper. Officer--Continental Microwave (Holdings) Plc, Luton, United Kingdom; *Int'l*, pg. 1289
Clifford, Patrick, Chm. Bd.--Mosby-Year Book, Inc., Saint Louis, MO; *U.S. Public*, pg. 1616
Clifford, Richard P., Mng. Dir.--BetzDearborn B.V., Mijdrecht, Netherlands; *U.S. Public*, pg. 227
Clift, Mark F., Pres.--Marithe and Francois Girbaud N.A., Greensboro, NC; *U.S. Public*, pg. 1702
Clifton, M.A., Pres.--Meadows Resources, Inc., Albuquerque, NM; *U.S. Public*, pg. 1339
Clifton, Matthew P., Chief Oper. Officer--Holly Petroleum, Inc., Dallas, TX; *U.S. Public*, pg. 830
Clifton, Paul H., Jr., Pres.--BenefitAmerica, Columbia, SC; *U.S. Public*, pg. 1699
Clijsters, Jos, Admin.--Banque de La Poste, Brussels, Belgium; *Int'l*, pg. 547
Climent, Carlos, Gen. Mgr.--Signode Spain, Barcelona, Spain; *U.S. Public*, pg. 869
Clinch, Colin, Div. Mgr.--ITW Fixfast AB, Goteborg, Sweden; *U.S. Public*, pg. 868
Clinch, D. S., Mng. Dir.--De La Rue Services (Malaysia) Sdn Bhd, Petaling Jaya, Malaysia; *Int'l*, pg. 387
Cline, Bob L., Chief Oper. Officer--Custom Colorants, Inc., Dalton, GA; *U.S. Public*, pg. 1052
Clingen, Jerry, Mgr.--Surplus Warehouse-Lake Charles, Lake Charles, LA; *U.S. Private*, pg. 119
Clinton, Mark, Gen. Mgr.--Master Data Center, Southfield, MI; *U.S. Private*, pg. 778
Clipez, Patrice, Pres.--Synergie, Puteaux, France; *Int'l*, pg. 601
Clissman, Helmut, Div. Dir.--UPM-Kymmene Ireland, Dublin, Ireland; *Int'l*, pg. 1430
Clitheroe, Lord, Chm. Bd.--Yorkshire Bank, Leeds, United Kingdom; *Int'l*, pg. 906
Clodi, Alexander, Mgr.--GGK Salzburg, Salzburg, Austria; *Int'l*, pg. 1335
Cloes, Philippe, Mng. Dir.--Credit Lyonnais Belgium, Brussels, Belgium; *Int'l*, pg. 344
Cloney, Richard M., Pres.--Susque-Bancshares Leasing Co., Inc., Lititz, PA; *U.S. Public*, pg. 1542
Clooe, J. P., Chief Oper. Officer--S.A. Polytuil, Herstal, Belgium; *Int'l*, pg. 301
Close, Graham, Chief Oper. Officer--Aladdin Industries Pty. Ltd., Westgate, Australia; *U.S. Private*, pg. 31
Close, James, Gen. Mgr.--AlliedSignal Guidance & Control, Cheshire, CT; *U.S. Public*, pg. 50
Close, John W., Pres.--Harris Bank Wilmette N.A., Wilmette, IL; *Int'l*, pg. 154
Close, R.C., Pres.--Kodak Electronic Printing Systems, Billerica, MA; *U.S. Public*, pg. 551
Close, Richard, Pres.--Electronic Printing Systems, Bedford, MA; *U.S. Public*, pg. 551
Close, Robert, Pres.--Magnedyne Div., Vista, CA; *U.S. Private*, pg. 999
Closset, Roger, Plant Mgr.--Armstrong International, S.A., Liege, Belgium; *U.S. Private*, pg. 83
Cloud, Don, Pres.--Tampo Industries Inc., San Antonio, TX; *Int'l*, pg. 1420
Cloud, Ronald E., Pres. & Chief Exec. Officer--Resin Formulators, Culver City, CA; *U.S. Private*, pg. 935
Clough, Ronald L., Plant Mgr.--Power Distribution Div., Cleveland, TN; *U.S. Public*, pg. 557
Clouse, Rod, Gen. Mgr.--Hydraulic Valve Div., Elyria, OH; *U.S. Public*, pg. 1261
Clouston, Robert A.R., Pres. & Gen. Mgr., Consumer Prods--Warner-Lambert Canada, Inc., Scarborough, Canada; *U.S. Public*, pg. 1739
Cloutier, Alain, Pres.--Publicis BCP Promotion Inc., Montreal, Canada; *Int'l*, pg. 116
Clowe, C. Thomas, Pres. & Chief Oper. Officer-Missouri Gas Energy--Southern Union Company, Austin, TX; *U.S. Public*, pg. 1491
Clowes, Mike, Editor--Pensions & Investments, Chicago, IL; *U.S. Private*, pg. 285
Clowes, R.J., Chief Exec.-GKN Sankey Division--GKN Sankey Ltd., Telford, United Kingdom; *Int'l*, pg. 534
Cloyd, G. Gilbert, V.P.-Pharmaceuticals--Norwich Div., Cincinnati, OH; *U.S. Public*, pg. 1330
Cloyd, G.G., V.P.-Pharmaceuticals-U.S.--Procter & Gamble Pharmaceuticals, Inc., Cincinnati, OH; *U.S. Public*, pg. 1331
Cluss, Veit, Rep.--Representacion del Deutsche Bank AG (Santiago), Santiago, Chile; *Int'l*, pg. 405
Clutterbuck, Howard C., Pres. & Chief Exec. Officer--American Journal of Nursing Company, New York, NY; *Int'l*, pg. 1513
Clyburn, Bill, Mgr.-Production--McCormick Ingredients, Hunt Valley, MD; *U.S. Public*, pg. 1066
Clymans, Frans, Plant Mgr.--Beringen, Beringen, Belgium; *Int'l*, pg. 1341
Clymans, Frans, Plant Mgr.--Nivelles, Nivelles, Belgium,; *Int'l*, pg. 1342
Clymans, Luc, Mgr.-Opers.--Sensormatic (Belgium) S.A., Groot-Bijgaarden, Belgium; *U.S. Public*, pg. 1457
Coackley, Robert, Pres.--Telenex, Mount Laurel, NJ; *U.S. Public*, pg. 727
Coackley, Robert, Pres.--General Signal Networks, Shelton, CT; *U.S. Public*, pg. 727
Coady, Michael F., Pres.--Children's Business, New York, NY; *U.S. Public*, pg. 513
Coady, Michael F., Pres.--Footwear News, New York, NY; *U.S. Public*, pg. 513
Coakley, David, Mng. Dir.--AEP/Borden Global Packaging (U.K.) Ltd., North Braddesley, United Kingdom; *U.S. Public*, pg. 5
Coakley, Gerard, Gen. Mgr.--Butterworths Ireland, Dublin, Ireland; *Int'l*, pg. 1095
Coape-Arnold, D.A., Chm. Bd. & Chief Exec. Officer--Dunhill Personnel System, Inc., Hauppauge, NY; *U.S. Public*, pg. 1746
Coate, John P., Sr., Pres.--Flowers Baking Co. of Bradenton, Inc., Sarasota, FL; *U.S. Public*, pg. 657
Coates, David A., Dr., Gen. Mgr.--Johnson & Johnson Poland, Sp.z.o.o., Warsaw, Poland; *U.S. Public*, pg. 931
Coates, John, Mgr.-Opers.--Neer Manufacturing Company Inc., Lexington, OH; *U.S. Public*, pg. 727
Coates, Jon P., Pres. & Chief Exec. Officer--Key Bank of Colorado, Fort Collins, CO; *U.S. Public*, pg. 954
Coates, Michael B., Pres. & Chief Exec. Officer-Canada--Hill and Knowlton, Inc., New York, NY; *Int'l*, pg. 1483
Coats, Max M., Pres. & Chief Exec. Officer--Washburn Direct Marketing, Inc., Charlotte, NC; *U.S. Public*, pg. 291
Cobb, Bill, Pres.--QS/1 Data Systems Div., Spartanburg, SC; *U.S. Private*, pg. 1008
Cobb, D.W., Chief Oper. Officer--Magco Ltd., Stourport, United Kingdom; *Int'l*, pg. 473
Cobb, G.L., Jr., Pres.--Alcoa Recycling Co., Knoxville, TN; *U.S. Public*, pg. 61
Cobb, William, Gen. Mgr.--U S West Communications Federal Services Inc., Englewood, CO; *U.S. Public*, pg. 1689
Cobb, William G., Pres. & Gen. Mgr.--Kysor/Westran, Byron, IL; *U.S. Public*, pg. 968
Cobbett, Paula, Mgr.--Stewart Smith West, Inc., San Francisco, CA; *Int'l*, pg. 1508
Coberly, Ernest D., Chief Oper. Officer--Ross Aluminum Foundries, Sidney, OH; *U.S. Private*, pg. 355
Cobery, Thomas J., Pres.--Label Art, Inc., Wilton, NH; *U.S. Private*, pg. 782
Coblentz, Joanne, V.P. & Gen. Mgr.--WAXY (FM), Fort Lauderdale, FL; *U.S. Public*, pg. 925
Coburn, Al, Exec. V.P. & Chief Oper. Officer--Salem Sportswear, Hudson, NH; *U.S. Public*, pg. 686
Coburn, Patrick, Publr.--Lincoln Courier, Lincoln, IL; *U.S. Private*, pg. 275
Coc, Bedo, Chief Exec. Officer--AxPro Axel Johnson GesmbH, Graz, Austria; *Int'l*, pg. 710
Coccari, Greg, Pres. & Chief Exec. Officer--Teleflora, LLC, Los Angeles, CA; *U.S. Private*, pg. 941
Cocchiola, Mark, Chm. Bd., Pres. & Chief Exec. Officer--Suprema Specialties Northeast, Inc., Ogdensburg, NY; *U.S. Public*, pg. 1541
Cocci, Chuck, Dir.-Fritz Air Freight--Fritz Air Freight, Irving, TX; *U.S. Public*, pg. 683
Coccia, C.M., Pres. & Mng. Dir.--Alcan Alluminio S.p.A., Pieve Emanuele, Italy; *Int'l*, pg. 50
Cocheteux, Jean-Bernard, Chm. Bd. & Chief Exec. Officer--Microturbo Division, Toulouse, France; *Int'l*, pg. 786
Cochran, Gary, Plant Mgr.--Glass Plant, Clairton, PA; *U.S. Private*, pg. 486
Cochran, James G., Pres.--ReliaStar Employer Financial Services Company, Arlington, VA; *U.S. Public*, pg. 1376
Cochran, Russell G., Chm. Bd., Pres. & Chief Exec. Officer--United Missouri Bank of Joplin, Joplin, MO; *U.S. Public*, pg. 1655
Cochran, Terry G., Publr.--Dodge City Daily Globe, Dodge City, KS; *U.S. Private*, pg. 995
Cochran, Terry G., Publr.--Dodge City Shopper's Weekly, Dodge City, KS; *U.S. Private*, pg. 995
Cochrane, Charles, Publr.--Walla Walla Union Bulletin, Walla Walla, WA; *U.S. Private*, pg. 980
Cochrane, James M.T., Mng. Dir.--E.R. Squibb & Sons Ltd., Hounslow, United Kingdom; *U.S. Public*, pg. 256
Cochrane, James M.T., Mng. Dir.--E.R. Squibb & Sons Ltd., Wirral, United Kingdom; *U.S. Public*, pg. 256
Cochrane, Len, Pres. & Chief Oper. Officer--The Family Channel Inc., Toronto, Canada; *Int'l*, pg. 1482
Cochrane, Richard M., V.P. & Gen. Mgr.--GNI Chemical Corporation, Deer Park, TX; *U.S. Public*, pg. 694
Cocker, Gail, Sr. V.P.--Bank of Montreal - Winnipeg, Winnipeg, Canada; *Int'l*, pg. 153
Cockrell, Alan E., Pres.--Fluids Handling Group, Springfield, OH; *U.S. Public*, pg. 1393
Cocozzo, Joseph A., Publisher--The News-Herald (Lake County), Willoughby, OH; *U.S. Public*, pg. 935
Coder, P. Jerry, Pres.--EKC Technology, Inc., Hayward, CA; *U.S. Public*, pg. 344
Coder, Stephen, Pres.--Ring King Visibles, Inc., Muscatine, IA; *Int'l*, pg. 460
Codron, Herve, Mgr.--Nordia S.A., Pontcharra, France; *Int'l*, pg. 421
Cody, Keith D., Pres.--Risk Planners, Inc., Hopkins, MN; *U.S. Public*, pg. 1541
Cody, Kevin, Pres.--Pace Mechanical Services, Inc, Westland, MI; *U.S. Public*, pg. 572
Coe, Martyn, Mng. Dir.--Sanderson Computers New Zealand Ltd., Ponsonby, New Zealand; *Int'l*, pg. 1185
Coelho, Edeson, Gen. Dir.--DPZ, Rio de Janeiro, Brazil; *Int'l*, pg. 352
Coelho, J.M., Chief Exec. Officer--Zurich Life Insurance Company, Lisbon, Portugal; *Int'l*, pg. 1530
Coelho, J.M., Chief Exec. Officer--Companhia de Seguros Metropole S.A., Lisbon, Portugal; *Int'l*, pg. 1531
Coey, Ken, Mng. Dir.--Esselte Meto Ltd., Bracknell, United Kingdom; *Int'l*, pg. 461
Coffey, Larry R., Pres.--Landmark Community Newspapers, Inc., Shelbyville, KY; *U.S. Private*, pg. 648
Coffey, Mark, Plant Mgr.--Dold Foods, Wichita, KS; *U.S. Public*, pg. 840
Coffey, R.L., Pres.--Vigortone AG Products, Inc., Cedar Rapids, IA; *Int'l*, pg. 1357
Coffin, Louise, Dir.-Sls.--FaceMate Corp., Somersworth, NH; *U.S. Private*, pg. 391
Coffin, Steve, Div. Mgr.--Mosinee Industrial Forest Division, Solon Springs, WI; *U.S. Public*, pg. 1747

Coffman, Gregory M., Pres. & Chief Exec. Officer--Downey, Inc., Milwaukee, WI; *U.S. Private*, pg. 602
Coffman, Richard S., Pres.--Coscan Land, Inc., Vienna, VA; *Int'l*, pg. 228
Cofield, Charles D., Pres.--American Emulsions Co., Inc., Dalton, GA; *U.S. Public*, pg. 1357
Cofield, Charles D., Pres.--Chemical Specialties Manufacturing Corp., Baltimore, MD; *U.S. Public*, pg. 1357
Cofsky, Stewart, V.P. & Controller--Finora Company, Inc., Englewood, CO; *U.S. Private*, pg. 802
Cogan, John F., Jr., Pres.--Pioneering Management Corporation, Boston, MA; *U.S. Public*, pg. 1298
Coggiani, Carlos, Gen. Mgr.--Sermatech Southeast, Boynton Beach, FL; *U.S. Public*, pg. 1570
Coghlan, John, Pres.--Beam Industries, Webster City, IA; *Int'l*, pg. 440
Cogliati, Carlo, Pres.--Ausimont S.p.A., Bollate, Italy; *Int'l*, pg. 324
Cohan, Richard, Sr. V.P.--Healthcare Application Systems Services, Atlanta, GA; *U.S. Public*, pg. 1156
Cohen Tervaert, Dirk G., Chm. Bd. & Pres.--N.V. Deli-Universal, Rotterdam, Netherlands; *U.S. Public*, pg. 1695
Cohen, A.H.E., Mng. Dir.--AAH Consumer Products Ltd., Warrington, United Kingdom; *Int'l*, pg. 591
Cohen, A.L., Pres.--Cumberland Engineering-Europe, Stroud, United Kingdom; *Int'l*, pg. 774
Cohen, Ahren, Pres.--Cumberland Eng. Div., Attleboro, MA; *Int'l*, pg. 773
Cohen, Ahren, Pres.--Cumberland Engineering, Attleboro, MA; *Int'l*, pg. 774
Cohen, Avi, Chief Oper. Officer--Octel Communications (Israel) Ltd., Yehuda, Israel; *U.S. Public*, pg. 1018
Cohen, Barbara, Office Mgr.--Summit Specialty Chemicals Corporation, Fort Lee, NJ; *Int'l*, pg. 1312
Cohen, Betty, Pres.--The Cartoon Network, Atlanta, GA; *U.S. Public*, pg. 1614
Cohen, Bob, V.P. & Gen. Mgr.--KAJA-FM, San Antonio, TX; *U.S. Public*, pg. 384
Cohen, Bob, V.P. & Gen. Mgr.--KQXT Radio, San Antonio, TX; *U.S. Public*, pg. 384
Cohen, Brian, Chm. & Chief Exec. Officer--Technology Solutions Inc., New York, NY; *U.S. Private*, pg. 1157
Cohen, David, First V.P. & Mgr.--Bank Hapoalim (San Francisco), San Francisco, CA; *Int'l*, pg. 149
Cohen, David, Publr.--Golf for Women, Des Moines, IA; *U.S. Public*, pg. 1094
Cohen, G., Gen. Mgr.--Production Division/Commercial Aircraft Group, Israel; *Int'l*, pg. 690
Cohen, Gary, Pres.--ACI Telecentrics Inc., Lombard, IL; *U.S. Public*, pg. 3
Cohen, Gary, Pres.--Becton Dickinson VACUTAINER Systems, Franklin Lakes, NJ; *U.S. Public*, pg. 199
Cohen, Gordon, Chm. Bd. & Chief Oper. Officer--Jeneric/Pentron Corp., Wallingford, CT; *U.S. Private*, pg. 298
Cohen, Harold, Co-Chm.--Somerville Lumber & Supply Co., Somerville, MA; *U.S. Public*, pg. 1268
Cohen, Harvey, Mgr.--Stephen Gould of Ohio, Corp., Cincinnati, OH; *U.S. Private*, pg. 467
Cohen, Ira D., Pres.--TransCor Waste Service, Inc., Tampa, FL; *U.S. Public*, pg. 960
Cohen, Larry, Pres.--The Hotsy Corporation, Englewood, CO; *U.S. Private*, pg. 500
Cohen, Melvin S., Pres.--National Defense Corp., Eau Claire, WI; *U.S. Public*, pg. 1159
Cohen, Melvin S., Pres.--Century Leasing & Liquidating, Inc., Minneapolis, MN; *U.S. Public*, pg. 1159
Cohen, Melvin S., Pres.--Presto Export Ltd., Saint Croix, VI; *U.S. Public*, pg. 1159
Cohen, Mordechay, First V.P. & Mgr.--Bank Hapoalim (Miami), Miami Beach, FL; *Int'l*, pg. 149
Cohen, R., Pres.--Scarborough Research Corporation, New York, NY; *Int'l*, pg. 1447
Cohen, Robert, Pres.--IMA of Colorado Inc., Denver, CO; *U.S. Private*, pg. 565
Cohen, Robert, Chief Oper. Officer & Gen. Mgr.-Pharmaceuticals--Berlex Laboratories Inc., Wayne, NJ; *Int'l*, pg. 1204
Cohen, Ronnie, Pres.--AyerDirect, New York, NY; *U.S. Private*, pg. 104
Cohen, Tim, Mgr.-Office--Woodward-Clyde, Santa Barbara, CA; *U.S. Public*, pg. 1657
Cohen, Warren, Pres.--Fanta Furniture, Philadelphia, PA; *U.S. Private*, pg. 35
Cohen, William, Pres.--Andrews & Clark, Inc., New York, NY; *U.S. Public*, pg. 1593
Cohlst, C.G., Pres.-Mktg. & Sls.--UBO Verzekeringen, Utrecht, Netherlands; *Int'l*, pg. 26
Cohn, Gerald, Pres.--E.J. Footwear Corp., Endicott, NY; *U.S. Public*, pg. 1684
Cohn, Gerald M., Pres.--Georgia/Durango Boot Company, Franklin, TN; *U.S. Public*, pg. 1684
Cohn, Mark, Pres.--Texas Telemarketing, Inc., Minneapolis, MN; *U.S. Public*, pg. 478
Cohn, Mark, Pres.--Damark Financial Services, Inc., Minneapolis, MN; *U.S. Public*, pg. 478
Cohn, Richard, Pres.--Pyrofuse, Mount Vernon, NY; *U.S. Private*, pg. 250
Cohn, Richard, Pres.--Medwire, Mount Vernon, NY; *U.S. Private*, pg. 250
Cohn, Robert, Chm. Bd. & Chief Exec. Officer--Octel Messaging Division, Milpitas, CA; *U.S. Public*, pg. 1017
Cohon, George A., Sr. Chm.--McDonald's Restaurants of Canada Ltd., Toronto, Canada; *U.S. Public*, pg. 1069
Cohrs, Fred W., Pres.--Thorstenberg Materials Co., Inc., Denver, CO; *Int'l*, pg. 628
Coia, Ron, V.P.-Chicago--Harwick Standard Distribution Corp., Elk Grove Village, IL; *U.S. Private*, pg. 509
Coimbra, Roberto, Exec. V.P., Pres. & CEO-JWT/Venezuela--J. Walter Thompson Company, New York, NY; *Int'l*, pg. 1483
Coimbra, T., Gen. Mgr.--Kodak Portuguesa, Ltd., Carnaxide, Portugal; *U.S. Public*, pg. 554
Coine, Alain, Mng. Dir.--Rhone-Poulenc Japan, Ltd., Tokyo, Japan; *Int'l*, pg. 1113
Cointet, Luc, Gen. Mgr.--Credit Commercial de France, Thessaloniki, Greece; *Int'l*, pg. 342
Coit, Donna, Branch Admin.--Limbach Co., Pontiac, MI; *Int'l*, *pg. 322*
Cojuangco, Antonio O., Chm.--Mabuhay Philippines Satellite Corp., Makati, Philippines; *Int'l*, pg. 1051
Colaccino, Frank, Pres. & Chief Exec. Officer--Dairy Mart, Inc., Enfield, CT; *U.S. Public*, pg. 476
Colaluca, C., Mng. Dir.--Driver-Harris Australia, Epping, Australia; *Int'l*, pg. 723
Colaninno, Roberto, Mgr. Dir.--FRAM Filter S.p.A., Castelfranco Veneto, Italy; *U.S. Public*, pg. 53
Colas, Ady, Dr., Mng. Dir.--Wuestenrot International Management-Gesellschaft AG, Luxembourg, Luxembourg; *Int'l*, pg. 1514
Colas, J., Gen. Mgr.--Signode France, Paris, France; *U.S. Public*, pg. 869
Colas, Javier, Mgr.-Spain--Medtronic Hispania S.A., Madrid, Spain; *U.S. Public*, pg. 1083
Colasacco, Domenic, Chm. Bd. & Pres.--United States Trust Company, Boston, MA; *U.S. Public*, pg. 1660
Colavito, L.M., Mgr.--Distillation Products Industries, Rochester, NY; *U.S. Public*, pg. 551
Colbert, C.J., Gen. Mgr.--CHEMCENTRAL/San Francisco, Hayward, CA; *U.S. Private*, pg. 232
Colbert, J.A., Mng. Dir.--APV Chemical Machinery Limited, Stoke on Trent, United Kingdom; *Int'l*, pg. 1240
Colbert, Jack L., Pres.--United Southwest Bank, Washington, IN; *U.S. Public*, pg. 1217
Colbert, M.W., Pres.--DFC Ceramics Inc., Canon City, CO; *Int'l*, pg. 893
Colbran, Scott, Pres.--Rogers Cable Systems, Etobicoke, Canada; *Int'l*, pg. 1123
Colcord, Harry, Chief Oper. Officer--Wausau Metals Corp., Wausau, WI; *U.S. Public*, pg. 120
Cole, Bob, Gen. Mgr.--Stocko Corp., La Habra, CA; *Int'l*, pg. 1301
Cole, C. David, Pres.--RainSoft Water Treatment Systems, Elk Grove Village, IL; *U.S. Private*, pg. 78
Cole, Chris, Pres.--The Buschman Company, Cincinnati, OH; *U.S. Private*, pg. 866
Cole, Christopher C., Grp. V.P.--Cincinnati Milacron Industrial Systems Division, Cincinnati, OH; *U.S. Public*, pg. 368
Cole, Dale, Pres. & Chief Exec. Officer--NationsBank of Newark, Newark, AR; *U.S. Public*, pg. 1164
Cole, Dale, Pres. & Chief Exec. Officer--NationsBank of Batesville, Batesville, AR; *U.S. Public*, pg. 1164
Cole, David, Pres.--Century Cellunet, Inc., Monroe, LA; *U.S. Public*, pg. 330
Cole, David L., Pres.--Virginia Surety Co., Inc., Chicago, IL; *U.S. Public*, pg. 118
Cole, Don, V.P. & Reg. Mgr.--Bergen Brunswig Medical Corporation, Atlanta, GA; *U.S. Public*, pg. 214
Cole, Eddie, Pres.--Answer Products, Inc., Valencia, CA; *U.S. Private*, pg. 639
Cole, Edward M., Pres.--Cigna Insurance Company of Illinois, Chicago, IL; *U.S. Public*, pg. 366
Cole, G., Mgr.-Opers.--Lips Propellers West/Coast Operations, Oakland, CA; *Int'l*, pg. 812
Cole, Gary, Pres.--Playboy Models, Inc., Beverly Hills, CA; *U.S. Public*, pg. 1310
Cole, George P., V.P.-Exploration--Cominco American Incorporated, Spokane, WA; *Int'l*, pg. 308
Cole, Jeff, Gen. Mgr.--Barton's of Harrisburg, Harrisburg, AR; *U.S. Private*, pg. 119
Cole, John, Pres.--PolyPhaser Corporation, Minden, NV; *Int'l*, pg. 1268
Cole, Michael, Pres.--RJ Leasing, Inc., Saint Petersburg, FL; *U.S. Public*, pg. 923
Cole, Nick, Pres.--Spicer Off-Highway Axle Div., Fort Wayne, IN; *U.S. Public*, pg. 479
Cole, R.D., Chm. Bd., Pres. & Chief Exec. Officer--The Dosco Corp., Abingdon, VA; *Int'l*, pg. 124
Cole, Richard E., Jr., Chm. Bd.--The Insurance Corp. of New York, New York, NY; *U.S. Public*, pg. 336
Cole, Scott, Mng. Dir.--Cole, Sherman & Associates Ltd., Thornhill, Canada; *U.S. Public*, pg. 1657
Cole, Sidney J., V.P. & Gen. Mgr., Systems--Landis & Gyr Systems, Inc., San Jose, CA; *Int'l*, pg. 800
Cole, Stephan W., Pres.--Cole Consumer Products, Solon, OH; *U.S. Private*, pg. 1142
Cole, Tom, Pres.--Federated Logistics, Secaucus, NJ; *U.S. Public*, pg. 618
Coleman, Bernard, Gen. Mgr.--Caribbean Cement Co., Ltd., Kingston, Jamaica; *Int'l*, pg. 1201
Coleman, Bob, Chm.--Wittnauer International, Inc., New Rochelle, NY; *U.S. Public*, pg. 273
Coleman, Dennis, V.P.-Engrng.--AMETEK Dixson Division, Grand Junction, CO; *U.S. Public*, pg. 100
Coleman, Gregory G., Gen. Mgr. & V.P.-U.S. Magazines & Publr.-U.S. Reader's Digest Mag--Reader's Digest Publications-US Sales Div., New York, NY; *U.S. Public*, pg. 1367
Coleman, Jeff, V.P. & Gen. Mgr.--Interstate Container Corporation, Reading, PA; *U.S. Private*, pg. 573
Coleman, Jim, Pres. & Chief Exec. Officer--Coleman Cable Systems, Inc., North Chicago, IL; *U.S. Public*, pg. 968
Coleman, John, Plant Mgr.--Bose Ireland, Carrickmacross, Ireland; *U.S. Private*, pg. 161
Coleman, John R., Reg. V.P.--RLI Northern California Regional Office, San Francisco, CA; *U.S. Public*, pg. 1356
Coleman, John R., Reg. V.P.--RLI Southern California Regional Office, Los Angeles, CA; *U.S. Public*, pg. 1356
Coleman, Ken, Chief Admin. Officer--Capital American Finance, Cleveland, OH; *U.S. Public*, pg. 433
Coleman, Lou, Warden--Lake City Correctional Facility, Lake City, FL; *U.S. Public*, pg. 450
Coleman, Lynword, Mgr.--White Electrical Construction Co, Savannah, GA; *U.S. Private*, pg. 1172
Coleman, Marvin, Mgr.--Century Printing & Publishing Co., Monroe, LA; *U.S. Public*, pg. 330
Coleman, Michael, Pres. & Publisher--Cape Publications, Inc., Melbourne, FL; *U.S. Public*, pg. 700
Coleman, Mike, Pres.--North Star Steel Co., Wayzata, MN; *U.S. Private*, pg. 210
Coleman, Richard C., Pres.--Container Port Group, Cleveland, OH; *U.S. Private*, pg. 1191
Coleman, Steven S., Pres.--Magnus Metals, Fremont, NE; *U.S. Private*, pg. 394
Coleman, Th. B., Mng. Dir.--International-Matex Tank Terminals, New Orleans, LA; *Int'l*, pg. 758
Coler, Gregory, Pres.-Govt. Transactions--Transactive Corporation, Austin, TX; *U.S. Public*, pg. 767
Coles, Charles W., Gen. Mgr.--Mississauga Plant St. Lawrence Cement, Mississauga, Canada; *Int'l*, pg. 629
Coles, Kenneth J., Gen. Mgr.--Santa Fe Drilling Co. of Venezuela, C.A., Anaco, Venezuela; *Int'l*, pg. 765
Coles, R.W., Mng. Dir.--Ultra Electronics Ocean Systems, Weymouth, United Kingdom; *Int'l*, pg. 1431
Coletta, Antoine, Pres.--Charmilles Technologies (South East Asia) Pte. Ltd., Singapore, Singapore; *Int'l*, pg. 489
Coletta, R.E., V.P. & Gen. Mgr.--Buick Motor Div. General Motors Corp., Flint, MI; *U.S. Public*, pg. 720
Coley, Bill A., Pres.--Tower Printing Company, Atlanta, GA; *U.S. Public*, pg. 1736
Coley, Thomas H., Pres. & Chief Exec. Officer--SouthTrust Bank of Georgia, Atlanta, GA; *U.S. Public*, pg. 1492
Colfer, N.T.J., Mng. Dir.--The Jardine Engineering Corporation Ltd., Hong Kong, Hong Kong; *Int'l*, pg. 704
Colgan, Robert T., Exec. V.P. & Asst. Mgr.-Natl. Sls.--Jefferies & Company, Inc., Los Angeles, CA; *U.S. Public*, *pg. 925*
Colgan, Thomas, Gen. Mgr.--Whitehall Laboratories Limited, Dublin, Ireland; *U.S. Public*, pg. 82
Colglazien, Mike, Acct. Supvr.--Fogarty Klein & Partners, Dallas, TX; *U.S. Private*, pg. 416
Colgrove, Bob, Div. Mgr.--Southwest Division, Tolleson, AZ; *U.S. Public*, pg. 39
Colhag, Klas, Chief Oper. Officer--Hagglunds Drives Ltd, Singapore, Singapore; *Int'l*, pg. 670
Colignon, F., Chief Oper. Officer--Elf Aquitaine Angola, Courbevoie, France; *Int'l*, pg. 444
Colitti, Marcello, Pres.--Enichem S.p.A., Milan, Italy; *Int'l*, pg. 428
Coll, Edward, Pres.--Chaps By Ralph Lauren, New York, NY; *U.S. Public*, pg. 1738
Coll, Edward W., Gen. Mgr.--Deutsche Bank AG (Columbo, Sri Lanka), Colombo, Sri Lanka; *Int'l*, pg. 404
Collado, H., Mng. Dir.--Goodyear de Colombia S.A., Cali, Colombia; *U.S. Public*, pg. 753
Collantes, Francisco Javier Salas, Chm. & Chief Exec. Officer--Sepi, Madrid, Spain; *Int'l*, pg. 1224
Collard, Jerry, Mgr.--INX Incorporated/Pressroom, Orlando, FL; *Int'l*, pg. 1311
Collart, J., Mng. Dir.--S.A. Chaussures Bally Schoenen N.V., Brussels, Belgium; *Int'l*, pg. 997
Collatz, Edward T.G., Exec. Dir.--Johnson & Johnson Professional Products (Pty) Ltd., Transvaal, South Africa; *U.S. Public*, pg. 931
Colle, Dr. B., Dir.--Fiat Auto S.p.A., Milan, Italy; *Int'l*, pg. 481
Colledge, Anthony V., Plant Mgr.--CTS of Canada, Ltd., Streetsville, Canada; *U.S. Public*, pg. 286
Colley, Blanaid, Mng. Dir.--Shandwick Public Relations Ltd., London, United Kingdom; *Int'l*, pg. 1226
Colley, Blanaid, Mng. Dir.--TPS Public Relations Ltd., London, United Kingdom; *Int'l*, pg. 1226
Colley, Blanaid, Mng. Dir.--Fleet PR Ltd., London, United Kingdom; *Int'l*, pg. 1227
Colley, Brian, Chief Oper. Officer--Fabdec Ltd., Ellesmere Port, United Kingdom; *U.S. Private*, pg. 301
Colley, Walter M., Pres.--Pacific Clay Products, Corona, CA; *U.S. Private*, pg. 831
Colliander, Alan C., Pres.--A & B Plastics, Inc., Yakima, WA; *Int'l*, pg. 232
Collier, Bill, Jr., Gen. Mgr.--E.D. Collier & Son, Woodbury, NJ; *U.S. Private*, pg. 122
Collier, Emil, Pres.--Scandura Ohio Inc., Port Clinton, OH; *Int'l*, pg. 113
Collier, Peter, Mng. Dir.--System Sensor Canada, Toronto, Canada; *U.S. Public*, pg. 1307
Colligan, Paul, Mng. Dir.--FCS Currency Management, Dublin, Ireland; *Int'l*, pg. 219
Colligan, Philip P., V.P.-Eastern Region--Analysts International, Eastern Region, New York, NY; *U.S. Public*, pg. 110
Collin, Dan, Publr.--The York News-Times, York, NE; *U.S. Private*, pg. 995
Collinet, All, Plant Mgr.--Ash Grove Cement-Western Region Lime Plant, Portland, OR; *U.S. Private*, pg. 88
Colling, Catharine, Admin.--Hillhaven-Lawton Convalescent Hospital, San Francisco, CA; *U.S. Public*, pg. 1713
Collingwool, J.A., Chief Exec. Officer-Americas--Tioxide Group Limited, London, United Kingdom; *Int'l*, pg. 663
Collins, Al, Gen. Mgr.--Phoenix Manufacturing, Inc., Phoenix, AZ; *U.S. Public*, pg. 441
Collins, Alan D., V.P. & Gen. Mgr.--Cox Communications-Spokane, Spokane, WA; *U.S. Public*, pg. 455
Collins, Brian P., Mng. Dir.--Bank of Ireland Securities Services Limited, Dublin, Ireland; *Int'l*, pg. 152
Collins, Dannie Joe, Pres.--Westvaco Development Corp., Summerville, SC; *U.S. Public*, pg. 1762
Collins, Dave, Supervisor-Prod.--Banta Global Turnkey, Colorado Springs, CO; *U.S. Public*, pg. 188
Collins, Dennis P., V.P. & Gen. Mgr.--WNWS (AM) & WLYF (FM), Miami, FL; *U.S. Public*, pg. 926
Collins, Don, V.P.-Sls.--Fairfield Sapphire Valley, Sapphire, NC; *U.S. Public*, pg. 611
Collins, Donald, Pres.--Conseco Risk Management, Inc., Carmel, IN; *U.S. Public*, pg. 433
Collins, Eric, Mng. Dir.--Gambro Ltd., Sidcup, United Kingdom; *Int'l*, pg. 668

Collins, Francis A., Pres. & Chief Exec. Officer--The Imperial Electric Company, Akron, OH; *U.S. Private*, pg. 598
Collins, Francis A., Pres.--The Scott Motors Company, Alamogordo, NM; *U.S. Private*, pg. 598
Collins, Frederick P., Chief Tech. Officer--Microwave Radio Communications, Chelmsford, MA; *U.S. Public*, pg. 294
Collins, Gary, Admin.--San Francisco Convalescent Center, San Francisco, CA; *U.S. Public*, pg. 1714
Collins, Herb, Plant Mgr.--American Natl. Can Co., Forest Park, GA; *Int'l*, pg. 1029
Collins, John A., III, Pres.--Paterson Stamp Works, Clifton, NJ; *U.S. Private*, pg. 59
Collins, John F., Pres.--Moog Automotive, Inc., Saint Louis, MO; *U.S. Public*, pg. 443
Collins, John G., Chm. Bd.--UJB Discount Brokerage, Ridgefield Park, NJ; *U.S. Public*, pg. 1528
Collins, Julie E., Treas. & Sec.--Continental Homes, Inc., Scottsdale, AZ; *U.S. Public*, pg. 440
Collins, Keith, Chief Exec. Officer--ChubbHealth New York/ New Jersey, New York, NY; *U.S. Public*, pg. 360
Collins, Ken, State Mgr.--National Mutual New South Wales, Sydney, Australia; *Int'l*, pg. 908
Collins, Marshall J., Jr., Pres. & Chief Exec. Officer--BI-LO Inc., Greenville, SC; *Int'l*, pg. 749
Collins, Michael W., Mng. Dir.--Dynex Technologies, Inc., Saint Peter Port, United Kingdom; *U.S. Public*, pg. 1591
Collins, Mike, Pres.--Donzi Marine Corporation, Sarasota, FL; *U.S. Private*, pg. 58
Collins, Pat, Pres. & Publisher--The Spectator, Hamilton, Hamilton, Canada; *Int'l*, pg. 631
Collins, Paul, Gen. Mgr.--Breckland Farms, Thetford, United Kingdom; *Int'l*, pg. 1170
Collins, R.P., Pres.--GE Fanuc Automation North America, Inc., Charlottesville, VA; *Int'l*, pg. 477
Collins, Richard, Pres. & Gen. Mgr.--The Tobin Corporation, North Ridgeville, OH; *U.S. Private*, pg. 102
Collins, Richard B., Pres. & Chief Exec. Officer--First Massachusettes Bank, N.A., Worcester, MA; *U.S. Public, pg. 187*
Collins, Robert L., Pres.--A.I. Credit Corp., New York, NY; *U.S. Public*, pg. 85
Collins, Robert T., Pres. & Publisher--Asbury Park Press, Inc., Neptune, NJ; *U.S. Public*, pg. 699
Collins, Robert T., Pres. & Publr.--Courier-Post, Cherry Hill, NJ; *U.S. Public*, pg. 700
Collins, Roger, Mng. Dir.--Chalmette Medical Center, Chalmette, LA; *U.S. Public*, pg. 1697
Collins, Ron, Pres. & Chief Exec. Officer--Stone Fort National Bank, Nacogdoches, Nacogdoches, TX; *U.S. Public*, pg. 630
Collins, Terry, V.P. & Gen. Mgr.--Engineering Research Associates, Vienna, VA; *U.S. Public*, pg. 1365
Collins, Walter, Pres.--Sea Ranch Properties, Fort Lauderdale, FL; *U.S. Private*, pg. 803
Collinson, Daniel S., Publr.--Blue Springs Examiner, Blue Springs, MO; *U.S. Private*, pg. 995
Collinson, Thomas H., Publr.--Pittsburg Morning Sun, Pittsburg, KS; *U.S. Private*, pg. 995
Collinsworth, Henry T., Chm. Bd.--NationsBank Trust, Atlanta, GA; *U.S. Public*, pg. 1165
Collinsworth, Henry T., Chm. Bd.--NationsBank Investment Advisors, Inc., Atlanta, GA; *U.S. Public*, pg. 1165
Colliver, Danielle, Pres.--N.W. Ayer & Partners Detroit, Detroit, MI; *U.S. Private*, pg. 104
Colloca, John, V.P. & Eastern Div. Mgr.--TriStar Pictures Eastern Division, New York, NY; *Int'l*, pg. 1283
Collura, Sam, Pres.--TIE Systems Arkansas/Gulfcoast, Little Rock, AR; *U.S. Private*, pg. 1085
Collura, Sam, Pres.--TIE Systems Florida (North), Tampa, FL; *U.S. Private*, pg. 1085
Collura, Sam, Pres.--TIE Systems Missouri, Saint Louis, MO; *U.S. Private*, pg. 1085
Colne, Nigel, Pres.--Marks & Spencer US Holdings Inc., New York, NY; *Int'l*, pg. 843
Colne, Nigel, Pres.--Marks & Spencer Services Inc., New York, NY; *Int'l*, pg. 843
Colombano, Jean-Pierre, Mgr.--Sandvik Tobler S.A., Paris, France; *Int'l*, pg. 1187
Colombatta, J., V.P.-Mfg.--Moore Response Graphics, Green Bay, WI; *Int'l*, pg. 890
Colombo, Giampero, Chief Oper. Officer--Bran & Luebbe S.r.l., Varese, Italy; *Int'l*, pg. 1380
Colombo, Gianpietro, Chm. Bd.--Immobiliare Maram S.r.l., Milan, Italy; *Int'l*, pg. 138
Colombo, Ing Luis, Gen. Mgr.--Nicoll Eterplast, Buenos Aires, Argentina; *Int'l*, pg. 430
Colombo, Robert, Mgr.-Opers.--S & W Construction Services Inc, Seattle, WA; *U.S. Private*, pg. 989
Colomer, Victor Serrato, Gen. Mgr.--TecniQuimia Mexicana S.A. de C.V., Monterrey, Mexico; *U.S. Public*, pg. 1347
Colonello, Alex, Chm. Bd.--Bayco Industries, Winnipeg, Canada; *Int'l*, pg. 395
Colquhoun, Ross K., Chief Oper. Officer--The Raymond Export Corporation, Saint Thomas, VI; *Int'l*, pg. 123
Colquitt, K., V.P.--Ranger Oil Company, Houston, TX; *Int'l*, pg. 1086
Colson, Alfred, Chief Oper. Officer--Neste Chemicals Belgium N.V., Brussels, Belgium; *Int'l*, pg. 914
Coltman, David A., Chm. Bd. & Pres.--Covia, LLC, Elk Grove Village, IL; *U.S. Public*, pg. 1653
Coltman, David A., Chm. Bd. & Pres.--United Vacations, Inc., Elk Grove Village, IL; *U.S. Public*, pg. 1653
Coltman, David A., Chm. Bd.--Milage Plus, Inc., Rolling Meadows, IL; *U.S. Public*, pg. 1653
Colton, Aaron, Chief Exec. Officer--Ceitronics, Inc., San Jose, CA; *U.S. Private*, pg. 1060
Colton, David A., Chm. Bd.--Mileage Plus Holdings, Inc., Elk Grove Village, IL; *U.S. Public*, pg. 1653
Colvert, Glen E., Exec. V.P.--NationsBank Services Corporation, Little Rock, AR; *U.S. Public*, pg. 1164
Colvin, Dennis, Mgr.--GES Inc., Forrest City, AR; *U.S. Private*, pg. 434
Colwell, John G., Jr., Pres.--Banta Information Services Group, Eden Prairie, MN; *U.S. Public*, pg. 188
Colwell, Kent L., Pres.--Transamerica Realty Services, Inc., San Francisco, CA; *U.S. Public*, pg. 1630
Combe, B., Chief Oper. Officer--The Kendall Co., Antony, France; *U.S. Public*, pg. 1647
Combe, Jean-Francois, Pres.--SKF France S.A., Clamart, France; *Int'l*, pg. 1158
Combe, Tony, Gen. Mgr.--Polarcup (Australia) Ltd., Bankstown, Australia; *Int'l*, pg. 638
Combeau, Pierre, Pres.--Campenon Bernard, Clichy, France; *Int'l*, pg. 321
Combette, Marc, Gen. Mgr.--ITW Spit, Bourg-les-Valence, France; *U.S. Public*, pg. 869
Combs, Charles S., Pres. & Chief Exec. Officer--Merchants National Bank, Terre Haute, IN; *U.S. Public*, pg. 1217
Combs, W.C., V.P. & Gen. Mgr.--Industrial Chemicals Div., Valley Forge, PA; *U.S. Private*, pg. 827
Comeau, David J., Gen. Mgr.--Marsa Kraft Jacobs Suchard Sabanci Gida Sanayi Ve Ticaret A.S, Istanbul, Turkey; *Int'l*, pg. 1168
Comeau, David J., Gen. Mgr.--Marsa Kraft Jacobs Suchard Sabanci Gida Sanayi Ve Ticaret A.S, Istanbul, Turkey; *U.S. Public*, pg. 1290
Comeau, Robert, Pres.--PacifiCare Life & Health Insurance Co., Costa Mesa, CA; *U.S. Public*, pg. 1251
Comer, Gordon, Gen. Mgr.--Raytex Finishing Co., Marion, SC; *U.S. Public*, pg. 430
Comer, John, Gen. Mgr.--St. Paul Plant, Saint Paul, MN; *U.S. Public*, pg. 1521
Comer, Ronald, Pres.--McCord Payen Inc., Wyandotte, MI; *Int'l*, pg. 1334
Comer, Tony, V.P. & District Sls. Mgr.--Life & Health--Willis Corroon Administrative Services Corporation, Cary, NC; *Int'l*, pg. 1505
Comey, Dale R., Chm. & Pres.--First State Insurance Company, Boston, MA; *U.S. Public*, pg. 794
Commander, Raymond L., Mgr.-Terminal--Pasadena Terminal, Pasadena, TX; *U.S. Public*, pg. 692
Commerot, Gerard, Pres. & New Bus. Contact--Ketchum Advertising France, Paris, France; *U.S. Private*, pg. 617
Commerro, Pietro, Mng. Dir.--Comtest Italy, Turin, Italy; *U.S.* Public, pg. 1596
Commette, William, Pres.--Middlesex Insurance, Westford, MA; *U.S. Private*, pg. 985
Commette, William E., Pres.--Middlesex Insurance Co., Stevens Point, WI; *U.S. Private*, pg. 985
Commons, Dave, Publr.--Roane County News, Kingston, TN; *U.S. Private*, pg. 648
Commons, David, Gen. Mgr.--Rockwood Times, Rockwood, TN; *U.S. Private*, pg. 648
Comoletti, Baldo, Mgr.--EG & G Sealol Inc., High Wycombe, United Kingdom; *U.S. Public*, pg. 544
Comora, Owen, Pres.--Owen Comora Associates, New York, NY; *U.S. Private*, pg. 985
Compitelo, Joseph, Pres.--International Envelope Company, Exton, PA; *U.S. Public*, pg. 70
Compton, James, Pres. & Chief Exec. Officer--Stewart Smith Southeast, Inc., Tampa, FL; *Int'l*, pg. 1508
Compton, Jimmy, Gen. Mgr.--Metro Auto Auction of Kansas City, Inc., Lees Summit, MO; *U.S. Public*, pg. 1649
Compton, Robert G., Pres.--Maescher Construction Co., Cincinnati, OH; *U.S. Private*, pg. 694
Compton, Robin, Mng. Dir.--Time-Life International Ltd., London, United Kingdom; *U.S. Public*, pg. 1615
Compton, Thomas A., Pres. & Chief Exec. Officer--EnviroSource-International Mill Service, Inc., Horsham, PA; *U.S. Public*, pg. 587
Comtet, M., Chief Oper. Officer--Elf Nigeria, Lagos, Nigeria; *Int'l*, pg. 446
Comtois, Claude, Pres.--AGRA Monenco Quebec, Inc., Montreal, Canada; *Int'l*, pg. 30
Conacher, J.C., Pres.--Halma Holdings Inc., Cincinnati, OH; *Int'l*, pg. 590
Conaerts, Marc, Chief Oper. Officer--SCA Packaging France S.A., Nantes, France; *Int'l*, pg. 1326
Conant, Douglas R., Exec. V.P. & Gen. Mgr.--Specialty Products Co., Parsippany, NJ; *U.S. Public*, pg. 1355
Conaty, James R., Pres.--H.B. Fuller Automotive Products, Madison Heights, MI; *U.S. Public*, pg. 687
Conchon, Francois, Mng. Dir.--DataCard France S.A., Bagnolet, France; *U.S. Private*, pg. 313
Concina, E., Dir.--Albacom SpA, Rome, Italy; *Int'l*, pg. 223
Conda, Joseph V., V.P.-Sls. & Mktg.--Owens-Brockway Glass Containers, Toledo, OH; *U.S. Public*, pg. 1238
Conde, Cristobal I., Pres.--SunGard Trading Systems Group, New York, NY; *U.S. Public*, pg. 1535
Conde, Victor, Dir.--International Marketing & Promotions Madrid, Madrid, Spain; *U.S. Private*, pg. 304
Condivi, Mario Torzi, Chief Exec. Officer--Maserati Automobiles, Incorporated, Baltimore, MD; *Int'l*, pg. 482
Condon, Brian, Superintendant--Fraser Paper Limited, Ashland, ME; *Int'l*, pg. 434
Condon, Dennis E., Pres.--Mentor H/S, Inc., Santa Barbara, CA; *U.S. Public*, pg. 1086
Condon, Gary, Chief Fin. Officer--Blue Streak-Hygrade Motor Products Ltd., Mississauga, Canada; *U.S. Public*, pg. 1503
Condon, Pierre, Pres.--Interavia Publishing Group, Geneva, Switzerland; *U.S. Public*, pg. 1601
Condon, Robert L., Gen. Mgr.--Ney Ultrasonics, Inc., Bloomfield, CT; *U.S. Public*, pg. 111
Condon, William P., Pres.--U.S. Specialty Insurance Co., Saint Peters, MO; *U.S. Public*, pg. 152
Condor, Daryl, Gen. Mgr.--Universal Studios Mfg., Pinckneyville, IL; *Int'l*, pg. 1216
Condria, Edward, Publr.--Troy Publishing Company, Inc., Troy, NY; *U.S. Public*, pg. 935
Conduff, J.F., Pres.--Badger Pipe Line Co., Tulsa, OK; *U.S. Public*, pg. 1584
Cone, George W., Pres. & Chief Oper. Officer--Virtual Vision, Inc., Redmond, WA; *U.S. Public*, pg. 1573
Conefry, John J., Jr., Chm. Bd.--Entrust Home Financing, Columbia, MD; *U.S. Public*, pg. 1013
Conen, Ulrich, Mng. Dir.--N.V. Maxon International S.A., Vilvoorde, Belgium; *U.S. Private*, pg. 717
Conesa, J.J., V.P. & Gen. Mgr.--Latin American Division, Miami, FL; *U.S. Public*, pg. 834
Confer, Jim, Gen. Mgr.--Corrugated Container Div.-Williamsport Plant, Williamsport, PA; *U.S. Public*, pg. 1521
Conger, H.M., Pres.--Phelps Dodge Morenci Inc., Morenci, AZ; *U.S. Public*, pg. 1287
Conger, Kelly, Gen. Mgr.--Northstar Auto Auction Inc., Shakopee, MN; *U.S. Public*, pg. 1649
Coniglio, Michel, Pres.--Carbone-Lorraine North America, Parsippany, NJ; *Int'l*, pg. 1028
Conine, Jim, Sr. V.P.-Real Estate--Minyard Properties, Inc., Coppell, TX; *U.S. Private*, pg. 752
Conine, Michael, Pres.--Stewart & Stevenson Power, Inc., City of Commerce, CA; *U.S. Public*, pg. 1518
Conine, Mike, Pres.--Stewart & Stevenson Holdings, Inc., Houston, TX; *U.S. Public*, pg. 1517
Conkin, Lorraine, Chief Oper. Officer--Kamyr Canada Inc., Ottawa, Canada; *Int'l*, pg. 35
Conklin, Keith H., Pres.--Nestle Foodservice Canada, Markham, Canada; *Int'l*, pg. 922
Conklin, Robert E., Pres. & Chief Exec. Officer--South Padre Land Co., Houston, TX; *U.S. Public*, pg. 77
Conklin, T., Gen. Mgr.--Menasha Corp., Printed Systems Div., Neenah, WI; *U.S. Private*, pg. 731
Conlan, James T., Pres.--Astro Aerospace Corp., Carpinteria, CA; *Int'l*, pg. 1288
Conlan, John, Pres.--ASEA BICC Capacitors Ltd., Ellesmere Port, United Kingdom; *Int'l*, pg. 7
Conley, E. A., Chief Oper. Officer--Guarantee American Life Company, Omaha, NE; *U.S. Public*, pg. 768
Conley, George M., Pres.--The Network of City Business Journals, Inc., Kansas City, MO; *U.S. Private*, pg. 19
Conley, Howard, Admin.--Fremont Mannor Nursing & Convalescent Home, Riverton, WY; *U.S. Public*, pg. 1712
Conley, J., Pres.--Photo Mechanix Inc., Carpentersville, IL; *U.S. Private*, pg. 891
Conley, Michael E., Pres. & Chief Exec. Officer--General Life Insurance Company Of America, Edwardsville, IL; *U.S. Private*, pg. 443
Conley, R. Michael, Pres.--NWNL Benefits Corp., Minneapolis, MN; *U.S. Public*, pg. 1375
Conly, Michael J., Pres. & Gen. Mgr.--Harte-Hanks Television, Inc. (KENS-TV), San Antonio, TX; *U.S. Public, pg. 794*
Conn, John L., V.P. & Gen. Mgr.--Semiconductor Manufacturing Division, Melbourne, FL; *U.S. Public*, pg. 792
Connally, Naomi, V.P. & Branch Mgr.--Las Vegas Branch, Las Vegas, NV; *U.S. Public*, pg. 1683
Connaly, Michael, Gen. Mgr.--SCI UK Ltd., Irvine, United Kingdom; *U.S. Public*, pg. 1417
Connaughton, Steve, Dir.--Program Water Technologies, Franklin Park, IL; *U.S. Private*, pg. 1006
Connavino, Nicholas A., Pres.--SuperValu, Inc.-Northeastern Reg., Burlington, MA; *U.S. Public*, pg. 1540
Connell, C. Willis, Jr., Chm. Bd. & Pres.--United Southern Bank, Clarksdale, MS; *U.S. Public*, pg. 1669
Connell, James R., Gen. Mgr.--Ropak Materials Handling Div., Elk Grove Village, IL; *Int'l*, pg. 812
Connell, Randy, Gen. Mgr.--American Cablevision of Carolina, Inc., Rockingham, NC; *U.S. Public*, pg. 1610
Connell, Randy, Gen. Mgr.--Rockingham-Hamlet, Inc., Rockingham, NC; *U.S. Public*, pg. 1610
Connell, Randy, Gen. Mgr.--Rockingham-Hamlet Cablevision, Inc., Rockingham, NC; *U.S. Public*, pg. 1610
Connell, William, Pres.--Aerospace Bearing Support, Inc., Moorpark, CA; *U.S. Public*, pg. 187
Connelly, Barry, Area Mgr.--High Prairie Division, High Prairie, Canada; *Int'l*, pg. 1395
Connelly, Jerry, Pres. & Gen. Mgr.--Chemineer, Inc., Dayton, OH; *U.S. Public*, pg. 1393
Connelly, Thomas, Office Mgr.--Korn/Ferry International, Miami, FL; *U.S. Private*, pg. 633
Conner, Robert, Pres.--OPW Fueling Components, Cincinnati, OH; *U.S. Public*, pg. 521
Conners, Gary, Chief Oper. Officer--Kodak Federal Systems Division, Rochester, NY; *U.S. Public*, pg. 555
Conners, Jack, Pres. & Gen. Mgr.--WICS-TV, Springfield, IL; *U.S. Private*, pg. 439
Connolley, John, Chm. Bd. & Chief Exec. Officer--G.E. American Communications, Inc., Princeton, NJ; *U.S. Public*, pg. 711
Connolly, Amanda, Mng. Dir.--Coley Porter Bell, London, United Kingdom; *Int'l*, pg. 1482
Connolly, Daryl, Pres. & Chief Exec. Officer--HCO Energy Ltd., Calgary, Canada; *U.S. Public*, pg. 782
Connolly, David, Media Dir.--Leo Burnett Limited, London, United Kingdom; *U.S. Private*, pg. 185
Connolly, John M., V.P. & Dir.--The Education Publishing Group, Reading, MA; *Int'l*, pg. 1026
Connolly, Kevin, Pres.--Excerpta Medica Inc., Belle Mead, NJ; *Int'l*, pg. 1100
Connolly, Michael, Pres.-U.S. Opers.--Waterford Foods USA, Inc., Wilmington, DE; *Int'l*, pg. 102
Connolly, Patrick, Gen. Mgr.--Dresdner Bank AG, New York, NY; *Int'l*, pg. 418
Connolly, Patrick, Pres.--Network Systems Integration, Lowell, MA; *U.S. Public*, pg. 711
Connolly, S., Chief Oper. Officer--Longman Botswana (Pty) Ltd., Gaborone, Botswana; *Int'l*, pg. 1025
Connolly, Sean, Mng. Dir.--Modem Media Hong Kong, Wan Chai, Hong Kong; *U.S. Public*, pg. 1641
Connor, Alan M., Pres. & Chief Exec. Officer--Cornerstone Real Estate, Hartford, CT; *U.S. Private*, pg. 712
Connor, Gary, Gen. Mgr.--Peterson Spring-Madison Heights Plant, Madison Heights, MI; *U.S. Private*, pg. 857
Connor, J.F., Mgr.--Queen Charlotte Division, Juskatla, Canada; *Int'l*, pg. 828
Connor, Jack, Gen. Mgr.--The HON Co., Winnsboro Plant, Winnsboro, SC; *U.S. Public*, pg. 772

Connor, Joseph, Pres.--Fiberlock Technologies, Inc., Cambridge, MA; *U.S. Private*, pg. 201
Connor, Mark, Chief Oper. Officer--Ferrosan International A/S, Soeborg, Denmark; *Int'l*, pg. 987
Connor, Mark, Mng. Dir.--Ferrosan International A/S, Soeborg, Denmark; *Int'l*, pg. 987
Connors, Ed, Chief Oper. Officer--Luxo Lamps Ltd., Laval, Canada; *Int'l*, pg. 821
Connors, Ed., Pres.--Luxo Ltd./Sverige Inc., Sainte-Therese-de-Blainville, Canada; *Int'l*, pg. 822
Connors, Jim J., Chief Oper. Officer--N.V. Weiser Europe, S.A., Saint-Niklaas, Belgium; *U.S. Public*, pg. 1055
Connors, John J., Publr.--Buffalo Law Journal, Buffalo, NY; *U.S. Private*, pg. 19
Connors, John J., Publisher--Business First of New York, LLC, Buffalo, NY; *U.S. Private*, pg. 19
Connors, Kevin P., Gen. Mgr.--Coherent, Inc.-Medical Group, Palo Alto, CA; *U.S. Public*, pg. 395
Conover, Donald E., Pres. & Chm. Bd.--Greystone Realty Corporation, Greenwich, CT; *U.S. Private*, pg. 795
Conrad, Phil, Pres.--Endevco Corporation, San Juan Capistrano, CA; *Int'l*, pg. 853
Conrad, Richard, Pres.--Castleberry Knits, Ltd., New York, NY; *U.S. Public*, pg. 989
Conrad, W. Richard, Pres.--Bell Atlantic Paging, Parsippany, NJ; *U.S. Public*, pg. 203
Conrad, William C., Pres. & Chief Exec. Officer--First American Capital Management, Inc., Newport Beach, CA; *U.S. Public*, pg. 625
Conrades, George H., Chm. Bd., Pres. & Chief Exec. Officer--GTE Internetworking, Cambridge, MA; *U.S. Public*, pg. 696
Conrades, George H., Sr. V.P. & Gen. Mgr.--IBM Enterprise Systems, Somers, NY; *U.S. Public*, pg. 895
Conran, Vincent, Mng. Dir.--International Thomson Business Publishing, London, United Kingdom; *U.S. Public*, pg. 1601
Conrekas, Anna, Branch Mgr.--Downey Savings & Loan Association, F.A., Downey, CA; *U.S. Public*, pg. 526
Conrick, Ken, Mng. Dir.--Thermon Australia, Bayswater, Australia; *U.S. Private*, pg. 1081
Conrold, Anne, Mgr.--Syntellect Technology Corp., Roswell, GA; *U.S. Public*, pg. 1550
Conron, Mark, V.P. & Gen. Mgr.--Wajax Pacific Fire Equipment Inc., Kent, WA; *Int'l*, pg. 1485
Conroy, Dan, Gen. Mgr.--Arrow/Schweber Electronics, Itasca, IL; *U.S. Public*, pg. 134
Conroy, John L., Sr. V.P. & Fin. Controller--Jefferies & Company, Inc., Los Angeles, CA; *U.S. Public*, pg. 925
Conroy, Patrick T., Pres.--GENXON Power Systems LLC, Mountain View, CA; *U.S. Public*, pg. 1776
Conroy, T.F., Pres.--Security Life of Denver Reinsurance Company, Denver, CO; *Int'l*, pg. 648
Conroy, Thomas E., Gen. Mgr.--Kvaerner Hymac Corporation, Roswell, GA; *Int'l*, pg. 770
Consdorf, Frank, Gen. Mgr.--AAR Defense Systems, Elk Grove Village, IL; *U.S. Public*, pg. 1
Conservo, Salvatore, Chm. Bd.--Banco di Sicilia International S.A., Luxembourg, Luxembourg; *Int'l*, pg. 141
Consonni, Marcello, Pres.--Hagglunds Drives Srl, Milan, Italy; *Int'l*, pg. 670
Constable, P.S., Chief Exec. Officer--Black Horse Agencies Ltd., Hatfield, United Kingdom; *Int'l*, pg. 813
Constable, Wes, Mgr.--Commercial Metals Company, Corpus Christi, TX; *U.S. Public*, pg. 413
Constable, Wes, Mgr.--Commercial Metals Company, Victoria, TX; *U.S. Public*, pg. 413
Constandse, Robert W.J., Mgr.-Sls.--Fasson Products (Pty) Ltd., Johannesburg, South Africa; *U.S. Public*, pg. 154
Constant, Dave, Mgr.-Branch--GAI Consultants, Inc., Fort Wayne, IN; *U.S. Private*, pg. 434
Constantine, Jerry, V.P. & Gen. Mgr.--AAR Engine Component Services, Windsor, CT; *U.S. Public*, pg. 1
Contalini, Carl, Pres.--Waterbury Companies, Inc., Waterbury, CT; *U.S. Public*, pg. 308
Conte, Pierre, Pres.-Europe--Johnson & Johnson Professional Products Ltd., Bracknell, United Kingdom; *U.S. Public*, pg. 931
Conte, Reynaldo, Media Dir.--Comunica Leo Burnett Panama, S.A., Panama, Panama; *U.S. Private*, pg. 184
Conti, Bruce A., Dir.-Asia Opers.--Asia Representative Office, Singapore, Singapore; *U.S. Public*, pg. 693
Conti, F., Chief Opers. Officer--Mead Management Services S.A., Zurich, Switzerland; *U.S. Public*, pg. 1076
Conti, Joseph J., First V.P.--Jefferies & Company, Inc., Los Angeles, CA; *U.S. Public*, pg. 925
Conti, Mark, Mgr.--Ripley Graphics, Ripley, TN; *U.S. Public*, pg. 78
Conti, Renato, Gen. Mgr.--Ansaldo Componenti srl, Genoa, Italy; *Int'l*, pg. 653
Contino, Frederic L., Pres.--Plastics, Inc., Saint Paul, MN; *U.S. Public*, pg. 1177
Contino, Frederic L., Pres.--Anchor Hocking Plastics, Saint Paul, MN; *U.S. Public*, pg. 1177
Contino, Frederic L., Pres.--Jareen Co., Saint Paul, MN; *U.S. Public*, pg. 1177
Contino, Rick, Pres.--Game Time, Inc., Fort Payne, AL; *U.S. Public*, pg. 1543
Contois, Michael S., Pres.--Pacific Tri-View Corporation, Rancho Cucamonga, CA; *U.S. Public*, pg. 990
Contreras, C. Armando, Gen. Mgr.--Nature's Sunshine Products de Venezuela, Caracas, Venezuela; *U.S. Public*, pg. 1166
Contreras, Fernando, Mng. Dir.--Johnson & Johnson de Mexico SA de CV, Mexico, Mexico; *U.S. Public*, pg. 930
Contreras, Mark, Pres. & Publisher--The Times Leader, Wilkes-Barre, PA; *U.S. Public*, pg. 963
Contreras, Mark, Pres. & Publr.--The Times Leader, Wilkes-Barre, PA; *U.S. Public*, pg. 964
Contzen, Ernst Wilhelm, Dir.--Deutsche Bank AG (Brussels), Brussels, Belgium; *Int'l*, pg. 403

Convers, Oscar, Gen. Mgr.--Marcam Corporation, Latin American Headquarters, Atlanta, GA; *U.S. Public*, pg. 1043
Conviser, Richard J., Chm. & Pres.--Harcourt Brace & Company Legal and Professional Publications, Inc., Chicago, IL; *U.S. Public*, pg. 783
Conviser, Richard J., Pres.--Miller Comprehensive CPA Review, Inc., Chicago, IL; *U.S. Public*, pg. 783
Conway, Allen, Pres.--Discount Labels, Inc., New Albany, IN; *U.S. Public*, pg. 70
Conway, C. V., V.P. & Gen. Mgr.--Fragrance Div., Springfield, NJ; *Int'l*, pg. 174
Conway, Don, Gen. Mgr.--Brierley Investments Ltd., Sydney, Australia; *Int'l*, pg. 215
Conway, J.M., Pres.--PTI Technolgies, Inc., Newbury Park, CA; *U.S. Public*, pg. 546
Conway, James E., Pres.--AmSouth Bank N.A., Dothan, AL; *U.S. Public*, pg. 105
Conway, James F. III, Pres.--Courier Westford, Inc., Westford, MA; *U.S. Public*, pg. 453
Conway, James F., III, Pres.--Courier Companies, Inc., Lowell, MA; *U.S. Public*, pg. 453
Conway, James J., Pres.--ISP Technologies Inc., Texas City, TX; *U.S. Public*, pg. 859
Conway, Joe, Mng. Dir.--A. Schulman, Inc., Grand Rapids, MI; *U.S. Public*, pg. 1441
Conway, John W., Pres.--Crown Cork & Seal, Americas Division, Philadelphia, PA; *U.S. Public*, pg. 463
Conway, Mike, Pres.--First American Title Co. of Florida, Inc., Tampa, FL; *U.S. Public*, pg. 625
Conway, Richard, V.P. & Gen. Mgr.--Logicon Geodynamics Central Division, Colorado Springs, CO; *U.S. Public*, pg. 1199
Conway, Ronald J., Pres.--TCV, Inc., Philadelphia, PA; *U.S. Public*, pg. 432
Coody, Marc, Gen. Mgr.--Aircraft Systems Division, Los Angeles, Hawthorne, CA; *U.S. Private*, pg. 71
Coogan, William, Sr. V.P.--Expeditors International Ocean, Inc., Seattle, WA; *U.S. Public*, pg. 600
Cook, Brian, V.P.--Bankers Trust Investment Management Ltd., London, United Kingdom; *U.S. Public*, pg. 186
Cook, Brian, Pres.--Famous Footwear, Madison, WI; *U.S. Public*, pg. 262
Cook, Brian, Dir.--Willis Corroon Credit Limited, Glasgow, United Kingdom; *Int'l*, pg. 1502
Cook, Charlie, Pres.--UPB of Middle Tennessee, Nashville, TN; *U.S. Public*, pg. 1669
Cook, Daniel, Dir.-Ford Bus. Unit--Bundy Corporation, Phoenix Center, Chesterfield, MI; *Int'l*, pg. 1340
Cook, Daniel L., Pres.--Overland Transportation System, Inc., Indianapolis, IN; *Int'l*, pg. 1469
Cook, David A., Resident Rep.--The World Bank, Harare, Zimbabwe; *U.S. Private*, pg. 1190
Cook, David G., Pres.--Stearns Manufacturing Company, Sauk Rapids, MN; *U.S. Public*, pg. 940
Cook, Gail, Pres.--Dana Buchman Div., New York, NY; *U.S. Public*, pg. 1006
Cook, Harold, Plant Mgr.--Hershey Chocolate U.S.A.-Stuarts Draft Plant, Stuarts Draft, VA; *U.S. Public*, pg. 812
Cook, Harold C., Plant Mgr.--Hershey Canada Inc.-Smith Falls Plant, Smiths Falls, Canada; *U.S. Public*, pg. 812
Cook, Ian, Pres.--Colgate U.S.A., New York, NY; *U.S. Public*, pg. 397
Cook, J. Mark, Pres.--Cyprus Foote Mineral Co., Kings Mountain, NC; *U.S. Public*, pg. 471
Cook, James W., Pres.--CMS Generation Co., Dearborn, MI; *U.S. Public*, pg. 280
Cook, Jeffrey, Exec. V.P.--Chapman Equipment Company, Cranston, RI; *U.S. Private*, pg. 334
Cook, Jim, Gen. Mgr.--Baltimore-Washington Auto Exchange Inc., Baltimore, MD; *U.S. Public*, pg. 1648
Cook, John J., Jr., Pres.--UAM Investment Services, Inc., Boston, MA; *U.S. Public*, pg. 1674
Cook, Joseph W., Pres. & Gen. Mgr.--WALA-TV, Mobile, AL; *U.S. Public*, pg. 1685
Cook, Keith, Pres.--Marvella Inc., New York, NY; *U.S. Private*, pg. 757
Cook, L. H., Chm.--Stanbic Bank Zimbabwe Limited, Harare, Zimbabwe; *Int'l*, pg. 1294
Cook, Leroy, Gen. Mgr.--Case Farms, Inc., Morganton, NC; *U.S. Private*, pg. 218
Cook, Matthew, Sr. V.P. & Branch Mgr.--Willis Corroon Melling Inc., Ottawa, Canada; *Int'l*, pg. 1509
Cook, Norman, Chief Oper. Officer & Pur. Dir.--Hang Ten, Montreal, Canada; *Int'l*, pg. 549
Cook, Peter, Mng. Dir.--PPA Design Ltd., Central, Hong Kong; *Int'l*, pg. 118
Cook, Peter, Mng. Dir.--Intermotor, Nottingham, United Kingdom; *U.S. Public*, pg. 1503
Cook, Randall, Sr. V.P.-Property & Casualty & Mgr.-N. Div.--Willis Corroon Administrative Services Corporation, Louisville, KY; *Int'l*, pg. 1504
Cook, Richard W., Pres.--Buena Vista Pictures Distribution Inc., Burbank, CA; *U.S. Public*, pg. 513
Cook, Roger A., Chief Exec. Officer--Colliers Jardine Holdings Ltd., Hong Kong, Hong Kong; *Int'l*, pg. 705
Cook, S., Mng. Dir.--Manor Bakeries Limited, Windsor, United Kingdom; *Int'l*, pg. 1396
Cook, Stephen, Chief Oper. Officer & Pur. Dir.--Kamik, Montreal, Canada; *Int'l*, pg. 549
Cook, Ted, Chm. Bd.--Ted Cook Tours Islands in the Sun, Costa Mesa, CA; *Int'l*, pg. 21
Cook, Tom, Fin. Dir.--Leo Burnett Kyodo Co. Ltd., Tokyo, Japan; *U.S. Private*, pg. 185
Cook, Tony, Mgr.-Mktg.--Schumann Sasol GmbH & Co KG, Hamburg, Germany; *Int'l*, pg. 1197
Cook, Walter R., Exec. V.P.--RNBNY Branch Office-Tokyo, Tokyo, Japan; *U.S. Public*, pg. 1381
Cooke, Amory J., V.P. & Gen. Mgr.--Sunical Land & Livestock Division, San Francisco, CA; *U.S. Private*, pg. 518
Cooke, Danny, Pres.--Signal Artwear, Wabash, IN; *U.S. Public*, pg. 1472

Cooke, Dr. C. John, Mng. Dir.--Tesa Metrology Limited, Telford, United Kingdom; *U.S. Public*, pg. 260
Cooke, J.M., Pres.--Northern Pigment, Toronto, Canada; *Int'l*, pg. 1150
Cooke, Jack Kent, Pres.--Cooke Media Group, Inc., Woodland Hills, CA; *U.S. Private*, pg. 273
Cooke, Mike, Mng. Dir.--DMG Business Media Ltd., Redhill, United Kingdom; *Int'l*, pg. 366
Cooke, Sergio de Burgos, Mgr.--Rio de Janeiro Branch, Rio de Janeiro, Brazil; *Int'l*, pg. 139
Cooke, Tim M., Mng. Dir.--Logica Communications and Electronic Systems Limited, London, United Kingdom; *Int'l*, pg. 814
Cookman, Michael A., Pres.--Flagg Brass, Stowe, PA; *U.S. Public*, pg. 63
Cookson, Dr. John T., Pres.--JTC Environmental Consultants, Inc., Rockville, MD; *U.S. Public*, pg. 694
Cookson, Michael, Gen. Mgr.--Aviva Sport, Inc., El Segundo, CA; *U.S. Public*, pg. 1058
Cooler, Charles, Sr. V.P. & Gen. Mgr.--BASES International Research Division, Westport, CT; *U.S. Private*, pg. 120
Cooley, George F., Pres.--Mercury Printing Company, Inc., Memphis, TN; *U.S. Public*, pg. 1736
Cooley, Horace, Gen. Mgr.--Servitex, Inc., Durham, NC; *U.S. Private*, pg. 782
Cooley, Roger, V.P. & Gen. Mgr.--Hallmark Art Products & International Div., Easton, PA; *U.S. Private*, pg. 496
Coolidge, Awson, Chief Oper. Officer--Milton Roy Company, Ivyland, PA; *U.S. Public*, pg. 1534
Coolier, Jean-Philippe, Regional Mgr.--Societe Generale, Chicago, IL; *Int'l*, pg. 1273
Coombi, V.A., Chief Oper. Officer--The Starflo Corporation, Manning, SC; *U.S. Private*, pg. 877
Coombs, D.A.L., Pres.--ICI Polyurethanes Group, Deptford, NJ; *Int'l*, pg. 664
Coon, James A., Gen. Mgr.--West Coast Redwood Sawmill, Fort Bragg, CA; *U.S. Public*, pg. 739
Cooney, C.E., Pres. & Gen. Mgr.--KPNX-TV, Phoenix, AZ; *U.S. Public*, pg. 702
Cooney, Jack, Pres. & Chief Exec. Officer--Advance Machine Company, Plymouth, MN; *Int'l*, pg. 932
Cooney, Kevin, V.P.--Whirlpool Corp., Clyde Div., Clyde, OH; *U.S. Public*, pg. 1765
Cooney, Robert J., Pres. & Chief Oper. Officer--X.L. Insurance Company, Ltd., Hamilton, Bermuda; *Int'l*, pg. 467
Cooney, Wilson C., Pres.-P&C Insurance--Property & Casualty Insurance, San Antonio, TX; *U.S. Private*, pg. 1114
Coopat, E. Thomas, Jr., Gen. Mgr.--Avon Cosmetics (Taiwan) Ltd., Taipei, Taiwan; *U.S. Public*, pg. 156
Cooper, A.J., Gen. Mgr.--ANZ Grindlays Bank plc United Arab Emirates, Dubai, United Arab Emirates; *Int'l*, pg. 99
Cooper, B. E., Pres. & Chief Exec. Officer--Kennecott Holdings Corporation, Magna, UT; *Int'l*, pg. 1119
Cooper, Benny R., Pres.--Affiliated Finance Inc., Amarillo, TX; *U.S. Private*, pg. 25
Cooper, Burton, Pres.--Green Bus Holding, Jamaica, NY; *U.S. Private*, pg. 477
Cooper, Charles B., Pres.--American Income Life Insurance Company, Waco, TX; *U.S. Public*, pg. 1622
Cooper, Debbie, Exec. V.P.--Turner Private Networks, Atlanta, GA; *U.S. Public*, pg. 1614
Cooper, Donald M., Chm. Bd., Pres. & Chief Exec. Officer--CoreStates Bank, Lancaster, PA; *U.S. Public*, pg. 446
Cooper, Ian G., Pres.--Bayex Incorporated, Albion, NY; *Int'l*, pg. 1170
Cooper, J. Fred, V.P. & Div. Mgr.--Quebecor Printing Hawkins, Church Hill, TN; *Int'l*, pg. 1076
Cooper, J. Patterson, Pres.--Bankers Trust Co. of Florida, N.A., West Palm Beach, FL; *U.S. Public*, pg. 185
Cooper, Jane, Pres. & Chief Exec. Officer--Paramount Parks, Charlotte, NC; *U.S. Private*, pg. 776
Cooper, John, Mgr.--General Employment Enterprises, Inc., Horsham, PA; *U.S. Public*, pg. 714
Cooper, John S., Sr. V.P. & Grp. Exec.-Railroad Group--Portec Inc., Railway Maintenance Products Div., Pittsburgh, PA; *U.S. Public*, pg. 1318
Cooper, Jonathan, Pres.--Tracer Products, Westbury, NY; *U.S. Private*, pg. 1024
Cooper, Larry, Chief Oper. Officer--Pool Insurance, Winnipeg, Canada; *Int'l*, pg. 1195
Cooper, M. Lynn, Chm. Bd., Pres. & Chief Exec. Officer--Citizens Bank of Illinois, Mount Vernon, IL; *U.S. Public*, pg. 280
Cooper, Martin, Pres. & Gen. Mgr.--AAR Cooper Aviation, Elk Grove Village, IL; *U.S. Public*, pg. 1
Cooper, Milton E., Pres.--Systems Group, Falls Church, VA; *U.S. Public*, pg. 423
Cooper, Murray W., Pres. & Chief Exec. Officer--Northern Telephone Limited, New Liskeard, Canada; *Int'l*, pg. 115
Cooper, Neal, Controller--U.S. Brick-San Antonio, San Antonio, TX; *Int'l*, pg. 699
Cooper, Ned, Pres. & Div. Mgr.--Batavia Wine Cellars, Batavia, NY; *U.S. Public*, pg. 300
Cooper, Ned, Pres.-Batavia Wine Cellars--Canandaigua Wine Co., Canandaigua, NY; *U.S. Public*, pg. 300
Cooper, P., Mng. Dir.--Racal Health & Safety, Inc., Frederick, MD; *Int'l*, pg. 1083
Cooper, Paul, Mgr.--Kvaerner Boving (ANZ) Pty Ltd, Auckland, New Zealand; *Int'l*, pg. 772
Cooper, Paul, Pres.--Peoples, Montreal, Canada; *Int'l*, pg. 843
Cooper, Paul A., Chm. Bd.--Australian Road Credit Limited, Melbourne, Australia; *U.S. Public*, pg. 665
Cooper, Paul A., Chm. Bd. & Mng. Dir.--Ford Credit SpA, Rome, Italy; *U.S. Public*, pg. 666
Cooper, Phil, Pres.--Polhemus Inc., Colchester, VT; *U.S. Private*, pg. 605
Cooper, Philip D., Pres.--ORIX Commercial Alliance Corporation, Secaucus, NJ; *Int'l*, pg. 1009
Cooper, R.H., Pres.--APV Gaulin Inc., Wilmington, MA; *Int'l*, pg. 1241

Cooper, Richard, Pres.--Finnfeeds International Ltd., Marlborough, United Kingdom; *Int'l*, pg. 349
Cooper, Richard, Gen. Mgr.--Columbia Medical, Inc., Redmond, OR; *U.S. Public*, pg. 1700
Cooper, Roger A., Pres.--Target Oilfield Pipe & Supply Company (TOPS), Canton, OH; *U.S. Private*, pg. 1078
Cooper, Ronald M., Pres.--Temple-Inland Mortgage Corporation, Austin, TX; *U.S. Public*, pg. 1575
Cooper, Sam, V.P. & Gen. Mgr.--Farm Bureau Casualty Insurance Co., Little Rock, AR; *U.S. Private*, pg. 82
Cooper, Sam, V.P. & Gen. Mgr.--Farm Bureau Mutual Insurance Co. of Arkansas, Little Rock, AR; *U.S. Private*, *pg. 82*
Cooper, Steve, V.P. & Gen. Mgr.--Sealright Mfg. West, Inc., San Leandro, CA; *U.S. Public*, pg. 1452
Cooper, Tom, Reg. Mgr.--Green Tree Acceptance, Inc., Las Vegas, NV; *U.S. Public*, pg. 762
Coopersmith, Jeff, Pres.--HMS-Direct Columbus, Columbus, OH; *U.S. Private*, pg. 492
Coopersmith, Jeffrey, Pres.--HMS Direct, Cincinnati, OH; *U.S. Private*, pg. 492
Coords, Robert H., Chm. Bd. & Chief Exec. Officer--SunTrust Bank, South Florida, N.A., Fort Lauderdale, FL; *U.S. Public*, pg. 1538
Coors, Jeffrey H., Pres.--Graphic Packaging Corporation, Wayne, PA; *U.S. Public*, pg. 3
Coors, Joseph, Jr., Pres. & Chief Exec. Officer--Coors Ceramics Company, Golden, CO; *U.S. Public*, pg. 3
Coosemans, J.F., Mng. Dir.--N.V. Wellcome S.A., Brussels, Belgium; *Int'l*, pg. 553
Coover, David B., Pres.--PNC Bank, South Central, Mechanicsburg, PA; *U.S. Public*, pg. 1243
Copage, Alan, Dir.--Carot Insight, London, United Kingdom; *Int'l*, pg. 1342
Cope, E., District Mgr.--A.M. Castle & Co., Fairless Hills, PA; *U.S. Public*, pg. 313
Cope, Laura, Mgr.--Southern Electric Supply Co., Inc., Fort Lauderdale, FL; *Int'l*, pg. 1107
Cope, Mike D., Mng. Dir.--Neste Chemicals UK Ltd., Stockport, United Kingdom; *Int'l*, pg. 914
Cope, Noah, Plant Mgr.--Ruetgers-Nease Corporation, Ross, OH; *Int'l*, pg. 1148
Cope, Peter, Pres.--Pall Ultrafine Filtration Company, Greenvale, NY; *U.S. Public*, pg. 1254
Cope, Richard N., Pres.--Victaulic Company of Canada Limited, Rexdale, Canada; *U.S. Private*, pg. 1138
Cope, Robert W., V.P. & Gen. Mgr.--Western Energy Company, Colstrip, MT; *U.S. Public*, pg. 1127
Cope, Roger, Mng. Dir.--Bestobell Service Co. Ltd., Maidenhead, United Kingdom; *Int'l*, pg. 853
Copeland, Claire, Pres.--Mappins Jewelers, Don Mills, Canada; *Int'l*, pg. 1036
Copeland, Claire, V.P.-Opers.--Peoples Jewelers, Don Mills, Canada; *Int'l*, pg. 1036
Copeland, Frederick C., Jr., Pres.--Aetna International, Inc., Hartford, CT; *U.S. Public*, pg. 26
Copenhaver, Mike, Plant Superintendant--General Shale Products Corp., Glasgow, VA; *Int'l*, pg. 844
Copete, Ignacio, V.P. & Representative--NationsBank (Colombia) Branch, Bogota, Colombia; *U.S. Public*, pg. 1166
Copijn, Lia M., Mng. Dir.--Copijn Utrecht Holding BV, Utrecht, Netherlands; *Int'l*, pg. 607
Copley, Helen K., Publisher--San Diego Union Tribune, San Diego, CA; *U.S. Private*, pg. 275
Copley, Michael, Mng. Dir.--Revertex-Americas, Saint Louis, MO; *U.S. Private*, pg. 324
Coplin, Gerry W., Plant Mgr.--Wedco, Inc., Fontana, CA; *U.S. Public*, pg. 854
Coppage, Robert, Pres.--VF Jeanswear-Europe, Brussels, Belgium; *U.S. Public*, pg. 1702
Coppedge, Ferrell L., Exec. V.P.--Southern Group, Atlanta, GA; *U.S. Public*, pg. 649
Coppel Luken, Enrique, Chm. Bd.--Coppel S.A. de C.V., Culiacan, Mexico; *Int'l*, pg. 330
Coppens, J., Mng. Dir.--Anco N.V., Turnhout, Belgium; *Int'l*, pg. 244
Coppersmith, Randall S., V.P.--Redgate Communications Corp., San Francisco, CA; *U.S. Public*, pg. 66
Coppersmith, S. James, Pres. & Gen. Mgr.--WCVB-TV, Boston, MA; *U.S. Private*, pg. 516
Coppieters, Yves, Mng. Dir.--Powerfin S.A., Brussels, Belgium; *Int'l*, pg. 1415
Copping, Dwight, Mgr.--Anixter Winnipeg, Winnipeg, Canada; *U.S. Public*, pg. 116
Copping, Harold, Pres. & Gen. Mgr.--Teleflex (Canada) Ltd., Vancouver, Canada; *U.S. Public*, pg. 1570
Copple, Frank, Pres.--Stinnes Interoil Inc., Red Bank, NJ; *Int'l*, pg. 1459
Coppola, Hector, Gen. Dir.--Marcam Argentina S.A., Buenos Aires, Argentina; *U.S. Public*, pg. 1043
Coppola, Joseph Skip, V.P.--Faneuil Hall Marketplace, Inc., Boston, MA; *U.S. Public*, pg. 1408
Coppola, Ralph, Pres.--Hill Phoenix, Colonial Heights, VA; *U.S. Public*, pg. 521
Coquoz, Christian, Mgr.--Ferrier Lullin Bank & Trust (Bahamas) Limited, Nassau, Bahamas; *Int'l*, pg. 480
Corapi, Gene, Chief Oper. Officer--Regency Engravers, Inc., Waynesboro, PA; *U.S. Public*, pg. 89
Corapi, Gene, Chief Oper. Officer--Regency Thermographers of Pa., Inc., Waynesboro, PA; *U.S. Public*, pg. 89
Corapi, Gene, Chief Oper. Officer--Value Stationery, Inc., Chambersburg, PA; *U.S. Public*, pg. 89
Corbel, Gary, Pres.--Welenco, Inc., Bakersfield, CA; *Int'l*, pg. 1019
Corbet, R., Chief Exec. Officer--AMEV General Insurance Company Limited, Dublin, Ireland; *Int'l*, pg. 499
Corbet, Tim, Pres.--Trimfoot Company, Farmington, MO; *U.S. Public*, pg. 1684
Corbett, Donald, Pres.--MDI Management Inc., Hickory, NC; *U.S. Private*, pg. 657
Corbett, Luke R., Pres.--Kerr-McGee Oil (U.K.) PLC, London, United Kingdom; *U.S. Public*, pg. 952
Corbett, Rick P., Chief Oper. Officer & V.P.--Foundation Health Benefit Life Insurance Company, Rancho Cordova, CA; *U.S. Public*, pg. 678
Corbett, Robin, Dir.--Willis Corroon Credit Limited, London, United Kingdom; *Int'l*, pg. 1502
Corbin, Larry, Dir.-Mfg.--Nestle Confectionery, Toronto, Canada; *Int'l*, pg. 922
Corbley, Paul, Gen. Mgr.--Poe & Brown of Florida, Melbourne, FL; *U.S. Public*, pg. 1312
Corbusier, Dave, Chm. Bd.--Fort Worth Division, Fort Worth, TX; *U.S. Public*, pg. 509
Corcoran, David, Pres. & Mng. Exec.--Northern Trust Bank of Florida, N.A., Bradenton, FL; *U.S. Public*, pg. 1196
Corcoran, E. Thomas, Pres.--Fort Dodge Animal Health, Overland Park, KS; *U.S. Public*, pg. 79
Corcoran, Jim, Pres.--Systems Tax Service, Inc., Fountain Valley, CA; *U.S. Public*, pg. 331
Corcoran, Thomas A., Pres.--Lockheed Martin Electronics Group, Bethesda, MD; *U.S. Public*, pg. 1006
Corcoran, Walter, Pres.--Philips Credit Corporation, New York, NY; *Int'l*, pg. 1055
Cordaro, Robert, Pres.--VF Asia Limited, Kowloon, Hong Kong; *U.S. Public*, pg. 1702
Cordeau, Francis, V.P.-Semiconductor Mfg. Opers.--Mitel Semiconductor AB, Jarfalla, Sweden; *Int'l*, pg. 870
Cordemans, Jan, Chief Exec. Officer-Creation & Production--Quattro DMB&B, Brussels, Brussels, Belgium; *U.S. Private*, pg. 305
Corder, Richard, Branch Mgr.--Zellerbach Division, Oakland, CA; *U.S. Public*, pg. 1076
Corder, Richard B., Branch Mgr.--Zellerbach Division, South San Francisco, CA; *U.S. Public*, pg. 1075
Corder, Sidney, Pres. & Chief Exec. Officer--MSC Corporation, Indianapolis, IN; *U.S. Public*, pg. 110
Cordes, Dr. Rainer, Mng. Dir.--Reise-und Verkehrs Verlag GmbH, Munich, Germany; *Int'l*, pg. 190
Cordes, E., Dr., Chief Oper. Officer--ABB-Daimler Benz Transportation (Adtranz), Berlin, Germany; *Int'l*, pg. 8
Cordes, Eugene H., Dr., Pres.--Sanofi Research Division, Malvern, PA; *Int'l*, pg. 445
Cordes, J. F., Chm. & Pres.--ANR Gasification Properties Co., Detroit, MI; *U.S. Public*, pg. 389
Cordes, William R., Pres.--Northern Natural Gas Co., Omaha, NE; *U.S. Public*, pg. 584
Cordido Valery, Carlos G., Pres. & Gen. Mgr.--Componentes Delfa, C.A., Caracas, Venezuela; *U.S. Public*, pg. 724
Cordola, J.P., Pres. & Gen. Mgr.--ITW de France SA, Beauchamp, France; *U.S. Public*, pg. 868
Cordon, Valentin Martinez, Gen. Mgr.--Cia. Espanola de Petroleos Atlantico, S.A., Madrid, Spain; *Int'l*, pg. 323
Cordova, Randy M., Pres.--World Dryer Corp., Berkeley, IL; *U.S. Public*, pg. 1497
Corey, Allen, Pres. Chief Exec. Officer--Big River Grille & Brewery Works, Chattanooga, TN; *U.S. Public*, pg. 1396
Corey, J., Pres.--Douglas Dynamics, Inc., Milwaukee, WI; *U.S. Public*, pg. 131
Corey, John, Pres.--Mechanics Tool Div., Dallas, TX; *U.S. Public*, pg. 1509
Corey, John, Pres.--National Hand Tools, Dallas, TX; *U.S. Public*, pg. 1509
Corey, R.L., Pres.--Molson Sports and Entertainment, Montreal, Canada; *Int'l*, pg. 887
Corey, Robin, V.P. & Editorial Dir.--Little Simon, New York, NY; *U.S. Private*, pg. 777
Corey, Robin, V.P. & Editorial Dir.--Rabbit Ears Book & Audio, New York, NY; *U.S. Private*, pg. 777
Corfield, George, Gen. Mgr.--XTEK/Arizona Division, Tempe, AZ; *U.S. Private*, pg. 1194
Cori, Tom, Chief Exec. Officer--Sigma Chemical Co., Saint Louis, MO; *U.S. Public*, pg. 1472
Coria, Julian, Gen. Mgr.--Circle Airfreight International de Mexico S.A. de C.V., Mexico, Mexico; *U.S. Public*, pg. 372
Corigliano, Jeff, Gen. Mgr.--San Antonio Auto Auction, San Antonio, TX; *U.S. Private*, pg. 283
Corish, Benjamin T., Pres. & Chief Exec. Officer--First Virginia Bank-Piedmont, Lynchburg, VA; *U.S. Public*, pg. 642
Corkeem, Nancy E., Chief Oper. Officer & V.P.--Immunobiology Research Institute, Annandale, NJ; *U.S. Public*, pg. 928
Corless, Brian, Opers. Dir.--The Gates Rubber Company Limited, Edinburgh, United Kingdom; *Int'l*, pg. 1397
Corlett, Glenn, Chief Oper. Officer--Ayer International, New York, NY; *U.S. Private*, pg. 104
Corley, James W., Co-Chief Exec. Officer & Chief Oper. Officer--Dave & Buster's, Dallas, TX; *U.S. Public*, pg. 488
Corley, Reynard A., V.P. & Gen. Mgr.--WXII-TV, Winston Salem, NC; *U.S. Public*, pg. 1344
Corley, Reynard A., V.P. & Gen. Mgr.--WXII-AM, Winston Salem, NC; *U.S. Public*, pg. 1344
Corliss, Pamela, Chief Exec. Officer--North Miami Beach Surgical Center, Miami, FL; *U.S. Public*, pg. 405
Cormier, Andy, Pres.--NB Coal Company Limited, Minto, Canada; *Int'l*, pg. 923
Corn, Larry, Pres.--Roadrunner Trucking, Inc., Albuquerque, NM; *U.S. Public*, pg. 911
Corn, Larry, Pres.--Roadrunner Distribution Systems, Inc., Indianapolis, IN; *U.S. Public*, pg. 911
Cornacchiulo, Frank, V.P.--W. Braun Co., Lyndhurst, NJ; *U.S. Private*, pg. 166
Cornale, P., Mng. Dir.--Nutricia S.p.A., Milan, Italy; *Int'l*, pg. 992
Corneil, Art, V.P. & Gen. Mgr.--Hedstrom Canada, Kitchener, Canada; *U.S. Private*, pg. 526
Corneille, E., Gen. Mgr.--Aer Lingus, Zurich, Switzerland; *Int'l*, pg. 28
Cornelis, H., Mng. Dir.--Toshiba Medical Systems NV/SA, Wijnegem, Belgium; *Int'l*, pg. 1407
Cornelison, Mike, Mng. Dir.--Forest View Psychiatric Hospital, Grand Rapids, MI; *U.S. Public*, pg. 1697
Cornelissen, Roger, Chief Exec. Officer--Alfa-Laval Agri N.V., Kortenberg, Belgium; *Int'l*, pg. 1379
Cornelius, Nigel, Dir.--Rolls-Royce Motor Cars Pacific Operations, Crewe, United Kingdom; *Int'l*, pg. 1467
Corneliussen, Arne, Mng. Dir.--Getinge Vaxjo A/S, Oslo, Norway; *Int'l*, pg. 552
Corneliussen, Leo, Chief Oper. Officer--Kvaerner Installasjon, Bergen Division, Sandsli, Norway; *Int'l*, pg. 769
Cornell, Alan D., Pres.--Korry Electronics Co., Seattle, WA; *U.S. Public*, pg. 594
Cornell, Larry, Mgr.-Plant--Star Building Systems, Monticello, IA; *U.S. Public*, pg. 1394
Cornell, William E., Pres.--Sea-3, Inc., Houston, Houston, TX; *U.S. Private*, pg. 1096
Cornella, Rick L., Pres.--Hevi-Duty Electric, Goldsboro, NC; *U.S. Public*, pg. 726
Cornet, A. G., Mng. Dir.--Electric Furnace Germany, GmbH, Kleve, Germany; *U.S. Private*, pg. 368
Cornett, Arlen C., Sr. V.P.--CR Minerals Corporation, Golden, CO; *U.S. Public*, pg. 302
Cornett, Ben, Pres.--Ademco Sensor Company, Louisville, KY; *U.S. Public*, pg. 1306
Cornett, Lee G., Dir.-Bus.--Mechanical Filter Products, Costa Mesa, CA; *U.S. Public*, pg. 1398
Cornick, James, Publr.--Successful Farming Magazine, Des Moines, IA; *U.S. Public*, pg. 1094
Cornick, Robert, Mng. Dir.--RAECO, Scoresby, Australia; *Int'l*, pg. 462
Corniglia, Renzo, Gen. Sls. Mgr. & Area Mgr.-Italy & Spain--Fasson Italia S.p.A., Varese, Italy; *U.S. Public*, pg. 154
Cornille, John, Pres.--Bracco Diagnostics, Inc., Princeton, NJ; *Int'l*, pg. 210
Cornish, Robin, Gen. Mgr.--Nokia Telecommunications Pty. Ltd., Melbourne, Australia; *Int'l*, pg. 954
Corno, Marco, Chief Oper. Officer--Candy Iberica S.A., Barcelona, Spain; *Int'l*, pg. 260
Cornog, R., Pres.--Broderick & Bascom Rope Co., Sedalia, MO; *U.S. Private*, pg. 68
Cornu, Jozef, Pres.--Alcatel Netherland, Hague, Netherlands; *Int'l*, pg. 55
Cornwall, Deborah, Mngng. Partner--Korn/Ferry Organizational Consulting, Boston, MA; *U.S. Private*, pg. 633
Cornwell, G. D., V.P. & Mgr.--Separation Systems Div., Denton, TX; *U.S. Public*, pg. 1269
Cornwell, Gary, Interim Div. Mgr.--Circuit Materials Division, Chandler, AZ; *U.S. Public*, pg. 1402
Cornwell, William, Pres.--Electroglas, Santa Clara, CA; *U.S. Public*, pg. 727
Cornwell, William J., Pres.--Electroglas, Inc., Santa Clara, CA; *U.S. Public*, pg. 727
Corona, Luis Rebollar, Chief Exec. Officer--Grupo Situr SA de CV, Guadalajara, Mexico; *Int'l*, pg. 576
Coronas, Jose, Mgr.--Kodak Bio-Products Division, Rochester, NY; *U.S. Public*, pg. 551
Corozza, Eugene J., Pres.--Certech, Inc., Wood Ridge, NJ; *U.S. Public*, pg. 307
Corp, William, Pres. & Chief Exec. Officer--Comstock Canada Ltd., Burlington, Canada; *U.S. Public*, pg. 572
Corporron, Randy J., Pres.--K-Tec Electronics, Sugar Land, TX; *U.S. Public*, pg. 951
Corradi, Adolfo, Gen. Mgr.--CPAC Italia, s.r.l./Chimifoto Ornano, Milan, Italy; *U.S. Public*, pg. 282
Corral, Jorge de, Gen. Mgr.--Grupo Agrogen S.A. de C.V., Mexico, Guadalajara, Mexico; *U.S. Public*, pg. 493
Correa, David, Dir.--Takenaka (U.K.) Ltd., Spain, Barcelona, Spain; *Int'l*, pg. 1352
Correa, Frank, Gen. Mgr.--Loctite Argentina, Buenos Aires, Argentina; *Int'l*, pg. 611
Correa, Jose G., Mgr.--Kodak Brasileira C.I.L., Porto Alegre, Brazil; *U.S. Public*, pg. 552
Correa, Jose Goncalves, Mgr.--Kodak Brasileira C.I.L., Rio de Janeiro, Brazil; *U.S. Public*, pg. 552
Correa, Wilson E., Gen. Mgr.--Home Products Inc., Guayaquil, Ecuador; *U.S. Public*, pg. 81
Correale, David, V.P. & Gen. Mgr.--Dentsply/Implant Division, Encino, CA; *U.S. Public*, pg. 499
Correll, Donald L., Chm. Bd. & Chief Exec. Officer--United Water Management & Services, Harrington Park, NJ; *U.S. Public*, pg. 1692
Corrigan-Davis, Mary Ann, Pres.--Summit Division, Cleveland, OH; *U.S. Public*, pg. 78
Corrigan, C. Rory, Exec. V.P. & Mgr.-N.Y. Sls. Mgr.--Jefferies & Company, Inc., Los Angeles, CA; *U.S. Public*, *pg. 925*
Corrigan, C. Rory, Mgr.--Jefferies & Company, Inc., New York, NY; *U.S. Public*, pg. 925
Corrigan, James H., V.P. & Gen. Mgr.--Falconbridge Dominicana, C. por A., Bonao, Dominican Republic; *Int'l*, *pg. 434*
Corrigan, Thomas J., Jr., Pres.--Corrigan Company Mechanical Contractors, Saint Louis, MO; *U.S. Private*, pg. 277
Corriveau, Alfred N., Pres.--Bombardier Real Estate Ltd., Montreal, Canada; *Int'l*, pg. 200
Corriveau, David O., Co-Chief Exec. Officer & Pres.--Dave & Buster's, Dallas, TX; *U.S. Public*, pg. 488
Corroon, James M., Chm. Bd.--Willis Corroon Corp. of Idaho, Boise, ID; *Int'l*, pg. 1506
Corry, Edward K., Pres. & Chief Oper. Officer--Southeastern Financial Services, Inc., Port Huron, MI; *U.S. Public*, pg. 1489
Corry, Martin G., Pres.--NationsBank Insurance Inc., Gaithersburg, MD; *U.S. Public*, pg. 1162
Corsentino, Charles J., Pres. & Chief Exec. Officer--Exhibitgroup/Giltspur, Roselle, IL; *U.S. Public*, pg. 1718
Corser, S.D., Chm.--North Whitfords Estates Pty. Ltd., Kallaroo, Australia; *Int'l*, pg. 1359
Corsie, Ian, Mng. Dir.--Pitkin Guides, Andover, United Kingdom; *Int'l*, pg. 1094
Corsiglia, Robert, Pres. & Chief Exec. officer--Hyre Electric Company of Indiana, Inc., Highland, IN; *U.S. Public*, pg. 572
Corso, Joseph D., Pres.--Birmingham Southeast, Cartersville, GA; *U.S. Public*, pg. 232

Corson, Robert, Pres.--Saline Investment Co., Saline, MI; *U.S. Private*, pg. 902
Cort, Fredric B., Reg. Pres.--Summit Bank, Bethlehem, PA; *U.S. Public*, pg. 1528
Cortazzi, William, Chief Exec. Officer--Dalgety Food Ingredients Ltd., London, United Kingdom; *Int'l*, pg. 376
Cortellini, Charles, Mgr.-Plant--Nestle Beverage Company, Suffolk, VA; *Int'l*, pg. 918
Cortes, Juan J., Reg. Dir.--Crown Cork Company (Spain) S.A., Madrid, Spain; *U.S. Public*, pg. 464
Cortez, Allen, Admin.--Hillhaven Healthcare, Phoenix, Phoenix, AZ; *U.S. Public*, pg. 1713
Cortez, Armando, Gen. Mgr.--Columbia Pictures of Argentina, Inc., Buenos Aires, Argentina; *Int'l*, pg. 1282
Cortez, Victor, Chief Oper. Officer--Tonka Corp., Juarez, Mexico; *U.S. Public*, pg. 798
Corti, Oscar, Pres.--Syremont S.p.A., Novara, Italy; *Int'l*, pg. 324
Cortilier, G., Mng. Dir.--S.A. Cockerill Mechanical Industries C.M.I., Seraing, Belgium; *Int'l*, pg. 301
Cortina, Cynthia, Bus. Mgr.--National Business Employment Weekly, Princeton, NJ; *U.S. Public*, pg. 524
Cortina, Fernando, Gen. Mgr.--Square D Company Centroamerica, S.A., San Jose, Costa Rica; *Int'l*, pg. 1209
Cortina, R. Martinez, Chm.--Banco NatWest Espana SA, Madrid, Spain; *Int'l*, pg. 911
Cortright, Lynn M., Pres.--Latin American Group, Cleveland, OH; *U.S. Public*, pg. 1262
Cortus, John W., Mng. Dir.--Nederman Inc., Westland, MI; *Int'l*, pg. 281
Corvi, Carolyn, V.P. & Gen. Mgr.--Propulsion Systems Division, Kent, WA; *U.S. Public*, pg. 240
Corvi, Lawrence, Pres. & Publr.--Oklahoma Press Publishing Co., Muskogee, OK; *U.S. Public*, pg. 701
Corvin, Joe, Pres.--CF & I Steel, L.P., Pueblo, CO; *U.S. Public*, pg. 1230
Corwin, Al, Pres.--Grohe America, Inc., Wood Dale, IL; *Int'l*, pg. 559
Corwin, Joe, Gen. Mgr.--Rich Products Corp., Buffalo, NY; *U.S. Private*, pg. 928
Corwin, W.C., Plant Mgr.--Precision Forming Facility, Sanford, NC; *Int'l*, pg. 535
Cory, Chappell, Gen. Mgr.--Computer Design & Applications Division, Peabody, MA; *U.S. Public*, pg. 109
Cory, Edward, Gen. Dir.--Steelcase Strafor (UK) Ltd., Poyle, United Kingdom; *Int'l*, pg. 569
Cory, Edward, Chief Exec. Officer--Steelcase-Strafor S.A., Strasbourg, France; *U.S. Private*, pg. 1038
Cory, J., Chief Oper. Officer--Instrumentos Bristol S.A., Mexico, Mexico; *Int'l*, pg. 473
Cos, J., Mgr.--Hosokawa Micron Espana S.A., Barcelona, Spain; *Int'l*, pg. 636
Cosetta, Michael, Asst. Landfill Mgr.--Browning-Ferris Industries of Oregon, Inc., Portland, OR; *U.S. Public*, pg. 264
Cosgrove, Dan, Pres.-Eyemark Media Sls.--CBS Enterprises Division, New York, NY; *U.S. Public*, pg. 274
Cosgrove, Jack D., Pres.--Avionics & Communications, Cedar Rapids, IA; *U.S. Public*, pg. 1397
Cosgrove, P., Mng. Dir.--Harvey Plant Limited, Bedworth, United Kingdom; *Int'l*, pg. 910
Cosgrove, T.A., Plant Mgr.--Alamance Facility, Mebane, NC; *Int'l*, pg. 535
Cosgrove, Timothy A., Div. Mgr.--Amcast Automotive-Wapakoneta Plant, Wapakoneta, OH; *U.S. Public*, pg. 63
Cosman, Les, Chm. Bd.--Genstar Development Company, San Diego, CA; *Int'l*, pg. 112
Cosner, J. L., Pres.--American Ingredients Company, Grandview, MO; *Int'l*, pg. 244
Cosner, J.L., Pres.--American Ingredients Company, Kansas City, KS; *Int'l*, pg. 244
Coss, Lawrence M., Chief Oper. Officer--Green Tree Agency of Nevada, Inc., Saint Paul, MN; *U.S. Public*, pg. 763
Cosse, M., Chief Oper. Officer--Elf Gabon, Port Gentil, Gabon; *Int'l*, pg. 446
Cosslett, Andrew, Pres.--Cottee's Foods, Liverpool, Australia; *Int'l*, pg. 248
Costa, Carlos, Chief Oper. Officer--BNP Factor - Portugal, Porto, Portugal; *Int'l*, pg. 163
Costa, Elizabeth Hargreaves, Rep.--Standard Chartered Bank (Brazil), Rio de Janeiro, Brazil; *Int'l*, pg. 1295
Costa, Giorgio, Chm. Bd.--Caboto Gestioni Sim S.p.A., Milan, Italy; *Int'l*, pg. 138
Costa, Gustavo, Gen. Mgr.--Boston Inversiones Servicios Y Administracion Ltda., Santiago, Chile; *U.S. Public*, pg. 185
Costa, Harry, Pres.--United Parking Services, Inc., Toronto, Canada; *U.S. Public*, pg. 326
Costa, Joe, Mgr.-Natl. Sls.--Sensormatic New Zealand Ltd., Auckland, New Zealand; *U.S. Public*, pg. 1458
Costa, Jose Maria, Pres.--J.M.C./Young & Rubicam, Caracas, Venezuela; *U.S. Private*, pg. 1200
Costa, M.B., Gen. Mgr.--CHEMCENTRAL/Minnesota, Lakeville, MN; *U.S. Private*, pg. 232
Costa, Michael A., Pres.--Kaufman and Broad Multi-Housing Group, Long Beach, CA; *U.S. Public*, pg. 945
Costa, Paulo, Pres. & Chief Oper. Officer--Janssen Pharmaceutica, Inc., Titusville, NJ; *U.S. Public*, pg. 928
Costanzo, Frank, Mng. Dir.--Avery Etichette Italia S.p.A., Milan, Italy; *U.S. Public*, pg. 153
Costas, Jose, Pres.--Volvo Vehiculos Industriales Espana, S.A., Madrid, Spain; *Int'l*, pg. 1478
Costello, Jim, Pres.--Oklahoma City Div., Oklahoma City, OK; *U.S. Public*, pg. 652
Costello, Jonathan, Treas.--Safeguard International Group, Wayne, PA; *U.S. Public*, pg. 1424
Costello, Peter, Gen. Mgr.--Akron Brass Company, Wooster, OH; *Int'l*, pg. 1068
Costello, Philip, Gen. Mgr.--Plunt Acrow Ltd., Slough, United Kingdom; *Int'l*, pg. 88
Coster, Peter, Pres.--Mercer Consulting Group, Inc., New York, NY; *U.S. Public*, pg. 1049
Coster, Peter, Chm. Bd.--Mercer Management Consulting, Inc., New York, NY; *U.S. Public*, pg. 1049
Costley, Greg, Pres.--Dole Citrus & Dole Deciduous, Bakersfield, CA; *U.S. Public*, pg. 515
Cota, Richard, Chief Oper. Officer--Continental Industries Inc., Tulsa, OK; *U.S. Public*, pg. 780
Cotanda, Jose Maria Carballo, Mng. Dir.--Banco Santander de Negocios, Madrid, Spain; *Int'l*, pg. 143
Cotaya, Steve, Gen. Mgr.--Snavely Forest Products, Inc., Chandler, AZ; *U.S. Private*, pg. 1010
Cote, Benoit, Plant Mgr.-Shawinigan--Bandag Canada, Ltd., Shawinigan, Canada; *U.S. Public*, pg. 178
Cote, David M., Pres. & Chief Exec. Officer--G.E. Appliances, Louisville, KY; *U.S. Public*, pg. 710
Cote, Gilles, Mill Mgr.--Scierie Parent Inc., Trois Rivieres, Canada; *Int'l*, pg. 761
Cote, Louis, Exec. V.P.--Cossette Communication-Marketing (Quebec) Inc., Quebec, Canada; *Int'l*, pg. 336
Cotler, Maynard L., V.P. & Gen. Mgr.--Pierce-All Div., Jamestown, NY; *U.S. Private*, pg. 889
Cotner, Donald, Div. Mgr.--Atlantic Homes Div., Central City, NE; *U.S. Public*, pg. 332
Cotran, Ralph, Sr. V.P.--Willis Corroon International/ Americas, Glendale, CA; *Int'l*, pg. 1507
Cotrel, Yves Paul, Dr., Chm. Bd.--Sofamor, S.N.C., Rang-du-Fliers, France; *U.S. Public*, pg. 1482
Cotter, Frank, Mgr.--General Employment Enterprises, Inc., Austin, TX; *U.S. Public*, pg. 715
Cotter, Stephen, Dir.--Laura Ashley Ltd., Maidenhead, United Kingdom; *Int'l*, pg. 804
Cotter, Stephen, Pres.--Laura Ashley Shops Ltd., Calgary, Canada; *Int'l*, pg. 804
Cotter, William E., Jr., Pres.--National Mines Corp., Lexington, KY; *Int'l*, pg. 903
Cotter, William R., Investment Dir.--IBI Investment Services Limited, Dublin, Ireland; *Int'l*, pg. 152
Cotter, William R., Chief Exec. Officer--Bank of Ireland Asset Management Limited, Dublin, Ireland; *Int'l*, pg. 152
Cotterill, D., Pres.--Senior Conflow Inc., Washington, PA; *Int'l*, pg. 1222
Cotterill, W.E., Chief Oper. Officer--Babcock Engineering Contractors (Pty) Ltd., Johannesburg, South Africa; *Int'l*, pg. 474
Cottle, William H., V.P.-International--Dictaphone Co. U.K. Ltd., Royal Leamington Spa, United Kingdom; *U.S. Private*, pg. 1045
Cotton, Eliane, Mgr.--Standard & Poor's International S.A., Brussels, Belgium; *U.S. Public*, pg. 1072
Cotton, M.W., Pres. & Chief Oper. Officer--Bergen Brunswig Medical Corporation, Montgomery, AL; *U.S. Public*, pg. 214
Cotton, Michelle, V.P.-Mid Atlantic Region--BSA Advertising, Inc., Philadelphia, PA; *U.S. Private*, pg. 108
Cotton, Michelle, V.P.-Mid Atlantic Region--BSA Advertising, Inc., Vienna, VA; *U.S. Private*, pg. 108
Cottrell, Christopher, Chief Exec. Officer--Fleming Fund Management (Luxembourg) S.A., Howald, Luxembourg; *Int'l*, pg. 493
Cottrell, James L., Chm. Bd.--Cape Coral National Bank, Cape Coral, FL; *U.S. Public*, pg. 607
Cottrell, Monty, V.P. & Gen. Mgr.--Allergan Australia (Pty.) Ltd., Artarmon, Australia; *U.S. Public*, pg. 46
Couch, Jerry, Gen. Mgr.--Containerboard & Paper Div.-Uncasville Mill, Uncasville, CT; *U.S. Public*, pg. 1520
Couch, John C., Chm. Bd. & Pres.--A & B-Hawaii, Inc., Honolulu, HI; *U.S. Public*, pg. 39
Couch, John C., Chm. Bd.--California & Hawaiian Sugar Company Inc., Crockett, CA; *U.S. Public*, pg. 39
Couch, Ken, Pres.--Smith Wholesale Drug Div., Spartanburg, SC; *U.S. Private*, pg. 1008
Couchman, Richard, Mng. Dir.--VTEL Europe, Ltd., Reading, United Kingdom; *U.S. Public*, pg. 1703
Coughlan, Bill, Chief Oper. Officer--Stewart Warner Corp. of Canada, Ltd., Belleville, Canada; *Int'l*, pg. 127
Coughlan, Frank, Mng. Dir.--Shell of Castle Donington, Derby, United Kingdom; *Int'l*, pg. 1139
Coughlin, Christopher J., Pres.--Nabisco International Incorporated, New York, NY; *U.S. Public*, pg. 1355
Coughlin, Jim, Mgr.-Plant--Sugar Creek Packing Co., Dayton, OH; *U.S. Private*, pg. 1049
Coughlin, Michael, Pres. & Chief Oper. Officer--Brooks Beverage Management, Inc., Columbus, OH; *U.S. Private*, pg. 142
Cougill, Dan, Pres. & Chief Oper. Officer--Riddell Sports, Inc., Chicago, IL; *U.S. Public*, pg. 1389
Couillard, Yves, Mng. Dir.--Packinox, Paris, France; *Int'l*, pg. 503
Couk, Marty D., Sr. V.P.-Pizza Hut Opers.--Pizza Hut Division, Pittsburg, KS; *U.S. Public*, pg. 1147
Couldwell, Paul D., Div. Mgr.--Thermal Processing Group Ltd. (Coventry), Exhall, United Kingdom; *Int'l*, pg. 1338
Coulibaly, T., Dir. Gen.--Societe Generale de Banques en Cote D'Ivoire, Abidjan, Cote d'Ivoire; *Int'l*, pg. 548
Couling, Gary, Pres.--E.R. Probyn Export Ltd., New Westminster, Canada; *Int'l*, pg. 1071
Coulombe, Cecile J., Pres.--Lawrence & Company, Lewiston, ME; *U.S. Private*, pg. 1173
Coulombe, Cecile J., Pres.--Maine Bottlers, Lewiston, ME; *U.S. Private*, pg. 1173
Coulombe, Raymond R., Pres.--Nuyens Liquor Importing, Inc., Syosset, NY; *U.S. Private*, pg. 1173
Coulson, M., District Mgr.--A.M. Castle & Co., Stockton, CA; *U.S. Public*, pg. 313
Coultas, Jeffrey B., Pres. & Chief Exec. Officer--Elliott State Bank, Jacksonville, IL; *U.S. Public*, pg. 643
Coultas, William H., Pres.--Old Kent Bank-Lansing, Lansing, MI; *U.S. Public*, pg. 1216
Coulter, David A., Pres. & Chief Exec. Officer--Bank of America California, San Francisco, CA; *U.S. Public*, pg. 180
Coulter, Glenn, Gen. Mgr.--Chase & Sons Division, Randolph, MA; *U.S. Public*, pg. 337
Coulter, John A. F. H., V.P. & Mng. Dir.--Tonka Europe, Limited, Henley-on-Thames, United Kingdom; *U.S. Public*, pg. 798
Coulthard, K., Representative--THORN EMI South Africa (Pty.) Limited, South Hills, South Africa; *Int'l*, pg. 428
Coulthard, Lee E., Pres.--Fort James Western Transportation, Portland, OR; *U.S. Public*, pg. 672
Counts, Randy, Div. Mgr.--ConAgra Turkey Company, Carthage, MO; *U.S. Public*, pg. 427
Coupe, C., Pres.--Haden Engineering Pty, Rosebery, Australia; *Int'l*, pg. 586
Couperthwaite, Larry, Pres.--Atlet, Inc., Schaumburg, IL; *Int'l*, pg. 97
Coupland, Gary, Mgr.-Opers.--Titan Wheel Corporation Of Ohio, Warren, OH; *U.S. Public*, pg. 1619
Coupland, Warren, Chm. Bd. & Chief Exec. Officer--GAB Robins North America, Inc., Parsippany, NJ; *Int'l*, pg. 1153
Courbon, Guy, Mng. Dir.--Bertrand Faure Sitztechnik GmbH & Co. KG, Stadthagen, Germany; *Int'l*, pg. 193
Couric, Charles, Pres.--Brita (USA), Inc., Oakland, CA; *U.S. Public*, pg. 387
Cournoyer, Rene, V.P. & Gen. Mgr.--Cott Corporatoin - North East Region (Quebec), Pointe-Claire, Canada; *Int'l*, pg. 337
Course, R.E., Gen. Mgr.--Algemene Bank Nederland, Manchester, United Kingdom; *Int'l*, pg. 11
Courson, Dennis, Plant Mgr.--Astor Products, Jacksonville, FL; *U.S. Public*, pg. 1772
Court, R.P., Pres.--Torcad Limited, Toronto, Canada; *Int'l*, pg. 1299
Courtemanche, Jack, Pres.--Country Coach, Inc., Junction City, OR; *U.S. Public*, pg. 1159
Courtemanche, Lee, Chief Oper. Officer--Ahlstrom Process Equipment Inc., Roswell, GA; *Int'l*, pg. 34
Courtiere, Jean, Mng. Dir.--Givenchy S.A., Paris, France; *Int'l*, pg. 780
Courtin, Gerard, Gen. Mgr.--Gunnebo Entrance Control SARL, Charenton-le-pont, France; *Int'l*, pg. 578
Courtney, Brian, Pres.--Oracle Corporation Canada, Mississauga, Canada; *U.S. Public*, pg. 1228
Courtney, M.; Chief Oper. Officer--Scholl Deutchland GmbH, Maintal, Germany; *Int'l*, pg. 1209
Coury, Bruce, V.P. & Publisher--Edwardsville Intelligencer, Edwardsville, IL; *U.S. Private*, pg. 517
Cousens, Rod, Chief Oper. Officer--Acclaim Entertainment, Ltd, London, United Kingdom; *U.S. Public*, pg. 15
Cousins, Dean, Pres.--Ferraz Corporation, Parsippany, NJ; *Int'l*, pg. 1028
Cousins, John F., Mng. Dir.--Deep Sea Seals Ltd., Havant, United Kingdom; *Int'l*, pg. 1339
Cousins, John F., Mng. Dir.--John Cranes Marine International, Havant, United Kingdom; *Int'l*, pg. 1339
Cousins, P.J., Dir.--AER Turas Teo, Dublin, Ireland; *Int'l*, pg. 28
Cousins, R.W., Pres.--Tenneco Aviation Limited, London, United Kingdom; *U.S. Public*, pg. 1580
Coutanceau, C., Mgr.--Eau et Feu, Reims, France; *Int'l*, pg. 1500
Coutancen, C., Mgr.--Societe des Etablissements Schiffers, Vernouillet, France; *Int'l*, pg. 1500
Couto, J., Mng. Dir.--De La Rue Systems Limited, Lisbon, Portugal; *Int'l*, pg. 387
Coutts, George, Gen. Mgr.--Weatherford Saudia Arabia Ltd., Al-Krabiyah, Saudi Arabia; *U.S. Public*, pg. 1750
Coutu, Michel, Pres.--The Jean Coutu (PJC) USA Inc., Warwick, RI; *Int'l*, pg. 340
Couture, George, Mgr.-Station--WDIO-TV, Duluth, MN; *U.S. Private*, pg. 544
Coutureau, Henri, Chief Oper. Officer--Bran & Luebbe S.a.r.l., Evron, France; *Int'l*, pg. 1380
Couzens, T. J., Gen. Mgr.--J & J Snack Foods Corp., Scranton, PA; *U.S. Public*, pg. 916
Covalt, Robert B., Pres.--Morton International Inc., Chicago, IL; *U.S. Public*, pg. 1135
Covalt, Robert R., Pres.--Specialty Chemicals Group, Chicago, IL; *U.S. Public*, pg. 1134
Covarrubias, Carlos Levy, Pres.--Acciones y Valores de Mexico, S.A. de C.V., Mexico, Mexico; *Int'l*, pg. 574
Cover, Thomas, Pres.--Mercantile Bank of Council Bluffs, Council Bluffs, IA; *U.S. Public*, pg. 1088
Coverdale, Maurice, Mgr.--Anixter Darlington, Darlington, United Kingdom; *U.S. Public*, pg. 115
Covert, Frank, Pres.--Broad, Vogt & Conant S.W., Inc., Bryant, AR; *U.S. Private*, pg. 170
Covert, Tom, Exec. V.P.--Vulcan Asphalt Refining Company, Cordova, AL; *U.S. Private*, pg. 915
Covette, Daniel, Country Sls. Mgr.--Trinova S.A.-Aeroquip Div., Chambery, France; *U.S. Public*, pg. 25
Covey, Harold D., Exec. V.P., Treas. & Chief Admin. Officer--State Farm Fire and Casualty Co., Bloomington, IL; *U.S. Private*, pg. 1036
Covey, Harold D., Exec. V.P., Treas. & Chief Admin. Officer--State Farm General Insurance Co., Bloomington, IL; *U.S. Private*, pg. 1036
Covey, Harold D., V.P. & Chief Admin. Officer--State Farm Lloyds, Inc., Dallas, TX; *U.S. Private*, pg. 1036
Coviello, Peter P., Branch Mgr.--Union-Transport Corporation-Philadelphia Office, Folcroft, PA; *U.S. Private*, pg. 1120
Covitz, Harvey, Plant Mgr.--AM General Corporation, Indianapolis, IN; *U.S. Private*, pg. 922
Cowan, Andrew, Mng. Dir.--SAIC UK Limited, Cambridge, United Kingdom; *U.S. Private*, pg. 976
Cowan, Brian C., Pres.--Chr. Hansen (UK) Ltd., Reading, United Kingdom; *Int'l*, pg. 289
Cowan, J.A., Pres.--Cable Tech Company Limited, Stouffville, Canada; *Int'l*, pg. 955
Cowan, Mike, Chm.--BOCM Silcock Ltd., Basingstoke, United Kingdom; *Int'l*, pg. 1434
Cowan, Ron, V.P. & Gen. Mgr.--Contadina Fresh, Glendale, CA; *Int'l*, pg. 918
Coward, Ray, Gen. Mgr.--S.I. De Mexico S.A. de C.V., Sonora, Mexico; *U.S. Public*, pg. 1507

Cowgill, F. Brooks, Pres.--New England Life Mortgage Funding Corp., Boston, MA; *U.S. Private*, pg. 738
Cowgill, F. Brooks, Pres.--TNE Funding Corporation, Boston, MA; *U.S. Private*, pg. 738
Cowles, Donald T., V.P. & Gen. Mgr.--Reynolds Aluminum Supply Co. Div., Richmond, VA; *U.S. Public*, pg. 1386
Cowles, Jim, V.P.-Life & Health & Dir.-Sls.--Willis Corroon Corporation of Louisville, Louisville, KY; *Int'l*, pg. 1505
Cowley, Christopher, Gen. Mgr.--Circle Freight International USA, Indianapolis, IN; *U.S. Public*, pg. 371
Cowley, Kenneth Edward, Chief Oper. Officer--News Limited Of Australia, Sydney, Australia; *Int'l*, pg. 925
Cowling, J.C., Mgr.-Mktg.--Casio Electronics Co., Ltd., London, United Kingdom; *Int'l*, pg. 274
Cowling, John, Dir.Sls.--Arthur Sanderson and Sons Ltd., Uxbridge, United Kingdom; *Int'l*, pg. 540
Cox, A. Paul, Jr., V.P. & Gen. Mgr.--Business Equipment and Systems Division, Dayton, OH; *U.S. Public*, pg. 1505
Cox, Barrie R., Pres.--ADM Food Additives Division, Decatur, IL; *U.S. Public*, pg. 127
Cox, D.C., Mng. Dir.--E.J. Cook SCD Partnership, London, United Kingdom; *Int'l*, pg. 336
Cox, D.G., Mng. Dir.--Babcock Energy Limited, Crawley, United Kingdom; *Int'l*, pg. 130
Cox, Daniel T., Chm. & Chief Exec. Officer--Godwins, Booke & Dickenson, Inc., Chicago, IL; *U.S. Public*, pg. 117
Cox, David M., Mng. Dir.--SHL Clarion Education, Finchampstead, United Kingdom; *Int'l*, pg. 1154
Cox, Dotty, V.P.-Casino Mktg.--Princess Casinos Inc., Miami, FL; *Int'l*, pg. 818
Cox, J. David, Pres.--Harris Trust Bank of Arizona, Scottsdale, AZ; *Int'l*, pg. 155
Cox, J. Robert, V.P. & G.M.--Cambridge-Lee Canada Ltd., Milton, Canada; *U.S. Private*, pg. 202
Cox, J.E., Mgr.--International Matex Tank Terminals, Bayonne, Bayonne, NJ; *Int'l*, pg. 758
Cox, J.E., Chm. Bd.--Taylor Woodrow-Towell Co. (LLC), Ruwi, Oman; *Int'l*, pg. 1360
Cox, Jim, Chief Oper. Officer--Knox Allright, Inc., Knoxville, TN; *U.S. Private*, pg. 43
Cox, John, Mng. Dir.--Scholastic Publications Ltd., Leamington Spa, United Kingdom; *U.S. Public*, pg. 1441
Cox, Keith, Admin.--Charter Hospital of Mobile, Inc., Mobile, AL; *U.S. Public*, pg. 1034
Cox, M.N., Fin. Dir.--Acco-Rexel Group Services PLC, West Drayton, United Kingdom; *U.S. Public*, pg. 674
Cox, Michele, Pres.--National Institute of Business Management, Inc., Mc Lean, VA; *U.S. Private*, pg. 785
Cox, Neil, Pres.--Ameritech Information Systems Inc., Chicago, IL; *U.S. Public*, pg. 98
Cox, Ralph, Pres. & Gen. Mgr.--Primark Tool Group, Louisville, KY; *U.S. Public*, pg. 575
Cox, Richard, V.P.-CIS Opers.--Weatherford U.S., Inc., Houston, TX; *U.S. Public*, pg. 1749
Cox, Robert G., Pres.--Summit Bank, Chatham, NJ; *U.S. Public*, pg. 1528
Cox, Ron, Pres. & Chief Exec. Officer--Learning International, Stamford, CT; *U.S. Public*, pg. 1617
Cox, Ron, Chief Exec. Officer-Times Mirror Training Grp.--Zenger-Miller, San Jose, CA; *U.S. Public*, pg. 1617
Cox, Rosie, Mng. Dir.--DYWIDAG Systems International, USA, Inc., Marietta, GA; *Int'l*, pg. 424
Cox, Sharon, Reservations Supvr.--Utell International-South Africa, Cape Town, South Africa; *Int'l*, pg. 1099
Cox, Simon, Mng. Dir.--ISS Mediclean Ltd., Slough, United Kingdom; *Int'l*, pg. 657
Cox, Stan, Gen. Mgr.--General Microcircuits, Inc., Mooresville, NC; *U.S. Public*, pg. 1107
Cox, Steve, Gen. Mgr.--Castlegate Inc., Pittsburg, KS; *Int'l*, pg. 1067
Cox, Winston H., Chief Exec. Officer--Showtime/The Movie Channel Inc. (U.K.), New York, NY; *U.S. Private*, pg. 779
Coxe, Donald G.M., Pres. & Chief Investment Officer--Harris Investment Management, Inc., Chicago, IL; *Int'l*, pg. 154
Coyle, Thomas E., V.P. & Gen. Mgr.--Owens-Brockway Prescription Products, Toledo, OH; *U.S. Public*, pg. 1238
Coyne, David, Gen. Mgr.--Axelrod Foods, Inc., Paterson, NJ; *Int'l*, pg. 752
Coyne, Frank J., Pres. & Chief Oper. Officer--The Camden Fire Insurance Assn., Philadelphia, PA; *Int'l*, pg. 543
Coyne, Frank J., Pres. & Chief Oper. Officer--General Assurance Company, Melville, NY; *Int'l*, pg. 543
Coyne, Michael, Sls. Mgr.--WWF Paper Corporation - N.E., East Hartford, CT; *U.S. Private*, pg. 1145
Cozier, James, Plant Mgr.--Milwaukee Container Div., Milwaukee, WI; *U.S. Public*, pg. 1289
Cozzani, Gian Carlo, Pres. & Chief Exec. Officer--Vesuvius U.S.A., Champaign, IL; *Int'l*, pg. 329
Crabtree, Cleo, Plant Mgr.--Carl A. Lowe Industries, Inc., Lebanon, MO; *U.S. Private*, pg. 478
Crabtree, Cleo, Plant Mgr.--Sea Nymph Inc., Lebanon, MO; *U.S. Private*, pg. 478
Crabtree, Condy, V.P. & Gen. Mgr.--Custom Extrusions, Connersville, IN; *U.S. Private*, pg. 567
Crabtree, Debbie, Mgr.--Echo Bay Mining Company, Reno, NV; *U.S. Public*, pg. 562
Crabtree, Jim, Reg. Mgr.--Century Telephone Enterprises, Inc., Alexandria, LA; *U.S. Public*, pg. 329
Crabtree, John, Pres.--Wilson Seeds Inc., Harlan, IA; *U.S. Private*, pg. 646
Crabtree, Larry, Gen. Mgr.--U.S. Filter/Polymetrics, Milpitas, CA; *U.S. Public*, pg. 1682
Crabtree, Ron, Gen. Mgr.--Livonia-Rubber & Plastics Div., Livonia, MI; *U.S. Public*, pg. 1176
Crack, Brian, Mng. Dir.--SICO Europe Limited, Ashford, United Kingdom; *U.S. Private*, pg. 997
Cracraft, Roger P., Asst. Branch Mgr.--Piper Jaffray Inc., Boulder, CO; *U.S. Public*, pg. 1302
Craddock, Barry F., V.P. & Gen. Mgr.--United Media Canada, Mississauga, Canada; *U.S. Public*, pg. 1448
Craddock, Michael, Gen. Mgr.--Advanced Polymers Division, Seattle, WA; *U.S. Public*, pg. 689
Craddock, Michael, Gen. Mgr.--Advanced Polymers Division - Kent Facility, Kent, WA; *U.S. Public*, pg. 689
Craddock, Roger, Pres.--CH & A Corporation, Kingwood, TX; *Int'l*, pg. 1153
Craddock, Steven L., Pres.--Tucson Div., Tucson, AZ; *U.S. Public*, pg. 1683
Craft, James, Pres. & Chief Oper. Officer--R.R. Donnelley, Limited-York, York, United Kingdom; *U.S. Public*, pg. 519
Craft, James, Mfg. Dir.--R.R. Donnelley U.K.-Gateshead Division, Gateshead, United Kingdom; *U.S. Public*, pg. 519
Craft, Joseph W. III, Pres.--Mapco Coal Inc., Tulsa, OK; *U.S. Public*, pg. 1042
Craft, Michael, Pres., Publr. & Editor--Jackson Sun, Inc., Jackson, TN; *U.S. Public*, pg. 701
Crager, Bruce L., Sr. V.P.--Oceaneering Production Systems, Houston, TX; *U.S. Public*, pg. 1211
Crahan, P.M., V.P. & Gen. Mgr.--Flexsteel Division, Dubuque, IA; *U.S. Public*, pg. 654
Craide, Carlos, Reg. Mgr.--Banco De Boston, Sao Paulo, Brazil; *U.S. Public*, pg. 184
Craig, Derek, Co-Creative Dir.--Leo Burnett/Connaghan & May (VIC.) Pty. Ltd., Melbourne, Australia; *U.S. Private*, pg. 185
Craig, Donald W., Pres. & Gen. Mgr.--Media General Cable of Fredericksburg, Inc., Fredericksburg, VA; *U.S. Public*, pg. 1078
Craig, Duncan, Mng. Dir.--Logica B.V., Rotterdam, Netherlands; *Int'l*, pg. 814
Craig, George, Pres. & Chief Exec. Officer--HarperCollins Publishers, New York, NY; *Int'l*, pg. 926
Craig, Jim, Chief Oper. Officer & V.P.--United States Name Plate, Philadelphia, PA; *U.S. Private*, pg. 640
Craig, John, Pres. & V.P.-Adams U.S.A.--Adams U.S.A., Morris Plains, NJ; *U.S. Public*, pg. 1739
Craig, Kim, Pres.--Laurel Trust Company, Johnstown, PA; *U.S. Public*, pg. 164
Craig, Nevin J., Pres.--Delta International Machinery Corp., Pittsburgh, PA; *U.S. Public*, pg. 1273
Craig, Ron, Plant Mgr.--Hydro Conduit Corp., Medley, FL; *Int'l*, pg. 246
Craig, Steve, Gen. Mgr.--Enercom Inc., Halifax, Canada; *Int'l*, pg. 971
Craighead, Dan, Pres.--Snap-on Tools International, Ltd., Kenosha, WI; *U.S. Public*, pg. 1481
Craigie, Cheryl, V.P. & Gen. Mgr.--WDTN Div., Dayton, OH; *U.S. Private*, pg. 516
Craigie, Cheryl A., V.P. & Gen. Mgr.--WDTN-TV, Dayton, OH; *U.S. Private*, pg. 516
Crain, C. William, Pres. & Chief Oper. Officer--London Fog Industries, Inc., New York, NY; *U.S. Private*, pg. 673
Crain, Keith E., Publisher--Crain's Detroit Business, Detroit, MI; *U.S. Private*, pg. 285
Crain, Rance, Pres. & Editor-in-Chief--Advertising Age, Chicago, IL; *U.S. Private*, pg. 284
Crain, Roy, Pilot--Business Air, Grosse Ile, MI; *U.S. Private*, pg. 539
Cram, Scott W., Pres.--CRSS Constructors, Inc., Denver, CO; *U.S. Public*, pg. 922
Cramer, Larry, Pres. & Chief Exec. Officer--Laser Diode Products, New Brunswick, NJ; *Int'l*, pg. 892
Cramme, Klaus-Peter, Chief Oper. Officer--Suddeutsche Brennstoffhandelsgesellschaft mbH, Mannheim, Germany; *Int'l*, pg. 1167
Cramoy, David, Gen. Mgr.--North Castle Direct, Stamford, CT; *U.S. Private*, pg. 804
Cramp, Colin, Gen. Mgr.--Rohr Industries, Riverside Plant, Riverside, CA; *U.S. Public*, pg. 752
Cramphorn, Alan, Mng. Dir.--TI Reynolds Rings Limited, Birmingham, United Kingdom; *Int'l*, pg. 1338
Crampton, B.A., Chief Oper. Officer--Stahl Div., Wooster, OH; *U.S. Public*, pg. 218
Crandell, Charles, Warden--Central Arizona Detention Center, Florence, AZ; *U.S. Public*, pg. 450
Crandell, D.R., Gen. Mgr.--Detrex Industrial Chemical Specialties Div., Redford, MI; *U.S. Public*, pg. 502
Crandell, D.R., Div. Pres.--Solvents & Environmental Services Div., Southfield, MI; *U.S. Public*, pg. 502
Crane, E.A., Chm. Bd.--California Reconveyance Co., Chatsworth, CA; *U.S. Public*, pg. 1741
Crane, Eileen, V.P.--Domaine Carneros, Napa, CA; *Int'l*, pg. 1348
Crane, K., Mng. Dir.--Senior Hargreaves Limited, Bury, United Kingdom; *Int'l*, pg. 1221
Crane, Lawrence L., Jr., Pres.--Piggly Wiggly Co., Memphis, TN; *U.S. Public*, pg. 653
Crane, Ralph, Pres.--John H. Harland Co. of Puerto Rico, San Juan, PR; *U.S. Public*, pg. 786
Crane, Ralph, Mng. Dir.--Preformed Line Products Canada, Cambridge, Canada; *U.S. Public*, pg. 1321
Cranstone, Peter, Mng. Dir.--Inamed Ltd., Wokingham, United Kingdom; *U.S. Public*, pg. 874
Crapper, Andy, V.P. & Gen. Mgr.--Mayfield Swain/Keller, Keller, TX; *U.S. Private*, pg. 686
Craspay, Gilbert, Chief Oper. Officer--T-Fal de Mexico S.A. de C.V., Mexico, Mexico; *Int'l*, pg. 568
Crassaris, Leonidas, Mng. Dir.--Rhone-Poulenc Hellas, Athens, Greece; *Int'l*, pg. 1113
Crassaris, Leonidas, Mng. Dir.--Rhone-Poulenc Rorer A.E.B.E., Athens, Greece; *Int'l*, pg. 1113
Craven, John, Chm.--Phoenix Securities Limited, London, United Kingdom; *Int'l*, pg. 405
Craven, Patrick, Sr. V.P.-Opers. & Branch Mgr.--W & D Securities, Inc., Jersey City, NJ; *U.S. Public*, pg. 925
Craven, Rex, V.P. & Gen. Mgr.--Quadrangle Management Company, Washington, DC; *U.S. Private*, pg. 898
Cravens, John E., Pres. & Gen. Mgr.--WPLT-FM, Detroit, MI; *U.S. Public*, pg. 512
Crawford, Albert Lee, Sole Administrator--Alambrados y Circuitos Electricos, S.A. De C.V., Mexico, Mexico; *U.S. Public*, pg. 721
Crawford, Bob, Gen. Mgr.--Church & Dwight Co., Inc. Ltd., Toronto, Canada; *U.S. Public*, pg. 356
Crawford, Brook, Pres.--Hilb, Rogal and Hamilton Company of Dallas, Dallas, TX; *U.S. Public*, pg. 827
Crawford, Curt J., Pres.--Lucent Technologies, Microelectronics Div., Berkeley Heights, NJ; *U.S. Public*, pg. 1017
Crawford, Dan, Chief Oper. Officer-Avantel S.A.--MCI Communications Corp., Atlanta, GA; *U.S. Public*, pg. 1023
Crawford, E.H., Chm. Bd.--Canada Life Assurance Company of Great Britain Limited, Potters Bar, United Kingdom; *Int'l*, pg. 255
Crawford, J. Dickson, Pres. & Chief Exec. Officer--Maritime Life Assurance Co., Halifax, Canada; *U.S. Private*, pg. 590
Crawford, James W., Pres.--Continental Dynamics, Inc., Herndon, VA; *U.S. Public*, pg. 110
Crawford, Kathy, Pres.-Western Direct--Western Direct, Phoenix, AZ; *U.S. Private*, pg. 1166
Crawford, Kathy, Sr. V.P. & Mng. Dir.--Western International Media Corporation, Phoenix, AZ; *U.S. Private*, pg. 1167
Crawford, Les, Pres.--Wellcraft Marine Corp., Sarasota, FL; *U.S. Private*, pg. 447
Crawford, Michael, Pres.--GTE Data Services Incorporated, Temple Terrace, FL; *U.S. Public*, pg. 696
Crawford, Paul, III, Pres. & Chief Exec. Officer--Interstate Billing Service, Inc., Decatur, AL; *U.S. Public*, pg. 1373
Crawford, Peter, Mng. Dir.--Willis Corroon North Limited, Sheffield, United Kingdom; *Int'l*, pg. 1503
Crawford, Randy, Pres.--Crawford & Crawford, Inc., Adair, IA; *U.S. Private*, pg. 16
Crawford, Robert P., Jr., Pres.--Chubb & Son, Inc., Warren, NJ; *U.S. Public*, pg. 355
Crawford, Russ, Plant Mgr.--Crescent/Xcelite, Sumter, SC; *U.S. Public*, pg. 444
Crawford, Tom, Pres.--Prudential Property & Casualty Insurance Company, Holmdel, NJ; *U.S. Private*, pg. 892
Crawford, Tom, Pres.--Prudential General Insurance Co., Holmdel, NJ; *U.S. Private*, pg. 892
Crawford, Tony, Mgr.--Frank Paxton Lumber Company, Fort Worth, TX; *U.S. Private*, pg. 585
Crawford, W.H., Jr., Mgr.--Tencarva Machinery Co., Columbia, SC; *U.S. Private*, pg. 1076
Crawford, William, Pres.--Steelcase Design Partnership, Kentwood, MI; *U.S. Private*, pg. 1038
Crawley, David, Deputy Gen. Mgr.--Young & Rubicam/Sovero, Moscow, Russia; *U.S. Private*, pg. 1199
Crawley, William H., V.P.-Asia--MTel International (Tokyo), Tokyo, Japan; *U.S. Public*, pg. 1120
Crawshaw, John, Area V.P.--Wattie's Limited, Parnell, New Zealand; *U.S. Public*, pg. 807
Crawshaw, John, Area V.P.--Heinz-Wattie's Australasia, Auckland, New Zealand; *U.S. Public*, pg. 807
Crean, A.J.B., Mng. Dir.--Pandoro Ltd., Fleetwood, United Kingdom; *Int'l*, pg. 1034
Crean, Timothy, Mng. Dir.--Sifco Turbine Components, Ltd., Cork, Ireland; *U.S. Public*, pg. 1471
Creber, Ernest B., Pres.--SAIC Canada, Ottawa, Canada; *U.S. Private*, pg. 976
Cree, Helen, Mng. Dir.--Shandwick Scotland Ltd., Glasgow, United Kingdom; *Int'l*, pg. 1226
Creech, Jack, Pres.--Color-Box, Inc., Richmond, IN; *U.S. Public*, pg. 347
Creed, Hilton, Gen Mgr.--Proctor-Silex, Mt. Airy Operations, Mount Airy, NC; *U.S. Public*, pg. 1149
Creed, Hilton, Gen Mgr.--Proctor-Silex, Southern Pines Operations, Southern Pines, NC; *U.S. Public*, pg. 1149
Creeden, Joseph M., Pres.--Intertrace Technology, Inc., Rancho Cucamonga, CA; *U.S. Public*, pg. 1101
Creel, Diane C., Chm. Bd., Pres. & Chief Exec. Officer--Earth Technology Corp. USA, Long Beach, CA; *U.S. Public*, pg. 1648
Creer, Bob, Mgr.-Sls.--Temco Fireplace Products, Inc. (Perris), San Bernardino, CA; *U.S. Public*, pg. 1576
Crees, Chris, Dir.-Sls.--Britannic Aviation Limited, Albourne, United Kingdom; *Int'l*, pg. 215
Creighton, P.R., V.P. & Gen. Mgr.--Turner Construction Co., Cleveland, OH; *U.S. Public*, pg. 1645
Cremer, Ernst, Sr. Mng. Dir.--Deutsche Bank AG (Bielefeld), Bielefeld, Germany; *Int'l*, pg. 402
Cremota, Ray, Gen. Mgr.--University Inn Associates, Salt Lake City, UT; *U.S. Public*, pg. 1537
Crepin, Philippe, Chief Exec. Officer--Axel Johnson Minerais & Metaux S.A.R.L., Paris, France; *Int'l*, pg. 711
Creson, Jerry, Country Mgr.--Autodesk AB, Goteborg, Sweden; *U.S. Public*, pg. 149
Crespel, Etienne, Chief Oper. Officer--Advanced Micro Devices (Overseas Corp.), Brussels, Belgium; *U.S. Public*, pg. 21
Crespi, Robert, Gen. Mgr.--Gillette South Africa Limited, Bedfordview, South Africa; *U.S. Public*, pg. 745
Crespin, Claude, Pres.--Generale de Banque Belge (France) SA, Paris, France; *Int'l*, pg. 548
Crespo-Setien, Adolfo, Pres.--Koipe S.A., San Sebastian, Spain; *Int'l*, pg. 324
Cress, George H., Chm. Bd., Pres. & Chief Exec. Officer--Society Bank, Michigan, Ann Arbor, MI; *U.S. Public*, pg. 954
Cresswell, J.C., Mng. Dir.--Everbright Fasteners Ltd., Gloucester, United Kingdom; *Int'l*, pg. 585
Cresswell, J.C., Mng. Dir.--Sandiacre Screw Ltd., Nottingham, United Kingdom; *Int'l*, pg. 585
Creten, Andre, Pres.--Mann & Hummel Hydromation N.V., Tongeren, Belgium; *Int'l*, pg. 484
Creten, Andre, Pres.--Hydromation France S.A.R.L., Paris, France; *Int'l*, pg. 484
Creveling, Robert, Dr., Pres.--Covance Inc., Indianapolis, IN; *U.S. Public*, pg. 454
Crew, Drummond, Pres.--Empire Candle, Inc., Kansas City, MO; *U.S. Private*, pg. 330
Crew, J. William, Mng. Dir.--Alcan Specialty Aerospace, Birmingham, United Kingdom; *Int'l*, pg. 51
Crew, J.G., Mng. Dir.--OCE Graphics (U.K.) Limited, Bristol, United Kingdom; *Int'l*, pg. 994

Crew, Walter, Plant Mgr.--Selkirk Metalbestos N.A., Nampa, ID; *U.S. Public*, pg. 1794
Crews, Art, V.P. & Gen. Mgr.--Gibson Container Division, Verona, MS; *U.S. Private*, pg. 1170
Crews, K.M., Mng. Dir.--Barclays Bank Finance Co. (Jersey) Ltd., Saint Helier, United Kingdom; *Int'l*, pg. 165
Crichfield, Douglas, Pres. & Chief Exec. Officer--Concord Savings Bank, Concord, NH; *U.S. Public*, pg. 278
Crichley, Keith, Pres. & Chief Exec. Officer--Printwest Communications Ltd., Regina, Canada; *Int'l*, pg. 1195
Crichton, Robert W., Pres. & Gen. Mgr.--The Morrill Press, Fulton, NY; *U.S. Public*, pg. 1486
Crider, Joe D., Chm. Bd. & Chief Exec. Officer--Metalcenter, Inc., Santa Fe Springs, CA; *U.S. Public*, pg. 1375
Criel, Eric, Mng. Dir.--Anixter Antwerp, Kontich, Belgium; *U.S. Public*, pg. 116
Crilly, John, Pres.--Ikon Office Solutions-Alabama, Birmingham, AL; *U.S. Public*, pg. 863
Crim, Jack C., Pres. & Chief Oper. Officer--Talley Industries, Inc., Phoenix, AZ; *U.S. Public*, pg. 307
Crim, Randy B., Pres.--Old Kent Bank of Petoskey, Petoskey, MI; *U.S. Public*, pg. 1217
Crim, Terence, Supvr.--Applied Industrial Technologies, Detroit, MI; *U.S. Public*, pg. 122
Crimmins, Alfred, Pres.--Dominion Textile International B.V., Zug, Switzerland; *Int'l*, pg. 415
Crimmins, Randy, Mgr.--Fogarty Klein & Partners Direct, Houston, TX; *U.S. Private*, pg. 416
Crimmins, Timothy P., Jr., Pres.--Bank of Western Massachusettes, Springfield, MA; *U.S. Public*, pg. 351
Cripe, Richard L., Treas. & Controller--Gohmann Asphalt & Construction of KY., Inc., Louisville, KY; *U.S. Private*, pg. 459
Crippen, Michael, Gen. Mgr.--Ceramic Tile International, Norcross, GA; *U.S. Private*, pg. 564
Criscolo, Charles, Pres.--Red Apple Companies Food Group, New York, NY; *U.S. Private*, pg. 915
Crisler, Bill, Sr. V.P. & Gen. Mgr.--Gould Paper Corporation, Dallas, TX; *U.S. Private*, pg. 467
Crisp, Bill, Gen. Mgr.--AAR Power Boss, Aberdeen, NC; *U.S. Public*, pg. 1
Crisp, David, Gen.-Mgr.--Bison Foods Company, Buffalo, NY; *U.S. Private*, pg. 1129
Crisp, Jimmy D., Pres.--SAIA Motor Freight Lines, Houma, LA; *U.S. Public*, pg. 1788
Crisp, M. Douglas, Pres.--Capitol Finance Group, Inc., Charlotte, NC; *U.S. Public*, pg. 640
Crispin, Janet, Mng. Dir.--Western Staff Services (U.K.) Ltd., Gloucester, United Kingdom; *U.S. Public*, pg. 1760
Cristini, Henri, V.P.-European Opers.--Compass Design Automation Inc., San Jose, CA; *U.S. Public*, pg. 1703
Cristofani, Enrique, Gen. Mgr.--Banco Santander Argentina, Buenos Aires, Argentina; *Int'l*, pg. 143
Cristofoli, Nino M., Sr. V.P.-Sls. & Mktg., Nestle Refigerated Food Co.--Nestle Frozen/Refrigerated Food Co., Solon, OH; *Int'l*, pg. 918
Cristovao, Joao Henrique de, Pres.--Banco de Montreal S.A., Rio de Janeiro, Brazil; *Int'l*, pg. 155
Criswell, R.J., Pres.--Amoco (U.K.) Exploration Company, London, United Kingdom; *U.S. Public*, pg. 102
Critchfield, Jack B., Chm. Bd.--Advanced Separation Technologies Incorporated, Lakeland, FL; *U.S. Public*, pg. 655
Critchlow, J.W., Div. Pres.--Winn-Dixie Raleigh, Inc., Raleigh, NC; *U.S. Public*, pg. 1771
Crivelli, Mario, Mng. Dir.--Ticino Societa d'Assicurazzioni Sula Vita, Breganzona, Switzerland; *U.S. Public*, pg. 85
Crivello, Frank, Gen. Mgr.--The Southland Corporation, Melville, NY; *Int'l*, pg. 694
Croasdale, Bill, V.P. & East Coast Mng. Dir.--Promotional Broadcast Services, New York, NY; *U.S. Private*, pg. 1166
Crocker, Charles, Chm. Bd.--BEI Sensors and Systems Company, Sylmar, CA; *U.S. Public*, pg. 160
Crocker, Douglas, II, Pres.--First Capital Financial Corp., Troy, MI; *U.S. Private*, pg. 473
Crocker, LeRoy, Gen. Mgr.--Corrugated Container Div.-Richmond Plant, Richmond, VA; *U.S. Public*, pg. 1520
Crocker, Mary Ann, Admin.--Guardian Care of Elizabeth City, Elizabeth City, NC; *U.S. Public*, pg. 1712
Crocker, Nicholas, Mng. Dir.--Rhone-Poulenc Polska, Varsovie, Poland; *Int'l*, pg. 1113
Croden, Peter, Pres.--Kenral Inc., Don Mills, Canada; *Int'l*, pg. 1049
Croden, Peter, Pres.--Pharmacia & Upjohn Company of Canada, Don Mills, Canada; *Int'l*, pg. 1049
Croe, Henri, Mng. Dir.--CINTA Compagnie Independante des Tabacs S.A., Brussels, Belgium; *Int'l*, pg. 1101
Croggon, Jeremy, Pres.--Omya, Inc., Proctor, VT; *Int'l*, pg. 1061
Croker, Rodney, Gen. Mgr.--Willis Corroon Hellas SA, Athens, Greece; *Int'l*, pg. 1509
Croker, Rodney, Gen. Mgr.--Willis Corroon Kendriki SA, Athens, Greece; *Int'l*, pg. 1509
Croland, Pierre, Chm. Bd.--Michelin Reifenwerke KGaA, Karlsruhe, Germany; *Int'l*, pg. 322
Crole, Peter V., Pres.--CIMatrix L.L.C., Canton, MA; *U.S. Public*, pg. 1395
Crolla, Tony, Mgr.-European Sls.--Ling Electronics Ltd., Suffolk, United Kingdom; *U.S. Public*, pg. 1077
Crombez, Jean-Luc, Mng. Dir.--Kvaerner Pulping SA, Saint Germain-en-Laye, France; *Int'l*, pg. 768
Crombez, Jean-Luc, Mng. Dir.--Kamyr S.A., Saint Germain-en-Laye, France; *Int'l*, pg. 771
Cromer, Richard F., Pres. & Chief Oper. Officer--Continental Energy Services, Inc., Butte, MT; *U.S. Public*, pg. 1127
Cromie, Bob, Plant Mgr.--American Natl. Can Co., Jacksonville, FL; *Int'l*, pg. 1029
Cromie, Scott J., Pres.--American Home Shield Corporation, Memphis, TN; *U.S. Public*, pg. 1461
Cromwell, James J., Chm. Bd.--Potomac Valley Bank, Gaithersburg, MD; *U.S. Public*, pg. 1089
Cromwell, Richard, Gen. Mgr.--Milgray/California, Inc., Thousand Oaks, CA; *U.S. Public*, pg. 206
Cronberg, Hakan, Chm. Reg. Bd.--ICA Handlarna Syd AB, Arlov, Sweden; *Int'l*, pg. 643
Crone, R.F., Gen. Mgr.--Tarmac Construction (Caribbean) Ltd., Couva, Trinidad & Tobago; *Int'l*, pg. 1355
Cronin, J.B., Mng. Dir.--GEC Alsthom N.V., Amsterdam, Netherlands; *Int'l*, pg. 56
Cronin, Thomas G., Chm. Bd.--First National Bank of Fort Myers, Fort Myers, FL; *U.S. Public*, pg. 608
Cronin, Timothy C., Pres.--Hilton Active Apparel, Lincolnwood, IL; *U.S. Public*, pg. 940
Cronk, David N., Pres.--Mercantile Bank of Clay County, Spencer, IA; *U.S. Public*, pg. 1088
Crook, Andy, Mgr.--EG & G Fiber Optics, Wokingham, United Kingdom; *U.S. Public*, pg. 544
Crook, Charles, Exec. V.P.--Ross Roy Communications Canada, Limited, Windsor, Canada; *U.S. Private*, pg. 946
Crook, David G., Mng. Dir.--Delta Circuit Protection & Controls Ltd., Birmingham, United Kingdom; *Int'l*, pg. 390
Crook, J., Gen. Mgr.--Moduline Industries, Inc., Chehalis, WA; *U.S. Public*, pg. 333
Crooke, Denzil, Mng. Dir.--Shell Antilles, Basseterre, Saint Kitts and Nevis; *Int'l*, pg. 1141
Croom, Judson H., Pres. & Chief Exec. Officer--CTX Mortgage Co., Inc., Dallas, TX; *U.S. Public*, pg. 323
Cropanese, Gerard, Gen. Mgr.--Lawson Products, Inc., Fairfield, NJ; *U.S. Public*, pg. 980
Cropper, Stephen L., Pres. & Chief Exec. Officer--Williams Pipe Line Co., Tulsa, OK; *U.S. Public*, pg. 1769
Crosby, Percy C., V.P.--Crown Cork de Argentina, S. A., Buenos Aires, Argentina; *U.S. Public*, pg. 464
Crosby, Ralph D., Jr., V.P.--Commercial Aircraft Division, Dallas, TX; *U.S. Public*, pg. 1198
Crosby, W.F., Mng. Dir.--Rentokil Pty. Ltd., Willoughby, Australia; *Int'l*, pg. 1286
Crosetto, Carl J., Pres.--Bowne International Inc., New York, NY; *U.S. Public*, pg. 248
Crosio, Michele, Gen. Mgr.--Alenia, Naples, Italy; *Int'l*, pg. 653
Crosno, Michael K., V.P. & Gen. Mgr.--Kodak Business Imaging Systems Division, Rochester, NY; *U.S. Public*, pg. 555
Cross, Burton, Pres.--Mercantile Bank of Chariton, Chariton, IA; *U.S. Public*, pg. 1088
Cross, Don, Pres.--Fanchem, Ltd., Oakville, Canada; *U.S. Private*, pg. 828
Cross, Jim, Pres. & Chief Exec. Officer--Thaw & Walrus, Inc., Seattle, WA; *U.S. Private*, pg. 914
Cross, Les, Pres.--Smith & Nephew DonJoy Inc., Carlsbad, CA; *Int'l*, pg. 1263
Cross, Mike, Exec. V.P. & Gen. Mgr.--Sea World of California, San Diego, CA; *U.S. Public*, pg. 114
Cross, Neil D., Gen. Mgr.--Elvins Equipment Sales Limited, Whitehorse, Canada; *Int'l*, pg. 1485
Cross, Rick, Pres.--Mr. Electric Corporation, Waco, TX; *U.S. Public*, pg. 538
Cross, Rick, Pres.--Aire Serve Heating & Air Conditioning, Inc., Waco, TX; *U.S. Public*, pg. 538
Cross, Rick, Pres.--Mr. Rooter Corporation, Waco, TX; *U.S. Public*, pg. 538
Cross, Timothy E., Pres. & Chief Exec. Officer--M & I Bank of Shawano, N.A., Shawano, WI; *U.S. Public*, pg. 1050
Crossley, Donald W., Chief Oper. Officer--Advance Packaging Corporation-Jackson Facility, Jackson, MI; *U.S. Private*, pg. 18
Crossman, Jim, Chief Exec. Officer--Caparo Merchant Bar plc, Scunthorpe, United Kingdom; *Int'l*, pg. 265
Crossman, R.E., Pres. & Gen. Mgr.--Bryant Grinder Corp., Springfield, VT; *U.S. Private*, pg. 461
Crossman, Richard, Pres.--Vermont USA Machine Tool Group, North Springfield, VT; *U.S. Private*, pg. 461
Crossman, William M., V.P. & Gen. Mgr.--Banta Catalog Group, Maple Grove, MN; *U.S. Public*, pg. 188
Croteau, Pierre, Pres. & Gen. Mgr.--Hudon et Deaudelin Ltee, Montreal, Canada; *Int'l*, pg. 1012
Crothers, William N., Pres.--Berlex Canada, Inc., Lachine, Canada; *Int'l*, pg. 1204
Crotty, Gerald R., Chm. Bd. & Chief Exec. Officer--ITT Information Services, Inc., New York, NY; *U.S. Public*, pg. 1512
Crouan, P., Pres.--Scholl SA, Sarcelles, France; *Int'l*, pg. 1210
Crouan, Patrice, Mng. Dir.--Scholl Belgique SA, Brussels, Belgium; *Int'l*, pg. 1209
Crouch, B.G., Dr., Pres.--Elf Sanofi Inc., New York, NY; *Int'l*, pg. 445
Crouch, C.H., Jr., Pres.--SouthTrust Securities Inc., Birmingham, AL; *U.S. Public*, pg. 1492
Croufer, Edouard, Dir. Gen.--UCB SA Pharma Sector, Braine-l'Alleud, Belgium; *Int'l*, pg. 1427
Crous, A., Chief Oper. Officer & Mng. Dir.--Hammerite Productos Especiales, Barcelona, Spain; *Int'l*, pg. 1501
Crouse, Ron, Gen. Mgr.--Kubota Tractor Corp., Columbus, OH; *Int'l*, pg. 762
Crouse, Steve, Gen. Mgr.--Allparts, Inc., Louisiana, MO; *U.S. Public*, pg. 919
Crouse, Ted L., Pres.--SuperValu, Inc.-Lewis Grocer Div., Indianola, MS; *U.S. Public*, pg. 1540
Crouse, Ted L., Pres.--SuperValu, Inc.-Southeast Div., Anniston, AL; *U.S. Public*, pg. 1541
Crouzer, Philippe, Pres.-Indus. Ceramics Div.--Quartz & Silice, Courbevoie, France; *Int'l*, pg. 1176
Crouzet, Philippe, Chief Oper Officer--Cristaleria Espanola S.A., Madrid, Spain; *Int'l*, pg. 1176
Crouzillard, Pierre, Chief Oper. Officer--Monofort, Buenos Aires, Argentina; *Int'l*, pg. 1177
Crow, Harlan, Mng. Partner--Trammell Crow Interests, Dallas, TX; *U.S. Public*, pg. 1628
Crow, Harry, Gen. Mgr.--Schwing America, Inc., Sludge Pump Div., Danbury, CT; *Int'l*, pg. 1211
Crow, Richard, Pres.--President Baking Inc., Birmingham, AL; *Int'l*, pg. 1069
Crow, Tony, Pres.--Koltex, Inc., Lawrenceville, GA; *Int'l*, pg. 1378
Crowdis, James H., III, Gen. Mgr.--Chattanooga Cable T.V. Company, Chattanooga, TN; *U.S. Public*, pg. 1447
Crowe, A Derrill, Pres.--Mutual Assurance, Inc., Birmingham, AL; *U.S. Public*, pg. 1080
Crowe, A. Derrill, Chm. Bd.--Medical Assurance of West Virginia, Charleston, WV; *U.S. Public*, pg. 1080
Crowe, Daniel, Pres. & Chief Exec. Officer--Dallas-Ft. Worth Suburban Newspapers, Inc., Arlington, TX; *U.S. Public*, pg. 209
Crowe, J., Chief Exec. Officer--Ascom Hasler Mailing Systems AG, Bern, Switzerland; *Int'l*, pg. 86
Crowe, M.R., Pres.--Fisons Western Corporation, Vancouver, Canada; *Int'l*, pg. 1111
Crowe, P. A., Pres.--Tolbiachim, Paris, France; *U.S. Public*, pg. 82
Crowe, Peter, Dir.-Systems Devel.--Mastercare Limited, Hemel Hempstead, United Kingdom; *Int'l*, pg. 414
Crowe, S.J., Pres.--Chevron Capital U.S.A. Inc., San Francisco, CA; *U.S. Public*, pg. 348
Crowe, Steve, Pres. & Chief Exec. Officer--SouthTrust Bank of Alexander City, Alexander City, AL; *U.S. Public*, pg. 1492
Crowely, Ed, Chief Oper. Officer--Empire Steel Castings, Inc., Laureldale, PA; *U.S. Public*, pg. 142
Crowl, John F., Gen. Mgr.--Koncor Industries Div., Wauseon, OH; *U.S. Public*, pg. 1617
Crowley, Daniel, Gen. Mgr.--Dekoron/Unitherm Division, Cape Coral, FL; *U.S. Public*, pg. 689
Crowley, Desmond, Mng. Dir.--Bank of Ireland Finance Ltd., Dublin, Ireland; *Int'l*, pg. 152
Crowley, Frank J., Pres. & Chief Oper. Officer--Commercial Union Life Assurance Company of Canada, Scarborough, Canada; *Int'l*, pg. 308
Crowley, Joseph P., Pres. & Chief Oper. Officer--Philadelphia American Life Insurance Company, Houston, TX; *U.S. Public*, pg. 853
Crowley, Kieran, Gen. Mgr.--A.T. Cross U.K. Ltd., Luton, United Kingdom; *U.S. Public*, pg. 461
Crown, Fred S., Jr., Pres.--Lee, Robinson & Steine, Inc., Nashville, TN; *U.S. Public*, pg. 624
Crown, Lester, Chm.--Material Service Corp., Chicago, IL; *U.S. Public*, pg. 709
Crowther, I.H., Gen. Mgr.--Fairfax Community Newspapers Pty. Limited, Condell Park, Australia; *Int'l*, pg. 477
Crowther, P., Chief Exec. Officer--Redland Distribution Limited, Worksop, United Kingdom; *Int'l*, pg. 1090
Croxton, G. Duke, Chief Exec. Officer--Magnus Software Corporation, Smyrna, GA; *U.S. Private*, pg. 795
Crozier, J., Mng. Dir.--Riley Advertising (London) Ltd., London, United Kingdom; *Int'l*, pg. 1117
Cruce, Carl, Gen. Mgr.--Nuclear Upgrade, Tulsa, OK; *U.S. Private*, pg. 55
Crudo, N. Robert, Pres.--BA Agency, Inc., San Francisco, CA; *U.S. Public*, pg. 180
Crudo, N. Robert, Pres.--BA Insurance Company, Inc., San Francisco, CA; *U.S. Public*, pg. 180
Cruger, Melvin E., Pres.--Teledyne Water Pik, Fort Collins, CO; *U.S. Public*, pg. 44
Cruikshank, Bruce, Pres.--Sealed Air Food Packaging Division, Patterson, NC; *U.S. Public*, pg. 1451
Crum, Gary, Gen. Mgr.--Frontier Communications-Schuyler, Inc., Rushville, IL; *U.S. Public*, pg. 684
Crum, Lynn, Chief Oper. Officer--Simkins Carton Div.-Cleveland, Cleveland, OH; *U.S. Private*, pg. 1000
Crum, Niles D., Publr.--ID Magazine, New York, NY; *Int'l*, pg. 1446
Crumley, James, Pres.--Proof Positive/Farrowlyne Associates, Inc., Evanston, IL; *U.S. Public*, pg. 503
Crump, John, Pres.--Sensall, Div. of Rosemount, Inc., Hauppauge, NY; *U.S. Public*, pg. 574
Crutchfield, Bill, Chm. Bd.--State First National Bank, Arkansas, Texarkana, AR; *U.S. Public*, pg. 630
Crutchfield, Bill, Chm. Bd., Pres. & Chief Exec. Officer--State First National Bank, Texas, Texarkana, TX; *U.S. Public*, pg. 630
Crutchfield, George, Plant Mgr.--Ash Grove Cement-Western Region Cement Plant, Leamington, UT; *U.S. Private*, pg. 88
Crutchfield, K.S., Pres.--Cyprus Cumberland Coal Corporation, Middlesboro, KY; *U.S. Public*, pg. 471
Crutchfield, K.S., Pres.--Cyprus Mountain Coals Corporation, Bulan, KY; *U.S. Public*, pg. 471
Crutchfield, K.S., Pres.--Cyprus Kanawha Corporation, Powellton, WV; *U.S. Public*, pg. 471
Crutchfield, Kevin, Pres.--Cannelton Industries, Inc., Charleston, WV; *U.S. Public*, pg. 471
Crutchfield, Kevin, Pres.--Cannelton Inc., Charleston, WV; *U.S. Public*, pg. 471
Crutchfield, S., Plant Mgr.--Square D Company-Assembly Operations, Clearwater, FL; *Int'l*, pg. 1208
Cruwell, Bernd, Dr., Chief Oper. Officer--Hesse, Rhineland-Palatinate & Saar Branch, Frankfurt/Main, Germany; *Int'l*, pg. 645
Cruz, Eduardo, Pres.--Crown Cork de Chile, S.A.I., Santiago, Chile; *U.S. Public*, pg. 464
Cruz, Eduardo, Pres.--Crown Cork de Chile S.A., Santiago, Chile; *U.S. Public*, pg. 464
Cruz, Fernando, Mng. Dir.--Colombiana Universal de Papeles S.A., Pereira, Colombia; *U.S. Public*, pg. 959
Cruz, Julio, Gen. Mgr.--Newell Puerto Rico, Ltd., Carolina, PR; *U.S. Public*, pg. 1177
Cruz, M., Mng. Dir.--Editorial Alhambra Mexicana S.A. de C.V., Mexico, Mexico; *Int'l*, pg. 1025
Cruz, Marcelino Correa, Plant Mgr.--Satellite Plant Juatuba, Juatuba, Brazil; *Int'l*, pg. 1342
Crye, Betty, Mgr.--Downey Savings & Loan Association, F.A., Lancaster, CA; *U.S. Public*, pg. 527
Crysler, D., Plant Mgr.--American Natl. Can Co., Minneapolis, MN; *Int'l*, pg. 1029
Csabai, B., Chief Exec. Officer--Bramac Kft, Veszprem, Hungary; *Int'l*, pg. 1092
Csiszar, Ernst N., Chm. Bd. & Chief Exec. Officer--Premium Budget Plan, Inc., Winston Salem, NC; *U.S. Public*, pg. 1453

Csiszar, Ernst N., Chm. Bd. & Chief Exec. Officer--The Innovative Company, Winston Salem, NC; *U.S. Public*, pg. 1454
Csiszar, Ernst N., Chm. Bd. & Chief Exec. Officer--Universal Insurance Co., Winston Salem, NC; *U.S. Public*, pg. 1454
Csomor, Laszlo, Mng. Dir.--EURO RSCG, Budapest, Hungary; *Int'l*, pg. 602
Csonka, Mark, V.P. & Gen. Mgr.--The Timms Spring Company, Elyria, OH; *U.S. Private*, pg. 880
Cuadra Barillas, Roberto, Gen. Mgr.--Publiciaa Cuadra Chamberlain, Managua, Nicaragua; *U.S. Private*, pg. 186
Cuadra Chamberlain, Vicente, Pres.--Publiciaa Cuadra Chamberlain, Managua, Nicaragua; *U.S. Private*, pg. 186
Cuadra, Gonzalo, Mng. Dir.--Chile Copper Ltd., London, United Kingdom; *Int'l*, pg. 303
Cuadra, Juan Roldao, Gen. Mgr.--CEPSA Cia. Portuguesa de Petroleos, Lda., Lisbon, Portugal; *Int'l*, pg. 323
Cuatrecasas, Pedro, Pres.--COFIR (Corporacion Financiera Reunida), Madrid, Spain; *Int'l*, pg. 240
Cubarsi, Rafael, Chief Oper. Officer--Vendo Iberia, S.A., Barcelona, Spain; *Int'l*, pg. 1184
Cubel, Jerry, Gen. Mgr.--Arrow Commercial Systems Div., Hayward, CA; *U.S. Public*, pg. 133
Cubillette, Luis Francisco, Representative--CUNA Mutual Group-Dominican Republic, Santo Domingo, Dominican Republic; *U.S. Private*, pg. 296
Cubukcu, Aydin I., Mng. Dir.--Beko Elektronik A.S., Istanbul, Turkey; *Int'l*, pg. 741
Cucarella, Alejandro, Gen. Mgr.--Wang Export Services, Inc., Buenos Aires, Argentina; *U.S. Public*, pg. 1738
Cucci, Frank, Mgr.--Finkel Outdoor Products, Inc., Garfield, NJ; *U.S. Private*, pg. 1094
Cuccurese, Giuseppe, Mgr.--Sanpaolo-New York Branch, New York, NY; *Int'l*, pg. 691
Cucinotta, P., Chief Oper. Officer--FATA Sud, San Marco Evangelista, Italy; *Int'l*, pg. 474
Cucuz, R., Pres. & Chief Oper. Officer--Acco Controls North America, Wixom, MI; *Int'l*, pg. 473
Cudd, Bobby Joe, Pres.--Cudd Pressure Control, Inc., Houma, LA; *U.S. Public*, pg. 1356
Cuddihy, Robert V., Jr., Chief Oper. Officer--Electronic Voting Systems, Inc., New York, NY; *U.S. Public*, pg. 771
Cuddihy, Tim, Exec. V.P. & Gen. Mgr.--Water Country USA, Williamsburg, VA; *U.S. Public*, pg. 114
Cudworth, J., Mng. Dir.--GEC Reinforced Plastics Ltd., Preston, United Kingdom; *Int'l*, pg. 544
Cuellar, Victor, Chief Oper. Officer--Hughes Tool Company, C.A., Maracaibo, Venezuela; *U.S. Public*, pg. 167
Cuello, Alfredo, G.M.--Avon Cosmetics de Venezuela, C.A., Caracas, Venezuela; *U.S. Public*, pg. 156
Cuello, Rafael, Pres.--Caribe Freight, Aguadilla, PR; *U.S. Private*, pg. 211
Cuello, Rafael, Pres.--Caribe Freight, Santo Domingo, Dominican Republic; *U.S. Private*, pg. 211
Cuesta, Armando, Pres.--ECI Telecom Americas Inc., Fort Lauderdale, FL; *Int'l*, pg. 643
Cueurachi, Francesca, Regional Dir.--Berlitz Language Centers, S.R.L., Rome, Italy; *U.S. Public*, pg. 222
Cuevas, Walter, V.P. & Gen. Mgr.--Medtronic Heart Valve Division, Irvine, CA; *U.S. Public*, pg. 1083
Cugnon, M., Pres.--Merck Sharp & Dohme (Asia) Inc., Wan Chai, Hong Kong; *U.S. Public*, pg. 1092
Cuilhe, Michel, Deputy Mng. Dir.--Framatome Connectors International, Courbevoie, France; *Int'l*, pg. 503
Culang, Michael S., Pres.--Somerset Knitting Mills, New York, NY; *U.S. Public*, pg. 1291
Culbertson, Edward D., Mgr.-Production--Industrial Bag Division - Kansas City Plant, Kansas City, MO; *U.S. Public*, pg. 1521
Culbertson, Steven R., Gen. Mgr.--EMPIRE METRO, Phoenix, AZ; *U.S. Private*, pg. 375
Culcchi, Paolo, Chief Oper. Officer--Italmaceri, Turin, Italy; *Int'l*, pg. 1327
Cullberg, B., Mng. Dir.--De La Rue Systems Asia Pacific Limited, Wan Chai, Hong Kong; *Int'l*, pg. 387
Cullen, Brian D., Gen. Mgr.--Intelligence, Information & Aircraft Integration Systems, Garland, TX; *U.S. Public*, pg. 1364
Cullen, Tom, Pres.--Sterling Steel Service Ltd., Chicago, IL; *U.S. Private*, pg. 345
Culleton, James E., Pres.--First Bank of California, Sacramento, CA; *U.S. Public*, pg. 626
Cullingworth, L. Ross, Chm. Bd.--Consolidated Carma Corporation, Calgary, Canada; *Int'l*, pg. 229
Cullis, Andrew, Mgr.--Elsevier Electronic Publishing Services, Lancaster, United Kingdom; *Int'l*, pg. 1100
Cullison, Rod, Sr. V.P. & Mgr.--First Security Processing Services, Inc., Salt Lake City, UT; *U.S. Public*, pg. 638
Culliton, John, V.P. & Gen. Mgr.--WCCO-TV, Minneapolis, MN; *U.S. Public*, pg. 275
Cullman, Lewis B., Pres.--Cullman Ventures, Inc., New York, NY; *U.S. Private*, pg. 295
Cullum, John D., Pres.--PHH Vehicle Management Services, United Kingdom, Swindon, United Kingdom; *U.S. Public*, pg. 322
Culotta, Tom, Div. Mgr.--ConAgra Broiler Co., Natchitoches, LA; *U.S. Public*, pg. 427
Culp, Jack, System Foreman--Rosita Plant/El Grullo, Freer, TX; *U.S. Public*, pg. 1759
Culver, George, Chief Oper. Officer--Allright Corpus Christi, Inc., Corpus Christi, TX; *U.S. Private*, pg. 42
Culver, George, Chief Oper. Officer--Allright San Antonio Parking, Inc., San Antonio, TX; *U.S. Private*, pg. 43
Culver, Harold, V.P. & Gen. Mgr.--KAIT-TV, Jonesboro, AR; *U.S. Public*, pg. 992
Culver, Ken, Area Dir.--AlliedSignal Aerospace Service Corporation, Sao Paulo, Brazil; *U.S. Public*, pg. 52
Cumberlidge, Robert, Chm. Bd.--Texas Utilities Australia, Melbourne, Australia; *U.S. Public*, pg. 1588
Cuminatti, L., Gen. Mgr.--Cariplo Madrid, Madrid, Spain; *Int'l*, pg. 275
Cumming, W.C., Sr. Representative--The Royal Bank of Scotland plc, New York, NY; *Int'l*, pg. 1133
Cummings, Barry, V.P. & Gen. Mgr.--TMP Worldwide, Inc., Cincinnati, OH; *U.S. Private*, pg. 1065
Cummings, Billy, Administrator--Hobbs Healthcare Center, Hobbs, NM; *U.S. Public*, pg. 838
Cummings, Bruce E., Exec. V.P.-Mktg.--Lotus Word Processing Division, Atlanta, GA; *U.S. Public*, pg. 896
Cummings, Daniel W., Principal Officer--LaSalle Advisors Limited, Chicago, IL; *U.S. Public*, pg. 979
Cummings, Frank T., V.P. & Gen. Mgr.--Logicon Strategic and Information Systems Division, San Pedro, CA; *U.S. Public*, pg. 1199
Cummings, Ian, Chief Fin. Officer-U.K.--Diversified Agency Services, New York, NY; *U.S. Public*, pg. 1223
Cummings, John, Pres.--Fishery Products International USA, Danvers, MA; *Int'l*, pg. 492
Cummings, P., Mng. Dir.--Hanimex Pty. Limited, Brookvale, Australia; *Int'l*, pg. 1115
Cummings, Phil, Div. Mgr.--Champion Home Builders Co., Lillington, NC; *U.S. Public*, pg. 332
Cummings, Robert S., Pres.--SAIC Engineering, Inc., Lakeville, MA; *U.S. Private*, pg. 976
Cummins, Andrew E., Pres.--Air Products Canada, Brampton, Canada; *U.S. Public*, pg. 31
Cummins, Bob, Pres.--Wellborn - DE Corp., Albuquerque, NM; *U.S. Private*, pg. 347
Cumo, Giorgio, Mng. Dir.--Olivetti de Chile S.A., Santiago, Chile; *Int'l*, pg. 1003
Cundiff, Daimon E., Asst. V.P.--IBP-Joslin, Geneseo, IL; *U.S. Public*, pg. 852
Cundiff, Robert, Mgr.--Shepler's San Antonio, San Antonio, TX; *U.S. Public*, pg. 413
Cuneo, Ronald E., Pres.--Wang Fed Inc., Mc Lean, VA; *U.S.* Public, pg. 1737
Cunliffe, A.G., Chief Exec. Officer--Hellermann Insuloid, Manchester, United Kingdom; *Int'l*, pg. 207
Cunliffe, S., Pres.--Pasta & Cheese, Inc., Glendale, CA; *Int'l, pg. 918*
Cunningham, A. Patrick, Pres.--Dovatech, Ltd., Beecher, IL; *U.S. Public*, pg. 520
Cunningham, Bill, Mgr.--Targ-It-Tronics Inc., Melbourne, FL; *Int'l*, pg. 713
Cunningham, Bruce T., V.P. & Gen. Mgr.--Olin Fabricated Metals Products, Inc., Bloomington, IL; *U.S. Public*, pg. 1219
Cunningham, C. Baker, Chm. Bd., Pres. & Chief Exec. Officer--Belden Wire & Cable Company, Richmond, IN; *U.S. Public*, pg. 201
Cunningham, C. Joseph, III, Chm. Bd., Pres. & Chief Exec. Officer--The Fidelity Bank, Frostburg, MD; *U.S. Public*, pg. 1089
Cunningham, Chuck, V.P.-Client Service--Total Research Corporation, Poughkeepsie, NY; *U.S. Public*, pg. 1625
Cunningham, E., Gen. Mgr.--Aer Lingus, Frankfurt, Germany; *Int'l*, pg. 28
Cunningham, E.L., V.P. & Gen. Mgr.--Marion Machine Company Division, Marion, NC; *U.S. Private*, pg. 1055
Cunningham, Gerel C., Pres.--Essex Corporation, New York, NY; *U.S. Public*, pg. 320
Cunningham, John W., Pres.--Crown Litometal, S.A., Medellin, Colombia; *U.S. Public*, pg. 465
Cunningham, Jonathan R., Exec. V.P. & Mgr.-N.Y. Reg. Sls.--Jefferies & Company, Inc., Los Angeles, CA; *U.S. Public*, pg. 925
Cunningham, Larry, Pres.--Gooch Foods, Inc., Lincoln, NE; *U.S. Public*, pg. 128
Cunningham, Larry H., Pres.--ADM Corn Processing Division, Decatur, IL; *U.S. Public*, pg. 127
Cunningham, Larry H., Pres.--ADM Protein Specialties, Decatur, IL; *U.S. Public*, pg. 128
Cunningham, Linda, V.P. & Dir.-Publishing--Harper Reference, New York, NY; *Int'l*, pg. 927
Cunningham, M.W., Exec. V.P.--ING North America Insurance Company, Atlanta, GA; *Int'l*, pg. 648
Cunningham, Maston N., Pres. & Gen. Mgr.--Occidental Exploration and Production Company, Quito, Ecuador; *U.S. Public*, pg. 1210
Cunningham, N.J., Pres. & Sec.--Atlantic Energy Technology, Inc., Pleasantville, NJ; *U.S. Public*, pg. 430
Cunningham, Phil, Pres.--Networking Products, Alexandria, VA; *U.S. Public*, pg. 1105
Cunningham, Ralph S., Pres. & Chief Exec. Officer--Citgo Petroleum Corporation, Tulsa, OK; *Int'l*, pg. 1045
Cunningham, Theodor R., Pres. & Mng. Dir.--Chrysler de Mexico S.A., Mexico, Mexico; *U.S. Public*, pg. 354
Cunningham, Theodore R., Pres. & Mng. Dir.--Chrysler de Mexico, Ramos Arizpe, Mexico; *U.S. Public*, pg. 354
Cunningham, Tom, Pres.--Bench Craft, Inc., Blue Mountain, MS; *U.S. Private*, pg. 432
Cunningham, William J., V.P.-Worldwide Mfg.--Data General Manufacturing Division, Westborough, MA; *U.S. Public*, pg. 485
Cuomo, Tom, Grp. V.P.--Drew Industrial, Boonton, NJ; *U.S. Public*, pg. 139
Cuppens, Louis, Mgr.--Sandvik Saws and Tools Benelux B.V., Helmond, Netherlands; *Int'l*, pg. 1187
Cuppini, James D., V.P. & Gen. Mgr.--Frontier Network Systems, Inc., Rochester, NY; *U.S. Public*, pg. 684
Cupps, Brian, Customer Base Representative--TIE Systems-Omaha/Des Moines, Omaha, NE; *U.S. Private*, pg. 1085
Cuppy, Donald, Mgr.--General Employment Enterprises, Inc., Phoenix, AZ; *U.S. Public*, pg. 714
Cureton, William, Pres.--C&W Refractories, Ltd., Hamilton, Canada; *U.S. Private*, pg. 194
Curiel, Francois, Dir.--Christie's (International) S.A., Geneva, Switzerland; *Int'l*, pg. 290
Curiel, Juan Carlos Lasa, Pres.--Juliana Constructora Gijonesa, S.A., Gijon, Spain; *Int'l*, pg. 1223
Curien, Thierry, Gen. Mgr.--ITW Fixations, Clichy, France; *U.S. Public*, pg. 868
Curington, Wayne, Pres.--Dan-Loc Bolt & Gasket, Inc., Houston, TX; *U.S. Private*, pg. 413
Curleigh, James, Pres.--Taylor Made (Great Britain) Ltd., Basingstoke, United Kingdom; *Int'l*, pg. 1181
Curler, Jeffrey H., Chm.--Curwood, Inc., Murphysboro, IL; *U.S. Public*, pg. 210
Curley, Dwight G., Pres.--Granite State Gas Transmission, Inc., Portsmouth, NH; *U.S. Public*, pg. 197
Curley, Thomas, Pres., Publr. & Chief Oper. Officer--USA Today, Arlington, VA; *U.S. Public*, pg. 700
Curran, B., Pres.--JC Penney Purchasing Corp., Dallas, TX; *U.S. Public*, pg. 917
Curran, D. Patrick, Chief Oper. Officer--Cook Composites & Polymers Inc., Orlando, FL; *Int'l*, pg. 1409
Curran, Denis, Pres.--Bank of Ireland Asset Management Limited, Greenwich, CT; *Int'l*, pg. 152
Curran, J.J., Pres.--Mizuno Golf Company, Norcross, GA; *Int'l*, pg. 885
Curran, James J., Chm. Bd. & Chief Exec. Officer N.W. Reg.--First Interstate Bank of Oregon, N.A., Portland, OR; *U.S. Public*, pg. 1753
Curran, John, Div. Mgr.--Wyle Electronics-Irvine, Irvine, CA; *Int'l*, pg. 1457
Curran, Leo, Gen. Mgr.-European Opers.--Tab Products Europa B.V., Amsterdam, Netherlands; *U.S. Public*, pg. 1559
Curran, Robert, Pres.--Wheel Tronic Inc., Mississauga, Canada; *U.S. Public*, pg. 1481
Currence, Richard M., Exec. V.P.--Pan-Marine International, Inc., New Orleans, LA; *U.S. Public*, pg. 1608
Currie, Brian, Gen. Mgr.--Tektronix Australia Pty. Limited, Sydney, Australia; *U.S. Public*, pg. 1567
Currie, D.A., Gen. Mgr.--Baring International Investment (Canada), Toronto, Canada; *Int'l*, pg. 648
Currie, D.J., Vice Chm.--Balfour Guthrie Forest Products Inc., Vancouver, Canada; *Int'l*, pg. 260
Currie, R.J., Pres.--Loblaw Companies Limited, North York, Canada; *Int'l*, pg. 1495
Currier, Bonnie J., V.P. & Barton Office Mgr.--Community National Bank, Derby, VT; *U.S. Public*, pg. 416
Currin, H. Randolph, Jr., Chief Oper. Officer--Currin & Associates, Inc., Cary, NC; *U.S. Public*, pg. 347
Curro, Phil, Asst. V.P.--Voest-Alpine International Corp.-Machine Tools Div., Fair Lawn, NJ; *Int'l*, pg. 1471
Curro, Sheryl, Lab Mgr.--Quest Diagnostic, Oneida, NY; *U.S.* Public, pg. 1351
Curry, C. E., Chm. Bd.-Saniserv-Korea--Saniserv-Korea, Seoul, Korea; *U.S. Private*, pg. 965
Curry, Craig, Pres.--POST Buckley Schuh & Jernigan, Dallas, TX; *U.S. Private*, pg. 826
Curry, James, Pres.--South Florida Land Division, Fort Myers, FL; *U.S. Public*, pg. 1683
Curry, K.P., Mng. Dir.--R&H Australia Pty. Ltd., Melbourne, Australia; *Int'l*, pg. 681
Curry, Kenneth O., Pres. & Chief Oper. Officer--Nelson Westerberg International Inc., Elk Grove Village, IL; *U.S. Private*, pg. 1164
Curry, Kim Anderson, Chief Oper. Officer--K&M Associates, Providence, RI; *U.S. Public*, pg. 69
Curry, Peter, Chief Exec. Officer--Unitech Plc, Reading, United Kingdom; *Int'l*, pg. 1241
Curry, Richard E., Pres.--ISS Mall Services, Inc., West Hartford, CT; *Int'l*, pg. 656
Curtas, William W., Chief Exec., Chief Oper. & Chief Fin. Officer & Exec. V.P.--Steego Corporation, West Palm Beach, FL; *Int'l*, pg. 216
Curtfeld, Brian, Mgr.-Opers.--Advance Circuits, Commercial Div., Roseville, MN; *Int'l*, pg. 713
Curtin, John, Co-Gen. Mgr.--WWF Paper Corporation - International, Greenwich, CT; *U.S. Private*, pg. 1145
Curtin, Paul C., Mng. Dir.--Stuart Entertainment, S.A. de C.V., Reynosa, Mexico; *U.S. Public*, pg. 1526
Curtis, Charlie, Pres.--Nana Development Corporation, Kotzebue, AK; *U.S. Private*, pg. 774
Curtis, D. G., Mng. Dir.--Irish Sewing Ltd., Dublin, Ireland; *Int'l*, pg. 299
Curtis, Edward, Pres.--Hobart/McIntosh Paper Company, Elk Grove Village, IL; *Int'l*, pg. 72
Curtis, John, Reg. Transportation Superintendent--MIGC, Inc., Denver, CO; *U.S. Public*, pg. 1758
Curtis, John, Regional Transportation Superintendent--MGTC, Inc., Gillette, WY; *U.S. Public*, pg. 1758
Curtis, Jonathan G., Pres.--CDM Federal Programs Corporation, Fairfax, VA; *U.S. Private*, pg. 204
Curtis, Lawrence, Pres.--Partlow Corporation, New Hartford, NY; *U.S. Public*, pg. 482
Curtis, S.W., Plant Mgr.--Longview Fibre Co. Western Container Division, Spanish Fork, UT; *U.S. Public*, pg. 1014
Cusack, Thomas J., Pres. & Chief Exec. Officer--Transamerica Life Companies, Los Angeles, CA; *U.S. Public*, pg. 1630
Cusano, Michael R., Pres.--Deepwater Chemicals, Inc., Woodward, OK; *Int'l*, pg. 1395
Cush, H. Terry, Sr. V.P. & Dir.--Bank of America NT&SA, Grand Cayman, Cayman Islands; *U.S. Public*, pg. 182
Cushing, James E., Jr., Pres. & Chief Oper. Officer--Wright Group Publishing, Inc., Bothell, WA; *U.S. Public*, pg. 1636
Cushing, Peter, Assoc. Dir.--Procter & Gamble Inc., Mississauga, Canada; *U.S. Public*, pg. 1332
Cushing, Robert, Pres. & Chief Exec. Officer--Pepsi-Cola General Bottlers, Inc., Rolling Meadows, IL; *U.S. Public*, pg. 1277
Cushman, Daniel H., Pres.--Triple Crown Services Company, Fort Wayne, IN; *U.S. Public*, pg. 432
Cusi, Gustavo, Commercial Mgr.--Dun & Bradstreet SA, Buenos Aires, Argentina; *U.S. Public*, pg. 536
Custer, Ernest, Mgr.-Opers.-Trucks--GTY Tire Co., Mount Vernon, IL; *Int'l*, pg. 327
Custis, Ken, Gen. Mgr.--Keystone Northern California Warehouse-Benicia, Benicia, CA; *U.S. Public*, pg. 955
Custode, J.V., Chief Oper. Officer--Welland Forge Div., Welland, Canada; *Int'l*, pg. 474
Cusumano, Carole, Branch Mgr.--Downey Savings & Loan Association, F.A., Palm Springs, CA; *U.S. Public*, pg. 527
Cusworth, Neville, Chm. & Chief Exec.--Reed Elsevier Legal Division, London, United Kingdom; *Int'l*, pg. 1095

Cusworth, Rodney, Pres.--MGI Pumps, Inc., Kenosha, WI; *Int'l*, pg. 1378

Cuthbert, Robert A., Pres.--Lambert-Kay Div., Princeton, NJ; *U.S. Public*, pg. 310

Cuthbertson, Thomas, Gen. Mgr.--The Coe Mfg. Ltd., Brampton, Canada; *U.S. Private*, pg. 249

Cuthill, Happy, Admin.--The Dun & Bradstreet Corporate Foundation, New Providence, NJ; *U.S. Public*, pg. 535

Cutie, James A., Pres.--The New York Times Information Services Group, New York, NY; *U.S. Public*, pg. 1174

Cutini, Jerauld J., Pres.--OnTrak Systems, Inc., San Jose, CA; *U.S. Public*, pg. 975

Cutler, Joel Bernard, Pres.--National Leisure Group, Boston, MA; *U.S. Public*, pg. 320

Cutlip, Michael, Dir.-Opers.--Certified Food Service of Orlando, Inc., Orlando, FL; *U.S. Public*, pg. 1529

Cutrone, L.D., Sr. V.P. & Mgr.-Branch--ABN AMRO Bank, N.V. (Pittsburgh), Pittsburgh, PA; *Int'l*, pg. 10

Cutshaw, Mark, Div. Mgr.--Marianna Div.-Florida Public Utilities, Marianna, FL; *U.S. Public*, pg. 655

Cutts-Watson, Malcolm, Mng. Dir.--Willis Corroon Management Limited-Guernsey, Saint Peter Port, United Kingdom; *Int'l*, pg. 1503

Cuvelier, Joseph, Pres. & Chief Exec. Officer--Gie ETEX Gestion, Vernouillet, France; *Int'l*, pg. 430

Cuyegkeng, Paul, Pres.--Dole Asia, Tokyo, Japan; *U.S. Public*, pg. 515

Cuyler, D., Pres.--Rank Video Services America Inc., Northbrook, IL; *Int'l*, pg. 1087

Cuzzer, Arturo, Gen. Mgr.--Elkem S.r.l., Milan, Italy; *Int'l*, pg. 447

Cybulski, M. P., Pres.-Japan--Bristol-Myers International Group, New York, NY; *U.S. Public*, pg. 254

Cypher, Al J., Mgr.--Citizens Utilities Company of Pennsylvania, New Bethlehem, PA; *U.S. Public*, pg. 380

Cyphert, Mary, Service Mgr.--ALLTEL Answering Service, Inc., Export, PA; *U.S. Public*, pg. 55

Cyr, Art, Gen. Mgr.--Marietta Canada, Inc., Toronto, Canada; *U.S. Private*, pg. 703

Cyr, Carol, Branch Mgr.--Troy Savings Bank, Watervliet, NY; *U.S. Private*, pg. 1106

Cyr, Eugene A., Gen. Mgr.--Givaudan-Roure Inc., Brampton, Canada; *Int'l*, pg. 1120

Cyr, Reginald J., Pres.--Sonatech, Inc., Santa Barbara, CA; *U.S. Private*, pg. 229

Cyrenne, Roland O., Pres. & Chief Oper. Officer--Trois-Rivieres Mill, Trois-Rivieres, Canada; *Int'l*, pg. 761

Cyrenne, Roland O., Pres. & Chief Oper. Officer--Place Turcot Mill, Montreal, Canada; *Int'l*, pg. 761

Cyrenne, Roland O., Pres. & Chief Oper. Officer--Ville LaSalle Plant, La Salle, Canada; *Int'l*, pg. 761

Cyrenne, Roland O., Pres. & Chief Oper. Officer--Rexdale Plant, Rexdale, Canada; *Int'l*, pg. 761

Czajkowski, John, Mgr.--Saugus Division, Saugus, CA; *U.S. Public*, pg. 1161

Czaus, Walt, Pres.--Otis Merla Systems, Garland, TX; *U.S. Public*, pg. 776

Czechowski, Claude, Pres.--French Division, Boulogne-Billancourt, France; *U.S. Public*, pg. 423

Czernakowski, W., Mng. Dir.--Romer-Britax Autogurte GmbH, Ulm, Germany; *Int'l*, pg. 217

Czerniak, Richard A., Pres.--DeVRY Institute of Technology, Columbus, OH; *U.S. Public*, pg. 504

Czul, Joseph, Pres.--Logan & Kanawha Coal Co., South Charleston, WV; *U.S. Private*, pg. 672

Czura, Antony, Pres. & Chief Exec. Officer--SGS North America Inc., New York, NY; *Int'l*, pg. 1153

Czyz, Lorence, Gen. Mgr.--Plastron, City of Industry, CA; *U.S. Private*, pg. 15

D-Alonzo, Thomas, Pres.--PPD Pharmaco, Inc., Wilmington, NC; *U.S. Public*, pg. 1285

d'Addario, Sandro, Country Mgr.--Berlitz Language Centers of Canada Ltd., Toronto, Canada; *U.S. Public*, pg. 222

D'Addio, L.J., Gen. Mgr.--Citizens Utilities Company of California, North Highlands, CA; *U.S. Public*, pg. 380

D'Agostini, Luigi, V.P.--VM Motori S.p.A., Cento, Italy; *Int'l*, pg. 654

d'Agostino, A., Dr., Chief Oper. Officer--Flo-con Italiana S.r.l., Milan, Italy; *Int'l*, pg. 1529

D'Agostino, J., Pres.--Lehrer McGovern Bovis Inc., New York, NY; *Int'l*, pg. 1035

D'Alatri, Paola, Rep.--Generale Bank, Ho Chi Minh City, Vietnam; *Int'l*, pg. 547

D'Alessandro, Dominic, Pres. & Chief Exec. Officer--Laurentian Trust of Canada, Montreal, Canada; *Int'l*, pg. 396

D'Alessandro, Dominic, Pres. & Chief Exec. Officer--Manulife Financial, Toronto, Canada; *Int'l*, pg. 840

D'Alessio, Frederick D., Pres. & Chief Exec. Officer--Bell Atlantic-MD, Baltimore, MD; *U.S. Public*, pg. 202

D'Alessio, Walter, Pres.--Latimer & Buck, Inc., Philadelphia, PA; *U.S. Public*, pg. 985

d'Aligny, Francois-Xavier, Dir.--Deutsche Bank AG (Paris), Paris, France; *Int'l*, pg. 404

D'Aloia, Paul, Pres. & Gen. Mgr.--Huffy Sports Company, Sussex, WI; *U.S. Public*, pg. 846

d'Amade, J., Pres.--Agences Maritime Associes, Le Havre, France; *Int'l*, pg. 682

d'Amade, J., Pres.--Agence Maritime et Conteneurs, Boulogne-Billancourt, France; *Int'l*, pg. 682

D'Ambra, Michael, Pres.--Birmingham Cable Communications, Inc., Birmingham, AL; *U.S. Public*, pg. 1610

D'Amecourt, Jean, Chief Exec.--GrandMet Foods Europe, Paris, France; *Int'l*, pg. 408

D'Amico, S., Administrator--Sumoto S.r.l., Montecchio Maggiore, Italy; *Int'l*, pg. 432

D'Amolo, Avvocato Carlo, Pres.--Italgas S.p.A., Turin, Italy; *Int'l*, pg. 428

D'Ancicco, K., Branch Mgr.--RHG New York, Kenilworth, NJ; *Int'l*, pg. 1151

D'Andrea, Paul, Pres. & Chief Exec. Officer--Mystic Color Lab, Inc., Mystic, CT; *Int'l*, pg. 501

D'Angelo, Frank G., V.P.-Information Systems--Diebold, Incorporated, Canton, OH; *U.S. Public*, pg. 506

D'Angelo, Joseph F., Pres.--North America Syndicate, Inc., New York, NY; *U.S. Private*, pg. 515

D'Angelo, Joseph F., Pres.--King Features Syndicate Division, New York, NY; *U.S. Private*, pg. 518

D'Angelo, Joseph F., Pres.--Volt Delta Resources, Inc., New York, NY; *U.S. Public*, pg. 1724

D'Angelo, Pasuqale, Mng. Dir.--Officine Aeronavali Venezia S.p.A., Tesero, Italy; *Int'l*, pg. 653

D'Angelo, Robert, Gen. Mgr.--Quebecor Printing Orlando, Orlando, FL; *Int'l*, pg. 1076

D'Angostino, Dominic, Mgr.--Anixter Vancouver, Richmond, Canada; *U.S. Public*, pg. 116

d'Anterroches, Ph., Pres.--SBS Valeurs S.A., Paris, France; *Int'l*, pg. 1331

D'Anton, Russell, Pres.--Charlie Brown's & The Office Restaurant Group, Mountainside, NJ; *U.S. Private*, pg. 219

D'Antona, Rosanna, Gen. Mgr.--Edelman Gruppo D', Milan, Italy; *U.S. Private*, pg. 363

D'Antuono, Dave, V.P. & Gen. Mgr.--WXXA-TV, Albany, NY; *U.S. Public*, pg. 385

D'Antuono, David, V.P.-Albany--Clear Channel Television, Inc., Minneapolis, MN; *U.S. Public*, pg. 383

D'Antuono, M., Pres.--Parsons Constructors Inc., Pasadena, CA; *U.S. Private*, pg. 842

D'Argent, Philippe, Gen. Mgr.--Lotus Development, SA, Saint Quentin-en-Yvelines, France; *U.S. Public*, pg. 896

D'Armour, Mead, V. P. & Gen. Mgr.--Nuclear and Advanced Technology Division, Monroeville, PA; *U.S. Public*, pg. 273

D'Augostino, Vincent, Pres.--Benefit Consultants, Inc. (CT), San Carlos, CA; *U.S. Public*, pg. 320

D'Cruz, Colin, Mgr.-Plant--Schnadig Corp., Corona, CA; *U.S. Private*, pg. 971

D'Epifanio, Luigi, Mng. Dir.--Johnson & Johnson Sihhi Malzeme Sanayi Ve Ticaret Ltd. Sti., Istanbul, Turkey; *U.S. Public*, pg. 931

d'Escury, F.A.G. Collot, Pres.--Akzo Zout Chemie B.V., Hengelo, Netherlands; *Int'l*, pg. 43

D'Hondt, Freddy, Chief Fin. Officer--Lee Europe N.V., Brussels, Belgium; *U.S. Public*, pg. 1702

D'Silva, Michael, V.P. & Chief Rep.--Westpac Banking Corporation (Columbus Representative Office), Columbus, OH; *Int'l*, pg. 1496

D'Urso, Giorgio, Pres. & Chief Exec. Officer--Diamedix Corporation, Miami, FL; *U.S. Public*, pg. 914

D'Urso, Giorgio, Pres.--Delta Biologicals, S.r.l., Rome, Italy; *U.S. Public*, pg. 915

Da Costa Noble, Christian, Pres.--Tailleur Industrie, Paris, France; *Int'l*, pg. 549

da Costa, M., Pres.--Tyton Hellermann do Brasil Industria e Comercio Ltda., Sao Paulo, Brazil; *Int'l*, pg. 209

da Costa, R., Gen. Mgr.--DeVilbiss Ransburg Brazil, Sao Paulo, Brazil; *U.S. Public*, pg. 867

da Costa, Vera Nobre, Pres.--Young & Rubicam (Portugal), Lisbon, Portugal; *U.S. Private*, pg. 1199

da Cruz, Rui Monteiro, Dir. Gen.-North America--TAP Air Portugal, Newark, NJ; *Int'l*, pg. 1418

da Silva, A.R., Gen. Mgr.--Hoover Electrica Portuguesa Ltda., Lisbon, Portugal; *Int'l*, pg. 260

da Silva, Alaecio Nascimento, Mgr.--Fortaleza Branch, Fortaleza, Brazil; *Int'l*, pg. 139

da Silva, F.E., Mng. Dir.--Instituto Pasteur de Lisboa, Lisbon, Portugal; *U.S. Public*, pg. 81

Daasch, Warren R., Pres.--Wright & Wilhelmy Co., Omaha, NE; *U.S. Private*, pg. 335

Dabah, Ezra, Chief Oper. Officer--Girl's Division, New York, NY; *U.S. Public*, pg. 686

Dabney, Barbara, Admin.--Pine Towers Convalescent Hospital, San Francisco, CA; *U.S. Public*, pg. 1714

Dabringhausen, Peter, Pres.--Nalco Chemical Process Chemicals Division, Naperville, IL; *U.S. Public*, pg. 1150

Dabrowski, H.J., V.P. & Gen. Mgr.--Senior TIFT, Inc., Union, NJ; *Int'l*, pg. 1222

DaCanal, Randy, Gen. Mgr.--P/M Bearing Div., Cherryville, NC; *U.S. Private*, pg. 619

Dachowski, Peter, Pres.-Insulation Div.--Isover Saint-Gobain, Courbevoie, France; *Int'l*, pg. 1176

Dachowski, Peter R., Chm. Bd.--Ludowici Roof Tile, Inc., New Lexington, OH; *Int'l*, pg. 1171

Dachowski, Peter R., Pres.--CertainTeed International, Inc., Valley Forge, PA; *Int'l*, pg. 1171

Dachowski, Peter R., Pres.--CertainTeed Manatee Insulation Ltd., Montreal, Canada; *Int'l*, pg. 1176

Dack, Lee, Div. Pres.--Kaynar/K-Fast/APS, Fullerton, CA; *U.S. Public*, pg. 940

Dacla, Francois, Pres.--BMG Ariola S.A. (France), Paris, France; *Int'l*, pg. 192

Dacosta, Otilia, Mgr.--Broad National Bank-Kearny, Kearny, NJ; *U.S. Public*, pg. 258

Dadario, Michael J., Div. Exec. V.P.-Stores & Opers.--Banana Republic, San Francisco, CA; *U.S. Public*, pg. 702

Dadd, R.F., Pres.--Construction Specialties of California, Cranford, NJ; *U.S. Private*, pg. 266

Dadd, R.F., Pres.--Datasphere, Inc., Cranford, NJ; *U.S. Private*, pg. 266

Dadon, Robert, Chief Oper. Officer--Nobel Electronique S.A.R.L., Paris, France; *Int'l*, pg. 1290

Daenen, Victor, Chief Oper. Officer--KONE Luxembourg S.a.r.l., Strassen, Latvia; *Int'l*, pg. 747

Daffy, Paul, Mng. Dir.--Challenge Properties Limited, Auckland, New Zealand; *Int'l*, pg. 495

Dagan, D., Gen. Mgr.--LAHAV Division/Military Aircraft Group, Israel; *Int'l*, pg. 690

Dager, Sergio, Mng. Dir.--Nova Trading, Sao Paulo, Brazil; *Int'l*, pg. 1389

Daggon, R.V., Chief Oper. Officer--Kidde Technologies Inc., Marlborough, MA; *Int'l*, pg. 1500

Dagnall, Dr. Roy, Chief Oper. Officer--Covance Laboratories, Madison, WI; *U.S. Public*, pg. 454

Dagnan, O.G., Chm. Bd. & Chief Exec. Officer--Centex Construction Products, Inc., Dallas, TX; *U.S. Public*, pg. 322

Dahan, Andre, Pres.--Dun & Bradstreet, Murray Hill, NJ; *U.S. Public*, pg. 535

Dahl, Aage, Mng. Dir.--A/S Mulva Grafiske Produkter, Vestby, Norway; *U.S. Public*, pg. 78

Dahl, Erik, Mng. Dir.--Ericsson Holding A/S, Nesbru, Norway; *Int'l*, pg. 1367

Dahl, H. Douglas, Pres.--Eastern Associated Coal Corp., Charleston, WV; *Int'l*, pg. 594

Dahl, H. Douglas, Pres.--Peabody Coal Co., Charleston, WV; *Int'l*, pg. 594

Dahl, Lars, Gen. Mgr.--Wisconsin Machining Division, Lake Mills, WI; *Int'l*, pg. 737

Dahl, Lars Gorvell, Dir.--Kvaerner Fjellstrand (S) Pte Ltd., Hong Kong Representative Office, Happy Valley, Hong Kong; *Int'l*, pg. 767

Dahl, Ole, Pres.--Time/System International A/S, Allerod, Denmark; *Int'l*, pg. 73

Dahl, Robert, Pres.--Curtis 1000, Inc., Atlanta, GA; *U.S. Public*, pg. 70

Dahl, Rolf Nagel, Mgr.--Norden Banking Group, Oslo, Norway; *Int'l*, pg. 1328

Dahlberg, Burt, Pres.--Kraus-Anderson Realty Company, Bloomington, MN; *U.S. Private*, pg. 635

Dahlberg, Kenneth, Pres. & Chief Oper. Officer--Raytheon Systems Company, Arlington, VA; *U.S. Public*, pg. 1364

Dahlberg, Lars, Chief Oper. Officer--ISAGA H.F., Reykjavik, Iceland; *Int'l*, pg. 14

Dahlin, Richard L., Pres.--Henry & Henry, Inc., Lancaster, NY; *Int'l*, pg. 244

Dahlka, Edward, Pres.--Sanwa General Equipment Leasing, Towson, MD; *Int'l*, pg. 1189

Dahlke, Michael, Pres.--Enron Americas, Inc., Houston, TX; *U.S. Public*, pg. 584

Dahlman, Fredrich, Gen. Mgr.--Sensormatic AB (Sweden), Stockholm, Sweden; *U.S. Public*, pg. 1457

Dahlman, Jules, Gen. Mgr.--Budde & Westermann, Montclair, NJ; *U.S. Private*, pg. 411

Dahlquist, Steve, Pres.--Bruner Water Treatment Systems, Milwaukee, WI; *U.S. Public*, pg. 467

Dahlstrom, Arne, Chief Oper. Officer--Granges International Mining, Stockholm, Sweden; *Int'l*, pg. 439

Dahlstrom, Christer, Pres.--Skandia Investment AB, Stockholm, Sweden; *Int'l*, pg. 1256

Dahm, Jose, Mng. Dir.--Ares S.A., Rodange, Luxembourg; *Int'l*, pg. 79

Dahne, Helmut, Dr., Mng. Dir.--Rowohlt Verlag GmbH, Reinbek, Germany; *Int'l*, pg. 1478

Daigle, Robert, Div. Mgr.--Microwave Materials Group-Microwave Materials Div., Chandler, AZ; *U.S. Public*, pg. 1402

Daikubara, Izumi, Pres.--GSI Exim America Inc., New York, NY; *Int'l*, pg. 578

Dailey, John R., Pres.--Quantic Industries Inc., Hollister, CA; *U.S. Private*, pg. 899

Daily, Curtis E., Pres. & Grp. V.P.--Flowserve Corporation, Rotating Equipment Grp., Dayton, OH; *U.S. Public*, pg. 658

Daily, Ralph, Branch Mgr.--Circle International, Indianapolis, IN; *U.S. Public*, pg. 371

Daimaru, Wayne, Asst. Branch Mgr.--Gasco, Inc., Kailua Kona, HI; *Int'l*, pg. 225

Daireaux, Carlos, Gen. Mgr.--Gillette do Brasil & Cia, Rio de Janeiro, Brazil; *U.S. Public*, pg. 744

Daisy, Edward, Pres.--Adhesive Research, Inc., Glen Rock, PA; *U.S. Private*, pg. 1091

Dakoske, D., Chief Oper. Officer--Augat, Inc., Automotive Components Division-Boyne City, Boyne City, MI; *U.S. Public*, pg. 1598

Daks, Peter A., Pres.--GTE Florida Incorporated, Tampa, FL; *U.S. Public*, pg. 697

Dalbin, Patrick, Mng. Dir.--CCCE Nelson/Babylone, Boulogne, France; *Int'l*, pg. 116

Dalby, Glenn, Mng. Dir.--Gencor ACP Ltd., Leicester, United Kingdom; *U.S. Public*, pg. 705

Dalcontres, Marcantonio Stagno, Gen. Mgr.--Banco di Sicilia, London, United Kingdom; *Int'l*, pg. 140

Dale, Bruce, Pres.--Aaron Brothers, Inc., City of Commerce, CA; *U.S. Public*, pg. 1104

Dale, Robert, Pres.--Windy Hill Pet Food Co., Perham, MN; *U.S. Private*, pg. 1182

Dalesio, Ronald, Gen. Mgr.--Interactive Instructional Systems Inc., Pittsburgh, PA; *Int'l*, pg. 1089

Daley, James C., Pres.--IMSAMET, Inc., Litchfield Park, AZ; *U.S. Public*, pg. 587

Daley, Joseph, V.P.-Ink Prods.--PAXAR Apparel Identification Systems, Rock Hill, SC; *U.S. Public*, pg. 1266

Daley, Keiran, Mng. Dir.--IGT-(Australia), Pty. Limited, Rosebery, Australia; *U.S. Public*, pg. 900

Dalglish, J., Mgr.--NSP-North Debate Region, Grand Forks, ND; *U.S. Public*, pg. 1195

Dalhoff, Wilhelm, Prof. Dr., Chm. Bd.--Krupp Maschinentechnik GmbH, Hamburg, Germany; *Int'l*, pg. 510

Daliakopoulos, N.S., Mng. Dir.--Goodyear Hellas S.A.I.C., Athens, Greece; *U.S. Public*, pg. 753

Dalichook, Igar, Mng. Dir.--Reemtsma Cherkassy Tyutyunova Fabrika, Cherkassy, Ukraine; *Int'l*, pg. 1101

Dall' Acqua, Charles, Pres.--Harte-Hanks Marketing Services, River Edge, NJ; *U.S. Public*, pg. 794

Dall'Acqua, Charles, Pres.--Harte-Hanks Direct Marketing Maryland, Baltimore, MD; *U.S. Public*, pg. 794

Dallal, Vera, Dir.--WF Corroon-Europe, London, United Kingdom; *Int'l*, pg. 1502

DallaPezze, J. R., Sr. V.P. & Gen. Mgr.--McCullough, An Atlas Wireline Services Operation, Houston, TX; *U.S. Public*, pg. 1004

Dalle, Phillipe, Pres.--Cosmair Canada Inc., Montreal, Canada; *Int'l*, pg. 819

Dalle, Roger, Mng. Dir.--Bekaert Benelux N.V., Zwevegem, Belgium; *Int'l*, pg. 183

Dallinger, Curtis C., Pres.--Natural Fuels Corporation, Denver, CO; *U.S. Public*, pg. 1170
Dallmayr, Patrick, Gen. Mgr.--Societe Financere de Geneve, Geneva, Switzerland; *Int'l*, pg. 240
Dalquist, H. David, III, Pres.--Nordic Ware Direct, Inc., Saint Louis Park, MN; *U.S. Private*, pg. 806
Dalsgaard, Carl-Johan, Pres.--Astra Pain Control AB, Sodertalje, Sweden; *Int'l*, pg. 93
Dalsjo, Age, Gen. Mgr.--Kvaerner Energy, Sorumsand, Sorumsand, Norway; *Int'l*, pg. 767
Dalton, James, Chief Oper. Officer--Tektronix Development Company, Wilsonville, OR; *U.S. Public*, pg. 1567
Dalton, James E., Pres.--Logicon R & D Associates, Los Angeles, CA; *U.S. Public*, pg. 1199
Dalton, Larry H., V.P.-Opers.--Guardsman Consumer Products Div., Grand Rapids, MI; *U.S. Public*, pg. 995
Dalton, Michaael J., Pres.--Concord Electric Company, Hampton, NH; *U.S. Public*, pg. 1692
Dalton, Michael J., Pres.--Exeter & Hampton Electric Co., Hampton, NH; *U.S. Public*, pg. 1692
Dalton, Michael J., Pres.--Fitchburg Gas and Electric Light Co., Fitchburg, MA; *U.S. Public*, pg. 1692
Dalton, Michael J., Sr. Exec. V.P.--UNITIL Service Corporation, Hampton, NH; *U.S. Public*, pg. 1693
Dalton, Tom, Gen. Mgr.--Plumley Companies, Paris, TN; *U.S. Public*, pg. 480
Dalton, Tom, Mgr.-Opers.--Geo-Con, Inc., Voorhees, NJ; *U.S. Public*, pg. 1657
Dalton, William, Pres.--SMC McEver Inc., Houston, TX; *U.S.* Public, pg. 1717
Daltrini, Bernardo, Mgr.--Banco do Brasil S.A.-Hong Kong Representative Office, Queensway, Hong Kong; *Int'l*, pg. 142
Daly, Ann, Pres.--Buena Vista Home Video, Burbank, CA; *U.S. Public*, pg. 513
Daly, Gerald R., V.P. & Gen. Mgr.--Harris Bank International Corp., New York, NY; *Int'l*, pg. 154
Daly, James G., Pres.--UNITIL Power Corporation, Hampton, NH; *U.S. Public*, pg. 1692
Daly, James G., Pres.--UNITIL Resources, Inc., Hampton, NH; *U.S. Public*, pg. 1692
Daly, James M., Plant Mgr.--Miller Brewing Company, Eden, NC; *U.S. Public*, pg. 1289
Daly, John F., Pres.--Karl Koch Erecting Co. Inc., Carteret, NJ; *Int'l*, pg. 1261
Daly, Kevin, Chm. Bd., Pres. & Chief Exec. Officer--ATL Products, Inc., Anaheim, CA; *U.S. Public*, pg. 1212
Daly, M.A., Gen. Mgr.--Baring Asset Management (France), Paris, France; *Int'l*, pg. 648
Daly, Ron E., Pres.--R.R. Donnelley Norwest Div.-Greeley, Greeley, CO; *U.S. Public*, pg. 518
Daly, Stephen J., V.P. & Gen. Mgr.--Lindenmeyr Munroe, Rutherford, NJ; *U.S. Private*, pg. 224
Daly, Terry, Pres.--Hermes Precisa Australia Pty Ltd., Sydney, Australia; *Int'l*, pg. 579
Daly, Thomas M., Pres.--C.J. Tower Inc., Buffalo, NY; *U.S. Public*, pg. 1071
Daly, Tom, Grp. V.P.--TMP Worldwide/Recruitment Division, Atlanta, GA; *U.S. Private*, pg. 1065
Daly, Vincent, Mng. Dir.--LM Ericsson Holdings Ltd., Dublin, Ireland; *Int'l*, pg. 1368
Dalzell, James, Mng. Dir.--Bridgeway Hospital, North Little Rock, AR; *U.S. Public*, pg. 1696
Dalziel, Mark W., V.P. & Mng. Exec.--Northern Trust Bank of Florida, N.A., Boca Raton, FL; *U.S. Public*, pg. 1196
Dambek, D.M., V.P. & Gen. Mgr.--Flexonics Hose, Westmont, IL; *Int'l*, pg. 1222
Dame, John, Distr. Mgr.--National Mine Service Company, Logan Div., Switzer, WV; *Int'l*, pg. 281
Dameron, John, Mgr.--Shepler's Austin, Austin, TX; *U.S. Public*, pg. 413
Dameron, John, Mgr.--Shepler's Waco, Waco, TX; *U.S. Public*, pg. 413
Dameron, John, Mgr.--Shepler's Round Rock, Round Rock, TX; *U.S. Public*, pg. 413
Damiano, Ray, Gen. Mgr.--Frankel & Company, Orange, CA; *U.S. Private*, pg. 424
Damico, Joseph F., Pres. & Chief Oper. Officer--Allegiance Healthcare International, McGaw Park, IL; *U.S. Public*, pg. 45
Damisch, Hans, Mng. Dir.--Beteiligungsgesellschaft fur die deutsche Wirtschaft GmbH, Frankfurt/Main, Germany; *Int'l*, pg. 418
Damkjaer, Erling, Chief Oper. Officer--A/S Vestfrost, Esbjerg, Denmark; *Int'l*, pg. 441
Damkjaer, Jorgen, Chief Oper. Officer--Scania Danmark A/S, Herlev, Denmark; *Int'l*, pg. 687
Damm, Helmut, Gen. Mgr.--Banco Nacional de Mexico, Toronto, Canada; *Int'l*, pg. 574
Damm, Karl Hans, Chief Exec. Officer--AEG Hausgerate AG, Nuremberg, Germany; *Int'l*, pg. 442
Dammeier, Brian, Vice Chm.--Print Northwest Company, L.P., Fife, WA; *Int'l*, pg. 1076
Dammerg, John, Chief Exec. Officer--Schering Pty. Ltd., Alexandria, Australia; *Int'l*, pg. 1204
Damonti, Giancarlo, Mgr.--Vickers Medical Italia S.p.A., San Giuliano Milanese, Italy; *Int'l*, pg. 1467
Damphousse, Roger, Pres.--Benchmark Electronics, Inc., Hudson, NH; *U.S. Public*, pg. 211
Dampman, J. Doug, Plant Mgr.--Pneu-Hydro Products, Inc., Wharton, NJ; *U.S. Public*, pg. 1593
Dan, Michael T., Pres. & Chief Exec. Officer--Brink's, Inc., Darien, CT; *U.S. Public*, pg. 1305
Dana, Donald C., Pres.--Sound Elevator, Kirkland, WA; *U.S.* Public, pg. 521
Danaher, B., Pres.--Phillips & Temro Industries Inc., Eden Prairie, MN; *Int'l*, pg. 1388
Danahy, James M., Pres.--Sysco Food Services of Connecticut, Rocky Hill, CT; *U.S. Public*, pg. 1551
Danahy, John F.nt, Chm.--Famous-Barr, Saint Louis, MO; *U.S. Public*, pg. 1063
Dancer, E., Mng. Dir.--Dartington Crystal, Torrington, United Kingdom; *Int'l*, pg. 124
Dancheck, Joseph M., Pres.--Harris Life Insurance Company, Scottsdale, AZ; *Int'l*, pg. 154
Danderidge, M., Sr. V.P. & Gen. Mgr.--Electronics & Systems Integration Division, Melbourne, FL; *U.S. Public*, *pg. 1198*
Dandes, Jonathan A., V.P. & Gen. Mgr.--B.R. Guest, Ltd., Buffalo, NY; *U.S. Private*, pg. 928
Dandridge, Linda Gail, Area Mgr.--American Cablevision of West Memphis, Inc., West Memphis, AR; *U.S. Public*, pg. 1610
Dandurand, Richard A., Pres.--Stanley Access Technologies, Farmington, CT; *U.S. Public*, pg. 1509
Danehy, R. James, Pres.--Centocor Diagnostics Div., Malvern, PA; *U.S. Public*, pg. 323
Danelli, Jose Carlos Gouveia, Gen. Mgr.--Banco do Brasil S.A.-Milan, Milan, Italy; *Int'l*, pg. 141
Danford, Dan, Pres.--Esprit Kids, San Francisco, CA; *U.S. Private*, pg. 383
Dang, Pran, Mgr.-Mfg.--Indian Shaving Products, Limited, New Delhi, India; *U.S. Public*, pg. 745
Dangerfield, Brian, Mng. Dir.--Union-Transport (HK) Ltd, Kowloon, Hong Kong; *U.S. Private*, pg. 1120
Dangerfield, W.F., Chief Exec. Officer--New Zealand Starch, Auckland, New Zealand; *Int'l*, pg. 555
Danhoff, Richard E., Div. Mgr.--Rail Products Division, Lancaster, SC; *U.S. Private*, pg. 65
Daniel, Charles, Pres. & Chief Exec. Officer--UPB of Girardeau Co., Cape Girardeau, MO; *U.S. Public*, pg. 1669
Daniel, Josef, Pres.--AGA GAS spol.s r.o., Prague, Czech Republic; *Int'l*, pg. 13
Daniel, Josef, Pres.--AGA GAS Spol.s r.o., Bratislava, Slovakia; *Int'l*, pg. 13
Daniel, Travis E., Mgr.-Branch--Lindenmeyr Munroe, Richmond, VA; *U.S. Private*, pg. 224
Daniels, D.A., Gen. Mgr.--CHEMCENTRAL/Orlando, Orlando, FL; *U.S. Private*, pg. 232
Daniels, George F., Pres.--McCord Winn Textron Company, Manchester, NH; *U.S. Public*, pg. 1590
Daniels, Mike, Pres.--SCT Government Systems, Lexington, KY; *U.S. Public*, pg. 1552
Daniels, Mitchell E., Jr., Pres.-N. American Pharmaceuticals Opers.--Pharmaceutical Division, Indianapolis, IN; *U.S. Public*, pg. 993
Daniels, Steven L., V.P.-Mktg.--Marketing & Project Development, Erie, PA; *U.S. Public*, pg. 1794
Daniels, Waynes, Pres.--Crown Moving & Storage Inc., Indianapolis, IN; *U.S. Private*, pg. 1171
Danielsen, Daniel, Chief Oper. Officer--Royal Copenhagen Retail A/S, Copenhagen, Denmark; *Int'l*, pg. 1134
Danielson, Robert, Dir.-Engrng.--AlliedSignal Automotive Proving Grounds, New Carlisle, IN; *U.S. Public*, pg. 51
Danielsson, Alrik, Mng. Dir.--SKF Loziska A.S., Prague, Czech Republic; *Int'l*, pg. 1159
Danielsson, Bengt, Chief Oper. Officer--Perstorp Formox, Perstorp, Sweden; *Int'l*, pg. 1038
Danielsson, Erik, Pres. & Chief Exec. Officer--Pharmacia & Upjohn Biosystems AB, Uppsala, Sweden; *Int'l*, pg. 1047
Danielsson, Goran, Pres.--Telub Inforum AB, Vaxjo, Sweden; *Int'l*, pg. 277
Danielsson, Nils-Erik, Chief Oper. Officer--AB Overums Fonsterfabrik, Overum, Sweden; *Int'l*, pg. 439
Daniher, Bill, Sr. Acct. Supvr.--The McClure Group/American Teledirect, Chicago, IL; *U.S. Private*, pg. 720
Danilson, Ron, Pres. & Chief Exec. Officer--Delaware Charter Guarantee & Trust Co., Wilmington, DE; *U.S. Private*, pg. 885
Daninger, Don, Engineer--Transico Inc., Membrane Switch Operations, Phoenix, AZ; *U.S. Public*, pg. 1631
Danio, John R., Pres.--CR Kendall Corporation, Hilger, MT; *U.S. Public*, pg. 302
Dann, L. Kevin, Sr. V.P.--Jefferies & Company, Inc., Los Angeles, CA; *U.S. Public*, pg. 925
Danneburg, John C., V.P. & Gen. Mgr.--BC Hydrotile Machinery Co., Sioux City, IA; *U.S. Private*, pg. 571
Dannenberg, John C., V.P. & Gen. Mgr.--McCracken, Sioux City, IA; *U.S. Private*, pg. 571
Dannenhauer, Daniel g., Pres.--Hilb, Rogal and Hamilton Company of Fort Myers, Fort Myers, FL; *U.S. Public*, pg. 827
Danner, Paul, Pres. & Chief Exec. Officer--Regions Bank/Citrus County, Inverness, FL; *U.S. Public*, pg. 1372
Dannestig, Per Olof, Mng. Dr.--Kalmar LMV AB, Ljungby, Sweden; *Int'l*, pg. 1421
Dansby, Ronald C., Pres.--Dixie Marine, Inc., Houston, TX; *U.S. Public*, pg. 962
Dansereau, Dick, Dir.-Opers.--Kimberly-Clark Tecnol, Fort Worth, TX; *U.S. Public*, pg. 959
Dantas, Ney, Chief Oper. Officer--Automatic Power RJ, Rio de Janeiro, Brazil; *Int'l*, pg. 1289
Dantoft, Jan-Erik, Chief Oper. Officer--Saab-Scania AB, Lulea, Sweden; *Int'l*, pg. 687
Danton, Ken, Pres.--The White Lily Foods Co., Knoxville, TN; *U.S. Private*, pg. 866
Dantuma, Klaas, Mng. Dir.--Koninklijke Gazelle BV, Dieren, Netherlands; *Int'l*, pg. 394
Danty, Natan, Dir.--Dacem S.A.R.L., Bondy, France; *Int'l*, pg. 734
Danz, Christian, Gen. Mgr.--Eagle-Picher Wolverine GmbH, Ohringen, Germany; *U.S. Private*, pg. 355
Danz, Christian, Chief Oper. Officer--Eagle-Picher Wolverine Gmbh, Ohringen, Germany; *U.S. Private*, pg. 355
Danzer, Rudolph, Country Mgr.--Autodesk GesmbH, Wels, Austria; *U.S. Public*, pg. 149
Danzi, Paul R., V.P.-Construction--Walsh Construction Company (West), Sacramento, CA; *U.S. Public*, pg. 143
Danzi, Paul R., V.P.--Walsh Power Group, Sacramento, CA; *U.S. Public*, pg. 143
Danzig, Robert J., V.P. & Gen. Mgr.--Hearst Newspapers, New York, NY; *U.S. Private*, pg. 517
Danziger, Jerry, Vice Chm.--KOB-TV, Inc., Albuquerque, NM; *U.S. Private*, pg. 544
Dapper, G. Steven, Pres. & Chief Exec. Officer--Rapp Collins Worldwide, New York, NY; *U.S. Public*, pg. 1224
Darby, Christopher, Pres. & Chief Exec. Officer--Caronet LLC, Raleigh, NC; *U.S. Public*, pg. 307
Darby, Jim, Chief Exec. Officer--Kearney Company, Fayetteville, AR; *U.S. Public*, pg. 444
Darby, Kenneth M., Chief Oper. Officer--Vicon Industries (U.K.) Ltd., Fareham, United Kingdom; *U.S. Public*, pg. 1719
Darby, O.C., Exec. Chm.--Bass Leisure, Burton on Trent, United Kingdom; *Int'l*, pg. 170
Darby, Warren A., Pres.--ServiceCare, Inc., Columbia, SC; *U.S. Public*, pg. 1436
Darcey, H. James, Pres. & Chief Exec. Officer--First Security Investment Management, Inc., Salt Lake City, UT; *U.S. Public*, pg. 638
Darcey, John, Chief Exec. Officer--Laminaire Corporation, Rahway, NJ; *U.S. Public*, pg. 1596
Darch, S.T., Pres.--ING Baring Sociedad de Bolsa (Argentina), Buenos Aires, Argentina; *Int'l*, pg. 649
Darche, Jean, Dir.--Eurolease-Factor (Elfa) SA, Luxembourg, Luxembourg; *Int'l*, pg. 548
Darcy, John M., Pres. & Gen. Mgr.--Penford Food Ingredients Company, Englewood, CO; *U.S. Public*, pg. 1269
Darcy, Randy G., Pres.--General Mills Operations, Inc., Minneapolis, MN; *U.S. Public*, pg. 718
Darcy, Thomas B., Mgr.-Reg. Sls.--Burgmann Seals America, Inc., Warwick, RI; *Int'l*, pg. 233
Dardaud, Jacques, Pres.--Laboratoires Bristol S.A., Paris, France; *U.S. Public*, pg. 256
Dardel, Pierre Emmanuel, Chm. Bd.--Sofineti, Paris, France; *Int'l*, pg. 344
Darden, Dan, Mgr.--Tandy Transportation, Fort Worth, TX; *U.S. Public*, pg. 1560
Dargatz, K.C., Pres.--Haden, Inc., Auburn Hills, MI; *Int'l*, pg. 586
Dargatz, K.C., Pres.--Nim-Cor, Inc., Auburn Hills, MI; *Int'l*, pg. 586
Darhoff, Gunnel, Gen. Mgr.--ESAB Representative Office, Moscow, Russia; *Int'l*, pg. 282
Dariano, Joseph, Chief Exec. Officer--Reed Technology and Information Services-Government Services, Horsham, PA; *Int'l*, pg. 1096
Darieu, M.C., Gen. Mgr.--Teletec SARL, Paris, France; *U.S. Private*, pg. 1074
Darimont, M., Chief Oper. Officer--IC Imtech NV, Brussels, Belgium; *Int'l*, pg. 681
Darkazanli, Serge, Pres.--Kelly Douglass Westfair Foods Ltd., Winnipeg, Canada; *Int'l*, pg. 1495
Darland, Stephen A., Exec. V.P.--J. Walter Thompson Company, New York, NY; *Int'l*, pg. 1483
Darling, Darrell, Pres. & Chief Exec. Officer--First National Bank of Crossville, Crossville, TN; *U.S. Public*, pg. 1669
Darlow, Mark H., Pres.--Unidigital/Cardinal Corp., New York, NY; *U.S. Public*, pg. 1664
Darlow, Richard A., Div. Pres.--HIAC/ROYCO Division, Silver Spring, MD; *U.S. Public*, pg. 1250
Darmisch, Hans E., Chief Exec.--Unternehmensbeteilgungsgesellschaft fur die deutsche Wirtschaft, Frankfurt/Main, Germany; *Int'l*, pg. 418
Darmon, Claude, Chm. & Chief Oper. Officer--SAFT, Romainville, France; *Int'l*, pg. 54
Darmstadt, Raymond, Mgr.-Div.--Bermco Paper Company, New York, NY; *U.S. Private*, pg. 467
Darmstadter, Ludwig, Mng. Dir.--Matchbox Spielwaren GmbH, Hosbach, Germany; *U.S. Public*, pg. 1059
Darnall, Robert J., Chm. Bd. & Chief Exec. Officer--Inland International, Inc., Chicago, IL; *U.S. Public*, pg. 879
Darpe, Max-J., Mng. Dir.--Deutsche Bank Lubeck AG, Lubeck, Germany; *Int'l*, pg. 402
Darpi, Abdul Vitri, V.P. & Dir.--P.T. Chase Leasing Indonesia, Jakarta, Indonesia; *U.S. Public*, pg. 339
Darragh, Kent J., Pres.--Cadillac Plastic & Chemical Co., Troy, MI; *U.S. Public*, pg. 781
Darriba, J.R., Chief Oper. Officer--Supermercados Mayoristas Makra S.A., Buenos Aires, Argentina; *Int'l*, pg. 1156
Darrouzet, Jean-Claude, Chief Oper. Officer--Evian, Evian-les-Bains, France; *Int'l*, pg. 381
Dart, L.K., Gen. Mgr.--ITT Jabsco, Costa Mesa, CA; *U.S. Public*, pg. 860
Dartevelle, Jacques, Chief Oper. Officer--Akerlund & Rausing S.A.R.L., Paris, France; *Int'l*, pg. 33
Dartnell, David, Pres.--David Dart, Chatsworth, CA; *U.S. Public*, pg. 948
Darty, Bernard, Chm. & Pres.--Establissments Darty & Fils S.A., Bondy, France; *Int'l*, pg. 734
Darty, Natan, Dir.--Caprofem S.A., Paris, France; *Int'l*, pg. 734
Darwin, Edward O., Pres.--Chubb Custom Market, Inc., Warren, NJ; *U.S. Public*, pg. 355
Darwin, Sidney, Chm. Bd.--Concord Miniatures, Rahway, NJ; *U.S. Private*, pg. 209
Darwish, Mougahed, Mng. Dir.--ICB Ingenieurs Conseils, Marin, Switzerland; *Int'l*, pg. 1160
Darwish, Mougahed, Mng. Dir.--EM Microelectronic-Marin S.A., Marin, Switzerland; *Int'l*, pg. 1160
Darwish, Mougahed, Mng. Dir.--SMH Automobile AG, Bienne, Switzerland; *Int'l*, pg. 1161
Darwish, Raouf, Mng. Dir.--Darwish Consulting Engineers, Cairo, Egypt; *Int'l*, pg. 606
Das, Gucharan C., V.P. & Gen. Mgr.--India--Procter & Gamble India, Mumbai, India; *U.S. Public*, pg. 1332
Das, Suprotik, Gen. Mgr.--Nordson India Private Limited, Mumbai, India; *U.S. Public*, pg. 1189
Dashnaw, Richard L., Pres.--Fairbanks Morse Engine Division, Beloit, WI; *U.S. Public*, pg. 401
Datt, Raymond, Pres.--Wells Manufacturing Canada Ltd., Mississauga, Canada; *U.S. Private*, pg. 1113
Dattilo, Tom, Pres.--Victor Products, Lisle, IL; *U.S. Public*, pg. 480
Dattoli, Joseph, V.P. & Gen. Mgr.--Perugina Brands of America, Saddle Brook, NJ; *Int'l*, pg. 917
Daub, Albert W., Pres.--Scarecrow Press, Inc., Metuchen, NJ; *Int'l*, pg. 794

Daubel, Jim, Pres., Publr. & Editor--Fremont News-Messenger, Fremont, OH; *U.S. Public*, pg. 700
Daubenspeck, Harold, Pres.--Togiak Fisheries Inc., Seattle, WA; *Int'l*, pg. 845
Daugherty, B.J., Vice Chm.--NationsBank of Conway, Conway, AR; *U.S. Public*, pg. 1164
Daugherty, Tim, Admin.--Greenery Health Care Center, Howell, MI; *U.S. Public*, pg. 837
Daul, Pierre, Mng. Dir.--Jet Chandler International, Rungis, France; *Int'l*, pg. 560
Daum, Gary C., Sr. V.P. & Gen. Mgr.--Quebecor Printing Fairfield Inc., Fairfield, PA; *Int'l*, pg. 1076
Daum, Gary C., Sr. V.P. & Gen. Mgr.--Quebecor Printing Martinsburg, Martinsburg, WV; *Int'l*, pg. 1076
Davaille, Jean-Pierre, Mng. Dir.--Janssen-Cilag S.A., Boulogne-Billancourt, France; *U.S. Public*, pg. 929
Davant, Jack, Sr. V.P.--Financial Aims Corporation, Great Falls, MT; *U.S. Private*, pg. 314
Davatzes, Nickolas, Pres. & Chief Exec. Officer--Arts & Entertainment Network/ABC/NBC, New York, NY; *U.S. Public*, pg. 512
Davatzes, Nickolas, Pres. & Chief Exec. Officer--A&E Television Networks, New York, NY; *U.S. Private*, pg. 515
Davatzes, Nickolas, Pres. & Chief Exec. Officer--Arts & Entertainment Network/ABC/NBC, New York, NY; *U.S. Private*, pg. 516
Davenport, D.A., Deputy Mng. Dir.--P&O Vending, London, United Kingdom; *Int'l*, pg. 1034
Davenport, Norman, Mng. Dir.--UPM-Kymmene UK plc, London, United Kingdom; *Int'l*, pg. 1430
Davenport, Vern, Reg. Mgr.--SMS-Ft. Lauderdale, Fort Lauderdale, FL; *U.S. Public*, pg. 1463
Davey, Don, Chief Oper. Officer--Onga Pty. Ltd., Toorak, Australia; *U.S. Public*, pg. 1767
Davey, Graham, Reg. Mng. Dir.--DHL International (Singapore) Pte. Ltd., Singapore, Singapore; *U.S. Private, pg. 302*
Davey, P., Mng. Dir.--European Cellars Ltd., Guildford, United Kingdom; *Int'l*, pg. 1499
David-Weill, Michel, Chm Bd. & Chief Exec. Officer--Lazard Freres & Co., New York, NY; *Int'l*, pg. 1027
David, Greg, Editor--Crain's New York Business, New York, NY; *U.S. Private*, pg. 285
David, P. J., Chief Exec. Officer--Pig Improvement Group Ltd., Abingdon, United Kingdom; *Int'l*, pg. 376
David, Popplewell, Pres.--Cincinnati Life Insurance Co., Fairfield, OH; *U.S. Public*, pg. 368
David, Rhys A., Publr.--Business Magazine, London, United Kingdom; *Int'l*, pg. 1025
David, Richard, Gen. Mgr.--Heinemann ELT-Central Europe, Prague, Czech Republic; *Int'l*, pg. 1479
Davidow, S., V.P. & Gen. Mgr.--Four Seasons Air Conditioning Div., Coppell, TX; *U.S. Public*, pg. 1503
Davidson, B.C., Pres.--Terminal Railroad Association of St. Louis, Granite City, IL; *U.S. Public*, pg. 1668
Davidson, Charles T., Chm. Bd., Pres. & Chief Exec. Officer--J.A. Jones, Inc., Charlotte, NC; *Int'l*, pg. 633
Davidson, Charles T., Chm. Bd., Pres. & Chief Exec. Officer--J. A. Jones Construction Company, Charlotte, NC; *Int'l*, pg. 633
Davidson, D. Dwayne, Pres. & Chief Exec. Officer--Liberty Mortgage Co., Oklahoma City, OK; *U.S. Public*, pg. 174
Davidson, Denis H., Pres. & Chief Exec. Officer--Clear Shield National, Inc., Wheeling, IL; *U.S. Public*, pg. 586
Davidson, Dewayne, Chm. Bd.--Liberty Property Management Co., Oklahoma City, OK; *U.S. Public*, pg. 174
Davidson, Donald, Pres.--Outdoor Systems, Inc., New York, NY; *U.S. Public*, pg. 1235
Davidson, Grant, Gen. Mgr.--Abbot Point Bulkcoal Pty. Ltd, Brisbane, Australia; *Int'l*, pg. 827
Davidson, Grant, Gen. Mgr.--Collinsville Coal Co. Pty. Ltd., Brisbane, Australia; *Int'l*, pg. 827
Davidson, Grant, Gen. Mgr.--Newlands Coal Pty. Ltd., Brisbane, Australia; *Int'l*, pg. 827
Davidson, Herbert S., Pres. & Chief Exec. Officer--Milgray/Atlanta, Inc., Norcross, GA; *U.S. Public*, pg. 206
Davidson, Ian, Mng. Dir.--OCLI Optical Coatings Ltd., Dunfermline, United Kingdom; *U.S. Public*, pg. 1227
Davidson, Jeff, Chm. Bd. & Pres.--Michael Weinig, Inc., Statesville, NC; *Int'l*, pg. 1488
Davidson, John, Pres.--Ericsson Components, Inc., Richardson, TX; *Int'l*, pg. 1364
Davidson, Leif, Chief Oper. Officer--Borens AB, Boras, Sweden; *Int'l*, pg. 821
Davidson, M.J., Gen. Mgr.-Sls.--Quality Bakers New Zealand Ltd., Auckland, New Zealand; *Int'l*, pg. 556
Davidson, Marcella, Plant Mgr.--H.B. Reese Candy Co., Hershey, PA; *U.S. Public*, pg. 812
Davidson, Martin, Plant Superintendent--General Shale Products Corp.-Cumberland Mountain Sand Div., Hillsboro, TN; *Int'l*, pg. 844
Davidson, Pat, Managing Partner--Power Business, Kansas City, MO; *U.S. Private*, pg. 146
Davidson, Pat, Managing Partner--Black & Veatch International-Energy, Kansas City, MO; *U.S. Private*, pg. 146
Davidson, Pat, Pres.--Peirone Produce Company, Spokane, WA; *U.S. Private*, pg. 1114
Davidson, Paul, Pres.--Tridon Inc., Nashville, TN; *U.S. Public*, pg. 11
Davidson, Paul E., Grp. Pres.-Refrigeration--Toromont Industries Ltd., Concord, Canada; *Int'l*, pg. 1400
Davidson, R., Mgr.-Sls.--Cooper Bearings, Virginia Beach, VA; *U.S. Public*, pg. 946
Davidson, R.K., Pres.--Southern Illinois and Missouri Bridge Co., Saint Louis, MO; *U.S. Public*, pg. 1668
Davidson, R.L., Chief Oper. Officer--CM Hoist Division, Damascus, VA; *U.S. Public*, pg. 405
Davidson, Robert, V.P.-European Sls. & Opers.--Vicorp, N.V., Utrecht, Netherlands; *U.S. Public*, pg. 1321
Davidson, Robert Sir, Mng. Dir.--GEC Alsthom N.V., Amsterdam, Netherlands; *Int'l*, pg. 56
Davidson, S.W., Gen. Mgr.--A-R Technologies, Richmond, Canada; *Int'l*, pg. 829
Davidson, Wayne, Pres.-Northern District--Holsum of Fort Wayne, Inc., Fort Wayne, IN; *U.S. Private*, pg. 665
Davidson, Wayne A., Pres.--Bristol-Myers Squibb Pharmaceutical & Nutritional Group, New York, NY; *U.S. Public*, pg. 254
Davidson, William, Pres.--Glass Plant, Atlanta, GA; *U.S. Private*, pg. 485
Davidson, William, Pres.--Glass Plant, Harvey, IL; *U.S. Private*, pg. 485
Davidson, William A., Pres.--Davidson Coscan Partners, San Diego, CA; *Int'l*, pg. 228
Davidsson, Lars, Pres.--Kvaerner Kamfab AB, Karlstad, Sweden; *Int'l*, pg. 767
Davidsson, Lars, Mng. Dir.--Kamfab AB, Karlstad, Sweden; *Int'l*, pg. 771
Davie, Andrew, Chief Oper. Officer, Sec. & Mgr.-Personnel--Campbell Distillers Limited, Brentford, United Kingdom; *Int'l*, pg. 567
Davie, Anne, Mng. Dir.--Griffin Bacal Publicidad, Mexico, Mexico; *U.S. Private*, pg. 480
Davies, A.G., Mng. Dir.--Bonded Fibre Fabric Ltd., Bridgwater, United Kingdom; *Int'l*, pg. 798
Davies, C.W., Jr., Pres.--Akom Ltd., Montego Bay, Jamaica; *U.S. Public*, pg. 1644
Davies, Carl, Area Mgr.--Gensym Ltd., Kingston upon Thames, United Kingdom; *U.S. Public*, pg. 731
Davies, Connally, V.P. & Dir.-Opers.--CUC Travel Services Inc., Nashville, TN; *U.S. Public*, pg. 320
Davies, Garry, Mgr.--Sandvik Hard Materials, Warren, MI; *Int'l*, pg. 1186
Davies, Geoff P., Pres.--Charterways Transportation Limited, London, Canada; *Int'l*, pg. 1213
Davies, Gregory T.H., Pres.--Jacobs Vehicle Equipment Company, Bloomfield, CT; *U.S. Public*, pg. 481
Davies, Harry, V.P.-Mfg.--Industrial Acoustics Company S.C. Inc., Moncks Corner, SC; *U.S. Public*, pg. 875
Davies, Hilton, Chm.--Boart International Limited, Sandton, South Africa; *Int'l*, pg. 76
Davies, Howard, Chief Oper. Officer--Uniroyal Englebert Tyres Ltd., Newbridge, United Kingdom; *Int'l*, pg. 327
Davies, J. A., Chief Oper. Officer--Lloyds International Ltd., Sydney, Australia; *Int'l*, pg. 813
Davies, J. Trefor, V.P. & Gen. Mgr.--Dentsply Latin American Export, York, PA; *U.S. Public*, pg. 499
Davies, J.A., Mng. Dir.--British Steel Seamless Tubes-Wednesfield Works, Wolverhampton, United Kingdom; *Int'l*, pg. 220
Davies, J.T., Dir.-Intl. Banking--Lloyds International Banking, London, United Kingdom; *Int'l*, pg. 813
Davies, Jack, Mng. Dir.--CitiBank Savings, London, United Kingdom; *U.S. Public*, pg. 378
Davies, Jim, Dir.--Con-Carriers Ltd., London, United Kingdom; *U.S. Public*, pg. 373
Davies, Jim, Chief Oper. Officer--Dow Jones Markets Canada, Inc., Toronto, Canada; *U.S. Public*, pg. 525
Davies, Jim, Pres.--J.J. Kenny Co., Inc., New York, NY; *U.S.* Public, pg. 1070
Davies, John, Reg. Mgr.--Green Tree Acceptance, Inc., Federal Way, WA; *U.S. Public*, pg. 762
Davies, John B., Mng. Dir.--Kemira Ince Ltd., Chester, United Kingdom; *Int'l*, pg. 728
Davies, John H., Pres.--Barringer Research Limited, Mississauga, Canada; *U.S. Public*, pg. 192
Davies, M.J., Reg. Dir.--Wimpey Alawi LLC, Ruwi, Oman; *Int'l*, pg. 1355
Davies, Marcus O., Pres.--Midrex Corp., Charlotte, NC; *Int'l, pg. 740*
Davies, P., Mgr.--ING Real Estate, London, United Kingdom; *Int'l*, pg. 650
Davies, Paul, Gen. Mgr.--Wynn's-Precision (U.K.)Ltd., Aldershot, United Kingdom; *U.S. Public*, pg. 1783
Davies, Paul T., Pres. & Chief Exec. Officer--F.W. Woolworth Co., New York, NY; *U.S. Public*, pg. 1777
Davies, Peter, Mng. Dir.-Middle East & Central Europe--Tamra DMB&B, Dubai, United Arab Emirates; *U.S. Private*, pg. 305
Davies, Philip, Mng. Dir.--Allied Domecq Leisure, Bourne, United Kingdom; *Int'l*, pg. 63
Davies, Phyl, Brdcst. Dir.--Western International Media Corporation, Vancouver, Canada; *U.S. Private*, pg. 1167
Davies, R.E., Pres.--Engineering-Test Services, Charleston, SC; *U.S. Public*, pg. 468
Davies, R.J., Chief Oper. Officer--Fletcher Smith Ltd., Derby, United Kingdom; *Int'l*, pg. 202
Davies, Richard, Mgr.--Lynchburg Service Center, Madison Heights, VA; *U.S. Private*, pg. 214
Davies, Robert M., Pres.--Hallwood Hotels Inc., Dallas, TX; *U.S. Public*, pg. 778
Davies, Sam, Gen. Mgr.--TML Metrology Centre for Bedford, Kempston, United Kingdom; *U.S. Public*, pg. 260
Davies, Tim, Chief Oper. Officer--National Information Services (NIS), Bethesda, MD; *Int'l*, pg. 1096
Davies, Tony, Dr., Chief Oper. Officer--Meggitt Petroleum Systems (UK), Blackburn, United Kingdom; *Int'l*, pg. 853
Davies, W.D. L., Chm. Bd.--Amersham Corporation, Arlington Heights, IL; *Int'l*, pg. 992
Davies, W.J.B., Pres. & Mng. Dir.--Trafalgar House Property, Inc., Trenton, NJ; *Int'l*, pg. 774
Davila Sola, Nestor D., Gen. Mgr.--John Crane Caribe, San Juan, PR; *Int'l*, pg. 1339
Davis, Alan, Div. Mgr.--TNP Enterprises, Inc.-Mountain Div., Silver City, NM; *U.S. Public*, pg. 1557
Davis, Alan B., Chief Oper. Officer--Princeville Realty Corporation, Princeville, HI; *U.S. Private*, pg. 885
Davis, Alfred M., Chm. Bd.--Halliburton Energy Services, Moorestown, NJ; *U.S. Public*, pg. 776
Davis, Ben, Plant Mgr.--Southern Phenix Textiles, Inc., Phenix City, AL; *U.S. Public*, pg. 933
Davis, Bill, Mgr.--Universal Telephone Co. of Colorado, Pagosa Springs, CO; *U.S. Public*, pg. 330
Davis, Bill, V.P. & Gen. Mgr.--A. Mindel & Son, Inc., Toledo, OH; *U.S. Private*, pg. 987
Davis, Brad, V.P.-Pacific North--Nordson Application Equipment, Inc., Sha Tin, Hong Kong; *U.S. Public*, pg. 1189
Davis, Brad, V.P.-Pacific North--Nordson China Co., Ltd., Shanghai, China; *U.S. Public*, pg. 1189
Davis, Charles, Branch Mgr.--Financial Collection Agencies, Birmingham, United Kingdom; *Int'l*, pg. 471
Davis, Charles H., Pres.--Midwestern Holdings, Inc., Chicago, IL; *Int'l*, pg. 155
Davis, Chris, Chief Oper. Officer--Maxpro Systems, Malaga, Australia; *U.S. Public*, pg. 1663
Davis, Christopher J., Pres.--Volvo Penta U.K. Ltd., Watford, United Kingdom; *Int'l*, pg. 1478
Davis, Clay M., Pres.--Hollywood Supply Company, Hollywood, CA; *U.S. Public*, pg. 1619
Davis, Clive, Pres.--Arista Records Inc., New York, NY; *Int'l, pg. 192*
Davis, D., V.P. & Gen. Mgr.--Dunlap Manufacturing Co., Unionville, MO; *U.S. Private*, pg. 1137
Davis, D. Drew, Div. V.P.--Commercial Care Division, Saint Paul, MN; *U.S. Public*, pg. 1605
Davis, D.D., Mng. Dir.--3M Italia SpA, Milan, Italy; *U.S. Public*, pg. 1607
Davis, D.R., Pres.--Hoffman-Miller Engineers, Inc., Tempe, AZ; *U.S. Private*, pg. 842
Davis, Dan, V.P.--Harwick Standard Distribution Corp., Pico Rivera, CA; *U.S. Private*, pg. 509
Davis, Darrel W., Pres.--TNL Flight Services, Inc., Austin, TX; *U.S. Public*, pg. 1638
Davis, Dave, Div. Mgr.--Johnston & Murphy Retail/Wholesale Stores, Nashville, TN; *U.S. Public*, pg. 728
Davis, David, Chm. Bd.--Dowty Aerospace Propellers, Gloucester, United Kingdom; *Int'l*, pg. 1337
Davis, David E., Jr., Editor & Dir.- Publications--Automobile Magazine, Ann Arbor, MI; *U.S. Public*, pg. 1328
Davis, David J., Chief Oper. Officer & Exec. V.P.--Kleer-Vu Plastics Corp., Compton, CA; *U.S. Public*, pg. 962
Davis, Dean, Gen. Mgr.--Alro Group, Jackson Plastics, Jackson, MI; *U.S. Private*, pg. 46
Davis, Denise J., Pres.--VASA Care, Indianapolis, IN; *Int'l*, pg. 464
Davis, Donald W., Pres. & Chief Exec. Officer--Sunbelt Nursery Group Inc., Fort Worth, TX; *U.S. Public*, pg. 715
Davis, E.W., Mng. Dir.--AAH Meditel Limited, Bromsgrove, United Kingdom; *Int'l*, pg. 591
Davis, Ed, Div. Mgr.--Industrial Coatings Div., Tinley Park, IL; *U.S. Public*, pg. 686
Davis, Ed, Div. Mgr.--Industrial Coatings Div., Oakdale, MN; *U.S. Public*, pg. 686
Davis, Edwin, V.P. & Gen. Mgr.--Micro USPD Inc., Watertown, MA; *U.S. Public*, pg. 1107
Davis, Edwin V., II, Pres. & Chief Exec. Officer--First Security Bank of Oregon, Salem, OR; *U.S. Public*, pg. 637
Davis, Elliott, Mgr.--Eclipse Combustion, Inc., Gilbertsville, PA; *U.S. Private*, pg. 360
Davis, G., Pres.--BookCrafters U.S.A. Inc., Chelsea, MI; *U.S.* Public, pg. 70
Davis, Garry, Sr. Mktg. Officer--Northwest Marketing Div., Federal Way, WA; *U.S. Private*, pg. 296
Davis, Gary, Pres.--BookCrafters U.S.A. Inc., Fredericksburg, VA; *U.S. Public*, pg. 70
Davis, Gary, Controller--South Shore Harbour Development, League City, TX; *U.S. Public*, pg. 88
Davis, Gary, Pres.--Flowers Baking Co. of Baton Rouge, Inc., Baton Rouge, LA; *U.S. Public*, pg. 657
Davis, Gene, Pres.--National Distributing Co., Inc., Tampa, FL; *U.S. Private*, pg. 781
Davis, Geoff, Mng. Dir.--Bomford Turner Limited, Evesham, United Kingdom; *U.S. Public*, pg. 35
Davis, George, Pres.--Timco, Inc., Ashland City, TN; *U.S. Private*, pg. 234
Davis, Gerald, Pres.--Merchants Distributors, Inc., Hickory, NC; *U.S. Private*, pg. 657
Davis, Graham, Dir.- Fin.--Ultra Electronics Controls, Greenford, United Kingdom; *Int'l*, pg. 1431
Davis, Greg, V.P. & Gen. Mgr.--Varian Australia Pty. Ltd., Melbourne, Australia; *U.S. Public*, pg. 1710
Davis, Ian, Pres.--Delta Education, Inc., Hudson, NH; *Int'l*, pg. 1402
Davis, Irwin, Pres.--Broan Limited, Mississauga, Canada; *U.S. Public*, pg. 1194
Davis, J.B., Pres.--Klaussner Furniture Industry, Asheboro, NC; *U.S. Private*, pg. 625
Davis, J.L., Mgr.--Morton Salt Division, Hutchinson, KS; *U.S.* Public, pg. 1135
Davis, J.R., Pres.--The Lakefront Dock & Railroad Terminal Co., Baltimore, MD; *U.S. Public*, pg. 432
Davis, Jack, Chm. Bd.--Dataproducts Corporation, Simi Valley, CA; *Int'l*, pg. 620
Davis, James C., Pres. & Chief Exec. Officer--FFG Trust, Inc., Springfield, IL; *U.S. Public*, pg. 644
Davis, James V., Ph.D., Chm. Bd. & Chief Exec. Officer--Willis Corroon Advanced Risk Management Services, Nashville, TN; *Int'l*, pg. 1505
Davis, James, Jr., Pres.--BCIS Services, Inc., Sherman Oaks, CA; *U.S. Public*, pg. 175
Davis, Jay A., V.P. & Gen. Mgr.--Military and Aerospace Division, Melbourne, FL; *U.S. Public*, pg. 792
Davis, Jeff, Mgr.-Sls.--PENCO-New Mexico, Albuquerque, NM; *Int'l*, pg. 1508
Davis, Jeffrey L., Pres.--McKenzie Technology, Fremont, CA; *Int'l*, pg. 776
Davis, Jerry, Chief Opr. Officer--Energy Systems Div., Waltham, MA; *U.S. Public*, pg. 1591
Davis, Jerry, Pres.--Thermo Energy Systems Corporation, Waltham, MA; *U.S. Public*, pg. 1593
Davis, Jerry B., Pres. & Chief Exec. Officer--Halliburton Energy Services, Carrollton, TX; *U.S. Public*, pg. 776
Davis, Jerry P., Pres.--TE Energy Systems, Inc., Waltham, MA; *U.S. Public*, pg. 1592

Davis, Jerry R., Pres. & Chief Oper. Officer--Union Pacific Railroad Company, Omaha, NE; *U.S. Public*, pg. 1668
Davis, John, Pres. & Chief Exec. Officer--Thomson Book/Reference Group, Stamford, CT; *U.S. Public*, pg. 1600
Davis, John H., Pres.--First Community Bank of Tifton, Tifton, GA; *U.S. Public*, pg. 1549
Davis, John L., Pres. & Chief Oper. Officer--The Wing Group, Woodlands, TX; *U.S. Public*, pg. 1760
Davis, John W., Pres.--Greenwood Development Co., Greenwood, SC; *U.S. Private*, pg. 479
Davis, Ken, Gen. Mgr.--James Jones Company, El Monte, CA; *U.S. Public*, pg. 1650
Davis, Kenneth C., Mng. Dir.--ConAgra Asia-Pacific, Singapore, Singapore; *U.S. Public*, pg. 429
Davis, L.L., Chm. & Chief Exec. Officer--Marley Mouldings Inc., Marion, VA; *Int'l*, pg. 843
Davis, Lee, Plant Mgr.--Waterjet Cutting Systems Div., Baxter Springs, KS; *U.S. Public*, pg. 877
Davis, Leila, V.P.--LDDS WorldCom, Louisville, KY; *U.S. Public*, pg. 1779
Davis, Malcolm, Gen. Mgr.--GEC Computer Services Ltd., Stafford, United Kingdom; *Int'l*, pg. 544
Davis, Margaret, Pres. & Chief Oper. Officer--Selective Insurance Company of South Carolina, Charlotte, NC; *U.S. Public*, pg. 1455
Davis, Margaret, Pres. & Chief Oper. Officer--Selective Insurance Company of the Southeast, Charlotte, NC; *U.S. Public*, pg. 1456
Davis, Mark D., Chm.--Ad Americas, Los Angeles, CA; *U.S. Private*, pg. 316
Davis, Mark D., Chm.--Ingalls Moranville Advertising, San Francisco, CA; *U.S. Private*, pg. 316
Davis, Melissa, Area Mgr.--TNP Enterprises, Inc.-Gulf Coast Region, Texas City, TX; *U.S. Public*, pg. 1557
Davis, Mike, Gen. Mgr.--Madison Industries Inc. of Georgia, Conyers, GA; *U.S. Private*, pg. 428
Davis, Mike, Mng. Dir.--Eurodis HB Electronics Limited, Bolton, United Kingdom; *Int'l*, pg. 1247
Davis, Nigel, Pres.--Dover Elevator International, Inc., Memphis, TN; *U.S. Public*, pg. 521
Davis, Nigel, Ph.D., Mng. Dir.--Innovir (UK) LTD, Cambridge, United Kingdom; *U.S. Public*, pg. 1703
Davis, Pat, Pres. & Chief Exec. Officer--UPB of Northeast MS, New Albany, MS; *U.S. Public*, pg. 1669
Davis, Paul, V.P.--Personal Communications Div., Fort Worth, TX; *Int'l*, pg. 1433
Davis, Paula, Mng. Dir.--Triclinica Inc., New York, NY; *U.S. Private*, pg. 679
Davis, Peter, Chm. Bd.--Jackson National Life Insurance Company, Lansing, MI; *Int'l*, pg. 1073
Davis, Peter, Sir, Grp. Chief Exec.--Prudential Corporation PLC, London, United Kingdom; *Int'l*, pg. 1073
Davis, Philip, Gen. Mgr.--Newly Weds Foods, Inc., Cleveland, TN; *U.S. Private*, pg. 797
Davis, Preston A., Pres.--Broadcast Operations & Engineering, New York, NY; *U.S. Public*, pg. 511
Davis, Randall K., Pres.--Operations Management Division, Reston, VA; *U.S. Public*, pg. 1516
Davis, Ray, Pres.--SunGard Employee Benefits Systems, Birmingham, AL; *U.S. Public*, pg. 1534
Davis, Reid, Plant Mgr.--Black Mountain Plant, Black Mountain, NC; *U.S. Public*, pg. 443
Davis, Reid, Plant Mgr.--Goldsboro Plant, Goldsboro, NC; *U.S. Public*, pg. 443
Davis, Richard, Admin.--Rosewood Manor, Galion, OH; *U.S.* Public, pg. 838
Davis, Richard, Mgr.--IBP-West Point, West Point, NE; *U.S. Public*, pg. 852
Davis, Richard A., Pres. & Chief Exec. Officer--Pentzer Corporation, Spokane, WA; *U.S. Public*, pg. 1744
Davis, Richard D., Pres.--Triangle Geophysical Co., Greenwich, CT; *U.S. Public*, pg. 808
Davis, Richard L., Exec. V.P. & Gen. Mgr.--American Drug Stores Inc., Oak Brook, IL; *U.S. Public*, pg. 93
Davis, Rick, Gen. Mgr.--Alro Group, Muncie, Muncie, IN; *U.S. Private*, pg. 46
Davis, Robert, V.P.--Custom Casting, Portland, OR; *U.S. Private*, pg. 383
Davis, Robert, V.P. & Gen. Mgr.--Winsted Precision Ball Co., Winsted, CT; *Int'l*, pg. 468
Davis, Robert, V.P. & Gen. Mgr.--Hayward Industrial Products-Strainer Div., Elizabeth, NJ; *U.S. Private*, pg. 513
Davis, Robert, Pres.--Hayward Industrial Products, Elizabeth, NJ; *U.S. Private*, pg. 513
Davis, Robert, Gen. Mgr.--Corrugated Container Div.-Martinsville Plant, Martinsville, VA; *U.S. Public*, pg. 1520
Davis, Robert C., Pres.--Bremson Data Systems, Inc., Lenexa, KS; *U.S. Public*, pg. 551
Davis, Robert H., Chief Oper. Officer & V.P.--Universal Financial Services, Memphis, TN; *U.S. Private*, pg. 1127
Davis, Robert J., Pres.--Sysco Food Services of Charlotte, Inc., Concord, NC; *U.S. Public*, pg. 1551
Davis, Ron, Gen. Mgr.--Microsemi Corp.-Colorado, Broomfield, CO; *U.S. Public*, pg. 1107
Davis, S., Branch Mgr.--Van Leeuwen Pipe & Tube Corp., Martinez, CA; *Int'l*, pg. 1450
Davis, Stephen J., Vice Chm.--Avco Financial Services, Costa Mesa, CA; *U.S. Public*, pg. 1589
Davis, Steve F., Mgr.--Ohio Utilities Company, Westerville, OH; *U.S. Public*, pg. 380
Davis, Thomas A., Pres., Chief Exec. Officer & Asst. Sec.--United HealthCare of Utah, Salt Lake City, UT; *U.S. Public*, pg. 1678
Davis, Thomas D., Pres. & Chief Oper. Officer--The Smithfield Packing Co., Inc., Smithfield, VA; *U.S. Public*, pg. 1479
Davis, Tim, Exec. V.P. & Global Bus. Dir.-Shell, Unilever--J. Walter Thompson Company, New York, NY; *Int'l*, pg. 1483
Davis, Tim B., Project Dir.--Messier-Dowty Customer Support Centre- Europe, Gloucester, United Kingdom; *Int'l*, pg. 1340
Davis, Tim L., Pres.--Bird Machine Company, South Walpole, MA; *U.S. Public*, pg. 166
Davis, Tom, Gen. Mgr.--Butler Auto Auction, Evans City, PA; *U.S. Private*, pg. 282
Davis, Tom, Pres.--Pentastar Aviation, Inc., Ypsilanti, MI; *U.S. Public*, pg. 354
Davis, W. Donald, Chm. Bd., Pres. & Chief Exec. Officer--SouthTrust Bank, Cullman County, Cullman, AL; *U.S. Public*, pg. 1491
Davis, W.S., Pres.--Amoco Madagascar Petroleum Company, Antanarivo, Madagascar; *U.S. Public*, pg. 102
Davis, W.S., Pres.--Amoco Abu Dhabi Exploration Co., Chicago, IL; *U.S. Public*, pg. 103
Davis, William, Pres. & Chief Exec. Officer--Uniroyal Goodrich Canada Inc., Kitchener, Canada; *Int'l*, pg. 322
Davison, M., District Mgr.--A.M. Castle & Co., Salt Lake City, UT; *U.S. Public*, pg. 313
Davison, William H., Chm. Bd. & Chief Exec. Officer--SunTrust Bank, East Central Florida, Daytona Beach, FL; *U.S. Public*, pg. 1537
Davisson, John Q., Mgr.--Eclipse Combustion, Inc., Charlotte, NC; *U.S. Private*, pg. 360
Davoli, Pier Paolo, Chief Exec. Officer--Finsiel, Rome, Italy; *Int'l*, pg. 654
Davoren, Peter J., V.P. & Gen. Mgr.--Turner Construction Co., New York, NY; *U.S. Public*, pg. 1645
Davy, J. Brian, Chm.--J & E Davy Holdings Limited, Dublin, Ireland; *Int'l*, pg. 152
Davyduke, Meroslav O., Gen. Mgr.--PCS Potash - Cory, Saskatoon, Canada; *Int'l*, pg. 1064
Dawdy, Richard A., Pres. & Chief Oper. Officer--UMB First National Bank, Collinsville, IL; *U.S. Public*, pg. 1654
Dawes, Alan, Mng. Dir.--General Combustion Ltd., Billingshurst, United Kingdom; *U.S. Public*, pg. 705
Dawes, Dexter B., Mng. Dir.--John Hancock Capital Growth Management, Inc., San Francisco, CA; *U.S. Private*, pg. 590
Dawkins, Enoch L., Pres.--Murphy Exploration & Production Co., New Orleans, LA; *U.S. Public*, pg. 1142
Dawley, Roger, Pres.--Swain Building Materials, Lewisville, TX; *U.S. Private*, pg. 686
Dawson, Art, Dr., Gen. Mgr.--Decco Div., Monrovia, CA; *Int'l*, pg. 446
Dawson, C.W., Pres. & Gen. Mgr.--Mirrlees Blackstone (Canada) Ltd., Oakville, Canada; *Int'l*, pg. 125
Dawson, Gaynor W., Pres. & Gen. Mgr.--EG & G Environmental, Inc., Pittsburgh, PA; *U.S. Public*, pg. 543
Dawson, George, Mng. Dir. & Dir.-Aviation & Engrng.--Industrial Acoustics Company, Ltd., Staines, United Kingdom; *U.S. Public*, pg. 875
Dawson, Jack, Pres.--First State Bank of Fayette Co., Somerville, TN; *U.S. Public*, pg. 1669
Dawson, James A., Pres. & Chief Exec. Officer--Quebecor Printing (USA) Corp., Boston, MA; *Int'l*, pg. 1076
Dawson, James A., Pres.--Quebecor Printing Kingsport Inc., Kingsport, TN; *Int'l*, pg. 1076
Dawson, James A., Pres.--Quebecor Printing Richmond Inc., Richmond, VA; *Int'l*, pg. 1078
Dawson, James A., Pres.--Quebecor Printing Buffalo Inc., Depew, NY; *Int'l*, pg. 1078
Dawson, James A., Pres.--Quebecor Printing Dickson Inc., Dickson, TN; *Int'l*, pg. 1078
Dawson, James A., Pres.--Quebecor Printing St. Paul Inc., Saint Paul, MN; *Int'l*, pg. 1078
Dawson, Jim, Pres.--Brunswick Outdoor Recreation Group, Tulsa, OK; *U.S. Public*, pg. 265
Dawson, John, Pres. & Gen. Mgr.--Indiana Broadcasting Co. (WISH), Indianapolis, IN; *U.S. Public*, pg. 11
Dawson, Lori, Gen. Mgr.--DSI Staff Connxions Southwest, Houston, TX; *U.S. Public*, pg. 508
Dawson, P.A., Chm. Bd.--Jardine Credit Insurance Ltd., London, United Kingdom; *Int'l*, pg. 705
Dawson, P.J., Area Mgr.--Ballast Wiltshier plc - North West Region, Kingswinford, United Kingdom; *Int'l*, pg. 135
Dawson, Rockleigh S., Jr., Pres.-Forged Prods.--Ameri-Forge Corporation, Houston, TX; *U.S. Public*, pg. 748
Dawson, Steve L., Plant Mgr.--Reeves Brothers, Inc. (Bishopville Div.), Bishopville, SC; *U.S. Private*, pg. 507
Day-Harper, Melinda, Pres. & Chief Oper. Officer--Wise & Associates/S&W Technical Services, San Antonio, TX; *U.S. Public*, pg. 1161
Day, Barry, Mgr.--Anixter Bristol, Bristol, United Kingdom; *U.S. Public*, pg. 116
Day, Don, Gen. Mgr.--R-2 KIT Mfg. Co., Caldwell, ID; *U.S. Public*, pg. 962
Day, Frank R., Chm. Bd.--Trustmark National Bank, Jackson, MS; *U.S. Public*, pg. 1643
Day, Gordon, Exec. Dir.--First Brands Africa (Pty) Ltd., Johannesburg, South Africa; *U.S. Public*, pg. 627
Day, James, Controller--Keystone Lines, Gary, IN; *U.S. Public*, pg. 1687
Day, James, Controller--TC Services, Gary, IN; *U.S. Public*, pg. 1687
Day, James L., Pres.--EUA Day, Victor, NY; *U.S. Public*, pg. 549
Day, Jeffrey B., Pres.--M & C Brokerage Services, Inc., Houston, TX; *U.S. Public*, pg. 366
Day, Joe, Chief Exec. Officer--Freudenberg NOK, Manchester, NH; *Int'l*, pg. 505
Day, John, Chief Oper. Officer--NIFE Australia Pty. Ltd., Willoughby, Australia; *Int'l*, pg. 54
Day, Joseph, Pres.--Freudenberg NOK, Bristol, NH; *Int'l*, pg. 507
Day, Karen C., Publisher--Charles Scribner's Sons Reference, New York, NY; *U.S. Private*, pg. 777
Day, Karen C., Publisher--Twayne Publishers, New York, NY; *U.S. Private*, pg. 777
Day, Ken, Pres.--Signal Science, Santa Clara, CA; *U.S. Public*, pg. 46
Day, Kim, Pres.--Zenith Products Corp., New Castle, DE; *U.S. Public*, pg. 1054
Day, L. S., Mng. Dir.--Barlows Equipment Co., Sandton, South Africa; *Int'l*, pg. 167
Day, LaVelle, Mgr.--CAP Gemini America (Portland Branch), Portland, OR; *Int'l*, pg. 264
Day, Michael, Comml. Dir.--ICI Colors, Wilmington, DE; *Int'l*, pg. 663
Day, R.F., Pres.--Lurgi Canada Ltd., Toronto, Canada; *Int'l*, pg. 861
Day, R.I., Area Mgr.--Ballast Wiltshier Plc - South West Region, Cardiff, United Kingdom; *Int'l*, pg. 135
Day, T., Plant Mgr.--Square D Co., Huntington, IN; *Int'l*, pg. 1208
Day, Tom, Gen. Mgr.--Waterville Valley Ski Area Ltd., Waterville Valley, NH; *U.S. Private*, pg. 62
Dayal, Ginger, Chief Oper. Officer--RC Communications, Inc., New York, NY; *U.S. Public*, pg. 1224
Dayan, Charles, Pres. & Chief Exec. Officer--Licensing Div., New York, NY; *U.S. Private*, pg. 156
Dayke, Darren, Mgr.-Opers.--General Magnaplate Wisconsin, Racine, WI; *U.S. Public*, pg. 717
Daylan, R., Mgr.--Mallinckrodt Medical, Lisses, France; *U.S. Public*, pg. 1040
Dayller, Jose, Mng. Dir.--Chilebras Metais Ltda., Sao Paulo, Brazil; *Int'l*, pg. 303
Days, B.M., Pres.--KINETCO, Charleston, SC; *U.S. Public*, pg. 468
Dazzi, G., Chief Oper. Officer--FATA USSR, Moscow, Russia; *Int'l*, pg. 474
de Aguilar, Milagros Plaza, Pres.--Creativity/Young & Rubicam Asociados, Lima, Peru; *U.S. Private*, pg. 1200
de Aguirre, Ignacio Maria Garcia, Pres.--SODIAN - Sociedad Para el Desarrollo Industrial de Analucia, S.A., Seville, Spain; *Int'l*, pg. 1225
de Albornoz Bonet, Carlos Martinez, Pres.--Empresa Auxiliar de la Industria, Auxini, S.A., Madrid, Spain; *Int'l*, pg. 1224
de Alvarez, Alicia, Dir.-Life Reassurance--Skandia S.A., Mexico, Mexico; *Int'l*, pg. 1256
De Andrade, Roberto Motta, Plant Mgr.--Elkem Aluminium Lista, Farsund, Norway; *Int'l*, pg. 446
de Andres, Felix Llorente, Pres.--T.G.I. - Tecnologia del Grupo INI, S.A., Madrid, Spain; *Int'l*, pg. 1225
De Angelo, Lawrence, Pres.--EMS Asia Pacific, Lan Tau Island, Hong Kong; *U.S. Public*, pg. 566
de Araoz, E.F., Representative--Morgan Grenfell (Spain), Madrid, Spain; *Int'l*, pg. 406
De Arce, Ausbert, Mng. Dir.--United Media Europe/Scripps, Amsterdam, Netherlands; *U.S. Public*, pg. 1448
de Athayde, Augusto, Pres.--Banco Espirito Santo do Oriente SARL (Besor), Macau, Macau; *Int'l*, pg. 142
de Azevedo Bonfim, Antonio, Gen. Mgr.--Banco do Brasil S.A.-Los Angeles, Los Angeles, CA; *Int'l*, pg. 141
de Bakker, Ferry, Pres. & Chief Exec. Officer-Europe (London)--Burson-Marsteller, New York, NY; *U.S. Private*, pg. 1197
de Barros Moraes, Neide, Gen. Mgr.--Cement Div., Sao Paulo, Brazil; *Int'l*, pg. 677
de Bedout, J.D., V.P. & Gen. Mgr.--Kimberly-Clark de Centro America S.A., Nueva San Salvador, El Salvador; *U.S. Public*, pg. 959
de Bedout, Juan E., Mng. Dir.--Colombiana Kimberly S.A., Medellin, Colombia; *U.S. Public*, pg. 959
De Beeck, Jan Op, Chief Oper. Officer--Antwerp Local Head Office, Antwerp, Belgium; *Int'l*, pg. 147
de Beer, H., Chief Oper. Officer--Volkswagen Overseas Finance N.V., Willemstad, Netherlands Antilles; *Int'l*, pg. 1475
de Belloy, Patrick, Pres.--Prolifix, Aubervilliers, France; *Int'l*, pg. 789
de Benedetti, Carlo, Chm. Bd.--Buitoni SpA, Perugia, Italy; *Int'l*, pg. 919
De Benedetti, Marco, Mng. Dir.--Olivetti Portuguesa S.A., Lisbon, Portugal; *Int'l*, pg. 1003
De Benedetti, R., Chief Oper. Officer--SAIA-Burgess SRL, Milan, Italy; *Int'l*, pg. 1501
de Beneditti, Alberto, Dir.--Finmeccanica S.p.A., New York, NY; *Int'l*, pg. 654
de Berand, Gabriel, Pres.--AlliedSignal Aftermarket Europe S.A., Drancy, France; *U.S. Public*, pg. 53
de Beuckelaer, Christian, Gen. Mgr.--Ohmeda BV, Bilthoven, Netherlands; *Int'l*, pg. 122
De Bey, Paul D., Mgr.-Branch--Piper Jaffray Inc., Sioux City, IA; *U.S. Public*, pg. 1302
De Biase, Dean, Pres. & Chief Exec. Officer--The Imagination Network, Burlingame, CA; *U.S. Public*, pg. 66
de Bie, Britt, Chief Oper. Officer--Todd-AO/Editworks, Atlanta, GA; *U.S. Public*, pg. 1619
de Blieck, Pieter, Mng. Dir.--Kredietbank (Nederland) N.V., Rotterdam, Netherlands; *Int'l*, pg. 761
de Boissieu, Ghislain, Mng. Dir.--Chapelle Darblay Grand Couronne, Grand Couronne, France; *Int'l*, pg. 1428
De Boon, T., Chief Oper. Officer--Raibobank do Brasil Ltda., Sao Paulo, Brazil; *Int'l*, pg. 1082
De Bosschere, M., Mng. Dir.--NRG Benelux B.V., s Hertogenbosch, Netherlands; *Int'l*, pg. 1116
De Bosschere, M., Mng. Dir.--NRG Belgium S.A., Brussels, Belgium; *Int'l*, pg. 1116
De Bourleuf, X., Gen. Mgr.--Rocol Limited, Gonesse, France; *Int'l*, pg. 893
de Boysson, Gaetan, Chm. Bd. & Chief Exec. Officer--Saint Dominique Finance, Paris, France; *Int'l*, pg. 344
de Bresser, Pierre, Pres.--Buss (Benelux) B.V., Rijen, Netherlands; *Int'l*, pg. 490
de Brito Lovrengo, Luiz Carlos, Gen. Mgr.--Banco do Brasil S.A.-Portugal, Lisbon, Portugal; *Int'l*, pg. 141
de Broglie, Frederic, Mng. Dir.--3i France, Neuilly, France; *Int'l*, pg. 1386
de Bruijn, A.W.J., Mng. Dir.--Nedlloyd Energy B.V., Rotterdam, Netherlands; *Int'l*, pg. 1144
de Bruijn, H., Chief Exec. Officer--Blackwood Hodge (Belgie) N.V., Vilvoorde, Belgium; *Int'l*, pg. 231
de Bruin, W., Div. Mgr.--Campina AG, Stuttgart, Germany; *Int'l*, pg. 254
de Bruyn, Han, Reg. Mgr.--Circle-ATS AG, Zurich, Switzerland; *U.S. Public*, pg. 372

de Buhr, Ted, Pres. & Chief Exec. Officer--Fox Photo, Inc., Saint Louis, MO; *U.S. Public*, pg. 283

De Buono, Peter, V.P. & Chief Oper. Officer--Compass Investment Services, Mineola, NY; *U.S. Public*, pg. 1194

de Caceres, Javier Monzon, Pres.--Ceselsa-Inisel, S.A., Madrid, Spain; *Int'l*, pg. 1224

de Campos, C. Martinez, Chm. Bd.--Barclays Bank SA-Madrid, Madrid, Spain; *Int'l*, pg. 166

De Candia, Humphrey, Pres.--Italtractor America Inc., Addison, IL; *Int'l*, pg. 654

de Caralt, Fernando, Chief Oper. Officer--Construcciones Aeronauticas, S.A. (CASA), Madrid, Spain; *U.S. Public*, pg. 1199

de Carbon, Axel Bourcier, Gen. Mgr.--Societe Francaise des Amortisseurs de Carbon S.A., La Garenne-Colombes, France; *U.S. Public*, pg. 725

de Cardona, R.P., Chief Oper. Officer--Rabofin Italia SpA, Milan, Italy; *Int'l*, pg. 1082

de Carmoy, Herve, Chm. Bd.--Parviland Gerance, Paris, France; *Int'l*, pg. 344

de Carvalho, Oswaldo, Mng. Dir.--Esselte Meto Ind. e. Com. Ltda., Sao Paulo, Brazil; *Int'l*, pg. 461

De Carvalho, Sergio Monteiro, Mng. Dir.--Ericsson do Brasil Comercio e Industria S.A., Sao Paulo, Brazil; *Int'l*, pg. 1366

De Carvalho, Sergio Monteiro, Mng. Dir.--Ericsson Amazonia S.A., Manaus, Brazil; *Int'l*, pg. 1366

De Castillo, Luis, Pres.--Sans, S.A., Barcelona, Spain; *U.S. Public*, pg. 1434

de Castro Esteves, Ivan, Pres.--Cobra-Computadores e Sistemas Brasileiros, Rio de Janeiro, Brazil; *Int'l*, pg. 142

de Castro, Donald J., Pres.--Cyanamid Latin America Group, Parsippany, NJ; *U.S. Public*, pg. 79

de Chabannes la Palice, Jean, Dir.--WF Corroon-France, Paris, France; *Int'l*, pg. 1502

de Chalendar, Pierre Andre, Chm. Bd., Pres. & Chief Exec. Officer--Norton Company, Worcester, MA; *Int'l*, pg. 1173

de Chalon, A. Sauty, Chm. Bd.--Gan Holding Pacifique, Paris, France; *Int'l*, pg. 564

de Charette, J.R, Mng. Dir.--Gan Portugal Seguros, Lisbon, Portugal; *Int'l*, pg. 564

De Clerck, Paul, Gen. Mgr.--CiMatrix NV/SA, Zaventem, Belgium; *U.S. Public*, pg. 1395

De Clerck, Yves, Dir. General--Generale Bank - Lisboa, Lisbon, Portugal; *Int'l*, pg. 547

de Clippele, Luc J., Gen. Sec.--Vlaamse Investeringsvennootschap (VIV), Zwijnaarde, Belgium; *Int'l*, pg. 547

de Combret, B., Chief Oper. Officer--SOCAP LTD Elf Trading SA, Courbevoie, France; *Int'l*, pg. 445

de Comeiras, Dominique, Gen. Mgr.--Skandia International Gestion de Reassurance SA, Paris, France; *Int'l*, pg. 1256

de Comtes, Harold, Mng. Dir.--VOEST-ALPINE STAHL Traisen Ges.m.b.H., Traisen, Austria; *Int'l*, pg. 1470

De Cort, Andre, Counsel--Skadden, Arps, Slate, Meagher & Flom LLP, Moscow, Russia; *U.S. Private*, pg. 1004

De Cristofaro, Dr. Gennaro Rino, Chief Oper. Officer--Alfa Romeo International S.A., Luxembourg, Luxembourg; *Int'l*, pg. 481

de Dardel, Claes, Gen. Dir., Committee Pres.--Banque Edouard Constant, Geneva, Switzerland; *U.S. Public*, pg. 1197

de Decker, D., Mng. Dir.--Getinge-D.S.E. NV, Antwerp, Belgium; *Int'l*, pg. 551

De Deo, Joseph E., Chm.-Latin America & Canada--Young & Rubicam Latam (Miami), Miami, FL; *U.S. Private*, pg. 1198

De Deygere, Luc, Gen. Mgr.--Colorprofil N.V., Geel, Belgium; *Int'l*, pg. 79

de Entrambasaguas, Guillermo Serrano, Pres.--Viva, Vuelos Internacionales de Vacaciones, S.A., Madrid, Spain; *Int'l*, *pg. 1225*

De Falco, Osvaldo, Sole Administrator--Vestiduras Fronterizas, S.A. de C.V., Mexico, Mexico; *U.S. Public*, pg. 724

de Filippo, John, Mgr.--CAP Gemini America (Houston Branch), Houston, TX; *Int'l*, pg. 264

De Filippo, Patrice, Dir.-Sls. & Gen. Mgr.--Milgray/Connecticut, Inc., Milford, CT; *U.S. Public*, pg. 206

de Florio, Vito, Controller--Bridgestone/Firestone Hispania S.A., Madrid, Spain; *Int'l*, pg. 214

De Franchis, Rosario, Rep.--Banco Di Napoli-Moscow, Moscow, Russia; *Int'l*, pg. 140

de Freitas, S.E., Chief Oper. Officer--Procter & Gamble of Peru, Lima, Peru; *U.S. Public*, pg. 1332

de Galembert, Antoine, Chief Oper. Officer--Compagnie Fermiere de L'Etablissement Thermal de Vichy, Paris, France; *Int'l*, pg. 919

De Geer, Johan, Chief Oper. Officer--SNC Alfa-Laval & Cie, Toulouse, France; *Int'l*, pg. 1379

de Gelis, Dominique, Gen. Mgr.--Audax Industries, S.A., Chateau-du-Loir, France; *U.S. Public*, pg. 787

de Gier, N.W.A., Mng. Dir.--Wolters Kluwer Germany, Kriftel, Germany; *Int'l*, pg. 1513

De Gier, Willem, Chief Oper. Officer--Deutsche Husqvarna GmbH, Schweinfurt, Germany; *Int'l*, pg. 442

de Glutz, Jean-Pierre, Mgr.--Commerzbank AG, Geneva, Switzerland; *Int'l*, pg. 311

De Goedereng, P., Mng. Dir.--Thailand Smelting & Refining, Co. Ltd., Bangkok, Thailand; *Int'l*, pg. 1140

de Graaf, Cees, Mng. Dir.--Anacomp (Nederland) B.V., Almere-Haven, Netherlands; *U.S. Public*, pg. 107

de Graaf, J., Mgr.--Delta-Bouw BV, Dokkum, Netherlands; *Int'l*, pg. 607

de Graaf, S, Dir.--Mabon B.V., Rijswijk, Netherlands; *Int'l*, pg. 630

de Graef, Matt H., Chief Exec. Officer--Eurotec Systemteile Gmbh, Botzingen, Germany; *Int'l*, pg. 737

de Groot, A., Mng. Dir.--Wolters Kluwer Trade Publishing, Utrecht, Netherlands; *Int'l*, pg. 1513

de Groot, A.J., Gen. Mgr.--AMEV Praktijkvoorziening N.V., Utrecht, Netherlands; *Int'l*, pg. 499

de Groot, C.A., Mng. Dir.--Big Balloon bv, Heemstede, Netherlands; *Int'l*, pg. 1445

De Groot, F.L., Gen. Mgr.--Johnson & Johnson GABA B.V., Almere, Netherlands; *U.S. Public*, pg. 930

de Groot, Herman, Mng. Dir.--ESAB Nederland B.V., Utrecht, Netherlands; *Int'l*, pg. 282

de Gruyter, L.P.J.M., Chief Oper. Officer--Otto Reichelt GmbH, Berlin, Germany; *Int'l*, pg. 1156

De Gryse, Bernard, Chief Oper. Officer--BBL Life, Brussels, Belgium; *Int'l*, pg. 147

De Gryse, Bernard, Chief Oper. Officer--BBL Insurance, Brussels, Belgium; *Int'l*, pg. 147

De Guzzis, Giovanni, Mng. Dir.--FATME Soc. per Az, Rome, Italy; *Int'l*, pg. 1368

De Haan, Gerrit, Mng. Dir.--ISS Hospital Service B.V., Utrecht, Netherlands; *Int'l*, pg. 657

De Haan, S., Pres.--ABB Simcon, Inc., Bloomfield, NJ; *Int'l*, pg. 5

de Haas, R., Dir.--TBS Soest, Soest, Netherlands; *Int'l*, pg. 134

De Haeyer, Frans, Mgr.--Kredietbank (Nederland) N.V., Breda, Netherlands; *Int'l*, pg. 761

de Hoon, Leo, Mng. Dir.--Ericsson Holding International B.V., Rijen, Netherlands; *Int'l*, pg. 1367

de Hoon, Leo, Mng. Dir.--Ericsson Holding Nederland B.V., Rijen, Netherlands; *Int'l*, pg. 1367

de Hoz, A. Martinez, Gen. Manager--Quimica S.C. Johnson & Son Chilena S.A.C.I., Vina del Mar, Chile; *U.S. Private*, *pg. 593*

de Ibarra, Felix Saez, Chief Exec.--Cementos Caribe C.A., Caracas, Venezuela; *Int'l*, pg. 629

de Jager, Jan, Mng. Dir.--Thomassen Stewart & Stevenson International B.V., Rheden, Netherlands; *U.S. Public*, pg. 1518

de Jarnac, Dominique, Gen. Mgr.--Conquest Europe S.A.R.L., Neuilly-sur-Seine, France; *Int'l*, pg. 1484

de Jesus Valdez, Jose, Pres.--Alpek, S.A. de C.V., Garza Garcia, Mexico; *Int'l*, pg. 56

de Jesus, C.R., Pres.--Esso Sociedad Anonima Petroleum Argentina, Buenos Aires, Argentina; *U.S. Public*, pg. 602

de Jong, Case, V.P. & Gen. Mgr.--Kindred Industries, Midland, Canada; *Int'l*, pg. 453

de Jong, J., Mng. Dir.--De Lampenier, Beesd, Netherlands; *Int'l*, pg. 750

de Jonge, Hans, Dir.--Starke Diekstra NV, Saint-Niklaas, Belgium; *Int'l*, pg. 608

de Jonge, J.C.A., Chief Oper. Officer--Makro Comercializadora S.A., Caracas, Venezuela; *Int'l*, pg. 1155

de Jonge, M.W., Mng. Dir.--Fisher-Price Spielwaren GmbH, Bruhl, Germany; *U.S. Public*, pg. 1058

de Jons, C., Mng. Dir.--Industrial Pharmaceutical Products Division, Delft, Netherlands; *Int'l*, pg. 1142

de Jorg, A.P.J., Chief Oper. Officer--Allianz Nederland N.V. (Rotterdam Office), Rotterdam, Netherlands; *Int'l*, pg. 60

de Jorry, B., Mgr.--F. Berger & Co. B.V., Amsterdam, Netherlands; *Int'l*, pg. 9

de Kan, W., Gen. Mgr.--Postbank Lease, Amsterdam, Netherlands; *Int'l*, pg. 647

de Keghel, Philippe, Mng. Dir.--Banque Internationale a Luxembourg BIL (Suisse) S.A., Lausanne, Switzerland; *Int'l*, pg. 162

De Keyser, Jean-Charles, Mng. Dir.--Bel RTL, Brussels, Belgium; *Int'l*, pg. 561

de Keyser, R.P., Area Mgr.--Ballast Nedam Industriebouw B.V., Amstelveen, Netherlands; *Int'l*, pg. 133

de Kimpe, Theo, Chief Oper. Officer--Alfa-Laval N.V., Amsterdam, Netherlands; *Int'l*, pg. 1380

de Klerk, Bram, Mng. Dir.--Natref, Sasolburg, South Africa; *Int'l*, pg. 1197

de Kleuver, J.M.F., Chief Oper. Officer--Dyas B.V., Utrecht, Netherlands; *Int'l*, pg. 1155

De Knijf, Alfons, Mng. Dir.--Bekaert-Tinsley, Hemiksem, Belgium; *Int'l*, pg. 183

De Knoop, Michel, Mng. Dir.--Union de Banques Congolaises, Kinshasa, Congo; *Int'l*, pg. 149

De Kock, David L., Pres.--Sysco Food Services of Grand Rapids, Inc., Grand Rapids, MI; *U.S. Public*, pg. 1551

de Kraker, Peter, Mng. Dir.--Ahold Finance Company (Nederlandse Antillen) NV, Curacao, Netherlands Antilles; *Int'l*, pg. 750

de Krassny, Alain, Chief Oper. Officer--Donau Chemie AG, Vienna, Austria; *Int'l*, pg. 1112

de la Baume, Francois, Chief Oper. Officer--Financiere Atlas S.A., Paris, France; *Int'l*, pg. 120

de la Calle, M., Mateos, Dir. Gen.--Williams & Humbert Ltd., Jerez de la Frontera, Spain; *Int'l*, pg. 751

De La Garza, George, Plant Supt.--General Felt Industries, Inc., Dallas, TX; *U.S. Private*, pg. 1095

de la Guardia, Ruben, Pres.--Phillips Petroleum International Corporation, Bartlesville, OK; *U.S. Public*, pg. 1291

de la M. Thompson, R. Julian, Chm. Bd.--Sotheby's Asia, London, United Kingdom; *U.S. Public*, pg. 1487

de la Maza, Fernado, Pres.--Jacuzzi (Chile) S.A., Santiago, Chile; *U.S. Public*, pg. 1684

de la Pascua, Rose, Dir.--Shandwick Spain, Madrid, Spain; *Int'l*, pg. 1228

De la Peza, Pablo, Pres.--Seguros Banamex-Aegon, S.A. de C.V., Mexico, Mexico; *Int'l*, pg. 574

De La Porte, Charles Andre, Dir.--Christie's Amsterdam B.V., Amsterdam, Netherlands; *Int'l*, pg. 290

de La Roer, Hubert, Pres.--Minnesota Rubber Europe S.A., Evreux, France; *U.S. Private*, pg. 898

de la Sal, Alberto Perez, Mng. Dir.--Tractebel Espana S.A., Madrid, Spain; *Int'l*, pg. 1416

de la Seigliere, B., Chm. Bd.--Credit Industriel de L'Ouest, Nantes, France; *Int'l*, pg. 564

de la Torre, J.R., Chm. Bd.--International Columbia Resources Corporation, Bogota, Colombia; *U.S. Public*, pg. 602

de Labouchere, Pierre, Pres. & Chief Exec. Officer--R.J. Reynolds Tobacco Intl., Inc., Geneva, Switzerland; *U.S. Public*, pg. 1355

de Laender, Daniel, Gen. Mgr.--CCF (Luxembourg) S.A., Luxembourg, Luxembourg; *Int'l*, pg. 342

de Lange, J., Pres.--Nicholas Turkey Breeding Farms, Sonoma, CA; *Int'l*, pg. 202

de Larminat, Pierre, Mng. Dir.--LM/Young & Rubicam, Nantes, France; *U.S. Private*, pg. 1199

de Launoit, Jean-Pierre, Pres.--RTL TVi, Brussels, Belgium; *Int'l*, pg. 562

De Leevin, Walter J., Sr. V.P. & Gen. Mgr.--Raytheon Environmental Services Company, Houston, TX; *U.S. Public*, pg. 1366

de Lima Mayer, Th., Chief Exec. Officer--OCE-Lima Mayer S.A., Lisbon, Portugal; *Int'l*, pg. 994

de Limelette, Gery, Chief Oper. Officer--Mexalit S.A., Mexico, Mexico; *Int'l*, pg. 1171

de Loor, Johannes, Chm. Bd.--Total South Africa (Pty.) Ltd., Johannesburg, South Africa; *Int'l*, pg. 1409

de Looze, S., Mng. Dir.--Scott Western Ltd., Mansfield, United Kingdom; *Int'l*, pg. 552

de los Angeles Alvarez, Maria, Rep.-Marketing--Singapore Tourist Promotion Board - Buenos Aires, Buenos Aires, Argentina; *Int'l*, pg. 1254

De Los Reyes, Roderigo, Pres. & Chief Exec. Officer--The Philippines American Assurance Co., Inc., Manila, Philippines; *U.S. Public*, pg. 85

de Lounoit, Jean-Pierre, Chm.--Royale Belge S.A., Brussels, Belgium; *Int'l*, pg. 562

De Luca, Daniele, Partner--Korn/Ferry International, Rome, Italy; *U.S. Private*, pg. 633

de Luca, Geoff, Dir.--International Public Relations, Pty. Ltd., Adelaide, Australia; *Int'l*, pg. 1227

de Lurdes, Maria, Dir.-Fin.--Sensormatic Lda., Lisbon, Portugal; *U.S. Public*, pg. 1458

de Maio, Mike, Pres.--Lois/EJL Advertising/Chicago, Chicago, IL; *U.S. Public*, pg. 1011

De Marco, Nicholas, Pres.--International Apparel Marketing Corp., New York, NY; *U.S. Public*, pg. 498

de Maria, Manuel Ortiz, Ing., Dir.--Pemex Exploracion y Produccion, Mexico, Mexico; *Int'l*, pg. 1046

de Matharel, M., Gen. Mgr.--Total Indonesie, Jakarta, Indonesia; *Int'l*, pg. 1409

De Medeiros, Wagner, Gen. Mgr.--Banco do Brasil S.A.-Miami, Miami, FL; *Int'l*, pg. 141

de Meeus d'Argenteuil , Daniel, Pres.--G-Securities, Brussels, Belgium; *Int'l*, pg. 547

de Mello, Geraldo Isnard, Gen. Mgr.--Campinas Branch, Campinas, Brazil; *Int'l*, pg. 139

De Mello, L.C.B., Pres.--Autolatina Brasil S.A., Sao Paulo, Brazil; *U.S. Public*, pg. 665

de Mendoga Almeida, Jose Augusto, Gen. Mgr.--Banco do Brasil S.A.-Bolivia, La Paz, Bolivia; *Int'l*, pg. 141

de Mey, G., Dir.--EMI Belgium SA, Brussels, Belgium; *Int'l*, pg. 427

de Mezerville, Eduardo, Chief Oper. Officer--Industrias Merrimac Incorporada, S.A., Heredia, Costa Rica; *U.S. Public*, pg. 1098

de Miguel, F., Dir.--Van Leer Embalagens Industriais do Brasil Ltda, Sao Paulo, Brazil; *Int'l*, pg. 1146

De Montalivet, Jean Pierre, Chm. Bd.--Henkel France S.A., Boulogne-Billancourt, France; *Int'l*, pg. 612

de Montebello, George L., Gen. Mgr.--J.P. Morgan (Suisse) S.A., Geneva, Switzerland; *U.S. Public*, pg. 1131

de Moraes Filho, Jose Emirio, Pres.--Cia. Nitroquimica Brasileira, Sao Miguel, Brazil; *Int'l*, pg. 677

de Murville, A. Couve, Mng. Dir.--Van Leeuwen Tubes SA, Chalette-sur-Loing, France; *Int'l*, pg. 1450

de Naeyer, Achilles, Chief Exec. Officer--FTK Holland B.V., Bleiswijk, Netherlands; *Int'l*, pg. 710

de Nanteuil, Baudouin, Mgr.--Radiometer S.A., Neuilly-Plaisance, France; *Int'l*, pg. 1084

de Neergaard, Claes, V.P.--European Investment Bank, Luxembourg, Luxembourg; *Int'l*, pg. 465

De Neve, J., Pres.--Bekaert Corporation, Rogers, AR; *Int'l*, pg. 184

de Ocio, Daniel, Pres.--Chr. Hansen-Lacta S.L., Madrid, Spain; *Int'l*, pg. 289

De Oliveira, Ararino Sallum, Pres.--Allianz-Bradesco Cia. Brasileira de Seguros, Sao Paulo, Brazil; *Int'l*, pg. 59

de Oliveira, Evandro Lopes, Chief Oper. Officer--BBBI Banco de Investimento, Rio de Janeiro, Brazil; *Int'l*, pg. 141

de Oliveira, Manuel, Chief Exec. Officer--Cimianto Sth SA, Vila Franca de Xira, Portugal; *Int'l*, pg. 430

De Oliveira, Manuel Ferreira, Chm.--Petrogal Espanola, S.A., Madrid, Spain; *Int'l*, pg. 1045

De Oliveira, Manuel Ferreira, Chm.--Sacor Maritima, S.A., Lisbon, Portugal; *Int'l*, pg. 1045

De Oliveira, Manuela Ferreira, Chm.--Comp. Logistica Combustiveis, S.A., Lisbon, Portugal; *Int'l*, pg. 1045

de Oliveira, Ricardo Sergio, Mgr.--Brasilian American Merchant Bank, Georgetown, Cayman Islands; *Int'l*, pg. 142

de Oliveira, Wagner Dognani, Mgr.--Curitiba Branch, Curitiba, Brazil; *Int'l*, pg. 139

de Panafieu, Guy, Chief Oper. Officer--Banque Hydro-Energie, Paris, France; *Int'l*, pg. 822

de Pena, Damaris Defillo, Pres.--Young & Rubicam Damaris, C. por A., Santo Domingo, Dominican Republic; *U.S. Private*, pg. 1200

de Penanros, Patrick, Mng. Dir.--Nouvelle Vague, Nantes, France; *Int'l*, pg. 116

de Picciotto, R., Mng. Dir.--Banque Cantrade Lausanne S.A., Lausanne, Switzerland; *Int'l*, pg. 1439

De Pietro, Patricia, Media Supvr.--Saint Jacques Vallee Young & Rubicam, Inc., Montreal, Canada; *U.S. Private*, pg. 1200

de Posson, Marina, Gen. Mgr.--Belgolaise, London, United Kingdom; *Int'l*, pg. 548

de Pracomtal, Henri, Mng. Dir.--Hine U.K., London, United Kingdom; *Int'l*, pg. 782

de Prat, Luis Perez, Pres.--Made Sistemas Electricos, S.A., Vicalvaro, Spain; *Int'l*, pg. 1224

De Pretis, Dario, Chm. Bd.--Banca Di Trento e Bolzano S.p.A., Trento, Italy; *Int'l*, pg. 138

de Preux, M., Mgr.--Societe de Banque Suisse, Geneva, Switzerland; *Int'l*, pg. 1329

de Preux, Thierry, Office Mgr.--Korn/Ferry International, Geneva, Switzerland; *U.S. Private*, pg. 633

de Priede, Javier Gimeno, Pres.--Cabinas Telefonicas, S.A. (Cabitel), Madrid, Spain; *Int'l*, pg. 1371

de Puppi, L., Chm.--Electrolux International S.p.A., Pordenone, Italy; *Int'l*, pg. 442

de Puppi, L., Chm.--Veneta Factoring S.p.A., Pordenone, Italy; *Int'l*, pg. 442

de Puppi, L., Chm.--P & O Centro Servizi S.p.A., Pordenone, Italy; *Int'l*, pg. 442

de Purton, Ron, Dir.--Caparo Insurance Ltd., Saint Peter Port, United Kingdom; *Int'l*, pg. 265

de Puzo, Julio J., Jr., Chief Exec. Officer--First Pacific Advisors, Inc., Los Angeles, CA; *U.S. Public*, pg. 1673

de Rassin, Jean Marc, Pres.--S.O.C.A.T.A.(Societe de Construction d'Avions de Tourismes et d'Affaires), Tarbes, France; *Int'l*, pg. 29

de Ries, P.A.C., Mng. Dir.--Droste B.V., Vaassen, Netherlands; *Int'l*, pg. 243

De Risi, Frank, Mng. Dir.--Dun & Bradstreet Ltd., Dublin, Ireland; *U.S. Public*, pg. 536

de Rivoyre, Antoine, Chief Oper. Officer--Imprimerie Wallon, Vichy, France; *Int'l*, pg. 919

de Roeck, Guy, Mgr.--Commerzbank AG Representative Office-Bratislava, Bratislava, Czech Republic; *Int'l*, pg. 311

de Roissard, Henri, Chm. & Chief Exec. Officer--Dumez-GTM, Nanterre, France; *Int'l*, pg. 823

de Rudder, Thierry, Pres.--Groupe Bruxelles Lambert S.A., Brussels, Belgium; *Int'l*, pg. 561

de Ruijter, G., Pres.--Robot Pompen B.V., Alphen aan den Rijn, Netherlands; *Int'l*, pg. 1421

de Ruijter, S.C.M., Mng. Dir.--Phenix Aluminium S.A., Ivoz-Ramet, Belgium; *Int'l*, pg. 755

de Saint-Remy, Gerard, Pres.--Alcan France, Toulouse, France; *Int'l*, pg. 51

de Salterain, Pablo, Gen. Mgr.--Abiatar S.A., Montevideo, Uruguay; *U.S. Public*, pg. 208

De Sauvage, Marc, Mng. Dir.--Bekaert Engineering, Zwevegem, Belgium; *Int'l*, pg. 183

De Schutter, Richard U., Chm. Bd. & Pres.--Searle & Co., Skokie, IL; *U.S. Public*, pg. 1125

De Schutter, Richard U., Chief Exec. Officer--Searle Laboratories, Skokie, IL; *U.S. Public*, pg. 1125

de Schutter, W., Dr., Mng. Dir.--Wuestenrot Finance B.V., Amsterdam, Netherlands; *Int'l*, pg. 1514

de Sentmenat, Carlos Guell, Mng. Dir.--Asland S.A., Madrid, Spain; *Int'l*, pg. 790

de Seze, Amaury-Daniel, Pres.--Volvo European Corporate Office S.A., Paris, France; *Int'l*, pg. 1477

de Silva e Sousa, Alvaro, Mng. Dir.--Hyster Brasil Limitada, Santo Amaro, Brazil; *U.S. Public*, pg. 1149

De Simone, Lawrence E., Pres.--CSW Communications, Inc., Dallas, TX; *U.S. Public*, pg. 324

de Smedt, Hubert, Gen. Mgr.--Analog Devices International Inc., Antwerp, Belgium; *U.S. Public*, pg. 108

De Smedt, P.A., Chief Oper. Officer--S.A. Volkswagen Bruxelles N.V., Brussels, Belgium; *Int'l*, pg. 1475

De Smet, Andre, Reg. Dir.--Crown Cork Company (Holland) B.V., Rotterdam, Netherlands; *U.S. Public*, pg. 464

De Socio, Peter, Plant Mgr.--Eljer Industries, Ford City, PA; *U.S. Public*, pg. 1795

De Solombrino, Virginia, Opers. Mgr. & Service Coord.--Leo Burnett Comunica S.A., Guatemala, Guatemala; *U.S. Private*, pg. 185

de Soto, Maria Isabel, Pub. Rels. Dir. & Promo. Dir.--Leo Burnett Inc., Santo Domingo, Dominican Republic; *U.S. Private*, pg. 185

de Sousa, Herculano, Gen. Mgr. & Agent--Banco Totta & Acores, New York, NY; *Int'l*, pg. 145

de Sousa, J.A., Chief Oper. Officer--Zurich Chapultepec, Mexico, Mexico; *Int'l*, pg. 1532

de Sousa, Lincoln Barros, Gen. Mgr.--Banco do Brasil S.A.-Chile, Santiago, Chile; *Int'l*, pg. 141

De Souza, F.J. Guidao, Pres.--Air Products Gases Industriais Ltda., Sao Paulo, Brazil; *U.S. Public*, pg. 31

de Spirlet, Louis, Chm. Bd.--Techspace Aero, Milmort, Belgium; *Int'l*, pg. 1166

De Stefano, Daniel, Pres.--Deerskin Trading Post, Inc., North Bergen, NJ; *U.S. Public*, pg. 879

De Sutter, W., Mng. Dir.--S.A. Brother International (Belgium) N.V., Brussels, Belgium; *Int'l*, pg. 229

de Tinguy, Ch., Mng. Dir. & Gen. Mgr.--Gan Italia S.p.A., Rome, Italy; *Int'l*, pg. 564

de Torey, Maurice, Pres.--AGA S.A., Toulouse, France; *Int'l*, *pg. 13*

de Tray, Dennis N., Country Dir.--The World Bank, Jakarta, Indonesia; *U.S. Private*, pg. 1189

De Tuoni, C., Mgr.--ABN Leasing Italia S.p.A., Milan, Italy; *Int'l*, pg. 11

De Val, Javier, Dir.--ELVIAseg. S.A., Madrid, Spain; *Int'l*, pg. 60

de Valk, G., Chief Oper. Officer--Sobelease N.V., Zaventem, Belgium; *Int'l*, pg. 1082

de Vallois, Patrick, Mng. Dir.--Rhone-Poulenc Bucarest, Bucharest, Romania; *Int'l*, pg. 1112

de Vaucleroy, Gui, Chm. & Chief Exec. Officer--Delhaize The Lion America, Inc., Atlanta, GA; *Int'l*, pg. 463

De Vaucleroy, Jacques, Head-BBL/Central Region--BBL Central Region, Brussels, Belgium; *Int'l*, pg. 147

De Vecchi, Francesco, Chm.--Ambroveneto International Bank Ltd., Grand Cayman, Cayman Islands; *Int'l*, pg. 138

De Vecchi, Francesco, Chm. Bd.--Caboto Sim S.p.A., Milan, Italy; *Int'l*, pg. 138

De Verdier, Lars, Pres.--Atlas Copco Rockdrilling Equipment, Stockholm, Sweden; *Int'l*, pg. 96

De Vicq, Arnod, Mng. Dir.--154 Testa, Brussels, Belgium; *Int'l*, pg. 1377

de Villelongue, Thierry, Mng. Dir.--PT Sagita Dumez, Jakarta, Indonesia; *Int'l*, pg. 823

de Villelongue, Thierry, Mng. Dir.--Dumez-GTM Jakarta, Jakarta, Indonesia; *Int'l*, pg. 823

de Villiers, D.J.J., Chief Oper. Officer & Mng. Dir.--Sasol Oil (Pty) Ltd., Randburg, South Africa; *Int'l*, pg. 1197

de Villiers, Etienne, Mng. Dir.--The Walt Disney Company Ltd., London, United Kingdom; *U.S. Public*, pg. 514

de Vogeler, Ines, V.P. & Plng. Dir.--Leo Burnett Venezuela, C.A., Caracas, Venezuela; *U.S. Private*, pg. 186

de Vogt, Karl F., Mng. Dir.--Universal Studios TV (Television) G.m.b.H., Munich, Germany; *Int'l*, pg. 1217

de Vries, H. R., Chm.--Grabowsky & Poort International Consultants, Hague, Netherlands; *Int'l*, pg. 607

de Vries, J.R., Dir.--Ingenieursbureau Grabowsky & Poort BV, Hague, Netherlands; *Int'l*, pg. 607

de Vries, Max, Mng. Dir.--Mecatool AG, Flawil, Switzerland; *Int'l*, pg. 489

De Vries, R.R.D., V.P. & Mng Dir.--Varco BJ Oil Tools B.V., Etten-Leur, Netherlands; *U.S. Public*, pg. 1709

de Vries, S., Chief Oper. Officer--Imtech Projects Noord-Oost bv, Coevorden, Netherlands; *Int'l*, pg. 681

de Waard, D., Dir.--HBW, Hollandsche Beton en Waterbouw B.V., Gouda, Netherlands; *Int'l*, pg. 630

De Waardt, B., Chief Oper. Officer--Van Leeuwen Pipe & Tube Corp., Carson, CA; *Int'l*, pg. 1450

de Wilde, Louk, Gen. Dir.--Compagnie de Gestion et de Banque Gonet SA, Geneva, Switzerland; *Int'l*, pg. 548

de Wildt, H.R., Chm.--Hoogovens Aluminium NV, Duffel, Belgium; *Int'l*, pg. 755

de Wilt, W., Mng. Dir.--Uitgeverij Spaarnestad bv, Haarlem, Netherlands; *Int'l*, pg. 1445

de Winter, Marcel, Chief Oper. Officer--MacGREGOR (BEL) N.V., Antwerp, Belgium; *Int'l*, pg. 670

De Wite, Lieven, Mgr.-Commercial--Gamatex N.V, Antwerp, Belgium; *U.S. Public*, pg. 692

De Witt, Marianne, Mng. Dir.--Arte Film, Turin, Italy; *Int'l*, pg. 1377

de Woot, Fernand, Mng. Dir.--Compagnie Immobiliere de Belgique S.A., Brussels, Belgium; *Int'l*, pg. 1415

de Xouza, A.A., Chief Exec. Officer--Sangam Books Ltd., London, United Kingdom; *Int'l*, pg. 1026

De-Cardenas, Gilbert, Pres.--Cacique, City of Industry, CA; *U.S. Public*, pg. 995

De-Hui, Yu, Mng. Dir.--Burgmann Shanghai Ltd., Shanghai, China; *Int'l*, pg. 234

Deadman, G.J., Gen. Mgr.--Commonwealth Bank-Tokyo, Tokyo, Japan; *Int'l*, pg. 313

Deal, Steven C., Pres. & Chief Exec. Officer--Hilb, Rogal and Hamilton Company of Virginia, Glen Allen, VA; *U.S. Public*, pg. 827

Deale, Johannes, Mng. Dir.--Olin (Proprietary) Limited, Johannesburg, South Africa; *U.S. Public*, pg. 1220

Dean, Andrew R., District Office Mgr.--Aquaterra Environmental Consultants, Leeds, United Kingdom; *U.S.* Public, pg. 697

Dean, Art, Pres.--Evergreen Mills Inc., Ada, OK; *U.S. Private*, pg. 1134

Dean, Barrie, Mng. Dir.--Florasynth Australasia Pty. Ltd., Caringbah, Australia; *Int'l*, pg. 173

Dean, Howard M., Pres.--McArthur Dairy, Inc., Sunrise, FL; *U.S. Public*, pg. 491

Dean, Jim, Pres.--Four Corners Aviation, Inc., Farmington, NM; *U.S. Public*, pg. 1099

Dean, Kenny Ray, Acct. Exec.--Zimmerman & Partners Advertising, Inc., Grand Prairie, TX; *U.S. Private*, pg. 1206

Dean, Lawrence, Sr. Exec.--Fine Pitch Technology, Inc., San Jose, CA; *U.S. Public*, pg. 1483

Dean, Mike, Pres.--Business Machine Center, Inc. (NSL), Albuquerque, NM; *U.S. Public*, pg. 863

Dean, Ray, Plant Mgr.--Liberty Fabrics-Gordonsville Division, Gordonsville, VA; *Int'l*, pg. 340

Dean, Robert J., Gen. Mgr.--Summit Gravure Ltd., Preston, United Kingdom; *Int'l*, pg. 498

Dean, Robert W., Sr. V.P.-Admin. & Advanced Bus. Devel.--Ball Systems Engineering Operations, San Diego, CA; *U.S. Public*, pg. 171

Dean, T. Richard, Chm. Bd.--Regions Bank/Middle Tennessee, Nashville, TN; *U.S. Public*, pg. 1372

Deane, John C., Pres.--Banc One Leasing Co., Milwaukee, WI; *U.S. Public*, pg. 173

Deane, John C., Pres.--Banc One Leasing Corporation, Columbus, OH; *U.S. Public*, pg. 175

Deane, Kenny, Pres.--Alltel Missouri, Inc., Bolivar, MO; *U.S. Public*, pg. 56

Deane, T.E., Chm. & Chief Exec. Officer--Automotive Products USA Inc., Sterling Heights, MI; *Int'l*, pg. 113

Dearman, Timothy, Gen. Mgr.--Park Newspapers of Statesville, Inc., Statesville, NC; *U.S. Public*, pg. 1078

Dearman, Timothy, Gen. Mgr.--Statesville Record and Landmark, Statesville, NC; *U.S. Public*, pg. 1078

Dearman, Timothy, Gen. Mgr.--Park Newspapers of Iredell, Inc., Statesville, NC; *U.S. Public*, pg. 1078

Deasey, Stephen M., Pres. & Chief Oper. Officer--The Sygma Network, Inc.-Columbus Central Division, Columbus, OH; *U.S. Public*, pg. 1550

Deasy, William J., Pres.--T.L. James & Co., Inc., Saint Rose, LA; *U.S. Private*, pg. 580

DeBacker, D., Mng. Dir.--Mobrey SA-NV, Brussels, Belgium; *Int'l*, pg. 854

DeBacker, Werner, Pres.--Becton Dickinson Europe, Meylan, France; *U.S. Public*, pg. 200

DeBard, Daniel L., Chm. Bd.--Clinton State Bank, Clinton, IN; *U.S. Public*, pg. 1217

DeBari, Brien, Pres.--ALK Laboratories, Inc., Wallingford, CT; *Int'l*, pg. 288

DeBartelo, Louis, Pres.--Computer Products, National Accounts Division, Fremont, CA; *U.S. Public*, pg. 422

DeBartelo, Louis R., Pres.--Power Conversion, Boston, MA; *U.S. Public*, pg. 422

DeBartelo, Louis R., Acting Pres.--Power Conversion North America, Boston, MA; *U.S. Public*, pg. 422

DeBartolo, Lou, Pres.--Power Conversion-North America West, Fremont, CA; *U.S. Public*, pg. 422

DeBastiani, Donald, V.P. & Gen. Mgr.--Steering Wheel Systems North America, Yaphank, NY; *U.S. Public*, pg. 1558

Debater, Raphael Castejon, Gen. Mgr.--Terminals Portuarias, S.A., Barcelona, Spain; *U.S. Public*, pg. 693

DeBell, Gary, Pres.--Spectra-Physics Optics Corp., Mountain View, CA; *U.S. Public*, pg. 1594

DeBenedictis, Nicholas, Chm.--Utility & Municipal Services, Inc., Bryn Mawr, PA; *U.S. Public*, pg. 1287

DeBergh, Richard R., Mgr.--Scott & Stringfellow, Inc., Winchester, VA; *U.S. Public*, pg. 1446

DeBerry, Tim, Gen. Mgr.--Colorado Springs Auto Auction Inc., Colorado Springs, CO; *U.S. Public*, pg. 1648

DeBerry, William R., Chm. Bd., Pres. & Chief Oper. Officer--NationsBank/Chattanooga, Chattanooga, TN; *U.S. Public*, pg. 1163

Debievre, Georges, Pres. & Mng. Dir.--Anciens Establissements Goyot et Cie, Bellegarde-sur-Valserine, France; *U.S. Public*, pg. 1507

Debievre, Georges, V.P. & Gen. Mgr.--Keller-Dorian Graveurs, Div. of Roehlen Industries/Europe, Lyon, France; *U.S. Public*, pg. 1507

Debnar, Miro, Office Mgr.--Korn/Ferry International, Prague, Czech Republic; *U.S. Private*, pg. 634

DeBoer, Randall D., Pres.--Ikon Office Solutions-Michigan, Grand Rapids, MI; *U.S. Public*, pg. 863

DeBoer, Robert, Pres.--DeBoer's Fabrieken B.V., Amsterdam, Netherlands; *Int'l*, pg. 594

DeBolt, Marion L., Pres. & Gen. Mgr.--All American Homes, Inc., Decatur, IN; *U.S. Public*, pg. 388

DeBone, Louis J., Pres.--Bertek, Inc., Saint Albans, VT; *U.S.* Public, pg. 1143

DeBord, Brady L., Gen. Mgr.--TCA Cable of Amarillo, Inc., Amarillo, TX; *U.S. Public*, pg. 1553

Debrot, Larry L., V.P. & Gen. Mgr.--Product Support Division, Wichita, KS; *U.S. Public*, pg. 241

Debrun, Philippe, Chm.--Revima, Roissy, France; *Int'l*, pg. 560

DeBruyne, Walter, Country Mgr.--BMC Software Belgium N.V.-S.A., Zaventem, Belgium; *U.S. Public*, pg. 162

Decaillet, Pierre, Pres.--Sakata Seed Europe B.V., Rijssen, Netherlands; *Int'l*, pg. 1178

DeCamella, David, Admin.--Palmer House Healthcare, Palmer, MA; *U.S. Public*, pg. 1714

DeCarlo, D.J., V.P.--Bronze Div., Pittsburgh, PA; *U.S. Public*, *pg. 1059*

DeCarlo, D.J., Pres.--Matthews International Memorial Division, Pittsburgh, PA; *U.S. Public*, pg. 1059

DeCaro, Angelo A., Jr., Pres.--Xetel Corporation, Austin, TX; *Int'l*, pg. 1125

DeCastro, Herbert, Pres.--Pittra, Elizabeth, NJ; *U.S. Private*, pg. 94

DeCessaro, Al, Plant Mgr.--Sealy Mattress Company - Denver, Denver, CO; *U.S. Private*, pg. 979

Deceuninck, Paul, Mgr.--CAE Trislot N.V., Waregem, Belgium; *Int'l*, pg. 238

Deck, Howard, Pres.--AOTEC, Southbridge, MA; *U.S. Private*, pg. 60

Deck, N., Pres.--Claritas, Inc., Arlington, VA; *Int'l*, pg. 1447

Decker, C. David, Pres.--GTE Laboratories Incorporated, Waltham, MA; *U.S. Public*, pg. 697

Decker, Dwight W., V.P. & Gen. Mgr.--Rockwell Semiconductor Systems, Newport Beach, CA; *U.S. Public*, pg. 1398

Decker, Dwight W., Pres.--3ockwell Semiconductor Systems, Newport Beach, CA; *U.S. Public*, pg. 1398

Decker, Dwight W., Pres.--Brooktree Rockwell Semiconductor Systems Div., San Diego, CA; *U.S. Public*, pg. 1398

Decker, Gayle, Exec. V.P.--Blumenthal/Lansing Company, Lansing, IA; *U.S. Public*, pg. 1187

Decker, Jeff, Pres.--Greenberg Financial Insurance Services, Inc., Palm Desert, CA; *U.S. Public*, pg. 1334

Decker, Steven, Gen. Mgr.--Giesecke & Devrient Engineering, Inc., Bedford, MA; *U.S. Private*, pg. 452

Decker, T.E., Pres. & Chief Oper. Officer--AC & S Inc., Lancaster, PA; *U.S. Public*, pg. 913

Decker, Thomas A., Pres.--CertainTeed Foreign Sales Corp., Valley Forge, PA; *Int'l*, pg. 1171

Decker, William, Pres.--PVS Chemicals, Inc., Buffalo, NY; *U.S. Private*, pg. 828

Decker, William, Pres.--PVS Chemicals, Inc., Chicago, IL; *U.S. Private*, pg. 828

Decker, Yvonne, Mgr.--Sugar Valley Telephone Co., Loganton, PA; *U.S. Public*, pg. 1572

Deckman, Joe, Pres.--Window Fabrication Div., Wausau, WI; *U.S. Public*, pg. 120

DeClemente, Thomas, Gen. Mgr.--AMP Italia S.p.A., Turin, Italy; *U.S. Public*, pg. 9

DeCook, Ray, Plant Mgr.--American Natl. Can Co., Saint Louis, MO; *Int'l*, pg. 1029

Decot, Roger, Chm. Bd.--Eurofip (Madrid), Madrid, Spain; *Int'l*, pg. 163

Decourcelle, Gerard, Chm.--BNP SIM S.P.A., Genoa, Italy; *Int'l*, pg. 164

DeCruz, Wasy, Pres.--American Banknote Holographics, Elmsford, NY; *U.S. Public*, pg. 68

Decurtins, Arthur, Mng. Dir.--Union de Banques Suisses (Luxembourg) S.A., Luxembourg, Luxembourg; *Int'l*, pg. 1441

Dedayan, Louis, Pres.--Vibratechniques STV, Fontenay-sous-Bois, France; *Int'l*, pg. 1420

Dedehayir, Fevzi, Mng. Dir.--Valmet-Boustead Pty. Ltd., Braybrook, Australia; *Int'l*, pg. 1449

Dedeluk, Ken, Pres.--Auto-trol Technology (Canada) Ltd., Calgary, Canada; *U.S. Public*, pg. 148

Dedoyard, Raoul, Head-BBL/Flemish Region--BBL Flemish Region, Antwerp, Belgium; *Int'l*, pg. 147

Dee-luca, Pitro, V.P. & Mgr.--Banca Nazionale Del Lavoro (Chicago), Chicago, IL; *Int'l*, pg. 136

Dee, Jimmy, Gen. Mgr.--CMC Fareast Limited, Hong Kong, Hong Kong; *U.S. Public*, pg. 413

Deed, Peter, Mgr.--Newcastle Wire Mill, Mayfield, Australia; *Int'l*, pg. 226

Deeds, David C., Dir.-Sls.--Solvay Polymers Inc., Houston, TX; *Int'l*, pg. 1278

Deeg, L., Mgr.--Hercules Inc.-Jefferson, West Elizabeth, PA; *U.S. Public*, pg. 810

Deege, Peter, Chief Oper. Officer--Carrefour Nederland B.V., Rotterdam, Netherlands; *Int'l*, pg. 273

Deekens, John, Plant Mgr.--Triwood, Inc., Ridgeway, VA; *U.S. Public*, pg. 193

Deekens, John, Plant Mgr.--Triwood, Inc., Ridgeway, VA; *U.S. Private*, pg. 538

Deekens, John, Plant Mgr.--Triwood, Inc., Ridgeway, VA; *U.S. Public*, pg. 1343

Deeks, H. R., Pres--Molson Saskatchewan Brewery Ltd., Regina, Canada; *Int'l*, pg. 887

Deel, Jerry, Pres.--Portec, Inc.-Construction Equipment Div., Yankton, SD; *U.S. Public*, pg. 1318

Deelen, Jan, Chief Exec. Officer--Timac B.V., Fijnaart, Netherlands; *Int'l*, pg. 712

Deeley, Steven, Branch Mgr.--Downey Savings & Loan Association, F.A., Burbank, CA; *U.S. Public*, pg. 527

Deems, T.F., Pres.--United Clays, Inc., Brentwood, TN; *Int'l, pg. 1487*

Deeney, Gerald, Chief Fin. Officer--KOB-TV, Inc., Albuquerque, NM; *U.S. Private*, pg. 544

Deeney, Gerald D., Chief Fin. Officer--United States Satellite Broadcasting, Co., Saint Paul, MN; *U.S. Private, pg. 544*

Deer, P. W., Reg. Mng. Dir.--National Westminster Bank Plc, Hong Kong, Hong Kong; *Int'l*, pg. 911

Deering, Joseph W., Pres.--Hobart Corporation, Troy, OH; *U.S. Public*, pg. 1322

Defauw, Robert, Mgr.-Oper.--Middleville Mfg. Div., Middleville, MI; *U.S. Public*, pg. 1475

DeFay, C., Mng. Dir.--Ascom HPF SA, Bonneville, France; *Int'l*, pg. 87

Defelice, Norm, Gen. Mgr.--Bass Block & Building Supplies, Beamsville, Canada; *Int'l*, pg. 629

DeFeo, Ronald J., Pres.--Wholesale Glass Fabricators Inc., Wilmington, NC; *Int'l*, pg. 616

Deffebach, Harry L., V.P. & Gen. Mgr.--Government Communication Systems Division, Melbourne, FL; *U.S. Public*, pg. 792

Deffis, J.P., Gen. Mgr.--Font Vella, Barcelona, Spain; *Int'l*, pg. 381

Deffren, John, Gen. Mgr.--Paxton Beautiful Woods, New Orleans, LA; *U.S. Private*, pg. 585

DeFilippis, Grace, Mgr.--Special Instruments, Chicago, IL; *U.S. Private*, pg. 132

deFlines, Egbert W., Gen. Mgr.--USB Pharma B.V., Nijmegen, Netherlands; *U.S. Public*, pg. 1681

DeFlorio, V., Controller--Bridgestone/Firestone Italia S.p.A., Milan, Italy; *Int'l*, pg. 214

DeFlorio, Victor, Pres.--Bridgestone/Firestone de la Argentina S.A.I.C., Buenos Aires, Argentina; *Int'l*, pg. 214

Deford, Bill, Gen. Mgr.--WWF National, Boston, MA; *U.S. Private*, pg. 1145

Defraigne, Jacques, Mng. Dir.--Aquinter S.A., Brussels, Belgium; *Int'l*, pg. 1415

DeFreitas, Teresa, Admin., Opers. & Systems--TMP Worldwide Ltd., Toronto, Canada; *U.S. Private*, pg. 1065

Degail, Jean-Jacques, Country Mgr.--Circle Freight International France, S.A., Roissy Charles de Gaulle, France; *U.S. Public*, pg. 372

DeGeer, Ross, Vice Chm. & Dir.--GPC Government Policy Consultants (Ontario), Toronto, Canada; *U.S. Public*, pg. 1225

Degelman, Roland, Mgr.-Sls.--Hylar Metal Products, Regina, Canada; *Int'l*, pg. 388

Degen, A.P., Pres.--Vamco, Cumberland, RI; *U.S. Public*, pg. 1706

Degen, A.P., Pres.--Valley Gas Co., Cumberland, RI; *U.S. Public*, pg. 1706

Degenring, Horst W., Chief Oper. Officer--Homburger Papierfabrik Wilhelm Geldmacher GmbH & Co. KG, Numbrecht, Germany; *Int'l*, pg. 35

DeGeorge, Cynthia, V.P. & Gen. Mgr.-Mid-Atlantic Reg.--Pennsylvania Cellular Telephone Corp., Harrisburg, PA; *U.S. Public*, pg. 1708

DeGeorge, Cynthia L., V.P. & Gen. Mgr.-Southern Penn. Opers.--Pennsylvania Cellular Telephone Corp., Chambersburg, PA; *U.S. Public*, pg. 1708

Degerman, A., Chief Fin. Officer--Scholl Danmark A/S, Copenhagen, Denmark; *Int'l*, pg. 1209

Degerman, A., Chief Fin. Officer--Scholl (Sverige) SA, Stockholm, Sweden; *Int'l*, pg. 1210

Deges, John A., Chief Oper. Officer--First Brands (Europe) Ltd., Wokingham, United Kingdom; *U.S. Public*, pg. 627

Degginger, Lou, Pres.--Lubbock Div., Lubbock, TX; *U.S. Public*, pg. 652

Degler, Sandra C., Pres.--Tax Management, Inc., Washington, DC; *U.S. Private*, pg. 182

Degnan, Gerard A., Pres.--ADM Arkady, Olathe, KS; *U.S. Public*, pg. 127

Degnan, John J., Pres.--Chubb Insurance Company of New Jersey, Warren, NJ; *U.S. Public*, pg. 355

Degnan, Thomas J., Pres.--Universal Foods Corporation-Bakery Products Div., Milwaukee, WI; *U.S. Public*, pg. 1696

Degni, Ralf, Chief Fin. Officer--Young & Rubicam South Africa, Johannesburg, South Africa; *U.S. Private*, pg. 1198

Degos, Philippe, Mng. Dir.--Constructora Dumez de Chile, Santiago, Chile; *Int'l*, pg. 823

Degos, Philippe, Mng. Dir.--Dumez-GTM, Buenos Aires, Argentina; *Int'l*, pg. 823

deGraauw, John S., Pres.--Premier Securities Corporation, Baton Rouge, LA; *U.S. Public*, pg. 173

DeGregorio, Guido, V.P. & Gen. Mgr.--Display Technologies Electrohome Inc., Carthage, MO; *Int'l*, pg. 438

Degremont, Samuel, Administrative Rep.--GTMI (M) Sdn Bhd, Kuala Lumpur, Malaysia; *Int'l*, pg. 823

Degroote, Odilo, Mgr.--Soges-Fiducem S.A., Brussels, Belgium; *Int'l*, pg. 147

Deguerry, P., Chm. Bd.--Banque Regionale De L'Ain, Bourg-en-Bresse, France; *Int'l*, pg. 563

DeGuzman, Bobby, Mng. Dir.--Woodward-Clyde International, Manila, Philippines; *U.S. Public*, pg. 1658

DeHaven, Bud, Pres.--Electronica Condor De Mexico, S.A., Cuauhtemoc, Mexico; *U.S. Public*, pg. 1419

Dehler, A.P., Branch Mgr.--CHEMCENTRAL/Odessa, Odessa, TX; *U.S. Private*, pg. 232

Dehn, Wulf H., Dr., Mgr.--Hapag-Lloyd (Asia) Pte. Ltd., Singapore, Singapore; *Int'l*, pg. 596

Dehne, John S., Pres.--Lockheed Martin Infared Imaging Systems, Lexington, MA; *U.S. Public*, pg. 1008

Dehner, James B., Pres.--Southern Group, Inc., Kansas City, MO; *U.S. Public*, pg. 944

DeHont, Raymond, Gen. Mgr.--Flex-Kleen Corporation, Chicago, IL; *U.S. Public*, pg. 29

DeHont, Raymond, Gen. Mgr.--Flex-Kleen Corporation, Itasca, IL; *U.S. Public*, pg. 29

DeHont, Raymond J., V.P. & Gen. Mgr.--Fybroc Division, Telford, PA; *U.S. Public*, pg. 1100

Deieso, Donald A., Pres.--EA Global, Inc., Hunt Valley, MD; *U.S. Public*, pg. 541

Deines, Don, Gen. Mgr.--Dyna-Pak Div., Kennewick, WA; *U.S. Private*, pg. 832

Deininger, Larry R., Grp. V.P.--Aerospace-Marine-Defense Group, Maumee, OH; *U.S. Public*, pg. 24

Deisenroth, Clint, Pres.--Whittaker Electronic Systems, Simi Valley, CA; *U.S. Public*, pg. 1767

Deitch, Mordecai, Pres.--Deitsch Plastic Export Co., New York, NY; *U.S. Private*, pg. 321

Deitzer, Harry J., Pres.--Besser Canada, Ltd., Bramalea, Canada; *U.S. Private*, pg. 139

DeJaeger, K.L., Pres.--Industrial Plastics Company, Fort Smith, AR; *U.S. Public*, pg. 56

Dejardin, Pierre, Pres.-Exec. Bd.--Banque Piguet & Cie S.A., Yverdon, Switzerland; *Int'l*, pg. 160

DeJidas, Gary M., Pres.--GAI Consultants-Southeast, Inc., Orlando, FL; *U.S. Private*, pg. 434

Dejonekhere, Janice E., Branch Mgr.--Financial Collection Agencies, Ottawa, Canada; *Int'l*, pg. 470

Dejonghe, W., Plant Mgr.--Bekaert Corporation, Dyersburg, TN; *Int'l*, pg. 184

DeJoseph, Thomas, Pres.--Sperry Rail Services, Danbury, CT; *U.S. Public*, pg. 75

Dekis, Jeffrey, Plant Mgr.--Hygeia Sciences, Inc., Newton, MA; *U.S. Public*, pg. 310

Dekker, Alan N., Pres.--Buckeye Union Insurance Co., Columbus, OH; *U.S. Public*, pg. 1010

Dekker, Ben, Gen. Mgr.--Esselte BV, Woerden, Netherlands; *Int'l*, pg. 461

Dekker, Ben, Gen. Mgr.--Kadee Delft BV, Delft, Netherlands; *Int'l*, pg. 461

Dekker, Ben, Gen. Mgr.--SA Letraset Belgium NV, Brussels, Belgium; *Int'l*, pg. 461

Dekker, Leendert W., Rep.--Kredietbank Representative Office (Arcadia), Pretoria, South Africa; *Int'l*, pg. 760

DeKoven, Lindy, V.P.-Movies & Miniseries--Lorimar Television, Burbank, CA; *U.S. Public*, pg. 1611

del Alcuaz, J., Plant Mgr.--Bridgford Frozen-Rite Foods, Dallas, TX; *U.S. Public*, pg. 252

Del Bondio, Bryan, Pres.--Markham Vineyards, Saint Helena, CA; *Int'l*, pg. 858

del Cueto Legaspi, Roberto, Pres.--Banco Nacional de Mexico, S.A. (Banamex), Mexico, Mexico; *Int'l*, pg. 574

del Cueto, Benito, Chief Oper. Officer--Desarrollos Multiples Insulares, Inc., San Juan, PR; *U.S. Public*, pg. 1342

del Olmo Alonso, Carlos, Mng. Dir.--Igemisa, Madrid, Spain; *Int'l*, pg. 608

Del Olmo, J., Gen. Mgr.--La Familia, Barcelona, Spain; *Int'l*, pg. 380

del Peral, Javier Revuelta, Pres.--Telefonica Publicidad e Informac., Madrid, Spain; *Int'l*, pg. 1372

del Rio, A., Gen. Mgr.--Davy McKee Chile Ltda., Santiago, Chile; *Int'l*, pg. 775

Del Rio, Jorge, Sr. V.P.--Banco de la Nacion Argentina, Miami, FL; *Int'l*, pg. 140

del Rosal, Roberto, Pres. & Chief Exec. Officer--Bacardi Corporation, San Juan, PR; *Int'l*, pg. 131

Del Rossi, Paul R., Chm. Bd.--General Cinema Theatres, Inc., Chestnut Hill, MA; *U.S. Public*, pg. 693

Del Rossi, Paul R., Pres.--GC International, Inc., Chestnut Hill, MA; *U.S. Public*, pg. 693

Del Tufo, Robert J., Partner--Skadden, Arps, Slate, Meagher & Flom LLP, Newark, NJ; *U.S. Private*, pg. 1004

Del Valle, Fulvio, Gen. Mgr.--AMP de Mexico, S. A., Tlalnepantla, Mexico; *U.S. Public*, pg. 8

Del Valle, Hector, Pres.--Caribbean Cement Carriers Corporation, San Juan, PR; *U.S. Public*, pg. 1342

del Valle, Oscar, Owner--Sun City Redi-Mix Inc., El Paso, TX; *Int'l*, pg. 573

Del Vecchio, Claudio, Pres. & Chief Exec. Officer--Petite Sophisticate Outlet, Enfield, CT; *U.S. Private*, pg. 219

del Villar, Gonzalo, V.P. & Fin. Dir.--Leo Burnett Chile, Santiago, Chile; *U.S. Private*, pg. 185

del Villar, Pablito S., Jr., Chief Oper. Officer--Induplex, Inc., Legaspi, Philippines; *U.S. Private*, pg. 904

Delaforge, Gerard, Sr. Officer--Banque Indosuez, Geneva, Switzerland; *Int'l*, pg. 314

Delage, D.D., V.P. & Div. Mgr.--Century Fence Co., Forest Lake, MN; *U.S. Private*, pg. 226

DeLagrange, Lawrence, Mng. Dir.--Society Francais Pour Le Developpement de la Porcelaine d'Art, Paris, France; *U.S. Public*, pg. 1609

Delahanty, P., Chief Oper. Officer--J & B Products, Inc., South Bend, IN; *U.S. Private*, pg. 399

Delahaut, Robert J., Gen. Mgr.--MKRD-Laser Service, Hopedale, MA; *U.S. Private*, pg. 685

Delaney, Claude J., Chief Oper. Officer--Frigoscandia Food Process Systems Inc., Guelph, Canada; *U.S. Public*, pg. 607

Delaney, James R., Pres.--Lincoln Electric Mexicana S.A. de C.V., Mexico, Mexico; *U.S. Public*, pg. 997

Delaney, Jerry, Country Mgr.--Raychem SDN Berhad, Petaling Jaya, Malaysia; *U.S. Public*, pg. 1363

Delaney, Jerry, Mgr.-Reg.--Raychem Singapore Pte Ltd, Singapore, Singapore; *U.S. Public*, pg. 1363

Delaney, John M., Pres.--The Dometic Corporation, Elkhart, IN; *Int'l*, pg. 440

Delaney, Paul, Plant Mgr.--Tabuchi Electric de Mexico S.A. de C.V., Tijuana, Mexico; *Int'l*, pg. 1346

Delanghe, Jean-Claude, Chief Rep.--Generale Bank, Tokyo, Japan; *Int'l*, pg. 547

Delano, Steve, Chief Oper. Officer--BMS On-Line Services, Inc., Randolph, MA; *U.S. Public*, pg. 647

Delanoe, Jacques, Co-Mgr.--Etoile Bleue, Nantes, France; *Int'l*, pg. 600

Delanoe, Jacques, Assoc. Gen. Mgr.--Etoile Bleue, Rennes, France; *Int'l*, pg. 600

DeLarosa, Valerie, Gen. Mgr.--Friendly Holidays Inc.-West, Costa Mesa, CA; *U.S. Private*, pg. 429

Delattre, Yves, Chief Oper. Officer--France Transfo, Maizieres-les-Metz, France; *Int'l*, pg. 706

Delaye, Dennis, Pres.--UniSea Foods, Inc., Redmond, WA; *Int'l*, pg. 940

Delbard, Francois, Mng. Dir.--Georges Delbard S.A., Paris, France; *Int'l*, pg. 780

DelBoccio, L., Mgr.--Daher Golden Eagle - Chicago, Elk Grove Village, IL; *U.S. Public*, pg. 749

Delbrook, James, Pres.--Arizona Elevator, Inc., Phoenix, AZ; *U.S. Public*, pg. 521

Delcour, Gerard, Mng. Dir.--Cosmeurop S.A., Strasbourg, France; *Int'l*, pg. 295

Delean, Alain, Chm. Bd. & Mng. Dir.--Ford Italiana S.p.A., Rome, Italy; *U.S. Public*, pg. 666

Delendas, Jerome, Exec. Chm.--Allianz General Insurance Company S.A., Athens, Greece; *Int'l*, pg. 59

Delendas, Jerome, Exec. Chm.--Allianz Life Insurance Company S.A., Athens, Greece; *Int'l*, pg. 59

DeLeo, Dennis, Chief Oper. Officer--Kodak Bioscience / Emerging Business Division, Rochester, NY; *U.S. Public, pg. 551*

DeLeo, Dennis, Chief Oper. Officer--Eastman Technology Inc., Rochester, NY; *U.S. Public*, pg. 551

DeLeo, Dennis, V.P. & Gen. Mgr.--Image Acquisition Products Division, Rochester, NY; *U.S. Public*, pg. 555

DeLeo, Richard, Pres.--Countrywide Title Corporation, Pasadena, CA; *U.S. Public*, pg. 453

Delepine, Robert, Pres. & Mng. Dir.--Duquesne-Purina S.A., Montigny-le-Bretonneux, France; *U.S. Public*, pg. 1360

Deletang, Bruno, Exec. V.P.--CGG American Services Inc., Houston, TX; *Int'l*, pg. 241

Deletang, D., Mgr.--Compania Mexicana de Geofisica, Mexico, Mexico; *Int'l*, pg. 241

Deleva, John, Mng. Dir.--Dudley Sports Co. Division, Chicopee, MA; *U.S. Private*, pg. 629

Delforge, J.L., Gen. Mgr.--SmithKline Beecham Diergeneeskundige Producten B.V., Zoetermeer, Netherlands; *Int'l*, pg. 1266

Delfosse, J., Chief Exec. Officer--Redland Koramic Bricks N.V., Malle, Belgium; *Int'l*, pg. 1093

DelFranco, Michael, Mgr.--Meyer Wire & Cable Company, Hamden, CT; *U.S. Private*, pg. 251

Delgado, Juan March, Pres.--Corporacion Financiera Alba S.A., Madrid, Spain; *Int'l*, pg. 136

Delgado, Luis, Gen. Mgr.--Amway de Portugal, Inc., Carnaxide, Portugal; *U.S. Private*, pg. 69

Delgado, Mark, Admin.--Las Cruces Nursing Center, Las Cruces, NM; *U.S. Public*, pg. 838

Deli, Steven F., Chm. & Chief Exec. Officer--Eaglemark Financial Services, Inc., Chicago, IL; *U.S. Public*, pg. 786

Delian, Lu, Pres.--Casco Signal Ltd., Shanghai, China; *Int'l*, pg. 1195

Delight, Guy, Pres.--ABB Hafo Inc., San Diego, CA; *Int'l*, pg. 4

Delinikolov, Saso, Chief Oper. Officer--Novo Nordisk A/S, Skopje, Macedonia; *Int'l*, pg. 988

DeLisle, Richard H., Pres.--Scott Aviation, Lancaster, NY; *U.S. Public*, pg. 622

Delius, Carlos E., Pres. & Gen. Mgr.--Occidental Peruana, Inc., Lima, Peru; *U.S. Public*, pg. 1210

Dell, G., Area Mgr.--The Foundation Company - Halifax, Halifax, Canada; *Int'l*, pg. 118

Dell, Mary Ann, Gen. Mgr.--Capintec Instruments Inc., Pittsburgh, PA; *U.S. Private*, pg. 205

Della Noce, Joseph, Pres. & Chief Oper. Officer--Richfood Pennsylvania, Harrisburg, PA; *U.S. Public*, pg. 1389

della Torre, Augusto, Dir.--Banca d'America e d'Italia S.p.A. (Mestre), Mestre, Italy; *Int'l*, pg. 403

Della Torre, G., Chief Fin. Officer--Olivetti Australia Pty. Ltd., Silverwater, Australia; *Int'l*, pg. 1003

Della-Porta, Pierre, Fin. Dir.--Robertson Leo Burnett Pty. Ltd., Adelaide, Australia; *U.S. Private*, pg. 186

Dellas, G.J., Plant Mgr.--Huntsville Electronics Div., Huntsville, AL; *U.S. Public*, pg. 353

Delling, David, Pres.--Tenneco Minerals Co., Lakewood, CO; *U.S. Public*, pg. 1579

Delloye, Philippe, Pres.--Corning France, S.A., Avon, France; *U.S. Public*, pg. 449

Delman, Steven, Chief Oper. Officer--Splendor Form Brassiere, Inc., Long Island City, NY; *U.S. Private*, pg. 792

Delmar, Jack, Pres. & Chief Oper. Officer--Brascan Brazil, Rio de Janeiro, Brazil; *Int'l*, pg. 435

Delmar, Steve, Chm. Bd.--Old Dominion Systems of Maryland, Germantown, MD; *U.S. Public*, pg. 1105

DeLong, Al, V.P.-Mfg.--Spartanburg Steel Products, Spartanburg, SC; *U.S. Private*, pg. 300

DeLong, Phillip, Div. Pres.--Boehringer Mannheim Biochemicals Div., Indianapolis, IN; *Int'l*, pg. 331

DeLorenzo, Matt, Editor--AutoWeek, Detroit, MI; *U.S. Private*, pg. 284

Delorme, Jean-Louis, Mng. Dir.--Pochentong Airport Construction JV, Phnom Penh, Kampuchea; *Int'l*, pg. 823

DeLoughry, Jim, Mgr.--Crawal, Indianapolis, IN; *U.S. Private, pg. 177*

Delport, W.A., Mgr.--Leeudoorn Division, Leeudoorn, South Africa; *Int'l*, pg. 738

DelSanto, Mary Elicia, Banking & Fin. Svcs. Officer--Troy Savings Bank-Albany, Albany, NY; *U.S. Private,* pg. 1106
DeLuca, J.M., Pres.--JMD Development Corporation, San Francisco, CA; *U.S. Private,* pg. 976
DeLuca, John, V.P. & Gen. Mgr.--Vortec, Cincinnati, OH; *U.S. Public,* pg. 865
DeLuca, Robert, Pres. & Chief Exec. Officer--Air Crafters Inc., Ronkonkoma, NY; *U.S. Private,* pg. 24
DeLuca, Robert A., Pres.--Enzyme Bio-Systems, Ltd., Beloit, WI; *U.S. Public,* pg. 448
DeLuca, Roberta, Pres. & Chief Exec. Officer--Lab Crafters Inc., Ronkonkoma, NY; *U.S. Private,* pg. 24
DeLue, Robert S., Pres. & Chief Exec. Officer--ACSIA, Burlingame, CA; *Int'l,* pg. 499
Delusinne, Philippe, Pres., Mng. Dir. & Chief Exec. Officer--Young & Rubicam Belgium S.A., Brussels, Belgium; *U.S. Private,* pg. 1199
Delva, Luc, Chief Oper. Officer--Bank Brussels Lambert (Singapore) Ltd., Singapore, Singapore; *Int'l,* pg. 148
Delvaux, S., Mng. Dir.--S.C. Corporations Efficiency Growth Through Information Systems CEGIS, Ougree, Belgium; *Int'l,* pg. 301
DelVecchio, Gary, Chief Exec. Officer--Doubleday Book Shops, Inc., New York, NY; *U.S. Public,* pg. 189
DelVecchio, George, Gen. Mgr.--Milgray/Florida, Inc., Lake Mary, FL; *U.S. Public,* pg. 206
Delyzer, Dave, V.P. & Gen. Mgr.--North Safety Products Siebe North Canada Ltd., Etobicoke, Canada; *Int'l,* pg. 1243
Delzer, R., Mgr.-West Coast--CGG American Services, Inc., Walnut Grove, CA; *Int'l,* pg. 241
Demand, G., Chief Oper. Officer--VW Kraftwerk GmbH, Wolfsburg, Germany; *Int'l,* pg. 1474
Demangel, Pierre J., Resident Rep.--Banque Mondiale, Brazzaville, Congo; *U.S. Private,* pg. 1189
Demarais, Charlie, Branch Mgr.--Circle International, Huntington Beach, CA; *U.S. Public,* pg. 372
Demaray, S., Asst. V.P. & Gen. Mgr.--Manulife Bank of Canada-Regional Lending Unit, Toronto, Canada; *Int'l,* pg. 840
DeMarco, Carol, Admin.--Carriage House Manor, Fullerton, CA; *U.S. Private,* pg. 733
Demarest, Clifford J., Pres. & Chief Exec. Officer--Starboard Data Services, Inc., King of Prussia, PA; *U.S. Private,* pg. 86
Demaret, Jean-Pierre, Mgr.--Kredietbank (Nederland) N.V., Maastricht, Netherlands; *Int'l,* pg. 761
DeMaria, Claudio, Mng. Dir.--PDA International/Italy, Turin, Italy; *U.S. Public,* pg. 1031
DeMaria, Roberto, Chief Oper. Officer--Elevadores Kone Sabiem S.A. de C.V., Mexico, Mexico; *Int'l,* pg. 747
DeMars, Dan R., Pres.--Geupel DeMars, Inc., Indianapolis, IN; *U.S. Private,* pg. 450
DeMars, Jerry, V.P. & Gen. Mgr.--Nucor Fasteners, Saint Joe, IN; *U.S. Public,* pg. 1205
Demarthe, J.M., Pres. & Chief Exec. Officer--Minemet Recherche, Trappes, France; *Int'l,* pg. 661
DeMartino, F.A., Pres.--Parsons Infrastructure & Technology Group Inc., Pasadena, CA; *U.S. Private,* pg. 842
Demel, Herbert, Dr., Chm. Bd.--Audi AG, Ingolstadt, Germany; *Int'l,* pg. 1473
Demel, Richard, Chief Oper. Officer--Rowenta-Vertriebsgesellschaft mbH, Vienna, Austria; *Int'l,* pg. 569
DeMere, John, Pres.--Colonial Marine Industries, Inc., Savannah, GA; *U.S. Private,* pg. 254
Demeritt, Stephen R., Chief Exec. Officer--Cereal Partners Worldwide, Morges, Switzerland; *U.S. Public,* pg. 718
Demeritt, Stephen R., Chief Exec. Officer--Cereal Partners Worldwide, Morges, Switzerland; *Int'l,* pg. 916
DeMerritt, Ted C., Chief Exec. Officer--Olsy North America Inc., Liberty Lake, WA; *Int'l,* pg. 1002
Demers, Richard P., Pres.--EnergyNorth Propane, Inc., Concord, NH; *U.S. Public,* pg. 582
Demetrieus, John, Pres.--Sunkyong America, Inc., New York, NY; *Int'l,* pg. 1320
DeMeulenaere, Robert L., Chief Exec. Officer--Brenton Bank, Des Moines, IA; *U.S. Public,* pg. 251
DeMey, Luc, V.P.-European Opers.--BancTec Benelux B.V., Amsterdam, Netherlands; *U.S. Public,* pg. 177
Demharter, Stephan, Area Mgr.--Louis Creek Division, Louis Creek, Canada; *Int'l,* pg. 1395
DeMicco, Frank J., Pres.--United Water New Jersey, Inc., Harrington Park, NJ; *U.S. Public,* pg. 1692
DeMichiei, J.M., Pres.--Cyprus Emerald Resources Corporation, Waynesburg, PA; *U.S. Public,* pg. 471
DeMichiei, J.M., Pres.--Cyprus Empire Corporation, Craig, CO; *U.S. Public,* pg. 471
DeMichiei, J.M., Pres.--Cyprus Plateau Mining Corporation, Price, UT; *U.S. Public,* pg. 471
DeMichiei, J.M., Pres.--Cyprus Shoshone Coal Corporation, Hanna, WY; *U.S. Public,* pg. 471
DeMiecoo, Frank J., Pres.--United Water Mid-Atlantic, Succasunna, NJ; *U.S. Public,* pg. 1692
DeMille, Wallace J., Exec. V.P. & Chief Oper. Officer--Monumental Life Insurance Company, Baltimore, MD; *Int'l,* pg. 27
Demiresi, Tahsin, Gen. Dir.--IBM Turk Limited Sirketi, Istanbul, Turkey; *U.S. Public,* pg. 1043
Demirjian, Abraham, Mgr.-Sls., West Coast--Kuwait Airways, West Coast Region, Los Angeles, CA; *Int'l,* pg. 764
Demjan, Zoltan, Chief Exec.--Hirocem a.s., Rohoznik, Slovenia; *Int'l,* pg. 629
Demko, Don, Pres.--The Holden Group, Los Angeles, CA; *Int'l,* pg. 435
Demmer, Jurgen, Mng. Dir.--Krupp Stahl Kaltform GmbH, Leverkusen, Germany; *Int'l,* pg. 508
Demmin, Dave, Mgr.--Quest Diagnostic-Amherst, Amherst, NY; *U.S. Public,* pg. 1351
Demone, Henry E., Pres. & Chief Exec. Officer--National Sea Products Incorporated, Portsmouth, NH; *Int'l,* pg. 909
DeMone, Robert S., Chm., Pres. & Chief Exec. Officer--Canadian Pacific Hotels & Resorts Inc., Toronto, Canada; *Int'l,* pg. 258
Demonte, Filippo, Chief Oper. Officer--Olivetti Canon Industriale, Aglie, Italy; *Int'l,* pg. 1002
DeMorette, Don, Pres.--TL Systems Corporation, Minneapolis, MN; *Int'l,* pg. 205
DeMoulin, Raymond H., V.P. & Gen. Mgr.--Kodak Professional Photography Division, Rochester, NY; *U.S. Public,* pg. 555
Demoulins, Jean, Chief Oper. Officer--Ahlstrom-Hanssen S.A., Bordeaux, France; *Int'l,* pg. 34
DeMoura, Brian, Pres.--Guilford of Maine, Inc., Guilford, ME; *U.S. Public,* pg. 889
Dempsey, Charles, Pres.--Buccaneer Homes, Inc., Hamilton, AL; *U.S. Public,* pg. 318
Dempsey, Jack D., Gen. Mgr.--WJHL-TV, Johnson City, TN; *U.S. Public,* pg. 1078
Dempsey, Kenneth L., Pres.--Masland Carpets, Inc., Saraland, AL; *U.S. Public,* pg. 514
Dempsey, Robert, Gen. Mgr.--Warren Tool Group, Garrettsville, OH; *U.S. Private,* pg. 1181
Den Hert, Cesar, Grp. V.P.-European Opers.--Bailey-Fischer & Porter N.V., Wilrijk, Belgium; *Int'l,* pg. 449
den Toom, J.W.R., Mng. Dir.--Corporate New Business Development Div., Delft, Netherlands; *Int'l,* pg. 1142
Den Yuen, F., Pres.--Honolulu Fueling Facilities Corp., Honolulu, HI; *Int'l,* pg. 700
Denardo, Donna, Pres. & Chief Oper. Officer--Vitalink Pharmacy Services, Inc., Naperville, IL; *U.S. Public,* pg. 1041
DeNardo, Donna, Pres.--Vitalink Pharmacy Services, Inc., Atlanta, GA; *U.S. Public,* pg. 1042
Denaro, Giorgio, Dir.--Gambro S.p.A., Latina Scalo, Italy; *Int'l,* pg. 668
Dench, Robert Graham, Chm. Bd. & Mng. Dir.--Barclays Insurance Brokers International Ltd., London, United Kingdom; *Int'l,* pg. 164
Denchfield, Dwayne, Pres. & Gen. Mgr.--DataCard Service, Minnetonka, MN; *U.S. Private,* pg. 312
Denecke, Martin, Mng. Dir.--GGK Basel, Zurich, Switzerland; *Int'l,* pg. 1335
Dengate, Steve, Pres.--Anixter Canada, Mississauga, Canada; *U.S. Public,* pg. 115
Dengler, Jean-Michel, Mng. Dir.--Stahlwerk Thuringen GmbH, Unterwellenborn, Germany; *Int'l,* pg. 79
Denham, Art, Mgr.-Distr.--Weatherford US Inc., Santa Maria, CA; *U.S. Public,* pg. 1749
Denholm, John, Mng. Dir.--The Leith Agency, Edinburgh, United Kingdom; *U.S. Private,* pg. 1152
Denig, Thomas H., Pres.--Trus Joist MacMillan Limited, Surrey, Canada; *Int'l,* pg. 829
Denig, Thomas H., Pres. & Chief Exec. Officer--Trus Joist MacMillan, Boise, ID; *Int'l,* pg. 829
Denig, Thomas H., Pres.--Trus Joist MacMillan Limited, Surrey, Canada; *U.S. Public,* pg. 1556
Denig, Thomas H., Pres.--Trus Joist (Western) Ltd., Surrey, Canada; *U.S. Public,* pg. 1556
Denig, Thomas H., Pres.--Norco Windows, Inc., Boise, ID; *U.S. Public,* pg. 1556
Denig, Thomas H., Pres. & Chief Exec. Officer--Trus Joist MacMillan, Boise, ID; *U.S. Public,* pg. 1556
Deniger, John, Pres.--Prostrollo Motor Sales, Inc., Huron, SD; *U.S. Private,* pg. 891
Dening, A.R.J., Mng. Dir.--Jaguar Cars Finance Limited, Coventry, United Kingdom; *Int'l,* pg. 910
Denis, Pierre, Dist. Mgr.--Flowserve Duriron Canada Inc., Laval, Canada; *U.S. Public,* pg. 659
Denisco, Ralph A., Chief Exec. Officer--Noise Dairy Systems, LP, Columbus, OH; *U.S. Private,* pg. 249
Denisco, Ralph A., Pres.-Nestle Ice Cream Company--Nestle Frozen/Refrigerated Food Co., Solon, OH; *Int'l,* pg. 918
Denisco, Ralph A., Pres.--NDS, Columbus, OH; *Int'l,* pg. 918
Denison, Mike, Gen. Mgr.--Surplus Warehouse-Nacogdoches, Nacogdoches, TX; *U.S. Private,* pg. 120
Denk, Gregory P., Pres. Chief Exec. Officer & Chief Oper. Officer--Kitchell CEM, Inc., Phoenix, AZ; *U.S. Private,* pg. 624
Denkl, Heinz, Pres.--Services Conselis Dowell, Montrouge, France; *U.S. Public,* pg. 1439
Denkwirth, Joachim, Chief Oper. Officer--Nema Warmetauscher GmbH, Netzschkau, Germany; *Int'l,* pg. 399
Denlea, Leo, Chm. Bd. & Chief Exec. Officer--Farmers Group, Inc., Los Angeles, CA; *Int'l,* pg. 110
Denley, James H., Pres. & Editor--Birmingham Post-Herald Company, Birmingham, AL; *U.S. Public,* pg. 1447
Denman, Richard, Pres.--M & S Systems, Inc., Dallas, TX; *U.S. Public,* pg. 1193
Denmark, Lee, Publr.--Morgan Hill Times, Morgan Hill, CA; *U.S. Public,* pg. 1065
Denmark, Stelio, Pres.--ABB Robotics AB, Vasteras, Sweden; *Int'l,* pg. 7
Denne, Donald, Pres.--Alba-Waldensian Health Products Div., Valdese, NC; *U.S. Public,* pg. 36
Dennehy, Glyn, Gen. Mgr.--Augat Ltd., Telford, United Kingdom; *U.S. Public,* pg. 1598
Dennehy, John, V.P. & Gen. Mgr.--Cott Corporation - South Central Region, Irving, TX; *Int'l,* pg. 337
Dennehy, John, V.P. & Gen. Mgr.--Cott Corporation - South Central Region, San Antonio, TX; *Int'l,* pg. 337
Dennett, Matt, Mgr.--Downey Savings & Loan Association, F.A., Redlands, CA; *U.S. Public,* pg. 527
Denney, Chris, Chief Exec. Officer--CCL Industries Limited, Grimsby, United Kingdom; *Int'l,* pg. 239
Denney, Christopher, Pres.--Kolmar Laboratories, Inc., Port Jervis, NY; *Int'l,* pg. 239
Denney, James, Pres.--Nabors Alaska Drilling, Inc., Anchorage, AK; *U.S. Public,* pg. 1148
Denning, Gene, Mgr.--AFS Insurance Services, Inc., Salt Lake City, UT; *U.S. Private,* pg. 90
Denning, R.F., Pres. & Chief Exec. Officer--Risk Sciences Group, Inc., Atlanta, GA; *U.S. Public,* pg. 458
Denningham, Wayne, V.P.--Rocky Mountain Division, Aurora, CO; *U.S. Public,* pg. 38
Dennis, Andrew, Mng. Dir.--Willis Faber (Underwriting Management) Limited, Ipswich, United Kingdom; *Int'l,* pg. 1504
Dennis, Barry, Mng. Dir.--EMAP Pursuit Publishing, Peterborough, United Kingdom; *Int'l,* pg. 451
Dennis, Chris, Mng. Dir.--LifeScan Canada Ltd., Burnaby, Canada; *U.S. Public,* pg. 931
Dennis, Jim W., Pres.--Pacesetter Inc., Sylmar, CA; *U.S. Public,* pg. 1428
Dennis, Lorne, Gen. Mgr.--Lakeside Processors, Wynyard, Canada; *Int'l,* pg. 1195
Dennis, Nicholas, Pres.--Bell & Howell Acceptance Corporation, Skokie, IL; *U.S. Public,* pg. 201
Dennis, P., Mng. Dir.--Barclays Unicorn Ltd., London, United Kingdom; *Int'l,* pg. 165
Dennis, Ron, Pres.--Kash N Karry Food Stores, Inc., Tampa, FL; *Int'l,* pg. 463
Dennison, S., Pres.--Van Leer New Zealand Ltd., East Tamaki, New Zealand; *Int'l,* pg. 1147
Dennler, Bruce, V.P. & Gen. Mgr.--Carat ICG (San Francisco), San Francisco, CA; *U.S. Private,* pg. 208
Denny, Clinton, Pres.--Lockheed Martin Space Information Systems, Houston, TX; *U.S. Public,* pg. 1009
Denny, Robert M., Pres.--CSC Credit Services, Inc., Houston, TX; *U.S. Public,* pg. 423
Denoma, Mike, V.P.--Abrasive Systems Division, Saint Paul, MN; *U.S. Public,* pg. 1605
Denrich, Louis, Pres.--Valu Foods Inc., Baltimore, MD; *U.S. Private,* pg. 1012
Densen, Larry, V.P.--Worksafe, Inc., Huntington Station, NY; *U.S. Public,* pg. 548
Densen, Larry, Gen. Mgr.--Eastco Glove Technologies, Huntington Station, NY; *U.S. Public,* pg. 548
Denson, Richard E., Gen. Mgr.--Exchange Div., Dallas, TX; *U.S. Private,* pg. 823
Denter, Borje, Chief Oper. Officer--Skandia Leben AG, Zurich, Switzerland; *Int'l,* pg. 1258
Denton, Edward W., Gen. Mgr.--Westvaco Canada, Ltd., Mississauga, Canada; *U.S. Public,* pg. 1762
Denton, Jill, Office Mgr.--Korn/Ferry International - High Technology Research Center, Dallas, TX; *U.S. Private,* pg. 633
Denton, Leet E., Pres.--Denton Concrete Services Inc., Grosse Pointe Woods, MI; *U.S. Private,* pg. 325
Denton, Tom, Mgr.--Asbury Graphite Inc. of California, Rodeo, CA; *U.S. Private,* pg. 87
Denton, Tom, Mgr.--Asbury Fluxmaster, Clearfield, UT; *U.S. Private,* pg. 87
Denton, Tony, Gen. Mgr.--WCPS, Tarboro, NC; *U.S. Private,* pg. 297
Denyer, Peter, Mng. Dir.--Vision Group plc, Edinburgh, United Kingdom; *U.S. Public,* pg. 519
Depa, Ray, Station Mgr.--KMAZ, Las Cruces, NM; *U.S. Public,* pg. 983
DePalma, P., V.P. & Gen. Mgr.--ITT Bell & Gossett, Morton Grove, IL; *U.S. Public,* pg. 860
DePauw, R., V.P. & Gen. Mgr.--Texaco Services (Europe) Ltd., Brussels, Belgium; *U.S. Public,* pg. 1584
DePerro, Don, Publr.--American City Business Journals, Inc., Jacksonville, FL; *U.S. Private,* pg. 19
DePhillips, Fred C., Pres.--Bettigole, Andrews & Clark, Inc., Hackensack, NJ; *U.S. Public,* pg. 1593
Depoil, Francois, Pres.--Laboratoires Fumouze S.A., Saint Denis, France; *U.S. Public,* pg. 310
Depositio, A.J., Pres.--Society Equipment Leasing Corporation, Cleveland, OH; *U.S. Public,* pg. 955
Deppe, Scott, Gen. Mgr.--Dolet Hills Mining Venture, Mansfield, LA; *Int'l,* pg. 337
Depperman, Klaus-Peter, Chief Oper. Officer--Flender Engineering & Service Antriebstechnik GmbH, Herne, Germany; *Int'l,* pg. 400
Deprienzo, Ken, Div. V.P.--All Star Gas, Inc., Lebanon, MO; *U.S. Private,* pg. 35
Deprins, Jacques, Chm.--Bernheim-Comofi, Brussels, Belgium; *Int'l,* pg. 562
DePrinzio, Ken, V.P.-Sls.--All Star Gas Co.-Region VII, Lebanon, MO; *U.S. Private,* pg. 35
Depth, James, Gen. Mgr.--Interactive Media, Inc., Cedar Rapids, IA; *U.S. Private,* pg. 442
Depto, David J., Branch Mgr.--Zellerbach Division, Orlando, FL; *U.S. Public,* pg. 1075
Deputy, Howard, Branch Mgr.--Bergen Brunswig Medical Corporation, Carrollton, TX; *U.S. Public,* pg. 214
Derbes, Daniel W., Chm. Bd.--San Diego Gas & Electric Company, San Diego, CA; *U.S. Public,* pg. 584
Derbin, L., Mgr.--Daher Golden Eagle - Denver, Aurora, CO; *U.S. Public,* pg. 749
Derby, Crispin, Mng. Dir.--LGC Communications Ltd., London, United Kingdom; *Int'l,* pg. 451
Deretchin, S.J., Mgr.--E.L. Mansure Div., Clinton, SC; *U.S. Private,* pg. 1094
Derfler, Gerhard, Chief Oper. Officer--Alfa-Laval Industrietechnik G.m.b.H., Hamburg, Germany; *Int'l,* pg. 1379
Derge, Klaus, V.P. & Mng. Dir.--OCLI Optical Coating Laboratory GmbH, Reinheim, Germany; *U.S. Public,* pg. 1227
Derham, Ken, Mng. Dir., Plenum Publishing Company Ltd.--Plenum Publishing Company, Ltd., London, United Kingdom; *U.S. Public,* pg. 1311
Derhofer, George, Pres.--Bassett-Walker, Martinsville, VA; *U.S. Public,* pg. 1702
Dericke, Roger, Plant Mgr.--H.S. Crocker Co., Inc., Exton, PA; *U.S. Private,* pg. 290
Deriso, Jr., Walter M., Pres.--Security Bank and Trust Company, Albany, GA; *U.S. Public,* pg. 1549
Derksen, R., Plant Mgr.--Square D Co., Oshkosh, WI; *Int'l,* pg. 1208
Dermul, Walter, Chief Exec. Officer-Organization & Fin.--Quattro DMB&B, Brussels, Brussels, Belgium; *U.S. Private,* pg. 305
Dernsbourg, J., Pres.--Honda France S.A., Paris, France; *Int'l,* pg. 635

DeRoeck, Walter A., Pres.--Palladin Financial, Inc., Austin, TX; *U.S. Public*, pg. 1554
DeRoeck, Walter A., Pres.--Barton Creek Capital, Inc., Austin, TX; *U.S. Public*, pg. 1554
DeRoin, Larry L., Pres.--Northern Plains Natural Gas Co., Omaha, NE; *U.S. Public*, pg. 584
Deromedi, Roger, Pres.-W. Europe & Exec. V.P.--Kraft Jacobs Suchard AG, Zurich, Switzerland; *U.S. Public*, pg. 1288
Deromedi, Roger K., Pres.-Western Europe--Kraft Foods International, Rye Brook, NY; *U.S. Public*, pg. 1288
DeRoode, Fredrick, Mgr.--Hotel Inter-Continental, New York, NY; *Int'l*, pg. 1178
DeRosa, Patricia, Pres.--GapKids Division, San Bruno, CA; *U.S. Public*, pg. 702
DeRosa, Paul R., Pres. & Chief Exec. Officer--Eastbridge Holdings Inc., New York, NY; *Int'l*, pg. 933
DeRosa, Paul R., Pres.--Eastbridge Asset Management Inc., New York, NY; *Int'l*, pg. 933
DeRosa, Terrence, Exec. V.P.--DRS Electronic Systems, Inc., Gaithersburg, MD; *U.S. Public*, pg. 474
DeRose, Pete, Reg. Mgr.--Oriental Motor U.S.A. Corp., Schaumburg, IL; *Int'l*, pg. 1008
Derow, Peter A., Pres.--Institutional Investor, Inc., New York, NY; *U.S. Public*, pg. 513
Derr Dulk, W., Pres.--Europe Combined Terminals B.V., Rotterdam, Netherlands; *Int'l*, pg. 682
Derrah, Frank A., Gen. Mgr.--Havelock Lime Div., Havelock, Canada; *Int'l*, pg. 243
Derrick, Donald E., V.P.--Loctite Luminescent Europe, Leuven, Belgium; *Int'l*, pg. 611
Derrick, K.G., Mng. Dir.--Hamworthy Marine Limited, Poole, United Kingdom; *Int'l*, pg. 1065
Derrough, Neil, Gen. Mgr.--KNSD-TV, San Diego, CA; *U.S. Public*, pg. 712
Derville, T., Chief Oper. Officer--Liebig Maille Amora, Dijon, France; *Int'l*, pg. 380
Derwing, Jan, Dir.--Iglo Industrias de Gelados, Lda., Lisbon, Portugal; *Int'l*, pg. 1437
Derx, Jan, Publr.--Audet Tijdschriften, Arnhem, Netherlands; *Int'l*, pg. 1099
Dery, Alain, Plant Mgr.--Bridgeston/Firestone Tire Manufacturing Operations-Joliette, Quebec, Canada; *Int'l*, *pg. 213*
Derycke, Douglas, Chief Oper. Officer--Koch Container, Victor, NY; *U.S. Private*, pg. 177
des Dorides, Philippe, Chief Opers. Officer & Gen. Mgr.--SAFA, Madrid, Spain; *Int'l*, pg. 1114
des Isnards, T., Chm. Bd.--Texaco France S.A., Puteaux, France; *U.S. Public*, pg. 1584
Des Marais, Pierre, II, Pres. & Chief Exec. Officer--Unimedia Inc., Montreal, Canada; *Int'l*, pg. 632
Desanges, H.Y., Dir. Gen.--EPPC Polyplastic S.A., Rueil-Malmaison, France; *U.S. Public*, pg. 752
DeSantis, Gerry, Pres.--Honeywell Leeds & Northrup International, Horsham, PA; *U.S. Public*, pg. 834
DeSantis, J., Branch Mgr.--Van Leeuwen Pipe & Tube Corp., Chester, VA; *Int'l*, pg. 1450
DeSantis, Robert, Treas. & Fin. Admin. Officer--Citizens Resources Company, Stamford, CT; *U.S. Public*, pg. 380
DeSantis, Robert, Treas. & Fin. Admin. Officer--CU CapitalCorp, Stamford, CT; *U.S. Public*, pg. 380
DeSanto, Christopher, Pres.--Santo Tours & Travel, Inc., Buffalo, NY; *U.S. Private*, pg. 23
DeSanto, John, V.P. & Acct. Dir.--Western International Media Corporation, Cherry Hill, NJ; *U.S. Private*, pg. 1167
Desautels, Marc P., Chm. Bd.--General Electric Capital Aviation Services, San Francisco, CA; *U.S. Public*, pg. 712
Deschamps, Mario, V.P. & Gen. Mgr.--Dentsply Canada, Woodbridge, Canada; *U.S. Public*, pg. 499
DeSchepper, James L., V.P. & Gen. Mgr.--WSLS-TV, Roanoke, VA; *U.S. Public*, pg. 1078
Descoteaux, Denise, Branch Mgr.--Circle International, Columbus, OH; *U.S. Public*, pg. 371
Desforges, Olivier, Gen. Mgr.--CPC France, Clamart, France; *U.S. Public*, pg. 225
Desgeorges, Jean-Pierre, Chm. Bd.--GEC Alsthom N.V., Amsterdam, Netherlands; *Int'l*, pg. 56
Desi, Fred, Gen. Mgr.--Elixir Industries, Mesa, AZ; *U.S. Private*, pg. 371
DeSimone, L.D., Chm. Bd.--Electronic Products Division, Austin, TX; *U.S. Public*, pg. 1605
Desmarais, Pierre, V.P. & Mng. Dir.--WF Corroon-Ontario, Toronto, Canada; *Int'l*, pg. 1502
Desmarais, Rene, Pres. & Chief Oper. Officer--CFCF 12, Montreal, Canada; *Int'l*, pg. 241
Desmazes, F., Mng. Dir. & Gen. Mgr.--Gan Espana Seguros Generales y Vida, Madrid, Spain; *Int'l*, pg. 564
Desmazes, F., Mng. Dir.--Uniseguros Vida y Pensiones (UNIVYP), Madrid, Spain; *Int'l*, pg. 565
Desmet, Luc, Mng. Dir.--Bose N.V., Ternat, Belgium; *U.S. Private*, pg. 161
Desmond, Daniel F., Pres.--Electro Optical Div., Northampton, MA; *U.S. Public*, pg. 965
Despain, Eric, V.P.--Christensen Products, Salt Lake City, UT; *U.S. Public*, pg. 981
Despiegelaere, Marc, Mng. Dir.--Suomen 3M Oy, Espoo, Finland; *U.S. Public*, pg. 1606
Despointes, Nicolas, Mng. Dir.--Cohiba, Lamentin, Martinique; *Int'l*, pg. 117
Desprez, Martin, Chm. Bd., Pres., Chief Exec. Officer & Dir. General--Editions du Juris-Classeur, Paris, France; *Int'l*, pg. 1095
Desproges, Patrick, Chief Exec. Officer--Comark Communications, Inc., Chalfont, PA; *Int'l*, pg. 1383
Desriac, J. L., Chief Exec. Officer--OCE Graphics France S.A., Creteil, France; *Int'l*, pg. 994
Desroche, Eric, Pres.--Measurement Science, Inc., Englewood, CO; *U.S. Private*, pg. 826
DesRoche, Jerald, Pres.--ABB Commercial Engineering Canada, Gloucester, Canada; *Int'l*, pg. 5
Desrues, F., Pres.--Societe Francaise de Protection Juridique (S.F.P.J.), Courbevoie, France; *Int'l*, pg. 565
Desselles, Tony, Mgr.--Southern Electric Supply Co., Inc., Harahan, LA; *Int'l*, pg. 1108
Dessers, Jos, Mgr.-Pub. Rels.--Tessenderlo Plant, Tessenderlo, Belgium; *U.S. Public*, pg. 1291
Dessimoz, Richard E., Chief Exec. Officer--Wabash National Finance Corp., Arlington Heights, IL; *U.S. Public*, pg. 1730
Dessinger, Ted, Gen. Mgr.--Double H Boot Co., Womelsdorf, PA; *U.S. Public*, pg. 217
DeStefano, John J., Pres.--KLT Investments, Kansas City, MO; *U.S. Public*, pg. 943
Destin, Raymond, Gen. Dir.-Europe--Bioter-Biona S.A., Madrid, Spain; *U.S. Public*, pg. 429
Destin, Raymond, Gen. Dir.--ConAgra Spain, La Coruna, Spain; *U.S. Public*, pg. 429
Destin, Raymond R., Exec. V.P.-Europe--ConAgra-Europe, Inc., Brussels, Belgium; *U.S. Public*, pg. 429
Deswaef, Luc, Chief Oper. Officer--Gambro N.V./S.A., Leuven, Belgium; *Int'l*, pg. 668
Detampel, Donald, Pres.--ConferTech International, Westminster, CO; *U.S. Public*, pg. 683
Detassis, Frank, Gen. Mgr.--Precision Resource Florida Div., Fort Lauderdale, FL; *U.S. Private*, pg. 880
Detert, D., Dr., Gen. Mgr.--Wellcome GmbH, Burgwedel, Germany; *Int'l*, pg. 553
Detharding, Herbert, Chief Oper. Officer--Wintershall Gas GmbH, Kassel, Germany; *Int'l*, pg. 105
Dethere, Jacques, V.P.-Sls. & Mktg.--Francia-Lotus S.A., Brussels, Belgium; *U.S. Public*, pg. 672
Detjen, Larry L., Pres.--Valvoline Instant Oil Change, Inc., Lexington, KY; *U.S. Public*, pg. 139
Detrez, Guido, Gen. Mgr.--Segal s.c.r.l., Ivoz-Ramet, Belgium; *Int'l*, pg. 79
Detrez, J.M., Gen. Mgr.--Vandamme - Pie Qui Chante, Wattignies, France; *Int'l*, pg. 380
Detsch, Hanspeter, Chief Exec. Officer--Impuls Advertising, Bern, Switzerland; *Int'l*, pg. 666
Detter, Dwayne, Mgr.-Station--KSNK, Oberlin, KS; *U.S. Public*, pg. 984
Detter, Gerald L., Pres. & Chief Exec. Officer--Con-Way Transportation Services, Palo Alto, CA; *U.S. Public*, pg. 281
Detter, Jarl, Chief Oper. Officer--Wirsbo AG, Lucerne, Switzerland; *Int'l*, pg. 444
Dettmann, Harold R., Pres.--Mutual Savings & Loan Association, Pasadena, CA; *U.S. Public*, pg. 217
Dettmer, Cord, Dir.-Admin.--Storm van Bentem & Kluyver B.V., Wormer, Netherlands; *U.S. Public*, pg. 756
Deuer, Jim, Pres.--Deuer Manufacturing, Inc., Dayton, OH; *U.S. Public*, pg. 1455
Deupree, William W., Jr., Pres.--Morgan Keegan & Company, Inc., Memphis, TN; *U.S. Public*, pg. 1131
Deupree, William W., Jr., Pres.--Morgan Keegan Insurance Agency of Louisiana, Inc., Memphis, TN; *U.S. Public*, pg. 1131
Deutch, Andrew, Pres.--Grey Direct, New York, NY; *U.S. Public*, pg. 764
Deutsch, Jeffrey A., Pres.--Machinery Acceptance Corp., Houston, TX; *U.S. Public*, pg. 1517
Deutsch, Jeffrey A., Pres.--Machinery Acceptance Corporation, Houston, TX; *U.S. Public*, pg. 1517
Deutsch, Les, Gen. Mgr.--Simkins Maryland Board, Baltimore, MD; *U.S. Private*, pg. 1000
Deutsch, Mitchell, Pres.--Warner Audio Publishing, New York, NY; *U.S. Public*, pg. 1614
Devane, John, Dr., Pres. & Chief Oper. Officer--Elan Pharmaceutical Research Corp., Gainesville, GA; *Int'l*, pg. 436
Devaney, Steve, Mng. Dir.--Kintetsu Euro Transport Ltd., Slough, United Kingdom; *Int'l*, pg. 735
Devanna, Leonard R., Pres. & Chief Oper. Officer--COM/Energy Resources Inc., Cambridge, MA; *U.S. Public*, pg. 414
Devanna, Leonard R., Pres. & Chief Oper. Officer--COM/Energy Enterprises, Cambridge, MA; *U.S. Public*, pg. 414
Deveau, Joseph, Admin.--Franklin House Healthcare, Franklin, MA; *U.S. Public*, pg. 1712
Devereaux, David G., Pres.--Coordinated Healthcare Systems, San Diego, CA; *U.S. Public*, pg. 361
Devereaux, Lance, Pres.--Wausau Metals, Nanik Division, Wausau, WI; *U.S. Public*, pg. 1500
Deverell, Thomas J., Pres.--Ikon Office Solutions-San Diego, San Diego, CA; *U.S. Public*, pg. 864
Devereux, T.J., Gen. Mgr.--Haden King Limited, Birmingham, United Kingdom; *Int'l*, pg. 585
DeVico, Tony, Gen. Mgr.--Arrow/Schweber Electronics, San Diego, CA; *U.S. Public*, pg. 134
Deville, Pat, Pres.--Erie County Cablevision, Sandusky, OH; *U.S. Private*, pg. 147
Devine, C.R., Pres.--KCS Resources, Inc., Houston, TX; *U.S. Public*, pg. 939
Devine, Donald R., V.P.--Bonded Abrasives, Worcester, MA; *Int'l*, pg. 1174
Devine, I.C., Mgr.--Seal Sands Storage Ltd., Middlesbrough, United Kingdom; *Int'l*, pg. 1251
Devine, Jim, Dir.--International Public Relations, Pty Ltd., Canberra, Australia; *Int'l*, pg. 1227
Devine, John A., Pres.--Boston Overseas Holding Corp., Boston, MA; *U.S. Public*, pg. 184
Devine, Richard, Gen. Mgr.--Circon GmbH, Taufkirchen, Germany; *U.S. Public*, pg. 374
Devine, William, Chief Oper. Officer--Vorelco, Inc., Troy, MI; *Int'l*, pg. 1474
Devineni, Bob, Plant Mgr.--Oxford Automotive, Howell Industries Div., Masury, OH; *U.S. Private*, pg. 825
DeVink, Lodewink J.R., Pres. & Chief Oper. Officer-Warner-Lambert Co.--Warner-Lambert Consumer Healthcare, Morris Plains, NJ; *U.S. Public*, pg. 1739
DeVira, James E., Publisher--Southern Accents, Inc., Birmingham, AL; *U.S. Public*, pg. 1613
Devish, Mary J., Pres. & Publr.--Sioux Falls Argus Leader, Sioux Falls, SD; *U.S. Public*, pg. 701
DeVito, Vince, Pres.--Adam Technology Co., Union, NJ; *U.S. Public*, pg. 1101
DeVivo, Sal, Chief Oper. Officer--The Daily Journal (NJ), Vineland, NJ; *U.S. Public*, pg. 700
Devlin, Bill, V.P.--Products Research & Chemical Corp., Semco Division, Glendale, CA; *Int'l*, pg. 339
Devlin, Frederick, Chief Exec. Officer--Lambert Smith Hampton, Dublin, Ireland; *Int'l*, pg. 797
Devlin, Marcia, Dir.-Telephone Opers.--Total Research Corporation, Tampa, FL; *U.S. Public*, pg. 1625
Devlin, Robert M., Chm. Bd.--The Franklin Life Insurance Company, Springfield, IL; *U.S. Public*, pg. 76
Devlin, Robert M., Chm. Bd. & Chief Exec. Officer--The American Franklin Life Insurance Co., Springfield, IL; *U.S. Public*, pg. 76
Devlin, Robert M., Chm., Pres. & Chief Exec. Officer--National Public Service Ins. Co., Waco, TX; *U.S. Public*, pg. 77
Devonport, B., Mgr.--Warwick Finspa Limited, West Bromwich, United Kingdom; *Int'l*, pg. 426
DeVore, Ron, Chief Exec. Officer--Terumo Medical Corporation, Somerset, NJ; *Int'l*, pg. 1376
DeVore, Ron, Pres.--Terumo Medical Corp., Somerset, NJ; *Int'l*, pg. 1376
DeVore, W.A., Pres.--Catalyst Resources, Inc, Houston, TX; *U.S. Public*, pg. 1039
DeVoto, Richard H., Pres.--CR Briggs Corporation, Trona, CA; *U.S. Public*, pg. 302
DeVries, Dick, Mgr.--L.H. Sowles Company, Inc., Billings, MT; *U.S. Private*, pg. 1019
DeVries, Jim, V.P. & Gen. Mgr.-DLP & Cardiac Surgery Ventures--Medtronic DLP, Grand Rapids, MI; *U.S. Public*, *pg. 1083*
DeVries, Peter, V.P.-Sls.--Bergquist ITC, GmbH, Pinneberg, Germany; *U.S. Private*, pg. 135
DeVries, Peter, V.P.-Sls.--Bergquist UK. Limited, Milton Keynes, United Kingdom; *U.S. Private*, pg. 135
DeWaele, Jerry, Gen. Mgr.--Jefferson Chevrolet, Grosse Pointe Park, MI; *U.S. Private*, pg. 584
Dewar-Durie, A. M., Mng. Dir.--Wm. Teacher & Sons Limited, Dumbarton, United Kingdom; *Int'l*, pg. 63
Deware, Peter, V.P. & Gen. Mgr.--Cott Corporation - North East US Region, Wyomissing, PA; *Int'l*, pg. 337
DeWet, Pieter, Mng. Dir.--Joy Manufacturing Company (Africa) (Pty) Ltd. Johannesburg Plant, Johannesburg, South Africa; *U.S. Public*, pg. 789
Dewey, Christopher C., Exec. V.P.--Jefferies & Company, Inc., Los Angeles, CA; *U.S. Public*, pg. 925
Dewey, Don, V.P.--Sealright Mfg. West, Inc., Los Angeles, CA; *U.S. Public*, pg. 1452
Dewey, R., Mng. Dir.--Penny & Giles Position Sensors Ltd., Christchurch, United Kingdom; *Int'l*, pg. 207
Dewey, R. Gene, V.P. & Pres.-Molycorp, Inc.--Unocal Carbon & Minerals, Brea, CA; *U.S. Public*, pg. 1698
Dewhurst, C.G., Gen. Mgr.--Morganite Carbon Division, Alexandria, Australia; *Int'l*, pg. 895
Dewin, Robert M., Mgr.--John Crane Middle East- Central Region, Dubai, United Arab Emirates; *Int'l*, pg. 1339
DeWitt, Steve, Publr.--Iowa Farmer Today, Cedar Rapids, IA; *U.S. Private*, pg. 442
Dewitt, T.J., V.P. & Gen. Mgr.--Morgantown Machine & Hydraulics, Inc., Morgantown, WV; *Int'l*, pg. 280
Dewsbery, Colin, Dir.--Clydesdale Jones Co., Walsall, United Kingdom; *Int'l*, pg. 265
Dexeus, C., Chm. & Pres.--SBS Espanan S.A., Madrid, Spain; *Int'l*, pg. 1331
Dexter, Richard, Pres.--Dexter Axle Div., Elkhart, IN; *Int'l*, pg. 1396
DeYoreo, Sal, Pres. & Chief Oper. Officer--Flowtron/Galaxie Division, Melrose, MA; *U.S. Public*, pg. 131
DeYoung, Jim, V.P.-Sls.--All Star Gas Co.-Region IV, Lebanon, MO; *U.S. Private*, pg. 35
Dezaly, B.J., Gen. Mgr.--La Johnson Francaise S.A., Cergy-Pontoise, France; *U.S. Private*, pg. 593
Dhabi, Mohammed, Chm. Bd. & Chief Exec. Officer--Faugere & Jutheau S.A., Paris, France; *U.S. Public*, pg. 1049
Dhaere, G., Mng. Dir.--Eurasem B.V., Nijmegen, Netherlands; *Int'l*, pg. 1133
Dham, Guy, Chief Oper. Officer--Eurolysine SA, Paris, France; *Int'l*, pg. 41
Dhanvarjor, Opart, Mng. Dir.--Siam Furukawa Co., Ltd., Bangkok, Thailand; *Int'l*, pg. 1238
Dhar, Subhash K., Pres. & Chief Oper. Officer--Ovonic Battery Company, Inc., Troy, MI; *U.S. Public*, pg. 581
Dholakia, Pratap, Plant Mgr.--General Felt Industries, Inc., Pico Rivera, CA; *U.S. Private*, pg. 1094
di Chio, Augusto, Mng. Dir.--Foster Wheeler Iberia S.A., Madrid, Spain; *U.S. Public*, pg. 677
Di Comite, Emilio, Chm. Bd.--Locazioni Finanziarie S.p.A., Brescia, Italy; *Int'l*, pg. 138
Di Domenica, Nicola, Branch Mgr.--Banco di Napoli-Madrid, Madrid, Spain; *Int'l*, pg. 140
Di Giacomo, Thomas A., Chm. Bd.--ManuLife Investment Management Corporation, Toronto, Canada; *Int'l*, pg. 840
Di Luigi, Edward D., Gen. Mgr.-Opers--UNC Airwork, Millville, NJ; *U.S. Public*, pg. 710
di Macco, Saverio, Mng. Dir.--Cantieri Italiani Navali (FINCANTIERI), Trieste, Italy; *Int'l*, pg. 652
Di Maria, Charles E., Pres. & Chief Exec. Officer--Foster Wheeler Ltd. (Canada), Niagara on the Lake, Canada; *U.S. Public*, pg. 677
di Pace, Elio, Chief Exec. Officer & Mng. Dir.--Eurocom Concato di Pace Srl, Milan, Italy; *Int'l*, pg. 603
Di Rosa, G., Chief Oper. Officer--FATA European Group S.p.A., Pianezza, Italy; *Int'l*, pg. 474
Di Stefano, Robby, Mng. Dir.--Olivetti Canada Ltd., Markham, Canada; *Int'l*, pg. 1003
Di Stefano, Rodolfo, Pres.--ABB Asea, Milan, Italy; *Int'l*, pg. 8
Diament, Thomas, P., Pres.--John J. McMullen Associates, New York, NY; *U.S. Public*, pg. 308

Diamond, B.P., Mng. Dir.--Barlow Motor Investments Ltd., Rivonia, South Africa; *Int'l*, pg. 167
Diamond, Christopher S., Mng. Dir.--Mount Snow Resort, Mount Snow, VT; *U.S. Private*, pg. 61
Diamond, Gerald, Chm. Bd., Chief Exec. Officer & Pres.--Southern Electronics Distributors International, Tucker, GA; *U.S. Public*, pg. 1490
Dias, Carlos, Pres.--ABB SACE Limitada, Guarulhos, Brazil; *Int'l*, pg. 8
Dias, Ronald, V.P.--Teradyne Connection Systems, Inc., Nashua, NH; *U.S. Public*, pg. 1581
Diaz-Gonzalez, Antonio, Mng. Dir.--Repsol Derivados, Madrid, Spain; *Int'l*, pg. 1104
Diaz-Llanos, Federico A. Reyes, Dir.--Bayerische Vereinsbank AG, Caracas, Venezuela; *Int'l*, pg. 180
Diaz, Alberto, Mng. Dir.--McCormick de Venezuela, C.A., Caracas, Venezuela; *U.S. Public*, pg. 1067
Diaz, Julio, Mgr.-Sls.--Braun Transworld Corp., Caracas, Venezuela; *Int'l*, pg. 765
Diaz, Lou, Mgr.-Plant--Nestle Beverage Company, New Orleans, LA; *Int'l*, pg. 917
Diaz, Michael, Pres.--APL Land Transport Service Inc., Oakland, CA; *Int'l*, pg. 912
Diaz, Mike, V.P.-Opers--Duro-Test Intl. Corp., Fairfield, NJ; *U.S. Private*, pg. 349
Diaz, Ofelia, Country Mgr.--Instituto de Idiomas Colombia, S.A., Bogota, Colombia; *U.S. Public*, pg. 222
Diaz, Peter, Pres. & Gen. Mgr.--KHOU-TV Inc., Houston, TX; *U.S. Public*, pg. 209
Diaz, R., Chm.--Dairy Industries (Jamaica) Ltd., Kingston, Jamaica; *Int'l*, pg. 923
Diaz, Robert, V.P.--Regional Aircraft Services, Reading, PA; *U.S. Public*, pg. 1099
Dibbs, Dick, Pres.--Stein Inc., Sandusky, OH; *Int'l*, pg. 13
DiBella, Richard D., Pres.--Pulte Virginia Division, Fairfax, VA; *U.S. Public*, pg. 1345
DiBenedetto, George, Pres.--Hiram Walker, Southfield, MI; *Int'l*, pg. 63
Dicapo, Rick, Chief Exec. Officer--Medical Center of Baton Rouge, Baton Rouge, LA; *U.S. Public*, pg. 405
Dichak, Pete, Mgr.-Sls.--Southern Post Company, Houston, TX; *U.S. Public*, pg. 412
DiChio, A., Chm. Bd.--Foster Wheeler Chile, S.A., Santiago, Chile; *U.S. Public*, pg. 677
Dick, Christopher W., Pres. & Treas.--Pioneer Associates Inc., Boston, MA; *U.S. Public*, pg. 1298
Dick, Dan, Mgr.--Hotel Mead Corp., Wisconsin Rapids, WI; *U.S. Public*, pg. 436
Dick, Garry T., V.P.--OUB Manulife Pte. Ltd., Singapore, Singapore; *Int'l*, pg. 841
Dick, John, Gen. Mgr.--Anchor Stampings, Waterbury, CT; *U.S. Public*, pg. 865
Dick, Malcolm G., Gen. Mgr. & Area Mgr.--Fasson Adhesive Products, Ltd., Hemel Hempstead, United Kingdom; *U.S. Public*, pg. 154
Dick, Roger, Dir.-Chain Opers.--York Plant, York, PA; *U.S. Public*, pg. 444
Dick, Wolfgang, Chm. Bd.--EvoBus GmbH Setra Omnibusse, Ulm, Germany; *Int'l*, pg. 368
Dickard, Lester R., V.P. & Gen. Mgr.--Fasson Industrial (U.S.) Div., Painesville, OH; *U.S. Public*, pg. 153
Dickason, Elly, Assoc. Publisher--Macmillan Reference USA, New York, NY; *U.S. Private*, pg. 777
Dickens, Jackie, Reg. Dir.-Strategic Plng.--Leo Burnett Worldwide Asia/Pacific Hdqtrs., Hong Kong, Hong Kong; *U.S. Private*, pg. 186
Dickens, Kevin, Pres.--ACC Long Distance, Ltd., Etobicoke, Canada; *U.S. Public*, pg. 3
Dickens, Rory, Pres.--D.C. Division, Silver Spring, MD; *U.S. Public*, pg. 1682
Dickens, William A., V.P.& Mng. Dir.--State Street GmbH, Munich, Germany; *U.S. Public*, pg. 1513
Dickenson, J. T., Chief Oper. Officer--Nocona Boot Co., Nocona, TX; *U.S. Public*, pg. 937
Dickenson, J.A.S., Tech. Dir.--Salem Automation Limited, Rotherham, United Kingdom; *U.S. Private*, pg. 962
Dicker, D.G., Gen. Mgr.--Thomas De La Rue Lanka (Pte) Limited, Colombo, Sri Lanka; *Int'l*, pg. 386
Dickerman, George, Pres.--Spalding, Chicopee, MA; *U.S. Private*, pg. 629
Dickerson, Michael A., Pres. & Chief Exec. Officer--The National Bank of Sussex County, Branchville, NJ; *U.S. Public*, pg. 826
Dickerson, Robert E., Pres. & Chief Exec. Officer--Baltimore Trust Company, Selbyville, DE; *U.S. Public*, pg. 1088
Dickey, David, Mgr.--Adamsville Telephone Co., Adamsville, TN; *U.S. Public*, pg. 329
Dickey, Robert, Publr.--The Desert Sun, Palm Springs, CA; *U.S. Public*, pg. 700
Dickieson, C.W., Pres.--Indiana Harbor Belt Railroad Co., Hammond, IN; *U.S. Public*, pg. 432
Dickinson, Elizabeth, Admin.--Hillhaven Convalescent Hospital Menlo Park, Menlo Park, CA; *U.S. Public*, pg. 1713
Dickinson, Gary W., Pres. & Chief Exec. Officer--Delco Electronics Corporation, Kokomo, IN; *U.S. Public*, pg. 720
Dickinson, John F., Pres.--Compac Corporation, Netcong, NJ; *U.S. Public*, pg. 1054
Dickinson, John F., II, Pres.--US Steel Mining Co., Inc., Pittsburgh, PA; *U.S. Public*, pg. 1662
Dickinson, R.P., Gen. Mgr.--Thomas De La Rue (Malta) Limited, Zejtun, Malta; *Int'l*, pg. 386
Dickinson, Roy, Pres.--Bayco Industries, Winnipeg, Canada; *Int'l*, pg. 395
Dickinson, S., Mng. Dir.--P.C. Henderson Limited, Romford, United Kingdom; *Int'l*, pg. 615
Dickinson, Terri, V.P.--Simon Marketing Consulting (Canada) Ltd., Toronto, Canada; *U.S. Private*, pg. 1001
Dicks, J., Mng. Dir.--Pork Farms/Bowyers, Nottingham, United Kingdom; *Int'l*, pg. 968
Dickson, Bruce, Pres.--Continental Homes of Austin, L.P., Austin, TX; *U.S. Public*, pg. 441
Dickson, Carol, Chief Oper. Officer--Brink's Home Security, Inc., Irving, TX; *U.S. Public*, pg. 1305
Dickson, G.G., Chm. Bd.--Scottish Brewers Limited, Edinburgh, United Kingdom; *Int'l*, pg. 1212
Dickson, Gary D., Publr.--Glenwood Post, Glenwood Springs, CO; *U.S. Private*, pg. 995
Dickson, Harold A., Jr., Chm. Bd., Pres. & Chief Exec. Officer--SouthTrust Bank, Sylacauga, Sylacauga, AL; *U.S. Public*, pg. 1492
Dickson, Hearon F., V.P. & Gen. Mgr.--Dillard, A ResourceNet International Company, Morrisville, NC; *U.S. Public*, pg. 902
Dickson, James H., Pres.--Consolidated Group, Inc., Charlotte, NC; *U.S. Private*, pg. 351
Dickson, James H., Pres.--Consolidated Engravers-East, Inc., Charlotte, NC; *U.S. Private*, pg. 351
Dickson, James H., Pres.--Consolidated Screen-Makers, Inc., Charlotte, NC; *U.S. Private*, pg. 351
Dickson, Jim, V.P. & Gen. Mgr.--Cott Corporation - North East Region (Ontario), Mississauga, Canada; *Int'l*, pg. 337
Diclemente, Lucio, V.P.-Fin.--Thrifty Canada, Ltd., Mississauga, Canada; *U.S. Public*, pg. 354
DiCola, Frank E., Pres.--Atlantic Thermal Systems, Inc., Pleasantville, NJ; *U.S. Public*, pg. 430
Diddle, L.E., Pres.--Bulab Realty Of Missouri, LLC, Memphis, TN; *U.S. Private*, pg. 180
Didier, Remi, Gen. Mgr.--Merloni Electromenagers S.A., Marne la Vallee, France; *Int'l*, pg. 860
Didion, James J., Co-Chm. Bd.--CB Commercial Real Estate Group, Inc., Los Angeles, CA; *U.S. Public*, pg. 272
Didmer, Fred, Chm.--Radio TV Steiner AG, Bern, Switzerland; *Int'l*, pg. 330
DiDomenico, Mario, Mgr.-Opers.--Warren Pumps Inc., Warren, MA; *U.S. Public*, pg. 857
DiDominicis, Dennis F., Pres.--Ryka Incorporated, King of Prussia, PA; *U.S. Public*, pg. 1414
DiDonna, D., V.P. & Gen. Mgr.--Hercules Inc., Paper Technology Group, Wilmington, DE; *U.S. Public*, pg. 810
Didula, J. W., Mgr.--SASKFOR MacMillan, Regina, Canada; *Int'l*, pg. 829
Didur, N.J., Pres.--Centra Gas Inc., Vancouver, Canada; *Int'l*, pg. 1492
Dieck, Walter, Dr., Dir.--Bayerische Handelsbank AG, Munich, Germany; *Int'l*, pg. 179
Dieckbernd, Dale, Plant Mgr.--Interlake Material Handling, Pontiac, IL; *U.S. Public*, pg. 893
Diederich, John L., Pres.--Alcoa Proppants, Inc., Fort Smith, AR; *U.S. Public*, pg. 61
Diego, Guillermo, Chm., Pres. & Chief Exec. Officer-Y&R Spain--Young & Rubicam, S.A., Madrid, Spain; *U.S. Private*, pg. 1199
Dieguez, Carlos, Chief Oper. Officer--H.B. Fuller Mexico, S.A. de C.V., Mexico, Mexico; *U.S. Public*, pg. 687
Diehl, R. U., Mng. Dir.--Glaxo Wellcome GmbH, Namburg, Germany; *Int'l*, pg. 553
Diekmann, Michael, Mng. Dir.--Allianz Asia Pacific, Singapore, Singapore; *Int'l*, pg. 59
Diener, I. Howard, Pres. & Chief Oper. Officer--The Cosmetic Center Inc., Columbia, MD; *U.S. Private*, pg. 689
Diercks, Ardyth, Pres. & Gen. Mgr.--KVUE-TV, Inc., Austin, TX; *U.S. Public*, pg. 702
Diercks, Marcel, Dir. Gen.--Ford Werke AG - Genk Branch, Genk, Belgium; *U.S. Public*, pg. 666
Dierickx, Peter A., Pres.--The William Dierickx Company, Bellevue, WA; *U.S. Public*, pg. 863
Diessner, Dennis G., Gen. Mgr.--Kraus-Anderson Insurance, Burnsville, MN; *U.S. Private*, pg. 635
Dieter, Polt, Mng. Dir.--Hermann Wagner, GmbH, Reutlingen, Germany; *Int'l*, pg. 1418
Dieterle, Hal, V.P.-Southwest Region--Circle International, Inglewood, CA; *U.S. Public*, pg. 371
Dietert, Achim, Div. Mgr.--Standex International GmbH, Mold-Tech South, Öhringen, Germany; *U.S. Public*, pg. 1507
Dietlin, Francois, Mng. Dir.--Sulzer del Peru S.A., Lima, Peru; *Int'l*, pg. 1306
Dietrich, E., Mng. Dir.--Merck Balzers AG, Balzers, Liechtenstein; *Int'l*, pg. 997
Dietrich, Peter W., V.P.--IES Investments Inc., Cedar Rapids, IA; *U.S. Public*, pg. 855
Dietz, Joachim, Gen. Mgr.--Moog S.A.R.L., Rungis, France; *U.S. Public*, pg. 1128
Dietz, Thomas J., Pres.--Medical Professional Liability Agency, Ltd., Bedford Hills, NY; *U.S. Public*, pg. 685
Dietzel, Dan, Pres.-Distr.--Norandex Vinyl Products Co., Macedonia, OH; *U.S. Public*, pg. 1237
Diez, Javier, Chief Oper. Officer--COBE Iberica S.A., Barcelona, Spain; *Int'l*, pg. 667
DiFeo, Samuel X., Jr., Pres. & Chief Oper. Officer--United Auto Group, Inc., New York, NY; *U.S. Private*, pg. 1095
Diffley, Robert G., Pres.--Malama Pacific Corp., Honolulu, HI; *U.S. Public*, pg. 800
DiGaetano, Frank, Gen. Mgr.--Builders Material Company, Jonesboro, AR; *U.S. Private*, pg. 119
Digenis, Sofoclis, Mgr.--Det Norske Veritas, Mumbai, India; *Int'l*, pg. 398
Digenis, Sofoclis, Reg. Mgr.--Det Norske Veritas, Dubai, United Arab Emirates; *Int'l*, pg. 398
Digenis, Xenophon A., Mng. Dir.--ISS Servisystem S.A., Amarousion, Greece; *Int'l*, pg. 657
DiGeso, Amy, Pres.-U.S. Opers.--Mary Kay, Inc., Dallas, TX; *U.S. Private*, pg. 711
Diggins, John, Pres. & Chief Exec. Officer--Pilot Software, Cambridge, MA; *U.S. Private*, pg. 872
DiGiovanna, Charles, Pres. & Chief Exec. Officer--Continental Plastic Containers, Inc., Norwalk, CT; *U.S. Public*, pg. 440
DiGiovanni, Rico, Sr. V.P. & Mng. Dir.--IMPACT/FCB, Toronto, Canada; *U.S. Private*, pg. 389
Dijkman, H., Gen. Mgr.--Ventilex Milieutechniek B.V., Heerde, Heerde, Netherlands; *Int'l*, pg. 681
Dijner, Christer, Pres.--Componenta Kranlyft AB, Goteborg, Sweden; *Int'l*, pg. 1419
Dike, Buddy, Chm. Bd.--Willis Corroon, Fort Worth, TX; *Int'l*, pg. 1504
Dikken, A.B., Mgr.--ABN-AMRO Australia Limited, Sydney, Australia; *Int'l*, pg. 11
Dil, Jan G., V.P. & Gen. Mgr.--Vitatron--Vitatron Medical B.V., Velp, Netherlands; *U.S. Public*, pg. 1084
Dilacqua, John, Pres.--Philip Metals Inc., Cleveland, OH; *Int'l*, pg. 1050
Dilda, E.C., Pres.--Stancom Home Center, Inc., Wilson, NC; *U.S. Public*, pg. 1502
Dilger, Chris E., Gen. Mgr.--DMI Furniture, Inc., Huntingburg, IN; *U.S. Public*, pg. 473
DiLiello, Danny, V.P. & Gen. Mgr.--Ilco Unican Inc. (Capitol Division), Montreal, Canada; *Int'l*, pg. 1432
Dilissen, Theo, Mng. Dir.--ISS Airport Services S.A.-N.V., Brussels, Belgium; *Int'l*, pg. 657
Dilissen, Theo, Mng. Dir.--ISS Healthcare S.A.-N.V., Brussels, Belgium; *Int'l*, pg. 657
Dilissen, Theo, Mng. Dir.--ISS Luxembourg S.A., Luxembourg, Luxembourg; *Int'l*, pg. 657
Dill, Jerry R., Pres.--DeVRY Institute of Technology, Addison, IL; *U.S. Public*, pg. 504
Dill, Louise, V.P. & Mng. Exec.--Northern Trust Bank of Florida, N.A., Fort Lauderdale, FL; *U.S. Public*, pg. 1196
Dill, Mike, Plant Mgr.--Interlake Conveyor Systems, Shepherdsville, KY; *U.S. Public*, pg. 893
Dill, S. L., Chm. Bd.--Coutts & Co Trust Holdings Limited, Nassau, Bahamas; *Int'l*, pg. 911
Dill, Sir Bayard, Chm. Bd. & Pres.--Watlington Waterworks Limited, Hamilton, Bermuda; *U.S. Public*, pg. 912
Dillard, Edwin, V.P. & Gen. Mgr.--Dillard, A ResourceNet International Company, Lynchburg, VA; *U.S. Public*, pg. 902
Dillard, Mike, Chm. Bd.--Little Rock Division, Little Rock, AR; *U.S. Public*, pg. 509
Dille, T.M., Grp. V.P. & Gen. Mgr.--Rhone-Poulenc, Agrochemical Division, Research Triangle Park, NC; *Int'l*, pg. 1109
Dillella, D.M., Pres.--Berwind Property Group, Inc., Philadelphia, PA; *U.S. Private*, pg. 138
Dilley, George, District Mgr.--Wright & Lopez, Inc., Louisville, KY; *U.S. Private*, pg. 843
Dillingham, Robert, V.P. & Pub. Rels.--Popular Mechanics, New York, NY; *U.S. Private*, pg. 517
Dillingham, William A., Pres. & Chief Oper. Officer--Aspen Imaging International, Inc., Cleveland, OH; *U.S. Public*, pg. 1339
Dillinham, William A., Pres.--Kroy Inc., Scottsdale, AZ; *U.S. Public*, pg. 1339
Dillman, Ron, Chief Exec. Officer & Gen. Mgr.--The Virgin Islands Daily News, Saint Thomas, VI; *U.S. Public*, pg. 702
Dillon, Daniel P., Pres. & Chief Exec. Officer--Welch Foods Inc., A Cooperative, Concord, MA; *U.S. Private*, pg. 784
Dillon, Donald F., Pres.--Information Technology, Inc., Lincoln, NE; *U.S. Public*, pg. 647
Dillon, Gary G., Chm. Bd., Pres. & Chief Exec. Officer--Schwitzer, Inc., Indianapolis, IN; *U.S. Public*, pg. 968
Dillon, Jack, Mgr.--Anixter St. Johns, Saint John, Canada; *U.S. Public*, pg. 116
Dillon, Jack, Dir.-Intl. Tech & Mfg.--General Tire Intl. Co., Akron, OH; *Int'l*, pg. 327
Dillon, John R., Pres.--Cox Communications, Inc., Atlanta, GA; *U.S. Private*, pg. 282
Dillon, John T., Chief Exec. Officer--Hammermill Papers, Memphis, TN; *U.S. Public*, pg. 902
Dillon, Joseph, Pres. & Chief Oper. Officer--Matsushita Services Co. Div., Secaucus, NJ; *Int'l*, pg. 847
Dillon, Vincent, Mng. Dir.--Livingston UK Limited, Dublin, Ireland; *Int'l*, pg. 212
Dilts, Stephen R., Dir.--J&H Marsh & McLennan Management Services (Cayman) Ltd., Georgetown, Cayman Islands; *U.S. Public*, pg. 1049
DiLuzio, Robert G., Gen. Mgr.--EG & G Dynatrend, Fairfax, VA; *U.S. Public*, pg. 544
Dilworth, John R., Pres.--The Psychological Corp., San Antonio, TX; *U.S. Public*, pg. 784
Dimacopoulos, Gregory, Pres.--Astra Hellas S.A., Athens, Greece; *Int'l*, pg. 93
DiMaria, Peter, Chief Oper. Officer & Pres.--Accu-Time System, Ellington, CT; *U.S. Private*, pg. 11
DiMartino, George, Pres.--Piher International Corporation, Mount Prospect, IL; *Int'l*, pg. 853
DiMartino, Joseph S., Pres. & Chief Oper. Officer--The Dreyfus Corporation, New York, NY; *U.S. Public*, pg. 1085
DiMeglio, Mario, Pres.--Process & Industrial Division, Philadelphia, PA; *U.S. Private*, pg. 317
DiMeola, Richard, Pres.--Premium Products Division, Fort Lauderdale, FL; *U.S. Private*, pg. 690
DiMicco, Dan, V.P. & Gen. Mgr.--Nucor-Yamato Steel Company, Blytheville, AR; *U.S. Public*, pg. 1206
Dimich, Daniel L., Pres.--General Coach, Oliver, Canada; *U.S. Public*, pg. 1602
Dimitriou, A., Chief Exec. Officer--B&D Instruments and Avionics, Inc., Valley Center, KS; *Int'l*, pg. 208
Dimling, John A., Pres. & Chief Oper. Officer--Nielsen Media Research, New York, NY; *U.S. Public*, pg. 395
Dimmick, Donald, Pres.--Simplimatic Engineering Co., Lynchburg, VA; *U.S. Public*, pg. 463
Dimou, Aphrodite, Mng. Dir.--Progress Advertising, Athens, Greece; *Int'l*, pg. 470
Dina, Dino, M.D., Pres.--The Biocine Company, Emeryville, CA; *U.S. Public*, pg. 350
Dinaman, Saya, Mng. Dir.--Middle East Bank Kenya Ltd., Nairobi, Kenya; *Int'l*, pg. 548
DiNardo, John N., V.P.--K N Gas Gathering, Inc., Lakewood, CO; *U.S. Public*, pg. 937
Dinares, Jorge, Country Mgr.--BMC Software, S.A., Madrid, Spain; *U.S. Public*, pg. 163
Dinda, Bruce, Chief Oper. Officer--Fabricon Products, River Rouge, MI; *U.S. Private*, pg. 355

Dineen, Pat, Pres.--National Baking, Chicago, IL; *U.S. Private*, pg. 1022
Dinesen, Vagn A., Pres.--Extract-oil, S.A., Santa Ana, Spain; *Int'l*, pg. 288
Dinesen, Vagn A., Pres.--Xantoflor, S.A., Tudela, Spain; *Int'l*, pg. 289
Dingee, Michael S., Gen. Mgr.--Molinos Caracas Maracaibo S.A., Caracas, Venezuela; *Int'l*, pg. 411
Dingel, Siegfried, Chief Oper. Officer--Granges Aluminium GmbH, Dusseldorf, Germany; *Int'l*, pg. 442
Dingley, G.A., Mng. Dir.--Pentax U.K. Ltd., Langley, United Kingdom; *Int'l*, pg. 85
Dingmans, Ir. S., Pres.--DSM Resins B.V., Zwolle, Netherlands; *Int'l*, pg. 353
Dings, John L., V.P.--Wellman Man-Made Fibers Div., Johnsonville, SC; *U.S. Public*, pg. 1752
Dingus, David H., Pres.--Reedrill Inc., Denison, TX; *Int'l*, pg. 1325
DiNicola, Robert J., Chm. Bd. & Chief Exec. Officer--Zale Delaware, Inc., Irving, TX; *U.S. Public*, pg. 1789
Dinkelacker, Fred, Branch Mgr.--Circle Freight International USA, Valley Stream, NY; *U.S. Public*, pg. 370
Dinmore, Fred, Mng. Dir.--Ark Life Assurance Company Limited, Dublin, Ireland; *Int'l*, pg. 64
Dinos, John L., V.P.-Sls. & Mktg.--Southern Tea Co., Marietta, GA; *Int'l*, pg. 1377
Dinovitz, Paul, V.P. & Gen. Mgr.--KMBC Division, Kansas City, MO; *U.S. Private*, pg. 516
Dinovitz, Paul, V.P. & Gen. Mgr.--KMBC-TV, Kansas City, MO; *U.S. Private*, pg. 516
Dinsdale, Chris, Pres.--Tillamook Food Sales, Tigard, OR; *U.S. Private*, pg. 1086
Dintaman, James L., Pres.--Food Division, Solon, OH; *Int'l*, pg. 916
Dintaman, James L., Pres.--Nestle Frozen, Refrigerated, and Ice Cream Companies, Solon, OH; *Int'l*, pg. 918
Diodati, James, V.P. & Gen. Mgr.--The Ontario Produce Co., Bradford, Canada; *Int'l*, pg. 1012
Diodati, James, V.P. & Gen. Mgr.--The Ontario Produce Co., Toronto, Canada; *Int'l*, pg. 1012
Dioios, Ike, Mgr.--Kern Livestock Supplement Co., Inc., Bakersfield, CA; *U.S. Private*, pg. 46
Dion, Robert, Pres.--Three Branches, Inc., Plaistow, NH; *U.S. Private*, pg. 215
Dionne, Denis, Pres.--Capital Communications CDPQ, Montreal, Canada; *Int'l*, pg. 249
Dionne, Denis, Pres.--Sofinov, Montreal, Canada; *Int'l*, pg. 249
Dionne, Mario, Gen. Mgr.--J.B. Dionne Ltd., Quebec, Canada; *Int'l*, pg. 1074
DiOrio, Darryl, Pres.--Johnstown Wire Technologies, Inc., Johnstown, PA; *U.S. Private*, pg. 344
DiPietro, Robert, Pres.-Marine Group--TFX Marine, Hagerstown, MD; *U.S. Public*, pg. 1570
DiPietro, Robert M., Pres.--Teleflex Marine, Limerick, PA; *U.S. Public*, pg. 1569
DiPippo, Gerry, Pres.--Volt Directory Services, Blue Bell, PA; *U.S. Public*, pg. 1724
Diracles, John, Jr., V.P., Treas. & Sec.--Radisson Hotel Corporation, Minneapolis, MN; *U.S. Private*, pg. 212
Dirkes, Christiane, Mng. Dir.--Shandwick Lutz Bohme Public Relations GmbH, Hamburg, Germany; *Int'l*, pg. 1227
Dirnberger, Kenneth, Pres.--Konami Corporation of America Inc., Buffalo Grove, IL; *Int'l*, pg. 746
Dirom, N.A., Mgr.--Somass Division, Port Alberni, Canada; *Int'l*, pg. 828
DiRomualdo, Robert, Chm. Bd. & Chief Exec. Officer--Borders Group, Inc., Ann Arbor, MI; *U.S. Public*, pg. 245
Dirrett, Steven D., V.P.--Balcron Oil Division, Billings, MT; *U.S. Public*, pg. 589
Dirti, Arnold, Chief Exec. Officer--Hedstrom Holding Co., Mount Prospect, IL; *U.S. Private*, pg. 526
Disbrow, Cliff, Sr. V.P.-Technical Opers.--Glaxo Wellcome Inc., Zebulon, NC; *Int'l*, pg. 552
Dischi, Franco, Gen. Mgr.--Notifier Italia S.r.l., Milan, Italy; *U.S. Public*, pg. 1307
Disenborg, Ann-Marie, Chief Oper. Officer--Svensk Teknisk Byra AB, Stockholm, Sweden; *Int'l*, pg. 709
Dishman, Rosemarie, Pres.--DeVRY Institute of Technology, Pomona, CA; *U.S. Public*, pg. 504
DiSibio, Ralph R., Pres.--Parsons Development Company, Pasadena, CA; *U.S. Private*, pg. 842
DiSimone, G., Deputy Mgr.--Banca Nazionale Del Lavoro (Atlanta), Atlanta, GA; *Int'l*, pg. 136
Disler, Benno, Rep. Officer--Ferrier Lullin & Cie SA, Singapore, Singapore; *Int'l*, pg. 480
Disney, Michael G., V.P. & Gen. Mgr.--WCKG, Inc., Chicago, IL; *U.S. Public*, pg. 274
Distefano, Timmy, Gen. Mgr.--Capitol Steel, Inc., Baton Rouge, LA; *U.S. Public*, pg. 412
Distefano, Timmy, Gen. Mgr.--Capitol Steel-Slidell, Slidell, LA; *U.S. Public*, pg. 412
Ditmar, Edele, Editor--Eden News, Eden, NC; *U.S. Public*, pg. 1078
Ditner, Anton, Acting Mng. Dir.--Becker, Karlsbad, Germany; *U.S. Public*, pg. 787
Ditomassi, George R., Jr., Chief Oper. Officer--Hasbro International, Inc., Springfield, MA; *U.S. Public*, pg. 797
Ditri, Arnold, Chief Exec. Officer--Hedstrom Corporation, Mount Prospect, IL; *U.S. Private*, pg. 526
Ditri, Arnold, Chief Exec. Officer--ERO Industries, Inc., Mount Prospect, IL; *U.S. Private*, pg. 526
Ditter, James J., Pres.--Norlight Telecommunications Inc., Brookfield, WI; *U.S. Private*, pg. 601
Dittmer, Thomas, Pres.--Refco Inc., Chicago, IL; *U.S. Private*, pg. 917
Dittmore, Michael, Pres.--Ikon Office Solutions-Arizona, Tempe, AZ; *U.S. Public*, pg. 863
Dittrich, Roger, Exec. V.P.--T & D Metal Products, Wasco, IL; *U.S. Private*, pg. 638
Ditz, George R., Gen. Mgr.--Aeroquip Division, Vickers Systems Pty. Ltd., Mulgrave, Australia; *U.S. Public*, pg. 25
Divine, Thomas L., Mgr.--Piper Jaffray Inc., Ames, IA; *U.S. Public*, pg. 1301
Dix, Jan F., Pres. & Chief Exec. Officer--OCE USA, Inc., Chicago, IL; *Int'l*, pg. 994
Dix, William L., Chm. Bd. & Mng. Dir.--Foral Service Proprietary Limited, Campbellfield, Australia; *U.S. Public*, pg. 665
Dix, William L., Chm. & Mng. Dir.--Ford Sales Company of Australia Limited, Campbellfield, Australia; *U.S. Public*, pg. 666
Dixon, Bill, Plant Mgr.--Transmission Div., Shelbyville, TN; *U.S. Public*, pg. 556
Dixon, C.O., Pres.--Seven Seas Limited, Hull, United Kingdom; *Int'l*, pg. 593
Dixon, Donna, Pres.--The Hair Cuttery, Falls Church, VA; *U.S. Private*, pg. 287
Dixon, Frank, Fin. Controller--Autodesk Australia Pty. Ltd., North Ryde, Australia; *U.S. Public*, pg. 149
Dixon, Gene, Chm. Bd. & Pres.--Cavalier Hotel Corp., Virginia Beach, VA; *U.S. Private*, pg. 638
Dixon, George, Chief Oper. Officer--Binks-Bullows, Ltd., Walsall, United Kingdom; *U.S. Public*, pg. 229
Dixon, J. E., Pres.--JE Merit Constructors, Inc., Houston, TX; *U.S. Public*, pg. 921
Dixon, J.R., Mng. Dir.--Air UK (Leisure) Ltd., Stansted, United Kingdom; *Int'l*, pg. 39
Dixon, James A., Chief Oper. Officer--Allright Louisville Co., Inc., Louisville, KY; *U.S. Private*, pg. 42
Dixon, James D., Chief Oper. Officer--Euroclean Canada Inc., Cambridge, Canada; *Int'l*, pg. 441
Dixon, Jim, Chief Oper. Officer--Ferodo Ltd., Stockport, United Kingdom; *Int'l*, pg. 1334
Dixon, John, Pres. & Chief Exec. Officer--Mutual Service Corporation, North Palm Beach, FL; *U.S. Private*, pg. 831
Dixon, John T., Pres.--Quality Markets, Inc., Jamestown, NY; *U.S. Public*, pg. 1270
Dixon, M.C., Gen. Mgr.--Flexsteel Division, Dublin, GA; *U.S. Public*, pg. 654
Dixon, Norval W. Jr., Chm. Bd.--Rockville National Bank, Rockville, IN; *U.S. Public*, pg. 1217
Dixon, Peter, Mng. Dir.--CNT International, Uxbridge, United Kingdom; *U.S. Public*, pg. 421
Dixon, Peter, Mng. Dir.--Ultra GmbH, Hilden, Germany; *U.S. Public*, pg. 421
Dixon, Rafe, Branch Mgr.--Continental/Murray, Augusta, GA; *U.S. Private*, pg. 268
Dixon, Scott, Dir.-Opers.--Sensormatic Canada, Inc., Mississauga, Canada; *U.S. Public*, pg. 1457
Dixon, Steve, Chief Exec. Officer--La Palma Intercommunity Hospital, La Palma, CA; *U.S. Private*, pg. 1118
Dixon, Wendell L., Chm.--Merit Life Insurance Co., Evansville, IN; *U.S. Public*, pg. 77
Dizon, Romeo, Reg. Mgr.--Velsicol Chemical Corp., Manila, Philippines; *U.S. Private*, pg. 1135
Djumaeva, Stora V., Chief Exec.--Novo Nordisk A/S, Tashkent, Uzbekistan; *Int'l*, pg. 987
Djurle, Gunilla, Sls. & Mktg. Mgr.--Whitehall Sweden, Stockholm, Sweden; *U.S. Public*, pg. 82
Dlaska, Hubert, Gen. Mgr.--Bombardier-Wien Schienenfahrzeuge AG, Vienna, Austria; *Int'l*, pg. 200
do Carmo, Jorge, Chief Oper. Officer--Sharp do Brasil S.A. Industria de Equipamentos Electronicos, Manaus, Brazil; *Int'l*, pg. 1229
Dobat, Hans, Chief Oper. Officer--VOTEX GmbH, Dreieichenhain, Germany; *Int'l*, pg. 1474
Dobbeaere, Rik, Gen. Mgr.--Browning SA, Herstal, Belgium; *Int'l*, pg. 617
Dobbie, A.A., Dr., Mng. Dir.--Kelco International Ltd., London, United Kingdom; *U.S. Public*, pg. 1091
Dobbie, Clare, Dir.-Communications--Nike (U.K.) Limited, Sunderland, United Kingdom; *U.S. Public*, pg. 1184
Dobbie, S. J., Chm. Bd.--NatWest Financial Products plc, London, United Kingdom; *Int'l*, pg. 910
Dobbin, Alvin, Pres. & Chief Exec. Officer--Giant of Salisbury, Inc., Hyattsville, MD; *U.S. Public*, pg. 741
Dobbin, Alvin, Pres. & Chief Exec. Officer--Shaw Community Supermarket, Hyattsville, MD; *U.S. Public*, pg. 741
Dobbin, Alvin, Pres.--Giant of Cherry Hill, Inc., Hyattsville, MD; *U.S. Public*, pg. 741
Dobby, J.M., Dir.--Meyer Forest Products Ltd, London, United Kingdom; *Int'l*, pg. 864
Dobe, Nobuyuki, Chief Rep.--Bain & Company Ltd. (Tokyo), Tokyo, Japan; *Int'l*, pg. 406
Doberneck, John, Plant Mgr.--Sealy Mattress Company - Clarion, Richmond, CA; *U.S. Private*, pg. 979
Dobler, Sven C., Gen. Mgr.--Orlandi Inc., Farmingdale, NY; *Int'l*, pg. 1269
Dobloug, Mikkel, Pres.--Swix Sport, Lillehammer, Norway; *Int'l*, pg. 1390
Dobranski, Dennis, Gen. Mgr.--NuArc Western Div., Santa Fe Springs, CA; *U.S. Private*, pg. 809
Dobrez, John G., Pres.--Industrial Laundry Group of Amerclean, Midlothian, IL; *U.S. Private*, pg. 337
Dobrindt, Eckhard, Mng. Dir.--Costar GmbH, Bodenheim, Germany; *U.S. Public*, pg. 448
Dobson, M.W.R., Chm.--Morgan Grenfell Asset Management Limited, London, United Kingdom; *Int'l*, pg. 405
Dobson, Michael, Grp. Chief Exec. Officer--Morgan Grenfell Group PLC, London, United Kingdom; *Int'l*, pg. 405
Dobson, P.O., Mgr.--Chemainus Sawmill Division, Chemainus, Canada; *Int'l*, pg. 828
Dobson, T., Mng. Dir.--Shell Fuel Supplies, Saint Helier, United Kingdom; *Int'l*, pg. 1141
Dockery, J. Glenn, Sr. V.P.--Willis Corroon Financial Services Corp., Atlanta, GA; *Int'l*, pg. 1507
Doctor, John, Mgr.--Champaign-Urbana Communications, Inc., Urbana, IL; *U.S. Public*, pg. 1610
Dodd, Dave, V.P.-Sls.--Whiteville Apparel Corp., Whiteville, NC; *U.S. Public*, pg. 796
Dodd, James R., Pres.--Citizens Trust Company of Indiana, N.A., Evansville, IN; *U.S. Public*, pg. 280
Dodd, Leon, V.P.-Opers.--Rospatch Jessco, Inc., Dowagiac, MI; *U.S. Public*, pg. 98
Dodds, P., Mng. Dir.--Sovereign Chemical Industries Limited, Barrow-in-Furness, United Kingdom; *Int'l*, pg. 802
Dodge, James H., Chm., Pres. & Chief Exec. Officer--Providence Gas Co., Providence, RI; *U.S. Public*, pg. 1337
Dodge, Steven F., Chief Oper. Officer--Nitro Steel Div., Pleasant Prairie, WI; *U.S. Public*, pg. 1349
Dodic, Martin, Chief Oper. Officer--Novo Nordisk A/S, Bratislava, Slovakia; *Int'l*, pg. 987
Dodig, Victor G., Pres. & Chief Exec. Officer--Atlas Asset Management Inc., Toronto, Canada; *Int'l*, pg. 865
Dodosh, Mark, Editor--Crain's Cleveland Business, Cleveland, OH; *U.S. Private*, pg. 285
Dods, Walter A., Jr., Chm. Bd. & Chief Exec. Officer--First Hawaiian Bank, Honolulu, HI; *U.S. Public*, pg. 634
Dods, Walter A., Jr., Chm. Bd.--Pacific One Bank, Portland, OR; *U.S. Public*, pg. 635
Dodson, D.K., Pres. & Chief Exec. Officer--John Brown E & C Corporate Offices (U.S.), Houston, TX; *Int'l*, pg. 774
Dodson, D.K., Mng. Dir.--Trafalgar House Inc., Attleboro, MA; *Int'l*, pg. 774
Dodson, Edmond O., Pres.--Farmers State Bank, Liberty, IN; *U.S. Public*, pg. 633
Dodson, John, Gen. Mgr.--Adolphus Hotel, Dallas, TX; *U.S. Private*, pg. 800
Dodyk, Lou, Plant Mgr.--Cambridge Industries, Inc., Marion, IN; *U.S. Private*, pg. 202
Doelder, Jay L., Pres.--Pak-Sak Industries, Inc., Sparta, MI; *U.S. Public*, pg. 1061
Doepper, Walter, Prof. Dr., Chief Exec. Officer--Kennametal Hertel AG, Furth, Germany; *U.S. Public*, pg. 951
Doerflinger, G., Mng. Dir.--OMRON Electronics S.A., Madrid, Spain; *Int'l*, pg. 1006
Doering, Hans, Vice Chm. & Chief Exec. Officer--Siemens Ltd., Johannesburg, South Africa; *Int'l*, pg. 1247
Doering, John, V.P. & Gen. Mgr.--Dover Mills Limited, Halifax, Canada; *Int'l*, pg. 417
Doerner, Ewald, General Mgr.--Dresdner Bank Mexico S.A., Mexico, Mexico; *Int'l*, pg. 419
Doerner, Frank, Pres.--Northfield Metal Products Ltd., Waterloo, Canada; *U.S. Public*, pg. 987
Doerr, Franz, Mng. Dir.--Lurgi (Australia) Pty. Ltd., Melbourne, Australia; *Int'l*, pg. 861
Doerr, Harvey, Pres.--Murphy Oil Co., Ltd., Calgary, Canada; *U.S. Public*, pg. 1142
Doerre, W. Richard, Pres.--Voest-Alpine Steel Corp., New York, NY; *Int'l*, pg. 1471
Doggett, Christopher, Gen. Mgr.--AMP Packaging Systems, Inc., Round Rock, TX; *U.S. Public*, pg. 8
Dognin, Bruno, Mgr.--Barden SARL, Malakoff, France; *Int'l*, pg. 468
Doherty, Edward D., Chm. Bd. & Chief Exec. Officer--Kaneb Pipe Line Partners, L.P., Richardson, TX; *U.S. Public*, pg. 942
Doherty, J.A., V.P. & Gen. Mgr.--Nucor Steel-Nebraska, Norfolk, NE; *U.S. Public*, pg. 1205
Doherty, John P., Pres.--American Southern Financial Group, Miami, FL; *U.S. Private*, pg. 618
Dohi, Masao, Mng. Dir.--ORIX Maritime Corporation, Tokyo, Japan; *Int'l*, pg. 1009
Dohring, Ed, Pres.--SVG Lithography Systems, Wilton, CT; *U.S. Public*, pg. 1474
Dohrman, Fred, Pres. & Chief Exec. Officer--Winnebago Acceptance Corp., Forest City, IA; *U.S. Public*, pg. 1772
Doi, Hiroyuki, Chief Rep.--Daiwa Bank-Sydney, Sydney, Australia; *Int'l*, pg. 374
Doi, Hisato, Mng. Dir.--Sumitomo Life International (UK) Limited, London, United Kingdom; *Int'l*, pg. 1315
Doi, Katunari, Pres.--The Green Cross Corp.-New York Representative Office, New York, NY; *Int'l*, pg. 558
Doi, Tsuguo, Mng. Dir.--Nippon Express Hawaii Inc., Honolulu, HI; *Int'l*, pg. 934
Doig, George, Pres. & Chief Exec. Officer--Johnson Yokogawa Corporation, Newnan, GA; *Int'l*, pg. 1521
Dojny, Richard, Pres.--Prentice Hall Education, Career & Technology, Upper Saddle River, NJ; *U.S. Private*, pg. 778
Dokken, Wade, Chief Mktg. Officer--American Skandia Marketing, Inc., Shelton, CT; *Int'l*, pg. 1257
Dokter, Ernst, Mng. Dir.--Caliqua AG, Basel, Switzerland; *Int'l*, pg. 1306
Dolan, Don, Pres.--Custom Direct Inc., Cincinnati, OH; *Int'l*, pg. 1076
Dolan, J. Mitchell, Pres. & Gen. Mgr.--WPLJ-FM Radio, Inc., New York, NY; *U.S. Public*, pg. 512
Dolan, John, Country Mgr.--Compaq Computer Mfg. Ltd., Bishopston, United Kingdom; *U.S. Public*, pg. 418
Dolan, Paul, Pres.--Fetzer Vineyards California Wines, Hopland, CA; *U.S. Public*, pg. 261
Dolan, Ronald V., Pres. & Chief Exec. Officer--First Colony Life Insurance Co., Lynchburg, VA; *U.S. Public*, pg. 711
Dolcetti, Daniel J., Pres.--The Wheatley Group, Inc., Stamford, CT; *U.S. Public*, pg. 152
Dole, Benjamin, Pres.--BCS Richland Inc., Richland, WA; *U.S. Public*, pg. 241
Dolen, Mike, Gen. Mgr.--Antennacraft Co., Burlington, IA; *U.S. Public*, pg. 1560
Dolwick, Jim, Plant Mgr.--General Tire Div., Mount Vernon, IL; *Int'l*, pg. 327
Doman, Nico, Mng. Dir.--Sasol Engineering Division, Secunda, South Africa; *Int'l*, pg. 1197
Doman, Walt, Gen. Mgr.--Republic Automotive Parts Sales, Inc., Des Moines, IA; *U.S. Public*, pg. 1378
Dombek, Gerard M., Pres. & Gen. Mgr.--Precoat Metals Division, Saint Louis, MO; *U.S. Public*, pg. 1458
Dombkowski, Edwin H., Pres.--Cigna Life Insurance Company of Canada, Toronto, Canada; *U.S. Public*, pg. 362
Dombroski, Rick, Pres.--Hamlin Steel Products, Akron, OH; *U.S. Private*, pg. 299

Domenici, Mary Anne, Branch Mgr.--Downey Savings & Loan Association, F.A., Saratoga, CA; *U.S. Public*, pg. 527

Domeniconi, R., Dr., Chm. Bd.--Coutts & Co AG, Zurich, Switzerland; *Int'l*, pg. 911

Domes, Anton, Dr., Chm. Bd.--Heraeus Kulzer GmbH, Hanau, Germany; *Int'l*, pg. 616

Domey, Alice K., Controller--Sunhill Food Of Vermont, Inc., Swanton, VT; *Int'l*, pg. 1464

Domingues, Ariel, Chief Oper. Officer--Fundiciones Metalicas, S.A., Mexico, Mexico; *Int'l*, pg. 1244

Dominguez, J. A., Pres.--Compania de Financiacion Case, S.A., Madrid, Spain; *U.S. Public*, pg. 1579

Dominguez, Jose, Dir.--Poclain Hispana S.A., Madrid, Spain; *U.S. Public*, pg. 1580

Dominguez, Pilar, Mgr.--Broad National Bank-Elizabeth, Elizabeth, NJ; *U.S. Public*, pg. 257

Dominguez, Ron, Gen. Mgr.--Mitsubishi Silicon America-Southwest Regional Sales Office, Dallas, TX; *Int'l*, pg. 875

Dominik, Chris, V.P.--Coca-Cola Bottling Co. of West Virginia, Inc., Charleston, WV; *U.S. Public*, pg. 392

Dominioni, Angelo M., Pres. & Chief Exec. Officer--Cucina Classica Italiana Inc., Lakewood, NJ; *U.S. Public*, pg. 1435

Domo, James F., Pres.--Joslyn Hi-Voltage Corporation, Cleveland, OH; *U.S. Public*, pg. 481

Domont, John J., Pres.--Symbol, Santa Fe, NM; *U.S. Public*, *pg. 1546*

Domsch, Stefan, Mng. Dir.--Bronborger & Kessler Handelsgesellschaft GmbH, Munich, Germany; *Int'l*, pg. 428

Dona, J.C., Pres.--Brabant Pers bv, s Hertogenbosch, Netherlands; *Int'l*, pg. 1445

Donadio, Robert, Pres.--CVD Incorporated, Woburn, MA; *U.S. Public*, pg. 1135

Donahue-Dalton, Ellen, Pres.-Game Design--GameScape, Inc., Coventry, RI; *U.S. Public*, pg. 767

Donahue, Daniel W., Jr., Chm. Bd.--Donahue Schriber, Newport Beach, CA; *Int'l*, pg. 253

Donahue, Dennis, Pres.--Enviromental Products Inc., Orrville, OH; *U.S. Private*, pg. 1177

Donahue, Glenda, Admin.--Winter Haven, Houston, TX; *U.S. Public*, pg. 839

Donahue, J.A., Pres. & Gen. Mgr.--Delta Design, Inc., San Diego, CA; *U.S. Public*, pg. 396

Donahue, Raymond, Pres. & Chief Oper. Officer--Red-E-Crete, Inc., Sun Valley, CA; *Int'l*, pg. 818

Donahue, Robert, Gen. Mgr.--KMOL Television, Inc., San Antonio, TX; *U.S. Public*, pg. 352

Donahue, William J., V.P. & Gen. Mgr.--KJRH, Tulsa, OK; *U.S. Public*, pg. 1448

Donald, Odie C., Pres.--BellSouth Mobility, Inc., Atlanta, GA; *U.S. Public*, pg. 208

Donaldson, Fred, Publr.--Intercounty Newspaper, Philadelphia, PA; *U.S. Public*, pg. 935

Donaldson, Hugh, Chief Exec. Officer--Spillers Foods, New Malden, United Kingdom; *Int'l*, pg. 376

Donaldson, J. Harold, Pres. & Chief Exec. Officer--Regions Bank/Marianna, Marianna, FL; *U.S. Public*, pg. 1372

Donaldson, James, Pres.--Ford Industria e Comercio Ltda., San Paulo, Brazil; *U.S. Public*, pg. 666

Donaldson, Nigel, Chm. & Pres.--United Advertising Publications, Inc., Dallas, TX; *Int'l*, pg. 1443

Donati, Franco, Mng. Dir.--Delta Trading Co. Ltd., Tel Aviv, Israel; *Int'l*, pg. 1003

Donaubauer, Franz, Gen. Mgr.--Analog Devices GmbH, Munich, Germany; *U.S. Public*, pg. 108

Donaway, Carl D., Pres. & Chief Exec. Officer--ABX Air, Inc., Wilmington, OH; *U.S. Public*, pg. 33

Dondero, Harvey, Pres.--Maitland-Smith U.S., Inc., High Point, NC; *U.S. Private*, pg. 432

Donelan, Patrick, Chm. Bd.--Kleinwort Benson North America Inc., New York, NY; *Int'l*, pg. 420

Dong-Run, Park, Gen. Dir.--New Computer Service Co., Ltd. (NCS), Seoul, Korea; *U.S. Public*, pg. 1043

Donlon, Liam, Exec. Dir.--KB Financial Services (Ireland) Unltd., Dublin, Ireland; *Int'l*, pg. 761

Donnell, Jack, Div. Mgr.--AgTec Inc., Minnetonka, MN; *U.S. Public*, pg. 6

Donnell, Thomas, Pres.--Cain's Coffee Co., Oklahoma City, OK; *U.S. Public*, pg. 351

Donnelly, Clifford W., Pres.--PCA Life Reinsurance, Miami, FL; *U.S. Public*, pg. 1293

Donnelly, John J., Pres.--DRS Laurel Technologies, Johnstown, PA; *U.S. Public*, pg. 475

Donnelly, Kevin, Chief Oper. Officer--Allright Toledo, Inc., Toledo, OH; *U.S. Private*, pg. 43

Donnelly, Richard, Dir.-Safety--Tilcon Tomasso Services Inc., North Branford, CT; *U.S. Private*, pg. 1086

Donner, Clifford L., Pres.--M & I Bank Southwest, Spring Green, WI; *U.S. Public*, pg. 1050

Donner, Lynn A., V.P. & Gen. Mgr.--First American Title Co. of Nevada, Las Vegas, NV; *U.S. Public*, pg. 625

Donohue, Brendan, Mng. Dir.--BIAM Australia Pty Ltd., Melbourne, Australia; *Int'l*, pg. 153

Donohue, Michael, Pres.--Associated Sand & Gravel Co., Inc., Everett, WA; *Int'l*, pg. 245

Donoso, Boris, Chief Oper. Officer--Novo Nordisk, Buenos Aires, Argentina; *Int'l*, pg. 987

Donoughue, Peter C., Mng. Dir.--Jacaranda Wiley Ltd., Milton, Australia; *U.S. Public*, pg. 1768

Donovan, D. X., Chm. Bd.--Eaton Leasing Corp., Cleveland, OH; *U.S. Public*, pg. 558

Donovan, Dan, Gen. Mgr.--Burke Fuel & Heating Co., Hawthorne, NY; *U.S. Private*, pg. 729

Donovan, Donna, Pres. & Publr.--Utica Observer-Dispatch, Utica, NY; *U.S. Public*, pg. 700

Donovan, Gerry, Plant Mgr.--Bose S.A. de C.V., Sonora, Mexico; *U.S. Private*, pg. 161

Donovan, Michael, Gen. Mgr.--KBSG/KNDD-AM/FM, Seattle, WA; *U.S. Private*, pg. 378

Donovan, Michael, Gen. Mgr.-Sls.--Republic Automotive Parts Sales, Inc., Charlotte, NC; *U.S. Public*, pg. 1378

Donovan, Nancy S., Pres.--NOVUS Financial Corporation, Riverwoods, IL; *U.S. Public*, pg. 1132

Donovan, Patrick X., Pres.--Eaton International Corp., Wilmington, DE; *U.S. Public*, pg. 558

Donovan, Peter, Pres.--Worldscope/Disclosure, LLC, Bethesda, MD; *U.S. Public*, pg. 1325

Donovan, Stephen P., Jr., V.P.--Procter & Gamble Beverage Div., Cincinnati, OH; *U.S. Public*, pg. 1330

Donovan, Stephen P., Jr., Pres.--Procter & Gamble Food Products Div., Cincinnati, OH; *U.S. Public*, pg. 1331

Donovan, William, Chief Oper. Officer--Imperial Die Casting, Easley, SC; *U.S. Private*, pg. 903

Dontas, P., Gen. Mgr.--ING Bank Athens, Athens, Greece; *Int'l*, pg. 648

Donze, B., Gen. Rep.--Gan Incendie Accidents Switzerland, Lausanne, Switzerland; *Int'l*, pg. 564

Donze, B., Chm.--Zenith Vie, Pully, Switzerland; *Int'l*, pg. 565

Doodson, Tony, Mng. Dir.--SKF Philippines Inc., Manila, Philippines; *Int'l*, pg. 1160

Dooher, Terry, Chief Oper. Officer--Barry Controls Industrial/Defense, Brighton, MA; *U.S. Public*, pg. 124

Doolen, Dennis G., Mgr.-Opers.--Granger Container Service, Lansing, MI; *U.S. Private*, pg. 469

Doolen, Dennis G., Mgr.-Opers.--Granger Land Development Co., Lansing, MI; *U.S. Private*, pg. 469

Doolen, Dennis G., Mgr.-Opers.--Granger Waste Management Co., Lansing, MI; *U.S. Private*, pg. 469

Dooley, David M., Pres.--Duni Inc., Milwaukee, WI; *Int'l*, pg. 421

Dooley, Graham, Dir.-Australia--North West Water Australia Pty. Ltd., Sydney, Australia; *Int'l*, pg. 1444

Dooley, Kenneth J., Chief Oper. Officer--Holland Sweetener North America, Inc., Atlanta, GA; *Int'l*, pg. 1407

Dooley, Larry W., Pres. & Chief Exec. Officer--Regions Bank-Cedartown/Rockmart, Cedartown, GA; *U.S. Public*, *pg. 1372*

Dooling, John, Publisher--Silver Burdett Division, Parsippany, NJ; *U.S. Private*, pg. 778

Doolittle, Dennis, Mng. Dir.--Autologic Information International, Inc., Oakville, Canada; *U.S. Public*, pg. 1724

Doolittle, Don, V.P.--Coca-Cola Bottling Co. of Roanoke, Roanoke, VA; *U.S. Public*, pg. 392

Doolittle, James H., Pres. & Chief Oper. Officer--Time Warner Cable, Stamford, CT; *U.S. Public*, pg. 1610

Doordan, John, Regional Mgr. Asia-Pacific--qad.australia pty ltd, Hunters Hill, Australia; *U.S. Public*, pg. 1345

Doordan, John M., Reg. Mgr. Asia-Pacific--qad.japan k.k., Yokohama, Japan; *U.S. Public*, pg. 1345

Dooris, Floyd F., Pres.--Central Hudson Cogeneration, Inc., Poughkeepsie, NY; *U.S. Public*, pg. 325

Dora, Aysegul, Chm. Bd. & Chief Exec. Officer--Penajans DMB&B Ticaret, Istanbul, Turkey; *U.S. Private*, pg. 305

Doraisamy, E.C., Gen. Mgr.--Oral-B Laboratories Pty. Limited, Sydney, Australia; *U.S. Public*, pg. 745

Doran, Daniel J., Pres.--Ace Doran Brokerage, Cincinnati, OH; *U.S. Private*, pg. 340

Doran, Janis, Admin.--Hillhaven Convalescent Hospital San Rafael, San Rafael, CA; *U.S. Public*, pg. 1713

Doran, Lindsay, Pres.--United Artists Pictures, Inc., Santa Monica, CA; *U.S. Public*, pg. 1102

Doran, Terry, Chief Oper. Officer--Hudson General Aviation Services, Inc., Dorval, Canada; *U.S. Public*, pg. 846

Doran, Wayne, Chm. Bd.--Ford Motor Land Development Corporation, Dearborn, MI; *U.S. Public*, pg. 663

Doran, Wayne S., Chm. Bd. & Pres.--Greenfield Properties, Inc., Dearborn, MI; *U.S. Public*, pg. 663

Doran, Wayne S., Pres.--Fordson Coal Company, Dearborn, MI; *U.S. Public*, pg. 664

Dorau, Siegfried, Mng. Dir.--ISS Servisystem GmbH, Hamburg, Germany; *Int'l*, pg. 657

Dore, Brook, Reg. Acct. Dir.--RP alpha/Denver, Aurora, CO; *U.S. Private*, pg. 950

Dore, Gerald, Gen. Mgr.--Ortho Clinical Diagnostic S.A., Roissy, France; *U.S. Public*, pg. 931

Dore, Roland, Gen. Mgr.--Uniboard Division Val d'Or, Val d'Or, Canada; *Int'l*, pg. 1431

Dore, Roland, Gen. Mgr.--Uniboard Division Unires, Val d'Or, Canada; *Int'l*, pg. 1431

Dorey, Ray C., Mng. Dir.-Northern Territories--John Crane EAA, Slough, United Kingdom; *Int'l*, pg. 1338

Dorfman, Eliezer, V.P. & Gen. Mgr.--Thorn Apple Valley-Deli & Smoked Meats Division, Detroit, MI; *U.S. Public*, pg. 1603

Dorfman, Neil, Mgr.-Plant--FIDCO (Food Ingredient Development Company), New Milford, CT; *Int'l*, pg. 917

Dorfman, S.D., V.P. & Grp. Pres.--Hughes Space & Communications Group, Los Angeles, CA; *U.S. Public*, pg. 721

Dorfs, Joachim, Mng. Dir.--VDI-Verlag GmbH, Dusseldorf, Germany; *Int'l*, pg. 1479

Doria, C., Mng. Dir.--Distribuidores Concesionarios S.A., Bilbao, Spain; *Int'l*, pg. 615

Doria, Joseph, Pres. & Chief Exec. Officer--The Lincoln Electric Co. of Canada Ltd., Toronto, Canada; *U.S. Public*, pg. 997

Dorig, Werner, Gen. Mgr.--Siegling (Schweiz) A.G., Laufenburg, Switzerland; *Int'l*, pg. 497

Doriga, Ramon Eduardo Garcia Lopez, Pres.--CTE - Compania Trasatlantica Espanola, S.A., Madrid, Spain; *Int'l*, pg. 1224

Doring, Holger, Commercial Dir.--Mead Empaques S.A. de C.V., Mexico, Mexico; *U.S. Public*, pg. 1076

Dorion, George, Pres.--Analytical Technologies, Inc., San Juan, PR; *Int'l*, pg. 131

Dorion, George, Pres. & Chief Oper. Officer--Biotechnical Processes Inc., Catano, PR; *Int'l*, pg. 132

Dorkhom, G.H., Mng. Dir.--Contraves Inc., Pittsburgh, PA; *Int'l*, pg. 998

Dorkin, John, Pres. & Gen. Mgr.--Independence Television Co., Louisville, KY; *U.S. Private*, pg. 147

Dorman, Lawrence B., Pres.--American International Adjustment Company, Livingston, NJ; *U.S. Public*, pg. 85

Dormer, Michael, Pres.--DePuy, Inc., Warsaw, IN; *Int'l*, pg. 331

Dorming, John, Gen. Mgr.--California Auto Dealers Exchange, Inc., Anaheim, CA; *U.S. Private*, pg. 282

Dorminy, Jon L., Gen. Mgr.--Ramparts Div., Sand Springs, OK; *U.S. Public*, pg. 754

Dorn, Gordon H., Dir.-Pur.--Chr. Hansen, Inc., Milwaukee, WI; *Int'l*, pg. 288

Dorn, Wolfgang, Chm.--Deutsche Babcock Handel GmbH, Oberhausen, Germany; *Int'l*, pg. 401

Dornau, Peter, Pres.--Kinpak, Inc., Montgomery, AL; *U.S. Public*, pg. 1211

Dornemann, Michael, Pres., Chief Exec. Officer, & Chm. of Bertelsmann Music Grp.--BMG/Music, New York, NY; *Int'l*, pg. 191

Dornhaus, Ulrich, Mng. Dir.--Buckau-Walther AG, Essen, Germany; *Int'l*, pg. 516

Dornia, M., Dr., Mng. Dir.--Haniel Baustoff-Industrie GmbH, Duisburg, Germany; *Int'l*, pg. 592

Dorrance, Roy G., Pres.--USX Engineers & Consultants, Inc., Pittsburgh, PA; *U.S. Public*, pg. 1662

Dorris, Joe, V.P. & Gen. Mgr.--Futaba Corporation of America, Schaumburg, IL; *Int'l*, pg. 531

Dorris, Joe M., Pres.--Futaba Corporation of America, Irvine, CA; *Int'l*, pg. 531

Dorsa, Peter A., Pres.--Epoxylite Corporation-Equipment Div., Irvine, CA; *U.S. Private*, pg. 379

Dorsey, John, Gen. Mgr.--Hyundai Motor America Western Regional Office, Fountain Valley, CA; *Int'l*, pg. 641

Dorsey, Patrick B., Dir.--Tiffany & Co., London, United Kingdom; *U.S. Public*, pg. 1609

Dorwart, Paul, Pres.--Linear Products Inc., Vancouver, WA; *U.S. Public*, pg. 687

dos Santos, Elisio Alexandre Soares, Chief Exec. Officer--YMR, Lisbon, Portugal; *Int'l*, pg. 750

Dosher, Sheila, Administrator--Van Ark Care Center, Tucumcari, NM; *U.S. Public*, pg. 838

Doshida, T., Gen. Mgr.--Toshiba International Corp. Industrial Div., Houston, TX; *Int'l*, pg. 1405

Doshier, Alan, V.P. & Gen. Mgr.--Greenville Div., Greenville, TX; *U.S. Public*, pg. 1365

Dosho, Koichi, Pres.--NMB Minebea GmbH, Langen, Germany; *Int'l*, pg. 868

Dosho, Koichi, Pres.--Precision Motors - Deutsche Minebea GmbH, Spaichingen, Germany; *Int'l*, pg. 869

Doss, Charles Edward, Mgr.--Batson Mill LP, Batson, TX; *U.S. Public*, pg. 1179

Doss, Wayne, Pres.--Keller Ladders Inc., Fort Lauderdale, FL; *U.S. Public*, pg. 1684

Dossa, P.J., Gen. Mgr.--BFCE Brazil, Sao Paulo, Brazil; *Int'l*, *pg. 161*

Dossaer, Ben, Dir. General--Generale Bank - Milano, Milan, Italy; *Int'l*, pg. 547

Dossche, Piet, Pres.--Beaulieu United, Dalton, GA; *U.S. Private*, pg. 128

Dossi, Giuseppe, Gen. Mgr.--Dexter Aerospace Materials Division, Treviso, Italy; *U.S. Public*, pg. 505

Dot, Jose Maria, Dir. Gen.--Seguros Genesis, S.A., Madrid, Spain; *U.S. Private*, pg. 738

Dot, Jose Maria, Dir. Gen.--Seguros Genesis, S.A., Lisbon, Portugal; *U.S. Private*, pg. 738

Dotson, George S., Chief Oper. Officer--Helmerich & Payne International Drilling Co., Tulsa, OK; *U.S. Public*, pg. 808

Dotson, John L. Jr., Pres. & Publisher--The Beacon Journal Publishing Company, Akron, OH; *U.S. Public*, pg. 963

Dott, Bernhard Klaus, Dr., Sr. Mng. Dir.--Deutsche Bank AG (Frankfurt), Frankfurt/Main, Germany; *Int'l*, pg. 402

Dotti, Pietro, Mng. Dir.-Torino--Armando Testa S.p.A, Rome, Italy; *Int'l*, pg. 1377

Dottor, Lawrence J., Pres.--Lehigh Securities Corporation, Whitehall, PA; *U.S. Public*, pg. 1528

Douay, Michel, Pres.--Clestra Hauserman, Strasbourg, France; *Int'l*, pg. 569

Doucet, Jeau Pierre, Chief Oper. Officer--Cellatex, Lyon, France; *Int'l*, pg. 1109

Doucet, John, Pres. & Chief Oper. Officer--Day & Ross Inc., Hartland, Canada; *Int'l*, pg. 850

Doucette, David, Office Mgr.--Pentax Canada-Vancouver, Vancouver, Canada; *Int'l*, pg. 85

Douez, Marc, Gen. Mgr.--Siegling France S.A., Lomme, France; *Int'l*, pg. 498

Dougan, J., Pres.--BFC Buildings, Scarborough, Canada; *Int'l*, pg. 118

Dougan, J., Pres.--BFC Frontier, Lynnwood, WA; *Int'l*, pg. 118

Dougan, Paul M., Pres.--Symskaya Exploration, Inc., Salt Lake City, UT; *U.S. Public*, pg. 590

Dougherty, B.D., Chief Fin. Officer--The Rawlplug Company Limited, Glasgow, United Kingdom; *Int'l*, pg. 925

Dougherty, David F., Pres. & Chief Exec. Officer--MATRIXX Marketing Inc., Cincinnati, OH; *U.S. Public*, pg. 368

Dougherty, N.D., Mgr.--Martin's Uniforms Div.-San Antonio/Houston, San Antonio, TX; *U.S. Public*, pg. 1539

Dougherty, Peter, Mng. Dir.--PMI Motion Technologies Div., Commack, NY; *U.S. Public*, pg. 965

Doughty, David, Pres.--Clark Boardman Company, Ltd., New York, NY; *U.S. Public*, pg. 1602

Doughty, Patricia, Mgr.-Division--Liberia Mfg. Co., Bossier City, LA; *U.S. Public*, pg. 491

Doughty, Robert T., Div. V.P.--Home Care Division, Saint Paul, MN; *U.S. Public*, pg. 1605

Douglas-Home, D.A.C., Chm.--Morgan Grenfell (Scotland) Limited, Edinburgh, United Kingdom; *Int'l*, pg. 405

Douglas, Donald, Chm. Bd.--M&W, Gibson City, IL; *U.S. Public*, pg. 35

Douglas, Edna, Gen. Mgr.--Park Newspapers of Moore County, Inc., Aberdeen, NC; *U.S. Public*, pg. 1079

Douglas, James, Pres.-Regional--Citizens Bank of Kentucky, Morganfield, KY; *U.S. Public*, pg. 280

Douglas, M. Valoise, V.P. & Gen. Mgr.--Harris Trust Company of California, Los Angeles, CA; *Int'l*, pg. 155

Douglas, Michael, Mgr.-Terminal--Wymondham Oil Storage Company Limited, Wymondham, United Kingdom; *U.S. Public*, pg. 693

Douglas, R. Gordon, M.D., Pres.--Merck Vaccine Division, Rahway, NJ; *U.S. Public*, pg. 1091

Dournel, Patrick, Mng. Dir.--Dumez-GTM, Hanoi, Vietnam; *Int'l*, pg. 823

Dourney, Martin W., Pres.--Omaha Property and Casualty Insurance Co., Omaha, NE; *U.S. Private*, pg. 770

Doutre, P., Pres.--Racal Filter Technologies, Inc., Brockville, Canada; *Int'l*, pg. 1083

Douville, Arthur J., Pres.--Unisource (North East), Windsor, CT; *U.S. Public*, pg. 1671

Dove, Nicholas, Pres.--Hudson Reinsurance Company Limited, Hamilton, Bermuda; *Int'l*, pg. 1257

Dove, Nicholas, Pres.--Hudson Underwriting Ltd., Hamilton, Bermuda; *Int'l*, pg. 1257

Dover, Eli, Mgr.--GGK Tel Aviv, Tel Aviv, Israel; *Int'l*, pg. 1336

Dover, J.D., Pres.--Zeolyst International, Houston, TX; *U.S. Private*, pg. 827

Dow, David, V.P. & Gen. Mgr.--Brambles Equipment Services Inc., Perrysburg, OH; *Int'l*, pg. 211

Dow, Kerr, Chm. Bd.--Custom Foods Limited, Dundalk, Ireland; *U.S. Public*, pg. 806

Dow, Philip L., V.P.-Mfg. & Engrng.--Philips Elmet Corporation, Lewiston, ME; *Int'l*, pg. 1055

Dow, Stephen, Mng. Dir.--Cyclam SA, Amiens, France; *Int'l*, pg. 1339

Dowbek, B.S., Pres. & Chief Exec. Officer--Siemens A.E., Athens, Greece; *Int'l*, pg. 1247

Dowd, Chuck, Chief Oper. Officer--Delta Faucet Corporation, Indianapolis, IN; *U.S. Public*, pg. 1053

Dowd, James F., Pres. & Chief Exec. Offcier--Hudson Insurance Company, New York, NY; *Int'l*, pg. 1258

Dowd, Kenneth L., Jr., Pres.--Albuquerque Capital Management, Inc., New York, NY; *U.S. Public*, pg. 337

Dowd, Peter, Mng. Dir.--Bank of Ireland, Frankfurt, Germany; *Int'l*, pg. 153

Dowd, Peter, Rep.--Bank of Ireland, Frankfurt/Main, Germany; *Int'l*, pg. 153

Dowd, Philip L., Chief Exec. Officer--Sungard Trust & Shareholder Systems Group, Hinsdale, IL; *U.S. Public*, pg. 1535

Dowd, Steve, V.P. & Mgr.-Life & Health Sls.--Willis Corroon Corporation of Lexington, Lexington, KY; *Int'l*, pg. 1505

Dowdy, Sherman, Mgr.--Logan Manufacturing, Chapmanville, WV; *U.S. Private*, pg. 1032

Dowdy, William C., Pres.--ServiceMaster Healthcare Management Services, Inc., Downers Grove, IL; *U.S. Public*, pg. 1462

Dowell, Gary R., Pres. & Chief Exec. Officer--Reistertown Federal Savings Bank, Baltimore, MD; *U.S. Public*, pg. 1543

Dowers, John D., V.P.-Mktg., Nestle Ice Cream Co.--Nestle Frozen/Refrigerated Food Co., Solon, OH; *Int'l*, pg. 918

Dowes, Richard, Pres.--Etablissements Bez S.A., Paris, France; *Int'l*, pg. 62

Dowey, James, Pres.--Akron Standard Division, Akron, OH; *U.S. Public*, pg. 865

Dowlan, James R., Pres.--Westhrift Life Insurance Company, Irvine, CA; *U.S. Public*, pg. 1757

Dowlen, James, Gen. Mgr.--NuArc Southwestern Div., Grand Prairie, TX; *U.S. Private*, pg. 809

Dowling, D.H., Mgr.--Estevan Division, Port Alberni, Canada; *Int'l*, pg. 828

Dowling, John, Pres.--Sunwest Bank of Gallup, Gallup, NM; *U.S. Public*, pg. 1165

Dowling, Peter, V.P.-Mfg./Europe--Loctite (Ireland) Ltd., Dublin, Ireland; *Int'l*, pg. 611

Dowling, Robert, Publisher--The Hollywood Reporter, Hollywood, CA; *Int'l*, pg. 1446

Dowling, Steve, Mng. Dir.--Meggit Mobrey Ltd., Slough, United Kingdom; *Int'l*, pg. 853

Dowling, Steven, Pres.--Harcourt Brace & Company Media Systems Corporation, Orlando, FL; *U.S. Public*, pg. 783

Dowling, Steven A., Sr. V.P.--Holt, Rinehart and Winston School Division, Austin, TX; *U.S. Public*, pg. 783

Dowling, Steven A., Pres.--Macmillan/McGraw-Hill School Publishing Company, New York, NY; *U.S. Public*, pg. 1070

Dowling, Tim, Pres.--Sunwest Bank of Raton, N.A., Raton, NM; *U.S. Public*, pg. 1165

Downe, Bill, Exec. V.P.-Noth American Corp. Banking--Bank of Montreal - Chicago, Chicago, IL; *Int'l*, pg. 154

Downes, Laurence M., Pres.--NJR Energy Services Corporation, Wall, NJ; *U.S. Public*, pg. 1172

Downes, Laurence M., Chm. Bd. & Chief Fin. Officer--New Jersey Natural Gas Co., Wall, NJ; *U.S. Public*, pg. 1172

Downess, John W., Dir.--GSI Engineering, Inc., Columbus, OH; *U.S. Public*, pg. 1780

Downey, G. Lowell, Pres.--Collingwood Grain, Inc., Hutchinson, KS; *U.S. Public*, pg. 128

Downey, James, Gen. Mgr.--Long Beach Learning Center, Long Beach, CA; *U.S. Public*, pg. 218

Downey, L., Gen. Mgr.--Becton Dickinson & Co., Ltd., Dun Laoghaire, Ireland; *U.S. Public*, pg. 200

Downey, Thomas, Gen. Mgr.--Arrow/Schweber Electronics, Wallingford, CT; *U.S. Public*, pg. 134

Downie, Mike, Mng. Dir.--BICC Cables Limited, Chester, United Kingdom; *Int'l*, pg. 120

Downin, R.D., Chief Oper. Officer--Fireye, Inc., Derry, NH; *Int'l*, pg. 1500

Downing, Donald S., Pres.--SunTrust Mortgage Inc., Atlanta, GA; *U.S. Public*, pg. 1538

Downing, Gary, Mng. Partner--Raymond James Capital, Saint Petersburg, FL; *U.S. Public*, pg. 923

Downing, Jeffrey P., V.P. & Gen. Mgr.--Nucor Bearing Products, Inc., Wilson, NC; *U.S. Public*, pg. 1206

Downing, Kathryn, Pres. & Chief Exec. Officer--Matthew Bender & Company, Incorporated, New York, NY; *U.S. Public*, pg. 1616

Downing, Robert, Mng. Dir.--Logica Pty., Melbourne, Australia; *Int'l*, pg. 815

Downing, Robert, Pres.--Maytag Financial Services Corp., Newton, IA; *U.S. Public*, pg. 1065

Downs, David, Chm. Bd. & Pres.--Norwest Bank Nevada, N.A., Las Vegas, NV; *U.S. Public*, pg. 1202

Downs, Linda, Gen. Mgr.--Poe & Brown of Florida, Maitland, FL; *U.S. Public*, pg. 1312

Downs, Ryan A., Co-Gen. Mgr.--Great Lakes Kraut Co., L.L.C., Rochester, NY; *U.S. Private*, pg. 887

Downs, Ryan A., Gen. Mgr.--Great Lakes Kraut Co., Bear Creek, WI; *U.S. Private*, pg. 887

Dowsett, L., Pres. & Gen. Mgr.--Mentholatum Canada Ltd., Fort Erie, Canada; *Int'l*, pg. 1126

Doxsee, Tucker, Pres.--Heraeus Instruments Inc., South Plainfield, NJ; *Int'l*, pg. 616

Doyle, D., Gen. Mgr.--ABN International Financial Services Co., Dublin, Ireland; *Int'l*, pg. 11

Doyle, Declon, Mng. Dir.--Irish Cement Ltd., Stillorgan, Ireland; *Int'l*, pg. 242

Doyle, Gerald L., V.P. & Gen. Mgr.--Harris Corp., Digital Telephone Systems Div., Novato, CA; *U.S. Public*, pg. 791

Doyle, J. A., Chief Oper. Officer--Novo Nordisk Bioindustrie S.A., Nanterre, France; *Int'l*, pg. 989

Doyle, J. Aelred, Chief Oper. Officer--Novo Nordisk Bioindustrie SA, Europe, Nanterre, France; *Int'l*, pg. 989

Doyle, James F., Pres.--Stokely-Van Camp, Inc., Chicago, IL; *U.S. Public*, pg. 1348

Doyle, Kevin, Pres.--Wassall USA Inc., Southport, CT; *Int'l*, pg. 1486

Doyle, Larry, Pres.--PVC Compounders, Kendallville, IN; *U.S. Private*, pg. 484

Doyle, Mary, Pres. & Principal--HSC Securities Corporation, Dallas, TX; *U.S. Public*, pg. 778

Doyle, Mary E., Mgr.--Struers Division, Westlake, OH; *Int'l*, pg. 1084

Doyle, P., Mng. Dir.--Coutts & Co (Guernsey) Limited, Saint Peter Port, United Kingdom; *Int'l*, pg. 910

Doyle, P., Mng. Dir.--NatWest International Trust Corporation (Guensey) Limited, Saint Peter Port, United Kingdom; *Int'l*, pg. 911

Doyle, Patrick, Mng. Dir.--AlliedSignal Ireland Ltd., Waterford, Ireland; *U.S. Public*, pg. 53

Doyle, Patrick, Mng. Dir.--Gunnebo Ireland Ltd., Dublin, Ireland; *Int'l*, pg. 578

Doyle, Patrick J., Pres. & Chief Exec. Officer--Willis Corroon Corp. of Missouri, Saint Louis, MO; *Int'l*, pg. 1506

Doyle, Robert, Chief Oper. Officer--Hudson General Corp., Ronkonkoma, NY; *U.S. Public*, pg. 845

Doyle, Robert E., Pres.--Simplex Products, Adrian, MI; *U.S. Public*, pg. 940

Doyle, Tim, Gen. Mgr.--Newburgh Auto Auction, Newburgh, NY; *U.S. Private*, pg. 282

Doyle, Walter, Pres.--Eaton IDT, Westerville, OH; *U.S. Public*, pg. 558

Drabant, Terry, Pres.--Lockheed Martin Federal Systems-Gaithersburg, Gaithersburg, MD; *U.S. Public*, pg. 1008

Drabinsky, C.R., Pres.--Deluxe Toronto Limited, Toronto, Canada; *Int'l*, pg. 1087

Drabinsky, Cyril, Pres.--Deluxe Laboratories, Inc., Hollywood, CA; *Int'l*, pg. 1087

Draeger, D.M., Sr. V.P.-Specialty Alloys Opers.--Carpenter Specialty Alloys Operations, Reading, PA; *U.S. Public*, pg. 307

Draeger, D.M., Sr. V.P.-Specialty Alloys Opers.--Carpenter Steel Div., Orangeburg, SC; *U.S. Public*, pg. 307

Draeger, D.M., Sr. V.P.-Steel Opers.--Carpenter Steel Div., Fryeburg, ME; *U.S. Public*, pg. 307

Draeger, Kenneth, Pres.--AGFA EPS Division, Wilmington, MA; *Int'l*, pg. 172

Draetta, Ugo R., V.P. & Sr. Counsel--General Electric International Operations, London, United Kingdom; *U.S. Public*, pg. 713

Drafz, William, Mfg. Mgr.--Fuel Systems Textron (Harvard Plant), Harvard, IL; *U.S. Public*, pg. 1589

Drago, Franklin J., Pres.--Bison Canning Co., Inc., Angola, NY; *U.S. Private*, pg. 468

Draheim, Edward R., Chief Exec. Officer--Faultless Caster, Evansville, IN; *Int'l*, pg. 473

Drain, Ted, Gen. Mgr.--Washington Manufacturing Company, Inc., Washington, IA; *U.S. Public*, pg. 612

Drainer, Terry, Plant Mgr.--Ropak Central Inc., Elk Grove Village, IL; *Int'l*, pg. 811

Draisbach, Walter H., Joint Acting Pres.--Dresdner Bank Luxembourg S.A., Luxembourg, Luxembourg; *Int'l*, pg. 419

Draisma, H., Mgr.--Laporte Absorbents-Holland, Raamsdonksveer, Netherlands; *Int'l*, pg. 803

Drake, Edward, Pres.--Designers Knitting Mills, New York, NY; *U.S. Public*, pg. 778

Drake, John E., Pres.--Crest Ridge Homes, Inc., Breckenridge, TX; *U.S. Public*, pg. 333

Drake, Michael, Chief Oper. Officer--Analogic Ltd., White Waltham, United Kingdom; *U.S. Public*, pg. 109

Drake, Robert, Base Mgr.--Mercury Air Center, Atlanta, GA; *U.S. Public*, pg. 1093

Drake, Robin A., Mng. Dir.--Derby Industries (Pty.) Ltd., Sandton, South Africa; *Int'l*, pg. 394

Dralle, Robert, Mgr.--General Employment Enterprises, Inc., Indianapolis, IN; *U.S. Public*, pg. 714

Draney, Robert, Chm. Bd.--Entertainment Partners, Burbank, CA; *U.S. Private*, pg. 554

Dranginis, Frank G., Pres.--Cigna Capital Brokerage, Inc., Bloomfield, CT; *U.S. Public*, pg. 357

Drango, B.F., Branch Mgr.--CHEMCENTRAL/Spokane, Spokane, WA; *U.S. Private*, pg. 232

Dransart, G., Plant Mgr.--Saint Marcellin Factory, Saint-Marcellin-en-Forez, France; *Int'l*, pg. 894

Dransfield, Jim, V.P.--AGRA Earth & Environmental, Inc., Kirkland, WA; *Int'l*, pg. 31

Draper, E. Linn, Jr., Dr., Chm. Bd., Pres. & Chief Exec. Officer--American Electric Power Service Corp., Columbus, OH; *U.S. Public*, pg. 72

Draper, James, Plant Mgr.--Huls America Inc., South Holland, IL; *Int'l*, pg. 1455

Draper, Michael, Pres.--Sauer-Sundstrand Company, Ames, IA; *Int'l*, pg. 1198

Draper, Paul, Chm. Bd.--Ridge Vineyards Inc., Cupertino, CA; *Int'l*, pg. 1013

Draper, Thomas F., V.P.--Wellman Wool Div., Johnsonville, SC; *U.S. Public*, pg. 1753

Draude, Rich, Div. Mgr.--Transilwrap Company, Inc., Santa Fe Springs, CA; *U.S. Private*, pg. 1097

Dravail, Michael, Dir. Gen.--Lux International S.A., Evry, France; *Int'l*, pg. 993

Draves, Craig, V.P. & Gen. Mgr.--IMI Cornelius, Inc. (IA), Mason City, IA; *Int'l*, pg. 646

Drayss, Ernst-Ludwig, Mng. Dir.--Deutsche Asset Management G.m.b.H., Frankfurt/Main, Germany; *Int'l*, pg. 402

Drayton, Edward R., III, Gen. Mgr.--Sonoco Forest Products Division, Hartsville, SC; *U.S. Public*, pg. 1486

Drazin, Avrum I., Pres.--Canlyte Incorporated, Lachine, Canada; *U.S. Public*, pg. 730

Dreblow, Lutz, Area Sls.--Analog Devices GMBH - Technisches Buero Nord, Buchholz, Germany; *U.S. Public*, pg. 108

Drechsel, James, Pres.--Atlas Tag & Label Inc., Neenah, WI; *U.S. Private*, pg. 145

Dreher, John A., Pres.--Nooter Construction Co., Saint Louis, MO; *U.S. Private*, pg. 801

Drennan, Robert, Pres.--Unichema U.S.A., Chicago, IL; *Int'l*, pg. 1436

Dresnick, Stephen J., M.D., Pres. & Chief Exec. Officer--Sterling Healthcare Group, Inc., Miami, FL; *U.S. Public*, pg. 608

Dresselhaus, Paul, V.P. & Mng. Exec.--Northern Trust Bank of Florida, N.A., Saint Petersburg, FL; *U.S. Public*, pg. 1197

Drew, Bill, V.P. & Gen. Mgr.--Time Products, Inc., Atlanta, GA; *U.S. Private*, pg. 1079

Drew, Bruce, Gen. Mgr.--Rhone-Poulenc Rorer Ltd., West Malling, United Kingdom; *Int'l*, pg. 1110

Drew, Ernest, Grp. Pres.--Hoechst Specialty Chemicals Group, Somerville, NJ; *Int'l*, pg. 624

Drew, Richard J., Pres.--Aspen Laboratories, Inc., Englewood, CO; *U.S. Public*, pg. 431

Drew, Robert, Pres.--Lockheed Martin Fairchild Imaging Sensors, Milpitas, CA; *U.S. Public*, pg. 1008

Drewry, John T., Pres.--Advanced Marine Enterprises, Inc., Arlington, VA; *U.S. Public*, pg. 1182

Dreyezhner, John, Mgr.-Regional--Alimak Elevator Company, Glenview, IL; *U.S. Private*, pg. 34

Dreyfus-Cloarec, Claire, Chief Oper. Officer--Serese (Service de Restauration du Sud Est), Paris, France; *Int'l*, pg. 560

Dreyfus, Paul, Pres.--Somfy S.A., Cluses, France; *Int'l*, pg. 376

Dreyfuss, Ted, Sr. Officer--The Chase Manhattan Trust Corporation Limited, Santiago, Chile; *U.S. Public*, pg. 341

Driesens, Doeke, Mng. Dir.--Iggesund Paper & Board Service B.V., Maarssen, Netherlands; *Int'l*, pg. 886

Driesse, Henry J., Pres. & Gen. mgr.--ITT Avionics Division, Clifton, NJ; *U.S. Public*, pg. 859

Driessen, A.J., Pres.--Wavin Bv, Zwolle, Netherlands; *Int'l*, pg. 1135

Driggers, Gary, Pres. & Chief Oper. Officer--Midcoast Aviation, Inc., Saint Louis, MO; *U.S. Private*, pg. 959

Driscoll, David W., Reg. V.P.--RLI Southeast Regional Office, Alpharetta, GA; *U.S. Public*, pg. 1356

Driscoll, Joe Ross, Warden--Cleveland Pre-Release Center, Cleveland, TX; *U.S. Public*, pg. 450

Driscoll, Mike, Chief Exec. Officer--IPC Technologies, Inc., Austin, TX; *Int'l*, pg. 651

Driscoll, Susan, Pres.--Worth Publisher Inc., New York, NY; *Int'l*, pg. 1479

Driscoll, Walter, Mng. Dir.--DYWIDAG Systems International, USA, Inc., Baltimore, MD; *Int'l*, pg. 424

Driscoll, William, Gen. Mgr.--Tremont Nail Co., Wareham, MA; *U.S. Private*, pg. 718

Driskell, Joe R., Administrator--Liberty County Jail/Juvenile Center, Liberty, TX; *U.S. Public*, pg. 450

Driven, Michael, Mng. Dir.--Avnet Access Ltd., Letchworth, United Kingdom; *U.S. Public*, pg. 155

Driver, Adrian, Pres.--CSR Central, Houston, TX; *Int'l*, pg. 245

Driver, Frank L. IV, Pres.--Driver-Harris Alloys, Inc., Harrison, NJ; *U.S. Public*, pg. 530

Driver, Frank L., IV, Mng. Dir.--Irish Driver-Harris Co., Ltd., Walkinstown, Ireland; *U.S. Public*, pg. 530

Driver, Philip L., Pres.--Berkley Care Network, Inc., Greensboro, NC; *U.S. Public*, pg. 216

Droege, Arthur, Pres.--Oilfree Air Division, Wilrijk, Belgium; *Int'l*, pg. 96

Drohan, Gregory J., Pres.--Carter Products, Canada, Mississauga, Canada; *U.S. Public*, pg. 310

Droin, Michel, Reg. Pres.--Melitta Societe de Distribution Bentz & Cie, Paris, France; *Int'l*, pg. 857

Drolet, Claude, Pres.--National Bearings Limited, Montreal, Canada; *Int'l*, pg. 1485

Drolet, Gerry, Mng. Dir.--Barringer Asia-Pacific, Kuala Lumper, Malaysia; *U.S. Public*, pg. 192

Drometer, W.G., V.P.--High Proformance Industrial Doors, Lawrenceville, GA; *U.S. Public*, pg. 36

Dronsfield, K., Chief Oper. Officer--AD Plastics Ltd., Blackpool, United Kingdom; *U.S. Public*, pg. 499

Drook, Garry G., Pres.--Ameritech Publishing, Inc., Troy, MI; *U.S. Public*, pg. 98

Drossaert, Jacques, Chief Exec. Officer--PanEuroLife, Luxembourg, Luxembourg; *Int'l*, pg. 323

Drost, W., Div. Pres.--Sun Ray Products, Inc., Miami, FL; *Int'l*, pg. 752

Drouillard, Neil R., Pres. & Chief Exec. Officer--F/N Group, Inc., Oak Park, MI; *U.S. Public*, pg. 84

Drouilly, B., Chief Oper. Officer--Thermo Electric S.A., Limiel Brevannes, France; *U.S. Private*, pg. 1080

Droz, Henry, Pres.--WEA Corp., Burbank, CA; *U.S. Public*, pg. 1612

Drozd, Andrew, Gen. Mgr.--Miller Brands, Inc., Portland, OR; *U.S. Public*, pg. 1289

Drucker, George, Gen. Mgr. & Dir., Events Worldwide--Edelman Worldwide, Inc., Los Angeles, CA; U.S. Private, pg. 362
Drucker, Jean, Chm. & Chief Exec. Officer--M6, Paris, France; Int'l, pg. 561
Drucker, Jean, Chm.--Serie Club, Paris, France; Int'l, pg. 562
Drucker, Martin, V.P.-Sls.--Nu Horizons International Corp., Amityville, NY; U.S. Public, pg. 1205
Druehl, Bradley P., Pres.--HRH Insurance Services of Northern California, Inc., San Rafael, CA; U.S. Public, pg. 827
Drueppel, Don, Gen. Mgr.--Henningsen Foods, Inc., David City, NE; Int'l, pg. 1074
Druggs, M., Sec.--Oerlikon Buhrle USA, Inc., New York, NY; Int'l, pg. 998
Druitt, R.J., Mng. Dir.--Queensland Alumina Limited, Brisbane, Australia; Int'l, pg. 52
Druitt, R.J., Mng. Dir.--Queensland Alumina Limited, Brisbane, Australia; U.S. Public, pg. 1063
Drum, James R., Grp. V.P.-Systems Furniture--The HON Co. Systems Furniture Plant, Muscatine, IA; U.S. Public, pg. 772
Drum, Robert P., Pres.--Fleet Services Corp., Providence, RI; U.S. Public, pg. 650
Drumgool, James E., Pres.--Martin Marietta International, Inc., Bethesda, MD; U.S. Public, pg. 1009
Drumm, Curtis, Pres.--Monarch Ware, Inc., Algoma, WI; U.S. Private, pg. 735
Drumm, Gerard F., Mng. Dir.--ITW Magnaflux Limited, Swindon, United Kingdom; U.S. Public, pg. 868
Drumm, Milton, V.P.-Fin.--Spartan Showcase, Inc., Union, MO; U.S. Private, pg. 904
Drumm, Wesley, Pres.--Nesco Ameican Harvest Inc., Chaska, MN; U.S. Private, pg. 735
Drummond, Clif, Pres. & Chief Exec. Officer--Parker Kinetic Designs, Austin, TX; U.S. Public, pg. 1259
Drummond, Jere A., Pres. & Chief Exec. Officer--BellSouth Telecommunications, Inc., Atlanta, GA; U.S. Public, pg. 209
Drummond, Jim, Dir.-Mktg.--Hitachi Home Electronics (America) Inc., Norcross, GA; Int'l, pg. 622
Drummond, Robert J., Pres. & Chief Exec. Officer--Epsilon, Burlington, MA; U.S. Public, pg. 74
Drummond, W.T., Chief Exec. Officer--Linhas Corrente Ltda., Ipiranga, Brazil; Int'l, pg. 301
Drury, David, Chm. Bd. & Chief Exec. Officer--Principal Mutual Life Insurance Co., Des Moines, IA; U.S. Private, pg. 886
Druse, Loise, Pres.--Bristol-Myers S.A.E., Madrid, Spain; U.S. Public, pg. 255
Dryburg, Doug, Pres.--Izod, New York, NY; U.S. Public, pg. 1292
Dryburgh, R.H.R., Pres. & Chief Exec. Officer--Jannock Steel Fabricating Company, Oakville, Canada; Int'l, pg. 698
Dryburgh, R.H.R., Pres.--Jenisys Engineered Products, Oakville, Canada; Int'l, pg. 698
Dryburgh, R.H.R., Pres.--Jenisys Engineered Products, Inc., Louisville, KY; Int'l, pg. 698
Dryden, Robert C., Chm. Bd.--Caterpillar Industrial Products, Inc., Peoria, IL; U.S. Public, pg. 316
Dryden, Trip, Pres.--Dryden Oil of New England, Worcester, MA; Int'l, pg. 235
Drysdale, J. Keith, Gen. Mgr.--AMP of Great Britain Limited, Stanmore, United Kingdom; U.S. Public, pg. 9
Drysdale, Robert H., Pres.--Crestar Securities Corporation, Richmond, VA; U.S. Public, pg. 458
Drysdale, Robert H., Chm. Bd. & Pres.--PNC Securities Corp., Pittsburgh, PA; U.S. Public, pg. 1244
du Bois, G.B., Mng. Dir.--Spadel SA, Brussels, Belgium; Int'l, pg. 1287
Du Bois, Willy, Rep.--Banque Commerciale Zairoise, Johannesburg, South Africa; Int'l, pg. 547
du Boullay, E., Chief Exec. Officer--Zurich Compagnie d'assurances sur la vie, Paris, France; Int'l, pg. 1529
du Boullay, E., Chief Exec. Officer--Zurich Epargne, Paris, France; Int'l, pg. 1531
du Boullay, E., Chief Exec. Officer--Zurich International (France) S.A., Paris, France; Int'l, pg. 1532
Du Buc, Stephano, Chief Oper. Officer--Allright Parking Washington, Inc., Washington, DC; U.S. Private, pg. 43
du Chatelier, Bernard, Pres.--Cyanamid Iberica, S.A., Madrid, Spain; U.S. Public, pg. 81
du Columbier, Xavier, Chief Oper. Officer--Rhone-Poulenc Kimyevi Maddeler Ltd., Istanbul, Turkey; Int'l, pg. 1113
du Laney, Chris, Exec. Dir.--QualMed Plans for Health-Washington, Bellevue, WA; U.S. Public, pg. 678
Du Peloux, Cyrille, Pres. & Dir. Gen.--Multivision, Paris, France; Int'l, pg. 561
du Toit, J.S., Mgr.-Mktg.--Sasol Phenolics, Rosebank, South Africa; Int'l, pg. 1196
Du, W.J., Gen. Mgr.--Wrigley Chewing Gum Company Ltd., Guangzhou, China; U.S. Public, pg. 1781
Duarte, Decio, Chief Oper. Officer--Perstorp do Brasil Industria e Comercio Ltda.-Div. Chemitec, Sao Bernardo do Campo, Brazil; Int'l, pg. 1037
Duarte, Gilberto, Jr., Pres.--Inktel Marketing, Miami, FL; U.S. Private, pg. 101
Duarte, Janie, Mgr.-Credit--Jones Financial Services, McAllen, TX; U.S. Private, pg. 596
Duarte, Valentine, Pres.--Jacuzzi do Brasil, Itu, Brazil; U.S. Public, pg. 1684
Duato, Joaquin, Gen. Mgr.--Janssen-Cilag S.p.A., Milan, Italy; U.S. Public, pg. 929
Duban, John, Acct. Supvr.--Louis London Dallas, Dallas, TX; U.S. Private, pg. 674
Dubau, Jean-Jacques, Chief Oper. Officer--Rowenta Italia S.p.A., Milan, Italy; Int'l, pg. 569
Dubault, Pierre, Mng. Dir.--Programmes Marketing Annuaires (PMA), Paris, France; U.S. Private, pg. 1065
Dubay, Eugene, Pres.--Kansas Gas Service, Overland Park, KS; U.S. Public, pg. 1226
Dubbeld, Peter, Mgr.--H. Albert de Bary & Co. N.V. (Rotterdam), Rotterdam, Netherlands; Int'l, pg. 404
Dubbeling, Ph., Mng. Dir.--P.T. Ballast Indonesia Construction, Jakarta, Indonesia; Int'l, pg. 134
Dube, Jean-Marie, Pres.--Willis Corroon Aerospace of Canada Ltd., Montreal, Canada; Int'l, pg. 1509
Dube, Roland, Gen. Mgr.--Groendyk, Inc., Buchanan, VA; U.S. Private, pg. 56
Dubes, Michael J., Pres. & Chief Exec. Officer--Northern Life Insurance Company, Seattle, WA; U.S. Public, pg. 1375
Dubicki, Norm, Plant Supervisor--Automatic Metal Blanking, Inc., Sparrows Point, MD; U.S. Private, pg. 300
Dubiel, Robert S., Pres. & Chief Exec. Officer--Cobra Golf Incorporated, Carlsbad, CA; U.S. Public, pg. 675
Dubin, Dan, Chief Exec. Officer--Penguin Air Conditioning Corp., Brooklyn, NY; U.S. Public, pg. 572
Dubin, Leslie, Publisher--Diversion, New York, NY; U.S. Private, pg. 516
Dublin, Steve, Chief Oper. Officer--Major Pharmaceuticals, Murray, KY; U.S. Private, pg. 475
DuBois, Christian, Chm. Bd.--Castorama Italia, Bollate, Italy; Int'l, pg. 276
Dubois, Colette, Gen. Mgr.-Sls. & Mktg./France, Switzerland, Benelux & Africa--Utell International-France, Paris, France; Int'l, pg. 1098
DuBois, Gonzague, Exec. Dir.--Societe Civile Immobiliere, Lesquin, France; Int'l, pg. 275
Dubois, Lieven, Sr. Tech. Engr.--Gensym B.V., Leiden, Netherlands; U.S. Public, pg. 731
Dubois, Marcel, Gen. Mgr.--Altra Marine Products, Inc., Princeville, Canada; U.S. Private, pg. 479
DuBose, Terry, Chm. Bd., Pres. & Chief Exec. Officer--SouthTrust Bank of Northwest Florida, Marianna, FL; U.S. Public, pg. 1492
Dubout, Louis, Gen. Mgr.--Service Genetiques S.A.R.L., Auxonne, France; U.S. Public, pg. 1299
Dubow, Craig, Pres. & Gen. Mgr.--WXIA-TV, Atlanta, GA; U.S. Public, pg. 702
Dubow, Phil, Pres.--Empire Clothing, Kewanee, IL; U.S. Private, pg. 387
Dubray, Srew, Gen. Mgr.--Pacific Heater Corporation, Pacific, MO; U.S. Private, pg. 1153
Dubrovolsky, Pavel, Gen. Mgr.--Dentsply Stomadent, Moscow, Russia; U.S. Public, pg. 500
Dubuke, Larry, Chief Oper. Officer--Web Graphics, Inc., Glens Falls, NY; U.S. Public, pg. 89
Duca, John, Gen. Mgr.--Los Angeles Dealers Auto Auctions, Rosemead, CA; U.S. Private, pg. 282
Ducas, Don, Mgr.--Anixter Montreal, Lachine, Canada; U.S. Public, pg. 115
Duchange, Jean-Francois, Gen. Mgr.--Canadian Imperial Bank of Commerce (International) S.A., Paris, France; Int'l, pg. 257
Ducharme, Alain, Gen. Mgr.--Cascades Dominion Inc., Brantford, Canada; Int'l, pg. 273
Duchaussoy, Elisabeth, Gen. Mgr.--Unicom, Rennes, France; Int'l, pg. 601
Ducher, H.P., Chief Exec. Officer--Getranke-Dienst AG, Dietikon, Switzerland; Int'l, pg. 479
Duchman, Mendel, Pres.--Allou Personal Care Corp., Saugus, CA; U.S. Public, pg. 55
Duckert, Jan, Mng. Dir.--Wibroe, Duckert & Partners, Copenhagen, Denmark; U.S. Private, pg. 678
Duckworth, Gary, Pres. & Gen. Mgr.--Outdoor Systems, Inc. of Northern California, Berkeley, CA; U.S. Public, pg. 1235
Duclos, Brenda, Branch Mgr.--Downey Savings & Loan Association, F.A., Elk Grove, CA; U.S. Public, pg. 526
Ducos, Georges, Mng. Dir.--Siebret, Redon, France; Int'l, pg. 192
DuCoty, Chuck, V.P. & Gen. Mgr.--WISN-AM, Milwaukee, WI; U.S. Public, pg. 1418
DuCoty, Chuck, V.P. & Gen. Mgr.--WLTQ-FM, Milwaukee, WI; U.S. Public, pg. 1418
Ducret, Daniel, Chief Oper. Officer--Rhone-Poulenc Senegal-SSPT, Dakar, Senegal; Int'l, pg. 1114
Duda, D., Pres.--Valley Onions, McAllen, TX; U.S. Private, pg. 344
Duda, Joseph A., Pres.--The Viera Company, Melbourne, FL; U.S. Private, pg. 344
Dudas, Nicholas, Pres.--Klockner-Moeller Corp., Franklin, MA; Int'l, pg. 736
Duddingston, Charles N., Sr., Mgr.--Piper Jaffray Inc., Bloomington, MN; U.S. Public, pg. 1301
Duddy, John, Sr. V.P. & Gen. Mgr.--Directory Services Group, Cleveland, OH; U.S. Private, pg. 667
Duderstadt, Stefan, Chief Oper. Officer--Dresdner Bank AG, London, United Kingdom; Int'l, pg. 419
Duderstaedt, Hans, Mng. Dir.--Wuestenrot Lebensversicherungs-AG, Ludwigsburg, Germany; Int'l, pg. 1514
Dudik, J. Robert, Pres.-Dental Div.--Allied Diagnostic Imaging Resources, Inc., Norcross, GA; U.S. Public, pg. 282
Dudley, Charles, Pres.--NationsBank of Arkansas, Little Rock, AR; U.S. Public, pg. 1164
Dudley, Charles B., III, Chm. & Pres.--NationsBank of Tennessee, Memphis, TN; U.S. Public, pg. 1165
Dudley, Ernie, Sls. Mgr.--Arrow/Schweber Electronics, Cedar Rapids, IA; U.S. Public, pg. 134
Dudley, Glenn, Mng. Dir.--Metal Manufactures Limited, Sydney, Australia; Int'l, pg. 120
Dudot, Gilles, Gen. Mgr.--Habitat International, Le Pecq, France; Int'l, pg. 659
Dudson, Eric C., Gen. Mgr.--Cayeli Bakir Isletmeleri, Cayeli, Turkey; Int'l, pg. 862
Dueck, Ernie, V.P. & Gen. Mgr.--Fleet Industries, Fort Erie, Canada; Int'l, pg. 829
Dueffert, Gregory, Pres. & Treas.--Lincoln Industries, Inc., Boonville, IN; U.S. Private, pg. 1207
Dueholm, John, Mng. Dir.--ISS Rengoringsservice, Copenhagen, Denmark; Int'l, pg. 656
Duenas, Arthur M., V.P. & Div. Mgr.--Bindley Western, Southern California Division, San Dimas, CA; U.S. Public, pg. 229
Duerden, John, Chm. Bd., Pres. & Chief Exec. Officer--Dictaphone Corp., Stratford, CT; U.S. Private, pg. 1045
Duerk, Barry S., Pres.--Beechwood Insurance Agency, Inc., Chatham, NJ; U.S. Public, pg. 1528
Dueser, F. Scott, Pres. & Chief Exec. Officer--First National Bank of Abilene, Abilene, TX; U.S. Public, pg. 633
Dueser, Fred F., Chief Exec. Officer--Breck Operating Corp., Breckenridge, TX; U.S. Private, pg. 1037
Duff, Andrew S., Pres. & Chief Oper. Officer--Piper Jaffray, Inc., Minneapolis, MN; U.S. Public, pg. 1303
Duff, Charles B., Chief Exec. Officer--Security Lawn & Garden Co., Phoenix, AZ; U.S. Private, pg. 397
Duff, Dennis, Pres.--DSM Sheffield Plastics, Sheffield, MA; Int'l, pg. 354
Duff, Frank F. Jr., V.P. & Gen. Mgr.--AmeriSource-Chattanooga Div., Chattanooga, TN; U.S. Public, pg. 97
Duff, Jim, Editor--On Track, Charlotte, NC; U.S. Private, pg. 19
Duff, Philip N., Pres. & Chief Exec. Officer--Van Kampen/American Capital Inc., Oak Brook Terrace, IL; U.S. Public, pg. 1132
Duff, Sam, Pres.--Amtech Lighting Services Co., South El Monte, CA; U.S. Public, pg. 2
Duffin, Iain, Pres.--ITT Cannon, Santa Ana, CA; U.S. Public, pg. 859
Dufft, Klaus, Dir.--Van Leer Verpackungen GmbH, Cologne, Germany; Int'l, pg. 1147
Duffy, B.C., Mng. Dir.--Guinness Northern Ireland Limited, Belfast, United Kingdom; Int'l, pg. 412
Duffy, Bill, Chief Oper. Officer & Exec. V.P.--Barnes & Noble Direct, Rockleigh, NJ; U.S. Public, pg. 189
Duffy, E. Patrick, Pres.--Bowater Coated Paper & Pulp Div., Catawba, SC; U.S. Public, pg. 248
Duffy, Gary, Mng. Dir.--Power Conversion Europe, Youghal, Ireland; U.S. Public, pg. 422
Duffy, Kevin, Head-Bus. Devel./Continental Europe--Bank of Ireland Asset Management, Frankfurt/Main, Germany; Int'l, pg. 153
Duffy, Marty, Pres.--Concrete Service Co., Fayetteville, NC; Int'l, pg. 166
Duffy, Philip, Gen. Mgr.--Suntester (Australia) Pty. Ltd., Seven Hills, Australia; U.S. Public, pg. 1481
Duffy, Roger G., Pres.--Manchester Tool Company, Akron, OH; U.S. Public, pg. 617
Duffy, S., Mgr.--Kodak Limited-Chemical Division, Liverpool, United Kingdom; U.S. Public, pg. 553
Duffy, Steven F., Mgr.-Property & Casualty Claims--Willis Corroon Administrative Services Corporation, Bettendorf, IA; Int'l, pg. 1504
Duffy, Timothy B., Mng. Dir. & Gen. Mgr.--PictureTel International Corporation-Europe/Middle East/Africa, Slough, United Kingdom; U.S. Public, pg. 1295
Dufour, Bruce, Pres. & Gen. Mgr.--Kysor Cooling Systems, Cadillac, MI; U.S. Public, pg. 968
Dufour, Guy, Mng. Dir.--Habitat France SA, Orgeval, France; Int'l, pg. 659
Dufour, Jacques-Henry, Chief Exec. Officer--Messier S.A., Paris, France; Int'l, pg. 1166
DuFour, Mr., Chm. Bd.--GEC Alsthom-Intermagnetics S.A., Belfort, France; Int'l, pg. 56
DuFour, Mr., Chm. Bd.--GEC Alsthom-Intermagnetics S.A., Belfort, France; U.S. Public, pg. 894
Dufour, Robert M., Pres.--National Card Control, Inc., Crozier, VA; U.S. Public, pg. 321
Dufresne, Michel, Mgr.-Raglan Proj. & Quebec Nickel Exploration--Falconbridge Explorations, Rouyn-Noranda, Canada; Int'l, pg. 433
Dugan, D., Gen. Mgr.--Burns & Roe Industrial Services Company, Fairfax, VA; U.S. Private, pg. 187
Dugan, D.R., Pres.--American Finance Group, Inc., Boston, MA; U.S. Public, pg. 1241
Dugan, Frances, Pres.--Dugan & Meyers Construction Co., Cincinnati, OH; U.S. Private, pg. 345
Dugan, J., Chief Exec. Officer--Swiss Bank Corporation, Chicago, IL; Int'l, pg. 1329
Dugan, James A., Pres.--DeVRY Institute of Technology, Phoenix, AZ; U.S. Public, pg. 504
Dugan, Jerry, Gen. Mgr.--Hood Industries Inc., Bakersfield, CA; U.S. Private, pg. 215
Dugan, Michael, Pres.--Henredon Upholstery, High Point, NC; U.S. Private, pg. 432
Dugan, Michael K., Pres.--Henredon Furniture Industries, Inc., Morganton, NC; U.S. Private, pg. 432
Duggal, Arun, Sr. V.P. & Country Mgr.--Bank of America NT&SA, Tokyo, Japan; U.S. Public, pg. 182
Duggan, Edwin L., Sr., Pres.--Ace Iron & Metal Div., Dallas, TX; U.S. Private, pg. 345
Duggan, J., Pres.--NMB Precision Inc., Mississauga, Canada; Int'l, pg. 868
Duggan, Jackie, Pres.--Crankshaft Machine Group, Jackson, MI; U.S. Private, pg. 102
Duggan, Robert, Chief Oper. Officer--Louisiana Industries Div., Monroe, LA; U.S. Public, pg. 1585
Duggan, Robert, Gen. Mgr.--Louisiana Industries Div., Perry, LA; U.S. Public, pg. 1585
Dugger, Tom, Pres.--Firestone Tube Company, Russellville, AR; Int'l, pg. 214
Duggins, Dean, Supervisor-Property & Casualty Claims--Willis Corroon Administrative Services Corporation, Birmingham, AL; Int'l, pg. 1504
Duh, Leonard, Chief Oper. Officer--Electrolux (Far East) Ltd., Taipei, Taiwan; Int'l, pg. 444
Duhame, Janice, Sales Rep.--Singapore Airlines Ltd., Phoenix, AZ; Int'l, pg. 1374
Duhem, J.C., Gen. Mgr.--Generale Traiteur, Lyon, France; Int'l, pg. 380
Duhne, Jaap M., Mng. Dir.--Esselte Meto BV, Nieuwegein, Netherlands; Int'l, pg. 461
Duhnkrack, Thomas, Dr., Gen. Mgr.--Deutsche Bank AG (Osaka), Osaka, Japan; Int'l, pg. 404

Duhrkop, Klaus, Allianz Representative--Allianz AG (EU Representative Office), Brussels, Belgium; *Int'l*, pg. 59
Duignan, Brian W., Mng. Dir.-New Zealand--Moore Business Forms & Systems Ltd., Auckland, New Zealand; *Int'l*, pg. 889
Duke, Dwight, Acting Gen. Mgr.--Scientific-Atlanta Canada, Inc., Scarborough, Canada; *U.S. Public*, pg. 1443
Duke, Ellen, Gen. Mgr.--Bio Enterics Corporation, Carpinteria, CA; *U.S. Public*, pg. 873
Duke, Michael T., Pres.--Volvo Finance North America, Inc., Montvale, NJ; *Int'l*, pg. 1477
Dukes, William, Pres.--KDA/HEPY, P.C., Denver, CO; *U.S. Private*, pg. 503
Dukhaikh, M.A., Acting Div. Dir.--Al-Jubail Petrochemical Company, Tareet, Saudi Arabia; *U.S. Public*, pg. 601
Dukich, Joe, Mgr.-Property & Casualty Claims--Willis Corroon Administrative Services Corporation, Wichita, KS; *Int'l*, pg. 1504
Dulac, Cindy, Branch Mgr.--Zellerbach Division, Wenatchee, WA; *U.S. Public*, pg. 1076
Dulgeroglu, Erkan, Mng. Dir.--Ege Ferro Kimya Sanayi ve Ticarret, Istanbul, Turkey; *U.S. Public*, pg. 619
Dulin, Patrick, Gen. Mgr.--API Harowe, West Chester, PA; *U.S. Public*, pg. 90
Dulin, Patrick, Gen. Mgr.--Vernitron Controls Div., San Diego, CA; *U.S. Public*, pg. 158
Dulin, Patrick J., Gen. Mgr.--Magnet Controls Div., San Diego, CA; *U.S. Public*, pg. 157
Duling, Thomas, Mgr.-Sls.--Klockner-Moeller, Concord, CA; *Int'l*, pg. 736
Dulmes, Gary, Gen. Mgr.--Mainline Industrial Distributors, Inc., Milwaukee, WI; *U.S. Public*, pg. 123
Dumais, Michel E., Pres.--Securespace Inc., Beauport, Canada; *Int'l*, pg. 253
Dumas, Brad, Mfg. Mgr.--Cohart De Mexico, S.A. DE C.V., Tijuana, Mexico; *U.S. Public*, pg. 1749
Dumas, Guy, Pres.--Matra-Harris Semiconducteurs S.A., Nantes, France; *U.S. Public*, pg. 791
Dumas, Guy, Chief Oper. Officer--Matra Harris Semiconducteurs, Nantes, France; *Int'l*, pg. 793
Dumas, James, Branch Mgr.--Downey Savings & Loan Association, F.A., Carlsbad, CA; *U.S. Public*, pg. 526
Dumas, Russel, Admin.--Colony House Healthcare, Abington, MA; *U.S. Public*, pg. 1712
Dumay, Jean-Midul, Pres.--Coflexip & Services Inc., Houston, TX; *Int'l*, pg. 304
DuMee, Robert, Pres.--Quest International Fragrances Inc., Budd Lake, NJ; *Int'l*, pg. 1436
Dummigan, J. Patrick, Sr. V.P. & Gen. Mgr.--Ball Telecommunication Products Division, Broomfield, CO; *U.S. Public*, pg. 171
Dumont, Daniel, Pres. & Chief Oper. Officer--Joslyn Canada Inc., Lachine, Canada; *U.S. Public*, pg. 482
Dumont, Serge, Pres.- Greater China--Edelman Worldwide China, Beijing, China; *U.S. Private*, pg. 363
Dumortier, Michel, Gen. Mgr.--Tournai Local Head Office, Tournai, Belgium; *Int'l*, pg. 147
Dun, Richard H., Pres.--Transistor Devices Europe Ltd., Cork, Ireland; *U.S. Private*, pg. 1097
Dunagan, Rick D., Plant Mgr.--AC Rochester Division (Sao Paulo), Sao Paulo, Brazil; *U.S. Public*, pg. 721
Dunah, Richard E., Pres.--Precision Lamp, Inc., Cotati, CA; *U.S. Public*, pg. 856
Dunand, Bernard, Exec. Officer-Argentina--Carrefour Argentine S.A., Buenos Aires, Argentina; *Int'l*, pg. 272
Dunand, Yves, Chief Oper. Officer--GEKA, S.A., Chatenay-Malabry, France; *U.S. Public*, pg. 1722
Dunaway, Oscar, Branch Mgr.--Burns & Wilcox - Tampa Office, Tampa, FL; *U.S. Private*, pg. 610
Dunbar, Bill, Pres. & Chief Exec. Officer--CellularVision Canada Ltd., Vancouver, Canada; *Int'l*, pg. 1482
Dunbar, Donald, Plant Mgr.--Tulon de Mexico, S.A. de C.V., Guadalajara, Mexico; *U.S. Public*, pg. 594
Dunbar, Jim, Pres.--GSW Pump Company, Fergus, Canada; *Int'l*, pg. 538
Dunbar, Thomas E., Gen. Mgr.--Vermont American Canada, Inc., Mississauga, Canada; *U.S. Public*, pg. 578
Dunbar, William F., Pres. & Chief Oper. Officer--Allied Capital Corporation II, Washington, DC; *U.S. Public*, pg. 47
Duncan, Bill, Mng. Dir.--Amway of Australia Pty. Ltd., Castle Hill, Australia; *U.S. Private*, pg. 70
Duncan, D. F., Pres.--Toromont Process Systems Inc., Houston, TX; *Int'l*, pg. 1401
Duncan, D.F., Pres.--Toromont Process Systems, Calgary, Canada; *Int'l*, pg. 1400
Duncan, Dale, Pres. & Publisher--Great Lakes Media, Inc., Pontiac, MI; *U.S. Public*, pg. 513
Duncan, Dave, Pres.--Imprimerie Quebecor Canada, Woodbridge, Canada; *Int'l*, pg. 1077
Duncan, G., Mng. Dir.--Ferro (Thailand) Co. Ltd., Sara Buri, Thailand; *U.S. Public*, pg. 619
Duncan, George A., Mng. Dir.--Deltronicos de Matamoros S.A. de C.V., Mexico, Mexico; *U.S. Public*, pg. 721
Duncan, Gregory A., Pres. & Chief Exec. Officer--Citizens National Bank of Southern Pennsylvania, Greencastle, PA; *U.S. Public*, pg. 1542
Duncan, Jay, Pres.--Duncan & Hill Division, Niles, IL; *U.S. Public*, pg. 773
Duncan, Jeff, Chief Oper. Officer--Allright L.R., Inc., Little Rock, AR; *U.S. Private*, pg. 42
Duncan, Joe, Chief Oper. Officer--Lemons Waste Systems Inc., Dexter, MO; *U.S. Public*, pg. 49
Duncan, John A., V.P. & Gen. Mgr.--Glen Raven Mills, Inc.-Textured Mills Group, Glen Touch Div., Glen Raven, NC; *U.S. Private*, pg. 456
Duncan, Jon, Pres.--Birdair, Inc., Amherst, NY; *Int'l*, pg. 1348
Duncan, M. David, Pres.--Physicians Insurance Company of Indiana, Indianapolis, IN; *U.S. Public*, pg. 1080
Duncan, Mike, Mgr.-Division--Gould Paper Corporation-NJ, Edison, NJ; *U.S. Private*, pg. 467
Duncan, William A.M., Dr., Chm.--R.W. Johnson Pharmaceutical Research Institute, Raritan, NJ; *U.S. Public*, pg. 928
Duncan, William W., Jr., Pres. & Chief Exec. Officer--St. Michaels Bank, Saint Michaels, MD; *U.S. Public*, pg. 1089
Dundas, J.R., Pres. & Chief Exec. Officer--Canadian Roxy Petroleum Ltd., Calgary, Canada; *Int'l*, pg. 1492
Dundas, Joseph R., Pres. & Chief Exec. Officer--Westcoast Petroleum Ltd., Calgary, Canada; *Int'l*, pg. 1492
Dundon, Brian R., Pres.--Magnetek Motors & Generators, Saint Louis, MO; *U.S. Public*, pg. 1037
Dundon, Peter, Oper. Group Leader--Woodward-Clyde, Milton, Australia; *U.S. Public*, pg. 1657
Dunford, Robert A., Chm. Bd.--Great Lakes Power Inc., Toronto, Canada; *Int'l*, pg. 433
Dunford, Stanley, Pres.--Laidlaw Carriers Inc., Woodstock, Canada; *Int'l*, pg. 328
Dungate, D., Mng. Dir.--Shell UK Oil (Birmingham), Birmingham, United Kingdom; *Int'l*, pg. 1139
Dunham, Archie, Chief Exec. Officer--Conoco, Houston, TX; *U.S. Public*, pg. 531
Dunham, Duane R., Pres.--Bethlehem Steel-Sparrows Point Division, Sparrows Point, MD; *U.S. Public*, pg. 226
Dunham, Michael D., Chief Oper. Officer--EMS Central Regional Office (Corporate), Milwaukee, WI; *U.S. Public*, pg. 565
Dunkailo, Peter, Dir.-Tech.--Schuller Intl. Inc., Toledo, OH; *U.S. Public*, pg. 927
Dunlap, Angela O., Pres.-MCI Consumer Markets--MCI Telecommunications Corp., Washington, DC; *U.S. Public*, pg. 1024
Dunlap, Angela O., Pres.--MCI Mass Markets, Arlington, VA; *U.S. Public*, pg. 1024
Dunlap, Charles L., Pres.--Hawaiian Independent Refinery, Inc., Honolulu, HI; *Int'l*, pg. 225
Dunlap, Frederick C., Pres.--United HealthCare of Florida, Inc., Coral Gables, FL; *U.S. Public*, pg. 1678
Dunlap, Rex H., Pres.--Bank Building, Manchester, MO; *U.S. Private*, pg. 407
Dunlap, William H., Pres.--Ikon Office Solutions-North New England, Bedford, NH; *U.S. Public*, pg. 863
Dunlap, William H., Pres.--Ikon Office Solutions-North New England, Portland, ME; *U.S. Public*, pg. 864
Dunlop, G.D.S., Chm. Bd. & Mng. Dir.--P&O European Ferries Ltd., Dover, United Kingdom; *Int'l*, pg. 1033
Dunlop, Robert P., Pres.--Mutual Travel, Inc., Seattle, WA; *U.S. Public*, pg. 1742
Dunmire, Philip L., Pres.--First Wisconsin Trust Company of Florida, West Palm Beach, FL; *U.S. Public*, pg. 643
Dunmire, Ron, Pres.--Standard Havens, Kansas City, MO; *U.S. Public*, pg. 1365
Dunn, Bill, Mng. Dir.--BMC Software (Australia) Pty. Ltd., Hawthorn, Australia; *U.S. Public*, pg. 162
Dunn, Dennis G., Pres.--Pennsylvania National Bank, Pottsville, PA; *U.S. Public*, pg. 956
Dunn, G.D., Pres.--Willson Stationers, Mississauga, Canada; *Int'l*, pg. 1150
Dunn, G.J., V.P.--BP North America Petroleum Inc., Cleveland, OH; *Int'l*, pg. 220
Dunn, Gordon, Pres.--Transworld Systems, Inc., Rohnert Park, CA; *U.S. Public*, pg. 1667
Dunn, J.R., Pres.-Yeargin, Inc.--Raytheon Engineers & Constructors, Inc., Englewood, CO; *U.S. Public*, pg. 1366
Dunn, James W., Pres. & Chief Exec. Officer--Willis Corroon Corp. of Florida, Tampa, FL; *Int'l*, pg. 1505
Dunn, Jim, Gen. Mgr.--Wilsey Foods, Inc., Salem, OR; *Int'l*, pg. 879
Dunn, Jim, Pres.--Lockheed Martin Fairchild Systems, Syosset, NY; *U.S. Public*, pg. 1008
Dunn, Jim, Chm.--TPS Public Relations Ltd., London, United Kingdom; *Int'l*, pg. 1226
Dunn, Larry, Pres.--Elco Precision Stamping Div., Logansport, IN; *U.S. Public*, pg. 1590
Dunn, Peter, Mgr.--Tesa Reference Standards Div., Leicester, United Kingdom; *U.S. Public*, pg. 260
Dunn, Peter, Pres.--Componenta International Ltd., Manchester, United Kingdom; *Int'l*, pg. 1421
Dunn, Raymond, Pres.--Sunflower Carriers, York, NE; *U.S. Private*, pg. 289
Dunn, Raymond W., Pres.--Weir Floway Inc., Fresno, CA; *Int'l*, pg. 1489
Dunn, Stephen D., Pres., Chief Exec. Officer & Treas.--Dunn Reality, Inc., Kansas City, MO; *U.S. Private*, pg. 347
Dunn, Terrence P., Pres. & Chief Exec. Officer--J.E. Dunn Construction Co., Kansas City, MO; *U.S. Private*, pg. 347
Dunn, Thomas R., Chm. & Chief Oper. Officer--M & I First American Bank, Wausau, WI; *U.S. Public*, pg. 1050
Dunn, Tom, Reg. Mgr.--SMS-Atlanta, Atlanta, GA; *U.S. Public*, pg. 1463
Dunn, Tom, Reg. Mgr.--SMS-Nashville, Brentwood, TN; *U.S. Public*, pg. 1463
Dunn, W. Byron, Pres.--Lone Star Steel Company, Dallas, TX; *U.S. Public*, pg. 1012
Dunne, George, Pres.--Kohl & Madden Printing Ink Corp. Div., Fort Lee, NJ; *Int'l*, pg. 370
Dunne, Harry, Mng. Dir.--TFM, Middlesbrough, United Kingdom; *Int'l*, pg. 452
Dunne, Robert, Gen. Mgr.--Fluke Electronics Canada Inc., Mississauga, Canada; *U.S. Public*, pg. 659
Dunnet, Kenneth E., Joint Mng. Dir.--D.R. Johnston Group Pty. Ltd., Sydney, Australia; *U.S. Public*, pg. 429
Dunnigan, T. Kevin, Pres.--Thomas & Betts Caribe, Inc., Bayamon, PR; *U.S. Public*, pg. 1598
Dunning, Forest B., Mgr.--Piper Jaffray Inc., Sheridan, WY; *U.S. Public*, pg. 1302
Dunning, Forest B., Mgr.-Branch--Piper Jaffray Inc., Gillette, WY; *U.S. Public*, pg. 1303
Dunsworth, Robert A., Chief Oper. Officer--Lafarge Concrete Ltd., Vancouver, Canada; *Int'l*, pg. 789
Dunton, Tom, Country Mgr.--Standard Chartered Bank Australia Limited, Sydney, Australia; *Int'l*, pg. 1294
Dupin, Jean-Michel, Gen. Mgr.--Tektronix S.A., Les Ulis, France; *U.S. Public*, pg. 1568
Duplantis, Dan, Mgr.-Opers.--Raceland Raw Sugar Corp., Raceland, LA; *U.S. Private*, pg. 843
Dupont-Willemin, Albert-Louis, Chm.--Coop Geneve, Vernier, Switzerland; *Int'l*, pg. 329
Dupont, Bertrand, Chief Oper. Officer--SEB Developpement S.A., Ecueille, France; *Int'l*, pg. 568
Dupont, Charles, Chief Oper. Officer--Nouvelle Societe Victoria, Lausanne, Switzerland; *Int'l*, pg. 298
DuPont, F.I., Pres.& Chief Exec. Officer--SouthTrust Bank of Jacksonville, Jacksonville, FL; *U.S. Public*, pg. 1492
Dupont, Francis, Mng. Dir.--McCain Espana S.A. (Spain), Burgos, Spain; *Int'l*, pg. 850
Dupont, P., Chief Exec. Officer--Coverland S.A., Rueil-Malmaison, France; *Int'l*, pg. 1092
Dupont, Phillip A., Chief Oper. Officer--Emons Railroad Group, Inc., York, PA; *U.S. Public*, pg. 578
Dupont, Phillip A., Chief Oper. Officer--Emons Logistics Services Inc., York, PA; *U.S. Public*, pg. 578
Dupre, B., Chief Oper. Officer--Mead-Emballage S.A., Chateauroux, France; *U.S. Public*, pg. 1076
Dupre, Claude V., Mng. Dir.--Driver-Harris, S.A., Mantes-la-Jolie, France; *Int'l*, pg. 723
Dupree, Tom, Pres.--Flow-Quip Texas, Inc., Irving, TX; *U.S. Private*, pg. 162
Dupuy, J., Pres. & Mng. Dir.--Marchon France S.A., Saint Mihiel, France; *U.S. Public*, pg. 1580
Duquemin, Philip, Mng. Dir.--Gestetner Asia Pacific Limited, Saint Sampson, United Kingdom; *Int'l*, pg. 1114
Durame, Jean, Pres.--Credit Industriel de Normandie, Rouen, France; *Int'l*, pg. 564
Duran, Alvaro Bilbao, Pres.--Bilbao/Y&R, Asuncion, Paraguay; *U.S. Private*, pg. 1200
Durand, Alain, Chief Oper. Officer--Parfums Laura Ashley SA, Fribourg, Switzerland; *Int'l*, pg. 804
Durand, Bernard, Mng. Dir.--SKF Abidjan S.A.R.L., Abidjan, Cote d'Ivoire; *Int'l*, pg. 1158
Durand, Claude, Chief Oper. Officer--Librairie Artheme Fayard, Paris, France; *Int'l*, pg. 792
Durand, Emile, Chief Oper. Officer--Matra Electronique, Paris, France; *Int'l*, pg. 793
Durand, Gary, V.P.-Mfg.--Quebecor Printing Semline Inc., Braintree, MA; *Int'l*, pg. 1078
Durant, James E., Pres. & Chief Exec. Officer--Trautman & Shreve, Inc., Denver, CO; *U.S. Public*, pg. 572
Durant, Kenneth F., Pres.--CH2M Hill Industrial Design Corp., Portland, OR; *U.S. Private*, pg. 195
Durante, Raffaele, Pres.--Siemens S.p.A., Milan, Italy; *Int'l*, pg. 1248
Durante, Salvatore, V.P. & Gen. Mgr.--KVVU Broadcasting Corporation, Henderson, NV; *U.S. Public*, pg. 1094
Durbin, Denny, Admin.--Bay County Jail, Panama City, FL; *U.S. Public*, pg. 450
Durbin, William, Mgr.-Office--Woodward-Clyde, Saint Louis, MO; *U.S. Public*, pg. 1656
Durcan, Kelly, Mng. Dir.--Partners & Shevack Public Relations, New York, NY; *U.S. Private*, pg. 842
Durden, Hugh M., Pres.--Wachovia Corporate Services, Inc., Atlanta, GA; *U.S. Public*, pg. 1730
Duren, D. Ronald, Pres. & Chief Oper. Officer--Telecom Solutions, San Jose, CA; *U.S. Public*, pg. 1547
Durfee, Dr. Robert L., Pres.--GEOMET Technologies, Inc., Germantown, MD; *U.S. Public*, pg. 1717
Durham, Kenneth, Mgr.--Asbury Equipment, Roanoke, VA; *U.S. Private*, pg. 87
Durham, Larry K., Pres.--Durham Transportation Inc., Rosemead, CA; *U.S. Private*, pg. 348
Durham, Michael J., Pres. & Chief Exec. Officer--The SABRE Group Holdings, Inc., Fort Worth, TX; *U.S. Public*, pg. 10
Durham, Timothy S., Pres. & Chief Exec. Officer--Carpenter Industries, Inc., Richmond, IN; *U.S. Private*, pg. 215
Durhan, Michael D., Chm., Pres. & Chief Exec. Officer--SunTrust Bank, West Florida, Pensacola, FL; *U.S. Public*, pg. 1538
Durhein, Rich, Pres.--McHugh Software International, Waukesha, WI; *U.S. Private*, pg. 866
Durkee, Ed, Pres.--Accudyne Corporation, Janesville, WI; *U.S. Public*, pg. 47
Durling, Ricardo, Pres.--McDonald's Panama, Panama, Panama; *U.S. Public*, pg. 1069
Duroche, Mike, Gen. Mgr.--American Packaging Corporation, Columbus, WI; *U.S. Private*, pg. 60
Duroux, Axel, Pres.--RTL 2, Paris, France; *Int'l*, pg. 561
Durr, Jim, Mgr.-Mfg.--Bayley/Fan Group, Lebanon, IN; *Int'l*, pg. 1398
Durr, Jim, V.P. & Gen. Mgr.--Industrial Air Div., Lebanon, IN; *Int'l*, pg. 1398
Durrant, Monica, Mng. Dir.--Dynex Technologies Ltd. (U.K.), Billingshurst, United Kingdom; *U.S. Public*, pg. 1591
Durton, J., Gen. Mgr.--Baring Trustee (Guernsey) Ltd., Saint Peter Port, United Kingdom; *Int'l*, pg. 648
Dusa, Jerry A., Pres.--Eagle Technology, San Jose, CA; *U.S. Public*, pg. 1105
Dusek, Joe, V.P.--Opus South Construction Corporation, Tampa, FL; *U.S. Private*, pg. 818
Dusel, Henry F., V.P.--Crown Crafts Home Furnishings of Illinois, Inc., Chicago, IL; *U.S. Public*, pg. 465
Dusil, K.S., Gen. Mgr.--MOLY-COP Canada, Kamloops, Canada; *Int'l*, pg. 1300
Dussart, Marc, Pres.--MACtac Europe S.A., Soignies, Belgium; *U.S. Public*, pg. 210
Dussault, C., Pres. & Chief Oper. Officer--Le Groupe Commerce, Saint-Hyacinthe, Canada; *Int'l*, pg. 650
Dutcher, Charles, Gen. Mgr.--CONUS Communication Company Limited Partnership, Saint Paul, MN; *U.S. Private*, pg. 544
Duthoit, Stephane, Dir. Gen.--Charles River France S.A., Saint Aubin, France; *U.S. Public*, pg. 195
Dutilloy, Daniel, Gen. Mgr.--Johnson & Johnson S.A., Colombes, France; *U.S. Public*, pg. 931
Dutley, P., Chief Oper. Officer--Sunkist (Europe) S.A., Lausanne, Switzerland; *U.S. Private*, pg. 1053

Dutscher, Dominique, Mng. Dir.--Dominique Dutscher, S.A., Brumath, France; *U.S. Public*, pg. 448
Dutscher, Gerard, Plant Mgr.--Harrison Radiator Division, Donchery, France; *U.S. Public*, pg. 725
Dutta, R.K., Exec. Dir.--Assam Oil Division, Assam, India; *Int'l*, pg. 673
Dutton, Mitchell L., Gen. Mgr.--AST Bearings Division, Montville, NJ; *U.S. Public*, pg. 157
Duursma, W.S., Mng. Dir.--MSA Nederland B.V., Hoorn, Netherlands; *U.S. Public*, pg. 1115
Duvall, Stephen R., Dir.-Opers.--Techsonic Industries, Inc., Eufaula, AL; *U.S. Public*, pg. 1570
Duvall, William A., Chm. Bd. & Chief Exec. Officer--Bliss Manufacturing Company, Youngstown, OH; *U.S. Public*, pg. 771
Duvar, I.E.H., Chm. Bd. & Chief Exec. Officer--Maritime Telegraph & Telephone Company, Ltd., Halifax, Canada; *Int'l*, pg. 116
Duxbury, Robert, Dir. & Chief Oper. Officer--Hardings Machine Tools, Ltd., Exeter, United Kingdom; *U.S. Private*, pg. 502
Duyn, Rene, Mng. Dir.--Coastal (Rotterdam) B.V., Rotterdam, Netherlands; *U.S. Public*, pg. 390
Duyser, Peter A., Chief Exec. Officer--OCE-Australia Limited, Cheltenham, Australia; *Int'l*, pg. 994
Duyzer, C., Chief Oper. Officer--Hoogovens Aluminium Geveltechniek BV, Capelle aan den Ijssel, Netherlands; *Int'l*, pg. 753
Dvernberger, Nancy, Mgr.--DWF of Milwaukee, Inc., Milwaukee, WI; *U.S. Private*, pg. 326
Dvir, Dov, Gen. Mgr.--Medtronic World Trade Corp., Herzliyya, Israel; *U.S. Public*, pg. 1084
Dvoracek, Deane, V.P. & Gen. Mgr.--California Pretzel Company, San Leandro, CA; *U.S. Private*, pg. 434
Dvorak, E., Plant Mgr.--Mathews International, Sun City, CA; *U.S. Public*, pg. 1059
Dvorak, Petr, Gen. Mgr.--City Radio, Prague, Czech Republic; *Int'l*, pg. 561
Dwarshuis, Henk E., Gen. Mgr.--Ford Credit B.V., Amsterdam, Netherlands; *U.S. Public*, pg. 665
Dwight, John, V.P. & Gen. Mgr.--Wavetek Communications Div., Indianapolis, IN; *U.S. Private*, pg. 1155
Dwight, John K., Pres. & Sr. Portfolio Mgr.--Dwight Asset Management Company, Burlington, VT; *U.S. Public*, pg. 1673
Dworak, Peter, Mng. Dir.--Janssen/Cilag Pharmaceutica GmbH, Vienna, Austria; *U.S. Public*, pg. 929
Dworak, Peter, Dr., Mgr. Dir.--Janssen/Cilag G.m.b.H., Vienna, Austria; *U.S. Public*, pg. 929
Dworman, Alvin, Chm. Bd. & Pres.--Great Universal Capital Corp., New York, NY; *U.S. Private*, pg. 658
Dwyer, Bill, Reg. Mgr.--SMS-Dallas, Richardson, TX; *U.S. Public*, pg. 1463
Dwyer, Jerry, Res. Sls. Rep-Philadelphia--Singapore Airlines Ltd., Princeton, NJ; *Int'l*, pg. 1374
Dwyer, Kevin, Gen. Mgr.--An American Place, New York, NY; *U.S. Public*, pg. 130
Dwyer, M.A., Pres. & Chief Exec. Officer--Daubert Chemical Company, Inc., Chicago, IL; *U.S. Private*, pg. 313
Dwyer, Robert, Chief Oper. Officer--Production Management Corporation, Houston, TX; *U.S. Private*, pg. 889
Dwyer, T.P., Pres.--CG Projects, Inc., Philadelphia, PA; *U.S. Public*, pg. 432
Dwyer, W., V.P.-Opers.--Litton Solid State, Santa Clara, CA; *U.S. Public*, pg. 1003
Dwyre, Lauren, Fin. Dir.--Leo Burnett Warsaw SP.Z.O.O., Warsaw, Poland; *U.S. Private*, pg. 186
Dye, William G., Pres.--Air Cargo Equipment Corporation, Rancho Dominguez, CA; *U.S. Public*, pg. 1791
Dyer, Bruce, Pres.--BFD Productions, Inc., Las Vegas, NV; *U.S. Public*, pg. 1321
Dyer, Chris, Chief Oper. Officer--Rhone-Poulenc Danmark A/S, Soeborg, Denmark; *Int'l*, pg. 1112
Dyer, Cliff, Pres.--Merisel Latin America, Miami, FL; *U.S. Public*, pg. 1096
Dyer, M., Gen. Mgr.--Senior TIFT Pte. Ltd., Jurong, Singapore; *Int'l*, pg. 1223
Dyer, Max, V.P.-Opers.--E-Z Serve Convenience Stores, Inc.-Panama City Market, Panama City, FL; *U.S. Public*, pg. 540
Dyer, Robert W., Plant Mgr.--Engine Components Div., Kearney, NE; *U.S. Public*, pg. 557
Dyer, Tony, Dir.--Willis Corroon Scotland Limited, Aberdeen, United Kingdom; *Int'l*, pg. 1503
Dyess, R. Steve, Pres.--ALLTEL Mississippi, Inc., Florence, MS; *U.S. Public*, pg. 56
Dygert, Dave, Gen. Mgr.--Dygert Seating, Elkhart, IN; *U.S. Public*, pg. 654
Dyke, Frank, Pres.--Fourth Generation Technology Inc., La Jolla, CA; *U.S. Public*, pg. 1199
Dyke, Greg, Chief Exec. Officer--Pearson Television Ltd., Teddington, United Kingdom; *Int'l*, pg. 1026
Dyke, Robert W., Pres.--Acme Packaging Corporation, Riverdale, IL; *U.S. Public*, pg. 16
Dykema, John, Plant Mgr.--SASIB Packaging North America Inc.-Wrapper Division, De Pere, WI; *Int'l*, pg. 1194
Dykes, James, Chief Oper. Officer--IFC Non Wovens, Bound Brook, NJ; *U.S. Public*, pg. 1782
Dykgraaf, Steven, Gen. Mgr.--W. Braun Co., Dallas, TX; *U.S. Private*, pg. 166
Dykstra, J.D., Mng. Dir.--LASMO Mineraria SpA, Rome, Italy; *Int'l*, pg. 804
Dykstra, Tom, Chief Oper. Officer--EMS-Michigan, Novi, MI; *U.S. Public*, pg. 565
Dylor, Paul, Gen. Mgr.--Sensormatic A/S (Denmark), Herlev, Denmark; *U.S. Public*, pg. 1457
Dymond, Robert C., Pres.--Layne-Western Co., Inc., Mission Woods, KS; *U.S. Public*, pg. 981
Dynna, Harold, Plant Mgr.--Firestone Fibers & Textiles Company-Woodstock Plant, Woodstock, Canada; *Int'l*, pg. 214
Dyos, Brita C., Dir.--Skandia Advisory Company SA, Luxembourg, Luxembourg; *Int'l*, pg. 1258
Dyott, Stephen, Pres.--American Color Graphics, Brentwood, TN; *U.S. Public*, pg. 1132
Dyring, Henrik, Country Mgr.--Nielsen Marketing Research A/S, Copenhagen, Denmark; *U.S. Public*, pg. 1184
Dyrnes, J.H., Mng. Dir.--Uni-Cardan Norge A/S, Vestby, Norway; *Int'l*, pg. 536
Dyson, Marvin, Pres.--WGCI-AM/FM, Chicago, IL; *U.S. Public*, pg. 335
Dyson, Robert R., Chm. & Chief Exec. Officer--Burner Systems International, Inc., Chattanooga, TN; *U.S. Private*, pg. 351
Dyszynski, Adam, Country Mgr.--Heinz Polska Sp., Warsaw, Poland; *U.S. Public*, pg. 806
Dytor, G.W., Mng. Dir.--Boral (UK) Ltd., Hemel Hempstead, United Kingdom; *Int'l*, pg. 203
Dytrich, W., Mng. Dir.--GKN Service-Austria GmbH, Vienna, Austria; *Int'l*, pg. 536
Dziedzic, Tom, Gen. Mgr.--Flexmag Industries, Marietta, OH; *U.S. Public*, pg. 1420
Dziubek, Paul, Chief Oper. Officer--Fuji Securities Inc.-Chicago, Chicago, IL; *Int'l*, pg. 519
Dzuryachko, Thomas A., Pres.--United Concordia Companies Inc., Camp Hill, PA; *U.S. Private*, pg. 529
Each, Thomas C., Pres.--Chemifax, Santa Fe Springs, CA; *U.S. Private*, pg. 774
Eades, E.D.M., Pres.--ICI Polyester Polymer, Wilmington, DE; *Int'l*, pg. 664
Eady, Michele Jessie, Terminal Mgr.--Kintetsu World Express Inc., Atlanta, GA; *Int'l*, pg. 734
Eager, Tony, Publisher--Plastics News, Akron, OH; *U.S. Private*, pg. 285
Eagle, David A., Chm.--Ford Finance Company of Japan, Limited, Tokyo, Japan; *U.S. Public*, pg. 666
Eaker, Alan C., Pres.--GTE Alaska Incorporated, Anchorage, AK; *U.S. Public*, pg. 697
Eaker, Woody, Gen. Mgr.--M.D. Industries, Inc., Northbrook, IL; *U.S. Public*, pg. 352
Eakes, W. E., Pres.--N.C. Products Corp., Raleigh, NC; *Int'l*, pg. 242
Eakins, J. G., V.P.--Ecolab Canada, Mississauga, Canada; *U.S. Public*, pg. 562
Eales, John C., Mng. Dir.--McCormick Glentham (Pty), Midrand, South Africa; *U.S. Public*, pg. 1067
Eanes, Jr., Joseph C., Chm Bd.--Fidelity & Deposit Company of Maryland, Baltimore, MD; *Int'l*, pg. 1530
Earl, J.G.G., Dir. & Gen. Mgr.--Santa Fe Braun (U.K.) Ltd., Milton Keynes, United Kingdom; *Int'l*, pg. 765
Earl, Robert M., Pres. & Chief Oper. Officer--Earl Construction Company, West Sacramento, CA; *U.S. Private*, pg. 1051
Earle, Randolph A., Pres. & Gen. Mgr.--Mrs. Giles Country Kitchens, Inc., Lynchburg, VA; *U.S. Public*, pg. 596
Earley, Pat, Pres.--Ameritech Communications, Inc., Rosemont, IL; *U.S. Public*, pg. 98
Earlougher, R.C., Pres.--Pan Ocean Energy Company, Findlay, OH; *U.S. Public*, pg. 1662
Earls, Joseph F., Plant Mgr.--Lifesavers Plant, Hamilton, Canada; *U.S. Public*, pg. 812
Early, Jeffrey B., V.P. & Mng. Exec.--Northern Trust Bank of Texas, N.A., Houston, TX; *U.S. Public*, pg. 1197
Early, Kathy, V.P.--AT&T Business Communications Services, Bridgewater, NJ; *U.S. Public*, pg. 10
Early, Kathy, V.P.--AT&T Networked Commerce Services, Parsippany, NJ; *U.S. Public*, pg. 11
Earnheart, Aubrey, Pres. & Chief Exec. Officer--First State Bank, Brownsville, TN; *U.S. Public*, pg. 1669
Earwood, Dale C., Pres.--NorAm Field Services Corp., Shreveport, LA; *U.S. Public*, pg. 843
Easley, Dan, Pres.--Sunrise Medical Respiratory Products Division, Somerset, PA; *U.S. Public*, pg. 1536
Eason, Forrest K., V.P.-Sls.--Crown Cork & Seal, Southwest Div., Abilene, TX; *U.S. Public*, pg. 463
East, Charles, Pres. & Chief Exec. Officer--Regions Bank/Rockdale County, Conyers, GA; *U.S. Public*, pg. 1372
East, David, Mng. Dir.--Anixter UK, Colnbrook, United Kingdom; *U.S. Public*, pg. 116
East, F. Howard, Pres.--Bell Packaging Corporation-Marion Div., Marion, IN; *Int'l*, pg. 1066
East, Keith, Chief Oper. Officer--Allright Pensacola Parking, Pensacola, FL; *U.S. Private*, pg. 43
Easter, James, Gen. Mgr.--NAO, Spring, TX; *U.S. Private*, pg. 771
Easter, Rayford E., Pres.--CDI Engineering Group, Inc., Kingsport, TN; *U.S. Public*, pg. 277
Easterling, Jack, Chief Oper. Officer--CEGF (USA) Inc., Plant City, FL; *U.S. Public*, pg. 606
Eastham, Tom, Gen. Mgr.--Empire Cheese, Inc., Cuba, NY; *U.S. Private*, pg. 474
Eastin, Mark, III, Chm., Chief Exec. Officer & Pres.--Liberty National Bank of Western Kentucky, Hopkinsville, KY; *U.S. Public*, pg. 173
Eastlake, R.W., Pres.--Kaw Pipeline Co., Houston, TX; *U.S. Public*, pg. 1584
Eastlake, R.W., Pres.--Olympic Pipe Line Co., Dallas, TX; *U.S. Public*, pg. 1584
Eastly, Arthur C., Pres.--Canadian Forest Oil Ltd., Calgary, Canada; *U.S. Public*, pg. 670
Eastman, Michael, Publr.--Hollister Free Lance, Hollister, CA; *U.S. Private*, pg. 225
Easton, Harry M., Pres.--Berwind Coal Sales Company, Philadelphia, PA; *U.S. Private*, pg. 138
Easton, John, Mng. Dir.--Raybestos Reibtechnik, Leverkusen, Germany; *U.S. Public*, pg. 1364
Easton, John J., Pres.--Raybestos Products Co., Crawfordsville, IN; *U.S. Public*, pg. 1363
Easton, Robert G., Pres. & Chief Exec. Officer--Stockton Holdings Limited, Hamilton, Bermuda; *Int'l*, pg. 1010
Eastwood, S., Sr. Mng. Dir.--Scholl (Asia) Limited, Wan Chai, Hong Kong; *Int'l*, pg. 1209
Eastwood, Steve, Sr. Mng. Dir.--Scholl International (ANZ) Pty. Ltd., Dingley, Australia; *Int'l*, pg. 1209
Eatherley, P.C., Mng. Dir.--Tate & Lyle Specialty Sweeteners, Reading, United Kingdom; *Int'l*, pg. 1356
Eatock, William H., Gen. Mgr.--PCS Potash - Lanigan, Lanigan, Canada; *Int'l*, pg. 1064
Eaton, Charles, V.P.-Sls.--Shorewood Packaging Company of Illinois, Inc., Palatine, IL; *U.S. Public*, pg. 1468
Eaton, Edwin H., Jr., Mng. Dir.--Richardson-Vicks (Overseas) Finance N.V., Curacao, Netherlands Antilles; *U.S. Public*, pg. 1333
Eaton, F., Regional Chm.--Barratt Central, Halesowen, United Kingdom; *Int'l*, pg. 168
Eaton, Jerry, V.P. & Gen. Mgr.--KPIX-TV, San Francisco, CA; *U.S. Public*, pg. 275
Eaton, John, Gen. Mgr.--GCI Boston, Inc., Boston, MA; *U.S. Private*, pg. 470
Eaton, John, Gen. Mgr.--Hawkins Terminal I, Saint Paul, MN; *U.S. Public*, pg. 800
Eaton, John A., Pres.--Lockwood Kessler & Bartlett, Inc., Syosset, NY; *U.S. Public*, pg. 440
Eaton, John C., V.P. & Gen. Mgr.--The Mudge Paper Co., Hyattsville, MD; *U.S. Public*, pg. 902
Eaton, Max S., Mgr.--Piper Jaffray Inc., Bozeman, MT; *U.S. Public*, pg. 1301
Eaton, Maynard S., Mng. Dir.--Du Pont de Nemours (Nederland) B.V., Dordrecht, Netherlands; *U.S. Public*, pg. 532
Ebbers, Bernard J., Pres. & Chief Exec. Officer--LDDS WorldCom Inc., East Rutherford, NJ; *U.S. Public*, pg. 1779
Ebbert, William A., Chm. Bd. & Mng. Dir.--Vauxhall Motors Limited, Luton, United Kingdom; *U.S. Public*, pg. 724
Ebel, Dr. Claus, Co-Chief Oper. Officer--Modellkraftwerk Voelklingen GmbH, Saarbruecken, Germany; *Int'l*, pg. 1167
Ebel, Horst, Mng. Dir.--Media EMAP Verlag GmbH, Vienna, Austria; *Int'l*, pg. 451
Ebeling, Michael P., Gen. Mgr.--Ikon Office Solutions-Milwaukee, Pewaukee, WI; *U.S. Public*, pg. 863
Eben, Hans, Gen. Mgr.--Productos Gillette Chile Limitada, Santiago, Chile; *U.S. Public*, pg. 745
Ebenezer, Duke, Mng. Dir.--M4 Data Ltd., Camberley, United Kingdom; *U.S. Public*, pg. 1523
Eberhardt, U., Mng. Dir.--Swiss Bank Corporation, London, United Kingdom; *Int'l*, pg. 1330
Eberle, Robert W., Chm. Bd.--BMCA Insulation Products, Inc., Ontario, CA; *U.S. Private*, pg. 433
Eberle, Urban, V.P.--LGT Finanz Aktiengesellschaft, Vaduz, Liechtenstein; *Int'l*, pg. 809
Eberling, Jean Claude, Chief Oper. Officer--Osram S.A., Molsheim, France; *Int'l*, pg. 1244
Ebersole, George D., Pres.--Energy Absorption Systems, Inc., Chicago, IL; *U.S. Public*, pg. 1353
Ebersole, George D., Pres.--Spin-Cast Plastics, Inc., South Bend, IN; *U.S. Public*, pg. 1353
Ebert, Don E., Pres.--Roll Coater, Inc., Kingsbury, IN; *U.S. Public*, pg. 137
Ebert, Donald E., Pres.--Roll Coater, Inc., Greenfield, IN; *U.S. Public*, pg. 137
Ebert, Douglas, Pres. & Chief Exec. Officer--Michigan National Corporation, Farmington Hills, MI; *Int'l*, pg. 906
Ebert, Fred, Pres.--Kuehne & Nagel Inc., Jersey City, NJ; *Int'l*, pg. 763
Ebert, John H., Pres. & Chief Exec. Officer--M & I Bank South Central, Watertown, WI; *U.S. Public*, pg. 1050
Ebert, Larry, Pres.--Flowers Snack of Tennessee, Inc., Crossville, TN; *U.S. Public*, pg. 657
Ebert, Mike, Plant Mgr.--Safety-Kleen Oil Recovery Co., East Chicago, IN; *U.S. Public*, pg. 1426
Ebetino, Charles A., Jr., Pres. & Chief Oper. Officer--Simco, Inc., Columbus, OH; *U.S. Public*, pg. 72
Ebetino, Charles A., Jr., Pres. & Chief Oper. Officer--Blackhawk Coal Co., Salt Lake City, UT; *U.S. Public*, pg. 72
Ebetino, Charles A., Jr., Pres. & Chief Oper. Officer--Price River Coal Co., Inc., Fort Wayne, IN; *U.S. Public*, pg. 72
Ebetino, Charles A., Jr., Pres. & Chief Oper. Officer--Conesville Coal Preparation Co., Columbus, OH; *U.S. Public*, pg. 72
Ebetino, Charles A., Jr., Pres. & Chief Oper. Officer--Central Ohio Coal Co., Canton, OH; *U.S. Public*, pg. 73
Ebetino, Charles A., Jr., Pres. & Chief Oper. Officer--Southern Ohio Coal Co., Canton, OH; *U.S. Public*, pg. 73
Ebetino, Charles A., Jr., Pres. & Chief Oper. Officer--Windsor Coal Co., Canton, OH; *U.S. Public*, pg. 73
Ebker, Gerald W., V.P.--IBM Systems Integration Div., Bethesda, MD; *U.S. Public*, pg. 896
Ebner, Alan M., V.P. & Gen. Mgr.-Western Opers.--Raytheon Engineers & Constructors, Inc., Boston, MA; *U.S. Public*, pg. 1366
Ebright, John, Chief Acctg. Officer--IES Transportation, Inc., Cedar Rapids, IA; *U.S. Public*, pg. 855
Ebright, John, Chief Acctg. Officer--IES Investments Inc., Cedar Rapids, IA; *U.S. Public*, pg. 855
Ebright, John, Chief Acctg. Officer--Industrial Energy Applications, Cedar Rapids, IA; *U.S. Public*, pg. 855
Eby, Clifford C., Pres.--Barton-Aschman Associates, Inc., Evanston, IL; *U.S. Private*, pg. 841
Eccles, C., Mng. Dir.--Essilor Limited, Bristol, United Kingdom; *Int'l*, pg. 462
Eccleston, Wayne, Gen. Mgr.--Velvet Drive Transmissions, New Bedford, MA; *U.S. Public*, pg. 1370
Echevarria, Agatha, Gen. Mgr.--Finanz Charterhouse Iberica, SA, Madrid, Spain; *Int'l*, pg. 343
Echevarria, Guido, Mng. Dir.--NRG Distribution Corporation, Guaynabo, PR; *Int'l*, pg. 1115
Echolds, Mike, Pres.--Tropitone Furniture, Irvine, CA; *U.S. Private*, pg. 1105
Echols, James E., Pres.--Hohenberg Bros. Company, Memphis, TN; *U.S. Private*, pg. 210
Echols, Rebecca S., Pres. & Chief Exec. Officer--Regions Bank/Douglas County, Douglasville, GA; *U.S. Public*, pg. 1372
Echstein, H., Gen. Mgr.--Uta Finanz und Leasing, Kleinostheim, Germany; *Int'l*, pg. 651
Eck, Chuck, Gen. Mgr.--Minneapolis Auto Auction, Maple Grove, MN; *U.S. Private*, pg. 282

Eckardt, Carl R., Pres. & Chief Oper. Officer--ISP Chemicals Inc., Calvert City, KY; *U.S. Public*, pg. 858
Eckart, John E., Pres.--Indiana-American Water Co., Inc., Greenwood, IN; *U.S. Public*, pg. 95
Eckburg, Richard, Plant Mgr.--Kawai America Mfg. Inc., Lincolnton, NC; *Int'l*, pg. 725
Ecke, Patricia, Publisher--TimesFax, New York, NY; *U.S. Public*, pg. 1174
Eckel, J.S., Dir.--Flabeg GmbH, Furth, Germany; *Int'l*, pg. 1056
Eckenschwiller, Conrad, Gen. Mgr.--Viscosuisse S.A., Emmen, Switzerland; *Int'l*, pg. 1114
Ecker, William, Pres.--Redmond Products, Inc., Chanhassen, MN; *U.S. Public*, pg. 254
Eckerle, David E., Pres. & Chief Exec. Officer--Dubois County Bank, Jasper, IN; *U.S. Public*, pg. 1217
Eckersmann, Dan, Pres.--Le Tourneau, Inc., Longview, TX; *U.S. Public*, pg. 1410
Eckert, David D., Pres.--Rhone-Poulenc Basic Chemicals Co., Shelton, CT; *Int'l*, pg. 1110
Eckert, Michael J., Pres. & Chief Exec. Officer--Broadcast and Video Enterprises Div., Atlanta, GA; *U.S. Private*, pg. 647
Eckert, P., Chief Exec. Officer--Zurich Insurance Company, Glattbrugg, Switzerland; *Int'l*, pg. 1529
Eckert, Ulrich, Mgr.--Commerzbank AG Representative Office-St. Petersburg, Saint Petersburg, Russia; *Int'l*, pg. 312
Eckerwall, Ake, Chief Oper. Officer--Geodimeter of Australia Pty. Ltd., Brookvale, Australia; *Int'l*, pg. 1290
Eckerwall, Ake, Chief Oper. Officer--K.K. Geotronics, Omiya, Japan; *Int'l*, pg. 1290
Eckerwall, Ake, Chief Oper. Officer--Geotronics AB, Pasay, Philippines; *Int'l*, pg. 1290
Eckes, Harold, Mng. Dir.--Chantre & Cie GmbH, Nieder-Olm, Germany; *Int'l*, pg. 433
Eckhart, Glen E., Pres.--The Sabine Mining Co., Hallsville, TX; *U.S. Public*, pg. 1149
Eckhoff, Bruce, Pres.--Telos Consulting Services, Santa Clara, CA; *U.S. Public*, pg. 1573
Eckley, Gary, Gen. Mgr.--Midland Forge Division, Cedar Rapids, IA; *U.S. Public*, pg. 406
Eckloff, Richard, Pres.--BioChem ImmunoSystems, Inc., Allentown, PA; *Int'l*, pg. 196
Eckman, Leo T., Pres.--Krepe-Kraft, Inc., Blasdell, NY; *U.S. Public*, pg. 142
Eckman, Rich, Gen. Mgr.--American Yard Products Inc., Swainsboro, GA; *Int'l*, pg. 440
Eckstein, G., Chief Oper. Officer--Universal Transport GmbH, Kelsterbach, Germany; *Int'l*, pg. 1034
Ecles, Reg, Mng. Dir.--Ord Minnett Group Limited, London, United Kingdom; *Int'l*, pg. 1497
Eddington, Thomas, Pres.--Weststar Engineering Inc., San Diego, CA; *U.S. Public*, pg. 65
Eddis, Gerald, Pres.--Garry Precision Screw Machine, New Brunswick, NJ; *U.S. Private*, pg. 1184
Eddis, Gerald, Pres.--Garry Electronics, Salem, NJ; *U.S. Private*, pg. 1184
Eddis, Gerald, Pres.--General Connector, Salem, NJ; *U.S. Private*, pg. 1184
Eddis, Gerald, Pres.--Viking Electronics, Inc., Chatsworth, CA; *U.S. Private*, pg. 1184
Ede, Terence, Pres.--Communication Techniques, Inc., Whippany, NJ; *U.S. Public*, pg. 521
Edel, Patrick H., Gen. Mgr.--European Carbon Black Div.--Carbon Black Div., Boston, MA; *U.S. Public*, pg. 289
Edel, Patrick H., V.P. & Gen. Mgr.--Cabot Europe Limited, Neuilly-sur-Seine, France; *U.S. Public*, pg. 289
Edelen, James L., Publr.--Sentinel-News, Shelbyville, KY; *U.S. Private*, pg. 648
Edelhart, Michael, Publ.--PC Computing, Foster City, CA; *Int'l*, pg. 1276
Edelkoort, Robert, Gen. Mgr.--Cognos B.V., Nieuwegein, Netherlands; *Int'l*, pg. 306
Edelmann, Hansueli, Pres.--CS Life, Zurich, Switzerland; *Int'l*, pg. 345
Edelmann, Klaus, Pres. & Chief Oper. Officer--KHD Humboldt Wedag AG, Cologne, Germany; *Int'l*, pg. 408
Edelmann, Michael S., Pres.--SBC-Asset Management Inc., Saint Louis, MO; *U.S. Public*, pg. 1416
Edelmann, Pierre, Dr., Gen. Mgr.--Bayerische Landesbank (Schweiz) AG, Zurich, Switzerland; *Int'l*, pg. 176
Edelson, A.M., Dr., Ph.D., Pres.--J.B. Lippincott Company, Philadelphia, PA; *Int'l*, pg. 1513
Edem, Bassly, Vice Chm.--Pamol (Nigeria) Ltd., Lagos, Nigeria; *Int'l*, pg. 1438
Eden, R. W., Chief Exec. Officer--Guthrie Canadian Investments Limited, Toronto, Canada; *Int'l*, pg. 113
Edenfield, J. Michael, Chief Exec. Officer--Logility, Inc., Atlanta, GA; *U.S. Public*, pg. 91
Edens, Jim B., Chm. Bd. & Pres.--Huttig Sash & Door Co., Chesterfield, MO; *U.S. Public*, pg. 457
Eder, George, Gen. Mgr.--Reska Spline Products Inc., Warren, MI; *U.S. Public*, pg. 1054
Edgar, Bill, Gen. Mgr.--Barton's of Portageville, Portageville, MO; *U.S. Private*, pg. 119
Edgar, M., Mng. Dir.--Tasman Chile S.A., Santiago, Chile; *Int'l*, pg. 495
Edgar, Marvin, V.P. & Gen. Mgr.--Dominion Controls Company, Stratford, Canada; *Int'l*, pg. 473
Edgar, R.J., Mng. Dir.--Esanda Finance Corporation Limited, Melbourne, Australia; *Int'l*, pg. 98
Edgecomb, Kari, Gen. Mgr.--America Cafe, Washington, DC; *U.S. Public*, pg. 130
Edgerton, Brenda, Mng. Dir.--Bons N.V., Zoetermeer, Netherlands; *U.S. Public*, pg. 299
Edgington, Robert, Dir.-Mktg.--Woven Products Div., Corbin, KY; *U.S. Public*, pg. 1161
Edgren, Anders, Mng. Dir.--Oy Jotun Scanpol AB, Helsinki, Finland; *Int'l*, pg. 715
Edholm, Uno, Gen. Mgr.--Svenska Handelsbanken Hong Kong, Central, Hong Kong; *Int'l*, pg. 1327
Edinger, Daniel J., Pres.--Telmark, Inc., Syracuse, NY; *U.S. Private*, pg. 27
Edison, David, Pres.--Westinghouse Communications, Inc. (WesComm), Pittsburgh, PA; *U.S. Public*, pg. 273
Edlinger, Gerard, Chief Oper. Officer--Tratel, Saint Denis, France; *Int'l*, pg. 292
Edlund, Andy, Mgr.--Uddeholm Corporation, Fairfield, NJ; *Int'l*, pg. 1471
Edlund, Hans, Pres.--Pronesto, Solna, Sweden; *Int'l*, pg. 687
Edman, W.D., Pres.--Chevron Standard Limited, Calgary, Canada; *U.S. Public*, pg. 348
Edman, William D., Pres.--Chevron Canada Resources Limited, Calgary, Canada; *U.S. Public*, pg. 348
Edmond, Dewey, V.P. & Gen. Mgr.--Dentsply New Image, Carlsbad, CA; *U.S. Public*, pg. 499
Edmonds, Charlie, Grp. Gen. Mgr.--Tandy Cable Products, Fort Worth, TX; *U.S. Public*, pg. 1560
Edmonds, Charlie, Grp. Gen. Mgr.--Tandy Wire Fabrication, Fort Worth, TX; *U.S. Public*, pg. 1560
Edmonds, Frank, Gen. Mgr.--EDL Industries Ltd., Rugeley, United Kingdom; *Int'l*, pg. 821
Edmonds, Stephen N., Branch Mgr.--Piper Jaffray Inc., Lawrence, KS; *U.S. Public*, pg. 1302
Edmondson, Sam, Jr., Pres.--National Old Line Insurance Co., Little Rock, AR; *Int'l*, pg. 27
Edmunds, Alan M., Pres.--BNA International Inc., London, United Kingdom; *U.S. Private*, pg. 182
Edmunds, Terrell, Plant Mgr.--Cambridge Industries, Inc., Lapeer, MI; *U.S. Private*, pg. 202
Edris, Rojali, Gen. Mgr.--Avon Cosmetics (Malaysia) Sdn. Bhd., Petaling Jaya, Malaysia; *U.S. Public*, pg. 156
Edsell, Patrick, Pres.--Spectra-Physics Lasers, Inc., Mountain View, CA; *U.S. Public*, pg. 1594
Edson, A.H., Mng. Dir. & Sec.--Senior Engineering (Pty) Limited-South Africa, Vereeniging, South Africa; *Int'l*, pg. 1223
Edstrom, Gustaf, Mng. Dir.--Esselte Chrono AB, Solna, Sweden; *Int'l*, pg. 459
Edwall, Lars, Mgr. Dir.--General Motors Nordiska AB, Haninge, Sweden; *U.S. Public*, pg. 722
Edward, David, Pres.--The Body Shop, Cedar Knolls, NJ; *Int'l*, pg. 199
Edward, Gary, Gen. Mgr.--Statesville Auto Auction, Statesville, NC; *U.S. Private*, pg. 283
Edwards, Alasdair, Chief Exec. Officer--IRPC Hinton Limited, Hinckley, United Kingdom; *Int'l*, pg. 1502
Edwards, Annette, Pres.--Insulate LLC, Auburn, WA; *Int'l*, pg. 1171
Edwards, Anthony, Plant Mgr.--Peter Paul, Naugatuck, CT; *U.S. Public*, pg. 812
Edwards, Barrie, Pres.--Associated Music Publishers, New York, NY; *U.S. Private*, pg. 768
Edwards, Barrie, Pres.--G. Schirmer, Inc., New York, NY; *U.S. Private*, pg. 768
Edwards, Benjamin F., III, Chm. Bd., Pres. & Chief Exec. Officer--A.G. Edwards & Sons, Inc., Saint Louis, MO; *U.S. Public*, pg. 565
Edwards, Bill, Sr. V.P. & Branch Mgr.--Burns & Wilcox - San Diego Office, San Diego, CA; *U.S. Private*, pg. 610
Edwards, Briand D., Pres.--Ikon Office Solutions-Indiana, Indianapolis, IN; *U.S. Public*, pg. 863
Edwards, Bryn, Pres. & Chief Exec. Officer--Automation Software, Inc., Farmington, MI; *U.S. Public*, pg. 110
Edwards, C. Webb, Pres.--Norwest Services, Inc., Minneapolis, MN; *U.S. Public*, pg. 1202
Edwards, Chris, Pres.--Hurd Locks, Greeneville, TN; *U.S. Private*, pg. 102
Edwards, Clarence, Gen. Mgr.--Signature Flight Support, Clearwater, FL; *Int'l*, pg. 114
Edwards, D.G., Mng. Dir.--British Alcan Rolled Products Limited, Newport, United Kingdom; *Int'l*, pg. 51
Edwards, D.J., Chief Exec. Officer--Readymix Gulf Ltd., Sharjah, United Arab Emirates; *Int'l*, pg. 1092
Edwards, David J., Mng. Dir.--Computer Power Support Group, Swindon, United Kingdom; *U.S. Public*, pg. 576
Edwards, Doug, Country Mgr.--Circle Airfreight Intl. (Thailand) Ltd., Bangkok, Thailand; *U.S. Public*, pg. 372
Edwards, Douglas W., Plant Mgr.-Batteries--Delco Remy Division, Sarreguemines, France; *U.S. Public*, pg. 725
Edwards, Gary, Supervisor of R.R. Opers.--Somerset Railroad Corp., Ithaca, NY; *U.S. Public*, pg. 1173
Edwards, H.R., Gen. Mgr.--CHEMCENTRAL/Grand Rapids, Wyoming, MI; *U.S. Private*, pg. 232
Edwards, John, Mgr.--Amano Cincinnati - Toronto Branch Office, Mississauga, Canada; *Int'l*, pg. 71
Edwards, John, Pres. & Chief Exec. Officer--Sachs Boge of America, Westlake, OH; *Int'l*, pg. 835
Edwards, John, Pres.--Milford Fabricating Co., Detroit, MI; *Int'l*, pg. 1388
Edwards, John, Gen. Mgr.--The Resin Exchange, Cape Girardeau, MO; *U.S. Public*, pg. 1496
Edwards, John D., Gen. Mgr.--Atlas Alchem Plastics, Inc., Goddard, KS; *U.S. Public*, pg. 1496
Edwards, John K., Pres.--Onan Corporation, Minneapolis, MN; *U.S. Public*, pg. 468
Edwards, Johnathan, Chm. Bd. & Chief Exec. Officer--IPC Interactive, Inc., Novato, CA; *Int'l*, pg. 651
Edwards, Kurt, Pres.--Odessa Exploration, Inc., Odessa, TX; *U.S. Public*, pg. 953
Edwards, L.A., Chief Exec. Officer--Dowty Aerospace, Abingdon, United Kingdom; *Int'l*, pg. 1337
Edwards, L.A., Chm. Bd. & Chief Exec. Officer--Messier-Dowty, Abingdon, United Kingdom; *Int'l*, pg. 1340
Edwards, L.A., Chm. Bd. & Chief Exec. Officer--Messier-Dowty International, Velizy-Villacoublay, France; *Int'l*, pg. 1340
Edwards, L.D., Gen. Mgr.--Braden Company, Tulsa, OK; *U.S. Public*, pg. 924
Edwards, Marc, Pres. & Gen. Mgr.--KFSN-TV, Fresno, CA; *U.S. Public*, pg. 512
Edwards, Michael, Pres.--Meyer Laminates, Inc., West Palm Beach, FL; *Int'l*, pg. 864
Edwards, N.J., Chief Oper. Officer--Makro Cash and Carry Wholesale S.A., Piraeus, Greece; *Int'l*, pg. 1155
Edwards, Paul, Chief Exec. Officer--The Henley Centre, London, United Kingdom; *Int'l*, pg. 1482
Edwards, Peter, Mgr.--Sandvik Australia Pty. Ltd., Sydney, Australia; *Int'l*, pg. 1187
Edwards, Tom, Pres.--Ruskin Div., Grandview, MO; *Int'l*, pg. 1398
Edwards, Tom, Pres.--Swartwout Industries, Grandview, MO; *Int'l*, pg. 1398
Edwards, William E., III, V.P. & Controller--GTE California Incorporated, Irving, TX; *U.S. Public*, pg. 697
Edwards, William G., Pres.--Golden West Homes, Mesa, AZ; *U.S. Public*, pg. 1209
Edwards, William H., Pres. & Chief Exec. Officer--Lockwood Greene Technologies, Oak Ridge, TN; *Int'l*, pg. 633
Ee, Chia Shing, Gen. Mgr.--Albright & Wilson (Malaysia) Sdn. Bhd., Petaling Jaya, Malaysia; *Int'l*, pg. 49
Eertmans, Michel, Head-BBL/London Branch--Bank Brussels Lambert, London Branch, London, United Kingdom; *Int'l*, pg. 147
Effendl, Yaseen, Office Mgr.--Utell International-Oman, Muscat, Oman; *Int'l*, pg. 1098
Eftekhar, Zia, Pres.--Lightolier Division, Fall River, MA; *U.S. Public*, pg. 730
Egan, Barbara, Admin.--Parkview Acres, Dillon, MT; *U.S. Public*, pg. 1714
Egan, Bruce, Mgr.-Opers.--Woodward-Clyde, Lexington, MA; *U.S. Public*, pg. 1657
Egan, David, Publisher--BYTE Publications, Peterborough, NH; *U.S. Public*, pg. 1070
Egan, J., Mng. Dir.--Bally Schoenhandel B.V., Hague, Netherlands; *Int'l*, pg. 997
Egan, J., Mng. Dir.--Bally Group (UK) Limited, London, United Kingdom; *Int'l*, pg. 997
Egan, J.G., Mng. Dir.--Bally UK Sales Ltd., London, United Kingdom; *Int'l*, pg. 997
Egan, Jack, Pres.--American Bldg. Maintenance Co., San Francisco, CA; *U.S. Public*, pg. 2
Egan, Jack, Pres. & Chief Exec. Officer--RehabWorks Inc., Clearwater, FL; *U.S. Public*, pg. 839
Egan, Jack, Chief Exec. Officer--CMS Therapies, Inc., Charlotte, NC; *U.S. Public*, pg. 839
Egan, James J., Pres.--The CIT Group/Sales Financing, Inc., Livingston, NJ; *Int'l*, pg. 360
Egan, John M., Pres.--Anixter Cable TV, Rolling Meadows, IL; *U.S. Public*, pg. 115
Egan, Michael A., Pres. & Chief Exec. Officer--CheckRite International, Midvale, UT; *U.S. Public*, pg. 484
Egan, Raymond C., Pres.--Bristol-Myers Squibb U.S., Evansville, IN; *U.S. Public*, pg. 254
Egan, Tom, V.P.-Sls.--Wolf Range Co., Compton, CA; *U.S. Public*, pg. 1322
Egawa, N., Pres.--Yamaha Corporation of America, Buena Park, CA; *Int'l*, pg. 1516
Egawa, Yasuhiro, Chief Oper. Officer--The Sri Muang Insurance Co., Ltd., Bangkok, Thailand; *Int'l*, pg. 1392
Ege, H. Ray, Gen. Mgr.--Chicago Plant, Chicago, IL; *U.S. Public*, pg. 443
Egeland, Erik, Asst. V.P.--Willis Corroon Aerospace-Midwest Region, Chicago, IL; *Int'l*, pg. 1505
Eger, E., Mng. Dir.--Albany International Feltros E Telas Industrias Ltda., Indaial, Brazil; *U.S. Public*, pg. 37
Egerot, Curt, Chief Oper. Officer--AB Elektroservice, Stockholm, Sweden; *Int'l*, pg. 439
Egert, Dana, Chm. Bd.--Durst Corporation, Mountainside, NJ; *U.S. Private*, pg. 349
Egerton, John, Pres.--Lambert Smith Hampton, San Diego, CA; *Int'l*, pg. 797
Egerton, K.R., Chm. Bd. & Mng. Dir.--Taylor Woodrow Property Company Ltd., London, United Kingdom; *Int'l*, pg. 1359
Eggebrecht, Jerry J., Pres.-Colorado Div.--The Sygma Network, Inc.-Denver Central, Lakewood, CO; *U.S. Public*, pg. 1551
Eggenschwiler, Walter A., Branch Mgr.--Union Bank of Switzerland, Hong Kong Branch, Hong Kong, Hong Kong; *Int'l*, pg. 1440
Eggers, Claus, Mng. Dir.--Valley Hospital Medical Center, Las Vegas, NV; *U.S. Public*, pg. 1697
Eggers, Harald, Chief Oper. Officer--Siemens Microelectronics Center GmbH & Co., Dresden, Germany; *Int'l*, pg. 1245
Eggert, Albert E., Div. V.P.--Health Care Services Division, Saint Paul, MN; *U.S. Public*, pg. 1605
Eggleton, Wally, Gen. Mgr.--Quebecor Merrill Canada Inc., Vancouver, Canada; *Int'l*, pg. 1077
Egioff, Peter, Pres.--Sulzer Ruti Inc., Spartanburg, SC; *Int'l*, pg. 1307
Egle, Gert, Dr., Pres.--Thera Cosmetic GmbH, Dusseldorf, Germany; *Int'l*, pg. 610
Egler, James T., Chief Oper. Officer--Equitable Gas Co., Pittsburgh, PA; *U.S. Public*, pg. 589
Egli, Felix, Gen. Mgr.--Wisconsin Fineblanking, Deerfield, WI; *Int'l*, pg. 737
Eglin, Peter B., Chm. Bd., Pres. & Chief Exec. Officer--Mellon Bank, N.A.-Northeastern Region, Wilkes-Barre, PA; *U.S. Public*, pg. 1085
Eglinton, W.M., Chm.--Sunbelt Mining Co., Inc., Albuquerque, NM; *U.S. Public*, pg. 1340
Egmar, S., Mng. Dir.--EMI Music Publishing (Sweden) AB, Bromma, Sweden; *Int'l*, pg. 427
Egstrand, Bjarne, Pres.--Saab Sweden AB, Nykoping, Sweden; *Int'l*, pg. 687
Egstrand, Bjarne, Chief Oper. Officer--Saab Danmark A/S, Kvistgaard, Denmark; *Int'l*, pg. 687
Ehle, J.A., Dir.--Pilkington Visioncare, Menlo Park, CA; *Int'l*, pg. 1056
Ehlers, J. Steven, Mgr.-Branch--Piper Jaffray Inc., Burnsville, MN; *U.S. Public*, pg. 1302
Ehlers, Kurt-Peters, Chief Oper. Officer--Stolberger Metallwerke GmbH & Co. KG, Stolberg, Germany; *Int'l*, pg. 719
Ehmke, B.S., Pres. & Chief Exec. Officer--Forney Corporation, Carrollton, TX; *Int'l*, pg. 1500

Ehmke, Lane, Pres.--Bridgestone/Firestone Credit Services Company, Brook Park, OH; *Int'l*, pg. 213
Ehn, Gunnar, Chief Oper. Officer--Electrolux International Sales AB, Stockholm, Sweden; *Int'l*, pg. 438
Ehr, Robert, Pres.--Smiths Industries Aerospace & Defense Systems Inc.-Grand Rapids Operation, Grand Rapids, MI; *Int'l*, pg. 1268
Ehrat, Rodolphe, Mng. Dir.--Sulzer Australia Pty. Limited, Hornsby, Australia; *Int'l*, pg. 1306
Ehrengart, Bernd, Mng. Dir.--Bang & Olufsen G.m.b.H., Gilching, Germany; *Int'l*, pg. 146
Ehrich, O., Chief Oper. Officer--Dataschalt Gesellschaft fur Industrielle Daten-Mess-Und Antriebstechnik mGH, Lubeck, Germany; *Int'l*, pg. 473
Ehrlen, Olle, Pres.--NCC Building, Stockholm, Sweden; *Int'l*, *pg. 898*
Ehrlich, Klaus, Chief Oper. Officer--Novo Nordisk Pharma GmbH, Mainz, Germany; *Int'l*, pg. 988
Ehrlichman, John, Sr. V.P.--Law Companies Group, Atlanta, GA; *U.S. Private*, pg. 653
Ehrlinger, Erich, Dr., Chief Oper. Officer--Boehme Chemie Gesellschaft mbH, Dusseldorf, Germany; *Int'l*, pg. 609
Ehrnberg, Jan, Chief Oper. Officer--Alfa-Laval S.A. de C.V., Mexico, Mexico; *Int'l*, pg. 1380
Ehrnrooth, Rolf, Pres.--Oy Volvo-Auto Ab, Vantaa, Finland; *Int'l*, pg. 1477
Ehster, R.J., Div. Pres.--Winn-Dixie Stores Inc.-Miami Div., Pompano Beach, FL; *U.S. Public*, pg. 1771
Eiba, K., Gen. Mgr.--Gervais Danone AG, Munich, Germany; *Int'l*, pg. 380
Eiborn, Jan, Pres.--FFV Aerotech AB, Arboga, Sweden; *Int'l*, pg. 277
Eichberg, Catherine M., Admin.--Twin Palms Care Center, Artesia, CA; *U.S. Private*, pg. 733
Eiche, James, Mng. Dir.--DMB&B Taiwan, Taipei, Taiwan; *U.S. Private*, pg. 304
Eichenberger, J.Y., Chm. Bd.--Sacem, Casablanca, Morocco; *Int'l*, pg. 662
Eichenfield, Samuel L., Chm. Bd., Pres. & Chief Exec. Officer--FINOVA Capital Corporation, Phoenix, AZ; *U.S. Public*, pg. 624
Eicher, Henry V., Chm. & Pres.--Unisys Eletronica Ltda., Rio de Janeiro, Brazil; *U.S. Public*, pg. 1671
Eichler, Frank, Pres.--Rollman Supply Company, Mount Joy, PA; *U.S. Private*, pg. 407
Eichmann, M., Chief Exec. Officer--Zurich Insurance Company, Tokyo, Japan; *Int'l*, pg. 1531
Eichorn, Mark R., Pres.--Anchor Hocking Consumer Glass, Lancaster, OH; *U.S. Public*, pg. 1177
Eichorn, Mark R., Pres.--Anchor Hocking Corporation, Freeport, IL; *U.S. Public*, pg. 1177
Eide, R., Exec. V.P. & Mng. Dir.-Benelux--Dun & Bradstreet Eurinform SA-NV, Brussels, Belgium; *U.S. Public*, pg. 536
Eide, Rolv, Mng. Dir.--Dun & Bradstreet B.V., Rotterdam, Netherlands; *U.S. Public*, pg. 536
Eiden, Manfred, Gen. Mgr.--KONE Aufzug GmbH, Hannover, Germany; *Int'l*, pg. 747
Eidhagen, Bjorn, Chief Oper. Officer--Electrolux Philippines, Inc., Manila, Philippines; *Int'l*, pg. 443
Eifuku, Keigo, Pres.--Nippon Chemical Handling, Tokyo, Japan; *U.S. Public*, pg. 693
Eiger, Richard, V.P. & Publisher--The World Almanac, Mahwah, NJ; *U.S. Public*, pg. 1328
Eigruber, Horst, Pres.--American Maplan Corporation, Mc Pherson, KS; *Int'l*, pg. 825
Eiler, Frank, Intl. Chief Exec. Officer--Eiler & Riemel - Testa, Munich, Germany; *Int'l*, pg. 1377
Eilers, Daniel L., Pres. & Chief Exec. Officer--Claris Corporation, Santa Clara, CA; *U.S. Public*, pg. 121
Eilers, Ron, Pres.--PaperDirect, Inc., Secaucus, NJ; *U.S. Public*, pg. 498
Eilingsen, Ken, Pres.--Aegis Safety Holdings, Inc., Weehawken, NJ; *U.S. Public*, pg. 782
Eimbcke, Fernando, Mng. Dir.--Codelco-Kupferhandel GmbH, Dusseldorf, Germany; *Int'l*, pg. 303
Einhorn, Dominique, Mgr.-Brazil--Raychem Produtos Irradiados Ltda, Sao Paulo, Brazil; *U.S. Public*, pg. 1363
Einstein, Clifford, Chm. Bd. & Creative Dir.--Dailey & Associates, West Hollywood, CA; *U.S. Public*, pg. 909
Eio, Peter, Pres.--LEGO Systems, Inc., Enfield, CT; *Int'l*, pg. 805
Eipp, Donald, Exec. V.P.-Dairy Plant Opers.--Richfood Dairy, Richmond, VA; *U.S. Public*, pg. 1389
Eiritz, Per, V.P.-Tissue Machines--Valmet-Karlstad AB, Karlstad, Sweden; *Int'l*, pg. 1448
Eisele, Klaus, Pres.--Baden-Wurttemberg Branch, Stuttgart, Germany; *Int'l*, pg. 645
Eisen, Don, Branch Mgr.--Cushman & Wakefield, East Rutherford, NJ; *Int'l*, pg. 873
Eisen, Juan Carlos, Pres.-Latin American Grp.--Griffith Colombia S.A., Medellin, Colombia; *U.S. Private*, pg. 481
Eisen, Juan Carlos, Chief Oper. Officer--Laboratorios Griffith de Centro America S.A., San Jose, Costa Rica; *U.S. Private*, pg. 481
Eisen, Paul, Pres.--Jeans West, Inc., Saint Louis, MO; *U.S. Public*, pg. 563
Eisen, Paul, Pres.--Coda, Saint Louis, MO; *U.S. Public*, pg. 563
Eisen, Paul, Pres.--Oaktree, Saint Louis, MO; *U.S. Public*, pg. 564
Eisenbury, Wayne, Mgr.-Sls.--Apex Data, Fremont, CA; *U.S. Public*, pg. 1476
Eisenegger, Otto, Mng. Dir.--Media Daten AG, Zurich, Switzerland; *Int'l*, pg. 451
Eisentraeger, G., Gen. Mgr.--Endevco Vertriebs GmbH, Heidelberg, Germany; *Int'l*, pg. 854
Eiserman, Fred, Mgr.-Office--Woodward-Clyde, Casper, WY; *U.S. Public*, pg. 1656
Eisner, Robert A., V.P.--Jefferies & Company, Inc., Los Angeles, CA; *U.S. Public*, pg. 925
Eistert, Michael, Pres.--Babcock Sempell AG, Korschenbroich, Germany; *Int'l*, pg. 399
Eiswerth, Leon R., Pres.--Park Drop Forge Div., Cleveland, OH; *U.S. Public*, pg. 1258
Eitan, Shalom, Chm. Bd.--Power Spectrum Technology Ltd., Kiryat Bialick, Israel; *U.S. Public*, pg. 740
Eitel, Karl, Dr., Mng. Dir.--Vorwerk & Co. Elektrowerke KG., Wuppertal, Germany; *Int'l*, pg. 1480
Eizenga, Gary, Pres.--Americable, Inc., Eden Prairie, MN; *U.S. Public*, pg. 585
Ejima, M., Gen. Mgr.--Mitsui & Co. (U.S.A.), Inc., San Francisco, CA; *Int'l*, pg. 879
Ejlerskov, Allan, Gen. Mgr.--Cinet Danmark A/S, Glostrup, Denmark; *Int'l*, pg. 710
Ejlerskov, Allan, Mng. Dir.--Cinet Periferi A/S, Glostrup, Denmark; *Int'l*, pg. 710
Ek, Lennart, Mgr.--Sandvik Stal Forsaljnings AB, Kista, Sweden; *Int'l*, pg. 1185
Ekberg, Bengt, Chief Oper. Officer--Perstorp Form, Perstorp, Sweden; *Int'l*, pg. 1037
Ekberg, D.C., Sr. V.P. & Mgr.-Branch--ABM AMRO Bank, N.V. (Boston), Boston, MA; *Int'l*, pg. 10
Ekberg, Sven, Chief Oper. Officer--Granges Hedlund AB, Stockholm, Sweden; *Int'l*, pg. 439
Ekedahl, S.A.V., Gen. Mgr.--Glaxo Wellcome AB, Molndal, Sweden; *Int'l*, pg. 553
Ekegren, John W., Pres.--Atlantic Guest, Inc., Meriden, CT; *U.S. Public*, pg. 1705
Ekeland, Bruno, Chief Oper. Officer--Waco Jonsereds AB, Halmstad, Sweden; *Int'l*, pg. 1421
Ekelund, Bengt, Gen. Mgr.--Kodak A/S, Tastrup, Denmark; *U.S. Public*, pg. 552
Ekelund, Erik, Chief Oper. Officer--Perstorp Unidur, Inc., Greensboro, NC; *Int'l*, pg. 1038
Ekfeldt, Sune, Gen. Mgr.--Command & Control Systems, Vaxjo, Sweden; *Int'l*, pg. 277
Ekholm, Markku, Mng. Dir.--Suomen Unipol Oy, Helsinki, Finland; *Int'l*, pg. 15
Ekholm, Thomas, Chief Fin. Officer--Swedish Rail System SRS, Ystad, Sweden; *Int'l*, pg. 1199
Ekins, W. Leo, Pres. & Chief Exec. Officer--AgrEvo USA Company, Wilmington, DE; *Int'l*, pg. 1203
Eklof, Rolf, Chief Oper. Officer--Husqvarna Pty. Ltd., Sydney, Australia; *Int'l*, pg. 440
Eklund, B., Gen. Mgr.--Kodak AB, Jakobsberg, Sweden; *U.S. Public*, pg. 552
Eklund, Henrik, Pres.--Sanitec Ltd. Oy, Ratingen, Germany; *Int'l*, pg. 863
Eklund, Jorgen, Mng. Dir.--Logica Svenska AB, Solna, Sweden; *Int'l*, pg. 815
Eklund, Stig, Pres.--Pernovo, Perstorp, Sweden; *Int'l*, pg. 1036
Ekstedt, Lennart, Gen. Mgr. & Dir.--Dexter Nonwovens AB, Kopparberg, Sweden; *U.S. Public*, pg. 505
Ekstrand, Arne, Mgr.--Duni AB-Nordic Division, Halmstad, Sweden; *Int'l*, pg. 421
Ekstrom, Bojre, Chief Oper. Officer--AB Lidingo Verkstader, Lidingo, Sweden; *Int'l*, pg. 1377
Ekstrom, Carl, Chief Oper. Officer--Alfa-Laval S.A.C.I., Santiago, Chile; *Int'l*, pg. 1379
Ekstrom, Hans, Mng. Dir.--Telefonaktiebolaget LM Ericsson China, Beijing, China; *Int'l*, pg. 1370
Ekstrom, Kaj, Chief Oper. Officer--Hagglunds Drives Oy, Helsinki, Finland; *Int'l*, pg. 670
Ekyamp, William, Pres.--Koch Membrane Systems, Wilmington, MA; *U.S. Private*, pg. 628
El Nenaei, Maged, Mng. Dir.--Johnson & Johnson (Egypt) S.A.E., Cairo, Egypt; *U.S. Public*, pg. 930
El-Din, M. Hussam, Gen. Mgr.--Jotun Polymer Inc., Dubai, United Arab Emirates; *Int'l*, pg. 715
El-Hage, Nabil, Chm. Bd. & Chief Exec. Officer--Jeepers! Inc., Waltham, MA; *U.S. Private*, pg. 222
El-Sayed, Mustafa, Plant Mgr.--Rhone-Poulenc Specialty Chemicals, Newark, NJ; *Int'l*, pg. 1110
El-Zayat, Khaled, Resident Mgr.--ESAB Egypt, Cairo, Egypt; *Int'l*, pg. 282
Elbirt, Carlos, Resident Rep.--The World Bank, Tirana, Albania; *U.S. Private*, pg. 1189
Elbourne, J. K., Mng. Dir.--TSB Trust Co. Ltd., Andover, United Kingdom; *Int'l*, pg. 813
Elbourne, John, Mng. Dir.--Prudential Assurance Co. Ltd., London, United Kingdom; *Int'l*, pg. 1073
Elden, Gerald P., Pres.-Textile Group--Celanese Canada Textile Group, Kingston, Canada; *Int'l*, pg. 625
Elder, Andy, Pres.--Stratis Corporation, Indianapolis, IN; *U.S. Private*, pg. 862
Elder, Edwin W., III, Pres.--American Country Insurance Co., Chicago, IL; *U.S. Private*, pg. 1030
Elder, Edwin W., III, Pres.--American Country Financial Services Corp., Chicago, IL; *U.S. Private*, pg. 1030
Elder, Josef I., Chm.--Hartmann & Braun AG, Frankfurt/Main, Germany; *Int'l*, pg. 835
Elder, Wayne, Gen. Mgr.--Textron Compressor Components, Odessa, TX; *U.S. Public*, pg. 1590
Elders, Al, Chief Oper. Officer--Globe Business Furniture, Inc., Hendersonville, TN; *U.S. Private*, pg. 512
Eldred, P., Mgr.--Rockware Glass Ltd.-Wigan Factory, Wigan, United Kingdom; *Int'l*, pg. 124
Eldridge, Dave, Gen. Mgr.--Henry County Local, Eminence, KY; *U.S. Private*, pg. 648
Eldridge, Ed, Mgr.--American Eagle Lines, Dallas, TX; *U.S. Public*, pg. 685
Elenbaas, Ronald A., Pres.--Stryker Corporation Endoscopy, San Jose, CA; *U.S. Public*, pg. 1526
Elfner, Anders, Pres.--Skanska Stockholm Malardalen, Danderyd, Sweden; *Int'l*, pg. 1260
Elford, John, Gen. Mgr.--Turtle Bay Hilton Golf & Tennis Resort, Kahuku, HI; *U.S. Public*, pg. 829
Elfstrom, Bertil, Chief Oper. Officer--Fuji Film Sverige AB, Stockholm, Sweden; *Int'l*, pg. 708
Elfstrom, Tony, Mgr.--Dormer Tools (Sheffield) Ltd., Sheffield, United Kingdom; *Int'l*, pg. 1186
Elgar, Clint, Mng. Dir.--Kvaerner Process Systems Asia Pacific Sdn Bhd., Raja Chulan, Malaysia; *Int'l*, pg. 768
Elhalwagy, M.E., Gen. Mgr.--Johnson Wax Research and Development, Egham, United Kingdom; *U.S. Private*, pg. 593
Elia, Claudio, Pres.--Anjou International Company, New York, NY; *Int'l*, pg. 321
Elia, Claudio, Chief Oper. Officer--Limbach Constructors, Inc., Pittsburgh, PA; *Int'l*, pg. 322
Elia, Clemi, First V.P.--RNBNY Representative Office-Caracas, Caracas, Venezuela; *U.S. Public*, pg. 1381
Elias, Arthur G., Pres.--Hayhurst Elias Dudek, Inc., Winnipeg, Canada; *U.S. Public*, pg. 827
Elias, Arturo Segundo, Administrator--General Motors de Venezuela C.A., Caracas, Venezuela; *U.S. Public*, pg. 722
Elias, Craig, Pres.--Pan Canadian Energy Services, Houston, TX; *Int'l*, pg. 259
Elias, Elmer J., Pres. & Chief Exec. Officer--B.M.J. Financial Corp., Bordentown, NJ; *U.S. Public*, pg. 1528
Elias, R.T., Mgr.--Ballast Nedam Suriname N.V., Paramaribo, Suriname; *Int'l*, pg. 134
Elias, Richard, Pres.--Transitions Optical, Inc., Pinellas Park, FL; *U.S. Public*, pg. 1245
Elio, Alvaro, Dir. General--Generale Bank - Banco Belga, Madrid, Spain; *Int'l*, pg. 547
Elizando, Cesar, Pres.--Corporacion E.G., S.A. de C.V., Monterrey, Mexico; *Int'l*, pg. 395
Elizondo, Cesar, Pres.--Ruhrpumpen GmbH, Witten, Germany; *Int'l*, pg. 395
Elkin, Kenneth, Pres. & Chief Exec. Officer--SGS U.S. Testing Company, Inc., Fairfield, NJ; *Int'l*, pg. 1153
Elkin, Kenneth, Pres. & Chief Exec. Officer--SGS Industrial Services, Iselin, NJ; *Int'l*, pg. 1153
Elkins, Alan A., Mng. Exec.--Northern Trust Bank of Arizona, N.A., Scottsdale, AZ; *U.S. Public*, pg. 1196
Elkins, Scott, Plant Mgr.--Block Products Plant, Corpus Christi, TX; *U.S. Public*, pg. 936
Elkuch, Erwin, Rep.--Riunione Adriatica di Sicurta, Vaduz, Liechtenstein; *Int'l*, pg. 61
Ellefsen, Ellen, Gen. Mgr.--Elkem Tana, Tana, Norway; *Int'l*, *pg. 448*
Ellefson, Chris S., Mgr.--San Juan Mine, Waterflow, NM; *Int'l*, pg. 224
Ellender, John E., Sec.--Cigna Reinsurance Company (U.K.) Limited, London, United Kingdom; *U.S. Public*, pg. 363
Eller, Timothy R., Pres. & Chief Exec. Officer--Centex Real Estate Corp./Centex Homes, Dallas, TX; *U.S. Public*, pg. 323
Ellerbrook, Niel, Pres. & Chief Oper. Officer--IEI Services, LLC, Indianapolis, IN; *U.S. Public*, pg. 875
Ellerman, Mike, Pres.--Yuasa-Exide, Inc., Reading, PA; *Int'l*, pg. 1522
Ellett, Bob R., Mgr.--The Rytex Company, Indianapolis, IN; *U.S. Private*, pg. 62
Ellett, Phil D., Pres. & Chief Exec. Officer--Gates/Arrow Commercial Systems Div., Greenville, SC; *U.S. Public*, pg. 133
Ellickson, David G., Mgr.--Waunakee Telephone Co., Inc., Waunakee, WI; *U.S. Public*, pg. 1572
Elliff, Mark J., Pres. & Chief Exec. Officer--United Missouri Bank of Boonville, Boonville, MO; *U.S. Public*, pg. 1654
Elliman, Donald M., Jr., Pres. & Publisher-Sports Illustrated--Time Inc., New York, NY; *U.S. Public*, pg. 1612
Elliman, Donald M., Jr., Pres.--Sports Illustrated, New York, NY; *U.S. Public*, pg. 1613
Ellingsen, Ken, Pres.-Catalog--LWI Holdings Inc., Cleveland, OH; *U.S. Public*, pg. 782
Ellingson, Chester W., III, Pres.--Weather Strip Division, Rosemount, MN; *U.S. Private*, pg. 916
Ellingson, Robert T., Pres.--Plastic Division, Rosemount, MN; *U.S. Private*, pg. 916
Elliot, Fred, Pres.--Dussek Campbell Ltd., Belleville, Canada; *Int'l*, pg. 236
Elliott, B.L., Pres.--Eastman Savings & Loan Association, Rochester, NY; *U.S. Public*, pg. 551
Elliott, D.E., Mng. Dir.--Oliver Rubber Europa Ltd., Grantham, United Kingdom; *U.S. Public*, pg. 1505
Elliott, J. Mark, Chm. Bd. & Chief Exec. Officer--QST Environmental Inc., Peoria, IL; *U.S. Public*, pg. 367
Elliott, J. Mark, Pres. & Chief Oper. Officer--QST Enterprises Inc., Peoria, IL; *U.S. Public*, pg. 367
Elliott, J. Mark, Chm. Bd. & Chief Exec. Officer--QST Energy, Inc., Peoria, IL; *U.S. Public*, pg. 367
Elliott, James A., Pres.--Mackay, Inc., Florence, KY; *U.S. Public*, pg. 210
Elliott, John, Exec. V.P.--BetzDearborn Hydrocarbon Process Group, Woodlands, TX; *U.S. Public*, pg. 226
Elliott, John E., Pres.--Thermotech Systems Corporation, Orlando, FL; *U.S. Public*, pg. 705
Elliott, Jordan, Chm.--Lowell Shoe, Inc., Hudson, NH; *U.S. Public*, pg. 217
Elliott, Joseph, Pres.--Encyclopaedia Britannica Educational Corporation, Chicago, IL; *U.S. Private*, pg. 375
Elliott, Joseph W., Pres.--Cornhusker Casualty Co., Omaha, NE; *U.S. Public*, pg. 221
Elliott, Marc G., Pres.--General Combustion Corporation, Orlando, FL; *U.S. Public*, pg. 705
Elliott, Sheila, Mng. Dir.--Aetna International (Australia) Pty. Ltd., Chatswood, Australia; *U.S. Public*, pg. 27
Elliott, T.L., Mng. Dir.--Senior Heat Treatment Limited, Dunstable, United Kingdom; *Int'l*, pg. 1221
Ellis, B. Herbert, Pres.--Barnes & Reinecke, Inc., Arlington Heights, IL; *U.S. Public*, pg. 49
Ellis, Barry, Pres. of Gen. Partner & Mngng. Dir.--Blair Tower Limited Partnership, Bella Vista, AR; *U.S. Private*, pg. 274
Ellis, Barry W., Pres.--Apartment Ventures, Inc., Bella Vista, AR; *U.S. Private*, pg. 274
Ellis, Bert, Mgr.--Chicago South Financial Center, Chicago, IL; *U.S. Public*, pg. 1196
Ellis, Bryan, Mng. Dir.--Hasbro Europe UK Limited, Uxbridge, United Kingdom; *U.S. Public*, pg. 797
Ellis, Darren, Mgr.-Office--Woodward-Clyde International, Hackney, Australia; *U.S. Public*, pg. 1658

Ellis, Dayle B., V.P. & Div. Mgr.--SCR Division, Dallas, TX; *U.S. Public*, pg. 1268

Ellis, E. Addison, III, Pres. & Chief Exec. Officer--Glencoe/Mc-Graw Hill, Westerville, OH; *U.S. Public*, pg. 1070

Ellis, Fred K., Pres. & Chief Inv. Officer--Skandia Investment Management, Inc., New York, NY; *Int'l*, pg. 1257

Ellis, G.H.G., Chm. Bd. & Dir.-Lube Mktg.--Mobil Oil Company, Ltd., Milton Keynes, United Kingdom; *U.S. Public*, pg. 1119

Ellis, J. Ronald, Pres. & Chief Exec. Officer--Willis Corroon Corp. of Nashville, Nashville, TN; *Int'l*, pg. 1506

Ellis, John, Gen. Mgr.--McClatchy Printing Service, Clovis, CA; *U.S. Public*, pg. 1066

Ellis, John E., V.P.--Global Special Risks, Inc. of New York, New York, NY; *Int'l*, pg. 1503

Ellis, K.M., Mng. Dir.--Cosmetic Products Pty, Ltd., Somersby, Australia; *Int'l*, pg. 1490

Ellis, Mary, Plant Mgr.--Champion Valley Farms, Bloomsburg, PA; *U.S. Public*, pg. 806

Ellis, Michael, Rep.--Mead Packaging Poland Sp.z O.O., Warsaw, Poland; *U.S. Public*, pg. 1076

Ellis, Milton, Gen. Mgr. & Publisher--The Standard-Freeholder, Cornwall, Canada; *Int'l*, pg. 631

Ellis, N.A., Dir. & Gen. Mgr.--Hamworthy Combustion Systems Limited, Poole, United Kingdom; *Int'l*, pg. 1065

Ellis, Par, Mng. Dir.--Gypsum Industries plc., Dublin, Ireland; *Int'l*, pg. 123

Ellis, Paula Lynn, Pres. & Publr.--The Sun News, Myrtle Beach, SC; *U.S. Public*, pg. 964

Ellis, Paula Lynn, Pres. & Publr.--Sun Publishing Company, Inc., Myrtle Beach, SC; *U.S. Public*, pg. 964

Ellis, Robert, Pres.--Haviland Telephone Company, Inc., Haviland, KS; *U.S. Public*, pg. 1021

Ellis, Robert F., Pres.--Austron Inc., Austin, TX; *U.S. Public*, pg. 488

Ellis, Royan, Mng. Dir.--Westpac Banking Corporation (Jersey) Ltd., Saint Helier, United Kingdom; *Int'l*, pg. 1497

Ellis, Stephen, Gen. Mgr.--Loctite Asia Ltd., Wan Chai, Hong Kong; *Int'l*, pg. 611

Ellis, Tony, Facility Mgr.--Square D Company Ireland, Galway, Ireland; *Int'l*, pg. 1209

Ellis, Willen, Pres.--ATIO Corporation USA, Inc., Hopkins, MN; *U.S. Public*, pg. 1716

Ellis, William B., Chm. Bd. & Chief Oper. Officer--Connecticut Yankee Atomic Power Co., Berlin, CT; *U.S. Public*, pg. 325

Ellison, Bruce, Chief Oper. Officer--Liqui-Box Acquisition Corporation, New Albany, IN; *U.S. Public*, pg. 1000

Ellison, Dave, Editor--Fishing Tackle Retailer, Montgomery, AL; *U.S. Private*, pg. 105

Ellison, Francis, Mng. Dir.--Bank of Ireland Investment Managers Limited, London, United Kingdom; *Int'l*, pg. 153

Ellison, Francis, Mng. Dir.--Bank of Ireland Asset Management (UK) Limited, London, United Kingdom; *Int'l*, pg. 153

Ellison, Nick, Country Mgr.--Standard Chartered Bank (Qatar), Doha, Qatar; *Int'l*, pg. 1295

Ellison, Richard D., Pres.--TRC Environmental Solutions, Inc., Irvine, CA; *U.S. Public*, pg. 1558

Ellisor, Steve, Gen. Mgr.--Mustang Power Systems, Houston, TX; *U.S. Private*, pg. 769

Ellithrpe, Randy, Gen. Mgr.--Connelly Paper Mill, Philadelphia, PA; *U.S. Private*, pg. 264

Ellspermann, W.R., Pres. & Chief Exec. Officer--Security Pacific Information Services Corporation, San Diego, CA; *U.S. Public*, pg. 182

Ellsworth, Jennifer, V.P.-Mdsg.--Hold Everything, Inc., San Francisco, CA; *U.S. Public*, pg. 1770

Ellsworth, Ron, Mgr.-Reg. Sls.--Edward Don & Company-Clarkston Branch, Clarkston, GA; *U.S. Private*, pg. 339

Ellwinger, Imogene, Admin.--Rehabilitation & Nursing Care Center, Fremont, CA; *U.S. Private*, pg. 733

Ellwood, Jeffrey, V.P.--Univar Europe N.V., Croydon, United Kingdom; *Int'l*, pg. 1147

Elmer, A., III, Pres.--Sea River Maritime, Inc., Houston, TX; *U.S. Public*, pg. 601

Elmer, Wesley, Pres.--Coca-Cola Northern New England, Inc., Bedford, NH; *Int'l*, pg. 736

Elms, Darryl, Mgr.--Norwich ParK Mine, Dysart, Australia; *Int'l*, pg. 223

Elo, Arto, Chief Oper. Officer--Ahlstrom Recovery Inc., Roswell, GA; *Int'l*, pg. 34

Elphick, Anthony J., Chief Oper. Officer--Novo Nordisk A/S, Bagsvaerd, Denmark; *Int'l*, pg. 987

Elrod, Allen, Mgr.-Western Div.--Columbia Pictures Western Division, Culver City, CA; *Int'l*, pg. 1281

Elsasser, J.T., V.P.-Bearings-Europe, Africa & West Asia--British Timken Div., Northampton, United Kingdom; *U.S. Public*, pg. 1617

Elsasser, J.T., V.P.-Bearings-Europe, Africa & W. Asia--Timken Italia S.r.l., Milan, Italy; *U.S. Public*, pg. 1618

Elsayed, Salama, Plant Mgr.--AEP Industries, Inc., Chino, CA; *U.S. Public*, pg. 5

Elsenstaedt, Bob, Mgr.--F & F Productions, Inc., Saint Petersburg, FL; *U.S. Private*, pg. 544

Elsey, D.J., Gen. Mgr.--Laporte Wood Preservation, Widnes, United Kingdom; *Int'l*, pg. 802

Elsey, John H., Pres.--Dairyland County Mutual Insurance Co., Austin, TX; *U.S. Private*, pg. 985

Elshorst, Guenter, Chm. Bd.--Klockner-Pentaplast GmbH, Montabaur, Germany; *Int'l*, pg. 737

Elslander, M. Dick, Mng. Dir.--General Biscuits Belgie N.V., Herentals, Belgium; *Int'l*, pg. 380

Elsner, Bernd, Mng. Dir.--Haniel EnvirService GmbH, Duisburg, Germany; *Int'l*, pg. 592

Elson, Irwin L., Pres.--JLK America Inc., Livonia, MI; *U.S. Public*, pg. 951

Elstad, Tore, Mng. Dir.--Autologic Information International AB, Sollentuna, Sweden; *U.S. Public*, pg. 1724

Elster, Robert, Publisher--Taft Group, Rockville, MD; *U.S. Public*, pg. 1601

Elswick, Lloyd C, Pres.--Bendix Security Systems, Pasadena, MD; *U.S. Public*, pg. 51

Elten, Hartwig, Mng. Dir.--Neste Chemicals GmbH, Dusseldorf, Germany; *Int'l*, pg. 914

Elton, S., Mng. Dir.--Smythson of Bond Street, London, United Kingdom; *Int'l*, pg. 707

Eltringham, Lou, Gen. Mgr.--Mohawk Plastics, Inc., Bernardston, MA; *U.S. Private*, pg. 755

Elvidge, Jim, V.P.-Americas Opers.--Vicorp Interactive Systems, Inc., Boston, MA; *U.S. Public*, pg. 1321

Ely, Timothy, Pres.--Highfield Manufacturing Co., Bridgeport, CT; *Int'l*, pg. 127

Ema, Naoki, Mng. Dir.--NLI International Australia Limited, Sydney, Australia; *Int'l*, pg. 936

Emanuel, A., Exec. V.P.--Coil-Tec Corporation, Bessemer, AL; *Int'l*, pg. 79

Embden, Claus, Co-Chm. Bd.--Krupp Metalurgica Campo Limpo Ltda., Sao Paulo, Brazil; *Int'l*, pg. 508

Emberton, Dave, Mng. Dir.--Gestetner Limited, Nairobi, Kenya; *Int'l*, pg. 1115

Embrechts, Rene, Mng. Dir.--Saproma S.A., Brussels, Belgium; *U.S. Private*, pg. 212

Embry, Carroll, V.P. & Gen. Mgr.--Northwestern Resources Company, Jewett, TX; *U.S. Public*, pg. 1127

Embry, Mark, Reg. Mgr.--SMS-Boston, Wakefield, MA; *U.S. Public*, pg. 1463

Emch, Eric, Gen. Mgr.--Ohio Engine Power, Broadview Heights, OH; *U.S. Private*, pg. 813

Emeny, Colin, Mng. Dir.--SPS Technologies Limited, Smethwick, United Kingdom; *U.S. Public*, pg. 1420

Emerson, Barry K., Chm. Bd., Pres. & Chief Exec. Officer--Texas National Bank, Southlake, TX; *U.S. Public*, pg. 633

Emerson, Bob, Country Mgr.--NBS Limited-Card Services Division, Weybridge, United Kingdom; *Int'l*, pg. 898

Emerson, Brian, Chief Oper. Officer--Continental Microwave Technology Ltd., Luton, United Kingdom; *Int'l*, pg. 1289

Emerson, Thomas E., Chief Exec. Officer--Norwest Audit Services, Inc., Minneapolis, MN; *U.S. Public*, pg. 1201

Emert, Bonnie M., Pres.--Norwest Financial Coast, Inc., Signal Hill, CA; *U.S. Public*, pg. 1202

Emery, Brian, Chief Oper. Officer--AGRA Cambrian Inc., Oakville, Canada; *Int'l*, pg. 30

Emery, David, V.P. & Mng. Dir.-Asian/India Region--Dun & Bradstreet (Singapore) Pte. Ltd., Singapore, Singapore; *U.S. Public*, pg. 537

Emery, David J., Mng. Dir.--Dun & Bradstreet Schweiz AG, Urdorf, Switzerland; *U.S. Public*, pg. 537

Emery, Merl, Pres.--Multi-Plex, Inc., Howe, IN; *U.S. Private*, pg. 315

Emhiser, William, Pres.--Amicon, Inc., Beverly, MA; *U.S. Public*, pg. 1113

Emigh, Michael, Acting Pres.--Valley Fig Growers, Fresno, CA; *U.S. Private*, pg. 1051

Emilsson, Kare, Chief Oper. Officer--Perstorp Components, Hogsater, Sweden; *Int'l*, pg. 1040

Emkes, Mark, Pres.--Bridgestone/Firestone de Mexico, S.A. de C.V., Mexico, Mexico; *Int'l*, pg. 214

Emling, John R., V.P.-Opers.--Barden Precision Bearings, Danbury, CT; *Int'l*, pg. 468

Emm, David, Gen. Mgr.--Rusch, Duluth, GA; *U.S. Public*, pg. 1569

Emmenegger, Charles E., Pres.--Bull Moose Tube Company, Chesterfield, MO; *Int'l*, pg. 265

Emmens, Matthew W., Pres.--Astra Merck Inc., Wayne, PA; *Int'l*, pg. 93

Emmerling, Paul, Pres.--Marston Ring Div., Wolverhampton, United Kingdom; *U.S. Private*, pg. 425

Emmes, Olle, Mng. Dir.--Oy Nautor AB, Pietarsaari, Finland; *Int'l*, pg. 1428

Emmons, Don, Pres.--Prescolite Moldcast Lighting Company, San Leandro, CA; *U.S. Public*, pg. 1684

Emmons, Robert J., Dr., Chm. Bd.--Casino U.S.A., Inc., Santa Barbara, CA; *Int'l*, pg. 563

Emmons, Robert, Dr., Chm. Bd.--Smart & Final, Vernon, CA; *Int'l*, pg. 563

Emo, Brian, Pres.--Brian Controls, Mississauga, Canada; *Int'l*, pg. 1489

Emo, Glen, Pres.--Wandel & Goltermann Inc., Scarborough, Canada; *Int'l*, pg. 1486

Emola, Al, Pres.--Flexmedics Corporation, Minnetonka, MN; *U.S. Private*, pg. 862

Emondts, M.H.P.J., Dir. Gen.--Bols Benelux B.V., Zoetermeer, Netherlands; *Int'l*, pg. 751

Emori, S., Chief Oper. Officer--Shiseido Deutschland GmbH, Dusseldorf, Germany; *Int'l*, pg. 1235

Emrich, John A., Pres.--Guilford Mills (Automotive & Upholstery Fabrics), Kenansville, NC; *U.S. Public*, pg. 769

Emrich, John A., Pres.--Guilford Mills (Automotive & Upholstery Fabrics), Southfield, MI; *U.S. Public*, pg. 769

Emrich, Pat, Mgr.-Plant--Nestle Frozen/Refrigerated Food Co., Gaffney, SC; *Int'l*, pg. 918

Emsell, Brian, Grp. Opers. Dir.-U.K.--Diversified Agency Services, New York, NY; *U.S. Public*, pg. 1223

Emsermann, M., Dr., Chief Exec. Officer--Ascom Frako GmbH, Teningen, Germany; *Int'l*, pg. 87

Ence, Ralf, Gen. Mgr.--Skandinaviska Enskilda Banken, Copenhagen, Copenhagen, Denmark; *Int'l*, pg. 1259

Enck, Richard, Pres.--Kevex Instruments, Valencia, CA; *U.S. Public*, pg. 1594

Endaya, V.M., Gen. Mgr.--Van Melle-(Phils.) Inc., Manila, Philippines; *Int'l*, pg. 1451

Ender, Christoph, Mng. Dir.--Sulzer Shanghai Eng. and Mach. Works Ltd., Shanghai, China; *Int'l*, pg. 1306

Enderle, Marvin, Gen. Mgr.--Park Newspapers of Rockingham, Inc., Rockingham, NC; *U.S. Public*, pg. 1079

Enderle, Marvin, Gen. Mgr.--Aberdeen Citizen News-Record, Aberdeen, NC; *U.S. Public*, pg. 1079

Enderli, Willi, Gen. Mgr.--Micarna AG, Bazenheid, Switzerland; *Int'l*, pg. 865

Enders, Larry J., Pres. & Chief Exec. Officer--Oliver Rubber Co., Athens, GA; *U.S. Public*, pg. 1504

Enderweit, Fritz, Base Mgr.--Weatherford Australia Pty. Ltd., Adelaide, Australia; *U.S. Public*, pg. 1750

Endicott, Samuel L., Pres.--NationsBank Equity Mortgage Corporation, Richmond, VA; *U.S. Public*, pg. 1163

Endicott, Thomas A., Pres.--Duffy Tool & Stamping, Inc., Muncie, IN; *U.S. Private*, pg. 169

Endler, Talito, Pres. & Chief Exec. Officer--TNT Participacoes Ltda., Sao Paulo, Brazil; *Int'l*, pg. 1343

Endo, Atsushi, Gen. Mgr.--The Industrial Bank of Japan, Limited (Dalian), Dalian, China; *Int'l*, pg. 675

Endo, Hiro, Dir.--Nihon Exabyte K.K., Tokyo, Japan; *U.S. Public*, pg. 597

Endo, Takuro, Pres.--Nissan Diesel Motor Co., Ltd., Ageo, Japan; *Int'l*, pg. 944

Endo, Toshio, Gen. Mgr.--The Sumitomo Trust & Banking Co., Ltd., Singapore, Singapore; *Int'l*, pg. 1318

Endrass, B., Mng. Dir.--Schwarz Extrusionswerkzeuge GmbH, Wolfratshausen, Germany; *Int'l*, pg. 825

Endres, Ronald J., Pres., Chief Oper. Officer & Treas.--Southern Union Gas Co., Austin, TX; *U.S. Public*, pg. 1491

Endresen, Axel, Pres.--Norcem a.s., Oslo, Norway; *Int'l*, pg. 42

Endresen, Edvin B., Pres.--Kvaerner Installasjon a.s., Hundvag, Norway; *Int'l*, pg. 769

Endung, Roar, Pres.--Kvaerner Ships Equipment a.s, Lier, Norway; *Int'l*, pg. 770

Eng, M., Mng. Dir.--Quality Bakers (Asia) Pte Ltd., Singapore, Singapore; *Int'l*, pg. 555

Engdahl, Peter, Pres.--Handelsbanken Fonder AB, Stockholm, Sweden; *Int'l*, pg. 1327

Engel, Clyde W., Chief Oper. Officer--Telco Capital Corp., Chicago, IL; *U.S. Private*, pg. 903

Engel, Clyde W., Pres.--Hickory Furniture Company, Chicago, IL; *U.S. Private*, pg. 903

Engel, David, Exec. V.P.--Dynarad Corporation, Deer Park, NY; *U.S. Public*, pg. 494

Engel, Ed, Plant Mgr.-Griffin--Tread Rubber Plant, Griffin, GA; *U.S. Public*, pg. 177

Engel, Horst, Mgr.--Commerzbank (Switzerland) AG, Zurich, Switzerland; *Int'l*, pg. 311

Engel, James D., Pres.--Recovery Services International, Inc., Philadelphia, PA; *U.S. Public*, pg. 366

Engel, Jorge, Pres. & Chief Exec. Officer--Berlex Laboratories Inc., Wayne, NJ; *Int'l*, pg. 1204

Engel, R.U., Pres.--F&S Incorporated, New York, NY; *Int'l*, pg. 1458

Engelbrecht, Horst P., Pres.--Lightnin Mixers, Rochester, NY; *U.S. Public*, pg. 726

Engelbrecht, S., Mng. Dir.--S.A. Paper Chemicals (Proprietary), Limited, Parklands, South Africa; *U.S. Public*, pg. 1580

Engelhardt, Harald, Gen. Mgr.--CiMatrix GmbH, Friedrichsdorf, Germany; *U.S. Public*, pg. 1395

Engelhardt, Irl F., Chm. Bd. & Chief Exec. Officer--Peabody Holding Company, Inc., Saint Louis, MO; *Int'l*, pg. 594

Engelke, Arno, Chief Oper. Officer--Gambro Dialysatoren GmbH & Co KG, Hechingen, Germany; *Int'l*, pg. 667

Engels, Robert, Mng. Dir.--Cognos Ltd., Bracknell, United Kingdom; *Int'l*, pg. 306

Engels, Thomas R., Div. V.P.--Medical Device Division, Ann Arbor, MI; *U.S. Public*, pg. 1605

Engert, Gert, Mng. Dir.--Rammer Deutschland GmbH, Wiesbaden, Germany; *Int'l*, pg. 1352

Engibons, Thomas J., Pres.--Texas Instruments Semiconductor Group, Dallas, TX; *U.S. Public*, pg. 1586

England, A.D., Mng. Dir.--P&O Property Holdings Ltd., London, United Kingdom; *Int'l*, pg. 1034

England, D.T., Gen. Mgr.--Fleetguard, Inc., Cookeville, TN; *U.S. Public*, pg. 468

England, Gordon, Pres.--Lockheed Fort Worth Company, Fort Worth, TX; *U.S. Public*, pg. 1007

England, John K., Mgr.--Beenup Mine, Karridale, Australia; *Int'l*, pg. 224

England, Peter W., Pres. & Chief Exec. Officer--Elizabeth Arden Company, New York, NY; *Int'l*, pg. 1435

England, R., Dir.-Gateshead Mfg. Div.--R.R. Donnelley, Limited-York, York, United Kingdom; *U.S. Public*, pg. 519

England, Rodney, Pres.--England/Corsair, New Tazewell, TN; *U.S. Public*, pg. 972

Engle, C.J., Pres.--Gared Sports Inc., Saint Louis, MO; *U.S. Private*, pg. 799

Engle, Clyde Wm., Chm. Bd. & Pres.--Bank of Lincolnwood, Lincolnwood, IL; *U.S. Private*, pg. 436

Engle, Dick, Mgr.-Service Center--Gulf Coast Service Center, La Porte, TX; *U.S. Private*, pg. 1180

Engle, H. Joseph, Pres.--AlliedSignal Technical Service, Columbia, MD; *U.S. Public*, pg. 50

Engle, Phillip R., Pres.--Bergen Brunswig Drug Company, Orange, CA; *U.S. Public*, pg. 213

Engle, Robert, V.P. & Gen. Mgr.--Banta Book Group-Harrisonburg, Harrisonburg, VA; *U.S. Public*, pg. 188

Engle, Robert C., Pres.--Waldom Electronics, Inc., Chicago, IL; *U.S. Public*, pg. 944

English, Charlotte Moore, V.P. & Gen. Mgr.--KSHB-TV, Kansas City, MO; *U.S. Public*, pg. 1448

English, Gerry, V.P. & Mng. Dir.--Option One, Minneapolis, MN; *U.S. Private*, pg. 710

English, Lawrence P., Pres.--Connecticut General Life Insurance Company, Bloomfield, CT; *U.S. Public*, pg. 360

English, Marc A., Pres. & Chief Exec. Officer--Cleo Inc., Memphis, TN; *U.S. Public*, pg. 284

English, Robert W., Mgr.-Branch--Piper Jaffray Inc., Butte, MT; *U.S. Public*, pg. 1302

Engsted, Michael, Pres.--AGA Gas Ltd., Coventry, United Kingdom; *Int'l*, pg. 13

Engstrom, Juan, Rep.--Svenska Handelsbanken Tokyo, Tokyo, Japan; *Int'l*, pg. 1327

Engstrom, Leif, Pres.--Forss-Parator, Mjolby, Sweden; *Int'l*, pg. 1420

Engvik, Terje H., Mgr.--Kvaerner Pulp Equipment a.s, Lier, Norway; *Int'l*, pg. 769

Enigk, Asmus, Chief Oper. Officer--Alfa-Laval Agrar G.m.b.H., Hamburg, Germany; *Int'l*, pg. 1377

Enker, Michael, Mng. Dir.--Amway GmbH, Puchheim, Germany; *U.S. Private*, pg. 70
Ennen, Richard L., Pres.--Only Deals, Inc., New Hope, MN; *U.S. Public*, pg. 1697
Ennerfelt, Goran, Pres.--Axel Johnson AB, Stockholm, Sweden; *Int'l*, pg. 708
Ennest, John W., Chm. Bd. & Chief Exec. Officer--Commercial National Bank of Berwyn, Berwyn, IL; *U.S. Public*, pg. 379
Ennis, Donald, Pres.--Nicholson Steam Trap, Walden, NY; *U.S. Public*, pg. 1747
Ennis, John M., Pres.--MacGregor Golf Ireland, Ltd., Dublin, Ireland; *Int'l*, pg. 73
Ennis, Thomas P., Pres.--Firstar Mortgage Corporation, Milwaukee, WI; *U.S. Public*, pg. 643
Ennit, Tony, Mng. Dir.-Mgmt. Committee--FinansSkandic AB, Stockholm, Sweden; *Int'l*, pg. 1259
Enoch, Jack, Gen. Mgr.--South Bend Perishables Division, South Bend, IN; *U.S. Private*, pg. 948
Enoki, Hiroshi, Chief Oper. Officer--Makita Corporation of America, Buford, GA; *Int'l*, pg. 831
Enomoto, T., Chief Oper. Officer--P.T. Irian Marine Product Development, Buru, Indonesia; *Int'l*, pg. 948
Enright, James, Pres.--Harte-Hanks Shopper Miami, Miami, FL; *U.S. Public*, pg. 794
Enriquez, Augustine, Gen. Mgr.--Bandag de Mexico S.A. de C.V., Leon, Mexico; *U.S. Public*, pg. 178
Enriquez, Engardo C., Pres.--Astra Pharmaceuticals (Philippines) Inc., Manila, Philippines; *Int'l*, pg. 94
Ensch, Thomas, Pres.--Champion Motor Coach, Inc., Imlay City, MI; *U.S. Public*, pg. 332
Ensch, Thomas, Gen. Mgr.--Commercial Vehicle Div., Imlay City, MI; *U.S. Public*, pg. 333
Ensenat, Ramon, Dir. Gen.--Mantequerias Arias S. A., Madrid, Spain; *Int'l*, pg. 201
Ensign, Bill, Pres.--Goldstrike Hotel, Jean, NV; *U.S. Public*, pg. 375
Ensiki, Akira, Mgr.--BB Europe-Banco do Brasil N.V., Brussels, Belgium; *Int'l*, pg. 141
Ensor, Charles E., Sr., Chm. Bd.--Sparks State Bank, Sparks, MD; *U.S. Public*, pg. 1089
Ensor, Eric F., Pres.--Bellsouth Personal Communications, Inc., Atlanta, GA; *U.S. Public*, pg. 208
Ensor, Kevin, Mgr.-Branch--Douglaston Electric, West Nyack, NY; *U.S. Private*, pg. 1110
Ent, W., Dir.--TBS Soest, Soest, Netherlands; *Int'l*, pg. 134
Enters, S., Mng. Dir.--Nihon Balzers K.K., Hiratsuka, Japan; *Int'l*, pg. 997
Entringer, James W., Chm. Bd., Pres & Chief Exec. Officer--Selective Insurance Company of America, Branchville, NJ; *U.S. Public*, pg. 1455
Entwhistle, Gordon, Gen. Mgr.--Castle Rubber Co., East Butler, PA; *U.S. Public*, pg. 1258
Entwhistle, Ray, Chief Exec. Officer--Adam & Company Group plc, Edinburgh, United Kingdom; *Int'l*, pg. 1132
Eoff, Robert H., Pres.--WREG-TV, Memphis, TN; *U.S. Public*, pg. 1174
Epifanio, Carlos, Dr., Dr.--Deutsche Bank de Investimento, S.A. (Porto), Porto, Portugal; *Int'l*, pg. 405
Epley, Glen, Gen. Mgr.--Poe & Brown of Florida, Saint Petersburg, FL; *U.S. Public*, pg. 1312
Epp, Peter, Chief Fin. Officer--Dixie Union Verpackungen GmbH, Kempten, Germany; *U.S. Public*, pg. 440
Epple, Steve, Plant Mgr.--The Binkley Co., Dumas Plant, Dumas, AR; *U.S. Private*, pg. 534
Epps, David, Pres.--Counce Finance Corporation, Houston, TX; *U.S. Public*, pg. 1578
Epry, Maurice, Chief Oper. Officer--Societe Generale de Grandes Sources Eaux Minerales, Paris, France; *Int'l*, pg. 919
Erana, Lic. Eugenio G., Chief Oper. Officer--Toshiba de Mexico, S.A. de C.V., Mexico, Mexico; *Int'l*, pg. 1406
Erasmus, D., Chief Exec. Officer--Morganite Consumer Products (MCP), Johannesburg, South Africa; *Int'l*, pg. 895
Erazim, John M., Pres.--Yarway Corporation, Blue Bell, PA; *U.S. Public*, pg. 1650
Erb, Melinda, Branch Mgr.--Downey Savings & Loan Association, F.A., Irvine, CA; *U.S. Public*, pg. 526
Erb, Rachelle, Branch Mgr.--The Commercial Bank-Cole St. Branch, Lima, OH; *U.S. Public*, pg. 410
Erb, Richard, V.P. & Gen. Mgr.--Nice Specialty Bearings, Kulpsville, PA; *Int'l*, pg. 1157
Erbes, William, Pres.--LINC Equipment Services, Lincolnshire, IL; *U.S. Public*, pg. 996
Erdman, Rick, Gen. Mgr.-Mfg.--Tylan General, Inc.-Flow Division, Compton, CA; *U.S. Public*, pg. 1112
Erdmann, Rainer, Mng. Dir.--Helaba Switzerland Ltd., Zurich, Switzerland; *Int'l*, pg. 799
Erdtman, Urban, Chief Oper. Officer--Scania France S.A., Saint Ouen-l'Aumone, France; *Int'l*, pg. 687
Eredini, James R., Pres.--J. Gordon Gaines of Texas, Inc., Irving, TX; *U.S. Public*, pg. 1623
Erener, Serdar, Chief Exec. Officer & Mng. Dir.--Young & Rubicam Turkey, Istanbul, Turkey; *U.S. Private*, pg. 1200
Erennalm, Stattan, Pres. & Chief Exec. Officer--AB Akerlund & Rausing Group, Lund, Sweden; *Int'l*, pg. 33
Erensen, George B., Chief Oper. Officer--Olin Export Trading Corporation, Saint Thomas, VI; *U.S. Public*, pg. 1219
Erfeling, Erwin, Chief Oper. Officer--Granges Metalock GmbH, Munich, Germany; *Int'l*, pg. 442
Erfert, Reiner, Vice Chm.-Europe, Middle East & Africa--Michael Conrad & Leo Burnett GmbH, Frankfurt/Main, Germany; *U.S. Private*, pg. 184
Ergun, R. Sukru, Mng. Dir.--Jotun Polisan Boya Tic A.S., Istanbul, Turkey; *Int'l*, pg. 715
Erhardt, Ed, Publisher--Advertising Age, New York, NY; *U.S.* Private, pg. 284
Erhardt, Ingo, Exec. V.P.--Embraco North America, Inc., Norcross, GA; *U.S. Public*, pg. 1765
Erhardt, Mary C., Pres. & Gen. Mgr.--Mark Antenna Products, Inc., Des Plaines, IL; *U.S. Public*, pg. 424
Erichsen, Jan Erik, Pres.--Norcem Cement A/S, Oslo, Norway; *Int'l*, pg. 42
Erichsen, Klaus, Gen. Mgr.--Florasynth GMBH, Norderstedt, Germany; *Int'l*, pg. 173
Erichsen, Thorbjorn, Gen. Mgr.--Indiana Tube Danmark A/S, Kolding, Denmark; *U.S. Public*, pg. 780
Erickson, D.L., Pres.--Consolidated Communications, Mattoon, IL; *U.S. Public*, pg. 1073
Erickson, David, Pres.--ITW Deltar, Glenview, IL; *U.S. Public*, pg. 866
Erickson, Donovan, Pres.--Holiday Station Stores, Inc., Minneapolis, MN; *U.S. Private*, pg. 534
Erickson, Dr. Paul, Pres.--New England Research, Inc., Worcester, MA; *U.S. Private*, pg. 724
Erickson, Edward H., Div. V.P.--Medical-Surgical Division, Saint Paul, MN; *U.S. Public*, pg. 1605
Erickson, Eric, Gen. Mgr.-Voice Prod.--Dukane Communications Systems Div., Saint Charles, IL; *U.S. Private*, pg. 346
Erickson, James, Mgr.-Sls. & Cargo Mktg.--Kuwait Airways, Northeast Region, Jamaica, NY; *Int'l*, pg. 764
Erickson, Jimmy, Pres.--Consolidated Network, Inc., Saint Louis, MO; *U.S. Public*, pg. 1073
Erickson, John, Chief Oper. Officer--John Rickson Properties, Vadnais Heights, MN; *U.S. Private*, pg. 553
Erickson, R., Mgr.-Adv.--Power Distribution Division, Milwaukee, WI; *U.S. Public*, pg. 557
Erickson, R.D., Pres. & Gen. Mgr.--Amoco Norway Oil Co., Stavanger, Norway; *U.S. Public*, pg. 102
Erickson, Robert D., Chm. Bd. & Pres.--Amoco Canada Petroleum Company Ltd., Calgary, Canada; *U.S. Public*, pg. 103
Erickson, Robert R., Gen. Mgr.--Mokon, Buffalo, NY; *U.S. Public*, pg. 1045
Erickson, Rolin, Gen. Mgr.--Montana Tunnels Mining, Inc., Jefferson City, MT; *U.S. Public*, pg. 1269
Erickson, Stanford, Publr.--Traffic World, New York, NY; *Int'l*, pg. 1026
Erickson, Terry C., Pres.--National Yellow Pages Monitor (NYPM), San Francisco, CA; *U.S. Public*, pg. 1146
Erickson, Theresa, Pres.--Old Kent Bank of Ludington, Ludington, MI; *U.S. Public*, pg. 1217
Erickson, Tom, Gen. Mgr.--Full Circle, Saint Paul, MN; *U.S. Private*, pg. 222
Erickson, Walter W., Exec. V.P. & Gen. Mgr.--Carlson Promotion Division, Minneapolis, MN; *U.S. Private*, pg. 212
Ericson, Claus H., Gen. Mgr.-Nordic Countries--CPC Foods AB, Kristianstad, Sweden; *U.S. Public*, pg. 225
Ericson, Hans F., Mng. Dir.--KONE Rulltrappor A.B., Kista, Sweden; *Int'l*, pg. 748
Ericson, Nils, Pres.--Logicon Syscon Corporation, Falls Church, VA; *U.S. Public*, pg. 1199
Ericson, Per, Mgr.--AB Sandvik Steel, Sandviken, Sweden; *Int'l*, pg. 1185
Ericsson, Anders, Pres.--Asea Brown Boveri Ltd., Dublin, Ireland; *Int'l*, pg. 8
Ericsson, Bengt, Gen. Mgr.--Conquest Europe, Stockholm, Sweden; *Int'l*, pg. 1483
Ericsson, Bjorn, Pres.--Astra Pharmaceuticals (HK) Ltd., Kwai Chung, Hong Kong; *Int'l*, pg. 94
Ericsson, Holger, Chief Oper. Officer--AB Pharos Marine, Stockholm, Sweden; *Int'l*, pg. 1289
Eriksen, Pelle, Mng. Dir.--SKF (Thailand) Ltd., Bangkok, Thailand; *Int'l*, pg. 1159
Eriksen, Vern, Pres.--Nooter/Eriksen, Inc., Saint Louis, MO; *U.S. Private*, pg. 801
Eriksen, Viljen, Chief Oper. Officer--Husqvarna Elektro A/S, Sarpsborg, Norway; *Int'l*, pg. 443
Erikson, Robert W., Pres.--Insituform East, Inc., Hyattsville, MD; *U.S. Public*, pg. 330
Erikson, Tim, Gen. Mgr.--GATX Logistics, Inc.-California (Kellogg), Walnut, CA; *U.S. Public*, pg. 691
Eriksson, Anders, Gen. Mgr.--Polaroid AB, Stockholm, Sweden; *U.S. Public*, pg. 1314
Eriksson, Azke, Chief Oper. Officer--SAPA AG, Zug, Switzerland; *Int'l*, pg. 443
Eriksson, Bengt, Pres.--Ballast Stockholm AB, Upplands Vasby, Sweden; *Int'l*, pg. 899
Eriksson, H.G., Mng. Dir.--Hellermann Scandinavia AB, Jarfalla, Sweden; *Int'l*, pg. 209
Eriksson, J.E., Mng. Dir.--AB Tegma, Malmo, Sweden; *U.S. Public*, pg. 1114
Eriksson, Jan, Pres.--Thai-Swedish Assembly Co. Ltd., Bangkok, Thailand; *Int'l*, pg. 1476
Eriksson, Jyrki, Mng. Dir.--Norvista, North York, Canada; *Int'l*, pg. 486
Eriksson, K. Harry, Mng. Dir.--Kalmar Verkstad AB, Kalmar, Sweden; *Int'l*, pg. 1421
Eriksson, Orjan, Gen. Mgr.--Systems Support, Vaxjo, Sweden; *Int'l*, pg. 277
Eriksson, Peter, Pres.--Alnab Armatur AB, Partille, Sweden; *Int'l*, pg. 678
Eriksson, Rolf, Mng. Dir.--Hagglunds Drives Inc., Columbus, OH; *Int'l*, pg. 670
Eriksson, Soren, Chief Oper. Officer--C E Johansson GmbH, Weiterstadt, Germany; *Int'l*, pg. 1290
Eriksson, Ulf S., Mng. Dir.--RPM Belgium N.V., Tielt, Belgium; *U.S. Public*, pg. 1357
Erixon, Steve, Admin.--Bay Area Medical Center, Corpus Christi, TX; *U.S. Public*, pg. 404
Erkaya, Cumhur, Chief Oper. Officer--Frigoscandia Food Process Systems International AB, Istanbul, Turkey; *U.S.* Public, pg. 607
Erken, Tore, Mng. Dir.--MoDo Skog AB, Ornskoldsvik, Sweden; *Int'l*, pg. 887
Erkeneff, Richard R., Pres. & Chief Exec. Officer--AAI Corporation, Hunt Valley, MD; *U.S. Public*, pg. 1679
Erlandsson, Anders, Chief Oper. Officer--Axel Johnson Petroleum AB, Stockholm, Sweden; *Int'l*, pg. 709
Erlandsson, Krister, Mng. Dir.--Ericsson European Support Centre, Brussels, Belgium; *Int'l*, pg. 1366
Ermatinger, Francis, Chm.--Coop Neuchatel, Neuchatel, Switzerland; *Int'l*, pg. 329
Ermold, John D., Pres.--MD Pneumatics, Springfield, MO; *U.S. Private*, pg. 1111
Ernest, David, Publr.--The Lancaster News, Lancaster, SC; *U.S. Private*, pg. 648
Ernesto Solitto, Roberto Felix, Pres.--Independencia Compania Argentina de Seguros, S.A., Buenos Aires, Argentina; *U.S. Public*, pg. 216
Ernst, Matthias, Gen. Mgr.--Sensormatic Ges.m.b.H, Salzburg, Austria; *U.S. Public*, pg. 1457
Ernst, Paul W., Pres. & Chief Exec. Officer--Carter Day International, Inc., Minneapolis, MN; *U.S. Private*, pg. 217
Ernst, Paul W., Pres.--Carter Day Industries (Canada) Ltd., Winnipeg, Canada; *U.S. Private*, pg. 217
Ernst, Peter, Mgr.--General Employment Enterprises, Inc., Woburn, MA; *U.S. Public*, pg. 714
Erol, Adil, Gen. Mgr.--Oysa Nidge Cimento Sanayi Ve Ticaret A.S., Nigde, Turkey; *Int'l*, pg. 1168
Erondy, Pamela, Branch Mgr.--Troy Savings Bank-Latham, Latham, NY; *U.S. Private*, pg. 1106
Erra, Mercedes, Co-Chief Exec. Officer--EURO RSCG Babinet, Erra, Tong Cuong, Levallois-Perret, France; *Int'l, pg. 600*
Erskine, E. Perry, Gen. Mgr.--Blancett, Fort Worth, TX; *U.S. Private*, pg. 906
Ertas, Semih, Mng. Dir.--Corro-Coat Toz Boya San.ve Tic. A.S., Istanbul, Turkey; *Int'l*, pg. 715
Ertel, Louis, V.P.-Gen. Mgr.--Foote-Jones/Illinois Gear, Chicago, IL; *U.S. Public*, pg. 1370
Ertun, Aybars, Chief Exec.--KONE Asansor Sanayi ve Ticaret A.S., Istanbul, Turkey; *Int'l*, pg. 747
Ertun, Aybars, Chief Oper. Officer--Tekimal Asanor Sanayi ve Ticaret A.S., Istanbul, Turkey; *Int'l*, pg. 748
Ertze, Juan Antonio, Pres.--Wallace & Tiernan de Mexico SA de CV, Mexico, Mexico; *U.S. Public*, pg. 61
Erussard, Michel, Pres.--Renault USA, Southfield, MI; *Int'l*, pg. 1102
Ervanian, Armen, Pres.--Viad Realty Corp., Phoenix, AZ; *U.S. Public*, pg. 1718
Ervesun, Enrique, Pres. & Gen. Mgr.--Cyanamid de Venezuela CA, Caracas, Venezuela; *U.S. Public*, pg. 80
Ervin, Robert E., Pres.--Consumers Service Company, Boardman, OH; *U.S. Public*, pg. 439
Erwin, W.E., Pres.--Chandeleur Pipe Line Co., San Ramon, CA; *U.S. Public*, pg. 348
Esa, Ahmad, Dir.--MTPB - Sabah Region, Kota Kinabalu, Malaysia; *Int'l*, pg. 833
Esaki, Kiyoshi, Pres.--GEOSTR Corporation, Tokyo, Japan; *Int'l*, pg. 763
Escalona, V.B., Mgr.--Nalco Chemical Co. (Philippines), Inc., Manila, Philippines; *U.S. Public*, pg. 1150
Escande, J. P., Pres.--Societe Bordelaise de Cic, Bordeaux, France; *Int'l*, pg. 565
Escandon Cusi, Pablo, Chm. & Dir.--Nadro S.A. de C.V., Mexico, Mexico; *U.S. Public*, pg. 1073
Escantra, Enrique Schacht, Dir.--Industrias Cydsa Bayer, S.A. de C.V., Garza Garcia, Mexico; *Int'l*, pg. 246
Escantra, Enrique Schacht, Ing., Dir.--Industria Quimica del Istmo, S.A. de C.V., Garza Garcia, Mexico; *Int'l*, pg. 246
Escario, Carlos, Mng. Dir.--Servicios Logisticos Integrados S.A., Madrid, Spain; *U.S. Private*, pg. 1120
Eschbach, C. Scott, Gen. Mgr.--Bioplexus Corporation, Las Vegas, NV; *U.S. Public*, pg. 874
Esche, Michael, Co-Chief Oper. Officer--Daarberg-Oekotechnik GmbH, Saarbruecken, Germany; *Int'l*, pg. 1167
Eschrich, Robert W., Pres. & Chief Exec. Officer--WM Life Insurance Company, Seattle, WA; *U.S. Public*, pg. 1742
Escobar, Miguel, Gen. Mgr.--Wackenhut El Salvador, S.A., San Salvador, El Salvador; *U.S. Public*, pg. 1731
Escosura, Luis, Mng. Dir.--Bertrand Faure Componentes SA, Madrid, Spain; *Int'l*, pg. 193
Escudie, Christian, Reg. Mgr.--Air France (Southwestern Region), Houston, TX; *Int'l*, pg. 561
Eshelmam, Bryon, Admin.--Crestwood Care Center, Shelby, OH; *U.S. Public*, pg. 838
Eskew, Robert, Admin.--Hillhaven Convalescent Center Salt Lake City, Salt Lake City, UT; *U.S. Public*, pg. 1713
Eskildsen, John, Pres.--United States National Bank of Oregon, Portland, OR; *U.S. Public*, pg. 1681
Eskola, Seppo, Chief Oper. Officer--Ahlstrom Machinery Salo Works, Salo, Finland; *Int'l*, pg. 34
Esmeyer, Hank, Chief Oper. Officer--Semitec, Inc., Santa Clara, CA; *U.S. Public*, pg. 969
Espen, Robert W., Pres.--Miether Bearing Products, Inc., Odessa, TX; *U.S. Private*, pg. 33
Espinola, Emilio, Gen. Mgr.--Grinnell Sistemas de Proteccion Contra Incendio S.A. de C.V., Mexico, Mexico; *U.S. Public*, pg. 1651
Espinosa, Jacobo Hernandez, Pres.--Repsol Derivados, Madrid, Spain; *Int'l*, pg. 1104
Espinosa, Manuel, Jr., Gen. Mgr.--Economy International Service Inc., Hato Rey, PR; *U.S. Private*, pg. 6
Espinoza, Manuel, Gen. Mgr.--Productos Avon S.A., Lima, Peru; *U.S. Public*, pg. 156
Esplen, Mike, Mng. Dir.--Heinemann English Language Teaching, Oxford, United Kingdom; *Int'l*, pg. 1479
Esposito, Andrew, Pres.--FiberCote Industries, Inc., Waterbury, CT; *U.S. Public*, pg. 1258
Esquivel, C., Gen. Mgr.--Laboratorios Wyeth Inc., Santiago, Chile; *U.S. Public*, pg. 81
Esseiva, P., Chief Exec. Officer--WAGO Contact SA, Domdidier, Switzerland; *Int'l*, pg. 209
Esser, Peter J., III, Publr.--The Oak Ridger, Oak Ridge, TN; *U.S. Private*, pg. 995
Esser, R., Mgr.--De La Rue Fortronic GmbH, Morfelden, Germany; *Int'l*, pg. 387
Essex, R.I., Gen. Mgr.--GKN Sankey Engineering Products, Telford, United Kingdom; *Int'l*, pg. 535
Essick, Skip, Gen. Mgr.--WBCT-FM, Grand Rapids, MI; *U.S.* Public, pg. 384
Essick, Skip, Gen. Mgr.--WOOD-AM/FM, Grand Rapids, MI; *U.S. Public*, pg. 385

Essingler, John J., Pres. & Chief Oper. Officer--Enron Capital & Trade Resources, Houston, TX; *U.S. Public*, pg. 584
Essink, Robert, V.P. & Reg. Mgr.--Kaiser Permanente, Central East Division, Rockville, MD; *U.S. Private*, pg. 605
Essl, Gerald J., Pres.--Texas-Lehigh Cement Co., Buda, TX; *U.S. Public*, pg. 323
Essoka, Ebenezer, Country Mgr.--Standard Chartered Bank Uganda Ltd., Kampala, Uganda; *Int'l*, pg. 1295
Esson, J. Douglas, Chief Exec. Officer--King Cotton Foods, Memphis, TN; *U.S. Public*, pg. 1433
Estenfelder, L.G., Pres.--Gates Europe, Erembodegem, Belgium; *Int'l*, pg. 1396
Estenson, Noel, Pres. & Chief Exec. Officer--Cenex/Land O'Lakes, Inc., Fort Dodge, IA; *U.S. Private*, pg. 646
Estepp, Larry, Reg. Pres.--First Tennessee Bank - Greeneville, Greeneville, TN; *U.S. Public*, pg. 639
Estes, A.H., Pres.--Haeger Potteries of Macomb, Inc., Macomb, IL; *U.S. Private*, pg. 493
Estes, Bill, Pres. & Chief Exec. Officer--McKesson Corporation, Carrollton, TX; *U.S. Public*, pg. 1073
Estes, Laura R., Pres. & Mng. Dir.--Aetna Financial Services Inc., Hartford, CT; *U.S. Public*, pg. 26
Estes, Phil, Plant Mgr.--Bridgestone/Firestone Tire Manufacturing Operations-Warren County, Morrison, TN; *Int'l*, pg. 213
Estes, Rick, Gen. Mgr.--Trelleborg YSH, Inc.-Carmi Mixing Division, Carmi, IL; *Int'l*, pg. 1422
Estes, S.E., Warden--Venus Pre-Release Center, Venus, TX; *U.S. Public*, pg. 451
Esteva, M., Chief Oper. Officer--Skis Rossignol de Espana S.A., Barcelona, Spain; *Int'l*, pg. 1127
Esteva, P., Chm.--National Westminster Bank s.a., Paris, France; *Int'l*, pg. 911
Esteve, Manuel, Chm. Bd.--Viva, Madrid, Spain; *Int'l*, pg. 575
Esteve, Rafael, Gen. Mgr.--Vinizius/Young & Rubicam, S.A., Barcelona, Spain; *U.S. Private*, pg. 1199
Estourgie, M.R.M., Dir.--HCG industrieservice bv, Rijswijk, Netherlands; *Int'l*, pg. 630
Estrada, J.s., Chm. Bd.--Hughes Microelectronics Europa Espana S.A., Correos, Spain; *U.S. Public*, pg. 725
Estrade, Javier de Ozamiz, Pres.--Defover, S.A., Panama, Panama; *Int'l*, pg. 1224
Estrade, Jean-Michel, Dir.--Etablissement de Martignas, Martignas-sur-Jalle, France; *Int'l*, pg. 383
Estroff, Allan, Mgr.--Service Uniforms Div., Atlanta, GA; *U.S. Public*, pg. 1539
Estroff, Allan, Mgr.--Southern Uniforms Div., Memphis, TN; *U.S. Public*, pg. 1539
Etchenique, Hugo, Pres.--Empresa Brasileira de Compressores S.A. (Embraco), Joinville, Brazil; *U.S. Public*, pg. 1765
Etelaaho, Jaakko, Rep.--Nokia Representative Office, Moscow, Russia; *Int'l*, pg. 953
Eterovic, Cedomir, Pres.--Dana South American Operations, Fort Lauderdale, FL; *U.S. Public*, pg. 480
Etheridge, Brian N., V.P. & Gen. Mgr.--Martin Marietta Air Traffic Systems, Washington, DC; *U.S. Public*, pg. 1007
Etheridge, Frank S., III, Pres.--SunTrust Bank, West Georgia, N.A., Columbus, GA; *U.S. Public*, pg. 1538
Etheridge, Jeff D., Regional Pres.--BB&T Regional Headquarters, Whiteville, NC; *U.S. Public*, pg. 160
Etheridge, Oliver, V.P.-Pur.--Lea Industries, Greensboro, NC; *U.S. Public*, pg. 974
Etheridge, P.W., Mng. Dir.--Edgars Stores Ltd., Crown Mines, South Africa; *Int'l*, pg. 1287
Ethington, A., Pres.--Rentokil Initial Pest Control, Duluth, GA; *Int'l*, pg. 1285
Ethridge, J.B., Pres.--Struthers Wells Corp., Warren, PA; *U.S. Private*, pg. 1048
Ethridge, Mark III, Publr.--Business Journals of North Carolina, LLC, Charlotte, NC; *U.S. Private*, pg. 19
Ethridge, Roger, Mgr.-Opers.--GATX Logistics, Inc.-Texas, Desoto, TX; *U.S. Public*, pg. 692
Ethridge, Will, Pres.--Prentice Hall Engineering, Science & Math, Upper Saddle River, NJ; *U.S. Private*, pg. 778
Etienne, Larry, Gen. Mgr.--Reed Travel Publishing-Omaha, Omaha, NE; *Int'l*, pg. 1097
Etienne, Marc, Chief Oper. Officer--Rhone-Poulenc de Venezuela, Caracas, Venezuela; *Int'l*, pg. 1113
Etienne, Philippe, V.P.--Fleishman-Hillard Brussels, Brussels, Belgium; *U.S. Private*, pg. 411
Etournaud, Denis, Gen. Mgr.--BHP Steel Building Products New Caledonia SA, Noumea, New Caledonia; *Int'l*, pg. 226
Etter, Christoph, Mng. Dir.--Sulzer International Ltd., Winterthur, Switzerland; *Int'l*, pg. 1306
Etter, H.J., Mng. Dir.--Contraves GmbH, Stockach, Germany; *Int'l*, pg. 998
Etter, Richard A., Chm. & Pres.--Bank of America Nevada, Reno, NV; *U.S. Public*, pg. 180
Ettie, G., Gen. Mgr.--Hosokawa Micron Powder Systems, Summit, NJ; *Int'l*, pg. 636
Ettie, Gordon, Pres.--Bepex Corporation, Minneapolis, MN; *Int'l*, pg. 636
Ettie, Gordon, V.P. & G.M.--Pelleting Systems Division-Crawfordsille, Nashua, NH; *U.S. Public*, pg. 705
Ettinger, Melvin A., Pres.--Du Pont Printing & Publishing, Wilmington, DE; *U.S. Public*, pg. 531
Ettlinger, Roy, Group Dir.--The Arbour Hospital, Boston, MA; *U.S. Public*, pg. 1696
Ettlinger, Roy, Grp. Dir.--HRI Hospital, Brookline, MA; *U.S. Public*, pg. 1697
Ettori, Francois M., Resident Rep.--The World Bank, Bucharest, Romania; *U.S. Private*, pg. 1189
Etzweiler, William D., Corp. Sr. V.P. & Chief Oper. Officer--Heckett MultiServ, Butler, PA; *U.S. Public*, pg. 793
Eubank, Frank, Pres.--Envirovac, Inc., Rockford, IL; *Int'l*, pg. 439
Eubank, T.W., Pres.--Taurus Energy Corp., Dallas, TX; *U.S. Public*, pg. 584
Eubel, Peter, Mng. Dir.--Walter Hundhausen GmbH & Co KG, Schwerte, Germany; *Int'l*, pg. 508
Eukovich, Robert, V.P.-Sls. & Mktg.--Pullman/Holt Corp., Tampa, FL; *U.S. Private*, pg. 1173
Eul, Chris, Mgr.--Shade/Allied, Inc., De Pere, WI; *U.S. Public*, pg. 89
Eulenberg, Tony, Liaison Officer--E/B/D/Interpartners, Dusseldorf, Germany; *U.S. Private*, pg. 1152
Eulich, John, Pres.--Mark Andy, Inc., Chesterfield, MO; *U.S. Public*, pg. 521
Eunson, Jack T., Pres.--Zurn Balke-Durr, Inc., Tampa, FL; *Int'l*, pg. 401
Eustace, Harry F., Pres.--California Microwave Navigation Systems, Inc., Washington, DC; *U.S. Public*, pg. 293
Eustace, R.R., Gen. Mgr.--Interplastic Distribution Group, San Antonio, TX; *U.S. Private*, pg. 572
Eustace, Royston K., Pres.--TECO Coalbed Methane, Inc., Tampa, FL; *U.S. Public*, pg. 1565
Evan, George, Pres.--Magnetics Data, Inc., Eden Prairie, MN; *U.S. Private*, pg. 696
Evans, A.A.J., Vice Chm.--Klaxon Signals Limited, Stanmore, United Kingdom; *Int'l*, pg. 590
Evans, A.N., Gen. Mgr.--Comalco (UK) Limited, London, United Kingdom; *Int'l*, pg. 307
Evans, Andrew, Chief Oper. Officer--Leonard Lifts Ltd., London, United Kingdom; *Int'l*, pg. 748
Evans, B., Gen. Mgr.--Newcastle Newspapers Pty. Limited, Newcastle, Australia; *Int'l*, pg. 477
Evans, C.L., Jr., Pres. & Chief Exec. Officer--Unisource, Doraville, GA; *U.S. Public*, pg. 1671
Evans, Carol, Pres.--Stagebill, New York, NY; *U.S. Public*, pg. 1328
Evans, Christer, Mgr.--Sandvik Polska Ltd., Warsaw, Poland; *Int'l*, pg. 1186
Evans, Clive, Mng. Dir.--Zitel International Corp., Thatcham, United Kingdom; *U.S. Public*, pg. 1794
Evans, David, Pres.--Carolina By-Products Co. Greensboro Division, Greensboro, NC; *U.S. Private*, pg. 192
Evans, David, Chm. & Chief Exec. Officer--Grass Roots Group plc, Tring, United Kingdom; *Int'l*, pg. 1482
Evans, Don S., Pres.--Operations Management International, Inc., Englewood, CO; *U.S. Private*, pg. 195
Evans, Dwight H., Pres. & Chief Exec. Officer--Mississippi Power Co., Gulfport, MS; *U.S. Public*, pg. 1490
Evans, Ed, Mng. Dir.--Robinson Cone, Burlington, Canada; *Int'l*, pg. 417
Evans, Eric P., Chm. Bd.--Integra Resort Management, Inc., Dallas, TX; *U.S. Public*, pg. 778
Evans, Eric P., Chm. Bd.--Condo, Hotel & Resort Management, Dallas, TX; *U.S. Public*, pg. 778
Evans, Frank, Gen. Mgr.--20th Century Insurance Co. of Arizona, Phoenix, AZ; *U.S. Public*, pg. 85
Evans, G.F., Gen. Mgr.--Denstree Corporation Ltd., Auckland, New Zealand; *Int'l*, pg. 703
Evans, Gary, Chief Oper. Officer--Hudson General Aviation Services Inc., Saint John, Canada; *U.S. Public*, pg. 846
Evans, George W., Pres. & Chief Exec. Officer--Regions Bank/Banks County, Homer, GA; *U.S. Public*, pg. 1371
Evans, Harold, Publisher--Villard Books, New York, NY; *U.S. Private*, pg. 21
Evans, Howel T., Branch Mgr.--Bear, Stearns & Co. Inc., Boston, Boston, MA; *U.S. Public*, pg. 198
Evans, Hywel, Chief Oper. Officer--Novo Nordisk Pharmaceuticals Ltd., Crawley, United Kingdom; *Int'l*, pg. 988
Evans, J. William III, V.P. & Gen. Mgr.--Charleston Television, Inc., Mount Pleasant, SC; *U.S. Public*, pg. 1078
Evans, Jack, Chief Opers. Mgr.--Ground Flat Stock Div., Mount Airy, NC; *U.S. Public*, pg. 1511
Evans, James E., Pres.--Lancaster Colony Commercial Products, Inc., Columbus, OH; *U.S. Public*, pg. 977
Evans, James, Dr., Pres.--SRC Vision, Medford, OR; *U.S. Public*, pg. 20
Evans, Jennie, Assoc. Publr.--Ziff-Davis Consumer Media Group, New York, NY; *Int'l*, pg. 1276
Evans, John P., Chief Exec. Officer--Associated Bank North, Wausau, WI; *U.S. Public*, pg. 140
Evans, John S., Chm. Bd.--Commerce Finance Company, Memphis, TN; *U.S. Public*, pg. 1155
Evans, Larry, V.P.-Mfg.--Lamina Inc., Bellaire Plant, Bellaire, MI; *Int'l*, pg. 75
Evans, Larry, V.P. & Gen. Mgr.--Prime Systems Group, Tampa, FL; *U.S. Public*, pg. 1329
Evans, Leslie, Chief Oper. Officer--Flymo Ltd., Darlington, United Kingdom; *Int'l*, pg. 444
Evans, Leslie R., Pres.--Electro Rent Corporation-ESD, Inc., Elk Grove Village, IL; *U.S. Public*, pg. 568
Evans, Leslie R., Pres.--Equipment Sales Division, Van Nuys, CA; *U.S. Public*, pg. 568
Evans, Mark E., Pres.--Wiltron Company, Morgan Hill, CA; *Int'l*, pg. 77
Evans, Michael, Chief Oper. Officer--Ferrosan Operations Ltd., Lewes, United Kingdom; *Int'l*, pg. 989
Evans, N.R., Representative--Morgan Grenfell (Kenya), Nairobi, Kenya; *Int'l*, pg. 405
Evans, Nicolas, Co-Mgr.--EURO RSCG Novation, Marseilles, France; *Int'l*, pg. 601
Evans, P.S., Div. Mgr.--Dan River Inc.-Riverside Div., Danville, VA; *U.S. Public*, pg. 479
Evans, Patricia D., Pres.--Prentice Hall of Australia Pty., Ltd., Brookvale, Australia; *U.S. Private*, pg. 778
Evans, Phillip A., Mng. Dir.--TAB Products Pty. Ltd., Auburn, Australia; *U.S. Public*, pg. 1559
Evans, R., Chief Oper. Officer--PSM International, Willenhall, United Kingdom; *Int'l*, pg. 852
Evans, Randy, Mgr.-Plant--Arizona Galvanizing Inc., Goodyear, AZ; *U.S. Public*, pg. 159
Evans, Raymond, Chief Oper. Officer & Exec. V.P.--State Auto Life Insurance Company, Columbus, OH; *U.S. Public*, pg. 622
Evans, Richard W., Jr., Chm. Bd.--Frost National Bank, San Antonio, TX; *U.S. Public*, pg. 467
Evans, Richard W., Jr., Chm. Bd.--Daltex General Agency, San Antonio, TX; *U.S. Public*, pg. 467
Evans, Stuart M., Pres. & Chief Exec. Officer--Amtech Europe Limited, Cambridge, United Kingdom; *U.S. Public*, pg. 106
Evans, T., Gen. Mgr.--Penny & Giles Electronic Components Ltd., Newport, United Kingdom; *Int'l*, pg. 207
Evans, T.J., Chm. Bd.--Birtley Engineering Ltd., Chesterfield, United Kingdom; *Int'l*, pg. 1139
Evans, T.J., Chm. Bd.--Taylor Woodrow Management & Engineering Limited, Southall, United Kingdom; *Int'l*, pg. 1358
Evans, T.J., Chm. Bd.--Birtley Engineering Ltd., Chesterfield, United Kingdom; *Int'l*, pg. 1359
Evans, Thomas E., Pres.--Tenneco Automotive, Deerfield, IL; *U.S. Public*, pg. 1577
Evans, Tom, Pres.--Walker Manufacturing Co., Deerfield, IL; *U.S. Public*, pg. 1578
Evans, Trevor, Dir.-Export--Export Sales & Distribution, Birmingham, United Kingdom; *Int'l*, pg. 390
Evans, Trevor, Mng. Dir.--Wiggins Arjo Ireland (Holdings) Ltd., Dublin, Ireland; *Int'l*, pg. 567
Evans, William A., Pres. & Chief Executive Officer--Regions Bank/Choctaw County, Butler, AL; *U.S. Public*, pg. 1372
Evans, William H., Chm. Bd., Pres. & Chief Exec. Officer--SunTrust Bank, North Central Florida, Ocala, FL; *U.S. Public*, pg. 1537
Evanson, Julius, Dep. Gen. Mgr.--Daniel J. Edelman Sdn. Bhd., Kuala Lumpur, Malaysia; *U.S. Private*, pg. 363
Evanson, Robert E., Chm.--Harcourt Brace & Company Farm Publications Inc., Orlando, FL; *U.S. Public*, pg. 783
Evanson, Robert E., Chm. Bd. & Pres.--The Dryden Press, a Division of Holt, Rinehart and Winston College Division, Fort Worth, TX; *U.S. Public*, pg. 783
Evanson, Robert E., Chm. Bd.--Gary Wood Associates, Inc., Valley Stream, NY; *U.S. Public*, pg. 783
Evarts, Don, Gen. Mgr.--ITT Barton Instruments, City of Industry, CA; *U.S. Public*, pg. 860
Evceg, I.J., Gen. Mgr.--New Zealand Starch, Auckland, New Zealand; *Int'l*, pg. 555
Evelyn, Carol, Gen. Mgr.--Harowe Servo Controls, Basseterre, Saint Kitts and Nevis; *U.S. Public*, pg. 90
Everard, John D., V.P. & Gen. Mgr.-Europe, Middle East & Africa Reg.--Newbridge Networks Corporation, Kanata, Canada; *Int'l*, pg. 924
Everett, Graham, Pres.--Caleb Brett USA Inc., Houston, TX; *Int'l*, pg. 671
Everett, Larry, V.P.-Reilly Foods--Reily Foods & Co., Knoxville, TN; *U.S. Private*, pg. 919
Everett, Steve, Gen. Mgr.--American Cablevision of Orange, Inc., Orange, CA; *U.S. Public*, pg. 1610
Everitt, David, Chm.--Chamberlain John Deere Pty. Ltd., Melbourne, Australia; *U.S. Public*, pg. 492
Everitt, David, Chm. Bd. & Mng. Dir.--John Deere (Pty.) Ltd., Nigel, South Africa; *U.S. Public*, pg. 493
Evers, D., Mng. Dir.--Automobielbedrijven Hoogenboom B.V., Rotterdam, Netherlands; *Int'l*, pg. 216
Evers, Heinz, Gen. Mgr.--Nicolet Instrument GmbH, Offenbach/Main, Germany; *U.S. Public*, pg. 1594
Evershed, Jeffrey A., Chm. Bd., Pres. & Chief Exec. Officer--Society Mortgage Company, Cleveland, OH; *U.S. Public*, pg. 955
Eversoll, Bob, Mgr.-Mktg.--Ecology System Dept., Grand Island, NE; *U.S. Private*, pg. 236
Everson, William, V.P. & Treas.--Premier Farnell, Cleveland, OH; *Int'l*, pg. 1068
Eversull, Andrew, Mgr.-Office--Woodward-Clyde, Jackson, MS; *U.S. Public*, pg. 1656
Evertse, Jan, Gen. Mgr.--Raychem (Nederland) BV, Amstelveen, Netherlands; *U.S. Public*, pg. 1362
Eves, Russell, Mng. Dir.--McCormick Foods Australia Pty. Ltd., Clayton, Australia; *U.S. Public*, pg. 1067
Evon, Joe M., Pres. & Gen. Mgr.--BHP Petroleum Ltd., London, United Kingdom; *Int'l*, pg. 225
Evoy, William, Pres.--Canadian Building Systems Inc., Burlington, Canada; *Int'l*, pg. 698
Ewanchuk, Boris, Gen. Mgr.-East Coast Opers.--Noble Drilling (Canada) Ltd., Saint Johns, Canada; *U.S. Public*, pg. 1187
Ewart, Alan D., Joint Mng. Dir.--London & Scandinavian Metallurgical Co. Limited, London, United Kingdom; *U.S. Private*, pg. 735
Ewart, G., Dr., Chief Oper. Officer--ICI India Limited, New Delhi, India; *Int'l*, pg. 665
Ewaschuk, Harry D., Gen. Mgr.--PCS Potash - Patience Lake, Saskatoon, Canada; *Int'l*, pg. 1064
Ewell, Ken, Pres.--Proto-Power Corporation, Groton, CT; *U.S. Public*, pg. 965
Ewen, Daniel C., Dir.--First Trust Company of Montana, National Association, Billings, MT; *U.S. Public*, pg. 1681
Ewerhart, Christoph M., Gen. Mgr.--Deutsche Bank AG (China), Beijing, China; *Int'l*, pg. 404
Ewers, Gene, Pres.--King of the Road, Russell, KS; *U.S. Private*, pg. 236
Ewers, Horst, Div. Mgr.--Standex International GmbH, Mold-Tech I North (Germany), Krefeld, Germany; *U.S. Public*, pg. 1507
Ewers, Lennart, Chief Oper. Officer--V.A.G. Sverige AB, Sodertalje, Sweden; *Int'l*, pg. 1474
Ewing, Christopher, V.P.--FCA Transaction Services, Inc., Norristown, PA; *Int'l*, pg. 471
Ewing, Edward, Pres. & Chief Oper. Officer--Southwest Marine, Inc., San Diego, CA; *U.S. Private*, pg. 213
Ewing, Larry, V.P. & Gen. Mgr.--Badger Meter, PMI, Tulsa, OK; *U.S. Public*, pg. 165
Ewing, Lee W., Opers. Mgr.--Delco Remy Division, Sao Caetano do Sul, Brazil; *U.S. Public*, pg. 721
Ewing, M., Pres.--Hood Corporation, Whittier, CA; *U.S. Private*, pg. 673
Ewington, M., Mng. Dir.--Gestetner Private Limited, Singapore, Singapore; *Int'l*, pg. 1115
Ewington, M. E., Mng. Dir.--Gestetner Malaysia Sdn Bhd, Petaling Jaya, Malaysia; *Int'l*, pg. 1115

Ewun-Tohna, I.D., Chm.--Taysec Construction Ltd., Osu, Ghana; *Int'l*, pg. 1360
Exec. Dir., Exec. Dir.--McAllen Medical Center, McAllen, TX; *U.S. Public*, pg. 1697
Exon, J., Mng. Dir.--Butterley Engineering Ltd., Ripley, United Kingdom; *Int'l*, pg. 585
Exposito, Daisy, Pres. & Chief Creative Officer--The Bravo Group, New York, NY; *U.S. Private*, pg. 1197
Eyerton, Keith, Chm. & Mng. Dir.--Costain Homes Limited, Marlow, United Kingdom; *Int'l*, pg. 336
Eynon, K., V.P.-Fin.--Curtiss-Wright Flight Systems, Inc., Fairfield, NJ; *U.S. Public*, pg. 469
Eysel, Jurgen, Mng. Dir.--Hoesch Rothe Erde AG, Dortmund, Germany; *Int'l*, pg. 509
Eytcheson, Rick, V.P.--KFBK (AM) & KAER (FM) Radio, Sacramento, CA; *U.S. Public*, pg. 335
Eytel, Lawrence, Pres.--ABB Environmental Services Inc., Portland, ME; *Int'l*, pg. 4
Ezcurra, Gus, V.P.-Worldwide Sls.--Harris Corp. Broadcast Div., Quincy, IL; *U.S. Public*, pg. 791
Ezring, Ron, Acting Regional Mgr.--CAP Gemini America (St. Louis Branch), Saint Louis, MO; *Int'l*, pg. 264
Fa, L., Gen. Mgr.--HP Foods, Market Harborough, United Kingdom; *Int'l*, pg. 380
Faas, Loni, Branch Mgr.--Zimmer Orthopaedic Implant Division, Warsaw, IN; *U.S. Public*, pg. 254
Faasse, A., Mng. Dir.--Van Leeuwen Precision BV, Deventer, Netherlands; *Int'l*, pg. 1449
Faba, Jose Luis, Chief Oper. Officer--Klippan Espana, Barcelona, Spain; *Int'l*, pg. 443
Fabbri, Mark, Pres.--Kvaerner FSSL Ltd., London, United Kingdom; *Int'l*, pg. 767
Fabbri, Mark, Pres.--FSSL Ltd., London, United Kingdom; *Int'l*, pg. 772
Fabeck, Pierre, Gen. Mgr.--S.A. Durco Europe N.V., Brussels, Belgium; *U.S. Public*, pg. 659
Fabeck, Pierre, Gen. Mgr.--S.A. Durco Europe N.V., Petit-Rechain, Belgium; *U.S. Public*, pg. 659
Fabert, Christian, Dir.--Banque Cogeba-Gonet Luxembourg SA, Senningerberg, Luxembourg; *Int'l*, pg. 547
Fabian, Jeffrey B., V.P.--Tesoro Refining, Marketing & Supply Co., Seattle, WA; *U.S. Public*, pg. 1582
Fabian, Mary Ann, Dir.-Personnel--Process Equipment, Congers, NY; *Int'l*, pg. 1283
Fabian, Peter J., Gen. Mgr.--Fansteel VR/Wesson-Lexington, Lexington, KY; *U.S. Public*, pg. 612
Fabian, R., Mgr.--Lindberg Heat Treating Co., Berlin, CT; *U.S. Public*, pg. 999
Fabian, R.J., Mgr.--Lindberg Heat Treating Co., Waterbury, CT; *U.S. Public*, pg. 999
Fabiano, Andrea, Gen. Mgr.--Watlow Italy, Milan, Italy; *U.S. Private*, pg. 1154
Fabiano, Joseph, Chief Oepr. Officer--Computer Enterprises, Inc., Newton, MA; *U.S. Private*, pg. 1072
Fabiano, P., Chm. & Mng. Dir.--Enichem Finance (Overseas) Ltd., Grand Cayman, Cayman Islands; *Int'l*, pg. 429
Fabre, Emmanuel, Chief Oper. Officer--NAPS France S.A., Lens, France; *Int'l*, pg. 913
Fabre, Roland, Pres.--Techlam SA, Cernay, France; *Int'l*, pg. 1166
Fabri, Dr., Pres.--SME International, Novara, Italy; *Int'l*, pg. 655
Fabri, Franz, Mng. Dir.--Touraine & Jacobi GmbH, Dortmund, Germany; *Int'l*, pg. 597
Fabris, James D., Pres.--Hurco Manufacturing Company, Indianapolis, IN; *U.S. Public*, pg. 850
Fabry, Georges, Mng. Dir.--Esselte NV Produktion, Saint-Niklaas, Belgium; *Int'l*, pg. 461
Fabulich, J.A., Chief Oper. Officer--Parker Paint Manufacturing Co. Inc., Tacoma, WA; *Int'l*, pg. 1501
Fache, Jean-Louis, Dir.--Engins Tactiques Div., Chatillon, France; *Int'l*, pg. 29
Fadel, Ali A., Pres.--Associated Spring, Bristol, CT; *U.S. Public*, pg. 190
Fadel, Toufic, Mng. Dir.--Fouad & Toufic Fadel & Co., Beirut, Lebanon; *Int'l*, pg. 458
Fadie, M. Jean, Chief Oper. Officer--Societe Toulousaine de Minoterie a Revel, Paris, France; *Int'l*, pg. 557
Fadiga, Antonio, Pres. & Co-Exec. Officer--Young & Rubicam Brazil, Sao Paulo, Brazil; *U.S. Private*, pg. 1200
Fagan, Anthony F., Mng. Dir.--Ethyl Petroleum Additives Ltd., Bracknell, United Kingdom; *U.S. Public*, pg. 595
Fagan, Bob, V.P.--Club Med, Scottsdale, AZ; *Int'l*, pg. 298
Fagan, James J., Pres. & Chief Exec. Officer--ILA Financial Services, Inc., Phoenix, AZ; *U.S. Public*, pg. 680
Fagan, R.J., Pres.--Quaker Chemical Corp., Wilmington, DE; *U.S. Public*, pg. 1346
Fagan, Robert W., Mng. Dir.--AC Rochester Luxembourg S.A., Luxembourg, Luxembourg; *U.S. Public*, pg. 723
Fagerholm, Stig H., Pres.--Opel Oy, Espoo, Finland; *U.S. Public*, pg. 723
Fagerlin, Mark, Pres.--Burns & Roe Services Corp., Oradell, NJ; *U.S. Private*, pg. 187
Fagerlind, Olof, Chief Oper. Officer--Ahlstrom Machinery AB-Recovery Processes, Stockholm, Sweden; *Int'l*, pg. 35
Fagerstrom, Hans, Gen. Mgr.--Det Norske Veritas, Jakarta, Indonesia; *Int'l*, pg. 397
Fagerstrom, Thor, Chief Oper. Officer--Neste Air, Vantaa, Finland; *Int'l*, pg. 913
Fagerstrom, Thor, Chief Oper. Officer--Neste Aviation and Marine Sales, Espoo, Finland; *Int'l*, pg. 913
Faget, Andre, Reg. Dir.--Pioneer Overseas, GES.mbH., Parndorf, Austria; *U.S. Public*, pg. 1299
Fagg, Terry, Gen. Mgr.--Pinson Mine, Winnemucca, NV; *Int'l*, pg. 169
Faggin, G., Supervisor--Kodak S.p.A., Padua, Italy; *U.S. Public*, pg. 554
Fagioli, Hugo, Gen. Mgr.--Medtronic Latin America, Inc., Buenos Aires, Argentina; *U.S. Public*, pg. 1084
Fahey, Frank, Gen. Mgr.--MTI Systems Div., Itasca, IL; *U.S. Public*, pg. 135
Fahey, John M., Jr., Pres. & Chief Exec. Officer--Time-Life, Inc., Alexandria, VA; *U.S. Public*, pg. 1613
Fahey, Mike, Pres.-Mfg.--Norandex Vinyl Products Co., Macedonia, OH; *U.S. Public*, pg. 1237
Fahlbusch, Fritz, Mng. Dir.--Dresdner Bank AG, Beirut, Lebanon; *Int'l*, pg. 419
Fahnenstich, Heiner, Chief Officer--Deutsche Babcock International Vetriebs-GmbH, Oberhausen, Germany; *Int'l*, pg. 401
Fahnenstich, Klaus, Mng. Dir.--Excellon Europa GmbH, Dietzenbach, Germany; *U.S. Public*, pg. 594
Fahner, Jan, Gen. Mgr.--John Crane Holland B.V., Barendrecht, Netherlands; *Int'l*, pg. 1339
Fahnrich, Eberhard, Mng. Dir.--LBB Service Gesellschaft mbH, Berlin, Germany; *Int'l*, pg. 160
Fahr, Rickey, Gen. Mgr.--Surplus Warehouse-Jonesboro, Jonesboro, AR; *U.S. Private*, pg. 120
Fahs, Jurgen, Mng. Dir.--ALLSPANN, Allgemeine Spannbeton GmbH, Puchheim, Germany; *Int'l*, pg. 423
Faijean, Francois, Dir. Gen.--IMS, Neuilly-sur-Seine, France; *Int'l*, pg. 571
Fair, C.B., III, Pres. & Chief Exec. Officer--Regions Bank/Paulding County, Dallas, TX; *U.S. Public*, pg. 1372
Fair, Eddie, Gen. Mgr.--Surplus Warehouse-Monroe, Monroe, LA; *U.S. Private*, pg. 120
Fairbairn, Will, Mng. Dir.--Ashdown Press Ltd., London, United Kingdom; *Int'l*, pg. 1226
Fairbank, C.E., Pres.--MC2 Inc., Lombard, IL; *U.S. Public*, pg. 1210
Fairbanks, Walter, Grp. V.P.--Cubic Defense Systems, San Diego, CA; *U.S. Public*, pg. 466
Fairchild, Alan, Gen. Mgr.--DeVilbiss Ransburg Spray Equipment, Barrie, Canada; *U.S. Public*, pg. 868
Faire, Phillippe, Dir.--Hatton et Cookson S.A., Libreville, Gabon; *Int'l*, pg. 1437
Fairholm, Don, Chief Oper. Officer--Nurre Caxton, Sunrise, FL; *Int'l*, pg. 460
Fairnington, Alan, Exec. V.P., Pres.-JWT/Asia Pacific--J. Walter Thompson Company, New York, NY; *Int'l*, pg. 1483
Fait, George A., Pres.--Capitol Facilities Corp., Madison, WI; *U.S. Public*, pg. 302
Faithfull, R., Pres.--Scott National, Calgary, Canada; *Int'l*, pg. 1012
Fajolle, B., Area Mgr.--Compania General de Geofisica S.A., Madrid, Spain; *Int'l*, pg. 241
Fakkert, A.A., Gen. Mgr.-Netherlands--Fortis International N.V., Utrecht, Netherlands; *Int'l*, pg. 499
Faksvaag, Svein Oue, Managing Dir.--Borregaard NEA, Lysaker, Norway; *Int'l*, pg. 1011
Falb, John, Chief Oper. Officer--NationsBank of Texas National International Co., Dallas, TX; *U.S. Public*, pg. 1163
Falce, Lou, Gen. Mgr.--Semicon Associates, Lexington, KY; *U.S. Public*, pg. 330
Falciola, Giuseppe, Chief Oper. Officer--Societa Alfa-Laval, S.p.A., Monza, Italy; *Int'l*, pg. 1378
Falck, Sven T., Mng. Dir.--Grenland Industriutvikling A/S, Porsgrunn, Norway; *Int'l*, pg. 959
Falco, Neil M., Pres.--InterLake Papers, Inc., Stamford, CT; *U.S. Public*, pg. 436
Falcone, Frank J., Regional Project Mgr.--Air Conditioning Co., Inc., San Diego, CA; *U.S. Private*, pg. 28
Faldt, Bertil, Chief Oper. Officer--Gambro Engstrom AB, Bromma, Sweden; *Int'l*, pg. 667
Falenius, Tor, Chief Oper. Officer--Oy Electrolux Ab-HUSQVARNA, Tampere, Finland; *Int'l*, pg. 441
Fales, Raymond, Reg. Mgr.--Det Norske Veritas, Rio de Janeiro, Brazil; *Int'l*, pg. 396
Falk, Anton, Adm. Leader--Springborn Testing & Inspection (Europe) AG, Horn, Switzerland; *U.S. Private*, pg. 1027
Falk, Patrice, Mgr.--Incognito, Clermont-Ferrand, France; *Int'l*, pg. 601
Falk, Raymond B., Chm. Bd.--Willis Corroon Corp. of Louisiana, New Orleans, LA; *Int'l*, pg. 1506
Falke, Goran, Pres.--Componenta Tools AB, Karlskoga, Sweden; *Int'l*, pg. 1421
Falke, Holger, Representative--Deutsche Bank AG (Istanbul), Istanbul, Turkey; *Int'l*, pg. 404
Falkenberg, J., Chief Exec. Officer--Dan Tegl Tag A/S, Aalborg, Denmark; *Int'l*, pg. 1092
Falkie, T. V., Pres.--Berwind Natural Resources Corporation, Philadelphia, PA; *U.S. Private*, pg. 138
Falkland, Johan, Mng. Dir.--Avesta Prefab AB, Avesta, Sweden; *Int'l*, pg. 221
Falkman, Edwin G., Chm. Bd.--Waste Management International plc, London, United Kingdom; *U.S. Public*, pg. 1745
Falkowski, Patricia A., Pres. & Chief Investment Officer--Fiduciary Management Associates, Inc., Chicago, IL; *U.S. Public*, pg. 1673
Fallon, Donald M., Chm. Bd.--Lehigh Portland Cement Company, Allentown, PA; *Int'l*, pg. 605
Fallon, Michael C.J., Pres.--United Properties Group, Fairfield, NJ; *U.S. Public*, pg. 1692
Fals, Peter, Chm. Bd.--Schweizerische Bankgesellschaft (Deutschland) AG, Frankfurt/Main, Germany; *Int'l*, pg. 1440
Faludy, Thomas, Pres.--Carefree of Colorado, Broomfield, CO; *U.S. Public*, pg. 217
Famechon, Rene, Dir. General--Micronyl-Wedco S.A., Montereau, France; *U.S. Public*, pg. 854
Famechon, Rene, Gen. Dir.--Wedco, Beaucaire, France; *U.S. Public*, pg. 854
Familia, Richard, Pres.--Giant Resource Recovery Company (Grr!), Harleyville, SC; *U.S. Public*, pg. 741
Fancher, Donald, Pres.--Waukesha Bearings Corp., Waukesha, WI; *U.S. Public*, pg. 521
Fandes, M., Dir.--Brother Industrial Espana S.A., Valencia, Spain; *Int'l*, pg. 229
Fanelli, Richard G., Pres. & Chief Exec. Officer--Enthone-OMI, Inc., West Haven, CT; *U.S. Public*, pg. 138
Fankhauser, Urs, V.P.--Sulzer Chemtech Pte. Ltd., Singapore, Singapore; *Int'l*, pg. 1308
Fanning, John, Pres.--PRO, Woodbury, NY; *U.S. Public*, pg. 409
Fanning, John, Pres.--THISCO, Woodbury, NY; *U.S. Public*, pg. 409
Fanning, John, Pres.--SOCO Thomasville, Inc.; Fort Worth, TX; *U.S. Public*, pg. 1482
Fanning, John, Pres.--SOCO California Properties, Inc., Fort Worth, TX; *U.S. Public*, pg. 1482
Fannon, Don, Div. Mgr.--Century Telephone of Claiborne, Inc., New Tazewell, TN; *U.S. Public*, pg. 330
Fanshawe, Douglas G., Chief Oper. Officer--Allright West Palm Beach, Inc., West Palm Beach, FL; *U.S. Private*, pg. 43
Fanthorpe, David C., Mng. Dir.--Black & Decker International, Slough, United Kingdom; *U.S. Public*, pg. 234
Fantin, Orlando, Mng. Dir.--Zimmermann & Jansen S.A. (Pty.) Ltd., Vanderbijlpark, South Africa; *Int'l*, pg. 1529
Fantola, Carlo Ignazio, Chief Oper. Officer--ESSPA-Edilizia Siciliana S.p.A., Milan, Italy; *Int'l*, pg. 170
Fantone, Lee C., Mgr.-Opers.--Centric Clutch Co., Woodbridge, NJ; *U.S. Public*, pg. 1794
Fantozzi, Joseph, V.P. & Gen. Mgr.--White Rose Dairy, Woodbridge, NJ; *U.S. Private*, pg. 330
Fantozzi, Joseph J., Pres.--McArdle Printing Co., Inc., Upper Marlboro, MD; *U.S. Private*, pg. 182
Farber, Bill, Chief Exec. Officer--Major Pharmaceuticals Corp., Auburn Hills, MI; *U.S. Private*, pg. 475
Farber, Sam, Chief Exec. Officer--OXO International, New York, NY; *U.S. Public*, pg. 716
Fardon, R.S.H., Exec. Gen. Mgr.--Mineral Resources--M.I.M. Exploration Pty. Ltd., Brisbane, Australia; *Int'l*, pg. 827
Farebrother, M., Chief Exec. Officer--Cape Plc., Uxbridge, United Kingdom; *Int'l*, pg. 280
Fariello, Frank A., Pres.--EDO Western Corporation, Salt Lake City, UT; *U.S. Public*, pg. 542
Farina, George, Mgr. Dir.--Wadsworth International, Belmont, CA; *U.S. Public*, pg. 1600
Farina, Gino, Chief Oper. Officer--Sabiem S.r.L., Bologna, Italy; *Int'l*, pg. 748
Farina, Joseph C., Pres.--Nynex Network Systems Company, Brussels, Belgium; *U.S. Public*, pg. 204
Faris, Mustapha, Chief Exec. Officer--BMCI Morocco, Casablanca, Morocco; *Int'l*, pg. 163
Farish, William S., Chm. Bd.--Anderson Park, Inc., Louisville, KY; *U.S. Public*, pg. 356
Farish, William S., Chm. Bd.--Churchill Downs Management Co., Louisville, KY; *U.S. Public*, pg. 356
Farkas, Joseph, Pres.--Standard Products Industrial, Bezons, France; *U.S. Public*, pg. 1505
Farkas, Melanie, Admin.--Fifth Avenue Convalescent House, San Rafael, CA; *U.S. Public*, pg. 1712
Farkas, Peter, Mgr.--Willis Corroon Hungary Kft, Budapest, Hungary; *Int'l*, pg. 1509
Farley, Claire S., Pres.--Getty Oil Exploration Co., Universal City, CA; *U.S. Public*, pg. 1583
Farley, D.W., Sec.--NGE Enterprises, Inc., Binghamton, NY; *U.S. Public*, pg. 1173
Farley, Joseph J., Pres.--Teletrak Advanced Technology Systems, Inc., Greenwich, CT; *U.S. Public*, pg. 808
Farlin, Diane, Exec. Editor--Sarasota Herald-Tribune, Sarasota, FL; *U.S. Public*, pg. 1175
Farling, Robert J., Chm. Bd. & Chief Exec. Officer--The Toledo Edison Company, Toledo, OH; *U.S. Public*, pg. 645
Farlow, Jeff, Pres.--Envirotrol Inc., Greensboro, NC; *U.S. Private*, pg. 378
Farm, Kaj, Pres.--Oy Scan-Auto AB, Helsinki, Finland; *Int'l*, pg. 686
Farman, Richard D., Pres.--Southern California Gas Tower, Los Angeles, CA; *U.S. Public*, pg. 1249
Farmer, Bruce J., Pres. & Chief Exec. Officer--Farmers Marine Copper Works, Galveston, TX; *U.S. Private*, pg. 422
Farmer, Bruce J., Sr., Pres.--Farmers Copper & Industrial Supply, Galveston, TX; *U.S. Private*, pg. 422
Farmer, Bruce, Dr., Chm. Bd.--Allied Colloids Group Plc., Bradford, United Kingdom; *Int'l*, pg. 62
Farmer, Donald, Pres.--Great Western Metals Inc., Houston, TX; *U.S. Private*, pg. 422
Farmer, Forest J., Pres.--Acustar, Inc., Troy, MI; *U.S. Public*, pg. 353
Farmer, Frank A., Pres.--Highland Propane Company, Roanoke, VA; *U.S. Public*, pg. 1393
Farmer, John R., Chm. Bd., Pres. & Chief Exec. Officer--SouthTrust Bank, Tuscaloosa County, Tuscaloosa, AL; *U.S. Public*, pg. 1492
Farmer, Larry E., Pres.--Brown & Root Energy Services, London, United Kingdom; *U.S. Public*, pg. 775
Farmer, Patrick, Mng. Dir.--C & J Clark Canada, Ltd., Oakville, Canada; *Int'l*, pg. 297
Farmer, William J., Chief Oper. Officer--Hills Precision Components Ltd., Stoke on Trent, United Kingdom; *Int'l*, pg. 1021
Farnam, Walter E., Chm. Bd. & Chief Exec. Officer--General Accident Insurance, Philadelphia, PA; *Int'l*, pg. 543
Farnsworth, Harold R., Pres.--E.J. Bartells Material Management Co., Renton, WA; *U.S. Private*, pg. 118
Farnsworth, Jack, Pres.--Primedia Information Inc., Hightstown, NJ; *U.S. Public*, pg. 1328
Farnsworth, Jack, Pres. & Chief Exec. Officer--Primedia Informatin Group, New York, NY; *U.S. Public*, pg. 1328
Farnsworth, James T., Plant Mgr.--Wolverine Technologies Inc., Jackson, MI; *Int'l*, pg. 1171
Farnsworth, Ross N., Pres.--Farnsworth Development Co., Mesa, AZ; *U.S. Private*, pg. 397
Farquet, Simon, Gen. Mgr.--Seba Aproz S.A., Sion, Switzerland; *Int'l*, pg. 866
Farquhar, Robert, Div. Pres.--Movie Star Factory Outlet Stores, Poplarville, MS; *U.S. Public*, pg. 1141
Farquharson, G., Pres.--Nanisivik Mines Ltd., Toronto, Canada; *Int'l*, pg. 1138
Farquiav, James D., Sls. Mgr.--Elkem Sales & Marketing Service, Hamilton, Canada; *Int'l*, pg. 448

Farr, Edward, Pres.--Northwest Pacific Indemnity Co., Portland, OR; *U.S. Public*, pg. 355

Farr, Frank, Gen. Mgr.--Southland Corporation - Canada National Office, Burnaby, Canada; *Int'l*, pg. 694

Farr, William, III, Pres.--Georgia Federal Bank, FSB, Atlanta, GA; *U.S. Public*, pg. 640

Farraker, Stephen, Exec. Dir.--WF Corroon-Manchester, Manchester, United Kingdom; *Int'l*, pg. 1502

Farrar, Clarence, V.P.--Goldblatt's Department Stores, Chicago, IL; *U.S. Public*, pg. 917

Farrar, David, Chief Exec. Officer--Allied Colloids Ltd., Bradford, United Kingdom; *Int'l*, pg. 62

Farrar, G.D., Pres. & Chief Exec. Officer--Barclays Bank of Canada, Toronto, Canada; *Int'l*, pg. 165

Farrar, Roger L., Pres.--Vanguard Bank & Trust Company, Valparaiso, FL; *U.S. Public*, pg. 1549

Farrell, Gary, Branch Mgr.--Saunders Oil Co., Inc., Charlottesville, VA; *U.S. Private*, pg. 968

Farrell, J.E., Pres.--Chrysler Credit Corp., Southfield, MI; *U.S. Public*, pg. 354

Farrell, James L., Jr., Chm.--Farrell Wako Global Investment Management, Inc., New York, NY; *Int'l*, pg. 1485

Farrell, Jerald F., Pres.--Hughes Communications, Inc., Long Beach, CA; *U.S. Public*, pg. 721

Farrell, Michael J., Pres.--Wide-Lite, San Marcos, TX; *U.S. Public*, pg. 730

Farrell, Nora, Mng. Dir.--The PR Centre Limited, Edinburgh, United Kingdom; *Int'l*, pg. 1226

Farrell, Patrick, V.P. & Gen. Mgr.--Ivex Packaging Corporation-Industrial Products Division, Newton, MA; *U.S. Public*, pg. 915

Farrell, Rick, Pres.--Hoyle Products, Saint Paul, MN; *U.S. Private*, pg. 172

Farrell, Robert, Gen. Mgr.--Mitchell-Bradford International, Waterbury, CT; *U.S. Private*, pg. 544

Farrenkopf, John, Plant Mgr.--Dayton Superior Corp., Oregon, IL; *U.S. Private*, pg. 932

Farrens, Gene, Reg. Mgr.--Green Tree Acceptance of Montana, Inc., Missoula, MT; *U.S. Public*, pg. 762

Farrington, Chuck, Plant Mgr.--Bunge Foods, Fort Worth, TX; *Int'l*, pg. 753

Farrington, Hugh G., Pres.--Progressive Distributors, Inc., Winthrop, ME; *U.S. Public*, pg. 782

Farrington, J.S., Chm. Bd. & Chief Exec. Officer--Texas Utilities Fuel Co., Dallas, TX; *U.S. Public*, pg. 1588

Farrington, J.S., Chm. Bd. & Chief Exec. Officer--Texas Utilities Mining Co., Dallas, TX; *U.S. Public*, pg. 1588

Farrington, P.D., Gen. Mgr.--Haden Drysys Environmental Ltd., Birmingham, United Kingdom; *Int'l*, pg. 585

Farrington, Stanley, Pres.--The Robert Carter Corp., Oak Park, MI; *U.S. Public*, pg. 1676

Farris, Allen, Pres. & Chief Exec. Officer--United Missouri Bank N.A., Kansas City, MO; *U.S. Public*, pg. 1654

Farris, Bruce, Gen. Mgr.--Pressure Pak Container, Inc., Paducah, KY; *U.S. Private*, pg. 300

Farris, David J., Pres. & Chief Exec. Officer--Beneficial Management Corporation, Peapack, NJ; *U.S. Public*, pg. 211

Farris, David J., Pres. & Chief Exec. Officer--Beneficial Management Corporation of America & Affiliated Corps., Wilmington, DE; *U.S. Public*, pg. 211

Farris, G. Stephen, Pres.--The Phoenix Resource Companies, Inc., Oklahoma City, OK; *U.S. Public*, pg. 119

Farris, John R., Pres.--Peabody TecTank, Inc., Parsons, KS; *U.S. Public*, pg. 1477

Farro, Angelo, Pres.--Deutsch Metal Components, Gardena, CA; *U.S. Private*, pg. 328

Farstad, Atle, Mgr.--Kvaerner Invest a.s., Oslo, Norway; *Int'l*, pg. 769

Farter, John, Mng. Dir.--Applied Magnetics (Malaysia) Sdn. Bhd., Penang, Malaysia; *U.S. Public*, pg. 123

Faruffini, G., Dr., Mng. Dir.--Balzers-Silmax S.p.A., Milan, Italy; *Int'l*, pg. 997

Faruque, A., Chm. Bd.--Mackinnon Mackenzie & Co. of Pakistan (Private) Ltd., Karachi, Pakistan; *Int'l*, pg. 1035

Farwell, I.S., Pres.--Rheem Water Heater, Montgomery, AL; *Int'l*, pg. 1022

Fasel, Dr. Juergen, Chief Exec. Officer--CHEMETALL GMBH Gesellschaft fuer chemisch technische Verfahren, Frankfurt/Main, Germany; *Int'l*, pg. 861

Fasel, Rolf-Dieter, Dir.--Deutsche Bank AG (Cairo), Cairo, Egypt; *Int'l*, pg. 404

Fasick, Ross W., Grp. V.P.--Du Pont Automotive Products, Wilmington, DE; *U.S. Public*, pg. 531

Fasolo, Joseph, Pres.--Baum Printing House, Inc., Philadelphia, PA; *U.S. Public*, pg. 1735

Fasquelle, Jean-Claude, Chief Oper. Officer--Editions Grasset-Fasquelle, Paris, France; *Int'l*, pg. 792

Fassati, Ariberto, Sr. Officer--Banque Indosuez, Milan, Italy; *Int'l*, pg. 314

Fassi, Johnny, Mng. Dir.--Tyco Toys (Italy) S.p.A., Milan, Italy; *U.S. Public*, pg. 1059

Fassler, Joseph K., Pres. & Chief Exec. Officer--Restaura, Inc., Phoenix, AZ; *U.S. Public*, pg. 1718

Fast, Larry, V.P. & Gen. Mgr.-Cord Prods.--Belden Wire & Cable Company, Richmond, IN; *U.S. Public*, pg. 201

Fast, Ole, Gen. Mgr.--Perstrup Beton Industri A/S, Kolind, Denmark; *Int'l*, pg. 1199

Fast, Robert B., Pres.--Claims Service International, Inc., Portland, ME; *U.S. Public*, pg. 1699

Fasth, Lars-Goran, Chief Oper. Officer--AB Overums Bruk, Overum, Sweden; *Int'l*, pg. 439

Fatemieh, S.M.H., Chief Rep.--Tehran Representative Office, Tehran, Iran; *Int'l*, pg. 520

Fathi, Ferri, Admin.--Victorian Convalescent Hospital, San Francisco, CA; *U.S. Public*, pg. 1715

Fatouris, Michael, Mgr.--Radiometer Pacific Pty. Ltd., Terrey Hills, Australia; *Int'l*, pg. 1084

Fatum, Arthur L., Pres. & Mng. Dir.-AT&T Capital Europe--AT&T Capital Corporation, Morristown, NJ; *Int'l*, pg. 924

Faubion, Charles M., V.P.--British Telecom Tymnet, San Jose, CA; *Int'l*, pg. 223

Faucett, Bill, Gen. Mgr.--Macklanburg-Duncan Co., Gainesville, GA; *U.S. Private*, pg. 692

Faucher, Richard R., Pres. & Gen. Mgr.--Falconbridge Dominicana, C. por A., Bonao, Dominican Republic; *Int'l*, pg. 434

Faude, Rudolf, Mng. Dir.--Ballinger Schalttechnik G.m.b.H., Balingen, Germany; *U.S. Public*, pg. 1366

Faudel, Gerald B., V. P.-Safety & Environmental Affairs--Wainoco Oil & Gas Company, Houston, TX; *U.S. Public*, pg. 1732

Faulhaber, Robert, Plant Mgr.--Wagner Lighting Products-Sparta Facility, Sparta, TN; *U.S. Public*, pg. 442

Faulk, Richard D., Pres.--Indimac Manufactured Housing Division, San Diego, CA; *U.S. Public*, pg. 857

Faulkner, David, Vice Chm. & Chief Fin. Officer--Memorex Telex Corp., Irving, TX; *Int'l*, pg. 857

Faulkner, John, Gen. Mgr.--Synflex Division, Mantua, OH; *U.S. Public*, pg. 689

Faulkner, Phillip G., Pres. & Chief Exec. Officer--USLIFE Real Estate Services Corp., Dallas, TX; *U.S. Public*, pg. 77

Faulkner, Ray, Mng. Dir.--Precision Moulds, Ltd., Kowloon, Hong Kong; *U.S. Public*, pg. 1059

Faupel, A., Gen. Mgr.--ACI Gateway, Saint Louis, MO; *Int'l*, pg. 891

Fauquet-Lemaitre, Arnaud, Mgr.--EURO RSCG Media, Moscow, Russia; *Int'l*, pg. 603

Fauquier, Chris F., Reg. Dir.--AlliedSignal Aerospace Canada Ocean Defense Systems, Ottawa, Canada; *U.S. Public*, pg. 53

Fauran, F., Pres.--Laboratoires Wyeth France, Paris, France; *U.S. Public*, pg. 81

Faure, Jeam Luc, Gen. Mgr.--Mepps S.A., Contes, France; *U.S. Private*, pg. 992

Faure, Jean-Pierre, Chm. & Exec. Mng. Dir.--Faure Vadon Forest, Paris, France; *Int'l*, pg. 601

Faure, Philippe, Sr. Country Officer--Banque Indosuez, London, United Kingdom; *Int'l*, pg. 314

Faus, Alberto, Chm.--Sharp Electronica Espana S.A. (Barcelona), Barcelona, Spain; *Int'l*, pg. 1229

Fausel, Chuck, Pres. & Chief Exec. Officer--Lester B. Knight Facilities Management, Inc., Chicago, IL; *U.S. Private*, pg. 627

Fausett, Jeff, Pres.--GKN Westland Aerospace North America Inc., Compton, CA; *Int'l*, pg. 535

Faust, Charles, Chief Oper. Officer--GeoTrans, Inc., Sterling, VA; *U.S. Public*, pg. 1582

Faust, Klaus, Chief Oper. Officer--BMW Technik GmbH, Munich, Germany; *Int'l*, pg. 177

Faver, June, Admin.--Silver Springs Nursing & Rehabilitation Center, Houston, TX; *U.S. Public*, pg. 839

Favereau-Forestier, Michel, Pres.--Chr. Hansen France S.A., Arpajon, France; *Int'l*, pg. 289

Favier, James G., Jr., Pres.--Olin Microelectronic Materials, Inc., Norwalk, CT; *U.S. Public*, pg. 1219

Favini, Carlo, Pres.--Elga Ronal S.r.l., Milan, Italy; *U.S. Public*, pg. 982

Favre-Bulle, F., Mgr.--Societe de Banque Suisse, Neuchatel, Switzerland; *Int'l*, pg. 1329

Favre, Jacques, Mng. Dir.--Banque Bruxelles Lambert (Jersey) Ltd., Saint Helier, United Kingdom; *Int'l*, pg. 148

Favre, Martin, Pres.--Bernina of America Inc., Aurora, IL; *Int'l*, pg. 189

Favro, David A., Acct. Mgr.--EMPIRE Machinery - Show Low, Show Low, AZ; *U.S. Private*, pg. 375

Fawcett, Gerald A., Pres.--Kaiser Eagle Mountain, Inc., Ontario, CA; *U.S. Public*, pg. 941

Fawcett, Gerald A., Pres.--Lake Tamarisk Development Corporation, Ontario, CA; *U.S. Public*, pg. 941

Fawcett, Rae, Acting District Mgr.--Circle Freight International USA, Linthicum Heights, MD; *U.S. Public*, pg. 371

Fawcett, Rae, V.P. & Mgr.-East Coast--Circle International, Linthicum Heights, MD; *U.S. Public*, pg. 371

Fawer, Samuel, Plant Mgr.--Swissmetal Plant Dornach, Dornach, Switzerland; *Int'l*, pg. 1427

Faxon, Bradford J., Pres.--Fall River Gas Appliance Co., Inc., Fall River, MA; *U.S. Public*, pg. 612

Fay, Luke, Gen. Mgr.--Diasonics Pty. Ltd., Lane Cove, Australia; *Int'l*, pg. 644

Fayard, Christian, Pres.--Siemens S.A., Saint Denis, France; *Int'l*, pg. 1247

Fayet, Luc, Pres.--Schweppes France S.A., Levallois-Perret, France; *Int'l*, pg. 248

Faym Catharine, Gen. Mgr.--A.C. Nielsen (N.Z.) Limited, Auckland, New Zealand; *U.S. Public*, pg. 1183

Fayne, Ed, Gen. Mgr.--A.E. Staley Manufacturing Co., Lafayette, IN; *Int'l*, pg. 1357

Fazio, Rob, Mgr.-Opers.--Inland Concrete Constructors, Riverside, CA; *U.S. Private*, pg. 332

Fazollahi, Dariush, Mng. Dir.--Dresdner Bank AG, Tehran, Iran; *Int'l*, pg. 419

Feabel, Doug, Sr. Prod. Mgr.--Consolidated Communications Mobile Services, Inc., Mattoon, IL; *U.S. Public*, pg. 1073

Fearn, David, Mng. Dir.--Lambeth Commutators Ltd., Bath, United Kingdom; *Int'l*, pg. 390

Featherston, Bob, Plant Mgr.--AMP Recycling, Austin, TX; *U.S. Public*, pg. 413

Featherstone, Diane L., Pres.--Constellation Energy Source, Inc., Baltimore, MD; *U.S. Public*, pg. 172

Feaver, Ed, Pres.--Prescription Solutions, Costa Mesa, CA; *U.S. Public*, pg. 1251

Febles, Alberto, Mgr.-Terminal--Barcelona Terminal, Barcelona, Spain; *U.S. Public*, pg. 692

Febles, I., Gen. Mgr.--S.C. Johnson & Son, S.A. de C.V., Mexico, Mexico; *U.S. Private*, pg. 593

Fechner, Hana, Dr., Chm.--Babcock Prozessautomation GmbH, Oberhausen, Germany; *Int'l*, pg. 398

Fechter, G.A., Chief Oper. Officer--Affiliated Building Services, Inc., Pittsburgh, PA; *Int'l*, pg. 322

Fecteau, T.P., Gen. Mgr.--Flexsteel Division, Lancaster, PA; *U.S. Public*, pg. 654

Fedak, Jerzy, Liaison Officer--E/B/D/Interpartners Warszawa, Warsaw, Poland; *U.S. Private*, pg. 1152

Fedchyshyn, J. Roman, Sr. V.P.--Manulife Bank of Canada, Waterloo, Canada; *Int'l*, pg. 840

Feder, F.B., Representative Dir.--Elgin Brother Industrial Ltda., Sao Paulo, Brazil; *Int'l*, pg. 230

Fedesna, Kenneth J., V.P. & Gen. Mgr.--Williams Electronics Games, Inc., Chicago, IL; *U.S. Public*, pg. 1727

Fedewa, R.E., Pres.--Transport USA, Inc., West Mifflin, PA; *U.S. Public*, pg. 389

Fedrick, Dee, Pres.--C.R. Fedrick, Inc., Novato, CA; *U.S. Private*, pg. 1052

Fedus, Cynthia, Pres.--Victoria's Secret Catalog, Columbus, OH; *U.S. Public*, pg. 995

Fee, Robert, Mng. Dir.--Turner South America, Sao Paulo, Brazil; *U.S. Public*, pg. 1646

Fee, Robert E., Pres.--Turner Construction Company, New York, NY; *U.S. Public*, pg. 1645

Feenan, R.J., Gen. Mgr.--Thomas De La Rue (Kenya) Limited, Nairobi, Kenya; *Int'l*, pg. 386

Feeney, Ed, Pres.-Liebert North America--Liebert Corporation, Columbus, OH; *U.S. Public*, pg. 573

Feeney, James K., Pres.--Windmoeller & Hoelscher Corp., Lincoln, RI; *Int'l*, pg. 1511

Feeney, Robert, Chief Oper. Officer--Systems Management & Development, Newton, MA; *U.S. Private*, pg. 1072

Feeney, William, Pres.--Dole Europe, S.A., Paris, France; *U.S. Public*, pg. 515

Fees, John A., Pres.-B&W Federal Svcs., Inc.--Babcock & Wilcox Co., Barberton, OH; *U.S. Public*, pg. 1068

Feese, Richard P., Plant Mgr.--IMO Pump, Columbia, KY; *U.S. Public*, pg. 857

Feffer, F. M., Jr., Pres.--Chemonics Fire-Trol, Inc., Phoenix, AZ; *U.S. Public*, pg. 591

Feffer, Frank M., Jr., Pres.--Chemonics Industries (Canada) Ltd., Kamloops, Canada; *U.S. Public*, pg. 591

Feghali, Charles, V.P. & Gen. Mgr.--Interstate Container Corporation, Reading, PA; *U.S. Private*, pg. 573

Fegler, James T., Pres.--Equitable Resources Marketing Company, Pittsburgh, PA; *U.S. Public*, pg. 590

Fehlandt, Ricardo, Exec. Pres.--Bayer de Chile S.A., Santiago, Chile; *Int'l*, pg. 175

Fehr, Hans-Peter, Mgr.-Switzerland--Fasson Vertriebs, AG, Dubendorf, Switzerland; *U.S. Public*, pg. 154

Fehr, Jeffrey F., Pres.--Warren Rupp, Inc., Mansfield, OH; *U.S. Public*, pg. 862

Fehr, Paul, Pres.--Georg Fischer Rohrverbindungstechnik Gmbh, Singen, Germany; *Int'l*, pg. 490

Fehr, Rick, Gen. Mgr.--Favorite Foods, Inc., Fullerton, CA; *U.S. Public*, pg. 1527

Fehrenbach, Dan, Pres. & Chief Exec. Officer--Citizens Bank of Western Indiana, Terre Haute, IN; *U.S. Public*, pg. 280

Fehring, Patrick J., Jr., Pres.--The Fifth Third Bank of Columbus, Columbus, OH; *U.S. Public*, pg. 621

Feierelsen, Andre, Mng. Dir.--Ewald Giebel Luxembourg G.m.b.H., Dudelange, Luxembourg; *Int'l*, pg. 79

Feigenwinter, Mr., Gen. Dir.--INTEL DATA AG, Switzerland; *U.S. Public*, pg. 1043

Feighner, Mark S., Pres.--GTE Mobile Communications Incorporated, Atlanta, GA; *U.S. Public*, pg. 696

Feightner, Ted, Mgr.--Home Products. Div., Stamford, CT; *Int'l*, pg. 1054

Feinberg, John R., Pres.--Dyno Merchandise Corp., Pompano Beach, FL; *U.S. Public*, pg. 428

Feinberg, Steve, V.P. & Gen. Mgr.--Outdoor Systems, Inc.-New York, New York, NY; *U.S. Public*, pg. 1235

Feinblum, R.M., Mng. Dir.--Conshu Holdings Ltd., Benmore, South Africa; *Int'l*, pg. 1287

Feinstein, Alan, Pres.--Micro Slides Div., Hauppauge, NY; *U.S. Private*, pg. 125

Feinstein, Jack B., Mng. Dir.--Sulzer Pumps (PTE) Ltd., Singapore, Singapore; *Int'l*, pg. 1306

Feinstein, Ronald, Pres.--Dennison Stationery Products Company, Holyoke, MA; *U.S. Public*, pg. 153

Feipel, Edouard, Pres.--TrefiLARBED Arkansas Inc., Pine Bluff, AR; *Int'l*, pg. 80

Feitler, Jr., Robert, Chief Oper. Officer--Adler Shoe Shops, Great Neck, NY; *U.S. Public*, pg. 1764

Feitler, Robert, Chief Oper. Officer--Stacy Adams Shoe Co., Milwaukee, WI; *U.S. Public*, pg. 1763

Feito, Marisa, Mng. Dir.--SKF Espanola S.A., Madrid, Spain; *Int'l*, pg. 1158

Felber, Neil, Mgr.--Public Service Company of Oklahoma-Eastern Div., McAlester, OK; *U.S. Public*, pg. 324

Felcht, Dr. Utz, V.P. & Grp. Pres.--Hoechst Celanese Advanced Technology, Short Hills, NJ; *Int'l*, pg. 625

Feld, Kenneth, Pres.--Ice Follies & Holiday on Ice, Vienna, VA; *U.S. Private*, pg. 400

Felder, Anton, Chm.--Arni AG, Lyss, Switzerland; *Int'l*, pg. 329

Felder, Anton, Chm.--Nutrex AG, Busswil, Switzerland; *Int'l*, pg. 330

Felder, Anton, Chm.--Panofina AG, Wallisellen, Switzerland; *Int'l*, pg. 330

Felder, Anton, Chm.--Pasta Gala SA, Morges, Switzerland; *Int'l*, pg. 330

Felder, Anton, Chm.--Schweizerische Genpssenschaft fur Gemusebau, Kersers, Switzerland; *Int'l*, pg. 330

Felder, Mariano, Mng. Dir.--Banco Interfinanzas S.A., Buenos Aires, Argentina; *Int'l*, pg. 347

Felder, Rolf, Mng. Dir.--BWH Koutschur GmbH, Marl, Germany; *Int'l*, pg. 1454

Feldman, D., Mng. Dir.--Churchill PPS-KK, Tokyo, Japan; *Int'l*, pg. 1025

Feldman, J., Pres.--NPDC-AS101, Inc., New Brunswick, NJ; *U.S. Public*, pg. 694

Feldman, Jeffrey, Pres.--Yellow Cab Co., Chicago, IL; *U.S. Private*, pg. 1030

Feldman, M.J., Gen. Mgr.--Wood Products Division, Harrison, AR; *U.S. Public*, pg. 654

Feldman, Noel, Pres.--West Mill Clothes, Tuxedo Accessories Div., Bristol, PA; *U.S. Private*, pg. 1163

Feldman, Steve, Pres.--Pulte Puerto Rican Operations, Bayamon, PR; *U.S. Public*, pg. 1345
Feldman, Steven J., Pres.--Pulte South Florida Division, Deerfield Beach, FL; *U.S. Public*, pg. 1345
Felicella, Frank, Pres. & Chief Exec. Officer--Builders Square, Inc., San Antonio, TX; *U.S. Private*, pg. 477
Felisa, Ana, Gen. Mgr.--Grace Colombia S.A., Bogota, Colombia; *U.S. Public*, pg. 755
Felix, Antonio G., Pres.--Felicitaciones Nacionales S.A. de C.V, Mexico, Mexico; *U.S. Public*, pg. 78
Felix, Bernard, Chief Oper. Officer--Matra Transport, Paris, France; *Int'l*, pg. 793
Felix, Hans, Chm. Bd. & Mng. Dir.--Scholl AG, Reinach, Switzerland; *Int'l*, pg. 1209
Felix, Maria, Country Mgr.--Utell International-Portugal, Lisbon, Portugal; *Int'l*, pg. 1098
Felker-White, Tammy, Gen. Mgr.--Salt Lake City Buzz, Salt Lake City, UT; *U.S. Private*, pg. 751
Felker, W. R., Mng. Dir.--First Chicago Futures, Inc., Chicago, IL; *U.S. Public*, pg. 628
Fell, A.S., Chm. Bd. & Chief Exec. Officer--RBC Dominion Securities Ltd., Toronto, Canada; *Int'l*, pg. 1131
Feller, H., Gen. Mgr.--Plus Leben, Neu-Isenburg, Germany; *Int'l*, pg. 565
Feller, H., Gen. Mgr.--Plus Allgemeine, Neu-Isenburg, Germany; *Int'l*, pg. 565
Feller, Raymond, Pres.--Rowman & Littlefield Publishers, Inc., Lanham, MD; *U.S. Private*, pg. 1128
Feller, Thomas W., Pres.--Sterimatics Corporation, Bedford, MA; *U.S. Public*, pg. 1113
Fellerman, Linden, Pres.--Telecredit Service Corp., Tampa, FL; *U.S. Public*, pg. 588
Fellerman, Linden J., V.P.--Telecredit Collection Service, Los Angeles, CA; *U.S. Public*, pg. 588
Fello, William, Pres.--Xerox Computer Services, Los Angeles, CA; *U.S. Public*, pg. 1784
Fellows, George, Pres. & Chief Oper. Officer--Revlon International Corporation, New York, NY; *U.S. Private*, pg. 690
Fellows, J., Chief Exec. Officer--GD Express Worldwide NV, Amsterdam, Netherlands; *Int'l*, pg. 720
Fellows, Steve, Chief Oper. Officer--Glendale Memorial Hospital and Medical Center, Glendale, CA; *U.S. Private*, *pg. 1118*
Felsch, Kurt, Sr. Mng. Dir.--Deutsche Bank-Kreditbank AG (Halle), Halle, Germany; *Int'l*, pg. 402
Felsted, John, Pres.--Chr. Hansen Pty. Ltd., Greenacres, Australia; *Int'l*, pg. 289
Feltham, Donald, Regional Mgr.--Jaco Electronics, Inc., Coral Springs, FL; *U.S. Public*, pg. 921
Felthuis, D., Dir.--Rademakers Gieterij B.V., Klazienaveen, Netherlands; *Int'l*, pg. 134
Felton, Edgar C., Chm. & Pres.--Bank of Bermuda (New York) Limited, New York, NY; *Int'l*, pg. 151
Felton, Peter E., Chm.--William M. Mercer Limited, London, United Kingdom; *U.S. Public*, pg. 1049
Feltrin, Antonio, Mgr.--Vendo (Italy) S.p.A., Casale Monferrato, Italy; *Int'l*, pg. 1184
Feltrin, C., Gen. Mgr.--VMC, Reims, France; *Int'l*, pg. 381
Fenby, Richard, Dr., Mng. Dir.--Rank Brimar Ltd., Manchester, United Kingdom; *Int'l*, pg. 1087
Fender, David, Plant Mgr.--AlliedSignal General Aviation Avionics, Lawrence, KS; *U.S. Public*, pg. 50
Fendig, J.G., Gen. Mgr.-Woodlands Div.--Union Camp Woodlands Div., Savannah, GA; *U.S. Public*, pg. 1666
Fendrich, George, Div. Mgr.--Raven Industries Sportswear Div., Sioux Falls, SD; *U.S. Public*, pg. 1361
Fenech, Derek, Mng. Dir.--Crown Advertising Ltd., Valetta, Malta; *U.S. Private*, pg. 303
Fenna, David, Dir.--Willis Faber Consulting (Far East) Ltd., Wan Chai, Hong Kong; *Int'l*, pg. 1502
Fenner, Ken, Area Mgr.--Lavington Planer Division, Vernon, Canada; *Int'l*, pg. 1395
Fennessy, Jim, Mgr.--Dayton Superior Canada Ltd., Rexdale, Canada; *U.S. Private*, pg. 932
Fennie, Bruce W., V.P. & Gen. Mgr.--Harris Corp., RF Communications Group Marketing Division, Rochester, NY; *U.S. Public*, pg. 792
Fennimore, Robert T., Pres.--Rainbow Advertising Sales Corporation (RASCO), Woodbury, NY; *U.S. Public*, pg. 288
Fennings, Roger, Mng. Dir.--Intermarkets Public Relations (ME), Dubai, United Arab Emirates; *Int'l*, pg. 680
Fenolgio, Walter, Dr., Chief Oper. Officer--U.I.C.A. S.p.A., Turin, Italy; *Int'l*, pg. 481
Fensgard, Oyund, Mng. Dir.--Corro-Coat (Thailand) Ltd., Bangkok, Thailand; *Int'l*, pg. 715
Fenster, R.F., V.P. & Gen. Mgr.--Automotive, Wayne, NJ; *Int'l*, pg. 234
Fenstermacher, Richard L., Exec. Dir.--NAAO Marketing, Dearborn, MI; *U.S. Public*, pg. 662
Fenton, Barry, Mng. Dir.--Jones Environmental (Ireland) Ltd., Dublin, Ireland; *Int'l*, pg. 1444
Fenton, Chris, Chief Oper. Officer--Alfa-Laval Hamilton Pty Ltd., Melbourne, Australia; *Int'l*, pg. 1379
Fenton, Robert, Dir. & Mgr.--AlliedSignal Aerospace Limited, Waterloo, Australia; *U.S. Public*, pg. 52
Fenton, T., Chief Oper. Officer--Huwood International, Gateshead, United Kingdom; *Int'l*, pg. 473
Fenwick, Robert, Dr., Chm. Bd. & Chief Exec. Officer--On Command Video, Santa Clara, CA; *U.S. Public*, pg. 138
Fer, Claude, Gen. Mgr.--Storage Technology Switzerland AG, Zurich, Switzerland; *U.S. Public*, pg. 1523
Feraco, Frank, Pres. & Sector Exec.--Sterling Plumbing Group, Inc., Rolling Meadows, IL; *U.S. Private*, pg. 630
Ferdausi, H., Gen. Mgr.--Burroughs Wellcome & Co (Bangladesh) Ltd, Dhaka, Bangladesh; *Int'l*, pg. 553
Ferdinandtsen, G.R., Chm. Bd. & Pres.--American National Life Insurance Co. of Texas, Galveston, TX; *U.S. Public*, pg. 87
Ferfer, Gottfried, Chief Officer--Generale Bank & Co., Monchengladbach, Germany; *Int'l*, pg. 548
Fergen, P.A., Gen. Mgr.--Hunter Douglas Fabrication Company, Kent, WA; *Int'l*, pg. 639
Ferger, Lawrence A., Pres.--IEI Investments, Inc., Indianapolis, IN; *U.S. Public*, pg. 875
Ferger, Lawrence A., Pres.--Energy Realty, Inc., Indianapolis, IN; *U.S. Public*, pg. 875
Fergus, Dan, Pres.--Genesee Stamping, Grand Prairie, TX; *U.S. Private*, pg. 446
Fergus, Jeff, Grp. Pres.-Europe, Middle East, Africa & Asia/Pacific--Leo Burnett Greater China, Quarry Bay, Hong Kong; *U.S. Private*, pg. 185
Fergus, Jeff, Grp. Pres.-Europe, Middle EAst, Africa & Asia-Pacific--Leo Burnett Worldwide Asia/Pacific Hdqtrs., Hong Kong, Hong Kong; *U.S. Private*, pg. 186
Fergus, M.P., Chief Exec. Officer--Allied Van Lines, Inc., Naperville, IL; *Int'l*, pg. 901
Ferguson, Brian, Sr. V.P.-Dana Europe--Dana Distribution U.K., Swindon, United Kingdom; *U.S. Public*, pg. 480
Ferguson, C. David, Pres.--Gould Electronics Inc., Foil Division, Eastlake, OH; *U.S. Public*, pg. 1592
Ferguson, Colin, V.P. & Gen. Mgr.--Palmer Jarvis Advertising, Winnipeg, Canada; *Int'l*, pg. 1022
Ferguson, D. R., Div. Mgr.--Eve River Division, Sayward, Canada; *Int'l*, pg. 828
Ferguson, D.C., Exec. Dir.-North American Opers.--Brambles Holdings Limited, Sydney, Australia; *Int'l*, pg. 211
Ferguson, Daniel S., Mgr.--Canadian Imperial Bank of Commerce (Suisse) S.A., Geneva, Switzerland; *Int'l*, pg. 258
Ferguson, Darrel R., Pres. & Chief Exec. Officer--NationsBank of Troy, Troy, MO; *U.S. Public*, pg. 1165
Ferguson, Dwight, Pres. & Chief Oper. Officer--Florimex Worldwide, Inc., Danville, VA; *U.S. Public*, pg. 510
Ferguson, Gary L., Pres. & Treas.--Dearborn Capital Corporation, Dearborn, MI; *U.S. Public*, pg. 663
Ferguson, Gerry, Pres., Chief Exec. Officer & Chief Oper. Officer--Binning's Building Products, Inc., Lexington, NC; *U.S. Public*, pg. 67
Ferguson, Jerry, Mgr.-Opers.--Key Perfuracoes Maritimas Limitada, Rio de Janeiro, Brazil; *Int'l*, pg. 765
Ferguson, John, Pres.--U.S. Elevator, Spring Valley, CA; *Int'l*, pg. 1387
Ferguson, John, Gen. Mgr.--Thousand Oaks News-Chronicle, Thousand Oaks, CA; *U.S. Public*, pg. 1448
Ferguson, Ken, Mng. Dir.--MRNI, Bangor, United Kingdom; *Int'l*, pg. 554
Ferguson, Mary Ann, Admin.--Hillhaven Convalescent Hospital Claremont, Claremont, CA; *U.S. Public*, pg. 1713
Ferguson, Rex, V.P.--Sentrol Controls Group, Hickory, NC; *U.S. Private*, pg. 139
Ferguson, Robert, Pres.--Bankers Trust Australia Limited, Sydney, Australia; *U.S. Public*, pg. 185
Ferguson, Robert, Pres.--Continental Airline Holdings, Inc., Houston, TX; *Int'l*, pg. 1202
Ferguson, Robert J., Pres.--Royal Life Insurance Company of Canada, Oakville, Canada; *Int'l*, pg. 1130
Ferguson, Whitworth, Pres. & Dir.--Ferguson Electric Equipment Corporation, Buffalo, NY; *U.S. Private*, pg. 401
Ferguson, Whitworth, Pres.--Ferguson Electric Service Co., Inc., Buffalo, NY; *U.S. Private*, pg. 401
Fergusson, Ann, Gen. Mgr.--Shelby Williams Textiles, Morristown, TN; *U.S. Public*, pg. 1465
Fergusson, Ewen, Sir, Chm.--Coutts & Co., London, United Kingdom; *Int'l*, pg. 910
Ferioli, Vilmo, Gen. Mgr.--VM Motori S.p.A., Cento, Italy; *Int'l*, pg. 654
Ferkany, Edward A., Grp. V.P.--Worthington Steel Co., Columbus, OH; *U.S. Public*, pg. 1780
Ferlauto, Dominic, Pres.--The Keds Corporation, Lexington, MA; *U.S. Public*, pg. 1525
Ferlecki, G.M., Pres.--Hull-Thomson Limited, Windsor, Canada; *Int'l*, pg. 1150
Fermin, Mendizabal, Chief Oper. Officer--Mayc S.A., Berga, Spain; *Int'l*, pg. 260
Fern, David, Publr.--Business Week, New York, NY; *U.S. Public*, pg. 1069
Fern, Nicholas, Chief Oper. Officer--Crompton & Knowles Tertre SA., Brussels, Belgium; *U.S. Public*, pg. 460
Fernandes, Gary, Sr. V.P.--EDS, International, Commercial and Communications Groups, Dallas, TX; *U.S. Public*, pg. 570
Fernandes, Jay, Pres.--Whittaker Controls, Inc., North Hollywood, CA; *U.S. Public*, pg. 1767
Fernandes, Leo, Gen. Mgr.--Quality Hotel Downtown, Washington, DC; *U.S. Private*, pg. 1067
Fernandes, Lester L., Gen. Mgr.--Cominco (Peru) S.R.L., Lima, Peru; *Int'l*, pg. 307
Fernandes, Melania Medeiros, Gen. Mgr.--Banco do Brasil S.A.-Panama, Panama, Panama; *Int'l*, pg. 141
Fernandes, Miguel, Mng. Dir.--Donaldson do Brasil, Ltda., Diadema, Brazil; *U.S. Public*, pg. 517
Fernandez Rodriguez, Antonio, Chm. & Pres.--Grupo Modelo S.A., Mexico, Mexico; *U.S. Public*, pg. 115
Fernandez, Anthony G., Chm.--ARCO Chemical Co., Newtown Square, PA; *U.S. Public*, pg. 144
Fernandez, Braulio, Mng. Dir.--Ferro Ecuatoriana S.A., Cuenca, Ecuador; *U.S. Public*, pg. 619
Fernandez, Carlos, Gen. Mgr.--Re-Mi Foods Inc., Elk Grove Village, IL; *U.S. Private*, pg. 158
Fernandez, Dario, Gen. Mgr.--Empresa de Refractarios Colombianos S.A., Medellin, Colombia; *U.S. Private*, pg. 903
Fernandez, Dario, Gen. Mgr.--Materiales Industriales S.A., Bogota, Colombia; *U.S. Private*, pg. 904
Fernandez, David, Gen. Mgr.--TN Media, Caracas, Venezuela; *U.S. Public*, pg. 1641
Fernandez, Domingo Soto, Gen. Mgr.--Telefonica Chile, S.A., Santiago, Chile; *Int'l*, pg. 1372
Fernandez, Eleuterio Juarez, Mng. Dir.--FoxVideo (Espanola) S.A., Madrid, Spain; *Int'l*, pg. 926
Fernandez, Fausto B., Mng. Dir.--Kimberly-Clark International, S.A., Panama, Panama; *U.S. Public*, pg. 959
Fernandez, Fernando, Country Mgr.--Grace Venezuela S.A., Valencia, Venezuela; *U.S. Public*, pg. 756
Fernandez, Fernando Rubio, Pres.--INESPAL - Industria Espanola del Aluminio, S.A., Madrid, Spain; *Int'l*, pg. 1225
Fernandez, Florencio, Gen. Mgr.--Security Plastics Caribe, Inc., Rio Grande, PR; *U.S. Private*, pg. 981
Fernandez, Geuillermo, Pres.--Colgate-Palmolive Co. Anonima, Caracas, Venezuela; *U.S. Public*, pg. 398
Fernandez, Gregorio Rodriguez, Gen. Mgr.--Binter Finance, B.V., Hoofddorp, Netherlands; *Int'l*, pg. 1225
Fernandez, Guillermo, Mng. Dir.--Grace Portuguesa Lda., Savcavem, Portugal; *U.S. Public*, pg. 756
Fernandez, Guillermo, Mng. Dir.--Grace, S.A., Barcelona, Spain; *U.S. Public*, pg. 756
Fernandez, J., Mng. Dir.--Alconor S.A., Itapissuma, Brazil; *U.S. Public*, pg. 62
Fernandez, J., Mng. Dir.--Alumar Consortium, Sao Luis, Brazil; *U.S. Public*, pg. 62
Fernandez, Jaime, Branch Mgr.--Mallinckrodt Caribe, Inc., Catano, PR; *U.S. Public*, pg. 1039
Fernandez, James N., Mng. Dir.--Tiffany & Co. Overseas Finance B.V., Amsterdam, Netherlands; *U.S. Public*, pg. 1609
Fernandez, Javier, Gen. Dir.--Compania Latinoamerica de Software (LASC), Medellin, Colombia; *U.S. Public*, pg. 1043
Fernandez, John Viney, Pres.--PDV Marina, S.A., Caracas, Venezuela; *Int'l*, pg. 1045
Fernandez, Jorge, Pres.--Fleck Controls, Milwaukee, WI; *U.S. Public*, pg. 1273
Fernandez, Jose Luis, Gen. Mgr.--Consumer Opers.--Refinacoes de Milho, Brasil Ltda., Sao Paulo, Brazil; *U.S.* Public, pg. 448
Fernandez, L.M., Chief Oper. Officer--Makro Autoservico Grossista, S.A., Lisbon, Portugal; *Int'l*, pg. 1155
Fernandez, Luis, Pres.--Bustelo Coffee Roasting Co., Bronx, NY; *Int'l*, pg. 1377
Fernandez, Luis Garza T., Pres.--Galvak S.A., San Nicolas, Mexico; *Int'l*, pg. 56
Fernandez, Manuel, Mgr.--Alpine Center, s.r.l. (Berlitz), Milan, Italy; *U.S. Public*, pg. 221
Fernandez, Manuel, Mgr.--Alps Institute s.r.l. (Berlitz), Rome, Italy; *U.S. Public*, pg. 221
Fernandez, Mirta, Pres.--Cavexsa (U.S.A.) Inc., Calumet City, IL; *U.S. Private*, pg. 694
Fernandez, Nelly, Reg. Dir.-Mexico, Cuba & Central America--Utell International-Mexico, Mexico, Mexico; *Int'l*, *pg. 1098*
Fernandini, Fernando, Gen. Mgr.--Alimentos y Productos de Maiz S.A., Callao, Peru; *U.S. Public*, pg. 447
Ferneyhough, Butch, Pres.--Pall (Canada) Ltd., Mississauga, Canada; *U.S. Public*, pg. 1254
Fernstrom, Gunnar, Chief Oper. officer--Molnlycke Absorbant Products Supply AB, Molnlycke, Sweden; *Int'l*, *pg. 1326*
Fernvik, Hakan, Bus. Area Mgr.--Cementa AB, Danderyd, Sweden; *Int'l*, pg. 1198
Feroz, Mehtabuddin, Pres.--Otsuka Pakistan Ltd., Karachi, Pakistan; *Int'l*, pg. 1014
Ferran, Xavier, Chm. Bd. & Pres.--Bacardi-Martini Belgium, Brussels, Belgium; *U.S. Private*, pg. 109
Ferrantee, Michael A., Gen. Mgr.--Busch Gmbh, Duren, Germany; *U.S. Public*, pg. 1124
Ferrantee, Michael A., Gen. Mgr.--Busch U.S., Sidney, OH; *U.S. Public*, pg. 1124
Ferrar, Angelo, Chm.--AGIP Petroli International B.V., Amsterdam, Netherlands; *Int'l*, pg. 429
Ferrara, Cheryl, Publisher--Marco Island Eagle, Marco Island, FL; *U.S. Public*, pg. 1175
Ferrara, Dominico, Mng. Dir.--Siciliana Electronica & Telecomunicazioni S.p.A., Palermo, Italy; *Int'l*, pg. 1370
Ferrari, Alpino, Mgr.-Opers.--Siria Officine Meccaniche SpA, Modena, Italy; *U.S. Public*, pg. 1619
Ferrari, Angelo, Pres.--AGIP Petroli, Rome, Italy; *Int'l*, pg. 428
Ferrari, Claudio, Chm. Bd. & Chief Exec. Officer--Foster Wheeler Power Systems, Inc., Clinton, NJ; *U.S. Public*, pg. 677
Ferrari, Claudio, Chm. Bd. & Mng. Dir.--Foster Wheeler Italiana S.P.A. (Italy), Milan, Italy; *U.S. Public*, pg. 677
Ferrari, Claudio, Chm. Bd. & Chief Exec. Officer--Foster Wheeler Facilities Management, Inc., Clinton, NJ; *U.S. Public*, pg. 677
Ferrari, Gabriele, Mng. Dir.--CCP Positioning S.R.L., Milan, Italy; *Int'l*, pg. 394
Ferrari, Mario, Fin. Dir.--Leo Burnett Co. Inc., Buenos Aires, Argentina; *U.S. Private*, pg. 185
Ferrari, Richard J., Pres.--Textron Automotive Interiors Company, Dover, NH; *U.S. Public*, pg. 1590
Ferrarin, E., Chm. & Mng. Dir.--ECP - Enichem Polymers Netherlands B.V., Amsterdam, Netherlands; *Int'l*, pg. 429
Ferrario, Franco, Gen. Mgr.--Banca Briantea Spa, Merate, Italy; *Int'l*, pg. 137
Ferraro, Domenico, Mng. Dir.--Olivetti Peruana S.A., Lima, Peru; *Int'l*, pg. 1003
Ferraro, Greg, V.P.--R&R Advertising, Reno, NV; *U.S. Private*, pg. 902
Ferraz, Jose Maria Fita, Vice Pres.--ERZ - Electricas Reunidas de Zaragoza, S.A., Zaragoza, Spain; *Int'l*, pg. 1224
Ferre Rangel, Antonio L., Chief Oper. Officer--Ponce Cement Div., Ponce, PR; *U.S. Public*, pg. 1342
Ferre, Rich, Plant Mgr.--Hydro Conduit Corp., Reno, NV; *Int'l*, pg. 245
Ferre, Serge F., Mng. Dir.--Nokia Mobile Phones France, Romainville, France; *Int'l*, pg. 952
Ferrebee, David, Admin.--Colonial Manor, Youngstown, OH; *U.S. Public*, pg. 838
Ferreira-Pero, Marta, Chm.--JMCT Publicidad, New York, NY; *U.S. Private*, pg. 599
Ferreira, Carlos, Chief Fin. Officer--Delco Remi-Componentes Electronicos, Lda., Seixal, Portugal; *U.S. Public*, pg. 721

Ferreira, D., Mng. Dir.--EMI-Valentini de Carvalho Musica Lda., Lisbon, Portugal; *Int'l*, pg. 427
Ferreira, Israel Magalhaes, Asst. Mgr.--Brasilia Branch, Brasilia, Brazil; *Int'l*, pg. 139
Ferreira, Wolney Bonfim, Gen. Mgr.--Banco do Brasil S.A.-New York, New York, NY; *Int'l*, pg. 141
Ferreiro, Juan, Pres.--Cronos/DMB&B, San Salvador, El Salvador; *U.S. Private*, pg. 303
Ferreiro, Maria H., Pres.--Union Carbide Argentina S.A.I.C.S., Buenos Aires, Argentina; *U.S. Public*, pg. 1667
Ferrell, James, Chm.--Ferrellgas Houston, Houston, TX; *U.S. Public*, pg. 618
Ferrell, Red, Plant Mgr.--Wing Industries South Central, Greenville, TX; *U.S. Private*, pg. 1183
Ferrer-Vidal, J. Gay de Montella, Gen. Mgr.--ABN, Sucursal en Espana (Barcelona), Barcelona, Spain; *Int'l*, pg. 11
Ferrer, A., Processing Lab Mgr.--Kodak S.A., Barcelona, Spain; *U.S. Public*, pg. 554
Ferrer, A., Mgr.--Kodak S.A., Palma de Mallorca, Spain; *U.S. Public*, pg. 554
Ferrer, Felix E., Mng. Dir.--DYWIDAG Systems International, USA, Inc., Eastern Div., Lincoln Park, NJ; *Int'l*, pg. 424
Ferrera, Kenneth, Chief Oper. Officer--First United Small Business Investment Co., Canton, MA; *U.S. Private*, pg. 402
Ferretti, Tom, Gen. Mgr.--America, New York, NY; *U.S. Public*, pg. 130
Ferreyra, E., Gen. Mgr.--Kodak Columbiana, Ltd., Bogota, Colombia; *U.S. Public*, pg. 553
Ferreyra, E., Gen. Mgr.--Kodak America, Ltda., Lima, Peru; *U.S. Public*, pg. 554
Ferrier, A.A., Pres.--Redpath Industries Ltd., Toronto, Canada; *Int'l*, pg. 1357
Ferries, Chuck, Pres. & Chief Exec. Officer--Scott U.S.A., Ketchum, ID; *U.S. Private*, pg. 977
Ferries, John C., Pres.-Americas--D'Arcy Masius Benton & Bowles, New York, NY; *U.S. Private*, pg. 303
Ferrill, Harve A., Chm. Bd.--Europe Tax-Free Shopping Ltd., Chicago, IL; *U.S. Public*, pg. 320
Ferrington, Lars, Mng. Dir.--G Cederholms Verkstad AB, Malmo, Sweden; *Int'l*, pg. 281
Ferris, Douglas W., Jr., Pres.--National Commerce Bank Services, Inc., Memphis, TN; *U.S. Public*, pg. 1155
Ferris, Pete, Mgr.-Plant--Nestle Chocolate & Confections Company, Burlington, WI; *Int'l*, pg. 917
Ferris, Richard P., Chm. & Chief Exec. Officer--Norwest Bank International, Minneapolis, MN; *U.S. Public*, pg. 1202
Ferris, Robert, Gen. Mgr.--Cook Moving Systems, Inc. (Florida Corporation), Saint Petersburg, FL; *U.S. Private*, pg. 273
Ferris, Steve, Pres.--Apache Canada Ltd., Calgary, Canada; *U.S. Public*, pg. 119
Ferris, William, Pres. & Chief Exec. Officer--PM Group Life Insurance Company, Fountain Valley, CA; *U.S. Private*, pg. 831
Ferro, David R., Publr.--Argus-Courier, Petaluma, CA; *U.S. Public*, pg. 1343
Ferro, Dennis H., Representative Dir.--Cigna International Investment Advisors K.K., Tokyo, Japan; *U.S. Public*, pg. 357
Ferro, J.J., V.P.--J.M. Huber, Clay Div., Macon, GA; *U.S. Private*, pg. 545
Ferroglio, Enrico, Pres.--Componenta International S.P.A., Arluno, Italy; *Int'l*, pg. 1421
Ferrucci, Mark, Chief Oper. Officer--The New Galveston Company, Wilmington, DE; *U.S. Public*, pg. 467
Fersch, Richard T., Pres.--Eddie Bauer, Inc., Redmond, WA; *U.S. Public*, pg. 1499
Fertig, Robert F., Pres.--North Florida Div., Spring Hill, FL; *U.S. Public*, pg. 1683
Fesenmeyer, Robert, V.P. & Gen. Mgr.--Spicer Driveshaft Div., Toledo, OH; *U.S. Public*, pg. 479
Fesperman, John, Pres.--J.C. Penney Life Insurance Company, Plano, TX; *U.S. Public*, pg. 917
Fest, H., Regional Mng. Dir.--EMI Electrola GmbH, Cologne, Germany; *Int'l*, pg. 427
Festa, John R., Pres.--Buypass Corporation, Atlanta, GA; *U.S. Public*, pg. 446
Festa, Oscar, Chief Exec. Officer--EURO RSCG, Buenos Aires, Argentina; *Int'l*, pg. 602
Festre, Marcel J., Mgr.--Westvaco Europe, S.A., Brussels, Belgium; *U.S. Public*, pg. 1762
Fetal, Alain, Dir. Gen.--Darty Alsace Lorraine, Moulins, France; *Int'l*, pg. 734
Fethke, Wayne G., Pres.--Fiskars Inc., Wausau, WI; *Int'l*, pg. 492
Fetterly, Elden, Gen. Mgr.--Chase Canada, Winnipeg, Canada; *U.S. Public*, pg. 337
Fetterman, Bert M., Pres.--Kvaerner National, Inc. Canadian Division, Edmonton, Canada; *Int'l*, pg. 768
Fetterman, Lewis M., Pres.--Tomahawk Farms, Inc., Dunn, NC; *U.S. Private*, pg. 681
Fettig, Jeff M., Pres.--Whirlpool Europe B.V., Comerio, Italy; *U.S. Public*, pg. 1765
Fetting, Mark, Pres.--Prudential Defined Contribution Services, Florham Park, NJ; *U.S. Private*, pg. 892
Fetxer, Brian, Pres.--Steelastic Co., Akron, OH; *U.S. Private*, pg. 860
Fetzer, Gunther, Dr., Mng. Dir.--Droemersche Verlagsanstalt Th. Knaur Nachf. GmbH & Co., Munich, Germany; *Int'l*, pg. 1478
Fetzer, Gunther, Dr., Mng. Dir.--Scherz Verlag GmbH, Bern, Switzerland; *Int'l*, pg. 1480
Fetzner, Carl G., V.P. & Mgr.-Opers.--Cast Metals Operations, Erie, PA; *U.S. Public*, pg. 1794
Feuillat, Guy, Pres. & Dir. General--Banque de L'Aquitaine, Bordeaux, France; *Int'l*, pg. 548
Feulner, Andreas, Mng. Dir.--Astra GmbH, Wedel, Germany; *Int'l*, pg. 93
Fevre, Gaetan Le, Gen. Mgr.--Forbo Krommenie S.A., Brussels, Belgium; *Int'l*, pg. 497
Fevre, Philippe, Chm. Bd.--SEB Internationale, Chemin-du-Petit-Bois, France; *Int'l*, pg. 568
Fewings, Don, Mng. Dir.--GN Rathdown, Ascot, United Kingdom; *Int'l*, pg. 537
Fey, John T., Chm. Bd.--CertainTeed Corporation, Valley Forge, PA; *Int'l*, pg. 1170
Feyen, Pat, Pres.--PacifiCare of Oklahoma, Tulsa, OK; *U.S. Public*, pg. 1251
Feyen, Pat, Pres.--PacifiCare of Texas, Dallas, TX; *U.S. Public*, pg. 1251
Feyerabend, Angela, Mgr.--Outdoor Services, Atlanta, GA; *U.S. Private*, pg. 1166
Fezer, Ulrich, Mgr.--Sandvik Rock Tools, Dusseldorf, Germany; *Int'l*, pg. 1187
Fezer, Ulrich, Mgr.--Sandvik Steel, Dusseldorf, Germany; *Int'l*, pg. 1187
Ffoulkes-Jones, Robert, Chm. Bd.--BSL Limited, Manchester, United Kingdom; *Int'l*, pg. 212
Fiaschetti, Michael, Pres. & Chief Oper. Officer--HealthAmerica of Central Pennsylvania, Harrisburg, PA; *U.S. Public*, pg. 454
Fiato, George, Pres.--Revlon Research Center, Inc., Edison, NJ; *U.S. Private*, pg. 690
Fick, Paul R., Pres.--Harza Northeast, Inc., Utica, NY; *U.S. Private*, pg. 509
Fiddis, Richard, Gen. Mgr.--Marcam U.K., Headquarters, Warwick, United Kingdom; *U.S. Public*, pg. 1043
Fiden, Elizabeth M., Div. Pres.--Dukane Audio Visual Div., Saint Charles, IL; *U.S. Private*, pg. 346
Fidler, F., Chief Oper. Officer--Metal Box plc., Research & Development Div., Wantage, United Kingdom; *Int'l*, pg. 267
Fidler, John Raymond, Gen. Mgr.--Adriatic Life Ltd., Melbourne, Australia; *Int'l*, pg. 61
Fiebig, Phil, Chief Exec. Officer--Leo Burnett Advertising SDN.BHD., Kuala Lumpur, Malaysia; *U.S. Private*, pg. 184
Fiedler, Hans, Dr., Dir.--GETAC Instrumentebau GmbH, Mainz, Germany; *Int'l*, pg. 1111
Fiedler, Lee F., Pres. & Chief Exec. Officer--The Kelly-Springfield Tire Company, Cumberland, MD; *U.S. Public*, pg. 753
Fiehler, Robert M., Asst. V.P.--IBP-Emporia, Emporia, KS; *U.S. Public*, pg. 852
Fiehrer, Ronald A., Pres.--Unisource (Midwest Region), Broadview, IL; *U.S. Public*, pg. 1671
Fiehrer, Ronald A., Pres.-Midwest--Unisource, Denver, CO; *U.S. Public*, pg. 1671
Field, Arthur, Pres.--NCC Specialty Publications, Dartmouth, Canada; *Int'l*, pg. 924
Field, H. James, Jr., Chm. & Chief Exec. Officer--Fleet Trust Co. of Florida, N.A., Stuart, FL; *U.S. Public*, pg. 649
Field, Joe, Pres.--Pony U.S.A., Nashville, TN; *Int'l*, pg. 1036
Field, Martin J., Plant Mgr.--AlliedSignal Limited Truck Brake Systems, Bristol, United Kingdom; *U.S. Public*, pg. 54
Field, Martyn R., Mng. Dir.--UNUM Limited, Dorking, United Kingdom; *U.S. Public*, pg. 1700
Field, Mike, Mng. Dir.--Lambert Smith Hampton, Slough, United Kingdom; *Int'l*, pg. 797
Field, Peter, Gen. Mgr.--Didde Web Press, Emporia, KS; *U.S. Private*, pg. 331
Field, R.L., Chief Oper. Officer--Toyota New Zealand Ltd., Johnsonville, New Zealand; *Int'l*, pg. 1414
Field, Thomas C., Pres.--Schlage Lock Company, Colorado Springs, CO; *U.S. Public*, pg. 876
Fielder, Jerry, Pres.--Exel Microelectronics, Inc., San Jose, CA; *Int'l*, pg. 1125
Fielding, Bill, Pres.--Excel Corp., Wichita, KS; *U.S. Private*, pg. 210
Fielding, L.A., Grp. Mng. Dir.--HSS Hire Service Group PLC, Mitcham, United Kingdom; *Int'l*, pg. 385
Fields, Edwin, Pres.--Fields & Devereaux/HEPY, Inc., Los Angeles, CA; *U.S. Private*, pg. 503
Fields, Gary L., V.P.-Southwest Region--Wall Street Deli, Inc., Houston, TX; *U.S. Public*, pg. 1734
Fields, George, Publisher--American Home Style, New York, NY; *Int'l*, pg. 190
Fields, Joe, Pres.--Mitre Sports (U.S.), Nashville, TN; *Int'l*, pg. 1036
Fields, Wendell E., V.P.-Opers.--Martin Marietta Uranium Enrichment Operations, Oak Ridge, TN; *U.S. Public*, pg. 1007
Fielke, Neville, Mng. Dir.--H.J. Heinz Company Australia Ltd., Dandenong, Australia; *U.S. Public*, pg. 807
Fien, Robert, Plant Mgr.--Klenasha Carton Plant, Menasha, WI; *U.S. Public*, pg. 671
Fierens, Robert, Mng. Dir.--BBL Ireland, Dublin, Ireland; *Int'l*, pg. 148
Fierens, Robert L., Mng. Dir.--Bank Brussels Lambert - Dublin, Dublin, Ireland; *Int'l*, pg. 148
Fiers, Alan, Pres.--MEGTEC, De Pere, WI; *U.S. Public*, pg. 1459
Fieweger, Tom E., III, Mgr.-Sls.--American Flow Control, Birmingham, AL; *U.S. Private*, pg. 52
Fife, Scott, Pres. & Chief Exec. Officer--Citizens First Bank, Fordyce, AR; *U.S. Public*, pg. 630
Fifield, J.G., Pres. & Chief Exec. Officer--EMI Music, New York, NY; *Int'l*, pg. 427
Fifield, Ralph E., Pres. & Chief Oper. Officer--United States Pipe & Foundry Company, Inc., Birmingham, AL; *U.S. Public*, pg. 1736
Figas, Larry, Mgr.--Sandvik Canada Inc., Mississauga, Canada; *Int'l*, pg. 1188
Figeac, Michel, Chief Exec. Officer (Southern Europe)--McCain Alimentaire SA, Harnes, France; *Int'l*, pg. 850
Figert, Dan, V.P. & Gen. Mgr.--Marshall Erdman & Assoc., Inc., Richardson, TX; *U.S. Private*, pg. 380
Figgins, Stan, Gen. Mgr.--Premdor Wood Products, Corning, CA; *Int'l*, pg. 1067
Figore, Daniel P., Mng. Dir.--Crown Cork & Seal (Thailand) Co., Ltd., Samutprakan, Thailand; *U.S. Public*, pg. 464
Figueinas, R., Chief Oper. Officer--Dentsply Brazil, Petropolis, Brazil; *U.S. Public*, pg. 499
Figueroa, C., Chm. Bd.--Figueroa, Madrid, Spain; *Int'l*, pg. 662
Figueroa, Ignacio, Gen. Mgr.--Unbrako Mexicana, S.A. de C.V., Ixtapalapa, Mexico; *U.S. Public*, pg. 1420
Figueroa, Julie, Chm.--Infocom Technologies, Inc., Pasig, Philippines; *Int'l*, pg. 1051
Figueroa, Nelson, Mng. Dir.--Compania Ericsson de Chile S.A., Santiago, Chile; *Int'l*, pg. 1365
Figueroa, Roman, Chief Oper. Officer-Construction Sand & Gravel--Louisiana Industries Div., Alexandria, LA; *U.S. Public*, pg. 1585
Fihri, Chakir Fassi, Mng. Dir.--SAGA Communications, Casablanca, Morocco; *U.S. Private*, pg. 305
Fike, William, Pres.--Atoma International, Inc., Markham, Canada; *Int'l*, pg. 829
Fike, William F., Chm. Bd. & Pres.--Ford Plastic & Trim Products International, Inc., Dearborn, MI; *U.S. Public*, pg. 662
Fike, William H., Pres.--Favesa S.A. de C.V., (Mexico), El Paso, TX; *U.S. Public*, pg. 982
Fila, Wiktor, Gen. Mgr.--Scholl (Polska) Sp zoo, Warsaw, Poland; *Int'l*, pg. 1210
Filecia, P., Dir.-Fin.--Herr Voss Ltd., Derby, United Kingdom; *U.S. Private*, pg. 962
Filer, Jim, Pres.--Apex, Raleigh, NC; *U.S. Public*, pg. 1306
Files, Glenn, Pres. & Chief Exec. Officer--West Texas Utilities Co., Abilene, TX; *U.S. Public*, pg. 324
Filho, Acacio Rosa de Queiroz, Pres.--Sumare Processamento E Servicos S.A., Rio de Janeiro, Brazil; *U.S. Public*, pg. 363
Filho, Acacio Rosa de Queiroz, Gen. Mgr.--Cigna Brasil Empreendimentos Ltda., Rio de Janeiro, Brazil; *U.S. Public*, pg. 363
Filho, Antonio W. Landulfo, Mgr.--Salvador Branch, Salvador, Brazil; *Int'l*, pg. 139
Filice, Bert, V.P. & Gen. Mgr.--Anchor Hocking Canada Div., Richmond Hill, Canada; *U.S. Public*, pg. 1178
Filice, Pete, Chief Fin. Officer--KTXL Channel 40, Sacramento, CA; *U.S. Public*, pg. 1636
Filipacchi, Daniel, Chief Oper. Officer--Hachette Filipacchi Presse, Levallois-Perret, France; *Int'l*, pg. 794
Filipov, Fil, Pres.--Terex Cranes, Conway, SC; *U.S. Public*, pg. 1581
Filkins, Mike, Pres.--Lectro Products, Inc., Athens, GA; *Int'l*, pg. 126
Filkins, Ron, Publr.--Perry County News, Tell City, IN; *U.S. Private*, pg. 648
Filkowski, J., Mgr.--Lindberg Heat Treating Co., Houston, TX; *U.S. Public*, pg. 999
Fillmore, Morris, V.P. & Gen. Mgr.--Boeing Georgia Inc., Macon, GA; *U.S. Public*, pg. 241
Fillon, Oliver, Chief Oper. Officer--Hospal B.V., Uden, Netherlands; *Int'l*, pg. 668
Fillon, Oliver, Chief Oper. Officer--Hospal-COBE Renal N.V., Zaventem, Belgium; *Int'l*, pg. 668
Filmer, O.A., Gen. Mgr.--Comalco Aluminium (Bell Bay) Limited, Bell Bay, Australia; *Int'l*, pg. 307
Filmeridis, John, Country Mgr.--Standard Chartered Bank, Dubai, United Arab Emirates; *Int'l*, pg. 1294
Filotas, William, Pres.--Crown Cork de Mexico, S.A., El Salto, Mexico; *U.S. Public*, pg. 464
Filowitz, Dr. Mark S., Pres.--Wynn Oil Company, Azusa, CA; *U.S. Public*, pg. 1782
Filshill, Robert, Gen. Mgr.--Young & Rubicam S.A., Cali, Colombia; *U.S. Private*, pg. 1200
Filson, Theodore A., Pres.--Advance Transformer Co., Rosemont, IL; *Int'l*, pg. 1054
Finas, Pierre, Mng. Dir.--Credit Lyonnais S.A., Seoul, Korea; *Int'l*, pg. 344
Finch, Fred, Mng. Dir.--Excellon U.K., Littlehampton, United Kingdom; *U.S. Public*, pg. 594
Finch, G., Gen. Mgr.--ITW Electronic Component Packaging, Basingstoke, United Kingdom; *U.S. Public*, pg. 868
Finch, John, Pres.--Wyoming Concrete Products Co., Casper, WY; *U.S. Private*, pg. 208
Finch, Kenneth J., Pres.--Edwards & Broughton Company, Raleigh, NC; *U.S. Public*, pg. 1735
Finch, R.J., Mng. Dir.--Plant Construction Plc, Thamesmead, United Kingdom; *Int'l*, pg. 585
Fincher, Joseph, Exec. V.P. & Gen. Mgr.--Adventure Island, Tampa, FL; *U.S. Public*, pg. 114
Fincher, Joseph, Exec. V.P. & Gen. Mgr.--Busch Gardens Tampa, Tampa, FL; *U.S. Public*, pg. 114
Fincher, Steve, Plant Mgr.--Acme Brick Co., Bridgeport, TX; *U.S. Public*, pg. 936
Finder, Pedro, Chief Oper. Officer--Alfa-Laval S.A., Buenos Aires, Argentina; *Int'l*, pg. 1379
Finders, Jake, Gen. Mgr.--Arrow/Schweber Electronics, Bellevue, WA; *U.S. Public*, pg. 134
Findlay-Shirras, Alasdair, Mng. Dir.--BV Financial (Ireland) Ltd., Dublin, Ireland; *Int'l*, pg. 180
Findlay, J. Duncan, Mgr.-Branch--Shannon & Wilson, Inc., Seattle, WA; *U.S. Private*, pg. 989
Findlay, J. Duncan, Pres.--Shannon & Wilson Intl., Seattle, WA; *U.S. Private*, pg. 989
Findlay, John R., Chief Oper. Officer--Computer Design, Inc., Grand Rapids, MI; *U.S. Public*, pg. 1053
Findlay, Scott F., V.P.-Ontario Div.--Mike's Mart, Barrie, Canada; *Int'l*, pg. 1249
Findlay, William, Controller--Avex Electronics Ltd., East Kilbride, United Kingdom; *U.S. Private*, pg. 545
Findlay, William, Pres. & Publisher--The Expositor, Brantford, Canada; *Int'l*, pg. 631
Findley, Jack, Pres. & Publr.--Long Beach Press-Telegram, Long Beach, CA; *U.S. Private*, pg. 727
Fine, Alan, Chief Oper. Officer--Toy Biz, International, New York, NY; *U.S. Public*, pg. 1626
Fine, Henri, Gen. Mgr.--Howmet-Cercast Inc., Montreal, Canada; *U.S. Private*, pg. 213
Fine, Henri, Gen. Mgr.--Ciral, Evron, France; *U.S. Private*, pg. 213
Fine, Michael, Pres.--Bakers/Leeds Shoe Stores, Saint Louis, MO; *U.S. Public*, pg. 563

Fine, Michael, Pres.--Size 5-7-9 Shops, Inc., Saint Louis, MO; *U.S. Public*, pg. 564
Fine, Michael, Pres.--The Wild Pair, Saint Louis, MO; *U.S. Public*, pg. 564
Fink, Jean-Marie, Pres.--Roulement Service S.A., Strasbourg, France; *Int'l*, pg. 212
Fink, Marvin H., Pres. & Chief Exec. Officer--Teledyne Electronic Technologies, Los Angeles, CA; *U.S. Public*, pg. 43
Fink, William C., Mng. Dir.--GM Singapore Pte. Limited, Singapore, Singapore; *U.S. Public*, pg. 721
Finkel, Paul A., Pres.-Domestic Life Companies--Delaware American Life Insurance Co., Wilmington, DE; *U.S. Public*, pg. 84
Finkelstein, James A., Pres.--National Law Publishing Co., New York, NY; *Int'l*, pg. 956
Finkelstein, James A., Pres.--New York Law Journal, New York, NY; *Int'l*, pg. 956
Finkle, Ray, Chief Oper. Officer--Waste King, Los Angeles, CA; *U.S. Public*, pg. 1053
Finklea, Terry, Gen. Mgr.--Sterling Electronics, Austin, TX; *U.S. Public*, pg. 1051
Finlay, Francis, Co-Chm. & Chief Exec. Officer--Clay Finlay Inc., New York, NY; *U.S. Public*, pg. 1673
Finlay, G.T., Gen. Mgr.--A.C. Nielsen Co. of Canada, Ltd., Markham, Canada; *U.S. Public*, pg. 1183
Finlay, Keith, Gen. Mgr.--Select Gauges, Torpoint, United Kingdom; *U.S. Public*, pg. 260
Finlay, William G., Reg. Mgr.-Atlanta--Dowty Aerospace North America, Atlanta, GA; *Int'l*, pg. 1337
Finlayson, Allistair, Mng. Dir.--SmithKline Beecham of Ireland Ltd., Dublin, Ireland; *Int'l*, pg. 1266
Finlayson, D.J.M., Mng. Dir.--RoyScot Trust plc, Cheltenham, United Kingdom; *Int'l*, pg. 1132
Finlayson, Robert, Gen. Mgr.--KFW Canada, Inc., Orillia, Canada; *Int'l*, pg. 1338
Finley, A.K., Pres.--Town & Country Homes, Fort Worth, TX; *U.S. Public*, pg. 319
Finley, Fred J., Pres. & Chief Oper. Officer--GTE Reinsurance Company Limited, Hamilton, Bermuda; *U.S.* Public, pg. 697
Finley, J.H., Pres.--Craft-Co Enterprises Inc., Morton, MS; *Int'l*, pg. 955
Finley, Jon L., Pres.--Gold Medal Div., Minneapolis, MN; *U.S. Public*, pg. 718
Finley, Peggy, Pres.--American Antenna Corp, Elgin, IL; *U.S.* Private, pg. 207
Finn, Billy, Mng. Dir.--AIB Finance & Leasing Ltd., Dublin, Ireland; *Int'l*, pg. 64
Finn, G.G., Mgr.-Sls.--Morgan Matroc Inc.-West Coast Sales Division, El Toro, CA; *Int'l*, pg. 893
Finn, J., Pres.--Metal Stamping Equip. Div., Bloomfield, CT; *U.S. Private*, pg. 825
Finn, Richard H., Pres. & Chief Exec. Officer--Transamerica Finance Group, Inc., Los Angeles, CA; *U.S. Public*, pg. 1630
Finn, Timothy, Gen. Mgr.--Athletic Express, New York, NY; *U.S. Public*, pg. 1777
Finnbraaten, Terje, Mng. Dir.--ISS Catering a.s., Oslo, Norway; *Int'l*, pg. 656
Finne, Harald, Mng. Dir.--Wisapak Oy Ab, Pietarsaari, Finland; *Int'l*, pg. 1429
Finnegan, Seamus, Mng. Dir.--Elsevier Reed Finance Ireland, Dublin, Ireland; *Int'l*, pg. 1093
Finney, Bill, Mng. Dir.--National Distributing Co., Inc., Orlando, FL; *U.S. Private*, pg. 781
Finney, Donald J., Admin. Asst.--Rehabilitative Health Services, Inc., Fort Myers, FL; *U.S. Public*, pg. 405
Finney, Mike, Area Sls. Mgr. Comp.--Analog Devices Ltd., Halesowen, United Kingdom; *U.S. Public*, pg. 108
Finrud, Kris, Mng. Dir.--Plastic Padding A/S, Oslo, Norway; *Int'l*, pg. 611
Finucane, Mike, Gen. Mgr.--Nichols Aluminum, Lincolnshire, IL; *U.S. Public*, pg. 1350
Fiondella, Robert W., Chm. Bd., Pres. & Chief Exec. Officer--Phoenix Home Life Mutual Insurance Co., Hartford, CT; *U.S. Private*, pg. 863
Fiorani Piero, Jian, Mng. Dir.--Banca Mercantile S.p.A., Florence, Italy; *Int'l*, pg. 784
Fiore, Jim, Dir.-Opers.--Olympic Mill Services, Glassport, PA; *U.S. Private*, pg. 1108
Fiore, N.F., Sr. V.P.-Engineered Products Group--Carpenter Special Products Corp., El Cajon, CA; *U.S. Public*, pg. 307
Fiorentino, Carl F., Pres.--Tiger Direct, Inc. (d/b/a Tiger Software, Inc.), Miami, FL; *U.S. Public*, pg. 747
Fiorenza, Jim, Mgr.--Shepler's Beaumont, Beaumont, TX; *U.S. Public*, pg. 413
Fiori, Pamela, Editor-in-Chief--Town & Country, New York, NY; *U.S. Private*, pg. 517
Fiorina, Carly, Jr., Pres.--Lucent Technologies, Consumer Products Div., Parsippany, NJ; *U.S. Public*, pg. 1017
Firchow, Claus G., Mng. Dir.--Spektrum der Wissenschaft Verlagsgesellschaft mbH, Heidelberg, Germany; *Int'l*, pg. 1478
Firestone, Brooks, Gen. Partner--The Firestone Vineyard, Los Olivos, CA; *Int'l*, pg. 1321
Firestone, Leonard L., Pres. & Gen. Mgr.--Allbritton Jacksonville, Inc, Jacksonville, FL; *U.S. Private*, pg. 854
Firm, Donald, Pres.--Davenport Machine Tool Div., Rochester, NY; *U.S. Public*, pg. 520
Fischbeck, Thomas, Sr. Mng. Dir.--Deutsche Bank-Kreditbank AG (Magdeburg), Magdeburg, Germany; *Int'l*, pg. 402
Fischer-Knudsen, Jorgen, Chief Oper. Officer--Jacobs Suchard Kaffe A/S, Odense, Denmark; *U.S. Public*, pg. 1289
Fischer, Bill, Pres.--Dean Pickle & Specialty Products, Atkins, AR; *U.S. Public*, pg. 490
Fischer, Bill, Pres.--Mayfield Dairy Farms Inc., Athens, TN; *U.S. Public*, pg. 490
Fischer, C., Pres.--OWL AG Logistik-Systeme, Buchs, Switzerland; *Int'l*, pg. 490
Fischer, Charles W., Chief Oper. Officer & Exec. V.P.--Canadian Occidental Petroleum Ltd., Calgary, Canada; *U.S. Public*, pg. 1210
Fischer, Chris, Branch Mgr.--Building Products Inc. of S.D., Sioux Falls, SD; *U.S. Private*, pg. 180
Fischer, Christian O., Dr., Chief Officer--Tela Versicherung AG, Munich, Germany; *Int'l*, pg. 58
Fischer, Christoph, Exec. V.P.--Mannesmann Demag Corporation, Cleveland, OH; *Int'l*, pg. 837
Fischer, Craig A., Pres.--American River Transportation Co., Decatur, IL; *U.S. Public*, pg. 128
Fischer, David, Sr. Mgr.--Australian Guarantee Corporation Limited - South Australia, Adelaide, Australia; *Int'l*, pg. 1496
Fischer, Douglas J., Chief Exec. Officer--J. Richard Industries, L.P., Toledo, OH; *U.S. Private*, pg. 249
Fischer, Earl, Pres.--Western Kentucky Gas Co., Owensboro, KY; *U.S. Public*, pg. 146
Fischer, Erwin, Pres.--Flender Austria Antriebstechnik AG, Spielberg, Austria; *Int'l*, pg. 400
Fischer, Francois, Chief Oper. Officer--Saarbach, Cologne, Germany; *Int'l*, pg. 796
Fischer, Fred, V.P.--All-Pro Imaging, Hicksville, NY; *U.S. Private*, pg. 28
Fischer, Hans, V.P.--Dana Europe Industrial, Lausanne, Switzerland; *U.S. Public*, pg. 480
Fischer, Hans Erich, Mng. Dir.--WM Wirtschafts-Medien AG, Zurich, Switzerland; *Int'l*, pg. 1480
Fischer, John, Branch Mgr.--Union-Transport Corporation-San Francisco Office, Burlingame, CA; *U.S. Private*, pg. 1120
Fischer, John A., Pres.--Egan Mechanical Contractors Inc., Minneapolis, MN; *U.S. Private*, pg. 366
Fischer, K., Mgr.-Sls.--Getranke-Dienst AG, Dietikon, Switzerland; *Int'l*, pg. 479
Fischer, Kelly, Pres.--Parachute, Inc., Minneapolis, MN; *U.S.* Private, pg. 242
Fischer, Meinrad, Gen. Mgr.--AMP (Schweiz) AG, Steinach, Switzerland; *U.S. Public*, pg. 9
Fischer, Neal, Pres.--Watsco Components, Inc., Hialeah, FL; *U.S. Public*, pg. 1746
Fischer, Neal, Pres.--Cam-Stat, Inc., Hialeah, FL; *U.S. Public*, pg. 1746
Fischer, Robert A., Pres.--Agway Agricultural Products (AAP), Syracuse, NY; *U.S. Private*, pg. 27
Fischer, Stephen H., Pres. & Chief Exec. Officer--PrimeVest Financial Services, Inc., Saint Cloud, MN; *U.S. Public*, pg. 1376
Fischer, Tilman, Gen. Mgr.--Sauer Sundstrand Gmbh & Co., Neumunster, Germany; *Int'l*, pg. 1198
Fischer, Ulrich, Dr., Chief Oper. Officer--Industrie-Beteiligungs Gesellschaftmbh, Frankfurt/Main, Germany; *Int'l*, pg. 119
Fisette, Robert A., V.P.--Martin Marietta International, Inc., Brussels, Belgium; *U.S. Public*, pg. 1010
Fish, Graham, Grp. Mng. Dir.--Alberto-Culver Company (U.K.) Limited, Basingstoke, United Kingdom; *U.S. Public*, *pg. 38*
Fish, Lawrence K., Chm., Pres. & Chief Exec. Officer--Citizens Financial Group, Inc., Providence, RI; *Int'l*, pg. 1132
Fish, Martin, Country Mgr.--Standard Chartered Bank, Mumbai, India; *Int'l*, pg. 1294
Fish, Vance, Gen. Mgr.--Greenwood Plant, Greenwood, SC; *U.S. Private*, pg. 1044
Fisher, A. Derek, Gen. Mgr.--Martin Marietta International, Inc., Taipei, Taiwan; *U.S. Public*, pg. 1010
Fisher, Al, Pres.--Summit-Beers Construction Company, Scottdale, GA; *Int'l*, pg. 1261
Fisher, Brad C., Mgr.-Branch--Piper Jaffray Inc., Kennewick, WA; *U.S. Public*, pg. 1303
Fisher, Brad C., Mgr.-Branch--Piper Jaffray Inc., Walla Walla, WA; *U.S. Public*, pg. 1303
Fisher, Bradley, Gen. Mgr.--Ashland Oil (Nigeria) Co., Ltd., Lagos, Nigeria; *U.S. Public*, pg. 140
Fisher, David G., Sr. V.P.--Automotive Original Equipment Div., Auburn Hills, MI; *U.S. Public*, pg. 1045
Fisher, Dean, Branch Mgr.--Duellman Electric Supply, Inc., Cleveland, OH; *Int'l*, pg. 1107
Fisher, Gary, Pres.--Saunders Valve, Inc., Houston, TX; *Int'l*, *pg. 1379*
Fisher, George M.C., Chm. Bd. & Chief Exec. Officer--Eastman Kodak Company, Rochester, NY; *U.S. Public*, pg. 550
Fisher, Jack, Gen. Mgr.--Boomtown-Reno, Verdi, NV; *U.S. Public*, pg. 831
Fisher, James, Gen. Mgr.--Airflex Div. Eaton Corp., Cleveland, OH; *U.S. Public*, pg. 556
Fisher, Kevin, Mng. Dir.--Dowty Woodville Polymer, Swadlincote, United Kingdom; *Int'l*, pg. 1338
Fisher, Leo R., Pres.--M & I Bank of Mayville, Mayville, WI; *U.S. Public*, pg. 1050
Fisher, Mike, Jr., Mgr.--Fisher Graphic Industries, Modesto, CA; *U.S. Private*, pg. 267
Fisher, P.S., Pres.--Amoco Leasing Corporation, Chicago, IL; *U.S. Public*, pg. 102
Fisher, Paul E., Chm.--The Fifth Third Bank of Western Ohio, National Association, Piqua, OH; *U.S. Public*, pg. 622
Fisher, Rayburn J., Jr., Pres. & Chief Exec. Officer--Regions Bank/Atlanta, Sandy Springs, GA; *U.S. Public*, pg. 1371
Fisher, Richard B., Pres. & Chief Oper. Officer--Morgan Stanley & Co. Incorporated, New York, NY; *U.S. Public*, pg. 1132
Fisher, Rob, Publr.--Business Journal Publications, Inc., Phoenix, AZ; *U.S. Private*, pg. 19
Fisher, Stephen N., Jr., Pres.--Seagram Beverage Co., New York, NY; *Int'l*, pg. 1215
Fisher, Todd, Mgr.--Stephen Gould of Tennessee, Inc., Knoxville, TN; *U.S. Private*, pg. 468
Fisher, Tom, Gen. Mgr.--Sterilization Services of Tennessee, Memphis, TN; *U.S. Private*, pg. 46
Fisher, W., Chief Oper. Officer--Precipitair Pollution Control, Longview, TX; *U.S. Public*, pg. 320
Fisher, W., Chief Oper. Officer--Advance Ross Steel Co., Chicago, IL; *U.S. Public*, pg. 320
Fisher, W. Patrick, Sr. V.P.--ABN AMRO Bank, N.V. (Atlanta), Atlanta, GA; *Int'l*, pg. 10
Fisher, William E., Pres. & Chief Exec. Officer--Applied Communications, Inc., Omaha, NE; *U.S. Public*, pg. 1629
Fisher, Wm. M. Jr., Chief Oper. Officer--Advance Ross Electronics Corp., Chicago, IL; *U.S. Public*, pg. 320
Fishkellar, Paul, Pres.--Casa Bonita, Inc., Carrollton, TX; *U.S. Public*, pg. 278
Fishman, Martin, Mng. Dir.--Merisel Switzerland, Nyon, Switzerland; *U.S. Public*, pg. 1096
Fisk, Paul, Pres.--N.D.T. Engineering Inc., Westborough, MA; *U.S. Private*, pg. 989
Fisler, B., Chief Exec. Officer--Societa Italiana Assicurazioni e Reassicurazioni S.p.A., Rome, Italy; *Int'l*, pg. 1531
Fitch, J. D., Chm. Bd.--Rover Finance Holding Limited, Solihull, United Kingdom; *Int'l*, pg. 911
Fitch, Laura W., Chm. & Pres.--Bank of America New Mexico, Albuquerque, NM; *U.S. Public*, pg. 180
Fithowski, Gene, Gen. Mgr.--Michigan Spring Company, Muskegon, MI; *U.S. Private*, pg. 880
Fitschen, Jurgen, Gen. Mgr.--Deutsche Bank AG (Tokyo), Tokyo, Japan; *Int'l*, pg. 405
Fitton, Chris, Mgr.--Ampex Great Britain Limited, Basingstoke, United Kingdom; *U.S. Public*, pg. 104
Fitton, Michael, Pres.--Unified Systems Solutions Inc., Mountain Lakes, NJ; *U.S. Public*, pg. 421
Fitts, J., Pres.--Williams & Mackie, Vancouver, Canada; *Int'l*, *pg. 1150*
Fitts, Robert L., Pres.--S.P. Richards Co., Smyrna, GA; *U.S.* Public, pg. 732
Fitze, Manfred, Sr. Mng. Dir.--Deutsche Bank-Kreditbank AG (Rostock), Rostock, Germany; *Int'l*, pg. 402
Fitzgerald, Barry, Pres.--American Nucleonics Corp., Westlake Village, CA; *U.S. Public*, pg. 556
Fitzgerald, Brian, Mng. Dir.--Nira Australia Pty. Ltd., Waterloo, Australia; *Int'l*, pg. 1369
Fitzgerald, C. P., Pres.--C & L Marketing Inc., Hollywood, CA; *Int'l*, pg. 428
Fitzgerald, Carol, Pres.--Pulte Chesapeake Division, Silver Spring, MD; *U.S. Public*, pg. 1344
Fitzgerald, Gary, V.P. & Chief Oper. Officer--EG & G Special Projects, Las Vegas, NV; *U.S. Public*, pg. 543
Fitzgerald, Gary, Mgr.--EC III, Yuma, AZ; *U.S. Public*, pg. 543
Fitzgerald, Gwen, Pres.--TSI Washington Laboratories, Rockville, MD; *U.S. Public*, pg. 733
Fitzgerald, Hugh, Pres.--The Quadrant Corporation, Bellevue, WA; *U.S. Public*, pg. 1764
Fitzgerald, J.W., II, Gen. Mgr.--Kodak New Zealand Ltd., Auckland, New Zealand; *U.S. Public*, pg. 554
Fitzgerald, James, V.P.--Earth Station Div., Reston, VA; *U.S.* Public, pg. 46
Fitzgerald, James, Publisher--Sailing Business, Newport, RI; *U.S. Public*, pg. 1174
FitzGerald, James W., Grp. Pres.--Sports/Leisure Magazines Group, Trumbull, CT; *U.S. Public*, pg. 1174
Fitzgerald, James W., Pres.--The New York Times Magazine Company Group, Trumbull, CT; *U.S. Public*, pg. 1174
Fitzgerald, John, Gen. Mgr.--International Moskow Bank, Moscow, Russia; *Int'l*, pg. 181
Fitzgerald, Joseph P., Pres.--Landstar Ligon, Inc., Madisonville, KY; *U.S. Public*, pg. 978
Fitzgerald, Kathleen, Mng. Dir.--Ilco Unican (SA) (PTY) Ltd., Benoni, South Africa; *Int'l*, pg. 1432
Fitzgerald, Mark, Pres. & Chief Exec. Officer--Willis Corroon Construction Services Corp., New Hyde Park, NY; *Int'l*, pg. 1504
Fitzgerald, Michael J., Pres.--The Riggs National Bank of Maryland, Rockville, MD; *U.S. Public*, pg. 1390
Fitzgerald, Robert, Gen. Mgr.--Precision Resource California Div., Huntington Beach, CA; *U.S. Private*, pg. 880
Fitzgerald, Robert W., Plant Mgr.--Commercial Intertech Corp., Benton, AR; *U.S. Public*, pg. 411
Fitzgerald, T.C., Pres.--Griffin Pipe Products Co., Downers Grove, IL; *U.S. Private*, pg. 68
Fitzgerald, Thomas H., V.P. & Gen. Mgr.--Silicone Products Div., Waterford, NY; *U.S. Public*, pg. 711
Fitzgibbon, David A., Pres.--Bardes Corp., Cincinnati, OH; *U.S. Private*, pg. 558
Fitzgibbon, Jim, V.P. & Gen. Mgr.--Las Colinas Inn & Conference Center, Irving, TX; *Int'l*, pg. 502
Fitzgibbons, Jack, Mng. Dir.--C & M Europe, Laois, Ireland; *U.S. Private*, pg. 192
Fitzhugh, B.J., Branch Mgr.--Zellerbach Division, Raleigh, NC; *U.S. Public*, pg. 1075
Fitzhugh, James, Branch Pres.--First State Bank N.A., Abilene, Abilene, TX; *U.S. Public*, pg. 874
Fitzpatrick, Charles, Chief Fin. Officer--Commercial Union Corporation, Boston, MA; *Int'l*, pg. 308
Fitzpatrick, Charles R., Chief Fin. Officer & First Sr. V.P.--Commercial Union Insurance Company, Boston, MA; *Int'l*, pg. 308
Fitzpatrick, Mark S., Mng. Dir.--AES Electric, Richmond, United Kingdom; *U.S. Public*, pg. 5
Fitzpatrick, Thomas J., Pres.--Spring Financial Services, Mount Laurel, NJ; *U.S. Public*, pg. 176
Fitzsimmons, C. F., Pres.--Bridon American Corp., Wilkes-Barre, PA; *Int'l*, pg. 215
Fitzsimmons, Joe, Pres.--UMI, Ann Arbor, MI; *U.S. Public*, pg. 201
Fitzsimmons, Joe, Gen. Mgr.--UMI Data Courier, Louisville, KY; *U.S. Public*, pg. 201
FitzSimmons, John, Gen. Mgr.--The Doe Run Company, Herculaneum, MO; *U.S. Private*, pg. 922
Fitzsimmons, Wayne, V.P.-Americas/Far East--Data General Singapore Pte. Ltd., Singapore, Singapore; *U.S. Public*, pg. 486
FitzSimons, Dennis J., Pres.--Tribune Broadcasting Company, Chicago, IL; *U.S. Public*, pg. 1636
Fitzwater, John, Publisher--Gainesville Sun Publishing Company, Gainesville, FL; *U.S. Public*, pg. 1175

Fiumano, Frank, V.P.--Sperber-Peterman Company, Union, NJ; *U.S. Private*, pg. 107
Fivash, John, Mng. Dir.--Quaker Chemical Limited, Stroud, United Kingdom; *U.S. Public*, pg. 1347
Fix, R.L., Pres.--Xomox Corp., Cincinnati, OH; *U.S. Public*, pg. 574
Fix, Roger L., Pres.-John Crane N. America--John Crane North America, Morton Grove, IL; *Int'l*, pg. 1339
Fjallstrom, Roland, Pres.--Celleco Hedemora, Lawrenceville, GA; *Int'l*, pg. 1378
Fjelstul, Dean M., Pres. & Treas.--Jim Walter Computer Services, Inc., Tampa, FL; *U.S. Public*, pg. 1737
Fjose, Oddbjorn, Mgr.--Caravelle Technology AS, Stavanger, Norway; *Int'l*, pg. 731
Flaa, Dag, Pres.--Hydro Aluminium A/S, Stabekk, Norway; *Int'l*, pg. 959
Flack, Alan, Pres.--Atomi Corp., Farmington, NM; *U.S. Private*, pg. 345
Flack, Gary, Gen. Mgr.--Graham Manufacturing Co., Marshfield, WI; *Int'l*, pg. 18
Fladeland, Harvey T., Mgr.-Branch--Piper Jaffray Inc., Sun City, AZ; *U.S. Public*, pg. 1301
Flagezil, Jean-Pierre, Chief Fin. Officer--Rainbow Technologies, Neuilly-sur-Seine, France; *U.S. Public*, pg. 1359
Flagg, Mark R., V.P. & Mng. Exec.--Northern Trust Bank of Texas, N.A., Dallas, TX; *U.S. Public*, pg. 1197
Flahaux, Jose, Pres.--Supply Point, Inc., Fremont, CA; *U.S. Public*, pg. 541
Flahavin, G. Thomas, Pres.--Columbia Lighting, Inc., Spokane, WA; *U.S. Public*, pg. 1684
Flaherty, William, Chm. Bd.--Horsehead Resource Development Co., Inc., New York, NY; *Int'l*, pg. 860
Flamein, Jean-Michel, Mng. Dir.--Battenfeld France S.A., Villepinte, France; *Int'l*, pg. 825
Flamingo, J.M., V.P. & Gen. Mgr.--General Cable Apparatus Division, Westminster, CO; *Int'l*, pg. 1487
Flamingo, Joseph, Pres. & Chief Exec. Officer--International Wire Group Inc., Saint Louis, MO; *U.S. Private*, pg. 526
Flamingo, Joseph, Pres. & Chief Exec. Officer--Harness Division, Saint Louis, MO; *U.S. Private*, pg. 526
Flamingo, Joseph, Pres. & Chief Exec. Officer--Non-Insulated Division, Camden, NY; *U.S. Private*, pg. 526
Flamingo, Joseph, Pres. & Chief Exec. Officer--Insulated Division, Avilla, IN; *U.S. Private*, pg. 526
Flamingo, Joseph, Pres.--General Cable Co., Highland Heights, KY; *Int'l*, pg. 1487
Flammang, Bob, Plant Mgr.--Donaldson Co., Inc., Stevens Point, WI; *U.S. Public*, pg. 517
Flanagan, Alawoise, Admin.--Guardian Care of Farmville, Farmville, NC; *U.S. Public*, pg. 1712
Flanagan, Chris, Chief Oper. Officer--SDRC Engineering Services Inc., San Diego, CA; *U.S. Public*, pg. 1525
Flanagan, David J., Co-Gen. Mgr.--Great Lakes Kraut Co., L.L.C., Rochester, NY; *U.S. Private*, pg. 887
Flanagan, David J., Jr., Gen. Mgr.--Great Lakes Kraut Co., Bear Creek, WI; *U.S. Private*, pg. 887
Flanagan, David T., Pres.--Central Securities Corp., Augusta, ME; *U.S. Public*, pg. 325
Flanagan, David T., Pres.--Cumberland Securities Corp., Augusta, ME; *U.S. Public*, pg. 325
Flanagan, Joseph P., Chief Oper. Officer--Impact Communications Group, Chicago, IL; *U.S. Public*, pg. 1641
Flanagan, P.J., Pres.--Swift and Company Ltd., Sydney, Australia; *Int'l*, pg. 682
Flanagan, Paul, Site Mgr.--Quinlan Pretzel Co., Inc., Denver, PA; *U.S. Private*, pg. 158
Flanagan, Richard, Pres.--Borders, Inc., Ann Arbor, MI; *U.S.* Public, pg. 245
Flanagan, Richard L., Pres.--Planet Music, Inc., Ann Arbor, MI; *U.S. Public*, pg. 245
Flanagan, Terry M., Ph.D., Pres. & Chief Exec. Officer--Jacor Networks Inc., San Diego, CA; *U.S. Private*, pg. 584
Flanagan, Tom, Gen. Mgr.--Capstone Electronics Div., Wilmington, MA; *U.S. Public*, pg. 134
Flanders, Scott, Pres.--Macmillan Computer Publishing USA, Indianapolis, IN; *U.S. Private*, pg. 777
Flanders, Scott N., Pres.--Macmillan Publishing USA, Indianapolis, IN; *U.S. Private*, pg. 777
Flandin, Pierre, Pres.--NEPA, Paris, France; *Int'l*, pg. 239
Flannery, Mark, Gen. Mgr.--Nielsen Logistics Co, Cincinnati, OH; *U.S. Private*, pg. 799
Flannery, William, Pres.--Edlon Products, Inc., Avondale, PA; *U.S. Public*, pg. 1393
Flaskey, Mike, V.P.-Sls.--Fairfield Orlando at Cypruss Palms, Kissimmee, FL; *U.S. Public*, pg. 611
Flaten, Alfred N., Pres.--T.J. U.S. Company, Statesboro, GA; *U.S. Public*, pg. 1152
Flaten, Alfred N., Pres.--Piggly Wiggly Northland Corp., Minneapolis, MN; *U.S. Public*, pg. 1152
Flatgard, Bjorn, Pres.--Elopak A/S, Lierstranda, Norway; *Int'l*, pg. 1389
Flatley, William F., Pres.--Bristol-Myers Health Care Group, New York, NY; *U.S. Public*, pg. 253
Flatow, Mike, Pres. & Chief Exec. Officer--Champion Products Inc., Winston Salem, NC; *U.S. Public*, pg. 1433
Flatt, Tolly, Reg. Mgr.--Green Tree Acceptance, Inc., Davenport, IA; *U.S. Public*, pg. 762
Flaum, Sander A., Pres. & Chief Exec. Officer--Robert A. Becker, New York, NY; *Int'l*, pg. 601
Flavel, P., Mng. Dir.--National Australia Financial Management Ltd., Melbourne, Australia; *Int'l*, pg. 906
Flavio, Guacelli, Chief Oper. Officer--Groupe SEB Do Brasil, Sao Paulo, Brazil; *Int'l*, pg. 568
Flaxman, Michael, Pres.--Groupe Accor of Canada Inc., Toronto, Canada; *Int'l*, pg. 21
Flay, Paul, V.P. & Treas.--J.L. de Ball-Girmes of America, Inc., Montreal, Canada; *Int'l*, pg. 552
Flechner, H., Pres--Bayer Argentina S.A., Munro, Argentina; *Int'l*, pg. 175
Fleck, Dennis M., Pres.--Sam Dick Industries, Inc., Seattle, WA; *U.S. Private*, pg. 360
Flecther, Arthur, Mng. Dir.--Kvaerner National Ltd., Aberdeen, United Kingdom; *Int'l*, pg. 768
Fleetwood, Christopher, Chief Exec. Officer--Whessoe Computing Systems Ltd., Darlington, United Kingdom; *Int'l*, pg. 1498
Fleisch, Jack, Publr.--Meredith Publishing Services, Des Moines, IA; *U.S. Public*, pg. 1094
Fleischer, Chuck, Pres.--Kyocera Canada, Inc., Mississauga, Canada; *Int'l*, pg. 776
Fleischer, Helmut, Pres.--H.F.&P. Munchen GmbH, Munich, Germany; *Int'l*, pg. 394
Fleischer, J., Chief Exec. Officer--Neumeyer Fliesspressen GmbH, Nuremberg, Germany; *Int'l*, pg. 755
Fleischer, Michael, Chief Exec. Officer--Agro Barter United AB, Moscow, Russia; *Int'l*, pg. 710
Fleischhackei, M., Chief Exec. Officer--Zurich Poistovna sluzby s.r.o., Bratislava, Slovakia; *Int'l*, pg. 1532
Fleishman, Donna, Gen. Mgr.--Edelman Worldwide, Inc., Atlanta, GA; *U.S. Private*, pg. 362
Fleishman, E., Pres.--Magazine Group, New York, NY; *U.S. Public*, pg. 1440
Fleishman, Stanley, Chief Exec. Officer--Jetro Cash & Carry, Philadelphia, PA; *U.S. Private*, pg. 587
Fleiss, R. A., Pres.--Nicholas, Fayette & Greenbrier RR Co., Baltimore, MD; *U.S. Public*, pg. 432
Fleissner, Gerhart, Gen. Mgr.--Thyssen Haniel Logistic International GmbH, Kelsterbach, Germany; *Int'l*, pg. 1388
Fleming, Adam, Mng. Dir.--Robert Fleming (South Africa) (Pty) Limited, Johannesburg, South Africa; *Int'l*, pg. 494
Fleming, Brian L., Pres. & Chief Oper. Officer--Santa Anita Enterprises, Inc., Arcadia, CA; *U.S. Public*, pg. 1081
Fleming, J. D., Vice Chm.--Coutts & Co. (Trustees) SA, Geneva, Switzerland; *Int'l*, pg. 911
Fleming, J. Gordon, Chm. & Pres.--Canada Life Mortgage Services Ltd., Toronto, Canada; *Int'l*, pg. 255
Fleming, Joe, Pres.--Formex, Inc. - Permanent Steel Forms, Richmond, VA; *U.S. Public*, pg. 1222
Fleming, John, Pres.--Saft Batteries Ltd., Scarborough, Canada; *Int'l*, pg. 55
Fleming, Malcolm, Sr. Mng. Dir.--Banque Internationale a Luxembourg BIL (Asia) Ltd., Singapore, Singapore; *Int'l*, pg. 162
Fleming, Michael J., Pres.--Topeka Div., Topeka, KS; *U.S. Public*, pg. 652
Fleming, P.J., Chm. & Pres.--Getty Gas Gathering, Inc., New Orleans, LA; *U.S. Public*, pg. 1583
Fleming, Patrick B., Gen. Mgr.--Alchem Plastics Corp.-Indiana, Richmond, IN; *U.S. Public*, pg. 1495
Fleming, Patrick B., Gen. Mgr.--Alchem Plastics Corp.-Michigan, Clare, MI; *U.S. Public*, pg. 1495
Fleming, Paul J., Pres.--Monitor Surety Managers, Inc., New York, NY; *U.S. Public*, pg. 215
Fleming, R.A., Mng. Dir.--Angus Fire Armour Limited, Thame, United Kingdom; *Int'l*, pg. 1500
Fleming, Scott T., Chm. Bd.--Spectrum Asset Management, Inc., Stamford, CT; *U.S. Public*, pg. 1674
Flemings, James, Gen. Mgr.--Stand-Cote Industrial Coatings Div., Houston, TX; *U.S. Private*, pg. 1032
Flemming, James B., Chm. Bd. & Chief Exec. Officer--Bank of Tuscaloosa, Tuscaloosa, AL; *U.S. Public*, pg. 1549
Flengsburg, Peter, Mng. Dir.--Ericsson Reinsurance S.A., Luxembourg, Luxembourg; *Int'l*, pg. 1367
Flenniken, Tom, Pres. & Chief Exec. Officer--UPB of Chattanooga, Chattanooga, TN; *U.S. Public*, pg. 1669
Fletcher, Adrian H., Exec. V.P., Gen. Mgr. & Chief Oper. Officer--Republic National Bank of New York (U.K.), London, United Kingdom; *U.S. Public*, pg. 1381
Fletcher, Arnold B., Pres.--Talbots, New York, NY; *Int'l*, pg. 28
Fletcher, David A., Pres. & Chief Oper. Officer--Deposition Technologies, Inc., San Diego, CA; *U.S. Public*, pg. 1056
Fletcher, Donald J., Pres.--George S. May Canada, Ltd., Montreal, Canada; *U.S. Private*, pg. 717
Fletcher, Harold J., Chief Oper. Officer & Exec. V.P.--Federal Home Loan Bank of New York, New York, NY; *U.S. Private*, pg. 399
Fletcher, Herman E., Gen. Mgr.--Greenwood Plant, Greenwood, SC; *U.S. Public*, pg. 443
Fletcher, J.W.S., Chm. & Mgr.--Trafalgar House Corporate Development Ltd., London, United Kingdom; *Int'l*, pg. 773
Fletcher, R.J., Dep. Mng. Dir.--Simon-Carves Australia, Sydney, Australia; *Int'l*, pg. 1252
Fletcher, Robert, Pres.--Ilford Inc., Paramus, NJ; *U.S. Public*, pg. 904
Fletcher, Robert D., Grp. V.P.--Avery International Converting Group, Azusa, CA; *U.S. Public*, pg. 152
Fletcher, Terry, Plant Superintendant--General Shale Products Corp., Kingsport, TN; *Int'l*, pg. 844
Fletcher, W.L., Pres.--FHI Benefit Systems, Inc., San Diego, CA; *U.S. Private*, pg. 343
Fletcher, William, Pres. & Chief Exec. Officer--Teva USA - Biocraft, Fair Lawn, NJ; *Int'l*, pg. 1381
Fletcher, William C., Pres.--Independence Investment Associates, Inc., Boston, MA; *U.S. Private*, pg. 589
Fleury, Daniel, Gen. Dir.--Procter & Gamble Laundry Cleaning & Paper Products Benelux, Brussels, Belgium; *U.S. Public*, pg. 1332
Fleury, Guy, Pres. & Chief Exec. Officer--Stolt Comex Seaway S.A., Marseilles, France; *Int'l*, pg. 1302
Fleury, Ronald R., V.P. & Gen. Mgr.--National Meats Inc., Etobicoke, Canada; *Int'l*, pg. 1207
Flick, Manfred, Chief Oper. Officer--Ahlstrom Alcore GmbH-Dusseldorf Core Plant, Dusseldorf, Germany; *Int'l*, pg. 33
Flick, Rainer, Chief Fin. Officer--Esselte Meto International Produktions GmbH, Hirschhorn, Germany; *Int'l*, pg. 461
Flieger, Berg, Gen. Mgr.--Forbo Wallcoverings Inc., Bridgeport, NJ; *Int'l*, pg. 497
Flieger, Bert, Gen. Mgr.--Siegling America Inc., Huntersville, NC; *Int'l*, pg. 497
Flieth, Holger, Pres. & Chief Opr. Officer--Thyssen Specialty Steels, Inc., Carol Stream, IL; *Int'l*, pg. 1388
Fligg, J.E., Pres.--Amoco Chemical Holding Co., Chicago, IL; *U.S. Public*, pg. 102
Fligg, Loren L., Pres. & Chief Oper. Officer--Hawkeye Security Insurance Company, West Des Moines, IA; *Int'l*, *pg. 543*
Fligg, Loren L., Chm. & Chief Exec. Officer--Hawkeye-Security Insurance Co., West Des Moines, IA; *Int'l*, pg. 543
Flinders, Leon, Chief Fin. Officer--Bally's Grand Inc. (Las Vegas), Las Vegas, NV; *U.S. Public*, pg. 829
Flinkerbusch, R., Mgr.-Pub. Rels.--Ballast Nedam Dredging, Zeist, Netherlands; *Int'l*, pg. 133
Flint, R. D., Mng. Dir.--Lucas-TVS Ltd., Padi, India; *Int'l*, pg. 820
Flint, R.A., Chief Oper. Officer--Thermo Electric Intl. Ltd., Sittingbourne, United Kingdom; *U.S. Private*, pg. 1080
Fliss, Michael C., Pres. & Chief Exec. Officer--AMCORE Bank N.A., Rock River Valley, Sterling, IL; *U.S. Public*, pg. 64
Floch, George, Chief Oper. Officer--Instron S.A., Paris, France; *U.S. Public*, pg. 883
Flock, H.H., Pres.--Tuthill Pump, Alsip, IL; *U.S. Private*, pg. 1111
Flock, Henry, Pres.--Ikon Office Solutions/D.C. Hey, Mendota Heights, MN; *U.S. Public*, pg. 863
Flock, Michael, Pres.--Dun & Bradstreet Canada Ltd., Mississauga, Canada; *U.S. Public*, pg. 536
Flocken, Jeff, Chief Exec. Officer--Northridge Hospital-Roscoe Blvd. Campus, Northridge, CA; *U.S. Private*, pg. 1118
Floeckher, Peter W., Pres. & Chief Exec. Officer--The Citizens National Bank, Laurel, MD; *U.S. Public*, pg. 1089
Flohr, Fred, Resident Mgr.--Dixie Cutlery Plant, Leominster, MA; *U.S. Public*, pg. 671
Flohr, Jurgen, Gen. Mgr.--Dresdner Bank AG, Milan, Italy; *Int'l*, pg. 419
Flood, Bill, Gen. Mgr.--Clarinda Color L.L.C., Saint Paul, MN; *U.S. Private*, pg. 206
Flood, Patrick O., Operations Mgr.--McGhan Limited, Arklow, Ireland; *U.S. Public*, pg. 874
Flood, Peter D., Chm. & Chief Exec. Officer--Multi-Arc Inc., Rockaway, NJ; *Int'l*, pg. 1198
Flood, Teresa, Mng. Dir. & Brdcst. Dir.--Western International Media Corporation, Springfield, MO; *U.S. Private*, pg. 1167
Flook, Roger D., Mng. Dir.--Crown Cork & Seal (West Indies) Ltd., Port of Spain, Trinidad & Tobago; *U.S. Public*, pg. 464
Floore, Less, Mgr.-Plant--Carriage Hill Foods, Salem, OR; *U.S. Private*, pg. 427
Florczuk, Marek, Gen. Mgr.--Amway Poland, Warsaw, Poland; *U.S. Private*, pg. 70
Florence, F., Chief Oper. Officer--Transalme Sociedade de Representacoes Administracao e Organizacao Ltda., Sao Bernardo do Campo, Brazil; *Int'l*, pg. 1475
Florence, Frank, Pres.--Parallax Graphics, Inc., Santa Clara, CA; *U.S. Public*, pg. 539
Florence, Leonard, Pres.--Towle Manufacturing Corporation, East Boston, MA; *U.S. Private*, pg. 1061
Florence, Leonard, Pres.--Leonard Florence Associates, East Boston, MA; *U.S. Private*, pg. 1061
Flores-Estrada, Fernando, Mng. Dir.--Causa Publicidad, Lima, Peru; *U.S. Private*, pg. 184
Flores, C L., Grp. V.P. & Mgr.--Packard Hughes Interconnect, Irvine, CA; *U.S. Public*, pg. 719
Flores, Rafael Gomez, Chm. Bd.--Motor Coach Industries International, Inc., Phoenix, AZ; *Int'l*, pg. 326
Flores, Raul Quintero, Exec. V.P.--Hylsa S.A.-Technology Division, San Nicolas, Mexico; *Int'l*, pg. 56
Florin, Gerd, Mng. Dir.--Sulzer Chemtech GmbH, Ravensburg, Germany; *Int'l*, pg. 1308
Florio, Charles J., Acting V.P. & Gen. Mgr.--High-Lites, Inc., Waterbury, CT; *Int'l*, pg. 821
Florio, Nick, V.P. & Branch Mgr.--California State Bank-Beaumont, Beaumont, CA; *U.S. Public*, pg. 294
Florjancic, Frederick J., Pres.--Brunswick Bowling & Billiards Corp., Muskegon, MI; *U.S. Public*, pg. 265
Florjancic, Frederick J., Pres.--Brunswick Indoor Recreation Group, Lake Forest, IL; *U.S. Public*, pg. 265
Florsheim, T. W., Chief Oper. Officer--Morgan-Hayes Div., Houston, TX; *U.S. Public*, pg. 1764
Flotron, B.E., Mgr.--Schweizerischer Bankverein, Winterthur, Switzerland; *Int'l*, pg. 1329
Flowers, John W., Chief Exec. Officer-UK & Ireland--Moore Business Forms U.K. Ltd., London, United Kingdom; *Int'l*, *pg. 889*
Floyd, Jack C., Pres.--Bank of Hazlehurst, Hazlehurst, GA; *U.S. Public*, pg. 1549
Floyd, James G., Pres. & Chief Exec. Officer--The Houston Exploration Company, Houston, TX; *U.S. Public*, pg. 259
Floyd, John, Pres.--GCO Minerals Co., Houston, TX; *U.S. Public*, pg. 902
Floyd, Susan, Gen. Mgr.--Centra 2000, Inc., Houston, TX; *U.S. Public*, pg. 148
Fluffer, J.R., Pres.--Enka bv, Arnhem, Netherlands; *Int'l*, pg. 45
Flum, O., Mng. Dir.--Gestetner Buromaschinen-Verkaufsgesellschaft m.b.H., Vienna, Austria; *Int'l*, pg. 1115
Flurey, George, Div. Mgr.--The Chantland Company Division, Humboldt, IA; *Int'l*, pg. 830
Flury, P., Rep.--Swiss Bank Corporation, Seoul, Korea; *Int'l*, pg. 1330
Flury, Peter, Dir.--Spectra-Physics AG, Basel, Switzerland; *Int'l*, pg. 1290
Flury, R.H., Rep.--Swiss Bank Corporation, Singapore, Singapore; *Int'l*, pg. 1330
Flynn, Bill, Plant Mgr.--Industrial Bag Division - Jacksonville Plant, Jacksonville, AR; *U.S. Public*, pg. 1521
Flynn, Chris, V.P. & Branch Mgr.--D.C. Branch Office, Silver Spring, MD; *U.S. Public*, pg. 1683
Flynn, Edward, Pres.--Foster Wheeler Caribe Corporation, C.A., Caracas, Venezuela; *U.S. Public*, pg. 677

Flynn, J., Chief Oper. Officer--Fred Perry Sportswear Ltd., London, United Kingdom; Int'l, pg. 620
Flynn, James F., Pres.--Union Carbide Inter-America, Inc., Danbury, CT; U.S. Public, pg. 1667
Flynn, Maurice J., Mng. Dir.--Delmex de Juarez S.A. de C.V., Mexico, Mexico; U.S. Public, pg. 721
Flynn, Michael, Publr.--The Seattle Business Journal, Inc., Seattle, WA; U.S. Private, pg. 20
Flynn, Robert, Div. Mgr.--Bluffton Mfg. Div., Bluffton, IN; U.S. Public, pg. 1475
Flynn, Terence M., Pres.--Portal Publications, Ltd., Corte Madera, CA; U.S. Public, pg. 503
Flynn, William R., Pres.--Michell NBD Limited, Adelaide, Australia; U.S. Public, pg. 628
Fobert, Ernest M., Mgr.-New England Branch--NuArc Northeastern Div., Chelsea, MA; U.S. Private, pg. 809
Focht, Michael H., Sr., Pres.--Tenet HealthSystem Medical, Inc., Dallas, TX; U.S. Public, pg. 1577
Focht, Michael H., Sr., Gen. Mgr.--Tenet HealthSystem HealthCorp, Dallas, TX; U.S. Public, pg. 1577
Focke, H., Chief Exec. Officer--Zurich Lebenversicherungs-Gesellschaft, Frankfurt/Main, Germany; Int'l, pg. 1529
Focke, H., Chief Exec. Officer--Zurich Versicherungs-Gesellschaft, Frankfurt/Main, Germany; Int'l, pg. 1531
Focke, H., Chief Exec. Officer--Agrippina Lebensversicherung Aktiengesellschaft, Cologne, Germany; Int'l, pg. 1531
Focke, H., Chief Exec. Officer--Agrippina Rechtsschutzversicherung AG, Cologne, Germany; Int'l, pg. 1531
Focke, H., Chief Exec. Officer--Agrippina Versicherung Aktiengesellschaft, Cologne, Germany; Int'l, pg. 1531
Focke, H., Chief Exec. Officer--DA Deutsche Allgemeine Versicherungs-Aktiengesellschaft, Frankfurt/Main, Germany; Int'l, pg. 1531
Focke, H., Chief Exec. Officer--Patria Versicherung Aktiengesellschaft, Cologne, Germany; Int'l, pg. 1531
Focke, H., Chief Exec. Officer--Zeta Finanza S.p.A., Milan, Italy; Int'l, pg. 1531
Focke, H., Chief Exec. Officer--Zurich International (Deutschland) Versicherungs-Aktiengesellschaft, Frankfurt/Main, Germany; Int'l, pg. 1532
Focke, H., Chief Exec. Officer--Zurich Kautions-und Kreditversicherungs-Aktiengesellschaft, Frankfurt/Main, Germany; Int'l, pg. 1532
Focke, H., Chief Exec. Officer--Zurich Rechtsschutzverischerungs-Aktiengesellschaft, Frankfurt/Main, Germany; Int'l, pg. 1532
Fodor, Random, Div. Pres.--Clifford Metal, Providence, RI; U.S. Private, pg. 651
Foegele, George, Pres. & Chief Exec. Officer--Transamerica Life Insurance Co.-Canada, Scarborough, Canada; U.S. Public, pg. 1630
Fogarty, Thomas, Pres.--Distribution Services, New York, NY; U.S. Private, pg. 777
Fogel, Thomas, Exec. V.P.--Allied Security Inc., Burlington, MA; U.S. Private, pg. 40
Fogelstrom, Anders, Chief Oper. Officer--Geotronics S.A.R.L., Lagny, France; Int'l, pg. 1290
Fogelstrom, Lennert, Pres.--ABB Atom AB, Vasteras, Sweden; Int'l, pg. 7
Fogg, James W., Pres.--Banta Catalog Group, Saint Paul, MN; U.S. Public, pg. 188
Fogle, Frank, Mgr.-Opers.--Waterworks Equipment Co. (WECO) Div., Corona, CA; U.S. Public, pg. 1682
Fogle, Glenn, Plant Mgr.--Crescent Genlyte, Barrington, NJ; U.S. Public, pg. 730
Fogliata, Ezio, Mgr.--Sandvik Rock Tools S.N.C., Viriat, France; Int'l, pg. 1187
Fogliata, Ezio, Mgr.--Sandvik Rock Tools, Milan, Italy; Int'l, pg. 1187
Fohlmeister, Klaus J., Mng. Dir.--KG Allgemeine Leasing GmbH & Co., Grunwald, Germany; Int'l, pg. 418
Fohrer, Alan J., Pres.--SCE Capital Company, Rosemead, CA; U.S. Public, pg. 564
Fohrman, Neal, Pres. & Chief Exec. Officer--Red Calliope & Associates, Inc., Los Angeles, CA; U.S. Public, pg. 465
Fok, Terry, Mng. Dir.--Kim Eng Securities (Hong Kong) Limited, Central, Hong Kong; Int'l, pg. 733
Foks, W.H., Exec. Chm.--GESTRA (U.K.) Ltd., Hitchin, United Kingdom; Int'l, pg. 550
Folan, Stephen B., Gen. Mgr.--Container Div. (New Hartford), New Hartford, NY; Int'l, pg. 1269
Folds, G. Thomas, Pres.--VASA North Atlantic Insurance Company, Indianapolis, IN; Int'l, pg. 464
Foley, Ann, Chief Fin. Officer--Foley Tractor Company, Inc., Wichita, KS; U.S. Private, pg. 416
Foley, Dwayne F., Pres.--Oregon Natural Gas Development Corp., Portland, OR; U.S. Public, pg. 1200
Foley, E. Wayne, Pres. & Gen. Mgr.--Stanley Air Tools Div., Cleveland, OH; U.S. Public, pg. 1509
Foley, Gerald F., Pres. & Chief Exec. Officer--Teleglobe Marine Inc., Montreal, Canada; Int'l, pg. 1373
Foley, James, Exec. V.P.--Dentsu Young & Rubicam/Seoul, Seoul, Korea; U.S. Private, pg. 325
Foley, Kirk W., Pres.--HMI Incorporated, Toronto, Canada; U.S. Public, pg. 771
Foley, Max, Branch Mgr.--Skandia America Reinsurance Corp., Atlanta Branch Office, Atlanta, GA; Int'l, pg. 1257
Foley, Mike, Plant Mgr.--Ropak Atlantic Inc., Dayton, NJ; Int'l, pg. 811
Foli, Dan, Pres.--L & L Plant Soil Division, Fife, WA; U.S. Private, pg. 638
Folk, James C., Pres.--SL Montevideo Technology, Inc., Montevideo, MN; U.S. Public, pg. 1419
Folkers, Onno Wilfried, Chief Oper. Officer--BHF Finance (Netherlands) B.V., Amsterdam, Netherlands; Int'l, pg. 119
Follett, C.R., Jr., Pres.--Follett Software Company, McHenry, IL; U.S. Private, pg. 417
Follett, K.A., Pres.--Follett Educational Services, Chicago, IL; U.S. Private, pg. 417
Follett, Lori, Dir.--Columbia Back Institute, El Paso, TX; U.S. Public, pg. 404
Follett, R.C., Pres.--Follett Library Resources, Crystal Lake, IL; U.S. Private, pg. 417
Follows, Robert, Pres.--Maritz Canada Inc., Mississauga, Canada; U.S. Private, pg. 704
Folts, Norm, Plant Mgr.--Dean Foods Vegetable Company, Darien, WI; U.S. Public, pg. 490
Fondren, Neal, Gen. Mgr.--Scripps Howard Cable of Northwest Georgia, Rome, GA; U.S. Public, pg. 1448
Fondy, Phil, Gen. Mgr.--DeVilbiss Spray Booth Products, Barrie, Canada; U.S. Public, pg. 868
Fondy, Philip, Gen. Mgr.--DeVilbiss Spray Booth Div., Atlanta, GA; U.S. Public, pg. 866
Fong, Chew Weng, Mng. Dir.--Monsanto Singapore Company (Pte.) Ltd., Singapore, Singapore; U.S. Public, pg. 1126
Fong, Wong Ai, Gen. Mgr.--F.J. Benjamin Multimedia Pte Ltd., Singapore, Singapore; Int'l, pg. 187
Fonseca Adeodato, Carlos Persandro, Gen. Mgr.--Banco do Brasil S.A.-Paris, Paris, France; Int'l, pg. 141
Font, Salvador, Gen. Mgr.--CEPSA Estaciones de Servicio, S.A., Madrid, Spain; Int'l, pg. 323
Fontaine, George, Gen. Mgr.--Sandpiper Cove Div., Destin, FL; U.S. Private, pg. 895
Fontan, Maria, Mgr.--Broad National Bank-Jackson, Newark, NJ; U.S. Public, pg. 258
Fontana Filho, Walter, Pres.-Exec. Bd.--Sadia Concordia S.A. Industria e Comercio, Concordia, Brazil; Int'l, pg. 1168
Fontana Filho, Walter, Pres.-Exec. Bd.--Frigobras Companhia Brasileira de Frigorificos, Toledo, Brazil; Int'l, pg. 1168
Fontana Filho, Walter, Pres. Exec. Bd.--Sadia Mato Grosso S/A, Sao Paulo, Brazil; Int'l, pg. 1168
Fontana Filho, Walter, Pres.-Exec. Bd.--Lapa Alimentos S/A, Bauru, Brazil; Int'l, pg. 1168
Fontana Filho, Walter, Pres.-Exec. Bd.--Sadia Agroavicola S/A Industria E Comercio, Bauru, Brazil; Int'l, pg. 1168
Fontana Filho, Walter, Pres.-Exec. Bd.--Sadia Oeste S.A. Industria e Comercio, Varzea Grande, Brazil; Int'l, pg. 1169
Fontana, Cesar, Pres.--Cia. AGA del Peru S.A., Lima, Peru; Int'l, pg. 13
Fontana, Fiorinda, Chief Oper. Officer--Spectra-Physics S.R.L., Cascina, Italy; Int'l, pg. 1290
Fontana, Rizieri, Rep.--Sanpaolo-Istanbul Representative Office, Istanbul, Turkey; Int'l, pg. 691
Fontana, Roland, Gen. Mgr.--Banque Bruxelles Lambert (Suisse)-Lausanne, Lausanne, Switzerland; Int'l, pg. 148
Fontana, Victor, Pres., Chief Exec. Officer & Treas.--Autranet, Inc., New York, NY; U.S. Public, pg. 589
Fontana, Vincenzo, Mng. Dir.--Metalchimica srl, Turin, Italy; U.S. Private, pg. 735
Fontanazza, William C., Pres.--Wisconsin Wire & Steel, Brookfield, WI; U.S. Public, pg. 1061
Fontein, Hans, Mng. Dir.--H. Albert de Bary & Co. N.V. (Amsterdam), Amsterdam, Netherlands; Int'l, pg. 404
Fontenot, Al, Pres.--ATAPCO Office Products Group, Saint Louis, MO; U.S. Private, pg. 64
Fonville, Ken, Pres.--Pennsylvania House Casegoods, Lewisburg, PA; U.S. Public, pg. 975
Foo, K.K., Mng. Dir.--McCormick Ingredients Southeast Asia Pvt., Ltd., Jurong, Singapore; U.S. Public, pg. 1067
Foo, Larry, Chief Oper. Officer--Clarins Pte Ltd., Singapore, Singapore; Int'l, pg. 295
Foo, Theresa, Country Mgr.--Standard Chartered Futures (Singapore) Pte Limited, Singapore, Singapore; Int'l, pg. 1295
Foo, Vivian, Pres. & Mng. Dir.--Simon Marketing, Ltd., Wan Chai, Hong Kong; U.S. Private, pg. 1001
Foo, Yin Yee, Gen. Mgr.--John Crane Tianjin Ltd., Tianjin, China; Int'l, pg. 1339
Foody, William, Mgr.-Plant--David & Sons, Saint Louis, MO; Int'l, pg. 917
Fook, Chong Teng, Gen. Mgr.--Mortgage & Finance Berhad, Bandar Seri Begawan, Brunei Darussalam; Int'l, pg. 583
Fooksman, Mark, Mr., Gen. Mgr.--Gema, Indianapolis, IN; U.S. Public, pg. 866
Foong, S.S., Chief Fin. Officer--Olivetti Singapore Pte. Ltd., Singapore, Singapore; Int'l, pg. 1003
Foot, B., Chief Oper. Officer--Laing Oman LLC, Ruwi, Oman; Int'l, pg. 797
Foot, Silas B., III, Pres.--S.B. Foot Tanning Co., Red Wing, MN; U.S. Private, pg. 915
Foote, William D., Mng. Dir.--Southwest Diversified Coscan Partnerships, Irvine, CA; Int'l, pg. 228
Footman, J.W., Gen. Mgr.--Heating Replacement Parts and Controls Ltd., Leyland, United Kingdom; Int'l, pg. 1511
Footman, J.W., Mng. Dir.--Chandlers Printers Ltd., Bexhill-on-Sea, United Kingdom; Int'l, pg. 1511
Footman, J.W., Gen. Mgr.--Plant & Tools Ltd., Tunbridge Wells, United Kingdom; Int'l, pg. 1512
Footman, J.W., Mng. Dir.--D. Rowe & Co. Ltd., Chichester, United Kingdom; Int'l, pg. 1512
Footman, John W., Chief Exec. Officer--Wolseley Building Distribution - Europe, Droitwich, United Kingdom; Int'l, pg. 1511
Foran, W.J., Chm. Bd.--Cyanamid Canada Inc., Markham, Canada; U.S. Public, pg. 80
Forayce, Dave, Plant Mgr.--Hydro Conduit Corp., Denver, CO; Int'l, pg. 245
Forbers, Jack, Plant Mgr.--Industrial Bag Division - Cantonment Plant, Cantonment, FL; U.S. Public, pg. 1521
Forbes, A., Dir.--THORN Business Communications Ltd., Reading, United Kingdom; Int'l, pg. 1385
Forbes, A.D., Mng. Dir.--Ladybird Books Ltd., Loughborough, United Kingdom; Int'l, pg. 1025
Forbes, Darius, Chm.--Sempell Valves Pvt. Ltd., Pune, India; Int'l, pg. 401
Forbes, Farhad, Dir.--Moore Controls Pvt. Limited, Kasarwadi, India; U.S. Public, pg. 1128
Forbes, Gary, Mng. Dir.--Sundstrand Pacific Aerospace (Pte) Ltd., Singapore, Singapore; U.S. Public, pg. 1534
Forbes, James L., Pres.--Badger Meter de Mexico, S.A. de C.V., Nogales, Mexico; U.S. Public, pg. 165
Forbes, Jim, Pres.--The American Meat Packing Corp., Chicago, IL; U.S. Private, pg. 575
Forbes, John, Sr. V.P.-Operations--Citizen Watch Co. of America, Inc., Los Angeles, CA; Int'l, pg. 294
Forbes, Jon, Chief Oper. Officer--Artistic Brass, South Gate, CA; U.S. Public, pg. 1053
Forbes, Jon, Chief Oper. Officer--Jensen Industries, Los Angeles, CA; U.S. Public, pg. 1193
Forbes, Nancy, Mgr.-Customer Service--AMICO-Riverside, Kansas City, MO; U.S. Private, pg. 30
Forbes, Probyn, Plant Mgr.--Huls Canada Inc., Brampton, Canada; Int'l, pg. 1455
Forbes, R.H.A., Sec.--Baco Leisure Products, Gerrards Cross, United Kingdom; Int'l, pg. 51
Forbes, Timothy, Chief Oper. Officer--Forbes Investors Advisory Institute, Inc., New York, NY; U.S. Private, pg. 418
Forcella, P., Mng. Dir.--Ascom Automation S.r.l., Milan, Italy; Int'l, pg. 86
Forch, Hubert, Dr., Mng. Dir.--Oldenburgische Landesbank AG, Oldenburg, Germany; Int'l, pg. 418
Ford, Allyn, Pres.--Roseburg Resources Co., Dillard, OR; U.S. Private, pg. 905
Ford, Allyn, Pres.--Scott Timber Co., Dillard, OR; U.S. Private, pg. 905
Ford, Andy, Gen. Dir.--CSSL (M) Sdn Bhd, Kuala Lumpur, Malaysia; U.S. Public, pg. 1043
Ford, Bill, Reg. Mgr.--Green Tree Acceptance, Inc., Hendersonville, TN; U.S. Public, pg. 762
Ford, Bob, Pres. & Gen. Mgr.--WLFI-TV, West Lafayette, IN; U.S. Private, pg. 148
Ford, Brad, V.P. & Gen. Mgr.--Wabash Fibre Box Company-Chicago Plant, Chicago, IL; U.S. Private, pg. 1170
Ford, Brent, Pres.--Sub Sea International, Aberdeen, United Kingdom; U.S. Public, pg. 529
Ford, D.G., Gen. Mgr. & Dir.--Aylesbury Automation Ltd., Aylesbury, United Kingdom; Int'l, pg. 297
Ford, Darcy, Gen. Mgr.-Asian Opers.--Westpac Banking Corporation-Asian Div., Hong Kong, Hong Kong; Int'l, pg. 1497
Ford, Dee, Mng. Dir.--Viking Radio, Hull, United Kingdom; Int'l, pg. 452
Ford, Edsel B., II, Pres. & Chief Oper. Officer--Ford Motor Credit Company, Dearborn, MI; U.S. Public, pg. 663
Ford, Edsel B., II, Pres. & Chief Oper. Officer--Ford Motor Credit Company International, Dearborn, MI; U.S. Public, pg. 664
Ford, Gerald J., Chm. Bd.--First Gibraltar Bank, Irving, TX; U.S. Public, pg. 181
Ford, Henry, Pres.--Sequridad Tecnica, S.A., Panama, Panama; U.S. Public, pg. 1731
Ford, Henry A., Plant Mgr.--Fort Worth Container Div., Fort Worth, TX; U.S. Public, pg. 1289
Ford, James, Mgr.-Sls.--Uniroyal Chemical Co., Inc,, Fresno, CA; U.S. Public, pg. 460
Ford, John, Gen. Mgr.--Oral-B Laboratories Inc., Mississauga, Canada; U.S. Public, pg. 745
Ford, Judy, Chief Exec. Officer--Medical Park Diagnostic Center, Miami, FL; U.S. Public, pg. 405
Ford, Richard Q., Chief Exec. Officer-Life & Health Programs Div.--Willis Corroon Administrative Services, Inc., Nashville, TN; Int'l, pg. 1504
Ford, Steve, Mgr.--Lapham Hickey Steel (WI), Oshkosh, WI; U.S. Private, pg. 651
Ford, Steve, Pres.--Knurr (UK) Ltd., Saint Ives, United Kingdom; Int'l, pg. 739
Ford, Tom, Pres. & Chief Exec. Officer--Grossman's, Inc., Stoughton, MA; U.S. Private, pg. 585
Ford, W. Douglas, Pres.--Amoco Oil Company, Chicago, IL; U.S. Public, pg. 102
Ford, William Clay, Jr., Gen. Mgr.--Ford Climate Control Division, Dearborn, MI; U.S. Public, pg. 662
Forde, Patrick, Gen. Mgr.--Devcon Ltd., Shannon, Ireland; U.S. Public, pg. 867
Forde, Sherland, Exec. V.P. & Media Dir.--Bensimon Byrne DMB&B Toronto, Toronto, Canada; U.S. Private, pg. 303
Forde, W.D., Chief Exec. Officer--Readymix Qatar WLL & The Quatar Quarry Co. WLL, Doha, Qatar; Int'l, pg. 1092
Fordham, Michael, Chief Oper. Officer--Northumberland Group Ltd., Richmond, United Kingdom; Int'l, pg. 162
Fordham, Sharon, Pres.--LifeSavers Company, Parsippany, NJ; U.S. Public, pg. 1355
Fording, Edmund H., Pres.--Dyes & Chemicals Div., Reading, PA; U.S. Public, pg. 459
Fore, Dewey, Reg. Mgr.-Sls.--Ash Grove Cement Company Sales Office, Little Rock, AR; U.S. Private, pg. 87
Forem, Linda, V.P. & Gen. Mgr.--WRVQ-FM, Richmond, VA; U.S. Public, pg. 385
Foreman, Glen, Gen. Mgr.--Seaboard Farms of Chattanooga, Chattanooga, TN; U.S. Public, pg. 1449
Foreman, James, Mgr.-Div.--Aramark Sports & Entertainment Services Group Inc., Tampa, FL; U.S. Private, pg. 79
Foreman, Joe, Gen. Mgr.--Watlow Process Systems, Inc., Troy, MO; U.S. Private, pg. 1153
Foreman, Wayne, Pres.--Bank One Venture Corporation, Milwaukee, WI; U.S. Public, pg. 174
Foremberd, Christian, Pres.--Reifenhauser Ind. de Maquinas Ltda., Diadema, Brazil; Int'l, pg. 1101
Forese, James J., V.P. & Grp. Exec.--IBM World Trade Americas/Far East Corporation, North Tarrytown, NY; U.S. Public, pg. 896
Foresio, Fabrizio, Pres.--Aermacchi S.p.A., Varese, Italy; Int'l, pg. 653
Forest, Harvey, Pres.--Solarex Corporation, Frederick, MD; U.S. Public, pg. 103
Forest, Lynn, Reg. Mgr.--Green Tree Acceptance of North Carolina, Inc., Raleigh, NC; U.S. Public, pg. 762
Forester, David, Chief Oper. Officer--Bio-Rad Laboratories Ltd., Hemel Hempstead, United Kingdom; U.S. Public, pg. 230

Forestier, Yves, Gen. Mgr.--Skandia International Gestion de Reassurance Vie, Le Mans, France; *Int'l*, pg. 1258

Forgach, John, Plant Mgr.--Ringier America, Charlotte Division, Charlotte, NC; *U.S. Public*, pg. 1778

Forgan, Eric, Chief Oper. Officer--Armstrong Screws & Fixings Ltd., Birmingham, United Kingdom; *Int'l*, pg. 265

Forgie, James L., Pres.--Waltec Components, Wallaceburg, Canada; *Int'l*, pg. 453

Forgie, James L., Pres.--Waltec American Forgings, Inc., Port Huron, MI; *Int'l*, pg. 453

Forgie, James L., Pres.--Emco Custom Products Group, Wallaceburg, Canada; *Int'l*, pg. 453

Forguez, M. William, Pres.--Information Dimensions, Dublin, OH; *U.S. Private*, pg. 465

Foriska, Charles, Gen. Mgr.--Halstead Industrial Prods. Div., Wynne, AR; *U.S. Private*, pg. 497

Forjaz, Duarte, Chief Exec. Officer--DMB&B Lisbon, Lisbon, Portugal; *U.S. Private*, pg. 304

Forker, Michelle, Branch Mgr.--TMP Worldwide/Recruitment Division, Portland, OR; *U.S. Private*, pg. 1065

Forkner, Colin M., V.P. & Mng. Dir.--Northern Trust Bank of California, N.A., Newport Beach, CA; *U.S. Public*, pg. 1196

Forlenza, Vincent A., Pres.--Becton Dickinson Microbiology Systems, Sparks, MD; *U.S. Public*, pg. 199

Forman, Tom, Admin.--Indian Creek Nursing Center, Overland Park, KS; *U.S. Public*, pg. 837

Formhals, David G., V.P. & Gen. Mgr.--Wynn's Canada, Ltd., Mississauga, Canada; *U.S. Public*, pg. 1783

Formhals, P.K., Rep.--Barclays Bank PLC, Bangkok, Thailand; *Int'l*, pg. 166

Formica, Mark J., Pres. & Chief Exec. Officer--Citizens Savings Bank, Providence, RI; *Int'l*, pg. 1132

Formica, Mark J., Pres. & Chief Exec. Officer--Citizens Trust Company, Providence, RI; *Int'l*, pg. 1132

Formica, Mark J., Chm. & Chief Exec. Officer--Citizens Mortgage Corporation, Atlanta, GA; *Int'l*, pg. 1132

Formis, Stefano, Mgr.--AlliedSignal Automotive Italia S.p.A., Turbocompressori Garrett, Milan, Italy; *U.S. Public*, pg. 53

Fornataro, A.A., Pres. & Chief Exec. Officer--Salem Corporation, Pittsburgh, PA; *U.S. Private*, pg. 961

Fornataro, A.A., Pres.--Salem Asset Management Corp., Wilmington, DE; *U.S. Private*, pg. 961

Fornataro, A.A., Pres.--Salem Foreign Sales Corp., Charlotte Amalie, VI; *U.S. Private*, pg. 961

Fornell, Karl-Valter, Pres.--Maskin AB Rapid, Varnamo, Sweden; *Int'l*, pg. 678

Fornell, Sten, Mng. Dir.--Ericsson Mobile Communications AB, Stockholm, Sweden; *Int'l*, pg. 1364

Forni, Paola, Dir.--Vista Multi National, Bologna, Italy; *U.S. Public*, pg. 222

Foroni Lo Faro, V., Gen. Mgr.--Bankhaus Loebbecke & Co., Berlin, Germany; *Int'l*, pg. 275

Forquer, David, Gen. Mgr.--Alro Group, Lansing, Lansing, MI; *U.S. Private*, pg. 46

Forrest, Alan, Mng. Dir.--DOM AG Sicherheitstechnik, Altendorf, Switzerland; *U.S. Public*, pg. 233

Forrest, Gregory J., Pres. & Chief Exec. Officer--Bank of America Capital, Costa Mesa, CA; *U.S. Public*, pg. 180

Forrest, H. Miles, Publisher--The Houma Courier Newspaper Corporation, Houma, LA; *U.S. Public*, pg. 1175

Forrest, Jackie, Pres.--Flowers Baking Co. of Lynchburg, Inc., Lynchburg, VA; *U.S. Public*, pg. 657

Forrest, Peter, Mng. Dir.--Pringle of Scotland Ltd, Hawick, United Kingdom; *Int'l*, pg. 385

Forrest, Peter, V.P.-Sls.--VWR Canlab, Mississauga, Canada; *U.S. Public*, pg. 1704

Forrester, G. Nelson, Jr., Regional Pres.--First Tennessee Bank - Cookeville, Cookeville, TN; *U.S. Public*, pg. 639

Forrey, Jim, Gen. Mgr.--Corrugated Container Div.-Los Angeles Plant, City of Industry, CA; *U.S. Public*, pg. 1520

Fors, Borje, Chief Officer--Akademibokhandelsgruppen, Stockholm, Sweden; *Int'l*, pg. 718

Forsberg, Benny, Chief Oper. Officer--DAB Dental AB, Sundsvall, Sweden; *Int'l*, pg. 711

Forsberg, Karl Erik, Mgr.--AB Sandvik Hand Tools, Bollnas, Sweden; *Int'l*, pg. 1185

Forsberg, Stig, Mng. Dir.--Tele-ekonomi AB, Bandhagen, Sweden; *Int'l*, pg. 29

Forsee, Gary D., Pres.--Sprint's Long Distance Division, Dallas, TX; *U.S. Public*, pg. 1501

Forssell, Arne, Chief Oper. Officer--Vyncolit N.V., Gent, Belgium; *Int'l*, pg. 1037

Forssell, Harry, Pres.--Sodipan S.A., Saint Etienne-du-Rouvray, France; *U.S. Public*, pg. 673

Forssio, Jan-Erik, Chief Oper. Officer--Electrolux (Far East) Ltd., Hong Kong, Hong Kong; *Int'l*, pg. 442

Forsslof, Johan, Chief Oper. Officer--SCA Recycling, Aylesford, United Kingdom; *Int'l*, pg. 1327

Forst, Eric, Gen. Mgr.--Evans Ball Brass & Aluminum Foundry, Auburn, IN; *U.S. Private*, pg. 385

Forst, John, Gen. Mgr.--International Travel Associates Corp., Des Moines, IA; *U.S. Private*, pg. 555

Forster, Frank L., Chief Oper. Officer & Sr. V.P.--Hawaiian Airlines, Inc., Honolulu, HI; *U.S. Public*, pg. 799

Forster, Gordon, Gen. Mgr.--GPC Communications (Calgary), Calgary, Canada; *U.S. Public*, pg. 1225

Forster, Jurgen, Gen. Mgr.--Southern Fineblanking, Spartanburg, SC; *Int'l*, pg. 737

Forster, Lou, Gen. Mgr.--Poe & Brown of Florida, Miami, FL; *U.S. Public*, pg. 1312

Forston, Marion, Pres.--Lisa Motor Lines, Inc., Fort Worth, TX; *U.S. Public*, pg. 685

Forston, Marion, Pres.--Middleton Transportation Co., Fort Worth, TX; *U.S. Public*, pg. 685

Forsyth, Don, Mng. Dir.--Kvaerner Paladon Ltd., Hampton, United Kingdom; *Int'l*, pg. 768

Forsyth, Robert, Pres.--FKG Oil Company, Belleville, IL; *U.S. Private*, pg. 764

Forsyth, S., Mng. Dir.--Hexcel, U.K., Swindon, United Kingdom; *U.S. Public*, pg. 824

Forsyth, Stephen, Gen. Mgr.--Hexcel, S.A., Welkenraedt, Belgium; *U.S. Public*, pg. 824

Forsythe, F.S., Pres.--Cliffs Mining Company, Cleveland, OH; *U.S. Public*, pg. 386

Fort, L., Pres.--Greening Donald Co. Ltd., Orangeville, Canada; *Int'l*, pg. 1389

Forte, Luis Monteiro, Chm.--Galp International Corporation, Panama, Panama; *Int'l*, pg. 1045

Fortenbaugh, Bill, Pres.--Christal Radio, New York, NY; *U.S. Public*, pg. 335

Fortenberry, Carey, Chief Oper. Officer--Comet Rice, Inc.-Stuttgart, Stuttgart, AR; *U.S. Public*, pg. 591

Forter, Rod, Pres.--Nordberg-Read, Inc., Middleboro, MA; *Int'l*, pg. 1428

Fortes, M. Roy, Mgr.--Parker Hannifin Argentina SAIC, San Martin, Argentina; *U.S. Public*, pg. 1263

Fortes, Martin, V.P.--Perimeter Mall Management Corp., Atlanta, GA; *U.S. Public*, pg. 1408

Fortgens, Henk, Pres.--AGA Gas B.V., Amsterdam, Netherlands; *Int'l*, pg. 13

Fortgens, Henk, Chief Oper. Officer--AGA nv/sa, Brussels, Belgium; *Int'l*, pg. 13

Forti, Edwin, Pres.--Burrell/DFA Advertising, New York, NY; *U.S. Private*, pg. 188

Forti, Serge, Gen. Mgr.--PT Bank BNP Lippo Indonesia, Jakarta, Indonesia; *Int'l*, pg. 164

Fortier, Levis, V.P. & Controller--Peerless Carpet, Acton Vale, Canada; *Int'l*, pg. 1032

Fortino, John, Pres.--Fortino's Supermarkets Ltd., Hamilton, Canada; *Int'l*, pg. 1495

Fortmann, G., Mng. Dir.--Kytta-Werk Sauter GmbH, Alpirsbach, Germany; *U.S. Public*, pg. 81

Fortmann, Guenter, Mng. Dir.--Wyeth-Pharma GmbH, Munster, Germany; *U.S. Public*, pg. 82

Fortner, Richard, Pres.--AAR Landing Gear Center, Miami, FL; *U.S. Public*, pg. 1

Fortney, Jay, Pres. & Gen. Mgr.--Charles Town Races, Charles Town, WV; *U.S. Public*, pg. 1270

Fortun, Wayne M., Pres.--Hutchinson Technology Inc., Hutchinson, MN; *U.S. Public*, pg. 851

Fortunado, Edmundo G., Mng. Dir.--Analog Devices (PHILS), Inc., Manila, Philippines; *U.S. Public*, pg. 108

Fortune, Brian, Partner & Gen. Mgr.--CKS Partners/London, Bracknell, United Kingdom; *U.S. Private*, pg. 195

Fortune, Ronald F., Pres. & Chief Exec. Officer--Computer Curriculum Corporation, Sunnyvale, CA; *U.S. Private*, pg. 778

Forward, Gordon E., Pres. & Chief Exec. Officer--Chaparral Steel Co., Midlothian, TX; *U.S. Public*, pg. 1585

Foscante, Robert E., Dr., Grp. Pres.--Ameron B.V., Protective Coatings Division-Europe, Geldermalsen, Netherlands; *U.S. Public*, pg. 99

Fosdahl, Richard G., Chief Oper. Officer--Maskin A/S Zeta, Oslo, Norway; *Int'l*, pg. 1380

Foshee, Douglas L., V.P. & Mgr.--Texas Bank N.A., Houston, TX; *U.S. Public*, pg. 626

Foshee, Mike, Plant Mgr.--Hydro Conduit Corp., Oklahoma City, OK; *Int'l*, pg. 245

Fosnaugh, Charles B., Chief Oper. Officer--Market Development Co., Kentwood, MI; *U.S. Private*, pg. 1021

Foss, Kjell, Gen. Mgr.--Kvaerner Kleven Forde A/S, Forde, Norway; *Int'l*, pg. 769

Foss, T.A.G., Chm.--Societe Anonyme Industrielle De Resines, Gironde, France; *U.S. Public*, pg. 1580

Foss, T.A.G., Chm.--Tenneco Organics Ltd., Bristol, United Kingdom; *U.S. Public*, pg. 1580

Fossati, Renzo, Pres.--Chr. Hansen S.p.A., Milan, Italy; *Int'l*, *pg. 289*

Fosse, Finn E., Pres.--Kvaerner Insurance A/S, Oslo, Norway; *Int'l*, pg. 769

Fossett, W. Curtis, Chief Fin. Officer--Publishing Div., Tulsa, OK; *U.S. Public*, pg. 565

Fossett, W. Curtis, Chief Fin. Officer--Home Party Plan Div., Tulsa, OK; *U.S. Public*, pg. 565

Fossileus, Henry, Chief Oper. Officer--Auto-trol Technology AB, Sollentuna, Sweden; *U.S. Public*, pg. 148

Foster, Bruce J., Exec. V.P.--Leslie Paper, Minneapolis, MN; *U.S. Public*, pg. 903

Foster, D., Mng. Dir.--Gestetner Limited, Blantyre, Malawi; *Int'l*, pg. 1115

Foster, Dana, Gen. Mgr.--CDF Northeast, White River Junction, VT; *U.S. Public*, pg. 298

Foster, Dennis P., Pres.--Gifford-Hill Cement Company of South Carolina, Dallas, TX; *Int'l*, pg. 593

Foster, Duke, Office Mgr.--Korn/Ferry International, Stamford, CT; *U.S. Private*, pg. 633

Foster, Fred, Pres. & Publisher--Independent Publishing Company, Anderson, SC; *U.S. Public*, pg. 794

Foster, Greg, District Mgr.--Acme Brick Co., New Orleans, LA; *U.S. Public*, pg. 936

Foster, Henry L., Sr. V.P.--Charles River Laboratories-ME, Windham, ME; *U.S. Public*, pg. 194

Foster, Henry L., D.V.M., Chm. Bd.--Charles River Biotechnical Services, Inc., Wilmington, MA; *U.S. Public*, pg. 194

Foster, J.H., Chief Oper. Officer--Siemens Components Snd. Bhd., Melaka, Malaysia; *Int'l*, pg. 1247

Foster, Jack C., Chief Oper. Officer--Melitta Canada Inc., Rexdale, Canada; *Int'l*, pg. 857

Foster, James, Pres.--Universal Foot Care Products, Northbrook, IL; *U.S. Public*, pg. 1437

Foster, James C., Pres. & Chief Exec. Officer--Charles River Laboratories, Inc., Wilmington, MA; *U.S. Public*, pg. 194

Foster, James G., V.P. & Gen. Mgr.-Heart Valves Bus.--Medtronic Heart Valve Division, Minneapolis, MN; *U.S. Public*, pg. 1083

Foster, Joe B., Chm. Bd.--Tennessee Gas Transmission Co., Houston, TX; *U.S. Public*, pg. 567

Foster, Kim, Chief Fin. Officer--Pacific Brands, Hawthorn, Australia; *Int'l*, pg. 1021

Foster, Leland, Ph.D., Pres. & Chief Exec. Officer--HyClone Laboratories Inc., Logan, UT; *Int'l*, pg. 1037

Foster, M.E., Chm. Bd. & Mng. Dir.--Esso Malaysia Berhad, Kuala Lumpur, Malaysia; *U.S. Public*, pg. 602

Foster, M.E., Chm.--Esso Production Malaysia Inc., Kuala Lumpur, Malaysia; *U.S. Public*, pg. 602

Foster, Mark, Chief Oper. Officer--Medical Innovations Corp., Pocatello, ID; *U.S. Public*, pg. 171

Foster, Matthew, Reg. Chief Exec Officer--Milk Products Holdings (Australia) Pty Ltd, Rowville, Australia; *Int'l*, pg. 923

Foster, Mike, Pres.--MoorMan's Feed Division, Quincy, IL; *U.S. Private*, pg. 760

Foster, Mike, Chief Exec.--The Grand Pub Company Limited, Thame, United Kingdom; *Int'l*, pg. 956

Foster, Mike, Chief Exec. Officer--Inntrepreneur Pub Company Limited, Thame, United Kingdom; *Int'l*, pg. 956

Foster, Patrick, Div. Mgr.--Fernandina Div.-Florida Public Utilities, Fernandina Beach, FL; *U.S. Public*, pg. 655

Foster, R., V.P.-Electrical Distribution Sector--Square D Company United Kingdom Limited, Swindon, United Kingdom; *Int'l*, pg. 1209

Foster, Robert, Pres. & Gen. Mgr.--Medtronic Avalon Laboratories, Inc., Rancho Dominguez, CA; *U.S. Public*, pg. 1083

Foster, Robert F., Dr., Gen. Mgr.--Materials Research Corporation, Phoenix, AZ; *Int'l*, pg. 1283

Foster, S.F., Area V.P. & Gen. Mgr.--ITT Sheraton Hotels, Toronto, Canada; *U.S. Public*, pg. 1512

Foster, Scott, Mgr.-Adv.--D & S Marketing, Pequannock, NJ; *U.S. Private*, pg. 130

Foster, Thomas, V.P. & Dir.-Opers.--Reed Elsevier Business Information-Denver, Highlands Ranch, CO; *Int'l*, pg. 1095

Foster, Vickey, Admin--Hillhaven Topeka, Topeka, KS; *U.S. Public*, pg. 1714

Foster, Wenche Marshall, Chief Exec. Officer--Perrier UK Ltd., London, United Kingdom; *Int'l*, pg. 919

Fote, Charles T., Pres.--First Data Corporation, Englewood, CO; *U.S. Public*, pg. 631

Fothergill, G.P., Chm.--Fisons Consumer Health Plc, Witham, United Kingdom; *Int'l*, pg. 1110

Fouche, Yves, Chm. Bd.--Sogitec, Suresnes, France; *Int'l*, pg. 383

Foudree, Charles M., Pres.--Harmon Industries-Lees Summit, Lees Summit, MO; *U.S. Public*, pg. 788

Foudree, Charles M., Pres.--Vale-Harmon Enterprises, Ltd., Montreal, Canada; *U.S. Public*, pg. 788

Fougere, Richard J., Pres.--Kollmorgen Virtual Motion Group, Blacksburg, VA; *U.S. Public*, pg. 965

Foujlhac, Charles, Chief Exec. Officer--Credit Agricole (CNCA) Madrid, Madrid, Spain; *Int'l*, pg. 341

Fouks, Stephane, Gen. Mgr.--EURO RSCG Institutionnel, Levallois-Perret, France; *Int'l*, pg. 601

Foulas, Stephane, Mng. Dir.--EURO RSCG Institutionnel, Levallois-Perret, France; *Int'l*, pg. 600

Foulis, Ian, Mng. Dir.--Union Air Transport Inc., Mississauga, Canada; *U.S. Private*, pg. 1120

Foulkes, Hilary S., Partner--Skadden, Arps, Slate, Meagher & Flom LLP, Frankfurt/Main, Germany; *U.S. Private*, pg. 1004

Foulkes, Mike, Sr. V.P. & Gen. Mgr.--Fogarty Klein & Partners, San Antonio, TX; *U.S. Private*, pg. 416

Fountain, Jack, Pres.--Burgmann Seals America, Inc., Houston, TX; *Int'l*, pg. 233

Fouque, Alain, Mng. Dir.--Baldwin France Sarl, Verneuil en Halatte, France; *U.S. Public*, pg. 170

Fourman, Harold, Gen. Mgr.--Champaign Landmark, Mechanicsburg, OH; *U.S. Private*, pg. 227

Fournelle, Jorg W., Dir.--Banque Internationale de Credit et de Gestion Monaco, Monaco, Monaco; *Int'l*, pg. 180

Fournier, Andre, Mng. Dir.--Quadrant International Pty. Ltd., Sydney, Australia; *Int'l*, pg. 528

Fournier, Bernard, Mng. Dir.--Rank Xerox Limited, Marlow, United Kingdom; *Int'l*, pg. 1087

Fournier, Bernard, Mng. Dir.--Rank Xerox Limited, Marlow, United Kingdom; *U.S. Public*, pg. 1785

Fournier, D.E., Gen. Mgr.--CHEMCENTRAL/Fort Wayne, Fort Wayne, IN; *U.S. Private*, pg. 232

Fournier, David E., Gen. Mgr.--Martin Marietta International, Inc., Ankara, Turkey; *U.S. Public*, pg. 1010

Fournier, G.J., Pres.--Gold Circle Insurance Co., Toronto, Canada; *Int'l*, pg. 558

Fournier, James, Dir.--Associates Diversified Investments Ltd., Hamilton, Bermuda; *U.S. Public*, pg. 665

Fournier, Jean, Chief Oper. Officer--Elf Congo, Brazzaville, Congo; *Int'l*, pg. 446

Fournier, Thomas J., Pres.--Triumph Industries, Bridgeview, IL; *U.S. Public*, pg. 1641

Foursans, Louis, Chief Oper. Officer--Sucos Refrigerantes Aguas Minerais Industria E Comercia, Rio de Janeiro, Brazil; *Int'l*, pg. 919

Fourtean, Patrick, Pres.--St. Jude Medical Europe, Inc., Brussels, Belgium; *U.S. Public*, pg. 1428

Fouse, William L., Chm.--Mellon Capital Management Corporation (MFSC 1085

Foust, David B., V.P. & G.M.--Bekaert Associates, Inc., Marietta, GA; *Int'l*, pg. 184

Foust, Larry, Gen. Mgr.--Consolidated Wholesale Lumber Co., Austin, TX; *U.S. Private*, pg. 200

Fouts, Craig C., II, Pres.--Ikon Office Solutions-Columbus, Dublin, OH; *U.S. Public*, pg. 863

Fouts, Jerry J., Pres.--Old Kent Bank of Big Rapids, Big Rapids, MI; *U.S. Public*, pg. 1216

Fowler, Caleb L., Pres.--INA Corporation, Philadelphia, PA; *U.S. Public*, pg. 362

Fowler, E., Mgr.--Radio-Holland de Venezuela S.A., Caracas, Venezuela; *Int'l*, pg. 1152

Fowler, John, Joint Chief Exec. Officer--Westcan Chromalox, Cambridge, Canada; *Int'l*, pg. 554

Fowler, John P. II, Pres.--Goodkind & O'Dea, Inc., Rutherford, NJ; *U.S. Private*, pg. 329

Fowler, Mark, Pres.--First Bank of Arkansas, Jonesboro, AR; *U.S. Public*, pg. 630

Fowler, Newton, Jr., Chief Exec. Officer--Philip Morris U.S.A., Cabarrus Mfg. Center, Concord, NC; *U.S. Public*, pg. 1290

Fowler, Paul, Mng. Dir.--Tasman Forestry Limited, Rotorua, New Zealand; *Int'l*, pg. 495

Fowler, R., Mng. Dir.--Simon Petroleum Technology Ltd., Swanley, United Kingdom; *Int'l*, pg. 1251
Fowler, Richard M., Chief Fin. Officer--Southwestern Financial Corp., Dallas, TX; *U.S. Public*, pg. 1585
Fowler, Robert G., Pres. & Chief Oper. Officer--Enserch Shirley, Wilmington, DE; *U.S. Public*, pg. 1587
Fowode, B., Gen. Mgr.--Johnson Wax Nigeria Limited, Ikeja, Nigeria; *U.S. Private*, pg. 593
Fox, A.J., Jr., Gen. Mgr.--Union Camp Ireland, Ashbourne, Ireland; *U.S. Public*, pg. 1666
Fox, Alan, Mng. Dir.--Process Equipment, Manchester, United Kingdom; *Int'l*, pg. 1444
Fox, Andy, Gen. Mgr.--Wabash Fibre Box Company, Kansas City, MO; *U.S. Private*, pg. 1170
Fox, Brad, Pres.--Fox International Ltd., Inc., Cleveland, OH; *U.S. Public*, pg. 1720
Fox, Brad, Pres.--GMB Sales, Setauket, NY; *U.S. Public*, pg. 1720
Fox, Brendan P., D.V.M., Pres.--Elanco Animal Health, Indianapolis, IN; *U.S. Public*, pg. 993
Fox, David, Pres.--Behavioral Health Services, Winfield, IL; *U.S. Private*, pg. 223
Fox, David, III, Sr. V.P.--McJunkin - Appalachain, Charleston, WV; *U.S. Private*, pg. 722
Fox, Dennis, Plant Mgr.-Abilene--Tread Rubber Plant, Abilene, TX; *U.S. Public*, pg. 177
Fox, Dick, Mgr.--Century Telephone, Region III, La Crosse, WI; *U.S. Public*, pg. 329
Fox, E.G., Gen. Mgr.--Kinepak, Incorporated, Dallas, TX; *Int'l*, pg. 664
Fox, Ed, Pres.--North Star BHP Steel LLC, Delta, OH; *Int'l*, pg. 226
Fox, Edward, Admin.--Roswell Nursing Center, Roswell, NM; *U.S. Public*, pg. 838
Fox, Grahame, V.P.--Weatherford Oil Tool (Pte.) Ltd., Loyang Crescent, Singapore; *U.S. Public*, pg. 1750
Fox, Gwen, Gen. Mgr.--ATCO Travel, Calgary, Canada; *Int'l*, pg. 95
Fox, Herbert A., Jr., Pres.--Murphy Oil Trading Co. (Eastern), El Dorado, AR; *U.S. Public*, pg. 1142
Fox, Herbert A., Jr., Pres.--Murphy Oil USA, Inc., El Dorado, AR; *U.S. Public*, pg. 1142
Fox, Jim, Gen. Mgr.--Royale Coach, Elkhart, IN; *U.S. Public*, pg. 1123
Fox, John L., Gen. Mgr.--Bostik, Inc., Middleton, MA; *Int'l*, pg. 1409
Fox, Jonathan E., Chief Exec. Officer, Exec. V.P.-Intl. & Reg. Dir.-Asia Pacific--Grey Asia Pacific, Quarry Bay, Hong Kong; *U.S. Public*, pg. 765
Fox, Keith, Gen. Mgr.--Master Mold, Erie, PA; *U.S. Private*, pg. 870
Fox, Larry H., Pres.--Powder River Coal Company, Gillette, WY; *Int'l*, pg. 594
Fox, Marea, Mng. Dir.--International Public Relations, Pty Ltd., Hobart, Australia; *Int'l*, pg. 1227
Fox, Mark, Gen. Mgr.--Mystic Stamp Company, Camden, NY; *U.S. Private*, pg. 671
Fox, Mitchell B., Publisher--Details Magazine, New York, NY; *U.S. Private*, pg. 20
Fox, Richard, Mgr.--Century Telephone of Wisconsin, Inc., La Crosse, WI; *U.S. Public*, pg. 329
Fox, Richard, Mgr.--Century Area Long Lines Inc., La Crosse, WI; *U.S. Public*, pg. 330
Fox, Richard, Pres.-Warner Bros. Intl.--Warner Bros. Studios, Inc., Burbank, CA; *U.S. Public*, pg. 1611
Fox, Robert, Pres.--Conax Buffalo Corporation, Buffalo, NY; *Int'l*, pg. 646
Fox, Scott, Reg. Acct. Dir.--RP alpha/New Jersey, Moorestown, NJ; *U.S. Private*, pg. 950
Fox, Sheila, Pres.--Chapman Warwick Inc., San Diego, CA; *U.S. Private*, pg. 1152
Fox, William A., Pres.--The Peoples Natural Gas Co., Pittsburgh, PA; *U.S. Public*, pg. 435
Fox, William A., Jr., Pres.--Hope Gas, Inc., Clarksburg, WV; *U.S. Public*, pg. 435
Foxx, S. Dell, Pres. & Chief Exec. Officer--County Banking & Trust Company, Elkton, MD; *U.S. Public*, pg. 1089
Foy, Bruce, Mng. Dir.--BBL Australia Limited, Sydney, Australia; *Int'l*, pg. 148
Foy, Thomas, Pres. & Chief Exec. Officer--Action Industries, Inc., Tupelo, MS; *U.S. Public*, pg. 688
Foyle, R.C., Pres.--Heraeus/Kulzer, Inc. - Dental Products Div., South Bend, IN; *Int'l*, pg. 616
Fraback, Alan, Sr. V.P. & Mng. Dir.--Western International Media Corporation, Seattle, WA; *U.S. Private*, pg. 1167
Frachey, Enrico, Pres.--Fila USA, Sparks, MD; *Int'l*, pg. 484
Fradlin, Lucien, Div. V.P.-Large Accounts & Distr.-Europe--Data General Europe, Inc., Paris, France; *U.S. Public*, pg. 486
Frady, James, Plant Mgr.--Hydro Conduit Corp., Apopka, FL; *Int'l*, pg. 246
Fraefel, Peter, Chm.--Coop Zentralschweiz, Kriens, Switzerland; *Int'l*, pg. 329
Fraggstedt, Anders, Pres.--ABB Relays AB, Vasteras, Sweden; *Int'l*, pg. 7
Fragle, Brian, Mng. Dir.--Willis Corroon North Limited, Manchester, United Kingdom; *Int'l*, pg. 1503
Fragle, Brian, Mng. Dir.--Willis Corroon North Limited, Preston, United Kingdom; *Int'l*, pg. 1503
Fraher, James, V.P.--Land O'Lakes, Inc., Southampton, PA; *U.S. Private*, pg. 646
Fraim, Richard, Pres. & Gen. Mgr.--KLAS, Inc., Las Vegas, NV; *U.S. Private*, pg. 647
Frain, William T., Jr., Pres. & Chief Oper. Officer--Public Service Company of New Hampshire, Manchester, NH; *U.S. Public*, pg. 1195
Fraka, D. Lyle, V.P. & G.M.--Electronia Dale de Mexico S.A. de C.V., Juarez, Mexico; *U.S. Public*, pg. 1722
Frame, Cary G., Gen. Mgr.--VAC Data Management, Inc., Louisville, KY; *U.S. Public*, pg. 575
Frame, W. Douglas, Pres.--National-Oilwell/Dreco, Edmonton, Canada; *U.S. Public*, pg. 1158
Framji, Kaikhosrou K., Resident Rep.--The World Bank, Accra, Ghana; *U.S. Private*, pg. 1189
Framp, Paul, Gen. Mgr.--Britannia Refined Metals Ltd., Gravesend, United Kingdom; *Int'l*, pg. 827
Franca, Jair, Mgr.--Franca Branch, Franca, Brazil; *Int'l*, pg. 139
Frances, Dr. F., Chief Oper. Officer--Siemens S.A., Madrid, Spain; *Int'l*, pg. 1248
Francese, Peter, Pres. & Publisher--American Demographics, Inc., Ithaca, NY; *U.S. Private*, pg. 281
Francese, Steve, Gen. Mgr.--Acme Chemicals & Insulation Co., New Haven, CT; *U.S. Private*, pg. 565
Franchi, Luigi, Mng. Dir.--SASIB Packaging Italia S.r.l., Pistoia, Italy; *Int'l*, pg. 1194
Franchise Direcer, Jorge Rorg, Chief Oper. Officer--Johnson & Johnson Productos, Barcelona, Spain; *U.S. Public*, pg. 928
Francis, Dennis, Pres.--Patrician Associates, Inc., Des Moines, IA; *U.S. Private*, pg. 885
Francis, Dennis, Pres.--Petula Associates, Ltd., Des Moines, IA; *U.S. Private*, pg. 885
Francis, Dennis, Pres.--Principal Development Associates, Inc., Des Moines, IA; *U.S. Private*, pg. 885
Francis, Martin S., V.P. & Mng. Dir.--LTX (Europe) Limited, Woking, United Kingdom; *U.S. Public*, pg. 972
Francis, R.J., Mng. Dir.--T.H.E., Newcastle under Lyme, United Kingdom; *Int'l*, pg. 707
Francis, R.J., Mng. Dir.--The Games, Eastleigh, United Kingdom; *Int'l*, pg. 707
Francisco, Gerald, Gen. Mgr.--H.E.I.L.L., Phoenix, AZ; *U.S. Public*, pg. 521
Francke, Richard, Gen. Mgr.--ITW Panel Switches and Systems, Chicago, IL; *U.S. Public*, pg. 866
Franco, Agustin, Gen. Dir.--Cryolnfra S.A. de C.V., Mexico, Mexico; *U.S. Public*, pg. 32
Franco, Anthony F., Exec. V.P. & Gen. Mgr.--Banca Popolare di Milano, New York, NY; *Int'l*, pg. 137
Franco, Carol, Pres. & Publisher--Ballinger Publishing Co., Cambridge, MA; *Int'l*, pg. 927
Franco, Donna S., Pres. & Chief Oper. Officer--Melrose, Chatsworth, CA; *U.S. Public*, pg. 948
Franco, Felipe, V.P.-Mortgage Loans--Mortgage Loan Div., Hato Rey, PR; *U.S. Public*, pg. 175
Franco, J. M., G.M.--Avon Cosmetics, Inc., Pasay, Philippines; *U.S. Public*, pg. 156
Franco, J.O. Junquera, Mng. Dir.--Quaker Brasil, Ltda., Rio de Janeiro, Brazil; *U.S. Public*, pg. 1348
Franco, M., Chief Oper. Officer--Teledinamica LDA., Maia, Portugal; *Int'l*, pg. 474
Franco, Richard, V.P. & Gen. Mgr.--Cerenex Pharmaceuticals, Research Triangle Park, NC; *Int'l*, pg. 553
Francoeur, M., Pres. & Chief Exec. Officer--Stelco-McMaster Ltee, Contrecoeur, Canada; *Int'l*, pg. 1299
Francois-Poncet, Gerard, Gen. Mgr.--Olin S.A., Roissy Charles de Gaulle, France; *U.S. Public*, pg. 1220
Francois, Jacques, Mng. Dir.--Nira S.A., Nanterre, France; *Int'l*, pg. 1369
Francois, Jean, Mng. Dir.--Bertrand Faure Argentina SA, Cordoba, Argentina; *Int'l*, pg. 193
Francois, Jean, Mng. Dir.--PAB SA, Cordoba, Argentina; *Int'l*, pg. 193
Francq, W., Mng. Dir.--N.V. Galenco, Paal, Belgium; *Int'l*, pg. 991
Frandsen, Henning Korsbaek, Mng. Dir.--Kelly Vikarer, Copenhagen, Denmark; *U.S. Public*, pg. 949
Frandsen, Lau, Chief Oper. Officer--Damixa Armaturen, GmbH, Dusseldorf, Germany; *U.S. Public*, pg. 1054
Frandsen, Lau, Chief Oper. Officer--Damixa Ltd., Brentford, United Kingdom; *U.S. Public*, pg. 1055
Frangenberg, Bernd, Pres. & Chief Exec. Officer--Continental General Tire, Inc., Charlotte, NC; *Int'l*, pg. 327
Frangi, Pierre, Chief Exec. Officer--Fotolabo Club S.A., Lausanne, Switzerland; *Int'l*, pg. 501
Frank, Alan, Gen. Mgr.--Post-Newsweek Stations, Michigan, Inc., Detroit, MI; *U.S. Public*, pg. 1743
Frank, Alan, Gen. Mgr.--WDIV-TV, Detroit, MI; *U.S. Public*, pg. 1743
Frank, Dale, Mgr.-Sls.--Illinois Auto Central Div., Chicago, IL; *U.S. Private*, pg. 558
Frank, Forest C., Exec. V.P.--Provident Commercial Group, Inc., Cincinnati, OH; *U.S. Public*, pg. 1338
Frank, H. Alan, Chief Exec. Officer--Admiral Packaging, Inc., Providence, RI; *U.S. Private*, pg. 1119
Frank, H. Alan, Chief Exec. Officer--Union Paper Co., Providence, RI; *U.S. Private*, pg. 1119
Frank, J.L., Pres.--Marathon Ashland Petroleum LLC, Findlay, OH; *U.S. Public*, pg. 139
Frank, J.W., Chief Oper. Officer--Georg Jensen Silver (NSW) Pty. Ltd, Sydney, Australia; *Int'l*, pg. 1134
Frank, James, Editor--Golf Magazine, New York, NY; *U.S. Public*, pg. 1617
Frank, Jeffrey, Div. Pres.--Sanmark Group, New York, NY; *U.S. Public*, pg. 1141
Frank, John B., Pres. & Chief Exec. Officer--SunTrust Bank, Middle Georgia, N.A., Macon, GA; *U.S. Public*, pg. 1538
Frank, Russell, Mgr.--Shepler's Conroe, Conroe, TX; *U.S. Public*, pg. 413
Franke, Arthur G., Pres.--Acme Printing Ink Co., Inc., Elk Grove Village, IL; *Int'l*, pg. 1311
Franke, J.P., Pres. & Chief Exec. Officer--Syndesis Development Corp., Milwaukee, WI; *U.S. Public*, pg. 1773
Franke, Klaus, Sr. Mng. Dir.--Deutsche Bank-Kreditbank AG (Erfurt), Erfurt, Germany; *Int'l*, pg. 402
Franke, Thomas S., Pres. & Chief Oper. Officer--Raymond James & Associates, Inc., Saint Petersburg, FL; *U.S. Public*, pg. 923
Frankel, Robert, Pres.--Gerber Agri Inc., New York, NY; *U.S. Private*, pg. 449
Frankenfield, Donald E., Pres.--Philadelphia International Investment Corp., Philadelphia, PA; *U.S. Public*, pg. 447
Frankfort, Lew, Chm. Bd. & Chief Exec. Officer--Coach, New York, NY; *U.S. Public*, pg. 1433
Frankfurt, George, Dir.-North Europe--AlliedSignal Aerospace Service Corporation, Southall, United Kingdom; *U.S. Public*, pg. 52
Frankland, James G., Pres.--New Castle Industries, Inc., New Castle, PA; *U.S. Public*, pg. 104
Franklin, A.J.D., Chm. Bd.--Costain International Limited, Woking, United Kingdom; *Int'l*, pg. 336
Franklin, Boyd, Branch Mgr.--Bergen Brunswig Medical Corporation, Boise, ID; *U.S. Public*, pg. 214
Franklin, Bruce, Pres.--International Correspondence Schools (New Zealand) Limited, Wellington, New Zealand; *U.S. Public*, pg. 784
Franklin, Dick, Pres.--PT BHP Steel Building Products Indonesia, Jakarta, Indonesia; *Int'l*, pg. 226
Franklin, Gary A., Pres. & Chief Fin. Officer--ServiceMaster of Canada Ltd., Mississauga, Canada; *U.S. Public*, pg. 1462
Franklin, George, Chief Oper. Officer--Design Concepts Integration, Inc., Bloomington, MN; *U.S. Private*, pg. 572
Franklin, H. Allen, Pres. & Chief Exec. Officer--Georgia Power Co., Atlanta, GA; *U.S. Public*, pg. 1490
Franklin, H. Allen, Pres.--Southern Company Services, Inc., Atlanta, GA; *U.S. Public*, pg. 1490
Franklin, J., V.P. & Gen. Mgr.--McDermott Scotland, Inverness, United Kingdom; *U.S. Public*, pg. 1068
Franklin, Joy, Exec. Editor--Times-News, Hendersonville, NC; *U.S. Public*, pg. 1175
Franklin, W.E., Pres.--Weyerhaeuser Japan Ltd., Tokyo, Japan; *U.S. Public*, pg. 1764
Franklin, William E., Pres.--Weyerhaeuser (Far East) Ltd., Wan Chai, Hong Kong; *U.S. Public*, pg. 1764
Frankovic, Richard, Pres. & Chief Oper. Officer--The Rugby Group, Inc., Rockville Centre, NY; *Int'l*, pg. 625
Franks, Martin D., Sr. V.P. & Pres.-CBS Foundation--CBS, New York, NY; *U.S. Public*, pg. 273
Franks, R.G., Mng. Dir.--Teamwork Corporation Sdn Bhd, Kuala Lumpur, Malaysia; *Int'l*, pg. 1360
Franks, Richard M., Chm. Bd. & Pres.--Dispatch Consumer Services, Westerville, OH; *U.S. Private*, pg. 335
Franks, Richard M., Chm. Bd. & Pres.--CNS-Community News Service Weekly Newspapers, Columbus, OH; *U.S. Private*, pg. 335
Frankulin, R., Pres. & Chief Oper. Officer--Frankulin Tool & Mfg. Co., New Berlin, WI; *U.S. Private*, pg. 1192
Franssen, P.J.G., Mng. Dir.--Ballast Nedam & Industrie & Toelevering B.V., Soest, Netherlands; *Int'l*, pg. 133
Frantz, Christine, Branch Mgr.--Downey Savings & Loan Association, F.A., Fullerton, CA; *U.S. Public*, pg. 526
Frantz, Pat, Pres. & Publr.--Elmira Star-Gazette, Elmira, NY; *U.S. Public*, pg. 700
Frantz, Richard, Pres. & Chief Exec. Officer--Peoples Federal Savings Bank, Wooster, OH; *U.S. Public*, pg. 647
Frantzen, Gaston, Gen. Mgr.--MecanARBED Dommeldange S.a.r.l., Dudelange, Luxembourg; *Int'l*, pg. 80
Franz, A.R., Mng. Dir.--Whitehall Laboratories Pty. Limited, Lidcombe, Australia; *U.S. Public*, pg. 82
Franz, Elizabeth T., Pres. & Publr.--Great Falls Tribune, Great Falls, MT; *U.S. Public*, pg. 700
Franz, J.E., Pres.--Zephyer Properties, Inc., Dayton, OH; *U.S. Public*, pg. 1076
Franz, Peter, Mng. Dir.--Battenfeld Chen Extrusion Systems Ltd., Guangdong, China; *Int'l*, pg. 825
Franz, William H., V.P.--XTRA Lease, Inc., Saint Louis, MO; *U.S. Public*, pg. 1786
Franz, Wurm, Pres.--Agrolinz Melamin Italia S.r.l., Castellanza, Italy; *Int'l*, pg. 356
Franza, Alberto, Pres.--NEC Electronics Italiana s.r.l., Milan, Italy; *Int'l*, pg. 900
Franzen, Neil, Representative--Banco di Sicilia, Chicago, IL; *Int'l*, pg. 140
Franzen, Peter, Mng. Dir.--MMI Insurance Group, Sydney, Australia; *Int'l*, pg. 60
Franzen, Pieter, Mng. Dir.--Anglo-Elementar Versicherungs-AG, Vienna, Austria; *Int'l*, pg. 60
Franzgrote, Joseph, Pres. & Gen. Mgr.--KUSA-TV, Denver, CO; *U.S. Public*, pg. 702
Frascari, Dr. Giuliano, Mng. Dir.--SMET, Milan, Italy; *U.S. Private*, pg. 1065
Frase, David M., Pres. & Gen. Mgr.--Kysor Panel Systems, Fort Worth, TX; *U.S. Public*, pg. 1445
Fraser, A., Mng. Dir.--Riley Advertising (Edinburgh) Ltd., Edinburgh, United Kingdom; *Int'l*, pg. 1117
Fraser, A., Mng. Dir.--Riley Advertising (Scotland) Ltd., Glasgow, United Kingdom; *Int'l*, pg. 1117
Fraser, A., Mng. Dir.--Riley Advertising (Aberdeen) Ltd., Aberdeen, United Kingdom; *Int'l*, pg. 1117
Fraser, Allan, Chief Rep.--Westpac Banking Corporation-Bahrain, Manama, Bahrain; *Int'l*, pg. 1497
Fraser, C., Gen. Mgr.--Ballast Wiltshier Plc - South East Region, Maidstone, United Kingdom; *Int'l*, pg. 135
Fraser, Don C., Pres.--BHP Steel Canada Inc., Vancouver, Canada; *Int'l*, pg. 227
Fraser, Duncan, Pres.--Consolidated Graphic Communications, Bridgeville, PA; *U.S. Public*, pg. 333
Fraser, E.L., V.P. & Sec.--ILA Financial Services, Inc., Phoenix, AZ; *U.S. Public*, pg. 680
Fraser, Graham, Gen. Mgr.--Nicolet Limited, Warwick, United Kingdom; *U.S. Public*, pg. 1594
Fraser, I., Mng. Dir.--TNT Australia Pty. Limited, Mascot, Australia; *Int'l*, pg. 1343
Fraser, Iain, Base Mgr.--Weatherford U.K. Ltd., Great Yarmouth, United Kingdom; *U.S. Public*, pg. 1750
Fraser, J. Robert, Pres.--Frank W. Horner Inc. (Canada), Montreal, Canada; *U.S. Public*, pg. 310
Fraser, Robert, Chief Oper. Officer--Engine Control Systems, Ltd., Newmarket, Canada; *U.S. Public*, pg. 1016
Fraser, Stuart G., Pres.--Empire Theaters Limited, Stellarton, Canada; *Int'l*, pg. 454
Fraser, W.W., Joint Mng. Dir.--P&O (New Zealand) Ltd., Wellington, New Zealand; *Int'l*, pg. 1035
Frasso, Peter, V.P. & Gen. Mgr.--Vacuum Products, Lexington, MA; *U.S. Public*, pg. 1710

Frater, Steve, Gen. Mgr.--COFINEC (Compagnie Financiere pour l'Europe Centrale), Vienna, Austria; *Int'l*, pg. 240
Fratto, Frank, Sr. V.P.--Garment Center Region, Los Angeles, CA; *U.S. Public*, pg. 872
Frauenhofer, V.H., Chm., Pres. & Chief Exec. Officer--ENI Gas Services, Inc., Hartford, CT; *U.S. Public*, pg. 285
Frauenhofer, Victor H., Chm. Bd. & Chief Exec. Officer--Energy Networks, Inc. (ENI), Hartford, CT; *U.S. Public*, pg. 285
Frauenhofer, Victor H., Chm., Pres. & Chief Exec. Officer--CNG Realty Co., Hartford, CT; *U.S. Public*, pg. 285
Fravel, J.C., Chm., Pres. & Chief Exec. Officer--Syroco Inc., Peabody, MA; *Int'l*, pg. 844
Frawley, John R., Pres.--Merrill Lynch Investment Partners, Inc., New York, NY; *U.S. Public*, pg. 1098
Frayle, Jose-Luis, Mng. Dir.--Asientos de Castilla Leon SA, Valladolid, Spain; *Int'l*, pg. 193
Frazer, R.W., Chief Exec. Officer--Blackwood Hodge (South Africa) (Pty.) Ltd., Boksburg, South Africa; *Int'l*, pg. 231
Frazho, Paul R., Mgr.-Sls. & Admin.--Fastcut Tool Corporation, Troy, MI; *U.S. Public*, pg. 368
Frazier, D., Mgr.--M&N Valve, Aurora, CO; *Int'l*, pg. 1449
Frazier, Edward C., Pres.--Liberty Sports, Inc., Englewood, CO; *U.S. Public*, pg. 1555
Frazier, George, Opers. Mgr.--United Graphics, Inc., Kent, WA; *U.S. Public*, pg. 188
Frazier, John L.D., Chm. Bd. & Chief Exec. Officer--Full Service Beverage Company, Wichita, KS; *U.S. Private*, pg. 34
Frazier, Reid, V.P. & Gen. Mgr.--Aqualon, Wilmington, DE; *U.S. Public*, pg. 810
Frecha, Patricio, Mng. Dir.--Dart do Brasil Industria e Comercio Ltda., Sao Paulo, Brazil; *U.S. Public*, pg. 1322
Frechette, Peter L., Pres.--Direct Dental Supply Co., Sparks, NV; *U.S. Public*, pg. 1265
Frechette, Robert, Pres.--Safecard Services, Inc., Jacksonville, FL; *U.S. Public*, pg. 320
Freddi, Davide, Pres.--Frigoscandia Food Process Systems S.R.L., Milan, Italy; *U.S. Public*, pg. 607
Freddura, Manny, Administrator--Greenery Rehabilitation & Skilled Nursing Center, Hyannis, MA; *U.S. Public*, pg. 837
Frede, D.J., Gen. Mgr.--CHEMCENTRAL/Chicago, Bedford Park, IL; *U.S. Private*, pg. 232
Frederick, Donald A., Pres.--Pennzoil Exploration & Production Co., Houston, TX; *U.S. Public*, pg. 1272
Frederick, James, Sr. V.P. & Gen. Mgr.--Intalco Aluminum Corp., Ferndale, WA; *U.S. Public*, pg. 60
Frederick, Ray, V.P. & Gen. Mgr.--Weatherhead Brake Div., Fort Wayne, IN; *U.S. Public*, pg. 480
Frederick, Rick, Pres.--Ikon Office Solutions, Oklahoma City, OK; *U.S. Public*, pg. 863
Frederick, Tom, Pres.--The Plexus Group, Sunnyvale, CA; *U.S. Public*, pg. 177
Fredericks, Eric, Exec. V.P.--Young & Rubicam Europe, Zurich, Switzerland; *U.S. Private*, pg. 1199
Fredericks, James, Gen. Mgr.--Benson Corp., Weyauwega, WI; *U.S. Private*, pg. 443
Fredericks, Michael, Pres.--NCC Publishing, Tillsonburg, Canada; *Int'l*, pg. 924
Fredericks, Ray, Gen. Mgr.--Gresen Hydraulics Div., Greenville, SC; *U.S. Public*, pg. 479
Fredericksen, Dennis, Chief Oper. Officer--Hubbard Feeds, Rapid City, SD; *Int'l*, pg. 1116
Fredericksen, Paul H., V.P. & Gen. Mgr.--KCCI Television, Inc., Des Moines, IA; *U.S. Public*, pg. 1343
Frederiksen, Flemming, V.P. & Gen. Mgr.--Laitram Machinery Inc., Harahan, LA; *U.S. Private*, pg. 643
Frederiksen, Peter, Mng. Dir.--Ferrosan Danmark A/S, Soeborg, Denmark; *Int'l*, pg. 987
Fredheim, Kjell, Exec. V.P. & Chief Oper. Officer--SAS Airline, Stockholm, Sweden; *Int'l*, pg. 1201
Frediani, M., Chief Oper. Officer--A.I. Ocean (Australia) Pty. Ltd., Mascot, Australia; *Int'l*, pg. 14
Fredrickson, C.T., Chief Exec. Officer--Agribank, FCB, Saint Paul, MN; *U.S. Private*, pg. 398
Fredrickson, Robert, Pres.--The Chase Manhattan Bank (USA), NA, Wilmington, DE; *U.S. Public*, pg. 338
Fredrickson, Tony, Pres.--Titan Research & Technology, San Diego, CA; *U.S. Public*, pg. 1618
Fredrikson, Kurt, Dir.--Dickursby Farg AB, Spangenas, Sweden; *Int'l*, pg. 729
Fredryk, Mike, Branch Mgr.--New Balance Canada Inc., Mississauga, Canada; *U.S. Private*, pg. 792
Freeborough, Chris, Mng. Dir.--Royal Bank Leasing Ltd., Cheltenham, United Kingdom; *Int'l*, pg. 1132
Freed, Robert, Pres.--Kaufman and Broad-South Bay Inc., Fremont, CA; *U.S. Public*, pg. 945
Freedhoff, Harry, Pres.--Tyco Canada Ltd., Mississauga, Canada; *U.S. Public*, pg. 1059
Freedman, D., Gen. Mgr.--The Jacob's Bakery Ltd., Liverpool, United Kingdom; *Int'l*, pg. 381
Freedman, David N., Chief Oper. Officer--Giant Construction Co., Inc., Hyattsville, MD; *U.S. Public*, pg. 741
Freedman, Eugene, Pres. & Chief Exec. Officer--Enesco Corporation, Itasca, IL; *U.S. Public*, pg. 1508
Freeh, John J., Pres. & Gen. Mgr.--KAPL, Inc., Schenectady, NY; *U.S. Public*, pg. 1007
Freeland, David, Pres.--Texas Sunbelt Cement, Corpus Christi, TX; *U.S. Public*, pg. 323
Freeland, T. B., Chief Oper. Officer--Melben Products Inc., Harrison, OH; *U.S. Public*, pg. 218
Freeman, Alan, Mgr.--Darwin Bakery Pty. Ltd., Winnellie, Australia; *Int'l*, pg. 1074
Freeman, Bob, Pres.--William Penn Life Insurance Co. of New York, New Hyde Park, NY; *Int'l*, pg. 805
Freeman, Bruce, Pres.--AEC, Inc., Wood Dale, IL; *U.S. Private*, pg. 500
Freeman, Bruce, Pres.--Nelmor Co., Inc., North Uxbridge, MA; *U.S. Private*, pg. 1041
Freeman, Bruce, Pres.--AEC/Application Engineering Corporation, Wood Dale, IL; *U.S. Private*, pg. 1041
Freeman, Bruce, Admin.--Salemhaven, Salem, NH; *U.S. Public*, pg. 1714
Freeman, Carrie L., Pres.--Freeman Exhibit Co., Dallas, TX; *U.S. Private*, pg. 426
Freeman, Cliff, Chm. & Chief Creative Officer--Cliff Freeman & Partners, New York, NY; *U.S. Public*, pg. 1422
Freeman, David, Chm. & Chief Exec. Officer--Loctite Corporation, Rocky Hill, CT; *Int'l*, pg. 611
Freeman, E., Dir. of Ports--Killingholme Wharfage Co. Ltd., Grimsby, United Kingdom; *Int'l*, pg. 1251
Freeman, Edmund J., Pres.--Joy Energy Systems Inc., Charlotte, NC; *U.S. Public*, pg. 789
Freeman, Edward H., Pres. & Chief Exec. Officer--USLIFE Agency Services, Inc., Schaumburg, IL; *U.S. Public*, pg. 77
Freeman, Eugene R., V.P. & Gen. Mgr.--Power Products Div., Somerville, NJ; *U.S. Public*, pg. 792
Freeman, Gerald M., Sr. V.P. & Gen. Mgr.--Forest Products Division, Chicago, IL; *U.S. Public*, pg. 1521
Freeman, Henry, Pres. & Publr.--Courier-News Co., Bridgewater, NJ; *U.S. Public*, pg. 700
Freeman, Jeff, V.P.--Jani King of California, Inc., San Mateo, CA; *U.S. Private*, pg. 581
Freeman, John, Pres.--UPB of Northeast Arkansas, Jonesboro, AR; *U.S. Public*, pg. 1669
Freeman, M W., Chm.--Miller Freeman PTE Ltd., Singapore, Singapore; *Int'l*, pg. 1443
Freeman, Marshall, Chm. Bd.--Miller Freeman PLC, London, United Kingdom; *Int'l*, pg. 1443
Freeman, Patrick S., Chief Oper. Officer--The Goldfield Consolidated Mines Co., Melbourne, FL; *U.S. Public*, pg. 750
Freeman, Patrick S., Chief Oper. Officer--St. Cloud Mining Co., Truth Or Consequences, NM; *U.S. Public*, pg. 750
Freeman, R.R., Mng. Dir.--Rank Taylor Hobson Limited, Leicester, United Kingdom; *Int'l*, pg. 1087
Freeman, S. David, Gen. Mgr.--The Los Angeles Department of Water and Power (DWP), Los Angeles, CA; *U.S. Private*, pg. 676
Freeman, Thomas E., Pres.--Fleet Real Estate, Inc., Providence, RI; *U.S. Public*, pg. 650
Freeman, William A., Pres.--Navajo Western Land Co., Walsenburg, CO; *U.S. Private*, pg. 1153
Freeman, William A., Pres.--Watkins Associated Developers, Atlanta, GA; *U.S. Private*, pg. 1153
Freer, Kenneth, Pres.--The Fonda Group, Inc., Saint Albans, VT; *U.S. Private*, pg. 421
Freericks, Charles J., Jr., Pres.--Talley Realty Group, Phoenix, AZ; *U.S. Public*, pg. 308
Frega, Ben, Pres. & Chief Exec. Officer--Comstock Michigan Fruit, Rochester, NY; *U.S. Private*, pg. 887
Frei, Chris, Terminal Mgr.--Kintetsu World Express Inc., El Paso, TX; *Int'l*, pg. 735
Frei, Jurgen, Branch Mgr.--Union-Transport Corporation-Salt Lake City Office, Salt Lake City, UT; *U.S. Private*, pg. 1120
Frei, K., Rep.--Swiss Bank Corporation, Mexico, Mexico; *Int'l*, pg. 1330
Frei, Philipp A., Mng. Dir.--Swiss Life International Services, Ridgewood, NJ; *Int'l*, pg. 1332
Freiberg, Patty, V.P. & Branch Mgr.--Minnesota Branch Office, Minneapolis, MN; *U.S. Public*, pg. 1683
Freibergs, Janis, Pres.--Talsi Building Materials Ltd., Talsi, Latvia; *Int'l*, pg. 1201
Freidel, G. Kathleen, Admin.--Hillhaven Extended Care, Santa Cruz, CA; *U.S. Public*, pg. 1713
Freimath, Steven P., Pres.--VanFed Appraisal Company, Seattle, WA; *U.S. Public*, pg. 1742
Freimuth, Stan, V.P. & Gen. Mgr.--Fuji Graphic Arts Div., Itasca, IL; *Int'l*, pg. 524
Freire, Amable Dopico, Gen. Mgr.--Renosa - Remolcadores del Noroeste, S.A., Fene, Spain; *Int'l*, pg. 1223
Freireich, G.T., Mgr.--Morton Chemical Div., Greenville, SC; *U.S. Public*, pg. 1135
Freischmidt, Peter, Grp. Gen. Mgr.--Oral-B Laboratories GmbH, Frankfurt/Main, Germany; *U.S. Public*, pg. 745
Freitag, Ivens, Chief Oper. Officer--Consul S.A., Joinville, Brazil; *U.S. Public*, pg. 1765
Freitag, Miles, Pres.--Solvay Animal Health, Inc., Mendota Heights, MN; *Int'l*, pg. 1277
Fremont, A., Gen. Mgr.--Laiterie de Villecomtal, Mielan, France; *Int'l*, pg. 379
Fremont, Enrique, Mgr.--Grupo Termoindustrial ECA, S.A. de C.V., Queretaro, Mexico; *U.S. Private*, pg. 361
Fremont, Jacky, Pres.--Photocentron Inc., Novato, CA; *Int'l*, pg. 462
French, Bill, Div. Mgr.--Century Telephone of Arkansas, Inc., Hardy, AR; *U.S. Public*, pg. 329
French, Daniel E., Sr. V.P.--A.H. Robins Co., Operations Division, Richmond, VA; *U.S. Public*, pg. 80
French, David, Gen. Mgr.--Computer Products Division, Norwood, MA; *U.S. Public*, pg. 108
French, David, Mgr.--BI Commercial Finance Limited, Croydon, United Kingdom; *Int'l*, pg. 153
French, David, Gen. Mgr.--Poe & Brown of Florida, Miami, FL; *U.S. Public*, pg. 1312
French, David C., V.P.--Citizens Utilities Company, Kingman, AZ; *U.S. Public*, pg. 380
French, Gary L., Pres.--UAM Fund Services Inc., Boston, MA; *U.S. Public*, pg. 1674
French, M.R., Div. Mng. Dir.--Metal Box plc Beverage Can Div., Reading, United Kingdom; *Int'l*, pg. 267
French, Philip, Pres.--Farbest Inc., Indianapolis, IN; *U.S. Private*, pg. 279
Frendigoun, E.R., Chm. Bd.--Jonathan James Limited, Rainham, United Kingdom; *Int'l*, pg. 1358
Frenner, Markus, Dr., Mng. Dir.--Wirtschaftswoche Zeitschriften-Verlagsgesellschaft m.b.H. & Co. KG, Vienna, Austria; *Int'l*, pg. 1479
Frere, Baron, Chm.--Electrafina, Brussels, Belgium; *Int'l*, pg. 562
Frere, John, Pres.--World Book Publishing, Chicago, IL; *U.S. Public*, pg. 218
Frere, John, Pres.--World Book International, Chicago, IL; *U.S. Public*, pg. 218
Frescura, T. F., Chief Oper. Officer--Triangle Mining Equipment Co. Inc., Cedar Bluff, VA; *Int'l*, pg. 473
Frese, Juergen-Hinrich, Gen. Mgr.--Deutsche Bank AG (Bombay), Mumbai, India; *Int'l*, pg. 404
Frese, M., Mng. Dir.--Hoogovens Packaging Steel, Ijmuiden, Netherlands; *Int'l*, pg. 756
Frette, Tharald, Gen. Mgr.--Danisco Paper, Grena, Denmark; *Int'l*, pg. 378
Fretz, Kent F., Chief Oper. Officer--The Pittman Company, Harleysville, PA; *U.S. Public*, pg. 1270
Freudenberger, Wilfred, Exec. V.P. & Gen. Mgr.--Bayerische Landesbank - New York Branch, New York, NY; *Int'l*, pg. 176
Frew, D., Mng. Dir.--Crowcon Detection Instruments Limited, Abingdon, United Kingdom; *Int'l*, pg. 589
Frew, Dale, Dir.-Canadian Opers.--General Instrument of Canada Ltd., Mississauga, Canada; *U.S. Public*, pg. 716
Frey, Fredric, Chm. Bd.--Great West Casualty Company, South Sioux City, NE; *U.S. Public*, pg. 1218
Frey, Hans F.W., Chief Oper. Officer--Banque Veuve Morin-Pons, Paris, France; *Int'l*, pg. 419
Frey, J.R., Pres.--Alberta Power Limited, Edmonton, Canada; *Int'l*, pg. 95
Frey, Keith G., Pres.--IL USA, Inc., Stratford, CT; *U.S. Public*, pg. 856
Frey, Tom, Mng. Dir.--Howell Packaging, Burlington, Canada; *Int'l*, pg. 417
Freyer, Lewis E., Pres.--Harris Bank Glencoe-Northbrook, N.A., Glencoe, IL; *Int'l*, pg. 154
Freyou, Ernest, Pres. & Chief Exec. Officer--Regions Bank/New Iberia, New Iberia, LA; *U.S. Public*, pg. 1372
Friars, Eileen M., Chm. Bd.--NationsBank Investment Corporation, Richmond, VA; *U.S. Public*, pg. 1163
Frias, Fernan, Pres.--ARS/DMB&B, Caracas, Venezuela; *U.S. Private*, pg. 303
Frick, Per Erik, Mng. Dir.--Iggesund Timber AB, Hudiksvall, Sweden; *Int'l*, pg. 886
Frick, Raymond A., Pres.--Quebecor Printing Semline Inc., Braintree, MA; *Int'l*, pg. 1078
Frick, Raymond A., Pres.--Quebecor Printing Federated Inc., Providence, RI; *Int'l*, pg. 1078
Frick, Urs, Mng. Dir.-Madrid, Creative & Pub. Rels. Dir.--Grupo Barro Testa, Madrid, Spain; *Int'l*, pg. 1377
Fricke, T. E., Property Mgr.--Flowing Wells, Inc., Stamford, CT; *U.S. Public*, pg. 380
Fricke, Tom E., Gen. Mgr.--Citizens Utilities Company of Illinois, Addison, IL; *U.S. Public*, pg. 380
Frickel, Jack, Pres.--Zero Plastics, Monson, MA; *U.S. Public*, pg. 1791
Frickel, Jack, Pres.--Zero Stantron Cabinets, Pacoima, CA; *U.S. Public*, pg. 1791
Frickel, Jack, Pres.--Stantron/PFT/EMI, Pacoima, CA; *U.S. Public*, pg. 1791
Frid, Erik, Chief Oper. Officer--Granges Aluminium AB, Avesta, Sweden; *Int'l*, pg. 439
Frid, Svante, Mng. Dir.--AGA Gas AB, Sundbyberg, Sweden; *Int'l*, pg. 12
Fridlund, M., Mng. Dir.--Ascom Tateco AB, Goteborg, Sweden; *Int'l*, pg. 87
Frie, Bernie, Mng. Dir.--Granit-Bronz, Inc., Cold Spring, MN; *U.S. Private*, pg. 251
Frieder, Israel, Pres. & Chief Oper. Officer--Telematics Inc., Fort Lauderdale, FL; *Int'l*, pg. 643
Frieder, L. Peter, Jr., Pres.--Gentex Optics, Inc., Simpson, PA; *Int'l*, pg. 462
Friederich, Baldur, Pres.--Filtros Mann S.A. de C.V., Tlalnepantla, Mexico; *Int'l*, pg. 484
Friedland, Gayle, Pres.-Boston Division--Forest City Commercial Construction Company, Inc., Cleveland, OH; *U.S. Public*, pg. 668
Friedlich, James L., Mng. Dir.--Handelsblatt-Dow Jones GmbH, Frankfurt/Main, Germany; *Int'l*, pg. 1479
Friedlund, Harold, Gen. Mgr.--Duo-Fast Corporation, Cleveland, MS; *U.S. Private*, pg. 348
Friedman, Alan, Gen. Mgr.--Corrugated Container Div.-Atlanta (West) Plant, Atlanta, GA; *U.S. Public*, pg. 1520
Friedman, Ira, Pres.--Snell Acoustics, Peabody, MA; *U.S. Public*, pg. 246
Friedman, Jay, Pres.--Claiborne Menswear Div., New York, NY; *U.S. Public*, pg. 1006
Friedman, Mike, Mgr.--Hughes-Peters, Inc., Lorain, OH; *U.S. Private*, pg. 547
Friedman, Ronald, Gen. Mgr.--Life Sciences-Meissner & Wurst, Stuttgart, Germany; *U.S. Private*, pg. 317
Friedman, Seymour, Sr. V.P. & Exec. Production Mgr.--Columbia TriStar Television, Culver City, CA; *Int'l*, pg. 1282
Friedman, Vicki, Gen. Mgr.--Columbus Bakery, New York, NY; *U.S. Public*, pg. 130
Friedman, Victor, Pres.--Miller-Friedman Advertising, Waldwick, NJ; *U.S. Private*, pg. 746
Friedrich-Rust, Dr. Hilmar, Chief Oper. Officer--Dresdner Bank AG, Central, Hong Kong; *Int'l*, pg. 419
Friedrich, Axel, Chief Oper. Officer--N.V. Schering S.A./Belgien, Mechelen, Belgium; *Int'l*, pg. 1204
Friedrich, P. F., Pres.--Thermador, Los Angeles, CA; *U.S. Public*, pg. 1054
Friel, Sean, Reg. Mgr.--SMS-New Jersey, Edison, NJ; *U.S. Public*, pg. 1463
Friemel, Michael, Works Mgr.--Nichols Aluminum, Davenport, IA; *U.S. Public*, pg. 1350
Friendly, Ian M., Pres.--Yoplait USA, Minneapolis, MN; *U.S. Public*, pg. 718
Friends, Barry G., Pres.--Deaktor/Sysco Food Services Co., Harmony, PA; *U.S. Public*, pg. 1551
Frierson, Paul K., Pres.--Candlewick Group, Dalton, GA; *U.S. Public*, pg. 514
Frierson, Phil, Pres.--MagnaView Inc., Dallas, TX; *U.S. Public*, pg. 1720
Fries, Regis, Chief Oper. Officer--Societe de Distribution et d'Exportation Automobiles - SODEXA, Courbevoie, France; *Int'l*, pg. 1020

Fries, Robert, Pres.--Stratton Corporation, Stratton Mountain, VT; *Int'l*, pg. 685
Fries, Theodore S., Pres.--Emergency One, Inc., Ocala, FL; *U.S. Public*, pg. 617
Friese, Marianne, Partner & Global Brand Mktg. Dir.--Ketchum Public Relations, GmbH, Munich, Germany; *U.S. Private*, pg. 617
Friesen, Abe, Pres.--Pope & Talbot Ltd., Grand Forks, Canada; *U.S. Public*, pg. 1317
Friess, Gregory J., Pres.--Culbro Land Resources, Inc., Windsor, CT; *U.S. Public*, pg. 708
Friezkin, Richard, Pres.--Monarch Industries, Inc., Ridgefield, NJ; *U.S. Public*, pg. 153
Frigo, Fred, Plant Mgr.--Boston Operations, Brighton, MA; *U.S. Public*, pg. 443
Frigo, Fred V., Plant Mgr.--Headlamp Facility, Boyertown, PA; *U.S. Public*, pg. 442
Frima, Maija-Liisa, Pres.--Gyproc Oy, Kirkkonismmi, Finland; *Int'l*, pg. 1200
Frings, Jurgen, Chief Exec. Officer--Radiometer International A/S, Roedovre, Denmark; *Int'l*, pg. 1083
Friou, Philip, Pres.--American Family Life Assurance Company of New York, Albany, NY; *U.S. Public*, pg. 28
Frisch, Diane, Gen. Mgr.--Idaho Independent Television, Inc., Nampa, ID; *U.S. Private*, pg. 147
Frischman, Howard, Opers. Mgr.--Abrasives, Inc., Grand Rapids, MI; *U.S. Private*, pg. 884
Frisk, C.E., Pres.--Air-Shields Inc., Hatboro, PA; *Int'l*, pg. 1468
Fristad, Kenneth A., Pres. & Gen. Mgr.--Boss Manufacturing Company, Kewanee, IL; *U.S. Private*, pg. 1142
Fritchman, F., Service Center Mgr.--Square D Co., Atlanta, GA; *Int'l*, pg. 1208
Frith, Bud F., Chief Oper. Officer--MACE Products, Upland, CA; *U.S. Public*, pg. 1234
Frith, R., Mgr.--Immingham Storage Co. Ltd., Grimsby, United Kingdom; *Int'l*, pg. 1251
Fritsch, Bill, Pres.--CF2GS, Seattle, WA; *U.S. Private*, pg. 194
Fritscher, Hans-Peter, Chief Exec. Officer--Procter & Gamble AG, Geneva, Switzerland; *U.S. Public*, pg. 1332
Fritscher, Willie, Plant Mgr.--Guild Music Division, Westerly, RI; *U.S. Private*, pg. 400
Fritschi, Alfred, Chief Oper. Officer--Gambro AG, Hunenberg, Switzerland; *Int'l*, pg. 667
Fritz, Andre, Sr. V.P.-Opers.--AM General Corporation, Mishawaka, IN; *U.S. Private*, pg. 922
Fritz, Darwin, V.P. & Gen. Mgr.--Shade Pasta, Inc., Fremont, NE; *U.S. Private*, pg. 802
Fritz, Fred, Pres. & Chief Oper. Officer--The Coleman Company, Inc., Golden, CO; *U.S. Private*, pg. 690
Fritz, Frederick M., Pres.--BancBoston Capital, Inc., Boston, MA; *U.S. Public*, pg. 184
Fritz, Gunther, Dir.-Far East--Circle Freight International (H.K.), Wan Chai, Hong Kong; *U.S. Public*, pg. 372
Fritz, Jerry L., Pres.--Precision Foods, Inc., Saint Louis, MO; *U.S. Private*, pg. 1134
Fritz, Lorenz, V.P.--Alcatel Austria A.G., Vienna, Austria; *Int'l*, pg. 55
Fritz, Steve, Pres.--Jantzen, Portland, OR; *U.S. Public*, pg. 1702
Fritz, Wayne, Pres.--Saladmaster, Inc., Arlington, TX; *U.S. Private*, pg. 917
Fritz, William, Branch Mgr.--Bear, Stearns & Co. Inc., Dallas, Dallas, TX; *U.S. Public*, pg. 198
Fritzen, J. M., Chief Oper. Officer--V.A.G. Transport GmbH Co. DHG, Wolfsburg, Germany; *Int'l*, pg. 1473
Frixiug, Roland, Gen. Mgr.--Cregelux SA, Luxembourg, Luxembourg; *Int'l*, pg. 162
Frizoni, Patrick, V.P.-Asia--Avnet WKK Components, Kowloon, Hong Kong; *U.S. Public*, pg. 155
Frizzell, J.D., Vice Chm. & Mng. Dir.--NatWest International Trust Holdings Limited, Nassau, Bahamas; *Int'l*, pg. 911
Frodl, Hans, Chm.--Mannesmann Rexroth GmbH, Lohra, Germany; *Int'l*, pg. 838
Froelle, David, Mng. Dir.--ISS Energy Services, Inc., New York, NY; *Int'l*, pg. 656
Frohlich, Christoph, Mng. Dir.--Rex-Rotary AG, Bern, Switzerland; *Int'l*, pg. 1116
Frohnaple, David, Pres.--Collier-Keyworth, Inc., Liberty, NC; *U.S. Public*, pg. 985
Froidevaux, Joseph, Mng. Dir.--Kammer Vannes, La Chaux de Fonds, Switzerland; *U.S. Public*, pg. 658
Froidevaux, Pierre A., Chief Exec.--Apasco S.A. de C.V., Mexico, Mexico; *Int'l*, pg. 629
Froissant, Andre, Pres. & Chief Exec. Officer--Credit Lyonnais Canada, Montreal, Canada; *Int'l*, pg. 344
Frolich, Bruce D., Pres.--Chevron Research and Technology Company, Richmond, CA; *U.S. Public*, pg. 348
Frolich, D., Mgr.--M&N Valve, Bakersfield, CA; *Int'l*, pg. 1449
Frolich, Ib, Chief Oper. Officer--A/S Scan-Atlas Husholdningsapparater, Lyngby, Denmark; *Int'l*, pg. 441
Frolich, Ottheinrich, Dr., Chm.-Bd. of Mgmnt.--Bayerische Versicherungsbank-AG, Munich, Germany; *Int'l*, pg. 58
From, Jeffrey E., Plant Mgr.--AlliedSignal Turbos Automatrices, S.A. de C.V., Mexicali, Mexico; *U.S. Public*, pg. 54
From, Mogens, Mng. Dir.--Thrige Electric, Odense, Denmark; *Int'l*, pg. 1387
From, Mogens, Mng. Dir.--Thrige Electric GmbH, Berching, Germany; *Int'l*, pg. 1387
Froman, John, Pres.--Circuit City Central Div., Richmond, VA; *U.S. Public*, pg. 374
Froman, Lawrence M., Gen. Mgr.--Panalarm Products, Ametek, Inc., Skokie, IL; *U.S. Public*, pg. 100
Fromer, Harvey, Pres.--Lockheed Martin Electronic Defense Systems, Yonkers, NY; *U.S. Public*, pg. 1008
Fromknecht, Robert A., Pres.--PNC Bank Mortgage Center, Erie, PA; *U.S. Public*, pg. 1243
Froning, Daniel, Mgr.--Dicalite Corporation, Burney, CA; *U.S. Private*, pg. 903
Fronk, Mike, V.P.--Food Ingredients, Minneapolis, MN; *U.S. Private*, pg. 646
Frooman, Robert J., Pres.--Sysco Food Services, Cincinnati, OH; *U.S. Public*, pg. 1551
Frost, Charles, Mgr.--Chief Industries UK Ltd., Maldon, United Kingdom; *U.S. Private*, pg. 236
Frost, Charles, Chief Oper. Officer--Innco Management Corp., Knoxville, TN; *U.S. Private*, pg. 392
Frost, Chas, Mng. Dir.--Chief Industries UK Ltd, Maldon, United Kingdom; *U.S. Private*, pg. 236
Frost, Chester R., Pres.--Newbury Insurance Co., Hamilton, Bermuda; *U.S. Private*, pg. 738
Frost, D.M., Mng. Dir.--Schenectady Pratteln A.G., Pratteln, Switzerland; *U.S. Private*, pg. 970
Frost, Don, Publisher--American Artist, New York, NY; *Int'l*, pg. 1446
Frost, Herb, Supvr.--Kezar Falls Division, Kezar Falls, ME; *U.S. Public*, pg. 438
Frost, Jack M., Mng. Dir.--Oxford Instruments-Medical Systems Div., Clearwater, FL; *Int'l*, pg. 1018
Frost, Michael, Pres.--Burner Systems International, Inc., Chattanooga, TN; *U.S. Private*, pg. 351
Froud, Susan, Mng. Dir.--Oxford University Press Canada, Don Mills, Canada; *Int'l*, pg. 1019
Frova, C.M., Chief Oper. Officer--Beckman Industrial Corporation, Fullerton, CA; *U.S. Public*, pg. 574
Frowein, Gunter, Dr., Sr. Mng. Dir.--Deutsche Bank AG (Mannheim), Mannheim, Germany; *Int'l*, pg. 402
Fruend, Robert A., Chm. Bd.--American National Property & Casualty Co., Springfield, MO; *U.S. Public*, pg. 87
Fruend, Robert A., Chm. Bd.--American National General Insurance Company, Springfield, MO; *U.S. Public*, pg. 88
Frugone, Adriana, Rep.--Singapore Tourist Promotion Board - Santiago, Santiago, Chile; *Int'l*, pg. 1254
Fruh, Kathy, Branch Mgr.--Downey Savings & Loan Association, F.A., Fullerton, CA; *U.S. Public*, pg. 526
Fruit, R.E., V.P. & Gen. Mgr.--Diversey Water Technologies, Inc., Chagrin Falls, OH; *U.S. Public*, pg. 1150
Frumento, Massimo, Mng. Dir.--DYWIT S.p.A., Milan, Italy; *Int'l*, pg. 425
Frutig, Fredy, Country Mgr.--Compaq Computer AG, Bassersdorf, Switzerland; *U.S. Public*, pg. 418
Fry, Dennis, Gen. Mgr.--ITW Proffitt & Co. Ltd., Walsall, United Kingdom; *U.S. Public*, pg. 869
Fry, Gary, V.P. & Gen. Mgr.--ICI Explosives, Gillette, WY; *Int'l*, pg. 664
Fry, Jef, Gen. Mgr.--Stelpipe Ltd., Welland, Canada; *Int'l*, pg. 1299
Fry, John, Pres.--Dun & Bradstreet Ltd., High Wycombe, United Kingdom; *U.S. Public*, pg. 536
Fry, Keith, Dir.-Foreign Language Pub.--Foreign Language Div., Lincolnwood, IL; *U.S. Public*, pg. 1635
Fry, Keith A., Pres. & Chief Oper. Officer--Lake States Insurance Co., Traverse City, MI; *U.S. Public*, pg. 787
Frydrych, Melvyn J., Pres.--Fleet Precious Metals, Inc., Providence, RI; *U.S. Public*, pg. 650
Frye, Charles, Mgr.--Interstate Core Pack, Cambridge, MD; *U.S. Private*, pg. 573
Frye, Paul, Gen. Mgr.--Duro Paper Bag Mfg. Co., Hudson, WI; *U.S. Private*, pg. 349
Fryer, C.W.B., Chm. Bd.--ZSR Corporation Ltd., Harare, Zimbabwe; *Int'l*, pg. 1357
Fryer, George A., Gen. Mgr.--Standex International Limited, Stockport, United Kingdom; *U.S. Public*, pg. 1507
Fryer, Robert L., Chm. Bd.--Hopper Soliday & Co., Inc., Lancaster, PA; *Int'l*, pg. 65
Fryer, Rupert, Gen. Mgr.--Robert Fleming (Switzerland) S.A., Geneva, Switzerland; *Int'l*, pg. 494
Frymark, John R., Pres.--Guardian Products, Inc., Simi Valley, CA; *U.S. Public*, pg. 1535
Fucciolo, Eduardo Wanderley, Gen. Mgr.--Universal Studios Filmes do Brazil LTDA, Sao Paulo, Brazil; *Int'l*, pg. 1216
Fuchida, Kyo, Exec. Mng. Dir.--Yuasa-Ionics Co., Ltd., Tokyo, Japan; *U.S. Public*, pg. 912
Fuchs, Benjamin J., Dr., Gen. Mgr.--Design-Tuft DT GmbH, Bad Hersfeld, Germany; *Int'l*, pg. 497
Fuchs, Eduard, Pres.--H. Krantz-TKT GmbH, Bergisch Gladbach, Germany; *Int'l*, pg. 399
Fuchs, Jay R., Pres.--American Bankers Life Assurance Co. of Florida, Miami, FL; *U.S. Public*, pg. 67
Fuchs, Joachim G., Mgr.--Commerzbank AG-Shanghai, Shanghai, China; *Int'l*, pg. 311
Fuchs, Karl-Hans, Mng. Dir.--LeaRonal GmbH, Birkenfeld, Germany; *U.S. Public*, pg. 982
Fuciu, George N., Pres.--Technology Services, Overland Park, KS; *U.S. Public*, pg. 1501
Fudge, Thomas F., Mgr.--Lucky Friday Unit, Mullan, ID; *U.S. Public*, pg. 804
Fuelling, Thomas N., Pres. & Chief Exec. Officer--Lawry's Foods, Inc., Monrovia, CA; *Int'l*, pg. 1435
Fuentes, Ricardo, Mng. Dir.--Reemtsma Espana S.A., Madrid, Spain; *Int'l*, pg. 1101
Fuentes, Ricardo, Mng. Dir.--EMESTA Empressa Espanola de Tabacos S.L., Madrid, Spain; *Int'l*, pg. 1101
Fugalli, Gualberto, Country Mgr.--Ethicon S.p.A., Rome, Italy; *U.S. Public*, pg. 929
Fugate, Cecil, Mgr.-Opers.--Fremont Mfg. Div., Fremont, IN; *U.S. Public*, pg. 1475
Fugazy, Roy, Pres.--Fugazy International Corporation, New York, NY; *U.S. Private*, pg. 430
Fugazzi, Pamela, Acting Warden--Houston Processing Center, Houston, TX; *U.S. Public*, pg. 450
Fugelsang, George N., Pres.--Dresdner Securities (USA) Inc., New York, NY; *Int'l*, pg. 418
Fugelsang, George N., Chief Exec. Officer--Dresdner Bank AG, New York, NY; *Int'l*, pg. 418
Fuglesang, Bent, Managing Dir.--Orkla Foods AS, Trollasen, Norway; *Int'l*, pg. 1011
Fuhlman, James O., V.P. & Gen. Mgr.--The HON Co., Cedartown Plant, Cedartown, GA; *U.S. Public*, pg. 772
Fuhrman, Joseph, Facilities Mgr.--Huls America Inc., Chestertown, MD; *Int'l*, pg. 1455
Fuhrman, Robert A., Chm.--Bank of the West, Walnut Creek, CA; *Int'l*, pg. 163
Fujii, Hideyuki, Pres.--Gigalex Co., Ltd., Osaka, Japan; *Int'l*, pg. 1125
Fujii, Hirofumi, Mng. Dir.--IBJ-CA Consult Handels-und Investitionsberatungsgesellschaft m.b.H., Vienna, Austria; *Int'l*, pg. 347
Fujii, Juntaro, Chief Exec. Offier & Mng. Dir.--Tokyo-Mitsubishi International plc, London, United Kingdom; *Int'l*, pg. 158
Fujii, Kazuhide, Gen. Mgr.--The Sumitomo Bank, Ltd.-Guangzhou Branch, Guangzhou, China; *Int'l*, pg. 1309
Fujii, Kazuo, Mng. Dir.--Bank of Tokyo-Mitsubishi (UK) Limited, London, United Kingdom; *Int'l*, pg. 158
Fujii, Kimio, Pres.--Cirrus Logic K.K., Tokyo, Japan; *U.S. Public*, pg. 375
Fujii, Kunito, Pres.--Wako Electric Co., Ltd., Okayama, Japan; *Int'l*, pg. 1125
Fujii, Mutsuhisa, Chief Rep.--IBJ Schroder Bank & Trust Company (Cayman Branch), Georgetown, Cayman Islands; *Int'l*, pg. 675
Fujii, Tatsuya, Chief Rep.--Nippon Life - Taipei Representative Office, Taipei, Taiwan; *Int'l*, pg. 936
Fujikawa, Tadahiro, Pres.--Fukushima Hakuhodo Inc., Fukushima, Japan; *Int'l*, pg. 587
Fujikawa, Tadahiro, Pres.--Fukushima Hakuhodo, Inc., Koriyama, Japan; *Int'l*, pg. 587
Fujikuna, Yoichi, Chief Rep. & Gen. Mgr.-China--The Sakura Bank - Beijing Representative Office, Beijing, China; *Int'l*, pg. 1179
Fujimaki, Minoru, Pres.--Rheometrics Scientific Far East Ltd., Tokyo, Japan; *U.S. Public*, pg. 1387
Fujimatsu, Tadao, Chm. Bd.--JAL International Services, New York, NY; *Int'l*, pg. 700
Fujimori, Toshiyuki, Sr. Exec. V.P.--The Book Club Finance and Securities Public Company Ltd., Bangkok, Thailand; *Int'l*, pg. 816
Fujimoto, H., Office Chief--Man Nen Sha, Inc., Kyoto, Japan; *Int'l*, pg. 834
Fujimoto, Mamoru, Mng. Dir.--Dai-ichi Life International (H.K.) Limited, Wan Chai, Hong Kong; *Int'l*, pg. 362
Fujimoto, Michikazu, Chief Rep.--The Sakura Bank - Milan Representative Office, Milan, Italy; *Int'l*, pg. 1180
Fujimoto, Shuji, Exec. Dir.--Kyoei Fire & Marine Insurance Co. (U.K.) Ltd., London, United Kingdom; *Int'l*, pg. 777
Fujimura, Enji, Pres.--Hakuhodo I.O. Co. Ltd., Tokyo, Japan; *Int'l*, pg. 588
Fujimura, T., Chief Oper. Officer--Man Nen Sha Agency, Inc., Osaka, Japan; *Int'l*, pg. 834
Fujine, Junichi, Pres.--Phoenix Technologies K.K., Tokyo, Japan; *U.S. Public*, pg. 1292
Fujino, Hirotake, Chm.--Takugin Bank (Schweiz) AG, Zurich, Switzerland; *Int'l*, pg. 627
Fujio, Satoshi, Chief Rep.--Asahi Bank Bangkok Representative Office, Bangkok, Thailand; *Int'l*, pg. 83
Fujio, Tadashi, Pres.--Daihatsu Deutschland GmbH, Tonisvorst, Germany; *Int'l*, pg. 365
Fujioka, Craig, Branch Mgr.--Handleman Company of Canada Ltd., Scarborough, Canada; *U.S. Public*, pg. 780
Fujisawa, Hiroshi, Mgr.--Kobe Terminal, Kobe, Japan; *U.S. Public*, pg. 693
Fujisawa, Susumu, Gen. Mgr. & Exec. Dir.--NMB Precision Tool & Die (Pte) Ltd., Singapore, Singapore; *Int'l*, pg. 868
Fujisawa, Yoshihiro, Pres. & Chief Exec. Officer--Daiwa-MKB (Hungary) Investment and Securities Co. Ltd., Budapest, Hungary; *Int'l*, pg. 376
Fujiseki, Katsuhiro, Pres.--Seiyo, Ltd., Tokyo, Japan; *Int'l*, pg. 1178
Fujishima, Takashi, Gen. Mgr. & Dir.--The Sakura Bank - Cayman Branch, Georgetown, Cayman Islands; *Int'l*, pg. 1179
Fujishima, Takashi, Gen. Mgr. & Dir.--Sakura Bank - New York Branch, New York, NY; *Int'l*, pg. 1179
Fujita, A., Mng. Dir.--Ebara Pumpen GmbH, Dietzenbach, Germany; *Int'l*, pg. 432
Fujita, Eisaku, Mng. Dir.--Hakuhodo Inc., Toyama, Japan; *Int'l*, pg. 587
Fujita, Fred, Chief Oper. Officer--DataCard Japan Ltd, Tokyo, Japan; *U.S. Private*, pg. 313
Fujita, K., Chief Oper. Officer--Furukawa Saudi Arabia, Ltd. (FSA), Jeddah, Saudi Arabia; *Int'l*, pg. 531
Fujita, Naohisa, Pres.--Mitsubishi Rayon America, Inc., New York, NY; *Int'l*, pg. 876
Fujita, Shuji, Pres.--Hakuhodo Office Services Co., Ltd., Tokyo, Japan; *Int'l*, pg. 588
Fujita, Yosuke, Gen. Mgr.--The Sumitomo Trust & Banking Co., Ltd., London, United Kingdom; *Int'l*, pg. 1318
Fujitani, K., Pres.--Toshiba Electronics Italiana S.R.L., Milan, Italy; *Int'l*, pg. 1406
Fujiwara, Kota, Chief Oper. Officer--Kyowa Hakko Europe GmbH, Dusseldorf, Germany; *Int'l*, pg. 778
Fujiwara, Kota, Co.-Chief Oper. Officer--Kyowa Hakko U.K. Ltd., London, United Kingdom; *Int'l*, pg. 778
Fujiwara, Nobuo, Gen. Mgr.--Fukuchiyama Branch Office, Fukuchiyama, Japan; *Int'l*, pg. 1491
Fujiwara, Yasuyuki, Chief Oper. Officer--Makita Singapore PTE. LTD., Singapore, Singapore; *Int'l*, pg. 832
Fujiwara, Yutaka, Gen. Mgr.--Chicago Branch, Chicago, IL; *Int'l*, pg. 1520
Fujiwasa, Masaki, Chief Rep.--Toray Industries, Inc.-Seoul Office, Seoul, Korea; *Int'l*, pg. 1400
Fukada, Ikumasa, Chief Opr. Officer--Babcock-Hitachi K.K., Tokyo, Japan; *Int'l*, pg. 621
Fukada, Michio, Pres.--Fukada-Kidde Co., Ltd., Tokyo, Japan; *Int'l*, pg. 594
Fukada, Ryoji, Mng. Dir.--Elsevier Science Japan, Tokyo, Japan; *Int'l*, pg. 1100
Fukai, Kiyoshi, Pres.--P.T. Otsuka Indonesia, Jakarta, Indonesia; *Int'l*, pg. 1014
Fukai, Kiyoshi, Chm. Bd.--Otsuka Pakistan Ltd., Karachi, Pakistan; *Int'l*, pg. 1014
Fukase, Masaru, Pres.--Komatsu do Brasil Ltda., Sao Paulo, Brazil; *Int'l*, pg. 744
Fukawatase, Tohsifumi, Pres.--Minebea Onkyo Co., Ltd., Yamanashi, Japan; *Int'l*, pg. 868
Fukawatase, Toshifumi, Pres.--Hwan Chong Enterprise Co., Ltd., Kao-hsiung, Taiwan; *Int'l*, pg. 868

Fukaya, Y., Pres.--Mitsubishi Cable America, Inc., New York, NY; *Int'l*, pg. 870
Fukazawa, Yoji, Chm.--Non Ferrous International Corp., New York, NY; *Int'l*, pg. 872
Fukubayashi, Masami, Chief Oper. Officer--The Tokio Marine & Fire Insurance Company (U.K.) Limited, London, United Kingdom; *Int'l*, pg. 1392
Fukuchi, Hideo, Pres. & Chief Exec. Officer--Nikon Inc., Melville, NY; *Int'l*, pg. 931
Fukuda, Fumihiro, Chief Rep.--Asahi Bank Sydney Branch, Sydney, Australia; *Int'l*, pg. 82
Fukuda, Fumihiro, Mng. Dir.--Asahi Finance (Australia) Ltd., Sydney, Australia; *Int'l*, pg. 83
Fukuda, Hidenori, Pres.--Dai Nippon Book Binding Co., Ltd., Tokyo, Japan; *Int'l*, pg. 363
Fukuda, Hiromu, Pres.--Hitachi Semiconductor (America), Inc., Irving, TX; *Int'l*, pg. 622
Fukuda, Hisao, Mng. Dir.--Hirayama Manufacturing Ltd., Kasukabe, Japan; *Int'l*, pg. 1306
Fukuda, K., Pres. & Chief Oper. Officer--Ikegami Electronics (U.S.A.), Inc., Maywood, NJ; *Int'l*, pg. 660
Fukuda, Kazuhiko, Chief Exec.--Nittetsu Shoji Co., Ltd., Tokyo, Japan; *Int'l*, pg. 939
Fukuda, Kazuro, V.P. & Branch Mgr.--Dai-Ichi Kangyo Bank of California-San Jose, San Jose, CA; *Int'l*, pg. 360
Fukuda, Kiyofumi, Chief Representative--Daiwa Bank-Paris, Paris, France; *Int'l*, pg. 374
Fukui, Kikuo, Pres.--Tiffany & Co. K.K. (Japan), Tokyo, Japan; *U.S. Public*, pg. 1609
Fukui, Kikuo, Pres.--Tiffany & Co. Japan Inc., New York, NY; *U.S. Public*, pg. 1609
Fukui, Kikuo, Pres.--Tiffany & Co. Japan Inc. - Japan Branch, New York, NY; *U.S. Public*, pg. 1609
Fukui, Makoto, Gen. Mgr.--Nihon Wang K.K., Tokyo, Japan; *U.S. Public*, pg. 1737
Fukui, Sagorogei, Pres.--Renishaw K.K., Nagoya, Japan; *Int'l*, pg. 1103
Fukui, Sagurogei, Pres.--Renishaw K.K., Tokyo, Japan; *Int'l*, pg. 1103
Fukumoto, Takeo, Mng. Dir.--Nanto Credit Guarantee Co., Ltd., Nara, Japan; *Int'l*, pg. 905
Fukunishi, Masumi, Mng. Dir.--Nanto Computer Service Co., Ltd., Nara, Japan; *Int'l*, pg. 905
Fukuoka, Yoshihiko, Dir.--Explosives Div., Tokyo, Japan; *Int'l*, pg. 934
Fukushige, Y., Chief Oper. Officer--Littelfuse KK, Yokohama, Japan; *U.S. Public*, pg. 1001
Fukushima, Akira, Pres.--Hakuhodo Incentive Promotions Inc., Tokyo, Japan; *Int'l*, pg. 588
Fukushima, Akira, Chm.--ORIX Auto Leasing Corporation, Tokyo, Japan; *Int'l*, pg. 1008
Fukushima, Kaoru, Chief Rep.--Nanjing Representative Office, Nanjing, China; *Int'l*, pg. 520
Fukushima, Sumio, Chief Exec. Officer--Sumitomo Finance International plc, London, United Kingdom; *Int'l*, pg. 1310
Fukuzawa, Mutsuo, Chm.--Sanwa Business Credit Corporation, Chicago, IL; *Int'l*, pg. 1189
Fuld, Richard S., Pres. & Co-Chief Exec. Officer--Lehman Brothers, New York, NY; *U.S. Public*, pg. 987
Fulenwider, Claire, Pres.--Heartland Energy Services, Inc., Madison, WI; *U.S. Public*, pg. 1728
Fulenwider, Claire, Pres.--Heartland Energy Group, Inc., Madison, WI; *U.S. Public*, pg. 1728
Fulford, Greg, Gen. Mgr.--fp Packaging, Inc., South San Francisco, CA; *U.S. Private*, pg. 411
Fulford, R.S., Chm. Bd.--London Brick Company Ltd., Bedford, United Kingdom; *Int'l*, pg. 593
Fulk, Mike, Exec. Dir.--QualMed Plans for Health-Denver, Denver, CO; *U.S. Public*, pg. 678
Fullagar, E.J., Chief Exec. Officer--Sandoz Pharmaceuticals Corp., East Hanover, NJ; *Int'l*, pg. 974
Fullbeck, Dieter, Gen. Mgr.--Avery Maschinen GmbH, Hamburg, Germany; *U.S. Public*, pg. 153
Fullelove, W.R., Chief Mgr.--Lloyds Associated Air Leasing Ltd., London, United Kingdom; *Int'l*, pg. 813
Fullem, Gary L., Pres.--UNIRISC, Inc., Washington, DC; *U.S. Public*, pg. 117
Fullenkamp, Steve, Sr. Officer--The Chase Manhattan Bank, N.A., Manama, Bahrain; *U.S. Public*, pg. 339
Fuller, Brenton, Mng. Dir.--Dexion (Australia) Pty. Ltd., Blacktown, Australia; *U.S. Public*, pg. 893
Fuller, Charles, Branch Mgr.--National Mine Service Company, Madisonville Div., Madisonville, KY; *Int'l*, pg. 281
Fuller, D. Ward, Pres. & Chief Exec. Officer--General American Transportation Corporation, Chicago, IL; *U.S. Public*, pg. 692
Fuller, Gary T., Pres. & Chief Exec. Officer--Woolworth Overseas Corp., New York, NY; *U.S. Public*, pg. 1778
Fuller, Gary W., Pres. & Treas.--Jamieson Film Company, Inc., Dallas, TX; *U.S. Public*, pg. 551
Fuller, Glenn, Pres.--Sovex Natural Foods, Collegedale, TN; *U.S. Private*, pg. 723
Fuller, J., Mgr.--Hollingsworth & Vose Co. U.K. Ltd., Cheltenham, United Kingdom; *U.S. Private*, pg. 535
Fuller, Jack, Pres.--Tribune Publishing Company, Chicago, IL; *U.S. Public*, pg. 1636
Fuller, Jerry, Chief Oper. Officer--Frank Paxton Lumber Company, Kansas City, MO; *U.S. Private*, pg. 585
Fuller, Lawrence R., Pres. & Publr.--The Honolulu Advertiser, Honolulu, HI; *U.S. Public*, pg. 701
Fuller, Michael B., Pres.--Sprint's Local Telecommunication Division, San Diego, CA; *U.S. Public*, pg. 1500
Fuller, Ned, Pres.--C & J Clark Retail, Inc., Kennett Square, PA; *Int'l*, pg. 297
Fuller, P.D., Mng. Dir.--Omnifit Ltd., Cambridge, United Kingdom; *Int'l*, pg. 589
Fuller, Robert E., V.P.--Car Brite, Inc., Indianapolis, IN; *U.S. Private*, pg. 352
Fuller, Rod, Mgr.--Eclipse Combustion, Inc., South Windham, CT; *U.S. Private*, pg. 360
Fuller, Warren D., Pres.--International Rehabilitation Associates, Inc., Berwyn, PA; *U.S. Public*, pg. 362
Fuller, William E., V.P.--The Wurlitzer Company, Holly Springs, MS; *U.S. Public*, pg. 169
Fullerton, James H., Pres. & Chief Exec. Officer--M & I Bank of LaCrosse, La Crosse, WI; *U.S. Public*, pg. 1050
Fullmer-Chin, Ann, V.P. & Acct. Supvr.--Carat ICG (Portland, OR), Beaverton, OR; *U.S. Private*, pg. 207
Fullmer, William F., G.M.--Laimbeer Packaging, Detroit, MI; *U.S. Public*, pg. 1521
Fullmer, William F., Gen. Mgr.--Laimbeer Packaging, Melvindale, MI; *U.S. Public*, pg. 1521
Fullwood, Stanley, Mng. Dir.--Security Insurance Co. (U.K.) Ltd., London, United Kingdom; *U.S. Public*, pg. 1232
Fulps, Dan, Pres.--Curtis Equipment Co., Inc., Tulsa, OK; *U.S. Private*, pg. 494
Fulton, Bill, Pres.--Fleming-Potter Co., Peoria, IL; *U.S. Private*, pg. 411
Fulton, Robert J., Pres.--Hoeganaes Corp., Riverton, NJ; *U.S. Public*, pg. 893
Fulton, Sandy M., Pres.--Pacific Forest Products Limited, Vancouver, Canada; *Int'l*, pg. 102
Fulton, Thomas B., Pres.--Cade Composites, Inc., San Diego, CA; *U.S. Public*, pg. 290
Fumachi, Dirceu, Mng. Dir.--Bobst Brasil Ltda., Itatiba, Brazil; *Int'l*, pg. 198
Fumagalli, Luigi, Gen. Mgr.--Officine Aeronavali Venezia S.p.A., Tesero, Italy; *Int'l*, pg. 653
Fumizono, Yoshiro, Pres.--NSK-RHP France S.A., Voisins-le-Bretonneux, France; *Int'l*, pg. 904
Fumosa, John J., V.P. & Gen. Mgr.--Turner Construction Company, Somerset, NJ; *U.S. Public*, pg. 1645
Funaoki, Robert, Gen. Mgr.--Kokusai Electric Co., Ltd. America, El Segundo, CA; *Int'l*, pg. 743
Funes, Victor, Dir.-Sls.--Turner Construction Co., Houston, TX; *U.S. Public*, pg. 1645
Funk, Albert, Pres.--Modern Hilift Equipment Co., West Conshohocken, PA; *U.S. Private*, pg. 755
Funk, John, Pres.--TCR Corporation, Minneapolis, MN; *U.S. Public*, pg. 1632
Funker, Wolfgang, Pres.--Luxo Leuchten GmbH, Hildesheim, Germany; *Int'l*, pg. 821
Funkhouser, Elmer N., Pres.-Engr. Prods. Div.--Sealed Air Engineered Products Division, Danbury, CT; *U.S. Public*, pg. 1451
Funt, Yigal, Dir. Gen.--Raychem Ltd., Givatayim, Israel; *U.S.* Public, pg. 1362
Funton, John, Mng. Dir.--British Aerospace (Consultancy Services) Limited, Warrington, United Kingdom; *Int'l*, pg. 217
Furbacher, Stephen A., Pres.--Warren Petroleum Company, Houston, TX; *U.S. Public*, pg. 1146
Furchner, Jim, Chief Oper. Officer--Anixter Sudbury, Sudbury, Canada; *U.S. Public*, pg. 116
Furebotten, Tohan, Pres.--Kvaerner Kimek a.s., Kirkenes, Norway; *Int'l*, pg. 770
Furgada, Enrico, Mng. Dir.--Per Transport S.p.A, Italy; *U.S. Private*, pg. 1120
Furger, R.J., Pres.--Dynmark Plastics Inc., Brampton, Canada; *Int'l*, pg. 1397
Furlong, Dan, Pres.--Compass Distribution, Clearwater, FL; *U.S. Private*, pg. 838
Furlonger, Robert A., V.P.-Mktg.--Grolier Limited, Toronto, Canada; *Int'l*, pg. 794
Furman, James E., Pres.--ECO Resources, Inc., Sugar Land, TX; *U.S. Public*, pg. 1494
Furman, Roy L., Pres.--Furman Selz Holding Corporation, New York, NY; *U.S. Public*, pg. 1785
Furness, Terence N., Pres.--Zimmer, Inc., Warsaw, IN; *U.S. Public*, pg. 254
Furness, Terence N., Pres.--Microtek Medical, Inc., Columbus, MS; *U.S. Public*, pg. 914
Furniss, Don, Pres.--Atochem Canada Inc., Oakville, Canada; *Int'l*, pg. 446
Furr, Cynthia M., Pres.--Beneficial Savings Bank, FSB, Tampa, FL; *U.S. Public*, pg. 211
Furst, Rafael, Pres., Treas. & Sec.--The El-Bee Chargit Corp., Dayton, OH; *U.S. Private*, pg. 367
Furubayashi, R., Dr., Chief Oper. Officer--Gemini Science, Inc., La Jolla, CA; *Int'l*, pg. 736
Furuhata, Shunichi, Mng. Dir.--Toyo Trust Asia Limited, Hong Kong, Hong Kong; *Int'l*, pg. 1411
Furuhjelm, Johan, Mng. Dir.--Kymi Paper Mills Ltd., Kuusankoski, Finland; *Int'l*, pg. 1428
Furui, Masahiko, Mng. Dir. & Gen. Mgr.--Sanwa-DSP Credit Limited, Central, Hong Kong; *Int'l*, pg. 1190
Furuichi, Takeshi, Pres.--NLI International, New York, NY; *Int'l*, pg. 935
Furukawa, Tadayasu, Chief Oper. Officer--Nutri-Quest, Inc., Chesterfield, MO; *Int'l*, pg. 778
Furuta, Makoto, Exec. Dir.--Dentsu Young & Rubicam Inc. (Tokyo), Tokyo, Japan; *U.S. Private*, pg. 325
Furuya, O., Pres.--AMP Technologies Japan, Tokyo, Japan; *U.S. Public*, pg. 9
Furuyama, Satoshi, Pres.--Corning Japan K.K., Shizuoka, Japan; *U.S. Public*, pg. 449
Fusche, John-Harald, Gen. Mgr.--Jac. O. Lyngaas & Co. A/S (Cornhill), Tonsberg, Norway; *Int'l*, pg. 60
Fusco, Ippolito, Chief Oper. Officer--Alfa Romeo Veicoli Comm. e Lav Mecc. S.p.A., Naples, Italy; *Int'l*, pg. 481
Fusco, Ray, Admin.--Columbia Diagnostic Center, El Paso, TX; *U.S. Public*, pg. 404
Fusco, Ray, Admin.--Physical Therapy Center, El Paso, TX; *U.S. Public*, pg. 405
Fuse, Takashi, Pres.--Nissho Iwai (Thailand) Limited Partnership, Bangkok, Thailand; *Int'l*, pg. 948
Fuselier, David, Publisher--Muscatine Journal, Muscatine, IA; *U.S. Public*, pg. 984
Fusetti, Alvaro, Gen. Administrator--A.C. Nielsen Company S.A., Madrid, Spain; *U.S. Public*, pg. 1183
Fusetti, Alvaro, Gen. Mgr.--A.C. Nielsen Italia S.p.A., Milan, Italy; *U.S. Public*, pg. 1183
Fushimi, Kenjiro, Sr. Rep.--Nippon Credit Bank Ltd.-Frankfurt, Frankfurt/Main, Germany; *Int'l*, pg. 933
Fusilli, Donald P., Jr., Pres. & Gen. Mgr.--Baker/MO Services, Inc., Cypress, TX; *U.S. Public*, pg. 168
Fust, Erich, Mng. Dir.--Tyco Toys (Schweiz/Suisse) AG/SA, Dubendorf, Switzerland; *U.S. Public*, pg. 1059
Fusting, Fred, Pres.--Professional Learning Systems, Baltimore, MD; *U.S. Public*, pg. 1748
Fusz, Lou, Jr., Pres.--Lou Fusz Motor Company, Saint Louis, MO; *U.S. Private*, pg. 432
Fuszard, Curtis J., Pres.--Associated Financial Center, Ltd., Menomonee Falls, WI; *U.S. Public*, pg. 140
Fuszard, Curtis J., Pres. & Chief Exec. Officer--Associated Investment Services, Inc., Green Bay, WI; *U.S. Public*, pg. 140
Futchko, Andrew R., Pres.--Bethlehem Steel-PA Steel Technologies Inc., Steelton, PA; *U.S. Public*, pg. 226
Futerman, Eli N., Pres.--Professional Auto Warehouse, Rochester, NY; *U.S. Public*, pg. 774
Futerman, Mike, Chief Exec. Officer--Professional Auto Warehouse, Rochester, NY; *U.S. Public*, pg. 774
Fuyuno, K., Chief Exec. Officer--Nippon Monier Co. Ltd., Osaka, Japan; *Int'l*, pg. 1092
Fyfe, David, Pres.--Harris Specialty Chemical, Jacksonville, FL; *U.S. Private*, pg. 505
Fyfe, Nick, Mgr.--Bain Securities, Inc., New York, NY; *Int'l*, pg. 406
Fynes, D.M.S., Pres.--Castell Interlocks Inc., Erlanger, KY; *Int'l*, pg. 590
Gaard, Jens Maj, Pres.--Andelssmar A.m.b.a., Viby, Denmark; *Int'l*, pg. 826
Gaasche, Ted L., Pres.--SunGard Planning Solutions Inc., Wayne, PA; *U.S. Public*, pg. 1535
Gabaldon, Richard, V.P.--Viking Entertainment, Troy, MI; *U.S. Public*, pg. 780
Gabaldon, S.J., Mng. Dir.--First Philippine Industrial Corp., Manila, Philippines; *Int'l*, pg. 1140
Gabayzadeh, Mehdi, Pres.--American Tissue, Inc., Mechanicville, NY; *U.S. Private*, pg. 63
Gable, Mike, Chief Oper. Officer--Southern Beauty Enterprises, Birmingham, AL; *U.S. Private*, pg. 128
Gabriel, N., Chief Exec. Officer--OCE (Far East) Pte. Ltd., Singapore, Singapore; *Int'l*, pg. 994
Gabriel, Zbynek, Media Dir.--Leo Burnett Advertising Spol.SR.O, Prague, Czech Republic; *U.S. Private*, pg. 184
Gabrielson, Chuck, Publr.--USA Weekend, New York, NY; *U.S. Public*, pg. 701
Gabriola, Sharon, Branch Mgr.--Yoh Scientific, Orange, CA; *U.S. Private*, pg. 317
Gabutina, Lorenz, Mng. Dir.--Marketforce Advertising Philippines Inc., Manila, Philippines; *U.S. Private*, pg. 325
Gaby, Barb, Pres.--Amway Hotel Corporation, Grand Rapids, MI; *U.S. Private*, pg. 69
Gadberry, James F., Pres.-Southwest Region--ALLTEL Arkansas, Inc., Little Rock, AR; *U.S. Public*, pg. 55
Gaddo, Donald, V.P. & Gen. Mgr.--Heartland Building Products, Inc., Booneville, MS; *Int'l*, pg. 699
Gade, Bill, V.P. & Gen. Mgr.--Protein Blenders, Iowa City, IA; *Int'l*, pg. 1116
Gadow, Rainer, Dr., Pres.--euroflamm GmbH, Bremen, Germany; *Int'l*, pg. 400
Gadsby, R.E., Pres.--ICI Chemicals & Polymers, Wilmington, DE; *Int'l*, pg. 663
Gaeng, J. Brian, Pres. & Chief Exec. Officer--Fredericktown Bank & Trust Co., Frederick, MD; *U.S. Public*, pg. 1089
Gaerttling, Sieghart, Mng. Dir.--Wuestenrot Staedtebau- und Entwicklungsgesellschaft mbH, Ludwigsburg, Germany; *Int'l*, pg. 1514
Gaffin, C. Harold, V.P. & Gen. Mgr.--Kodak Graphics Imaging Systems Division, Rochester, NY; *U.S. Public*, pg. 551
Gaffney, M. Gaffney, Sr. V.P.--United Missouri Bank N.A., Kansas City, MO; *U.S. Public*, pg. 1654
Gaffney, T.C., Pres.--Performance Products Division, New York, NY; *U.S. Public*, pg. 1500
Gagaon, Gary, Gen. Mgr.--Prime Tanning Corp., Saint Joseph, MO; *U.S. Private*, pg. 884
Gage, David, Plant Mgr.--Sargento Foods, Inc., Tampa, FL; *U.S. Private*, pg. 966
Gage, Duncan, Pres.--Lafarge, Southfield, MI; *Int'l*, pg. 788
Gage, Duncan, V.P.--Lafarge (Whitehall), Whitehall, PA; *Int'l*, pg. 788
Gage, Duncan, Mng. Dir.--Fondarge (Pty.) Ltd., Sandton, South Africa; *Int'l*, pg. 790
Gage, John, Reg. V.P.--Subaru Southwest Region, San Antonio, TX; *Int'l*, pg. 523
Gagg, J.W., Mng. Dir.--United Flexible, Merthyr Tydfil, United Kingdom; *Int'l*, pg. 1221
Gagliano, John, Pres.--Alfa Romeo Distributors of North America, Orlando, FL; *Int'l*, pg. 481
Gagliarducci, James P., Pres. & Chief Exec. Officer--Sunmark Inc., Saint Louis, MO; *Int'l*, pg. 917
Gaglione, Thomas, Pres.--Bank One, International Services Corporation, Milwaukee, WI; *U.S. Public*, pg. 173
Gagnaire, Francois, Dir. General--Banque Regionale du Nord, Lille, France; *Int'l*, pg. 548
Gagne, C., Chief Oper. Officer--Rawl S.A., Goussainville, France; *Int'l*, pg. 925
Gagne, Steve, Pres.--Dana Commercial Credit Corporation, Troy, MI; *U.S. Public*, pg. 479
Gagnier, Charles E., Pres. & Chief Exec. Officer--AMCORE Bank N.A., Rockford, Rockford, IL; *U.S. Public*, pg. 64
Gagnon, David, V.P.-Consulting--TRI-S Environmental Consulting, Brattleboro, VT; *U.S. Public*, pg. 546
Gagnon, Denis, V.P.-Intl. Opers.--Sta-Rite Foreign Sales Company, Delavan, WI; *U.S. Public*, pg. 1767
Gagnon, J. G., Mgr.--Camco Inc., Montreal, Canada; *U.S. Public*, pg. 713
Gagnon, Michael, Gen. Mgr.--Transplantation & Industrial Products Div., Wilmington, MA; *U.S. Public*, pg. 108
Gagnum, Hilge, Pres.--Greiter AG, Altstatten, Switzerland; *U.S. Public*, pg. 929
Gahungu, Athanese, Admin.--Banque de Credit de Bujumbura, Bujumbura, Burundi; *Int'l*, pg. 547
Gai, Luigi, Chief Oper. Officer--Bosso Carte Speciali S.p.A., Mathi, Italy; *Int'l*, pg. 35

Gaida, Blair, V.P. & Gen. Mgr.--Skydyne Div., Port Jervis, NY; *U.S. Public*, pg. 1

Gaillard, Pascal, Co-Mgr.--Unicom, Nantes, France; *Int'l*, pg. 601

Gaillard, Roger R., Pres. & Chief Exec. Officer--Williams & Company, Inc., Pittsburgh, PA; *U.S. Private*, pg. 1055

Gailly, Pierre-Antoine, Mng. Dir.--Desfosses International, Paris, France; *Int'l*, pg. 780

Gaines, Larry, Pres.--Media Play, Inc., Minnetonka, MN; *U.S. Public*, pg. 1142

Gainey, H.G., Gen. Mgr.--Liquid Coatings & Dispersions Division, Plymouth, IN; *U.S. Public*, pg. 619

Gainey, Mitch, Mng. Dir.--Machinery Manufacturing, Hartsville, SC; *U.S. Public*, pg. 1486

Gainsburg, Roy, Pres.--St. Martins Press, Inc., New York, NY; *Int'l*, pg. 1479

Gaiser, Charles, Gen. Mgr.--Castrol Industrial, Chicago, IL; *Int'l*, pg. 235

Gaisford, John, Publr. & Mng. Dir.--George Philip Limited, London, United Kingdom; *Int'l*, pg. 1093

Gaitan, Antonia, Chief Oper. Officer--Everest & Jennings de Mexico S.A. de C.V., Guadalajara, Mexico; *U.S. Public*, pg. 758

Gaites, Robert, Chief Exec. Officer--Architectural Wall Systems, LLC, Edison, NJ; *U.S. Private*, pg. 403

Gaites, Robert J., Pres.--The Strober Organization, Inc., Brooklyn, NY; *U.S. Private*, pg. 403

Gaitewaite, Richard L., Pres.--A.L. Hyde Company, Grenloch, NJ; *U.S. Public*, pg. 481

Gaither, John S., Pres.--Reichhold Limited, Mississauga, Canada; *Int'l*, pg. 370

Gaither, Thomas A., Pres.--Sunlink Corporation, Atlanta, GA; *U.S. Public*, pg. 208

Gaither, Tom, V.P.-Mktg.--Epsilon/West, San Francisco, CA; *U.S. Public*, pg. 74

Gajewski, Dennis, Sls. Promo Mgr.--Rolfs, Milwaukee, WI; *U.S. Private*, pg. 7

Galacz, Lajos, Gen. Mgr.--Scholl Kft, Budapest, Hungary; *Int'l*, pg. 1210

Galagaza, Mark, Dir.-Western Hemisphere Sls. & Oper.--Varco BJ Oil Tools, Houston, TX; *U.S. Public*, pg. 1709

Galagaza, Mark, Gen. Mgr.--Varco Best Products, Houston, TX; *U.S. Public*, pg. 1709

Galaggi, Jonathan, Editor-In-Chief--Noonday Press, New York, NY; *Int'l*, pg. 1479

Galaggi, Jonathan, Editor-In-Chief--North Point Press, New York, NY; *Int'l*, pg. 1479

Galais, Philippe, Mgr.--Network Systems France S.A., Neuilly-sur-Seine, France; *U.S. Public*, pg. 1523

Galamba, A.J.M., Dr., Mng. Dir.--The Standard Bank of South Africa Limited Representative Office, Maputo, Mozambique; *Int'l*, pg. 1294

Galan, Bob, Gen. Mgr.--Colgate-Palmolive Portuguese Ltda, Queluz, Portugal; *U.S. Public*, pg. 398

Galanski, Stan, Pres.--New Hampshire Insurance Group, New York, NY; *U.S. Public*, pg. 84

Galante, G., Gen. Mgr.--Cariplo Banque S.A., Paris, France; *Int'l*, pg. 275

Galante, Joseph, Pres.--RCA Records U.S., New York, NY; *Int'l*, pg. 192

Galante, Rick, Gen. Mgr.--Olympic Steel - Chicago Division, Schaumburg, IL; *U.S. Public*, pg. 1221

Galardi, Mario, Mng. Dir.--Olivetti de Venezuela C.A., Caracas, Venezuela; *Int'l*, pg. 1003

Galarreta, Jesus Peralta, Pres.--SODICAL - Sociedad Para el Desarrollo Industrial de Castilla y Leon, S.A., Valladolid, Spain; *Int'l*, pg. 1225

Galasso, Maria, Mgr.--Yoh Staffing Services, Philadelphia, PA; *U.S. Private*, pg. 317

Galbraith, Evan Griffith, Chm. Bd.--LVMH Moet Hennessy Louis Vuitton, New York, NY; *Int'l*, pg. 781

Galceran, J.P., Mng. Dir.--BBGR SA, Paris, France; *Int'l*, pg. 462

Gale, Simon, Gen. Mgr.--Roltech, Cambridge, United Kingdom; *Int'l*, pg. 462

Galea, Chris, Gen. Mgr.--Griffin Bacal International B.V., London, United Kingdom; *U.S. Private*, pg. 480

Galeazzi, Enrico P., Chm. Bd.--BMG Ariola Musica S.p.A., Rome, Italy; *Int'l*, pg. 192

Galenza, Len, V.P. & Controller--Weatherford Canada Ltd., Nisku, Canada; *U.S. Public*, pg. 1750

Galermo, Steve, Controller--Data Business Forms, Edmonton, Canada; *Int'l*, pg. 384

Galili, N., Gen. Mgr.--RAMTA Division/BEDEK Aviation Group, Beersheba, Israel; *Int'l*, pg. 690

Galili, U., Gen. Mgr.--Bank Leumi (UK) P.L.C., London, United Kingdom; *Int'l*, pg. 150

Galindo, Rodolfo, Pres.--Kolmar de Mexico, S.A., Tlalnepantla, Mexico; *Int'l*, pg. 239

Galioni, M., Mng. Dir.--Wolters Kluwer Italy, Milan, Italy; *Int'l*, pg. 1513

Galizia, Paul, Pres.--Bealls Outlet Inc., Bradenton, FL; *U.S. Private*, pg. 126

Galla, Helmut, Gen. Mgr.--Langenberg Kupfer und Messingwerke GmbH, Velbert, Germany; *U.S. Public*, pg. 1219

Gallacher, J.D. Stirling, Chm. Bd. & Mng. Dir.--P&O Vending, London, United Kingdom; *Int'l*, pg. 1034

Gallagher, Bob, Pres.--Six Flags Hurricane Harbor, Arlington, TX; *U.S. Public*, pg. 1611

Gallagher, Bob, Pres.--Wet-N-Wild, A Six Flags Water Park, Arlington, TX; *U.S. Public*, pg. 1612

Gallagher, Connell, Gen. Mgr.--Framlington Asset Management Russia, Moscow, Russia; *Int'l*, pg. 343

Gallagher, Daniel J., Pres.--Protection Technology, Philadelphia, PA; *U.S. Private*, pg. 317

Gallagher, E. Barry, Reg. Mgr.--BHP Steel Europe Middle East Ltd., Dubai, United Arab Emirates; *Int'l*, pg. 227

Gallagher, H. James, Chief Fin. Officer--CalMat Leasing Co., Los Angeles, CA; *U.S. Public*, pg. 295

Gallagher, J., Branch Mgr.--Van Leeuwen Pipe & Tube Corp., South Plainfield, NJ; *Int'l*, pg. 1450

Gallagher, James F., Jr., Pres.--International Benefit Service Corporation, Fort Worth, TX; *U.S. Public*, pg. 362

Gallagher, John S., Pres.--Pulte Carolina Division, Cary, NC; *U.S. Public*, pg. 1344

Gallagher, Raymond V., Gen. Mgr.--Rubber Molding Division, Norwich, CT; *U.S. Private*, pg. 355

Gallagher, Thomas J., Pres.--CG Equity Ventures, Inc., Bloomfield, CT; *U.S. Public*, pg. 365

Gallahan, Patricia, Gen. Mgr.--Diamond Paper Corporation, Sterling, VA; *U.S. Private*, pg. 467

Gallamore, Chuck, Reg. Mgr.--SMS-New Orleans, Metairie, LA; *U.S. Public*, pg. 1463

Gallano, I. Soroa, Gen. Mgr.--Seguros Orbita S.A., Madrid, Spain; *Int'l*, pg. 499

Gallant, Jean Phillipe, Pres.--Solectron France, S.A., Cestas, France; *U.S. Public*, pg. 1483

Gallant, R. Paul, Pres.--Compass Foods, Inc., Montvale, NJ; *Int'l*, pg. 1375

Gallant, S., Mng. Dir.--Diesel ReCon de Mexico, S.A. de C.V., Juarez, Mexico; *U.S. Public*, pg. 469

Gallegos, Jose Ramon, Gen. Mgr.--John Crane Brasil, Sao Paulo, Brazil; *Int'l*, pg. 1340

Gallello, Claude, Mng. Dir. & Mgr.-U.S. Network Country--Willis Corroon International/Americas, New York, NY; *Int'l*, pg. 1507

Gallery, Robert E., Mng. Dir.--Bank of Boston Ltd, London, United Kingdom; *U.S. Public*, pg. 184

Gallery, Robert E., Gen. Mgr.--Banque De Boston S.A., Paris, France; *U.S. Public*, pg. 185

Galli, Enrico, Mgr.--Sandvik Hard Materials A/S, Espergaerde, Denmark; *Int'l*, pg. 1186

Galli, Euvico, Technical Dir.--Sandvik Hard Materials A/S, Espergaerde, Denmark; *Int'l*, pg. 1186

Galli, Guido, Dir.--Houghton Italia S.p.A., Genoa, Italy; *U.S. Private*, pg. 541

Galli, Joseph, Pres.--Black & Decker Inc., Towson, MD; *U.S. Public*, pg. 234

Galligan, Kay A., V.P. & Gen. Mgr.--Cox Communications-Quad Cities, Moline, IL; *U.S. Public*, pg. 455

Gallimore, David A., Pres.--Lancaster Glass Corporation, Lancaster, OH; *U.S. Public*, pg. 977

Gallin, Philippe, Pres. & Dir. Gen.--AlliedSignal Turbo S.A., Thaon-les-Vosges, France; *U.S. Public*, pg. 53

Gallina, Joseph, V.P. & Gen. Mgr.--Castrol Inc., Specialty Products Div., Irvine, CA; *Int'l*, pg. 235

Gallman, Bob, Sr. Mktg. Officer--Southwest Marketing Div., Dallas, TX; *U.S. Private*, pg. 296

Gallo, Eugenio, Pres. & Chief Exec. Officer--Italia Di Navigazione S.p.A., Genoa, Italy; *Int'l*, pg. 653

Gallo, Jonathan, Pres.--J.L. DeGraffenreid & Sons, Inc., Springfield, MO; *U.S. Private*, pg. 301

Gallo, Robert J., Pres.--Missouri-American Water Co., Saint Joseph, MO; *U.S. Public*, pg. 95

Gallo, Robert J., Pres.--Ohio-American Water Co., Marion, OH; *U.S. Public*, pg. 95

Gallo, Robert J., Pres.--Iowa-American Water Co., Davenport, IA; *U.S. Public*, pg. 95

Gallo, Robert J., Pres.--Michigan-American Water Company, Calumet, MI; *U.S. Public*, pg. 95

Gallo, Roberto, Gen. Mgr.--Esselte S.P.A., Cascina, Italy; *Int'l*, pg. 461

Gallo, Terry, Mgr.--Redgate Communications Corp., Cambridge, MA; *U.S. Public*, pg. 66

Gallo, Vincenzo Antonio, Gen. Mgr.--Cariplo London, London, United Kingdom; *Int'l*, pg. 275

Gallois, Louis, Pres.--Aeroassurances, Paris, France; *Int'l*, pg. 29

Galloway, Bob, Chief Oper. Officer--Hubbard Petfood, Mankato, MN; *Int'l*, pg. 1116

Galloway, David, Chm. Bd.--Silhouette Books, New York, NY; *Int'l*, pg. 1402

Galloway, Harvey S., Jr., Pres.--Nationwide HMO, Inc., Columbus, OH; *U.S. Private*, pg. 789

Galloway, Lowell D., Pres. & Chief Exec. Officer--Regions Bank/Albertville/Guntersville/Arab, Albertville, AL; *U.S. Public*, pg. 1371

Gallu, Christopher T., V.P. & Gen. Mgr.--KKLT-FM, Phoenix, AZ; *U.S. Public*, pg. 1344

Gallu, Christopher T., V.P. & Gen. Mgr.--KMVP-AM, Phoenix, AZ; *U.S. Public*, pg. 1344

Galluccio, Michael, Gen. Mgr.--EG & G Sealol Engineered Products Division, Warwick, RI; *U.S. Public*, pg. 542

Galluccio, Mike, Mgr.--EG & G Sealol-Industrial Division, Cranston, RI; *U.S. Public*, pg. 543

Gallup, Charles A., Pres.--Gal Corp., Ann Arbor, MI; *Int'l*, pg. 1249

Gallup, Frank, Pres.--Markhon Industries, Inc, Wabash, IN; *U.S. Private*, pg. 614

Gallus, Gregory F., Chm. Bd. & Pres.--Foodland Distributors, Livonia, MI; *U.S. Public*, pg. 1541

Galluzzo, Massimo, Mng. Dir.--FEMSA S.p.A., Mesero, Italy; *Int'l*, pg. 283

Galmon, Charles R., Plant Mgr--Moultrie Container Div., Moultrie, GA; *U.S. Public*, pg. 1289

Galotti, Donna Kalajian, Sr. V.P. & Publr.--Cosmopolitan, New York, NY; *U.S. Private*, pg. 517

Galotti, Ronald, Publisher--Vogue Magazine, New York, NY; *U.S. Private*, pg. 20

Galpin, Brian, Admin.--Hearthstone of Northern Nevada, Sparks, NV; *U.S. Public*, pg. 837

Galssini, F.S., Pres.--Superior Linkage Division, New Haven, IN; *U.S. Private*, pg. 1111

Galt, Jeffrey S., Exec. V.P.--The DIALOG Corporation, Mountain View, CA; *Int'l*, pg. 412

Galt, Martin, Chief Exec. Officer--Boatmen's Trust Company, Inc., Little Rock, AR; *U.S. Public*, pg. 1164

Galusha, Jack, Mgr.--Lincoln Graphics Inc., Lincoln, NE; *U.S. Public*, pg. 503

Galvez, Mr., Gen. Mgr.--ScanData S.A., Marne la Vallee, France; *U.S. Public*, pg. 177

Galvin, E.P., Dr., Chm. Bd.-Crystal Div.--Waterford Crystal Ltd., Kilbarry, Ireland; *Int'l*, pg. 1487

Galvin, Neal, Pres.--Callanan Industries, Inc., Albany, NY; *Int'l*, pg. 242

Galvin, R.E., Pres.--Chevron USA Production Co., Houston, TX; *U.S. Public*, pg. 348

Galvin, Stephen J., Pres.--Educational Finance Group, Hyannis, MA; *U.S. Public*, pg. 1679

Galway, Byron, V.P. & Gen. Mgr.--TMP Worldwide, Inc., Atlanta, GA; *U.S. Private*, pg. 1064

Galyean, Tommy, V.P.--Newell Paper Co. of Meridian, Meridian, MS; *U.S. Private*, pg. 579

Gamache, Brian, Pres. & Chief Oper. Officer--WHG Resorts & Casinos, Carolina, PR; *U.S. Public*, pg. 1265

Gamache, Brian, Pres.--Williams Hospitality Group Inc., Carolina, PR; *U.S. Public*, pg. 1265

Gamaggio, Uberto, Mng. Dir.--Thomas & Betts GmbH, Egelsbach, Germany; *U.S. Public*, pg. 1598

Gamatero, Delilah, V.P. & Mgr.--City National Bank - Olympic Plaza Regional Office, Los Angeles, CA; *U.S. Public*, pg. 381

Gamba, John F., Pres.--Bell Atlantic Network Services, Inc., Arlington, VA; *U.S. Public*, pg. 202

Gambarota, Mario G., Dir.--Cigna Insurance New Zealand Limited, Auckland, New Zealand; *U.S. Public*, pg. 364

Gamberale, Vito, Chief Exec. Officer--Telecom Italia Mobile, Rome, Italy; *Int'l*, pg. 1363

Gambill, Mark M., Pres.--Wheat First Butcher Singer, Inc., Richmond, VA; *U.S. Public*, pg. 640

Gamble, Bob, Mng. Dir.--Nationwide Bearings Pty. Ltd., Dingley, Australia; *Int'l*, pg. 1157

Gamble, Dolores R., V.P. & Mng. Officer--Northern Trust Bank of Florida, N.A., Naples, FL; *U.S. Public*, pg. 1196

Gamble, F., Mng. Dir.--ANZ Grindlays Bank plc Bangladesh, Dhaka, Bangladesh; *Int'l*, pg. 98

Gamble, Richard, Grp. Exec. Officer--Royal & Sun Alliance Insurance Group, London, United Kingdom; *Int'l*, pg. 1130

Gambow, N.E., Pres.--Post Glover Resistors Inc., Erlanger, KY; *Int'l*, pg. 590

Gambrel, William, Sr. Officer--The Chase Manhattan Bank, N.A., Buenos Aires, Argentina; *U.S. Public*, pg. 340

Gambrill, Anthony, Chief Exec. Officer & Bus. Devel./Information--CGR Communications, Kingston, Jamaica; *U.S. Public*, pg. 1422

Gamm, Ulrich, Mng. Dir.--Nokia Audio Electronics GmbH, Straubing, Germany; *Int'l*, pg. 954

Gammill, Lee, Pres.--New York Life Insurance and Annuity Corporation, New York, NY; *U.S. Private*, pg. 795

Gammon, David, Mng. Dir.--Robert Fleming Spain SA, Madrid, Spain; *Int'l*, pg. 494

Gammon, Richard, Mng. Dir.--Fiserv Europe Limited, Uxbridge, United Kingdom; *U.S. Public*, pg. 647

Gamot, M., Chief Oper. Officer--SAIA-Burgess, Gennevilliers, France; *Int'l*, pg. 1500

Gamper, Albert R., Jr., Pres. & Chief Exec. Officer--The CIT Group Holdings, Inc., New York, NY; *Int'l*, pg. 360

Gan, K.C., Sr. V.P. & Country Mgr.--Bank of America NT&SA, Jakarta, Indonesia; *U.S. Public*, pg. 182

Gan, K.S., Dr., Mng. Dir.--Methode Electronics FarEast PTE, Ltd., Jurong, Singapore; *U.S. Public*, pg. 1101

Gan, Yian Cheng, Chief Oper. Officer--Novo Nordisk Pharma (Taiwan) Ltd., Taipei, Taiwan; *Int'l*, pg. 988

Ganasevici, Joan, Chief Fin. Officer--General Motors Venezolana, C.A., Caracas, Venezuela; *U.S. Public*, pg. 723

Gandel, Priscilla, Dir.--Epsilon Direct, New York, NY; *U.S. Public*, pg. 74

Gandhi, Mukesh, Chief Oper. Officer--Axel Johnson & Co. (India) Ltd., Calcutta, India; *Int'l*, pg. 711

Gandini, Osvaldo, Gen. Mgr.--Formica Italia S.r.1., Milan, Italy; *Int'l*, pg. 129

Gandionco, Perlita, Mgr.--Downey Savings & Loan Association, F.A., Fremont, CA; *U.S. Public*, pg. 527

Gandy, Roland, Admin.--Hillhaven Convalescent Hospital Palo Alto, Palo Alto, CA; *U.S. Public*, pg. 1713

Ganem, Jacques, Chief Oper. Officer--Krauss-Maffei France S.a.r.l., Gennevilliers, France; *Int'l*, pg. 836

Ganier, Jim, Dir.--Morgan Keegan, Inc.-Branch Div., Memphis, TN; *U.S. Public*, pg. 1131

Ganin, Bruce, V.P.--Reynolds Tire & Rubber, Brooklyn, NY; *U.S. Private*, pg. 439

Ganis, David R., Pres.--Northern Futures Corporation, Chicago, IL; *U.S. Public*, pg. 1196

Ganis, Sid, Pres.-Mktg. & Distr.--Sony Pictures Studios, Culver City, CA; *Int'l*, pg. 1283

Ganley, Jack, Pres.--Burlington House Fabrics Group, New York, NY; *U.S. Public*, pg. 268

Ganly, Neal J., Pres.--Bemis Polyethylene Packaging Div., Terre Haute, IN; *U.S. Public*, pg. 210

Gann, John W., Chief Oper. Officer--Allright Baltimore, Inc., Baltimore, MD; *U.S. Private*, pg. 42

Gannaway, Michael T., Pres.-Fragrance Grp.--Charles of the Ritz Group Ltd., New York, NY; *U.S. Private*, pg. 689

Gannerud, Per, Pres.--AB Ljungby Stalgjuteri, Ljungby, Sweden; *Int'l*, pg. 1419

Gannon, James A., Mgr.-Branch--Piper Jaffray Inc., Twin Falls, ID; *U.S. Public*, pg. 1301

Gannon, Jim A., Mgr.--Piper Jaffray Inc., Boise, ID; *U.S. Public*, pg. 1301

Gannon, John J., Pres.--Physician Practice Management, Northbrook, IL; *U.S. Public*, pg. 1082

Gannon, Joseph P., Pres.--Maine/Sysco, Inc., Newport, ME; *U.S. Public*, pg. 1551

Gannon, Mike, V.P.-Admin.--Dana Commercial Credit Small Tkt, Troy, MI; *U.S. Public*, pg. 480

Gannon, R.P., Pres.--Canadian-Montana Pipeline Co., Butte, MT; *U.S. Public*, pg. 1127

Gannon, R.P., Pres.--Glacier Gas Company, Butte, MT; *U.S. Public*, pg. 1127

Ganote, Len, Pres.--Hawaiian Pacific Elevator Company, Honolulu, HI; *U.S. Public*, pg. 521

Gantcher, Nathan, Pres. & Co-Chief Exec. Officer--CIBC Oppenheimer Corp., New York, NY; *Int'l*, pg. 257

Gantchev, Galin Iordanov, Mng. Dir.--Jotun Bulgaria Ltd., Sofia, Bulgaria; *Int'l*, pg. 715

Gantert, F., Dr., Chief Exec. Officer--Ascom Autelca AG, Gumligen, Switzerland; *Int'l*, pg. 86

Gantz, John G., Pres. & Chief Oper. Officer--AIG Risk Management, Inc., New York, NY; *U.S. Public*, pg. 85

Ganucheau, Frank P., III, Pres.--GSB Investment Management, Inc., Fort Worth, TX; *U.S. Public*, pg. 1673

GaNung, Mark A., Pres.--Keystone Brokerage, Inc., Williamsport, PA; *U.S. Public*, pg. 956

Ganyo, Richard A., Pres.--BKG Finishing Systems, Inc., Minneapolis, MN; *U.S. Public*, pg. 865

Ganz, J.C., Gen. Mgr.--ING Bank Bratislava, Bratislava, Slovakia; *Int'l*, pg. 649

Ganz, Jochen, Mgr.--Pracht Spedition & Logistik GmbH, Haiger, Germany; *Int'l*, pg. 596

Ganzi, Victor F., Sr. V.P. & Group Head--Hearst Books/ Business Publishing Group, New York, NY; *U.S. Private*, pg. 515

Garaets, Gerard, V.P.-Opers. & Gen. Mgr.--De Zaan Far East Pte. Ltd., Singapore, Singapore; *U.S. Public*, pg. 128

Garando, Gallon, Pres.--Sedec s.a.r.l., Kinshasa, Congo; *Int'l*, pg. 1438

Garavaglia, M., Mng. Dir.--Ascom Safnat SpA, Milan, Italy; *Int'l*, pg. 87

Garbagnati, Furio, Chm. & Chief Exec. Officer--Shandwick Corporate Communications S.p.A., Milan, Italy; *Int'l*, pg. 1227

Garbarski, Eddie, Pres.--Garbarski EURO RSCG, Brussels, Belgium; *Int'l*, pg. 603

Garbee, Richard E., Pres.--Hayward Pool Products, Inc., Elizabeth, NJ; *U.S. Private*, pg. 513

Garber, C. Stedman, Jr., Pres.--Santa Fe Minerals Inc., Dallas, TX; *Int'l*, pg. 765

Garber, Mark, Publisher--Springfield News, Springfield, OR; *U.S. Public*, pg. 984

Garber, Nancy D., M.D., Orthopedic Surgeon--Orthopaedic Rehabilitation Center of Atlanta, Hapeville, GA; *U.S. Public*, pg. 1715

Garbett, Gerald S., Mgr.--Sandvik Process Systems Ltd., Birmingham, United Kingdom; *Int'l*, pg. 1187

Garby, Gage, Pres.--Senetics, Boulder, CO; *U.S. Public*, pg. 1755

Garces, Jorge J., Pres.--John Crane Latin America, Codigo, Mexico; *Int'l*, pg. 1339

Garcha, Ranjit, Plant Mgr.--Goshen Rubber of Canada Ltd., Brampton, Canada; *U.S. Private*, pg. 466

Garcia Cisneros, Teresa, Gen. Mgr.--Spanish Executive Information Services (SEIS), Madrid, Spain; *U.S. Private*, pg. 617

Garcia Hijonoso, Rene, Pres.--Protexa Industrias S.A. de C.V., Santa Catarina, Mexico; *Int'l*, pg. 576

Garcia-Marato, Antonio, Mng. Dir.--McGraw Hill Interamericana de Espana S.A., Madrid, Spain; *U.S. Public*, pg. 1072

Garcia-Maroto, Antonio, Mng. Dir.--McGraw-Hill Interamericana de Portugal, Ltda, Lisbon, Portugal; *U.S. Public*, pg. 1072

Garcia-Mella, Nelson, Gen. Mgr.--Colgate-Palmolive S.A.E., Madrid, Spain; *U.S. Public*, pg. 399

Garcia-Morales, Alejandro, V.P. & Agent--Banca Serfin, S.N.C., Los Angeles Agency, Los Angeles, CA; *Int'l*, pg. 138

Garcia, Angelo R., III, Pres.--Arrow Freight Corporation, Bulacan, Philippines; *Int'l*, pg. 186

Garcia, Anita, Branch Mgr.--Downey Savings & Loan Association, F.A., Los Alamitos, CA; *U.S. Public*, pg. 526

Garcia, Antonio, Mgr.-Country--Sensormatic Lda., Lisbon, Portugal; *U.S. Public*, pg. 1458

Garcia, Antonio Valcarce, Pres.--ENCE - E.N. de Celulosas, S.A., Madrid, Spain; *Int'l*, pg. 1224

Garcia, Augustin, Gen. Mgr.--Polarcup S.A., Nules, Spain; *Int'l*, pg. 638

Garcia, Augustin, Gen. Mgr.--Polarcup Portugal, Setubal, Portugal; *Int'l*, pg. 639

Garcia, Carlos M., Chief Fin. Officer--Countrywide Capital Markets, Inc., Pasadena, CA; *U.S. Public*, pg. 453

Garcia, Eduardo Abellan, Pres.--HUNOSA - E.N. Hulleras del Norte, S.A., Oviedo, Spain; *Int'l*, pg. 1224

Garcia, Emilio Gasco, Mng. Dir.--MB Espana, S.A., Quart de Poblet, Spain; *U.S. Public*, pg. 798

Garcia, Enrique M., Gen. Mgr.--Albany International S.A. de C.V., Cuautitlan, Mexico; *U.S. Public*, pg. 37

Garcia, Francisco, Pres.--Pall Biomedical Puerto Rico, Fajardo, PR; *U.S. Public*, pg. 1254

Garcia, Gregorio D. III, Mng. Dir. & Chief Creative Officer--Hemisphere-Leo Burnett, Inc., Manila, Philippines; *U.S. Private*, pg. 184

Garcia, J.M.A., Mng. Dir.--Sociedad Gestora de Fundos de Pensoes SA, Lisbon, Portugal; *Int'l*, pg. 565

Garcia, Jean, Chief Oper. Officer--Basic Chemicals Div., Courbevoie, France; *Int'l*, pg. 1109

Garcia, Jesus, Gen. Mgr.--D'Arcy Masius Benton & Bowles, S.A., Barcelona, Spain; *U.S. Private*, pg. 304

Garcia, Jose, Mng. Dir.--Industrias Cousin Freres, Burlada, Spain; *Int'l*, pg. 193

Garcia, Jose L., Gen. Mgr.--Iberia, Madrid, Spain; *Int'l*, pg. 574

Garcia, Jose L., Gen. Mgr.--Iberia Cargo, Madrid, Spain; *Int'l*, pg. 574

Garcia, Jose L., Gen. Mgr.--Iberia Air Lines of Spain, Boston, MA; *Int'l*, pg. 575

Garcia, Jose L., Gen. Mgr.--Iberia Air Lines of Spain, Washington, DC; *Int'l*, pg. 575

Garcia, Jose Luis Alvarez, Pres.--Foarsa Forjas Y Aceros De Reinosa, S.A., Reynosa, Mexico; *Int'l*, pg. 1225

Garcia, Julio Lander, Pres.--Wackenhut de Venezuela, S.A., Caracas, Venezuela; *U.S. Public*, pg. 1731

Garcia, Luis Alberto Arias, Pres.--Cigna Compania de Seguros de Panama S.A., Panama, Panama; *U.S. Public, pg. 364*

Garcia, Luis Alberto Arias, Pres.--Delpanama S.A., Panama, Panama; *U.S. Public*, pg. 364

Garcia, Luzzie, V.P. & Fin. Dir.--Leo Burnett Inc., Hato Rey, PR; *U.S. Private*, pg. 185

Garcia, M. Perez, Mng. Dir.--Van Leeuwen Tubos Espana S.A.E., Madrid, Spain; *Int'l*, pg. 1450

Garcia, Manuel Fernandez, Pres.--Productos Tubulares, S.A., Vizcaya, Spain; *Int'l*, pg. 1224

Garcia, Paul R., Pres. & Chief Exec. Officer--NaBANCO, Sunrise, FL; *U.S. Public*, pg. 631

Garcia, Pete, Pres. & Chief Exec. Officer--University Mechanical & Engineering Contractors, Inc., San Diego, CA; *U.S. Public*, pg. 572

Garcia, Salvador, Portraits Mgr.--LOOK, Santiago, Chile; *U.S. Public*, pg. 553

Garcia, Ted, Gen. Mgr.--Watlow de Mexico S.A. de C.V., Queretaro, Mexico; *U.S. Private*, pg. 1153

Gardas, Peter, Mng. Dir.--Amway Hungaria Marketing KFT., Budapest, Hungary; *U.S. Private*, pg. 70

Gardea, Brad, Base Mgr.--Mercury Air Center, Costa Mesa, CA; *U.S. Public*, pg. 1093

Gardehall, Hans, Pres.--NCC Prefab AB, Sollentuna, Sweden; *Int'l*, pg. 899

Garden, R.I., Exec. Dir.--P.T. Multinational Finance Corporation, Jakarta, Indonesia; *Int'l*, pg. 1133

Gardiner, Cheri, Mng. Dir.--Western International Media Corporation, Cleveland, OH; *U.S. Private*, pg. 1167

Gardiner, Jim, Chm. & Chief Exec. Officer--Fording Coal Ltd., Calgary, Canada; *Int'l*, pg. 259

Gardiner, R., Gen. Mgr.--ITW Hi-Cone Ltd., Mallow, Ireland; *U.S. Public*, pg. 868

Gardner, Dave, Plant Mgr.--Robinson Nugent (Scotland) Limited, Renfrew, United Kingdom; *U.S. Public*, pg. 1395

Gardner, Frank, Gen. Mgr.--Robert Fleming Holdings Limited, Manama, Bahrain; *Int'l*, pg. 494

Gardner, George D., Pres. & Mng. Dir.--Grocers Specialty Co., Los Angeles, CA; *U.S. Private*, pg. 227

Gardner, George D., Pres.--Grocers General Merchandise Co., Los Angeles, CA; *U.S. Private*, pg. 227

Gardner, Gerald, Mgr.--Continental Telephone Co., Continental, OH; *U.S. Public*, pg. 1571

Gardner, J. S., Pres.--Principal Marketing Services, Inc., Des Moines, IA; *U.S. Private*, pg. 886

Gardner, J.L., Chm. Bd.--Invesco Inc., Boston, MA; *Int'l*, pg. 685

Gardner, M. Dozier, Pres.--Eaton Vance Management, Boston, MA; *U.S. Public*, pg. 559

Gardner, Marilyn, Admin.--Guardian Care of Elkin, Elkin, NC; *U.S. Public*, pg. 1712

Gardner, Mike, Pres.--Whittaker Communications, Inc., Santa Clara, CA; *U.S. Public*, pg. 1767

Gardner, Myrna, Pres.--Hudson Street Partners, New York, NY; *U.S. Public*, pg. 1422

Gardner, Peter R., Gen. Mgr.--Bundy Tubing Co. (Australia) Pty. Ltd., Adelaide, Australia; *Int'l*, pg. 1341

Gardner, R.J.M., Mng. Dir.--De La Rue Payment Systems Division, Basingstoke, United Kingdom; *Int'l*, pg. 387

Gardner, Ralph H., Pres.--Milkco, Inc., Asheville, NC; *U.S. Public*, pg. 878

Gardner, Rick, Chm. Bd. & Chief Exec. Officer--First Commercial Mortgage Co., Little Rock, AR; *U.S. Public*, pg. 630

Gardner, Tim, Plant Mgr.--BMB Company, Holton, KS; *U.S. Public*, pg. 35

Gardner, William R., Dir.--Pharmacia & Upjohn, Hartland, WI; *Int'l*, pg. 1048

Gardnier, J. L., Dir. Gen.--Case Tracteurs, S.A., Les Ulis, France; *U.S. Public*, pg. 1579

Gardo, Lars, Chief Oper. Officer--AxTrade AB, Stockholm, Sweden; *Int'l*, pg. 708

Garel, John R., Pres. & Chief Exec. Offcier--Cadmus Journal Services, Inc., Linthicum Heights, MD; *U.S. Public*, pg. 291

Garet, Bernard, Mng. Dir.--Limagrain Genetics Corp., Kirkland, IL; *Int'l*, pg. 566

Garfinckle, David, Pres.--Paramount Productions, Inc., Toronto, Canada; *U.S. Private*, pg. 777

Garfinkle, Jeff, Mgr.--SMS-Santa Barbara, Santa Barbara, CA; *U.S. Public*, pg. 1463

Garfunkel, Margaret D., Pres.--MBIA Municipal Investors Service Corporation, Armonk, NY; *U.S. Public*, pg. 1023

Gargan, R., Mgr.-Sls. Office--VG Quadrupoles Ltd., Middlewich, United Kingdom; *Int'l*, pg. 1111

Garguilo, L., Sr. V.P.--Daher Golden Eagle - New York, Jamaica, NY; *U.S. Public*, pg. 749

Gargus, Robert, Pres. & Gen. Mgr.--Atalla Corporation, San Jose, CA; *U.S. Public*, pg. 417

Garian, Rick C., Exec. V.P.--Everex Systems Inc., Fremont, CA; *Int'l*, pg. 498

Garland, H. Julian, Mng. Dir.--Salem Engineering Co., Ltd., Derby, United Kingdom; *U.S. Private*, pg. 962

Garland, Wallace, Mng. Dir.--Cadbury Kenya Limited, Nairobi, Kenya; *Int'l*, pg. 248

Garlick, Ralph W., Pres.--Old Kent Bank-East, Southfield, MI; *U.S. Public*, pg. 1216

Garlick, Ron, Chief Oper. Officer--New Zealand Controls Ltd., Masterton, New Zealand; *Int'l*, pg. 1244

Garlington, Dub, Pres. & Chief Oper. Officer--Affiliated Funding Inc., Amarillo, TX; *U.S. Private*, pg. 25

Garlock, John, Pres.--Porter-Cable Corporation, Jackson, TN; *U.S. Public*, pg. 1274

Garlock, Leo, Mgr.--A. Schulman, Inc., Akron, OH; *U.S. Public*, pg. 1441

Garlow, James F., Pres.--John W. Hancock Jr., Inc., Salem, VA; *U.S. Public*, pg. 1392

Garman, M.L., Chm. Bd.--ECP Incorporated, Westchester, IL; *U.S. Private*, pg. 313

Garmsen, Richard, Gen. Mgr.--Reclamation Div. (Sacramento), Sacramento, CA; *Int'l*, pg. 1271

Garndiner, Richard, Pres.--R-Cubed Composites Inc., West Jordan, UT; *Int'l*, pg. 1037

Garneau, Simon N., Pres.--Teleglobe Insurance Systems, Richmond Hill, Canada; *Int'l*, pg. 1373

Garner, Don, Pres.--Dixie Type & Supply Co., Inc., Birmingham, AL; *U.S. Public*, pg. 1329

Garner, Jack, Pres.--UPB of Central Mississippi, Jackson, MS; *U.S. Public*, pg. 1669

Garner, Jerry N., V.P. & Gen. Mgr.--Industrial & Retail Bag Division, Chicago, IL; *U.S. Public*, pg. 1521

Garner, John F., Pres.--Flavorite Laboratories, Horn Lake, MS; *U.S. Private*, pg. 1090

Garner, Ken, Pres.--United Litho, Inc., Ashburn, VA; *U.S. Private*, pg. 993

Garner, T.J., Pres.--Ekco Canada, Inc., Niagara Falls, Canada; *U.S. Public*, pg. 566

Garner, Terry, Pres.--Grayson Electronics Corporation, Forest, VA; *U.S. Public*, pg. 46

Garner, Terry R., V.P. & Gen. Mgr.--Elkhart Products Corporation-Industrial Division, Geneva, IN; *U.S. Public*, pg. 63

Garnet, Anthony, Dir.--Fleming Martin Limited, London, United Kingdom; *Int'l*, pg. 493

Garnett, William A., Pres.--Jones Capital Corporation, Charlotte, NC; *Int'l*, pg. 633

Garnham, Francisco, Pres.--AGA de Mexico S.A. de C.V., Tlalnepantla, Mexico; *Int'l*, pg. 13

Garnier, Bernard, V.P.--Sulzer Pompes France S.A., Mantes-la-Jolie, France, Mantes-la-Jolie, France; *Int'l*, pg. 1306

Garnier, Jean-Pierre, Pres.--SmithKline Beecham Pharmaceuticals, Philadelphia, PA; *Int'l*, pg. 1265

Garnish, Ian, Chief Exec. Officer--Saunders Valve Co. Ltd., Cwmbran, United Kingdom; *Int'l*, pg. 1379

Garnjost, Joachim, Dr., Chm.--Mannesmann Anlagenbau AG, Dusseldorf, Germany; *Int'l*, pg. 836

Garoche, Jean, Pres.--Paretan Garoche, Santeny, France; *Int'l*, pg. 789

Garofalo, Richard, Pres. & Chief Oper. Officer--Health Acquisition Corp., Jamaica, NY; *U.S. Public*, pg. 1157

Garofolo, Joe, V.P.--Arrow Commercial Systems Div., Wilmington, MA; *U.S. Public*, pg. 133

Garoklanian, Charles F., Sr. Bus. Devel. Officer--Northeast Marketing-New York Business Center, New York, NY; *U.S. Public*, pg. 649

Garrasso, Mario, Pres.--Exor America, New York, NY; *Int'l*, pg. 467

Garren, Jerry L., V.P.--La-Z-Boy Utah, Tremonton, UT; *U.S. Public*, pg. 973

Garret, M., Dir.--GTM Caraibes, Fort-de-France, Martinique; *Int'l*, pg. 823

Garretsen, Reinier, Gen. Mgr.--Muva Greetings S.A., Zonhoven, Belgium; *U.S. Public*, pg. 78

Garretson, Richard C., Pres.--OREO Corporation, Cleveland, OH; *U.S. Public*, pg. 955

Garretson, Wade, Mgr.-Dist. Sls.--Thai Airways Intl. Ltd.-Chicago, Chicago, IL; *Int'l*, pg. 1381

Garrett, Bob, Mgr.-Exploration--Hunt Oil Gulf Coast Exploration Division, Houston, TX; *U.S. Private*, pg. 548

Garrett, Ellie, Admin.--Cherry Creek Village Retirement Center, Wichita, KS; *U.S. Public*, pg. 837

Garrett, Frank, Branch Mgr.--Continental/Murray, Memphis, TN; *U.S. Private*, pg. 268

Garrett, Frantz, Branch Mgr.--Continental/Murray, Rayville, LA; *U.S. Private*, pg. 268

Garrett, James C., V.P. & Gen. Mgr.--ECI Div., Saint Petersburg, FL; *U.S. Public*, pg. 1365

Garrett, Sam L., Pres.--Ikon Office Solutions-Dallas, Dallas, TX; *U.S. Public*, pg. 863

Garrett, Steve O., Pres.--Sunwest Bank of Farmington, Farmington, NM; *U.S. Public*, pg. 1165

Garrett, Thomas H., V.P. &. Gen. Mgr.--Eastern Engraving, Stirling, NJ; *U.S. Public*, pg. 1506

Garrett, Todd A., Pres.--Procter & Gamble Health & Beauty Care Belgium, Brussels, Belgium; *U.S. Public*, pg. 1332

Garrett, Todd A., Pres.--Procter & Gamble Health & Beauty Care Germany, Mainz, Germany; *U.S. Public*, pg. 1332

Garrett, William, Pres.--Delta Mills Marketing Company, New York, NY; *U.S. Public*, pg. 498

Garrido, Edgar Lenis, Chm. Bd.--Aluminio Reynolds, Santo Domingo, S.A., Barranquilla, Colombia; *U.S. Public*, pg. 1386

Garrido, Juan, Mng. Dir.--Battenfeld Iberica S.A., Montcada, Spain; *Int'l*, pg. 826

Garriga Torres, Jorge, Mng. Dir.--Fibroco S.A., Barcelona, Spain; *Int'l*, pg. 1368

Garriga, J., Mng. Dir.--Howard S.A., Barcelona, Spain; *Int'l*, pg. 1387

Garriott, Richard, Co-Founder, V.P. & Dir.-Devel.--Origin Systems, Inc., Austin, TX; *U.S. Public*, pg. 569

Garripy, Morris, Mgr.--Anixter Toronto, Brampton, Canada; *U.S. Public*, pg. 116

Garrison, F.S., Pres. & Chief Exec. Officer--American Freightways, Inc., Harrison, AR; *U.S. Public*, pg. 76

Garrison, James, Chief Oper. Officer--Gooch Packing Co., Inc., Abilene, TX; *U.S. Private*, pg. 909

Garrison, S. Jack, Mgr.--Barnardsville Telephone Co., Barnardsville, NC; *U.S. Public*, pg. 1571

Garrity, Monique P., Resident Rep.--The World Bank, Lome, Togo; *U.S. Private*, pg. 1190

Garrott, Thomas M., Chief Exec. Officer--National Bank of Commerce, Memphis, TN; *U.S. Public*, pg. 1155

Garrott, Thomas M., Chm. Bd.--Monroe Properties, Inc., Memphis, TN; *U.S. Public*, pg. 1155

Garrou, Victor H., Chief Oper. Officer--Pilot Research Corp., Valdese, NC; *U.S. Public*, pg. 36

Garrucho, Clemente, Chief Exec. Officer--Gerber Products Co Singapore, Singapore, Singapore; *Int'l*, pg. 973

Garry, G. R., Pres.--Fiber Optic Services, Inc., Melbourne, FL; *U.S. Public*, pg. 750

Garschagen, D.H., Exec. V.P. & Reg. Mgr.--Bank of America NT&SA, Hong Kong, Hong Kong; *U.S. Public*, pg. 182

Garson, Donald, Pres.--Dakota Pork Industries, Green Bay, WI; *U.S. Private*, pg. 54

Garsow, Donald, Pres.--Green Bay Dressed Beef Company, Green Bay, WI; *U.S. Private*, pg. 54

Garten, E.A., V.P. & Gen. Mgr.--Milupa Company, Darien, CT; *Int'l*, pg. 991

Gartner, Hans, Dr., Chief Oper. Officer--Wackenhut Central Europe GmbH, Offenbach/Main, Germany; *U.S. Public*, pg. 1731

Gartner, Hartmut, Mng. Dir.--Sodra Cell GmbH, Hamburg, Germany; *Int'l*, pg. 1276

Gartner, Pedro, Pres.--AGA Argentina SACIFIMR, Buenos Aires, Argentina; *Int'l*, pg. 13

Gartner, Pedro, Chief Oper. Officer--AGA Gaz Sp.z.o.o., Warsaw, Poland; *Int'l*, pg. 13
Garton, Daniel P., Pres.--AMR Eagle, Inc., Fort Worth, TX; *U.S. Public*, pg. 9
Garufi, Michele, Chief Oper. Officer--Recordati-Elmu S.L., Madrid, Spain; *Int'l*, pg. 1090
Garvey, Chris, Mgr.--Stephen Gould of Carolina, Inc./ Charlotte Div., Charlotte, NC; *U.S. Private*, pg. 467
Garvey, Denis, Plant Mgr.--General Tire Div., Charlotte, NC; *Int'l*, pg. 327
Garvey, Eddie, Mng. Dir.--Rouse Thompson & Lloyd Ltd., Birmingham, United Kingdom; *Int'l*, pg. 391
Garvey, Howard, Pres.--Northern Telecom Japan Inc., Tokyo, Japan; *Int'l*, pg. 970
Garvey, James W., Pres.--Builders Development Inc., Wichita, KS; *U.S. Private*, pg. 440
Garvey, Michael, Pres. & Chief Oper. Officer--Moxness Products, Inc., Racine, WI; *U.S. Public*, pg. 124
Garvey, Mike, Pres.--Mox-Med, Inc., Portage, WI; *U.S. Public*, pg. 124
Garvey, Neil, Pres.--Simplex Technologies, Inc., Portsmouth, NH; *U.S. Public*, pg. 1648
Garvey, Willard W., Pres.--Builders Inc., Wichita, KS; *U.S. Private*, pg. 440
Garvin, Ed, Exec. V.P. & Gen. Mgr.--South Carolina Steel, Taylors, SC; *U.S. Public*, pg. 412
Garwood, John, Gen. Mgr.--WPLG-TV, Miami, FL; *U.S. Public*, pg. 1743
Gary, Michael, Gen. Mgr.--Arrow/Schweber Electronics, Columbia, MD; *U.S. Public*, pg. 133
Gary, Samuel, Chm. Bd.--Gary-Williams Energy Corporation, Denver, CO; *U.S. Private*, pg. 440
Garza de la Garza, Jorge, Pres.--Compania Minera Las Cuevas S.A. de C.V., San Luis Potosi, Mexico; *Int'l*, pg. 575
Garza Delgado, Roberto, Pres.--Versax, S.A. de C.V., Garza Garcia, Mexico; *Int'l*, pg. 56
Garza, Jorge, Pres.--Aceros Camesa S.A. de C.V., Mexico, Mexico; *Int'l*, pg. 575
Garzone, Max, Mng. Dir.--MacDermid Italiana SRL, Cavaglia, Italy; *U.S. Public*, pg. 1030
Gasbarro, Robert, V.P. & Gen. Mgr.--H.F. Coors China Co., Inglewood, CA; *U.S. Public*, pg. 1506
Gascoyne, John, Pres.--Hubbard Farms, Inc., Walpole, NH; *U.S. Public*, pg. 1092
Gascoyne, John, Pres.--Hubbard Farms, Inc., Walpole, NH; *Int'l*, pg. 1114
Gasiorski, Peter R., Pres.--Baron Drawn Steel Corp., Toledo, OH; *U.S. Private*, pg. 922
Gaskell, Kevin, Chief Oper. Officer--Porsche Cars Great Britain Ltd., Reading, United Kingdom; *Int'l*, pg. 1063
Gaspar, Raul, Mng. Dir.--SKF Argentina S.A., Buenos Aires, Argentina; *Int'l*, pg. 1158
Gasparini, Mauro, Gen. Mgr.--Nordson Italia SpA, Milan, Italy; *U.S. Public*, pg. 1189
Gasparkova, Jindrinska, Mng. Dir.--ISS Servisystem s.r.o., Prague, Czech Republic; *Int'l*, pg. 657
Gasparutti, Daniel, Mng. Dir.--Ferro de Venezuela, C.A., Valencia, Venezuela; *U.S. Public*, pg. 619
Gasper, Dick M., Pres.--North Star Print Group Inc., Milwaukee, WI; *U.S. Private*, pg. 601
Gasper, Joseph J., Pres.--Nationwide Life Insurance Co., Columbus, OH; *U.S. Private*, pg. 789
Gasperson, Bill, Pres.--Flowers Baking Co. of West Virginia, Bluefield, WV; *U.S. Public*, pg. 657
Gass, Hans, Mgr.--Sandvik Hard Materials S.A., Epinouze, France; *Int'l*, pg. 1186
Gass, Hans, Mgr.--Sandvik Asia Ltd., Pune, India; *Int'l*, pg. 1187
Gassert, H., Dr., Chm. Bd.-Gerhard Grp.--Asea Brown Boveri Aktiengesellschaft, Mannheim, Germany; *Int'l*, pg. 2
Gassian, Jean-Pierre, Mng. Dir.--Clecim, Cergy-Pontoise, France; *Int'l*, pg. 774
Gassner, Ernst-Peter, Representative--Allianz Lebensversicherung (Schweiz) AG, Vaduz, Liechtenstein; *Int'l*, pg. 59
Gassner, Ernst-Peter, Representative--Allianz Versicherung (Schweiz) AG, Vaduz, Liechtenstein; *Int'l*, pg. 60
Gassner, Rudolf, Div. V.P.--AMP Capital Goods, Harrisburg, PA; *U.S. Public*, pg. 7
Gastiaux, G., Mng. Dir.--De Vaderlandsche Spaarbank N.V., Antwerp, Belgium; *Int'l*, pg. 648
Gastineau, Herve, Co-Mgr.--Etoile Bleue, Nantes, France; *Int'l*, pg. 600
Gastman, T.R., Chm. Bd.--Florida Division, Saint Petersburg, FL; *U.S. Public*, pg. 509
Gaston, Gerald N., Chm. Bd. & Chief Oper. Officer--American Bankers Insurance Co. of Florida, Miami, FL; *U.S. Public*, pg. 67
Gaston, Gerald N., Chm. Bd. & Chief Oper. Officer--American Bankers Life Assurance Co. of Florida, Miami, FL; *U.S. Public*, pg. 67
Gaston, Gerald N., Chief Exec. Officer--Voyager Indemnity Insurance Company, Fort Worth, TX; *U.S. Public*, pg. 68
Gaston, Gerald N., Chm. Bd.--Voyager Service Warranties, Inc., Fort Worth, TX; *U.S. Public*, pg. 68
Gaston, Gerald N., Chief Exec. Officer--Voyager Life Insurance Company, Fort Worth, TX; *U.S. Public*, pg. 68
Gatehouse, Ian R., Chief Oper. Officer--Mead Packaging Ltd., Bristol, United Kingdom; *U.S. Public*, pg. 1077
Gatehouse, Rihcard, Pres.--Halsey Taylor, Oak Brook, IL; *U.S. Private*, pg. 372
Gates, Adrian, Mng. Dir.--Fotolab Limited, London, United Kingdom; *Int'l*, pg. 1389
Gates, Bill, Mgr.-Service Center--Barber Industries Ltd.-Service Center, Slave Lake, Canada; *Int'l*, pg. 164
Gates, H., Sls. Mgr.--North Killingholme Cargo Terminal, Killingholme, United Kingdom; *Int'l*, pg. 1251
Gates, John, Pres.--Lancaster Foods, Inc., Jessup, MD; *U.S. Private*, pg. 487
Gates, Robert W., Jr., Pres.--R & R Uniforms, Nashville, TN; *Int'l*, pg. 635
Gates, Walter, Pres. & Chief Exec. Officer--THORN Americas, Wichita, KS; *Int'l*, pg. 1385
Gatewood, Dudley, Dir.-Florescent Opers.--Metalux Lighting, Americus, GA; *U.S. Public*, pg. 443
Gathman, David D., Chief Oper. Officer--Integrated Systems Consulting Group, Wayne, PA; *U.S. Public*, pg. 1425
Gathright, Jack, Pres.--Graysonia, Nashville & Ashdown Railroad Co., Nashville, AR; *Int'l*, pg. 628
Gathright, Richard E., Pres. & Chief Exec. Officer--Transmontaigne, Fayetteville, AR; *U.S. Public*, pg. 1631
Gati, George, Gen. Mgr.--Kent Plant, Kent, OH; *U.S. Private*, pg. 1044
Gatlin, James, Reg. V.P.--Union-Transport Corporation-Memphis Office, Memphis, TN; *U.S. Private*, pg. 1119
Gatlin, Wade, Plant Mgr.-Griffin--Tread Rubber Plant, Chino, CA; *U.S. Public*, pg. 177
Gatti, R., Pres. & Chief Oper. Officer--IG Autotrim, Inc., Chicago, IL; *Int'l*, pg. 1117
Gattis, Jerry D., Pres. & Chief Oper. Officer--Cagle's Farms Inc., Dalton, GA; *U.S. Public*, pg. 292
Gatto, Vincent, Acting Mng. Dir.--Wormald Holdings N.Z. Limited, New Lynn, New Zealand; *U.S. Public*, pg. 1651
Gatto, Vincent, Acting Mgr.--Grinnell Asia Pacific Pty Limited, Chatswood, Australia; *U.S. Public*, pg. 1651
Gaubier, Alain, Sr. V.P.--Dumez-GTM, Singapore, Singapore; *Int'l*, pg. 823
Gaucher, Michel, Chm. Bd. & Chief Exec. Officer--Steinberg Inc., Montreal, Canada; *Int'l*, pg. 1272
Gauci, Peter, Gen. Mgr.--Dictaphone International AG, Killwangen, Switzerland; *U.S. Private*, pg. 1045
Gaudenzi, D., Mgr.--M&N Valve, Benicia, CA; *Int'l*, pg. 1449
Gaudig, Frieder, Mgr.-Facilities--Cardiotron Medizintechnik GmbH, Halle, Germany; *U.S. Public*, pg. 1083
Gaudin, Jean-Luc Viard, Gen. Mgr.--Grapheme Inc., Montreal, Canada; *Int'l*, pg. 336
Gauger, Hans Siegfried, Mng. Dir.--ITT Flygt GmbH, Langenhagen, Germany; *U.S. Public*, pg. 860
Gauldin, John E., III, Chm. Bd.--First Tennessee Bank - Dyersburg, Dyersburg, TN; *U.S. Public*, pg. 639
Gaullier, J.P., Pres.--Gan Sante, Paris, France; *Int'l*, pg. 565
Gault, Bob, Chief Oper. Officer & Exec. V.P.--Universal Studios Japan, Ltd., Tokyo, Japan; *Int'l*, pg. 1216
Gaultney, Bruce, Exec. Editor--Ocala Star-Banner, Ocala, FL; *U.S. Public*, pg. 1175
Gaunt, James R., Pres.--The Fifth Third Bank of Kentucky, Paris, KY; *U.S. Public*, pg. 621
Gaunt, Joseph P., Pres.--NationsBank of Lebanon, Lebanon, MO; *U.S. Public*, pg. 1164
Gauntlett, M.V., Chm.--Aston Martin Lagonda Group Limited, Newport Pagnell, United Kingdom; *U.S. Public*, pg. 665
Gauss, Cal, Pres.--Boye Needle, Chicago, IL; *U.S. Private*, pg. 1192
Gauss, Cal, Pres.--EZ International, West Warren, MA; *U.S. Private*, pg. 1192
Gaussmann, Peter, Chief Oper. Officer--NIFE GmbH Stromversorgungssysteme, Berlin, Germany; *Int'l*, pg. 54
Gauthier, Carl P., V.P. & Gen. Mgr.--Paramount Development Assocs., Inc., Framingham, MA; *U.S. Public*, pg. 1278
Gauthier, Noel, Pres.--SNECMA Services International (SSI), Paris, France; *Int'l*, pg. 1166
Gauthier, Pierre, Plant Mgr.--Elkem Chicoutimi, Chicoutimi, Canada; *Int'l*, pg. 448
Gauthier, Raoul J., Gen. Mgr.--PCS Potash - Allan, Allan, Canada; *Int'l*, pg. 1064
Gauthier, Robert, Chief Oper. Officer--Lafarge Aluminates Co. Ltd., Grays, United Kingdom; *Int'l*, pg. 790
Gautier, C., Gen. Mgr.--ING Baring Securities (France), Paris, France; *Int'l*, pg. 650
Gautier, Jean-Bernard, Chief Oper. Officer--Rhone-Poulenc Belgique S.A., Brussels, Belgium; *Int'l*, pg. 1112
Gautier, Robert, V.P. & Mgr.--Bank of America (Jersey) Ltd., Saint Helier, United Kingdom; *U.S. Public*, pg. 182
Gautier, Tony, Gen. Mgr.--Reed Exhibition Companies-The Netherlands, Amsterdam, Netherlands; *Int'l*, pg. 1097
Gauvin, Ray, V.P. & Gen. Mgr.--Baldwin Dampening Systems, Naugatuck, CT; *U.S. Public*, pg. 170
Gauvreau, Paul R., Pres.--Pittway Real Estate, Wesley Chapel, FL; *U.S. Public*, pg. 1306
Gavazzi, Dr. Roberto, Chm.--Continentale Allgemeine Versicherungs-AG, Zurich, Switzerland; *Int'l*, pg. 61
Gavazzi, Michele, Dir.--Banca d'America e d'Italia S.p.A. (Bologna), Bologna, Italy; *Int'l*, pg. 403
Gavazzi, Roberto, Pres.--Allianz Via Assurances, Charenton-le-Pont, France; *Int'l*, pg. 60
Gavazzi, Roberto, Dr., Pres.--Allianz Subalpina S.p.A., Turin, Italy; *Int'l*, pg. 60
Gavazzi, Roberto, Dr., Pres.--Allianz Via Vie-Compagnie d'Assurances sur la Vie, Charenton-le-Pont, France; *Int'l*, pg. 60
Gavazzi, Roberto, Dr., Pres. Dir. Gen.--Compagnie Generale de Prevoyance, Strasbourg, France; *Int'l*, pg. 60
Gavazzi, Roberto, Dr., Gen. Dir.--ELVIA Versicherungen, Zurich, Switzerland; *Int'l*, pg. 60
Gavazzi, Roberto, Dr., Pres. Dir. Gen.--Rhin et Moselle Assurances Compagnie d' Assurances sur la vie Societe Anonyme, Strasbourg, France; *Int'l*, pg. 61
Gavazzi, Roberto, Dr., Chm.--Continental Lebensversicherungsgesellschaft, Zurich, Switzerland; *Int'l*, pg. 61
Gavelin, Bengt, Gen. Mgr.--Elkem Sverige, Stockholm, Sweden; *Int'l*, pg. 447
Gavin, Michael P., Pres.--Atlantic Federal Savings Bank, Baltimore, MD; *U.S. Public*, pg. 1543
Gavin, Sara, Mng. Dir.--Shandwick Minneapolis, Minneapolis, MN; *Int'l*, pg. 1227
Gavlinski, T.P., Mgr.--Morton Chemical Div., Paterson, NJ; *U.S. Public*, pg. 1135
Gawler, David, Mng. Dir.--Trafalgar House Group Services Ltd., London, United Kingdom; *Int'l*, pg. 773
Gawlik, Rick, Pres.--SierraCom, Hopkinton, MA; *U.S. Private*, pg. 999
Gawronski, Robert A., National Sls. Mgr.--Alumax Primary Materials Management National Sales Office, Mentor, OH; *U.S. Public*, pg. 60
Gay, Andrew J., Chm. Bd. & Chief Exec. Officer--Drake & Scull Engineering Ltd., Kew Bridge, United Kingdom; *U.S. Public*, pg. 572
Gay, B.R., Pres.--Bard Interventional Products, Tewksbury, MA; *U.S. Public*, pg. 189
Gay, Cynthia, Sr. V.P.--Allan Schneider Associates, Southampton, NY; *U.S. Private*, pg. 971
Gay, P., Mng. Dir.--Glenco SA, Paris, France; *Int'l*, pg. 536
Gay, Tan Chen, Mng. Dir.--Ssangyong Cement (Singapore) Ltd., Singapore, Singapore; *Int'l*, pg. 1293
Gay, Tan Cheng, Pres.--Pacific Technology Private ltd., Singapore, Singapore; *Int'l*, pg. 1292
Gay, W. Ross, Mktg. Mgr.--Bleached Board Folding Carton Div., Newark, DE; *U.S. Public*, pg. 1762
Gayle, Norman W., III, Pres. & Chief Exec. Officer--The Shelby Insurance Companies, Shelby, OH; *U.S. Public*, pg. 1718
Gaynor, Dan, Pres. & Publisher--The St. Catharines Standard, Saint Catharines, Canada; *Int'l*, pg. 631
Gaynor, Jim, V.P. & Gen. Mgr.--Spectrum Control Technology Inc., New Orleans, LA; *U.S. Public*, pg. 1497
Gaytan, James, Pres.--Cigna Reaseguros, S.A., Panama, Panama; *U.S. Public*, pg. 364
Gaytan, James, Pres.--Cigna de Venezuela Intermediarios de Reaseguros, S.A., Caracas, Venezuela; *U.S. Public*, pg. 364
Gazmararian, Dickran, Mng. Dir.--Mase Westpac Limited, London, United Kingdom; *Int'l*, pg. 1497
Gazpio, F., Mng. Dir.--Comercial Papelera Aldi S.A., Madrid, Spain; *Int'l*, pg. 886
Gazzola, D., V.P. & Gen. Mgr.--WD-40 Products (Canada) Ltd., Etobicoke, Canada; *U.S. Public*, pg. 1726
Gburek, John, Pres.--Precision Imaged Products Group, Tully, NY; *U.S. Public*, pg. 162
Ge'de'on, Tony, Chief Oper. Officer--Ahlstrom Machinery Canada Inc., Saint Laurent, Canada; *Int'l*, pg. 35
Gea, Jerry, V.P.--Olympic Steel - Philadelphia Division, Lester, PA; *U.S. Public*, pg. 1221
Gear, Charles W., Pres. & Dir.--NEC Research Institute, Inc., Princeton, NJ; *Int'l*, pg. 900
Gearhart, Greg, Plant Mgr.--Vernay Manufacturing, Inc., Griffin, GA; *U.S. Private*, pg. 1137
Gearon, Colin, Mng. Dir.--Xyvision Limited, Slough, United Kingdom; *U.S. Public*, pg. 1787
Gebbe, Rainer, Mng. Dir.--CB Beteiligungs Und Verwaltungsgesellschaft mbH, Frankfurt/Main, Germany; *U.S. Public*, pg. 339
Gebert, K. R., Pres.--Dickerson Realty Florida, Inc., Stuart, FL; *U.S. Private*, pg. 331
Gebhardt, Christian, Pres.--Neuwiesen Immobilien AG, Winterthur, Switzerland; *Int'l*, pg. 1305
Gebhardt, Scott W., Pres. & Chief Exec. Officer--PG&E Energy Services, San Francisco, CA; *U.S. Public*, pg. 1241
Gebhart, Jeff, Branch Mgr.--Broughton Foods Company, Old Washington, OH; *U.S. Public*, pg. 260
Gebler, David, Pres.--United States Airlease, Incorporated, San Francisco, CA; *U.S. Public*, pg. 664
Gebler, David B., Chief Oper. Officer--Airlease Management Services, Inc., San Francisco, CA; *U.S. Public*, pg. 33
Geddes, James H., Pres. & Chief Oper. Officer--Barnett International/PAREXEL, Media, PA; *U.S. Public*, pg. 1258
Geddes, John W.H., Chief Oper. Officer--Dresser Wheatley Division, Calgary, Canada; *U.S. Public*, pg. 529
Gedge, D., Pres.--Deep Sea Clam Company Limited, Lunenburg, Canada; *Int'l*, pg. 909
Gee, David, Pres. & Chief Exec. Officer--Marsulex Inc., North York, Canada; *Int'l*, pg. 599
Gee, Helen, Mng. Dir.--Shandwick North Ltd., Manchester, United Kingdom; *Int'l*, pg. 1227
Gee, Robert, Mgr.-Plant & Sls.--Golden Sun Feeds, Inc., Estherville, IA; *U.S. Private*, pg. 895
Geener, Anthony, Chief Exec. Officer--Guinness Enterprises Ltd., London, United Kingdom; *Int'l*, pg. 412
Geer, Charles, Gen. Mgr.--Wichita Cessna Learning Center, Wichita, KS; *U.S. Public*, pg. 219
Geer, P.C., Dir.-Asean--Barclays Bank PLC, Singapore, Singapore; *Int'l*, pg. 165
Geerst, Frank, Chief Oper. Officer--Axel Johnson & Co. N.V. Marin Division, Antwerp, Belgium; *Int'l*, pg. 711
Geerts, F., Gen. Mgr.--Muller Liner Agencies N.V., Antwerp, Antwerp, Belgium; *Int'l*, pg. 682
Geggie, Thomas H., Pres.--Cardinal Redevelopment Corporation, Dearborn, MI; *U.S. Public*, pg. 663
Gehl, William D., Pres.--Gehl Power Products, Inc., Yankton, SD; *U.S. Public*, pg. 704
Gehr, John, Gen. Mgr.--Frontier Communications of Pennsylvania, Inc., New Holland, PA; *U.S. Public*, pg. 684
Gehrels, J., Chief Oper. Officer--Siemens plc, Sunbury, United Kingdom; *Int'l*, pg. 1247
Gehrig, B. Dr., Mng. Dir.--Cantrade Private Ltd., Zurich, Switzerland; *Int'l*, pg. 1439
Gehring, Fred, Pres.--Cargo Furniture & Accents, Fort Worth, TX; *U.S. Public*, pg. 1561
Gehrlein, Edward J., Pres. & Chief Oper. Officer--Bedford Associates, Inc., Norwalk, CT; *Int'l*, pg. 219
Gehrmann, Dieter, Dr., Co-Chief Oper. Officer--S-Beteiligungsgesellschaft Hessen- Thuringen mbH, Frankfurt/Main, Germany; *Int'l*, pg. 799
Geier, Mitch, Plant Mgr.--Dayton Superior Corporation, Orlando, FL; *U.S. Private*, pg. 932
Geiger, Claudio, Pres. & Dir.--Sherwin-Williams do Brasil Industria e Comercio Limitada, Sao Paulo, Brazil; *U.S. Public*, pg. 1466
Geiger, James, Chief Oper. Officer--The Universal Steel Co., Cleveland, OH; *U.S. Private*, pg. 256
Geiger, James, Chief Oper. Officer--Universal Steel of Pennsylvania, Conshohocken, PA; *U.S. Private*, pg. 256

Geiger, Julian R., Pres.--Aeropostale/Charter Club, New York, NY; *U.S. Public*, pg. 618

Geiger, Karl, Pres.--Dennison Transoceanic Corporation, Rogersville, TN; *U.S. Public*, pg. 153

Geiger, Paul, Mill Mgr.--Gien Mill, Gien, France; *U.S. Public*, *pg. 673*

Geiger, S.C., Div. Mgr.--Curtis 1000, Inc., West Hartford, CT; *U.S. Public*, pg. 70

Geiger, W., Pres.--Carole Fabrics Corp., Martinez, GA; *Int'l*, pg. 639

Geillochet, Bertran, V.P. & Gen. Mgr.--NIKE France S.A.R.L., Saint Ouen-l'Aumone, France; *U.S. Public*, pg. 1184

Geiman, Edgar, Gen. Mgr.--Michigan CA-TV Company, Sturgis, MI; *U.S. Public*, pg. 287

Geis, Kevin Z., Pres.--Brenton Savings Bank, FSB, Ames, IA; *U.S. Public*, pg. 251

Geiser, Edgar, Mng. Dir.--SMH (UK) Ltd., Eastleigh, United Kingdom; *Int'l*, pg. 1161

Geiser, Gerhart, Mgr.--American Fabrics Co., Bogalusa, LA; *U.S. Private*, pg. 53

Geisinger, Norbert, Mng. Dir.--Packard Elektrik Sistemleri Limited Sirketi, Istanbul, Turkey; *U.S. Public*, pg. 723

Geismar, Ulf, Gen. Mgr.--Santander Direkt Bank A.G., Frankfurt/Main, Germany; *Int'l*, pg. 144

Geiss, Heinz, V.P. & Gen. Mgr.-Charlotte, NC--Colorants & Auxiliaries, Bridgewater, NJ; *Int'l*, pg. 626

Geisselhardt, Emil, Chief Oper. Officer--Walter & Bruynzeel AG, Balterswil, Switzerland; *Int'l*, pg. 444

Geissinger, Frederick W., Chm. Bd., Pres. & Chief Exec. Officer--Yosemite Insurance Co., Evansville, IN; *U.S. Public*, pg. 77

Geissleler, Guanrice, Mng. Dir.--Coates Brothers PLC, Saint Mary Cray, United Kingdom; *Int'l*, pg. 1409

Geissler, Rolf, Branch Mgr.--Klockner-Moeller, Lincoln Park, NJ; *Int'l*, pg. 736

Geitz, W., Chief Oper. Officer--Hoogovens Aluminium GmbH, Dusseldorf, Germany; *Int'l*, pg. 755

Gelain, Ronaldo, Mng. Dir.--The West Company Brasil Ltda., Sao Paulo, Brazil; *U.S. Public*, pg. 1755

Gelber, Abe, Pres.--Forest City Management, Inc., Cleveland, OH; *U.S. Public*, pg. 668

Gelber, Abe, Chief Oper. Officer--Forest City Apartment Mngmt. Div., Cleveland, OH; *U.S. Public*, pg. 668

Gelber, Robert M., V.P. & Gen. Mgr.--Coherent, Inc.-Auburn Group, Auburn, CA; *U.S. Public*, pg. 395

Gelbmann, Christoph, Chief Oper. Officer--Skandia Leben AG, Vienna, Austria; *Int'l*, pg. 1258

Geldart, Scott, Gen. Mgr.--Colgate-Palmolive (Fiji) Ltd., Suva, Fiji; *U.S. Public*, pg. 398

Gelder, James R., Pres.--Washington Square Securities, Minneapolis, MN; *U.S. Public*, pg. 1376

Gelder, Philippe, Liaison Officer--Equinox Communications, Brussels, Belgium; *U.S. Private*, pg. 1152

Geldmacher, Henner, Chm. Bd.--Krupp Hoesch International GmbH, Essen, Germany; *Int'l*, pg. 513

Geldmacher, Horst, V.P.-Overseas Business Dev.--Dexter Europe, Brussels, Belgium; *U.S. Public*, pg. 505

Gelhaus, Paul, Pres.--Figi's, Inc., Marshfield, WI; *U.S. Public*, pg. 623

Geller, Gunter, Mng. Dir.--Deutsche Bank-Kreditbank AG, Berlin, Germany; *Int'l*, pg. 402

Geller, Larry, Pres.--URM Insurance Agency, Spokane, WA; *U.S. Private*, pg. 1114

Geller, Martha Ferro, V.P.-Acct. Services--YAR West, Burlingame, CA; *U.S. Private*, pg. 1195

Geller, Yair, Gen. Mgr.--Geller Nessis/DMB&B Tel Aviv, Tel Aviv, Israel; *U.S. Private*, pg. 304

Gellerstedt, L.L., III, Chm. & Chief Exec. Officer--Beers Construction Company, Atlanta, GA; *Int'l*, pg. 1261

Gelton, Rolf, Gen. Mgr.--Forbo Forshaga AB, Goteborg, Sweden; *Int'l*, pg. 497

Gemine, Robert, Dir. General--Alpha Life SA, Brussels, Belgium; *Int'l*, pg. 546

Gemmel, Charlotte, Chief Exec. Officer--Creative Publications, Mountain View, CA; *U.S. Private*, pg. 288

Gemmel, Douglas, Mng. Dir.--Meggitt Avionics, Fareham, United Kingdom; *Int'l*, pg. 853

Gemmel, William A., Gen. Mgr.--Bank of Boston, Seoul, Korea; *U.S. Public*, pg. 184

Genard, Michel, Dir.--Integrated Systems, Inc., S.A., Jouy-en-Josas, France; *U.S. Public*, pg. 886

Gencade, Antonio, Pres.--AlliedSignal Materiaux de Friction S.A., Barcelona, Spain; *U.S. Public*, pg. 54

Gendebien, Louis, Mng. Dir.--BDDP Belgique, Brussels, Belgium; *Int'l*, pg. 117

Gendron, Bruce, Admin.--Bancroft House Healthcare, Worcester, MA; *U.S. Public*, pg. 1711

Gendron, Bruce, Admin.--Hanover Terrace Healthcare, Hanover, NH; *U.S. Public*, pg. 1713

Gendron, Michel, Dir.--Mil Intermodal, Levis, Canada; *Int'l*, pg. 385

Gendron, William T., V.P. & Gen. Mgr.--Thomas Lighting-C&I Outdoor Division, San Leandro, CA; *U.S. Public*, pg. 1599

Geneczko, Robert M., V.P.--Pennsylvania Power & Light Company-Susquehanna Div., Montoursville, PA; *U.S. Public*, pg. 1244

Genetempo, John, Pres.--ADT Security Systems Southwest, Dallas, TX; *U.S. Public*, pg. 1649

Gengenbach, Benno, Co-Pres.--Schroff, Straubenhardt, Germany; *U.S. Public*, pg. 1274

Genier, Bob, Pres.--Atwood & Morrill Co., Inc., Salem, MA; *Int'l*, pg. 1489

Genin, Claude, Gen. Mgr.--Hexcel (Lyon) S.A., Villeurbanne, France; *U.S. Public*, pg. 824

Gennaro, Ellen M., Mgr.-West Coast--Los Angeles Division, Los Angeles, CA; *U.S. Public*, pg. 1613

Genoud, Michel, Mgr.-Opers.--Woodward-Clyde International, Lyon, France; *U.S. Public*, pg. 1658

Genova, Ricardo, Mgr.-Office--Woodward-Clyde/Limnos, S.A. Barcelona, Barcelona, Spain; *U.S. Public*, pg. 1658

Genovese, Anthony, Exec. V.P.--HRH Construction Interiors, Inc., New York, NY; *U.S. Private*, pg. 1035

Genovese, Peter J., Chm. Bd. & Chief Exec. Officer--United Missouri Bank of St. Louis, Saint Louis, MO; *U.S. Public*, *pg. 1655*

Genovese, Rocco C., Pres. & Chief Exec. Officer--Burke Flooring Products Div., San Jose, CA; *U.S. Private*, pg. 183

Genovese, Rocco C., Pres. & Chief Exec. Officer--Custom Process, San Jose, CA; *U.S. Private*, pg. 183

Genrich, Hans-Dieter, Pres.--EFEKA Friedrich & Kaufmann GmbH & Co., Isernhagen, Germany; *U.S. Public*, pg. 81

Gensior, Eckehard, Co-Chief Oper. Officer--BHF & IKB Baumanagement GmbH, Dusseldorf, Germany; *Int'l*, pg. 645

Gentil, F.B., Gen. Mgr.--ING Bank Sao Paulo, Sao Paulo, Brazil; *Int'l*, pg. 649

Gentil, F.B., Gen. Mgr.--ING Baring Corretora de Valores Mobiliaros, Sao Paulo, Brazil; *Int'l*, pg. 649

Gentil, F.B., Gen. Mgr.--ING Guilder, Sao Paulo, Brazil; *Int'l*, *pg. 650*

Gentil, F.B., Gen. Mgr.--Regional Office South Latin America, Sao Paulo, Brazil; *Int'l*, pg. 651

Gentine, Larry, Pres.--Sargento Foods Inc.- Food Service Div., Plymouth, WI; *U.S. Private*, pg. 966

Gentine, Lee, Pres. & Chief Exec. Officer--Sargento Foods Inc., Plymouth, WI; *U.S. Private*, pg. 966

Gentles, G., Gen. Mgr.--Lafarge Platreurope S.A., Isle-sur-la-Sorgue, France; *Int'l*, pg. 788

Gentles, R.G., Pres. & Mng. Dir.--Blue Circle America Inc., Marietta, GA; *Int'l*, pg. 197

Gentry, Frank, Pres.--Harbor Financial/New America, Walnut Creek, CA; *U.S. Public*, pg. 644

Gentry, Gary, Dir.-Mktg.--Seagate Control Data, Oklahoma City, OK; *U.S. Public*, pg. 1450

Gentry, Marvin D., Chm. Bd. & Pres.--New Fortis Corp., King, NC; *U.S. Public*, pg. 843

Gentry, W., Pres.--ALTO Papers Company, Carrollton, TX; *U.S. Private*, pg. 164

Geoffrey, Vincent, Chief Oper. Officer--Sherle Wagner International, Inc., New York, NY; *U.S. Public*, pg. 1054

Geoga, Doug, Pres.--Hyatt Hotels Corporation, Chicago, IL; *U.S. Private*, pg. 551

Georg, Rudolf, Pres.--Mannesmann Pipe & Steel Corp., Houston, TX; *Int'l*, pg. 838

Georgalos, Juan Pablo, Gen. Mgr.--Topps Argentina S.A., Buenos Aires, Argentina; *U.S. Public*, pg. 1622

George, Boyd L., Pres.--Capital Resources, Inc., Hickory, NC; *U.S. Private*, pg. 657

George, Boyd L., Pres.--Merchants Transport of Hickory, Hickory, NC; *U.S. Private*, pg. 657

George, D. T., Plant Mgr.--Case CE Div.-Wausau, Wausau, WI; *U.S. Public*, pg. 311

George, D. T., Plant Mgr.--Case CE Wichita Div., Wichita, KS; *U.S. Public*, pg. 311

George, David, Mgr.--Friona Feed Yard, Friona, TX; *U.S. Private*, pg. 429

George, Dennis, Pres. & Gen. Mgr.--Bridgestone/Firestone Information Services Company, Akron, OH; *Int'l*, pg. 213

George, Gordon, Mng. Dir.--Elida Faberge, Kingston upon Thames, United Kingdom; *Int'l*, pg. 1434

George, H.D., Mgr.--Tencarva Machinery Co., Greer, SC; *U.S. Private*, pg. 1076

George, John W., Pres.--Autocon Technologies, Inc., Farmington, MI; *U.S. Public*, pg. 850

George, Keith L., Pres.--Grolier Interstate, Inc., Danbury, CT; *Int'l*, pg. 794

George, Laurie, Chief Mgr.--Westpac Banking Corp. - Taiwan, Taipei, Taiwan; *Int'l*, pg. 1497

George, Leslie, Jr., Chief Exec. Officer--Distributor Concepts, Ann Arbor, MI; *U.S. Private*, pg. 620

George, Richard, V.P.--Bergen Brunswig Medical Corporation, Birmingham, AL; *U.S. Public*, pg. 214

George, Robert, Pres.--Pioneer Snacks, Farmington Hills, MI; *U.S. Private*, pg. 730

George, Thomas D., Pres.--Motorola Semiconductor Products Sector, Phoenix, AZ; *U.S. Public*, pg. 1137

Georges-Picot, Bruno, Chm. Bd.--Banque Indosuez Luxembourg, Luxembourg, Luxembourg; *Int'l*, pg. 314

Georges, Francois M., Pres.--Elf Aquitaine Asphalt, Inc., Saint Louis, MO; *Int'l*, pg. 445

Georgescu, Dino, Mng. Dir.--American Appraisal Italia S.r.l., Milan, Italy; *U.S. Private*, pg. 50

Georgi, Peter, Mng. dir.--Georg Fischer, Inc., Lavalle, Argentina; *Int'l*, pg. 488

Georgiades, Vankelis, Chief Exec. Officer--Geo-Young & Rubicam, Athens, Greece; *U.S. Private*, pg. 1199

Georgiadis, Gus P., Pres.--Alliance Ventures, Inc., Pittsburgh, PA; *U.S. Private*, pg. 529

Georgine, R.A., Chm. & Chief Exec. Officer--Trust Fund Advisors, Inc., Washington, DC; *U.S. Private*, pg. 1116

Georgine, R.A., Chm. & Chief Exec. Officer--Unioncare, Inc., Washington, DC; *U.S. Private*, pg. 1116

Georgine, R.A., Chm. & Chief Exec. Officer--ULICO Casualty Company, Washington, DC; *U.S. Private*, pg. 1116

Georgine, Robert A., Chm. Bd. & Chief Exec. Officer--The Union Labor Life Insurance Co., Washington, DC; *U.S. Private*, pg. 1116

Georgine, Robert A., Chm. Bd. & Chief Exec. Officer--AMI Capital Inc., Bethesda, MD; *U.S. Private*, pg. 1116

Georgscu, Calin, Mng. Dir.--Young & Rubicam Bucharest, Bucharest, Romania; *U.S. Private*, pg. 1199

Georyer, M., Chief Oper. Officer--Elf Suisse S.A., Geneva, Switzerland; *Int'l*, pg. 446

Gerad, R.P., Pres.--Brunswick Square Ltd., Saint John, Canada; *Int'l*, pg. 230

Geraghty, James, Chief Exec. Officer--TSI Corporation, Milford, MA; *U.S. Public*, pg. 733

Geraghty, Michael, Mng. Dir.--Bank of Ireland (Jersey) Limited, Saint Helier, United Kingdom; *Int'l*, pg. 153

Gerald, Patrick N., Chm. Bd.--First National Bank of Sweetwater, Sweetwater, TX; *U.S. Public*, pg. 633

Geraldino, Pedro, Gen. Mgr. & Sr. V.P.--Chilton Research Services, Radnor, PA; *Int'l*, pg. 1096

Gerard, Hipolito, Pres.--Kaufman y Broad de Mexico SA de CV, Mexico, Mexico; *U.S. Public*, pg. 945

Gerard, Luis, Chm.--Central de Industrias, S.A., Mexico, Mexico; *U.S. Public*, pg. 982

Gerard, Michel, Pres. & Chief Oper Officer--Cegelec, Levallois-Perret, France; *Int'l*, pg. 52

Gerard, S., Pres. & Chief Exec. Officer--Crown Lance, Inc., Stamford, CT; *U.S. Private*, pg. 155

Gerarder, S., Chm. Bd. & Chief Exec. Officer--Crown Lance Italia Srl, Rome, Italy; *U.S. Private*, pg. 155

Gerardi, C., Gen. Mgr.--Square D Co., Harrisburg, PA; *Int'l*, pg. 1208

Gerardin, Yahn, Dir.--BNP Arbitrage, Paris, France; *Int'l*, pg. 163

Gerber, C. Allen, Pres.--Emerald Industries Inc., Florence, KY; *U.S. Public*, pg. 657

Gerber, Ch. Heinz, Gen. Mgr.--American Home Assurance Company New York, Swiss Branch, Zurich, Switzerland; *U.S. Public*, pg. 85

Gerber, Charles J., Jr., Pres.--Alcor Envelope Co., Hamburg, NY; *U.S. Public*, pg. 1666

Gerber, John, V.P.-Sls.--American Drew, Greensboro, NC; *U.S. Public*, pg. 974

Gerber, Kirk B., Pres.--HSC Controls, Buffalo, NY; *U.S. Public*, pg. 1776

Gerber, Lea, Mgr.--Garden Insurance Companies, Gardena, CA; *U.S. Private*, pg. 371

Gerber, M., Chief Oper. Officer--General Engineers Limited, Herzliyya, Israel; *Int'l*, pg. 645

Gerber, S., Pres.--Simon-Atlantico Inc., Emmaus, PA; *Int'l*, pg. 1252

Gerber, William G., M.D., Pres.--Chiron Diagnostics, Emeryville, CA; *U.S. Public*, pg. 350

Gerber, William G., M.D., Pres.--Chiron Diagnostics, Emeryville, CA; *Int'l*, pg. 974

Gerborg, Bengt, Pres.--VWS, Inc., Cleveland, OH; *Int'l*, pg. 440

Gerdelman, John W., Pres.--NetworkMCI Services, Richardson, TX; *U.S. Public*, pg. 1024

Gerdes, Mary, Pres.--Western Nebraska National Bank, North Platte, NE; *U.S. Public*, pg. 629

Gerhard, E.H., Pres.--Crane Defense Systems, Conroe, TX; *U.S. Public*, pg. 456

Gerhardsson, Lars, Mng. Dir.--AB Cerbo, Trollhattan, Sweden; *Int'l*, pg. 1423

Gerhardsson, Peter, Chief Oper. Officer--Novo Nordisk Pharma AB, Malmo, Sweden; *Int'l*, pg. 988

Gerhart, Don, Plant Mgr.--Ervin Amasteel Div., Butler, PA; *U.S. Private*, pg. 382

Gerhart, Phil, Mgr.-Office--Woodward-Clyde, Midvale, UT; *U.S. Public*, pg. 1656

Gerin-Jean, Pierre, Chm. Bd.--Predil-Pertusola, Rome, Italy; *Int'l*, pg. 662

Geringer, Steven I., Pres. & Chief Exec. Officer--PCS Health Systems, Inc., Scottsdale, AZ; *U.S. Public*, pg. 993

Gerke-Doemamann, Moritz, Gen. Mgr.--Marcam Germany GmbH, Dusseldorf, Germany; *U.S. Public*, pg. 1043

Gerlach, John B., Pres.--Waycross Molded Products, Inc., Waycross, GA; *U.S. Public*, pg. 977

Gerlach, John B., Jr., Pres.--Canida Rubber Company, Elkhart, IN; *U.S. Public*, pg. 976

Gerlach, John B., Jr., Pres.--Jackson Corp., Jackson, OH; *U.S. Public*, pg. 977

Gerlach, K., Mng. Dir.--Agfa-Gevaert AG, Leverkusen, Germany; *Int'l*, pg. 174

Gerlach, Manfred, Mng. Dir.--Coron Verlag Monika Schoeller & Co., Lachen, Switzerland; *Int'l*, pg. 1479

Gerlach, N. Erich, Pres.--The Braas Group, Oberursell, Germany; *Int'l*, pg. 1091

Gerlach, N.E., Chief Exec. Officer--Braas GmbH, Oberursell, Germany; *Int'l*, pg. 1091

Gerlach, Thomas B., V.P. & Gen. Mgr.--Turner Construction Co., Seattle, WA; *U.S. Public*, pg. 1645

Germain-Thomas, B., Gen. Mgr.--Volvic, Bourg-la-Reine, France; *Int'l*, pg. 381

Germaine, Robert, V.P.-Opers.--Bickford's Family Restaurants, Brighton, MA; *U.S. Public*, pg. 545

German, Linda Larsen, Pres.--Lizsport Division, New York, NY; *U.S. Public*, pg. 1006

Germann, Karl, Chm.--Stadtmuhle CMZ Zurich, Zurich, Switzerland; *Int'l*, pg. 330

Germano, I., Opers. Mgr.--Square D Company Italia, S.P.A., Arenzano, Italy; *Int'l*, pg. 1209

Germino, Pete, Gen. Mgr.--Arrow/Schweber Electronics, Deerfield Beach, FL; *U.S. Public*, pg. 134

Germosen, Cecilia, Yellow Pages Dir.--Paradigm National Yellow Pages Group, Tampa, FL; *U.S. Private*, pg. 838

Gernert, Douglas P., Chief Oper. Officer & Exec. V.P.--Totes Incorporated, Loveland, OH; *U.S. Private*, pg. 111

Gernow, Per, Chief Oper. Officer--Novo Nordisk A/S, Santurce, PR; *Int'l*, pg. 987

Geronimo, M.R., Pres.--Locus, Inc., State College, PA; *U.S. Public*, pg. 942

Gerrard, Chris, Mng. Dir.--Ciprico Intertnational Ltd., Newbury, United Kingdom; *U.S. Public*, pg. 370

Gerrard, David, Mng. Dir.--Harman Audio, Borehamwood, United Kingdom; *U.S. Public*, pg. 787

Gerrard, Francois, Chm. & Chief Exec. Officer--SIAS - MPA, Paris, France; *Int'l*, pg. 566

Gerrard, Jim, Gen. Mgr.--Frank Paxton Lumber Company, Louisville, KY; *U.S. Private*, pg. 585

Gerretsen, Wob, Chm.--Costain Civil Engineering Ltd., Maidenhead, United Kingdom; *Int'l*, pg. 336

Gerretsen, Wob, Chm. Bd. & Mng. Dir.--Costain Engineering & Construction Limited, London, United Kingdom; *Int'l*, pg. 336

Gerrie, John, Dir.--Shandwick Scotland Ltd., Edinburgh, United Kingdom; *Int'l*, pg. 1226

Gerritsen, A.W., Gen. Mgr.--Look-o-Look BV, Ridderkerk, Netherlands; *Int'l*, pg. 1451

Gerry, Gordon R., Pres.--AGRA International Limited, Oakville, Canada; *Int'l*, pg. 30

Gerry, Mike, Gen. Mgr.--Arrow/Schweber Electronics, Huntsville, AL; *U.S. Public*, pg. 134

Gersh, Gary, Pres.--Capitol Records, Inc., Hollywood, CA; *Int'l*, pg. 428
Gershel, Seth, Sr. V.P. & Publisher--Simon & Schuster Audio, New York, NY; *U.S. Private*, pg. 778
Gershom, P.O., Chief Oper. Officer--GPT Holdings Ltd., London, United Kingdom; *Int'l*, pg. 1248
Gershon, Norman B., Managing Dir.--Oil-Dri S.A., Zurich, Switzerland; *U.S. Public*, pg. 1215
Gerstall, A. Frederick, Pres.--Hidden Valley Coal Company, Los Angeles, CA; *U.S. Public*, pg. 296
Gerstein, Jorg, Pres.--Rudolf Muller & Co. G.m.b.H., Pohlheim, Germany; *Int'l*, pg. 289
Gerstell, A. Frederick, Pres.--CalMat Co. of Arizona, Los Angeles, CA; *U.S. Public*, pg. 295
Gerstell, A. Frederick, Chief Oper. Officer--CalMat of Central California, Los Angeles, CA; *U.S. Public*, pg. 295
Gerstell, A. Frederick, Pres.--Allied Concrete, Inc., Los Angeles, CA; *U.S. Public*, pg. 295
Gerstell, A. Frederick, Pres.--Azusa Rock, Inc., Los Angeles, CA; *U.S. Public*, pg. 295
Gerstell, A. Frederick, Pres.--Kirst Construction Co., Inc., Los Angeles, CA; *U.S. Public*, pg. 296
Gerstell, A. Frederick, Pres.--Rio Norte Este Co., Los Angeles, CA; *U.S. Public*, pg. 296
Gerstell, A. Frederick, Pres.--River Bend Corp., Los Angeles, CA; *U.S. Public*, pg. 296
Gerstell, A. Frederick, Pres.--Sanger Rock and Sand, Los Angeles, CA; *U.S. Public*, pg. 296
Gerstell, A. Frederick, Pres.--Triangle Rocks Products, Inc., Los Angeles, CA; *U.S. Public*, pg. 296
Gerster, Donald, Pres.--Protective Closures Co., Inc., Buffalo, NY; *U.S. Public*, pg. 1045
Gerstl, Cindy B., Exec. Dir.--Northridge Surgery Center, Northridge, CA; *U.S. Public*, pg. 1715
Gerstner, Joseph, Chief Exec. Officer--Duewag AG, Krefeld, Germany; *Int'l*, pg. 1244
Gerstner, R.T., V.P. & Gen. Mgr.--IBM Personal Systems, White Plains, NY; *U.S. Public*, pg. 895
Gertner, Jane S., Pres.--Chocolate Products Co. Ltd., Toronto, Canada; *Int'l*, pg. 1495
Gertz, S., V.P.--PNC Discount Brokerage, Philadelphia, PA; *U.S. Public*, pg. 1242
Gerutti, Giancarlo, Mng. Dir.--ATA S.p.A., Milan, Italy; *Int'l*, pg. 170
Gervais, J. Ronald, Dir.--AlliedSignal Turbocharging & Truck Brake Systems, London, Canada; *U.S. Public*, pg. 53
Gervais, Rene, G.M.--Newport Electronique, S.A.R.L., Trappes, France; *U.S. Private*, pg. 816
Gervais, Russell, Pres.--Silgan Plastic Corp., Chesterfield, MO; *U.S. Public*, pg. 1473
Gervasi, Enrico, Chm., Chief Exec. Officer & Fin. Dir.--Young & Rubicam Italia, S.p.A., Milan, Italy; *U.S. Private*, pg. 1199
Gervasi, Enrico, Chm. & Chief Exec. Officer-Milan--Young & Rubicam Roma SRL, Rome, Italy; *U.S. Private*, pg. 1199
Gerza, Milan, Mng. Dir.--CAC Leasing a.s., Prague, Prague, Czech Republic; *Int'l*, pg. 348
Gescheider, Bruce A., Chm. Bd. & Chief Exec. Officer--Day-Timers, Inc., East Texas, PA; *U.S. Public*, pg. 674
Geschwind, R. McRae, Pres. & Chief Exec. Officer--Southwestern Bell Yellow Pages Inc., Saint Louis, MO; *U.S. Public*, pg. 1415
Geske, Larry D., Pres.--Montana Sun, Inc., Great Falls, MT; *U.S. Public*, pg. 581
Geske, Larry D., Pres.--Energy West Resources, Great Falls, MT; *U.S. Public*, pg. 581
Gespo, R. Garcia, Chief Oper. Officer--Kodak S.A., Barcelona, Spain; *U.S. Public*, pg. 554
Gestaut, Larry, Mng. Dir.--Heraeus De Nora Inc., Union, NJ; *Int'l*, pg. 616
Gestetner, G., Chief Oper. Officer & Mng. Dir.--Aqualisa Products Limited, Westerham, United Kingdom; *Int'l*, pg. 925
Gestin, Jean-Yves, Mgr.-Admin.--Calcia, Guerville, France; *Int'l*, pg. 292
Gething, Chris, Mng. Dir.--Rhone-Poulenc Chemicals Thailand (Ltd.), Bangkok, Thailand; *Int'l*, pg. 1112
Gething, R. Chris, Chief Oper. Officer--May & Baker Nigeria Ltd., Lagos, Nigeria; *Int'l*, pg. 1112
Gette, Anthony R., Pres.--Mentor Urology, Inc., Santa Barbara, CA; *U.S. Public*, pg. 1086
Gettier, Glenn H., Jr., Pres. & Chief Exec. Officer--Southwestern Life Insurance Company, Dallas, TX; *U.S. Private*, pg. 1018
Gettlefinger, Andrew J., Chm. Bd., Pres. & Chief Exec. Officer--Pride Oil Co., Inc., Knoxville, TN; *U.S. Private*, pg. 613
Gettler, Benjamin, Chief Oper. Officer--Vulcan Corporation, Clarksville, TN; *U.S. Public*, pg. 1725
Getty, Mary Ellen, Admin.--Hillhaven-Orange Nursing Center, Durham, NC; *U.S. Public*, pg. 1713
Geul, B., Gen. Mgr.--Kalkzandsteenfabriek Rijsbergen B.V., Huizen, Netherlands; *Int'l*, pg. 1199
Geurts, Red, Gen. Mgr.--ProGold, Wahpeton, ND; *U.S. Private*, pg. 53
Gevers, Walter, Chief Oper. Officer--Datapoint Belgium S.A., Brussels, Belgium; *Int'l*, pg. 384
Geweke, R.A., Mgr.--Citizens Utilities Company, Bullhead City, AZ; *U.S. Public*, pg. 380
Gey, Robert, Pres.--Lincoln Automotive, Saint Louis, MO; *U.S. Public*, pg. 1273
Geyer, Detlef, Mng. Dir.--Knurr-Taunus GmbH, Alfeld, Germany; *Int'l*, pg. 739
Geyer, James P., Gen. Mgr.--Zortman Mining Inc., Zortman, MT; *U.S. Public*, pg. 1269
Geyer, Richard D., Pres.--Williams Bridge Co., Manassas, VA; *U.S. Public*, pg. 1770
Geysen, R., Mgr.-Mktg.--Nourypharma Nederland B.V., Oss, Netherlands; *Int'l*, pg. 44
Gezelius, Goran, Mgr.--AB Sandvik Saws & Tools, Sandviken, Sweden; *Int'l*, pg. 1185
Gezon, David, Pres.--Midwest Mezzanine Fund, Chicago, IL; *Int'l*, pg. 10
Ghaleb, Kahlil, Pres.--Hagglunds Drives SARL, Grenoble, France; *Int'l*, pg. 670
Ghassemian, Mojtaba, Pres.--U.K. Division, Farnborough, United Kingdom; *U.S. Public*, pg. 423
Ghelfi, Brent, Pres.--SunBuilt Homes, Inc., Phoenix, AZ; *U.S. Public*, pg. 323
Ghelfi, Gregg, Pres.--National Security Containers, Phoenix, AZ; *U.S. Public*, pg. 323
Gherardini, Mike, Mng. Dir.--Auburn General Hospital, Auburn, WA; *U.S. Public*, pg. 1696
Ghergo, H. Jorge, Chief Oper. Officer--DeKalb Argentina, S.A., Buenos Aires, Argentina; *U.S. Public*, pg. 493
Ghia, Jitendra R., Pres.--Harza Environmental Services, Inc., Chicago, IL; *U.S. Private*, pg. 509
Ghibellini, Sergio, Dir. Gen.--Allianz Mexico S.A. Compania de Seguros, Mexico, Mexico; *Int'l*, pg. 59
Ghibellini, Sergio, Dir. Gen.--Aseguradora Cuauhtemoc S.A., Mexico, Mexico; *Int'l*, pg. 61
Ghibellini, Sergio, Pres. & Ger. Gen.--Compania Aseguradora Argentina S.A., Buenos Aires, Argentina; *Int'l*, pg. 61
Ghida, Giovanni, Mgr.--Banque Indosuez, Lugano, Switzerland; *Int'l*, pg. 314
Gho, Cesare, Dir.--Banca d'America e d'Italia S.p.A. (Padova), Padua, Italy; *Int'l*, pg. 403
Ghorawat, Sunil, Mng. Dir.--Structural India Private, Limited, Goa, India; *U.S. Public*, pg. 593
Ghosh, Asoke, Mng. Dir.--Prentice-Hall of India Private Ltd., New Delhi, India; *U.S. Private*, pg. 778
Ghouti, Pierre, Dir. & Gen. Mgr.--Dataproducts S.A.R.L., Le Buisson, France; *Int'l*, pg. 621
Giachetti, Edward J., Mng. Dir.--COBE Cardiovascular Inc., Arvada, CO; *Int'l*, pg. 667
Giacometti, Jacques, Chief Fin. Officer--Olivetti (Schweiz) AG, Wallisellen, Switzerland; *Int'l*, pg. 1003
Giacometti, William, Mng. Dir.--SASIB Bakery Holland N.V., Asperen, Netherlands; *Int'l*, pg. 1194
Giacomuzzi-Moore, Lionello, Gen. Mgr.--Letraset Italia Srl, Milan, Italy; *Int'l*, pg. 462
Giallovrakis, George, Gen. Mgr.--Matt Construction Services, Inc., Cleveland, OH; *U.S. Private*, pg. 256
Giambrone, Angelo, Pres.--Unimed Management Services, Burbank, CA; *U.S. Private*, pg. 1118
Giancola, James J., Chm.--Citizens Information Systems, Inc., Evansville, IN; *U.S. Public*, pg. 281
Giangreco, Michael, Publr.--The Napa Valley Register, Napa, CA; *U.S. Public*, pg. 1343
Giannelli, S.P., Pres.--Toromont Process Systems Inc., Malden, MA; *Int'l*, pg. 1401
Giannini, Luigi Petrillo, Chief Oper. Officer--Rubinetterie Mariani S.p.A., Zingonia, Italy; *U.S. Public*, pg. 1055
Giannone, Richard, Pres.--D&Z Microelectronics, Philadelphia, PA; *U.S. Private*, pg. 317
Giannotti, Alberto, Dir.--Banca d'America e d'Italia S.P.A. (Catania), Catania, Italy; *Int'l*, pg. 403
Gianotten, Frans, Pres.--Simon & Schuster International (UK) Limited, Hemel Hempstead, United Kingdom; *U.S. Private*, pg. 778
Gianotten, Frans, Pres.--Simon & Schuster International, Upper Saddle River, NJ; *U.S. Private*, pg. 778
Gianotten, Frans, Chief Oper. Officer--Addison-Wesley Publishers B.V., Amsterdam, Netherlands; *Int'l*, pg. 1027
Giaquinto, Eleanor, Admin.--River Terrace Healthcare, Lancaster, MA; *U.S. Public*, pg. 1714
Giardino, F., Mng. Dir.--Mosler SA de C.D., Mexico, Mexico; *U.S. Private*, pg. 763
Giasson, Jean, Mgr.--Cascades East Angus Inc., East Angus, Canada; *Int'l*, pg. 273
Giayvia, Max, Chief Oper. Officer--Hudson Aviation Services Inc., Delaware, Baltimore, MD; *U.S. Public*, pg. 845
Gibb, Ian Buchan, V.P.--Industra Thermal Service Corporation, New Westminster, Canada; *Int'l*, pg. 74
Gibb, R.G., Pres.--Federal Signal International Ltd., Urbana, IL; *U.S. Public*, pg. 616
Gibb, Richard G., Pres.--Federal Signal Corporation, Signal Div., University Park, IL; *U.S. Public*, pg. 616
Gibb, W.K., Chief Oper. Officer--Aquaconsult S.A. de C.V., Polanco, Mexico; *Int'l*, pg. 474
Gibbes, A.H., Pres. & Treas.--SCANA, Columbia, SC; *U.S. Public*, pg. 1436
Gibbes, Asbury H., Pres.--South Carolina Pipeline Corporation, Columbia, SC; *U.S. Public*, pg. 1436
Gibbins, Roger N., Mng. Dir.--Signfix Ltd., Bristol, United Kingdom; *U.S. Public*, pg. 862
Gibbons, Charles H., Chm. Bd., Pres. & Chief Exec. Officer--Intellisource, Fairfield, CT; *U.S. Public*, pg. 1425
Gibbons, David, Mng. Dir.--Abbott Laboratories Ltd., Maidenhead, United Kingdom; *U.S. Public*, pg. 14
Gibbons, Ronald W., Pres. & Chief Exec. Officer--First National Bank, Harrisburg, IL; *U.S. Public*, pg. 1217
Gibbs, Bryan, V.P. & Mgr.--First National Bank of Edmond, Edmond, OK; *U.S. Public*, pg. 174
Gibbs, C.L., Pres.--Standard Pipe Line Co., San Ramon, CA; *U.S. Public*, pg. 348
Gibbs, Charles W., Pres.--Gibbs Wire & Steel Company of Canada Ltd., Brampton, Canada; *U.S. Private*, pg. 451
Gibbs, David, Pres.--Todd-AO Filmatic Ltd., London, United Kingdom; *U.S. Public*, pg. 1619
Gibbs, H.J., Pres.--Basic Resources, Inc., Dallas, TX; *U.S. Public*, pg. 1587
Gibbs, H.J., Pres.--Chaco Energy Co., Dallas, TX; *U.S. Public*, pg. 1587
Gibbs, James M., Pres.--Marley Pump, Overland Park, KS; *U.S. Public*, pg. 1676
Gibbs, Jarrell, Pres.--TU Services, Dallas, TX; *U.S. Public*, pg. 1588
Gibbs, Mike, Gen. Mgr.--Surplus Warehouse-West Memphis, West Memphis, AR; *U.S. Private*, pg. 120
Gibbs, R., Gen. Mgr.--ANZ Grindlays Bank plc Greece, Athens, Greece; *Int'l*, pg. 99
Giberg, Peter, Chief Exec. Officer--Circle Freight International USA, Lester, PA; *U.S. Public*, pg. 370
Giberson, Cyril, Pres.--McCain Fertilizers Limited, Florenceville, Canada; *Int'l*, pg. 850
Gibert, Peter, Pres.--Circle Freight International (U.S.A.), San Francisco, CA; *U.S. Public*, pg. 370
Gibli, Shoshana, V.P. & Gen. Mgr.--SAR U.S.A. Incorporated, Hackensack, NJ; *U.S. Public*, pg. 125
Giblin, James, Editor & Publr.--Clarion Books, New York, NY; *U.S. Public*, pg. 841
Gibson, Ann, Div. Mgr.--Montana Power Bozeman Div., Bozeman, MT; *U.S. Public*, pg. 1126
Gibson, Brad, Gen. Mgr.--BIC Inc., Downsview, Canada; *Int'l*, pg. 1273
Gibson, C., Mng. Dir.--Builders Merchants--AAH Builders Supplies Limited, Lincoln, United Kingdom; *Int'l*, pg. 591
Gibson, Charles, Gen. Mgr.--Chief Financial Services, Grand Island, NE; *U.S. Private*, pg. 236
Gibson, Chip, Pres. & Publr.--Crown Publishers, Inc., New York, NY; *U.S. Private*, pg. 21
Gibson, Dennis, Pres.--Secoroc Inc., Commerce City, CO; *Int'l*, pg. 96
Gibson, Don, Mgr.--Broken Bow Gas Co., Payson, AZ; *U.S. Public*, pg. 581
Gibson, John R., Pres.--AMPAC Development Company, Las Vegas, NV; *U.S. Public*, pg. 88
Gibson, John R., Pres.--Halotron, Inc., Cedar City, UT; *U.S. Public*, pg. 88
Gibson, John R., Jr., Pres.--American Azide Corporation, Cedar City, UT; *U.S. Public*, pg. 88
Gibson, Mike, Branch Mgr.--Lindenmeyr Munroe, Westbrook, ME; *U.S. Private*, pg. 224
Gibson, P., Mng. Dir.--Hanovia Limited, Slough, United Kingdom; *Int'l*, pg. 589
Gibson, Randy, Pres.--Lockley Manufacturing Division, Danville, VA; *U.S. Private*, pg. 378
Gibson, S. Baily, Chief Exec. Officer--Zurich Life Insurance Company, Dubai, United Arab Emirates; *Int'l*, pg. 1529
Gibson, Shirley, Gen. Mgr.--Johnson County Title Company, Inc., Buffalo, WY; *U.S. Public*, pg. 626
Gibson, Tim, Mng. Dir.--Ohmeda Ltd., Swindon, United Kingdom; *Int'l*, pg. 121
Gibson, Tim, Pres.--New Zealand Milk Products (North Asia) Ltd, Tokyo, Japan; *Int'l*, pg. 923
Gibson, Timothy P.S., Chief Exec. Officer--Alexander & Alexander (Hong Kong) Holdings Ltd., Central, Hong Kong; *U.S. Public*, pg. 117
Gibson, Willis, Warden--Northeast Ohio Correctional Facility, Youngstown, OH; *U.S. Public*, pg. 451
Gicquiaux, Yvon, Chief Oper. Officer--Novo Nordisk Ferment AG, Esentepe, Turkey; *Int'l*, pg. 988
Gidwitz, James G., Pres.--Continental Catalina, Inc., Chicago, IL; *U.S. Public*, pg. 441
Giegerich, John R., Pres.--Kathryn Beich, Inc., Bloomington, IL; *Int'l*, pg. 917
Gielis, Laurent, Chief Oper. Officer--KONE Belgium S.A., Awans, Belgium; *Int'l*, pg. 747
Gielisse, Jan, Gen. Mgr.--Tektronix Holland N.V., Heerenveen, Netherlands; *U.S. Public*, pg. 1567
Gielow, Derry, Gen. Mgr.--Arrow/Schweber Electronics, Tustin, CA; *U.S. Public*, pg. 134
Gierow, Arvid, Pres.--Frigoscandia AB, Helsingborg, Sweden; *U.S. Public*, pg. 606
Gies, Aida, Dir.--WestWayne - Miami, Miami, FL; *U.S. Private*, pg. 1170
Giese, T.P., Grp. Pres.--Ameron Concrete & Steel Pipe (Northern Div.), Tracy, CA; *U.S. Public*, pg. 99
Giese, T.P., Grp. Pres.--Concrete & Steel Pipe Group (Southern Div.), Rancho Cucamonga, CA; *U.S. Public*, pg. 99
Giesecke, Reini, Gen. Mgr.--Sterling Electronics, San Diego, CA; *U.S. Public*, pg. 1051
Giesel, Ronald D., Mng. Dir.--DYWIDAG Systems International, USA, Inc., Long Beach, CA; *Int'l*, pg. 424
Giesen, J.A.W., Mng. Dir.--Hosokawa Micron B.V., Doetinchem, Netherlands; *Int'l*, pg. 636
Gieskes, Hans, Pres. & Chief Exec. Officer--LEXIS-NEXIS, Miamisburg, OH; *Int'l*, pg. 1096
Giesler, Rolf Dieter, Chief Oper. Officer--Electrolux-Constructor GmbH, Siegen, Germany; *Int'l*, pg. 442
Giesler, Rolf-Dieter, Chief Oper. Officer--Electrolux Siegen GmbH, Siegen, Germany; *Int'l*, pg. 442
Gifford, Roger, Head of Unit--Skandinaviska Enskilda Banken, Tokyo, Japan; *Int'l*, pg. 1259
Gifstad, Walther, Pres.--Aker Verdal a.s., Verdal, Norway; *Int'l*, pg. 42
Gigandet, C.F., V.P. & Gen. Mgr.--Industrial Service Div., Saint Louis, MO; *U.S. Public*, pg. 573
Gigandet, C.F., Exec. V.P.--Micro Devices Div., Mansfield, OH; *U.S. Public*, pg. 573
Gigou, Michel, Pres. & Chief Exec. Officer--Mack Trucks, Inc., Allentown, PA; *Int'l*, pg. 1102
Gil Antillon, Oscar Robles, Exec. V.P.--Hylsa Bekaert, Tultitlan, Mexico; *Int'l*, pg. 56
Gil, Dionisio R., Jr., Gen. Mgr.--Gillette (Philippines), Inc., Manila, Philippines; *U.S. Public*, pg. 745
Gil, Fernando Iturriete, Mgr. Gen.--Intercontinental Quimica, S.A. (INTERQUISA), Madrid, Spain; *Int'l*, pg. 323
Gil, Granado J.A., Mgr.--ABN Leasing Espana, S.A., Madrid, Spain; *Int'l*, pg. 11
Gil, R., Reg. Mng. Dir.--EMI Music Group, Madrid, Spain; *Int'l*, pg. 427
Gilbane, Robert V., Pres.--Gilbane Properties, Inc., Providence, RI; *U.S. Private*, pg. 453
Gilbert, Anne, Mng. Dir.--Principal Investment Management Ltd., Sevenoaks, United Kingdom; *Int'l*, pg. 1020
Gilbert, Bob, Pres.--Infinet Operations, Norfolk, VA; *U.S. Private*, pg. 649
Gilbert, Carl A., Pres.--Dravo Lime Company, Pittsburgh, PA; *U.S. Public*, pg. 527
Gilbert, Dave, Pres.--Golin/Harris Communications, Inc., Chicago, IL; *Int'l*, pg. 1226
Gilbert, David, Mng. Dir.--Currys Group plc, Hemel Hempstead, United Kingdom; *Int'l*, pg. 414
Gilbert, Donald M., Pres.--Suffolk Capital Management, New York, NY; *U.S. Public*, pg. 1674

Gilbert, Hans W., Gen. Mgr.--Crown Cork Company (Germany) G.m.b.H., Frankenthal, Germany; *U.S. Public*, pg. 464
Gilbert, Jackson B., Pres.--Banco Espirito Santo Sa. (Bessa), Madrid, Spain; *Int'l*, pg. 142
Gilbert, John, Pres.--Bioplex Corp., Montvale, NJ; *U.S. Public*, pg. 487
Gilbert, John, Pres.--Datascope Collagen Products Division, Montvale, NJ; *U.S. Public*, pg. 487
Gilbert, John F., Sr. V.P.-Opers.--Bolt Research Division, Norwalk, CT; *U.S. Public*, pg. 244
Gilbert, Richard, Pres.--Quartet Manufacturing Co., Skokie, IL; *U.S. Public*, pg. 707
Gilbert, Richard S., Pres.--Kentrox Industries, Inc., Portland, OR; *U.S. Public*, pg. 4
Gilbert, Robert, Mgr.--Somerset Telephone Co., North Anson, ME; *U.S. Public*, pg. 1572
Gilbert, Suzel, Mng. Dir.--SEO Achat d'Espace, Paris, France; *Int'l*, pg. 116
Gilbertson, David, Mng. Dir.--The Lancet Limited, London, United Kingdom; *Int'l*, pg. 1100
Gilbertson, J.E., V.P. & Gen. Mgr.--Metal Division, Dubuque, IA; *U.S. Public*, pg. 654
Gilbertson, John, V.P.--AVX Leaded Products Div., Myrtle Beach, SC; *Int'l*, pg. 775
Gilbertson, John, Mng. Dir.--Ericsson Communications Ltd., Napier, New Zealand; *Int'l*, pg. 1366
Gilbertson, K., Pres.--Brown Shoe Co. of Canada Ltd., Perth, Canada; *U.S. Public*, pg. 262
Gilchrist, Allan, Mng. Dir.--Nokia Products Ltd., Ajax, Canada; *Int'l*, pg. 952
Gilchrist, David M., Jr., Pres.--VP Buildings, Memphis, TN; *U.S. Public*, pg. 972
Gilchrist, David, Jr., Pres. & Chief Oper. Officer--Varco-Pruden Buildings, Memphis, TN; *U.S. Public*, pg. 1677
Gilchrist, Grace, Gen. Mgr.--WXYZ TV - Channel 7 of Detroit, Inc., Southfield, MI; *U.S. Public*, pg. 1448
Gilchrist, Patrick, Mgr.--General Employment Enterprises, Inc., Woodland Hills, CA; *U.S. Public*, pg. 715
Giles, A.H., Pres.--Zinc Products Company, Greeneville, TN; *U.S. Public*, pg. 57
Giles, Glenn, Branch Mgr.--Keane Federal Systems, Rockville, MD; *U.S. Public*, pg. 946
Giles, Peter, V.P. & Gen. Mgr.--Kodak Mass Memory Division, Rochester, NY; *U.S. Public*, pg. 555
Giles, Richard A., Pres.--Jordan's Foods-Westbrook Division, Westbrook, ME; *U.S. Private*, pg. 599
Giles, Rick, Pres.--John Wieland Homes of Jacksonville, Inc., Jacksonville, FL; *U.S. Private*, pg. 1175
Giles, T. Phillipe, Mng. Dir.--A.B. Dick S.A., Brussels, Belgium; *U.S. Private*, pg. 791
Gilgen, Markus, Mgr.-County Franchise--Johnson & Johnson Medical G.m.b.H., Norderstedt, Germany; *U.S. Public*, pg. 931
Gilger, David, Sr. V.P. & Mgr.--Logica Inc., San Francisco, CA; *Int'l*, pg. 814
Gili, Massimo, Rep.--Sanpaolo-Bombay Representative Office, Mumbai, India; *Int'l*, pg. 691
Gilis, Willy, Admin.--Grace S.A., Nanterre, France; *U.S. Public*, pg. 756
Gilje, K.O., Chm., Pres. & Chief Exec. Officer--Esso Norge a.s., Oslo, Norway; *U.S. Public*, pg. 602
Gill, Anthony A., Chm.--Canmakers (Nigeria) Ltd., Ikeja, Nigeria; *U.S. Public*, pg. 463
Gill, Anthony A., Chm.--Crown Cork & Seal Company (Nigeria) Ltd., Ikeja, Nigeria; *U.S. Public*, pg. 464
Gill, David, Mng. Dir.--Fischer & Porter Ltd., Workington, United Kingdom; *Int'l*, pg. 449
Gill, David, Mng. Dir.--RHM Ingredient Supplies Limited, Ossett, United Kingdom; *Int'l*, pg. 1396
Gill, Emanuel, Chm. Bd. & Chief Exec. Officer--Diasonics Ultra Sound, Inc., Santa Clara, CA; *Int'l*, pg. 644
Gill, Emmanuel, Pres. & Chief Exec. Officer--Elbit Computers Ltd., Haifa, Israel; *Int'l*, pg. 644
Gill, James A., Pres.--Citizens Bank and Trust of West Georgia, Carrollton, GA; *U.S. Public*, pg. 1549
Gill, Jerry, V.P.-New Product Devel.--Varco BJ Drilling Systems, Houston, TX; *U.S. Public*, pg. 1709
Gill, Luther, V.P.-Sls.--All Star Gas Co.-Region VIII, Lebanon, MO; *U.S. Private*, pg. 35
Gill, Mark, Pres.-Mktg.--Miramax Films, Inc., New York, NY; *U.S. Public*, pg. 514
Gill, Robert, Mng. Dir.--Nokia Telecommunications NZ Limited, Parnell, New Zealand; *Int'l*, pg. 953
Gill, Robert B., Pres.--Bergen Cable Technologies, Inc., Lodi, NJ; *U.S. Public*, pg. 1056
Gill, Robert B., Pres.--Valpey-Fisher Corporation, Hopkinton, MA; *U.S. Public*, pg. 1056
Gill, Stephen M., Pres.--Wilson USA Inc., Cranford, NJ; *Int'l*, pg. 124
Gill, W.H., Pres.--American Limestone Co., Knoxville, TN; *U.S. Public*, pg. 138
Gillam, T. Scott, Jr., V.P. & Gen. Mgr.--Glen Raven Mills, Inc.-Filament Fabrics Division, Burnsville, NC; *U.S. Private*, pg. 456
Gillard, S.H., Dir. & Gen. Mgr.--G.E.-Thorn Lamps Presscaps Division, Enfield, United Kingdom; *U.S. Public*, pg. 713
Gillenwater, Kelso, Pres. & Publr.--The News Tribune, Tacoma, WA; *U.S. Public*, pg. 1066
Gillenwater, Kelso, Publisher--Tri-City Herald, Pasco, WA; *U.S. Public*, pg. 1066
Gilleo, Peter, Pres.--ABB Energy Ventures Inc., Princeton, NJ; *Int'l*, pg. 4
Giller, James M., Pres. & Chief Exec. Officer--Woodstock National Bank, Woodstock, VT; *U.S. Public*, pg. 187
Gilles, G., Pres.--Micropolish, Greasque, France; *Int'l*, pg. 803
Gillespie, A.W., Hon., Chm. Bd.--National Westminster Bank of Canada, Toronto, Canada; *Int'l*, pg. 911
Gillespie, Bernard M., Pres.--Mobil Solar Energy Corporation, Billerica, MA; *U.S. Public*, pg. 1119
Gillespie, Bill, V.P. & Gen. Mgr.--GAC Color Graphics, Atlanta, GA; *U.S. Public*, pg. 1038
Gillespie, Clyde, V.P.--Alcoa Forged Products, Cleveland, OH; *U.S. Public*, pg. 60
Gillespie, George E., Pres.--Pyron Corp., Niagara Falls, NY; *Int'l*, pg. 1524
Gillespie, George E., Pres.--Pyron Metal Powders, Inc., Greenback, TN; *Int'l*, pg. 1524
Gillespie, Michael, Pres.-Asia--The Lincoln Electric Company (Asia Pacific) Pte. Ltd., Singapore, Singapore; *U.S. Public*, pg. 996
Gillespie, Mike, Reg. Dir.-Asia/Pacific--ESAB Asia/Pacific Pte Ltd., Singapore, Singapore; *Int'l*, pg. 282
Gillespie, Ralph, Pres.--Milliken Industrial Div., Spartanburg, SC; *U.S. Private*, pg. 749
Gillespie, Roger, Admin.--Casa Real Health Care Center, Santa Fe, NM; *U.S. Public*, pg. 838
Gillespie, William, MD, Pres.--Kaiser Permanente, Southwest Division, Dallas, TX; *U.S. Private*, pg. 605
Gillett, Alistair, Mng. Dir.--M/B Interactive, New York, NY; *U.S. Private*, pg. 740
Gillette, E. Peter, Chm. Bd. & Pres.--Piper Trust Company, Minneapolis, MN; *U.S. Public*, pg. 1303
Gillette, Frank, V.P. & Gen. Mgr.--International Operations, Richmond, VA; *Int'l*, pg. 1243
Gillette, Patricia, Mng. Dir.--Brimax Books Limited, Newmarket, United Kingdom; *Int'l*, pg. 1093
Gilley, Gary, Gen. Mgr.--San Diego Auto Auction Inc., Oceanside, CA; *U.S. Public*, pg. 1649
Gilley, Nick R., Gen. Mgr.--Sherman Wire of Caldwell, Inc., Caldwell, TX; *U.S. Public*, pg. 955
Gilli, Davide, Mgr.--UTA Milano SpA, Milan, Italy; *Int'l*, pg. 1509
Gilliam, Doyle, Gen. Mgr.--E.C.B. Brokerage, Jonesboro, AR; *U.S. Private*, pg. 119
Gilliam, Greg, Supervisor-Property & Casualty Claims--Willis Corroon Administrative Services Corporation, Dublin, OH; *Int'l*, pg. 1505
Gilliam, Mike, Warden--Winn Correctional Center, Winnfield, LA; *U.S. Public*, pg. 451
Gillies, Duncan A., Exec. V.P.--Trinity Leasing, Dallas, TX; *U.S. Public*, pg. 1639
Gilligan, Kevin, Pres.-Solutions & Svcs.--Home and Building Control, Minneapolis, MN; *U.S. Public*, pg. 833
Gilligan, Patrick J., Pres.--Nord Photo Engineering, Inc., Minneapolis, MN; *U.S. Public*, pg. 1292
Gillihan, Michael, Gen. Mgr.--Tube Division, Cleveland, OH; *U.S. Public*, pg. 1221
Gillingham, David, Mng. Dir.--New Zealand Milk Products (CIS) AO, Moscow, Russia; *Int'l*, pg. 923
Gillingham, Peter, Gen. Mgr.--ITW Fastex, Basingstoke, United Kingdom; *U.S. Public*, pg. 868
Gillings, Ritson, Mng. Dir.--A. Schulman Inc. Limited, Newport, United Kingdom; *U.S. Public*, pg. 1441
Gillis, A.E., Pres.--Milltronics, Peterborough, Canada; *Int'l*, pg. 1150
Gillis, Derek G., Mgr.-Terminal--Belfast Terminal, Belfast, United Kingdom; *U.S. Public*, pg. 692
Gillis, Robert, Pres. & Chief Exec. Officer--First Vermont Bank & Trust Company, Brattleboro, VT; *U.S. Public*, pg. 187
Gilmore, C.M., Pres.--LumenX Company, Mogadore, OH; *U.S. Public*, pg. 56
Gilmore, Debbie, Clinic Mgr.--Stockbridge, Stockbridge, GA; *U.S. Public*, pg. 1716
Gilmore, Thomas K., Mng. Dir.--Notifier Middle East, Amman, Jordan; *U.S. Public*, pg. 1307
Gilmore, Tom, Gen. Mgr.--National Surface Cleaning-New Jersey Div., Elmwood Park, NJ; *U.S. Public*, pg. 1208
Gilmore, Wanda, Plant Mgr.--Barry Distribution of San Angelo, San Angelo, TX; *U.S. Public*, pg. 192
Gilmour, Alan, Rep.--Sanpaolo-Sydney Representative Office, Sydney, Australia; *Int'l*, pg. 692
Gilmour, J.J., Pres.--Boeing Japan, Tokyo, Japan; *U.S. Public*, pg. 242
Gilmour, L.D., Chief Oper. Officer--Australian Char Holding Pty., Ltd., Prahran, Australia; *Int'l*, pg. 947
Gilotti, Stephen A., Pres.--Textron Financial Corporation, Providence, RI; *U.S. Public*, pg. 1590
Gilpin, Kim, V.P. & Gen. Mgr.--Steelcase Inc./Western Div., Tustin, CA; *U.S. Private*, pg. 1038
Gilreath, Emily, Exec. Editor--BNA Human Resources & Labor Services Div., Washington, DC; *U.S. Private*, pg. 182
Gilroy, Rosalind, Co-Mng. Dir.--International Correspondence Schools (Australasia) Limited, Lane Cove, Australia; *U.S. Public*, pg. 784
Gilson, Bob, Pres.--Anthracite Industries, Inc., Sunbury, PA; *U.S. Private*, pg. 87
Gilstring, Kare, Gen. Mgr.--Storage Technology Sweden, Stockholm, Sweden; *U.S. Public*, pg. 1523
Gilway, B., Chief Exec. Officer--Assurance Company of America, Baltimore, MD; *Int'l*, pg. 1530
Gilway, B., Chief Exec. Officer--Maine Bonding & Casualty Company, Baltimore, MD; *Int'l*, pg. 1530
Gilway, B., Chief Exec. Officer--Maryland Insurance Company, Baltimore, MD; *Int'l*, pg. 1530
Gilway, B., Chief Exec. Officer--National Standard Insurance Company, Baltimore, MD; *Int'l*, pg. 1530
Gilway, B., Chief Exec. Officer--Valiant Insurance Company, Baltimore, MD; *Int'l*, pg. 1530
Gimbus, Thomas, Plant Mgr.--Great Lakes Terminal & Transport of Pennsylvania, Industry, PA; *U.S. Private*, pg. 435
Gimenez, Victor, Gen. Mgr.--Skandia Correduria de Reaseguros SA, Madrid, Spain; *Int'l*, pg. 1256
Gimpel, John, Gen. Mgr.--Hayes-Dana Filter, Fitting & Gasket Div., Ayr, Canada; *U.S. Public*, pg. 480
Ginciene, Marco A., Gen. Mgr.--AMP do Brasil, Sao Paulo, Brazil; *U.S. Public*, pg. 8
Ginestet, Roger, Plant Mgr.--Ethone OMI-Warren, Warren, MI; *U.S. Public*, pg. 138
Gingl, Manfred, Pres. & Chief Exec. Officer--Tesma International Inc., Concord, Canada; *Int'l*, pg. 830
Gingue, R., Mng. Dir.--Alphagary Corporation, Leominster, MA; *Int'l*, pg. 802
Ginman, Tom, Mng. Dir.--Young & Rubicam Finland Oy, Helsinki, Finland; *U.S. Private*, pg. 1199
Ginn, R.J., Jr., Pres.--Southern Plastics Co., West Columbia, SC; *Int'l*, pg. 233
Ginn, Robert M., Pres.--BPI Inc., Kent, WA; *U.S. Public*, pg. 772
Ginnings, Robert M., Pres.--Hekimian Laboratories, Inc., Rockville, MD; *Int'l*, pg. 709
Ginsberg, Allan, Chief Oper. Officer--Empress Handbags, West New York, NJ; *U.S. Public*, pg. 920
Ginsberg, Randy, Pres.--George Rice & Sons, Los Angeles, CA; *U.S. Public*, pg. 1779
Ginsburg, Allan, Chief Oper. Officer--Aetna Handbags, West New York, NJ; *U.S. Public*, pg. 920
Ginsburg, Allan, Chief Oper. Officer--Bonnie International, West New York, NJ; *U.S. Public*, pg. 920
Ginsburg, Allan, Chief Oper. Officer--JLN, West New York, NJ; *U.S. Public*, pg. 920
Ginsburg, Michael, Co-Mgr.--Legion Paper Corporation, New York, NY; *U.S. Private*, pg. 467
Ginter, Michael R., Pres.--First American Bank Wisconsin, Menomonie, WI; *U.S. Private*, pg. 167
Ginter, Piet, Chief Oper. Officer--Boart Longyear GmbH, Celle, Germany; *Int'l*, pg. 76
Ginther, Jim, Sr., Pres.--Firstaff, Inc., Bloomington, MN; *U.S. Public*, pg. 15
Ginwala, Kymus, V.P. & Gen. Mgr.--Northern Research & Engineering Corp., Woburn, MA; *U.S. Public*, pg. 877
Giocopinelli, Enzo, Mng. Dir.-Rome--Armando Testa S.p.A, Rome, Italy; *Int'l*, pg. 1377
Giogio, Robert, Pres.--Day & Zimmermann International, Inc., Philadelphia, PA; *U.S. Private*, pg. 317
Gioia, Craig, Pres.--Zynolyte Products Company, Carson, CA; *Int'l*, pg. 663
Giordano, Joseph, Chm. Bd.--Eastern Sales & Manufacturing, Gloucester City, NJ; *Int'l*, pg. 339
Giordano, Lou, Pres. & Gen. Mgr.--Outdoor Systems, Inc. of New Jersey, Fairfield, NJ; *U.S. Public*, pg. 1235
Giordano, Michael, Mng. Dir.--Fedders Asia Pte. Ltd., Singapore, Singapore; *U.S. Public*, pg. 615
Giordano, Robert R., Pres.--EnergyNorth Natural Gas, Inc., Manchester, NH; *U.S. Public*, pg. 582
Giordano, Ron, Exec. V.P.--H.S. Crocker Co., Inc., Huntley, IL; *U.S. Private*, pg. 290
Giordano, Sal, III, Pres.--Melcor Corporation, Trenton, NJ; *U.S. Public*, pg. 615
Giorgini, Cyril, Mng. Dir.--Auditoire, Paris, France; *Int'l*, pg. 116
Giorgio, Pier, Exec. V.P. & Reg. Mgr.--Bank of America NT&SA, Milan, Italy; *U.S. Public*, pg. 182
Giorgio, Robert J., Pres.--Life Sciences International, Philadelphia, PA; *U.S. Private*, pg. 317
Giosa, P., Chief Oper. Officer--Lee Spring Company, Brooklyn, NY; *U.S. Private*, pg. 1118
Giovannini, Alberto, Mng. Dir.--Premark Italia SpA, Milan, Italy; *U.S. Public*, pg. 1323
Giovannini, Georges, Exec. Mgr.--Ocye S.A., Buenos Aires, Argentina; *Int'l*, pg. 823
Gipson, Hayward R., Pres. & Chief Exec. Officer--Playtex Apparel, Inc., Stamford, CT; *U.S. Public*, pg. 1433
Girard, Henri, Mgr.--Anixter Rouyn, Rouyn-Noranda, Canada; *U.S. Public*, pg. 116
Girard, Richard, Pres.--Fenwal Electronics, Inc., Milford, MA; *U.S. Public*, pg. 1341
Girardi, Romano, Pres.--Portable Air Division, Wilrijk, Belgium; *Int'l*, pg. 96
Giraud, Jacques, Chief Oper. Officer--Club Mediterranee Investissements, Paris, France; *Int'l*, pg. 298
Giraudet, Jean Paul, Pres.--Elf Exploration Inc., Houston, TX; *Int'l*, pg. 445
Girdlestone, Brian A., Pres.-Hoover N.A.--Hoover Company, Canton, OH; *U.S. Public*, pg. 1065
Girling, Adrian, Mng. Dir.--Lloyd Instruments Ltd., Fareham, United Kingdom; *U.S. Public*, pg. 100
Giroldi, S., Pres.--Interappia Publicita S.p.A., Novara, Italy; *Int'l*, pg. 751
Giroletti, Luigi, Pres.--Italiana Luce S.r.l., Settimo Milanese, Italy; *U.S. Public*, pg. 856
Girsault, Herve, Chief Exec. Officer--Gerber France, Taverny, France; *Int'l*, pg. 973
Girsky, Charles, Exec. V.P.--Jaco Electronics, Inc., Westlake Village, CA; *U.S. Public*, pg. 921
Girvin, Phil, Gen. Mgr.--ITW Engineered Polymers Businesses, Danvers, MA; *U.S. Public*, pg. 866
Gisbertz, Maureen, Mgr.--Downey Savings & Loan Association, F.A., Bakersfield, CA; *U.S. Public*, pg. 527
Gisbon, Les, Country Mgr.--Standard Chartered Bank Botswana Limited, Gaborone, Botswana; *Int'l*, pg. 1294
Gisi, John J., Chm. Bd. & Chief Exec. Officer--National Bank of Arizona, Tucson, AZ; *U.S. Public*, pg. 1793
Giske, Arnfinno, Pres. & Chief Exec. Officer--Westwood Shipping Lines, Federal Way, WA; *U.S. Public*, pg. 1764
Gisslin, Jeffrey, Chief Oper. Officer--All Size Corrugated, Lancaster, PA; *U.S. Private*, pg. 177
Gisvold, Rune, Pres.--Kvaerner Venture a.s, Oslo, Norway; *Int'l*, pg. 770
Gittelman, Michael, Mng. Dir.--Florida Medical Center South, Fort Lauderdale, FL; *U.S. Public*, pg. 1577
Gitter, David J., Pres. & Chief Exec. Officer--M & I Bank Fox Valley, Appleton, WI; *U.S. Public*, pg. 1050
Gittins, Stephen N., V.P.-Information Tech.--Manulife Financial, Toronto, Canada; *Int'l*, pg. 840
Gitz, E., Mng. Dir.--Ascom Teletron B.V., Nieuwegein, Netherlands; *Int'l*, pg. 87
Gitz, E., Mng. Dir.--Ascom Hasler BV, Arnhem, Netherlands; *Int'l*, pg. 87
Giubertoni, A., Mng. Dir.--OMRON Electronics S.p.A., Milan, Italy; *Int'l*, pg. 1006
Giudici, Angela, Gen. Mgr.--Bipiemme Fiduciaria Spa, Milan, Italy; *Int'l*, pg. 137
Giuffre, Giuseppe, Mng. Dir.--Giuffre Editore SpA, Milan, Italy; *Int'l*, pg. 1095
Giuliano, Louis J., Pres. & Chief Exec. Officer--ITT Defense & Electronics, Inc., Mc Lean, VA; *U.S. Public*, pg. 859

Giuliano, Louis J., Chm. Bd.--ITT Federal Services Corporation, Colorado Springs, CO; *U.S. Public*, pg. 859
Giulietti, Gary J., Vice Chm.-Eastern Div.--Willis Corroon Construction Svcs. Corp. of CT, Farmington, CT; *Int'l*, pg. 1504
Giuntini, Philip M., Chm.--AMS Operations Corporation, Inc., Lakewood, CO; *U.S. Public*, pg. 86
Giuox, Pierre, Mgr.--SEA, Vernon, France; *Int'l*, pg. 430
Giuria, Alfredo, Pres.--Viceversa/Young & Rubicam, Montevideo, Uruguay; *U.S. Private*, pg. 1200
Giuseppe, Migliorino, Pres.--Termosud S.p.A., Gioia del Colle, Italy; *Int'l*, pg. 653
Given, J.B., Chm. Bd.--Fibras Ceramicas, Inc., Ponce, PR; *Int'l*, pg. 893
Givliano, Klaus, Mgr.--Incor of Alabama, Birmingham, AL; *U.S. Private*, pg. 309
Gjers, A., Mng. Dir.--THORN Svenska AB, Solna, Sweden; *Int'l*, pg. 1386
Glading, D., Chief Oper. Officer--Binks-Bullows (Aust.) Pty, Ltd., Mona Vale, Australia; *U.S. Public*, pg. 229
Gladstone, David, Chm. Bd.--Allied Development Corp., Washington, DC; *U.S. Public*, pg. 48
Gladstone, Margery, Publisher--Fitness, New York, NY; *Int'l*, *pg. 190*
Gladstone, Rea, Pres.--ALLTEL Tennessee, Inc., Powell, TN; *U.S. Public*, pg. 380
Gladys, Kendall, Pres.--International Tool & Supply Company, Inc., Houston, TX; *Int'l*, pg. 684
Glaese, O., Dir.--Raulf Bau GmbH, Gottingen, Germany; *Int'l*, pg. 630
Glah, R.A., Pres.--Alcoa Packaging Machinery, Inc., Englewood, CO; *U.S. Public*, pg. 60
Glaizal, F., Gen. Mgr.--Agnesi SpA, Imperia, Italy; *Int'l*, pg. 380
Glamazdine, Michael, Mng. Dir.--Bettis France, Villemomble, France; *U.S. Public*, pg. 483
Glanville, Peter E., Pres.--Lowry Hill Investment Advisors, Inc., Minneapolis, MN; *U.S. Public*, pg. 1201
Glasco, R.G., Mng. Dir.--UPM-Kymmene Canada, Toronto, Canada; *Int'l*, pg. 1430
Glascock, Tom, Exec. V.P.--B.I. Transportation, Inc., Burlington, NC; *U.S. Public*, pg. 268
Glascott, Benjamin J., Mgr.--Cornhill Insurance PLC, Dublin, Ireland; *Int'l*, pg. 60
Glaser, Gary A., Chm. Bd.--National City Bank, Cleveland, OH; *U.S. Public*, pg. 1154
Glasgow, Andrew, Chm.--International Water Limited, Manchester, United Kingdom; *Int'l*, pg. 1444
Glasner, Ulrich, Reg. Mgr.--Check Point Software Technologies GmbH, Unterfoehring, Germany; *U.S. Public*, pg. 342
Glass, Carol J., Gen. Mgr.--Global Processing & Recycling Group, Shied-Tech Cambridge, Cambridge, Canada; *U.S.* Public, pg. 748
Glass, Curtis, Pres.--Bailey Hats, Fort Worth, TX; *U.S. Private*, pg. 155
Glass, J.A., Gen. Mgr.-Divisional--Bluebird Foods Ltd, Manukau, New Zealand; *Int'l*, pg. 556
Glass, Jean, Gen. Mgr.--Olan Mills Inc. of Ohio, Springfield, OH; *U.S. Private*, pg. 749
Glass, Ryan, Gen. Mgr.--City Meats & Provisions - San Diego, San Diego, CA; *U.S. Private*, pg. 244
Glasse, J.M., Chief Oper. Officer--Columbus Dixon Ltd., Luton, United Kingdom; *Int'l*, pg. 444
Glasson, Keith, Gen. Mgr.--Pioneer Hi-Bred Australia Pty. Ltd., Toowoomba, Australia; *U.S. Public*, pg. 1299
Glatthard, Kaspar, Dir.-Mkt.--ETA S.A. Fabriques D'Ebauches, Grenchen, Switzerland; *Int'l*, pg. 1160
Glauberman, Carl, Chief Oper. Officer--Ozone Industries Inc., Ozone Park, NY; *Int'l*, pg. 113
Glave, F.E., V.P. & Gen. Mgr.--Pulse Communications, Inc., Herndon, VA; *U.S. Public*, pg. 844
Glave, Jan-Gunnar, Pres.--Skanska Anlaggning AB, Malmo, Sweden; *Int'l*, pg. 1260
Glazer, Dennis L., Asst. V.P.--Collective Mortgage Services, Inc., Wilmington, DE; *U.S. Public*, pg. 1528
Glazer, Michael, Pres. & Chief Exec. Officer--Kay-Bee Toy & Hobby Shops, Inc., Pittsfield, MA; *U.S. Public*, pg. 437
Glazewski, Kazimierz, Rep.--Bayerische Landesbank Girozentrale, Warsaw, Poland; *Int'l*, pg. 177
Glazier-Sinkowski, Gayle, Admin.--Willowbrook Manor, Flint, MI; *U.S. Public*, pg. 837
Gleacher, Eric, Chief Oper. Officer--Gleacher Morgan Grenfell Inc., New York, NY; *Int'l*, pg. 405
Gleason, D. H., Pres.--Amfac Property Investment Corp., Lahaina, HI; *U.S. Private*, pg. 577
Gleason, D. H., Pres.--Kaanapali Water Corporation, Lahaina, HI; *U.S. Private*, pg. 578
Gleason, Dana, Pres.--Dana Design, Bozeman, MT; *U.S. Public*, pg. 940
Gleason, Larry, Pres.-Worldwide Theater, Dist.--MGM/UA Distribution Co., Santa Monica, CA; *U.S. Public*, pg. 1102
Gleason, Robert, Pres.--Rottlund Homes of Florida, Inc., Fort Myers, FL; *U.S. Public*, pg. 1406
Gleed, William H., Chief Exec. Officer--The Citadel Assurance Companies, Toronto, Canada; *Int'l*, pg. 346
Gleeman, Marsha, Pres.--MGM/UA Music, Santa Monica, CA; *U.S. Public*, pg. 1102
Gleeson, John, V.P. & Gen. Mgr.--Acme Electronics Division, Cuba, NY; *U.S. Public*, pg. 16
Gleichenstein, Viktor von, Mng. Dir.--Dresdner Bank AG, Melbourne, Australia; *Int'l*, pg. 419
Gleie, Axel, Mng. Dir.--Verlag Der Tagesspiegel, Berlin, Germany; *Int'l*, pg. 1479
Gleim, Richard, Pres.--Federated Fry Metals, Inc., Altoona, PA; *Int'l*, pg. 328
Gleisner, Mark, Pres.--Hayes Brake, Mequon, WI; *U.S. Private*, pg. 299
Gleizes, Jean-Louis, Dir. Gen.--Bayerische Landesbank - Succursale de Paris, Paris, France; *Int'l*, pg. 176
Glen, Suzanne Tang, Mng. Dir.--The Asian Wall Street Journal Weekly, New York, NY; *U.S. Public*, pg. 524
Glendenin, Charles D., Mng. Dir.-Trust & Banking Opers.--American National Bank & Trust Co. of Chicago, Chicago, IL; *U.S. Public*, pg. 628
Glendinning, Paul, Pres.--Glendinning Marine Products, Inc., Conway, SC; *U.S. Public*, pg. 1705
Glenn, Brad, Mng. Dir.--Industrial Rubber Goods, Saint Joseph, MI; *U.S. Private*, pg. 229
Glenn, Leslie, V.P. & Gen. Mgr.--WLVI-TV, Boston, MA; *U.S. Public*, pg. 1636
Glenn, Robert, Gen. Mgr.--Cook Moving Systems, Inc. (Illinois Corporation), Elk Grove Village, IL; *U.S. Private*, pg. 273
Glenn, Robert, Pres.--Morgan Asset Management, Inc., Memphis, TN; *U.S. Public*, pg. 1131
Glenn, Victor, Pres.--Grundy Worldwide, London, United Kingdom; *Int'l*, pg. 1025
Glenne, Tore, Mng. Dir.--Gorud, Oslo, Norway; *Int'l*, pg. 18
Glez del Peral, A., Mng. Dir.--SAB WABCO Dimetal Equipos Ferroviarrios, Madrid, Spain; *Int'l*, pg. 271
Glicker, Al, Gen. Mgr.--Elof Hansson Wood Products, Inc., Los Angeles, CA; *Int'l*, pg. 595
Glickman, Marshall L., Pres. & Mng. Dir.--Jewett International Corp., Buffalo, NY; *U.S. Private*, pg. 952
Gligsberg, Victor, Chief Oper. Officer--Advanced Micro Devices, S.A., Paray-Vielle-Poste, France; *U.S. Public*, pg. 21
Glime, Ronald, Pres.--Warrantech Automotive, Inc., Euless, TX; *U.S. Public*, pg. 1740
Glisson, Britton L., Pres. & Chief Oper. Officer--Essex Insurance Co., Glen Allen, VA; *U.S. Public*, pg. 1046
Glleden, Hans Hermann, Pres.--TrefilARBED Korea Co. Ltd., Yangsan, Korea; *Int'l*, pg. 80
Globerman, Oren, V.P. & Gen. Mgr.--In Stent Israel, Holon, Israel; *U.S. Public*, pg. 1083
Gloor, Rolf, Plant Mgr.--Littelfuse AG, Grenchen, Switzerland; *U.S. Public*, pg. 1001
Glore, Jodie, Pres. & Chief Oper. Officer--Reliance Electric, Cleveland, OH; *U.S. Public*, pg. 1397
Glosser, Roy J., Pres.--American Locker Co., Inc., Jamestown, NY; *U.S. Public*, pg. 86
Glosser, Roy J., Pres.--American Locker Co. of Canada Ltd., Scarborough, Canada; *U.S. Public*, pg. 86
Glosser, Roy J., Pres.--Canadian Locker Co., Ltd., Scarborough, Canada; *U.S. Public*, pg. 86
Glossop, Michael, Mng. Dir.--AP & T Ltd., Oxford, United Kingdom; *U.S. Public*, pg. 620
Glover, G., Jr., Mng. Dir.--Haden Schweitzer Canada Inc., Toronto, Canada; *Int'l*, pg. 586
Glover, Ronald, V.P. & Div. Mgr.--Bindley Western, Carolina Division, Charlotte, NC; *U.S. Public*, pg. 228
Glover, William, Pres. & Gen. Mgr.--TENERA Rocky Flats, LLC, Louisville, CO; *U.S. Public*, pg. 1576
Glowacki, John, V.P. & Gen. Mgr.--General Machinery Co., Millville, NJ; *Int'l*, pg. 68
Glowacki, John, Exec. V.P.--Wheaton Plastic Products, Mays Landing, NJ; *Int'l*, pg. 68
Gluckman, Michael J., Pres. & Chief Exec. Officer--TriStar Ventures Corporation, Wilmington, DE; *U.S. Public*, pg. 403
Gluckstern, S.M., Chief Exec. Officer--Zurich Reinsurance Centre, New York, NY; *Int'l*, pg. 1530
Glueck, Walter, Country Mgr.--Network Systems (Schweiz) AG, Zurich, Switzerland; *U.S. Public*, pg. 1523
Glusac, William L., Pres.--Vulcan Materials Company-Midwest Div., Lombard, IL; *U.S. Public*, pg. 1726
Glycerio, George, Gen. Mgr.--Equipamentos Cientificos Instron Ltd., Sao Paulo, Brazil; *U.S. Public*, pg. 883
Glynn, Robert D., Jr., Chm. Bd.--Pacific Gas & Electric Company, San Francisco, CA; *U.S. Public*, pg. 1241
Glynn, William C., Pres.--Intermountain Gas Co., Boise, ID; *U.S. Private*, pg. 568
Gmehlin, Fred, V.P.--H.A. Schlatter, Inc., Rockford, IL; *Int'l*, pg. 1206
Gmeiner, Ted, Gen. Mgr.--Ice Cream Specialties, Inc., Saint Louis, MO; *U.S. Private*, pg. 879
Gnadinger, P., Mng. Dir.--Georg Fischer Leichtmetall AG, Schaffhausen, Switzerland; *Int'l*, pg. 490
Gnaegi, A., Rep.--Swiss Bank Corporation (Overseas) S.A., Lima, Peru; *Int'l*, pg. 1330
Gnath, Ulrich, Chief Oper. Officer--Helaba International Finance plc, Dublin, Ireland; *Int'l*, pg. 799
Gnazzo, Patrick J., Pres.--United Technologies International Corp., Hartford, CT; *U.S. Public*, pg. 1690
Goathe, Bob, Pres.--Gulf State Mortgage, Inc., Atlanta, GA; *Int'l*, pg. 1133
Gobayzadeh, Mehdi, Pres.--American Tissue Mills of Greenwich, Middle Falls, NY; *U.S. Private*, pg. 63
Gobbers, Jean, Chief Exec. Officer--AxPro France S.A., Villefranche-sur-Saone, France; *Int'l*, pg. 710
Gobbi, Fausto, Chm. Bd.--I.S.A. Istituto Atesino di Sviluppo S.p.A., Trento, Italy; *Int'l*, pg. 138
Gobel, Andre, Pres.--Leaf Norway A/S, Skare, Norway; *Int'l*, *pg. 638*
Gobeli, Larry, Gen. Mgr.--Hendrickson Stamping, Joliet, IL; *U.S. Private*, pg. 155
Gockel, Helmut, Mng. Dir.--Dresdner Bank AG, Istanbul, Turkey; *Int'l*, pg. 419
Goda, Shoji, Dir.--Takenaka Europe GmbH, Frankfurt, Frankfurt, Germany; *Int'l*, pg. 1351
Godard, Alain, Pres.--Rhone-Poulenc Agrochimie, Lyon, France; *Int'l*, pg. 1109
Godard, E., Mng. Dir.--S.A. Cockerill Forges and Ringmill C.F.R., Seraing, Belgium; *Int'l*, pg. 301
Godber, Steve, Mng. Dir.--Medelec Limited, Old Woking, United Kingdom; *Int'l*, pg. 1467
Goddard, G. Gary, Pres.--Handy & Harman Tube Co., Inc., Norristown, PA; *U.S. Public*, pg. 780
Goddard, Terry, Chm. Bd.--Dimplex UK, Southampton, United Kingdom; *Int'l*, pg. 554
Godel, D., Chief Oper. Officer--Schlatter do Brasil, Sao Bernardo do Campo, Brazil; *Int'l*, pg. 1206
Godel, Jean-Claude, Mng. Dir.--Sulzer Canada Inc., Pointe-Claire, Canada; *Int'l*, pg. 1306
Godfrey, Bruce, Chief Fin. Officer--RCN Long Distance, Princeton, NJ; *U.S. Public*, pg. 1354
Godfrey, Paul, Pres.--The Toronto Sun Publishing Corporation, Toronto, Canada; *Int'l*, pg. 1320
Godfrey, Ragan E., Pres. & Chief Exec. Officer--Regions Bank/Gadsden, Gadsden, AL; *U.S. Public*, pg. 1372
Godfrey, Scott, Gen. Mgr.--Econolite Canada, Inc., Scarborough, Canada; *U.S. Private*, pg. 362
Godi, Jewel, Plant Mgr.--Acme Brick Co., Garrison, TX; *U.S.* Public, pg. 936
Godinez, Emilio, Mgr.--Grupo Termoindustrial ECA, S.A. de C.V., Guadalajara, Mexico; *U.S. Private*, pg. 361
Godoy, Michael, Project Mgr.--Wackenhut Belize, Ltd., Belize, Belize; *U.S. Public*, pg. 1731
Godsey, Edward P., Pres. & Gen. Mgr.--Chesapeake Packaging Co./Baltimore, Baltimore, MD; *U.S. Public*, pg. 346
Godshall, Jonathan H., Pres.--Igloo Products Corporation, Houston, TX; *U.S. Public*, pg. 265
Godson, Don, Chief Exec. Officer--Oldcastle, Inc., Los Angeles, CA; *Int'l*, pg. 242
Godwin, J.H., Pres. & Chief Exec. Officer--SouthTrust Bank, Ozark, Ozark, AL; *U.S. Public*, pg. 1492
Godwin, Michael E., Pres.--Harris Bank Libertyville, Libertyville, IL; *Int'l*, pg. 154
Goebbert, Luanne, Mgr.--Successories, Palatine, IL; *U.S. Private*, pg. 1049
Goebel, Richard, Gen. Mgr.--Weatherford Oil Tool Co. (1983) Ltd., Edmonton, Canada; *U.S. Public*, pg. 1750
Goebes, Bill, Gen. Mgr.--Arrow/Schweber Electronics, Indianapolis, IN; *U.S. Public*, pg. 134
Goecke, Joseph M., Pres.--Valmont Irrigation Division, Valley, NE; *U.S. Public*, pg. 1707
Goeckmann, Klaus, Dr., Chm. Bd.--Norddeutsche Affinerie AG, Hamburg, Germany; *Int'l*, pg. 861
Goedeke, Edward R., Pres. & Chief Oper. Officer--Manufacturers Railway Company, Saint Louis, MO; *U.S. Public*, pg. 114
Goedert, Philip H., Pres.--Interplan, Denver, CO; *U.S. Private*, pg. 905
Goeing, Peter, Pres.--PTG Plasma-Oberflachentechnik GmbH, Horb am Neckar, Germany; *Int'l*, pg. 400
Goeke, Tom, Gen. Mgr.--Klockner Barrier Films, Gordonsville, VA; *Int'l*, pg. 737
Goekjian, Christopher, Chief Exec. Officer--Credit Suisse Financial Products, London, United Kingdom; *Int'l*, pg. 345
Goell, Jim, Gen. Mgr.--Microwave Signal, Inc., Clarksburg, MD; *U.S. Public*, pg. 8
Goeller, William A., Pres. & Chief Exec. Officer--Hatzel & Buehler, Inc., Wilmington, DE; *U.S. Private*, pg. 266
Goelman, Lawrence, Pres.--Cost Care, Inc., Huntington Beach, CA; *U.S. Private*, pg. 589
Goelz, Ron, Gen. Mgr.--Folding Carton (Morris), Morris, IL; *Int'l*, pg. 1270
Goeman, Pete, Gen. Mgr.--Lunstead, A Haworth Co., Kent, WA; *U.S. Private*, pg. 512
Goer, Ernest J., Chm. Bd. & Chief Exec. Officer--Goer Manufacturing Co., Charleston, SC; *U.S. Private*, pg. 904
Goergen, R.M., Pres.--American Appraisal Capital Services, Inc., Milwaukee, WI; *U.S. Private*, pg. 50
Goerlich, Joe, Pres.--Fitzsimons Manufacturing Co., Detroit, MI; *U.S. Public*, pg. 1045
Goerth, Wolfgang J., Mng. Dir.--Heidelberg Graphic Equipment Ltd.-Heidelberg UK, Brentford, United Kingdom; *Int'l*, pg. 605
Goethals, James, Pres.--Sturgis Foundry Corp., Sturgis, MI; *U.S. Private*, pg. 83
Goethals, Ludovic, Gen. Mgr.--Shandwick S.A. Infopublic N.V., Brussels, Belgium; *Int'l*, pg. 1228
Goethals, M., Dir.-Brico & Garden GB--GIEE Brico International, Brussels, Belgium; *Int'l*, pg. 533
Goethe, Robert A., Pres. & Chief Oper. Officer--Citizens Mortgage Corporation, Atlanta, GA; *Int'l*, pg. 1132
Goethe, Robert A., Chm. Bd., Pres. & Chief Exec. Officer--Regions Mortgage, Inc., Montgomery, AL; *U.S. Public*, pg. 1373
Goetsch, Gary, Pres.--Wheeled Coach Industries, Inc., Hutchinson, KS; *U.S. Public*, pg. 400
Goetsch, Gary G., Pres.--Wheeled Coach Industries, Inc., Winter Park, FL; *U.S. Public*, pg. 400
Goetschel, Arthur W., Pres.--Griffin Wheel Co., Chicago, IL; *U.S. Private*, pg. 68
Goetschi, Pierre, Pres.--Switzerland Cheese Association, Inc., Valley Cottage, NY; *Int'l*, pg. 1211
Goetter, Robert W., Pres. & Chief Exec. Officer--Harris Futures Corporation, Chicago, IL; *Int'l*, pg. 154
Goetz, John, Mgr.--Bio-Rad ECS Division, Anaheim, CA; *U.S. Public*, pg. 230
Goetze, William, Sr. V.P.-Gen. Mgr.--Mazda Motor of America, Inc. Western Region, Irvine, CA; *Int'l*, pg. 849
Goetzen, Johann, Area Sls.--Analog Devices GMBH - Techniches Buero West, Cologne, Germany; *U.S. Public*, pg. 108
Goff, Dick, Pres.--Rockford International Group, Rockford, IL; *U.S. Private*, pg. 938
Goff, Neal, Chief Oper. Officer & Sr. V.P.--R.R. Bowker, New Providence, NJ; *Int'l*, pg. 1096
Goffin, Claire, Acct. Dir.--Conquest Europe S.A., Brussels, Belgium; *Int'l*, pg. 1484
Gofortu, Jess, Mgr.--Clements Vinegar Company, Oklahoma City, OK; *U.S. Private*, pg. 245
Gogan, James W., Pres.--Kepec Resources Limited, Stellarton, Canada; *Int'l*, pg. 454
Gogel, Mark, Plant Mgr.--DMI Furniture, Inc., Huntingburg, IN; *U.S. Public*, pg. 473
Goggin, Zane, Pres.--Dixie Industries, Inc., Chattanooga, TN; *U.S. Public*, pg. 406
Goggins, Colleen A., Pres.--Johnson & Johnson Consumer Products, Skillman, NJ; *U.S. Public*, pg. 928
Goguikian, Michel, Gen. Mgr.--Valores Santander, S.A., Caracas, Venezuela; *Int'l*, pg. 144
Goh, Han Hian, Mng. Dir.--AlliedSignal (Ltd.) Singapore, Jurong, Singapore; *U.S. Public*, pg. 53

Goh, Han Hian, Mng. Dir.--Dowty Aerospace Aviation Services Pte Ltd, Singapore, Singapore; *Int'l*, pg. 1337
Goh, Hup Jin, Pres.--Sanwa Foods, Inc., City of Industry, CA; *U.S. Public*, pg. 299
Goh, R., Chief Exec. Officer--OCE Systems (Malaysia) Sdn. Bhd., Petaling Jaya, Malaysia; *Int'l*, pg. 995
Gohausen, Hans-Jurgen, Dr., Mng. Dir.--Lixton Spezialreiniger GmbH, Dusseldorf, Germany; *Int'l*, pg. 610
Goicoechea, Angel Frances, Gen. Mgr.--Campos Velazguez, S.A., Madrid, Spain; *Int'l*, pg. 1224
Goins, F. Winslow, Pres.--Fast Food Merchandisers Inc., Rocky Mount, NC; *U.S. Public*, pg. 278
Goins, Gary, H&TP Svcs. Mgr.--TDW Services, Inc., Tulsa, OK; *U.S. Private*, pg. 1180
Goins, Gary, Mgr.-HT&P Services--Mid-Continent Service Center, Tulsa, OK; *U.S. Private*, pg. 1180
Goins, Gary, Mgr.-HT&P Services--East Coast Service Ctr., Newark, DE; *U.S. Private*, pg. 1180
Goischke, Rainer, Mgr.--Commerzbank AG-Mexico Representative Office, Mexico, Mexico; *Int'l*, pg. 311
Goitia, Fernando, V.P.--Crown Cork del Peru, S.A., Lima, Peru; *U.S. Public*, pg. 464
Goity, Gregorio R., Pres.--Boston Inversora De Valores S.A., Buenos Aires, Argentina; *U.S. Public*, pg. 185
Gokli, Kash, V.P.--Amano Cincinnati - Cincinnati Branch Office, Loveland, OH; *Int'l*, pg. 70
Goksel, Attila, Pres.--Serpo AS, Istanbul, Turkey; *Int'l*, pg. 1200
Golabek, Alex, Mgr.--CPC Industrial Products, Nairobi, Kenya; *U.S. Public*, pg. 225
Golabowski, Paul, Mgr.--General Employment Enterprises, Inc., Indianapolis, IN; *U.S. Public*, pg. 715
Golacinski, M., V.P.--Consumer Audio & Video Sales, Fair Lawn, NJ; *Int'l*, pg. 622
Gold Frank, Jack C., Pres.--Mead Coated Board Division, Columbus, GA; *U.S. Public*, pg. 1074
Gold, Christina A., Pres.--Avon Canada, Inc., Pointe-Claire, Canada; *U.S. Public*, pg. 156
Gold, Daniel, Pres.--Cable Television Division, New Canaan, CT; *U.S. Public*, pg. 329
Gold, Ian, Gen. Mgr.-Fin.--Woolworths Limited, Yennora, Australia; *Int'l*, pg. 676
Gold, Stanley P., Pres.--Shamrock Holdings Of California, Inc., Burbank, CA; *U.S. Private*, pg. 989
Goldberg, A.H., Gen. Mgr.--ING Bank Luxembourg, Strassen, Luxembourg; *Int'l*, pg. 649
Goldberg, Danny, Pres. & Chief Exec. Officer & Chm. Bd.-Mercury Grp.--Polygram N.V., Baarn, Netherlands; *Int'l*, pg. 1051
Goldberg, H., Mng. Dir.--Philip Morris Limited, Moorabbin, Australia; *U.S. Public*, pg. 1290
Goldberg, Linda P., Pres. & Chief Exec. Officer--Dental Health Alliance, L.L.C., New York, NY; *Int'l*, pg. 499
Goldberg, Michael A., Chm. Bd.--National Indemnity Company of Mid-America, Omaha, NE; *U.S. Public*, pg. 221
Goldberg, Stanley, Chm. Bd., Pres. & Chief Exec. Officer--Dexol, Torrance, CA; *U.S. Public*, pg. 1390
Goldblatt, M., Pres.--Fers et Metaux Recycles Ltee., La Prairie, Canada; *Int'l*, pg. 1299
Goldbloom, Michael, Pres. & Publisher--The Gazette, Montreal, Canada; *Int'l*, pg. 631
Goldcamp, John, V.P. & Gen. Mgr.--Sheaffer Inc., Fort Madison, IA; *Int'l*, pg. 542
Golden, Ed, Pres.--Barton Brands of Georgia, Inc., Atlanta, GA; *U.S. Public*, pg. 300
Golden, Ed, Pres.--Barton Brands of California, Inc., Carson, CA; *U.S. Public*, pg. 300
Golden, Ed, Pres.--Barton Brands, Ltd., Chicago, IL; *U.S. Public*, pg. 300
Golden, J., Mng. Dir.--Ascom Timeplex SA, Montigny-le-Bretonneux, France; *Int'l*, pg. 87
Golden, Stephen, Chief Oper. Officer--Northern SC Paper Corporation, New York, NY; *U.S. Public*, pg. 1174
Golden, Stephen C., Pres.--New York Times Company Forest Products Group, New York, NY; *U.S. Public*, pg. 1174
Goldman, Bernard, Pres.--BLFC Securities Corporation, San Mateo, CA; *U.S. Public*, pg. 377
Goldman, Ed, V.P. & Gen. Mgr.-TV & Radio--WBZ Radio & WBZ-TV, Boston, MA; *U.S. Public*, pg. 275
Goldman, Jim, Mng. Dir.--Westpac Financial Services Group Limited, Sydney, Australia; *Int'l*, pg. 1496
Goldman, Robert I., Chm. & Chief Exec. Officer--Congress Financial Corp., New York, NY; *U.S. Public*, pg. 447
Goldman, S. I., Pres.--Southeast Fire Sprinkler Company, Longwood, FL; *U.S. Private*, pg. 462
Goldner, Karl-Ludwig, Mgr.--Deutsche Bank (Swiss) S.A., Geneva, Switzerland; *Int'l*, pg. 405
Goldpy, Willy, Pres.--Philips Danmark A/S, Copenhagen, Denmark; *Int'l*, pg. 1055
Goldring, Jeff, Pres.--Republic Beverage Company, Houston, TX; *U.S. Private*, pg. 149
Goldring, Jeff, Pres.--Republic Beverage Co., Dallas, TX; *U.S. Private*, pg. 150
Goldsberry, Ronald E., Pres.--Carplastic S.A. de C.V., Monterrey, Mexico; *U.S. Public*, pg. 665
Goldsmith, Howard, Pres.--Todd Enterprises, Cranston, RI; *U.S. Private*, pg. 231
Goldsmith, Russell, Chm. Bd. & Chief Exec. Officer--City National Bank, Beverly Hills, CA; *U.S. Public*, pg. 381
Goldstein, Bill, Dir.-Opers.--Rexam Medical Packaging, Inc., Mount Holly, NJ; *Int'l*, pg. 1106
Goldstein, Charles, Die.--Becton Dickinson Research Center, Research Triangle Park, NC; *U.S. Public*, pg. 199
Goldstein, Ed, Publisher--Crain Associated Enterprises, Chicago, IL; *U.S. Private*, pg. 285
Goldstein, Gary P., Gen. Mgr.--Shepard's, Colorado Springs, CO; *Int'l*, pg. 1095
Goldstein, Gary P., Gen. Mgr.--Shepard's, Colorado Springs, CO; *U.S. Public*, pg. 1616
Goldstein, Guy, V.P.-Res. & Devel.--JA/MONT N.V. - Technology Office, Muntzenheim, France; *U.S. Public*, pg. 673
Goldstein, I., Dir. Gen.--International Telecommunications Satellite Organization (INTELSAT), Washington, DC; *Int'l*, pg. 223
Goldstein, K.T., Pres. & Chief Exec. Officer--Universal Underwriters Insurance Co., Overland Park, KS; *Int'l*, pg. 1530
Goldstein, K.T., Chief Exec. Officer--Universal Underwriters of Texas, Overland Park, KS; *Int'l*, pg. 1530
Goldstein, Leonard, Mgr.--AFA Protective Systems, Inc., Syosset, NY; *U.S. Public*, pg. 5
Goldstein, Morris, Pres.--Information Access Co., Foster City, CA; *U.S. Public*, pg. 1600
Goldstein, Richard A., Pres. & Chief Exec. Officer--Unilever United States Inc., New York, NY; *Int'l*, pg. 1435
Goldstein, Richard J., V.P.-Sls. & Mktg.--Industrial Electronics Division, Collinsville, CT; *Int'l*, pg. 204
Goldthorp, William R., Gen. Mgr.--Soabar Systems (Hong Kong) Ltd., Quarry Bay, Hong Kong; *U.S. Public*, pg. 154
Goldworn, Jill, Pres.--Interplay OEM, Inc., Irvine, CA; *U.S. Private*, pg. 573
Goldwyn, John, Pres.--Paramount Pictures Corporation, Los Angeles, CA; *U.S. Private*, pg. 776
Golemme, Joe, Pres.--Federal Products Co., Providence, RI; *U.S. Public*, pg. 594
Golhofer, Jim, Pres.--Grolsch Importers Inc., Atlanta, GA; *Int'l*, pg. 559
Golin, Alvin, Chm. Bd.--Golin/Harris Communications, Inc., Chicago, IL; *Int'l*, pg. 1226
Golinelli, Walter, Sr. Exec. V.P.--Banca Nazionale Del Lavoro (New York), New York, NY; *Int'l*, pg. 136
Golinkin, Alexandra, Publisher--Allure, New York, NY; *U.S. Private*, pg. 20
Golinvaux, Louis A., Chm.--Berkley Risk Services, Inc., Minneapolis, MN; *U.S. Public*, pg. 215
Gollady, Steve, V.P.--Columbus Coca-Cola Bottling Co., Columbus, GA; *U.S. Public*, pg. 392
Golleher, George, Pres.--Food 4 Less, Inc., Compton, CA; *U.S. Private*, pg. 1202
Gollek, Dieter, Pres.--Clausen & Bosse GmbH, Leck, Germany; *Int'l*, pg. 1478
Gollmann, Raul E.A., Gen. Mgr.--Extremultus Industria de Correias Ltda., Itapeva, Brazil; *Int'l*, pg. 497
Gollwitz, Tom, Plant Mgr.--American Natl. Can Co., Bishopville, SC; *Int'l*, pg. 1029
Golm, Louis C., Pres.--AirTouch International, Walnut Creek, CA; *U.S. Public*, pg. 34
Golonski, Thomas W., Pres.--National City Bank, Pennsylvania, Pittsburgh, PA; *U.S. Public*, pg. 1154
Goltzman, Joseph L., Chm. Bd., Pres. & Chief Exec. Officer--Anheuser-Busch Recycling Corporation, Saint Louis, MO; *U.S. Public*, pg. 114
Golub, Harvey, Chm. Bd.--American Express Europe Limited, London, United Kingdom; *U.S. Public*, pg. 74
Golub, Neil, Pres. & Chief Oper. Officer--Price Chopper Operating Co., Inc., Schenectady, NY; *U.S. Private*, pg. 463
Gomendio, Pedro, Mng. Dir.--Lukcor, S.A., Larache, Morocco; *U.S. Public*, pg. 1067
Gomersall, J. E., Mng. Dir.--Pretoria Portland Cement Co. Ltd., Johannesburg, South Africa; *Int'l*, pg. 167
Gomes, Carlos A. Meireles, Chief Oper. Officer--Frigoscandia Food Process Systems S.A., Pinhal Novo, Portugal; *U.S. Public*, pg. 607
Gomes, Jose Reinaldo, V.P.-Media Opers.--Leo Burnett Publicidade, Ltda., Sao Paulo, Brazil; *U.S. Private*, pg. 185
Gomez, Alain, Chm. Bd. & Chief Exec. Officer--Thomson-CSF S.A., Paris, France; *Int'l*, pg. 1383
Gomez, Daniel J., Pres.--Bell Atlantic Directory Graphics, Inc., Valley Forge, PA; *U.S. Public*, pg. 203
Gomez, Dennis, Chief Oper. Officer--Sierra Pacific Industries-Burney Division, Burney, CA; *U.S. Private*, pg. 998
Gomez, Ernesto Ortega, Gen. Mgr.--Aceromex-Atlas S.A. DE C.V., Tepetlacalco, Mexico; *Int'l*, pg. 1118
Gomez, Flavio, Chm.--SBG Enterprise, San Francisco, CA; *Int'l*, pg. 1483
Gomez, Francisco, Gen. Mgr.--Four Seasons Hotel, Houston, TX; *Int'l*, pg. 502
Gomez, J. Hoyos, Mgr.--Owens Corning Andercol Tuberias, Medellin, Colombia; *U.S. Public*, pg. 1237
Gomez, J. Paul, Dir.-Washington Opers.--AM General Corporation, Arlington, VA; *U.S. Private*, pg. 922
Gomez, Jesus Cayetano B., Mng. Dir.--Electrodos Monterrey S.A. de C.V., Monterrey, Mexico; *Int'l*, pg. 281
Gomez, Jose, Supvr.-Electronic Banking--Corporate Services Div., Redondo Beach, CA; *U.S. Public*, pg. 871
Gomez, Jose Federico, Chief Oper. Officer--La Rural del Paraguay S.A. , Paraguaya de Seguros, Asuncion, Paraguay; *Int'l*, pg. 1392
Gomez, Louis, Plant Mgr.--Waterbury Companies, Inc.-Independence Div., Independence, LA; *U.S. Public*, pg. 308
Gomez, Marco A., Sr. V.P. & Country Mgr.--Bank of America NT&SA, Santiago, Chile; *U.S. Public*, pg. 182
Gomez, Milton, Chief Oper. Officer--Kativo Nicaragua, S.A., Managua, Nicaragua; *U.S. Public*, pg. 687
Gomez, Richard, V.P.-E. Div. U.S. & Lat. America--Singapore Airlines Ltd., New York, NY; *Int'l*, pg. 1374
Gomez, Roberto, Gen. Mgr.--WWF de Mexico, S.A. de C.V., Mexico, Mexico; *U.S. Private*, pg. 1145
Gomo, Anthony, Mgr.-Opers.--Bay City Forge Operations, Erie, PA; *U.S. Public*, pg. 1794
Gondek, Robert J., Pres.--M/D Totco Instrumentation, Cedar Park, TX; *U.S. Public*, pg. 1709
Gongas, John C., Pres.--Nora Transmission Co., Pittsburgh, PA; *U.S. Public*, pg. 590
Gongas, John C., Jr., Pres.--Kentucky West Virginia Gas Co., Ashland, KY; *U.S. Public*, pg. 590
Gongaware, Don, Pres.--Transport Holdings Inc., Fort Worth, TX; *U.S. Public*, pg. 433
Gongaware, Don, Pres.--Transport Life Insurance Co., Fort Worth, TX; *U.S. Public*, pg. 433
Gongaware, Don, Pres.--Continental Life Insurance Company, Fort Worth, TX; *U.S. Public*, pg. 433
Gongaware, Donald F., Chief Oper. Officer--Bankers National Life Insurance Co., Carmel, IN; *U.S. Public*, pg. 433
Gongaware, Donald F., Chief Oper. Officer--National Fidelity Life Insurance Co., Carmel, IN; *U.S. Public*, pg. 433
Gongaware, Donald F., Pres. & Chief Exec. Officer--Bankers Life & Casualty Company, Chicago, IL; *U.S. Public*, pg. 433
Gongaware, Donlad F., Chief Oper. Officer--Lincoln American Life Insurance Co., Carmel, IN; *U.S. Public*, pg. 433
Gonima, Ivan, Gen. Mgr.--Rorer De Ecuador, S.A., Quito, Ecuador; *Int'l*, pg. 1111
Gonior, Martin, Mgr.-Oper.--SIFCO Custom Machining, Minneapolis, MN; *U.S. Public*, pg. 1471
Gonis, Arthur P., Pres. & Chief Exec. Officer--Ragu Foods, Inc., Trumbull, CT; *Int'l*, pg. 1436
Gonnella, Joseph E., Grp. V.P.--Automotive Emission Systems, Iselin, NJ; *U.S. Public*, pg. 582
Gonnella, Ken, Pres.--Gonnella Frozen Products, Schaumburg, IL; *U.S. Private*, pg. 463
Gonome, Akira, Pres.--Synergy Computer Graphics Corporation, Santa Clara, CA; *Int'l*, pg. 594
Gonon, Jean Francois, Mgr. & Area Mgr.-France--Organisation de Vente des Produits Fasson S.a.r.l., Blanc Mesnil, France; *U.S. Public*, pg. 154
Gonsalves, Ernest, Gen. Mgr.--Colgate-Palmolive (Guyana) Ltd., Georgetown, Guyana; *U.S. Public*, pg. 398
Gonzales, Ernesto, Pres.--Motor Wheel de Mexico, Monterrey, Mexico; *U.S. Private*, pg. 513
Gonzales, Ignacio, Mng. Dir.--Ericsson de Guatemala, S.A., Guatemala, Guatemala; *Int'l*, pg. 1366
Gonzales, L., Gen. Mgr.--Aer Lingus, Madrid, Spain; *Int'l*, pg. 28
Gonzales, Manuel, Mgr.--Elasco International Corp., Manila, Philippines; *U.S. Private*, pg. 361
Gonzales, Manvel, Gen. Mgr.--Nicolet Instrument S.A.R.L., Trappes, France; *U.S. Public*, pg. 1594
Gonzales, Walter, V.P.--Volt-Autologic Directories S.A., Montevideo, Uruguay; *U.S. Public*, pg. 1724
Gonzalez Cuevas, Jose Antonio, Dir.--FCA!BMZ CID Barcelona, Barcelona, Spain; *Int'l*, pg. 469
Gonzalez-Adalid Garcia-Zozaya, Antonio, Pres.--Repsol Exploracion, Madrid, Spain; *Int'l*, pg. 1104
Gonzalez-Rivas, Joseph I., Gen. Mgr.--Nashua Imaging Supplies Div., Nashua, NH; *U.S. Public*, pg. 1152
Gonzalez-Rivas, Joseph I., Pres. & Gen. Mgr.--Patton, Moorestown, NJ; *U.S. Public*, pg. 1486
Gonzalez, Angel, Gen. Mgr.--Jacuzzi Universal, S.A., Monterrey, Mexico; *U.S. Public*, pg. 1684
Gonzalez, Claudio X., Chm. Bd. & Mng. Dir.--Kimberly-Clark de Mexico, S.A. de C.V., Mexico, Mexico; *U.S. Public*, pg. 960
Gonzalez, Clemente, V.P. & Client Services Dir.--Leo Burnett Chile, Santiago, Chile; *U.S. Private*, pg. 185
Gonzalez, Daniel, Pres.--Union des Assurances Federales, Paris, France; *Int'l*, pg. 344
Gonzalez, Eddie, Grp. Mng. Dir.-Hong Kong & China--Dentsu Young & Rubicam Limited (Hong Kong), Hong Kong, Hong Kong; *U.S. Private*, pg. 325
Gonzalez, Emilio, Pres.-Latin America & Canada Div.--Bristol-Myers International Group, New York, NY; *U.S. Public*, pg. 254
Gonzalez, Federico Sada, Pres.--Vitro, Sociedad Anonima - Containers Div., Garza Garcia, Mexico; *Int'l*, pg. 1469
Gonzalez, Frederico, Gen. Dir.--Arrendadora Comermex S.A. de C.V., Mexico, Mexico; *U.S. Public*, pg. 182
Gonzalez, J.L., Chief Oper. Officer--Andrew Corporation (Mexico) S.A. de C.V., Zapopan, Mexico; *U.S. Public*, pg. 113
Gonzalez, Javier, Dir.-Spain--Raychem SA, Alcobendas, Spain; *U.S. Public*, pg. 1363
Gonzalez, Jesse, Pres.--Singleton Seafood Co., Tampa, FL; *U.S. Public*, pg. 427
Gonzalez, Joe, Gen. Mgr.--The West Company of Puerto Rico, Inc., Vega Alta, PR; *U.S. Public*, pg. 1755
Gonzalez, Jose E., Mng. Dir.--Petroleos De Canarias, S.A. (PETROCAN), Las Palmas, Spain; *Int'l*, pg. 323
Gonzalez, Pablo de Bergia, Pres.--Casa Aircraft USA Incorporated, Chantilly, VA; *Int'l*, pg. 1224
Gonzalez, Rafael, Pres.--AGA Chile S.A., Maipu, Chile; *Int'l*, pg. 13
Gonzalez, Rafael, Gen. Mgr.--Chuquicamata Division, Chuquicamata, Chile; *Int'l*, pg. 302
Gonzalez, Raul, Gen. Mgr.--GATX Logistics, Inc.-New York, Bronx, NY; *U.S. Public*, pg. 691
Gonzalez, Raul, Gen. Mgr.--GATX Logistics, Inc.-N.Y., Bronx, NY; *U.S. Public*, pg. 691
Gonzalez, Rogelio A., Pres.--Astra Chemicals S.A., Mexico, Mexico; *Int'l*, pg. 93
Gonzalez, Rolando, Chief Oper. Officer--VARTA Batterie AG, Miami, FL; *Int'l*, pg. 1452
Gonzalez, Sixto, Mgr.--Caribbean Outerwear Corp., Yabucoa, PR; *U.S. Private*, pg. 1032
Good, Bill, Mgr.--Sandvik Steel U.K., Birmingham, United Kingdom; *Int'l*, pg. 1187
Good, Bill, Mgr.--Sterling Tubes Ltd., Walsall, United Kingdom; *Int'l*, pg. 1187
Good, Chester G., Pres.--GM Allison Japan Limited, Tokyo, Japan; *U.S. Public*, pg. 721
Good, Edward, Mng. Dir.--Rosella Lipton Pty. Ltd., Richmond, Australia; *Int'l*, pg. 1438
Good, Jeff, Chief Fin. Officer--Esselte Pendaflex Canada, Inc., Mississauga, Canada; *Int'l*, pg. 460
Good, R., Mgr.-Recycling--Rockware Glass Reclamation Centre, Northampton, United Kingdom; *Int'l*, pg. 124
Good, Tim, V.P. & Div. Mgr.--Cody Gas Division, Cody, WY; *U.S. Public*, pg. 581
Goodacre, Daniel, V.P.-Mfg.--Pandrol Jackson, Inc., Ludington, MI; *Int'l*, pg. 280

Goodall, Oakley C., V.P. & Gen. Mgr.--GAICO, Reading, PA; *U.S. Private*, pg. 841
Goodall, Peter, Mng. Dir.--Tiffany & Co. (New York) Pty Limited, Sydney, Australia; *U.S. Public*, pg. 1609
Goodall, Thomas M., Mng. Dir.--Morton International Limited, Warrington, United Kingdom; *U.S. Public*, pg. 1135
Goode, Earl A., Pres.--GTE Information Services Incorporated, Dallas-Fort Worth Airport, TX; *U.S. Public*, pg. 696
Goode, K. Edward, Chm. Bd.--Bank of Ferrum, Ferrum, VA; *U.S. Public*, pg. 1038
Goode, R.C., Pres.--M.W. Kellogg Limited, Wembley, United Kingdom; *U.S. Public*, pg. 528
Goode, Richard, Office Mgr.--Korn/Ferry International, Moscow, Russia; *U.S. Private*, pg. 634
Goode, Richard, Office Mgr.--Korn/Ferry International, Saint Petersburg, Russia; *U.S. Private*, pg. 634
Goodell, B. Douglas, V.P.--Machinery Div., Baltimore, MD; *U.S. Public*, pg. 463
Goodell, Kent, Admin.--Las Palma Nursing Center, Anaheim, CA; *U.S. Public*, pg. 1714
Goodell, Leon, Chief Oper. Officer--Marine Communications Div., Fort Worth, TX; *Int'l*, pg. 1433
Gooden, Robert, Pres.--Seacore Limited, Helston, United Kingdom; *Int'l*, pg. 31
Goodfellow, David W., Pres.--American Pfauter Corp., Loves Park, IL; *Int'l*, pg. 617
Goodger, Mitchell, Plant Mgr.--Acme Brick Co., Malvern, AR; *U.S. Public*, pg. 936
Goodhard, Bill, Project Mgr.--Echo Bay Alaska Inc., Juneau, AK; *U.S. Public*, pg. 562
Gooding, Paul H., Pres.--Ascend Financial Services, Saint Paul, MN; *U.S. Private*, pg. 750
Gooding, Thomas L., Chm. Bd. & Pres.--NationsBank of Central IL, Hillsboro, IL; *U.S. Public*, pg. 1164
Gooding, Thomas L., Mr., Chm. Bd. & Pres.--NationsBank of Central IL., Benld, IL; *U.S. Public*, pg. 1164
Goodlick, William H., Pres.--SuperValu, Inc.-Food Marketing Div., Fort Wayne, IN; *U.S. Public*, pg. 1540
Goodloe, John, V.P. & Gen. Mgr.--Chesapeake Packaging Co./Roanoke, Roanoke, VA; *U.S. Public*, pg. 347
Goodman, Adam, V.P. & Gen. Mgr.--G-2 Office Furniture Market, Phoenix, AZ; *U.S. Private*, pg. 464
Goodman, Andrew P., Pres.--Minipack Systems Limited, Southampton, United Kingdom; *U.S. Public*, pg. 1067
Goodman, Bill, Gen. Mgr.--Barton's of Pine Bluff, Pine Bluff, AR; *U.S. Private*, pg. 119
Goodman, Dana, V.P.--Dani Michaels, Inc., New York, NY; *U.S. Private*, pg. 309
Goodman, Ellis M., Pres.--Barton Distillers Import Corp., Rockville Center, NY; *U.S. Public*, pg. 300
Goodman, Fredric, Chief Exec. Officer--Welsbach Electric Corp., College Point, NY; *U.S. Public*, pg. 572
Goodman, L.D., Chief Oper. Officer--Jardine (Lloyd's Underwriting Agents) Ltd., London, United Kingdom; *Int'l*, *pg. 705*
Goodman, Larry, Exec. V.P.-CNN Sls.--CNN Headline News, Atlanta, GA; *U.S. Public*, pg. 1614
Goodman, Louis A., Partner--Skadden, Arps, Slate, Meagher & Flom LLP, Boston, MA; *U.S. Private*, pg. 1004
Goodman, Louis J., Pres. & Chief Exec. Officer--J.C. Higgins Corp., Stoughton, MA; *U.S. Public*, pg. 572
Goodman, Peter A., Chm. & Chief Exec. Officer--A.J. Brandon, Vernon, CA; *U.S. Public*, pg. 948
Goodrich, Clifford C., Pres. & Chief Oper. Officer--Los Angeles Turf Club, Inc., Arcadia, CA; *U.S. Public*, pg. 1081
Goodson, Kenneth, Pres.--Integrated Metal Technologies, Inc., Spring Lake, MI; *U.S. Public*, pg. 1112
Goodson, R.M., Branch Mgr.--Zellerbach Division, Charlotte, NC; *U.S. Public*, pg. 1075
Goodspeed, Paul, Chief Exec. Officer--Safer, Ltd., Scarborough, Canada; *U.S. Public*, pg. 1390
Goodwill, Dan, Pres.--Sunac America, Etobicoke, Canada; *Int'l*, pg. 924
Goodwin, G.F., Pres.--CLAM Petroleum Co., Hague, Netherlands; *U.S. Public*, pg. 1662
Goodwin, H. Clark, Pres. & Chief Exec. Officer--Bank of Union, Monroe, NC; *U.S. Public*, pg. 627
Goodwin, Harry, Pres.--Crest Fruit Co., Alamo, TX; *U.S. Public*, pg. 1506
Goodwin, John E., Pres.--Texas Homestead Mortgage Co., San Antonio, TX; *U.S. Public*, pg. 945
Goodwin, Morris, Pres. & Treas.--IDS Deposit Corp., Midvale, UT; *U.S. Public*, pg. 73
Goodwin, Peter, Pres.--Tarmac Texas, Fort Worth, TX; *Int'l*, pg. 1356
Goodwin, Peter J., Pres.--Miller & Co., Chicago, IL; *Int'l*, pg. 1458
Goodwin, Peter J., Pres.--The Feldspar Corp., Atlanta, GA; *Int'l*, pg. 1523
Goodwin, Peter J., Pres.--Suzorite Mica Products Inc., Boucherville, Canada; *Int'l*, pg. 1523
Goodwin, Peter J., Pres.--Suzorite Mineral Products, Inc., Spruce Pine, NC; *Int'l*, pg. 1524
Goodyear, William M., Chm. & Pres.--Bank of America Illinois Trust Company of Florida, N.A., Boca Raton, FL; *U.S. Public*, pg. 181
Google, Charles H., Area V.P.--Avon Sales & Distribution Branch, Newark, DE; *U.S. Public*, pg. 156
Goos, Roel, Chief Oper. Officer--Kjellbergs Successors B.V., Ter-Apel, Netherlands; *Int'l*, pg. 712
Goossen, John D., Publr.--The Grand Island Daily Independent, Grand Island, NE; *U.S. Private*, pg. 995
Gopaiakrishnan, C.G., Gen. Dir.--Square D Software Limited, Madras, India; *U.S. Public*, pg. 1043
Goraleski, Michael, Pres.--GLENFED Brokerage Services, Glendale, CA; *U.S. Public*, pg. 747
Goralnick, L. Arnold, Exec. V.P.--Keith Highlanders Shoes, Bridgewater, MA; *U.S. Private*, pg. 612
Goransson, Claes, Mgr.--Cardo Door AB, Malmo, Sweden; *Int'l*, pg. 269
Gorbea, Carlos, Chief Oper. Officer--Tefal Mexicana S.A. de C.V., Miguel Hidalgo, Mexico; *Int'l*, pg. 568
Gorder, Mark, Pres.--RTI Export, Inc. (Barbados), Arden Hills, MN; *U.S. Public*, pg. 1455
Gordian, Santiago, Mng. Dir.--Grupo Barro Testa, Barcelona, Spain; *Int'l*, pg. 1377
Gordon, Arthur, Chief Exec. Officer--E.N.C., City of Commerce, CA; *U.S. Public*, pg. 948
Gordon, Bernard, Chm. Bd.--Analogic Scientific, Peabody, MA; *U.S. Public*, pg. 109
Gordon, Bernard M., Pres.--Anadventure II Corporation, Peabody, MA; *U.S. Public*, pg. 109
Gordon, Bruce, Pres.--Paramount Television International Services Ltd., Hamilton, Bermuda; *U.S. Private*, pg. 777
Gordon, David G., Pres.--Dexter Nonwovens Division, Windsor Locks, CT; *U.S. Public*, pg. 504
Gordon, Elizabeth, V.P. & Publr., Junior Books--HarperCollins Junior Books Division, New York, NY; *Int'l*, *pg. 927*
Gordon, Ellen R., Pres.--Tri-Mass., Inc., Wellesley Hills, MA; *U.S. Public*, pg. 1621
Gordon, Elliot, Office Mgr.--Korn/Ferry International, Newport Beach, CA; *U.S. Private*, pg. 633
Gordon, Irv, Gen. Mgr.--Poe & Brown of Pennsylvania, Newtown Square, PA; *U.S. Public*, pg. 1312
Gordon, Janine, Pres.--Waring LaRosa Gordon Public Relations, New York, NY; *U.S. Private*, pg. 1150
Gordon, Jerry A., Chief Oper. Officer--GW Services, Inc., Carlsbad, CA; *U.S. Public*, pg. 745
Gordon, Jerry A., Chief Oper. Officer--Glacier Water Services, Inc., Carlsbad, CA; *U.S. Public*, pg. 745
Gordon, Kenneth A., Pres.--Reader's Digest Latinoamerica S.A., Coral Gables, FL; *U.S. Public*, pg. 1367
Gordon, Martin S., V.P.--Data Conversion Products, Wakefield, MA; *U.S. Public*, pg. 109
Gordon, Melvin J., Chief Exec. Officer--Henry Eisen Adv. Agency, Inc., Chicago, IL; *U.S. Public*, pg. 1621
Gordon, Melvin J., Chief Opr. Officer--TRI International Co., Chicago, IL; *U.S. Public*, pg. 1621
Gordon, Melvin J., Chief Exec. Officer--Tootsie Rolls-Latin America, Inc., Chicago, IL; *U.S. Public*, pg. 1621
Gordon, Mona, Gen. Mgr.--Butterworth of Puerto Rico Inc., San Juan, PR; *Int'l*, pg. 1095
Gordon, Mona, Mng. Dir.--Lexis Law Publishing, San Juan, PR; *Int'l*, pg. 1096
Gordon, P., Reg. Mgr.--Birmingham Field Office, Atlanta, GA; *Int'l*, pg. 840
Gordon, Pat, Gen. Mgr.--McKissick Products Co., Tulsa, OK; *Int'l*, pg. 473
Gordon, Paul, Gen. Mgr.--Sequoia, Washington, DC; *U.S. Public*, pg. 130
Gordon, Peter, Chm. Bd.--Crystal Geyser Water Company, Calistoga, CA; *Int'l*, pg. 1013
Gordon, Peter, Pres.--Crystal Geyser Roxane Water L.P., Olancha, CA; *Int'l*, pg. 1013
Gordon, R.J., Pres. & Chief Oper. Officer-Ohio & Kentucky--Columbia Gas Distribution Companies, Columbus, OH; *U.S. Public*, pg. 402
Gordon, Richard, Gen. Mgr.--GATX Logistics, Inc.-California (Quaker), Stockton, CA; *U.S. Public*, pg. 691
Gordon, Robert D., Pres.--Systems Strategies, Inc., New York, NY; *U.S. Public*, pg. 120
Gordon, Roy, Mgr.-Plant--Schnadig Corp., Montoursville, PA; *U.S. Private*, pg. 971
Gordon, S., Mgr.-Natl. Sls.--Crane National Vendors Co., Ltd., Scarborough, Canada; *U.S. Public*, pg. 456
Gordon, Stuart, Pres.--Votaw Precision Technologies, Santa Fe Springs, CA; *U.S. Private*, pg. 605
Gordono, Michael, Pres.--Beehive Machinery Co., Sandy, UT; *U.S. Private*, pg. 1160
Gordonsmith, John, Pres.--Financial Collection Agencies (International) Inc., Westmount, Canada; *Int'l*, pg. 470
Gordonsmith, John, Pres.--Financial Collection Agencies (International) Inc., Mississauga, Canada; *Int'l*, pg. 470
Gordonsmith, John, Pres.--Financial Collection Agencies, Edmonton, Canada; *Int'l*, pg. 470
Gordonsmith, John, Pres.--Financial Collection Agencies (International) Inc., Brantford, Canada; *Int'l*, pg. 470
Gore, David E., Mng. Dir.--Triton Oil Co. of Thailand (Bangkok), Bangkok, Thailand; *U.S. Public*, pg. 1640
Gore, James L., Pres. & Chief Oper. Officer--Southern Health Services, Inc., Richmond, VA; *U.S. Public*, pg. 454
Gore, James R., M.D., Medical Dir.--Stockbridge, Stockbridge, GA; *U.S. Public*, pg. 1716
Gore, Jeff, Pres.--Franklin Press, San Bernardino, CA; *U.S. Private*, pg. 268
Gore, Randy, V.P.-Hospital Div.--Kentucky Medical Insurance Company, Hospital Division, Louisville, KY; *U.S. Private*, pg. 741
Gorecki, J., V.P. & Gen. Mgr.--Esquire Novelty Co., Amsterdam, NY; *U.S. Private*, pg. 1047
Gorel, Hans P., Mng. Dir.--Braun (U.K.) Ltd., Sunbury, United Kingdom; *U.S. Public*, pg. 744
Gorell, Franklyn, Chm. Bd. & Chief Exec. Officer--Season-All Industries, Inc., Indiana, PA; *Int'l*, pg. 267
Gorewitz, D. M., Plant Mgr.--Longview Fibre Co., Merchandise, Grocery & Specialty Bag Div., Waltham, MA; *U.S. Public*, pg. 1014
Gorga, Joseph L., Pres.--CMI Industries Inc.-Finished Fabrics Division, Greensboro, NC; *U.S. Private*, pg. 195
Gorgi, Habib Y., Pres.--Fleet Equity Partners, Providence, RI; *U.S. Public*, pg. 650
Gorham, Brian L., Pres. & Chief Exec. Officer--Hilb, Rogal and Hamilton Insurance Services of Central California, Inc., Fresno, CA; *U.S. Public*, pg. 827
Gorian, Jim, Gen. Mgr.--Dekoron Division, Aurora, OH; *U.S. Public*, pg. 689
Gorin, David, Branch Mgr.--Rathbone, King & Seeley Insurance Services, Encino, CA; *U.S. Private*, pg. 610
Gorin, Michael, Pres.--Aeroflex Systems Corp., Saint Leonard, MD; *U.S. Public*, pg. 24
Gorini, R., Mng. Dir.--Toshiba Medical Systems S.R.L., Rome, Italy; *Int'l*, pg. 1407
Goris, Paul C., Chm. Bd.--Antwerpese Diamantbank N.V., Antwerp, Belgium; *Int'l*, pg. 147
Gorla, Carlo, Pres.--Computational Systems Inc., Knoxville, TN; *U.S. Public*, pg. 572
Gorlitz, Werner, Chief Oper. Officer--Krauss-Maffei Verkehrstechnik GmbH, Munich, Germany; *Int'l*, pg. 836
Gorman, Christopher, Chief Exec. Officer--Jardine Fleming Ord Minnett Pty Limited, Sydney, Australia; *Int'l*, pg. 494
Gorman, Jeffrey S., V.P. & Gen. Mgr.--Mansfield Div., Mansfield, OH; *U.S. Public*, pg. 754
Gorman, P.O., Gen. Mgr.--Kodak (Thailand) Ltd., Bangkok, Thailand; *U.S. Public*, pg. 555
Gorman, Peter, Pres.--PennySaver, Brea, CA; *U.S. Public*, pg. 794
Gorman, Tim, Gen. Mgr.--Dynagen Inc., Odessa, TX; *Int'l*, pg. 327
Gorrell, Leroy, Publr.--Gilroy Dispatch, Gilroy, CA; *U.S. Private*, pg. 225
Gorria, J. Romeo, Chm.--CAM, Madrid, Spain; *Int'l*, pg. 662
Gorski, Donald J., Pres. & Chief Oper. Officer--Devon Publishing Group, Novato, CA; *U.S. Public*, pg. 503
Gorski, P. Paul, Pres.--Siouxland Galvanizing Corp., Sioux City, IA; *U.S. Private*, pg. 656
Gorsky, Alec, Mgr.--Victaulic International, Easton, PA; *U.S. Private*, pg. 1138
Gorstoiago, Jose Antonio, Mng. Dir.--Asientos del Norte SA (ANSA), Pamplona, Spain; *Int'l*, pg. 193
Gorsuch, Terry, Gen. Mgr.--United States Aluminum-Carolina, Rock Hill, SC; *U.S. Public*, pg. 895
Gortazar Landecho, Ignacio, Gen. Mgr.--Voith Tolosa S.A., Tolosa, Spain; *Int'l*, pg. 1473
Gorton, M.G., Mng. Dir.--A.C. Nielsen Co., Ltd., Oxford, United Kingdom; *U.S. Public*, pg. 1183
Goschke, Doug, V.P. & Gen. Mgr.--The HON Co., Oak Street Plant No. 1, Muscatine, IA; *U.S. Public*, pg. 772
Gose, G., Chief Exec. Officer--Zurich Life Insurance Company, Zurich, Switzerland; *Int'l*, pg. 1529
Goshko, Nester, Mgr.--Lufkin Machine Co. Ltd., Nisku, Canada; *U.S. Public*, pg. 1019
Goslyn, H.I., Mng. Dir.--Remtox (Chemicals) Limited, Kingswinford, United Kingdom; *Int'l*, pg. 802
Gosper, Brett, Chief Exec. Officer--EURO RSCG Wnek Gosper, London, United Kingdom; *Int'l*, pg. 603
Goss, Allan, Chief Oper. Officer--Chris-Craft Industrial Products, Inc., Trenton, NJ; *U.S. Public*, pg. 351
Goss, C. H., Pres.--R.I. Development & Exploration Co., Cumberland, RI; *U.S. Public*, pg. 1706
Goss, C. H., Pres.--Valley Propane, Inc., Cumberland, RI; *U.S. Public*, pg. 1706
Goss, David, Gen. Mgr.--Hercules Energy Corp., Oklahoma City, OK; *U.S. Public*, pg. 970
Goss, John, Mgr.-Sls.--PENCO-Georgia, Atlanta, GA; *Int'l*, pg. 1508
Goss, Robert T., Gen. Mgr.--Custodis-Cottrell, Inc., Somerville, NJ; *U.S. Public*, pg. 29
Gosselin, Yves, Div. Gen. Mgr.--Northern Telecom Canada Limited, Network Access Div., Aylmer, Canada; *Int'l*, pg. 969
Gosselink, Jerry D., Pres.-Natl. Div. & Chief Oper. Officer--The Weitz Company, Inc., Des Moines, IA; *U.S. Private*, pg. 1160
Gossett, Forrest, Publr.--Wichita Business Journal, Inc., Wichita, KS; *U.S. Private*, pg. 20
Gosslim, Wayne, Plant Mgr.--Data Business Forms, Regina, Canada; *Int'l*, pg. 384
Gossner, Alfred, Dr., Chief Exec. Officer--Allianz Versicherungs-AG, Hamburg, Germany; *Int'l*, pg. 58
Gothard, Tom, Plant Mgr.--Forge Division, South Bend, IN; *U.S. Public*, pg. 557
Gotkin, Bob, Branch Mgr.--Union-Transport Corporation-New York Office, Jamaica, NY; *U.S. Private*, pg. 1120
Goto, Kazuhiro, Gen. Mgr.--Office Products Div., Ramsey, NJ; *Int'l*, pg. 869
Goto, Kunio, Dir.--Dyestuffs Div., Tokyo, Japan; *Int'l*, pg. 934
Goto, Masaru, Pres.--Honda International Trading Co. (H.I.T.), Torrance, CA; *Int'l*, pg. 634
Goto, Mitsuo, Pres.--Nomura Wasserstein Perella Co., Ltd., Tokyo, Japan; *Int'l*, pg. 956
Goto, Naohide, Rep.--Aichi Steel Works, Ltd., Lexington, KY; *Int'l*, pg. 36
Gotoh, Kazuhiko, Pres.--Pasco Corp. of America, Torrance, CA; *Int'l*, pg. 1231
Gotoh, Masao, Pres.--Hakuhodo Corporate Sound Design Co., Ltd., Tokyo, Japan; *Int'l*, pg. 587
Gott, Wolfgang, Chief Oper. Officer--GLS Gesellschaft fur Logistischen Service mbH, Munich, Germany; *Int'l*, pg. 836
Gottdenker, Michael, Exec V.P.--Commonwealth Telephone Co., Dallas, PA; *U.S. Public*, pg. 415
Gotter, Steve A., Mgr.-Branch--Piper Jaffray Inc., Lake Oswego, OR; *U.S. Public*, pg. 1302
Gottesman, Charles E., Pres.--Unisource, City of Commerce, CA; *U.S. Public*, pg. 1671
Gottheil, Julio J. R., Gen. Mgr.--Rorer Argentina S.A., Buenos Aires, Argentina; *Int'l*, pg. 1111
Gotthelf, Michael, Dr., Mng. Dir.--Metallbank GmbH, Frankfurt/Main, Germany; *Int'l*, pg. 861
Gotti-Tedeschi, Ettore, Gen. Mgr.--Santander Investment SpA, Milan, Italy; *Int'l*, pg. 144
Gottlieb, Terry, Pres. & Chief Exec. Officer--Talent Partners, Chicago, IL; *U.S. Private*, pg. 554
Gottmann, Henry D., Chief Admin. Officer--Lehman Brothers, Inc., New York, NY; *U.S. Public*, pg. 987
Gottschalk, Carlos A., Grp. Chm.--Johnson & Johnson Ltda., Sao Paulo, Brazil; *U.S. Public*, pg. 931
Gottsche, Graham, Gen. Mgr.--Kvaerner R J Brown Pty Ltd, Chatswood, Australia; *Int'l*, pg. 767
Gottsche, Michael, V.P.--Pirella Gottsche Lowe, Milan, Italy; *U.S. Private*, pg. 678
Gottschlich, Jim, Gen. Mgr.--Dayco Molded Products, Mebane, NC; *U.S. Public*, pg. 1045
Gouby, Philippe, V.P.--OCG Microelectronic Materials S.A., Roissy Charles de Gaulle, France; *U.S. Public*, pg. 1220

Goucher, Bob, Pres.--Starmark, Inc., Sioux Falls, SD; *U.S. Public*, pg. 1054
Goucher, Robert, Pres. & Chief Exec. Officer--Ryobi Outdoor Products, Chandler, AZ; *Int'l*, pg. 1151
Goudriaan, John, Pres.--Georg Fischer WAGA N.V., Epe, Netherlands; *Int'l*, pg. 490
Gough, Leland, Pres.--Peoples Bank, Senatobia, MS; *U.S. Public*, pg. 639
Gough, Malcolm, Mng. Dir.--EMAP Nationals, Peterborough, United Kingdom; *Int'l*, pg. 451
Gougoux, Yves, Pres. & Chief Exec. Officer--Publicis BCP Montreal Inc., Montreal, Canada; *Int'l*, pg. 116
Goulay, Jean-Claude, Chm. Bd.--Initiative & Finance Investissement, Paris, France; *Int'l*, pg. 344
Gould, B. D., V.P. & Gen. Mgr.--Saft America, Power Sources Div., Valdosta, GA; *Int'l*, pg. 55
Gould, F.J., Chm.--Investment Research Company, Rancho Santa Fe, CA; *U.S. Public*, pg. 1673
Gould, P.R., Joint Mng. Dir.--Bovis International Ltd., London, United Kingdom; *Int'l*, pg. 1032
Gould, Wayne, Unit Mgr.--Weatherford Inc. P.R.C., Hong Kong, Hong Kong; *U.S. Public*, pg. 1750
Gouldey, William, Mgr.--General Employment Enterprises, Inc., Philadelphia, PA; *U.S. Public*, pg. 714
Gouldie, Peter J., Pres. & Mng. Dir.--Inco Pacific Sales Limited, Taipei, Taiwan; *Int'l*, pg. 673
Goulding, Paul, Chief Oper. Officer--Addison-Wesley (Singapore) Pvt. Ltd., Singapore, Singapore; *Int'l*, pg. 1027
Gouldney, David, Gen. Mgr.--Bristol Brewery, Bristol, United Kingdom; *Int'l*, pg. 1212
Gourbin, Jean-Louis, Mng. Dir.--Kellogg (Aust.) Proprietary Ltd., Pagewood, Australia; *U.S. Public*, pg. 947
Gourd, Alain, Pres. & Chief Exec. Officer--Canadian Satellite Communications Inc., Mississauga, Canada; *Int'l*, pg. 1481
Gourgeon, Pierre-Henri, Chm.--Groupe Servair (Compagnie d'Exploitation des Services Auxiliairies Aeriens), Roissy, France; *Int'l*, pg. 560
Gourlay, John, Gen. Mgr.--BHP Steel Building Products Vietnam Ltd., An Bien, Vietnam; *Int'l*, pg. 227
Gournay, Patrick, Pres. & Chief Exec. Officer--The Dannon Co., Tarrytown, NY; *Int'l*, pg. 379
Goust, Dominique, Chief Oper. Officer--Librairie Generale Francaise, Paris, France; *Int'l*, pg. 792
Gouvars, X., Dir.--Domaines Michel Bernard SA, Orange, France; *Int'l*, pg. 752
Gouwens, Bob, Pres.--Worldwide Foods, Inc., Chicago, IL; *U.S. Private*, pg. 640
Gouyou Beauchamps, Xavier, Pres.--Telediffusion de France, Paris, France; *Int'l*, pg. 503
Govan, G.R., Chief Oper. Officer--Babcock Contractors Ltd., Crawley, United Kingdom; *Int'l*, pg. 471
Gove, Kenneth, Dr., Mgr.-Oper.--SIFCO Turbine Component Services, Tampa, FL; *U.S. Public*, pg. 1471
Gover, D.L., Plant Mgr.--Dunlop Tire Corporation (Huntsville), Huntsville, AL; *Int'l*, pg. 1317
Govern, G.R., Chief Oper. Officer--Babcock Minerals Engineering Ltd., Gloucester, United Kingdom; *Int'l*, pg. 472
Govern, G.R., Chief Oper. Officer--Bulk Handling Division, Gloucester, United Kingdom; *Int'l*, pg. 472
Gowan, Damon, Pres. & Chief Exec. Officer--Gowan, Inc., Houston, TX; *U.S. Public*, pg. 572
Goward, Jim, Mgr.-Sls., W. Coast Opers.--LeaRonal, Inc., Orange, CA; *U.S. Public*, pg. 982
Gowdy, Bob G., Pres. & Chief Exec. Officer--Commercial Union Corporation, Boston, MA; *Int'l*, pg. 308
Gower, Dennis, Div. Pres.--SLACAN, Brantford, Canada; *Int'l*, pg. 1262
Gower, Peter, Dir.--Willis Corroon Construction Risks Limited, Billericay, United Kingdom; *Int'l*, pg. 1502
Gowin, Wallace, Gen. Mgr.--Wackenhut Thailand Co., Ltd., Bangkok, Thailand; *U.S. Public*, pg. 1732
Gowlik, Mark, Pres.--Ace Novelty Company, Inc., Woodinville, WA; *U.S. Public*, pg. 1309
Goyeneche, Marcel, Gen. Mgr.--CCF Quito, Quito, Ecuador; *Int'l*, pg. 342
Goyenechea, Juan-Carlos, Rep.--Generale Bank, Mexico, Mexico; *Int'l*, pg. 547
Goyette, Joe, Plant Mgr.--Brockway Standard Inc., Homerville, GA; *U.S. Public*, pg. 164
Goyette, R.A., Opers. Mgr.--Hubbell Diecasting, Moultrie, GA; *U.S. Public*, pg. 844
Goyette, Tom J., Gen. Mgr.--Martin Marietta International, Inc., London, United Kingdom; *U.S. Public*, pg. 1010
Goytia, G., Mng. Dir.--Marchon Espanola S.A., Tarragona, Spain; *U.S. Public*, pg. 1580
Graae, Niels, Exec. Dir.--Icopal-Siplast GmbH, Werne, Germany; *Int'l*, pg. 659
Graaff, Jurgen, Mng. Dir.--Telefunken Sendertechnik GmbH, Berlin, Germany; *U.S. Public*, pg. 1563
Graarud, Thorbjorn, Mng. Dir.--ISS Norge a.s., Oslo, Norway; *Int'l*, pg. 656
Graban, Th.J.M., Dir. Gen.--Luijckx BV Chocolade, Zundert, Netherlands; *Int'l*, pg. 751
Grabenhofer, Emil, Pres.--Componenta International GmbH, Vienna, Austria; *Int'l*, pg. 1421
Graber, Marcel, Dr., Gen. Mgr.--Secura Insurance Companies, Zurich, Switzerland; *Int'l*, pg. 866
Graber, W.R., Chief Oper. Officer--Mead Timber Co., Dayton, OH; *U.S. Public*, pg. 1076
Graber, Werner, Chief Oper. Officer--Alfa-Laval AG, Sursee, Switzerland; *Int'l*, pg. 1380
Grabner, George J., Jr., Pres.--American Recreation Products, Inc., Saint Louis, MO; *U.S. Public*, pg. 948
Grabs, Ingolf, Mgr.--Deutsche Bank AG (Macau), Macau, Macau; *Int'l*, pg. 404
Grace, Bob, Editor--Plastics News, Akron, OH; *U.S. Private*, *pg. 285*
Grace, J. Peter, Chm. Bd. & Chief Exec. Officer--W.R. Grace & Co.-Conn., New York, NY; *U.S. Public*, pg. 755
Grace, James N., Chief Oper. Officer--CCH Canadian Ltd., North York, Canada; *Int'l*, pg. 1513
Grace, Kevin, Pres. & Chief Oper. Officer--Spring Engineers of Houston Ltd., Houston, TX; *U.S. Private*, pg. 956
Grace, Patrick P., Pres.--Grace Logistics Services, Greenville, SC; *U.S. Public*, pg. 755
Grace, Perry R., Pres.--Dynachem Div., Tustin, CA; *U.S. Public*, pg. 1135
Grace, Richard, Chief Oper. Officer--Warner-Jenkinson Cosmetic Colors, South Plainfield, NJ; *U.S. Public*, pg. 1696
Grad, John, Pres.--Landis & Staefa, Inc., Buffalo Grove, IL; *Int'l*, pg. 800
Grad, John, Pres.--Landis & Staefa Inc., Buffalo Grove, IL; *Int'l*, pg. 800
Grad, Richard, Pres.--Five Star Group, Inc., East Hanover, NJ; *U.S. Public*, pg. 694
Gradman, Per, Mng. Dir.--Neopac A/S, Randers, Denmark; *Int'l*, pg. 864
Grady, John, Pres. & Chief Exec. Officer--XRE Corporation, Littleton, MA; *U.S. Public*, pg. 1595
Graf Kerssenbrock, Valentin N., Dir.--DG European Securities Corporation, New York, NY; *Int'l*, pg. 352
Graf, A. Jay, Pres.--Guidant Corporation-Cardiac Rhythm Management Group, Saint Paul, MN; *U.S. Public*, pg. 768
Graf, Guenther, Gen. Mgr.--Tektronix GesmbH, Schwechat, Austria; *U.S. Public*, pg. 1567
Graf, John A., Pres.--Western National Corporation, Houston, TX; *U.S. Public*, pg. 76
Graf, John A., Pres. & Chief Exec. Officer--Western National Life Insurance Co., Houston, TX; *U.S. Public*, pg. 76
Graf, W.J., Dr., Chm.--Hoogovens Aluminium Profiltechnik GmbH, Vogt, Germany; *Int'l*, pg. 755
Graf, Wilfried H., Mgr.--Commerzbank AG London Branch, London, United Kingdom; *Int'l*, pg. 311
Graff, Curtis, Pres.--NationsBank of Butler, Butler, MO; *U.S.* Public, pg. 1164
Graff, Curtis, Pres.--NationsBank of Southwest Missouri, Carthage, MO; *U.S. Public*, pg. 1164
Graffeo, Christopher, Pres. & Chief Exec. Officer--National City Bank, Indiana, Indianapolis, IN; *U.S. Public*, pg. 1154
Grafton, Daniel, Exec. V.P.--Beech Aerospace Services, Inc., Madison, MS; *U.S. Public*, pg. 1365
Graham, Alex, Pres.--Western Pool Terminals Limited, Vancouver, Canada; *Int'l*, pg. 1195
Graham, C., Pres.--Smithbooks, Toronto, Canada; *Int'l*, pg. 1150
Graham, Charles A., Chm., Pres. & Chief Exec. Officer--Regions Bank/Baldwin County, Bay Minette, AL; *U.S. Public*, pg. 1371
Graham, Conn, Gen. Mgr.--HMT Rubber Glas Ltd., High Wycombe, United Kingdom; *U.S. Public*, pg. 914
Graham, David, Chm. Bd.--Sunwest Bank of El Paso, El Paso, TX; *U.S. Public*, pg. 1165
Graham, Don A., Pres.-Rollform--Trinity-Structural Steel, Montgomery, AL; *U.S. Public*, pg. 1639
Graham, Doug, Gen. Mgr.--Wabash Fibre Box Co.-Montgomery, Prattville, AL; *U.S. Private*, pg. 1170
Graham, Edward J., Pres.--SJ EnerTrade, Folsom, NJ; *U.S. Public*, pg. 1488
Graham, Edward S., Pres.--Noramco, Inc., Athens, GA; *U.S.* Public, pg. 929
Graham, Gary, Gen. Mgr.--Bear Island Paper Co., Ashland, VA; *U.S. Private*, pg. 166
Graham, Gary, Gen. Mgr.--Bear Island Paper Co., Ashland, VA; *U.S. Public*, pg. 525
Graham, Gordon L., Pres.--Sysco Food Services of Southeast Florida, Inc., Riviera Beach, FL; *U.S. Public*, pg. 1552
Graham, H. D., Jr., Treas. & Fin. Admin. Officer--Electric Energy Export Corp., Stamford, CT; *U.S. Public*, pg. 380
Graham, H. D., Jr., Treas. & Fin. Admin. Officer--Southwestern Investments, Inc., Stamford, CT; *U.S. Public*, pg. 380
Graham, H. D., Jr., Treas. & Fin. Admin. Officer--Utilities Advances Corporation, Stamford, CT; *U.S. Public*, pg. 380
Graham, J.D., Pres.--Canadian Western Natural Gas Company Limited, Calgary, Canada; *Int'l*, pg. 95
Graham, James, Gen. Mgr.--Erdle Perforating Co. Ltd., Fort Erie, Canada; *U.S. Private*, pg. 380
Graham, James C., Pres.--Mid-Central/Sysco Food Services, Inc., Olathe, KS; *U.S. Public*, pg. 1551
Graham, Jimmy, Plant Mgr.--Retail Bag Division - Richmond Plant, Richmond, VA; *U.S. Public*, pg. 1521
Graham, John, Plant Mgr.--Formica Corp., Rocklin, CA; *Int'l*, *pg. 129*
Graham, John, Chief Exec. Officer--Fleishman-Hillard, Saint Louis, MO; *U.S. Private*, pg. 411
Graham, John, Pres. & Gen. Mgr.--Molded Fiber Glass Co., Union City, PA; *U.S. Private*, pg. 756
Graham, John G., Pres.--General Portfolios Corp., Wilmington, DE; *U.S. Public*, pg. 695
Graham, Kenneth, Pres. & Chief Exec. Officer--Thyssen Inc., Detroit, MI; *Int'l*, pg. 1389
Graham, Mark, Pres.--Southern Division, Norcross, GA; *U.S.* Public, pg. 1255
Graham, Michael, Plant Mgr.--Retail Bag Division - Savage Plant, Savage, MD; *U.S. Public*, pg. 1521
Graham, Mike, Mng. Partner--RTCdirect, Washington, DC; *Int'l*, pg. 1483
Graham, Paul, Pres.--3 dbm, Inc., Camarillo, CA; *U.S. Public*, pg. 534
Graham, Richard W., V.P. & Gen. Mgr.--Jefferson Smurfit Folding Carton & Boxboard Mills Div., Saint Louis, MO; *Int'l*, pg. 1270
Graham, Robert J., Controller--Hynautic, Sarasota, FL; *U.S. Public*, pg. 857
Graham, Stuart, Mng. Dir.--ISS Servisystem Com. E. Ind. Ltda., Sao Paulo, Brazil; *Int'l*, pg. 657
Graham, Stuart, Pres.--Slattery Associates Inc., Whitestone, NY; *Int'l*, pg. 1261
Graham, Stuart, Pres. & Chief Exec. Officer--Skanska E&C, Carmel, IN; *Int'l*, pg. 1261
Graham, Stuart E., Chm.--Sordoni Skanska Construction Co., Parsippany, NJ; *Int'l*, pg. 1261
Graham, Suzanne, Pres.--Rauland-Borg Corporation of Florida, Altamonte Springs, FL; *U.S. Private*, pg. 911
Graham, Thomas, V.P.--Florida Tile Ceramic Centers, Inc., Lakeland, FL; *U.S. Public*, pg. 1322
Grahn, Sven-Otto, Mgr.--Athena AB, Malmo, Sweden; *Int'l*, pg. 666
Grainger, John R., Pres.--Laidlaw Transit, Inc, Van Nuys, CA; *Int'l*, pg. 259
Grajales, Eduardo, Mng. Dir.--Publispana/BDDP, Mexico, Mexico; *Int'l*, pg. 118
Gram, Torleif, Pres.--Aker Contracting a.s., Stavanger, Norway; *Int'l*, pg. 41
Gran, Dieter, Gen. Mgr.--BNP-AK Dresdner Bank A.S., Istanbul, Turkey; *Int'l*, pg. 420
Granade, Marshall, Gen. Mgr.--Finishline Industries Inc. of Georgia, Conyers, GA; *U.S. Private*, pg. 428
Granados, Juan, Mgr. Gen.--Petroquimica Espanola, S.A. (PETRESA), Madrid, Spain; *Int'l*, pg. 323
Granata, John P., Sr. V.P. & Gen. Mgr.-Australia--CUNA Mutual Group-Australia, Pennant Hills, Australia; *U.S. Private*, pg. 296
Granath, Herbert A., Pres.--ABC Cable & International Broadcast, Inc., New York, NY; *U.S. Public*, pg. 512
Granberg, Egil, Mng. Dir.--Rammer Norge A/S, Langhus, Norway; *Int'l*, pg. 1352
Granberg, Johan, Chief Oper. Officer--A. Ahlstrom Corporation-Stromfors Works, Ruotsinpyhtaa, Finland; *Int'l*, pg. 32
Granberry, William R., Pres. & Chief Oper. Officer--Tom Brown, Inc., Englewood, CO; *U.S. Public*, pg. 262
Granborg, Mogens, Pres.--Danisco Sugar, Copenhagen, Denmark; *Int'l*, pg. 378
Grand, Andre, Pres. & Chief Oper. Officer--Servirail, Paris, France; *Int'l*, pg. 560
Grandall, Arthur J., Pres.--Ikon Office Systems, Elmsford, NY; *U.S. Public*, pg. 864
Grande, Raymond E., Pres.--LFE Instruments, Chesterland, OH; *U.S. Public*, pg. 482
Grande, Rene, Pres.--Goulds Pumps (Phil.) Inc., Manila, Philippines; *U.S. Public*, pg. 861
Grandeza, R., Mng. Dir.--Gestetner do Brasil, S.A. Sistemas Reprographicos, Rio de Janeiro, Brazil; *Int'l*, pg. 1115
Grandgeorge, Michael, Pres.--Mercantile Bank of Ankeny, Ankeny, IA; *U.S. Public*, pg. 1087
Grandinetti, Anthony A., Pres.--Ball Packaging Holdings Corp., Westminster, CO; *U.S. Public*, pg. 171
Grandinetti, James R., Plant Mgr.--Miller Brewing Company, Fort Worth, TX; *U.S. Public*, pg. 1289
Grandle, Ralph W., Exec. V.P.--Tricon Electromechanical Div., Downers Grove, IL; *U.S. Private*, pg. 1103
Grandsagne, Pierre, Pres.--Dynapac S.A., Tournan-en-Brie, France; *Int'l*, pg. 1420
Grandval, B., Gen. Mgr.--Toshiba Electronics France S.A.R.L., Rosny-sous-Bois, France; *Int'l*, pg. 1406
Grandy, Jeff, Sr. Corp. Fin. Dir.--Citicorp Investment Bank Ltd., London, United Kingdom; *U.S. Public*, pg. 379
Grandy, Richard, Pres.--Easy Gardener Inc., Waco, TX; *U.S.* Public, pg. 1682
Grandy, Richard, Pres.--Weatherly Consumer Products, Paris, KY; *U.S. Public*, pg. 1682
Grandy, Robert D., Pres.--Merrill Lynch Canada Inc., Toronto, Canada; *U.S. Public*, pg. 1098
Granel, Horacio Sanchez, Gen. Mgr.--Boston Compania Argentina de Seguros S.A., Buenos Aires, Argentina; *U.S. Public*, pg. 1700
Grangaard, Paul D., Chm. Bd.--Piper Jaffray Ventures Inc., Minneapolis, MN; *U.S. Public*, pg. 1303
Granger, Alain, Mng. Dir.--Hogamed S.A., Lyon, France; *Int'l*, pg. 668
Granger, Alain, Chief Oper. Officer--Hospal International Marketing, Lyon, France; *Int'l*, pg. 668
Granger, Alain, Chief Oper. Officer--Hospal Ltd., Basel, Switzerland; *Int'l*, pg. 668
Granger, Gordon F., Pres.--CPC Latin American Consumer Foods Division, Englewood Cliffs, NJ; *U.S. Public*, pg. 447
Granger, John, Pres.--APPX Software Inc., Richmond, VA; *U.S. Public*, pg. 1634
Granger, Steve, Gen. Mgr.--Unitog Company, Warrensburg, MO; *U.S. Public*, pg. 1693
Granget, Michel, Pres.--FBFC, Paris, France; *Int'l*, pg. 503
Grangis, Claude, Pres.--Banque de Nouvelle Caledonie, Noumea, New Caledonia; *U.S. Public*, pg. 1248
Grangis, Claude, Pres.--Banque de Tahiti, Papeete, French Polynesia; *U.S. Public*, pg. 1248
Granjean, Michel, chief Exec. Offcier--Mediapolis France, Puteaux, France; *U.S. Private*, pg. 1199
Granjon, D., Chm. Bd.--Simura, Paris, France; *Int'l*, pg. 662
Granmann, Jeorg, Pres. & Chief Exec. Officer--Nihon Schering K.K., Osaka, Japan; *Int'l*, pg. 1204
Grann, Phillis, Pres.--Penguin Putnam Inc., New York, NY; *Int'l*, pg. 1027
Grannan, Ken, Pres. & Gen. Mgr.--Electromechanical Systems, Inc., Largo, FL; *U.S. Public*, pg. 424
Granrud, Ragnar, Mng. Dir.--Esselte Meto A/S, Oslo, Norway; *Int'l*, pg. 461
Granse, Hans-Hermann, Mgr.--Didier Saurebau GmbH, Konigswinter, Germany; *Int'l*, pg. 1464
Granstrom, Rolf, Mng. Dir.--Ericsson Communications (Hong Kong) Ltd., Hong Kong, Hong Kong; *Int'l*, pg. 1366
Grant, Barry, Pres.--Phoenix Div., Tempe, AZ; *U.S. Public*, pg. 1683
Grant, Cynthia, Mng. Dir.--CF2GS, Portland, OR; *U.S. Private*, pg. 194
Grant, David, Pres.--Sight Systems, Inc., Newbury Park, CA; *U.S. Public*, pg. 1795
Grant, Douglas M., Gen. Mgr.--Isco Environmental Division, Lincoln, NE; *U.S. Public*, pg. 914

Grant, Gary, Pres.--United TransNet, Inc., Roswell, GA; *U.S. Public*, pg. 449
Grant, Graham, Mng. Dir.--Mallinckrodt Australia Pty. Ltd., Nottingham, Australia; *U.S. Public*, pg. 1040
Grant, Hal, Facility Mgr.--Square D Co.-Transformer Bus. Div., Milwaukee, WI; *Int'l*, pg. 1208
Grant, Ian J., Pres.--Poli-Twine Canada (Belleville), Belleville, Canada; *Int'l*, pg. 1361
Grant, Ian S., Dir.--BNP - Jersey Trust Corp. Limited, Saint Helier, United Kingdom; *Int'l*, pg. 163
Grant, J.E., Grp. Pres. & V.P.--Industrial Electronics Group, Torrance, CA; *U.S. Public*, pg. 1364
Grant, M. A., Mgr.--Bank of Commerce Trust Company Barbados Limited, Bridgetown, Barbados; *Int'l*, pg. 257
Grant, Margaret, Mng. Dir.--Cascade Land Leasing Co., Seattle, WA; *U.S. Public*, pg. 311
Grant, Martin, Mng. Dir.--Allied Domecq Leisure, Birmingham, United Kingdom; *Int'l*, pg. 63
Grant, Martin, Oper. Mgr.--Gem, Byhalia, MS; *U.S. Private*, pg. 510
Grant, R.C.S., Rep.--ING Bank Kiev, Kiev, Ukraine; *Int'l*, pg. 649
Grant, Susan, V.P.-Southeastern Region--Columbia Tri-Star Television Distribution - Atlanta, Atlanta, GA; *Int'l*, pg. 1282
Grant, Thomas W., Jr., Pres.--Durex Consumer Products, Norcross, GA; *Int'l*, pg. 815
Grant, Thomas W., Jr., Pres.--Marigold Glove Division, Norcross, GA; *Int'l*, pg. 815
Grant, W. Thomas II, Chm. Bd., Pres. & Chief Exec. Officer--Lab One, Lenexa, KS; *U.S. Public*, pg. 1449
Grantham, William P., V.P. & Gen. Mgr.--Dillard, A ResourceNet International Company, Winston Salem, NC; *U.S. Public*, pg. 902
Grantland, Charles R., V.P.--Great Southern Plywood, Cedar Springs, GA; *U.S. Public*, pg. 736
Granus, Lee, Gen. Mgr.--Supreme Truck Bodies of California, Inc., Moreno Valley, CA; *U.S. Public*, pg. 1542
Grapin, Philippe, Chief Oper. Officer--Santa Marina, Sao Paulo, Brazil; *Int'l*, pg. 1177
Grappe, Steve, Admin.--Horizon Specialty Hospital - Lubbock, Lubbock, TX; *U.S. Public*, pg. 839
Gras, Dieter, Pres.--Werner & Pfleiderer Corporation, Ramsey, NJ; *Int'l*, pg. 511
Grasha, James D., Mng. Dir.--A.O. Smith-Water Products Co., Veldhoven, Netherlands; *U.S. Public*, pg. 1477
Grasley, M.H., Pres.--Shell Chemical Co., Houston, TX; *Int'l*, *pg. 1136*
Grass, David, Pres.--Firestone Industrial Products Co., Carmel, IN; *Int'l*, pg. 214
Grasshoff, Hans Wilhelm, Dr., Chm. Bd.--Krupp Hoesch Stahl AG - Dortmund, Dortmund, Germany; *Int'l*, pg. 512
Grassie, Dr. A., Pres.--Wyeth S.A. de C.V., Mexico, Mexico; *U.S. Public*, pg. 82
Grassley, Raymond W., Chief Oper. Officer--XTRA International Ltd., San Francisco, CA; *U.S. Public*, pg. 1786
Grasso, Jo-Ann, Administrator--Lake Eustis Care Center, Eustis, FL; *U.S. Public*, pg. 837
Grau, Juan, Mng. Dir.--TBWA Barcelona, Barcelona, Spain; *U.S. Private*, pg. 1063
Grauman, Gary, Pres.--Rocco Quality Foods, Timberville, VA; *U.S. Private*, pg. 937
Gravel, Michael M., Pres.--Baum USA, Sidney, OH; *Int'l*, pg. 1293
Gravell, John, Base Mgr.--Mercury Air Center, Corpus Christi, TX; *U.S. Public*, pg. 1093
Gravelle, David, Principal--Richards/Gravelle, Dallas, TX; *U.S. Private*, pg. 929
Gravelle, Frederick H., Pres.--NBD Trust Company of Florida N.A., North Palm Beach, FL; *U.S. Public*, pg. 628
Graves, Anthony, Mgr.--Anixter Warrington, Warrington, United Kingdom; *U.S. Public*, pg. 116
Graves, Carol, Gen. Mgr.--EA Engineering, Science & Technology, Inc., Silver Spring, MD; *U.S. Public*, pg. 541
Graves, Earl J., Pres.--Earl G. Graves Publishing Co., Inc., New York, NY; *U.S. Private*, pg. 471
Graves, Herbert, Pres. & Chef Exec. Officer--Standard Steel, Burnham, PA; *U.S. Private*, pg. 425
Graves, J. Anthony, Pres.--Concord Computing Corp., Elk Grove Village, IL; *U.S. Public*, pg. 429
Graves, Richard, V.P.-Saudi Programs & Gen. Mgr.-Riyadh Office--General Dynamics International Corporation, Riyadh, Saudi Arabia; *U.S. Public*, pg. 709
Graving, Bruce, Pres. & Gen. Mgr.--Horizon Coal Services, Inc., Butte, MT; *U.S. Public*, pg. 1127
Gravino, Richard R., Pres.--Provident Consumer Financial Services, Cincinnati, OH; *U.S. Public*, pg. 1338
Gravsam, Michael, Pres.--Grovenberg, Williamsport, PA; *U.S. Private*, pg. 1077
Gravsam, Mike, Pres.--Lunaire Environmental, Williamsport, PA; *U.S. Private*, pg. 1077
Grawe, Jim, Gen. Mgr.--Keystone Buffalo Warehouse, Buffalo, NY; *U.S. Public*, pg. 955
Grawert, Ronald R., Pres.--GTE Mobilnet Incorporated, Atlanta, GA; *U.S. Public*, pg. 696
Gray, David, Pres.--Astra Pharmaceuticals (Malaysia) Sdn Bhd., Kuala Lumpur, Malaysia; *Int'l*, pg. 94
Gray, David, Mng. Dir.--Caledonian Paper Plc, Irvine, United Kingdom; *Int'l*, pg. 1430
Gray, Fred, Chief Oper. Officer--NationsBank of Texas National Money Orders Inc, Dallas, TX; *U.S. Public*, pg. 1163
Gray, Glenn, Gen. Mgr.--Meritex Plastics Industries, Inc., Arlington, TX; *U.S. Public*, pg. 867
Gray, Glenn, Gen. Mgr.--ITW Thielex Plastics Corp., Piscataway, NJ; *U.S. Public*, pg. 867
Gray, H.M.V., Chief Exec.--NatWest U.K., London, United Kingdom; *Int'l*, pg. 910
Gray, James B., Pres.--Monroe Clevite, Milan, OH; *U.S. Public*, pg. 1577
Gray, James K., Pres.--Canadian Hunter Exploration Ltd., Calgary, Canada; *Int'l*, pg. 433
Gray, John, Regional Mgr.--Sumitomo Machinery Corp. of America, Glendale Heights, IL; *Int'l*, pg. 1314
Gray, John, Pres.--Bran & Luebbe Inc., Buffalo Grove, IL; *Int'l*, pg. 1378
Gray, John R., Pres.--Philips Information Systems, Dallas, TX; *Int'l*, pg. 1055
Gray, Josef E., Pres.--Seafirst Corporation, Seattle, WA; *U.S. Public*, pg. 181
Gray, Linda, Gen. Mgr.--WXIN, Indianapolis, IN; *U.S. Public*, *pg. 1636*
Gray, M.F., Dep. Mng. Dir.--Simon-Carves Ltd., Hulme, United Kingdom; *Int'l*, pg. 1251
Gray, Peter M., Exec. Chm.--Jardine Securicor Ltd., Kowloon, Hong Kong; *Int'l*, pg. 705
Gray, Richard L., Chief Oper. Officer--Ahlstrom Filtration, Inc., Chattanooga, TN; *Int'l*, pg. 35
Gray, Robert, Gen. Mgr.-Opers.--Republic Automotive Parts Sales, Inc., Raleigh, NC; *U.S. Public*, pg. 1378
Gray, Ronald G., Chm.--Lever Brothers Ltd., Kingston upon Thames, United Kingdom; *Int'l*, pg. 1434
Gray, Steve, Mng. Dir.--Batey Kazoo, Sydney, Australia; *Int'l*, pg. 117
Gray, Trevor, Mng. Dir.--VMark Asia-Pacific Pty. Ltd., Bondi Junction, Australia; *U.S. Public*, pg. 129
Gray, W. Keith, Exec. V.P.--Green Line Investor Service, Toronto, Canada; *Int'l*, pg. 1401
Gray, Wayne, Plant Mgr.--Certified Apparel Services of Honduras, S.A., San Pedro Sula, Honduras; *U.S. Private*, *pg. 625*
Gray, William J., Chief Oper. Officer--Montana Refining Co., Black Eagle, MT; *U.S. Public*, pg. 830
Gray, William J., Chief Oper. Officer--Navajo Pipeline Co., Artesia, NM; *U.S. Public*, pg. 830
Gray, William J., Chief Oper. Officer--Navajo Holdings, Inc., Dallas, TX; *U.S. Public*, pg. 830
Gray, William J., Chief Oper. Officer--Navajo Western Asphalt Company, Dallas, TX; *U.S. Public*, pg. 830
Graybill, Cheryl, R.N., Fac. Mgr.--Grandview Surgery Center, Camp Hill, PA; *U.S. Public*, pg. 803
Grayson, Brenda, Gen. Mgr.--Olan Mills Inc. of Texas, Waco, TX; *U.S. Private*, pg. 749
Grayson, Patrick, Pres.--Kent Meters, Inc., Isabela, PR; *Int'l*, *pg. 4*
Grayuski, Frank, Plant Mgr.--East Stroudsburg Plant, East Stroudsburg, PA; *U.S. Public*, pg. 443
Graziadio, George L., Pres. & Chief Exec. Officer--Imperial Bank, Inglewood, CA; *U.S. Public*, pg. 871
Grazier, David, Plant Mgr.--C.C.K., Inc., Tyrone, PA; *U.S. Private*, pg. 637
Grazier, George, Pres.--Farmland Foods, Inc., Kansas City, MO; *U.S. Private*, pg. 396
Grazier, George, Pres. & Treas.--FDL Foods, Inc., Dubuque, IA; *U.S. Private*, pg. 396
Grealis, William J., Pres.--Cinergy Investments, Inc., Indianapolis, IN; *U.S. Public*, pg. 369
Grealis, William J., Pres.--Power Equipment Supply Company, New Washington, IN; *U.S. Public*, pg. 369
Grealis, William J., Pres.--PSI Power Resource Development, Inc., Indianapolis, IN; *U.S. Public*, pg. 369
Grealis, William J., Pres.--PSI Power Resource Operations, Indianapolis, IN; *U.S. Public*, pg. 369
Grealis, William J., Pres.--CGE Eck, Inc., Cincinnati, OH; *U.S. Public*, pg. 369
Grealis, William J., Pres.--CG&E Resource Marketing, Inc., Cincinnati, OH; *U.S. Public*, pg. 369
Grealis, William J., Pres.--Tri-State Improvement Co., Cincinnati, OH; *U.S. Public*, pg. 369
Greanias, Stanley L., Pres. & Chief Exec. Officer--Superior Coffee and Foods, Bensenville, IL; *U.S. Public*, pg. 1434
Greason, Robert J., V.P.--Hickman, Williams de Mexico S.A. de C.V., Monterrey, Mexico; *U.S. Private*, pg. 525
Greason, Robert J., Pres.--Hickman, Williams Canada, Inc., Cambridge, Canada; *U.S. Private*, pg. 525
Greathouse, Steve, Pres. & Chief Exec. Officer--Casino Electronics, Inc., Las Vegas, NV; *U.S. Public*, pg. 47
Greaves, David, Mng. Dir.--Brockhouse C & F Machining Limited, West Bromwich, United Kingdom; *Int'l*, pg. 426
Grebe, Manfred, Mng. Dir.--Circulo de Leitores, Lisbon, Portugal; *Int'l*, pg. 192
Grebenstein, Hermann, Pres.--Projidata A.G., Neuendorf, Switzerland; *Int'l*, pg. 489
Greblo, G.A., Pres.--Portland Terminal Railroad Co., Portland, OR; *U.S. Public*, pg. 1668
Grecco, Mike, Gen. Mgr.--ITW Norwood Marking Systems, Downers Grove, IL; *U.S. Public*, pg. 866
Greciet, Francois, Chief Oper. Officer--Rhone-Poulenc Maroc, Casablanca, Morocco; *Int'l*, pg. 1113
Greco Clow, Maryann, Publication Mgr.--Expecting, New York, NY; *Int'l*, pg. 190
Greco, Rosemarie B., Pres. & Chief Exec. Officer--CoreStates Bank, N.A., Philadelphia, PA; *U.S. Public*, pg. 446
Greczyn, Robert, Chief Exec. Officer--Healthsource North Carolina, Inc., Morrisville, NC; *U.S. Public*, pg. 360
Greed, Thomas, Gen. Mgr.--Triple S Plastics, Southwest, Tucson, AZ; *U.S. Public*, pg. 1640
Greehey, William E., Chm. Bd. & Chief Exec. Officer--Valero Refining Company, San Antonio, TX; *U.S. Public*, pg. 1704
Greely, F.J., Jr., Pres. & Chief Exec. Officer--Regions Bank/ Central Louisiana, New Roads, LA; *U.S. Public*, pg. 1372
Green Martin, Chief Oper. Officer--TRU-LON Printed Circuits (Royston) Limited, Royston, United Kingdom; *Int'l*, pg. 1290
Green, A., Gen. Mgr.--Bleakley Fine Chemicals, Silverwater, Australia; *Int'l*, pg. 803
Green, Anthony H., Reg. Mgr.--Falconbridge Explorations, Falconbridge, Canada; *Int'l*, pg. 433
Green, B.J., Pres.--Solutia Inc., Foley, AL; *U.S. Public*, pg. 1484
Green, Bill, Gen. Mgr.--Sterling Rubber & Gasket, Houston, TX; *U.S. Private*, pg. 1032
Green, Bob, Pres.--Leone Food Service Corp., Livonia, MI; *U.S. Private*, pg. 244
Green, Brian, Mng. Dir.--BOC Process Plants Ltd., Guildford, United Kingdom; *Int'l*, pg. 121
Green, C.H., Chm. Bd.--Rolls-Royce-Commercial Aero Engines Ltd., Derby, United Kingdom; *Int'l*, pg. 1127
Green, Christine, Branch Mgr.--Downey Savings & Loan Association, F.A., Palm Desert, CA; *U.S. Public*, pg. 527
Green, Clay S., Pres. & Chief Exec. Officer--First Midwest Mortgage Corporation, Joliet, IL; *U.S. Public*, pg. 636
Green, Dave, Pres.--Linotype-Hell Company, Hauppauge, NY; *Int'l*, pg. 604
Green, Dave, Mng. Dir.--Logica SA/NV, Brussels, Belgium; *Int'l*, pg. 815
Green, David, Pres.--Dole Northwest, East Wenatchee, WA; *U.S. Public*, pg. 515
Green, David L., Plant Mgr.--Miller Brewing Company, Fulton, NY; *U.S. Public*, pg. 1289
Green, Don, Pres.--Capacity of Texas, Inc., Longview, TX; *U.S. Public*, pg. 400
Green, Gary, Pres.--Comair Aviation Academy, Inc., Sanford, FL; *U.S. Public*, pg. 406
Green, George, Pres. & Gen. Mgr.--KABC-AM Radio, Inc., Los Angeles, CA; *U.S. Public*, pg. 512
Green, Jack, Gen. Mgr.--Bay Cities Auto Auction, Hayward, CA; *U.S. Private*, pg. 282
Green, Jeffrey W., Pres.--HTI Export Ltd., Bridgetown, Barbados; *U.S. Public*, pg. 851
Green, Jerome K., Pres.--Case Engine Holding Company, Inc., Racine, WI; *U.S. Public*, pg. 311
Green, Jim, Mng. Dir.--Ademco MicroTech Limited, Glasgow, United Kingdom; *U.S. Public*, pg. 1307
Green, Jim, Mng. Dir.--Ademco Microtech Security Ltd., East Kilbride, United Kingdom; *U.S. Public*, pg. 1307
Green, Johnathan D., Pres. & Chief Exec. Officer--Rockefeller Center Management Corporation, New York, NY; *Int'l*, pg. 873
Green, Judson, Pres.--Walt Disney Attractions Division, Anaheim, CA; *U.S. Public*, pg. 511
Green, Judson, Pres.--Lake Buena Vista Communities, Inc., Lake Buena Vista, FL; *U.S. Public*, pg. 513
Green, Judson, Pres.--Reedy Creek Energy Services, Inc., Lake Buena Vista, FL; *U.S. Public*, pg. 514
Green, Ken, V.P.-Prod. Mdsg. & Procurement--National Produce Div., Montvale, NJ; *Int'l*, pg. 1375
Green, Kenneth, Pres.--Revlon International Corporation, London, United Kingdom; *U.S. Private*, pg. 690
Green, Kurt, Pres.--Asea Brown Boveri Sdn. Bhd., Kuala Lumpur, Malaysia; *Int'l*, pg. 8
Green, M.J., Mng. Dir.--Century Life, London, United Kingdom; *Int'l*, pg. 685
Green, Malcolm, Gen. Mgr.--Martin Marietta International, Inc., Singapore, Singapore; *U.S. Public*, pg. 1010
Green, Michael B., Mgr.--CVG Aviation, Cincinnati, OH; *U.S. Public*, pg. 406
Green, Michael W., Pres.--Miesel/Sysco Food Service Co., Canton, MI; *U.S. Public*, pg. 1551
Green, Mike, Pres. & Chief Exec. Officer-Inpower--Integral Systems, Inc., Walnut Creek, CA; *Int'l*, pg. 242
Green, Mike, Pres. & Chief Oper. Officer--InPower Inc., San Francisco, CA; *Int'l*, pg. 242
Green, Owen, Sir, Chm. Bd.--Dunlop Holdings plc, London, United Kingdom; *Int'l*, pg. 124
Green, Paul, Mgr.-Opers.--Titan Wheel International Ltd., Newton-le-Willows, United Kingdom; *U.S. Public*, pg. 1619
Green, R. W., Plant Mgr.--Waterbury Companies, Inc., Randolph, VT; *U.S. Public*, pg. 308
Green, R.L., Gen. Mgr.--Abtco, Inc., Middlebury, IN; *Int'l*, pg. 20
Green, Ray, Chief Oper. Officer--Paradigm Learning, Tampa, FL; *U.S. Private*, pg. 838
Green, Richard L., Chm. Bd., Pres. & Chief Exec. Officer--General Shale Products Corp., Johnson City, TN; *Int'l*, pg. 843
Green, Richard L., Chm. Bd., Pres. & Chief Exec. Officer--General Shale Products Corp., Elizabethton, TN; *Int'l*, pg. 843
Green, Robert E., Mng. Dir.--W.R. Grace Ltd., London, United Kingdom; *U.S. Public*, pg. 756
Green, Steve, Pres.--Flowers Baking Co. of Tyler, Inc., Tyler, TX; *U.S. Public*, pg. 657
Green, Terence, Chief Oper. Officer--Tappan International Sales Ltd., Manchester, United Kingdom; *Int'l*, pg. 444
Green, William, Principal--Nadel Architects Inc. & Marvin Fitch, Chicago, IL; *U.S. Private*, pg. 773
Green, William B., V.P. & Publisher--Laredo Morning Times, Laredo, TX; *U.S. Private*, pg. 517
Greenacre, Martyn, Chm.--SmithKline Beecham Pharmaceuticals, European Division, Brussels, Belgium; *Int'l*, pg. 1264
Greenacre, Tom, Pres.--Dukane SeaCom Division, Saint Charles, IL; *U.S. Private*, pg. 346
Greenawald, Mike, Mgr.-Project--Cupertino Electric, Inc., Phoenix, AZ; *U.S. Private*, pg. 1060
Greenbaum, Bruce, Pres.--Brice Manufacturing Company, Inc., Pacoima, CA; *U.S. Public*, pg. 534
Greenberg, Arthur, Chief Oper. Officer--SIFCO Selective Plating, Cleveland, OH; *U.S. Public*, pg. 1471
Greenberg, Arthur, Chief Oper. Officer--SIFCO Selective Plating, Monrovia, CA; *U.S. Public*, pg. 1471
Greenberg, Jeffrey W., Chm. Bd. & Chief Exec. Officer--Marsh & McLennan Risk Capital Corp., Greenwich, CT; *U.S. Public*, pg. 1049
Greenberg, Karen R., Pres.--Elisabeth Division, New York, NY; *U.S. Public*, pg. 1006
Greenberg, Marty, Pres.--AVW Audiovisual, Inc., Dallas, TX; *U.S. Private*, pg. 426
Greenberg, Maurice, Chm. Bd.--Transatlantic Holdings Inc., New York, NY; *U.S. Public*, pg. 84
Greenberg, Michael, Exec. V.P.--Vinylweld Division, Chicago, IL; *U.S. Private*, pg. 848
Greenberg, Richard L., Pres.--Wadsworth Publishing Co., Belmont, CA; *U.S. Public*, pg. 1600
Greenberg, Robert, Chm. & Chief Exec. Officer--R/GA Interactive, New York, NY; *U.S. Public*, pg. 1641

Greenblatt, Alfred A., Pres.--Guilford Mills (Apparel, Home & Industrial Fabrics), New York, NY; *U.S. Public*, pg. 769

Greenblatt, Alfred A., Pres.--Guilford Mills (Apparel, Home & Industrial Fabrics), Northfield, IL; *U.S. Public*, pg. 769

Greene, Bruce E., Pres.--Environ, Inc., Dearborn, MI; *U.S. Public*, pg. 664

Greene, Edward, Pres.--Carl Zeiss Optical, Inc., Petersburg, VA; *Int'l*, pg. 1523

Greene, Gerald, Gen. Mgr.--Kodak Brasileira C.I.L., Sao Paulo, Brazil; *U.S. Public*, pg. 552

Greene, Gordon J., Pres.--Sheldon Good & Company Auctions, Chicago, IL; *U.S. Private*, pg. 464

Greene, H. Lyle, Pres.--Peters Machinery Co., Chicago, IL; *U.S. Public*, pg. 944

Greene, Jaime, Mng. Dir.--Leo Burnett Publicidade, Ltda., Sao Paulo, Brazil; *U.S. Private*, pg. 185

Greene, M. Anthony, Pres.--Investment Management & Research, Inc., Saint Petersburg, FL; *U.S. Public*, pg. 923

Greene, Marc J., Pres. & Chief Exec. Officer--Regions Bank/White County, Cleveland, GA; *U.S. Public*, pg. 1373

Greener, Anthony, Chm. Bd. & Chief Exec. Officer--Guinness Plc, London, United Kingdom; *Int'l*, pg. 412

Greener, George, Chm. Bd.--Eagle Star, London, United Kingdom; *Int'l*, pg. 110

Greener, Stewart, V.P. & Gen. Mgr.--Barbeque King, Reading, United Kingdom; *U.S. Public*, pg. 1507

Greenfield, David, Gen. Mgr.--Fisax, Tewkesbury, United Kingdom; *U.S. Private*, pg. 103

Greenfield, Janet, R.N., Fac. Mgr.--Inland Surgery Center, Redlands, CA; *U.S. Public*, pg. 803

Greenfield, Jim, V.P. & Branch Mgr.--Burns & Wilcox - Indianapolis Office, Indianapolis, IN; *U.S. Private*, pg. 610

Greenfield, Richard, Mng. Dir.--National Mutual Funds Management Ltd., Melbourne, Australia; *Int'l*, pg. 908

Greenhalgh, Nigel, Mng. Dir.--Dumez S.A. Emirates, Abu Dhabi, United Arab Emirates; *Int'l*, pg. 823

Greenhouse, Harold, Gen. Mgr.--Spring Lake Feed Yard, Earth, TX; *U.S. Private*, pg. 429

Greenhow, Richard, Pres.--Premier Drywall Tool Company, Stockton, CA; *U.S. Private*, pg. 613

Greenlee, Jim, Chief Oper. Officer--Pyro Mining Co., Sturgis, KY; *Int'l*, pg. 337

Greenlee, Rich, Mgr.-Office--Woodward-Clyde, Middleton, WI; *U.S. Public*, pg. 1656

Greenlee, Richard, Mgr.-Office--Woodward-Clyde, Minneapolis, MN; *U.S. Public*, pg. 1656

Greenlee, Stewart M., Pres. & Chief Exec. Officer--The Fifth Third Bank of Southern Ohio, Hillsboro, OH; *U.S. Public*, pg. 622

Greenman, John, Publisher--The Columbus Ledger & Enquirer, Columbus, GA; *U.S. Public*, pg. 964

Greenshields, R., Mng. Dir.--AMP Asset Management Plc, London, United Kingdom; *Int'l*, pg. 100

Greenstein, Michael K., Exec. V.P. & Gen. Mgr.-Avon Books--Avon Books, New York, NY; *U.S. Private*, pg. 515

Greenwald, Richard, Pres.--Interstate Div., Troy, MI; *U.S. Public*, pg. 779

Greenwood, Barry, Pres.--Bosch Packaging Machinery Division, South Plainfield, NJ; *Int'l*, pg. 204

Greenwood, John, Mgr.-Sls.--WCPO-TV, Cincinnati, OH; *U.S. Public*, pg. 1448

Greenwood, L., Pres.--Davis Tool & Engineering Co., Detroit, MI; *U.S. Private*, pg. 315

Greenwood, Nigel, Dr., Chief Exec.--Forkardt International GmbH, Erkrath, Germany; *Int'l*, pg. 1484

Greenwood, Nigel, Dr., Pres.--Buck Forkardt, Inc., Portage, MI; *Int'l*, pg. 1484

Greenzalis, Bill, Pres.--Buckeye Biscuit Company, Walton Hills, OH; *Int'l*, pg. 1069

Greer, C. Scott, Pres.--United Technologies Automotive, Dearborn, MI; *U.S. Public*, pg. 1691

Greer, Carol G., Pres. & Chief Exec. Officer-Specialty Footwear--Woolworth Corporation, New York, NY; *U.S. Public*, pg. 1777

Greer, Freddy C., Pres.--The Citizens Bank, Fort Valley, GA; *U.S. Public*, pg. 1549

Greer, K.J., Dir.-Opers.--Meneba N.V., Hague, Netherlands; *Int'l*, pg. 555

Greer, P.C., Reg. Chief Exec. Officer-East Asia--Barclays Bank PLC, Hong Kong, Hong Kong; *Int'l*, pg. 165

Greer, Paul, Pres.--D&Z Utility Services, Philadelphia, PA; *U.S. Private*, pg. 317

Grefe, Peter, Pres.--Shur-Lok International, Petit-Rechain, Belgium; *U.S. Private*, pg. 997

Grefski, Sharon, Branch Mgr.--Valley National Bank, Vernon, NJ; *U.S. Public*, pg. 1706

Gregath, Tim, V.P. & Gen. Mgr.--Quebecor Printing Nashville, Nashville, TN; *Int'l*, pg. 1076

Gregersen, Chris, Gen. Mgr.--ProFormance Awards Inc,, West Des Moines, IA; *U.S. Private*, pg. 555

Gregg, D.E., Pres.--Conoco Norway, Inc., Stavanger, Norway; *U.S. Public*, pg. 531

Gregg, David E., V.P. & Mgr.-Mdsg.--Noland Electrical Div., Newport News, VA; *U.S. Public*, pg. 1187

Gregg, David E., V.P. & Mgr.-Mdsg.--Noland Industrial Div., Newport News, VA; *U.S. Public*, pg. 1187

Gregg, Jeffrey L., Pres.--Bretlin, Inc., Calhoun, GA; *U.S. Public*, pg. 514

Gregg, Ray, Pres.--WCI Machine Tools & Systems, Cincinnati, OH; *Int'l*, pg. 440

Grego, Claudio, Sr. V.P.--RNBNY Branch Office-Milan, Milan, Italy; *U.S. Public*, pg. 1381

Gregoire, Jean, Mng. Dir.--Carlton Cards France, Paris, France; *U.S. Public*, pg. 78

Gregoire, Pierre, Mng. Dir.--Pittway Corp. of Canada, Saint-Laurent, Canada; *U.S. Public*, pg. 1307

Gregor, Charles W., Pres.--Magnet Wire Insulation Sector, Fort Wayne, IN; *U.S. Public*, pg. 593

Gregor, Robert J., Pres.--Woodlands License Management/ Fibre Procurement, Marathon, Canada; *U.S. Public*, pg. 672

Gregori, S.R., Chm. & Mng. Dir.--Texaco Overseas (Nigeria) Petroleum Co., Lagos, Nigeria; *U.S. Public*, pg. 1584

Gregory, Bill, Gen. Mgr.--BRC Weldmesh (Vietnam) Ltd., Ho Chi Minh City, Vietnam; *Int'l*, pg. 227

Gregory, Bruce, Mng. Dir.--Plantronics Ltd., Wootton Bassett, United Kingdom; *U.S. Public*, pg. 1308

Gregory, Harry, Pres. & Gen. Mgr.--AAR Allen Aircraft, Elk Grove Village, IL; *U.S. Public*, pg. 1

Gregory, Joe, Pres.--Perfection Corporation, Madison, OH; *Int'l*, pg. 1149

Gregory, Joel, Gen. Mgr.--Day & Zimmermann Kansas Division, Parsons, KS; *U.S. Private*, pg. 317

Gregory, Jon, Pres.--Quarries Division, Barre, VT; *U.S. Public*, pg. 1396

Gregory, Jon, V.P.--Pennsylvania Granite Corp., Saint Peters, PA; *U.S. Public*, pg. 1396

Gregory, Jon, V.P.--Autumn Rose Quarry, Inc., Mill Creek, OK; *U.S. Public*, pg. 1396

Gregory, Kim, Pres.--Hansen Mechanical Contractors, Inc., Las Vegas, NV; *U.S. Public*, pg. 572

Gregory, R., Chief Exec. Officer-Asia Pacific--Tioxide Group Limited, London, United Kingdom; *Int'l*, pg. 663

Gregory, R.A., Mng. Dir.--Kyle Stewart Ltd., London, United Kingdom; *Int'l*, pg. 630

Gregory, William R., Pres.--Edison Sault Electric Company, Sault Sainte Marie, MI; *U.S. Public*, pg. 592

Greiner, Charles H., Jr., Sr. V.P.--Union Camp Fine Paper Div., Franklin, VA; *U.S. Public*, pg. 1666

Greiner, G.R., Pres.--Genesis Underwriting Management Company, Stamford, CT; *U.S. Public*, pg. 725

Greinke, Bruce, Pres. & Gen. Mgr.--Magnetics International, Inc., Chesterton, IN; *U.S. Public*, pg. 879

Greisch, John J., Pres.--Interlake Material Handling Div., Naperville, IL; *U.S. Public*, pg. 893

Greisen, K. G., Mng. Dir.--Rex-Rotary S.A., Sarcelles, France; *Int'l*, pg. 1116

Greisen, Ken, Mng. Dir.--Lance International S.A., Sarcelles, France; *Int'l*, pg. 1116

Greisiger, W., Controller--DeVilbiss Automotive Refinishing Products, Maumee, OH; *U.S. Public*, pg. 865

Greisinger, James, Pres.--Dean Pickle & Specialty Products Co., Green Bay, WI; *U.S. Public*, pg. 490

Greisinger, James, Pres.--Dean Pickles & Specialty Products, Plymouth, IN; *U.S. Public*, pg. 490

Greller, Andrew H., Pres.--TPT Transportation Company, Baton Rouge, LA; *U.S. Public*, pg. 962

Grellet, Jose Luiz, Gen. Mgr.--ADD Agency, Sao Paulo, Brazil; *U.S. Private*, pg. 1200

Gremillion, Robert, Pres. & Chief Exec. Officer--Sun-Sentinel Company, Fort Lauderdale, FL; *U.S. Public*, pg. 1636

Grenacher, Hans, Chm.--Coop Aargau, Lenzburg, Switzerland; *Int'l*, pg. 329

Grenier, M., Pres.--Primes de Luxe Inc., Neuville, Canada; *Int'l*, pg. 1150

Grenon, Jean-Francois, Pres.-Digital Division--Microwave Radio Communications, Chelmsford, MA; *U.S. Public*, pg. 294

Gres, John, Pres.--Lyall Assemblies, Inc., Albion, IN; *U.S. Private*, pg. 484

Gres, John, Pres.--Pent Plastics, Inc., Avilla, IN; *U.S. Private*, pg. 484

Gres, John, Pres.--Pent Assemblies, Inc., Kendallville, IN; *U.S. Private*, pg. 484

Gres, John, Pres.--Garrett Products, Inc., Garrett, IN; *U.S. Private*, pg. 484

Gres, John, Pres.--Dekko Technical Center, Laotto, IN; *U.S. Private*, pg. 484

Gresh, Philip, V.P. & Gen. Mgr.--ITW Hi-Cone, Itasca, IL; *U.S. Public*, pg. 866

Gresley, John, Gen. Mgr.--Fort Wayne Vehicle Auction Inc., Fort Wayne, IN; *U.S. Public*, pg. 1649

Gressel, Alan, Chief Oper. Officer--Research Trucking Company, Inc., Cleveland, OH; *U.S. Private*, pg. 924

Gressel, Alan, Chief Oper. Officer--Great Lakes Environmental Services, Inc., Cleveland, OH; *U.S. Private*, pg. 924

Gressel, Alan, Chief Oper. Officer--Research Oil Co., Cleveland, OH; *U.S. Private*, pg. 924

Gressette, L.M., Jr., Chm. Bd. & Chief Exec. Officer--South Carolina Generating Co., Inc., Columbia, SC; *U.S. Public*, *pg. 1436*

Gressette, L.M., Jr., Chm. Bd. & Chief Exec. Officer--SCANA Resources, Inc., Columbia, SC; *U.S. Public*, pg. 1436

Gressier, C., Chm. Bd. & Mng. Dir.--CTT Sceta, Paris, France; *Int'l*, pg. 1163

Gressingh, Jack L., V.P. & Gen. Mgr.--Electromagnetic Systems Div., Goleta, CA; *U.S. Public*, pg. 1364

Grethe, Wilhelm, Mgr.--Commerzbank AG Representative Office-Cairo, Cairo, Egypt; *Int'l*, pg. 311

Greubel, William P., V.P. & Gen. Mgr.--AlliedSignal Environmental Catalysts, Catoosa, OK; *U.S. Public*, pg. 51

Greubel, William P., Pres.--Accuride Corp., Henderson, KY; *U.S. Public*, pg. 1286

Greulich, Joseph D., Pres.--D & S Plastics International, Auburn Hills, MI; *Int'l*, pg. 1277

Greuter, Ruedi, Gen. Mgr.--Tektronix International AG, Zug, Switzerland; *U.S. Public*, pg. 1568

Grew, Jim, Pres.--Tri State Tank Corp., Kansas City, KS; *U.S. Private*, pg. 1066

Grey, Bob, Pres.--Gene Jackson Farms, Oxnard, CA; *U.S. Private*, pg. 344

Grey, David, V.P. & Gen. Mgr.--Varitronic Systems, Inc., Brooklyn Park, MN; *U.S. Public*, pg. 250

Grey, Linda, Pres.--Ballantine Books, New York, NY; *U.S. Private*, pg. 21

Gribbin, M.C.D., Chm. Bd. & Chief Exec. Officer--Jardine Insurance Brokers International Limited, London, United Kingdom; *Int'l*, pg. 705

Gribble, Richard N., Pres. & Chief Oper. Officer--Premium Service Corp., Columbia, SC; *U.S. Public*, pg. 1454

Grice, G. Max, III, Chief Oper. Officer--Texas Central Railroad, Gorman, TX; *U.S. Private*, pg. 145

Griebel, James D., Pres.--Treated Water Outsourcing, Naperville, IL; *U.S. Public*, pg. 1150

Griebel, R. Nelson, Pres.--Bank of Boston Connecticut, Hartford, CT; *U.S. Public*, pg. 184

Griech, Frederick G., Pres.--ALLTEL Service Corporation, Hudson, OH; *U.S. Public*, pg. 56

Grieger, Jurgen, Dr., Dir.--Deutsche Hypothekenbank (Actien-Gesellschaft), Hannover, Germany; *Int'l*, pg. 119

Grier, Kathleen T., Pres.--Cosmoflex, Inc., Hannibal, MO; *U.S. Public*, pg. 753

Grierson, B.J., Chm. Bd.--QIT-Fer Et Titane, Montreal, Canada; *Int'l*, pg. 1119

Gries, Louis, Pres.--James Hardie Building Products Inc., Fontana, CA; *Int'l*, pg. 597

Griesbaum, Horst, Gen. Mgr.--Precision Resource-Kentucky Div., Mount Sterling, KY; *U.S. Private*, pg. 880

Griesedieck, Chris R., Pres. & Chief Exec. Officer--Colonial Bank, Des Peres, MO; *U.S. Public*, pg. 643

Griessel, Richard, Pres.--Semikron Inc., Hudson, NH; *Int'l*, pg. 1220

Griessler, Lilith, Dir.--Euro Synergies Management SA, Paris, France; *Int'l*, pg. 181

Griffin, Alfred, Mgr.-Sls., Western--Atlanta Mfg. Facility, Douglasville, GA; *U.S. Private*, pg. 976

Griffin, Bernard, Pres. & Publr.--Press & Sun-Bulletin, Binghamton, NY; *U.S. Public*, pg. 700

Griffin, Bobby, Exec. V.P.-Pacing Bus.--Pacing Business Unit, Minneapolis, MN; *U.S. Public*, pg. 1083

Griffin, Emmett G., Pres.--High State/Investors Guaranty, Columbus, OH; *Int'l*, pg. 110

Griffin, G. Lee, Chief Exec. Officer--Premier Bank N.A., Baton Rouge, LA; *U.S. Public*, pg. 173

Griffin, Greggory E., Gen. Mgr.--Scripps Howard Cable Company, Longmont, CO; *U.S. Public*, pg. 1448

Griffin, Ian, Mng. Dir.--EMAP Response Ltd., Peterborough, United Kingdom; *Int'l*, pg. 451

Griffin, Ian, Gen. Mng. Dir.--CAP Nationwide Motor Research, Skipton, United Kingdom; *Int'l*, pg. 451

Griffin, Ian, Gen. Mng. Dir.--Sewells International Ltd., Totnes, United Kingdom; *Int'l*, pg. 451

Griffin, James, Pres.--AlliedSignal Fluid Systems, Tempe, AZ; *U.S. Public*, pg. 50

Griffin, James, Plant Mgr.--Deep South Products, Gainesville, GA; *U.S. Public*, pg. 1772

Griffin, James A., Pres. & Chief Exec. Officer--The Old Line Life Insurance Co. of America, Milwaukee, WI; *U.S. Public*, pg. 77

Griffin, James W., Pres.--Old Kent Bank of Brighton, Brighton, MI; *U.S. Public*, pg. 1216

Griffin, Jerry, Plant Mgr.--Block Plant, Las Cruces, NM; *U.S. Public*, pg. 936

Griffin, Jerry, Pres.--Master-Bilt Products, New Albany, MS; *U.S. Public*, pg. 1506

Griffin, Jerry, Pres.--United Service Equipment Company, Murfreesboro, TN; *U.S. Public*, pg. 1507

Griffin, John J., Pres.--Seagram Asia Pacific/Global Duty Free, New York, NY; *Int'l*, pg. 1217

Griffin, Merv, Chm. & Chief Exec. Officer--Merv Griffin Enterprises, Beverly Hills, CA; *Int'l*, pg. 1282

Griffin, Randall M., Pres.--Constellation Real Estate Group Inc., Baltimore, MD; *U.S. Public*, pg. 172

Griffin, Richard M., Chm. Bd.--Nippon Credit Australia Limited, Sydney, Australia; *Int'l*, pg. 933

Griffin, T. J., Mgr.--Morton Salt Division, Silver Springs, NY; *U.S. Public*, pg. 1135

Griffin, W. Boyd, Pres.--Retirement Advisors, Inc., Garden City, NY; *U.S. Private*, pg. 516

Griffin, William, Pres.--CNF Constructors Inc., Meriden, CT; *U.S. Public*, pg. 950

Griffiss, Don, Pres.--Stella Foods, Inc., Hinesburg, VT; *U.S. Private*, pg. 1040

Griffith, Bill, Pres. & Chief Exec. Officer--Kockums Cancar Corp., Savannah, GA; *Int'l*, pg. 124

Griffith, Dan, Pres.--Harig Products, Elgin, IL; *U.S. Public*, pg. 252

Griffith, Dan, Pres.--Harig Grinders, Elgin, IL; *U.S. Public*, pg. 252

Griffith, Edward L., Jr., Chief Oper. Officer--EMCON Southwest, Inc., Burbank, CA; *U.S. Public*, pg. 571

Griffith, Edward L., Jr., Chief Oper. Officer--EMCON Associates, Concord, CA; *U.S. Public*, pg. 571

Griffith, Edward L., Jr., Chief Oper. Officer--EMCON Southwest, Inc., Phoenix, AZ; *U.S. Public*, pg. 571

Griffith, Gary R., Pres.--Acordia Northeast, Boston, MA; *Int'l*, *pg. 671*

Griffith, John, V.P. & Gen. Mgr.--Cott Corporation - Mid-Atlantic Region, Wilson, NC; *Int'l*, pg. 338

Griffith, John W., V.P.-Finished Prods. Grp.--Naheola Board, Pennington, AL; *U.S. Public*, pg. 671

Griffith, P., Chm. Bd.--Standard Products Limited, Huntingdon, United Kingdom; *U.S. Public*, pg. 1505

Griffith, Robert, V.P.-Govt. & Military--Dataproducts New England, Inc., Wallingford, CT; *Int'l*, pg. 621

Griffiths, Dave, Gen. Mgr.-U.K. South--Nordson U.K., Ltd., Thame, United Kingdom; *U.S. Public*, pg. 1189

Griffiths, Frank W., Vice Chm.--Allarcom Pay Television Limited, Edmonton, Canada; *Int'l*, pg. 1481

Griffiths, Frank W., Vice Chm.--WIC Television Ltd., Vancouver, Canada; *Int'l*, pg. 1482

Griffiths, Frank W., Vice Chm.--WIC Entertainment Ltd., Vancouver, Canada; *Int'l*, pg. 1482

Griffiths, Frank W., Vice Chm.--Western Broadcast Sales Ltd., Toronto, Canada; *Int'l*, pg. 1482

Griffiths, Frank W., Vice Chm.--Canadian Broadcast Sales, Toronto, Canada; *Int'l*, pg. 1482

Griffiths, Gordon, Grp. Pres.--Imprimeries Quebecor Canada, Richmond Hill, Canada; *Int'l*, pg. 1077

Griffiths, Jeff, Gen. Mgr.--ITW Irathane Intl. Ltd., Wellingborough, United Kingdom; *U.S. Public*, pg. 868

Griffiths, William C., Pres.--Waukesha Cherry-Burrell, Delavan, WI; *U.S. Public*, pg. 1677
Griffitus, P.L., Mgr.-Distr.--Kodak Limited, Hemel Hempstead, United Kingdom; *U.S. Public*, pg. 553
Grigal, Dennis, Mng. Dir.--Donaldson Micro Pore S.A. de C.V., Aguascalientes, Mexico; *U.S. Public*, pg. 517
Grigas, Breck, Pres.--Worldwide Produce, Inc., Chicago, IL; *U.S. Private*, pg. 640
Grigg, Phyllis, Gen. Mgr.--M.F. Neal & Co.,Inc., Richmond, VA; *U.S. Private*, pg. 689
Grigg, Richard R., Jr., Pres., Chief Oper. Officer & Chief Nuclear Officer--Wisconsin Electric Power Company, Milwaukee, WI; *U.S. Public*, pg. 1773
Grigg, Ted, Pres.--William Cook Direct Marketing, Inc., Jacksonville, FL; *U.S. Private*, pg. 273
Griggs, Doyle, Pres.--Professional Aviation Associates, Inc., Atlanta, GA; *U.S. Public*, pg. 187
Griggs, Gary E., Pres.--Parsons Brinckerhoff Quade & Douglas, Inc., New York, NY; *U.S. Private*, pg. 841
Griggs, Hedley P., Contact--Banco Norchem, S.A., Sao Paulo, Brazil; *U.S. Public*, pg. 339
Griggs, Hedley P., Contact--BNCI Comercial Exportadora Ltda., Sao Paulo, Brazil; *U.S. Public*, pg. 339
Griggs, Hedley P., Contact--NC Comercial Exportadora Ltda., Sao Paulo, Brazil; *U.S. Public*, pg. 339
Griggs, Hedley P., Contact--Norchem Distribuidora de Titulos e Valores Mobiliarios S.A., Sao Paulo, Brazil; *U.S.* Public, pg. 339
Griggs, Hedley P., Contact--Noroeste Chemical S.A. Arrendamento Mercantil Norchem, Sao Paulo, Brazil; *U.S. Public*, pg. 341
Griggs, Hedley P., Contact--Chemical Administracao e Consultoria Economico Financeira Ltda., Sao Paulo, Brazil; *U.S. Public*, pg. 341
Griggs, Hedley P., Contact--Palupe-Comercio, Participacao e Servicos Ltda., Sao Paulo, Brazil; *U.S. Public*, pg. 341
Griggs, Stephen P., Pres. & Chief Oper. Officer--RoTech Medical Corporation, Orlando, FL; *U.S. Public*, pg. 884
Grigsby, E.K., Pres.--Phillips Petroleum International Investment Company, Reno, NV; *U.S. Public*, pg. 1291
Grigsby, Edd K., Pres.--Phillips Investment Company, Reno, NV; *U.S. Public*, pg. 1291
Grigsby, James A., Pres.--Cigna Insurance Company (Hellas) S.A., Athens, Greece; *U.S. Public*, pg. 364
Grigsby, Sam, Pres.--Bank of East Tennessee, Morristown, TN; *U.S. Public*, pg. 1669
Grijalbo, Estaban, Mgr.-Country--Encore Computer Espana S.A., Madrid, Spain; *U.S. Public*, pg. 580
Grijns, L.C., Chm.--ING (U.S.) Financial Services kk, New York, NY; *Int'l*, pg. 648
Grill, Gerhard, Mng. Dir.--Pitney Bowes Ges.b.H., Vienna, Austria; *U.S. Public*, pg. 1304
Grill, Robert, Pres.--Menasco Aerosystems Division, Euless, TX; *U.S. Public*, pg. 402
Grill, Robert, V.P.--Menasco California Operation, Burbank, CA; *U.S. Public*, pg. 402
Grillenmeier, Berthold, Mng. Dir.--Constructora ALMEX S.A., Mexico, Mexico; *Int'l*, pg. 424
Grilli, Donald A., Pres.--Johnson & Johnson Professional, Inc., Raynham, MA; *U.S. Public*, pg. 928
Grimaldi, Joseph A., Pres.--BNY Financial Corporation, New York, NY; *U.S. Public*, pg. 178
Grimes, B.G., Reg. Mng. Dir.--Ballast Wiltshier Plc-South West Div., Reading, United Kingdom; *Int'l*, pg. 135
Grimes, B.G., Reg. Mng. Dir.--Ballast Wiltshier Plc - South West Region, Winchester, United Kingdom; *Int'l*, pg. 135
Grimes, Doug, Gen. Mgr.--Forbo Wallcoverings Inc., Bridgeport, NJ; *Int'l*, pg. 497
Grimm, Charlie, Pres.--Pall Aerospace, New Port Richey, FL; *U.S. Public*, pg. 1253
Grimm, Dick, G.M.--KGMB-TV, Honolulu, HI; *U.S. Public*, pg. 983
Grimmer, Terry, Mgr.--Kvaerner Humberoak Ltd., Lowestoft, United Kingdom; *Int'l*, pg. 767
Grimshaw, Stuart, Mgr.-Northwestern Branch--NuArc Northwestern Div., Sumner, WA; *U.S. Private*, pg. 809
Grimsmo, Nils, Mng. Dir.--Ericsson Telecom A/S, Billingstad, Norway; *Int'l*, pg. 1367
Grinder, Dan, Pres. & Chief Exec. Officer--Hood Communications, Inc., Grand Terrace, CA; *U.S. Private*, pg. 673
Grindstaff, E.D., Pres.--Procter & Gamble Inc., North York, Canada; *U.S. Public*, pg. 1331
Gringarten, Alain C., Dr., Exec. V.P.--Scientific Software-Intercomp, Inc.-Exploration and Production Products Div., Denver, CO; *U.S. Public*, pg. 1443
Grinstead, Steve R., Pres.--Lone Star Produce Acquisition Corp., Austin, TX; *U.S. Public*, pg. 682
Grippa, Vincent V., Sr. V.P. & Mng. Dir.--State Street Canada, Inc., Toronto, Canada; *U.S. Public*, pg. 1513
Gripper, Raymond A., Mng. Dir.--Johnson & Johnson Central/East Africa, Harare, Zimbabwe; *U.S. Public*, pg. 930
Griscom, Thomas C., Exec. V.P.-External Rels.--RJR Tobacco Company, Inc., Winston Salem, NC; *U.S. Public*, pg. 1355
Griscti, Walter, Gen. Mgr.--Amway Uruguay, Montevideo, Uruguay; *U.S. Private*, pg. 70
Grissner, A., Dr., Mng. Dir.--Allianz of South Africa (Pty.) Ltd., Johannesburg, South Africa; *Int'l*, pg. 60
Grissom, Paul, Mgr.--Filtrol Corporation, Los Angeles, CA; *Int'l*, pg. 47
Griswold, Patrick, Gen. Mgr.--General Tyre East Africa Ltd., Arusha, Tanzania; *Int'l*, pg. 327
Grizzle, Lamar, Plant Mgr.--Rockmart Operations, Rockmart, GA; *Int'l*, pg. 897
Groag, Tony, Country Mgr.--Standard Chartered Bank Kenya Limited, Nairobi, Kenya; *Int'l*, pg. 1294
Grob, Christian, Chief Oper. Officer--SEB Asia, Kowloon, Hong Kong; *Int'l*, pg. 568
Groce, Michael, Pres.--Carolina Maiden Corp., Maiden, NC; *U.S. Private*, pg. 214
Groce, Vicki, Branch Mgr.--Downey Savings & Loan Association, F.A., Sunnyvale, CA; *U.S. Public*, pg. 527
Grodem, Halvard, Plant Mgr.--Jotun A/S, Fredrikstad, Norway; *Int'l*, pg. 714
Groehl, Cornelia, Mng. Dir.--Johnson & Johnson G.m.b.H., Norderstedt, Germany; *U.S. Public*, pg. 930
Groenbaek, K., Mng. Dir.--Dansk Uni-Cardan A/S, Ballerup, Denmark; *Int'l*, pg. 535
Groenendaal, Alain, V.P.-Bus. Devel.--Leo Burnett Publicidade, Ltda., Sao Paulo, Brazil; *U.S. Private*, pg. 185
Groeninger, Robert, Chief Oper. Officer--Strober Bros., Inc. Building Supply Centers, Brooklyn, NY; *U.S. Private*, pg. 403
Groesch, Gerhard, Gen. Mgr.--Forbo Uli-Chemie GmbH, Schenklengsfeld, Germany; *Int'l*, pg. 498
Groflin, H., Mgr.-Sls.--Tuflin AG, Basel, Switzerland; *U.S. Public*, pg. 578
Grogono, Andrew J., Mng. Dir.--Ampep P.l.c., Clevedon, United Kingdom; *Int'l*, pg. 1157
Groh, Laurie, Mng. Dir.--Triumph Releasing Corporation - Great Lakes Territory, Des Plaines, IL; *Int'l*, pg. 1282
Groh, Richard, Dr., Gen. Mgr.--Bayerische Hypotheken-und Wechsel-Bank A.G., London, United Kingdom; *Int'l*, pg. 176
Groh, Thomas M., Pres.--McAlpin's, Lexington, KY; *U.S. Public*, pg. 1090
Groh, Thomas N., Pres.--J. Bacon & Sons, Louisville, KY; *U.S. Public*, pg. 1090
Groh, Thomas N., Pres.--Lion, Toledo, OH; *U.S. Public*, pg. 1090
Groh, Thomas N., Pres.--Root Dry Goods Company, Inc., Terre Haute, IN; *U.S. Public*, pg. 1090
Groman, William C., Div. Mgr.--Barton Brands of California, Inc., Carson, CA; *U.S. Public*, pg. 300
Gromek, Josheph, Pres. & Chief Exec. Officer--Brooks Brothers, New York, NY; *Int'l*, pg. 843
Gromer, J., Gen. Mgr.--AMP Deutschland GmbH, Langen, Germany; *U.S. Public*, pg. 8
Gromer, Jurgen, Gen. Mgr.--AMP Hungary Trading Kft., Budapest, Hungary; *U.S. Public*, pg. 8
Gromer, Jurgen, Gen. Mgr.--AMP Polska Sp. Z.o.o., Poznan, Poland; *U.S. Public*, pg. 9
Gromer, Klaus, Chm.--Loher AG, Rott, Germany; *Int'l*, pg. 400
Gronau, Kurt, Mngng. Dir.--Sulzer Papertec Euskirchen GmbH, Euskirchen, Germany; *Int'l*, pg. 1305
Gronbarj, Klaus, Head of Unit--Skandinaviska Enskilda Banken Helsinki, Helsinki, Finland; *Int'l*, pg. 1259
Gronberg, Erik, Pres. & Chief Exec. Officer--Deminex (Canada) Ltd., Calgary, Canada; *Int'l*, pg. 1461
Gronberg, Per, Chief Oper. Officer--Neste Kemi Danmark A/S, Horsholm, Denmark; *Int'l*, pg. 915
Gronberg, Per Erik, Gen. Mgr.--Storage Technology Finland, Helsinki, Finland; *U.S. Public*, pg. 1523
Grondal, Steinar, Chief Oper. Officer--Pharmacia & Upjohn A/S, Oslo, Norway; *Int'l*, pg. 1049
Gronen, Christoph, Officer-Bd. of Mgmnt. & Gen. Mgr.--Ford Bank AG, Cologne, Germany; *U.S. Public*, pg. 665
Groner, Robert, Gen. Mgr.--California Drop Forge, Los Angeles, CA; *U.S. Public*, pg. 612
Gronfors, Harry, Mng. Dir.--W.R. Grace Oy, Helsinki, Finland; *U.S. Public*, pg. 756
Grongvist, Erkki, Chief Oper. Officer--Neste Oy, Shipping, Espoo, Finland; *Int'l*, pg. 913
Gronholm, Janina, Mgr.--Nordbanken Banking Group, Helsinki, Finland; *Int'l*, pg. 1328
Gronlund, Jan, Mng. Dir.--Avesta ABE AB, Ornskoldsvik, Sweden; *Int'l*, pg. 221
Gronlund, Klas, Chief Oper. Officer--Alfa-Laval Agri Scandinavia AB, Sodertalje, Sweden; *Int'l*, pg. 1377
Gronmark, Bjarne, Mng. Dir.--Wisaforest (UK) Ltd., Uxbridge, United Kingdom; *Int'l*, pg. 1429
Gronner, Erik M., Gen. Mgr.--Kvaerner Eureka, Moss Division, Moss, Norway; *Int'l*, pg. 767
Gronow, C.W., Dr., Mng. Dir.--ECC International Ltd., Theale, United Kingdom; *Int'l*, pg. 455
Gronqvist, Leif, V.P.--Valmet Corporation - Air Systems, Turku, Finland; *Int'l*, pg. 1448
Groom, Arthur, Mgr.--Network Systems Limited, Manchester, United Kingdom; *U.S. Public*, pg. 1522
Groom, P.J., Mng. Dir.--TP Manipulations, Oldbury, United Kingdom; *Int'l*, pg. 1222
Groome, Harry C., III, Pres.--SmithKline Beecham Clinical Laboratories, Inc., King of Prussia, PA; *Int'l*, pg. 1264
Grooms, David, Pres.--Kyocera America, Inc., San Diego, CA; *Int'l*, pg. 775
Groos, Hubertus, Mng. Dir.--Creditanstalt Bankverein AG, Munich, Germany; *Int'l*, pg. 348
Groos, Michael, Gen. Mgr.--Nordson Engineering GmbH, Luneburg, Germany; *U.S. Public*, pg. 1189
Gropp, Louis, Editor-in-Chief--House Beautiful, New York, NY; *U.S. Private*, pg. 517
Grosche, Karl-Rudolf, Chief Oper. Officer--Dresdner Bank AG, Central, Hong Kong; *Int'l*, pg. 419
Groseclose, Richard, Chm. & Chief Exec. Officer--GFG Corporation, Milwaukee, WI; *Int'l*, pg. 395
Grosklaus, James G., Sector Pres.--North American Pulp & Paper Sector, Roswell, GA; *U.S. Public*, pg. 958
Grosman, Abraham D., Chief Exec. Officer--Meditrust Operating Company, West Palm Beach, FL; *U.S. Public*, pg. 1081
Grosman, Leo, Mgr.-Sls.--Sensormatic (Belgium) S.A., Groot-Bijgaarden, Belgium; *U.S. Public*, pg. 1457
Grospitsch, Diethard, Gen. Mgr.--Gillette Deutschland G.m.b.H., Berlin, Germany; *U.S. Public*, pg. 744
Gross, David P., Pres.--Franklin Properties, Inc., San Mateo, CA; *U.S. Public*, pg. 680
Gross, Detlef, Mng. Dir.--Otto Scheurmann Bank-KG, Berlin, Germany; *Int'l*, pg. 418
Gross, Gerhard, Gen. Mgr.--Forbo Helmitin GmbH, Pirmasens, Germany; *Int'l*, pg. 497
Gross, Glen, Chief Oper. Officer--Hudson General Corp., Flushing, NY; *U.S. Public*, pg. 845
Gross, John F., Gen. Mgr.--Lamosa S.A. de C.V., (Mexico), Nuevo Laredo, Mexico; *U.S. Public*, pg. 667
Gross, Joseph A., Mgr.--General Employment Enterprises, Inc., Southfield, MI; *U.S. Public*, pg. 714
Gross, Peter, Publisher--Golf World, Trumbull, CT; *U.S. Public*, pg. 1174
Gross, Robert, Pres.--Capro, Inc., Willis, TX; *U.S. Public*, pg. 1569
Gross, Robert, Pres.--First Interstate Bank of Utah, N.A., Salt Lake City, UT; *U.S. Public*, pg. 1753
Grossberg, Jess, Publr.--Foodservice Director, New York, NY; *Int'l*, pg. 1446
Grosse, Helmut, Pres.--Voigt & Co. Baugesellschaft GmbH, Berlin, Germany; *Int'l*, pg. 1261
Grosset, Marc, Pres.--SAGEM Corporation, Derry, NH; *Int'l*, pg. 1273
Grossett, Jeff, Chm. Bd.--Owens-Corning Canos S.A., Buenos Aires, Argentina; *U.S. Public*, pg. 1237
Grossman, Janice, V.P. & Grp. Publr.--Seventeen Magazine, New York, NY; *U.S. Public*, pg. 1328
Grossman, Peter, Pres.--Nunn-Bush Shoe Co., Milwaukee, WI; *U.S. Public*, pg. 1763
Grossman, Todd A., Branch Mgr.--Zellerbach Division, Akron, OH; *U.S. Public*, pg. 1075
Grossmann, Axel, Pres.--Filtros Mann Ltda., Indaial, Brazil; *Int'l*, pg. 484
Grosso, G., Mng. Dir.--Oki Systems (Italia) S.p.A., Lacchiarella, Italy; *Int'l*, pg. 1000
Grosso, R., Chief Oper. Officer--Andrew S.R.L., Milan, Italy; *U.S. Public*, pg. 113
Grossrieder, Albert, Chief Oper. Officer--Menalux S.A., Murten, Switzerland; *Int'l*, pg. 443
Grostad, Eivind, Reg. Mgr.--Det Norske Veritas, Hong Kong, Hong Kong; *Int'l*, pg. 397
Grosz, Meir, Gen. Mgr.--Bank Leumi Le-Israel (Switzerland), Zurich, Switzerland; *Int'l*, pg. 150
Grote, Gary, Pres.--Mercantile Bank of Maquoketa, Maquoketa, IA; *U.S. Public*, pg. 1088
Grotenfelt, Sten, Chm. Bd.--Sodexi, Roissy, France; *Int'l*, pg. 560
Grotloh, Karlheinz, Mng. Dir.--Sulzer-Burckhardt Engineering Works Ltd., Basel, Switzerland; *Int'l*, pg. 1305
Grotloh, Karlheinz, V.P.--Sulzer-Burckhardt Engineering Works ltd., Basel, Switzerland; *Int'l*, pg. 1307
Grott, E., Mgr.--Lindberg Heat Treating Co., Tulsa, OK; *U.S.* Public, pg. 999
Grott, E., Mgr.--Lindberg Heat Treating Company, Batson Div., Wichita, KS; *U.S. Public*, pg. 999
Grottke, Gary, Pres.--Amfac/JMB Hawaii, Inc., Honolulu, HI; *U.S. Private*, pg. 577
Grottke, Gary, Pres.--Amfac Agribusiness, Inc., Honolulu, HI; *U.S. Private*, pg. 578
Grottke, Gary, Pres.--Kekaha Sugar Company, Limited, Kekaha, HI; *U.S. Private*, pg. 578
Grottke, Gary, Pres.--The Lihue Plantation Company, Limited, Lihue, HI; *U.S. Private*, pg. 578
Grottke, Gary, Pres.--Kauai Sugar Storage Co., Lihue, HI; *U.S. Private*, pg. 578
Grottke, Gary, Pres.--Waiahole Irrigation Co., Ltd., Waipahu, HI; *U.S. Private*, pg. 578
Grottke, Gary, Pres.--Pioneer Mill Company, Ltd., Lahaina, HI; *U.S. Private*, pg. 578
Grottke, Gary, Pres. & Mgr.--Puna Sugar Co., Ltd., Keaau, HI; *U.S. Private*, pg. 578
Grottke, Gary, Pres.--Amfac Sugar and Agribusiness, Inc., Honolulu, HI; *U.S. Private*, pg. 578
Grounds, Kenneth, Gen. Mgr.--Harley Gauge & Instrument Co., Tulsa, OK; *U.S. Public*, pg. 880
Grouse, Charles, Pres.--L3 Communications Advanced Recorders Div., Sarasota, FL; *U.S. Private*, pg. 638
Grout, Daniel, Chief Oper. Officer--Rhone-Poulenc Taiwan Ltd., Taipei, Taiwan; *Int'l*, pg. 1114
Grove-Rasmussen, Steen, Mgr.--Domestic Sales Division, Roedovre, Denmark; *Int'l*, pg. 1083
Groven, Darrol N., Pres.--Heavy Civil Construction, Boise, ID; *U.S. Public*, pg. 1134
Grover, William, Pres.--Comdial Enterprise Systems, Inc., Charlottesville, VA; *U.S. Public*, pg. 407
Groves, C.D., Sec.--MSA Zimbabwe (Pvt.) Limited, Harare, Zimbabwe; *U.S. Public*, pg. 1115
Groves, G., Pres.--Meridian Environmental Services, Inc., Detroit, MI; *U.S. Public*, pg. 1095
Groves, Robert L., Chief Oper. Officer--Flexible Lamps Ltd., Epping, United Kingdom; *U.S. Private*, pg. 1113
Grow, Daniel M., Pres.--Drexel Heritage Furnishings Inc., Drexel, NC; *U.S. Private*, pg. 432
Grubb, Albany D., Pres.--BOC Coating Technologies, Fairfield, CA; *Int'l*, pg. 121
Grubb, Christopher, Gen. Mgr.--Jardine Fleming Securities Limited, Tokyo, Japan; *Int'l*, pg. 494
Grubb, John W., Mng. Dir.--Ok Tedi Mining Limited, Kiunga, Papua New Guinea; *Int'l*, pg. 228
Grubb, Lauren, Mgr.--General Employment Enterprises, Inc., Scottsdale, AZ; *U.S. Public*, pg. 715
Grubbs, Robert, Gen. Mgr.--Skyline Port Newark Facility, Newark, NJ; *U.S. Public*, pg. 1648
Gruben, Juan G., Mng. Dir.--Dresdner Bank AG, Lisbon, Portugal; *Int'l*, pg. 419
Gruber, Alan, Pres.--Jabawwat, Inc., New York, NY; *U.S. Public*, pg. 1231
Gruber, Alan R., Pres.--Orion Properties Corp., New York, NY; *U.S. Public*, pg. 1231
Gruber, Alan R., Pres.--EFC Property Management, Inc., New York, NY; *U.S. Public*, pg. 1231
Gruber, Alan R., Pres.--Independent Financial Planners Corp., New York, NY; *U.S. Public*, pg. 1231
Gruber, Reinhard, Mng. Dir.--Battenfeld Kunststoffmaschinen Ges. m.b.H., Kottingbrunn, Austria; *Int'l*, pg. 825
Gruen, Heinrich, V.P.-European Grp.--Loctite Deutschland G.m.b.H., Munich, Germany; *Int'l*, pg. 611
Gruenberg, Don, Pres.--Thermal-Care Div., Niles, IL; *U.S. Public*, pg. 1026
Gruenberg, Paul T., Chm. & Chief Exec. Officer--NYT Video News International, Philadelphia, PA; *U.S. Public*, pg. 1174

Gruenewald, David, Pres.--Arvey Paper & Office Products, Chicago, IL; *U.S. Public*, pg. 903
Gruenewald, Gerd, Chief Oper. Officer--Deutsche Goodyear GmbH, Cologne, Germany; *U.S. Public*, pg. 753
Grum, Clifford J., Chm. Bd., Pres. & Chief Exec. Officer--Temple-Inland Forest Products Corporation, Diboll, TX; *U.S. Public*, pg. 1575
Grun, Christian, Dr., Gen. Partner--Weberbank Berliner Industriebank KGaA, Berlin, Germany; *Int'l*, pg. 160
Grunder, Eitel, Chief Oper. Officer--CC-Bank, A.G., Monchengladbach, Germany; *Int'l*, pg. 144
Grundhofer, Jerry A., Chm. Bd., Pres. & Chief Exec. Officer--Star Bank, N.A., Cincinnati, OH; *U.S. Public*, pg. 1510
Grundy, Walter, Mng. Dir.--Johnson & Johnson de Venezuela, S.A., Caracas, Venezuela; *U.S. Public*, pg. 930
Grune, George V., Pres.--Ardee Music Publishing, Inc., Pleasantville, NY; *U.S. Public*, pg. 1367
Grune, George V., Pres.--Pleasantville Music Publishing, Inc., Pleasantville, NY; *U.S. Public*, pg. 1367
Grune, George V., Pres.--RD Publications, Inc., New York, NY; *U.S. Public*, pg. 1367
Grune, George V., Pres.--W.A. Publications, Inc., Pleasantville, NY; *U.S. Public*, pg. 1368
Grunert, Heribert H., Pres.--CPC Asia Consumer Foods Division, Hong Kong, Hong Kong; *U.S. Public*, pg. 224
Grunewald, Fred, Pres. & Chief Oper. Officer--The Genie Company, Alliance, OH; *U.S. Private*, pg. 823
Grunfeld, Ernie, Pres.--New York Knickerbockers, New York, NY; *U.S. Public*, pg. 288
Grunfeld, Tommy, Pres.--Sharplan Lasers GmbH, Freising, Germany; *Int'l*, pg. 429
Grunig, Arthur, Chief Oper. Officer--Widag AG, Zurich, Switzerland; *Int'l*, pg. 444
Grunnet-Jepsen, Jes, Chief Oper. Officer--ISA Internationale Schiffahrts-Agentur GmbH, Hamburg, Germany; *Int'l*, pg. 711
Grunstein, Laurence R., Pres.--Citizen Watch Co. of America, Inc., Lyndhurst, NJ; *Int'l*, pg. 294
Gruntker, Herbert Hans, Co-Chief Oper. Officer--Helaba Trust Beratungs-und Management Gesellschaft mbH, Frankfurt/Main, Germany; *Int'l*, pg. 799
Grunwald, John, Dr., Chief Oper. Officer--MacDermid Israel Ltd., Tel Aviv, Israel; *U.S. Public*, pg. 1030
Grunwaldt, Charlene, Publr.--Business Journals of North Carolina, LLC, Raleigh, NC; *U.S. Private*, pg. 19
Grunzke, Henry R., Chm. Bd.--Standard Wool, Inc., North Oxford, MA; *U.S. Public*, pg. 1502
Grush, John T., Pres. & Chief Oper. Officer--USF Re Insurance Company, Costa Mesa, CA; *U.S. Public*, pg. 328
Grutschnig, Karl, Gen Mgr--Dresdner Bank AG, Tokyo, Japan; *Int'l*, pg. 419
Gruver, Jacob, Mng. Dir.--Katharine Gibbs School, Inc., New York, NY; *U.S. Private*, pg. 209
Gruver, Robert, Plant Mgr.--Hickson Corporation, Conley, GA; *Int'l*, pg. 619
Grvejwald, G.M., V.P. & Gen. Mgr.--Lighting Div., Christiansburg, VA; *U.S. Public*, pg. 844
Grynkewicz, Frank M., Gen. Mgr.--SRI-Soil & Rock Instrumentation, Newton, MA; *U.S. Public*, pg. 697
Gryszkiewicz, Andrew, V.P.--Cluett International Group, New York, NY; *Int'l*, pg. 194
Gryszko, Stanley J., Admin.--Hillhaven Convalescent Center Akron, Akron, OH; *U.S. Public*, pg. 1713
Grywalski, Frank, Gen. Mgr.--Marcam Corporation, North American Operations, Newton, MA; *U.S. Public*, pg. 1043
Grzyb, Malagorzata, Media Dir.--Leo Burnett Warsaw SP.Z.O.O., Warsaw, Poland; *U.S. Private*, pg. 186
Grzybowski, J.R., Pres.--PDM Bridge, Wausau, WI; *U.S. Public*, pg. 1305
Grzybowski, J.R., Pres.--PDM Bridge, Eau Claire, WI; *U.S. Public*, pg. 1305
Gschaider, Bernd, Plant Mgr.--Bundy Systemwerk, Neunkirchen, Germany; *Int'l*, pg. 1342
Gschaider, Peter, Dr., Gen. Mgr.--Forbo Wiener Teppichfabrik GmbH, Pottendorf, Austria; *Int'l*, pg. 498
Gu, D.L., Pres.--Yantai Ebara Air Conditioning Equipment Co., Ltd., Yantai, China; *Int'l*, pg. 432
Guadagno, Angelo, V.P.-Americas Sls. & Service--Data General Customer Service Division, Southborough, MA; *U.S. Public*, pg. 485
Guadagno, Angelo, V.P.-Americas Sls. & Mktg.--Data General Chile C.A., Santiago, Chile; *U.S. Public*, pg. 485
Guadagno, Angelo, V.P.-Sls. & Mktg.-Americas--Data General del Peru, S.A., Lima, Peru; *U.S. Public*, pg. 486
Gualtieri, Albert L., Pres.--Powerine Oil Company, Santa Fe Springs, CA; *U.S. Public*, pg. 314
Gualtieri, Edwin D., Pres. & Gen. Mgr.--Vanguard Division, Farmington, CT; *Int'l*, pg. 917
Guan, Ming-Der, Pres.--Heinz Win Chance Ltd., Samutprakan, Thailand; *U.S. Public*, pg. 807
Guan, W., Mgr.--Suzhou Littelfuse OVS Co. Ltd., Suzhou, China; *U.S. Public*, pg. 1001
Guarnero, P., Chief Oper. Officer--Fataluminium, Rivoli, Italy; *Int'l*, pg. 474
Guatelli, Fabio Enrico, Mng. Dir.--Rhone-Poulenc Rorer, Varese, Italy; *Int'l*, pg. 1113
Guay, Bernard M., Gen. Mgr.--Stelfil Ltee., Lachine, Canada; *Int'l*, pg. 1299
Gubala, Thomas J., Pres.--ARGOSystems, Inc., Sunnyvale, CA; *U.S. Public*, pg. 240
Gubesch, M.M., Pres.--Janesville Products, Norwalk, OH; *U.S. Public*, pg. 924
Gueddas, Hayder, Gen. Mgr.--Sicoac, Jebel Jeloud, Tunisia; *Int'l*, pg. 430
Guedon, Philippe, Chief Oper. Officer--Matra Automobile, Paris, France; *Int'l*, pg. 792
Guehler, Paul F., Div. V.P.--Safety & Security Systems Division, Saint Paul, MN; *U.S. Public*, pg. 1605
Guelke, Hans-Georg, Mng. Dir.--Wustenrot Hypothekenbank Aktiengesellschaft, Ludwigsburg, Germany; *Int'l*, pg. 1514
Guell, Francisco, Gen. Mgr.--Witco Espana S.L., Barcelona, Spain; *U.S. Public*, pg. 1774
Guella, L., Chm.--Montepolimeri Belgio S.A., Nivelles, Belgium; *Int'l*, pg. 429
Guemey, Malcom, Gen. Mgr.--BancTec (Canada), Inc., Mississauga, Canada; *U.S. Public*, pg. 177
Guenthardt, Lukas, Mng. Dir.--K-Tron Switzerland-Soder Division, Niederlenz, Switzerland; *U.S. Public*, pg. 938
Guenther, Benjamin R., Pres.--Mercantile Bank, Boone, IA; *U.S. Public*, pg. 1087
Guenther, C., Pres.--Ampco Metal S.A., Fribourg, Switzerland; *U.S. Private*, pg. 67
Guenther, Hans, V.P. & Gen. Mgr.--Peterson Spring-Georgia Plant, Athens, GA; *U.S. Private*, pg. 857
Guenther, Jack, Pres.--Mercantile Bank of Centerville, N.A., Centerville, IA; *U.S. Public*, pg. 1088
Guenther, Lutz, Dr., Pres. & Chief Oper. Officer--Copper Range Company, White Pine, MI; *Int'l*, pg. 862
Guenther, Robert, V.P.--Ghafari Associates, Inc., Detroit, MI; *U.S. Private*, pg. 450
Guerault, P., Gen. Mgr.--Gorcy S.A., Mirebeau, France; *Int'l*, pg. 380
Guerin, Philippe, Pres.--Total Transport Maritime, Puteaux, France; *Int'l*, pg. 1409
Guerini, Bernard, Pres. Dir.--Prodair, S.A., Saint Denis, France; *U.S. Public*, pg. 32
Guerra, F.F., III, Gen. Mgr.--S.C. Johnson & Son, Ltd., Bangkok, Thailand; *U.S. Private*, pg. 593
Guerra, Fernando, Mng. Dir.--Anchor Foods Limited, Swindon, United Kingdom; *Int'l*, pg. 923
Guerra, Gabriel, Gen. Mgr.--Edelman PR Worldwide, Mexico, Mexico; *U.S. Private*, pg. 363
Guerrein, Rich, Publr.--Cardinal Business Media, Vision Care Grp., Norwalk, CT; *U.S. Private*, pg. 1116
Guerreluo, Anabela, House Mgr.--Bela Vista Limitada, Macau, Macau; *Int'l*, pg. 704
Guerrero, Alejandro, Mng. Dir.--Ericsson de Costa Rica, San Jose, Costa Rica; *Int'l*, pg. 1366
Guerrero, Ben, Mgr.--Southern Iron & Metal Co., Beaumont, TX; *U.S. Public*, pg. 413
Guerrero, Juan O., V.P.-Investments--Investments Div., Hato Rey, PR; *U.S. Public*, pg. 175
Guerrero, Ramon, Dir. Gen.--PEMEX, Houston, TX; *Int'l*, pg. 1046
Guerrero, Regulo, Gen. Mgr.--Optimizacion ADD, Caracas, Venezuela; *U.S. Private*, pg. 1200
Guerrovich, Erwin, Gen. Mgr.--Intermarkets Advertising/Lebanon, Beirut, Lebanon; *Int'l*, pg. 680
Guertin, Timothy E., Pres.--Oncology Systems, Palo Alto, CA; *U.S. Public*, pg. 1710
Guerts, Euguen, V.P.--Richco Structures, De Pere, WI; *U.S. Private*, pg. 929
Guest, Capt. Eugene, Dir.--MarineSafety International, Flushing, NY; *U.S. Public*, pg. 218
Guest, Howard, V.P.-Tech.--Oughtibridge Mill, Sheffield, United Kingdom; *U.S. Public*, pg. 672
Guetzlaff, John, Gen. Mgr.--Spang & Company-Booneville Plant, Booneville, AR; *U.S. Private*, pg. 1020
Guevara Llinas, Carlos, V.P.--Central Zone Office, San Luis Potosi, Mexico; *Int'l*, pg. 573
Guffey, John, Jr., Chm. Bd. & Chief Exec. Officer--Coltec Industries Inc., Charlotte, NC; *U.S. Public*, pg. 401
Gugenberger, Ernst, Mng. Dir.--ESAB AG, Dietikon, Switzerland; *Int'l*, pg. 282
Guggenheim, Jacques, Chief Oper. Officer--Locatel, Poissy, France; *Int'l*, pg. 54
Guggenheim, Richard, Pres.--G-B Miller, New York, NY; *U.S. Private*, pg. 746
Gugliemi, Peter, Chief Oper. Officer--Tellabs International, Inc., Bolingbrook, IL; *U.S. Public*, pg. 1573
Gugman, Thomas, Reg. Mgr.-Latin America--AlliedSignal Fluorocarbons, Aventura, FL; *U.S. Public*, pg. 51
Guibout, Jean-Louis, Mgr.--EURO RSCG Nord, Roubaix, France; *Int'l*, pg. 601
Guibout, Jean-Louis, Gen. Mgr.--EURO RSCG Nord, Metz, France; *Int'l*, pg. 601
Guida, Mark E., Pres.--The Business Outlet, Inc., Reading, PA; *Int'l*, pg. 9
Guidi, Fabrizio, Dir.--Banca d'America e d'Italia S.p.A. (Chiavari), Chiavari, Italy; *Int'l*, pg. 403
Guido, R., Pres.--Inco United States Inc., New York, NY; *Int'l*, pg. 672
Guidry, Lyman, Pres. & Chief Exec. Officer--Electric Research and Manufacturing Cooperative, Inc. (ERMCO), Dyersburg, TN; *U.S. Private*, pg. 82
Guige, Alain, Pres.--Unilaser, Boulogne-Billancourt, France; *Int'l*, pg. 29
Guihereuf, Marc, Mgr.-Opers.--Donnelly Euro Glas Systems, Langres, France; *U.S. Public*, pg. 519
Guilbert, Dominique, Mng. Dir.--Bertrand Faure Equipements SA, Lure, France; *Int'l*, pg. 192
Guilbert, Dominique, Mng. Dir.--Bertrand Faure Equipements SA, Magny, France; *Int'l*, pg. 192
Guildea, Fred, Mng. Dir.--Mallinckrodt Medical, Athlone, Ireland; *U.S. Public*, pg. 1040
Guilemany, Xavier, Mng. Dir.--Commestsa, Barcelona, Spain; *Int'l*, pg. 193
Guilfoyle, Dick, Pres.--USF Insurance Company, Philadelphia, PA; *U.S. Public*, pg. 328
Guilkey, Don, Plant Mgr.--Firestone Industrial Products Company-Williamsburg, Williamsburg, KY; *Int'l*, pg. 214
Guillard, Robert, Mng. Dir.--Dyckerhoff & Widmann Baugesellschaft mbH, Deggendorf, Germany; *Int'l*, pg. 423
Guillaume, Christian, Dir.--CFCI S.A., Abidjan, Cote d'Ivoire; *Int'l*, pg. 1436
Guillaume, Marnix L.K., Chm. Bd. & Mgr.-Latin & S. America--Willis Corroon International/Americas, Minneapolis, MN; *Int'l*, pg. 1507
Guille, R.O., Mng. Dir.--P&O Harbours Ltd., Felixstowe, United Kingdom; *Int'l*, pg. 1034
Guillemot, Jean-Claude, Gen. Mgr.--BFCE Ho Chi Minh City, Ho Chi Minh City, Vietnam; *Int'l*, pg. 161
Guillen, L. Alejandro, Pres.--EA Engineering, Science & Technology de Mexico, S.A. de C.V., Colonia, Mexico; *U.S. Public*, pg. 541
Guillenette, Larry, Gen. Mgr.--Balcrank Products, Weaverville, NC; *U.S. Public*, pg. 707
Guillin, Pierre, Pres. & Chief Exec. Officer--Sanders, Athis-Mons, France; *Int'l*, pg. 459
Guillon, Alain, Pres.--Elf France, Paris, France; *Int'l*, pg. 445
Guillot, Jean, Chief Exec.--Groupe Origny S.A., Paris, France; *Int'l*, pg. 629
Guilmil, J., Mng. Dir.--Claudius Peters (Iberica) S.A., Madrid, Spain; *Int'l*, pg. 131
Guimbourg, Jacques, V.P.--Alcatel ATFH, Levallois-Perret, France; *Int'l*, pg. 55
Guimond, David, Plant Mgr.--Whitefield Power & Lighting, Whitefield, NH; *U.S. Public*, pg. 1593
Guinasso, Vic A., Pres. & Chief Oper. Officer--DHL Airways, Inc., Redwood City, CA; *U.S. Private*, pg. 302
Guinddeau, Jean-Luc, Mng. Dir.--Gestetner Services S.A., Paris, France; *Int'l*, pg. 1115
Guindo, Julio Alcaide, Pres.--Cargosur, S.A., Madrid, Spain; *Int'l*, pg. 1225
Guinot, Francois, Pres.--Fine Inorganic Chemicals, Courbevoie, France; *Int'l*, pg. 1109
Guinsberg, Sydney, Dir.-Eastern Region--USA Network, New York, NY; *U.S. Public*, pg. 1686
Guis, J., Pres.--VNU Magazine Group International bv, Haarlem, Netherlands; *Int'l*, pg. 1445
Guit, Leo, Chief Oper. Officer--Halm Industries International, Warmond, Netherlands; *U.S. Private*, pg. 496
Gulas, Ivan, Dr., Co-Chm.--Pacific Title/Mirage, Hollywood, CA; *U.S. Public*, pg. 1425
Gulasy, Dennis, V.P.--Simulation Systems Division, Broken Arrow, OK; *U.S. Public*, pg. 218
Gulbas, Bruce, Pres.--Interfab, El Paso, TX; *U.S. Private*, pg. 786
Gulbrandsen, Paul, Mng. Dir.--A/S Scandia Kjemiske, Oslo, Norway; *Int'l*, pg. 715
Gulden, Frank, Acting Pres.--Avdel Textron, Hertford, United Kingdom; *U.S. Public*, pg. 1590
Gulick, Robert, Pres.--New York Institiute of Finance, New York, NY; *U.S. Private*, pg. 778
Gulledge, Bill R., Publr.--The Middlesex News, Framingham, MA; *U.S. Public*, pg. 794
Gullestad, R., Mng. Dir.--THORN Norge A/S, Oslo, Norway; *Int'l*, pg. 1386
Gulliford, James W., V.P. & Gen. Mgr.--AMSCO, Rice Lake, WI; *U.S. Public*, pg. 1350
Gulliford, Mike, Mng. Dir.--Burgmann Middle East, Dubai, United Arab Emirates; *Int'l*, pg. 234
Gulliksson, Anders, Mng. Dir.--Korn/Ferry International, Stockholm, Sweden; *U.S. Private*, pg. 634
Gully, Jay, Chief Oper. Officer--JPS Converter & Industrial Corp., Greenville, SC; *U.S. Private*, pg. 578
Guloien, Donald, Pres.--ManuLife Financial Services Limited, Toronto, Canada; *Int'l*, pg. 840
Gultormsen, Arne B., Gen. Mgr.--Jotun (Deutschland) GmbH, Hamburg, Germany; *Int'l*, pg. 715
Gummer, Charles L., Pres. & Chief Exec. Officer--Comerica Bank Texas, Dallas, TX; *U.S. Public*, pg. 409
Gummere, John, Chief Oper. Officer--PM Holdings, Inc., Hartford, CT; *U.S. Private*, pg. 863
Gummere, John, Pres.--Phoenix American Life Ins. Co., Hartford, CT; *U.S. Private*, pg. 863
Gummeson, Sune, Gen. Mgr.--Kvaerner Kimek a.s, Arkhangelsk Office, Arkhangelsk, Russia; *Int'l*, pg. 772
Gump, David F., Pres.--Bell & Howell Publication Systems Company, Wooster, OH; *U.S. Public*, pg. 201
Gundermann, Peter J., Pres.--Flex-Key Corporation, Gloucester, MA; *U.S. Public*, pg. 142
Gundersen, Lars Erik, Mgr.--Frionor Danmark A/S, Viborg, Denmark; *Int'l*, pg. 516
Gunderson, B.C., Mng. Dir.--CIBC New Zealand Limited, Auckland, New Zealand; *Int'l*, pg. 258
Gunderson, Craig, Gen. Mgr.--Frontier Communications of Georgia, Inc., Statesboro, GA; *U.S. Public*, pg. 683
Gunderson, Gene, Pres.--Banta Healthcare Products, Neenah, WI; *U.S. Public*, pg. 188
Gundry, Stanley N., V.P. & Publ. Academic Books & Electronic Publ.--The Zondervan Corporation, Grand Rapids, MI; *Int'l*, pg. 927
Gunji, Hiromi, Chm. Bd., Pres. & Chief Exec. Officer--Brother International Corporation, Somerset, NJ; *Int'l*, pg. 229
Gunlock, T.W., Pres.--Sabre Systems & Service Inc., Miamisburg, OH; *Int'l*, pg. 890
Gunn, G. James, Pres.--AMR Services Corporation, Dallas-Fort Worth Airport, TX; *U.S. Public*, pg. 9
Gunn, I.C.E.H., Chm. Bd.--The Canada Life Assurance Company of Ireland Limited, Blackrock, Ireland; *Int'l*, pg. 255
Gunn, Neil E., Gen. Mgr.--Winstone Wallboards Limited, Auckland, New Zealand; *Int'l*, pg. 495
Gunn, Peter M., Gen. Mgr.--Forbo Nairn Ltd., Kirkcaldy, United Kingdom; *Int'l*, pg. 497
Gunn, Robert, Mng. Dir.--VMark Software, Ltd., Bracknell, United Kingdom; *U.S. Public*, pg. 129
Gunn, Robert J., Pres.--Roins Holdings Limited, Toronto, Canada; *Int'l*, pg. 1131
Gunn, Sandra, V.P. & Gen. Mgr.--Lotus Engineering & Scientific Products Div., Cambridge, MA; *U.S. Public*, pg. 896
Gunning, David, Gen. Mgr.--Tellabs Wireless Systems, Burlington, MA; *U.S. Public*, pg. 1573
Gunnison, Robert, Pres.--Fireman's Fund Insurance Co. of Georgia, Atlanta, GA; *Int'l*, pg. 59
Guns, Jan, Gen. Mgr.--Nordson Belgium N.V., Zaventem, Belgium; *U.S. Public*, pg. 1189
Gunston, W.G., Mng. Dir.--Integrated Network for Computer Administration Ltd., Hook, United Kingdom; *Int'l*, pg. 591
Gunter, H., Mng. Dir.--Ascom Hongkong Ltd., Hong Kong, Hong Kong; *Int'l*, pg. 87

Gunther, A., Chief Oper. Officer--Square D Company (Deutschland) GmbH, Volperhausen, Germany; *Int'l*, pg. 1209
Gunther, Ray, Pres.--Phoenix Division, Phoenix, AZ; *U.S. Public*, pg. 652
Gunther, Stephen J., Pres.--AGL Energy Services, Inc., Atlanta, GA; *U.S. Public*, pg. 7
Gunti, Ray C., Pres.--ALLTEL Supply, Inc., Norcross, GA; *U.S. Public*, pg. 55
Guont, James R., Chm., Pres. & Chief Exec. Officer--The Fifth Third Bank of Kentucky, Louisville, Louisville, KY; *U.S. Public*, pg. 621
Guoqing, Paul Liu, Mng. Dir.--Grand Generale Asia Ltd., Hong Kong, Hong Kong; *Int'l*, pg. 548
Gupte, Anil M., Chief Rep.--Generale Bank, Mumbai, India; *Int'l*, pg. 547
Guralnick, Miles, Pres.--Vespa Laboratories, Inc., Spring Mills, PA; *Int'l*, pg. 288
Gurchiek, Bill, Gen. Mgr.--Domestic Uniform Rental, Detroit, MI; *U.S. Private*, pg. 338
Guren, Clifford, Gen. Mgr.--Quebecor Interactive Electronic Publishing Group, Bellevue, WA; *Int'l*, pg. 1076
Gurgold, Steven, Chief Oper. Officer--Power Plastics Inc., Paterson, NJ; *U.S. Private*, pg. 1086
Gurgovits, Stephen J., Chief Oper. Officer--Mortgage Service Corporation, Hermitage, PA; *U.S. Public*, pg. 607
Gurian, Kenneth J., Chm. Bd. & Chief Exec. Officer--BGM Health Communications, Inc., Los Angeles, CA; *U.S. Public*, pg. 1223
Gurin, Richard S., Pres. & Chief Exec. Officer--Binney & Smith Inc., Easton, PA; *U.S. Private*, pg. 496
Gurtner, Thomas, Gen. Mgr.--Four Seasons Hotel, Newport Beach, CA; *Int'l*, pg. 502
Gurvitch, William M., Pres.--Harcourt Brace & Company Intl. Corp., Orlando, FL; *U.S. Public*, pg. 783
Gushue, Jerry, Mgr.--Anixter Halifax, Dartmouth, Canada; *U.S. Public*, pg. 115
Gust, James F., Pres.--Stacoswitch, Inc., Costa Mesa, CA; *U.S. Private*, pg. 260
Gustafson, James E., Pres.--GRC Realty Corp., Stamford, CT; *U.S. Public*, pg. 725
Gustafson, James E., Pres. & Chief Exec. Officer--General Re Services Corp., Stamford, CT; *U.S. Public*, pg. 725
Gustafson, Robert, Sr. V.P.--UNC Accessory Services, Annapolis, MD; *U.S. Public*, pg. 710
Gustafson, S. Reid, Pres.--Shea Homes Northern California, San Jose, CA; *U.S. Private*, pg. 991
Gustafson, Tom-Henrik, Mng. Dir.--Pargas Plant, Pargas, Finland; *Int'l*, pg. 1198
Gustafson, William R., Grp. V.P. & Gen. Mgr.--Petroleum Catalysts, Iselin, NJ; *U.S. Public*, pg. 582
Gustafsson, Bengt, Pres.--Skanska Installation AB, Sundbyberg, Sweden; *Int'l*, pg. 1260
Gustafsson, Bengt, Pres.--Industriventilation Svenska AB, Vaxjo, Sweden; *Int'l*, pg. 1261
Gustafsson, Bernt, Pres.--Danisco Sugar AB, Malmo, Sweden; *Int'l*, pg. 378
Gustafsson, Bo, Mng. Dir.--Conductores Latincasa S.A. de C.V., Mexico, Mexico; *Int'l*, pg. 1365
Gustafsson, Claes, Pres.--Skanska Bygg AB, Danderyd, Sweden; *Int'l*, pg. 1260
Gustafsson, Goran, Mng. Dir.--SKF Bearing Services Taiwan Ltd., Taipei, Taiwan; *Int'l*, pg. 1158
Gustafsson, Kjell, Chief Oper. Officer--ICA Forlaget AB, Vasteras, Sweden; *Int'l*, pg. 643
Gustafsson, Lennart, Pres.--Tecfor Inc., Itasca, IL; *Int'l*, pg. 440
Gustafsson, Olof, Mng. Dir.--Pharmacia & Upjohn Risk Management Service AB, Stockholm, Sweden; *Int'l*, pg. 1048
Gustafsson, Ronald, Mng. Dir.--ESAB Tech AB, Vastra Frolunda, Sweden; *Int'l*, pg. 281
Gustafsson, Rune, Chief Oper. Officer--Gothia Pulp & Paper AB, Goteborg, Sweden; *Int'l*, pg. 708
Gustar, Chris, Chief Exec.--GKN Westland Aerospace Limited, East Cowes, United Kingdom; *Int'l*, pg. 535
Gustarsson, Jakob, Mng. Dir.--AGA RE, Lidingo, Sweden; *Int'l*, pg. 13
Gustin, Mike, V.P.-Northern Region--Chambers USA Waste, Inc., North Huntingdon, PA; *U.S. Public*, pg. 1686
Guston, Tim, Pres.--DecisionMark, Cedar Rapids, IA; *U.S. Private*, pg. 442
Gut, H., Gen. Mgr.--ADT/Proegur, S.A., Madrid, Spain; *U.S. Public*, pg. 1649
Gut, Jean, Mng. Dir., President-Director General, France--EuroKasco, Torcy, France; *U.S. Public*, pg. 165
Gutbub, Rolf, Gen. Mgr.--Wang (Schweiz) AG, Wallisellen, Switzerland; *U.S. Public*, pg. 1738
Guth, Albert E., Pres.--Astec Financial Services, Inc., Chattanooga, TN; *U.S. Public*, pg. 141
Guthinger, George, Publr.--Business First of New York, Inc., Albany, NY; *U.S. Private*, pg. 19
Guthire, Alexander, Pres.--Davis Electric, Wallingford, CT; *Int'l*, pg. 1240
Guthrie, Bob, Chief Exec. Officer--Willis Corroon Limited, Kingston upon Thames, United Kingdom; *Int'l*, pg. 1502
Guthrie, Don, Chief Oper. Officer--Milky Way, Inc., Yakima, WA; *U.S. Private*, pg. 683
Guthrie, John F., Jr., Pres.--Newport, Boston, MA; *U.S. Private*, pg. 738
Guthy, Bil, Co-Pres.--Guthy-Renker Corp., Santa Monica, CA; *U.S. Private*, pg. 488
Gutierrez, Bernardo, Mgr.--Jugos del Valle Distribution, San Antonio, TX; *Int'l*, pg. 716
Gutierrez, David, Gen. Mgr.--Avon Products Manufacturing, Inc., Manila, Philippines; *U.S. Public*, pg. 156
Gutierrez, Fernando, Gen. Mgr.--Avon Cosmetics, S.A., Madrid, Spain; *U.S. Public*, pg. 156
Gutierrez, Gabriel, Mng. Dir.--3i Spain, Madrid, Spain; *Int'l*, pg. 1386
Gutierrez, Joe, Mgr.-Admin.--Santa Fe Detention Center, Santa Fe, NM; *U.S. Public*, pg. 451
Gutierrez, Jose Maciel, Exec. V.P.--Hylsa S.A.-Mining and Pelletiing Division, Cuauhtemoc, Mexico; *Int'l*, pg. 56
Gutierrez, Julian Serrano, Chief Exec. Officer--Cadena Comercial Oxxo, S.A. de CV, Monterrey, Mexico; *Int'l*, pg. 496
Gutierrez, Luis, Gen. Mgr.--Colgate-Palmolive (Central America) S.A., Guatemala, Guatemala; *U.S. Public*, pg. 398
Gutierrez, Manuel, Dir--CID FCA!BMZ Sevilla, Seville, Spain; *Int'l*, pg. 469
Gutierrez, Mario, Gen. Mgr.--Moore Products de Mexico, S.A. de C.V., Mexico, Mexico; *U.S. Public*, pg. 1129
Gutierrez, Tom, Pres. & Chief Exec. Officer--Exide Electronics Group, Inc., Raleigh, NC; *Int'l*, pg. 126
Gutierrez, Victor, Vice Chm. & Chief Fin. Officer-Nw YOrk--Young & Rubicam Latam (Miami), Miami, FL; *U.S. Private*, pg. 1198
Gutting, Bernd, Dr., Mng. Dir.--Allianz Asset Management (Hong Kong) Ltd., Hong Kong, Hong Kong; *Int'l*, pg. 59
Guttman, James L., Pres.--Mon River Towing Inc., Belle Vernon, PA; *U.S. Private*, pg. 489
Guttman, Richard M., Pres.--Guttman Oil, Inc., Belle Vernon, PA; *U.S. Private*, pg. 489
Guttmann, Ron, Gen. Mgr.--Israel Edible Products Ltd., Herzliyya, Israel; *U.S. Public*, pg. 225
Guttner, Gunter, Mng. Dir.--BV-Consult, Berlin, Germany; *Int'l*, pg. 178
Gutwein, Richard, Plant Mgr.--Grand Forks Plant, Grand Forks, ND; *U.S. Public*, pg. 1521
Gutzler, Marc, Gen. Mgr.--UNC ARTEX, Addison, TX; *U.S. Public*, pg. 710
Guudling, Ralph, Dr., Chief Oper. Officer--Siemens K.K., Tokyo, Japan; *Int'l*, pg. 1247
Guy, C.U., Gen. Mgr.--Chemicals Division, Ashtabula, OH; *U.S. Public*, pg. 501
Guy, G. C., Mng. Dir.--Australian Thread Pty. Ltd., Sydney, Australia; *Int'l*, pg. 299
Guy, Geoff I., V.P.--Manulife Financial, Toronto, Canada; *Int'l*, pg. 840
Guy, Geoffry, Pres.--ManuLife Investment Holdings Limited, Toronto, Canada; *Int'l*, pg. 840
Guyette, James M, Chm. Bd. & Pres.--Air Canada, New York, NY; *Int'l*, pg. 36
Guzik, William, Chief Fin. Officer & V.P.--Goldblatt's Department Stores, Chicago, IL; *U.S. Public*, pg. 917
Guzlas, D.L., Plant Mgr.--Silgan Containers, Waukegan, IL; *U.S. Public*, pg. 1473
Guzman, Julia Lucia, Dir.--Florasynth Ltda., Bogota, Colombia; *Int'l*, pg. 173
Guzman, Kathleen, Pres.--Christie's East, New York, NY; *Int'l*, pg. 290
Guzman, Samuel, Pres. & Chief Exec. Officer--Young & Rubicam Bogota, Bogota, Colombia; *U.S. Private*, pg. 1200
Guzner, N., Mgr.-Sls., U.K. & Scandinavia--OCG Microelectronic Materials Limited, Worcester, United Kingdom; *U.S. Public*, pg. 1220
Guzzetti, William L., Pres.--Hallwood Realty Corporation, Dallas, TX; *U.S. Public*, pg. 778
Guzzetti, William L., Pres.--Hallwood Realty Investors Inc., Dallas, TX; *U.S. Public*, pg. 778
Guzzetti, William L., Pres.--Hallwood Commercial Real Estate, Inc., Dallas, TX; *U.S. Public*, pg. 778
Guzzle, Timothy L., Chm. Bd. & Chief Exec. Officer--Tampa Electric Co., Tampa, FL; *U.S. Public*, pg. 1565
Gwangwadza, Earnest, Gen. Mgr.--Johnson & Johnson (Zambia) Ltd., Ndola, Zambia; *U.S. Public*, pg. 931
Gwinn, J. Campbell, Chm. Bd.--National Bank of Summers, Hinton, WV; *U.S. Public*, pg. 836
Gwyn, Peter, Pres.--Bird-Johnson Company, Walpole, MA; *Int'l*, pg. 709
Gwynne, Russell, Plant Mgr.--Alumax Aluminum Corp., Mill Products, Lancaster, PA; *U.S. Public*, pg. 59
Gyarfas, Tamas, Pres.--NAP-TV, Budapest, Hungary; *Int'l*, pg. 394
Gyde, Dick, Pres.--Childcraft Education Corporation, Lancaster, PA; *U.S. Public*, pg. 513
Gyenes, Peter, V.P. & Gen. Mgr.-Intl.--Data General International Sales Corporation, Westborough, MA; *U.S. Public*, pg. 485
Gygi, Richard W., Pres.--CPS Corporation, Franklin, TN; *U.S. Private*, pg. 422
Gyllenberg, Bengt-Ake, Mng. Dir.--Nokia Mobile Phones Italia S.r.l., Rome, Italy; *Int'l*, pg. 952
Gyllstrom, Gregory, Pres. & Chief Exec. Officer--Industrial Coatings Group, Inc., Chicago, IL; *U.S. Private*, pg. 434
Gynn, John, Gen. Mgr.--Inspectorate Plc, Witham, United Kingdom; *Int'l*, pg. 679
Gynne, Goran, Chief Officer--AB Tidningen Vi, Stockholm, Sweden; *Int'l*, pg. 718
Gyorkonyi, T., Gen. Mgr.-Sls.--Scitel Telematics Ltd., Budapest, Hungary; *Int'l*, pg. 1195
Gyouda, Haruhiko, Sr. V.P., Gen. Mgr. & Dir.--Tokio Marine Management Inc. - Western Regional Office, Pasadena, CA; *Int'l*, pg. 1392
Gyssler, George, Pres.--ABB Power Generation Inc., Midlothian, VA; *Int'l*, pg. 3
Ha Moud, Ammar Ben, Chm.--Impol SA, Tunis, Tunisia; *Int'l*, *pg. 429*
Ha, Young-jun, Pres.--Hyosung Aluminum Co., Ltd., Seoul, Korea; *Int'l*, pg. 640
Haab, Larry D., Pres.--Illinois Power Fuel Co., Decatur, IL; *U.S. Public*, pg. 869
Haab, Larry D., Pres.--IP Gas Supply Co., Decatur, IL; *U.S. Public*, pg. 869
Haab, Larry D., Chm.--Illinova Energy Partners, Inc., Oak Brook, IL; *U.S. Public*, pg. 870
Haaften, V., Mng. Dir.--Toshiba Medical Systems AG, Oetwil am See, Switzerland; *Int'l*, pg. 1407
Haag, Daniel S., Pres.--Major Sysco Food Services Inc., Modesto, CA; *U.S. Public*, pg. 1551
Haag, Joachim, Mng. Dir.--Bohlin Instruments Vetriebs GmbH, Muhlacker, Germany; *Int'l*, pg. 208
Haag, William, Mng. Dir.--Fanner-PLP, Northmead, Australia; *U.S. Public*, pg. 1321
Haakonsson, Henrick, Mng. Dir.--Bruel & Kjaer Measurements A/S, Naerum, Denmark; *Int'l*, pg. 14
Haank, Derk, Chief Exec.--Bonaventura, Amsterdam, Netherlands; *Int'l*, pg. 1099
Haank, Derk, Chief Exec.--Elsevier Bedrijfinformatie B.V., Doetinchem, Netherlands; *Int'l*, pg. 1099
Haank, Derk J., Chief Exec. Officer--Elsevier Business Information, Amsterdam, Netherlands; *Int'l*, pg. 1099
Haapala, Jorma, Chief Oper. Officer--Neste Resins Oy, Hamina, Finland; *Int'l*, pg. 913
Haapanen, Pekka, Exec. V.P.--Valmet Inc.- Appleton Division, Appleton, WI; *Int'l*, pg. 1448
Haapavaara, Mikko, Chief Oper. Officer--Neste Singapore Holdings Pte. Ltd., Singapore, Singapore; *Int'l*, pg. 915
Haarstick, Kathrin, Media Dir.--Michael Conrad & Leo Burnett GmbH, Frankfurt/Main, Germany; *U.S. Private*, pg. 184
Haas-Wittmuess, Hans-Jurgen, Pres.--Banque Veuve Morin-Pons, Lyon, France; *Int'l*, pg. 419
Haas, Andrew, Branch Mgr.--Bear, Stearns & Co. Inc., Los Angeles, Los Angeles, CA; *U.S. Public*, pg. 198
Haas, B.K., Pres.--Bud West, Inc., Phoenix, AZ; *U.S. Private*, pg. 178
Haas, F. Eugene, Pres.--General Merchandise Distributors, Inc., Topeka, KS; *U.S. Public*, pg. 653
Haas, Gerhard, Chief Oper. Officer--Krauss-Maffei Wehrtechnik GmbH, Munich, Germany; *Int'l*, pg. 836
Haas, Josef, Gen. Mgr.--ANA Hotel, San Francisco, CA; *Int'l*, pg. 57
Haas, Madame, Chief Oper. Officer--Societe Anonyme des Eaux Minerales de Ribeauville, Ribeauville, France; *Int'l*, pg. 919
Haas, Peter, Mng. Dir.--Amoco Fabrics (U.K.) Ltd., London, United Kingdom; *U.S. Public*, pg. 103
Haas, R. H., Gen. Mgr.--Curacao Trading Company (Dominicana) C. Por A., Santo Domingo, Dominican Republic; *Int'l*, pg. 280
Haase, Daniel, Sr. V.P. & Mng. Dir.--BankAmerica Trust & Banking Corp. (Cayman) Ltd., Georgetown, Cayman Islands; *U.S. Public*, pg. 183
Haase, Michael M., Mgr.--Stockbridge & Sherwood Telephone Co., Inc., Sherwood, WI; *U.S. Public*, pg. 1572
Haass, James B., Mgr.-Branch--Piper Jaffray Inc., Denver, CO; *U.S. Public*, pg. 1303
Habaieb, Taofik, Mng. Dir.--TH Com, Tunis, Tunisia; *U.S. Private*, pg. 305
Habeggar, Richard J., V.P. & Gen. Mgr.--Technical Motor Div., Kent, OH; *U.S. Public*, pg. 100
Habegger, Christian, Mng. Dir.--Sulzer Hydro AG, Kriens, Switzerland; *Int'l*, pg. 1307
Haber, Barry, Gen. Mgr.--Cuisinart Inc., Stamford, CT; *U.S. Private*, pg. 261
Haber, Dr. P., Mng. Dir.--PBZ Privatbank Zurich, Zurich, Switzerland; *Int'l*, pg. 1440
Haber, Edgar, M.D., Pres.--The Squibb Institute for Medical Research, Princeton, NJ; *U.S. Public*, pg. 254
Haberberger, Arthur A., Pres.--American Commercial Credit Corp., Reading, PA; *Int'l*, pg. 9
Haberberger, Arthur A., Pres.--AEL Leasing Co., Inc., Reading, PA; *Int'l*, pg. 9
Haberstroh, Jorns, Area Gen. Mgr.--Nokia Telecommunications GmbH, Dusseldorf, Germany; *Int'l*, pg. 953
Haberzeth, Heinz, Dr., Chm. Bd. & Mng. Dir.--Ford Motor Co. (Switzerland) S.A., Zurich, Switzerland; *U.S. Public*, pg. 666
Habib, Laurent, Mng. Dir.--EURO RSCG Institutionnel, Levallois-Perret, France; *Int'l*, pg. 600
Habib, M.S., Dr., Mng. Dir.--Wellcome Pakistan Ltd, Karachi, Pakistan; *Int'l*, pg. 553
Habig, John, Chief Oper. Officer--Kimball Electronics Group, Jasper, IN; *U.S. Public*, pg. 957
Hable, Bob, Chief Oper. Officer--Louisiana Industries Div., Bossier City, LA; *U.S. Public*, pg. 1585
Hacala, John, Chm. & Chief Exec. Officer--Spencer Gifts, Inc., Egg Harbor Township, NJ; *Int'l*, pg. 1216
Hacas, M.K., Gen. Mgr.--CHEMCENTRAL/Houston, Houston, TX; *U.S. Private*, pg. 232
Haccour, Raf, Gen. Mgr.--Leuven Local Head Office, Leuven, Belgium; *Int'l*, pg. 147
Hach, Kathryn C., Pres.--Hach International, Inc., Loveland, CO; *U.S. Public*, pg. 773
Hack, Frank, Pres.--Componenta International A/S, Eidanger, Norway; *Int'l*, pg. 1421
Hacker, Douglas A., Pres.--United Worldwide Corporation, Tumon, GU; *U.S. Public*, pg. 1653
Hacker, Mike, Mgr.--Circuit Foil U.K. Ltd., Carlisle, United Kingdom; *Int'l*, pg. 80
Hacker, Rodney J., Gen. Mgr.--Fresno Auto Dealers Auction, Fresno, CA; *U.S. Private*, pg. 282
Hackett, David, Chief Exec. Officer--Airport '82 Associates Ltd., Pigeon Forge, TN; *U.S. Private*, pg. 392
Hackett, David, Chief Oper. Officer--Profit Management Corp., Kingston, TN; *U.S. Private*, pg. 393
Hackett, David, Chief Exec. Officer--Tri-Management Corp., Pigeon Forge, TN; *U.S. Private*, pg. 393
Hackett, John J., Pres.--TIE Systems, Inc. New England, Needham, MA; *U.S. Private*, pg. 1085
Hackler, B.J., Pres.--Trans Louisiana Gas Co., Lafayette, LA; *U.S. Public*, pg. 145
Hacklin, Pertti, Chief Representative Officer--Union Bank of Switzerland, Moscow, Russia; *Int'l*, pg. 1441
Hackman, Roger, Vice Chm.--TABS Direct (Operating Div.), Stafford, TX; *U.S. Private*, pg. 482
Hackney, F. Ray, Pres.--Duall Plastics, Inc., Athol, MA; *Int'l*, *pg. 233*
Hackney, Hodges, Pres.--Hackney International, Washington, NC; *U.S. Private*, pg. 1097
Hackney, Steve, Pres.--Las Vegas Div., Las Vegas, NV; *U.S. Public*, pg. 1683
Hacksell, Uli, Pres.--Astra Draco AB, Lund, Sweden; *Int'l*, pg. 93

Hackwell, David J., Mng. Dir.--Esselte UK Ltd., Feltham, United Kingdom; *Int'l*, pg. 461

Hadala, Richard J., Pres.--Westinghouse Communication & Information Systems, Pittsburgh, PA; *U.S. Public*, pg. 273

Hadani, Ron, Pres.--DRS Medical Systems, Mahwah, NJ; *U.S. Public*, pg. 475

Hadaway, Mike, Pres.--Merit Distribution Services, Inc., Temple, TX; *U.S. Public*, pg. 1733

Hadaway, R.H., Mng. Dir.--Alcan Consumer Products, Amersham, United Kingdom; *Int'l*, pg. 51

Hadberg, Preben, Area Mgr.-Scandinavia--Fasson A/S, Copenhagen, Denmark; *U.S. Public*, pg. 154

Hadberg, Preben, Area Mgr.-Scandinavia--Fasson AB, Malmo, Sweden; *U.S. Public*, pg. 154

Hadberg, Preben, V.P. & Gen. Mgr.--N.V. Fasson Indus. Div., Turnhout, Belgium; *U.S. Public*, pg. 154

Haddad, Bishara, Reg. Mgr.--Skandia Insurance (UK Contact Office) Ltd., London, United Kingdom; *Int'l*, pg. 1258

Haddad, Jamil, Rep.--Mead Packaging Chile Limitada, Santiago, Chile; *U.S. Public*, pg. 1076

Haddad, Jamil, Jr., Commercial Dir.--Mead Embalagens LTDA, Sao Paulo, Brazil; *U.S. Public*, pg. 1076

Hadden, Abel, Mng. Dir.--Daniel J. Edelman Ltd., London, United Kingdom; *U.S. Private*, pg. 363

Hadden, Richard, Pres.--Cossette Communication-Marketing (Vancouver) Inc., Vancouver, Canada; *Int'l*, pg. 336

Hadding, Gunther, Dr., Chief Exec. Officer--Bertelsmann Lexikothek Verlag GmbH, Gutersloh, Germany; *Int'l*, pg. 189

Haddix, George, Pres.--Cable Services Group, Omaha, NE; *U.S. Public*, pg. 283

Haddock, John, Pres.--Manchem Inc., Princeton, NJ; *Int'l*, pg. 1110

Hadenfeldt, Claus-Detlef, Mng. Dir.--Vectur GmbH, Dusseldorf, Germany; *U.S. Private*, pg. 1129

Hadfield, Frederick W., Pres. & Chief Exec. Officer--Ingersoll-Dresser Pump Company, Liberty Corner, NJ; *U.S. Public*, pg. 529

Hadfield, Jay, Pres.--Utimaco Safeware, Inc., Windsor, CT; *Int'l*, pg. 1444

Hadfield, Noel J., Reg. Mgr.--AlliedSignal Aerospace Service Corporation, Melbourne, Australia; *U.S. Public*, pg. 52

Hadl, Gunawan, Mng. Dir.--Simon & Schuster (Asia) Pte. Ltd., Singapore, Singapore; *U.S. Private*, pg. 778

Hadley, Chris, Mng. Dir.--International Business Analysis Proprietary Limited, Sydney, Australia; *Int'l*, pg. 1496

Hadrys, Helmut G., Chm.--Hoesch Rothe Erde GmbH, Lippstadt, Germany; *Int'l*, pg. 509

Hadrys, Helmut G., Dr., Pres.--Krupp Hoesch Stahlexport GmbH, Aurora, OH; *Int'l*, pg. 515

Hadsell, James, Gen. Mgr.--Napco Plastics Co., Napoleon, OH; *Int'l*, pg. 440

Hadwich, Ingomar, Mng. Dir.--Dyckerhoff & Widmann Gesellschaft m.b.H., Vienna, Austria; *Int'l*, pg. 424

Haegerty, Robert, V.P.-Sls.--All Star Gas Co.-Region XII, Lebanon, MO; *U.S. Private*, pg. 35

Haeggblom, Sten, Pres.--Asea Brown Boveri Aktiengesellschaft mbH, Vienna, Austria; *Int'l*, pg. 8

Haemmerle, Andre, Pres.--Intermedics S.A., Le Locle, Switzerland; *Int'l*, pg. 1307

Haemmerle, Walter, V.P. & Group Gen. Mgr.--Unisys Deutschland GmbH, Sulzbach, Germany; *U.S. Public*, pg. 1672

Haenel, Hans-Dieter, Dr., Mng. Dir.--Betriebswintschaft Licher Verlag Dr. Th. Gabler GmbH, Wiesbaden, Germany; *Int'l*, pg. 189

Haenelt, Stefan, Chief Oper. Officer--Wirsbo Pex GmbH, Heusenstamm, Germany; *Int'l*, pg. 442

Haener, William J., Pres.--American Natural Offshore Co., Detroit, MI; *U.S. Public*, pg. 389

Haeng, Cho-Kwan, Chief Exec. Officer--POSAM New York Office, New York, NY; *Int'l*, pg. 1062

Haenig, G., Dr., Mng. Dir.--Grillo-Werke AG, Duisburg, Germany; *Int'l*, pg. 861

Haentjens, Peter, Gen. Mgr.--Hazleton Pumps Inc., Hazleton, PA; *Int'l*, pg. 967

Haertel, Rainer M., Mng. Dir.--Loctite Europa Gesellschaft mbH, Vienna, Austria; *Int'l*, pg. 611

Haessler, J., Pres.--Assurity Life Inc., Lincoln, NE; *U.S. Private*, pg. 1187

Haf, Wolfgang, Reg. Dir.--Wunderman Cato Johnson Singapore, Singapore, Singapore; *U.S. Private*, pg. 326

Hafele, Carl W., Principal & Mng. Dir.--National Asset Management Corporation, Louisville, KY; *U.S. Public*, pg. 1154

Hafer, Fred D., Pres. & Chief Exec. Officer--GPU Service Corp., Parsippany, NJ; *U.S. Public*, pg. 695

Hafer, Fred D., Pres. & Chief Oper. Officer--Metropolitan Edison Co., Reading, PA; *U.S. Public*, pg. 695

Hafer, Marc, Pres.--Lester Buildings Division, Lester Prairie, MN; *U.S. Public*, pg. 271

Hafez, Hassan, Chm. & Mng. Dir.--Arab International Insurance Company, Cairo, Egypt; *Int'l*, pg. 61

Hafez, Hassan, Chief Oper. Officer--Electrolux Saudi Services, Ltd., Riyadh, Saudi Arabia; *Int'l*, pg. 443

Hafez, Hassan M., Chief Oper. Officer--The Arab-Eastern Insurance Company Limited E.C., Manama, Bahrain; *Int'l*, *pg. 1392*

Haffen, Bill, Reg. Dir.--Atlanta Regional Office, Atlanta, GA; *U.S. Public*, pg. 1715

Haffey, Kevin, Mng. Dir.--SKF New Zealand Ltd., Auckland, New Zealand; *Int'l*, pg. 1159

Hafkesbrink, Werner, Mgr.--Adrema Leasing Corporation, Heppenheim, Germany; *U.S. Public*, pg. 1304

Haflidson, John, Mine Mgr.--Holt-McDermott Mine, Kirkland Lake, Canada; *Int'l*, pg. 169

Hafner, Anton, Mng. Dir.--NeoTecha Ag, Hombrechtikon, Switzerland; *U.S. Public*, pg. 1651

Hafner, F., Mgr.--Swiss Bank Corporation, Madrid, Spain; *Int'l*, pg. 1330

Hafner, F., Pres.--SBS Sociedad de Valores S.A., Madrid, Spain; *Int'l*, pg. 1331

Hafner, Ingo, Mng. Partner--Curtis 1000 Europe GmbH, Andernach, Germany; *U.S. Public*, pg. 70

Hafner, J.A., Jr., Pres. & Chief Exec. Officer--Riviana International Inc., Houston, TX; *U.S. Public*, pg. 1392

Haft, Robert M., Pres.--Crown Books East Corporation, Landover, MD; *U.S. Public*, pg. 484

Haga, Magne, Head of Unit--Skandinaviska Enskilda Banken Oslo, Oslo, Norway; *Int'l*, pg. 1259

Hagaman, John, Pres.--Dow Elanco, Indianapolis, IN; *U.S. Public*, pg. 522

Hagaman, John, Pres. & Chief Oper. Officer--Dow Elanco, Indianapolis, IN; *U.S. Public*, pg. 523

Hagan, John I., Pres.--Line Equipment Sales Co., Inc., Charleston, SC; *U.S. Private*, pg. 1130

Hagan, Michael C., Pres. & Chief Exec. Officer--American Commercial Lines Inc., Jeffersonville, IN; *U.S. Public*, pg. 284

Hagan, R.L., Pres.--Filtrona Richmond Company, Richmond, VA; *Int'l*, pg. 232

Hageboeck, Leo, Pres.--Sperrholz Koch GmbH, Coesfeld, Germany; *Int'l*, pg. 1491

Hagedorn, David j., Gen. Mgr.--Emirates Can Company Ltd., Dubai, United Arab Emirates; *U.S. Public*, pg. 465

Hagedorn, Fritz, Dir.--Desowag-Bayer Holzschutz GmbH, Dusseldorf, Germany; *Int'l*, pg. 172

Hagedorn, Robert Leo, Gen. Mgr.--DMI Furniture, Inc., Ferdinand, IN; *U.S. Public*, pg. 473

Hagel, Rauno, Mng. Dir.--Valmet Dura Oy, Jarvenpaa, Finland; *Int'l*, pg. 1448

Hagelstein, Robert, Pres.--Greenwood Publishing Group Inc., Westport, CT; *Int'l*, pg. 1094

Hageman, James A., Chm.--May Merchandising Company, Saint Louis, MO; *U.S. Public*, pg. 1064

Hagemann, F., Gen. Mgr.--ING Baring Securities do Brazil, Sao Paulo, Brazil; *Int'l*, pg. 649

Hagen, David F., Gen. Mgr.--Ford Engine Division, Dearborn, MI; *U.S. Public*, pg. 662

Hagen, Greg, Plant Mgr.--Lucas Body Systems - Lake Center Industries, Winona, Winona, MN; *Int'l*, pg. 820

Hagen, John, Pres.--DACAM Corp., Madison Heights, VA; *U.S. Private*, pg. 814

Hagen, Stein Erik, Chief Oper. Officer--Hakon Gruppen AS, Oslo, Norway; *Int'l*, pg. 643

Hagens, Jack, Mng. Dir.--Tukkers Milieu-onderzoek BV, Woerden, Netherlands; *Int'l*, pg. 607

Hager, Edward B., Chief Oper. Officer--Vineland Laboratories Inc., Vineland, NJ; *U.S. Public*, pg. 855

Hager, Edward B., M.D., Chief Oper. Officer--EVSCO Pharmaceuticals, Buena, NJ; *U.S. Public*, pg. 855

Hager, Edward B., M.D., Chief Exec. Officer--Molecular Packaging Systems, Inc., Vineland, NJ; *U.S. Public*, pg. 855

Hager, J.L., Pres. & Chief Exec. Officer--WRR Environmental Services Co., Inc., Eau Claire, WI; *U.S. Public*, pg. 1792

Hagerty, James J., Pres.--ReliaStar Financial Marketing Corp., Seattle, WA; *U.S. Public*, pg. 1376

Hagesather, Osvald, Chief Oper. Officer--A/S SAPA, Lillestrom, Norway; *Int'l*, pg. 443

Haggarty, Michael C., Pres. & Chief Exec. Officer--The Auburn State Bank, Auburn, IN; *U.S. Public*, pg. 674

Haggert, Sonja, V.P. & Gen. Mgr.--Keystone Filter Division, Hatfield, PA; *U.S. Public*, pg. 1100

Haggerty, Daniel J., Pres. & Chief Exec. Officer--Norwest Venture Capital Management, Inc., Minneapolis, MN; *U.S. Public*, pg. 1202

Haggerty, Gretchen R., Pres.--USX Credit, Pittsburgh, PA; *U.S. Public*, pg. 1661

Haggerty, Sherman, Pres.--Sacramento Div., Gold River, CA; *U.S. Public*, pg. 1683

Haggett, Christopher, V.P. & Gen. Mgr.--I.D.M. Electronics Ltd., Reading, United Kingdom; *U.S. Public*, pg. 946

Hagglund, Bjorn, Pres.--Stora Forest AB, Falun, Sweden; *Int'l*, pg. 1303

Hagie, John, Pres.--Palco MFG., Clarion, IA; *U.S. Private*, pg. 493

Hagihara, Masomi, V.P. & Gen. Mgr.--Day-Lee Foods Inc., Santa Fe Springs, CA; *Int'l*, pg. 936

Hagiwara, Y., Mng. Dir.--Thermometrics Japan Co. Ltd., Tokyo, Japan; *Int'l*, pg. 209

Hagley, John, Mng. Dir.--John Hagley Communications, Singapore, Singapore; *Int'l*, pg. 117

Haglund, Ake, Mgr.--Guldsmedshytte Bruks AB, Guldsmeds-hyttan, Sweden; *Int'l*, pg. 1185

Haglund, Christer, Chief Oper. Officer--Molnlycke Toiletries AB, Goteborg, Sweden; *Int'l*, pg. 1326

Haglund, Mark, Pres.-Automotive--STP Corporation, Danbury, CT; *U.S. Public*, pg. 627

Haglund, Mark E., Pres.--STP Products, Inc., Danbury, CT; *U.S. Public*, pg. 627

Hague, Mark H., Gen. Mgr.--Electronic Materials & Refractory Metals Div., Boyertown, PA; *U.S. Public*, pg. 289

Hahn-Petersen, Vilhelm, Mng. Dir.--FLS Aerospace Engineering Ltd., Stansted, United Kingdom; *Int'l*, pg. 475

Hahn, Ed, V.P.-No. Opers.--Albany International/Press Fabrics Division, Albany, NY; *U.S. Public*, pg. 36

Hahn, Joe, Gen. Mgr.--ITW Magnaflux, Glenview, IL; *U.S. Public*, pg. 866

Hahn, Kenneth, Exec. V.P.--Hahn Equipment Co., Evansville, IN; *U.S. Public*, pg. 1624

Hahn, Richard C., Pres. & Chief Exec. Officer--Farmers National Company, Omaha, NE; *U.S. Private*, pg. 738

Hahn, Robert B., Pres.--Aerochem, Inc., Orange, CA; *U.S. Public*, pg. 534

Hahn, T. Marshall, Chief Exec. Officer--Aztec Trading Company, S.A., Port Wentworth, GA; *U.S. Public*, pg. 736

Hahn, Thomas M., Pres. & Chief Oper. Officer--Garden State Paper Co., Inc., Elmwood Park, NJ; *U.S. Public*, pg. 1078

Hahn, Yea Sun, Pres.--Korea Development Leasing Corporation, Seoul, Korea; *Int'l*, pg. 1010

Hahne, Hakan, Chief Oper. Officer--Ledu International AB, Bohus, Sweden; *Int'l*, pg. 821

Hahnmann, Paul F., V.P. & Gen. Mgr.--Schuller GmbH, Wertheim, Germany; *U.S. Public*, pg. 927

Hahs, Dwain L., Pres.--Eyewear Division, Rochester, NY; *U.S. Public*, pg. 194

Haidinger, Robert N., Chm. Bd., Pres. & Chief Exec. Officer--JJI Lighting Group Inc., Greenwich, CT; *Int'l*, pg. 821

Haidlmair, J., Chief Exec. Officer--Schiedel Kaminwerke GmbH, Wartberg, Austria; *Int'l*, pg. 1092

Haigh, Brian, Pres.--Organon Inc., West Orange, NJ; *Int'l*, pg. 48

Haight, George, V.P. & Gen. Mgr.--Wynn's-Precision, Inc., Arizona Div., Tempe, AZ; *U.S. Public*, pg. 1783

Haile, William B., Pres. & Chief Exec. Officer--SunTrust Bank, Savannah, N.A., Savannah, GA; *U.S. Public*, pg. 1538

Hainer, Goetz E., Mng. Dir.--Lorenz & Lihn Obst-Edel-Erzeugnisse GmbH, Monchengladbach, Germany; *Int'l*, pg. 433

Haines, Debby L., Pres.--Simian Company, Inc., Santa Cruz, CA; *U.S. Public*, pg. 1357

Haines, Jerry, Dir.-Oper.--Harris Protocall, Inc., Atlanta, GA; *U.S. Public*, pg. 792

Haines, Peter, Pres. & Chief Exec. Officer--Cybex International, Inc., Medway, MA; *U.S. Private*, pg. 1114

Haines, Richard, Chief Oper. Officer--Waterbury Headers, Inc., Waterbury, CT; *U.S. Private*, pg. 984

Haines, Richard, Pres.--Maytag Company, Newton, IA; *U.S. Public*, pg. 1064

Haines, Scott, Pres.--Windsor Service, Inc., Reading, PA; *U.S. Private*, pg. 494

Hainley, Dennis, V.P. & Gen. Mgr.--Ceco Building Systems-Midwestern Region, Mount Pleasant, IA; *U.S. Private*, pg. 221

Hainley, Gary, Pres.--The Shannon Group, Brentwood, TN; *U.S. Public*, pg. 1041

Hainley, John D.H., Sole Administrator--Rimir, S.A. de C.V., Mexico, Mexico; *U.S. Public*, pg. 723

Haiplik, T.W., Pres. & Chief Exec. Officer--MacMillan Bathurst Inc., Mississauga, Canada; *Int'l*, pg. 20

Haire, Larry, Pres. & Chief Oper. Officer--Kilgore First National Bank, Kilgore, TX; *U.S. Public*, pg. 630

Haishimoto, Takashi, Pres.--Mitsui T & B Options Inc., New York, NY; *Int'l*, pg. 883

Hajek, David J., Pres. & Chief Exec. Officer--Cadmus Journal Services, Richmond, VA; *U.S. Public*, pg. 291

Haji, Hiroshi, Chief Oper. Officer--COBE Laboratories, K.K., Tokyo, Japan; *Int'l*, pg. 667

Hajme, Suzuki, Pres.--Applied Super Conetics, Inc., San Diego, CA; *Int'l*, pg. 1405

Hakala, Heikki, Pres. & Chief Exec. Officer--Rauma Ltd., Helsinki, Finland; *Int'l*, pg. 1428

Hakanson, Staffan, Mgr.--SAB WABCO Holdings B.V., Heerhugowaard, Netherlands; *Int'l*, pg. 271

Hakansson, Gunnar, Mng. Dir.--Telefonaktiebolaget LM Ericsson Delagation Technique du Projet au Maroc, Rabat, Morocco; *Int'l*, pg. 1370

Hakansson, Kurt, Pres.--ABB Distribution AB, Vasteras, Sweden; *Int'l*, pg. 7

Hakata, Kazuyasu, Mng. Dir.--Fuji International Finance (HK) Limited, Central, Hong Kong; *Int'l*, pg. 521

Hake, William D., Sr. V.P.-Coal--Kerr-McGee Coal Corp., Oklahoma City, OK; *U.S. Public*, pg. 952

Hakhu, Jai K., Bus. Dir.--Rockwell Semiconductor Systems, Newbury Park, CA; *U.S. Public*, pg. 1398

Hakim, B.H., Pres.--P.T. Caltex Pacific Indonesia, Jakarta, Indonesia; *U.S. Public*, pg. 348

Hakim, George N., Jr., Pres.--Crowntuft Manufacturing Co., New York, NY; *U.S. Public*, pg. 948

Hakimoglu, Demirhan, Chief Exec. Officer--Aydin Yazilim ve Elektronik Sanayii A.S. (AYES AS), Ankara, Turkey; *U.S. Public*, pg. 158

Hakkarainen, Ari, Pres.--TrioVing a.s., Hoyden, Norway; *Int'l*, *pg. 18*

Hakooz, Samir A., Pres.--Plasma Energy Corporation, Raleigh, NC; *U.S. Public*, pg. 344

Haladun, Tony, Gen. Mgr.--Intergraph Canada Ltd., Calgary, Canada; *U.S. Public*, pg. 891

Halahel, Ted, Gen. Mgr.--Engelhard Canada Limited, Aurora, Canada; *U.S. Public*, pg. 582

Halamoda, Jurgen, Pres.--Astra Ges. m.b.H., Lienz, Austria; *Int'l*, pg. 93

Haland, Yngve, Chief Oper. Officer--Autoliv Development AB, Vargarda, Sweden; *Int'l*, pg. 438

Halano, Hiroshi, Chief Exec. Officer--GS Battery (U.S.A.), Inc., City of Industry, CA; *Int'l*, pg. 702

Halberda, Michael, Chief Oper. Officer--Comprehensive Care Integration, Corona Del Mar, CA; *U.S. Public*, pg. 419

Halbrook, Jack, Gen. Mgr.--American Bread Co., Huntsville, AL; *U.S. Public*, pg. 547

Hale, Dan, Pres.--Chase Manhattan Leasing, Montvale, NJ; *U.S. Public*, pg. 338

Hale, David, Branch Mgr.--Willis Corroon Corp. of Fairbanks, Fairbanks, AK; *Int'l*, pg. 1505

Hale, Don, V.P. & Gen. Mgr.--Dillard, A ResourceNet International Company, Bristol, VA; *U.S. Public*, pg. 902

Hale, Elden A., Jr., Pres.--NYT Video Productions, Scranton, PA; *U.S. Public*, pg. 1174

Hale, Elden A., Jr., Pres.--WTKR-TV, Norfolk, VA; *U.S. Public*, pg. 1174

Hale, G. W., Mgr.-Mktg. Communications--Du Pont Biomedicals Department, Wilmington, DE; *U.S. Public*, pg. 531

Hale, Jeffrey, Pres.-Media Information Grp.--Competitive Media Reporting, New York, NY; *Int'l*, pg. 1447

Hale, Jim, Plant Mgr.--Norandal U.S.A., Newport, AR; *Int'l*, pg. 434

Hale, John, Pres.--RTS Systems, Minneapolis, MN; *U.S. Private*, pg. 1074

Hale, John, Dir.-Southern Mfg.--Frito-Lay Inc., Charlotte, NC; *U.S. Public*, pg. 1277

Hale, Lee, Gen. Mgr.--Poli-Twine Western Inc., Clearfield, UT; *Int'l*, pg. 1362
Hale, R.D., Pres. & Chief Oper. Officer--Cancarb Limited, Medicine Hat, Canada; *Int'l*, pg. 1417
Hale, Rodney L., Pres. & Chief Exec. Officer--Academy Life Insurance Co., Alpharetta, GA; *Int'l*, pg. 27
Hale, W. R., Mng. Dir.--Anglesey Aluminium Limited, Holyhead, United Kingdom; *U.S. Public*, pg. 1063
Hale, W. R., Mng. Dir.--Anglesey Aluminium Limited, Holyhead, United Kingdom; *Int'l*, pg. 1119
Hale, W.T., Pres.--Hale Brothers, Inc., Morristown, TN; *U.S. Public*, pg. 1278
Halecky, E., Pres.--PDM Steel Service Center-Stockton, Stockton, CA; *U.S. Public*, pg. 1305
Halef, Besim, Pres.--MM Industra, Ltd., Dartmouth, Canada; *Int'l*, pg. 74
Halenda, John, Pres.--Wynn's-Precision, Inc., Lebanon, TN; *U.S. Public*, pg. 1783
Halenke, Torsten, Chief Oper. Officer--BHF-Bank Representative Office, Madrid, Spain; *Int'l*, pg. 120
Hales, Antony J., Chm.--Allied Domecq Retailing Limited, Burton on Trent, United Kingdom; *Int'l*, pg. 63
Hales, Brent, Div. Mgr.--Wyle Electronics-Salt Lake City, Salt Lake City, UT; *Int'l*, pg. 1458
Haleski, L.B., Pres.--Ikselah Corporation, Tullytown, PA; *U.S. Public*, pg. 1339
Haley, Bill, Plant Mgr.--Hydro Conduit Corp., Gainesville, GA; *Int'l*, pg. 246
Haley, Daniel J., Chm. Bd.--Weather Barrier Inc., Conshohocken, PA; *U.S. Private*, pg. 406
Haley, Daniel J., Chm. Bd.--Spring Mill Corp., Conshohocken, PA; *U.S. Private*, pg. 406
Haley, Linda, Div. Mgr.--Transilwrap Co., Inc., Kansas City, MO; *U.S. Private*, pg. 1097
Haley, Mark, Pres.--Almond Roca International, Tacoma, WA; *U.S. Private*, pg. 173
Haley, Michael P., Pres.--American Furniture Company, Incorporated, Martinsville, VA; *U.S. Public*, pg. 974
Haley, Robert, Gen. Mgr.--Scandura Canada Inc., Bracebridge, Canada; *Int'l*, pg. 114
Haley, Robert G., Pres.--BellSouth Information Systems, Inc. (BIS), Atlanta, GA; *U.S. Public*, pg. 208
Halfacre, Van, Gen. Mgr.--Rohr Industries, Heber Springs Plant, Heber Springs, AR; *U.S. Public*, pg. 752
Halferty, James J., Pres.--Chatas Glass Co., Inc., Vineland, NJ; *U.S. Public*, pg. 1341
Halfon, Jacques, Chm.--Elf Aquitaine (Production), Paris, France; *Int'l*, pg. 444
Halford, T.E., Pres. & Mng. Dir.--Equifax Europe, London, United Kingdom; *U.S. Public*, pg. 588
Halinen, Juho, Gen. Mgr.--Nokia Mobile Phones (Gulf), Dubai, United Arab Emirates; *Int'l*, pg. 952
Halkema, A.R.T., Mng. Dir.--Nutricia S.A., Madrid, Spain; *Int'l*, pg. 992
Halko, George A., Pres.--Temtrol, Inc., Okarche, OK; *U.S. Public*, pg. 1193
Hall, A.C., Chief Oper. Officer--Downings Steel Ltd., Middlesbrough, United Kingdom; *Int'l*, pg. 1450
Hall, A.C., Mgr.--Van Leeuwen Tubes Ltd., Middlesbrough, United Kingdom; *Int'l*, pg. 1450
Hall, Andrew J., Pres.--Phibro Division of Salomon Inc., Westport, CT; *U.S. Public*, pg. 1633
Hall, B., Mng. Dir.--Timken Argentina S.R.L., Buenos Aires, Argentina; *U.S. Public*, pg. 1617
Hall, Bjorn, Chm. Bd.--Skandia Asia Ltd., Central, Hong Kong; *Int'l*, pg. 1258
Hall, Bradley C., Pres.--UGI Enterprises, King of Prussia, PA; *U.S. Public*, pg. 1653
Hall, Brian, Pres.--Specialty Underwriters Reinsurance Facility, Hamilton, Bermuda; *U.S. Private*, pg. 741
Hall, Brian H., Pres.--West Information Publishing Group, Saint Paul, MN; *U.S. Public*, pg. 1602
Hall, Charles A., Dr., Pres.--Martin Marietta Specialty Components, Inc., Largo, FL; *U.S. Public*, pg. 1007
Hall, Conrad M., Pres. & Chief Exec. Officer--Trader Publishing Company, Norfolk, VA; *U.S. Private*, pg. 649
Hall, D.A., Sr. V.P.-Great Lakes Chemical Corp.--WIL Research Laboratories, Inc., Ashland, OH; *U.S. Public*, pg. 760
Hall, David, Mng. Dir.--Exquisite Form Brassiere (GB) Ltd., London, United Kingdom; *Int'l*, pg. 14
Hall, Derek, Gen. Mgr.--Addison-Wesley Publishers Pty. Ltd., Sydney, Australia; *Int'l*, pg. 1027
Hall, Don, Div. Mgr.--ConAgra Broiler Co., Gainesville, GA; *U.S. Public*, pg. 427
Hall, Don, Sr. V.P.--Helen of Troy (Far East) Ltd., Kowloon, Hong Kong; *U.S. Public*, pg. 807
Hall, E.W., Pres.--Frigoscandia Ltd., Hoddesdon, United Kingdom; *U.S. Public*, pg. 607
Hall, Ed, Mgr.--Sterling Steel Company, Houston, TX; *U.S. Public*, pg. 412
Hall, Edward R., Pres.-Hydraulics--Parker Hannifin Corporation, Hemel Hempstead, United Kingdom; *U.S. Public*, pg. 1263
Hall, Gary, Plant Mgr.--Solvay Interox America, Longview, WA; *Int'l*, pg. 1278
Hall, Geoff, Chief Oper. Officer--Ceatron Technology Ltd., Warwick, United Kingdom; *U.S. Public*, pg. 148
Hall, George, Gen. Mgr.--International Window-Northern California, Hayward, CA; *U.S. Public*, pg. 895
Hall, George, Co-Mgr.--Automatic Music Service of Billings, Inc., Billings, MT; *U.S. Public*, pg. 1319
Hall, Gordon, Publr.--Midland Daily News, Midland, MI; *U.S. Private*, pg. 517
Hall, Graham, Pres.--Todd-AO U.K., London, United Kingdom; *U.S. Public*, pg. 1619
Hall, Graham, Pres.--Todd-AO Europe Holding Ltd., London, United Kingdom; *U.S. Public*, pg. 1619
Hall, Herbert A., Chm.--Sigma Investment Management Systems Limited, Kingston, Jamaica; *Int'l*, pg. 156
Hall, Herbert A., Chm.--Sigma Unit Trust Managers Limited, Kingston, Jamaica; *Int'l*, pg. 156
Hall, J.E., Mng. Dir.--NatWest International Trust Corporation (Cayman) Limited, Georgetown, Cayman Islands; *Int'l*, pg. 911
Hall, James A., Chief Oper. Officer--Allright Tenn. Inc., Chattanooga, TN; *U.S. Private*, pg. 43
Hall, James N., Pres.--Dacco, Inc., Cookeville, TN; *U.S. Private*, pg. 598
Hall, Jim, Reg. Mgr.--Green Tree Acceptance, Inc., Tulsa, OK; *U.S. Public*, pg. 762
Hall, Jim A., Div. Mgr.--Megamarkets, Inc., Memphis, TN; *U.S. Public*, pg. 653
Hall, John, Pres.-Time-Life Books--Time-Life, Inc., Alexandria, VA; *U.S. Public*, pg. 1613
Hall, John, Sir, Mng. Dir.--European Brazilian Bank Ltd., London, United Kingdom; *U.S. Public*, pg. 183
Hall, John, Sir, Chm.--The Nikko Bank (UK) Plc, London, United Kingdom; *Int'l*, pg. 930
Hall, K.H., Mng. Dir.-S.E. Asia--Ingersoll Rand S.E. Asia (Private) Limited, Singapore, Singapore; *U.S. Public*, pg. 878
Hall, Ken, V.P. & Mng. Dir.--ABC-Ademco Security Products, Saint-Laurent, Canada; *U.S. Public*, pg. 1306
Hall, Nigel, Mng. Dir.--Ginn & Co. Limited, Aylesbury, United Kingdom; *Int'l*, pg. 1094
Hall, Pamela S., Pres.--Normandeau Associates, Inc., Bedford, NH; *U.S. Public*, pg. 1594
Hall, Phillip G., Chm. Bd.--CH2M Hill, Inc., Greenwood Village, CO; *U.S. Private*, pg. 195
Hall, Ray, Pres.--Sulzer Papertec Inc., Middletown, OH; *Int'l*, pg. 1305
Hall, Ray C., Pres.--AVEMCO Insurance Co., Frederick, MD; *U.S. Public*, pg. 152
Hall, Rick, Sr. Mgr.-Opers.--Consolidated Communications Operator Services, Inc., Mattoon, IL; *U.S. Public*, pg. 1073
Hall, Robert, Pres.--Lenox Brands, Lawrenceville, NJ; *U.S. Public*, pg. 261
Hall, Robert, Pres.--Lenox Brands, Langhorne, PA; *U.S. Public*, pg. 261
Hall, Robert, Sr. V.P.--Grolier Educational Corporation, Danbury, CT; *Int'l*, pg. 794
Hall, Robert, Publisher--Philadelphia Newspapers, Inc., Philadelphia, PA; *U.S. Public*, pg. 964
Hall, Robert J., Chm. & Publr.--Philadelphia Daily News, Philadelphia, PA; *U.S. Public*, pg. 964
Hall, Roger A., Mng. Dir.--Bain Hogg Insurance Management Guernsey Ltd., Saint Peter Port, United Kingdom; *Int'l*, pg. 671
Hall, Stuart, Pres.--Liberty Northwest Insurance Corp., Portland, OR; *U.S. Private*, pg. 666
Hall, Thomas E., Mgr.-Branch--Piper Jaffray Inc., Brookings, SD; *U.S. Public*, pg. 1300
Hall, Thomas E., Mgr.-Branch--Piper Jaffray Inc., Sioux Falls, SD; *U.S. Public*, pg. 1302
Hall, Thomas H., Pres.--Butler Real Estate, Kansas City, MO; *U.S. Public*, pg. 271
Hall, Thomas L., Pres. & Chief Exec. Officer--International Women's Apparel Group, Easton, PA; *U.S. Public*, pg. 796
Hall, Thomas. W., Pres.--GTE Southwest Incorporated, Irving, TX; *U.S. Public*, pg. 697
Hall, Troy, Gen. Mgr.--Creative Media Products, Mason, OH; *U.S. Private*, pg. 1055
Hall, W. Reginald, V.P. & Gen. Mgr.--FMC Food Machinery Group, Chicago, IL; *U.S. Public*, pg. 605
Hall, William, Pres.--Sight & Sound, Wilsonville, OR; *U.S. Public*, pg. 780
Hall, William E., Pres.--Parsons Process Group Inc., Houston, TX; *U.S. Private*, pg. 842
Hall, William K., Pres. & Chief Exec. Officer--Eagle Industries, Inc., Chicago, IL; *U.S. Private*, pg. 473
Hall, Willie, Gen. Mgr.--Taylor Home Health Inc., Beaumont, TX; *U.S. Public*, pg. 885
Hallal, John, Gen. Mgr.--Martin Marietta Automations Systems, Daytona Beach, FL; *U.S. Public*, pg. 1007
Hallam, Gary, Gen. Mgr.--Triple S Plastics, Battle Creek, Battle Creek, MI; *U.S. Public*, pg. 1640
Hallam, Stuart, Chief Exec. Officer--Brite Voice Systems Europe, Cambridge, United Kingdom; *U.S. Public*, pg. 257
Hallamore, Jeffrey J., Gen. Mgr.--BRENNTAG Interchem, Inc., Trevose, PA; *Int'l*, pg. 1458
Hallard, Jose, Mng. Dir.--DMR Group (Belgium) S.A.-N.V., Brussels, Belgium; *Int'l*, pg. 528
Hallatt, A.P., Mng. Dir.--Master Foods, Kings Lynn, United Kingdom; *U.S. Private*, pg. 707
Hallberg, Per, Pres.--Optiroc AB, Sollentuna, Sweden; *Int'l*, pg. 1200
Halldorf, Anders, Chief Oper. Officer--Saab-Scania AB, Oskarshamn, Sweden; *Int'l*, pg. 687
Halle, Alfredo G., Mng. Dir.--Elaboradora Argentina de Cereales, S.A., Buenos Aires, Argentina; *U.S. Public*, pg. 1348
Hallenbeck, Christopher, Pres.--Pepsi-Cola West, Irvine, CA; *U.S. Public*, pg. 1277
Haller, Donald, V.P.--TABC, Inc., Long Beach, CA; *Int'l*, pg. 1412
Haller, Federico G., Pres.--ATS Omega de Mexico, S.A. de C.V., Tlalnepantla, Mexico; *U.S. Public*, pg. 1222
Haller, J., Pres. & Chief Exec. Officer--PNC Bank, Cincinnati, OH; *U.S. Public*, pg. 1242
Hallet, Jim, Pres. & Chief Exec. Officer--Adesa Inc., Indianapolis, IN; *U.S. Public*, pg. 1116
Halley-Wright, Andy, Reg. Strategic Plng. Dir. & Res. Dir.--Young & Rubicam Latam (Miami), Miami, FL; *U.S. Private*, pg. 1198
Halley, David, V.P./Gen. Mgr.--Air Traffic Control Systems Division, Melbourne, FL; *U.S. Public*, pg. 792
Halley, J.A., Mng. Dir.--HDA Forgings Ltd., Redditch, United Kingdom; *Int'l*, pg. 126
Hallgren, Kenneth, Pres. & Chief Oper. Officer--Hurd Millwork Company, Inc., Medford, WI; *U.S. Private*, pg. 1113
Halliday, Darryl L., Mgr.--Peak Downs Mine, Moranbah, Australia; *Int'l*, pg. 223
Hallmann, Harry, Gen. Mgr.--Geonex, Chatsworth, CA; *U.S. Private*, pg. 448
Halloin, Mike, Gen. Mgr.--Parker Hannifin SA NV, Brussels, Belgium; *U.S. Public*, pg. 1263
Halloran, Michael, Gen. Mgr.--Westpac Banking Corp. - Western Samoa, Apia, Samoa; *Int'l*, pg. 1497
Halloran, Michael J., Gen. Mgr.--Pacific Commercial Bank Limited, Apia, Samoa; *U.S. Public*, pg. 1248
Hallowell, Chris, Sr. V.P. & Mng. Dir.--The Program Exchange, New York, NY; *U.S. Public*, pg. 1422
Hallstrom, Ulf, Chief Exec. Officer & Mng. Dir.--D'Arcy Masius Benton & Bowles AB, Stockholm, Sweden; *U.S. Private*, pg. 304
Halluitte, Blaise, Pres.--Rhodia Nordeste, Sao Paulo, Brazil; *Int'l*, pg. 1109
Halpain, Joseph, V.P.--Scientific Communications, Inc., Garland, TX; *U.S. Public*, pg. 112
Halper, Norman A., Chief Oper. Officer--First Republic Corp., Real Estate Div., New York, NY; *U.S. Public*, pg. 637
Halper, Norman A., Pres.--The First Republic Building Corp., New York, NY; *U.S. Public*, pg. 637
Halpern, Morris S., Pres.--Colony Glass, New York, NY; *U.S. Public*, pg. 976
Halpern, S., Exec. V.P.--Dongbu Aetna Life Insurance Co., Ltd., Seoul, Korea; *U.S. Public*, pg. 27
Halpin, Charles, Mng. Dir.--Bowker-Saur Ltd., East Grinstead, United Kingdom; *Int'l*, pg. 1094
Hals, Bjorn, Gen. Mgr.--Oceaneering A/S, Stavanger, Norway; *U.S. Public*, pg. 1211
Halsey, A.W., Pres.--Texaco Petroleos de Angola S.A.R.L., Luanda, Angola; *U.S. Public*, pg. 1584
Halstead, C.W., Chief Oper. Officer--Mack Trucks Australia Pty. Ltd., Darra, Australia; *Int'l*, pg. 1103
Halula, John R., Grp. V.P.--Worthington Custom Plastics, Columbus, OH; *U.S. Public*, pg. 1780
Halvorsen, Arne, Mng. Dir.--Nodest A/S, Drammen, Norway; *Int'l*, pg. 715
Halvorson, William, Pres.--Amador Motors, Sutter Creek, CA; *U.S. Private*, pg. 891
Hama, Fudeji, Chief Oper. Officer--The Tokio (New York) Corporation, New York, NY; *Int'l*, pg. 1392
Hamaberg, Bob, Chief Exec. Officer--BTR Aerspace Group, Winnipeg, Canada; *Int'l*, pg. 127
Hamad, Samuel, Pres.-Asia/Australasia Div.--Bristol-Myers International Group, New York, NY; *U.S. Public*, pg. 254
Hamada, Yuji, Chief Rep.--Daiwa Bank-Bangkok, Bangkok, Thailand; *Int'l*, pg. 373
Hamalainen, Antti, Mng. Dir.--SKF Tohmac Transmission Oy, Tohmajarvi, Finland; *Int'l*, pg. 1159
Hamalainen, Risto, Chief Oper. Officer--Ahlstrom Machinery Savonlinna Engineering Works, Savonlinna, Finland; *Int'l*, pg. 34
Hamamoto, Masao, Mgr.--Tokio Marine Management Inc. - San Francisco, San Francisco, CA; *Int'l*, pg. 1392
Hamanaka, Hideo, Pres.--Thai Hakuhodo Co., Ltd., Bangkok, Thailand; *Int'l*, pg. 589
Hamano, Y., Chief Oper. Officer--Toshiba (Australia) Pty., Ltd., Sydney, Australia; *Int'l*, pg. 1406
Hamaya, Mike, Pres.--Bridgestone/Firestone Technology Company, Akron, OH; *Int'l*, pg. 213
Hamazaki, Yasuhiro, Mng. Dir.--NEC Home Electronics (Malaysia) Sdn. Bhd., Sungai Petani, Malaysia; *Int'l*, pg. 900
Hamberg, Goran, Pres.--Hercules Grandlaggning AB, Kista, Sweden; *Int'l*, pg. 899
Hamblenne, Bernard, Mng. Dir.--Moduwall N.V., Geel, Belgium; *Int'l*, pl. 80
Hambleton, J., Mng. Dir.--Eagle Aviation Ltd., Hamilton, New Zealand; *Int'l*, pg. 38
Hamblin, Brian, Reg. Mgr.--Green Tree Acceptance, Inc., Indianapolis, IN; *U.S. Public*, pg. 762
Hamblin, Steve, Country Mgr.--Compaq Computer Asia Pte Ltd., Singapore, Singapore; *U.S. Public*, pg. 418
Hamburger, Ernst, Dir.--Helly-Hansen (Suisse) SA, Wallisellen, Switzerland; *Int'l*, pg. 1011
Hamburger, Manfred, Mng. Dir.--Deutsche Bank AG (Sao Paulo), Sao Paulo, Brazil; *Int'l*, pg. 404
Hamel, William J., Mng. Dir.--General Motors-Holden's Automotive Limited, Melbourne, Australia; *U.S. Public*, pg. 723
Hamer, M.D., Chief Exec. Officer--Centre Reinsurance Representative Limited, London, United Kingdom; *Int'l*, pg. 1530
Hamer, M.D., Chief Exec. Officer--Centre Reinsurance International Company, Dublin, Ireland; *Int'l*, pg. 1531
Hamer, Norman, Chief Oper. Officer--Williamhouse Sales Corp., Bloomfield, NJ; *U.S. Public*, pg. 89
Hamers, G.L.M., Dr., Pres.--Fokker Aircraft Services B.V., Hoogerheyde, Netherlands; *Int'l*, pg. 1304
Hamers, Jac, Gen. Mgr.--Thermo Instrument Systems B.V., Breda, Netherlands; *U.S. Public*, pg. 1596
Hamershock, Larry, Chief Oper. Officer--Strober Building Supply Centers, Inc., Kingston, PA; *U.S. Private*, pg. 403
Hames, Harlin, Mgr.--Century Telephone, Region II, Hardy, AR; *U.S. Public*, pg. 329
Hames, Rodney D., Mgr.-Office--Woodward-Clyde, Mobile, AL; *U.S. Public*, pg. 1656
Hamid, A., Gen. Mgr.--ANZ Grindlays Bank plc Pakistan, Karachi, Pakistan; *Int'l*, pg. 99
Hamid, En Mohamed Ishak Abdul, Mng. Dir.--Sime Aircraft Tyre Company Sdn. Bhd., Petaling Jaya, Malaysia; *Int'l*, pg. 1250
Hamid, Mohamed Nor Abdul, Div. Dir.--Sime Darby Berhad Insurance Services Division, Kuala Lumpur, Malaysia; *Int'l*, pg. 1250
Hamil, Jack, Mgr.--Hi-Pro Feed, Friona, TX; *U.S. Private*, pg. 429
Hamilton, B., Tech. Dir.--Rockware Glass Technical Centre, Knottingley, United Kingdom; *Int'l*, pg. 124
Hamilton, Barry, Country Mgr.--Standard Chartered Bank Zimbabwe Limited, Harare, Zimbabwe; *Int'l*, pg. 1295

Hamilton, Carl, V.P. & Gen. Mgr.--KBXX-FM, Houston, TX; *U.S. Public*, pg. 384
Hamilton, Dan, Pres.--Venture Engineering Inc., Carrollton, TX; *U.S. Public*, pg. 757
Hamilton, David R., Pres. & Chief Exec. Officer-Chemical Leaman Corp.--Chemical Leaman Tank Lines, Inc., Exton, PA; *U.S. Private*, pg. 233
Hamilton, Fred, Pres. & Publr.--The Olympian, Olympia, WA; *U.S. Public*, pg. 701
Hamilton, I.M., Chief Oper. Officer--Siam Makro Ltd., Bangkok, Thailand; *Int'l*, pg. 1156
Hamilton, John, Plant Mgr.--Industrial Bag Division - Quincy Plant, Quincy, IL; *U.S. Public*, pg. 1521
Hamilton, Josh, Pres.--CMI Industries, Inc., Geneva, AL; *U.S. Private*, pg. 195
Hamilton, Murray, Mng. Dir.--Butterworths Australia, Sydney, Australia; *Int'l*, pg. 1095
Hamilton, N., Plant Mgr.--Viskase Canada Inc., Lindsay, Canada; *U.S. Public*, pg. 586
Hamilton, P.R., Gen. Mgr.-America--Commonwealth Bank of Australia, New York, NY; *Int'l*, pg. 313
Hamilton, R.W., Gen. Mgr.--Container Div. (Frankfort), Frankfort, IN; *Int'l*, pg. 1269
Hamilton, Robert F., V.P.--ECC Financial Group, Cleveland, OH; *U.S. Public*, pg. 558
Hamilton, Robert T., V.P. & Gen. Mgr.--Kodak Health Sciences Division, Rochester, NY; *U.S. Public*, pg. 551
Hamilton, Thomas, Mng. Dir.--Tin Plate Containers, Ltd., Twyford, United Kingdom; *Int'l*, pg. 1126
Hamlin, Ben, Dir.-Opers.--Ash Instruments Division, Dentsply Ltd., Plymouth, United Kingdom; *U.S. Public*, pg. 499
Hamlin, Craig, Pres.--ADM Milling Co. - Rice Division, Shawnee Mission, KS; *U.S. Public*, pg. 128
Hamlin, Craig, Pres.--ADM Milling Co. - Valley Grain, Overland Park, KS; *U.S. Public*, pg. 128
Hamlin, Craig L., Pres. & Chief Exec. Officer--ADM Milling Co., Overland Park, KS; *U.S. Public*, pg. 128
Hamlin, Staffan, Gen. Mgr.--John Crane Finland, Porvoo, Finland; *Int'l*, pg. 1339
Hamling, L., Pres.--Berwind Industries, Inc., Nashville, TN; *U.S. Private*, pg. 138
Hamm, Charles S., Pres.--Bellsouth Mobile Systems Group, Atlanta, GA; *U.S. Public*, pg. 208
Hamm, Charles S., Pres.--Bellsouth Cellular National Marketing, Inc., Atlanta, GA; *U.S. Public*, pg. 208
Hamm, John W., Pres.--Sprecher & Schuh N. America, Houston, TX; *U.S. Public*, pg. 1397
Hamm, Willi, Pres.--Canadian Energy Services, New Westminster, Canada; *Int'l*, pg. 74
Hamm, Willi, Pres.--Industra Thermal Service Corporation, New Westminster, Canada; *Int'l*, pg. 74
Hamm, Willi, Chief Oper. Officer--Industra Inc., Seattle, WA; *Int'l*, pg. 74
Hamm, Willi, Chief Oper. Officer--Industra Inc., Portland, OR; *Int'l*, pg. 74
Hamm, Willi, Chief Oper. Officer--Industra Inc., Greenville, SC; *Int'l*, pg. 74
Hammaker, Ronald A., V.P. & Gen. Mgr.--Cox Communications-Cleveland, Cleveland, OH; *U.S. Public*, pg. 454
Hammar, Orjan, Mng. Dir.--Gunnebo Baltic Sp z o o, Gdynia, Poland; *Int'l*, pg. 578
Hammarskjold, Ulf, Pres.--Elof Hansson Pulp, Inc., Elmsford, NY; *Int'l*, pg. 595
Hammarstedt, Jan, Pres.--GPA Plast AB, Hjarnarp, Sweden; *Int'l*, pg. 678
Hammarstrom, Hakan, Chief Oper. Officer--NIFE AB, Oskarshamn, Sweden; *Int'l*, pg. 53
Hammel, Bent, Pres.--Kvaerner a.s. Fast Ferries, Oslo, Norway; *Int'l*, pg. 766
Hammell, Randy, Pres.--Peacock Inc., La Salle, Canada; *Int'l*, pg. 1489
Hammer, C., Mng. Dir.--Lancer S.A., Tournefeuille, France; *Int'l*, pg. 552
Hammer, C. LaRoy, Pres.--Stewart & Stevenson Vehicle Services, Inc., Houston, TX; *U.S. Public*, pg. 1518
Hammer, Gary, Plant Superintendant--General Shale Products Corp.-Arkalite Products Div., West Memphis, AR; *Int'l*, pg. 844
Hammer, John, Pres.--Revlon-Realistic Professional Products, Inc., New York, NY; *U.S. Private*, pg. 690
Hammer, Thomas James, Pres.--Quail Piping Products, Inc., Magnolia, AR; *U.S. Public*, pg. 137
Hammer, W., Chief Fin. Officer--Scholl AG, Reinach, Switzerland; *Int'l*, pg. 1209
Hammerberg, David L., V.P.-Opers.--Reames Foods Inc., Clive, IA; *U.S. Public*, pg. 977
Hammerstein, Michael, Gen. Mgr.--Wang Deutschland GmbH, Neu-Isenburg, Germany; *U.S. Public*, pg. 1737
Hammerton, Mark, Mng. Dir.--Carefree Camping Limited, Chesire, United Kingdom; *Int'l*, pg. 465
Hammill, Kenneth O., V.P. & Gen. Mgr.--Blount Canada Ltd., Guelph, Canada; *U.S. Public*, pg. 239
Hammill, Roy, Chief Rep.--Westpac Banking Corp. - China, Beijing, China; *Int'l*, pg. 1497
Hammond, Graham, Chief Oper. Officer--MacDermid New Zealand, Ltd., Auckland, New Zealand; *U.S. Public*, pg. 1030
Hammond, Jack A., Sr. V.P. & Gen. Mgr.--Bleached Board Div., New York, NY; *U.S. Public*, pg. 1762
Hammond, John, Mng. Dir.--Enesco Limited, Carlisle, United Kingdom; *U.S. Public*, pg. 1508
Hammond, Michael, Mng. Dir.--The Victoria Wine Company Limited, Woking, United Kingdom; *Int'l*, pg. 63
Hammond, N.W., Dir.-Commercial--Gammon Construction Ltd., Quarry Bay, Hong Kong; *Int'l*, pg. 775
Hammond, P., Mng. Dir.--Edwards Dunlop & Co. Pty. Ltd., Mulgrave, Australia; *Int'l*, pg. 72
Hammond, P., Pres.--American Tech Manufacturing Corporation, Glenolden, PA; *Int'l*, pg. 590
Hammond, Richard, Plant Mgr.--Bekaert Corporation, Rome, GA; *Int'l*, pg. 184
Hammond, T.L., Pres.--Southern Graphics Systems, Louisville, KY; *U.S. Public*, pg. 1386
Hammond, Thomas L., Pres.--GSE, Inc., Farmington, MI; *U.S. Public*, pg. 1676
Hammond, Tom, Grp. V.P.-Central Region--Jacobs Engineering Group Inc., Houston, TX; *U.S. Public*, pg. 921
Hamnes, Kare Angel, Pres.--Kvaerner Fjellstrand (S) Pte Ltd., Singapore, Singapore; *Int'l*, pg. 771
Hampson, M., Mng. Dir.--Air Movement Group Ltd., Dudley, United Kingdom; *Int'l*, pg. 1267
Hampton, Bruce, Pres.--Railroad Pass Casino, Henderson, NV; *U.S. Public*, pg. 375
Hampton, Bruce, Pres.--Value Priced Clothing Inc., Culver City, CA; *U.S. Public*, pg. 1086
Hampton, Hiram, Pres. & Chief Oper. Officer--Lykes Insurance Inc., Tampa, FL; *U.S. Private*, pg. 682
Hampton, John C., Chm. Bd. & Pres.--Willamina Lumber Co. Inc., Portland, OR; *U.S. Private*, pg. 498
Hampton, Paul, Pres.--Vickers Medical France S.A., Bordeaux, France; *Int'l*, pg. 1467
Hamre, Ebbe, Mng. Dir.--Jotun-Danmark A/S, Kolding, Denmark; *Int'l*, pg. 714
Hamre, Tor G., Station Mgr.--Det Norske Veritas, Dunkirk, France; *Int'l*, pg. 397
Hamrick, C. Rush, III, Pres.--Bindley Western, Kendall Division, Shelby, NC; *U.S. Public*, pg. 228
Hamstreet, Richard, Mgr.-Sls.--Pick's Cove Marina, Tacoma, WA; *U.S. Private*, pg. 865
Hamway, Ezra, Pres.--Remco Toys, New York, NY; *U.S. Public*, pg. 923
Han, Eng Juan, Mng. Dir.--Banque Internationale a Luxembourg BIL (Asia) Ltd., Singapore, Singapore; *Int'l*, pg. 162
Han, K.H., Branch Mgr.--Medtronic Asia, Ltd., Seoul, Korea; *U.S. Public*, pg. 1083
Han, Keun Taek, Gen. Mgr.--Cho Hung Bank of New York - Flushing Branch, Flushing, NY; *Int'l*, pg. 288
Han, M.S., Exec. V.P.--Applied Magnetics Korea, Ltd., Seoul, Korea; *U.S. Public*, pg. 123
Han, Moo-Wang, Mng. Dir.--Cho Hung Finance Limited, Central, Hong Kong; *Int'l*, pg. 288
Hana, Bob, Chief Oper. Officer--River Ranch - Los Angeles, Los Angeles, CA; *Int'l*, pg. 491
Hanada, Susumu, Pres.--Tokyo-Mitsubishi Derivative Products (USA), Inc., New York, NY; *Int'l*, pg. 157
Hanada, Teruo, Chief Rep.--The Japan Development Bank (New York), New York, NY; *Int'l*, pg. 701
Hanajima, Kyozo, Chief Oper. Officer--The Tokio Marine & Fire Insurance Company (Singapore) Pte. Limited, Singapore, Singapore; *Int'l*, pg. 1392
Hanajima, Kyozo, Chief Oper. Officer--Tokio Management Services (Asia) Pte. Ltd., Singapore, Singapore; *Int'l*, pg. 1392
Hanaoka, T., Pres.--Don Juan Sportswear, Inc., New York, NY; *Int'l*, pg. 845
Hancharick, Steve, Mgr.-Sls.--PENCO-North Carolina, Raleigh, NC; *Int'l*, pg. 1508
Hancke, Marek, Gen. Mgr.--EURO RSCG Poland, Warsaw, Poland; *Int'l*, pg. 603
Hancock, Barry, Plant Mgr.--Griffin Div., Griffin, GA; *U.S. Public*, pg. 1599
Hancock, Gary, Pres.--Helena Chemical Company, Memphis, TN; *Int'l*, pg. 845
Hancock, George, Pres.--Thomas Kemper Lager, Seattle, WA; *U.S. Public*, pg. 1345
Hancock, George, Pres.--Thomas Kemper Soda Company, Seattle, WA; *U.S. Public*, pg. 1345
Hancock, Paul C., V.P.--Pool California Energy Services, Inc., Bakersfield, CA; *U.S. Public*, pg. 1316
Hancox, R., Chm.--The Reader's Digest Association (Canada) Ltd., Westmount, Canada; *U.S. Public*, pg. 1368
Hand, Don, Gen. Mgr.--Dawn Food Products Frozen Div., Crown Point, IN; *U.S. Private*, pg. 316
Hand, Kerry, Pres. & Chief Exec. Officer--Communicorp, Inc., Columbus, GA; *U.S. Public*, pg. 28
Hand, Kevin, Pres.--EMAP France, Paris, France; *Int'l*, pg. 451
Hand, Melvin R., Pres.--Los Angeles Die Casting, Los Angeles, CA; *U.S. Public*, pg. 142
Handel-Nazzetti, H., Chief Oper. Officer--Hospal Med Tech GmbH, Nuremberg, Germany; *Int'l*, pg. 668
Handel, J., Grp. Mng. Dir.--Countdown Clean Systems Limited, Alfreton, United Kingdom; *Int'l*, pg. 802
Handel, Manfred, Mgr.--Barden Corporation GmbH, Munich, Germany; *Int'l*, pg. 468
Handelsman, Jay, Gen. Mgr.--Regency-Sonnell Greetings, Sylmar, CA; *U.S. Public*, pg. 89
Handl, Mag. Stephan, Mng. Dir.--Deutsche Bank AG (Vienna), Vienna, Austria; *Int'l*, pg. 405
Handler, N., Mgr.-Sls.--Penny & Giles Inc., Santa Monica, CA; *Int'l*, pg. 208
Handler, Richard B., Exec. V.P.--Jefferies & Company, Inc., Stamford, CT; *U.S. Public*, pg. 925
Handley, M., Mng. Dir.--British Bakeries Limited, Windsor, United Kingdom; *Int'l*, pg. 1396
Handman, E., Gen. Mgr.--De La Rue Faraday - West, Livermore, CA; *Int'l*, pg. 387
Handman, Howard, Sr. V.P.--Northeast Loan Administration, Glastonbury, CT; *U.S. Public*, pg. 649
Handy, David G., Pres. & Chief Exec. Officer--Associated Bank, National Association, Neenah, WI; *U.S. Public*, pg. 140
Haneda, Jiro, Gen. Mgr.--Dai-Ichi Kangyo Bank, Ltd.-Hong Kong, Central, Hong Kong; *Int'l*, pg. 360
Haneline, Richard L., Pres.--American West Insurance Company, Grand Forks, ND; *U.S. Public*, pg. 216
Haner, Derek J., Pres.--Power Indusries Ltd., Mississauga, Canada; *U.S. Private*, pg. 878
Hanert, E., Dir.--Von Roll AG Departement Armaturen, Oensingen, Switzerland; *Int'l*, pg. 1480
Hanert, E., Dir.--Von Roll AG Departement Druckrohre, Choindez, Switzerland; *Int'l*, pg. 1480
Hanert, E., Dir.--Von Roll AG Departement Maschinen & Fordertechn, Bern, Switzerland; *Int'l*, pg. 1480
Hanes, James H., Pres.--C.S. McKee & Company, Inc., Pittsburgh, PA; *U.S. Public*, pg. 1673
Hanewald, Richard H., Pres.--The International Metals Reclamation Company, Inc., Ellwood City, PA; *Int'l*, pg. 672
Haney, J. Whitney, Pres.--PAR Microsystems Corporation, New Hartford, NY; *U.S. Public*, pg. 1256
Haney, Michael H., Pres.--Seneca Foods-Central Div., Janesville, WI; *U.S. Public*, pg. 1456
Haney, R. Lee, Pres.--Saddle River Holdings Corp., Pearl River, NY; *U.S. Public*, pg. 1229
Hanford, John, Dir.--General Mills Europe Limited, London, United Kingdom; *U.S. Public*, pg. 718
Hanft, Jeffrey, Chm. Bd. & Chief Exec. Officer--Carifone, Miami, FL; *U.S. Public*, pg. 1275
Hanik, Peter P., Pres. & Chief Oper. Officer--Millennium Petrochemicals Inc., Cincinnati, OH; *U.S. Public*, pg. 1111
Hanka, Erina, Pres.--Suspa, Inc., Grand Rapids, MI; *Int'l*, pg. 1322
Hanke, James, V.P.--Viking Entertainment, Troy, MI; *U.S. Public*, pg. 780
Hankey, D., Gen. Mgr.--Electronic Materials Div., Santa Barbara, CA; *U.S. Public*, pg. 619
Hanlay, Ed, Pres.--Healthsource, Inc., Hooksett, NH; *U.S. Public*, pg. 360
Hanley, Bryant M., Jr., Pres.--Barrow, Hanley, Mewhinney & Strauss, Inc., Dallas, TX; *U.S. Public*, pg. 1672
Hanley, C., District Mgr.--A.M. Castle & Co., Kennesaw, GA; *U.S. Public*, pg. 313
Hanley, Declan, V.P.-Sls., Europe--Koss Europe, Stabio, Switzerland; *U.S. Public*, pg. 966
Hanley, Steve, V.P. & Gen. Mgr.--Systems Assembly Div., Wyomissing, PA; *U.S. Public*, pg. 479
Hanlin, R.L., Pres.--SunMac Hawaii, Ltd., Honolulu, HI; *U.S. Private*, pg. 1053
Hanlon, Jerry, Pres.--AGRA Marine Construction Limited, Richmond, Canada; *Int'l*, pg. 30
Hanlon, Jerry, Pres.--AGRA Foundations (Pacific) Limited, Richmond, Canada; *Int'l*, pg. 30
Hanlon, Jerry, Pres.--MCL Pile Driving, Richmond, Canada; *Int'l*, pg. 30
Hann-Yeh, Ho, Gen. Mgr.--China Airlines Ltd., San Francisco, CA; *Int'l*, pg. 285
Hanna, D.A. II, Sr. V.P. & Mgr.--ABN AMRO Bank, N.V. (Houston), Houston, TX; *Int'l*, pg. 10
Hanna, Don, Pres.--Eberline Instrument Corporation, Santa Fe, NM; *U.S. Public*, pg. 1593
Hanna, Don, Pres.--National Nuclear Corporation, Sunnyvale, CA; *U.S. Public*, pg. 1594
Hanna, E. Michael, Pres.--Peters-Revington Corp., Delphi, IN; *U.S. Public*, pg. 352
Hanna, J. Terrance, Pres.--Pulte Northern California Division, Pleasanton, CA; *U.S. Public*, pg. 1345
Hanna, R.G.C., Chm. Bd.--Ervin Amasteel Uk. LP, Tipton, United Kingdom; *U.S. Private*, pg. 382
Hanna, T., Mgr.--Canadian White Pine Division, Vancouver, Canada; *Int'l*, pg. 828
Hanna, Tim, V.P. & Gen. Mgr.--Spring Tools Company, Portage, MI; *U.S. Private*, pg. 857
Hannah, John C., Grp. Gen. Mgr.--BHP Coal, Brisbane, Australia; *Int'l*, pg. 223
Hannah, Tom, Pres.--Milliken Finished Apparel Div., Spartanburg, SC; *U.S. Private*, pg. 748
Hannan, Brian N.B., Mng. Dir.--Fletcher Challenge Methanol Limited, Auckland, New Zealand; *Int'l*, pg. 495
Hannaway, Terence, Mng. Dir.--Bank of Ireland (IOM) Limited, Douglas, United Kingdom; *Int'l*, pg. 153
Hannell, Geoff, Publr.--Harper Audio, New York, NY; *Int'l*, pg. 926
Hannemann, Timothy W., Exec. V.P. & Gen. Mgr.--TRW Space & Electronics Group, Redondo Beach, CA; *U.S. Public*, pg. 1558
Hanney, L.D., Mng. Dir.--Simon Engineering (Australia) Pty Ltd., Sydney, Australia; *Int'l*, pg. 1252
Hanngren, Per, Mng. Dir.--SKF del Peru S.A., Lima, Peru; *Int'l*, pg. 1158
Hanninen, Juhani, Chief Oper. Officer--Ahlstrom Machinery Pumps Inc., Karhula, Finland; *Int'l*, pg. 33
Hanning, Franz, Pres. & Chief Exec. Officer--Vacation Break USA, Fort Lauderdale, FL; *U.S. Public*, pg. 611
Hannon, John W., Chm. Bd.--Rollins Hudig Hall of Indiana, Inc., Indianapolis, IN; *U.S. Public*, pg. 117
Hanoka, Maurice, Mng. Dir.--Lumiere, Paris, France; *U.S. Private*, pg. 1199
Hanon, Darlene, Acct. Mgr.--BSA Advertising, Inc., Tampa, FL; *U.S. Private*, pg. 108
Hanrahan, Paul T., Mng. Dir.--AES China Generating, Beijing, China; *U.S. Public*, pg. 5
Hanrahan, Thomas E., Pres.--Gessner/Miller Corporation, Worcester, MA; *U.S. Private*, pg. 435
Hans, Jean-Pierre, Pres.--Astra Luxembourg S.A.R.L., Ehlange, Luxembourg; *Int'l*, pg. 94
Hansberry, Edward, Gen. Plant Mgr.--Kellogg Convenience Food Plant, Rossville, TN; *U.S. Public*, pg. 947
Hansen, Bill, V.P. & Gen. Mgr.--Barko Hydraulics, Superior, WI; *U.S. Private*, pg. 859
Hansen, Charles, Pres.--U.S. Pulp and Newsprint, Coosa Pines, AL; *U.S. Public*, pg. 959
Hansen, Darryl D., Pres. & Chief Exec. Officer--Central Property & Casualty Insurance Company, West Des Moines, IA; *U.S. Private*, pg. 880
Hansen, David, Gen. Mgr.--Interplastic Corporation, Pryor, OK; *U.S. Private*, pg. 572
Hansen, Don, Pres.--Koch Engineering Company, Inc., Akron, OH; *U.S. Private*, pg. 628
Hansen, Egon Friis, Pres.--AGA A/S, Copenhagen, Denmark; *Int'l*, pg. 13
Hansen, Flemming, Chief Oper. Officer--Kjellbergs Successors A/S, Charlottenlund, Denmark; *Int'l*, pg. 712
Hansen, Frank, Mng. Dir.--TA Control A/S, Albertslund, Denmark; *Int'l*, pg. 670

Hansen, Hans, V.P.--Metal & Catalyst Division, South Plainfield, NJ; *Int'l*, pg. 388
Hansen, Irving, Chm. Bd. & Pres.--M & I Northern Bank, Brookfield, WI; *U.S. Public*, pg. 1050
Hansen, John, Chief Oper. Officer--KPTV Television, Inc., Portland, OR; *U.S. Public*, pg. 352
Hansen, John, Pres.--MD Foods Sverige AB, Malmo, Sweden; *Int'l*, pg. 826
Hansen, John C., Mng. Dir.--Industrial Galvanizers Corporation Pty. Ltd., Brisbane, Australia; *Int'l*, pg. 391
Hansen, L.A., Chief Tech. Officer--AGRA Earth & Environmental, Inc., Phoenix, AZ; *Int'l*, pg. 31
Hansen, Lee, Pres.--Alcon (Puerto Rico) Inc., Humacao, PR; *Int'l*, pg. 916
Hansen, Nils B., Mng. Dir.--Jotun Protective Coatings B.V., Rotterdam, Netherlands; *Int'l*, pg. 715
Hansen, Otto, Pres.--A/S Ruko, Herlev, Denmark; *Int'l*, pg. 18
Hansen, Poul, Chm. Bd.--Chr. Hansen, Inc., Milwaukee, WI; *Int'l*, pg. 288
Hansen, Poul, Pres.--Chr. Hansen A/S, Horsholm, Denmark; *Int'l*, pg. 288
Hansen, Ragnar E., Gen. Mgr.--Det Norske Veritas, Seoul, Korea; *Int'l*, pg. 397
Hansen, Richard D., Chm. Bd., Pres. & Chief Exec. Officer--M & I Bank of Eagle River, Eagle River, WI; *U.S. Public*, pg. 1050
Hansen, Robert, V.P. & Gen. Mgr.--Connector Division America and Asia, Elk Grove Village, IL; *Int'l*, pg. 786
Hansen, Robert L., Pres.--AHF-Ducommun Incorporated, Gardena, CA; *U.S. Public*, pg. 534
Hansen, Stephen, V.P. & Gen. Mgr.--S & J Industries, Kennesaw, GA; *U.S. Private*, pg. 803
Hansen, Svein H., Mng. Dir.--ESAB Middle East, Dubai, United Arab Emirates; *Int'l*, pg. 282
Hansen, Terry, Mng. Dir.--Camtec Electronic Ltd., Leicester, United Kingdom; *Int'l*, pg. 1365
Hansen, Tom, Gen. Mgr.--ITW Shakeproof/Industrial Products, Elgin, IL; *U.S. Public*, pg. 867
Hansen, Torbjorn, Mgr.--Langasjonas Paper Mill, Kisa, Sweden; *Int'l*, pg. 421
Hansen, Vagn, Dir.--Kemira Danmark A/S, Fredericia, Denmark; *Int'l*, pg. 728
Hanson, Anders, V.P. & Gen. Mgr.--NIKE International Ltd.-Sweden, Solna, Sweden; *U.S. Public*, pg. 1184
Hanson, D., Pres.--Chemetics International Company Ltd Vancouver Operations, Vancouver, Canada; *Int'l*, pg. 774
Hanson, David M., Chm. & Chief Exec. Officer--M & I Bank S.S.B., Sheboygan, WI; *U.S. Public*, pg. 1050
Hanson, Donald W., V.P.--Vision-Ease Lens, Saint Cloud, MN; *U.S. Public*, pg. 162
Hanson, Graham, Mng. Dir.--Comtext International, London, United Kingdom; *Int'l*, pg. 537
Hanson, James C., Pres.--Chandler Products, Inc., Cleveland, OH; *U.S. Private*, pg. 370
Hanson, Ken, Chief Oper. Officer--Flo-Pac Southeast, East Point, GA; *U.S. Private*, pg. 414
Hanson, L., Pres.--Sani-Matic Systems, Madison, WI; *U.S. Private*, pg. 301
Hanson, Larry L., Pres. & Publr.--Daily Herald Co., Everett, WA; *U.S. Public*, pg. 1743
Hanson, Leroy, Dr., Pres.--Insta-Pro International, Ltd., Des Moines, IA; *U.S. Private*, pg. 1104
Hanson, Linda S., Mgr.-Branch--Piper Jaffray Inc., Brainerd, MN; *U.S. Public*, pg. 1302
Hanson, Russell, Pres. & Gen. Mgr.--Flexible Assembly Systems Division, Bridgman, MI; *Int'l*, pg. 204
Hanson, Steven E., Pres.--Calcitek, Inc., Carlsbad, CA; *Int'l, pg. 1307*
Hanssel, Roland, Mng. Dir.--Manus Presse GmbH, Stuttgart, Germany; *Int'l*, pg. 1478
Hanssen, Knut, Mng. Dir.--Jotun U.A.E. Ltd., Dubai, United Arab Emirates; *Int'l*, pg. 716
Hanssen, Peter Jul, Pres.--Norcem Betong A/S, Fredrikstad, Norway; *Int'l*, pg. 42
Hanssens, M. Ignace, Mng. Dir.--General Biscuits Espana (GBE), Barcelona, Spain; *Int'l*, pg. 381
Hansson, Bertil, Chief Oper. Officer--DAB Dental AB, Goteborg, Sweden; *Int'l*, pg. 711
Hansson, Birger, Exec. V.P.--Jimek, Arlov, Sweden; *U.S. Public*, pg. 170
Hansson, Jarl, Mgr.--Sandvik Latin America, Inc., Coral Gables, FL; *Int'l*, pg. 1185
Hansson, Per. Ulf, Mng. Dir.--Wilhelmstal-Werke GmbH Papiersackfabriken, Achern, Germany; *Int'l*, pg. 759
Hantila, I., Chief Exec. Officer--Ascom Energy Systems, Bern, Switzerland; *Int'l*, pg. 86
Hanway, H.E., Pres.--Cigna Worldwide, Incorporated, Philadelphia, PA; *U.S. Public*, pg. 363
Hanway, Harry E., Chm. Bd.--Cigna Insurance Company of Europe, S.A.-N.V., Brussels, Belgium; *U.S. Public*, pg. 364
Hanway, Harry E., Chm. Bd.--Cigna Insurance Australia Limited, Sydney, Australia; *U.S. Public*, pg. 364
Happ, Scott T., Pres. & Chief Exec. Officer--M & I Mortgage Corp., Cedarburg, WI; *U.S. Public*, pg. 1051
Happel, Joe, Pres.--Ampco Saftey Tools, Dallas Div., Garland, TX; *U.S. Private*, pg. 67
Happel, R.W., V.P. & Gen. Mgr.--Electro-Motive Division, La Grange, IL; *U.S. Public*, pg. 719
Happola, Kai, Mng. Dir.--Parker Hannifin Oy Finn Filter Division, Urjala, AS, Finland; *U.S. Public*, pg. 1263
Happy, Randy, Branch Mgr.--Zellerbach Division, Lexington, KY; *U.S. Public*, pg. 1075
Haque, M. S., Chief Oper. Officer--The General Electric Company of Bangladesh Ltd., Motijheel, Bangladesh; *Int'l*, pg. 546
Hara, A., Acting Mng. Dir.--Baldwin Printing Controls Ltd., Hong Kong, Hong Kong; *U.S. Public*, pg. 170
Hara, Akira, Pres.--Baldwin Japan Ltd., Tokyo, Japan; *U.S. Public*, pg. 170
Hara, Akira, Pres.--Baldwin Printing Control Equipment (Beijing) Company, Ltd., Beijing, China; *U.S. Public*, pg. 170
Hara, Akira, Pres.--Baldwin Asia Pacific Ltd., Hong Kong, Hong Kong; *U.S. Public*, pg. 170
Hara, Akira, Pres.--Baldwin Graphic Equipment Pty., Balmain, Australia; *U.S. Public*, pg. 170
Hara, Akira, Pres.--Baldwin Printing Control Equipment (Beijing) Co., Ltd., Shanghai, China; *U.S. Public*, pg. 170
Hara, Daiji, Chief Oper. Officer--America Latina Companhia de Seguros, Sao Paulo, Brazil; *Int'l*, pg. 1392
Hara, Kazuo, Gen. Mgr.--The Mitsui Trust and Banking Company - London, London, United Kingdom; *Int'l*, pg. 883
Hara, Masanori, Mng. Dir.--Mitsui Trust Finance (Australia) Ltd., Sydney, Australia; *Int'l*, pg. 883
Hara, Takashi, Pres.--Toray Engineering Co., Ltd., Osaka, Japan; *Int'l*, pg. 1399
Harada, Eiko, Pres.--Apple Computer Japan, Inc., Tokyo, Japan; *U.S. Public*, pg. 121
Haraldsson, Sigg, Mng. Dir.--Alfa-Laval Thermal AB, Lund, Sweden; *Int'l*, pg. 1378
Haranger, M., Chief Exec. Officer--OCE-France Financement S.A., Saint Cloud, France; *Int'l*, pg. 994
Haratuman, M., Chm. Bd. & Chief Exec. Officer--STV Incorporated, New York, NY; *U.S. Public*, pg. 1421
Haratunian, M., Pres--STV Environmental, Douglassville, PA; *U.S. Public*, pg. 1421
Haratunian, M., Pres. & Chief Exec. Officer--STV Architects, Douglassville, PA; *U.S. Public*, pg. 1421
Harbauer, Werner, Chief Oper. Officer--Vacuumschmelze GmbH, Hanau, Germany; *Int'l*, pg. 1245
Harbaugh, Rick, Pres.--The Overland National Bank, Grand Island, NE; *U.S. Public*, pg. 629
Harbin, Henry, Pres. & Chief Exec. Officer--Merit Behavioral Care Corp., Park Ridge, NJ; *U.S. Public*, pg. 1036
Harbing, L.P., Mng. Dir.--Getinge International Inc., Lakewood, NJ; *Int'l*, pg. 551
Harbing, Lars-Peter, Pres. & Chief Exec. Officer--Getinge/Castle Inc., Rochester, NY; *Int'l*, pg. 551
Harbison, Gregory A., Pres., Chief Exec. & Trust Officer--Rockville National Bank, Rockville, IN; *U.S. Public*, pg. 1217
Harborn, Mats, V.P.--Svenska Handelsbanken Beijing, Beijing, China; *Int'l*, pg. 1327
Harbour, Ken, Chief Fin. Officer--Cleveland Electric Co., Atlanta, GA; *U.S. Private*, pg. 246
Harcarufka, John J., Pres.--Hiram Walker & Sons Limited, Windsor, Canada; *Int'l*, pg. 63
Harcourt, R., Pres.--Angus Fire Limited, Mississauga, Canada; *Int'l*, pg. 1500
Harcourt, R.M., Chief Oper. Officer--Angus Fire Armour Corp., Angier, NC; *Int'l*, pg. 1500
Harcourt, R.M., Pres.--Flexline Hose Inc., Fuquay Varina, NC; *Int'l*, pg. 1500
Hardan, Richard, Pres.--Compass Group, Inc., Spokane, WA; *U.S. Public*, pg. 1681
Hardeman, S.J., Gen. Mgr.--Clevedon Rivets & Tools Ltd., Sutton Coldfield, United Kingdom; *Int'l*, pg. 297
Harden, David, Chief Oper. Officer--Akerlund & Rausing, Godalming, United Kingdom; *Int'l*, pg. 33
Harden, Joe W., V.P. & Gen. Mgr.--Buckeye Steel Castings Company, Columbus, OH; *U.S. Public*, pg. 1780
Harden, Robert, V.P. & Gen. Mgr.--The Climatic Corporation, Little Rock, AR; *U.S. Private*, pg. 246
Hardesty, D., V.P.-Atlanta--Harwick Standard Distribution Corp., Norcross, GA; *U.S. Private*, pg. 509
Hardesty, Sharon, Mgr.--Broad National Bank-East Orange, East Orange, NJ; *U.S. Public*, pg. 257
Hardie, David, Chm. & Chief Exec. Officer--International Distillers & Vintners Ltd., London, United Kingdom; *Int'l*, pg. 409
Hardie, Graham, Pres.--Aker Contracting plc, Aberdeen, United Kingdom; *Int'l*, pg. 42
Hardiman, Chm. Bd.--Ford-Werke AG & Co., Cologne, Germany; *U.S. Public*, pg. 666
Hardiman, R.F., Mgr.--Morton Salt Division, Grand Saline, TX; *U.S. Public*, pg. 1135
Hardin, Leonard, Pres.--National City Bank, Kentucky, Louisville, KY; *U.S. Public*, pg. 1154
Hardin, Linda B., V.P.--Augusta Mall, Inc., Augusta, GA; *U.S. Public*, pg. 1408
Hardind, Nick, Mng. Dir.--H.J. Heinz Foodservice, Hayes, United Kingdom; *U.S. Public*, pg. 806
Harding, A.B., Chief Oper. Officer--Gloucester Railway Carriage & Wagon Company Ltd., Cardiff, United Kingdom; *Int'l*, pg. 473
Harding, A.B., Mng. Dir.--Powell Duffryn Standard Limited, Cardiff, United Kingdom; *Int'l*, pg. 1065
Harding, Andrew B., Mng. Dir.--Methode Mikon Limited, Haverhill, United Kingdom; *U.S. Public*, pg. 1101
Harding, Enoch Jr., Chm. Bd.--Kellwood Sportswear, Rutherford, TN; *U.S. Public*, pg. 948
Harding, Janie, Branch Mgr.--Downey Savings & Loan Association, F.A., La Quinta, CA; *U.S. Public*, pg. 526
Harding, L.G., Pres.--Maple Leaf Meats, Winnipeg, Canada; *Int'l*, pg. 841
Harding, Paul, Gen. Mgr., Gen. Mgr.--ITW Compular, Ewell, United Kingdom; *U.S. Public*, pg. 868
Harding, Richard, Gen. Mgr.--Rogers Cable TV-Kitchener, Kitchener, Canada; *Int'l*, pg. 1122
Harding, Richard, Mgr.--Xtek Canada, Ltd., Rexdale, Canada; *U.S. Private*, pg. 1194
Hardison, Jerry, Pres.--Lone Star Container Sales Corp., Irving, TX; *U.S. Private*, pg. 674
Hardison, Marshall, Mgr.--Braswell Concrete Products, Inc., Shreveport, LA; *Int'l*, pg. 628
Hardjanto, Rudyanto, Chief Oper. Officer--P.T. Toyota-Astra Motor, Jakarta, Indonesia; *Int'l*, pg. 1413
Hardman, Graham, Chief Oper. Officer--Neste (UK) Ltd., London, United Kingdom; *Int'l*, pg. 915
Hardman, Gregory S., Pres.--Warsteiner Importers Agency, Lombard, IL; *Int'l*, pg. 1486
Hardman, Henry J., Pres.--Waddell & Reed Investment Mngmt. Co., Kansas City, MO; *U.S. Public*, pg. 1623
Hardman, Michael, Pres.--iCatcher, Cleveland, OH; *U.S. Private*, pg. 1194
Hardman, Roger R., Plant Mgr.--AlliedSignal Ltd. Turbochargers, Skelmersdale, United Kingdom; *U.S. Public*, pg. 53
Hardorp, Hans Hinrich, Chm. Bd.--BOHLER Ges.m.b.H., Kapfenberg, Austria; *Int'l*, pg. 1470
Hardt, David, Pres.--Data-Tronics Corp., Fort Smith, AR; *U.S. Public*, pg. 130
Hardt, Wolfgang, Co-Chief Oper. Officer--Saarberg Handel GmbH, Saarbruecken, Germany; *Int'l*, pg. 1167
Hardy, Carolyn, Mgr.--Smucker Memphis Plant, Memphis, TN; *U.S. Public*, pg. 1480
Hardy, Don C.A.M., Mng. Dir.--ENVIRAS, Deurne, Belgium; *Int'l*, pg. 608
Hardy, E. Russell, Pres.--Services Division, Sunnyvale, CA; *U.S. Public*, pg. 293
Hardy, Ed, Pres.--Yosemite Concession Services Co., Yosemite National Park, CA; *Int'l*, pg. 1216
Hardy, John R., Mgr.--Ampex Data Systems Corporation, Ramona, CA; *U.S. Public*, pg. 104
Hardy, Timothy, V.P.--Terrestrial Microwave Services Div., Reston, VA; *U.S. Public*, pg. 46
Hare, Ed, Mgr.-Intl. Mktg.--Noble Drilling International, Inc., Houston, TX; *U.S. Public*, pg. 1186
Hare, John, Pres. & Gen. Mgr.--WBAP-AM--WBAP-KSCS Radio, Inc., Arlington, TX; *U.S. Public*, pg. 512
Hare, Richard, Pres.--National Fuel Gas Supply Corp., Erie, PA; *U.S. Public*, pg. 1156
Hare, Ronald R., Pres.--Stop In Food Stores, Roanoke, VA; *U.S. Private*, pg. 859
Hare, Walt, Gen. Mgr.--O'Brien International, Inc., Redmond, WA; *U.S. Private*, pg. 689
Haresh, R., Gen. Mgr.--TVS Cherry Private Limited, Madurai, India; *U.S. Public*, pg. 346
Harg, Morten, Chief Exec. Officer--D'Arcy Masius Benton & Bowles, Oslo, Norway; *U.S. Private*, pg. 304
Hargens, Roger, Plant Mgr.--Copperweld Metallon Div., Pawtucket, RI; *Int'l*, pg. 662
Hargil, E., Mng. Dir.--Witco Ltd., Haifa, Israel; *U.S. Public*, pg. 1774
Hargrave, Milton I., Gen. Mgr.--Containerboard & Paper Div.-Hopewell Mill, Hopewell, VA; *U.S. Public*, pg. 1520
Hargrave, Robert L., Dir.--Stewart & Stevenson (U.K.) Limited, Houston, TX; *U.S. Public*, pg. 1518
Hargrave, Robert L., Pres. & Treas.--Takumei Kumiai Holdings, Inc., Houston, TX; *U.S. Public*, pg. 1518
Hargraves, William B., Mng. Dir.--Delnosa, S.A. De C.V., Mexico, Mexico; *U.S. Public*, pg. 721
Hargrett, Betty J., Admin.--Hillhaven Convalescent Center Savannah, Savannah, GA; *U.S. Public*, pg. 1713
Hargrove, Basil, Chief Exec. Officer--McCain Foods (Australia) Pty. Ltd., Ballarat, Australia; *Int'l*, pg. 850
Hargrove, Max, Plant Mgr.--Eastern Div.-Plymouth, Plymouth, FL; *U.S. Public*, pg. 463
Hari, Shunichi, Mng. Dir.--Yamaichi Bank Nederland N.V., Strawinskylaan, Netherlands; *Int'l*, pg. 1517
Hari, Shunichi, Mng. Dir.--Yamaichi Bank Nederland Custody N.V., Amsterdam, Netherlands; *Int'l*, pg. 1517
Harigan, J., V.P.-Opers.--Automotive Opers., Belleville, MI; *U.S. Public*, pg. 1134
Harimoto, Masahiro, Chief Oper. Officer--Toho Electronics Co., Ltd., Tokorozawa, Japan; *Int'l*, pg. 999
Harinck, S.P., Gen. Mgr.--Algemene Zeeuwse Verzekering Maatschappij N.V., Middelburg, Netherlands; *Int'l*, pg. 647
Haring, Wolfgang, Dr., Mgr.--Commerzbank AG-Moscow Representative Office, Moscow, Russia; *Int'l*, pg. 311
Harithaitavorw, Surapong, Mng. Dir.--The CPAC Concrete Products Co., Ltd., Nonthaburi, Thailand; *Int'l*, pg. 1237
Harjehausen, Ed, Pres.--ADM Ethanol Sales, Decatur, IL; *U.S. Public*, pg. 127
Harjuvaara, Heikki, Chief Oper. Officer--Akerlund & Rausing Oy, Kauttua, Finland; *Int'l*, pg. 32
Harjuvaava, Heikki, Chief Oper. Officer--Ahlstrom Consumer Products Ltd., Helsinki, Finland; *Int'l*, pg. 32
Harker, Albert P., Pres.--LaSalle Bank Westmont, Westmont, IL; *Int'l*, pg. 10
Harker, John, Resident Mgr.--Adams Mill, Adams, MA; *U.S. Public*, pg. 465
Harker, Richard A., Pres.--Conversion Systems, Inc., Horsham, PA; *U.S. Public*, pg. 587
Harkey, Roy, Gen. Mgr.--Clarion Sales Corporation, Gardena, CA; *Int'l*, pg. 296
Harkey, William, Jr., Gen. Mgr.--Dixie Reel & Box Co., Charlotte, NC; *U.S. Private*, pg. 674
Harkies, Mike, Area Mgr.--Nicola Division, Merritt, Canada; *Int'l*, pg. 1395
Harkins, J.J., Mgr.--Morton Salt Division, Painesville, OH; *U.S. Public*, pg. 1135
Harkinson, Scott, Chief Oper. Officer--Atlas Roofing Corp., Franklin, OH; *U.S. Private*, pg. 96
Harkki, Pekka, Managing Dir.--Corenso United Oy Ltd., Lahti, Finland; *Int'l*, pg. 456
Harkness, J. Scott, Pres.--First Wisconsin Asset Management, Inc., Madison, WI; *U.S. Public*, pg. 643
Harkness, Marianne, Publisher--Vegetarian Times, Oak Park, IL; *U.S. Private*, pg. 281
Harkness, Peter, Editor & Publr.--Governing Magazine, Washington, DC; *U.S. Private*, pg. 1088
Harl, R. Randall, Pres.-Services--Brown & Root Inc., Alhambra, CA; *U.S. Public*, pg. 775
Harl, R. Randall, Pres.--Brown & Root Industrial Services, Houston, TX; *U.S. Public*, pg. 775
Harlacher, Meredith, Pres. & Chief Exec. Officer--Atlantic Electric Co., Pleasantville, NJ; *U.S. Public*, pg. 430
Harlan, Jimmy, Chief Oper. Officer--AxTrade Korea Ltd., Seoul, Korea; *Int'l*, pg. 710
Harlan, Joyce, Admin.--Convalescent Center of The Palm Beaches, West Palm Beach, FL; *U.S. Public*, pg. 1712
Harland, Paul, Div. Mgr.--Gaylord Div., Gaylord, MI; *U.S. Public*, pg. 1504
Harless, Katherine J., Pres.--GTE Airfone Incorporated, Oak Brook, IL; *U.S. Public*, pg. 696
Harley, Nigel, Chm. Bd.--Continental Reinsurance Corp., New York, NY; *U.S. Public*, pg. 1011

Harlfinger, Charles, Pres.--T.W. Kutter, Inc., Avon, MA; *Int'l*, pg. 1378
Harlin, James, Pres.--Mid-Continent Life Insurance Company, Oklahoma City, OK; *U.S. Public*, pg. 655
Harling, Ben, Mgr.--Autocomp, Inc., Atlanta, GA; *U.S. Public*, pg. 1735
Harlow, John, Office Mgr.--Korn/Ferry International, Palo Alto, CA; *U.S. Private*, pg. 633
Harlow, John, Office Mgr.--Korn/Ferry International, San Francisco, CA; *U.S. Private*, pg. 633
Harlow, John M., Pres.--Intervest-Mortgage Investment Company, Lake Oswego, OR; *U.S. Public*, pg. 1516
Harman, G.K., Chief Exec. Officer--Morganite Industrial Carbon (MIC), Johannesburg, South Africa; *Int'l*, pg. 895
Harman, Mike, Pres.--MW Manufacturers Inc., Rocky Mount, VA; *Int'l*, pg. 593
Harmon, Bob, Plant Mgr.--Square D Middletown Plant, Middletown, OH; *Int'l*, pg. 1208
Harmon, Run, Gen. Mgr.--Reyco-Canada, Inc., Grimsby, Canada; *U.S. Private*, pg. 926
Harmon, Todd, Mgr.--Stephen Gould of Texas, Inc., Dallas, TX; *U.S. Private*, pg. 468
Harmon, Tom, Mgr.-West Coast Service Center--Concord Service Ctr., Concord, CA; *U.S. Private*, pg. 1180
Harmon, Tom, Mgr.-West Coast Service Center--Signal Hill Service Center, Signal Hill, CA; *U.S. Private*, pg. 1180
Harmon, W. Henry, Pres.--Columbia Coal Gasification Corp., Ashland, KY; *U.S. Public*, pg. 402
Harmon, W. Henry, Pres. & Chief Exec. Officer--Columbia Natural Resources, Inc., Charleston, WV; *U.S. Public*, pg. 403
Harms, John E., Gen. Mgr.--BHP South Pacific, Inc., Honolulu, HI; *Int'l*, pg. 225
Harms, Robert L., Pres. & Gen. Mgr.--3M Canada Inc., London, Canada; *U.S. Public*, pg. 1606
Harms, Ronald, Chief Exec. Officer--Healthsource New York, De Witt, NY; *U.S. Public*, pg. 360
Harnal, Vimal, Gen. Mgr.--South West Asia--Singapore Tourist Promotion Board - Mumbai, Mumbai, India; *Int'l*, pg. 1254
Harned, Richard, Gen. Mgr.--Hydromatic Pumps, Ashland, OH; *U.S. Public*, pg. 726
Harnetty, Michael C., Div. V.P.--Protective Chemical Products Div., Saint Paul, MN; *U.S. Public*, pg. 1605
Harnisch, Jurgen, Chm. Bd.--Krupp Hoesch Automotive GmbH, Bochum, Germany; *Int'l*, pg. 507
Harper, Bill, Pres.--Lambert Smith Hampton, Beverly Hills, CA; *Int'l*, pg. 797
Harper, Colin, Chm., Pres. & Chief Exec. Officer--Camco Inc., Mississauga, Canada; *U.S. Public*, pg. 713
Harper, Gladyce, Laboratory Mgr.--Quest Diagnostic-Rome, Rome, NY; *U.S. Public*, pg. 1351
Harper, Gregory S., V.P.-Opers.--Chancellor Corporation, Boston, MA; *U.S. Public*, pg. 335
Harper, John, Reg. Mgr.--Federal Products U.K. Ltd., London, United Kingdom; *U.S. Public*, pg. 594
Harper, Mark, Gen. Mgr.--Surplus Warehouse-Longview, Longview, TX; *U.S. Private*, pg. 120
Harper, Mike, Gen Mgr.--O-Ring Div., Lexington, KY; *U.S. Public*, pg. 1262
Harper, Paul, Mgr.-Plant--Anvil Products, Fort Worth, TX; *U.S. Public*, pg. 1651
Harper, Rich, Plant Mgr.--E.J. Brach, Inc., Davenport, IA; *U.S. Private*, pg. 163
Harper, Rick, Mgr.--DWF of North Kansas City, North Kansas City, MO; *U.S. Private*, pg. 326
Harper, William, Mgr.--Bio-Rad Laboratories (Canada) Ltd., Mississauga, Canada; *U.S. Public*, pg. 230
Harpkopf, Scott, Pres.--Brayton International Inc., High Point, NC; *U.S. Private*, pg. 1038
Harreld, M., Chm. Bd. & Chief Exec. Officer--PNC Bank, Louisville, KY; *U.S. Public*, pg. 1242
Harreld, Michael N., Pres.--PNC Bank, Louisville, KY; *U.S. Public*, pg. 1242
Harrell, Michael K., Pres.--Bellsouth Mobile Data, Inc., Atlanta, GA; *U.S. Public*, pg. 208
Harrell, Samual S., Chm. Bd.--E & D Grain Marketing Co, Covington, KY; *U.S. Private*, pg. 353
Harrelson, Ronald S., Pres.--CFE Company, Phoenix, AZ; *U.S. Public*, pg. 51
Harrera, Dickie, Admin.--Kaiser Electronics, San Francisco, CA; *U.S. Private*, pg. 605
Harrill, Laurie, V.P. & Gen. Mgr.--Dillard Paper Co. of Miami, Medley, FL; *U.S. Public*, pg. 902
Harring, Steve, Div. Mgr.--Goldsboro Div., Goldsboro, NC; *U.S. Public*, pg. 1504
Harrington, A. Leigh, V.P. & Gen. Mgr.--Rinn Corporation, Elgin, IL; *U.S. Public*, pg. 499
Harrington, Allan, Gen. Mgr.--Forbo Wallcoverings Ltd., Woodbridge, Canada; *Int'l*, pg. 498
Harrington, Bryce, Plant Mgr.--Cambridge Industries, Inc., Lenoir, NC; *U.S. Private*, pg. 202
Harrington, Daniel M., Pres.--Allentown Cement Co. Inc., Blandon, PA; *Int'l*, pg. 1201
Harrington, Don, Chief Operating Officer--Fleet Bank NH, Littleton, NH; *U.S. Public*, pg. 649
Harrington, Douglas, M.D., Chief Exec. Officer--ChromaVision Medical Systems, Inc., San Juan Capistrano, CA; *U.S. Public*, pg. 1424
Harrington, Larry, Mgr.--Stoutland Telephone Company, Stoutland, MO; *U.S. Public*, pg. 1572
Harrington, Mark, Gen. Mgr.--BFCE Houston, Houston, TX; *Int'l*, pg. 161
Harrington, Matthew, Exec. V.P. & Gen. Mgr.--Edelman Worldwide, Inc., San Francisco, CA; *U.S. Private*, pg. 362
Harrington, Richard J., Pres. & Chief Exec. Officer--Thomson Professional Publishing, Stamford, CT; *U.S. Public*, pg. 1601
Harris, A., Chm.--Scaw Metal Ltd., Johannesburg, South Africa; *Int'l*, pg. 76
Harris, Anthony B., Mng. Dir.--Kimberly-Clark GmbH, Koblenz, Germany; *U.S. Public*, pg. 959
Harris, Ben, Pres.--Jarman Shoe Co., Nashville, TN; *U.S. Public*, pg. 728
Harris, Bill, Mgr.--Eclipse Combustion, Inc., West Memphis, AR; *U.S. Private*, pg. 360
Harris, Bren, Plant Mgr.--Vibration Automotive Division, Ligonier, IN; *U.S. Private*, pg. 428
Harris, Brian, Mgr.--Yale Europe Materials Handling Corporation Ltd., Wolverhampton, United Kingdom; *U.S. Public*, pg. 1150
Harris, Bryn, Gen. Mgr.--Westpac Banking Corp. - Tonga, Nuku'alofa, Tonga; *Int'l*, pg. 1497
Harris, Chris, Mgr.-Opers.--CR Minerals Corporation, Fernley, NV; *U.S. Public*, pg. 302
Harris, David J., Pres. & Chief Exec. Officer--M & I Bank Northeast, Green Bay, WI; *U.S. Public*, pg. 1050
Harris, Don, Chief Oper. Officer--7-UP of Victoria, Victoria, TX; *U.S. Private*, pg. 470
Harris, Elmer B., Pres. & Chief Exec. Officer--Alabama Power Co., Birmingham, AL; *U.S. Public*, pg. 1489
Harris, Elmer B., Pres.--Southern Electric Generating Co., Birmingham, AL; *U.S. Public*, pg. 1490
Harris, Elvon, Mng. Dir.--ManuLife Holdings (Hong Kong) Limited, Hong Kong, Hong Kong; *Int'l*, pg. 841
Harris, Fred, Jr., Div. V.P.--Personal Care & Related Products Division, Saint Paul, MN; *U.S. Public*, pg. 1605
Harris, G. Dennis, Pres.--North Bros. Co., Atlanta, GA; *U.S. Private*, pg. 853
Harris, G.M., Chief Oper. Officer--LBI Finance (Hong Kong) Ltd., Hong Kong, Hong Kong; *Int'l*, pg. 813
Harris, G.M., Plant Mgr.--Sundor Brands Inc./Lincoln, Chicopee, MA; *U.S. Public*, pg. 1331
Harris, Geoff, Pres. & Chief Exec. Officer--American Aggregates Corp., Dayton, OH; *Int'l*, pg. 245
Harris, George, Pres.--Evenflo Company, Inc., Canton, GA; *U.S. Private*, pg. 629
Harris, George, Pres.--Evenflo Company, Inc., Piqua, OH; *U.S. Private*, pg. 629
Harris, Graeme, Partner--Goldsack Harris Thompson Advertising, Wellington, New Zealand; *U.S. Private*, pg. 184
Harris, James A., Pres. & Chief Exec. Officer--Eljer Plumbingware, Dallas, TX; *U.S. Public*, pg. 1794
Harris, Jay, Chm. Bd. & Publisher--San Jose Mercury News, San Jose, CA; *U.S. Public*, pg. 964
Harris, Jeremy C., Gen. Mgr.--Olin UK Ltd., Droitwich, United Kingdom; *U.S. Public*, pg. 1220
Harris, Jerold L., Pres.--Farm Credit Bank of Wichita, Wichita, KS; *U.S. Private*, pg. 398
Harris, Jerold L., V.P.-Fin.--Farm Credit Council Services, Bloomington, IL; *U.S. Private*, pg. 398
Harris, Jim D., Mgr.--MMI General Insurance (N.Z.) Ltd., Auckland, New Zealand; *Int'l*, pg. 60
Harris, Joe, Gen. Mgr.--Hollis & Eastern Railroad Co., Duke, OK; *U.S. Public*, pg. 1378
Harris, John, Pres.--Harris Rebar, Stoney Creek, Canada; *Int'l*, pg. 598
Harris, John, Mng. Dir.--The Aluminum Powder Company, Sutton Coldfield, United Kingdom; *U.S. Private*, pg. 735
Harris, John, V.P. & Gen. Mgr.--Friskies PetCare Div., Glendale, CA; *Int'l*, pg. 917
Harris, K., Mgr.-Natl. Sls. & Mktg.--Goodman Fielder Mills (NZ) Ltd., Auckland, New Zealand; *Int'l*, pg. 556
Harris, L. Elvon, Chm.--The Manufacturers (Pacific Asia) Insurance Co. Ltd., Hong Kong, Hong Kong; *Int'l*, pg. 841
Harris, Larry, Plant Mgr.--Crackin' Good Bakers, Valdosta, GA; *U.S. Public*, pg. 1772
Harris, Lloyd, Mng. Dir.--Bondware, Toronto, Canada; *Int'l*, pg. 417
Harris, Lou, Reg. Mgr.--Accu-Sort Canada, Lachine, Canada; *U.S. Private*, pg. 11
Harris, Louis A., Pres. & Chief Exec. Officer--First Security Leasing Co., Salt Lake City, UT; *U.S. Public*, pg. 638
Harris, Mel, Pres.--Sony Pictures Entertainment Television Group, Culver City, CA; *Int'l*, pg. 1282
Harris, Mike, V.P.--Great Atlantic Management Co. Inc., Hampton, VA; *U.S. Private*, pg. 473
Harris, P. J., Chief Oper. Officer--Babcock Electrical Projects Ltd, Gloucester, United Kingdom; *Int'l*, pg. 471
Harris, Randolph L. P., Resident Rep.--The World Bank, Kampala, Uganda; *U.S. Private*, pg. 1190
Harris, Randy, V.P. & Div. Mgr.--Brevard Div., Rockledge, FL; *U.S. Public*, pg. 1148
Harris, Randy, Pres.--Sunwest Bank of Clovis, N.A., Clovis, NM; *U.S. Public*, pg. 1165
Harris, Raymond A., Plant Mgr.--Nicholson File, Cullman, AL; *U.S. Public*, pg. 444
Harris, Richard, Pres.--BA Leasing & Capital Corporation, San Francisco, CA; *U.S. Public*, pg. 181
Harris, Richard, Pres.--Western Indemnity Insurance Company, Houston, TX; *U.S. Public*, pg. 685
Harris, Richard M., Pres.--Predicasts, Cleveland, OH; *U.S. Public*, pg. 1600
Harris, Richard S., Sr. V.P.--Manufacturers Life Property Corporation, Toronto, Canada; *Int'l*, pg. 840
Harris, Rob, Pres.--GSW Heating Products Company, Stoney Creek, Canada; *Int'l*, pg. 538
Harris, Rob, Pres.--GSW Jackes-Evans Manufacturing Co., Saint Louis, MO; *Int'l*, pg. 538
Harris, Rob, Mng. Dir.-Europe--NDC International Ltd., Inc., London, United Kingdom; *U.S. Public*, pg. 1156
Harris, Robert, Branch Mgr.--Bergen Brunswig Medical Corporation, Tulsa, OK; *U.S. Public*, pg. 214
Harris, Robert, Pres.--Konica Manufacturing USA, Inc., Whitsett, NC; *Int'l*, pg. 749
Harris, Robert, Pres.--Universal Television Div., Universal City, CA; *Int'l*, pg. 1216
Harris, Robert R., Pres.--Armtec Defense Products Co., Coachella, CA; *U.S. Public*, pg. 594
Harris, S., Gen. Mgr.--Wellcome Norge AS, Oslo, Norway; *Int'l*, pg. 553
Harris, Steve, Gen. Mgr.--Westinghouse Cubic Limited, Merstham, United Kingdom; *U.S. Public*, pg. 466
Harris, Steve, Pres.--Frontier Transport Corporation, Indianapolis, IN; *Int'l*, pg. 1469
Harris, Steve, Admin.--Guardian Care of New Bern, New Bern, NC; *U.S. Public*, pg. 1713
Harris, Steven M., V.P.-Broadcasting--Maclean Hunter Broadcasting, Toronto, Canada; *Int'l*, pg. 1123
Harris, Stuart G., Chm. Bd. & Pres.--S&H Citadel, Inc., Hillside, IL; *U.S. Public*, pg. 990
Harris, Terry, Gen. Mgr.--ITW Red Head, Glasgow, United Kingdom; *U.S. Public*, pg. 869
Harris, Thomas E., Pres. & Chief Exec. Officer--Commonwealth Gas Services, Inc., Richmond, VA; *U.S. Public*, pg. 403
Harris, Tim, Pres.--Armour Food Company, Downers Grove, IL; *U.S. Public*, pg. 427
Harris, Tim, Pres.--Princess Cruise Lines, Los Angeles, CA; *Int'l*, pg. 1035
Harris, Tim, Exec. V.P.--Witt Products Division, Cincinnati, OH; *U.S. Private*, pg. 1185
Harris, Tony, Mng. Dir.--EMAP Computing Ltd., London, United Kingdom; *Int'l*, pg. 451
Harrison, A., Pres.--Racal NCS Inc., Houston, TX; *Int'l*, pg. 1083
Harrison, Ben, Pres.--John Wieland Homes of South Carolina, Inc., Mount Pleasant, SC; *U.S. Private*, pg. 1175
Harrison, Brian, Mng. Dir.--Dentsu Young & Rubicam/Singapore, Singapore, Singapore; *U.S. Private*, pg. 325
Harrison, Carl, Pres.--McCain Refrigerated Foods Inc., Oakville, Canada; *Int'l*, pg. 850
Harrison, Charles P., V.P. & Gen. Mgr.--Lambda Novatronics Inc., Pompano Beach, FL; *Int'l*, pg. 1241
Harrison, D., Gen. Mgr.--Exsil, Inc., San Jose, CA; *Int'l*, pg. 802
Harrison, Dean, Pres.--Titan Tool, Inc., Oakland, NJ; *U.S. Private*, pg. 500
Harrison, Denise S., Pres.--Equifax Center for Information Research, Atlanta, GA; *U.S. Public*, pg. 588
Harrison, Fiona, Mng. Dir.--Jaeger Holdings Limited, London, United Kingdom; *Int'l*, pg. 300
Harrison, Gary, Pres. & Chief Oper. Officer--Mrs. Smith's Bakeries, Inc., Thomasville, GA; *U.S. Public*, pg. 657
Harrison, Gui, V.P. & Gen. Mgr.--Peterson Spring-Kingsville Plant, Kingsville, Canada; *U.S. Private*, pg. 857
Harrison, Ian, V.P. & Gen. Mgr.--Leasing Solutions International, Ltd., Woking, United Kingdom; *U.S. Public*, pg. 983
Harrison, Ian, Regional Gen. Mgr.--Bill Acceptance Corporation Limited - Queensland, Brisbane, Australia; *Int'l*, pg. 1496
Harrison, J. Dan, Pres. & Chief Oper. Officer--Schott's Bakery, Inc., Houston, TX; *U.S. Public*, pg. 658
Harrison, J. R., Property Mgr.--CVC of Ohio, Stamford, CT; *U.S. Public*, pg. 380
Harrison, Jack E., Div. V.P.--Technology Engineering, Atlanta, GA; *U.S. Public*, pg. 1520
Harrison, John, Pres. & Chief Exec. Officer--Chemical Bank Key State, Owosso, MI; *U.S. Public*, pg. 345
Harrison, John, State Mgr.--National Mutual Queensland, Brisbane, Australia; *Int'l*, pg. 908
Harrison, John E., V.P.--Electronics and Systems Integration Division, Bethpage, NY; *U.S. Public*, pg. 1198
Harrison, John J., Pres.--DiMark, Inc., Langhorne, PA; *U.S. Public*, pg. 793
Harrison, Mike, Gen. Mgr.--Data General Limited, Brentford, United Kingdom; *U.S. Public*, pg. 486
Harrison, Neil, Gen. Mgr.--CBFC Limited, Sydney, Australia; *Int'l*, pg. 313
Harrison, Neil, Pres.--Weight Watchers Gourmet Food Company, Pittsburgh, PA; *U.S. Public*, pg. 806
Harrison, O.R., Pres.--Exxon Pipeline Company, Houston, TX; *U.S. Public*, pg. 601
Harrison, P., Chm. Bd.--Alpha Airports Group Plc, London, United Kingdom; *Int'l*, pg. 65
Harrison, Patrick W., Dir.--Tennessee Valley Life Insurance Co., Nashville, TN; *U.S. Public*, pg. 1163
Harrison, R.J., Sls. Mgr. Canada--AlliedSignal Chemicals Canada Inc., Mississauga, Canada; *U.S. Public*, pg. 52
Harrison, Richard, Pres.--Atlantic Auto Finance Corp., Fairport, NY; *U.S. Private*, pg. 1095
Harrison, Richard, Pres.--Parametric Technology Corporation, Bedford, MA; *U.S. Public*, pg. 1257
Harrison, Richard E., Plant Mgr.--Industrial Bag Division - Wellsburg Plant, Wellsburg, WV; *U.S. Public*, pg. 1521
Harrison, Ridgley W., III, Pres.--Minwax Company Div., Upper Saddle River, NJ; *U.S. Public*, pg. 1466
Harrison, Ridgley, III, Pres. & Chief Exec. Officer--The Thompson-Minwax Company, Upper Saddle River, NJ; *U.S. Public*, pg. 1466
Harrison, Ritchie J., Mng. Dir.--Reemtsma Japan Ltd., Tokyo, Japan; *Int'l*, pg. 1101
Harrison, Ritchie J., Mng. Dir.--Reemtsma International Far East Pte. Ltd., Singapore, Singapore; *Int'l*, pg. 1101
Harrison, Robert R., Mgr.-Admin.--Charter-Provo School, Inc., Provo, UT; *U.S. Public*, pg. 1035
Harrison, S.C., Pres. & Dir.--P.T. Burroughs Wellcome Indonesia, Jakarta, Indonesia; *Int'l*, pg. 553
Harrison, Thomas B., Div. V.P.--Pharmaceuticals Division, Saint Paul, MN; *U.S. Public*, pg. 1605
Harrison, Tom, Chm. & Chief Exec. Officer--Harrison Wilson & Associates, Parsippany, NJ; *U.S. Public*, pg. 1224
Harrison, W.A., Area Mgr.--Milchem Venezuela Corporation, Maracaibo, Venezuela; *U.S. Public*, pg. 167
Harrison, Warren, Mng. Dir.--DYWIDAG Systems International, USA, Inc., Parker, CO; *Int'l*, pg. 424
Harrison, Wayne, Mng. Dir.--Kollmorgen Tandon India, Mumbai, India; *U.S. Public*, pg. 966
Harrison, William B., Jr., Chm., Pres. & Treas.--Chatham Ventures, Inc., New York, NY; *U.S. Public*, pg. 338
Harrison, William J., Chief Oper. Officer--Kenhar Corporation, Guelph, Canada; *U.S. Public*, pg. 311
Harrison, William, Jr., V.P. & Gen. Mgr.--U.S. Brick, Inc.-Sipple Brick Division, Stanton, KY; *Int'l*, pg. 699

Harrold, Jim, Dir.-Sls.--Sensormatic CamEra Ltd., Warwick, United Kingdom; *U.S. Public*, pg. 1457

Harrold, John, Mgr.-Branch--American Inks & Coatings Corp., Ink Division, Winston Salem, NC; *U.S. Private*, pg. 56

Harrop, R. O., Mng. Dir.--Tenneco Malros Ltd., Bristol, United Kingdom; *U.S. Public*, pg. 1580

Harsh, John, Exec. V.P.--Safari Tool, Bridgeport, CT; *U.S. Private*, pg. 879

Harshman, Richard R., Pres. & Chief Exec. Officer--Storck U.S.A., L.P., Chicago, IL; *Int'l*, pg. 1304

Harss, Richard, Gen. Mgr.--Glass Plant, Fort Lauderdale, FL; *U.S. Private*, pg. 486

Hart-Stephens, Ruth, Gen. Mgr.--Toronto Auto Auction, Milton, Canada; *U.S. Private*, pg. 283

Hart, Betty, Gen. Mgr.--Securall, Inc., Sanford, NC; *U.S. Private*, pg. 309

Hart, Edward, Pres.--Wabash Magnetics, Huntington, IN; *U.S. Private*, pg. 351

Hart, Fred C., Pres.--McLaren/Hart Environmental Engineering Corp., Warren, NJ; *Int'l*, pg. 1465

Hart, James N., Mng. Dir.--Wallace & Tiernan Pacific Pty. Ltd., Artarmon, Australia; *U.S. Public*, pg. 61

Hart, James W. Jr., Pres. & Chief Oper. Officer--Reeves International, Spartanburg, SC; *U.S. Private*, pg. 507

Hart, James W. Jr., Pres. & Chief Oper. Officer--Reeves Brothers, Inc., Spartanburg, SC; *U.S. Private*, pg. 507

Hart, Jan't, Mng. Dir.--Tennant Holding B.V., Uden, Netherlands; *U.S. Public*, pg. 1577

Hart, Jeff R., Mng. Dir.--Swiss Re Life Company America, New York, NY; *Int'l*, pg. 1333

Hart, Jim, Mgr.-Sls.--Bergen Brunswig Medical Corporation, Murray, UT; *U.S. Public*, pg. 214

Hart, John W., Mng. Dir.--Bermuda Trust (Cook Islands) Limited, Rarotonga, Cook Islands; *Int'l*, pg. 151

Hart, Jonathan, Mng. Dir.--Dixons Stores Group Ltd., Hemel Hempstead, United Kingdom; *Int'l*, pg. 414

Hart, Kenneth A., Pres., Chief Oper. Officer & Sec.--First Trust and Savings Bank of Taylorville, Taylorville, IL; *U.S. Public*, pg. 644

Hart, Malcolm, Dir.--Rolls-Royce Motor Cars Limited Sales & Marketing, Crewe, United Kingdom; *Int'l*, pg. 1467

Hart, Mike, Reg. Pres.--Capstone Electronics Div., San Jose, CA; *U.S. Public*, pg. 134

Hart, Milledge A., III, Chm. Bd.--DocuCorp International, Dallas, TX; *U.S. Public*, pg. 1425

Hart, Philip, Mng. Dir.--Soundcraft Electronics, Ltd, Potters Bar, United Kingdom; *U.S. Public*, pg. 787

Hart, Robert, Pres.--Sierracin/Sylmar Corporation, Sylmar, CA; *U.S. Private*, pg. 999

Hart, Robert, V.P. & Gen. Mgr.-Paper Board--Paperboard Div., Atlanta, GA; *U.S. Public*, pg. 1391

Hart, Ron, Pres.--Nelco Products, Inc., Fullerton, CA; *U.S. Public*, pg. 1258

Hart, Roy, Gen. Mgr.--Metz Baking Co., Dubuque, IA; *U.S. Private*, pg. 1022

Hart, Sandy, Div. Mgr.--Concrete Service Co., Wilmington, NC; *Int'l*, pg. 166

Hart, Tom, Pres.--Astra Pharmaceuticals (New Zealand) Ltd., Auckland, New Zealand; *Int'l*, pg. 94

Hart, W. Jeffery, Pres.--Mapco Petroleum Inc., Tulsa, OK; *U.S. Public*, pg. 1042

Harte, Maurice, Mng. Dir.--AIB Investment Managers Ltd., Dublin, Ireland; *Int'l*, pg. 64

Hartenfels, Markus, Gen. Mgr.--Pornon Et Cie, S.A.R.L., Diou, France; *Int'l*, pg. 1488

Hartermann, Rolf, Chief Oper. Officer--V.A.G. Synko GmbH, Braunschweig, Germany; *Int'l*, pg. 1473

Hartery, John C., Pres.--Stora Forest Industries, Port Hawkesbury, Canada; *Int'l*, pg. 1304

Hartford, L.L., Pres.--Centra Gas Alberta Inc., Leduc, Canada; *Int'l*, pg. 1492

Hartford, Tom, V.P. & Gen. Mgr.--Tidewater Compression Service, Inc., Houston, TX; *U.S. Public*, pg. 1608

Hartigan, Norm, Plant Mgr.--Ringier America, Dresden Division, Dresden, TN; *U.S. Public*, pg. 1778

Hartigan, William N., Mng. Dir.--Ford Motor Co. of New Zealand Ltd., Lower Hutt, New Zealand; *U.S. Public*, pg. 666

Hartinger, Robert, Mgr.--MKTS, Moscow, Russia; *Int'l*, pg. 1186

Hartl, Richard J., Grp. V.P.--Specialty Tapes and Adhesives Group, Pasadena, CA; *U.S. Public*, pg. 153

Hartle, Gerald, Gen. Mgr.--International Window Corp., South Gate, CA; *U.S. Public*, pg. 895

Hartley, Dan, Chief Oper. Officer--Flowers Baking Co. of South Carolina, Inc., Spartanburg, SC; *U.S. Public*, pg. 657

Hartley, E., Mgr.--Daher Golden Eagle - Las Vegas, Las Vegas, NV; *U.S. Public*, pg. 749

Hartley, J.M., Mng. Dir.--Bally Shoe Co. Ltd., London, United Kingdom; *Int'l*, pg. 997

Hartley, John, Gen. Mgr.--Hansen Plastics Division, Clearwater, FL; *U.S. Private*, pg. 1110

Hartley, Sharon, Grp. Mgr.--Playskool, Inc., Pawtucket, RI; *U.S. Public*, pg. 797

Hartley, Sonia, Resident V.P.--Fireman's Fund Insurance Co. of Louisiana, Metairie, LA; *Int'l*, pg. 59

Hartley, T.P., Regional Chm.--Barratt Southern, Wallington, United Kingdom; *Int'l*, pg. 168

Hartley, Todd, Reg. Mgr.--Green Tree Acceptance, Inc., San Diego, CA; *U.S. Public*, pg. 762

Hartlieb, A., Gen. Mgr.--OAG Gruppe A.G., Vienna, Austria; *Int'l*, pg. 1511

Hartman, David, Pres.--Midwest Products, Inc., Strafford, MO; *U.S. Public*, pg. 849

Hartman, Donald, V.P. & Gen. Mgr.--PAXAR Apparel Identification Systems, Sayre, PA; *U.S. Public*, pg. 1266

Hartman, Douglas, V.P.--Y & S Candies, Lancaster, PA; *U.S. Public*, pg. 812

Hartman, Douglas S., Gen. Mgr.--Aviation Product Support Inc., Mentor, OH; *U.S. Public*, pg. 1569

Hartman, F., Chief Fin. Officer & V.P.--National Vendors, Bridgeton, MO; *U.S. Public*, pg. 457

Hartman, Gerald, Pres.--Burnup & Sims ComTec, Inc., Tampa, FL; *U.S. Public*, pg. 1056

Hartman, Gerald, Pres.--Burnup & Sims of California, Inc., North Highlands, CA; *U.S. Public*, pg. 1056

Hartman, Horst, Chief Oper. Officer--Saarberg-Hoelter-Lurgi GmbH, Saarbruecken, Germany; *Int'l*, pg. 1167

Hartman, Jack, Pres. & Chief Exec. Officer--SunTrust Bank, Southeast Georgia, N.A., Brunswick, GA; *U.S. Public*, pg. 1538

Hartman, Rick, Mgr.-Opers.--Simpson Pasadena Paper Co., Pasadena, TX; *U.S. Private*, pg. 1003

Hartman, William C., Pres.--Cigna Holdings, Inc., Wilmington, DE; *U.S. Public*, pg. 357

Hartman, William C., Pres.--Malrosian, Inc., Wilmington, DE; *U.S. Public*, pg. 357

Hartmann, Andreas, Chm.--Coop Rechtsschutz, Aarau, Switzerland; *Int'l*, pg. 330

Hartmann, Bruce, Gen. Mgr.--Knoxville News-Sentinel Company, Knoxville, TN; *U.S. Public*, pg. 1448

Hartmann, Edward G., Pres. & Chief Exec. Officer--BA Investment Managers, Los Angeles, CA; *U.S. Public*, pg. 180

Hartmann, M., Exec. V.P. & Gen. Mgr.--Deutsche Babcock Technologies, Inc., Duluth, GA; *Int'l*, pg. 401

Hartmann, Rudolf, Mng. Dir.--Grace G.m.b.H., Norderstedt, Germany; *U.S. Public*, pg. 755

Hartmann, Udo B., Mng. Dir.--BB-Kapitalbeteiligungs gesellschaft GmbH, Berlin, Germany; *Int'l*, pg. 159

Hartnett, Brian, Dr., Mng. Dir.--Tasmanian Alkaloids Pty. Ltd., Westbury, Australia; *U.S. Public*, pg. 932

Hartnett, Richard, Publisher--Battle Creek Enquirer, Battle Creek, MI; *U.S. Public*, pg. 700

Hartog, D.R., Chief Oper. Officer--P.T. Rabobank Duta Indonesia, Jakarta, Indonesia; *Int'l*, pg. 1082

Hartsfield, Wayne, Pres.--First National Bank of Searcy, Searcy, AK; *U.S. Public*, pg. 630

Hartsuck, Dick, Gen. Mgr.--Pirelli Armstrong Midwest Division, Des Moines, IA; *Int'l*, pg. 1058

Hartt, Stanley H., Chm. Bd.--Camdev Properties Inc., Toronto, Canada; *Int'l*, pg. 993

Hartung, Horst, Chm. Bd.--Krupp Mak Maschinenbau GmbH, Kiel, Germany; *Int'l*, pg. 509

Hartwell, Bob, Gen. Mgr.--Nestle Dairy Systems-Packaging/ Machinery Division, Columbus, OH; *Int'l*, pg. 918

Hartzel, Fred, Plant Mgr.--A. Goodman & Sons, Inc., Deer Park, NY; *U.S. Private*, pg. 158

Haruki, Warren H., Pres.--GTE Hawaiian Telephone Company Incorporated, Irving, TX; *U.S. Public*, pg. 697

Harvey, Carter, Pres.--Fleming Co. of Nebraska, Inc., Lincoln, NE; *U.S. Public*, pg. 653

Harvey, Claude, Pres.--Central Plants, Inc., Los Angeles, CA; *U.S. Public*, pg. 1249

Harvey, David, Chief Oper. Officer--Notifier Ltd., Brighton, United Kingdom; *U.S. Public*, pg. 1307

Harvey, David C., Mng. Dir.--System Sensor Ltd., Horsham, United Kingdom; *U.S. Public*, pg. 1307

Harvey, Dennis D., Pres. & Chief Exec. Officer--United Missouri Bank of Jefferson City, Jefferson City, MO; *U.S. Public*, pg. 1655

Harvey, F.L. Mike, Pres.--Applications Management Group, Plano, TX; *U.S. Public*, pg. 1516

Harvey, Francis J., Chief Oper. Officer--Westinghouse Industries & Technologies Group, Pittsburgh, PA; *U.S. Public*, pg. 273

Harvey, Gregg, Mng. Dir.--CTS Singapore Pte., Ltd., Singapore, Singapore; *U.S. Public*, pg. 286

Harvey, James, Pres.--Logicon Eagle Technology, Inc., Winter Park, FL; *U.S. Public*, pg. 1199

Harvey, James F., V.P. & Gen. Mgr.--Logicon Tactical and Training Systems Division, San Diego, CA; *U.S. Public*, pg. 1199

Harvey, Larry, Pres.--Zimmer Patient Care Systems Division, Statesville, NC; *U.S. Public*, pg. 254

Harvey, Len, Gen. Mgr.--Polarcup (N.Z.) Limited, Henderson, New Zealand; *Int'l*, pg. 638

Harvey, Michael, Pres.--Gulfstar Energy, Inc., Houston, TX; *U.S. Public*, pg. 516

Harvey, Michael, Chm. & Chief Exec. Officer--Habitat Group, London, United Kingdom; *Int'l*, pg. 660

Harvey, Niel, Chm.--Amquip (Proprietary) Limited, Isando, South Africa; *Int'l*, pg. 76

Harvey, Randy, Mgr.--Laboratory Supply Company, Jacksonville, FL; *U.S. Private*, pg. 642

Harvey, Sue, Chief Oper. Officer--Luncheon Vouchers Ltd., London, United Kingdom; *Int'l*, pg. 21

Harvey, Tom, Pres.--Consumer Audio Products Co., Park Ridge, NJ; *Int'l*, pg. 1281

Harwood, A.R., Gen. Mgr.--Australian Mutual Provident Society, Wellington, New Zealand; *Int'l*, pg. 100

Harwood, Brett, Pres. & Chief Oper. Officer--Square Industries, Inc., Jersey City, NJ; *U.S. Public*, pg. 326

Harwood, Bud, Reg. Mgr.--Green Tree Acceptance, Inc., Syracuse, NY; *U.S. Public*, pg. 762

Harwood, Jim, Chief Exec. Officer--City National Bank of Fort Smith, Fort Smith, AR; *U.S. Public*, pg. 641

Harz, Klaus Hermann, Chief Oper. Officer--Schmidt & Hagen GmbH & Co. KG, Uetersen, Germany; *Int'l*, pg. 610

Hasan, Malik A., M.D., Chm. Bd.--Qual-Med, Inc., Pueblo, CO; *U.S. Public*, pg. 678

Hasatani, Toichi, Country Mgr.--Grace Japan K.K., Tokyo, Japan; *U.S. Public*, pg. 756

Hascall, James G., Pres.--Olin Specialty Metals Corporation, East Alton, IL; *U.S. Public*, pg. 1219

Hasch, J. Bruce, Pres. & Chief Oper. Officer--The Peoples Gas Light & Coke Co., Chicago, IL; *U.S. Public*, pg. 1275

Hasegawa, Mitsuaki, Pres.--Dai-ichi Life (U.S.A.) Inc., New York, NY; *Int'l*, pg. 362

Hasegawa, Noboru, Pres.--MacGregor Golf (Japan) Ltd., Tokyo, Japan; *Int'l*, pg. 73

Hasegawa, Noboru, Gen. Mgr.--Dai-Ichi Kangyo Bank, Ltd.-Atlanta, Atlanta, GA; *Int'l*, pg. 359

Hasegawa, Nobuhisa, Pres.--Banco Sumitomo Brasileiro S.A., Sao Paulo, Brazil; *Int'l*, pg. 1310

Hasegawa, Ryoichi, Pres. & Dir.--P.T. Bank Sumitomo Niaga, Jakarta, Indonesia; *Int'l*, pg. 1310

Hasegawa, Sachiyuki, Chief Fin. Officer--Eurogenetics N.V., Tessenderlo, Belgium; *Int'l*, pg. 1408

Hasegawa, Sueyoshi, Chm.--Harima M.I.D., Inc., Osaka, Japan; *U.S. Public*, pg. 1077

Hasegawa, Takehiko, Pres. & Representative Dir.--Yamaha Motor Co., Ltd., Iwata, Japan; *Int'l*, pg. 1516

Haseltine, G.K., Site Co-Ordinator--Butachimie, Chalampe, France; *U.S. Public*, pg. 533

Haselwander, Jack G., Gen. Mgr.--Salem Carpet Mills, Ringgold, GA; *U.S. Public*, pg. 1464

Haselwander, Mark, Gen. Mgr.--Ashley Carpet, Ringgold, GA; *U.S. Public*, pg. 1464

Hashagen, John P., Chm. & Chief Exec. Officer--SunTrust Bank, Miami, N.A., Miami, FL; *U.S. Public*, pg. 1537

Hashim, Hashim, Media Mgr.--Targets-Leo Burnett Advertising, Jeddah, Saudi Arabia; *U.S. Private*, pg. 186

Hashimi, F.A., Mng. Dir.--Gestetner (Private) Limited, Karachi, Pakistan; *Int'l*, pg. 1115

Hashimoto, A., Pres.--Nichimen America, Inc., New York, NY; *Int'l*, pg. 927

Hashimoto, Akira, Pres.--Micro-Mech. Inc., Ipswich, MA; *Int'l*, pg. 578

Hashimoto, Clark, Pres.--Glory USA, Inc., West Caldwell, NJ; *Int'l*, pg. 554

Hashimoto, Kazuo, Gen. Mgr.--The Sakura Bank - New Delhi Branch, New Delhi, India; *Int'l*, pg. 1179

Hashimoto, Kyosuke, Partner--Brown Brothers Harriman & Co., Tokyo, Tokyo, Japan; *U.S. Private*, pg. 173

Hashimoto, Takashi, Pres.--Mitsui Trust Bank (U.S.A.), New York, NY; *Int'l*, pg. 883

Hashimoto, Takashi, Mng. Dir.--Yamaichi Australia Ltd., Sydney, Australia; *Int'l*, pg. 1517

Hashimoto, Takayuki, Pres.--Toto (Beijing) Co., Ltd., Beijing, China; *Int'l*, pg. 1410

hashimoto, Tomoaki, Pres.--Amano Partners U.S.A. Inc. (A.P.U.), Roseland, NJ; *Int'l*, pg. 71

Hashimoto, Toru, Pres.--Haseko Development Inc., Osaka, Japan; *Int'l*, pg. 600

Hashizaki, J., Pres.--Sharp Electronics of Canada Ltd., Mississauga, Canada; *Int'l*, pg. 1230

Hasimoto, Shozo, Pres.--Nomura Research Institute, Ltd., Tokyo, Japan; *Int'l*, pg. 956

Haskell, Gregory W., Pres. & Chief Oper. Officer--XL Vision Inc., Sebastian, FL; *U.S. Public*, pg. 1424

Haskin, Douglas N., Plant Mgr.--Bundy Corporation, Marine City Plant, Marine City, MI; *Int'l*, pg. 1340

Haskin, Douglas N., Plant Mgr.--Bundy Corporation, Warren Plant, Warren, MI; *Int'l*, pg. 1341

Haskins, Elizabeth, Pres.--Lazerdata, Sanford, FL; *Int'l*, pg. 127

Haslam, James A., 111, Dir.--Pilot Receivables Corporation, Knoxville, TN; *U.S. Private*, pg. 865

Hasler, Oliver, Mgr.--Oneida Mexicana, S.A., Toluca, Mexico; *U.S. Public*, pg. 1226

Haslimann, Patzi, Mng. Dir.--Haslimann Taylor, Sutton Coldfield, United Kingdom; *Int'l*, pg. 1226

Hass, Donald R., Pres.--First American Bank, Detroit Lakes, MN; *U.S. Private*, pg. 167

Hassanein, Richard C., Pres.--Todd-AO Studios West, Santa Monica, CA; *U.S. Public*, pg. 1619

Hassell, Bill, Pres.--Engineered Polymers Corporation, Mora, MN; *Int'l*, pg. 328

Hasselo, William, Branch Mgr.--Union-Transport Corporation-Orlando Office, Orlando, FL; *U.S. Private*, pg. 1120

Hasselsweiler, Benno, Dir.--Schulverlag Vieweg GmbH, Dusseldorf, Germany; *Int'l*, pg. 190

Hassler, Sterling L., Div. V.P. & Gen. Mgr.--Super Abrasives, Worcester, MA; *Int'l*, pg. 1174

Hasson, John D., V.P. & Gen. Mgr.--Stelco Fasteners Ltd., Brantford, Canada; *Int'l*, pg. 1299

Hastey, Joe A., Pres.--Piedmont Olsen Hensley, Inc., Greenville, SC; *Int'l*, pg. 607

Hasting, John, Pres.--Litho-Krome Company, Columbus, GA; *U.S. Private*, pg. 496

Hastings, Shaun, Gen. Mgr.--Forbo UK Ltd., Cramlington, United Kingdom; *Int'l*, pg. 498

Hasty, Alan E., Pres.--Sysco Food Services of Virginia, Inc., Harrisonburg, VA; *U.S. Public*, pg. 1552

Hasty, Rick, Branch Mgr.--CAP Gemini America (Tampa Branch), Tampa, FL; *Int'l*, pg. 264

Hata, Fumio, Pres.--Daihatsu America, Inc., Los Alamitos, CA; *Int'l*, pg. 365

Hatakeyama, Shigemitsu, Pres.--The Inctec Inc., Yokohama, Japan; *Int'l*, pg. 363

Hatanaka, Takeshi, Pres.--Sumikin Bussan International (Australia) Pty. Ltd., Melbourne, Australia; *Int'l*, pg. 1308

Hatch, Harold, Pres. & Chief Exec. Officer--United Missouri Mortgage Company, Kansas City, MO; *U.S. Public*, pg. 1655

Hatch, Ralph, Gen. Mgr.--Coca-Cola/Dr. Pepper Bottling Co. Of South Arkansas, Pine Bluff, AR; *U.S. Public*, pg. 393

Hatcher, Robert V., III, Sr. V.P.--Willis Faber North America, Inc.-Pennsylvania, Radnor, PA; *Int'l*, pg. 1504

Hatchett, A.G., Chm. Bd.--P&O Harbours Ltd., Felixstowe, United Kingdom; *Int'l*, pg. 1034

Hatfield, C. Donald, V.P. & Publisher--Citizen Publishing Co., Tucson, AZ; *U.S. Public*, pg. 700

Hatfield, Dave, System Supervisor--Lincoln Road Gas Plant, Green River, WY; *U.S. Public*, pg. 1759

Hatfield, Joseph P., Sr. V.P. & Gen. Mdsg. Mgr.--Wal-Mart Home/Seasonal Div., Bentonville, AR; *U.S. Public*, pg. 1733

Hathaway, Dan, Gen. Mgr.--Performance Elastomers Division, Sunnyvale, CA; *U.S. Public*, pg. 689

Hathaway, Dan, Gen. Mgr.--Performance Elastomers Division, Fremont, CA; *U.S. Public*, pg. 689

Hathorn, J., Rep.--Swiss Bank Corporation, Johannesburg, South Africa; *Int'l*, pg. 1330

Hathorn, Samuel C., Jr., Chief Oper. Officer--Trendmaker Homes Inc., Houston, TX; *U.S. Public*, pg. 1764

Hathorn, Samuel, Jr., Pres.--Centennial Homes Inc., Dallas, TX; *U.S. Public*, pg. 1764

Hatki, Basilio P., Gen. Mgr.--Cigna Compania de Seguros (Chile) S.A., Santiago, Chile; *U.S. Public*, pg. 363

Hatley, Mike, Plant Mgr.--The Lamson & Sessions Co., Woodland, CA; *U.S. Public*, pg. 976

Hatsopoulos, G.N., Chm. Bd.--Peter Brotherhood Ltd., Peterborough, United Kingdom; *U.S. Public*, pg. 1596

Hatt, Jean-Denis, Dir.-Mexico--North West Water (Mexico), Mexico, Mexico; *Int'l*, pg. 1444

Hatta, Mr., Chief Oper. Officer--Sharp Corporation Brussels Office, Brussels, Belgium; *Int'l*, pg. 1229

Hatta, Nobuo, Chm.--Rohm Electronics (U.K.) Limited, Milton Keynes, United Kingdom; *Int'l*, pg. 1125

Hattem, E., Gen. Mgr.--Components Division/BEDEK Aviation Group, Israel; *Int'l*, pg. 690

Hattemer, James C., Pres. & Gen. Mgr.--Graphic Resources, Inc., Cold Spring, KY; *U.S. Public*, pg. 1486

Hatter, Bryan E., Chief Oper. Officer--Saab Great Britain Ltd., Marlow, United Kingdom; *Int'l*, pg. 687

Hattersley, J.B., Mng. Dir.--Hawker de Havilland Ltd., Bankstown, Australia; *Int'l*, pg. 128

Hattori, Hideaki, Pres. & Chief Exec. Officer--Pacific Guardian Life Insurance, Honolulu, HI; *Int'l*, pg. 854

Hattori, Kazuo, Gen. Mgr.--Kyodo Advertising Co., Ltd., Fukuoka, Japan; *Int'l*, pg. 776

Hattori, Kirk, Pres.--Canadian Kawasaki Motors Inc., Don Mills, Canada; *Int'l*, pg. 726

Hattori, Masami, Mng. Dir.--Wako International (Europe) Limited, London, United Kingdom; *Int'l*, pg. 1485

Hattori, Mikihiko, Gen. Mgr.--The Industrial Bank of Japan, Limited (Milan), Milan, Italy; *Int'l*, pg. 675

Hattori, Osamu, Pres.--Rohm Electronics (Philippines) Sales Corporation, Cavite, Philippines; *Int'l*, pg. 1125

Hattori, Satoshi, Chief Oper. Officer--Tosoh Medics, Inc., Foster City, CA; *Int'l*, pg. 1407

Hattori, Yoshio, Pres.--Sanyo Sales & Supplies (USA) Corporation, Bensenville, IL; *Int'l*, pg. 1191

Hatziantoniou, Michalis, Chief Oper. Officer--Novo Nordisk Hellas Ltd., Athens, Greece; *Int'l*, pg. 988

Hau, Andy, Chief Oper. Officer--MacGREGOR (HKG), Ltd., Kowloon, Hong Kong; *Int'l*, pg. 671

Haub, Christian W.E., Pres. & Co-Chief Exec. Officer--The Great Atlantic & Pacific Tea Company, Inc., Montvale, NJ; *Int'l*, pg. 1375

Hauber, Earl, Pres.--Environmental Construction, Inc. (ECI), Plantation, FL; *Int'l*, pg. 607

Hauch, Helmut, Co-Chief Oper. Officer--Saarberg Brennstoffhandel GmbH, Saarbruecken, Germany; *Int'l*, pg. 1167

Hauck, Bob, Mgr.-Sls.--PENCO-Kentucky, Louisville, KY; *Int'l*, pg. 1508

Hauck, Richard E., Pres.--Allegheny Gear Corporation, Orchard Park, NY; *U.S. Public*, pg. 142

Hauck, Richard E., Pres.--Rodgard Corporation, Buffalo, NY; *U.S. Public*, pg. 142

Hauck, Steve, Mng. Dir.--A. Schulman, Inc., Piscataway, NJ; *U.S. Public*, pg. 1441

Hauensack, Lane, Pres.--ABS Quality Evaluations, Inc., Houston, TX; *U.S. Private*, pg. 51

Hauer, Daniel, Pres. & Chief Exec. Officer--S MOS Systems, Inc., San Jose, CA; *Int'l*, pg. 1219

Hauff, A., Mng. Dir.--Ebara Germany GmbH, Hanau, Germany; *Int'l*, pg. 432

Haug, Trygve, V.P.--Kvaerner Energy a.s. South East Asia Representative Office, Singapore, Singapore; *Int'l*, pg. 767

Haug, W., Gen. Mgr.--Wellcome Pharmaceuticals BV, Utrecht, Netherlands; *Int'l*, pg. 553

Haugan, Jens, V.P.-Air Freight--Circle Leman Air Freight, Kastrup, Denmark; *U.S. Public*, pg. 373

Hauge, Anders, V.P. & Mgr.-Office--Harland Bartholomew & Associates Inc., Sacramento, CA; *U.S. Private*, pg. 842

Hauge, Stig, Gen. Mgr.--Kvaerner Energy, Agotnes, Agotnes, Norway; *Int'l*, pg. 767

Haugen, Dave, V.P.--Lynden Incorporated, Anchorage, AK; *U.S. Private*, pg. 683

Haugen, Donald, Pres.--Waterous Company, South Saint Paul, MN; *U.S. Private*, pg. 52

Haugen, Rolf E., Pres. & Chief Exec. Officer--Farm Credit Leasing Services Corporation, Minneapolis, MN; *U.S. Private*, pg. 398

Hauglund, Jorgen, Mng. Dir.--ISS Finans A/S, Holte, Denmark; *Int'l*, pg. 656

Hauhe, Dutch, Gen. Mgr.--St. Louis Auto Auction, Bridgeton, MO; *U.S. Private*, pg. 283

Haukkasalo, Paula, Acct. Mgr.--International Marketing & Promotions Helsinki, Helsinki, Finland; *U.S. Private*, pg. 304

Haun, Glenn, Gen. Mgr.--Schlumberger Industries, Owenton, KY; *U.S. Public*, pg. 1439

Haun, Monica, Chief Oper. Officer--Hawkeye Quality Service Corporation, West Des Moines, IA; *U.S. Public*, pg. 1087

Haun, S. Wesley, V.P.--K N Gas Marketing, Inc., Lakewood, CO; *U.S. Public*, pg. 937

Hauner, Axel, Pres.--Telair International Cargo Systems, Oxnard, CA; *U.S. Public*, pg. 1570

Hauner, Axel H.R., Pres.--Telair International, Oxnard, CA; *U.S. Public*, pg. 1570

Haunschild, Frank, Pres.--Pulte Phoenix Division, Tempe, AZ; *U.S. Public*, pg. 1345

Haupt, Rudiger, Dr., Chief Oper. Officer--Babcock Feuerungssysteme GmbH, Oberhausen, Germany; *Int'l*, pg. 398

Hauptli, Martin, Gen. Mgr.--Production AG Meilen, Meilen, Switzerland; *Int'l*, pg. 866

Hauser, Gustave M., Chm. Bd.--Orion Network Systems Incorporated, Rockville, MD; *Int'l*, pg. 218

Hauser, Helmut, Mng. Dir.--Sudkurier GmbH, Konstanz, Germany; *Int'l*, pg. 1478

Hauser, Joshua A., Pres. & Chief Exec. Officer--Lambda Electronics Inc., Melville, NY; *Int'l*, pg. 1241

Hausler, Yvette M., Mgr.-Fin.--APD Cryogenics Inc., Allentown, PA; *U.S. Public*, pg. 894

Hausmann, Carl, Chm. Bd. & Pres.--Central Soya Company, Inc., Fort Wayne, IN; *Int'l*, pg. 324

Hausmann, Judy, Gen. Mgr.--Casco Cable Television Inc., Brunswick, ME; *U.S. Private*, pg. 860

Hautcoeur, J. L., Chm. Bd.--Assu-Vie, Paris, France; *Int'l*, pg. 563

Hautcoeur, Jean-Louis, Chm.--NATIO-VIE, Paris, France; *Int'l*, pg. 163

Hautop, Ken, Plant Mgr.--Advanced Polymers Division, Mundelein, IL; *U.S. Public*, pg. 689

Havander, Goran, Mng. Dir. & Grp. Chief Exec.--Cederroth International AB, Upplands Vasby, Sweden; *U.S. Public*, pg. 38

Havelaar, Cor, Chief Oper. Officer--Eclipse Combustion B.V., Gouda, Netherlands; *U.S. Private*, pg. 361

Havelka, Josef, Mng. Dir.--Leo Burnett Advertising Spol.SR.O, Prague, Czech Republic; *U.S. Private*, pg. 184

Havens, Theodore A., Chief Fin. Officer--Pac-Fab, Inc./ East, Sanford, NC; *U.S. Public*, pg. 593

Havenstein, Ralph, Mng. Dir.--Sasol Chemical Industries Ltd., Sasolburg, South Africa; *Int'l*, pg. 1196

Haverbeke, Peter, Mng. Dir.--Keystone Valve (Europa) B.V., Breda, Netherlands; *U.S. Public*, pg. 1650

Havermans, A., Gen. Mgr.--N.V. Vereenigde Glasfabrieken, Schiedam, Netherlands; *Int'l*, pg. 381

Havers, Charles, Pres.-Supply Div.--Crescent Genlyte, Barrington, NJ; *U.S. Public*, pg. 730

Havers, Chuck, Pres.--Stonco Genlyte, Union, NJ; *U.S. Public*, pg. 730

Haverstick, M., Mng. Dir.--Yale Industrial Products, Forrest City, AR; *U.S. Public*, pg. 406

Haverty, Michael R., Pres. & Chief Exec. Officer--The Kansas City Southern Railway Co., Kansas City, MO; *U.S. Public*, pg. 944

Haveus, Peter, Mng. Dir.--AB Tvattman Textil Service, Malmo, Sweden; *Int'l*, pg. 1286

Haviland, E. Bernard, Pres.--Haviland Products, Grand Rapids, MI; *U.S. Private*, pg. 511

Havill, Chuck, Pres. & Gen. Mgr.--Door Closer Division, Princeton, IL; *U.S. Public*, pg. 876

Havill, Rick, V.P. & Gen. Mgr.--WWF-Canada, Inc., Montreal, Canada; *U.S. Private*, pg. 1145

Havre, Art, Gen. Mgr.--Haviland Consumer Products, Inc., Grand Rapids, MI; *U.S. Private*, pg. 511

Haw, Claude, V.P.-Fast Packet Networks--Newbridge Networks Corporation, Kanata, Canada; *Int'l*, pg. 924

Hawes, Brian, Gen.-Mgr.--Wildon Industries, Inc., Mount Bethel, PA; *Int'l*, pg. 129

Hawes, Howard H., Pres.--ALLTEL Telephone Services Corporation, Little Rock, AR; *U.S. Public*, pg. 56

Hawes, Peter, Pres.--Design Professional Insurance Co., Monterey, CA; *U.S. Public*, pg. 1231

Hawk, Barry E., Partner--Skadden, Arps, Slate, Meagher & Flom LLP, 1050 Brussels, Belgium; *U.S. Private*, pg. 1004

Hawk, Bob, Chief Oper. Officer--Valu-Fare Foods, Inc., Tulsa, OK; *U.S. Private*, pg. 494

Hawk, Jerry, Gen. Mgr.--Tandy Cabinets, Fort Worth, TX; *U.S. Public*, pg. 1560

Hawk, Robert, Pres.--Foodland, Inc., Tulsa, OK; *U.S. Private*, pg. 494

Hawk, Robert, Pres.--WildHawk, Inc., Wisconsin Rapids, WI; *U.S. Public*, pg. 1197

Hawken, Sue, Mng. Dir.--EMAP Elan, London, United Kingdom; *Int'l*, pg. 451

Hawkins, A.J., Gen. Mgr.--Kodak Canada Inc., Vancouver, Canada; *U.S. Public*, pg. 553

Hawkins, Andrew, Chm. & Chief Exec. Officer--GGK London Ltd., London, United Kingdom; *Int'l*, pg. 1335

Hawkins, Bruce, Pres.--Sunbird Boat Co., Inc., Columbia, SC; *U.S. Private*, pg. 478

Hawkins, Dan, Pres. & Chief Exec. Officer--Bank of Goodlettsville, Goodlettsville, TN; *U.S. Public*, pg. 1669

Hawkins, David, Country Mgr.--Standard Chartered Bank (Indonesia), Jakarta, Indonesia; *Int'l*, pg. 1295

Hawkins, Forrest, Chief Oper. Officer--Express 1 Stop, Baton Rouge, LA; *U.S. Private*, pg. 1050

Hawkins, James T., Pres. & Chief Exec. Officer--Weasler Engineering Inc., West Bend, WI; *U.S. Private*, pg. 249

Hawkins, R.W., Pres.--Tifton Aluminum Co., Inc., Tifton, GA; *U.S. Public*, pg. 61

Hawkins, Roger N., Publisher--The Gadsden Times, Gadsden, AL; *U.S. Public*, pg. 1175

Hawkins, Russell B., Pres.--VM Software Division, Reston, VA; *U.S. Public*, pg. 1516

Hawkins, S.M., Mng. Dir.--British United Turkeys Ltd., Chester, United Kingdom; *U.S. Public*, pg. 1091

Hawkins, William, Pres.--Sherwood-Davis & Geck, Saint Louis, MO; *U.S. Public*, pg. 80

Hawkins, William A., Sr. V.P.--Griffin Financial Services, Santa Fe Springs, CA; *U.S. Public*, pg. 29

Hawkins, William A., Pres.--Ethicon Endo-Surgery, Inc., Cincinnati, OH; *U.S. Public*, pg. 928

Hawks, Lawrence F., Pres. & Chief Oper. Officer--Marketing Communications, Lenexa, KS; *U.S. Public*, pg. 794

Hawksworth, Keith, Pres.--Parsons Brinckerhoff International, Pte. Ltd, Singapore, Singapore; *U.S. Private*, pg. 841

Hawley, Norman, Plant Mgr.--Madison Plant, Madison, ME; *U.S. Public*, pg. 444

Hawley, Ron K., Chm. Bd. & Pres.--NationsBank River Valley, Lexington, MO; *U.S. Public*, pg. 1164

Hawley, Ron K., Chm. Bd. & Pres.--NationsBank of River Valley, Richmond, MO; *U.S. Public*, pg. 1164

Haworth, Dave, Mgr.--Smith Specialty Metals, Phoenix, AZ; *U.S. Private*, pg. 1009

Haworth, Gordon, Pres.--Costain Holdings, Inc., Chicago, IL; *Int'l*, pg. 337

Haworth, Gordon, Pres.--Costain Process Inc., Dallas, TX; *Int'l*, pg. 337

Hawthorne, Lawrence, Pres.--Henningson, Durham & Richardson Inc., Omaha, NE; *Int'l*, pg. 207

Hay, Alec J., Pres.--Poly-Bond Inc., Waynesboro, VA; *Int'l*, pg. 415

Hay, John F., V.P.-Govt. Opers.--Westinghouse Government Operations, Washington, DC; *U.S. Public*, pg. 273

Hay, R. Allan, Mng. Dir.--Nederman Canada Ltd., Mississauga, Canada; *Int'l*, pg. 283

Hay, W.A., Mng. Dir.--BMMI Engineering Services, Manama, Bahrain; *U.S. Public*, pg. 1128

Hayakawa, Katsumi, Pres.--Kumagai International USA Corporation, Irving, TX; *Int'l*, pg. 764

Hayakawa, Katsumi, Pres.--KG Land California Corporation, Belmont, CA; *Int'l*, pg. 764

Hayakawa, Riko, Stryper Prod. Dir.--Sony Music Entertainment (Japan) Inc., Tokyo, Japan; *Int'l*, pg. 1281

Hayakawa, Susumu, Pres.--Marsiling Ltd., Kowloon, Hong Kong; *Int'l*, pg. 579

Hayakawa, Y., Pres.--Hino Diesel Trucks (U.S.A.), Inc., Orangeburg, NY; *Int'l*, pg. 620

Hayama, Akira, Gen. Mgr.--Skandia International Insurance Co., Tokyo, Japan; *Int'l*, pg. 1258

Hayashi, Akiya, Gen. Dir.--Mizuno (France) S.A.R.L., Gentilly, France; *Int'l*, pg. 885

Hayashi, Junichi, Gen. Mgr.--Kyodo Advertising Co., Ltd., Sapporo, Japan; *Int'l*, pg. 776

Hayashi, Keiichi, Exec. V.P.--Alyeska Seafoods, Inc., Unalaska, AK; *Int'l*, pg. 845

Hayashi, Keiji, Dir.--Takenaka (U.S.A.) Corporation, New York Office, New York, NY; *Int'l*, pg. 1351

Hayashi, Koji, Pres.--Kajima Engineering and Construction Inc., Pasadena, CA; *Int'l*, pg. 722

Hayashi, Kosaku, Mng. Dir.--Daiwa Finance Australia Limited, Sydney, Australia; *Int'l*, pg. 373

Hayashi, Shinichi, Gen. Mgr.--Labuan Branch, Jalan Merdeka, Malaysia; *Int'l*, pg. 82

Hayashi, Shuhei, Pres.--Japan Ajax Magnethermic Co. Ltd., Tokyo, Japan; *Int'l*, pg. 113

Hayashi, Sumio, Chief Rep.--Daiwa Bank-Shanghai, Shanghai, China; *Int'l*, pg. 374

Hayashi, T., Pres.--Komatsugawa Koki Co., Ltd., Ichikawa, Japan; *Int'l*, pg. 946

Hayashi, Toshihiko, Dir.--Kyodo Advertising Co., Ltd., Nagoya, Japan; *Int'l*, pg. 776

Hayden, D.A., Pres.--Arnold Public Relations, Boston, MA; *U.S. Private*, pg. 84

Hayden, Donald J., V.P. & Gen. Mgr.--Mead Johnson Laboratories, Evansville, IN; *U.S. Public*, pg. 254

Hayden, J. P., III, Pres. & Chief Oper. Officer--M/G Transportation Services, Inc., Amelia, OH; *U.S. Public*, pg. 1111

Hayden, John W., Chm. Bd. & Chief Exec. Officer--C S Crable Sportswear, Inc., Batavia, OH; *U.S. Public*, pg. 1111

Hayek, G. Nicolas, Jr., Mng. Dir.--SMH Italia S.P.A., Rozzano, Italy; *Int'l*, pg. 1161

Hayeno, Stephanie, V.P.--Quencher Div., Farmingdale, NY; *U.S. Public*, pg. 494

Hayes, A. Wallace, Dr., V.P.-Corporate Product Integrety--Corporate Product Integrity, Boston, MA; *U.S. Public*, pg. 744

Hayes, C.D., V.P.-Southern Region--Benjamin Moore & Co., Pell City, AL; *U.S. Private*, pg. 133

Hayes, Christopher, Gen. Mgr.--James Burn International AB, Malmo, Sweden; *U.S. Public*, pg. 1507

Hayes, Daryl, Pres.--Marks & Spencer Canada Inc., Mississauga, Canada; *Int'l*, pg. 843

Hayes, Edward J., Pres.--Equitable Holding Corporation, Secaucus, NJ; *U.S. Public*, pg. 589

Hayes, Everett, Gen. Mgr.--Southwest Chemical/Services, Houston, TX; *U.S. Public*, pg. 781

Hayes, Forrest D., Pres.--The Payne Investment Company, Cleveland, OH; *U.S. Private*, pg. 169

Hayes, Greg, Pres.--Southcorp U.S.A., Inc., Atlanta, GA; *Int'l*, pg. 1287

Hayes, John, Pres. & Chief Exec. Officer--Ellis Communications, Montgomery, AL; *U.S. Private*, pg. 912

Hayes, Judith W., Pres.--Consumers Maine Water, Rockport, ME; *U.S. Public*, pg. 438

Hayes, Kevin, Gen. Mgr.--Corrugated Container Div.-Mishawaka Plant, Mishawaka, IN; *U.S. Public*, pg. 1520

Hayes, Lacey L., III, Pres.--Pneumatic Products Corp., Ocala, FL; *U.S. Public*, pg. 1676

Hayes, Lacy L., III, Pres.--Flair Corporation, Ocala, FL; *U.S. Public*, pg. 1676

Hayes, Lacy L., III, Pres.--Dollinger Corporation, Rich Creek, VA; *U.S. Public*, pg. 1676

Hayes, Michael, Gen. Mgr.--Spirol Ind. Ltd., Windsor, Canada; *U.S. Private*, pg. 1026

Hayes, Peter J., Sr. V.P. & Gen. Mgr.--Chem-Trend Incorporated, Howell, MI; *Int'l*, pg. 235

Hayes, Philip M., Pres.--The Kent Company, Elkhart, IN; *Int'l*, pg. 440

Hayes, R.H., Gen. Mgr.--American Natl. Can Co., Bedford Park, IL; *Int'l*, pg. 1029

Hayes, Roger H., Pres.--Springfield Manufacturing LLC, Clover, SC; *U.S. Private*, pg. 546

Hayes, S., Mng. Dir.--G.E. Lighting (Ireland) Ltd., Dublin, Ireland; *U.S. Public*, pg. 713

Hayes, Samuel B., III, Chm. Bd., Pres. & Chief Exec. Officer--NationsBank of St. Louis, Saint Louis, MO; *U.S. Public*, pg. 1164

Hayes, Stephen L., Pres.--Aerospace Group, Irvine, CA; *U.S. Public*, pg. 1259

Hayes, Steven C., Mgr.--Eclipse Combustion, Inc., Greenville, SC; *U.S. Private*, pg. 360

Hayes, Todd S., Pres.--Interact Accessories, Inc., Hunt Valley, MD; *U.S. Public*, pg. 1369

Hayes, W.C., Pres.--Crane Resistoflex/Industrial, Marion, NC; *U.S. Public*, pg. 457

Hayes, W.M., Pres.--Placer Dome Latin America, Santiago, Chile; *Int'l*, pg. 1060

Hayhow, Joyce, Publr.--ACBJ Business Journals, Inc., Kansas City, MO; *U.S. Private*, pg. 19

Hayko, Leonard J., Chief Oper. Officer & V.P.--Elkins-Sinn, Inc.-Lederle, Saint Davids, PA; *U.S. Public*, pg. 79
Haymaker, George T., Jr., Chm. Bd. & Chief Exec. Officer--Kaiser Aluminum Corporation, Houston, TX; *U.S. Public*, pg. 1062
Haymann, E., Mgr.--Molto AG, Villmergen, Switzerland; *Int'l, pg. 1501*
Haymon, M.R., Chm. Bd.--Tennessee River Pulp & Paper Co., Counce, TN; *U.S. Public*, pg. 1579
Haymon, Monte R., Pres. & Chief Exec. Officer--S.D. Warren Co., Boston, MA; *Int'l*, pg. 1193
Hayner, Pamela, Pres.--The Family Mortgage Banking Co., Inc., Troy, NY; *U.S. Private*, pg. 1106
Haynes, Dave, V.P. & Gen. Mgr.--Sauer-Sundstrand, Freeport, IL; *Int'l*, pg. 1198
Haynes, Herbert L., V.P. & G.M.--United Cities Gas Co., IL/TN/MO Div., Franklin, TN; *U.S. Public*, pg. 146
Haynes, J.D., Mng. Dir.--Senior TIFT Australia Pty Limited, Rockdale, Australia; *Int'l*, pg. 1223
Haynes, Joseph V., Dir.-Champion--Champion Modular Restaurant Company, Clearwater, FL; *U.S. Public*, pg. 343
Haynes, R. G. A., Chm.--Stelrad Div., Henley-on-Thames, United Kingdom; *Int'l*, pg. 267
Haynes, R.G.A., Chief Oper. Officer--Stelrad Group Limited, Henley-on-Thames, United Kingdom; *Int'l*, pg. 267
Haynes, Rollin F., V.P.--Dead River Properties, South Portland, ME; *U.S. Private*, pg. 318
Haynes, William E., Pres. & Chief Exec. Officer--Lyondell-Citgo Refining Company, Ltd., Houston, TX; *U.S. Public*, pg. 1022
Hays, David, Pres.--Institutional Services, Inc., Fort Worth, TX; *U.S. Public*, pg. 1482
Hays, Dennis G., Branch Mgr.--Circle International, Vandalia, OH; *U.S. Public*, pg. 371
Hays, Jack, Branch Mgr.--RHG Mobile, Mobile, AL; *Int'l*, pg. 1151
Hays, Robert A., Chief Oper. Officer--Capitol Concrete Division, Jacksonville, FL; *U.S. Public*, pg. 656
Haysman, Paul, Chief Oper. Officer--Philmac Pty Limited, Clayton, Australia; *Int'l*, pg. 555
Hayt, John T., Chief Exec. Officer--EquiCredit Corporation, Jacksonville, FL; *U.S. Public*, pg. 1162
Hayter, Fred W., Pres.--Tri-State Concrete Products Co., Inc., Kingsport, TN; *Int'l*, pg. 843
Hayter, Freddie W., Gen. Mgr.--Bristol Concrete Prods. Corp., Bristol, VA; *Int'l*, pg. 843
Hayutin, Murray P., Pres.--Hilb, Rogal and Hamilton Company of Denver, Denver, CO; *U.S. Public*, pg. 827
Hayward, Allen, Co-Pres.--Kidd Creek Division, Timmins, Canada; *Int'l*, pg. 433
Hayward, Anna, Sls. Mgr.--Utell International-New Zealand, Auckland, New Zealand; *Int'l*, pg. 1098
Hayward, Charles W., Pres. & Chief Oper. Officer--Chicago Union Station Company, Chicago, IL; *U.S. Private*, pg. 69
Hayward, David, V.P.--Sierracin/Trans Tech, Sylmar, CA; *U.S. Private*, pg. 999
Hayward, J., Mng. Dir.--Laporte Hygiene, Cheadle, United Kingdom; *Int'l*, pg. 802
Hayward, John C., Pres.--Michael Baker, Jr., Inc., Beaver, PA; *U.S. Public*, pg. 168
Hayward, Kenneth, Mng. Dir.--CSA, Ltd., Rochester, United Kingdom; *U.S. Public*, pg. 424
Hayward, Les, Mng. Dir.--ISS Contract Clean Midlands Ltd., Milton Keynes, United Kingdom; *Int'l*, pg. 657
Hayward, P.M., Chief Oper. Officer--Victoria Joinery Ltd., London, United Kingdom; *Int'l*, pg. 796
Hayward, Rich, Plant Mgr.--Crestar Foods Inc., Washington Court House, OH; *U.S. Public*, pg. 805
Hayward, Ross, Gen. Mgr. & Mgr.-Plant Opers.--H.S.C. Canada Inc., Burlington, Canada; *U.S. Private*, pg. 505
Hayward, S.P., Mgr.--Nalco Chemicals India Limited, Calcutta, India; *U.S. Public*, pg. 1150
Haywood, Don, Chief Oper. Officer--Comet Rice of California, Maxwell, CA; *U.S. Public*, pg. 591
Haywood, John, Dir.-Natl. Parts Opers.--Whirlpool Corp., La Porte Div., La Porte, IN; *U.S. Public*, pg. 1765
Haywood, Lee, Pres. & Gen. Mgr.--First American Title Insurance Agency of Mohave, Inc., Kingman, AZ; *U.S. Public*, pg. 626
Haywood, Robert, Plant Mgr.--Applied Coatings, Wayne, NJ; *U.S. Private*, pg. 130
Hazan, Paul, Mgr.--Bank Leumi Le-Israel (Switzerland), Geneva, Switzerland; *Int'l*, pg. 150
Hazelbaker, Steven R., Chief Fin. Officer--Meridian Security Insurance Company, Indianapolis, IN; *U.S. Public*, pg. 1095
Hazelhorst, Jan, Chief Exec. Officer--Al-Techniek Benelux B.V., Almere, Netherlands; *Int'l*, pg. 710
Hazell, Colin, Mgr.--GATX Finance (UK) Ltd., Kingston upon Thames, United Kingdom; *U.S. Public*, pg. 691
Hazelwood, C.T., Pres.--Northwood Pulp & Timber Ltd., Prince George, Canada; *Int'l*, pg. 434
Hazelwood, C.T., Pres.--Northwood Forest Industries, Ltd., Prince George, Canada; *U.S. Public*, pg. 1076
Hazelwood, C.T., Pres.--Northwood Pulp & Timber Ltd., Prince George, Canada; *U.S. Public*, pg. 1076
Hazelwood, Gary, Gen. Mgr.--Steel Form Div., New Braunfels, TX; *U.S. Private*, pg. 932
Hazen, Richard C., Pres.--Green Bay Supply Co., Inc., Hatfield, PA; *U.S. Public*, pg. 307
Hazeyama, Nobuhiro, Chief Rep.--Daiwa Bank-Beijing, Beijing, China; *Int'l*, pg. 373
Head, Don, Mgr.--Otis International, Ltd., Abu Dhabi, United Arab Emirates; *U.S. Public*, pg. 777
Head, J. Michael, Pres.--Mark Risk Management, Inc., Kansas City, MO; *U.S. Public*, pg. 1046
Head, J. Michael, Pres.--Mark VII Transportation Solutions, Inc., Kansas City, MO; *U.S. Public*, pg. 1046
Head, Mike, Mng. Dir.--Johnson & Johnson Limited, Maidenhead, United Kingdom; *U.S. Public*, pg. 930
Headey, Blake, Plant Mgr.--AlliedSignal Aerospace Canada, Electronic Systems, Cornwall, Canada; *U.S. Public*, pg. 54
Heagle, Jim, Pres.--Calgon Corporation, Pittsburgh, PA; *Int'l, pg. 455*
Heald, Francis J., Pres.--Green Mountain Propane Gas Co., Burlington, VT; *U.S. Public*, pg. 761
Healey, J., Chief Oper. Officer--Mosler Electronic Systems Div., Wayne, NJ; *U.S. Private*, pg. 763
Healey, Matthew, Chm. & Chief Exec. Officer--Execution Services Incorporated, New York, NY; *Int'l*, pg. 675
Healy, Ben, Pres.--Raytheon Infrastructure Incorporated, New York, NY; *U.S. Public*, pg. 1366
Healy, David, Mng. Dir.--ISS Contract Cleaners Ltd., Dublin, Ireland; *Int'l*, pg. 657
Healy, Declan, Mng. Dir.--Bradstock Insurance Brokers Limited, Dublin, Ireland; *Int'l*, pg. 210
Healy, Gail, Publr.--Country America Magazine, Des Moines, IA; *U.S. Public*, pg. 1094
Healy, J., Pres.--R & C Inc., Montvale, NJ; *Int'l*, pg. 1090
Healy, James J., V.P.--Jacobs International Limited, Inc., Dublin, Ireland; *U.S. Public*, pg. 922
Healy, John, Gen. Mgr.--Pro Shop (Fairfield, NJ), Fairfield, NJ; *U.S. Public*, pg. 861
Healy, John T., V.P.--ABC Cable & International Broadcast, Inc., New York, NY; *U.S. Public*, pg. 512
Healy, Mary, Mgr.--Sandvik Ireland Limited, Dublin, Ireland; *Int'l*, pg. 1186
Healy, Michael, Pres. & Chief Exec. Officer--Sordoni Skanska Construction Co., Parsippany, NJ; *Int'l*, pg. 1261
Healy, Ray, Mgr.-Division--Gould's Paper House, Inc., Tampa, FL; *U.S. Private*, pg. 467
Healy, Rick, Branch Mgr.--Nikon Inc., Torrance, CA; *Int'l*, pg. 931
Healy, Stephen D., Pres.--Cochrane Furniture Co., Inc., Lincolnton, NC; *U.S. Public*, pg. 352
Healy, Thomas J., Pres.--Chemgraphics Systems, Inc., Secaucus, NJ; *U.S. Public*, pg. 338
Hean, Scott B., Mng. Dir.--Corporate & Institutional Financial Services - Vancouver, Vancouver, Canada; *Int'l*, pg. 153
Heard, Billy, Plant Mgr.--Fostercoat Div., Doraville, GA; *U.S. Public*, pg. 676
Heard, Billy, Plant Mgr.--L.B. Foster Company-Doraville Yard/Coated Pipe, Norcross, GA; *U.S. Public*, pg. 676
Heard, Frank, Gen. Mgr.--ITW Construction Products, Scarborough, Canada; *U.S. Public*, pg. 868
Heard, Grayson, Sr. V.P.-Mining--Consolidation Coal Co.-Mid-Continent Region, Saint Louis, MO; *U.S. Public*, pg. 531
Heard, Larry, Gen. Mgr.--Murray Canada, Brampton, Canada; *Int'l*, pg. 1397
Heard, William T., Pres.--Bill Heard Oldsmobile Company, Columbus, GA; *U.S. Private*, pg. 515
Hearn, D., Mng. Dir.--Bowthorpe (NZ) Limited, Christchurch, New Zealand; *Int'l*, pg. 208
Hearn, Laurence M., Gen. Mgr. & Dir.--ITW Switches-Europe, Portsmouth, United Kingdom; *U.S. Public*, pg. 869
Hearne, William A., Sr., Landman--Hunt Oil Lafayette Land Office, Lafayette, LA; *U.S. Private*, pg. 548
Hearnshaw, David, Mng. Dir.--Preformed Line Products(Great Britain) Ltd., Andover, United Kingdom; *U.S. Public*, pg. 1321
Hearshman, W.R., Pres.--ResourceNet International, Shawnee Mission, KS; *U.S. Public*, pg. 903
Hearst, George R., Jr., V.P.-Grp. Head--Hearst Real Estate Division, Paso Robles, CA; *U.S. Private*, pg. 518
Hearst, Randolph A., Pres.--San Francisco Examiner, San Francisco, CA; *U.S. Private*, pg. 518
Heath, E., Gen. Mgr.--Wood Products Div., New York, NY; *U.S. Public*, pg. 903
Heath, Evans A., V.P. & Gen. Mgr.--Nevamar Division, Odenton, MD; *U.S. Public*, pg. 903
Heath, Frank, Pres.--Houghton Canada Inc., Toronto, Canada; *U.S. Private*, pg. 541
Heath, James A., Pres.--Energy Investors Management, Inc., Boston, MA; *U.S. Private*, pg. 589
Heath, Raymond J., Pres.--Riverside/Bi-Lo Division, Du Bois, PA; *U.S. Public*, pg. 1270
Heath, Richard W., Pres.--JLH Advertising, Inc., Dallas, TX; *U.S. Public*, pg. 198
Heatley, J.M., Gen. Mgr.--Flexibox Inc., Houston, TX; *Int'l*, pg. 426
Heavenridge, David L., Pres.--Rincon Securities, Inc., Richmond, VA; *U.S. Public*, pg. 516
Heavisides, Henry, Mng. Dir.--Lands' End Direct Merchants UK Limited, Rutland, United Kingdom; *U.S. Public*, pg. 978
Hebbelinck, D., Mgr.--Kodak S.A., Renens, Switzerland; *U.S. Public*, pg. 554
Hebble, Jeffrey, Mng. Dir.--Stamford Food Industries Sdn. Berhad, Petaling Jaya, Malaysia; *U.S. Public*, pg. 447
Heber, Jim, Chief Oper. Officer--Design Systems Inc., Bellevue, WA; *U.S. Public*, pg. 606
Hebert, Lawrence I., Pres.--Allbritton News Bureau, Inc., Washington, DC; *U.S. Private*, pg. 854
Hebert, Michel, Mng. Dir.--Jump, Lyon, France; *Int'l*, pg. 116
Hebert, Roger, V.P.-Admin.--Canadian Forest Products Ltd., Vancouver, Canada; *Int'l*, pg. 260
Hebiguchi, Hirotaka, Gen. Mgr.--Bank of Tokyo-Mitsubishi Ltd., Zurich Representative Office, Zurich, Switzerland; *Int'l*, pg. 158
Hebling, Robert, Pres.--Surgitek, Racine, WI; *U.S. Public*, pg. 253
Hechler, Robert, Pres. & Chief Exec. Officer--Waddell & Reed, Inc., Shawnee Mission, KS; *U.S. Public*, pg. 1623
Hechler, Robert L., Pres.--Waddell & Reed Services Co., Kansas City, MO; *U.S. Public*, pg. 1623
Hecht, William F., Pres.--Realty Co. of Pennsylvania, Allentown, PA; *U.S. Public*, pg. 1244
Hecht, William F., Pres.--CEP Group, Inc., Allentown, PA; *U.S. Public*, pg. 1244
Hecht, William F., Chm. Bd. & Chief Exec. Officer--Power Markets Development Company, Allentown, PA; *U.S. Public*, pg. 1244
Heck, Helmut, Gen. Mgr.--Amerford France S.A., Paris, France; *Int'l*, pg. 1388
Heck, J.A., Pres.--ATT Network Sistems International, B.V., Hilversum, Netherlands; *Int'l*, pg. 1373
Heck, Warren, Pres.--Insurance Company of Greater New York, New York, NY; *U.S. Private*, pg. 476
Heckel, Anton, Pres.--Georg Fischer S.A., Madrid, Spain; *Int'l*, pg. 490
Heckel, Vincent, Mng. Dir.--Bureau Rhone-Poulenc SA, Budapest, Hungary; *Int'l*, pg. 1112
Heckler, Robert D., Chm. Bd.--Sunwest Bank of Las Cruces, N.A., Las Cruces, NM; *U.S. Public*, pg. 1165
Heckman, Gregory A., Gen. Mgr.--ConAgra Feed Ingredient Merchandising Company, Omaha, NE; *U.S. Public*, pg. 428
Heckmann, Dick, Pres. & Chief Exec. Officer--U.S. Filter, Palm Desert, CA; *U.S. Public*, pg. 61
Heckmann, Dr. Nicolas, Chief Oper. Officer--Schott Glass Technologies, Inc., Duryea, PA; *Int'l*, pg. 1523
Hecox, Kurt, Gen. Mgr.--Nicolet Biomedical, Madison, WI; *U.S. Public*, pg. 1593
Hecquet, J.L., Chief Oper. Officer--Binks International, France, Roissy-en-Brie, France; *U.S. Public*, pg. 229
Hector, P. Holcomb, V.P. & Gen. Mgr.--Diamondhead Div., Diamondhead, MS; *U.S. Private*, pg. 895
Hedbecker, Robert, Pres.--Gotaverken Energy Systems Inc., Charlotte, NC; *Int'l*, pg. 770
Hedberg, Christer, Mng. Dir.--Telefonaktiebolaget LM Ericsson Iraq Branch, Baghdad, Iraq; *Int'l*, pg. 1370
Hedberg, Kai, Chief Oper. Officer--Enso Danmark A/S, Copenhagen, Denmark; *Int'l*, pg. 457
Hedblom, O.G., Gen. Mgr.--J.I. Case Sweden AB, Malmo, Sweden; *U.S. Public*, pg. 1580
Heddema, Ton, Mng. Dir.--Euroconsult BV, Arnhem, Netherlands; *Int'l*, pg. 606
Heddema, Ton, Mng. Dir.--ILIS International Land Information Services CV, Arnhem, Netherlands; *Int'l*, pg. 606
Hedemark, E. James, Pres.--Continental Auxiliary Company Trustee, Orange, CA; *U.S. Public*, pg. 181
Heden, Hakan, Chief Oper. Officer--Alfa-Laval Iran Co., Tehran, Iran; *Int'l*, pg. 1380
Hedenstedt, Jan, Mgr.--Siluett Nordia AB, Kristinehamn, Sweden; *Int'l*, pg. 421
Hedenstrom, Anders, Mng. Dir.--S-E-Banken Fonder AB, Stockholm, Sweden; *Int'l*, pg. 1259
Hederstrom, Stefan, Chief Oper. Officer--Electrolux S.A., Sao Paulo, Brazil; *Int'l*, pg. 441
Hedfors, Bo, Pres.--Ericsson North America, Inc., Richardson, TX; *Int'l*, pg. 1364
Hedges, Andrew, Pres.--Reckitt & Colman Canada Inc., Toronto, Canada; *Int'l*, pg. 1090
Hedges, Arthur J., Jr., V.P.--IBM Real Estate & Construction Div., White Plains, NY; *U.S. Public*, pg. 896
Hedges, Peter, Pres.--Taylor Woodrow of California Inc., San Francisco, CA; *Int'l*, pg. 1359
Hedges, Robbin, Sr. V.P.--McDonald's France SA, Guayancourt, France; *U.S. Public*, pg. 1069
Hedley, R.J.G., Mng. Dir.--Alcan Chemicals Europe, Gerrards Cross, United Kingdom; *Int'l*, pg. 51
Hedlund, Hans, Chief Oper. Officer--Scania Argentina S.A., San Miguel de Tucuman, Argentina; *Int'l*, pg. 687
Hedlund, Larry, Gen. Mgr.--Capstone Electronics Div., Tustin, CA; *U.S. Public*, pg. 134
Hedlund, Lars, Chief Oper. Officer--AB Axel Christiernsson, Nol, Sweden; *Int'l*, pg. 708
Hedlund, Thomas, Pres.--Ballast Nord AB, Umea, Sweden; *Int'l*, pg. 899
Hedman, Hans, Pres.--Karlskronavarvet AB, Karlskrona, Sweden; *Int'l*, pg. 277
Hedman, Stig, Mng. Dir.--UPM-Kymmene Papir A/S, Hellerup, Denmark; *Int'l*, pg. 1430
Hedri, Hassine, Gen. Mgr.--CPC Maghreb S.A., Casablanca, Morocco; *U.S. Public*, pg. 225
Hedstrom, Bo S., Chm. Bd.--Sodra Skogagarna, Vaxjo, Sweden; *Int'l*, pg. 1275
Hedvold, Ralf, Mng. Dir.--Berendsen Components AB, Stockholm, Sweden; *Int'l*, pg. 1284
Hee, Lee Yeon, Pres.--The Panther Car Co., Ltd., Harlow, United Kingdom; *Int'l*, pg. 1292
Hee, Song Soon, Pres.--Burgmann Malaysia SDN BHD, Petaling Jaya, Malaysia; *Int'l*, pg. 233
Heel, Doug, Mgr.-Opers.--Triumph Machine Co., Hackettstown, NJ; *U.S. Public*, pg. 35
Heenan, D.A., Pres. & Chief Exec. Officer--Theo. H. Davies & Co., Ltd, Honolulu, HI; *Int'l*, pg. 704
Heenpok, Michael Lim, Chief Oper. Officer--UMW Toyota Motor Sdn. Bhn., Petaling Jaya, Malaysia; *Int'l*, pg. 1414
Heer, Dr. Rudolph, V.P.--Henkel Corporation Textile Chemicals, Charlotte, NC; *Int'l*, pg. 610
Heeremans, C.R., Pres.--Monsanto Overseas, S.A., Panama, Panama; *U.S. Public*, pg. 1126
Heese, Steven, Mgr.--Alphabet European Sales Office, Eschborn, Germany; *U.S. Private*, pg. 1045
Heeter, William B., Pres. & Chief Oper. Officer--The Paper Factory of Wisconsin, Inc., Appleton, WI; *U.S. Public*, pg. 742
Heffels, G.H., Chief Oper. Officer--Robbe Radiatoren B.V., Gorinchem, Netherlands; *Int'l*, pg. 267
Heffer, John, Pres. & Chief Exec. Officer--Republic Factors Corp., New York, NY; *U.S. Public*, pg. 1380
Hefferman, Liam, Pres.--Timar (Culturas em Agua), Lda., Olhao, Portugal; *Int'l*, pg. 1390
Heffernan, Gerard E., Pres.--Stratton Monthly Dividend Shares, Inc., Plymouth Meeting, PA; *U.S. Private*, pg. 1046
Heffernan, J.J., Gen. Mgr.--Clarendon Imports Inc., North York, Canada; *Int'l*, pg. 1130
Heffernan, John, Gen. Mgr.--Litton Instruments & Life Support, Davenport, IA; *U.S. Public*, pg. 1003
Heffernan, Thomas, Mgr.--EG & G Rotron Industrial Division, Saugerties, NY; *U.S. Public*, pg. 543

Heffner, Lowell S., V.P. & Gen. Mgr.--Pipe Fabricating & Supply Company, Woods Cross, UT; *U.S. Private*, pg. 867
Heffron, Bob, V.P. & Gen. Mgr.--Grayson Controls Div., Long Beach, CA; *Int'l*, pg. 1243
Heffron, Thomas L., Pres.--Raytech Industries Division, Middletown, CT; *U.S. Private*, pg. 683
Heflebower, Jeffrey N., Pres. & Chief Exec. Officer--The Peoples Bank of Maryland, Denton, MD; *U.S. Public*, pg. 1089
Heflin, Hugh, Pres. & Chief Oper. Officer--Belwith International Div., City of Industry, CA; *Int'l*, pg. 473
Hefner, James R., III, V.P. & Gen. Mgr.--WTAE-TV, Pittsburgh, PA; *U.S. Private*, pg. 516
Hefner, Linda, Pres.--L'eggs Products, Inc., Winston Salem, NC; *U.S. Public*, pg. 1434
Heft, Kathy, Gen. Mgr.--Frank Paxton Lumber Company, Chicago, IL; *U.S. Private*, pg. 585
Hefter, Harry O., Chm. Bd. & Pres.--HOH Engineers, Inc., Chicago, IL; *U.S. Private*, pg. 492
Hefti, Dr. Walter, Chm.--Sais, Zurich, Switzerland; *Int'l*, pg. 1438
Hefti, Hans, Mng. Dir.--Harrington International Insurance Ltd., Hamilton, Bermuda; *Int'l*, pg. 1333
Hegarty, Adrian, Dir.--Premier Banking, Dublin, Ireland; *Int'l*, pg. 152
Hegarty, Kieran, Chief Oper. Officer--Ludlow-Saylor Inc., Warrenton, MO; *Int'l*, pg. 1066
Hegbrant, Jorgen, Mng. Dir.--Park Dialys AB, Lund, Sweden; *Int'l*, pg. 667
Hegde, A.R., Pres.--Astra-IDL Ltd., Bangalore, India; *Int'l*, pg. 93
Hege, Rick, V.P.-Mktg.--J.R. Technical, Lake Zurich, IL; *U.S. Private*, pg. 85
Hegedus, Tony, Mng. Dir.--Interbath-Australia, Pty. Ltd., Mulgrave, Australia; *U.S. Private*, pg. 566
Hegel, Fernando, Gen. Mgr.--Wackenhut de Guatemala, S.A., Guatemala, Guatemala; *U.S. Public*, pg. 1731
Hegel, Tom, V.P. & Gen. Mgr.--Kelso-Burnett Zion Branch, Zion, IL; *U.S. Private*, pg. 613
Hegeler, U., Mgr.--Bowthorpe GmbH, Pinneberg, Germany; *Int'l*, pg. 208
Heger, Otto, Mng. Dir.--Dresdner (S.E. Asia) Ltd., Singapore, Singapore; *Int'l*, pg. 420
Heggestad, David, Pres.--Swift & Co., Greeley, CO; *U.S. Public*, pg. 426
Hegglin, Hans Peter, Gen. Mgr.--Mesotex S.A., Lachen, Switzerland; *Int'l*, pg. 497
Heglund, Forrest E., Chm. Bd. & Chief Exec. Officer--Enron Oil & Gas Co., Houston, TX; *U.S. Public*, pg. 584
Hegna, Gary, Pres.--Fujitsu Networks Industries, Stamford, CT; *Int'l*, pg. 529
Hegstrom, Robert, Chief Oper. Officer--Green Tree Agency, Inc., Saint Paul, MN; *U.S. Public*, pg. 763
Hegstrom, Robert A., Chief Oper. Officer--Green Tree Life Insurance Co., Saint Paul, MN; *U.S. Public*, pg. 763
Hegyi, Mary E., V.P.--Latin America Operation, Plano, TX; *U.S. Public*, pg. 1516
Hehir, Peter, Chm.--Countrywide Porter/Novelli, Banbury, United Kingdom; *U.S. Public*, pg. 1225
Hehl, Mike, Pres.--Nelco Products Pte. Ltd., Jurong, Singapore; *U.S. Public*, pg. 1258
Heide, Robert, Exec. V.P.--Vitt Media International, Inc. - Los Angeles, Los Angeles, CA; *U.S. Private*, pg. 1142
Heide, Y.B., Chief Oper. Officer--Elf Aquitaine Norge A/S, Stavanger, Norway; *Int'l*, pg. 445
Heidgen, J., Gen. Mgr.--Ford Versicherungs-Vermittlungs GmbH, Cologne, Germany; *U.S. Public*, pg. 666
Heidman, T., Mng. Dir.--Gall & Gall, Hoofddorp, Netherlands; *Int'l*, pg. 749
Heidsieck, Horst, Dr., Chief Exec. Officer--Balzers, Balzers, Switzerland; *Int'l*, pg. 997
Heidt, Larry P., Pres.--Nabors Drilling & Energy Services UK, Ltd., Aberdeen, United Kingdom; *U.S. Public*, pg. 1149
Heigl, Gerhard, Gen. Mgr.--Deutsche Bank AG (Bangkok), Bangkok, Thailand; *Int'l*, pg. 404
Heikkila, Matti, Chief Oper. Officer--Ahlstrom Machinery Ecomachinery, Helsinki, Finland; *Int'l*, pg. 33
Heikkila, Tapio, Mgr.-Private Mobile Radio--Nokia Telecommunications, Espoo, Finland; *Int'l*, pg. 952
Heikkonen, Mikko, Mgr.-Networks & Access Systems--Nokia Telecommunications, Espoo, Finland; *Int'l*, pg. 952
Heikkonen, Mikko, Pres.--Nokia Network and Access Systems, Espoo, Finland; *Int'l*, pg. 953
Heikonen, Pekka, Pres.--Detec International Oy, Lahti, Finland; *Int'l*, pg. 1352
Heil, Michael, Pres.--Consumer Display Products Co., Park Ridge, NJ; *Int'l*, pg. 1281
Heil, Michael J., Pres. & Gen. Mgr.-Los Angeles Cellular Telephone Co., L.A.--LIN Cellular Group, Kirkland, WA; *U.S. Public*, pg. 11
Heil, Thomas A., Gen. Mgr.--Reclamation Div. (Louisville), Louisville, KY; *Int'l*, pg. 1271
Heil, William H., Chm. & Chief Exec. Officer--AllEnergy Marketing Company, L.L.C., Waltham, MA; *U.S. Public*, pg. 549
Heiliger, Klaus A., Mng. Dir.--Bankgesellschaft Berlin International S.A., Luxembourg, Luxembourg; *Int'l*, pg. 159
Heilman, Gerald W., Pres. & Gen. Mgr.--TV Alabama, Inc., Birmingham, AL; *U.S. Private*, pg. 854
Heilman, Rick, Gen. Mgr.--WGBR, Goldsboro, NC; *U.S. Private*, pg. 297
Heim, Donald J., Chief Oper. Officer--Brandywood Estates, Inc., Washington, DC; *U.S. Public*, pg. 1741
Heim, Donald J., Chief Oper. Officer--Shenandoah Gas Co., Winchester, VA; *U.S. Public*, pg. 1741
Heim, Knut, Chief Oper. Officer--K/S Kaldnes de Groot A/S, Tonsberg, Norway; *Int'l*, pg. 965
Heim, Lee, District Mgr.--Circle Freight International USA, Cleveland, OH; *U.S. Public*, pg. 371
Heiman, Donald M., Pres.--Reactor Experiments, Inc., Sunnyvale, CA; *U.S. Public*, pg. 1594
Heiman, Richard I., Pres.--Campbell Hausfeld Division of Scott Fetzer, Harrison, OH; *U.S. Public*, pg. 217
Heimann, Juergen, District Sls. Mgr.--Medtronic GmbH, Hamburg, Germany; *U.S. Public*, pg. 1083
Heimann, Klaus-Peter, Chief Oper. Officer--Osram do Brasil Companhia de Lampadas Eletricas S.A., Osasco, Brazil; *Int'l*, pg. 1244
Heimbuch, Babette, Chief Exec. Officer--Seaside Financial Corporation, Santa Monica, CA; *U.S. Public*, pg. 646
Heimers, Edward F., Sr. V.P.-Natl. Bus. Opers. Rx.--Sandoz Pharmaceuticals Corp., East Hanover, NJ; *Int'l*, pg. 974
Heimes, Peter T., Mng. Dir.--Super RTL, Cologne, Germany; *Int'l*, pg. 562
Heimpel, Grant J., Pres.--Zehrmart Inc., Cambridge, Canada; *Int'l*, pg. 1495
Hein, Larry, Pres.--FMC-Smith Meter Co., Erie, PA; *U.S. Public*, pg. 605
Hein, R.J., Mng. Dir.--P&O Australia Ltd., Sydney, Australia; *Int'l*, pg. 1035
Hein, Raymond, Sir, Chm.--Union Commercial Bank S.A., Antananarivo, Madagascar; *Int'l*, pg. 1294
Heine-Geldern, Thomas, Chief Oper. Officer--K & P Leykam Austria, Gratkorn, Austria; *Int'l*, pg. 757
Heine, Chuck, Pres.--Dana Asia/Pacific, Hong Kong, Hong Kong; *U.S. Public*, pg. 480
Heine, Spencer H., Acting Pres.--The Signature Group, Schaumburg, IL; *U.S. Private*, pg. 758
Heinemann, Scott, Pres.--Conway Import Co. Inc., Elmsford, NY; *U.S. Private*, pg. 272
Heinen, Richard H., Gen. Mgr.--Western Ag-Minerals Company (Mine Office), Carlsbad, NM; *U.S. Public*, pg. 856
Heiner, Dennis G., Pres.--Kwikset Corporation, Irvine, CA; *U.S. Public*, pg. 233
Heines, Martine, Gen. Mgr.--Amway France, Antony, France; *U.S. Private*, pg. 69
Heines, Martine, Gen. Mgr.--Amway Italia s.r.l., Milan, Italy; *U.S. Private*, pg. 70
Heinig, Lutz, Mng. Dir.--Datapoint Deutschland GmbH, Neu-Isenburg, Germany; *Int'l*, pg. 384
Heinle, Charles, Pres.--Heinle & Heinle Publishers, Inc., Boston, MA; *U.S. Public*, pg. 1600
Heinrich, John P., Pres.--Oncomembrane, Inc., Seattle, WA; *Int'l*, pg. 1013
Heinrich, John P., Pres.--Otsuka Electronics (U.S.A.) Inc., Fort Collins, CO; *Int'l*, pg. 1013
Heinrichs, Arlene, Mng. Dir.--BHP Steel SE Asia Pte Ltd., Singapore, Singapore; *Int'l*, pg. 227
Heins, John, Pres. & Chief Exec. Officer--Gruner + Jahr USA Publishing, Inc., New York, NY; *Int'l*, pg. 190
Heinsch, M., Gen. Mgr.--Axson GmbH, Dietzenbach, Germany; *Int'l*, pg. 103
Heinson, R. Conrad, Pres.--Allied Tire Co., Omaha, NE; *U.S. Private*, pg. 39
Heinz, Terry J., Pres.--Huntco Steel Co., Springfield, MO; *U.S. Public*, pg. 849
Heinzelman, Charles, Pres.--Jamestown Metal Products, Inc., Jamestown, NY; *U.S. Private*, pg. 169
Heiroth, Claes U., Chief Oper. Officer--AB Stockholms-Brandskyddskonsulenter, Stockholm, Sweden; *Int'l*, pg. 35
Heischmann, Wilhelm, Mng. Dir.--Dresdnerbank Asset Management S.A., Senningerberg, Luxembourg; *Int'l*, pg. 420
Heise, Hans, Pres.--Pall Biomedizin GmbH, Dreieichenhain, Germany; *U.S. Public*, pg. 1254
Heiskanen, Risto, Mng. Dir.--Raisio Polska Foods Sp. z.o.o., Warsaw, Poland; *Int'l*, pg. 1085
Heiskanen, Risto T., Mng. Dir.--Oy McCormick Ab, Helsinki, Finland; *U.S. Public*, pg. 1067
Heiss, Harry, Sr. Mng. Dir.--Scholl Oesterreich GmbH, Vienna, Austria; *Int'l*, pg. 1210
Heiss, R.S., Gen. Mgr.--Albright & Wilson GmbH (Germany), Neu-Isenburg, Germany; *Int'l*, pg. 49
Heissel, Mgr.-Sls.--Uddeholm Corporation, Itasca, IL; *Int'l*, pg. 1471
Heitmann, William, Pres.--Bell Atlantic Funding Company, New York, NY; *U.S. Public*, pg. 202
Heitner, Andrew, Dir.--Banta Integrated Media, Cambridge, MA; *U.S. Public*, pg. 188
Heitsch, J., Pres.--Atlantic Scientific Corporation, Melbourne, FL; *Int'l*, pg. 208
Heitt, James D., Pres.--Iowa Precision Industries, Cedar Rapids, IA; *U.S. Public*, pg. 1100
Heitt, James D., V.P.--Lockformer Company, Lisle, IL; *U.S. Public*, pg. 1100
Heitzler, Colleen, Gen. Mgr.--Country Sampler Store, Saint Charles, IL; *U.S. Private*, pg. 963
Heitzman, Michael, Mgr.-Sls.--Timber Products Co., Germantown, TN; *U.S. Private*, pg. 1086
Hejmelaeus, Hannu, Chief Oper. Officer--Tampere EPS Plant, Tampere, Finland; *Int'l*, pg. 863
Helaby, Sir Alan, Chm. Bd.--P&O (New Zealand) Ltd., Wellington, New Zealand; *Int'l*, pg. 1035
Helander, Mikko, Chief Oper. Officer--Valmet Corporation Calenders, Jarvenpaa, Finland; *Int'l*, pg. 1448
Helander, Veh-Pekka, Chief Oper. Officer--Neste Yrityspalvelu Oy, Espoo, Finland; *Int'l*, pg. 913
Helbert, Jeff, Plant Superintendant--General Shale Products Corp., Fairdale, KY; *Int'l*, pg. 844
Held, A. Peter, Pres.--Cooper Power Tools Division, Lexington, SC; *U.S. Public*, pg. 444
Held, Robert, Pres.--Seely Equipment & Supply Co., Inc., Wall, NJ; *U.S. Private*, pg. 755
Held, Tomas, Chief Oper. Officer--BHF-Bank Representative Office, Bogota, Colombia; *Int'l*, pg. 120
Helderman, Frank, Jr., Publisher--TSP Newspapers, Inc., Florence, AL; *U.S. Public*, pg. 1175
Heldman, K.A., Mng. Dir.--Euryza International AG, Zug, Switzerland; *Int'l*, pg. 244
Heldman, Lou, Pres. & Publr.--Nittany Printing & Publishing Co., State College, PA; *U.S. Public*, pg. 964
Heldman, Lou, Publisher--Centre Daily Times, Inc., State College, PA; *U.S. Public*, pg. 964
Heldman, Roger, Mgr.--Fechheimer Bros. Co., Cincinnati, OH; *U.S. Public*, pg. 217
Heldrich, John, Pres. & Chief Exec. Officer--Swift Textiles, Inc., Atlanta, GA; *Int'l*, pg. 415
Heldring, Ernst M., V.P. & Branch Mgr.--Bank of Montreal - Korea, Seoul, Korea; *Int'l*, pg. 155
Helenbrook, George H., Chief Oper. Officer--Regency Thermographers of Buffalo, Inc., Buffalo, NY; *U.S. Public*, pg. 89
Helf, Peter J., Chief Oper. Officer & Exec. V.P.--Marcus Restaurants Inc., Milwaukee, WI; *U.S. Public*, pg. 1044
Helgesen, Oscar, Dir.--Monsanto Norge A/S, Hovik, Norway; *U.S. Public*, pg. 1126
Helgeson, Donald P., Pres.--Gold'n Plump Poultry, Saint Cloud, MN; *U.S. Private*, pg. 577
Helgeson, Donald P., Pres.--Gold'n Plump Poultry, Inc., Arcadia, WI; *U.S. Private*, pg. 577
Helgeson, Ulf, Mng. Dir.--ScanDust AB, Landskrona, Sweden; *Int'l*, pg. 1157
Helinski, Leo, Pres. & Chief Exec. Officer--El Dorado Chemical, Oklahoma City, OK; *U.S. Public*, pg. 970
Hell, Manfred, Pres.--Jack Wolfskin, Idstein, Germany; *U.S. Public*, pg. 933
Hellberg, Bengt, Pres.--Valmet Svenska AB, Eskilstuna, Sweden; *Int'l*, pg. 1449
Heller, Arnold, Gen. Mgr.--Freightliner Enterprise Corp., Bluefield, VA; *Int'l*, pg. 368
Heller, Chester M., Sr., Pres.--Manufacturing Div., Philadelphia, PA; *U.S. Private*, pg. 706
Heller, Chester M., Sr., Pres.--Piping Design Div., Philadelphia, PA; *U.S. Private*, pg. 706
Heller, Daniel J., Pres.--Websource, New York, NY; *U.S. Public*, pg. 1671
Heller, Darl H., Chm. Bd.--The Russell National Bank, Lewistown, PA; *U.S. Public*, pg. 1222
Heller, Fred, Chief Oper. Officer--Anedco, Inc., Houston, TX; *U.S. Public*, pg. 1016
Hellman, H. Carl, Pres.--Ceco Door Products, Brentwood, TN; *U.S. Public*, pg. 1676
Hellman, Kurt, Pres.--Basic American Metal Products, Oshkosh, WI; *U.S. Public*, pg. 404
Hellmold, Aloys, Dir.--Prisma Verlag GmbH, Munich, Germany; *Int'l*, pg. 190
Hellsten, Kalevi, Mgr.--Suomen Sandvik Oy, Helsinki, Finland; *Int'l*, pg. 1187
Hellums, C. E., Pres. & G.M.--Peoria & Pekin Union Railway Co., Creve Coeur, IL; *U.S. Public*, pg. 432
Hellwig, Peter, Mng. Dir.--BRC Weldmesh (SEA) Pte Ltd., Jurong, Singapore; *Int'l*, pg. 227
Helm, Brian, Mgr.--Electronic Display Systems (Kallego), Grand Island, NE; *U.S. Private*, pg. 236
Helm, D., Pres.--Thermo Environmental Instrument Inc., Franklin, MA; *U.S. Public*, pg. 1593
Helm, Lothar, Mng. Dir.--BV Capital Markets (Asia) Ltd., Hong Kong, Hong Kong; *Int'l*, pg. 180
Helm, M. R., Gen. Mgr.--Macungie Div., Macungie, PA; *Int'l*, pg. 1103
Helm, Michael J., Pres.--Kaufman and Broad Central Valley Div., Modesto, CA; *U.S. Public*, pg. 945
Helm, W. Don, Pres.--Delco Electronics Overseas Corporation, Detroit, MI; *U.S. Public*, pg. 721
Helmberg, Hans-Dieter, Chief Oper. Officer--Binks Deutschland GmbH, Mulheim an der Ruhr, Germany; *U.S. Public*, pg. 229
Helmer, Svend, Mng. Dir.--Danisco Distillers, Copenhagen, Denmark; *Int'l*, pg. 378
Helmich, Karl W., Chief Oper. Officer--Sea Containers GmbH, Hamburg, Germany; *Int'l*, pg. 1214
Helmroth, A.V., V.P. & Gen. Mgr.--Albany International B.V., Dieren, Netherlands; *U.S. Public*, pg. 37
Helmroth, Anders, V.P. & Gen. Mgr.--Albany International S.A., Riberac, France; *U.S. Public*, pg. 37
Helms, George, Pres.--MascoTech Coatings, Saint Clair, MI; *U.S. Public*, pg. 1055
Helms, Lois, Publr.--Opinion-Tribune, Glenwood, IA; *U.S. Private*, pg. 648
Helms, W. Edd, Jr., Chief Oper. Officer--Edd Helms Electrical, Inc., Miami, FL; *U.S. Private*, pg. 521
Helms, W. Edd, Jr., Chief Oper. Officer--Edd Helms Electrical Service, Inc., Miami, FL; *U.S. Private*, pg. 521
Helmy, H.H., Pres.--Egan Machinery Division, Somerville, NJ; *Int'l*, pg. 774
Helmy, Hassan A., Dr., Mng. Dir.--R.P. Scherer Egypt, Alexandria, Egypt; *U.S. Public*, pg. 1438
Helomaa, Jouku, Mng. Dir.--Merita Capital Ltd., Helsinki, Finland; *Int'l*, pg. 859
Helpern, Joan, Pres. & Chief Exec. Officer--Joan & David Helpern, Inc., Everett, MA; *U.S. Private*, pg. 521
Helppie, Richard D., Pres. & Chief Exec. Officer--Superior Consultant Company, Inc., Southfield, MI; *U.S. Public*, pg. 1539
Helsley, Dana, V.P.-Contract Opers.--Pandrol Jackson, Inc., East Syracuse, NY; *Int'l*, pg. 280
Helsley, Robert C., Publr.--The Yankton Printing Company, Yankton, SD; *U.S. Private*, pg. 995
Helstrom, Mikael, Gen. Mgr.--Huhtamaki Finance Oy, Espoo, Finland; *Int'l*, pg. 638
Helton, Bob, Mgr.--J and O Diesel, Columbus, MS; *U.S. Private*, pg. 1101
Helton, James E., Pres. & Chief Exec. Officer--M & M Precision Systems Corporation, Carrollton, OH; *U.S. Public*, pg. 482
Helton, James E., Pres.--Ball Screws & Actuators Co., Inc., San Jose, CA; *U.S. Public*, pg. 482
Hemeyer, Terry, Exec. V.P. & Gen. Mgr.--Edelman Worldwide, Inc., Houston, TX; *U.S. Private*, pg. 362
Hemlin, Rolf, Mgr.--AB Sandvik Belts, Sandviken, Sweden; *Int'l*, pg. 1185
Hemmer, William, Chm. Bd. & Pres.--Amway (Japan) Limited, Tokyo, Japan; *U.S. Private*, pg. 70
Hemmerle, Glen, Pres.--Harvey Electronics, New York, NY; *U.S. Public*, pg. 796

Hemminghaus, Roger R., Chief Exec. Officer--Diamond Shamrock Credit Card Center, Amarillo, TX; *U.S. Public*, pg. 1663
Hemphill, William J., Pres.--Bristol Laboratories International, S.A., Colon, Panama; *U.S. Public*, pg. 255
Hemstad, Bjorn, Pres.--Ericsson Network Systems, Inc., Richardson, TX; *Int'l*, pg. 1364
Hench, Kurt, Mng. Dir.--Tylan GmbH, Eching, Germany; *U.S. Public*, pg. 1113
Hendel, M., Pres.--Commodore Aviation, Miami, FL; *Int'l*, pg. 690
Henderson, D.A., Chief Exec. Officer--Scottisch Equitable, Edinburgh, United Kingdom; *Int'l*, pg. 28
Henderson, David, Chief Oper. Officer--Manus (Great Britain) Ltd., Moreton-in-Marsh, United Kingdom; *Int'l*, pg. 1380
Henderson, Don, Chief Oper. Officer--John Deere Horicon Works, Horicon, WI; *U.S. Public*, pg. 492
Henderson, Donald, Chm. Bd., Pres. & Chief Exec. Officer--Citation National Insurance Company, San Jose, CA; *U.S. Public*, pg. 376
Henderson, Donald, Chm. Bd. & Chief Exec. Officer--Madison Acceptance Corporation, San Jose, CA; *U.S. Public*, pg. 376
Henderson, Donald, Chm. Bd., Pres. & Chief Exec. Officer--Citation Insurance Company, San Jose, CA; *U.S. Public*, pg. 376
Henderson, Douglas A., Pres.--Polysar Rubber Corporation, Toronto, Canada; *Int'l*, pg. 175
Henderson, Frederick A., Pres. & Mng. Dir.--General Motors do Brasil Ltda., Sao Caetano do Sul, Brazil; *U.S. Public*, pg. 722
Henderson, Grant W., Pres. & Chief Fin. Officer--Coda Energy, Inc., Dallas, TX; *U.S. Public*, pg. 584
Henderson, Gregory M., Pres.--SuperValu, Inc.-Des Moines Div., Des Moines, IA; *U.S. Public*, pg. 1540
Henderson, James A., Pres.--Atlas Copco Wagner Inc., Portland, OR; *Int'l*, pg. 96
Henderson, James A., Chm. Bd. & Chief Exec. Officer--Cummins Engine Company, Inc., Columbus, IN; *U.S. Public*, pg. 467
Henderson, Joe, Pres.--Sunwest Bank of Hobbs, N.A., Hobbs, NM; *U.S. Public*, pg. 1165
Henderson, Keith, Mng. Dir.--Seal Sands Chemicals Ltd., Middlesbrough, United Kingdom; *U.S. Public*, pg. 297
Henderson, Keith, Dr., Mng. Dir.--Pentagon Chemicals limited, Workington, United Kingdom; *Int'l*, pg. 88
Henderson, Kevin, Div. Pres.--Fifth Quarter, Nashville, TN; *U.S. Public*, pg. 1467
Henderson, Michael, V.P.-Sls. & Mktg.--Northern Telecom Inc., Bracknell, United Kingdom; *Int'l*, pg. 970
Henderson, Mike, Chief Oper. Officer--Rhone-Poulenc Chemicals (India), Mumbai, India; *Int'l*, pg. 1112
Henderson, Nina Z., Pres.--CPC Specialty Markets Group, Englewood Cliffs, NJ; *U.S. Public*, pg. 224
Henderson, R. Phillip, V.P. & Gen. Mgr.--Information Systems Division, Melbourne, FL; *U.S. Public*, pg. 792
Henderson, Robert, Chief Oper. Officer--Hudson General Corp., Fort Lauderdale, FL; *U.S. Public*, pg. 845
Henderson, Rowe, Plant Mgr.--Firestone Fibers & Textiles Company-Kings Mountain, Kings Mountain, NC; *Int'l*, pg. 214
Henderson, Terry, Exec. V.P.--Mahlo America Inc., Spartanburg, SC; *Int'l*, pg. 830
Henderson, William P., Mgr.-Branch--Piper Jaffray Inc., Saint Louis, MO; *U.S. Public*, pg. 1301
Hendin, David, Sr. V.P.--Newspaper Enterprise Assoc., New York, NY; *U.S. Public*, pg. 1448
Hendley, Ray, Mgr.--BHP Steel Sankey, Mayfield, Australia; *Int'l*, pg. 227
Hendrata, Leo, Gen. Mgr.--PT John Crane Indonesia, Jakarta, Indonesia; *Int'l*, pg. 1339
Hendrick, J., Chief Exec. Officer--RBB NV, Tessenderlo, Belgium; *Int'l*, pg. 1092
Hendrick, J.R. III, Pres.--Hendrick Imports, Charlotte, NC; *U.S. Private*, pg. 522
Hendricks, Albert L., Pres.--Wisconsin Protective Coatings Corp., Green Bay, WI; *U.S. Public*, pg. 1358
Hendricks, Albert L., Pres.--Briner Paint Manufacturing Co., Inc., Corpus Christi, TX; *U.S. Public*, pg. 1358
Hendricks, J.R., III, Pres.--Hendrick Motorsports, Harrisburg, NC; *U.S. Private*, pg. 522
Hendricks, Patrick T., V.P. & Gen. Mgr.--Thoroughbred Plastics Corp., Louisville, KY; *U.S. Public*, pg. 261
Hendricks, Thomas L., Pres. & Chief Exec. Officer--USLIFE Systems Corporation, Dallas, TX; *U.S. Public*, pg. 77
Hendricks, Thomas L., Pres. & Chief Exec. Officer--USLIFE Insurance Services Corporation, Dallas, TX; *U.S. Public*, pg. 77
Hendricks, Warren, Dist. Mgr.--ENSCO Drilling (Venezuela), S.A., Los Morochas, Venezuela; *U.S. Public*, pg. 585
Hendrickson, Buck, V.P.-Opers.--Doehler-Jarvis, Pottstown Inc., Stowe, PA; *U.S. Public*, pg. 796
Hendrickson, John J., Mng. Dir.--Securitas Capital Partners I, L.P., Hamilton, Bermuda; *Int'l*, pg. 1333
Hendrickx, Luc, Pres.--Industrial Air Division, Wilrijk, Belgium; *Int'l*, pg. 96
Hendriksen, F., Dir.--THORN Denmark, Hvidovre, Denmark; *Int'l*, pg. 1386
Hendrikson, Eddie L., Pres.--SAFECO Properties, Inc., Seattle, WA; *U.S. Public*, pg. 1423
Hendrix, William J., Gen. Mgr.--HI Property, Inc., Dallas, TX; *U.S. Private*, pg. 537
Hendry, B.W., Chm. Bd.--Taylor Woodrow Construction Corp., New York, NY; *Int'l*, pg. 1359
Hendry, Robert, Pres. & Chief Exec. Officer--Saab Automobile AB, Nykoping, Sweden; *Int'l*, pg. 687
Hendry, Robert, Pres. & Chief Exec. Officer--Saab Automobile AB, Nykoping, Sweden; *U.S. Public*, pg. 725
Henein, Rafick, Ph.D., Pres. & Chief Exec. Officer--Zenith Goldline Pharmaceuticals, Miami, FL; *U.S. Public*, pg. 915
Henel, Robert E., Jr., Pres. & Chief Exec. Officer--The Annapolis Banking & Trust Co., Annapolis, MD; *U.S. Public*, pg. 1088
Henery, Maurice D., Chm. & Chief Exec. Officer--Marblehead Lime Co., Chicago, IL; *U.S. Public*, pg. 709
Heng, Roger K.K., Sr. Representative--Bank of Montreal - China, Beijing, China; *Int'l*, pg. 155
Henge, Karlheinz, Dr., Chief Exec. Officer--Badenia Bausparkasse AG, Karlsruhe, Germany; *Int'l*, pg. 15
Henkel, Gerd, Mng. Dir.--Morton International G.m.b.H., Bremen, Germany; *U.S. Public*, pg. 1135
Henkel, Hans-Olaf, Pres.--IBM Deutschland GmbH, Stuttgart, Germany; *U.S. Public*, pg. 897
Henley, Barry S., Mng. Dir.--Chubb Singapore Private Limited, Singapore, Singapore; *Int'l*, pg. 1250
Henley, Peter, Sr. Mgr.--Australian Guarantee Corporation Limited - Tasmania, Hobart, Australia; *Int'l*, pg. 1496
Henli, Larry, Chief Oper. Officer--Upper Rock Island County Landfill, East Moline, IL; *U.S. Public*, pg. 49
Henmi, Shinzo, Pres.--Liaoning Liao Bian Advanced Fashion Garments Co., Ltd., Dalian, China; *Int'l*, pg. 579
Henn, R.A., V.P.--Greer Limestone Co., Morgantown, WV; *U.S. Private*, pg. 479
Henn, Steve, Gen. Mgr.--ITW Fluid Products Group, Norcross, GA; *U.S. Public*, pg. 866
Hennecke, Hans Peter, Pres.--Dolomitwerke GmbH, Wulfrath, Germany; *Int'l*, pg. 1388
Hennecke, Hans Peter, Dr., Pres.--Rheinische Kalksteinwerke GmbH, Wulfrath, Germany; *Int'l*, pg. 1388
Hennel, Alfonso Brandao, Pres.--Semp Toshiba Amazonas S.A., Manaus, Brazil; *Int'l*, pg. 1406
Hennessey, B.J., Mng. Dir.--Decoflex Limited, Hartlepool, United Kingdom; *Int'l*, pg. 889
Hennessey, J., Mng. Dir.--Ascom Timeplex Ltd. (New Zealand), Wellington, New Zealand; *Int'l*, pg. 87
Hennessey, Mike J., Pres. & Chief Exec. Officer--Jumping Jacks, Monett, MO; *U.S. Private*, pg. 767
Hennig, Peter, Dr., Mgr.--Commerzbank AG, Brussels, Belgium; *Int'l*, pg. 311
Henning, John J., Pres.--Symtron Systems, Inc., Fair Lawn, NJ; *U.S. Public*, pg. 1679
Henning, K.M., Pres.--Marathon Petroleum Indonesia, Ltd., Jakarta, Indonesia; *U.S. Public*, pg. 1662
Henning, Martin, Mng. Dir.--Hartung, Kuhn, & Co., Maschinenfabrik GmbH, Essen, Germany; *Int'l*, pg. 511
Henning, Martin, Dir.--Krupp Stahl Wohnungsbau GmbH, Essen, Germany; *Int'l*, pg. 512
Henninger, Christian, Mng. Dir.--Sulzer International (Deutschland) GmbH, Ravensburg, Germany; *Int'l*, pg. 1308
Henningsen, John S., Pres.--Amycel, Inc., San Juan Bautista, CA; *U.S. Private*, pg. 758
Henningson, Ray C., Jr., Chm. Bd.--Willis Corroon Corp. of Minnesota, Minneapolis, MN; *Int'l*, pg. 1506
Henpf, Erhard K., Chief Oper. Officer--Schmidt & Hagen GmbH & Co. KG, Uetersen, Germany; *Int'l*, pg. 610
Henri-Drevon, Pierre, Dir.--BT France SNC, Paris, France; *Int'l*, pg. 223
Henricsson, Wiking, Pres.--Perstorp Plastic Systems, Perstorp, Sweden; *Int'l*, pg. 1037
Henrie, Robert A., Exec. V.P.--R&R Advertising, Salt Lake City, UT; *U.S. Private*, pg. 902
Henriksen, Bjoern, Chief Oper. Officer--MacGREGOR (NOR) A/S, Oslo, Norway; *Int'l*, pg. 671
Henriksen, Freddie, Dir.-Admin.--Castrol A/S, Copenhagen, Denmark; *Int'l*, pg. 235
Henriksen, Lars, Gen. Mgr.--AMP Danmark, Viby, Denmark; *U.S. Public*, pg. 8
Henriksen, Oskar, Mgr.--Digitale Kartsystemer, Lysaker, Norway; *Int'l*, pg. 766
Henriksson, Bertel, Chief Oper. Officer--Axel Johnson Oy, Helsinki, Finland; *Int'l*, pg. 712
Henriksson, Lars, Chief Oper. Officer--Equipos Agricolas Alfa-Laval S.A., Madrid, Spain; *Int'l*, pg. 1377
Henrion, Romain, Mng. Dir.--ProfilARBED, Esch-sur-Alzette, Luxembourg; *Int'l*, pg. 79
Henrique, Edgar, Mgr.--Joinville Branch, Joinville, Brazil; *Int'l*, pg. 139
Henriques, Antonio Veiga, Chm.--Carbogal-Carbonos de Portugal, S.A., Lisbon, Portugal; *Int'l*, pg. 1045
Henrot, Jacques, Mng. Dir.--ETCD, Casablanca, Morocco; *Int'l*, pg. 823
Henry, Austin, Gen. Mgr.--Farah (Exports) Ireland, Galway, Ireland; *U.S. Public*, pg. 613
Henry, Barbara A., Pres. & Publr.--Des Moines Register & Tribune Co., Des Moines, IA; *U.S. Public*, pg. 700
Henry, Charles L., Grp. V.P.--Du Pont Electronics, Wilmington, DE; *U.S. Public*, pg. 531
Henry, Dennis, Mgr.-Zone--Safemal Drilling Sdn. Bhd., Miri, Malaysia; *Int'l*, pg. 765
Henry, H.C., Jr., Pres.--BellSouth Resources, Inc., Atlanta, GA; *U.S. Public*, pg. 208
Henry, Peter, Reg. Sales Mgr.--Briggs & Stratton Australia Pty. Limited, Springvale, Australia; *U.S. Public*, pg. 252
Henry, Todd, Mgr.-Facility--Lawson Products, Inc., Addison, IL; *U.S. Public*, pg. 980
Hensel, Neil, Pres.--Titan Systems, Inc., San Diego, CA; *U.S. Public*, pg. 1618
Henshall, Alan R., Mng. Dir.--Commercial Hydraulics Pty. Ltd., Melbourne, Australia; *U.S. Public*, pg. 411
Hensing, Willem, Dir.--Generale Bank - Eindhoven, Eindhoven, Netherlands; *Int'l*, pg. 547
Hensley, David, V.P.--Eckerd Drug Co., Charlotte, NC; *U.S. Public*, pg. 917
Hensley, Richard R., Pres.--SuperValu, Inc.-Ryans Div., Billings, MT; *U.S. Public*, pg. 1541
Henson, Arnold R., Pres.--Farm Credit Bank of Texas, Austin, TX; *U.S. Private*, pg. 398
Henson, C.A., Plant Mgr.--Block Plant, Abilene, TX; *U.S. Public*, pg. 936
Henson, Gary, Plant Mgr.--General Motors Canada Ste. Therese Div., Boisbriand, Canada; *U.S. Public*, pg. 722
Henson, Gary Lloyd, Mng. Dir.--General Motors de Mexico, S.A. de C.V., Mexico, Mexico; *U.S. Public*, pg. 722
Henson, Gary Lloyd, Mng. Dir.--General Motors de Mexico, S.A. de C.V., Ramos Arizpe, Mexico; *U.S. Public*, pg. 722
Henson, Lisa, Pres.-Worldwide Production--Sony Pictures Studios, Culver City, CA; *Int'l*, pg. 1283
Henson, Ted, Pres.--Summit Performance Dist. Inc., Channelview, TX; *U.S. Public*, pg. 1233
Henstra, R., Mng. Dir.--Hoogovens Steel Primary Products, Ijmuiden, Netherlands; *Int'l*, pg. 756
Henthorne, Michael, Pres.--Ellwood Texas Forge, Inc., Houston, TX; *U.S. Private*, pg. 373
Hentschel, David A., Chm. Bd. & Chief Exec. Officer--Occidental Oil & Gas Corporation, Bakersfield, CA; *U.S. Public*, pg. 1210
Henwood, Derek, Pres.--Great Lakes Gas Transmission Co., Detroit, MI; *Int'l*, pg. 1417
Henzl, David, Sr. Sls. Engineer--Kvaerner Hydro Power, Inc.-West Coast Sales Division, San Francisco, CA; *Int'l*, pg. 770
Hepburn, Jim, Chief Exec. Officer--Milk Products Holdings (North America) Inc., Santa Rosa, CA; *Int'l*, pg. 923
Hepburn, Vic C., Pres.--Jannock Brick Group-Head Office, Streetsville, Canada; *Int'l*, pg. 698
Hepher, M.L., Chm. Bd. & Mng. Dir.--Lloyds Abbey Life PLC, Weybridge, United Kingdom; *Int'l*, pg. 813
Hepher, Michael, Chm. & Chief Exec. Officer--Charterhouse Bank Ltd., London, United Kingdom; *Int'l*, pg. 342
Hepplestone, Clive, Mgr.--New England Laminates (U.K.) Ltd., Skelmersdale, United Kingdom; *U.S. Public*, pg. 1258
Heppner, Michael, Gen. Mgr.--Farman Brothers Pickle Company, Renton, WA; *U.S. Private*, pg. 887
Herb, Matt, Mgr.--Barenbrug Research USA, Tangent, OR; *Int'l*, pg. 166
Herberg, Gotz, Dr., Chm. Bd.--Holstein and Kappert GmbH, Dortmund, Germany; *Int'l*, pg. 737
Herbert, Bart, Pres.--Creditor Resources, Inc., Atlanta, GA; *Int'l*, pg. 27
Herbert, Bill, Gen. Mgr.--Macromeric Division, Aurora, OH; *U.S. Public*, pg. 689
Herbert, Charles J., V.P. & Gen. Mgr.--Government Aerospace Systems Division, Melbourne, FL; *U.S. Public*, pg. 792
Herbert, Charles J., V.P. & Gen. Mgr.--Government Aerospace Systems Division, Syosset, NY; *U.S. Public*, pg. 792
Herbert, Charles J., V.P. & Gen. Mgr.--Government Aerospace Systems Division-Orlando Operations, Orlando, FL; *U.S. Public*, pg. 792
Herbert, Don, Mng. Dir.--Carter Holt Harvey Timber Limited, Auckland, New Zealand; *U.S. Public*, pg. 904
Herbert, Laurence, Pres.--Intertext Group, Ltd., Glasgow, United Kingdom; *U.S. Public*, pg. 784
Herbert, Laurence, Pres.--The School of Accountancy, Glasgow, United Kingdom; *U.S. Public*, pg. 784
Herbert, Lawrence, Pres.--International Correspondence Schools Ltd., Glasgow, United Kingdom; *U.S. Public*, pg. 784
Herbert, Lawrence, Mng. Dir.--International Correspondence Schools (Overseas) Limited, Glasgow, United Kingdom; *U.S. Public*, pg. 784
Herbert, M., Chm. Bd.--The Tussauds Group Limited, London, United Kingdom; *Int'l*, pg. 1026
Herbert, Mike, Mng. Dir.--Phildas Ltd., Pontefract, United Kingdom; *Int'l*, pg. 585
Herbert, Paul, Chief Oper. Officer-Zanders--International Paper Company, Purchase, NY; *U.S. Public*, pg. 901
Herbert, Richard K., Pres.--Howell Petroleum Corp., Houston, TX; *U.S. Public*, pg. 844
Herbison, Claude, Mgr.--Westco Products/Phoenix, Phoenix, AZ; *Int'l*, pg. 244
Herbison, Steve, Chief Exec. Officer--URM Development Corp., Spokane, WA; *U.S. Private*, pg. 1114
Herbst, Hans Jurgen, Chm. Bd.--Krupp Anlagenbau GmbH, Duisburg, Germany; *Int'l*, pg. 511
Herbst, Thomas C., Pres.--Abello Deutschland Pharma GmbH, Bornheim, Germany; *Int'l*, pg. 288
Herbster, Keith, Gen. Mgr.--Desoutter, Inc., Farmington Hills, MI; *Int'l*, pg. 96
Herdin, Clas, Chief Oper. Officer--Electrolux S.A., Madrid, Spain; *Int'l*, pg. 443
Heredia, Thomas, Gen. Mgr.--Ionics Ultrapure Water Corporation, Campbell, CA; *U.S. Public*, pg. 912
Hering, Tony, Gen. Mgr.--ABB Process Analytics, Burlington, Canada; *Int'l*, pg. 5
Heritage, B., Chm. Bd.--Myton Limited, Hayes, United Kingdom; *Int'l*, pg. 1358
Herkstroton, Rudolf, Chief Oper. Officer--Husqvarna Vertriebs GmbH, Hamburg, Germany; *Int'l*, pg. 442
Herl, James C., Gen. Mgr.--Chemical Group, Gibsonburg, OH; *U.S. Public*, pg. 345
Herlaar, Will, Chief Exec.--Sulzer Metco (Benelux) B.V., Breda, Netherlands; *Int'l*, pg. 1308
Herlihy, Michael, Pres. & Chief Exec. Officer--Advest Bank, Hartford, CT; *U.S. Public*, pg. 23
Herman, Bernard, Pres.--Star Video Entertainment, L.P., Jersey City, NJ; *U.S. Private*, pg. 1132
Herman, David J., Pres. & Chief Exec. Officer--Saab Automobile AB, Trollhattan, Sweden; *Int'l*, pg. 687
Herman, David J., Pres. & Chief Exec. Officer--Saab Automobile AB, Trollhattan, Sweden; *U.S. Public*, pg. 720
Herman, David J., Chm. Bd & Mng. Dir.--Adam Opel AG, Russelsheim, Germany; *U.S. Public*, pg. 721
Herman, F. H., Mgr.--Franklin River Division, Port Alberni, Canada; *Int'l*, pg. 828
Herman, Howard L., Pres.--Great Pacific Insurance Company, San Bruno, CA; *U.S. Public*, pg. 1158
Herman, Mike, Pres.--Comdisco Electronics Group, San Diego, CA; *U.S. Public*, pg. 408
Herman, Mike, Pres.--Comdisco Laboratory & Scientific Group, Canton, MA; *U.S. Public*, pg. 408

Herman, Pal, Gen. Mgr.--A.E. Staley Manufacturing Co., Loudon, TN; *Int'l*, pg. 1357
Herman, Roy, Gen. Mgr.--UNR-Leavitt Div., Chicago, IL; *U.S. Public*, pg. 1404
Herman, Scott, V.P. & Gen. Mgr.--WINS Radio, New York, NY; *U.S. Public*, pg. 274
Herman, Timm, Gen. Mgr.--J.H. Williams, Columbus, GA; *U.S. Public*, pg. 1481
Herman, Wes, Pres. & Gen. Mgr.--Chesapeake Packaging Co./North Tonawanda, North Tonawanda, NY; *U.S. Public*, pg. 347
Herman, Will, Pres.--Viewlogic Systems Group, Marlborough, MA; *U.S. Public*, pg. 1548
Hermance, Dave, Gen. Mgr.--Toyota Technical Center, U.S.A., Inc., Ann Arbor, MI; *Int'l*, pg. 1413
Hermaniati, Lisa, Mgr.--Utell International-Indonesia, Jakarta, Indonesia; *Int'l*, pg. 1098
Hermann, Jesse, Pres.--BWD Automotive, North Brunswick, NJ; *U.S. Public*, pg. 560
Hermann, Rudolf, Pres. & Chief Exec. Officer--Dover Resources Inc., Tulsa, OK; *U.S. Public*, pg. 521
Hermans, R., Gen. Mgr.--ING Lease Vastgoed, Amsterdam, Netherlands; *Int'l*, pg. 647
Hermanson, Terry, Pres.--Mr. Christmas Limited, Kowloon, Hong Kong; *U.S. Private*, pg. 765
Hermansson, Hakan, Mgr.--Boliden Intermarket AB, Stockholm, Sweden; *Int'l*, pg. 1422
Hermansson, Michael, Mgr.--Sandvik Bahco Argentina S.A.C.el., Buenos Aires, Argentina; *Int'l*, pg. 1187
Hermelin, Victor M., Chm.--Particle Dynamics, Inc., Saint Louis, MO; *U.S. Public*, pg. 941
Hermenet, E.W., Pres.--Brooks Foods, Mount Summit, IN; *U.S. Private*, pg. 887
Hermesdorf, J., Chief Oper. Officer--Devro-Teepak, Inc., Westchester, IL; *Int'l*, pg. 408
Hermoni, Avner, V.P. & Mng. Dir.--Kulicke & Soffa (Israel) Ltd., Haifa, Israel; *U.S. Public*, pg. 969
Hermoso, Jose Manuel Garcia, Pres.--A.H.V. Ensidesa Capital, S.A., Madrid, Spain; *Int'l*, pg. 1223
Hermoso, Jose Manuel Garcia, Pres.--C.S.I. Corporacion Siderurgia Integral, S.A., Madrid, Spain; *Int'l*, pg. 1224
Hernan, Fernando Guerrero, Pres.--TAUSA - Trasatlantica Agency USA Inc., New York, NY; *Int'l*, pg. 1224
Hernandez, Anne, Mgr.-Pur.--Ceco Door Products, Milan, TN; *U.S. Public*, pg. 1676
Hernandez, Artemio, Chief Exec. Officer--Adriatica-Sociedad Anonima de Seguros y Reaseguros, Madrid, Spain; *Int'l*, pg. 61
Hernandez, Artemio, Office Mgr.--Korn/Ferry International, Madrid, Spain; *U.S. Private*, pg. 633
Hernandez, G., Gen. Mgr.--Texaco Mexicana S.A. de C.V., Mexico, Mexico; *U.S. Public*, pg. 1584
Hernandez, James A. Jr., Pres. & Chief Exec. Officer--3 Score, Inc., Tucker, GA; *U.S. Public*, pg. 291
Hernandez, M.O., Chief Oper. Officer--FATA SA, Llica de Vall, Spain; *Int'l*, pg. 474
Hernandez, Michael, V.P. & Gen. Mgr.--Certified Poultry & Egg Co., Inc., Fort Lauderdale, FL; *U.S. Public*, pg. 1529
Hernandez, R., Gen. Mgr.--Kodak Uruguaya, Ltd., Montevideo, Uruguay; *U.S. Public*, pg. 555
Herndon, D. Alton, Pres.--Hatteras Yachts, New Bern, NC; *U.S. Private*, pg. 447
Herndon, Hubert G., Pres. & Chief Exec. Officer--Bank of Morgan County, Madison, GA; *U.S. Public*, pg. 1371
Heroman, Paul, Plant Mgr.--American Natl. Can Co., Batavia, IL; *Int'l*, pg. 1029
Heron, Michael G., Mng. Dir.--Unilever U.K. Central Resources Ltd., London, United Kingdom; *Int'l*, pg. 1434
Heron, T.A., Chm. Bd.--Robert Bryce & Co., Ltd., Abbotsford, Australia; *Int'l*, pg. 682
Herpin, Greg, Gen. Mgr.--Guaranty Broadcasting, Baton Rouge, LA; *U.S. Private*, pg. 485
Herr, Gary P., Pres.--Sysco Food Services of Iowa, Inc., West Des Moines, IA; *U.S. Public*, pg. 1551
Herrara, J., Gen. Mgr.--Nalco Ecuador S.A., Quito, Ecuador; *U.S. Public*, pg. 1150
Herrara, Joaquin, Mgr.--Quimica Nalco de Colombia, S.A., Bogota, Colombia; *U.S. Public*, pg. 1151
Herrbach, Ralph W., Pres.--Cedarapids, Inc., Cedar Rapids, IA; *U.S. Public*, pg. 1365
Herrenknecht, Max-Eugen, Gen. Mgr.--Dresdner Bank AG, New York, NY; *Int'l*, pg. 418
Herrera, Frank E., Pres.--International Circulation Distributors, New York, NY; *U.S. Private*, pg. 517
Herrera, H., Mgr.--Lange Ballast Contractors Ltd., Port of Spain, Trinidad & Tobago; *Int'l*, pg. 135
Herrera, Luis, Mgr.--Lehigh Press-Puerto Rico, Juncos, PR; *U.S. Private*, pg. 659
Herrera, Manuel O., Pres.--Molinas de Puerto Rico, San Juan, PR; *U.S. Public*, pg. 426
Herrick, Donald T. Jr., Pres.--Dominion Lands, Inc., Richmond, VA; *U.S. Public*, pg. 516
Herrick, Glenn W., V.P.--Technical Services Division, Buffalo, NY; *U.S. Public*, pg. 419
Herries, Robert, Dir.--Jardine Fleming Bank Limited, Central, Hong Kong; *Int'l*, pg. 494
Herrill, Doug, Mng. Dir.--Trimble Navigation Europe Ltd., Hook, United Kingdom; *U.S. Public*, pg. 1638
Herriman, David, Gen. Mgr.--Barton's of Osceola, Osceola, AR; *U.S. Private*, pg. 119
Herriman, M. Davis, Pres.--Maryland Concession & Vending Company, Hyattsville, MD; *U.S. Public*, pg. 741
Herring, G. F., Mng. Dir.--Tootal Thread Malacca Sdn Bdn, Melaka, Malaysia; *Int'l*, pg. 299
Herring, Gregg, V.P.--Intertec Publishing, Garland, TX; *U.S. Public*, pg. 1328
Herring, James, Pres.-Actg.--Friona Agriculture Credit Corp., Amarillo, TX; *U.S. Private*, pg. 429
Herrington, Douglas, Pres.--Chemical Bank Thumb Area, Caro, MI; *U.S. Public*, pg. 345
Herrington, Glenn, Mgr.--Southern Electric Supply Co., Inc., Birmingham, AL; *Int'l*, pg. 1107
Herrington, Glenn, Mgr.--Southern Electric Supply Co., Inc., Montgomery, AL; *Int'l*, pg. 1107
Herrington, Glenn, Mgr.--Southern Electric Supply Co., Inc., Tuscaloosa, AL; *Int'l*, pg. 1107
Herrloff, Tommy, Mng. Dir.--Skanska London, London, United Kingdom; *Int'l*, pg. 1261
Herrman, Jim, Pres.--Gardner Abrasives, South Beloit, IL; *U.S. Public*, pg. 1699
Herrman, Robert, Chief Oper. Officer--Micronics Technology, Inc., Glen Cove, NY; *Int'l*, pg. 1289
Herrman, Tom, Reg. Mgr.--Green Tree Acceptance, Inc., Mesa, AZ; *U.S. Public*, pg. 762
Herrmann, Erik, Pres.--STAL Refrigeration AB, Norrkoping, Sweden; *Int'l*, pg. 7
Herrmann, Henry J., Sr. V.P. & Chief Investment Officer--Waddell & Reed Asset Mngmt. Co., Kansas City, MO; *U.S. Public*, pg. 1623
Herrmann, Joachim, Mng. Dir.--DYWIT S.p.A., Milan, Italy; *Int'l*, pg. 425
Herron, G.T., V.P.--Dan River Cotton Co., Inc., Danville, VA; *U.S. Public*, pg. 479
Herron, J.T., Mgr.--Dan River Inc.-Home Furnishings & Related Prods., Div. I, Danville, VA; *U.S. Public*, pg. 479
Herron, Kevin E., Mgr.--Scott & Stringfellow, Inc., Greensboro, NC; *U.S. Public*, pg. 1446
Herron, M.B., V.P. & District Mgr.--A.M. Castle & Co., Paramount, CA; *U.S. Public*, pg. 313
Herron, Tom, Branch Mgr.--Bergen Brunswig Medical Corp., Tigard, OR; *U.S. Public*, pg. 214
Herrring, James E., Pres.--United Knitting, Inc., Cleveland, TN; *U.S. Public*, pg. 538
Hersch, Ronald G., Ph.D., Pres.--Comprehensive Behavioral Care, Inc., Tampa, FL; *U.S. Public*, pg. 419
Hersh, Harry, Pres. & Chief Exec. Officer--Pepcom Industries, Inc., Raleigh, NC; *Int'l*, pg. 1321
Hersh, Mark, Plant Mgr.--Household Products Co., Chicago, IL; *U.S. Public*, pg. 387
Hershberger, Terry, Mgr.--Amana Society Service Co., Amana, IA; *U.S. Private*, pg. 48
Hershey, Robert V., Pres.--Duluth & Northeastern Railroad Co., Cloquet, MN; *U.S. Public*, pg. 1318
Herskind, Carl C., Jr., Gen. Mgr.--Transit Mix Concrete Co., Colorado Springs, CO; *U.S. Public*, pg. 441
Herskovitz, Stephen, Mng. Dir.--MC2 Adams, New York, NY; *U.S. Private*, pg. 679
Herskowitz, Ron, Exec. V.P.--Refractive Centers International, Waltham, MA; *U.S. Public*, pg. 1529
Herslow, John H., Pres. & Chief Exec. Officer--Sillcocks Plastics, Inc., Berkeley Heights, NJ; *U.S. Private*, pg. 63
Herson, Gerald, Pres. & Chief Exec. Officer--Delair Group, L.L.C., Delair, NJ; *U.S. Private*, pg. 47
Herson, Steven J., Pres.--TeleRep, Incorporated, New York, NY; *U.S. Private*, pg. 282
Hertel, Frederick C., Gen. Mgr.--Creditanstalt Finance Inc.-New York, New York, NY; *Int'l*, pg. 347
Herteman, Jean-Paul, Chm. Bd.--SNECMA Inc., Dover, DE; *Int'l*, pg. 1166
Herter, Walter, Mng. Dir.--Sulzer (Thailand) Ltd., Bangkok, Thailand; *Int'l*, pg. 1307
Hertwig, James R., Pres.--Landstar ITCO, Inc., Jacksonville, FL; *U.S. Public*, pg. 978
Hertwig, James R., Pres.--Landstar Logistics, Inc., Jacksonville, FL; *U.S. Public*, pg. 978
Hertz, Benny, Sr. V.P. & Mgr.--Bank Leumi le-Israel B.M., Chicago, IL; *Int'l*, pg. 150
Hertz, J.E., Pres.--Alandco Inc., North Palm Beach, FL; *U.S. Public*, pg. 608
Hertzberg, Matts, Mng. Dir.--Ewos AB, Sollentuna, Sweden; *Int'l*, pg. 349
Heruzd, R., Mng. Dir.--Babcock Holding (Deutschland) GmbH, Buxtehude, Germany; *Int'l*, pg. 131
Hervert, Jean, Mng. Dir --J.V. Laing-GTM Europe, Bristol, United Kingdom; *Int'l*, pg. 823
Hervieux, Phillippe, Chief Fin. Officer--Roulement Service S.A., Strasbourg, France; *Int'l*, pg. 212
Herzberg, David H., Pres.--Shakespeare Monofilament, Columbia, SC; *U.S. Public*, pg. 940
Herzog, Joseph, V.P. & Gen. Mgr.--Automax, Inc., Cincinnati, OH; *U.S. Public*, pg. 658
Herzog, Paul, Chief Exec. Officer--Columbia Medical Center-East, El Paso, TX; *U.S. Public*, pg. 404
Herzog, Siegfried, Gen. Mgr.--Ueberseebank AG, Zurich, Switzerland; *U.S. Public*, pg. 85
Heselton, James, Gen. Mgr.--Pneutronics Div., Hollis, NH; *U.S. Public*, pg. 1262
Heske, Douglas C., Reg. Dir.--Piper Jaffray Inc., San Francisco, CA; *U.S. Public*, pg. 1301
Heske, Douglas C., Reg. Dir.--Piper Jaffray Inc., Sonoma, CA; *U.S. Public*, pg. 1303
Hesketh, Kim, Gen. Mgr.--Rogers CJVI-AM, Victoria, Canada; *Int'l*, pg. 1123
Hesler, Ray, Mgr.--Midland Color Company, North Little Rock, AR; *Int'l*, pg. 1311
Hespe, Harald, Mng. Dir.--S.A. ESAB N.V., Brussels, Belgium; *Int'l*, pg. 282
Hess, Blaine R., Pres. & Chief Exec. Officer--Thomas J. Lipton Company, Englewood Cliffs, NJ; *Int'l*, pg. 1435
Hess, J. Daniel, Pres. & Chief Oper. Officer--Takatta Inc., Auburn Hills, MI; *U.S. Private*, pg. 528
Hess, Jean Pierre, Gen. Mgr.--PromoPub/DMB&B Kuwait, Kuwait, Kuwait; *U.S. Private*, pg. 305
Hess, Karsten A., Chief Oper. Officer--Rimi Svenska AB, Bromma, Sweden; *Int'l*, pg. 643
Hess, Mary, Publr.--Business Journal Publications, Inc., San Francisco, CA; *U.S. Private*, pg. 19
Hess, Norbert A., Jr., Pres. & Gen. Mgr.--Coachmen Automotive, Elkhart, IN; *U.S. Public*, pg. 388
Hess, William, Pres.--Senco Products, Inc., Cincinnati, OH; *U.S. Private*, pg. 984
Hesse, D.R., Pres.--AT&T Network Systems International, Hilversum, Netherlands; *U.S. Public*, pg. 11
Hesse, Daniel, Pres.--AT&T Wireless Services, Kirkland, WA; *U.S. Public*, pg. 11
Hesse, Holger, Gen. Mgr.--Notifier Deutschland GmbH, Hilden, Germany; *U.S. Public*, pg. 1307
Hesse, K.F., Pres.--Wm. Haughton & Co. Ltd., Melbourne, Australia; *Int'l*, pg. 501
Hesse, Kenneth, Gen. Mgr.--Atlanta Learning Center, College Park, GA; *U.S. Public*, pg. 218
Hessell, Andy, Gen. Mgr.--Nickel Ads, Portland, OR; *U.S. Public*, pg. 984
Hesselman, James, Gen. Mgr.--Frontier Communications of Mondovi, Inc., Mondovi, WI; *U.S. Public*, pg. 684
Hessendahl, H., Mng. Dir.--Gestetner AB, Spanga, Sweden; *Int'l*, pg. 1115
Hesser, Dan, Chm. Bd. & Pres.--Invesco Funds Group, Denver, CO; *Int'l*, pg. 685
Hessey, Kevin, Pres.--Hebco Products, Bucyrus, OH; *U.S. Public*, pg. 1055
Hessler, Pierre, Chm. Bd. & Chief Exec. Officer--Gemini Consulting, Morristown, NJ; *Int'l*, pg. 264
Hestand, J. Don, Chief Oper. Officer--Hackney Inc., Dallas, TX; *U.S. Public*, pg. 1639
Hester, Evelyn, Pres.--Dover Handbag Co., Inc., New York, NY; *U.S. Private*, pg. 1042
Hester, Mark W., Pres.--Telos Field Engineering, Bountiful, UT; *U.S. Public*, pg. 1573
Hester, Mark W., Pres.--Telos Systems Solutions, Bountiful, UT; *U.S. Public*, pg. 1573
Hester, Willie, Gen. Mgr.--Elixir Industries, Fitzgerald, GA; *U.S. Private*, pg. 371
Hestler, R., Chief Oper. Officer--Vorelco Ltd., Ajax, Canada; *Int'l*, pg. 1475
Heston, Russell, Chief Oper. Officer--Hach Europe, S.A./N.V., Namur, Belgium; *U.S. Public*, pg. 773
Heston, W. Craig, Chm. & Chief Exec. Officer--Utica National Insurance Group, New Hartford, NY; *U.S. Private*, pg. 1130
Heszheimer, Dr. Alfred, Dir.--BV Financial Management GmbH, Munich, Germany; *Int'l*, pg. 178
Hete, Joseph, Chief Oper. Officer & Sr. V.P.-Admin.--ABX Air, Inc., Wilmington, OH; *U.S. Public*, pg. 33
Hetherington, Robert H., Pres.--Mueller International Sales Corp., Springfield, MO; *U.S. Public*, pg. 1141
Hetterick, John F., Pres.--Tonka International Division, Beverly, MA; *U.S. Public*, pg. 797
Hetterschijt, F., Mng. Dir.--A.C. Nielsen (Nederland) B.V., Diemen, Netherlands; *U.S. Public*, pg. 1183
Hettinga, Martin, Chm.--HLPB, Amsterdam, Netherlands; *Int'l*, pg. 1377
Hettinger, Jon E., Pres.--Grocery & Specialty Products Division, Columbus, OH; *U.S. Private*, pg. 157
Hettinger, Robert, Gen. Mgr.--ITW Coding Products, Kalkaska, MI; *U.S. Public*, pg. 867
Hetzer, Peter H., Mng. Dir.--Kodak S.A., Lausanne, Switzerland; *U.S. Public*, pg. 554
Heuer, Martina, Gen. Mgr.--Edelman/Heuer & Partner, GmbH, Hamburg, Germany; *U.S. Private*, pg. 363
Heuer, William H., Pres.--Yashica, Inc., Somerset, NJ; *Int'l*, pg. 776
Heukels, D.F., Chief Oper. Officer--NS Holdings NV, Curacao, Netherlands Antilles; *Int'l*, pg. 1082
Heusala, Pekka, Exec. Dir.--Icopal OY, Espoo, Finland; *Int'l*, pg. 659
Heuser, Eberhard, Mng. Dir.--Eldon GmbH, Neuss, Germany; *Int'l*, pg. 436
Heusler, Andreas K., Chief Exec.--Cemento Polpaico S.A., Santiago, Chile; *Int'l*, pg. 629
Heutink, R., Mng. Dir.--Nutricia Cujik B.V., Cuyk, Netherlands; *Int'l*, pg. 991
Heuze, J.C.P.R., Pres.--Prochimar S.A., Paris, France; *Int'l*, pg. 682
Hewett, Peter J., Pres.--MB America, Inc., Westport, CT; *Int'l*, pg. 267
Hewing, Tony, Div. Mgr.--ConAgra Feed Mill, Arcadia, LA; *U.S. Public*, pg. 427
Hewins, William C., V.P.-Intl. Opers.--Welch's International Div., Concord, MA; *U.S. Private*, pg. 784
Hewitson, J. W., Chm. & Mng. Dir.--Albright & Wilson Northern Ireland, Ltd., Belfast, United Kingdom; *Int'l*, pg. 49
Hewitson, J.W., Mng. Dir.--Albright & Wilson Ireland, Ltd., Dublin, Ireland; *Int'l*, pg. 49
Hewitt, Jack, Div. Mgr.--Titan Homes, Inc., Sangerfield, NY; *U.S. Public*, pg. 332
Hewitt, Thomas F., Pres.--Carnival Hotels & Casinos, Miami, FL; *U.S. Public*, pg. 1265
Hewitt, William B., Chm. Bd.--Capital Credit Corporation, Jacksonville, FL; *U.S. Public*, pg. 1667
Hewlett, Brian A., Mgr.--Glasgow Terminal, Glasgow, United Kingdom; *U.S. Public*, pg. 693
Hewlett, P.C., Mgr.--Exxon Computing Services Company, Houston, TX; *U.S. Public*, pg. 601
Hewson, Jeffrey, Pres. & Chief Exec. Officer--Beckley Cardy Group, Mansfield, OH; *U.S. Private*, pg. 190
Hey, Dr., Mng. Dir.--Robert Bosch Produktie NV, Brussels, Belgium; *Int'l*, pg. 206
Hey, John C., Pres.--D.C. Hey Company, Minneapolis, MN; *U.S. Public*, pg. 863
Heydt, Mason, Pres.--Marine Air Systems, Inc., Pompano Beach, FL; *U.S. Private*, pg. 1071
Heying, R., Supvr.--Vancouver Distribution Center, Vancouver, WA; *U.S. Public*, pg. 654
Heykoop, J.D., Mng. Dir.--MB Group plc Engineering Div., Wantage, United Kingdom; *Int'l*, pg. 267
Heymans, Alfonse, Mng. Dir.--Reinshagen Tournai S.A., Tournai, Belgium; *U.S. Public*, pg. 723
Heystek, H.B., Mng. Dir.--Gis Munsters B.V., Erp, Netherlands; *Int'l*, pg. 1133
Heyus, Erna, Mgr.--Butterworths South Africa, Sandton, South Africa; *Int'l*, pg. 1095
Heyward, Andrew, Pres.--CBS News, New York, NY; *U.S. Public*, pg. 274
Heyward, Andrew, Pres.--DIC Entertainment, Burbank, CA; *U.S. Public*, pg. 513
Heyworth, Anthony, Chm. Bd. & Chief Exec. Officer--Society National Bank, Indiana, South Bend, IN; *U.S. Public*, pg. 954

Hiatt, John, V.P. & Gen. Mgr.-KLTR-FM--CBS Radio Div., New York, NY; *U.S. Public*, pg. 274
Hiatt, Robert N., Chm.--Maybelline, Inc., New York, NY; *Int'l*, pg. 819
Hiatt, Russ, Pres. & Chief Exec. Officer--The Citizens State Bank, Williamsport, IN; *U.S. Public*, pg. 1217
Hiatt, W. Harrison, Gen. Mgr.--Alchem Plastics Inc.-California, La Mirada, CA; *U.S. Public*, pg. 1495
Hiatt, W. Harrison, Gen. Mgr.--Atlas-Alchem Plastics-Oregon, McMinnville, OR; *U.S. Public*, pg. 1496
Hibberd, Robin S., Mng. Dir.--BNS International (Hong Kong) Limited, Hong Kong, Hong Kong; *Int'l*, pg. 156
Hibbs, Warren, Mng. Dir.--J. Jarvis & Sons P.L.C., London, United Kingdom; *Int'l*, pg. 705
Hibino, Yukihiko, Mgr.-Japan--Singapore Tourist Promotion Board - Osaka, Osaka, Japan; *Int'l*, pg. 1254
Hibler, Kim, Div. Mgr.--Wyle Electronics-Los Angeles, Calabasas, CA; *Int'l*, pg. 1457
Hibler, Terry, Gen. Mgr.--LaGuardia Learning Center, Flushing, NY; *U.S. Public*, pg. 218
Hibnick, Phillip, Admin.--Vegas Valley Convalescent Center, Las Vegas, NV; *U.S. Public*, pg. 837
Hibon, Louis, Mgr.--Induplast, Vernouillet, France; *Int'l*, pg. 430
Hickam, Wade, Gen. Mgr.--ITW Ransburg Electrostatic Systems, Indianapolis, IN; *U.S. Public*, pg. 867
Hickerson, David, Pres.--Morris Merchants, Inc., Canton, MA; *U.S. Public*, pg. 1706
Hickerson, John T., Pres.--Con-Way Southern Express, Inc., Fort Worth, TX; *U.S. Public*, pg. 281
Hickert, Thomas C., Pres.--WCI Machine Tools, Bridgeport, CT; *Int'l*, pg. 440
Hickey, Joel, Pres.--Dow Corning S.T.I., Plymouth, MI; *U.S. Public*, pg. 523
Hickey, John, Pres.--RPR Correspondant Clearing, Saint Louis, MO; *U.S. Public*, pg. 476
Hickey, John M., Pres.--Associates Insurance Group, Inc., Dallas, TX; *U.S. Public*, pg. 663
Hickey, John M., Pres.--Associates Financial Life Insurance Company, Dallas, TX; *U.S. Public*, pg. 663
Hickey, John M., Pres.--Associates Insurance Company, Dallas, TX; *U.S. Public*, pg. 663
Hickey, John M., Pres.--Commercial Guaranty Insurance Company, Dallas, TX; *U.S. Public*, pg. 663
Hickey, John T., Gen. Mgr.--Planes Moving & Storage Of Indianapolis, Inc., Indianapolis, IN; *U.S. Private*, pg. 869
Hickey, Walter B.D., Jr., Chm. & Chief Policy Officer--Hickey-Freeman/Bobby Jones, Rochester, NY; *U.S. Public*, pg. 795
Hickin, S. Vance, Pres.--F.B. Beattie & Company, Inc., Seattle, WA; *U.S. Public*, pg. 1423
Hickman, J.C., Pres. & Publisher--The Bellingham Herald, Bellingham, WA; *U.S. Public*, pg. 700
Hickman, Roy, V.P.-Prod. Devel.--Lotus Carpet Division, Phenix City, AL; *U.S. Private*, pg. 257
Hicks, Dwain, Pres.--L.J. Smith, Inc., Bowerston, OH; *U.S. Private*, pg. 706
Hicks, George, Gen. Mgr.--Peterson Spring-Three Rivers Plant, Three Rivers, MI; *U.S. Private*, pg. 857
Hicks, Joseph D., Pres. & Chief Exec. Officer--Siecor Corporation, Saskatoon, Canada; *U.S. Public*, pg. 449
Hicks, Lenord, Plant Mgr.--Acme Brick Co., Weir, KS; *U.S. Public*, pg. 936
Hicks, N.W., V.P. & Mgr.--Tencarva Machinery Co., Nashville, TN; *U.S. Private*, pg. 1075
Hicks, Richard, Plant Mgr.--Electron Corp., Blackwell, OK; *U.S. Private*, pg. 370
Hicks, Todd, Gen. Mgr.--Alro Specialty Metals, Charlotte, Charlotte, NC; *U.S. Private*, pg. 46
Hickson, P., Dir.--Lonrho Textiles Ltd., Cramlington, United Kingdom; *Int'l*, pg. 817
Hidaka, Satoshi, Mgr.--Marumoto K.K. Ltd., Tokyo, Japan; *Int'l*, pg. 1084
Hidaka, Toshiaki, Pres.--Toray Fibers (Thailand), Ltd., Bangkok, Thailand; *Int'l*, pg. 1400
Hidalgo, Enrique, Mng. Dir.--Datapoint Iberica S.A., Madrid, Spain; *Int'l*, pg. 384
Hidalgo, Franklin, Gen. Mgr.--Crown Cork CentroAmericana S.A., San Jose, Costa Rica; *U.S. Public*, pg. 464
Hidalgo, Hector Santacruz, Chief Oper. Officer--Wackenhut del Ecuador, S.A., Quito, Ecuador; *U.S. Public*, pg. 1731
Hidalgo, Hector Santacruz, Gen. Mgr.--Seguridad Movil del Ecuador, S.A., Quito, Ecuador; *U.S. Public*, pg. 1731
Hidalgo, Roberto, Chm. Bd.--Cigna Insurance Company of Puerto Rico, Hato Rey, PR; *U.S. Public*, pg. 364
Hidalgu, Tony, Plant Mgr.--Block Products Plant, El Paso, TX; *U.S. Public*, pg. 936
Hiderson, Tim, S.E. Reg. Mgr.--Jaco Electronics, Inc., Raleigh, NC; *U.S. Public*, pg. 920
Hieaux, Bertrand, Dir.--Banque Hieaux, Dreux, France; *Int'l*, pg. 548
Hiekintalo, Mauri, Pres.--Artek oy ab, Helsingfors, Finland; *Int'l*, pg. 1072
Hiel, Georges, Gen. Mgr.--MoDo Paper Benelux BV, Kallo, Belgium; *Int'l*, pg. 887
Hienrich, Edi, Gen. Mgr.--Herbalife International Israel (1990) Ltd., Holon, Israel; *U.S. Public*, pg. 809
Hierneis, Gunter, Dir.--Bayerische Vereinsbank AG, Rio de Janeiro, Brazil; *Int'l*, pg. 180
Hierner, Dieter, Representative--Deutsche Bank AG (Nigeria) Ltd., Lagos, Nigeria; *Int'l*, pg. 404
Hiester, Thomas R., Mng. Dir.--Zurn Thailand, Bangkok, Thailand; *U.S. Public*, pg. 1795
Hifti, Dr. Walter H., Dir.--Unilever (Schweiz) AG, Zurich, Switzerland; *Int'l*, pg. 1439
Higano, Yoshiaki, Gen. Mgr.--Ashikaga Bank-International Division, Tokyo, Japan; *Int'l*, pg. 88
Higashi, Shuntaro, Gen. Mgr.--The Sumitomo Bank, Ltd.-Hong Kong Branch, Central, Hong Kong; *Int'l*, pg. 1309
Higashi, Tadao, Chief Oper. Officer--Miyazaki Oki Electric Co., Ltd., Miyazaki, Japan; *Int'l*, pg. 999
Higashidani, Chieko, Branch Mgr.--Nikko Europe Plc.-Amsterdam Branch, Amsterdam, Netherlands; *Int'l*, pg. 930
Higashimoto, Akira, Pres.--Teichiku Records Co., Ltd., Nara, Japan; *Int'l*, pg. 846
Higashio, Takeshi, Pres.--Haseko (New York) Inc., New York, NY; *Int'l*, pg. 600
Higashio, Takeshi, Chief Fin. Officer--Haseko (USA) Corporation, Los Angeles, CA; *Int'l*, pg. 600
Higashio, Takeshi, Chief Oper. Officer--Haseko Realty (California), Inc., Los Angeles, CA; *Int'l*, pg. 600
Higashiyama, Akiyuki, Pres.--Oversea Courier Service Co., Ltd., Tokyo, Japan; *Int'l*, pg. 929
Higbee, Ann, Mng. Partner--EMA Public Relations Services, Inc., Syracuse, NY; *U.S. Private*, pg. 765
Higbee, D., Pres.--Sawhill Tubular Div., Sharon, PA; *U.S. Public*, pg. 131
Higdon, Danny, V.P.-Sls.--Fairfield Nashville, Nashville, TN; *U.S. Public*, pg. 611
Higgenbotham, H., Mgr.--B.F. Goodrich Chemical (Far East) Ltd., Hong Kong, Hong Kong; *U.S. Public*, pg. 752
Higginbotham, Richard, Pres.--Bowen Tools, Houston, TX; *U.S. Public*, pg. 858
Higgins, Archibald, Gen. Mgr.--Printer Operations-Storage Tek, Palm Bay, FL; *U.S. Public*, pg. 1523
Higgins, Bruce, Pres.--FAMEX, Inc., Novato, CA; *Int'l*, pg. 59
Higgins, Clive, Dir.-Mktg.--Fisons Instruments USA, Beverly, MA; *Int'l*, pg. 1111
Higgins, Donald E., Gen. Mgr.--Boehmers, Kitchener, Canada; *Int'l*, pg. 629
Higgins, Glenn F., Pres.--Comtech Antenna Systems, Inc., Saint Cloud, FL; *U.S. Public*, pg. 425
Higgins, Harold, Publr.--Boulder Publishing, Inc., Boulder, CO; *U.S. Public*, pg. 1447
Higgins, Jack, Pres.--Katz Continental Television, New York, NY; *U.S. Public*, pg. 335
Higgins, James, Chm. Bd., Pres. & Chief Exec. Officer--Charter Builders, Inc., Dallas, TX; *Int'l*, pg. 896
Higgins, Kathy, Pres.--Sachs Properties, Chesterfield, MO; *U.S. Private*, pg. 959
Higgins, Patrick B., Mng. Dir.--Sun Electric U.K. Limited, Kings Lynn, United Kingdom; *U.S. Public*, pg. 1481
Higgins, Richard A, Mng. Dir.--Systems Integration, U.K., Camberley, United Kingdom; *Int'l*, pg. 1154
Higgins, Robert J., Pres. & Chief Exec. Officer--Fleet National Bank, Providence, RI; *U.S. Public*, pg. 649
Higgins, Tom, Mgr.--CCF International Finance Corp., New York, NY; *Int'l*, pg. 342
Higgins, Tom, Mgr.--Sharp Electronics Corporation, Alexandria, VA; *Int'l*, pg. 1229
Higgins, Tom, Gen. Mgr.--Paul Revere Insurance Group, Syracuse, NY; *U.S. Public*, pg. 1338
Higgs, Derek, Chm. Bd.--Prudential Portfolio Managers Limited, London, United Kingdom; *Int'l*, pg. 1073
Highland, Joseph, Chief Exec. Officer--ENVIRON International, Arlington, VA; *U.S. Public*, pg. 1285
Highmark, David, Pres.--Northern Trust Bank of Florida, N.A., Naples, FL; *U.S. Public*, pg. 1196
Hightower, C.S., Mgr.-Sls.--American Steel Pipe Div., Birmingham, AL; *U.S. Private*, pg. 52
Hightower, Lloyd A., Pres. & Chief Exec. Officer--Williams Field Services, Tulsa, OK; *U.S. Public*, pg. 1769
Hightower, Ron, Plant Mgr.--Townsends, Millsboro, DE; *U.S. Private*, pg. 1094
Higo, Yoshinari, Pres.--Kawasho International (H.K.) Ltd., Hong Kong, Hong Kong; *Int'l*, pg. 727
Higuchi, Masanori, Mng. Dir.--Chuo Trust Asia Limited, Hong Kong, Hong Kong; *Int'l*, pg. 291
Higuchi, Takeshi, Pres.--Nikkei Research, Inc., Tokyo, Japan; *Int'l*, pg. 929
Higurashi, Takeshi, Chm. Bd., Pres. & Chief Exec. Officer--Subaru of America, Inc., Cherry Hill, NJ; *Int'l*, pg. 523
Hiigel, Hugh, Mgr.--Woodward Governor (Reguladores) Ltda., Campinas, Brazil; *U.S. Public*, pg. 1777
Hijmans, K., Mng. Dir.--Kaagro B.V., Zoetermeer, Netherlands; *Int'l*, pg. 991
Hikosaka, K., Pres.--Nissho Iwai Foods Corp., Tokyo, Japan; *Int'l*, pg. 946
Hilb, Robert H., Pres.--Hilb, Rogal and Hamilton Company of Canada, Limited, Winnipeg, Canada; *U.S. Public*, pg. 828
Hilbert, Stephen, Chm. Bd., Pres. & Chief Exec. Officer--CHIC, Carmel, IN; *U.S. Public*, pg. 433
Hilbert, Stephen, Chm. Bd., Pres. & Chief Exec. Officer--Intermediate Holdings, Inc., Carmel, IN; *U.S. Public*, pg. 433
Hilbert, Stephen, Chm. Bd., Pres. & Chief Exec. Officer--THD, Inc., Carmel, IN; *U.S. Public*, pg. 433
Hilbert, Steve, Chief Exec. Officer--Conseco Capital Partners II, L.P., New York, NY; *U.S. Public*, pg. 432
Hilbert, Steven, Chm. Bd.--American Life Holding Corp., Des Moines, IA; *U.S. Public*, pg. 432
Hilbert, William M., Sr., Pres. & Chief Exec. Officer--PHB Machining Division, Fairview, PA; *U.S. Private*, pg. 826
Hilbert, William M., Sr., Pres. & Chief Oper. Officer--PHB Tool & Die, Girard, PA; *U.S. Private*, pg. 826
Hilbert, William M., Sr., Pres. & Chief Exec. Officer--PHB Plastic & Rubber Molding Division, Fairview, PA; *U.S. Private*, pg. 826
Hildebrand, E.H., Pres.--CR Quality Services, Inc., Philadelphia, PA; *U.S. Public*, pg. 432
Hildebrand, Ken, Gen. Mgr.--Shell Aerocentre, Calgary, Canada; *Int'l*, pg. 1138
Hildebrand, Michael, Chief Fin. Officer--Compack Douwe Egberts RT, Budapest, Hungary; *U.S. Public*, pg. 1434
Hildebrand, W.R., Pres. & Chief Oper. Officer--Fiatallis North America, Inc., Carol Stream, IL; *Int'l*, pg. 483
Hildebrand, Willard R., Pres. & Chief Exec. Officer--Great Dane Trailers, Inc., Savannah, GA; *U.S. Private*, pg. 1030
Hildebrandt, Andreas, Mgr.--Rickmers-Linie GmbH, Hamburg, Germany; *Int'l*, pg. 596
Hildebrandt, Bernd, Pres.--CCC Steel, Inc., Rancho Dominguez, CA; *U.S. Public*, pg. 1375
Hildebrandt, John, Mgr.--Stephen Gould of Indiana, Inc., Indianapolis, IN; *U.S. Private*, pg. 467
Hildestad, Terry D., Pres. & Chief Exec. Officer--Knife River Coal Mining Company, Bismarck, ND; *U.S. Public*, pg. 1025
Hilding, Greg, Pres.--First American Bank & Trust, Willmar, MN; *U.S. Private*, pg. 167
Hildingsson, Bo, Mng. Dir.--Ericsson Thai Networks Company Ltd., Bangkok, Thailand; *Int'l*, pg. 1368
Hildrew, P. D., Mng. Dir.--Garny AG, Morfelden, Germany; *Int'l*, pg. 387
Hildyard, N., Mng. Dir.--Smith & Nephew Medical Ltd., Kingston-upon-Hull, United Kingdom; *Int'l*, pg. 1263
Hilfiker, Andre, Dr., Mng. Dir.--CIBA-GEIGY Colombiana S.A., Bogota, Colombia; *Int'l*, pg. 976
Hilger, D., Pres.--Trane Europe, Epinal, France; *U.S. Public*, pg. 92
Hill-Reid, M.J., Mng. Dir.--Cyrus J. Lawrence (UK) Limited, London, United Kingdom; *Int'l*, pg. 405
Hill, Allen M., Pres. & Chief Exec. Officer--Dayton Power & Light Co., Dayton, OH; *U.S. Public*, pg. 473
Hill, Brent, Plant Gen. Mgr.--Quebecor Printing Concord, Concord, Canada; *Int'l*, pg. 1077
Hill, Brian, Pres.-Worldwide Seed--Cargill Seed Div., Minneapolis, MN; *U.S. Private*, pg. 210
Hill, C., Gen. Mgr.--Guernsey International Fund Managers Limited, Saint Peter Port, United Kingdom; *Int'l*, pg. 648
Hill, Chuck, Mgr.--AAllied Die Casting Mfg., Inc., Rutherfordton, NC; *U.S. Private*, pg. 903
Hill, Colin, V.P.--Earthmoving Equipment Div., Portland, OR; *U.S. Private*, pg. 383
Hill, Craig, Unit Mgr.--Weatherford Australia Pty. Ltd., Malaga, Australia; *U.S. Public*, pg. 1750
Hill, Dan J., Pres.--Cosbel Petroleum Corp., Houston, TX; *U.S. Public*, pg. 390
Hill, Dan J., Pres. & Chief Exec. Officer--Coastal Tug & Barge, Inc., Miami, FL; *U.S. Public*, pg. 390
Hill, Dave, Gen. Mgr.--Albuquerque Auto Auction Inc., Albuquerque, NM; *U.S. Public*, pg. 1648
Hill, David C., Pres.--AlliedSignal Fibers, Petersburg, VA; *U.S. Public*, pg. 51
Hill, David F., Chief Oper. Officer--Pierce National Life Insurance Co., Greenville, SC; *U.S. Public*, pg. 992
Hill, David F., Chm. Bd.--Washington Square Securities, Minneapolis, MN; *U.S. Public*, pg. 1376
Hill, David F., Pres.--SAFECO Services Co., Seattle, WA; *U.S. Public*, pg. 1423
Hill, David F., Pres.--SAFECO Securities, Inc., Seattle, WA; *U.S. Public*, pg. 1423
Hill, David F., Pres.-SAFECO Mutual Funds--SAFECO Asset Management Company, Seattle, WA; *U.S. Public*, pg. 1423
Hill, David F., Pres.--SAFECO Mutual Funds, Seattle, WA; *U.S. Public*, pg. 1423
Hill, Dieter, Pres.--Turbo-Lufttechnik GmbH, Zweibrucken, Germany; *Int'l*, pg. 399
Hill, Elmer W., Pres.--Litton Precision Gear Div., Chicago, IL; *U.S. Public*, pg. 1003
Hill, Ian, Pres.--Berendsen Fluid Power, Inc., Tulsa, OK; *Int'l*, pg. 1284
Hill, Irving S., Gen. Mgr.--Golf Grip Division, Laurinburg, NC; *U.S. Public*, pg. 557
Hill, J.S., Chief Exec. Officer--MG Natural Gas Corporation, Houston, TX; *Int'l*, pg. 862
Hill, James, Pres.--Superior Emergency Vehicles, Ltd., Red Deer, Canada; *U.S. Public*, pg. 617
Hill, James, Pres.--Nitro Steel Div., Pleasant Prairie, WI; *U.S. Public*, pg. 1349
Hill, Joel, Admin.--McKinley Manor, Gallup, NM; *U.S. Public*, pg. 838
Hill, John, Rep.--Singapore Tourist Promotion Board - Auckland, Auckland, New Zealand; *Int'l*, pg. 1254
Hill, John, Mgr.--Trans-American Steamship Agency, Houston, TX; *Int'l*, pg. 1418
Hill, John, Consultant--Standex Electronics, Cincinnati, OH; *U.S. Public*, pg. 1507
Hill, John, Consultant--Standex Electronics (U.K.) Ltd., Tonbridge, United Kingdom; *U.S. Public*, pg. 1507
Hill, Julie, Pres.--Costain Homes Inc., Newport Beach, CA; *Int'l*, pg. 337
Hill, Kevin R., Pres.--Oxford Health Plans (IL), Inc., Rosemont, IL; *U.S. Public*, pg. 1239
Hill, Lewis, Pres.--First American Tax Valuation, Irving, TX; *U.S. Public*, pg. 625
Hill, Mitch, Mgr.-Large Sls.--PENCO-Nevada, Reno, NV; *Int'l*, pg. 1508
Hill, O., Mng. Dir.--Toshiba Medical Systems GmbH, Neuss, Germany; *Int'l*, pg. 1407
Hill, Paul H., Pres.--Dryvit Systems, Inc., West Warwick, RI; *U.S. Public*, pg. 1357
Hill, R.G., Grp. Gen. Mgr.--Swan Hill Milk Distributors Pty. Ltd., Bendigo, Australia; *Int'l*, pg. 1074
Hill, R.L., Pres.--Amtech Logistics Corporation, Dallas, TX; *U.S. Public*, pg. 432
Hill, Raymond, Grp. Gen. Mgr.--Q.U.F. Milk Marketing, Brisbane, Australia; *Int'l*, pg. 1074
Hill, Richard T., Pres.--HT&T Company, Inc., Hilo, HI; *U.S. Private*, pg. 190
Hill, Robert, Mng. Dir.--Matchbox Collectibles Pty. Ltd., Castle Hill, Australia; *U.S. Public*, pg. 1059
Hill, Robert O., Mgr.-Branch--Piper Jaffray Inc., Durango, CO; *U.S. Public*, pg. 1301
Hill, Rod, Mng. Dir.--Liverpool Airport Public Limited Company, Liverpool, United Kingdom; *Int'l*, pg. 217
Hill, Steven, Pres.--Heritage Asset Management, Inc., Saint Petersburg, FL; *U.S. Public*, pg. 923
Hill, Thomas A., Chm. Bd., Pres. & Chief Exec. Officer--United Missouri Bank of Warsaw, Warsaw, MO; *U.S. Public*, pg. 1655
Hill, William R., Pres. & Chief Exec. Officer--OAO Technology Solutions, Inc., Greenbelt, MD; *U.S. Public*, pg. 1425
Hillary, Sudha, Gen. Mgr.--TMP Worldwide/Recruitment Division, Annandale, VA; *U.S. Private*, pg. 1065
Hillback, Elliott D., Jr., Pres. & Chief Exec. Officer--IG Laboratories, Inc., Framingham, MA; *U.S. Public*, pg. 733

Hillebrand, G., Mng. Dir.--Fuchs' Sche Tongruben GmbH & Co. Ltd., Ransbach-Baumbach, Germany; Int'l, pg. 1488
Hillegass, Bonnie, Pres.--Family Healthcare Services, Inc., Las Vegas, NV; U.S. Public, pg. 1469
Hillen, C.A., Pres. & Gen. Mgr.--Olin Pantex, Inc, Saint Petersburg, FL; U.S. Public, pg. 1219
Hillen, Chip, Gen. Mgr.--Penn Erie Div., Erie, PA; U.S. Private, pg. 870
Hiller, Manfred, Chief Oper. Officer--Neste Oel GmbH, Hamburg, Germany; Int'l, pg. 915
Hiller, Robert G., Pres.--Telecommunications Group, Gaithersburg, MD; U.S. Public, pg. 1745
Hilleshiem, Deb, Mgr.--Williams Fastener & Supply Co., Cedar Rapids, IA; U.S. Private, pg. 1178
Hillgard, Allan, Chief Oper. Officer--AG Alfa-Laval, Vienna, Austria; Int'l, pg. 1379
Hillgath, Tristan, Mng. Dir.--Invesco Europe Ltd., London, United Kingdom; Int'l, pg. 685
Hillhouse, R., Dr., Mng. Dir.--VG Laboratory Systems Ltd., Altrincham, United Kingdom; U.S. Public, pg. 1595
Hillier-Brook, Jan, Gen. Mgr.--Storage Technology Limited, Woking, United Kingdom; U.S. Public, pg. 1523
Hillis, John D., Pres.--Allnewsco, Inc., Springfield, VA; U.S. Private, pg. 854
Hillis, Kelly, Pres. & Chief Exec. Officer--Regions Bank/ Carroll County, Carrollton, GA; U.S. Public, pg. 1372
Hillius, Gustan, Pres.--Automotive Accessory Co., Ltd., Winnipeg, Canada; U.S. Private, pg. 1113
Hillowitz, Les, Mng. Dir.--Rhone-Poulenc Agrichem S.A. (Pty) Ltd, Onderstepoort, South Africa; Int'l, pg. 1112
Hillstrom, David G., Chm. Bd., Pres. & Chief Exec. Officer--Precision Steel Warehouse, Inc., Franklin Park, IL; U.S. Public, pg. 217
Hillukkala, Jukka, Chief Oper. Officer--Raisio Group plc, Vihanti, Finland; Int'l, pg. 1085
Hilmes, Jerome B., Pres.--Applied Technology Division, Falls Church, VA; U.S. Public, pg. 423
Hilpert, Jochen, Chief Oper. Officer--LBS Immobilien GmbH, Frankfurt/Main, Germany; Int'l, pg. 799
Hiltgen, Bill, Chief Oper. Officer--Nebraska Engineering Co., Omaha, NE; U.S. Private, pg. 1064
Hilton, Avery, Pres. & Gen. Mgr.--SMI Steel South Carolina, Cayce, SC; U.S. Public, pg. 412
Hilton, James C., Pres.-Wayne Div.--Dresser Industries Wayne Division, Austin, TX; U.S. Public, pg. 528
Hilton, John R., Mng. Dir.--Delta Fasteners Pty. Ltd., Welshpool, Australia; Int'l, pg. 391
Hilton, Ross, Mgr.--Spectra-Physics Canada, Inc., Mississauga, Canada; Int'l, pg. 1290
Hilton, Tim, Pres.--Fidelity Capital, Boston, MA; U.S. Private, pg. 403
Hilty, Gerald A., Mgr.-Mktg.--Material Handling Systems Div., Chalfont, PA; U.S. Public, pg. 605
Himatsingka, B., Chm. Bd.--Assam Carbon Products Limited, Calcutta, India; Int'l, pg. 891
Himes, Donald A., Pres.--Nordco, Inc., Milwaukee, WI; U.S. Public, pg. 1209
Hin, Chong Siong, Pres. & Gen. Mgr.--Xian-Janssen Pharmaceutical Ltd., Xian, China; U.S. Public, pg. 932
Hin, Tan Siew, Dir.--Building Products Division, Kuala Lumpur, Malaysia; Int'l, pg. 1250
Hinchcliff, Richard H., Mng. Dir.--General Re Europe Limited, London, United Kingdom; U.S. Public, pg. 726
Hinchcliffe, William A., V.P. & Div. Mgr.--Bindley Western, Middletown Division, Middletown, PA; U.S. Public, pg. 228
Hinchliffe, Allan, Chief Oper. Officer--Mikron Corp. Anderson, Anderson, SC; Int'l, pg. 866
Hinchman, David F., Pres. & Chief Exec. Officer--U.S. Precision Lens Inc., Cincinnati, OH; U.S. Public, pg. 448
Hinckley, Jim, Pres.--Club Corporation of America, Dallas, TX; U.S. Private, pg. 247
Hind, A.J., Mng. Dir.--Horstman Timers & Controls Limited, Bath, United Kingdom; Int'l, pg. 297
Hind, David, Mng. Dir.--Ortho Clinical Diagnostic Systems Limited, Amersham, United Kingdom; U.S. Public, pg. 931
Hind, Michael, District Mgr.--AirMate, Oak Brook, IL; U.S. Private, pg. 317
Hinderaker, P., Pres.--DEC Alkar Div., Lodi, WI; U.S. Private, pg. 301
Hindi, Riyadh, Plant Mgr.--Continental Can of Saudi Arabia, Dammam, Saudi Arabia; U.S. Public, pg. 465
Hindle, Tony, Superintendant--Runcorn Terminal, Runcorn, United Kingdom; U.S. Public, pg. 693
Hindman, Arthur, Gen. Mgr.--Instron Japan Co., Ltd., Canton, MA; U.S. Public, pg. 882
Hindman, Arthur, Gen. Mgr.--Instron Asia, Ltd., Canton, MA; U.S. Public, pg. 882
Hindman, Craig, Gen. Mgr.--ITW Buildex, Itasca, IL; U.S. Public, pg. 866
Hindman, Harold, Trustee--Instron Realty Trust, Canton, MA; U.S. Public, pg. 883
Hindman, Harold, Chm. Bd.--Wilson/Shore Instruments, Canton, MA; U.S. Public, pg. 883
Hinds, Cameron, Pres.--First Commerce Investors, Lincoln, NE; U.S. Public, pg. 629
Hinds, Susan C., Asst. Sec.--IES Investments Inc., Cedar Rapids, IA; U.S. Public, pg. 855
Hinds, Thomas M., Chm. Bd., Pres. & Chief Exec. Officer--Regions Bank/Mobile, Mobile, AL; U.S. Public, pg. 1372
Hindson, R.C., Dir.--BT Limited, London, United Kingdom; Int'l, pg. 222
Hiner, Dave, Div. Mgr.--ConAgra Broiler Co., Athens, AL; U.S. Public, pg. 427
Hiner, Roger, Plant Mgr.--Lloydaire/Eljer Inc., Mississauga, Canada; U.S. Public, pg. 1795
Hines, David, Mgr.--Bob Ostrow Co., San Francisco, CA; U.S. Public, pg. 75
Hines, J.B., Pres.--SLI International Corp., Stamford, CT; Int'l, pg. 1268
Hines, Peter S., Chief Oper. Officer--Ronson Aviation, Inc., Trenton, NJ; U.S. Public, pg. 1405
Hines, Richard D., Grp. V.P.--Associated Spring, Bristol, CT; U.S. Public, pg. 190
Hines, Richard L., Pres.--Johnson & Johnson Finance Corporation, New Brunswick, NJ; U.S. Public, pg. 928
Hines, Tom, Mgr.-Division--Specialty Window Coverings, Elkhart, IN; U.S. Public, pg. 491
Hinfey, John K., Pres. & Chief Exec. Officer--United Planners' Financial Services of America, Scottsdale, AZ; U.S. Private, pg. 831
Hinish, Samuel L., Chm.--First National Bank of Saxton, Allentown, PA; U.S. Public, pg. 1222
Hinish, Samuel L., Chm. Bd.--Penn Central National Bank, Huntingdon, PA; U.S. Public, pg. 1222
Hink, Wally, V.P. & Gen. Mgr.--D & K Healthcare Resources-Minneapolis Division, Minneapolis, MN; U.S. Public, pg. 472
Hinkaty, Charles, Pres.--Del Pharmaceuticals, Inc., Farmingdale, NY; U.S. Public, pg. 494
Hinkaty, Charles M., Pres.--Del International, Farmingdale, NY; U.S. Public, pg. 494
Hinkle, Donald, Gen. Mgr.--Rohr Industries, Sheridan Plant, Sheridan, AR; U.S. Public, pg. 752
Hinkle, Harry W., V.P. & Gen. Mgr.--Cardox Division, Walnut Creek, CA; Int'l, pg. 37
Hinkley, Robert C., Partner--Skadden, Arps, Slate, Meagher & Flom LLP, Central, Hong Kong; U.S. Private, pg. 1004
Hinman, Wayne A., Pres.--Air Products Ref-fuel Holding Corp., Allentown, PA; U.S. Public, pg. 31
Hino, Takahiro, Gen. Mgr., Exec. V.P.--Nippon Steel U.S.A., Inc., Houston, TX; Int'l, pg. 940
Hinojosa, Joe, Administrator--Laredo Processing Center, Laredo, TX; U.S. Public, pg. 450
Hinojosa, Santiago, Chm. & Mng. Dir.--DMB&B S.A. de C.V., Mexico, Mexico; U.S. Private, pg. 304
Hinrichs, Horst, Sr. V.P.-Automotive Products--WABCO Automotive Products Group, Hannover, Germany; U.S. Public, pg. 92
Hinrichs, Marlon, Reg. Mgr.--Green Tree Acceptance, Inc., Little Rock, AR; U.S. Public, pg. 762
Hinrup, Peter, Mng. Dir.--Dancall Telecom A/S, Pandrup, Denmark; Int'l, pg. 206
Hinson, Charlie, Pres.--Limited Store Planning, Columbus, OH; U.S. Public, pg. 995
Hinson, Laura K., Chief Fin. Officer--Winterthur U.S. Holdings Inc., Wilmington, DE; Int'l, pg. 345
Hinson, Richard E., Pres. & Gen. Mgr.--Searle Canada Inc., Oakville, Canada; U.S. Public, pg. 1126
Hinterleuthner, Richard, Rep.--Bayerische Landesbank Girozentrale, Milan, Italy; Int'l, pg. 177
Hintikka, Martti, Pres.--ExClay Suomi Oy, Helsinki, Finland; Int'l, pg. 1200
Hintikka, Pentti-Juhani, Pres.--Wartsila Diesel International Ltd. Oy, Strasbourg, France; Int'l, pg. 863
Hintz, Donald, Pres.--Entergy Operations, Inc., Jackson, MS; U.S. Public, pg. 586
Hintz, Donald C., Pres. & Chief Exec. Officer--System Energy Resources, Inc., Jackson, MS; U.S. Public, pg. 586
Hintze, A.A., Mng. Dir.--Purac Sinteses, Rio de Janeiro, Brazil; Int'l, pg. 245
Hinz, William J., Pres.--AlliedSignal Aerospace GmbH, Raunheim, Germany; U.S. Public, pg. 52
Hipkiss, Keith, Gen. Mgr.--Vickers Systems Div., Telford, United Kingdom; U.S. Public, pg. 25
Hippler, John D., Pres. & Chief Exec. Officer--Bank of America, Coeur D'Alene, ID; U.S. Public, pg. 180
Hirabayashi, Ryoji, Gen. Mgr.--Fuji Bank, Dusseldorf Branch, Dusseldorf, Germany; Int'l, pg. 520
Hirai, Naohiko, Chief Rep.--Bank of Yokohama Shanghai, Shanghai, China; Int'l, pg. 159
Hirai, Yoshifumi, Pres.--Yamato Transport USA, Inc., Flushing, NY; Int'l, pg. 1519
Hiraiwa, Masao, Chief Rep.--Madrid Representative Office, Madrid, Spain; Int'l, pg. 816
Hirakawa, Akira, Chief Rep.--Daiwa Bank-Sao Paulo, Sao Paulo, Brazil; Int'l, pg. 374
Hirano, Haruo, Gen. Mgr.--The Emmac, Inc., Gardena, CA; Int'l, pg. 364
Hirano, Keiichiro, Gen. Mgr.-Fund & Foreign Exchange Dept., London--Daiwa Bank-International Treasury Division, Tokyo, Japan; Int'l, pg. 373
Hirano, Kenichiro, Dep. Gen. Mgr.--Daiwa Bank-London, London, United Kingdom; Int'l, pg. 373
Hirano, Kohei, Gen. Mgr.--Dai Nippon Printing (Europa) GmbH, Dusseldorf, Germany; Int'l, pg. 363
Hirano, Masahiro, Chief Rep.--The Industrial Bank of Japan, Limited (Beijing), Beijing, China; Int'l, pg. 675
Hirano, Sadayoshi, Chief Oper. Officer--Makita Sp. Z O.O., Bielsko-Biala, Poland; Int'l, pg. 832
Hirano, Sadayoshi, Chief Oper. Officer--Makita S.R.O., Brno, Czech Republic; Int'l, pg. 832
Hirano, Sadayoshi, Chief Oper. Officer--Makita Kft., Szekesfehervar, Hungary; Int'l, pg. 832
Hiraoka, Akikazu, Gen. Mgr.--Sakura Bank - Chicago Branch, Chicago, IL; Int'l, pg. 1179
Hirasa, Takeshi, Gen. Mgr.--Dentsu Inc. Taipei, Taipei, Taiwan; Int'l, pg. 393
Hirasawa, Takashi, Branch Mgr.--Analog Devices K.K., Osaka, Japan; U.S. Public, pg. 108
Hirashima, Tomoyoshi, Pres.--Circle Freight International Japan Ltd., Funibashi, Japan; U.S. Public, pg. 372
Hirata, N., Pres.--Nihon Shokuhin Kako Co., Ltd., Tokyo, Japan; U.S. Public, pg. 447
Hirata, Nobuo, Pres.--Dentsu Kyushu, Fukuoka, Japan; Int'l, pg. 393
Hirata, Takashi, Chief Rep.--The Sakura Bank - Dalian Representative Office, Dalian, China; Int'l, pg. 1179
Hirata, Yasuaki, Mng. Dir.--Kobe Steel Europe, Ltd., London, United Kingdom; Int'l, pg. 741
Hirata, Yukio, Mng. Dir.--Chuo Trust International Limited, London, United Kingdom; Int'l, pg. 291
Hirayama, Shinji, Pres. & Chief Exec. Officer--The Fuji Bank & Trust Co., New York, NY; Int'l, pg. 519
Hird, Stephen C., Mgr.-Branch--Piper Jaffray Inc., Madison, WI; U.S. Public, pg. 1301
Hirgi, Murad, Chief Fin. Officer--Western Cooperative Fertilizers Limited (WCFL), Calgary, Canada; Int'l, pg. 1195
Hirko, Joe, Pres.--Tule Hub Services Co., Portland, OR; U.S. Public, pg. 585
Hirl, J. Roger, Pres. & Chief Exec. Officer--Occidental Chemical Corporation, Dallas, TX; U.S. Public, pg. 1210
Hirlinger, Franz-Hermann, Chief Rep.--Bayerische Landesbank Girozentrale, Tokyo, Japan; Int'l, pg. 177
Hirosawa, Steve, Branch Mgr.--Noritake Co., Inc.-Table Top Div., Dallas, Dallas, TX; Int'l, pg. 959
Hirose, Kazuhiro, Chm.--Toshiba Electronics Asia (Singapore) Pte. Ltd., Singapore, Singapore; Int'l, pg. 1406
Hirose, Masashi, Pres.--Miura Boiler Co. Ltd., Northbrook, IL; Int'l, pg. 884
Hirose, Shuji, V.P.--Sumitomo Corporation of America, Southfield, MI; Int'l, pg. 1312
Hirota, Akira, Pres.--Nippon Keystone Corporation, Kobe, Japan; U.S. Public, pg. 1650
Hiroyuki, Hatasa, Mgr.--AA Japan Co., Tokyo, Japan; U.S. Private, pg. 50
Hirs, James, Pres.--AmSouth Bank N.A., Mobile, AL; U.S. Public, pg. 105
Hirsch, Brad, Pres.--Shane Handbags, New York, NY; U.S. Public, pg. 920
Hirsch, Henry C., Pres. & Chief Oper. Officer--Williams Telecommunications Systems, Inc., Houston, TX; U.S. Public, pg. 1769
Hirsch, Howard, Pres.--Forest Electric Corp., New York, NY; U.S. Public, pg. 571
Hirsch, Robert, Branch Mgr.--Zellerbach Division, Glendale, AZ; U.S. Public, pg. 1076
Hirsch, Robert A., Pres.--Baldwin Steel Company, Jersey City, NJ; Int'l, pg. 401
Hirschauer, Tom, Pres.--EvansGroup, Indianapolis, IN; U.S. Private, pg. 385
Hirschberg, Henry, Pres.--Higher Education Division, Upper Saddle River, NJ; U.S. Private, pg. 778
Hirschmann, Joseph L., Pres.--First DataBank, San Bruno, CA; U.S. Private, pg. 515
Hirshson, William R., Pres.--Coscan Waterways, Inc., Aventura, FL; Int'l, pg. 228
Hirsig, Alan R., Pres. & Chief Exec. Officer--ARCO Chemical Co., Newtown Square, PA; U.S. Public, pg. 144
Hirst, James T., Div. Mgr.--Glassboro Div., Glassboro, NJ; U.S. Public, pg. 1488
Hirt, David J., Pres. & Chief Exec. Officer--Batesville Casket Company, Inc., Batesville, IN; U.S. Public, pg. 828
Hirvensalo, Mikko, Chief Oper. Officer--Ahlstrom Machinery Mantta Pump Factory, Mantta, Finland; Int'l, pg. 33
Hisamitsu, Tatsuhiko, Pres.--Haseko Urbest Inc., Tokyo, Japan; Int'l, pg. 600
Hisano, Ryomin, Pres.--Shin-Wako Securities Investment Trust and Management Co., Ltd., Tokyo, Japan; Int'l, pg. 1485
Hiscock, Derek, Pres.--Robinson-Blackmore Express, Saint Johns, Canada; Int'l, pg. 924
Hislof, Ian, Pres. & Chief Exec. Officer--Capital Controls Company Inc., Colmar, PA; Int'l, pg. 1226
Hitchcock, John G., Jr., Pres. & Sr. Trust Officer--Franklin Templeton Trust Company, San Mateo, CA; U.S. Public, pg. 680
Hitchcock, Kenneth W., Chm. Bd. & Chief Exec. Officer--The Whyte & Mackay Group Plc., Glasgow, United Kingdom; U.S. Public, pg. 675
Hitchings, Jeff, Gen. Mgr.--Effron Fuel Oil Co., Inc., Poughkeepsie, NY; U.S. Private, pg. 729
Hitesman, Timothy E., Pres.--Osborn Manufacturing, Cleveland, OH; U.S. Public, pg. 924
Hitesy, Agnes, Repr.--Kredietbank Representative Office (Budapest), Budapest, Hungary; Int'l, pg. 760
Hitsman, A.E., Pres.--Boeing Electronics, Inc., Irving, TX; U.S. Public, pg. 240
Hively, Robert J., Publr.--The Topeka Capital-Journal, Topeka, KS; U.S. Private, pg. 995
Hixon, Fred, Plant Mgr.--Selkirk Metalbestos N.A., Logan, OH; U.S. Public, pg. 1794
Hixon, Fred, Plant Mgr.--Selkirk Canada Ltd., Brockville, Canada; U.S. Public, pg. 1795
Hixon, John, V.P.--Alliant Techsystems-Rocket Center, Keyser, WV; U.S. Public, pg. 47
Hixon, Thomas, Chm. Bd., Pres. & Chief Exec. Officer--Gulf South Medical Supply, Inc., Ridgeland, MS; U.S. Public, pg. 1294
Hixson, David M., Asst. V.P.--IBP-Finney County, Holcomb, KS; U.S. Public, pg. 852
Hjelle, Bjorn, Gen. Mgr.--Kvaerner Eureka, Alesund Division, Alesund, Norway; Int'l, pg. 767
Hjelle, Bjorn, Gen. Mgr.--Kvaerner Fish Process Technology a.s - Kvaerner Kulde, Alesund, Norway; Int'l, pg. 768
Hjerpe, William, Pres.--Honeywell Europe S.A., Brussels, Belgium; U.S. Public, pg. 834
Hjertaas, Klaus Erik, Mgr.--Tyri A/S, Kroderen, Norway; Int'l, pg. 421
Hjertstedt, Gouran, Mng. Dir.--SKF Mekan AB, Katrineholm, Sweden; Int'l, pg. 1157
Hjort, Hans Henning, Pres.--Asea Brown Boveri Lda., Lisbon, Portugal; Int'l, pg. 8
Hjorth, John, Gen. Mgr.--TMP Worldwide Pty Ltd., Melbourne, Australia; Int'l, pg. 1342
Hjorth, Sven-Gunnar, Mng. Dir.--SAS Mediapartner AB, Stockholm, Sweden; Int'l, pg. 1202
Hjorth, Tomy, Pres.--Kockums AB, Malmo, Sweden; Int'l, pg. 277
Hladik, Milan, Rep.--Fleming Investments Limited, Prague, Czech Republic; Int'l, pg. 494
Hlavac, Jozef, Mng. Dir.--Istropolitana/DMB&B Bratislava, Bratislava, Slovakia; U.S. Private, pg. 304
Hlavacek, Jim, Pres.--American Trans Air Training Corp., Indianapolis, IN; U.S. Public, pg. 106

Hnat, D., District Mgr.--A.M. Castle & Co., Charlotte, NC; *U.S. Public*, pg. 313
Hnatuk, John, Chief Oper. Officer--Anixter Saskatoon, Saskatoon, Canada; *U.S. Public*, pg. 116
Ho Kee, Lim, Sr. V.P. & Branch Mgr.--Union Bank of Switzerland, Singapore Branch, Singapore, Singapore; *Int'l*, pg. 1440
Ho, Adrian, Country Mgr.--Circle Freight (Maylaysia) SDN BHD, Penang, Malaysia; *U.S. Public*, pg. 373
Ho, Anthony, Chief Exec. Officer--The Universal Hardware and Plastic Fty. Ltd., Kowloon, Hong Kong; *Int'l*, pg. 430
Ho, Bernard, Chief Oper. Officer--Royal Copenhagen Singapore Pte. Ltd., Singapore, Singapore; *Int'l*, pg. 1135
Ho, David, Mng. Dir.--Sime Travel (Singapore) Private Limited, Singapore, Singapore; *Int'l*, pg. 1251
Ho, Geoff, Mgr.--Commerzbank AG-Labuan, Labuan, Malaysia; *Int'l*, pg. 311
Ho, Kim Ki, Pres.--Ssangyong Heavy Industries Co., Ltd., Seoul, Korea; *Int'l*, pg. 1292
Ho, Patrick, Mgr.--Corcom Far East Ltd., Kwai Chung, Hong Kong; *U.S. Public*, pg. 446
Ho, Raymond, Pres.--Astra (Wuxi) Pharmaceutical, Wuxi, China; *Int'l*, pg. 94
Ho, S., Mng. Dir.--Hanimex Vivitar (H.K.) Ltd., Kowloon, Hong Kong; *Int'l*, pg. 1061
Ho, S.O., Mng. Dir.--Wellcome Singapore Private Ltd., Singapore, Singapore; *Int'l*, pg. 553
Ho, Steven, Gen. Mgr.--Diodes Co. Ltd., Taipei, Taiwan; *U.S. Public*, pg. 510
Ho, Tan Swee, Gen. Mgr.--Bank Brussels Lambert, Labuan, Labuan, Malaysia; *Int'l*, pg. 148
Hoadley, James, Gen. Mgr.-Sls. & Mktg.--ITW Screen Process Specialist, Ltd., Plymouth, WI; *U.S. Public*, pg. 867
Hoadley, Thomas C., Chief Oper. Officer & Exec. V.P.--Lanai Co., Ltd., Lanai City, HI; *U.S. Public*, pg. 313
Hoag, James, Chief Exec. Officer--Meridian Sports/Water Sports Group, New York, NY; *U.S. Private*, pg. 689
Hoag, Peter J., Gen. Mgr.--J.J. Tourek Co., Elk Grove Village, IL; *U.S. Private*, pg. 1111
Hoag, Thomas R., Pres. & Chief Exec. Officer--ScanTron Corporation, Tustin, CA; *U.S. Public*, pg. 786
Hoak, Scott, Gen. Mgr.--Adcom of Iowa, Inc., Grant City, MO; *U.S. Private*, pg. 1137
Hoar, Paul, Pres.--Crown Cork de Guatemala, S.A., Guatemala, Guatemala; *U.S. Public*, pg. 464
Hoare, C.J., Gen. Mgr.--Johnson's Wax (East Africa) Ltd., Nairobi, Kenya; *U.S. Private*, pg. 593
Hoare, Toby, Chief Exec. Officer-Y&R London--Young & Rubicam Holdings Ltd., London, United Kingdom; *U.S. Private*, pg. 1199
Hobbs, Andrew, Chm. Bd.--Kim Eng Securities (London) Limited, London, United Kingdom; *Int'l*, pg. 733
Hobbs, Craig S., Pres.--Composite Research & Management Company, Seattle, WA; *U.S. Public*, pg. 1742
Hobbs, J.E., V.P. & Gen. Mgr.--General Latex & Chemical Corp (N.C.), Charlotte, NC; *U.S. Private*, pg. 444
Hobbs, John S., Pres.--W.E. O'Neil Construction Company of Arizona, Phoenix, AZ; *U.S. Private*, pg. 817
Hobbs, Mixon, Pres.--Homestead Homes, Cordele, GA; *U.S.* Public, pg. 318
Hobby, Ric, Opers. Mgr.--Herbalife (UK) Limited, Slough, United Kingdom; *U.S. Public*, pg. 809
Hoberman, Alan, Gen. Mgr.--TSI Argus Research Laboratories & Center for Photobiology, Horsham, PA; *U.S. Public*, pg. 733
Hobratschk, A., Pres.--Hamworthy USA, Inc., Forest Park, GA; *Int'l*, pg. 1066
Hobson, Bill, Gen. Mgr.--Tradewind Technologies, Inc., Phoenix, AZ; *U.S. Public*, pg. 937
Hobson, Brian, Gen. Mgr.--CA Capital Management Limited, Central, Hong Kong; *Int'l*, pg. 347
Hobson, Derry, Gen. Mgr.--Sequoia-Pacific Systems Corp., Exeter, CA; *Int'l*, pg. 1270
Hobson, Ed, Div. Mgr.--Bindley Western, Orange Division, Orange, CT; *U.S. Public*, pg. 228
Hobson, Harry, Plant Mgr.--York Intl./Reco, San Antonio, TX; *U.S. Public*, pg. 1789
Hobson, Michael, Gen. Mgr.--President Baking-Marietta, Marietta, OK; *Int'l*, pg. 1069
Hoch, John L., Chm.--Van Deventer & Hoch, Glendale, CA; *U.S. Public*, pg. 339
Hochberg, Mitchell C., Pres. & Chief Exec. Officer--Spectrum Skanska Inc., Greenwich, CT; *Int'l*, pg. 1261
Hochenberry, Barry, Pres.--Berryville Graphics Inc., Berryville, VA; *Int'l*, pg. 191
Hochfelder, James L., Pres.--Pierre Cardin Knits, New York, NY; *U.S. Public*, pg. 520
Hochfelder, Thomas G., Pres.--Knitmaker Division, New York, NY; *U.S. Public*, pg. 520
Hochleitner, A., Chief Oper. Officer--Siemens AG Oesterreich, Vienna, Austria; *Int'l*, pg. 1247
Hochner, Gad, Gen. Mgr.--Elscint (GB) Limited, Watford, United Kingdom; *Int'l*, pg. 450
Hochstrasser, Bruno, Mng. Dir.--Studer, Regensdorf, Switzerland; *U.S. Public*, pg. 788
Hock, Wilson Tan Poh, Mgr.-Commercial--Singapore Airport Terminal Services, Singapore, Singapore; *Int'l*, pg. 1374
Hockenberg, Werner, Mng. Dir.--Flexaust G.m.b.H., Mulheim an der Ruhr, Germany; *U.S. Public*, pg. 394
Hocker, Ronald J., Pres.--National Attorneys' Title Assurance Fund, Inc., Vevay, IN; *U.S. Private*, pg. 98
Hockman, Carol, Pres.--Liz Claiborne Outlet Division, Secaucus, NJ; *U.S. Public*, pg. 1006
Hockridge, Lance E., Grp. Gen. Mgr.--BHP Transport, Melbourne, Australia; *Int'l*, pg. 225
Hoctor, James B., Pres.--DCA of Texas, Inc., Houston, TX; *U.S. Public*, pg. 988
Hod, E., Mng. Dir.--Gestetner (Israel) Limited, Tel Aviv, Israel; *Int'l*, pg. 1115
Hodapp, Siegfried, Pres. & Chief Oper. Officer--Metallgesellschaft Corp., New York, NY; *Int'l*, pg. 861
Hodapp, Siegfried, Chm. & Chief Exec. Officer--MG Refining & Marketing, Inc., Houston, TX; *Int'l*, pg. 862
Hoddinott, Geoff, Mgr.--Remington Consumer Products, Ltd., Northampton, United Kingdom; *U.S. Private*, pg. 921
Hodenberg, Claus, Pres. & Gen. Mgr.--Vermont GMBH, Starnberg, Germany; *U.S. Public*, pg. 578
Hodes, Bernard S., Pres.--Bernard Hodes Group, New York, NY; *U.S. Public*, pg. 1224
Hodge, Luther H., Pres.--Fleet Trust Co. of Florida, N.A., Stuart, FL; *U.S. Public*, pg. 649
Hodgen, Paul J., V.P.-Fin.--Sandvik Coromant Company, Fair Lawn, NJ; *Int'l*, pg. 1185
Hodges, Brian, Gen. Mgr.--ANI Strata Products, Bennetts Green, Australia; *Int'l*, pg. 100
Hodges, C.C., Chief Oper. Officer--Lincoln Big Three, Inc., Baton Rouge, LA; *Int'l*, pg. 37
Hodges, Don, Plant Mgr.--Crowley Tubing Div., Crowley, TX; *U.S. Public*, pg. 159
Hodges, Jim, V.P. & Gen. Mgr.--Pirelli Jerome Inc., Beaufort, SC; *Int'l*, pg. 1059
Hodges, John, Div. Mgr.--Huls America Inc., Miplom Division, Elizabeth, NJ; *Int'l*, pg. 1455
Hodges, Larry, Pres. & Chief Exec. Officer--Pretzel Time Inc., Salt Lake City, UT; *U.S. Private*, pg. 688
Hodgkins, R.J.J., Grp. Pres.-Asia Pacific--Keystone Pacific Pty. Ltd., Nowra, Australia; *U.S. Public*, pg. 1650
Hodgkinson, Geoffrey, Mng. Dir.--Mase Westpac Australia Limited, Sydney, Australia; *Int'l*, pg. 1496
Hodgkinson, Patricia, Chief Oper. Officer & Dir.-Admin.--Charter Clinic Nightingale, London, United Kingdom; *U.S.* Public, pg. 1036
Hodgson, Alistair, Mng. Dir.--British Aerospace Australia Limited, The Levels, Australia; *Int'l*, pg. 218
Hodgson, R.J., Pres.--Technical Coatings Co., Flanders, NJ; *U.S. Private*, pg. 133
Hodin, Donald, Pres.--Waltec Engineering, Wallaceburg, Canada; *Int'l*, pg. 453
Hodnett, M.M., Pres.--Lockheed Aeromod Center, Inc., Greenville, SC; *U.S. Public*, pg. 1007
Hodowal, John R., Chm. Bd. & Chief Exec. Officer--Mid-America Capital Resources, Inc., Indianapolis, IN; *U.S. Public*, pg. 913
Hodowal, John R., Chm. Bd.--Mid-America Energy Resources, Indianapolis, IN; *U.S. Public*, pg. 913
Hodowal, John R., Chm. Bd. & Chief Exec. Officer--Cleveland Thermal Energy Corporation, Cleveland, OH; *U.S. Public*, pg. 913
Hodowal, John R., Chm. Bd. & Chief Exec. Officer--Cleveland District Cooling Corp., Cleveland, OH; *U.S. Public*, pg. 913
Hodsdon, Kenneth, Gen. Mgr.--Pinkham Lumber, Ashland, ME; *U.S. Public*, pg. 248
Hodson, Robert C., Gen. Plant Mgr.--UTA Grabill Plant, Grabill, IN; *U.S. Public*, pg. 1691
Hoe, Tan Kian, Mgr.--Sandvik Malaysia Sdn. Bhd., Kuala Lumpur, Malaysia; *Int'l*, pg. 1187
Hoecker, B.W., Pres.--NationsBank of Columbia, Columbia, MO; *U.S. Public*, pg. 1165
Hoed, Hoediatmo, Pres.--P.T. Freeport Indonesia Co., New Orleans, LA; *U.S. Public*, pg. 681
Hoefler, Dieter, Country Mgr.--Autodesk GmbH, Munich, Germany; *U.S. Public*, pg. 149
Hoefler, Stefan, Gen. Mgr.--IPC Corporation (Germany), Siegsdorf, Germany; *Int'l*, pg. 651
Hoefmans, Arno, Dir. Gen.--Bristol-Myers Belgium S.A N.V., Brussels, Belgium; *U.S. Public*, pg. 255
Hoefner, P., Chief Oper. Officer--Osram Argentina S.A.C.I., Buenos Aires, Argentina; *Int'l*, pg. 1244
Hoeft, Jack, Chm. Bd. & Chief Exec. Officer--Bantam Doubleday Dell Publishing Group, Inc., New York, NY; *Int'l*, pg. 191
Hoeg, Steinar, Pres.--Astra Norge A/S, Skare, Norway; *Int'l*, pg. 94
Hoek, Hein, Chief Oper. Officer--NCT Singapore Pte. Ltd., Singapore, Singapore; *Int'l*, pg. 914
Hoeksema, Timothy E., Chm. Bd. & Chief Exec. Officer--K-C Aviation Inc., Neenah, WI; *U.S. Public*, pg. 959
Hoeksema, Timothy E., Chm. Bd., Pres. & Chief Exec. Officer--Midwest Express Airlines, Inc., Oak Creek, WI; *U.S. Public*, pg. 1111
Hoekstra, Karl E., V.P. & Gen. Mgr.--Dentsply Ransom & Randolph, Los Angeles, CA; *U.S. Public*, pg. 499
Hoekstra, Karl E., Dr., V.P. & Gen. Mgr.--Ransom & Randolph Division, Maumee, OH; *U.S. Public*, pg. 499
Hoel, Lars, Mng. Dir.--Skega GmbH, Muhlacker, Germany; *Int'l*, pg. 1323
Hoel, Roar, Managing Dir.--Bakers AS, Oslo, Norway; *Int'l*, pg. 1010
Hoelter, Heinrich, Co.-Chief Oper. Officer--ENERGAS Gesellschaft zur Energiegewinnung aus Mull und Kohle mbH, Berlin, Germany; *Int'l*, pg. 1166
Hoem, Oistein, Mng. Dir.--Corro-Coat A/S, Larvik, Norway; *Int'l*, pg. 714
Hoenigsberg, Peter, V.P. & Dir.-Intl. Publishing--The International Publishing Group, Reading, MA; *Int'l*, pg. 1027
Hoenigsberg, Peter, Chief Oper. Officer--Addison-Wesley Publishers Ltd., Wokingham, United Kingdom; *Int'l*, pg. 1027
Hoenshell, R. Craig, Chm. Bd. & Chief Exec. Officer--Avis Car Leasing, Garden City, NY; *U.S. Public*, pg. 321
Hoeppner, Joerg, Dir.--Elbe Transport G.m.b.H., Hamburg, Germany; *Int'l*, pg. 1436
Hoeppner, Tom, Pres.--Kraft Foods Inc., Glenview, IL; *U.S. Public*, pg. 1288
Hoerig, Jerry, Pres.--Syntex Chemicals, Inc., Boulder, CO; *Int'l*, pg. 1120
Hoerl, Thelma, R.N., Fac. Mgr.--Central Maryland Surgery Center, Baltimore, MD; *U.S. Public*, pg. 803
Hoerster, E., Pres.--Industrial Coatings Div., Wichita, KS; *U.S. Public*, pg. 1466
Hoesterey, R., Pres.--Para Systems Inc., Carrollton, TX; *U.S. Private*, pg. 260
Hoevelmann, Dr. Paul, V.P.-Grp.--Henkel Corporation Functional Products Div., La Grange, IL; *Int'l*, pg. 610
Hoeven, Pvander, Chief Oper. Officer--Vonk Systems, Coevorden, Netherlands; *Int'l*, pg. 681
Hofer, Judith K., Pres. & Chief Exec. Officer--Filene's, Boston, MA; *U.S. Public*, pg. 1063
Hofer, Jurg, Mng. Dir.--Nokia Telecommunications AG, Dubendorf, Switzerland; *Int'l*, pg. 953
Hoff, D., Chief Oper. Officer--Mill-Log Equipment Co., Inc., Coburg, OR; *U.S. Public*, pg. 1646
Hoff, D.K., Gen. Mgr.--CHEMCENTRAL/Los Angeles, Santa Fe Springs, CA; *U.S. Private*, pg. 232
Hoff, H.M., Pres.--Flow Control Equipment, Tomball, TX; *U.S. Public*, pg. 1393
Hoff, Walter, Pres.--First Data Resources, Omaha, NE; *U.S.* Public, pg. 631
Hofferth, L.M., V.P. & Gen. Mgr.--McGill Mfg. Co. Bearing Division, Valparaiso, IN; *U.S. Public*, pg. 573
Hoffman-Petersen, Erik, Mng. Dir.--FLS Miljo A/S, Valby, Denmark; *Int'l*, pg. 475
Hoffman, Brent, Admin.--North Las Vegas Care Center, Las Vegas, NV; *U.S. Public*, pg. 837
Hoffman, Brian, Service Center Mgr.--Square D Co., Mercer Island, WA; *Int'l*, pg. 1208
Hoffman, Bruno, Pres.--Hoffman Laces, Ltd., Cobleskill, NY; *U.S. Public*, pg. 769
Hoffman, Charles, Pres.--Litton Applied Technology, San Jose, CA; *U.S. Public*, pg. 1003
Hoffman, Dave, Pres.--ALZA, Ltd., Palo Alto, CA; *U.S. Public*, pg. 62
Hoffman, David, Reg. V.P.--Arrow/Schweber Electronics, Salt Lake City, UT; *U.S. Public*, pg. 134
Hoffman, David, Chm. Bd.--Freeman Products, Elmwood Park, NJ; *U.S. Private*, pg. 1105
Hoffman, Dieter, Mng. Dir.--Allgemeine Privatkundenbank AG, Hannover, Germany; *Int'l*, pg. 159
Hoffman, Dirk, Dr., Mng. Dir.--G. Drauz GmbH & Co., Heilbronn, Germany; *Int'l*, pg. 507
Hoffman, Dr. Paul R., Pres.--Textron Systems Corporation, Lowell, MA; *U.S. Public*, pg. 1589
Hoffman, F. David, Jr., V.P.-Petroleum Operations--Hawaii Independent Refinery, Honolulu, HI; *Int'l*, pg. 225
Hoffman, G.M., Pres.--Centra Gas Manitoba Inc., Winnipeg, Canada; *Int'l*, pg. 1492
Hoffman, George W., Pres.--Keystone Industries, Inc., Naperville, IL; *U.S. Public*, pg. 1711
Hoffman, George W., Pres.--Keystone Railway Equipment Company, Camp Hill, PA; *U.S. Public*, pg. 1711
Hoffman, Gregory R., Mgr.--Piper Jaffray Inc., Fargo, ND; *U.S. Public*, pg. 1301
Hoffman, James L., Gen. Mgr.--DMI Furniture, Inc., Huntingburg, IN; *U.S. Public*, pg. 473
Hoffman, Jeff, Pres.--The Acorn, Kalamazoo, MI; *U.S. Private*, pg. 454
Hoffman, Kenneth A., Pres. & Chief Exec. Officer--Hart Schaffner & Marx Clothes, Chicago, IL; *U.S. Public*, pg. 795
Hoffman, M., Pres.--Sterling Instrument Div., New Hyde Park, NY; *U.S. Private*, pg. 327
Hoffman, Mark H., Pres.--Transport, Inc., Madison, AL; *U.S. Public*, pg. 482
Hoffman, Nito, Chief Oper. Officer--Bank Leumi (Luxembourg) S.A., Senningerberg, Luxembourg; *Int'l*, pg. 150
Hoffman, Oswald, Mng. Dir.--Corcom GmbH, Martinsried, Germany; *U.S. Public*, pg. 446
Hoffman, Pam, Branch Mgr.--Downey Savings & Loan Association, F.A., Laguna Niguel, CA; *U.S. Public*, pg. 526
Hoffman, Patty, V.P. & Mng. Dir.--Western International Media Corporation, Sacramento, CA; *U.S. Private*, pg. 1167
Hoffman, R.L., Pres.--Flowserve Corporation, Valve Div., Cookeville, TN; *U.S. Public*, pg. 658
Hoffman, Ray, Administrator--Butte Park Royal, Butte, MT; *U.S. Public*, pg. 837
Hoffman, Richard J., Dir.-Matls. Mngmt.--Sphere Supply, Inc., Houston, TX; *Int'l*, pg. 765
Hoffman, Richard R., Pres.--HAWG Hauling & Disposal, Inc., Buckhannon, WV; *U.S. Public*, pg. 403
Hoffman, Ulrich, Chief Oper. Officer--Volta Electrogenerate Vertriebs GmbH, Stuttgart, Germany; *Int'l*, pg. 442
Hoffman, W., Gen. Mgr.--GKN Technology US, Auburn Hills, MI; *Int'l*, pg. 535
Hoffman, Wayne, Gen. Mgr.--Siegling America Inc., Huntersville, NC; *Int'l*, pg. 497
Hoffmann, Allen J., Pres. & Gen. Mgr.--Carlisle Engineered Products, Chardon, OH; *U.S. Public*, pg. 305
Hoffmann, David R., Pres. & Chief Fin. Officer--ALZA Development Corporation, Palo Alto, CA; *U.S. Public*, pg. 62
Hoffmann, Ken, Pres.--Adapt Electronic Publishing, San Francisco, CA; *Int'l*, pg. 191
Hoffmann, M.R., Chief Oper. Officer--Babcock International Investments Ltd., London, United Kingdom; *Int'l*, pg. 472
Hoffmann, Peter, Chief Oper. Officer--Lang Apparatebau GmbH, Siegsdorf, Germany; *Int'l*, pg. 610
Hoffmann, Rolf, Pres.--Magdeburger Armaturenwerke MAW AG, Magdeburg, Germany; *Int'l*, pg. 400
Hoffmaster, Howard, Publisher--Winona Daily News, Winona, MN; *U.S. Public*, pg. 984
Hofman, E., Mng. Dir.--General Motors Hungary (Distribution) Ltd., Budapest, Hungary; *U.S. Public*, pg. 722
Hofman, George W., Pres. & Chief Oper. Officer--Teleflex Automotive, Troy, MI; *U.S. Public*, pg. 1569
Hofman, Ted, Plant Mgr.--Metform, Inc., Savanna, IL; *U.S. Private*, pg. 692
Hofmann, C.B., Pres.--Amecom Div., College Park, MD; *U.S.* Public, pg. 1002
Hofmann, Ernst A., Mng. Dir.--General Motors Hungary, Budapest, Hungary; *U.S. Public*, pg. 722
Hofmann, Hartmut, Gen. Mgr.--CM Chemical, Berkeley Heights, NJ; *Int'l*, pg. 861

Hofmann, Herbert C., Pres. & Chief Exec. Officer--Bulova Corporation, Woodside, NY; U.S. Public, pg. 1010

Hofmann, Ivan T., Pres.--RPS Inc., Coraopolis, PA; U.S. Public, pg. 604

Hofmann, Werner, Pres.-North America--Intercosmetics, Inc., New York, NY; Int'l, pg. 1489

Hofschulz, Robert, Pres.--Intercare Technologies, Inc., Waukesha, WI; U.S. Public, pg. 459

Hofstra, Johan, Pres.-DMB&B Eur., Mid. East, Africa, India, Pakistan& IMP Europe--DMB&B/Worldwide Communications Amsterdam, Amsterdam, Netherlands; U.S. Private, pg. 304

Hofvander, Per, Pres.--Skanska International Civil Engineering AB, Danderyd, Sweden; Int'l, pg. 1260

Hogan, Dan W., Pres. & Chief Exec. Officer--NBC Bank, FSB (Knoxville), Knoxville, TN; U.S. Public, pg. 1155

Hogan, Daug, Pres.--Teledyne Advanced Materials, Huntsville, AL; U.S. Public, pg. 43

Hogan, Gerald P., Pres.--Automobile Club Insurance Company, Columbus, OH; U.S. Private, pg. 51

Hogan, J.E., Gen. Mgr.--MSA de Mexico, S.A. de C.V., Mexico, Mexico; U.S. Public, pg. 1114

Hogan, John E., V.P. & Gen. Mgr.--WPCH-FM, Atlanta, GA; U.S. Public, pg. 923

Hogan, Kenneth W., Chief Fin. Officer, Sr. V.P. & Sec.--Bristol & Warren Gas Company, Bristol, RI; U.S. Public, pg. 1706

Hogan, Michael, Pres.--Componenta International Ltd., Brampton, Canada; Int'l, pg. 1421

Hogan, Michael J.C., Pres.--SaskPower Commercial, Regina, Canada; Int'l, pg. 1196

Hogan, P. J., Chief Dir.--Balfour, Williamson & Co. Ltd., London, United Kingdom; Int'l, pg. 817

Hogan, Patrick J., V.P.--Nortel Limited, Maidenhead, United Kingdom; Int'l, pg. 970

Hogan, Paul, Gen. Mgr.--Commissary Div., West Palm Beach, FL; U.S. Private, pg. 823

Hogan, Robert F., Jr., Pres.--AmerCable, Eldorado, TX; U.S. Private, pg. 91

Hogan, Terrance J., Pres.--Alumitech, Inc., Streetsboro, OH; Int'l, pg. 1523

Hogan, William, Chief Oper. Officer--Nippon Silica Glass Europe Ltd., Stanley, United Kingdom; Int'l, pg. 1408

Hogarty, Daniel J., Jr., Pres.--TS Capital Corp., Troy, NY; U.S. Private, pg. 1106

Hogberg, Goran, Gen. Mgr.--Esselte Wensbo AB, Malmo, Sweden; Int'l, pg. 459

Hogbin, W., Chm. Bd.--Taylor Woodrow International Ltd., Southall, United Kingdom; Int'l, pg. 1358

Hogenson, Bill E., Mgr.-Bus. Unit--Forest Oil New Ventures, Houston, TX; U.S. Public, pg. 670

Hogestyn, H.M., V.P.-Wood Prods.-Europe--Weyerhaeuser, S.A., Brussels, Belgium; U.S. Public, pg. 1764

Hogg, A.M., Mng. Dir.--IRD Mechanalysis (U.K.) Limited, Chester, United Kingdom; U.S. Public, pg. 790

Hogg, J., Gen. Mgr.--Albright & Wilson Intertrade Ltd., Oldbury, United Kingdom; Int'l, pg. 49

Hogg, Michael, Chm. Bd. & Chief Exec. Officer--Michael Hogg-Young & Rubicam (Pvt.) Ltd., Harare, Zimbabwe; U.S. Private, pg. 1198

Hogg, Peter, Mng. Dir.--Willis Faber (Far East) Limited, Wan Chai, Hong Kong; Int'l, pg. 1510

Hogge, Jack, Pres.--Northern Trust Securities, Inc., Chicago, IL; U.S. Public, pg. 1197

Hogge, John, Pres.--Northern Trust Securities, Inc., Chicago, IL; U.S. Public, pg. 1196

Hoglund, Kurt, Pres.--FFV Test Systems AB, Stockholm, Sweden; Int'l, pg. 277

Hoglund, Raymond C., Mng. Dir.--ESAB Equipment/ Automation, Florence, SC; Int'l, pg. 281

Hohage, Frederick W., Pres.--Bosch Sales Group, Broadview, IL; Int'l, pg. 205

Hohenbrink, Kelli, Branch Mgr.--Downey Savings & Loan Association, F.A., Redwood City, CA; U.S. Public, pg. 527

Hohlfeld, Michael, Div. Mgr.--Bindley Western, Tennessee Wholesale Division, Nashville, TN; U.S. Public, pg. 229

Hohling, Heinrich, Mng. Dir.--ISS Food Hygiene Service GmbH, Flensburg, Germany; Int'l, pg. 657

Hohling, Heinrich, Mng. Dir.--ISS Holzl GmbH Servisystem, Munich, Germany; Int'l, pg. 657

Hohman, Jeffrey L., Pres.--Micropump Corporation, Vancouver, WA; U.S. Public, pg. 862

Hohmann, Klaus, Mng. Dir.--DEGI Deutsche Gesellschaft fur Immobilenfonds mbH, Frankfurt/Main, Germany; Int'l, pg. 418

Hohn, Rudolf, Pres.--IBM Brasil-Industria Maquinas e Servicos Ltda., Rio de Janeiro, Brazil; U.S. Public, pg. 896

Hohorst, W., Pres.--WAGO Contact i.Gr, Wipperfurth, Germany; Int'l, pg. 209

Hoiden, John, Chief Oper. Officer--Husqvarna A/S, Lyngby, Denmark; Int'l, pg. 441

Hoiden, John, Mng. Dir.--Getinge Vaxjo A/S, Lyngby, Denmark; Int'l, pg. 552

Hoien, Thomas L., Pres.--NationsBank of Mount Vernon, Mount Vernon, IL; U.S. Public, pg. 1164

Hoikkala, Juhani, Chief Oper. Officer--Ahlstrom Machinery Paivarinne Works, Varkaus, Finland; Int'l, pg. 33

Hoketsu, Hiroshi, Pres. & Mng. Dir.--Ortho Clinical Diagnostic Systems K.K., Tokyo, Japan; U.S. Public, pg. 931

Holaas, A., Sr. V.P.--Elkem Mangan, Oslo, Norway; Int'l, pg. 447

Holaday, Alan M., V.P.--Whirlpool Corp., Ft. Smith Div., Fort Smith, AR; U.S. Public, pg. 1765

Holaday, G.S., Plantation Gen. Mgr.--Hawaiian Commercial & Sugar Co., Puunene, HI; U.S. Public, pg. 39

Holaday, G.S., Chief Oper. Officer--Kauai Commercial Company, Inc., Puhi, HI; U.S. Public, pg. 39

Holbek, Karsten, Pres.--AGA Gas GmbH, Hamburg, Germany; Int'l, pg. 13

Holbird, Bill, Mgr.-Sls.--Futaba Corporation of America, Plymouth, MI; Int'l, pg. 531

Holbrook, Darrell, V.P.-Opers.--Reyna Capital Corp., Dayton, OH; U.S. Public, pg. 1385

Holbrook, George T., Jr., Pres. & Chief Exec. Officer--Reliance Surety Corp., Philadelphia, PA; U.S. Public, pg. 1374

Holbrook, Kathy, Cargo Agent--Baltimore Office, Glen Burnie, MD; U.S. Public, pg. 749

Holckner, David, Gen. Mgr.--Smorgon Fencing, Melbourne, Australia; Int'l, pg. 1269

Holcomb, Benjamin F., Pres.--American Cellular Communications Corporation, Atlanta, GA; U.S. Public, pg. 208

Holcomb, Jim, Admin.--Washoe Care Center, Sparks, NV; U.S. Public, pg. 838

Holcombe, James, Admin.--Medicenter, Tampa, Tampa, FL; U.S. Public, pg. 1714

Holcombe, Tony, Pres.--Comdata Corporation, Brentwood, TN; U.S. Public, pg. 331

Holcroft, P.R., Chief Exec. Officer--Robert Fleming Insurance Brokers Limited, London, United Kingdom; Int'l, pg. 493

Holdaway, Murray, Gen. Dir.--Madison Systems Ltd., Auckland, New Zealand; U.S. Public, pg. 1043

Holden, Barry W., Pres.--Hoover Treated Wood Products, Inc., Thomson, GA; U.S. Public, pg. 1193

Holden, J. P., Chief Oper. Officer--SKA Storkokken, Ishoj, Denmark; Int'l, pg. 441

Holden, William, Pres.--Hallsmith-Sysco Food Services, Norton, MA; U.S. Public, pg. 1550

Holden, Win, Editor & Publr.--Phoenix Magazine, Phoenix, AZ; U.S. Private, pg. 685

Holder, Daniel, Mng. Dir.--Telefonaktiebolaget LM Ericsson Technical Office, Panama, Panama; Int'l, pg. 1370

Holder, George H., Pres.--Syntex Agribusiness, Inc., Palo Alto, CA; Int'l, pg. 1120

Holder, Ken, Plant Mgr.--Trenton Mills, Trenton, TN; U.S. Public, pg. 538

Holder, Ronald, V.P. & Mgr.--Dresdner Bank AG, Chicago, IL; Int'l, pg. 418

Holderness-Roddam, T., Mng. Dir.--United Molasses Company, London, United Kingdom; Int'l, pg. 1356

Holding, Frank, Jr., Pres.--First Citizens Bank & Trust Co., Raleigh, NC; U.S. Public, pg. 629

Holding, J., Mng. Dir.--Texaco Exploration Norway A/S, Oslo, Norway; U.S. Public, pg. 1584

Holding, R. Earl, Pres.--Little America Refining, Inc., Evansville, WY; U.S. Private, pg. 1003

Holdredge, Ernest C., V.P.-Mfg.--Structural Foam Plastics, Inc., Winchester, KY; U.S. Private, pg. 1048

Holdrege, J.H., Gen. Mgr.--Kato Engineering Div., North Mankato, MN; U.S. Public, pg. 1398

Holdsworth, Robert, Mgr.-Distr. Center--Herbalife Australasia Pty. Ltd., Camden Park, Australia; U.S. Public, pg. 809

Holdsworthy, Geoff, Gen. Mgr.--WD-40 Company (Australia), Epping, Australia; U.S. Public, pg. 1726

Holgate, Fred, Pres.--Prestige Stations Inc., Cerritos, CA; U.S. Public, pg. 144

Holgate, John, Chief Oper. Officer--NIFE Silcon Ltd., Kowloon, Hong Kong; Int'l, pg. 54

Holguin R., Juan Manuel, Pres.--Vitro, Sociedad Anonima - Glassware Div., Garza Garcia, Mexico; Int'l, pg. 1469

Holiczki, Walter, Gen. Mgr.--Conquest Europe, Vienna, Austria; Int'l, pg. 1483

Holifield, G., Gen. Mgr.--Aguadilla Shoe Div., Aguadilla, PR; U.S. Public, pg. 1775

Holifield, Gary, G.M.--Wolverine Boot Co., Aguadilla, PR; U.S. Public, pg. 1775

Holland, Del, Pres.--Six Flags Magic Mountain & Six Flags Hurricane Harbor, Valencia, CA; U.S. Public, pg. 1611

Holland, Dennis, Gen. Mgr.--Tampa Bay Moving Systems Inc., Tampa, FL; U.S. Private, pg. 273

Holland, Edward W., Pres.--HWC Distribution Corp., Houston, TX; U.S. Public, pg. 55

Holland, Egil, Chief Oper. Officer--Bulklift A/S, Tonsberg, Norway; Int'l, pg. 965

Holland, G. Ed, Jr., Pres. & Chief Exec. Officer--Savannah Electric & Power Co., Savannah, GA; U.S. Public, pg. 1490

Holland, John, Mng. Dir.--Edelman Public Relations Worldwide Pte. Ltd., Singapore, Singapore; U.S. Private, pg. 363

Holland, John, Mgr.--Commercial Metals Company, Fort Worth, TX; U.S. Public, pg. 413

Holland, John B., Chm. Bd. & Pres.--Durum Energy Corp., Sucursal Del Peru, Vancouver, Canada; Int'l, pg. 422

Holland, John B., Chm. Bd. & Pres.--Durum (Australia) Pty. Ltd., Vancouver, Canada; Int'l, pg. 422

Holland, John L., Pres.--BetzDearborn Water Management Group, Horsham, PA; U.S. Public, pg. 226

Holland, Linda, Dir.--Hummingbird Specialized Solutions, Chicago, IL; U.S. Private, pg. 497

Holland, Michael C., Pres. & Chief Exec. Officer--Mojave Pipeline Company, Bakersfield, CA; U.S. Public, pg. 567

Holland, Richard F., Pres. & Chief Exec. Officer--D/B Cameras Microcheck Division, Fullerton, CA; U.S. Private, pg. 5

Holland, Richard F., Pres. & Chief Exec. Officer--Electro-Mechanical Instruments Div., Fullerton, CA; U.S. Private, pg. 5

Holland, Richard F., Pres. & Chief Exec. Officer--Precision Power Div., Fullerton, CA; U.S. Private, pg. 5

Hollander, Bob, Gen. Mgr.--Poe & Brown of Florida, Aventura, FL; U.S. Public, pg. 1312

Hollands, John, Pres.--Sony Magnetic Products Co., Park Ridge, NJ; Int'l, pg. 1281

Hollar, Bob, Chief Oper. Officer--CRX Inc., Fremont, NE; U.S. Public, pg. 49

Hollen, Larry D., Pres.--Employee Benefits Insurance Company, Farmington, CT; U.S. Public, pg. 1231

Hollen, Larry D., Pres.--EBI Indemnity Company, Farmington, CT; U.S. Public, pg. 1231

Hollen, Larry D., Pres.--Security Insurance Co. of Hartford, Farmington, CT; U.S. Public, pg. 1231

Holler, J., Pres. & Chief Exec. Officer--PNC Bank, Cincinnati, OH; U.S. Public, pg. 1242

Holleran, Edward P., Pres.--Robert F. Coleman, Inc., Wilmington, DE; U.S. Public, pg. 366

Holleran, J.W., Pres.--Jefferson Square, Inc., Boise, ID; U.S. Public, pg. 243

Holleran, J.W., Pres.--JPB General Placerville Corporation, Boise, ID; U.S. Public, pg. 243

Holleran, J.W., Pres.--Voyageur Panel Limited, Boise, ID; U.S. Public, pg. 243

Hollering, L. Karl, V.P.--Sterno, Inc., New York, NY; U.S. Public, pg. 397

Hollern, Michael P., Pres.--Awbrey Glen Golf Club, Inc., Bend, OR; U.S. Private, pg. 172

Hollerscmid, Manfred, Chief Oper. Officer--Hospal Medizintechnische Produkte Ges.m.b.H, Vienna, Austria; Int'l, pg. 668

Hollett, Grant T., Jr., Pres.--Cherry Electrical Products, Waukegan, IL; U.S. Public, pg. 346

Holley, Edward E., V.P. & Branch Mgr.--California State Bank-Victorville, Victorville, CA; U.S. Public, pg. 294

Holley, R.E., V.P. & Gen. Counsel--High Density Film Prods. Div., Hartsville, SC; U.S. Public, pg. 1486

Holliday, Brian, Mng. Dir.--Denison Colour Limited, Guiseley, United Kingdom; U.S. Public, pg. 78

Holliday, Jessica J., Pres.--Prodair Corporation, Wilmington, DE; U.S. Public, pg. 31

Holliday, Ralph K., Pres. & Chief Exec. Officer--Security Pacific Bank Alaska, N.A., Anchorage, AK; U.S. Public, pg. 180

Hollidge, Gregg M., Mgr.--Scott & Stringfellow, Inc., Charlotte, NC; U.S. Public, pg. 1446

Hollidge, R., Mng. Dir.--Lloyds Development Capital Ltd., London, United Kingdom; Int'l, pg. 813

Hollier, Robert, Pres.--OSCA, Lafayette, LA; U.S. Public, pg. 760

Holliger, Frederic L., Pres. & Chief Exec. Officer--Giant Exploration & Production Co., Farmington, NM; U.S. Public, pg. 742

Hollindale, Ian, Mng. Dir.--Gold Coast Milk Pty. Ltd., Labrador, Australia; Int'l, pg. 1074

Hollings, Earle, Admin.--Clifton House Rehabilitation Center, New Haven, CT; U.S. Public, pg. 836

Hollingsed, William, Mgr.--Jenks (INMETCO), Orlando, FL; U.S. Private, pg. 559

Hollingsworth, A., Mng. Dir.--The Davy Roll Co. Ltd., Sheffield, United Kingdom; Int'l, pg. 773

Hollingsworth, David, Pres.--Gates, McDonald & Co., Hilliard, OH; U.S. Private, pg. 789

Hollingsworth, Fred IV, Pres.--OFI Technology, Inc., Sarasota, FL; U.S. Public, pg. 915

Hollins, Arthur, III, Chm. Bd.--The First National Bank of Lake Charles, Lake Charles, LA; U.S. Public, pg. 630

Hollins, Peter, Gen. Mgr.--Grace Construction Products, Slough, United Kingdom; U.S. Public, pg. 755

Hollis, Charles E., Pres.--Ikon Office Solutions-Houston, Houston, TX; U.S. Public, pg. 863

Hollis, S., Chief Fin. Officer--ING Barings Southern Africa (Proprietary), Sandton, South Africa; Int'l, pg. 650

Holloran, John, Chief Exec.--Reed Books, London, United Kingdom; Int'l, pg. 1093

Holloway, C.G., Pres.--Wedge Dia-Log, Pearland, TX; U.S. Private, pg. 1158

Holloway, D.N., V.P. & Gen. Mgr.--Vulcraft Div., Norfolk, NE; U.S. Public, pg. 1206

Holloway, Gary F., Vice Chm.--Greenwich Capital Markets, Inc., Greenwich, CT; Int'l, pg. 911

Holloway, J.G., Chm. & Mng. Dir.--Exxon Chemical Limited, Farnham, United Kingdom; U.S. Public, pg. 602

Holloway, J.G., Chm. & Pres.--Exxon Chemical Olefins Inc., Fareham, United Kingdom; U.S. Public, pg. 602

Holloway, J.G., Chief Exec. Officer--Humberside Holdings Ltd, Grimsby, United Kingdom; Int'l, pg. 1065

Holloway, Mark, Gen. Mgr.--Keystone Automotive Industries, Inc.-Dallas, Dallas, TX; U.S. Public, pg. 955

Holloway, Richard A., Pres.--Teledyne Brown Engineering, Huntsville, AL; U.S. Public, pg. 43

Holloway, W. Robert, V.P.-Intl.--Symbol Technologies International, Inc., Brussels, Belgium; U.S. Public, pg. 1546

Hollows, J.A., Sr. Mgr.--Barclays Bank PLC, Taipei, Taiwan; Int'l, pg. 165

Hollwood, David J., Chief Exec. Officer--Livingston UK Ltd., Teddington, United Kingdom; Int'l, pg. 212

Holly, Andrew, Mgr.--Tekra Corp., West Coast Div., Orange, CA; U.S. Private, pg. 1073

Holly, Brian, Pres. & Chief Exec. Officer--ITK Telecommunications, Inc., Chelmsford, MA; U.S. Private, pg. 556

Holly, Jim, Plant Mgr.--Elkem Alloy, Alloy, WV; Int'l, pg. 447

Holm, Christel, Chief Oper. Officer--Douglas Management Company, Seattle, WA; U.S. Private, pg. 683

Holm, Christian, Gen. Dir.--IBM Danmark A/S, Lyngby, Denmark; U.S. Public, pg. 1043

Holm, Egon, Mng. Dir.--Metsa-Serla Tissue A/S, Tastrup, Denmark; Int'l, pg. 864

Holm, Johan, Mgr.--Sandvik Hard Materials Norden AB, Stockholm, Sweden; Int'l, pg. 1185

Holm, John, Gen. Mgr.--Wichita Learjet Learning Center, Wichita, KS; U.S. Public, pg. 219

Holm, Kim R., Exec. V.P.--Salem Carpet Mills, Ringgold, GA; U.S. Public, pg. 1464

Holm, Leif, Chief Oper. Officer--Ericsson Mobile Data Inc., Paramus, NJ; Int'l, pg. 1365

Holm, Lennart, Pres.--Stora Cell AB, Gavle, Sweden; Int'l, pg. 1303

Holm, Magnus, Pres.--Optiroc Oy AB, Helsinki, Finland; Int'l, pg. 1200

Holm, Mats, Mng. Dir.--SKF Specialty Products AB, Goteborg, Sweden; Int'l, pg. 1157

Holm, Pelle, Pres.--Isaberg Rapid AB, Hestra, Sweden; Int'l, pg. 678

Holman, Darrell, Gen. Mgr.--Cameo Container Corporation, Chicago, IL; U.S. Public, pg. 1520

Holman, W.H., Jr., Chm. Bd., Chief Exec. & Chief Oper. Officer--Southern Jitney-Jungle, Inc., Jackson, MS; *U.S. Private*, pg. 588

Holman, W.H., Jr., Chm. Bd., Chief Exec. & Chief Oper. Officer--Jitney-Jungle Bakery, Inc., Jackson, MS; *U.S. Private*, pg. 588

Holman, W.H., Jr., Pres.--Pump and Save, Inc., Jackson, MS; *U.S. Private*, pg. 588

Holmen, Jan Ove, Pres.--Kvaerner Doris Offshore Concrete A/S, Lysaker, Norway; *Int'l*, pg. 766

Holmen, Reidar Erik, Chm.--BNP Finans A/S - Norway, Oslo, Norway; *Int'l*, pg. 163

Holmen, Stein, Chief Oper. Officer--Ahlstrom A/S Ahlstrom Machinery, Drammen, Norway; *Int'l*, pg. 34

Holmes, A. Glen, Pres.--Ikon Office Solutions-Mississippi, Columbus, MS; *U.S. Public*, pg. 863

Holmes, Brian W., Pres.--The Northern Trust Company of New York, New York, NY; *U.S. Public*, pg. 1197

Holmes, D.J., Pres.--CIBC Mortgage Corporation, Toronto, Canada; *Int'l*, pg. 256

Holmes, Edith, Pres.--FCW Publishing Corp., Falls Church, VA; *U.S. Private*, pg. 569

Holmes, Everett, Country Mgr.--A.C. Nielsen Company-Taiwan Branch, Taipei, Taiwan; *U.S. Public*, pg. 1183

Holmes, George, Pres.--D & H Piping, Chicago, IL; *U.S. Private*, pg. 338

Holmes, Gordon A., Sec.--Alcan Ireland Ltd., Limerick, Ireland; *Int'l*, pg. 51

Holmes, Houston E., Jr., Pres. & Chief Oper. Officer--Cullum Development Co., Dallas, TX; *U.S. Private*, pg. 909

Holmes, John B., Jr., Pres.--Sonat Exploration GOM Inc., Houston, TX; *U.S. Public*, pg. 1485

Holmes, Jonathan, Mgr.--Inland Steel Mining Co., Virginia, MN; *U.S. Public*, pg. 879

Holmes, Mike, V.P.-Fin.--Guilford Rail System, North Billerica, MA; *U.S. Private*, pg. 487

Holmes, Ramsay R., Pres. & Chief Exec. Officer--The Bank of Nova Scotia Trust Company, Toronto, Canada; *Int'l*, pg. 155

Holmes, Roger, Mng. Dir.--McLean Europe, Smethwick, United Kingdom; *U.S. Public*, pg. 1791

Holmes, T.R., Mgr.--Port McNeill Div., Port McNeill, Canada; *Int'l*, pg. 828

Holmes, Warren, Pres.--Sudbury Division, Falconbridge, Canada; *Int'l*, pg. 433

Holmgren, Anders, Mng. Dir.--SKF Chilena S.A.I.C., Santiago, Chile; *Int'l*, pg. 1158

Holmgren, Bjorn, Chief Oper. Officer--Saab-Scania AB, Sibbhult, Sweden; *Int'l*, pg. 687

Holmgren, Kenneth, Mng. Dir.--SKF Multitec A/S, Oslo, Norway; *Int'l*, pg. 1159

Holmgren, Kenneth D., Pres.--Automotive Safety Products, Ogden, UT; *U.S. Public*, pg. 1134

Holmsen, Cato A., Pres.--Scancem International ANS, Oslo, Norway; *Int'l*, pg. 1201

Holmstrom, Stig, Mng. Dir.--Avesta Valbruna AB, Karlstad, Sweden; *Int'l*, pg. 221

Holmstrom, Tom, Pres. & Chief Exec. Officer--Corporate Express Office Products, Arden Hills, MN; *U.S. Public*, pg. 449

Holmstrom, Tom, Pres. & Chief Exec. Officer--Corporate Express Office Products, Duluth, MN; *U.S. Public*, pg. 449

Holmstrom, Veikko, Mng. Dir.--ZAO KONE Lifts St. Petersburg, Saint Petersburg, Russia; *Int'l*, pg. 748

Holsapple, Jerry L., Pres. & Chief Exec. Officer--Bright National Bank, Flora, IN; *U.S. Public*, pg. 633

Holstad, Neil, Pres.--Advanced Energy Technologies, Tucson, AZ; *U.S. Public*, pg. 1670

Holstad, Neil, Chief Oper. Officer--Global Solar Energy, Tucson, AZ; *U.S. Public*, pg. 1670

Holsted, Tom, Dir.-Real Estate--Dade Lease Management, Inc., Scottsville, KY; *U.S. Public*, pg. 515

Holsteen, Jon F., Pres.--Chicago Asset Management Company, Chicago, IL; *U.S. Public*, pg. 1672

Holston, J.B., Div. Head--Ziff-Davis International Media Group, New York, NY; *Int'l*, pg. 1276

Holsworth, William C., Pres. & Chief Exec. Officer--FINAST, Maple Heights, OH; *Int'l*, pg. 750

Holt, Charles, Div. Mgr.--Alabama Div., Florence, AL; *U.S. Private*, pg. 180

Holt, D., V.P. & Gen. Mgr.--Beloit Manhattan Inc., Clarks Summit, PA; *U.S. Public*, pg. 789

Holt, D.B., V.P. & Gen. Mgr.--Jewel Osco Southwest, Inc., Albuquerque, NM; *U.S. Public*, pg. 93

Holt, Dennis F., Chm. Bd. & Chief Exec. Officer--Western Motivational Incentives Group, Inc., Los Angeles, CA; *U.S. Private*, pg. 1167

Holt, Henry H., Jr., Chm. Bd.--Denver Chemical (PR) Inc., Humacao, PR; *U.S. Public*, pg. 310

Holt, Howard W., V.P. & Gen. Mgr.--Central Carolina Bank, Salisbury, NC; *U.S. Public*, pg. 276

Holt, John R., Mgr.--Decatur Telephone Company, Decatur, AR; *U.S. Public*, pg. 1571

Holt, Larry O., Pres. & Chief Exec. Officer--Regions Bank/Cullman/Walker County, Cullman, AL; *U.S. Public*, pg. 1372

Holt, Lonnie, G.M.--First American Title Co. of Thurston County, Olympia, WA; *U.S. Public*, pg. 625

Holt, Stephen L., Chief Exec. Officer-IL Weeklies--Highland News-Leader, Highland, IL; *U.S. Public*, pg. 964

Holt, Stephen L., Chief Exec. Officer-IL Weeklies--O'Fallon Progress, O Fallon, IL; *U.S. Public*, pg. 964

Holt, Tim, Plant Mgr.--Heck Cellars Winery, Di Giorgio, CA; *U.S. Private*, pg. 632

Holteman, Bob, Plant Mgr.--Hydro Conduit Corp., El Paso, TX; *Int'l*, pg. 245

Holter-Sorensen, Erik, Chief Oper. Officer--Ivaran Agencies Inc., Jersey City, NJ; *Int'l*, pg. 696

Holthaus, Gerard E., Pres. & Chief Oper. Officer--Williams Scotsman, Inc., Baltimore, MD; *U.S. Private*, pg. 976

Holthaus, J., Mng. Dir.--Holec Machines & Apparaten B.V., Ridderkerk, Netherlands; *Int'l*, pg. 1133

Holthaus, J.C.C., Chief Oper. Officer--Lips B.V., Drunen, Netherlands; *Int'l*, pg. 812

Holthouse, Michael H., Pres.--Sprint Paranet, Houston, TX; *U.S. Public*, pg. 1501

Holton, Earl, Pres.--Meijer Wholesale Inc., Lansing, MI; *U.S. Private*, pg. 729

Holton, Mike, Plant Mgr.--Cambridge Industries, Inc., Shelbyville, IN; *U.S. Private*, pg. 202

Holton, Rick, Chief Oper. Officer--Automation Finishing Inc., Cleveland, OH; *U.S. Private*, pg. 426

Holtschlag, J., Dir.--Red Band Susswaren Vertriebs GmbH, Bocholt, Germany; *Int'l*, pg. 244

Holtshousen, B.W., Exec. Gen. Mgr.-Gold--Carpentaria Gold Pty. Ltd., Brisbane, Australia; *Int'l*, pg. 827

Holtsnider, William, V.P. & Gen. Mgr.--Dennison International Co., Framingham, MA; *U.S. Public*, pg. 153

Holtvoigt, Werner, Mng. Dir.--Stalo Chemicals GmbH, Lohne, Germany; *Int'l*, pg. 610

Holtz, Richard, Pres. & Publr.--Journal & Courier, Lafayette, IN; *U.S. Public*, pg. 701

Holtzman, Bernard, Pres.--Harve Benard Ltd., New York, NY; *U.S. Private*, pg. 508

Holub, William J., Pres.--Vineland Transit Mix Concrete Co., Inc., Marlton, NJ; *Int'l*, pg. 1201

Holwerda, R., Mng. Dir.--Baars Kaas B.V., Schoonrewoerd, Netherlands; *Int'l*, pg. 752

Holz, Bodo, Dir.--Management Engineers GmbH, Dusseldorf, Germany; *U.S. Private*, pg. 162

Holz, Tim, Pres.--Plant Maintenance, Inc., Martinez, CA; *U.S. Private*, pg. 1011

Holzenthaler, John W., Gen. Mgr.-Refinery--Phelps Dodge Refining Corp., El Paso, TX; *U.S. Public*, pg. 1287

Holzer, Anthony, V.P. & Gen. Mgr.--Precision Disc Corp., Knoxville, TN; *U.S. Private*, pg. 803

Holzer, Edwin H., Chm. Bd., Chief Exec. Officer & Mng. Dir.--Lois/EJL Chicago, Chicago, IL; *U.S. Public*, pg. 1011

Holzer, Henry, Pres. & Chief Exec. Officer--SGS Government Programs Inc., New York, NY; *Int'l*, pg. 1153

Holzhauer, George, Pres. & Chief Exec. Officer--Central DuPage Hospital Association, Winfield, IL; *U.S. Private*, pg. 223

Hom, Tony, Admin.--Sunshine Haven, Lordsburg, NM; *U.S. Public*, pg. 838

Homan, Hendrik, Pres.--AKG Acoustics, Vienna, Austria; *U.S. Public*, pg. 787

Homan, Paul M., Pres. & Chief Exec. Office--Riggs Bank N.A., Washington, DC; *U.S. Public*, pg. 1390

Homburg, Axel, Dr., Chm. Bd.--Dynamit Nobel AG, Troisdorf, Germany; *Int'l*, pg. 861

Homeier, David M., V.P.-Div. Mgr.--Bindley Western, Dallas Division, Dallas, TX; *U.S. Public*, pg. 228

Homer, Charles, Pres.--LePage's Limited, Brampton, Canada; *Int'l*, pg. 613

Homitsu, Toshiro, Branch Mgr.--Dai-Ichi Kangyo Bank, Ltd.-Munich, Munich, Germany; *Int'l*, pg. 360

Homma, Mitsuru, Pres.--Sanyo Fisher Home Appliance & Consumer Products Div., Little Ferry, NJ; *Int'l*, pg. 1191

Homma, Toichi, Gen. Mgr.--The Hokkaido Takushoku Bank, Ltd. (Shenzhen), Shenzhen, China; *Int'l*, pg. 627

Hon, Noel, Mng. Dir.--NEC Singapore Pte. Ltd., Singapore, Singapore; *Int'l*, pg. 900

Hon, William T.Y., Dir. & Branch Mgr.--Bank of Montreal - Singapore, Singapore, Singapore; *Int'l*, pg. 155

Honaker, Mark, Mgr.-Sls.--PENCO-Florida, Altamonte Springs, FL; *Int'l*, pg. 1508

Honda, Keikichi, Chm. & Pres.--The Bank of Tokyo-Mitsubishi, Ltd., Chicago, IL; *Int'l*, pg. 157

Honda, Mitsuo, Pres.--President Inc., Tokyo, Japan; *U.S. Public*, pg. 1615

Honda, Shinichi, Gen. Mgr.--The Daishi Bank, Ltd., Hong Kong, Hong Kong; *Int'l*, pg. 373

Hondlik, Frank R., Pres.--Kilroy Structural Steel, Cleveland, OH; *U.S. Public*, pg. 1640

Honegger, Arthur, Pres.--DRS Ahead Technology, Inc., San Jose, CA; *U.S. Public*, pg. 475

Honegger, John, Gen. Mgr.--Portland Auto Auction, Portland, OR; *U.S. Private*, pg. 283

Honer, Eckart F., Mgr.--Hapag-Lloyd Kreuzfahrten GmbH, Bremen, Germany; *Int'l*, pg. 596

Honeycutt,Ann, Mgr.-Admin.--Stuart Circle Hospital Corporation, Atlanta, GA; *U.S. Public*, pg. 1036

Honeywell, Paul, Chief Oper. Officer--Price/Stern/Publishers, Ltd., Northampton, United Kingdom; *Int'l*, pg. 1215

Hong, Frank, V.P.--Jardine Fleming Taiwan Securities Limited, Taipei, Taiwan; *Int'l*, pg. 494

Hong, Glenn K.Y., Pres.--Hawaiian Tug & Barge Corp., Honolulu, HI; *U.S. Public*, pg. 800

Hong, Glenn K.Y., Pres.--Young Brothers, Ltd., Honolulu, HI; *U.S. Public*, pg. 800

Hong, Peter, Pres.--Positech Corporation, Laurens, IA; *U.S. Public*, pg. 406

Hong, Woo-Shik, Pres. & Chief Exec. Officer--Seoul DMB&B, Inc., Seoul, Korea; *U.S. Private*, pg. 305

Hong, Yee Jee, Chm.--Singapore Factory Development Ltd., Singapore, Singapore; *Int'l*, pg. 351

Honig, Raul, V.P. & Gen. Mgr.--Rorer de Mexico, S.A. de C.V., Mexico, Mexico; *Int'l*, pg. 1111

Honjo, Junji, Representative--Union Bank of Switzerland, Osaka, Japan; *Int'l*, pg. 1441

Honma, Masakazu, Pres.--Hitachi Consumer Products of America, Inc., Anaheim, CA; *Int'l*, pg. 622

Honoki, Koji, Pres.--Nikkei Media Marketing, Inc., Tokyo, Japan; *Int'l*, pg. 929

Honor, Richard G., Chief Oper. Officer--CCH Australia Limited, Sydney, Australia; *Int'l*, pg. 1513

Honour, D.M., Sr. V.P.--Jannock Steel Fabricating, Inc., Danville, KY; *Int'l*, pg. 699

Honour, Ric, Gen. Mgr.--GATX Logistics, Inc.-Georgia (Atlas), Atlanta, GA; *U.S. Public*, pg. 691

Hood, Bruce, Chief Oper. Officer--Shiseido N.Z. Ltd., Auckland, New Zealand; *Int'l*, pg. 1235

Hood, Elizabeth, Dir.-Corp. Rels.--Continental Europe, West Drayton, United Kingdom; *Int'l*, pg. 1442

Hood, Jeanne, Pres.--Elsinore Shore Associates, Atlantic City, NJ; *U.S. Public*, pg. 570

Hood, Ken, Gen. Mgr.--Beijing Ji Tong-Bellsouth Communication & Information Engineering Co., Ltd., Beijing, China; *U.S. Public*, pg. 208

Hood, Larry, Chief Oper. Officer--Hamlet Group, Inc., Los Angeles, CA; *U.S. Public*, pg. 966

Hood, Nigel, Gen. Mgr.--Valtek New Zealand, Ltd., Auckland, New Zealand; *U.S. Public*, pg. 659

Hood, Robert R., Pres. & Chief Exec. Officer--M & I Community State Bank, Eau Claire, WI; *U.S. Public*, pg. 1050

Hood, Stephen, Gen. Mgr.--Crouse-Hinds (Australia) Pty. Ltd., Sydney, Australia; *U.S. Public*, pg. 445

Hoofe, Erich, Area V.P.-Continental Europe--Circle Freight International Speditionsgesellschaft mbH, Kelsterbach, Germany; *U.S. Public*, pg. 373

Hoogakker, B., Gen. Mgr.--Electric Protection Services (EPS), Brussels, Belgium; *U.S. Public*, pg. 1650

Hoogendoorn, Jaap, Mng. Dir.--Horticom BV, De Lier, Netherlands; *Int'l*, pg. 1099

Hoogenkamp, Derk A.J., Chief Oper. Officer--Hufvudstaden Nederland B.V., Amsterdam, Netherlands; *Int'l*, pg. 478

Hoogenraat, P. W., Mng. Dir.--City Com B.V., Rotterdam, Netherlands; *Int'l*, pg. 681

Hoogers, Paul, Chief Oper. Officer--Binks International, S.A., Waterloo, Belgium; *U.S. Public*, pg. 229

Hoogeveen, Jack, Pres.--Mercantile Bank of Lyon County, Rock Rapids, IA; *U.S. Public*, pg. 1088

Hoogewijs, Dr. G., Gen. Mgr.--Wyeth Laboratoria B.V., Hoofddorp, Netherlands; *U.S. Public*, pg. 82

Hoogewijs, G., Gen. Mgr.--Libamedi S.A., Brussels, Belgium; *U.S. Public*, pg. 81

Hoogewijs, G., Gen. Mgr.--Wyeth S.A., Brussels, Belgium; *U.S. Public*, pg. 82

Hooi, Teoh Tee, Sr. V.P.-Americas--Singapore Airlines, Los Angeles, CA; *Int'l*, pg. 1374

Hook, Claes, Pres.--Euronord WTM AB, Gavle, Sweden; *Int'l*, pg. 678

Hook, Jerry, Gen. Mgr.--The Southland Corporation, Pleasanton, CA; *Int'l*, pg. 694

Hook, Richard A., V.P. & Gen. Mgr.--Cox Communications-Omaha, Omaha, NE; *U.S. Public*, pg. 455

Hooker, Robert, Pres.--Mazda Distributors (Great Lakes), Inc., Grand Rapids, MI; *Int'l*, pg. 849

Hooley, Jay, Pres. & Chief Oper. Officer--Boston Financial Data Services, Inc., Quincy, MA; *U.S. Public*, pg. 944

Hoon, Soh Chee, Dr., Pres.--MMC-GTM Bina Sama, Kuala Lumpur, Malaysia; *Int'l*, pg. 823

Hoon, Soh Chee, Dr., Pres.--GTM Wan Soon Pte Ltd., Singapore, Singapore; *Int'l*, pg. 823

Hoong, Leong Mun, Mng. Dir.--Strombecker (HK) Ltd., Kowloon, Hong Kong; *U.S. Private*, pg. 1047

Hooper, Calvin A., Pres.--Wallace & Tiernan Canada, Inc., Scarborough, Canada; *U.S. Public*, pg. 61

Hooper, John, Mgr.--Century Telephone of Michigan, Inc., Pinconning, MI; *U.S. Public*, pg. 329

Hooper, Michael, Pres.--The Crown Divisions, Wooster, OH; *U.S. Public*, pg. 1631

Hooper, Steven, Pres.--Land Title Insurance Co. of St. Louis, Des Peres, MO; *U.S. Public*, pg. 626

Hoopis, Michael P., Pres.--Black & Decker Household Products Group, Shelton, CT; *U.S. Public*, pg. 234

Hooson, Greg, Pres.--Jered Brown Brothers Inc., Brunswick, GA; *Int'l*, pg. 1468

Hoover, J.E., Mng. Dir.--Australian Timken Proprietary Ltd., Ballarat, Australia; *U.S. Public*, pg. 1617

Hoover, Jerry, Gen. Mgr.--Stewart-Warner South Wind Corp., Indianapolis, IN; *Int'l*, pg. 127

Hoover, Jerry D., V.P. & Chief Oper. Officer--Staple Cotton Discount Corporation, Greenwood, MS; *U.S. Private*, pg. 1033

Hoover, Mark, Reg. Mgr.--SMS-Cleveland, Independence, OH; *U.S. Public*, pg. 1463

Hoover, Mark, Reg. Mgr.--SMS-Columbus, Columbus, OH; *U.S. Public*, pg. 1463

Hoover, Tom, Dir.-Opers.--Max Food & Drug Div., Long Beach, CA; *U.S. Public*, pg. 38

Hoover, W., Pres.--Data Aire, Inc., Garden Grove, CA; *U.S. Private*, pg. 266

Hoover, William C., Pres.--PRC, Inc., Mc Lean, VA; *U.S. Public*, pg. 1003

Hooykaas, Henricus, Pres.--Royal Nederland Levensverzekering N.V., Utrecht, Netherlands; *Int'l*, pg. 16

Hop, Henk, Gen. Mgr.--Gillette Finance B.V., Rijswijk, Netherlands; *U.S. Public*, pg. 744

Hopcraft, Lawrence J., Pres.--Climate & Industrial Controls Group, Cleveland, OH; *U.S. Public*, pg. 1260

Hope, Bill, Pres.--Work Wear Canada, Mississauga, Canada; *U.S. Public*, pg. 690

Hope, Frank, Dr., Mng. Dir.--Ultra Electrics, Cheltenham, United Kingdom; *Int'l*, pg. 1431

Hope, Jeff, Gen. Mgr.--Servitex, Inc., Macon, GA; *U.S. Private*, pg. 781

Hope, Michael, Pres.--Utell International, Brentford, United Kingdom; *Int'l*, pg. 1098

Hope, Svein Erik, Gen. Mgr.--Forbo A/S, Asker, Norway; *Int'l*, pg. 497

Hopkins, Clyde C., Pres.--Martin Marietta Energy Group, Oak Ridge, TN; *U.S. Public*, pg. 1007

Hopkins, Dale, V.P.-Prod. Devel.--Atalla Corporation, San Jose, CA; *U.S. Public*, pg. 417

Hopkins, Donald W., V.P. & Gen. Mgr.--Hearst Enterprises Division, New York, NY; *U.S. Private*, pg. 516

Hopkins, Jim, Pres.--Chromatic Technologies, Inc., Franklin, MA; *Int'l*, pg. 417

Hopkins, Jim, Pres.--Helix/Hi-Temp Cables, Inc., Franklin, MA; *Int'l*, pg. 417

Hopkins, M., Mng. Dir.--Wellcome Thailand Ltd., Bangkok, Thailand; *Int'l*, pg. 553

Hopkins, Michael B., Pres.--First American Equity Loan Services, Cleveland, OH; U.S. Public, pg. 625
Hopkins, Mike, V.P. & Gen. Mgr.--Unitog Company, Brookfield Div., Kansas City, MO; U.S. Public, pg. 1693
Hopkins, Ron, Gen. Mgr.--NuArc Southern Div., Fort Lauderdale, FL; U.S. Private, pg. 809
Hopkins, Roy M., Mng. Dir.--Magellan Petroleum Australia Ltd., Brisbane, Australia; U.S. Public, pg. 1037
Hopkins, Sheldon, V.P. & Gen. Mgr.--General Latex & Chemical Corp (Ohio), Ashland, OH; U.S. Private, pg. 444
Hopkins, Steve, Chief Oper. Officer--Auto-trol Technology Australia, Sydney, Australia; U.S. Public, pg. 148
Hopkinson, Alan, Chief Oper. Officer--Solvay Pharma Deutschland GmbH, Hannover, Germany; Int'l, pg. 1280
Hopkinson, Mark R., Chief Fin. Officer--White Pigeon Paper Company, White Pigeon, MI; U.S. Private, pg. 87
Hoppe, Victor, Mgr.--W.C. Caye & Co., Lawrenceville, GA; U.S. Private, pg. 220
Hoppenjans, A.J., Pres.--Turner Electric Corporation, Fairview Heights, IL; U.S. Public, pg. 1705
Hopper, Andy, Mng. Dir.--Olivetti Research Ltd., Cambridge, United Kingdom; Int'l, pg. 1003
Hopper, Jefferson C., Pres.--Coscan Florida, Inc., Boca Raton, FL; Int'l, pg. 228
Hopping, Malcolm, V.P.-European Opers.--Network Systems Limited, Ascot, United Kingdom; U.S. Public, pg. 1522
Hopping, Malcolm, V.P.-Europe--NSC European Operations, Ascot, United Kingdom; U.S. Public, pg. 1522
Hopps, Jim, Plant Mgr.--American Natl. Can Co., Monmouth Junction, NJ; Int'l, pg. 1029
Hopsicker, Michael, Pres.--Agway Energy Products (AEP), Syracuse, NY; U.S. Private, pg. 27
Hopwood, Jan, Mng. Dir.--Schiess (UK) Ltd., Barnsley, United Kingdom; Int'l, pg. 860
Hora, Charles, Pres.--Lord Corporation, Mechanical Products Division, Erie, PA; U.S. Private, pg. 676
Horak, H. Lynn, Pres.--Norwest Bank Iowa, N.A., Des Moines, IA; U.S. Public, pg. 1202
Horan, Mike, V.P. & Gen. Mgr.--Cox Communications-Cedar Rapids, Cedar Rapids, IA; U.S. Public, pg. 454
Horan, Niall, Pres. & Gen. Mgr.--Royer Industries, Inc., Kingston, PA; Int'l, pg. 1066
Horan, Phil, Chief Oper. Officer--Bank of America Nevada, Reno, NV; U.S. Public, pg. 180
Horano, T., Chief Oper. Officer--Nippon Selas Co., Ltd., Tokyo, Japan; U.S. Public, pg. 1455
Hord, Fenton, Pres.--Carolina Builders Corporation, Raleigh, NC; Int'l, pg. 1512
Hore, G., Mng. Dir.--S.A. Societe Caroloregienne de Cokefaction CARCOKE, Terte, Belgium; Int'l, pg. 301
Horeau, Hubert, Gen. Mgr.--CiMatrix S.A., Cormeilles-en-Parisis, France; U.S. Public, pg. 1395
Horgan, Paul J., V.P.-Opers.--Textron Automotive Trim Operations, Athens, TN; U.S. Public, pg. 1590
Hori, Hiroaki, Mng. Dir.--Daiko Communications Asia Co., Ltd., Hong Kong, Hong Kong; Int'l, pg. 366
Hori, Kenya, Terminal Mgr.--Kintetsu World Express Inc., Stoneham, MA; Int'l, pg. 734
Hori, Tetsusaburo, Pres.--Sintyal Otsuka Pharmaceutical S.A., Buenos Aires, Argentina; Int'l, pg. 1014
Horie, Akira, Deputy Gen. Mgr.--China Universal Leasing Co., Ltd., Beijing, China; Int'l, pg. 1190
Horie, Tetsuya, Chm. Bd.--Long-Term Credit Bank of Japan (Schweiz) AG, Zurich, Switzerland; Int'l, pg. 816
Horiguchi, Hitoshi, Pres.--Sumitomo Sitix Europe Plc., London, United Kingdom; Int'l, pg. 1317
Horii, Masaaki, Gen. Mgr. & Dir.--The Chiba Bank, Ltd.-International Divison, Tokyo, Japan; Int'l, pg. 283
Horiko, Yoshikazu, Chief Oper. Officer--Tosoh America, Inc., Atlanta, GA; Int'l, pg. 1407
Horiko, Yoshikazu, Chief Oper. Officer--Tosoh USA, Inc., Atlanta, GA; Int'l, pg. 1408
Horine, J., District Mgr.--A.M. Castle & Co., Grand Prairie, TX; U.S. Public, pg. 313
Horiuchi, Junji, Chief Repsentative--Daihatsu Motor Co., Ltd., Zaventem, Belgium; Int'l, pg. 365
Horiuchi, Senji, Gen. Mgr.--The Sumitomo Trust & Banking Co., Ltd., Los Angeles, CA; Int'l, pg. 1317
Horlick, Allan, Pres. & Gen. Mgr.-WRC-TV--National Broadcasting Co., Inc., New York, NY; U.S. Public, pg. 712
Horman, David, V.P.--Dharmala Manulife, Jakarta, Indonesia; Int'l, pg. 841
Horn, Andreas, Partner--Transnational Korn/Ferry, Paris, France; U.S. Private, pg. 634
Horn, Boyd F., Jr., Pres. & Chief Exec. Officer--Regions Bank/Dothan, Dothan, AL; U.S. Public, pg. 1372
Horn, Carl, Mgr.-Plant--The L.J. Minor Corporation, Celina, OH; Int'l, pg. 917
Horn, James C., Exec. V.P. & Gen. Mgr.--Acme Markets, Malvern, PA; U.S. Public, pg. 93
Horn, Larry, Pres.--Quincy Soybean Co., Quincy, IL; U.S. Private, pg. 760
Horn, Ralph, Chm. Bd., Pres., Chief Exec. & Oper. Officer--First Tennessee Bank National Association, Memphis, TN; U.S. Public, pg. 639
Horn, Robert E., Pres.--McCormick Pesa, S.A. de C.V., Mexico, Mexico; U.S. Public, pg. 1067
Horn, William B., Pres.--Gorman-Rupp of Canada Ltd., Saint Thomas, Canada; U.S. Public, pg. 754
Hornady, Steve, Pres.--Hornady Ammunition, Grand Island, NE; U.S. Private, pg. 540
Hornbacher, Dean P., Pres.--Hornbachers, Fargo, ND; U.S. Public, pg. 1541
Hornbaker, R.W., Pres.--Garlock Bearings Division, Thorofare, NJ; U.S. Public, pg. 402
Hornbech, Friedrich Dr., Chief Oper. Officer--Kloeckner Ionon of America, Inc., Charlotte, NC; Int'l, pg. 737
Hornberger, Glenn O., Pres.--Floquil-Polly S Color Corp., Amsterdam, NY; U.S. Public, pg. 1357
Hornberger, Glenn O., Pres.--Chemical Coatings, Inc., Hudson, NC; U.S. Public, pg. 1357
Hornberger, Glenn O., Pres.--Star Finishing Products, Inc., Hinsdale, IL; U.S. Public, pg. 1358
Hornbuckle, William J., Pres. & Chief Oper. Officer--Caesars Palace, Las Vegas, NV; U.S. Public, pg. 1512
Hornbuckley, William J., Pres. & Chief Exec. Officer--GNL, Corp., Laughlin, NV; U.S. Public, pg. 1116
Hornby, Darell, Pres.--Clarke Transport, Concord, Canada; Int'l, pg. 924
Hornby, John, Pres.--Kato Cranes (UK) Ltd., Avonmouth, United Kingdom; Int'l, pg. 1420
Horne, D.O., Chm. Bd. & Chief Exec. Officer--Lloyds Merchant Bank Ltd., London, United Kingdom; Int'l, pg. 813
Horne, Eugene B., Pres.--PH Holding, Sanford, NC; U.S. Private, pg. 837
Horne, James, Pres.--Clarostat Centers & Controls Group, El Paso, TX; Int'l, pg. 127
Horne, Rex, Plant Mgr.--The JPM Company, Beaver Springs, PA; U.S. Public, pg. 919
Horne, Steve, Gen. Mgr.--Alro Group, Fort Wayne, Fort Wayne, IN; U.S. Private, pg. 46
Horne, Tony, Gen. Mgr.--ANI Wear Resistant Products, Waratah, Australia; Int'l, pg. 100
Horner, Donald G., Pres. & Chief Exec. Officer--Pacific One Dealer Center, Inc., Costa Mesa, CA; U.S. Public, pg. 635
Horner, Kenneth D., Pres.--North Pacific Insurance Company, Portland, OR; Int'l, pg. 543
Horner, Maurice O., Pres. & Chief Exec. Officer--Willis Corroon Corp. of Chattanooga, Chattanooga, TN; Int'l, pg. 1505
Horner, Nick, Pres. & Chief Exec. Officer--Citizens First Bank, El Dorado, AR; U.S. Public, pg. 630
Horner, Robert, Chm.--Citicorp Mortgage, Inc., Saint Louis, MO; U.S. Public, pg. 378
Horner, Russ, Mng. Dir.--Australian Newsprint Mills, Hobart, Australia; Int'l, pg. 495
Hornfeld, Arnold, Chief Oper. Officer--Simko Ticaret ve Sanayi A.S., Karakoy, Turkey; Int'l, pg. 1248
Hornfeldt, Bjorn, Chief Oper. Officer--C.A. Electrolux, Quito, Ecuador; Int'l, pg. 441
Hornfeldt, Jan, Pres.--ABB Industria AB, Barbera del Valles, Spain; Int'l, pg. 7
Horngvist, Hans, Pres.--Skanska Norr AB, Sundsvall, Sweden; Int'l, pg. 1260
Hornick, Gerald C., Pres.--Advanced Structures, Inc., Escondido, CA; U.S. Public, pg. 592
Hornick, Gerald C., Pres.--Structural North America, Chardon, OH; U.S. Public, pg. 593
Horning, Jane, Global Mgr.--BanRenta Compania de Seguros de Vida S.A., Santiago, Chile; U.S. Private, pg. 886
Horning, John I., Pres.--Dubai Petroleum Company, Dubai, United Arab Emirates; U.S. Public, pg. 533
Hornsby, Tommy, Exec. Editor--Lake City Reporter, Lake City, FL; U.S. Public, pg. 1175
Hornung, Karlheinz, Dir.--KS Winston Ltd., Maidenhead, United Kingdom; Int'l, pg. 861
Hornyak, George T., Jr., Pres. & Chief Exec. Officer--Pulse Savings Bank, South River, NJ; U.S. Public, pg. 1344
Horo, Kaarlo, Chief Oper. Officer--Ahlstrom Process Equipment Inc., Easley, SC; Int'l, pg. 34
Horowitz, J.M., Pres.--Clarins USA Inc., New York, NY; Int'l, pg. 295
Horowitz, Robert, Exec. V.P.--Lamb-Weston, Boise, ID; U.S. Public, pg. 427
Horowitz, Zach, Pres.--MCA Records, Inc., Universal City, CA; Int'l, pg. 1215
Horras, Doug, Gen. Mgr.--Hillshire Farm Company, New London, WI; U.S. Public, pg. 1433
Horrigan, John F., III, Pres.--American Real Estate Investment & Development Co., Chicago, IL; Int'l, pg. 9
Horrighs, Wolfgang, Dr., Chief Oper. Officer--Chema Balcke-Durr Verfahrenstechnik GmbH Rudisleben, Rudisleben, Germany; Int'l, pg. 399
Horrocks, Steven E., Plant Mgr.--Eaton Corp., Supercharger Div., Athens, GA; U.S. Public, pg. 556
Horsch, Gerd R., Dir.-Production--Cuyk Mill, Cuyk, Netherlands; U.S. Public, pg. 672
Horsfield, John, Mng. Dir.--AMEC Development Ltd., Manchester, United Kingdom; Int'l, pg. 16
Horsfman, Paul, Pres.--Industrial & Automotive Fasteners, Inc., Royal Oak, MI; U.S. Public, pg. 919
Horsler, T., Chief Oper. Officer--Longman France SA, Paris, France; Int'l, pg. 1025
Horsley, R. Scott, Pres.--Ameritech Capital Services, Rolling Meadows, IL; U.S. Public, pg. 98
Horsmtein, Per, Chief Oper. Officer--Ahlstrom Pulp & Paper Engineering S.A., Barcelona, Spain; Int'l, pg. 35
Horst, A. Ter, Chief Oper. Officer--Gist-Brocades, Lda., Matosinhos, Portugal; Int'l, pg. 1143
Horst, Charles, Pres.--Associated Aviation Underwriters, Chicago, IL; U.S. Public, pg. 355
Horsten, Wit, Mgr.--Sandvik Hard Materials, Dusseldorf, Germany; Int'l, pg. 1186
Horstman, A.C.J., Chm. Bd.--Tiel Utrecht, Utrecht, Netherlands; Int'l, pg. 647
Horstman, M., Mng. Dir.--Hepworth Minerals and Chemicals S.A., Bourron, France; Int'l, pg. 615
Horstmann, Hans-Jurgen, Dir.--Deutsche Bank AG (Campinas), Campinas, Brazil; Int'l, pg. 404
Hort, Erich, Gen. Mgr.--Migros Bank, Zurich, Switzerland; Int'l, pg. 866
Horthrop, Bill, V.P.-Sls.--Spartanburg Steel Products, Spartanburg, SC; U.S. Private, pg. 300
Hortin, Ian, Base Supvr.--Weatherford Australia Pty. Ltd., Winnellie, Australia; U.S. Public, pg. 1750
Horton, Ann N., Chief Fin. Officer--Penn Virginia Coal Company, Duffield, VA; U.S. Public, pg. 1271
Horton, Ann N., Treas. & Sec.--Penn Virginia Oil & Gas Company, Kingsport, TN; U.S. Public, pg. 1271
Horton, C. C., Chief Oper. Officer--Rolls-Royce & Associates Limited, Derby, United Kingdom; Int'l, pg. 472
Horton, Duncan, Pres.--ASSA Ltd., Croydon, United Kingdom; Int'l, pg. 17
Horton, E. M., Pres.--NationsBank of Camden, Camden, AR; U.S. Public, pg. 1164
Horton, Gary, Pres.--Nationwide Commercial Co., Phoenix, AZ; U.S. Private, pg. 49
Horton, Gary, Plant Mgr.--Salem Carpet Mills, La Fayette, GA; U.S. Public, pg. 1464
Horton, H.K., Chief Oper. Officer--Mead KK, Tokyo, Japan; U.S. Public, pg. 1076
Horton, H.K., Chief Oper. Officer--Mead Packaging Korea, Inc., Seoul, Korea; U.S. Public, pg. 1076
Horton, Jim, Pres.--Hagglunds Drives Pty Ltd, Canning Vale, Australia; Int'l, pg. 670
Horton, John, Chief Oper. Officer & V.P.--Heath Company, Benton Harbor, MI; Int'l, pg. 317
Horton, Keith D., Pres.--Penn Virginia Coal Company, Duffield, VA; U.S. Public, pg. 1271
Horton, M. Dean, Mgr.--Cash & Carry Div., Topeka, KS; U.S. Public, pg. 652
Horton, Richard B., Pres.--Melling Forging Company, Lansing, MI; U.S. Private, pg. 102
Horton, William, V.P. & Gen. Mgr.--Johnson Controls, Inc., Battery Group, Milwaukee, WI; U.S. Public, pg. 932
Hortsock, Robert, V.P. & Gen. Mgr.--Pacord, National City, CA; U.S. Private, pg. 957
Horvath, Alexander L., Dr., Pres.--Martin Marietta Ocean, Radar & Sensor Systems, Syracuse, NY; U.S. Public, pg. 1007
Horwitz, Martin, Pres. & Chief Exec. Officer--Stewart Smith Mid America, Inc., Chicago, IL; Int'l, pg. 1508
Horwitz, Phillip, Pres.--Liberty Paper & Bag Co., Auburn Hills, MI; Int'l, pg. 233
Horwitz, Susan, Pres. & Chief Exec. Officer--Aurora National Bank, Aurora, IL; U.S. Public, pg. 760
Horwood, B., Chief Oper. Officer--Dampier Salt Ltd., Perth, Australia; Int'l, pg. 947
Horwood, Les, Gen. Mgr.--Education & Entertainment, Salt Lake City, UT; U.S. Public, pg. 596
Hosaka, Taira, Mng. Dir. & Gen. Mgr.--Dai-Ichi Kangyo Bank, Ltd.-London, London, United Kingdom; Int'l, pg. 360
Hose, Paul, Sales & Mktg.--Amicon Ltd., Stonehouse, United Kingdom; U.S. Public, pg. 1113
Hoshiba, Hideo, Exec. V.P.--Dentsu USA-Los Angeles, Santa Monica, CA; Int'l, pg. 393
Hoshino, Hiroaki, Pres.--Kajima International, Inc., Englewood Cliffs, NJ; Int'l, pg. 722
Hoshino, Tadashi, Gen. Mgr.--Cherry Automotive-Japan, Yokohama, Japan; U.S. Public, pg. 346
Hosking, Doug, Pres.--IPC Communication Services, Saint Joseph, MI; U.S. Private, pg. 601
Hoskins, Britt, Gen. Mgr.--Daleville Learning Center, Daleville, AL; U.S. Public, pg. 218
Hoskins, Gregory J., Pres. & Chief Exec. Officer--Refined Sugars, Inc., Yonkers, NY; Int'l, pg. 699
Hosoki, Dairoku, Dir. & Gen. Mgr.--Tokyo Subaru Motors Co., Ltd., Tokyo, Japan; Int'l, pg. 523
Hossack, G.M., Chm. & Mng. Dir.--GKN Chep SA (Pty) Ltd., Wandsbeck, South Africa; Int'l, pg. 536
Hosseinian, Amir, Gen. Mgr.--Harrison Div., Burbank, CA; U.S. Private, pg. 999
Hossom, Chuck, V.P. & Gen. Mgr.--Dayton Rogers of Ohio, Columbus, OH; U.S. Private, pg. 318
Hostenskey, Dale, Mgr.-Exploration--Hunt Oil Central Exploration Division, Dallas, TX; U.S. Private, pg. 548
Hostetler, Dan, Mng. Dir.--George S. May International, S.P.A., Brienza, Italy; U.S. Private, pg. 717
Hostetter, W. Richard, Gen. Mgr.--Cladwood Div. (Philomath), Philomath, OR; Int'l, pg. 1270
Hotaling, Reid, Pres.--K. Hovnanian Companies of Florida, Inc., West Palm Beach, FL; U.S. Public, pg. 843
Hotan, Ernst, Mng. Dir.--Crown Obrist AG, Reinach, Switzerland; U.S. Public, pg. 465
Hotchkiss, Jeffrey, V.P.--Teradyne Assembly Test/East Division, Boston, MA; U.S. Public, pg. 1581
Hott, Ray, Pres.--Nehring Electrical Works Company, De Kalb, IL; U.S. Public, pg. 968
Hotta, Masao, Mgr.-Acctg.--Nanometrics Japan Ltd., Tokyo, Japan; U.S. Public, pg. 1151
Hotta, Michihisa, Pres.--Dongguan Sanxing Socks Co., Ltd., Tung Guan, China; Int'l, pg. 579
Hotta, Toshinobu, Pres.--Nikkeisha, Inc., Tokyo, Japan; Int'l, pg. 929
Hottman, Norman D., Pres.--Tokheim & Gasboy of Canada Limited, Brighton, Canada; U.S. Public, pg. 1620
Houben, Peter, Mng. Dir.--LB Rheinland Pfalz Finance B.V., Amsterdam, Netherlands; Int'l, pg. 799
Houche, Bernard, Mng. Dir.--O.K. Personnel, Neuchatel, Switzerland; U.S. Public, pg. 949
Houchens, Ruel, Pres.--Houchens Markets, Bowling Green, KY; U.S. Private, pg. 541
Houck, J.C., Pres.--Texaco Development Corp., White Plains, NY; U.S. Public, pg. 1583
Houdement, J.C., Dir. Gen.--Selectpack SA, Val-de-Reuil, France; Int'l, pg. 753
Houdkamp, Jaap, Mng. Dir.--Costar Europe, Ltd., Badhoevedorp, Netherlands; U.S. Public, pg. 448
Houdmont, B.W.C., Mng. Dir.--Wolters Kluwer Spain, Madrid, Spain; Int'l, pg. 1514
Houdmont, Bruno, Gen. Mgr.--Bank Brussels Lambert Hong Kong Branch, Central, Hong Kong; Int'l, pg. 148
Hougaard, Helge, Pres.--Volvo Personvage Danmark A/S, Brondby, Denmark; Int'l, pg. 1478
Houge, Mark, Pres.--AP Technology Management Inc., Saint Paul, MN; U.S. Private, pg. 18
Hougendober, John, Gen. Mgr.--ADM Milling Co., Jackson, TN; U.S. Public, pg. 128
Hougenkamp, Daj, Chief Oper. Officer--Carrefour Nederland B.V., Rotterdam, Netherlands; Int'l, pg. 273
Hough, Nick, Mng. Dir.--Lowe Kuiper & Schouten, Amsterdam, Netherlands; U.S. Private, pg. 678
Hough, Paul, Pres.--Van Waters & Rogers, Kirkland, WA; Int'l, pg. 1147

Hough, Paul, Pres.--Van Waters & Rogers Inc., Kirkland, WA; *Int'l*, pg. 1147
Hough, Paul H., Pres.--Van Waters & Rogers Ltd., Richmond, Canada; *Int'l*, pg. 1147
Hough, S. Lachlan, Pres. & Chief Exec. Officer--Security Pacific Asian Bank, Ltd., Central, Hong Kong; *U.S. Public*, pg. 183
Houghton, Alf, Commercial Dir.--Wisaforest (UK) Ltd., Altrincham, United Kingdom; *Int'l*, pg. 1430
Houghton, C.B., Jr., V.P.- Admin.--Encoat-North Arlington, Inc., Wilmington, DE; *U.S. Public*, pg. 1020
Houghton, Peter E., Pres.--Fiduciary Trust International of the South, Miami, FL; *U.S. Public*, pg. 621
Houghton, Richard, Mng. Dir.--Prime Communications Ltd., London, United Kingdom; *Int'l*, pg. 1226
Houghton, Robert M., V.P. & Gen. Mgr.--WGST-AM, Atlanta, GA; *U.S. Public*, pg. 923
Houillon, T., Gen. Mgr.--Delisle Foods Ltd., Boucherville, Canada; *Int'l*, pg. 380
Houk, Keith D., Chm. Bd.--PSA Airlines, Inc., Vandalia, OH; *U.S. Public*, pg. 1680
Houlding, A.J., Mgr.--ING Bank Harare, Harare, Zimbabwe; *Int'l*, pg. 649
Houlditch, Lee C., Pres.--Sloss Industries Corporation, Birmingham, AL; *U.S. Public*, pg. 1736
Houlihan, B., Mng. Dir.--Andrew Australia, Campbellfield, Australia; *U.S. Public*, pg. 113
Hourcade, Xavier, Dir. Gen.--Conforama, Paris, France; *Int'l, pg. 98*
Hourfar, Parviz, Mng. Dir.--SIMCO Ericsson Ltd., Tehran, Iran; *Int'l*, pg. 1370
Hourihane, Paul, Gen. Mgr.--Wunderman Cato Johnson Singapore, Singapore, Singapore; *U.S. Private*, pg. 326
Hourselt, G.L., V.P. & Gen. Mgr.--Flexonics Expansion Joints, New Braunfels, TX; *Int'l*, pg. 1222
Hourselt, Gary L., Pres.--Huck International Aerospace Fastener Division, Carson, CA; *U.S. Public*, pg. 1597
Housand, Jonathan W., Jr., Pres. & Chief Oper. Officer--Society National Bank, Elkhart, IN; *U.S. Public*, pg. 955
House, David, Pres.--James Hardie Gypsum Washington, Seattle, WA; *Int'l*, pg. 597
House, David L., Sr. V.P. & Pres.-Microcomputer Components Group--Intel Microcomputer Group, Santa Clara, CA; *U.S. Public*, pg. 887
House, Deloris, Administrator--Colonial Manor of Whitefish, Whitefish, MT; *U.S. Public*, pg. 837
House, Frank, Jr., Chm. Bd. & Reg. Construction Mng. Dir.--Willis Corroon Corp. of Birmingham, Birmingham, AL; *Int'l*, pg. 1505
House, George, Chief Oper. Officer--QF, Inc., Bayou La Batre, AL; *Int'l*, pg. 940
House, H.D., Pres.--Centex American Gypsum Co., Albuquerque, NM; *U.S. Public*, pg. 322
House, James F., Pres. & Chief Exec. Officer--SouthTrust Bank, Dothan, Dothan, AL; *U.S. Public*, pg. 1491
Houser, George G., Pres.--Raytheon Systems Co., Kirkwood, NY; *U.S. Public*, pg. 1364
Housman, Edward L., Pres.--Automatic Radio International, Melrose, MA; *U.S. Public*, pg. 131
Housman, Kenneth L., Chief Oper. Officer--Echovision Division, Melrose, MA; *U.S. Public*, pg. 131
Houssels, J.K., Chm. Bd.--Showboat Operating Co., Las Vegas, NV; *U.S. Public*, pg. 1469
Houssin, P., Pres.--Kraft Jacobs Suchard, Velizy-Villacoublay, France; *U.S. Public*, pg. 1290
Houston, Alfred D., Pres.--New England Energy, Inc., Westborough, MA; *U.S. Public*, pg. 1171
Houston, Alfred D., Pres.--New England Power Service Co., Westborough, MA; *U.S. Public*, pg. 1171
Houston, B. Ord, Sec.--Bethlehem Intl. Sales Corp., Easton, PA; *U.S. Public*, pg. 226
Houston, D., Mgr.-Worldwide Bus.--Silver-Weibull, Aurora, CO; *U.S. Public*, pg. 705
Houston, Dwight, Pres.--Houston Products, Waverly, TN; *Int'l*, pg. 74
Houston, Paul A., Chm.--Scott's Food Services Inc., Markham, Canada; *Int'l*, pg. 1213
Houston, Paul A., Pres.--Scott's Management Services Inc., Markham, Canada; *Int'l*, pg. 1213
Houston, Robert A., V.P. & Gen. Mgr.--Hydrolectric Lift Trucks Inc., Wilmington, OH; *U.S. Public*, pg. 61
Houtz, Jim H., Chief Exec. Officer--CyData, Inc., Scottsdale, AZ; *U.S. Public*, pg. 770
Houzlet, William, Gen. Mgr.--Colgate-Palmolive CIA, Cali, Colombia; *U.S. Public*, pg. 398
Hovarter, F.M., V.P.--Valley Forest Resources Co., Marcell, MN; *U.S. Private*, pg. 1140
Hove, Larry, Pres.--Entwistle, Fort Worth, TX; *U.S. Private*, pg. 378
Hoven, Gordon E., Mgr.-Branch--Piper Jaffray Inc., Helena, MT; *U.S. Public*, pg. 1303
Hoverson, Robert L., Pres.--Provident Commercial Group, Inc., Cincinnati, OH; *U.S. Public*, pg. 1338
Hovind, Knut, Chief Oper. Officer--KONE A/S, Oslo, Norway; *Int'l*, pg. 747
Hoving, Jan-Willem, Chief Oper. Officer--KONE Starlift B.V., Leidschendam, Netherlands; *Int'l*, pg. 748
Howalt, F. Harvey, Jr., Pres.--Perpetual Machine, Dalton, GA; *U.S. Private*, pg. 1079
Howard-Jonese, Peter, Mng. Dir.--Rayovac/Vidor Limited, Maidstone, United Kingdom; *U.S. Private*, pg. 912
Howard, Al, Pres. & Gen. Mgr.--WFAA-TV, Dallas, TX; *U.S. Public*, pg. 209
Howard, Albert, Dir. & Gen. Mgr.--Almetex, Saint Helens, United Kingdom; *Int'l*, pg. 51
Howard, Alfred J., Pres.--RehabCare Outpatient Services, Inc., Jacksonville, FL; *U.S. Public*, pg. 1373
Howard, Allen E., III, Pres. & Gen. Mgr.--KXTV Inc., Sacramento, CA; *U.S. Public*, pg. 209
Howard, Anthony, Gen. Mgr.--Wang New Zealand Limited, Auckland, New Zealand; *U.S. Public*, pg. 1738
Howard, C. Sammy, Pres.--CB & T Bank of Russell County, Phenix City, AL; *U.S. Public*, pg. 1549
Howard, D.L., Pres. & Chief Oper. Officer--Kaman Instrumentation Corp., Colorado Springs, CO; *U.S. Public*, pg. 942
Howard, Don, V.P. & Gen. Mgr.--United Cities Gas Co., Great River Div., Keokuk, IA; *U.S. Public*, pg. 146
Howard, Donald L., V.P. & G.M.--United Cities Gas Co., KS/IA/MO Div., Overland Park, KS; *U.S. Public*, pg. 146
Howard, Ginger L., Pres.--Guidant Corporation-Vascular Intervention Group, Santa Clara, CA; *U.S. Public*, pg. 768
Howard, Greg, Mgr.-Distr. Center--Herbalife (N.Z.) Limited, Penrose, New Zealand; *U.S. Public*, pg. 809
Howard, James L., Pres.--Kvaerner Moss, Inc., New York, NY; *Int'l*, pg. 770
Howard, Jim L., Mgr.--Stainless Products, Unanderra, Australia; *Int'l*, pg. 227
Howard, K.A., Mng. Dir.--Concrete Industries Sector, Auckland, New Zealand; *Int'l*, pg. 495
Howard, Mary Jane, Pres.--Public Storage Commercial Properties Group, Inc., Glendale, CA; *U.S. Public*, pg. 1341
Howard, Morgan S., Mgr.-Opers.--Wilkins-Regulator Div., Paso Robles, CA; *U.S. Public*, pg. 1794
Howard, Peter, Pres.--Leaf River Forest Products, Inc., New Augusta, MS; *U.S. Public*, pg. 736
Howard, Richard R., Pres.--Genesis ElderCare, Philadelphia, PA; *U.S. Public*, pg. 728
Howard, Robert, Pres.--Alcoa Fujikura, Troy, MI; *U.S. Public, pg. 61*
Howard, W.R., Pres. & Treas.--Saddlebag Lake Resorts, Inc., La Belle, FL; *U.S. Public*, pg. 41
Howarth, J.F., Exec. Dir.--Travelstrength Limited, Sydney, Australia; *Int'l*, pg. 313
Howarth, Peter, Mng. Dir.--Royal Mail, London, United Kingdom; *Int'l*, pg. 1064
Howatt, Thomas J., V.P. & Gen. Mgr.--Wausau Papers - Printing & Writing Div., Brokaw, WI; *U.S. Public*, pg. 1747
Howatt, Thomas J., V.P. & Gen. Mgr.-Printing & Writing Div.--Wausau Papers of New Hampshire, Inc., Groveton, NH; *U.S. Public*, pg. 1748
Howden, Maria, Gen. Mgr.--Dealers Auto Auction of Sanford, Inc., Sanford, FL; *U.S. Public*, pg. 1649
Howe, David, General Mgr.--TecSyn P.M.P. Inc., Huntsville, AL; *Int'l*, pg. 1362
Howe, Donald J., V.P. & Gen. Mgr.--KRFX-FM, Denver, CO; *U.S. Public*, pg. 922
Howe, Fletcher S., Jr., Pres.--Bancorp Investment Group, Ltd., Honolulu, HI; *U.S. Public*, pg. 1248
Howe, Gene, Gen. Mgr.--Telemation Productions Inc., Ontario, CA; *U.S. Public*, pg. 1686
Howe, Hubbard C., Chm. Bd. & Pres.--A.P.S., Memphis, TN; *U.S. Public*, pg. 10
Howe, J., Gen. Mgr.--Anglo-Austrian Magnesite, Ltd., Sunningdale, United Kingdom; *U.S. Private*, pg. 903
Howe, Michael V., Chm. Bd.--Mileage Plus Marketing, Inc., Elk Grove Village, IL; *U.S. Public*, pg. 1653
Howe, R.W., Mng. Dir.--Goodyear Malaysia Berhad, Kuala Lumpur, Malaysia; *U.S. Public*, pg. 753
Howe, Stephen, Mgr.-Mktg.--Cerner Corporation Pty Ltd., Milsons Point, Australia; *U.S. Public*, pg. 331
Howe, Travis L., Mng. Dir.--Meto, USA, Morris Plains, NJ; *Int'l*, pg. 460
Howe, Willis E., Pres.--SuperValu, Inc.-Keene Div., Keene, NH; *U.S. Public*, pg. 1540
Howell, A. Leo, Pres.--Howell Metal Company, New Market, VA; *U.S. Public*, pg. 413
Howell, D.A., Chief Oper. Officer--Scott Tobacco, Bowling Green, KY; *U.S. Private*, pg. 272
Howell, David, Mng. Dir.--EURO RSCG Partnership, Bangkok, Thailand; *Int'l*, pg. 602
Howell, Donald E., Pres.--NationsBank Leasing Corp., Charlotte, NC; *U.S. Public*, pg. 1165
Howell, Edwin C., Pres.--Baker Oil Tools, Houston, TX; *U.S.* Public, pg. 167
Howell, Hilton H., Jr., Chm. Bd.--Self-Insurance Administrators, Inc., Stone Mountain, GA; *U.S. Public*, pg. 144
Howell, James, V.P. & Gen. Mgr.--National Steel Corp., Great Lakes Division, Ecorse, MI; *Int'l*, pg. 903
Howell, Jay, Mgr.--Harley Valve & Instrument, Beaumont, TX; *U.S. Public*, pg. 880
Howell, John A., III, V.P. & Gen. Mgr.--WPXI Inc., Pittsburgh, PA; *U.S. Private*, pg. 282
Howell, John R., Chm. Bd., Pres. & Chief Exec. Officer--Summit Bank, Bethlehem, PA; *U.S. Public*, pg. 1528
Howell, Judith, Mgr.--David Levin Co., Peru, IN; *U.S. Private, pg. 1048*
Howell, Mark, Pres. & Chief Exec. Officer--First Security Business Investment Corp., Salt Lake City, UT; *U.S. Public*, pg. 637
Howell, R.G., Chm. Bd.--Fruehauf Finance Company, Dallas, TX; *U.S. Public*, pg. 663
Howell, Terrence, Pres. & Gen. Mgr.--Beacon Press, Inc., Richmond, VA; *U.S. Public*, pg. 1077
Howell, Warren R., V.P. & Gen. Mgr.--Bio-Rad Digilab Div., Cambridge, MA; *U.S. Public*, pg. 230
Howells, Hank, Pres.--Westinghouse Residential Security Systems, Irving, TX; *U.S. Public*, pg. 273
Howenstein, William K., Pres.--Copper & Brass Sales, Inc., Eastpointe, MI; *Int'l*, pg. 1389
Howes, Bob, Pres.--Carpentry & Hardware Services, Columbia, MD; *U.S. Private*, pg. 503
Howes, Mike, Mng. Dir.--John Crane (Pty) Ltd., Transvaal, South Africa; *Int'l*, pg. 1339
Howes, R., Pres.--Racal Canada Inc., Vancouver, Canada; *Int'l*, pg. 1083
Howeth, Robert W., Pres.--Fairfield Acceptance Corporation, Little Rock, AR; *U.S. Public*, pg. 611
Howlett, Brian, Chief Oper. Officer--COBE Laboratories Ltd., Gloucester, United Kingdom; *Int'l*, pg. 667
Howse, Karl, V.P. & Gen. Mgr.--Cook Chocolate Canada Ltd., Campbellford, Canada; *U.S. Private*, pg. 1191
Howse, Karl, V.P. & Gen. Mgr.--World's Finest Chocolate Canada Ltd., Campbellford, Canada; *U.S. Private*, pg. 1191
Hoyem, Tor Jakob, Mng. Dir.--Ericsson Components A/S, Oslo, Norway; *Int'l*, pg. 1366
Hoyle, John, Chief Oper. Officer--United Eco Systems, High Point, NC; *Int'l*, pg. 74
Hoylman, D.L., Pres.--Industrial Resources, Inc., Fairmont, WV; *U.S. Private*, pg. 961
Hoyne, W., Chief Exec. Officer--Brinks-Allied, Dublin, Ireland; *Int'l*, pg. 81
Hoyos, Alexander, Chm.-Bd. of Mgmnt.--Wiener Allianz Versicherungs-AG, Vienna, Austria; *Int'l*, pg. 62
Hoyos, Alexander, Dr., Chm.-Bd. of Mngmt.--Wiener Allianz Lebensversicherungs-AG, Vienna, Austria; *Int'l*, pg. 62
Hoysentruyt, Paul, Mng. Dir.--Bekintex N.V., Wetteren, Belgium; *Int'l*, pg. 183
Hoyt, Brad, Chief Oper. Officer--Hoyt Development, Plymouth, MN; *U.S. Private*, pg. 543
Hoyt, Everett E., Pres. & Chief Oper. Officer--Black Hills Power & Light Company, Rapid City, SD; *U.S. Public*, pg. 235
Hoyt, Harry E., Pres.--INA Special Risk Facilities, Inc., Philadelphia, PA; *U.S. Public*, pg. 366
Hoyt, Marty, Mgr.--The Walling Co., Inc., Davenport, IA; *U.S.* Private, pg. 360
Hozaki, Hideo, Gen. Mgr.--Sanko Peterson Corporation, Madison Heights, MI; *U.S. Private*, pg. 857
Hrabchak, Dennis, Pres.--Precision Power, Inc., Hamden, CT; *U.S. Public*, pg. 1678
Hrach, R. Joseph, Div. Mgr.--Ohio Edison Co.-Stark Div., Massillon, OH; *U.S. Public*, pg. 645
Hribar, Herb, Pres.--Ameritech Cellular and Paging Services, Hoffman Estates, IL; *U.S. Public*, pg. 98
Hrizuk, Michael, Plant Mgr.--Ash Grove Cement-Western Region Cement Plant, Durkee, OR; *U.S. Private*, pg. 88
Hromas, Loni, Media Dir.--Western International Media Corporation, Houston, TX; *U.S. Private*, pg. 1167
Hrushetska, Layna, Mng. Dir.--Leo Burnett Kyiv, Ukraine; *U.S. Private*, pg. 185
Hruska, John R., Mng.-Bus. Unit--Airborne Div., Elyria, OH; *U.S. Public*, pg. 1262
Hruska, John R., Mgr.-Bus. Unit--Aircraft Wheel & Brake Div., Avon, OH; *U.S. Public*, pg. 1262
Hsin, Lo Ta, Pres.--Mandarin Airlines, Taipei, Taiwan; *Int'l*, pg. 284
Hsiung, Richard, Mng. Dir.--Dentsu Young & Rubicam/ Taipei, Taipei, Taiwan; *U.S. Private*, pg. 325
Hsu, Chao Chi, Chief Exec. Officer--President Foods Co., Ltd., Ping-tung, Taiwan; *Int'l*, pg. 1069
Hsu, David, Pres.--Jardine Fleming Taiwan Investment Management Limited, Taipei, Taiwan; *Int'l*, pg. 494
Hsu, Fu-Chien, V.P. & G.M.--RISC Div., Santa Clara, CA; *U.S. Public*, pg. 884
Hsu, Julia, Chief Oper. Officer--Royal Copenhagen (Taiwan) Ltd., Taipei, Taiwan; *Int'l*, pg. 1135
Hsu, P.T., Chm.--Kuo Hua Inc., Taipei, Taiwan; *Int'l*, pg. 394
Hu, Jerome S., Jr., Representative & V.P.--First RepublicBank Dallas, N.A. Representative Office, Taipei, Taiwan; *U.S. Public*, pg. 1165
Hu, L.R., Pres.--Gains Investment Corporation, Kao-hsiung, Taiwan; *Int'l*, pg. 285
Hu, Longmen, Chm.--Dentsu (Taiwan) Inc., Taipei, Taiwan; *Int'l*, pg. 394
Hu, M.K., Gen. Mng.--S.C. Johnson & Son Taiwan Ltd., Taipei, Taiwan; *U.S. Private*, pg. 593
Hua, Zhou Yong, Gen. Mgr.--Wuhan Bundy Fluid Systems Co. Ltd., Wuhan, China; *Int'l*, pg. 1341
Huang, Wen-Hsiung, V.P. & Gen. Mgr.--The International Commercial Bank of China, Colon, Panama; *Int'l*, pg. 683
Huang, Yukon, Country Dir.--The World Bank, Beijing, China; *U.S. Private*, pg. 1189
Hubacker, Fred L., Pres.--Textron Automotive Company, Troy, MI; *U.S. Public*, pg. 1590
Hubbard, Allan B., Pres.--E & A Investors, L.P., Indianapolis, IN; *U.S. Private*, pg. 352
Hubbard, D.F., Mgr.--Tencarva Machinery Co., Knoxville, TN; *U.S. Private*, pg. 1075
Hubbard, Don, Gen. Mgr.--BancTec Technologies, Oklahoma City, OK; *U.S. Public*, pg. 177
Hubbard, E. J., Gen. Mgr.--Seraphic Division, Beverly, Australia; *Int'l*, pg. 1057
Hubbard, Paul, Gen. Mgr.--Alro Group, South Bend, South Bend, IN; *U.S. Private*, pg. 46
Hubbard, R.D., Pres. & Chief Exec. Officer--Turf Paradise, Inc., Phoenix, AZ; *U.S. Public*, pg. 831
Hubbard, Robert W., Pres.-TV Grp.--KSTP-TV, Saint Paul, MN; *U.S. Private*, pg. 544
Hubbard, Samuel T., Jr., Pres. & Chief Exec. Officer--The Ailing & Cory Company, Rochester, NY; *U.S. Public*, pg. 1666
Hubbard, Stanley E., Pres. & Chief Exec. Officer--United States Satellite Broadcasting Co., Saint Paul, MN; *U.S. Private*, pg. 544
Hubbard, Stanley S., Chm. Bd.--United States Satellite Broadcasting, Co., Saint Paul, MN; *U.S. Private*, pg. 544
Hubbard, Ward M., V.P. & Gen. Mgr.--Wabash Fibre Box Company-Terre Haute Plant, Terre Haute, IN; *U.S. Private*, pg. 1170
Hubble, Don W., Chm. Bd.--National Linen & Uniform Service, Atlanta, GA; *U.S. Public*, pg. 1160
Hubble, Don W., Pres.--Zep Manufacturing, Dorval, Canada; *U.S. Public*, pg. 1160
Hubble, Don W., Dir.--Zep Europe B.V., Rungis, France; *U.S. Public*, pg. 1160
Huber, Albert F., Pres.--Patterson Pump Company, Toccoa, GA; *U.S. Public*, pg. 754
Huber, Chris J., V.P. & Gen. Mgr.--WSBA AM/FM, York, PA; *U.S. Private*, pg. 860
Huber, Daniel, Dir.-Acctg.--Eurodis AG, Regensdorf, Switzerland,; *Int'l*, pg. 1247

Huber, Franz, Mng. Dir.--Cerner Solutions Center -SNI Health Solutions Div., Pfeffenhausen, Germany; *U.S. Public*, pg. 331
Huber, Fred R., Pres.--Melamine Chemicals, Inc., Donaldsonville, LA; *U.S. Public*, pg. 344
Huber, John, Pres.--Phoenix Chemical Company, East Dubuque, IL; *U.S. Public*, pg. 856
Huber, Joseph, Mgr.-Sls.--Fasson Gesellschaft GmbH, Vienna, Austria; *U.S. Public*, pg. 154
Huber, K., Chief Oper. Officer--SAIA-Burgess Ges.mbH, Salzburg, Austria; *Int'l*, pg. 1501
Huber, L., Gen. Mgr.--Moore Paragon (Suisse) S.A., Lausanne, Switzerland; *Int'l*, pg. 890
Huber, Oliver, Branch Mgr.--Union-Transport Corporation-Charlotte Office, Charlotte, NC; *U.S. Private*, pg. 1119
Huber, Robert, Pres. & Gen. Mgr.--LLE, Rastatt, Germany; *U.S. Public*, pg. 1045
Huber, Sigfried, Chief Oper. Officer--Alfa Romeo Vertriebsges m.b.H., Frankfurt/Main, Germany; *Int'l*, pg. 481
Huber, Thomas G., Vice Chmn.--JEOL (U.S.A.), Inc., Peabody, MA; *Int'l*, pg. 697
Huber, Willy, Dir.-Switzerland--Raychem AG, Baar, Switzerland; *U.S. Public*, pg. 1362
Hubers, David, Chm. Bd., Chief Exec. Officer & Pres.--IDS Financial Services, Inc., Minneapolis, MN; *U.S. Public*, pg. 73
Hubert, Einar, Mgr.--Kvaerner Engineering, Stavanger Division, Stavangor, Norway; *Int'l*, pg. 766
Hubert, Roger, Pres.--Manoir Industries, Paris, France; *Int'l*, pg. 570
Hubert, Th. J., Gen. Mgr.--Zwolsche Algemeene N.V., Nieuwegein, Netherlands; *U.S. Public*, pg. 795
Hubert, Wanda, Admin.--Park Avenue Villa, Mansfield, OH; *U.S. Public*, pg. 838
Hubler, Peter, Chief Oper. Officer--DEC AG, Zug, Switzerland; *U.S. Private*, pg. 301
Hublick, Jana, Clinical Evaluator--MedTrac, Inc., Wichita, KS; *Int'l*, pg. 1504
Hubling, C.L., Pres.--Hubbell Canada Inc., Pickering, Canada; *U.S. Public*, pg. 845
Hubner, Eric, Pres.--Allied Felt Group, Bloomingdale, NJ; *U.S. Private*, pg. 224
Hubregtse, Robin, Mgr.--General Employment Enterprises, Inc., Irvine, CA; *U.S. Public*, pg. 714
Huby, Bart J., Assoc. Dir.--WF Corroon-Bristol, Bristol, United Kingdom; *Int'l*, pg. 1501
Huckel, Dr. Hubert E., Grp. Pres.--Hoechst Celanese Life Sciences Group, Somerville, NJ; *Int'l*, pg. 626
Hudak, A., Mgr.--ING Bank Kosice, Kosice, Slovakia; *Int'l*, pg. 649
Hudak, Paul, V.P. & Gen. Mgr.-Opers.--Fuji Photographic Products Div., Elmsford, NY; *Int'l*, pg. 524
Hudd, Neil, Pres.--N.B.S. Inc., Lachine, Canada; *Int'l*, pg. 898
Huddleston, Ray, Pres. & Chief Exec. Officer--Citizens First Bank, Springhill, LA; *U.S. Public*, pg. 630
Hudkins, Jerry H., Pres.--Leggett Wire Company, Jacksonville, FL; *U.S. Public*, pg. 986
Hudler, Carol, Pres. & Publr.--Macon Telegraph Publishing Company, Macon, GA; *U.S. Public*, pg. 964
Hudler, Donald W., Chm. Bd. & Pres.--The Saturn Corporation, Troy, MI; *U.S. Public*, pg. 721
Hudson-Smith, Eric, Mgr.-Office--Woodward-Clyde, Perth, Australia; *U.S. Public*, pg. 1657
Hudson, A. Carman K., Chm. & Mng. Dir.--Scotia Jamaica Insurance Agency Limited, Kingston, Jamaica; *Int'l*, pg. 156
Hudson, Bill, Pres.--NVR Settlement Services, Pittsburgh, PA; *U.S. Public*, pg. 1148
Hudson, Bob, Head-Nordic Sls.--Skandia Life Assurance Co. Ltd. - Helsinki, Helsinki, Finland; *Int'l*, pg. 1256
Hudson, C. B., Jr., Chm. Bd. & Chief Exec. Officer--United American Insurance Co., Dallas, TX; *U.S. Public*, pg. 1623
Hudson, Carl R., Gen. Mgr.--Rorer Australia Pty. Ltd., Arncliffe, Australia; *Int'l*, pg. 1111
Hudson, Chuck, Pres.--Brawn of California, Inc., San Diego, CA; *U.S. Public*, pg. 782
Hudson, D., Dir.--Baring Brothers, Central, Hong Kong; *Int'l*, *pg. 648*
Hudson, Desmond F., Chm. Bd.--Nortel Limited, Maidenhead, United Kingdom; *Int'l*, pg. 970
Hudson, Don, Pres.--Hathaway Process Instrumentation, Carrollton, TX; *U.S. Public*, pg. 799
Hudson, Donald H., Gen. Mgr.--Alchem Plastics Corp.-Georgia, Atlanta, GA; *U.S. Public*, pg. 1495
Hudson, Eric, Mng. Dir.--Angelica International Ltd., Warrington, United Kingdom; *U.S. Public*, pg. 113
Hudson, Gary, Gen. Mgr.--Allegheny Heat Treating, Chicora, PA; *U.S. Public*, pg. 412
Hudson, John B., Chm.--Hilb, Rogal and Hamilton Company of Victoria, Victoria, TX; *U.S. Public*, pg. 827
Hudson, Kent O., Pres. & Chief Exec. Officer--SRS, Raleigh, NC; *U.S. Public*, pg. 307
Hudson, M.R., Chm. & Pres.--Meta Oil Inc., Westwood, KS; *U.S. Private*, pg. 408
Hudson, Michael, Pres.--Bourns Integrated Technologies Division, Logan, UT; *U.S. Private*, pg. 161
Hudson, Michael J., Corp. V.P.--Convertors/Custom Sterile, McGaw Park, IL; *U.S. Public*, pg. 44
Hudson, P.M.G., Mng. Dir.--De La Rue Holographics Limited, Basingstoke, United Kingdom; *Int'l*, pg. 387
Hudson, R., Pres.--BFC Industrial Nicholls-Radtke, Cambridge, Canada; *Int'l*, pg. 118
Hudson, R.J., Pres.--Mikropul Environmental Systems Div., Summit, NJ; *Int'l*, pg. 636
Hudson, Roger, Pres.--Hosokawa Micron Ltd., Brampton, Canada; *Int'l*, pg. 636
Hudyka, Diane, Branch Mgr.--Circle International, Cleveland, OH; *U.S. Public*, pg. 371
Huebler, F., Chief Exec. Officer--Bramac Dachsysteme International GmbH, Pochlarn, Austria; *Int'l*, pg. 1092
Huebner, Hans J., Mng. Dir.--Gesellschaft fur Gerotebau mbH, Dortmund, Germany; *Int'l*, pg. 594
Huebner, Margaret A., Pres.--Grocers Development Co., Los Angeles, CA; *U.S. Private*, pg. 227
Huecker, Wally, Gen. Mgr.--Elixir Industries, Meridian, ID; *U.S. Private*, pg. 371
Huecker, Wally, Gen. Mgr.--Elixir Industries, Aurora, OR; *U.S. Private*, pg. 371
Huelsman, Howare, Pres. & Gen. Mgr.--Casco Products Corporation, Bridgeport, CT; *U.S. Public*, pg. 1458
Huemer, David A., Chief Exec. Officer--New York Switch Corporation, Fort Lee, NJ; *U.S. Public*, pg. 339
Huenber, Ralfr, Gen. Mgr.--ITW Oberflachentechnk GmbH, Dietzenbach, Germany; *U.S. Public*, pg. 869
Hueppi, Rolph, Chm. Bd.--Zurich American Insurance Company of Illinois, Schaumburg, IL; *Int'l*, pg. 1530
Hueston, Elizabeth, Chief Oper. Officer--Guest International (Canada) Ltd., Mississauga, Canada; *U.S. Public*, pg. 768
Huet, J., Gen. Mgr.--Cic Paris, Paris, France; *Int'l*, pg. 564
Huete, Pedro Guardeno, Pres.--ASTANDER - Astilleros de Santander S.A., El Astillero, Spain; *Int'l*, pg. 1223
Huey, David, Pres.--Buckeye Cablevision, Toledo, OH; *U.S. Private*, pg. 147
Huey, John, Mng. Editor--Fortune, New York, NY; *U.S. Public*, pg. 1613
Huey, Rob, Gen. Mgr.--TDK Electronics, Western Region, Gardena, CA; *Int'l*, pg. 1336
Huff, Eric, Pres.--Call Interactive, Omaha, NE; *U.S. Public*, pg. 631
Huff, Glen E., Pres.--ITW Electronic Component Packaging, Arlington, TX; *U.S. Public*, pg. 866
Huff, Jackson, Pres. & Chief Exec. Officer--UPB of Louisiana, Baton Rouge, LA; *U.S. Public*, pg. 1669
Huff, John R., Chm. Bd., Pres. & Chief Exec. Officer--Oceaneering International, Inc., Morgan City, LA; *U.S. Public*, pg. 1211
Huff, Jonathan, Plant Mgr.--Finishing Div., Thomaston, GA; *U.S. Public*, pg. 1599
Huff, Ronald E., Chief Fin. Officer--Peake Energy, Inc., Ravenswood, WV; *U.S. Private*, pg. 1078
Huff, Sam, Gen. Mgr.--Vulcraft Div., Grapeland, TX; *U.S. Public*, pg. 1206
Huff, Wayne, Pres. & Chief Exec. Officer--Cegelec AEG Automation Systems Corp., Canonsburg, PA; *Int'l*, pg. 52
Huffman, Robert Y., Pres. & Chief Exec. Officer--Liberty Management Services, Inc., Birmingham, AL; *U.S. Public*, *pg. 1622*
Huffnagel, R.A., Chief Rep.--ING Insurance International, Beijing, China; *Int'l*, pg. 650
Hufford, Chuck, Pres.--Midwest Agri-Commodities, Corte Madera, CA; *U.S. Private*, pg. 53
Hufford, Donald M., Sr. V.P. & Grp. Publisher--Car and Driver, New York, NY; *Int'l*, pg. 795
Hufford, Greg, Gen. Mgr.--Barton's of Leachville, Leachville, AR; *U.S. Private*, pg. 119
Hufnagl, Brunhilde, Gen. Mgr.--National Indemnity Co., Omaha, NE; *U.S. Public*, pg. 221
Hug, Klaus, Chief Exec.--Protek GmbH, Freiburg, Germany; *Int'l*, pg. 1307
Hug, Luzius, Pres.--Cerberus AG, Manneforf, Switzerland; *Int'l*, pg. 1246
Huga, Akira, Terminal Mgr.--Kintetsu World Express Inc., Taylor, MI; *Int'l*, pg. 735
Hugas, William, V.P.--Dayflex Plastics, Dayton, OH; *U.S. Public*, pg. 1045
Hugdal, Jan, Gen. Mgr.--Kvaerner Engineering, Trondheim, Trondheim, Norway; *Int'l*, pg. 766
Hugenot, Verle, Chm. Bd., Pres. & Chief Exec. Officer--United Missouri Bank Northeast, Monroe City, MO; *U.S. Public*, pg. 1654
Huges, Grady, Mgr.-Opers.--Trademark Press, Inc., Corpus Christi, TX; *U.S. Public*, pg. 794
Huget, Larry, Pres.--Bucyrus Blades Inc., Bucyrus, OH; *U.S. Private*, pg. 383
Hugger, Michael, Pres.--Katz American Television, New York, NY; *U.S. Public*, pg. 335
Huggins, Alan, V.P. & G.M.--FIFO Division, San Jose, CA; *U.S. Public*, pg. 884
Huggins, Alan, V.P. & Gen. Mgr.--Static RAM Div., Salinas, CA; *U.S. Public*, pg. 884
Huggins, Charles N., Pres.--See's Candy Shops, Inc., South San Francisco, CA; *U.S. Public*, pg. 221
Huggins, Frederick A., Jr., Pres. & Chief Exec. Officer--We Care Hair, Minneapolis, MN; *U.S. Private*, pg. 115
Huggins, Rinald W., Mng. Dir.--Kimberly-Clark Limited, Larkfield, United Kingdom; *U.S. Public*, pg. 959
Hughes, Arturo, Mgr.--Evenflo, Manila, Philippines; *U.S. Private*, pg. 630
Hughes, Bill, Pres.--Howe Sound Pulp & Paper Limited, Vancouver, Canada; *Int'l*, pg. 260
Hughes, Calvin D., V.P.--Wellman Engineering Resins Div., Johnsonville, SC; *U.S. Public*, pg. 1752
Hughes, Catherine, Gen. Mgr.--Radio One of Maryland, Baltimore, MD; *U.S. Private*, pg. 906
Hughes, Christopher D., Pres.--Booth/Crystal Tips, Dallas, TX; *U.S. Public*, pg. 1445
Hughes, David H., Pres.--H. Venture Corp., Orlando, FL; *U.S. Public*, pg. 847
Hughes, Don A., Gen. Mgr.--Reclamation Div. (Maplewood), Maplewood, MO; *Int'l*, pg. 1271
Hughes, Donal, Mng. Dir.--Chilton Electric, Dunleer, Ireland; *Int'l*, pg. 554
Hughes, Edward B., V.P.-Grp. Publisher--Healthcare Group, New York, NY; *U.S. Private*, pg. 515
Hughes, Hugh, Chief Exec. Officer--Societe Generale Equities International, London, United Kingdom; *Int'l*, pg. 1274
Hughes, J.H., Pres.-U.K.--GKN North America Services Inc., Memphis, TN; *Int'l*, pg. 535
Hughes, James E., Pres.--Financial Protection Marketing Inc., Indianapolis, IN; *U.S. Public*, pg. 1336
Hughes, Jim, Chief Exec. Officer--Star Container, Co., Phoenix, AZ; *U.S. Private*, pg. 1071
Hughes, John, Chief Oper. Officer--Volclay Limited, Wallasey, United Kingdom; *U.S. Public*, pg. 64
Hughes, John, Pres. & Chief Exec. Officer--Volclay Standard Pty. Ltd., Geelong, Australia; *U.S. Public*, pg. 64
Hughes, John, Mgr.--Gould Paper Corporation of New York, Inc., Rochester, NY; *U.S. Private*, pg. 467
Hughes, John, Mng. Dir.--THORN Australia Pty Ltd., Sydney, Australia; *Int'l*, pg. 1386
Hughes, K., Chief Oper. Officer--Longman Italia SRL, Milan, Italy; *Int'l*, pg. 1025
Hughes, Keith W., Chm. Bd. & Chief Exec. Officer--Associates First Capital Corporation, Dallas, TX; *U.S. Public*, pg. 662
Hughes, Kenneth M., Div. Mgr.--Westpac - Australian Capital Territory, Barton, Australia; *Int'l*, pg. 1496
Hughes, Linda, Pres. & Publisher--The Edmonton Journal, Edmonton, Canada; *Int'l*, pg. 631
Hughes, Luois R., Pres.--General Motors (Europe) AG, Glattbrugg, Switzerland; *U.S. Public*, pg. 721
Hughes, Marvin B., Pres.-Railcar Repair--Trinity Railcar Leasing, Dallas, TX; *U.S. Public*, pg. 1639
Hughes, Michael, Gen. Mgr.--AAR Pacific Pte. Ltd., Singapore, Singapore; *U.S. Public*, pg. 1
Hughes, R., Pres.--Laporte Absorbents Europe, Widnes, United Kingdom; *Int'l*, pg. 802
Hughes, R.G., Mng. Dir.--P&O Cruises Limited, London, United Kingdom; *Int'l*, pg. 1033
Hughes, Robert S., II, Pres.--Alcoa Fujikura Ltd., Brentwood, TN; *U.S. Public*, pg. 60
Hughes, Robert S., II, Pres.--Alcoa Fujikura Ltd., Brentwood, TN; *Int'l*, pg. 525
Hughes, S. Anderson, Pres. & Chief Exec. Officer--First Virginia Bank-Colonial, Richmond, VA; *U.S. Public*, pg. 641
Hughes, Sean, Pres.--P T Jardine Fleming Nusantara, Jakarta, Indonesia; *Int'l*, pg. 494
Hughes, Simon, Chief Fin. Officer--Mothercare World UK Ltd., Watford, United Kingdom; *Int'l*, pg. 1304
Hughes, Terry, Pres. & Chief Exec. Officer--InfoWorks, Mississauga, Canada; *U.S. Public*, pg. 1225
Hughes, Victor A., Sr., Chief Fin. Officer--Southeast Properties Holding Corporation, Inc., Jacksonville, FL; *U.S. Public*, pg. 965
Hughes, W.J., Pres.--American Life & Casualty Insurance Co., Des Moines, IA; *U.S. Public*, pg. 433
Hughes, Wesley E., Jr., Pres. & Chief Exec. Officer--Bank of Southern Maryland, La Plata, MD; *U.S. Public*, pg. 1088
Hughes, William E., Chief Opr. Officer--Crown Door Corp., Mobile, AL; *Int'l*, pg. 1067
Hughey, Bob, Gen. Mgr.--Fansteel VR/Wesson-Plantsville, Plantsville, CT; *U.S. Public*, pg. 612
Hughey, David, Gen. Mgr.--Fuchs-Montgomery Company, Inc., Cambridge, Canada; *Int'l*, pg. 518
Hugill, Herbert L., Pres.--R.P. Scherer North America, Saint Petersburg, FL; *U.S. Public*, pg. 1438
Hugo-Martinez, Albert J., Pres & Chief Exec. Officer--Valor Electronics, Inc., San Diego, CA; *U.S. Public*, pg. 768
Hugo, Nigel, Gen. Mgr.--Norman Levy Associates Overseas, Coventry, United Kingdom; *U.S. Private*, pg. 664
Huguet, John, Pres. & Gen. Mgr.--Commonwealth Construction Co., Burnaby, Canada; *U.S. Public*, pg. 143
Hugunin, Mike, Mgr.--Cablevision of Shreveport, Shreveport, LA; *U.S. Public*, pg. 1610
Huh, Suk-Beom, Pres.--Hokuryu Cement Corp., Hokkaido, Japan; *Int'l*, pg. 1291
Huhne, Wolfgang, Gen. Mgr.--Bayerische Landesbank - Tokyo Branch, Tokyo, Japan; *Int'l*, pg. 176
Huhta, Steve, Pres.--ADD, Inc., Waupaca, WI; *U.S. Private*, pg. 601
Hui, Benny, Gen. Mgr.--DMB&B Shanghai, Shanghai, China; *U.S. Private*, pg. 304
Hui, Hong Chong, Mng. Dir.--Inoue-Nissei Engineering Pte Ltd., Singapore, Singapore; *Int'l*, pg. 1322
Hui, Y.C., Chief Fin. Officer--ISC Systems Asia Pacific Ltd., Hong Kong, Hong Kong; *Int'l*, pg. 1003
Huibers, S.C., Chm.--The PFH Group, Diemen, Netherlands; *Int'l*, pg. 750
Huie, Glenn G., Chm. Bd., Pres. & Chief Exec. Officer--SouthTrust Bank of Anniston, Anniston, AL; *U.S. Public*, pg. 1492
Huiskes, A., Dir.--Ballast Nedam Milieutechniek B.V., Amstelveen, Netherlands; *Int'l*, pg. 134
Huisman, J.B.A.A., Gen. Mgr.--ING Bank Zurich, Zurich, Switzerland; *Int'l*, pg. 649
Huisman, J.R., Chm.--de Bijenkorf B.V., Amsterdam, Netherlands; *Int'l*, pg. 750
Huisman, R.J., Chm. Bd.--Monsanto (Malaysia) Sendirian Berhad, Petaling Jaya, Malaysia; *U.S. Public*, pg. 1126
Huizenga, H. Wayne, Chm., Pres. & Chief Exec. Officer--Blockbuster Video Limited Partnership, Burr Ridge, IL; *U.S. Private*, pg. 776
Huizinga, Hans, Gen. Mgr.--Mefiag Nederland B.V., Heerenveen, Netherlands; *U.S. Public*, pg. 1100
Hujts, H., Chief Oper. Officer--Rhenania Transport B.V., Rotterdam, Netherlands; *Int'l*, pg. 1034
Hulber, Loren J., Pres. & Chief Exec. Officer--NovaCare Employee Services, Inc., Norristown, PA; *U.S. Public*, pg. 1203
Hulbert, A.J., Gen. Mgr.--Morgan Matroc Limited Transducer Products Division, Southampton, United Kingdom; *Int'l*, pg. 893
Hulick, William, Pres.--Air Engineering Co., Inc., Honolulu, HI; *U.S. Public*, pg. 65
Hulit, E. Addison, Pres.--Addison Insurance Agency, Lombard, IL; *U.S. Public*, pg. 1677
Hull, Dan A., Admin.--Wasatch Villa Convalescent Nursing Home, Salt Lake City, UT; *U.S. Public*, pg. 1715
Hull, David, Mng. Dir.--Nederman Ltd., Preston, United Kingdom; *Int'l*, pg. 283
Hull, Donald N., Sr. V.P. & Gen. Mgr.--Crawford & Company Insurance Adjusters Ltd., Toronto, Canada; *U.S. Public*, pg. 458

Hull, Edward M., Pres.-J-P Sports--Jefferson-Pilot Communications Company, Greensboro, NC; *U.S. Public, pg. 925*
Hull, Edward M., Pres.-Jefferson-Pilot Sports--Jefferson-Pilot Communications Co. of Virginia, Richmond, VA; *U.S. Public*, pg. 926
Hull, Hardwood Campbell, Mng. Dir.--Leo Burnett Co. Inc., Buenos Aires, Argentina; *U.S. Private*, pg. 185
Hull, John, Chief Oper. Officer--Ahlstrom Process Equipment Inc., Bracey, VA; *Int'l*, pg. 34
Hull, John, Chief Fin. Officer--CAE Electronics plc, Burgess Hill, United Kingdom; *Int'l*, pg. 238
Hull, John, Pres.--Hanover Shoe Co., Hanover, PA; *Int'l*, pg. 297
Hull, John C., Chm. Bd. & Chief Exec. Officer--Pratt Casino Corporation, Dallas, TX; *U.S. Public*, pg. 761
Hull, John L., Pres.--Hull/Finmac, Inc., Warminster, PA; *U.S. Private*, pg. 547
Hull, Keith M., Pres. & V.P.--Avondale Mills Fabric Div., Sylacauga, AL; *U.S. Private*, pg. 102
Hull, Robert, Pres. & Publisher--The Nugget, North Bay, Canada; *Int'l*, pg. 631
Hullander, Steve, V.P.--Orkin Lawn Care, Atlanta, GA; *U.S. Public*, pg. 1405
Hulme, Jack, Chief Oper. Officer--MacDermid G.B., Ltd., Telford, United Kingdom; *U.S. Public*, pg. 1030
Huls, John F., Mgr.--Piper Jaffray Inc., Saint Cloud, MN; *U.S. Public*, pg. 1302
Huls, John F., Mgr.-Branch--Piper Jaffray Inc., Fergus Falls, MN; *U.S. Public*, pg. 1303
Hulse, Ted, Gen. Mgr.--Triumph Releasing Corporation - Canadian Territory, Toronto, Canada; *Int'l*, pg. 1282
Hulse, W. Michael, Pres.--Murphy Eastern Oil Co., London, United Kingdom; *U.S. Public*, pg. 1142
Hulse, W. Michael, Chief Oper. Officer--Murco Petroleum Ltd., London, United Kingdom; *U.S. Public*, pg. 1142
Hulse, W. Michael, Chief Oper. Officer--Murphy Petroleum Ltd., London, United Kingdom; *U.S. Public*, pg. 1142
Hulsewe, Anthonie F., Dir.--H.J. Heinz B.V., Elst, Netherlands; *U.S. Public*, pg. 806
Hulsizer, Richard L., Pres.--First Security Thrift, Orange, CA; *U.S. Public*, pg. 626
Hulsman, James, Pres.--Trayco of S.C., Inc., Florence, SC; *U.S. Private*, pg. 352
Hult, Lennart, Mng. Dir.--Kalmar Nohab AB, Trollhattan, Sweden; *Int'l*, pg. 1421
Hult, Staffan, Mng. Dir.--Telefonaktiebolaget LM Ericsson Egypt, Cairo, Egypt; *Int'l*, pg. 1370
Hultberg, Hans, Pres.--AB BINAB, Kista, Sweden; *Int'l*, pg. 899
Hultner, Wolfgang, Gen. Mgr.--Mandarin Oriental, San Francisco, San Francisco, CA; *Int'l*, pg. 704
Hultstroem, Goesta, Mng. Dir.--Fischer & Porter AB, Stockholm, Sweden; *Int'l*, pg. 449
Hulzer, K. H., Oper. Officer--Rhenania Umschlag und Lagerei GmbH, Kehl, Germany; *Int'l*, pg. 1034
Humbart, M., Mng. Dir.--Klockner Maschinen - UND Anglagenbau GMBH, Hirtscheid, Germany; *Int'l*, pg. 131
Humbert, Georges, Co-Mgr.--EURO RSCG Quartet, Annecy, France; *Int'l*, pg. 601
Humbert, Michel, Company Head--SKF European Distribution Centre, Tongeren, Belgium; *Int'l*, pg. 1158
Humbet, Christian, Dr., Dir.--Bankhaus Gebruder Bethmann, Frankfurt/Main, Germany; *Int'l*, pg. 179
Humby, N., Pres. & Chief Oper. Officer--Soo Line Mills Limited, Winnipeg, Canada; *Int'l*, pg. 1495
Hume, F.R., V.P.--Keithley Test Instrumentation Group, Cleveland, OH; *U.S. Public*, pg. 946
Hume, John, Pres.--John Fyfe Ltd., Aberdeen, United Kingdom; *Int'l*, pg. 166
Humeny, Don, Chief Oper. Officer--Aeroservices J.T. Inc., Dorval, Canada; *U.S. Public*, pg. 845
Humke, Ramon L., Pres. & Chief Oper. Officer--Indianapolis Power & Light Company, Indianapolis, IN; *U.S. Public*, pg. 913
Huml, D.S., Chm. & Pres.--Lake Keowee Country Club, Inc., Valley Forge, PA; *Int'l*, pg. 1171
Hummel, R. Scott, Chief Oper. Officer--Shield Insurance, Grand Rapids, MI; *U.S. Private*, pg. 1021
Hummer, John, Mng. Dir.--River Parishes Hospital, La Place, LA; *U.S. Public*, pg. 1697
Hummers, William S., III, Pres.--CF Investment Company, Greenville, SC; *U.S. Public*, pg. 306
Hummitzsch, Siegfried, Dr., V.P. & Gen. Mgr.--Du Pont de Nemours (Deutschland) GmbH, Bad Homburg, Germany; *U.S. Public*, pg. 532
Humphrey, Bill, Pres.--Milliken Fine Goods Div., Spartanburg, SC; *U.S. Private*, pg. 748
Humphrey, Bruce, Pres.--Wearguard Corp., Norwell, MA; *U.S. Private*, pg. 79
Humphrey, Colin, Chief Oper. Officer--Perwakilan Bureau Technique Rhone-Poulenc, Jakarta, Indonesia; *Int'l*, pg. 1112
Humphrey, D.A., Mng. Dir.--Nutricia (Asia-Pacific) Ltd., Wan Chai, Hong Kong; *Int'l*, pg. 992
Humphrey, Ian, Chief Oper. Officer--Modern Structural Plastics Ltd., Cumbernauld, United Kingdom; *Int'l*, pg. 444
Humphrey, Stewart, Pres.--Scandinaviska Enskilda Banken London, London, United Kingdom; *Int'l*, pg. 1259
Humphreys, Bob, Chief Oper. Officer--Stevcoknit Fabrics Company, Greer, SC; *U.S. Public*, pg. 498
Humphreys, D.S., Gen. Mgr.--Star Export Services Inc., Pearlington, MS; *Int'l*, pg. 664
Humphreys, Ed, Mng. Dir.--Nestle Lyons Maid, York, United Kingdom; *Int'l*, pg. 918
Humphreys, Julie, Gen. Mgr.--Classic Nissan, Orlando, FL; *U.S. Private*, pg. 8
Humphreys, Sidney, Mng. Dir.--Korn/Ferry International, Toronto, Canada; *U.S. Private*, pg. 633
Humphreys, Stuart G., Gen. Mgr.--Velcro Australia Pty. Ltd., Rowville, Australia; *Int'l*, pg. 1462
Humphries, G. Kent, Pres.--Smelkinson Sysco Food Services, Inc., Jessup, MD; *U.S. Public*, pg. 1550
Humphries, Larry, Pres.--Prior Data Sciences Ltd., Kanata, Canada; *Int'l*, pg. 1288
Hun, Cheah Kin, V.P.--Tourism Malaysia - L.A. Office, Los Angeles, CA; *Int'l*, pg. 833
Hunckler, Yves, Gen. Mgr.--SepelCom, Lyon, France; *Int'l*, pg. 1097
Hundertmark, Gerd, Gen. Mgr.--Ernst Siegling GmbH & Co., Hannover, Germany; *Int'l*, pg. 497
Hung, Aaron, Reg. Dir.-United Kingdom--Singapore Tourist Promotion Board - London, London, United Kingdom; *Int'l*, pg. 1254
Hung, Philip, Pres. & V.P.-Mktg.--Braun, North America, Woburn, MA; *U.S. Public*, pg. 743
Hung, Willy Lee Wai, Gen. Mgr.--Singapore Petroleum Co. (HK) Ltd., Wan Chai, Hong Kong; *U.S. Public*, pg. 102
Hunger, Walter, Pres.--Hunger Hydraulics, Limited, Rossford, OH; *Int'l*, pg. 639
Hungerbuhler, Beat, Gen. Mgr.--CPC Export (Africa/Middle East) AG, Zurich, Switzerland; *U.S. Public*, pg. 225
Hungs, Dieter, Dir.--Generale Bank & Co., Aachen, Germany; *Int'l*, pg. 548
Hunkin, J.S., Pres. & Chief Oper. officer--The CIBC Wood Gundy Corporation, Toronto, Canada; *Int'l*, pg. 256
Hunn, Michael, Mng. Dir.--Del Amo Hospital, Torrance, CA; *U.S. Public*, pg. 1697
Hunner, Brad, Dir.--Studio 70, Eden Prairie, MN; *U.S. Public, pg. 1541*
Hunnicutt, David, Work Center Supvr.--Mustang Telephone Co., Port Aransas, TX; *U.S. Public*, pg. 329
Hunot, Pete, Plant Mgr.--Hydro Conduit Corp., Tualatin, OR; *Int'l*, pg. 246
Huns, Adrian J., Pres.--Carter-Wallace International Div., Princeton, NJ; *U.S. Public*, pg. 310
Huns, Adrian J.L., Mng. Dir.--Carter-Wallace Limited (United Kingdom), Folkestone, United Kingdom; *U.S. Public*, pg. 310
Hunsberger, William, Pres. & Publr.--Hattiesburg American, Hattiesburg, MS; *U.S. Public*, pg. 701
Hunsinger, Peter King, Publisher--Gourmet, New York, NY; *U.S. Private*, pg. 20
Hunsunger, Jerome, V.P. & Gen. Mgr.--Ambassador Office Equipment, Inc., Schaumburg, IL; *Int'l*, pg. 262
Hunt, Brian, Pres.--PHH Vehicle Management Services Canada, Mississauga, Canada; *U.S. Public*, pg. 321
Hunt, C., Gen. Mgr.--Perq Research Corporation, Wilton, CT; *Int'l*, pg. 1447
Hunt, Colin, Dir.-Opers., U.K.--Vickers Systems Div., Havant, United Kingdom; *U.S. Public*, pg. 25
Hunt, Dan, Plant Mgr.--Abbott Critical Care Systems, Morgan Hill, CA; *U.S. Public*, pg. 13
Hunt, Donald K., Pres.--Sysco Food Services of Horseheads, Horseheads, NY; *U.S. Public*, pg. 1551
Hunt, Edward, Mng. Dir.--Sulzer Papertec Manchester Ltd., Manchester, United Kingdom; *Int'l*, pg. 1306
Hunt, Fred, Mng. Dir.--CR Industries Pty. Ltd., Mentone, Australia; *Int'l*, pg. 1157
Hunt, Harold, Plant Mgr.--Farr Company, Jonesboro, AR; *U.S. Public*, pg. 614
Hunt, James H., Chief Exec. Officer--Barnett Bank of Southeast Georgia, N.A., Brunswick, GA; *U.S. Public*, pg. 1162
Hunt, James K., Pres.--SunAmerica Corporate Finance, Houston, TX; *U.S. Public*, pg. 1533
Hunt, Jim, Pres.--L.A. Gauge Co., Sun Valley, CA; *U.S. Public*, pg. 1640
Hunt, John G., Gen. Mgr.--BHP Steel N Asia Ltd. - Taiwan Branch, Kao-hsiung, Taiwan; *Int'l*, pg. 227
Hunt, Kevin, Pres.--Bremner, Inc., Saint Louis, MO; *U.S. Public*, pg. 1359
Hunt, Mark, Gen. Mgr.--Cosworth Engineering, Wellingborough Plant, Wellingborough, United Kingdom; *Int'l*, pg. 1467
Hunt, Mitchell W., Jr., Chm. Bd., Pres. & Chief Exec. Officer--SouthTrust Bank of Columbus, Columbus, GA; *U.S. Public*, pg. 1492
Hunt, P.J., Chm. Bd.--Land Securities Properties Limited, London, United Kingdom; *Int'l*, pg. 798
Hunt, P.J., Chm. Bd.--Ravenseft Properties Limited, London, United Kingdom; *Int'l*, pg. 798
Hunt, P.J., Chm. Bd.--Ravenseft Industrial Estates Limited, London, United Kingdom; *Int'l*, pg. 798
Hunt, P.J., Chm. Bd.--The City of London Real Property Company Limited, London, United Kingdom; *Int'l*, pg. 798
Hunt, R.G., Asst. Chief Exec. Officer--Huber, Hunt & Nichols, Inc., Phoenix, AZ; *U.S. Private*, pg. 548
Hunt, Randy, Mgr.--Southern States Steel Company, Beaumont, TX; *U.S. Public*, pg. 412
Hunt, Ray, Plant Mgr.--Huls Canada Inc., Toronto, Canada; *Int'l*, pg. 1455
Hunt, Rocklyn, Pres. & Chief Exec. Officer--Regions Bank/Forsyth County, Cumming, GA; *U.S. Public*, pg. 1372
Hunt, Ronald, V.P. & Chief Oper. Officer--Nationwide HMO, Inc., Columbus, OH; *U.S. Private*, pg. 789
Hunt, Steve, Gen. Mgr.--Quality Food Oils, Inc., New Milford, CT; *Int'l*, pg. 92
Hunt, T.H., Pres.--Apollo Gas Co., Pittsburgh, PA; *U.S. Public*, pg. 1661
Hunt, T.H., Pres.--Carnegie Natural Gas Co., Pittsburgh, PA; *U.S. Public*, pg. 1661
Hunt, Terrence M., Pres.--Futronix Systems, Houston, TX; *U.S. Public*, pg. 951
Hunt, W. Kenneth, III, Pres.--Liberty Life Insurance Company, Greenville, SC; *U.S. Public*, pg. 992
Hunt, William, Sr. V.P.--State Street Trust & Banking Company, Ltd., Tokyo, Japan; *U.S. Public*, pg. 1513
Hunte, Henry F., Pres. & Chief Oper. Officer--Pre-Mix Concrete Co., San Diego, CA; *U.S. Private*, pg. 400
Hunter, Alan, Mgr.--EG & G Management Systems Inc.-Albuquerque Operations, Albuquerque, NM; *U.S. Public*, pg. 543
Hunter, Alan, Mgr.--EG & G Management Systems, Albuquerque, NM; *U.S. Public*, pg. 543
Hunter, Bill, Publisher--Sandy Post, Sandy, OR; *U.S. Public*, pg. 984
Hunter, Dan, Gen. Mgr.--Alro Group, Alpena, Alpena, MI; *U.S. Private*, pg. 46
Hunter, Dave, Gen. Mgr.--Welland Pipe Ltd., Welland, Canada; *Int'l*, pg. 1299
Hunter, F.O., Div. Mgr.--Curtis 1000, Inc., Saint Paul, MN; *U.S. Public*, pg. 70
Hunter, Harold C., Chief Oper. Officer--NationsBank of Texas National Leasing Corp., Dallas, TX; *U.S. Public*, pg. 1163
Hunter, John, Mng. Dir.--Croner-Tyco Toys Pty. Ltd., Maidstone, Australia; *U.S. Public*, pg. 1059
Hunter, John F.B., Chm. Bd.--SmithKline Beecham Consumer Brands, Brentford, United Kingdom; *Int'l*, pg. 1264
Hunter, John, III, Gen. Mgr.--Redco, Inc., Peoria, IL; *U.S. Public*, pg. 926
Hunter, Lance, Pres.--World Book Financial Services, Columbus, OH; *U.S. Public*, pg. 218
Hunter, Lane, Gen. Mgr.--Corrugated Container Div.-Torrington Plant, Torrington, CT; *U.S. Public*, pg. 1521
Hunter, Michael, Gen. Mgr.--Forbo Contract Fabrics Ltd., Lancaster, United Kingdom; *Int'l*, pg. 497
Hunter, Michael T., Pres.--Lone Star Pipeline Company, Dallas, TX; *U.S. Public*, pg. 1587
Hunter, R.J., Pres.--Otis Canada Inc., Oakville, Canada; *U.S. Public*, pg. 1691
Hunter, Robert G., Pres.--Carrier Canada Ltd., Mississauga, Canada; *U.S. Public*, pg. 1691
Hunter, Robert V., V.P.--Florida Medical Collection Services, Inc., Orlando, FL; *U.S. Public*, pg. 404
Hunter, W. Alex, Dir.-Production--Invercon Papermills Ltd., Larne, United Kingdom; *U.S. Public*, pg. 672
Hunter, W. Alex, Dir.-Production--Curran Plant, Larne, United Kingdom; *U.S. Public*, pg. 672
Hunter, W. Alex, Dir.-Production--Inver Mill, Larne, United Kingdom; *U.S. Public*, pg. 672
Hunter, Wayne, Pres.--Milliken Interior Furnishings Div., Spartanburg, SC; *U.S. Private*, pg. 749
Huntington, James F., Pres.--School Annual Publishing Co., Coshocton, OH; *U.S. Private*, pg. 598
Huntington, Jim, Pres.--Gitano Fashions Ltd., Bowling Green, KY; *U.S. Public*, pg. 686
Huntington, Jim, Pres.--Bushnell Corporation, Overland Park, KS; *U.S. Private*, pg. 1191
Huntington, Tom, Chm. Bd., Pres. & Chief Exec. Officer--EVCON Industries, Wichita, KS; *U.S. Public*, pg. 1788
Huntley, David J., Pres.--Mammoth, Inc., Chaska, MN; *U.S. Public*, pg. 1193
Huntley, David J., Pres.--Commercial Environmental Systems Group, Inc., Chaska, MN; *U.S. Public*, pg. 1193
Huntsman, Jon M., Chm. Bd. & Chief Exec. Officer--Huntsman Corporation, Salt Lake City, UT; *U.S. Private*, pg. 549
Huntzinger, George S., Pres.--CSC Healthcare Systems, Farmington, MI; *U.S. Public*, pg. 423
Hunziker, Fredy W., Mng. Dir.--LeaRonal AG, Littau, Switzerland; *U.S. Public*, pg. 982
Hunziker, Fredy W., Chm. Bd.--LeaRonal S.E. Asia Ltd., Kowloon, Hong Kong; *U.S. Public*, pg. 982
Huostila, Markku, Sr. V.P.-Tech.--Nokia Mill, Nokia, Finland; *U.S. Public*, pg. 673
Huotelin, Martti, Mng. Dir.--Helsingen Pantti-Osakeyhtio, Helsinki, Finland; *Int'l*, pg. 859
Huras, Lynn, V.P. & Asst. Sec.--Trans-Lux Canada Ltd., Mississauga, Canada; *U.S. Public*, pg. 1629
Hurban, Jim, Gen. Mgr.--Hyundai Motor America Southern Regional Office, Lithia Springs, GA; *Int'l*, pg. 641
Hurcomb, Thomas J., Sr. V.P.--Smart Energy Services, Inc., Rutland, VT; *U.S. Public*, pg. 328
Hurd, Ruth, Publr.--Thomas Register, New York, NY; *U.S. Private*, pg. 1082
Hurdwell, Robert E., Dir.--KS Winston Ltd., Maidenhead, United Kingdom; *Int'l*, pg. 861
Hurkmans, Thomas, Pres.--Duquesne Enterprises, Pittsburgh, PA; *U.S. Public*, pg. 474
Hurley, Donald, Div. V.P.-Canada/Latin America--Medtronic of Canada, Mississauga, Canada; *U.S. Public*, pg. 1084
Hurley, Doug, Gen. Mgr.--Keystone Northeast Warehouse-Bethlehem, Bethlehem, PA; *U.S. Public*, pg. 955
Hurley, G. John, Pres.--Idex Investor Services, Inc., Largo, FL; *Int'l*, pg. 27
Hurley, Jim, Mng. Dir.--Tylan (UK) Ltd., Swindon, United Kingdom; *U.S. Public*, pg. 1113
Hurley, K., Chief Exec. Officer--Kaye Instruments, Inc., Bedford, MA; *Int'l*, pg. 208
Hurley, Kevin, Pres.--Springhouse Corporation, Spring House, PA; *Int'l*, pg. 1100
Hurley, Mark, Pres.--Chr. Hansen Ireland Limited, Little Island, Ireland; *Int'l*, pg. 289
Hurley, Paul J., Pres.--International Turbine Engine Corporation (ITEC), Phoenix, AZ; *U.S. Public*, pg. 51
Hurley, Smith, Gen. Mgr.--Strydel, Inc., Stryker, OH; *U.S. Public*, pg. 1214
Hurley, Tom M., V.P. & Gen. Mgr.--20th Century Products Div., Los Angeles, CA; *U.S. Public*, pg. 153
Hurlimann, Rene R., Co-Owner & Pres.--Eurad RSCG, Zurich, Switzerland; *Int'l*, pg. 602
Hurni, Marcel, Chm.--Coop Ostschweiz, Gossau, Switzerland; *Int'l*, pg. 329
Hurst, F.B., V.P.-Marine Coatings--International Paint Southwest Div., Houston, TX; *Int'l*, pg. 339
Hurst, L.M., Pres.--Hurst Manufacturing, Princeton, IN; *U.S. Public*, pg. 573
Hurst, Mary, Exec. Editor--The News-Leader, Fernandina Beach, FL; *U.S. Public*, pg. 1175
Hurst, Randall, Pres.--Mining Controls, Inc., Beckley, WV; *U.S. Private*, pg. 370
Hurst, Robert G., V.P. & Gen. Mgr.--Lloyd Electric Apparatus Co., Seattle, WA; *U.S. Private*, pg. 672
Hurt, Michael L., Pres.--T B Wood's Volkmann Controls, Greensboro, NC; *U.S. Public*, pg. 1562

Hurt, Randy, Chief Oper. Officer--Chemrock Corporation, Nashville, TN; *U.S. Private*, pg. 903

Hurt, Randy, Chief Oper. Officer--Chemrock Corporation, Lafayette, IN; *U.S. Private*, pg. 903

Hurt, Randy, Chief Oper. Officer--Chemrock Corporation, Thomaston, ME; *U.S. Private*, pg. 903

Hurtubise, Lionel P., Mng. Dir.--Ericsson Communications, Inc., Montreal, Canada; *Int'l*, pg. 1366

Hurtubise, Lionel P., Mng. Dir.--Ericsson GE Mobile Communications Canada, Inc., Mississauga, Canada; *Int'l*, pg. 1371

Hurvig, T., Mng. Dir.--FLS Maskinteknik A/S, Valby, Denmark; *Int'l*, pg. 475

Hurwitt, D. F., V.P & Gen. Mgr.--Breakfast Foods Div., White Plains, NY; *U.S. Public*, pg. 1287

Husby, Paul, Pres.--3M Do Brasil Ltda., Sao Paulo, Brazil; *U.S. Public*, pg. 1606

Huse, A. R., Pres.--BS & B Safety Systems, Tulsa, OK; *U.S. Private*, pg. 572

Huse, Richard, Gen. Mgr.--Williamhouse of Colorado, Inc., Denver, CO; *U.S. Public*, pg. 89

Huseboe, S., Mgr.-Marine Opers.--CGG Norge A/S, Naersnes, Norway; *Int'l*, pg. 241

Husein, Ahmad, Pres.--P.T. KADI International, Jakarta, Indonesia; *Int'l*, pg. 764

Husek, Vladimir, Pres.--Chr. Hansen Czech Republic, s.r.o, Prague, Czech Republic; *Int'l*, pg. 289

Huser, Lawrence, V.P. & Gen. Mgr.--Aircraft Products Company, Jacksonville, FL; *U.S. Public*, pg. 159

Huseth, Merle H., Pres.--K. Hovnanian Companies Northeast, Inc., Edison, NJ; *U.S. Public*, pg. 843

Hushovd, Oyvind, Mng. Dir.--Falconbridge Nikkelverk A/S, Kristiansand, Norway; *Int'l*, pg. 434

Huskins, Walter E., Pres.--UST Leasing Corporation, Boston, MA; *U.S. Public*, pg. 1660

Huslip, Nicholas, Chm.--Dallas Semiconductor Corporation Ltd., Birmingham, United Kingdom; *U.S. Public*, pg. 478

Husmo, Odd, Plant Mgr.--Elkem Mangan PEA, Porsgrunn, Norway; *Int'l*, pg. 447

Husmo, Odd, Plant Mgr.--Bjolvefossen, Alvik, Norway; *Int'l*, pg. 448

Hussain, Imtiaz, Sr. V.P. & Gen. Mgr.--Habib Bank Ltd., Khartoum, Sudan; *Int'l*, pg. 584

Hussein, Abdul Razzak Mulla, Chief Oper. Officer--Kuwait Foreign Petroleum Exploration Co. KSC, Safat, Kuwait; *Int'l*, pg. 765

Husseini, Tony, Mng. Dir.-Dubai--Tamra DMB&B, Dubai, United Arab Emirates; *U.S. Private*, pg. 305

Hussey, Leo J., Pres.--Southeastern Printing Company Inc., Stuart, FL; *U.S. Public*, pg. 1056

Hussman, Walter E., Jr., Pres.--Wehco Video Inc., Little Rock, AR; *U.S. Private*, pg. 1159

Husson, F., Gen. Mgr.--Groupe SEB Argentina, Buenos Aires, Argentina; *Int'l*, pg. 568

Husson, Jean-Claude, Pres.--Alcatel Espace, Nanterre, France; *Int'l*, pg. 56

Hustad, Paul, Pres.--Burns & McDonnell Waste Consultants, Inc., Kansas City, MO; *U.S. Private*, pg. 187

Husted, Don, Plant Mgr.--Central States Can Co. of Puerto Rico, Inc., Mayaguez, PR; *U.S. Public*, pg. 463

Huston, James, Pres.--First Recovery, Lexington, KY; *U.S. Public*, pg. 139

Huta, Henry N., Pres. & Chief Exec. Officer--Pacific Diversified Capital Company, Santa Ana, CA; *U.S. Public, pg. 584*

Hutchens, Jim, V.P.-Sls.--Foamex International-Consumer Products Division, Saint Louis, MO; *U.S. Private*, pg. 1094

Hutchens, Leon E., Pres.--Kaneb Pipe Line Co., Wichita, KS; *U.S. Public*, pg. 942

Hutcherson, David, Gen. Mgr.--Littlefield Feed Yard, Littlefield, TX; *U.S. Private*, pg. 429

Hutcheson, Alan G., Pres.--Communications Technology Corporation, Dallas, TX; *U.S. Public*, pg. 480

Hutchias, Thomas M., Mgr.--Maurexco Exporters, Laurel, MD; *U.S. Private*, pg. 715

Hutchin, James W., Dir.-Natl. Mktg.--Willis Corroon International/Americas, Radnor, PA; *Int'l*, pg. 1507

Hutchings, Clifton, Grp. V.P.--Pall Industrial Hydraulics Ltd., Portsmouth, United Kingdom; *U.S. Public*, pg. 1254

Hutchins, B., Plant Mgr.--National Spinning Co., Warsaw, NC; *U.S. Private*, pg. 787

Hutchins, Buford, Plant Mgr.--National Spinning Co., Whiteville, NC; *U.S. Private*, pg. 787

Hutchins, Burleigh M., Chm. Bd. & Chief Tech. Officer--Zymark Corporation, Hopkinton, MA; *U.S. Private*, pg. 139

Hutchins, Cecil, Mgr.-Plant--Arkansas Galvanizing Inc., Prairie Grove, AR; *U.S. Public*, pg. 159

Hutchins, D., V.P.--Whirlpool Corp., La Vergne Div., La Vergne, TN; *U.S. Public*, pg. 1765

Hutchins, Dave, Mgr.--Anixter Harlow, Harlow, United Kingdom; *U.S. Public*, pg. 115

Hutchins, Marcus, Pres.--Fenchurch Capital Management Limited, Chicago, IL; *Int'l*, pg. 420

Hutchins, P., Chief Oper. Officer--Chloride Power Electronics Inc., Burgaw, NC; *Int'l*, pg. 287

Hutchinson, Brad, Facility Mgr.--Pro Shop (Baton Rouge, LA), Denham Springs, LA; *U.S. Public*, pg. 861

Hutchinson, David, Mgr.--Australian Guarantee Corporation Limited - Northern Territory, Darwin, Australia; *Int'l*, pg. 1496

Hutchinson, F. James, Chm. Bd.--BNY Holdings (New Jersey) Corp., West Paterson, NJ; *U.S. Public*, pg. 178

Hutchinson, John H., Jr., Pres.-TV Div.--Jefferson-Pilot Communications Company, Greensboro, NC; *U.S. Public, pg. 925*

Hutchinson, Larry M., Pres.--Mercantile Bank of Marshalltown, Marshalltown, IA; *U.S. Public*, pg. 1088

Hutchinson, Lexie, Admin.--Hillhaven Convalescent Center El Paso, El Paso, TX; *U.S. Public*, pg. 1713

Hutchinson, Peter, Pres.--Onexa, S.A. de C.V., Garza Garcia, Mexico; *Int'l*, pg. 56

Hutchinson, Richard, Pres.--Consolidated Industries Corp., Lafayette, IN; *Int'l*, pg. 188

Hutchinson, W.R., Pres.--AmProp Finance Company, Chicago, IL; *U.S. Public*, pg. 103

Hutchison, James, Mgr.-Office--Woodward-Clyde, Jakarta, Indonesia; *U.S. Public*, pg. 1657

Hutchison, John H., Jr., Pres.-Television Div. & Gen. Mgr.-WBTV--Jefferson-Pilot Communications Co. of Virginia, Richmond, VA; *U.S. Public*, pg. 926

Hutin, Patrice, Pres.--Roger Cleveland Golf Company, Paramount, CA; *Int'l*, pg. 1127

Hutson, Alan R., Pres.--Lehigh Safety Shoe Co., Endicott, NY; *U.S. Public*, pg. 1684

Hutson, Don, Pres.--TIG Insurance Co., Woodland Hills, CA; *U.S. Public*, pg. 1556

Hutson, Joe, Plant Mgr.--Block Plant, Round Rock, TX; *U.S. Public*, pg. 936

Hutson, Paul, Chm. Bd.--Griffin Bacal Ltd., London, United Kingdom; *U.S. Private*, pg. 480

Hutson, T.G., Mng. Dir.--International Factors Limited, Brighton, United Kingdom; *Int'l*, pg. 813

Hutt, Kenneth D., V.P.-Intl.--McGraw-Hill Information Systems Co. of Canada Ltd., North York, Canada; *U.S. Public*, pg. 1072

Huttaporn, Preecha, Pres.--The Siam Sanitary Fittings Co., Ltd., Pathum Thani, Thailand; *Int'l*, pg. 1239

Huttaporn, Preecha, Pres.--The Siam Sanitary Fittings Co., Ltd., Bangkok, Thailand; *Int'l*, pg. 1410

Hutter, Heidi, Mng. Dir.--Swiss Re America Corporation, New York, NY; *Int'l*, pg. 1333

Huttle, Larry, Pres.--Airstream, Inc., Jackson Center, OH; *U.S. Public*, pg. 1602

Huttner, Bill, Pres.--Textile Chemical Co., Inc., Reading, PA; *Int'l*, pg. 1458

Hutto, Mike, V.P.-Sls.--Fairfield Ocean Ridge, Edisto Island, SC; *U.S. Public*, pg. 610

Hutton, A.S., Gen. Mgr.--Prodorite Ltd., Wednesbury, United Kingdom; *U.S. Public*, pg. 99

Hutton, Andrew, Deputy Mng. Dir.--Alex Lawrie Factors Ltd., Banbury, United Kingdom; *Int'l*, pg. 813

Hutton, Andrew J., Mng. Dir.--Wolseley Centers Ltd., Ripon, United Kingdom; *Int'l*, pg. 1511

Hutton, David, Plant Mgr.--West Agro, Inc.-Des Plaines, Des Plaines, IL; *Int'l*, pg. 1379

Hutton, David R., Sr. Representative--Bank of Montreal - Australia, Sydney, Australia; *Int'l*, pg. 155

Hutton, Douglas, Chief Oper. Officer--Perstorp Components Werk Lambrecht, Lambrecht, Germany; *Int'l*, pg. 1040

Huttonen, Jussi, Mng. Dir.--Enso Marketing Co. Ltd., Orpington, United Kingdom; *Int'l*, pg. 457

Hutzel, Donald, V.P.-Mfg.--Angstrohm Precision, Inc., Hagerstown, MD; *U.S. Public*, pg. 1722

Huumonen, Jouka, Chief Oper. Officer--Neste Oy, Porvoo Refinery, Porvoo, Finland; *Int'l*, pg. 914

Huurinainen, Arto, Chief Oper. Officer--Saimaa Procurement Area, Savonlinna, Finland; *Int'l*, pg. 455

Huurman, B.N.J., Mng. Dir.--Hak B.V., Giessen, Netherlands; *Int'l*, pg. 244

Huvanandana, Umyos, Rep.--Generale Bank, Bangkok, Thailand; *Int'l*, pg. 547

Huwer, Doug, Pres.--Daimler-Benz Capital Inc., Wilmington, DE; *Int'l*, pg. 368

Huxforff, K., V.P.-Opers.--Square D Company (Deutschland) GmbH, Marienheide, Germany; *Int'l*, pg. 1209

Huxtable, Peter, Gen. Mgr.--Laporte Minerals, Sheffield, United Kingdom; *Int'l*, pg. 802

Huysentruyt, Paul, Mng. Dir.--N.V. Bekaert S.A., Zwevegem, Belgium; *Int'l*, pg. 183

Huysman, Marc, Mng. Dir.--S.M.P., Prague, Czech Republic; *Int'l*, pg. 823

Hwa, Lui Man, Gen. Mgr.--NSSP Malaysia Sdn. Bhd., Petaling Jaya, Malaysia; *U.S. Public*, pg. 1166

Hwan, Chang Ji, Pres.--Ssangyong Engineering & Construction Co., Ltd., Seoul, Korea; *Int'l*, pg. 1291

Hwang, Chy Yung, Mng. Dir.--Sulzer International (Hong Kong) Limited, Hong Kong, Hong Kong; *Int'l*, pg. 1306

Hwang, George, Pres.--Regal Korea, Seoul, Korea; *U.S. Private*, pg. 917

Hwang, H.T., Exec. V.P.-N. America--Hanjin Co., Ltd., Paramus, NJ; *Int'l*, pg. 592

Hwang, I.H., Exec. V.P. & Gen. Mgr.--Goldstar of America, Inc., Huntsville, AL; *Int'l*, pg. 779

Hwang, Kyu Sang, Chief Rep.--Cho Hung Bank, Ho Chi Minh Representative Office, Ho Chi Minh City, Vietnam; *Int'l*, pg. 288

Hwang, Show-Loong, V.P. & Gen. Mgr.--The International Commercial Bank of China, Panama, Panama; *Int'l*, pg. 683

Hyatt, Arnold, Pres. & Chief Exec. Officer--Stride Rite Footwear, Inc., Lawrence, MA; *U.S. Public*, pg. 1525

Hyatt, Harry J., Chief Oper. Officer & Mng. Dir.--Sasol Alpha Olefins, Rosebank, South Africa; *Int'l*, pg. 1196

Hyatt, Kenneth E., Pres.--Mid-State Homes, Inc., Tampa, FL; *U.S. Public*, pg. 1736

Hyatt, Kenneth E., Pres.--Cardem Insurance Co., Ltd., Tampa, FL; *U.S. Public*, pg. 1736

Hyatt, T.L., Pres.--HyCon, Inc., Harpersville, AL; *U.S. Public, pg. 1304*

Hyatt, William, Gen. Mgr.--Watlow Anafaze, Watsonville, CA; *U.S. Private*, pg. 1153

Hyatt, William W., Jr., Chief Exec. Officer--The Central Press of Miami, Inc., Pompano Beach, FL; *U.S. Public*, pg. 1735

Hyde, D.W., Mng. Dir.--Alcan Metal Centres, Tipton, United Kingdom; *Int'l*, pg. 51

Hyde, Harry, Mng. Dir.--Escalade International Ltd., Swansea, United Kingdom; *U.S. Public*, pg. 591

Hyde, James D., Mgr.-Opers.--Constar International, Inc., Charlotte, NC; *U.S. Public*, pg. 463

Hyde, James R., Pres.--Grace Davison, Baltimore, MD; *U.S. Public*, pg. 755

Hyde, LeGrande, III, Pres. & Gen. Mgr.--Screen Art, Knoxville, TN; *U.S. Public*, pg. 1486

Hyde, Mark, Dir.--WF Corroon (Private) Limited, Harare, Zimbabwe; *Int'l*, pg. 1502

Hyde, Milo, Gen. Mgr.--EDO Combat Systems, Chesapeake, VA; *U.S. Public*, pg. 542

Hyde, R., Pres.--Smith Engineering Co., Ontario, CA; *Int'l*, pg. 586

Hyde, Rollie D., V.P. & Publisher--Plainview Daily Herald, Plainview, TX; *U.S. Private*, pg. 517

Hyde, William, Mgr.--Brambles Div. of Brambles Equipment Services Inc., Jackson, MS; *Int'l*, pg. 211

Hyder, Hartley, Pres.--J.W. Window Components, Inc., Elizabethton, TN; *U.S. Public*, pg. 1736

Hyer, Edward T. C., Plant Mgr.--Surfactant Dept. Plant, Winder, GA; *U.S. Public*, pg. 1514

Hyjek, Ed, Pres. & Chief Exec. Officer--Bridgestone/Firestone Canada Inc., Mississauga, Canada; *Int'l*, pg. 214

Hyjek, Ed, Pres.--Bridgestone/Firestone Canada, Inc., Mississauga, Canada; *Int'l*, pg. 214

Hylla, Volkswirt Helge, Pres.--Deutsche PostConsult, Bonn, Germany; *Int'l*, pg. 407

Hylton, E., Pres.--Ebara International Corp., Sparks, NV; *Int'l*, pg. 431

Hyman, Richard, Pres.--Milgray Electronics, Inc., Farmingdale, NY; *U.S. Public*, pg. 205

Hyman, Richard, Chief Oper. Officer & Exec. V.P.--Milgray/Atlanta, Inc., Norcross, GA; *U.S. Public*, pg. 206

Hyman, Richard, Chief Oper. Officer & Exec. V.P.--Milgray/Connecticut, Inc., Milford, CT; *U.S. Public*, pg. 206

Hyman, Richard, Chief Oper. Officer & Exec. V.P.--Birnbach Company, Inc., Farmingdale, NY; *U.S. Public*, pg. 207

Hymes, William W., Pres.--Banking Systems Division, Dallas, TX; *U.S. Public*, pg. 1516

Hynes, Bob, Pres.--CMS Gilbreth Packaging Systems, Bensalem, PA; *U.S. Private*, pg. 558

Hynes, Chuck, Gen. Mgr.--Container Div. (Jacksonville), Jacksonville, FL; *Int'l*, pg. 1269

Hyodo, Toshio, Joint Gen. Mgr. & Agent--Dai-Ichi Kangyo Bank, Ltd.-San Francisco, San Francisco, CA; *Int'l*, pg. 359

Hyoto, Isamu, Gen. Mgr.--Yonago Branch Office, Yonago, Japan; *Int'l*, pg. 1491

Hypponen, Heikki, Mng. Dir.--Merita Real Estate Ltd., Helsinki, Finland; *Int'l*, pg. 859

Hysell, Charles, Plant Mgr.--Dayton Superior Corp., Hialeah, FL; *U.S. Private*, pg. 932

Hyvarinen, Matti, Chief Oper. Officer--Ahlstrom Machinery (Asia-Pacific) Pte Ltd., Jakarta, Indonesia; *Int'l*, pg. 35

Hyvonen, Tuula, Mng. Dir.--ZAO Norvista - St. Petersburg, Saint Petersburg, Russia; *Int'l*, pg. 486

Hyytiainen, Matti, Mng. Dir.--PT KSB Indonesia, Java, Indonesia; *Int'l*, pg. 721

Iacherri, Don M., Chief Opr. Officer--BankAmerica Trust Co. of New York, New York, NY; *U.S. Public*, pg. 181

Iacobelli, Olindo, Branch Mgr.--Mead Europe Engineering, S.A.R.L., Chateauroux, France; *U.S. Public*, pg. 1076

Iacobelli, Olindo, Chief Oper. Officer--Mead Holdings S.A., Paris, France; *U.S. Public*, pg. 1076

Iacobellis, Rocco, Gen. Mgr.--Outdoor Systems, Inc.-New York, Detroit, MI; *U.S. Public*, pg. 1235

Ialenti, Pascal, Pres.--Venmar Ventilation, Inc., Drummondville, Canada; *U.S. Public*, pg. 1194

Iammarino, Craig, Pres.--Welded Tube, Chicago, IL; *Int'l*, pg. 101

Iandoli, Gerald, Mgr.--AFA Protective Systems, Inc., Boston, MA; *U.S. Public*, pg. 5

Ianello, P., Pres. & Chief Exec. Officer--SBC Capital Markets Inc., New York, NY; *Int'l*, pg. 1329

Iannuzzi, Joseph, Pres.--Wella Canada Inc., Oakville, Canada; *Int'l*, pg. 1489

Ianuario, Dr. Ing. Enzo, Mng Dir--Alfa Romeo Veicoli Comm. e Lav Mecc. S.p.A., Naples, Italy; *Int'l*, pg. 481

Ianuario, Enzo, Mng. Dir. & Gen. Mgr.--Italtractor ITM S.p.A., Potenza, Italy; *Int'l*, pg. 654

Ianuzzi, L., Chief Exec. Officer--OCE-Italia S.p.A., Milan, Italy; *Int'l*, pg. 994

Ibanez, Jose L., Chief Oper. Officer--Ladeco S.A., Santiago, Chile; *Int'l*, pg. 575

Ibargaray, Juan Carlos Garay, Gen. Dir.--Deutsche Bank AG (Madrid), Madrid, Spain; *Int'l*, pg. 404

Ibarrando, Pedro, Mng. Dir.--Ademco-Sontrix Espana, S.A., Madrid, Spain; *U.S. Public*, pg. 1307

Ibbitson, Ian R., Gen. Mgr.--Architectural Landscape Lighting, Santa Ana, CA; *Int'l*, pg. 821

Ibbotson, Brian J., Pres.--AMSTED Industries International, Chicago, IL; *U.S. Private*, pg. 68

Ibison, J., Mng. Dir.--Riley Advertising (Manchester) Ltd., Manchester, United Kingdom; *Int'l*, pg. 1117

Ibrahim, Mohd Taib, Dir.--Tourism Malaysia - Perth Office, Perth, Australia; *Int'l*, pg. 833

Icart, Jose Maria, Mng. Dir.--Icart S.A., Barcelona, Spain; *U.S. Public*, pg. 310

Iceman, T.L., Pres.--Stamping Division, Wooster, OH; *U.S. Public*, pg. 1780

Icenogle, C. Marlin, Mgr.--Smucker Woodburn Plant, Woodburn, OR; *U.S. Public*, pg. 1480

Icenogle, Marlin, Mgr.--Smucker Grandview Plant, Grandview, WA; *U.S. Public*, pg. 1480

Ichige, S., Exec. V.P.--California MEC, Inc., Los Angeles, CA; *Int'l*, pg. 873

Ichikawa, Akira, Pres.--Shinsho Corporation, Osaka, Japan; *Int'l*, pg. 740

Ichikawa, Katsuhiko, Mng. Dir.--Central Japan Railway Company-Sydney Office, Sydney, Australia; *Int'l*, pg. 279

Ichikawa, Susumu, Pres.--Advanced Micro Devices, KK, Tokyo, Japan; *U.S. Public*, pg. 21

Ichikawa, Tetsuo, Pres.--Dai-ichi Seimei America Corp., New York, NY; *Int'l*, pg. 362

Ichimura, Kentaro, Pres.--Kawasaki Motors Pty. Ltd., Rydalmere, Australia; *Int'l*, pg. 726

Ichinoki, Nori, Pres.--JAE Electronics, Inc., Irvine, CA; *Int'l*, pg. 701

Ichiyanagi, Yoshiki, Mng. Dir.--Dai Nippon Printing Co. (Australia) Pty. Ltd., Sydney, Australia; *Int'l*, pg. 363

Icke, Mike, Gen. Mgr.--Energy Control Products, Ross-on-Wye, United Kingdom; *Int'l*, pg. 1338
Ickes, David, Pres.--Sky Bros. Inc., Allentown, PA; *U.S. Public*, pg. 918
Ida, K., Gen. Mgr.--Taiwan Hokuriku Co., LTD., Tao-yuan, Taiwan; *Int'l*, pg. 628
Ida, S., Mng. Dir.--Tabuchi Electric U.K. Ltd., Stockton on Tees, United Kingdom; *Int'l*, pg. 1346
Ida, Takao, Chief Rep.--Nippon Life - Beijing Representative Office, Beijing, China; *Int'l*, pg. 936
Iddles, Alan M C, Assoc. Dir.--WF Corroon-Glasgow, Glasgow, United Kingdom; *Int'l*, pg. 1501
Ide, Christopher G., Mng. Dir.--Swiss Life (UK) Group, Sevenoaks, United Kingdom; *Int'l*, pg. 1332
Ide, Hidehiko, Gen. Mgr.--Fuji Bank, London Branch, London, United Kingdom; *Int'l*, pg. 520
Ide, Joichi, Chief Oper. Officer--Red Robin International Inc., Irvine, CA; *Int'l*, pg. 1262
Ide, Magane, Mng. Dir.--Fuji Investment Management Company (Europe) Limited, London, United Kingdom; *Int'l*, pg. 521
Idelson, Charles K., Pres. & Chief Exec. Officer--SunTrust Bank, Southwest Florida, Fort Myers, FL; *U.S. Public*, pg. 1538
Ido, I., Pres.--Yamatake-Honeywell Company Ltd., Tokyo, Japan; *U.S. Public*, pg. 835
Idres, Abdul Jalil, Mng. Dir.--Johnson & Johnson Medical Mfg., Sdn. Bhd., Shah Alam, Malaysia; *U.S. Public*, pg. 931
Idris, Abdul Jalil, Mng. Dir.--Johnson & Johnson Sdn. Bhd., Petaling Jaya, Malaysia; *U.S. Public*, pg. 931
Ienaga, Takahiro, Pres.--Mitsui & Co. (Thailand) Ltd., Bangkok, Thailand; *Int'l*, pg. 882
Igarashi, Motoyuki, Pres.--K.G. System Construction Co., Ltd., Tokyo, Japan; *Int'l*, pg. 763
Igarashi, Sadaaki, Pres.--Beijing Toto Co., Ltd., Beijing, China; *Int'l*, pg. 1410
Igarashi, Tadayoshi, Mng. Dir.--Nippon Express (Belgium) N.V./S.A., Zaventem, Belgium; *Int'l*, pg. 934
Igbal, M. Javed, V.P. & Mgr.--Habib Bank Ltd., Paris, France; *Int'l*, pg. 584
Igd, Werner, Mng. Dir.--UPM-Kymmene Deutschland GmbH, Dorpen, Germany; *Int'l*, pg. 1430
Igel, Anders, Mng. Dir.--Swedish Ericsson Company Ltd., Horsham, United Kingdom; *Int'l*, pg. 1370
Iglesias-Enriquez, Avelina, Gen. Mgr.-Sls. & Mktg./ Mediterranean & Middle East--Utell International-Spain, Madrid, Spain; *Int'l*, pg. 1099
Iglesias, R., Chief Exec. Officer--SBS Ibersuizas S.A., Madrid, Spain; *Int'l*, pg. 1332
Ignacio, Jose E., Chief Oper. Officer--Boart Longyear Inc., Manila, Philippines; *Int'l*, pg. 76
Ignasiak, Michael F., V.P. & Gen. Mgr.--Turco Products Division, Marion, OH; *Int'l*, pg. 446
Ignatoski, Joseph, Pres.--ISK BioSciences, Memphis, TN; *Int'l*, pg. 689
Iguchi, Akira, Chief Representative--Berlin Representative Office, Berlin, Germany; *Int'l*, pg. 1517
Iguchi, Haruhiro, Mng. Dir.--Cheil Communications, Inc., Seoul, Korea; *Int'l*, pg. 588
Ihamuotila, Jaako, Chief Oper. Officer--Neste Oy International Trading & Supply, Espoo, Finland; *Int'l*, pg. 913
Ihan, Atok, Gen. Mgr.--Turk Philips Sanayi A.S., Istanbul, Turkey; *Int'l*, pg. 1055
Ihatsu, Rauno, Mng. Dir.--Roxon Komponentit Oy, Hollola, Finland; *Int'l*, pg. 1353
Ihenen, Ronald James, Mng. Dir.--Leiner-Davis International Limited, Gladesville, Australia; *Int'l*, pg. 555
Ihori, M., Chief Oper. Officer--Toshiba Europe (I.E.) G.m.b.H., Neuss, Germany; *Int'l*, pg. 1406
Ihre, Torbjorn, Pres.--The Ericsson Corporation, Arlington, VA; *Int'l*, pg. 1364
Ihrig, Ronald, Exec. V.P.--FilmTec Corporation, Minneapolis, MN; *U.S. Public*, pg. 523
Iida, H., Office Chief--Man Nen Sha, Inc., Sapporo, Japan; *Int'l*, pg. 834
Iida, Kazuoi, Gen. Mgr.--The Industrial Bank of Japan Trust Company (Atlanta Agency), Atlanta, GA; *Int'l*, pg. 675
Iida, Masayuki, Mng. Dir. & Gen. Mgr.--Sumitomo Trust International Plc., London, United Kingdom; *Int'l*, pg. 1318
Iida, Tetsuo, Pres.--Honda Europe N.V., Gent, Belgium; *Int'l*, pg. 635
Iijima, H., Gen. Mgr.--Sanyo Laser Products, Inc., Richmond, IN; *Int'l*, pg. 1191
Iiori, John, Pres.--American National Can Canada Inc., Brampton, Canada; *Int'l*, pg. 1029
Iitsuka, Nobuo, Pres.--Dai Nippon Shoji Co., Ltd., Tokyo, Japan; *Int'l*, pg. 363
Iizima, M., Pres.--Minebea Credit Co., Ltd., Tokyo, Japan; *Int'l*, pg. 868
Iizuka, Kohji, Pres.--Dow Corning Toray Silicon Co., Ltd., Tokyo, Japan; *Int'l*, pg. 1400
Ijichi, Seibi, Chief Representative--Sumitomo Trust & Banking (Deutschland) AG, Frankfurt/Main, Germany; *Int'l*, pg. 1318
Ijsselsteijn, Bert, Reg. Dir.--Sensormatic B.V., Bunnik, Netherlands; *U.S. Public*, pg. 1457
Ijuin, M., Pres.--Nissho Iwai Steel Leasing Co. Ltd., Tokyo, Japan; *Int'l*, pg. 947
Ijuin, M., Chief Oper. Officer--Nissho Iwai Coal Development (Canada) Ltd., Vancouver, Canada; *Int'l*, pg. 948
Ikavalko, Pentti, Area Mgr.--Leaf Baltics, Tallinn, Estonia; *Int'l*, pg. 638
Ikawa, Yasuji, Gen. Mgr.--Fuji Bank, Madrid Branch, Madrid, Spain; *Int'l*, pg. 520
Ikebata, Katsuhiko, Pres.--DNP Denmark A/S, Karlslunde, Denmark; *Int'l*, pg. 363
Ikeda, Mitsuaki, Pres.--Kawasaki Precision Machinery (UK) Ltd., Plymouth, United Kingdom; *Int'l*, pg. 726
Ikeda, Satoru, Pres.--Capy U.S.A. Inc., Culver City, CA; *Int'l*, pg. 253
Ikeda, Tsutomu, Terminal Mgr.--Kintetsu World Express Inc., Portland, OR; *Int'l*, pg. 735
Ikegami, Kazuyuki, Chief Representative--Washington, D.C. Representative Office, Washington, DC; *Int'l*, pg. 519
Ikegami, Kunio, Mng. Dir.--Daiwa Europe (Spain) Sociedad de Valores S.A., Madrid, Spain; *Int'l*, pg. 375
Ikehara, Toshiro, Mng. Dir.--Dai-Ichi Kangyo Australia Limited, Sydney, Australia; *Int'l*, pg. 361
Ikehashi, Masayuki, Pres.--Daihatsu Motor (H.K.) Ltd., Hong Kong, Hong Kong; *Int'l*, pg. 365
Ikehata, A. T., Pres.--Spalding Japan Inc., Tokyo, Japan; *U.S. Private*, pg. 630
Ikekita, K., Chief Oper. Officer--Nisco Steel Services, Inc., Memphis, TN; *Int'l*, pg. 947
Ikram, Khalid, Country Dir.--The World Bank, Cairo, Egypt; *U.S. Private*, pg. 1189
Ikuma, Masayuki, Pres.--CAMI Automotive, Inc., Ingersoll, Canada; *U.S. Public*, pg. 722
Ikuta, M., Pres.--Mikuni Adec., Iwate, Japan; *Int'l*, pg. 867
Ikuta, Masaki, Chm.--Mikuni American Corporation, Northridge, CA; *Int'l*, pg. 867
Ikuta, Shigemi, Mng. Dir.--The Meiji Life Insurance Company Frankfurt Office, Frankfurt, Germany; *Int'l*, pg. 854
Ikuta, Shigemi, Chief Rep.--The Meijiseimei Property Germany GmbH, Frankfurt/Main, Germany; *Int'l*, pg. 855
Iles, D.A., Pres. & Chief Oper. Officer--Western Union Insurance Co., Calgary, Canada; *Int'l*, pg. 651
Ilgner, Dr. Hans Peter, Chief Oper. Officer--Ernst Michalke GmbH, Langweid, Germany; *Int'l*, pg. 624
Ilhan, Atok, Gen. Mgr.--Turk Philips Ticaret A.S., Istanbul, Turkey; *Int'l*, pg. 1055
Ilkka, Eero, Mng. Dir.--Huoneistomarkkinointi Oy, Helsinki, Finland; *Int'l*, pg. 858
Illi, Klaus, Office Mgr.--Thermo Instrument Systems GmbH, Dortmund, Germany; *U.S. Public*, pg. 1596
Illingsworth, John K., Gen. Mgr.--Winstone Aggregates Limited, Auckland, New Zealand; *Int'l*, pg. 495
Ilstam, Anders, Mgr.--CTT Management GmbH, Frankfurt/ Main, Germany; *Int'l*, pg. 1186
Ilvessalo, Seppo, Mng. Dir.--Merita Life Assurance Ltd., Espoo, Finland; *Int'l*, pg. 859
Ilzarbe, Miguel Angel, Mng. Dir.--Heinemann Iberia SA, Madrid, Spain; *Int'l*, pg. 1094
Imai, Fumio, Chief Rep.--The Industrial Bank of Japan, Limited (Rio de Janeiro), Rio de Janeiro, Brazil; *Int'l*, pg. 675
Imai, H., Branch Mgr.--Mitrans Corporation, Houston, TX; *Int'l*, pg. 874
Imai, Kazuhiko, Mng. Dir.--Thai Fuji Finance and Securities Company Ltd., Bangkok, Thailand; *Int'l*, pg. 521
Imai, Kozo, Pres.--Analog Devices K.K., Tokyo, Japan; *U.S. Public*, pg. 108
Imai, Naomi, Pres.--Toshiba de Panama, S.A., Panama, Panama; *Int'l*, pg. 1406
Imamura, Fumihiko, Pres. & Chief Exec. Officer--The Sumitomo Trust & Banking Co., Ltd., New York, NY; *Int'l*, pg. 1317
Imamura, Yoshinobu, Chief Oper. Officer--Hitachi Kiden Kogyo, Ltd., Amagasaki, Japan; *Int'l*, pg. 621
Imanishi, Teruyo, Dir.--John Crane (Japan), Inc., Osaka, Japan; *Int'l*, pg. 1339
Imanse, Andy, Pres.--El Dorado National, Chino, CA; *U.S. Public*, pg. 1602
Imanse, Andy, Pres.--El Dorado National, Salina, KS; *U.S. Public*, pg. 1602
Imaoka, Zenjiro, Mgr.--Nippon PDA Engineering K.K., Tokyo, Japan; *U.S. Public*, pg. 1031
Imazato, Eisaku, Deputy Pres.--Nikko Bank (Switzerland) Ltd., Zurich, Switzerland; *Int'l*, pg. 930
Imazeki, Kazuo, Dir. Gen.--Tecnologias NEC de Mexico, S.A. de C.V., Guadalajara, Mexico; *Int'l*, pg. 901
Imazoto, Eisaku, Deputy Pres.--Nikko Bank (Switzerland) Ltd., Zurich, Switzerland; *Int'l*, pg. 930
Imbellone, Oscar A., Gen. Mgr.-Consumer Opers.--Refinerias de Maiz S.A.I.C.F., Buenos Aires, Argentina; *U.S. Public*, pg. 448
Imbordino, Ronald, Reg. V.P.--Ruppman Marketing Technologies, Inc., Lisle, IL; *U.S. Private*, pg. 952
Imeson, Jo, Mng. Dir.--CineBooks, Inc., New York, NY; *Int'l*, pg. 925
Imhof, Heinz, Dir.--Sandoz Agro Ltd., Muttenz, Switzerland; *Int'l*, pg. 972
Imhoff, Jochem, Mng. Dir.--Plaza y Janes S.A., Barcelona, Spain; *Int'l*, pg. 192
Imholz, Alfred W., V.P. & Agency Mgr.--Union Bank of Switzerland, Houston, TX; *Int'l*, pg. 1440
Imorde, H., Pres.--Wintershall Canada Ltd., Calgary, Canada; *Int'l*, pg. 110
Imoto, Yoshihide, Dir.--Showpla (M) Sdn. Bhd., Nilai, Malaysia; *Int'l*, pg. 1237
Impellizeri, Marisa, Mng. Dir.--Norvista S.R.L., Milan, Italy; *Int'l*, pg. 486
Imperiali, Clemente, Rep.--Banco Di Napoli-Los Angeles, Los Angeles, CA; *Int'l*, pg. 140
Imrie, Ian, Pres.--Asea Brown Boveri Pty. Ltd., Lilydale, Australia; *Int'l*, pg. 8
Imura, Akiya, Pres.--Pitney Bowes Japan, Tokyo, Japan; *U.S. Public*, pg. 1304
Imura, Hideaki, Chief Oper. Officer--Nishimatsu Construction Co., Ltd.-London Office, London, United Kingdom; *Int'l*, pg. 943
Inaba, H., Pres.--Fanuc USA Corp., Elk Grove Village, IL; *Int'l*, pg. 477
Inaba, Hirotsugu, Pres.--Nippo Marketing & Advertising, Inc., Torrance, CA; *Int'l*, pg. 932
Inaba, Michinori, Chief Rep.--Daiwa Bank-Guangzhou, Guangzhou, China; *Int'l*, pg. 373
Inaba, Yoji, Chief Representative--The Japan Development Bank-Washington, D.C. Representative Office, Washington, DC; *Int'l*, pg. 702
Inada, Shigetoshi, Pres.--The Haokkaido Takushoku Securities Co. (Sapporo), Sapporo, Japan; *Int'l*, pg. 626
Inada, Tetsushi, Chief Oper. Officer--Kyowa Pharmaceutical Inc., New York, NY; *Int'l*, pg. 778
Inagaki, Naoki, Branch Mgr.--Noritake Co., Inc.-Table Top Div., Atlanta, Atlanta, GA; *Int'l*, pg. 959
Inagawa, Tatsunori, Gen. Mgr.--The Bank of Tokyo-Mitsubishi, Ltd. (New York Branch), New York, NY; *Int'l*, pg. 157
Inai, Takayoshi, Pres.--Matsushita Kotobuki Electronics Industries, Ltd., Takamatsu, Japan; *Int'l*, pg. 846
Inami, Tomoyuki, Dir. Gen.--Besshi-Niihama District Div., Ehime, Japan; *Int'l*, pg. 1316
Inborr, Jan, Grp. Exec. V.P.--A. Ahlstrom Corporation, Helsinki, Finland; *Int'l*, pg. 32
Incrocci, C. Joseph, Pres.--Alkco Lighting Company, Franklin Park, IL; *Int'l*, pg. 821
Inerney, Michael M., Pres. & Chief Exec. Officer--Gibson Electric Co., Oak Brook, IL; *U.S. Public*, pg. 572
Infanger, Walter, Mng. Dir.--Banque Ferrier Lullin (Luxembourg) SA, Luxembourg, Luxembourg; *Int'l*, pg. 480
Infantino, Bob, Pres.--Bostonian Shoe Co., Newton, MA; *Int'l*, pg. 297
Infantino, Ray, Pres.--Hilb, Rogal and Hamilton Insurance Services of Orange County, Inc., Placentia, CA; *U.S. Public*, pg. 827
Infeld, Gregors, Chief Oper. Officer--Tefal UK Ltd., Slough, United Kingdom; *Int'l*, pg. 569
Ingall, Geoff, Mng. Dir.--Young & Rubicam Mattingly, Richmond, Australia; *U.S. Private*, pg. 1198
Ingalls, Clyde, Regional Pres.--First Tennessee Bank - Nashville, Nashville, TN; *U.S. Public*, pg. 639
Inge, Clifton C., Chm. Bd.--Willis Corroon Corp. of Mobile, Mobile, AL; *Int'l*, pg. 1506
Ingebrethsen, Cathy, Mgr.-Import--Circle International, Lawrence, NY; *U.S. Public*, pg. 372
Ingebrigtsen, K.A., Pres.--Sonotron Holding AG, Zug, Switzerland; *Int'l*, pg. 644
Ingersoll, Ted, Principal--The Ingersoll Group, Dallas, TX; *U.S. Private*, pg. 651
Ingham, Clive, Mng. Dir.--Moore Europe, Lausanne, Switzerland; *Int'l*, pg. 889
Inglessi, J.-Ch., Chief Oper. Officer--Compagnie des Gaz de Petrole Primagaz S.A., Paris, France; *Int'l*, pg. 1155
Inglis, R., Mng. Dir.--Air Nelson, Nelson, New Zealand; *Int'l*, pg. 38
Ingold, Urs, Mng. Dir.--Reed Exhibition Companies-Switzerland, Fallanden, Switzerland; *Int'l*, pg. 1097
Ingolfsson, Eirikur, Mng. Dir.--ISS pjonustan hf., Reykjavik, Iceland; *Int'l*, pg. 657
Ingram, Darrell, Mgr.--Circle Freight International (Bahrain) Ltd., Sitra, Bahrain; *U.S. Public*, pg. 372
Ingram, E.W., III, Pres. & Chief Exec. Officer--White Castle International Company, Columbus, OH; *U.S. Private*, pg. 1172
Ingram, James J., Mgr.-Branch--Piper Jaffray Inc., Davenport, IA; *U.S. Public*, pg. 1303
Ingram, R.W., Plant Superintendant--General Shale Products Corp., Huntsville, AL; *Int'l*, pg. 844
Ingram, Robert A., Pres. & Chief Exec. Officer--Glaxo Wellcome Inc., Research Triangle Park, NC; *Int'l*, pg. 552
Ingram, Robert B., Gen. Mgr.--John Crane Inc., Vandalia, IL; *Int'l*, pg. 1338
Ingrando, Leonard V., Chief Oper. Officer & Exec. V.P.--Crowley Foods, Inc., Binghamton, NY; *Int'l*, pg. 752
Ingrassia, Lawrence, London Bureau Chief--The Wall Street Journal Europe, London, United Kingdom; *U.S. Public*, pg. 525
Ingrassia, Paul, Exec. Editor, V.P. & Chief Oper. Officer-News Services--AP-Dow Jones News Service, New York, NY; *U.S. Public*, pg. 524
Ings, D.M., Pres.--Solar Turbines Incorporated, San Diego, CA; *U.S. Public*, pg. 316
Ingvoldstad, Stein, Chief Oper. Officer--Scania Australia Pty. Ltd., Campbellfield, Australia; *Int'l*, pg. 687
Inkpen, James Dr., Mng. Dir.--SmithKline Beecham Clinical Laboratories, Saint Louis, MO; *Int'l*, pg. 1265
Inkpen, Ross, Pres. & Chief Exec. Officer--Richard De Boo Publishers, Scarborough, Canada; *U.S. Public*, pg. 1601
Inman, Darrel F., Pres.--Blount, Inc. Sporting Equipment Group, Lewiston, ID; *U.S. Public*, pg. 238
Inman, William J., Pres.--NVR Mortgage, Mc Lean, VA; *U.S.* Public, pg. 1148
Inman, William J., Pres. & Chief Exec. Officer--NVR Financial Services, Inc., Mc Lean, VA; *U.S. Public*, pg. 1148
Innes, W.R.K., Pres.--Esso Sekiyu Kabushiki Kaisha, Tokyo, Japan; *U.S. Public*, pg. 602
Innocenti, Ing. C., V.P. & Mng. Dir.--Fiat Auto S.p.A., Milan, Italy; *Int'l*, pg. 481
Inomata, Noriaki, V.P.--BHP Japan, Tokyo, Japan; *Int'l*, pg. 226
Inoue, Hideaki, Pres.--NLI Asset Management Corporation, New York, NY; *Int'l*, pg. 935
Inoue, Junichi, Chief Rep.--The Sumitomo Bank, Ltd.-Mexico Representative Office, Mexico, Mexico; *Int'l*, pg. 1310
Inoue, M., Pres.--Nissho Iwai General Merchandise Corp., Tokyo, Japan; *Int'l*, pg. 946
Inoue, M., Exec. V.P.--Sanyo E & E Corporation, San Diego, CA; *Int'l*, pg. 1191
Inoue, Makoto, Sr. V.P.--ORIX USA Corporation-Los Angeles, Los Angeles, CA; *Int'l*, pg. 1009
Inoue, Masanori, Mng. Dir.--Nittsu Shoji Co., Ltd., Tokyo, Japan; *Int'l*, pg. 934
Inoue, Michinobu, V.P. & Gen. Mgr.--Biokyowa Inc., Chesterfield, MO; *Int'l*, pg. 778
Inoue, Nagaharu, Mng. Dir.--Oki (Thailand) Co., Ltd., Ayutthaya, Thailand; *Int'l*, pg. 1000
Inoue, Osamu, Pres.--Fuji Photo Film U.S.A., Inc., Elmsford, NY; *Int'l*, pg. 524
Inoue, Seijiro, Pres.--Toto Industries (Atlanta), Inc., Atlanta, GA; *Int'l*, pg. 1410
Inoue, Shinichi, Dep. Gen. Mgr.--International Business Division (Toyko), Tokyo, Japan; *Int'l*, pg. 373

Inoue, T., Pres.--Bando Manufacturing of America, Inc., Bowling Green, KY; *Int'l*, pg. 145
Inoue, T., Gen. Mgr.--Marubeni America Corporation, Houston Branch, Houston, TX; *Int'l*, pg. 844
Inoue, Tadayuki, Pres. & Chief Oper. Officer--Panasonic Consumer Electric Co., Secaucus, NJ; *Int'l*, pg. 847
Inoue, Takami, Gen. Mgr.--Dentsu Inc. Seoul Office, Seoul, Korea; *Int'l*, pg. 393
Inoue, Tim, Mgr.--Tesa Seimitsu Co., Ltd., Tokyo, Japan; *U.S. Public*, pg. 261
Inoue, Tsuyohito, Pres.--Rohm Fuji Co., Ltd., Yamanashi, Japan; *Int'l*, pg. 1125
Inoue, Tsuyoshi, Pres.--Kobe-Midrex Research, Research Triangle Park, NC; *Int'l*, pg. 740
Inoue, Yutaka, Chief Representative--The Sumitomo Trust & Banking Co., Ltd., Toronto, Canada; *Int'l*, pg. 1318
Inove, Shigeo, Mng. Dir.--Japan Universal Securities (Hong Kong) Limited, Hong Kong, Hong Kong; *Int'l*, pg. 1444
Inpyn, Bob, Dir.-Opers.--Basic Vegetable Products, Modesto, CA; *U.S. Private*, pg. 121
Insetta, Victor, Chief Oper. Officer--Phase Components Ltd., Horsham, United Kingdom; *U.S. Public*, pg. 93
Insetta, Victor, Pres.--ATC International Technical Ceramics, Inc., Huntington Station, NY; *U.S. Public*, pg. 93
Inskeep, C., Chief Exec. Officer--Monitor Products Company Inc., Oceanside, CA; *Int'l*, pg. 208
Interno, Antonio, Mng. Dir.--Meridian Diagnostics Europe s.r.l., Milan, Italy; *U.S. Public*, pg. 1095
Inthaler, Horst, Gen. Mgr.--Crown Cork Company (Austria), GmbH, Schwanenstadt, Austria; *U.S. Public*, pg. 464
Inui, Wataru, Chief Representative--Beijing Representative Office, Beijing, China; *Int'l*, pg. 1517
Inurritegui, Jose, Dir.--Humanasegur SA, Lima, Peru; *Int'l*, pg. 1502
Invester, Doug, Gen. Mgr.--WWF Paper Corporation - Southeast, Atlanta, GA; *U.S. Private*, pg. 1145
Inzantino, Robert J., Pres.--Clarks Cos. N.A., Newton, MA; *Int'l*, pg. 297
Iordanou, C., Chief Exec. Officer--American Guarantee & Liability Insurance Company, Schaumburg, IL; *Int'l*, pg. 1530
Iordanou, C., Chief Exec. Officer--American Zurich Insurance Company, Schaumburg, IL; *Int'l*, pg. 1530
Iordanou, C., Chief Exec. Officer--Steadfast Insurance Company, Schaumburg, IL; *Int'l*, pg. 1530
Iordanou, C., Chief Exec. Officer--Zurich American Insurance Company of Illinois, Schaumburg, IL; *Int'l*, pg. 1530
Iordanou, C., Chief Exec. Officer--Zurich American Lloyds, Schaumburg, IL; *Int'l*, pg. 1530
Iott, Wallace D., Chief Oper. Officer--Buckeye Specialties Division, Toledo, OH; *U.S. Public*, pg. 1453
Iovino, Steve, Pres.--Chase Education Finance, Tampa, FL; *U.S. Public*, pg. 338
Iozzo, Riccardo, Rep.--Sanpaolo-Brussels Branch, Brussels, Belgium; *Int'l*, pg. 692
Ipjian, Ron, Pres. & Gen. Mgr.--Outdoor Systems, Inc.-Chicago, Chicago, IL; *U.S. Public*, pg. 1235
Ipsen, Sven, Mng. Dir.--ISS Scandinavia A/S, Copenhagen, Denmark; *Int'l*, pg. 656
Ipsen, Sven, Mng. Dir.--ISS Specialservice, Copenhagen, Denmark; *Int'l*, pg. 656
Iqbal, Manzar, Gen. Mgr.--BHP Steel N Asia Ltd., Central, Hong Kong; *Int'l*, pg. 227
Ira, Steven D., Pres.--Property Asset Management, Tampa, FL; *U.S. Private*, pg. 891
Ira, Steven D., Pres.--Property Asset Management, Altamonte, FL; *U.S. Private*, pg. 891
Irani, Dr. Ray R., Chm. Bd.--Canadian Occidental Petroleum Ltd., Calgary, Canada; *U.S. Public*, pg. 1210
Iranzo, Iciar, Mgr.--Griffith Laboratories Iberia S.A., Valls, Spain; *U.S. Private*, pg. 481
Iraola, Manuel J., Pres.--Phelps Dodge Industries, Phoenix, AZ; *U.S. Public*, pg. 1286
Iraola, Manuel J., Pres.--Phelps Dodge & Alcoa Fios e Cabos Electricos S.A., Sao Paulo, Brazil; *U.S. Public*, pg. 1286
Ireland, John J., Gen. Mgr.--Specialty Coated Products, Merrimack, NH; *U.S. Public*, pg. 1152
Irie, Hiroshi, Pres.--Asatsu Hong Kong Ltd., Causeway Bay, Hong Kong; *Int'l*, pg. 86
Irion, Guido, Mng. Dir.--Sulzer Infra (Schweiz) AG, Winterthur, Switzerland; *Int'l*, pg. 1306
Irisa, Junji, Chief Oper. Officer--Suita Institute, Osaka, Japan; *Int'l*, pg. 1019
Irisawa, Koji, Mng. Dir.--The Sakura Bank (Luxembourg) S.A., Luxembourg, Luxembourg; *Int'l*, pg. 1180
Irisawa, Ryuichi, Gen. Mgr.--Dentsu Europe-Paris, Paris, France; *Int'l*, pg. 393
Iriyama, Yosuke, Exec. V.P.--Sanken Electric U.S.A. Corp., Worcester, MA; *Int'l*, pg. 1188
Irlinger, F., Gen. Mgr.--Morgan Matroc S.A., Collegien, France; *Int'l*, pg. 893
Irvin, John, Pres.--Fitel Lucent, Carrollton, GA; *Int'l*, pg. 530
Irvin, John, Pres.--Fitel Lucent, Carrollton, GA; *U.S. Public*, pg. 1019
Irvine, Charles, Opr. Mgr.--Furman Wholesale Lumber Branch, Orlando, FL; *U.S. Private*, pg. 431
Irvine, George A., Pres.--Steel Ceilings Inc., Coshocton, OH; *U.S. Private*, pg. 29
Irvine, I.J., Dir.--George Outram & Company Ltd., Glasgow, United Kingdom; *Int'l*, pg. 817
Irvine, R., Chief Exec. Officer--Zurich Insurance Company, Dublin, Ireland; *Int'l*, pg. 1531
Irving, Bob, Gen. Mgr.--ANI Bradken, Waratah, Australia; *Int'l*, pg. 100
Irving, Carol, Gen. Mgr.--Ervins Group, Warren, MI; *U.S. Private*, pg. 13
Irving, Ian, Natl. Sls. Mgr.--Battery Products Div., Fair Lawn, NJ; *Int'l*, pg. 622
Irving, M. G., Mng. Dir.--CIBC Australia Limited, Sydney, Australia; *Int'l*, pg. 257
Irwin, Arnold B., Chief Oper. Officer--Kenner Products (Canada) Limited, Toronto, Canada; *U.S. Public*, pg. 798
Irwin, C.C., Mng. Dir.--Guinness Publishing Ltd., London, United Kingdom; *Int'l*, pg. 412
Irwin, David K., Pres.--Cadbury Beverages Canada Inc., Mississauga, Canada; *Int'l*, pg. 248
Irwin, Joe R., Chm. & Chief Exec. Officer--PNC Funding Corp., Pittsburgh, PA; *U.S. Public*, pg. 1243
Irwin, John R., Pres.--Atwood Oceanics Drilling Co., Houston, TX; *U.S. Public*, pg. 146
Irwin, John R., Pres.--Eagle Oceanics, Inc., Houston, TX; *U.S. Public*, pg. 146
Irwin, John R., Pres.--Swiftdrill, Inc., Houston, TX; *U.S. Public*, pg. 146
Irwin, John R., Pres.--Atwood Oceanics Australia Pty. Ltd., O'Connor, Australia; *U.S. Public*, pg. 146
Irwin, John R., Pres.--Clearways Drilling (M) SDN BHD, Kuala Lumpur, Malaysia; *U.S. Public*, pg. 146
Irwin, K., Mgr.--De La Rue Smurfit (NI) Ltd., Lisburn, United Kingdom; *Int'l*, pg. 386
Irwin, Michael L., Pres. & Chief Exec. Officer--Cadmus Direct Marketing, Inc., Charlotte, NC; *U.S. Public*, pg. 290
Irwin, Paul, Mng. Dir.--Thermon France, Rosny-sous-Bois, France; *U.S. Private*, pg. 1081
Irwin, Sean T., Mng. Dir.--Kimberly-Clark Australia Pty. Ltd., Milsons Point, Australia; *U.S. Public*, pg. 959
Isaac, Gregory, Pres.--Belmont Plastics Co., Irvine, CA; *U.S. Private*, pg. 415
Isaacs, George, Pres.--Aydin Europe Ltd., Hitchin, United Kingdom; *U.S. Public*, pg. 158
Isaacs, Ken, Pres.--Graycor Industrial Constructors Inc., Homewood, IL; *U.S. Private*, pg. 472
Isaacs, Ken, Pres.--Graycor Construction Company Inc., Homewood, IL; *U.S. Private*, pg. 472
Isaacs, Ken, Pres.--Graycor Blasting Company Inc., Chicago, IL; *U.S. Private*, pg. 472
Isacsson, Curt, Pres.--Skanska Maskin AB, Danderyd, Sweden; *Int'l*, pg. 1261
Isaka, Satoru, Chief Rep.--The Hokkaido Takushoku Bank, Ltd. (Beijing), Beijing, China; *Int'l*, pg. 627
Isakson, Michael, Pres.--ServiceMaster Residential/Commercial Services Co., Memphis, TN; *U.S. Public*, pg. 1461
Isaksson, Kurt, Chief Oper. Officer--Saab Marine Electronics AB, Goteborg, Sweden; *Int'l*, pg. 686
Isaksson, Thomas, Pres.--Ericsson Radio Systems, Richardson, TX; *Int'l*, pg. 1365
Isbel, George, Pres.--M & I Marshall & Ilsley Trust Company of Arizona, Phoenix, AZ; *U.S. Public*, pg. 1051
Isbell, Larry, Mgr.--Southern Electric Supply Co., Inc., Gadsden, AL; *Int'l*, pg. 1107
Isberg, Gary, Chief Oper. Officer--EMAB Canada Div., Peterborough, Canada; *Int'l*, pg. 441
Ischreyt, Mark, Co-Chief Oper. Officer--BHF-Bank, London, United Kingdom; *Int'l*, pg. 119
Isden, R.F., Mng. Dir.--Grupo Sitra, S.A. DE C.V., Piso, Mexico; *Int'l*, pg. 775
Isejima, Isao, Mng. Dir.--Shiseido (Australia) Pty. Limited, Pyrmont, Australia; *Int'l*, pg. 1235
Iseki, Hirofumi, Dep. Gen. Mgr.--International Business Division (Toyko), Tokyo, Japan; *Int'l*, pg. 373
Isenberg, Howard, Pres. & Chief Exec. Officer--CCL Custom Manufacturing, Niles, IL; *Int'l*, pg. 238
Isenhart, Leslie, Asst. V.P. & Branch Mgr.--California State Bank-Glendora, Glendora, CA; *U.S. Public*, pg. 294
Isenhour, Fred, Gen. Mgr.--National Mount Airy, Bassett, VA; *U.S. Public*, pg. 193
Iserman, Bruce D., Pres.--First American Bank North Dakota, Lisbon, ND; *U.S. Private*, pg. 167
Iseto, Yoshihiko, Gen. Mgr.--International Business Division (Toyko), Tokyo, Japan; *Int'l*, pg. 373
Ishak, Hasanvsi, Gen. Mgr.--P.T. Circle Freight International Indonesia, Jakarta, Indonesia; *U.S. Public*, pg. 372
Isham, Rick, V.P., Opers.--D.L. Blair Inc., Blair, NE; *U.S. Private*, pg. 148
Ishee, Robert R., Pres.--MACtac North America, Brampton, Canada; *U.S. Public*, pg. 210
Ishi, K., Gen. Mgr.-Technical Ctr.--Fujitsu Ten Corp. of America, Torrance, CA; *Int'l*, pg. 526
Ishi, S., Gen. Mgr.--Bank of Tokyo-Mitsubishi, Ltd., Portland, OR; *Int'l*, pg. 157
Ishibashi, Katsuhiko, Pres.--Flender Ishibashi Co. Ltd., Fukuoka, Japan; *Int'l*, pg. 400
Ishibashi, Ko, Gen. Mgr.--Nippon Credit Bank Ltd., Los Angeles, Los Angeles, CA; *Int'l*, pg. 932
Ishibashi, Taro, Pres.--Matsushita Battery Industrial Co., Ltd., Mariguchi, Japan; *Int'l*, pg. 846
Ishida, Etsuo, Gen. Mgr.--Ashikaga Bank-London Branch, London, United Kingdom; *Int'l*, pg. 88
Ishida, J., Chm. Bd. & Chief Exec. Officer--Sumitomo Sitix Silicon, Inc., Fremont, CA; *Int'l*, pg. 1317
Ishida, Ken, Mgr.--NJC Engineering, Tokyo, Japan; *U.S. Private*, pg. 361
Ishida, Nobuyuki, Mng. Dir.--Shizuoka Bank (Europe) S.A., Brussels, Belgium; *Int'l*, pg. 1236
Ishida, Tateaki, Mng. Dir.--Tokai Capital Markets Limited, London, United Kingdom; *Int'l*, pg. 1391
Ishida, Tsunejiro, Mgr.--Commerzbank AG-Osaka, Osaka, Japan; *Int'l*, pg. 311
Ishida, Y., Pres.--NextLevel Systems (Japan), Tokyo, Japan; *U.S. Public*, pg. 716
Ishigaki, T., Chief Oper. Officer--Asahi Komag Company Limited, Yamagata, Japan; *U.S. Public*, pg. 966
Ishihara, K., Pres.--NI Tubulars, Inc., Houston, TX; *Int'l*, pg. 947
Ishihara, Toru, Mng. Dir.--The Fuji Futures (Singapore) Pte., Limited, Singapore, Singapore; *Int'l*, pg. 521
Ishii, Hideo, Pres.--Nissan Motor Deutschland GmbH, Neuss, Germany; *Int'l*, pg. 945
Ishii, Hugo, Dir.--Mizuno Corporation Niederlassung Deutschland, Munich, Germany; *Int'l*, pg. 885
Ishii, Junpei, Gen. Mgr.--The Sakura Bank - London Branch, London, United Kingdom; *Int'l*, pg. 1179
Ishii, K., Pres.--Suzuki Canada Inc., Richmond Hill, Canada; *Int'l*, pg. 1323
Ishii, Kentaro, Dir. & Gen. Mgr.--Fuji Heavy Industries, Ltd., Rolling Stock Div., Utsunomiya, Japan; *Int'l*, pg. 523
Ishii, Takafumi, Pres. & Chief Exec. Officer--Nippon Credit Trust Company, New York, NY; *Int'l*, pg. 933
Ishikawa, Hidesato, Pres.--NMB Corporation, Chatsworth, CA; *Int'l*, pg. 868
Ishikawa, Kozo, Mng. Dir.--The Nikko Merchant Bank (Singapore) Ltd., Singapore, Singapore; *Int'l*, pg. 931
Ishikawa, Ryoji, Gen. Mgr.--Dentsu Moscow Office, Moscow, Russia; *Int'l*, pg. 393
Ishikawa, S., Pres.--Q & B Foods, Inc., Irwindale, CA; *Int'l*, pg. 1074
Ishikawa, Taizo, Gen. Mgr.--Fuji Bank, Houston, Houston, TX; *Int'l*, pg. 519
Ishikura, S., Pres.--Sharp Technology (Taiwan) Corporation, Taipei, Taiwan; *Int'l*, pg. 1230
Ishimatsu, Takao, Pres.--Rohm Amagi Co., Ltd., Fukuoka, Japan; *Int'l*, pg. 1125
Ishioka, Jun, Reg. Mgr.--K.K. Raychem, Yokohama, Japan; *U.S. Public*, pg. 1362
Ishitani, Akira, Pres.--Toray Research Center, Inc., Tokyo, Japan; *Int'l*, pg. 1399
Ishizaka, Akira, Pres.--John Crane (Japan) Inc., Shiga, Japan; *Int'l*, pg. 1339
Ishizaka, Yoshio, Pres. & Chief Exec. Officer--Toyota Motor Sales, U.S.A., Inc., Torrance, CA; *Int'l*, pg. 1412
Ishizuka, H., Mng. Dir.--Toshiba Electronics Malaysia Sdn. Bhd., Kuala Langat, Malaysia; *Int'l*, pg. 1406
Ishizuka, Hisai, Pres.--Foster Wheeler k.k., Tokyo, Japan; *U.S. Public*, pg. 677
Ishizumi, Tad, Pres.--Reed Exhibition Companies-Asia North, Tokyo, Japan; *Int'l*, pg. 1096
Isley, John, Pres.--Prentice Hall Canada, Inc., Scarborough, Canada; *U.S. Private*, pg. 778
Isley, Loren, Chief Oper. Officer--NTS Detroit, Detroit, MI; *U.S. Public*, pg. 1161
Ismail, Yusca, Pres., Gen. Mgr. & Dir.--Perwanal/D'Arcy Masius Benton & Bowles, Jakarta, Indonesia; *U.S. Private*, pg. 305
Ismail, Zalizam, Asst. Dir.--Tourism Malaysia - Hong Kong Office, Hong Kong, Hong Kong; *Int'l*, pg. 833
Isogai, Kazuyoshi, Gen. Mgr.--Yazaki Sabanci Otomotiv Kablo Donanimi San. Ve Tic. A.S., Sakarya, Turkey; *Int'l*, *pg. 1168*
Isogai, Masaharu, Pres.--Jusco USA, Inc., New York, NY; *Int'l*, pg. 28
Isohata, Kemichi, Exec. V.P. & Gen. Mgr.--Shuwa Corp. of New York, New York, NY; *Int'l*, pg. 1237
Isokpan, Osaro, Gen. Mgr.--Nigerian-American Merchant Bank Ltd, Lagos, Nigeria; *U.S. Public*, pg. 185
Isola, Frnak J., Pres.--Franklin Templeton Investor Services, Inc., San Mateo, CA; *U.S. Public*, pg. 680
Isomura, Nobuaki, Chief Oper. Officer--Zimbabwe Project Office, Harare, Zimbabwe; *Int'l*, pg. 943
Isomura, Yoji, Dir.--West Japan Railway Company, Paris, France; *Int'l*, pg. 1491
Isono, Yasuo, Dir.--Brother Industries (Australia) Pty. Ltd., Sydney, Australia; *Int'l*, pg. 229
Isotalo, Jukka, Pres.--Valmet Chile Ltda., Santiago, Chile; *Int'l*, pg. 1448
Israel, Charles, Pres.--Pitkin County Bank & Trust Company, Aspen, CO; *U.S. Public*, pg. 1793
Israel, David, Pres.--SuperValu, Inc.-Greenville Div., Greenville, KY; *U.S. Public*, pg. 1540
Israel, Henrique, Chief Oper. Officer--Ahlstrom Equipamentos Ltda., Curitiba, Brazil; *Int'l*, pg. 34
Issac, Bill, Pres.--Texas Apparel, El Paso, TX; *U.S. Public*, pg. 1429
Issakainen, Markku, Chief Exec. Officer--VPV EURO RSCG, Helsinki, Finland; *Int'l*, pg. 603
Issenmann, Nico, Gen. Mgr.--Jacobs Suchard Tobler AG, Neuchatel, Switzerland; *U.S. Public*, pg. 1288
Isshiki, Toru, Pres.--Taiwan Toto Co., Ltd., Taipei, Taiwan; *Int'l*, pg. 1410
Issler, Robert, Controller--Chris-Craft Industrial Products, Inc., Trenton, NJ; *U.S. Public*, pg. 351
Issoupov, Valery, Fin. Dir.--Leo Burnett & Moradpour/Moscow, Moscow, Russia; *U.S. Private*, pg. 184
Itabashi, Masashi, Chief Rep.--Nippon Life - Shanghai Representative Office, Shanghai, China; *Int'l*, pg. 936
Itagaki, Osamu, Chief Oper. Officer--S.A. Makita N.V., Vilvoorde, Belgium; *Int'l*, pg. 832
Itakura, T., Chief Exec. Officer--Japan Airlines, Geneva, Switzerland; *Int'l*, pg. 700
Itameri, Harry, Chief Oper. Officer--Novo Nordisk A/S, Moscow, Russia; *Int'l*, pg. 987
Itaya, Norman, Pres.--United Australian Automotive Industries Ltd., Saint Kilda, Australia; *U.S. Public*, pg. 725
Itaya, Norman, Pres.--United Australian Automotive Industries Ltd., Saint Kilda, Australia; *Int'l*, pg. 1414
Itayama, M., Pres.--Sanyo Industries Canada Inc., Montreal, Canada; *Int'l*, pg. 1192
Ito, Hajime, Chief Rep.--The Sumitomo Bank, Ltd.-Sydney Representative Office, Sydney, Australia; *Int'l*, pg. 1310
Ito, Hironobu, Pres.--Dai-Ichi Kikaku Co. Ltd., Tokyo, Japan; *Int'l*, pg. 357
Ito, J., Pres.--Sambow Plastics Co., Ltd., Osaka, Japan; *Int'l*, pg. 947
Ito, Kenichi, Pres.--Shanghai Office, Shanghai, China; *Int'l*, pg. 578
Ito, Kotaro, Chief Oper. Officer--Disco Hi-Tec America Inc., Santa Clara, CA; *Int'l*, pg. 413
Ito, Naoaki, Chief Rep.--Bank of Yokohama Bangkok, Bangkok, Thailand; *Int'l*, pg. 159
Ito, Shigemasa, Plant Mgr.--Hitachi Consumer Products de Mexico, Tijuana, Mexico; *Int'l*, pg. 622
Ito, Shinichi, Pres.--Sumitomo Bank of New York Trust Company, New York, NY; *Int'l*, pg. 1309
Ito, Takeshi, Mng. Dir.--The Meijiseimei Investment Singapore Pte. Ltd., Singapore, Singapore; *Int'l*, pg. 854
Ito, Tetsuya, Mng. Dir.--Nippon Express (Nederland) B.V., Schiphol, Netherlands; *Int'l*, pg. 934

Ito, Yukihiro, Dir.--Takenaka Hungaria kft, Budapest, Hungary; *Int'l*, pg. 1351
Itoh, H., Gen. Mgr.--Ransburg Industrial Finishing, Tokyo, Japan; *U.S. Public*, pg. 869
Itoh, John, V.P. & Gen. Mgr.--Sumitomo Corporation of America, Pittsburgh, PA; *Int'l*, pg. 1312
Itoh, Koichi, Mng. Dir.--Handy & Harman International, Ltd., Tokyo, Japan; *U.S. Public*, pg. 780
Itoh, Mikio, Mng. Dir.--Toyo Trust & Banking (Europe) S.A., Brussels, Belgium; *Int'l*, pg. 1411
Itoh, Yasutaka, Chief Oper. Officer--Bamiyan Co., Ltd., Tokyo, Japan; *Int'l*, pg. 1262
Itoh, Yoshiaki, Mgr.--Deutsche Bank AG (Nagoya), Nagoya, Japan; *Int'l*, pg. 404
Itomine, N., Gen. Mgr.--Fujitsu Ten Corp. of America/ Rushville, Rushville, IN; *Int'l*, pg. 526
Itosaka, Minoru, Gen. Mgr.--Fuji Bank, Hong Kong Branch, Central, Hong Kong; *Int'l*, pg. 520
Itterly, Robert, Resident Mgr.--Milford Mill, Milford, NJ; *U.S. Public*, pg. 465
Iturbe, Eglen, Mgr.--PDV America Corp., New York, NY; *Int'l*, pg. 1045
Ivancich, Joe, Mgr.-Plant--Chicago Steel & Wire, Chicago, IL; *U.S. Private*, pg. 686
Ivans, Alicia, Publr.--Computer Shopper, New York, NY; *Int'l*, pg. 1276
Ivansson, Kenneth, Pres.--NCC Uddevalla, Uddevalla, Sweden; *Int'l*, pg. 899
Iversen, Arve, Pres.--Kvaerner Professional Services Limited, Slough, United Kingdom; *Int'l*, pg. 768
Iversen, Arve, Pres.--Kvaerner Professional Services Ltd., Aberdeen, United Kingdom; *Int'l*, pg. 768
Iversen, Bruno, Chm. Bd.--Schumann Sasol International AG, Hamburg, Germany; *Int'l*, pg. 1196
Iversen, Karsten, Chief Oper. Officer--Fischer Imaging Europe, Hamburg, Germany; *U.S. Public*, pg. 647
Iversen, Ole Chr., Chief Exec. Officer--Cinet A/S, Oslo, Norway; *Int'l*, pg. 710
Iversen, Willy, Managing Dir.--Saetre AS, Kolbotn, Norway; *Int'l*, pg. 1011
Iverson, Ann, Chm. Bd. & Chief Exec. Officer--Laura Ashley (USA) Inc., Boston, MA; *Int'l*, pg. 804
Iverson, Robert I., Pres.--Maritime Leisure Corporation, Fort Lauderdale, FL; *Int'l*, pg. 21
Ives, Christopher L., Ph.D., Mng. Dir.--PolyMedica Industries UK, Ltd., Tarvin, United Kingdom; *U.S. Public*, pg. 1315
Ivester, Ann, Pres.--Cornerstone Title Company, Columbia, MD; *U.S. Public*, pg. 1414
Ivester, M. Douglas, Pres.--The Coca-Cola Export Corporation, Atlanta, GA; *U.S. Public*, pg. 392
Ivester, M. Douglas, Pres.--Coca-Cola Interamerican Corp., Atlanta, GA; *U.S. Public*, pg. 392
Ivey, Dick, Mgr.--Health Care Div., Stamford, CT; *Int'l*, pg. 1053
Ivey, Gerry, Gen. Mgr.--Liqui-Box Corp., Elkton, MD; *U.S. Public*, pg. 1000
Ivins, Robert, Pres.--Silver Furniture Co., Inc., Knoxville, TN; *U.S. Public*, pg. 352
Ivstan, Shaul, Gen. Mgr.--Klil Industries Ltd., Kiryat Motzkin, Israel; *Int'l*, pg. 644
Ivy, Jim, Pres. & Chief Exec. Officer--Gestetner Corporation, Greenwich, CT; *Int'l*, pg. 1115
Iwagaki, Ken, Pres. & Chief Oper. Officer--Matsushita Television Co., Elgin, IL; *Int'l*, pg. 847
Iwagami, K., Chief Oper. Officer--Compania NHK Cimebra-Comercial Industrial e Mecanica Brasileira, Rio de Janeiro, Brazil; *Int'l*, pg. 947
Iwai, M., Pres.--Nissho Iwai Aerospace Corp., Tokyo, Japan; *Int'l*, pg. 946
Iwai, Toshiyuki, Pres.--Nomura Land & Building Co. Ltd., Tokyo, Japan; *Int'l*, pg. 956
Iwai, Yasushi, Pres.--ORIX Baseball Club, Kobe, Japan; *Int'l*, pg. 1008
Iwaki, Masayasu, Pres.--Nippon Koshuha Steel Co., Ltd., Tokyo, Japan; *Int'l*, pg. 740
Iwakura, Joe, Pres.--Wako Bank (Schweiz) AG, Zurich, Switzerland; *Int'l*, pg. 1485
Iwama, Yoichiro, Chm.--Tokio Marine Investment Services, Limited, Hong Kong, Hong Kong; *Int'l*, pg. 1393
Iwama, Youichiro, Chief Oper. Officer--Tokio Marine Asset Management New York Co., Ltd., New York, NY; *Int'l*, pg. 1392
Iwamitsu, Naoki, Gen. Mgr.--Cognos Japan KK, Tokyo, Japan; *Int'l*, pg. 306
Iwamoto, Gunn, Mgr.--Autodesk Ltd., Tokyo, Japan; *U.S. Public*, pg. 149
Iwamura, H., Pres.--Kubota America Corp., New York, NY; *Int'l*, pg. 762
Iwamura, Mr., Pres.--Honda Deutschland GmbH, Offenbach/Main, Germany; *Int'l*, pg. 635
Iwano, Shunpei, Pres.--Konica Photo Service U.S.A., Inc., East Hartford, CT; *Int'l*, pg. 748
Iwasa, Toshiyuki, Gen. Mgr.-Intl. Opers. Center--International Business Division (Toyko), Tokyo, Japan; *Int'l*, pg. 373
Iwasaki, T., Pres.--Noritake Co., Inc., Secaucus, NJ; *Int'l*, pg. 959
Iwasaki, Tetsuo, Chm. Bd.--Applied Materials Japan, Inc., Chiba, Japan; *U.S. Public*, pg. 123
Iwashita, Hiroyoshi, Pres. & Rep. Dir.--Asahi-Penn Chemical Company Limited, Tokyo, Japan; *U.S. Public*, pg. 1245
Iwashita, Kenneth M., Pres. & Chief Oper. Officer-Lubrizol Foundation--The Lubrizol Corporation, Wickliffe, OH; *U.S. Public*, pg. 1016
Iwashito, Isao, Pres.--SEH America Inc., Vancouver, WA; *Int'l*, pg. 1234
Iwata, Saiji, Chief Oper. Officer--Makita Werkzeug GmbH, Duisburg, Germany; *Int'l*, pg. 832
Iwata, Yukihisa, Dir.--Worldsec International Limited, Central, Hong Kong; *Int'l*, pg. 158
Iwatake, Katsuji, Mng. Dir.--Brother International (Singapore) Pte. Ltd., Singapore, Singapore; *Int'l*, pg. 230
Iwerebon, Felix A., Mng. Dir.--Longman Nigeria Ltd., Lagos, Nigeria; *Int'l*, pg. 1027
Iyama, Hideki, Chief Oper. Officer--The Taiyo Mutual Life Insurance Co., New York, NY; *Int'l*, pg. 1349
Izabelle, Alain, Chief Exec. Officer--ACCO France S.A., Savigny-le-Temple, France; *U.S. Public*, pg. 675
Izaguirre, Pablo, Mgr.--Raychem de Venezuela, CA, Caracas, Venezuela; *U.S. Public*, pg. 1362
Izawa, Shuhei, Mng. Dir.--SEC (Soft, Event & Promotion) Planning, Inc., Tokyo, Japan; *Int'l*, pg. 588
Izumi, H., Mng. Dir.--Toshiba Electronics (UK) Ltd., Camberley, United Kingdom; *Int'l*, pg. 1406
Izumi, Masaharu, Pres.--United Asset Management (Japan), Inc., Tokyo, Japan; *U.S. Public*, pg. 1674
Jaatinen, Veikko, Resident Mgr.--Pellos Mills, Pellosniemi, Finland; *Int'l*, pg. 1429
Jaben, Jan, Editor--Business Marketing, Chicago, IL; *U.S. Private*, pg. 285
Jack, Donna K., Mgr.-Bank--Liberty Bank & Trust of Oklahoma City, Oklahoma City, OK; *U.S. Public*, pg. 174
Jack, Ross, Mgr.-Tech.--Rod & Bar Products Division, Mayfield, Australia; *Int'l*, pg. 227
Jackman, Bobby, Gen. Mgr.--Tandy Packaging, Fort Worth, TX; *U.S. Public*, pg. 1560
Jackman, Joseph R., Pres.--Shaw-Perkins, Inc., West Pittsburg, PA; *U.S. Private*, pg. 913
Jackman, P., Mng. Dir.--Swish Products Ltd., Tamworth, United Kingdom; *Int'l*, pg. 925
Jackman, Robert L., Mng. Dir.--Bendix Mintex Pty., Ltd., Ballarat, Australia; *U.S. Public*, pg. 54
Jackson, Alexander III, Grp. V.P.--Barnes Group Aerospace Components, Windsor, CT; *U.S. Public*, pg. 190
Jackson, Anthony Howland, Mng. Dir.--Structured Compensation Ltd., London, United Kingdom; *Int'l*, pg. 671
Jackson, Bernie, Gen. Mgr.--Balco, Inc., San Jose, CA; *U.S. Public*, pg. 1480
Jackson, Bruce, Pres.--Coast Steel Fabricators Ltd., Port Coquitlam, Canada; *Int'l*, pg. 31
Jackson, Charlie E., Pres. & Chief Exec. Officer--AirTouch Paging, Dallas, TX; *U.S. Public*, pg. 34
Jackson, Cliff, Mgr.-Warehouse--Norwich, Norwich, CT; *U.S. Public*, pg. 730
Jackson, D.G., Dir.--Tradinco Instrumenten-Apparaten B.V., Berkel, Netherlands; *Int'l*, pg. 590
Jackson, Dale P., Gen. Mgr.--PCS Potash - Rocanville, Rocanville, Canada; *Int'l*, pg. 1064
Jackson, David, Pres.--C. Lee Cook Div., Louisville, KY; *U.S. Public*, pg. 521
Jackson, David, Pres.--EPS/Entertainment Programming Services Ltd., Toronto, Canada; *Int'l*, pg. 1282
Jackson, David N., Pres. & Gen. Mgr.--Williams Detroit Diesel-Allison Midwest, Inc., Brunswick, OH; *U.S. Private*, pg. 1179
Jackson, Dick, Pres.--Pedus Building Services, Los Angeles, CA; *U.S. Private*, pg. 846
Jackson, Dick, Pres.--Pedus Security Services, Los Angeles, CA; *U.S. Private*, pg. 846
Jackson, Dick, Pres.--Pedus Office Services, Los Angeles, CA; *U.S. Private*, pg. 846
Jackson, Dick, Pres.--Pedus Food Services, Los Angeles, CA; *U.S. Private*, pg. 846
Jackson, E.V., Chm. Bd. & Pres.--Reynolds Metals Company-Illinois, Mc Cook, IL; *U.S. Public*, pg. 1385
Jackson, Eddie L., Pres.-Lil' Champs--Lil'Champ/Food Stores Inc., Jacksonville, FL; *U.S. Private*, pg. 837
Jackson, Eldon, Pres.--Premark Canada Inc., North York, Canada; *U.S. Public*, pg. 1323
Jackson, Eric, Pres.--Shieldalloy Metallurgical Corportation, Newfield, NJ; *U.S. Private*, pg. 735
Jackson, Harold W., Gen. Mgr.--Lever Brothers Industrial Division, New York, NY; *Int'l*, pg. 1436
Jackson, J., Plant Mgr.--Long Mile Rubber Company, Dallas, TX; *U.S. Public*, pg. 1504
Jackson, J., Plant Mgr.--Oliver Rubber Co., Dallas, TX; *U.S. Public*, pg. 1505
Jackson, J. Andrew, Pres.--Optiroc Ltd., Manchester, United Kingdom; *Int'l*, pg. 1200
Jackson, J.A., Gen. Mgr.--Euroc Brick Ltd., Manchester, United Kingdom; *Int'l*, pg. 1199
Jackson, James A., V.P. & Gen. Mgr.--All American Homes of Iowa Inc., Dyersville, IA; *U.S. Public*, pg. 388
Jackson, Jim, Pres.--DeSoto Inc., Joliet, IL; *U.S. Public*, pg. 956
Jackson, John, Gen. Mgr.--All-State Ford Truck Sales, Louisville, KY; *U.S. Private*, pg. 524
Jackson, John E., Sr. V.P.--Nordson North American Div., Duluth, GA; *U.S. Public*, pg. 1188
Jackson, K., Mgr.--Velva Liquids Ltd., North Shields, United Kingdom; *Int'l*, pg. 1251
Jackson, Kenneth, Mgr.-Distr.--Weatherford US Inc., Vernal, UT; *U.S. Public*, pg. 1749
Jackson, Lawrence, Pres.--Linatex Canada Inc., Montreal, Canada; *Int'l*, pg. 599
Jackson, Mary Anne, Pres.--J&M Company, Deerfield, IL; *U.S. Private*, pg. 770
Jackson, Meryl, Pres.--Almega Corporation, Bensenville, IL; *U.S. Public*, pg. 546
Jackson, P., Mng. Dir.--De La Rue Cash Handling Product Group, Havant, United Kingdom; *Int'l*, pg. 387
Jackson, Penny, Pres.--Nevada Landing, Jean, NV; *U.S. Public*, pg. 375
Jackson, R.S., Gen. Mgr.--Morgan Matroc Limited Unilator Division, Wrexham, United Kingdom; *Int'l*, pg. 893
Jackson, Ralph, Gen. Mgr.--Rathbone, King & Seeley Insurance Services, Inc., San Francisco, CA; *U.S. Private*, pg. 610
Jackson, Richard L., Pres.--Quest Staffing, Atlanta, GA; *U.S. Public*, pg. 45
Jackson, Richard L., Pres.--Surgical Information Systems, Atlanta, GA; *U.S. Public*, pg. 45
Jackson, Ron, Mgr.--General Employment Enterprises, Inc., Dallas, TX; *U.S. Public*, pg. 715
Jackson, T., Gen. Mgr.--Baring Asset Management (Bahrain) Ltd., Manama, Bahrain; *Int'l*, pg. 648
Jackson, T.A., Pres.--The Trust Company of Bank of Montreal, Toronto, Canada; *Int'l*, pg. 153
Jackson, Thomas, Reg. Mgr.--Kredietbank Representative Office (Los Angeles), Los Angeles, CA; *Int'l*, pg. 760
Jackson, V. Charles, Sr. V.P.--Mellon Financial Services, Los Angeles, CA; *U.S. Public*, pg. 1085
Jackson, Valton T., Mgr.-Branch--Piper Jaffray Inc., Provo, UT; *U.S. Public*, pg. 1301
Jackson, W. Ronald, Chm. Bd. & Pres.--Cleveland Chair Company, Cleveland, TN; *U.S. Private*, pg. 579
Jackson, W.A., Pres.--Esso Brasileira de Petroleo Limitada, Rio de Janeiro, Brazil; *U.S. Public*, pg. 602
Jacob, Norman A., Pres. & Chief Exec. Officer--The Huntington Trust Co., N.A., Columbus, OH; *U.S. Public*, pg. 850
Jacob, Steve M., Mgr.-Mid-South Service Center--Mid-South Service Center, Baton Rouge, LA; *U.S. Private*, pg. 1180
Jacobi, Fritz, Pres. & Publr.--The Springfield News Leader, Springfield, MO; *U.S. Public*, pg. 701
Jacobina, Luiz Eduardo, Mgr.--Banco do Brasil S.A.-San Isidro Representative Office, San Isidro, Peru; *Int'l*, pg. 142
Jacobs, Allan, Exec. V.P.--Burlington House Area Rugs, New York, NY; *U.S. Public*, pg. 268
Jacobs, Bruce, Pres.--Grede Transport, Inc., Milwaukee, WI; *U.S. Private*, pg. 476
Jacobs, Daniel L., Pres.--Jacobs Asset Management, Fort Lauderdale, FL; *U.S. Public*, pg. 1673
Jacobs, Francis B., Pres.--EA Financial, Inc., Wilmington, DE; *U.S. Public*, pg. 541
Jacobs, George W., Publr.--Cynthiana Democrat, Cynthiana, KY; *U.S. Private*, pg. 648
Jacobs, Glyn, Mgr.--Alitalia, Atlanta, GA; *Int'l*, pg. 652
Jacobs, Herman, Pres.--Allou Distributors Inc., Brentwood, NY; *U.S. Public*, pg. 55
Jacobs, J.L., Pres.--Deepwater Operating Co., Pleasantville, NJ; *U.S. Public*, pg. 430
Jacobs, Jerry, Pres. & Chief Exec. Officer--First National Bank, Nashville, Nashville, AR; *U.S. Public*, pg. 630
Jacobs, John M., Pres. & Chief Exec. Officer--Dillingham Construction Corp., Pleasanton, CA; *U.S. Private*, pg. 333
Jacobs, Joop C., Mgr.--Hutchinson Technology Inc., Leiden, Netherlands; *U.S. Public*, pg. 851
Jacobs, Leonard, V.P.--Perry Machinery Poland, Przedstawickel, Poland; *U.S. Private*, pg. 855
Jacobs, Leonard, V.P.--Perry Machinery Czech S.R.O., Prague, Czech Republic; *U.S. Private*, pg. 855
Jacobs, Leonard J., Pres.--Jet Spray International, Norwood, MA; *U.S. Private*, pg. 587
Jacobs, Mark E., Pres.--Pulte Southern California Division, Newport Beach, CA; *U.S. Public*, pg. 1345
Jacobs, Michael, Dir.--Generale Bank & Co., Cologne, Germany; *Int'l*, pg. 548
Jacobs, Michael, V.P. & Publisher--The Free Press, New York, NY; *U.S. Private*, pg. 777
Jacobs, Michael, Admin.--Hillhaven Convalescent Center Las Vegas, Las Vegas, NV; *U.S. Public*, pg. 1713
Jacobs, Norman, Pres.--World Publishing Company, Evanston, IL; *U.S. Private*, pg. 226
Jacobs, Paul, Pres. & Chief Exec. Officer--IsoQuest, Inc., Fairfax, VA; *U.S. Private*, pg. 958
Jacobsen, A. Ronald, V.P. & Gen. Mgr.--Logicon Geodynamics Western Division, Torrance, CA; *U.S. Public*, pg. 1199
Jacobsen, Aage, Pres.--Chr. Hansen Argentina S.A.I.C., Quilmes, Argentina; *Int'l*, pg. 289
Jacobsen, Bob, V.P. & Gen. Mgr.--Missouri Valley Steel Co., Sioux City, IA; *U.S. Private*, pg. 824
Jacobsen, Cai Toft, Chief Oper. Officer--A/S Ernst Voss Fabrik, Fredericia, Denmark; *Int'l*, pg. 441
Jacobsen, E. P., Exec. V.P.--Curver B.V., Goirle, Netherlands; *Int'l*, pg. 352
Jacobsen, Finn, Mng. Dir.--KE-Burgmann A/S, Vejen, Denmark; *Int'l*, pg. 234
Jacobsen, Haye, Mng. Dir.--Quimica Henkel S.A. de C.V., Morelos, Mexico; *Int'l*, pg. 613
Jacobsen, J.J., Mng. Dir.--Nedlloyd Bulk B.V., Rotterdam, Netherlands; *Int'l*, pg. 1144
Jacobsen, Joseph T., Pres.--International Exploration, Inc., Doylestown, PA; *U.S. Public*, pg. 546
Jacobsen, Pat, Sr. V.P.-Human Resources & Corp. Services--Manulife Financial, Toronto, Canada; *Int'l*, pg. 840
Jacobsen, Uwe, Pres.--Neckura Versicherungs AG, Oberursell, Germany; *U.S. Private*, pg. 789
Jacobsen, Uwe, Pres.--Saarbrucker Zeitung Verlag und Druckerei GmbH, Saarbruecken, Germany; *Int'l*, pg. 1478
Jacobson, Bryan, Pres.--Pirelli Jacobson, Inc., Seattle, WA; *Int'l*, pg. 1059
Jacobson, Edwin, Pres.--Avatar Properties Inc., Miami, FL; *U.S. Public*, pg. 151
Jacobson, Edwin, Pres.--Avatar Realty, Inc., Coral Gables, FL; *U.S. Public*, pg. 151
Jacobson, Jack, V.P. & Gen. Mgr.--KTTU-TV, Tucson, AZ; *U.S. Public*, pg. 384
Jacobson, Max M., Pres.--Harris Building Services Corporation, Chicago, IL; *Int'l*, pg. 154
Jacobson, Rick, Gen. Mgr.--Norpac Services, Inc., Lake Oswego, OR; *U.S. Private*, pg. 802
Jacobson, Rick, Gen. Mgr.--Stone Mill Foods, Portland, OR; *U.S. Private*, pg. 802
Jacobsson, Gunnar, Chief Oper. Officer--Alfa-Laval S.A., Lima, Peru; *Int'l*, pg. 1380
Jacobsson, Leif, Pres.--Skanska Stalteknik AB, Kalmar, Sweden; *Int'l*, pg. 1261
Jacobus, Phillip R., Pres.--Hartger & Willard Mortgage Associates, Inc., Grand Rapids, MI; *U.S. Public*, pg. 1216
Jacoby, Douglas, Pres.--Millipore Process Div., Bedford, MA; *U.S. Public*, pg. 1112
Jacoby, Jeff, Gen. Mgr.--WMYU-FM, Knoxville, TN; *U.S. Public*, pg. 923
Jacoby, Klaus, Chief Exec. Officer--Cosmos Versicherung AG, Saarbruecken, Germany; *Int'l*, pg. 15

Jacoby, Klaus, Chief Exec. Officer--Cosmos Lebensversicherung AG, Saarbruecken, Germany; *Int'l*, pg. 15
Jacoby, Klaus, Chief Exec. Officer--Cosmos Krankenversicherung AG, Saarbruecken, Germany; *Int'l*, pg. 15
Jacoby, L. Phillip, V.P. & Gen. Mgr.--Elco Precision Forming Div., Rockford, IL; *U.S. Public*, pg. 1590
Jacoby, Thomas, Pres.--JBL Consumer, Woodbury, NY; *U.S. Public*, pg. 787
Jacokes, Thomas R., V.P. & Gen. Mgr.--Lindenmeyr Munroe, Jessup, MD; *U.S. Private*, pg. 224
Jacomin, J.C., Gen. Mgr.--Britannia Brands (Malaysia) SON BHD, Tampoi, Malaysia; *Int'l*, pg. 380
Jacot, H. Dean, Chm. Bd.--The Coteau Properties Co., Beulah, ND; *U.S. Public*, pg. 1149
Jacqmarcq, Guillaume, Mgr.--Devimco, Evry, France; *Int'l*, pg. 20
Jacuzzi, Roy A., Pres.--Jacuzzi, Inc., Walnut Creek, CA; *U.S. Public*, pg. 1684
Jadelis, Tom, Sr. V.P.--Advanced Risk Management Services, New York, NY; *Int'l*, pg. 1505
Jadow, Henry C., Exec. V.P.--Krazy Glue Inc., New York, NY; *U.S. Private*, pg. 158
Jaech, David, Gen. Mgr.--Folding Carton Div., Memphis, TN; *U.S. Public*, pg. 902
Jaeger, Bill, Pres.--Kraus-Anderson Construction Company, Minneapolis, MN; *U.S. Private*, pg. 635
Jaeger, Rolf, Pres.--Kvaerner Hydrotech a.s., Hundvag, Norway; *Int'l*, pg. 769
Jaeggi, Anton, Chief Oper. Officer--BHF-Bank Representative Office, Zurich, Switzerland; *Int'l*, pg. 120
Jaekel, Fred, Pres.--Cosma International Inc., Concord, Canada; *Int'l*, pg. 829
Jaen, Juan Pedro Gomez, Pres.--Suria K, S.A., Madrid, Spain; *Int'l*, pg. 1225
Jaernefelt, Mr., Chief Oper. Officer--Siemens Osakeytioe, Helsinki, Finland; *Int'l*, pg. 1247
Jaffe, Ira, Pres.-Famous Music--Paramount Pictures Corporation, Los Angeles, CA; *U.S. Private*, pg. 776
Jaffee, Keith, Pres.--Amco Corporation, Chicago, IL; *U.S. Public*, pg. 985
Jaffri, Shafeeg H., Chief Exec. Officer--Habib Bank Ltd., New York, NY; *Int'l*, pg. 584
Jagadisan, T.V., Mng. Dir.--Monsanto Chemicals of India Limited, Mumbai, India; *U.S. Public*, pg. 1125
Jagenberg, Axel, Chief Oper. Officer--Ferd. Jagenberg & Sohne GmbH & Co. KG, Altenkirchen, Germany; *Int'l*, pg. 35
Jagenberg, Christian, Mgr.--Commerzbank Aktiengesellschaft Los Angeles Office, Los Angeles, CA; *Int'l*, pg. 310
Jager, Hans H., Dr., Chief Exec. Officer--Volksfursorge Holding AG, Hamburg, Germany; *Int'l*, pg. 15
Jager, Hans, Dr., Chief Exec. Officer--Volksfursorge Deutsche Lebensversicherung AG, Hamburg, Germany; *Int'l*, pg. 16
Jager, Hans, Dr., Chief Exec. Officer--Volksfursorge Deutsche Sachversicherung, Hamburg, Germany; *Int'l*, pg. 16
Jaggard, Ian, Mng. Dir.--Check Technology Limited, Crawley, United Kingdom; *U.S. Public*, pg. 342
Jagger, B.J., Plant Mgr.--Dayton Superior Corporation, Seattle, WA; *U.S. Private*, pg. 932
Jaggs, S., Mng. Dir.--Pinewood Studios Limited, Iver, United Kingdom; *Int'l*, pg. 1086
Jagnert, Kent, Mng. Dir.--SKF (Zambia) Ltd., Kitwe, Zambia; *Int'l*, pg. 1159
Jagt, J., Pres.--H.A. Astlett & Co. Ltd., Toronto, Canada; *Int'l*, pg. 682
Jahanger, Salim, Gen. Mgr.--Pakistan International Airlines Corporation, New York, NY; *Int'l*, pg. 1022
Jahn, Mikael O.F., Mng. Dir.--Svenska Skumslacknings Aktiebolaget, Kungalv, Sweden; *Int'l*, pg. 595
Jaidar, Roberto, Chief Oper. Officer--Fama de Durango, S.A. de C.V., Durango, Mexico; *U.S. Public*, pg. 613
Jaime, Antonio, Pres.--Construcciones Agrometalicas Levante, S.A. (Calsa), Zaragoza, Spain; *U.S. Public*, pg. 1579
Jain, Nirmal, Grp. V.P.--Polymer Chemicals Group, Greenwich, CT; *U.S. Public*, pg. 1774
Jaine, Olivier, Co-Mgr.--EURO RSCG Novation, Villeneuve-Loubet, France; *Int'l*, pg. 601
Jakel, F., Gen. Mgr.--Steelweld Division-Zweigniederlassung Bonn der Ambac B.V., Gauting, Germany; *Int'l*, pg. 71
Jakobsen, Jesper H., Mng. Dir.--DanTransport A/S, Glostrup, Denmark; *Int'l*, pg. 476
Jakobsen, Ole, Pres.--Tamrock Oy, Tampere, Finland; *Int'l*, pg. 1352
Jakobsson, Pauli, Mng. Dir.--Oy Bang & Olufsen ab, Helsinki, Finland; *Int'l*, pg. 146
Jakosa, Marty, Plant Mgr.--ConAgra Turkey Co., Turlock, CA; *U.S. Public*, pg. 427
Jakubowski, G.F., Branch Mgr.--Zellerbach Division, Milwaukee, WI; *U.S. Public*, pg. 1075
Jalanonen, T., Mng. Dir.--Consilium Bulk Oy, Rauma, Finland; *Int'l*, pg. 131
Jali, Tajuddin, Dr., Chm.--Reed Exhibition Companies-Malaysia, Kuala Lumpur, Malaysia; *Int'l*, pg. 1097
Jallier, Roland, Gen. Mgr.--Fairchild Fasteners France, Cergy-Pontoise, France; *U.S. Public*, pg. 610
Jalluddin, Tuan Haji Bin, Mng. Dir.--Fima Metal Box Berhad, Petaling Jaya, Malaysia; *Int'l*, pg. 267
Jalos, Francisco, Mgr. Gen.--Distribuidora de Productos Petroliferos, S.A. (DISPESA), Madrid, Spain; *Int'l*, pg. 323
Jamal, Mustafa, Sr. V.P. & Chief Mgr.--Habib Bank Limited, Karachi, Pakistan; *Int'l*, pg. 584
Jamaluddin, Zaiton, Chief Oper. Officer--Novo Nordisk A/S, Petaling Jaya, Malaysia; *Int'l*, pg. 988
Jamar, John P., Chief Oper. Officer--Klungess Electronic supply, Iron Mountain, MI; *U.S. Private*, pg. 197
James, Carl, Pres.--Riverchase Homes, Haleyville, AL; *U.S. Public*, pg. 319
James, David, Mng. Dir.--Acuson Ltd., Uxbridge, United Kingdom; *U.S. Public*, pg. 18
James, Don, Mgr.--A. Schulman, Inc., Evansville, IN; *U.S. Public*, pg. 1441
James, Donald M., Pres.--Vulcan Materials Company-Southern Div., Birmingham, AL; *U.S. Public*, pg. 1726
James, Elliott D., V.P. & Group Exec.--Enterprise Service Solutions, Carrollton, TX; *U.S. Public*, pg. 729
James, G.P.H., Chief Oper. Officer--Husqvarna Ltd., Luton, United Kingdom; *Int'l*, pg. 444
James, Guo Jin Zhi, Chief Exec. Officer--KONE Elevators (Shenzhen) Co. Ltd., Shenzhen, China; *Int'l*, pg. 747
James, Jeff, Regional Mgr.--Allen & Hoshall, Irving, TX; *U.S. Private*, pg. 36
James, Jerry, V.P.--Olympic Steel - Minneapolis Division, Plymouth, MN; *U.S. Public*, pg. 1221
James, John D., Pres.--Health Care Institutional Services, Rockville, MD; *U.S. Public*, pg. 1156
James, Juanita, Pres.--Newbridge Communications, Inc., New York, NY; *Int'l*, pg. 191
James, Lawrence E., Pres.--ReliaStar Mortgage Company, West Des Moines, IA; *U.S. Public*, pg. 1376
James, Lisa, Admin.--Casa Del Sol, Las Cruces, NM; *U.S. Public*, pg. 838
James, M., Branch Mgr.--Mack Valves-NSW, Smithfield, Australia; *Int'l*, pg. 1223
James, Matt, Pres. & Gen. Mgr.--KTVE, Inc., Channel 10, Monroe, LA; *U.S. Public*, pg. 759
James, Neil, Mng. Partner--Potentia Healthcare Communications Partners, Chicago, IL; *U.S. Public*, pg. 1224
James, Opie, Division Mgr.--Horizon Technology Group - Wyandotte Division, Wyandotte, MI; *U.S. Private*, pg. 539
James, P.G., Pres.--Hydro Conduit Corp., Houston, TX; *Int'l*, pg. 245
James, Paul, Dir.--BNP Private Bank & Trust Cayman Limited, Grand Cayman, Cayman Islands; *Int'l*, pg. 164
James, Phillip, Mgr.--DWF of Salt Lake, Inc., Salt Lake City, UT; *U.S. Private*, pg. 326
James, R. J., Chief Oper. Officer--DSS Engineers, Inc., Plantation, FL; *U.S. Public*, pg. 1519
James, Ronald, Pres.--Ceridian Employer Services, Bloomington, MN; *U.S. Public*, pg. 331
James, S., Mng. Dir.--Rossing Uranium Ltd., Windhoek, Namibia; *Int'l*, pg. 1119
James, Steve, District Mgr.--Central Texas District Office, Brenham, TX; *U.S. Private*, pg. 150
James, Ted, Chief Oper. Officer--BTR Med/Vet, Tempe, AZ; *Int'l*, pg. 127
James, Ted, Pres.--Veterinary Companies of America, Topeka, KS; *U.S. Public*, pg. 397
James, Thomas A., Chm. Bd.--RJ Credit Partners, Saint Petersburg, FL; *U.S. Public*, pg. 923
James, Thomas A., Chm. Bd.--Raymond James Partners, Inc., Saint Petersburg, FL; *U.S. Public*, pg. 923
James, Thomas A., Chm. Bd.--RJ Realty, Inc., Saint Petersburg, FL; *U.S. Public*, pg. 923
James, Thomas A., Chm. Bd.--Raymond James Realty Advisors, Inc., Saint Petersburg, FL; *U.S. Public*, pg. 923
James, William J., Pres.--Northrop Grumman International, Inc., Arlington, VA; *U.S. Public*, pg. 1198
Jameson, Teena, Mng. Dir.--AIS Media Brisbane, Brisbane, Australia; *Int'l*, pg. 15
Jamieson, Diarmid, Mgr.-Opers.--Woodward-Clyde International, Windsor, United Kingdom; *U.S. Public*, pg. 1658
Jamieson, E., Mgr.--Lindberg Heat Treating Co., New Berlin, WI; *U.S. Public*, pg. 999
Jamieson, G.A., Gen. Mgr.--LASMO Runtu Ltd., Jakarta, Indonesia; *Int'l*, pg. 804
Jamieson, Michael, Pres.--Mission Linen Supply, Santa Barbara, CA; *U.S. Private*, pg. 753
Jamison, Dave, Chief Oper. Officer--Service Products Buildings, Inc., Toledo, OH; *U.S. Public*, pg. 1645
Jamison, Jayne, Publr.--Redbook, New York, NY; *U.S. Private*, pg. 517
Jamison, R.H., V.P.--Nutter Engineering, Tulsa, OK; *U.S. Public*, pg. 793
Jamison, Richard, Div. Mgr.--ConAgra Broiler Co., El Dorado, AR; *U.S. Public*, pg. 427
Jamme, Norbert, Mng. Dir.--Rhone-Poulenc Rorer Philippines Inc., Manila, Philippines; *Int'l*, pg. 1111
Jamme, Norbert, Mng. Dir.--Rhone-Poulenc Philippines Inc., Manila, Philippines; *Int'l*, pg. 1113
Jammet, Bernard, V.P.--MICROS-Fidelio Software Deutschland GmbH, Dusseldorf, Germany; *U.S. Public*, pg. 1106
Jamsen, Lauri, Chief Oper. Officer--Raision Lateksi Oy, Kaipiainen, Finland; *Int'l*, pg. 1085
Jan van Rijnbach, Pieter, Mgr.--Woodward Governor Germany GmbH, Elbe, Germany; *U.S. Public*, pg. 1777
Janaczek, Stephen J., Pres.--Power Piping Company, Pittsburgh, PA; *U.S. Public*, pg. 1029
Janas, Adam, Pres.--Delta-Unibus Corp., Franklin Park, IL; *U.S. Public*, pg. 1319
Janasko, Greg M., Pres.--Norwest Financial Leasing, Inc., Des Moines, IA; *U.S. Public*, pg. 1202
Janatello, A. Peter, Gen. Mgr.--Schult Homes Corporation, Plainville, KS; *U.S. Public*, pg. 1442
Janczyk, W., Mng. Dir.--Business Management & Finance International Ltd., Warsaw, Poland; *Int'l*, pg. 1332
Jandorf, Bruce, V.P. & Gen. Mgr.--Rosemount Analytical, Inc., Irvine, CA; *U.S. Public*, pg. 574
Janego, Tim, Gen. Mgr.--Greater Tampa Bay Auto Auction, Tampa, FL; *U.S. Private*, pg. 282
Janelle, Andy, Gen. Mgr.--Cablelink, Incorporated, Kings Mountain, NC; *U.S. Public*, pg. 1394
Janelle, Claude, Div. Mgr.--Belgo Div., Shawinigan, Canada; *Int'l*, pg. 19
Janelle, Claude, Pres. & Chief Oper. Officer--Stone Container (Canada), Bathurst, Canada; *U.S. Public*, pg. 1522
Janes, John, Country Mgr.--Standard Chartered Bank Zambia Ltd., Lusaka, Zambia; *Int'l*, pg. 1295
Janes, Michael A., Pres.--Hilb, Rogal and Hamilton Company of Arizona, Phoenix, AZ; *U.S. Public*, pg. 827
Janitz, John, Pres.--Randall Textron, Troy, MI; *U.S. Public*, pg. 1590
Janjak, Vinko, Pres.--Jotul a.s., Fredrikstad, Norway; *Int'l*, pg. 42
Janke, Robert F., Chief Oper. Officer--TosoHaas Company, Montgomeryville, PA; *U.S. Public*, pg. 1403
Janke, Robert F., Chief Oper. Officer--TosoHaas Company, Montgomeryville, PA; *Int'l*, pg. 1408
Janke, Robert F., Chief Oper. Officer--TosoHaas GmbH, Stuttgart, Germany; *Int'l*, pg. 1408
Janks, Arlene A., Adv. Coord.--Acustar, Inc., Engineered Products Group, Troy, MI; *U.S. Public*, pg. 353
Janmohamed, M., V.P.--Celfortec Inc., Valleyfield, Canada; *Int'l*, pg. 698
Jannes, Zantero, Chief Oper. Officer--Gasum Oy, Espoo, Finland; *Int'l*, pg. 913
Janosa-McMahon, Stilla, Gen. Mgr.--Spencer County Journal-Democrat, Rockport, IN; *U.S. Private*, pg. 648
Janowiak, Mary, Travel Trade Mgr.--Utell International-Dallas, Dallas, TX; *Int'l*, pg. 1098
Jans, Thomas, Pres.--Recognition Division, Memphis, TN; *U.S. Public*, pg. 934
Jansen, Guy, Chief Oper. Officer--Bering Marine Corporation, Seattle, WA; *U.S. Private*, pg. 683
Jansen, Hans, Chief Exec. Officer--Atlet-Multicar BV, Enschede, Netherlands; *Int'l*, pg. 97
Jansen, Henry, Chief Oper. Officer--LTI, Inc., Lynden, WA; *U.S. Private*, pg. 683
Jansen, Jerry, Gen. Mgr.--Federal Industries, Inc., Belleville, WI; *U.S. Public*, pg. 1506
Jansen, Louis P., Gen. Mgr.--Dicalite Europe Nord, S.A., Brussels, Belgium; *U.S. Private*, pg. 903
Jansen, Raymond A., Pres., Chief Exec. Officer & Publr.--Newsday, Melville, NY; *U.S. Public*, pg. 1616
Jansen, Steve, Chief Oper. Officer--Knik Construction Co., Inc., Seattle, WA; *U.S. Private*, pg. 683
Jansen, W. David, Pres.& Chief Exec. Officer--WJW Constructors, LLC, Mesa, AZ; *U.S. Private*, pg. 1187
Janson, Peter S., Pres.--ABB Inc., Norwalk, CT; *Int'l*, pg. 3
Janssen, Erik, Country Mgr.--Compaq Computer N.V./S.A., Zaventem, Belgium; *U.S. Public*, pg. 418
Janssen, H. J., Chief Oper. Officer--Ferrosan Benelux B.V., Barneveld, Netherlands; *Int'l*, pg. 989
Janssen, Peter, Publr. & Editor-in-Chief--Motor Boating & Sailing, New York, NY; *U.S. Private*, pg. 517
Janssen, V., Pres.--Sara Lee/DE, Utrecht, Netherlands; *U.S. Public*, pg. 1434
Janssens, Chester G., Pres.--Crusader Marine Engines, Sterling Heights, MI; *U.S. Public*, pg. 1591
Janssens, Chris, Dir.--Takenaka Belgium S.A., Diegem, Belgium; *Int'l*, pg. 1351
Janssens, H.J., Mng. Dir.--Amoco Chemical Belgium N.V., Geel, Belgium; *U.S. Public*, pg. 103
Jansson, Christian W., Pres.--Ellos AB, Boras, Sweden; *Int'l*, pg. 643
Jansson, Harri, Exec. V.P.-Central Ontario Div./Personal & Comml. Banking--Bank of Montreal - Ottawa, Ottawa, Canada; *Int'l*, pg. 153
Jansson, Harri, Exec. V.P.-Central Ontario Div./Personal & Comml. Banking--Bank of Montreal - Vancouver, Vancouver, Canada; *Int'l*, pg. 153
Jansson, Lars, Chief Oper. Officer--Electrolux Elmotor A/S, Aalborg, Denmark; *Int'l*, pg. 441
Jansson, Nils-Holger, Mng. Dir.--SMT Machine Company AB, Vasteras, Sweden; *Int'l*, pg. 1421
Jansson, Roger, Mgr.--Sandvik Czechoslovakia s.r.o., Prague, Czech Republic; *Int'l*, pg. 1186
Janstow, Steven, Pres.--Beta Tube, Toledo, OH; *U.S. Public*, pg. 17
Janstow, Steven G., Pres.--Alpha Tube, Holland, OH; *U.S. Public*, pg. 17
Jantti, Kari, Mng. Dir.--Pitney Bowes Oy, Helsinki, Finland; *U.S. Public*, pg. 1304
Janush, Joseph, Gen. Mgr.--KVB, Irvine, CA; *U.S. Public*, pg. 29
Janzen, George, Dr., Pres. & Chief Oper. Officer--Mineral San Sebastian S.A., San Salvador, El Salvador; *U.S. Public*, pg. 410
Jaques, Frederick M., Pres.--Kellogg Canada Inc., Rexdale, Canada; *U.S. Public*, pg. 947
Jaquet, Andre, Mng. Dir.--Sulzer Industries France S.A., Paris, France; *Int'l*, pg. 1306
Jaquet, Andre, Mng. Dir.--Sulzer Belgium S.A., Brussels, Belgium; *Int'l*, pg. 1306
Jaquith, Bill, Publisher--National Telegraph, Hudson, NH; *U.S. Private*, pg. 559
Jaramillo, Socorro, Gen. Mgr.--Y&R Medellin, Medellin, Colombia; *U.S. Private*, pg. 1200
Jarboe, Cletus B., V.P. & Div. Mgr.--Bindley Western, Southwestern Division, Houston, TX; *U.S. Public*, pg. 229
Jarboe, Thomas L., Plant Mgr.--Teleflex Automotive Manufacturing Corp., Waterbury, CT; *U.S. Public*, pg. 1569
Jardin, M., Mng. Dir.--OMRON Electronics S.a.r.L., Fontenay-sous-Bois, France; *Int'l*, pg. 1006
Jardine, D. Colin, Pres.--Alcan Price Extrusions Ltd., Calgary, Canada; *Int'l*, pg. 50
Jardine, David, V.P. & Bus. Unit Exec.--Valmet Automation (USA) Inc. - Sage Systems Division, Houston, TX; *Int'l*, pg. 1449
Jarding, J.L., Mng. Dir.--Phillips Petroleum Singapore Chemicals Pte. Ltd., Singapore, Singapore; *U.S. Public*, pg. 1291
Jardis, Paul, V.P. & Grp. Gen. Mgr.--Prince Foods Canning Div., Merchantville, NJ; *U.S. Private*, pg. 158
Jarling, C.E., Gen. Mgr.--Turner Construction Co., Detroit, MI; *U.S. Public*, pg. 1645
Jarmain, Eric, Pres.--BAIC International, Bluffton, IN; *Int'l*, pg. 478
Jarman, Colin, Gen. Mgr.--BancTec Ltd., Colnbrook, United Kingdom; *U.S. Public*, pg. 177

Jarman, David W., Pres.--Dresser Drilling & Production Services, Aberdeen, United Kingdom; *U.S. Public*, pg. 529
Jarman, Peter, Dir.-Fin.--Sensormatic CamEra Ltd., Warwick, United Kingdom; *U.S. Public*, pg. 1457
Jarman, Richard S., Pres.--Butler Buildings Division, Kansas City, MO; *U.S. Public*, pg. 271
Jarnfeldt, Curt, Mgr.--Boliden Ore & Metals, Stockholm, Sweden; *Int'l*, pg. 1422
Jaro, Vic, Factory Supt.--Amalgamated Sugar Co., Twin Falls, ID; *U.S. Private*, pg. 48
Jarrard, Richard, Chief Oper. Officer--Hudson General Corp., Boise, ID; *U.S. Public*, pg. 845
Jarrell, Gary, Mgr.--Southern Electric Supply Co., Inc., Ocala, FL; *Int'l*, pg. 1107
Jarrold, Tom, Mgr.-Mktg. Communications--Cincinnati Milacron Plastics Machinery Group, Batavia, OH; *U.S. Public*, pg. 368
Jarry, Gilles, Sr. V.P.-Quebec Div.--Bank of Montreal - Montreal, Montreal, Canada; *Int'l*, pg. 153
Jarskog, Lars, Mng. Dir.--Consilium CMH-Babcock AB, Bjuv, Sweden; *Int'l*, pg. 131
Jarveneaux, Ed, Div. Supt.--Otis Nigeria, Ltd., Lagos, Nigeria; *U.S. Public*, pg. 777
Jarvie, Andrew, Mgr.--Victoria Branch, Noble Park, Australia; *Int'l*, pg. 226
Jarvinen, Alpo, Chief Oper. Officer--Oy Alfa-Laval Zeta AB, Helsinki, Finland; *Int'l*, pg. 1379
Jarvinen, Ilkka, Pres.--Bretec Oy, Lahti, Finland; *Int'l*, pg. 1352
Jarvinen, Tapio, Chief Oper. Officer--Latvian Traffic Service, Riga, Latvia; *Int'l*, pg. 914
Jarvinen, Teemu, Chief Oper. Officer--Melia Ltd., Raisio, Finland; *Int'l*, pg. 1085
Jarvis, David, Pres.--Astro Polyfoam Ltd., Mississauga, Canada; *Int'l*, pg. 756
Jarvis, Doug, Gen. Mgr.--DeVilbiss Distributed Products Division, Bournemouth, United Kingdom; *U.S. Public*, pg. 867
Jarvis, J. Paul, Mng. Dir.--Anacomp (Canada) Ltd., Markham, Canada; *U.S. Public*, pg. 107
Jarvis, John, Sr. V.P.-Europe & Mng. Dir.-Wiley Europe Ltd.--Wiley Europe Limited, Chichester, United Kingdom; *U.S. Public*, pg. 1768
Jarvis, Neville, Mng. Dir.--Buckhorn Ltd., Witney, United Kingdom; *U.S. Public*, pg. 1143
Jarvis, Paul, Mng. Dir.--Desoutter Brothers (Holdings) plc, London, United Kingdom; *Int'l*, pg. 96
Jarvis, Ron, Pres. & Chief Oper. Officer--Technicolor, Inc., North Hollywood, CA; *Int'l*, pg. 272
Jasick, Thomas A., Pres.--Berkley Information Services, Luverne, MN; *U.S. Public*, pg. 216
Jaskolski, Jurgen, Mng. Dir.--Dresdner Bank AG, Jakarta, Indonesia; *Int'l*, pg. 419
Jasmann, Dwight E., Pres. & Gen. Mgr.--COMSAT International Ventures, Bethesda, MD; *U.S. Public*, pg. 425
Jason-Stampe, Bjorn, Pres.--Nobel Consumer Goods AB, Stockholm, Sweden; *Int'l*, pg. 48
Jason, Haig, Chief Oper. Officer--Fischer Imaging Australia Pty. Ltd., Dingley, Australia; *U.S. Public*, pg. 647
Jasurda, Bruce, Pres. & Chief Oper. Officer--David Cravit & Associates Advertising, Chicago, IL; *U.S. Private*, pg. 287
Jaudenes, Jose, Gen. Mgr.--Olympia International, Pittsburgh, PA; *U.S. Public*, pg. 1221
Jaume, Feliciano Fuster, Chm. Bd. & Pres.--ENDESA - Empresa Nacional de Electricidad, S.A., Madrid, Spain; *Int'l*, pg. 1224
Jauring, Arvid, Mng. Dir.--FACOMEC S.A., Cali, Colombia; *Int'l*, pg. 1368
Javier, Antero B., Jr., Chm.--Dentsu Young & Rubicam-Alcantara Inc. (Manila), Manila, Philippines; *U.S. Private*, pg. 325
Javier, Conrado, Sls. Rep.--Columbia Pictures International Television, Manila, Philippines; *Int'l*, pg. 1282
Javier, Leandro D., Chief Exec.--Iligan Cement Corporation, Manila, Philippines; *Int'l*, pg. 629
Jawola, P.E.R., Mng. Dir.--Vernons Pools Limited, Liverpool, United Kingdom; *Int'l*, pg. 787
Jayes, Mike A., Dir. & Gen. Mgr.--Dowty Aerospace Hydraulics, Cheltenham, Cheltenham, United Kingdom; *Int'l*, pg. 1337
Jaynes John, Pres.--Scandura Inc., Charlotte, NC; *Int'l*, pg. 113
Jean, Christian, Mng. Dir.--Bundy SNC, Amboise, France; *Int'l*, pg. 1342
Jean, R.L., Chief Exec. Officer--Indiana Insurance Company, Indianapolis, IN; *Int'l*, pg. 648
Jean, Raymond, Mng. Dir.--Walter Herzog G.m.b.H., Lauda, Germany; *U.S. Public*, pg. 1711
Jeanmart, Pierre, Chief Oper. Officer--New Vanden Boore S.A., Brussels, Belgium; *Int'l*, pg. 441
Jeannerat, Francois E.P., Sr. Mgr.--UBS Representative Office Ltd., Johannesburg, South Africa; *Int'l*, pg. 1441
Jeannin, Gerard, Sr. Officer--Banque Indosuez, New York, NY; *Int'l*, pg. 313
Jeans, Michael D., Pres.--Nashua Photo Products Div., Nashua, NH; *U.S. Public*, pg. 1152
Jebsen, Finn, Managing Dir.--A/S Denofa og Lilleborg Fabriker, Oslo, Norway; *Int'l*, pg. 1010
Jeckering, Thomas E., Pres.--Polychem Corporation, Mentor, OH; *U.S. Private*, pg. 169
Jefferson, Frederick D., Pres.--Commercial Bank, Thomasville, GA; *U.S. Public*, pg. 1549
Jeffrey, Galian V., Mng. Dir.-Asia--Forum Asia Ltd., Central, Hong Kong; *U.S. Private*, pg. 420
Jeffries, Mary, Mng. Dir.--Shandwick Minneapolis, Minneapolis, MN; *Int'l*, pg. 1227
Jeffries, Michael, Pres. & Chief Exec. Officer--Abercrombie & Fitch, Reynoldsburg, OH; *U.S. Public*, pg. 995
Jeffs, Thomas H. II, Pres. & Chief Oper. Officer--NBD Bank (Michigan), Troy, MI; *U.S. Public*, pg. 628
Jeger, Bernard, Assoc. Gen. Mgr.--EURO RSCG Communicance, Reims, France; *Int'l*, pg. 600
Jelensperger, Francis, Exec. V.P.--HDR Inc., Omaha, NE; *Int'l*, pg. 206
Jellinek, Frank H., Pres.--Erie Scientific Co., Portsmouth, NH; *U.S. Public*, pg. 1545
Jellison, B.D., V.P. & G.M.--Exit Device Division, Indianapolis, IN; *U.S. Public*, pg. 876
Jeltsch, Dr. Werner, Mng. Dir.--ALLSPANN, Allgemeine Spannbetongesellschaft m.b.H., Salzburg, Austria; *Int'l*, pg. 424
Jen, Shek Chuen, Mng. Dir.--DBS Investment Research Pte. Ltd., Singapore, Singapore; *Int'l*, pg. 350
Jenckes, A.C., Pres.--H.W. Jencks, Inc., Ferndale, MI; *U.S. Private*, pg. 328
Jendahl, Staffan, Pres.--Gyproc Balsta Plant, Balsta, Sweden; *Int'l*, pg. 1200
Jender, Bo, Pres.--ABB Selfa AB, Nykoping, Sweden; *Int'l*, pg. 7
Jenkin, J.G., Mng. Dir.--Carter Holt Harvey Plastic Products Group Limited, Hamilton, New Zealand; *U.S. Public*, pg. 904
Jenkin, Tom, Chief Oper. Officer--Ahlstrom Machinery, Glens Falls, NY; *Int'l*, pg. 34
Jenkins, Anthony, V.P. & Gen. Mgr.-Atlas Van Lines Intl.--Atlas Van Lines Intl., Evansville, IN; *U.S. Private*, pg. 97
Jenkins, B. Larry, Pres.--Monumental Life Insurance Company, Baltimore, MD; *Int'l*, pg. 27
Jenkins, Benjamin P., III, Pres. & Chief Oper. Officer--First Union National Bank of Virginia, Roanoke, VA; *U.S. Public*, pg. 640
Jenkins, Christopher D., Pres.--Todd-AO Studios, Hollywood, CA; *U.S. Public*, pg. 1619
Jenkins, Christopher D., Pres.--Todd-AO Preservation Services, Hollywood, CA; *U.S. Public*, pg. 1619
Jenkins, David, Mng. Dir.--Abu Garcia (UK) Ltd., Middlewich, United Kingdom; *U.S. Private*, pg. 822
Jenkins, David, Group Exec. Officer--Millward Brown International, Warwick, United Kingdom; *Int'l*, pg. 1482
Jenkins, G., Pres.--Fill-Rite Div., Fort Wayne, IN; *U.S. Private*, pg. 1111
Jenkins, George P., Pres.--Fill-Rite Division, Fort Wayne, IN; *U.S. Private*, pg. 1110
Jenkins, John R., Pres.--Inner City, Inc., Boston, MA; *U.S. Public*, pg. 1313
Jenkins, M.J.W., Mng. Dir.--Mills Manufacturing Technology, Norwich, United Kingdom; *Int'l*, pg. 585
Jenkins, Robert, Branch Mgr.--Circle International, Charlotte, NC; *U.S. Public*, pg. 371
Jenkins, Robert, District Mgr.--Circle Freight International USA, Charlotte, NC; *U.S. Public*, pg. 371
Jenkins, Robert L., Pres. & Chief Oper. Officer--Lennox Global Ltd., Richardson, TX; *U.S. Private*, pg. 659
Jenkins, Roy, Mng. Dir.--D. Anderson & Son Ltd., Stretford, United Kingdom; *Int'l*, pg. 659
Jenkins, Samuel P., Jr., Pres.--The Boeing Travel Company, Irvine, CA; *U.S. Public*, pg. 241
Jenkins, Stephen, Pres.--KLT Power Inc., Kansas City, MO; *U.S. Public*, pg. 943
Jenkins, Terry R., Pres. & Gen. Mgr.--Chesapeake Packaging Co./Louisville, Louisville, KY; *U.S. Public*, pg. 346
Jenkins, Wayne, Mgr.-Opers.--Pepsi-Cola Bottling Company of Richmond, Inc., Richmond, VA; *U.S. Public*, pg. 1277
Jenkinson, D.J., Pres.--Early Learning Centre, Swindon, United Kingdom; *Int'l*, pg. 707
Jenkinson, Paul, V.P.-Human Resources & Admin.--McGraw-Hill International Publications Co. Ltd., Maidenhead, United Kingdom; *U.S. Public*, pg. 1072
Jenks, Richard, Pres.--Pall Puerto Rico, Inc., Fajardo, PR; *U.S. Public*, pg. 1254
Jenmett, Christopher M., Chm.--UAC International Ltd., London, United Kingdom; *Int'l*, pg. 1434
Jenne, P., Mgr.-Sls.--Penny & Giles Controls Inc., Attleboro, MA; *Int'l*, pg. 208
Jennens, Dave, Dir.--Jenesis Advertising, Durban, South Africa; *U.S. Public*, pg. 1422
Jenner, C.R., Pres. & Chief Oper. Officer--A.Y. McDonald Supply Co. Inc., Dubuque, IA; *U.S. Private*, pg. 721
Jenner, Karl-Heinz, Chief Oper. Officer--Suddeutsche Brennstoffhandelsgesellschaft mbH, Mannheim, Germany; *Int'l*, pg. 1167
Jenness, K., Pres.--Shreve, Crump & Low Co., Boston, MA; *Int'l*, pg. 197
Jennings, Bill, V.P.-Western Hemisphere--Noble Drilling (U.S.) Inc., Houston, TX; *U.S. Public*, pg. 1186
Jennings, C., Mgr.--Baring, Houston & Saunders, London, United Kingdom; *Int'l*, pg. 648
Jennings, Donald, Mng. Dir.--American Ingredients Company, Dolton, IL; *Int'l*, pg. 244
Jennings, Gary, Pres.--Zimmer of Canada Limited, Mississauga, Canada; *U.S. Public*, pg. 257
Jennings, John, Gen. Mgr.--Great Lakes Cheese of New York, Inc., Adams, NY; *U.S. Private*, pg. 474
Jennings, Philip F., Mgr.--Universal Paper Goods, Los Angeles, CA; *Int'l*, pg. 460
Jennings, R. E., Mng. Dir.--Ajax Magnethermic U.K. Ltd., Oxton, United Kingdom; *Int'l*, pg. 113
Jennings, R.D., Pres--Federal Construction Co., Saint Petersburg, FL; *Int'l*, pg. 774
Jennings, W. H., Mng. Dir.--Coutts & Co (Bahamas) Limited, Nassau, Bahamas; *Int'l*, pg. 911
Jensen, Benny Balle, Mng. Dir.--Pedershaab A/S, Bronderslev, Denmark; *Int'l*, pg. 475
Jensen, Bjarne Skov, Pres.--Danisco Seed, Holeby, Denmark; *Int'l*, pg. 378
Jensen, Bo W., Dir.--Nevi Finans A/S, Hvidovre, Denmark; *Int'l*, pg. 1257
Jensen, Brian, Gen. Mgr.--Kahler Park Hotel, Hibbing, MN; *U.S. Public*, pg. 1537
Jensen, Chris, Pres.--El Paso Times, Inc., El Paso, TX; *U.S. Public*, pg. 700
Jensen, Daryl D., Vice Chm. & Pres.--Sunset Life Insurance Co. of America, Olympia, WA; *U.S. Public*, pg. 943
Jensen, Dick, Chief Oper. Officer--Salem Carpet Mills, Elk Grove Village, IL; *U.S. Public*, pg. 1464
Jensen, Erik, Chief Oper. Officer--Alfa-Laval Agri Scandinavia A/S, Vejle, Denmark; *Int'l*, pg. 1379
Jensen, F. Rolf, Pres.--Ikon Office Solutions-Oregon, Portland, OR; *U.S. Public*, pg. 864
Jensen, Finn O., Grp. Exec. V.P.--Jotun Powder Coatings Pty. Ltd., Brooklyn, Australia; *Int'l*, pg. 715
Jensen, Henrik, Chief Oper. Officer--Novo Nordisk A/S, Levent, Turkey; *Int'l*, pg. 989
Jensen, Jeff, Assoc. Dir.--Pharmaco International Holdings, Inc., Brussels, Belgium; *U.S. Public*, pg. 1285
Jensen, Jens Aage, Mgr.--Sandvik A/S, Copenhagen, Denmark; *Int'l*, pg. 1186
Jensen, Jes Northard, Mng. Dir.--Lever & Kitchen Pty. Ltd., Sydney, Australia; *Int'l*, pg. 1437
Jensen, Jim, Gen. Mgr.--Surveying Div., Englewood, CO; *Int'l*, pg. 85
Jensen, Jorgen, Mng. Dir.--Shell of Esbjerg, Esbjerg, Denmark; *Int'l*, pg. 1138
Jensen, Jorgen Mata, Chief Oper. Officer--Neste Thermisol A/S, Hedensted, Denmark; *Int'l*, pg. 915
Jensen, K.R., Chm. Bd.--First Trust Corporation, Denver, CO; *U.S. Public*, pg. 647
Jensen, Kaare Vagner, Pres.--ABB Motors A/S, Odense, Denmark; *Int'l*, pg. 8
Jensen, Keith, Gen. Mgr.--Liqui-Box Corp., Houston, TX; *U.S. Public*, pg. 1001
Jensen, Kurt, Chief Oper. Officer--Electrolux A/S, Lyngby, Denmark; *Int'l*, pg. 441
Jensen, Magnus, Chief Oper. Officer--Electrolux Rengjo/ringsmaskiner A/S, Oslo, Norway; *Int'l*, pg. 443
Jensen, Marc, Gen. Mgr.--Blue Fox Tackle Co., Cambridge, MN; *U.S. Private*, pg. 802
Jensen, Oystein, Mng. Dir.--Kalmar LMV A/S, Oslo, Norway; *Int'l*, pg. 1421
Jensen, Per, Chief Oper. Officer--Novo Nordisk Bioindustriale Srl, Anagni, Italy; *Int'l*, pg. 989
Jensen, Roland, Chm. & Chief Exec. Officer--NRG Group, Inc., Minneapolis, MN; *U.S. Public*, pg. 1195
Jensen, Roland J., Pres.--Cormorant Corp., Helena, MT; *U.S. Public*, pg. 1195
Jensen, Roland J., Pres.--United Power & Land Co., Minneapolis, MN; *U.S. Public*, pg. 1195
Jensen, Roy A., Pres.--Simrad Optronics A/S, Oslo, Norway; *Int'l*, pg. 770
Jensen, Tom, Pres.--Mary Maxim, Ltd., Paris, Canada; *U.S. Private*, pg. 716
Jensen, Torben, Pres.--Luxo Danmark A/S, Ballerup, Denmark; *Int'l*, pg. 821
Jenson, Robert M., Pres.--Sysco Food Services of Seattle, Inc., Kent, WA; *U.S. Public*, pg. 1552
Jenssen, Per Sture, Mng. Dir.--Madshus A/S, Biri, Norway; *U.S. Public*, pg. 940
Jentoft, Eva, Chief Representative--Christiania Bank Luxembourg S.A.-Representacion en Espana, Fuengirola, Spain; *Int'l*, pg. 289
Jeppesen, Henrik, Gen. Mgr.--Nordson Danmark A/S, Albertslund, Denmark; *U.S. Public*, pg. 1189
Jeppsson, Bert, Sr. V.P-Mktg.--Ericsson Components AB, Stockholm, Sweden; *Int'l*, pg. 1363
Jepsen, C.J., Gen. Mgr.--Glaxo Danmark a/s, Copenhagen, Denmark; *Int'l*, pg. 553
Jeremias, Carl, Pres.--Transico Inc., Key Pad Div., Santa Ana, CA; *U.S. Public*, pg. 1630
Jerlow, D.A., Pres.--Tamco, Rancho Cucamonga, CA; *U.S. Public*, pg. 99
Jermihou, N., Mgr.--Industrial Instruments Div., Loves Park, IL; *Int'l*, pg. 1242
Jernemyr, Sven-Eric, Chm. Reg. Bd.--ICA Handlarna Mellansverige AB, Vasteras, Sweden; *Int'l*, pg. 642
Jernigan, Yvonne, Admin.--Guardian Care of Ahoskie, Ahoskie, NC; *U.S. Public*, pg. 1712
Jeska, Philip K., Pres.--Allsteel, Inc., Aurora, IL; *U.S. Public*, pg. 772
Jeske, Roy, Chief Oper. Officer--Allright Sacramento, Sacramento, CA; *U.S. Private*, pg. 43
Jespersen, C.K., Pres.--Nova Gas International Ltd., Calgary, Canada; *Int'l*, pg. 971
Jespersen, Jim, Prod. Mgr.--Rubber Group, Niles, MI; *U.S. Public*, pg. 1160
Jespersen, Niels, Chief Oper. Officer--Lydig of Scandinavia A/S, Ringkobing, Denmark; *U.S. Public*, pg. 787
Jesse, Klaus, Chief Oper. Officer--Maxitrol Company M.B.H., Senden, Germany; *U.S. Private*, pg. 716
Jesse, W.C., Pres. & Chief Exec. Officer--Tangram Enterprise Solutions, Inc., Cary, NC; *U.S. Public*, pg. 1424
Jestadt, Gerhard, General Area Mgr.--Time-Life International GmbH, Munich, Germany; *U.S. Public*, pg. 1615
Jestaedt, Alberecht, Mng. Dir.--Braun Ireland Ltd., Carlow, Ireland; *U.S. Public*, pg. 744
Jester, John R., Pres. & Chief Exec. Officer--Muzak Limited Partnership, Seattle, WA; *U.S. Private*, pg. 222
Jester, L.T., III, Pres.--Plantation Pipe Line Co., Atlanta, GA; *U.S. Public*, pg. 348
Jester, Thomas L., Pres.--CRSS Civil Engineers, Inc., Chicago, IL; *Int'l*, pg. 1415
Jett, Dennis D., Pres. & Chief Exec. Officer--Oklahoma National Bank of Duncan, Duncan, OK; *U.S. Public*, pg. 630
Jett, Donald W., Pres.--CDI Marine Company, Jacksonville, FL; *U.S. Public*, pg. 277
Jeurling, Lars, Chief-Regional Mission--The World Bank, Riga, Latvia; *U.S. Private*, pg. 1189
Jewell, Donald, Pres.--Engineering & Information Systems Div., Alexandria, VA; *U.S. Public*, pg. 773
Jewell, G. Bernard, Grp. V.P. & Gen. Mgr.--B/E Aerospace Seating Products, Winston Salem, NC; *U.S. Public*, pg. 159
Jewell, Thompson B., Pres.--Amoco Oman Petroleum Company, Oman; *U.S. Public*, pg. 102
Jewett, C.E., Pres. & Chief Exec. Officer--Solvay Technologies Inc, New York, NY; *Int'l*, pg. 1277

Jewett, Steven R., Pres.--First American Co. of Alaska, Anchorage, AK; *U.S. Public*, pg. 625
Jezuit, L., Pres.--Robertshaw Controls Company, Richmond, VA; *Int'l*, pg. 1243
Ji, Yang Liang, Gen. Mgr.--Beijing Huade Lining Materials Industry Co. Ltd., Beijing, China; *Int'l*, pg. 1322
Jicinsky, Gerhard, Chief Oper. Officer--Novo Nordisk A/S, Vienna, Austria; *Int'l*, pg. 989
Jilek, R. F., Pres.--Voith Inc., Appleton, WI; *Int'l*, pg. 1473
Jilk, Lawrence T., Jr., Chm. Bd.--National Penn Bank, Boyertown, PA; *U.S. Public*, pg. 1159
Jimenez, Abby, Joint Chief Exec. Officer--Jimenez/DMB&B, Manila, Philippines; *U.S. Private*, pg. 304
Jimenez, Ramon, Joint Chief Exec. Officer--Jimenez/DMB&B, Manila, Philippines; *U.S. Private*, pg. 304
Jin, N., Pres.--Kellogg (Japan) K.K., Tokyo, Japan; *U.S. Public*, pg. 948
Jin, W.K., Pres.--Lucky-Goldstar International (America), Englewood Cliffs, NJ; *Int'l*, pg. 779
Jinks, Nigel, Gen. Mgr.--Lumonics Limited, Rugby, United Kingdom; *Int'l*, pg. 1315
Jiorgetti, J. Giacamo, Gen. Mgr.--Electroform S.A., Bioggio, Switzerland; *U.S. Public*, pg. 1598
Jirathiyur, V., Mng. Dir.--EMI (Thailand) Limited/Audiovision Limited, Bangkok, Thailand; *Int'l*, pg. 427
Jiricek, Jaroslav, Chief Exec.--Ceva Prachovice a.s., Prachovice, Czech Republic; *Int'l*, pg. 629
Jis-Norgaar, Jensen, Pres. & Gen. Mgr.--Lever S.A., Levallois-Perret, France; *Int'l*, pg. 1438
Jiu, Xu Yong, Chief Officer--Shanghai Pulong Concrete Products Co., Ltd., Shanghai, China; *Int'l*, pg. 1293
Jiumtipanat, Somlak, Mng. Dir.--Siam Compressor Industry Co., Ltd., Ban Si Racha, Thailand; *Int'l*, pg. 1238
Jiun, Sieh Kok, Representative--Morgan Grenfell (Malaysia), Kuala Lumpur, Malaysia; *Int'l*, pg. 405
Jiura, Raoul, Pres.--Tuftex, Santa Fe Springs, CA; *U.S. Private*, pg. 900
Joaansson, Gora K., Pres.--Kvaerner Ships Equipment AB, Goteborg, Sweden; *Int'l*, pg. 771
Joachim, Michael, Pres.--Pocahontas Foods, USA, Richmond, VA; *U.S. Public*, pg. 1278
Joaquin, Antonia H., V.P.-Fin. & Admin.--Hemisphere-Leo Burnett, Inc., Manila, Philippines; *U.S. Private*, pg. 184
Joast, Fred, V.P.-Opers.--Bones/Lincolnwood, Lincolnwood, IL; *U.S. Private*, pg. 661
Jobard, George, Mng. Dir.--Clextral, Firminy, France; *Int'l*, pg. 503
Jobe, Jan, Pres.--Principal International, Inc., Des Moines, IA; *U.S. Private*, pg. 886
Jochem, W.M., Mgr.--Radio Holland Group Singapore, Singapore, Singapore; *Int'l*, pg. 1152
Jockenhofer, Gisbert, Mng. Dir.--BNP-Dresdner Bank (CR) a.s., Prague, Czech Republic; *Int'l*, pg. 418
Jocson, George L., Pres.--Philippine Cocoa Estates Corporation, Davao, Philippines; *Int'l*, pg. 187
Jodes, Fred R., Pres.--ABB Financial Services Inc., Stamford, CT; *Int'l*, pg. 4
Joel, David, Mng. Dir. & Publ.--The Macmillan Co. of New Zealand Ltd., Takapuna, New Zealand; *Int'l*, pg. 1480
Joel, Lyons B., Jr., Pres.--Selig Chemical Industries, Atlanta, GA; *U.S. Public*, pg. 1160
Joergensen, Palle O., Pres.--F.L. Smidth & Co. A/S, Copenhagen, Denmark; *Int'l*, pg. 475
Joffe, Paul, Natl. Strategy Dir.--Leo Burnett/Connaghan & May Pty. Ltd., Sydney, Australia; *U.S. Private*, pg. 185
Joffrin, Alain, Pres. & Dir. Gen.--Kodak Pathe S.A., Paris, France; *U.S. Public*, pg. 554
Johannesson, Nils-Erik, Pres.--Bengtssons Maskin AB, Arlov, Sweden; *Int'l*, pg. 678
Johannsen, James P., Pres. & Chief Exec. Officer--PNC Trust Company of Florida, N.A., Tampa, FL; *U.S. Public*, pg. 1244
Johannsen, Tony, Pres.--James Burn Intl., Poughkeepsie, NY; *U.S. Public*, pg. 1506
Johannsen, Tony, Pres.--James Burn International Limited, Esher, United Kingdom; *U.S. Public*, pg. 1507
Johannsson, Fridrik, Pres.--Vatryggingarfelagid Skandia HF, Reykjavik, Iceland; *Int'l*, pg. 1258
Johansen, Bjarne, Mng. Dir.--SKF Japan Ltd., Tokyo, Japan; *Int'l*, pg. 1159
Johansen, Bjorn Viggo, Mng. Dir.--AS ESAB, Larvik, Norway; *Int'l*, pg. 281
Johansen, Jan Martin, Gen. Mgr.--Sensormatic A/S, Oslo, Norway; *U.S. Public*, pg. 1457
Johansen, Nils-Erik, Pres.--J.S. Hemkopskedjan AB, Falun, Sweden; *Int'l*, pg. 272
Johansen, Per, Chief Oper. Officer--Royal Copenhagen Norge A/S, Oslo, Norway; *Int'l*, pg. 1135
Johansen, Roger, Mng. Dir.--Getinge Disinfection Inc., Toms River, NJ; *Int'l*, pg. 551
Johansen, Tor, Mng. Dir.--Jotun NOF Singapore Pte. Ltd., Jurong, Singapore; *Int'l*, pg. 715
Johansen, Tore, Rep.--Kvaerner Shipping Manila, Representative Office, Manila, Philippines; *Int'l*, pg. 772
Johanson-Hedberg, B., Mng. Dir.--Wolters Kluwer Sweden, Stockholm, Sweden; *Int'l*, pg. 1514
Johansson-AX, Lennard, Dir. & Gen. Mgr.--Bundy AB, Linkoping, Sweden; *Int'l*, pg. 1341
Johansson, Anders, Mgr.--Duni/Finess Hygiene, Kisa, Sweden; *Int'l*, pg. 421
Johansson, Anders, Pres.--Componenta Parts AB, Taby, Sweden; *Int'l*, pg. 1421
Johansson, Bengt, Pres.--Stora Purchasing & Transport, Falun, Sweden; *Int'l*, pg. 1303
Johansson, Bert, Chief Oper. Officer--Perstorp Analytical AB-Distribution HQ, Helsingborg, Sweden; *Int'l*, pg. 1039
Johansson, Claes, Chief Oper. Officer--Alfa-Laval (Malaysia) Sdn Bhd, Kuala Lumpur, Malaysia; *Int'l*, pg. 1380
Johansson, Erik, Gen. Mgr.--Alrashid-Abetong Co. Ltd., Riyadh, Saudi Arabia; *Int'l*, pg. 1199
Johansson, Hans, Pres.--ASSA AB, Eskilstuna, Sweden; *Int'l*, pg. 17
Johansson, Hans, Pres.--ASSA Industrie AB, Eskilstuna, Sweden; *Int'l*, pg. 17
Johansson, Hans, Pres.--Mecel AB, Amal, Sweden; *Int'l*, pg. 686
Johansson, Henry, Pres.--Kvaerner Ships Equipment Inc., New Orleans, LA; *Int'l*, pg. 770
Johansson, IngeLill, Chief Oper. Officer--DAB Ortodonti AB, Upplands Vasby, Sweden; *Int'l*, pg. 711
Johansson, Jan Ingvar, Pres.--FFV AvioComp AB, Linkoping, Sweden; *Int'l*, pg. 276
Johansson, Kjell, Pres.--Astra Pharmaceutical Production AB, Sodertalje, Sweden; *Int'l*, pg. 93
Johansson, Kurt J., Mng. Dir.--Dayco Europe AB, Solvesborg, Sweden; *U.S. Public*, pg. 1045
Johansson, Kurt S., Pres.--Mark IV Automotive, Solvesborg, Sweden; *U.S. Public*, pg. 1045
Johansson, Lars, Mng. Dir.--Telefonaktiebolaget LM Ericsson Bureaux Techniques de Tunisie, Tunis, Tunisia; *Int'l*, pg. 1370
Johansson, Lars Olof, Mgr.--Ahlsell AB, Sollentuna, Sweden; *Int'l*, pg. 1422
Johansson, Leif, Mng. Dir.--Skega Far East Pte. Ltd., Singapore, Singapore; *Int'l*, pg. 1323
Johansson, Leif, Mng. Dir.--Telecomponentes Ericsson S.A. de C.V., Tlalnepantla, Mexico; *Int'l*, pg. 1370
Johansson, Lennart, Mng. Dir.--SKF Bearing Mfrs. Pty. Ltd., Uitenhage, South Africa; *Int'l*, pg. 1158
Johansson, Nils-Erik, Pres.--J S Hemkopskedjan AB, Falun, Sweden; *Int'l*, pg. 708
Johansson, Nils-Erik, Chief Oper. Officer--Saroph Holdings B.V., Amsterdam, Netherlands; *Int'l*, pg. 1290
Johansson, Olle, Pres.--Falconbridge Europe S.A., Brussels, Belgium; *Int'l*, pg. 434
Johansson, Roger, Mng. Dir.--Baldwin Europe Consolidated, Inc., Geldrop, Netherlands; *U.S. Public*, pg. 170
Johansson, Roger, Chm. Bd.--AMAL AB, Amal, Sweden; *U.S. Public*, pg. 170
Johansson, S., Mng. Dir.--Nordiska Balzers AB, Kungsbacka, Sweden; *Int'l*, pg. 998
Johansson, S. Roger, Mng. Dir.--Baldwin Graphic Equipment BV, Geldrop, Netherlands; *U.S. Public*, pg. 170
Johansson, Stig, Chief Oper. Officer--TA Control Oy, Vantaa, Finland; *Int'l*, pg. 670
Johansson, Stig, Mng. Dir.--Cia. Argentina de Telefonos, S.A., Buenos Aires, Argentina; *Int'l*, pg. 1365
Johansson, Sveneric, Chief Oper. Officer--ICA Utbildningar AB, Vasteras, Sweden; *Int'l*, pg. 643
Johansson, Ulf, Pres.--ABB Metallurgy AB, Vasteras, Sweden; *Int'l*, pg. 7
Johansson, Ulf, Mgr.--Kvaerner Eureka, Tromso Division, Tromso, Norway; *Int'l*, pg. 767
Johansson, Ulf, Gen. Mgr.--Kvaerner Fish Process Technology a.s - Kvaerner Kulde, Tromso, Norway; *Int'l*, pg. 768
Johansson, Ulf, Pres.--NCC Building, Linkoping, Sweden; *Int'l*, pg. 898
Johansson, Ulf H., Mng. Dir.--Ericsson Network Engineering Pte. Ltd., Singapore, Singapore; *Int'l*, pg. 1367
Johansson, Willy, Mng. Dir.--Ericsson (Hellas) Telecommunications Equipment S.A., Athens, Greece; *Int'l*, pg. 1366
Johari, Mazita, Dir.--Tourism Malaysia - Singapore Office, Singapore, Singapore; *Int'l*, pg. 833
John, Christopher, Mng. Dir.--Krafft, S.A., Andoain, Spain; *Int'l*, pg. 323
John, David E., Div. Mgr.--Thermal Processing Group Ltd. (Skelmersdale), Skelmersdale, United Kingdom; *Int'l*, pg. 1338
John, R., Gen. Mgr.--Burroughs Wellcome (Far East) Ltd, Taipei, Taiwan; *Int'l*, pg. 553
Johncock, G., Mgr.--Colinta Holdings Pty. Ltd., Brisbane, Australia; *Int'l*, pg. 827
Johns, Bob, V.P. & Gen. Mgr.--PSB Co., Columbus, OH; *U.S. Private*, pg. 1172
Johns, R.W., Jr., Mng. Dir.--Electronic Tele-Communications, Inc., Atlanta, GA; *U.S. Public*, pg. 570
Johns, Richard G., Pres.--Wright Plastic Products, Inc., Sheridan, MI; *U.S. Public*, pg. 1061
Johnsen, Bent M., Chief Oper. Officer--Novo Nordisk A/S, Warsaw, Poland; *Int'l*, pg. 988
Johnsmeyer, William L., Pres.--Bucon, Inc., Kansas City, MO; *U.S. Public*, pg. 271
Johnson, A.D., Mng. Dir.--Joy Manufacturing Company (UK) Ltd., East Kilbride Plant, East Kilbride, United Kingdom; *U.S. Public*, pg. 789
Johnson, Allan R., Pres.--Agricultural Publishing Group, Carol Stream, IL; *U.S. Public*, pg. 512
Johnson, Allan R., Pres.--Farm Progress Publications, Carol Stream, IL; *U.S. Public*, pg. 513
Johnson, Allen, Gen. Mgr.--Houston Learning Center, Houston, TX; *U.S. Public*, pg. 218
Johnson, Art, Pres.--Lockheed Martin Air Traffic Management, Rockville, MD; *U.S. Public*, pg. 1008
Johnson, Arve K., Mng. Dir.--Carl Jonsson Papir A/S, Oslo, Norway; *Int'l*, pg. 864
Johnson, Barry L., Sr. Business Devel. Officer--Southeast Marketing-Richmond Business Center, Powhatan, VA; *U.S. Public*, pg. 650
Johnson, Bill, Admin.--Horizon Specialty Hospital - Albuquerque, Albuquerque, NM; *U.S. Public*, pg. 838
Johnson, Billy J., V.P. & Gen. Mgr.--Sherman Wire, Sherman, TX; *U.S. Public*, pg. 955
Johnson, Bruce, Gen. Mgr.--Mid-Western of Alabama Division, Leesburg, AL; *U.S. Private*, pg. 60
Johnson, C., Chief Oper. Officer--Hughes Tool Company (Far East) Pte. Ltd., Singapore, Singapore; *U.S. Public*, pg. 167
Johnson, C. Lee, Pres. Emeritus--Limited Distribution Services, Columbus, OH; *U.S. Public*, pg. 995
Johnson, Carl, Grp. Mng. Dir.--Simons Palmer Denton Clemmow & Johnson Ltd., London, United Kingdom; *Int'l*, pg. 1252
Johnson, Carl P., Pres.--Diamond Energy Operating Co., Dallas, TX; *U.S. Public*, pg. 584
Johnson, Charles, V.P.--Abisko Mfg., Inc., Richmond Hill, Canada; *U.S. Private*, pg. 412
Johnson, Charles, Plant Mgr.--Data General Corporation, Clayton, NC; *U.S. Public*, pg. 485
Johnson, Charles, Pres.--IMC Magnetics Corp., Tempe, AZ; *Int'l*, pg. 868
Johnson, Charles, Mgr.-Office--Woodward-Clyde, Del City, OK; *U.S. Public*, pg. 1656
Johnson, Charles E., V.P. & Div. Mgr.--Westvaco Worldwide, New York, NY; *U.S. Public*, pg. 1762
Johnson, Clif A., Pres.--Hytek Finishes Co., Kent, WA; *U.S. Public*, pg. 594
Johnson, Coe, Gen. Mgr.--National Frozen Foods Corporation - Chehalis, Chehalis, WA; *U.S. Private*, pg. 783
Johnson, Craig A., V.P. & Treas.--Jefferies & Company, Inc., Los Angeles, CA; *U.S. Public*, pg. 925
Johnson, D., Pres. & Chief Exec. Officer--Blandin Paper Company, Grand Rapids, MN; *Int'l*, pg. 495
Johnson, D.A., Mng. Dir.--Bovis Urban Renewal Ltd., London, United Kingdom; *Int'l*, pg. 1032
Johnson, D.P., Chief Oper. Officer--Wire Machinery Div., Bolton, United Kingdom; *Int'l*, pg. 473
Johnson, Dave, Mng. Dir.--Aero Engine Equipment Group, Birmingham, United Kingdom; *Int'l*, pg. 127
Johnson, Dave, Pres.--Cenex/Land O'Lakes, Inc., Inver Grove Heights, MN; *U.S. Private*, pg. 222
Johnson, David, Pres.--Atlas Copco AFS Inc., Sterling Heights, MI; *Int'l*, pg. 96
Johnson, David, Pres.--Howden Compressors, Bloomfield, CT; *Int'l*, pg. 636
Johnson, David W., Pres. & Chief Exec. Officer--Campbell Sales Company, Camden, NJ; *U.S. Public*, pg. 299
Johnson, David W., Pres.--Joseph Campbell Company, Camden, NJ; *U.S. Public*, pg. 299
Johnson, David, Jr., Chief Oper. Officer & Mgr.-Opers.--B & R Foods, Dover, FL; *U.S. Public*, pg. 1278
Johnson, Dennis, Pres.--Arnolds Interiors, Inc., San Diego, CA; *U.S. Private*, pg. 546
Johnson, Dennis A., Pres. & Chief Exec. Officer--St. Paul Bank for Cooperatives, Saint Paul, MN; *U.S. Private*, pg. 398
Johnson, Don, Pres.--Georgia Woodlands Railroad Co., Washington, GA; *U.S. Private*, pg. 171
Johnson, Don, Gen. Mgr.--Geonex, Sacramento, CA; *U.S. Private*, pg. 448
Johnson, Don, Pres.--Johnson Printing Co., Kittery, ME; *U.S. Private*, pg. 592
Johnson, Don H., Pres.-Syro, Inc.--Trinity-Structural Steel, Montgomery, AL; *U.S. Public*, pg. 1639
Johnson, Donald R., Pres.--Airfoil Technologies International LLC, Cincinnati, OH; *U.S. Public*, pg. 1569
Johnson, Donna, Branch Mgr.--Downey Savings & Loan Association, F.A., Norwalk, CA; *U.S. Public*, pg. 527
Johnson, Doug, V.P. & Gen. Mgr.--Sparton Electronics Florida, Inc., De Leon Springs, FL; *U.S. Public*, pg. 1496
Johnson, Douglas, Pres.--Noah Howden, Inc., Corona, CA; *Int'l*, pg. 636
Johnson, Douglas, Pres.--Mercantile Bank of Vinton, Vinton, IA; *U.S. Public*, pg. 1088
Johnson, Edward, Pres.--Perstorp Analytical Inc. Division Alpkem, Wilsonville, OR; *Int'l*, pg. 1039
Johnson, Edward C., Chief Exec. Officer--FMR Corp., Boston, MA; *U.S. Private*, pg. 403
Johnson, Edward G., Sr. V.P. & Resident Mgr.--Willis Faber North America, Inc.-Georgia, Atlanta, GA; *Int'l*, pg. 1503
Johnson, Elden, Gen. Mgr.--SMI Rebar South Carolina, Columbia, SC; *U.S. Public*, pg. 412
Johnson, Elroy, Plant Mgr.--Dean Foods Vegetable Company, Brillion, WI; *U.S. Public*, pg. 490
Johnson, Erich, Dir.-Mfg.--BHA Group, Folkston, GA; *U.S. Public*, pg. 161
Johnson, Frank, V.P.--Cleveland Electric Company of Arkansas, Little Rock, AR; *U.S. Private*, pg. 246
Johnson, Fred, Mgr.-Office--Woodward-Clyde, Chicago, IL; *U.S. Public*, pg. 1656
Johnson, Fred T., Pres.--Support Terminal Services, Inc., Dallas, TX; *U.S. Public*, pg. 942
Johnson, G. D, Pres.--Mack Canada Inc., Toronto, Canada; *Int'l*, pg. 1103
Johnson, Gary, Mgr.-Bus.--EIS, Inc., Salt Lake City, UT; *U.S. Private*, pg. 368
Johnson, Geoff, Mng. Dir.--Coherent (U.K.) Ltd., Cambridge, United Kingdom; *U.S. Public*, pg. 396
Johnson, Gilbert F., Pres.--California Microwave, Inc.-Government Grp., Sunnyvale, CA; *U.S. Public*, pg. 293
Johnson, Glendon E., Pres. & Chief Exec. Officer--John Alden Life Insurance Company, Miami, FL; *U.S. Public*, pg. 39
Johnson, Gordon, V.P. & Mng. Dir.--National Distributing Co., Inc., Savannah, GA; *U.S. Private*, pg. 781
Johnson, Gordon P., Pres.--Deerfield Urethane, Inc., South Deerfield, MA; *Int'l*, pg. 173
Johnson, Graham, Mng. Dir.--Paper Agencies (Aust.) Pty. Ltd., Hawthorn, Australia; *Int'l*, pg. 458
Johnson, Greg, Gen. Mgr.--ADM Milling Co., Portland, OR; *U.S. Public*, pg. 128
Johnson, Greg, Pres.--Franklin/Templeton Distributors, Inc., San Mateo, CA; *U.S. Public*, pg. 680
Johnson, Harold O., Pres.--Contact Lens Division, Rochester, NY; *U.S. Public*, pg. 194
Johnson, Harold O., Sr. V.P.--Bausch & Lomb Contact Lens Division-FL, Sarasota, FL; *U.S. Public*, pg. 194
Johnson, Harvey R., Chief Oper. Officer--Piedmont Metal Products, Inc., Bedford, VA; *U.S. Public*, pg. 1770
Johnson, Horace M., Jr., Exec. V.P. & Reg. Mgr.--Willis Faber North America, Inc.-North Carolina, Greensboro, NC; *Int'l*, pg. 1503
Johnson, I. M., Deputy Chm.--D & D Tolhurst Ltd., Melbourne, Australia; *Int'l*, pg. 257
Johnson, J., Plant Mgr.--Square D Co., Secaucus, NJ; *Int'l*, pg. 1208
Johnson, J.A., Pres.--Elometa Corporation, Thomaston, CT; *U.S. Private*, pg. 1098

Johnson, J.C.H., Pres. & Chief Exec. Officer--American International Co. Ltd., Pembroke, Bermuda; *U.S. Public*, pg. 85
Johnson, James, V.P.-Sls.-Seating Div.--Fixtures Furniture, Kansas City, MO; *U.S. Private*, pg. 581
Johnson, James C., Gen. Mgr.--HMT Tonkawa Tank Company, Inc., Tonkawa, OK; *U.S. Public*, pg. 914
Johnson, Jennie M., Pres.--Pierce National Life Insurance Co., Greenville, SC; *U.S. Public*, pg. 992
Johnson, Jerome T., Pres. & Chief Exec. Officer--Natural Gas Odorizing, Baytown, TX; *U.S. Public*, pg. 1210
Johnson, Jerry W., Pres.--American Baler Co., Bellevue, OH; *U.S. Private*, pg. 102
Johnson, Jim, Pres. & Gen. Mgr.--KFXX/KGON, Inc., Portland, OR; *U.S. Private*, pg. 378
Johnson, Jim, V.P.-Sls.-Seating Division--Harter, Middlebury, IN; *U.S. Private*, pg. 581
Johnson, Jim, Gen. Mgr.--Signode Fasteners, Montreal, Canada; *U.S. Public*, pg. 869
Johnson, Jim, Pres. & Chief Exec. Officer--Anspach Grossman Enterprise, New York, NY; *Int'l*, pg. 1483
Johnson, John, Gen. Mgr.--Fluid Product Sales Div., Maumee, OH; *U.S. Public*, pg. 479
Johnson, John, Chm. Bd. & Pres.--Harvest State Feed, Inc., Snohomish, WA; *U.S. Private*, pg. 508
Johnson, John, Pres.--Cooper Smith, Inc., Mobile, AL; *U.S. Public*, pg. 547
Johnson, John, Pres.--DOD Electronics Corporation, Sandy, UT; *U.S. Public*, pg. 787
Johnson, John K., Pres.--Seoul-Heinz Ltd., Inchon, Korea; *U.S. Public*, pg. 807
Johnson, Joseph, Pres. & Gen. Mgr.--CPC/AJI (Taiwan) Ltd., Taipei, Taiwan; *U.S. Public*, pg. 225
Johnson, Joseph C. H., Pres.--American International Underwriters Overseas Ltd., Hamilton, Bermuda; *U.S. Public*, pg. 85
Johnson, Joseph H., Pres. & Chief Exec. Officer--Security Pacific Bank Oregon, Portland, OR; *U.S. Public*, pg. 182
Johnson, Keith, Mng. Dir.--Cogsdill-Nuneaton, Ltd., Nuneaton, United Kingdom; *U.S. Private*, pg. 250
Johnson, Keith, Mng. Dir.--Shefcut Tool & Engineering Ltd., Sheffield, United Kingdom; *U.S. Private*, pg. 250
Johnson, Ken, Gen. Mgr.--Filbert Corp., Altamonte Springs, FL; *U.S. Private*, pg. 1140
Johnson, Kenley, Mgr.-Retail Branch--First National Bank of East Grand Forks, East Grand Forks, MN; *U.S. Public*, pg. 1681
Johnson, Kenneth D., Pres. & Treas.--Signet Star Reinsurance Company, Florham Park, NJ; *U.S. Public*, pg. 216
Johnson, Kjell-David, Pres.--Dynapac Mfg. Inc., Hackettstown, NJ; *Int'l*, pg. 1420
Johnson, Larry, Plant Mgr.--Air Control Products, Roxboro, NC; *U.S. Public*, pg. 556
Johnson, Lawrence, Chm. Bd., Pres., Chief Exec. Officer & Gen Counsel--Kelley Dock Systems, Milwaukee, WI; *U.S.* Private, pg. 612
Johnson, Lawrence M., Chm. Bd. & Chief Exec. Officer--Bank of Hawaii, Honolulu, HI; *U.S. Public*, pg. 1248
Johnson, Lee, Admin.--Sharp Electronics Corporation, Dallas, TX; *Int'l*, pg. 1229
Johnson, Leif, Chief Oper. Officer--Bauer Hiss AB, Frolunda, Sweden; *Int'l*, pg. 747
Johnson, Lloyd, Pres.--Roberts & Schaefer Co., Chicago, IL; *U.S. Private*, pg. 371
Johnson, Lloyd, Pres.--Thompson-Starrett Construction Company, Inc., Chicago, IL; *U.S. Private*, pg. 371
Johnson, Lou, Mgr.-Mktg.--Military Products Div., Sunnyvale, CA; *Int'l*, pg. 1054
Johnson, M., Gen. Mgr.--Sara Lee/DE, Utrecht, Netherlands; *U.S. Public*, pg. 1434
Johnson, Marilyn D., V.P.--Delta Life & Annuity Co., Memphis, TN; *U.S. Private*, pg. 59
Johnson, Mark, Gen. Mgr.--W. Heath & Co., Los Angeles, CA; *U.S. Public*, pg. 84
Johnson, Mark, Pres.--Comdisco Integrated Services, Minnetonka, MN; *U.S. Public*, pg. 408
Johnson, Mark K., Pres.--Security Van Lines, Kenner, LA; *U.S. Private*, pg. 594
Johnson, Mark K., Pres.--Denver Moving & Storage Co., Denver, CO; *U.S. Private*, pg. 594
Johnson, Mike, V.P. & Gen. Mgr.--Rust Craft Canada, Inc., Toronto, Canada; *U.S. Public*, pg. 78
Johnson, Nigel, Mng. Dir.--Excerpta Medica Medical Communications BV, Amsterdam, Netherlands; *Int'l*, pg. 1099
Johnson, O.B., III, Pres.--White Star Steel, Houston, TX; *U.S. Private*, pg. 775
Johnson, Pamela, Pres.-Pub. Rels. Div.--Serino Coyne Public Relations, New York, NY; *U.S. Private*, pg. 985
Johnson, Patricia, Chief Fin. Officer & Gen. Mgr.--MGM Grand Australia Pty, Ltd., Darwin, Australia; *U.S. Public*, pg. 1027
Johnson, Patrick L., Pres. & Chief Oper. Officer--ServiCenter USA, Deerfield Beach, FL; *U.S. Public*, pg. 1201
Johnson, Paul, Gen. Mgr.--Vloc, Tarpon Springs, FL; *U.S. Public*, pg. 1647
Johnson, Peter, V.P.--Bankers Trust New York Corporation, Cairo, Egypt; *U.S. Public*, pg. 186
Johnson, Phillip, Mgr.--Commercial Metals Company, Odessa, TX; *U.S. Public*, pg. 413
Johnson, Quentin, Pres.--Northern Trust Bank of Arizona, N.A., Phoenix, AZ; *U.S. Public*, pg. 1196
Johnson, Quentin, Pres.--Northern Trust Bank of Arizona, N.A., Tucson, AZ; *U.S. Public*, pg. 1196
Johnson, R. Larry, Pres.--Oxford Slacks Division, New York, NY; *U.S. Public*, pg. 1239
Johnson, R.A., Pres.--Alphagaz Division, Walnut Creek, CA; *Int'l*, pg. 37
Johnson, R.L., V.P.--Dillingham Construction N.A., Inc., Long Beach, CA; *U.S. Private*, pg. 333
Johnson, R.R., Gen. Mgr.--GMOC Japan, Tokyo, Japan; *U.S. Public*, pg. 723
Johnson, Ralph W., Pres.--Turner International Industries, Inc., New York, NY; *U.S. Public*, pg. 1646
Johnson, Ralph W., Chief Oper. Officer--Turner International U.K. Ltd., London, United Kingdom; *U.S. Public*, pg. 1646
Johnson, Randall, Mng. Dir.--Corporate & Institutional Financial Services - Calgary, Calgary, Canada; *Int'l*, pg. 153
Johnson, Raymond, Pres. & Chief Oper. Officer--Republic American Corporation, Van Nuys, CA; *U.S. Public*, pg. 75
Johnson, Richard, V.P. & Gen. Mgr.--Banta Publications Group, Liberty, MO; *U.S. Public*, pg. 188
Johnson, Richard, Pres.--Banta Merchandising Products, Milwaukee, WI; *U.S. Public*, pg. 188
Johnson, Richard E., Pres. & Chief Exec. Officer--The Stratevest Group, N.A., Burlington, VT; *U.S. Public*, pg. 187
Johnson, Robert D., Pres. & Mng. Dir.--G.E. (U.S.A.) Aviation Service Operation Pte. Ltd., Singapore, Singapore; *U.S. Public*, pg. 713
Johnson, Robert D., Pres.--Imperial Adhesives & Chemicals, Inc., Cincinnati, OH; *U.S. Public*, pg. 1147
Johnson, Robert J., Pres.--BET West Coast Media/Affiliate Sales & BET Action Pay Per View, Santa Monica, CA; *U.S. Public*, pg. 235
Johnson, Robert L., Pres. & Chief Exec. Officer--Action Pay-Per-View, Washington, DC; *U.S. Public*, pg. 235
Johnson, Robert L., Pres.--BET Cable Network Operations, Washington, DC; *U.S. Public*, pg. 235
Johnson, Robert L., Pres.--BET West Coast Operations, Burbank, CA; *U.S. Public*, pg. 235
Johnson, Robert L., Pres.--BET New York Media Sales, New York, NY; *U.S. Public*, pg. 235
Johnson, Robert L., Pres.--BET Midwest Media/Affiliate Sales, Chicago, IL; *U.S. Public*, pg. 235
Johnson, Robert L., Pres.--BET Media Sales, Southfield, MI; *U.S. Public*, pg. 235
Johnson, Robert L., Sole Administrator--Sistemas Electricos Y Conmutadores, S.A. de C.V., Mexico, Mexico; *U.S. Public*, pg. 724
Johnson, Robin, Mgr.-Division--Haleyville Drapery Manufacturing Division, Haleyville, AL; *U.S. Public*, pg. 491
Johnson, Rodney N.M., Pres.--Jaeger Sportswear Ltd., New York, NY; *Int'l*, pg. 299
Johnson, Roger M., Pres.--Camerz Photo Products, Minneapolis, MN; *U.S. Public*, pg. 1292
Johnson, Ron, V.P. & Gen. Mgr.--Goldstrike Mine, Elko, NV; *Int'l*, pg. 169
Johnson, Ronald, Gen. Mgr.--Sterling Electronics, Wallingford, CT; *U.S. Public*, pg. 1051
Johnson, Ronald F., Pres.--Stonewall Insurance Co., Birmingham, AL; *U.S. Public*, pg. 75
Johnson, S. Brooks, Pres. & Publr.--The Sun Co., San Bernardino, CA; *U.S. Public*, pg. 701
Johnson, S. Curtis III, Gen. Partner--Johnson Venture Capital, Inc., Racine, WI; *U.S. Private*, pg. 592
Johnson, Steven M., V.P.--Trase-Miller, Oak Brook, IL; *U.S. Private*, pg. 688
Johnson, Susan, Mgr.--Pella Travel Inc., Pella, IA; *U.S. Private*, pg. 555
Johnson, Terry, Gen. Mgr.--Crane Inspection & Certification Bureau, Orlando, FL; *Int'l*, pg. 1153
Johnson, Thomas A., Pres.--AlliedSignal Aircraft Landing Systems, South Bend, IN; *U.S. Public*, pg. 50
Johnson, Thomas E., Pres.--Tom Johnson Investment Management, Inc., Oklahoma City, OK; *U.S. Public*, pg. 1673
Johnson, Thomas S., Mgr.--Piper Jaffray Inc., Rochester, MN; *U.S. Public*, pg. 1302
Johnson, Thomas S., Mgr.-Branch--Piper Jaffray Inc., Albert Lea, MN; *U.S. Public*, pg. 1302
Johnson, Thomas W., Pres.--Coastal (Bermuda) Petroleum Limited, Hamilton, Bermuda; *U.S. Public*, pg. 390
Johnson, Tom, Plant Mgr.--Kenworth Truck Co., Renton, WA; *U.S. Public*, pg. 1246
Johnson, Tom, Pres.-CNN--CNN Headline News, Atlanta, GA; *U.S. Public*, pg. 1614
Johnson, Tor, Chief Oper. Officer--Scania-Vabis del Peru S.A., Lima, Peru; *Int'l*, pg. 687
Johnson, Van, Pres. & Chief Exec. Officer--First Citizens Bank of Hohenwald, Hohenwald, TN; *U.S. Public*, pg. 1669
Johnson, Vicki, Admin.--Valley Manor Care Center, Concord, CA; *U.S. Private*, pg. 733
Johnson, W. Ben, V.P. & Gen. Mgr.--Dentsply Tulsa, Johnson City, TN; *U.S. Public*, pg. 499
Johnson, Wade, Pres.--Agvestments, Inc., Atlanta, GA; *U.S.* Private, pg. 459
Johnson, Wilbur G., Pres. & Gen. Mgr.--Hing Around Products, Inc., Prattville, AL; *U.S. Public*, pg. 1210
Johnsson, Jan Ake, Chief Oper. Officer--Perstorp Railite S.A. Decorative Laminate, Valencia, Spain; *Int'l*, pg. 1038
Johnsson, Stefan, Pres.--Volvo Group Finance Sweden AB, Goteborg, Sweden; *Int'l*, pg. 1476
Johnston, A., Mng. Dir.--Heatric Ltd., Poole, United Kingdom; *Int'l*, pg. 853
Johnston, A.B., Mng. Dir.--Compoflex, Oldham, United Kingdom; *Int'l*, pg. 1221
Johnston, Bob, Pres.--Pie Piper Products, Ltd., Chicago, IL; *U.S. Private*, pg. 1140
Johnston, Brian G., Pres. & Chief Exec. Officer--Cigna Insurance Company of Canada, Toronto, Canada; *U.S. Public*, pg. 366
Johnston, Charles, Pres.--Philip Laser Magnetic Storage, Colorado Springs, CO; *Int'l*, pg. 1054
Johnston, David, Mng. Dir.--BHA Group, Newport News, VA; *U.S. Public*, pg. 161
Johnston, David, Pres.--Highland Valley Copper, Logan Lake, Canada; *Int'l*, pg. 308
Johnston, Dennis N., Pres.--Norwest Financial Business Credit, Inc., Des Moines, IA; *U.S. Public*, pg. 1202
Johnston, Diane, V.P.--USA Network, Troy, MI; *U.S. Public*, pg. 1686
Johnston, Dixon R., Pres.--Consumer Products Div., Valdese, NC; *U.S. Public*, pg. 36
Johnston, Doug, Gen. Mgr.--Folding Carton (Middletown), Middletown, OH; *Int'l*, pg. 1270
Johnston, Fred B., II, Chief Exec. Officer--Weisz Graphics, Chapin, SC; *U.S. Private*, pg. 595
Johnston, Gary E., Pres.--Acme Frame Products, Inc., Cleveland, OH; *U.S. Public*, pg. 78
Johnston, Gary E., Pres.--Wilhold Inc., Cleveland, OH; *U.S. Public*, pg. 78
Johnston, Gayle, Pres.--Thin Film Technology Division, Rochester, NY; *U.S. Public*, pg. 194
Johnston, George G., Pres.--Delco Chassis Overseas Corporation, Detroit, MI; *U.S. Public*, pg. 723
Johnston, Graham S., Chm. & Mng. Dir.--W.A. Deutsher Pty. Ltd., Melbourne, Australia; *U.S. Public*, pg. 867
Johnston, Ian, Mgr.--Anixter Thunder Bay, Thunder Bay, Canada; *U.S. Public*, pg. 116
Johnston, Ian D., Mng. Dir.--Cadbury International Limited, Birmingham, United Kingdom; *Int'l*, pg. 248
Johnston, Jerry, V.P.--The Kingsford Products Company, Oakland, CA; *U.S. Public*, pg. 387
Johnston, Jim, Sr. V.P.-Acct. Services--Western International Media Corporation, Las Vegas, NV; *U.S. Private*, pg. 1167
Johnston, John E., Pres. European Opers.--Combined Ins. Co. of America, Kingston upon Thames, United Kingdom; *U.S. Public*, pg. 118
Johnston, Mark, Dir.--Nicolet Japan Corp.-Osaka, Osaka, Japan; *U.S. Public*, pg. 1594
Johnston, Max, Mng. Dir.--Johnson & Johnson Pacific Pty. (New Zealand) Ltd., East Tamaki, New Zealand; *U.S. Public*, pg. 931
Johnston, Norm, Mng. Dir.--Modem Media U.K., London, United Kingdom; *U.S. Public*, pg. 1641
Johnston, Peter D., Joint Mng. Dir.--D.R. Johnston Group Pty. Ltd., Sydney, Australia; *U.S. Public*, pg. 429
Johnston, Richard, Publisher--Southern Illinoisan, Carbondale, IL; *U.S. Public*, pg. 984
Johnston, Richard W., Exec. V.P.--Pierce & Stevens Corp., Buffalo, NY; *U.S. Private*, pg. 1019
Johnston, Robert P., V.P. & Gen. Mgr.--Emco Supply Central Region, Weston, Canada; *Int'l*, pg. 453
Johnston, Skeeter, Pres.-East Grp.--The Coca-Cola Bottling Co. of New York, Inc., Hawthorne, NY; *U.S. Public*, pg. 393
Johnston, William, Publisher--Decatur Herald & Review, Decatur, IL; *U.S. Public*, pg. 983
Johnston, William, Pres.--Salt Group, Chicago, IL; *U.S. Public*, pg. 1134
Johnston, William, Pres.--Morton Salt, Chicago, IL; *U.S. Public*, pg. 1135
Johr, Roger, V.P.--Earth Technology Corp., Grand Rapids, MI; *U.S. Public*, pg. 1648
Johsonbaugh, Rich, V.P.-Production--Oil-Dri Corporation of Georgia, Ochlocknee, GA; *U.S. Public*, pg. 1215
Joint, Anthony, Mng. Dir.--Aladdin Industries, Ltd., Hemel Hempstead, United Kingdom; *U.S. Private*, pg. 31
Jokelainen, Ari, Chief Oper. Officer--Exel Oy, Mantyharju, Finland; *Int'l*, pg. 913
Jokinen, Kari, Chief Oper. Officer--Raisio Group plc-Margarine, Raisio, Finland; *Int'l*, pg. 1085
Jokinen, Pentti, Resident Mgr.--Joensuu Mill, Joensuu, Finland; *Int'l*, pg. 1429
Joldersma, Becky, Mgr.--GLS of Indiana, Goshen, IN; *U.S. Private*, pg. 435
Jolkkonen, Pentti, Mng. Dir.--Metsa-Serla AG, Zurich, Switzerland; *Int'l*, pg. 864
Joll, Richard W.S., Mng. Dir.--The Bank of Nova Scotia Asia Limited, Singapore, Singapore; *Int'l*, pg. 156
Jolley, Richard, Gen. Mgr.--EG & G Florida, Kennedy Space Center, FL; *U.S. Public*, pg. 544
Jollin, David A., Chm. Bd. & Chief Exec. Officer--Willis Corroon Corp. of Massachusetts, Boston, MA; *Int'l*, pg. 1506
Jolly, Ken, Mng. Dir.--Ashton/Scholastic Pty. Ltd., Gosford, Australia; *U.S. Public*, pg. 1440
Jolstedt, Anders, Mng. Dir.--Grafiskt Paper & Norden AB, Vallingby, Sweden; *Int'l*, pg. 864
Joly, Christian, Dir.--Hachette Canada, Montreal, Canada; *Int'l*, pg. 795
Joly, Jean-Pierre, Gen. Dir.--Banque Diamantaire Anversoise (Suisse) SA, Geneva, Switzerland; *Int'l*, pg. 548
Jomeirson, Peter, Gen. Mgr.--Technophone Manufacturing (H.K.) Ltd., Yuen Long, Hong Kong; *Int'l*, pg. 952
Jon, Roger, Chief Oper. Officer--Technip Clepian, Sao Paulo, Brazil; *Int'l*, pg. 1361
Jonas, Cheryl, Mgr.-Underwriting--Burns & Wilcox - Sacramento Office, Sacramento, CA; *U.S. Private*, pg. 610
Jonas, Ed, Gen. Mgr.--Rosendorf/Evans, Mc Lean, VA; *U.S.* Public, pg. 597
Jonas, Ed, Gen. Mgr.--Rosendorf/Evans, Washington, DC; *U.S. Public*, pg. 597
Jonas, Ed, Gen. Mgr.--Rosendorf/Evans, Bethesda, MD; *U.S. Public*, pg. 597
Jonas, M., Mng. Dir.--Getinge GmbH, Langenfeld, Germany; *Int'l*, pg. 551
Jonas, Matthew G., Pres.--Kansas City Div., North Kansas City, MO; *U.S. Public*, pg. 652
Joncas, Richard, Plant Mgr.--Cascades Industries Inc., Rockingham, NC; *Int'l*, pg. 274
Jones, A.D., Mng. Dir.--TNT U.K. Limited, Atherstone, United Kingdom; *Int'l*, pg. 1343
Jones, A.K., Dir.-Food--Pauls plc, Ipswich, United Kingdom; *Int'l*, pg. 598
Jones, Alan W., Area Mgr.--Raytheon Overseas Ltd., London, United Kingdom; *U.S. Public*, pg. 1366
Jones, Allan, Branch Dir.--N.G. Bailey & Co. Ltd.-Leeds Branch, Leeds, United Kingdom; *Int'l*, pg. 132

Jones, Allen N., Pres.--Merrill Lynch Insurance Group, Inc., Plainsboro, NJ; *U.S. Public*, pg. 1098
Jones, Arthur, Chief Oper. Officer--Allright Parking Charlotte, Inc., Charlotte, NC; *U.S. Private*, pg. 43
Jones, B.C., Chief Oper. Officer--Parsons Chain Company Ltd., Stourport, United Kingdom; *Int'l*, pg. 473
Jones, B.R.S., Dr., Chm. Bd.--Archer Technicoat Limited, High Wycombe, United Kingdom; *Int'l*, pg. 893
Jones, Barry, Pres.-DMB&B Asia/Pacific North--DMB&B/Hong Kong, Quarry Bay, Hong Kong; *U.S. Private*, pg. 303
Jones, Barry, Pres.-DmB&B Asisa/Pacific Nroth--DMB&B/Hong Kong, Quarry Bay, Hong Kong; *U.S. Private*, pg. 303
Jones, Barry, Pres.-DMB&B Asia Pacific South--DMB&B Asia Pacific North, Quarry Bay, Hong Kong; *U.S. Private*, *pg. 303*
Jones, Barry, Gen. Mgr. & Exec. V.P.--Paramount Canada's Wonderland, Vaughan, Canada; *U.S. Private*, pg. 776
Jones, Bill, Reg. Mgr.--Green Tree Acceptance of Texas, Inc., Arlington, TX; *U.S. Public*, pg. 763
Jones, Brad, Gen. Mgr.--JM Television Productions, Carlsbad, CA; *U.S. Private*, pg. 584
Jones, Brian, Pres.-West Coast Division--Forest City Commercial Construction Company, Inc., Cleveland, OH; *U.S. Public*, pg. 668
Jones, Brian R., Pres.--AirTouch Cellular, Walnut Creek, CA; *U.S. Public*, pg. 34
Jones, Calvin K., Sr. V.P.--HSC Export Corporation, Sugar Land, TX; *U.S. Public*, pg. 872
Jones, Catesby ap R., Chm. Bd., Pres. & Chief Exec. Officer--Regions Bank/Selma, Selma, AL; *U.S. Public*, pg. 1372
Jones, Catherine, Mgr.-Office--Jani King of New Jersey, Inc., Parsippany, NJ; *U.S. Private*, pg. 582
Jones, Charles E., Pres.--Pennsylvania Power Co., New Castle, PA; *U.S. Public*, pg. 645
Jones, Charlie, V.P.-Sls.--All Star Gas Co.-Region X, Lebanon, MO; *U.S. Private*, pg. 35
Jones, Chuck, Mgr.-Office--Woodward-Clyde, Sacramento, CA; *U.S. Public*, pg. 1656
Jones, D. Paul, Jr., Chm. Bd. & Chief Exec. Officer--Compass Bank, Plano, TX; *U.S. Public*, pg. 419
Jones, D.A., Mng. Dir.--Baker Perkins Proprietary Limited, Springvale, Australia; *Int'l*, pg. 1240
Jones, D.H., Pres.--Morganite Inc., Dunn, NC; *Int'l*, pg. 893
Jones, D.H., Chm. Bd.--Morgan Matroc S.A., Barcelona, Spain; *Int'l*, pg. 893
Jones, Dan, Pres.--Hayssen, Duncan, SC; *U.S. Private*, pg. 118
Jones, Dan F., Pres.--Automatic Castings Division, Green Forest, AR; *U.S. Public*, pg. 986
Jones, David, Gen. Mgr.--Spectrum Molding, Erie, PA; *U.S. Private*, pg. 870
Jones, David, Dir.--Takenaka (U.K.) Ltd., Birmingham, Birmingham, United Kingdom; *Int'l*, pg. 1352
Jones, David D., Pres.--Mercury Marine, Fond Du Lac, WI; *U.S. Public*, pg. 265
Jones, David K., Gen. Mgr.--Chomerics Europe/U.K., Marlow, United Kingdom; *U.S. Public*, pg. 1262
Jones, Evan Y., Mgr.--La Plata Mine, La Plata, NM; *Int'l*, pg. 224
Jones, F. Clark, Pres.--First Commercial Bank, Huntsville, AL; *U.S. Public*, pg. 1549
Jones, G., Mng. Dir.--Walsall Conduits Ltd., West Bromwich, United Kingdom; *Int'l*, pg. 80
Jones, G.H., Plant Mgr.--Curtis 1000, Inc., Duluth, GA; *U.S. Public*, pg. 70
Jones, George, Pres.--TA Mfg. Co., Glendale, CA; *U.S. Public*, pg. 594
Jones, Glenn, Pres.--GREFCO, Inc., Torrance, CA; *U.S. Private*, pg. 903
Jones, Glenn R., Chm., Pres. & Chief Exec. Officer--Jones Spacelink, Ltd., Englewood, CO; *U.S. Private*, pg. 597
Jones, Gordon, Sr. V.P. & Mng. Dir.--Allergan Limited, High Wycombe, United Kingdom; *U.S. Public*, pg. 46
Jones, Graham D., Pres.--Shamrock Aggregates, Inc., Shawnee Mission, KS; *U.S. Private*, pg. 88
Jones, Greg, Gen. Mgr.--Coastal Lumber Company, Hazelton, WV; *U.S. Private*, pg. 248
Jones, Gregory L., Branch Mgr.--Zellerbach Division, Louisville, KY; *U.S. Public*, pg. 1075
Jones, H.C.C., Mng. Dir.--Oki Systems (UK) Ltd., Slough, United Kingdom; *Int'l*, pg. 999
Jones, Harrison P., Pres.--Vincent Metals Division, Minneapolis, MN; *Int'l*, pg. 1118
Jones, Harrison P., Exec. V.P.--Vincent Metal Goods-Northern Division, Coon Rapids, MN; *Int'l*, pg. 1118
Jones, Harry D., Pres.--Boyles Galvanizing Co., Hurst, TX; *U.S. Public*, pg. 960
Jones, Harry D., Pres.--Lake River Corporation, Berwyn, IL; *U.S. Public*, pg. 961
Jones, Herbert D., Mgr.-St. Louis Office--Light Helicopter Turbine Engine Company (LHTEC), Saint Louis, MO; *U.S. Public*, pg. 51
Jones, J., Chm. Bd.--Rollins Hudig Hall of Northern California, Inc., Palo Alto, CA; *U.S. Public*, pg. 117
Jones, J., Pres.--Blue Devil Industries, Inc., San Diego, CA; *Int'l*, pg. 802
Jones, J.P., Pres.--NEO Industries, Burlington, Canada; *Int'l*, *pg. 1150*
Jones, J.R., Chief Oper. Officer--Bristol Instruments Div., Waterbury, CT; *Int'l*, pg. 472
Jones, James C., Pres.--Airco Commercial Services, Inc., Sacramento, CA; *U.S. Private*, pg. 29
Jones, James C., Gen. Mgr.--A-R Technologies, Richmond, Canada; *Int'l*, pg. 604
Jones, James M., Jr., Chm., Pres. & Chief Exec. Officer--Peoples & Union Bank, Lewisburg, TN; *U.S. Public*, pg. 639
Jones, James R., Pres.--Warnaco Inc.-International Div., New York, NY; *U.S. Public*, pg. 1738
Jones, Jeff, Terminal Mgr.--Kintetsu World Express Inc., Commerce City, CO; *Int'l*, pg. 735
Jones, Joseph L., III, Pres.--Stanley Tools Div., New Britain, CT; *U.S. Public*, pg. 1509
Jones, Keith, Chief Exec.--Reed Business Information, Sutton, United Kingdom; *Int'l*, pg. 1094
Jones, Keith, Mgr.-Office--Woodward-Clyde, Seattle, WA; *U.S. Public*, pg. 1657
Jones, Keith W., Pres.--Republic Franklin Insurance Co., Columbus, OH; *U.S. Private*, pg. 1130
Jones, Kenneth, Gen. Mgr.--New Albany Gazette, New Albany, MS; *U.S. Private*, pg. 648
Jones, Lawrence M., Chm.--New Coleman Holdings Inc., Wichita, KS; *U.S. Private*, pg. 690
Jones, Lewis, Mgr.--Southern Electric Supply Co., Inc., Greenville, MS; *Int'l*, pg. 1108
Jones, Lewis, Mgr.--Southern Electric Supply Co., Inc., Greenwood, MS; *Int'l*, pg. 1108
Jones, Lloyd W., Pres.--International Container Systems, Tampa, FL; *Int'l*, pg. 685
Jones, M. David, Pres.--Fleetguard Inc., Nashville, TN; *U.S. Public*, pg. 468
Jones, M. David, Pres.--Fleetguard Inc., Lake Mills, IA; *U.S. Public*, pg. 468
Jones, Marvin, Mgr.--Valley Air, Charleston, WV; *U.S. Private*, pg. 672
Jones, Marvin E., Publr.--Chillicothe Newspapers, Chillicothe, OH; *U.S. Public*, pg. 700
Jones, Merv, Mgr.-Office--Woodward-Clyde, Auckland, New Zealand; *U.S. Public*, pg. 1657
Jones, Millard H., Pres.--HMT Inc., Houston, TX; *U.S. Public*, pg. 914
Jones, Neil, Chief Mgr.--Westpac - Northern Territory, Darwin, Australia; *Int'l*, pg. 1496
Jones, Owen, Gen. Mgr.--McAlester Publishing Co., McAlester, OK; *U.S. Public*, pg. 1078
Jones, Owen, Gen. Mgr.--McAlester News-Capital & Democrat, McAlester, OK; *U.S. Public*, pg. 1078
Jones, Paul, Pres. & Chief Exec. Officer--Rule Industries, Inc., Gloucester, MA; *U.S. Public*, pg. 950
Jones, Paul A., Pres.--Glenview State Bank, Glenview, IL; *U.S. Private*, pg. 295
Jones, Peter, Pres.--American Council for International Studies, Boston, MA; *U.S. Private*, pg. 57
Jones, Peter D., Chief Oper. Officer--SAPA Ltd., Derby, United Kingdom; *Int'l*, pg. 444
Jones, R., Chief Oper. Officer--Willenhall Manufacturing, Willenhall, United Kingdom; *Int'l*, pg. 265
Jones, R., Dir.--Imperial Tobacco Ltd., Liverpool Trading Div., Liverpool, United Kingdom; *Int'l*, pg. 666
Jones, R. Terry, V.P.-Opers.--Southern Instruments, Inc., Baton Rouge, LA; *U.S. Public*, pg. 921
Jones, R. Terry, V.P.-Opers.--Jacobs Maintenance, Inc., Baton Rouge, LA; *U.S. Public*, pg. 921
Jones, R. Terry, V.P.-Opers.--Southern Instruments, Inc., Lima, OH; *U.S. Public*, pg. 921
Jones, R.L., Gen. Mgr.--CHEMCENTRAL/Kansas City, Kansas City, MO; *U.S. Private*, pg. 232
Jones, R.N., Mng. Dir.--Cussons (U.K.) LTD., Cheadle, United Kingdom; *Int'l*, pg. 1024
Jones, Randy, V.P. & Gen. Mgr.--Dillard, A ResourceNet International Company, Tampa, FL; *U.S. Public*, pg. 902
Jones, Randy B., Jr., Pres.--Sumter Bank and Trust Company, Americus, GA; *U.S. Public*, pg. 1549
Jones, Rex, Pres.--Schilling Motors, Inc., Germantown, TN; *U.S. Private*, pg. 970
Jones, Richard H., Pres.--Coventry Health & Life Insurance, Fort Worth, TX; *U.S. Public*, pg. 454
Jones, Robert, Chief Fin. Officer--Irving Tanning Co., Hartland, ME; *U.S. Private*, pg. 575
Jones, Robert, V.P.--General Physics Finance Inc., Columbia, MD; *U.S. Public*, pg. 694
Jones, Robert, Gen. Mgr.--Container Div. (Miami), Miami, FL; *Int'l*, pg. 1270
Jones, Robert L., Pres. & Chief Exec. Officer--First National Bank of Magnolia, Magnolia, AR; *U.S. Public*, pg. 641
Jones, Ronald, Pres. & Chief Exec. Officer--Royal Doulton USA Inc., Somerset, NJ; *Int'l*, pg. 1135
Jones, S. F., Mng. Dir.--MB International B.V., Mijdrecht, Netherlands; *Int'l*, pg. 267
Jones, Scott, Mgr.--Jefferies & Company, Inc., Chicago, IL; *U.S. Public*, pg. 925
Jones, Shelby L., Pres.--Continental Western Insurance Company, Urbandale, IA; *U.S. Public*, pg. 215
Jones, Skip, Mgr.--J and O Diesel, Jonesboro, AR; *U.S. Private*, pg. 1101
Jones, Steve, Pres.--Princor Management Corporation, Des Moines, IA; *U.S. Private*, pg. 886
Jones, Steve, Pres.--Princor Financial Services Corporation, Des Moines, IA; *U.S. Private*, pg. 886
Jones, T., V.P. & Gen. Mgr.--Gerber Products, S.A. de C.V., Queretaro, Mexico; *Int'l*, pg. 973
Jones, Ted, Gen. Mgr.--Antique Trader Publications, Dubuque, IA; *U.S. Private*, pg. 649
Jones, Ted, Jr., Pres.--California-American Water Co., Chula Vista, CA; *U.S. Public*, pg. 95
Jones, Ted, Jr., Chief Oper. Officer--Paradise Valley Water Co., Scottsdale, AZ; *U.S. Public*, pg. 95
Jones, Ted, Jr., Pres.--New Mexico-American Water Co., Clovis, NM; *U.S. Public*, pg. 95
Jones, Thomas H., Gen. Mgr.--Bell & Howell Document Management Products Company, Lincolnwood, IL; *U.S. Public*, pg. 201
Jones, Tim, Pres.--Bank and Office Interiors, Seattle, WA; *U.S. Private*, pg. 107
Jones, Trevor Edward, Chm.--Highveld Steel & Vanadium Corporation, Witbank, South Africa; *Int'l*, pg. 76
Jones, W. David, Pres. & Chief Exec. Officer--SunTrust Bank, South Central Tennesse, N.A., Pulaski, TN; *U.S. Public*, pg. 1538
Jones, W.C., Pres.--Eastman Gelatine Corp., Peabody, MA; *U.S. Public*, pg. 551
Jones, Wallace A., Pres. & Chief Exec. Officer--El Chico Restaurants, Inc., Dallas, TX; *U.S. Private*, pg. 283
Jones, Warren, Dir.-Opers.--Rhone-Poulenc Walsh, Gastonia, NC; *Int'l*, pg. 1110
Jones, Wayne, V.P.--City National Bank - Newport Beach Regional Office, Newport Beach, CA; *U.S. Public*, pg. 381
Jones, Wayne, Plant Mgr.--Vicksburg Plant, Vicksburg, MS; *U.S. Public*, pg. 444
Jones, Wayne, Plant Mgr.--Prestec, Preston, GA; *U.S. Public*, pg. 444
Jones, Will, Pres.--Lau Div., Dayton, OH; *Int'l*, pg. 1398
Jones, William H., Chm. Bd. & Pres.--Foster Wheeler Energy Corporation, Clinton, NJ; *U.S. Public*, pg. 676
Jones, Wm. F., V.P.-Southern Grp.--Wabash Fibre Box Co., Jonesboro, AR; *U.S. Private*, pg. 1170
Jonge, K., Dr., Mng. Dir.--AE Goetze GmbH, Burscheid, Germany; *Int'l*, pg. 1334
Jongebloed, John, V.P. & Gen. Mgr.--New England Laminates Co., Inc., Walden, NY; *U.S. Public*, pg. 1258
Jongeling, George B., Pres.--Pace Power Constructors, Inc., Worcester, MA; *Int'l*, pg. 401
Jongeling, George B., Mgr.--Riley Stoker Corporation, Worcester, MA; *Int'l*, pg. 401
Jonker, Bjorn C.W., Mng. Dir.--DG Finance Company B.V., Amsterdam, Netherlands; *Int'l*, pg. 352
Jonker, Bjorn C.W., Rep.--DG Bank-Amsterdam, Amsterdam, Netherlands; *Int'l*, pg. 352
Jonkhans, G. A., Mng. Dir.--Purac Far East, Singapore, Singapore; *Int'l*, pg. 245
Jonson, Jim, Pres. & Chief Oper. Officer--Gulfstream Aerospace Corporation, Savannah, GA; *U.S. Private*, pg. 419
Jonson, Rupert H., Jr., Pres.--Franklin Advisers, Inc., Fort Lee, NJ; *U.S. Public*, pg. 680
Jonsson, Anders, Mng. Dir.--Cementa AB (Skovde), Skovde, Sweden; *Int'l*, pg. 1199
Jonsson, Gosta, Pres.--Astra Arcus AB, Sodertalje, Sweden; *Int'l*, pg. 93
Jonsson, Hans, Mng. Dir.--SKF Maintenance Products B.V., Mijdrecht, Netherlands; *Int'l*, pg. 1159
Jonsson, Ingvar, Dir.--Svenska Unilever Forvaltnings AB, Stockholm, Sweden; *Int'l*, pg. 1438
Jonsson, Kent, Pres.--Skanska Fastigheter Goteborg AB, Goteborg, Sweden; *Int'l*, pg. 1260
Jonsson, Kenth-Ake, Pres.--Telub AB, Vaxjo, Sweden; *Int'l*, pg. 277
Jonsson, Per, Mng. Dir.--Stora Dalum A/S, Odense, Denmark; *Int'l*, pg. 1303
Jonsson, Per-Ingvar, Mgr.--Swedish Tyre Tube AB, Helsingborg, Sweden; *Int'l*, pg. 1422
Jonsson, Peter, Pres.--Stabilator AB, Danderyd, Sweden; *Int'l*, pg. 1261
Jonsson, Sture, Gen. Mgr.--Lincoln Svetshuset AB, Lidkoping, Sweden; *U.S. Public*, pg. 997
Jonsson, Sture, Pres.--Dynapac (UK) Ltd., Reading, United Kingdom; *Int'l*, pg. 1420
Jonsson, Uwe, Gen. Mgr.--Tanzania Portland Cement Company Ltd., Dar es Salaam, Tanzania; *Int'l*, pg. 1201
Joost, Frank, Gen. Mgr.--Carpenter Rigging, San Francisco, CA; *U.S. Private*, pg. 215
Joosten, B.P.A., Works Dir.--Vierverlaten Sugar Factory, Groningen, Netherlands; *Int'l*, pg. 244
Joosten, Mark, Mng. Dir.--DMB&B Prague, Prague, Czech Republic; *U.S. Private*, pg. 304
Jorda, Hans, Office Mgr.--Korn/Ferry International, Vienna, Austria; *U.S. Private*, pg. 634
Jordal, Anders, Pres.--Kvaerner Fjellstrand A/S, Omastrand, Norway; *Int'l*, pg. 768
Jordan, A.F.S., Mng. Dir.--Bovis Construction Ltd., Harrow, United Kingdom; *Int'l*, pg. 1032
Jordan, Alfred, Pres.--Commerce Capital Management, Inc., Memphis, TN; *U.S. Public*, pg. 1155
Jordan, Anthony, Mng. Dir.--Severn Furnaces Limited, Bristol, United Kingdom; *U.S. Public*, pg. 883
Jordan, D., Gen. Sls. Mgr.--ITW Paslode, Swansea, United Kingdom; *U.S. Public*, pg. 869
Jordan, Dan, Plant Mgr.--AVX Conway Plant, Conway, SC; *Int'l*, pg. 775
Jordan, David, Plant Superintendant--General Shale Products Corp.-McMinnville Concrete Div., McMinnville, TN; *Int'l*, pg. 844
Jordan, Ennis, Pres.--CSR West, Las Vegas, NV; *Int'l*, pg. 245
Jordan, Gerald R., Jr., Pres.--Hellman, Jordan Management Company, Inc., Boston, MA; *U.S. Public*, pg. 1673
Jordan, Hamilton, Pres.--Whittle Communications L.P., Knoxville, TN; *U.S. Public*, pg. 1614
Jordan, Hugh, Reg. Mgr.--Green Tree Acceptance, Inc., Tallahassee, FL; *U.S. Public*, pg. 762
Jordan, J. Gary, Pres.--Cordis, a Johnson & Johnson Company, Miami, FL; *U.S. Public*, pg. 928
Jordan, J. Gary, Pres.--Cordis, a Johnson & Johnson Company, Warren, NJ; *U.S. Public*, pg. 928
Jordan, James R., Pres.--Merchant & Planters Bank N.A. of Camden, Camden, AR; *U.S. Public*, pg. 641
Jordan, Jennifer, Gen. Mgr.--El Rio Grande, New York, NY; *U.S. Public*, pg. 130
Jordan, Lester C., Chm. Bd.--Robert Skeels & Co., Compton, CA; *U.S. Public*, pg. 1782
Jordan, Mary B., Pres.--Candian Regional Airlines, Etobicoke, Canada; *Int'l*, pg. 256
Jordan, Ralph, Foreman--Hunt Oil Cotton Valley District, Cotton Valley, LA; *U.S. Private*, pg. 548
Jordan, Reggie, V.P. & Gen. Mgr.--WTVR-AM/FM, Richmond, VA; *U.S. Public*, pg. 385
Jordan, Roger, Chief Exec. Officer--Hanson Amalgamated Industries, Stevenage, United Kingdom; *Int'l*, pg. 592
Jordi, Emilio Gomariz, Chm. Bd.--Industrias Gomariz, S.A., Navarra, Spain; *U.S. Public*, pg. 1387
Jordi, Walter, Chief Exec. Officer--Maloya Fredestein, Gelterkinden, Switzerland; *Int'l*, pg. 505
Jordis-Lohausen, Alexander, Dir.--Credit Agricole (Deutschland) AG Handelsberatung, Frankfurt/Main, Germany; *Int'l*, pg. 341
Jorg, Klaus, Gen. Mgr.--Max Gruenhut International Canada Inc, Rexdale, Canada; *U.S. Public*, pg. 373

Jorgensen, Charles J., Gen. Mgr.--Angar Scientific Co., Inc., Cedar Knolls, NJ; *U.S. Public*, pg. 574
Jorgensen, Erik, Dir.--Kemira Danmark A/S, Noerresundby, Denmark; *Int'l*, pg. 728
Jorgensen, Jad, Mng. Dir.--NuEar Electronics, San Diego, CA; *U.S. Private*, pg. 1035
Jorgensen, Jorn Ole, Dir.-Admin.--Kgl. Brand A/S, Hvidovre, Denmark; *Int'l*, pg. 1257
Jorgensen, Ole Asboe, Mgr.--Medical Division, Willich, Germany; *Int'l*, pg. 1084
Jorgensen, Robert M., Pres. & Chief Exec. Officer--Bank of America, San Diego, CA; *U.S. Public*, pg. 180
Jorgenson, Gorden, Sr. V.P.--Corporate Cash Management Div., Los Angeles, CA; *U.S. Public*, pg. 871
Jorgenssen, O.A., Chief Oper. Officer--O.G. Hoyer A/S, Århus, Denmark; *Int'l*, pg. 1378
Jornov, Mike, Plant Mgr.--Dayton Superior Corp., Folcroft, PA; *U.S. Private*, pg. 932
Josef, M., Mng. Dir.--Albany International Ltd., Bury, United Kingdom; *U.S. Public*, pg. 37
Joseph, Alex A., Acting Pres.--Qualitrol Corp., Fairport, NY; *U.S. Public*, pg. 482
Joseph, Alex A., Pres.--Namco Controls Corporation, Highland Heights, OH; *U.S. Public*, pg. 482
Joseph, Daniel S., Pres.--Donnelly Optics Corporation, Tucson, AZ; *U.S. Public*, pg. 519
Joseph, Eileen Z., Exec. Editor--BNA Environment & Safety Services Div., Washington, DC; *U.S. Private*, pg. 182
Joseph, F., Mng. Dir.--GKN Walterscheid Presswerk GmbH, Trier, Germany; *Int'l*, pg. 536
Joseph, Gary, Pres.--Heraeus Precious Metals Management Inc., New York, NY; *Int'l*, pg. 616
Joseph, I., Pres.--Crosby Canada Ltd., Brampton, Canada; *Int'l*, pg. 473
Joseph, Jeffrey F., Pres.--Presidential Continental Gardens Corp., White Plains, NY; *U.S. Public*, pg. 1323
Joseph, Jeffrey F., Pres.--Presidential Realty of Iowa, Inc., White Plains, NY; *U.S. Public*, pg. 1324
Joseph, John, Pres.-USA--Ketchum Directory Advertising/Chicago, Chicago, IL; *U.S. Private*, pg. 616
Joseph, Judith, Pres.--Van Nostrand Reinhold Co., New York, NY; *U.S. Public*, pg. 1600
Joseph, Rishya, Mng. Dir. & V.P.-Reg. Mgr.--Dentsu Young & Rubicam Sdn. Bhd. (Kuala Lumpur), Kuala Lumpur, Malaysia; *U.S. Private*, pg. 325
Joseph, Thomas, Pres.--Bankers Standard Fire & Marine Company, Irving, TX; *U.S. Public*, pg. 365
Josephi, M., Chief Oper. Officer--Volkswagen de Mexico S.A. de C.V., Puebla, Mexico; *Int'l*, pg. 1475
Josephson, Jack, Pres.--Sellers & Josephson, Norwood, NJ; *U.S. Public*, pg. 1465
Josephson, John E., Pres. & Chief Exec. Officer--Big Bear Stores Company, Columbus, OH; *U.S. Public*, pg. 1270
Joshi, Shriniwas K., Mng. Dir.--Sulzer India Ltd., Mumbai, India; *Int'l*, pg. 1306
Joslin, Bill, Gen. Mgr.--Fo-Mac Division, Tulsa, OK; *U.S. Public*, pg. 689
Joslin, Bill, Gen. Mgr.--Grover Piston Ring Division, Milwaukee, WI; *U.S. Public*, pg. 689
Joslin, Bill, Gen. Mgr.--Structural Bearings Div., Athens, TX; *U.S. Public*, pg. 689
Joslin, Donald E., Pres. & Chief Exec. Officer--Monitor Life Insurance Company of New York, Utica, NY; *U.S. Private*, pg. 258
Jost, Fritz, Chm.--Coop Oberaargau-Thal/Gau, Lagenthal, Switzerland; *Int'l*, pg. 329
Jost, Jack H., Sr. Representative--Union de Bancos Suizos, Mexico, Mexico; *Int'l*, pg. 1441
Jouanno, P., Gen. Mgr.--Kilometrage S.A., Neuilly-sur-Seine, France; *Int'l*, pg. 650
Jouassain, Christian, Gen. Mgr.--MSA de France, Cergy-Pontoise, France; *U.S. Public*, pg. 1114
Joubert, Charles, Pres.--Newpark Environmental Services, Inc., Lafayette, LA; *U.S. Public*, pg. 1179
Joubert, P.E., Chief Oper. Officer--African Oxygen Ltd., Johannesburg, South Africa; *Int'l*, pg. 121
Joubert, Todd, Gen. Mgr.--United States Aluminum Corp.-Texas, Waxahachie, TX; *U.S. Public*, pg. 895
Jouett, Larry R., Exec. V.P. & Chief Oper. Officer--ANR Freight System, Inc., Golden, CO; *U.S. Public*, pg. 389
Jouffray, Guy, Mill Mgr.--Kunheim Consumer Products Div., Muntzenheim, France; *U.S. Public*, pg. 673
Jouin, Patrice, Mng. Dir.--Devimco Ltd., London, United Kingdom; *Int'l*, pg. 21
Journalist, John, Gen. Mgr.--CTS Corp. Frequency Controls, Sandwich, IL; *U.S. Public*, pg. 285
Joutsjoki, Jukka, V.P.--Valmet Corporation Roll Handling, Hollola, Finland; *Int'l*, pg. 1448
Jovanovich, Peter, Pres.--Books for Professionals, Inc., San Diego, CA; *U.S. Public*, pg. 783
Jovanovich, Peter, Chm. Bd. & Pres.--Harcourt Brace & Company Media Systems Corporation, Orlando, FL; *U.S.* Public, pg. 783
Jovanovich, Peter, Chm. & Pres.--Academic Press International Corp., Orlando, FL; *U.S. Public*, pg. 783
Jovanovich, Peter, Chm.--AP Journals, Inc., Orlando, FL; *U.S. Public*, pg. 783
Jovanovich, Peter, Pres.--Holt, Rinehart and Winston, Inc., Orlando, FL; *U.S. Public*, pg. 783
Jovanovich, Peter, Pres.--HBC Informational and Instructional Services, Inc., New York, NY; *U.S. Public*, pg. 783
Jovanovich, Peter, Chmn.--The Psychological Corp., San Antonio, TX; *U.S. Public*, pg. 784
Jovanovich, Peter, Chm. & Pres.--Miller Accounting Publications, Inc., San Diego, CA; *U.S. Public*, pg. 784
Jovanovich, Peter, Chm. Bd.--W.B. Saunders Company, Philadelphia, PA; *U.S. Public*, pg. 784
Jovanovich, Peter, Chm. & Chief Exec. Officer--Addison-Wesley Longman Ltd., Harlow, United Kingdom; *Int'l*, pg. 1027
Jovanovich, Peter, Pres.--Educational & Professional Publishing Group, New York, NY; *U.S. Public*, pg. 1070
Jovick, Tom, Exec. Dir.--QualMed Plans for Health-Oregon, Portland, OR; *U.S. Public*, pg. 678
Joyce, J., District Mgr.--A.M. Castle & Co., Tulsa, OK; *U.S. Public*, pg. 313
Joyce, K.R., Pres. & Chief Exec. Officer--Texas-New Mexico Power Co., Fort Worth, TX; *U.S. Public*, pg. 1557
Joyce, Terry, Chief Oper. Officer--MacDermid Chemicals Inc., Mississauga, Canada; *U.S. Public*, pg. 1030
Joyet, Alain, Gen. Mgr.--Societe Generale, New York, NY; *Int'l*, pg. 1273
Joyner, F. Belton, III, Pres.--Williamsburg Foods, Inc., Toano, VA; *U.S. Public*, pg. 1479
Joynson, Antony, Mng. Dir.--Samuel Groves & Co., Ltd., Birmingham, United Kingdom; *U.S. Public*, pg. 1791
Joynt, John D., Branch Mgr.--Financial Collection Agencies, Moncton, Canada; *Int'l*, pg. 470
Jozoff, Malcolm, Chm. Bd. & Chief Exec. Officer--Lenox, Incorporated, Lawrenceville, NJ; *U.S. Public*, pg. 261
Jozwiak, Daniel, Pres. & Chief Oper. Officer--Drummond American Corporation, Vernon Hills, IL; *U.S. Public*, pg. 980
Jreidini, Ramzi T., Pres.--Ikon Office Solutions, Orlando, FL; *U.S. Public*, pg. 863
Ju, David, Gen. Mgr.--Squibb (Far East) Ltd., Causeway Bay, Hong Kong; *U.S. Public*, pg. 256
Juai, ReiJane, Gen. Mgr.--Cheyenne, Roslyn Heights, NY; *U.S. Public*, pg. 420
Juanarena, Douglas B., Pres. & Chief Exec. Officer--Pressure Systems, Inc., Hampton, VA; *Int'l*, pg. 1130
Jubert, L., Gen. Mgr.--Heudebert, Athis-Mons, France; *Int'l*, pg. 380
Juch, D.R., Mng. Dir.--Kulk & Kramer Kantoorsystemen B.V., Zoetermeer, Netherlands; *Int'l*, pg. 1116
Juday, Floyd J., V.P.-Mktg.--MacMillan Bloedel Inc., Alpharetta, GA; *Int'l*, pg. 829
Judd, John E., Pres.--Vibra-Metrics, Inc., Hamden, CT; *U.S. Private*, pg. 622
Judd, L.F., V.P. & Gen. Mgr.--Falls Church Div., Falls Church, VA; *U.S. Public*, pg. 1365
Judd, Paul, Plant Mgr.--General Motors Canada Transmission Div., Windsor, Canada; *U.S. Public*, pg. 722
Judd, Richard, Pres.--San Antonio Div., San Antonio, TX; *U.S. Public*, pg. 652
Jude, Peter, Dir.-Opers.--First Health Center, Miami, FL; *U.S. Public*, pg. 404
Judge, Fred, Pres. & Chief Exec. Officer--Titan Information Systems, San Diego, CA; *U.S. Public*, pg. 1618
Juelich, Richard J., Pres.--AmClyde Engineered Products Co., Inc., Saint Paul, MN; *U.S. Public*, pg. 778
Juhl, Daniel L., Pres.--Stanhope Products Company, Brookville, OH; *U.S. Private*, pg. 169
Juhn, Jun-Yong, Pres.--Shinryu Cement Corp., Osaka, Japan; *Int'l*, pg. 1291
Juliano, Mark, Pres. & Chief Oper. Officer--Boardwalk Regency Corporation, Atlantic City, NJ; *U.S. Public*, pg. 1512
Juliber, Lois D., Pres.--Colgate-Palmolive Household Products Div., New York, NY; *U.S. Public*, pg. 397
Julien, Gary, V.P.--Molded Fiber/North Carolina, Morganton, NC; *U.S. Private*, pg. 756
Julier, H.S., Pres.--Carter Rice, Boston, MA; *U.S. Public*, pg. 903
Jumisco, Don, Mgr.-Detroit--Metro-Puck Comics Network, New York, NY; *U.S. Private*, pg. 739
Jummati, Michael, Chief Oper. Officer--Regency Thermographers of Ill., Inc., Chicago, IL; *U.S. Public*, pg. 89
Junck, Mary, Chief Exec. Officer & Publisher--The Baltimore Sun Newspapers, Baltimore, MD; *U.S. Public*, pg. 1616
Junck, Roland, Pres.--TrefilARBED Bissen S.a.r.l, Bissen, Luxembourg; *Int'l*, pg. 80
Junck, Roland, Gen. Mgr.--TrefilARBED Luxembourg/Saarbrucken S.a.r.l., Luxembourg, Luxembourg; *Int'l*, pg. 80
Junco, Gary J., Pres. & Chief Oper. Officer--Enserch International Exploration, Inc., Dallas, TX; *U.S. Public*, pg. 1587
Juneau, Paul, Pres.--Acces Capital, Montreal, Canada; *Int'l*, pg. 249
Juneau, Paul, Pres.--Acces Capital Quebec, Montreal, Canada; *Int'l*, pg. 249
Junek, Adolph, Mgr.--Houston Steel Service Company of Texas, Houston, TX; *U.S. Public*, pg. 412
Jung-Senssfelder, Dr. Ottheinz, Dir.--Simon AG, Dusseldorf, Germany; *Int'l*, pg. 180
Jung, Helmut, Mgr.--Commerzbank AG Representative Office-Thailand, Bangkok, Thailand; *Int'l*, pg. 312
Jung, J. D., Pres.--Samsung Electron Devices Co., Ltd., Seoul, Korea; *Int'l*, pg. 1181
Jung, Peter, Mng. Dir.--Bertrand Faure Sitztechnik GmbH & Co. kg, Stadthagen, Germany; *Int'l*, pg. 193
Jung, Seon-Ki, Pres.--Ssangyong Paper Co., Ltd., Seoul, Korea; *Int'l*, pg. 1292
Jung, Steve, Sr. Representative--Bank of Montreal - Taiwan, Taipei, Taiwan; *Int'l*, pg. 155
Junge, Morten, Gen. Mgr.--Distributoren Interelko A/S, Karlslunde, Denmark; *Int'l*, pg. 710
Jungers, Blaine, V.P. & Gen. Mgr.--Hush Puppies Retail, Inc., Lombard, IL; *U.S. Public*, pg. 1775
Jungers, Blaine C., Pres.--WWW Retail, Inc., Rockford, MI; *U.S. Public*, pg. 1775
Jungjohann, Heinz Gunther, Mng. Dir.--Dresdner (S.E. Asia) Ltd., Singapore, Singapore; *Int'l*, pg. 420
Jungmeier, Gunther, Gen. Mgr.--Refractories Consulting & Engineering GmbH, Vienna, Austria; *U.S. Private*, pg. 904
Jungwirth, Dan, Plant Mgr.--St. Jude Medical Ltd., Saint-Hyacinthe, Canada; *U.S. Public*, pg. 1428
Junkunc, James, Plant Mgr.--The Producto Machine Co., Franklin Park, IL; *U.S. Private*, pg. 889
Juoy, A., Mgr.-Mfg.--Industria Fotografica Interamericana S.A. de C.V., Guadalajara, Mexico; *U.S. Public*, pg. 554
Jupp, E. C. J., Mng. Dir.--Amerford Intl. (U.K.) Ltd., Hounslow, United Kingdom; *Int'l*, pg. 1388
Juraska, Jayson R., V.P. & Gen. Mgr.--Cox Communications-Greater Hartford, Manchester, CT; *U.S. Public*, pg. 454
Jurgensen, John C., Pres.--John R. Jurgensen Co., Cincinnati, OH; *U.S. Private*, pg. 1131
Juris, David S., V.P. & Gen. Mgr.--Tribune Denver Radio, Inc., Denver, CO; *U.S. Public*, pg. 1636
Juris, David S., V.P. & Gen. Mgr.--KOSI-FM, Denver, CO; *U.S. Public*, pg. 1636
Juris, David S., V.P. & Gen. Mgr.--KEZW-AM, Denver, CO; *U.S. Public*, pg. 1636
Juris, David S., V.P. & Gen. Mgr.--KKHK, Denver, CO; *U.S. Public*, pg. 1636
Justafre, G., Deputy Gen. Mgr.--Algemene Bank Nederland (Suisse), Geneva, Switzerland; *Int'l*, pg. 12
Justice, David, Mgr.-Property & Casualty Claims--Willis Corroon Administrative Services Corporation, Pikeville, KY; *Int'l*, pg. 1504
Justice, Gary, V.P. & Gen. Mgr.--Ohio Gear/Richmond Gear - Liberty Div., Liberty, SC; *U.S. Public*, pg. 1370
Justino, Jose A., Mng. Dir.--Johnson & Johnson de Colombia S.A., Cali, Colombia; *U.S. Public*, pg. 930
Juszli, Mark P., V.P. & Gen. Mgr.--Oglebay Norton Industrial Sands, Inc., Cleveland, OH; *U.S. Public*, pg. 1213
Juteau, Olivier, Chief Exec. Officer-Western Europe--Moore Nederland B.V., Amsterdam, Netherlands; *Int'l*, pg. 890
Jutte, A.J., Gen. Mgr.--The Netherlands Insurance, Belait, Singapore; *Int'l*, pg. 651
Juul, Arne, Mng. Dir.--Bates Emballage A/S, Noerresundby, Denmark; *Int'l*, pg. 476
Kaarnakari, Matti, Chief Oper. Officer--Neste Polyester S.A., Sauveterre, France; *Int'l*, pg. 915
Kaarnasaari, Jussi, Chief Oper. Officer--NCT Norden AB, Espoo, Finland; *Int'l*, pg. 913
Kaartinen, Kalevi, Mng. Dir.--Nokia Mobile Phones GmbH, Dusseldorf, Germany; *Int'l*, pg. 952
Kabala, Stanely J., Chief Exec. Officer--Rogers Cantel Mobile Communications Inc., Saint-Laurent, Canada; *Int'l*, pg. 1122
Kabala, Stanley J., Chief Oper. Officer-Telecommunications-Rogers Communications, Inc., Toronto, Canada; *Int'l*, pg. 1122
Kabb, Marsha, Office Mgr.--Leo Burnett U.S.A., Los Angeles, CA; *U.S. Private*, pg. 184
Kabe, Junichi, Pres.--Toray Industries (America) Inc., New York, NY; *Int'l*, pg. 1400
Kabe, Toshiaki, Gen. Mgr.--The Sakura Bank, Tokyo, Japan; *Int'l*, pg. 1179
Kabel, Steve, Pres.--Richmond American Homes, Inc., Phoenix, AZ; *U.S. Public*, pg. 1025
Kabus, Alan S., Pres. & Chief Exec. Officer--Bentley Mills, Inc., City of Industry, CA; *U.S. Public*, pg. 889
Kacer-Hanley, Bonnie, Reg. Acct. Mgr.--Utell International-Miami, Miami, FL; *Int'l*, pg. 1098
Kach, Victor, Gen. Mgr.--Isomedix Operations Inc., El Paso, TX; *U.S. Public*, pg. 1515
Kaczynski, Jim, Div. Mgr.--Campbell Plastics Div., Schenectady, NY; *U.S. Public*, pg. 1504
Kaczynski, Jim, Div. Mgr.--Reid Products Div., Cleveland, OH; *U.S. Public*, pg. 1504
Kadak, Andrew, Pres. & Chief Oper. Officer--Yankee Atomic Electric Co., Bolton, MA; *U.S. Public*, pg. 325
Kaderli, Ernst, Mgr.--Radiometer RSCH GmbH, Thalwil, Switzerland; *Int'l*, pg. 1084
Kadiri, Hamid, Chief Exec. Officer--Klem EURO RSCG, Casablanca, Morocco; *Int'l*, pg. 603
Kadlec, Rudy, Pres.--Geophysical Survey Systems, Inc., Salem, NH; *Int'l*, pg. 1019
Kadrowski, Ryan, Mgr.-Division--Southern Interiors, Memphis, TN; *U.S. Public*, pg. 491
Kady, Tom, Pres.--Handex of New Jersey, Inc., Morganville, NJ; *U.S. Private*, pg. 499
Kaeding, Uwe, Branch Mgr.--Union-Transport Corporation-Chicago Office, Elk Grove Village, IL; *U.S. Private*, pg. 1119
Kaelin, Heinz, Dir.--Dresdner Forfaitierungs Aktiengesellschaft, Zurich, Switzerland; *Int'l*, pg. 419
Kaemmer, D., Chm. Bd. & Chief Exec. Officer--GEHE AG, Stuttgart, Germany; *Int'l*, pg. 591
Kaempfer, J.W., Jr., Pres.--BAA Mc Arthur-Glen Europe, Washington, DC; *U.S. Private*, pg. 604
Kaentz, M., Mng. Dir.--Jurid N.V. (S.A.), Zaventem, Belgium; *U.S. Public*, pg. 53
Kaenzig, J. Gary, Pres.--Grace Packaging, Duncan, SC; *U.S. Public*, pg. 755
Kafer, Siegfried, Gen. Mgr.--Tokheim GmbH, Weilheim, Germany; *U.S. Public*, pg. 1620
Kafry, Mordechay, V.P.-Far East Opers.--Kirkstone Company Ltd., Kowloon, Hong Kong; *U.S. Public*, pg. 336
Kagami, Shigeru, Dir.--Takenaka Europe GmbH, Dusseldorf, Dusseldorf, Germany; *Int'l*, pg. 1351
Kagan, Jonathan M., Pres.--Novel Biomedical, Plymouth, MN; *U.S. Public*, pg. 401
Kagawa, Kozaburo, Pres.--Hebron S.A., Barcelona, Spain; *Int'l*, pg. 1014
Kage, Yuji, Chm. Bd.--LTCB and F&C Investment Management Co. Limited, London, United Kingdom; *Int'l*, *pg. 816*
Kageyama, Kenji, Mng. Dir.--Ilco Unican Mexico S.A. de C.V., Tlalnepantla, Mexico; *Int'l*, pg. 1432
Kageyama, Koichiro, Pres.--Nissho Iwai Australia Ltd., Sydney, Australia; *Int'l*, pg. 948
Kageyama, Yoshio, Pres.--Toray Plastics (America), Inc., North Kingstown, RI; *Int'l*, pg. 1400
Kahana, Aron, Chm. Bd. & Pres.--Israel Discount Bank of New York, New York, NY; *Int'l*, pg. 645
Kahari, Jorma, Mng. Dir.--Viljavuuspalvelu Oy, Mikkeli, Finland; *Int'l*, pg. 728
Kaharu, S., Pres.--Fuji Bondstrand Co., Ltd., Shizuoka, Japan; *U.S. Public*, pg. 99

Kahl, Darrell G., Gen. Mgr.--Container Div. (Jonesboro), Jonesboro, AR; *Int'l*, pg. 1270
Kahl, Harold J., Chm. Bd., Pres. & Chief Exec. Officer--Calvert Bank & Trust Co., Prince Frederick, MD; *U.S. Public*, pg. 1088
Kahl, Richard W., Editor-in-Chief--Skiing, New York, NY; *U.S. Public*, pg. 1617
Kahl, Robert, Plant Mgr.--Silgan Containers, Hoopeston, IL; *U.S. Public*, pg. 1473
Kahl, Trevor, Branch Mgr.--Roehlen Industries Pty. Ltd. Mold-Tech Div., Mordialloc, Australia; *U.S. Public*, pg. 1507
Kahl, Trevor, Branch Mgr.--Roehlen Industries Pty. Ltd. Procon Pump Div., Mordialloc, Australia; *U.S. Public*, pg. 1507
Kahmeyer, Heinrich, Co-Mng. Dir.--Krupp Hoesch Dienstleistigungen GmbH, Essen, Germany; *Int'l*, pg. 512
Kahn, Harold D., Chm. Bd. & Chief Exec. Officer--Macy's East, New York, NY; *U.S. Public*, pg. 618
Kahn, Jan, Pres., Sls. & Mktg.--Caron International, De Kalb, IL; *U.S. Private*, pg. 786
Kahn, Jenette, Pres. & Editor-In-Chief--DC Comics, Inc., New York, NY; *U.S. Public*, pg. 1614
Kahn, P., Chief Exec.--Longman Group UK Ltd., Harlow, United Kingdom; *Int'l*, pg. 1025
Kahot, Barry, Plant Mgr.--Union Electric Steel Corp., Valparaiso, IN; *U.S. Public*, pg. 104
Kai, K., Chief Oper. Officer--NIC Resources, Inc., Calgary, Canada; *Int'l*, pg. 948
Kai, M., Mng. Dir.--International Video Products Pte. Ltd., Singapore, Singapore; *Int'l*, pg. 1405
Kai, Masaru, Chief Oper. Officer--Nippon Oil (U.S.A.) Limited - New York Office, New York, NY; *Int'l*, pg. 937
Kaija, Matti, Mng. Dir.--A. Jalander Oy, Muurla, Finland; *Int'l*, *pg. 727*
Kaikhosrovi, M., Mng. Dir.--ESAB International AB, Tehran, Iran; *Int'l*, pg. 282
Kailbourne, Erland E., Chm. & Chief Exec. Officer--Fleet Bank, Albany, NY; *U.S. Public*, pg. 649
Kailly, Darshan S., Pres.--Canadian Freightways Ltd., Calgary, Canada; *U.S. Public*, pg. 435
Kain, Bruce E., Chief Oper. Officer--Pool Arabia, Ltd., Al-Khobar, Saudi Arabia; *U.S. Public*, pg. 1316
Kaines, Don, Chief Oper. Officer--The Terminix International Company, Memphis, TN; *U.S. Public*, pg. 1461
Kaino, Tomotaka, Chief Oper. Officer--Hitachi Seiko, Ltd., Kanagawa, Japan; *Int'l*, pg. 622
Kairakbayev, Bakhyt, Mng. Dir.--EurAsia Consult, Almaty, Kazakhstan; *Int'l*, pg. 606
Kaiser, James, Gen. Mgr.--Isomedix Operations Inc., Whippany, NJ; *U.S. Public*, pg. 1515
Kaiser, Lori, Gen. Mgr.--Port Chatham Packing Company, Seattle, WA; *U.S. Private*, pg. 556
Kaiser, Marshall J., Pres. & Chief Exec. Officer--Safe Harbor Water Power Corp., Conestoga, PA; *U.S. Public*, pg. 172
Kaiser, Marshall J., Pres. & Chief Exec. Officer--Pennsylvania Power & Light Company-Northeast Div., Wilkes-Barre, PA; *U.S. Public*, pg. 1244
Kaiser, Marshall J., Pres. & Chief Exec. Officer--Safe Harbor Water Power Corp., Conestoga, PA; *U.S. Public*, pg. 1244
Kaiser, Susan, V.P.--Magna Bank, St. Clair Region, Belleville, IL; *U.S. Public*, pg. 1037
Kaizerman, Dalia, Branch Mgr.--Bank Hapoalim (Luxembourg) Ltd., Luxembourg, Luxembourg; *Int'l*, pg. 149
Kajinski, Shogo, Pres.--ORIX Computer Systems Corporation, Tokyo, Japan; *Int'l*, pg. 1008
Kakavis, Nick, Pres.--MCS, Inc., Pittsburgh, PA; *U.S. Public*, pg. 1099
Kakehi, Nabuo, Pres.--Taito Co., Ltd., Kobe, Japan; *Int'l*, pg. 878
Kakiage, Masatoshi, Pres. & Chief Exec. Officer--Mitsui Fudosan (USA), Inc., New York, NY; *Int'l*, pg. 882
Kakimi, Mitsuo, Chief Rep.--Dai-Ichi Kangyo Bank, Ltd.-Beijing, Beijing, China; *Int'l*, pg. 361
Kaldellis, Emanuel, Chm. Bd., Pres. & Chief Exec. Officer--Copais Food & Beverage Company S.A., Athens, Greece; *U.S. Public*, pg. 806
Kalin, Edward L., Pres.--Kalin Financial Division, Sarasota, FL; *U.S. Private*, pg. 606
Kalinske, Thomas, Pres. & Chief Exec. Officer--Sega of America Inc., Redwood City, CA; *Int'l*, pg. 1218
Kalinta, Nond, Mgr.-Dist. Sls.--Thai Airways Intl. Ltd.-San Francisco, San Francisco, CA; *Int'l*, pg. 1381
Kalish, William B., Pres.--IPD Printing & Distributing, Inc., Chamblee, GA; *U.S. Public*, pg. 1735
Kalka, Michael, Dr., Chief Exec. Officer--Aachener und Muenchener Lebensversicherung, Aachen, Germany; *Int'l*, pg. 15
Kalkbrenner, Karl, Gen. Mgr.-Mfg.--Retail Bag Division - Elizabeth Plant, Elizabeth, NJ; *U.S. Public*, pg. 1521
Kalkman, A., Dir.--Snijbrandcentrum Roermond, Roermond, Netherlands; *Int'l*, pg. 754
Kalkman, B., Mng. Dir.--ABN-AMRO Bank (Sverige) AB, Stockholm, Sweden; *Int'l*, pg. 11
Kalksma, J.P.B., Div. Mgr.--Melkunie, Woerden, Netherlands; *Int'l*, pg. 254
Kall, Terry, Pres.--General Felt Industries, Inc., Linwood, PA; *U.S. Private*, pg. 1094
Kallas, Constantine, Pres. & Gen. Mgr.--Ariston, Hillside, NJ; *U.S. Public*, pg. 1486
Kallay, Istvan, Mng. Dir.--SKF Sved Golyoscsapagy Reszvenytarsasag, Budapest, Hungary; *Int'l*, pg. 1159
Kallay, Michael, Publr.--Crossroads Press, Inc., Honolulu, HI; *U.S. Private*, pg. 19
Kallbom, Lennart, Pres.--Motala Tank, Motala, Sweden; *Int'l*, pg. 1420
Kalldert, Arne, Chief Oper. Officer--ICA Butiksfinans AB, Goteborg, Sweden; *Int'l*, pg. 643
Kallen, M.J., V.P. & Mng. Dir.-Europe & Africa--Monsanto Europe S.A., Brussels, Belgium; *U.S. Public*, pg. 1125
Kallenius, Jan, Chief Exec. Officer--S.A. Cebelor, Brussels, Belgium; *Int'l*, pg. 710
Kaller, Ronald, V.P & Gen. Mgr.--Red Seal Quality Foods, Inc., Denver, CO; *U.S. Private*, pg. 158
Kallery, D., Gen. Mgr.--Hitchiner Mfg. Co., Inc., O Fallon, MO; *U.S. Private*, pg. 531
Kalliala, Kari, Mng. Dir.--Papeteries de Docelles, Docelles, France; *Int'l*, pg. 1430
Kallicragas, Jim, Plant Mgr.--Sweetheart Cup Company Inc., Dallas, TX; *U.S. Private*, pg. 1058
Kallioniemi, Esko, Mng. Dir.--Combitrans Oy, Lappeenranta, Finland; *Int'l*, pg. 1428
Kalloren, H., Mng. Dir.--Finnish Chemicals Oy, Aetsa, Finland; *Int'l*, pg. 954
Kalls, Kjell, Gen. Mgr.--Norrkopings Sand AB, Norrkoping, Sweden; *Int'l*, pg. 1200
Kallstrom, Curt, Chief Oper. Officer--AxTrade Flow AB, Stockholm, Sweden; *Int'l*, pg. 708
Kallstrom, Willy, Mng. Dir.--ITT Flygt Werk GmbH, Pforzheim, Germany; *U.S. Public*, pg. 860
Kalma, Ludvik, ing., Chm. Bd.--SKODA, Automobilova a.s., Mlada Boleslav, Czech Republic; *Int'l*, pg. 1475
Kalmbach, Lisa, Pres.--Kaufman and Broad of Northern California, Inc., San Ramon, CA; *U.S. Public*, pg. 945
Kalmet, John, Pres.--North American Metals Corp., Vancouver, Canada; *Int'l*, pg. 1498
Kalogris, Michael J., Pres. & Gen. Mgr.-Metrophone, Philadelphia--LIN Cellular Group, Kirkland, WA; *U.S. Public*, pg. 11
Kalosis, Stephen, Pres.-Bldg. Prods. Div.--Libbey Owens Ford Co., Toledo, OH; *Int'l*, pg. 1056
Kalsbeek, P., Dir.--CEF Safety Systems B.V., Rijswijk, Netherlands; *Int'l*, pg. 590
Kalsson, Klas-Goran, Mill Mgr.--Metsa-Serla AB (Paulistrom Mill), Paulistrom, Sweden; *Int'l*, pg. 864
Kaltenegger, Wolf-Dieter, Chief Oper. Officer--Frankfurt-Trust Investment GmbH, Frankfurt/Main, Germany; *Int'l*, pg. 119
Kalthaus, Christine, Reg. Opers. Mgr.-Germany, Austria & Central Europe--Utell International-Germany, Dusseldorf, Germany; *Int'l*, pg. 1098
Kaltman, Dennis, Gen. Mgr.--Queens Group Kentucky, Inc., Louisville, KY; *U.S. Private*, pg. 900
Kalverkamp, D.G., Dir.--Tebodin BV Consultants & Engineers, Hague, Netherlands; *Int'l*, pg. 630
Kalvik, Jan-Tore, Mng. Dir.--Hagglunds Drives A/S, Sandvika, Norway; *Int'l*, pg. 670
Kam, C. Robert, Mng. Dir.--First Brands Asia, Wan Chai, Hong Kong; *U.S. Public*, pg. 627
Kam, C.K., Laboratory Dir.--Springborn Testing & Research (Singapore) Pte Ltd., Singapore, Singapore; *U.S. Private*, *pg. 1027*
Kam, Sam, Lab. Dir.--Springborn Testing & Research (Taiwan) Ltd., Taipei, Taiwan; *U.S. Private*, pg. 1027
Kaman, C. William, II, Pres.--Kaman Music Corp., Bloomfield, CT; *U.S. Public*, pg. 942
Kaman, Greg, Plant Mgr.--Bundy Corporation, Cynthiana Plant, Cynthiana, KY; *Int'l*, pg. 1340
Kamarata, Dale, Mgr.-Tucson Div.--Smith Pipe & Steel, Tucson, AZ; *U.S. Private*, pg. 1009
Kamareddine, Imad, V.P. & Gen. Mgr.--Flow Europe, Darmstadt, Germany; *U.S. Public*, pg. 656
Kambak, Keith, Pres.--WCO Port Properties, Inc., Long Beach, CA; *U.S. Public*, pg. 514
Kambara, Akio, Dir.--West Japan Railway Company, New York, NY; *Int'l*, pg. 1491
Kambara, M., Mng. Dir.--Moore Products Co. (Japan) K.K., Tokyo, Japan; *U.S. Public*, pg. 1129
Kambara, Steve, Chief Rep.--Nokia Japan K.K. Ltd., Tokyo, Japan; *Int'l*, pg. 954
Kambli, R., Mng. Dir.--Bally Hong Kong Ltd., Kowloon, Hong Kong; *Int'l*, pg. 997
Kameyama, Kazunori, Chief Rep.--LTCB Atlanta, Atlanta, GA; *Int'l*, pg. 816
Kameyama, Ken, Mng. Dir.--Dentsply Japan, Tokyo, Japan; *U.S. Public*, pg. 499
Kamigori, Katsuhiko, Joint Mng. Dir.--Dentsu Europe Ltd.-London, London, United Kingdom; *Int'l*, pg. 393
Kamin, P.D., Pres.--Ortman Fluid Power Division, Hammond, IN; *U.S. Public*, pg. 402
Kamin, Robert, Pres.--Aydin Raytor Div., Montgomeryville, PA; *U.S. Public*, pg. 158
Kaminaga, Hitoshi, Pres.--Oki Semiconductores (Puerto Rico) Inc., Hato Rey, PR; *Int'l*, pg. 1000
Kaminski, Mark, Pres.--Commonwealth Aluminum-Lewisport, Lewisport, KY; *U.S. Public*, pg. 415
Kaminski, Mark V., Pres. & Chief Exec. Officer--Alflex, Long Beach, CA; *U.S. Public*, pg. 415
Kaminski, Robert S., Oper. Partner--International Pin, Park Forest, IL; *U.S. Private*, pg. 269
Kamio, Kazuo, Pres.--Fuji Bank International, Inc., San Francisco, CA; *Int'l*, pg. 519
Kamio, Kazuo, Gen. Mgr.--Fuji Bank, San Francisco, San Francisco, CA; *Int'l*, pg. 520
Kamishima, M., Pres.--Ebara UK Ltd., Hounslow, United Kingdom; *Int'l*, pg. 432
Kamm, J.O., Chm. & Chief Exec. Officer--Wilkinson Company, Inc., Stow, OH; *U.S. Private*, pg. 368
Kamman, Gerald J., Pres.--Dixie-Narco, Inc., Williston, SC; *U.S. Public*, pg. 1065
Kamminga, Peter, Chief Oper. Officer--Hermedico BV, Doesburg, Netherlands; *Int'l*, pg. 987
Kamnikar, Michael, Pres.--Ellwood Crankshaft & Machine Company, Hermitage, PA; *U.S. Private*, pg. 373
Kamo, Ryuzo, Mng. Dir.--IGT-Japan K.K., Tokyo, Japan; *U.S. Public*, pg. 900
Kamono, Akira, Pres.--Mitsui Matsushima Co., Ltd., Fukuoka, Japan; *Int'l*, pg. 877
Kamoto, T., Gen. Mgr.--Hanwa American Corp., New York, NY; *Int'l*, pg. 595
Kamphuis, Ceec, Mng. Dir.--Woodward Governor France S.A.R.L., Venissieux, France; *U.S. Public*, pg. 1777
Kamphuis, Robert D., V.P. & Gen. Mgr.--Gilman, Janesville, WI; *Int'l*, pg. 1389
Kamppinen, Pentti, Mng. Dir.--Nokia Telecommunications B.V., Leidschendam, Netherlands; *Int'l*, pg. 953
Kampson, S.J., Branch Mgr.--Zellerbach Division, Fresno, CA; *U.S. Public*, pg. 1075
Kamstra, Garrett A., Pres.--Hutch Sports USA, Inc., Hebron, KY; *U.S. Public*, pg. 1354
Kamusui, Damsi, Pres.--P.T. Merapi Utama Pharma, Jakarta, Indonesia; *Int'l*, pg. 1014
Kan, Yiu Hei, Mng. Dir.--Macmillan Publishers (China) Ltd., Central, Hong Kong; *Int'l*, pg. 1480
Kanai, Senki, Mng. Dir.--OMRON Europe G.m.b.H., Hamburg, Germany; *Int'l*, pg. 1006
Kanakubo, Hide, V.P.-Satellite Div.--Satellite Technology Group, Fort Worth, TX; *Int'l*, pg. 1433
Kanaler, Stifab, Mgr.--Stifab, Jonkoping, Sweden; *Int'l*, pg. 1422
Kanaley, James E., Pres.--Bausch & Lomb Personal Products Division-NY, Rochester, NY; *U.S. Public*, pg. 194
Kanaly, Tim, V.P.-Pur.--VICOM Production and Distribution Co., Denver, CO; *U.S. Public*, pg. 1719
Kanamori, K., Pres.--NYK Line (North America) Inc., Secaucus, NJ; *Int'l*, pg. 941
Kanary, James R., Chm. Bd., Pres. & Chief Exec. Officer--Grayling State Bank, Grayling, MI; *U.S. Public*, pg. 379
Kanaya, Mitsuo, Vice Chm. & Mng. Dir.--Dai Nippon Printing Co. (Hong Kong) Ltd., Tsuen Wan, Hong Kong; *Int'l*, pg. 363
Kanazawa, Takehisa, Pres.--Brother International Corporation (Canada) Ltd., Dollard des Ormeaux, Canada; *Int'l*, pg. 229
Kanbara, Isao, Dir.--P.T. Astra Daihatsu Motor, Jakarta, Indonesia; *Int'l*, pg. 365
Kanbe, Toru, Pres.--Calsonic Climate Control, Inc., Irvine, CA; *Int'l*, pg. 944
Kanda, Takafumi, Chm. Bd. & Dir.--ORIX Asia Limited, Hong Kong, Hong Kong; *Int'l*, pg. 1009
Kanda, Takafumi, Pres.--ORIX Hotels International Private Limited, Hong Kong, Hong Kong; *Int'l*, pg. 1009
Kandel, Jerry, Pres.--Hinkle Easter Products, Baltimore, MD; *U.S. Private*, pg. 666
Kandel, Svante, Gen Mgr.--Euroc Capital B.V., Neuchatel, Switzerland; *Int'l*, pg. 1200
Kandil, El Sayed Ahmed Mahmoud, Acctg. Gen. Mgr.--Alexandria Automotive Company SAE, Alexandria, Egypt; *U.S. Public*, pg. 665
Kandus, Marhan, Mng. Dir.--Banka Creditanstalt d.d., Ljubljana, Slovenia; *Int'l*, pg. 347
Kane, Brian L., Mng. Dir.--Bristol-Myers Company Limited, Uxbridge, United Kingdom; *U.S. Public*, pg. 255
Kane, Dennis B., Pres. & Chief Exec. Officer--ABC/Kane Productions International, Inc., Washington, DC; *U.S. Public*, pg. 511
Kane, Edward W., Mng. Dir.--John Hancock Venture Capital Management, Inc., Boston, MA; *U.S. Private*, pg. 590
Kane, Francis, V.P. & Gen. Mgr.--National Metal Industries, West Springfield, MA; *U.S. Public*, pg. 1506
Kane, Joseph R., Jr., Pres. & Chief Exec. Officer--Days Inns of America, Inc., Parsippany, NJ; *U.S. Public*, pg. 321
Kane, Richard C., Sr. V.P. & Mgr.-San Francisco Sls.--Jefferies & Company, Inc., Los Angeles, CA; *U.S. Public*, *pg. 925*
Kane, Richard C., Mgr.--Jefferies & Company, Inc., San Francisco, CA; *U.S. Public*, pg. 925
Kane, Thomas P., Pres. & Gen. Mgr.--WPVI-TV, Philadelphia, PA; *U.S. Public*, pg. 512
Kane, William E., Chm. Bd.--First National Bank in Marlinton, Marlinton, WV; *U.S. Public*, pg. 836
Kaneb, John, Mng. Partner--Gulf Oil, Chelsea, MA; *U.S. Private*, pg. 220
Kanegawa, C., Pres.--Shintech Inc., Houston, TX; *Int'l*, pg. 1234
Kanehann, William M., Pres.--INAC Corp., Philadelphia, PA; *U.S. Public*, pg. 366
Kanehann, William M., Pres.--INAC Corp. of California, Rancho Cordova, CA; *U.S. Public*, pg. 366
Kanehira, Yasuhiro, Chief Rep.--The Sakura Bank - Representative Office for the Middle East, Manama, Bahrain; *Int'l*, pg. 1180
Kaneko, K., Branch Mgr.--Kodak Far East Purchasing Co. Inc., Tokyo, Japan; *U.S. Public*, pg. 552
Kaneko, Masato, Chm., Pres. & Chief Exec. Officer--Manufacturers Bank, Los Angeles, CA; *Int'l*, pg. 1179
Kaneko, Mitsunori, Dir.--Agrochemicals Div., Tokyo, Japan; *Int'l*, pg. 934
Kaneto, Akinori, Chief Oper. Officer--P.T. Asuransi Tokio Marine Indonesia, Jakarta, Indonesia; *Int'l*, pg. 1392
Kang, Bong Sup, Mgr.--Willis Faber & Dumas Limited, Seoul, Korea; *Int'l*, pg. 1510
Kang, H.J., Mng. Dir.--Van Leeuwen Pipe and Tube Korea Ltd., Seoul, Korea; *Int'l*, pg. 1450
Kang, Shin Jung, Chief Rep.--Cho Hung Bank, Moscow Representative Office, Moscow, Russia; *Int'l*, pg. 288
Kangas, Eero, Mng. Dir.--Oy Skega Ab, Tampere, Finland; *Int'l*, pg. 1323
Kangas, Jorma, Mgr.--Enocell Oy, Uimaharju, Finland; *Int'l*, pg. 455
Kangas, Markku, Pres.--Valmet Automation Inc., Helsinki, Finland; *Int'l*, pg. 1449
Kangas, Seppo, Dir.-Sawmill--Kaukas Sawn Goods Industry, Lappeenranta, Finland; *Int'l*, pg. 1428
Kankin, Jerome, Gen. Mgr.--Miller Thermal, Inc., Appleton, WI; *U.S. Public*, pg. 867
Kann, Constance, Gen. Mgr.--Edelman Europe, Brussels, Belgium; *U.S. Private*, pg. 363
Kanner, Edwin, Pres.--American Insulated Wire Corp., Pawtucket, RI; *U.S. Private*, pg. 663
Kanner, Edwin, Pres.--Pacific Electricord Co., Gardena, CA; *U.S. Private*, pg. 663
Kanner, Robert H., Pres.--Buxton & Skinner Printing Company, Cleveland, OH; *U.S. Public*, pg. 1339
Kanngiesser, D., Gen. Mgr.--Baring Private Equity Partners, Frankfurt/Main, Germany; *Int'l*, pg. 648

Kanning, Rolf D., Mng. Dir.--Dresdner Bank AG, Beijing, China; *Int'l*, pg. 419

Kanno, Yukihiro, Pres.--P.T. Nikko Securities Indonesia, Jakarta, Indonesia; *Int'l*, pg. 931

Kanode, Pauline, Gen. Mgr.--First American Title Guaranty Agency of Crook County, Sundance, WY; *U.S. Public*, pg. 625

Kanode, Robert L., Pres. & Gen. Mgr.--VARTA Batteries Inc., Elmsford, NY; *Int'l*, pg. 1452

Kanoff, Chris M., Exec. V.P. & Dir.-Fin.--Jefferies & Company, Inc., Los Angeles, CA; *U.S. Public*, pg. 925

Kant, Robert, Mng. Dir.--Time-Life Books B.V., Amsterdam, Netherlands; *U.S. Public*, pg. 1615

Kantarci, Hazim, Gen. Mgr.--Toyotasa A.S., Istanbul, Turkey; *Int'l*, pg. 1168

Kantor, David, Pres.--ABC Radio Network, Inc., New York, NY; *U.S. Public*, pg. 512

Kanuckel, Jack, V.P. & Gen. Mgr.--Clow Water Systems Corp., Coshocton, OH; *U.S. Private*, pg. 725

Kanyama, Davis, Gen. Mgr.--Johnson & Johnson (Kenya) Ltd., Nairobi, Kenya; *U.S. Public*, pg. 930

Kanzaki, Yasuhiko, Chief Oper. Officer--Euro Makita Corporation B.V., Amsterdam, Netherlands; *Int'l*, pg. 831

Kanzaki, Yasuhiko, Chief Oper. Officer--Makita International Europe Ltd., Milton Keynes, United Kingdom; *Int'l*, pg. 832

Kanzi, Rudolph, Gen. Mgr.--Oesterreichisch Heraklith, A.G., Radenthein, Austria; *U.S. Private*, pg. 904

Kapalla, Elizabeth, Exec. V.P.--Health Education Technologies (HET) Div., New York, NY; *U.S. Public*, pg. 1224

Kapalla, Elizabeth A., Exec. V.P.--PRISM International, New York, NY; *U.S. Public*, pg. 1224

Kapash, Richard, Pres.--Symbol Technologies, Portable Systems Division, Costa Mesa, CA; *U.S. Public*, pg. 1546

Kapelowski, Tom, Mgr.-Division--Haleyville Drapery, Bloomsburg, PA; *U.S. Public*, pg. 491

Kaper, C.N., Mng. Dir.--Witco B.V., Haarlem, Netherlands; *U.S. Public*, pg. 1774

Kaper, C.N., Mng. Dir.--Witco B.V., Koog aan de Zaan, Netherlands; *U.S. Public*, pg. 1774

Kaplan, Arnold H., Pres.--APCI (U.K.), Inc., Allentown, PA; *U.S. Public*, pg. 30

Kaplan, Harley B., Pres.--Koehler Manufacturing Company, Marlborough, MA; *U.S. Private*, pg. 706

Kaplan, Ian, V.P.--BSA Advertising, Inc., North Miami, FL; *U.S. Private*, pg. 108

Kaplan, Ira, V.P.--EDO Marine and Aircraft Systems, College Point, NY; *U.S. Public*, pg. 542

Kaplan, J.G., Pres.-Plastics--AlliedSignal Inc., AlliedSignal Plastic, Morristown, NJ; *U.S. Public*, pg. 51

Kaplan, James A., Pres.--Capital Management Sciences, Los Angeles, CA; *U.S. Public*, pg. 484

Kaplan, Larry, Chief Exec. Officer--Shandwick Americas, New York, NY; *Int'l*, pg. 1226

Kaplan, Matthew, Sr. V.P. & Gen. Mgr.--Corrugated Container Div., Chicago, IL; *U.S. Public*, pg. 1520

Kaplan, Richard W., Pres.--Cigna Healthcare of Connecticut, Inc., Enfield, CT; *U.S. Public*, pg. 359

Kaplan, Richard W., Pres.--Cigna Healthcare of Massachusetts, Inc., Framingham, MA; *U.S. Public*, pg. 360

Kaplan, Richard W., Pres.--Cigna Healthcare of New York, Inc., Great Neck, NY; *U.S. Public*, pg. 360

Kaplan, Richard W., Pres.--Cigna Healthcare of Northern New Jersey, Inc., Denville, NJ; *U.S. Public*, pg. 360

Kaplan, Ron D., V.P.-Capital Markets--Street Retail, Inc., Rockville, MD; *U.S. Public*, pg. 616

Kaplan, Ronald W., Exec. V.P.--Plant City Steel Co., Plant City, FL; *U.S. Public*, pg. 793

Kaplan, Ronald W., Pres.--Taylor-Wharton Gas Equipment, Camp Hill, PA; *U.S. Public*, pg. 793

Kapoon, Raman, V.P. & Gen. Mgr.--Dentsply India, New Delhi, India; *U.S. Public*, pg. 499

Kapp, Michael, Pres.--Warner Special Products, Burbank, CA; *U.S. Public*, pg. 1612

Kapp, Pat, V.P.--POST Buckley Schuh & Jernigan, Irvine, CA; *U.S. Private*, pg. 826

Kappauf, Donald W., Pres.--Digital Staff ConnXions, Somerset, NJ; *U.S. Public*, pg. 508

Kappeler, Gerhard, Mng. Dir.--Hosokawa MikroPul GmbH, Cologne, Germany; *Int'l*, pg. 636

Kappeli, Rene, Mng. Dir.--Shannon Turbine Technologies Ltd., Shannon, Ireland; *Int'l*, pg. 1308

Kappler, George, Chm. Bd. & Pres.--Kappler USA, Guntersville, AL; *U.S. Private*, pg. 607

Kappus, Gerd, Pres.--Filterwerk Mann & Hummel GmbH, Speyer, Germany; *Int'l*, pg. 484

Kapur, A., Gen. Mgr.--Algemene Bank Nederland, Mumbai, India; *Int'l*, pg. 11

Kapur, Anil, Chief Oper. Officer--Novo Nordisk (India) Pvt Ltd, Bangalore, India; *Int'l*, pg. 988

Kapur, S.N., Gen. Mgr., Deputy Gen. Mgr.-India--Deutsche Bank AG (New Delhi), New Delhi, India; *Int'l*, pg. 404

Kapur, Sudhir, Dr., Chief Oper Officer--Flender Macneill Gears Ltd., Calcutta, India; *Int'l*, pg. 401

Kapusta, George, Pres.--Commerce Bank, College Park, MD; *U.S. Public*, pg. 1038

Kar, Maharaj, Chief Exec.--Sulzer Flovel Hydro Ltd., New Delhi, India; *Int'l*, pg. 1308

Karachuk, Halina L., Pres.--MONY Brokerage, Inc., Harrisburg, PA; *U.S. Private*, pg. 769

Karaffa, Corwin J., Pres.--Preferred Public Storage Co., Los Angeles, CA; *U.S. Private*, pg. 227

Karagianis, L.P., V.P. & Gen. Mgr.--Xerox Special Information Systems, Pasadena, CA; *U.S. Public*, pg. 1784

Karahan, Sabri, Gen. Mgr.--Cominco Madencilik Sanayi A.S., Ankara, Turkey; *Int'l*, pg. 307

Karai, D. Puthu, V.P.-Direct Mktg.--B.M.G. Music Service, New York, NY; *Int'l*, pg. 1383

Karalis, P.A., Gen. Mgr.--ING Bank Greece, Athens, Greece; *Int'l*, pg. 649

Karalis, P.A., Gen. Mgr.--Nationale-Nederlanden, Athens, Greece; *Int'l*, pg. 650

Karam, Thomas, Pres. & Chief Exec. Officer--PG Energy, Inc., Wilkes-Barre, PA; *U.S. Public*, pg. 1271

Karam, Victor A., V.P.-Footwear--McRae Footwear Div., Mount Gilead, NC; *U.S. Public*, pg. 1073

Karamercan, Erdal, Gen. Mgr.--Ipek Kagit Sanayi ve Ticaret A.S., Istanbul, Turkey; *U.S. Public*, pg. 673

Karamercan, Erdal, Gen. Mgr.--Karamursel Mill, Izmit, Turkey; *U.S. Public*, pg. 673

Karanian, Ralph E., Gen. Mgr.--Pratt & Whitney, Plainville, CT; *U.S. Public*, pg. 1128

Karas, Dean, Plant Mgr.--Farr Company, Crystal Lake, IL; *U.S. Public*, pg. 614

Karasawa, Hiroshi, Pres.--Niko Co., Ltd., Tokyo, Japan; *Int'l*, pg. 883

Karasawa, M., Mng. Dir.--Nippon Donaldson Ltd., Tokyo, Japan; *U.S. Public*, pg. 517

Karasawa, M., Gen. Mgr.--Marubeni America Corporation, Dallas Branch, Dallas, TX; *Int'l*, pg. 844

Karasawa, Shinji, Pres.--Daiwa Europe (France) S.A., Paris, France; *Int'l*, pg. 375

Kardos, Andy, Pres.--Publicis BCP Direct Inc., Toronto, Canada; *Int'l*, pg. 116

Kardos, Paul J., Pres.--Allegiance Insurance Company, Springfield, IL; *U.S. Public*, pg. 362

Karekallas, Markku, Chief Oper. Officer--Perstorp IKI Oy Decorative Laminate, Kolho, Finland; *Int'l*, pg. 1038

Karhio, Matti, Resident Mgr.--Jyvaskyla Mills, Jyvaskyla, Finland; *Int'l*, pg. 1429

Karhunen, Kimmo, Gen. Mgr.--Tektronix Oy, Helsinki, Finland; *U.S. Public*, pg. 1568

Karisson, Carl-Ake, Mng. Dir.--Jotun Sverige A.B., Vastra Frolunda, Sweden; *Int'l*, pg. 715

Karjalainen, Markku, Mng. Dir.--Kalso-Teollisuus Oy, Vuohijarvi, Finland; *Int'l*, pg. 1428

Karjaluoto, Johan, Mng. Dir.--Wisaforest Oy Ab, Pietarsaari, Finland; *Int'l*, pg. 1429

Karkhanis, P.S., Mng. Dir.--Simpson Industries, Inc., Pune, India; *U.S. Public*, pg. 1475

KarKinkead, Karl, V.P. & Gen. Mgr.--Ansul Incorporated, Marinette, WI; *U.S. Public*, pg. 1648

Karklins, George J., V.P. & Treas.--CoreStates Capital Corp., Philadelphia, PA; *U.S. Public*, pg. 446

Karkonen, Kalevi, Chief Oper. Officer--Oy Electrolux Ab-TAMMERMATIC, Tampere, Finland; *Int'l*, pg. 441

Karkosky, Jim, Gen. Mgr.--Golden State Foods-Northwest Div., Sumner, WA; *U.S. Private*, pg. 460

Karl, Dr. Otfried, Co-Chief Oper. Officer--INDUSTRIE-RING Sach-und Versicherungs-Vermittlungsgesellschaft mbH, Saarbruecken, Germany; *Int'l*, pg. 1166

Karl, J. Don, Chief Exec. Officer--Healthcare Diagnostics Centers, El Paso, TX; *U.S. Public*, pg. 405

Karl, Klaus, Mng. Dir.--Pitney Bowes Deutschland G.m.b.H., Heppenheim, Germany; *U.S. Public*, pg. 1304

Karl, Paul M., Country Rep.--IPOK, Zrenjanin, Serbia; *U.S. Public*, pg. 447

Karlen, Jorgen, Chief Oper. Officer--A/S Drommekjokkenet, Oslo, Norway; *Int'l*, pg. 443

Karlen, Stig, Div. Mgr.--AB Sture Ljungdahl, Nybro, Sweden; *Int'l*, pg. 1423

Karlin, Miriam, Mgr.-Admin.--Florida Health Facilities, Inc., Lutz, FL; *U.S. Public*, pg. 1035

Karlsen, Arne, Admin. Dir.--Intel Norway, Skjetten, Norway; *U.S. Public*, pg. 887

Karlsen, Ivan G., Pres.--Frigoscandia A/S, Lysaker, Norway; *U.S. Public*, pg. 606

Karlsen, Terje, Pres.--Lysaker Reisebyra a.s., Lysaker, Norway; *Int'l*, pg. 769

Karlson, Arne, Chief Oper. Officer--Scania-Bussar AB, Katrineholm, Sweden; *Int'l*, pg. 687

Karlsson, Bjorn, Chief Oper. Officer--Perstorp Components, Amotfors, Sweden; *Int'l*, pg. 1040

Karlsson, Bjorn, Mgr.--Sandvik Obergue-Limas e Mecanica Lda., Vila do Conde, Portugal; *Int'l*, pg. 1186

Karlsson, Carl-Goran, Gen. Mgr.--EleComp, Helsinki, Finland; *Int'l*, pg. 746

Karlsson, Christer, Mng. Dir.--Pharmacia & Upjohn Data AB, Uppsala, Sweden; *Int'l*, pg. 1048

Karlsson, Christer, Chief Oper. Officer--Dataliner AB, Eskilstuna, Sweden; *Int'l*, pg. 1289

Karlsson, Ingvar, Mng. Dir.--SKF Belgium S.A., Brussels, Belgium; *Int'l*, pg. 1158

Karlsson, Jerry, Mng. Dir.--Lidkoping Machine Tools AB, Linkoping, Sweden; *Int'l*, pg. 1157

Karlsson, Klas-Goran, Mill Mgr.--Metsa-Serla AB (Nyboholm Mill), Kvillsfors, Sweden; *Int'l*, pg. 864

Karlsson, Mats, Chief Oper. Officer--Granges Nigeria Ltd., Lagos, Nigeria; *Int'l*, pg. 443

Karlsson, Paul, Reg. Dir.-Eastern Europe--ESAB International AB, Goteborg, Sweden; *Int'l*, pg. 281

Karlsson, Stefan, Mng. Dir.--SKF Norge A/S, Oslo, Norway; *Int'l*, pg. 1159

Karlsson, Sune, Pres.--ABB Transformers AB, Ludvika, Sweden; *Int'l*, pg. 7

Karlsson, Tommy, Chief Oper. Officer--Hufvudstaden France S.A., Paris, France; *Int'l*, pg. 478

Karlsson, Tommy H., Pres.--Crown Cork & Seal, European Division, Paris, France; *U.S. Public*, pg. 464

Karlstrom, Arne, Chief Oper. Officer--Scania Belgium sa-nv, Diegem, Belgium; *Int'l*, pg. 687

Karman, Dale, Pres.--ADP Fluor Daniel, Tucson, AZ; *U.S. Public*, pg. 660

Karnatz, Robert, Admin.--Hillhaven Convalescent Hospital Orange, Orange, CA; *U.S. Public*, pg. 1713

Karnes, Chuck, Gen. Mgr.--Barton's of Monticello, Monticello, AR; *U.S. Private*, pg. 119

Karnes, Gary A., Pres.--Appleton Electric Co., Chicago, IL; *U.S. Public*, pg. 572

Karns, Randy, V.P. & Gen. Mgr.--BKI, Simpsonville, SC; *U.S. Public*, pg. 1506

Karp, John, Chief Oper. Officer--Shiseido U.K. Co., Ltd., London, United Kingdom; *Int'l*, pg. 1236

Karppinen, Lassi, Mng. Dir.--Perimistoimisto Contant Oy, Turku, Finland; *Int'l*, pg. 859

Karr, Gary, Gen. Mgr.--TransAmerican Refining Corp., New Sarpy, LA; *U.S. Private*, pg. 1096

Karros, George A., Pres. & Chief Exec. Officer--Union Bank of California, San Diego, CA; *Int'l*, pg. 157

Karsholm, Bjorn, Mng. Dir.--Kvaerner Installasjon, Kristiansund Division, Kristiansand, Norway; *Int'l*, pg. 769

Karskens, Paulus, Mng. Dir.--IGT-Europe b.v., Hoofddorp, Netherlands; *U.S. Public*, pg. 900

Kartau, Madis, Mng. Dir.--AS Neopac-Elkson, Maakond, Estonia; *Int'l*, pg. 863

Kartaun, M., Chief Oper. Officer--Grunzweig & Hartmann und Glasfaser AG, Ludwigshafen, Germany; *Int'l*, pg. 1176

Karter, E.M., Pres.--Forest Kraft Company, Dayton, OH; *U.S. Public*, pg. 1076

Karube, Kenji, Chief Oper. Officer--Makita U.S.A., Inc., La Mirada, CA; *Int'l*, pg. 831

Karuklis, Walter, Branch Mgr.--Union-Transport Corporation-Houston Office, Houston, TX; *U.S. Private*, pg. 1119

Karutz, P., Mng. Dir.--Ascom GmbH, Frankfurt, Germany; *Int'l*, pg. 87

Karuula, Matti, Chief Oper. Officer--Karelia Procurement Area, Uimaharju, Finland; *Int'l*, pg. 455

Karvonen, Jim, Gen. Mgr.--Republic Automotive Parts Sales, Inc., Duluth, MN; *U.S. Public*, pg. 1378

Karwoski, Glenn, V.P. & Mng. Dir.--Karwoski & Courage, Minneapolis, MN; *U.S. Private*, pg. 710

Kasahara, Kazuto, Pres.--Nippon Gatx Co., Ltd., Tokyo, Japan; *U.S. Public*, pg. 693

Kasahara, Y., Chief Oper. Officer--IMC Associates, Inc., Tokyo, Japan; *Int'l*, pg. 834

Kasai, Y., Dir. & Gen. Mgr.--Fuji Heavy Industries, Ltd., Mitaka Plant, Tokyo, Japan; *Int'l*, pg. 523

Kasai, Yutaka, Pres.--Kawasaki Heavy Industries (Europe) B.V., Amsterdam, Netherlands; *Int'l*, pg. 726

Kasarcik, Don, Plant Mgr.--Enthone OMI-Bridgeview, Bridgeview, IL; *U.S. Public*, pg. 138

Kase, Rolf, Chief Oper. Officer--Dentsply Gmbh, Konstanz, Germany; *U.S. Public*, pg. 499

Kaselau, Rainer, Dr., Mgr.--Deutsche Flugzeugvermietungs AG, Stapelburg, Germany; *Int'l*, pg. 596

Kasen, Keith, Exec. V.P. & Gen. Mgr.--Busch Gardens Williamsburg, Williamsburg, VA; *U.S. Public*, pg. 114

Kash, J., Pres.--Dresser-Rand Co. (Wellsville), Wellsville, NY; *U.S. Public*, pg. 529

Kash, Lawrence S., Pres. & Chief Exec. Officer--Laurel Capital Advisors, Pittsburgh, PA; *U.S. Public*, pg. 1085

Kashi, Akira, Chm. Bd.--ORIX Ireland Limited, Dublin, Ireland; *Int'l*, pg. 1009

Kashima, Toshiyuki, Pres.--Sumitomo Bank Capital Markets, Inc., New York, NY; *Int'l*, pg. 1308

Kashnow, Richard A., Pres.--Manville Sales Corporation, Denver, CO; *U.S. Public*, pg. 927

Kashnow, Richard A., Pres.--Schuller International, Inc., Denver, CO; *U.S. Public*, pg. 927

Kasinger, Roy, Branch Mgr.--Weatherford US Inc., Rancho Dominguez, CA; *U.S. Public*, pg. 1749

Kasior, Michael, Mng. Dir.--Norfi Exhaust Extraction Systems GmbH, Ratekau, Germany; *Int'l*, pg. 283

Kaskel, Roy R., Pres.--Enron Liquids Services Corp., Houston, TX; *U.S. Public*, pg. 584

Kaskel, Roy R., Chm. Bd. & Chief Exec. Officer--Enron Liquid Services Corp., Houston, TX; *U.S. Public*, pg. 584

Kasko, Heikki, Mng. Dir.--Nokia Telecommunications (Thailand) Ltd., Bangkok, Thailand; *Int'l*, pg. 954

Kasmer, Anthony, Pres.--Tri-Lite Plastics, Inc., Fallsington, PA; *Int'l*, pg. 233

Kaspar, Franz, Pres.--Parker Hannifin Corporation, Hemel Hempstead, United Kingdom; *U.S. Public*, pg. 1261

Kasputis, David, Plant Mgr.--Hoeganaes Corp., Gallatin, TN; *U.S. Public*, pg. 893

Kasputys, Joseph E., Pres. & Chief Exec. Officer--Primark Storage Leasing Corporation, Mc Lean, VA; *U.S. Public*, pg. 1325

Kass, Ron, Chief Exec. Officer--Robert Allen Ametek, Mansfield, MA; *U.S. Private*, pg. 432

Kass, Ron, Chief Exec. Officer--Ametex Fabrics, Inc., Mansfield, MA; *U.S. Private*, pg. 432

Kass, Warren, Mng. Dir.--Partners & Shevack Design, New York, NY; *U.S. Private*, pg. 842

Kassa, Kelley, V.P. & Gen. Mgr.--Technology Solutions Inc., Boston, MA; *U.S. Private*, pg. 1157

Kassab, Robert, Pres.--Play Systems, Deerfield Beach, FL; *U.S. Private*, pg. 1029

Kassin, Raymond, V.P.--RNBNY Representative Office-Montevideo, Montevideo, Uruguay; *U.S. Public*, pg. 1381

Kassin, Raymond, V.P.--RNBNY Representative Office-Uruguay, Punta del Este, Uruguay; *U.S. Public*, pg. 1381

Kassis, May, V.P.--Clouston Foods Canada, Lachine, Canada; *Int'l*, pg. 492

Kast, Gerhard, Mng. Dir.--DYWIDAG Systems International, USA, Inc., Abbotsford, Canada; *Int'l*, pg. 424

Kastel, August, Pres.--Matrix Science Corporation, Torrance, CA; *U.S. Public*, pg. 8

Kastel, August P., Div. V.P.--AMP Aerospace/Government Systems Division, Harrisburg, PA; *U.S. Public*, pg. 7

Kasten, Stan, Pres.--Atlanta Braves, Inc., Atlanta, GA; *U.S. Public*, pg. 1614

Kasticky, Johannes, Member of the Bd.--VOEST-ALPINE Stahlhandel AG, Lienz, Austria; *Int'l*, pg. 1470

Kastner, Erich, Asst. V.P.-Hydro Div.--Voest-Alpine International Corp.-Hydro Division, Berlin, NJ; *Int'l*, pg. 1470

Kastner, Winifried, Reg. V.P.-Asia/Pacific North--Procter & Gamble (Malaysia), Petaling Jaya, Malaysia; *U.S. Public*, pg. 1332

Kasuya, Masonori, Central Div. Mgr.--Pentel Central Regional Office, Elk Grove Village, IL; *Int'l*, pg. 1035

Kat, J., Chief Oper. Officer--Rabobank Trust Company, Luxembourg, Luxembourg; *Int'l*, pg. 1082

Katagiri, T., Pres.--Achilles USA, Inc., Everett, WA; *Int'l*, pg. 22

Katajamaki, Seppo, V.P.--Kyro Board Mill, Kyroskoski, Finland; *Int'l*, pg. 863

Kataoka, K., Mgr.--Tokio Marine Management Inc. - Houston, Houston, TX; *Int'l*, pg. 1392

Katayama, A., Pres.--Simco Japan Inc., Kobe, Japan; *U.S. Public*, pg. 869

Katayama, Hideaki, Gen. Mgr.--Chubu Electric Power Co., Inc. (London Office), London, United Kingdom; *Int'l*, pg. 290

Katayama, Hiroshi, Chief Oper. Officer--Nissho Iwai de Venezuela C.A., Caracas, Venezuela; *Int'l*, pg. 948

Katayama, Takazi, Mng. Dir.--Sun Electric do Brasil Comercio e. Industria Limitada, Sao Paulo, Brazil; *U.S. Public*, pg. 1481

Katayama, Wayne K., Pres.--Hawaiian Fruit Specialties Co., Ltd., Kalaheo, HI; *U.S. Private*, pg. 190

Kate, Nancy Ten, Mng. Editor--American Demographics, Inc., Ithaca, NY; *U.S. Private*, pg. 281

Kathmann, Michael A., Pres.--Hilb, Rogal and Hamilton Company of Grand Rapids, Grand Rapids, MI; *U.S. Public*, pg. 827

Katler, Gary, V.P. & Gen. Mgr.--LIT America Inc., Chicago, IL; *U.S. Public*, pg. 181

Kato, Akira, Pres.--Kumagai Properties Inc., Honolulu, HI; *Int'l*, pg. 764

Kato, Hiromichi, Chief Oper. Officer--Kyowa Hakko Kogyo Co., Ltd., Beijing, China; *Int'l*, pg. 778

Kato, Isaoio, Mng. Dir. & Gen. Mgr.--Fashion Business Group, Nagoya, Japan; *Int'l*, pg. 229

Kato, K., Pres.--Nippon Suisan U.S.A., Redmond, WA; *Int'l*, pg. 940

Kato, Kenji, Gen. Mgr.--The Sakura Bank - Tianjin Branch, Tianjin, China; *Int'l*, pg. 1179

Kato, Masahiko, Chm. & Chief Exec. Officer--Otsuka America, Inc., San Francisco, CA; *Int'l*, pg. 1013

Kato, Masahiko, Chm. Bd.--Otsuka America Pharmaceutical, Inc., Rockville, MD; *Int'l*, pg. 1013

Kato, R., Eastern Div. Mgr.--Pentel Eastern Regional Office, Fairfield, NJ; *Int'l*, pg. 1035

Kato, S., Pres.--MSA Japan Ltd., Tokyo, Japan; *U.S. Public*, *pg. 1115*

Kato, Shinji, Pres.--DKB Financial Futures Corp., Chicago, IL; *Int'l*, pg. 360

Kato, Y., V.P. & Gen. Mgr.--Noritake Co., Inc.-Abrasive Division, Secaucus, NJ; *Int'l*, pg. 959

Kato, Yuji, Chief Representative--The Sumitomo Trust & Banking Co., Ltd., Jakarta, Indonesia; *Int'l*, pg. 1318

Kato, Yuzo, V.P.--Nissan Motor Parts Centre (Europe) B.V., Amsterdam, Netherlands; *Int'l*, pg. 945

Katrak, B.J., Mng. Dir.--SAB Electronic Devices Ltd., Sahibabad, India; *Int'l*, pg. 1369

Katrus, Anton A., Pres.--Brody Co. Div., Cincinnati, OH; *U.S. Public*, pg. 976

Katsaras, Vassilios, Mgr.--National Bank of Greece Chicago Branch, Chicago, IL; *Int'l*, pg. 907

Katsoudas, Harry, Mgr.--Amano Cincinnati - Atlanta Branch Office, Roswell, GA; *Int'l*, pg. 70

Katsoulas, George, Sr. Mng. Dir.--Scholl Hellas SA, Athens, Greece; *Int'l*, pg. 1209

Katsu, Shiego, Country Dir.--The World Bank, Abidjan, Cote d'Ivoire; *U.S. Private*, pg. 1189

Katsumata, Mark, Pres.--Indo-Pacific Energy Ltd., Vancouver, Canada; *Int'l*, pg. 422

Katsumoto, Malolm T., Chm. Bd.--Toray Composites (America), Inc., Tacoma, WA; *Int'l*, pg. 1400

Katsushima, I., Mng. Dir.--NatWest Investment Management Japan Limited, Tokyo, Japan; *Int'l*, pg. 911

Katsuya, Yoshiro, Mng. Dir.--The Nikko Securities Co., (Asia) Limited, Central, Hong Kong; *Int'l*, pg. 931

Kattar, Jorge A., Chief Exec.--CIMINAS-Cimento Nacional de Minas S.A., Sao Paulo, Brazil; *Int'l*, pg. 629

Kattar, Richard J., Pres.--New England CRInc., Chelmsford, MA; *U.S. Public*, pg. 1753

Katz, Donald L., Pres.--Capitol Manufacturing Co., Westerville, OH; *U.S. Public*, pg. 793

Katz, Howard, V.P.-Opers.--Tucci Benucch, Chicago, IL; *U.S. Private*, pg. 661

Katz, Howard, V.P.-Opers.--Avanzare, Chicago, IL; *U.S. Private*, pg. 661

Katz, Howard, V.P.-Opers.--Tucchetti, Phoenix, AZ; *U.S. Private*, pg. 661

Katz, Howard, V.P.-Opers.--Tucci Benucch, Bloomington, MN; *U.S. Private*, pg. 661

Katz, Howard, V.P.-Opers.--Food Life, Chicago, IL; *U.S. Private*, pg. 661

Katz, Howard, V.P.-Opers.--Tucci Benucch, Seattle, WA; *U.S. Private*, pg. 661

Katz, Howard, V.P.-Opers.--Twin City Diner, Bloomington, MN; *U.S. Private*, pg. 662

Katz, J.G., Pres.--SABRE Travel Information Network, Fort Worth, TX; *U.S. Public*, pg. 10

Katz, Joel, Pres. & Chief Exec. Officer--Boatmen's National Mortgage Inc., Memphis, TN; *U.S. Public*, pg. 1165

Katz, Matthew, Chm. & Gen. Mgr.--EURO RSCG, Warsaw, Poland; *Int'l*, pg. 602

Katz, Milton, Chm. Bd.--Chase Financial Services Corp., Cleveland, OH; *U.S. Public*, pg. 338

Katz, Milton, Pres.--Chase Financial Management Corp., Cleveland, OH; *U.S. Public*, pg. 338

Katz, Nart, Chief Oper. Officer--Quinton Electro Physiology, Richmond Hill, Canada; *U.S. Public*, pg. 82

Katz, Nathan, Pres.--Dana Lighting, Inc., Easton, MA; *U.S. Public*, pg. 314

Katz, Neil J., Pres.--Liz Claiborne Cosmetics, Inc., New York, NY; *U.S. Public*, pg. 1006

Katz, Warren, Chm. Bd.--Manhattan Factory, New York, NY; *U.S. Public*, pg. 1429

Katzenberger, George, Pres.--Upright, Saint Louis, MO; *U.S. Private*, pg. 1128

Katzman, Fred, Pres.--Nielsen & Bainbridge, Cranbury, NJ; *Int'l*, pg. 460

Kaudopoulos, Paula, Gen. Mgr.--Arrow Hellas AEE, Athens, Greece; *U.S. Public*, pg. 135

Kauffman, Beat, Grp. Mng. Dir.--Schiesser Eminence Holding AG, Stein, Switzerland; *Int'l*, pg. 618

Kauffman, J.B., Pres.--Jen-Coat Inc., Westfield, MA; *U.S. Public*, pg. 70

Kauffman, James B., Jr., Pres.--Northern Central Bank, Williamsport, PA; *U.S. Public*, pg. 956

Kauffman, Larry, Plant Mgr.--GRN Corp., Gothenburg, NE; *U.S. Private*, pg. 466

Kauffman, Michael L., Pres.--Nobel/Sysco Food Services Company-Denver, Denver, CO; *U.S. Public*, pg. 1551

Kaufman, Derek, Chief Exec. Officer--Diesel Technology Company, Wyoming, MI; *Int'l*, pg. 205

Kaufman, Harry, Mgr.-Opers.--Troy Operations, Troy, OH; *U.S. Public*, pg. 1475

Kaufman, Jeffrey V., V.P.-Central Region--Wall Street Deli, Inc., Chicago, IL; *U.S. Public*, pg. 1734

Kaufman, Jerry M., Pres.--Nationwide Credit, Marietta, GA; *U.S. Public*, pg. 631

Kaufman, Linda, Branch Mgr.--Zellerbach Division, Yakima, WA; *U.S. Public*, pg. 1075

Kaufman, Michael, Pres.--Kaufel America Inc., Baldwin, NY; *Int'l*, pg. 725

Kaufman, Michael, Pres. & Chief Exec. Officer--Ponderosa Steakhouse, Dallas, TX; *U.S. Private*, pg. 736

Kaufman, Ray, Pres.--J.R. Simplot Co.-Diversified Products Group, Caldwell, ID; *U.S. Private*, pg. 1002

Kaufman, Stephen P., Pres. & Chief Exec. Officer--MTI Systems Corp., Melville, NY; *U.S. Public*, pg. 134

Kaufmann, David, Pres.--The Vacation Store, Virginia Beach, VA; *U.S. Private*, pg. 649

Kaufmann, J., Mgr.--Schweizerischer Bankverein, Bern, Switzerland; *Int'l*, pg. 1329

Kaufmann, J., Pres.--Swiss Bank & Trust Corporation Ltd., Georgetown, Cayman Islands; *Int'l*, pg. 1332

Kaufmann, M., Mng. Dir.--Oerlikon Singapore Pte. Ltd., Singapore, Singapore; *Int'l*, pg. 998

Kaufmann, Michael C., V.P. & Gen. Mgr.--National PharmPak Services, Inc., Zanesville, OH; *U.S. Public*, pg. 304

Kaufmann, O.A., Mng. Dir.--GKN Birfield SpA, Bruneck, Italy; *Int'l*, pg. 535

Kaul, David, Gen. Mgr.-North America--Cab-o-Sil Div. Cabot Corp., Tuscola, IL; *U.S. Public*, pg. 289

Kaupas, Jan P., Mng. Dir.--ISS Building Maintenance, Inc., New York, NY; *Int'l*, pg. 656

Kauppila, Jarmo, Pres.--Sensodec Oy, Kajaani, Finland; *Int'l*, pg. 1449

Kauppila, Jussi, V.P.--Tako Board Mill, Tampere, Finland; *Int'l*, pg. 863

Kaur, Jaswinder, Media Dir.--Kreasindo Advertising & Marketing Consultants, Jakarta, Indonesia; *U.S. Private*, pg. 184

Kauranen, Jouko, Mng. Dir.--Mecakone Oy, Joensuu, Finland; *Int'l*, pg. 1353

Kauranen, Timo, Chief Exec. Officer & Mng. Dir.--Foster Wheeler Energia Oy, Helsinki, Finland; *U.S. Public*, pg. 677

Kaurisa, C.V., Chm.--Stanbic Bank Namibia Limited, Windhoek, Namibia; *Int'l*, pg. 1293

Kausman, Carl, Pres.--Kenneth Gordon IAG, Inc., New Orleans, LA; *U.S. Private*, pg. 581

Kautonen, Harri, Sawmill Mgr.--Kitee Sawmill, Puhos, Finland; *Int'l*, pg. 456

Kautz, J.H., Chm. Bd. & Chief Exec. Officer--Grain Processing Corp., Muscatine, IA; *U.S. Private*, pg. 1134

Kavalsky, Basil G., Contry Dir.--The World Bank, Warsaw, Poland; *U.S. Private*, pg. 1189

Kavanah, John, Chm. Bd., Pres. & Chief Exec. Officer--Marketing Corp. of America, Westport, CT; *U.S. Private*, pg. 704

Kavanaugh, Penn, Pres. & Chief Exec. Officer--Shieffelin Somerset Co., New York, NY; *Int'l*, pg. 412

Kavanaugh, Steve, Plant Mgr.--Power Control Div., Bowling Green, KY; *U.S. Public*, pg. 556

Kavourakis, Sam, Mng. Dir.--National Mutual Funds Management (Global) Ltd., Melbourne, Australia; *Int'l*, pg. 908

Kawabarayashi, Seji, Chm. & Mng. Dir.--Mitsui & Co. (Australia), Brisbane, Australia; *Int'l*, pg. 880

Kawabata, A., Pres.--Toshiba Electronics Europe GmbH, Dusseldorf, Germany; *Int'l*, pg. 1406

Kawabata, Yoshihiko, Chief Rep.--The Sumitomo Bank, Ltd.-Chongqing Representative Office, Chongqing, China; *Int'l*, pg. 1309

Kawachi, Akio, Mng. Dir. & Gen. Mgr.--Bank of Yokohama (Europe) S.A., Brussels, Belgium; *Int'l*, pg. 159

Kawachi, Matt, Dir.-Engrng.--Mitsubishi Electric Mfg., Mason, OH; *Int'l*, pg. 872

Kawaguchi, Akio, Gen. Mgr.--MSC Japan Ltd., Kyoto, Japan; *U.S. Public*, pg. 1032

Kawaguchi, Gary, V.P.--Fishking Processors, Inc., Los Angeles, CA; *Int'l*, pg. 940

Kawaguchi, Hirotada, Chief Oper. Officer--Hitachi Power Engineering Co., Ltd., Hitachi, Japan; *Int'l*, pg. 621

Kawaguchi, Shozo, V.P. & Gen. Mgr.--Inco Limited, Japan Branch, Tokyo, Japan; *Int'l*, pg. 672

Kawaharada, S., Pres.--Tokuyama Europe GmbH, Dusseldorf, Germany; *Int'l*, pg. 1394

Kawai, H., Pres.--Toshiba Semiconductor G.m.b.H., Braunschweig, Germany; *Int'l*, pg. 1407

Kawai, Kazuyoshi, Pres.--Western Alaska Fisheries Inc., Seattle, WA; *Int'l*, pg. 845

Kawai, Kazuyoshi, Pres.--Trans Ocean Products, Inc., Bellingham, WA; *Int'l*, pg. 845

Kawajiri, Yoshihisa, Chief Rep.--The Sakura Bank - Manila Representative Office, Manila, Philippines; *Int'l*, pg. 1180

Kawakami, Fumio, Chief Exec.--Sulzer Metco (Japan) Ltd., Tokyo, Japan; *Int'l*, pg. 1308

Kawakami, Tetsuji, Gen. Mgr.--The Chiba Bank, Ltd.-New York Branch, New York, NY; *Int'l*, pg. 283

Kawakami, Yoshiaki, Mng. Dir. & Gen. Mgr.--Daiwa Bank (Capital Management) Ltd., London, United Kingdom; *Int'l*, pg. 373

Kawamori, Kiyoshi, Chief Oper. Officer--Makita, S.A., Madrid, Spain; *Int'l*, pg. 832

Kawamoto, Jun, Chief Rep.--Taipei Representative Office, Taipei, Taiwan; *Int'l*, pg. 1485

Kawamoto, Toshio, Chief Exec. Officer--Willis Corroon Japan Limited, Tokyo, Japan; *Int'l*, pg. 1509

Kawamura, Hajime, Pres.--Tomen America Inc., New York, NY; *Int'l*, pg. 1395

Kawamura, Kazuhisa, Terminal Mgr.--Kintetsu World Express Inc., Newark, NJ; *Int'l*, pg. 734

Kawamura, Koji, Chief Oper. Officer--Makita (New Zealand) Ltd., Auckland, New Zealand; *Int'l*, pg. 832

Kawamura, M., Pres.--Juki Union Special, Inc., Wayne, NJ; *Int'l*, pg. 716

Kawamura, Seidhiro, Country Mgr.--Standard Chartered Bank (Japan), Tokyo, Japan; *Int'l*, pg. 1295

Kawamura, Takeo, Pres.--Taisei America Corp., Long Beach, CA; *Int'l*, pg. 1347

Kawamura, Yoshinori, Pres.--ARS Chemical (Thailand) Co., Ltd., Bangkok, Thailand; *Int'l*, pg. 1014

Kawanaka, Katsuo, Pres.--Y.O. Machinery Leasing Co., Ltd., Tokyo, Japan; *Int'l*, pg. 1009

KAwanata, Yoshitaka, V.P.--Shiseido Cosmetics (America) Ltd., Oakland, NJ; *Int'l*, pg. 1235

Kawanishi, Isao, Chief Rep.--The Sumitomo Trust & Banking Co., Ltd., Chicago, IL; *Int'l*, pg. 1317

Kawano, Hiroshi, Mng. Dir.--Fuji Bank (Deutschland) AG, Frankfurt/Main, Germany; *Int'l*, pg. 521

Kawarabayashi, Seiji, Chm.--Mitsui & Co. (N.Z.) Ltd., Wellington, New Zealand; *Int'l*, pg. 882

Kawarasaki, Atsuhi, Pres.--Mitsui Mining Co., Ltd., Tokyo, Japan; *Int'l*, pg. 878

Kawasaki, Yasushi, Pres.--Nihon Building Co. Ltd., Tokyo, Japan; *Int'l*, pg. 702

Kawasaki, Yutaka, Chm. Bd.--Nanto Investment Management Co., Ltd., Nara, Japan; *Int'l*, pg. 905

Kawashima, Yukio, Chief Oper. Officer--Honda International Sales Corp., Tokyo, Japan; *Int'l*, pg. 634

Kawauchi, Tsuneno, Pres.--AP Techno Glass Company, Bellefontaine, OH; *Int'l*, pg. 84

Kawer, Sheldon, Exec. V.P.--Vitt Media Direct, New York, NY; *U.S. Private*, pg. 1142

Kay, Brian, Pres. & Chief Exec. Officer--Connecting Point Computer Services, Canton, OH; *U.S. Private*, pg. 471

Kay, Jay, Pres.--Phoenix Technologies Ltd., Norwood, MA; *U.S. Public*, pg. 1292

Kay, R., Pres.--Filtertek Inc., Hebron, IL; *U.S. Public*, pg. 546

Kay, Steve, Reg. Mgr.--Green Tree Acceptance, Inc., Rancho Cucamonga, CA; *U.S. Public*, pg. 762

Kay, Tony, Chief Oper. Officer--Hagglunds Drives Ltd, York, United Kingdom; *Int'l*, pg. 670

Kayashi, Mr., Mgr.--Mitsubishi Oil America, New York, NY; *Int'l*, pg. 876

Kayatz, Carsten, Mgr.--Commerzbank Rio de Janeiro Servicos Ltda. Representative Office, Rio de Janeiro, Brazil; *Int'l*, pg. 312

Kaye, Debra, Mng. Dir.--BDDP Mancebo Kaye, Madrid, Spain; *Int'l*, pg. 117

Kaye, Issac, Chm. Bd. & Chief Exec. Officer--Norton Healthcare Limited, Harlow, United Kingdom; *U.S. Public*, *pg. 915*

Kaye, Leonard, Div. Pres.--Malone & Hyde, Inc.-Southaven, Southaven, MS; *U.S. Public*, pg. 653

Kaye, Michael S., Pres.--Secomerica, Inc., Newport Beach, CA; *Int'l*, pg. 1217

Kayho, Kimmo, Pres.--Esselte Oy, Helsinki, Finland; *Int'l*, pg. 461

Kayon, Don, Gen. Mgr.--Marshall Erdman & Assoc., Inc., Newington, VA; *U.S. Private*, pg. 380

Kaysen, Richard L., Pres.--Cheyenne Light, Fuel & Power Co., Cheyenne, WY; *U.S. Public*, pg. 1170

Kayser, Ferd, Gen. Mgr.--CLT Deutschland, Cologne, Germany; *Int'l*, pg. 561

Kaywork, E. Lee, Pres. & Gen. Mgr.-Metro One Cellular Telephone Co., N.Y.--LIN Cellular Group, Kirkland, WA; *U.S. Public*, pg. 11

Kaywork, E. Lee, Pres. & Gen. Mgr.--AT&T Wireless Services, Paramus, NJ; *U.S. Public*, pg. 11

Kazama, Hiroshi, Chief Rep.--Miami Representative Office, Miami, FL; *Int'l*, pg. 519

Kazama, Hitoshi, Mgr.--Fujitsu Limited, New York, NY; *Int'l*, pg. 526

Kazmi, Iftikhar, Grp. V.P.--Superior Industries-Fayetteville, Fayetteville, AR; *U.S. Public*, pg. 1539

Kealey, Darwin, Pres.--GPC Communications (Ontario), Toronto, Canada; *U.S. Public*, pg. 1225

Kean, Charles T., V.P. & Gen. Mgr.--Dentsply Asia, Aberdeen, Hong Kong; *U.S. Public*, pg. 499

Kean, D. Bruce, Pres.--Multifoods Specialty Distribution Inc., Denver, CO; *U.S. Public*, pg. 901

Kean, Marjorie, Office Mgr.--Korn/Ferry International, Caracas, Venezuela; *U.S. Private*, pg. 633

Kean, Robert W., Chm. Bd.--E'town Properties Inc., Westfield, NJ; *U.S. Public*, pg. 540

Keane, Charles E., Sr. V.P.--Mellon Mortgage Company, Cleveland, OH; *U.S. Public*, pg. 1085

Keane, Kevin T., Chief Oper. Officer--E-L Products Company, East Aurora, NY; *U.S. Public*, pg. 142

Kearney, Daniel P., Pres.--Aeltus Investment Management, Inc., Hartford, CT; *U.S. Public*, pg. 27

Kearney, John, Chief Oper. Officer--Kvaerner Earl and Wright, Inc., Aberdeen, United Kingdom; *Int'l*, pg. 771

Kearney, Joseph P., Pres. & Chief Exec. Officer--PG&E Gas Transmission, San Francisco, CA; *U.S. Public*, pg. 1241

Kearney, M., Chief Exec. Officer--Blackwood Hodge (Ghana) Ltd., Accra, Ghana; *Int'l*, pg. 231

Kearney, Matthew B., Pres.--GGRI, Inc., Hollywood, FL; *U.S. Private*, pg. 480

Kearns, Gerald D., V.P. & Gen. Mgr.--Materiel Division, Lynnwood, WA; *U.S. Public*, pg. 240

Kearns, James F., Grp. V.P.--Du Pont Fibers, Wilmington, DE; *U.S. Public*, pg. 531

Kearns, John P., Pres.--TECO Manufacturing, Inc., Alvin, TX; *U.S. Public*, pg. 1562
Kearns, Walter J., Pres. & Chief Exec. Officer--Data Documents Holdings, Inc., Omaha, NE; *U.S. Public*, pg. 449
Kearns, Walter J., Pres. & Chief Exec. Officer--Data Documents, Inc., Omaha, NE; *U.S. Public*, pg. 449
Keast, John J., Pres.--Mil Systems Engineering, Ottawa, Canada; *Int'l*, pg. 385
Keat, Lim Hong, Mng. Dir.--Metal Box Singapore Limited, Singapore, Singapore; *Int'l*, pg. 267
Keating, Brendan, Pres.--Bowne Business Communications, Inc., New York, NY; *U.S. Public*, pg. 248
Keating, Brian, Mng. Dir.--CEM Computers Limited, Belfast, United Kingdom; *Int'l*, pg. 1247
Keating, Dr. Patrick, Dir. & Gen. Mgr.--AlliedSignal Microelectronics & Technology Center, Columbia, MD; *U.S. Public*, pg. 50
Keating, James J., Pres.--Petro-Diamond, Inc., Irvine, CA; *Int'l*, pg. 872
Keating, P.W., Zone Gen. Mgr.-Australian Capital Territory--Commonwealth Bank of Australia-Australian Capital Territory, Canberra, Australia; *Int'l*, pg. 312
Keating, Paul J., Chief Exec. Officer--Keating Materials, Dracut, MA; *U.S. Private*, pg. 611
Keating, Phillip J., Pres.--Rieke Corporation, Auburn, IN; *U.S. Public*, pg. 1054
Keating, Susan, Pres. & Chief Exec. Officer--Dauphin Deposit Bank and Trust Company, Harrisburg, PA; *Int'l*, pg. 64
Keating, Susan C., Pres.--First Maryland Credit Corp., Baltimore, MD; *Int'l*, pg. 64
Keating, Susan C., Pres.--The York Bank and Trust Company, York, PA; *Int'l*, pg. 65
Keatinge, Richard, Mng. Dir.--IBI Corporate Finance Limited, Dublin, Ireland; *Int'l*, pg. 152
Keatinge, W.D., Gen. Mgr.--Barclays Bank PLC, Amsterdam, Netherlands; *Int'l*, pg. 166
Keaton, C.M., Pres.--McEwen Lumber Company, High Point, NC; *U.S. Public*, pg. 903
Keats, Harvey F., Asst. Gen. Mgr.--Falconbridge Chile S.A., Santiago, Chile; *Int'l*, pg. 434
Keaveney, W.J., Mgr.-Global Sls./Steel Div.--Carpenter Technology (Canada) Ltd., Mississauga, Canada; *U.S. Public*, pg. 308
Keay, Jim, Pres.--Morflex, Inc., Greensboro, NC; *U.S. Private*, pg. 919
Keck, Daniel, Mng. Dir.--Steelcase Strafor AG, Basel, Switzerland; *Int'l*, pg. 569
Keck, Valarie, Admin.--Lincoln Nursing Center, Inc., Lincolnton, NC; *U.S. Public*, pg. 1714
Keddy, Patrick, Pres.--PB Leasing Ltd., London, United Kingdom; *U.S. Public*, pg. 1304
Kedrowski, Leonard, Pres.--North Coast Mortgage, Inc., Roseville, MN; *U.S. Public*, pg. 1406
Kedrowski, Tony, Mgr.-Division--Liberia Mfg. Co., Abbotsford, WI; *U.S. Public*, pg. 491
Kedwell, Barry H., Pres.--Curwood Packaging (Canada) Ltd., Georgetown, Canada; *U.S. Public*, pg. 210
Kee, Joseph L., Chm. Bd. & Pres.--General American Door Company, Montgomery, IL; *U.S. Private*, pg. 732
Kee, Wee Bon, Reg. Mgr.--Scott & English Limited, Singapore, Singapore; *Int'l*, pg. 603
Keebaugh, M.D., V.P. & Gen. Mgr.--HRB Systems, State College, PA; *U.S. Public*, pg. 1365
Keeble, Stephen, Pres.--CDA Investment Technologies, Inc., Rockville, MD; *U.S. Public*, pg. 1600
Keef, John M., Chief Oper. Officer--Ahlstrom Filtration, Inc.-Chattanooga Mill, Chattanooga, TN; *Int'l*, pg. 35
Keefe, Gary, Pres.--Consolidated Device Inc., City of Industry, CA; *U.S. Public*, pg. 1481
Keefe, Mark, Pres.--PrimeNet Marketing Services, Saint Paul, MN; *U.S. Private*, pg. 602
Keefe, Mary Patricia, Grp. V.P. & Gen. Counsel--Elizabethtown Gas Co., Union, NJ; *U.S. Public*, pg. 1147
Keefe, Paul F., Exec. V.P.--Montreal Trustco-Financial Operations & Control Div., Montreal, Canada; *Int'l*, pg. 155
Keefe, Tom, Pres.--GH Hensley Industries, Inc., Dallas, TX; *U.S. Private*, pg. 439
Keegan, Joseph, Pres.--Becton Dickinson Labware, Franklin Lakes, NJ; *U.S. Public*, pg. 199
Keegan, Mike, Gen. Mgr.--Fraser Valley Forest Products Limited, Mission, Canada; *Int'l*, pg. 1067
Keegan, R.J., Gen. Mgr.--Kodak S.A., Las Rozas, Spain; *U.S. Public*, pg. 554
Keegan, R.J., Gen. Mgr.--Kodak S.A., Madrid, Spain; *U.S. Public*, pg. 554
Keegel, R.H., Area Mgr.--Recycling Maatschappij Feniks B.V., Alkmaar, Netherlands; *Int'l*, pg. 134
Keehan, Ed, Chief Exec. Officer--Damart, Rollinsford, NH; *Int'l*, pg. 376
Keel, Lenz, Mng. Dir.--Swiss Re Southern Africa Ltd., Johannesburg, South Africa; *Int'l*, pg. 1333
Keelean, John S., Chief Oper. Officer--Owen-Ames-Kimball Engineering, Inc., Grand Rapids, MI; *U.S. Private*, pg. 824
Keeler, D.J., Pres.--Keeler Instruments Inc., Broomall, PA; *Int'l*, pg. 590
Keeley, Rupert, Country Mgr.--Standard Chartered Bank (Bahrain), Manama, Bahrain; *Int'l*, pg. 1295
Keeling, Ian, Mng. Dir.--Fine Organics Limited, Middlesbrough, United Kingdom; *Int'l*, pg. 802
Keen, Gerald S., Pres.--MGS Storage Services, Inc., Mobile, AL; *U.S. Public*, pg. 1120
Keenan, A.H., Pres.--Regal Greetings & Gifts, Toronto, Canada; *Int'l*, pg. 1150
Keenan, Dennis, Terminal Mgr.--Kintetsu World Express Inc., Sharon Hill, PA; *Int'l*, pg. 735
Keenan, Joe, Branch Mgr.--Hughes-Peters, Inc., Columbus, OH; *U.S. Private*, pg. 547
Keenan, Michael E., Mng. Dir.--Western International Media Corporation, New York, NY; *U.S. Private*, pg. 1166
Keenan, Mike, Gen. Mgr.--Fraser Valley Forest Inc., Kent, WA; *Int'l*, pg. 1067
Keenan, Paul, Mng. Dir.--EMAP Fashion Ltd., London, United Kingdom; *Int'l*, pg. 451
Keenan, Ray, Pres.--Sharps Pixley Inc., New York, NY; *Int'l*, *pg. 403*
Keenan, Roy, Mng. Dir.--Bank of Ireland Home Morgages Limited, Reading, United Kingdom; *Int'l*, pg. 153
Keenan, Thomas J., Pres.--General Dynamics Land Systems Div., Muskegon, MI; *U.S. Public*, pg. 709
Keenan, Tom, Gen. Mgr.--ITW Shippers Paper, Mount Pleasant, TN; *U.S. Public*, pg. 867
Keene, David L., Pres.--Fiduciary Trust International of California, Los Angeles, CA; *U.S. Public*, pg. 621
Keene, Richard, Gen. Mgr.--Grow Group Canada Ltd., Dartmouth, Canada; *Int'l*, pg. 663
Keeney, John, Admin.--Greenery Rehabilitation & Skilled Nursing Center, Middleboro, MA; *U.S. Public*, pg. 837
Keep, D.J., Mng. Dir.--Yale Security Products, Ltd., Wolverhampton, United Kingdom; *Int'l*, pg. 1499
Keepers, William L., Pres., Chief Exec. & Chief Oper. Officer--Sierra Pacific Power Co., Reno, NV; *U.S. Public*, pg. 1470
Keereweer, Jean, Mng. Dir.--AGA-Cryo AB, Goteborg, Sweden; *Int'l*, pg. 12
Keersmaecker, Guido de, Chief Oper. Officer--Henkel Belgium S.A., Brussels, Belgium; *Int'l*, pg. 612
Keesan, Barry, Pres.--Logical Operations, Rochester, NY; *Int'l*, pg. 1276
Keeshan, Robert J., Pres.--Robert Keeshan Associates, Inc., New York, NY; *U.S. Private*, pg. 554
Keesler, Pat, Traffic Mgr.--Flanagan Bros. Trucking Co., Bear Creek, WI; *U.S. Private*, pg. 887
Keethler, Robert, Chief Oper. Officer & Gen. Mgr.--CMI Group, Inc., Milwaukee, WI; *U.S. Public*, pg. 1462
Keever, Lynda, Publr.--Florida Trend Magazine, Saint Petersburg, FL; *U.S. Private*, pg. 1088
Kefalas, Paul T., Pres. & Chief Exec. Officer--ABB in Canada, Saint-Laurent, Canada; *Int'l*, pg. 7
Keg, Gertjen, Dir.--The E.F. MacDonald Verkaufsforderung GmbH, Cologne, Germany; *U.S. Private*, pg. 212
Kegerreis, Kenneth M., Pres.--SuperValu, Inc.-Denver Div., Denver, CO; *U.S. Public*, pg. 1540
Kegg, John, Mng. Dir.--Blue Coral Quaker State International, Newport, United Kingdom; *U.S. Public*, pg. 1348
Kegler, Dennis P., Pres. & Chief Oper. Officer--Great Lakes Coal and Dock Company, Saint Paul, MN; *U.S. Public*, pg. 139
Kegley, Michael, Admin.--Birchwood Care Center, Marne, MI; *U.S. Public*, pg. 837
Kehal, Gerry, Natl. Sls. Mgr.--Bio-Rad Semiconductor Systems Div., Cambridge, MA; *U.S. Public*, pg. 230
Kehlbeck, Fritz, Dr., Co-Chief Oper. Officer--BHF & IKB Baumanagement GmbH, Dusseldorf, Germany; *Int'l*, pg. 645
Kehoe, John M., Pres. & Chief Exec. Officer--Wheelabrator Technologies Inc., Hampton, NH; *U.S. Public*, pg. 1745
Keiffer, E.G., Chm. Bd. & Chief Exec. Officer--ESY Export Co., Inc., Dallas, TX; *U.S. Public*, pg. 1365
Keigel, Ch., Mng. Dir.--Bally Gesellschaft mbH, Vienna, Austria; *Int'l*, pg. 997
Keijzer, Peter, Chief Oper. Officer--Scandex Aluminium N.V., Hoogezand-Sappeemeer, Netherlands; *Int'l*, pg. 443
Keila, Gerson Sergio, Pres. & Gen. Mgr.--Donuts Comercio de Produtos Alimenticios, Ltda., Sao Paulo, Brazil; *Int'l*, pg. 64
Keimatsu, Shunsuke, Chm. Bd. & Chief Exec. Officer-IMS Cognizant Japan--I.M.S. International, Inc., Totowa, NJ; *U.S. Public*, pg. 395
Keine, Erik, Mgr.--Newport B.V., Bunnik, Netherlands; *U.S. Public*, pg. 1179
Keiper, William C., Chief Exec. Officer--MicroAge International Inc., Tempe, AZ; *U.S. Public*, pg. 1104
Keir, G, Mng. Dir.--De La Rue Fortronic Limited, Dunfermline, United Kingdom; *Int'l*, pg. 387
Keirght, Claudio, Ing., Gen. Dir.--Plasticos Rex. S.A. de C.V., Garza Garcia, Mexico; *Int'l*, pg. 246
Keirle, G.G., Gen. Mgr.--Papua-New Guinea Division, Summer Hill, Australia; *Int'l*, pg. 556
Keiser, A. W., Pres.--Canadian Imperial Bank of Commerce (New York), New York, NY; *Int'l*, pg. 257
Keiser, Donald M., Pres. & Chief Exec. Officer--SunTrust Bank, Northwest Georgia, N.A., Rome, GA; *U.S. Public*, pg. 1538
Keiser, F., Mgr.--Schweizerischer Bankverein, Aarau, Switzerland; *Int'l*, pg. 1329
Keiser, Jack, Pres.--Bird Products Corporation, Palm Springs, CA; *U.S. Public*, pg. 1591
Keisling, Gary, Pres.--International Correspondence Schools, Inc., Scranton, PA; *U.S. Public*, pg. 783
Keisling, Gary, Pres.--National Learning Systems, Inc., Scranton, PA; *U.S. Public*, pg. 783
Keisling, Gary, Pres.--NBD Incorporated, Scranton, PA; *U.S.* Public, pg. 783
Keisling, Gary M., Mng. Dir.--International Correspondence Schools (New Zealand) Limited, Wellington, New Zealand; *U.S. Public*, pg. 784
Keith, Dean, Gen. Mgr.--Lawson Products, Inc., Dallas, TX; *U.S. Public*, pg. 980
Keith, John, V.P.--Rock of Ages Memorials LLC, Elizabethtown, KY; *U.S. Public*, pg. 1396
Keith, Kenneth L., Pres.--FISI Madison Financial Corporation, Nashville, TN; *U.S. Public*, pg. 320
Keith, Lee R., Pres. & Chief Exec. Officer--United Missouri Bank Northwest, Saint Joseph, MO; *U.S. Public*, pg. 1654
Keith, Matt, Gen. Mgr.--Samuel Specialty Metals Inc., Houston, TX; *U.S. Private*, pg. 964
Keith, R. Drake, Pres.--Entergy Arkansas, Inc., Little Rock, AR; *U.S. Public*, pg. 586
Keith, Richard, Pres.--Scottish & Newcastle Importers Co., San Francisco, CA; *Int'l*, pg. 1212
Keith, Robert, Pres. & Chief Exec. Officer--ServiceMaster Management Services Corporation, Downers Grove, IL; *U.S. Public*, pg. 1462
Keith, Robert E., Pres. & Chief Exec. Officer--TL Ventures, Wayne, PA; *U.S. Public*, pg. 1424
Keith, Robert E., Jr., Chm. Bd.--Internet Capital Group, Wayne, PA; *U.S. Public*, pg. 1425
Keith, William R., V.P.-Sls.--Crown Cork & Seal, Southern Div., Arden, NC; *U.S. Public*, pg. 463
Kelbel, Craig, Pres.--US Benefits Insurance Services, Inc., Costa Mesa, CA; *U.S. Public*, pg. 328
Kelberg, George, Mng. Dir.--Styx & Leo Burnett, Almaty, Kazakhstan; *U.S. Private*, pg. 186
Kelchen, Steve, Gen. Mgr.--Folding Carton (Pacific), Pacific, MO; *Int'l*, pg. 1270
Kellar, Marshal M., Pres.--West Texas Wholesale Supply Co., Abilene, TX; *U.S. Private*, pg. 335
Kellaway, Martin G., Gen. Mgr.--Forbo CP Ltd., Cramlington, United Kingdom; *Int'l*, pg. 497
Kellaway, R.J., Mng. Dir.--GATX Terminals Ltd., Maidenhead, United Kingdom; *U.S. Public*, pg. 693
Kelleher, Daniel L., Pres.--New Jersey-American Water Co., Haddon Heights, NJ; *U.S. Public*, pg. 95
Kelleher, Daniel L., Pres.--New Jersey-American Resources Company, Haddon Heights, NJ; *U.S. Public*, pg. 95
Kelleher, Kevin, Pres. & Chief Exec. Officer--HFS Mobility Services, Danbury, CT; *U.S. Public*, pg. 321
Kelleher, Mike, V.P.--Eastern Div., Middletown, CT; *U.S. Public*, pg. 732
Keller, Charles E., Chief Exec. Officer--Acordia Northeast, Boston, MA; *Int'l*, pg. 671
Keller, Chris, Gen. Mgr.--Oar Bar & Grill, Boston, MA; *U.S. Public*, pg. 130
Keller, Chris, Gen. Mgr.--The Marketplace Cafe, Boston, MA; *U.S. Public*, pg. 130
Keller, Daniel R., Gen. Mgr.--Worlds of Fun & Oceans of Fun, Kansas City, MO; *U.S. Public*, pg. 319
Keller, David, Plant Mgr.--L.B. Foster Company-Ephrata Plant, Ephrata, PA; *U.S. Public*, pg. 676
Keller, David, Pres. & Chief Exec. Officer--UPB of Mid-Missouri, Columbia, MO; *U.S. Public*, pg. 1669
Keller, David H., Pres. & Gen. Mgr.--Lucas Body Systems - North America, Winona, MN; *Int'l*, pg. 820
Keller, Gary, Gen. Mgr.--SoniForm, Inc., El Cajon, CA; *U.S. Private*, pg. 689
Keller, Hans Peter, Mgr.--Network Systems Corporation, Mississauga, Canada; *U.S. Public*, pg. 1523
Keller, Isaac Rodrigo, Mng. Dir.--Arte y Cemento SA, Bilbao, Spain; *Int'l*, pg. 1099
Keller, J. Frank, Pres.--Barrett Fuels Corporation, Denver, CO; *U.S. Public*, pg. 191
Keller, Larry, Chief Exec. Officer--Dewberry Design Group, Oklahoma City, OK; *U.S. Private*, pg. 329
Keller, R. E., Exec. V.P.--Invista Capital Management Inc., Des Moines, IA; *U.S. Private*, pg. 885
Keller, R. E., Chm.--Principal Portfolio Services, Inc., Costa Mesa, CA; *U.S. Private*, pg. 886
Keller, Richard D., Pres. & Chief Exec. Officer--Electric Fuel Corp., Saint Petersburg, FL; *U.S. Public*, pg. 655
Keller, S.S., Mng. Dir.--Ascom Automation Inc., Philadelphia, PA; *Int'l*, pg. 86
Keller, Shirley P., Admin.--Colonial Manor Nursing & Convalescent Hospital, Madison, WI; *U.S. Public*, pg. 1712
Keller, Thomas, Pres. & Gen. Mgr.--Thermoplastics, Inc., Mishawaka, IN; *U.S. Public*, pg. 1590
Keller, Thomas M., Pres.--Time Insurance, Milwaukee, WI; *Int'l*, pg. 499
Keller, Thomas M., Pres.--Fortis Life, Milwaukee, WI; *Int'l*, pg. 499
Keller, W. Richard, Mgr.--Medical Division, Westlake, OH; *Int'l*, pg. 1084
Kellerfors, Bo, Mng. Dir.--RYDS Batindustri AB, Ryds, Sweden; *U.S. Private*, pg. 479
Kellett, John W., Jr., Mgr.-Engrng.--Ocean Spray Cranberries-Bordentown Plant, Bordentown, NJ; *U.S. Private*, pg. 811
Kelley, B.O., Chm. Bd.--Dosimeter Corporation of America, Cincinnati, OH; *Int'l*, pg. 892
Kelley, Daniel M., V.P. & Publr.--McGraw-Hill Healthcare Publications Group, Minneapolis, MN; *U.S. Public*, pg. 1071
Kelley, Daniel M., Publisher--The Physician and Sportsmedicine, Minneapolis, MN; *U.S. Public*, pg. 1071
Kelley, Donald, V.P.-Opers.--ROPER Corporation, La Fayette, GA; *U.S. Public*, pg. 710
Kelley, E.W., Chm. Bd.--SNS Investment Company, Indianapolis, IN; *U.S. Public*, pg. 436
Kelley, Edward W., Chief Exec. Officer-Europe--Korn/Ferry International, London, United Kingdom; *U.S. Private*, pg. 633
Kelley, J. Randy, V.P.--Industrial Products Div., Hartsville, SC; *U.S. Public*, pg. 1486
Kelley, James M., Pres.--Dixie Crystals Brands, Inc., Savannah, GA; *U.S. Public*, pg. 872
Kelley, James M., Pres.--Savannah Investment Company, Wilmington, DE; *U.S. Public*, pg. 873
Kelley, Joe, Pres. & Chief Exec. Officer--AGC Life Insurance Co., Nashville, TN; *U.S. Public*, pg. 76
Kelley, Kevin, Pres.--Lexington Insurance Co., Boston, MA; *U.S. Public*, pg. 84
Kelley, Kevin P., V.P. & Div. Mgr.--Quebecor Printing Sherwood, Kingsport, TN; *Int'l*, pg. 1076
Kelley, Larry, Sr. V.P. & Dir.--Fogarty Klein & Partners, Houston, TX; *U.S. Private*, pg. 416
Kelley, Mike, Pres.--Richards Industries Valve Group, Cincinnati, OH; *U.S. Private*, pg. 929
Kelley, Perry M., Plant Mgr.--Tompkinsville Plant, Tompkinsville, KY; *U.S. Public*, pg. 201
Kelley, R.A., Pres.--Electric Energy, Inc., Joppa, IL; *U.S. Public*, pg. 870
Kelley, Scott, Pres.--Natvar Company, Clayton, NC; *U.S. Private*, pg. 528

Kelley, Thomas M., Pres.--First American Title Co. of Los Angeles, Glendale, CA; *U.S. Public*, pg. 625
Kelley, William, Plant Mgr.--Power Distribution Div., Lincoln, IL; *U.S. Public*, pg. 557
Kelley, William, Pres. & Mgr.-Opers.--Fiber-Resin Corporation, Chatsworth, CA; *U.S. Public*, pg. 686
Kelley, William M., Chm. Bd.--Hill-Rom Company, Inc., Batesville, IN; *U.S. Public*, pg. 828
Kelley, William T., V.P. & Gen. Mgr.--Micro-Precision Operations, Berne, IN; *U.S. Public*, pg. 1589
Kellgren, Bengt, Mng. Dir.--Ericsson Telecommunicatie B.V., Rijen, Netherlands; *Int'l*, pg. 1367
Kellman, Mildred, Chm. Bd. & Pres.--Assurance Glass Co. of Alabama, Selma, AL; *U.S. Private*, pg. 458
Kellond, A.W., Plant Mgr.--Dayton Superior Corp., Houston, TX; *U.S. Private*, pg. 932
Kells, R.D., Chm.--Ulster Bank Trust Company, Belfast, United Kingdom; *Int'l*, pg. 911
Kelly, A. Thomas III, Pres.--SNET Systems Inc., New Haven, CT; *U.S. Public*, pg. 1491
Kelly, A.P., Mng. Dir.--Gelman Sciences Pty. Ltd., Sydney, Australia; *U.S. Public*, pg. 1253
Kelly, B.O., Chm. Bd.--TGM Detectors Inc., Waltham, MA; *Int'l*, pg. 892
Kelly, Brian, Managing Dir.--Softrans International, Ltd., Dublin, Ireland; *U.S. Public*, pg. 222
Kelly, Christopher H., Mng. Dir.--Johnson & Johnson Korea, Ltd., Seoul, Korea; *U.S. Public*, pg. 930
Kelly, Curtis, Gen. Mgr.--Sterling Electronics, Englewood, CO; *U.S. Public*, pg. 1052
Kelly, D.J., Mng. Dir.--Senior Entex, Nottingham, United Kingdom; *Int'l*, pg. 1220
Kelly, Dennis, Pres.--Baxter Tube Company, Warrensville Heights, OH; *U.S. Public*, pg. 1632
Kelly, Desmond, M.D., Chm.-Priory Hospitals Group--Community Psychiatric Centers of London (Unlimited), London, United Kingdom; *U.S. Public*, pg. 1716
Kelly, Don, Regional Mgr.--CAP Gemini America (NJ Commercial Branch), Edison, NJ; *Int'l*, pg. 264
Kelly, Don, Pres.--North Central Division, Norcross, GA; *U.S. Public*, pg. 1255
Kelly, Donald F., Pres.--Maine Electric Power Co., Inc., Augusta, ME; *U.S. Public*, pg. 325
Kelly, E.F., Pres. & Chief Oper. Officer--Liberty Mutual Fire Insurance Co., Boston, MA; *U.S. Private*, pg. 666
Kelly, Ed, V.P. & Publr.--Food & Wine, New York, NY; *U.S. Public*, pg. 74
Kelly, Ed, V.P. & Publr.--Travel & Leisure, New York, NY; *U.S. Public*, pg. 74
Kelly, Edmund F., Pres. & Chief Admin. Officer--Liberty Life Assurance Company of Boston, Dover, NH; *U.S. Private*, *pg. 666*
Kelly, Fernando, Pres.--Search Organization de Seguridad, S.A., Buenos Aires, Argentina; *U.S. Public*, pg. 1731
Kelly, J., Mng. Dir.--Ferro Mexicana S.A. de C.V., Mexico, Mexico; *U.S. Public*, pg. 619
Kelly, James M., V.P. & Gen. Mgr.--Western Syncoal Company, Billings, MT; *U.S. Public*, pg. 1127
Kelly, John D., Pres. & Chief Exec. Officer--Na-Churs Plant Food Company, Marion, OH; *U.S. Private*, pg. 1096
Kelly, John J., Pres. & Chief Exec. Officer--Willis Corroon Corp. of New York, New York, NY; *Int'l*, pg. 1506
Kelly, John J., Pres.--Textron Marine & Land Systems, New Orleans, LA; *U.S. Public*, pg. 1589
Kelly, John L., Pres.--CWC Textron Company, Muskegon, MI; *U.S. Public*, pg. 1590
Kelly, John L., Pres.--CWC Castings Textron, Muskegon, MI; *U.S. Public*, pg. 1590
Kelly, John M., Pres.--Midvale Plaza, Madison, WI; *U.S. Private*, pg. 784
Kelly, Joseph B., Pres.--Randolph Computer Corporation, Boston, MA; *U.S. Public*, pg. 184
Kelly, Ken, Mgr.--Hay Point Export Terminal, Mackay, Australia; *Int'l*, pg. 223
Kelly, Linda, Pres.--Astra Pharmaceuticals Ltd., Kings Langley, United Kingdom; *Int'l*, pg. 94
Kelly, Mary E., Dir.--BNA PLUS, Washington, DC; *U.S. Private*, pg. 182
Kelly, Michael N., Pres.--Tera Pharmaceuticals, Buena Park, CA; *U.S. Public*, pg. 196
Kelly, Michael V., Auction Mgr.--Manheim's Oshawa Dealers Exchange, Newcastle, Canada; *U.S. Private*, pg. 283
Kelly, Patrick C., Chief Oper. Officer & Gen. Mgr.--Ozone Research & Equipment Corp., Phoenix, AZ; *U.S. Public*, pg. 1234
Kelly, Patrick T., Pres.--BancBoston Leasing Inc., Boston, MA; *U.S. Public*, pg. 184
Kelly, Peter, Sr. V.P.-Sls.--Hasbro, Cincinnati, OH; *U.S. Public*, pg. 797
Kelly, Peter H., Pres. & Chief Oper. Officer--LaVaca Realty Co., Austin, TX; *U.S. Public*, pg. 1491
Kelly, Regan E., Pres.--Western Financial Auto Loans 2, Inc., Irvine, CA; *U.S. Public*, pg. 1757
Kelly, Richard C., Pres.--E Prime, Inc., Denver, CO; *U.S. Public*, pg. 1170
Kelly, Robert, Pres. & Gen. Mgr.--Helene Curtis UK, Inc., Oldsleworth, United Kingdom; *Int'l*, pg. 1434
Kelly, Robert J., Pres.--Bull HN Information Systems Inc., Billerica, MA; *Int'l*, pg. 316
Kelly, Robert, Jr., Pres.--MacSteel Div., Jackson, MI; *U.S. Public*, pg. 1349
Kelly, Robert, Jr., Pres.--MacSteel Div., Fort Smith, AR; *U.S.* Public, pg. 1349
Kelly, T., Mgr.--Van Leeuwen Pipe & Tube (Canada) Inc., Calgary, Canada; *Int'l*, pg. 1450
Kelly, Terry, Pres.--Baker Distributing Company, Jacksonville, FL; *U.S. Public*, pg. 1746
Kelly, Thomas J., Chm. Bd.--Exchange Insurance Company, Buffalo, NY; *U.S. Public*, pg. 1455
Kelly, Timothy, Pres.--Mercury Adjustment Bureau, Inc., Lynbrook, NY; *U.S. Private*, pg. 406
Kelly, Tom, Gen. Mgr.--Four Seasons Hotel, Philadelphia, PA; *Int'l*, pg. 502
Kelly, Tom, Gen. Mgr.--Four Seasons Hotel, Austin, TX; *Int'l*, pg. 502
Kelly, Tom, Plant Superintendent--Toca Plant, Saint Bernard, LA; *U.S. Public*, pg. 1759
Kelly, William, Exec. Dir.--Filene Research Institute, Madison, WI; *U.S. Private*, pg. 288
Kelly, William R., Pres. & Chief Oper. Officer--Enserch Development Corporation, Florham Park, NJ; *U.S. Public*, *pg. 1587*
Kelly, William T., Mng. Dir.--Bensons International Systems, Mississauga, Canada; *Int'l*, pg. 460
Kelman, J. M., Exec. V.P. & G.M.--Davy International, Pittsburgh, PA; *Int'l*, pg. 773
Kelman, J.M., Pres.--Kvaerner Davy, Pittsburgh, PA; *Int'l*, pg. 774
Kelman, J.M., Pres.--Davy International, San Francisco, San Ramon, CA; *Int'l*, pg. 774
Kelner, Judy, Publr.--ACBJ Business Journals, Inc., Miami, FL; *U.S. Private*, pg. 19
Kelsey, Greg, V.P. & Gen. Mgr.--Quebecor Printing Hazleton Inc., Hazleton, PA; *Int'l*, pg. 1076
Kelso, Bill, Mgr.-Kitchen Appliances--Coffeemaker Div., Stamford, CT; *Int'l*, pg. 1053
Keltner, Charles, Gen. Mgr.--Unitog Company, Warsaw, MO; *U.S. Public*, pg. 1693
Keltz, Martin J., Pres.--Scholastic Productions Inc., New York, NY; *U.S. Public*, pg. 1440
Kemmish, Kirk C., Pres.--Phelps Dodge Magnet Wire Co., Fort Wayne, IN; *U.S. Public*, pg. 1286
Kemna, Ralf, Chief Fin. Officer--Scanvest Olivetti A/S, Oslo, Norway; *Int'l*, pg. 1004
Kemp, Axel, Gen. Mgr.--Aeroquip Iberica S.A. (Automotive Group), Alcala de Henares, Spain; *U.S. Public*, pg. 25
Kemp, J. A., Mng. Dir.--Tate & Lyle Reinsurance Ltd., Hamilton, Bermuda; *Int'l*, pg. 1357
Kemp, Melvin T., Pres.--Bowman & Kemp Steel & Supply Company, Ogden, UT; *U.S. Private*, pg. 105
Kemp, Melvin T., Pres.--Bowman & Kemp Rebar, Ogden, UT; *U.S. Private*, pg. 105
Kemp, N., Opers. Supvr.--Kodak Canada Inc., Montreal, Canada; *U.S. Public*, pg. 553
Kemp, S.D., Mgr.--Sutton Bridge Wharfage Co. Ltd., Spalding, United Kingdom; *Int'l*, pg. 1251
Kemp, Stephen, Gen. Mgr.--Racal Avionics, Inc., Silver Spring, MD; *Int'l*, pg. 1082
Kemp, Steven E., Pres. & Chief Exec. Officer--Regions Bank/Rome, Rome, GA; *U.S. Public*, pg. 1372
Kemp, Thomas, Chm. Bd. & Chief Exec. Officer--Penton Publishing, Inc., Cleveland, OH; *U.S. Public*, pg. 1306
Kemp, William, Jr., Gen. Mgr.--Republic Automotive Parts Sales, Inc., El Centro, CA; *U.S. Public*, pg. 1378
Kempel, M., Mng. Dir.--Robert Bosch A/S, Ballerup, Denmark; *Int'l*, pg. 205
Kemper, Frank, Mgr.-Opers.--Flowserve Corporation, Engineered Plastic Products Div., Springboro, OH; *U.S. Public*, pg. 658
Kemper, Heinz Armin, Co-Chief Oper. Officer--INDUSTRIE-RING Sach-und Versicherungs-Vermittlungsgesellschaft mbH, Saarbruecken, Germany; *Int'l*, pg. 1166
Kemper, Jonathan M., Chm. Bd., Pres. & Chief Exec. Officer--Commerce Bank N.A., Kansas City, MO; *U.S. Public*, pg. 409
Kemper, Michael J., Pres. & Chief Exec. Officer--Northern Pipeline Construction Co., Phoenix, AZ; *U.S. Public*, pg. 1493
Kempinski, Chester F., Pres.--McCoy Electronics Co., Mount Holly Springs, PA; *U.S. Public*, pg. 1209
Kempner, Brian, Pres.--The New York Observer, New York, NY; *U.S. Private*, pg. 993
Kempson, Fred C., Mng. Dir.--Security Pacific Limited, Sydney, Australia; *U.S. Public*, pg. 183
Kempster, John, Pres.--Hallmark Cards Canada, Willowdale, Canada; *U.S. Private*, pg. 496
Kemsley, M., Mgr.--Yale Electronics Asia - Pacific Limited, Causeway Bay, Hong Kong; *Int'l*, pg. 1499
Kemsley, M.A., Chief Oper. Officer & Mng. Dir.--Yale Security Products (Hong Kong) Ltd., Causeway Bay, Hong Kong; *Int'l*, pg. 1499
Kenagy, Donald, Pres.--Thermo Materials, Scottdale, GA; *U.S. Public*, pg. 330
Kendall, Kennett R., Jr., Chm. Bd. & Chief Exec. Officer--Willis Corroon Corp. of New Hampshire, Rochester, NH; *Int'l*, pg. 1506
Kendell, Ross E., Pres. & Chief Exec. Officer--Key Bank of Utah, Salt Lake City, UT; *U.S. Public*, pg. 954
Kendle, Paul, Pres.--Norwest Bank Wisconsin Green Bay N.A., Green Bay, WI; *U.S. Public*, pg. 1203
Kendrick, Graham, Mng. Dir.--Scottish Courage Limited, Staines, United Kingdom; *Int'l*, pg. 1212
Keneally, T.P., V.P. & Gen. Mgr.--Union Camp Flexible Packaging, Wayne, NJ; *U.S. Public*, pg. 1666
Kenjo, Nobuyuki, Mng. Dir.--Kintetsu World Express (Australia) Pty. Ltd., Matraville, Australia; *Int'l*, pg. 735
Kenlon, John, Pres. & Chief Oper. Officer--Scott's Miracle-Gro Products, Inc., Port Washington, NY; *U.S. Public*, pg. 1447
Kenmochi, Yoshikazu, Chief Exec. Officer--Kyowa Hakko U.S.A., Inc., New York, NY; *Int'l*, pg. 778
Kennedy, Alan W., Gen. Mgr.--General Motors Chile S.A., Industria Automotriz, Santiago, Chile; *U.S. Public*, pg. 721
Kennedy, Barham F., V.P.--Du Pont Japan Ltd., Tokyo, Japan; *U.S. Public*, pg. 533
Kennedy, Brian J., Pres.--FMC Gold Co., Reno, NV; *U.S. Public*, pg. 605
Kennedy, C., Rep.--Cariplo (Chicago), Chicago, IL; *Int'l*, pg. 275
Kennedy, D., Chief Oper. Officer--Power Development, Taunton, United Kingdom; *Int'l*, pg. 207
Kennedy, D., Chief Exec. Officer--Bowthorpe Thermometrics, Taunton, United Kingdom; *Int'l*, pg. 207
Kennedy, D.P., Chm. Bd.--First American Title Insurance Co., Santa Ana, CA; *U.S. Public*, pg. 625
Kennedy, David E., Pres.--Radio Indianapolis, Inc., Indianapolis, IN; *U.S. Private*, pg. 860
Kennedy, David E., Pres.--Radio Metroplex Inc., Dallas, TX; *U.S. Private*, pg. 860
Kennedy, Donald D., Jr., Pres.--Providian Life & Health Insurance Co., Valley Forge, PA; *Int'l*, pg. 27
Kennedy, Elizabeth, Mng. Dir.--Michael de Kretser Consultants, Singapore, Singapore; *Int'l*, pg. 117
Kennedy, Eric, Sls. Exec.--Circle Freight International, Houston, TX; *U.S. Public*, pg. 370
Kennedy, Eric, Gen. Mgr.--Circle International, Houston, TX; *U.S. Public*, pg. 371
Kennedy, Faye M., Admin.--Hillhaven Convalescent Center Wilmington, Wilmington, NC; *U.S. Public*, pg. 1713
Kennedy, Frank, Pres.--Equator Holdings Ltd., Glastonbury, CT; *Int'l*, pg. 580
Kennedy, Frank, Mng. Dir.--Tarmac Construction Intl., Brentford, United Kingdom; *Int'l*, pg. 1355
Kennedy, Howard, Gen. Mgr.--KMTV-3, Omaha, NE; *U.S. Public*, pg. 983
Kennedy, Iain, Mng. Dir.--Solectron Scotland Limited, Dunfermline, United Kingdom; *U.S. Public*, pg. 1483
Kennedy, J.R., Chief Oper. Officer--ECI Telecom Inc., Altamonte Springs, FL; *Int'l*, pg. 643
Kennedy, J.S., JR., Gen. Mgr.--Orley Meyer, Big Bend, WI; *U.S. Public*, pg. 1041
Kennedy, Jack, Gen. Mgr.--Service Motor Co., New Franken, WI; *U.S. Private*, pg. 986
Kennedy, Jack P., Gen. Mgr. & V.P.--Flamingo Products, Inc., Hialeah, FL; *U.S. Private*, pg. 382
Kennedy, James A., Pres. & Chief Exec. Officer--National Starch and Chemical Company, Bridgewater, NJ; *Int'l*, pg. 1435
Kennedy, John, Gen. Mgr. & Dir.-Adv.--Park Newspapers of Concord, Inc., Concord, NC; *U.S. Public*, pg. 1078
Kennedy, John, Gen. Mgr. & Dir.-Adv.--The Concord Tribune, Inc., Concord, NC; *U.S. Public*, pg. 1078
Kennedy, John C., Pres.--Autocam Acquisition, Inc., Hayward, CA; *U.S. Public*, pg. 148
Kennedy, John C., Pres.--Autocam Laser Technologies, Inc., Hayward, CA; *U.S. Public*, pg. 148
Kennedy, John C., Pres.--Autocam-Pax, Inc., Dowagiac, MI; *U.S. Public*, pg. 148
Kennedy, John C., Pres.--Autocam South Carolina, Inc., Gaffney, SC; *U.S. Public*, pg. 148
Kennedy, John L., Mng. Dir.--Ericsson Business Communications Ltd., Dublin, Ireland; *Int'l*, pg. 1366
Kennedy, John R., Pres. & Chief Exec. Officer--Federal Paper Board Company, Inc., Montvale, NJ; *U.S. Public*, pg. 903
Kennedy, John T., Pres.--Graphic Direct, Inc., Elmhurst, IL; *U.S. Public*, pg. 1735
Kennedy, John W., V.P. & Southern Div. Mgr.--TriStar Pictures Southern Division, Dallas, TX; *Int'l*, pg. 1283
Kennedy, Keith, Pres.--Sullivan Transfer Co., Dallas, TX; *U.S. Private*, pg. 426
Kennedy, Lee, Pres.--Telecredit Service Center, Inc., Los Angeles, CA; *U.S. Public*, pg. 588
Kennedy, M., Chief Oper. Officer--Printed Motors Ltd., Borden, United Kingdom; *Int'l*, pg. 448
Kennedy, Mark A., Mgr.-Branch--Piper Jaffray Inc., Pueblo, CO; *U.S. Public*, pg. 1301
Kennedy, Nancy, Chief Oper. Officer--Bank of Boston Trust Co. (Bahamas) Limited, Nassau, Bahamas; *U.S. Public*, pg. 185
Kennedy, Paul, V.P. & G.M.--United Cities Gas Co., VA/ETN Div., Johnson City, TN; *U.S. Public*, pg. 146
Kennedy, Phil, Pres.--Mercantile Bank of Humboldt County, Humboldt, IA; *U.S. Public*, pg. 1088
Kennedy, Rod, Mng. Dir.--Beazer Homes (Yately) Limited, Camberley, United Kingdom; *Int'l*, pg. 182
Kennedy, Tim, Pres.--Tim's Cascade Style Potato Chips, Auburn, WA; *U.S. Private*, pg. 887
Kennedy, Tom, Gen. Mgr.--KKND, New Orleans, LA; *U.S. Public*, pg. 384
Kennedy, Tom, Gen. Mgr.--WNOE, New Orleans, LA; *U.S. Public*, pg. 385
Kennedy, Vincent, Pres.--Applied Industrial Materials Corporation, Stamford, CT; *U.S. Public*, pg. 1736
Kennedy, W., Plant Mgr.--FPC, Inc., Mountain City, TN; *U.S.* Public, pg. 551
Kennedy, W. Keith, Jr., Pres.--Watkins-Johnson International, Palo Alto, CA; *U.S. Public*, pg. 1745
Kennelly, P.E.M., Chief Exec. Officer--Delmon Ready Mixed Concrete & Products Co. W.L.L. (Bahrain), Manama, Bahrain; *Int'l*, pg. 1092
Kennely, Thomas, Controller--Steiger Tractor, Fargo, ND; *U.S. Public*, pg. 311
Kenner, Bernie, Gen. Mgr.--Arrow/Schweber Electronics, Duluth, GA; *U.S. Public*, pg. 133
Kennerly, Lynn, Export Rep.--Export Services, Houston, TX; *U.S. Private*, pg. 1032
Kenneway, Ernest, Gen. Mgr.--Dunkley Intl., Kalamazoo, MI; *U.S. Private*, pg. 234
Kenney, Judy, Gen. Mgr.--WSYM-TV, Lansing, MI; *U.S. Private*, pg. 601
Kenney, Martin E., Jr, Pres.--Simon & Schuster Education Technology Group, New York, NY; *U.S. Private*, pg. 778
Kennis, Harry, Gen. Mgr.--AMP Belgium, Brussels, Belgium; *U.S. Public*, pg. 8
Kenny, Michael J., Pres.-Specialty Products Div.--Church & Dwight Specialty Products Division, Princeton, NJ; *U.S. Public*, pg. 356
Kenny, Robert, Gen. Mgr.--Boston Wharf Company, Boston, MA; *Int'l*, pg. 1035
Kensington, Larry, Plant Mgr.--Bananza Air Management Systems, Inc., Kentwood, MI; *U.S. Private*, pg. 910
Kent, Conrad S., Chief Oper. Officer--Delamine B.V., Amersfoort, Netherlands; *Int'l*, pg. 1408
Kent, Conrad S., Chief Oper. Officer--Delamine B.V.-Delfzijl Plant, Delfzijl, Netherlands; *Int'l*, pg. 1408
Kent, Gage A., Pres.--Grain Processing Corp., Muscatine, IA; *U.S. Private*, pg. 1134

Kent, Harvey R., V.P. & Gen. Mgr.--Agency & Rep. Services Div.--Jefferson-Pilot Data Services, Inc., Memphis, TN; U.S. Public, pg. 925
Kent, Jerald, Pres.--CCT Holdings Corp., Saint Louis, MO; U.S. Private, pg. 230
Kent, K. Colin, Pres.--Rosemount Instruments Ltd., Calgary, Canada; U.S. Public, pg. 577
Kent, N. W., Mng. Dir.--Hellas Can S.A., Athens, Greece; Int'l, pg. 267
Kent, Roger A., Gen. Mgr.--Dowty Palmer-Chenard, Somersworth, NH; Int'l, pg. 1338
Kentner, Pat, Gen. Mgr. & Dir.--Railway Educational Bureau, Omaha, NE; U.S. Private, pg. 1000
Kenton, James, Pres.--Futuro Inc., Milford, OH; Int'l, pg. 182
Kenton, James A., Pres.--Beiersdorf, Inc., Norwalk, CT; Int'l, pg. 182
Kenworthy, Harry, Div. V.P.--Poron Materials Unit, East Woodstock, CT; U.S. Public, pg. 1403
Kenworthy, Harry W., Div. Mgr.--Elastomer Components Unit, South Windham, CT; U.S. Public, pg. 1402
Kenyon, Alfred, Pres. & Chief Oper. Officer--Lumbermen's Mutual Casualty Company, Long Grove, IL; U.S. Private, pg. 614
Kenyon, Alfred, Pres. & Chief Oper. Officer--American Manufacturers Mutual Insurance Company, Long Grove, IL; U.S. Private, pg. 614
Kenyon, Ian, Chief Fin. Officer--The Music and Video Club Limited, Harrow, United Kingdom; Int'l, pg. 733
Kenyon, Jeff, Mgr.-Mktg. Communications--Keithley Test Instrumentation Group, Cleveland, OH; U.S. Public, pg. 946
Kenyon, Peter, Pres.--Carlson Marketing Group Japan Co. Ltd., Tokyo, Japan; U.S. Private, pg. 212
Kenyon, Peter, Gen. Mgr.--Carlson Marketing Group Japan KK, Tokyo, Japan; U.S. Private, pg. 212
Kenyon, T.J., Mgr.--T.J. Kenton & Company, Stevenage, United Kingdom; U.S. Public, pg. 552
Keogh, C.J., Pres.--Niedner Limited, Coaticook, Canada; Int'l, pg. 1485
Keogh, Denis, G.M.--Martin Merkel Ireland Ltd., Dublin, Ireland; Int'l, pg. 860
Keogh, J., Gen. Mgr.--Aer Lingus, Dusseldorf, Germany; Int'l, pg. 28
Keohane, Sean, Pres.--Banta Global Turnkey Group, Cork, Ireland; U.S. Public, pg. 189
Keosayian, Raymond, Pres.--Holmes Protection of Long Island, Inc., Islandia, NY; U.S. Public, pg. 1649
Keown, Marcus G., Gen. Mgr.--WDEF-TV, Chattanooga, TN; U.S. Public, pg. 1078
Kepecs, G., Mng. Dir.--AB-AEGON Altalanos Biztosito Rt, Budapest, Hungary; Int'l, pg. 28
Kepford, R.P., Pres.--Western Ash Company, Phoenix, AZ; Int'l, pg. 203
Kepner, M. James, Plant Mgr.--Bosch Braking Systems-North America, Sumter, SC; Int'l, pg. 205
Keppel, Steven C., Plant Mgr.--Industrial Bag Division - Salt Lake City Plant, Salt Lake City, UT; U.S. Public, pg. 1521
Keppler, Ulrich, V.P.--Sulzer (Japan) Ltd., Tokyo, Japan; Int'l, pg. 1306
Kera, Takeshi, Chief Oper. Officer--Honda Austria G.m.b.H., Vienna, Austria; Int'l, pg. 635
Keranen, Ulla-Maija, Mng. Dir.--Fidenta Oy, Espoo, Finland; Int'l, pg. 859
Kerckhove, Goerge H., Sr. V.P.-Plumbing Prods.--American Standard Plumbing Products, Piscataway, NJ; U.S. Public, pg. 92
Kerins, Donald J., Pres.--Government Electronics Div., Woodland Hills, CA; U.S. Public, pg. 293
Kerkman, Donald L., Mgr.--Burlington, Brighton & Wheatland Telephone Co., Burlington, WI; U.S. Public, pg. 1571
Kerl, Jon F., Reg. Dir.--Piper Jaffray Inc., Portland, OR; U.S. Public, pg. 1302
Kerley, Gary, Pres.--SMI Rail, Seguin, TX; U.S. Public, pg. 413
Kerman, Harold M., Pres.--Steiner Electric Company, Chicago, IL; U.S. Private, pg. 1039
Kern, Dave, Gen. Mgr.--Starboard Industries, Inc., East Tawas, MI; U.S. Public, pg. 919
Kern, David, Gen. Mgr.--American Camper, Lenexa, KS; U.S. Public, pg. 265
Kern, Ellis, Pres.--Ivy Hill Corporation, New York, NY; U.S. Public, pg. 1611
Kern, Jim, V.P.--Armin Plastics, Tyco Labs, Tulsa, OK; U.S. Public, pg. 1647
Kern, Karl Heinz, Gen. Mgr.--New York Branch, New York, NY; Int'l, pg. 139
Kern, Karl-Heinz, Mgr.-Reg. Sls.--Robinson-Nugent GmbH, Stuttgart, Germany; U.S. Public, pg. 1395
Kern, Lawrence A., Pres.--Dole Fresh Vegetables, Salinas, CA; U.S. Public, pg. 515
Kern, Robert, Mgr.--Westco Products, Sparks, NV; Int'l, pg. 244
Kernan, Richard M., Jr., Chm. Bd. & Chief Exec. Officer--New York Life International Investment, New York, NY; U.S. Private, pg. 795
Kerns, Gerald, Branch Mgr.--National Mine Service Company, Morgantown, WV; Int'l, pg. 281
Kerns, Richard A., Plant Mgr.--Troy Mills, Inc., Harrisville, WV; U.S. Private, pg. 1106
Kerns, William M., Plant Mgr.--Central New York Bottle Co., Auburn, NY; U.S. Public, pg. 1289
Keromnes, Leon, Mng. Dir.--The Lincoln Electric Co. (France) S.A., Grand Quevilly, France; U.S. Public, pg. 996
Kerr, A., Area Mgr.--Van Leeuwen Pipe and Tube Eastern Australia Pty. ltd., Salisbury, Australia; Int'l, pg. 1450
Kerr, Charles, Pres.--Trans-American Steamship Agency, San Pedro, CA; Int'l, pg. 1418
Kerr, Donald J., Pres. & Chief Exec. Officer--Crestar Food Products, Inc., Brentwood, TN; U.S. Public, pg. 805
Kerr, Ian, Mng. Dir.--Hepworth Minerals and Chemicals Limited, Sandbach, United Kingdom; Int'l, pg. 615
Kerr, John R., Exec. Dir.--Carboindustrial, Rio de Janeiro, Brazil; Int'l, pg. 447
Kerr, Laurence, Chm.--International Public Relations, Pty. Ltd., Melbourne, Australia; Int'l, pg. 1227
Kerr, Mark, Joint Mng. Dir.--International Public Relations, Pty. Ltd., Melbourne, Australia; Int'l, pg. 1227
Kerr, Mike, Pres.--Huber, Hunt & Nichols, Inc., Indianapolis, IN; U.S. Private, pg. 548
Kerr, Paul, Joint Mng. Dir.--International Public Relations, Pty. Ltd., Melbourne, Australia; Int'l, pg. 1227
Kerr, Stephen R., Exec. V.P.--Holstein-Friesian Services, Inc., Brattleboro, VT; U.S. Private, pg. 536
Kerr, William, Pres.--Professional Loss Control, Kingston, TN; U.S. Public, pg. 795
Kerr, William A., Gen. Mgr.--ITW New Zealand, Ltd., Avondale, New Zealand; U.S. Public, pg. 868
Kerry, Alan E., Pres.--American Trading Real Estate Properties, Inc., Baltimore, MD; U.S. Private, pg. 64
Kers, F.M., Pres.--TFA - Trans-maritime Freight Agencies B.V., Rotterdam, Netherlands; Int'l, pg. 682
Kers, Jon H., Mng. Dir.--Quaker Oats B.V., Zwijndrecht, Netherlands; U.S. Public, pg. 1348
Kersels, George, V.P. & Mgr.--Tektronix U.K. Limited, Marlow, United Kingdom; U.S. Public, pg. 1568
Kersey, Don, Gen. Mgr.--Tele Scripps Cable, Bluefield, WV; U.S. Public, pg. 1448
Kersh, Russell A., Chief Fin. Officer & Chief Oper. Officer--Adidas America, Spartanburg, SC; Int'l, pg. 24
Kershaw, G.K., Gen. Mgr.--Commonwealth Bank-Hong Kong, Central, Hong Kong; Int'l, pg. 313
Kershaw, Roger, Gen. Mgr.--Scotch Premium Meat, Gorgie, United Kingdom; U.S. Public, pg. 607
Kershaw, William, Chief Oper. Officer--Camloc International, Leicester, United Kingdom; U.S. Public, pg. 610
Kersting, Kurt, V.P.-Sls. & Mktg.--Duro-Test Intl. Corp., Fairfield, NJ; U.S. Private, pg. 349
Kersulis, Bernard, Pres.--Zephyr Mfg. Co., Inglewood, CA; U.S. Private, pg. 1032
Kertesz, George, Pres.--The Schebler Co., Bettendorf, IA; U.S. Private, pg. 366
Kertz, James, Pres.--Melroe Company, Fargo, ND; U.S. Public, pg. 877
Kertzman, Kris, Admin.--Alvarado Convalescent & Rehabilitation Hospital San Diego, San Diego, CA; U.S. Public, pg. 1711
Kertzman, Mitchell, Pres.--Sybase Professional Services, Burlington, MA; U.S. Public, pg. 1544
Kertzman, Mitchell, Pres.--Sybase Inc., Concord, MA; U.S. Public, pg. 1544
Kerwin, J.P., M.D., Pres.--Krug Life Sciences Inc., Houston, TX; U.S. Public, pg. 968
Kese, John, Mng. Dir.--Ericsson GE Mobile Communications Inc., Lynchburg, VA; Int'l, pg. 1365
Keskasemsook, Anant, Mng. Dir.--Siam Guardian Glass Co., Ltd., Nong Khae, Thailand; Int'l, pg. 1238
Kesl, James R., Pres. & Chief Exec. Officer--Willis Corroon Corp. of Seattle, Seattle, WA; Int'l, pg. 1507
Kesler, Steven D., Pres.--Constellation Investments, Inc., Baltimore, MD; U.S. Public, pg. 172
Kesman, Anthony K., Corp. V.P.--Distribution, McGaw Park, IL; U.S. Public, pg. 44
Kesper, Carl, V.P. & Gen. Mgr.--Raypak Canada, Ltd., Mississauga, Canada; Int'l, pg. 1022
Kesper, Klaus-Martin, Chief Officer--Generale Bank & Co., Wuppertal, Germany; Int'l, pg. 548
Kespohl, Horst, Mng. Dir.--Bertrand Faure Sitztechnik GmbH & Co. KG, Geiselhoring, Germany; Int'l, pg. 193
Kesselman, Ronald C., Chm.--Wise Foods, Inc., Parsippany, NJ; U.S. Private, pg. 157
Kesselman, Ronald C., Chm.--Elmer's Products, Inc., Columbus, OH; U.S. Private, pg. 158
Kesselring, Markus, Gen. Mgr.--Johnson Wax AG, Dietikon, Switzerland; U.S. Private, pg. 593
Kessen, George, Mgr.--General Employment Enterprises, Inc., Tampa, FL; U.S. Public, pg. 714
Kessissoglou, J., Mng. Dir.--Forest Products S.A., Maroussi, Greece; Int'l, pg. 458
Kessler, Eric, Sr. V.P.-Mktg.--HBO Video, Inc., New York, NY; U.S. Public, pg. 1612
Kessler, Hanspeter, Dir.--CAP Rechtsschutz, Geneva, Switzerland; Int'l, pg. 60
Kessler, Oswald, Gen. Mgr.--Mifa AG, Frenkendorf, Switzerland; Int'l, pg. 866
Kessler, Paul, Pres.--Toledo Stamping & Manufacturing Co., Toledo, OH; U.S. Public, pg. 707
Kesteloot, Thomas M., Pres.--Sysco Intermountain Food Services, Inc., Salt Lake City, UT; U.S. Public, pg. 1552
Keswick, Henry, Chm. Bd.--Jardine Strategic Holdings Ltd., Hamilton, Bermuda; Int'l, pg. 703
Keswick, Simon, Chm. Bd.--Dairy Farm International Holdings Limited, Hamilton, Bermuda; Int'l, pg. 703
Ketcham, Hank, Pres.--Revelstoke Home Centers, Surrey, Canada; Int'l, pg. 1490
Ketelsen, J. L., Chm. Bd. & Pres.--Tenneco Sudan, Inc., Houston, TX; U.S. Public, pg. 1578
Ketner, William O., Jr., Pres. & Sec.--Exclusive Healthcare, Inc., Omaha, NE; U.S. Private, pg. 770
Ketscher, Gerhard, Chief Oper. Officer--Chemserv Industrie Service Ges.m.b.H., Lienz, Austria; Int'l, pg. 356
Kett, Bill, Gen. Mgr.--JPE Canada Inc., Peterborough, Canada; U.S. Public, pg. 919
Kettemann, Tim, Mng. Dir.--Bankgesellschaft Berlin Investment GmbH, Berlin, Germany; Int'l, pg. 159
Kettemann, Tim, Mng. Dir.--BB-Asset Management Vermogensverwaltung GmbH, Berlin, Germany; Int'l, pg. 159
Kettler, Richard A., Pres.--Lucas-Milhaupt, Inc., Cudahy, WI; U.S. Public, pg. 780
Kettler, Richard A., V.P. & Gen. Mgr.--Lucas Milhaupt - Europe, Stevenage, United Kingdom; U.S. Public, pg. 780
Kettlewell, Jennie, Chief Exec.--Shandwick Communications Ltd., London, United Kingdom; Int'l, pg. 1226
Keun-Sun, Choi, Pres.--Lucky Ltd., Seoul, Korea; Int'l, pg. 779
Keup, Rick E., Pres. & Chief Oper. Officer--Ames Company, Parkersburg, WV; U.S. Public, pg. 1683
Keup, Tom, Mgr.-Opers.--Mercer Products Co., Umatilla, FL; Int'l, pg. 802
Keusch, Hubert, V.P.--LGT Bank in Liechtenstein AG Hong Kong, Central, Hong Kong; Int'l, pg. 810
Keville, Tim J., Assoc. Dir.--WF Corroon-Belfast, Belfast, United Kingdom; Int'l, pg. 1501
Kewitz, S., Chief Oper. Officer--Churrasco Steak-Restaurant GmbH, Dusseldorf, Germany; Int'l, pg. 1499
Key, Frank S., Jr., Pres.--Socar, Inc., Florence, SC; U.S. Public, pg. 1392
Key, James Richard, Pres. & Chief Exec. Officer--Regions Bank/Chilton County, Thorsby, AL; U.S. Public, pg. 1372
Key, John, Pres. & Chief Exec. Officer--Clinton State Bank, Clinton, IN; U.S. Public, pg. 1217
Key, John L., Mng. Dir.--Red Dog, Kotzebue, AK; Int'l, pg. 308
Keyder, Emine, Chm.--A4 Reklamcilik, Istanbul, Turkey; U.S. Private, pg. 1062
Keyes, Bob, Plant Superintendant--General Shale Products Corp., Corbin, KY; Int'l, pg. 844
Keyes, Jim, Pres.--President Homes, Minneapolis, MN; U.S. Private, pg. 970
Keyes, Warren, Jr., Gen. Mgr.--Schult Homes Corporation, Elkton, MD; U.S. Public, pg. 1442
Keys, Chandler, V.P.--National Cattlemen's Beef Association, Washington, DC; U.S. Private, pg. 780
Keys, David N., Chief Fin. Officer--Western Electrochemical Company, Cedar City, UT; U.S. Public, pg. 88
Keys, Tom, Mgr.-Sls.--Temco Fireplace Products, Inc. (Manchester), Manchester, TN; U.S. Public, pg. 1576
Keys, Wesley, Mng. Dir.--Heil Europe, Dunfermline, United Kingdom; U.S. Public, pg. 521
Keyser, R.P., Area Mgr.--Ballast Nedam Beton en Waterbouw B.V., Amstelveen, Netherlands; Int'l, pg. 133
Keyser, Richard L., Pres.--Grainger, Lincolnshire, IL; U.S. Public, pg. 758
Kezsbom, Arnold, V.P.--Ambico, Lake Mary, FL; U.S. Public, pg. 1369
Kezuka, Tomio, Pres.--Nomura Satellite Communications Co., Ltd., Tokyo, Japan; Int'l, pg. 956
Kfouri, Fernando, Pres.--Seagram Latin America, Coral Gables, FL; Int'l, pg. 1217
Khalid, Muhammad, Sr. V.P. & Gen. Mgr.--Habib Bank Ltd., Colombo, Sri Lanka; Int'l, pg. 584
Khan, A., Mng. Dir.--Wyeth Laboratories (Pakistan) Ltd., Karachi, Pakistan; U.S. Public, pg. 82
Khan, Anis, Office Mgr.--Weatherford Inc., Mumbai, India; U.S. Public, pg. 1750
Khan, Kamran, Dir.--Excalibur Technologies International, Ltd., Windsor, United Kingdom; U.S. Public, pg. 598
Khan, Mohammed, Chm.--Enterprise Nexus Communications, Mumbai, India; U.S. Private, pg. 678
Khan, Nazir, Mng. Dir.--PCS Nitrogen-Trinidad, Couva, Trinidad & Tobago; Int'l, pg. 1064
Khan, Saeed U., Pres.--Kvaerner R J Brown Pte. Ltd., Singapore, Singapore; Int'l, pg. 767
Khanna, M.K. "Mike", Exec. V.P., Area Dir.-Central Asia & CEO Hindustan Thompson--J. Walter Thompson Company, New York, NY; Int'l, pg. 1483
Khanna, Ravi, Pres.--India Photographic Company Limited, Mumbai, India; U.S. Public, pg. 552
Khasitsakul, Decha, Mng. Dir.--Asset Development Co., Ltd., Bangkok, Thailand; Int'l, pg. 677
Khawaja, Tanveer A., Mr., Sr. V.P. & Chief Mgr.--Habib Bank Ltd., Istanbul, Turkey; Int'l, pg. 585
Khayat, B., Mng. Dir.--Oasis-Ameron, Ltd., Dammam, Saudi Arabia; U.S. Public, pg. 99
Kheng, Oliver TanKok, Chm.--NDC Merchant Bank Ltd., Singapore, Singapore; Int'l, pg. 351
Kheong, Ng Chee, Gen. Mgr.--ORIX Car Rentals Sdn. Bhd., Kuala Lumpur, Malaysia; Int'l, pg. 1009
Khiang, Ang Miah, Deputy Gen. Mgr.--Heller Factoring (Singapore) Ltd., Singapore, Singapore; Int'l, pg. 521
Khilnari, Dipi, Mng. Dir.--Donaldson Filter Systems Pvt. Ltd., New Delhi, India; U.S. Public, pg. 517
Khin, Kwan Wai, Chief Oper. Officer--MacGREGOR (SGP) Pte. Ltd., Singapore, Singapore; Int'l, pg. 671
Khoman, Thanat, Dr., Chm. Bd.--Securities One Limited, Bangkok, Thailand; Int'l, pg. 485
Khoo, Richard, Chief Exec. Officer & Gen. Mgr.--SATS Passenger Services Pte. Ltd., Singapore, Singapore; Int'l, pg. 1374
Khor, Charles, Mng. Dir.--Sime Diamond Leasing (Malaysia) Sdn. Bhd., Kuala Lumpur, Malaysia; Int'l, pg. 158
Khossoussi, I., Mng. Dir.--A.H. Robins (Iran) Company, Tehran, Iran; U.S. Public, pg. 82
Khourie, Matt, Chief Exec. Officer-Texas & Houston--Trammell Crow Company, Dallas, TX; U.S. Public, pg. 1628
Khoury, Carlos, Chief Exec.--Societe des Ciments Libanais, Beirut, Lebanon; Int'l, pg. 629
Khoury, George, Pres.--Riyad Insurance Company Ltd., Hamilton, Bermuda; U.S. Public, pg. 363
Khowry, Majed, Mgr.-Office--Woodward-Clyde, New York, NY; U.S. Public, pg. 1656
Khunnah, Madan, Pres.--Pioneer Biogene, Pvt. Ltd., Janakpur, India; U.S. Public, pg. 1299
Kibler, Michael E., Pres.--Blue & Gray Brokerage, Gary, IN; U.S. Public, pg. 1687
Kida, Setsuo, Gen. Mgr.--Tektronix Industria e Comercio Ltda., Sao Paulo, Brazil; U.S. Public, pg. 1568
Kidajo, Setsuo, Gen. Mgr.--Tektronix S.A. de C.V., Mexico, Mexico; U.S. Public, pg. 1568
Kidd, Daniel, Mng. Dir.--KeyStone Center, Chester, PA; U.S. Public, pg. 1697
Kidd, Don, V.P. & Gen. Mgr.--Ringier America, Pontiac Division, Pontiac, IL; U.S. Public, pg. 1778
Kidder, C. Robert, Chm. Bd. & Chief Exec. Officer--Borden, Inc., Columbus, OH; U.S. Private, pg. 157

Kidder, C. Robert, Chm. Bd. & Chief Exec. Officer--Cracker Jack Division, Northbrook, IL; *U.S. Private*, pg. 157
Kidder, R. Perry, V.P. & Gen. Mgr.--WFRV-TV, Green Bay, WI; *U.S. Public*, pg. 275
Kidder, Richard, Gen. Plant Mgr.--Bayou Cogeneration, Pasadena, TX; *Int'l*, pg. 37
Kidell, Sten-Soren, Gen. Mgr.--Forbo Parkett AB, Tibro, Sweden; *Int'l*, pg. 497
Kidner, Raymond L., Chief Oper. Officer--Tosoh SMD, Inc., Grove City, OH; *Int'l*, pg. 1407
Kieckhafer, Thomas W., Pres.--The West Bend Co., West Bend, WI; *U.S. Public*, pg. 1322
Kiefer, Edward S., Mng. Dir.--General Motors Austria Ges.m.b.H., Vienna, Austria; *U.S. Public*, pg. 721
Kiefer, John, Pres.--Capital Factors, Inc., Fort Lauderdale, FL; *U.S. Public*, pg. 1669
Kieffer, Dominique, Pres.--Polarcup France S.A., Auneau, France; *Int'l*, pg. 638
Kieffer, Tom, Gen. Mgr.--Connect Computer, Minneapolis, MN; *U.S. Public*, pg. 1192
Kieffer, William, Gen. Mgr.--Komori America Corporation, Allendale, NJ; *Int'l*, pg. 745
Kiehm, John, Pres.--PAR Vision Systems Corporation, New Hartford, NY; *U.S. Public*, pg. 1256
Kielhoz, Rolf, Chief Exec. Officer--Alpina Insurance Company, Zurich, Switzerland; *Int'l*, pg. 1529
Kielty, Robin, Reg. Acct. Dir.--RP alpha/Boston, Waltham, MA; *U.S. Private*, pg. 950
Kiely, Jeremiah, Plant Mgr.--Amicon Ireland Limited, Limerick, Ireland; *U.S. Public*, pg. 1113
Kiely, Leonard, Mng. Dir.--SPS International Ltd., Shannon, Ireland; *U.S. Public*, pg. 1420
Kiene, Wilfried, Gen. Mgr.--Bailey Fischer & Porter GmbH, Gottingen, Germany; *Int'l*, pg. 449
Kiepper, Alan F., Pres.--New York City Transit Authority, Brooklyn, NY; *U.S. Private*, pg. 739
Kiepper, Alan F., Pres.--Manhattan and Bronx Surface Transit Operating Authority, Brooklyn, NY; *U.S. Private*, pg. 739
Kierce, Diane, Mng. Dir.--IMG Communications, Harrison, NY; *U.S. Private*, pg. 566
Kiernan, Charles E., Pres.--Duracell U.S.A., Bethel, CT; *U.S. Public*, pg. 743
Kiernan, Edward C., V.P. & Gen. Mgr.--WBAL-AM, Baltimore, MD; *U.S. Private*, pg. 516
Kiernan, Edward C., V.P. & Gen. Mgr.--WIYY-FM, Baltimore, MD; *U.S. Private*, pg. 516
Kiesling, Richard, Pres.--Belmont Telephone Company, Madison, WI; *U.S. Public*, pg. 1022
Kieta, D.L., Pres.--Century Contractors West Inc., Kingwood, TX; *U.S. Public*, pg. 950
Kiewel, Bill, Gen. Mgr.--National Frozen Foods Corporation - Albany, Albany, OR; *U.S. Private*, pg. 783
Kight, J.A., Pres.--Therm-O-Disc Inc., Mansfield, OH; *U.S. Public*, pg. 573
Kihara, Kazuhiko, Chief Oper. Officer--Hospal Ltd., Tokyo, Japan; *Int'l*, pg. 668
Kihara, Terutaka, Pres.--Descente America Inc., Englewood, CO; *Int'l*, pg. 395
Kiiski, Antti, Gen. Mgr.--Bailey-Fischer & Porter Oy, Espoo, Finland; *Int'l*, pg. 449
Kikendall, Thomas R., V.P.--Nordson Sang San Engineering Co., Kyonggi-do, Korea; *U.S. Public*, pg. 1190
Kikkawa, Akikazu, Pres. & Chief Exec. Officer--Ajinomoto U.S.A., Inc., Teaneck, NJ; *Int'l*, pg. 40
Kikuchi, Hidehiro, Chm. Bd.--BTM Finanziaria (Italia) S.p.A., Milan, Italy; *Int'l*, pg. 158
Kikuchi, Koichi, Chief Oper. Officer--P.T. Standard Toyo Polymer-Merak Plant, Jawa, Indonesia; *Int'l*, pg. 1408
Kikuchi, Kuninori, Joint Gen. Mgr.--Dai-Ichi Kangyo Bank, Ltd.-Taipei, Taipei, Taiwan; *Int'l*, pg. 361
Kikuchi, Kyo, Chm. & Pres.--Yasuda Bank and Trust Company (U.S.A.), New York, NY; *Int'l*, pg. 1520
Kikuchi, Saburo, Pres.--Lotus Development Japan Limited, Tokyo, Japan; *U.S. Public*, pg. 896
Kikuchi, Yukio, Pres.--Brighton Corporation, Chiba, Japan; *Int'l*, pg. 600
Kikura, Keiichi, Pres.--Hakuhodo Services Co., Ltd., Tokyo, Japan; *Int'l*, pg. 588
Kilbane, J. Kevin, Pres.--Lowara S.p.A, Montecchio Maggiore, Italy; *U.S. Public*, pg. 861
Kilberg, Steven, Plant Mgr.--Sweetheart Cup Company Inc., Owings Mills, MD; *U.S. Private*, pg. 1058
Kilbride, William, Pres.--American Rug Craftsmen, Sugar Valley, GA; *U.S. Public*, pg. 1121
Kilburn, Michael, Chief Oper. Officer--Commerce Drug Canada Ltd., Barrie, Canada; *U.S. Public*, pg. 494
Kilburn, Michael, Chief Oper. Officer--Del Laboratories (Canada) Ltd., Barrie, Canada; *U.S. Public*, pg. 494
Kilburn, Michael, Gen. Mgr.--Theon Co. Ltd., Barrie, Canada; *U.S. Public*, pg. 494
Kilby, David K., V.P.--Cousins Subs Systems, Inc., Menomonee Falls, WI; *U.S. Private*, pg. 280
Kilby, Leonard, Pres.--SASIB Bakery North America Inc., Plano, TX; *Int'l*, pg. 1194
Kilchman, Patrick, Pres.--Frigorex AG fur Kaltetechnik, Lucerne, Switzerland; *Int'l*, pg. 1306
Kilduff, Jack, Pres. & Chief Oper. Officer--Dr. Pepper Co., Dallas, TX; *Int'l*, pg. 248
Kiley, Mike, V.P.--D&Z Construction Services, Philadelphia, PA; *U.S. Private*, pg. 317
Kilfeather, Terry D., Pres.--Fibo ExClay Ltd., Tilbury, United Kingdom; *Int'l*, pg. 1200
Kilgore, H. Dustin, III, Gen. Mgr.--Sermatech Maine, Biddeford, ME; *U.S. Public*, pg. 1570
Kilian, Horst, Mgr.--Hapag-Lloyd Tours GmbH, Bremen, Germany; *Int'l*, pg. 596
Kilkenny, J., Pres.--Monsanto Enviro-Chem. Systems, Inc., Saint Louis, MO; *U.S. Public*, pg. 1125
Kill, Ted, Gen. Mgr.--Magnetoelastic Devices Inc. (MDI), Carthage, IL; *U.S. Public*, pg. 1101
Killebrew, Don, Plant Mgr.--Ash Grove Cement-Western Region Cement Plant, Inkom, ID; *U.S. Private*, pg. 88
Killeen, Allen, Gen. Mgr.--Kimberly-Clark Italiana S.r.l., Milan, Italy; *U.S. Public*, pg. 959
Killeen, Eugene T., Chief Oper. Officer--Allright Parking of Cleveland, Inc., Cleveland, OH; *U.S. Private*, pg. 43
Killen, Denis, Pres.--Lockheed Martin Western Development Labs, San Jose, CA; *U.S. Public*, pg. 1009
Killian, Raymond L., Jr., Chm. Bd.--Investment Technology Group, Inc., New York, NY; *U.S. Public*, pg. 924
Killinger, Gerhard, Gen. Mgr.--Hampshire Chemical GmbH, Heidelberg, Germany; *U.S. Private*, pg. 498
Killinger, Kerry K., Pres.--WM Financial, Inc., Seattle, WA; *U.S. Public*, pg. 1742
Killingsworth, Cleve, Jr., Pres.--Kaiser Permanente, Central East Division, Rockville, MD; *U.S. Private*, pg. 605
Killion, Dennis, Pres.--Onondaga Litho Supply Co., Inc., Henrietta, NY; *U.S. Public*, pg. 1329
Killoran, Dermot E., Sr. Mng. Dir.--Bank of Ireland - Tokyo Representative Office, Tokyo, Japan; *Int'l*, pg. 153
Kilpatrick, Dale, Plant Mgr.--Setzer Forest Products-Oroville Plant, Oroville, CA; *U.S. Private*, pg. 988
Kilpatrick, John, Pres.--Tam Ceramics Inc., Niagara Falls, NY; *Int'l*, pg. 329
Kilpatrick, K.R., Pres.--ASTEC America Corp., Oceanside, CA; *U.S. Public*, pg. 573
Kilpatrick, Kenneth R., Pres.--Elgar Corporation, San Diego, CA; *U.S. Public*, pg. 789
Kilpelainen, Jukka, Mng. Dir.--Tervakoski Oy, Tervakoski, Finland; *Int'l*, pg. 456
Kilpelainen, Markku, Gen. Mgr.--Hissi-Ala Oy, Turku, Finland; *Int'l*, pg. 746
Kilpi, Tapio, Mng. Dir.--Oy Finnterminals AB, Kotka, Finland; *Int'l*, pg. 1428
Kilpinen, Esko, Mng. Dir.--KONE Elevators Poland Sp.zo.o., Warsaw, Poland; *Int'l*, pg. 747
Kim, A., Pres.--SBC Portfolio Management International K.K., Tokyo, Japan; *Int'l*, pg. 1330
Kim, Chang-Ho, Gen. Mgr.--Cho Hung Bank, London Branch, London, United Kingdom; *Int'l*, pg. 288
Kim, Chee, Pres.--GATX Terminals (Pte.) Ltd., Singapore, Singapore; *U.S. Public*, pg. 693
Kim, Christopher D., Pres.--Bolt Geophysical Corporation, Englewood, CO; *U.S. Public*, pg. 244
Kim, Chul-Woong, Mng. Dir.--Awabed - Ssangyong Contracting Co., Dhahran, Saudi Arabia; *Int'l*, pg. 1292
Kim, Chwee, Pres.--GATX Private Ltd., Jurong, Singapore; *U.S. Public*, pg. 693
Kim, D.H., Mgr.--Unbrako Inc., Kyongki, Korea; *U.S. Public*, pg. 1420
Kim, Dae-Young, Pres.--Ssangyong Finance Inc., Seoul, Korea; *Int'l*, pg. 1292
Kim, Dong-Kwan, Chief Rep.--The Export-Import Bank of Korea, Abidjan, Cote d'Ivoire; *Int'l*, pg. 467
Kim, Hyun Tae, Grp. Acct. Dir.--SangAm Communications Co., Ltd., Seoul, Korea; *U.S. Public*, pg. 765
Kim, I. H., Pres.--Chonju Paper Mfg. Co., Ltd., Seoul, Korea; *Int'l*, pg. 1181
Kim, J. D., Pres.-Saniserv-Korea--Saniserv-Korea, Seoul, Korea; *U.S. Private*, pg. 965
Kim, J.H., Mng. Dir.--Thermon Korea Ltd., Seoul, Korea; *U.S. Private*, pg. 1081
Kim, Jae Koo, Pres. & Chief Exec. Officer--Cho Hung Bank of Canada, Toronto, Canada; *Int'l*, pg. 288
Kim, Jeong-Hwan, Pres.--Ssangyong Investment & Finance Co., Ltd., Inchon, Korea; *Int'l*, pg. 1292
Kim, Jhoung-ung, Pres.--Daewoo Motor Company, Ltd., Inchon, Korea; *Int'l*, pg. 357
Kim, Johnmin, Pres.--Pall Korea Limited, Seoul, Korea; *U.S. Public*, pg. 1254
Kim, Jong-Kwan, Pres.--Daewoo Sang Sa, Seoul, Korea; *Int'l*, pg. 357
Kim, Keith, Owner & Pres.--Granny Goose Foods, Inc., Oakland, CA; *U.S. Private*, pg. 469
Kim, Ken, Chm. Bd.--Kabuto International Phoenix Inc., San Francisco, CA; *Int'l*, pg. 721
Kim, Kun Hong, V.P. & Dir.--Global Rental Corporation, Seoul, Korea; *Int'l*, pg. 1009
Kim, Lee Kok, Mgr.--Keppel FELS Baltech Ltd., Varna, Bulgaria; *Int'l*, pg. 731
Kim, S.W., Pres.--Korea Bundy Corporation, Kyongki, Korea; *Int'l*, pg. 1341
Kim, Se-Yung, Pres.--TrefilARBED Korea Co. Ltd., Yangsan, Korea; *Int'l*, pg. 80
Kim, Senyon, Chm.--Leo Burnett Sonyon Inc., Seoul, Korea; *U.S. Private*, pg. 185
Kim, Seung-Hwan, Chief Officer--Qingdao Ssangyong Apparel Co., Ltd., Qingdao, China; *Int'l*, pg. 1291
Kim, Song-woong, Chief Rep.--The Export-Import Bank of Korea, Los Angeles, CA; *Int'l*, pg. 467
Kim, Suk-Dong, Pres.--Ssangyong Investment & Securities Co., Ltd., Seoul, Korea; *Int'l*, pg. 1292
Kim, Sun-Dong, Pres.--Ssangyong Oil Refining Co. Ltd., Seoul, Korea; *Int'l*, pg. 1292
Kim, Sung-Choong, Mng. Dir.--Delkor Battery Company, Gumi, Korea; *U.S. Public*, pg. 724
Kim, T.H., Pres.--IPC Corporation (Korea) Ltd., Seoul, Korea; *Int'l*, pg. 651
Kim, Tai Hwan, Pres.--Dong-A Otsuka Co., Ltd., Anyang, Korea; *Int'l*, pg. 1014
Kim, Woo-Choong, Pres.--Daewoo Shipbuilding & Heavy Machinery, Ltd., Seoul, Korea; *Int'l*, pg. 357
Kim, Xong-Han, Counrty Mgr.--A.C. Nielsen Company of Korea, Seoul, Korea; *U.S. Public*, pg. 1183
Kim, Y. D., Station Chief--Sun Microsystems of California Ltd., Seoul, Korea; *U.S. Public*, pg. 1532
Kim, Y.H., Pres. & Chief Exec. Officer--Hyundai Electronics America, San Jose, CA; *Int'l*, pg. 641
Kim, Y.Y., Sls. Mgr.--Analog Devices Korea, Ltd., Seoul, Korea; *U.S. Public*, pg. 108
Kim, Yong-Won, Pres.--Daewoo Electronics Co., Ltd., Seoul, Korea; *Int'l*, pg. 357
Kim, Young Chong, Gen. Mgr.--K.S., Seoul, Korea; *Int'l*, pg. 303
Kim, Young Han, Pres. & Chief Oper. Officer--Daewoo Securities (America) Inc., New York, NY; *Int'l*, pg. 359
Kim, Young Pyo, Gen. Mgr.--Cho Hung Bank, Tianjin Branch, Tianjin, China; *Int'l*, pg. 288
Kim, Young-ho, Pres.--Goldstar Precision Industries Ltd., Seoul, Korea; *Int'l*, pg. 779
Kimball, David J., Pres.--Market Entry Omega, Bothell, WA; *U.S. Public*, pg. 1222
Kimball, John G., Pres.--Old Kent Bank-Southwest, Kalamazoo, MI; *U.S. Public*, pg. 1217
Kimball, Richard, Pres.--Granite Prods. Div., Barre, VT; *U.S. Public*, pg. 1396
Kimball, Richard, Pres.--Rock of Ages Canada, Inc., Beebe, Canada; *U.S. Public*, pg. 1396
Kimball, Steven L., Mgr.--Willis Faber EC, Manama, Bahrain; *Int'l*, pg. 1510
Kimbell, John S., Pres. & Chief Exec. Officer--Vermont Gas Systems, Inc., South Burlington, VT; *Int'l*, pg. 542
Kimbro, J. Kirk, Pres.--Overseas Commodex Corp., Rocky Mount, NC; *Int'l*, pg. 1390
Kimbrough, James H., Pres. & Chief Exec. Officer--SunTrust Bank, Nature Coast, Brooksville, FL; *U.S. Public*, pg. 1537
Kime, Jeff, Pres.--Four Wind International Corp., Elkhart, IN; *U.S. Public*, pg. 1602
Kimes, John, Chief Oper. Officer--Computerized Security Systems, Inc., Costa Mesa, CA; *U.S. Public*, pg. 1053
Kimizuka, Masakazu, Chief Oper. Officer--Hirose Cherry Precision Company Ltd., Kawasaki, Japan; *U.S. Public*, pg. 346
Kimlin, R.P., Pres.--National Electrical Carbon Corporation, Greenville, SC; *Int'l*, pg. 891
Kimmer, Gregory C., Gen. Mgr.--Duall Division, Owosso, MI; *U.S. Public*, pg. 1100
Kimmet, Daniel E., Grp. V.P.--Automotive Group, Mount Clemens, MI; *U.S. Public*, pg. 24
Kimmo, Osmo, Mng. Dir.--Tietokesko Oy, Helsinki, Finland; *Int'l*, pg. 732
Kimmons, W. Arnold, V.P.--Oneida Foodservice Division, Oneida, NY; *U.S. Public*, pg. 1226
Kimoto, Ted, Mgr.--South Island Woodlands, Nanoose Bay, Canada; *Int'l*, pg. 828
Kimoto, Yasuyuki, Pres.--Sumitomo Bank Financial Services, Inc., New York, NY; *Int'l*, pg. 1308
Kimpe, V., Gen. Mgr.--Saval N.V., Antwerp, Belgium; *Int'l*, pg. 681
Kimpton, Geoffrey H., Gen. Mgr.--Westpac - Victoria, Melbourne, Australia; *Int'l*, pg. 1496
Kimpton, Graham, Chief Oper. Officer--Remington Australia, Noble Park, Australia; *U.S. Private*, pg. 921
Kimsey, Gary, Pres.--Gemtron Corporation, Sweetwater, TN; *Int'l*, pg. 1523
Kimura, Fumio, Pres.--Japan Business Services Co., Ltd., Tokyo, Japan; *Int'l*, pg. 702
Kimura, Hideo, Chief Oper. Officer--Honda de Mexico, S.A. de C.V., El Salto, Mexico; *Int'l*, pg. 635
Kimura, Hirokazu, Chief Oper. Officer--Hitachi Medical Corporation, Tokyo, Japan; *Int'l*, pg. 621
Kimura, Makoto, Mng. Dir.--Dai-ichi Life International (Australia) Limited, Sydney, Australia; *Int'l*, pg. 362
Kimura, O., Pres.--New United Motor Manufacturing Inc., Fremont, CA; *U.S. Public*, pg. 721
Kimura, O., Pres.--New United Motor Manufacturing Inc., Fremont, CA; *Int'l*, pg. 1413
Kimura, Osamu, Dir.--Takenaka (U.S.A.) Corporation, Indianapolis Office, Greenwood, IN; *Int'l*, pg. 1351
Kimura, Tadashi, Chief Exec.--Sumitrust Ivory & Sime Limited, Edinburgh, United Kingdom; *Int'l*, pg. 1318
Kimura, Ted, Pres. & Chief Exec. Officer--Yamaha Motor Corp., U.S.A., Cypress, CA; *Int'l*, pg. 1516
Kinane, Pat, Gen. Mgr.--Watlow Batavia, Inc., Batavia, IL; *U.S. Private*, pg. 1153
Kinard, David, Pres.--Pacificare of Nevada, Las Vegas, NV; *U.S. Public*, pg. 1251
Kinard, Jane, Admin.--Hillhaven Rehabilitation Convalescent, Norfolk, VA; *U.S. Public*, pg. 1713
Kinas, John, Gen. Mgr.--United States Aluminum Corp., Vernon, CA; *U.S. Public*, pg. 895
Kinblonz, Jeffrey, Gen. Mgr.--NYCO Minerals, Willsboro, NY; *Int'l*, pg. 259
Kincaid, Brent B., Pres. & Chief Exec. Officer--Broyhill Furniture Industries, Inc., Saint Louis, MO; *U.S. Public*, pg. 688
Kincaid, Steven M., Pres.--Kincaid Furniture Co., Inc., Hudson, NC; *U.S. Public*, pg. 972
Kincer, Jim A., Pres.--Ikon Office Solutions-Kentucky, Louisville, KY; *U.S. Public*, pg. 863
Kindberg, Jack, Pres.--Culver Studios, Culver City, CA; *Int'l*, pg. 1283
Kinder, Jim, Gen. Mgr.--Shorewood Packaging Corporation Of Alabama, Andalusia, AL; *U.S. Public*, pg. 1468
Kindinger, Wolfgang, Mng. Dir.--Burgmann Seals Australia Pty. Ltd., Sydney, Australia; *Int'l*, pg. 234
Kindlund, Newton C., Chief Oper. Officer--Holiday RV Rental/Leasing, Inc., Orlando, FL; *U.S. Public*, pg. 829
Kindlund, Newton C., Chief Oper. Officer--Holiday RV Superstores West, Inc., Sacramento, CA; *U.S. Public*, pg. 830
Kindlund, Newton C., Chief Oper. Officer--Holiday RV Superstores of New Mexico Inc., Las Cruces, NM; *U.S. Public*, pg. 830
Kindness, Ken, Gen. Mgr.--Interconnect Products Division, Rolling Meadows, IL; *U.S. Public*, pg. 1101
Kindt, Robert J., Pres.--Monarch Cortland Div., Cortland, NY; *U.S. Public*, pg. 1124
Kindt, Robert J., Pres.--Monarch Wetkzengmaschinen GmbH, Duren, Germany; *U.S. Public*, pg. 1124
Kindt, Robert J., Pres.--Stamco (U.K.) Ltd., Walsall, United Kingdom; *U.S. Public*, pg. 1124
Kindt, Robert J., Pres.--Stamco-Depiereux GMBH, Dueren, Germany; *U.S. Public*, pg. 1124
Kindt, Robert J., Pres.--Busch Gmbh, Duren, Germany; *U.S. Public*, pg. 1124
Kindt, Robert J., Pres.--Busch U.S., Sidney, OH; *U.S. Public*, pg. 1124

Kines, John D., Exec. V.P.--Fleet Leasing Division, Chicago, IL; *U.S. Public*, pg. 663
King, A. Philip, Mng. Dir.--Delta Fluid Products Ltd., Saint Helens, United Kingdom; *Int'l*, pg. 391
King, Alan, Gen. Mgr.--Analog Devices, Santa Clara, CA; *U.S. Public*, pg. 108
King, Alan, Pres.--Analog Devices, Santa Clara, Santa Clara, CA; *U.S. Public*, pg. 108
King, Aldin S., Mgr.--Scott & Stringfellow, Inc., Warrenton, VA; *U.S. Public*, pg. 1446
King, Brian, Pres.-Unit Rig--Terex Trucks, Tulsa, OK; *U.S. Public*, pg. 1581
King, Burt, Pres. & Chief Exec. Officer--Gibson County Bank, Princeton, IN; *U.S. Public*, pg. 1217
King, C.G., Pres.--Boeing Advanced Systems, Seattle, WA; *U.S. Public*, pg. 240
King, C.Y., Dir.--Hyosung America, Inc., New York, NY; *Int'l*, pg. 641
King, Carolyn, Pres.--Provident National Assurance Co., Chattanooga, TN; *U.S. Public*, pg. 1338
King, Charles, Pres.--NationsBank Securities, Inc., Charlotte, NC; *U.S. Public*, pg. 1165
King, D.R., Pres.--Ferguson Machine Co., Saint Louis, MO; *U.S. Public*, pg. 457
King, David A., Pres.--NationsBank Funding Corporation, Norfolk, VA; *U.S. Public*, pg. 1163
King, Desmond B., Chief Exec. Officer--Premier Power Ltd., Antrim, United Kingdom; *Int'l*, pg. 119
King, Douglas, Pres.--Gunther Mele Packaging, Inc., Buffalo, NY; *Int'l*, pg. 578
King, Edith, Branch Mgr.--Troy Savings Bank-Schenectady, Schenectady, NY; *U.S. Private*, pg. 1106
King, Edward L., Jr., Chm. Bd. & Chief Exec. Officer--Regions Bank/Okaloosa/Bay County, Fort Walton Beach, FL; *U.S. Public*, pg. 1372
King, G., Chief Oper. Officer--Boral Gas Limited, Sydney, Australia; *Int'l*, pg. 203
King, G., Gen. Mgr.--Standard Coffee Service, New Orleans, LA; *U.S. Private*, pg. 919
King, George, Pres.--Real Time Solutions, Napa, CA; *U.S. Private*, pg. 866
King, George F., Pres. & Chief Exec. Officer--Associated Building Systems, Portland, TN; *Int'l*, pg. 699
King, Gerry, Pres.--Catalog Resources, Inc., Dover, DE; *U.S. Public*, pg. 970
King, Gilman R., Pres. & Chief Exec. Officer--AEC/Application Automation, Inc., Wood Dale, IL; *U.S. Private*, pg. 1041
King, Gregory P., Dir.-Opers.--The Toro Co., Windom, MN; *U.S. Public*, pg. 1624
King, Harvey C., Pres.--PENCO-Hawaii, Honolulu, HI; *Int'l*, pg. 1508
King, Helen M., Mgr.--Scott & Stringfellow, Inc., Culpeper, VA; *U.S. Public*, pg. 1446
King, John F., Pres.--Brown Brothers Harriman Trust Co. of New York, New York, NY; *U.S. Private*, pg. 173
King, Judy, Chief Oper. Officer--Wieland Financial Services, Inc., Atlanta, GA; *U.S. Private*, pg. 1175
King, Ken, Pres. & Publisher--Calgary Herald, Calgary, Canada; *Int'l*, pg. 631
King, Kenneth, Pres.--Editors Press, Inc., Hyattsville, MD; *U.S. Private*, pg. 623
King, Linda, Branch Mgr.--Ace Glass Incorporated-Midwest Div., Louisville, KY; *U.S. Private*, pg. 12
King, Maclellan E., Jr., Pres. & Chief Exec. Officer--Nevada Bell, Reno, NV; *U.S. Public*, pg. 1416
King, Marla, V.P. & Mgr.--City National Bank - San Diego Regional Office, La Jolla, CA; *U.S. Public*, pg. 381
King, Michael, Exec. V.P. & Gen. Mgr.--Bayerische Landesbank - Singapore Branch, Singapore, Singapore; *Int'l*, pg. 176
King, Michael, Pres. & Chief Exec. Officer--King World Productions, Los Angeles, CA; *U.S. Public*, pg. 961
King, Ng, Chief Oper. Officer--NIFE Power Systems Pte Ltd., Singapore, Singapore; *Int'l*, pg. 54
King, Nuala M., Pres.--Coca-Cola Financial Corporation, Atlanta, GA; *U.S. Public*, pg. 392
King, Patrick J., Pres. & Chief Exec. Officer--Adriatic Insurance Company of Canada, Montreal, Canada; *Int'l*, pg. 61
King, R.E., Pres.--Mount Vernon Mills, Inc., LaFrance Industries, La France, SC; *U.S. Private*, pg. 835
King, R.L., Jr., Pres.--Mount Vernon Dryer Fabrics, Greenville, SC; *U.S. Private*, pg. 835
King, Ralph, V.P.--CAP Gemini America (Management Consulting Branch), Vienna, VA; *Int'l*, pg. 264
King, Ray C., Mng. Dir.--Mildara Blass Wines, Albert Park, Australia; *Int'l*, pg. 501
King, Richard, Pres.--The Canadian Salt Co. Ltd., Pointe-Claire, Canada; *U.S. Public*, pg. 1135
King, Robert J., Pres.--The Fifth Third Bank of Northwestern Ohio, National Association, Toledo, OH; *U.S. Public*, pg. 622
King, Ron, Pres. & Chief Exec. Officer--BlueLincs HMO, Tulsa, OK; *U.S. Private*, pg. 152
King, Ron, Pres. & Chief Exec. Officer--Member Service Life Insurance Co., Tulsa, OK; *U.S. Private*, pg. 152
King, Steve, Mng. Dir.--Scitex America Corp., Bedford, MA; *Int'l*, pg. 644
King, T. Eugene, Chm., Pres. & Chief Exec. Officer--First Security Service Company, Salt Lake City, UT; *U.S. Public*, pg. 638
King, T.H., Pres. & Chief Exec. Officer--Federal Industries Transport Group, Winnipeg, Canada; *Int'l*, pg. 1150
King, T.S., Pres. & Gen. Mgr.--Sherwin-Williams Consumer Brands Division, Cleveland, OH; *U.S. Public*, pg. 1466
King, Timothy J., Pres.--Norwest Insurance, Inc., Minneapolis, MN; *U.S. Public*, pg. 1202
King, Tom, Editor--El Paso Herald-Post, El Paso, TX; *U.S. Public*, pg. 1447
King, Van, Pres. & Publisher--News & Record, Greensboro, NC; *U.S. Private*, pg. 649
King, Winston, Chm. Bd.--Aroaima Bauxite Company Ltd., Bridgetown, Barbados; *U.S. Public*, pg. 1386
King, Winston M., Chm. Bd.--Aroaima Mining Company Limited, Georgetown, Guyana; *U.S. Public*, pg. 1386
Kingdom, Scott, Office Mgr.--Korn/Ferry International, Chicago, IL; *U.S. Private*, pg. 633
Kingery, Daniel, Pres.--Reeves-Hoffman Div., Carlisle, PA; *U.S. Public*, pg. 286
Kingham, David, Chief Exec. Officer--Wydawnictwa Prawnicze PWN, Warsaw, Poland; *Int'l*, pg. 1095
Kingham, R.C., Mng. Dir.--Barclays Bank Szarl, Kinshasa, Congo; *Int'l*, pg. 166
Kingma, R.V., Pres.--Delft Instruments International B.V., Delft, Netherlands; *Int'l*, pg. 389
Kingston, J., Plant Mgr.--The Kingsford Products Co., Belle, MO; *U.S. Public*, pg. 387
Kinkead-Weekes, R.C., Mng. Dir.--Comalco Minerals & Alumina, Brisbane, Australia; *Int'l*, pg. 307
Kinkead, Karl, V.P. & Gen. Mgr.--Ansul Fire Protection, Marinette, WI; *U.S. Public*, pg. 1650
Kinkel, Hans-Peter, Mng. Dir.--Nederman GmbH, Kronberg, Germany; *Int'l*, pg. 283
Kinnan, Frank, Pres.--Underground Technologies, Byron, CA; *U.S. Public*, pg. 1598
Kinnear, Anthony, Mng. Dir.--Butterworths Asia, Singapore, Singapore; *Int'l*, pg. 1095
Kinney, Barry P., Pres.--Fore Line Security, Tampa, FL; *U.S. Private*, pg. 917
Kinney, Bob, Plant Mgr.--Square D Company Manufacturing (Thailand) Ltd., Samutprakan, Thailand; *Int'l*, pg. 1209
Kinney, Ed, Mgr.-Sls.--McKenzie Towables By Monaco, Springfield, OR; *U.S. Public*, pg. 1123
Kinney, Michael J., Pres.--Philip Morris Capital Corporation, Rye Brook, NY; *U.S. Public*, pg. 1289
Kinney, Neil, Mng. Dir.--Westpac Bank - PNG Limited, Port Moresby, Papua New Guinea; *Int'l*, pg. 1497
Kinney, Tom, Mgr.-Mfg.--Advanced Polymers Division, North Bennington, VT; *U.S. Public*, pg. 689
Kinnie, R.H., Chm. Bd. & Pres.--Canada Safeway Limited, Calgary, Canada; *U.S. Public*, pg. 1426
Kinning, Jon L., Mgr.-Division--Performance Building System, Denver, CO; *U.S. Private*, pg. 905
Kinnunen, Matti, Mng. Dir.--D. Carnegie AB, Stockholm, Sweden; *Int'l*, pg. 272
Kino, Tsuneo, Gen. Mgr.--Bank of Yokohama Singapore, Singapore, Singapore; *Int'l*, pg. 159
Kinoshita, Kunio, Mng. Dir.--Sakura Bank (Deutschland) GmbH, Frankfurt/Main, Germany; *Int'l*, pg. 1180
Kinoshita, M., Mng. Dir.--Toshiba-EMI Limited, Tokyo, Japan; *Int'l*, pg. 427
Kinsch, J., Pres.--Circuit Foil Luxembourg S.A., Wiltz, Luxembourg; *Int'l*, pg. 80
Kinsel, Raymond L., Pres.--Besser/APPCO, San Antonio, TX; *U.S. Private*, pg. 139
Kinsella, P.J., Mng. Dir.--Cow & Gate Nutricia (Ireland) Ltd., Dublin, Ireland; *Int'l*, pg. 991
Kinsey, Jerry, Gen. Mgr.--Christy Halsey Oil Co., Chester, NJ; *U.S. Private*, pg. 729
Kinsey, Jerry, Gen. Mgr.--Meenan Oil Div., Clinton, NJ; *U.S. Private*, pg. 729
Kinsey, Wayne R., Pres.--Motion Control Industries, Inc., Ridgway, PA; *U.S. Public*, pg. 305
Kinsey, Wayne R., Pres.--Motion Control Industries, Inc., Bloomington, IN; *U.S. Public*, pg. 305
Kinsley, R.J., Resident Mgr.--CLAM Petroleum Co., Hague, Netherlands; *U.S. Public*, pg. 1662
Kinslow, E., Chief Oper. Officer--Augat, Inc., Interconnection Products-Sanford Plant, Sanford, ME; *U.S. Public*, pg. 1598
Kint, Daniel, Pres.--Atlantic Machine Tools Inc., Houston, TX; *Int'l*, pg. 585
Kinzel, Richard L., Pres & Chief Exec. Officer--The Cedar Point Transportation Co., Sandusky, OH; *U.S. Public*, pg. 319
Kinzler, Alexander C., Pres.--Barnwell Hawaiian Properties, Inc., Honolulu, HI; *U.S. Public*, pg. 191
Kinzler, Morton H., Pres.--Barnwell Geothermal Corporation, Honolulu, HI; *U.S. Public*, pg. 191
Kiola, Dan, Gen. Mgr.--Elkay Plastics Co., Inc., Stock Service Center, Bensenville, IL; *U.S. Private*, pg. 372
Kipec, Anita, Pres. & Chief Exec. Officer--Steck-Vaughn Publishing Corporation, Austin, TX; *U.S. Public*, pg. 784
Kipling, J.L., Mng. Dir.--Firestone Tire & Rubber Co. of New Zealand, Ltd., Christchurch, New Zealand; *Int'l*, pg. 214
Kipp, Larry, Pres.--Universal Tool & Stamping, Butler, IN; *U.S. Public*, pg. 17
Kipp, Louis D., Pres.--Quipp Systems, Inc., Hialeah, FL; *U.S. Public*, pg. 1353
Kippenberger, Hanns, Dr., Sr. Mng. Dir.--Deutsche Bank AG (Hamburg), Hamburg, Germany; *Int'l*, pg. 402
Kipperman, Robert, V.P. & Gen. Mgr.-CBS Radio Networks--CBS Radio Div., New York, NY; *U.S. Public*, pg. 274
Kipperman, Robert, Pres. & Gen. Mgr.-CBS Radio Networks--CBS Radio, New York, NY; *U.S. Public*, pg. 274
Kippur, Stephen, Exec. V.P. & Grp. Pres.--Professional Reference & Trade Group, New York, NY; *U.S. Public*, pg. 1768
Kirano, Akira, Mng. Dir.--Nikko Bank (Luxembourg) S.A., Luxembourg, Luxembourg; *Int'l*, pg. 930
Kirberg, Ralf, Mng. Dir.--LHI Leasing fur Handel und Industrie GmbH, Munich, Germany; *Int'l*, pg. 160
Kirbis, Reinhard, Chief Oper. Officer--Kammerer GmbH, Osnabruck, Germany; *Int'l*, pg. 35
Kirby, Dan L., Co.-Chm. Bd., Exec. V.P., Gen. Counsel & Sec.--Western Surety Company, Sioux Falls, SD; *U.S. Public*, pg. 303
Kirby, R. L., Branch Mgr.--American Inks & Coatings Corp., Ink Division, Richmond, VA; *U.S. Private*, pg. 56
Kirby, Robert, Pres.--Westmoreland Energy, Inc., Charlottesville, VA; *U.S. Public*, pg. 1761
Kirby, Ron, Jr., V.P. & Gen. Mgr.--ADT Truck & Equipment Auctions, Inc., Nashville, TN; *U.S. Public*, pg. 1648
Kirch, David, District Mgr.--W. Braun Co., Saint Paul, MN; *U.S. Private*, pg. 166
Kirch, Hermann, Gen. Mgr.--Cross (Deutschland) GmbH, Mainz, Germany; *U.S. Public*, pg. 461
Kirch, Robert J., Pres.--Aspen Pet Products, Inc., Denver, CO; *U.S. Public*, pg. 566
Kircheis, F., Mng. Dir.--Ascom Hasler SpA, Milan, Italy; *Int'l*, pg. 87
Kirchen, Steve, Gen. Mgr.--Alro Group, Louisville, Louisville, KY; *U.S. Private*, pg. 46
Kirchner, D., Chm. Bd. of Supervisory Dirs.--OCE-Deutschland GmbH, Mulheim, Germany; *Int'l*, pg. 994
Kirchner, Vinson E., Pres. & Chief Oper. Officer--Owens Country Sausage, Inc., Richardson, TX; *U.S. Public*, pg. 596
Kircuval, Murat, Acct. Mgr.--Nokia Telecommunications, Ankara, Turkey; *Int'l*, pg. 953
Kirihara, S., Mng. Dir.--OMRON Taiwan Electronics Inc., Taipei, Taiwan; *Int'l*, pg. 1006
Kirinovie, Milan, Dr., Gen. Mgr.--Willis Corroon s.r.o., Prague, Czech Republic; *Int'l*, pg. 1509
Kirk, Ian, Mng. Dir.--Gillette Internile S.A.E., Cairo, Egypt; *U.S. Public*, pg. 745
Kirk, J. Philip, Jr., Pres.--DST Realty, Inc., Kansas City, MO; *U.S. Public*, pg. 943
Kirk, James D., Pres. & Chief Exec. Officer--AgAmerica, FCB, Spokane, WA; *U.S. Private*, pg. 398
Kirk, James L., Pres.--OHM Remediation Services Corp., Findlay, OH; *U.S. Public*, pg. 1208
Kirk, Ken, Gen. Mgr.--Poe & Brown of Arizona, Phoenix, AZ; *U.S. Public*, pg. 1312
Kirk, Larry, Gen. Mgr.--Innisbrook/Hilton Resort, Tarpon Springs, FL; *U.S. Private*, pg. 1036
Kirk, M.D., Mng. Dir.--SPS Technologies Limited, Leicester, United Kingdom; *U.S. Public*, pg. 1420
Kirk, P., Chief Exec.--Dalgety Agriculture, Limited, Bristol, United Kingdom; *Int'l*, pg. 376
Kirk, P.T., V.P. & Gen. Mgr.--Kaydon Corporation, Bearings Division, Muskegon, MI; *U.S. Public*, pg. 946
Kirk, Paul, Pres.--United Communications Corporation of Louisiana, Inc., Baton Rouge, LA; *U.S. Public*, pg. 1675
Kirk, Philip, Mng. Dir.--Butterworths New Zealand, Wellington, New Zealand; *Int'l*, pg. 1095
Kirk, Robert A., V.P. & Gen. Mgr.--Humphrey Fluid Power Ltd., Markham, Canada; *U.S. Private*, pg. 548
Kirk, Robert L., Chm. Bd., Pres. & Chief Exec. Officer--British Aerospace Holdings Inc., Chantilly, VA; *Int'l*, pg. 218
Kirk, Simon, Mng. Dir.--British Gas Energy Centres Ltd., Nottingham, United Kingdom; *Int'l*, pg. 279
Kirk, Tony, Pres.--Genesee A & B, Inc., Old Hickory, TN; *U.S. Private*, pg. 446
Kirk, Ulrich, Dir.--Bayerische Landesbank International S.A., Luxembourg, Luxembourg; *Int'l*, pg. 176
Kirkbride, B.D., Mgr.--New Westminster Division, New Westminster, Canada; *Int'l*, pg. 828
Kirkby, R. W., Grp. Gen. Mgr.--Rod & Bar Products Division, Port Waratah, Australia; *Int'l*, pg. 227
Kirkendall, Bill, Pres.-Etonic--Tretorn AB, Helsingborg, Sweden; *Int'l*, pg. 1072
Kirkham, Jay, Mgr.--Hercules Inc.-Oxford, Covington, GA; *U.S. Public*, pg. 810
Kirkland, Gerry P., Pres.--CTR Manufacturing, Inc., Union Grove, NC; *U.S. Public*, pg. 238
Kirkland, J., Area Mgr.--Northside Div., Thomaston, GA; *U.S. Public*, pg. 1599
Kirkland, Kenyon R., Pres. & Chief Exec. Officer--Regions Bank/Shelby County, Pelham, AL; *U.S. Public*, pg. 1373
Kirkle, Phil, Gen. Mgr.--Skinner Macaroni, Omaha, NE; *U.S. Public*, pg. 812
Kirkle, Phil, Plant Mgr.--American Beauty Macaroni, Kansas City, KS; *U.S. Public*, pg. 812
Kirkman, M., Dir.--MB Overseas Limited, Reading, United Kingdom; *Int'l*, pg. 267
Kirkman, Stephen A., Pres.--American Risk Associates, Ltd., Philadelphia, PA; *U.S. Private*, pg. 317
Kirkpatrick, Brad, Mng. Dir.--Express Scripts Vision, Earth City, MO; *U.S. Public*, pg. 601
Kirkpatrick, Ian, Gen. Mgr.--ESAB Automation Ltd., Andover, United Kingdom; *Int'l*, pg. 282
Kirkpatrick, John R., Dir.--Standard Wool (Australia) Pty. Ltd., Fremantle, Australia; *U.S. Public*, pg. 1502
Kirkpatrick, Raymond, Dir.-Mktg.--Hewlett Packard Product Division, Louisville, OH; *U.S. Public*, pg. 816
Kirkpatrick, Simon C., Mng. Dir.--SHL Learning Technologies, Camberley, United Kingdom; *Int'l*, pg. 1154
Kirkup, Thomas J., Gen. Mgr.--Reynolds Metals Co.-Flexible Packaging Products Division, Richmond, VA; *U.S. Public*, pg. 1386
Kirkwood, R., V.P. & Gen. Mgr.--Pyroil Canada Limited, Mississauga, Canada; *Int'l*, pg. 955
Kirps, Georges, Mng. Dir.--ISSCO Luxembourg S.A., Esch-sur-Alzette, Luxembourg; *Int'l*, pg. 80
Kirsch, Dieter, Mng. Dir.--BB-Leasing GmbH, Frankfurt/Main, Germany; *Int'l*, pg. 159
Kirsch, Eugene, V.P.--Anacomp Magnetics Wales Ltd., Brynmawr, United Kingdom; *U.S. Public*, pg. 107
Kirsch, Ken, Pres.--Snowcrest Packers Ltd., Abbotsford, Canada; *Int'l*, pg. 990
Kirschfink, Fred, Mgr.--TSI GMBH, Aachen, Germany; *U.S. Public*, pg. 1559
Kirschner, Stuart, Pres.--Value Line, East Rutherford, NJ; *U.S. Private*, pg. 137
Kirshner, Hal, Pres. & Chief Exec. Officer--Trex Medical Corporation, Danbury, CT; *U.S. Public*, pg. 1595
Kirsten, Harald A., Mng. Dir.--Miller Intl. Schallplatten G.m.b.H., Quickborn, Germany; *Int'l*, pg. 1216
Kirzner, Stu, Branch Mgr.--Randy International, Kearny, NJ; *U.S. Private*, pg. 909
Kisanuki, Yutaka, Pres.--Nippon Novellus KK, Tokyo, Japan; *U.S. Public*, pg. 1204
Kiser, W.W., Pres.--USX Realty Development, Pittsburgh, PA; *U.S. Public*, pg. 1661
Kish, Thomas, Exec. Mgr.--Douglas y Lomason de Mexico S.A. de C.V., Acuna, Mexico; *Int'l*, pg. 830

Kish, Thomas G., Exec. Mgr.--Douglas & Lomason Company, Del Rio, TX; *Int'l*, pg. 830
Kish, Tom, Exec. Mgr.--Douglas & Lomason Company, Orangeville, Canada; *Int'l*, pg. 830
Kishi, Fusao, Pres.--Hughes-JVC Technology Corp., Carlsbad, CA; *U.S. Public*, pg. 721
Kishi, Fusao, Pres.--Hughes-JVC Technology Corp., Carlsbad, CA; *Int'l*, pg. 846
Kishida, R., Chief Rep. Officer--The Kansai Electric Power Co. - Washington Office, Washington, DC; *Int'l*, pg. 723
Kishimoto, Kiyokazu, Pres.--Toray Italia S.r.l., Milan, Italy; *Int'l*, pg. 1400
Kishimoto, Muneo, Chm. Bd.--Mazda (North America), Inc., Irvine, CA; *Int'l*, pg. 849
Kishimoto, Victor, Fin. Dir.--Causa Publicidad, Lima, Peru; *U.S. Private*, pg. 184
Kisiel, Boguslaw, Pres.--Bosta Beton Sp.z.o o., Warsaw, Poland; *Int'l*, pg. 1200
Kissack, Joe, Mgr.-Syndication, Southwestern Region--Columbia Tri-Star Television Distribution - Dallas, Dallas, TX; *Int'l*, pg. 1282
Kissel, W. Craig, V.P. & Grp. Exec.--The Trane Company, Unitary Products Group, Tyler, TX; *U.S. Public*, pg. 92
Kissling, Walter, Pres.--F.A.I. Trading Company, Pompano Beach, FL; *U.S. Public*, pg. 686
Kissling, Walter, Pres.--H.B. Fuller International Inc., Saint Paul, MN; *U.S. Public*, pg. 687
Kissman, Preston, Mgr.--Public Service Company of Oklahoma-Mantulsa Div., Tulsa, OK; *U.S. Public*, pg. 324
Kissner, Matthew, Pres.--Pitney Bowes Financial Services, Norwalk, CT; *U.S. Public*, pg. 1303
Kissner, Matthew, Pres. & Chief Exec. Officer--Pitney Bowes Real Estate Financing Corporation, Norwalk, CT; *U.S. Public*, pg. 1303
Kissner, Udo, Mgr.--Commerzbank AG-Jakarta Representative Office, Jakarta, Indonesia; *Int'l*, pg. 311
Kistler, Dr. F., Mng. Dir.--BDL Banco di Lugano, Lugano, Switzerland; *Int'l*, pg. 1439
Kistler, M.R., V.P. & Chief Oper. Officer--Logo 7, Inc., Indianapolis, IN; *U.S. Public*, pg. 1644
Kistner, Charles, Pres.--Buffalo Pumps, Inc., North Tonawanda, NY; *U.S. Public*, pg. 103
Kit, Li Ching, Gen. Mgr.--DMB&B Guangzhou, Guangzhou, China; *U.S. Private*, pg. 303
Kita, Yasuo, Dir. & Gen. Mgr.--Fuji Heavy Industries, Ltd., Engine & Machinery Div., Omiya, Japan; *Int'l*, pg. 523
Kitadai, Seiki, Sr. V.P. & Gen. Mgr.--Sumitomo Corporation of America, San Francisco, CA; *Int'l*, pg. 1312
Kitagawa, Keiyu, Gen. Mgr.--Dai-Ichi Kangyo Bank, Ltd.-Madrid, Madrid, Spain; *Int'l*, pg. 360
Kitagawa, Yoshiaki, Mng. Dir.--Hakuhodo Inc., Takamatsu, Japan; *Int'l*, pg. 587
Kitahara, Kunio, Pres.--Kawasaki do Brazil Industria E Comercio Ltda., Sao Paulo, Brazil; *Int'l*, pg. 726
Kitahara, Mamoru, Mng. Dir.--Wako International (Hong Kong) Limited, Hong Kong, Hong Kong; *Int'l*, pg. 1485
Kitahara, Tsuyoshi, Mng. Dir.--Neste Chemicals (Japan) Co., Ltd., Tokyo, Japan; *Int'l*, pg. 914
Kitahara, Yoshitaka, Pres.--Nanjing Toto Co., Ltd., Nanjing, China; *Int'l*, pg. 1410
Kitajima, Hiroyuki, Mng. Dir.--Nippon Express do Brasil Transportes Internacionais Ltda., Sao Paulo, Brazil; *Int'l*, pg. 934
Kitajima, Yoshitoshi, Pres.--Hokkaido Coca-Cola Bottling Co., Ltd., Sapporo, Japan; *Int'l*, pg. 363
Kitamine, M., Mng. Dir.--Sharp Manufacturing Corporation (M) Sdn. Bhd., Batu Pahat, Malaysia; *Int'l*, pg. 1230
Kitamura, Katsuhiko, Mng. Dir.--Daiwa Bank (Deutschland) GmbH, Frankfurt, Germany; *Int'l*, pg. 373
Kitamura, Masato, Pres.--Toto Dalian Co., Ltd., Dalian, China; *Int'l*, pg. 1410
Kitamura, Michio, Chief Oper. Officer--Asian Honda Motor Co., Ltd., Bangkok, Thailand; *Int'l*, pg. 635
Kitanishi, Yasuhiko, Pres.--The Kyoei Life Insurance Co., Ltd.-New York Office, New York, NY; *Int'l*, pg. 776
Kitano, Toshio, Pres.--Toto USA, Inc., Morrow, GA; *Int'l*, pg. 1410
Kitano, Toshio, Pres.--Toto Kiki USA, Inc., Morrow, GA; *Int'l*, *pg. 1410*
Kitayama, Teisuke, Dir.--Sakura Capital Funding (Cayman) Limited, Grand Cayman, Cayman Islands; *Int'l*, pg. 1180
Kitayama, Teisuke, Dir.--Sakura Finance (Cayman) Limited, Grand Cayman, Cayman Islands; *Int'l*, pg. 1180
Kitchen, D., Pres.--Labatt Breweries of Canada, Toronto, Canada; *Int'l*, pg. 679
Kitchen, Michael B., Chief Exec. Officer--CUMIS Insurance Society, Inc., Madison, WI; *U.S. Private*, pg. 296
Kitchen, Michael B., Chief Exec. Officer--CUNA Mutual Insurance Agency, Inc., Madison, WI; *U.S. Private*, pg. 296
Kitchen, Michael B., Chief Exec. Officer--CUNA Mutual Investment Corporation, Madison, WI; *U.S. Private*, pg. 296
Kitchen, Michael B., Chief Exec. Officer--Members Life Insurance Company, Waverly, IA; *U.S. Private*, pg. 296
Kitchen, Michael B., Chief Exec. Officer--League General Insurance Company, Bingham Farms, MI; *U.S. Private*, pg. 296
Kitchen, Michael B., Pres.--CMG Mortgage Insurance Company, Madison, WI; *U.S. Private*, pg. 296
Kitchen, Michael B., Chief Exec. Officer--CUNA Mutual Life Insurance Co., Waverly, IA; *U.S. Private*, pg. 296
Kitchen, Robert, Pres.--Freedom Textiles Chemicals Co., Charlotte, NC; *U.S. Private*, pg. 425
Kitchener, Brian, Mng. Dir.--Gas-Fired Products (U.K.) Ltd., Ipswich, United Kingdom; *U.S. Private*, pg. 440
Kitching, Peter, Mng. Dir.--Colin Stewart Minchem Limited, Winsford, United Kingdom; *Int'l*, pg. 858
Kite, J., Property Mgr.--Citizens Utilities Company, Kingman, AZ; *U.S. Public*, pg. 380
Kite, J., Asst. Mgr.-Arizona--Citizens Communications Services, Inc., Stamford, CT; *U.S. Public*, pg. 380
Kitiyakara, M.R. Sarisdiguna, Mng Dir.--Shell Company of Thailand Ltd, Bangkok, Thailand; *Int'l*, pg. 1140
Kitner, Don, Div. Mgr.--Deland District-Florida Public Utilities, De Land, FL; *U.S. Public*, pg. 655
Kitner, Don, Mgr.-Mid-Florida Div.--Mid-Florida Div.-Florida Public Utilities, Sanford, FL; *U.S. Public*, pg. 655
Kitsuda, Yoshikazu, Pres.--Nomura Finance Co., Ltd., Tokyo, Japan; *Int'l*, pg. 955
Kitteridge, David, Pres.--Fields Stores, Richmond, Canada; *Int'l*, pg. 637
Kittle, D. Dwayne, Co-Mgr.--Scott & Stringfellow, Inc., Blacksburg, VA; *U.S. Public*, pg. 1446
Kittscher, Gerhard, Pres.--Bankenunion Aktiengesellschaft, Frankfurt, Germany; *Int'l*, pg. 504
Kitziller, James K., Pres.-Concrete Prods.--Gifford-Hill Concrete Products Inc., Richmond, VA; *Int'l*, pg. 593
Kitzmiller, Mike, Pres. & Gen. Mgr.--Crest Cadillac, Inc., Nashville, TN; *U.S. Private*, pg. 712
Kiuchi, Takashioshi, Chm.--Mitsubishi Electronics America, Cypress, CA; *Int'l*, pg. 872
Kivenko, Ken, Pres. & Chief Exec. Officer--AlliedSignal Aerospace Canada, Etobicoke, Canada; *U.S. Public*, pg. 53
Kivenko, Ken, Pres. & Chief Exec. Officer--NBS Technologies Inc., Mississauga, Canada; *Int'l*, pg. 898
Kiyohara, Eisuke, Chief Oper. Officer--Neste Chemicals (Japan) Co., Ltd., Tokyo, Japan; *Int'l*, pg. 914
Kiyohara, Haruo, Gen. Mgr.--The Hokkaido Takushoku Bank, Ltd. (Singapore), Singapore, Singapore; *Int'l*, pg. 627
Kiyokawa, Akira, Pres.--The Nomura Trust and Banking Co., Ltd., Tokyo, Japan; *Int'l*, pg. 956
Kiyokawa, Mitsuo, Pres.--P.T. Daiwa Indonesia Securities, Jakarta, Indonesia; *Int'l*, pg. 375
Kiyozuka, Kazuo, Chief Oper. Officer--Ahlstrom Daiichi Co., Ltd., Tokyo, Japan; *Int'l*, pg. 34
Kizer, Robert, Pres.--Corson Lime Company, Plymouth Meeting, PA; *U.S. Public*, pg. 1685
Kizer, Robert, Pres. & Chief Exec. Officer--Texas Lime Co., Cleburne, TX; *U.S. Public*, pg. 1685
Kizirakos, Nikolaos, Chief Exec. Officer--Galileo Hellas, Athens, Greece; *Int'l*, pg. 1004
Kjaer-Rasmussen, Ove, Mng. Dir.--Aktieselikabet ESAB, Copenhagen, Denmark; *Int'l*, pg. 281
Kjaeroe, Stig, Mng. Dir.--ESS-FOOD USA Inc., Hollywood, FL; *Int'l*, pg. 429
Kjeldmann, Henning, Sr. V.P.--RNBNY Branch Office-Hong Kong, Central, Hong Kong; *U.S. Public*, pg. 1381
Kjellberg, Lennart, Mgr.--Forsakringsaktiebolaget Allianz Nordeuropa (RAS), Stockholm, Sweden; *Int'l*, pg. 60
Kjellgren, Hans, Pres.--NCC Industry, Solna, Sweden; *Int'l*, pg. 899
Kjellin, Bertil, Pres.--Skanska Prefab AB, Malmo, Sweden; *Int'l*, pg. 1261
Kjellman, Jan, Pres.--Ikea North America, Inc., Plymouth Meeting, PA; *Int'l*, pg. 660
Kjellstrom, David, Pres.--Kjellstrom & Lee, Inc., Richmond, VA; *U.S. Private*, pg. 453
Kjosen, Rolan, Gen. Mgr.--DeVilbiss Ransburg Industrial Liquid Systems (OH), Toledo, OH; *U.S. Public*, pg. 866
Klanderud, Barry, Pres.--Valmont Industries, Inc., Springville, UT; *U.S. Public*, pg. 1707
Klar, Walter, Mgr.--Gensym GmbH, Unterfoehring, Germany; *U.S. Public*, pg. 731
Klasen, Joachim, Mng. Dir.--Volksfreund-Druckerei Nikolaus Koch GmbH & Co. KG, Trier, Germany; *Int'l*, pg. 1479
Klasener, Ralf, Pres.--Koralle Verlag GmbH, Berlin, Germany; *Int'l*, pg. 102
Klasky, Jack, Pres.--Leadtec Systems, Inc., Canoga Park, CA; *U.S. Private*, pg. 1177
Klass, Winfried, Gen. Mgr.--Data Translation GmbH, Bietigheim-Bissingen, Germany; *U.S. Public*, pg. 1079
Klassen, R., Far East Area Mng. Dir.--Ferro Far East Ltd., Kowloon, Hong Kong; *U.S. Public*, pg. 619
Klassen, R.L., Far East Area Mng. Dir.--Ferro Industrial Products Ltd., Tao-yuan, Taiwan; *U.S. Public*, pg. 619
Klasson, Eric, Chief Exec. Officer--River Ranch - Salinas, Salinas, CA; *Int'l*, pg. 491
Klaus, Gallos, Pres.--Charmilles Technologies Ltd. Spb St. Petersburg, Saint Petersburg, Russia; *Int'l*, pg. 489
Klausman, Michael, V.P.--CBS/MTM Company, Studio City, CA; *U.S. Public*, pg. 275
Klaverkamp, Robert B., Publisher--Asiaweek Ltd., New York, NY; *U.S. Public*, pg. 1613
Klayman, Ron, Pres.--KTBC, Austin, TX; *Int'l*, pg. 926
Klebba, Robert H., Pres.--Fillauer, Inc., Chattanooga, TN; *U.S. Public*, pg. 214
Kleckley, Thomas, Gen. Mgr.--SMI-Owen Supply Company, Columbia, SC; *U.S. Public*, pg. 412
Klee, A., Mng. Dir.--Raybestos Industrie-Produkte GmbH, Morbach, Germany; *U.S. Public*, pg. 1364
Kleerekoper, D.J., Pres. & Dir.--Bols Milani Ltd., Sao Paulo, Brazil; *Int'l*, pg. 751
Kleiberg, A.B.M., Mng. Dir.--Van Leeuwen Pipe and Tube Eastern Australia Pty. Ltd., Girraween, Australia; *Int'l*, pg. 1450
Kleijn, Bert, Chief Oper. Officer--Datapoint Nederland B.V., Gouda, Netherlands; *Int'l*, pg. 384
Klein, A., Rep.-Mexico--Bank Hapoalim (Mexico City), Mexico, Mexico; *Int'l*, pg. 149
Klein, B., Gen. Mgr.--ING Bank Vienna, Vienna, Austria; *Int'l*, pg. 649
Klein, Burkhart, Dir.--Deutsche Bank AG (Bahrain), Manama, Bahrain; *Int'l*, pg. 404
Klein, Dr., Mng. Dir.--Union Werkzeugmaschinenfabrik Gera GmbH, Gera, Germany; *Int'l*, pg. 860
Klein, Francis, Sr. Country Officer--Marcard Stein & Co., Hamburg, Germany; *Int'l*, pg. 315
Klein, Gottfried, Pres.--Voest-Alpine Trading U.S.A. Corp., Houston, TX; *Int'l*, pg. 1471
Klein, Hans Rudolf, Mng. Dir.--Dyckerhoff & Widmann Baugesellschaft mbH, Deggendorf, Germany; *Int'l*, pg. 423
Klein, John, Dir.-Opers.--The Sherrill Corp., Mexico, IN; *U.S. Private*, pg. 298
Klein, John, Chm.--Steelcase Financial Services, Inc., Grand Rapids, MI; *U.S. Private*, pg. 1038
Klein, Jonathan, Gen. Mgr.--WCBS-TV, New York, NY; *U.S. Public*, pg. 275
Klein, Kurt, Mng. Dir.--Deutsche Heraklith A.G., Simbach, Germany; *U.S. Private*, pg. 903
Klein, Ludwig, Mng. Dir.--Hartek Beverage Handling GmbH, Radevormwald, Germany; *U.S. Public*, pg. 1445
Klein, Mary, Gen. Mgr.--Falcon-Belding, Belding, MI; *U.S. Public*, pg. 611
Klein, Norbert, Mng. Dir.--Skandinaviska Enskilda Banken, Luxembourg, Luxembourg; *Int'l*, pg. 1259
Klein, Patrick, Mng. Dir.--Visea THORN, Tassin-la-Demi-Lune, France; *Int'l*, pg. 1386
Klein, Paul, V.P. & Gen. Mgr.--Sun Chemical Pigments Div., Cincinnati, OH; *Int'l*, pg. 370
Klein, Peter-Jorg, Dr., Chief Oper. Officer--Dresdner Bank AG, Tokyo, Japan; *Int'l*, pg. 419
Klein, Sherwin J., Div. Mgr.--Martin's Uniforms Div., Tampa, FL; *U.S. Public*, pg. 1539
Klein, Stephen, Pres. & Gen. Counsel--Encore Clubs, Inc., Lanham, MD; *U.S. Public*, pg. 580
Klein, Stephen, Pres. & Gen. Counsel--E.M.I. Travel Center, Inc., Lanham, MD; *U.S. Public*, pg. 580
Klein, Stephen, Pres. & Gen. Counsel--Encore Group, Inc., Lanham, MD; *U.S. Public*, pg. 580
Klein, Stephen, Pres. & Gen. Counsel--Quality Services International, Inc., Lanham, MD; *U.S. Public*, pg. 580
Kleinbergen, J.J., Chief Oper. Officer--Zwjsen B.V., Hendrik-Ido-Ambacht, Netherlands; *Int'l*, pg. 754
Kleine, R. G., Gen. Mgr.--John Deere Harvester Works, East Moline, IL; *U.S. Public*, pg. 492
Kleine, R.G., Pres.--John Deere Technologies International, Inc., Moline, IL; *U.S. Public*, pg. 492
Kleiner, Arnold J., V.P. & Gen. Mgr.--WMAR-TV, Baltimore, MD; *U.S. Public*, pg. 1448
Kleinert, Robert, Pres.--Dade Behring-Microscan Div., Sacramento, CA; *U.S. Private*, pg. 110
Kleinlein, Bruce, Pres.--Illinois Fruit & Produce Corp., Streator, IL; *U.S. Public*, pg. 918
Kleinman, Kees S., Dir.--Grabowsky & Poort Zuid BV, Eindhoven, Netherlands; *Int'l*, pg. 607
Kleinman, L.F., Pres.--Metal Lubricants Co., Harvey, IL; *Int'l*, *pg. 518*
Kleinman,Richard, Chief Oper. Officer--AFA Mass., Inc., Boston, MA; *U.S. Public*, pg. 6
Kleisner, Ted, Pres. & Mng. Dir.--The Greenbrier, White Sulphur Springs, WV; *U.S. Public*, pg. 284
Kleist, Brenda, Acct. Representative--Circle Freight International USA, Milwaukee, WI; *U.S. Public*, pg. 370
Kleivan, Lars, Pres.--Diners Club Nordic A/S, Oslo, Norway; *Int'l*, pg. 1202
Klements, Rabbe, Mgr.--EG & G Wallac Oy, Turku, Finland; *U.S. Public*, pg. 544
Klemenz, Hans, Plant Mgr.--Dexter Midland Co. Ltd., Tokyo, Japan; *U.S. Public*, pg. 505
Klemenz, Hans, Plant Mgr.--Dexter Magnetic Materials GmbH, Garching, Germany; *U.S. Public*, pg. 505
Klemp, P., Mng. Dir.--Ascom Nordic A/S, Brondby, Denmark; *Int'l*, pg. 87
Klemperer, Victor von, Mng. Dir.--Dresdner International Financial Markets (Australia) Ltd., Sydney, Australia; *Int'l*, *pg. 419*
Klenz, Walter, Chm. Bd. & Chief Exec. Officer--Beringer Wine Estates Holdings, Inc., Saint Helena, CA; *U.S. Private*, pg. 1078
Klenz, Walter T., Pres.--Wine World Estates Company, Saint Helena, CA; *Int'l*, pg. 917
Klerx, Henry, Pres.--Information Systems Co., Park Ridge, NJ; *Int'l*, pg. 1281
Klesse, Richard C., Pres.--Beneficial Credit Services, Inc., Wilmington, DE; *U.S. Public*, pg. 211
Kletz, Selwyn J., Pres.--Laurentian Financial Services, Toronto, Canada; *Int'l*, pg. 396
Kleven, Bjornar, Gen. Mgr.--Kvaerner Eureka Inc., Seattle, WA; *Int'l*, pg. 770
Kleyn, Hendrik J.C., Mng. Dir.--Heraeus Electro-Nite International N.V., Houthalen, Belgium; *Int'l*, pg. 616
Klich, William R., Chm. Bd. & Chief Exec. Officer--SunTrust Bank, Gulf Coast, Sarasota, FL; *U.S. Public*, pg. 1537
Kliem, M., Mng. Dir.--Pfrimmer Nutricia GmbH & Co. KG, Erlangen, Germany; *Int'l*, pg. 992
Kliemann, Michael, Chief Oper. Officer--Gambro Vertriebsgesellschaft m.b.H., Vienna, Austria; *Int'l*, pg. 668
Klien, David, Editor--Electronic Media, Chicago, IL; *U.S. Private*, pg. 285
Klifa, Pierre, Mgr.--EURO RSCG Est, Mulhouse, France; *Int'l*, pg. 601
Kliger, Jack, Publisher--Glamour, New York, NY; *U.S. Private*, pg. 20
Klimp, Jack, Plant Mgr.--L.B. Foster Company-Pomeroy Plant, Pomeroy, OH; *U.S. Public*, pg. 676
Klimuc, Thomas M., Acting Mgr.--CAP Gemini (New Jersey Technologies), Cranford, NJ; *Int'l*, pg. 264
Kline, Clifford, V.P.-Customer Service & Distr.--John Wiley & Sons, Inc., Somerset, NJ; *U.S. Public*, pg. 1768
Kline, Dennis, V.P.--R.X.D., Inc., Norfolk, NE; *U.S. Public*, pg. 1376
Kline, Kevin, Plant Mgr.--Bundy Corporation, Winchester Tool Plant, Winchester, KY; *Int'l*, pg. 1341
Kling, Goran, Pres.--Volvo Data Corporation, Goteborg, Sweden; *Int'l*, pg. 1476
Kling, Lewis, V.P. & Gen. Mgr.--Electronic Systems Division, Melbourne, FL; *U.S. Public*, pg. 792
Kling, Richard, Chm. Bd.--IDS Life Insurance Co. of New York, Albany, NY; *U.S. Public*, pg. 73
Kling, Richard, Chm. Bd.--IDS Property Casualty Insurance Company, Minneapolis, MN; *U.S. Public*, pg. 73
Kling, Richard C., Pres.--Bell Atlantic Properties, Inc., Philadelphia, PA; *U.S. Public*, pg. 203
Klinga, Leif, Chief Oper. Officer--AB Celleco, Stockholm, Sweden; *Int'l*, pg. 1378

Klingeman, J.S., Chief Oper. Officer--Van Leeuwen Buizen Belgium N.V., Vilvoorde, Belgium; *Int'l*, pg. 1450
Klingensmith, Michael J., Pres.--Entertainment Weekly Inc., New York, NY; *U.S. Public*, pg. 1613
Klingspor, Horst, Gen. Mgr.--Associated Spring, Ltd., Burlington, Canada; *U.S. Public*, pg. 190
Klinkby-Silver, Paul, Gen. Mgr.--Data Translation Networking Limited, Wokingham, United Kingdom; *U.S. Public*, pg. 1079
Klinsky, Arnold, V.P. & Gen. Mgr.--WHEC-TV, Rochester, NY; *U.S. Private*, pg. 544
Klippa, Edmund, Pres.--Details, New York, NY; *U.S. Private*, *pg. 1038*
Klisiewicz, Jerry, Div. Mgr.--Transilwrap Manufacturing Division, Chicago, IL; *U.S. Private*, pg. 1097
Klitten, M.R., Pres.--Chevron Stations, Inc., San Francisco, CA; *U.S. Public*, pg. 348
Klodnicki, Z.G., Gen. Mgr.--Bank of Montreal Trust Company, New York, NY; *Int'l*, pg. 154
Klohr, Frank, Gen. Mgr.--Forbo Siegling Singapore Pte. Ltd., Singapore, Singapore; *Int'l*, pg. 498
Klomp, C.A., Dir.--Automatiseringcentrum Ideta B.V., Amsterdam, Netherlands; *Int'l*, pg. 750
Klonne, Michael, Pres.--Ato-Findley, Inc., Wauwatosa, WI; *Int'l*, pg. 445
Kloosterman, Johan, Mgr.--NEDCO (Newport European Distribution Co.), Nieuwegein, Netherlands; *U.S. Public*, pg. 1179
Klopfer, Kurt, Mng. Dir.--Ericsson AG, Bruttisellen, Switzerland; *Int'l*, pg. 1366
Kloska, Ronald F., Pres.--Homette Corporation, Elkhart, IN; *U.S. Public*, pg. 1476
Kloska, Ronald F., Pres.--Layton Homes Corp., Elkhart, IN; *U.S. Public*, pg. 1476
Kloska, Ronald F., Pres.--Skyline Homes, Inc., Elkhart, IN; *U.S. Public*, pg. 1476
Kloss, Hans, Pres.--Bally Gaming Inc., Las Vegas, NV; *U.S. Public*, pg. 47
Kloss, Peter, Mng. Dir.--Tyco Toys (Deutschland) GmbH, Nuremberg, Germany; *U.S. Public*, pg. 1059
Kloster, Karl, Pres. & Chief Oper. Officer--McCarthy Brothers Co., Saint Louis, MO; *U.S. Private*, pg. 719
Klosterman, Brian, Pres.--StarSight Telecast, Inc., Fremont, CA; *U.S. Public*, pg. 705
Klotzbuchen, Friedrich, Chief Oper. Officer--COBE Laboratories GmbH, Planegg, Germany; *Int'l*, pg. 667
Klug, Mark, Pres.--Palomar Systems, Inc., Escondido, CA; *U.S. Public*, pg. 569
Kluge, Alexander, Mng. Dir.--Development Company for TV-Program GmbH, Dusseldorf, Germany; *Int'l*, pg. 394
Kluge, Peter, Mng. Dir.--Scotiabank (Ireland) Limited, Dublin, Ireland; *Int'l*, pg. 156
Kluge, Robert, V.P. & Gen. Mgr.--Varian X-Ray Tube Products, Salt Lake City, UT; *U.S. Public*, pg. 1710
Klugh, John, Gen. Mgr.--Mount Vernon Mills, Inc., Commerce, GA; *U.S. Private*, pg. 835
Klumb, Uwe, Dr., Mng. Dir.--Grillo-Werke AG, Duisburg, Germany; *Int'l*, pg. 861
Kluneberg, H., Dr., Reg. Gen. Mgr.--Amersham Buchler GmbH & Co. KG, Braunschweig, Germany; *Int'l*, pg. 992
Klus, Steven E., Pres.--Seneca Foods-Eastern Div., Marion, NY; *U.S. Public*, pg. 1456
Kluth, Gerhard, Dr., Chief Oper. Officer--Siemens Finanzierungsgesellschaft fur Informationstechnik GmbH, Munich, Germany; *Int'l*, pg. 1245
Kluzer, Silvio, Chm. & Pres.--Cerestar Holding B.V., Sas-van-Gent, Netherlands; *Int'l*, pg. 324
Klym, Richard W., Chief Exec. Officer--Toledo Commutator Co., Owosso, MI; *U.S. Private*, pg. 623
Klyvis, Dalius, Chief Oper. Officer--AGA UAB, Vilnius, Lithuania; *Int'l*, pg. 14
Kmet, W.A., Pres.--ATCO Structures Inc., Calgary, Canada; *Int'l*, pg. 95
Knackstedt, Walter, Chief Oper. Officer--Hagglunds Drives GmbH, Haan, Germany; *Int'l*, pg. 670
Knaebel, Stephen P., Pres.--Cummins de Mexico S.A., Mexico, Mexico; *U.S. Public*, pg. 468
Knaisch, Karl E., Gen. Mgr.--Voith Turbo GmbH & Co. KG, Crailsheim, Germany; *Int'l*, pg. 1473
Knap, Arne Hj, Mgr.--Kvaerner Engineering, Miljo, Sandefjord, Norway; *Int'l*, pg. 766
Knape, Susan, Pres.--The Knape Group, Dallas, TX; *U.S. Private*, pg. 651
Knapp, John M., Grp. V.P.--Bowman Distribution, Cleveland, OH; *U.S. Public*, pg. 190
Knapp, Seaman A., III, Pres.--Riverside Book & Bible House, Inc., Iowa Falls, IA; *U.S. Private*, pg. 598
Knapper, W., Mng. Dir.--GKN Gelenkwellenbau GmbH, Essen, Germany; *Int'l*, pg. 536
Knaur, Hans-Juergen, Dr., Chief Exec. Officer--Stinnes AG, Mulheim, Germany; *Int'l*, pg. 1458
Knaus, Dr. Albrecht, Mng. Dir.--Albrecht Knaus Verlag, Munich, Germany; *Int'l*, pg. 190
Knaus, T., Gen. Mgr.--De La Rue Faraday - Midwest, Naperville, IL; *Int'l*, pg. 387
Knavle, Bill, Plant Mgr.--Brown & Williamson Tobacco Corp.-Macon Plant, Macon, GA; *Int'l*, pg. 111
Kneale, J.C., Dist. V.P.-Tulsa--Tulsa District, Tulsa, OK; *U.S. Public*, pg. 1226
Kneeland, James R., Pres.--Aeroquip Mexicana S.A. De C.V., Mexico, Mexico; *U.S. Public*, pg. 25
Knefel, Raymond, V.P.-Sls.--Diversified Compounders, Los Angeles, CA; *U.S. Private*, pg. 324
Knesz, Margo, Gen. Mgr.--Atco/East-West Records, New York, NY; *U.S. Public*, pg. 1611
Knesz, Peter, Chief Oper. Officer--Leu & Gygax AG, Birmenstorf, Switzerland; *Int'l*, pg. 356
Knetzger, Edwin L., III, Pres. & Chief Exec. Officer--Greenwich Capital Markets, Inc., Greenwich, CT; *Int'l*, pg. 911
Kniberg, Gunnar, Chief Oper. Officer--Electrolux (Japan) Ltd., Tokyo, Japan; *Int'l*, pg. 443
Kniebihler, Maurice J., Mng. Dir.--General Motors France Automobiles S.A., Argenteuil, France; *U.S. Public*, pg. 722
Kniehl, Dr. Hans Joachim, Mng. Dir.--D & W Capital Corp., Lincoln Park, NJ; *Int'l*, pg. 424
Kniep, James, Chief Oper. Officer--Allright Columbus Parking, Inc., Columbus, OH; *U.S. Private*, pg. 42
Knigen, Melvin, Div. Pres.--Cinema Etoile Division, New York, NY; *U.S. Public*, pg. 1141
Knight, Allen C., Chief Oper. Officer--Wilshire Oil of Canada, Ltd., Calgary, Canada; *U.S. Public*, pg. 1770
Knight, Andrew, Mng. Dir.--Information Trust Corporation (Pty.) Ltd., Johannesburg, South Africa; *U.S. Public*, pg. 537
Knight, Dennis, Pres.--Medusa Aggregate Co., Cleveland, OH; *U.S. Public*, pg. 1084
Knight, Gloria S., V.P.--Rouse-Carillon Shopping Center, Inc., Houston, TX; *U.S. Public*, pg. 1409
Knight, Kenneth Y., Pres.--Little America Hotels, Salt Lake City, UT; *U.S. Private*, pg. 1003
Knight, Larry, Reg. V.P.--Subaru Mid-America, Inc., Addison, IL; *Int'l*, pg. 523
Knight, Leo E., Pres. & Chief Exec. Officer--National City Mortgage Co., Miamisburg, OH; *U.S. Public*, pg. 1154
Knight, Lyle R., Pres. & Chief Exec. Officer--US Bank, Las Vegas, NV; *U.S. Public*, pg. 181
Knight, Max, Gen. Mgr.--BHP Steel Building Products (NZ) Ltd., Tauranga, New Zealand; *Int'l*, pg. 226
Knight, Paul, Mng. Dir.--Gunnebo Ltd., Redditch, United Kingdom; *Int'l*, pg. 578
Knight, R., Mng. Dir.--ANZ Bank (Guernsey) Limited, Saint Peter Port, United Kingdom; *Int'l*, pg. 98
Knight, Thomas, Mng. Dir.--Cathodic Protection Services Company, Houston, TX; *U.S. Private*, pg. 297
Knight, Thomas, Mng. Dir.--Cathodic Protection Services Company, Houston, TX; *U.S. Public*, pg. 1213
Knight, Thomas O., Mng. Dir.--General DataComm Limited, Wokingham, United Kingdom; *U.S. Public*, pg. 708
Knight, Tommy, Div. Mgr.--ConAgra Broiler Co., Enterprise, AL; *U.S. Public*, pg. 427
Knight, William, Mng. Dir.--Hopkins & Bailey Ltd., Birmingham, United Kingdom; *Int'l*, pg. 1226
Knights, Kieran, Div. Head--Rogers & Cowan Brand Placement, London, United Kingdom; *Int'l*, pg. 1226
Knights, Roger T., Gen. Mgr.--Banco Santander (Guernsey) Ltd., Saint Peter Port, United Kingdom; *Int'l*, pg. 144
Knipphals, H., Chief Oper. Officer--VW-Versicherungsvermittlungs-GmbH, Wolfsburg, Germany; *Int'l*, pg. 1474
Knipple, Glenn, Canadian Reg. Mgr.--Baker Oil Tools of Canada, Ltd., Calgary, Canada; *U.S. Public*, pg. 167
Knisely, P.W., Pres.--Emerson Power Transmission Co., Maysville, KY; *U.S. Public*, pg. 573
Knitt, Peter W., Pres.--M & I Merchants Bank, Rhinelander, WI; *U.S. Public*, pg. 1050
Knobel, Guido, Representative--Union Bank of Switzerland, Calgary, Canada; *Int'l*, pg. 1441
Knocz, I., Mng. Dir.--Consulting and Engineering Agrober Company, Budapest, Hungary; *Int'l*, pg. 607
Knodler, Ottmar, Mgr.-Sls.--Velcro GmbH, Sachsenheim, Germany; *Int'l*, pg. 1462
Knok, Lawrence, Mgr.--Sandvik Hong Kong Ltd., Kowloon, Hong Kong; *Int'l*, pg. 1187
Knol, Jan-Dirk, Mng. Dir.--UPM-Kymmene (Nederland) B.V., Amsterdam, Netherlands; *Int'l*, pg. 1430
Knoll, Erich, Gen. Mgr.--Siegling-Austria Ges.m.b.H., Vienna, Austria; *Int'l*, pg. 498
Knoll, Fred, Gen. Mgr.--Daniel Canada, Calgary, Canada; *U.S. Public*, pg. 483
Knoll, Jack L., Pres.--Home Telephone Co., Inc., Waldron, IN; *U.S. Public*, pg. 1571
Knoller, S., Gen. Mgr.--C.D. Packaging Systems Ltd., Petah Tiqwa, Israel; *Int'l*, pg. 75
Knoop, P., Pres.--Van Leer Metallized Products Ltd., Caerphilly, United Kingdom; *Int'l*, pg. 1147
Knop, U., Mng. Dir.--TPS, Krefeld, Germany; *Int'l*, pg. 1145
Knopfel, Thomas, Chief Exec.--Cementos Boyaca S.A., Bogota, Colombia; *Int'l*, pg. 629
Knorr, Hanns, Mgr.--Sandvik Chile S.A., Santiago, Chile; *Int'l*, pg. 1187
Knorr, John A., Chief Oper. Officer--Navajo Northern Inc., Artesia, NM; *U.S. Public*, pg. 830
Knostman, Rick, Pres.--Gesco International, San Antonio, TX; *U.S. Public*, pg. 189
Knoth, Karl H., V.P. & Gen. Mgr.--ASC Weinsberg Karosseriewerke Weinsberg GmbH, Weinsberg, Germany; *U.S. Private*, pg. 8
Knott, Joseph, Pres.--Fisons Corporation Limited, Pickering, Canada; *Int'l*, pg. 1111
Knott, Roland, Mng. Dir.--Berendsen Fluid Power Ltd., Tamworth, United Kingdom; *Int'l*, pg. 1284
Knowles, B. S., Mng. Dir.--P.T. Tootal Thread Wdongsla, Surabaya, Indonesia; *Int'l*, pg. 299
Knowles, David, Pres.--M.A. Hanna Resin Distribution, Lemont, IL; *U.S. Public*, pg. 781
Knowles, David, Pres.--M.A. Hanna Resin Distribution, Kent, WA; *U.S. Public*, pg. 781
Knowles, David, Pres.--M.A. Hanna Resin Distribution, Ayer, MA; *U.S. Public*, pg. 781
Knowles, G. Michael, Pres.-Kiwi Brands--Kiwi Brands, Douglassville, PA; *U.S. Public*, pg. 1433
Knowles, Kenneth, Gen. Mgr.--AVX Tantalum Div., Biddeford, ME; *Int'l*, pg. 775
Knowles, Robert, Pres.--Lockheed Martin Microwave-FSI, Chelmsford, MA; *U.S. Public*, pg. 1008
Knowles, Roger E., Pres. & Chief Exec. Officer--Willis Corroon Corp. of Texas, Dallas, TX; *Int'l*, pg. 1507
Knowlton, Thomas A., Pres.--Kellogg North America Division, Battle Creek, MI; *U.S. Public*, pg. 947
Knowlton, Thomas A., Pres.--Kellogg USA Inc., Battle Creek, MI; *U.S. Public*, pg. 947
Knox, Andrew, Office Mgr.--Korn/Ferry International, Los Angeles, CA; *U.S. Private*, pg. 633
Knox, Eirv, Country Mgr.--Standard Chartered Bank (Philippines), Makati, Philippines; *Int'l*, pg. 1295
Knox, Fred, Pres.--Varon, Hialeah, FL; *U.S. Public*, pg. 233
Knox, Fred, Chief Oper. Officer--Mercer Company, Sharon, PA; *U.S. Private*, pg. 256
Knox, James, Pres.--Billiards Div. of Brunswick, Bristol, WI; *U.S. Public*, pg. 265
Knox, John, Jr., Pres.--Universal Surety of America, Houston, TX; *U.S. Public*, pg. 303
Knox, Larry, Regional Mgr.--Higgins Las Vegas Operations, Las Vegas, NV; *U.S. Private*, pg. 527
Knox, Mike, Area Foreman--Talisman Energy Inc., Warburg, Canada; *Int'l*, pg. 1352
Knox, Paul, Gen. Mgr.--Mack Printing Group (Ephrata Div.), Ephrata, PA; *U.S. Private*, pg. 692
Knox, Stephen W., Pres.--Brewer Environmental Industries, LLC, Honolulu, HI; *U.S. Private*, pg. 190
Knox, Tim, Gen. Mgr.--The Worthington Steel Company-Pennsylavnia, Malvern, PA; *U.S. Public*, pg. 1780
Knox, Tony, Chm. Bd.--Financial Dynamics Ltd., London, United Kingdom; *Int'l*, pg. 117
Knox, W.C., Plant Mgr.--Lips Propeller Inc., Portland, OR; *Int'l*, pg. 812
Knox, William, Gen. Mgr.--Miller Brands, Inc., Fort Myers, FL; *U.S. Public*, pg. 1289
Knudsen, Ebbe, Dir.-Admin.--Beiersdorf (Denmark) A/S, Birkerod, Denmark; *Int'l*, pg. 183
Knudsen, K.C., Mgr.--Kemira Danmark A/S, Copenhagen, Denmark; *Int'l*, pg. 728
Knudsen, Lars Secher, Mng. Dir.--Radiometer GmbH, Willich, Germany; *Int'l*, pg. 1084
Knudsen, Preben, Chief Oper. Officer--Nordisk Elektronics A/S, Herlev, Denmark; *Int'l*, pg. 712
Knudsen, William, Pres.--Knudsen & Sons, Inc., Chico, CA; *U.S. Public*, pg. 1480
Knue, Paul, Editor--The Cincinnati Post, Cincinnati, OH; *U.S. Public*, pg. 1447
Knue, Paul, Editor--The Kentucky Post, Covington, KY; *U.S. Public*, pg. 1447
Knueppel, Henry W., Pres.--Marathon Electric Manufacturing Corp., Wausau, WI; *U.S. Public*, pg. 1371
Knupfer, Hans-Georg, Admin. Dir.--Hypobank International S.A., Luxembourg, Luxembourg; *Int'l*, pg. 176
Knuts, Per, Chm.--FPB Holding AG, Dusseldorf, Germany; *Int'l*, pg. 1303
Knutzen, Donald L., V.P. & Gen. Mgr.--General Mills, Marketing Services Div., Minneapolis, MN; *U.S. Public*, pg. 718
Knuutinen, Reijo, Mng. Dir.--Merita Securities Ltd., Helsinki, Finland; *Int'l*, pg. 859
Ko, Stephen, Opers. Mgr.--Herbalife International-Hong Kong, Wan Chai, Hong Kong; *U.S. Public*, pg. 809
Ko, W.T., Mgr.--Eclipse Combustion China Ltd., Kowloon, Hong Kong; *U.S. Private*, pg. 361
Koach, John H., Dir.--R.J. Reynolds Tobacco Co. (Asia Pacific) Limited, Hong Kong, Hong Kong; *U.S. Public*, pg. 1355
Koba, Yukio, Mng. Dir.--LTCB Merchant Bank (Singapore) Limited, Singapore, Singapore; *Int'l*, pg. 816
Kobacker, Edward J., Pres. & V.P./Gen. Mgr.--Land & Timber--IP Forest Resources Company, Purchase, NY; *U.S. Public*, pg. 904
Kobao, Giorgio, Mng. Dir.--Vitruvio/Leo Burnett, Barcelona, Spain; *U.S. Private*, pg. 186
Kobar, Peter J., Chief Oper. Officer--Universal Steel Tube Co. Limited, Birmingham, United Kingdom; *U.S. Private*, pg. 873
Kobasyashi, Atsushi, Pres.--Lion Henkel Corporation, Tokyo, Japan; *Int'l*, pg. 614
Kobau, Renato, Gen. Mgr.--SelmaBipiemme Leasing SpA, Milan, Italy; *Int'l*, pg. 137
Kobayashi, Eiichi, Pres.--Kobe Welding (Singapore) Pte. Ltd., Jurong, Singapore; *Int'l*, pg. 741
Kobayashi, Hideo, Pres.--Rohm Logistec Co., Ltd., Okayama, Japan; *Int'l*, pg. 1125
Kobayashi, Hiroji, Pres.--Minebea Electronics & Hi-Tech Components (Shanghai) Ltd., Shanghai, China; *Int'l*, pg. 868
Kobayashi, Hiromi, Mng. Dir.--ORIX Investment and Management Private Limited, Singapore, Singapore; *Int'l*, *pg. 1009*
Kobayashi, Katsuhiko, Pres.--Oyo Corporation U.S.A., Houston, TX; *Int'l*, pg. 1019
Kobayashi, Katsuhiko, Mng. Dir.--Sanwa International Finance Limited, Central, Hong Kong; *Int'l*, pg. 1190
Kobayashi, M., Pres.--Sanyo E.T. Canada Inc., Toronto, Canada; *Int'l*, pg. 1192
Kobayashi, Masayuki, Gen. Mgr.--Sakura Bank - Atlanta Agency, Atlanta, GA; *Int'l*, pg. 1179
Kobayashi, Sadaya, Mng. Dir.--Central Japan Railway Company-London Office, London, United Kingdom; *Int'l*, pg. 279
Kobayashi, Shigeru, Co.-Chief Oper. Officer--Kyowa Hakko U.K. Ltd., London, United Kingdom; *Int'l*, pg. 778
Kobayashi, T., Pres.--HND Corporation, Katsuta, Japan; *Int'l*, pg. 620
Kobayashi, T., Pres.--Hamamatsu Kohan Kako Co., Ltd., Shizuoka, Japan; *Int'l*, pg. 946
Kobayashi, Tadao, Chm. Bd.--Calhac, Inc., Cerritos, CA; *Int'l*, pg. 634
Kobayashi, Takaji, Pres.--Shuwa Investments Corp., Los Angeles, CA; *Int'l*, pg. 1237
Kobayashi, Takashi, Chief Mgr.--The Bank of Tokyo-Mitsubishi, Ltd. (Frankfurt Branch), Frankfurt/Main, Germany; *Int'l*, pg. 158
Kobayashi, Takuya, Pres.--Sanyo Office Automation, Chatsworth, CA; *Int'l*, pg. 1191
Kobayashi, Tatsuo, Gen. Mgr.--Japan Gamma Asset Management Ltd, Tokyo, Japan; *Int'l*, pg. 343
Kobayashi, Toshihiro, Chm. Bd.--Rheem Manufacturing Co., New York, NY; *Int'l*, pg. 1022
Kobayashi, Yonezo, Chief Rep.--The Industrial Bank of Japan, Limited (Frankfurt), Frankfurt/Main, Germany; *Int'l*, pg. 675

Kobayashi, Yoshiaki, Mng. Dir.--Turk Sakura Bank A.S., Istanbul, Turkey; Int'l, pg. 1180
Kobayashi, Yotaro, Pres.--Fuji Xerox Company Ltd., Tokyo, Japan; U.S. Public, pg. 1785
Kobe, E., Pres.--Waterous Detroit Diesel-Allison Inc., Edmonton, Canada; Int'l, pg. 1485
Kobel, Andrei, Dir.-Mktg.--Nihon Microtec Research, Tokyo, Japan; U.S. Public, pg. 1087
Kobel, Bernhard, Representative Asst.--UBS Representative Office, Bogota, Colombia; Int'l, pg. 1441
Kobel, Greg, Gen. Mgr.--Greater Chicago Auto Auction, Chicago, IL; U.S. Private, pg. 282
Kobenter, W., Mng. Dir.--Getinge GmbH, Murzzuschlag, Austria; Int'l, pg. 551
Kober, Roger W., Pres.--Energyline Corporation, Rochester, NY; U.S. Public, pg. 1396
Koblish, Bruce, Pres.--Reunion Records, Nashville, TN; Int'l, pg. 1529
Kobuna, Kunio, Exec. Dir.--Yamaichi Securities (Singapore) Pte. Ltd., Singapore, Singapore; Int'l, pg. 1518
Kocass, W., Grp. Mng. Dir.--Gammon Construction Ltd., Quarry Bay, Hong Kong; Int'l, pg. 775
Kocela, Erin, Exec. V.P.-Creative Services--Frankel & Company, Orange, CA; U.S. Private, pg. 424
Koch, Benoit H., Chief Exec.--S.A. Obourg, Obourg, Belgium; Int'l, pg. 629
Koch, Brent R., Mng. Dir.--DYWIDAG Systems International, USA, Inc., Fremont, CA; Int'l, pg. 424
Koch, Carl, Gen. Mgr.--Puget Sound Auto Auction, Inc., Auburn, WA; U.S. Public, pg. 1649
Koch, Carl, Gen. Mgr.--Tri-City Auto Auction, Inc., Pasco, WA; U.S. Public, pg. 1649
Koch, Charles John, Pres.--Charter One Bank, Cleveland, OH; U.S. Public, pg. 336
Koch, Craig, Pres.--Hertz Equipment Rental Corp., Park Ridge, NJ; U.S. Public, pg. 664
Koch, Craig, Pres.--Hertz Corporation, Trenton, NJ; U.S. Public, pg. 664
Koch, Egon, V.P.-Intl.-Europe--Air Canada, Hounslow, United Kingdom; Int'l, pg. 37
Koch, H., Pres.--Sharp Electronics (Schweiz) AG, Dallikon, Switzerland; Int'l, pg. 1230
Koch, Hans Peter, Mng. Dir.--Sulzer Informatik AG, Winterthur, Switzerland; Int'l, pg. 1306
Koch, Hans-Wolfgang, Pres. & Chief Exec. Officer--BDAG Balcke-Durr AG, Ratingen, Germany; Int'l, pg. 399
Koch, Jean-Claude, V.P. & Mng. Dir.--State Street Bank (Luxembourg) S.A., Luxembourg, Luxembourg; U.S. Public, pg. 1513
Koch, John E., Pres. & Chief Exec. Officer--M & I Citizens American Bank, Merrill, WI; U.S. Public, pg. 1050
Koch, Jurgen, Pres.--IMAS S.A., Volos, Greece; Int'l, pg. 298
Koch, K.G., Gen. Mgr.-Europe--Commonwealth Bank of Australia, London, United Kingdom; Int'l, pg. 313
Koch, Paul, Sr. V.P. & Mgr.--ABN AMRO Bank, N.V. (Miami), Miami, FL; Int'l, pg. 10
Koch, Stevan J., Mng. Dir.--Genie Mechanique Zairose, S.A.R.L, Kinshasa, Congo; U.S. Public, pg. 724
Koch, William A., V.P. & Gen. Mgr.--Kodak Motion Picture & Audiovisual Products Division, Rochester, NY; U.S. Public, pg. 555
Kocher, Carl, Gen. Mgr.--Poe & Brown of Florida, Winter Haven, FL; U.S. Public, pg. 1312
Kocher, James R., Chm. Bd.--Huntington Bancshares Indiana, Inc., Indianapolis, IN; U.S. Public, pg. 850
Kochi, M., Pres.--Ebara America Corporation, Foster City, CA; Int'l, pg. 431
Kochman, Michael, Pres.--Sharplan Lasers, Inc., Allendale, NJ; Int'l, pg. 429
Kochy, Tom, Pres.--Western Division, Norcross, GA; U.S. Public, pg. 1255
Kockum, Frans Henrik, Mng. Dir.--Svenska Handelsbanken Luxembourg, Luxembourg, Luxembourg; Int'l, pg. 1328
Kocsis, D., Dr., Mng. Dir.--Reemtsma Debreceni Dohanygyar Kft, Debrecen, Hungary; Int'l, pg. 1101
Kocsis, Margit, Media Dir.--Leo Burnett Budapest KFT, Budapest, Hungary; U.S. Private, pg. 185
Kodama, Ryuzo, Dir. & Gen. Mgr.--The Sumitomo Bank, Ltd.-New York Branch, New York, NY; Int'l, pg. 1309
Kodama, Tadahiro, Pres.--Bridgestone Cycle (U.S.A.), Inc., San Leandro, CA; Int'l, pg. 213
Koeberl, M., Mng. Dir.--O&K Antriebstechnik GmbH, Hattingen Works, Hattingen, Germany; Int'l, pg. 516
Koedijk, Dirk Stephan, Chief Oper. Officer--Thompson GmbH, Dusseldorf, Germany; Int'l, pg. 610
Koehler, H.C., Gen. Mgr.--Ameron (Pte) Ltd., Singapore, Singapore; U.S. Public, pg. 99
Koehler, James, V.P.-Sls.--Edward Don & Company-Mt. Laurel Branch, Mount Laurel, NJ; U.S. Private, pg. 339
Koehler, Rick, Pres.--PinnAcle Media, Cleveland, OH; U.S. Private, pg. 1194
Koehn, George W., Chm. Bd., Pres. & Chief Exec. Officer--SunTrust, Orlando, FL; U.S. Public, pg. 1537
Koehn, George W., Pres. & Chief Exec. Officer--SunTrust Bank, Central Florida, N.A, Orlando, FL; U.S. Public, pg. 1537
Koehn, Michael, Pres. & Chief Exec. Officer--Analytic TSA Global Asset Management Inc., Los Angeles, CA; U.S. Public, pg. 1672
Koehring, William, Station Mgr.--Limagrain Genetics Corp., Kirkland, IL; Int'l, pg. 566
Koelling, Klaus, Asst. V.P.--Voest-Alpine International Corp.-Railroad Products Div., New York, NY; Int'l, pg. 1471
Koenen, E.A.N., Chie Oper. Officer--De Lage Landen Factors GmbH, Dusseldorf, Germany; Int'l, pg. 1082
Koeniegseder, James A., V.P.--Wal-Mart Jewelry Div., Bentonville, AR; U.S. Public, pg. 1733
Koenig, Douglas B., Pres.--Wenco Inc., Hamburg, PA; U.S. Public, pg. 1754
Koenig, Howard, Pres.--American White Cross, Dayville, CT; U.S. Public, pg. 694
Koenig, Jean Claude, Dir.--Banque Veuve Morin-Pons, Strasbourg, France; Int'l, pg. 419
Koenig, Paul, Chief Oper. Officer--Trayco, Inc., Lapeer, MI; U.S. Public, pg. 1054
Koenig, Steve, V.P. & Gen. Mgr.--Nutrius Dairy Feed Supplements Div., Kingsburg, CA; U.S. Private, pg. 145
Koenig, Walter E., Chief Exec. Officer--Gummiwerke Fulda, Fulda, Germany; U.S. Public, pg. 753
Koenigsaecker, George J., Pres.--Jacobs Brake Division, Bloomfield, CT; U.S. Public, pg. 481
Koenigsfeld, Christian, Rep.--DG Bank - Brazil, Rio de Janeiro, Brazil; Int'l, pg. 352
Koennecke, Margarita, Country Mgr.--Lotus Development GmbH, Munich, Germany; U.S. Public, pg. 896
Koepnick, Jim, Pres.--The Weitz Company, Inc., West Palm Beach, FL; U.S. Private, pg. 1161
Koerner, Scott F., Sr. V.P.--Creative Computers, Inc., Elk Grove Village, IL; U.S. Public, pg. 458
Koether, Albert, Mng. Dir.--Kalso S.A., Hortes, France; Int'l, pg. 1428
Koether, Robert E., Pres.--Infincom, Tempe, AZ; U.S. Public, pg. 864
Koetzier, C., Mng. Dir.--Hoogovens Ijmuiden Verkoopkantoor B.V., Ijmuiden, Netherlands; Int'l, pg. 754
Kofalt, James A., Pres.--Cablevision, Woodbury, NY; U.S. Public, pg. 288
Koffend, Frank S., Pres.--Akrosil, Menasha, WI; U.S. Public, pg. 903
Koga, Hiroaki, Pres.--Hakuhodo Photo Creative Inc., Tokyo, Japan; Int'l, pg. 588
Koga, Ryozo, Gen. Mgr.--Asahi Bank Guam Branch, Agana, GU; Int'l, pg. 82
Kogan, Warren O., Pres.--H. Sand & Co., Inc., Westbury, NY; Int'l, pg. 1261
Kogstad, R.E., Pres.--Norsk Hydro USA Inc., New York, NY; Int'l, pg. 961
Kogumazaka, M., Pres.--Shin-Meito Co., Ltd., Chiba, Japan; Int'l, pg. 947
Kogune, Satoshi, Chief Rep.--Shenzhen Representative Office, Shenzhen, China; Int'l, pg. 85
Koh, Kenneth, Gen. Mgr.--UFE Pte Ltd, Singapore, Singapore; U.S. Private, pg. 1112
Koh, Mark, Gen. Mgr.--BMI Pte. Ltd., Singapore, Singapore, Singapore; Int'l, pg. 187
Kohama, S., Office Chief--Man Nen Sha, Inc., Okinawa, Japan; Int'l, pg. 834
Kohan, Raul E., Pres.--Schering-Plough Animal Health, Union, NJ; U.S. Public, pg. 1438
Kohara, Hidetsugu, Mng. Dir.--Pioneer Electronics Manufacturing NV, Erpe, Belgium; Int'l, pg. 1058
Kohata, Florencio, Mng. Dir.--Dun & Bradstreet SA, Lima, Peru; U.S. Public, pg. 537
Kohl, J., Dr., Chm.-Bd. of Mngmt.--Wacker-Chemie GmbH, Munich, Germany; Int'l, pg. 625
Kohl, Richard, Mgr.-Opers.--Titan Wheel Corporation of WI, Slinger, WI; U.S. Public, pg. 1619
Kohlbrunner, P. E., Chief Oper. Officer--Therma AG, Schwanden, Switzerland; Int'l, pg. 444
Kohle, Peter, Mng. Dir.--Minco International AB, Trelleborg, Sweden; Int'l, pg. 1423
Kohler, Hajo, Chief Oper. Officer--North German Branch, Hamburg, Germany; Int'l, pg. 645
Kohler, John M., Jr., Mgr.--Kohler Co. (SC), Spartanburg, SC; U.S. Private, pg. 630
Kohler, Manfred W., Exec. V.P.--Dun & Bradstreet Schimmelpfeng GmbH, Vienna, Austria; U.S. Public, pg. 537
Kohler, W. Manfred, Exec. V.P.--Dun & Bradstreet Deutschland GmbH, Frankfurt/Main, Germany; U.S. Public, pg. 536
Kohlhaupt, Fritz, Mng. Dir.--Gebruder Sulzer-Escher Wyss-Kaltetechnik GmbH, Lauterach, Austria; Int'l, pg. 1306
Kohlhaupt, Fritz, Chief Exec.--Sulzer Escher Wyss Kaltetchnik G.m.b.H., Lauterach, Austria; Int'l, pg. 1306
Kohli, Lee, Gen. Mgr.--Case Farms of Ohio, Winesburg, OH; U.S. Private, pg. 218
Kohlmann, E., Oper. Officer--Rhenania Umschlag und Lagerei GmbH, Mannheim, Germany; Int'l, pg. 1034
Kohlmeyer, Michael, Pres.--1st Source Insurance, South Bend, IN; U.S. Public, pg. 638
Kohlrusch, Dietmar, Mng. Dir.--KKW, Kulmbach, Germany; Int'l, pg. 554
Kohn, Jacques, Chief Oper. Officer--Balsa Development Corporation, Northvale, NJ; U.S. Public, pg. 171
Kohn, Jacques, Chief Oper. Officer--C.K. Trading Corp., Northvale, NJ; U.S. Public, pg. 172
Kohn, Jean, Chief Oper. Officer--Baltek Ltd., Croydon, United Kingdom; U.S. Public, pg. 172
Kohn, Jean, Chief Oper. Officer--Baltek S.A., Paris, France; U.S. Public, pg. 172
Kohn, Mathias, Mng. Dir.--ISS Hospital Service AG, Oberentfelden, Switzerland; Int'l, pg. 657
Kohn, Paul, Pres.--Pall Trinity Micro Corp., Cortland, NY; U.S. Public, pg. 1254
Kohn, Robin, Plant Mgr.--Washington Scientific Industries, Long Lake, MN; U.S. Public, pg. 1744
Kohn, Thomas W., Pres.--Chemical Bank Montcalm, Stanton, MI; U.S. Public, pg. 345
Kohno, Sukeo, Chief Opr. Officer--Hitachi Metals, Ltd., Tokyo, Japan; Int'l, pg. 621
Kohrs, Kenneth K., V.P.--Car Product Development, Dearborn, MI; U.S. Public, pg. 662
Kohrs, Richard, V.P.-Intl. Activities, Dir.-Intl. Aerospace Co-Operation--Anser, Moscow, Russia; U.S. Private, pg. 76
Kohut, Hershal, Pres.--ARCO Marine, Incorporated, Long Beach, CA; U.S. Public, pg. 144
Kohut, William, Pres.--Figgie Properties Inc., Cleveland, OH; U.S. Public, pg. 622
Kohzuki, Hidetoshi, Chief Oper. Officer--Isuzu Motors Co., (Thailand) Ltd., Samutprakan, Thailand; Int'l, pg. 693
Koike, Kunio, Exec. Dir.-Gen. Affairs--Leo Burnett Kyodo Co. Ltd., Tokyo, Japan; U.S. Private, pg. 185
Koike, Yasushi, Chief Rep.--The Sakura Bank - Tashkent Representative Office, Tashkent, Uzbekistan; Int'l, pg. 1180
Koiso-Kanttila, Kimmo, Pres.--Oy Saab-Auto Ab, Helsinki, Finland; Int'l, pg. 1449
Koistinen, Mikael, Chief Oper. Officer--Axtec AB, Stockholm, Sweden; Int'l, pg. 708
Koivisto, Pekka, V.P. & Gen. Mgr.--Kuusanniemi Pulp Mill, Kuusankoski, Finland; Int'l, pg. 1428
Koivunen, Kari, Pres.--Lohja Abetoni Oy AB, Perttila, Finland; Int'l, pg. 1199
Koizumi, Takashi, Pres.--ORIX Aircraft Corporation, Tokyo, Japan; Int'l, pg. 1008
Koizumi, Takashi, Pres.--ORIX Maritime Corporation, Tokyo, Japan; Int'l, pg. 1009
Koizumi, Toshio, Dep. Gen. Mgr.--Daiwa Bank-Singapore, Singapore, Singapore; Int'l, pg. 373
Kojima, Akira, Mng. Dir.--Brother Finance (Netherlands) B.V., Amsterdam, Netherlands; Int'l, pg. 229
Kojima, Hiroshi, Mng. Dir.--Oki (UK) Ltd., Cumbernauld, United Kingdom; Int'l, pg. 999
Kojima, Okinari, Pres.--Amano Deutschland GmbH, Erkrath, Germany; Int'l, pg. 71
Kojima, Seiichi, Pres.--Shinko Wire Co., Ltd., Amagasaki, Japan; Int'l, pg. 740
Kojima, T., Mng. Dir.--Tyton Hellermann Asia Pacific Ltd., Singapore, Singapore; Int'l, pg. 209
Kojima, Taijiro, Pres.--Sanwa Singapore Limited, Singapore, Singapore; Int'l, pg. 1190
Kojima, Tsugumasa, Mng. Dir. & Chief Exec. Officer--Sakura Finance International Limited, London, United Kingdom; Int'l, pg. 1180
Kojima, Tsugumasa, Chief Exec. & Mng. Dir.--Sakura Trust Internaional Limited, London, United Kingdom; Int'l, pg. 1180
Kojima, Yoji, Gen. Mgr.--Kubota America Corp., Los Angeles, CA; Int'l, pg. 762
Kok, Ronald, Pres.--Componenta International B.V., Alphen aan den Rijn, Netherlands; Int'l, pg. 1421
Kok, W.J., Dr., Chm. Bd.--Escap Limited, Sandton, South Africa; Int'l, pg. 459
Kok, William, Chm.--Mattessons Walls Ltd., Banbury, United Kingdom; Int'l, pg. 1434
Kokheel, Marcel, Chief Oper. Officer--Ahold Vastgoed B.V., Zaandam, Netherlands; Int'l, pg. 749
Kokkinen, Heikki, Pres.--Nokia Multimedia Network Terminals, Helsinki, Finland; Int'l, pg. 952
Kokubo, Masaaki, Mng. Dir.--Fuji International Finance (Australia) Limited, Sydney, Australia; Int'l, pg. 521
Kokubun, Haito, Chief Rep.--The Sakura Bank - Taipei Representative Office, Taipei, Taiwan; Int'l, pg. 1180
Kokuma, Atsushi, Pres.--Durakut International Corp., Farmingdale, NY; Int'l, pg. 740
Kolade, Christopher, Dr., Chm. Bd.--Cadbury Nigeria PLC, Ikeja, Nigeria; Int'l, pg. 248
Kolakowski, Ronald, V.P. & Gen. Mgr.--Acco Controls, Milan, TN; Int'l, pg. 472
Kolasinski, Edward M., Pres.--Pryon Corporation, Menomonee Falls, WI; U.S. Public, pg. 1336
Koldenhof, Jan, Mng. Dir.--Vectur B.V., Apeldoorn, Netherlands; U.S. Private, pg. 1129
Koles, William, Pres.--Carlisle Container Manufacturing Company, Saint Augustine, FL; U.S. Public, pg. 305
Kolff, C. L., Gen. Mgr.--Ferro (Holland) B.V., Rotterdam, Netherlands; U.S. Public, pg. 619
Kolino, M.A., V.P.-Central Region--Benjamin Moore & Co., Melrose Park, IL; U.S. Private, pg. 133
Koljonen, Markku, V.P.--Steel Structure Division, Helsinki, Finland; Int'l, pg. 1088
Kollberg, Bjorn, Pres.--Asea Brown Boveri S.A., Buenos Aires, Argentina; Int'l, pg. 8
Kollberg, Lars, Mgr.--Boliden Bergsoe AB, Landskrona, Sweden; Int'l, pg. 1422
Kolle, Peter O., Sr. V.P.--Vereinsbank Capital Corporation, New York, NY; Int'l, pg. 180
Koller, Karl, Mng. Dir.--Ancra Jungfalk GmbH, Engen, Germany; U.S. Private, pg. 71
Koller, Tim, Chief Fin. Officer--WPMT Channel 43, York, PA; U.S. Public, pg. 1636
Kollisch, Herbert, Mng. Dir.--Intercord Tongesellschaft mbH, Stuttgart, Germany; Int'l, pg. 428
Kollisch, Richard, Pres.--Sopur Medizintechnik GmbH, Maisach, Germany; U.S. Public, pg. 1536
Kolloff, Jean, Pres.--Burberrys Shirts, New York, NY; Int'l, pg. 194
Kolmann, E., Chief Oper. Officer--Rhenania Container GmbH, Mannheim, Germany; Int'l, pg. 1033
Kolody, Phil, Pres.--Lummi Fisheries Supply, Bellingham, WA; U.S. Public, pg. 429
Kolonko, D., Chief Oper. Officer--SAIA-Burgess Electronics GmbH, Dreieichenhain, Germany; Int'l, pg. 1501
Koloszar, G., Chief Exec. Officer--Zurich Biztosito Rt., Budapest, Hungary; Int'l, pg. 1532
Kolowratnik, P., Exec. V.P.--Braas GmbH, Oberursell, Germany; Int'l, pg. 1091
Kolowratnik, P., Chief Exec. Officer--Braas Italia S.p.A., Bolzano, Italy; Int'l, pg. 1092
Kolpin, Marc, Pres.--Physics International Co., San Leandro, CA; U.S. Public, pg. 1219
Kolsky, Kenneth, Chief Oper. Officer--ICF Incorporated, Fairfax, VA; U.S. Public, pg. 853
Koltin, Allan D., Pres.--Practice Development Institute, Chicago, IL; U.S. Private, pg. 428
Komai, M., Pres.--Toner Product Division, Mitchell, SD; Int'l, pg. 1405
Komai, Shigeharu, Pres.--Duskin USA, Inc., Hacienda Heights, CA; Int'l, pg. 422
Komai, Yoshiaki, Dep. Chm.--ORIX Australia Corporation Limited, Double Bay, Australia; Int'l, pg. 1009
Komatsu, Kyoichi, Pres.--Otsuka Packaging Industries Ltd., Tokushima, Japan; Int'l, pg. 1013
Komeda, M., V.P. & Gen. Mgr.--Nichimen America, Inc., Chicago Branch, Chicago, IL; Int'l, pg. 928
Kominami, I., Pres. & Chief Exec. Officer--Toyo Aluminium K.K., Osaka, Japan; Int'l, pg. 52
Kominami, Shigeharu, Chief Oper. Officer--Makita S.p.A., San Vittore Olona, Italy; Int'l, pg. 832

Komiya, Yozo, Mng. Dir.--Nippon Express (Malaysia) Sdn. Bhd., Petaling Jaya, Malaysia; *Int'l*, pg. 934
Komiyama, Tetsuji, Mng. Dir.--ORIX Rentec (Singapore) Pte. Limited, Singapore, Singapore; *Int'l*, pg. 1010
Komlen, Roger, Chief Fin. Officer--Romeo Rim Inc., Romeo, MI; *U.S. Private*, pg. 300
Kommers, Win, Chm.--Tenneco Nederland B.V., Amstelveen, Netherlands; *U.S. Public*, pg. 1580
Kommerstad, Robert, Chm. Bd. & Pres.--Provident Investment Counsel, Inc., Pasadena, CA; *U.S. Public*, pg. 1674
Kommerwell, Ronald, Pres.--Decca International, London, United Kingdom; *Int'l*, pg. 1053
Komnath, J., Gen. Mgr.--Corning Canada Inc., Richmond Hill, Canada; *U.S. Public*, pg. 448
Komolov, Alexey, Media Dir.--Leo Burnett & Moradpour/Moscow, Moscow, Russia; *U.S. Private*, pg. 184
Komori, Shuichi, Chm. Bd. & Chief Exec. Officer--Daiwa Securities America Inc., New York, NY; *Int'l*, pg. 375
Komori, Y., Pres.--Tomen Transportgeraete GmbH, Erkrath, Germany; *Int'l*, pg. 1412
Kompan, Jack, Publr.--Cahners Publishing-Hong Kong, Chai Wan, Hong Kong; *Int'l*, pg. 1096
Komura, Kazuro, Pres.--The Meijiseimei Asset Management of America, Ltd., New York, NY; *Int'l*, pg. 854
Komura, Kazuro, Pres.--The Meijiseimei Realty of America, Inc., New York, NY; *Int'l*, pg. 854
Konarski, Robert, Resident Mgr.--ESAB Przedstawicielstwo w. Polsce, Warsaw, Poland; *Int'l*, pg. 282
Konczak, Kevin, Pres.--Romeo Rim Inc., Romeo, MI; *U.S. Private*, pg. 300
Kondoh, Akira, Chm. Bd.--Sumitomo Bank Leasing & Finance, Inc., New York, NY; *Int'l*, pg. 1308
Kondoh, Akira, Chm. Bd.--Sumitomo Bank of California, San Francisco, CA; *Int'l*, pg. 1309
Kondoh, Y., Mng. Dir.--Sharp Thebnakorn Co., Ltd. (Bangkok), Bangkok, Thailand; *Int'l*, pg. 1230
Kondoh, Y., Pres.--Sharp Thebnakorn Manufacturing (Thailand), Nakornpathom, Thailand; *Int'l*, pg. 1230
Kondziolka, David, Exec. V.P.-Western U.S.--AGRA Earth & Environmental, Inc., Albuquerque, NM; *Int'l*, pg. 31
Kone, Anne, Co-Chief Oper. Officer--Cofhylux SA, Luxembourg, Luxembourg; *Int'l*, pg. 162
Konejung, Hans, Mng. Dir.--Wisaforest Deutschland GmbH, Dusseldorf, Germany; *Int'l*, pg. 1429
Kong, Do-shik, Chief Rep.--The Export-Import Bank of Korea, Tokyo, Japan; *Int'l*, pg. 467
Kong, John, Mgr.--BHP Steel Building Products Singapore Pte Ltd., Jurong, Singapore; *Int'l*, pg. 226
Kong, Liau Hong, Chm.--NDC Merchant Bank Nominees Pte Ltd., Singapore, Singapore; *Int'l*, pg. 351
Kong, Stanley, Gen. Mgr.-Sls.--Sensormatic Hong Kong Limited, Kowloon, Hong Kong; *U.S. Public*, pg. 1458
Kongsteien, Tor, Gen. Mgr.--Jotun L.L.C., Muscat, Oman; *Int'l*, pg. 716
Konicek, Joel, Pres.--Northern Computers Inc., Milwaukee, WI; *U.S. Private*, pg. 64
Konings, Hans P., Pres.--Sysco/Konings Wholesale, Port Coquitlam, Canada; *U.S. Public*, pg. 1552
Konishi, Sam, Pres.--Coil Plus-Illinois Inc., Plainfield, IL; *Int'l*, *pg. 872*
Kono, Yasushi, Chief Oper. Officer--Nippon Oil (U.K.) Public Limited Company, London, United Kingdom; *Int'l*, pg. 937
Kono, Yoshio, Pres.--Nozaki America, Inc., New York, NY; *Int'l*, pg. 990
Konopik, M. Gene, Pres.--Federal Systems Group, Mc Lean, VA; *U.S. Public*, pg. 1516
Konrad, Robert, Mng. Dir.--Sulzer Betriebsliegenschaften AG, Winterthur, Switzerland; *Int'l*, pg. 1307
Konstantinos, Keith, V.P. & Gen. Mgr.--Outdoor Systems, Inc.-Kansas City, Kansas City, MO; *U.S. Public*, pg. 1235
Kontogouris, Venetia, Pres.--Cognizant Enterprises, Inc., Westport, CT; *U.S. Public*, pg. 395
Konynendyk, Adrian, Mng. Dir.--Willis Corroon Scheuer, Amsterdam, Netherlands; *Int'l*, pg. 1509
Koo, John, Pres.--LG Group Inc., Englewood Cliffs, NJ; *Int'l*, *pg. 779*
Koo, Pyong Hwoi, Vice. Chm. & Pres.--Honam Oil Refinery Co. Ltd., Seoul, Korea; *Int'l*, pg. 779
Koob, Hans Konrad, Mng. Dir.--Koob & Partner/The Corporate Company, Mulheim an der Ruhr, Germany; *Int'l*, pg. 117
Koob, Mark, Pres.--Bumble Bee Seafoods Inc., San Diego, CA; *U.S. Private*, pg. 526
Kooger, Jaap, Mng. Dir.--Du Pont de Nemours (Belgium) S.A., Brussels, Belgium; *U.S. Public*, pg. 532
Koogle, Tim, Pres.--Intermec Technologies Corporation, Everett, WA; *U.S. Public*, pg. 1699
Kooi, Koay Gaik, Mng. Dir.--Longman Malaysia Sdn. Bhd., Petaling Jaya, Malaysia; *Int'l*, pg. 1025
Kook, Werner, Dir.--Langnese-Iglo G.m.b.H., Hamburg, Germany; *Int'l*, pg. 1437
Koon, Dan, Pres.--Pacificare of Guam, Tamuning, GU; *U.S. Public*, pg. 1251
Koon, David, Lease & Rental Mgr.--DSU Leasing, Inc., Portland, OR; *U.S. Private*, pg. 306
Koon, Ivan, Pres.--S.Two Systems Corporation, Dallas, TX; *U.S. Public*, pg. 1524
Koon, Richard D., Pres. & Chief Exec. Officer--Cubic Worldwide Technical Services, Inc., San Diego, CA; *U.S. Public*, pg. 466
Koonce, Don, Chief Fin. Officer--Schlegel Carolina Div., Chester, SC; *Int'l*, pg. 128
Koons, Fred, Pres.--Chase Home Mortgage Corporation, Tampa, FL; *U.S. Public*, pg. 338
Koons, John L., Pres.--Landstar T.L.C., Inc., Saint Clair, MO; *U.S. Public*, pg. 978
Koop, Robin, Pres.--AMI Metals, Inc., Fontana, CA; *U.S. Public*, pg. 1375
Koos, Tom, Pres.--BernzOmatic, Medina, NY; *U.S. Public*, pg. 1177
Kopald, Ken, V.P. & Gen. Mgr.--Fuji Micrographics Div., Elmsford, NY; *Int'l*, pg. 524
Kopchinsky, Billy, Chm. Bd. & Pres.--Ensueno-Tyco (Mexico) S.A. de C.V., Tlalnepantla, Mexico; *U.S. Public*, pg. 1059
Kopec, Anita, Pres.--Steck-Vaughn Company, Austin, TX; *U.S. Public*, pg. 784
Kopec, Anita, Pres.--Steck-Vaughn Distribution Company, Austin, TX; *U.S. Public*, pg. 784
Kopec, Michael J., Pres.--Carter-Wallace Manufacturing Div., Cranbury, NJ; *U.S. Public*, pg. 310
Kopecek, Lubomir, Chief Oper. Officer--Gambro-Meopta S.R.O., Prerov, Czech Republic; *Int'l*, pg. 668
Koper, M.A., Mng. Dir.--Ebara Pumps United Kingdom Limited, Hounslow, United Kingdom; *Int'l*, pg. 432
Koper, R.M., V.P. & Gen. Mgr.--Svedala Bulk Materials Handling Engineered Products, Pittsburgh, PA; *Int'l*, pg. 1326
Koperdraat, J., Mng. Dir.--Prenatal B.V., Almere, Netherlands; *Int'l*, pg. 750
Koperski, P., Mgr.--Harris Metals, Cookeville, TN; *U.S. Public*, pg. 999
Kopetzky, W., Chief Fin. Officer--Olivetti Austria G.m.b.H., Vienna, Austria; *Int'l*, pg. 1003
Kopfle, Karl-Heinz, Gen. Mgr.--Lufthansa CityLine GmbH, Kriftel, Germany; *Int'l*, pg. 407
Kopittke, Frederico, Gen. Mgr.--Bandag Do Brasil Ltda., Campinas, Brazil; *U.S. Public*, pg. 178
Koplovitz, Kay, Pres. & Chief Exec. Officer--USA Networks, New York, NY; *U.S. Public*, pg. 1686
Koponen, Matti, Mng. Dir.--SAMAB Cia. Industria e Comercio de Papel, Sao Paulo, Brazil; *Int'l*, pg. 458
Koponen, Pentti, Mgr.-Special Systems--Nokia Telecommunications, Espoo, Finland; *Int'l*, pg. 952
Kopp, Antoine, Pres.--AKO Armaturen - Vertrieks GmbH, Trebur, Germany; *Int'l*, pg. 710
Kopp, Wolf-Ulrich, Mgr.--Struers Division, Willich, Germany; *Int'l*, pg. 1084
Koppel, M.P., Mng. Dir.--Bank Rohner Ltd., Saint Gallen, Switzerland; *Int'l*, pg. 1439
Koppel, Ulrich, Mng. Dir.--Amway (Schweiz) AG, Kestenholz, Switzerland; *U.S. Private*, pg. 70
Koppensteiner, Walter, Pres. & Mng. Dir.--AGA Ges.m.b.H., Vienna, Austria; *Int'l*, pg. 13
Kopperud, Dean C., Pres.--Fortis Financial Group, Woodbury, MN; *Int'l*, pg. 499
Koptev, Sergey, Chief Exec. Officer, Mng. Dir.--DMB&B Moscow, Moscow, Russia; *U.S. Private*, pg. 304
Koptev, Sergey, Chm. & Chief Exec. Officer--DMB&B St. Petersburg, Saint Petersburg, Russia; *U.S. Private*, pg. 304
Korab, W., V.P. & Gen. Mgr.--Beverage Div., White Plains, NY; *U.S. Public*, pg. 1287
Korach, Dan, V.P. & Gen. Mgr.--Materials Handling Equipment, Marietta, GA; *U.S. Private*, pg. 1156
Korach, Dan, V.P. & Gen. Mgr.--Jervis B. Webb Co. of Georgia, Marietta, GA; *U.S. Private*, pg. 1157
Korach, Jeffrey L., Pres.--Tremco, Inc., Beachwood, OH; *U.S. Public*, pg. 1358
Korach, Kenneth W., Pres.--The Euclid Chemical Company, Cleveland, OH; *U.S. Public*, pg. 1358
Korbel, Rene, Mng. Dir.--Halten GmbH & Co. KG, Dusseldorf, Germany; *Int'l*, pg. 592
Korbell, Charles, Pres.--Clarke American Corp., San Antonio, TX; *Int'l*, pg. 267
Kordas, Dimitri, Gen. Mgr.--Conquest Europe, Athens, Greece; *Int'l*, pg. 1484
Koreeda, Atsushi, Pres.--Nikkei Newspaper Marketing, Inc., Tokyo, Japan; *Int'l*, pg. 929
Korell, Brad, Pres.--National Bank of Commerce, Lincoln, NE; *U.S. Public*, pg. 629
Koreman, Cornelius, Pres. & Gen. Mgr.--Ford Motor de Venezuela, S.A., Valencia, Venezuela; *U.S. Public*, pg. 666
Koren, Gideon, Gen. Mgr.--ITW Mapri Industria e Comercio Ltda., Sao Paulo, Brazil; *U.S. Public*, pg. 868
Koren, Mike, Gen. Mgr.--Keystone New England Warehouse-Norwood, Norwood, MA; *U.S. Public*, pg. 955
Korialos, John, Gen. Mgr.--SASIB Hellas Signaling Systems I.C.S.A., Athens, Greece; *Int'l*, pg. 1195
Korinek, Dr. George J., Pres.--Hermann C. Starck, Inc., New York, NY; *Int'l*, pg. 175
Korinek, George J., Dr., Pres.--NRC Inc., Newton, MA; *Int'l*, pg. 173
Korman, Cornelius, Mng. Admin.--Productos Industriales, C.A., Valencia, Venezuela; *U.S. Public*, pg. 666
Korn, Joel, Sr. V.P. & Area Gen. Mgr.--Bank of America NT&SA, Sao Paulo, Brazil; *U.S. Public*, pg. 182
Kornblum, Ruediger, Gen. Mgr.--NUS Deutschland GmbH, Dusseldorf, Germany; *U.S. Private*, pg. 787
Kornbrekke, Henning, Pres. & Gen. Mgr.--Stanley Hardware Div., New Britain, CT; *U.S. Public*, pg. 1509
Korner, Peter, Gen. Mgr.--GD-Golvdepan i Sverige AB, Jonkoping, Sweden; *Int'l*, pg. 498
Korning, J., Mng. Dir.--Ericsson Radio Systems B.V., Emmen, Netherlands; *Int'l*, pg. 1367
Kornswiet, Neil, Pres. & Chief Exec. Officer--One Stop Mortgage, Inc., Costa Mesa, CA; *U.S. Public*, pg. 12
Korologos, Tom, Pres.--Timmons & Company Inc., Washington, DC; *Int'l*, pg. 1483
Korp, Gunter, Rep.--Bayerische Landesbank Girozentrale, Vienna, Austria; *Int'l*, pg. 177
Korpan, Richard, Pres. & Chief Exec. Officer--Progress Capital Holdings, Inc., Saint Petersburg, FL; *U.S. Public*, pg. 655
Korphage, George J., Chm. Bd.--Pike & Fischer, Bethesda, MD; *U.S. Private*, pg. 182
Korsia, Guy, Gen. Mgr.-Pharmacy--Wuhrlin-Soplamed S.A., Courbevoie, France; *U.S. Public*, pg. 673
Korslin, William R., Pres.--American Pharmaceutical Services, Inc., Naperville, IL; *U.S. Public*, pg. 1257
Korssjoem, Y. Jam Erek, Chief Exec. Officer--Simrad Norge AF, Horten, Norway; *Int'l*, pg. 1252
Korte, Doug, Mgr.--Ampex Corporation, Canyon Country, CA; *U.S. Public*, pg. 104
Korte, Ralph, Gen. Mgr.--Simkins Carton Div.-Chicago, Cicero, IL; *U.S. Private*, pg. 1000
Korte, Steven, Pres.--Rigby Education, Crystal Lake, IL; *Int'l*, pg. 1094
Kortelainen, Tito, Mng. Dir.--Kesped Ltd., Vantaa, Finland; *Int'l*, pg. 732
Kortemeier, Carole, Admin.--East Moore Nursing Center, Moore, OK; *U.S. Public*, pg. 839
Kortemeyer, Peter, Pres.--Ensley Tool Co. Inc., North Kansas City, MO; *Int'l*, pg. 1129
Korth, Harald, Chm. Bd.--Markantstahl GmbH, Hagen, Germany; *Int'l*, pg. 79
Kosaka, Hiroshi, Gen. Mgr.--EG & G Japan, Tokyo, Japan; *U.S. Public*, pg. 544
Kosaza, Daizo, Rep.--The Industrial Bank of Japan, Limited (Sydney), Sydney, Australia; *Int'l*, pg. 675
Koschel, Peter Jurgen, Pres.--Babcock Rohrleitungsbau GmbH, Oberhausen, Germany; *Int'l*, pg. 399
Koscher, Edward R., V.P. & Gen. Mgr.--Plastic Sales Div., Pittsfield, MA; *U.S. Public*, pg. 711
Koscik, R., Gen. Mgr.--ITW Deltar-Fasteners, Frankfort, IL; *U.S. Public*, pg. 866
Kosh, James, Pres.--Alberta Oil Tool Div., Edmonton, Canada; *U.S. Public*, pg. 522
Koshiba, S., Chief Oper. Officer--Royal Copenhagen Japan Ltd., Tokyo, Japan; *Int'l*, pg. 1135
Koshida, N., Pres.--Kobelco America Inc., Houston, TX; *Int'l*, *pg. 740*
Koshiishi, Kazuhide, Chm. Bd.--LTCB Australia Limited, Sydney, Australia; *Int'l*, pg. 816
Koshima, D., Pres.--Sharp Manufacturing Company of U.K., Wrexham, United Kingdom; *Int'l*, pg. 1230
Koshimura, Yoshio, Gen. Mgr.--Hills Colgate Japan Ltd., Tokyo, Japan; *U.S. Public*, pg. 399
Koshino, Hidemasa, Pres.--Josephine Cosmetics, Inc., Osaka, Japan; *Int'l*, pg. 1126
Kosht, Jon A., Pres., Chief Oper. Officer, Sec. & Treas.--Michigan Gas Company, Three Rivers, MI; *U.S. Public*, pg. 1489
Koshy, Varghese T., Pres.--AKAY Flavours & Aromatics Ltd., Kerala, India; *Int'l*, pg. 288
Kosin, Osot, Chm. Bd.--Thana One Finance and Securities Limited, Bangkok, Thailand; *Int'l*, pg. 485
Kosinski, James, Plant Mgr.--The Producto Machine Co., Paramount, CA; *U.S. Private*, pg. 889
Kosonen, Markku, Chief Oper. Officer--Ahlstrom Machinery Chemical Recovery, Savonlinna, Finland; *Int'l*, pg. 33
Koss, John, Jr., V.P.-Sls.--Koss Classics Ltd., Milwaukee, WI; *U.S. Public*, pg. 966
Koss, Michael J., Pres., Chief Exec. Officer & Chief Fin. Officer--Koss Classics Ltd., Milwaukee, WI; *U.S. Public*, pg. 966
Koss, Michael J., Pres.--Koss Europe, Stabio, Switzerland; *U.S. Public*, pg. 966
Kost, Arvo, Chief Fin. Officer--AS Kandur, Tallinn, Estonia; *Int'l*, pg. 748
Kostadinov, Peter, Chief Exec.--Sulzer Praha s.r.o., Prague, Czech Republic; *Int'l*, pg. 1306
Kostas, Evans, Pres.--King Press Corporation, Joplin, MO; *U.S. Public*, pg. 1341
Kostelni, James C., Chm. Bd.--Bontex International (F.S.C.), Buena Vista, VA; *U.S. Public*, pg. 734
Kostoryz, J.A., Pres.--TECO Properties, Inc., Tampa, FL; *U.S. Public*, pg. 1565
Kostrzewa, Siegfried, Pres.--Deutsche Babcock Energie-und Umwelttechnik AG, Oberhausen, Germany; *Int'l*, pg. 398
Kostrzewa, Siegfried, Pres.--Babcock Lentjes Kraftwerkstechnik, Oberhausen, Germany; *Int'l*, pg. 398
Kostveit, Trond, Gen. Mgr.--Societe des Ciments du Congo S.A., Brazzaville, Congo; *Int'l*, pg. 1200
Kosuge, Juno, Chief Rep.--Asahi Bank Mexico Representative Office, Mexico, Mexico; *Int'l*, pg. 83
Kosuge, Kazuhiro, Gen. Mgr.--The Sakura Bank - Singapore Branch, Singapore, Singapore; *Int'l*, pg. 1179
Kotaka, Hiromi, Pres.--Kiriu Machine Mfg. Co., Ltd., Tochigi, Japan; *Int'l*, pg. 944
Kotake, Nobuhide, Representative Dir.--Goodman Fielder (Japan) KK, Tokyo, Japan; *Int'l*, pg. 556
Kotani, Yukihito, Mng. Dir.--NLI International Singapore Pte. Ltd., Singapore, Singapore; *Int'l*, pg. 936
Kotentopf, David D., Pres. & Chief Exec. Officer--Steiger Australia, Ltd., Woodville, Australia; *U.S. Public*, pg. 1580
Kothari, H.M., Mgr.--Swiss Bank Corporation, Mumbai, India; *Int'l*, pg. 1330
Kothari, Vikas, Chief Oper. Officer--Ahlstrom Machinery, New Delhi, India; *Int'l*, pg. 34
Kothoda, Toyoaki, Pres. & Gen. Mgr.--ITW Nifco, Inc., Hilliard, OH; *U.S. Public*, pg. 867
Kothoda, Toyoaki, Pres. & Gen. Mgr.--ITW Nifco, Inc., Hilliard, OH; *Int'l*, pg. 929
Kotkamp, Ruediger, Dr., Pres. & Chief Oper. Officer--Rheinische Olefinwerke GmbH, Wesseling, Germany; *Int'l*, pg. 105
Kotler, Steven, Pres.--Schroder & Co. Inc., New York, NY; *Int'l*, pg. 1210
Kott, Gary L., Pres. & Chief Oper. Officer--Global Marine Drilling Co., Houston, TX; *U.S. Public*, pg. 748
Kott, Jim, Pres.--Southwest Title & Trust Company, Oklahoma City, OK; *U.S. Public*, pg. 626
Kott, Kevin, Mgr.--EG & G Instruments, Oak Ridge, TN; *U.S. Public*, pg. 543
Kottkamp, David, Pres.--Nike Latin American Headquarters, Beaverton, OR; *U.S. Public*, pg. 1184
Kottmann, Bernd, Chief Officer--Deutsche Babcock Bau GmbH, Oberhausen, Germany; *Int'l*, pg. 401
Kouchi, Kenji, Chm. Bd--Olympus America Inc., Melville, NY; *Int'l*, pg. 1005
Kouck, Alain, Pres.--Diffulivre, Saint Sulpice, Switzerland; *Int'l*, pg. 795
Koudijs, Renee, Mng. Dir.--High Voltage Engineering B.V., Amersfoort, Netherlands; *U.S. Private*, pg. 528
Koukoullis, Dino, Fin.--Leo Burnett/Connaghan & May (VIC.) Pty. Ltd., Melbourne, Australia; *U.S. Private*, pg. 185

Koumoutsakis, John, Sls. Representative--Brian Controls Division, Moncton, Canada; Int'l, pg. 711
Kouno, Yeru, Pres.--Allstate Automobile & Fire Insurance Co., Ltd., Tokyo, Japan; Int'l, pg. 1178
Kourad, Hans Martin, Chief Oper. Officer--BHF-Bank, Central, Hong Kong; Int'l, pg. 119
Kourcia, Roger, Chm. Bd.--Gelazur S.A., Nice, France; U.S. Public, pg. 429
Kourkoumelis, Dan, Pres.--Hughes Family Markets, Inc., Irwindale, CA; U.S. Public, pg. 1349
Koury, James N., Chm. Bd. & Chief Exec. Officer--Security Pacific State Bank, Irvine, CA; U.S. Public, pg. 182
Koutras, Apostolos, Plant Mgr.--Achoia Papermill S.A., Patras, Greece; U.S. Public, pg. 672
Koutsogiorgas, Yorgo, V.P.-Opers.--Paragus, Chicago, IL; U.S. Private, pg. 661
Kouzuma, Makoto, Chief Oper. Officer, Exec. V.P. & Gen. Mgr.--SpeedFam Co Ltd., Ayase, Japan; U.S. Public, pg. 1498
Kovac, Gary W., Pres.--MariTrend, Inc., New Orleans, LA; U.S. Private, pg. 1135
Kovach, Albert F., Pres.--Stamping & Frame Div., Rochester, MI; Int'l, pg. 1388
Kovach, Cindy, Branch Mgr.--Downey Savings & Loan Association, F.A., Arcadia, CA; U.S. Public, pg. 526
Kovach, Paul F., Jr., Pres.--American General Securities Incorporated, Houston, TX; U.S. Public, pg. 76
Kovacs, Peter, Chm. Bd.--BritCair, Ltd., Aldershot, United Kingdom; U.S. Public, pg. 1091
Kovacs, Peter, Pres.--The NutraSweet Company, Deerfield, IL; U.S. Public, pg. 1125
Kovacs, Peter, Pres.--The NutraSweet Kelco Company, San Diego, CA; U.S. Public, pg. 1125
Kovalaski, Ray, Pres.--Tube-Fab Ltd., Mississauga, Canada; U.S. Public, pg. 771
Kovalenko, Yuri, Deputy Dir.-USSR Affairs--Abbott Laboratories-Moscow Sales Office, Moscow, Russia; U.S. Public, pg. 14
Kovalski, Ray, Pres.--Tube Form, Inc., Cleveland, OH; U.S. Public, pg. 771
Kovar, Lyle, Plant Mgr.--Square D Company, Cedar Rapids, IA; Int'l, pg. 1208
Kovary, Anton, Gen. Mgr.--Gates/Arrow Commercial Systems Div., Melville, NY; U.S. Public, pg. 133
Kovchis, Sam S., V.P.--Florida Division, Pompano Beach, FL; Int'l, pg. 518
Kovensky, Sheldon, Mng. Dir.--Allergan Inc., Markham, Canada; U.S. Public, pg. 46
Kow, G.C.M., Mng. Dir.--Glaxo Wellcome China Ltd., Wan Chai, Hong Kong; Int'l, pg. 553
Kowal, Peter, Pres.--Camisus de Juarez, S.A. de C.V., Col. Juarez, Mexico; U.S. Public, pg. 933
Kowal, W., Pres.--Senior Flexonics Inc., Bartlett, IL; Int'l, pg. 1222
Kowalewska, Nina, Gen. Mgr.--Young & Rubicam Poland, Warsaw, Poland; U.S. Private, pg. 1199
Kowalski, Edward, Mgr.-Prods.--ITW Deltar, Lakeville, CT; U.S. Public, pg. 866
Kowalski, Jeff, Pres.--SVG Thermco Systems, Orange, CA; U.S. Public, pg. 1474
Kowalski, John, Gen. Mgr.--Technitrol Component, Philadelphia, PA; U.S. Public, pg. 1564
Kowalski, John, Pres. & Chief Exec. Officer--Pulse Engineering, Inc., San Diego, CA; U.S. Public, pg. 1564
Kowalski, Michael J., Dir.--Tiffany & Co. Watch Center S.A., Morges, Switzerland; U.S. Public, pg. 1609
Kowalski, Michael J., Chm. Bd.--Tiffco Korea, Ltd., Seoul, Korea; U.S. Public, pg. 1609
Kowalski, Wojciech, Pres.--Foster Wheeler Energy Fakop, Ltd., Sosnowiec, Poland; U.S. Public, pg. 677
Kowar, Klaus, Mng. Dir.--Tyco Toys (Osterreich) Ges.m.b.H., Vienna, Austria; U.S. Public, pg. 1059
Kowert, Douglas, Pres. & Chief Exec. Officer--Moran Company, Alhambra, CA; U.S. Public, pg. 84
Kowinsky, Barbara, Mgr.-Opers.--Kolmar Laboratories, Corona, CA; Int'l, pg. 239
Koyama, H., Pres.--Koyo International Inc. of America, Hauppauge, NY; Int'l, pg. 760
Koyama, Hiromi, Representative--Banque Internationale a Luxembourg S.A.-Tokyo Representative Office, Tokyo, Japan; Int'l, pg. 162
Koyama, K., Sr. V.P.--American Honda Motor Co., Inc. Motorcycle Division, Torrance, CA; Int'l, pg. 634
Koyama, Koki, Chief Oper. Officer--Littelfuse do Brasil, Sao Paulo, Brazil; U.S. Public, pg. 1001
Koyama, M., Chief Representative--Singapore Representative Office, Singapore, Singapore; Int'l, pg. 1444
Koyama, Yuta, Gen. Mgr.--Fuji Bank, Brussels Branch, Brussels, Belgium; Int'l, pg. 520
Koyanagi, Kazuc, Pres.--Hakuhodo Singapore Pte. Ltd., Singapore, Singapore; Int'l, pg. 588
Kozacki, J., Pres.--Total Plastic Inc., Kalamazoo, MI; U.S. Public, pg. 313
Kozak, Dennis F., Gen. Mgr.--Park Newspapers of Honesdale, Inc., Honesdale, PA; U.S. Public, pg. 1078
Kozak, Dennis F., Gen. Mgr.--Wayne Independent, Honesdale, PA; U.S. Public, pg. 1078
Koziel, Mike, Plant Mgr.--Firmenich Incorporated, Plainsboro, NJ; Int'l, pg. 486
Kozlow, Walter R., Pres.--Kaman Aerospace Corp., Bloomfield, CT; U.S. Public, pg. 942
Kozlowski, M., Chief Exec. Officer--OCE-Poland Limited, Sp. z o.o., Warsaw, Poland; Int'l, pg. 995
Kozlowski, R.E., V.P. & Gen. Mgr.--McGill Mfg. Co., Inc. Electrical Division, Valparaiso, IN; U.S. Public, pg. 573
Kozy, William A., Pres.--Becton Dickinson Division, Franklin Lakes, NJ; U.S. Public, pg. 199
Kraan, George F., Mgr.--Kimberly-Clark Sales Corporation, Veenendaal, Netherlands; U.S. Public, pg. 959
Kraemer, Arthur T., Chm. Bd. & Chief Exec. Officer--M & I Lake Country Bank, Hartland, WI; U.S. Public, pg. 1050
Kraemer, G., Dir.--Penny & Giles GmbH, Ingolstadt, Germany; Int'l, pg. 209
Kraemer, Gerd, Co-Chief Oper. Officer--Saarberg Brennstoffhandel GmbH, Saarbruecken, Germany; Int'l, pg. 1167
Kraemer, Jack, V.P. & Gen. Mgr.--Cost Management Services, McGaw Park, IL; U.S. Public, pg. 44
Kraemer, Robert, Mng. Dir.--National Dehydration Company, Cairo, Egypt; U.S. Public, pg. 1067
Kraemer, Robert P., Pres.--Gilroy Energy Company, Gilroy, CA; U.S. Public, pg. 296
Krafcik, Robert J., Pres.--Durel Corporation, Chandler, AZ; U.S. Public, pg. 1403
Kraft, Bernie, Pres.--Demeter, Inc., Folwer, IN; U.S. Public, pg. 127
Kraft, Burnell D., Pres.--ADM/GROWMARK, Bloomington, IL; U.S. Public, pg. 128
Kraft, Jean-Marie, Rep.--DG Bank-Paris, Paris, France; Int'l, pg. 352
Kraft, Jerry, Gen. Mgr.--Evans St. Clair, Marysville, MI; U.S. Private, pg. 385
Kraft, Nils, Pres.--Iberica AGA S.A., Cadiz, Spain; Int'l, pg. 14
Kraft, Raymond E., Mgr.-Opers.--South Seas Drilling Co., Sale, Australia; Int'l, pg. 766
Kraft, Robert, Chm. Bd.--Carmel Container Systems Ltd., Petah Tiqwa, Israel; Int'l, pg. 75
Kraftsow, Stanley A., Chm. Bd. & Pres.--Craftmatic Organization, Inc., Trevose, PA; U.S. Private, pg. 284
Krafty, Linda, Branch Mgr.--Downey Savings & Loan Association, F.A., Los Gatos, CA; U.S. Public, pg. 526
Kragsterman, Cecilia, Pres.--Skandialink Livforsakrings AB, Stockholm, Sweden; Int'l, pg. 1258
Krahn, Dr., Chief Oper. Officer--Ascur Mannheim Versicherungsvermittlungsges. GmbH, Mannheim, Germany; Int'l, pg. 331
Kraima, Dick B., Gen. Mgr.--Forbo Parade Tapijt B.V., Soest, Netherlands; Int'l, pg. 497
Krajewski, D., Plant Mgr.--OMC Calhoun, Calhoun, GA; U.S. Private, pg. 478
Krajicek, Michael J., V.P. & Gen. Mgr.--Serv-Tech, Inc., Eastern Area, Lake Charles, LA; U.S. Public, pg. 1460
Krajniak, Ron, Branch Mgr.--Union-Transport Corporation-Milwaukee Office, Cudahy, WI; U.S. Private, pg. 1120
Krajny, David, Mgr.-Czechoslovakian Opers.--Wrigley Czechoslovakia, Ltd., Prague, Czech Republic; U.S. Public, pg. 1781
Krakaver, Leonard, Pres.--Pall Rai, Inc., Hauppauge, NY; U.S. Public, pg. 1254
Krakowsky, Robert, Pres.--Kropp Forge Co., Cicero, IL; U.S. Private, pg. 1064
Kralik, Doug, Plant Mgr.--Rawlings Costa Rica, Turrialba, Costa Rica; U.S. Public, pg. 1362
Kralik, Ralph, Chief Oper. Officer--Hudson General Aviation Services, Inc., Mississauga, Canada; U.S. Public, pg. 846
Kramer, Arnold J., Jr., Pres.--Trimfit Company Limited, Rexdale, Canada; U.S. Private, pg. 1103
Kramer, Gerald, Plant Mgr.--Alemite Div., Johnson City, TN; Int'l, pg. 127
Kramer, Hans B., Dr., Pres. & Chief Exec. Officer--Solvay Performance Chemicals, Greenwich, CT; Int'l, pg. 1278
Kramer, Heinz, Mng. Dir.--Skandinaviska Enskilda Banken, Hamburg, Germany; Int'l, pg. 1260
Kramer, Horst, Chief Oper. Officer--ENERGAS Gesellschaft zur Energiegewinnung aus Mull und Kohle mbH, Berlin, Germany; Int'l, pg. 1166
Kramer, J. Matthew, Exec. V.P. & Gen. Mgr.--Commercial Metals Co.-Dallas Trading Div., Dallas, TX; U.S. Public, pg. 413
Kramer, Joan, Gen. Mgr.--Quest Diagnostic-North Hornell, Hornell, NY; U.S. Public, pg. 1351
Kramer, Joel, Pres. & Publisher--Star Tribune, Minneapolis-St. Paul, Minneapolis, MN; U.S. Private, pg. 281
Kramer, Joseph J., Pres.--Busch Creative Services Corporation, Saint Louis, MO; U.S. Public, pg. 114
Kramer, L.D., Pres.--Kester Solder, Des Plaines, IL; U.S. Public, pg. 1003
Kramer, Richard, Pres.--Leslie Fay Sportswear, New York, NY; U.S. Public, pg. 989
Kramp, Harry, Exec. V.P., Chm. & Chief Creative Officer-PPGH/JWT-Netherlands--J. Walter Thompson Company, New York, NY; Int'l, pg. 1483
Krampe, Brian, Branch Mgr.--Zellerbach Division, Dayton, OH; U.S. Public, pg. 1075
Kranendoch, J., Mng. Dir.--Jamin, Oosterhout, Netherlands; Int'l, pg. 749
Kranert, Wolfgang, Dr., Chm. Bd.--Groschopp, Inc., Sioux Center, IA; Int'l, pg. 559
Krangel, Stan E., Pres.--Lenox Collections, Langhorne, PA; U.S. Public, pg. 261
Krantz, Barry, Pres.-Mexican Div.--El Torito Restaurants Inc., Irvine, CA; U.S. Private, pg. 393
Krantz, K. Theodor, Pres.--Velcro Group Corporation, Manchester, NH; Int'l, pg. 1462
Krantz, Lee, Plant Mgr.--Cambridge Industries, Inc., Dearborn, MI; U.S. Private, pg. 202
Kranyc, Stan, Plant Mgr.--Lancia-Bravo Foods, Toronto, Canada; U.S. Private, pg. 159
Kranzler, Hans G., Mng. Dir.--Dynisco Gerate G.m.b.H., Heilbronn, Germany; U.S. Private, pg. 139
Krapek, Karl J., Pres.--Pratt & Whitney Operations, East Hartford, CT; U.S. Public, pg. 1690
Krarec, Raphael, Dir.-Mktg.--Geoffrey Beene Fragrances, Miami, FL; U.S. Public, pg. 681
Krarup, Paul J., Gen. Mgr.--Stanfast, Inc., Doraville, GA; U.S. Public, pg. 1505
Krasnoff, Eric, Exec. V.P.--Pall Biomedical Products Corp., Greenvale, NY; U.S. Public, pg. 1254
Krasnoff, Eric, Exec. V.P.--Pall Biosupport Division, Greenvale, NY; U.S. Public, pg. 1254
Krasnov, Mikhail, Dir. Gen.--Merisel CAT, Ltd., Moscow, Russia; U.S. Public, pg. 1096
Krasnow, Robert, Chm. Bd.--Elektra Entertainment, New York, NY; U.S. Public, pg. 1612
Krass, Robert P., Pres.--UCAR Carbon Company Inc., Danbury, CT; Int'l, pg. 871
Kratochvil, Ed, Gen. Mgr.--Portland Plant, Portland, IN; U.S. Private, pg. 1044
Krattenmaker, Kelly, Pres.--Young Gas Storage Company, Denver, CO; U.S. Public, pg. 1170
Krattli, E., Chief Exec. Officer--Ascom Finanz AG, Bern, Switzerland; Int'l, pg. 86
Kratz, Bernd, Co-Chief Oper. Officer--Winschermann West GmbH, Recklinghausen, Germany; Int'l, pg. 1167
Kratzer, Kurt A., Exec. V.P.--Rurbanc Data Services, Inc., Defiance, OH; U.S. Public, pg. 1413
Krauer, Alex, Chm. Bd. & Mng. Dir.--CIBA-GEIGY AG, Grenzach-Wyhlen, Germany; Int'l, pg. 975
Kraus, Dieter, Chief Exec. Officer & Exec. V.P.--Union Air Transport GmbH, Dusseldorf, Germany; U.S. Private, pg. 1120
Kraus, Doug, V.P.-Sls.--BancTec, Inc.-New York, Hauppauge, NY; U.S. Public, pg. 177
Kraus, Eileen S., Chm. Bd.--Fleet National Bank of Connecticut, Hartford, CT; U.S. Public, pg. 649
Kraus, Werner, Gen. Mgr.--Semperit Reifen AG, Traiskirchen, Austria; Int'l, pg. 328
Kraus, William, Grp. Pres.--Aviation & Performance Chemicals Division, Philadelphia, PA; Int'l, pg. 446
Kraus, William, Grp. Pres.-Specialty Chemical--Specialty Chemicals, Philadelphia, PA; Int'l, pg. 446
Krause, Barry, Pres.--Hal Riney & Partners Heartland, Chicago, IL; U.S. Private, pg. 931
Krause, Gary W., Pres.--Kasser/Laird Distilling Co., Horsham, PA; U.S. Private, pg. 643
Krause, J.G., Mgr.-Production-Central Container Div.--Longview Fibre Co. Central Container Div., Milwaukee, WI; U.S. Public, pg. 1014
Krause, James W., Pres. & Gen. Mgr.--Sherwin-Williams Automotive Division, Cleveland, OH; U.S. Public, pg. 1465
Krause, R., Chief Fin. Officer--Olivetti Germany, Frankfurt/Main, Germany; Int'l, pg. 1003
Krauser, Larry, Mgr.--L.H. Sowles Company, Inc., Spokane, WA; U.S. Private, pg. 1019
Krauss, Axel, Pres.--Best Foods, Englewood Cliffs, NJ; U.S. Public, pg. 224
Krauss, Kent, Publr.--Business Journal Publications, Inc., San Antonio, TX; U.S. Private, pg. 19
Kravcik, J.W., Pres.--Minelco, Inc., Thomaston, CT; U.S. Public, pg. 308
Kravitz, Harry, Pres.--Shannock Quebec Audio and Video Inc., Montreal, Canada; Int'l, pg. 1343
Kravitz, Richard H., Pres. & Publr.--Panel Publishers, Inc., New York, NY; Int'l, pg. 1513
Kravscik, J.W., Pres.--Electrodynamics, Inc., Rolling Meadows, IL; U.S. Public, pg. 308
Krawack, Willy, Chm.--Ford Motor Company A/S, Copenhagen, Denmark; U.S. Public, pg. 666
Krawack, Willy, Chm.--Ford Credit A/S, Copenhagen, Denmark; U.S. Public, pg. 666
Kraxner, Dr. Gerhard, Mng. Dir.--BOHLER Ybbstalwerke Ges.m.b.H., Bohlerwerk, Austria; Int'l, pg. 1470
Krbec, J.R., Mng. Dir.--Bausch & Lomb G.m.b.H., Pforzheim, Germany; U.S. Public, pg. 195
Krbec, Jerry, Pres.--Dahlberg, Inc., Golden Valley, MN; U.S. Public, pg. 194
Krchnavy, Jon A., V.P.-Mfg.--The Producto Machine Co., Bridgeport, CT; U.S. Private, pg. 889
Krebec, J., Mng. Dir.--Toshiba Medical Systems Gesellschaft GmbH, Wiener Neustadt, Austria; Int'l, pg. 1407
Krebel, Albert D., Pres.--Reed & Barton Silversmiths, Taunton, MA; U.S. Private, pg. 916
Krebs, Andreas, Mng. Dir.--Bayerische Vereinsbank AG, Tehran, Iran; Int'l, pg. 180
Krebs, Rolf, Prof. Dr., Gen. Mgr.--Boehringer Ingelheim, Ingelheim, Germany; Int'l, pg. 199
Krebser, Jurg, Dr., Pres.--Georg Fischer Rohrleitungssysteme (Schweiz) A.G., Schaffhausen, Switzerland; Int'l, pg. 489
Krecklow, Robert L., Publr.--The Hannibal Courier-Post, Hannibal, MO; U.S. Private, pg. 995
Kreczmer, Lawrence J., Pres.--Harris Bank Argo, Summit Argo, IL; Int'l, pg. 154
Kreeker, Rudi, Pres.--Whiting Equipment Canada, Inc., Welland, Canada; U.S. Private, pg. 1173
Kreft, Ira J., Sr. V.P.--Central Marketing-Chicago Business Center, Chicago, IL; U.S. Public, pg. 649
Kreh, Kent Q., Pres. & Chief Exec. Officer--Weight Watchers International, Inc., Woodbury, NY; U.S. Public, pg. 806
Kreick, Dr. John R., Pres.--Sanders, A Lockheed Martin Company, Nashua, NH; U.S. Public, pg. 1008
Kreidel, Richard S., Pres.--Quadrastat Corp., City of Industry, CA; U.S. Private, pg. 17
Kreider, Louis S., Div. Mgr.--Lake Erie Division, Mentor, OH; U.S. Public, pg. 438
Kreigenfeld, Friedrich, Mng. Dir.--O&K Mining GmbH, Dortmund Works, Dortmund, Germany; Int'l, pg. 516
Kreikemeier, K.G., Pres.--Sverdrup Facilities, Inc., Saint Louis, MO; U.S. Private, pg. 1057
Kreikemeier, Ken, V.P.-Sls.--J-M Manufacturing Co., Inc., Livingston, NJ; Int'l, pg. 498
Kreilick, Thomas K., Pres.--Candle Corporation of America, Des Plaines, IL; U.S. Public, pg. 239
Krein, Fred, Pres.--Williams Healthcare Systems, Elgin, IL; U.S. Public, pg. 1507
Kreiner, Rolf, Sr. V.P.--McDonald's Deutschland GmbH, Munich, Germany; U.S. Public, pg. 1069
Kreis, W., Chief Exec. Officer--Ascom Ericsson Transmission AG, Bern, Switzerland; Int'l, pg. 86
Kreisler, Jerold A., Pres.--MCC Behavioral Care of California, Inc., Glendale, CA; U.S. Public, pg. 362
Kreissl, Karl-Heinz, Gen. Mgr.--Dresdner Bank AG, New York, NY; Int'l, pg. 418
Kreiter, Abe E., Chief Oper. Officer--Type Founders of Chicago, Skokie, IL; U.S. Private, pg. 219
Kreiter, Abe E., Chief Oper. Officer--Castcraft Software Optifont, Skokie, IL; U.S. Private, pg. 219

Kreiter, Herbert M., V.P.--Type Films of Chicago Co., Skokie, IL; *U.S. Private*, pg. 219
Kreiter, Herbert M., V.P.--Transfertech, Inc., Skokie, IL; *U.S. Private*, pg. 219
Kreiter, John, Plant Mgr.--Household Products, Fairfield, CA; *U.S. Public*, pg. 387
Kreitinger, Kenneth, Pres.--Richardton Mfg. Co., Richardton, ND; *U.S. Public*, pg. 1676
Krejci, Jim, Pres.--IGT-International Corp. Development, Reno, NV; *U.S. Public*, pg. 900
Krels, David P., Plant Mgr.--Bosch Braking Systems-North America, Clarksville, TN; *Int'l*, pg. 204
Krem, Guy, Sr. V.P. & Branch Mgr.-Frase Valley--Willis Corroon Melling Ltd., White Rock, Canada; *Int'l*, pg. 1509
Kremer, Gilbert, Pres.--TrefilARBED Bettembourg S.a.r.l, Bettembourg, Luxembourg; *Int'l*, pg. 80
Kremer, Juergen, Chief Fin. Officer--The Ore & Chemical Corp., New York, NY; *Int'l*, pg. 862
Kremer, M., Chief Oper. Officer--Sciaky GmbH, Wiesbaden, Germany; *Int'l*, pg. 1211
Kremer, Michael A., Mng. Dir.--DB Export Leasing G.m.b.H., Frankfurt/Main, Germany; *Int'l*, pg. 402
Kreminski, Jan, V.P. & Gen. Mgr.--ABB Environmental Systems (ABBES), Knoxville, TN; *Int'l*, pg. 4
Kreminski, Stan, Plant Mgr.--Calgon Carbon Corp., Neville Island, Pittsburgh, PA; *U.S. Public*, pg. 293
Kremmel, Hans S., Mng. Dir.--Mei Hoy Sports Co. Ltd., Kowloon, Hong Kong; *Int'l*, pg. 885
Krenich, J.M., Sec.--Australian Aluminium (Australuco) Limited, Sydney, Australia; *Int'l*, pg. 51
Krenz, Keith, Pres.--Technology Systems Corporation, Bethlehem, PA; *U.S. Public*, pg. 1425
Kreppel, Robert J., Pres.--National Fuel Resources, Buffalo, NY; *U.S. Public*, pg. 1156
Kresko, Daniel A., Pres.--Sani-Dairy Div., Johnstown, PA; *U.S. Public*, pg. 1271
Kress, Robert, Co-Chief Oper. Officer--SIPEC Ste Internationale de Petrole et de Chimie a r.l., Strasbourg, France; *Int'l*, pg. 1167
Kretsos, James, Gen. Mgr.--Pico-Matic Inc., Evanston, IL; *U.S. Private*, pg. 813
Kretz, Rolf, Mgr.--Commerzbank AG-Teheran Representative Office, Tehran, Iran; *Int'l*, pg. 312
Kretzer, Adolf, Chief Oper. Officer--Electrolux-Cramer GmbH, Siegen, Germany; *Int'l*, pg. 442
Kretzer, William T., Pres.--Unifi International Service, Inc., Greensboro, NC; *U.S. Public*, pg. 1665
Kreulitsch, Heribert, Chm. Bd.--VOEST-ALPINE STAHL Linz Ges.m.b.H., Lienz, Austria; *Int'l*, pg. 1470
Kreutz, Richard, Plant Mgr.--RAYOVAC Corporation, Fennimore, WI; *U.S. Private*, pg. 912
Kreutzer, David, Gen. Mgr.--Twin Rivers Towing Co., Elizabeth, PA; *U.S. Public*, pg. 531
Kreutzman, Erik, Pres.--Valmet-Como S.p.A., Maslianico, Italy; *Int'l*, pg. 1449
Kreuzhage, Jurgen, Mng. Dir.--Wilhelm Goldmann Verlag GmbH, Munich, Germany; *Int'l*, pg. 190
Krevtzer, Jeffrey, Plant Mgr.--Engineered Fasteners Div., Massillon, OH; *U.S. Public*, pg. 557
Krevzroither, Fritz, Chief Oper. Officer--A. Ahlstrom Ges.m.b.H., Vienna, Austria; *Int'l*, pg. 34
Krezan, Michael, Chief Pharmacist--FlexRx, North Versailles, PA; *U.S. Public*, pg. 1091
Kribel, Jerry, Gen. Mgr.--Isomedix Operations, Inc., Chester, NY; *U.S. Public*, pg. 1515
Krick, Mike, Pres.--Mrs. Smith's Bakery of Pennsylvania, Pottstown, PA; *U.S. Public*, pg. 658
Krief, Bernard, Pres.--Bernard Krief Motivation, S.A., Carlson Marketing Group, Paris, France; *U.S. Private*, pg. 212
Krieg, Mark, Mng. Dir.--Sulzer South Africa Ltd., Elandsfontein, South Africa; *Int'l*, pg. 1306
Kriegel, Ralf, Mng. Dir.--Schabmuller GmbH, Berching, Germany; *Int'l*, pg. 1387
Krieger, Ellen, V.P. & Editorial Dir.--Aladdin Paperbacks, New York, NY; *U.S. Private*, pg. 777
Krieger, Joseph Halby, Pres.--Canadian Art Prints, Richmond, Canada; *U.S. Public*, pg. 503
Krieger, M. Thomas, Pres.--Fleming Foods of Tennessee, Inc., Johnson City, TN; *U.S. Public*, pg. 653
Kriekle, Dean, Sr. V.P.-Eastern & Northern Ontario Div.--Bank of Montreal - Ottawa, Ottawa, Canada; *Int'l*, pg. 153
Kries, Harold, Pres. & Dir.-MKtg.--Humphrey, Inc., San Diego, CA; *U.S. Public*, pg. 1376
Kries, W., Chief Exec. Officer--Ascom Hasler AG, Bern, Switzerland; *Int'l*, pg. 86
Krieser, Thomas P., Pres.--Kvaerner Hymac Inc., Laval, Canada; *Int'l*, pg. 770
Kriess, F.L., Jr., Gen. Mgr.--Sun City Water Company, Sun City, AZ; *U.S. Public*, pg. 380
Krikava, Hans, Gen. Mgr.--Erste Bank - New York Branch, New York, NY; *Int'l*, pg. 459
Kring, Jerry, Plant Mgr.--Rhone-Poulenc Agrochemical Div., Mount Pleasant, TN; *Int'l*, pg. 1111
Kringel, John G., Pres.--Abbott Hospital Products Division, North Chicago, IL; *U.S. Public*, pg. 13
Kringer, Scott, Gen. Mgr.--North Specialty Products, Brea, CA; *Int'l*, pg. 1243
Krishnan, N., Pres.--State Bank of India (Canada), Toronto, Canada; *Int'l*, pg. 1297
Krist, Sven Ljnng, Chief Fin. Officer--Abetong Prefab AB, Vaxjo, Sweden; *Int'l*, pg. 1199
Kristensen, Per Herbert, Pres.--Kvaerner Arctic Offshore A/S, Lysaker, Norway; *Int'l*, pg. 769
Kristiansen, F., Dir.--K. Loegager A/S, Kvistgard, Germany; *Int'l*, pg. 859
Kristiansen, Knut, Pres.--Aker Subsea a.s., Stord, Norway; *Int'l*, pg. 42
Kristiansen, Thor, Pres.--Fine Chemicals, Oslo, Norway; *U.S. Public*, pg. 58
Kristiansson, Lars-Inge, Chief Oper. Officer--Ahlstromforetagen Svenska AB-Markaryd Core Plant, Markaryd, Sweden; *Int'l*, pg. 33
Kristiansson, Rune, Chief Oper. Officer--Granges Metalock AB, Goteborg, Sweden; *Int'l*, pg. 439
Kristich, Rudolph, Pres.--Basco Div., Buffalo, NY; *U.S. Public*, pg. 90
Kristich, Rudolph, Pres.--Air Technologies Division, Arcade, NY; *U.S. Public*, pg. 90
Kristov, Stojan, Resident Mgr.--ESTESA, Sofia, Bulgaria; *Int'l*, pg. 283
Kritzinger, Wikus, Div. Mgr.--Sasol Gas, Randburg, South Africa; *Int'l*, pg. 1197
Krivkovich, Peter G., Pres.--Cramer-Krasselt, Chicago, IL; *U.S. Private*, pg. 285
Krodel, Ken, Plant Mgr.--GNC Corp, Wilson, NC; *U.S. Private*, pg. 466
Kroef, J.J.A., Chm. Bd.--Electrical Carbon Limited, Sheffield, United Kingdom; *Int'l*, pg. 891
Kroeger, Barney, Pres.--A & A Associates, Santa Fe Springs, CA; *U.S. Private*, pg. 1206
Kroeger, Claus F., V.P. & Gen. Mgr.--Cox Communications-Middle Georgia, Macon, GA; *U.S. Public*, pg. 455
Kroeger, Kevin, Mng. Dir.--Heinemann Publishers (Pty) Ltd., Johannesburg, South Africa; *Int'l*, pg. 1094
Kroeger, Mike, Plant Mgr.--Firestone Industrial Products Company-Dyersburg, Dyersburg, TN; *Int'l*, pg. 214
Kroes, Kees, Mng. Dir.--SKF Bearings India Ltd., Mumbai, India; *Int'l*, pg. 1158
Kroes, P., Mng. Dir.--P.T. Nutricia Indonesia Sejaharta, Jakarta, Indonesia; *Int'l*, pg. 992
Kroesbergen, A.P., Mng. Dir.--BW Industrial Products B.V., Winterswijk, Netherlands; *Int'l*, pg. 198
Krogius, Tristan E. G., Chm. Bd. & Pres.--Kern County Land Co., Bakersfield, CA; *U.S. Public*, pg. 1578
Krogsgaard, Povl, Pres.--Mejeriernes Produktionsselskab A.m.b.a., Viby, Denmark; *Int'l*, pg. 826
Krohmer, Dr. Peter, Mng. Dir.--Bodenseewerk Perkin-Elmer & Co. G.m.b.H., Ueberlingen, Germany; *U.S. Public*, pg. 1279
Krohn, Klaus, Mgr.--Kautschuk-Gesellschaft Gmbh, Frankfurt/Main, Germany; *Int'l*, pg. 862
Krohn, Rasmus, Mng. Dir.--Andrex Radiation Products A/S, Copenhagen, Denmark; *U.S. Public*, pg. 867
Kronborg, Jens, Mng. Dir.--Nyborg Plast International A/S, Nyborg, Denmark; *Int'l*, pg. 476
Krone, John, Mng. Dir.--Amerford Intl. (PTY) Ltd., Johannesburg, South Africa; *Int'l*, pg. 1388
Krone, T., Chief Oper. Officer--Anchor Die Cast, Harrison, AR; *U.S. Private*, pg. 687
Kronenwetter, Donald R., V.P. & Gen. Mgr.--Philips E.C.G., Waltham, MA; *Int'l*, pg. 1054
Kronheim, Laszlo, Dir.--Deutsche Bank AG (Budapest), Budapest, Hungary; *Int'l*, pg. 404
Kronick, Susan, Chm. Bd. & Chief Exec. Officer--Burdines, Miami, FL; *U.S. Public*, pg. 618
Kronlof, Tom, Chief Oper. Officer--Raisio Svenska AB, Surte, Sweden; *Int'l*, pg. 1086
Kronquest, Steve, V.P. & Gen. Mgr.--WIXT-TV, East Syracuse, NY; *U.S. Public*, pg. 16
Kronschnabel, Robert J., Pres.--Grain Systems Division, Kansas City, MO; *U.S. Public*, pg. 271
Krook, Jorgen, Pres.--Atlas Copco Berema AB, Nacka, Sweden; *Int'l*, pg. 96
Kroon, Richard E., Pres. & Chief Exec. Officer--DLJ Capital Corp., New York, NY; *U.S. Public*, pg. 589
Kropf, Gary, Plant Mgr.--Northwestern States Portland Cement, Mason City, IA; *Int'l*, pg. 628
Kropf, Omer G., Pres. & Chief Exec. Officer--Supreme Corporation, Goshen, IN; *U.S. Public*, pg. 1542
Kropf, Omer G., Pres.--Supreme Corporation of Texas, Cleburne, TX; *U.S. Public*, pg. 1542
Kropf, Omer G., Pres.--Supreme MidAtlantic Corporation, Jonestown, PA; *U.S. Public*, pg. 1542
Kropf, Omer G., Pres.--Supreme Murphy Corp., Wilson, NC; *U.S. Public*, pg. 1542
Krossoy, Hans, Gen. Mgr.--Storage Technology Norway, Bergen, Norway; *U.S. Public*, pg. 1523
Krouch, Leslie M., Gen. Mgr.--Per Pak (Brook), Brook, IN; *Int'l*, pg. 1270
Kroworz, Rudolf, Chief Oper. Officer--Graphischer Maschinenbau, Berlin, Germany; *Int'l*, pg. 742
Kroyer, Steen, Pres.--Astra Pharmaceuticals (Pty.) Ltd., Bryanston, South Africa; *Int'l*, pg. 94
Kruczek, Gratien, Gen. Mgr.--Loews Monte Carlo, Monaco, Monaco; *U.S. Public*, pg. 1011
Krueger, Dennis, V.P.--Whirlpool Corp., Findlay Div., Findlay, OH; *U.S. Public*, pg. 1765
Krueger, Douglas, Gen. Mgr.--Sterling Electronics, Albuquerque, NM; *U.S. Public*, pg. 1051
Krueger, Jeffrey, Gen. Mgr.--Bodolay/Pratt Div., Lakeland, FL; *U.S. Private*, pg. 832
Kruela, Seppo, Pres.--Outokumpu Copper Products Oy, Espoo, Finland; *Int'l*, pg. 1016
Kruet, Chief Oper. Officer--Hestia-Pharma GmbH, Mannheim, Germany; *Int'l*, pg. 331
Kruft, David R., V.P. & Gen. Mgr.--Durable Specialties Division, Quakertown, PA; *U.S. Public*, pg. 620
Kruger, J.M., Mng. Dir.--R&R Tobacco Limited, Cape Town, South Africa; *Int'l*, pg. 1129
Kruger, K.P., Mng. Dir.--Timken South Africa Proprietary Ltd., Transvaal, South Africa; *U.S. Public*, pg. 1618
Kruger, Konrad R., Co-Pres. & Co-Chief Exec. Officer--Greenwich Capital Markets, Inc., Greenwich, CT; *Int'l*, pg. 911
Kruger, Mark, Exec. V.P. & Gen. Mgr.--Pragmaton, Chicago, IL; *U.S. Public*, pg. 1224
Kruger, Marvin J., Pres. & Chief Exec. Officer--Continental Bank New York Trust Company, New York, NY; *U.S. Public*, pg. 181
Kruger, Roger, Dir.-Mktg.--AGRA Monenco, Inc., Houston, TX; *Int'l*, pg. 31
Kruger, Siegmar, Gen. Mgr.--Ost-West Allianz, Moscow, Russia; *Int'l*, pg. 61
Kruger, Udo, Mng. Dir.--Allianz Insurance (Singapore) Pte. Ltd., Singapore, Singapore; *Int'l*, pg. 59
Kruiskamp, J., Dr., Mng. Dir.--Wuestenrot Finance B.V., Amsterdam, Netherlands; *Int'l*, pg. 1514
Krukoff, Yrjo, Chief Rep.--NOKO-Nokia Representative Office, Moscow, Russia; *Int'l*, pg. 953
Krum, Frank, Chief Exec. Officer--Golden Cat Corporation, Saint Louis, MO; *U.S. Public*, pg. 1360
Krumm, Peter, Pres.--EnviroTech PumpSystems, Salt Lake City, UT; *Int'l*, pg. 1489
Krumme, Dwane, Exec. V.P. & Gen. Mgr.--JCB International Credit Card Co., Ltd., Los Angeles, CA; *Int'l*, pg. 696
Krupa, Ray, Mgr.-Opers.--Van Gorp Corp., Pella, IA; *U.S. Public*, pg. 573
Kruse, Bernt, Sr. V.P.--Stockholm Regional Office, Kista, Sweden; *Int'l*, pg. 899
Kruse, David, Gen. Mgr.--American Glassmith, Inc., Columbus, OH; *U.S. Public*, pg. 67
Kruse, Erich, Gen. Mgr.--ITW Befestingungssysteme (Hattersheim) GmbH, Hattersheim, Germany; *U.S. Public*, pg. 868
Kruse, Gregory, Pres.--Sagebrush Sales Company, Albuquerque, NM; *U.S. Public*, pg. 1193
Kruse, Jeff, V.P.--ID Solutions, Lynnwood, WA; *U.S. Private*, pg. 566
Kruse, Kenneth, Pres.--COMSAT RSI, Richardson, TX; *U.S. Public*, pg. 424
Kruse, Michael, V.P.--Bankers Trust New York Corporation, Caracas, Venezuela; *U.S. Public*, pg. 186
Kruse, Thomas, Chief Oper. Officer--Berlin Branch, Berlin, Germany; *Int'l*, pg. 645
Kruse, Udo, Chm. Bd. & Mng. Dir.--Ford Motor Company (Belgium) N.V., Antwerp, Belgium; *U.S. Public*, pg. 666
Kruse, Udo, Chm. Bd.--Ford Credit N.V., Antwerp, Belgium; *U.S. Public*, pg. 666
Kruuse, Anders, Chief Oper. Officer--Axel Johnson Credit AB, Stockholm, Sweden; *Int'l*, pg. 708
Kruyer, Peter J., Pres.--Sandhills Inc., Wilmington, DE; *U.S. Private*, pg. 837
Kruyer, Peter J., Pres.--TC Capital Management Inc., Wilmington, DE; *U.S. Private*, pg. 837
Kruzel, Gerry, Pres.--Shelter Products Group, Elkhart, IN; *Int'l*, pg. 1396
Kruzick, Dave, Mgr.-Plant--Palmer International, Inc., Skippack, PA; *U.S. Private*, pg. 835
Kryger, Giles T., Chief Exec.--Ord Minnett Group Limited, Sydney, Australia; *Int'l*, pg. 1496
Krysak, David, Pres.--G.E. Fanuc Automation Canada, Mississauga, Canada; *U.S. Public*, pg. 713
Krysakowski, John, Pres.--Wackenhut Airline Services, Inc., Coral Gables, FL; *U.S. Public*, pg. 1731
Krysiak, Brian T., Pres.--Aeroquip Inoac Company, Mount Clemens, MI; *U.S. Public*, pg. 24
Krythe, R.M.L., Chief Oper. Officer--NedShip International, Inc., New York, NY; *Int'l*, pg. 1082
Ku, Charles K., Pres.--Lucky Goldstar International America, Inc., New York, NY; *Int'l*, pg. 779
Ku, Richard, Mng. Dir.--GP Battery Marketing (HK) Ltd., Kwai Chung, Hong Kong; *Int'l*, pg. 537
Ku, Richard Y.H., Dir. & Gen. Mgr.--GPI International Limited, Kwai Chung, Hong Kong; *Int'l*, pg. 537
Kubacki, K.J., Pres.--AAA Investment Company, Wilmington, DE; *U.S. Private*, pg. 51
Kubala, Raymond, Pres.--Burnup & Sims of TX, Austin, TX; *U.S. Public*, pg. 1056
Kube, F., Gen. Mgr.--Much Pharma, Bad Soden am Taunus, Germany; *U.S. Public*, pg. 81
Kubena, Bruce, Chief Oper. Officer--Allright Parking Corporation, Fort Worth, TX; *U.S. Private*, pg. 43
Kubisch, John, Pres.--Becton Dickinson Pharmaceutical Systems, Franklin Lakes, NJ; *U.S. Public*, pg. 199
Kubit, Dennis M., Pres.--Trans-General Life & Casualty Group, Inc., Pittsburgh, PA; *U.S. Private*, pg. 529
Kubit, Dennis M., Pres.--Trans-General Life Insurance Company, Pittsburgh, PA; *U.S. Private*, pg. 529
Kubota, Hiromichi, Pres.--Universal Public Relations Inc., Tokyo, Japan; *Int'l*, pg. 1228
Kubota, Hiroshi, Chief Oper. Officer--Nagase-Alfa K. K., Osaka, Japan; *Int'l*, pg. 1380
Kubota, S., Pres.--Fuji Seito Co., Ltd., Shimizu, Japan; *Int'l*, pg. 947
Kubota, T., Pres.--Toshiba Compressor (Taiwan) Corp., Tao-yuan, Taiwan; *Int'l*, pg. 1406
Kubota, Teruhisa, Mng. Dir.--Nippon Truck Co., Ltd., Tokyo, Japan; *Int'l*, pg. 934
Kubota, Yoshifumi, Pres.--Daicel Chemical Industries Ltd., Osaka, Japan; *Int'l*, pg. 877
Kuboyama, Akio, Branch Mgr.--Yamaichi Securities Co., Ltd.-Taipei Branch, Taipei, Taiwan; *Int'l*, pg. 1517
Kubrik, Geri, Chief Exec. Officer--Kenyon Industries, Inc., Kenyon, RI; *U.S. Public*, pg. 778
Kucharik, John, Pres.--Aurora Pump, North Aurora, IL; *U.S. Public*, pg. 726
Kuchenbrandt, Ingo, Mng. Dir.--Danisco Sugar GmbH, Anklam, Germany; *Int'l*, pg. 378
Kucik, John, Chief Oper. Officer--Discus Electronic Training, Rochester, NY; *U.S. Public*, pg. 551
Kuciukyan, A., Rep.--Cariplo (Bruxelles), Brussels, Belgium; *Int'l*, pg. 275
Kuck, Dennis, Gen. Mgr.--Vermont American Australia, Ltd., Springvale, Australia; *U.S. Public*, pg. 578
Kuckertz, Wilhelm, Mgr.--Rappold, Hermann & Co. GmbH, Duren, Germany; *Int'l*, pg. 1464
Kuckuck, William F., Exec. V.P.--Ralston Purina Canada Agri-Division, Woodstock, Canada; *U.S. Public*, pg. 1360
Kucsma, Geza, Dir.-USA--Malev Hungarian Airlines, U.S. Office, New York, NY; *Int'l*, pg. 834
Kuczwanski, John, Chief Exec. Officer--Loan America Financial Corp., Jacksonville, FL; *U.S. Public*, pg. 1162
Kudena, Jaroslav, Representative--Deutsche Bank AG (Prague), Prague, Czech Republic; *Int'l*, pg. 404
Kudo, Kazuyoshi, Dir. & Gen. Mgr.--Kyoto Branch Office, Kyoto, Japan; *Int'l*, pg. 1491

Kudo, Yasushi, Rep.--Dai-Ichi Kangyo Bank, Ltd.-Kuala Lumpur, Kuala Lumpur, Malaysia; *Int'l*, pg. 361
Kudoh, Kiyohiko, Chief Oper. Officer--Finetech Co., Ltd., Tokyo, Japan; *Int'l*, pg. 1262
Kuebelbeck, Al, Pres.--Crestliner, Inc., Little Falls, MN; *U.S. Private*, pg. 447
Kuebler, Charles H., Pres.--United States Auto Club, Motoring Division, Inc., Dallas, TX; *U.S. Public*, pg. 663
Kuebler, John, Gen. Mgr.--Meenan Oil Pennsylvania Div., Tullytown, PA; *U.S. Private*, pg. 729
Kuebler, William E., Pres.--Pyramid Services, Inc., Ridgefield, CT; *U.S. Public*, pg. 118
Kuebrich, Frederick W., Pres.--Northwest Industries, Inc., Albany, OR; *U.S. Public*, pg. 1640
Kuecker, John, Mgr.-Opers.--Thomas Industries Inc., Monroe, LA; *U.S. Public*, pg. 1599
Kuefer, Yapie, Chief Fin. Officer--Olivetti Africa Pty. Ltd., Johannesburg, South Africa; *Int'l*, pg. 1003
Kueheke, John, V.P. & Gen. Mgr.--KSDK, Inc., Saint Louis, MO; *U.S. Public*, pg. 702
Kuehne, W., Chief Oper. Officer--BPC Division, Bristol, IN; *Int'l*, pg. 618
Kuehnert, Marty, Club Pres.--Birmingham Baseball Club, Inc., Birmingham, AL; *Int'l*, pg. 1321
Kueng, Walter, Mgr.--EG & G Reticon, Munich, Germany; *U.S. Public*, pg. 544
Kuepers, J.W., Gen. Mgr.--Johnson Nederland B.V., Mijdrecht, Netherlands; *U.S. Private*, pg. 593
Kuest, Dieter, Dir.--Schafft Fleischwerke G.m.b.H., Ansbach, Germany; *Int'l*, pg. 1438
Kuester, D.J., Pres.--M & I Marshall & Ilsley Bank, Milwaukee, WI; *U.S. Public*, pg. 1050
Kuesters, Gottfried, V.P. & Gen. Mgr.--PTR-Precision Technologies, Inc., Enfield, CT; *Int'l*, pg. 679
Kuhagen, Jim, Resident Mgr.--Ypsilanti Mill, Ypsilanti, MI; *U.S. Public*, pg. 466
Kuhara, Masaharu, Chief Rep.--Long-Term Credit Bank of Japan, Limited - Chicago, Chicago, IL; *Int'l*, pg. 816
Kuhfahl, John, Gen. Mgr.--Watlow Industries, Inc., Hannibal, MO; *U.S. Private*, pg. 1153
Kuhfahl, John, Gen. Mgr.--Watlow St. Louis, Inc., Saint Louis, MO; *U.S. Private*, pg. 1153
Kuhl, H., Chief Oper. Officer--Burgess GmbH, Oldenburg, Germany; *Int'l*, pg. 1500
Kuhl, H., Mgr.--Micro-Tec Schalr-und Verbindungselemente Gmbh, Oldenburg, Germany; *Int'l*, pg. 1500
Kuhl, Richard G., Dir. Gen.--Velcromex S.A. de C.V., Agua Prieta, Mexico; *Int'l*, pg. 1462
Kuhlman, J.T., Pres.--Inter-Continental Hotels & Resorts Corporation, New York, NY; *Int'l*, pg. 1178
Kuhlmann, A., Chief Exec. Officer & Gen. Mgr.--ING Trust Company of Canada, North York, Canada; *Int'l*, pg. 650
Kuhlmann, Doug, Plant Mgr.--Ropak Northwest Inc., Kent, WA; *Int'l*, pg. 812
Kuhlmann, William, Pres.--General Physics Ohio Corporation, Columbia, MD; *U.S. Public*, pg. 694
Kuhlmann, William E., Pres.--General Physics Mohawk Corporation, Columbia, MD; *U.S. Public*, pg. 694
Kuhlmann, William F., Pres.--General Physics Niagara Corporation, Columbia, MD; *U.S. Public*, pg. 694
Kuhlmann, William F., Pres.--General Physics Philadelphia Corporation, Columbia, MD; *U.S. Public*, pg. 694
Kuhn, Frank, Pres.--Albright & Wilson, Inc., Ashland, VA; *Int'l*, pg. 49
Kuhn, H.J., Pres.--Danzas (Canada) Ltd., Mississauga, Canada; *Int'l*, pg. 382
Kuhn, Hans-Heinrich, Gen. Mgr.--Forbo Novilon GmbH, Frankfurt/Main, Germany; *Int'l*, pg. 497
Kuhn, Jack R., Pres.-Office Building Division--Forest City Commercial Mngmt. Div., Cleveland, OH; *U.S. Public*, pg. 668
Kuhn, John, Chief Oper. Officer--Oshkosh B'Gosh Hosiery Co., Niles, IL; *U.S. Private*, pg. 525
Kuhn, P.E., Plant Mgr.--American Natl. Can Co., Cleveland, OH; *Int'l*, pg. 1029
Kuhne, Bruno, Chm.--Coop Zurichsee-Linth, Hinwil, Switzerland; *Int'l*, pg. 329
Kuhne, K.M., Pres.--Kuehne & Nagel (AG & Co.), Bremen, Germany; *Int'l*, pg. 763
Kuhne, K.M., Pres.--Kuehne & Nagel GmbH, Vienna, Austria; *Int'l*, pg. 763
Kuhne, Peter, Mng. Dir.--Nokia Telecommunications Ltd., Huntingdon, United Kingdom; *Int'l*, pg. 953
Kuhnell, Roy E., Pres. & Treas.--Dempsey & Siders Insurance Agency, Cincinnati, OH; *U.S. Public*, pg. 75
Kuhnert, David, Pres.--Trammochem Division, Darien, CT; *U.S. Private*, pg. 1096
Kuhnert, Walter R., Mng. Dir.--Triumph International, Sacavem, Portugal; *Int'l*, pg. 1424
Kuhns, Dennis R., Pres.--Maryland Specialty Wire, Inc., Hunt Valley, MD; *U.S. Public*, pg. 780
Kuhre, Dave, Plant Mgr.--Admiral Remco, Inc., Oakland, CA; *U.S. Public*, pg. 1505
Kuijpers, J.F.C., Mng. Dir.--Van Leeuwen Tubes Ltd., Barnsley, United Kingdom; *Int'l*, pg. 1450
Kuijvenhoven, Pieter, Chief Exec. Officer--ARA/BDDP, Rotterdam, Netherlands; *Int'l*, pg. 117
Kuijvenhoven, Pieter, Mng. Dir.--Navar BDDP, Rotterdam, Netherlands; *Int'l*, pg. 117
Kuikka, Leona, Grp. Dir.--Young & Rubicam Finland Oy, Helsinki, Finland; *U.S. Private*, pg. 1199
Kuins, John, Mng. Dir.--G.E. Plastic Canada, Mississauga, Canada; *U.S. Public*, pg. 713
Kuipers, Willem, Mng. Dir.--Ancra CHS, Boxtel, Netherlands; *U.S. Private*, pg. 71
Kuisma, Aimo, Chief Oper. Officer--Valmet Corporation Production, Jarvenpaa, Finland; *Int'l*, pg. 1448
Kuivkaev, Harri, Pres.--Rae Betoon AS, Maakond, Estonia; *Int'l*, pg. 1201
Kujaiwen, John R., Chief Oper. Officer--Amite Foundry and Machine, Inc., Amite, LA; *U.S. Public*, pg. 142
Kujawa, John R., Chief Oper. Officer--Atchison/St. Joe Division, Atchison, KS; *U.S. Public*, pg. 142
Kujovich, Lawrence R., V.P.-Irrigation Products Div.--The Toro Company Irrigation Products, Riverside, CA; *U.S. Public*, pg. 1624
Kuk, Kenneth U., Pres. & Chief Exec. Officer--Washington Square Advisors, Inc., Minneapolis, MN; *U.S. Public*, pg. 1376
Kukk, Toomas J., Pres. & Chief Exec. Officer--Chempower, Inc., Akron, OH; *Int'l*, pg. 74
Kukkonen, Kosti, Dir.--Kaskinen Mill, Kaskinen, Finland; *Int'l*, pg. 863
Kuklenski, Charles, Mgr.-Sls.--Ericsson, Inc., Overland Park, KS; *Int'l*, pg. 1364
Kula, Joseph, Mgr.-Office--Woodward-Clyde, Gaithersburg, MD; *U.S. Public*, pg. 1656
Kulczyeki, George, V.P.-Community Oper.--Port Saint Lucie, Port Saint Lucie, FL; *U.S. Public*, pg. 144
Kulenkampf, Arnfred, Pres. & Chief Exec. Officer--TLT-Babcock, Inc., Akron, OH; *Int'l*, pg. 401
Kulenkampff, Georg, Chief Exec. Officer--Raab Karcher AG, Essen, Germany; *Int'l*, pg. 1457
Kulik, David G., Pres.--Customized Transportation, Inc., Jacksonville, FL; *U.S. Public*, pg. 284
Kulikovskis, Andrejs, Company Head--SKF Riga, Riga, Latvia; *Int'l*, pg. 1159
Kulka, Jonathan, First V.P. & Mgr.--Bank Hapoalim (Philadelphia), Philadelphia, PA; *Int'l*, pg. 149
Kull, Laurie, V.P. & Chief Oper. Officer--Land O'Lakes, Inc., Kiel, WI; *U.S. Private*, pg. 646
Kulovic, George, City Mgr.--Circle Freight International USA - Latin America, Miami, FL; *U.S. Public*, pg. 371
Kulovic, George, Gen. Mgr.--Circle Freight International USA - Free Zone Office, Miami, FL; *U.S. Public*, pg. 371
Kulovic, George, District Mgr.--Circle International, Miami, FL; *U.S. Public*, pg. 371
Kulow, Fred, Pres.--Bioriginal Food & Science Corp., Saskatoon, Canada; *Int'l*, pg. 1195
Kumada, Fukuhisa, Mng. Dir.--Sumitomo Life Investment Singapore Limited, Singapore, Singapore; *Int'l*, pg. 1315
Kumagai, Naohiko, Chm. & Mng. Dir.--Mitsui & Co. Europe Ltd., London, United Kingdom; *Int'l*, pg. 880
Kumagai, Shigeru, Chief Rep.--Bahrain Representative Office, Manama, Bahrain; *Int'l*, pg. 520
Kumagai, Shigeru, Chief Representative--Fuji Bank, Berlin Representative Office, Dusseldorf, Germany; *Int'l*, pg. 520
Kumaki, Yoshiro, Gen. Mgr.--The Industrial Bank of Japan, Limited (Hong Kong Branch), Central, Hong Kong; *Int'l*, pg. 675
Kumakura, Takashi, Gen. Mgr.--Sony/Tektronix Corporation, Tokyo, Japan; *U.S. Public*, pg. 1568
Kuman, Peg, Ms., Pres.--The Power Line, Port Washington, NY; *U.S. Private*, pg. 893
Kumar, Karthik, V.P.--Rediffusion-Dentsu, Young & Rubicam (Calcutta), Calcutta, India; *U.S. Private*, pg. 326
Kumasaka, Yuzo, Chief Economist--NLI Research Institute, New York, NY; *Int'l*, pg. 935
Kumita, Tetsuya, Pres.--LeaRonal Japan Inc., Tokyo, Japan; *U.S. Public*, pg. 982
Kumm, Larry, Mgr.-Sls.--Penny Saver, Cedar Rapids, IA; *U.S. Private*, pg. 442
Kummant, Alex, Pres.--Sweco, Florence, KY; *U.S. Public*, pg. 574
Kummer, Bernd W., Co.-Chief Oper. Officer--BHF-Bank, London, United Kingdom; *Int'l*, pg. 119
Kummer, Fred, Pres.--Hospital Building & Equipment Co., Saint Louis, MO; *U.S. Private*, pg. 489
Kummer, Fred, Pres.--Adam's Mark Hotels & Resorts, Saint Louis, MO; *U.S. Private*, pg. 489
Kummer, Fred, Pres.--HBE Adam's Rib, Saint Louis, MO; *U.S. Private*, pg. 489
Kummer, Glenn F., Chief Oper. Officer--Fleetwood Folding Trailers, Inc., Somerset, PA; *U.S. Public*, pg. 651
Kummer, Glenn F., Chief Oper. Officer--Fleetwood Homes of Texas, Inc., Waco, TX; *U.S. Public*, pg. 651
Kummer, Glenn F., Chief Oper. Officer--Fleetwood Homes of Arizona, Inc., Glendale, AZ; *U.S. Public*, pg. 651
Kummer, Glenn F., Chief Oper. Officer--Fleetwood Homes of Georgia, Inc.-Southwest-Industrial Park, Douglas, GA; *U.S. Public*, pg. 651
Kummer, Glenn F., Chief Oper. Officer--Fleetwood Homes of Alabama, Inc., Hamilton, AL; *U.S. Public*, pg. 651
Kummer, Glenn F., Chief Oper. Officer--Fleetwood Homes of Georgia, Inc.-Fitzgerald, Fitzgerald, GA; *U.S. Public*, pg. 651
Kummer, Glenn F., Chief Oper. Officer--Fleetwood Homes of Indiana, Inc., Garrett, IN; *U.S. Public*, pg. 651
Kummer, Glenn F., Chief Oper. Officer--Fleetwood Homes of North Carolina, Inc.-Lumberton, Lumberton, NC; *U.S. Public*, pg. 651
Kumoda, Yasuo, Pres.--Morinaga Nutritional Foods, Inc., Torrance, CA; *Int'l*, pg. 895
Kumonjo, Masashige, Pres.--House of Lloyd Japan, Inc., Osaka, Japan; *Int'l*, pg. 422
Kumpulainen, Kari, Mng. Dir.--Enso Trading AB, Uppsala, Sweden; *Int'l*, pg. 457
Kung, Andrew, Property & Casualty Adjuster--Willis Corroon Administrative Services Corporation, Las Vegas, NV; *Int'l*, pg. 1504
Kung, Edward Y., Pres.--Trans Asian Insurance Services, Inc., Anaheim, CA; *U.S. Public*, pg. 366
Kung, Ziang-Mien, Chm. & Chief Mgr.--Chekiang First Bank Ltd., Hong Kong, Hong Kong; *Int'l*, pg. 361
Kunii, Toshio, Pres.--Toyota Canada Inc., Scarborough, Canada; *Int'l*, pg. 1414
Kunisch, Robert D., Pres. & Chief Exec. Officer--PHH Corporation, Hunt Valley, MD; *U.S. Public*, pg. 321
Kunishi, Toshihiko, V.P.--Sumitomo Metal U.S.A. Corp., Houston, TX; *Int'l*, pg. 1316
Kunitomo, Hidehiro, Chief Oper. Officer--NEC Electronics (Germany) GmbH, Dusseldorf, Germany; *Int'l*, pg. 901
Kunitzsch, Eberhard, Mng. Dir.--Knurr-Lommatec GmbH & Co. KG, Lommatzsch, Germany; *Int'l*, pg. 739
Kunitzsch, Eberhard, Pres.--Knurr-Lommatec Beteiligungs-u. Verw Gmbh, Munich, Germany; *Int'l*, pg. 739
Kunk, Stephen E., Pres. & Chief Exec. Officer--Provident Bank of Florida, Sarasota, FL; *U.S. Public*, pg. 1338
Kunkel, Helmut, Publ.--Ziff-Davis Germany, Munich, Germany; *Int'l*, pg. 1276
Kunnen, F.R., Pres.--Sharp Electronics Benelux B.V., Houten, Netherlands; *Int'l*, pg. 1229
Kuno, Hiro, Pres.--Viacom Japan, Inc., Tokyo, Japan; *U.S. Private*, pg. 779
Kunoth, Peter D., V.P. & Gen. Mgr.--K & M Products Division, Torrance, CA; *U.S. Public*, pg. 152
Kunsch, Matthias, Mng. Dir.--Creditanstalt Rt., Budapest, Hungary; *Int'l*, pg. 348
Kunstner, Uwe, Mng. Dir.--Jetbag GmbH, Neumarkt, Germany; *Int'l*, pg. 436
Kunth, Wolfgang, Mng. Dir.--GeoCenter Verlagsvertrieb GmbH, Munich, Germany; *Int'l*, pg. 190
Kuntz, Curtis, Chief Oper. Officer--Hudson General Aviation Services Inc., Calgary, Canada; *U.S. Public*, pg. 846
Kuntz, Lawrence G., Pres.--Dielectric Polymers, Inc., Holyoke, MA; *U.S. Public*, pg. 1258
Kuntz, Randy, Plant Mgr.--The Coleman Company, New Braunfels, TX; *U.S. Private*, pg. 691
Kunz, Hansruedi, Chief Oper. Officer--Metallica SA, Crissier, Switzerland; *Int'l*, pg. 1427
Kunz, Heidi, Chief Fin. Officer & Sr. V.P.--ITT Industries, Inc., White Plains, NY; *U.S. Public*, pg. 859
Kunz, Kerry, Gen. Mgr.--International Sea Drilling Ltd., Sale, Australia; *U.S. Public*, pg. 1316
Kunz, T., Chief Oper. Officer--Danone de Mexico, Mexico, Mexico; *Int'l*, pg. 379
Kunz, Walter, Mng. Dir.--PAXAR Deutschland GmbH, Lohne, Germany; *U.S. Public*, pg. 1266
Kunze, David A., Chief Oper. Officer--NationsBank of Rolla, Rolla, MO; *U.S. Public*, pg. 1164
Kunze, Matthias, Mgr.--Systhema Verlag GmbH, Munich, Germany; *Int'l*, pg. 1479
Kunzel, H., Mng. Dir.--Nedlloyd Districenters International, Amsterdam, Netherlands; *Int'l*, pg. 1144
Kunzig, Louis A., Chief Oper. Officer--Sciaky Electric Welding Machines Ltd., Slough, United Kingdom; *Int'l*, pg. 1211
Kunzler, James, Pres.--TrustCorp Mortgage Company, South Bend, IN; *U.S. Public*, pg. 638
Kunzler, Jurgen, Dr., Exec. V.P.--Balcke-Durr Kuhlturmbau Leipzig GmbH, Leipzig, Germany; *Int'l*, pg. 400
Kuo, Richard, Gen. Mgr.--Signode International Trading Corporation, Tai-chung, Taiwan; *U.S. Public*, pg. 869
Kuoh-Moukouri, Manga, Resident Rep.--The World Bank, Ouagadougou, Burkina Faso; *U.S. Private*, pg. 1189
Kuozogi, Ervin, Pres.--Apex International, Inc., Passaic, NJ; *U.S. Public*, pg. 1720
Kuozogi, Ervin, Pres.--Chroma Video, Inc., White Mills, PA; *U.S. Public*, pg. 1720
Kupchunos, Richard H., Pres.--Silver Brook Real Estate Development Company, Bloomfield, CT; *U.S. Public*, pg. 358
Kuperhand, J., Chief Exec. Officer--Autronics Corporation, Arcadia, CA; *Int'l*, pg. 208
Kupfer, Peter, Pres.--The Private Bank Group, Zurich, Switzerland; *Int'l*, pg. 345
Kupien, Dieter, Mng. Dir.--ISS Holding GmbH, Munich, Germany; *Int'l*, pg. 657
Kurahashi, Yoshihito, Pres.--Rohm LSI Systems Inc., San Jose, CA; *Int'l*, pg. 1125
Kuramoto, Masahiro, Gen. Mgr.--The Sumitomo Bank, Ltd.-Atlanta Agency, Atlanta, GA; *Int'l*, pg. 1309
Kuramoto, Masahiro, Chief Rep.--The Sumitomo Bank, Ltd.-Ho Chi Minh Representative Office, Ho Chi Minh City, Vietnam; *Int'l*, pg. 1310
Kuranz, John, Gen. Mgr.--Find/SVP Published Products, Inc., New York, NY; *U.S. Public*, pg. 623
Kuras, Paul, Exec. V.P.-London Office--Shoppers Drug Mart, Ltd., London, Canada; *Int'l*, pg. 112
Kurata, M., Office Chief--Man Nen Sha, Inc., Nagoya, Japan; *Int'l*, pg. 834
Kurebayashi, Takeshi, Dir.--Takenaka Hong Kong Ltd., Central, Hong Kong; *Int'l*, pg. 1351
Kurelayashi, Hiroshi, Gen. Mgr.--Dentsu Europe-Amsterdam, Amsterdam, Netherlands; *Int'l*, pg. 393
Kuribayashi, Hiroshi, Mng. Dir.--Pioneer Electronics Asia Centre Pte. Ltd., Singapore, Singapore; *Int'l*, pg. 1058
Kurihara, Toshiaki, Joint Gen. Mgr.--Dai-Ichi Kangyo Bank, Ltd.-Atlanta, Atlanta, GA; *Int'l*, pg. 359
Kurinij, Wasyl, Pres.--Edgington Oil Company, Long Beach, CA; *U.S. Private*, pg. 77
Kurishima, Shigekazu, Pres.--Nikko International Capital Management Co., Ltd., New York, NY; *Int'l*, pg. 930
Kurisu, Tokuo, V.P. & Branch Mgr.--Bank of Montreal - Japan, Tokyo, Japan; *Int'l*, pg. 155
Kurisu, Toshio, Chief Rep.--Harris Trust & Savings Bank, Tokyo, Japan; *Int'l*, pg. 154
Kurita, Shoji, Pres.--P.T. Fuji Bank International Indonesia, Jakarta, Indonesia; *Int'l*, pg. 521
Kurkel, A. Bruce, Gen. Mgr.--Paul Revere Insurance Group, Gaithersburg, MD; *U.S. Public*, pg. 1338
Kurlak, Ray, Pres.--Hamilton Standard, Windsor Locks, CT; *U.S. Public*, pg. 1690
Kurniawan, Tanto, Pres.--P.T. Jaya Fuji Leasing Pratama, Jakarta, Indonesia; *Int'l*, pg. 521
Kuroda, Keiji, Mng. Dir.--The Meiji Life Insurance Company Sydney Office, Sydney, Australia; *Int'l*, pg. 854
Kuroda, Keiji, Mng. Dir.--The Meijiseimei Property Australia Ltd., Sydney, Australia; *Int'l*, pg. 854
Kuroki, Shigeo, Dir.--T and S Servicos Industrias S/C Ltda., Bela Vista, Brazil; *Int'l*, pg. 1406
Kuromizu, Hirokimi, Pres.--DKB Leasing (Thailand) Co., Ltd., Bangkok, Thailand; *Int'l*, pg. 362
Kuronya, G., Chief Oper. Officer--WAGO Kontakttechnik Ges mbH, Vienna, Austria; *Int'l*, pg. 209
Kurosawa, Yoh, Chm.--The Industrial Bank of Japan, Limited (Canada), Toronto, Canada; *Int'l*, pg. 675
Kurose, Sugayoshi, Pres.--ORIX COMMODITIES Corporation, Tokyo, Japan; *Int'l*, pg. 1008

Kurose, Tadashi, Chief Oper. Officer--Asahi Kogyo Co., Ltd., Toyohashi, Japan; *Int'l*, pg. 621
Kurstein-Jensen, Peter, Pres.--Radiometer Medical A/S, Bronshoj, Denmark; *Int'l*, pg. 1083
Kurten, Christian, Mgr.-Base Stations--Nokia Telecommunications, Espoo, Finland; *Int'l*, pg. 952
Kurtenbach, Matt, Pres.--Star Circuits, Brookings, SD; *U.S. Public*, pg. 478
Kurth, C. William, Gen. Mgr.--Container Div. (Milwaukee), Milwaukee, WI; *Int'l*, pg. 1269
Kurth, Hans, Mng. Dir.--Omega SA, Bienne, Switzerland; *Int'l*, pg. 1160
Kurth, Hans, Mng. Dir.--SMH Australia Ltd., Windsor, Australia; *Int'l*, pg. 1161
Kurth, Wolfgang, Mgr.--Hapag-Lloyd Fluggesellschaft mbH, Hannover, Germany; *Int'l*, pg. 596
Kurtz, Grant W., Pres.--Advest, Inc., Hartford, CT; *U.S. Public*, pg. 23
Kurtzhalts, Jody, Pres.--Robicon, New Kensington, PA; *U.S.* Private, pg. 528
Kuruvilla, Jolly, Mgr.--BB&T International, Charlotte, NC; *U.S. Public*, pg. 160
Kurz, Andreas, Pres.--Hugo Boss USA, Inc., New York, NY; *Int'l*, pg. 637
Kusa, A., Chief Exec. Officer--WAGO Company of Japan Limited, Tokyo, Japan; *Int'l*, pg. 209
Kusakabe, Etsuji, Chief Oper. Officer--Furukawa Aluminum Co., Ltd., Tokyo, Japan; *Int'l*, pg. 530
Kusakai, Hiroyuki, Pres.--Nissho Iwai Hong Kong Corporation Limited, Hong Kong, Hong Kong; *Int'l*, pg. 948
Kusano, M., Dir. & Mgr.--GPI (Japan) Limited, Tokyo, Japan; *Int'l*, pg. 537
Kusano, Seiichi, Pres. Dir.--P.T. Daiwa Lippo Leasing Corporation, Jakarta, Indonesia; *Int'l*, pg. 374
Kusch, Dr. Ing Gerhard, Co-Chief Oper. Officer--Saar-Gummiwerk GmbH, Wadern, Germany; *Int'l*, pg. 1167
Kushiyama, Hisao, Mng. Dir.--NEC Electronics Singapore Pte. Ltd., Singapore, Singapore; *Int'l*, pg. 901
Kushmaul, Bill, Pres.--Tech Mold, Tempe, AZ; *U.S. Private*, pg. 1071
Kushnir, Israel, Mng. Dir.--George S. May International Co., San Jose, CA; *U.S. Private*, pg. 717
Kuss, B. Ann, Mng. Dir.--Inland Valley Regional Medical Center, Wildomar, CA; *U.S. Public*, pg. 1697
Kustich, Karen, Mgr.-Sls.--A.M. Castle & Co., Cheswick, PA; *U.S. Public*, pg. 313
Kusumi, Gary, Pres.--National Continental Insurance Co., Beachwood, OH; *U.S. Public*, pg. 1335
Kusumoto, Sadahei, Chm. Bd. & Chief Exec. Officer--Minolta Corporation, Ramsey, NJ; *Int'l*, pg. 869
Kutchoukov, Dontcho, Mng. Dir.--Bayerische-Bulgarische Handelsbank GmbH, Munich, Germany; *Int'l*, pg. 179
Kutella, Ronald J., Pres.--Sedgwick, Inc., Memphis, TN; *Int'l*, *pg. 1218*
Kutsche, Ron A., Pres.--BetzDearborn Paper Process Group, Jacksonville, FL; *U.S. Public*, pg. 226
Kutsuma, Shiro, Mng. Dir.--Daiwa Middle East E.C., Manama, Bahrain; *Int'l*, pg. 375
Kuula, Timo, V.P.--Winpac B.V., Winschoten, Netherlands; *Int'l*, pg. 864
Kuwana, David, Country Mgr.--Standard Chartered Bank Gambia Ltd., Banjul, Gambia; *Int'l*, pg. 1294
Kuwao, Kentaro, Mng. Dir.--Kwe-Kintetsu World Express(S)Pte Ltd., Singapore, Singapore; *Int'l*, pg. 735
Kuwata, Yasuhiro, Dir.--Takenaka (U.K.) Ltd., London, London, United Kingdom; *Int'l*, pg. 1352
Kuykendall, W.R., Gen. Mgr.--Graybar International, Inc., Saint Louis, MO; *U.S. Private*, pg. 472
Kuyper, Ruud, Gen. Mgr.--Eurocol B.V., Wormerveer, Netherlands; *Int'l*, pg. 497
Kuze, Kazunori, Chief Rep.--Chubu Electric Power Co., Inc. (Washington Office), Washington, DC; *Int'l*, pg. 290
Kuzeppa, Michael S., Pres.--Dial Bank, Sioux Falls, SD; *U.S.* Public, pg. 1202
Kuzina, Donald, V.P.--Video King Gaming Systems, Inc., Littleton, CO; *U.S. Public*, pg. 1526
Kuzma, Tim L., V.P. & Gen. Mgr.--Feeny Manufacturing Company, Muncie, IN; *U.S. Public*, pg. 963
Kuznetsov, Evgeni, Chief Oper. Officer--MacGREGOR (UKR) A/O, Ilyichevsk City, Russia; *Int'l*, pg. 671
Kvalo, Bjorn, Mgr.-Opers.--Jotun A/S, Manger, Norway; *Int'l*, *pg. 714*
Kvangarsnes, Hallstein, Gen. Mgr.--Kvaerner Kleven Rovde A/S, Rovde, Norway; *Int'l*, pg. 769
Kvarnback, Bengt, Pres.--Atlas Copco Electric Tools, Winnenden, Germany; *Int'l*, pg. 96
Kvarnstrom, Ann-Christin, Pres.--Astra Production Liquid AB, Sodertalje, Sweden; *Int'l*, pg. 93
Kvisle, Hal, Pres.--Fletcher Challenge Petroleum Inc., Calgary, Canada; *Int'l*, pg. 495
Kvist, Anders, Pres.--Skandia Life Insurance Company Ltd., Stockholm, Sweden; *Int'l*, pg. 1257
Kwa, C.S., Chm. & Mng. Dir.--Esso Singapore Private Limited, Singapore, Singapore; *U.S. Public*, pg. 602
Kwak, A.C., Chm.--BolsWessanen Nederland BV, Amstelveen, Netherlands; *Int'l*, pg. 751
Kwak, A.C., Mng. Dir.--Delicia B.V., Tilburg, Netherlands; *Int'l*, pg. 752
Kwan, Tsang, Dir.--GP Battery Marketing (Singapore) Pte Ltd., Singapore, Singapore; *Int'l*, pg. 537
Kwan, Yip Kwok, Chm.--DBS Securities Nominees (HK) Ltd., Queensway, Hong Kong; *Int'l*, pg. 351
Kwan, Yip Kwok, Chm.--DBS Securities Philippines, Inc., Manila, Philippines; *Int'l*, pg. 351
Kwanchaithanya, Suraphol, Pres.--Siam City Syndicate Finance & Securities Co., Ltd., Bangkok, Thailand; *Int'l*, pg. 1239
Kwasek, Matthew J., Jr., Pres. & Chief Exec. Officer--Freezer Queen Foods Inc., Buffalo, NY; *Int'l*, pg. 340
Kwasny, Tom, Pres.--SuperValu, Inc.-Reading Div., Temple, PA; *U.S. Public*, pg. 1540
Kwinn, Dave, V.P.-Mktg.--CR Services, Elgin, IL; *Int'l*, pg. 1157
Kwok, Arthur C.S., Mgr.--Wackenhut Security (H.K.), Ltd., Kowloon, Hong Kong; *U.S. Public*, pg. 1732
Kwok, Francis, Reg. Mgr.--CUNA Mutual Group-Hong Kong, Kowloon, Hong Kong; *U.S. Private*, pg. 296
Kwok, W. H., Lab. Dir.--Springborn Testing & Research (Hong Kong) Ltd., Kwai Chung, Hong Kong; *U.S. Private, pg. 1027*
Kwok, W. H., Dir.-Laboratory--STR Shanghai Office, Shanghai, China; *U.S. Private*, pg. 1027
Kwon, H.S., Pres.--Doosan Crown Can Mfg. Co. Ltd., Seoul, Korea; *U.S. Public*, pg. 465
Kwon, T.Y., Chief Oper. Officer--Gambro Korea Co., Ltd, Seoul, Korea; *Int'l*, pg. 668
Kwon, Tony, Gen. Mgr.--Bundy Systems Korea, Ansan, Korea; *Int'l*, pg. 1341
Kwong, K.H., Chief Exec. Officer--A. Johnson Corp (HK) Ltd., Wan Chai, Hong Kong; *Int'l*, pg. 711
Kwong, Raymond, Rep. Officer--Merita Bank Ltd., Hong Kong Representative Office, Central, Hong Kong; *Int'l*, pg. 859
Kyle, Douglas, Branch Mgr.--Zellerbach Division, Sacramento, CA; *U.S. Public*, pg. 1075
Kyle, M.H., Chief Oper. Officer--Commonwealth Bank-Jakarta, Jakarta, Indonesia; *Int'l*, pg. 313
Kyle, Robert, Pres.--Longman Group USA Inc., Chicago, IL; *Int'l*, pg. 1026
Kylmala, Jukka, Chief Oper. Officer--ZAO KONE Lifts, Moscow, Russia; *Int'l*, pg. 748
Kympton, Howard W., III, V.P. & Gen. Mgr.-McCormick Flavor Div. USA--McCormick Flavor Division-U.S.A., Hunt Valley, MD; *U.S. Public*, pg. 1066
Kynnersley, P., Chief Exec. Officer--Mytton's Limited, Bundoora, Australia; *Int'l*, pg. 216
Kyriacou, K., Mng. Dir.--Bally Australia Pty. Ltd., Camperdown, Australia; *Int'l*, pg. 997
Kyu, Mong, Chm. Bd.--Hyundai Motor Company, Seoul, Korea; *Int'l*, pg. 641
Kyytsonen, Matti, Mng. Dir.--ISS Suomi Oy, Helsinki, Finland; *Int'l*, pg. 656
Kyzer, Floyd W., V.P.-Natl. Accts.--Winston Carpet Co., Ringgold, GA; *U.S. Public*, pg. 1464
Kyzer, Floyd W., V.P.-Natl. Accts.--Majestic Carpet Mills, Ringgold, GA; *U.S. Public*, pg. 1464
L'Arnaud, J. C., Chm. Bd.--Banque Bonnasse, Marseilles, France; *Int'l*, pg. 563
L'Esperance, Thomas F., Pres.-Commercial Laundry Div.--Raytheon Appliances, Ripon, WI; *U.S. Public*, pg. 1366
L'homme, Jean-Claude, Dir.-Encyclofidies--Hachette Latino America S.A. de C.V., Mexico, Mexico; *Int'l*, pg. 796
L'Orange, Raoul, Dr., Gen. Mgr.--Mibelle AG, Buchs, Switzerland; *Int'l*, pg. 865
L'Orsa, Arturo Matossi, V.P.--Sulzer Italia S.p.A., Milan, Italy; *Int'l*, pg. 1306
La Cour, Leif, Admin. Dir.--Duni A/S, Roedovre, Denmark; *Int'l*, pg. 421
La Cruise, Kenneth R., Chief Oper. Officer--CIBA-GEIGY Foreign Sales Corporation Ltd, Kingston, Jamaica; *Int'l*, pg. 976
La Grouw, J.C., Grp. V.P. & Dir.-Wines & Spirits--Bols Royal Distilleries, Nieuw-Vennep, Netherlands; *Int'l*, pg. 751
La Monica, Filippo, Pres.--EuroCetus, Amsterdam, Netherlands; *U.S. Public*, pg. 350
La Page, Jean, Pres.--Total Outre-Mer, Puteaux, France; *Int'l*, pg. 1409
La Porte, Dominique, Chief Oper. Officer--Sovcor, SA, Le Vesinet, France; *U.S. Public*, pg. 1722
La Porte, Gary, V.P. & Div. Mgr.--Bindley Western, Orlando Division, Orlando, FL; *U.S. Public*, pg. 228
La Russo, Rosa, Mgr.-Adv.--Rubbermaid Canada Inc. Consumer Products, Mississauga, Canada; *U.S. Public*, pg. 1411
La Russo, William, Pres.--Polyflon Company, New Rochelle, NY; *U.S. Public*, pg. 457
La Tour d'Artaise, Thierry, Chm. Bd.--Calor S.A., Lyon, France; *Int'l*, pg. 568
La Valle, Pier Giorgio, Chm. Bd.--Caboto Holding Societa di Intermediazione Mobiliare S.p.A., Milan, Italy; *Int'l*, pg. 138
Laag, Thorbjorn, Chief Oper. Officer--Unifridge AG, Gattikon, Switzerland; *Int'l*, pg. 444
Laaksonen, Tero, Mgr.-Systems Platforms & CS--Nokia Telecommunications, Espoo, Finland; *Int'l*, pg. 952
Laalo-Ristila, Seija, Chief Oper. Officer--Valmet Trade Promotion Office, Moscow, Russia; *Int'l*, pg. 1449
Laan, S P., Mng. Dir.--California B.V., Harderwijk, Netherlands; *Int'l*, pg. 243
Laanemets, Allan, Pres.--Rexcan Circuits Inc., Belleville, Canada; *Int'l*, pg. 628
Laas, Madis, Chief Exec. Officer & Mng. Dir.--Kontuur-Leo Burnett/Estonia, Tallinn, Estonia; *U.S. Private*, pg. 184
Labadie, Fran, V.P.--Favesa S.A. de C.V., (Mexico), El Paso, TX; *U.S. Public*, pg. 982
Labadie, Julio, Pres.--Refractarios Mexicanos S.A. de C.V. (REFMEX), Coahuila, Mexico; *U.S. Public*, pg. 748
Laband, P.A.K., Mng. Dir.--National Australia Asset Management, Melbourne, Australia; *Int'l*, pg. 906
LaBarge, C. E., Pres.--LaBarge Electronics, Saint Louis, MO; *U.S. Public*, pg. 973
Labathari, M., Mng. Dir.--Nutricia Hellas S.A., Athens, Greece; *Int'l*, pg. 992
Labergere, Alain, Pres.--CPC Europe Consumer Foods Division, Brussels, Belgium; *U.S. Public*, pg. 224
Labonte, J.M. Francois, 1st. V.P. & Branch Mgr.--Union Bank of Switzerland (Canada), Montreal, Canada; *Int'l*, pg. 1441
Laboon, Jr., James L., Chm. Bd. & Chief Exec. Officer--Athens First Bank & Trust Co., Athens, GA; *U.S. Public*, pg. 1549
Laborerio, Stephen, Pres.--Koch Otto H. York Co., Inc., Parsippany, NJ; *U.S. Private*, pg. 628
Labosky, Bonnie, V.P.-Promeon Components--Medtronic Promeon, Brooklyn Center, MN; *U.S. Public*, pg. 1083
LaBrecque, Normand, Dir.--Earle M. Jorgensen Company/Quebec, Laval, Canada; *U.S. Private*, pg. 600
Labrecque, R.J., Pres.--ITT Fluid Transfer Division, Midland Park, NJ; *U.S. Public*, pg. 860
Labrecque, Richard J., Pres. & Chief Exec. Officer--ITT Fluid Technology Corporation, Midland Park, NJ; *U.S. Public*, pg. 860
Labrecque, Richard J., Pres. & Chief Exec. Officer--ITT Fluid Handling, Morton Grove, IL; *U.S. Public*, pg. 860
Labreque, Richard J., Pres. & Chief Exec. Officer--Goulds Pumps, Incorporated, Fairport, NY; *U.S. Public*, pg. 860
Labriola, F.J., Pres.--Pimalco Inc., Chandler, AZ; *U.S. Public*, pg. 61
Labroue, Jean-Noel, Pres. & Chief Exec. Officer--Le Groupe Darty, Bondy, France; *Int'l*, pg. 734
LaButti, Gerald, Pres.--Aerospace Avionics Inc., Bohemia, NY; *Int'l*, pg. 126
LaCamera, Paul, V.P. & Gen. Mgr.--WCVB Division, Boston, MA; *U.S. Private*, pg. 516
LaCarrpa, Vincent, Gen. Mgr.--RS Electronics, Hauppauge, NY; *U.S. Private*, pg. 905
Lace, John, Mng. Dir.--Babcock Turnkey Operations Ltd., Crawley, United Kingdom; *Int'l*, pg. 472
Lacerda Villaga, Antonio Carlos, Gen. Mgr.--Banco do Brasil S.A.-Paraguay, Ciudad del Este, Paraguay; *Int'l*, pg. 141
Lacerda, Flavio, Reg. Mgr.-Latin America--Loctite Brasil Ltda., Sao Paulo, Brazil; *Int'l*, pg. 611
Lacey, Kelley, Gen. Mgr.--Frontier Communications of Fairmount, Inc., Fairmount, GA; *U.S. Public*, pg. 683
Lacey, Robert Mark, Resident Rep.--The World Bank, Yaounde, Cameroon; *U.S. Private*, pg. 1189
Lacey, Roger H.D., Div. V.P.--Telecom Systems Division, Austin, TX; *U.S. Public*, pg. 1605
Lacey, Tudor N., Mgr.-Branch--Piper Jaffray Inc., Tucson, AZ; *U.S. Public*, pg. 1301
LaChapolle, George, Plant Mgr.--Aerospace & Commercial Controls Division, Sarasota, FL; *U.S. Public*, pg. 557
Lachaume, Philippe, Pres.--Damart Serviposte S.A., Robaix, France; *Int'l*, pg. 376
Lachaux, Michel, Chief Oper. Officer--Land Instruments Sarl, Bailly, France; *Int'l*, pg. 798
Lachonius, Leif, Mng. Dir.--Flex-Link Systems AB, Goteborg, Sweden; *Int'l*, pg. 1157
Lack, Michael L., Pres.--Integrated Circuits Division, San Jose, CA; *U.S. Public*, pg. 290
Lackman, Les M., Pres.--Boeing North America, North American Aircraft Division, Seal Beach, CA; *U.S. Public*, pg. 241
Lackner, Egon, Chief Oper. Officer--Bohlerit Ges.m.b.H., Kapfenberg, Austria; *Int'l*, pg. 1470
LaClare, John, Gen. Mgr.--Heartland Livestock Services, Regina, Canada; *Int'l*, pg. 1195
Lacomis, Bernard J., Pres. & Chief Exec. Officer--Arthur D. Little Enterprises, Inc., Cambridge, MA; *U.S. Private*, pg. 670
Lacourciere, Paul A., Pres.--Watts Regulator Co., Andover, MA; *U.S. Public*, pg. 1747
Lacourrege, Michel, Chief Oper. Officer--Saint-Gobain Vitro Italia, Pisa, Italy; *Int'l*, pg. 1173
Lacroix, Georges, Gen. Mgr.--Raychem SA, Cergy-Pontoise, France; *U.S. Public*, pg. 1363
LaCross, David, Chief Exec. Officer--Risk Management Technologies, Berkeley, CA; *U.S. Public*, pg. 610
LaCrosse, Randy F., Exec. V.P. & Gen. Mgr.--Cleveland Shiprepair Company, Cleveland, OH; *U.S. Public*, pg. 1041
Lacson, Joselito L., Chief Oper. Officer--Griffith Laboratories (Phils.) Inc., Manila, Philippines; *U.S. Private*, pg. 481
Lacy, Mark, Media Dir.--Leo Burnett/Connaghan & May (QLD.) Pty. Ltd., Milton, Australia; *U.S. Private*, pg. 185
Lacy, Ray, Mng. Dir.--Switchgear & Instrumentation Ltd., Bradford, United Kingdom; *Int'l*, pg. 133
Lacy, William H., Chm. Bd. & Chief Exec. Officer--Mortgage Guaranty Insurance Corporation, Milwaukee, WI; *U.S. Public*, pg. 1026
Ladbrook, Peter, Dir.-Sls. Opers.--Bio-Logic Systems Corporation Ltd., Chipping Norton, United Kingdom; *U.S.* Public, pg. 230
Ladd, Alan, Jr., Chm. Bd., Pres., Chief Exec. & Chief Oper. Officer--MGM Entertainment Company, Culver City, CA; *U.S. Public*, pg. 1614
Ladd, Jeffrey, Chm. Bd.--Metra, Commuter Rail Service Board, Chicago, IL; *U.S. Private*, pg. 919
Ladden, Jack, Pres.--CANA Inc., Malvern, PA; *Int'l*, pg. 55
Ladden, Paul, Chief Oper. Officer--Genzyme Diagnostics, Medix Biotech, San Carlos, CA; *U.S. Public*, pg. 733
Lade, Brian G., V.P. & Gen. Mgr.--Riverwalk, New Orleans, LA; *U.S. Public*, pg. 1408
Ladell, Peter W., Pres.--Hoechst Marion Roussel North America, Kansas City, MO; *Int'l*, pg. 625
Ladet, Jean, Pres.--Sefcal S.A., Saint Julien de Peyrolas, France; *Int'l*, pg. 289
Ladinig, U., Chief Oper. Officer--Molto Ges.m.b.H., Salzburg, Austria; *Int'l*, pg. 1501
Ladinig, V., Mgr.--Commenda Hungaria Kpt., Budapest, Hungary; *Int'l*, pg. 1501
Ladinig, V., Mng. Dir.--Commenda Baustoff A.G., Vienna, Austria; *Int'l*, pg. 1501
Lador, Rami, Rep.-Hong Kong--Bank Hapoalim (Hong Kong), Central, Hong Kong; *Int'l*, pg. 149
LaDue, Jack W., Pres. & Treas.--Rochester Gauges Inc. Of Texas, Dallas, TX; *U.S. Private*, pg. 440
Laehy, Timothy P., Pres.--Leasing Solutions Receivables, Inc., San Jose, CA; *U.S. Public*, pg. 983
Laelage, Armand, Plant Mgr.--Hennepin Division, Exolon-Esk, Hennepin, IL; *U.S. Public*, pg. 600
Laengrich, Arthur R., Pres.--OEL, Ltd., Midland, TX; *U.S. Public*, pg. 568
Laento, Kari, Mng. Dir.--Neste Alfa Oy, Espoo, Finland; *Int'l*, *pg. 914*
Laethem, Kevin, Mgr.--B & W Farm Center, Breckenridge, MI; *U.S. Private*, pg. 105
Laferner, Dan, Div. Pres.--Winn-Dixie Louisville, Inc., Louisville, KY; *U.S. Public*, pg. 1771
Laferriere, Pierre, Pres. & Chief Oper. Officer--Teleglobe International Inc., Montreal, Canada; *Int'l*, pg. 1373

Lafever, Dan, Pres.-Midwest Div.--Thriftway, Inc., Louisville, KY; U.S. Public, pg. 1771
Lafevre, J., V.P.-Human Resources-Alcon Building Prods.--The Stolle Corporation, Sidney, OH; U.S. Public, pg. 61
Laffan, M., Mng. Dir.--Skala Home Electronics, s Hertogenbosch, Netherlands; Int'l, pg. 1386
Laffey, J., Gen. Mgr.--Augat Pty Ltd., Warriewood, Australia; U.S. Public, pg. 1598
LaFleur, Dennis J., Pres.--Chemical Bank Michigan, Clare, MI; U.S. Public, pg. 345
LaFleur, Kevin, Pres.--Monfort, Inc., Greeley, CO; U.S. Public, pg. 427
LaFleur, Paul D., Pres.--John Hancock Networking Insurance Agency, Boston, MA; U.S. Private, pg. 590
LaFollette, Larry, Pres.--Rocky Mountain Prestress, Denver, CO; U.S. Private, pg. 861
Lafontaine, T., District Mgr.--A.M. Castle & Co., Franklin Park, IL; U.S. Public, pg. 313
Lafontaine, Yves, Mgr.--Cascades Niagara Falls, Niagara Falls, NY; Int'l, pg. 274
Laforte, Pierre, Chief Oper. Officer--Ascenseurs Drolet KONE Inc., Quebec, Canada; Int'l, pg. 747
LaFourcade, Olivier, Dir.--Banco Mundial, Mexico, Mexico; U.S. Private, pg. 1189
Laftwein, Engelbert, Pres.--Krantz America, Inc., Charlotte, NC; Int'l, pg. 401
Lagally, Dr. Hermann, Gen. Mgr.--H.B. Fuller Austria GesmbH, Wels, Austria; U.S. Public, pg. 687
Lagally, Hermann, Dr., V.P.-Opers.--H.B. Fuller Belgium N.V./S.A., Kontich, Belgium; U.S. Public, pg. 687
Lagares, Victor, Chief Oper. Officer--Electrolux Lagares C. por A., Santo Domingo, Dominican Republic; Int'l, pg. 441
Lageard, D.A., Chief Oper. Officer--Parsons Chain Europe SA, Melun, France; Int'l, pg. 473
Lagergren, Bo, Pres.--Dynapac GmbH, Wardenburg, Germany; Int'l, pg. 1420
Lagerstrom, Nils, Mng. Dir.--Nokia Telecommunications AB, Kista, Sweden; Int'l, pg. 953
Lagerwall, Staffan, Chief Oper. Officer--Electrolux-Martin S.A., Brussels, Belgium; Int'l, pg. 441
Laghi, Franco, Pres.--Bondioli & Pavesi Inc., Ashland, VA; Int'l, pg. 201
Lagno, Robert A., Pres.--Airtron, Morris Plains, NJ; U.S. Public, pg. 1003
Lagorce, Michel, Chief Exec. Officer--Fabrications Mecaniques de l'Atlantique (FAMAT SA), Saint Nazaire, France; Int'l, pg. 1166
Laguercia, Alessandro, Gen. Mgr.--Banco di Sicilia, Los Angeles, CA; Int'l, pg. 140
LaHaie, Steve, V.P.-Opers.--Shaw's Deerfield, Deerfield, IL; U.S. Private, pg. 661
LaHaie, Steve, V.P.-Opers.--Mity Nice Grill, Chicago, IL; U.S. Private, pg. 661
Lahar, David, Pres.--Aurora Electronics, San Diego, CA; U.S. Public, pg. 147
Lahav, Gideon, Chm. Bd.--Israel Discount Bank Ltd., Tel Aviv, Israel; Int'l, pg. 645
Lahdesmaki, Tuomo, Pres. & Chief Exec. Officer--Leiras Oy, Turku, Finland; Int'l, pg. 639
Lahe, C.R., Mng. Dir.--Wyman-Gordon Limited, Livingston, United Kingdom; U.S. Public, pg. 1782
Lahey, Joseph P., Pres.--Furmanite Worldwide, Inc., Richardson, TX; U.S. Public, pg. 942
LaHood, Dennis J., V.P.-Country Prods. Group--Country Products Group, Syracuse, NY; U.S. Private, pg. 27
Lahr, K.O., Chief Oper. Officer--Siemens Ltd., Richmond, Australia; Int'l, pg. 1247
Lahteenmaki, Risto, Mng. Dir. & Chief Exec. Officer--Schauman Wood Oy, Lahti, Finland; Int'l, pg. 1428
Lahteenmaki, Risto, Mng. Dir.--Schauman Wood AB, Stockholm, Sweden; Int'l, pg. 1429
Lahtinen, Antero, Deputy Mng. Dir.--Norvista, London, United Kingdom; Int'l, pg. 486
Lai, Anthony N.S., Pres. & Gen. Mgr.--California Mfg. Co., Inc., Manila, Philippines; U.S. Public, pg. 225
Lai, Charles, Gen. Mgr.-North Asia--Utell International-Hong Kong, Chai Wan, Hong Kong; Int'l, pg. 1098
Lai, Chi-Sun, Gen. Mgr.--Motorola China, Inc., Schaumburg, IL; U.S. Public, pg. 1138
Lai, Glament, Gen. Mgr.--IPC Corporation (HK) Ltd., Kowloon, Hong Kong; Int'l, pg. 651
Lai, H.Y, Plant Mgr.--Microsemi (H.K.) Ltd., Sha Tin, Hong Kong; U.S. Public, pg. 1107
Lai, Peter, Pres.--Rohm Electronics (H.K.) Co., Ltd., Kowloon, Hong Kong; Int'l, pg. 1125
Lai, S.Y., Pres.--China Steel Structure Co., Ltd., Kao-hsiung, Taiwan; Int'l, pg. 286
Lai, Shiow-Shyong, Sr. V.P. & Gen. Mgr.--The International Commercial Bank of China, Tokyo, Japan; Int'l, pg. 683
Laibach, Robert, Gen. Mgr.--Mabamex S.A., Tijuana, Mexico; U.S. Public, pg. 1059
Laible, Charles, Chief Exec. Officer--Willis Corroon Aerospace, New York, NY; Int'l, pg. 1505
Laidig, Marc, Dir.-Trading & Sls.--Nasinsa Securities, New York, NY; Int'l, pg. 904
Laidlaw, W., Pres.--Claudius Peters Inc., Dallas, TX; Int'l, pg. 131
Laidley, Ron, Pres.--Yale E Key, Inc., Midland, TX; U.S. Public, pg. 953
Laido, Olavi, Pres.--Hansa Kindlustus, Tallinn, Estonia; Int'l, pg. 1425
Laiho, Jarmo, Mng. Dir.--Merita Finance Ltd., Helsinki, Finland; Int'l, pg. 859
Laine-Tuominen, Nina, Office Mgr.--Utell International-Finland, Helsinki, Finland; Int'l, pg. 1098
Laine, Jorma, V.P.--Lielahti CTMP Mill, Tampere, Finland; Int'l, pg. 863
Laing, Bert, Pres. & Chief Exec. Officer--LINC Anthem Inc., Chicago, IL; U.S. Public, pg. 996
Laing, Bert, Pres.--LINC Quantum Analytics, Foster City, CA; U.S. Public, pg. 996
Laing, Tim, Chief Fin. Officer--Young & Rubicam Australia/New Zealand, Sydney, Australia; U.S. Private, pg. 1198
Laipenieks, Maris, Pres.--Acapulco Restaurants, Long Beach, CA; U.S. Private, pg. 925
Laird, E.T., Sr. V.P. & Mgr.-Atlanta Sls.--Jefferies & Company, Inc., Los Angeles, CA; U.S. Public, pg. 925
Laird, E.T., Mgr.--Jefferies & Company, Inc., Atlanta, GA; U.S. Public, pg. 925
Laird, Thomas, Pres. & Chief Exec. Officer--Woods Equipment Company, Oregon, IL; U.S. Private, pg. 249
Laivins, Peter, Chief Exec. Officer--Norrkoping AxTrade AB, Riga, Latvia; Int'l, pg. 712
Laize, Georges, Chief Oper. Officer--Hospal Industrie S.A., Meyzieu, France; Int'l, pg. 668
Lake, David, Pres.--Quebecor Printing MIL Inc., Don Mills, Canada; Int'l, pg. 1077
Lake, Munro, Pres.--TIE Systems, Inc. Illinois, Arlington Heights, IL; U.S. Private, pg. 1085
Lake, Munro, Pres.--TIE Systems-Farmington Hills, Farmington, MI; U.S. Private, pg. 1085
Lake, Munro, Pres.--TIE Systems, Inc. Mississippi Valley, Moline, IL; U.S. Private, pg. 1085
Lake, P.A., Chief Oper. Officer--Addison Saws Limited, Dudley, United Kingdom; Int'l, pg. 448
Lake, R.D., Pres.--NFC International Holdings (U.S.A.) Inc., Dover, DE; Int'l, pg. 901
Lake, Stephen, Pres.--Super Sagless Corp., Tupelo, MS; U.S. Public, pg. 986
Lakin, Judy, V.P. & Gen. Mgr.--KPEZ-FM, Austin, TX; U.S. Public, pg. 384
Lal, Jagdish, Mgr.-Mktg., The Americas--Kuwait Airways, Canada, Toronto, Canada; Int'l, pg. 764
Lalain, Bob, Gen. Mgr.--Detroit Auto Auction, Inc., Taylor, MI; U.S. Public, pg. 1649
Lalande, Marcel, V.P.--Brookfield Homes Development Corporation, Gloucester, Canada; Int'l, pg. 228
Lallande, Mark, Pres.--Telecredit Marketing Services, Tampa, FL; U.S. Public, pg. 588
Lallemand, A., Gen. Mgr.--ING Immobilier, Paris, France; Int'l, pg. 650
Laloi, G., Gen. Mgr.--Panzalim, Paris, France; Int'l, pg. 381
Lalonde, Claude, Chief Oper. Officer--Hudson General Aviation Services Inc., Ottawa, Canada; U.S. Public, pg. 846
Lam Lo, Yuk, Pres.--Bio-Rad Pacific, Hong Kong, Hong Kong; U.S. Public, pg. 230
Lam, C.C., Mng. Dir.--Wayfoong Finance Ltd., Wan Chai, Hong Kong; Int'l, pg. 584
Lam, Gilbert, Assoc. Dir.--Du Pont Pharmaceuticals, Newark, DE; U.S. Public, pg. 531
Lam, J.K.K., Reg. Mgr. Asia--AlliedSignal Performance Additives, Kowloon, Hong Kong; U.S. Public, pg. 53
Lam, K.C., Mgr.--THORN-EMI Hong Kong Ltd., North Point, Hong Kong; Int'l, pg. 428
Lam, Mike, Mng. Dir.--Notifier Far East, Kowloon, Hong Kong; U.S. Public, pg. 1306
Lam, N.H., Gen. Mgr.--Ademco-Sontrix (Far East), Kowloon, Hong Kong; U.S. Public, pg. 1307
Lam, N.H., Gen. Mgr.--Ademco Hong Kong Ltd., Tsuen Wan, Hong Kong; U.S. Public, pg. 1307
Lam, Tan Eng, Exec. Dir.--Sime Diamond Leasing (Singapore) Pte. Ltd., Singapore, Singapore; Int'l, pg. 1251
Lamagrande, S. Hernandez, Chief Exec. Officer--Redland Iberica S.A., Madrid, Spain; Int'l, pg. 1093
Lamancusa, Mark, Plant Mgr.--Bundy Corporation, Hebron Plant, Hebron, OH; Int'l, pg. 1340
Lamar, Phil, Gen. Mgr.--Lexis Law Publishing, Charlottesville, VA; Int'l, pg. 1096
Lamattina, Larry, Pres. & Chief Exec. Officer--All American Television, Inc., New York, NY; U.S. Public, pg. 41
Lamb, Isabelle S., Pres.--Meridian Machine Works, Inc., Meridian, MS; U.S. Private, pg. 378
Lamb, J. Brian, Chief Oper. Officer--Sevcon, Inc., Burlington, MA; U.S. Public, pg. 1563
Lamb, Ritchie, Mng. Dir.--Skega (PTY) Ltd., Dunswart, South Africa; Int'l, pg. 1324
Lamb, Simon, Mng. Dir.--Eldon Electric Ltd., Rotherham, United Kingdom; Int'l, pg. 436
Lamb, Stewart, Dir. & Mgr.--Crown Cork Company (Zambia) Ltd., Ndola, Zambia; U.S. Public, pg. 464
Lamb, Tim, Country Mgr.--H.J. Heinz Company C.I.S., Moscow, Russia; U.S. Public, pg. 806
Lambe, Frank, Chief Oper. Officer--Forest Fasteners, Pontypridd, United Kingdom; Int'l, pg. 265
Lambert, D., Mng. Dir.--Gestetner (Pvt) Limited, Harare, Zimbabwe; Int'l, pg. 1115
Lambert, D.N., Chief Exec. Officer--La Garantie Generale Marocaine (G.G.M.), Casablanca, Morocco; Int'l, pg. 1531
Lambert, Gayle, Mgr.-Midwest--Midwest Division, Chicago, IL; U.S. Public, pg. 1613
Lambert, Henry A., Pres. & Chief Exec. Officer--Reliance Development Group Inc., New York, NY; U.S. Public, pg. 1374
Lambert, J.H., Gen. Mgr.--CHEMCENTRAL/St. Louis, Maryland Heights, MO; U.S. Private, pg. 232
Lambert, James L., Pres. & Chief Exec. Officer--Artecon, Inc., Carlsbad, CA; U.S. Private, pg. 409
Lambert, Jean-Michel, Chief Exec. Officer & Dir.--Nicoll, Cholet, France; Int'l, pg. 430
Lambert, John, Natl. Media Dir.--Leo Burnett/Connaghan & May Pty. Ltd., Sydney, Australia; U.S. Private, pg. 185
Lambert, Liam, Gen. Mgr.--The Excelsior Hotel, Hong Kong, Causeway Bay, Hong Kong; Int'l, pg. 704
Lambert, Peter, Mng. Dir.--Nordson Australia Pty., Ltd., Seven Hills, Australia; U.S. Public, pg. 1189
Lambert, Peter, Mng. Dir.--Nordson Australia Pty. Limited., Melbourne, Australia; U.S. Public, pg. 1189
Lambert, Phelps L., Chm. Bd.--Farmers Bank & Trust Co., Henderson, KY; U.S. Public, pg. 1217
Lambert, Thomas W., Chm. Bd.--Camtronics Ltd., Hartland, WI; U.S. Public, pg. 109
Lambert, Timothy, Pres.--VF International, Wyomissing, PA; U.S. Public, pg. 1702
Lambert, W., Mng. Dir.--Kerry Ultrasonics Limited, Hitchin, United Kingdom; Int'l, pg. 589
Lamberth, Richard, V.P.--ICIS LOR-USA, Houston, TX; Int'l, pg. 1094
Lambin, Serge, Gen. Mgr.--Rheometric Scientific France SARL, Marne la Vallee, France; U.S. Public, pg. 1387
Lambourne, R. E., Mng. Dir.--Hepworth Refractories Ltd., Alfreton, United Kingdom; Int'l, pg. 615
Lambrecht, Michel, Dir.--ELVIA Assurances S.A., Brussels, Belgium; Int'l, pg. 60
Lambrechts, Antoon, Chief Exec. Officer--Considar Europe S.A., Luxembourg, Luxembourg; Int'l, pg. 79
Lambri, Claudio, Chief Oper. Officer--Aviocart S.p.A., Borghetto, Italy; U.S. Public, pg. 1076
Lamden, John, Mgr.--Wing Industries North Central, Addison, IL; U.S. Private, pg. 1183
Lameiras, Jose, Gen. Mgr.--Ceras Johnson de Portugal, Lda., Oeiras, Portugal; U.S. Private, pg. 592
Lamer, Gerald, Pres.--Kewaunee Engineering Corp., Kewaunee, WI; U.S. Private, pg. 703
Lamer, Gerald, Pres.--MTI Leasing, Ltd., Sturgeon Bay, WI; U.S. Private, pg. 703
Lamer, Gerald, Pres.--Shuttlelift, Inc., Sturgeon Bay, WI; U.S. Private, pg. 703
Lamesch, Fred, Pres.--TrefilARBED Inc., New York, NY; Int'l, pg. 79
Lammam, Fouad, Chief Oper. Officer--Electrolux Middle East S.a.r.l., Beirut, Lebanon; Int'l, pg. 443
Lammers, Melissa, Gen. Mgr.--Young & Rubicam Puerto Rico, Inc., Guaynabo, PR; U.S. Private, pg. 1198
Lammert, Marilyn, Pres.--FFG Investments, Inc., Springfield, IL; U.S. Public, pg. 644
Lamminpaa, Osmo, Mng. Dir.--Valmet-Gorizia S.p.A., Gorizia, Italy; Int'l, pg. 1448
Lammot, Brooke, Dir.-Sls.--Clayton Manufacturing Div., Dynamic Equipment, El Monte, CA; U.S. Private, pg. 245
Lamneck, Ken, V.P. & Mng. Dir.--Anthem Technology, San Jose, CA; U.S. Public, pg. 134
Lamons, Robert G., Pres. & Chief Exec. Officer--First American National Bank, Jackson, TN; U.S. Public, pg. 624
Lamont, Dennis D., Pres. & Chief Exec. Officer--Bank of America Auto Lease Center, Westlake Village, CA; U.S. Public, pg. 181
Lamont, Dennis D., V.P.--Citicorp Acceptance Co., Inc., Saint Louis, MO; U.S. Public, pg. 378
Lamothe, Howard, Chief Oper. Officer--Williamhouse Sales Corporation, Appleton, WI; U.S. Public, pg. 89
Lamothe, Jean, Pres.--Capital International CDPQ, Montreal, Canada; Int'l, pg. 249
Lamotte, C., Chm. Bd.--Banque Scalbert Dupont, Lille, France; Int'l, pg. 563
Lampe, Jerry, Chief Exec. Officer--Innovative Health Alliances, Overland Park, KS; U.S. Public, pg. 839
Lampe, John, Pres.--Bridgestone/Firestone Tire Sales Company, Nashville, TN; Int'l, pg. 213
Lampe, Peter, Pres.--Thyssen Immobilien GmbH, Oberhausen, Germany; Int'l, pg. 1388
Lampert, Albert, Pres.--Aspen Systems Corp., Rockville, MD; Int'l, pg. 1513
Lampert, Andrew H., V.P.--Harris-Nesbitt Thomson Securities, Inc., Chicago, IL; Int'l, pg. 155
Lampert, David, Jr., Pres.--Swix Sport USA Inc., Wilmington, MA; Int'l, pg. 1390
Lampert, Joseph, Gen. Supervisor--Brake Fluid Operations, Berkeley, MO; U.S. Public, pg. 443
Lamphere, George, Pres. & Treas.--Chas. H. Tompkins Co., Washington, DC; Int'l, pg. 633
Lampila, Jorma, Chief Oper. Officer--Neste Oy, Naantali Refinery, Naantali, Finland; Int'l, pg. 914
Lampinen, Kari, Chief Oper. Officer--Noptor Oy, Espoo, Finland; Int'l, pg. 913
Lampinen, Paavo, Mng. Dir.--SO Oviteollisuus OY, Kuopio, Finland; Int'l, pg. 1302
Lampl, F.W., Joint Chm.--Bovis Urban Renewal Ltd., London, United Kingdom; Int'l, pg. 1032
Lampl, Frank, Chm. Bd.--Bovis Construction Ltd., Harrow, United Kingdom; Int'l, pg. 1032
Lampl, Frank, Chm. Bd.--Bovis Inc., New York, NY; Int'l, pg. 1033
Lampman, Michael, Pres.--Williams Constructors, Richmond, VA; U.S. Private, pg. 1178
Lamprecht, Hannes A., Office Rep.--UBS Representative Office, San Francisco, CA; Int'l, pg. 1440
Lamus, John, Chief Fin. Officer--Harveys of Bristol Limited, Bristol, United Kingdom; Int'l, pg. 63
Lamy, Jean, Mgr.--Sandvik Process Systems S.A., Paris, France; Int'l, pg. 1187
Lan, Chien-Min, V.P. & Gen. Mgr.--The International Commercial Bank of China, Paris, France; Int'l, pg. 683
Lan, S., Chief Exec. Officer--Zurich Insurance Company (Asia) Limited, Quarry Bay, Hong Kong; Int'l, pg. 1532
Lanary, R.S., Mng. Dir.--Hamworthy Combustion Equipment Limited, Poole, United Kingdom; Int'l, pg. 1065
Lancaster, B. Allen, Pres. & Chief Exec. Officer--Regions Bank/Raybun County, Clayton, GA; U.S. Public, pg. 1372
Lancaster, Charles L., Mng. Dir.--LABSCO, Indianapolis, IN; U.S. Private, pg. 642
Lancaster, Scott, Base Mgr.--Mercury Air Center, Burbank, CA; U.S. Public, pg. 1093
Lance, Robert, Facilities Mgr.--Huls America Inc., Theodore, AL; Int'l, pg. 1455
Lancelot, Jean Luc, Mng. Dir.--Acieries De Ploermel, Ploermel, France; U.S. Public, pg. 1711
Lancester, Charles, Mng. Dir.--Shandwick PTE Ltd., Singapore, Singapore; Int'l, pg. 1227
Lanciani, Rudolfo, Gen. Mgr.--Tektronix SpA, Vinodrone, Italy; U.S. Public, pg. 1568
Land, A., Gen. Mgr.--General Biscuits GmbH (GBG), Kempten, Germany; Int'l, pg. 381
Land, Eric, Gen. Mgr.--WEYI, Inc., Clio, MI; U.S. Private, pg. 389

Land, John, Chm. Bd.--M.M. Cohn Co., Inc., Little Rock, AR; *U.S. Private*, pg. 346
Land, Raymond J., Pres.--Citation Plastics, Co., Pleasantville, NJ; *U.S. Public*, pg. 1755
Land, Raymond J., Pres.--The West Company of Delaware, Inc., Wilmington, DE; *U.S. Public*, pg. 1755
Land, Raymond J., Pres.--West International Sales Corporation, Charlotte Amalie, VI; *U.S. Public*, pg. 1755
Land, Stanley, Sr. V.P. & Gen. Mgr.--EFG Technologies, Inc., Winston Salem, NC; *U.S. Public*, pg. 1679
Landa, Clayton L., V.P. & Gen. Mgr.--Mercur Mine, Tooele, UT; *Int'l*, pg. 169
Landau, Charles, Gen. Mgr.--E.B. Malone Corp., Lake Wales, FL; *U.S. Public*, pg. 193
Landau, Henry V., Pres.--Measurements Group, Inc., Raleigh, NC; *U.S. Public*, pg. 1722
Landau, Herbert, Chief Oper. Officer--Research Publications, Inc., Woodbridge, CT; *U.S. Public*, pg. 1600
Landau, Howard, Pres.--Wyse-Landau Public Relations, Cleveland, OH; *U.S. Private*, pg. 1194
Landau, Richard S., Pres.--Bear Stearns Mortgage Capital Corporation, New York, NY; *U.S. Public*, pg. 198
Landeau, Guy, Gen. Sls. Mgr.--Moore Products Co. (France) SARL, Romans, France; *U.S. Public*, pg. 1129
Landell-Mills, Pierre M., Country Dir.--The World Bank, Dhaka, Bangladesh; *U.S. Private*, pg. 1189
Landemar, Lars, Chief Oper. Officer--AxTrade East AB, Stockholm, Sweden; *Int'l*, pg. 708
Lander, Greg, Pres.--TransCapacity, L.P., Peabody, MA; *U.S. Public*, pg. 550
Lander, Howard, Publisher & Pres.--Billboard Magazine, New York, NY; *Int'l*, pg. 1446
Landers, R.D., Plant Mgr.--Artee-Wrap Spun, Wetumpka, AL; *U.S. Public*, pg. 467
Landes, Barbara, Pres.--Pinelands, Inc., Secaucus, NJ; *U.S.* Public, pg. 352
Landes, Jim, Pres. & Gen. Mgr.--DataCard Plastic Card Services, Minnetonka, MN; *U.S. Private*, pg. 312
Landgraf, Kurt, Pres. & Chief Exec. Officer--The Du Pont Merck Pharmaceutical Company, Wilmington, DE; *U.S. Public*, pg. 531
Landgren, Ulf, Mng. Dir.--Carlson Marketing Group Scandinavia Motivation Service AB, Djursholm, Sweden; *U.S. Private*, pg. 212
Landguth, Daniel P., Pres.--Wyodak Resources Development Corp., Rapid City, SD; *U.S. Public*, pg. 236
Landguth, Daniel P., Pres.--Western Production Company, Rapid City, SD; *U.S. Public*, pg. 236
Landich, Jurgen, Gen. Mgr.--OCG Microelectronic Materials GmbH, Ratingen, Germany; *U.S. Public*, pg. 1219
Landich, Jurgen, Gen. Mgr.--Olin GmbH, Ratingen, Germany; *U.S. Public*, pg. 1220
Landis, John, Mgr.-Property & Casualty Claims--Willis Corroon Administrative Services Corporation, Stockton, CA; *Int'l*, pg. 1504
Landmer, Bengt, Mgr.--Binks-Bullows Sweden AB, Partille, Sweden; *U.S. Public*, pg. 229
Lando, David, V.P.-Engrng. & Environmental Tech.--Lucent Technologies Engineering Research Center, Princeton, NJ; *U.S. Public*, pg. 1018
Landon, Barry, Gen. Mgr.--Lawrence Technology, Lawrence, KS; *U.S. Public*, pg. 298
Landon, David E., Pres.--Pardee Construction Company, Los Angeles, CA; *U.S. Public*, pg. 1764
Landon, R. Kirk, Pres.--Financial Exchange, Inc., Miami, FL; *U.S. Public*, pg. 67
Landon, R. Kirk, Pres.--American Bankers Life Agents Services, Inc., Miami, FL; *U.S. Public*, pg. 67
Landon, Richard, Pres. & Chief Oper. Officer--The Marley Cooling Tower Co., Overland Park, KS; *U.S. Public*, pg. 1676
Landoni, Luigi Battista, Mgr.--Sanpaolo-Tokyo Branch, Tokyo, Japan; *Int'l*, pg. 692
Landry, Bryan, Pres.--SECO Industries, Inc., Metairie, LA; *U.S. Public*, pg. 1460
Landry, Donald J., Pres.--Manor Healthcare Corp., Gaithersburg, MD; *U.S. Public*, pg. 1041
Landry, G.Y., Pres. & Chief Exec. Officer--Chrysler Canada Ltd., Windsor, Canada; *U.S. Public*, pg. 354
Landry, Lamar, Facility Mgr.--Pro Shop (Houston, TX), Houston, TX; *U.S. Public*, pg. 861
Landry, Thomas H., Pres.--A.J. Etkin Construction Co., Farmington, MI; *U.S. Private*, pg. 384
Lands, Jim, Plant Mgr.--Stride Rite Footwear, Inc., Fulton, MO; *U.S. Public*, pg. 1525
Landsberger, David, Pres.--Maddak Inc., Pequannock, NJ; *U.S. Private*, pg. 130
Landsittel, Thomas A., Mgr.--Scott & Stringfellow, Inc., Raleigh, NC; *U.S. Public*, pg. 1446
Landsman, Steven N., V.P.-Baltimore Fin.--CAP Gemini America (Baltimore Branch), Baltimore, MD; *Int'l*, pg. 263
Landstad, Charles K., Gen. Mgr.--Viking Computer Services, Minneapolis, MN; *U.S. Public*, pg. 472
Landstrom, John B., Pres.--Sony Trans Com Systems Inc., Costa Mesa, CA; *Int'l*, pg. 1281
Landwehr, Steven J., Gen. Mgr.--Automotive Aftermarket Div., Saint Paul, MN; *U.S. Public*, pg. 1605
Landy, Rona, Gen. Mgr.--WLTW-FM, New York, NY; *U.S. Private*, pg. 779
Lane, Alan, Pres.--Pacific Pride Bakeries, Escondido, CA; *Int'l*, pg. 575
Lane, Alan, Dir.--Willis Corroon Credit Limited, Manchester, United Kingdom; *Int'l*, pg. 1502
Lane, Albert, Jr., Pres.--Rome Research Corporation, New Hartford, NY; *U.S. Public*, pg. 1256
Lane, Buck, District Mgr.--Morgantown Machine Anderson Mavor, Lucernemines, PA; *Int'l*, pg. 281
Lane, Charles, Chief Oper. Officer--Allright Boston Parking, Inc., Boston, MA; *U.S. Private*, pg. 42
Lane, Clifford, Pres.--ILC Data Device, Bohemia, NY; *U.S. Private*, pg. 555
Lane, Daniel D.(Ron), Chief Exec. Officer--Boston Pacific, Inc., Anaheim, CA; *U.S. Public*, pg. 278
Lane, Davina C., Pres. & Chief Exec. Officer--HealthCare USA, Jacksonville, FL; *U.S. Public*, pg. 454
Lane, Graeme, Gen. Mgr.--Colgate-Palmolive Philippines Inc., Manila, Philippines; *U.S. Public*, pg. 398
Lane, James A., Jr., Pres.--Chaparral Boats, Nashville, GA; *U.S. Public*, pg. 1356
Lane, John M., Jr., Pres.--Potomac Graphic Industries, Inc., New York, NY; *Int'l*, pg. 699
Lane, John S., Chm. Bd.--Sun Life Distribution Services Inc., Toronto, Canada; *Int'l*, pg. 1319
Lane, Joseph C., Pres.--GATX Financial Services, San Francisco, CA; *U.S. Public*, pg. 690
Lane, Joseph C., Pres. & Chief Exec. Officer--GATX Capital Corporation, San Francisco, CA; *U.S. Public*, pg. 690
Lane, M.A., Chief Exec. Officer--WAGO Corporation, Brown Deer, WI; *Int'l*, pg. 209
Lane, R.W., Chief Oper. Officer--Productos para Escuela y Oficina, S.A. de C.V., Nuevo Laredo, Mexico; *U.S. Public*, pg. 1077
Lane, Ray, V.P. & Gen. Mgr.--Jervis B. Webb Company of Canada Ltd., Hamilton, Canada; *U.S. Private*, pg. 1157
Lane, Richard, Pres.--International Petroleum Corporation of Lafayette, Lafayette, LA; *U.S. Public*, pg. 906
Lane, Rod, Gen. Mgr.--ANI Engineering, Karrabin, Australia; *Int'l*, pg. 100
Lane, Ron, Gen. Mgr.--BHP Steel Building Products Papua New Guinea Pty Ltd., Lae, Papua New Guinea; *Int'l*, pg. 226
Lane, Russell S., Pres.--Atlas Weathering DSET Laboratories, Phoenix, AZ; *U.S. Private*, pg. 96
Lane, Tim, V.P. & Gen. Mgr.--Uddeholm Corporation, Santa Fe Springs, CA; *Int'l*, pg. 1472
Lane, W.R., Dir.-Sls. & Mktg.--Edward Barber & Co., London, United Kingdom; *U.S. Public*, pg. 1651
Laner, Jerry, Pres.--Jimmy Dean Foods, Cordova, TN; *U.S. Public*, pg. 1433
Lanes, Michael M., Pres.--Power Systems Inc., Bloomfield, CT; *Int'l*, pg. 868
Laney, Herbert, Pres.-Catalogs--Playboy Preferred, Inc., Itasca, IL; *U.S. Public*, pg. 1310
Laney, Herbert, Pres.-Catalogs--Critics' Choice Video, Inc., Itasca, IL; *U.S. Public*, pg. 1310
Laney, Skip, Mgr.--W.C. Caye & Co., Charleston, SC; *U.S. Private*, pg. 220
Lanfermann, Theodor, Representative--Deutsche Bank AG (Tehran), Tehran, Iran; *Int'l*, pg. 405
Lanford, Nathan Adrian, Pres.--Lufthansa Systems GmbH, Kelsterbach, Germany; *Int'l*, pg. 407
Lang, Dietrich, Dr., Chief Oper. Officer--BK Ladenburg GmbH, Ladenburg, Germany; *Int'l*, pg. 626
Lang, Donald G., Pres.--CCL Custom Manufacturing, Rosemont, IL; *Int'l*, pg. 238
Lang, Everett, Pres. & Chief Exec. Officer--National Discount Brokers, New York, NY; *U.S. Public*, pg. 1467
Lang, G.F.J., Mng. Dir.--Liberty of London Prints Limited, London, United Kingdom; *Int'l*, pg. 807
Lang, Gerhard, Co-Chief Oper. Officer--UNISPED Spedition und Transportgesellschaft mbH, Saarbruecken, Germany; *Int'l*, pg. 1167
Lang, Jordan, Chief Oper. Officer--OfB Grundstuecksverwaltungs GmbH, Frankfurt/Main, Germany; *Int'l*, pg. 799
Lang, Jordan, Chief Oper. Officer--OfB Bauvermittlungs und Gewerbebau Gesellschaft mbH, Frankfurt/Main, Germany; *Int'l*, pg. 799
Lang, Jordan, Chief Oper. Officer--GKH Gesellschaft fuer Kommunalbau in Hessen mbH, Frankfurt/Main, Germany; *Int'l*, pg. 799
Lang, K., Mng. Dir.--Hermann H.C. Starck Berlin GbmH & Co. KG, Berlin, Germany; *Int'l*, pg. 174
Lang, Keith, Chm. Bd.--Steketee Paul & Sons Company, Inc., Grand Rapids, MI; *U.S. Private*, pg. 346
Lang, Leo J., Asst. V.P.--IBP-Lexington, Lexington, NE; *U.S.* Public, pg. 852
Lang, Richard, Chief Oper. Officer--Geodimeter of Canada Ltd., Toronto, Canada; *Int'l*, pg. 1290
Langagne, Jean Paul, Mng. Dir.--Plasma-Technik S.A., Villefontaine, France; *Int'l*, pg. 1308
Langagne, Jean Paul, Mng. Dir.--Sulzer Metco (France) S.A., Vaulx, France; *Int'l*, pg. 1308
Langan, P.R., Pres. & Treas.--CENTIN Corporation, Strongsville, OH; *U.S. Public*, pg. 913
Langballe, Hakon, Pres.--Petrokjemi/Petrochemicals, Oslo, Norway; *Int'l*, pg. 960
Langbein, T.K., Pres.--Medicore Inc., Hialeah, FL; *U.S. Public*, pg. 1080
Langbein, T.K., Pres.--Dialysis Corporation of Harrisburg, Lemoyne, PA; *U.S. Public*, pg. 1080
Langdal, Ole, Pres.--Kvaerner Kincaid Ltd., Greenock, United Kingdom; *Int'l*, pg. 772
Langdale, Mark, Pres.--Posadas USA Inc., Dallas, TX; *Int'l*, pg. 576
Lange, A Robert, Pres.--Midlantic Commercial Co., Inc., West Paterson, NJ; *U.S. Public*, pg. 1242
Lange, Donald E., Pres. & Chief Exec. Officer--Weyerhaeuser Mortgage Company, Woodland Hills, CA; *U.S. Public*, pg. 1764
Lange, Fred J., Jr., Pres.--The Toledo Edison Company, Toledo, OH; *U.S. Public*, pg. 645
Lange, George W., Jr., Pres.--Marshall & Ilsley Trust Company of Florida, Naples, FL; *U.S. Public*, pg. 1051
Lange, Klas, Pres.--Componenta International Scandinavia AB, Sodertalje, Sweden; *Int'l*, pg. 1421
Lange, Klas, Pres.--Weda Pump AB, Sodertalje, Sweden; *Int'l*, pg. 1421
Lange, Manfred, Gen. Mgr.--CPC Deutschland GmbH, Heilbronn, Germany; *U.S. Public*, pg. 225
Lange, Richard W., Pres.--Bemis Paper Bag Division, Memphis, TN; *U.S. Public*, pg. 210
Lange, Wolfgang, Mng. Dir.--Emil Schlemper G.m.b.H., Solingen, Germany; *U.S. Public*, pg. 17
Langelaang, Rick, Chm.--Communicatie & Design, Wassemaar, Netherlands; *Int'l*, pg. 1335
Langenfeld, Hans, Sr. Mng. Dir.--Deutsche Bank AG (Dusseldorf), Dusseldorf, Germany; *Int'l*, pg. 402
Langenskiold, Bertel, Pres.--Tampella Power Inc., Tampere, Finland; *Int'l*, pg. 1353
Langenus, John C., Pres.--Cigna Direct Marketing Company, Inc., Philadelphia, PA; *U.S. Public*, pg. 362
Langenus, John C., Pres.--Cigna Road & Travel Club, Inc., Philadelphia, PA; *U.S. Public*, pg. 362
Langenus, John C., Pres.--Alaska Pacific Assurance Company, Anchorage, AK; *U.S. Public*, pg. 366
Langer, Jack, Pres. & Chief Exec. Officer--City Gas Company of Florida, Hialeah, FL; *U.S. Public*, pg. 1147
Langer, Ralph, Pres.--Blumenthal/Lansing Company, Lansing, IA; *U.S. Public*, pg. 1187
Langer, Robert R., Chief Oper. Officer--Only Deals, Inc., New Hope, MN; *U.S. Public*, pg. 1697
Langerak, Hans, Chief Oper. Officer--Hagglunds Drives GmbH, Gorinchem, Netherlands; *Int'l*, pg. 670
Langford, Vivien, Grp. Fin. Controller--Shandwick International Plc, London, United Kingdom; *Int'l*, pg. 1226
Langgartner, Claus, Pres.--Buss (America) Inc., Bloomingdale, IL; *Int'l*, pg. 490
Langhan, Terri, Pres. & Chief Oper. Officer--First Strategic Group, Whittier, CA; *U.S. Public*, pg. 1157
Langhorn, Brian L., Dir.--Flouro-Precision Coatings, Cranleigh, United Kingdom; *Int'l*, pg. 1338
Langley, Edward, Gen. Mgr.--The Weetabix Company, Inc., Clinton, MA; *Int'l*, pg. 1488
Langley, Jim, Plant Mgr.--CBP Resources, Strawberry Plains, TN; *U.S. Private*, pg. 192
Langley, Mike, Gen. Mgr.--Panama City Coca-Cola Bottling Co., Panama City, FL; *U.S. Public*, pg. 392
Langley, Sharon E., Pres. & Chief Exec. Officer--NationsBank of Vandalia, Vandalia, MO; *U.S. Public*, pg. 1165
Langlois-Meurinne, Aimery, Gen. Mgr.--Parfinance S.A., Paris, France; *Int'l*, pg. 562
Langlois, Norman, Chief Fin. Officer & Exec. V.P.--Butterworth-Heinemann USA, Newton, MA; *Int'l*, pg. 1094
Langlois, Robert, Gen. Mgr.--Salomon Sports Ltd., Dorval, Canada; *Int'l*, pg. 1181
Langly, Scott, Div. Mgr.--Wall Street Deli, Inc., Birmingham, AL; *U.S. Public*, pg. 1734
Langner, Karl-Heinz, Station Mgr.--Weatherford Services S.A., Port Harcourt, Nigeria; *U.S. Public*, pg. 1750
Langness, Cliff, Pres.--Scenic Air Lines, Las Vegas, NV; *U.S. Public*, pg. 1476
Langness, Cliff N., Pres.--Scenic Airlines Inc., Saint George, UT; *U.S. Public*, pg. 1476
Langone, Vincent P., Pres.--Formica Corporation, Wayne, NJ; *Int'l*, pg. 129
Langs, Frank N., Pres.--Pferd, Inc., Leominster, MA; *Int'l*, pg. 1046
Langston, John, Pres.--Regency Insurance Company, Charlotte, NC; *U.S. Public*, pg. 685
Langston, W.P., Vice Chm.--Barber Pure Milk Co., Birmingham, AL; *U.S. Private*, pg. 115
Langton, B.D., Chm. Bd.--Trusthoase Forte plc, London, United Kingdom; *Int'l*, pg. 170
Langton, Bryan D., Chm. Bd. & Chief Exec. Officer--Holiday Inn Worldwide, Atlanta, GA; *Int'l*, pg. 170
Lanier, D., Gen. Mgr.--Sanford Facility, Sanford, NC; *Int'l*, pg. 535
Lanier, J. R., Gen. Mgr.--Parmart Stores, Nashville, TN; *U.S.* Private, pg. 840
Lanier, Julian, Pres.--Sprauge Energy Corp. Southeast Operations, Wilmington, NC; *Int'l*, pg. 710
Lankford, C. Frederick, Pres.--Lankford-Sysco Food Services, Inc., Pocomoke City, MD; *U.S. Public*, pg. 1551
Lankford, H. Raymond, Jr., Pres.--All American Agency Facilities, Inc., Redmond, WA; *U.S. Public*, pg. 216
Lankford, James E., Pres.--Sysco Food Services Company, Harrisburg, PA; *U.S. Public*, pg. 1551
Lankford, James E., Pres.--Sysco Food Services of Philadelphia, Inc., Philadelphia, PA; *U.S. Public*, pg. 1552
Lanman, Jonathan, V.P. & Assoc. Publisher--Atheneum Books for Young Readers, New York, NY; *U.S. Private*, pg. 777
Lannebo, Anders, Pres.--Robur, Stockholm, Sweden; *Int'l*, pg. 1328
Lannert, George, Gen. Mgr.--ITW Linx, Elk Grove Village, IL; *U.S. Public*, pg. 866
Lannig, Gary, Plant Mgr.--Hydro Conduit Corp., Phoenix, AZ; *Int'l*, pg. 245
Lanning, Ed, Mgr.--Commercial-Levin, Burlington, NC; *U.S. Public*, pg. 413
Lannoye, Lee D., Pres.--VanFed Investment Services, Inc., Seattle, WA; *U.S. Public*, pg. 1742
Lano, James D., V.P. & Assoc. Gen. Counsel--Rouse Legal Div., Columbia, MD; *U.S. Public*, pg. 1407
Lanoix, Margaret L., Pres.--Marlborough Capital Advisors, Inc., Boston, MA; *U.S. Private*, pg. 737
Lanoue, Robert, Plant Mgr.--Starrett Granite Surface Plate Division, Mount Airy, NC; *U.S. Public*, pg. 1511
Lanoue, Robert, Plant Mgr.--Coordinate Measuring Machine Div., Mount Airy, NC; *U.S. Public*, pg. 1511
Lansbergen, W.N., Mgr.-Fishery Equip. Grp.--Radio Holland Group-Fishery Equip., Ijmuiden, Netherlands; *Int'l*, pg. 1151
Lansche, Wayne, Pres. & Gen. Mgr.--KBAK-TV, Bakersfield, CA; *U.S. Private*, pg. 1170
Lanscombe, M., Mng. Dir.--Beazer Homes (Doncaster) Limited, Doncaster, United Kingdom; *Int'l*, pg. 182
Lanshe, Margaret M., Pres.--Synertech, Harrisburg, PA; *U.S.* Private, pg. 529
Lanson, Elliott, Gen. Mgr.--Akzo LanChem Corp., East Saint Louis, IL; *Int'l*, pg. 47
Lanston, Greg, V.P.--Square D Company Mexico, S.A. de C.V., Ixtapalapa, Mexico; *Int'l*, pg. 1209
Lanthier, Armand, Dir.-Montreal & Eastern Reg.--Imprimerie Quebecor Inc. Division Cheques, Saint Leonard, Canada; *Int'l*, pg. 1077

Lanthorne, Rodney, Pres.--Kyocera International, Inc., San Diego, CA; *Int'l*, pg. 775
Lanton, Gene E., Pres.--Central Florida Div., Clearwater, FL; *U.S. Public*, pg. 1682
Lantto, Reijo, Pres.--Nokia Display Products Inc., Salo, Finland; *Int'l*, pg. 951
Lantto, Reijo, Gen. Mgr.--Nokia Display Products Oy, Salo, Finland; *Int'l*, pg. 951
Lantz, Randy, V.P.--AFG Industries, Inc., Kingsport, TN; *Int'l*, pg. 84
Lanwermeyer, Louis F., Pres.--Harriscorp Finance, Inc., Chicago, IL; *Int'l*, pg. 155
Lanz, Joaquin, Gen. Mgr.--Florasynth S.A. de C.V., Cuautitlan, Mexico; *Int'l*, pg. 174
Lanz, Ruedi, Mng. Dir.--K-Tron France, Boissy-Saint-Leger, France; *U.S. Public*, pg. 938
Lanzani, Emanuele, Mng. Dir.--CastelMAC, S.p.A., Castelfranco Veneto, Italy; *U.S. Public*, pg. 1445
Lanzani, Emanuele, Mng. Dir.--Frimont, S.p.A., Bettolino di Pogliano, Italy; *U.S. Public*, pg. 1445
Lanzi, Raymond J., Div. Pres.--Lydall Southern Products, Richmond, VA; *U.S. Public*, pg. 1021
Lanzi, Raymond J., Pres.-Div.--Lydall Southern Products, Jacksonville, FL; *U.S. Public*, pg. 1021
Lanzi, Raymond J., Pres.-Div.--Lydall Westex, Columbus, OH; *U.S. Public*, pg. 1021
Lanzi, Raymond J., Pres.-Div.--Lydall Westex, Rockwell, NC; *U.S. Public*, pg. 1021
Lap, Hans, Office Mgr.--Korn/Ferry International, Dusseldorf, Germany; *U.S. Private*, pg. 634
LaPan, Karl, Pres.--NBS Imaging Systems, Inc., Fort Wayne, IN; *Int'l*, pg. 898
Lapayre, J.M., Jr., Pres.--Lapeyre Stair, Inc., Harahan, LA; *U.S. Private*, pg. 643
Lapelle, Brian, Pres.--Dutch Housing, Inc., White Pigeon, MI; *U.S. Public*, pg. 333
Laphen, Michael W., Pres.--Integrated Systems Division, Moorestown, NJ; *U.S. Public*, pg. 423
Lapicola, John J., Pres.--AVO Multi-Amp Institute, Dallas, TX; *Int'l*, pg. 1335
Lapid, A.B., Chief Oper. Officer--Pan-Malayan Insurance Corporation, Manila, Philippines; *Int'l*, pg. 1392
LaPierre, Roland H., Pres.--Main Street South Corp., Bridgeport, CT; *U.S. Public*, pg. 126
Lapin, Byron, Pres.--Clayton Metals Corp., Fenton, MO; *U.S. Private*, pg. 244
Lapin, Byron, Pres.--Clayton Plastics Corp., Fenton, MO; *U.S. Private*, pg. 244
Lapin, Byron, Pres.--Convenience Products, Inc., Fenton, MO; *U.S. Private*, pg. 244
Lapin, Phil, Pres.--William B. Bliss Div., Somerville, NJ; *U.S. Private*, pg. 392
Lapin, Phil, Pres.--Edwal Scientific Products Div., Somerville, NJ; *U.S. Private*, pg. 392
Lapin, Steve, Pres.--First International Reinsurance Company, New York, NY; *U.S. Private*, pg. 446
Lapinski, Valerie, Gen. Mgr.--ITW Dynatec, Hendersonville, TN; *U.S. Public*, pg. 867
LaPointe, Bill, Mng. Dir.--Andover Controls Corp., Andover, MA; *Int'l*, pg. 120
Lapointe, Paul, V.P. & Gen. Mgr.--Roehlen Engraving, Rochester, NY; *U.S. Public*, pg. 1506
Laponder, Charles, Mng. Dir.--Berendsen PMC B.V., Rijswijk, Netherlands; *Int'l*, pg. 1285
LaPorte, Steve, V.P. & Gen. Mgr.--CardioRhythm, San Jose, CA; *U.S. Public*, pg. 1083
Lapp, Peter J., Pres.--Bird-Johnson Company-Gulf Coast Operations, Pascagoula, MS; *Int'l*, pg. 709
Lappen, Michael, Gen. Mgr.--Wang Australia Pty. Ltd., Frenchs Forest, Australia; *U.S. Public*, pg. 1737
Lapple, Robert C, V.P.--Engelhard Metals AG, Zug, Switzerland; *U.S. Public*, pg. 582
Laprade, Ed, Pres.--Sullair Corporation, Michigan City, IN; *U.S. Public*, pg. 1534
Lapsys, Michael T., Pres.--ConAgra Feed Ingredient, Knoxville, TN; *U.S. Public*, pg. 426
Lara, Carlos, Chief Oper. Officer--Tubetec, Mexico, Mexico; *U.S. Private*, pg. 873
Lara, Juan Jose, Vice Chm., Exec. V.P. & Chief Exec. Officer--Durakon Mexicana, S.A. de C.V., Lerma, Mexico; *U.S. Public*, pg. 537
Laraway, Steven D., Pres. & Chief Exec. Officer--First American Trust Company of Minnesota, Saint Cloud, MN; *U.S. Private*, pg. 167
Laraya, R.G., Chm.--BenguetCorp. International Ltd., Hong Kong, Hong Kong; *Int'l*, pg. 187
Laraya, R.G., Pres.--Benguet Ebara Real Estate Corporation, Manila, Philippines; *Int'l*, pg. 432
Laraya, Rogelio G., Chm. Bd.--Benguet Ebara Real Estate Corp., Laguna, Philippines; *Int'l*, pg. 187
Larbiere, J., Chief Oper. Officer--Goodyear-Luxembourg, Colmar, Luxembourg; *U.S. Public*, pg. 753
Larder, E., Mng. Dir.--Riley Advertising (Birmingham) Ltd., Birmingham, United Kingdom; *Int'l*, pg. 1117
Larder, P. H., Mng. Dir.--CIBC Bank and Trust Company (Cayman) Limited, Georgetown, Cayman Islands; *Int'l*, pg. 257
Lardino, Mary, Gen. Mgr.--Poe & Brown of Nevada, Las Vegas, NV; *U.S. Public*, pg. 1312
Lardner, M. Thomas, Pres. & Chief Exec. Officer--The L & B Group, Dallas, TX; *U.S. Public*, pg. 1673
Lardner, Peter, Chm. Bd., Pres. & Chief Exec. Officer--Bituminous Casualty Corp., Rock Island, IL; *U.S. Public*, pg. 1218
Lardner, Peter, Chm. Bd.--Bituminous Fire and Marine Insurance Co., Rock Island, IL; *U.S. Public*, pg. 1218
Larena, J.M. Alvear, Gen. Mgr.--BILBAO Compania Anonima de Seguros y Reaseguros, Neguri, Spain; *Int'l*, pg. 499
Largen, Joseph, Pres. & Chief Oper. Officer--Brodart Sales Co., Williamsport, PA; *U.S. Private*, pg. 170
Largen, Joseph, Chief Oper. Officer--Brodart, Brantford, Canada; *U.S. Private*, pg. 170
Largen, Joseph, Chief Oper. Officer--Dart Realty Co. Ltd., Brantford, Canada; *U.S. Private*, pg. 170
Larielle, Gail, Mng. Dir.--Shandwick France, Paris, France; *Int'l*, pg. 1227
Lariot, J., Pres. & Gen. Mgr.--Industrias Wyeth S.A., Caracas, Venezuela; *U.S. Public*, pg. 81
Lariviere, Louis F., V.P.--Promotion Blitz Inc., Quebec, Canada; *Int'l*, pg. 336
Lariviere, Ray, Mng. Dir.--Bently Nevada Canada Ltd., Nisku, Canada; *U.S. Private*, pg. 134
LaRiviere, Stephen, Mng. Dir.--DYWIDAG Systems International, USA, Inc., Portland, OR; *Int'l*, pg. 424
Lark, E., Mng. Dir.--Consilium Bulk-Babcock, Kvanum AB, Kvanum, Sweden; *Int'l*, pg. 131
Larkin, J.P., Pres.--Spectra Marketing Systems, Chicago, IL; *Int'l*, pg. 1447
Larkins, Gary L., Chief Exec. Officer--So Fro Fabrics, Inc., Sherman Oaks, CA; *U.S. Public*, pg. 842
Larkins, Mary L., Pres.--CitFed Mortgage Corporation of America, Dayton, OH; *U.S. Public*, pg. 376
LaRocco, J.L., Chief Oper. Officer--AquaMatic, Rockford, IL; *U.S. Public*, pg. 1234
LaRoche, Calvin, Pres. & Chief Exec. Officer-Mtel. International--MTel International, Washington, DC; *U.S. Public*, pg. 1120
Larocque, Robert, Site Mgr.--Black & Decker Holdings (Canada) Inc., Brockville, Canada; *U.S. Public*, pg. 234
Larrabure, R.L., Sr. V.P. & Mgr.--ABN AMRO Bank, N.V. (San Francisco), San Francisco, CA; *Int'l*, pg. 10
Larracoechea, Ignacio, Mng. Dir.--Johnson & Johnson S.A. Consumer, Madrid, Spain; *U.S. Public*, pg. 931
Larrain, German, Gen. Mgr.--Mueblas Andes, Santiago, Chile; *U.S. Public*, pg. 553
Larrain, Mauricio, Chief Rep.--Banco Santander Chile, S.A., Santiago, Chile; *Int'l*, pg. 144
Larrain, Nicolas, Pres.--ADN/ADD, Santiago, Chile; *U.S. Private*, pg. 1200
Larrick, Steve, Pres.--Chernin's Shoe Outlet, Chicago, IL; *U.S. Private*, pg. 233
Larricq, E. P., Gen. Mgr.--Purina Alimentos Ltda., Sao Paulo, Brazil; *U.S. Public*, pg. 1360
Larroche, Michel, Gen. Mgr.--H.J. Heinz SARL, Paris, France; *U.S. Public*, pg. 806
Larroque, J.M., Gen. Rep.--Gan Incendie Accidents Japan, Tokyo, Japan; *Int'l*, pg. 564
Larsen, Bent, Pres.--Brodrene Dahl A/S, Glostrup, Denmark; *Int'l*, pg. 359
Larsen, Dale E., Chief Oper. Officer--Pool Arctic Alaska, Anchorage, AK; *U.S. Public*, pg. 1316
Larsen, Fred, Gen. Mgr.--Sterling Electronics, Salt Lake City, UT; *U.S. Public*, pg. 1051
Larsen, Jorgen, Mng. Dir.--Sony Music International Ltd., London, United Kingdom; *Int'l*, pg. 1284
Larsen, Kolbjorn K., Gen. Mgr.--NOF Jotun (H.K.) Ltd., Wan Chai, Hong Kong; *Int'l*, pg. 716
Larsen, Kris, Sr. V.P. & Mng. Dir.--Interbrand Schechter, Chicago, IL; *U.S. Public*, pg. 1224
Larsen, Lee, V.P. & Gen. Mgr.--KOA-AM, Denver, CO; *U.S. Public*, pg. 922
Larsen, Marshall O., Pres.--B.F. Goodrich Aerospace, Akron, OH; *U.S. Public*, pg. 751
Larsen, Mogens, Mng. Dir.--Contl. Europe--Western Service A/S, Copenhagen, Denmark; *U.S. Public*, pg. 1760
Larsen, Ojvind, Gen. Mgr.--Forsikringsaksjeselskapet Allianz Nordeuropa, Lysaker, Norway; *Int'l*, pg. 60
Larsen, Ole-Johannes, Pres.--Kvaerner Rosenberg Newfoundland Ltd., Saint Johns, Canada; *Int'l*, pg. 768
Larsen, Palle, Gen. Mgr.--Storage Technology Denmark, Copenhagen, Denmark; *U.S. Public*, pg. 1523
Larsen, Per Henrik, Chief Oper. Officer--Novo Nordisk (China) Biotechnology Co. Ltd., Tianjin, China; *Int'l*, pg. 989
Larsen, Steen, Chief Oper. Officer--Novo Nordisk A/S, Singapore, Singapore; *Int'l*, pg. 987
Larsen, W.T., Gen. Mgr.--Svanehoj International A/S, Aalborg, Denmark; *Int'l*, pg. 1065
Larson, Bob, Gen. Mgr.--Masury Paint, Wheeling, IL; *U.S. Public*, pg. 1707
Larson, Carl, Gen. Mgr.--General Nutrition Services, Inc., Pittsburgh, PA; *U.S. Public*, pg. 725
Larson, Clay, Pres.--First National Bank of Central California, Salinas, CA; *U.S. Public*, pg. 1248
Larson, D. Scott, Div. Mgr.--Western Div., Santa Fe Springs, CA; *U.S. Public*, pg. 70
Larson, Dan, Pres.--Speedway Development Corp., Ontario, CA; *U.S. Public*, pg. 941
Larson, Dan, Pres.--Eagle Mountain Reclamation, Inc., Ontario, CA; *U.S. Public*, pg. 941
Larson, Dan, Pres.--Fontana Water Resources, Inc., Ontario, CA; *U.S. Public*, pg. 941
Larson, Dan, Pres.--Kaiser Recycling Corp., Ontario, CA; *U.S. Public*, pg. 941
Larson, Daniel N., Pres.--Kaiser Steel Corporation, Ontario, CA; *U.S. Public*, pg. 941
Larson, Daniel N., Pres.--Kaiser Steel Land Development, Inc., Ontario, CA; *U.S. Public*, pg. 941
Larson, Daniel N., Pres.--Kaiser Waste Treatment, Inc., Ontario, CA; *U.S. Public*, pg. 941
Larson, Dave, Pres.--Cargill Animal Nutrition Div., Minneapolis, MN; *U.S. Private*, pg. 210
Larson, Dean, Pres.--PVS Chemicals, Inc., Copley, OH; *U.S. Private*, pg. 828
Larson, Duane, Pres.--Aramark Educational Resources Inc. Inc., Golden, CO; *U.S. Private*, pg. 79
Larson, Eric W., Mgr.-Branch--Piper Jaffray Inc., Torrance, CA; *U.S. Public*, pg. 1301
Larson, Jay M., Mgr.-Branch--Piper Jaffray Inc., Fresno, CA; *U.S. Public*, pg. 1303
Larson, Johan H., Pres.--SkandiaBanken Fonder AB, Stockholm, Sweden; *Int'l*, pg. 1257
Larson, John D., Pres.--NGL Investment Services Inc., Madison, WI; *U.S. Private*, pg. 784
Larson, Keith, Pres.--Vibration Mountings & Controls, Inc., Bloomingdale, NJ; *U.S. Public*, pg. 24
Larson, Ken, Gen. Mgr.--Mastergear Division, Roscoe, IL; *U.S. Public*, pg. 1370
Larson, Lee, Gen. Mgr.--KHOW-AM/FM, Denver, CO; *U.S. Public*, pg. 922
Larson, LeRoy, Pres.--Saskatchewan Wheat Pool, Regina, Canada; *Int'l*, pg. 1195
Larson, M.A., Mng. Dir.--De La Rue Systems AB, Stockholm, Sweden; *Int'l*, pg. 387
Larson, Michael, Admin.--Heritage Country Manor, Sherman, TX; *U.S. Public*, pg. 839
Larson, R.N., Gen. Mgr.--Amersham Denmark ApS, Birkerod, Denmark; *Int'l*, pg. 993
Larson, Richard W., Chm. Bd. & Chief Exec. Officer--Bank of America Alaska, N.A., Anchorage, AK; *U.S. Public*, pg. 180
Larson, Rick, Reg. Mgr.--Factory Automation--Aromat Northwestern Sales Office, San Jose, CA; *Int'l*, pg. 848
Larson, Steve, Admin.--Heritage Manor Longview, Longview, TX; *U.S. Public*, pg. 839
Larson, Steven C., Plant Mgr.--The Albia Division, Albia, IA; *U.S. Public*, pg. 349
Larson, Susan S., Mgr.--CAP Gemini America (Denver Branch), Englewood, CO; *Int'l*, pg. 264
Larson, Tom, V.P.--CENEX Supply & Marketing, Saint Paul, MN; *U.S. Private*, pg. 222
Larsson, Ake, Mng. Dir.--Gambro K.K., Shiga, Japan; *Int'l*, pg. 668
Larsson, Ake, Mng. Dir.--Gambro K.K., Tokyo, Japan; *Int'l*, pg. 668
Larsson, Anders, Mng. Dir.--Avesta Calamo AB, Molkom, Sweden; *Int'l*, pg. 221
Larsson, Annika, Chief Fin. Officer--Knurr-Norge AS, Oslo, Norway; *Int'l*, pg. 739
Larsson, Annika, Chief Fin. Officer--Knurr Sverige AB, Kista, Sweden; *Int'l*, pg. 739
Larsson, Bjorn, Mng. Dir.--Lowe Brindfors, Stockholm, Sweden; *U.S. Private*, pg. 678
Larsson, Bjorn, Pres.--Volvo Bus Corporation, Goteborg, Sweden; *Int'l*, pg. 1476
Larsson, Carl Goran, Exec. V.P.-Network Services Div.--Telia Nattganster Division, Farsta, Sweden; *Int'l*, pg. 1373
Larsson, Goran, Mng. Dir.--Young & Rubicam Business Communications S.A., Geneva, Switzerland; *U.S. Private*, pg. 1199
Larsson, Hakan, Mgr.--Dormer Tools AB, Halmstad, Sweden; *Int'l*, pg. 1185
Larsson, Jan-Olov, Gen. Mgr.--IVT Graphics, Tranas, Sweden; *U.S. Public*, pg. 170
Larsson, Lars Olof, Chief Oper. Officer--Perstorp Components Inc., Plymouth, MI; *Int'l*, pg. 1040
Larsson, Lars Olov, Pres.--Perstorp Components, Lambrecht, Germany; *Int'l*, pg. 1040
Larsson, Lars-Borje, Mng. Dir.--NCT Norden AB, Malmo, Sweden; *Int'l*, pg. 915
Larsson, Lennart, Mng. Dir.--ESTA Fastighets AB, Goteborg, Sweden; *Int'l*, pg. 281
Larsson, Olov, Pres.--Hydrauto AB, Skelleftea, Sweden; *Int'l*, pg. 678
Larsson, Per, Pres.--Astra Export & Trading AB, Sodertalje, Sweden; *Int'l*, pg. 93
Larsson, Per Yngve, Mng. Dir.--AB Ph. Nederman & Co., Helsingborg, Sweden; *Int'l*, pg. 281
Larsson, Staffan, Mgr.--AB Sandvik Metal Saws, Lidkoping, Sweden; *Int'l*, pg. 1185
Larsson, Sune, Chief Oper. Officer--Saab Automation AB, Jonkoping, Sweden; *Int'l*, pg. 686
Larsson, Sune, Mng. Dir.--Telefonaktiebolaget LM Ericsson Technical Office Oman, Muscat, Oman; *Int'l*, pg. 1371
Larsson, Thorbjorn, Chief Oper. Officer--Electrolux-Wascator AB, Ljungby, Sweden; *Int'l*, pg. 439
Larsson, Uno, Mng. Dir.--Iggesund Paperboard Inc., Southport, CT; *Int'l*, pg. 886
LaRuffa, Richard A., Pres.--Value Engineering & Management, Inc., Morristown, NJ; *U.S. Private*, pg. 365
LaSalla, Francis J., Chief Oper. Officer--BHF Securities Corp., New York, NY; *Int'l*, pg. 119
Lascaris, Reg, Mng. Dir.--Hunt Lascaris/TBWA, Sandton, South Africa; *U.S. Private*, pg. 1062
Laseen, Jan, Chief Oper. Officer--Electrolux S.A. de C.V., Mexico, Mexico; *Int'l*, pg. 443
Laseen, Jan, Pres.--Health-Mor Mexicana S.A. de C.V., Mexico, Mexico; *U.S. Public*, pg. 771
Lasier, D.W., Pres.--Door Hardware Group, San Francisco, CA; *U.S. Public*, pg. 876
Laskey, Bill, V.P. & Gen. Mgr.--Wix Div., Gastonia, NC; *U.S. Public*, pg. 479
Laskey, John, Pres.--Port Lawrence Title & Trust Co., Toledo, OH; *U.S. Public*, pg. 626
Laskoski, Richard, Pres.--Print-O-Stat, Inc., York, PA; *U.S. Private*, pg. 830
Lasky, David, Pres.--Bresler's Industries, Inc., Des Plaines, IL; *Int'l*, pg. 1520
Lasky, David, Pres.--Larry's Industries, Inc., Des Plaines, IL; *Int'l*, pg. 1520
Lasky, David, Pres.--Pro Portion Industries, Inc., Des Plaines, IL; *Int'l*, pg. 1520
Lasky, Stephen, Publr.--Locksmith Publishing Corp., Park Ridge, IL; *Int'l*, pg. 1432
Lasnik, R., Mgr.-Opers.--Leisure Time Industries, Irwindale, CA; *Int'l*, pg. 802
Lasquellec, Alain, Mgr.-Fin. & Admin.--Medtronic France S.A., Fourmies, France; *U.S. Public*, pg. 1083
Lassahn, Sonnich, Mng. Dir. & Spokesman--Wuestenrot Bank AG, Ludwigsburg, Germany; *Int'l*, pg. 1514
Lassally, Stacey, Pres.-Production--TriStar Pictures, Culver City, CA; *Int'l*, pg. 1283
Lassen, Peter, Gen. Mgr.--CPC Foods A/S, Billingstad, Norway; *U.S. Public*, pg. 225
Lassen, T., Mng. Dir.--Gestetner A/S, Vaerlose, Denmark; *Int'l*, pg. 1115
Lasser, Lawrence J., Pres. & Chief Exec. Officer--Putnam Investments, Inc., Boston, MA; *U.S. Public*, pg. 1049

Lassos, Andrew, Mgr.--GGK Athens, Athens, Greece; *Int'l*, pg. 1335
Last, Billy, Mng. Dir.--Butterworths South Africa, Durban, South Africa; *Int'l*, pg. 1095
Lasvignes, Pierre, Gen. Mgr.--Colgate-Palmolive C.I.S.A., Abidjan, Cote d'Ivoire; *U.S. Public*, pg. 398
Lataif, Louis E., Pres.--Ford Truck Operations, Dearborn, MI; *U.S. Public*, pg. 662
Lataif, Louis E., Pres.--Ford of Europe, Incorporated, Dearborn, MI; *U.S. Public*, pg. 664
Latella, Robert N., Exec. V.P.--The Genesee Brewing Company, Inc., Rochester, NY; *U.S. Public*, pg. 728
Latham, George, Mng. Dir.--R.P. Scherer Limited, Swindon, United Kingdom; *U.S. Public*, pg. 1438
Latham, John, Pres. & Chief Exec. Officer--Colony Insurance Company, Richmond, VA; *U.S. Private*, pg. 430
Lathrop, Peter, Pres.--Hartmann Luggage & Leather Goods Group, Lebanon, TN; *U.S. Public*, pg. 261
Lathrop, Thomas C., Pres. & Chief Exec. Officer--M & I Thunderbird Bank, Phoenix, AZ; *U.S. Public*, pg. 1050
Latif, Hugh, Gen. Mgr.--A.C. Nielsen Co., Paris, France; *U.S. Public*, pg. 1183
Latimer, E.J., Pres.--Monarch Development Corporation, Willowdale, Canada; *Int'l*, pg. 1359
Latimer, E.J., Pres.--The Monarch Group, Willowdale, Canada; *Int'l*, pg. 1359
Latimer, Garry, Gen. Mgr.--Allied Clinical Laboratories, Inc., Saint Petersburg, FL; *U.S. Public*, pg. 973
Latiolais, Rene L., Pres., Chief Exec. Officer--Freeport-McMoRan Resource Partners, Ltd., New Orleans, LA; *U.S. Public*, pg. 681
Latiolais, Ron, Pres.--SOLOCO, Inc., Lafayette, LA; *U.S. Public*, pg. 1179
LaTrobe, D., Chief Exec. Officer--Bowthorpe-Hellermann Distributors, Walsall, United Kingdom; *Int'l*, pg. 207
Latrous, T., Pres.--Industries Mecaniques Maghrebines, Tunis, Tunisia; *Int'l*, pg. 693
Latshaw, Jim, Plant Mgr.--Justin Boot Company, Cassville, MO; *U.S. Public*, pg. 937
Latta, Paul I., Sr. V.P. & Dir.-Retail Opers.--Rouse Operating Properties Div., Columbia, MD; *U.S. Public*, pg. 1407
Latta, Stephen C., Sr. V.P.--Bioproducts, Inc., Aurora, MO; *U.S. Private*, pg. 145
Latta, Stephen C., Sr. V.P.--Bioproducts, Inc., Louisville, KY; *U.S. Private*, pg. 145
Latter, P.F., Gen. Mgr.--Automould (Pty) Limited, Pinetown, South Africa; *Int'l*, pg. 895
Latthanan, Pornlert, Pres.--SCF Finance & Securities Co., Ltd., Bangkok, Thailand; *Int'l*, pg. 1239
Lattimore, W., Pres.--The Branigar Organization, Inc., Savannah, GA; *U.S. Public*, pg. 1666
Lattimore, W., Jr., Pres.--Transtates Properties, Inc., Savannah, GA; *U.S. Public*, pg. 1666
Lattman, Jurg, Gen. Mgr.--Keithley Instruments S.A., Dubendorf, Switzerland; *U.S. Public*, pg. 947
Lattuada, Daniele, Mng. Dir.--Basinform-Bastogi Servizi Informativi S.p.A., Milan, Italy; *Int'l*, pg. 170
Latulippe, Michel, Gen. Mgr.--Premdor Inc.-Quebec Division, Ville d'Anjou, Canada; *Int'l*, pg. 1067
Latumahina, F.P., Pres.--ING Insurance Indonesia, Jakarta, Indonesia; *Int'l*, pg. 650
Latuske, Rudi, Gen. Mgr.--ARS Integrated Systems Gmbh, Munich, Germany; *U.S. Public*, pg. 886
Latz, Dr. Hans, Co-Chief Oper. Officer--Winschermann Berlin GmbH, Berlin, Germany; *Int'l*, pg. 1167
Latz, Dr. Hans, Co-Chief Oper. Officer--SIPEC Ste Internationale de Petrole et de Chimie a r.l., Strasbourg, France; *Int'l*, pg. 1167
Latz, Gert, Mng. Dir.--Kommunalconsult Gesellschaft fur die Beratung de Offentlichen Hand mbH, Berlin, Germany; *Int'l*, pg. 160
Latzer, Richard, Pres. & Chief Exec. Officer--Transamerica Investment Services, Inc., Los Angeles, CA; *U.S. Public*, pg. 1630
Latzka, Ernst, Chm.--Leo Burnett & Wirz, Vienna, Austria; *U.S. Private*, pg. 184
Lau, Allan, Logistics Mgr.--Sun Microsystems of California Ltd., Kowloon, Hong Kong; *U.S. Public*, pg. 1532
Lau, Chai Yau, Mng. Dir.--Johore Mining & Stevedoring Co., Johor Baharu, Malaysia; *Int'l*, pg. 52
Lau, Chris, Pres.--Towne Development Of Hawaii, Inc., Honolulu, HI; *U.S. Private*, pg. 1206
Lau, Clifford, Mgr.--Bain & Company Pte. Ltd. (Singapore), Singapore, Singapore; *Int'l*, pg. 406
Lau, Connie, Grp. Mgr.-Fin.--Jardine Shipping Agencies (Hong Kong) Ltd., Quarry Bay, Hong Kong; *Int'l*, pg. 704
Lau, Dan, Mgr.--Public Service Company of Oklahoma-Western Div., Lawton, OK; *U.S. Public*, pg. 324
Lau, David, Mgr.-Plant--National-Standard Co. Canada, Guelph, Canada; *U.S. Public*, pg. 1161
Lau, John C.S., Chief Exec. Officer--Husky Oil Operations Ltd., Calgary, Canada; *Int'l*, pg. 640
Lau, John C.S., Chief Exec. Officer--Husky Oil Intl. Ltd., Calgary, Canada; *Int'l*, pg. 640
Lau, Lawrence, Gen. Mgr.--Kredietbank Taipei Branch, Taipei, Taiwan; *Int'l*, pg. 760
Lau, Richard, Pres.--Go-Gro Industries, Ltd., Kowloon Bay, Hong Kong; *U.S. Public*, pg. 314
Lau, Tommy, Chief Oper. Officer--MTS Systems China Ltd., Beijing, China; *U.S. Public*, pg. 1029
Lau, Winston, Pres.--Waldes Truarc/Industrial Retaining Ring, Somerset, NJ; *U.S. Public*, pg. 1632
Laube, Hans, Mng. Dir.--Sun Electric Deutschland, Mettmann, Germany; *U.S. Public*, pg. 1481
Lauchert, F.N., Pres.--Elf Atochem North America, Fluorochemical Div., Philadelphia, PA; *Int'l*, pg. 446
Lauchert, F.N., Grp. Pres.-Industrial Chemicals--Elf Atochem North America, Basic Chemicals Div., Philadelphia, PA; *Int'l*, pg. 446
Laucirica, Louis, Pres., Chief Exec. Officer & Chief Oper. Officer--Norton Performance Plastics, Wayne, NJ; *Int'l*, pg. 1174
Laucirica, Louis F., Pres.--Halogen Insulator & Seal Corp., Elk Grove Village, IL; *Int'l*, pg. 1174
Laud, Paul J., Sr. V.P.--CIT Group/Equity Investments, Livingston, NJ; *Int'l*, pg. 360
Laudadio, Jim, Mgr.--Shepler's Corpus Christi, Corpus Christi, TX; *U.S. Public*, pg. 413
Lauder, Arthur W., Pres.--Bettis Canada Limited, Edmonton, Canada; *U.S. Public*, pg. 483
Lauderbauch, S.L., Chief Oper. Officer--Barcroft Co., Lewes, DE; *Int'l*, pg. 1110
Lauer, Charles S., Publisher--Modern Healthcare, Chicago, IL; *U.S. Private*, pg. 285
Lauer, Clinton D., V.P.--Ford Purchasing & Supply Staff, Dearborn, MI; *U.S. Public*, pg. 664
Lauer, Michael, Mgr.-Area Sls.--Gensym GmbH, Dortmund, Germany; *U.S. Public*, pg. 731
Lauer, Timothy C., Pres. & Gen. Mgr.--Unocal Indonesia, Ltd., Jakarta, Indonesia; *U.S. Public*, pg. 1698
Lauersdorf, William E., Gen. Mgr.--Miller Automation, Inc. (OH), Troy, OH; *U.S. Public*, pg. 867
Lauff, H., Chief Exec. Officer--Ruppkeramik GmbH, Buchen, Germany; *Int'l*, pg. 1093
Laughlin, Lyle H., V.P. & Gen. Mgr.--McNally Wellman Kansas Div., Pittsburg, KS; *Int'l*, pg. 1326
Laughlin, Robert N., Pres.--CitiCorp Del-Lease, Inc., San Mateo, CA; *U.S. Public*, pg. 377
Laughon, Kenneth C., Pres.--Carter Machinery Company, Inc., Salem, VA; *U.S. Public*, pg. 315
Laughton, A.W., Chm. Bd., Pres. & Mng. Dir.--British Trimmings Ltd., Stockport, United Kingdom; *U.S. Public*, pg. 434
Laugier-Negre, Jacques, Dir.-Opers.--Devimco, Evry, France; *Int'l*, pg. 20
Laukkonen, Ilkka, Chief Rep. Officer--Merita Bank Ltd., Tokyo Representative Office, Tokyo, Japan; *Int'l*, pg. 859
Laule, William J., Chief Exec. Officer--Bundy International, Warren, MI; *Int'l*, pg. 1340
Laulhere, Larry, Gen. Mgr.--Delta Contractor Equipment Rental, Inc., Whittier, CA; *U.S. Private*, pg. 673
Laumeyer, Hans-Dieter, Dr., Gen. Mgr.--Deutsche Bank AG (Seoul), Seoul, Korea; *Int'l*, pg. 404
Laune, Jean, Chief Oper. Officer--Societe des Boissons Gazeuses de Vergeze (Gard), Vergeze, France; *Int'l*, pg. 919
Lauren, Hakan, Pres.--Cultor Food Science Inc., New York, NY; *Int'l*, pg. 349
Lauren, Ollie, Mng. Dir.--Patons & Baldwins Limited, Darlington, United Kingdom; *Int'l*, pg. 300
Lauren, Ralph, Chm. Bd.--Polo/Ralph Lauren, Lyndhurst, NJ; *U.S. Private*, pg. 875
Laurent-Mazerolle, Louis, Mng. Dir.--Bang & Olufsen France S.A., Saint Denis, France; *Int'l*, pg. 146
Laurent, D.H., Mng. Dir.--Texaco Italiana SpA, Rome, Italy; *U.S. Public*, pg. 1584
Laurent, Jacques, Chm. Bd.--Sade, Paris, France; *Int'l*, pg. 321
Laurent, Jean-Louis, Mng. Dir.--Brambles Europe S.A., Brussels, Belgium; *Int'l*, pg. 212
Laurents, Kenneth, Gen. Mgr.--Canyon Roads, New York, NY; *U.S. Public*, pg. 130
Lauri, Furio, Pres.--Meteor Construzioni Aeronautiche ed Elettroniche S.p.A., Rome, Italy; *Int'l*, pg. 653
Lauridsen, Jorgen, Pres.--Colgate-Palmolive France, Courbevoie, France; *U.S. Public*, pg. 398
Laurie, Richard, Media Dir.--Robertson Leo Burnett Pty. Ltd., Adelaide, Australia; *U.S. Private*, pg. 186
Lauritzen, Peter, Pres.--MD Foods Ingriedients amba, Viby, Denmark; *Int'l*, pg. 826
Laursen, Allan, Pres.--A/S Fibo, Risskov, Denmark; *Int'l*, pg. 1200
Lautenschlager, Jack L., Pres.--Peabody Development Company, Saint Louis, MO; *Int'l*, pg. 594
Lauterbach, Klaus, Gen. Mgr.--Cherry Mikroschalter GmbH, Auerbach, Germany; *U.S. Public*, pg. 346
Lauterbach, Klaus, Chief Oper. Officer--Cherry SRO, Ostrava, Czech Republic; *U.S. Public*, pg. 346
Lautzenheiser, Karen R., V.P. & Gen. Mgr.--Image ReproGraphics, Philadelphia, PA; *U.S. Private*, pg. 317
Lauvias, Isak, Gen. Mgr.--Elkem International AS, Tokyo, Japan; *Int'l*, pg. 447
Laux, Andre, Mng. Dir.--Laminoir de Dudelange S.A., Dudelange, Luxembourg; *Int'l*, pg. 79
Laux, Helmut, Co-Chief Oper. Officer--Bavarian Branch, Munich, Germany; *Int'l*, pg. 645
Laux, Mike, Plant Mgr.--Three Rivers Refinery, Three Rivers, TX; *U.S. Public*, pg. 1663
Lauzon, D.A., Pres. & Chief Exec. Officer--Dow Chemical Canada, Inc., Sarnia, Canada; *U.S. Public*, pg. 523
Lav, Tom, Chief Oper. Officer--Littelfuse HK Ltd., Kowloon, Hong Kong; *U.S. Public*, pg. 1001
LaVallee, Charles, Exec. Dir.--Western Pennsylvania Caring Foundation, Inc., Pittsburgh, PA; *U.S. Private*, pg. 529
Lavan, Thomas J., Exec. V.P. & Gen. Mgr.--O'Donnell-Usen Fisheries Corp., Tampa, FL; *U.S. Public*, pg. 427
Lavanture, Al, V.P.--Airtex, Chicago, IL; *U.S. Private*, pg. 1113
LaVelle, Douglas C., V.P.--GTE Information Services Incorporated, Dallas-Fort Worth Airport, TX; *U.S. Public*, pg. 696
LaVelle, Michael J., V.P.-Southern Region--Analysts International, Southern Region, Atlanta, GA; *U.S. Public*, pg. 110
Lavelle, William M., Jr., Mgr.--Sandvik Saws & Tools Co., Throop, PA; *Int'l*, pg. 1185
Lavender, Fred C., Pres.--F.E. Myers, Ashland, OH; *U.S. Public*, pg. 1273
Laverman, Eugene A., Gen. Mgr.--Kemira Color B.V., Dordrecht, Netherlands; *Int'l*, pg. 729
Laveroni, Sherrie, Reg. V.P. & Mng. Dir.--Regency Hotel, New York, NY; *U.S. Public*, pg. 1011
Laverty, J., Mng. Dir.--Babcock Africa (Pty) Ltd., Johannesburg, South Africa; *Int'l*, pg. 131
Laverty, J.N., Mng. Dir.--Babcock Engineering Contractors (PTY) LTD, Johannesburg, South Africa; *Int'l*, pg. 131
Lavezzi, Charles, V.P.--Managed Properties, Inc., Chicago, IL; *U.S. Public*, pg. 1428
Lavezzo, Dario, Gen. Mgr.--Clorox Argentina S.A., Buenos Aires, Argentina; *U.S. Public*, pg. 387
Laviec, Gerard, Chm. Bd. & Chief Exec. Officer--CFM International SA, Paris, France; *Int'l*, pg. 1166
Lavin, Jesus Redondo, Pres.--I.C.S.A. - Internacional de Composites, S.A., Madrid, Spain; *Int'l*, pg. 1224
Lavin, Joseph J., Pres.--Sandoz Agro Corporation, Dallas, TX; *Int'l*, pg. 974
Lavington, Mike, Pres. & Chief Exec. Officer--Resorts USA Inc., Bushkill, PA; *Int'l*, pg. 1087
LaVoice, Richard, Branch Mgr.--Bear, Stearns & Co. Inc., San Francisco, San Francisco, CA; *U.S. Public*, pg. 198
Lavoie, C., Mng. Dir.--Monserco Limited, Brampton, Canada; *Int'l*, pg. 993
Lavoie, Jack, Gen. Mgr.--Henkel Leather Chemicals Div., Saugus, MA; *Int'l*, pg. 610
Lavoie, James R., Pres.--Integrated Performance Decisions, North Stonington, CT; *U.S. Public*, pg. 110
Lavoie, P., Exec. V.P.--Rose & Laflamme Co. Ltd., La Prairie, Canada; *Int'l*, pg. 1195
Lavonen-Ronkainen, Helga, Gen. Mgr.--KONE Finance Corporation, Helsinki, Finland; *Int'l*, pg. 746
LaVoy, Mark, Office Mgr.--Huber, Hunt & Nichols, Inc., Dallas, TX; *U.S. Private*, pg. 548
Law-Smith, David J., Chm. Bd., Pres. & Chief Exec. Officer--Caltex Petroleum Corporation, Irving, TX; *U.S. Public*, pg. 348
Law, A.J., Mng. Dir.--Standard Cressall Limited, Leicester, United Kingdom; *Int'l*, pg. 590
Law, C.W., Mng. Dir.--Dexter Asia Pacific Limited, Kowloon, Hong Kong; *U.S. Public*, pg. 505
Law, Douglas E., Plant Mgr--Reidsville Container Div., Reidsville, NC; *U.S. Public*, pg. 1289
Law, H.K., Gen. Mgr.--Alaron Asia Ltd., Kowloon, Hong Kong; *U.S. Private*, pg. 31
Law, Kerry, Div. Pres.--Fidelity Express Money Order Company Division, Sulphur Springs, TX; *U.S. Private*, pg. 436
Law, Ralph, Plant Mgr.--NavCom Defense Electronics, Inc., Warner Robins, GA; *U.S. Private*, pg. 789
Law, T.R., Mng. Dir.--Alumina Company Limited, Widnes, United Kingdom; *Int'l*, pg. 51
Lawhon, David, Pres.--TBAC - Prince Gardner, Inc., Arlington, TX; *U.S. Public*, pg. 1560
Lawhun, Del, Dir.-Opers.--Sheppard Foodservice, Inc., Auburndale, FL; *U.S. Public*, pg. 1529
Lawler, Jeff, Chief Oper. Officer--Orbex Inc., Circle Pines, MN; *U.S. Public*, pg. 238
Lawler, Joseph A., Pres.--Blue M Electric Co., Watertown, WI; *U.S. Public*, pg. 726
Lawler, Tim, Mgr.-Div.--Pittsburgh Stadium Concessions, Inc., Pittsburgh, PA; *U.S. Private*, pg. 79
Lawler, William H., V.P.--Military Aircraft Systems Division, El Segundo, CA; *U.S. Public*, pg. 1198
Lawless, Gregory, V.P.-Opers.--Wyman-Gordon Investment Castings, San Leandro, CA; *U.S. Public*, pg. 1782
Lawn, Terry, Assoc. Dir.--GATX Financial Services (Australia) PTY. Limited, Sydney, Australia; *U.S. Public*, pg. 691
Lawrence, A.L. John, Pres.--Phelps Dodge Exploration Corporation, Phoenix, AZ; *U.S. Public*, pg. 1287
Lawrence, D.M., Mng. Dir.--Firstcorp Merchant Bank Limited, Johannesburg, South Africa; *Int'l*, pg. 487
Lawrence, Fredrick D., Chief Exec. Officer--Comstream Corporation, San Diego, CA; *Int'l*, pg. 1288
Lawrence, G. Barry, Pres.--Gear Research Incorporated, Grand Rapids, MI; *U.S. Private*, pg. 598
Lawrence, H. Willard, V.P. & Branch Mgr.--Bergen Brunswig Medical Corporation, Mobile, AL; *U.S. Public*, pg. 214
Lawrence, Judy, Mgr.-Admin. & Risk--Canadian Pool Agencies Ltd., Winnipeg, Canada; *Int'l*, pg. 1195
Lawrence, Kenneth E., Pres.--Kelley Electric Company, Kennett, MO; *U.S. Private*, pg. 453
Lawrence, Larry, V.P.--Napa Pipe Corporation, Napa, CA; *U.S. Public*, pg. 1230
Lawrence, Mervyn, Mng. Dir.--Tyco Grinnell Asia Pacific (Thailand) Limited, Bangkok, Thailand; *U.S. Public*, pg. 1651
Lawrence, P.N. Kyle, Pres.--EZ Paintr Canada, Weston, Canada; *U.S. Public*, pg. 1178
Lawrence, Raymond, Jr., Distr. Mgr.--Browning-Ferris Industries of New Hampshire, Inc., Portsmouth, NH; *U.S. Public*, pg. 263
Lawrence, Steve, Pres.--California Custom Foods, Lodi, CA; *U.S. Private*, pg. 831
Lawrence, W., Mng. Dir.--PT IPCindo SISKOMDATA, Jakarta, Indonesia; *Int'l*, pg. 651
Lawrenson, C., Mgr.--Rockware Glass Ltd.-Worksop Factory, Worksop, United Kingdom; *Int'l*, pg. 124
Lawrenson, Stan, Mng. Dir.--L. Gardner Group PLC, Eccles, United Kingdom; *Int'l*, pg. 1381
Lawrenson, Stan, Mng. Dir.--L. Gardner & Sons Ltd., Eccles, United Kingdom; *Int'l*, pg. 1381
Lawrenson, Stan, Mng. Dir.--Gardner Avon, Eccles, United Kingdom; *Int'l*, pg. 1381
Laws, Dean R., Chm.--EJL Advertising/Los Angeles, Los Angeles, CA; *U.S. Private*, pg. 673
Laws, E.H., Pres.--Bayou City Barge Lines, Houston, TX; *U.S. Public*, pg. 19
Laws, E.H., Pres.--Ada Crude Oil Company, Houston, TX; *U.S. Public*, pg. 19
Laws, Ed, Chief Oper. Officer--Marketing Div., Houston, TX; *U.S. Public*, pg. 19
Lawson, Adrian, Pres.--Allied Colloids (Australia) Pty. Ltd., Wyong, Australia; *Int'l*, pg. 62
Lawson, Dan, Chief Oper. Officer--Allright Birmingham Inc., Mobile, AL; *U.S. Private*, pg. 42
Lawson, James, Pres.--Pneumatic Scale Corporation, Cuyahoga Falls, OH; *U.S. Private*, pg. 118
Lawson, John P., Jr., Pres.--The Otto Konigslow Mfg. Co., Cleveland, OH; *U.S. Public*, pg. 1640

Lawson, Paul, Pres.--Pepper-Lawson, Katy, TX; *U.S. Private*, pg. 851
Lawson, Phil, Plant Mgr.--Peerless Div., Thomaston, GA; *U.S. Public*, pg. 1599
Lawton, G.E., Chief Oper. Officer--Nutone Canada Inc., Mississauga, Canada; *Int'l*, pg. 1499
Lawton, Joe, Chief Oper. Officer--Kodak Commercial & Information Systems Marketing, Arlington, VA; *U.S. Public*, pg. 551
Lawton, John, Mng. Dir.--American Appraisal (U.K.) Ltd., Manchester, United Kingdom; *U.S. Private*, pg. 50
Lawton, Robert A., Pres.--LDI Auto Paint, Fort Lauderdale, FL; *U.S. Private*, pg. 639
Lax, Kevin, Exec. V.P.--Witt Galvanizing Division, Cincinnati, OH; *U.S. Private*, pg. 1185
Lay, B. Allen, Chm. Bd., Pres. & Chief Exec. Officer--Westbrae Natural, Inc., Carson, CA; *U.S. Public*, pg. 774
Lay, Charles, Pres. & Chief Exec. Officer--Geneva Pharmaceuticals, Inc., Broomfield, CO; *Int'l*, pg. 973
Lay, W. Sherman, Chief Exec. Officer--Philadelphia American Life Insurance Company, Houston, TX; *U.S. Public*, pg. 853
Laycock, M., Chm. Bd.--Taylor Woodrow Construction (Midlands) Ltd., Stafford, United Kingdom; *Int'l*, pg. 1358
Laycock, M., Chm. Bd.--Taylor Woodrow Construction Holdings Limited, Southall, United Kingdom; *Int'l*, pg. 1358
Layden, A.J., Jr., Chief Oper. Officer--Allright Parking of Texas, Inc., Houston, TX; *U.S. Private*, pg. 43
Layhon, Patrick, Mgr.--DWF of Seattle, Seattle, WA; *U.S. Private*, pg. 326
Layman, Harold E., Pres.--Blount Development Corp., Montgomery, AL; *U.S. Public*, pg. 239
Layman, Janice, Dir.--Parafax, Tampa, FL; *U.S. Private*, pg. 838
Layton, Richard A., Gen. Mgr.--Mohawk Flush Doors, Inc., Northumberland, PA; *Int'l*, pg. 1067
Layton, Rob, Area Mgr.--Quest Wood Division, Quesnel, Canada; *Int'l*, pg. 1395
Layton, Tim W., Pres. & Chief Exec. Officer--Medeco Security Locks, Inc., Salem, VA; *U.S. Public*, pg. 828
Layzell, P.A., Mng. Dir.--BMW (GB) Ltd., Bracknell, United Kingdom; *Int'l*, pg. 178
Lazarini, Gary L., Chm. Bd.--Commerce Investment Corporation, Memphis, TN; *U.S. Public*, pg. 1155
Lazdins, Arnis, Chief Oper. Officer--AGA SIA, Riga, Latvia; *Int'l*, pg. 14
Lazo, Samson C., Chief Oper. Officer--EEI-Marine Corp., Manila, Philippines; *Int'l*, pg. 426
Lazopoulas, Emanuel, V.P.--Fresh World, Eddystone, PA; *Int'l*, pg. 454
Le Blanc, Michele, Mgr.--General Employment Enterprises, Inc., Houston, TX; *U.S. Public*, pg. 714
Le Boutiellier, John, Pres.--Iron-Ore Company of Canada, Montreal, Canada; *Int'l*, pg. 967
Le Gall, Pierre, Gen. Mgr.--Richardson Franc SNC, Colombes, France; *U.S. Public*, pg. 1388
le Hodey, Patrice, Chief Exec. Officer--Claeys Semences, Annoeullin, France; *Int'l*, pg. 790
Le Houerou, Philippe H., Resident Rep.--Banque Mondiale, Antananarivo, Madagascar; *U.S. Private*, pg. 1189
Le Juerrne, Richard J., Pres.--Lamar Electro-Air, Wellington, KS; *U.S. Public*, pg. 1640
Le Louarn, A., Gen. Mgr.--ING Lease France, Paris, France; *Int'l*, pg. 650
Le Marquand, Phillip, Pres.--ALstrip East, Exton, PA; *U.S. Public*, pg. 43
Le Merrer, P., Gen. Mgr.--Steelweld France Sarl, Le Vesinet, France; *Int'l*, pg. 71
Le Metit, J.P., Gen. Mgr.--LTR Industries, Paris, France; *U.S. Public*, pg. 960
Le Morvan, Jacques, Mng. Dir.--Bertrand Faure Components Ltd., Mississauga, Canada; *Int'l*, pg. 193
Le Nir, Max, Mng. Dir.--CFG SA, Orleans, France; *Int'l*, pg. 608
Le Paire, M., Chief Oper. Officer--V.A.G. France S.A., Villers-Cotterets, France; *Int'l*, pg. 1475
Le Poidevin, Keith R., Mng. Dir.--Banque Belge Trust Company Ltd., Saint Peter Port, United Kingdom; *Int'l*, pg. 547
le Proux de la Riviere, Bruno, Mng. Dir.--Dun & Bradstreet France SA, Nanterre, France; *U.S. Public*, pg. 536
Le Roux, Herve, Mgr.--Sael Decors, Lavaur, France; *Int'l*, pg. 421
Le Roux, T., V.P.-Far East--Compagnie Generale de Geophysique (Far East), Singapore, Singapore; *Int'l*, pg. 241
Le Tissier, Anthony, Chief Oper. Officer--The First National Bank of Boston (Guernsey) Limited, Saint Peter Port, United Kingdom; *U.S. Public*, pg. 185
Le Vacon, Yannick, Pres.--Sfernice, S.A., Nice, France; *U.S. Public*, pg. 1722
Le, Luu, Sr. V.P. & Country Mgr.--Bank of America NT&SA, Hanoi, Vietnam; *U.S. Public*, pg. 182
Leach, Alan R., Pres.--Deposit Guaranty Investments, Inc., Jackson, MS; *U.S. Public*, pg. 501
Leach, Ed, Gen. Mgr.--Esselte Pendaflex, Union, MO; *Int'l*, pg. 460
Leach, J.W., Pres.--Tenneco United Kingdom, Inc., Richmond, United Kingdom; *U.S. Public*, pg. 1580
Leach, P.S., Mng. Dir.--Haden Drysys International Ltd., Birmingham, United Kingdom; *Int'l*, pg. 585
Leach, P.S., Mng. Dir.--Haden Drysys Ltd., Birmingham, United Kingdom; *Int'l*, pg. 585
Leach, R. K., Gen. Mgr.--Molson Saskatchewan Brewery Ltd., Regina, Canada; *Int'l*, pg. 887
Leach, Rodney, Chm. Bd.--JIB Group plc, London, United Kingdom; *Int'l*, pg. 705
Leadbeater, Seth, Pres.--Commerce Bank, N.A., Clayton, MO; *U.S. Public*, pg. 409
Leahey, Lynn, Editor-in-Chief--Soap Opera Digest, New York, NY; *U.S. Public*, pg. 1328
Leahy, Brian, Branch Mgr.--Bently Nevada Canada ltd., Markham, Canada; *U.S. Private*, pg. 134
Leahy, Terry, Pres. & Chief Exec. Officer--Stream International Holdings Inc., Canton, MA; *U.S. Public*, pg. 518
Leake, Lewis D., Asst. V.P.-Property & Casualty & Reg. Mgr.-N. Central--Willis Corroon Administrative Services Corporation, Saint Louis, MO; *Int'l*, pg. 1504
Leal, F.A., Pres.--Pharmacia & Upjohn Coordination Center N.V., Puurs, Belgium; *Int'l*, pg. 1049
Leal, Roberto, Exec. V.P., Pres. & CEO-JWT/Brazil--J. Walter Thompson Company, New York, NY; *Int'l*, pg. 1483
Leaman, Stephen, Pres.--Progressive Corp., Financial Services Div., Cleveland, OH; *U.S. Public*, pg. 1334
Leaman, Stephen, Pres.--Maryland Casualty Co., Baltimore, MD; *Int'l*, pg. 1530
Leaman, Stephen J., Pres.--United Financial Casualty Co., Cleveland, OH; *U.S. Public*, pg. 1335
Leano, Alberto M., Pres.--Ebara-Benguet, Inc., Laguna, Philippines; *Int'l*, pg. 187
Lear, Gene, Pres.--E & B Marine Supply, Inc., Edison, NJ; *U.S. Public*, pg. 1756
Learney, Mike, Mng. Dir.--Lambert Smith Hampton, Birmingham, United Kingdom; *Int'l*, pg. 797
Leary, Gerald J., Gen. Mgr.--Superior Valve Company, Washington, PA; *U.S. Public*, pg. 63
Leary, Mikel J., Pres.--Dairy Queen of Georgia, Inc., Decatur, GA; *U.S. Public*, pg. 220
Leary, Stephen, Chief Oper. Officer--GEC Engineering (Accrington) Ltd., Accrington, United Kingdom; *Int'l*, pg. 544
Leary, Thomas, Plant Superintendant--Quebecor Printing Semline Inc., West Bridgewater, MA; *Int'l*, pg. 1077
Leasure, Lukoki W., Pres.--L3 Communications Hycor Div., Woburn, MA; *U.S. Private*, pg. 638
Leath, Dale, Plant Mgr.--Dayton Superior Corp., Dallas, TX; *U.S. Private*, pg. 932
Leavell, Charlie, Mgr.--IBP-Boise, Boise, ID; *U.S. Public*, pg. 852
Leaver, John, Dir.--Helly-Hansen (UK) Ltd., Nottingham, United Kingdom; *Int'l*, pg. 1011
Leavitt, H. Huntington, Pres.--Spontex, Inc., Columbia, TN; *Int'l*, pg. 1409
Leavitt, Julian, Chm. Bd.--Springfield Sugar & Prod. Co., Windsor Locks, CT; *U.S. Public*, pg. 1541
LeBaron, Rogers D., Mng. Dir.--Deutsche Bank (Asia Pacific) Ltd., Singapore, Singapore; *Int'l*, pg. 405
Lebed, Hartzel Z., Chief Oper. Officer--Connecticut General Corporation, Bloomfield, CT; *U.S. Public*, pg. 358
Lebeer, Chris, Mng. Dir.--Delaware Industrial Services N.V., Zwijnaarde, Belgium; *Int'l*, pg. 183
Lebel, Andre, Pres. & Chief Exec. Officer--Teleglobe Canada Inc., Montreal, Canada; *Int'l*, pg. 1373
Leber, B.N., Gen. Mgr.--Wyeth AG, Basel, Switzerland; *U.S. Public*, pg. 82
Leber, T., V.P. & Gen. Mgr.--Wyeth-Suaco Laboratories, Inc., Manila, Philippines; *U.S. Public*, pg. 82
Lebeuf, M., Mgr.--Swiss Bank Corporation (Canada), Montreal, Canada; *Int'l*, pg. 1332
Leblanc, Daniel, Mng. Dir.--Capital International CDPQ inc., Hanoi, Vietnam; *Int'l*, pg. 249
LeBlanc, Edgar, Div. Mgr.--Chaleurs Div., New Richmond, Canada; *Int'l*, pg. 19
LeBlanc, James E., Chm. Bd. & Chief Exec. Officer--Whirlpool Financial Corp., Benton Harbor, MI; *U.S. Public*, pg. 1765
Leblanc, Jean-Yves, Pres. & Chief Oper. Officer--Transportation Equipment Group-North America, Saint-Bruno, Canada; *Int'l*, pg. 200
LeBlanc, John, Plant Mgr.--Donaldson Co., Inc., Frankfort, IN; *U.S. Public*, pg. 517
Lebobe, Eric, Mgr.--Dormer Tools S.A., Orleans, France; *Int'l*, pg. 1186
LeBoeuf, Robert, Mng. Dir.--DYWIDAG Systems International, USA, Inc., Saint-Laurent, Canada; *Int'l*, pg. 424
Lebovitz, Stephen D., Sr. V.P.--CBL & Associates Properties, Inc., Waltham, MA; *U.S. Public*, pg. 273
LeBrasseur, Richard, Pres.--Weekly Reader Corp., Middletown, CT; *U.S. Public*, pg. 1328
Lebreiro, P., Mng. Dir.--Nutricia Portugal L.D.A., Parede, Portugal; *Int'l*, pg. 992
LeCausi, Richard, Gen. Mgr.--Genco Distributing Div., Bohemia, NY; *U.S. Public*, pg. 730
Lecher, Theodore, Pres.--GB Electrical, Inc., Milwaukee, WI; *U.S. Public*, pg. 124
Lechner, F., Mng. Dir.--GKN Distribution GmbH, Rosrath, Germany; *Int'l*, pg. 536
Lechon, Damien, Mng. Dir.--Als Conseil, Toulouse, France; *Int'l*, pg. 116
Leckenby, J., Grp. Gen. Mgr.-Building Prods.--Email Limited-Building Products Group, Huntingdale, Australia; *Int'l*, pg. 450
Leclabart, Vincent, Chm. & Pres.--Australie, Levallois-Perret, France; *Int'l*, pg. 600
LeClaire, Jeffery D., Pres.--Pulte Mortgage Corporation, Greenwood Village, CO; *U.S. Public*, pg. 1345
Leclaire, Serge, Exec. V.P.--Montreal Trustco-Personal Services Division, Montreal, Canada; *Int'l*, pg. 155
Leclerc, Guy, Mng. Dir.--IRCON Pyrometers, Inc., Marne la Vallee, France; *Int'l*, pg. 1209
Leclere, Yves, Pres.--Messier-Bugatti S.A., Velizy-Villacoublay, France; *Int'l*, pg. 1165
Leclere, Yves, Pres.--Messier Services Inc., Sterling, VA; *Int'l*, pg. 1165
Lecomte, Jean, Pres.--Volvo Penta France S.A., Les Mureaux, France; *Int'l*, pg. 1478
Lecoq, Franck, Mng. Dir.--Bertrand Faure Componentes SA, Barcelona, Spain; *Int'l*, pg. 193
LeCouffe, Alonzo, V.P. & Gen. Mgr.--Canadian Stebbins Engineering & Mfg. Co. Ltd., Ottawa, Canada; *U.S. Private*, pg. 1037
Lecouvey, Alain, Mng. Dir.--Rhone-Poulenc Argentina S.A., Buenos Aires, Argentina; *Int'l*, pg. 1112
Lecumberri, Alfredo, Mng. Dir.--Tecnoconfort SA, Pamplona, Spain; *Int'l*, pg. 193
Ledbetter, Dale, Pres.--Shelter Distribution, Elkhart, IN; *U.S. Public*, pg. 953
Ledbetter, Tom, Plant Mgr.--Pirelli Cable, Fiber Optic Div., Lexington, SC; *Int'l*, pg. 1059
Leddy, William W., Mgr.-Branch--Piper Jaffray Inc., Montecito, CA; *U.S. Public*, pg. 1303
Leder, A., Chief Oper. Officer--Balzers Hochvakuum AG, Trubbach, Switzerland; *Int'l*, pg. 997
Lederer, Bertroui, Pres.--Teknor Color Company, Pawtucket, RI; *U.S. Private*, pg. 1073
Lederer, Frank B., Pres. & Chief Exec. Officer--Thomson Healthcare Communications, Scarborough, Canada; *U.S. Public*, pg. 1602
Lederman, Melvin M., Pres.--Special Services Company, Stamford, CT; *U.S. Public*, pg. 229
Ledet, Greg, Mgr.--Aaron Scrap Metals, Orlando, FL; *U.S. Public*, pg. 413
Ledezma, Fred, Gen. Mgr.--Houston Marine Containers Inc., Deer Park, TX; *Int'l*, pg. 1214
Ledford, Cynthia, Admin.--Horizon Specialty Center of Pensacola, Pensacola, FL; *U.S. Public*, pg. 836
Ledford, Lavoy, Mgr.--ADI, Nashville, TN; *U.S. Private*, pg. 1076
Ledgerwood, Tom, Gen. Mgr.--Golden State Foods-Rochester Div., Rochester, NY; *U.S. Private*, pg. 461
Ledieu, G., Mng. Dir.--GKN Florange SARL, Florange, France; *Int'l*, pg. 536
Ledieu, G., Mng. Dir.--GKN Glaenzer Spicer SA, Poissy, France; *Int'l*, pg. 536
Ledlie, D.H., Chm. & Mng. Dir.--Esso Standard Thailand Ltd., Bangkok, Thailand; *U.S. Public*, pg. 602
Leduc, Jean-Guy, Dir.--Earle M. Jorgensen Company/Ontario, Mississauga, Canada; *U.S. Private*, pg. 600
Lee, Alan, Pres.--Unity Sewing Supply Div., Carteret, NJ; *U.S. Private*, pg. 1177
Lee, Albert, Mgr.--Commercial Metals Company, Arcadia, CA; *U.S. Public*, pg. 412
Lee, Alfred, Mng. Dir.--IPC Systems (M) Sdn Bhd, Petaling Jaya, Malaysia; *Int'l*, pg. 651
Lee, Barry, Office Mgr.--Quaker Chemical Corp., Savannah, GA; *U.S. Public*, pg. 1346
Lee, Billy, Mgr.-Mktg.--Kvaerner Hong Kong R O for Kvaerner Singapore Pte Ltd, Sha Tin, Hong Kong; *Int'l*, pg. 772
Lee, Bobbie, Pres.--Superior Reprographics, Seattle, WA; *U.S. Private*, pg. 418
Lee, C., Gen. Mgr.--Wyeth Nordiska AB, Sollentuna, Sweden; *U.S. Public*, pg. 82
Lee, C.B., Gen. Mgr.--AMP Korea Limited, Seoul, Korea; *U.S. Public*, pg. 9
Lee, C.H., Gen. Mgr.--Shandong Zibo Kinhua-Chemferm Industrial Pharm. Ltd., Zibo, China; *Int'l*, pg. 1143
Lee, C.T., Pres.--Formosa Plastics Corp., U.S.A., Livingston, NJ; *Int'l*, pg. 498
Lee, Charles, Chm. Bd.--New Tai Milk Products Co. Ltd., Taipei, Taiwan; *Int'l*, pg. 923
Lee, Chong Haee, Chief Exec. Officer--C.I. Holdings Berhad, Kuala Lumpur, Malaysia; *Int'l*, pg. 1092
Lee, Chong-Jin, V.P.--AlliedSignal International, Inc., Seoul, Korea; *U.S. Public*, pg. 53
Lee, Chong-Won, Chief Oper. Officer--Novo Nordisk A/S, Kangnung, Korea; *Int'l*, pg. 988
Lee, Chong-Won, Chief Oper. Officer--Novo Nordisk Pharma Korea Limited, Seoul, Korea; *Int'l*, pg. 988
Lee, Chris, Gen. Mgr.--ANGUS Chemical (Singapore) Pte. Ltd., Singapore, Singapore; *U.S. Private*, pg. 75
Lee, D., Chief Fin. Officer--Olivetti U.K. Ltd., London, United Kingdom; *Int'l*, pg. 1003
Lee, D.K., Rep.--Swiss Bank Corporation (Luxembourg) Ltd., Seoul, Korea; *Int'l*, pg. 1330
Lee, D.S., Mgr.--Tencarva Machinery Company, Charleston, SC; *U.S. Private*, pg. 1076
Lee, Dan K., Pres. & Chief Exec. Officer--Willis Corroon Property & Casualty Programs Div., Nashville, TN; *Int'l*, pg. 1508
Lee, David, Chief Oper. Officer--Allright Beaumont Company, Beaumont, TX; *U.S. Private*, pg. 42
Lee, David, Gen. Mgr.--Vermont American Corporation-Fountain Inn, Fountain Inn, SC; *U.S. Public*, pg. 575
Lee, David, Mill Mgr.--Bergstrom Paper Div., Neenah, WI; *U.S. Public*, pg. 746
Lee, David, Mng. Dir.--The Anvil Consultancy, Marlow, United Kingdom; *U.S. Public*, pg. 1224
Lee, David W.S., V.P. & Gen. Mgr.--AlliedSignal Laminate Systems, Singapore, Singapore; *U.S. Public*, pg. 53
Lee, Dong Myun, Mng. Dir.--Cho Hung Bank (Deutschland) GmbH, Frankfurt/Main, Germany; *Int'l*, pg. 288
Lee, Doo-Hwan, Pres.--Ssangyong Uni-Charm Co., Ltd., Kumi, Korea; *Int'l*, pg. 1291
Lee, Doyle, Pres. & Chief Exec. Officer--Weatherford National Bank, Weatherford, TX; *U.S. Public*, pg. 633
Lee, E. T., Pres.--Samsung Shipbuilding & Heavy Industries Co. Ltd., Seoul, Korea; *Int'l*, pg. 1183
Lee, E.S.H., Dir.-Opers.--Taco Aloha, Inc., Honolulu, HI; *Int'l*, pg. 704
Lee, F.N., Gen. Mgr.--AMP Taiwan B.V., Taipei, Taiwan; *U.S. Public*, pg. 9
Lee, Gary D., Pres.--Lee-Rowan Company, Saint Louis, MO; *U.S. Public*, pg. 1177
Lee, George, Branch Mgr.--Gasco, Inc., Kahului, HI; *Int'l*, pg. 225
Lee, Gerald, V.P.-Canada--Singapore Tourist Promotion Board - Toronto, Toronto, Canada; *Int'l*, pg. 1254
Lee, Irmelin, Mgr.-Fin. & Admin.--Sensormatic New Zealand Ltd., Auckland, New Zealand; *U.S. Public*, pg. 1458
Lee, J. Tyler, Pres.--Royal Financial Services Inc., Southfield, MI; *Int'l*, pg. 1130
Lee, J.D., V.P.-Opers.--Living Centers of America, Houston, TX; *U.S. Public*, pg. 1257
Lee, J.K., Chief Oper. Officer--A & A International-Seoul Branch, Seoul, Korea; *U.S. Public*, pg. 1561

Lee, Jack R., Pres.--Tower Loan of Mississippi, Inc., Jackson, MS; *U.S. Private*, pg. 207
Lee, Jae-Wook, Mng. Dir.--TMC Company Ltd., Masan, Korea; *Int'l*, pg. 952
Lee, Jai Ryong, Gen. Mgr.--Cho Hung Bank, Chicago, IL; *Int'l*, pg. 287
Lee, James, Mng. Dir.--Burgmann Korea Ltd., Seoul, Korea; *Int'l*, pg. 233
Lee, James D., Chief Strategic Officer--Hamilton Communications Group, Inc., Chicago, IL; *U.S. Private*, pg. 497
Lee, James E., Pres. & Chief Exec. Officer--USLIFE Credit Life Insurance Co., Schaumburg, IL; *U.S. Public*, pg. 77
Lee, Jean, Mgr.--Golden Tiger, Los Angeles, CA; *U.S. Private*, pg. 1182
Lee, Jeffrey, Gen. Mgr.--WBIR, Inc., Knoxville, TN; *U.S. Public*, pg. 702
Lee, Jerry D., Pres.--Macpherson Meistergram, Inc., Greensboro, NC; *U.S. Private*, pg. 1177
Lee, John, Mng. Dir.--Toppan Moore Data Products Ltd., Wan Chai, Hong Kong; *U.S. Private*, pg. 313
Lee, John, V.P. & Gen. Mgr.--Cornwall & Stevens Co., Inc., Memphis, TN; *U.S. Private*, pg. 688
Lee, John, Pres.--Schwarz Pharma Manufacturing, Inc., Seymour, IN; *Int'l*, pg. 1211
Lee, John, Jr., Pres. & Treas.--Ireland Coffee Tea, Inc., Pleasantville, NJ; *U.S. Public*, pg. 351
Lee, Jong Dae, Pres.--YuHan-Kimberly, Ltd., Seoul, Korea; *U.S. Public*, pg. 960
Lee, Jong Young, Mng. Dir.--Alloy Rods Korea Corporation, Pusan, Korea; *Int'l*, pg. 281
Lee, Jong-Kyu, Pres.--Ssangyong Precision Industry Co., Ltd., Inchon, Korea; *Int'l*, pg. 1292
Lee, Jung-ki, Pres.--Hee Sung Co. Ltd., Seoul, Korea; *Int'l*, pg. 779
Lee, K.J., Chm.--Sharp Korea Corporation (Inchon), Inchon, Korea; *Int'l*, pg. 1230
Lee, K.S., Gen. Mgr.-Sls./Korea--Utell International-Korea, Seoul, Korea; *Int'l*, pg. 1098
Lee, K.T., Mng. Dir.--Safire Private Limited, Singapore, Singapore; *U.S. Public*, pg. 363
Lee, Kenneth, Pres.--Lawrence Division, Lawrence, MA; *U.S. Public*, pg. 27
Lee, Kevin, Mgr.-Natl. Sls.--Grace Taiwan, Inc., Tao-yuan, Taiwan; *U.S. Public*, pg. 756
Lee, Kheng Leong, Sr. Mgr.--DBS Factors Pte. Ltd., Singapore, Singapore; *Int'l*, pg. 350
Lee, Kimo, Chief Representative--The Sumitomo Trust & Banking Co., Ltd., Seoul, Korea; *Int'l*, pg. 1318
Lee, Kyung-Hoon, Pres.--Daewoo Heavy Industries, Ltd., Inchon, Korea; *Int'l*, pg. 357
Lee, Larry, Chief Oper. Officer--Regency Thermographers of Ga., Inc., Doraville, GA; *U.S. Public*, pg. 89
Lee, Lawrence, Mgr.--Mag-E Furnaces Pte Ltd., Singapore, Singapore; *U.S. Private*, pg. 361
Lee, Lawrence, Mng. Dir.--Regent Motors Limited, Singapore, Singapore; *Int'l*, pg. 1251
Lee, M., Mgr.--Thermo Instrument Systems (F.E.) Limited, Aberdeen, Hong Kong; *U.S. Public*, pg. 1596
Lee, Martin, Pres.--MacGregor Golf (Taiwan) Ltd., Taipei, Taiwan; *Int'l*, pg. 73
Lee, Martin, Mng. Dir.--Weyburn-Bartel Ltd., Godalming, United Kingdom; *Int'l*, pg. 1334
Lee, Mike, Pres.--Fiesta Restaurants, Inc., Oklahoma City, OK; *U.S. Public*, pg. 555
Lee, Monica, Mgr.--Utell International-Taiwan, Taipei, Taiwan; *Int'l*, pg. 1099
Lee, Paul, Chief Oper. Officer--Electronic Arts (Canada) Inc., Burnaby, Canada; *U.S. Public*, pg. 569
Lee, Phillip, Mng. Dir.--CMC International (S.E. Asia) Pte. Limited, Singapore, Singapore; *U.S. Public*, pg. 413
Lee, Preston, Mgr.-Opers.--Woodward-Clyde, Wilmington, DE; *U.S. Public*, pg. 1657
Lee, R. K., Gen. Mgr.--Circle Airfreight Intl. (Taiwan) Ltd., Taipei, Taiwan; *U.S. Public*, pg. 372
Lee, R.G., Joint Mng. Dir.--Jardine International Motor Holdings Ltd., Hong Kong, Hong Kong; *Int'l*, pg. 705
Lee, R.M., Mgr.--Tencarva Machinery Co., Chesapeake, VA; *U.S. Private*, pg. 1076
Lee, Ramon G., Pres.--Illinois-American Water Co., Belleville, IL; *U.S. Public*, pg. 95
Lee, Richard D., Pres.--Nesota Co., Saint Paul, MN; *U.S. Private*, pg. 750
Lee, Robert E., Pres. & Chief Exec. Officer--Millennium Inorganic Chemicals, Hunt Valley, MD; *U.S. Public*, pg. 1111
Lee, S., Pres.--Semiconductor Div., Mountain View, CA; *U.S. Public*, pg. 1365
Lee, S. B., Pres.--Cheil Foods & Chemicals Inc., Seoul, Korea; *Int'l*, pg. 1181
Lee, S. S., Mgr.--Control Instruments (M) Sdn. Bhd, Kuala Lumpur, Malaysia; *U.S. Private*, pg. 361
Lee, S.U., Dr., Pres.--Korea Industrial Gases Ltd., Seoul, Korea; *U.S. Public*, pg. 32
Lee, Sang Hun, Mng. Dir.--OPD Ltd. Hong Kong, Hong Kong, Hong Kong; *Int'l*, pg. 1003
Lee, Sang-On, Pres.--Ssangyong Fire & Marine Insurance Co., Ltd., Seoul, Korea; *Int'l*, pg. 1292
Lee, Sang-Won, Pres.--Ssangyong Shipping Co. Ltd., Seoul, Korea; *Int'l*, pg. 1292
Lee, Seung-Hyum, Pres.--Ssangyong (Hong Kong) Co., Ltd., Central, Hong Kong; *Int'l*, pg. 1291
Lee, Sharon, Exec. Dir. & Chief Rep.--Dentsu Young & Rubicam Advertising Co., Ltd. (Shanghai), Shanghai, China; *U.S. Private*, pg. 325
Lee, Simon, Mng. Dir.--Circle Airfreight International Korea, Seoul, Korea; *U.S. Public*, pg. 372
Lee, Simon, Mng. Dir.--MRI UK, London, United Kingdom; *U.S. Private*, pg. 727
Lee, T.H., Dir.--Northern Storage and Transportation Project and Construction Div., Taipei, Taiwan; *Int'l*, pg. 286
Lee, T.T., Pres.--King Car Otsuka Co., Ltd., Taipei, Taiwan; *Int'l*, pg. 1014
Lee, Tai Hsiung, V.P. & Gen. Mgr.--The International Commercial Bank of China, Amsterdam, Netherlands; *Int'l*, pg. 684
Lee, Tony, Mng. Dir.--Batey Ads Malaysia Sdn. Bhd., Kuala Lumpur, Malaysia; *Int'l*, pg. 117
Lee, Tony, Editor-in-Chief--National Business Employment Weekly, Princeton, NJ; *U.S. Public*, pg. 524
Lee, Victor, Gen. Mgr.--Bausch & Lomb (Singapore) Private Limited, Singapore, Singapore; *U.S. Public*, pg. 195
Lee, Victor, Dir.-Sls. & Opers.--Square D Company Singapore Pte. Ltd., Singapore, Singapore; *Int'l*, pg. 1209
Lee, W.Q., Gen. Mgr.--Window Furnishings Singapore Pte. Ltd., Singapore, Singapore; *Int'l*, pg. 640
Lee, Warren H.W., Pres.--Hawaii Electric Light Co., Inc., Hilo, HI; *U.S. Public*, pg. 800
Lee, Wesley D., Chief Oper. Officer--Minerals Div., Reno, NV; *U.S. Public*, pg. 355
Lee, William C., Plant Mgr.--Bundy Corporation, Marysville Plant, Marysville, MI; *Int'l*, pg. 1340
Lee, Y.I., Pres. & Chief Exec. Officer--Hyundai Motor America, Fountain Valley, CA; *Int'l*, pg. 641
Lee, Yoon Hee, Chm. & Mng. Dir.--Cho Hung Bank Luxembourg S.A., Luxembourg, Luxembourg; *Int'l*, pg. 288
Lee, Young C., Chief Oper. Officer--Novo Nordisk Bioindustrial, Korea, Seoul, Korea; *Int'l*, pg. 989
Lee, Young Ho, Pres.--NMB Korea Co., Ltd., Seoul, Korea; *Int'l*, pg. 868
Lee, Young Man, Mng. Dir.--Oriental Telecommunication Company Ltd., Kyonggi-do, Korea; *Int'l*, pg. 1369
Leebove, Roger, V.P.--Optech S.A.R.L., Farmington, MI; *Int'l*, pg. 1005
Leech, James W., Pres.--St. Clair Pipelines, Toronto, Canada; *Int'l*, pg. 1492
Leech, Steve, Mgr.--Amano Cincinnati - Dallas Branch Office, Carrollton, TX; *Int'l*, pg. 70
Leeds, A., Reg. Mgr.--Air France (Southeastern Region), Miami, FL; *Int'l*, pg. 561
Leeds, Paul T., Mng. Dir.--AIS Media South, Melbourne, Australia; *Int'l*, pg. 15
Leeflang, Karel, Mng. Dir.--Elsevier Science Ireland Limited, Shannon, Ireland; *Int'l*, pg. 1100
Leemans, Michel F., Pres.--IL (Stratford), Inc., Stratford, CT; *U.S. Public*, pg. 856
Leeming, R., Chief Exec. Officer--Pilkington Australasia Limited, Melbourne, Australia; *Int'l*, pg. 1057
Leemon, Daniel J., Pres.--Vulcan Materials Company-Midsouth Div., Knoxville, TN; *U.S. Public*, pg. 1726
Leenders, R.R., Gen. Mgr.--O.H. O'Brien Division, Wetherill Park, Australia; *Int'l*, pg. 895
Leeney, Brian, Exec. V.P.--AIB plc, New York, NY; *Int'l*, pg. 64
Leer, Steven F., Pres. & Chief Exec. Officer--Arch Coal, Inc., Saint Louis, MO; *U.S. Public*, pg. 139
Lees, James, V.P.-Europe--Newport Electronics Ltd., Stevenage, United Kingdom; *U.S. Private*, pg. 816
Lees, James, Gen. Mgr.--Newport Electronics B.V., Amstelveen, Netherlands; *U.S. Private*, pg. 816
Leese, Wolfgang, Chm. Bd.--Hoesch Hohenlimburg GmbH, Hagen, Germany; *Int'l*, pg. 508
Leesha, Pete, Gen. Mgr.--Bell Distributing, Sacramento, CA; *U.S. Private*, pg. 664
Leeson, D. B., Chief Oper. Officer--California Microwave Foreign Sales Corporation, Sunnyvale, CA; *U.S. Public*, pg. 293
Leeson, R.W., V.P. & Gen. Mgr.--CompAir Mako, Ocala, FL; *Int'l*, pg. 1242
Leete, Jack, Exec. V.P.-Opers.--Sundor Brands Inc., Mount Dora, FL; *U.S. Public*, pg. 1331
Leever, Thomas M., Pres.--MacDermid Systems, Inc., Waterbury, CT; *U.S. Public*, pg. 1030
Leeves, Paul, Exec. Creative Dir.--BST-BDDP, London, United Kingdom; *Int'l*, pg. 117
Lefebvre, Kenneth M., V.P. & Gen. Mgr.-New England Opers.--Atlantic Cellular Telephone Corp., Westbrook, ME; *U.S. Public*, pg. 1708
Lefebvre, Kenneth M., V.P. & Gen. Mgr.-New England Opers.--Piscataqua Cellular Telephone Corp., Dover, NH; *U.S. Public*, pg. 1708
Lefebvre, Marc, Chief Oper. Officer--Autoliv S.A., Seclin, France; *Int'l*, pg. 441
Lefelle, Philippe, Chief Exec. Officer--Euromezzanine Gestion, Paris, France; *Int'l*, pg. 344
Lefevre, Bernard, Mng. Dir.--SKF Slewing Bearings (RKS S.A), Avallon, France; *Int'l*, pg. 1159
Lefevre, Didier, Chief Oper. Officer--Peaudouce S.A. Baby Products, Linselles, France; *Int'l*, pg. 1326
LeFevre, Jacques P., Pres.--Indy Lighting, Inc., Indianapolis, IN; *U.S. Public*, pg. 935
Lefevre, Jean-Marie, Mng. Dir.--Champagne Pommery S.A., Reims, France; *Int'l*, pg. 780
Leffel, Kenneth E., Gen. Mgr.--Koneta Rubber Co. Div., Wapakoneta, OH; *U.S. Public*, pg. 976
Lefferts, Peter A., Chm. Bd.--IDS Trust Co., Minneapolis, MN; *U.S. Public*, pg. 73
Lefferts, Peter A., Pres.--Citicorp Savings of Florida, A Federal Savings & Loan Assn., Miami, FL; *U.S. Public*, pg. 378
Lefkariti, Despo, Mng. Dir.--De La Ma/TBWA, Nicosia, Cyprus; *U.S. Private*, pg. 1062
Lefkowicz, Anthony, Chief Oper. Officer--Augat, Inc., Wiring Systems & Components Group, Montgomery, AL; *U.S. Public*, pg. 1598
Lefkowicz, Anthony, Chief Oper. Officer--Augat, Inc., Wiring Systems, Montgomery, AL; *U.S. Public*, pg. 1598
Lefler, John, Pres.--Gulf States Steel, Inc., Gadsden, AL; *U.S. Private*, pg. 488
Lefort, Bernard, Mgr.--Credit Agricole (CNCA) Representative Office-Bangkok, Bangkok, Thailand; *Int'l*, pg. 341
LeFranc, Jean, Pres.--Bank of Boston S.A., Luxembourg, Luxembourg; *U.S. Public*, pg. 185
Legallet, Georges, Mng. Dir.--Simpson Industries E.U.R.L. (France), Lyon, France; *U.S. Public*, pg. 1475
Legallet, Georges, Mng. Dir.--Simpson Techniparts E.U.R.L. (France), Lyon, France; *U.S. Public*, pg. 1475
Legan, Gayland, V.P.-Retail Sls.--Family Smacks, Inc., Liberty, MO; *U.S. Private*, pg. 393
Legaz, Alfredo Llorente, Pres.--ENUSA - E.N. del Uranio, S.A., Madrid, Spain; *Int'l*, pg. 1224
Legeait, Noel-Jean, Dir.--Bull Ingenierie S.A., Le Pecq, France; *Int'l*, pg. 316
Leger, Buster, Pres.--Woolcan, Lachine, Canada; *U.S. Private*, pg. 1188
Leger, J.C., Pres. & Chief Exec. Officer--CGTX Inc., Mississauga, Canada; *Int'l*, pg. 604
Leger, Jacques, Pres.--CGTX, Inc., Montreal, Canada; *U.S. Public*, pg. 693
Leger, Richard F., Gen. Mgr.--Rathbone Precision Metals, Palmer, MA; *U.S. Public*, pg. 307
Legg, Mark, Chief Oper. Officer--Vivitar Corporation, Newbury Park, CA; *Int'l*, pg. 1060
Leggatt, John, V.P. & Gen. Mgr.--Palmer Jarvis Advertising, Edmonton, Canada; *Int'l*, pg. 1022
Legge, Brian E., Pres.--Intercon Security Limited, Toronto, Canada; *Int'l*, pg. 699
Legget, Terry J., Mng. Dir.--BNR Europe Limited, Harlow, United Kingdom; *Int'l*, pg. 969
Leggett, M.M., Pres.--Cummins Natural Gas Engines, Inc., Fort Worth, TX; *U.S. Public*, pg. 468
Leggetter, Barry, Pres., Sr. Partner, Mng. Dir. & Exec. V.P.--Fleishman-Hillard U.K. Limited, London, United Kingdom; *U.S. Private*, pg. 411
Legler, James, Pres.--Chem-tronics, Inc., El Cajon, CA; *U.S. Public*, pg. 893
Legnani, M., Gen. Mgr.--Axson-Italia, Saronno, Italy; *Int'l*, pg. 103
Legner, Alfred, Gen. Mgr.--DG Bank-London Branch, London, United Kingdom; *Int'l*, pg. 352
LeGoer, Jean-Luc, Chief Oper. Officer--Vishay Micro-Mesures, S.A., Malakoff, France; *U.S. Public*, pg. 1722
Legrain, Olivier, Mng. Dir.--Lafarge Materiaux de Specialites, Montrouge, France; *Int'l*, pg. 789
LeGrand, David J., Pres.--Nordyne Inc., Saint Louis, MO; *U.S. Public*, pg. 1193
LeGrand, Teresa, Pres. & Chief Exec. Officer--G.E. Capital Fleet Services, Eden Prairie, MN; *U.S. Public*, pg. 710
Legros, Georges, Mng. Dir.--Generale Bank Overseas (Belgium) - Belgian Bank, Hong Kong, Hong Kong; *Int'l*, pg. 548
Legros, Georges, Mng. Dir.--Wa Pei Finance Co. Ltd., Hong Kong, Hong Kong; *Int'l*, pg. 548
Lehane, Padraig, Gen. Mgr.-China--Dun & Bradstreet International Consultant (Shanghai) Ltd., Shanghai, China; *U.S. Public*, pg. 536
Lehman, Chris, V.P. & Publ. Dir.--Successful Farming Magazine, Des Moines, IA; *U.S. Public*, pg. 1094
Lehman, David A., Pres.--Dayton Operations, Dayton, OH; *Int'l*, pg. 644
Lehman, Jim, Gen. Mgr.--Pace Dairy Foods, Rochester, MN; *U.S. Public*, pg. 967
Lehman, John, Controller--Thomas Lighting-Sparta Opers., Sparta, TN; *U.S. Public*, pg. 1599
Lehman, Lester E., Pres.--Lehman Associates, Inc., New York, NY; *U.S. Private*, pg. 1125
Lehmann, B., Dir.--NatWest Securities Limited, Zurich, Switzerland; *Int'l*, pg. 911
Lehmann, Eckart, Dr., Chm. Bd.--Knorr-Bremse Systeme Fur Schienenfahrzeuge GmbH, Munich, Germany; *Int'l*, pg. 738
Lehmann, G., Mng. Dir.--Schweizerischer Bankverein AG, Frankfurt/Main, Germany; *Int'l*, pg. 1331
Lehmann, Guido W., Gen. Mgr.--Polaroid AG, Zurich, Switzerland; *U.S. Public*, pg. 1314
Lehmuskoski, Pekka, Pres.--Fiskars Power Systems, Espoo, Finland; *Int'l*, pg. 127
Lehnen, Gerhard, Pres.--Komatsu Hanomag AG, Hannover, Germany; *Int'l*, pg. 744
Lehner, Helmut, Chief Oper. Officer--DSM Chemie Linz North America Inc., Ridgefield Park, NJ; *Int'l*, pg. 356
Lehnert, Horst, Chief Oper. Officer--Flender Guss GmbH, Wittgensdorf, Germany; *Int'l*, pg. 400
Lehnhard, Mary Nell, V.P.-Office Govt. Rels.--Blue Cross and Blue Shield Assn. Government Relations, Washington, DC; *U.S. Private*, pg. 151
Lehning, D., Mng. Dir.--Deminex Syria GmbH, Essen, Germany; *Int'l*, pg. 1461
Lehodey, John, Pres.-Sofitel--Accor North America, Scarsdale, NY; *Int'l*, pg. 21
Lehrer, Eberhard, Gen. Mgr.--Florimex Worldwide GmbH, Nuremberg, Germany; *U.S. Public*, pg. 510
Lehrer, P.M., Vice Chm.--Bovis Construction Ltd., Harrow, United Kingdom; *Int'l*, pg. 1032
Lehrer, P.M., Pres.--Bovis Inc., New York, NY; *Int'l*, pg. 1033
Lehrer, Peter, Chm. Bd. & Chief Exec. Officer--Lehrer McGovern Bovis Inc., New York, NY; *Int'l*, pg. 1035
Lehtinen, Lasse, Mng. Dir.--Sesto, Helsinki, Finland; *Int'l*, pg. 1301
Lehto, Steve, Pres.--Hyde Park Markets, Fort Lauderdale, FL; *U.S. Public*, pg. 653
Lehtonen, Bill, Chief Oper. Officer--Allright San Diego Parking, Inc., San Diego, CA; *U.S. Private*, pg. 43
Lehtonen, Minna, Chief Rep.--Merita Bank Ltd., Paris Representative Office, Paris, France; *Int'l*, pg. 859
Lehtonen, Samuli, Gen. Mgr.--Polarcup Russia, Ivanteevka, Russia; *Int'l*, pg. 638
Lehtovaara, Ari, Mng. Dir.--Nokia Telecommunications Italia S.r.l., Gessate, Italy; *Int'l*, pg. 953
Leiberfarb, Warren, Pres.--Warner Home Video, Burbank, CA; *U.S. Public*, pg. 1611
Leibler, Kenneth, Pres.--Liberty Financial Companies, Boston, MA; *U.S. Private*, pg. 666
Leibovitz, Mitchell G., Pres.--The Pep Boys-Manny, Moe & Jack of California, Los Angeles, CA; *U.S. Public*, pg. 1276
Leibovitz, Stephen J., Sr. V.P. & Gen. Mgr.--Entertainment Industries Group, Beverly Hills, CA; *U.S. Public*, pg. 871

Leibovitz, Steven B., Mgr.--Omni-One, Des Plaines, IL; *U.S. Public*, pg. 715

Leibowitz, Del, V.P.-Mktg.--Naturistics, Farmingdale, NY; *U.S. Public*, pg. 494

Leibowitz, Irene S., Dir.--Samuel Montagu Inc., New York, NY; *Int'l*, pg. 580

Leifeld, Ellen, Publr.--Ithaca Journal, Ithaca, NY; *U.S. Public*, pg. 700

Leightman, Raymond H., V.P. & Mng. Exec.--Northern Trust Bank of Florida, N.A., Aventura, FL; *U.S. Public*, pg. 1196

Leighton, D.J., Mng. Dir.--Senior Moducel Limited, Stoke on Trent, United Kingdom; *Int'l*, pg. 1221

Leighty, D.A., Pres.--Perma Pure Inc., Toms River, NJ; *Int'l*, pg. 590

Leijdekker, Hans, Sr. V.P.--ADM Cocoa, Inc., Stamford, CT; *U.S. Public*, pg. 127

Leijon, Bo, Pres.--Componenta Gjuterier AB, Ljungby, Sweden; *Int'l*, pg. 1419

Leimer, Hans Jorg, Mng. Dir.--Neef Elektrotechnik GmbH & Co., Karlsruhe, Germany; *Int'l*, pg. 1306

Lein, Kurt, Pres.--Tab Products Europa B.V., Amsterdam, Netherlands; *U.S. Public*, pg. 1559

Leiner, H., Corp. Controller--Augat AG, Zug, Switzerland; *U.S. Public*, pg. 1598

Leingang, Jay, Mng. Dir.--Otis Elevator PLC, London, United Kingdom; *U.S. Public*, pg. 1691

Leinger, Mark, Chief Oper. Officer--Mid Pacific Air Corporation, New York, NY; *U.S. Private*, pg. 603

Leinonen, Esko, Chief Oper. Officer--Procurement Area South of Finland, Hamina, Finland; *Int'l*, pg. 455

Leinss, Edward A., Chief Oper. Officer--Ahlstrom Filtration, Inc., Roswell, GA; *Int'l*, pg. 35

Leinweber, John L., Pres. & Chief Oper. Officer--Funding Services Inc., La Grange, IL; *Int'l*, pg. 379

Leird, Alen, Dir.-Fin.--NORIT (UK) Ltd., Glasgow, United Kingdom; *Int'l*, pg. 958

Leirhol, Olav, Pres.--Volvo Lastebiler og Busser Norge AS, Kolbotn, Norway; *Int'l*, pg. 1477

Leirman, Etienne, Gen. Mgr.--Tailor Steel N.V., Genk, Belgium; *Int'l*, pg. 79

Leiser, G. Malcolm, Chm. Bd.--California Custom Foods, Lodi, CA; *U.S. Private*, pg. 831

Leiser, Todd P., V.P. & Gen. Mgr.--WWRM, Inc., Saint Petersburg, FL; *U.S. Private*, pg. 282

Leissner, Bernd, Chief Oper. Officer--TAS Tvornica Automobila Sarajevo, Sarajevo, Bosnia and Herzegovina; *Int'l*, pg. 1475

Leistner, Ralph, Pres. & Chief Exec. Officer--McAlear Associates, Inc., Grand Rapids, MI; *Int'l*, pg. 1508

Leitch, A.P., Chm. Bd.--Eagle Star, Cheltenham, United Kingdom; *Int'l*, pg. 110

Leite, Anisio, Jr., Gen. Mgr.--Banco do Brasil S.A.-Paraguay, Asuncion, Paraguay; *Int'l*, pg. 141

Leite, Luiz, Chief Oper. Officer--Novo Nordisk Farmaceutica do Brasil Ltda., Sao Paulo, Brazil; *Int'l*, pg. 988

Leite, Maria, Mgr.--Broad National Bank-Livingston, Livingston, NJ; *U.S. Public*, pg. 258

Leite, Roger, Chm. Bd.--Oy FORD Ab, Helsinki, Finland; *U.S. Public*, pg. 665

Leith, William T., Pres.--Quality Park Products, Saint Paul, MN; *U.S. Public*, pg. 1038

Leitman, Jack, V.P.--W. Braun International, Opa Locka, FL; *U.S. Private*, pg. 166

Leitman, Jack, V.P.-Southern Reg.--W. Braun Co., Opa Locka, FL; *U.S. Private*, pg. 166

Leitstein, Robert, Pres.--Halls Merchandising Inc., Kansas City, MO; *U.S. Private*, pg. 496

Leitzell, Tim, Pres.--ABS Marine Services, Inc., Houston, TX; *U.S. Private*, pg. 51

Leiweke, Tim, Pres.--Denver Nuggets Limited Partnership, Denver, CO; *U.S. Public*, pg. 138

Lejesone, Jean-Michael, V.P.--Alcatel Business Systems UK, Romford, United Kingdom; *Int'l*, pg. 55

Lekander, Monika, Mng. Dir.--Nordic Synthesis AB, Karlskoga, Sweden; *U.S. Public*, pg. 297

Lekich, Ivo, Dir.-Sls.--GDC Federal Systems, Inc., Reston, VA; *U.S. Public*, pg. 708

Lekkerkerk, J., Mng. Dir.--Trencon Vuurvast BV, Oude Tonge, Netherlands; *Int'l*, pg. 894

LeKovich, J., Plant Mgr.--A.O. Smith Water Products Company, Seattle, WA; *U.S. Public*, pg. 1477

Lelan, Jean-Claude, Gen. Mgr.--Batiroc, Villers-la-Montagne, France; *Int'l*, pg. 430

Leland, David A., Pres.--Jefferson-Pilot Investor Services, Inc., Greensboro, NC; *U.S. Public*, pg. 926

Leleu, Christian, Pres.--Gargiulo Inc., Naples, FL; *U.S. Public*, pg. 1124

Lelikov, Konstantin, Chief Oper. Officer--Akerlund & Rausing, Saint Petersburg, Russia; *Int'l*, pg. 33

Lells, Peter, Chief Oper. Officer--Spectra-Physics Laserplane AB, Malmo, Sweden; *Int'l*, pg. 1289

Leloir, Maximo Federico, Pres.--Vidrieria Argentina SA, Buenos Aires, Argentina; *Int'l*, pg. 1057

Lemaire, Alain, Pres. & Chief Exec. Officer--Rolland Inc., Saint-Jerome, Canada; *Int'l*, pg. 273

Lemaire, Daniel, Mng. Dir.--Transrol S.n.c., Chambery, France; *Int'l*, pg. 1160

Lemaire, Laurent, Pres. & Chief Exec. Offficer--Cascades, Inc., Kingsey Falls, Canada; *Int'l*, pg. 273

LeMaistre, David J., Gen. Mgr.--Crafts Technology, Inc., Elk Grove Village, IL; *U.S. Public*, pg. 307

Lemarie, J.P., Chief Exec. Officer--Blackwood Hodge (Cote d'Ivoire) S.A.R.L., Abidjan, Cote d'Ivoire; *Int'l*, pg. 231

Lemay, Denis, Pres. & Gen. Mgr.--Bolands Limited, Halifax, Canada; *Int'l*, pg. 1012

Lemay, Raymond, Chm. Bd.--Wilson & Lafleur, Limitee, Montreal, Canada; *Int'l*, pg. 1076

Lemay, Raymond, Pres.--Quebecor Communications, Inc., Montreal, Canada; *Int'l*, pg. 1076

Lembre, Hakan, Pres.--TAC Control AB, Malmo, Sweden; *Int'l*, pg. 670

Lemener, George, Mng. Dir.--IBL S.A., Paris, France; *Int'l*, pg. 21

Lemercier, Jean Luc, Gen. Mgr.--Cordis S.A., Paris, France; *U.S. Public*, pg. 928

Lemert, Paul, Gen. Mgr. & Dir.-Mktg.--Agri-Graphics, Inc., Pittsburg, KS; *U.S. Private*, pg. 46

Lemert, Paul, Gen. Mgr.--Harvest Brands, Inc., Pittsburg, KS; *U.S. Private*, pg. 46

Lemery, John D., Pres.--Paul Revere Investment Management Company Inc. (PRIMCO), Worcester, MA; *U.S. Public*, pg. 1338

Lemieux, Ed, Gen. Mgr.--Bose Canada, Inc., Sainte-Marie-Beauce, Canada; *U.S. Private*, pg. 161

Lemieux, J.F., Mng. Dir.--Oerlikon Aerospace, Inc., Saint Jean-sur-Richelieu, Canada; *Int'l*, pg. 998

Lemieux, James, Mng. Dir.--Tyco (Hong Kong) Ltd., Kwai Chung, Hong Kong; *U.S. Public*, pg. 1059

Lemieux, Paul R., V.P.--Norton-Alcoa Proppants, Fort Smith, AR; *U.S. Public*, pg. 61

Lemieux, Paul R., V.P.--Norton-Alcoa Proppants, Fort Smith, AR; *Int'l*, pg. 1174

Lemke, Ronald A.H., Pres. & Chief Exec. Officer--McLean McCarthy Limited, Toronto, Canada; *Int'l*, pg. 405

Lemke, Russ, V.P.--Schlegel Industrial Products Div., Rochester, NY; *Int'l*, pg. 128

Lemmon, D.L., Pres.--Amoco Pipeline Co., Oak Brook Terrace, IL; *U.S. Public*, pg. 102

Lemoine, M., Gen. Mgr.--Australia & New Zealand Banking Group Limited France, Paris, France; *Int'l*, pg. 99

Lemon, David, Mng. Dir.--Hepworth Building Products Limited, Stocksbridge, United Kingdom; *Int'l*, pg. 615

Lemon, Jim, Plant Mgr.--Ervin Amasteel Div., Adrian, MI; *U.S. Private*, pg. 382

Lemonnier, Jean-Pierre, Chief Oper. Officer--BNP (Mexico) SA, Mexico, Mexico; *Int'l*, pg. 164

Lempe, Hans J., Chief Oper. Officer--A. Johnson & Co. GmbH, Bremen, Germany; *Int'l*, pg. 711

Lemus Simon, Antonio, Gen. Mgr.--Lemusimun, S.A. de C.V./Y&R, San Salvador, El Salvador; *U.S. Private*, pg. 1200

Lenaburg, David S., Pres.--Banner Life Insurance Co., Rockville, MD; *Int'l*, pg. 805

Lenarduzzi, John, Mng. Dir.--Esselte S.P.A., Cusago, Italy; *Int'l*, pg. 461

Lenart, Deb, Pres.--Ameritech New Media, Chicago, IL; *U.S.* Public, pg. 98

Lenderman, Larry, Chief Oper. Officer--Allright Shreveport, Inc., Shreveport, LA; *U.S. Private*, pg. 43

LeNeav, Gregory M., Sr. Mktg. Officer--Southeast Marketing-Charlotte Business Center, Charlotte, NC; *U.S.* Public, pg. 650

Lenfant, D., Chief Oper. Officer--Zurich Compagnie d'Assurances, Abidjan, Cote d'Ivoire; *Int'l*, pg. 1531

Leng, Lee Le, Asst. Gen. Mgr.--Hwang-DBS Asset Management (Malaysia) Sdn. Bhd., Kuala Lumpur, Malaysia; *Int'l*, pg. 351

Lengnick, G.F., Pres.--Wacker Silicones Corporation, Adrian, MI; *Int'l*, pg. 625

Lenhart, Hans, Grp. Pres.--Cylinder Div., Parker Hannifin plc, Watford, United Kingdom; *U.S. Public*, pg. 1263

Lenhart, Ronald G., Pres.-Mount Morris Facility--AMCORE Bank, Rock River Valley, Mount Morris, IL; *U.S. Public*, pg. 64

Lenkel, Goran, Pres.--SkandiaBanken AB, Stockholm, Sweden; *Int'l*, pg. 1257

Lennart, Mark, Gen. Mgr.--Eaton Corporation, Tort Control Division, Marshall, MI; *U.S. Public*, pg. 557

Lennartsson, Lars, Mng. Dir.--John Crane Sverige AB, Goteborg, Sweden; *Int'l*, pg. 1339

Lennerhov, Boris, Chief Oper. Officer--ASK-Centralen AB, Helsingborg, Sweden; *Int'l*, pg. 708

Lennox, Andrew B., Pres.--The Bank of Nova Scotia Properties, Toronto, Canada; *Int'l*, pg. 155

Lennox, Andrew B., Pres.--Scotia Properties Quebec Inc., Toronto, Canada; *Int'l*, pg. 156

Lennox, Andrew B., Pres.--Scotia Realty Limited, Toronto, Canada; *Int'l*, pg. 156

Lennox, Roy, Gen. Mgr.-Employee Benefits Actuarial Svcs. & Mktg.--Employee Benefits Div., Rondebosch, South Africa; *Int'l*, pg. 77

Lenoci, V. William, Pres. & Chief Exec. Officer--Industrial Coated Fabrics Group, Spartanburg, SC; *U.S. Private*, pg. 507

Lenoci, Vito, Pres.--Reeves S.p.A., Milan, Italy; *U.S. Private*, pg. 507

Lenoir, Phillip, Pres.--Precismeca S.A., Saverne, France; *Int'l*, pg. 399

Lenotti, A., Chm. & Mng. Dir.--Ingersoll-Rand Italiana S.R.L., Milan, Italy; *U.S. Public*, pg. 878

Lenotti, Luciano, Mng. Dir.--SKF Industrie S.p.A., Rivoli, Italy; *Int'l*, pg. 1158

Lens, J.W., Mng. Dir.--N.V. Nutricia, Zoetermeer, Netherlands; *Int'l*, pg. 991

Lens, Karl G., Officer-Crest Foam--Crest-Foam Corporation, Moonachie, NJ; *U.S. Public*, pg. 986

Lento, Markku, Gen. Mgr.--Nokia Paging, Largo, FL; *Int'l*, pg. 952

Lentz, David J., V.P. & Gen. Mgr.--Medtronic Interventional Vascular, Danvers, MA; *U.S. Public*, pg. 1083

Lenway, Fred, Pres.--Aramark Uniform Services, Burbank, CA; *U.S. Private*, pg. 79

Lenz, Karl J., Mng. Dir.--Leitz Messtechnik GmbH, Wetzlar, Germany; *U.S. Public*, pg. 260

Lenz, Raoul, Chief Oper. Officer--International Fibre Sales, S.A., Geneva, Switzerland; *U.S. Public*, pg. 1077

Lenz, Sidney, Pres.--LandSafe Title Agency, Inc., Pasadena, CA; *U.S. Public*, pg. 453

Leon, Gilberto, Pres.--UCAR Polimeros y Quimicos C.A., Guayaquil, Ecuador; *U.S. Public*, pg. 1667

Leon, Jesus Gaban, Mng. Dir.--Petroleos Del Sur, S.A. (PETROSUR), Spain; *Int'l*, pg. 323

Leon, Ramon J., Representative--First RepublicBank Dallas, N.A. Representative Office, Sao Paulo, Brazil; *U.S. Public*, pg. 1165

Leonard, Bernard, Pres.--Burlington Denim, Greensboro, NC; *U.S. Public*, pg. 268

Leonard, C.E., Pres.--NMU Marketing Information Services, New York, NY; *Int'l*, pg. 1446

Leonard, Carey, Country Mgr.--Standard Chartered Bank (Sri Lanka), Colombo, Sri Lanka; *Int'l*, pg. 1296

Leonard, G.C., Chief Oper. Officer--Richardson-Vicks Ltd., Auckland, New Zealand; *U.S. Public*, pg. 1333

Leonard, J.B., Pres.--Bath Fashions Division, Fort Mill, SC; *U.S. Public*, pg. 1500

Leonard, James E., Pres.--ConAgra Poultry Foodservice Co., Omaha, NE; *U.S. Public*, pg. 427

Leonard, John, V.P. & Gen. Mgr.--Peabody Engineering Canada Ltd., Mississauga, Canada; *Int'l*, pg. 1066

Leonard, John F., Pres. & Chief Exec. Officer--Piedmont Airlines, Inc., Salisbury, MD; *U.S. Public*, pg. 1680

Leonard, John K., Pres.--Century Indemnity Company, Philadelphia, PA; *U.S. Public*, pg. 365

Leonard, Joseph P., Sr. V.P.--AlliedSignal Airline Services, Phoenix, AZ; *U.S. Public*, pg. 50

Leonard, K.E., Chief Exec. Officer--Surlean Meat Co., San Antonio, TX; *U.S. Private*, pg. 660

Leonard, Kevin, City Mgr.--Ideal Parking, Inc., Montreal, Canada; *U.S. Private*, pg. 44

Leonard, Michael, Pres.--Harman Automotive, Farmington Hills, MI; *U.S. Public*, pg. 796

Leonard, Michel, Dir.--Fromarsac SARL, Dordogne, France; *Int'l*, pg. 201

Leonard, Ron, Plant Mgr.--Bagcraft Corporation of America, Georgia Div., Forest Park, GA; *U.S. Public*, pg. 136

Leonard, Tom, Pres.--Lark Luggage Company, Inc., Denver, CO; *U.S. Public*, pg. 1430

Leonardis, Peter, Distr. Mgr.--Browning-Ferris Industries of New Jersey, Inc., Elizabeth, NJ; *U.S. Public*, pg. 263

Leonardo, Frank, Pres.--Deer Park Spring Water, Inc., Carlstadt, NJ; *Int'l*, pg. 919

Leone, Lucas G., Pres.--Ethical Nutriment, Inc., King of Prussia, PA; *U.S. Private*, pg. 366

Leone, Miguel, V.P. & Gen. Mgr.--Marietta, Inc., Olive Branch, MS; *U.S. Private*, pg. 703

Leone, Thomas H., V.P. & Gen. Mgr.--Cox Communications-Santa Barbara, Goleta, CA; *U.S. Public*, pg. 455

Leone, Vincenzo, Mng. Dir.--Alinord S.p.A., Milan, Italy; *Int'l*, pg. 170

Leonetti, Bernard, Mng. Dir.--John Crane France, Courbevoie, France; *Int'l*, pg. 1339

Leong, Bo, Pres.--Machinery North, Umea, Sweden; *Int'l*, pg. 899

Leong, Charles, Sr. V.P.-Americas--Singapore Tourist Promotion Board - Los Angeles, Beverly Hills, CA; *Int'l*, pg. 1254

Leong, Limchin, Chief Oper. Officer--Kyowa Hakko (Malaysia) SDN BHD., Petaling Jaya, Malaysia; *Int'l*, pg. 778

Leong, Margaret, Chief Oper. Officer--Clarins Ltd., Kowloon, Hong Kong; *Int'l*, pg. 295

Leong, Ng Kim, Chm.--DBS Finance Nominees Pte. Ltd., Singapore, Singapore; *Int'l*, pg. 350

Leong, Ng Kim, Chm.--DBSF Investments Pte. Ltd., Singapore, Singapore; *Int'l*, pg. 351

Leong, Ng Kim, Chm.--DBSF Holdings Pte Ltd., Singapore, Singapore; *Int'l*, pg. 351

Leong, Ng Kok, Dir.--Tourism Malaysia - Taiwan Office, Taipei, Taiwan; *Int'l*, pg. 833

Leong, Wong Chee, Pres. & Chief Exec. Officer--Bangkok Bank Berhad, Kuala Lumpur, Malaysia; *Int'l*, pg. 146

Leongnarktongdee, Boonlieng, Mng. Dir.--Thai Containers Ltd., Bangkok, Thailand; *Int'l*, pg. 1238

Leongnarktongdee, Boonlieng, Mng. Dir.--Thai Containers Industry Co., Ltd., Bangkok, Thailand; *Int'l*, pg. 1238

Leongnarktongdee, Boonlieng, Mng. Dir.--Thai Containers Ratchaburi (1989) Co., Ltd., Bangkok, Thailand; *Int'l*, pg. 1238

Leonhardt, David, Pres.--Frigo Cheese Corp., Lena, WI; *U.S. Private*, pg. 1040

Leonhardt, Thomas C., Pres. & Chief Exec. Officer--Rust Environment & Infrastructure, Inc., Greenville, SC; *U.S. Public*, pg. 1745

Leonhart, William, Pres.--Konica Business Machines Canada, Ltd., Pickering, Canada; *Int'l*, pg. 749

Leoni, Giulio, Mng. Dir. & Gen. Mgr.--Ansaldo Industria S.p.A., Genoa, Italy; *Int'l*, pg. 653

Leoni, Rino, Pres.--EUROIPEX, S.p.A., Milan, Italy; *U.S. Public*, pg. 593

Leopando, Oddie, Pres.--Datcon Instrument Co., East Petersburg, PA; *U.S. Private*, pg. 528

Lepage, Alphonse, Mng. Dir.--Swiss Re Life Canada, Toronto, Canada; *Int'l*, pg. 1333

Lepers, M., Mgr.--Amersham France SA, Les Ulis, France; *Int'l*, pg. 993

Lepeuple, Gerard, Chm. Bd.--SEP Inc., Wilmington, DE; *Int'l*, pg. 1166

Lepp, H.J., Pres. & Chief Exec. Officer--AltaSteel Ltd., Edmonton, Canada; *Int'l*, pg. 1299

Lepp, Raymond, V.P.-Opers.--Seattle WA Steel Division, Seattle, WA; *U.S. Public*, pg. 232

Leppaaho, Rauli, Chief Oper. Officer--Turku Plant, Turku, Finland; *Int'l*, pg. 863

LeQuemener, Michel, Gen. Mgr.--Lee Company S.A., Voisins-le-Bretonneaux, France; *U.S. Private*, pg. 657

Leray, Claude, Mgr.--Gunther S.A., Soultz, France; *Int'l*, pg. 1186

Leray, M., Fin. Controller--AEP/Borden Macaple S.A., Pithwiers, France; *U.S. Public*, pg. 5

Lercari, Franco, Mng. Dir.--KONE Elevators Overseas S.r.l., Bologna, Italy; *Int'l*, pg. 748

Lerchl, Joachim, Chief Oper. Officer--Atmos Lebensmitteltechnik G.m.b.H., Hamburg, Germany; *Int'l*, pg. 1379

Lereah, Paul, Gen. Mgr.--Harvey Electronics, New York, NY; *U.S. Public*, pg. 797

Lerique, Dominique, Chief Oper. Officer--Perstorp Analytical S.A., Bezons, France; *Int'l*, pg. 1040

Lerner, Martin, Chm. Bd., Pres. & Treas.--American List Corporation, Mineola, NY; *U.S. Public*, pg. 1481

Lerner, Robert C., Pres.--Wang Canada Limited, Scarborough, Canada; *U.S. Public*, pg. 1737
Lerouge, Michel, Mng. Dir.--Dumez-GTM Portugal, Lisbon, Portugal; *Int'l*, pg. 823
LeRoux, Jean-Jacques, Chief Oper. Officer--NIFE France S.A., Louviers, France; *Int'l*, pg. 54
LeRoux, Kevin, Pres. & Gen. Mgr.--WGGB-TV, Springfield, MA; *U.S. Private*, pg. 439
Leroux, Marc, Pres. & Chief Oper. Officer--Teleglobe World Mobility, Montreal, Canada; *Int'l*, pg. 1373
Leroy, A.J., Chm. Bd.--Palabora Mining Co. Ltd., Phalaborwa, South Africa; *Int'l*, pg. 1119
Leroy, J.M., Pres.--N.V. Johnson Wax Belgium S.A., Groot-Bijgaarden, Belgium; *U.S. Private*, pg. 593
LeRoy, Lamar, Pres.--Ikon Office Solutions-Central Georgia, Macon, GA; *U.S. Public*, pg. 863
LeRoy, Pierre, Pres.--John Deere Industrial Equipment Company, Moline, IL; *U.S. Public*, pg. 492
LeRoy, Steve, Reg. V.P.--Atlantic Region, Alexandria, VA; *Int'l*, pg. 693
LeSaffre, Tony, Pres.--Plastimo S.A., Lorient, France; *U.S. Public*, pg. 933
Lesaint, Philippe, Man. Dir.--Jotun Polymer France S.A., Lognes, France; *Int'l*, pg. 714
Lesar, David J., Pres. & Chief Exec. Officer--Brown & Root Inc., Alhambra, CA; *U.S. Public*, pg. 775
Lesard, Gilles, Chm. Bd.--McCain U.S.A. Inc., Oak Brook, IL; *Int'l*, pg. 850
Leschak, Ulrich, Mgr.--GGK Dusseldorf, Dusseldorf, Germany; *Int'l*, pg. 1335
Leser, Lawrence, Chief Oper. Officer--Scripps Howard Broadcasting, Cincinnati, OH; *U.S. Public*, pg. 1447
LeSieur, James G., III, Pres. & Chief Exec. Officer--Sunwest Bank, Tustin, CA; *U.S. Public*, pg. 1755
Lesinki, Hank, Gen. Mgr.--Hycroft Resources & Development, Winnemucca, NV; *U.S. Public*, pg. 1723
Leskinen, Eero, Pres.--IKON Cully S.A., Cully, Switzerland; *Int'l*, pg. 18
Leslie, Charles J., Pres.--Fuji Medical Systems USA, Inc., Stamford, CT; *Int'l*, pg. 524
Leslie, David, Sr. V.P. & Gen. Mgr.--Eastalco Aluminum Company, Frederick, MD; *U.S. Public*, pg. 60
Leslie, G.A., Reg. Mgr.--The Royal Bank of Scotland plc, Singapore, Singapore; *Int'l*, pg. 1133
Leslie, Mike, Dir.-Opers.--Sun City Produce, Inc., Pompano Beach, FL; *U.S. Public*, pg. 1529
Leslie, Steve, Pres.--Thomson Company, Inc., Atlanta, GA; *U.S. Public*, pg. 1429
Lessard, Fernand, Dir. Gen.--Imprimerie Quebecor Barclay, Montreal, Canada; *Int'l*, pg. 1077
Lessard, Yvon L., Mng. Dir.--The Bank of Nova Scotia Trust Company (Caribbean) Limited, Bridgetown, Barbados; *Int'l*, pg. 157
Lesser, Richard, Pres.--T.J. Maxx, Framingham, MA; *U.S. Public*, pg. 1557
Lesser, Richard, Pres.--The Marmax Group, Framingham, MA; *U.S. Public*, pg. 1557
Lessmann, Ulrich, Chief Oper. Officer--ELG Haniel GmbH, Duisburg, Germany; *Int'l*, pg. 591
Lestardo, Eugene, Pres.--Holmes Protection of New York, Incorporated, New York, NY; *U.S. Public*, pg. 1649
Lester, Carl J., Mgr.--Tellico Telephone Company, Inc., Tellico Plains, TN; *U.S. Public*, pg. 1572
Lester, David, Gen. Mgr.--Leo Burnett/Connaghan & May (QLD.) Pty. Ltd., Milton, Australia; *U.S. Private*, pg. 185
Lester, M.R., Chief Oper. Officer--JL Property Holdings Ltd., London, United Kingdom; *Int'l*, pg. 796
Lester, Simon, Exec. V.P.--Cott Europe (Pontefract), Pontefract, United Kingdom; *Int'l*, pg. 338
Lester, W. Howard, Pres.--Gardener's Eden, Inc., San Francisco, CA; *U.S. Public*, pg. 1770
Lester, W. Howard, Pres.--Williams-Sonoma, Inc., San Francisco, CA; *U.S. Public*, pg. 1770
LeStrange, Dennis P., Pres.--Ikon Office Solutions-New England, Glastonbury, CT; *U.S. Public*, pg. 863
Letak, Stephen P., Pres.--Berkley Administrators, Minneapolis, MN; *U.S. Public*, pg. 216
LeTarte, Joel, Plant Mgr.--Forest Industries, Inc., Fryeburg, ME; *U.S. Private*, pg. 968
Letcher, C.R., Chief Oper. Officer--Babcock Ames Crosta Div., Johannesburg, South Africa; *Int'l*, pg. 474
Leticia, Tony, V.P.--Maui Cup, Rochester Hills, MI; *U.S. Private*, pg. 661
Letke, Dave, Pres.--Preston Trucking Company, Inc., Preston, MD; *U.S. Public*, pg. 1788
Letmithe, Peter Bribeck, Pres.--Nestle S.A., Vevey, Switzerland; *Int'l*, pg. 915
Letten, Brian, Div. Mgr.--Industrials Division, Belcamp, MD; *U.S. Private*, pg. 195
Letter, Mark S., Pres.--Lands of Sierra, Reno, NV; *U.S. Public*, pg. 1470
Letts Ken, Opers. Mgr.--M/D Totco Instrumentation, Jurong, Singapore; *U.S. Public*, pg. 1709
Letwin, J.R., Chief Exec. Officer--Blackwood Hodge (Canada) Ltd., North York, Canada; *Int'l*, pg. 231
Letwin, Stephen J.J., Pres.--TransCanada Energy USA Inc., Houston, TX; *Int'l*, pg. 1417
Letzelter, Pierre, Mng. Dir.--Champagne Moet & Chandon, Epernay, France; *Int'l*, pg. 779
Leu, Peter, Gen. Mgr.--Pioneer Saaten, GmbH, Buxtehude, Germany; *U.S. Public*, pg. 1299
Leu, Randall, Chief Oper. Officer--KONE Elevators C&N Products Corporation, Taipei, Taiwan; *Int'l*, pg. 747
Leuchten, William, Sr. V.P.--Essex Specialty Products, Inc., Clifton, NJ; *U.S. Public*, pg. 523
Leuchten, William, Sr. V.P.--Essex Specialty Products Inc., Canada, Clifton, NJ; *U.S. Public*, pg. 523
Leuenberger, Rolf, Chm.--CWK AG, Winterthur, Switzerland; *Int'l*, pg. 329
Leuenberger, Rolf, Chm.--OK Coop AG, Allschwil, Switzerland; *Int'l*, pg. 330
Leuenberger, Rolf, Chm.--Konsum Verein Zurich AG, Zurich, Switzerland; *Int'l*, pg. 330
Leugler, Helmut, Chief Oper. Officer--Siemens A/S, Ballerup, Denmark; *Int'l*, pg. 1247
Leuhis, William, Chief Oper. Officer--Cable Productos de Chihuahua, S.A. de C.V., Chihuahua, Mexico; *U.S. Public*, pg. 1790
Leung Ding-Bong, Ronald, Chm. Bd.--Kwong On Bank, Limited, Central, Hong Kong; *Int'l*, pg. 521
Leung Ting-Mow, Kenneth, Sr. Mng. Dir.--Kwong On Bank, Limited, Central, Hong Kong; *Int'l*, pg. 521
Leung, Andrew, Mgr.--Western Navigational Global Limited, Kowloon, Hong Kong; *U.S. Public*, pg. 373
Leung, E.P., Mng. Dir.--De La Rue Systems Ltd, Wan Chai, Hong Kong; *Int'l*, pg. 387
Leung, J., Gen. Mgr.--AMP Products Pacific Limited, Kowloon, Hong Kong; *U.S. Public*, pg. 9
Leung, Johnson C., Pres. & Mng. Dir., Far East--Anheuser-Busch Asia, Inc., Tokyo, Japan; *U.S. Public*, pg. 115
Leung, P.T., Mgr.--Nalco Chemical (H.K.) Ltd., Kowloon, Hong Kong; *U.S. Public*, pg. 1150
Leung, Peter T., Mgr.--Nalco Chemical (Suzhou) Co., Ltd., Jiangsu, China; *U.S. Public*, pg. 1150
Leurs, P., Dir.--VEPO Aannemingsbedrijf B.V., Brunssum, Netherlands; *Int'l*, pg. 134
Leutenegger, Aldo, Chief Oper. Officer--Swissmetal Italia s.r.l., Milan, Italy; *Int'l*, pg. 1427
Leuthy, Fritz, Chm.--Coop Bern, Bern, Switzerland; *Int'l*, pg. 329
Leva, Renzo, Mng. Dir.--Avnet EMG SRL, Milan, Italy; *U.S. Public*, pg. 155
LeValley, C. Robert, Pres.--DeVRY Institute of Technology, Kansas City, MO; *U.S. Public*, pg. 504
Levan, David M., Chm. Bd., Pres. & Chief Exec. Officer--CRR Industries, Inc., Philadelphia, PA; *U.S. Public*, pg. 432
Levander, Yngve, Chief Oper. Officer--Oy Electrolux Ab-ELEKTRO HELIOS, Helsinki, Finland; *Int'l*, pg. 441
Levantin, Allen M., Chm. Bd. & Chief Exec. Officer--Todays Temporary, Inc., Dallas, TX; *U.S. Public*, pg. 277
Levasseur, Pierre, Gen. Mgr.--Temlam Inc., Ville Marie, Canada; *Int'l*, pg. 1375
LeVault, Donald, Pres.--GKN Sinter Metals Inc., Cleveland, OH; *Int'l*, pg. 535
Leven, Bo, Gen. Mgr.--Harper Freight International (Sweden) AB, Marsta, Sweden; *U.S. Public*, pg. 373
Levenhagan, David, Pres.--The Loan Store, Inc., Michigan City, IN; *U.S. Private*, pg. 539
Levenhagen, Thomas, Pres.--MFG Tray Co., Linesville, PA; *U.S. Private*, pg. 756
Levenick, Mark, Pres. & Chief Exec. Officer--Tidel Engineering, Inc., Carrollton, TX; *U.S. Public*, pg. 1608
Levenson, Ted, Pres.--Medical Management Associates, Inc., Thousand Oaks, CA; *U.S. Public*, pg. 839
Leventhal, Kathy, Publisher--Vanity Fair, New York, NY; *U.S. Private*, pg. 20
Leveque, Marie-Francoise, Mng. Dir.--L-TEC France SARL, Maurepas, France; *Int'l*, pg. 283
Leveque, Timothy J., Pres.--Alcoa Closure Systems, International, Richmond, IN; *U.S. Public*, pg. 60
Lever, A.J., Mng. Dir.--Palintest Limited, Gateshead, United Kingdom; *Int'l*, pg. 589
Lever, Roy, Chm. & Chief Exec. Officer--GAN General Insurance Company, Burlington, Canada; *Int'l*, pg. 564
Leveroni, Peter, V.P. & Gen. Mgr.--Cox Communications-Bakersfield, Bakersfield, CA; *U.S. Public*, pg. 454
Levert, John, Chief Oper. Officer--Howard Weil Labouisse Friedrichs, Inc., New Orleans, LA; *U.S. Public*, pg. 985
Levesley, Derek, Div. Mgr.--Thermal Processing Group Ltd. (Cambridge), Waterbeach, United Kingdom; *Int'l*, pg. 1338
Levesque, J. Paul, Chief Oper. Officer--J. Paul Levesque & Sons Inc, Ashland, ME; *Int'l*, pg. 434
Levett, B., Mng. Dir.--Bohlin Instruments Ltd., Gloucester, United Kingdom; *Int'l*, pg. 207
Levett, John L., Pres.--New England Electric Resources, Inc., Westborough, MA; *U.S. Public*, pg. 1171
Levi, D., Mng. Dir.--M&A Societa di Mergers & Acquisitions S.p.A., Milan, Italy; *Int'l*, pg. 1330
Levin, Cary, V.P.--South Bend Scrap & Processing, South Bend, IN; *U.S. Private*, pg. 1048
Levin, Edward, Gen. Mgr.--Private Brands, Chicago, IL; *U.S. Private*, pg. 508
Levin, Eric, Pres.--W.B. Homes, Inc., Sunrise, FL; *U.S. Public*, pg. 989
Levin, Eric M., Pres.--Leisure Technology, New Jersey Div., Lakewood, NJ; *U.S. Private*, pg. 659
Levin, Jerry, Chm. & Chief Exec. Officer--The Coleman Company, Inc., Golden, CO; *U.S. Private*, pg. 690
Levin, Jerry W., Chm.--Revlon, Inc., New York, NY; *U.S. Private*, pg. 689
Levin, Ralph, Pres.--Three Rivers Iron & Metal, Three Rivers, MI; *U.S. Private*, pg. 1048
Levin, Ralph, Pres.--Kalamazoo Scrap & Processing, Kalamazoo, MI; *U.S. Private*, pg. 1048
Levin, Ralph, Pres.--Elkhart Metals Division, Elkhart, IN; *U.S. Private*, pg. 1048
Levin, Shoshana, Rep.-Venezuela--Bank Hapoalim (Caracas), Caracas, Venezuela; *Int'l*, pg. 149
Levin, Starr, V.P.--Sturgis Iron & Metal, Elkhart Metals Division, Elkhart, IN; *U.S. Private*, pg. 1048
Levine, Alexander M., Pres.--Webster Wire, Inc., Carthage, MO; *U.S. Public*, pg. 986
Levine, Jesse, Pres. & Chief Exec. Officer--Los Angeles Times Syndicate, Los Angeles, CA; *U.S. Public*, pg. 1616
Levine, Kenneth M., Chief Exec. Officer--MONY Ventures, Inc., New York, NY; *U.S. Private*, pg. 769
Levine, Kenneth M., Pres.--MONY Funding, Inc., New York, NY; *U.S. Private*, pg. 769
Levine, Kenneth M., Chief Exec. Officer--MONY Realty Partners, Inc., New York, NY; *U.S. Private*, pg. 769
Levine, Len, Co-Mgr.--Legion Paper Corporation, New York, NY; *U.S. Private*, pg. 467
Levine, Marty R., Gen. Mgr.--Dodge Car/Truck Division, Auburn Hills, MI; *U.S. Public*, pg. 353
Levine, Sol, Pres.--Carrington Parfums Ltd., New York, NY; *U.S. Private*, pg. 689
Levine, Sol, Pres.--Environmental Fragrance Technologies, Ltd., New York, NY; *U.S. Private*, pg. 689
Levine, Sol, Pres.--Revlon (Puerto Rico), Inc., Caparra Heights, PR; *U.S. Private*, pg. 690
Levine, Sol, Pres.--Fila Fitness Ltd., New York, NY; *U.S. Private*, pg. 690
Levine, Sol, Pres.--Prestige Fragrance & Cosmetics, Inc., New York, NY; *U.S. Private*, pg. 690
Levine, Sol, Pres.--Ritz Corporation, New York, NY; *U.S. Private*, pg. 690
Levins, Joseph T., Pres.--Unisource, Philadelphia, PA; *U.S. Public*, pg. 1671
Levinson, Arthur D., Ph.D., Pres. & Chief Exec. Officer--Genentech, Inc., South San Francisco, CA; *Int'l*, pg. 1120
Levinson, Steven, Branch Mgr.--Downey Savings & Loan Association, F.A., Mission Viejo, CA; *U.S. Public*, pg. 527
Levitt, D.S., Pres.--Universal Telephone, Inc., Monroe, LA; *U.S. Public*, pg. 330
Levy-Ganz, Ellen, Pres.--Esprit Accessories, San Francisco, CA; *U.S. Private*, pg. 383
Levy, Bruce L., Pres.--Energy Initiatives, Inc., Parsippany, NJ; *U.S. Public*, pg. 695
Levy, Bruce L., Pres.--EI Energy, Inc., Parsippany, NJ; *U.S. Public*, pg. 695
Levy, Bruce L., Pres.--EI Power, Inc., Parsippany, NJ; *U.S. Public*, pg. 695
Levy, Claude, Dir.-Italy--Raychem S.p.A., Milan, Italy; *U.S. Public*, pg. 1363
Levy, D.J., V.P. & Gen. Mgr.--Union Camp Container Div., Wayne, NJ; *U.S. Public*, pg. 1666
Levy, Elio, Pres. & Chief Exec. Officer--Tech Data Canada, Inc., Mississauga, Canada; *U.S. Public*, pg. 1562
Levy, Frank L., Pres. & Chief Exec. Officer--L & L Environmental Services, Metairie, LA; *U.S. Private*, pg. 638
Levy, Gerard, Chief Oper. Officer--Sormel, Besancon, France; *Int'l*, pg. 793
Levy, Girard, Chm. Bd.--Air Liquide America Corporation, Houston, TX; *Int'l*, pg. 37
Levy, Harold, Div. Pres.--TMP Worldwide/Recruitment Division, New York, NY; *U.S. Private*, pg. 1065
Levy, Irving L., Pres.--National Chemsearch of Canada Ltd., Brampton, Canada; *U.S. Public*, pg. 1145
Levy, Joe, Pres.--CIO Publishing Corp., Framingham, MA; *U.S. Private*, pg. 569
Levy, Jonathan, Gen. Mgr.--C. Cakebread, Crayford, United Kingdom; *Int'l*, pg. 460
Levy, Jonathan, Gen. Mgr.--Whitecable, Liverpool, United Kingdom; *Int'l*, pg. 462
Levy, Lawrence J., Chm. Bd.--Levy Real Estate Partners, Chicago, IL; *U.S. Private*, pg. 664
Levy, Leslie W., Pres. & Chief Oper. Officer--Heritage Sportswear, Marion, SC; *U.S. Public*, pg. 1472
Levy, Mark A., Pres. & Chief Oper. Officer--Champion Realty, Inc., Delray Beach, FL; *U.S. Public*, pg. 1231
Levy, Mark S., Chm. Bd. & Pres.--Fire Lite Alarms, Inc./Notifier Co., Northford, CT; *U.S. Public*, pg. 1306
Levy, Myron, Pres.--Herley Vega Industry, Lancaster, PA; *U.S. Public*, pg. 811
Levy, Peter, Pres.--Labelon/Noesting Company, LLC, Mount Vernon, NY; *U.S. Private*, pg. 641
Levy, R. D., Chief Oper. Officer--Oriole Homes Corp. of Maryland, Lutherville, MD; *U.S. Public*, pg. 1231
Levy, R. D., Chief Oper. Officer--Seabreeze Properties, Inc., Lutherville, MD; *U.S. Public*, pg. 1231
Levy, Robert I., M.D., Pres.--Wyeth-Ayerst Laboratories-Research & Development, Radnor, PA; *U.S. Public*, pg. 80
Levy, Yehuda, Pres. & Publ.--Jerusalem Post Publications Ltd., Jerusalem, Israel; *Int'l*, pg. 632
Levyh, T.J., Mgr.--Morton Chemical Div., Santa Fe Springs, CA; *U.S. Public*, pg. 1135
Lew, Schaun, Mng. Dir.--Tiffany & Co. International (Taiwan), Taipei, Taiwan; *U.S. Public*, pg. 1609
Lew, Steven, Pres. & Chief Oper. Officer--Universal Studios Hollywood, Universal City, CA; *Int'l*, pg. 1216
Lewandowski, Edward E., Pres.--Cohutta Banking Company, Chatsworth, GA; *U.S. Public*, pg. 1549
Lewandowski, Larry, Mgr.-Production--Coated & Laminated Products, West Monroe, LA; *U.S. Public*, pg. 927
Lewek, Kathleen, V.P. & Mgr.--Financial Institutions Div., Los Angeles, CA; *U.S. Public*, pg. 871
Lewellen, Jim, Pres. & Gen. Mgr.--FRL, Inc., Los Banos, CA; *U.S. Public*, pg. 396
Lewerke, Curtis, Chief Oper. Officer--Fieldstone Cabinetry Inc., Northwood, IA; *U.S. Public*, pg. 1053
Lewerke, Curtis, Chief Oper. Officer--Fieldstone Transportation Company, Northwood, IA; *U.S. Public*, pg. 1053
Lewis-Gordon, Danna, Pres. & Chief Exec. Officer--Surfer Publications, Inc., Dana Point, CA; *U.S. Private*, pg. 417
Lewis, Alan, Mng. Dir.--Normalair-Garrett Mfg. Australia, Melbourne, Australia; *U.S. Public*, pg. 53
Lewis, Barbara, Gen. Mgr.--Scripps Howard Cable T.V. Company, Knoxville, TN; *U.S. Public*, pg. 1448
Lewis, Barry, Mgr.-Opers.--Sertech Laboratories, Inc./SSI, Watertown, MA; *U.S. Public*, pg. 1107
Lewis, Barry, Mng. Dir.--Schauman (UK) Ltd., Hemel Hempstead, United Kingdom; *Int'l*, pg. 1429
Lewis, Bill, Chm. Bd., Pres. & Chief Exec. Officer--Casa Lupita, Scottsdale, AZ; *U.S. Private*, pg. 393
Lewis, Bill, Chm. Bd., Pres. & Chief Exec. Officer--Garcia's Mexican Restaurants, Scottsdale, AZ; *U.S. Private*, pg. 393
Lewis, Bill, Gen. Mgr.--Desert Production Center, Phoenix, AZ; *U.S. Private*, pg. 685
Lewis, Bill, Gen. Mgr.--Park Newspapers of Lumberton, Inc., Lumberton, NC; *U.S. Public*, pg. 1078
Lewis, Bill, Gen. Mgr.--Robesonian, Lumberton, NC; *U.S. Public*, pg. 1078

Lewis, Brian, Chm.--Roltra-Morse S.p.A., Turin, Italy; *U.S. Public*, pg. 857

Lewis, Bryan L., Pres.--Teledyne Continental Motors, Mobile, AL; *U.S. Public*, pg. 43

Lewis, C. Stephen, Pres. & Chief Exec. Officer--Weyerhaeuser Real Estate Company, Federal Way, WA; *U.S. Public*, pg. 1764

Lewis, Carlyn, Pres.--Insurance Brokers & Managers, Inc., New Orleans, LA; *U.S. Public*, pg. 1677

Lewis, Christopher H., Pres.--Foreign Trade Division, Glendale, CA; *Int'l*, pg. 917

Lewis, Clark, Plant Mgr.--Donaldson Co., Inc., Grinnell, IA; *U.S. Public*, pg. 517

Lewis, Claude H., Chief Oper. Officer--Service Transport Company, Houston, TX; *U.S. Public*, pg. 19

Lewis, Clinton L., III, Mgr.--Rouse Fort Worth, Inc., Fort Worth, TX; *U.S. Public*, pg. 1409

Lewis, Conrad W., Exec. V.P.-Business Units--Newbridge Networks Corporation, Kanata, Canada; *Int'l*, pg. 924

Lewis, Dainty, Office Mgr.--TMP Worldwide Ltd., Toronto, Canada; *U.S. Private*, pg. 1065

Lewis, Dana, Chief Oper. Officer--Fairfax Building Systems, Culpeper, VA; *U.S. Private*, pg. 391

Lewis, David, Reg. Mgr.--Analytical Surveys, Inc. - Northeast Division, Sterling, VA; *U.S. Public*, pg. 110

Lewis, David, Mng. Dir.--Pasta Foods Limited, Saint Albans, United Kingdom; *Int'l*, pg. 1396

Lewis, Dennis J., Pres.--Ultimate Technology Corporation, Victor, NY; *U.S. Public*, pg. 1637

Lewis, Don, Mng. Dir.--Farah Australia Pty. Limited, Waterloo, Australia; *U.S. Public*, pg. 613

Lewis, Donald J., Pres.--Associated Testing Laboratories, Inc., Burlington, MA; *U.S. Public*, pg. 1341

Lewis, E.F., Pres.--Stone & Webster Oil Company, Inc., Houston, TX; *U.S. Public*, pg. 1519

Lewis, E.J., Mng. Dir.--Bestobell Aviation, Slough, United Kingdom; *Int'l*, pg. 853

Lewis, Eric, Pres.--Avica Inc., San Fernando, CA; *Int'l*, pg. 853

Lewis, Eric, Mng. Dir.--Avica, Hemel Hempstead, United Kingdom; *Int'l*, pg. 853

Lewis, Eric, Mng. Dir.--Meggitt Composites, Dudley, United Kingdom; *Int'l*, pg. 853

Lewis, Eric, Mng. Dir.--Silicone Engineering, Blackburn, United Kingdom; *Int'l*, pg. 853

Lewis, Freida Z., Pres. & Chief Exec. Officer--Fleet Brokerage Securities Corp., New York, NY; *U.S. Public*, pg. 649

Lewis, George, Chief Oper. Officer--Dutch Parking Inc., Corning, NY; *U.S. Private*, pg. 43

Lewis, J. Gary, Pres.--Bowman Distribution, Cleveland, OH; *U.S. Public*, pg. 190

Lewis, James C., Pres.--Lizwear Division, New York, NY; *U.S. Public*, pg. 1006

Lewis, James H., Gen. Mgr.--Stone Savannah River Pulp and Paper, Savannah, GA; *U.S. Public*, pg. 1520

Lewis, Jerald P., Pres. & Chief Exec. Officer--First American Trust Co., Santa Ana, CA; *U.S. Public*, pg. 626

Lewis, John, Jr., Gen. Mgr.--EG & G China Representative Office, Beijing, China; *U.S. Public*, pg. 544

Lewis, Joseph W., V.P. & Gen. Mgr.--Systems & Services Div., Milwaukee, WI; *U.S. Public*, pg. 932

Lewis, Kenneth D., Pres.--Gulfstream Leasing Corporation, Tampa, FL; *U.S. Public*, pg. 1162

Lewis, Larry F., V.P. & Gen. Mgr.--Cox Communications-Pensacola/Ft. Walton, Pensacola, FL; *U.S. Public*, pg. 455

Lewis, Larry F., V.P. & Gen. Mgr.--TWC Cable Partners, Fort Walton Beach, FL; *U.S. Public*, pg. 455

Lewis, Lemuel E., Pres. & Gen. Mgr.--WTVF, Nashville, TN; *U.S. Private*, pg. 647

Lewis, M., Chief Oper. Officer--Marinello Schools of Beauty, Santa Monica, CA; *U.S. Public*, pg. 1444

Lewis, M.D., Pres.--Grant, Inc., Huron, SD; *U.S. Public*, pg. 1201

Lewis, MaryAnn E., Sr. Business Devel. Officer--Western Marketing-Oakland Region, Oakland, CA; *U.S. Public*, pg. 650

Lewis, Michael, Pres. & Chief Exec. Officer--ILD Communications, Inc., Carrollton, TX; *U.S. Public*, pg. 887

Lewis, Michael D., Pres.--Kvaerner National Division of Kvaerner Singapore Pte. Ltd., Singapore, Singapore; *Int'l*, pg. 768

Lewis, Michael J., Pres.--S.C. Food Services (Canada) Inc., Markham, Canada; *Int'l*, pg. 1213

Lewis, Mitchell, Pres.--Liz Claiborne Shoe Division, New York, NY; *U.S. Public*, pg. 1006

Lewis, Nicholas, Gen. Mgr.--Arrendadora Gorvac S.A. de C.V., Mexico, Mexico; *U.S. Public*, pg. 1621

Lewis, Norm, Publisher--The Montana Standard, Butte, MT; *U.S. Public*, pg. 984

Lewis, Peter, Branch Dir.--N.G. Bailey & Co. Ltd.-Newcastle Branch, Newcastle upon Tyne, United Kingdom; *Int'l*, pg. 132

Lewis, Peter B., Pres.--Progressive Casualty Insurance Co., Cleveland, OH; *U.S. Public*, pg. 1334

Lewis, Price, Pres.--Roll Source, Inc., Minneapolis, MN; *U.S.* Public, pg. 1671

Lewis, Ralph, Gen. Mgr.--Ketchikan Pulp Co., Ketchikan, AK; *U.S. Public*, pg. 1015

Lewis, Randy, Gen. Mgr.--Tucson Learning Center, Tucson, AZ; *U.S. Public*, pg. 219

Lewis, Richard C., Chm. Bd.--Richard Lewis Paper Corporation, Northfield, IL; *U.S. Private*, pg. 467

Lewis, Richard S., Pres. & Chief Exec. Officer--Countrywide Partnership Investments, Inc., Pasadena, CA; *U.S. Public*, pg. 453

Lewis, Robert, Pres.--enterWorks.com, inc., Ashburn, VA; *U.S. Public*, pg. 1573

Lewis, Seth, Gen. Mgr.--Center Cafe, Washington, DC; *U.S.* Public, pg. 130

Lewis, Susan, V.P. & Gen. Mgr.--Dillard, A ResourceNet International Company, Greenville, SC; *U.S. Public*, pg. 902

Lewis, T.C., Mng. Dir.--Strategic Systems International Limited, Basingstoke, United Kingdom; *Int'l*, pg. 1065

Lewis, Thomas H., Pres.--Cash Flow, Inc., Norfolk, VA; *U.S.* Public, pg. 1163

Lewis, Timothy, Pres.--Bethlehem Steel-Structural Products Division, Bethlehem, PA; *U.S. Public*, pg. 226

Lewis, Valerie, Gen. Mgr.--Miller's Publications, Tenterden, United Kingdom; *Int'l*, pg. 1093

Lewis, William, Pres.--Career Blazers Agency, Inc., New York, NY; *U.S. Private*, pg. 209

Lewis, William, Pres.--Career Blazers Service Company, Inc., New York, NY; *U.S. Private*, pg. 209

Lewis, William, Pres.--Career Blazers Learning Center, New York, NY; *U.S. Private*, pg. 209

Lewis, William, Pres.--Career Blazers Temporary Personnel, New York, NY; *U.S. Private*, pg. 209

Lewis, William, Mng. Dir.--Toronto Dominion (Southeast Asia) Limited, Singapore, Singapore; *Int'l*, pg. 1402

Lewis, William L., Pres.--Ralston Purina Canada Inc., Mississauga, Canada; *U.S. Public*, pg. 1360

Lewit-Nirenberg, Julie, Publisher--Mademoiselle, New York, NY; *U.S. Private*, pg. 20

Lewitt, Bert, Pres.--Morley Construction Co., Inc., Santa Monica, CA; *U.S. Private*, pg. 762

Lewy, Glen S., Chief Exec. Officer--Fuji-Wolfensohn International, New York, NY; *Int'l*, pg. 519

Lexa, M., Chm. & Mng. Dir.--ANTEA SA, Orleans, France; *Int'l*, pg. 607

Ley, James A., Pres. & Chief Exec. Officer--First Vantage-Tennessee, Knoxville, TN; *U.S. Public*, pg. 641

Leydes, J., Mng. Dir.--Pluspoint, Rotterdam, Netherlands; *Int'l*, pg. 750

Leyland, A.E., Mng. Dir.--Wimpey Property Holdings Ltd., London, United Kingdom; *Int'l*, pg. 1510

Lhota, William J., Pres. & Chief Oper. Officer--Kingsport Power Co., Roanoke, VA; *U.S. Public*, pg. 72

Lhota, William J., Pres. & Chief Oper. Officer--Indiana Michigan Power Company, Fort Wayne, IN; *U.S. Public*, pg. 72

Lhota, William J., Pres. & Chief Oper. Officer--Ohio Power Company, Canton, OH; *U.S. Public*, pg. 72

Lhota, William J., Pres. & Chief Oper. Officer--Columbus Southern Power Company, Columbus, OH; *U.S. Public*, pg. 72

Lhota, William J., Pres. & Chief Oper. Officer--Appalachian Power Company, Roanoke, VA; *U.S. Public*, pg. 72

Lhulier, Larry P., Div. Mgr.--Cumberland Div., Millville, NJ; *U.S. Public*, pg. 1488

Li, David K.P., Chm. Bd.--Oakreed Financial Services Limited, Hong Kong, Hong Kong; *Int'l*, pg. 817

Li, H., Gen. Mgr.--Kodak (Far East) Limited, North Point, Hong Kong; *U.S. Public*, pg. 553

Li, H., Gen. Mgr.--Kodak (Export Sales) Limited, North Point, Hong Kong; *U.S. Public*, pg. 553

Li, Joseph, Mng. Dir.--DYWIDAG Systems International, USA, Inc., Calgary, Canada; *Int'l*, pg. 424

Li, Nelson, Mng. Dir.--Formica Asia Limited, Wan Chai, Hong Kong; *Int'l*, pg. 129

Li, S.T., Gen. Mgr.--Monsanto Far East Ltd., Hong Kong, Hong Kong; *U.S. Public*, pg. 1125

Lia, Trond, Gen. Mgr.--Chokwang Jotun Ltd., Pusan, Korea; *Int'l*, pg. 715

Lian, Tan Po, Mng. Dir.--P.T. Dunkin do Lestari, Jakarta, Indonesia; *Int'l*, pg. 64

Lian, Ted, Gen. Mgr.--Kidde Consumer Durables Corp., Taipei, Taiwan; *Int'l*, pg. 594

Liao, James, Asst. Gen. Mgr.--GP Battery Marketing (Taiwan) Ltd., Taipei, Taiwan; *Int'l*, pg. 537

Liao, K., Gen. Mgr.--Laporte (Taiwan) Limited, Taipei, Taiwan; *Int'l*, pg. 803

Libby, Dale, Chief Oper. Officer--Ahlstrom Process Equipment Inc. Pump Factory, Easley, SC; *Int'l*, pg. 34

Libby, Henry G., Chm. Bd. & Pres.--The Disston Co., Greensboro, NC; *U.S. Public*, pg. 950

Libell, Goran, Chief Oper. Officer--Alfa-Laval (Ireland) Ltd., Dublin, Ireland; *Int'l*, pg. 1380

Liberati, Tommaso, Dir.--Fiat Auto S.p.A., Milan, Italy; *Int'l*, pg. 481

Libero, Robeli J., Pres. & Gen. Mgr.--IBM Latin American Region S.A., Peru; *U.S. Public*, pg. 897

Libot, Guy, Gen. Mgr.--Kredietbank Singapore Branch, Singapore, Singapore; *Int'l*, pg. 760

Libratore, Mark, Pres.--Liberty Medical Supply, Inc., Palm City, FL; *U.S. Public*, pg. 1315

Licarsi, Arthur, Mgr.-Sls.--Northeast Division (Luscon), East Haven, CT; *Int'l*, pg. 518

Licata, Sal, Pres.--EMI-Manhattan Records, New York, NY; *Int'l*, pg. 428

Licavoli, Sam, Pres.--Textron Automotive Interiors Company, Troy, MI; *U.S. Public*, pg. 1590

Liccardo, James E., Pres.--The Summit Mortgage Company, Inc., Cranford, NJ; *U.S. Public*, pg. 1528

Lichtenauer, P.A., Mng. Dir.--bv Televizier, Amsterdam, Netherlands; *Int'l*, pg. 1445

Lick, Fred, Jr., Chm. Bd., Pres. & Chief Exec. Officer--Central Reserve Life of North America Insurance Co., Strongsville, OH; *U.S. Public*, pg. 326

Lick, Fred, Jr., Chm. Bd.--Western Reserve Administrative Services, Inc., Strongsville, OH; *U.S. Public*, pg. 326

Licklider, Bill, Gen. Mgr.--Rupp Automotive, Chillicothe, MO; *U.S. Public*, pg. 1378

Licon, Arturo, Service Mgr.--Herramientas Varco S.A.C.V., Villahermosa, Mexico; *U.S. Public*, pg. 1709

Liczkowski, Jack, Gen. Mgr.--CPC Amino S.P. ZO.O., Poznan, Poland; *U.S. Public*, pg. 225

Lida, Takaya, Gen. Mgr.--The Sumitomo Bank, Ltd.-Labuan Branch, Labuan, Malaysia; *Int'l*, pg. 1309

Lida, Tom, Mgr.--Mitsumi Electronics Corp., Arlington Heights, IL; *Int'l*, pg. 884

Liddell, John M., Mgr.--Hydraulic Turbine Division, Loveland, CO; *U.S. Public*, pg. 1776

Liddle, James B., V.P.--General Felt- Central Div., Chicago, IL; *U.S. Private*, pg. 1095

Liddy, Lucien, Pres.--Intergen Center for Diagnostic Products, Milford, MA; *U.S. Private*, pg. 567

Lidl, Rolf, Chief Oper. Officer--Krauss-Maffei Kunststofftechnik GmbH, Munich, Germany; *Int'l*, pg. 836

Lidow, Alexander, Chief Oper. Officer--Electronic Products Division, El Segundo, CA; *U.S. Public*, pg. 907

Lidow, Derek, Chief Oper. Officer--Power Products Division, El Segundo, CA; *U.S. Public*, pg. 907

Liebel, M., Pres. & Chief Oper. Officer--Wendy's Restaurants of Canada Inc., Malton, Canada; *U.S. Public*, pg. 1754

Liebenthal, Robert B., Resident Rep.--The World Bank, Lilongwe, Malawi; *U.S. Private*, pg. 1189

Lieberman, Bonnie, Sr. V.P. & Gen. Mgr.-College Div.--Educational Publishing, New York, NY; *U.S. Public*, pg. 1768

Lieberman, Drew, Pres.--Oak Grigsby, Sugar Grove, IL; *U.S.* Public, pg. 1209

Lieberman, Jay M., Pres.--Tangent Industries Ltd., Brooklyn, NY; *U.S. Private*, pg. 383

Liebetseder, Dieter, Gen. Mgr.--Hamburger Aluminium-Werk Gesellschaft Mit Beschrankter Haftung, Hamburg, Germany; *U.S. Public*, pg. 1387

Liebl, James P., Gen. Mgr.--Reclamation Div. (Nashville), Nashville, TN; *Int'l*, pg. 1271

Liebowitz, Leo, Pres.--Getty Terminals, Inc., Jericho, NY; *U.S. Public*, pg. 741

Liebson, Richard D., Pres.--Mechanical Drives Div., Erie, PA; *U.S. Public*, pg. 1794

Liedberg, John H., Mng. Dir.--Georg Jensen Silver Ltd., London, United Kingdom; *Int'l*, pg. 1134

Liedtke, M., Mng. Dir.--Robert Bosch Ltd., Uxbridge, United Kingdom; *Int'l*, pg. 205

Lien, B., Gen. Mgr.--Albright & Wilson A/S, Klofta, Norway; *Int'l*, pg. 49

Lienaerts, Joerg, Chief Oper. Officer--BHF Immobilien-GmbH, Frankfurt/Main, Germany; *Int'l*, pg. 119

Lieppe, Charles, Pres. & Chief Exec. Officer--Berol Corporation, Brentwood, TN; *U.S. Public*, pg. 1178

Lierheimer, Paul, Production Mgr.--Albany Mount Vernon Dryer Fabric, Olympia, WA; *U.S. Public*, pg. 36

Lies, Gregg A., Mgr.--GATX Terminals Corp., Seattle, WA; *U.S. Public*, pg. 692

Liess, David, Pres.--Dynamic Graphics Inc., Horsham, PA; *Int'l*, pg. 191

Liestmann, Wulf Dietrich, Dr., Chm.--Mannesmannrohren-Werke AG, Mulheim, Germany; *Int'l*, pg. 835

Lievens, Hugo, Mng. Dir.--Innovative Sputtering Technology IST, Zulte, Belgium; *Int'l*, pg. 183

Lievense, Richard, Pres.--Old Kent Bank of Holland, Holland, MI; *U.S. Public*, pg. 1217

Lievense, W. Oost, Chm. Bd.--ABN-AMRO Securities (USA) Inc., New York, NY; *Int'l*, pg. 11

Lieverdink, J., Plant Mgr.--Zelhem Plant, Zelhem, Netherlands; *U.S. Public*, pg. 672

Liew, Ken, Pres.--Mal Pacific Technology Sdn. Bhd., Kuala Lumpur, Malaysia; *Int'l*, pg. 1293

Liew, P.H., Plant Mgr.--Robinson Nugent, Sungai Petani, Malaysia; *U.S. Public*, pg. 1395

Liff, Michael A., Pres.--Media General Broadcasting, Inc. (WJWB-TV), Jacksonville, FL; *U.S. Public*, pg. 1078

Liff, Noah, Pres.--Philip Metals/Steiner-Liff, Nashville, TN; *Int'l*, pg. 1050

Liffner, Bo, Chief Oper. Officer--ICA Fastighets AB, Vasteras, Sweden; *Int'l*, pg. 643

Ligeti, Jack, Mng. Dir.--Sabiem Elevators (Pty.) Ltd., Johannesburg, South Africa; *Int'l*, pg. 748

Liggett, Gary, Pres.--Justin Boot Company, Fort Worth, TX; *U.S. Public*, pg. 937

Lighty, P. Bruce, Pres. & Gen. Mgr.--The Lux Co., Inc., Elkhart, IN; *U.S. Public*, pg. 388

Ligon, Ed D., Pres.--Orbit Valve Co., Little Rock, AR; *U.S. Private*, pg. 819

Ligon, W. Austin, Pres.--Car Max, Glen Allen, VA; *U.S. Public*, pg. 374

Lihereau, Harve, Chief Oper. Officer--D.L. Blair Europe, Boulogne-Billancourt, France; *U.S. Private*, pg. 148

Lihui, Li, Mgr.--The Industrial and Commercial Bank of China, Beijing, China; *Int'l*, pg. 1328

Lihvarcik, John M., V.P.--Southern Division, Erial, NJ; *U.S. Public*, pg. 438

Liinamaa, J., Gen. Mgr.--Liljendals Bruk A.B., Liljendal, Finland; *U.S. Public*, pg. 869

Likarish, John, Chief Exec. Officer--Encycle/Texas, Inc., Corpus Christi, TX; *U.S. Public*, pg. 138

Lilburn, Randy, Plant Mgr.--Sierra Pacific Industries-Susanville Division, Susanville, CA; *U.S. Private*, pg. 999

Liles, Dean, Pres.--Electronic Tax Systems, Inc., Carrollton, TX; *U.S. Public*, pg. 421

Liles, Dean, Pres.--Fast-Tax, Carrollton, TX; *U.S. Public*, pg. 421

Lilienfeld, Pedro, Pres.--MIE, Inc., Bedford, MA; *U.S. Public, pg. 1558*

Liljedahl, Bo, Dir.--Ejendomsselskabet Tretorn A/S, Helsingor, Denmark; *Int'l*, pg. 1257

Liljenqvist, Reinhold, Mgr.--Deutsche Duni GmbH, Bramsche, Germany; *Int'l*, pg. 421

Liljevall, Jan, Chief Oper. Officer--Pharmacia & Upjohn Ges.m.b.H., Vienna, Austria; *Int'l*, pg. 1050

Lill, John W., Pres.--Barrick Chile Ltda., Santiago, Chile; *Int'l*, pg. 169

Lill, Matthew W., Gen. Mgr.--Brambles Security Services Inc., Westport, CT; *Int'l*, pg. 211

Lillelien, Bjorn, Gen. Mgr.--Kvaerner Kleven Floro A/S, Floro, Norway; *Int'l*, pg. 769

Lilley, Denise, Pres.--The Voucher Corporation, Cypress, CA; *Int'l*, pg. 21

Lillig, George, Mgr.-Sls.--Lucent Technologies, Seattle, WA; *U.S. Public*, pg. 1017

Lillis, Charles, Pres. & Chief Exec. Officer--U S West Media Group, Englewood, CO; *U.S. Public*, pg. 1689

Lilly, Francis X., Pres.--Bear Stearns Fiduciary Services, Inc., Washington, DC; *U.S. Public*, pg. 198
Lilly, Mike, Plant Superintendant--General Shale Products Corp., Blue Ridge, VA; *Int'l*, pg. 844
Lilly, R., Mng. Dir.--Senior Bigwood Limited, West Bromwich, United Kingdom; *Int'l*, pg. 1220
Lim, Anthony, Reg. Mgr.--Check Point Software Technologies (Singapore) Ltd., Singapore, Singapore; *U.S. Public*, pg. 342
Lim, Barry, Mng. Dir.--Esselte Meto SDN BHD, Kuala Lumpur, Malaysia; *Int'l*, pg. 461
Lim, Chris, Pres.--Pall Fluid Filtration Pte. Ltd., Singapore, Singapore; *U.S. Public*, pg. 1254
Lim, Edwin R., Dir.--The World Bank, New Delhi, India; *U.S. Private*, pg. 1189
Lim, Eric Ang Teik, Chm.--DBS Nominees Pte. Ltd., Singapore, Singapore; *Int'l*, pg. 350
Lim, Eric Ang Teik, Chm.--DBS Trustee Ltd., Singapore, Singapore; *Int'l*, pg. 351
Lim, Fletcher, Gen. Mgr.--Dentsu Young & Rubicam Sdn. Bhd. (Kuala Lumpur), Kuala Lumpur, Malaysia; *U.S. Private*, pg. 325
Lim, H.P., Pres. & Chief Exec. Officer--Baker Engineering, NY, Inc., Elmsford, NY; *U.S. Public*, pg. 168
Lim, James Aw Swee, Chief Oper. Officer--Rhone-Poulenc Malaysia Sdn, Bhd, Petaling Jaya, Malaysia; *Int'l*, pg. 1113
Lim, Jerry, Mgr.--SICO Asia Pte Ltd., Singapore, Singapore; *U.S. Private*, pg. 997
Lim, Jong Moon, Mng. Dir.--Kum Yang Otsuka Chemical Co., Ltd., Ulsan, Korea; *Int'l*, pg. 1014
Lim, Ken Au Yun, Country Mgr.--Standard Chartered Bank (Macao), Macau, Macau; *Int'l*, pg. 1295
Lim, Yeap Tang, Pres. & Chief Exec. Officer--Spider/DMB&B, Petaling Jaya, Malaysia; *U.S. Private*, pg. 305
Lima, Helio, Pres. & Chief Oper. Officer--Citibank (Florida) N.A., Dania, FL; *U.S. Public*, pg. 377
Lima, Manuel Branco Ferreira, Chm. Bd.--TAP Air Portugal, Newark, NJ; *Int'l*, pg. 1418
Limay, Luis A., Mgr.--Commerce/Sanseb Joint Venture, Milwaukee, WI; *U.S. Public*, pg. 410
Limaye, Prakash V., Pres.--Harding Lawson Associates, Infrastructure, Inc., Bellevue, WA; *U.S. Public*, pg. 785
Limbrick, Alfred, Grp. Pres.--Kohl's Food Stores, Wauwatosa, WI; *Int'l*, pg. 1375
Limburg, C.J.P., Gen. Mgr.--Erasmus Press Publishing kft., Budapest, Hungary; *Int'l*, pg. 1445
Limongelli, Anthony, Pres.--Atlas Copco Compressors, Inc., Holyoke, MA; *Int'l*, pg. 96
Limouzineous, Alain, Pres.--Spontex S.A., Paris, France; *Int'l*, pg. 1409
Limpaitoon, Sirin, Gen. Mgr.--ESAB (Thailand) Ltd., Bangkok, Thailand; *Int'l*, pg. 282
Limpuangthip, Chin, Chief Oper. Officer--Novo Nordisk Pharma (Thailand) Ltd., Bangkok, Thailand; *Int'l*, pg. 988
Lin, Anthony, Mng. Dir.--Christie's Hong Kong Ltd., Hong Kong, Hong Kong; *Int'l*, pg. 290
Lin, Anthony, Mng. Dir.--Christie's Taiwan, Taipei, Taiwan; *Int'l*, pg. 290
Lin, C. L., Gen. Mgr.--John Crane (Taiwan) Co. Ltd., Kaohsiung, Taiwan; *Int'l*, pg. 1339
Lin, C.H., Mgr.--Taiwan Nalco Chemical Co Ltd., Taipei, Taiwan; *U.S. Public*, pg. 1151
Lin, Edwin, Gen. Mgr.--AMP Products (Malaysia) SDN. BHD., Kuala Lumpur, Malaysia; *U.S. Public*, pg. 9
Lin, Jackson, Gen. Mgr.--Wang Industrial Co., Ltd., Taipei, Taiwan; *U.S. Public*, pg. 1738
Lin, Jay, Mgr.--Leo Burnett (Shanghai) Advertising Co., Ltd., Shanghai, China; *U.S. Private*, pg. 185
Lin, Lynn Y.S., Dr., Pres.--BASES International, Covington, KY; *U.S. Private*, pg. 120
Lin, Michelle, Gen. Dir.--China Management Systems (CMS), Taipei, Taiwan; *U.S. Public*, pg. 1043
Lin, P.C., Pres.--T.G.U.S. Corp., Wilsonville, OR; *Int'l*, pg. 1348
Lin, P.C., Chm.--Qingdao Rolled Glass Co., Ltd., Qingdao, China; *Int'l*, pg. 1348
Lin, P.F., Chm.--Taiwan Autogalss Industries Corp., Taipei, Taiwan; *Int'l*, pg. 1348
Lin, Robin C.C., V.P. & Rep.--The International Commercial Bank of China, Houston, TX; *Int'l*, pg. 683
Lin, W.H., Chief Oper. Officer--Gambro Taiwan Ltd., Taipei, Taiwan; *Int'l*, pg. 668
Lin, Wen-Long, Sr. V.P. & Gen. Mgr.--The International Commercial Bank of China, New York, NY; *Int'l*, pg. 683
Lin, Y.C., Chm.--Qingdao Float Glass Co., Ltd., Qingdao, China; *Int'l*, pg. 1348
Lin, Y.C., Chm.--Chang Jiang Float Glass Co., Ltd., Jiangsu, China; *Int'l*, pg. 1348
Lin, Zhang Fu, Chief Exec.--Suzhou Hongda Enzyme Co. Ltd., Jiangsu, China; *Int'l*, pg. 989
Linard, Jay M., Pres.--Alumax Extrusions, Inc., Cressona, PA; *U.S. Public*, pg. 60
Linard, Jay M., Pres.--Alumax Engineered Metal Processes, Inc., Saint Louis, MO; *U.S. Public*, pg. 60
Linaries, Fernando, V.P.--City National Bank - Fairfax Regional Office, Los Angeles, CA; *U.S. Public*, pg. 381
Lincoln, Dave, Mng. Dir.--Piccadilly Radio, Manchester, United Kingdom; *Int'l*, pg. 452
Lincoln, Dave, Mng. Dir.--Red Rose Radio, Preston, United Kingdom; *Int'l*, pg. 452
Lincoln, David F., Mng. Dir.--EnerTech Capital Partners, Wayne, PA; *U.S. Public*, pg. 1424
Lincoln, John, Pres.--Revenue Collection Group, San Diego, CA; *U.S. Public*, pg. 466
Lincoln, John, Pres. & Chief Exec. Officer--Revenue Collection Group World Headquarters, San Diego, CA; *U.S. Public*, pg. 466
Lincoln, John, Gen. Mgr.--Newly Weds Foods, Inc., Watertown, MA; *U.S. Private*, pg. 797
Lindahl, Agneta, Chief Oper. Officer--Scandinavian Heart Center AB, Goteborg, Sweden; *Int'l*, pg. 670
Lindahl, Stig, Mng. Dir.--Otis Hiss AB, Solna, Sweden; *U.S. Public*, pg. 1691
Lindback, Eje, Div. Mgr.--Chapman Industries plc, Darwen, United Kingdom; *Int'l*, pg. 1420
Lindback, Lars-Erik, Pres.--ABB Drives AB, Vasteras, Sweden; *Int'l*, pg. 7
Lindberg, Bo, Mng. Dir.--ESAB-Csepel Kft, Mor, Hungary; *Int'l*, pg. 282
Lindberg, Daniel, Admin.--Terrace Villa Convalescent Center, Salt Lake City, UT; *U.S. Public*, pg. 1715
Lindberg, Robert J., V.P. & Gen. Mgr.--Joslyn Clark Controls, Inc., Lancaster, SC; *U.S. Public*, pg. 481
Lindberg, William P., Mgr.--System One Control, Saint Paul, MN; *U.S. Private*, pg. 851
Lindblad, Anders, Chief Oper. Officer & Mng. Dir.--Hagglunds Drives AB, Mellansel, Sweden; *Int'l*, pg. 670
Lindblad, Ernest V., Pres.--SNET Paging, Inc., New Haven, CT; *U.S. Public*, pg. 1491
Lindbladh, Knut, Chief Oper. Officer--Saab-Scania AB, Falun, Sweden; *Int'l*, pg. 687
Lindbloom, Paul, Chief Oper. Officer--Acrometal-Brainerd, Brainerd, MN; *U.S. Private*, pg. 14
Lindborg, Ed., Pres.--Brock Candy Co. (MN), Winona, MN; *U.S. Private*, pg. 163
Lindborg, M., Chief Fin. Officer--AB Ferrolegeringar, Stockholm, Sweden; *U.S. Private*, pg. 735
Lindborg, Sivert, Chief Oper. Officer--ICA Kopmannatjanst AB, Vasteras, Sweden; *Int'l*, pg. 643
Linde, K., Pres. & Chief Exec. Officer--Principal Health Care, Inc., Rockville, MD; *U.S. Private*, pg. 885
Linde, Ken, Pres.--Principal Behavioral Health Care, Inc., Rockville, MD; *U.S. Private*, pg. 885
Linde, Ken, Dir.-Sls.--Phase Linear, Lincolnshire, IL; *U.S. Public*, pg. 1369
Lindeberg, Arne, Pres.--Perstorp Specialty Chemicals, Perstorp, Sweden; *Int'l*, pg. 1038
Lindeen, Tomas, Chief Oper. Officer--Electrolux (Chile) Ltda., Santiago, Chile; *Int'l*, pg. 441
Lindekens, Jean-Louis, V.P.-North America--Sabena Belgian World Airlines, Manhasset, NY; *Int'l*, pg. 1168
Lindell, Aulis, Chief Oper. Officer--Neste Liikennepalvelu Oy, Espoo, Finland; *Int'l*, pg. 913
Lindell, Borje, Chief Oper. Officer--AB Mikro-Verktyg, Sodertalje, Sweden; *Int'l*, pg. 686
Lindell, Stephen A., Reg. V.P.--RLI Special Risk, Glastonbury, CT; *U.S. Public*, pg. 1356
Lindelof, Ulf, Mng. Dir.--Iggesund Paperboard Norden, Goteborg, Sweden; *Int'l*, pg. 886
Lindelow, Jan, Pres. & Chief Exec. Officer--Trivoli Systems Inc., Austin, TX; *U.S. Public*, pg. 896
Lindelow, Jan, Pres. & Chief Exec. Officer--Trivoli Systems, Indianapolis, IN; *U.S. Public*, pg. 896
Lindemann, Diedrich, Gen. Mgr.--Enesco Import, GmbH, Hildesheim, Germany; *U.S. Public*, pg. 1508
Lindemann, J.J, Pres.--Commercial Cam Div., Wheeling, IL; *U.S. Public*, pg. 573
Lindemuth, David K., Pres.--Circle International, Brisbane, CA; *U.S. Public*, pg. 372
Linden, Helmut, Mgr.--Duisburg Branch, Duisburg, Germany; *Int'l*, pg. 401
Linden, Jan H., Pres.--Spintab, Stockholm, Sweden; *Int'l*, pg. 1328
Linden, Thom, Chief Oper. Officer--Frigoscandia Food Process Systems AB, Japan Branch, Tokyo, Japan; *U.S. Public*, pg. 606
Lindenbergh, J.H.M., Chm.--Baring Brothers, London, United Kingdom; *Int'l*, pg. 648
Lindenbergh, J.M., Chm.--ING Baring Securities, London, United Kingdom; *Int'l*, pg. 649
Linder, Bengt, Mng. Dir.--Ericsson Telecommunications Sdn Bhd, Shah Alam, Malaysia; *Int'l*, pg. 1368
Linder, Bent, Gen. Mgr. & Dir.-Mktg.--Avery Etikettering A/S, Randers, Denmark; *U.S. Public*, pg. 153
Linder, David, V.P. & Gen. Mgr.--The HON Co., Owensboro Plant, Owensboro, KY; *U.S. Public*, pg. 772
Linder, Douglas, Pres.--Cargill Citro-America, Inc., Minneapolis, MN; *U.S. Private*, pg. 210
Linderman, Dean, Exec. V.P.--EDS, Financial and Insurance Group, Plano, TX; *U.S. Public*, pg. 570
Linderoth, Egon, Pres.--Bofors AB, Bofors, Sweden; *Int'l*, pg. 276
Linders, Lars-Olof, Chief Oper. Officer--Saab Instruments, Jonkoping, Sweden; *Int'l*, pg. 686
Lindfelt, Jerry, Pres.--Lockheed Martin Tactical Defense Systems (Arizona), Goodyear, AZ; *U.S. Public*, pg. 1009
Lindgren, Bo-Goran, Chm. Reg. Bd.--ICA Handlarna Norr AB, Umea, Sweden; *Int'l*, pg. 642
Lindgren, Erick C., Mng. Dir.--Hans Reitzels Forlag A/S, Copenhagen, Denmark; *Int'l*, pg. 197
Lindgren, Erik C., Mng. Dir.--Horst & Sons Forlag A/S, Copenhagen, Denmark; *Int'l*, pg. 197
Lindgren, Leif, Chief Oper. Officer--Electrolux Aterforsakrings AB, Stockholm, Sweden; *Int'l*, pg. 438
Lindgren, Lennard, Pres.--Sandvik Coromant Skandinavien AB, Stockholm, Sweden; *Int'l*, pg. 1185
Lindgren, Per Olof, Plant Mgr.--Elkem Salten, Straumen, Norway; *Int'l*, pg. 448
Lindgren, Raimo, Mng. Dir.--Ericsson Telecomunicaciones S.A., Madrid, Spain; *Int'l*, pg. 1368
Lindgren, Stig R., Pres.--Flakt, S.A. de C.V., Tlalnepantla, Mexico; *Int'l*, pg. 5
Lindh, Carl-Eric, Pres.--Alfred Berg Fondkommission AB, Stockholm, Sweden; *Int'l*, pg. 12
Lindh, Jan, Managing. Dir.--Orkla Media A.S, Lysaker, Norway; *Int'l*, pg. 1011
Lindhardt, Ivan, Mng. Dir.--Neproma Textiel Service B.V., Arnhem, Netherlands; *Int'l*, pg. 1285
Lindhe, Bo, Pres.--Ahlens AB, Stockholm, Sweden; *Int'l*, pg. 708
Lindhe, Jan, Mng. Dir.--SKF Canada Ltd., Scarborough, Canada; *Int'l*, pg. 1158
Lindhoff, Bjoern F., Mng. Dir.--ITT Flygt S.p.A., Milan, Italy; *U.S. Public*, pg. 860
Lindholm, Svante, Mgr.--Sandvik Benelux B.V., Sandviken, Sweden; *Int'l*, pg. 1185
Lindley, D.J., Gen. Mgr.--Settef SpA, Resana, Italy; *Int'l*, pg. 803
Lindner, Carl H., III, Pres.--Great American Holding Corporation, Cincinnati, OH; *U.S. Public*, pg. 74
Lindner, Carl H., III, Pres.--American National Fire Insurance Company, Cincinnati, OH; *U.S. Public*, pg. 74
Lindner, Horst, Co-Chief Oper. Officer--Winschermann West GmbH, Recklinghausen, Germany; *Int'l*, pg. 1167
Lindner, Luca, Chief Oper. Officer--Conquest S.P.A., Milan, Italy; *Int'l*, pg. 1484
Lindner, S. Craig, Sr. Exec. V.P.--American Money Management Corporation, Cincinnati, OH; *U.S. Public*, pg. 74
Lindo, Anthony B., Mng. Dir.--The Bank of Nova Scotia Jamaica Limited, Kingston, Jamaica; *Int'l*, pg. 156
Lindo, Anthony B., Mng. Dir.--Scotiabank Jamaica Trust and Merchant Bank Limited, Kingston, Jamaica; *Int'l*, pg. 156
Lindo, Anthony B., Mng. Dir.--The West India Company of Merchant Bankers Limited, Kingston, Jamaica; *Int'l*, pg. 156
Lindquist, Bill, Bus. Mgr.--Firestone Fibers & Textiles Company-Gastonia, Gastonia, NC; *Int'l*, pg. 214
Lindquist, Lennart, Mng. Dir.--Esselte Meto AB, Solna, Sweden; *Int'l*, pg. 459
Lindquist, Roy W., Pres.--J.W. Aluminum Company, Mount Holly, SC; *U.S. Public*, pg. 1736
Lindqvist, Per-Arne, Pres.--Skanska Bostader Stockholm AB, Solna, Sweden; *Int'l*, pg. 1260
Lindroos, Kaj, V.P.--Valmet Corporation Printing Paper Machines, Karhula, Finland; *Int'l*, pg. 1448
Lindroos, Satu, Mng. Dir.--Lowe Brindfors, Helsinki, Finland; *U.S. Private*, pg. 678
Lindsay, Gary, Mgr.-Opers.--Spice Plant, Hunt Valley, MD; *U.S. Public*, pg. 1066
Lindsay, George I., Assoc. Dir.--WF Corroon-Birmingham, Birmingham, United Kingdom; *Int'l*, pg. 1501
Lindsay, Rob, Gen. Mgr.--Sasol Mining Explosives (SMX), Randburg, South Africa; *Int'l*, pg. 1196
Lindsay, Steve, Pres.--Applied Materials Europe BV, Schiphol, Netherlands; *U.S. Public*, pg. 123
Lindsay, Tim, Chief Exec. Officer--Lowe Howard-Spink, London, United Kingdom; *U.S. Private*, pg. 678
Lindseth, John, Dir.--NutriLite Products, Inc., Buena Park, CA; *U.S. Private*, pg. 69
Lindsey, Ernie, V.P. & Gen. Mgr.--ITW Deltar-Insert Molded, Mokena, IL; *U.S. Public*, pg. 866
Lindsey, George, Pres.--Nelson Publications, Port Chester, NY; *U.S. Public*, pg. 1328
Lindskog, Erik, Mng. Dir.--P.T. Karya Yansantara Cakti, Jakarta, Indonesia; *Int'l*, pg. 283
Lindstorm, Steve, Pres.--Pacificare of Arizona, Phoenix, AZ; *U.S. Public*, pg. 1251
Lindstrand, Jorn, Gen. Mgr.--A/S Scancem Chemicals, Skare, Norway; *Int'l*, pg. 1199
Lindstrand, Kenneth, Chief Fin. Officer--Gyproc AB, Malmo, Sweden; *Int'l*, pg. 122
Lindstrom, Bjorn, Pres.--Oy Novatool AB, Vantaa, Finland; *Int'l*, pg. 678
Lindstrom, Seppo, Gen. Mgr.--Wisapak Oy Ab, Karhula Factory, Karhula, Finland; *Int'l*, pg. 1429
Lindvall, Bo, Pres.--Perstorp Components, Skara, Sweden; *Int'l*, pg. 1040
Line, Roy, Gen. Mgr.--Turtle Wax Manufacturing Ltd., Skelmersdale, United Kingdom; *U.S. Private*, pg. 1110
Linebaugh, Karl W., Pres.--Chemical Bank Central, Big Rapids, MI; *U.S. Public*, pg. 345
Linehan, Liam, Exec. V.P.--Canadian Imperial Bank of Commerce (California), Los Angeles, CA; *Int'l*, pg. 257
Lineman, Ron, Office Mgr.--Chicago Rivet & Machine Co.-Automated Assembly Systems, Norwell, MA; *U.S. Public*, pg. 349
Linford, James C., Pres.--Testronics, Freeport, TX; *U.S. Private*, pg. 487
Linford, James C., Pres.--GSI of California, Pittsburg, CA; *U.S. Private*, pg. 487
Ling-Vannerus, Peter, Representative--Skandinaviska Enskilda Banken - Sao Paulo, Sao Paulo, Brazil; *Int'l*, pg. 1259
Ling, John H., Pres.--Bettcher Manufacturing Corporation, Brook Park, OH; *U.S. Private*, pg. 169
Ling, John H., Pres.--Amherst Metal Products, Inc., Amherst, OH; *U.S. Private*, pg. 169
Ling, Kah Seng, Mgr.-Sls.--Vickers Systems Sendinian Berhad, Petaling Jaya, Malaysia; *U.S. Public*, pg. 25
Ling, Michael, Mng. Dir.--DMB&B/Warsaw, Warsaw, Poland; *U.S. Private*, pg. 304
Ling, W. O., Chm. Bd.--The Derbyshire (Isle of Man) Ltd., Douglas, United Kingdom; *Int'l*, pg. 395
Lingnau, Lutz, Pres. & Chief Exec. Officer--Schering Berlin Inc., Cedar Knolls, NJ; *Int'l*, pg. 1204
Lingner, L., Dr., Chief Oper. Officer--Balzers Dunnschicht-Komponenten GmbH, Geisenheim, Germany; *Int'l*, pg. 997
Lingquist, William F., V.P.-Exploration--Homestake Mining Co. of California, San Francisco, CA; *U.S. Public*, pg. 833
Linhart, Gottfried, Gen. Mgr.--Colgate-Palmolive GmbH, Vienna, Austria; *U.S. Public*, pg. 398
Link, Art, Div. Mgr.--Hunt Oil Gulf Coast Exploration Division, Houston, TX; *U.S. Private*, pg. 548
Link, Franklin R., Pres.--Dukane Ultrasonics Div., Saint Charles, IL; *U.S. Private*, pg. 346
Link, Guy, Plant Mgr.--Industrial Bag Division - Louisville Plant, Louisville, KY; *U.S. Public*, pg. 1521
Link, James, Pres.-BACI--Beech Acceptance Corp., Inc., Wichita, KS; *U.S. Public*, pg. 1365
Link, James F., Chm.--Texaco Capital Inc., White Plains, NY; *U.S. Public*, pg. 1583
Link, Max E., Chm. Bd.--Novartis Nutrition Corporation, Saint Louis Park, MN; *Int'l*, pg. 974
Link, Perry, Pres.--Bruner-Ivory Handle Company, Hope, AR; *U.S. Private*, pg. 669
Link, Perry, Pres.--Sequatchie Handle Works, Inc., Sequatchie, TN; *U.S. Private*, pg. 669

Link, Perry, Pres.--Turner, Day & Woolworth Handle Corp., Crossville, TN; *U.S. Private*, pg. 669
Link, William, V.P. & Chief Exec. Officer--Chiron Vision, Irvine, CA; *U.S. Public*, pg. 350
Linke, Dr. Heinz, Chief Oper. Officer--Kepec Chemische Fabrik GmbH, Siegburg, Germany; *Int'l*, pg. 610
Linkous, J. Ronald, Pres.--Con-Way Truckload Services, Fort Worth, TX; *U.S. Public*, pg. 281
Linn, Jean A., Pres.--Green Meadows, Ltd., Johnston, IA; *U.S. Public*, pg. 1299
Linnell, Jim, Pres.--Development Association, Inc., Fort Worth, TX; *U.S. Public*, pg. 1561
Lins e Silva, Carlos Eduardo Korder, Dir.--Omnia Minerios Ltda., Rio de Janeiro, Brazil; *U.S. Public*, pg. 1387
Lins, Del, Pres.--Berg Co., Madison, WI; *U.S. Private*, pg. 301
Linser, Herbert, Pres.--Ameri-Forge Corporation, Houston, TX; *U.S. Public*, pg. 748
Linsey, Malcolm, Reg. Mgr.--Bailey Maintenance Services, Newcastle upon Tyne, United Kingdom; *Int'l*, pg. 133
Linski, C.J., V.P. & Gen. Mgr.--Raco, Inc., South Bend, IN; *U.S. Public*, pg. 845
Linski, Taisto, Mng. Dir.--Lappeenranti Plant, Villmanstrand, Finland; *Int'l*, pg. 1198
Linsley, Patrick M., Exec. V.P.-Corp. Mktg.--The National Enquirer, New York, NY; *U.S. Public*, pg. 87
Linstrom, Bjorn, Pres.--Oy Colly Company AB, Vantaa, Finland; *Int'l*, pg. 678
Lintecum, Randall, Pres.--International Billing Services, El Dorado Hills, CA; *U.S. Public*, pg. 1659
Lintz, Richard P., Chm. Bd. & Pres.--Busch Properties, Inc., Saint Louis, MO; *U.S. Public*, pg. 114
Lintz, Robert C., Pres.--Great American Management Services, Inc., Cincinnati, OH; *U.S. Public*, pg. 75
Linver, Sid, Pres.--Logicon Technical Services Inc., Leavenworth, KS; *U.S. Public*, pg. 1199
Linville, Steve, Pres.--Playfield Industries Inc., Chatsworth, GA; *Int'l*, pg. 1362
Linzmayer, W. P., Div. Mgr.--Bridgewater Div., Ellesmere Port, United Kingdom; *Int'l*, pg. 20
Lioz, Michael, Pres.--General Microcircuits Corporation, Billerica, MA; *U.S. Public*, pg. 717
Lipari, Rachel, Pres. & Chief Oper. Officer--Standard Security Life Insurance Company of New York, New York, NY; *U.S. Private*, pg. 446
Lipes, Edward B., Pres.--Osteonics Corp., Allendale, NJ; *U.S. Public*, pg. 1526
Lipinski, Jack, Pres.--Coastal Refining & Marketing, Wichita, KS; *U.S. Public*, pg. 390
Lipman, Ira A., Chm. Bd.--Peoplemark, Inc., Memphis, TN; *U.S. Private*, pg. 486
Lipovsky, Ronald P., Pres.--Maritz Marketing Research, Inc., Fenton, MO; *U.S. Private*, pg. 704
Lipp, M., Pres.--Racal Communications, Inc., Rockville, MD; *Int'l*, pg. 1083
Lipp, Robert I., Chm. Bd. & Chief Exec. Officer--Travelers Property Casualty Corp., Hartford, CT; *U.S. Public*, pg. 1633
Lippert, Douglas, Pres.--Lippert Components, Inc., Alma, MI; *U.S. Public*, pg. 529
Lippmann, Gerd-Michael, Mng. Dir.--Bertram & Graf GmbH, Pansdorf, Germany; *U.S. Public*, pg. 165
Lippoff, David B., V.P. & Gen. Mgr.--Miami Valley Broadcasting Corporation, Dayton, OH; *U.S. Private*, pg. 282
Lippold, Eberhard, Gen. Mgr.--Lupos Gmbh, Huckelhoven, Germany; *Int'l*, pg. 430
Lipps, Ben, Pres.--Fresenius Medical Care (North America), Lexington, MA; *Int'l*, pg. 505
Lipps, Ben, Dr., Pres. & Chief Exec. Officer--Fresenius Medical Care, Inc., Lexington, MA; *Int'l*, pg. 505
Lipscomb, Michael, Pres.--J.C. Carter Company, Inc., Costa Mesa, CA; *U.S. Private*, pg. 81
Lipsey, Sanford, Pres.--Buffalo Evening News, Inc., Buffalo, NY; *U.S. Public*, pg. 217
Lipshultz, Louis, Pres.--Weinstein International Seafood, Minneapolis, MN; *U.S. Private*, pg. 54
Liptak, Greg, Chm.--Product Information Network, Englewood, CO; *U.S. Private*, pg. 597
Liptak, Robert G., Jr., Pres.--Shenango Valley Water Co., Sharon, PA; *U.S. Public*, pg. 439
Lipton, Ivan, Pres.--Waxie Maxie Quality Music Co., Milford, MA; *U.S. Private*, pg. 1047
LiPuma, Tommy, Pres.--GRP Records, New York, NY; *Int'l*, pg. 1215
Lira, Alejandro Escobedo, Gen. Dir.--DMB&B Chile S.A., Santiago, Chile; *U.S. Private*, pg. 303
Lira, Juan Carlos Escobedo, Gen. Mgr.--DMB&B Chile S.A., Santiago, Chile; *U.S. Private*, pg. 303
Lirette, Jerry R., Pres.--D-M-E Company, Madison Heights, MI; *U.S. Public*, pg. 368
Lirtzman, Kenneth, Mgr.--Vanco International, Inc., Waukegan, IL; *U.S. Public*, pg. 1720
Lisauskas, A.J., Pres. & Chief Exec. Officer--Spartech Plastics, Portage, WI; *U.S. Public*, pg. 1496
Lischer, Larry, Pres.--Medicalodges, Inc., Coffeyville, KS; *U.S. Private*, pg. 728
Liscomb, Clark N., Pres.--Corning International K.K., Tokyo, Japan; *U.S. Public*, pg. 449
Lise, Claude, Pres.--Deluxair Incorporated, Longueuil, Canada; *Int'l*, pg. 453
Lishak, John, Jr., Pres.--Commercial Realty & Resources Corp., Wall, NJ; *U.S. Public*, pg. 1172
Liskowski, Fred J., Pres. & Chief Exec. Officer--First Western Trust Services Co., New Castle, PA; *U.S. Public*, pg. 642
Liss, Hans Dieter, Chief Oper. Officer--Wella Friseurbedarf GmbH, Berlin, Germany; *Int'l*, pg. 1489
Liss, Robert, Pres.--Neptune Trucking, Inc., Memphis, TN; *U.S. Public*, pg. 1046
Liss, Walter C., Jr., Pres. & Gen. Mgr.--WABC T.V., New York, NY; *U.S. Public*, pg. 512
Lissner, Mike, Jr., Branch Mgr.--Jaco Electronics, Inc., Columbia, MD; *U.S. Public*, pg. 920
List, Raymond, Pres.--ICF Kaiser Engineers, Inc., Oakland, CA; *U.S. Public*, pg. 853
Lister, C., Mng. Dir.--Wyseplant Ltd., Bedford, United Kingdom; *Int'l*, pg. 1035
Lister, Gerald W., Chief Exec. Officer--Mid-American Financial Services Company, Loves Park, IL; *U.S. Public*, *pg. 65*
Lister, H., Dir.--Caparo Wire Company Ltd., Wrexham, United Kingdom; *Int'l*, pg. 265
Lister, Roy L., Exec. V.P.--Bazaar & Novelty, Saint Catharines, Canada; *U.S. Public*, pg. 1526
Listi, Frank, V.P.--Golden State Foods-City of Industry Div., City of Industry, CA; *U.S. Private*, pg. 460
Listi, Frank J., Jr., Pres.--Universal Flavors Corp., Indianapolis, IN; *U.S. Public*, pg. 1695
Liston, Edward, Pres.--EUA Cogenex Corporation, Lowell, MA; *U.S. Public*, pg. 549
Liston, Edward T., Pres.--Rendva, Smithfield, RI; *U.S. Public*, pg. 549
Liston, Edward T., Pres.--Northeast Energy Management, Lowell, MA; *U.S. Public*, pg. 549
Liter, Peter, Jr., Gen. Mgr.--Color Data East, Armonk, NY; *U.S. Public*, pg. 1437
Lithander, Lars, Pres.--Volvo Sudamericana SACI, Lopez, Argentina; *Int'l*, pg. 1478
Litke, Mike, Mgr.--SMS-Seattle, Bellevue, WA; *U.S. Public*, pg. 1463
Litman, Arthur, Pres.--Castelazo & Associates, Los Angeles, CA; *U.S. Public*, pg. 1071
Little, Carl H., V.P.-Opers.--Weber-Knapp Company, Jamestown, NY; *Int'l*, pg. 473
Little, Chris, Chief Exec. Officer--Century Life, London, United Kingdom; *Int'l*, pg. 685
Little, Chris, Chm. Bd.--Century Pensions Limited, London, United Kingdom; *Int'l*, pg. 685
Little, Christopher, Pres.-Magazine Grp.--Meredith Publishing Group, Des Moines, IA; *U.S. Public*, pg. 1094
Little, Dennis R., V.P. & Gen. Mgr.--Marine & Industrial Engines & Service Div., Cincinnati, OH; *U.S. Public*, pg. 710
Little, Don, Gen. Mgr.--Alcoa Fujikura Ltd., Duncan, SC; *Int'l*, pg. 525
Little, F. Colin, Gen. Mgr.--Jeddah Beverage Can Making Company Ltd., Jeddah, Saudi Arabia; *U.S. Public*, pg. 465
Little, H.L., Mng. Dir.--Powell Duffryn Tools Limited, Poole, United Kingdom; *Int'l*, pg. 1066
Little, J. Lanier, Pres.--Norwest Bank of Wisconsin, Milwaukee, WI; *U.S. Public*, pg. 1202
Little, James, Pres.--Casualty Insurance Co., Chicago, IL; *U.S. Public*, pg. 681
Little, James, Exec. V.P. & Gen. Mgr.--WWF Paper Corp.-New York, New York, NY; *U.S. Private*, pg. 1145
Little, Larry, Gen. Mgr.--Mycogen Crop Protection, San Diego, CA; *U.S. Public*, pg. 1142
Little, M., Mng. Dir.--Fox's Biscuits Ltd., Batley, United Kingdom; *Int'l*, pg. 968
Little, Paul, Mng. Dir.--Turner Construction Company, Atlanta, GA; *U.S. Public*, pg. 1645
Little, Roger G., Pres.--Spire International Sales Corporation, Bedford, MA; *U.S. Public*, pg. 1499
Littleboy, P.A.E., Mng. Dir.--Coutts & Co (Jersey) Limited, Saint Helier, United Kingdom; *Int'l*, pg. 910
Littlechild, John F., Mng. Dir.--Q-ARC Limited, Cambridge, United Kingdom; *U.S. Public*, pg. 856
Littlefield, Roslea, Plant Mgr.--Block Plant, Midland, TX; *U.S. Public*, pg. 936
Littlejohn, Peter J., Chief Exec. Officer--BHP Information Technology, Melbourne, Australia; *Int'l*, pg. 225
Littlejohn, William L., Jr., Admin.--Hillhaven Rehabilitation Convalescent Center, Durham, Durham, NC; *U.S. Public*, *pg. 1714*
Littman-Quinn, Jack, Sr. V.P.-Intl.--Merisel, Marlborough, MA; *U.S. Public*, pg. 1096
Littman, Dr. Peter, Mng. Dir.--Vorwerk & Co. Teppichwerke GmbH. & Co. KG., Hameln, Germany; *Int'l*, pg. 1480
Littman, Irv, Pres.--Clearfield Insurance, Ltd., Boise, ID; *U.S. Public*, pg. 243
Litton, Jim, Gen. Mgr.--Taystee Bakeries, Marquette, MI; *U.S. Private*, pg. 1022
Litus, Bruce J., Mgr.-Terminal--Staten Island Terminal, Staten Island, NY; *U.S. Public*, pg. 692
Litwin, Nicholas E., Pres.--Ellison Graphics, Jupiter, FL; *U.S. Private*, pg. 524
Litz, Eric E., Mgr.-SC--Governor's Square, Inc., Tallahassee, FL; *U.S. Public*, pg. 1408
Litzinger, Chuck, Plant Mgr.--Oliver Rubber Co., Export, PA; *U.S. Public*, pg. 1504
Litzsinger, R.M., Pres.--Follett Collegiate Graphics, River Grove, IL; *U.S. Private*, pg. 417
Liu, George, Mng. Dir.--American Appraisal Hong Kong Ltd., Wan Chai, Hong Kong; *U.S. Private*, pg. 50
Liu, George, Pres.--American Appraisal Asia, Inc., Milwaukee, WI; *U.S. Private*, pg. 50
Liu, George, Pres.--American Appraisal China, Inc., Milwaukee, WI; *U.S. Private*, pg. 50
Liu, J., Mng. Dir.--Life Investors Insurance Co., Taipei, Taiwan; *Int'l*, pg. 28
Liu, Jar-Raang, V.P. & Gen. Mgr.--The International Commercial Bank of China, Chicago, IL; *Int'l*, pg. 683
Liu, Lee, Pres.--IES Investments Inc., Cedar Rapids, IA; *U.S. Public*, pg. 855
Liu, Ming-Yung, V.P. & Gen. Mgr.--The International Commercial Bank of China, Toronto, Canada; *Int'l*, pg. 684
Liu, Philip, Mgr.--Utell International-China, Beijing, China; *Int'l*, pg. 1098
Liu, R.C.K., Dir.-Bus. Devel.--Gammon Construction Ltd., Quarry Bay, Hong Kong; *Int'l*, pg. 775
Liu, Ruey-Jen, Sr. V.P. & Gen. Mgr.--The International Commercial Bank of China, Bangkok, Thailand; *Int'l*, pg. 683
Liu, S.C., Pres., Chief Exec. & Chief Oper. Officer--Tatung Company of America, Long Beach, CA; *Int'l*, pg. 1357
Liu, T.P., Chm. Bd.--Ford Lio Ho Motor Co., Ltd., Taipei, Taiwan; *U.S. Public*, pg. 665
Liukkonen, Karen E., Pres.--John Hancock Capital Corporation, Boston, MA; *U.S. Private*, pg. 590
Livaditis, C., Gen. Mgr.--ADT Greece, S.A., Athens, Greece; *U.S. Public*, pg. 1649
Livanovics, Andrejs, Mng. Dir.--KONE Lifti Latvija Oy, Riga, Latvia; *Int'l*, pg. 747
Livecchi, Jim, Specialized Mktg. Dir.--SBC Specialized Marketing, Columbus, OH; *U.S. Private*, pg. 955
Lively, R. Luke, Pres. & Chief Admin. Officer--First Virginia Bank-Mountain Empire, Abingdon, VA; *U.S. Public*, pg. 642
Livet, R.G., Pres.--P.T. Agra Monenco, Jakarta, Indonesia; *Int'l*, pg. 31
Livet, R.G., Mng. Dir.--Monenco Nigeria Limited, Lagos, Nigeria; *Int'l*, pg. 31
Livingston, David, Gen. Mgr.--BellSouth Shanghai Centre, Ltd., Shanghai, China; *U.S. Public*, pg. 208
Livingston, Doug, Pres.--Western Interactive Media, Los Angeles, CA; *U.S. Private*, pg. 1166
Livingston, John, Pres.--Tishman Urban Development, New York, NY; *U.S. Private*, pg. 1089
Livingston, Phillip K., Chm. Bd. & Chief Exec. Officer--Deposit Guaranty National Bank of Louisiana, Hammond, LA; *U.S. Public*, pg. 500
Livingston, Robert W., Pres. & Mng. Dir.--American Marine Pte. Ltd., Jurong, Singapore; *Int'l*, pg. 531
Livingston, Robert W., Mng. Dir.--Grand Banks Yachts, Ltd., Southport, CT; *Int'l*, pg. 531
Livingston, Robert W., Chief Exec. Officer--Grand Banks Yachts Sdn. Bhd., Pasir Gudang, Malaysia; *Int'l*, pg. 531
Livingston, W. Curtis, Chief Exec. Officer--Western Asset Management, Pasadena, CA; *U.S. Public*, pg. 985
Livini, Franco, Chm. Bd.--Pirelli Cables SAIC, Buenos Aires, Argentina; *Int'l*, pg. 1059
Livnat, I., Gen. Mgr.--MLM Division/Electronics Group, Beer-Yaacov, Israel; *Int'l*, pg. 690
Livshitz, Stanley, Plant Mgr.--Titleflex Canada, Richmond Hill, Canada; *Int'l*, pg. 1341
Ljung, Ake, Mng. Dir.--Nokia Satellite Systems AB, Motala, Sweden; *Int'l*, pg. 954
Ljungberg, Bo, Chief Oper. Officer--Dinol AB, Hassleholm, Sweden; *Int'l*, pg. 981
Ljungqvist, Stig-Ove, Mng. Dir.--Industri AB Thule, Hillerstorp, Sweden; *Int'l*, pg. 436
Llaguno, Juan, Mng. Dir.--Korn/Ferry International, Monterrey, Mexico; *U.S. Private*, pg. 633
Llampatas, Genero, Chief Oper. Officer--Bansafina, Madrid, Spain; *Int'l*, pg. 143
Lleonart, J. Juliana, Dir.-Admin. & Fin.--Revlon, S.A., Madrid, Spain; *U.S. Private*, pg. 690
Llera-Leathers, Alina M., V.P.--Willis Corroon Financial Services Corp., Glendale, CA; *Int'l*, pg. 1507
Llobet, Eduardo I., Pres.--La Union Gremial Compania Argentina de Seguros S.A., Rosario, Argentina; *U.S. Public*, pg. 216
Llobregat, Patrick, Chief Oper. Officer--SEB Japan Co. Ltd., Tokyo, Japan; *Int'l*, pg. 568
Llop, Ralph J.Jr., V.P. & Mgr.--Banco Santander International Miami, Miami, FL; *Int'l*, pg. 143
Llorach, Gloria, Gen. Mgr.--Circle Freight Venezuela S.A., Caracas, Venezuela; *U.S. Public*, pg. 373
Lloyd, Charles, Mng. Dir.--CPC/AJI (Hong Kong) Ltd., Tai No, Hong Kong; *U.S. Public*, pg. 225
Lloyd, Gary E., Mgr.-Branch--Piper Jaffray Inc., Grand Forks, ND; *U.S. Public*, pg. 1301
Lloyd, J.R.C., Mng. Dir.--Powell Duffryn Storage Limited, Felixstowe, United Kingdom; *Int'l*, pg. 1065
Lloyd, Jack, Pres.--Blackeyed Pea Restaurants Inc., Scottsdale, AZ; *U.S. Public*, pg. 498
Lloyd, John, Chief Oper. Officer--Enfield Industrial Corp., Lake Bluff, IL; *Int'l*, pg. 554
Lloyd, L.D., V.P.--The Bank of Nova Scotia, Houston, TX; *Int'l*, pg. 156
Lloyd, Larry, Pres.--Southern Golf Distributors, Inc., Fayetteville, NC; *U.S. Private*, pg. 896
Lloyd, Stuart, Mng. Dir.--FCB Singapore, Singapore, Singapore; *U.S. Private*, pg. 389
Lmbert, Ken, Pres.-DMB&B Asia/Pacific South--DMB&B/ Hong Kong, Quarry Bay, Hong Kong; *U.S. Private*, pg. 303
Lo, A.C.K., Mng. Dir.--China Thread Development Co. Ltd., Teun Mun, Hong Kong; *Int'l*, pg. 299
Lo, C.C., Gen. Mgr.--Amicon (H.K.) Ltd., Kowloon Bay, Hong Kong; *U.S. Public*, pg. 1113
Lo, Michael K.C., Pres.--Gold Peak Industries (Taiwan) Ltd., Hsin-chu, Taiwan; *Int'l*, pg. 537
Lo, Paul C.W., Mng. Dir.--GP Electronics Limited, Kwai Chung, Hong Kong; *Int'l*, pg. 537
Lo, Peter, Mgr.-Opers.--Olin Industrial (Hong Kong) Limited, Kowloon, Hong Kong; *U.S. Public*, pg. 1220
Lo, Philip, Gen. Mgr.--Shanghai Crown Packaging Company Ltd., Shanghai, China; *U.S. Public*, pg. 465
Lo, Robert, Gen. Mgr.--Raychem (H.K.) Ltd., Kowloon, Hong Kong; *U.S. Public*, pg. 1362
Lo, Robert, Mgr.-People's Republic of China--Raychem-Shanghai Cable Accessories Limited, Shanghai, China; *U.S. Public*, pg. 1363
Lo, Stephen, Mng. Dir.--Neste Chemicals South East Asia Ltd., Kowloon, Hong Kong; *Int'l*, pg. 914
Lo, W.K., Mng. Dir.--Power Conversion Asia-Pacific, Sha Tin, Hong Kong; *U.S. Public*, pg. 422
Lo, Wen, Gen. Mgr.--CCF Kuala Lumpur, Kuala Lumpur, Malaysia; *Int'l*, pg. 342
Lo, Yvonne, Chm. Bd. & Pres.--Vitasoy (U.S.A.) Inc., South San Francisco, CA; *Int'l*, pg. 1469
Loader, Helen, Pres.--Sally Fourmy & Associates, Toronto, Canada; *U.S. Public*, pg. 113
Loader, Ray, Gateway Mgr.--Circle Freight International, Romulus, MI; *U.S. Public*, pg. 370
Loating, Chris, Chief Oper. Officer--Ahlstrom Filtration, Inc.-Mt. Holly Springs Mill, Mount Holly Springs, PA; *Int'l*, pg. 35

Lobao, Luiz, Pres.--Coca-Cola Industrias Ltda., Rio de Janeiro, Brazil; *U.S. Public*, pg. 392

Lobbestail, Mike, Pres.--Steelcase Canada Ltd., Markham, Canada; *U.S. Private*, pg. 1038

Lobeck, Alexander, Gen. Mgr.--Kansas Information Network, Topeka, KS; *U.S. Private*, pg. 995

Lober, Richard O., Pres.--Epstein Construction Inc., Chicago, IL; *U.S. Private*, pg. 379

Lobo, Richard, Pres. & Geng. Mgr.-WTVJ-TV--National Broadcasting Co., Inc., New York, NY; *U.S. Public*, pg. 712

Lobon, Mario Franz, Gen. Mgr.--John Crane Venezuela, Barquisimeto, Venezuela; *Int'l*, pg. 1340

Loc, Truong, Mng. Dir.--Vietnam Marketing Center, Ho Chi Minh City, Vietnam; *U.S. Private*, pg. 305

Locasale, Tom, Pres.--Aydin Telecom Division, Horsham, PA; *U.S. Public*, pg. 158

Lochmann, Lee, Pres. & Chief Oper. Officer--Armour Swift Eckrich, Downers Grove, IL; *U.S. Public*, pg. 426

Lock, David, Chm. Bd.--Militair Aviation Limited, Ringwood, United Kingdom; *Int'l*, pg. 215

Lock, Terry R., Pres.--Boise Cascade Asia Ltd., Boise, ID; *U.S. Public*, pg. 243

Locke, Joseph J., Pres.--USLIFE Financial Institution Marketing Group, Inc., Chicago, IL; *U.S. Public*, pg. 77

Locke, Melvin W., Jr., Sr. V.P. & Dir.-People Services--Jefferies & Company, Inc., Los Angeles, CA; *U.S. Public, pg. 925*

Locker, James, Gen. Mgr.--Raymond Industrial Equipment Ltd., Brantford, Canada; *Int'l*, pg. 123

Lockhart, H. Eugene, Pres.-Global Retail Bank--BankAmerica Corporation, San Francisco, CA; *U.S. Public*, pg. 179

Lockhart, J.W., Chm. Bd. & Chief Exec. Officer--Morgan Grenfell Laurie Ltd., London, United Kingdom; *Int'l*, pg. 405

Lockwood, Earl F., Pres. & Chief Exec. Officer--Betac Corporation, Alexandria, VA; *U.S. Private*, pg. 140

Lockwood, Mark, Mgr.--EG & G Structural Kinematics, Troy, MI; *U.S. Public*, pg. 544

Lockwood, Stephen, Mng. Dir.--Dawson Fur Fabrics Ltd, Huddersfield, United Kingdom; *Int'l*, pg. 385

Lockyer, Katie, Pres.--Handar, Inc., Sunnyvale, CA; *U.S. Public*, pg. 1559

Lodeizen, A. R., Dir.--BolsWessanen International BV, Amstelveen, Netherlands; *Int'l*, pg. 751

Loden, D. John, Pres. & Chief Exec. Officer--FCB HealthCare, San Francisco, CA; *U.S. Public*, pg. 1641

Lodewijk, D.T., Gen. Mgr.--Van Melle Nederland Verkoop B. V., Breda, Netherlands; *Int'l*, pg. 1451

Lodge, Michael L., Pres.--Castle Cement Limited, Birmingham, United Kingdom; *Int'l*, pg. 1201

Lodotto, Don, Gen. Mgr.--Oxford Furniture, Moonachie, NJ; *Int'l*, pg. 460

Lodrini, Ron, Chm.--IMG Services, Harrison, NY; *U.S. Private*, pg. 566

Loeb, Helmut, Reg. Dir.-Central Europe--AlliedSignal Aerospace Service Corporation, Frankfurt/Main, Germany; *U.S. Public*, pg. 52

Loebach, D.C., Pres.--P.T. Natra Raya, Jakarta, Indonesia; *U.S. Public*, pg. 317

Loebbe, Klaus-Peter, Chief Oper. Officer--BASF Coatings AG, Munster, Germany; *Int'l*, pg. 104

Loeder, David, Sr. V.P.--Kvaerner Earl and Wright, Inc., London, United Kingdom; *Int'l*, pg. 771

Loedtup, Hans, Chief Oper. Officer--Siemens A/S, Oslo, Norway; *Int'l*, pg. 1247

Loekholm, Leif, Acting Mng. Dir.--Kaldnes Industri A/S, Tonsberg, Norway; *Int'l*, pg. 965

Loepfe, Otto, Chm. Bd.--Crossair Ltd., Basel, Switzerland; *Int'l*, pg. 1334

Loepfe, Willi, Representative--Union de Bancos Suizos, Madrid, Spain; *Int'l*, pg. 1441

Loes, Renato, V.P.-Accts. & Gen. Mgr.--Young & Rubicam Brasil, Sao Paulo, Brazil; *U.S. Private*, pg. 1200

Loeschen, Micahel, Gen. Mgr.--ITW Angleboard, Glenview, IL; *U.S. Public*, pg. 866

Loewenguth, Alfred, Mng. Dir.--Schachenmann & Co. AG, Basel, Switzerland; *Int'l*, pg. 1306

Loez, Bernard, Sr. V.P.--Dumez-GTM Chine, Beijing, China; *Int'l*, pg. 823

Loez, Bernard, Sr. V.P.--Dumez-GTM Hong Kong, Hong Kong, Hong Kong; *Int'l*, pg. 823

Lofberg, Per G.H., Pres.--Merck Medco Managed Care, Des Moines, IA; *U.S. Public*, pg. 1091

Loffler, Dietmar, Gen. Mgr.--Jowa AG, Volketswil, Switzerland; *Int'l*, pg. 865

Loffler, Gerd, Dr., Mng. Dir.--Krupp Hoesch Berufsbildung GmbH, Essen, Germany; *Int'l*, pg. 512

Lofholm, Steve, Gen. Mgr.--EA Engineering, Science & Technology, Inc., Sacramento, CA; *U.S. Public*, pg. 541

Lofredo, Rudolph, Chm. Bd.--Karl Koch Erecting Co. Inc., Carteret, NJ; *Int'l*, pg. 1261

Lofstrand, Hans-Olaf, Mgr.-Regional--Alimak Elevator Company, Atlanta, GA; *U.S. Private*, pg. 34

Loft, Stanley C., Pres.--Johnson-Loft Engineering, Inc., San Rafael, CA; *Int'l*, pg. 1378

Loftin, H. Lamar, Pres.--Community Bank & Trust of S.E. Alabama, Fort Rucker, AL; *U.S. Public*, pg. 1549

Loftin, William L., Pres.--Sysco Food Services-Syracuse, Warners, NY; *U.S. Public*, pg. 1552

Loftis, Jerry, Gen. Mgr.--Postal Systems Inc., Chicago, IL; *U.S. Public*, pg. 201

Loftus, David J., V.P.-Fin.--TreeSource, Inc., Portland, OR; *U.S. Public*, pg. 1729

Loftus, P.M., Gen. Mgr.--CSD Dayton Office, Dayton, OH; *U.S. Public*, pg. 1689

Lofy, Jack, Pres.--CommAir Mechanical Services, Oakland, CA; *U.S. Public*, pg. 2

Logan, David, Pres.--Gerber Scientific Products, Manchester, CT; *U.S. Public*, pg. 740

Logan, J., Gen. Mgr.--Petrocorp Exploration Limited, New Plymouth, New Zealand; *Int'l*, pg. 495

Logan, John F., Pres.--Pioneer International Corporation, Boston, MA; *U.S. Public*, pg. 1298

Logan, Len, Pres.--P.T. Asuransi Jiwa Dharmala ManuLife, Jakarta, Indonesia; *Int'l*, pg. 841

Logan, Leonard, Pres. Dir.--PT MetLife Sejahtera, Jarkata, Indonesia; *U.S. Private*, pg. 738

Logan, Mark, Mgr.-Canadian Sls.--Parker Pen Canada Limited, Scarborough, Canada; *U.S. Public*, pg. 745

Logan, Marlan, Gen. Mgr.--Pioneer Sementes Ltda., Santa Cruz do Sul, Brazil; *U.S. Public*, pg. 1299

Logan, Marlan J., Gen. Mgr.--Pioneer Agricultura Ltda., Santa Cruz do Sul, Brazil; *U.S. Public*, pg. 1299

Logan, Raymond F., Chief Oper. Officer--Christiana Community Builders, San Diego, CA; *U.S. Public*, pg. 352

Loginov, N.M., Chief Exec. Officer--Donax J/V, Kromtau, Russia; *Int'l*, pg. 710

Logotheti-Lyra, Elisavet, Chief Oper. Officer--Christie's Hellas Ltd., Athens, Greece; *Int'l*, pg. 290

Logsdon, Duane, Pres.--LSP Specialty Products Co., Stanton, CA; *U.S. Public*, pg. 1145

Logsdon, Gary, Mgr.-Bus. Devel.--Santa Fe Offshore Construction Co., Rio de Janeiro, Brazil; *Int'l*, pg. 766

Logston, R.W., Pres.--Timken do Brasil S.A. Comercio e Industria Limitada, Sao Paulo, Brazil; *U.S. Public*, pg. 1618

Logue, Gerry, Pres.--Grey Entertainment Inc., New York, NY; *U.S. Public*, pg. 764

Loh, Adrian, Gen. Mgr.--Hong Leong Assurance Sdn. Bhd. (Non-Life Div), Kuala Lumpur, Malaysia; *Int'l*, pg. 60

Loh, Andrew, Gen. Mgr.--Liebert Far East Ltd., Singapore, Singapore; *U.S. Public*, pg. 577

Loharjun, Ton, Mgr.-Sls.--Thai Airways Intl. Ltd.-Washington, Washington, DC; *Int'l*, pg. 1381

Lohlein, Friedrich, Gen. Mgr.--Esselte Vertriebsges. mbH, Vienna, Austria; *Int'l*, pg. 461

Lohmann, Christopher, Gen. Mgr.--Kallista, Inc., San Leandro, CA; *U.S. Private*, pg. 630

Lohmann, Tom, Pres.--Taurus Energy Co., Dallas, TX; *U.S. Public*, pg. 584

Lohmeier, Paul, Dr., Gen. Mgr.--Knorr-Bremse Electronic GmbH, Munich, Germany; *Int'l*, pg. 738

Lohmeyer, Jeannie, R.N., Fac. Mgr.--Montgomery Surgery Center, Rockville, MD; *U.S. Public*, pg. 803

Lohr, Eugene S., Gen. Mgr.--Georgia-Pacific Nekoosa Operations, Port Edwards, WI; *U.S. Public*, pg. 736

Lohrom, Frederick, Pres.--Rhode Island Hospital Trust National Bank, Providence, RI; *U.S. Public*, pg. 184

Loikkanen, Hanna, Representative--Merita Bank Ltd. - St. Petersburg Representative Office, Saint Petersburg, Russia; *Int'l*, pg. 859

Lois, George, Co-Chm. Bd., Chief Exec. Officer & Worldwide Creative Dir.--Lois/EJL New York, New York, NY; *U.S. Public*, pg. 1011

Loizides, Luis, Chief Exec.--Cyprus Cement Company Ltd., Limassol, Cyprus; *Int'l*, pg. 629

Loizzo, Mary, Pres.--Lab Safety Supply Inc., Janesville, WI; *U.S. Public*, pg. 758

Loke, Chan Keng, Chief Oper. Officer--Kim Eng Securities USA Inc., New York, NY; *Int'l*, pg. 733

Lolas, George, Gen. Mgr.--CPC (Hellas) A.B.E.E., Kifissia, Greece; *U.S. Public*, pg. 225

Lolas, William, Pres.--Pony International Inc., Warren, NJ; *Int'l*, pg. 1036

Lomakin, I., Rep.--Morgan Grenfell (Soviet Union), Moscow, Russia; *Int'l*, pg. 406

Lomason, Harry A., II, Pres.--Magna Lomason Corp., Farmington Hills, MI; *Int'l*, pg. 830

Lomax, James A., Gen. Mgr.--IPT Division, Mansfield, OH; *U.S. Public*, pg. 754

Lombard, Alain, Dir. Gen.--Europe Auto Equipment, Pantin, France; *U.S. Public*, pg. 394

Lombard, George, Pres.--Lockheed Martin Information Display Systems, Atlanta, GA; *U.S. Public*, pg. 1008

Lombardi, Carlo, Dir.--Banca d'America e d'Italia S.p.A. (Lucca), Lucca, Italy; *Int'l*, pg. 403

Lombardi, Giuliano, Sr. V.P. & Mgr.--Banca Commerciale Italiana, Los Angeles, CA; *Int'l*, pg. 652

Lombardi, R., V.P. & Mgr.--Turner Construction Co., Columbus, OH; *U.S. Public*, pg. 1645

Lombardo, Aldo, Mgr.--Sanpaolo-Amsterdam Branch, Amsterdam, Netherlands; *Int'l*, pg. 692

Lombardo, Joseph A., V.P. & Gen. Mgr.--Thiokol Space Operations, Brigham City, UT; *U.S. Public*, pg. 1597

Lombardo, Philip J., Chief Oper. Officer--Coronet Communications, Bronxville, NY; *U.S. Public*, pg. 1021

Lombardo, Phillip, Mgr.--WHBF, Rock Island, IL; *U.S. Public, pg. 1021*

Lomburger, Dave, Gen. Mgr.--Outdoor Systems, Inc.-New York, Pittsburgh, PA; *U.S. Public*, pg. 1235

Lomeli, Lois, Branch Mgr.--Pacific Crest Investment & Loan (Beverly Hills Branch), Beverly Hills, CA; *U.S. Public*, pg. 1249

Lomelin, Carlos Salazar, Chief Exec. Officer--Femsa Cerveza S.A. de CV, Monterrey, Mexico; *Int'l*, pg. 496

Lommer, Mel, Mng. Dir.--Royal Melrose Granites, Cold Spring, MN; *U.S. Private*, pg. 251

Londchal, Marc, Pres. & Chief Exec. Officer--Tredi, Paris, France; *Int'l*, pg. 459

London, J.P., Dr., Mng. Dir.--CACI N.V., London, United Kingdom; *U.S. Public*, pg. 272

Lonergan, James D., Pres. & Publr.--Wichita Falls Times & Record News, Wichita Falls, TX; *U.S. Public*, pg. 794

Lonergan, John, Mgr.--Croscill Outlet Store Corp., New York, NY; *U.S. Private*, pg. 291

Lones, Chuck, Mgr.-Opers.--Circle International, Austin, TX; *U.S. Public*, pg. 372

Loney, D. Allen, Pres.--Canada Life Insurance Company of America, Atlanta, GA; *Int'l*, pg. 255

Long, A.E., Gen. Mgr.--Commonwealth Bank of Australia-Victoria & Tasmania, Melbourne, Australia; *Int'l*, pg. 313

Long, Bo, Gen. Mgr.-The Americas--FINNAIR, New York, NY; *Int'l*, pg. 485

Long, Bob, Pres.--Tektronix NewStar, Inc., Madison, WI; *U.S. Public*, pg. 1567

Long, D.L., Pres.--PDM Strocal, Inc., Stockton, CA; *U.S. Public*, pg. 1305

Long, Daniel E., Pres.--EMS-Illinois, Naperville, IL; *U.S. Public*, pg. 565

Long, Darrell L., Pres.--SuperValu, Inc.-Scott City Div., Scott City, MO; *U.S. Public*, pg. 1541

Long, Donald J., Pres.--Anderson Bakery Co., Inc., Lancaster, PA; *U.S. Private*, pg. 65

Long, F.A., Pres.--Pennsylvania Coal Resources Corp., Allentown, PA; *U.S. Public*, pg. 1244

Long, Francis A., Pres.--Interstate Energy Co., Allentown, PA; *U.S. Public*, pg. 1244

Long, Francis A., Pres.--BDW Corp., Allentown, PA; *U.S. Public*, pg. 1244

Long, G.L., Pres.--Turbine Engine Components Textron, Thomasville, GA; *U.S. Public*, pg. 1588

Long, Glen, Pres. & Chief Exec. Officer--BWI Fords Holmatic, Norcross, GA; *Int'l*, pg. 130

Long, Ina, Admin.--Hillhaven, Little Rock, Little Rock, AR; *U.S. Public*, pg. 1713

Long, J.R., Pres. & Chief Oper. Officer--Ladbroke Racing Corporation, Pittsburgh, PA; *Int'l*, pg. 788

Long, James L., III, Pres.--Wackenhut Services, Inc., Coral Gables, FL; *U.S. Public*, pg. 1731

Long, John, V.P.-Sls.--All Star Gas Co.-Region IX, Lebanon, MO; *U.S. Private*, pg. 35

Long, John, V.P. & Gen. Mgr.--WRTV, Indianapolis, IN; *U.S. Public*, pg. 1070

Long, John W., Pres.--First American Real Estate Information Services, Inc., Saint Petersburg, FL; *U.S. Public*, pg. 625

Long, Larry, Mng. Dir.--DIWIDAG Systems International, USA, Inc., Avon Lake, OH; *Int'l*, pg. 424

Long, Matthew, Div. Mgr.--Higgins Union City Operations, Union City, CA; *U.S. Private*, pg. 527

Long, Millard J., Mgr.-Central European Office--World Bank, Budapest, Hungary; *U.S. Private*, pg. 1189

Long, Richard, Pres.--Iowa Mold Tooling Co., Inc., Garner, IA; *U.S. Public*, pg. 894

Long, Robert, Pres.--SunTrust Bank, Atlanta, Atlanta, GA; *U.S. Public*, pg. 1538

Long, Robert A., Pres. & Chief Exec. Officer--J.E. Dunn Equities, Inc., Kansas City, MO; *U.S. Private*, pg. 347

Long, Roddy, Mng. Dir.--Lambert Smith Hampton, Guildford, United Kingdom; *Int'l*, pg. 797

Long, Steve, Refinery Mgr.--Total Petroleum, Inc., Ardmore, OK; *U.S. Public*, pg. 1663

Long, Theresa, Pres.--Merrill Lynch Group, Inc., New York, NY; *U.S. Public*, pg. 1097

Long, V.R., Pres.--Western States Energy, Lehi, UT; *Int'l*, pg. 664

Long, Van, Gen. Mgr.--Rhone-Poulenc Basic Chemicals Co., Green River, WY; *Int'l*, pg. 1110

Long, W.H., Gen. Mgr.--Cylinder Div., Des Plaines, IL; *U.S. Public*, pg. 1261

Long, William, Pres.--Talman Home Mortgage Corp. & Talman Insurance Services, Inc., Chicago, IL; *Int'l*, pg. 11

Long, William E., Pres.--Technologies Division, Joplin, MO; *U.S. Private*, pg. 355

Long, William J., Pres. & Chief Exec. Officer--Sprayroq, Inc., Birmingham, AL; *U.S. Public*, pg. 882

Long, Zelma, Chm. Bd., Pres. & Chief Exec. Officer--Simi Winery, Healdsburg, CA; *Int'l*, pg. 781

Longacre, Philip E., Pres.--Seagate Technology Korea, Inc., Seoul, Korea; *U.S. Public*, pg. 1450

Longaker, Sue, Branch Mgr.--Downey Savings & Loan Association, F.A., Torrance, CA; *U.S. Public*, pg. 527

Longchampt, Michel, Pres.--Francosteel Corporation, New York, NY; *Int'l*, pg. 572

Longenecker, Robert, Pres.--KB Alloys, Inc., Sinking Spring, PA; *U.S. Private*, pg. 249

Longfellow, Aileen, Mgr.-Property & Casualty Claims--Willis Corroon Administrative Services Corporation, Reno, NV; *Int'l*, pg. 1504

Longfield, Craig N., Chm. Bd., Pres. & Chief Exec. Officer--PacifiCorp Financial Services, Inc., Portland, OR; *U.S. Public*, pg. 1252

Longfield, Craig N., Pres.--PacifiCorp Aviation (Holdings), Inc., Portland, OR; *U.S. Public*, pg. 1252

Longfield, Ross N., Pres. & Chief Exec. Officer--Beneficial National Bank USA, Wilmington, DE; *U.S. Public*, pg. 211

Longfield, Ross N., Pres.--Beneficial Tax Masters Inc., Peapack, NJ; *U.S. Public*, pg. 211

Longinotti, Ron, Pres. & Gen. Mgr.--KOTV Inc., Tulsa, OK; *U.S. Public*, pg. 209

Longley, Charles, Chief Exec. Officer--DHL International (Hong Kong) Ltd., Wan Chai, Hong Kong; *U.S. Private*, pg. 302

Longley, D.R., Gen. Mgr.--Senior Luke Materials Handling Division, Wakefield, United Kingdom; *Int'l*, pg. 1221

Longo, A., Pres.--Van Leer Embalagens Industriais do Brazil Ltda., Rio de Janeiro, Brazil; *Int'l*, pg. 1146

Longo, Art, Mgr.--Regal, New York, NY; *U.S. Private*, pg. 49

Longo, Edward, Sr. V.P.-Info. Svcs. Div.--Information Services Division, Boston, MA; *U.S. Public*, pg. 946

Longo, Eugene S., Pres. & Chief Exec. Officer--Adams Industries, Inc., Suffield, CT; *U.S. Public*, pg. 187

Longo, Joseph T., V.P. & Gen. Mgr.--Science Center, Thousand Oaks, CA; *U.S. Public*, pg. 1398

Longo, Leonard, V.P.--Ohio Sealants Inc., Mentor, OH; *Int'l, pg. 802*

Longo, Thomas A., Mng. Dir.--Handy & Harman Manufacturing (Singapore) Pte. Ltd., Jurong, Singapore; *U.S. Public*, pg. 780

Longoria, Tina, Creative Dir.--JMCTtouch, New York, NY; *U.S. Private*, pg. 599

Longstaff, G. Geoffrey, Pres. & Chief Exec. Officer--Regions Bank/Orlando, Longwood, FL; *U.S. Public*, pg. 1372

Longstreet, Dennis, Pres.--Johnson & Johnson Health Care Systems Inc., Piscataway, NJ; *U.S. Public*, pg. 928

Longthorpe, P.L., Project Mgr.--Meta Services Inc., Seattle, WA; *U.S. Private*, pg. 363

Lonyay, Alexander, Mng. Dir.--GGK Occidental Holding AG, Vienna, Austria; Int'l, pg. 1335
Loo, C.D., Pres.--Yale Europe Materials Handling, BV, Netherlands; U.S. Public, pg. 1149
Loof, P.O., Chief Exec. Officer--AT&T ISTEL Limited, Redditch, United Kingdom; U.S. Public, pg. 11
Loomis, James R., Pres.--Raytheon Systems Company Electronics Systems, Fort Wayne, IN; U.S. Public, pg. 1365
Loomis, Ronald, Pres.--Collins Bus Corp., South Hutchinson, KS; U.S. Public, pg. 400
Loon, Oon Kum, Chm.--DBS Trading Pte. Ltd., Singapore, Singapore; Int'l, pg. 351
Looney, Arthur, V.P. & Gen. Mgr.--Block Drug Corporation, Jersey City, NJ; U.S. Public, pg. 237
Looney, David R., Assoc. V.P.--Toronto-Dominion (Texas), Inc., Houston, TX; Int'l, pg. 1401
Looney, Mark E., Exec. V.P.--Chemtech Products Inc., Saint Louis, MO; U.S. Private, pg. 39
Loop, Carl B., Jr., Pres.--Florida Farm Bureau Casualty Insurance Company, Gainesville, FL; U.S. Private, pg. 1016
Loop, Gary, Chief Oper. Officer--Neste Polyester Inc., Fort Smith, AR; Int'l, pg. 913
Looper, Gary, Chief Exec. Officer--Columbia-Bay Area, Corpus Christi, TX; U.S. Public, pg. 404
Lopatin, Sergei, Chief Oper. Officer--MacGREGOR (RUS) A/O, Saint Petersburg, Russia; Int'l, pg. 671
Lopatka, Lubos, Mng. Dir.--KONE Lifts s.r.o., Bratislava, Slovakia; Int'l, pg. 747
Loper, David, Pres.--Intermat, Biddeford, ME; U.S. Private, pg. 402
Lopes, J. Cerqueria, Chief Oper. Officer--Axel Johnson (Acose Equipamentos) Lda, Carnaxide, Portugal; Int'l, pg. 711
Lopes, Richard A., Gen. Mgr.--L & M Corrugated Container Corp., Zion, IL; U.S. Public, pg. 1521
Lopez Saco, Antonio, Mgr.--MacNeal-Schwendler Iberica S.A., Madrid, Spain; U.S. Public, pg. 1032
Lopez-Aparicio, Rafael, Gen. Mgr.--Kodak Kft. Hungary, Budapest, Hungary; U.S. Public, pg. 553
Lopez-Rama, Cesar, Gen. Mgr.--Laboratorios Americanos S.A., Montevideo, Uruguay; U.S. Public, pg. 81
Lopez, Alejandro, Gen. Mgr.--Bailey Mexico S.A. de C.V., Mexico, Mexico; Int'l, pg. 449
Lopez, Alvaro, Gen. Mgr.--Corn Refining Opers.--Maizena S.A., Cali, Colombia; U.S. Public, pg. 447
Lopez, Alvaro Munoz, Pres.--Musini, Sociedad Mutua de Seguros y Reaseguros a Prima Fija, Madrid, Spain; Int'l, pg. 1225
Lopez, Bill, Gen. Mgr.--Paramount Metalizing Div., Sullivan, MO; U.S. Private, pg. 631
Lopez, Eduardo, Country Mgr.--Circle Espana S.A., Madrid, Spain; U.S. Public, pg. 372
Lopez, Emilio, V.P.-Latin America--Medtronic, Inc., Deerfield Beach, FL; U.S. Public, pg. 1083
Lopez, Emilio Gonzalez, Pres.--Mead Johnson de Mexico, S.A. de C.V., Mexico, Mexico; U.S. Public, pg. 256
Lopez, Felipe, Gen. Mgr.--Castleton Beverage Corp., Jacksonville, FL; Int'l, pg. 132
Lopez, Fernando, Mng. Dir.--Tissu Canarias S.A., Telde, Spain; Int'l, pg. 864
Lopez, Francisco Fernandez, Chief Oper. Officer--Banco Santander, Mexico, Mexico; Int'l, pg. 144
Lopez, Frank, V.P. & Gen. Mgr.--Bob Saks Jeep-Eagle, Farmington, MI; U.S. Private, pg. 395
Lopez, Jaime, Gen. Mgr.--Loctite de Venezuela, C.A., Caracas, Venezuela; Int'l, pg. 611
Lopez, Joe, Mgr.--Fabrication Plant/Custom Products, Irvine, CA; U.S. Public, pg. 1177
Lopez, Juan Mata, Gen. Mgr.--Naviera Castellana, S.A., Madrid, Spain; Int'l, pg. 1223
Lopez, Monica, Mgr.--General Employment Enterprises, New York, NY; U.S. Public, pg. 714
Lopez, Ofelia, Branch Dir. V.P.--Tucson Branch Office, Tucson, AZ; U.S. Public, pg. 1683
Lopez, R., Chief Oper. Officer--PolyGram Record Operations Ltd., London, United Kingdom; Int'l, pg. 1053
Lopez, Ramon, Chm. & Chief Exec. Officer--WEA Intl., Inc., New York, NY; U.S. Public, pg. 1612
Lopez, Raul Perez, Gen. Mgr.--Banco Santander International, Miami, FL; Int'l, pg. 143
Lopina, Thomas J., Pres. & Chief Exec. Officer--Ingersoll Equipment Co., Inc., Winneconne, WI; Int'l, pg. 1129
Loppke, Herbert, Dir.-Admin.--Skandinavisk Henkel A/S, Copenhagen, Denmark; Int'l, pg. 614
Lopuszynski, Thomas W., V.P.--Elkem-American Carbide Company (Pittsburgh), Pittsburgh, PA; U.S. Public, pg. 33
Lorain, G., Mng. Dir.--Vilmorin Inc., Empire, CA; Int'l, pg. 566
Loran, Mike, Pres.--Associated Plastics, Inc., Riverside, CA; U.S. Private, pg. 417
Lorant, Francois, Mgr.-Plant--Sucrerie De Cagny, Gagny, France; Int'l, pg. 549
Lorayes, Roberto, Chief Oper. Officer--Kim Eng Securities Philippines Inc., Manila, Philippines; Int'l, pg. 733
Lorber, Howard M., Pres.--Hallman & Lorber, Inc., Valley Stream, NY; U.S. Public, pg. 783
Lord, John, Pres.--Carrier Corporation, Indianapolis, IN; U.S. Public, pg. 1689
Lord, Richard J., Chm.--The Lord Group, New York, NY; U.S. Private, pg. 325
Lord, W.S., Gen. Mgr.--SYTECH, Columbus, IN; U.S. Public, pg. 468
Lorenowich, Stan J., Chief Oper. Officer--Titanium Ltd/Ltdee, Saint-Laurent, Canada; Int'l, pg. 35
Lorentzen, Matthew, Pres.--Canadian Transport Company, Vancouver, Canada; U.S. Private, pg. 805
Lorenz, Brenda, Admin.--Parkwood Place, Lufkin, TX; U.S. Public, pg. 839
Lorenz, Gary, Sr. V.P. & Gen. Mgr.--Griffin Technology Inc., Amsec Div., Rancho Dominguez, CA; U.S. Public, pg. 506
Lorenz, Juan, Mng. Dir.--Ortho Diagnostic Systems G.m.b.H., Neckargemund, Germany; U.S. Public, pg. 932
Lorenz, W.W., Exec.-Chm.--Monsanto New Zealand, Ltd., Wellington, New Zealand; U.S. Public, pg. 1126
Lorenzi, Henri, V.P.--Loews Monte Carlo, Monaco, Monaco; U.S. Public, pg. 1011
Lorenzo, Jose Manuel, Gen. Mgr.--CEPSA Italia, S.p.A., Milan, Italy; Int'l, pg. 323
Lorenzo, Pedro, Chief Oper. Officer--Prakoll, S.A., Alicante, Spain; U.S. Public, pg. 687
Lorimar, Gary D., V.P.-Engrg.--Henningsen Foods, Inc., Omaha, NE; Int'l, pg. 1074
Lorimer, Desmond, Sir, Chm. Bd.--Northern Bank Limited, Belfast, United Kingdom; Int'l, pg. 906
Loring, John C., Chm. Bd.--Avest, Inc., Plainview, NY; U.S. Public, pg. 141
Lortie, Piere, Pres.--Bombardier Capital Inc., Colchester, VT; Int'l, pg. 200
Lortie, Pierre, Pres.--Bombardier Regional Aircraft Division, Downsview, Canada; U.S. Public, pg. 242
Lorton, Donald, Pres.--Maytag Cleveland Cooking Products, Cleveland, TN; U.S. Public, pg. 1064
Losciale, Carlos, Mng. Dir.--Kelko Quaker Chemical, S.A., Caracas, Venezuela; U.S. Public, pg. 1346
Losey, Charles, Chief Oper. Officer--United Wholesale Inc., Grand Rapids, MI; U.S. Private, pg. 1021
Losito, David J., Sr. V.P.--Jefferies & Company, Inc., Los Angeles, CA; U.S. Public, pg. 925
Lospinoso, Albert P., Pres.--Bestolife Corp., Dallas, TX; U.S. Private, pg. 900
Lospinoso, Albert P., Pres.--RSR Corporation, Dallas, TX; U.S. Private, pg. 900
Lospinoso, Albert P., Pres.--Quemetco, Inc., Dallas, TX; U.S. Private, pg. 900
Lospinoso, Albert P., Pres.--Environmental Service Insurance Co., Dallas, TX; U.S. Private, pg. 900
Lospinoso, Albert P., Pres.--Revere Smelting & Refining Corp., Dallas, TX; U.S. Private, pg. 901
Lospinoso, Albert P., Pres.--West Morris Properties, Inc., Dallas, TX; U.S. Private, pg. 901
Lothongkam, Poe, Pres.--Multichip Technology, San Jose, CA; U.S. Public, pg. 470
Lotman, Herb, Pres.--M & M Restaurant Supply, Dayton, OH; U.S. Private, pg. 619
Lott, Hamilton, V.P. & Gen. Mgr.--Vulcraft Div., Florence, SC; U.S. Public, pg. 1206
Lott, William, V.P. & Gen. Mgr.--Thorn Apple Valley-Transportation Division, Grand Rapids, MI; U.S. Public, pg. 1603
Lottman, Donna, Mgr.--A. Schulman, Inc., Saint Louis, MO; U.S. Public, pg. 1441
Lotts, James E., V.P. & Gen. Mgr.--Dillard, A ResourceNet International Company, Wilmington, NC; U.S. Public, pg. 902
Loud, Derek, Gen. Mgr.--Avon Products Pty. Ltd., Deewhy, Australia; U.S. Public, pg. 156
Loudemilk, Billy R., Pres. & Chief Exec. Officer--Regions Bank/Gilmer County, Ellijay, GA; U.S. Public, pg. 1372
Loudermilk, James, Chief Oper. Officer--Health Care Management Corp., Inc., Fort Wayne, IN; U.S. Public, pg. 405
Loudon, Stuart, Mng. Dir.--CFS New Zealand Ltd., Auckland, New Zealand; U.S. Public, pg. 372
Lough, D.K., Pres. & Chief Oper. Officer--The Halifax Insurance Company, Toronto, Canada; Int'l, pg. 648
Lough, K.G., Mng. Dir.--LASMO North Sea PLC, London, United Kingdom; Int'l, pg. 804
Louie, John Y., Mng. Dir.--Schindler Lifts (Hong Kong) Ltd., Quarry Bay, Hong Kong; Int'l, pg. 1205
Louly, J.F., Chief Fin. Officer--Van Melle-France S.A., Wasquehal, France; Int'l, pg. 1451
Loundsbery, Jim, Mgr.--Tru-Turn Corporation, Homer, MI; U.S. Private, pg. 513
Loupos, G.A., Mng. Dir.--Cussons International Ltd., Stockport, United Kingdom; Int'l, pg. 1024
Louras, P.N., V.P.--The Clorox International Co., Oakland, CA; U.S. Public, pg. 387
Lourenco, Dario, G.M.--Avon Cosmeticas, Lda., Lisbon, Portugal; U.S. Public, pg. 156
Lourenco, Dario, Pres. & Mng. Dir.--Avon Cosmetics, S.p.A., Olgiate Comasco, Italy; U.S. Public, pg. 156
Lourival da Silva, Mercio, Mgr.--Vitoria Branch, Vitoria, Brazil; Int'l, pg. 139
Loury, George C., Pres.--Norgren Co., Littleton, CO; Int'l, pg. 647
Louthien, Paul, Pres.--President Baking-Little Rock, North Little Rock, AR; Int'l, pg. 1069
Loutit, John, Gen. Mgr.--Kvaerner Pulping Pty Ltd., Hawthorn, Australia; Int'l, pg. 768
Loutit, John, Gen. Mgr.--Kamyr Pty Ltd., Hawthorn, Australia; Int'l, pg. 771
Lovas, Steve, Pres.--Pacific Telecom Cable, Inc., Vancouver, WA; Int'l, pg. 247
Lovass, Jahn Henry, Reg. Mgr.--Det Norske Veritas, Goteborg, Sweden; Int'l, pg. 396
Love, K.D., Mgr.--Tencarva Machinery Co.-Asheville, Arden, NC; U.S. Private, pg. 1076
Love, Robert, Pres.--RJ Properties, Inc., Saint Petersburg, FL; U.S. Public, pg. 923
Lovejoy, William J., Gen. Mgr.--Service Parts Operations, Flint, MI; U.S. Public, pg. 720
Lovelace, Jim, Admin.--Champion's Residential Treatment Center, Houston, TX; U.S. Public, pg. 404
Lovelady, Ernest, Pres.--In-Sink-Erator, Racine, WI; U.S. Public, pg. 573
Lovell, Byron, Pres.--Fleming Foods West - Sacramento Div., West Sacramento, CA; U.S. Public, pg. 653
Lovell, P.J., Pres.--Bantrel Inc., Calgary, Canada; Int'l, pg. 118
Lovell, William, Pres.--Sandvik/Milford Corporation, Branford, CT; Int'l, pg. 1185
Lovelock, Derrick, Mng. Dir.--Richard Shops Holdings Ltd., London, United Kingdom; Int'l, pg. 1217
Loveridge, David, Chief Oper. Officer--Spectra-Physics Holdings Plc, Brentford, United Kingdom; Int'l, pg. 1290
Lovett, Chris, Gen. Mgr.--Notifier Australia, Saint Kilda, Australia; U.S. Public, pg. 1307
Lovett, Donald R., Chm. Bd., Pres. & Chief Exec. Officer--AMCORE Bank, Rock River Valley, Dixon, IL; U.S. Public, pg. 64
Lovett, Jack, Mgr.--All American Recycling, Ocala, FL; U.S. Public, pg. 413
Lovett, Peter R., Mgr.--Radiometer Ltd., Crawley, United Kingdom; Int'l, pg. 1084
Lovette, Gene Allen, Chief Opr. Officer--Tyson Foods of Texas, Inc., Springdale, AR; U.S. Public, pg. 1652
Lovette, George R., Chm. Bd.--Omega Bank, N.A., State College, PA; U.S. Public, pg. 1222
Lovfald, Dorothy A., V.P. & Gen. Mgr.--Cox Communications-Humboldt Bay, Eureka, CA; U.S. Public, pg. 454
Lovless, Rick, Plant Mgr.--Dekoron Wire & Cable Division, Mount Pleasant, TX; U.S. Public, pg. 689
Lovold, Kjell, Chief Oper. Officer--Norfolier A/S & Co., Fjellhamar, Norway; Int'l, pg. 659
Lovold, Larry, Pres.--Lund Boats, New York Mills, MN; U.S. Private, pg. 447
Lovstrom, Jan T.R., Chm. Bd.--Ecophon CertainTeed, Inc., Valley Forge, PA; Int'l, pg. 1171
Low, Gak Beng, Mng. Dir.--Dresdner Bank AG, Bangkok, Thailand; Int'l, pg. 419
Low, Jeffrey, Gen. Mgr.--Spider/DMB&B, Petaling Jaya, Malaysia; U.S. Private, pg. 305
Lowam, David, Div. Pres.--Danly Die Set Division, Cicero, IL; U.S. Private, pg. 264
Lowback, T., Chm.--Pulimat S.p.A., Guardamiglio, Italy; Int'l, pg. 442
Lowd, Robert M., Pres.--Associated Aviation, Inc., Short Hills, NJ; U.S. Public, pg. 355
Lowden, D., Gen. Mgr.--New Zealand AMP Ltd., Auckland, New Zealand; U.S. Public, pg. 9
Lowden, Paul W., Pres.--Resort Marketing International, Las Vegas, NV; U.S. Public, pg. 1432
Lowden, Paul W., Pres. & Chief Exec. Officer--Casino Properties, Inc., Las Vegas, NV; U.S. Public, pg. 1432
Lowden, Paul W., Pres.--Hacienda Hotel Inc., Las Vegas, NV; U.S. Public, pg. 1432
Lowden, Paul W., Pres.--Hacienda Hawaiian Properties, Inc., Las Vegas, NV; U.S. Public, pg. 1432
Lowden, Paul W., Pres.--Sahara Resorts, Las Vegas, NV; U.S. Public, pg. 1432
Lowden, Paul W., Pres.--Sahara Illinois Corp., Las Vegas, NV; U.S. Public, pg. 1432
Lowden, Paul W., Pres.--Sahara Nevada Corp., Las Vegas, NV; U.S. Public, pg. 1432
Lowden, Paul W., Pres.--Santa Fe Coffee Company, Las Vegas, NV; U.S. Public, pg. 1432
Lowden, Paul W., Pres.--Santa Fe Hotel Inc., Las Vegas, NV; U.S. Public, pg. 1432
Lowden, Paul W., Pres.--Pioneer Finance Corp., Las Vegas, NV; U.S. Public, pg. 1432
Lowden, Paul W., Pres.--Sahara Mississippi Management Company, Inc., Las Vegas, NV; U.S. Public, pg. 1432
Lowden, Paul W., Pres.--Sahara Parkville, Inc., Las Vegas, NV; U.S. Public, pg. 1432
Lowden, Paul W., Pres.--Santa Fe Valley, Inc., Las Vegas, NV; U.S. Public, pg. 1432
Lowe, Carol, Admin.--Heritage Forest Lane, Dallas, TX; U.S. Public, pg. 839
Lowe, Frank, Chm.--The Lowe Group, London, United Kingdom; U.S. Private, pg. 678
Lowe, George R., V.P. & Gen. Mgr.--Newberg Div., Newberg, OR; Int'l, pg. 1269
Lowe, George R., Gen. Mgr.--Newsprint Div. (Newberg), Newberg, OR; Int'l, pg. 1270
Lowe, Gordon, Chief Exec. Officer--Caparo Steel Stockholders Ltd., Wardley, United Kingdom; Int'l, pg. 265
Lowe, Harry R., V.P. & Gen. Mgr.--Nucor Building Systems, Waterloo, IN; U.S. Public, pg. 1205
Lowe, J. Millar, Pres.--Kvaerner Boving (ANZ) Pty Ltd, Hawthorn, Australia; Int'l, pg. 772
Lowe, Ken, Pres.--Home & Garden Television, Knoxville, TN; U.S. Public, pg. 1447
Lowe, Peter J., V.P. & Gen. Mgr.-European Aerospace--Huck, Europe, Clos D' Asseville, France; U.S. Public, pg. 1597
Lowe, Robert L., Pres.--Atlanta Casualty Company, Norcross, GA; U.S. Public, pg. 75
Lowe, Tom, Chief Oper. Officer--Advanced Micro Devices, Sdn Bhd, Penang, Malaysia; U.S. Public, pg. 21
Lowe, Vernon, Pres.--Judd-Olin (U.K.) Limited, Coventry, United Kingdom; U.S. Public, pg. 1219
Lowe, William C., Exec. V.P.--Development and Manufacturing, Stamford, CT; U.S. Public, pg. 1784
Lowell, Ed, Gen. Mgr.--Watlow Winona, Inc., Winona, MN; U.S. Private, pg. 1153
Lowell, Ed, Gen. Mgr.--Watlow Gordon, Richmond, IL; U.S. Private, pg. 1153
Lowenfels, Jeff B., Pres. & Chief Exec. Officer--Yukon Pacific Corporation, Anchorage, AK; U.S. Public, pg. 284
Lowenkron, N. Michael, Pres.--JCP Realty, Inc., Plano, TX; U.S. Public, pg. 917
Lowenthal, A.G., Chm. Bd., Pres. & Chief Exec. Officer--Fahnestock & Co., Inc., New York, NY; Int'l, pg. 476
Lowenthal, A.G., Chm. Bd.--Freedom Investment, Omaha, NE; Int'l, pg. 476
Lower, Jan, Chief Exec. Officer--Alima-Gerber SA, Rzeszow, Poland; Int'l, pg. 973
Lowery, John, Gen. Mgr.--WWF Paper Corporation - Mid Atlantic, Richmond, VA; U.S. Private, pg. 1145
Lowery, Steve, Publisher--Kentucky Standard, Bardstown, KY; U.S. Private, pg. 648
Lowhagen, Lars, Pres.--Skanska Vast, Goteborg, Sweden; Int'l, pg. 1261
Lowman, D. J., Gen. Mgr.--Barclays Bank SA, Geneva, Switzerland; Int'l, pg. 166

Lowrance, Darrell J., Pres.--Eagle Electronics, Catoosa, OK; *U.S. Public*, pg. 1016

Lowrance, Darrell J., Pres.--Lowrance Avionics, Tulsa, OK; *U.S. Public*, pg. 1016

Lowrance, Debra, Mng. Dir.--Meridell Achievement Center, Liberty Hill, TX; *U.S. Public*, pg. 1697

Lowrie, William G., Pres.--Amoco Production Company, Chicago, IL; *U.S. Public*, pg. 102

Lowry, Burns M., Pres.--Merrill Lynch Life Agency Inc., Plainsboro, NJ; *U.S. Public*, pg. 1098

Lowry, Dan, V.P.-Opers.--Doehler-Jarvis, Greeneville Inc., Greeneville, TN; *U.S. Public*, pg. 796

Lowry, Stephen I., Practice Dir.--WF Corroon-Hemel Hempstead, Hemel Hempstead, United Kingdom; *Int'l*, pg. 1501

Loyd, Paul B. Jr., Chm. Bd., Pres. & Chief Exec. Officer--Reading & Bates Corporation, Houston, TX; *U.S. Public*, pg. 1354

Loyd, Tim, Mgr.--Woodward Governor Nederland B.V., Hoofddorp, Netherlands; *U.S. Public*, pg. 1777

Loyez, Jean-Hugues, Mng. Dir.--Sous Groupe Castorama, Templemars, France; *Int'l*, pg. 275

Lozano, J.J., Mgr.--Kodak S.A., Valencia, Spain; *U.S. Public*, pg. 554

Lozano, Maria L., Mng. Dir.--Electronica Pantera, S.A. de C.V., Zapopan, Mexico; *U.S. Public*, pg. 919

Lozano, Sergio, Gen. Dir.--Quimobasicos, S.A. de C.V., Monterrey, Mexico; *Int'l*, pg. 247

Lu, Eugene, Chm. Bd., Pres. & Chief Exec. Officer--Advanced Logic Research, Inc., Irvine, CA; *U.S. Public*, pg. 703

Lu, Fang-Ming, Gen. Mgr.--Cirrus Logic International Ltd., Taipei, Taiwan; *U.S. Public*, pg. 375

Lu, Henry, Gen. Mgr.--ITW Switches-Asia, Kao-hsiung, Taiwan; *U.S. Public*, pg. 868

Lu, Rudy, Mgr.--Sandvik Titan Pty. Ltd., Chung Li, Taiwan; *Int'l*, pg. 1187

Lu, Yo-chi, Gen. Mgr.--Ohmeda Ltd., Tokyo, Japan; *Int'l*, pg. 122

Lubbe, Glenn, Plant Mgr.--Regal Cutting Tools Div., Mitchell, IN; *U.S. Public*, pg. 1370

Lubbers, B., Mgr.-Branch--American Inks & Coatings Corp., Ink Division, Florence, KY; *U.S. Private*, pg. 56

Lubbert, Mario, Pres. & Creative Dir.--Prolam/Young & Rubicam S.A., Santiago, Chile; *U.S. Private*, pg. 1200

Lube, Dr. Frank, Mng. Dir.--Friedrich Vieweg & Sohn Verlagsgesellschaft mbH, Wiesbaden, Germany; *Int'l*, pg. 190

Lubli, Richard E., Mgr.-Engrng.--APD Cryogenics Inc., Allentown, PA; *U.S. Public*, pg. 894

Lubner, R., Chm. & Chief Exec. Officer--Plate Glass & Shutterprufe Industries Limited, Satonwold, South Africa; *Int'l*, pg. 1287

Lubrano, Al, Pres.--Technical Materials, Inc., Lincoln, RI; *U.S. Public*, pg. 266

Luby, Dallas W., Chm. Bd. & Pres.--Herbert Clough, Inc., New York, NY; *U.S. Public*, pg. 726

Luby, Harvey, Pres.--Premium Tank Line Inc., Jackson, MS; *U.S. Private*, pg. 329

Luca, Raymond J., Pres. & Chief Exec. Officer--LogEtronics Corporation, Springfield, VA; *U.S. Public*, pg. 6

Lucas, Bill, Pres.--Crown Power & Redevelopment Corp., Kansas City, MO; *U.S. Private*, pg. 496

Lucas, Dave, Pres.--Budgetel Inns, Inc., Milwaukee, WI; *U.S. Public*, pg. 1044

Lucas, Glenn R., Mng. Dir.--Aluminum Co. of Malaysia Berhad, Petaling Jaya, Malaysia; *Int'l*, pg. 51

Lucas, Gregory C., Pres.--Consumer Marketing Services, Inc., Indianapolis, IN; *U.S. Public*, pg. 628

Lucas, Gregory C., Chm. Bd.--NBD Life Insurance Company, Indianapolis, IN; *U.S. Public*, pg. 628

Lucas, James, V.P. & Gen. Mgr.--KKTV-TV, Colorado Springs, CO; *U.S. Public*, pg. 16

Lucas, Loftus S., Gen. Mgr.--Rorer B.V., Hoofddorp, Netherlands; *Int'l*, pg. 1111

Lucas, P., Gen. Mgr.--National Rejectors, Inc., G.m.b.H., Hamburg, Germany; *U.S. Public*, pg. 456

Lucas, P.N., Pres.--Glaxo Wellcome Inc., Mississauga, Canada; *Int'l*, pg. 553

Lucas, Peter, Mng. Dir.--Tegel Foods Limited, Newmarket, New Zealand; *U.S. Public*, pg. 807

Lucas, Rafael Tapia, Pres.--PUCARSA - Puerto de Carboneras, S.A., Madrid, Spain; *Int'l*, pg. 1224

Lucas, Rolf, Mng. Dir.--ZK Hospital Bedarfs GmbH, Oer-Erkenschwick, Germany; *Int'l*, pg. 552

Lucas, W., Mng. Dir.--Firma E. Lucas Med. Technik GmbH, Munster, Germany; *Int'l*, pg. 551

Lucchesi, Donald A., Pres.--Landstar Gemini, Inc., Jacksonville, FL; *U.S. Public*, pg. 978

Lucchesi, Ronald, Chief Oper. Officer--Gonnella Frozen Products, Schaumburg, IL; *U.S. Private*, pg. 463

Lucchini, Gherarda, Chm.--Shandwick Marketing Communication Srl, Milan, Italy; *Int'l*, pg. 1227

Lucchini, Luigi, Chm. Bd.--Montedison S.p.A., Milan, Italy; *Int'l*, pg. 324

Lucchini, Roberto Mario, Dir. Gen.--BAI Leasing S.p.A., Milan, Italy; *Int'l*, pg. 403

Lucci, Mike, Pres. & Chief Oper. Officer--Bally Total Fitness Corporation, Chicago, IL; *U.S. Public*, pg. 171

Luce, James, Pres.--Zenith Administrators, Inc., Washington, DC; *U.S. Private*, pg. 1116

Lucet, Catherine, Pres. Dir. Gen.--Editions Scientifiques et Medicales Elsevier, Paris, France; *Int'l*, pg. 1099

Lucey, Richard E., Pres.--Bell Atlantic Credit Company, New York, NY; *U.S. Public*, pg. 202

Lucey, Robert F., Pres.--Newell Window Furnishings Co., Prescott, Canada; *U.S. Public*, pg. 1178

Lucey, Thomas W., Pres. & Chief Exec. Officer--Recoll Management Corp., Boston, MA; *U.S. Public*, pg. 650

Luchai, Shane, Mng. Dir.--Siam Tyre Industry Co., Ltd., Nong Khae, Thailand; *Int'l*, pg. 1238

Luchesi, Scott, Pres.--Garden State Life Insurance Company, League City, TX; *U.S. Public*, pg. 88

Luchik, J. T., Mgr.-Mktg.--Lord Corp., Industrial Adhesives & Coatings Div., Erie, PA; *U.S. Private*, pg. 676

Luchinger, W.W., Gen. Mgr.--OMRON Electronics AG, Steinhausen, Switzerland; *Int'l*, pg. 1005

Luchtenberg, Daphne, Mktg. Mgr.-UK/Europe--Shandwick International Plc, London, United Kingdom; *Int'l*, pg. 1226

Lucido, Chester, Pres. & Chief Exec. Officer--South-Western Publishing Company, Cincinnati, OH; *U.S. Public*, pg. 1600

Lucien, Kent T., Pres.--Ka'u Agribusiness Co., Inc., Pahala, HI; *U.S. Private*, pg. 190

Lucien, Sajus, Chief Oper. Officer--Technip CLE, Paris, France; *Int'l*, pg. 1360

Luck, Dave, Pres.--American Tire & Service Company, Rolling Meadows, IL; *Int'l*, pg. 213

Luck, David, Pres.--Bridgestone/Firestone Inc. Retail Operations, Rolling Meadows, IL; *Int'l*, pg. 213

Luckoff, Michael, Pres. & Gen. Mgr.--KGO-AM Radio, Inc., San Francisco, CA; *U.S. Public*, pg. 512

Lucks, Paul, V.P. & Gen. Mgr.--PolyGram Records, Inc., Nashville, TN; *Int'l*, pg. 1052

Luczaj, Kenneth J., V.P. & G.M.--Lewis Engineering Company, Naugatuck, CT; *U.S. Public*, pg. 402

Ludchak, Ron, Pres.--Furnival/State Machinery Co., Hatfield, PA; *Int'l*, pg. 744

Luddington, S.J., Chief Oper. Officer--Polycell Products Limited, Welwyn Garden City, United Kingdom; *Int'l*, pg. 1501

Ludeckel, Frank, Mng. Dir.--AVE Gesellschaft fur Fernsehproduktion mbH, Unterfoehring, Germany; *Int'l*, pg. 1478

Luders, Gerd, Country Mgr.--Berlitz Escuelas de Idiomas Ltda., Santiago, Chile; *U.S. Public*, pg. 222

Ludes, John T., Chm. Bd. & Chief Exec. Officer--ABCO, Inc., Old Greenwich, CT; *U.S. Public*, pg. 674

Ludes, John T., Pres. & Chief Exec. Officer--MCM Products, Inc., Old Greenwich, CT; *U.S. Public*, pg. 675

Ludington, Donald H., Chief Admin. Officer & V.P.--Downtown Cogeneration Associates, Hartford, CT; *U.S. Public*, pg. 285

Ludlow, C., Pres.--Amercoat Mexicana S.A. de C.V., Tlalnepantla, Mexico; *U.S. Public*, pg. 99

Ludvigsen, Narve, Exec. Dir.-Roofing--Icopal as, Fjellhamar, Norway; *Int'l*, pg. 659

Ludwig, Bob, Mgr.--AMF Bowling Centers Inc., Kansas City, MO; *U.S. Private*, pg. 7

Ludwig, H. R., Pres. & Chief Oper. Officer--Pacific International Brokers, Ltd., San Francisco, CA; *Int'l*, pg. 1504

Ludwig, Peter, Area Sls.--Analog Devices GMBH - Technisches Buero Berlin, Berlin, Germany; *U.S. Public*, pg. 108

Ludwig, Richard E., Pres.--TECO Power Services, Inc., Tampa, FL; *U.S. Public*, pg. 1565

Ludwig, William, Pres.--RGA Products Inc., Sacramento, CA; *U.S. Private*, pg. 927

Lueck, H., Chief Oper. Officer--Siemens Components (Pte) Ltd., Singapore, Singapore; *Int'l*, pg. 1247

Luedtke, Lou, Pres.--Tuchenhagen North America, Inc., Columbia, MD; *Int'l*, pg. 1426

Luehrs, Robert, Chief Oper. Officer--Women's Sportswear Division, New York, NY; *U.S. Private*, pg. 998

Lueneberg, Olaf, Mng. Dir.--Ethicon G.m.b.H. & Co. KG, Norderstedt, Germany; *U.S. Public*, pg. 929

Luettge, Hans-Michael, Gen. Mgr.--Deutsche Bank AG (Karachi), Karachi, Pakistan; *Int'l*, pg. 404

Luff, R., Mng. Dir.--Aluminum Corporation, Dolgarrog, United Kingdom; *Int'l*, pg. 51

Luft, R.v.d., Pres.-Europe--Du Pont de Nemours International S.A., Geneva, Switzerland; *U.S. Public*, pg. 532

Lugal, H. Joachim, Gen. Mgr.--Bombardier-Rotax GmbH Motorenfabrik, Gunskirchen, Austria; *Int'l*, pg. 200

Luger, Donald R., Chm., Pres. & Chief Exec. Officer--Lockwood Greene Engineers, Inc., Spartanburg, SC; *Int'l*, pg. 633

Lugge, Klemens, Co-Chief Oper. Officer--Winschermann West GmbH, Recklinghausen, Germany; *Int'l*, pg. 1167

Lugli, Franco, Pres.--ENI International Holding, Amsterdam, Netherlands; *Int'l*, pg. 429

Luglio, Franco, Pres.--SOFID, Rome, Italy; *Int'l*, pg. 429

Lugo, Jose, Mgr.--Broad National Bank-Perth Amboy, Perth Amboy, NJ; *U.S. Public*, pg. 258

Luhmann, Karl-Heinz, Tech. Mgr.--Kermi GmbH, Plattling, Germany; *Int'l*, pg. 1069

Luigi, Pistelli, Pres--Olteco, Scarmagno, Italy; *Int'l*, pg. 1002

Luijendijk, Rob J.M., Dir.-European Opers. & Bus. Devel.--Continental European Representative Office, Rotterdam, Netherlands; *U.S. Public*, pg. 692

Luiting, Oege, Pres.--Iseli Company, Terryville, CT; *U.S. Public*, pg. 481

Luiting, Oege, Pres.--Iseli Company, Walworth, WI; *U.S. Public*, pg. 481

Luiz, Brian, V.P.--Transdyn Controls, Inc., Concord, CA; *U.S. Public*, pg. 1319

Lujambio, Ricardo, Pres--Herramientas Klein S.A. de C.V., Mexico, Mexico; *U.S. Private*, pg. 625

Lujambio, Ricardo, Mgr.--Devcon de Mexico, S.A., Mexico, Mexico; *U.S. Public*, pg. 867

Lujan, Adolfo Patron, Pres.--Electro Quimica Mexicana S.A. de C.V., Mexico, Mexico; *U.S. Public*, pg. 606

Lukaska, Kenneth F., Pres. & Chief Oper. Officer--Unisource, Minneapolis, MN; *U.S. Public*, pg. 1671

Lukehart, Scott, V.P.--POST Buckley International Inc., Englewood, CO; *U.S. Private*, pg. 826

Lukens, Max L., Pres.--Baker Hughes Production Tools, Inc., Houston, TX; *U.S. Public*, pg. 166

Lukens, Paul B., Chm. Bd.--Cigna International Special Investments Inc., Wilmington, DE; *U.S. Public*, pg. 357

Luker, M.J., Chief Exec. Officer--Qanbar Steetley (Saudi) Limited, Dammam, Saudi Arabia; *Int'l*, pg. 1092

Lukianov, Alexis V., Pres.--Danek Medical Inc., Memphis, TN; *U.S. Public*, pg. 1482

Lukkari, Jorma, Sr. V.P.--Engineering Division, Oulu, Finland; *Int'l*, pg. 1088

Lukow, Lynn D.W., Pres.--Jossey-Bass, Inc., San Francisco, CA; *U.S. Private*, pg. 778

Luksa, Robert A., Pres. & Chief Oper. Officer--Philadelphia Suburban Water Company, Bryn Mawr, PA; *U.S. Public*, pg. 1287

Lum, Gadi, V.P. & Reg. Mgr.--Bergen Brunswig Medical Corporation, Tampa, FL; *U.S. Public*, pg. 214

Lum, Markus, Reg. Dir.-Germany--Singapore Tourist Promotion Board - Frankfurt, Frankfurt, Germany; *Int'l*, pg. 1254

Lumatjarvi, Eiro H., Pres.--Lever y Asociados SACIF, Buenos Aires, Argentina; *Int'l*, pg. 1438

Lumbroso, Claude, Pres.--Bio-Rad S.A., Paris, France; *U.S. Public*, pg. 230

Lumley, David, Pres.--Brunswick Bicyles Div., Bannockburn, IL; *U.S. Public*, pg. 265

Lun, S., Mgr.--Armstrong World Industries (H.K.) Limited, Central, Hong Kong; *U.S. Public*, pg. 132

Luna, A., Gen. Dir.--Hoover Mexicana S.A. de C.V., Mexico, Mexico; *U.S. Public*, pg. 1065

Luna, Mac, V.P. & Mgr.--McWane Cast Iron Pipe Co., Birmingham, AL; *U.S. Private*, pg. 725

Lund, Christian, Sector Gen. Mgr.--Berendsen Components A/S, Soeborg, Denmark; *Int'l*, pg. 1284

Lund, Eilert, Mgr.--Kvaerner Ships Equipment a.s Marine Automation, Lier, Norway; *Int'l*, pg. 770

Lund, Jan, Mgr.--Industrifilter AB, Boras, Sweden; *Int'l*, pg. 1422

Lund, Jon, Pres.--Aker Stord a.s., Stord, Norway; *Int'l*, pg. 42

Lund, Mark, Pres.--LIC Care AB, Solna, Sweden; *Int'l*, pg. 551

Lund, Olof, Chm.--Celsius Invest AB, Eskilstuna, Sweden; *Int'l*, pg. 276

Lund, R.L., Plant Mgr.--Longview Fibre Co. Central Container Div., Rockford, IL; *U.S. Public*, pg. 1014

Lund, Richard, Pres. & Chief Exec. Officer--Farmington National Bank, Farmington, NH; *U.S. Public*, pg. 187

Lund, Richard A., Pres.--Auto-Air Composites, Inc., Lansing, MI; *U.S. Public*, pg. 290

Lund, Richard A., Pres.--Cade International, Inc., Lansing, MI; *U.S. Public*, pg. 290

Lund, Robert K., V.P. & Dir.--Thiokol Science and Engineering, Brigham City, UT; *U.S. Public*, pg. 1597

Lund, Soren H., Chief Exec. Officer--Novo Nordisk A/S, Kuala Lumpur, Malaysia; *Int'l*, pg. 989

Lundberg, Goran, Pres.--ABB Stal AB, Finspang, Sweden; *Int'l*, pg. 7

Lundberg, Kenneth, Pres.--Volvo Nutzfahrzeuge Deutschland GmbH, Dietzenbach, Germany; *Int'l*, pg. 1477

Lundberg, Leif, Mng. Dir.--Nokia Audio & Electronics AB, Motala, Sweden; *Int'l*, pg. 954

Lundberg, Olof, Dir. Gen.--International Maritime Satellite Organisation (INMARSAT), London, United Kingdom; *Int'l*, pg. 222

Lundberg, Rune, Pres.--Volvo Penta Asia Pacific Corporation, Tokyo, Japan; *Int'l*, pg. 1477

Lundblad, Jan, Chief Oper. Officer--Nordisk Elektronik AB, Kista, Sweden; *Int'l*, pg. 709

Lundblad, Olof, Mgr.--Sandvik Rock Tools, Inc., Houston, TX; *Int'l*, pg. 1185

Lundeberg, Steffan, Chief Oper. Officer--Electrolux Bedenpflegegerate Vertriebsgesellschaft GmbH, Vienna, Austria; *Int'l*, pg. 440

Lundell, Bill, Div. Mgr.--Montgomery Elevator Architectural Products Division, Arkansas City, KS; *Int'l*, pg. 746

Lundell, Claes, Mng. Dir.--Icopal ab, Malmo, Sweden; *Int'l*, pg. 659

Lunden, Gene, Gen. Mgr.--Jannock Steel Fabricating, Inc., Salem, OR; *Int'l*, pg. 699

Lunden, L., Chief Oper. Officer--Babcock-Bristol AB, Vasteras, Sweden; *Int'l*, pg. 473

Lundgren, Per S., Chief Oper. Officer--Novo Nordisk A/S, Sao Paulo, Brazil; *Int'l*, pg. 987

Lundgren, Per S., Chief Exec.--Novo Nordisk Pharmaceuticals, Inc., Plantation, FL; *Int'l*, pg. 987

Lundgren, Terry, Pres. & Chief Exec. Officer-The Neiman-Marcus Grp.--The Neiman-Marcus Group, Inc., Chestnut Hill, MA; *U.S. Public*, pg. 784

Lundgren, Terry J., Chm.--Federated Merchandising, New York, NY; *U.S. Public*, pg. 618

Lundh, Bernt, Mgr.--Akvamatik AB, Tranas, Sweden; *Int'l*, pg. 1422

Lundh, Peter, Mgr.--AB Sandvik Information Systems, Sandviken, Sweden; *Int'l*, pg. 1185

Lundholm, Hans, Pres.--Handelsbanken Hypotek, Stockholm, Sweden; *Int'l*, pg. 1327

Lundin, Goran, Mng. Dir.--Holmen Paper AB, Norrkoping, Sweden; *Int'l*, pg. 885

Lundin, Kjell, Chief Oper. Officer--Bjornklader AB, Solna, Sweden; *Int'l*, pg. 438

Lundin, Sten, Chief Oper. Officer--Saab France S.A., Nanterre, France; *Int'l*, pg. 687

Lundman, Claes, Chief Exec. Officer--Normaco Ltd., London, United Kingdom; *Int'l*, pg. 712

Lundquist, Ake, Chief Oper. Officer--Ericsson GE Mobile Communications Holding Inc., Paramus, NJ; *Int'l*, pg. 1365

Lundquist, Jan, Chief Oper. Officer--Attendor Industri och Handel AB, Stockholm, Sweden; *Int'l*, pg. 708

Lundqvist, Goran, Pres.--SAS Trading, Stockholm, Sweden; *Int'l*, pg. 1202

Lundqvist, Stefan, Mng. Dir.--Gunnebo do Brasil Ltda, Sao Paulo, Brazil; *Int'l*, pg. 578

Lundregan, Stephen, Pres.--Colonial Insurance Company of California, Anaheim, CA; *U.S. Private*, pg. 788

Lundsgard, Johan, Mgr.--Trellex AB, Gallivare, Sweden; *Int'l*, pg. 1324

Lundstedt, David, Pres. & Chief Exec. Officer--Prestone Products Corporation, Danbury, CT; *U.S. Public*, pg. 51

Lundstrom, Bengt, Chief Oper. Officer--Alfa-Laval Agri-Scandinavia OY, Helsinki, Finland; *Int'l*, pg. 1379
Lundstrom, Lars, Country Mgr.--Nokia Telecommunications, Prague, Czech Republic; *Int'l*, pg. 953
Lundy, Francis E., Pres.--Technical Instrument Company, Sunnyvale, CA; *U.S. Public*, pg. 1795
Lundy, Michael, Rep.--Sanpaolo-Toronto Representative Office, Toronto, Canada; *Int'l*, pg. 692
Luneburg, Karsten, Pres.--Scanstone GmbH, Hamburg, Germany; *Int'l*, pg. 1199
Lung, Jim, Chief Oper. Officer--Patrick Metals, Mishawaka, IN; *U.S. Public*, pg. 1265
Lunn, S., Chm.--Lucas Sumitomo Brakes Inc., Lebanon, OH; *Int'l*, pg. 819
Lunning, Steve, Pres.--Dallas Moving System Inc., Dallas, TX; *U.S. Private*, pg. 1171
Lunstroo, Fred, Financial Controller--Gestetner Holding BV, Diemen, Netherlands; *Int'l*, pg. 1115
Luntsford, Sam, Mgr.--Arden Plant, Arden, NC; *Int'l*, pg. 1055
Luoma, Pekka, Gen. Mgr.--Beijing Nokia Hang XingTelecoms Systems Co. Ltd., Beijing, China; *Int'l*, pg. 953
Lupberger, Edwin, Chm. Bd. & Chief Exec. Officer--Entergy New Orleans, Inc., New Orleans, LA; *U.S. Public*, pg. 586
Lupi, Giorgio, Dir.--Deutsche Bank (Svizzera) S.A. (Lugano), Lugano, Switzerland; *Int'l*, pg. 405
Lupica, Ben, Chief Fin. Officer--Prior Remanufacturers, Inc., Garland, TX; *U.S. Private*, pg. 300
Lupica, Robert, Gen. Mgr.--Buffalo China, Inc., Buffalo, NY; *U.S. Public*, pg. 1226
Lupien, R.W., Mgr.--Lindberg Heat Treating Co., Melrose Park, IL; *U.S. Public*, pg. 999
Lupinetti, Alexander, Pres.--Visions Systems, Billerica, MA; *U.S. Public*, pg. 283
Lupinski, Thomas, Chief Fin. Officer--Swiss Army Brands Ltd., Shelton, CT; *U.S. Public*, pg. 1544
Luporte, Michael, Chief Oper. Officer--Olsonite Corporation, Newnan, GA; *U.S. Private*, pg. 815
Luppert, Charles W., Pres. & Cashier--Williamsport National Bank, Williamsport, PA; *U.S. Public*, pg. 1543
Luraschi, Luigi, V.P.-Intl.--Paramount British Pictures Ltd., London, United Kingdom; *U.S. Private*, pg. 777
Lurati, M., Mng. Dir.--Robert Bosch AG, Otelfingen, Switzerland; *Int'l*, pg. 205
Lurcott, Robert A., Pres. & Chief Exec. Officer--Henkel Corporation, King of Prussia, PA; *Int'l*, pg. 610
Luria, Ernesto, Mng. Dir.--Evenflo Mexico S.A., Mexico, Mexico; *U.S. Private*, pg. 630
Luscher, B., Dr., Chief Exec. Officer--Ascom Tech AG, Bern, Switzerland; *Int'l*, pg. 86
Lusetti, Gianni, Mng. Dir.--Bundy SpA, Busalla, Italy; *Int'l*, pg. 1341
Lusic, Ronald, Pres. & Chief Exec. Officer--Fleming Company, Waukesha, WI; *U.S. Public*, pg. 653
Lusic, Ronald R., Pres.--Hub City Foods, Marshfield, WI; *U.S. Public*, pg. 653
Lusink, John, Pres.--Philips Electronics Ltd., Scarborough, Canada; *Int'l*, pg. 1055
Lusk, Bob, V.P.--Ross Roy Communications Canada, Limited, Windsor, Canada; *U.S. Private*, pg. 946
Lusk, Ron, Mng. Dir.--Check Technology Pty Limited, Hornsby, Australia; *U.S. Public*, pg. 342
Luskey, Alvin, Pres.--Ryon's Saddle & Ranch Supply, Fort Worth, TX; *U.S. Private*, pg. 681
Luskey, Alvin, Pres.--Tejas Western Outlet, Fort Worth, TX; *U.S. Private*, pg. 681
Luskin, M., Chief Oper. Officer--Dext Company, Santa Monica, CA; *U.S. Public*, pg. 1444
Luszcz, Franz R., Pres.--Fenn Manufacturing Co., Newington, CT; *U.S. Public*, pg. 1676
Lutch, Donald, Gen. Mgr.--EA Engineering, Science & Technology, Inc., Deerfield, IL; *U.S. Public*, pg. 541
Luter, Barry R.F., Pres.--The Bank of Nova Scotia Trust Company of New York, New York, NY; *Int'l*, pg. 156
Luter, Joseph W., III, Chm. Bd. & Chief Exec. Officer--Gwaltney of Smithfield, Ltd., Smithfield, VA; *U.S. Public*, pg. 1479
Lutes, William, Pres.--Premier Refractories (Canada) Ltd., Welland, Canada; *U.S. Public*, pg. 58
Luther, Jon, Pres.--Popeye's Chicken & Biscuits, Atlanta, GA; *U.S. Private*, pg. 5
Luther, Jorg-Michael, Representative--Allianz Beijing Representative Office, Beijing, China; *Int'l*, pg. 59
Luthringhauser, Daniel, V.P. & Gen. Mgr.-Far East--Medtronic International, Ltd., Wan Chai, Hong Kong; *U.S. Public*, pg. 1083
Luthringshausen, Wayne, Chm. Bd.--Options Clearing Corp., Chicago, IL; *U.S. Private*, pg. 62
Lutterloch, Jermey, Dir.--Utah Scientific/Artel, Newbury, United Kingdom; *U.S. Private*, pg. 86
Luttrell, Robert G., V.P.-Admin.--Temple-Inland Forest Products Corporation, Diboll, TX; *U.S. Public*, pg. 1575
Luttrull, W. Ray, Jr., Pres.--NationsBank of Kentucky, Hopkinsville, KY; *U.S. Public*, pg. 1163
Lutz, Alan, V.P.-Intergrated Network Systems--Digital Switching Div., Research Triangle Park, NC; *Int'l*, pg. 969
Lutz, Bernd, Dr., Mng. Dir.--J.B. Metzler Verlag, Stuttgart, Germany; *Int'l*, pg. 1478
Lutz, Christian F., Pres.--Allianz Fire and Marine Insurance Japan Ltd., Tokyo, Japan; *Int'l*, pg. 59
Lutz, Dr., Chief Oper. Officer--Elf Erdoel Underdgas Deutschland Gmbh, Dusseldorf, Germany; *Int'l*, pg. 446
Lutz, Gunther, Pres.--AGRA CI Power Limited, Oakville, Canada; *Int'l*, pg. 30
Lutz, Jochen, Mng. Dir.--Avnet E2000 GmbH, Munich, Germany; *U.S. Public*, pg. 155
Lutz, John M., Mgr.--Batesco Quarries Div., Buffalo, MO; *U.S. Private*, pg. 88
Lutz, John M., Mgr.--Batesco Quarries Div., Butler, MO; *U.S. Private*, pg. 88
Lutz, Michael J., Pres.--Central California Div., Riverside, CA; *U.S. Public*, pg. 1682
Lutz, Thomas A., Pres.--Creative Data Systems Divisions, Beachwood, OH; *U.S. Public*, pg. 1516
Lutz, Tony, Gen. Mgr.--AJL Park, Caracas, Venezuela; *U.S. Private*, pg. 389
Luukkainen, Timo, Pres.--ASEA Skandia Oy, Helsinki, Finland; *Int'l*, pg. 7
Lux, Pierre, Gen. Mgr.--Helmitin SA, Surbourg, France; *Int'l*, pg. 498
Luyckx, Ben, Mgr.--Dormer Tools N.V./S.A., Mortsel, Belgium; *Int'l*, pg. 1186
Luyk, Charles J. Th., Dir.--Exportslachterij Udema B.V., Gieten, Netherlands; *Int'l*, pg. 1437
Luyten, Johannes, Gen. Mgr.--Moog Do Brasil, Santo Amaro, Brazil; *U.S. Public*, pg. 1128
Luzum, James A., Chief Fin. Officer--Valley Forest Resources Co., Marcell, MN; *U.S. Private*, pg. 1140
Lydiard, John M., III, V.P.--Avionics, Nashua, NH; *U.S. Public*, pg. 1008
Lyke, Chuch, Gen. Mgr.--Dynapower/Stratopower, Jackson, MS; *U.S. Public*, pg. 24
Lyle, James E., Chief Oper. Officer--International Brake Industries, Inc., Lima, OH; *U.S. Public*, pg. 1055
Lyle, N.C., Acting Gen. Mgr.--Australian Guarantee Corporation Limited - New South Wales, Epping, Australia; *Int'l*, pg. 1496
Lyman, Roger, Chief Oper. Officer--Health Maintenance Oregon, Salem, OR; *U.S. Private*, pg. 918
Lynaugh, N., Dr., Chief Exec. Officer--VG Analytical Ltd., Manchester, United Kingdom; *Int'l*, pg. 1110
Lynch, Charles, Gen. Mgr.--Charles Levy Transportation Co., Chicago, IL; *U.S. Private*, pg. 664
Lynch, Chuck, Gen. Mgr.--ITW Components & Tools, Glenview, IL; *U.S. Public*, pg. 866
Lynch, David, V.P. & Gen. Mgr.--WRGB-TV, Schenectady, NY; *U.S. Private*, pg. 425
Lynch, G., Pres. & Chief Exec. Officer--EnRoute Card Inc., Montreal, Canada; *Int'l*, pg. 36
Lynch, Helen, Gen. Mgr.--Westpac - South Australia, Adelaide, Australia; *Int'l*, pg. 1496
Lynch, John, Pres.--LaSalle Northwest National Bank, Chicago, IL; *Int'l*, pg. 10
Lynch, John A., Publisher--Wilmington Star-News, Inc., Wilmington, NC; *U.S. Public*, pg. 1175
Lynch, John J., Jr., Pres.--CCH Legal Information Services, Inc., New York, NY; *Int'l*, pg. 1513
Lynch, K.N., Gen. Mgr.--Commonwealth Bank of Australia-Western Australia, Perth, Australia; *Int'l*, pg. 313
Lynch, Michael J., Mgr.-Volkswagen L.A. Zone--Volkswagen of America Administration Center West, Westlake Village, CA; *Int'l*, pg. 1474
Lynch, Michael P., Pres.--Kmart (Canada) Ltd., Brampton, Canada; *U.S. Public*, pg. 963
Lynch, Michael T., Mng. Dir.--Santa Fe Minerals (U.K.), Inc., London, United Kingdom; *Int'l*, pg. 766
Lynch, Patrick J., Pres.--Texaco International Financial Corp., White Plains, NY; *U.S. Public*, pg. 1583
Lynch, Randall D., Pres. & Chief Exec. Officer--The Kitchen Collection Inc., Chillicothe, OH; *U.S. Public*, pg. 1149
Lynch, Robin M., V.P.--Sea Containers Agencies Inc., New York, NY; *Int'l*, pg. 1214
Lynch, Thomas E., Mng. Dir.--State Street Bank-Hong Kong Branch, Hong Kong, Hong Kong; *U.S. Public*, pg. 1513
Lynch, Tom, Plant Mgr.--Jannock Steel Fabricating, Inc., Mount Vernon, OH; *Int'l*, pg. 699
Lynch, W.P., Exec. V.P. & Gen. Mgr.--Auburn Technology, Inc., Auburn, NY; *Int'l*, pg. 200
Lynds, Trevor, Mng. Dir.--Aetna Health (New Zealand) Limited, Auckland, New Zealand; *U.S. Public*, pg. 27
Lynett, Patricia, Chief Oper. Officer--Kelly Assisted Living Services, Inc., Troy, MI; *U.S. Public*, pg. 949
Lynkowski, Garry, Pres. & Chief Fin. Officer--Highwood Resources Ltd., Calgary, Canada; *U.S. Public*, pg. 1411
Lynn, Anthony J., Pres.--Playboy Entertainment Group, Inc., Beverly Hills, CA; *U.S. Public*, pg. 1310
Lynn, Anthony J., Pres.--Alta Loma Productions, Inc., Beverly Hills, CA; *U.S. Public*, pg. 1310
Lynn, Anthony J., Pres.--After Dark Video, Inc., Beverly Hills, CA; *U.S. Public*, pg. 1310
Lynn, Robert G., Pres. & Chief Exec. Officer--U.S. Woolworth Div., New York, NY; *U.S. Public*, pg. 1778
Lyon, D.P., Mgr.--Cumbrian Storage Ltd., Workington, United Kingdom; *Int'l*, pg. 1251
Lyon, David L., Pres.--Pacific Communication Sciences, Inc., San Diego, CA; *U.S. Public*, pg. 375
Lyon, Douglas Lawson, Mng. Dir.--Pearsalls Sutures, Taunton, United Kingdom; *Int'l*, pg. 215
Lyon, Gary, Pres.--Wetmore & Company, Houston, TX; *U.S. Public*, pg. 1736
Lyon, Harald, Chief Oper. Officer--KONE Sowitsch AG, Vienna, Austria; *Int'l*, pg. 748
Lyon, L. Max, Pres.--Bard Diagnostic Sciences, Redmond, WA; *U.S. Public*, pg. 189
Lyon, Russel T., Pres.-Carpet Div.--Buchanan Industries, Inc., Dalton, GA; *U.S. Public*, pg. 1052
Lyons, Bill, Mgr.--GESTRA Inc., Ontario, CA; *Int'l*, pg. 549
Lyons, Chuck, Pres.--The Gazette Newspapers, Inc., Gaithersburg, MD; *U.S. Public*, pg. 1743
Lyons, J. David, V.P.-European Opers.--Data General Europe, Inc., Paris, France; *U.S. Public*, pg. 486
Lyons, James E., Partner--Skadden, Arps, Slate, Meagher & Flom LLP, San Francisco, CA; *U.S. Private*, pg. 1004
Lyons, James F., Pres. & Chief Exec. Officer--GenRad Electronic Manufacturing Tests Systems, Westford, MA; *U.S. Public*, pg. 731
Lyons, Jed, Pres.--Biblio Distribution Ctr., Lanham, MD; *U.S. Private*, pg. 1128
Lyons, Joe, Mgr.-Division--Gould Paper Corporation-Mid Atlantic, Burlington, NJ; *U.S. Private*, pg. 467
Lyons, Kevin, Publisher--Lincoln News Messenger, Lincoln, CA; *U.S. Private*, pg. 167
Lyons, Paul, III, Chief Exec. Officer--Halcyon Underwriters, Maitland, FL; *U.S. Public*, pg. 1312
Lyons, Richard M., Pres.--Gap Stores Division, San Bruno, CA; *U.S. Public*, pg. 702
Lyons, Sam, Pres.--Bryant Financial Corp., Chatsworth, CA; *U.S. Public*, pg. 1741
Lyons, Thomas M., Mgr.-Branch--Piper Jaffray Inc., Bellevue, WA; *U.S. Public*, pg. 1301
Lyons, W. David, Pres.--Ocelot International Ltd., Saint Helier, United Kingdom; *Int'l*, pg. 996
Lyons, W. David, Pres.--Ocelot International U.K. Ltd., Guildford, United Kingdom; *Int'l*, pg. 996
Lyons, Wayne, Pres.--Lafarge Canada, Calgary, Canada; *Int'l*, pg. 788
Lysenko, Vladimir P., Chief Oper. Officer--Akerlund & Rausing, Kiev, Ukraine; *Int'l*, pg. 33
Lyssy, Fred, Dir.--Martin Marietta Field Services, Littleton, CO; *U.S. Public*, pg. 1007
Lystad, Endre, Service Mgr.--Kvaerner Ships Equipment a.s Gibraltar Branch, Gibraltar, Gibraltar; *Int'l*, pg. 768
Lyth, Boo, Chief Oper. Officer--Electrolux Canarias S.A., Las Palmas, Spain; *Int'l*, pg. 443
Lytle, L. Ben, Pres.--Anthem Health Companies, Indianapolis, IN; *U.S. Private*, pg. 76
Ma, D., Mng. Dir.--Wuxi Quaker Chemical Co. Ltd., Wuxi, China; *U.S. Public*, pg. 1347
Ma, Daniel, Mng. Dir.--Quaker Chemical Limited, Central, Hong Kong; *U.S. Public*, pg. 1347
Ma, Victor, Mng. Dir.--Kemet Electronics Asia Ltd., Kowloon Bay, Hong Kong; *U.S. Public*, pg. 949
Maag, J.G., Chief Exec. Officer--Zurich Insurance Services (Middle East) E.C., Manama, Bahrain; *Int'l*, pg. 1532
Maain, Bruce, Gen. Mgr.--A.T. Cross (France) S.A., Paris, France; *U.S. Public*, pg. 461
Maak, Jan-Olof, Pres.--Astra Production Tablets AB, Sodertalje, Sweden; *Int'l*, pg. 93
Maaloe, Jens, Pres. & Chief Exec. Officer--GN Nettest, Telecom Division, Brondby, Denmark; *Int'l*, pg. 536
Maaroufi, Abdallah El, Dir.--The World Bank, Paris, France; *U.S. Private*, pg. 1189
Maas, A.J.P.M., Gen. Mgr.--Lamic nv, Willemstad, Netherlands Antilles; *Int'l*, pg. 682
Maas, C., Pres.--Hartwell Commercial Division, Placentia, CA; *U.S. Private*, pg. 1168
Maas, E. P., Treas. Dir.--Dixons Finance Plc, London, United Kingdom; *Int'l*, pg. 414
Maas, G.L., Pres.--Grand Trunk Western Railroad, Inc., Detroit, MI; *Int'l*, pg. 258
Maas, Lori, Dir.-Mktg.--Parfums Van Cleef & Arpels, New York, NY; *Int'l*, pg. 445
Maas, Onno, Mng. Dir. & Chief Exec. Officer--DMB&B/Worldwide Communications Amsterdam, Amsterdam, Netherlands; *U.S. Private*, pg. 304
Maberly, M., Chm. Bd.--Lex Vehicle Leasing Limited, Marlow, United Kingdom; *Int'l*, pg. 910
Mabey, R.S., Joint Mng. Dir.--Bovis International Ltd., London, United Kingdom; *Int'l*, pg. 1032
Mabood, Faizle-e, Sr. Exec. V.P. & Gen. Mgr.--Habib Bank Ltd., Ruwi, Oman; *Int'l*, pg. 584
Mabry, Pam, Gen. Mgr.--Clearwater Auto Auction Inc., Clearwater, FL; *U.S. Public*, pg. 1648
Mabuchi, Tom, Pres.--Yamaha Motor Canada Ltd., North York, Canada; *Int'l*, pg. 1516
Mac Donald, David, Country Mgr.--Lotus Development B.V., Cloghran, Ireland; *U.S. Public*, pg. 896
Mac Fyfe, A., Gen. Mgr.--W.A. Deutsher Pty. Ltd., Melbourne, Australia; *U.S. Public*, pg. 867
Mac Phail, B.D., Chm. Bd.--Charlwood Alliance Holdings Ltd., London, United Kingdom; *Int'l*, pg. 1034
MacAdam, William, V.P.-Operations--Rhone-Poulenc Performance Resins & Coatings, Kennesaw, GA; *Int'l*, pg. 1110
Macaione, D.A., Pres.--Trafalgar House Construction Inc., Pittsburgh, PA; *Int'l*, pg. 774
Macaisa, Dante, Country Mgr.--Circle Freight International (Philippines) Ltd., Manila, Philippines; *U.S. Public*, pg. 373
Macalister, Kim, Exec. V.P., Pres. & Gen. Mgr.-JWT/Singapore--J. Walter Thompson Company, New York, NY; *Int'l*, pg. 1483
Macartney, J.W., Chief Fin. Officer--Ballievey Ltd., Banbridge, United Kingdom; *Int'l*, pg. 797
Macaskill, Bridget, Pres. & Chief Exec. Officer--Oppenheimer Funds, Inc., New York, NY; *U.S. Private*, pg. 712
Macaulay, C.A., Chm. Bd.--Rio Algom Mining Corp., Oklahoma City, OK; *Int'l*, pg. 1118
MacBride, Earl T., Pres.--Frankford Abstract Co., Philadelphia, PA; *U.S. Public*, pg. 956
MacBride, Vicki, Bus. Mgr.--Daily Press Leader, Farmington, MO; *U.S. Public*, pg. 1343
Macca, Andy, Pres.--Drug Guild Div., Secaucus, NJ; *U.S. Public*, pg. 1169
MacCalman, Duncan, Co-Div. Mgr.--Gould Paper Corporation-Albany, Albany, NY; *U.S. Private*, pg. 467
MacCanna, Peadar, Mng. Dir.--Bank of Ireland Commercial Finance Ltd., Dublin, Ireland; *Int'l*, pg. 152
MacClelland, Ken, Sr. V.P.--Willis Corroon Inspace, Inc., Bethesda, MD; *Int'l*, pg. 1507
MacConnell, Cynthia S., Chief Oper. Officer--Cincinnati Limousine Service Inc., Cincinnati, OH; *U.S. Private*, pg. 129
MacConnell, George A., Sr. V.P.-Distribution & Specialty Oper.--Georgia-Pacific Distribution Div., Atlanta, GA; *U.S. Public*, pg. 735
MacCurdy, Jean, Pres.--Hanna-Barbera Productions, Inc., Hollywood, CA; *U.S. Public*, pg. 1614
MacDevette, William, Pres.--Elof Hansson Paper & Board, Inc., Elmsford, NY; *Int'l*, pg. 595
MacDonald, Angus, Mng. Dir.--Blackwood Brothers Ltd, Kilmarnock, United Kingdom; *Int'l*, pg. 385
MacDonald, David, Mgr.--Sandvik Hard Materials Pty. Ltd., Newcastle, Australia; *Int'l*, pg. 1187
Macdonald, Deborah A., Pres.--Transwestern Pipeline Co., Houston, TX; *U.S. Public*, pg. 585

MacDonald, Gary, Pres.--Arthur-Jones Lithographing Limited, Mississauga, Canada; *Int'l*, pg. 698
MacDonald, Geoffrey A., Pres.--American Financial Group Securities Corp., Boston, MA; *U.S. Private*, pg. 380
Macdonald, James, Principal Officer--Combined Life Insurance Co. of Australia, Ltd., Sydney, Australia; *U.S. Public*, pg. 118
MacDonald, John, Dir.--Shandwick Scotland Ltd., Aberdeen, United Kingdom; *Int'l*, pg. 1226
MacDonald, John D., V.P.-Switching--Northern Telecom Canada Limited, Data Networks Div., Nepean, Canada; *Int'l*, pg. 969
MacDonald, John R., Chief Fin. Officer & V.P.--Investment Technology Group, Inc., New York, NY; *U.S. Public*, pg. 924
MacDonald, K., Chief Exec. Officer--Franklins Holdings Ltd., Chullora, Australia; *Int'l*, pg. 703
MacDonald, Lawrence P., Gen. Mgr.--Catskill Cement Plant Independent Cement Corp., Catskill, NY; *Int'l*, pg. 629
Macdonald, Malcolm, Dir. & Gen. Mgr.--Dowty Aerospace, Isle of Man, Onchan, United Kingdom; *Int'l*, pg. 1337
MacDonald, Mary, Chief Exec. Officer & Mng. Dir.--DMB&B/Yellow Pages, Northbrook, IL; *U.S. Private*, pg. 303
MacDonald, Peter, Pres.--James Hardie USA, Mission Viejo, CA; *Int'l*, pg. 597
MacDonald, R.V., Pres.--Butter Kernel Products, Faribault, MN; *U.S. Private*, pg. 393
MacDonald, R.V., Pres.--Kuner-Empson Company, Brighton, CO; *U.S. Private*, pg. 393
MacDonald, Ralph, Pres.--Hilroy, Toronto, Canada; *Int'l*, pg. 20
MacDonald, Walter, Chief Fin. Officer--Gandalf Canada Ltd., Nepean, Canada; *Int'l*, pg. 540
MacDonald, Wayne, Pres. & Publisher--The Record, Kitchener, Canada; *Int'l*, pg. 631
MacDonnell, James M., Mng. Dir.--Sheldon Good & Company-Colorado, Denver, CO; *U.S. Private*, pg. 464
MacDonnell, Kathleen, Pres.-Frozen Food & Specialty Foods--Campbell USA, Camden, NJ; *U.S. Public*, pg. 299
MacDonough, John N., Chm. Bd. & Chief Exec. Officer--Miller Brewing Company, Milwaukee, WI; *U.S. Public*, pg. 1289
MacDougall, D., Mng. Dir.--Thorn-Ericsson Telecommunications Limited, Horsham, United Kingdom; *Int'l*, pg. 1370
MacDougall, George, Reg. Mgr.-Southern Cone--Utell International-Argentina, Buenos Aires, Argentina; *Int'l*, pg. 1098
Mace, Eugene, Pres.--USMEDIA Group, Festus, MO; *U.S. Private*, pg. 225
Mace, Lesly, V.P.-Engrng.--Cascadia Technology Corporation, Redmond, WA; *U.S. Public*, pg. 1203
MacEachern, Angus, Gen. Mgr.--Premdor Inc.-Atlantic Division, Amherst, Canada; *Int'l*, pg. 1067
MacEachran, Angus, Pres. & Editor--The Commercial Appeal, Memphis, TN; *U.S. Public*, pg. 1447
MacFadyen, C.R., Sr. V.P.--AGRA Earth & Environmental, Inc., Anaheim, CA; *Int'l*, pg. 31
MacFadyen, C.R., Pres.--Moore & Taber Grouting Services, Anaheim, CA; *Int'l*, pg. 31
MacFarland, Peter, Pres.--Magikitch'n, Inc., Quakertown, PA; *U.S. Public*, pg. 1065
Macfarlane, F. Scott, Gen. Mgr. & V.P.--Carton Div., Saint Louis, MO; *Int'l*, pg. 1269
MacFarlane, John C., Pres.--Minnesota-Dakota Generating Co., Fergus Falls, MN; *U.S. Public*, pg. 1235
MacFarlane, Phil, Pres. & Chief Exec. Officer--OmniTRAX Inc., Chicago, IL; *U.S. Private*, pg. 171
MacFarlane, Phil, Pres.--Chicago Rail Link, Chicago, IL; *U.S. Private*, pg. 171
MacFarlane, Phil, Pres.--Chicago West Pullman & Southern Railroad, Chicago, IL; *U.S. Private*, pg. 171
MacGibbon, A. Terrence, Pres.--American Copper & Nickel Company, Inc., Wheat Ridge, CO; *Int'l*, pg. 672
MacGilvray, James R., Pres.--Camcar Textron, Rockford, IL; *U.S. Public*, pg. 1589
MacGregor-Sim, James C., Mgr.--Sandvik (Private) Ltd., Harare, Zimbabwe; *Int'l*, pg. 1187
MacGregor, C. Carpizo, Pres. & Gen. Mgr.--Compania Sherwin-Williams, S.A. de C.V., Mexico, Mexico; *U.S. Public*, pg. 1466
MacGregor, Ian, Pres.--Instron Schenck Testing Systems Limited, High Wycombe, United Kingdom; *U.S. Public*, pg. 883
MacGregor, John, Sr. V.P. & Mgr.--The Royal Bank of Scotland plc, San Francisco, CA; *Int'l*, pg. 1133
MacGregor, John, Gen. Mgr.--International Public Relations, Pty Ltd., Sydney, Australia; *Int'l*, pg. 1227
MacGregor, Michael, Pres.--Dillingham Construction International, Inc., Pleasanton, CA; *U.S. Private*, pg. 333
Macgregor, Robert, Pres.--Reed Exhibition Companies-Canada, Scarborough, Canada; *Int'l*, pg. 1096
Macher, Frank E., Gen. Mgr.--Ford Electronics Division, Dearborn, MI; *U.S. Public*, pg. 662
Macher, Frank E., Chm. Bd.--Ford Microelectronics, Inc., Colorado Springs, CO; *U.S. Public*, pg. 664
Macher, Frank E., Pres.--ITT Automotive, Inc., Auburn Hills, MI; *U.S. Public*, pg. 859
Machet, Anne-Marie, Gen. Mgr.--Credit Commercial de France, Bangkok, Thailand; *Int'l*, pg. 343
Machida, Katsuhiko, Pres.--Yamaichi Italia S.p.A. Societa di Intermediazione Mobiliare, Milan, Italy; *Int'l*, pg. 1518
Machida, Ryoji, Pres.--Mitsui Construction Co., Ltd., Tokyo, Japan; *Int'l*, pg. 877
Machida, Tomone, V.P. & Gen. Mgr.--Nichimen America, Inc., San Francisco Branch, San Francisco, CA; *Int'l*, pg. 928
Machiels, G., Chief Oper. Officer--Gomala Imtech NV, Alken, Belgium; *Int'l*, pg. 681
Machii, A., Pres.--Loctite (Japan) Corp., Yokohama, Japan; *Int'l*, pg. 611
Machin, Roger, Mgr.--Century Telephone, Region IV, Pinconning, MI; *U.S. Public*, pg. 329
Machny, Walter, Gen. Mgr.--Rogers CFAC-AM, Calgary, Canada; *Int'l*, pg. 1123
MacHold, Roland, Gen. Mgr.--Ernst Siegling Beteiligungs GmbH, Hannover, Germany; *Int'l*, pg. 497
Machold, Ronald, Gen. Mgr.--Siegling Gmbh, Hannover, Germany; *Int'l*, pg. 498
Machorro, Carlos, Pres.--Gates Rubber de Mexico, Tlalnepantla, Mexico; *Int'l*, pg. 1397
Machulak, Edward L., Pres.--San Sebastian Gold Mines, Inc., Santa Rosa de Lima, El Salvador; *U.S. Public*, pg. 410
Macias, Ernesto D., Plant Mgr.--The Lamson & Sessions Co., High Springs, FL; *U.S. Public*, pg. 976
Macias, Hector, Pres.--Walter Kidde de Mexico S.A., Mexico, Mexico; *Int'l*, pg. 594
Macias, Pedro Salcedo, Gen. Mgr.--Bristol-Myers Ecuatoriana, S.A., Guayas, Ecuador; *U.S. Public*, pg. 255
Macias, Pedro Salcedo, Gen. Mgr.--Laboratorios Bristol del Ecuador S.A., Guayas, Ecuador; *U.S. Public*, pg. 256
MacIlvaine, Joe, Pres.--Paramount Farming Company, Bakersfield, CA; *U.S. Private*, pg. 941
MacInnis, Ian W., F.C.A., Finance Dir.--Citicorp Insurance Group, London, United Kingdom; *U.S. Public*, pg. 378
MacIntosh, Archie, Gen. Mgr.--ITW Limited-Buildex Europe, Reading, United Kingdom; *U.S. Public*, pg. 868
MacIntyre, John A., V.P. & Gen. Mgr.--Giddings & Lewis Casting Technology, Menominee, MI; *Int'l*, pg. 1389
Maciver, W.K., Mng. Dir.--Lucas Aerospace, Solihull, United Kingdom; *Int'l*, pg. 819
Mack, F.W., Chief Oper. Officer--Torin Engineered Blowers, Chesterfield, MO; *Int'l*, pg. 125
Mack, Horst, Mgr.--TOP Prazisionswerkzeuge GmbH, Frankfurt/Main, Germany; *Int'l*, pg. 1187
Mack, John, Mng. Dir.--M.E. Mack Valves Pty. Limited, Bayswater, Australia; *Int'l*, pg. 1222
Mack, John E., III, Pres.--Central Hudson Enterprises, Poughkeepsie, NY; *U.S. Public*, pg. 325
Mack, Kurt, Gen. Mgr.--Life Technologies GMbH, Eggenstein, Germany; *U.S. Public*, pg. 505
Mack, Stephan J., Pres.--Holm Industries, Inc., Scottsburg, IN; *U.S. Public*, pg. 1504
Mack, Terry, Pres.--BA Cheque Corp., San Francisco, CA; *U.S. Public*, pg. 180
Mack, Thomas, Pres.--EMS-Togo, Taylor, MI; *Int'l*, pg. 981
Mack, Tim, Mgr.-Plant--Mack Printing Group (East Stroudsburg Div.), East Stroudsburg, PA; *U.S. Private*, pg. 692
Mack, Tony, Gen. Mgr.--Grace China Ltd., Shanghai, China; *U.S. Public*, pg. 755
Mackaij, Robert, Exec.--Lips Asia Pte Ltd., Singapore, Singapore; *Int'l*, pg. 812
MacKay, Allistair R. L., Mng. Dir.--Andrew Valentine Holdings Limited, Dundee, United Kingdom; *U.S. Public*, pg. 78
Mackay, Brian, Gen. Mgr.--Goulds Pumps Canada, Inc., Cambridge, Canada; *U.S. Public*, pg. 861
Mackay, Bruce, Gen. Mgr.--GESTRA, Inc., West Caldwell, NJ; *Int'l*, pg. 549
MacKay, Bruce, Div. Mgr.-West--Pier 1 Imports Canada, Toronto, Canada; *U.S. Public*, pg. 1295
MacKay, Carol, Gen. Mgr.--Fraser Paper Limited, Etobicoke, Canada; *Int'l*, pg. 434
Mackay, David J., Pres.--John Menzies (UK) Limited, Edinburgh, United Kingdom; *Int'l*, pg. 707
MacKay, Donald R., Sr. V.P.--Dana Canada Inc., Saint Catharines, Canada; *U.S. Public*, pg. 480
Mackay, I.A., Pres.--W.H. Smith Canada Ltd., Toronto, Canada; *Int'l*, pg. 1150
Mackay, Ian M., Mng. Dir.--Adams Rite (Europe) Ltd., Swanley, United Kingdom; *U.S. Private*, pg. 17
Mackay, Terry D., Mng. Dir.--KWB Controls Ltd., Tromode, United Kingdom; *Int'l*, pg. 391
MacKenzie, David, Dist. Mgr.--Flowserve Duriron Canada Inc., Edmonton, Canada; *U.S. Public*, pg. 659
MacKenzie, Dylan T., V.P.--Toronto Dominion (Illinois), Inc., Chicago, IL; *Int'l*, pg. 1401
MacKenzie, J. Gregory, Pres.--Hilb, Rogal and Hamilton Company of Orlando, Orlando, FL; *U.S. Public*, pg. 827
MacKenzie, Neil, Mng. Dir.--Prok Group Ltd., Morley, Australia; *Int'l*, pg. 1353
MacKewich, Joseph C., Pres.--Western Metal Lath, Riverside, CA; *Int'l*, pg. 845
Mackey, Paul N., Pres. & Chief Exec. Officer--Prym-Dritz Corporation, Spartanburg, SC; *Int'l*, pg. 1499
Macki, Elliot, Rep. for Rio de Janeiro--Bank Hapoalim (Rio de Janeiro), Rio de Janeiro, Brazil; *Int'l*, pg. 149
Mackie, J. James, V.P.-Bus. Devel.--Newbridge Networks Corporation, Kanata, Canada; *Int'l*, pg. 924
Mackie, T.M., Mng. Dir.--Ross & Catherall Limited, Sheffield, United Kingdom; *Int'l*, pg. 1467
Mackie, Tom, Grp. Pres.--Instrumentation Group, Cleveland, OH; *U.S. Public*, pg. 1261
Mackiewicz, Piotr, Gen. Mgr.--Esselte Polska Sp.z.o.o., Kozienice, Poland; *Int'l*, pg. 461
Mackii, Callum, Chief Oper. Officer--Protocall Ventures, Marlow, United Kingdom; *U.S. Public*, pg. 740
Mackin, Gary, Pres.--Manville Canada Inc., Etobicoke, Canada; *U.S. Public*, pg. 927
Mackin, Jeffrey, Pres.--Louisville Transportation, Louisville, KY; *U.S. Private*, pg. 567
Mackin, John H., Pres. & Chief Exec. Officer--SouthTrust Bank, Gadsden, Gadsden, AL; *U.S. Public*, pg. 1491
Mackin, Scott G., Pres. & Chief Oper. Officer--Ogden Energy Group, Inc., Fairfield, NJ; *U.S. Public*, pg. 1213
Mackin, Terry, V.P. & Eastern Region Mgr.--Columbia Tri-Star Television Distribution - New York Office, New York, NY; *Int'l*, pg. 1282
Mackinney, Harold A., Jr., Chm. Bd. & Chief Exec. Officer--Fleet Investment Advisors, Inc., Boston, MA; *U.S. Public*, *pg. 650*
Mackintosh, Lyal, Regional Mgr.--Westpac Banking Corp. - New Caledonia, Noumea, New Caledonia; *Int'l*, pg. 1497
Mackintosh, Ronald W., Pres.--European Group, Farnborough, United Kingdom; *U.S. Public*, pg. 423
Mackler, Paul, Pres.--Reed Exhibition Companies-North America, Norwalk, CT; *Int'l*, pg. 1096
Mackney, Richard, V.P.--Federal Laboratories, Saltsburg, PA; *U.S. Public*, pg. 1030
Macknis, B., Gen. Mgr.--Senior Engineering Co.-Eastern Region, King of Prussia, PA; *Int'l*, pg. 1222
MacLachlan, Neil T., Sr. V.P.-Asia Opers.--Barrick Power Gold Corporation of China Limited, Beijing, China; *Int'l*, pg. 169
MacLachlan, Thomas, Chief Oper. Officer--Dutch Parking, Inc., Syracuse, NY; *U.S. Private*, pg. 43
MacLaurin, Anthony, Pres.--Rexam DSI, South Hadley, MA; *Int'l*, pg. 1106
Maclay, Geoffrey G., Jr., Pres.--Elan Investment Services, Inc., Milwaukee, WI; *U.S. Public*, pg. 643
MacLean, Cyril, Gen. Mgr.--Rotex Canada Inc., Scarborough, Canada; *Int'l*, pg. 462
MacLean, John S., Pres.--Therakos, Inc., Exton, PA; *U.S. Public*, pg. 929
MacLean, Neil, Dir.--KEG Restaurants U.S., Inc., Wilmington, DE; *Int'l*, pg. 1499
MacLeod, Donald W., Pres.--IRT Management Company, Atlanta, GA; *U.S. Public*, pg. 858
Macleod, Donald W., Pres.--VW Mall, Inc., Atlanta, GA; *U.S. Public*, pg. 858
Macleod, I., Mng. Dir.--ABB Process Analytics Ltd., Huntingdon, United Kingdom; *Int'l*, pg. 7
MacLeod, S.D., Pres.-CIMCO Refrigeration--Toromont Industries Ltd., Concord, Canada; *Int'l*, pg. 1400
Macloce, Helen L., Pres.--Merrill Lynch Bank & Trust Co., Plainsboro, NJ; *U.S. Public*, pg. 1097
MacMachon, Thomas E., V.P.-Hoffmann LaRoche Inc. & Pres.-Diagnostics Div.--Hoffmann-La Roche Inc., Nutley, NJ; *Int'l*, pg. 1120
MacMahon, David M., Pres.--Gates Formed-Fibre Products, Auburn, ME; *Int'l*, pg. 1396
MacManamon, Owen P., Pres.--Quaker State Inc., Burlington, Canada; *U.S. Public*, pg. 1348
MacMillan, Bobby, Gen. Mgr.--Jasper Textile, Jasper, FL; *U.S. Private*, pg. 542
MacMillan, Thomas, Pres. & Chief Exec. Officer--Mellon Bank Canada, Toronto, Canada; *U.S. Public*, pg. 1086
MacMorran, Henry G., Pres. & Chief Exec. Officer--LaSalle Bank Lake View, Chicago, IL; *Int'l*, pg. 10
MacMorran, Henry G., Pres. & Chief Oper. Officer--LaSalle Cragin Bank, Chicago, IL; *Int'l*, pg. 10
MacNamee, Gordon, Mng. Dir.--Red Dragon Radio, Cardiff, United Kingdom; *Int'l*, pg. 452
MacNutt, James W., Mgr.-Publicity & Adv.--Cincinnati Milacron Industrial Systems Division, Cincinnati, OH; *U.S. Public*, pg. 368
MacPhail, Donald E.A., Pres.--Ocelot International Tanzania Ltd., Dar es Salaam, Tanzania; *Int'l*, pg. 996
MacPherson, D. C., Chm. Bd.--NatWest Markets Corporate Finance Limited, London, United Kingdom; *Int'l*, pg. 910
MacPherson, R., Mng. Dir.--Ascom Timeplex Inc., Richmond Hill, Canada; *Int'l*, pg. 87
MacQueen, Ken, Pres.--KTVI-TV, Inc., Saint Louis, MO; *Int'l*, *pg. 926*
MacRae, G.D., Mng. Dir.--Abru Aluminium Limited, Launceston, United Kingdom; *Int'l*, pg. 615
Macredie, D., Gen. Mgr.--Hotpac Reservations (NZ) Ltd., Auckland, New Zealand; *Int'l*, pg. 38
Macrez, Roland, Mng. Dir.--Davum-Armatures, Puteaux, France; *Int'l*, pg. 571
Macri, Rocco, Exec. V.P.--Associates Communications Div., Dallas, TX; *U.S. Public*, pg. 663
Macum, Karen, Mktg. Dir.-The Monster Board--TMP Worldwide/Interactive Division, Framingham, MA; *U.S. Private*, pg. 1065
Macumber, John, Branch Mgr.--Burns & Wilcox - Salt Lake City Office, Salt Lake City, UT; *U.S. Private*, pg. 610
Maczek, Helmut, Chm. Bd.--Rheinische Zinkgesellschaft GmbH, Duisburg, Germany; *Int'l*, pg. 861
Maczuzak, John, V.P. & Gen. Mgr.--National Steel Corp., Granite City Division, Granite City, IL; *Int'l*, pg. 902
Madar, Jean, Pres.--Jordache Fragrances & Cosmetics, New York, NY; *U.S. Public*, pg. 924
Madar, Jean, Pres.--Elite Parfums, Ltd., New York, NY; *U.S. Public*, pg. 924
Madarame, Rikihiro, Chm. & Chief Exec. Officer--Nemic-Lambda KK, Tokyo, Japan; *Int'l*, pg. 1242
Madarasz, Laszlo, Mng. Dir.--BNP-Dresdner Bank (Hungaria) Rt., Budapest, Hungary; *Int'l*, pg. 418
Madden, Don, Gen. Mgr.--Green Oaks Park Hotel, Fort Worth, TX; *U.S. Public*, pg. 1537
Madden, Joe, Chief Oper. Officer--Rex Supply Company, Houston, TX; *U.S. Private*, pg. 889
Madden, L. James, Pres.--Commercial Union Life Insurance Company of America, Quincy, MA; *Int'l*, pg. 308
Madden, Mick, Mgr.--Gregory Mine, Emerald, Australia; *Int'l*, *pg. 223*
Madden, Robert E., Pres.--Thermice Corporation, Thorofare, NJ; *U.S. Public*, pg. 1341
Madden, Timothy M., Pres.--Transportation Recoveries Inc., Cleveland, OH; *U.S. Public*, pg. 1335
Madden, Will, Pres.--CABVAL, Houston, TX; *U.S. Public*, pg. 801
Madder, D.C., Chief Oper. Officer--John Laing Services Ltd., London, United Kingdom; *Int'l*, pg. 796
Madder, John, Gen. Mgr.--Banque Commerciale du Rwanda S.A., Kigali, Rwanda; *Int'l*, pg. 148
Maddison, R., Mng. Dir.--Decorport Ltd., Nelson, United Kingdom; *Int'l*, pg. 124
Maddock, G.A., Plant Dir.--Keebler Cone Co., Chicago, IL; *U.S. Public*, pg. 657
Maddox, Elton, Sr. V.P. & Gen. Mgr.--Poultry Div., Gainesville, GA; *U.S. Private*, pg. 268
Maddox, L.E., Pres. & Chief Exec. Officer--PG&E Energy Trading, Houston, TX; *U.S. Public*, pg. 1241
Maddox, Landell, Pres. & Chief Oper. Officer--Brooklyn Interstate, Houston, TX; *U.S. Public*, pg. 259
Made, Bjorn, Chief Oper. Officer--Electrolux S.E.A. Private Ltd., Singapore, Singapore; *Int'l*, pg. 443

Mader, Helmut, Mng. Dir.--DB Capital Markets (Asia) Ltd. (Hong Kong), Central, Hong Kong; *Int'l*, pg. 404
Mader, Helmut, Mng. Dir. & Gen. Mgr.--DB Capital Markets (Asia) Ltd. (Tokyo), Tokyo, Japan; *Int'l*, pg. 404
Madero, Ricardo, Mng. Dir.--Gemisa S.A. de C.V., Tlalnepantla, Mexico; *Int'l*, pg. 614
Madewell, Gary, Gen. Mgr.--Trelleborg YSH, Inc.-Western Kentucky Division, Morganfield, KY; *Int'l*, pg. 1422
Madgwick, Peter B., Mng. Dir.--Doubleday Australia Pty. Ltd., Lane Cove, Australia; *Int'l*, pg. 192
Madia, William, Dir.--Battelle Pacific Northwest National Laboratory, Richland, WA; *U.S. Private*, pg. 123
Madigan, Mary Jean, Publr. & Editor--Hospitality Design, New York, NY; *Int'l*, pg. 1446
Madill, F.A., Mgr.-Northern--HFC Trust & Savings Ltd., Bracknell, United Kingdom; *U.S. Public*, pg. 842
Madill, Paul, Gen. Mgr.--Bernal Division, Rochester Hills, MI; *U.S. Public*, pg. 1517
Madison, Dick, Jr., V.P. & Gen. Mgr.--DCI of Utah Inc., Cedar City, UT; *U.S. Private*, pg. 301
Madison, R.P., Pres. & Chief Exec. Officer--North American Resources Co., Butte, MT; *U.S. Public*, pg. 1127
Madison, R.P., Pres.--Altana Exploration Company, Butte, MT; *U.S. Public*, pg. 1127
Madison, Thomas R., Jr., Pres. & Chief Exec. Officer--CSC Financial Services Group, Austin, TX; *U.S. Public*, pg. 422
Madison, W.F., Pres.--Marathon International Petroleum Supply Company, Findlay, OH; *U.S. Public*, pg. 1662
Madl, Frederick J., Jr., V.P. & Gen. Mgr.--Thomas Lighting-C&I Accent Division, Los Angeles, CA; *U.S. Public*, pg. 1599
Madonia, Paula, DivisionMgr.--Horizon Technology Group - Westland Division, Westland, MI; *U.S. Private*, pg. 539
Madrid, Bobby, Gen. Mgr.--Manulife - Philippines Branch, Manila, Philippines; *Int'l*, pg. 841
Madrid, German Lopez, Pres.--Volvo Penta Espana, S.A., Madrid, Spain; *Int'l*, pg. 1478
Madrigal, Diane, Mgr.-Parts--EMPIRE Machinery - Tucson, Tucson, AZ; *U.S. Private*, pg. 375
Madrinan, Ramon, Chm. Bd.--Cigna Seguros de Colombia S.A., Bogota, Colombia; *U.S. Public*, pg. 363
Madsen, Everett, Chief Oper. Officer--Flo-Pac Midwest, Minneapolis, MN; *U.S. Private*, pg. 414
Madsen, Henrik Overgaard, Reg. Mgr.--Det Norske Veritas, Hellerup, Denmark; *Int'l*, pg. 396
Madsen, Henrik Overgaard, Reg. Mgr.--Det Norske Veritas, Kobe, Japan; *Int'l*, pg. 397
Madsen, John A., Chief Oper. Officer--Greenlux A/S, Lyngby, Denmark; *Int'l*, pg. 441
Madsen, Kevin, Branch Mgr.--Sharp Electronics Corporation Midwest Regional Office, Romeoville, IL; *Int'l*, pg. 1229
Madsen, Per, Pres.--Aker Elementbygg a.s., Moss, Norway; *Int'l*, pg. 41
Madsen, Tom B., Gen. Mgr.--Esselte Meto A-S, Herlev, Denmark; *Int'l*, pg. 461
Maeda, Hiroshi, Gen. Mgr.--SBCM Limited Hong Kong Branch, Central, Hong Kong; *Int'l*, pg. 1310
Maeda, Isamu, Pres.--Valmet Japan Co., Ltd., Tokyo, Japan; *Int'l*, pg. 1448
Maeda, J., Gen. Mgr.--Akagane Kauin Sangyo Kabushiki Kaisha, Kobe, Japan; *Int'l*, pg. 187
Maeda, Y., Pres.--Nissho Iwai Real Estate Corp., Tokyo, Japan; *Int'l*, pg. 947
Maeda, Yoshimi, Gen. Mgr.--Asahi Bank Seoul Branch, Seoul, Korea; *Int'l*, pg. 82
Maeer, Derek, Chief Oper. Officer--Visual Simulation Systems Division, Saint Louis, MO; *U.S. Public*, pg. 218
Maehlmann, Peter, Pres.--Hamburger Sparkasse, Hamburg, Germany; *Int'l*, pg. 590
Maes, Christian, Mgr.--Barenbrug (Belgium) Maes NV/SA, Kortrijk, Belgium; *Int'l*, pg. 167
Maes, Jo, Chief Oper. Officer--Pharmacia & Upjohn S.A.N.V., Brussels, Belgium; *Int'l*, pg. 1050
Maestre, Joaquin, Pres.--Shandwick Barcelona, Barcelona, Spain; *Int'l*, pg. 1227
Maestri, Tom, Gen. Mgr.--Corrugated Container Div.-New Orleans Plant, New Orleans, LA; *U.S. Public*, pg. 1520
Maestroni, Angelo, Mng. Dir.--Costar Italia, s.r.l., Concorezzo, Italy; *U.S. Public*, pg. 448
Maeyama, Yoshito, Pres.--Komatsu Huanan Ltd., Hong Kong, Hong Kong; *Int'l*, pg. 744
Maeyama, Yoshito, Pres.--Komatsu (Shanghai) Ltd., Shanghai, China; *Int'l*, pg. 744
Maffei, Italo, Mng. Dir.--Swiss Life (Italia), Milan, Italy; *Int'l*, pg. 1332
Maffei, Italo, Mng. Dir.--Swiss Life (Italia) Infortuni e Malattie, Milan, Italy; *Int'l*, pg. 1332
Maffic, Michael O., Pres. & Chief Exec. Officer--Carson Water Co., Las Vegas, NV; *U.S. Public*, pg. 1493
Maffie, Michael O., Chief Exec. Officer--Utility Financial Corp., Las Vegas, NV; *U.S. Public*, pg. 1493
Maffie, Michael O., Pres. & Chief Exec. Officer--LNG Energy, Inc., Phoenix, AZ; *U.S. Public*, pg. 1493
Mafune, Koichiro, Gen. Mgr.--Asahi Bank Hong Kong Branch, Hong Kong, Hong Kong; *Int'l*, pg. 82
Magagnoli, Claudio, Gen. Mgr.--Banca Monte Dei Paschi Di Siena, London, United Kingdom; *Int'l*, pg. 136
Magalhaes, Andre Da Silva, Gen. Mgr.--MSA do Brasil, Ltda., Diadema, Brazil; *U.S. Public*, pg. 1115
Magalhaes, Carlos, V.P.-Latin America-South--Nordson do Brasil Industria e Comercio Ltda., Sao Paulo, Brazil; *U.S. Public*, pg. 1189
Magalska, Jim, Chief Oper. Officer--Employers Life Ins. Co. of Wausau, Wausau, WI; *U.S. Private*, pg. 789
Magano, Alessandro, Gen. Mgr.--Azzura-International Marketing & Promotions, Turin, Italy; *U.S. Private*, pg. 303
Magarity, Russell L., Reg. Mgr.--Bank of Boston, Singapore, Singapore; *U.S. Public*, pg. 184
Magasrevy, J., Chm. Bd.--Fibras Ceramicas, C.A., Valencia, Venezuela; *Int'l*, pg. 894
Magdelain, Robert, Pres.--Nilfisk of America Inc., Malvern, PA; *Int'l*, pg. 932
Magee, Brian, Pres.--Canac Kitchens Ltd, Thornhill, Canada; *U.S. Private*, pg. 630
Magee, John, Gen. Mgr.--Terumo (Australia) Pty. Ltd., Mordialloc, Australia; *Int'l*, pg. 1376
Magee, Kenneth D., V.P.--Parts Operations, Allentown, PA; *Int'l*, pg. 1103
Magee, Robert P., Pres.--Totem Ocean Trailer Express, Seattle, WA; *U.S. Private*, pg. 1092
Magerkurth, Fred A., Mgr.-Branch--Piper Jaffray Inc., Lees Summit, MO; *U.S. Public*, pg. 1301
Maggiacomo, Ronald, Pres.--Billings & Co., Inc., Hartford, CT; *U.S. Public*, pg. 23
Maggio, Claudio, Pres.--MAF S.p.A., Nembro, Italy; *Int'l*, pg. 1449
Maggioli, Joao, Gen. Mgr.--Nature's Sunshine Produtos Naturais Ltda., Sao Paulo, Brazil; *U.S. Public*, pg. 1167
Maggioli, Joao B., Pres.--Avon Cosmeticos, Ltda., Sao Paulo, Brazil; *U.S. Public*, pg. 156
Maggs, David, Pres.--Ebtec Corporation, Agawam, MA; *Int'l*, *pg. 1337*
Magi, Orazio, Mng. Dir.--Unical S.p.A., Cosenza, Italy; *Int'l*, pg. 1371
Magiera, Horst R., Mng. Dir.--Banque Europeenne pour l'Amerique Latine (BEAL) S.A., Brussels, Belgium; *Int'l*, pg. 1493
Magill, Roger L., V.P.-Sls. & Gen. Mgr.--Bates Div., Rockford, MI; *U.S. Public*, pg. 1775
Magill, Thomas A., Mng. Dir.--Hyster B.V., Nijmegen, Netherlands; *U.S. Public*, pg. 1149
Maginnis, Stephen K., Pres.--ALLTEL Carolina, Inc., Matthews, NC; *U.S. Public*, pg. 55
Maginnis, Stephen K., Pres.--Heins Telephone Company, Sanford, NC; *U.S. Public*, pg. 56
Magistra, F., Rep.--SBC Ltda., Montevideo, Uruguay; *Int'l*, pg. 1330
Magistra, F., Mgr.--SBC Ltda., Punta del Este, Uruguay; *Int'l*, pg. 1330
Magliacane, Debbie, Branch Mgr.--Circle International, Charleston, SC; *U.S. Public*, pg. 371
Magliocco, Joseph, Pres.--Chatham Imports, Inc., New York, NY; *U.S. Private*, pg. 847
Maglione, Marcelo, V.P.--Graffiti/DMB&B, Buenos Aires, Argentina; *U.S. Private*, pg. 304
Magnan, Jean-Francois, Dir. Gen.--Imphy S.A., Puteaux, France; *Int'l*, pg. 571
Magnan, Larry, Pres.--Premier Cruises, Miami, FL; *U.S. Private*, pg. 293
Magne, Daniel, Dir. & Gen. Mgr.--Bundy U.K. Ltd., Telford, United Kingdom; *Int'l*, pg. 1341
Magner, Neil, Chief Oper. Officer--Hughes Tool Company de Mexico, S.A. de C.V., Mexico, Mexico; *U.S. Public*, pg. 167
Magneson, Jane, Gen. Mgr.--Red Oak Express, Red Oak, IA; *U.S. Private*, pg. 648
Magnus, Ken, Gen. Mgr.--Jeffers Electronics, Nogales, AZ; *U.S. Public*, pg. 1722
Magnussen, Jonn-Borger, Pres.--Aker Singel & Grus a.s., Sandnes, Norway; *Int'l*, pg. 42
Magnusson, Bengt, Gen. Mgr.--Nordson Sverige AB, Stenungsund, Sweden; *U.S. Public*, pg. 1189
Magnusson, Bengt, Gen. Mgr.--Nordson Norge A/S, Oslo, Norway; *U.S. Public*, pg. 1189
Magnusson, Bengt, Gen. Mgr.--Nordson Sverige AB, Malmo, Sweden; *U.S. Public*, pg. 1189
Magnusson, Gerhard, Chief Oper. Officer--Alfa-Laval Separation A/S, Soeborg, Denmark; *Int'l*, pg. 1378
Magnusson, Jan, Chief Oper. Officer--Tunborg A/S, Sarpsborg, Norway; *Int'l*, pg. 443
Magnusson, Joachim, Gen. Mgr.--Bundy A/S, Ikast, Denmark; *Int'l*, pg. 1341
Magnusson, Jonn-Borger, Pres.--NorStone a.s, Sandnes, Norway; *Int'l*, pg. 1199
Magnusson, Urban, Mgr.--Varnamo Isolerduk, Varnamo, Sweden; *Int'l*, pg. 1422
Magoon, Robert, Pres.--Amelco, Inc., Honolulu, HI; *U.S. Public*, pg. 65
Magowan, Peter A., Chm. Bd.--Safeway U.S. Holdings, Inc., Oakland, CA; *U.S. Public*, pg. 1426
Magrath, Jr., George N., Pres.--Peoples Federal Savings & Loan Association, Conway, SC; *U.S. Public*, pg. 634
Magrath, Paul, Pres.--Pentax Precision Instrument Corp., Orangeburg, NY; *Int'l*, pg. 85
Magrini, Gus, Pres.--Midcoast Marketing Company, Muscle Shoals, AL; *U.S. Public*, pg. 1109
Magsubara, Steve, Gen. Mgr.--Hanwa American Corp., Seattle Branch, Seattle, WA; *Int'l*, pg. 595
Maguier, Mary, Controller--Quarterdeck International Limited, Dun Laoghaire, Ireland; *U.S. Public*, pg. 1351
Maguire, Bill, Editor--RCR Publications, Denver, CO; *U.S. Private*, pg. 285
Maguire, Patrick, Area V.P.--Avon Sales & Distribution Branch, Springdale, OH; *U.S. Public*, pg. 156
Maguire, Thomas, Gen. Mgr.--Letraset New Zealand Ltd., Auckland, New Zealand; *Int'l*, pg. 462
Mah, G.K.O., Gen. Mgr.--Associated Merchant Bank Pte. Ltd., Singapore, Singapore; *Int'l*, pg. 1133
Mahadeva, Kumar, Chm. Bd. & Chief Exec. Officer--Cognizant Technology Solutions Corp., New York, NY; *U.S. Public*, pg. 395
Mahaffey, Paul F., Pres. & Chief Exec. Officer--PLUM, Eden Prairie, MN; *Int'l*, pg. 1504
Mahagitsiri, P., Gen. Mgr.--Thai Soluble Coffee Company Ltd., Bangkok, Thailand; *Int'l*, pg. 922
Mahan, Steve, Gen. Mgr.--GATX Freight Systems-California, City of Commerce, CA; *U.S. Public*, pg. 691
Mahan, Steve, Gen. Mgr.--GATX Logistics, Inc.-California (Dupont), City of Commerce, CA; *U.S. Public*, pg. 691
Mahapun, Somgiat, Gen. Mgr.--Janssen Pharmaceutical Ltd., Bangkok, Thailand; *U.S. Public*, pg. 930
Maharay, Walter, Pres.--Universal Dairy Equipment, Inc., Kansas City, MO; *Int'l*, pg. 1379
Maharry, Anne, Pres. & Chief Fin. Officer--Bull, Inc., San Diego, CA; *U.S. Private*, pg. 976
Mahendroo, Vikeesh, Pres.--William M. Mercer Companies, Inc., New York, NY; *U.S. Public*, pg. 1049
Maher, B.A., Pres.--Exxon Insurance Holdings, Inc., Saint Georges, Bermuda; *U.S. Public*, pg. 602
Maher, Jack, Gen. Mgr.--LeFebure, South, Stafford, TX; *Int'l*, pg. 387
Maher, Joseph L. Jr., Div. V.P.--AMP Industrial Div., Harrisburg, PA; *U.S. Public*, pg. 7
Maher, M., Mgr.--Credit Agricole (CNCA) Representative Office-Beijing, Beijing, China; *Int'l*, pg. 341
Maheshwari, K., Advisor--Geoffrey Manners and Co., Ltd., Mumbai, India; *U.S. Public*, pg. 81
Mahieu, Fabienne, Gen. Mgr. & Dir.-Fin.--Titleflex Europe SA, Ozoir-la-Ferriere, France; *Int'l*, pg. 1341
Mahlik, Michael B., Pres. & Chief Exec. Officer--Associated Trust Company, Inc., Milwaukee, WI; *U.S. Public*, pg. 140
Mahlin, Don, Mgr.-Branch--Graphic Systems, Saint Louis, MO; *U.S. Public*, pg. 1060
Mahmood, Khalid, Mgr.--Fouad Supply & Services Division, Dammam, Saudi Arabia; *Int'l*, pg. 502
Mahmood, Shahid Waqar, Mgr.--Deutsche Bank AG (Lahore), Lahore, Pakistan; *Int'l*, pg. 404
Mahoney, Gerald F., Pres.--Pavey Envelope & Tag Corp., Jersey City, NJ; *U.S. Public*, pg. 1038
Mahoney, Gerald F., Pres.--Standard Tag Mfg. Co., Jersey City, NJ; *U.S. Public*, pg. 1038
Mahoney, John, Gen. Mgr.--Daniel J. Edelman Ireland, Ltd., Dublin, Ireland; *U.S. Private*, pg. 363
Mahoney, Michael, Pres.--ComVideo Systems, Inc./N.J., Princeton, NJ; *U.S. Public*, pg. 1354
Mahoney, Richard, Pres. & Chief Oper. Officer--Caesars World, Inc., Las Vegas, NV; *U.S. Public*, pg. 1512
Mahoney, Robert M., Pres.--Citizens Bank of Massachusetts, Fairhaven, MA; *Int'l*, pg. 1132
Mahoney, Thomas, Gen. Mgr.--Teterboro Learning Center, Moonachie, NJ; *U.S. Public*, pg. 219
Mahoney, Thomas E., Pres. & Gen. Mgr.--Stanley Customer Support Div., New Britain, CT; *U.S. Public*, pg. 1509
Mahoney, Thomas J., Mng. Dir.--Cigna Reinsurance Company S.A.-N.V., Brussels, Belgium; *U.S. Public*, pg. 365
Mahoney, William, Pres.--SCT Utilities Systems, Inc., Columbia, SC; *U.S. Public*, pg. 1552
Mahony, Ken, Mng. Dir.--Willis Corroon Ireland Limited, Dublin, Ireland; *Int'l*, pg. 1504
Mahony, T. Paul, Publr.--The Evening Call Publishing Co.-The Call, Woonsocket, RI; *U.S. Public*, pg. 934
Mahr, Rene, Pres. & Chief Exec. Officer--Paul Wurth S.A., Luxembourg, Luxembourg; *Int'l*, pg. 80
Mahugh, Greg, Gen. Mgr.--South Seattle Auto Auction, Kent, WA; *U.S. Private*, pg. 283
Maia, Clouis DeCampos, Pres.--Walter Kidde S.A. Industria e Comercio, Sao Paulo, Brazil; *Int'l*, pg. 594
Maia, Fatima, Mgr.--Broad National Bank-Millburn, Millburn, NJ; *U.S. Public*, pg. 258
Maibach, Benjamin C., III, Pres.--Barton Malow Co., Southfield, MI; *U.S. Private*, pg. 120
Maiberger, Mark S., Pres.--Speedring Systems, Inc., Rochester Hills, MI; *U.S. Public*, pg. 158
Maida, Jane, Interim Lab Mgr.--Quest Diagnostic-Wayne, Wayne, NJ; *U.S. Public*, pg. 1352
Maidenberg, Michael, Publr.--Grand Forks Herald, Incorporated, Grand Forks, ND; *U.S. Public*, pg. 964
Maier, Craig F., Pres.--Frisch Florida, Inc., Cincinnati, OH; *U.S. Public*, pg. 682
Maier, Craig F., Pres.--Frisch Kentucky, Inc., Cincinnati, OH; *U.S. Public*, pg. 682
Maier, Craig F., Pres.--Kip's of Oklahoma, Inc., Cincinnati, OH; *U.S. Public*, pg. 682
Maier, Craig F., Pres.--Frisch Ohio, Inc., Cincinnati, OH; *U.S. Public*, pg. 682
Maier, Craig F., Pres.--Frisch Indiana, Inc., Cincinnati, OH; *U.S. Public*, pg. 682
Maier, Karl W., Reg. Representative--Banque Internationale a Luxembourg S.A.-Represantanz fur die, Frankfurt/Main, Germany; *Int'l*, pg. 162
Maier, P.H., Chief Exec. Officer--Curamik Electronics GmbH, Eschenbach, Germany; *Int'l*, pg. 209
Maier, Richard, Pres.--Ikon Capital, Wilmington, DE; *U.S. Public*, pg. 863
Maier, Richard P., Pres.--Ikon Capital, Inc., Macon, GA; *U.S.* Public, pg. 863
Maier, Scott C., Mng. Dir.--Quality Hotel Central, Cincinnati, OH; *U.S. Public*, pg. 682
Maier, Scott C., Mng. Dir.--Quality Hotel Riverview, Covington, KY; *U.S. Public*, pg. 682
Maier, Walter, Pres.--Sandvik Sorting Systems, Louisville, KY; *Int'l*, pg. 1186
Maik, Peter, Pres. & Chief Exec. Officer--Doubleday Canada Ltd., Toronto, Canada; *Int'l*, pg. 192
Maile, Wolfgang, Dr., Mng. Dir.--Wuestenrot International Management-Gesellschaft AG, Luxembourg, Luxembourg; *Int'l*, pg. 1514
Mailer, Dee Jay, Sr. V.P. & Reg. Mgr.--Kaiser Permanente, Hawaii Division, Honolulu, HI; *U.S. Private*, pg. 605
Mailind, Jesper, Pres. & Chief Oper. Officer--GN Danavox A/S, Taastrup, Denmark; *Int'l*, pg. 537
Maillan, Jean Claude, Chm.--CAP Sesa Tertiaire, Paris, France; *Int'l*, pg. 263
Maillefer, Pierre-Luc, V.P. & Gen. Mgr.--Dentsply Maillefer, Ballaigues, Switzerland; *U.S. Public*, pg. 499
Mailleret, Michel, Chm. Bd. & Chief Exec. Officer--Filtrauto Division, Montigny-le-Bretonneux, France; *Int'l*, pg. 785
Main, Andrew, Dir.--Ord Minnett Group Limited, Paris, France; *Int'l*, pg. 1497
Main, Barry, Mgr.--Western Australia Branch, Osbourne Park, Australia; *Int'l*, pg. 226
Main, Raymond E., Pres.--Illinois Union Insurance Company, Chicago, IL; *U.S. Public*, pg. 365
Maingard, D., Deputy Gen. Mgr.--Luxlife, Luxembourg, Luxembourg; *Int'l*, pg. 565
Maini, Roshan, Mng. Dir.--Vascutek Limited, Glasgow, United Kingdom; *Int'l*, pg. 1307

Mainwaring, Les, Sr. Mgr.--Australian Guarantee Corporation Limited - Queensland, Brisbane, Australia; *Int'l*, pg. 1496
Maio, Ralph, V.P. & Gen. Mgr.--American Refractories Co., Reading, PA; *U.S. Private*, pg. 903
Maior, H. Angel Toletti, Dir. Gen.--Zimbra Industria e Comercio Ltda., Sao Paulo, Brazil; *U.S. Public*, pg. 257
Maire, Jean-Pierre, Mgr.--Sandvik Venezuela C.A., Caracas, Venezuela; *Int'l*, pg. 1188
Maisel, Howard M., Pres. & Chief Exec. Officer--Columbia Cement Co. Inc., Freeport, NY; *Int'l*, pg. 235
Maisey, G., Gen. Mgr.--Kenner Parker Toys, Amsterdam, Netherlands; *U.S. Public*, pg. 798
Maisey, Geoff, Gen. Mgr.--Kenner Parker Toys International, Rodgau, Germany; *U.S. Public*, pg. 798
Maitland, John, Pres.--Business Information Technology, Concord, CA; *U.S. Public*, pg. 356
Maitland, Randy, Gen. Mgr.--Alro Group, Grand Rapids, Grand Rapids, MI; *U.S. Private*, pg. 46
Maito, Gabriel, Chief Oper. Officer--Allright Parking El Paso, Inc., El Paso, TX; *U.S. Private*, pg. 43
Maitrepierre, Philippe, Chief Exec. Officer--Techalloy Co., Inc., Mahwah, NJ; *Int'l*, pg. 572
Maiwald, Peter, Pres.--Fittings Traisen Gmbh, Traisen, Austria; *Int'l*, pg. 490
Maizlisz, Maria Lidia, Pres.--Total Research Argentina, Buenos Aires, Argentina; *U.S. Public*, pg. 1625
Majava, Jorma, Gen. Mgr.--Valmet Corporation Roll Coatings, Riihimaki, Finland; *Int'l*, pg. 1449
Majerczak, Edward, Pres.--Berlin Industries, Inc., Elk Grove Village, IL; *U.S. Private*, pg. 136
Majerus, Larry G., Sr. V.P. & Gen. Mgr.--Polk Automotive Data Services Div., Detroit, MI; *U.S. Private*, pg. 874
Majocchi, Roberto, Country Mgr.--Det Norske Veritas, Milan, Italy; *Int'l*, pg. 397
Major, Berry F., V.P. & Gen. Mgr.--IMO Pump, Monroe, NC; *U.S. Public*, pg. 857
Major, Ed, Pres. & Publr.--News-Star Publishing Company, Monroe, LA; *U.S. Public*, pg. 700
Major, James, V.P. & Gen. Mgr.--WFTS-TV, Tampa, FL; *U.S. Public*, pg. 1448
Major, R. Odie, Chm. Bd.--SunTrust Bank, Northeast Tennessee, Johnson City, TN; *U.S. Public*, pg. 1538
Major, Robert, Pres.--NationsCredit, Allentown, PA; *U.S. Public*, pg. 1165
Majorin, Erkki, Mng. Dir.--S.A. Comptoir Finlandais N.V., Brussels, Belgium; *Int'l*, pg. 457
Majorin, Erkki, Mng. Dir.--S.A. Enso N.V., Brussels, Belgium; *Int'l*, pg. 457
Mak, Caroline, Mng. Dir.--Dantas Holdings Ltd., Sha Tin, Hong Kong; *Int'l*, pg. 704
Mak, Rosanna, Dir. & Gen. Mgr.--Jardine Matheson (China) Ltd., Beijing, China; *Int'l*, pg. 705
Makabe, Tetsuo, Gen. Mgr.--Long-Term Credit Bank of Japan - Americas Division, New York, NY; *Int'l*, pg. 816
Makarewicz, David C., Pres. & Chief Oper. Officer--J2, Inc., Deerfield, IL; *U.S. Private*, pg. 598
Makarewicz, Stephen E., Pres. & Chief Oper. Officer--J.M. Tull Metals Co., Inc., Norcross, GA; *U.S. Public*, pg. 879
Makarius, E., Mng. Dir.--OMRON Electronics Ges.m.b.H., Vienna, Austria; *Int'l*, pg. 1006
Makela, Erkki, Mng. Dir.--KONE Elevators, Kiev, Ukraine; *Int'l*, pg. 747
Makes, N.T., V.P. & Gen. Mgr.--Turner Construction Company, Shelton, CT; *U.S. Public*, pg. 1645
Maki, Glen, Pres.--Maki Home Center, Inc., Lunenburg, MA; *U.S. Private*, pg. 698
Maki, Koichi, Pres.--ORIX Insurance Services Corporation, Tokyo, Japan; *Int'l*, pg. 1008
Makimura, Ike, Gen. Mgr.--Sakata Inx USA Corp., Torrance, CA; *Int'l*, pg. 1311
Makin, Ed, Pres. & Chief Exec. Officer--Domino Sugar Corporation, New York, NY; *Int'l*, pg. 1356
Makinen, Eero, Pres.--Kvaerner Masa Marine Inc., Vancouver, Canada; *Int'l*, pg. 771
Makinen, Heikki, Mng. Dir.--Schauman Panels Ltd., Mersey, United Kingdom; *Int'l*, pg. 1429
Makinen, Heimo, Pres.--Montgomery Elevator International Company, Moline, IL; *Int'l*, pg. 746
Makinen, Risto, Mng. Dir.--Nokia Mobile Phones Produktions GmbH, Bochum, Germany; *Int'l*, pg. 952
Makino, Arata, Pres.--Japan Polychem Corp., Tokyo, Japan; *Int'l*, pg. 871
Makita, H., Gen. Mgr.--The Daiei, Inc., Shanghai, China; *Int'l*, pg. 364
Makita, Shinichiro, Pres.--GAEART Kumagai Co., Ltd., Tokyo, Japan; *Int'l*, pg. 763
Makitalo, Osten, Chief Exec. Officer--Telia Research AB, Haninge, Sweden; *Int'l*, pg. 1374
Makkonen, G., Pres.--Skanska Oy, Helsinki, Finland; *Int'l*, pg. 1261
Makowski, Dieter, Dir.-Adv.--Prisma-Verlag GmbH & Co. KG, Dusseldorf, Germany; *Int'l*, pg. 190
Makowski, Karen, Pres. & Chief Exec. Officer--Key Bank of Vermont, Burlington, VT; *U.S. Public*, pg. 954
Malach, Ken, Pres.--Stephen Gould of Arizona, Inc., Tempe, AZ; *U.S. Private*, pg. 467
Malafronte, Thomas J., Pres.--Amerchol Corporation, Edison, NJ; *U.S. Public*, pg. 1667
Malchow, Dennis, Pres.--The Martin-Brower Company, Lombard, IL; *Int'l*, pg. 376
Malcolm, Bruce, Pres.--Electro Optical Ind., Santa Barbara, CA; *U.S. Private*, pg. 228
Maldidier, Ch., Chief Oper. Officer--Elf Idrocarburi Italiana SPA, Rome, Italy; *Int'l*, pg. 446
Maldonado Elizondo, Carlos, Pres.--Industrial Papelera Mexicana S.A. de C.V., Uruapan, Mexico; *Int'l*, pg. 330
Maldonado Elizondo, Carlos, Pres.--Papelera de Chihuahua S.A. de C.V., Chihuahua, Mexico; *Int'l*, pg. 330
Maldonado, Hector, Mgr.--Shepler's Rio Grande Steel, Pharr, TX; *U.S. Public*, pg. 413
Malec, John W., Pres.--Great Western Steel, Chicago, IL; *U.S. Public*, pg. 1640
Malecki, Leszek, Chief Oper. Officer--AOK-Nerval Cosmetics & Perfumes GmbH, Dusseldorf, Germany; *Int'l*, pg. 609
Malecki, Steve, Branch Dir.--N.G. Bailey & Co. Ltd.-Sheffield Branch, Sheffield, United Kingdom; *Int'l*, pg. 132
Malenick, Donald H., Pres.--I.H. Schlezinger, Inc., Columbus, OH; *U.S. Public*, pg. 1780
Malerba, James J., Pres. & Chief Oper. Officer--Key Bank of Washington, Tacoma, WA; *U.S. Public*, pg. 954
Maleska, Martin, Pres.--Simon & Schuster International & Business & Professional Group, Paramus, NJ; *U.S. Private*, pg. 778
Malet, Jean Piere, Dir.-Mercure--Societe Internationale des Hotels Novotel, Evry, France; *Int'l*, pg. 21
Malhotra, Arun, Dr., Gen. Mgr.--Aiwa Research & Development, Fremont, CA; *Int'l*, pg. 1280
Malhotra, I.S., Chm. Bd. & Mng. Dir.--Keystone Valve (India) PVT. Ltd., Baroda, India; *U.S. Public*, pg. 1650
Malik, Gerald I., Pres. & Chief Exec. Officer--Ameritech Development Corporation, Chicago, IL; *U.S. Public*, pg. 98
Malizia, R., Mng. Dir.--Ballast Nedam Grond en Wegen Projecten B.V., Amstelveen, Netherlands; *Int'l*, pg. 133
Malka, Martti, Mng. Dir.--Nokia Mobile Phones Australia Pty. Ltd., Bondi Junction, Australia; *Int'l*, pg. 952
Malkasian, Greg, Gen. Mgr.--Corrugated Container Div.-Columbia Plant, Columbia, SC; *U.S. Public*, pg. 1520
Malkia, Hannu, V.P.--Valmet Corporation Winders, Jarvenpaa, Finland; *Int'l*, pg. 1448
Malkin, Alan, Mgr.--Stephen Gould of Ohio, Corp., Cleveland, OH; *U.S. Private*, pg. 467
Malkki, Raimo, Chief Oper. Officer--Lappeenranta Paper Mill, Lappeenranta, Finland; *Int'l*, pg. 1428
Mallace, Eric, Gen. Mgr.--Corro Clark Coatings Ltd., Scunthorpe, United Kingdom; *Int'l*, pg. 715
Mallandt, Peter, Pres.--Decibel Products, Inc., Dallas, TX; *U.S. Public*, pg. 46
Mallard, R., Mgr.-Bus. Unit--Long Manufacturing Ltd., Cambridge, Canada; *Int'l*, pg. 815
Mallardi, Michael P., Pres.--Capital Cities/ABC Broadcast Group, New York, NY; *U.S. Public*, pg. 511
Mallaret, J., Chief Oper. Officer--G.I.E. Ipedex International, Rueil-Malmaison, France; *Int'l*, pg. 1361
Mallas, Joseph T., Exec. Dir.--Industrial Clinic, Hapeville, GA; *U.S. Public*, pg. 1715
Malle, Volkar, Mng. Dir.--Water Engineering Ltd., Banbury, United Kingdom; *Int'l*, pg. 399
Mallee, Joseph P., Pres.--Stokes-Merrill, Bristol, PA; *Int'l*, pg. 1379
Mallen, Gianni, Mgr.--Sanpaolo-London Branch, London, United Kingdom; *Int'l*, pg. 692
Mallett, Rick, Chief Fin. Officer--Hancock Manufacturing, Toronto, OH; *U.S. Private*, pg. 299
Mallin, Ed, Pres.--Compilers Plus Inc., Montvale, NJ; *U.S. Public*, pg. 70
Malling, James E., Pres.--Cigna International Finance Inc., Bloomfield, CT; *U.S. Public*, pg. 357
Malling, Joachim, Mng. Dir.--Munksgaard International Booksellers & Publishers Ltd., Copenhagen, Denmark; *Int'l*, pg. 197
Mallinson, Harry, Mgr.--Lotus Development Ltd., Staines, United Kingdom; *U.S. Public*, pg. 896
Mallo de la Calzada, Jose R., Mng. Dir.--Sulzer Sistemas e Instalaciones S.A., Madrid, Spain; *Int'l*, pg. 1306
Malloch, Gary N., Pres.--Chesebrough-Pond's Mfg. Co., Las Piedras, PR; *Int'l*, pg. 1435
Mallon, Bill, Mng. Dir.--Brian Pulfrey Ltd., Bingham, United Kingdom; *U.S. Public*, pg. 1267
Malloy, Dan, Pres.--IVHS Technologies Inc., San Diego, CA; *U.S. Public*, pg. 558
Malloy, J.B., Chm.--Smurfit Packaging Corporation, Saint Louis, MO; *Int'l*, pg. 1271
Malloy, Jack B., Gen. Mgr.--Container Div. (Highland), Highland, IL; *Int'l*, pg. 1269
Malloy, Kevin, Gen. Mgr.--The Kahler Hotel, Rochester, MN; *U.S. Public*, pg. 1537
Malloy, Kevin, Gen. Mgr.--Kahler Inn & Suites, Rochester, MN; *U.S. Public*, pg. 1537
Malloy, Kevin, Gen. Mgr.--Kahler Plaza Hotel, Rochester, MN; *U.S. Public*, pg. 1537
Malm. Thomas, Pres.--Volvo Espana, S.A., Madrid, Spain; *Int'l*, pg. 1477
Malm, Goran S., Pres. & Chief Exec. Officer--GE Medical Systems Asia Ltd., Tokyo, Japan; *U.S. Public*, pg. 713
Malm, Timothy O., Pres.--Fleischmann Malting Company, Inc., Minneapolis, MN; *U.S. Public*, pg. 128
Malmberg, Lars, Pres.--Distribution AB Dagab, Solna, Sweden; *Int'l*, pg. 272
Malmgren, J., Pres.--SBC Arbitech AB, Stockholm, Sweden; *Int'l*, pg. 1330
Malms, Christoph, Pres. & Chief Exec. Officer--ISL Marketing A.G., Lucerne, Switzerland; *Int'l*, pg. 394
Malmstrom, Kari, Chief Oper. Officer--KONE Elevators Export, Helsinki, Finland; *Int'l*, pg. 746
Malnight, Robert, Mgr.--Hercules Inc.-Savannah, Savannah, GA; *U.S. Public*, pg. 810
Malo, Jean Claude, Gen. Mgr.--DEMIX Beton/Agregats, Lasalle, Canada; *Int'l*, pg. 629
Malolos, Emmanuel C., Mgr.--Sandvik Philippines, Inc., Manila, Philippines; *Int'l*, pg. 1187
Malone, D.R., Gen. Mgr.--CHEMCENTRAL/San Antonio, San Antonio, TX; *U.S. Private*, pg. 232
Malone, Joseph L., Pres. & Chief Exec. Officer--First Union National Bank of Maryland, Rockville, MD; *U.S. Public*, pg. 640
Malone, Joseph L., Pres. & Chief Exec. Officer--First Union National Bank of Washington, Washington, DC; *U.S. Public*, pg. 640
Malone, Kevin, V.P. & Gen. Mgr.--WMTX-AM, Tampa, FL; *U.S. Public*, pg. 385
Malone, Kevin, V.P. & Gen. Mgr.--WMTX-FM, Tampa, FL; *U.S. Public*, pg. 385
Malone, Ma, Chief Rep.--MetLife Beijing Representative Office, Beijing, China; *U.S. Private*, pg. 738
Malone, Mark, Gen. Mgr.--Bunzl Packaging Consultants Inc., Alsip, IL; *Int'l*, pg. 233
Malone, Pat, Pres.--Gucci America Inc., Secaucus, NJ; *Int'l*, pg. 686
Maloney, Raymond E., Pres. & Chief Exec. Officer--Intertec Publishing, Overland Park, KS; *U.S. Public*, pg. 1327
Maloney, Raymond E., Pres. & Chief Oper. Officer--Farm Press, Clarksdale, MS; *U.S. Public*, pg. 1328
Maloney, William J., Pres. & Chief Exec. Officer--Rockefeller Center Development Corporation, New York, NY; *Int'l*, pg. 873
Maloof, Richard C., Pres.--Bird Roofing Products, Inc., Norwood, MA; *Int'l*, pg. 1171
Maloof, Thomas A., Pres. & Chief Oper. Officer--Foundation Health, A California Health Plan, Rancho Cordova, CA; *U.S. Public*, pg. 678
Malori, Gerry, V.P.--New Process Gear Div., East Syracuse, NY; *U.S. Public*, pg. 353
Malott, T.J, Pres. & Chief Exec. Officer--Siemens Energy & Automation Inc., Alpharetta, GA; *Int'l*, pg. 1245
Malowanczyk, Leon, Gen. Mgr.--Banque Leumi France S.A., Paris, France; *Int'l*, pg. 150
Maloy, Foy, Publisher--Fernandina Beach News Leader, Inc., Fernandina Beach, FL; *U.S. Public*, pg. 1175
Malpas, Robert, Chm. Bd.--Eurotunnel Finance Limited, London, United Kingdom; *Int'l*, pg. 466
Malpas, Robert, Chm. Bd.--Le Shuttle Holidays Limited, London, United Kingdom; *Int'l*, pg. 466
Malsbender, Dr., Mng. Dir.--Geschaftsbereich Schiess-Wotan, Dusseldorf, Germany; *Int'l*, pg. 861
Malschaert, Alain, Chief Oper. Officer--Aalst Local Head Office, Aalst, Belgium; *Int'l*, pg. 147
Maltone, Buddy, Gen. Mgr.--Holiday RV Superstores West, Inc., Bakersfield, CA; *U.S. Public*, pg. 830
Maltos, Manuel Villar, Gen. Mgr.--Forjacero, Ramos Arizpe, Mexico; *Int'l*, pg. 66
Maltz, Alan, Exec. V.P.--TSL, New York, NY; *U.S. Public*, pg. 257
Malvaso, James J., Pres. & Chief Oper. Officer--The Raymond Corporation, Greene, NY; *Int'l*, pg. 123
Malyan, Richard H., Pres.-Europe, Middle East & Africa Div.--Bristol-Myers International Group, New York, NY; *U.S. Public*, pg. 254
Malys, G.J., Pres.--Amax Energy, Inc., Englewood, CO; *U.S. Public*, pg. 470
Mamiya, Teruo, Gen. Mgr.--The Sumitomo Bank, Ltd.-Dusseldorf Branch, Dusseldorf, Germany; *Int'l*, pg. 1309
Mamo, Dave, Chief Oper. Officer--LINC Financial Services, Inc., Chicago, IL; *U.S. Public*, pg. 996
Mamoli, F., Pres.--Merck Sharp & Dohme GmbH, Vienna, Austria; *U.S. Public*, pg. 1092
Mampell, P., Mng. Dir.--EMI Records (Switzerland) AG, Zurich, Switzerland; *Int'l*, pg. 427
Mamsch, Helmut, Chief Exec. Officer--BRENNTAG Eurochem GmbH, Essen, Germany; *Int'l*, pg. 1458
Mamsch, Helmut, Chm. Bd.--Stinnes Corporation, Tarrytown, NY; *Int'l*, pg. 1460
Man, Chang Siew, Mng. Dir.--Tractors Machinery International Pte. Ltd., Singapore, Singapore; *Int'l*, pg. 1251
Manabe, Ken, Gen. Mgr.--CAPCO U.S.A., Inc. (Detroit), Farmington Hills, MI; *Int'l*, pg. 279
Manabe, Nobukatsu, Mng. Dir.--NEC Semiconductors Singapore Pte. Ltd., Singapore, Singapore; *Int'l*, pg. 900
Manara, Guiseppe, Gen. Mgr.--Pioneer Hi-Bred Italia S.p.A., Sissa, Italy; *U.S. Public*, pg. 1299
Manassah, Edward E., Pres. & Publisher--The Courier-Journal Louisville Times Co., Louisville, KY; *U.S. Public*, pg. 700
Manasse, Robert S., Exec. V.P.-U.S. Opers.--Coe & Clerici, Inc., Washington, DC; *Int'l*, pg. 304
Manassei, Umberto, Acting Dir.--Vista Multi Method, Rome, Italy; *U.S. Public*, pg. 222
Manavanicharoen, V., Mng. Dir.--Johnson & Johnson Medical Thailand, Bangkok, Thailand; *U.S. Public*, pg. 931
Manby, Phillip, V.P.-Opers.--Culinary Foods Group, Glendale, CA; *Int'l*, pg. 917
Manca, Jimmy, Sls. Rep.--T.V. Overseas, S.R.L., Rome, Italy; *Int'l*, pg. 1282
Manceau, Claude, Chief Oper. Officer--Societe d'Etudes et de Constructions Electroniques (SECRE), Paris, France; *Int'l*, pg. 706
Manchester, Sherri, Gen. Mgr.--Koslow's, Dallas, TX; *U.S. Public*, pg. 597
Manchharam, Kumar, Dir.--Mecomb Singapore Limited, Singapore, Singapore; *Int'l*, pg. 1251
Mancinelli, Victor A., Pres.--Mustang Manufacturing Company, Inc., Owatonna, MN; *U.S. Public*, pg. 704
Mancini, Antonio, Chief Oper. Officer--Hospal S.p.A., Bologna, Italy; *Int'l*, pg. 668
Mancini, Antonio J.P., Pres. & Gen. Mgr.--AlliedSignal Automotive Ltda-Campinas Plant, Sao Paulo, Brazil; *U.S. Public*, pg. 53
Mancuso, Lauren, Sr. V.P. & Reg. Dir.--Arnold Advertising, Albany, NY; *U.S. Private*, pg. 84
Mancuso, Lauren, Sr. V.P. & Reg. Dir.--Arnold Advertising, Rochester, NY; *U.S. Private*, pg. 84
Mancuso, Paul A., Pres.--Calvin Klein Cosmetics Company, New York, NY; *Int'l*, pg. 1435
Mandarich, David D., Pres.--Richmond Homes, Inc. I, Denver, CO; *U.S. Public*, pg. 1025
Mandel, Leon, Publr.--AutoWeek, Detroit, MI; *U.S. Private*, pg. 284
Mandell, James M., V.P. & Gen. Mgr.--DENTSPLY Ceramco, Burlington, NJ; *U.S. Public*, pg. 499
Mandelot, Pedro, Pres.--Dynapac Equipamentos Industriais Ltd., Sao Paulo, Brazil; *Int'l*, pg. 1420
Mander, Christopher, Mng. Dir.--Inter-Continental Hotels Corporation, London, United Kingdom; *Int'l*, pg. 1178
Manderfield, Nick, Gen. Mgr.--New Market Foods, Haverhill, United Kingdom; *Int'l*, pg. 1170
Manders, J., Div. Mgr.--DMV International, Veghel, Netherlands; *Int'l*, pg. 254

Mandeville, C. Robert, Chief Opr. Officer--Investment Leasing Services, Inc., Chicago, IL; *U.S. Private*, pg. 1073

Mandeville, C. Robert, Chief Opr. Officer--NRG NuFuel Co., Chicago, IL; *U.S. Private*, pg. 1073

Mandeville, Reba, Chief Exec. Officer--First National Bank of Clifton Forge, Clifton Forge, VA; *U.S. Public*, pg. 1039

Mandorf, Kaj, Pres.--AB Kaj Mandorf, Molnlycke, Sweden; *Int'l*, pg. 678

Mandrup, John, Gen. Mgr.--Avia Radio A/S, Dragor, Denmark; *U.S. Public*, pg. 2

Mane, Jose Enrique L., Mgr.--Tarragona Terminal, Tarragona, Spain; *U.S. Public*, pg. 693

Maneely, Dan, Gen. Mgr.--Courtaulds Structural Composites Inc., Bennington, VT; *Int'l*, pg. 338

Manenbach, Robert, Mgr.-Office--Harland Bartholomew & Associates Inc., Chesterfield, MO; *U.S. Private*, pg. 842

Manene, L., Gen. Mgr.--NRI Iberica, S.A., Barcelona, Spain; *U.S. Public*, pg. 457

Maness, Priscilla E., V.P.--McRae Financial and Leasing Div., Mount Gilead, NC; *U.S. Public*, pg. 1073

Maney, Steven R., Pres. & Chief Exec. Officer--Regions Bank/Barrow County, Winder, GA; *U.S. Public*, pg. 1371

Manez, Raymond, Chief Oper. Officer--Dynarad Corporation, Deer Park, NY; *U.S. Public*, pg. 494

Mang, W.P.E., Pres. & Chief Exec. Officer--Federal Industries Metals Group, Etobicoke, Canada; *Int'l*, pg. 1150

Mangan, Daniel A., Pres.--Valex Corp., Ventura, CA; *U.S. Public*, pg. 1375

Mangano, Sandy, Mgr.-Division--Haleyville Drapery Manufacturing Division, Salisbury, NC; *U.S. Public*, pg. 491

Mangeot, J-P, Gen. Mgr.--Laboratories Wellcome S.A., Paris, France; *Int'l*, pg. 553

Mangini, Guillermo, Dir.--Reinter BC, Buenos Aires, Argentina; *Int'l*, pg. 1502

Mango, Joe, Gen. Mgr.--Guelph Products, Guelph, Canada; *U.S. Public*, pg. 354

Mangold, J., Dr., Pres. & Chief Exec. Officer--Daimler-Benz InterServices (debis) AG, Berlin, Germany; *Int'l*, pg. 367

Mangold, Klaus, Chief Exec.--Daimler-Benz InterServices (debis) AG, Stuttgart, Germany; *Int'l*, pg. 367

Mangold, Klaus, Gen. Mgr.--Rhodia A.G., Freiburg, Germany; *Int'l*, pg. 1112

Mangold, Stephen G., Pres.--Fleming Finance Corp., Oklahoma City, OK; *U.S. Public*, pg. 653

Mangold, Thomas, V.P. & Gen. Mgr.--Process & Analytical Instruments Div., Pittsburgh, PA; *U.S. Public*, pg. 100

Mangold, W. B., Pres.--Grabner Pacific Co., Santa Fe Springs, CA; *U.S. Private*, pg. 165

Mangs, Einor, Gen. Mgr.--Vickers Systems AB, Spanga, Sweden; *U.S. Public*, pg. 25

Manhas, Amar, V.P. & Mng. Dir.--M/A-COM Limited, Dunstable, United Kingdom; *U.S. Public*, pg. 8

Manhatton, R.A., Mgr.--Lindberg Heat Treating Co., Minneapolis, MN; *U.S. Public*, pg. 999

Manheimer, Robert, Pres. & Chief Exec. Officer--Bank of America, New York, NY; *U.S. Public*, pg. 180

Mani, R.S., Gen. Mgr.--India Photographic Company Limited, Bangalore, India; *U.S. Public*, pg. 552

Manickavasagam, Joe, Resident Rep.--The World Bank, Kathmandu, Nepal; *U.S. Private*, pg. 1189

Manilla, Francisco Perez, Chief Oper. Officer--Santander de Leasing, Madrid, Spain; *Int'l*, pg. 143

Manion, John P., Chm.--Periodical Publishers' Service Bureau, Inc., Sandusky, OH; *U.S. Private*, pg. 517

Maniscalco, Rosemary, Pres.--Uniforce Information Services, Woodbury, NY; *U.S. Public*, pg. 409

Manishi, Motoro, Chief Oper. Officer--Ahlstrom Sumiju K.K., Tokyo, Japan; *Int'l*, pg. 35

Mankert, Thomas, Gen. Mgr.--Kappler Europe, Ltd., Netherfield, United Kingdom; *U.S. Private*, pg. 607

Mankiewicz, D.J., Pres.--Amoco Australia Petroleum Company, Sydney, Australia; *U.S. Public*, pg. 102

Mankwa, Blaise, Country Mgr.--Standard Chartered Bank Tanzania Limited, Dar es Salaam, Tanzania; *Int'l*, pg. 1295

Manlay, Jacques, Chief Oper. Officer--Peugeot Automobile Nigeria Ltd., Kaduna, Nigeria; *Int'l*, pg. 1021

Manley, Mark, Mgr.-Plant--Gulf Coast Galvanizing Inc., Citronelle, AL; *U.S. Public*, pg. 159

Manley, Richard, Pres.--Vitro Services Corporation, Fort Walton Beach, FL; *U.S. Public*, pg. 1627

Manley, Wade, Branch Mgr.--Broder Bros. Co. of Dallas, Carrollton, TX; *U.S. Private*, pg. 171

Mann, Andrew, Pres.--The Cook Bates Division, Venice, FL; *Int'l*, pg. 815

Mann, Brian, Pres.--BA Futures, Incorporated, Chicago, IL; *U.S. Public*, pg. 180

Mann, Gary P., Gen. Mgr.--Martin Marietta Information Systems, Bethesda, MD; *U.S. Public*, pg. 1007

Mann, George, Plant Mgr.--Liqui-Box Film Div., Santa Ana, CA; *U.S. Public*, pg. 1000

Mann, Gerhard, Chief Exec. Officer & Gen. Mgr.--Bayerische Landesbank - London Branch, London, United Kingdom; *Int'l*, pg. 176

Mann, Godfrey, Mng. Dir.--TMD Direct, London, United Kingdom; *Int'l*, pg. 1342

Mann, H., Mng. Dir.--RHM Foods Limited, Windsor, United Kingdom; *Int'l*, pg. 1396

Mann, Ian, Gen. Mgr.--Nashua Photo Delmont Ltd., Newtownabbey, United Kingdom; *U.S. Public*, pg. 1152

Mann, J.C., Exec. Dir.--Morgan Grenfell (Guernsey, C.I.) Limited, Saint Peter Port, United Kingdom; *Int'l*, pg. 406

Mann, Jim, Pres.--Day International Textile Products, Greenville, SC; *U.S. Private*, pg. 56

Mann, John, Pres.--Soil Teq, Inc., Minnetonka, MN; *U.S. Public*, pg. 6

Mann, John, Jr., Pres.--Moline Accessories Company, Moline, IL; *Int'l*, pg. 746

Mann, Lindsay, Mng. Dir.--National Mutual Funds Management NZ Limited, Wellington, New Zealand; *Int'l*, pg. 909

Mann, M. J., Pres.--Alternative Remedial Technologies, Inc., Tampa, FL; *Int'l*, pg. 607

Mann, Marvin L., Chm. Bd.& Chief Exec. Officer--Lexmark International, Inc., Lexington, KY; *U.S. Public*, pg. 991

Mann, Paul, Pres.--First Tennessee Brokerage, Inc., Memphis, TN; *U.S. Public*, pg. 639

Mann, Peter, Gen. Mgr.--NBS Limited-Personalization Systems Division, Weybridge, United Kingdom; *Int'l*, pg. 898

Mann, Regan, Gen. Mgr.--Taylor Made Products, Gloversville, NY; *U.S. Private*, pg. 1070

Mann, Robert, Mgr.--Carolina Steel Service Center Plant, Versailles, KY; *U.S. Private*, pg. 214

Mann, Robert, Pres.--Hardman Division of Harcros Chemicals, Inc., Belleville, NJ; *Int'l*, pg. 598

Mann, Samuel J., Pres.--Inverness France, Paris, France; *U.S. Private*, pg. 574

Mann, Samuel J., Pres.--Inverness UK LTD., Slough, United Kingdom; *U.S. Private*, pg. 574

Mann, Samuel J., Pres.--ERI Laboratories, Fair Lawn, NJ; *U.S. Private*, pg. 574

Mann, Thomas, Gen. Mgr.--G.E. Capital Vendor Financial Services, Danbury, CT; *U.S. Public*, pg. 712

Mann, Timothy, Pres.--Swisher International Group, Inc., Darien, CT; *U.S. Public*, pg. 1543

Mann, Tom, Pres.--Pro/Mark, Manchester, CT; *U.S. Public*, pg. 867

Mann, Tom, Pres.--ITW Maple Roll Leaf, Windsor, Canada; *U.S. Public*, pg. 868

Mann, William J., Pres.--Southam Magazine and Information Group, North York, Canada; *Int'l*, pg. 631

Manna, Michael, V.P. & Gen. Mgr.--Grove Gear Div., Union Grove, WI; *U.S. Public*, pg. 1370

Manne, R., Opers. Mgr.--Senior Engineering Co.-Central Region, Florence, KY; *Int'l*, pg. 1222

Manne, Stanley, Chm. Bd. & Pres.--Brawny Plastics West, Santa Ana, CA; *U.S. Private*, pg. 166

Mannekens, R.D., Mng. Dir.--N.V. Nutricia Belgie, Bornem, Belgium; *Int'l*, pg. 992

Mannes, U., Dir.--Tyler Berlin GmbH, Berlin, Germany; *Int'l*, pg. 592

Mannesson, Magnus, Exec. Dir.--Machinery West, Hisings Karra, Sweden; *Int'l*, pg. 899

Mannesson, Magnus, Pres.--NCC Real Estate, Solna, Sweden; *Int'l*, pg. 899

Manning, Allan, Mng. Dir.--Denver Process Equipment, Ltd., Leatherhead, United Kingdom; *Int'l*, pg. 1326

Manning, Bill, V.P.--Boss de Mexico, S.A., Juarez, Mexico; *U.S. Private*, pg. 1142

Manning, Brien, Publisher--Irvine World News Newspaper Company, Irvine, CA; *U.S. Private*, pg. 575

Manning, Burt, Chm. Bd.--J. Walter Thompson Company, New York, NY; *Int'l*, pg. 1483

Manning, Lynne, Mng. Dir.--Kelly Services Canada, Ltd., Toronto, Canada; *U.S. Public*, pg. 949

Manning, Patrick J., Gen. Mgr.--Escast, Inc., Addison, IL; *U.S. Public*, pg. 612

Manning, Phil, Chief Fin. Officer--Willcox & Gibbs, Ltd., Braintree, United Kingdom; *U.S. Private*, pg. 1177

Manning, Thomas K., Pres. & Chief Exec. Officer--Titan Sales Corp., Kansas City, MO; *U.S. Public*, pg. 1391

Manning, Thomas K., Pres. & Chief Oper. Officer--Waverly Products Co., Kansas City, MO; *U.S. Public*, pg. 1391

Manning, Thomas K., Pres. & Chief Exec. Officer--Waverly Products Co., Ltd., Kansas City, MO; *U.S. Public*, pg. 1391

Mannix, P.C., Pres.--Eveready Battery Co., Saint Louis, MO; *U.S. Public*, pg. 1360

Mannlein, Bill, Gen. Mgr.--fp CameoColor, Inc., East Peoria, IL; *U.S. Private*, pg. 411

Mannola, Kari, Sr. Country Officer--Banque Indosuez, Helsinki, Finland; *Int'l*, pg. 314

Mannon, Wm., Chief Oper. Officer--Scope Energy Resources, Inc., Santa Monica, CA; *U.S. Public*, pg. 1444

Mannos, James, Pres.--Sony Microelectronics, San Jose, CA; *Int'l*, pg. 1284

Mano, Mitsutada, Pres.--Nissan Motor Corporation in Hawaii, Ltd., Honolulu, HI; *Int'l*, pg. 945

Manogue, R. A., Pres.--NextLevel Systems (Belgium), Brussels, Belgium; *U.S. Public*, pg. 716

Manos, Pete L., Pres. & Chief Exec. Officer--Leco Inc., Hyattsville, MD; *U.S. Public*, pg. 741

Manos, Pete L., Pres.--Cole Engineering, Inc., Hyattsville, MD; *U.S. Public*, pg. 741

Mansbach, Claude E., Mng. Dir.--S.A. John Crane Belgium N.V., Brussels, Belgium; *Int'l*, pg. 1339

Manscourt, Jacques, Dir. Gen.--NEC Electronics (France) S.A., Velizy-Villacoublay, France; *Int'l*, pg. 901

Manse, Dan, Pres.--KM Development Corp., Milwaukee, WI; *U.S. Private*, pg. 1206

Manse, Don, Pres.--Landmark Construction Corp., Milwaukee, WI; *U.S. Private*, pg. 1206

Mansell, Bill, Mgr.-Opers.--Furon Co., Bristol, RI; *U.S. Public*, pg. 689

Mansfield, Barry C., Pres.--BASF Ireland Limited, Blackrock, Ireland; *Int'l*, pg. 106

Mansfield, Mark, Mng. Dir.--Raymond Granite Co., Raymond, CA; *U.S. Private*, pg. 251

Mansfield, R.C., Mng. Dir.--Tyco Investments (Australia) Limited, Saint Leonards, Australia; *U.S. Public*, pg. 1651

Mansfield, Terry, Mng. Dir.--The National Magazine Company Ltd., London, United Kingdom; *U.S. Private*, pg. 518

Mansford, Keith R.L., Chm.--SmithKline Beecham Pharmaceuticals, Research Division, Betchworth, United Kingdom; *Int'l*, pg. 1264

Mansholt, Scott, Plant Mgr.--Sweetheart Cup Company Inc., Chicago, IL; *U.S. Private*, pg. 1058

Manson, Bob, Reg. Dir.--Custom Cheques of Canada, Vancouver, Canada; *Int'l*, pg. 1077

Manson, D.S., Mng. Dir.--MB Toyo Glass Nigeria Limited, Lagos, Nigeria; *Int'l*, pg. 267

Manson, David, Country Mgr.--Standard Chartered Bank (Vietnam), Hanoi, Vietnam; *Int'l*, pg. 1296

Manson, J.M., Gen. Mgr.--IRD Mechanalysis (Australia) Pty. Limited, Crows Nest, Australia; *U.S. Public*, pg. 790

Mansour, Juanita, Admin.--Guardian Care of Goldsboro, Goldsboro, NC; *U.S. Public*, pg. 1712

Mansson, Ola, Pres.--Skanska Teknik AB, Malmo, Sweden; *Int'l*, pg. 1261

Mansson, Rolf, Chief Oper. Officer--Osby Tvattutrusiningar AB, Osby, Sweden; *Int'l*, pg. 439

Manston, Harlan, Pres.--Square Butte Electric Cooperative, Grand Forks, ND; *U.S. Private*, pg. 751

Mantel, J.W., Gen. Mgr.--Marine Electronics Division, Rotterdam, Netherlands; *Int'l*, pg. 1151

Mantero, Ferdinando, Dir.--Alpine Center, s.r.l. (Berlitz), Milan, Italy; *U.S. Public*, pg. 221

Manuel, Jackie, Pres.--Travis County Title Company, Austin, TX; *U.S. Public*, pg. 441

Manuel, Patti S., Pres.--Sprint Business, Dallas, TX; *U.S. Public*, pg. 1501

Manuel, Thomas, Pres--Grain Flour Milling Co., Omaha, NE; *U.S. Public*, pg. 428

Manuel, Thomas L., Pres. & Chief Oper. Officer--ConAgra Trading Companies (CTC), Omaha, NE; *U.S. Public*, pg. 428

Manuel, Thomas L., Gen. Mgr.--Fruen Oat Milling Co., Omaha, NE; *U.S. Public*, pg. 428

Manuel, Tom, Pres.--ConAgra Trading & Processing Companies, Omaha, NE; *U.S. Public*, pg. 428

Manuel, Wes A., Mgr.-Opers.--Snyder-Crown, Inc., Marked Tree, AR; *U.S. Private*, pg. 1011

Manus, Sam, Plant Superintendant--General Shale Products Corp.-Woodbury Concrete Div., Woodbury, TN; *Int'l*, pg. 844

Manwaring, Jay R., Pres.--Zero Enclosures, North Salt Lake, UT; *U.S. Public*, pg. 1791

Manz, George, Pres. & Chief Oper. Officer--Data Control Systems, Gaithersburg, MD; *U.S. Public*, pg. 420

Manzagol, Jeff, Mng. Dir.--SKF South Africa (Pty.) Ltd., Boksburg, South Africa; *Int'l*, pg. 1159

Manzi, Anthony, Mng. Dir.--ESCO Pest Control Services, New York, NY; *Int'l*, pg. 656

Manzon, Ugo, Mng. Dir.-Milan--Armando Testa S.p.A, Rome, Italy; *Int'l*, pg. 1377

Maor, Galia, Chief Exec. Officer & Gen. Mgr.--Bank Leumi le-Israel B.M., Tel Aviv, Israel; *Int'l*, pg. 150

Maples, Gary D., Pres. & Chief Exec. Officer--M & I Bank, Superior, WI; *U.S. Public*, pg. 1050

Maples, Mary Jane, Exec. Editor-ESL--Bilingual/ESL Div., Lincolnwood, IL; *U.S. Public*, pg. 1635

Mapp, D., Mng. Dir.--Tom Cobleigh plc, Mansfield, United Kingdom; *Int'l*, pg. 1087

Mapp, David, Branch Mgr.--Circle Freight International USA, Carolina, PR; *U.S. Public*, pg. 370

Mapplebeck, J. R., Chm.--National Westminster Bank AG, Frankfurt/Main, Germany; *Int'l*, pg. 911

Marabut, Raul F., V.P. & Acct. Dir.--Hemisphere-Leo Burnett, Inc., Manila, Philippines; *U.S. Private*, pg. 184

Maraffi, Edoardo, Gen. Mgr.--Storage Technology Italia S.p.A., Rome, Italy; *U.S. Public*, pg. 1523

Maraffy, Patrick J., Chief Exec. Officer--Nexstar Pharmaceuticals, Inc., Boulder, CO; *U.S. Public*, pg. 1180

Marah, Edward A., Chief Exec. Officer--Irish Intercontinental Bank, Ltd., Dublin, Ireland; *Int'l*, pg. 761

Marain, Michel, Mill Mgr.--Houndouville Mill, Louviers, France; *U.S. Public*, pg. 673

Marais, Jean, Gen. Mgr.--PT Inter Pacific Bank, Jakarta, Indonesia; *Int'l*, pg. 343

Maran, S., Chief Oper. Officer--Lloyds Bowmaker Finance Ltd, Bournemouth, United Kingdom; *Int'l*, pg. 813

Marano, Antonio, Mng. Dir.--Creditanstalt Finanziaria S.p.A., Milan, Italy; *Int'l*, pg. 348

Maranon, Fernando, Dir.--Envases y Alimentacion Madrid, S.A., Madrid, Spain; *U.S. Public*, pg. 1386

Marantette, Lawrence R., Pres.--ANR Ren-Cen, Inc., Detroit, MI; *U.S. Public*, pg. 389

Marasca, Patrizia, Acting Dir.--Princeton Language Center, San Donato Milanese, Italy; *U.S. Public*, pg. 222

Marashlian, Zohrab B., Pres.--Perini-Metropolitan New York Div., Hawthorne, NY; *U.S. Public*, pg. 1278

Maraziti, Charles A., Pres. & Chief Exec. Officer--United Jersey Credit Life Insurance Company, Princeton, NJ; *U.S. Public*, pg. 1528

Marberg, William, Pres. & Chief Exec. Officer--Wilcox Electric, Inc., Kansas City, MO; *Int'l*, pg. 1384

Marble, Stephen C., Pres. & Chief Exec. Officer--Nielsen Dillingham Builders, Inc., San Diego, CA; *U.S. Private*, pg. 333

Marbler, A., Chief Oper. Officer--Europcar Autovermietung GmbH, Hamburg, Germany; *Int'l*, pg. 1473

Marburger, Asusmus, Pres.--Fire Protection Industries, Inc., Bensalem, PA; *Int'l*, pg. 321

Marc, Francois, Pres. & Chief Exec. Officer--Iveco-Unic S.A., Trappes, France; *Int'l*, pg. 484

Marcant, Christophe, Mgr.-Reg.--Gensym Corporation, Western Regional Office, Boulder, CO; *U.S. Public*, pg. 731

Marcella, Ron, Mgr.--Procter & Gamble Inc., Hamilton, Canada; *U.S. Public*, pg. 1332

Marcemmi, Romano, Chief Exec. Officer--CCF Milan, Milan, Italy; *Int'l*, pg. 342

Marcenac, Laurent, Gen. Mgr.--Carbone of America, Ultra Carbon Div., Bay City, MI; *Int'l*, pg. 1028

March, W., Branch Mgr.--Kodak Fotoservice Gesellschaft m.b.H., Dornbirn, Austria; *U.S. Public*, pg. 553

Marchal, Jean-Francois, Sr. Country Officer--Banque Indosuez Belgique, Brussels, Belgium; *Int'l*, pg. 314

Marchand, Gerard, Vice Chm. & Chief Oper. Officer--EMC-Belgique, Brussels, Belgium; *Int'l*, pg. 459

Marchand, Gerard, Chm. & Chief Exec. Officer--Tessenderlo Chemie, Tessenderlo, Belgium; *Int'l*, pg. 459

Marchant, T.R., Mng. Dir.--Modo Merchants Ltd., Byfleet, United Kingdom; *Int'l*, pg. 886

Marcheggiani, Marco, V.P. & Gen. Mgr.--Valmet Inc.-Enerdy Division, Knoxville, TN; *Int'l*, pg. 1448

Marchesini, Frank, Gen. Mgr.--Mars Aircraft Services Co. of New Jersey, Teterboro, NJ; *U.S. Public*, pg. 1

Marchetti, Tom, Reg. Mgr.--Green Tree Acceptance, Inc., Sioux Falls, SD; *U.S. Public*, pg. 762

Marchetti, Tullio, Mng. Dir. & Dir.-Fin.--Compania Nacional De Direcciones Automotrices, S.A. De C.V., Mexico, Mexico; *U.S. Public*, pg. 724

Marchetto, Maurizio, Dr., Gen. Mgr--DeKalb Italia, S.p.A., Venice, Italy; *U.S. Public*, pg. 493

Marchi, David, Pres. & Chief Oper. Officer--TLP East, Wilton, CT; *U.S. Public*, pg. 1224

Marchio, Angelo, Pres.--Riunione Adriatica di Sicurta S.p.A., Milan, Italy; *Int'l*, pg. 61

Marchioli, Nelson J., Pres. & Sr. V.P.--El Pollo Loco, Irvine, CA; *U.S. Public*, pg. 23

Marchioni, Allen, Chm. Bd., Pres. & Chief Exec. Officer--William Morrow & Co., Inc., New York, NY; *U.S. Private*, pg. 515

Marchioni, Allen A., Pres.--Wilmor Warehouse & Shipping Co., Inc., Fairfield, NJ; *U.S. Private*, pg. 516

Marcic, Irene S., Chief Fin. Officer--T.F. Cushing, Inc., West Springfield, MA; *U.S. Public*, pg. 141

Marcom, Mike, Mgr.--Rowan Drilling (U.K.) Limited, London, United Kingdom; *U.S. Public*, pg. 1410

Marconi, Robert C., Pres.--AAllied Die Casting Mfg., Inc., Franklin Park, IL; *U.S. Private*, pg. 903

Marconi, V., Mng. Dir.--NMB Italia S.r.l., Milan, Italy; *Int'l*, pg. 868

Marcos, Juan, Country Mgr.--Autodesk S.A., Barcelona, Spain; *U.S. Public*, pg. 149

Marcott, Wilbur, Gen. Mgr.--Ennis Business Forms of Kansas, Inc., Fort Scott, KS; *U.S. Public*, pg. 583

Marcotte, Brian W.G., Pres.--Unocal Thailand, Bangkok, Thailand; *U.S. Public*, pg. 1698

Marcovaldi, Maurizio, Mng. Dir.--CESI Centro Elaborazioni e Studi Informatici S.p.A., Rome, Italy; *Int'l*, pg. 1365

Marcum, Joseph L., Chm. Bd.--The Ohio Casualty Insurance Group, Hamilton, OH; *U.S. Public*, pg. 1214

Marcus, Barbara A., Pres.--Trumpet Book Clubs, New York, NY; *U.S. Public*, pg. 1440

Marcus, Jerry, V.P. & Gen. Mgr.--KRIV, Houston, TX; *Int'l*, pg. 926

Marcus, Leonard, Pres. & Chief Oper. Officer--Federated Merchandising, New York, NY; *U.S. Public*, pg. 618

Marcus, Roger, Chief Exec. Officer--Congoleum Corporation, Trenton, NJ; *U.S. Public*, pg. 69

Marcus, Roger S., Pres. & Chief Exec. Officer--Congoleum Corporation, Mercerville, NJ; *U.S. Public*, pg. 69

Marcus, Stephen, Pres.--SelectRehab, Mechanicsburg, PA; *U.S. Public*, pg. 839

Marcus, Steve, Pres.--Marcus Hotel Corp., Milwaukee, WI; *U.S. Public*, pg. 1044

Marcus, Steven, V.P.--Nutri-Tonic Div., Farmingdale, NY; *U.S. Public*, pg. 494

Marcus, Steven, V.P.--Rejuvia Prod. Group, Farmingdale, NY; *U.S. Public*, pg. 494

Marcussen, Jens M., Pres.--Kvaerner Incineration A/S, Gjeving, Norway; *Int'l*, pg. 769

Marcy, Raymond, Pres. & Chief Exec. Officer--Interim Services (Canada) Ltd., Montreal, Canada; *U.S. Public*, pg. 892

Marcyes, Alan D., Pres.--First American Bank N.A., Saint Cloud, MN; *U.S. Private*, pg. 167

Marden, James L., Pres.--D.P. Fitness, Opelika, AL; *U.S. Public*, pg. 1354

Marder, Michael, Gen. Mgr.--WHYN, Springfield, MA; *U.S. Public*, pg. 385

Mardis, Wilbur, Dir.-Research--Reichhold Chemicals Div., Buffalo, NY; *Int'l*, pg. 370

Mareck, Bill, Mgr.--Barrick Gold, Kirkland Lake, Canada; *Int'l*, pg. 169

Marek, Larry T., Pres.--Allen-Lewis Manufacturing Co., Inc., Denver, CO; *U.S. Public*, pg. 1554

Marengo, M., Reg. Mgr.--Gema Volstatic Industrial Powder Systems (Italy), Milan, Italy; *U.S. Public*, pg. 868

Mareno, Paul, Mgr.--Southern Electric Supply Co., Inc., Mobile, AL; *Int'l*, pg. 1107

Marenzi, Gary, Pres.--MGM/UA Telecommunications Group, Santa Monica, CA; *U.S. Public*, pg. 1102

Mares, Nick, Pres.--Cummings-Moore Graphite Co., Detroit, MI; *U.S. Private*, pg. 87

Mares, Raymond, Plant Mgr.--General Tire Div., Bryan, OH; *Int'l*, pg. 327

Marfadia, Nosh, Pres.--Topa Insurance Company, Los Angeles, CA; *U.S. Private*, pg. 1091

Margain, Carlos A., Chief Oper. Officer--Axel Johnson de Mexico SA de CV, Mexico, Mexico; *Int'l*, pg. 711

Margerison, Rick, Pres.--Briggs Weaver Vinson, Dallas, TX; *U.S. Private*, pg. 963

Margeuson, R. W., Pres.--Composite Thread Protectors, Inc., Houston, TX; *U.S. Private*, pg. 963

Margolis, David, Pres.--Winners Apparel Ltd., Toronto, Canada; *U.S. Public*, pg. 1557

Margossian, Kenneth M., Pres. & Chief Oper. Officer--Commonwealth Gas Co., Cambridge, MA; *U.S. Public*, pg. 415

Marguez, Jose-Antonio, Mng. Dir.--Nokia Mobile Phones, Madrid, Spain; *Int'l*, pg. 952

Marianetti, Ronald, Mng. Dir.--Delredo S.A. de C.V., Mexico, Mexico; *U.S. Public*, pg. 721

Mariani, Gary, Pres.--The Winn Art Group, Ltd., Seattle, WA; *U.S. Public*, pg. 503

Mariani, John, Chief Exec. Officer--Banfi Product Corp, Old Brookville, NY; *U.S. Private*, pg. 113

Mariani, M., Reg. Mgr.--Air France (Northeast Region), New York, NY; *Int'l*, pg. 560

Marianno, Eugenio, Mng. Dir.--ISS Sulamericana Comercial Ltda., Sao Paulo, Brazil; *Int'l*, pg. 657

Mariano, Robert, Pres. & Chief Exec. Officer--Dominick's Finer Foods, Northlake, IL; *U.S. Private*, pg. 1202

Mariategui, Francisco, Sr. Brand Mgr.--Gillette de Peru S.C., Lima, Peru; *U.S. Public*, pg. 744

Marichal, Jo, Pres.--Wossinger Zement, Walzbuchtal, Germany; *Int'l*, pg. 789

Marici, Edward, V.P., Dir.-Mktg.--Porta Systems Co., Charlotte, NC; *U.S. Public*, pg. 1317

Marie, Jacques, Chief Exec. Officer--Dim S.A., Lavallois Perret, France; *U.S. Public*, pg. 1434

Marien, Katherine C., Pres. & Chief Oper. Officer--Allied Capital Lending Corporation, Washington, DC; *U.S. Public*, pg. 48

Marienau, John, Pres.--ICI Katalco, Villa Park, IL; *Int'l*, pg. 664

Marier, Guy, Pres.--Telebec Ltee, Anjou, Canada; *Int'l*, pg. 116

Marin, Jon, Dir.--FCA!BMZ CID Bilbao, Bilbao, Spain; *Int'l*, pg. 469

Marin, Martha, V.P.-Media--Leo Burnett Columbiana, S.A., Bogota, Colombia; *U.S. Private*, pg. 185

Marin, Richard, Pres.--BT Private Clients Group, New York, NY; *U.S. Public*, pg. 185

Marine, Ignacio Bayon, Chm. & Chief Exec. Officer--Citroen Hispana S.A., Pontevedra, Spain; *Int'l*, pg. 1020

Marinelli, Davide, Mng. Dir.--Anacomp Italia, Milan, Italy; *U.S. Public*, pg. 107

Maringer, M., Mgr.-Fin.--Packard Electric Vas Kft, Szombathely, Hungary; *U.S. Public*, pg. 723

Maringer, Michael, Mng. Dir.--Packard Electric Burgenland Ges.m.b.H., Grosspetersdorf, Austria; *U.S. Public*, pg. 723

Marini, Alex P., Pres.--Hydromechanics Div., Erie, PA; *U.S. Public*, pg. 1794

Marini, Alex P., Pres.--Zurn Plumbing Products Group, Erie, PA; *U.S. Public*, pg. 1794

Marini, David P., Pres.--Trilog, Inc., Philadelphia, PA; *U.S. Public*, pg. 362

Marino, David J., Pres.--Penright!, Fremont, CA; *U.S. Public*, *pg. 1573*

Marino, John T., Pres.--United Metering Inc., Long Island City, NY; *U.S. Public*, pg. 1692

Marino, Louis, First V.P.--RNBNY-Buenos Aires Office, Buenos Aires, Argentina; *U.S. Public*, pg. 1381

Marino, Robert J., Pres. & Gen. Mgr.-Houston Cellular Telephone Co., Houston--LIN Cellular Group, Kirkland, WA; *U.S. Public*, pg. 11

Marino, V. James, V.P. & Head of Professional Channel--Helene Curtis U.S.A. Professional, Chicago, IL; *Int'l*, pg. 1434

Marino, V.J., Pres. & Chief Oper. Officer--Ullrich Copper, Inc., Kenilworth, NJ; *U.S. Public*, pg. 677

Mario, Pretti, Pres.--Sagit S.p.A., Milan, Italy; *Int'l*, pg. 1438

Mario, Ronald J., Pres.--COMSAT Mobile Communications, Clarksburg, MD; *U.S. Public*, pg. 424

Marion, Donald, V.P. & Gen. Mgr.-KRQR--CBS Radio Div., New York, NY; *U.S. Public*, pg. 274

Marion, Jean, Mgr.--Banque Indosuez, Central, Hong Kong; *Int'l*, pg. 314

Marion, Jesse R., Exec. V.P. & Dir.--Datatel, Inc., Houston, TX; *U.S. Public*, pg. 1454

Marion, Jesse R., Pres.--Seitel Data Corp., Houston, TX; *U.S. Public*, pg. 1454

Marion, Ron, Mgr.--Westco Products/Sacramento, Sacramento, CA; *Int'l*, pg. 244

Marioni, Fabio, Representative--Union de Banques Suisses, Monte Carlo, Monaco; *Int'l*, pg. 1441

Marischen, Robert J., Pres.--HSI Aviation, Inc., Springfield, MO; *U.S. Public*, pg. 849

Marischka, Gerhard, Mng. Dir.--ISS Central Europe GesmbH, Vienna, Austria; *Int'l*, pg. 656

Marius, Steen, Mng. Dir.--Elkem Materials, Kristiansand, Norway; *Int'l*, pg. 447

Mariwala, Sanjay, Mng. Dir.--Kancor Flavours and Extracts Limited, Cochin, India; *U.S. Public*, pg. 1067

Marjamaa, Ilpo, Div. Mgr.--Montgomery Escalator Division, Moline, IL; *Int'l*, pg. 746

Mark, Lothar, Mng. Dir.--Metallbank GmbH, Frankfurt/Main, Germany; *Int'l*, pg. 861

Markakis, Eva, V.P. & Mgr.--City National Bank - Studio City Office, Studio City, CA; *U.S. Public*, pg. 381

Markee, Richard L., Pres.--Kids "R" Us, Paramus, NJ; *U.S. Public*, pg. 1626

Markee, Richard L., Pres.--Babies "R" Us, Paramus, NJ; *U.S. Public*, pg. 1626

Marker, E.F. Ted, Mill Mgr.--Bridgend Paper Mill, Bridgend, United Kingdom; *U.S. Public*, pg. 672

Markert, William D., Gen. Mgr.--Frontier Communications of Viroqua, Inc., Viroqua, WI; *U.S. Public*, pg. 684

Markey, Jonathan H., Pres. & Chief Oper. Officer--Bergen Record Corp., Hackensack, NJ; *U.S. Private*, pg. 693

Markey, Jonathan H., Chief Oper. Officer--Magna Media Inc., Hackensack, NJ; *U.S. Private*, pg. 693

Markham, Charles R., Pres. & Chief Oper. Officer--State Gas & Oil Company Division, State College, PA; *U.S. Public*, pg. 1664

Markham, Lise, V.P. & Gen. Mgr.--KSWB-TV, Chula Vista, CA; *U.S. Public*, pg. 1636

Markhof, Theodor Mautner, Chief Exec.--Die Hager, Vienna, Austria; *U.S. Private*, pg. 678

Markin, David R., Pres.--CMC Kalamazoo Inc., Kalamazoo, MI; *U.S. Private*, pg. 1030

Markisohn, Jim, V.P. & Gen. Mgr.--Arrow/Schweber Electronics, Gaithersburg, MD; *U.S. Public*, pg. 134

Markle, Bill, Plant Mgr.--Worthington Cylinder Canada, Guelph, Canada; *U.S. Public*, pg. 1781

Markley, Buck, Gen. Mgr.--Manna Pro Partner L.P. (Limited Partnership), Denver, CO; *U.S. Private*, pg. 700

Markley, H. J., Mgr.--John Deere Dubuque Works, Dubuque, IA; *U.S. Public*, pg. 492

Markley, J. Thomas, Pres.--XEL Corporation, Aurora, CO; *U.S. Public*, pg. 1430

Markley, J.R., Chief Oper. Officer--R-V Chemicals Ltd., Nenagh, Ireland; *U.S. Public*, pg. 1332

Markley, Nolan, Gen. Mgr.--Dean Foods, Cambridge City, IN; *U.S. Public*, pg. 490

Markley, Thomas R., Sr. V.P.--CDI Corporation, Philadelphia, PA; *U.S. Public*, pg. 277

Marklin, George, Gen. Mgr.--Alliance Heater Company, Montgomery City, MO; *U.S. Private*, pg. 1153

Marklin, Hans-Rudolf, Chief Oper. Officer--Marklin AG, Liestal, Switzerland; *Int'l*, pg. 443

Marklund, Ingvar, Chief Oper. Officer--C.A. Electrolux, Caracas, Venezuela; *Int'l*, pg. 444

Marklund, Lena, Chief Officer--B&W Stormarknader AB, Stockholm, Sweden; *Int'l*, pg. 718

Marklund, Lief, Chief Oper. Officer--DAB Dental AB, Upplands Vasby, Sweden; *Int'l*, pg. 708

Marko, Neil, Pres.--Universal Industrial Products Co., Pioneer, OH; *U.S. Public*, pg. 1677

Markov, Miroslav, Mgr.--Sandvik-Bulgaria, Sofia, Bulgaria; *Int'l*, pg. 1186

Markowitz, Steven, Pres.--Rocky Mount Instruments, Inc., Rocky Mount, NC; *U.S. Public*, pg. 45

Markowitz, Steven, Pres.--VIR, Inc., Southampton, PA; *U.S. Public*, pg. 45

Markowitz, Steven, Pres.--Eastern Research, Inc., Moorestown, NJ; *U.S. Public*, pg. 45

Markowitz, Steven, Pres.--Linear Switch Corporation, Moorestown, NJ; *U.S. Public*, pg. 45

Markowsky, Don, Reg. Mgr.-Canada--Cruise Canada, Inc., Calgary, Canada; *U.S. Private*, pg. 178

Marks, David P., Pres.--Cigna Mezzanine Capital, Inc., Bloomfield, CT; *U.S. Public*, pg. 357

Marks, David P., Pres.--Cigna Advisory Partners, Inc., Bloomfield, CT; *U.S. Public*, pg. 357

Marks, E. Matthew, Pres. & Chief Exec. Officer--Intermodal Transportation Services, Inc., Parsippany, NJ; *Int'l*, pg. 1153

Marks, Francis, Chief Oper. Officer--Paris Securities, New York, NY; *U.S. Private*, pg. 839

Marks, Francis A., Pres.--Chem Free Corporation, Norcross, GA; *U.S. Public*, pg. 888

Marks, Frank, Pres.--Intelligent Enclosures Corp., Norcross, GA; *U.S. Public*, pg. 888

Marks, Horst, Mng. Dir.--O&K Rolltreppen GmbH, Hattingen Works, Hattingen, Germany; *Int'l*, pg. 516

Marks, P.J., Pres.--Gomar Manufacturing Co., Inc., Linden, NJ; *U.S. Public*, pg. 51

Marks, R. H., Chm.& Pres.--Tenneco International Finance Limited, London, United Kingdom; *U.S. Public*, pg. 1580

Marks, R.H., Chm.--Tenneco Europe, London, United Kingdom; *U.S. Public*, pg. 1580

Marks, Scott, Jr., Pres.--FCC National Bank, Wilmington, DE; *U.S. Public*, pg. 627

Marks, William L., Chm. Bd. & Chief Exec. Officer--Whitney National Bank, New Orleans, LA; *U.S. Public*, pg. 1766

Markson, Peter, Pres.--Baar & Beards, New York, NY; *U.S. Private*, pg. 839

Markus, Dennis W., Pres.--Transamerica HomeFirst, Inc., San Francisco, CA; *U.S. Public*, pg. 1630

Markwick, James C., Pres.--Manchester Guardian, New York, NY; *Int'l*, pg. 577

Markwort, Helmut, Editor-in-Chief--Focus Magazin Verlag, Munich, Germany; *Int'l*, pg. 233

Marlantes, Lorian L., Chm. Bd.--Rockefeller Group Telecommunications Services, Inc., New York, NY; *Int'l*, pg. 873

Marlar, Jerry L., Chief Oper. Officer--Intermedics Orthopedics, Inc., Austin, TX; *Int'l*, pg. 1307

Marlatt, James, Pres.--Titeflex Corporation, Springfield, MA; *Int'l*, pg. 1340

Marlatt, James W., Pres.--Titeflex Industrial Americas, Springfield, MA; *Int'l*, pg. 1340

Marlatt, James W., Pres.--VARI-FORM, Warren, MI; *Int'l*, pg. 1340

Marlatt, Terry L., Pres.--Carbomedics, Inc., Austin, TX; *Int'l*, pg. 1307

Marlborough, Donald J., Pres.--La Grange Foundry Inc., La Grange, MO; *U.S. Public*, pg. 142

Marler, Jim, Superintendant--Special Filaments Odenton, Odenton, MD; *U.S. Private*, pg. 77

Marlet, John, Country Mgr.--Compaq Computer A/S, Birkerod, Denmark; *U.S. Public*, pg. 418

Marlow, C.Guy, Pres.--Amersham Life Science, Inc., Arlington Heights, IL; *Int'l*, pg. 992

Marlow, J., Mgr.--Van Leeuwen Pipe and Tube Eastern Australia Pty. Ltd., Dandenong, Australia; *Int'l*, pg. 1450

Marlow, Paul, Mng. Dir.--Lambert Smith Hampton, Nottingham, United Kingdom; *Int'l*, pg. 797

Marlow, Ted, Pres.--Henri Bendel, New York, NY; *U.S. Public*, pg. 995

Marlowe, H.F., Jr., Plant Mgr.--Hickson Corporation, Hickory Grove, SC; *Int'l*, pg. 619

Marnati, Pietro, Chief Oper. Officer--BNP Leasing SPA, Milan, Italy; *Int'l*, pg. 164

Marohl, Rudolph O., Pres.--Central Research Laboratories, Red Wing, MN; *U.S. Public*, pg. 521

Marom, Chezi, Gen. Mgr.--Leumi Le-Israel (Latin America), Montevideo, Uruguay; *Int'l*, pg. 150

Marone, Joseph, Pres.--Sysco Food Services of Eastern Wisconsin, Jackson, WI; *U.S. Public*, pg. 1551

Maroney, Peter, Gen. Mgr.--KOIN-TV, Portland, OR; *U.S. Public*, pg. 983

Maroone, Michael E., Pres.-Car Div.--Maroone Automotive Group, Pembroke Pines, FL; *U.S. Public*, pg. 1379

Maroteaux, Patrick, Pres.--Societe Eurosucre S.N.C., Paris, France; *Int'l*, pg. 549

Marotta, N. G., Pres.--Custom Farm Seed, Momence, IL; *Int'l*, pg. 1435

Maroun, Joseph E., Pres.--Bristol-Myers International Group, New York, NY; *U.S. Public*, pg. 254

Marozsan, John R., Pres.--Aspen Publishers, Inc., Gaithersburg, MD; *Int'l*, pg. 1513

Marple, Allen C., Chm. Bd. & Pres.--Calvin Bullock, Ltd., Montreal, Canada; *Int'l*, pg. 1319

Marquardt, D., Gen. Mgr.--Stanley Drying Company, Stanley, WI; *U.S. Private*, pg. 301

Marquardt, Richard, Pres.--WEA Manufacturing, Olyphant, PA; *U.S. Public*, pg. 1612

Marquart, B., Mgr.--Swiss Bank Corporation, Buenos Aires, Argentina; *Int'l*, pg. 1330
Marquart, Clifford R., Pres.--East Smithfield Farms Inc., New Holland, PA; *Int'l*, pg. 201
Marquart, Donald E., Gen. Dir.--BMG Ariola S.A. de C.V. (Mexico), Mexico, Mexico; *Int'l*, pg. 192
Marques, A.S., Gen. Mgr.--Barclays Bank PLC, Lisbon, Portugal; *Int'l*, pg. 166
Marques, Albano Pires, Mng. Dir.--Esselte Meto Portugal LDA, Oeiras, Portugal; *Int'l*, pg. 461
Marques, Dr. Anibal, Chief Oper. Officer--Heller Factoring Portuguesa S.A., Lisbon, Portugal; *Int'l*, pg. 521
Marqueta, Alfonso Castro, Gen. Mgr.--Technoflow Iberica SA, Tauste, Spain; *Int'l*, pg. 1341
Marquez, Mike, Mng. Dir.--Wellington Regional Medical Center, West Palm Beach, FL; *U.S. Public*, pg. 1697
Marquez, Mila, Exec. Dir. & Chief Rep.--Dentsu Young & Rubicam Advertising Co., Ltd. (Guangzhou), Guangzhou, China; *U.S. Private*, pg. 325
Marquis, R., V.P.--Foundation Building West Inc., Burnaby, Canada; *Int'l*, pg. 118
Marr, G. Patrick, V.P.--Systems Engineering Division, Richardson, TX; *U.S. Public*, pg. 46
Marra, Ed, Pres.--Nestle Beverage Company, Glendale, CA; *Int'l*, pg. 917
Marra, Georgio, V.P. & Mgr.--Banca Nazionale Del Lavoro (Overseas), Los Angeles, CA; *Int'l*, pg. 136
Marraccino, A. S., Mgr.-Resident--Santa Fe Minerals (Asia) Inc., Hong Kong, Hong Kong; *Int'l*, pg. 766
Marrah, R.G., V.P. & Gen. Mgr.--Honeywell Defense Avionics Systems, Albuquerque, NM; *U.S. Public*, pg. 834
Marrakchi, Saad, Mng. Dir.--Sherazade Conseil, Casablanca, Morocco; *Int'l*, pg. 118
Marriott, John, Pres.--K & M Electronics, Inc., West Springfield, MA; *Int'l*, pg. 395
Marriott, John, Gen. Mgr.--Sasol Technology Division, Johannesburg, South Africa; *Int'l*, pg. 1197
Marriott, R., Pres.--Banister Majestic, Edmonton, Canada; *Int'l*, pg. 118
Marriott, R.F.C., Pres.--BFC Pipelines, Edmonton, Canada; *Int'l*, pg. 118
Marriott, Raymond, Pres.--Goody Canada Limited, Toronto, Canada; *U.S. Public*, pg. 1177
Marrison, Reg, Gen. Mgr.--A.C. Nielsen Co., Tokyo, Japan; *U.S. Public*, pg. 1183
Marron, Ashley, Chief Oper. Officer--Bermo Scotland, Ltd, Glenrothes, United Kingdom; *U.S. Private*, pg. 136
Marsal, Juan Jornet, Mng. Dir.--Sarrio Tisu S.A., Barcelona, Spain; *U.S. Public*, pg. 673
Marschall, Klaus, Gen. Mgr.--Commercial Metals Deutschland GmbH, Bergisch Gladbach, Germany; *U.S. Public*, pg. 414
Marsh, Alan, Mng. Dir.--Toyota Motor Corporation, London Representative Office, London, United Kingdom; *Int'l*, pg. 1413
Marsh, Charles L., Sr. Exec. V.P.-Pur. & Mktg.--Southern Electronics Distributors International, Tucker, GA; *U.S. Public*, pg. 1490
Marsh, Daniel C., Pres.--Marsh Products Co., Durand, MI; *U.S. Private*, pg. 881
Marsh, Daniel C., Pres.--Grand River Infrastructure, Inc., Grand Rapids, MI; *U.S. Private*, pg. 881
Marsh, David, Gen. Mgr.-Western Region--Cadillac Pipe, Cadillac, MI; *U.S. Private*, pg. 881
Marsh, J.B., Mng. Dir.--UBS Asset Management London Ltd., London, United Kingdom; *Int'l*, pg. 1440
Marsh, James G., V.P. & Gen. Mgr.--Dentsply Cavitron Plant, Long Island City, NY; *U.S. Public*, pg. 499
Marsh, Jeffrey, Pres.--Westwood-Squibb Pharmaceuticals Inc., Buffalo, NY; *U.S. Public*, pg. 255
Marsh, John, Chief Oper. Officer--SCA Transport, Ayelsford, United Kingdom; *Int'l*, pg. 1327
Marsh, Judith, Mng. Dir.--Triumph Releasing Corporation - Southeastern Territory, Duluth, GA; *Int'l*, pg. 1282
Marsh, N.F., Pres.--Bindicator Company, Port Huron, MI; *U.S. Private*, pg. 138
Marsh, R., Reg. Mng. Dir.--Ballast Wiltshier Plc - London Region, Barking, United Kingdom; *Int'l*, pg. 135
Marshall. Chris, Mgr.-Sls.--Richardson Electronics Canada Ltd., Mississauga, Canada; *U.S. Public*, pg. 1388
Marshall, A., Mng. Dir.--LASMO Nederland B.V., Beverwijk, Netherlands; *Int'l*, pg. 804
Marshall, B., Pres.--Hunter Douglas Metals, Homewood, IL; *Int'l*, pg. 639
Marshall, Bob, Product Support Rep.--EMPIRE Machinery - Yuma, Yuma, AZ; *U.S. Private*, pg. 375
Marshall, Bob, Gen. Mgr.--IER Division, Twinsburg, OH; *U.S. Public*, pg. 689
Marshall, Brent, Fin. Controller--AEP/Borden Global Packaging (U.K.) Ltd., Bridgwater, United Kingdom; *U.S. Public*, pg. 5
Marshall, Charles, Pres.--Tennessee Book Company, La Vergne, TN; *U.S. Private*, pg. 563
Marshall, Chris, Dir.-European Sls.--AAR Europa, Hounslow, United Kingdom; *U.S. Public*, pg. 1
Marshall, Curtis, Plant Mgr.--Bristol Lingerie, Bristol, VA; *U.S. Private*, pg. 542
Marshall, D. R., Pres.--Canadian Imperial Bank of Commerce (California), San Francisco, CA; *Int'l*, pg. 257
Marshall, David, Mng. Dir.--Willis Corroon South Limited, Bristol, United Kingdom; *Int'l*, pg. 1503
Marshall, Elmore, Mng. Dir.--SCI Operations Division, Sasolburg, South Africa; *Int'l*, pg. 1196
Marshall, Harold D., Vice Chm.--Associates Commercial Corporation, Dallas, TX; *U.S. Public*, pg. 663
Marshall, Harold D., Vice Chm.--Associates Real Estate Financial Services Company, Inc., Dallas, TX; *U.S. Public*, pg. 663
Marshall, J., Branch Mgr.--A.M. Castle & Co., Farmington Hills, MI; *U.S. Public*, pg. 313
Marshall, J., Country Mgr.--ING Baring Securities Indonesia, Jakarta, Indonesia; *Int'l*, pg. 650
Marshall, J. W., Pres.--Idaho Utility Products Company, Boise, ID; *U.S. Public*, pg. 862
Marshall, J. W., Pres.--IDACORP, INC., Boise, ID; *U.S. Public*, pg. 862
Marshall, J.W., Pres.--Idaho Energy Resources Co., Boise, ID; *U.S. Public*, pg. 862
Marshall, Janice, Pres.--USAA Buying Service, San Antonio, TX; *U.S. Private*, pg. 1114
Marshall, Jeffrey, Pres. & Chief Exec. Officer--Aluma Systems Corp., Toronto, Canada; *Int'l*, pg. 1423
Marshall, Jim, Mng. Dir.--The Media Centre, London, United Kingdom; *Int'l*, pg. 852
Marshall, John, Chief Fin. Officer--Duro-Test Canada, Rexdale, Canada; *U.S. Private*, pg. 349
Marshall, John, Pres.--Thermal Components, Inc., Montgomery, AL; *U.S. Public*, pg. 881
Marshall, Jon A., Pres.--Applied Drilling Technology Inc., Houston, TX; *U.S. Public*, pg. 748
Marshall, Raymond, Chief Exec. Officer--AmeriServe Food Distribution, Inc., Dallas, TX; *U.S. Private*, pg. 533
Marshall, Richard A., Pres.--International Imaging Materials, Inc., Amherst, NY; *U.S. Public*, pg. 1266
Marshall, Robert, Pres.--Raytheon Constructors, Inc.-Ebasco Construction, Lyndhurst, NJ; *U.S. Public*, pg. 1366
Marshall, S., Gen. Mgr.--Asian Bleaching Earth Co., Ltd., Bangkok, Thailand; *Int'l*, pg. 803
Marshall, S., Dr., Mng. Dir.--Potterton Myson, Warwick, United Kingdom; *Int'l*, pg. 197
Marshall, Stephen A., V.P. & Gen. Mgr.--Menasco Overhaul Division, Burlington, Canada; *U.S. Public*, pg. 402
Marshall, Tony, Mng. Dir.--Butlin's Limited, Hemel Hempstead, United Kingdom; *Int'l*, pg. 1086
Marshand, A.J., V.P. & Gen. Mgr.--The Beaver Wood Fiber Company Ltd., Thorold, Canada; *U.S. Public*, pg. 739
Marsiello, Lawrence A., Pres. & Chief Exec. Officer--The CIT Group/Commercial Services, New York, NY; *Int'l*, pg. 360
Marsinek, George E., Grp. Pres.--Lamb Electric Div., Kent, OH; *U.S. Public*, pg. 100
Marsland, D., Chief Oper. Officer--The Sunlight Service Group Ltd., Basingstoke, United Kingdom; *Int'l*, pg. 385
Marston, Deborah, Chief Oper. Officer--Allright Parking Virginia, Inc., Newport News, VA; *U.S. Private*, pg. 43
Marston, Robert, Pres.--Lakso Div., Leominster, MA; *U.S. Private*, pg. 832
Marston, Theodore U., Dr., Pres. & Chief Exec. Officer--P and G Specialty Insurance Services, Newport Beach, CA; *U.S. Private*, pg. 354
Marszalek, Anthony, Mgr.-Office--Woodward-Clyde, Darwin, Australia; *U.S. Public*, pg. 1657
Mart, Marcel, Pres.--Banque Generale du Luxembourg SA, Luxembourg, Luxembourg; *Int'l*, pg. 548
Martcia, Rick, Gen. Mgr.--Alro Group, Kalamazoo, Kalamazoo, MI; *U.S. Private*, pg. 46
Martel, Bob, Pres. & Chief Exec. Officer--Cerdec Corporation, Washington, PA; *Int'l*, pg. 292
Martelli, Paolo, Chm. Bd.--Fiscambi Leasing S.p.A., Milan, Italy; *Int'l*, pg. 138
Martello, Richard, Pres.--Rockwell Clutch Company, Troy, MI; *U.S. Public*, pg. 1096
Martellozzo, Pier Giorgio, Mgr.--Sandvik Steel, Milan, Italy; *Int'l*, pg. 1187
Martens, Herbert R., Pres. & Chief Exec. Officer--NatCity Investments, Inc., Cleveland, OH; *U.S. Public*, pg. 1154
Martens, John, Publisher--Ball Publishing, Batavia, IL; *U.S. Private*, pg. 188
Martens, Paul, Gen. Mgr.--Forbo Stamoid B.V., Soest, Netherlands; *Int'l*, pg. 498
Martens, Richard A., Chm. Bd. & Chief Exec. Officer--Security Pacific Oregon Bancorp, Portland, OR; *U.S. Public*, pg. 182
Martens, Tom, Plant Mgr.--American Beauty Macaroni, Fresno, CA; *U.S. Public*, pg. 812
Marterer, G.C., Chief Oper. Officer--Nicolet Paper Company, De Pere, WI; *U.S. Public*, pg. 903
Marti, Carlos Saez, Chm. Bd.--Envases y Alimentacion, S.A., Barcelona, Spain; *U.S. Public*, pg. 1387
Marti, Donald L., Mgr.-Term--Vancouver Terminal, Vancouver, WA; *U.S. Public*, pg. 692
Marti, Romaine, Gen. Mgr.--Conquest Europe, Zurich, Switzerland; *Int'l*, pg. 1484
Martin Bringas, Francisco Javier, Pres.--Tiendas de Descuento Sultana S.A. de C.V., Monterrey, Mexico; *Int'l*, pg. 1008
Martin, A.G., V.P.-Trenton--Harwick Chemical Corp., Trenton, NJ; *U.S. Private*, pg. 509
Martin, Adam W., Plant Mgr.--Miller Brewing Company, Albany, GA; *U.S. Public*, pg. 1289
Martin, Angel, Country Mgr.--Wang Latin America S.A., Caracas, Venezuela; *U.S. Public*, pg. 1738
Martin, Anthony J., Chief Exec. Officer--Bundy Asia Pacific, Adelaide, Australia; *Int'l*, pg. 1341
Martin, B.J., Pres.--Prime Option Services, Sandy, UT; *U.S. Public*, pg. 1132
Martin, B.W., Gen. Mgr.--The Royal Bank of Scotland AG, Zurich, Switzerland; *Int'l*, pg. 1133
Martin, Bea, Bldg. Mgr.--Bundy Properties, Los Angeles, CA; *U.S. Private*, pg. 941
Martin, Berthier, Mill Mgr.--Fraser Paper Limited, Madawaska, ME; *Int'l*, pg. 434
Martin, Bob, Mng. Dir.--Willis Corroon Asia Pacific Limited, Singapore, Singapore; *Int'l*, pg. 1509
Martin, C., Chm.--THORN EMI New Zealand, Auckland, New Zealand; *Int'l*, pg. 428
Martin, Clifton A., Gen. Mgr.--Plas-Techs, Inc., Oconto Falls, WI; *U.S. Public*, pg. 165
Martin, Craig, Publisher & Chief Exec. Officer--The Edmonton Sun, Edmonton, Canada; *Int'l*, pg. 1320
Martin, D.I., Pres.--Duperial S.A.I.C., Buenos Aires, Argentina; *Int'l*, pg. 664
Martin, Dan, Pres. & Publr.--News-Press Publishing Co., Fort Myers, FL; *U.S. Public*, pg. 701
Martin, Daniel, Mng. Dir.--Raschig AG (France), Paris, France; *U.S. Private*, pg. 827
Martin, Dave, V.P.--Longlac Wood Industries Inc., Mississauga, Canada; *Int'l*, pg. 761
Martin, David, Pres.--Blackwell Publishers, Inc., Cambridge, MA; *Int'l*, pg. 197
Martin, David B., V.P.--J.M. Huber, Oil & Gas Div., Houston, TX; *U.S. Private*, pg. 545
Martin, David W., Chief Fin. Officer & Dir.--Jardine Insurance Brokers Ltd., Hong Kong, Hong Kong; *Int'l*, pg. 705
Martin, Donald, Pres.--FFV Aerotech Inc., Nashville, TN; *Int'l*, pg. 276
Martin, Doug, V.P.--Adirondack Beverages, Scotia, NY; *U.S. Private*, pg. 873
Martin, E. J., Pres. & Gen. Mgr.--GKN Walterscheid Inc., Burr Ridge, IL; *Int'l*, pg. 536
Martin, Ed, Plant Mgr.--Fulton Container Div., Fulton, NY; *U.S. Public*, pg. 1289
Martin, Frank A., Pres.--St. Louis Metallizing Co., Saint Louis, MO; *U.S. Private*, pg. 801
Martin, Gary, Gen. Mgr.--Allied Advertising Public Relations Canada, Inc., Toronto, Canada; *U.S. Private*, pg. 38
Martin, Gary, Chief Oper. Officer--Hudson General Aviation Services Inc., Gloucester, Canada; *U.S. Public*, pg. 846
Martin, Gary, Pres.-Production Admin.--TriStar Pictures, Culver City, CA; *Int'l*, pg. 1283
Martin, Gary, Chief Oper. Officer--Virginia First Mortgage, Woodbridge, VA; *U.S. Public*, pg. 1721
Martin, George, Pres.--Pow Con, San Diego, CA; *U.S. Public*, pg. 867
Martin, Gordon, Mgr.--Nu-Way Energy (N.Z.) Ltd., Auckland, New Zealand; *U.S. Private*, pg. 361
Martin, H.E., Chief Oper. Officer--Babcock Engineering Ltd., Auckland, New Zealand; *Int'l*, pg. 474
Martin, Harold, V.P.--Glory USA, Inc., Schaumburg, IL; *Int'l*, pg. 554
Martin, Heino, Chm.--Deutsche Babcock Anlagen GmbH, Oberhausen, Germany; *Int'l*, pg. 398
Martin, Henry E., Pres.--Oxford Life Insurance Co., Phoenix, AZ; *U.S. Private*, pg. 49
Martin, Henry E., Pres. & Chief Exec. Officer--Ponderosa Holdings Inc., Phoenix, AZ; *U.S. Private*, pg. 49
Martin, Henry E., Pres.--Republic Western Insurance Co., Phoenix, AZ; *U.S. Private*, pg. 49
Martin, I., Mng. Dir.--GKN Ayra Durex SA, Zumaya, Spain; *Int'l*, pg. 535
Martin, Ian, Chm. Bd.--Newmond PLC, Tamworth, United Kingdom; *Int'l*, pg. 924
Martin, J. David, Pres. & Gen. Mgr.--WLW-AM, Cincinnati, OH; *U.S. Public*, pg. 922
Martin, J. Landis, Pres. & Chief Exec. Officer--Titanium Metals Corporation, Denver, CO; *U.S. Private*, pg. 270
Martin, Jack, Refinery Mgr.--Total Petroleum, Inc., Arkansas City, KS; *U.S. Public*, pg. 1663
Martin, Jean, Plant Mgr.--Nelco S.A., Mirebeau, France; *U.S. Public*, pg. 1258
Martin, Jean, Dir.--Blohorn S.A., Abidjan, Cote d'Ivoire; *Int'l*, pg. 1436
Martin, Jesus, Dir.-Fin. & Admin.--Valquimica, S.A., Madrid, Spain; *U.S. Public*, pg. 994
Martin, Jesus, Dir.-Fin. & Admin.--Elquiber, S.A., Madrid, Spain; *U.S. Public*, pg. 994
Martin, Jim, Gen. Mgr.--ICI Explosives, Newton, NJ; *Int'l*, pg. 663
Martin, Jim, Pres. & Chief Exec. Officer--UPB of the Cumberlands, Cookeville, TN; *U.S. Public*, pg. 1669
Martin, John C., Pres. & Chief. Exec. Officer--Outdoor Systems, Inc., Los Angeles, CA; *U.S. Public*, pg. 1235
Martin, Joshua W., III, Pres.--Bell Atlantic-DE, Wilmington, DE; *U.S. Public*, pg. 202
Martin, Judi, V.P. & Gen. Mgr.--Fogarty Klein & Partners Public Relations, Houston, TX; *U.S. Private*, pg. 416
Martin, Kenneth J., Pres.--Whitehall-Robins Healthcare, Madison, NJ; *U.S. Public*, pg. 80
Martin, Kirk, Mgr.--I.C. Thomasson Ass., Pinellas Park, FL; *U.S. Private*, pg. 1083
Martin, Lewis N., Div. Pres.--Spang Power Control, Sandy Lake, PA; *U.S. Private*, pg. 1020
Martin, Michael S., Chm. Bd.--Equitable Financial Consultants, Inc., New York, NY; *U.S. Public*, pg. 589
Martin, Michel, Gen. Mgr.--Nielsen Sarl, Strasbourg, France; *Int'l*, pg. 462
Martin, O., Mng. Dir.--Georg Fischer Fahrzeugtechnik AG, Schaffhausen, Switzerland; *Int'l*, pg. 488
Martin, Peter, Reg. V.P. & Gen. Mgr.--Four Seasons Olympic Hotel, Seattle, WA; *Int'l*, pg. 502
Martin, Richard, Chief Exec. Officer--Inchcape Berhad, Singapore, Singapore; *Int'l*, pg. 672
Martin, Richard, Controller--Outdoor Technologies - Canada, Portage la Prairie, Canada; *U.S. Pqivate*, pg. 822
Martin, Richard, Dir.--Takenaka (U.S.A.) Corporation, Los Angeles Office, Los Angeles, CA; *Int'l*, pg. 1351
Martin, Robert, Chief Oper. Officer--Sterling Machinery Co., Inc., Mena, AR; *Int'l*, pg. 746
Martin, Robert, Gen. Mgr.-Crude Supply--Ultramar Canada Inc.-London Office, London, United Kingdom; *U.S. Public*, pg. 1663
Martin, Robert C., Pres.--World Book Direct Marketing, Evanston, IL; *U.S. Public*, pg. 218
Martin, Rodney O., Pres. & Chief Exec. Officer--American General Life Insurance Company of New York, Syracuse, NY; *U.S. Public*, pg. 76
Martin, Ron, Gen. Mgr.--Lectrodryer Div., Ajax Magnethermic Corp., Richmond, KY; *Int'l*, pg. 113
Martin, Ron, Pres.--Meyer Laminates Georgia Inc., Atlanta, GA; *Int'l*, pg. 864
Martin, Roy, Chief Oper. Officer--Athens Brick Co., Athens, TX; *U.S. Public*, pg. 1585
Martin, Roy, Chief Oper. Officer--Athens Brick Co. (LA), Mooringsport, LA; *U.S. Public*, pg. 1585
Martin, S.G., Mgr.--Morton Chemical Div., Ringwood, IL; *U.S. Public*, pg. 1135

Martin, Sandra L., Branch Mgr.--Valley National Bank, Franklin, NJ; *U.S. Public*, pg. 1706
Martin, Scott, Pres.--Quality Chemicals, Inc., Tyrone, PA; *U.S. Public*, pg. 344
Martin, Scott, Pres.--Quality Chemicals, Inc., Dayton, OH; *U.S. Public*, pg. 345
Martin, Stephen C., Pres.--Arizona Refrigeration Supplies, Inc., Phoenix, AZ; *U.S. Private*, pg. 624
Martin, Stephen W., Pres.--Unisys Finance Corporation, Detroit, MI; *U.S. Public*, pg. 1671
Martin, T., Mgr.-Joint Ventures--Colgate-Clorox (Far East) Ltd., Kuala Lumpur, Malaysia; *U.S. Public*, pg. 387
Martin, T.A., Pres.--Landa Motor Lines, Kansas City, MO; *U.S. Public*, pg. 944
Martin, Theodore E., Pres.--Barnes Group Aerospace Components, Windsor, CT; *U.S. Public*, pg. 190
Martin, Thomas W., Pres.--Pacific Valves, Long Beach, CA; *U.S. Public*, pg. 457
Martin, Tom, Chm. Bd. & Chief Exec. Officer--First Commercial Bank, N.A. of Memphis, Memphis, TN; *U.S. Public*, pg. 630
Martin, William, Mgr.--A. Schulman, Inc., Pasadena, CA; *U.S. Public*, pg. 1441
Martinazzo, Jacques, Chief Oper. Officer--Rhone-Poulenc Sante C.I., Abidjan, Cote d'Ivoire; *Int'l*, pg. 1114
Martineau, Eugene, V.P. & Gen. Mgr.--Florida Mining & Materials Concrete Corp., Tampa, FL; *U.S. Public*, pg. 1489
Martineau, J. L., Chief Oper. Officer--Viracon of Illinois, Inc., Chicago, IL; *U.S. Public*, pg. 120
Martineau, J.L., Chief Oper. Officer--Viracon/Curvlite, Inc., Owatonna, MN; *U.S. Public*, pg. 120
Martineau, James, Pres. & Chief Exec. Officer--Viracon, Inc., Owatonna, MN; *U.S. Public*, pg. 120
Martineeli, J.W., Pres.--Chevron Pipe Line Company, San Ramon, CA; *U.S. Public*, pg. 348
Martinet, Pierre, Mng. Dir.-PRISM--Marcam France, Paris, France; *U.S. Public*, pg. 1043
Martinez Davila, Francisco J., V.P.--Western Zone Office, Guadalajara, Mexico; *Int'l*, pg. 573
Martinez, Adrian, Ing., Gen. Dir.--Derivados Acrilicos, S.A. de C.V., Garza Garcia, Mexico; *Int'l*, pg. 246
Martinez, Aldo, Fin. Dir.--Leo Burnett Inc., Santo Domingo, Dominican Republic; *U.S. Private*, pg. 185
Martinez, Alfonso, Gen. Dir.--Consulting Informatico S.A. (CINSA), Madrid, Spain; *U.S. Public*, pg. 1043
Martinez, Alvaro, Gen. Mgr.--Amway de Guatemala, S.A., Guatemala, Guatemala; *U.S. Private*, pg. 69
Martinez, Angel, Gen. Mgr.--Colgate-Palmolive Ltda., Sao Paulo, Brazil; *U.S. Public*, pg. 398
Martinez, Angel, Pres.--The Rockport Company, Marlborough, MA; *U.S. Public*, pg. 1370
Martinez, Axel, V.P. & Gen. Mgr.--Bancomer London Branch, London, United Kingdom; *Int'l*, pg. 145
Martinez, D. Francisco, Pres.--Servicios Teledistribucion, S.A. (St-Hilo), Madrid, Spain; *Int'l*, pg. 1371
Martinez, Diana, Sr. Claims Mgr.--Willis Corroon Administrative Services Corporation, Nashville, TN; *Int'l*, pg. 1505
Martinez, Edna Sofia, Res. Dir.--Leo Burnett Columbiana, S.A., Bogota, Colombia; *U.S. Private*, pg. 185
Martinez, Eliezer Galvan, Exec. V.P.--Acerex S.A., San Nicolas, Mexico; *Int'l*, pg. 56
Martinez, Eustacio, Gen. Mgr.--Sanitaria Mexicana S.A. de C.V., Mexico, Mexico; *Int'l*, pg. 614
Martinez, Francois, Gen. Mgr.--Trinova Aeroquip Div., Rungis, France; *U.S. Public*, pg. 25
Martinez, Frederico, Pres.--La Hacienda S.A. de C.V., Mexico, Mexico; *U.S. Public*, pg. 901
Martinez, Javier, Chief Oper. Officer--Estampaciones Noroeste S.A., Vigo, Spain; *Int'l*, pg. 265
Martinez, Joaquin Marinez, Pres.--Binter Canarias, S.A., Las Palmas, Spain; *Int'l*, pg. 1224
Martinez, Joe, Pres.--Kyocera Mexicana S.A. de C.V., Tijuana, Mexico; *Int'l*, pg. 776
Martinez, Jorge H., Chief Oper. Officer--Productos Avon de Guatemala S.A., Guatemala, Guatemala; *U.S. Public*, pg. 156
Martinez, Jorge H., Gen. Mgr.--Productos Avon, S.A., San Pedro Sula, Honduras; *U.S. Public*, pg. 156
Martinez, Juan Carlos, Gen. Mgr.--Avon Products, Inc., San Juan, PR; *U.S. Public*, pg. 156
Martinez, L.M., Gen. Mgr.--SmithKline Beecham Consumer Products, Hato Rey, PR; *Int'l*, pg. 1264
Martinez, Mario, Reg. Acct. Dir.--RP alpha/Portland, Portland, OR; *U.S. Private*, pg. 950
Martinez, Michael, V.P.--Norman Levy Associates, Inc., Marblehead, MA; *U.S. Private*, pg. 664
Martinez, Mike, Admin.--Red Rocks Care Center, Gallup, NM; *U.S. Public*, pg. 838
Martinez, Rafael, Mng. Dir.--FRAM Europe Ltd., Llantrisant, United Kingdom; *U.S. Public*, pg. 53
Martinez, Robert, Terminal Mgr.--Kintetsu World Express Inc., Phoenix, AZ; *Int'l*, pg. 735
Martinez, Roberto, Admin.--Spanish Meadow Nursing Center, Brownsville, TX; *U.S. Public*, pg. 839
Martinez, Tom, Pres.--Plateau Electric Construction Inc., Redmond, WA; *U.S. Public*, pg. 65
Martinho, Dr. Rui Leao, Pres.--Deutsche Bank de Investimento, S.A. (Lisbon), Lisbon, Portugal; *Int'l*, pg. 405
Martiningui, Paulo Raitwndo, Gen. Mgr.--Banco do Brasil S.A.-Madrid, Madrid, Spain; *Int'l*, pg. 141
Martino, Ralph, Gen. Mgr.--Crown Door Corp., Tampa, FL; *Int'l*, pg. 1067
Martino, Raymond, Pres.--Stanley Door Systems, Troy, MI; *U.S. Public*, pg. 1509
Martino, Raymond J., Pres. & Gen. Mgr.--Stanley Home Decor Div., New Britain, CT; *U.S. Public*, pg. 1509
Martino, William D., Pres.--Cooper Power Systems, Waukesha, WI; *U.S. Public*, pg. 443
Martinovich, P., Mng. Dir.--EMI (New Zealand) Ltd., Auckland, New Zealand; *Int'l*, pg. 427
Martins de Jesus, Jose Antonio, Dr., Chm.--Galpgeste, Lda., Lisbon, Portugal; *Int'l*, pg. 1045
Martins, A.J., Mgr.--Tagus-Dragagens Lda., Alges, Portugal; *Int'l*, pg. 135
Martins, Manuel Galo, Mng. Dir.--ESAB Lda., Lisbon, Portugal; *Int'l*, pg. 282
Martins, Newton, Mgr.--Nalco Brasil Ltda., Sao Paulo, Brazil; *U.S. Public*, pg. 1150
Martinsen, Morten Steen, V.P.--Kvaerner Engineering, Bergen, Sandsli, Norway; *Int'l*, pg. 766
Martinsen, Robert H., Sr.V.P.--Citicorp Industrial Credit, Inc., Harrison, NY; *U.S. Public*, pg. 378
Martinson, Allyn, Pres.--Mercantile Bank of Pella, Pella, IA; *U.S. Public*, pg. 1088
Martire, Luigino, Dir.--Banca d'America e d'Italia S.p.A. (Rome), Rome, Italy; *Int'l*, pg. 403
Martling, Len, Pres.--The Weitz Company, Inc., Omaha, NE; *U.S. Private*, pg. 1161
Martocci, James, Pres.--Special Program Management, Inc., Jersey City, NJ; *Int'l*, pg. 1504
Marton-Kimpton, Sylvie, Media Supvr.--Saint Jacques Vallee Young & Rubicam, Inc., Montreal, Canada; *U.S. Private*, pg. 1200
Marton, Drew, Chief Oper. Officer--Pathetek, Rochester, NY; *U.S. Public*, pg. 551
Martore, Albert V., Mng. Dir.--DYWIDAG Systems International, USA, Inc., Bedford, NH; *Int'l*, pg. 424
Marttinen, Jaakko, Pres.--Kymmene USA, Tarrytown, NY; *Int'l*, pg. 1430
Martyres, Raul J., Mng. Dir.--Access Advertising Limited, Nairobi, Kenya; *U.S. Private*, pg. 303
Martz, Ben L., Pres.--M.A.P. Builders Inc., Coral Springs, FL; *U.S. Public*, pg. 988
Martz, D. Stephen, Chm. Bd., Pres. & Chief Exec. Officer--Hollidaysburg Trust Company, Hollidaysburg, PA; *U.S. Public*, pg. 1222
Martz, Verle C., Mgr.-Office--Woodward-Clyde, Phoenix, AZ; *U.S. Public*, pg. 1656
Maruccilli, Stephen J., Pres.--First Hawaiian Leasing, Inc., Honolulu, HI; *U.S. Public*, pg. 635
Marui, Yashiro, Mng. Dir.--DKB Investment Management International Limited, London, United Kingdom; *Int'l*, pg. 362
Marunanen, Antero, Chief Oper. Officer--Ahlstrom Machinery Pump Industry After Sales, Karhula, Finland; *Int'l*, pg. 34
Maruska, Lawrence, Mgr.-Branch--Piper Jaffray Inc., Mankato, MN; *U.S. Public*, pg. 1301
Maruska, Lawrence, Mgr.-Branch--Piper Jaffray Inc., New Ulm, MN; *U.S. Public*, pg. 1303
Maruta, Yasuo, Branch Mgr.--Yamaichi International (America) Inc.-Chicago Branch, Chicago, IL; *Int'l*, pg. 1517
Maruyama, Kizou, Pres.--Calsonic Yorozu Corporation, Morrison, TN; *Int'l*, pg. 944
Maruyama, Ryoji, Sales Mgr.--Minebea Co., Ltd. - Kuala Lumpur Branch, Kuala Lumpur, Malaysia; *Int'l*, pg. 869
Maruyama, Takashi, Pres.--Otsuka Electronics Co., Ltd., Osaka, Japan; *Int'l*, pg. 1013
Marvelly, R. D., Exec. Dir.--Robert Bryce & Co., Ltd., Wellington, New Zealand; *Int'l*, pg. 682
Marwil, William, Pres.--Marwil Products Company, Fort Loramie, OH; *U.S. Public*, pg. 137
Marwood, Maurice E., V.P.--PROCHEM Mixing Equipment Ltd., Brampton, Canada; *U.S. Public*, pg. 1393
Marx, Carl, Gen. Mgr.--Colgate-Palmolive (Central America), Inc., San Jose, Costa Rica; *U.S. Public*, pg. 398
Marx, George, Gen. Mgr.--Jannock Steel Fabricating, Inc., Saint Joseph, MN; *Int'l*, pg. 699
Marx, O.B., III, Chm. Bd.--Ford Electronics & Refrigeration Corp., Dearborn, MI; *U.S. Public*, pg. 664
Marygold, M.S., Mgr.--GF Pacific Exports (NZ) Ltd., Auckland, New Zealand; *Int'l*, pg. 556
Marynissen, G.J., Gen. Mgr.--Van Buuren-Van Swaay Marine Airconditioning, Zoetermeer, Zoetermeer, Netherlands; *Int'l*, pg. 681
Marz, John F., Pres.--Dunn Reber Glenn Marz/Las Vegas, Las Vegas, NV; *U.S. Private*, pg. 347
Marziniak, Jurgen, Gen. Mgr.--Deutsche Bank AG (Jakarta), Jakarta, Indonesia; *Int'l*, pg. 404
Marzloff, Georges, Chief Oper. Officer--Neste Oy, Chemicals, Espoo, Finland; *Int'l*, pg. 913
Marzloff, Georges, Chief Oper. Officer--Neste Chemicals Holding France S.A., Rungis, France; *Int'l*, pg. 914
Marzo, J.M., Gen. Mgr.--Johnsonwax del Ecuador S.A., Guayaquil, Ecuador; *U.S. Private*, pg. 593
Marzullo, Pierluigi, Mng. Dir.--SIELTE Data Net S.p.A., Trieste, Italy; *Int'l*, pg. 1370
Mas, Frederico, Mng. Dir.--Turbinas y Equipos Industriales, S.A. de C.V., Morelia, Mexico; *Int'l*, pg. 1306
Mas, Frederico, Chief Exec.--Sulzer Hydro S.A. de C.V., Morelia, Mexico; *Int'l*, pg. 1308
Masachi, John E., V.P.-Industrial Wood Products--Georgia-Pacific Industrial Wood Products Div., Atlanta, GA; *U.S. Public*, pg. 735
Masaki, Junitsu, Mng. Dir.--Toyo Trust Australia Limited, Sydney, Australia; *Int'l*, pg. 1411
Masaki, Kozo, Gen. Mgr.--The Sumitomo Bank, Ltd.-San Francisco Branch, San Francisco, CA; *Int'l*, pg. 1309
Masamichi, Muraoka, Gen. Mgr.--The Sumitomo Bank, Ltd.-Seoul Branch, Seoul, Korea; *Int'l*, pg. 1309
Mascali, Rosemary, Pres.--Quantum Plus, New York, NY; *U.S. Public*, pg. 1224
Mascia, Frank R., Chm., Pres. & Chief Exec. Officer--United HealthCare of North Carolina, Inc., Greensboro, NC; *U.S. Public*, pg. 1678
Masco, John R., Pres. & Chief Exec. Officer--First National Bank of Ohio, Akron, OH; *U.S. Public*, pg. 646
Masek, Timothy A., Pres.--Bostrom Seating, Inc., Piedmont, AL; *U.S. Public*, pg. 933
Mashall, Stephen, Pres.--Meggitt Avionics Inc., Manchester, NH; *Int'l*, pg. 853
Masini, Massimo, Chief Exec. Officer--Stet International, Rome, Italy; *Int'l*, pg. 1363
Maskell, Tom, Gen. Mgr.--Corundite Refractories Div., Massillon, OH; *U.S. Public*, pg. 515
Maskell, Tom, Gen. Mgr.--New Castle Refractory Co., New Castle, PA; *U.S. Public*, pg. 515
Masmini, Arnold N., Reg. Mgr.-Africa--CUNA Mutual Group-Africa, Nairobi, Kenya; *U.S. Private*, pg. 296
Mason, Carl L., Pres.--Cone Finishing Company, Carlisle, SC; *U.S. Public*, pg. 430
Mason, Chris, Chief Exec. Officer--World Brands Duty Free, Brentford, United Kingdom; *Int'l*, pg. 567
Mason, Dan, Pres.--CBS Radio, New York, NY; *U.S. Public*, pg. 274
Mason, David, Branch Mgr.--Lindenmeyr Munroe, Lancaster, PA; *U.S. Private*, pg. 224
Mason, Douglas G., Pres.--Rockwell Plastic Products, Lenoir, NC; *Int'l*, pg. 113
Mason, George A., Mgr.--Turbine Engine Components Textron, Orlando, FL; *U.S. Public*, pg. 1589
Mason, Henry, Mng. Dir.--Haskel Energy Systems Ltd., Sunderland, United Kingdom; *U.S. Public*, pg. 798
Mason, J. Michael, Mgr.--CAP Gemini America (Atlanta Branch), Atlanta, GA; *Int'l*, pg. 263
Mason, James F., Pres.--Wagner Castings Company, Decatur, IL; *U.S. Public*, pg. 894
Mason, Linda, V.P.-Public Affairs Programming--CBS News, New York, NY; *U.S. Public*, pg. 274
Mason, Pam, Gen. Mgr.--Ernie's, New York, NY; *U.S. Public*, pg. 130
Mason, R.H.G., Exec. Dir.--BarclayTrust Investment Services Ltd., Nairobi, Kenya; *Int'l*, pg. 166
Mason, Roger, Company Head--Ovako Steel Ltd., Wolverhampton, United Kingdom; *Int'l*, pg. 1157
Mason, Ronald V., Pres.--Federal Cartridge Co., Anoka, MN; *U.S. Public*, pg. 239
Mason, Steve, Jr., Gen. Mgr.--Imperial Auto Auction, Lakeland, FL; *U.S. Private*, pg. 282
Mason, Steven J., Pres.--Ingram Library Services, Inc., La Vergne, TN; *U.S. Private*, pg. 563
Mason, Tom, Pres. & Chief Exec. Officer--Schwinn Cycling & Fitness Inc., Boulder, CO; *U.S. Private*, pg. 975
Mason, Wayne E., Jr., Chief Oper. Officer--North Central Florida Division, Gainesville, FL; *U.S. Public*, pg. 656
Masotti, David, Pres.--Spar Space Systems, Brampton, Canada; *Int'l*, pg. 1288
Massa, Julian, Mng. Dir.--Ericsson S.A., Madrid, Spain; *Int'l*, pg. 1367
Massa, Ronald E., Pres.--A.O. Smith Water Products Company, Irving, TX; *U.S. Public*, pg. 1477
Massarasky, Steven J., Pres. & Publr.--Acclaim Comics, New York, NY; *U.S. Public*, pg. 15
Massaro, Carl, Pres.--Ajax Manufacturing Company, Inc., Hillsborough, NJ; *U.S. Private*, pg. 1030
Masselink, Frederik, Gen. Mgr.--CPC-Monda N.V./S.A., Antwerp, Belgium; *U.S. Public*, pg. 224
Masselink, Frederik, Gen. Mgr.--CPC Benelux B.V., Hilversum, Netherlands; *U.S. Public*, pg. 225
Massengale, Jim E., Pres.--West Coast Life Insurance Co., San Francisco, CA; *U.S. Public*, pg. 1336
Massey, D.E., Pres. & Chief Exec. Officer--Massey Cadillac, Inc., Detroit, MI; *U.S. Private*, pg. 713
Massey, D.E., Pres. & Chief Exec. Officer--Massey Cadillac, Inc., Dallas, TX; *U.S. Private*, pg. 713
Massey, Dale, V.P.--Personal Finance Corp., Tupelo, MS; *U.S. Public*, pg. 176
Massey, Glenn, Sr. V.P. & Mng. Dir.--Western International Media Corporation, Dallas, TX; *U.S. Private*, pg. 1167
Massey, John, Pres.--Hilb, Rogal & Hamilton Company of Amarillo, Amarillo, TX; *U.S. Public*, pg. 827
Massey, Kenneth, Div. Mgr.--Dan River Inc.-Yarn Dyed Apparel Fabrics, Div. II, Danville, VA; *U.S. Public*, pg. 479
Massey, Larry, Chief Oper. Officer--Allright Miami, Inc., Miami, FL; *U.S. Private*, pg. 42
Massey, William J., III, Pres.--Neumaticos Goodyear SA, Buenos Aires, Argentina; *U.S. Public*, pg. 753
Massick, Cliff, Service Centre Mgr.--Barber Industries Ltd.-Service Center, Brooks, Canada; *Int'l*, pg. 164
Massing, Gunnar, Pres.--Nordiska Kompaniet (NK) AB, Stockholm, Sweden; *Int'l*, pg. 899
Massobrio, G., Pres.--Quebec Cartier Mining Co., Montreal, Canada; *Int'l*, pg. 414
Masson-Lecomte, Philippe, Gen. Mgr.--Reed Travel Group-France, Asnieres-sur-Seine, France; *Int'l*, pg. 1097
Masson, H., Pres.--SBS Gestion S.A., Paris, France; *Int'l*, pg. 1331
Masson, J.M., Dir. & Gen. Mgr.--Ultra Electronics Weapons Systems, United Kingdom; *Int'l*, pg. 1431
Masson, Jean-Francois, Gen. Mgr.--Whitehall Benelux S.A., Gembloux, Belgium; *U.S. Public*, pg. 82
Masson, Jean-Francois, Gen. Mgr.--Whitehall Laboratoria B.V., Amsterdam, Netherlands; *U.S. Public*, pg. 82
Masson, Jean-Pierre, Gen. Mgr.--BFCE New York, New York, NY; *Int'l*, pg. 161
Massot, Philippe, Gen. Mgr.--BFCE Indonesia, Jakarta, Indonesia; *Int'l*, pg. 161
Mast, C.A., Pres.--Amoco Supply & Trading Company, Chicago, IL; *U.S. Public*, pg. 103
Mast, Keith, Mgr.-Office--Woodward-Clyde, Solon, OH; *U.S. Public*, pg. 1656
Mast, Werner, Mgr.--Eastern Branch, Bitterfeld, Germany; *Int'l*, pg. 401
Mastej, Mike, Mng. Dir.--Victoria Regional Medical Center, Victoria, TX; *U.S. Public*, pg. 1697
Master, Rex, Chief Oper. Officer--BHF (Los Angeles), Los Angeles, CA; *Int'l*, pg. 119
Masters, C.R., Mng. Dir.--NatWest International Trust Corporation (Bahamas) Limited, Nassau, Bahamas; *Int'l*, pg. 911
Masters, Derek, Pres.--Asia Pacific Division, Frenchs Forest, Australia; *U.S. Public*, pg. 1516
Masters, Larry W., Pres.--South Florida Test Service, Miami, FL; *U.S. Private*, pg. 96
Masters, Melvin L., Pres.--Digital Typeface Corporation, Eden Prairie, MN; *U.S. Public*, pg. 979

Masters, Melvin L., Pres.--LaserMaster Export Corporation, Eden Prairie, MN; *U.S. Public*, pg. 979

Masters, Thomas A., Mgr.--Carteret Terminal, Carteret, NJ; *U.S. Public*, pg. 692

Masterson, Michael M., Pres.--NWNL Management Corp., Minneapolis, MN; *U.S. Public*, pg. 1375

Mastriani, John P., Chief Exec. Officer--Key Trust Company, Albany, NY; *U.S. Public*, pg. 954

Mastriani, John P., Pres. & Chief Exec. Officer--Society Investments, Inc., Cleveland, OH; *U.S. Public*, pg. 955

Mastrianni, Ron, Pres.--Harte-Hanks Direct Mail/California, Fullerton, CA; *U.S. Public*, pg. 794

Mastrogiacomo, Chris, V.P.--Hadco Corporation, Santa Clara, CA; *U.S. Public*, pg. 773

Mastromonaco, Lorenzo, Chief Oper. Officer--Novo Nordisk Farmaceutici Srl, Rome, Italy; *Int'l*, pg. 988

Mastropichro, Paolo, Gen. Mgr.--Polarcup s.r.l., Enza, Italy; *Int'l*, pg. 639

Mastrovito, Tony, Gen. Mgr.--Duro-Test Canada, Rexdale, Canada; *U.S. Private*, pg. 349

Masubuchi, Norio, Pres.--Showa Denko America, Inc., New York, NY; *Int'l*, pg. 1236

Masucci, James M., Pres. & Gen. Mgr.--KTRK Television, Inc., Houston, TX; *U.S. Public*, pg. 512

Masuda, Kohei, Exec. V.P. & Gen. Mgr.--Western Div.--The Sakura Bank (Canada), Vancouver Office, Vancouver, Canada; *Int'l*, pg. 1180

Masuda, Tadaaki, Gen. Mgr.--Nippon Polaroid K.K., Tokyo, Japan; *U.S. Public*, pg. 1314

Masuhari, Hiroshi, Gen. Mgr.--Kyodo Advertising Co., Ltd., Hiroshima, Japan; *Int'l*, pg. 776

Masuko, Mike K., Exec. V.P.--Bundy Japan Ltd., Nagoya, Japan; *Int'l*, pg. 1341

Masunari, Kaoru, Chief Rep.--The Sumitomo Bank, Ltd.-Istanbul Representative Office, Istanbul, Turkey; *Int'l*, pg. 1310

Masuno, Hiroyasu, Pres.--P.T. Multicor Securities, Jakarta, Indonesia; *Int'l*, pg. 817

Masuro, Miyake, Gen. Mgr.--Aisin World Corp. of America, Downers Grove, IL; *Int'l*, pg. 39

Masuzawa, Yasutoshi, Representative Dir.--Boeing Japan, Ltd., Tokyo, Japan; *U.S. Public*, pg. 242

Matagne, Robert, Mng. Dir.--Tractebel Engineering International S.A., Brussels, Belgium; *Int'l*, pg. 1415

Matalon, Joseph M., Chm.--British Caribbean Insurance Company Limited, Kingston, Jamaica; *Int'l*, pg. 156

Matalon, Joseph M., CHm.--Industrial Finance Holdings Limited, Kingston, Jamaica; *Int'l*, pg. 156

Matamoros, Agustin, Gen. Mgr.--Forbo Pavimentos SA, Barcelona, Spain; *Int'l*, pg. 498

Matamoros, Raul, Gen. Dir.--Cigarrera la Moderna, SA de CV, Monterrey, Mexico; *Int'l*, pg. 112

Matchael, Dick, Mng. Dir.--Laboratory Supply Company, Lees Summit, MO; *U.S. Private*, pg. 642

Matchett, Chris, Pres.--Hutchinson Wil-Rich Manufacturing Co., Dallas, TX; *U.S. Private*, pg. 1063

Matchett, Ken, Chief Exec. Officer--XCAN Grain Pool Ltd., Winnipeg, Canada; *Int'l*, pg. 1195

Mate, Bob, V.P. & Dir.-Publ.--Country America Magazine, Des Moines, IA; *U.S. Public*, pg. 1094

Mateer, Mike, Pres.--Mount Vernon Neon, Mount Vernon, IL; *U.S. Private*, pg. 386

Mateker, Emil J., Jr., Pres.--Aero Service Corp., Houston, TX; *U.S. Public*, pg. 1003

Matela, Matthew, Mng. Dir.--PAXAR Polska Sp.zo.o., Warsaw, Poland; *U.S. Public*, pg. 1267

Maten, Allen, V.P. & Gen. Mgr.--Solvay Automotive Inc., Troy, MI; *Int'l*, pg. 1277

Maten, Gerrit J., Mng. Dir.--KLM Aerocarto BV, Arnhem, Netherlands; *Int'l*, pg. 607

Mater, Robert F., Jr., Pres.--Reese Products, Inc., Elkhart, IN; *U.S. Public*, pg. 1054

Matheney, Keith, Gen. Mgr.--Weather-Seal Div., Barberton, OH; *U.S. Public*, pg. 1015

Mather, Ann, Controller--Paramount Pictures International, Amsterdam, Netherlands; *U.S. Private*, pg. 777

Mather, Donald, Gen. Mgr.--La-Z-Boy Leland, Leland, MS; *U.S. Public*, pg. 973

Mather, Duane A., Pres.--Nabors Drilling Limited, Nisku, Canada; *U.S. Public*, pg. 1149

Mather, Ernest F., V.P.--La-Z-Boy East, Florence, SC; *U.S. Public*, pg. 973

Mather, K., Gen. Mgr.--Wellcome Zambia Ltd, Lusaka, Zambia; *Int'l*, pg. 553

Mathers, John F., Pres. & Mng. Dir.--Imasco B.V., Amsterdam, Netherlands; *Int'l*, pg. 112

Mathers, John F., Mng. Dir.--Imasco B.V.-Fribourg Branch, Fribourg, Switzerland; *Int'l*, pg. 112

Mathers, Stephen R., Pres.--Sames Electrostatic, Inc., Livonia, MI; *U.S. Public*, pg. 229

Mathes, Heinrich-Wernr, Dr., Chm. Bd.--Lentjes AG, Dusseldorf, Germany; *Int'l*, pg. 861

Matheson, Greg, Pres.--Fibres International, Inc., Bellevue, WA; *U.S. Private*, pg. 269

Matheson, Jim, Controller--Weatherford Enterra Oilfield Rentals, Singapore, Singapore; *U.S. Public*, pg. 1750

Matheson, John, V.P. & Div. Mgr.--Transport International Pool of Canada Limited, Mississauga, Canada; *U.S. Public*, pg. 713

Matheson, Thomas A., V.P. & Gen. Mgr.-WBBM-FM--CBS Radio Div., New York, NY; *U.S. Public*, pg. 274

Matheus, Euler, Gen. Mgr.--Salles/DMB&B Publicidade S.A., Rio de Janeiro, Brazil; *U.S. Private*, pg. 305

Mathew, P.G., Dir.--Ascott International Management Pte. Ltd., Singapore, Singapore; *Int'l*, pg. 1212

Mathew, Sarrah, Mng. Dir.--O/E/N India Ltd., Cochin, India; *U.S. Public*, pg. 1209

Mathews, Francesca, V.P. & Gen. Mgr.--Cramer-Krasselt, Orlando, FL; *U.S. Private*, pg. 286

Mathews, Mark, Gen. Mgr.--Interstate Container Corporation, Lowell, MA; *U.S. Private*, pg. 573

Mathews, Phil, Chief Oper. Officer--Armstrong Fastenings Ltd., Darlaston, United Kingdom; *Int'l*, pg. 265

Mathews, Trevor, Mng. Dir.--Legal & General Assurance Holdings (Australia) Limited, Sydney, Australia; *Int'l*, pg. 805

Mathewson, John, Pres.--AGA Catalog Marketing & Design, New York, NY; *U.S. Private*, pg. 295

Mathias, P.A., Gen. Mgr.--Korea Johnson Co., Ltd., Seoul, Korea; *U.S. Private*, pg. 593

Mathiesen, Lars, Mng. Dir.--NY*BO*E, Copenhagen, Denmark; *Int'l*, pg. 993

Mathieu, Bernard, Mng. Dir.--Chapelle Darblay Grand Couronne S.A., Saint Etienne, France; *Int'l*, pg. 1430

Mathis, Daniel R., Reg. V.P.--Union Bank of California, Personal Trust, San Diego, CA; *Int'l*, pg. 157

Mathis, Keith, Gen. Mgr.--Nickel Nik, Spokane, WA; *U.S. Public*, pg. 984

Mathisen, Avild, Mng. Dir.--Pripps Ringnes a.s., Oslo, Norway; *Int'l*, pg. 1011

Mathisen, Erik, V.P. & Gen. Mgr.--NIKE International Ltd.-Norway, Lysaker, Norway; *U.S. Public*, pg. 1184

Mathison, Henry, Div. Mgr.--Wyle Electronics-Portland, Beaverton, OR; *Int'l*, pg. 1457

Mathoret, Jean-Francois, Mng. Dir.--CRMA, Elancourt, France; *Int'l*, pg. 560

Mathot, Jos, Mng. Dir.--Security House, Purmerend, Netherlands; *U.S. Public*, pg. 1307

Mathot, Jos, Mng. Dir.--Security House, Pumerend, Netherlands; *U.S. Public*, pg. 1307

Mathot, S.C., Chief Oper. Officer--MPB Corporation, Keene, NH; *U.S. Public*, pg. 1617

Mathur, Pracheesh, Pres.--Aerospace Operations Asia Pacific, Singapore, Singapore; *Int'l*, pg. 1337

Mathur, S.C., Exec. Dir.--Northern Region, New Delhi, India; *Int'l*, pg. 673

Mathys, Alain, Reg. Mgr.--Banco Mundial, La Paz, Bolivia; *U.S. Private*, pg. 1189

Matikainen, Martti, Pres.--Valmet-Xian Paper Machinery Co. Ltd., Xian, China; *Int'l*, pg. 1448

Matlack, Richard, Pres.--InfoCorp, Santa Clara, CA; *Int'l*, pg. 1276

Matlock, Dave, Pres.--Continental Homes of San Antonio, L.P., San Antonio, TX; *U.S. Public*, pg. 441

Matoba, Takemasa, Pres.--Nanto DC Card Co., Ltd., Nara, Japan; *Int'l*, pg. 905

Matola, Gerry, Plant Mgr.--Milwaukee Grey Iron, Milwaukee, WI; *U.S. Private*, pg. 579

Maton, M., Mng. Dir.--The Reader's Digest Association Pty. Limited, Sydney, Australia; *U.S. Public*, pg. 1368

Matons, J., Pres.--Amersham Corporation (Amersham QSA), Arlington Heights, IL; *Int'l*, pg. 992

Matorell, Fernando Abril, Pres.--Union Naval De Levante, S.A. (Madrid), Valencia, Spain; *Int'l*, pg. 1442

Matos, Francisco, Gen. Mgr.--Mold-Tech Portugal, Maia, Portugal; *U.S. Public*, pg. 1507

Matovcik, Victor, Mng. Dir.--Slovak International Tabak, a.s. (S.I.T.), Bratislava, Slovakia; *Int'l*, pg. 1101

Matricaria, Ronald A., Pres.--Eli Lilly International Corporation, Indianapolis, IN; *U.S. Public*, pg. 993

Matsas, M., Pres.--Minos EMI, Athens, Greece; *Int'l*, pg. 427

Matshushita, Hiroshi, Rep.--The Kyoei Mutual Fire & Marine Insurance Company, New York Representative Office, New York, NY; *Int'l*, pg. 777

Matsik, George A., Chief Oper. Officer--Ball Packaging Holdings Corp., Westminster, CO; *U.S. Public*, pg. 171

Matsko, Larry, Dir.--Custom Cheques of Canada, Winnipeg, Canada; *Int'l*, pg. 1077

Matson, John, Pres.--Hunt Refining Company, Tuscaloosa, AL; *U.S. Private*, pg. 549

Matson, Ronald, Pres. & Chief Exec. Officer--Cerberus Pyrotronics Inc., Cedar Knolls, NJ; *Int'l*, pg. 1246

Matsuba, Kiyoshi, Pres.--Daiwa Singapore Limited, Singapore, Singapore; *Int'l*, pg. 376

Matsubara, Mikio, Pres.--Seibu Allstate Life Insurance Co., Ltd., Tokyo, Japan; *Int'l*, pg. 1178

Matsubayashi, Isao, Chief Rep.--Dai-Ichi Kangyo Bank, Ltd.-Mexico City, Mexico, Mexico; *Int'l*, pg. 361

Matsuda, Seigo, Pres.--Nippon Jarrell-Ash Company, Ltd., Kyoto, Japan; *U.S. Public*, pg. 1596

Matsue, Shigeki, Pres. & Chief Exec. Officer--NEC Electronics Inc., Santa Clara, CA; *Int'l*, pg. 900

Matsueda, Masahiko, Pres.--Nisshin Steel USA, Inc., New York, NY; *Int'l*, pg. 946

Matsui, K., Chief Oper. Officer--Furukawa Electric Cables (Malaysia) Sdn. Bhd., Kuala Lumpur, Malaysia; *Int'l*, pg. 530

Matsui, Shigeru, Chief Oper. Officer--Daiko Advertising, Inc., Kyoto, Japan; *Int'l*, pg. 366

Matsui, Takashi, Mng. Dir.--NEC Taiwan Ltd., Taipei, Taiwan; *Int'l*, pg. 900

Matsui, Toru, Deputy Gen. Mgr.--Hino Motors, Ltd., Tokyo, Japan; *Int'l*, pg. 620

Matsukata, Ko, Pres.--Mitsui Marine & Fire Insurance Co., Ltd., Tokyo, Japan; *Int'l*, pg. 878

Matsumoto, Eiichi, Chm.--Bank of Tokyo-Mitsubishi Trust Company, New York, NY; *Int'l*, pg. 157

Matsumoto, Ernesto, Chief Oper. Officer--Tokio Marine Internacional Sociedad Anonima, Mexico, Mexico; *Int'l*, pg. 1393

Matsumoto, J., V.P.--Onkyo Corp., Osaka, Japan; *Int'l*, pg. 1403

Matsumoto, Munetoshi, Chief Rep.--Dai-Ichi Kangyo Bank, Ltd.-Sao Paulo, Sao Paulo, Brazil; *Int'l*, pg. 361

Matsumoto, Munetoshi, Exec. Dir. & Consultant--UNIBANCO-Uniao de Bancos Brasileiros S.A., Sao Paulo, Brazil; *Int'l*, pg. 362

Matsumoto, Sensaku, Pres.--Brother Industries (USA) Inc., Memphis, TN; *Int'l*, pg. 229

Matsumoto, T., Pres.--Component Products Co., New York, NY; *Int'l*, pg. 1281

Matsumoto, T.J., Mgr.--Tokio Marine Management Inc. - Atlanta, Atlanta, GA; *Int'l*, pg. 1392

Matsumoto, Teruomi, Mng. Dir.--Daiko Advertising, Inc., Osaka, Japan; *Int'l*, pg. 366

Matsumoto, Y., Pres.--P.T. Ebara Prima Indonesia, Serang, Indonesia; *Int'l*, pg. 432

Matsumoto, Yasushi, Chief Oper. Officer--Fresh Skylark Co., Ltd., Tokyo, Japan; *Int'l*, pg. 1262

Matsumura, Ken, Pres.--Nippon Paint (America) Corp., New York, NY; *Int'l*, pg. 937

Matsumura, Kimio, Chief Oper. Officer--Hitachi Ohira Industrial Co., Ltd., Tochigi, Japan; *Int'l*, pg. 621

Matsumura, Masaraka, Pres.--Nissan Motor Acceptance Corp., Torrance, CA; *Int'l*, pg. 945

Matsunaga, Jiro, Pres.--Rohm Mechatech Philippines, Inc., Cavite, Philippines; *Int'l*, pg. 1125

Matsunaga, T., Mgr.-Plant--NSK-AKS Precision Ball Company, Clarinda, IA; *Int'l*, pg. 903

Matsunaga, Yutaka, Chief Oper. Officer--Nippon Shipping Co., Ltd., Tokyo, Japan; *Int'l*, pg. 934

Matsuo, Junji, Pres.--Hakuhodo Hong Kong Ltd., Hong Kong, Hong Kong; *Int'l*, pg. 588

Matsuo, Kazuhiko, Chief Oper. Officer--Gunze Sangyo (Osaka), Osaka, Japan; *Int'l*, pg. 578

Matsuo, Tunji, Pres.--Hakuhodo Inc., Shanghai, China; *Int'l*, pg. 588

Matsuo, Y., Pres.--Silmax, Inc., Albuquerque, NM; *Int'l*, pg. 1317

Matsuo, Yoshio, Mng. Dir.--NEC Technologies (UK) Ltd., Telford, United Kingdom; *Int'l*, pg. 900

Matsuoka, Akifumi, Dir.--Takenaka (U.S.A.) Corporation, Atlanta Office, Atlanta, GA; *Int'l*, pg. 1351

Matsuoka, Iwao, Pres.--Laura Ashley Japan Co., Ltd., Tokyo, Japan; *Int'l*, pg. 28

Matsuoka, Jiro, Mgr.-Import Terminal--Kintetsu World Express Inc., Inglewood, CA; *Int'l*, pg. 734

Matsuoka, Michiya, Area Dir.-Asia & Oceania--Dentsu East Japan Inc., Tokyo, Japan; *Int'l*, pg. 393

Matsuoka, Michiya, Area Dir.--Area Headquarters-ASIA & OCEANIA, Tokyo, Japan; *Int'l*, pg. 393

Matsushima, Hiroshi, Deputy Representative--Union Bank of Switzerland, Osaka, Japan; *Int'l*, pg. 1441

Matsushima, Kunihiro, Deputy Reg. Dir.-East Asia--Dentsu Young & Rubicam Limited (Hong Kong), Hong Kong, Hong Kong; *U.S. Private*, pg. 325

Matsushita, Sheila, Pres.--A-Mold Corp., Mason, OH; *Int'l*, pg. 1427

Matsushita, Toshiharu, Pres.--PT Katsushiro Indonesia, Bekasi, Indonesia; *Int'l*, pg. 745

Matsuura, Isao, Pres. & Chief Exec. Officer--Sanwa Bank California, San Francisco, CA; *Int'l*, pg. 1189

Matsuura, Tamaki, Mng. Dir.--Dai-ichi Life Property (London) Limited, London, United Kingdom; *Int'l*, pg. 363

Matsuyama, Norio, Chief Oper. Officer--P.T. Standard Toyo Polymer, Jakarta, Indonesia; *Int'l*, pg. 1408

Matsuzaki, Toshiyuki, Pres.--P.T. Mesin Isuzu Indonesia, Tangerang, Indonesia; *Int'l*, pg. 693

Matsuzaki, Toshiyuki, Pres.--P.T. Mesin Isuzu Indonesia, Tangerang, Indonesia; *U.S. Public*, pg. 724

Matsuzawa, H., Pres.--Kasei Verbatim Corporation, Odawara, Japan; *U.S. Public*, pg. 552

Matsuzawa, Katsumi, Pres.--Sakura Trust Company, New York, NY; *Int'l*, pg. 1179

Matsuzawa, Katsumi, Pres.--Sakura Securities, New York, NY; *Int'l*, pg. 1179

Matsuzawa, Mitsuo, Pres.--INX Corporation, Elk Grove Village, IL; *Int'l*, pg. 1311

Matteo, Frank R., Pres.--CM Graphics, Cherry Hill, NJ; *U.S. Public*, pg. 1329

Matter, Heidi, Mng. Dir.--Janssen-Cilag Pharmaceutica AG, Baar, Switzerland; *U.S. Public*, pg. 929

Matteson, Hollis, Pres.--Burns & Roe Construction Group Inc., Oradell, NJ; *U.S. Private*, pg. 187

Matthew, John, Mng. Dir.--Reckitt & Colman Products Pty. Ltd., Ermington, Australia; *Int'l*, pg. 1090

Matthew, Mike, Chief Exec.--IPC Magazines Limited, London, United Kingdom; *Int'l*, pg. 651

Matthew, Mike, Chm.--Marketforce (UK) Limited, London, United Kingdom; *Int'l*, pg. 651

Matthews, A. Rabun, V.P. & Gen. Mgr.--WLKY-TV, Louisville, KY; *U.S. Public*, pg. 1344

Matthews, A. Rabun, V.P. & Gen. Mgr.--WLKY-AM, Louisville, KY; *U.S. Public*, pg. 1344

Matthews, B., Dir.-Mfg.--DuPont Merck Pharm, Garden City, NY; *U.S. Public*, pg. 1091

Matthews, Chris, Chief Exec.--Shandwick Consultants Ltd., London, United Kingdom; *Int'l*, pg. 1227

Matthews, Daniel, V.P.--Northwest Aircraft Inc., Saint Paul, MN; *U.S. Public*, pg. 1200

Matthews, Dave, Pres.--Brentwood Benson Publishing Group, Nashville, TN; *Int'l*, pg. 1529

Matthews, Don C., Mng. Dir.--Gould Electronics Ltd., Foil Div., Southampton, United Kingdom; *U.S. Public*, pg. 1592

Matthews, Harry, V.P. & Gen. Mgr.--The HON Co., Richmond Plant, Richmond, VA; *U.S. Public*, pg. 772

Matthews, J., Pres.--Dundridge College Limited, Totnes, United Kingdom; *Int'l*, pg. 544

Matthews, J.S., Pres.--Compressor Systems, Inc., Midland, TX; *Int'l*, pg. 1027

Matthews, L. W., Chief Oper. Officer--Electrolux Pty. Ltd., Glen Waverley, Australia; *Int'l*, pg. 440

Matthews, Leo L., Pres. & Chief Oper. Officer--Allied Construction Products, Inc., Cleveland, OH; *U.S. Public*, pg. 1339

Matthews, Linda, V.P.--Royal Insurance Ontario Regional Centre, Etobicoke, Canada; *Int'l*, pg. 1131

Matthews, Lynn O., Publisher--Sarasota Herald-Tribune Company, Sarasota, FL; *U.S. Public*, pg. 1175

Matthews, Robert, Pres.--Red Kap Industries, Nashville, TN; *U.S. Public*, pg. 1702

Matthews, Rudy, V.P.-Opers.--Electrolux Canada, Mississauga, Canada; *U.S. Private*, pg. 370

Matthews, Terence H., Chm. Bd. & Chief Exec. Officer--Newbridge Networks Corporation, Kanata, Canada; *Int'l*, pg. 924

Matthews, Terry, Gen. Mgr.--Microsep International Thailand, Ltd., Bangkok, Thailand; *U.S. Public*, pg. 143

Matthews, William E., Mng. Dir.--Southern Tree Surgeons, Ltd., Crawley, United Kingdom; *U.S. Private*, pg. 119
Matthias, Donald, Pres.--Little Falls Color Print, Little Falls, NY; *U.S. Private*, pg. 1050
Matthiensen, Ernst-Richard, Mng. Dir.--Dresdner International Finance plc, Dublin, Ireland; *Int'l*, pg. 419
Matthys, Paul, Chm. Bd.--TradeARBED S.A., Luxembourg, Luxembourg; *Int'l*, pg. 79
Mattiasson, Sture, Country Mgr.--Danzas AB, Molndal, Sweden; *Int'l*, pg. 382
Mattie, Richard J., Pres.--A-G Safety Sales, Inc., Baton Rouge, LA; *U.S. Public*, pg. 1650
Mattila, Markku, Chief Oper. Officer--MacGREGOR Group, Kaarina, Finland; *Int'l*, pg. 670
Mattila, Tapani, Mng. Dir.--Wisaforest Sverige AB, Stockholm, Sweden; *Int'l*, pg. 1429
Mattingly, David, Chm.--Young & Rubicam Mattingly, Richmond, Australia; *U.S. Private*, pg. 1198
Mattingly, John, Pres.--COMSAT World Systems, Bethesda, MD; *U.S. Public*, pg. 424
Mattinson, Graham, Mng. Dir.--PPP Beaumont PLC, High Wycombe, United Kingdom; *Int'l*, pg. 1020
Mattly, James, Pres.--Loomis-Fargo & Co., Houston, TX; *U.S. Public*, pg. 245
Mattola, Guy A., Pres.--Ikon Office Solutions-Pittsburgh, Pittsburgh, PA; *U.S. Public*, pg. 864
Mattoon, David S., Exec. V.P. & Asst. Mgr.-Natl. Sls.--Jefferies & Company, Inc., Los Angeles, CA; *U.S. Public*, *pg. 925*
Mattoon, David S., Mgr.--Jefferies & Company, Inc., Dallas, TX; *U.S. Public*, pg. 925
Mattos, William, Sr. Mgr.--EDE - Embraer Equipment Division, Sao Jose dos Campos, Brazil; *Int'l*, pg. 452
Mattot, E., Mng. Dir.--Inbar Computer Training Ltd., Tel Aviv, Israel; *Int'l*, pg. 1007
Mattson, Austin, Plant Mgr.--Barry of San Angelo, San Angelo, TX; *U.S. Public*, pg. 192
Mattson, Beverley, Pres.--Gellatly Hankey Marine Services, Houston, TX; *Int'l*, pg. 672
Mattson, Bradford C., Pres.--Bay Mills (Delaware), Inc., Wilmington, DE; *Int'l*, pg. 1170
Mattson, Bradford C., Pres.--Perma Glas-Mesh, Inc., Dover, OH; *Int'l*, pg. 1171
Mattson, Lorne K., Mng. Partner--Brookfield Homes Partners, Vancouver, Canada; *Int'l*, pg. 228
Mattson, Ralph S., V.P.-Opers.--Minera Rayrock Inc. Chile, Santiago, Chile; *Int'l*, pg. 1089
Mattsson, Ove, Pres.--Casco Nobel AB, Stockholm, Sweden; *Int'l*, pg. 48
Matusch, Antony H., Mng. Dir.--Dixie Benders Limited, London, United Kingdom; *U.S. Public*, pg. 672
Matusek, Brian, Pres.-SPOCA--Production Operators, Inc., Houston, TX; *U.S. Public*, pg. 298
Matyjek, Adam, Pres.--Chr. Hansen Poland Sp. z.o.o., Warsaw, Poland; *Int'l*, pg. 289
Matz, Roland, Pres.--Saba Trading AB, Arsta, Sweden; *Int'l*, *pg. 709*
Matzke, Richard, Pres.--Chevron Overseas Petroleum, Inc., San Ramon, CA; *U.S. Public*, pg. 348
Matzner, Erwin, Chief Oper. Officer--NIFE Ges.m.b.H., Vienna, Austria; *Int'l*, pg. 53
Matzner, H., Mgr.--Desowag GmbH, Dusseldorf, Germany; *Int'l*, pg. 1501
Mauch, Robert C., Pres.--AmeriGas, Inc., Valley Forge, PA; *U.S. Public*, pg. 1653
Mauer, Dieter, Editor-in-Chief--LR Medienverlag GmbH, Cottbus, Germany; *Int'l*, pg. 1478
Mauersberger, P., Chief Exec. Officer--Zurich Life Insurance Company Ltd., Quarry Bay, Hong Kong; *Int'l*, pg. 1530
Maughan, C.J.S., Mng. Dir.--Oerlikon Logistics Ltd., Faldingworth, United Kingdom; *Int'l*, pg. 998
Maughan, H.B., Chief Oper. Officer & Mng. Dir.--Kidde Thorn Fire Protection Limited, Oldham, United Kingdom; *Int'l*, pg. 1500
Maul, Peter, Pres.--Nanocor, Inc., Arlington Heights, IL; *U.S. Public*, pg. 64
Mauldin, Larry D., Chm., Pres. & Chief Exec. Officer--SunTrust Bank, East Tennessee, N.A., Knoxville, TN; *U.S. Public*, pg. 1538
Maule, Charles R. (Rick), Gen. Mgr.-Graphics Systems--Desktop Graphics, Salt Lake City, UT; *U.S. Public*, pg. 596
Maule, Helmut, Mng. Dir.--Hausbau Wuestenrot GmbH, Ludwigsburg, Germany; *Int'l*, pg. 1514
Maupay, Walter R., Jr., Pres.--Calgon Vestal Laboratories, Saint Louis, MO; *U.S. Public*, pg. 1515
Maurer, Claus, Country Mgr.--Skandia Versicherungs-AG, Neuisenburg, Germany; *Int'l*, pg. 1258
Maurer, Dr., Chief Oper. Officer--Galenus Chemicals GmbH, Mannheim, Germany; *Int'l*, pg. 331
Maurer, Jon, Plant Mgr.--Calgon Carbon Corp., Catlettsburg, Catlettsburg, KY; *U.S. Public*, pg. 293
Maurer, Kurt, Pres.--Knurr-Heinzinger Electronic GmbH, Rosenheim, Germany; *Int'l*, pg. 739
Maurer, Rolf W., Pres.--Clough Chemical Co., Ltd., Saint Jean-sur-Richelieu, Canada; *Int'l*, pg. 199
Maurer, Terrence, V.P. & Gen. Mgr.--Stroehmann Bakeries, Harrisburg, PA; *Int'l*, pg. 1495
Maurer, Warren, Chief Oper. Officer& Exec. V.P.--Shadow Broadcast Services, Bala Cynwyd, PA; *U.S. Public*, pg. 1763
Maurhofer, Fritz, Chief Exec. Officer--MBT Holding, Ltd., Zurich, Switzerland; *Int'l*, pg. 1465
Mauri, D., Mng. Dir.--NRG Comunicaciones S.A., Barcelona, Spain; *Int'l*, pg. 1116
Maurice, Samuel, Pres. & Chief Exec. Officer--London House, Rosemont, IL; *U.S. Public*, pg. 1070
Mauritz, F., Pres. & Gen. Mgr.--Bank Mendes Gans NV, Amsterdam, Netherlands; *Int'l*, pg. 647
Maury, Alain, Dir. Gen.--Groupe Strategies, Issy-les-Moulineaux, France; *Int'l*, pg. 1099
Mauser, Helmut, Co-Chm. Bd.--Krupp Metalurgica Campo Limpo Ltda., Sao Paulo, Brazil; *Int'l*, pg. 508
Mauzey, James J., Pres.--Bristol-Myers Squibb Pharmaceutical Division, Evansville, IN; *U.S. Public*, pg. 254
Mavrigian, M., Editor--Jobber Retailer, Akron, OH; *Int'l*, pg. 1446
Mavrikis, Costas, Dir.-Germany--Olympic Airways, New York, NY; *Int'l*, pg. 1004
Mawdsley, Jack, Chief Exec. Officer-Quarry Div.--Tarmac Roadstone Ltd., Matlock, United Kingdom; *Int'l*, pg. 1355
Mawer, Larry, Pres.--Taylor Products, Inc., Payne, OH; *U.S. Private*, pg. 1071
Max, M., Mng. Dir.--Reckitt & Colman Industrial Ltda., Sao Paulo, Brazil; *Int'l*, pg. 1090
Maxe, Claes, Pres.--Borel & Dunner, Inc., Novi, MI; *U.S. Public*, pg. 260
Maxfield, R.C., Dist. Sls. Mgr.--Singapore Airlines Ltd., Dallas, TX; *Int'l*, pg. 1374
Maxheim, John H., Pres.--Piedmont Energy Company, Charlotte, NC; *U.S. Public*, pg. 1295
Maxheim, John H., Pres.--Piedmont Intrastate Pipeline Company, Charlotte, NC; *U.S. Public*, pg. 1295
Maxheim, John H., Pres.--Piedmont Interstate Pipeline Company, Charlotte, NC; *U.S. Public*, pg. 1295
Maxson, Mark B., Sr. V.P.--Willis Faber North America, Inc.-California, San Francisco, CA; *Int'l*, pg. 1503
Maxson, Mike, Dir.-Opers.--Advance Circuits, Specialty Products, Minnetonka, MN; *Int'l*, pg. 713
Maxson, Richard, Exec. V.P. & Gen. Mgr.--Holman Boiler Works, Inc., Dallas, TX; *U.S. Private*, pg. 274
Maxted, John, Asst Mgr.-Opers.--Enterra Oil Field Services, Ltd., Norfolk, United Kingdom; *U.S. Public*, pg. 1750
Maxwell, Bonnie, V.P.--UMI Data Courier, Louisville, KY; *U.S. Public*, pg. 201
Maxwell, Carlyle, Jr., Pres.--SMI-Owen Steel Company, Columbia, SC; *U.S. Public*, pg. 413
Maxwell, Hamish, Chm. Bd.--WPP Group plc, London, United Kingdom; *Int'l*, pg. 1482
Maxwell, Harold C., Grp. V.P.--Temple-Inland Forest Products Corp.-Building Products Group, Diboll, TX; *U.S. Public*, pg. 1575
Maxwell, J. Gregory, Pres. & Chief Exec. Officer--Old-First National Bank in Bluffton, Bluffton, IN; *U.S. Public*, pg. 674
Maxwell, James, Partner & Chief Exec. Officer-Scope Ketchum--Scope Ketchum Communications Ltd., London, United Kingdom; *U.S. Private*, pg. 617
Maxwell, John, Distr. Mgr.--Westward Div., Troy, MI; *Int'l*, pg. 1244
Maxwell, Phillip, Gen. Mgr.--Cellular One Buffalo, Cheektowaga, NY; *U.S. Public*, pg. 1415
Maxwell, R., Gen. Mgr.--Burgess-SAIA Inc., Buffalo Grove, IL; *Int'l*, pg. 1500
Maxwell, R., Chief Oper. Officer--Burgess Saia Co. Inc., Scarborough, Canada; *Int'l*, pg. 1500
Maxwell, Robert O., Pres.--Security Life Insurance Company of America, Minnetonka, MN; *U.S. Private*, pg. 980
Maxwell, Robert O., Pres.--Congress Life Insurance Company, Minnetonka, MN; *U.S. Private*, pg. 980
May, Alan L., County Mgr.--Insurance Company of North America (U.K.) Limited, London, United Kingdom; *U.S. Public*, pg. 363
May, Alan L., County Mgr.--Cigna Services U.K. Limited, London, United Kingdom; *U.S. Public*, pg. 363
May, Alan L., Dir.--Ernest Linsdell Limited, London, United Kingdom; *U.S. Public*, pg. 363
May, Alfred K., Chm. Bd.--Ford Bank Aktiengesellschaft (Austria), Salzburg, Austria; *U.S. Public*, pg. 665
May, Bernard, Chief Oper. Officer--Granges Aluminium S.A., Paris, France; *Int'l*, pg. 441
May, Charles, Pres.--Transmix Corporation, Los Angeles, CA; *U.S. Public*, pg. 1489
May, George, Mng. Dir.-Civil Engrng. Div.--Costain Building & Civil Engineering Limited, Maidenhead, United Kingdom; *Int'l*, pg. 336
May, Jack B., Mgr.--Spalding Australia Pty. Ltd., Hawthorn, Australia; *U.S. Private*, pg. 630
May, Jim, Pres.--Heatec, Inc., Chattanooga, TN; *U.S. Public*, *pg. 141*
May, Melborne, Pres. & Gen. Mgr.--May Supply Company, Inc., Harrisonburg, VA; *U.S. Public*, pg. 1727
May, Milt, Mgr.--Du Pont Canada-Kingston Works, Kingston, Canada; *U.S. Public*, pg. 532
May, Milt, Mgr.--Du Pont Canada-Kingston Research, Kingston, Canada; *U.S. Public*, pg. 532
May, P. Thomas, Jr., Pres. & Chief Exec. Officer--First Virginia Mortgage Company, Falls Church, VA; *U.S. Public*, pg. 642
May, Phil, Exec. V.P. & Gen. Mgr.--Cramer-Krasselt/Direct, Chicago, IL; *U.S. Private*, pg. 286
May, Sam, Plant Mgr.--Acme Brick Co., Tulsa, OK; *U.S. Public*, pg. 936
May, Thomas O., Pres.--Weil-McLain, Michigan City, IN; *U.S. Public*, pg. 1676
May, Timothy J., Product Support Rep.--EMPIRE Machinery - California, Flagstaff, AZ; *U.S. Private*, pg. 375
Maya, Victor, Chief Exec. Officer--Kendall Regional Medical Center, Miami, FL; *U.S. Public*, pg. 405
Mayberry, Ted, Chief Oper. Officer--Polifin Limited, Randburg, South Africa; *Int'l*, pg. 1197
Maycock, Jerry C.R., Chief Exec.--Queensland Cement Ltd., Milton, Australia; *Int'l*, pg. 629
Maycock, Lan, Gen. Mgr.--Akzo Resins & Vehicles, Addison, IL; *Int'l*, pg. 48
Mayen, Donald, Mgr.--Multiform, Inc., Memphis, TN; *U.S. Private*, pg. 1193
Mayer, Guy L., Mng. Dir.--Zimmer Limited, Swindon, United Kingdom; *U.S. Public*, pg. 257
Mayer, Juan, Chief Oper. Officer--Titania Insurance Company of America, South Burlington, VT; *U.S. Public*, pg. 1731
Mayer, Martin A., Pres.--Maurin-Ogden Management Corporation, New Orleans, LA; *U.S. Private*, pg. 715
Mayer, Michael, Gen. Mgr.--El Al Israel Airlines, Ltd., New York, NY; *Int'l*, pg. 435
Mayer, Mike, Exec. Dir.--QualMed Plans for Health-New Mexico, Albuquerque, NM; *U.S. Public*, pg. 678
Mayer, Peter M., Pres.--NAL/Penguin Inc., New York, NY; *Int'l*, pg. 1027
Mayer, Richard, V.P.--Utica Lloyds of Texas, Dallas, TX; *U.S. Private*, pg. 1130
Mayer, Richard, V.P.--Utica National Insurance Co. of Texas, Dallas, TX; *U.S. Private*, pg. 1130
Mayer, Roger L., Pres.--Turner Entertainment Company, Los Angeles, CA; *U.S. Public*, pg. 1615
Mayer, Thomas, Gen. Mgr.--Reclamation Div. (Vancouver), Vancouver, WA; *Int'l*, pg. 1271
Mayer, Volker, Chm.--ASAL Ingenieure GmbH, Kaiserslautern, Germany; *Int'l*, pg. 608
Mayerhauser, D., Mng. Dir.--Hosokawa Micron International B.V., Amsterdam, Netherlands; *Int'l*, pg. 636
Mayersack, Joseph, Gen. Mgr.--Lockheed Martin Advanced Projects, Manassas, VA; *U.S. Public*, pg. 1008
Mayfield, Alan, Mgr.--Commercial Metals-Austin Inc., Austin, TX; *U.S. Public*, pg. 413
Mayfield, Sharolyn, Mgr.-Station--Target, Garden City, KS; *U.S. Public*, pg. 984
Mayhe, A., Plant Mgr.--Kenworth Truck Co., Chillicothe, OH; *U.S. Public*, pg. 1246
Mayhew, Adelaide K., Pres.--Prism-Dae, Inc., Mc Lean, VA; *U.S. Public*, pg. 110
Mayhew, Fred C., Chief Design Exec.--Ford North American Design, Dearborn, MI; *U.S. Public*, pg. 662
Mayle, Roger, Plant Mgr.--Brockway Standard Ohio, Inc., Solon, OH; *U.S. Public*, pg. 164
Maynard, Otto, Pres. & Chief Exec. Officer--Wolf Creek Nuclear Operating Corp., Burlington, KS; *U.S. Public*, pg. 1759
Maynard, Philip C., Pres. & Sec.--ICS Intangibles Holding Company, Irvine, CA; *U.S. Public*, pg. 783
Maynard, Robert E., Pres. & Chief Exec. Officer--Allianz Canada, Toronto, Canada; *Int'l*, pg. 59
Mayne, W.F.S., Dir.-Petfood--Pauls plc, Ipswich, United Kingdom; *Int'l*, pg. 598
Maynor, James E., Pres.--First Union Home Equity Corporation, Charlotte, NC; *U.S. Public*, pg. 640
Mayo, Earl, Gen. Mgr.--Industrial Packaging Div. (Crossett), Crossett, AR; *Int'l*, pg. 1270
Mayo, Earl, Gen. Mgr.--Industrial Packaging Div. (DeQuincy), De Quincy, LA; *Int'l*, pg. 1270
Mayo, J.H., Mng. Dir.--Australian Window Furnishings (NSW) Pty. Ltd., Sydney, Australia; *Int'l*, pg. 639
Mayo, John, V.P. & Gen. Mgr.--Florida Sun Publications, Inc., Bradenton, FL; *Int'l*, pg. 1026
Mayo, Larry S., Pres.--Ikon Office Solutions New York, New York, NY; *U.S. Public*, pg. 863
Mayor, J.J., V.P.-Eastern Region--Benjamin Moore & Co., Montvale, NJ; *U.S. Private*, pg. 133
Mayor, Manuel Plaza, Dir. Gen.--Stafford-Miller De Espana, Madrid, Spain; *U.S. Public*, pg. 237
Mayoral, Carmelo, Pres.--Repsol Distribucion, S.A., Madrid, Spain; *Int'l*, pg. 1104
Mayr, Ulrich, Chief Oper. Officer--Aupperle Aufzuge GmbH, Munich, Germany; *Int'l*, pg. 747
Mayrhofer, Josef, Mgr.--Voest-Alpine Services and Technologies Corp.-Baltimore, Baltimore, MD; *Int'l*, pg. 1471
Mayrhuber, Wolfgang, Chm.-Exec. Bd.--Lufthansa Technik AG, Hamburg, Germany; *Int'l*, pg. 407
Mayrose, Bill, Plant Mgr.--Hoechst Celanese Corp. Spunbond Products, Spartanburg, SC; *Int'l*, pg. 626
Mays, William G., Chief Oper. Officer--United Chemical Products, Indianapolis, IN; *U.S. Private*, pg. 718
Maytain, Ch., Mgr.--Societe de Banque Suisse, Petit-Lancy, Switzerland; *Int'l*, pg. 1329
Mazaika, M., V.P. & Gen. Mgr.--Lockheed Austin Division, Austin, TX; *U.S. Public*, pg. 1008
Mazany, Dan, Gen. Partner--Buildings Division, Kansas City, MO; *U.S. Private*, pg. 146
Mazhar, Ismail, Mgr.--John Crane Middle East - Western Region, Cairo, Egypt; *Int'l*, pg. 1339
Maziar, Harry, Pres.--Zep Manufacturing Company, Atlanta, GA; *U.S. Public*, pg. 1160
Mazur, Stefan, Pres.--General DataComm Intl. Corp., Middlebury, CT; *U.S. Public*, pg. 708
Mazure, Gerard R., Dir. Gen.--Dexter S.A., Tournus, France; *U.S. Public*, pg. 505
Mazurek, Ken, Plant Mgr.--W. H. Salisbury & Co., Chicago, IL; *Int'l*, pg. 1244
Mazza, Giorgio, Pres.--Standex International GmbH, Krefeld, Germany; *U.S. Public*, pg. 1507
Mazza, Nick, Branch Mgr.--Circle International, Saint Rose, LA; *U.S. Public*, pg. 371
Mazzaferro, Thomas M., Chief Fin. Officer--American Skandia Investment Services, Inc., Shelton, CT; *Int'l*, pg. 1257
Mazzarino, Pietro, Mng. Dir.--Finservizi S.p.A., Milan, Italy; *Int'l*, pg. 170
Mazzini, G., Chief Opr. Officer--New Hunter Engineering, Turin, Italy; *Int'l*, pg. 474
Mazzo, James, Mng. Dir.--Allergan S.p.A., Pomezia, Italy; *U.S. Public*, pg. 46
Mazzocchi, Rudy A., Pres.--Microvena Corporation, White Bear Lake, MN; *U.S. Private*, pg. 862
Mazzola, A., Pres.--B.F. Goodrich Chemical Italia SRL, Milan, Italy; *U.S. Public*, pg. 752
Mazzuca, Carl D., Pres.--Gas Tech, Newark, CA; *U.S. Public*, pg. 1593
Mc Bride, Vicki, Branch Mgr.--Union-Transport Corporation-Detroit Office, Taylor, MI; *U.S. Private*, pg. 1119
Mc Carrick, William P., V.P. & Gen. Mgr.--Kodak Processing Laboratories, Rochester, NY; *U.S. Public*, pg. 551
Mc Intyre, william, Admin.--Boca Raton Convalescent Center, Boca Raton, FL; *U.S. Public*, pg. 1712
Mc Rae, Neil, Mng. Dir.--The Reader's Digest Association Limited, London, United Kingdom; *U.S. Public*, pg. 1368
McAfee, Bob, V.P.--Dean Industries, Inc., Gardena, CA; *Int'l*, *pg. 188*

McAfee, Dwayne L., Pres. & Chief Exec. Officer--First Image Management Co., Atlanta, GA; *U.S. Public*, pg. 631
McAfee, Robert, Pres. & Chief Exec. Officer--Lincoln Foodservice Products, Inc., Fort Wayne, IN; *Int'l*, pg. 188
McAleer, Harry J., Mng. Dir.--Thermos Limited, Brentwood, United Kingdom; *Int'l*, pg. 938
McAleer, Ian, Mng. Dir.--Evode Group Ltd., Stafford, United Kingdom; *Int'l*, pg. 802
McAlhaney, W. Hardee, Chief Oper. Officer--Holiday RV Superstores, Inc.-Ft. Myers, Fort Myers, FL; *U.S. Public*, pg. 830
McAlhaney, W. Hardee, Chief Oper. Officer--Holiday RV Superstores, Inc.-Orlando, Orlando, FL; *U.S. Public*, pg. 830
McAllister, Duane, Publisher--The Clarion-Ledger, Jackson, MS; *U.S. Public*, pg. 700
McAllister, S., Chief Exec.--HMV Limited, Marlow, United Kingdom; *Int'l*, pg. 427
McAllister, Thomas, Div. Mgr.--Rocky Mount Div., Rocky Mount, NC; *U.S. Public*, pg. 1504
McAllister, Tom, Gen. Mgr.--Plastic Trim, Inc., Dayton, OH; *U.S. Public*, pg. 919
McAloon, Brian, Mng. Dir.--Analog Devices BV, Limerick, Ireland; *U.S. Public*, pg. 108
McAlpine, Ross, Pres.--Inter-Tel Leasing, Inc., Phoenix, AZ; *U.S. Public*, pg. 888
McAlpine, Ross E., Pres.--Inter-Tel Net Solutions, Phoenix, AZ; *U.S. Public*, pg. 888
McAnally, J., Mng. Dir.--Bally South Africa Ltd., Parklands, South Africa; *Int'l*, pg. 997
McAnally, James W., Pres.--Martin Marietta Astronautics, Denver, CO; *U.S. Public*, pg. 1007
McAnaney, M.T., Chief Exec. Officer--Blackwood Hodge (Tanzania) Limited, Dar es Salaam, Tanzania; *Int'l*, pg. 231
McAndrew, Mark S., Pres.--Globe Life And Accident Insurance Co., Oklahoma City, OK; *U.S. Public*, pg. 1622
McAndrew, Mark S., Pres.--Globe Life And Accident Insurance Co. of Oklahoma, Inc., Oklahoma City, OK; *U.S. Public*, pg. 1622
McAndrew, Nicholas, Chm. Bd.--Murray Johnstone Limited, Glasgow, United Kingdom; *U.S. Public*, pg. 1674
McAniff, Nora, Publr.--People, New York, NY; *U.S. Public*, pg. 1613
McAnoy, Colleen, Fin. Dir.--Bensimon Byrne DMB&B Toronto, Toronto, Canada; *U.S. Private*, pg. 303
McAra, Cynthia A., Pres.--Family Service Life Insurance Co., Dallas, TX; *U.S. Public*, pg. 1622
McArthur, J.C., Pres. & Chief Exec. Officer--Hartford Insurance Group of Canada, Willowdale, Canada; *U.S. Public*, pg. 794
McArthur, N., Chief Oper. Officer--Ames Crosta Babcock Ltd., Heywood, United Kingdom; *Int'l*, pg. 471
McArthur, Rawdon W., Chief Fin. Officer & Treas.--BellSouth International, Inc., Atlanta, GA; *U.S. Public*, pg. 208
McAtee, David, V.P. & Gen. Mgr.--WYFF-TV, Greenville, SC; *U.S. Public*, pg. 1344
McAuley, Barry, Chm.--Valley Fig Growers, Fresno, CA; *U.S. Private*, pg. 1051
McAuley, John T., Sr. V.P.--Sumitomo Marine Mgmt Services, Warren, NJ; *Int'l*, pg. 1314
McAvoy, Kevin, Sr. Acct. Exec.--CMI-Detroit, Birmingham, MI; *U.S. Private*, pg. 287
McBride, Allen, Pres.--Forged Products, Houston, TX; *U.S. Private*, pg. 299
McBride, David, Gen. Mgr.--Reclamation Div. (Ft. Lauderdale), Fort Lauderdale, FL; *Int'l*, pg. 1270
McBride, J.I., Mng. Dir.--Ducost Engineering Ltd., Birmingham, United Kingdom; *Int'l*, pg. 585
McBride, R. L., Jr., Chm. Bd. & Chief Exec. Officer--NationsBank/Marshall Co., Lewisburg, TN; *U.S. Public*, pg. 1163
McBride, Robert, Gen. Mgr.--Powerwinch Div., Bridgeport, CT; *U.S. Public*, pg. 218
McBride, T. Eugene, Pres. & Chief Exec. Officer--Dyersburg Fabric, Dyersburg, TN; *U.S. Public*, pg. 538
McCabe, Alan, Chief Oper. Officer--Axel Johnson Corp. (HK) Ltd., Wan Chai, Hong Kong; *Int'l*, pg. 711
McCabe, Kenneth T., Mng. Dir.--Acme United Ltd.-Surmanco Division, Sheffield, United Kingdom; *U.S. Public*, pg. 17
McCabe, Ray, Gen. Mgr.--American Cablevision of Monroeville, Inc., Monroeville, PA; *U.S. Public*, pg. 1610
McCabe, Virginia, Gen. Mgr.--Reclamation Div. (Oakland), Oakland, CA; *Int'l*, pg. 1271
McCafferty, George, Pres.--Holmes Protection of Philadelphia, Inc., Philadelphia, PA; *U.S. Public*, pg. 1649
McCaffery, James, V.P.-Sales & Mktg.--Mitsumi Electronics Corp., Irving, TX; *Int'l*, pg. 884
McCaffrey, Gary, Pres.--National Service Cleaning Corporation, South Windsor, CT; *U.S. Public*, pg. 1208
McCaffrey, Joseph J., Pres. & Chief Exec. Officer--United Jersey Bank Services Co, Paramus, NJ; *U.S. Public*, pg. 1528
McCaffrey, Joseph J., Pres. & Chief Exec. Officer--UJB Investor Services Company, Paramus, NJ; *U.S. Public*, pg. 1528
McCaffrey, P.G., Gen. Mgr.-Fin. & Admin.--Australian Poultry Ltd., Beresfield, Australia; *Int'l*, pg. 555
McCague, Beth, Chm. Bd., Pres. & Chief Exec. Officer--First Union National Bank of Tennessee, Nashville, TN; *U.S. Public*, pg. 640
McCain, James, Pres.--Oreck Manufacturing Company, Long Beach, MS; *U.S. Private*, pg. 819
McCall, J. Lash, V.P. & Mgr.--Chase Futures & Options, Inc., London, United Kingdom; *U.S. Public*, pg. 341
McCall, James, Mgr.--General Employment Enterprises, Inc., Palo Alto, CA; *U.S. Public*, pg. 715
McCall, John, Gen. Mgr.--Frank Paxton Lumber Company, Denver, CO; *U.S. Private*, pg. 585
McCall, Kerry, Gen. Mgr.--McCrometer Inc., Hemet, CA; *U.S. Public*, pg. 482
McCall, Michael, Mgr.-Opers.--Greenville Mfg. Div., Greenville, NC; *U.S. Public*, pg. 1475
McCall, Ron, Gen. Mgr.--Jones Lumber, Minneapolis, MN; *U.S. Private*, pg. 585
McCall, William, Pres.--Joseph Kirschner Co., Augusta, ME; *U.S. Private*, pg. 599
McCalla, John, Pres.--King Arthur Inc., Statesville, NC; *U.S. Public*, pg. 1465
McCallum, Craig L., Pres. & Chief Exec. Officer--Mission Viejo Company, Mission Viejo, CA; *U.S. Public*, pg. 1289
McCallum, Craig L., Pres. & Chief Exec. Officer-Mission Viejo Company--Philip Morris Capital Corporation, Rye Brook, NY; *U.S. Public*, pg. 1289
McCallum, Jim, Exec. V.P.--Lees Carpets, Greensboro, NC; *U.S. Public*, pg. 268
McCallum, John D., Pres.--Potomac Capital Investment Corporation, Washington, DC; *U.S. Public*, pg. 1319
McCallum, W.T., Pres.--Great-West Life & Annuity Insurance Co., Englewood, CO; *Int'l*, pg. 558
McCallum, William, Pres.--Long Prairie Packing Co., Long Prairie, MN; *U.S. Private*, pg. 945
McCann, Chris, Pres.--MCS Business Solutions, Inc., New York, NY; *Int'l*, pg. 262
McCann, Dave, Pres.--Toronto Dominion Securities (U.S.A.) Inc., New York, NY; *Int'l*, pg. 1401
McCann, Paul R., Pres. & Chief Exec. Officer--Mellon Bond Associates Corp., Pittsburgh, PA; *U.S. Public*, pg. 1085
McCann, Thomas, Pres.--Granite State Insurance Co., Manchester, NH; *U.S. Public*, pg. 84
McCann, Thomas, Pres.--Illinois National Insurance Co., Manchester, NH; *U.S. Public*, pg. 84
McCann, Thomas, Pres.--Inland National Ins. Co., Manchester, NH; *U.S. Public*, pg. 84
McCann, Thomas, Pres.--International Computer Services, Inc., Manchester, NH; *U.S. Public*, pg. 84
McCanto, Randy, Gen. Mgr.--Amador Ledger-Dispatch, Jackson, CA; *U.S. Private*, pg. 225
McCappin, Brian, Plant Dir.--Rolls-Royce Motor Cars Limited, Mulliner Park Ward, Crewe, United Kingdom; *Int'l*, pg. 1467
McCarley, Thomas D., Pres.--CommLink, Houston, TX; *U.S. Public*, pg. 809
McCarren, P.J., Mgr.--Alum-A-Therm, Westminster, CA; *U.S. Public*, pg. 999
McCarren, P.J., Mgr.--Lindberg Heat Treating Co., Los Angeles, CA; *U.S. Public*, pg. 999
McCarron, T. Robert, Pres.--Insurance Management Incorporated, New Haven, CT; *U.S. Public*, pg. 827
McCarter, Harvey, Gen. Mgr.--Seattle Airline Learning Center, Seattle, WA; *U.S. Public*, pg. 219
McCarter, James P., Pres.--Ikon Office Solutions-Atlanta, Norcross, GA; *U.S. Public*, pg. 863
McCarthy, Bill, Plant Mgr.--Kenlake Foods, Murray, KY; *U.S. Public*, pg. 967
McCarthy, C.M., Chm. Bd.--McCain Foods (GB) Limited, Scarborough, United Kingdom; *Int'l*, pg. 850
McCarthy, Charles B., Jr., Pres.--Energy Services, Inc., Rosemead, CA; *U.S. Public*, pg. 564
McCarthy, Charles H., Gen. Mgr.--Aqualon Canada Inc., Etobicoke, Canada; *U.S. Public*, pg. 810
McCarthy, Colm, Exec. V.P. & Reg. Mgr.--Bank of America NT&SA, Singapore, Singapore; *U.S. Public*, pg. 182
McCarthy, Daniel, Pres. & Chief Exec. Officer--Cowles Business Media, Inc., Stamford, CT; *U.S. Private*, pg. 281
McCarthy, Dennis, Pres.--Joern's Sunrise Medical, Stevens Point, WI; *U.S. Public*, pg. 1536
McCarthy, Des, Mng. Dir.--Willis Corroon Management Limited-Dublin, Dublin, Ireland; *Int'l*, pg. 1509
McCarthy, Gerald M., Pres.--Zenith Video Tech Corporation, Glenview, IL; *U.S. Public*, pg. 1790
McCarthy, H.R., Mgr.--Webb-Conveyor Company of Australia Pty. Ltd., Thomastown, Australia; *U.S. Private*, pg. 1157
McCarthy, J.T., Rep.--ING Bank Istanbul, Istanbul, Turkey; *Int'l*, pg. 649
McCarthy, James E., Pres.--Woodward-Clyde Federal Services, Denver, CO; *U.S. Public*, pg. 1657
McCarthy, Joan E., Asst. Branch Mgr.--Valley National Bank, Sparta, NJ; *U.S. Public*, pg. 1706
McCarthy, Kevin, Gen. Mgr.--Bay State Propane Division, Taunton, MA; *U.S. Public*, pg. 197
McCarthy, Kevin, Gen. Mgr.--Energy USA, Westborough, MA; *U.S. Public*, pg. 197
McCarthy, Kevin P., Pres.--UNUM Japan Accident Insurance Company Limited, Tokyo, Japan; *U.S. Public*, pg. 1700
McCarthy, M.C., Chief Exec. & Grp. Country Mgr.--Barclays Bank PLC, Tokyo, Japan; *Int'l*, pg. 165
McCarthy, Mike, Mgr.--Tri-State Mack Inc., Jackson, TN; *U.S. Private*, pg. 1101
McCarthy, Patrick, Plant Mgr.--Donaldson Co., Inc., Cresco, IA; *U.S. Public*, pg. 517
McCarthy, Peter, Chief Oper. Officer--A.T. Cross Ltd., Ballina, Ireland; *U.S. Public*, pg. 461
McCarthy, Roger, V.P. & Gen. Mgr.--Mont Tremblant Resort, Inc., Mont-Tremblant, Canada; *Int'l*, pg. 685
McCarthy, Ron, Dir.-Opers.--Primedica, Redfield, AR; *U.S. Public*, pg. 733
McCarthy, Terry, Mng. Dir.--Product Plus International, London, United Kingdom; *U.S. Public*, pg. 1225
McCarthy, William J., Pres.--Pepper Construction of Indiana, Inc. LLC, Indianapolis, IN; *U.S. Private*, pg. 851
McCartney, Daniel P., Chm. Bd. & Chief Exec. Officer--Healthcare Services Group, Inc., Huntingdon Valley, PA; *U.S. Public*, pg. 803
McCartney, J.J., Chief Exec. Officer--Empire Fire & Marine Insurance Co., Omaha, NE; *Int'l*, pg. 1530
McCartney, J.J., Chief Oper. Officer--Empire Indemnity Insurance Company, Omaha, NE; *Int'l*, pg. 1530
McCartney, John, Pres.-Client Access--3Com Corporation, Skokie, IL; *U.S. Public*, pg. 1604
McCarty, D.L., Pres.--Aquionics Inc., Erlanger, KY; *Int'l*, pg. 590
McCarty, Frederick R., V.P.--Atkinson Construction, Manila, Philippines; *U.S. Public*, pg. 143
McCarty, James L., Sr. V.P.--Ecolab Institutional Group, Saint Paul, MN; *U.S. Public*, pg. 562
McCaslin, William, V.P.--Harris Space Systems Corp., Rockledge, FL; *U.S. Public*, pg. 791
McCaughan, A.R., Pres.--Amoco Japan Ltd., Chicago, IL; *U.S. Public*, pg. 102
McCaughan, A.R., Pres.--Amoco Chemicals Far East, Ltd., Hong Kong, Hong Kong; *U.S. Public*, pg. 103
McCaul, Daniel, Pres.--Callaway Chemical Company, Columbus, GA; *U.S. Public*, pg. 1726
McCauley, D., Mng. Dir.--Coutts & Co (Isle of Man) Limited, Onchan, United Kingdom; *Int'l*, pg. 910
McCauley, Douglas A., Chief Oper. Officer--Mechanical Technology Inc.-Technology Grp.(Latham), Latham, NY; *U.S. Public*, pg. 1077
McCauley, J.T., Pres.--Avent, Inc., Tucson, AZ; *U.S. Public*, pg. 959
McCauley, James P., Gen. Mgr.--American Bank Note Co., Horsham, PA; *U.S. Public*, pg. 68
McCauley, Robert, Pres.--Devoe Paint, Cleveland, OH; *Int'l*, pg. 663
McCauley, Terry, V.P.-Western Region--Qualex Inc., Seattle, WA; *U.S. Public*, pg. 551
McCausland, Gary, V.P.--Domino's Pizza International, Inc., Ann Arbor, MI; *U.S. Private*, pg. 339
McCausland, Thomas, Pres. & Chief Exec. Officer--Siemens Medical Systems, Inc., Iselin, NJ; *Int'l*, pg. 1246
McCawley, Peter, Pres. & Chief Oper. Officer--Modern Building Cleaning Inc., Toronto, Canada; *U.S. Private*, pg. 79
McClain, B., Gen. Mgr.--Reclamation Div. (Augusta), Augusta, GA; *Int'l*, pg. 1270
McClain, Hugh, V.P.-Sls.--Harbinger Carpet, Atlanta, GA; *U.S. Public*, pg. 1121
McClain, Jerome G., Pres.--Key Community Development Corporation, Cleveland, OH; *U.S. Public*, pg. 954
McClain, Kenneth D., Pres.--McClain of Georgia, Inc., Macon, GA; *U.S. Public*, pg. 1065
McClain, Kenneth D., Pres.--Shelby Steel Processing Co., River Rouge, MI; *U.S. Public*, pg. 1065
McClain, M.F., Pres.--Rice-Carden Corp., Kansas City, MO; *U.S. Public*, pg. 944
McClanahan, D., Pres. & Chief Oper. Officer--Houston Lighting & Power Company, Houston, TX; *U.S. Public*, pg. 843
McClean, Murray R., Mng. Dir.--CMC (Australia) Pty. Limited, Sydney, Australia; *U.S. Public*, pg. 413
McClean, Richard, Chief Exec. Officer & Publisher--International Herald Tribune S.A., Neuilly-sur-Seine, France; *U.S. Public*, pg. 1176
McClean, Richard, Publisher & Chief Exec. Officer--International Herald Tribune, S.A., Neuilly-sur-Seine, France; *U.S. Public*, pg. 1743
McCleary, James W., Pres.--Facultative Resources, Inc., Stamford, CT; *U.S. Public*, pg. 215
McClellan, John, Pres. & Chief Exec. Officer--ASCG, Inc., Anchorage, AK; *U.S. Private*, pg. 80
McClellan, Michael, Div. Mgr.--FMC Food Ingredients Div., Philadelphia, PA; *U.S. Public*, pg. 605
McClelland, Jeffrey W., Pres.--Dexter Aerospace Materials Division, Pittsburg, CA; *U.S. Public*, pg. 504
McClelland, Kent, Chief Oper. Officer--Colorado Institutional Foods, Commerce City, CO; *U.S. Private*, pg. 989
McClelland, R., Pres. & Chief Oper. Officer--Dynamex Express, Mississauga, Canada; *Int'l*, pg. 36
McClenagan, Robert, Pres.--Ruby Tuesday Restaurants, Mobile, AL; *U.S. Public*, pg. 1412
McClennen, James C.A., Sr. Partner--Cooke & Bieler, Inc., Philadelphia, PA; *U.S. Public*, pg. 1673
McClintock, Michael, Mgr.--General Employment Enterprises, Inc., Naperville, IL; *U.S. Public*, pg. 714
McClintock, Royce, Pres.--M & H Dairy, Nashville, TN; *U.S. Public*, pg. 653
McCloskey, Victor R., V.P. & Gen. Mgr.--Applied Systems, York, PA; *U.S. Public*, pg. 1788
McClung, Conrad, V.P.--White Marsh Equities Corp., Baltimore, MD; *U.S. Public*, pg. 1409
McClung, Conrad D., V.P.--White Marsh Mall, Inc., Parkville, MD; *U.S. Public*, pg. 1409
McClung, Jim H., Pres.--Lithonia Lighting Co., Conyers, GA; *U.S. Public*, pg. 1160
McClung, Perry, Pres.--Universal Standard HealthCare of Michigan, Inc., Southfield, MI; *U.S. Public*, pg. 1698
McClung, Perry, Pres.--Universal Standard HealthCare of Ohio Inc., Southfield, MI; *U.S. Public*, pg. 1698
McClung, Perry, Pres.--Universal Standard HealthCare of Delaware, Inc., Southfield, MI; *U.S. Public*, pg. 1698
McClure, Alan, Pres.--Perfecseal, Inc., Mankato, MN; *U.S. Public*, pg. 210
McClure, B., Mng. Dir.--Ascom Nexion Inc., Acton, MA; *Int'l*, pg. 86
McClure, David, Gen. Mgr.--Bullfrog Mine, Elko, NV; *Int'l*, pg. 169
McClure, Kenneth A., Chief Oper. Officer--USAA Life Insurance Co., San Antonio, TX; *U.S. Private*, pg. 1115
McClure, Rex A., III, Pres.--Copperweld Miami Industries, Piqua, OH; *Int'l*, pg. 662
McClure, Robert, Gen. Mgr.--San Diego Wild Animal Park, Escondido, CA; *U.S. Private*, pg. 1207
McCluskey, Richard T., Pres.--Lubriplate Div. of Fiske Bros. Refining Co., Newark, NJ; *U.S. Private*, pg. 409
McColister, Russ, V.P. & Resident Mgr.--Camas Mill, Camas, WA; *U.S. Public*, pg. 671
McColl, Hugh L., Jr., Chm. Bd.--Superior Life Insurance Company, Charlotte, NC; *U.S. Public*, pg. 1165
McCollem, James, Pres.--Grumman Olson Division, Sturgis, MI; *U.S. Public*, pg. 1198
McColley, James R., Reg. Dir.--Piper Jaffray Inc., Seattle, WA; *U.S. Public*, pg. 1302
McCollough, Terry J., Publr.--Brainerd Daily Dispatch, Brainerd, MN; *U.S. Private*, pg. 995

McCollum, Jr., L. Gwaltney, Pres. & Chief Exec. Officer--First National Bank, Jasper, AL; *U.S. Public*, pg. 1549
McCollum, Robert, Pres.--Comtech Communications Corp., Tempe, AZ; *U.S. Public*, pg. 425
McCollum, William, Pres.--Harrington Industrial Plastics Inc., Chino, CA; *Int'l*, pg. 554
McComas, David, Pres.--Circuit City Western Div., Walnut, CA; *U.S. Public*, pg. 374
McComb, Dave, Gen. Mgr.--Utah Auto Auction, Midvale, UT; *U.S. Private*, pg. 283
McCombs, Rick, Pres.--Flowers Baking Co. of Norfolk, Inc., Norfolk, VA; *U.S. Public*, pg. 657
McConell, Pat, Gen. Mgr.--Golden State Foods-Phoenix Div., Phoenix, AZ; *U.S. Private*, pg. 460
McConnachie, Peter, Pres.--Moore International B.V., Leislen, Netherlands; *Int'l*, pg. 889
McConnell, Gerald, Pres.--A.B. Dick Company, Niles, IL; *U.S. Private*, pg. 791
McConnell, J. Steven, Pres.--AAR Aircraft Turbine Center, Elk Grove Village, IL; *U.S. Public*, pg. 1
McConnell, James A., Pres.--Northrop Grumman Allied Industries, Inc., Sturgis, MI; *U.S. Public*, pg. 1198
McConnell, Jim, Div. Mgr.--Transilwrap Co., Inc., Atlanta, GA; *U.S. Private*, pg. 1097
McConnell, Jim, Div. Mgr.--Transilwrap Co., Inc., Cleveland, OH; *U.S. Private*, pg. 1097
McConnell, John, Publisher--Peoria Journal Star, Inc., Peoria, IL; *U.S. Private*, pg. 275
McConnell, John, Pres. & Chief Exec. Officer--Medic Computer Systems, Inc., Raleigh, NC; *Int'l*, pg. 870
McConnell, Larry, Gen. Mgr.--Maestro Products Inc., Moreno Valley, CA; *U.S. Public*, pg. 895
McConnell, Paul R., Chm., Pres. & Chief Exec. Officer--Fleet Bank of Maine, Portland, ME; *U.S. Public*, pg. 649
McConnell, Thomas W., Pres.--Cigna Securities, Inc., Bloomfield, CT; *U.S. Public*, pg. 360
McConnell, W., Gen. Mgr.--Irish Biscuits-W & R Jacob, Dublin, Ireland; *Int'l*, pg. 381
McConnell, W.S., Pres.--Coastal Wood Products, Inc., City of Industry, CA; *U.S. Private*, pg. 720
McConney, F.O., Mng. Dir.--The Barbados Light & Power Co. Ltd., Bridgetown, Barbados; *U.S. Public*, pg. 990
McConville, Rick, Country Mgr.--IMSA S.A., Montevideo, Uruguay; *U.S. Public*, pg. 447
McCool, Pat, Dir.-Opers., Europe--Penn Racquet Sports, Mullingar, Ireland; *U.S. Public*, pg. 706
McCord, P.J., Chief Oper. Officer--Corbin Russwin, Inc., Berlin, CT; *Int'l*, pg. 1499
McCord, Patrick J., Pres.--Yale Security, Inc., Charlotte, NC; *Int'l*, pg. 1499
McCord, W. Shiles, Pres. & Chief Exec. Officer--City National Bank of Baton Rouge, Baton Rouge, LA; *U.S. Public*, pg. 629
McCorkindale, Douglas H., Chief Oper. Officer--Gannett Satellite Information Network, Inc., Arlington, VA; *U.S. Public*, pg. 700
McCorkindale, Neil M., Mng. Dir.--Sphinx Manufacturing Company, Ltd., Auckland, New Zealand; *U.S. Public*, pg. 53
McCormack, Robert, Branch Mgr.--Zellerbach Division, Miramar, FL; *U.S. Public*, pg. 1075
McCormick, Daniel J., Pres. & Chief Exec. Officer--NWNL Health Management Corp., Minneapolis, MN; *U.S. Public*, *pg. 1375*
McCormick, Douglas W., Chief Exec. Officer Officer--Lifetime Television/ABC, New York, NY; *U.S. Public*, pg. 512
McCormick, Douglas W., Chief Exec. Officer Officer--Lifetime Television/ABC, New York, NY; *U.S. Private*, pg. 516
McCormick, G. Roger, Pres. & Chief Exec. Officer--People's Bank & Trust Co., Mount Vernon, IN; *U.S. Public*, pg. 1217
McCormick, John, V.P.--Oconomowoc Canning Company, Oconomowoc, WI; *U.S. Public*, pg. 1519
McCormick, Larry, Chief Oper. Officer & Chief Fin. Officer--Automotive & Appliance Controls Div., Kendallville, IN; *U.S. Public*, pg. 556
McCormick, Mike, Gen. Mgr.--ITW Nifco, Inc., Hilliard, OH; *U.S. Public*, pg. 867
McCormick, Mike, Gen. Mgr.--ITW Nifco, Inc., Hilliard, OH; *Int'l*, pg. 929
McCormick, P.C., Mng. Dir.--Swiss Bank Corporation, New York, NY; *Int'l*, pg. 1329
McCormick, Rick M., Chief Oper. Officer--Corporate Express Delivery Systems Southwest, Inc., Houston, TX; *U.S. Public*, pg. 449
McCormick, Robert V., Pres. & Chief Exec. Officer--Laserscope Inc., San Jose, CA; *Int'l*, pg. 616
McCormick, Sheryl, Gen. Mgr.--Sterling Electronics, Fort Worth, TX; *U.S. Public*, pg. 1052
McCormick, Terrell A., Pres. & Chief Exec. Officer--Regions Bank/Athens/Lauderdale County/Florence, Athens, AL; *U.S. Public*, pg. 1371
McCormick, Thomas, Pres.--Carolina Mailing Service, Charlotte, NC; *U.S. Public*, pg. 1735
McCormick, Thomas, Pres.--Craftsman Printing Company, Charlotte, NC; *U.S. Public*, pg. 1735
McCormick, Wes, Gen. Mgr.--Frank Paxton Lumber Company, Oklahoma City, OK; *U.S. Private*, pg. 585
McCourt, K.W., Pres.--Buffalo Color Corporation, Buffalo, NY; *U.S. Private*, pg. 179
McCourtney, G.T., Chief Oper. Officer--MPC Minneapolis, Minneapolis, MN; *Int'l*, pg. 851
McCoy, Bill, Mgr.--IBP-Council Bluffs, Council Bluffs, IA; *U.S. Public*, pg. 852
McCoy, Chuck, Gen. Mgr.--Rogers CKKS-FM, Vancouver, Canada; *Int'l*, pg. 1123
McCoy, Glenn D., Chief Oper. Officer--Wachovia International Banking Corp., Winston Salem, NC; *U.S. Public*, pg. 1730
McCoy, Horacio, Office Mgr.--Korn/Ferry International, Mexico, Mexico; *U.S. Private*, pg. 633
McCoy, Larry, Distr. Mgr.--National Mine Service Company, Jenkins Div., Jenkins, KY; *Int'l*, pg. 281
McCoy, Neal S., Partner--Skadden, Arps, Slate, Meagher & Flom LLP, Washington, DC; *U.S. Private*, pg. 1004
McCoy, Phil, Plant Superintendant--General Shale Products Corp., Atlanta, GA; *Int'l*, pg. 844
McCoy, Tom, Dir.--Printing & Mailing Distribution, Bentonville, AR; *U.S. Public*, pg. 1733
McCoy, Ty W., V.P.--Thiokol Government Relations, Arlington, VA; *U.S. Public*, pg. 1597
McCracken, J.A., Area Mgr.--Milchem Canada Ltd., Calgary, Canada; *U.S. Public*, pg. 167
McCracken, Ken, Head of Discounting--Bank of Ireland Discounting, Croydon, United Kingdom; *Int'l*, pg. 153
McCracken, Richard P., Pres.--Alcoa Inter-America, Inc., Coral Gables, FL; *U.S. Public*, pg. 60
McCrank, Jerry, Gen. Mgr.--Echo Bay Mines-Lupin Operations, Edmonton, Canada; *U.S. Public*, pg. 562
McCrary, Leon E., Pres.--DynaVac, Hingham, MA; *U.S. Private*, pg. 1076
McCraw, Joan, Pres. & Publr.--Los Angeles Magazine, Inc., Los Angeles, CA; *U.S. Public*, pg. 513
McCray, Ronald D., Mgr.--Kimberly-Clark Computer Services, Inc., Neenah, WI; *U.S. Public*, pg. 959
McCready, P.R., Mng. Dir.--Johnson's Wax Espanola, S.A., Madrid, Spain; *U.S. Private*, pg. 593
McCready, Peter, Chief Exec. Officer--Inchcape Thailand Ltd., Bangkok, Thailand; *Int'l*, pg. 672
McCrone, Kevin E., V.P. & Pres.-The Delfield Company--Scotsman Industries, Inc., Vernon Hills, IL; *U.S. Public*, pg. 1444
McCrone, Kevin E., Pres.-The Delfield Company--Delfield Company, Mount Pleasant, MI; *U.S. Public*, pg. 1445
McCroskey, M.W., Pres.--American National Triflex Fund, Inc., Galveston, TX; *U.S. Public*, pg. 87
McCroskey, M.W., Pres. & Chief Exec. Officer--American National Growth Fund, Inc., Galveston, TX; *U.S. Public*, pg. 87
McCroskey, M.W., Pres. & Chief Exec. Officer--American National Income Fund, Inc., Galveston, TX; *U.S. Public*, pg. 87
McCroskey, Mike, Pres. & Chief Exec. Officer--Securities Management & Research, Galveston, TX; *U.S. Public*, pg. 88
McCrossan, Thomas, Pres.--Investors Fiduciary Trust Company, Kansas City, MO; *U.S. Public*, pg. 944
McCrummen, Ron, Mgr.--Grocery Supply of Paducah, Paducah, KY; *U.S. Private*, pg. 436
McCubben, T.A., V.P. & Gen. Mgr.--Ralston Purina Canada Eveready Div., Mississauga, Canada; *U.S. Public*, pg. 1360
McCue, James M., Chief Fin. Officer--Broadcort Capital Corp., New York, NY; *U.S. Public*, pg. 1097
McCue, Peter, Partner & Sr. V.P.--Fleishman-Hillard, Inc., New York, NY; *U.S. Private*, pg. 411
McCulla, John, Gen. Mgr.--Colonial Sugar, Inc. Refinery, Gramercy, LA; *U.S. Public*, pg. 872
McCullar, Cecil R., Pres. & Chief Exec. Officer--First American Federal Savings Bank, Bristol, VA; *U.S. Public*, *pg. 624*
McCullen, John, Admin.--Horizon's Bayside Manor, Pensacola, FL; *U.S. Public*, pg. 836
McCulley, Robert N., Pres. & Chief Oper. Officer--Southern Precision Corporation, Birmingham, AL; *U.S. Public*, pg. 1736
McCulloch, Carolyn H., Chm. Bd.--Bank of Raleigh, Beckley, WV; *U.S. Public*, pg. 836
McCulloch, Hugh, Gen. Sls. Mgr.--Dunkin' Donuts U.K. Limited, Bourne, United Kingdom; *Int'l*, pg. 63
McCulloch, Jim, Chief Oper. Officer--Prairie Farms Dairy Supply Corp., Carlinville, IL; *U.S. Private*, pg. 879
McCulloch, Kenneth, Pres.--AYP Canada, Inc., Mississauga, Canada; *Int'l*, pg. 440
McCullough, Charles F., Pres.--ALIC, Incorporated, Irving, TX; *U.S. Public*, pg. 364
McCullough, Charles F., Pres.--Cigna Insurance Company of Texas, Irving, TX; *U.S. Public*, pg. 365
McCullough, Charles F., Pres.--Coast to Coast Corporation, Irving, TX; *U.S. Public*, pg. 366
McCullough, Dan, Mgr.--Eclipse Combustion, Inc., Douglasville, GA; *U.S. Private*, pg. 360
McCullough, David, Gen. Mgr.--Intelledex Vision Products, Wilsonville, OR; *U.S. Public*, pg. 568
McCullough, Dick, V.P. & Gen. Mgr.--Thomas & Betts Reznor Division, Memphis, TN; *U.S. Public*, pg. 1598
McCullough, E., Plant Mgr.--Albany International Appleton Wire Div., Portland, TN; *U.S. Public*, pg. 36
McCullough, Eugene R., Pres.--Fidelity National Title Insurance Company of Tennessee, Knoxville, TN; *U.S. Public*, pg. 621
McCullough, Gary E., Pres.--SouthTrust Mortgage Corp., Birmingham, AL; *U.S. Public*, pg. 1492
McCullough, J.E., Pres. & Chief Exec. Officer--South Jersey Energy Co., Folsom, NJ; *U.S. Public*, pg. 1488
McCullough, Michael E., V.P. & Gen. Mgr.--Philadelphia Terminal, Philadelphia, PA; *U.S. Public*, pg. 692
McCullough, Michael E., Mgr.-Terminal--Paulsboro Terminal, Paulsboro, NJ; *U.S. Public*, pg. 692
McCullough, William J., Chief Oper. Officer--Cincinnati Bell Telephone Company, Cincinnati, OH; *U.S. Public*, pg. 367
McCune, John S., Jr., Pres.--Norwest Investment Services, Inc., Minneapolis, MN; *U.S. Public*, pg. 1202
McCurdy, Carl J., Exec. V.P.--Ionics, Incorporated, Bridgeville, PA; *U.S. Public*, pg. 912
McCurdy, D.W., Pres.--Marathon Monitors Incorporated, Cincinnati, OH; *Int'l*, pg. 590
McCurdy, Robert, Pres.--Katz Radio, New York, NY; *U.S. Public*, pg. 335
McCurdy, Scott, V.P. & Gen. Mgr.--City National Bank - Encino Regional Office, Encino, CA; *U.S. Public*, pg. 381
McCurley, F. Cedric, Pres.--American States Economy Insurance Co., Indianapolis, IN; *U.S. Public*, pg. 997
McCurley, F. Cedric, Pres. & Dir.--American States Insurance Co. of Texas, Indianapolis, IN; *U.S. Public*, pg. 997
McCurley, F. Cedric, Pres.--LINSCO Reinsurance Company, Indianapolis, IN; *U.S. Public*, pg. 998
McCutchen, Joan, Pres.--Yuba Heat Transfer Division, Tulsa, OK; *U.S. Private*, pg. 264
McCutcheon, Dan, V.P. & Mgr.--City National Bank - Pershing Square Regional Office, Los Angeles, CA; *U.S. Public*, pg. 381
McCutcheon, R. L.O., Mng. Dir.--Delta EMS Ltd., Walsall, United Kingdom; *Int'l*, pg. 391
McDaniel, Bobby, Pres.--Ultrasystems Defense, Irvine, CA; *U.S. Public*, pg. 1199
McDaniel, Gary, Gen. Mgr.--Laminating and Coating, Schaumburg, IL; *Int'l*, pg. 1270
McDaniel, Jim, Gen. Mgr.--Arrow/Schweber Electronics, Raleigh, NC; *U.S. Public*, pg. 134
McDaniel, Michael, Mgr.-Office--Woodward-Clyde, Baton Rouge, LA; *U.S. Public*, pg. 1656
McDaniel, Michael D., V.P. & Gen. Mgr.--Owens-Illinois Closure Inc., Toledo, OH; *U.S. Public*, pg. 1238
McDaniel, Ray, Pres. & Chief Oper. Officer--Flowers Baking Co. of Jacksonville, Inc., Jacksonville, FL; *U.S. Public*, pg. 657
McDaniel, Roger, Pres.--MEMC Electronic Materials, Inc., Saint Peters, MO; *Int'l*, pg. 1455
McDaniel, Skip, V.P. & Gen. Mgr.--Medtronic Cardiopulmonary, Anaheim, CA; *U.S. Public*, pg. 1083
McDaniel, Thomas R., Pres. & Chief Exec. Officer--Mission Land Company, Irvine, CA; *U.S. Public*, pg. 564
McDaniel, Thomas R., Pres.--Edison Capital, Irvine, CA; *U.S. Public*, pg. 564
McDavid, Randall S., Chm. Bd. & Pres.--Union Boiler Co., Nitro, WV; *U.S. Private*, pg. 262
McDavid, Tim, Pres.--Graver Tank & Mfg. Co., Inc., Pasadena, TX; *U.S. Public*, pg. 914
Mcdeiros, Maria C., Asst. V.P.-Retail Banking--The Bank of Bermuda Limited-Par-La-Ville Branch, Hamilton, Bermuda; *Int'l*, pg. 151
McDermott, D.J., Mng. Dir.--Australian Poultry Ltd., Beresfield, Australia; *Int'l*, pg. 555
McDermott, J.R., Gen. Mgr.--Kodak (Egypt) S.A., Cairo, Egypt; *U.S. Public*, pg. 553
McDermott, Kelly, V.P.--Western Interactive Media, Irving, TX; *U.S. Private*, pg. 1166
McDermott, Mike, Dir.--CMT Steels & Supplies, Audenshaw, United Kingdom; *Int'l*, pg. 265
McDermott, R.R., Gen. Mgr.--John Deere Waterloo Works, Waterloo, IA; *U.S. Public*, pg. 492
McDermott, Tammi, Admin.--Boulder City Care Center, Boulder City, NV; *U.S. Public*, pg. 837
McDill, James L., Plant Mgr.--Hydro Conduit Corp., Creve Coeur, MO; *Int'l*, pg. 245
McDoffie, Woodie, Pres.--Miller Intermodal Logistics Services Inc., Jackson, MS; *U.S. Private*, pg. 329
McDole, Gerald P., Pres.--Astra Pharma Inc., Mississauga, Canada; *Int'l*, pg. 94
McDonald-Kerr, A., Mng. Dir.--Dural Leeds Pty. Ltd., Tullamarine, Australia; *Int'l*, pg. 639
McDonald, Allan, Pres.--FIDCO, White Plains, NY; *Int'l*, pg. 916
McDonald, Bernard, Jr., Chief Oper. Officer--Exact Level, Alum Bank, PA; *U.S. Public*, pg. 1511
McDonald, Bob, Country Mgr.--Standard Chartered Bank, New York, NY; *Int'l*, pg. 1294
McDonald, C. Eugene, Pres.--National Auto Research, Gainesville, GA; *U.S. Private*, pg. 516
McDonald, D.E., Pres.--Caterpillar Americas Co., Peoria, IL; *U.S. Public*, pg. 315
McDonald, Daniel W., Pres.--Baker Support Services, Inc., Dallas, TX; *U.S. Public*, pg. 168
McDonald, Fred A., Pres. & Chief Exec. Officer--Cadmus Marketing Services, Atlanta, GA; *U.S. Public*, pg. 291
McDonald, Gene, V.P. & Gen. Mgr.--McCarty Foods, Inc., Jackson, MS; *U.S. Public*, pg. 1652
McDonald, J.M., III, Chm. Bd., Pres. & Chief Exec. Officer--A.Y. McDonald Industries, Inc., Dubuque, IA; *U.S. Private*, pg. 721
McDonald, Jack, Pres.--Southern Cotton Oil Co., Inc., Decatur, IL; *U.S. Public*, pg. 128
McDonald, Jack, Pres.--LASCO Fluid Distribution Products, Brownsville, TN; *Int'l*, pg. 1398
McDonald, John A., Exec. Dir.--Janssen/Cilag (Pty) Limited, Sandton, South Africa; *U.S. Public*, pg. 929
McDonald, John J., Pres. & Chief Exec. Officer--Casio, Inc., Dover, NJ; *Int'l*, pg. 274
McDonald, Michael, Mng. Dir.--Talisman Energy (U.K.) Limited, Aberdeen, United Kingdom; *Int'l*, pg. 1352
McDonald, Mike, Rep.--CSC, Saskatoon, Saskatoon, Canada; *Int'l*, pg. 1482
McDonald, Peter J., Pres.--Ameritech Advertising Services, Troy, MI; *U.S. Public*, pg. 97
McDonald, R.D., Chm. Bd. & Chief Exec. Officer--A.Y.M. Inc., Albia, IA; *U.S. Private*, pg. 721
McDonald, Rick, Plant Mgr.--Household Products, Los Angeles, CA; *U.S. Public*, pg. 387
McDonald, Robert, Pres.--Continental Electronics Corporation, Dallas, TX; *U.S. Public*, pg. 1563
McDonald, T.K., Mng. Dir.--Comalco New Zealand, Wellington, New Zealand; *Int'l*, pg. 307
McDonald, T.K., Chm. Bd.--Bank of New Zealand, Wellington, New Zealand; *Int'l*, pg. 906
McDonald, Tom, Dir.--Hehr Power Systems, Fort Worth, TX; *U.S. Private*, pg. 519
McDonald, W. O'Neill, Pres.--SuperValu, Inc.-Great Lakes Div.-Green Bay, Green Bay, WI; *U.S. Public*, pg. 1540
McDonell, Allan, Mgr.-Plant--Graphic Systems, Marietta, GA; *U.S. Public*, pg. 1060
McDonell, Michael B., Pres.--UMB Bank Colorado, Security, CO; *U.S. Public*, pg. 1654
McDonell, Terry, Editor-in-Chief & Publr.--Sports Afield, New York, NY; *U.S. Private*, pg. 517

McDoniels, Jim, Plant Mgr.--Dotco, Hicksville, OH; *U.S. Public*, pg. 444
McDonnell, Charlie, Joint Mng. Dir.--Quinn McDonnell Pattison DMB&B Dublin, Dublin, Ireland; *U.S. Private*, pg. 305
McDonnell, Christopher, Mng. Dir.--E Wood Limited, Northallerton, United Kingdom; *Int'l*, pg. 858
McDonnell, Edward F., Pres.--The Seagram Spirits and Wine Group, New York, NY; *Int'l*, pg. 1217
McDonnell, Gordon R., Exec. V.P.--Jefferies & Company, Inc., Los Angeles, CA; *U.S. Public*, pg. 925
McDonnell, James M., Pres. & Chief Exec. Officer--Liberty National Bank and Trust Company of Central Kentucky, Elizabethtown, KY; *U.S. Public*, pg. 173
McDonnell, Thomas A., Pres. & Chief Exec. Officer--DST Systems, Inc., Kansas City, MO; *U.S. Public*, pg. 943
McDonough, S., V.P. & Gen. Mgr.--Ludlow Laminating & Coating Div., Homer, LA; *U.S. Public*, pg. 1647
McDougall, Kenneth, Chief Oper. Officer--Ellis & McDougall Lifts Ltd., Glasgow, United Kingdom; *Int'l*, pg. 747
McDowall, G.D., Gen. Mgr.--Wellcome Taiwan Company Ltd., Taipei, Taiwan; *Int'l*, pg. 704
McDowell, James M., II, Plant Mgr.--Turbine Engine Components Textron, Santa Fe Springs, CA; *U.S. Public*, pg. 1588
McDowell, Thomas J., Chm. Bd.--NBD Insurance Agency, Inc., Troy, MI; *U.S. Public*, pg. 628
McDowell, Thomas J., Pres.--NBD Community Development Corporation, Detroit, MI; *U.S. Public*, pg. 628
McDowell, Thomas J., Pres.--NBD Mortgage Company, Troy, MI; *U.S. Public*, pg. 628
McDyre, Dan, Base Mgr.--Mercury Air Center, Reno, NV; *U.S. Public*, pg. 1093
McEachern, Ron, Pres. & Chief Exec. Officer--Pepsi-Cola Canada, Ltd., Toronto, Canada; *U.S. Public*, pg. 1277
McElderry, Margaret, V.P. & Publisher--Margaret K. McElderry Books, New York, NY; *U.S. Private*, pg. 777
McElhaney, George M., Pres.--Polaris Packaging Inc., Robbinsville, NJ; *U.S. Public*, pg. 1486
McElhatton, Jerry, Pres.--NationsBank of Texas National Bank Services Corporation, Dallas, TX; *U.S. Public*, pg. 1163
McElleney, James, Gen. Mgr.--Genus Inc.-Ion Technology Products, Newburyport, MA; *U.S. Public*, pg. 732
McElroy, Bill, Branch Mgr.-N. Div.--Air Liquide Northern Div., Grand Prairie, TX; *Int'l*, pg. 37
McElroy, Jack L., Sr. Mgr.--Geosafe Corporation, Richland, WA; *U.S. Private*, pg. 123
McElwain, Gary, Reg. Mgr.-Federal Systems--Wang Canada Ltd., Scarborough, Canada; *U.S. Public*, pg. 1737
McEniry, Robert G., Pres.--nexAir, Memphis, TN; *U.S. Private*, pg. 797
McEvers, Kent, Plant Mgr.--Four Corners Gas Plant, Blanding, UT; *U.S. Public*, pg. 1759
McEvers, Kent, Plant Supervisor--San Juan Gas Plant, Kirtland, NM; *U.S. Public*, pg. 1759
McEvoy, J.B., Chief Oper. Officer--Irish Bulk Liquid Storage Ltd., Foynes, Ireland; *Int'l*, pg. 1252
McEwan, J., Dir.--Simon Laboratories, Llandudno, United Kingdom; *Int'l*, pg. 1251
McEwen, Alton, Pres. & Chief Oper. Officer--Gloria Jean's and Coffee Plantation, Monterey, CA; *Int'l*, pg. 266
McEwen, James, Sr. V.P. & Publisher--The Family Circle, Inc., New York, NY; *Int'l*, pg. 190
McEwen, Joseph, Pres.--Moreco Inc., Bristol, PA; *U.S. Private*, pg. 755
McEwen, Neal, Pres.--Public Health Software Systems, Norcross, GA; *U.S. Public*, pg. 888
McEwen, Robert, Gen. Mgr.--Shandwick Detroit, Southfield, MI; *Int'l*, pg. 1227
McEwen, Robert R., Chief Oper. Officer--CSA Managed Gold Mutual Funds, Toronto, Canada; *Int'l*, pg. 243
McEwen, Robert R., Chm. & Chief Exec. Officer--Lexam Explorations Inc., Toronto, Canada; *Int'l*, pg. 243
McFadden, David, Chief Oper. Officer--Montgomery KONE Elevator Co. Ltd., Toronto, Canada; *Int'l*, pg. 748
McFadden, Derek, Mgr.-Office--Woodward-Clyde, Christchurch, New Zealand; *U.S. Public*, pg. 1657
McFadden, Gordon, Pres.--Helly-Hansen (US), Inc., Redmond, WA; *Int'l*, pg. 1010
McFadden, James W., V.P. & Mng. Officer--Northern Trust Bank of Florida, N.A., Fort Myers, FL; *U.S. Public*, pg. 1196
McFadden, Joel, Pres.--Stokes Vacuum Inc., Philadelphia, PA; *Int'l*, pg. 426
McFadyen, Hector J., Pres.--AEC Forest Products, Calgary, Canada; *Int'l*, pg. 48
McFall, Tom A., Jr., Pres.--Weatherly Securities Corp., New York, NY; *U.S. Private*, pg. 1156
McFarlan, Arthur, Gen. Mgr.--Aerochem, Inc./El Mirage, Adelanto, CA; *U.S. Public*, pg. 534
McFarland, Bill, Pres.--Comet American Marketing, Houston, TX; *U.S. Public*, pg. 591
McFarland, Brian, Pres.- Stationary Prod. Div.--Stationery Products Division, Boston, MA; *U.S. Public*, pg. 744
McFarland, Cole E., Pres.--Placer Dome U.S. Inc., San Francisco, CA; *Int'l*, pg. 1060
McFarland, David P., Gen. Mgr.--BNA Software, Washington, DC; *U.S. Private*, pg. 182
McFarland, Mike, Pres. & Chief Exec. Officer--Citizens First Bank, Arkadelphia, AR; *U.S. Public*, pg. 630
McFarland, Sheila, Sr. V.P.--Hilton Reservations Worldwide, Carrollton, TX; *U.S. Public*, pg. 829
McFarland, Stewart, Gen. Mgr.--Automax Controls, Inc., Woodbridge, Canada; *U.S. Public*, pg. 658
McFarland, Terry, Branch Mgr. & V.P.--TIE Systems Colorado, Denver, CO; *U.S. Private*, pg. 1085
McFarlane, G.B., Mng. Dir.--Outboard Marine Corporation Australia Pty. Ltd., Bankstown, Australia; *U.S. Private*, pg. 478
McFarlane, M.A., Branch Mgr.--Zellerbach Division, North Kansas City, MO; *U.S. Public*, pg. 1075
McFarlane, Ron, Mng. Dir.--SSB Advertising Brisbane, Brisbane, Australia; *Int'l*, pg. 394
McFarlin, James E., Pres. & Chief Exec. Officer--NationsBank/Union City, Union City, TN; *U.S. Public*, pg. 1163
McFerson, D.R., Chm. Bd. & Chief Exec Officer--Nationwide Mutual Insurance Co., Columbus, OH; *U.S. Private*, pg. 789
McGaha, Maria, Mgr.-Customer Service--AMICO-Greenville Distr. Center, Greenville, SC; *U.S. Private*, pg. 30
McGahan, Glenn, Mgr.--TN Media Inc., Auckland, New Zealand; *U.S. Public*, pg. 1642
McGann, James, V.P.--Outdoor Systems, Inc.-New York, Chicago, IL; *U.S. Public*, pg. 1235
McGara, J., Pres.--Revere Transducers Inc., Cerritos, CA; *U.S. Public*, pg. 790
McGarr, Amy, Branch Mgr.--Union-Transport Corporation-Saint Louis Office, Saint Ann, MO; *U.S. Private*, pg. 1120
McGarrity, William, Chief Oper. Officer--Telpar, Inc., Addison, TX; *Int'l*, pg. 890
McGarry, Jack, Mng. Dir.--Willis Corroon Harris Marrian Limited, Belfast, United Kingdom; *Int'l*, pg. 1502
McGarry, M.J., Dir.-Intl. Mktg./Europe & U.K.--Carpenter Technology (U.K.) Limited, Redditch, United Kingdom; *U.S. Public*, pg. 308
McGarry, Mike, Gen. Mgr.--Ipsen Ceramics, Pecatonica, IL; *Int'l*, pg. 1149
McGarry, Ron, Pres.--Elgin Sweeper Company, Elgin, IL; *U.S. Public*, pg. 617
McGary, Brendon, Chief Fin. Officer--City Machine & Wheel Co., Stow, OH; *U.S. Private*, pg. 299
McGaughey, William, Sr. V.P. & Treas.--Sierra West Bank, Truckee, CA; *U.S. Public*, pg. 1470
McGeary, Collin, Mgr.-Opers.--Littelfuse Ltd., Washington, United Kingdom; *U.S. Public*, pg. 1001
McGee, Patrick A., Pres.--First Valley Leasing, Inc., Bethlehem, PA; *U.S. Public*, pg. 1528
McGee, Robert M., Pres.--Occidental International Finance N.V., Curacao, Netherlands Antilles; *U.S. Public*, pg. 1210
McGee, T., Plant Dir.--Keebler Co./Denver Bakery, Denver, CO; *U.S. Public*, pg. 657
McGehee, Jefferson, Gen Mgr.--Frontier Communications of the South, Inc., Atmore, AL; *U.S. Public*, pg. 684
McGehee, Jefferson, Gen. Mgr.--Frontier Communications of Minnesota, Inc., Burnsville, MN; *U.S. Public*, pg. 684
McGehee, Scott, Pres. & Chief Exec. Officer--Fort Wayne Newspapers, Inc., Fort Wayne, IN; *U.S. Public*, pg. 964
McGerigle, John, Mgr.--Albuquerque Plant, Albuquerque, NM; *Int'l*, pg. 1054
McGhan, Jim J., Gen. Mgr.--Inamed Development Company, Carpinteria, CA; *U.S. Public*, pg. 873
McGill, Jay P., V.P. & Publisher--Country Living, New York, NY; *U.S. Private*, pg. 517
McGill, John, Pres.--Canadian Liquid Air Ltd.-Air Liquide Canada Ltee, Montreal, Canada; *Int'l*, pg. 37
McGill, John, Plant Mgr.--Engine Components Div., Saginaw, MI; *U.S. Public*, pg. 557
McGill, S.R., Pres.--Esso Inc., Brussels, Belgium; *U.S. Public*, pg. 602
McGill, Terrance L., Pres.--Columbia Gulf Transmission Co., Charleston, WV; *U.S. Public*, pg. 403
McGillis, E.G., Pres. & Chief Oper. Officer--Superior Water, Light & Power Company, Superior, WI; *U.S. Public*, pg. 1116
McGillivary, Christopher, Chief Exec. Officer--Waterford Crystal, Inc., Wall, NJ; *Int'l*, pg. 1487
McGinity, B.J., Chief Oper. Officer--Brake Cables Ltd, Lechlade, United Kingdom; *Int'l*, pg. 472
McGinley, Jack, V.P.--I.V. Systems Division, Round Lake, IL; *U.S. Public*, pg. 196
McGinley, John, Gen. Mgr.--Johnson Wax GmbH, Haan, Germany; *U.S. Private*, pg. 593
McGinn, M., Gen. Mgr.--Asgard Financial Services Ltd, Dublin, Ireland; *Int'l*, pg. 81
McGinn, Michael J., Gen. Mgr.--Kodak Caribbean Limited, Carolina, PR; *U.S. Public*, pg. 551
McGinn, Robb, Dir.-Area Opers.--Wendy's of Denver Inc., Denver, CO; *U.S. Public*, pg. 1754
McGinnis, Ana Maria, Chief Oper. Officer--Royal Copenhagen Porcelain Corporation, White Plains, NY; *Int'l*, pg. 1134
McGinnis, Daniel L., Chief Exec. Officer--Coherent Communications Systems Corp., Ashburn, VA; *U.S. Public*, pg. 1424
McGinnis, Dean, Gen. Mgr.--General Latex & Chemical Corporation, Cucamonga, CA; *U.S. Private*, pg. 444
McGinnis, Michael E., Pres. & Chief Exec. Officer--American Eco Corporation, Houston, TX; *Int'l*, pg. 74
McGinnis, William, Chief Oper. Officer--Acton Environmental Testing, Acton, MA; *U.S. Public*, pg. 1161
McGinty, Frederick W., Chief Exec.--Hilb, Rogal and Hamilton Company of St. Simons Island, Saint Simons Island, GA; *U.S. Public*, pg. 827
McGlinn, John S., V.P. & Gen. Mgr.--The HON Co., South Gate Plant, South Gate, CA; *U.S. Public*, pg. 772
McGlone, Gordon, Commercial Dir.--Elkes Biscuits, Uttoxeter, United Kingdom; *Int'l*, pg. 968
McGlynn, Dennis, Pres.--Brandywine Realty & Development, Inc., Wilmington, DE; *U.S. Private*, pg. 165
McGonagle, Patrick J., Pres. & Chief Exec. Officer--National Gas & Oil Corp., Newark, OH; *U.S. Public*, pg. 1157
McGory, Craig, Mgr.--Dixon Ticonderoga Company, Sandusky, OH; *U.S. Public*, pg. 515
McGough, George, Chm., Pres. & Chief Exec. Officer--Principal Financial Securities, Dallas, TX; *U.S. Private*, pg. 885
McGoun, Sam H., Pres. & Chief Exec. Officer--Willis Corroon Corp. of Michigan, Livonia, MI; *Int'l*, pg. 1506
McGovern, James, Pres.--Corona Clipper, Corona, CA; *U.S. Private*, pg. 506
McGovern, Ted, Mng. Dir.--ICS Building Society, Dublin, Ireland; *Int'l*, pg. 152
McGowan, David, Chief Exec. Officer--Bank of Ireland Corporate & International Banking, Belfast, United Kingdom; *Int'l*, pg. 153
McGowan, Donald J., Pres.--Flagship Bank & Trust Company, Worcester, MA; *U.S. Public*, pg. 351
McGowan, John, Dir.-Technical--Pegasus Engineering Ltd., Little Island, Ireland; *U.S. Public*, pg. 922
McGowan, John H., Pres.--BE & C Engineers Inc., Seattle, WA; *U.S. Public*, pg. 241
McGowan, Richard, Communications Dir.--Young & Rubicam Australia/New Zealand, Sydney, Australia; *U.S. Private*, pg. 1198
McGrah, E., Mng. Dir.--Bradstock Blunt & Thompson, London, United Kingdom; *Int'l*, pg. 210
McGrail, Michael, Pres. & Gen. Mgr.--Cabledata, Inc., Rancho Cordova, CA; *U.S. Public*, pg. 1659
McGranahan, Ron, Branch Mgr.--Weatherford US Inc., Bakersfield, CA; *U.S. Public*, pg. 1749
McGrath, Barry G., Pres.--The Pittsburg & Midway Coal Mining Co., Englewood, CO; *U.S. Public*, pg. 348
McGrath, Don J., Pres. & Chief Exec. Officer--Bank of the West, Walnut Creek, CA; *Int'l*, pg. 163
McGrath, John, Pres.--Bank of San Francisco Securities Brokerage, San Francisco, CA; *U.S. Public*, pg. 1430
McGrath, John P., Pres. & Chief Exec. Officer--Hilb, Rogal and Hamilton Company of Pittsburgh, Inc., Pittsburgh, PA; *U.S. Public*, pg. 827
McGrath, Judith, Pres.--MTV: Music Television, New York, NY; *U.S. Private*, pg. 779
McGrath, M.W., Bakery Dir.--Keebler Co./Cincinnati Bakery, Cincinnati, OH; *U.S. Public*, pg. 657
McGrath, Margaret H., Pres. & Chief Oper. Officer--PPG Canada Inc., Mississauga, Canada; *U.S. Public*, pg. 1245
McGrath, Michael, Pres.--Time Canada Ltd., Toronto, Canada; *U.S. Public*, pg. 1615
McGrath, Mike, Chief Oper. Officer--Cadbury Beverages Seven Up, Dallas, TX; *Int'l*, pg. 248
McGrattan, Ian, Mng. Dir.--Joseph Dawson Ltd, Bradford, United Kingdom; *Int'l*, pg. 385
McGraw, J. David, V.P. & Gen. Mgr.--NRD, Grand Island, NY; *U.S. Public*, pg. 1045
McGraw, Jim, Pres.--Viking Entertainment, Troy, MI; *U.S. Public*, pg. 780
McGraw, Josh, V.P-Jacksonville--Clear Channel Television, Inc., Minneapolis, MN; *U.S. Public*, pg. 383
McGraw, Josh, V.P. & Gen. Mgr.--WAWS-TV, Jacksonville, FL; *U.S. Public*, pg. 384
McGraw, Robert H., Pres.--Monumental General Insurance Company, Baltimore, MD; *Int'l*, pg. 27
McGraw, Robert P., Exec. V.P.--McGraw-Hill Professional Publishing Group, New York, NY; *U.S. Public*, pg. 1070
McGregor, Andy, V.P.-Sls. & Distr., N. America--Office Pavilion Division (Sls. & Mktg. Div.), Zeeland, MI; *U.S. Public*, pg. 1112
McGregor, Douglas A., Exec. V.P.-Devel. & Opers.--Rouse Office & Community Development Div., Columbia, MD; *U.S. Public*, pg. 1407
McGregor, G. W., Chief Exec. Officer & Exec. Gen. Mgr.--BHP Service Companies, Melbourne, Australia; *Int'l*, pg. 225
McGregor, I.C., Chief Exec. Officer--Redland Quarries Inc., Hamilton, Canada; *Int'l*, pg. 1093
McGregor, Robert, Pres.--Eighty Four Coal Co., Indiana, PA; *U.S. Public*, pg. 1395
McGregor, T.A., Grp. V.P.--Seibert-Oxidermo, Inc., Detroit, MI; *U.S. Public*, pg. 502
McGroarty, Bruce, Pres.--Azerty Incorporated, Orchard Park, NY; *Int'l*, pg. 20
McGruff, Edgar, Mgr.--McClellanville Telephone Co., Inc., McClellanville, SC; *U.S. Public*, pg. 1571
McGuigan, Brian, Chief Oper. Officer--Geotronics Ltd., Huntingdon, United Kingdom; *Int'l*, pg. 1290
McGuigan, J.W., Dir.-Division Sls.--Sunkist Growers, Inc.-Eastern Division, Chelsea, MA; *U.S. Private*, pg. 1052
McGuigan, Jack, V.P. & Gen. Mgr.--Harris Network Support Systems, Camarillo, CA; *U.S. Public*, pg. 792
McGuigan, Kate, Chief Oper. Officer--CFI Insurers, Ltd., Los Angeles, CA; *U.S. Public*, pg. 1475
McGuiness, Frank, Gen. Mgr.--Hesco, Inc., Teterboro, NJ; *U.S. Private*, pg. 524
McGuinness, Brian, Chief Oper. Officer--Mitchell Shackleton & Co. Ltd., Manchester, United Kingdom; *U.S. Private*, pg. 783
McGuire, Blanche, Sr. V.P.- Mktg. Strategy--Ketchum Directory Advertising/Pittsburgh, Pittsburgh, PA; *U.S. Private*, pg. 616
McGuire, Brett, Plant Mgr.--Sweetheart Cup Company Inc., Augusta, GA; *U.S. Private*, pg. 1058
McGuire, Gary, Pres.--Nortel Communications, San Ramon, CA; *Int'l*, pg. 969
McGuire, Gary, Pres.--Nortel Communications, San Ramon, CA; *U.S. Public*, pg. 1416
McGuire, Henry, Pres.--Outlander, New York, NY; *U.S. Public*, pg. 989
McGuire, James, Chief Exec. Officer--Twinco Services, Inc., Edison, NJ; *U.S. Private*, pg. 1111
McGuire, James, Chief Exec. Officer--Twinco Graphics, Edison, NJ; *U.S. Private*, pg. 1111
McGuire, James, V.P. & Gen. Mgr.--Smurfit Plastic Packaging Div., Wilmington, DE; *Int'l*, pg. 1271
McGuire, James J., Div. Head--KeyCorp Shareholder Services, Inc., Cleveland, OH; *U.S. Public*, pg. 955
McGuire, Michael, Pres.--T.F. Cushing, Inc., West Springfield, MA; *U.S. Public*, pg. 141
McGuire, Michael, Pres. & Chief Exec. Officer--Progress International Limited, Plainview, NY; *U.S. Public*, pg. 141
McGuire, Michael, Gen. Mgr.--DeKalb Canada Inc., Chatham, Canada; *U.S. Public*, pg. 493
McGuire, Michael, Pres.--MBIA Assurance S.A., Armonk, NY; *U.S. Public*, pg. 1023
McGuire, Paul A., Pres.--Electro-Voice, Inc., Buchanan, MI; *U.S. Private*, pg. 479
McGuire, Richard J., Jr., Pres.--TRC Mariah Associates, Inc., Laramie, WY; *U.S. Public*, pg. 1558
McGuire, William W., M.D., Chm. Bd., Pres. & Chief Exec. Officer--United HealthCare Services, Inc., Minnetonka, MN; *U.S. Public*, pg. 1678

McGuirk, Michael G., Pres.--PVS Technologies, Inc., Detroit, MI; *U.S. Private*, pg. 828
McGuirk, P.W., Pres. & Chief Exec. Officer--Kao Infosystems Company (MA), Plymouth, MA; *Int'l*, pg. 717
McGuirk, Terence F., Chm. Bd., Pres. & Chief Exec. Officer--Turner Broadcasting System Inc., Atlanta, GA; *U.S. Public*, pg. 1614
McGurk, John D., Pres.--Rothchild Realty Inc., New York, NY; *U.S. Private*, pg. 947
McHale, Hank, Pres.--GO/DAN Industries, New Haven, CT; *U.S. Public*, pg. 1631
McHale, Hank, Pres.--The G & O Manufacturing Co., New Haven, CT; *U.S. Public*, pg. 1631
McHale, J.W., V.P.-Trading--Texaco Oil Trading & Supply Company, White Plains, NY; *U.S. Public*, pg. 1583
McHale, Jim, Gen. Mgr.--LeFebure, Area West, Santa Fe Springs, CA; *Int'l*, pg. 387
McHale, John W., Pres.--Texaco International Trader Inc., White Plains, NY; *U.S. Public*, pg. 1583
McHale, Warren E., Pres.--Filtration Group, Cleveland, OH; *U.S. Public*, pg. 1260
McHenry, Daniel, Pres.--Oasis Outsourcing, Inc., Palm Beach Gardens, FL; *U.S. Public*, pg. 1731
McHugh, Arthur B., Pres.--Security Warranty Association of Florida, Altamonte Springs, FL; *U.S. Public*, pg. 1231
McHugh, Arthur B., Pres.--Connecticut Specialty Insurance Company, Farmington, CT; *U.S. Public*, pg. 1231
McHugh, C.R., Chm. Bd.--NatWest Futures Inc., Chicago, IL; *Int'l*, pg. 911
McHugh, Claire, Editor-in-Chief--New Woman Magazine, New York, NY; *U.S. Private*, pg. 939
McHugh, Gene, V.P. & Gen. Mgr.--WTTG, Washington, DC; *Int'l*, pg. 926
McHugh, J. Carey, Pres.--Texaco Bahamas Ltd., Nassau, Bahamas; *U.S. Public*, pg. 1584
McIlheney, Barry, Mng. Dir.--EMAP Metro, London, United Kingdom; *Int'l*, pg. 451
McIlnay, Donald R., Pres.--Newell Window Furnishings Co., Freeport, IL; *U.S. Public*, pg. 1177
McIlnay, Donald R., Pres.--Levolor, Greensboro, NC; *U.S. Public*, pg. 1177
McIlnay, Donald R., Pres.--Levolor Home Fashions, Westminster, CA; *U.S. Public*, pg. 1177
McIlroy, R., Mng. Dir.--Christie's Australia Pty. Ltd., Yarram, Australia; *Int'l*, pg. 290
McIlvaine, Glen E., Mgr.--Jefferies & Company, Inc., Los Angeles, CA; *U.S. Public*, pg. 925
McIlwaine, Steve, Pres.--Metcraft, Inc., Grandview, MO; *Int'l*, pg. 453
McIlwrath, John, Mng. Dir.--Ferro Chemicals S.A., Port-de-Bouc, France; *U.S. Public*, pg. 619
McIlwrick, Rod, Mng. Dir.--Rheometric Scientific, Inc., Bensheim, Germany; *U.S. Public*, pg. 1387
McInerney, James S., Pres.--BHC Company, Bridgeport, CT; *U.S. Public*, pg. 126
McInerney, James S., Pres.--Hydrocorp, Inc., Bridgeport, CT; *U.S. Public*, pg. 126
McInerney, James S., Jr., Pres.--Aquarion Management Services, Inc., Bridgeport, CT; *U.S. Public*, pg. 126
McInerney, Joseph A., Pres. & Chief Exec. Officer--Travelodge, El Cajon, CA; *U.S. Public*, pg. 322
McInerney, Robert J., Pres.--Arrow Commercial Systems Group, Melville, NY; *U.S. Public*, pg. 133
McInnes, Allen T., Chm. Bd.--Tenneco Ventures,Inc., Houston, TX; *U.S. Public*, pg. 1578
McInnes, Ross, Pres.--Cereol S.A., Neuilly-sur-Seine, France; *Int'l*, pg. 324
McIntire, E., Gen. Mgr.--Perrigo of Tennessee, Smyrna, TN; *U.S. Public*, pg. 1280
McIntire, Lee, Pres.--Bechtel National, Inc., San Francisco, CA; *U.S. Private*, pg. 128
McIntosh, Ian, Gen. Mgr.--PAXAR Canada, Ville Saint Laurent, Canada; *U.S. Public*, pg. 1266
McIntosh, J. David, V.P.-Strategic Bus.--Lawn-Boy Inc., Bloomington, MN; *U.S. Public*, pg. 1624
McIntosh, J.E., Dir.--NatWest Export Finance Limited, London, United Kingdom; *Int'l*, pg. 910
McIntosh, William, V.P. & Gen. Mgr.--NIKE Canada Ltd., Thornhill, Canada; *U.S. Public*, pg. 1184
McIntyre, Brookes, Chief Oper. Officer--Banco Santander International Miami, Miami, FL; *Int'l*, pg. 143
McIntyre, James, Cement Terminal Mgr.--Ideal Concrete, Houston, TX; *Int'l*, pg. 628
McIntyre, John, Gen. Mgr.--Maxus Southeast Sumatra, Jakarta, Indonesia; *Int'l*, pg. 1515
McIntyre, John Duncan, Mng. Dir.--Abbott AG, Cham, Switzerland; *U.S. Public*, pg. 13
McIntyre, Kathryn J., Publisher--Business Insurance, Chicago, IL; *U.S. Private*, pg. 285
McIntyre, Mark, V.P. & Dir.--Russ Reid Co., Washington, DC; *U.S. Private*, pg. 952
McIntyre, Matt, V.P.-Opers.--Claremont Flock, Leominster, MA; *U.S. Private*, pg. 242
McIntyre, Melissa E., RN, OCN, Pres. & Chief Oper. Officer--I.V. One, Altamonte Springs, FL; *U.S. Public*, pg. 229
McIntyre, Scott, Jr., Pres.--Crabtree Premium Finance, Lombard, IL; *U.S. Public*, pg. 1677
McIntyre, William, Pres.--The Optical Corporation, Oxnard, CA; *U.S. Public*, pg. 599
McIsaac, Larry, Pres.--Zebco, Tulsa, OK; *U.S. Public*, pg. 265
McIsaac, W.V., Pres.--White Pass Systems Ltd., Edmonton, Canada; *Int'l*, pg. 1150
McIvor, H., Mgr.--Anikem (Proprietary) Ltd., Kempton Park, South Africa; *U.S. Public*, pg. 1150
McIvor, Ron, Mgr.--Bain & Company New Zealand Ltd., Wellington, New Zealand; *Int'l*, pg. 406
McIvor, William, Pres.--Oxford Health Plans (FL), Inc., Sarasota, FL; *U.S. Public*, pg. 1239
McJeed, Sam, Exec. V.P & Gen. Mgr.--American Gasket & Rubber, Schaumburg, IL; *U.S. Private*, pg. 15
McKallor, Alex, Chief Oper. Officer--Alaska Marine Lines, Inc., Seattle, WA; *U.S. Private*, pg. 683
McKane, Tom, Pres. & Chief Exec. Officer--S-B Power Tool Company, Chicago, IL; *Int'l*, pg. 205
McKay, Alex R., Gen. Mgr.--Middle East Can Manufacturing Company, Amman, Jordan; *U.S. Public*, pg. 465
McKay, Barrie C., Chief Oper. Officer--CCH Editions Limited, Bicester, United Kingdom; *Int'l*, pg. 1514
McKay, D. A., Chief Oper. Officer--Richardson-Vicks Ltd., Bangkok, Thailand; *U.S. Public*, pg. 1333
McKay, David, Pres.--Puritan-Bennett Australia Pty. Ltd., Thomastown, Australia; *U.S. Public*, pg. 1040
McKay, Frederick, M.D., Chief Exec. Officer--Huntington Provider Management Services, Pasadena, CA; *U.S. Private*, pg. 1118
McKay, Jack D., Pres. & Chief Exec. Officer--Unigas, Calgary, Canada; *Int'l*, pg. 1492
Mckay, Keith, Chm.--Von Broembsen Marson Leo Burnett/Harare, Harare, Zimbabwe; *U.S. Private*, pg. 186
McKay, Mac, Chief Oper. Officer--Prior Gaskets Inc., Dallas, TX; *U.S. Private*, pg. 300
McKay, Norman, Mgr.-Office--Woodward-Clyde, Anchorage, AK; *U.S. Public*, pg. 1656
Mckay, Stuart S., Mng. Dir.-U.K. Opers.--Carlton Cards, Ltd., Dewsbury, United Kingdom; *U.S. Public*, pg. 78
McKean, M.H., Pres.--Wrigley Canada Inc., Don Mills, Canada; *U.S. Public*, pg. 1781
McKeand, Bert, Sr. Sls. Representative--PENCO-Virginia, Richmond, VA; *Int'l*, pg. 1508
McKechnie, B., Mng. Dir.--Babcock Construction Limited, Renfrew, United Kingdom; *Int'l*, pg. 130
McKechnie, B., Mng. Dir.--Babcock Construction Limited, Tipton, United Kingdom; *Int'l*, pg. 130
McKechnie, Brett, Area Foreman--Talisman Energy Inc., Grande Prairie, Canada; *Int'l*, pg. 1352
McKee-Anderson, Liz, Sr. V.P. & Gen. Mgr.--Centeon, L.L.C., King of Prussia, PA; *Int'l*, pg. 626
McKee, Daniel L., Chief Oper. Officer--Allright Colorado, Inc., Denver, CO; *U.S. Private*, pg. 42
McKee, Gregg, Pres.--Energy Products, San Diego, CA; *U.S. Public*, pg. 1061
McKee, Robert, Pres.--Brubaker Tool Corp., Millersburg, PA; *U.S. Public*, pg. 368
McKee, Robert E., III, Chm. Bd. & Mng. Dir.--Conoco (UK) Ltd., London, United Kingdom; *U.S. Public*, pg. 531
McKeehan, W. Dale, Gen. Mgr.--Ford Body & Assembly Operations, Dearborn, MI; *U.S. Public*, pg. 662
McKeighan, Mick, V.P. & Gen. Mgr.--Microsemi Corp.-Scottsdale, Scottsdale, AZ; *U.S. Public*, pg. 1107
McKenna, Bruce, Pres.--Exothermics-Eclipse, Inc., Toledo, OH; *U.S. Private*, pg. 360
McKenna, Charles, V.P. & Gen. Mgr.--Ion Implant Systems, Gloucester, MA; *U.S. Public*, pg. 1710
McKenna, Edward F., Pres.--CoreStates Bank of Delaware NA, Wilmington, DE; *U.S. Public*, pg. 447
McKenna, Gerald, Chief Oper. Officer--NAPS United Kingdom, Abingdon, United Kingdom; *Int'l*, pg. 913
McKenna, Gerald, Chief Oper. Officer--Neste Oil Services, Inc., Houston, TX; *Int'l*, pg. 914
McKenna, Gerald, Chief Oper. Officer--Neste Petroleum (Products), Inc., Houston, TX; *Int'l*, pg. 914
McKenna, Jim, Gen. Mgr.--East Florida Division, Orlando, FL; *Int'l*, pg. 693
McKenna, Joel, Gen. Mgr.--Mullen Testers, Chicopee, MA; *U.S. Public*, pg. 1506
McKenna, John P., Sr. V.P.-Opers., Eastern Div.--Manor Healthcare Corp., Gaithersburg, MD; *U.S. Public*, pg. 1041
McKenna, Matthew J., Pres.--Baltimore Aircoil Company, Jessup, MD; *U.S. Private*, pg. 68
McKenna, Michael J., Pres.--Crown Cork de Puerto Rico, Inc., Carolina, PR; *U.S. Public*, pg. 463
McKenna, Timothy, Rep.--Jardine Fleming International Securities Ltd., Singapore, Singapore; *Int'l*, pg. 494
McKenna, Timothy, Dir.--Jardine Fleming International Securities Limited, Singapore, Singapore; *Int'l*, pg. 494
McKenney, S.S., III, Pres.--Air Pro, Dallas, TX; *U.S. Public*, pg. 685
McKenny, Edward R., Pres.--Caterpillar World Trading Corporation, Peoria, IL; *U.S. Public*, pg. 316
McKenzie, Bob, Pres. & Publisher--The Prince George Citizen, Prince George, Canada; *Int'l*, pg. 631
McKenzie, Charles, V.P.--Bergen Brunswig Medical Corporation, Jacksonville, FL; *U.S. Public*, pg. 214
McKenzie, Christopher C., Pres.--General DataComm Ltd., Willowdale, Canada; *U.S. Public*, pg. 708
McKenzie, D. Barry, Sr. V.P.--Willis Corroon Marine & Energy, Glendale, CA; *Int'l*, pg. 1508
McKenzie, Dean, Chief Oper. Officer--Alaska-West Express, Inc., Anchorage, AK; *U.S. Private*, pg. 683
McKenzie, Douglas C., Mng. Dir.--Methode Electronics Europe Limited, Dumbarton, United Kingdom; *U.S. Public*, pg. 1101
McKenzie, Jack, Regional Mgr.--Peterbilt of Canada, Brampton, Canada; *U.S. Public*, pg. 1247
McKenzie, James, Pres. & Chief Exec. Officer--Leo Burnett Company Ltd., Toronto, Canada; *U.S. Private*, pg. 185
McKenzie, Robert J., Exec. V.P.--Brown Brothers Harriman Trust Co. of Texas, Dallas, TX; *U.S. Private*, pg. 173
McKeon, John S., Pres. & Chief Exec. Officer--Golden Valley Microwave Foods, Inc., Edina, MN; *U.S. Public*, pg. 427
McKeown, Louise, Div. Mgr.--Rogers Cable TV-Newmarket Div., Newmarket, Canada; *Int'l*, pg. 1122
McKeown, M., Mgr.--Rockware Glass Ltd.-Portland Factory, Irvine, United Kingdom; *Int'l*, pg. 124
McKernan, R.T., Pres.--Packard Instrument Co., Inc., Meriden, CT; *U.S. Private*, pg. 833
McKie, D., Gen. Mgr.--Caterpillar Belgium S.A., Gosselies, Belgium; *U.S. Public*, pg. 317
McKiernan, Edward, Pres.--SeaLand Technology, Big Prairie, OH; *U.S. Private*, pg. 1071
McKillen, Eric, Pres.--Dynapac Ltd., Hornby, Canada; *Int'l*, pg. 1420
McKillop, William, Admin.--Horizon Healthcare & Specialty Center, Daytona Beach, FL; *U.S. Public*, pg. 836
McKinley, Martin J., Pres.--Norwest Business Credit, Inc., Minneapolis, MN; *U.S. Public*, pg. 1202
McKinley, R.M., Chm. Bd.--British Aerospace Airbus Limited, Chester, United Kingdom; *Int'l*, pg. 217
McKinnerney, Floyd, Pres & Chief Oper. Officer--ConAgra Agri-Products Co., Greeley, CO; *U.S. Public*, pg. 426
McKinney, James A., Pres.--Federal Express Logistics, Inc., Memphis, TN; *U.S. Public*, pg. 604
McKinney, John B., Pres. & Chief Exec. Officer--Laclede Steel Company, Saint Louis, MO; *U.S. Public*, pg. 974
McKinney, Michael D., V.P. & Mgr.-Gen. Sls.--Champion Industries, Huntington, WV; *U.S. Public*, pg. 333
McKinney, Robert H., Chm. Bd. & Chief Exec. Officer--First Indiana Corporation, Indianapolis, IN; *U.S. Public*, pg. 1484
McKinney, Sonya, Gen. Mgr.--Forest Siding Supply, Inc., Oklahoma City, OK; *U.S. Private*, pg. 1080
McKinnon, Bruce, Gen. Mgr.--Arrow/Schweber Electronics, Beaverton, OR; *U.S. Public*, pg. 134
McKinnon, I., Mng. Dir.--Alcan Specialty Aerospace, Birmingham, United Kingdom; *Int'l*, pg. 51
McKinnon, John Q., Exec. V.P.-Comml. Banking--American National Bank & Trust Co. of Chicago, Chicago, IL; *U.S. Public*, pg. 628
McKinstry, Reginald, Pres.--Tech-Tran Corporation, Rancocas, NJ; *U.S. Private*, pg. 560
McKissack, Danny, Mgr.--Southern Electric Supply Co., Inc., Laurel, MS; *Int'l*, pg. 1108
McKissack, Danny, Mgr.--Southern Electric Supply Co., Inc., Meridian, MS; *Int'l*, pg. 1108
McKissick, Foster, III, Pres.--Fairway Ford of Anderson, Anderson, SC; *U.S. Private*, pg. 392
McKissick, J. Harold, Pres.--NationsBank Leasing Corporation, Pittsburgh, PA; *U.S. Public*, pg. 1163
McKitrick, James T., Pres. & Chief Exec. Officer--Central Tractor Farm & Country, Inc., Des Moines, IA; *U.S. Private*, pg. 237
McKitrick, Jim, Pres.--Country General Stores, Grand Island, NE; *U.S. Private*, pg. 237
McKnight, Paul J., Pres.--HCA-Florida Group, Tallahassee, FL; *U.S. Public*, pg. 403
McKnight, Ron, Exec. V.P.-Adv.--Franz Bakery, Portland, OR; *U.S. Private*, pg. 1124
McKnight, W.M., Pres.--McKnight Medical Communications, Northfield, IL; *U.S. Public*, pg. 1600
McKoen, Sondra, Co-Mgr.--Automatic Music Service of Billings, Inc., Billings, MT; *U.S. Public*, pg. 1319
McLachlan, J. Ross, V.P.--Oakite Canada, Ltd., Bramalea, Canada; *Int'l*, pg. 861
McLain, D., Mng. Dir.--Penny & Giles Studio Equipment Ltd., Blackwood, United Kingdom; *Int'l*, pg. 207
McLain, Jim, Pres.--Volt VIEWtech, Inc., Orange, CA; *U.S. Public*, pg. 1724
McLain, M., Plant Mgr.--Aztec Industries, Inc., Jackson, MS; *U.S. Public*, pg. 159
McLain, Mike A., Pres. & Chief Exec. Officer--DowBrands, L.P., Indianapolis, IN; *U.S. Public*, pg. 523
McLane, Don, V.P. & Gen. Mgr.--Nordson Pacific South Div., Amherst, OH; *U.S. Public*, pg. 1188
McLane, John, V.P.-Bus. Unit--Atlas Roll-Lite Door Corporation, Orlando, FL; *U.S. Public*, pg. 766
McLaren, Fred, Pres.--McLaren/Hart Environmental Engineering Company, Rancho Cordova, CA; *Int'l*, pg. 1465
McLaren, O., Chief Oper. Officer--Robertson Tooling Ltd., Kempston, United Kingdom; *Int'l*, pg. 449
McLaren, Tom, Gen. Mgr.--VR/Wesson Hydro Carbide, Latrobe, PA; *U.S. Public*, pg. 612
McLaren, Tom, Sr. V.P.-Western Canada--GPC Government Policy Consultants (Edmonton), Edmonton, Canada; *U.S. Public*, pg. 1225
McLaren, Tom, Sr. V.P.-Western Canada--GPC Government Policy Consultants (Calgary), Calgary, Canada; *U.S. Public*, pg. 1225
McLarty, Carroll, Pres.--Houston Div., Houston, TX; *U.S. Public*, pg. 652
Mclatchie, Colin, Mng. Dir. & Chief Info. Officer--PanAgora Asset Management Limited, London, United Kingdom; *Int'l*, pg. 936
McLaughlin, D., Pres.--Eureka Manufacturing Co., Inc., Norton, MA; *U.S. Private*, pg. 916
McLaughlin, Dennis, Pres.--Veterinary Medicine Publishing Co., Inc., Lenexa, KS; *U.S. Public*, pg. 1600
McLaughlin, J.J., Pres. & Chief Exec. Officer--DAP Inc., Tipp City, OH; *Int'l*, pg. 1486
McLaughlin, P., Pres.--Clover Produce Limited, Lakeside, Canada; *Int'l*, pg. 454
McLaughlin, P., Mng. Dir.--Getinge Australia Pty. Ltd., Bulimba, Australia; *Int'l*, pg. 551
McLaughlin, Rich, Pres.--Aliant Systems Inc., Lincoln, NE; *U.S. Public*, pg. 41
McLaughlin, Richard, V.P.--Goldblatt's Department Stores, Chicago, IL; *U.S. Public*, pg. 917
McLaughlin, Scott, Chief Oper. Officer--Ahlstrom Inc., Danvers, MA; *Int'l*, pg. 35
McLaughlin, William F., Pres. & Chief Exec. Officer--Sweetheart Cup Company Inc., Owings Mills, MD; *U.S. Private*, pg. 1058
McLay, William, Pres.--Ryobi Electric Tool Mfg., Anderson, SC; *Int'l*, pg. 1151
McLean, A., Mng. Dir.--Ballast Wiltshier Plc - Scotland, Berwick-upon-Tweed, United Kingdom; *Int'l*, pg. 135
McLean, Dan D., Pres.--SAFECO National Insurance Co., Seattle, WA; *U.S. Public*, pg. 1423
McLean, Dan D., Pres.--SAFECO Surplus Lines Insurance Co., Seattle, WA; *U.S. Public*, pg. 1423
McLean, Don, Pres.--General Insurance Co. of America, Seattle, WA; *U.S. Public*, pg. 1423
McLean, Donald A., Pres.--British Columbia Packers Limited, Vancouver, Canada; *Int'l*, pg. 1495
McLean, Donna, Mgr.-Property & Casualty Claims--Willis Corroon Administrative Services Corporation, Oklahoma City, OK; *Int'l*, pg. 1505

McLean, Edward L., Pres.--Connors Bros. Limited, Blacks Harbour, Canada; Int'l, pg. 1495
McLean, Ethyl, Admin.--Guardian Care of Kinston, Kinston, NC; U.S. Public, pg. 1712
McLean, Graham J., Pres.--Moore Business Forms & Systems Div., Lake Forest, IL; Int'l, pg. 890
McLean, James, Pres.--Jannock Imaging Companies Limited, Toronto, Canada; Int'l, pg. 698
McLean, Lachlan, Pres.--Boam Chemicals Co., Inc., Camden, NJ; U.S. Private, pg. 689
McLean, Robert, Mgr.-Property & Casualty Claims--Willis Corroon Administrative Services Corporation, San Jose, CA; Int'l, pg. 1504
McLean, Thomas, Chief Oper. Officer--Ahlstrom Filtration, Inc.-Madisonville Mill, Madisonville, KY; Int'l, pg. 35
McLean, W., Chief Oper. Officer--Yale-Corbin Canada Limited, Mississauga, Canada; Int'l, pg. 1499
McLellan, Paul M., V.P.-Prod. Opers.--Compass Design Automation Inc., San Jose, CA; U.S. Public, pg. 1703
McLelland, T.A., Gen. Mgr.--CHEMCENTRAL/Philadelphia, Morrisville, PA; U.S. Private, pg. 232
McLemore, Frank, Plant Mgr.--UTA Morganfield Plant, Morganfield, KY; U.S. Public, pg. 1691
McLemore, Fred B., Pres.--COMAV, Scottsdale, AZ; U.S. Public, pg. 1423
McLendon, James, Gen. Mgr.--WMAZ-WAYS Radio, Macon, GA; U.S. Public, pg. 699
McLennan, John T., Chm. Bd. & Chief Exec. Officer--Bell Mobility Paging Inc., Downsview, Canada; Int'l, pg. 115
McLennan, Lawrence, Pres.--DZIC, Schenectady, NY; U.S. Private, pg. 317
McLeod, Bill, Mng. Dir.--Crane Australia Pty. Ltd., Saint Marys, Australia; U.S. Public, pg. 457
McLeod, Morris, Pres.--Interstate Highway Sign, Little Rock, AR; U.S. Public, pg. 1045
McLeod, S.D., Pres.--CIMCO Refrigeration, Toronto, Canada; Int'l, pg. 1400
McLevish, Timothy R., Pres.--Mead Specialty Paper, South Lee, MA; U.S. Public, pg. 1074
McLoghlin, Peter David, Gen. Mgr.--The Uncle Toby's Company Ltd., Richmond, Australia; Int'l, pg. 555
McLornan, Brian, Mng. Dir.--Glen Electric, Newry, United Kingdom; Int'l, pg. 554
McLoughlin, Michael J., Pres.--Sysco Food Services of Portland, Inc., Wilsonville, OR; U.S. Public, pg. 1552
McLoughlin, Robert, Pres.--Blodgett Combi, Burlington, VT; U.S. Public, pg. 1064
McLuckey, John A., Pres.--Boeing North American, Seal Beach, CA; U.S. Public, pg. 241
McMahan, R.C., Pres.--Shell Pipe Line Corp., Houston, TX; Int'l, pg. 1136
McMahen, Charles E., Chm. Bd. & Chief Exec. Officer--Compass Bancshares, Inc., Houston, TX; U.S. Public, pg. 419
McMahon, Kevin J., Pres.--Edwards & Kelcey Wireless, Morristown, NJ; U.S. Private, pg. 364
McMahon, Raymond D., Pres.--Baldwin InLine Finishing, Willowbrook, IL; U.S. Public, pg. 170
McManus, James A., Pres. & Chief Exec. Officer--Radio City Productions, New York, NY; Int'l, pg. 873
McManus, Patrick J., Pres.--Raymond Leasing Corporation, Greene, NY; Int'l, pg. 123
McManus, Seamus, Gen. Mgr.--Mandarin Oriental, Hong Kong Limited, Central, Hong Kong; Int'l, pg. 704
McManus, Sean, Pres.--CBS Sports Div., New York, NY; U.S. Public, pg. 274
McMaster, Ian M., Grp. Gen. Mgr.--Sheet & Coil Products Division, Port Kembla, Australia; Int'l, pg. 227
McMaster, Jock, Chief Oper. Officer--Boart Longyear Ltd., Auckland, New Zealand; Int'l, pg. 76
McMaster, Lee P., Chm. Bd.--Union Carbide Asia Pacific Inc., Singapore, Singapore; U.S. Public, pg. 1667
McMeekin, H. Thomas, Pres.--Lincoln Investment Management Inc., Fort Wayne, IN; U.S. Public, pg. 998
McMeekin, H. Thomas, Pres.--Lincoln National Realty Corporation, Fort Wayne, IN; U.S. Public, pg. 998
McMeekin, H. Thomas, Pres.--Lincoln National Income Fund, Inc., Baltimore, MD; U.S. Public, pg. 998
McMeekin, William D., Pres. & Chief Exec. Officer--Granite Savings Bank & Trust Company, Barre, VT; U.S. Public, pg. 187
McMenemy, Cheryl, Publisher--Cobourg Daily Star, Cobourg, Canada; Int'l, pg. 631
McMillan, D.B., Gen. Mgr.--Kubota Tractor Corp. Engine Division, Schaumburg, IL; Int'l, pg. 762
McMillan, Doug, Gen. Mgr.--Tele Scripps Cable, Elizabethtown, KY; U.S. Public, pg. 1448
McMillan, Gary, Reg. V.P. & Gen. Mgr.--AIU Canada Ltd., Toronto, Canada; U.S. Public, pg. 85
McMillan, Gary, Reg. V.P. & Gen. Mgr.--Commerce & Industry Insurance Co. of Canada, Toronto, Canada; U.S. Public, pg. 85
McMillan, Hank, Plant Mgr.--Firestone Industrial Products Company-Noblesville Plant, Noblesville, IN; Int'l, pg. 214
McMillan, Harry, Exec. V.P.--Komori America Corporation, Rolling Meadows, IL; Int'l, pg. 745
McMillan, Howard L., Jr., Pres. & Chief Oper. Officer--Deposit Guaranty National Bank, Jackson, MS; U.S. Public, pg. 500
McMillan, Melvin, Mgr.-Branch--Piper Jaffray Inc., Aberdeen, WA; U.S. Public, pg. 1300
McMillan, Melvin A., Mgr.-Branch--Piper Jaffray Inc., Ocean Shores, WA; U.S. Public, pg. 1303
McMillan, Rae, V.P. & Mgr.--Northern Trust Bank of Arizona, N.A., Sun City, AZ; U.S. Public, pg. 1196
McMillan, Robert, Pres.--Progressive American Insurance Co., Tampa, FL; U.S. Public, pg. 1334
McMillan, Robert, Pres.--Progressive Southeastern Insurance Co., Tampa, FL; U.S. Public, pg. 1335
McMillan, Ross, Pres.-Americas Reg.--ICI Acrylics Inc., Cordova, TN; Int'l, pg. 663
McMillan, W.L., V.P.--Elkton DLV Operations, Elkton, MD; U.S. Public, pg. 1597
McMillan, William F., Jr., Pres. & Chief Exec. Officer--NCB Properties, Inc., Albany, NY; U.S. Public, pg. 955
McMillen, James E., Pres.--AeroThrust Corp., Miami, FL; Int'l, pg. 276
McMillen, Karl, Pres.--Todd Pipe & Supply-West L.A., Los Angeles, CA; U.S. Private, pg. 1090
McMillian, Robert T., Pres.--Bayside Underwriters Insurance Agency, Inc., Tampa, FL; U.S. Public, pg. 1334
McMillin, Robert J., Gen. Dir.--Delco Systems Operation, Goleta, CA; U.S. Public, pg. 720
McMullan, D.W., Chm.--SmithKline Beecham Pharmaceuticals, International Division, Brentford, United Kingdom; Int'l, pg. 1264
McMullen, Bob, Pres.--I.P.C., Tucker, GA; U.S. Public, pg. 484
McMullen, Kevin, Pres.--GenCorp Wallcovering Div., Salem, NH; U.S. Public, pg. 706
McMullen, Kevin, Pres.--GenCorp Decorative & Building Products Div., Maumee, OH; U.S. Public, pg. 706
McMullen, Kevin, Pres.--GenCorp Designed Product Div., Columbus, MS; U.S. Public, pg. 706
McMullen, Kevin, Pres.--GenCorp Designed Product Mfg. Div., Jeannette, PA; U.S. Public, pg. 706
McMullen, Kevin, Pres.--GenCorp Decorative Product Manufacturing Div., Auburn, PA; U.S. Public, pg. 706
McMullen, Tony, Mng. Dir.--Columbia Pictures Television Pty. Ltd., Sydney, Australia; Int'l, pg. 1282
McMunn, William H., Pres.--Indigo Development Inc., Daytona Beach, FL; U.S. Public, pg. 437
McMurray, Charley, Mng. Dir.--Advanced Filtration Systems, Inc., Champaign, IL; U.S. Public, pg. 316
McMurray, Darin, Pres.--Lee/Collier, Fort Myers, FL; U.S. Public, pg. 1683
McMurray, J. Patrick, Chm., Pres. & Chief Exec. Officer--First Security Bank of Idaho, N.A., Boise, ID; U.S. Public, pg. 637
McMurtrie, John, Mng. Dir.--UBS Australia Ltd., Sydney, Australia; Int'l, pg. 1440
McMurty, Peter, Mng. Dir.--Renishaw (Ireland) Limited, Dublin, Ireland; Int'l, pg. 1103
McNair, Carl H., Pres.--Enterprise Management, Reston, VA; U.S. Private, pg. 351
McNair, Gary, Gen. Mgr.--KSNT-TV, Topeka, KS; U.S. Public, pg. 983
McNally, J., Chm.--Ulster Bank Dublin Trust Company, Dublin, Ireland; Int'l, pg. 912
McNally, Joe, Country Mgr.--Compaq Computer Limited, Richmond, United Kingdom; U.S. Public, pg. 418
McNally, Robert, Pres.--Bridgestone/Firestone Off Road Tire Company, Nashville, TN; Int'l, pg. 213
McNally, Thomas M., Pres.--Abbott Chemical & Agricultural Products Division, Abbott Park, IL; U.S. Public, pg. 13
McNally, Timothy, V.P. & Gen. Mgr.--McNally Manufacturing, Pittsburg, KS; Int'l, pg. 1326
McNamara, Alveta, Admin.--Guardian Care of Rocky Mount, Rocky Mount, NC; U.S. Public, pg. 1713
McNamara, Austin T., Pres. & Chief Exec. Officer--General Cigar Company, Inc., Bloomfield, CT; U.S. Public, pg. 708
McNamara, James, Pres. & Chief Exec. Officer--New World Entertainment, Inc., Los Angeles, CA; Int'l, pg. 926
McNamara, John D., Pres.--ADM Processing Div., Decatur, IL; U.S. Public, pg. 127
McNamara, Joseph, Exec. V.P. & Gen. Mgr.--Edelman Worldwide, Inc., Dallas, TX; U.S. Private, pg. 362
McNamara, Michael, Exec. V.P. & Gen. Mgr.-Global Mktg. & U.S. Bus.--Neutrogena Corporation, Los Angeles, CA; U.S. Public, pg. 928
McNamara, Robert, Chief Exec. Officer--ADP Marshall Contractors Inc., Rumford, RI; U.S. Public, pg. 660
McNamara, Robert, Pres.--Bank of Dwight, Dwight, IL; U.S. Public, pg. 1316
McNamara, William P., III, Pres. & Chief Exec. Officer--Famous-Barr, Saint Louis, MO; U.S. Public, pg. 1063
McNamee, Gordon, Mng. Dir.--Kiss FM, London, United Kingdom; Int'l, pg. 452
McNaney, David, V.P.-Western Div. Mgr.--Worldvision Enterprises, Inc., Los Angeles, CA; U.S. Private, pg. 776
McNaughton, W., Chm. Bd.--British Aerospace Flying College Ltd., Prestwick, United Kingdom; Int'l, pg. 217
McNeel, R.L., Pres.--Amoco Performance Products, Inc., Alpharetta, GA; U.S. Public, pg. 102
McNeely, Gibbon, Dir.-Securities--Sea Island Services, Inc., Sea Island, GA; U.S. Private, pg. 978
McNeely, Larry, Mng. Dir.--Corro-Coat (Malaysia) Sdn. Bhd., Shah Alam, Malaysia; Int'l, pg. 715
McNeely, Larry, Man. Dir.--Corro-Coat U.A.E. Ltd., Dubai, United Arab Emirates; Int'l, pg. 715
McNeil, D., Pres.--Great Northern Paper, Inc., Millinocket, ME; U.S. Public, pg. 248
McNeil, Gordon H., Pres.--Magnetic Technologies Corporation, Rochester, NY; U.S. Public, pg. 1420
McNeill, C.A., Jr., Pres.--Susquehanna Power Co., Philadelphia, PA; U.S. Public, pg. 1268
McNeill, Carl, V.P. & Gen. Mgr.--WRVA-AM, Richmond, VA; U.S. Public, pg. 385
McNeill, Carl, V.P. & Gen. Mgr.--WRNL-FM, Richmond, VA; U.S. Public, pg. 385
McNeill, R.J.B., Mng. Dir.--Northern Ireland Carpets Ltd., Newtownards, United Kingdom; Int'l, pg. 797
McNeill, R.J.B., Mng. Dir.--B.H. McCleery & Co. Ltd., Newtownards, United Kingdom; Int'l, pg. 797
McNeill, R.J.B., Mng. Dir.--Hollybank Bleach & Dye Works Ltd., Ballyclare, United Kingdom; Int'l, pg. 798
McNeilly, R.J., Exec. Gen. Mgr. & Chief Exec. Officer--BHP Steel, Melbourne, Australia; Int'l, pg. 225
McNeilly, Robert E., III, Chm., Pres. & Chief Exec. Officer--SunTrust Bank, Alabama, N.A., Florence, AL; U.S. Public, pg. 1538
McNeilly, Robert E., Jr., Chm. Bd.--First American National Bank, Nashville, TN; U.S. Public, pg. 624
McNelis, T.J., V.P.--The Hunt Paving Company, Inc., Indianapolis, IN; U.S. Private, pg. 548
McNerney, W. James, Pres. & Chief Exec. Officer--Greenwich Air Services, Miami, FL; U.S. Public, pg. 710
McNew, Rex, Gen. Mgr.--Southwestern Explosives, Gonzales, TX; U.S. Private, pg. 100
McNichol, Jack, V.P.--Eastern Division, Pikeville, KY; Int'l, pg. 337
McNicoll, Donald, Chm. Bd.--Willis Corroon Limited, Auckland, New Zealand; Int'l, pg. 1509
McNiel, Bruce, Pres.--Dayco Products Inc., Miamisburg, OH; U.S. Public, pg. 1045
McNiel, Bruce A., Pres.--Dayco Swan Corporation, Worthington, OH; U.S. Public, pg. 1045
McNiel, Bruce A., Pres.--Mark IV Industrial, Dayton, OH; U.S. Public, pg. 1045
McNulty, James F., III, Pres.--Total Security Solutions, Chicago, IL; U.S. Public, pg. 245
McNulty, R.W. Roy, Pres.--Shorts Brothers PLC, Belfast, United Kingdom; Int'l, pg. 200
McPartland, Peter, Mng. Dir.--Radio Aire, Leeds, United Kingdom; Int'l, pg. 452
McPhail, B.D., Chm. Bd.--P&O Property Holdings Ltd., London, United Kingdom; Int'l, pg. 1034
McPhail, B.D., Chm. Bd.--CCL Ltd., London, United Kingdom; Int'l, pg. 1034
McPhail, Douglas J., Pres.--Productive Business Interiors, Indianapolis, IN; U.S. Private, pg. 560
McPhail, Gary, Pres.--AmerUS Life, Des Moines, IA; U.S. Private, pg. 59
McPhee, Jim, Pres.--FS Concepts, Inc., Anaheim, CA; U.S. Private, pg. 818
McPherson, D. Alex, Plant Mgr.--Bosch Braking Systems-North America, Saint Joseph, MI; Int'l, pg. 204
McPherson, G.S., Pres.--AlliedSignal Canada Inc., Automotive Aftermarket, Stratford, Canada; U.S. Public, pg. 52
McPherson, Ian, Chief Exec. Officer-Indus. Products--Aquaseal Ltd., Rochester, United Kingdom; Int'l, pg. 1355
McPherson, John, River Agent--The Union Water-Power Co., Lewiston, ME; U.S. Public, pg. 325
McPheters, Rebecca, Pres. & Chief Exec. Officer--Simmons, New York, NY; Int'l, pg. 1483
McQuade, John, Plant Mgr.--Bridgestone/Firestone Tire Manufacturing Operations-Lavergne, La Vergne, TN; Int'l, pg. 213
McQueary, C.E., Pres.--Lucent Technologies Advanced Technology Systems, Greensboro, NC; U.S. Public, pg. 1017
McQueeney, Daniel S., Mgr.--Scott & Stringfellow, Inc., Charleston, SC; U.S. Public, pg. 1446
McQueeney, Thomas A., Pres. & Publisher--Money Market Directories, Charlottesville, VA; U.S. Public, pg. 1071
McQuern, Marcia, Pres., Editor & Publr.--Press Enterprise Company, Riverside, CA; U.S. Public, pg. 209
McQueston, Robert, Sls. Representative--Brian Controls Division, Halifax, Canada; Int'l, pg. 711
McQuillan, J.J., Gen. Mgr.--CHEMCENTRAL/Atlanta, Doraville, GA; U.S. Private, pg. 232
McQuillan, J.J., Gen. Mgr.--CHEMCENTRAL/Greensboro, Jamestown, NC; U.S. Private, pg. 232
McQuillan, Paul J., Dir.-Sls.--R.R. Donnelley Pindar, London, United Kingdom; U.S. Public, pg. 519
McQuillan, Thomas, Exec. V.P. & Gen. Mgr.--Select Robinson Inc., Billerica, MA; Int'l, pg. 274
McQuillen, Harry A., Pres. & Chief Exec. Officer--K-III Media Group, New York, NY; U.S. Public, pg. 1328
McQuillen, James F., Gen. Mgr.--Connector Division, Chicago, IL; U.S. Public, pg. 1101
McQuinn, A.E., Pres.--Lor Al Products Inc, Benson, MN; U.S. Public, pg. 6
McRae, D. Gary, Pres.--Compsee, Inc., Mount Gilead, NC; U.S. Public, pg. 1073
McRae, D. Gary, Pres.--McRae Graphics, Inc., Mount Gilead, NC; U.S. Public, pg. 1074
McRann, Robert G., V.P. & Gen. Mgr.--Cox Communications-San Diego, San Diego, CA; U.S. Public, pg. 455
McReilly, Robert E., Jr., Chm.--First American Trust Company, N.A., Nashville, TN; U.S. Public, pg. 624
McReynolds, Malachy, Gen. Mgr.-Opers.--Leaf United Kingdom Ltd., Bristol, United Kingdom; Int'l, pg. 638
McReynolds, Sam, Pres.--Cleveland Bank & Trust Company, Cleveland, TN; U.S. Public, pg. 639
McShane, Denny, Facility Manager--Square D Co., Lincoln, NE; Int'l, pg. 1208
McSorley, Michael H.S., Chm. Bd.--Falconbridge International S.A., Brussels, Belgium; Int'l, pg. 434
McSwain, Ross, Gen. Mgr.--International Public Relations, Pty Ltd., Brisbane, Australia; Int'l, pg. 1227
McSweeney, Edward, Pres.--Norris Cylinder Company, Longview, TX; U.S. Public, pg. 1054
McSweeney, Rich, Asst. Branch Mgr.--Burns & Wilcox, Burlington, NJ; U.S. Private, pg. 609
McTague, John P., V.P. & Gen. Mgr.--Ford Technical Affairs & Operating Staffs, Dearborn, MI; U.S. Public, pg. 662
McVay, Edwin L., Plant Mgr.--Consumer Products Company, Muncie, IN; U.S. Public, pg. 56
McWalters, James G., Mng. Dir.--PM Realty Advisors Inc., Newport Beach, CA; U.S. Private, pg. 831
McWaters, Jeffrey L., Pres.--Cigna Healthcare Mid-Atlantic, Inc., Columbia, MD; U.S. Public, pg. 359
McWhinnie, Craig, Pres.--Summit-Canada, Toronto, Canada; U.S. Public, pg. 78
McWhorter, Anthony L., Pres.--Liberty National Life Insurance Co., Birmingham, AL; U.S. Public, pg. 1622
McWilliam, Alaiston C., Chief Oper. Officer--Armstrong Engineering Limited, Coventry, United Kingdom; Int'l, pg. 265
McWilliam, J. Donald, Pres.--BetzDearborn Canada, Inc., Mississauga, Canada; U.S. Public, pg. 227
Mead, Barbara, Acct. Exec.--U.S. Yellow Pages, Dallas, TX; U.S. Private, pg. 1168
Mead, D., Mng. Dir.--National Australia Trustees Ltd., Melbourne, Australia; Int'l, pg. 906

Mead, Dana, Chm. Bd.--Monroe Auto Equipment Co., Monroe, MI; *U.S. Public*, pg. 1577
Mead, Frank, Pres.--Tech Group Tempe Inc., Tempe, AZ; *U.S. Private*, pg. 1071
Meade, John, Pres. & Chief Exec. Officer--Hanover Bank, Mechanicsville, VA; *U.S. Public*, pg. 1039
Meade, Patrick, Chief Oper. Officer--Hi-Shear Corp., Torrance, CA; *U.S. Public*, pg. 825
Meades, Derek, Chief Fin. Officer--Hoskyns Group Plc, London, United Kingdom; *Int'l*, pg. 264
Meador, Thomas E., Pres. & Chief Oper. Officer--The Balcor Company, Bannockburn, IL; *U.S. Public*, pg. 74
Meadows, Arthur, Pres.--Erdle Perforating of Carolina, Charlotte, NC; *U.S. Private*, pg. 380
Meadows, George, Mgr.--Southern Electric Supply Co., Inc., Sanford, FL; *Int'l*, pg. 1108
Meadows, Roger, V.P.-Opers.--Dayflex Worldwide, Miamisburg, OH; *U.S. Public*, pg. 1045
Meadows, Vernon, Plant Mgr.--Nashua Photo Inc., Parkersburg, WV; *U.S. Public*, pg. 1152
Meakin, Timothy, Pres.--Bristol-Myers Squibb Canada Inc., Montreal, Canada; *U.S. Public*, pg. 256
Meakins, Keith, Chief Exec.-U.K. & Ireland--Fasson U.K. Ltd., Hemel Hempstead, United Kingdom; *U.S. Public*, pg. 154
Mealling, Bobbie, V.P. & Mng. Dir.--Standard Distributing Co. Inc., Brunswick, GA; *U.S. Private*, pg. 781
Meals, Pamela, Publr.--The Idaho Statesman, Boise, ID; *U.S. Public*, pg. 701
Means, Michael H., Pres. & Chief Oper. Officer--Arkla, Little Rock, AR; *U.S. Public*, pg. 843
Meany, William C., V.P. & Gen. Mgr.--Lindenmeyr Munroe, Wallingford, CT; *U.S. Private*, pg. 224
Meany, William F., Pres.--SAFECO Credit Company, Inc., Seattle, WA; *U.S. Public*, pg. 1423
Meara, Richard, V.P. & Gen. Mgr.--PAXAR Graphics, Vandalia, OH; *U.S. Public*, pg. 1266
Mears, W. Bruce, V.P. & Gen. Mgr.--Tar River Communications, Inc., Rocky Mount, NC; *U.S. Public*, pg. 701
Mears, William C., Pres.--CFX Funding, L.L.C., Keene, NH; *U.S. Public*, pg. 278
Meazzini, Vittorio, Pres.--Snam S.P.A., Milan, Italy; *Int'l*, pg. 428
Meazzini, Vittorio, Chm.--Snam International Holding A.G., Zurich, Switzerland; *Int'l*, pg. 429
Mebane, William deB., Publr.--Multimedia Publishing of South Carolina, Inc., Greenville, SC; *U.S. Public*, pg. 699
Mebane, William deB., Pres.--Multimedia Newspaper Company, Greenville, SC; *U.S. Public*, pg. 699
Meccariello, Joseph, Mgr.--Acessorios Electronicos (Bel Fuse Macao), Limitada, Taipa, Macau; *U.S. Public*, pg. 200
Meccia, Eduardo, Media Dir.--Leo Burnett Co. Inc., Buenos Aires, Argentina; *U.S. Private*, pg. 185
Mecham, Rex, V.P. & Gen. Mgr.--Material Handling Div., Salt Lake City, UT; *U.S. Private*, pg. 84
Mechanic, William, Pres.--Buena Vista International, Inc., Burbank, CA; *U.S. Public*, pg. 513
Mechigian, Robert, Pres.--Bob Saks Oldsmobile Inc., Farmington, MI; *U.S. Private*, pg. 395
Mechling, B.M., V.P. & Gen. Mgr.--Dillard, A ResourceNet International Company, Charlotte, NC; *U.S. Public*, pg. 902
Mechling, Barbara, Gen. Mgr.--Edelman Public Relations Worldwide, Tokyo, Japan; *U.S. Private*, pg. 363
Mechura, Frank, Pres. & Chief Exec. Officer--Crown Cork of Canada Ltd., Concord, Canada; *U.S. Public*, pg. 464
Mechura, Frank J., Pres. & Chief Exec. Officer--Constar International, Inc., Atlanta, GA; *U.S. Public*, pg. 463
Mechura, Frank J., Pres. & Chief Exec. Officer--Crown Cork & Seal Canada, Inc., Concord, Canada; *U.S. Public*, pg. 464
Mecili, Boussad, Resident Mgr.--ESAB Bureau de Liaison, Algiers, Algeria; *Int'l*, pg. 282
Meclot, Ludo, Chief Oper. Officer--Ferrosan Healthcrafts NV/SA, Brussels, Belgium; *Int'l*, pg. 989
Mecozzi, Walter, Gen. Mgr.--Governair Corporation, Oklahoma City, OK; *U.S. Public*, pg. 1193
Medart, Ch., Mng. Dir.--Ascom Hasler SA, Brussels, Belgium; *Int'l*, pg. 87
Medavoy, Michael, Chm. Bd.--Tri-Star Pictures, Inc., Culver City, CA; *Int'l*, pg. 1282
Medavoy, Mike, Chm. Bd.--TriStar Pictures, Culver City, CA; *Int'l*, pg. 1283
Meddaugh, Gary, Plant Mgr.--Apex Galvanizing Corp., Stewartsville, NJ; *U.S. Private*, pg. 1138
Medeiros, Paulo De Tarso, Mgr.--Banco do Brasil S.A.-Washington, Washington, DC; *Int'l*, pg. 141
Mederer, Dave, Gen. Mgr.--Omega Environmental Services, Lorton, VA; *U.S. Public*, pg. 1222
Medford, Larry D., Plant Mgr.--The Lamson & Sessions Co., Pasadena, TX; *U.S. Public*, pg. 976
Medica, Adolph J., Pres.--Space Transportation Systems, Washington, DC; *U.S. Public*, pg. 1690
Medica, John K., V.P.-Worldwide Procurement & Chief Oper. Officer-Japan--Dell Computer Corporation, Round Rock, TX; *U.S. Public*, pg. 495
Medico, William, Pres.--Action Lift, Wilkes-Barre, PA; *U.S. Private*, pg. 728
Medin, K.A., Pres.--Boeing North America, North American Aircraft Modification Division, Anaheim, CA; *U.S. Public*, pg. 241
Medina, A. Resino, Gen. Mgr.--Ferro Enamel Espanola, S.A., Castellon de la Plana, Spain; *U.S. Public*, pg. 619
Medina, Armando M., Pres. & Chief Exec. Officer--Rizal Commercial Banking Corporation, Makati, Philippines; *Int'l*, pg. 1190
Medina, Dionisio Garza, Chm. Bd.--Hylsamex, S.A. de C.V., San Nicolas, Mexico; *Int'l*, pg. 56
Medina, Felipe Garza, Exec. V.P.--Hylsa S.A.-Flat Rolled Division, San Nicolas, Mexico; *Int'l*, pg. 56
Medina, Sergio, Opers. Mgr.--Herbalife International de Mexico, S.A.D.C.V., Guadalajara, Mexico; *U.S. Public*, pg. 809
Medley, Ben, Pres.--Tracor Flight Systems, Inc., Mojave, CA; *U.S. Public*, pg. 1627
Medley, Rufus L., Mng. Dir.--Laboratory Supply Company, Nashville, TN; *U.S. Private*, pg. 642
Medley, Thomas, Plant Mgr.--Barton Brands of Georgia, Inc., Atlanta, GA; *U.S. Public*, pg. 300
Medlin, Bob, Gen. Mgr.--United Companies Mortgage of Florida, Inc., Tampa, FL; *U.S. Public*, pg. 1675
Medlin, Kenneth A., Sr., V.P. & Gen. Mgr.--Communication Systems Division, Richardson, TX; *U.S. Public*, pg. 1397
Medlin, Tom, Pres.--Marine Midland Mortgage Servicing Corporation, Charlotte, NC; *Int'l*, pg. 581
Medovic, Nikolaus, Mng. Dir.--Olivetti Sanay Ve Ticaret A.S., Istanbul, Turkey; *Int'l*, pg. 1003
Medrick, Cecil, Distr. Mgr.--Browning-Ferris Industries of Pennsylvania, Inc., Carnegie, PA; *U.S. Public*, pg. 264
Medvec, Bruce A., Pres.--Southwest Risk Services Inc., Phoenix, AZ; *U.S. Public*, pg. 215
Medved, Jon, Pres.--Walter Drake, Inc., Colorado Springs, CO; *U.S. Private*, pg. 421
Mee, George, Pres. & Chief Exec. Officer--Mallery Lumber Corp.-NY, Hancock, NY; *U.S. Private*, pg. 698
Meedman, Peter, Plant Mgr.--Elkem Bremanger, Svelgen, Norway; *Int'l*, pg. 448
Meehan, Andrew, Exec. Dir.--BIL Asia Holdings Ltd., Central, Hong Kong; *Int'l*, pg. 215
Meehan, Kerry, Chief Oper. Officer--Datapoint Corp. Pty. Ltd., Artarmon, Australia; *Int'l*, pg. 384
Meehan, M.R., Chief Fin.Officer--Vi-Spring Limited, Plymouth, United Kingdom; *Int'l*, pg. 925
Meehan, Peter J., Pres.--ESCOD Industries, Research Triangle Park, NC; *U.S. Public*, pg. 881
Meek, C. Agnew, Div. V.P.--Visual Systems Division, Austin, TX; *U.S. Public*, pg. 1605
Meek, C.M., Mng. Dir.--GEC Zambia Ltd., Ndola, Zambia; *Int'l*, pg. 546
Meek, Paul D., Chm. Bd.--Fina, Inc., Dallas, TX; *Int'l*, pg. 1044
Meek, Phillip J., Pres.--Capital Cities/ABC Publishing Group, New York, NY; *U.S. Public*, pg. 512
Meeker, Thomas H., Chm. Bd.--Hoosier Park Ltd., Anderson, IN; *U.S. Public*, pg. 356
Meelia, Richard D., Pres. & Chief Exec. Officer--The Kendall Company, Mansfield, MA; *U.S. Public*, pg. 1647
Meelia, Richard D., Pres.--Kendall Healthcare Products Company, Mansfield, MA; *U.S. Public*, pg. 1647
Meerloo, E.P., Gen. Mgr.--Medianet bv, Haarlem, Netherlands; *Int'l*, pg. 1445
Meers, P., Gen. Mgr. & Chief Exec. Rep.--Australia & New Zealand Banking Group Limited Singapore, Singapore, Singapore; *Int'l*, pg. 99
Meersseman, Jean Claude, Dir.--Takenaka Belgium S.A. - France Branch, Bagnolet, France; *Int'l*, pg. 1351
Meerstadt, Bert, Pres. & Chief Exec. Officer--PMSVW/ Young & Rubicam B.V., Amsterdam, Netherlands; *U.S. Private*, pg. 1199
Meert, Jacques, Gen. Mgr.-Mktg. & Sls.--H.J. Heinz Branch Belgium, Brussels, Belgium; *U.S. Public*, pg. 806
Meert, Jacques, Mng. Dir.--H.J. Heinz Central Europe S.A., Brussels, Belgium; *U.S. Public*, pg. 806
Meert, Jacques, Mng. Dir.--H.J. Heinz Northern Europe, Brussels, Belgium; *U.S. Public*, pg. 806
Meese, Gerhard, Pres.--Universal Instruments Corporation, Binghamton, NY; *U.S. Public*, pg. 522
Meeusen, Dan I., Mng. Dir.--Sulzer Pompen Benelux B.V., Hengelo, Netherlands; *Int'l*, pg. 1306
Meeusen, Dean, Plant Mgr.--Dean Foods Vegetable Company, Cedar Grove, WI; *U.S. Public*, pg. 490
Meeuwisse, J.M., Gen. Mgr.--Ballast Nedam Equipment Services Pte. Ltd., Singapore, Singapore; *Int'l*, pg. 134
Meffre, Jean-Marie, Mng. Dir.--Renishaw S.A., Marne la Vallee, France; *Int'l*, pg. 1103
Mefine, Andrew, Plant Mgr.--Enduro-Niagara Ltd., Beamsville, Canada; *U.S. Private*, pg. 935
Mega, John, Pres.--L3 Communications Narda-Microwave Div., Hauppauge, NY; *U.S. Private*, pg. 638
Meghani, Vijay, Chief Oper. Officer--BHF-Bank Representative Office, Mumbai, India; *Int'l*, pg. 120
Mehalchin, John J., Pres.--Highline Financial Services, Inc., Boulder, CO; *U.S. Public*, pg. 1785
Mehalik, Jan, V.P.--Ballantyne Cashmere USA Ltd., New York, NY; *Int'l*, pg. 386
Mehan, Monica, Pres. & Chief Exec. Officer--AT&T American Transtech Inc., Jacksonville, FL; *U.S. Public*, pg. 10
Mehdorn, Dr. Frank, Member of Bd.-Tech.--Spinnstofffabrik Zehlendorf AG, Berlin, Germany; *Int'l*, pg. 626
Mehlen, Jean-Pierre, Mgr.--Barenbrug Luxembourg SA, Diekirch, Luxembourg; *Int'l*, pg. 167
Mehler, Eckhart, Rep.--Bayerische Landesbank Girozentrale, Toronto, Canada; *Int'l*, pg. 177
Mehling, E., Mng. Dir.--VEM Erz und Stahl GmbH, Essen, Germany; *Int'l*, pg. 682
Mehner, Edward W., Chm. Bd. & Chief Exec. Officer--The Rugby Group, Inc., Rockville Centre, NY; *Int'l*, pg. 625
Mehrotra, Sunit, Mng. Dir.--TBWA Stockholm, Stockholm, Sweden; *U.S. Private*, pg. 1063
Mehta, Shailesh, Chm. Bd., Chief Exec. Officer & Pres.-Providian-Direct Insurance--National Liberty Corporation, Frazer, PA; *Int'l*, pg. 26
Mehta, Shailesh, Pres.-Direct Response Grp.--National Liberty Life Insurance Co., Valley Forge, PA; *Int'l*, pg. 27
Mehta, Sonny, Publisher & Editor-in-Chief--Alfred A. Knopf, Inc., New York, NY; *U.S. Private*, pg. 21
Mehta, V.K., Chief Exec. Officer--WAGO & Controls (India) Ltd., Nolda, India; *Int'l*, pg. 209
Meichsner, Christian, Mng. Dir.-Client Services--TBWA Hamburg GmbH, Hamburg, Germany; *U.S. Private*, pg. 1063
Meidenbauer, Arlen, Plant Mgr.--Eskimo Flavors, New Berlin, WI; *U.S. Public*, pg. 592
Meier Nolte, J. D., Mng. Dir.--Konatec Nassbaggertechnik GmbH, Monchengladbach, Germany; *Int'l*, pg. 608
Meier, Alan, Sr. V.P.--Central Loan Administration, Waukesha, WI; *U.S. Public*, pg. 649
Meier, Armand, Gen. Mgr.--Dietiker AG, Saint Gallen, Switzerland; *Int'l*, pg. 865
Meier, Bjorn, Pres.--ASEA Skandia Havemanns El A/S, Albertslund, Denmark; *Int'l*, pg. 7
Meier, Franz, Gen. Mgr.--Translastic A.G., Wallbach, Switzerland; *Int'l*, pg. 497
Meier, G.A., Mgr.--Alcan Aluminium Folienwerk Verwaltungs GmbH, Ludenscheid, Germany; *Int'l*, pg. 50
Meier, George, V.P.-Sls.--Autologic Information International Ltd. (Australia), Morabbin, Australia; *U.S. Public*, pg. 1724
Meier, Gerald, Pres.--Sunflower Mfg. Co., Inc., Beloit, KS; *U.S. Public*, pg. 1676
Meier, H., Mng. Dir.--Oerlikon-Contraves Pyrotec AG, Zurich, Switzerland; *Int'l*, pg. 998
Meier, K. H., Pres.--Noma (Hong Kong) Limited, Kowloon, Hong Kong; *Int'l*, pg. 955
Meier, K.H., Pres.--Noma Inc., Scarborough, Canada; *Int'l*, pg. 955
Meier, Paul, Pres.--Credit Suisse, Zurich, Switzerland; *Int'l*, pg. 345
Meier, Paul Gerhard, Chief Exec.--Sulzer Metco (Deutschland) GmbH, Hattersheim, Germany; *Int'l*, pg. 1307
Meier, Tom, Gen. Mgr.--Steiner Turf Equipment Inc., Orrville, OH; *Int'l*, pg. 1088
Meiers, Ronald J., Chief Oper. Officer & Sr. V.P.--Shopping Centre Group, Toronto, Canada; *Int'l*, pg. 253
Meije, Jose, Chief Oper. Officer--Hipotebansa, Madrid, Spain; *Int'l*, pg. 143
Meijer, Antonie, Mng. Dir.--SKF Kogellagerindustrie B.V., Veenendaal, Netherlands; *Int'l*, pg. 1159
Meijer, Emmo, Dr., Chief Oper. Officer--Holland Sweetener Company V.O.F., Maastricht, Netherlands; *Int'l*, pg. 1408
Meijer, Emmo, Dr., Chief Oper. Officer--Holland Sweetener Company, Geleen, Netherlands; *Int'l*, pg. 1408
Meijer, H.A., Mng. Dir.--Escher Holland B.V., Fijnaart, Netherlands; *Int'l*, pg. 1133
Meijer, M.C.J., Chm. Bd.--Quaker Chemical S.A., Villeneuve-la-Garonne, France; *U.S. Public*, pg. 1347
Meijer, Marc, V.P.-Europe--Quaker Chemical Europe B.V., Uithoorn, Netherlands; *U.S. Public*, pg. 1346
Meikle, Bruce F., Pres.--Rhein Chemie Corporation, Trenton, NJ; *Int'l*, pg. 173
Meili, Marcus, Mng. Dir.--A.C. Nielsen Management Services S.A., Buchrain, Switzerland; *U.S. Public*, pg. 1183
Meincke, Ronald, Mgr.-Plant--Mosinee Converted Products Div., Jackson, MS; *U.S. Public*, pg. 1747
Meinel, Helmut H., Sr. V.P.--Farah International, Inc., El Paso, TX; *U.S. Public*, pg. 613
Meinert, Greg, Mgr.-Plant--Pittsburgh Tube Jane Lew Div., Jane Lew, WV; *U.S. Private*, pg. 868
Meinhardt, Bradley, Reg. Dir.--Willis Corroon Aerospace-Western Region, Glendale, CA; *Int'l*, pg. 1505
Meinig, Walter P., Mng. Dir.--BNS International (Barbados) Limited, Saint Michael, Barbados; *Int'l*, pg. 156
Meinig, Walter P., Mng. Dir.--Scotia Insurance (Barbados) Limited, Saint Michael, Barbados; *Int'l*, pg. 156
Meishi, Takafumi, Regional Mgr.-Hawaii--Tokio Marine Management Inc. - Honolulu, Honolulu, HI; *Int'l*, pg. 1392
Meisner, D., Gen. Mgr.--Container Div. (Statesville), Statesville, NC; *Int'l*, pg. 1270
Meisser, F., Mgr.--Schweizerischer Bankverein, Chur, Switzerland; *Int'l*, pg. 1329
Meissner, Art, Pres.--600 Racing Inc., Harrisburg, NC; *U.S. Public*, pg. 1498
Meissner, Siegfried, Pres.--Nabors Drilling International Limited, Houston, TX; *U.S. Public*, pg. 1148
Meister, James, Pres. & Chief Exec. Officer--Kings Super Markets Inc., West Caldwell, NJ; *Int'l*, pg. 843
Meister, Peter, Mng. Dir.--Burgmann Seals South Africa (Pty) Ltd., Evendale, South Africa; *Int'l*, pg. 234
Meith, Mateland L., Jr., Pres.--GTE California Incorporated, Irving, TX; *U.S. Public*, pg. 697
Mejia, Sebastian Rodolfo Pastor, Pres. & Creative Dir.--Delfos/Y&R, Tegucigalpa, Honduras; *U.S. Private*, pg. 1200
Mejorada, Octavio Sanchez, Pres.--Campbell's de Mexico, S.A. de C.V., Villagran, Mexico; *U.S. Public*, pg. 299
Mekarporn, Phairuch, Mng. Dir.--Siam Kraft Industry Co., Ltd., Bangkok, Thailand; *Int'l*, pg. 1238
Mekarporw, Phairuch, Mng. Dir.--Thai Kraft Paper Industry Co., Ltd., Bangkok, Thailand; *Int'l*, pg. 1238
Mekler, Mark K., Reg. Dir.--Piper Jaffray Inc., Milwaukee, WI; *U.S. Public*, pg. 1302
Mektrakarn, Wicha, Pres.--Burgmann Thailand Co. Ltd., Rayong, Thailand; *Int'l*, pg. 234
Melamies, Pertti, Area Gen. Mgr.--Nokia Telecommunications Pty. Ltd., Sydney, Australia; *Int'l*, pg. 954
Melancon, Christine, Gen. Mgr.--Impact Recherche, Montreal, Canada; *Int'l*, pg. 336
Melancon, Rudy, Sls. & Service Mgr.--Varco BJ Oil Tools, New Iberia, LA; *U.S. Public*, pg. 1709
Melander, Bjorn, Chief Oper. Officer--Oy Raisional Ab, Raisio, Finland; *Int'l*, pg. 1085
Melani, Kenneth R., M.D., Pres.--Keystone Health Plan West, Inc., Pittsburgh, PA; *U.S. Private*, pg. 529
Melby, Larry, Chief Exec. Officer--Grant Center of Deering, Miami, FL; *U.S. Public*, pg. 405
Melcher, Ken, Sr. V.P. & Mgr.--City National Bank - Century City Regional Office, Los Angeles, CA; *U.S. Public*, pg. 381
Melchior, Jean, Mng. Dir.--Pittsburgh Corning Europe, N.V., Tessenderlo, Belgium; *U.S. Public*, pg. 449
Melchor, Joseph, Pres.--Gunther Nash Mining Construction, Saint Louis, MO; *U.S. Private*, pg. 32
Meldahl, Michael J., Pres. & Chief Oper. Officer--Tetragenics, Inc., Butte, MT; *U.S. Public*, pg. 1127

Meldahl, Michael J., Pres. & Chief Oper. Officer--TRI Touch America, Butte, MT; *U.S. Public*, pg. 1127
Meldahl, Phillip, V.P. & Gen. Mgr.--Outboard Marine de Mexico S.A. de C.V., Juarez, Mexico; *U.S. Private*, pg. 479
Meldrum, A.D., Chief Oper. Officer--GEC Australia Ltd., Sydney, Australia; *Int'l*, pg. 546
Meldrum, David L., First V.P. & Dir.-Tax Plng. & Admin.--Jefferies & Company, Inc., Los Angeles, CA; *U.S. Public*, pg. 925
Meldrum, Stephen T., Pres.--Lincoln National (China) Inc., Fort Wayne, IN; *U.S. Public*, pg. 998
Mele, Mario, Chief Exec. Officer-Mediapolis M&CS--Young & Rubicam Italia, S.p.A., Milan, Italy; *U.S. Private*, pg. 1199
Melendez, Blanca, Mng. V.P.--Danbury Pharmacal Puerto Rico Inc., Humacao, PR; *U.S. Private*, pg. 969
Melendez, E., Gen. Mgr.--DeVilbiss Ransburg Mexico, Tlalnepantla, Mexico; *U.S. Public*, pg. 868
Melendez, Eva, Opers. Mgr.-Cataluna--Utell International-Spain, Barcelona, Spain; *Int'l*, pg. 1099
Melendez, Luis, Plant Mgr.--Ransburg Mfg. Corp., Naguabo, PR; *U.S. Public*, pg. 865
Melgaard, J., Mng. Dir.--Livsforsikrings-Aktieselskabet Utrecht, Copenhagen, Denmark; *Int'l*, pg. 499
Melgaard, John, Pres.--Chr. Hansen G.m.b.H., Lubeck, Germany; *Int'l*, pg. 289
Melgar, Ismael, Pres.--Spicer Driveshaft Div., Toledo, OH; *U.S. Public*, pg. 479
Melgarejo, Ruben Ovelar, Gen. Mgr.--Senior Publicidad S.R.L., Asuncion, Paraguay; *U.S. Private*, pg. 305
Melham, Elie, Mng. Dir.--Nanjing Goulds Pumps Limited, Nanjing, China; *U.S. Public*, pg. 861
Melillo, Louis, Plant Mgr.--General Felt Industries, Inc., Philadelphia, PA; *U.S. Private*, pg. 1094
Melin, David, Chief Oper. Officer--Tech-Aerofoam Products, Inc., Miami, FL; *U.S. Private*, pg. 473
Melin, Judy, Admin.--Livingston Convalescent Center No. 434, Livingston, MT; *U.S. Public*, pg. 1714
Melina, Eduardo, Gen. Mgr.--PAXAR Iberia, S.A., Barcelona, Spain; *U.S. Public*, pg. 1267
Melkus, Thomas D., Mng. Dir.--CCL Security Products, New Britain, CT; *U.S. Public*, pg. 548
Melle, Jean-Louis, V.P. & Mng. Dir.--Groupe DMR S.A., Paris, France; *Int'l*, pg. 528
Mellen, R.L., V.P. & Gen. Mgr.--Bard Radiology Div., Covington, GA; *U.S. Public*, pg. 189
Mellen, Timothy J., Pres.--Edwards Systems Tech, Cheshire, CT; *U.S. Public*, pg. 726
Melley, W.P., Pres.--France Div., Fairview, TN; *U.S. Public*, pg. 217
Melling, A. Frederick, Pres. & Chief Exec. Officer--Willis Corroon Melling Inc., Montreal, Canada; *Int'l*, pg. 1509
Melling, Janet, Representative--CUNA Mutual Group-Great Britain, Birmingham, United Kingdom; *U.S. Private*, pg. 296
Melling, R. J., Dir. & Gen. Mgr.--Portals Ltd., Basingstoke, United Kingdom; *Int'l*, pg. 386
Mellis, Warren, Pres.--Golden Sun Feeds, Inc., Estherville, IA; *U.S. Private*, pg. 895
Mello, Robert L., Mng. Dir.--Bank of Montreal - New York, New York, NY; *Int'l*, pg. 154
Mellor, Terry D., Reg. Mgr.-Europe--Lord Corp. (Europe) Ltd., Aldershot, United Kingdom; *U.S. Private*, pg. 676
Mellow, James, Pres.--Draw-Tite, Inc., Canton, MI; *U.S. Public*, pg. 1054
Melo, M., Chief Oper. Officer--CPC-Companhia Petroquimica Camaccari Ltda., Camacari, Brazil; *Int'l*, pg. 947
Melocchi, Louis J., Pres.--Rimoldi of America Inc., Pittsburgh, PA; *Int'l*, pg. 1118
Meloon, Walter N., Pres.--Mid-Atlantic Correct Craft, Inc., Bloomsbury, NJ; *U.S. Private*, pg. 277
Meloon, Walter N., Pres.--Southeast Correct Craft, Inc., Orlando, FL; *U.S. Private*, pg. 277
Meloon, Walter N., Pres.--West Coast Correct Craft, Inc., Folsom, CA; *U.S. Private*, pg. 277
Melson, Jim, Mgr.--Ampex Data Systems Corporation, Los Angeles, CA; *U.S. Public*, pg. 104
Melton, D., V.P.--Wilsey Foods, Inc., Atlanta, GA; *Int'l*, pg. 879
Melton, George R., Pres.--Tracor Aerospace, Inc., Austin, TX; *U.S. Public*, pg. 1627
Melton, Jerry, Plant Mgr.--Reeves Brothers, Inc. (Chesnee Div.), Chesnee, SC; *U.S. Private*, pg. 507
Melton, Owen B., Jr., Pres. & Chief Oper. Officer--First Indiana Corporation, Indianapolis, IN; *U.S. Public*, pg. 1484
Meltz, Edward E., Chm. Bd., Chief Exec. Officer & Chief Fin. Officer--Carsen Group Inc., Markham, Canada; *U.S. Public*, pg. 301
Meltzer, Warren, V.P. & Gen. Mgr.--Lam Lighting Systems Inc., Santa Ana, CA; *Int'l*, pg. 821
Melville, James, Pres. & Chief Oper. Officer--Abraham Lincoln Insurance Co., Springfield, IL; *U.S. Private*, pg. 406
Melville, James, Pres. & Chief Oper. Officer--Universal Guarantee Life Insurance, Springfield, IL; *U.S. Private*, pg. 406
Melville, James E., Chief Oper. Officer--First Commonwealth Corporation, Springfield, IL; *U.S. Private*, pg. 406
Melville, Jo, Mng. Dir.--TML Reed Exhibitions (Pty.) Ltd.-Africa, Randburg, South Africa; *Int'l*, pg. 1097
Melvin, John, Branch Mgr.--Continental/Murray, Phoenix, AZ; *U.S. Private*, pg. 268
Melvin, John G., Pres.--Cone Drive Textron, Traverse City, MI; *U.S. Public*, pg. 1589
Melvin, T. Stephen, Pres. & Gen. Mgr.--Engineering Systems Co., Aston, PA; *U.S. Private*, pg. 313
Memmelaar, Jen, Gen. Mgr.--Frontier Communications of Seneca Gorham, Inc., Holcomb, NY; *U.S. Public*, pg. 684
Memmelaar, Jen, Gen. Mgr.--Frontier Communications of Slyvan Lake, Inc., Hopewell Junction, NY; *U.S. Public*, pg. 684
Menant, Claude, Gen. Mgr.--Cherry SARL, Paris, France; *U.S. Public*, pg. 346
Menard, Alain, Pres.--LeaRonal France, Lyon, France; *U.S. Public*, pg. 982
Menard, C., Chief Exec. & Grp. Country Mgr.--Barclays Bank SA, Paris, France; *Int'l*, pg. 166
Menard, Yves, Dir. Gen.--Imprimerie Quebecor Graphique-Couleur, La Salle, Canada; *Int'l*, pg. 1077
Mencacci, Dante, Mng. Dir.--EMAP Business International Ltd., London, United Kingdom; *Int'l*, pg. 451
Mence, Ian, Mng. Dir.--Ultra Electronics Magnetics, Cannock, United Kingdom; *Int'l*, pg. 1431
Menchace, Anthony L., Pres.--Comp-U-Card Division, Stamford, CT; *U.S. Public*, pg. 320
Mendell, D., III, Pres.--Exxon Upstream Technical Computing Company, Houston, TX; *U.S. Public*, pg. 601
Mendelson, Eric A., Chief Exec. Officer--Jet Avion Corporation, Hollywood, FL; *U.S. Public*, pg. 804
Mendelson, Eric A., Pres.--HEICO Aerospace Corporation, Hollywood, FL; *U.S. Public*, pg. 804
Mendenhall, C. Roy, Pres.--Balcrank Products, Weaverville, NC; *U.S. Public*, pg. 707
Mendenhall, Dave, Div. Mgr.--Cinti Fab, Erlanger, KY; *U.S. Private*, pg. 240
Mendes, Marfeide, Mgr.--Utell International-Brazil, Rio de Janeiro, Brazil; *Int'l*, pg. 1098
Mendes, Michael, Pres.--Diamond Walnut Growers, Inc., Stockton, CA; *U.S. Private*, pg. 1051
Mendez, Alvaro Morales, Pres.--Colcarga Transporte Internacional/Union-Transport, Bogota, Colombia; *U.S. Private*, pg. 1120
Mendez, Angel, Comptroller--Rorer (Caribbean) Corp., Hato Rey, PR; *Int'l*, pg. 1111
Mendez, Gonzalo D., V.P. & Gen. Mgr.--Ayerst-Wyeth Pharmaceuticals, Inc., Guayama, PR; *U.S. Public*, pg. 79
Mendez, Martin, Pres.--H.H. Robertson, Inc., Burlington, Canada; *U.S. Public*, pg. 1394
Mendez, Rafael, Dir. Sls. & Mktg.--AlliedSignal de Mexicano, S.A. de C.V., Mexico, Mexico; *U.S. Public*, pg. 54
Mendive, C., Gen. Mgr.--Amercoat Espana, S.A., Alcobendas, Spain; *U.S. Public*, pg. 99
Mendleski, Norbert, Pres.--Masterview Window Company, Inc., Phoenix, AZ; *U.S. Public*, pg. 1341
Mendola, Emanuel J., Pres.--The Chesapeake Life Insurance Co., Oklahoma City, OK; *U.S. Public*, pg. 1679
Mendoza, Dr. Francisco, Pres.--Multipak De Venezuela C.A., Caracas, Venezuela; *U.S. Public*, pg. 869
Mendoza, Emilio, Gen. Dir.--Spicer S.A., Mexico, Mexico; *U.S. Public*, pg. 480
Mendoza, Guillermo, Lic., Gen. Mgr.--Stafford-Miller de Mexico S.A. de C.V., Mexico, Mexico; *U.S. Public*, pg. 237
Mendoza, R., Mng. Dir.--Ascom Hasler SA, Madrid, Spain; *Int'l*, pg. 87
Mendrinos, Sotirios, Mng. Dir.--Grace Hellas Industrial & Commercial L.L.C., Athens, Greece; *U.S. Public*, pg. 756
Menechian, A., Pres.--AGRA Spectrocan Limited, Ottawa, Canada; *Int'l*, pg. 30
Menefee, Stephen W., Pres.--Arrow/Schweber Electronics Group, Melville, NY; *U.S. Public*, pg. 133
Menegazzi, Carmen, Mng. Dir.--Columbia Tri-Star Films (UK), London, United Kingdom; *Int'l*, pg. 1281
Meneghelli, Aldo, Country Mgr.--Compaq Computer S.P.A., Rozzano, Italy; *U.S. Public*, pg. 418
Meneguetti, Valdecio Guilherize, Chief Oper. Officer--BB Financeira S.A. Credito Financiamento e Investimento, Brasilia, Brazil; *Int'l*, pg. 141
Menendez, Francisco, Mng. Dir.--American Appraisal Consultores De Avaliacoa Limitada, Lisbon, Portugal; *U.S. Private*, pg. 50
Menendez, Frank, Gen. Mgr.--Abbott Laboratories de Mexico S.A., Mexico, Mexico; *U.S. Public*, pg. 13
Menerey, Robert J., Pres.--Baroid Drilling Fluids Division, Houston, TX; *U.S. Public*, pg. 528
Meng, Tan Siak, Pres.--Torita Corporation Ltd., Zhuhai, China; *Int'l*, pg. 651
Mengel, Art, Dir.--Teltron Technologies, Inc., Birdsboro, PA; *U.S. Public*, pg. 1720
Mengel, Richard R., Chief Exec. Officer--Glen-Gery Corporation, Wyomissing, PA; *Int'l*, pg. 658
Menger, Joe L., Pres.--The Machine Tool Group, Cleveland, OH; *U.S. Public*, pg. 503
Menges, James, Pres.--Mercantile Bank of Clinton County N.A., Clinton, IA; *U.S. Public*, pg. 1088
Menges, Werner, Mgr.--Commerzbank AG-Australia, Sydney, Australia; *Int'l*, pg. 311
Mengsha, Goitom, Chief Oper. Officer--Allright Parking Chicago, Inc., Chicago, IL; *U.S. Private*, pg. 43
Menholt, Dennis, Pres.--Denny Menholt Frontier Chevrolet, Billings, MT; *U.S. Private*, pg. 324
Menichini, John, V.P.--Pennsylvania Power & Light Company-Harrisburg Div., Harrisburg, PA; *U.S. Public*, pg. 1244
Menkel, William C., Chm. Bd. & Pres.--Nashville Bank of Commerce, Nashville, TN; *U.S. Public*, pg. 1155
Mennigfeld, Roland, Gen. Mgr.--Elkem Gmbh, Dusseldorf, Germany; *Int'l*, pg. 447
Menniti, Joseph, Pres.--DNE Systems, Inc., Wallingford, CT; *U.S. Public*, pg. 58
Menon, Balan, Gen. Mgr.--Dynagear Oil Pumps, Inc., Maquoketa, IA; *U.S. Private*, pg. 350
Menon, Jean-Jacques, Gen. Mgr.--Skandia International Insurance Co., Paris, France; *Int'l*, pg. 1258
Menon, N.R., Mgr.--Abdulla Fouad-Testrade Middle East, Dammam, Saudi Arabia; *Int'l*, pg. 502
Mensa, Jorge, Dir.--Harrod Devitt Sociedad Anonima, Barcelona, Spain; *U.S. Private*, pg. 893
Mensch, Veronica T., Pres.--Illinois Banc One Mortgage Corporation, Park Ridge, IL; *U.S. Public*, pg. 174
Mentre, F., Chief Oper. Officer--Agrotechnip S.A., Paris, France; *Int'l*, pg. 1360
Mentzer, Carl F., Chm. Bd., Pres. & Chief Exec. Officer--SunTrust Bank, Tampa Bay, Tampa, FL; *U.S. Public*, pg. 1538
Menzel, Brian, Pres. & Chief Oper. Officer--Desert Palace, Inc., Stateline, NV; *U.S. Public*, pg. 1512
Menzies, Evan, Pres.--Warren Gorham Lamont, New York, NY; *U.S. Public*, pg. 1602
Menzies, Henry W., Div. V.P.--Electrical Products Division, Austin, TX; *U.S. Public*, pg. 1605
Menzies, Jack, Pres.--Allmac Lumber Ltd., New Westminster, Canada; *Int'l*, pg. 1071
Menzies, Jack, Pres.--Probyn Log, Ltd., New Westminster, Canada; *Int'l*, pg. 1071
Menzies, James P., Pres. & Chief Exec. Officer--Key Bank of New York, Albany, NY; *U.S. Public*, pg. 954
Merber, Gene, Pres.--U.S. Lock, Brentwood, NY; *U.S. Public*, pg. 1748
Merbis, E., Pres. & Chief Exec. Officer--Banque ABN du Canada, Toronto, Canada; *Int'l*, pg. 12
Mercavage, John, Plant Mgr.--Bundy of Canada Ltd., Bramalea, Canada; *Int'l*, pg. 1341
Mercer, Buddy, Pres.--Flanders Precisionaire, Smithfield, NC; *U.S. Public*, pg. 648
Mercer, James B., V.P.--Enmark Stations, Inc., Savannah, GA; *U.S. Private*, pg. 254
Mercer, Robert, Pres.--Altegra Credit Company, Pittsburgh, PA; *U.S. Public*, pg. 1154
Mercer, William, Pres. & Chief Exec. Officer--ALARIS Medical Systems, Inc., San Diego, CA; *U.S. Public*, pg. 35
Merceron-Vicat, Jacques, Pres.--Vicat S.A., Paris, France; *Int'l*, pg. 606
Merchant, Ali, Mng. Dir.--Triton Communications, Mumbai, India; *Int'l*, pg. 118
Merchant, Shabbir, V.P. & Mng. Dir.-Simulation Div.--ETC Simulation Group, Orlando, FL; *U.S. Public*, pg. 587
Mercier, Claude Y., Chm. Bd.--Seabury & Smith, Inc., New York, NY; *U.S. Public*, pg. 1049
Mercier, Normand, Pres. & Gen. Mgr.--The Boiler Inspection & Insurance Co. of Canada, Toronto, Canada; *U.S. Public*, pg. 795
Mercier, Walter, Chief Oper. Officer--Hanora Spinning, Inc., Woonsocket, RI; *U.S. Public*, pg. 637
Merck, Herbert, Gen. Mgr.--Wyeth-Orfi S.A., Barcelona, Spain; *U.S. Public*, pg. 82
Merck, J. Wayne, Pres.--Shakespeare Composites & Electronics, Newberry, SC; *U.S. Public*, pg. 940
Mereau, J.P., Mng. Dir.--Claudius Peters S.A., Antony, France; *Int'l*, pg. 131
Meredith, J., Chief Oper. Officer--Shanks & McEwan (Southern Waste Services) Ltd, Milton Keynes, United Kingdom; *Int'l*, pg. 1228
Meredith, P.M., Chm.--UBS Phillips & Drew International Investment Ltd., London, United Kingdom; *Int'l*, pg. 1440
Merenyi, Eva, Mgr.--GGK Budapest, Budapest, Hungary; *Int'l*, pg. 1335
Meric, Jean-Paul, Pres.--Calcia, Guerville, France; *Int'l*, pg. 292
Merican, D.M. Jawhar, Reg. Mgr.--Kvaerner Engineering Sdn Bhd, Kuala Lumpur, Malaysia; *Int'l*, pg. 766
Merieux, Alain, Pres.--Pasteur Merieux Serums et Vaccins, Lyon, France; *Int'l*, pg. 1109
Merillat, Richard, Chief Oper. Officer--Merillat Industries Inc., Adrian, MI; *U.S. Public*, pg. 1053
Merillat, Richard, Chief Oper. Officer--Merillat Corporation, Adrian, MI; *U.S. Public*, pg. 1054
Merillat, Richard, Chief Oper. Officer--Merillat Transportation Company, Adrian, MI; *U.S. Public*, pg. 1054
Merino, Victor Aranguesen, Dir.--Frigo S.A., Barcelona, Spain; *Int'l*, pg. 1437
Meriwether, Heath, Publr.--Detroit Free Press, Detroit, MI; *U.S. Public*, pg. 965
Meriwether, J. Bruce, Chm. Bd. & Chief Exec. Officer--Mercantile Bank of Dubuque, N.A., Dubuque, IA; *U.S. Public*, pg. 1088
Merkel, P. Peter, Pres.--Band-It-Idex, Inc., Denver, CO; *U.S. Public*, pg. 862
Merkel, Steve, Pres.--Loctite Corp. North American Group, Rocky Hill, CT; *Int'l*, pg. 611
Merkle, Bob, Mgr.-Plant--Frigidaire Company Dishwasher Products, Kinston, NC; *Int'l*, pg. 439
Merkus, T.L., Mgr.--Radio Holland Group Carribbean, Willemstad, Netherlands Antilles; *Int'l*, pg. 1152
Merlet, Heinz, Chief Oper. Officer--Saarberg-Hoelter-Lurgi GmbH, Saarbruecken, Germany; *Int'l*, pg. 1167
Merlin, P., Mgr.--Amersham Iberica SA, Madrid, Spain; *Int'l*, pg. 993
Merlotti, Frank, Jr., Pres.--Metropolitan Furniture Corporation, Burlingame, CA; *U.S. Private*, pg. 1038
Mermilliod, M., Mng. Dir.--Robert Bosch (France) SA, Saint Ouen, France; *Int'l*, pg. 205
Mermoud, Roger, Mng. Dir.--Amdahl (Schweiz) AG, Zurich, Switzerland; *Int'l*, pg. 527
Merolla, Michael J., V.P. & Gen. Mgr.--Handy & Harman Precious Metals Products Division, East Providence, RI; *U.S. Public*, pg. 780
Meroni, Giuliano, Chief Oper. Officer--Advanced Micro Devices S.p.a., Milan, Italy; *U.S. Public*, pg. 21
Merrell, F.Max, Pres.--Mobil Mining & Minerals Company, Ashland, VA; *U.S. Public*, pg. 1118
Merrifield, Ann, Pres.--Genzyme Genetics Div., Santa Fe, NM; *U.S. Public*, pg. 733
Merrill, Keith E., Mgr.-Plant--GM Espana Fisher Guide, Logrono, Spain; *U.S. Public*, pg. 724
Merrill, Keniston P., Chm. Bd., Pres. & Chief Exec. Officer--Sentinel Advisors, Inc., Montpelier, VT; *U.S. Private*, pg. 785
Merrill, Keniston P., Chm., Pres. & Chief Exec. Officer--National Life Investment Management Co., Inc., Montpelier, VT; *U.S. Private*, pg. 785
Merrill, Lawrence G., Pres.--IPD Marketing Services, Inc., Cincinnati, OH; *U.S. Public*, pg. 1336

Merrill, Philip, Pres. & Publr.--Capital-Gazette Communications, Inc., Annapolis, MD; *U.S. Private*, pg. 649
Merrill, Rick, Pres.--The Prudential - Jon Douglas Company, Los Angeles, CA; *U.S. Private*, pg. 892
Merrill, Terry M., Pres.--Mar-Hyde Corporation, Cincinnati, OH; *U.S. Public*, pg. 1357
Merritt, Allen, Joint Mng. Dir.--Liberty Distributors Inc., Boston, MA; *U.S. Private*, pg. 666
Merritt, Robert J., Pres.--CIT Group/Industrial Financing, Livingston, NJ; *Int'l*, pg. 360
Merritt, S., Pres.--Van Leer (U.K.) Ltd., Cobham, United Kingdom; *Int'l*, pg. 1147
Merry, Bob, Pres. & Chief Exec. Officer--USDATA Corporation, Richardson, TX; *U.S. Public*, pg. 1425
Merry, Robert, Editor & Publr.--Congressional Quarterly, Washington, DC; *U.S. Private*, pg. 1088
Mersch, William, V.P. & Gen. Mgr.--Stiles-Kem Division, Waukegan, IL; *U.S. Public*, pg. 1100
Mersch, Wolfgang A., Mgr.--Toronto Dominion-Taipei Branch, Taipei, Taiwan; *Int'l*, pg. 1402
Mershad, Frederick J., Pres.--Proffitt's of Tri-Cities, Inc., Alcoa, TN; *U.S. Public*, pg. 1334
Mersky, Robert B., Pres.--Peregrine Capital Management, Inc., Minneapolis, MN; *U.S. Public*, pg. 1202
Merson, Andrew, Pres.--Command Web Offset Co., Secaucus, NJ; *U.S. Private*, pg. 693
Merten, Jost, Mng. Dir.--Merit-Malta Methode Ltd., Mriehel, Malta; *U.S. Public*, pg. 1101
Mervasto, Kalevi, Chief Oper. Officer--Nobel Elektroniikka Oy Ab, Espoo, Finland; *Int'l*, pg. 1290
Merx, Irene, Admin.--Hillhaven Convalescent Center Adrian, Adrian, MI; *U.S. Public*, pg. 1713
Merz, Dieter, Chief Oper. Officer--Scania (Great Britain) Ltd., Milton Keynes, United Kingdom; *Int'l*, pg. 687
Meschery, Ann, Sr. V.P., Media Dir.--Campbell Media Alliance, New York, NY; *U.S. Public*, pg. 1641
Meschiatti, Jose Luiz, Mgr.--Belo Horizonte Branch, Belo Horizonte, Brazil; *Int'l*, pg. 139
Meschkat, Reihard, Dr., Mng. Dir.--Bertrand Faure Sitztechnik GmbH & Co. KG, Neuburg an dew Donau, Germany; *Int'l*, pg. 193
Mesequet, Martin Crisco, Mgr.--Cia. Distribuidora de Petroleos, S.A. (CEDIPSA), Barcelona, Spain; *Int'l*, pg. 323
Mesick, R.E., Pres.--Southern Pacific Warehouse Co., San Francisco, CA; *U.S. Public*, pg. 1668
Mesirini, Rick, Administrator--Ridgecrest Care Center, Warren, OH; *U.S. Public*, pg. 838
Mesiti, Anthony, Pres.--National Surface Cleaning, Inc., Methuen, MA; *U.S. Public*, pg. 1208
Meske, James R., Gen. Mgr.--GREFCO, Inc., Crawfordsville, IN; *U.S. Private*, pg. 903
Meslow, John, Sr. V.P. & Pres.-Neurological Business--Medtronic Neurological Div., Minneapolis, MN; *U.S. Public*, pg. 1083
Messal, Edward C., V.P.--Whirlpool Corp., Marion Div., Marion, OH; *U.S. Public*, pg. 1765
Messenger, Irene, V.P. & Media Dir.--Western International Media Corporation-Detroit, Southfield, MI; *U.S. Private*, pg. 1167
Messer, A.W., Pres.-Columbia/Tri-Star Intl.--Tri-Star Pictures, Inc., Culver City, CA; *Int'l*, pg. 1282
Messer, Chester R., Pres.--Boston Gas Company, Boston, MA; *U.S. Public*, pg. 549
Messer, David, Pres.--Sempra Energy Trading, Greenwich, CT; *U.S. Public*, pg. 1249
Messier, John R., Pres.--GTE Government Systems Corporation, Needham, MA; *U.S. Public*, pg. 696
Messina, George, Pres. & Chief Exec. Officer--Burdick, Inc., Milton, WI; *U.S. Private*, pg. 181
Messina, Joseph J., Pres. & Chief Exec. Officer--Vendor Funding Co., Inc., New Hyde Park, NY; *Int'l*, pg. 153
Messina, Peter J., U.S. Regional Mgr.--Taca International Airlines, New Orleans, LA; *Int'l*, pg. 1346
Messitte, Anne, Dir.-Mktg.--Schocken Books, New York, NY; *U.S. Private*, pg. 21
Messmer, Daniel A., Pres.--Harvard Sports, Inc., Compton, CA; *U.S. Public*, pg. 591
Messmer, Daniel A., Pres.--Escalade Sports Sales & Marketing, Evansville, IN; *U.S. Public*, pg. 591
Metaxas, Leonidas, V.P. & Country Mgr.--Bank of America NT&SA, Athens, Greece; *U.S. Public*, pg. 182
Metcalf, B.S., Gen. Mgr.--Monorail, Inc., Auburn, NY; *U.S. Private*, pg. 256
Metcalf, M.E., Chief Exec.--THORN Group, Chertsey, United Kingdom; *Int'l*, pg. 1385
Metcalfe, David, Mng. Dir.--Trade Promotion Services Ltd., London, United Kingdom; *Int'l*, pg. 451
Metcalfe, Randolph, Pres.--U.S. Pipeline, Inc., Houston, TX; *Int'l*, pg. 31
Methline, Achim, European Sls. Dir.--Wavetek GmbH, Munich, Germany; *U.S. Private*, pg. 1155
Meton, Sonia, Chm. Bd. & Chief Exec. Officer--Turbomeca Microturbo Division, Bordes, France; *Int'l*, pg. 786
Metro, Anthony J., Pres.--Firstar Development Corporation, Milwaukee, WI; *U.S. Public*, pg. 643
Metscher, H. James, Pres.--Liz Claiborne Retail Division, New York, NY; *U.S. Public*, pg. 1006
Metta, F., Chief Oper. Officer--Kuehne & Nagel SpA, Milan, Italy; *Int'l*, pg. 763
Metz, Bob, Pres.--Haas Publishing Companies, Inc., Norcross, GA; *U.S. Public*, pg. 1327
Metz, Gerhard, Chm.--St. Johann Lagerhaus & Schiffahrts-Gesellschaft, Basel, Switzerland; *Int'l*, pg. 330
Metz, Gerhard, Dr., Chm.--CCB Co-op Bank Limited, Basel, Switzerland; *Int'l*, pg. 329
Metz, Gerhard, Dr., Chm.--Coop Lebensversicherungs Genossenschaft, Basel, Switzerland; *Int'l*, pg. 330
Metz, J. A., Pres.--Consumer Products Company, Muncie, IN; *U.S. Public*, pg. 56
Metzemaekers, D., Gen. Mgr.--AMP-Holland B.V., s Hertogenbosch, Netherlands; *U.S. Public*, pg. 8
Metzfield, William, Pres.--Gannett Supply Corp., Arlington, VA; *U.S. Public*, pg. 699
Metzger, Elisabeth, Mng. Dir.--Clarins SA, Les Plans, Switzerland; *Int'l*, pg. 295
Metzger, Hubert, Chief Oper. Officer--Perstorp S.A.-Div. Perstorp Stamp, Valmont, France; *Int'l*, pg. 1038
Metzger, Manfred, Gen. Mgr.--Viacom S.A., Zug, Switzerland; *U.S. Private*, pg. 779
Metzger, Michael, Pres. & Chief Exec. Officer--Willis Corroon Corp. of Arizona, Phoenix, AZ; *Int'l*, pg. 1505
Metzger, Richard, Pres.--Verson Division, Chicago, IL; *U.S. Public*, pg. 48
Metzger, Ron, Plant Mgr.--Hydro Conduit Corp., Napa, CA; *Int'l*, pg. 246
Metzler, Bill, Gen. Mgr.--Jaeger Baking Co., Milwaukee, WI; *U.S. Private*, pg. 1022
Metzler, Dave, Pres.-Europe--Colgate-Palmolive Belgium, Brussels, Belgium; *U.S. Public*, pg. 398
Metzler, Jean-Marie, Chief Oper. Officer--MTE, Puteaux, France; *Int'l*, pg. 706
Metzler, Kurt, Gen. Mgr.--M-Informatics AG, Dietikon, Switzerland; *Int'l*, pg. 865
Metzler, Richard, Gen. Mgr.--Great Lakes of Wisconsin, Plymouth, WI; *U.S. Private*, pg. 474
Metzler, Richard H., Pres.--Revlon Government Sales, Inc., New York, NY; *U.S. Private*, pg. 690
Metzler, Richard H., Pres.--Revlon Commissary Sales, Inc., New York, NY; *U.S. Private*, pg. 690
Meulnart, Alain, Chm.--Royal Champignon, Sauitur, France; *Int'l*, pg. 567
Meuwly, Haus-Ruedi, Gen. Mgr.--Commercial Metals (International) AG, Zug, Switzerland; *U.S. Public*, pg. 414
Meyer-Oertel, Henry C., Exec. V.P.--Gruner + Jahr International Marketing- and Media Services, Inc., New York, NY; *Int'l*, pg. 190
Meyer, A.C., Chief Oper. Officer--Carlon Chimes Co., Cleveland, OH; *U.S. Public*, pg. 976
Meyer, Bernhard, Mng. Dir.--Kaldnes Heavy Lift Trucks A/S, Tonsberg, Norway; *Int'l*, pg. 965
Meyer, Ch., Chief Exec. Officer--Geneva Life Insurance Company, Geneva, Switzerland; *Int'l*, pg. 1529
Meyer, Ch., Chief Exec. Officer--Geneva General Insurance Company, Geneva, Switzerland; *Int'l*, pg. 1529
Meyer, Charles, Gen. Mgr.--Tamura Corp. of America, Microtran Div., Valley Stream, NY; *U.S. Private*, pg. 1067
Meyer, D.D., Branch Mgr.--Zellerbach Division, Eureka, CA; *U.S. Public*, pg. 1075
Meyer, Dean, Pres.--Mercantile Bank of Osceola County, N.A., Sibley, IA; *U.S. Public*, pg. 1088
Meyer, Dick, Plant Mgr.--Acme Brick Co., Mc Queeney, TX; *U.S. Public*, pg. 936
Meyer, Douglas, Pres.-North America--Benckiser Consumer Products Inc., Greenwich, CT; *Int'l*, pg. 185
Meyer, Edward J., Pres.--ERI Services, Pittsburgh, PA; *U.S. Public*, pg. 589
Meyer, Fred, Mgr.--Westco Products/Northwest, Beaverton, OR; *Int'l*, pg. 244
Meyer, George G., Pres. & Chief Exec. Officer--Central Sprinkler Company, Lansdale, PA; *U.S. Public*, pg. 327
Meyer, Guido, Mng. Dir.--Pitney Bowes (Switzerland) AG, Effretikon, Switzerland; *U.S. Public*, pg. 1304
Meyer, Hans, Mng. Dir.--ITW Meypack GmbH, Nottuln, Germany; *U.S. Public*, pg. 868
Meyer, Jeffrey C., Chief Exec. Officer--Bemrose USA, Inc., Fort Wayne, IN; *Int'l*, pg. 185
Meyer, Jerry, Chief Exec. Officer--Optigraphics Inc., Dallas, TX; *U.S. Private*, pg. 866
Meyer, Jerry, Chief Exec. Officer--Pinnacle Trading Card Co., Dallas, TX; *U.S. Private*, pg. 866
Meyer, Jerry C., Pres.--SunBridge Assisted Living, Albuquerque, NM; *U.S. Public*, pg. 1531
Meyer, Lee, Sr. V.P. & Gen. Mgr.--Variform, Inc., Kearney, MO; *U.S. Public*, pg. 1193
Meyer, Lucas, V.P.--RNBNY Representative Office-Argentina, Buenos Aires, Argentina; *U.S. Public*, pg. 1381
Meyer, Lutz, Mng. Dir.--Shandwick Deutschland GmbH, Bonn, Germany; *Int'l*, pg. 1227
Meyer, M. J., Mng. Dir.--MacMillan Bloedel Meyer Ltd., Richmond, United Kingdom; *Int'l*, pg. 829
Meyer, Paul, Pres.--Knurr AG, Fallanden, Switzerland; *Int'l*, pg. 739
Meyer, Paula R., Pres. & Dir.-Mktg.--Piper Capital Management, Incorporated, Minneapolis, MN; *U.S. Public*, pg. 1303
Meyer, Philip J., Pres.--ChexSystems, Inc., Minneapolis, MN; *U.S. Public*, pg. 498
Meyer, Randy, Brewmaster--Russian River Brewing Company, Guerneville, CA; *U.S. Private*, pg. 632
Meyer, Raymond E., Pres.--Deltec, San Diego, CA; *Int'l*, pg. 126
Meyer, Richard, Pres.--Soligar GmbH, Stuttgart, Germany; *U.S. Private*, pg. 6
Meyer, Robert, Chm. Bd.--Midwest Mutual Insurance Co., West Des Moines, IA; *U.S. Private*, pg. 881
Meyer, Robert F., Pres.--Hammermill Papers Business, Erie, PA; *U.S. Public*, pg. 903
Meyer, Russell W., Jr., Chm. Bd. & Chief Exec. Officer--The Cessna Aircraft Co., Wichita, KS; *U.S. Public*, pg. 1589
Meyer, Stuart F., Pres. & Chief Exec. Officer--Civic Center Corporation, Saint Louis, MO; *U.S. Public*, pg. 114
Meyer, U.F., Gen. Mgr.--Detrex General Chemicals & Solvents Div., Ashtabula, OH; *U.S. Public*, pg. 501
Meyer, Uwe, Gen. Mgr.--ThermoTec Inc., Windsor Locks, CT; *U.S. Private*, pg. 360
Meyer, W. Darrell, Chm. Bd., Pres. & Chief Exec. Officer--Arkansas Bank & Trust, Hot Springs Village, AR; *U.S. Public*, pg. 630
Meyer, Wolfgang, Mng. Dir.--Battenfeld Canada Ltd., Mississauga, Canada; *Int'l*, pg. 825
Meyerholz, Kenneth, V.P. & Gen. Mgr.--The HON Co., Geneva Plant, Muscatine, IA; *U.S. Public*, pg. 772
Meyerrose, Sarah, Regional Pres.--First Tennessee Bank - Kingsport/Bristol, Kingsport, TN; *U.S. Public*, pg. 639
Meyers, A.J., Pres.--Bio-Chem Valve Inc., Boonton, NJ; *Int'l*, pg. 590
Meyers, Al, Sr. V.P.--ERA Aviation, Inc., Lake Charles, LA; *U.S. Public*, pg. 1410
Meyers, Bernard M., Pres.--Robern, Inc., Bristol, PA; *U.S. Private*, pg. 630
Meyers, Doug, Gen. Mgr.--Avon Manufacturing Lab., Morton Grove, IL; *U.S. Public*, pg. 156
Meyers, Hans W., Sr. V.P. & Gen. Mgr.--DG Bank-New York, New York, NY; *Int'l*, pg. 352
Meyers, Howard M., Pres.--Riteway Trucking, Dallas, TX; *U.S. Private*, pg. 900
Meyers, John, V.P. & Gen. Mgr.-Electrohydraulics--Sauer-Sundstrand, Plymouth, MN; *Int'l*, pg. 1198
Meyers, John R., Pres. & Chief Exec. Officer--Treadco, Inc., Fort Smith, AR; *U.S. Public*, pg. 131
Meyers, Louis A., Chm. Bd.--PNC Bank, Scranton, PA; *U.S. Public*, pg. 1243
Meyers, Raymond N., Pres.--Halliburton Energy Services, Huntington, IN; *U.S. Public*, pg. 776
Meyers, Richard W., Pres.--Hershey Canada Inc., Mississauga, Canada; *U.S. Public*, pg. 812
Meyers, Tom, V.P. & Gen. Mgr.--Lamplighter Homes, Inc., Lacey, WA; *U.S. Public*, pg. 333
Meyers, William, Mgr.--Stephen Gould of Connecticut Corp., Orange, CT; *U.S. Private*, pg. 467
Meyerson, A. Jay, Chief Exec. Officer--Key Bank USA N.A., Cleveland, OH; *U.S. Public*, pg. 954
Meyerson, George O., Pres.--System Sciences Division, Calverton, MD; *U.S. Public*, pg. 423
Meyne, John, Gen. Mgr.--Keystone Southern Warehouse-Atlanta, Atlanta, GA; *U.S. Public*, pg. 955
Meza, Jose, Chief Exec. Officer & Bus. Dir.--Quorum Publicidad, Lima, Peru; *U.S. Public*, pg. 1422
Mezger, Dieter, Pres.--VLSI Technology GmbH, Munich, Germany; *U.S. Public*, pg. 1703
Mezger, Jeffrey T., Pres.--Kaufman and Broad of Arizona, Inc., Phoenix, AZ; *U.S. Public*, pg. 945
Mezger, R. Theo, Gen. Mgr.--American Scandinavian Banking Corporation, New York, NY; *Int'l*, pg. 859
Mezger, R. Theo, Pres. & Gen. Mgr.--Merita Bank Ltd. New York Branch, New York, NY; *Int'l*, pg. 859
Mezo, Gyula, Fin. Dir.--Leo Burnett Budapest KFT, Budapest, Hungary; *U.S. Private*, pg. 185
Mezzano, Dario, Pres.--EURO RSCG Mezzano Costantini Mignani, Milan, Italy; *Int'l*, pg. 603
Michael, Dennis, Gen. Mgr.--Sawhill Tubular Div., Wheatland, PA; *U.S. Public*, pg. 131
Michael, Peter, Gen. Mgr.--ScanBeton Industrie GmbH, Roggentin, Germany; *Int'l*, pg. 1200
Michael, R.W., Pres.--Dixie Building Supplies, Inc., Tampa, FL; *U.S. Public*, pg. 1736
Michael, Steve, Pres.--AFGD, Marietta, GA; *Int'l*, pg. 84
Michael, Tony, Branch Mgr.--BSA Advertising, Inc., San Jose, CA; *U.S. Private*, pg. 108
Michaelevski, Kirill, Dr., Mgr.--Ost-West Allianz (St. Petersburg Office), Saint Petersburg, Russia; *Int'l*, pg. 61
Michaels, R.H., Pres.--Halma Asia Pte. Limited, Singapore, Singapore; *Int'l*, pg. 590
Michaelsen, Jacob, Pres.--Danfoss Inc., Mahwah, NJ; *Int'l*, pg. 377
Michalaros, Christa J., Pres.--Liz & Co., New York, NY; *U.S. Public*, pg. 1006
Michalik, R.J., Gen. Mgr.--CHEMCENTRAL/New Orleans, Jefferson, LA; *U.S. Private*, pg. 232
Michalka, Rod, Gen. Mgr.--Turner Construction Company, Kansas City, MO; *U.S. Public*, pg. 1645
Michalski, J.J., Chm. & Pres.--Esso International Shipping (Bahamas) Co. Limited, Florham Park, NJ; *U.S. Public*, pg. 601
Michaud, David E., Gen. Mgr.--Bell & Howell Mailmobile Co., Zeeland, MI; *U.S. Public*, pg. 201
Michaud, Jean-Paul, Dir. Gen.--Nouvelles Editions Marabout, Alleur, Belgium; *Int'l*, pg. 796
Michel, B., Pres.--Socapi, Paris, France; *Int'l*, pg. 565
Michel, Jacques, Gen. Mgr.--BFCE Singapore, Singapore, Singapore; *Int'l*, pg. 161
Michel, K., Mng. Dir.--Orca Bank Ltd., Geneva, Switzerland; *Int'l*, pg. 1440
Michel, Philippe, Pres. & Chief Exec. Officer--Bobst Group Inc., Roseland, NJ; *Int'l*, pg. 198
Micheleau, G., Gen. Mgr.--Stoeffler, Obernai, France; *Int'l*, pg. 380
Michelena, Juan A., III, Pres.--Corporate Services International, Inc., Key Biscayne, FL; *Int'l*, pg. 840
Michelet, Francis, Mng. Dir.--Korn/Ferry International, Luxembourg, Luxembourg; *U.S. Private*, pg. 633
Micheletta, Dr. Paolo, Gen. Mgr.--Alfa Romeo Auto S.p.A., Naples, Italy; *Int'l*, pg. 481
Michelini, F., Gen. Mgr.--Compania Scholl S.A., Madrid, Spain; *Int'l*, pg. 1209
Michell, S., Pres. & Chief Exec. Officer--Jardine Davies Inc., Manila, Philippines; *Int'l*, pg. 705
Michelman, Doug, Gen. Mgr.--Fleishman-Hillard, Inc., Los Angeles, CA; *U.S. Private*, pg. 411
Michelmore, J. D., Mng. Dir.--Rorer Health Care Ltd., Eastbourne, United Kingdom; *Int'l*, pg. 1112
Michels, Harold T., Pres.--LaQue Center for Corrosion Technology, Inc., Wrightsville Beach, NC; *Int'l*, pg. 672
Michelsen, Finn, Pres.--OYO Geosciences Corporation, Houston, TX; *Int'l*, pg. 1019
Michelson, Larry D., Pres. & Treas.--Sate-Lite Manufacturing Company, Niles, IL; *U.S. Private*, pg. 598
Michelson, Mogens, Pres.--Frigoscandia A/S, Hvidovre, Denmark; *U.S. Public*, pg. 606
Michelsson, Jorgen, Mng. Dir.--Thorn Finland Oy, Helsinki, Finland; *Int'l*, pg. 1386
Michiels, Baudouin, Pres.--Cote d'Or S.A., Brussels, Belgium; *U.S. Public*, pg. 1288
Michils, Marc, Chief Exec. Officer-Strategy & Creation--Quattro DMB&B, Brussels, Brussels, Belgium; *U.S. Private*, pg. 305
Michl, Ivan, Chief Exec. Officer--AxTrade Czechoslovakia, Prague, Czech Republic; *Int'l*, pg. 710

Michner, Karl, Pres.--J. Riggings, Saint Louis, MO; *U.S. Public*, pg. 564
Micik, Alan T., Pres.--AMCORE Investment Services, Inc., Rockford, IL; *U.S. Public*, pg. 64
Micke, Dave, Chief Fin. Officer--Beta Raven Inc., Bridgeton, MO; *U.S. Public*, pg. 1361
Mickels, Bror, Chief Oper. Officer--Novo Nordisk Farma OY, Espoo, Finland; *Int'l*, pg. 988
Mico, Richard D., V.P. & Gen. Mgr.--Sparton Technology, Inc., Rio Rancho, NM; *U.S. Public*, pg. 1496
Micoud, Pierre, Mng. Dir.--GESTRA S.A., Nogent-sur-Marne, France; *Int'l*, pg. 550
Micsky, William A., Pres.--BetzDearborn Metals Process Group, Horsham, PA; *U.S. Public*, pg. 226
Micyk, Rysard, Mng. Dir.--Willis Corroon Polska Spolka Akeyjna, Warsaw, Poland; *Int'l*, pg. 1509
Middaugh, John F., Pres.--Electronic Devices and Materials, San Carlos, CA; *U.S. Public*, pg. 1003
Middelmann, Ulrich, Dr., Chm. Bd.--O&K Orenstein & Koppel Aktiengesellschaft, Dortmund, Germany; *Int'l*, pg. 516
Middlebrook, Paul E., Pres.--Seneca Flight Oper., Penn Yan, NY; *U.S. Public*, pg. 1456
Middlebrooks, Bobby, Corp. Sr. V.P.--Bush Hog Division, Selma, AL; *U.S. Public*, pg. 48
Middlemiss, Chris, Reg. Mgr.--SMS-Pittsburgh, Pittsburgh, PA; *U.S. Public*, pg. 1463
Middlemiss, J.M., Reg. Mng. Dir.--Ballast Wiltshier Plc - Scotland, Glasgow, United Kingdom; *Int'l*, pg. 135
Middlesteadt, R., V.P. & Gen. Mgr.--Advanced Battery Systems Div., Hunt Valley, MD; *Int'l*, pg. 55
Middleton, C., Chief Exec. Officer--The Royal Bank of Scotland (Nassau) Limited, Nassau, Bahamas; *Int'l*, pg. 1133
Middleton, C.J., Mng. Dir.--Barclays Bank of Botswana Limited, Gaborone, Botswana; *Int'l*, pg. 165
Middleton, David, Mng. Dir.--Tonermex S.A. de C.V., Toluca, Mexico; *Int'l*, pg. 1116
Middleton, Frank, Dr., Chief Exec. Officer--Healthsource South Carolina, Inc., Charleston, SC; *U.S. Public*, pg. 360
Middleton, P.E., Mng. Dir.--Wayfarer Transit Systems Ltd., Poole, United Kingdom; *Int'l*, pg. 853
Middleton, R., Chief Exec. Officer--Wessex Advanced Switching Products Ltd., Havant, United Kingdom; *Int'l*, pg. 208
Middleton, Ron, Mng. Dir.--Sulzer New Zealand Limited, Auckland, New Zealand; *Int'l*, pg. 1306
Midgett, Leon A., Pres.-Metal Bev. Container Grp.--Ball Metal Beverage Container Corp., Westminster, CO; *U.S. Public*, pg. 171
Midgley, Alex, Mgr.-Opers.--Oceaneering International AG, Dubai, United Arab Emirates; *U.S. Public*, pg. 1211
Midgley, B. C., Chief Mgr.--The Standard Bank of South Africa Limited, Taipei, Taiwan; *Int'l*, pg. 1294
Midlam, Gary R., Pres.--ACG Componentes, S.A., Agoncillo, Spain; *U.S. Public*, pg. 724
Miears, Don, Exec. V.P. & Gen. Mgr.--Cedar Point, Sandusky, OH; *U.S. Public*, pg. 319
Mielchen, Wolfgang, Consultant--Berag GmbH, Munich, Germany; *Int'l*, pg. 1502
Miele, Arthur R., Pres.-Phelps Dodge Sales Company--Phelps Dodge Mining Company, Phoenix, AZ; *U.S. Public*, pg. 1286
Miele, Arthur R., Pres.--Phelps Dodge Sales Company, New York, NY; *U.S. Public*, pg. 1287
Miele, Jay, Chief Oper. Officer--Kamyr, Inc., Vancouver, WA; *Int'l*, pg. 34
Mier, Edward M.A., V.P.-European Opers.--Summa Four Limited, Slough, United Kingdom; *U.S. Public*, pg. 1527
Mier, Ruben, Mgr.-Parts--EMPIRE Machinery - Imperial, Imperial, CA; *U.S. Private*, pg. 375
Miercort, Clifford R., Pres. & Chief Exec. Officer--The North American Coal Corporation, Dallas, TX; *U.S. Public*, pg. 1149
Miers, J.H., Pres.--Amoco Espana Exploration Co., Madrid, Spain; *U.S. Public*, pg. 102
Mieszczak, Boguslaw, Mng. Dir.--TI Poland sp zo.o., Bielsko-Biala, Poland; *Int'l*, pg. 1341
Miettinen, Pekka, Mng. Dir.--Wisaforest France S.A.R.L., Lyon, France; *Int'l*, pg. 1429
Miettinen, Pekka, Mng. Dir.--Wisaforest Benelux B.V., Heerlen, Netherlands; *Int'l*, pg. 1429
Migdal, Alvin, Admin.--Heritage Place, Mesquite, TX; *U.S. Public*, pg. 839
Migirdicyan, Emig, Pres.--National Data Corporation of Canada Ltd., Don Mills, Canada; *U.S. Public*, pg. 1156
Migliazza, M., Mng. Dir.--Witco Italiana, Milan, Italy; *U.S. Public*, pg. 1774
Migliore, James, Pres.--Ohio Div., Hudson, OH; *U.S. Public*, pg. 1683
Migliori, Richard J., M.D., Pres. & Chief Exec. Officer--United HealthCare Plans of New England, Inc., Warwick, RI; *U.S. Public*, pg. 1678
Migliorino, Giuseppe, V.P. & Mng. Dir.--Ansaldo Componenti srl, Genoa, Italy; *Int'l*, pg. 653
Migliorino, M., Chm.--STAC Societe Technique D'application Chimique S.A., Strasbourg, France; *Int'l*, pg. 429
Mignacco, Dominique, Pres. Chief Oper. Officer--Farr Incorporated, Chomedey, Canada; *U.S. Public*, pg. 614
Mignault, Pierre L., Pres. & Chief Exec. Officer--Provigo Distribution, Montreal, Canada; *Int'l*, pg. 1073
Mignault, Pierre L., Pres. & Chief Exec. Officer--Loeb Inc., Ottawa, Canada; *Int'l*, pg. 1073
Migoya, Ing. Alfonso Gonzalez, Chief Oper. Officer--Cydsa S.A. Chemical Div., Garza Garcia, Mexico; *Int'l*, pg. 246
Miguel, Ricardo Mario, Pres. & Chief Fin. Officer--SmithKline Beecham Laboratorios Ltda., Rio de Janeiro, Brazil; *Int'l*, pg. 1266
Miguelon, Richard R., V.P. & Gen. Mgr.--American Biltrite (Canada) Ltd., Sherbrooke, Canada; *U.S. Public*, pg. 69
Mihaichuk, Garry P., Pres. & Chief Exec. Officer--TransCanada International Ltd., Calgary, Canada; *Int'l*, pg. 1417
Mihaly, Gabe, Pres. & Chief Exec. Officer--UnionTools, Inc., Columbus, OH; *U.S. Public*, pg. 17
Mihaylo, Steve, Pres.--Inter-Tel, Incorporated-New Jersey, Phoenix, AZ; *U.S. Public*, pg. 888
Mihaylo, Steven G., Pres.--Inter-Tel Japan, Inc., Tokyo, Japan; *U.S. Public*, pg. 888
Mii, Nobuo, V.P.--IBM Japan Sales Company, Ltd., Tokyo, Japan; *U.S. Public*, pg. 897
Mijangos, Victor, Mng. Dir.--Burgmann Mexico S.A. De C.V., Mexico, Mexico; *Int'l*, pg. 233
Mijer, J.C., Mgr.--Enthoven B.V., Zwaanshoek, Netherlands; *Int'l*, pg. 555
Mika, John J., Pres.--SFIC Properties, Inc., Alhambra, CA; *Int'l*, pg. 765
Mikalsen, Kjell, Pres.--Kvaerner Govan Ltd., Glasgow, United Kingdom; *Int'l*, pg. 772
Mikawa, Naoyoshi, Pres.--NYK Bulkship (USA) Inc., New York, NY; *Int'l*, pg. 941
Mikel, Steven, Pres.--Amerac Energy Corp., Houston, TX; *U.S. Public*, pg. 1490
Mikhailov, Vyacheslav, Production Dir.--Styx & Leo Burnett, Almaty, Kazakhstan; *U.S. Private*, pg. 186
Miki, Clemis, Pres.--AGA del Ecuador C.A., Quito, Ecuador; *Int'l*, pg. 13
Miki, Hirofumi, Chm. Bd.--Ferro Enamels (Japan) Ltd., Osaka, Japan; *U.S. Public*, pg. 619
Miki, S., Pres.--Nissho Iwai Building Materials Corp., Tokyo, Japan; *Int'l*, pg. 946
Miki, Yuzaburo, Pres.--Kikkoman International, Inc., San Francisco, CA; *Int'l*, pg. 733
Mikkelsen, Preben, Mgr.--International Sales Division, Roedovre, Denmark; *Int'l*, pg. 1083
Mikkola, Jussi, Chief Oper. Officer--Ahlstrom Recovery Inc.-Western Region, Camas, WA; *Int'l*, pg. 34
Mikon, Arnold, AIA Pres. & Chief Exec. Officer--Smith Hinchman Grylls Associates, Inc., Detroit, MI; *U.S. Private*, pg. 1010
Mikulak, John P., Pres.--CertainTeed Ventures, Inc., Valley Forge, PA; *Int'l*, pg. 1171
Mikulsky, Philip M., Pres. & Chief Exec. Officer--WPS Energy Services, Inc., Green Bay, WI; *U.S. Public*, pg. 1728
Mikunda, Steve, Mng. Dir.--Capstone Electronics Div., Carrollton, TX; *U.S. Public*, pg. 134
Mikuriya, F., Gen. Mgr.--Johnson Company, Ltd., Yokohama, Japan; *U.S. Private*, pg. 593
Miladinovic, Ratko, Chief Oper. Officer--Novo Nordisk A/S, Belgrade, Serbia; *Int'l*, pg. 988
Milam, M.E., Plant Mgr.--Detrex Equipment Div., Bowling Green, KY; *U.S. Public*, pg. 501
Milam, Mike, V.P.-Petrochemicals/NGLS--Natural Gas Liquids Marketing, Storage & Distribution, Houston, TX; *U.S. Public*, pg. 1663
Milan, Maureen, V.P. & Gen. Mgr.--New Jersey Transit Bus Operations, Maplewood, NJ; *U.S. Private*, pg. 794
Milan, Nigel, Chief Exec. Officer--Australian Radio Network, Seven Hills, Australia; *U.S. Public*, pg. 386
Milani, Mario, Pres.--Sogefi Industria de Autopecas Ltda., Sao Paulo, Brazil; *U.S. Public*, pg. 53
Milano, Gilbert, Mng. Dir.--SLE S.a.r.l., Nice, France; *U.S. Public*, pg. 1045
Milano, Marco, Mng. Dir.--Merloni Domestic Appliances Ltd, Uxbridge, United Kingdom; *Int'l*, pg. 860
Milas, Richard, V.P. & Gen. Mgr.--Pewaukee Plant, Pewaukee, WI; *U.S. Public*, pg. 443
Milawer, Teresa, Pres.--Lectorum Publications, New York, NY; *U.S. Public*, pg. 1440
Milczarek, Renata Eva, Dir.--Capital International CDPQ - Poland, Warsaw, Poland; *Int'l*, pg. 249
Milder, Mike, Mgr.-Plant & Sls.--Golden Sun Feeds, Inc., Grinnell, IA; *U.S. Private*, pg. 895
Milenekiotov, Georgia Garinois, Mng. Dir.--Neutrogena Corporation SARL, Paris, France; *U.S. Public*, pg. 928
Miles-Pickup, Arnold, Pres.--Canadian Western Trust, Vancouver, Canada; *Int'l*, pg. 259
Miles, Bob, Gen. Mgr.--Socar of Ohio, Inc., Continental, OH; *U.S. Public*, pg. 1392
Miles, C.V., Pres.--Westcode Semiconductors Inc. (U.S.A.), Long Beach, CA; *Int'l*, pg. 127
Miles, Geoff, State Mgr.--Valtek Australia/Perth, Perth, Australia; *U.S. Public*, pg. 659
Miles, Jerald, Gen. Mgr.--Mount Vernon Mills, Inc., Williamston, Williamston, SC; *U.S. Private*, pg. 835
Miles, Jim, Plant Mgr.--Acme Brick Co., Clinton, OK; *U.S. Public*, pg. 936
Miles, Jim, Plant Mgr.--Acme Brick Co., Edmond, OK; *U.S. Public*, pg. 936
Miles, John, Plant Mgr.--Teleflex Automotive, Van Wert, OH; *U.S. Public*, pg. 1569
Miles, John F., Div. Pres.--Hamilton Specialty Bar, Hamilton, Canada; *Int'l*, pg. 1262
Miles, John Greg, Pres.--Dorfile Company, Memphis, TN; *U.S. Public*, pg. 1177
Miles, Kim, Chief Oper. Officer--Rhone-Poulenc New Zealand Ltd., Wellington, New Zealand; *Int'l*, pg. 1113
Miles, Lyn, Chief Exec.--Barnett Merchant Services Corp., Jacksonville, FL; *U.S. Public*, pg. 1162
Miles, Nick, Chief Exec. Officer--Financial Dynamics Ltd., London, United Kingdom; *Int'l*, pg. 117
Miles, Richard F., Chm. Bd.--Syntron, Inc., Houston, TX; *U.S. Public*, pg. 1563
Miles, Richard J., Pres.--Hilb, Rogal & Hamilton Company of the Quad Cities, Moline, IL; *U.S. Public*, pg. 827
Miles, Ron, Plant Mgr.--Rhone-Poulenc Basic Chemicals Co., Freeport, TX; *Int'l*, pg. 1110
Miles, Ronald William Gordon, Pres. & Gen. Mgr.--Ceras Johnson Ltda., Rio de Janeiro, Brazil; *U.S. Private*, pg. 593
Miletti, M., Chief Oper. Officer--Luigi Fontana S.p.A., Milan, Italy; *Int'l*, pg. 1173
Milford, Peggy, Pres.--U S West Business Resources, Englewood, CO; *U.S. Public*, pg. 1689
Milhaud, Serge, Chm. Bd. & Chief Exec. Officer--Nestle Sources International S.A., Paris, France; *Int'l*, pg. 921
Milillo, Pasquale, Pres.--Eniricerche S.p.A., Milan, Italy; *Int'l*, pg. 428
Miliou, Elana, Chief Exec. Officer, Mng. Dir.--International Marketing & Promotions, Athens, Greece; *U.S. Private*, pg. 304
Miliou, Elena, Chief Exec. Officer & Mng. Dir.--DMB&B Athens, Athens, Greece; *U.S. Private*, pg. 303
Militello, Katey, V.P.-Opers.--Graphic Controls Medical, Buffalo, NY; *U.S. Private*, pg. 471
Militi, Ric, Pres.--Year 2K Communications, Los Angeles, CA; *U.S. Public*, pg. 1011
Mill, Mick, Chief Exec. Officer--EWA Ltd., Chelmsford, United Kingdom; *Int'l*, pg. 1482
Millan, Patricio, Resident Rep.--Banco Mundial, Buenos Aires, Argentina; *U.S. Private*, pg. 1189
Millar, I.W., Pres.--Mead Packaging, Atlanta, GA; *U.S. Public*, pg. 1074
Millar, James F., Grp. Pres.--Cardinal Distribution, Dublin, OH; *U.S. Public*, pg. 304
Millar, John, Exec. V.P.--American Graphite Co., Lakehurst, NJ; *U.S. Public*, pg. 515
Millar, John P., Mng. Dir.--Williams de Broe Holdings Ltd., London, United Kingdom; *Int'l*, pg. 148
Millard, Gene, V.P. & Gen. Mgr.--Interstate Paper Corporation, Riceboro, GA; *U.S. Private*, pg. 573
Millard, J.B., Dr., Pres. & Chief Exec. Officer-Mitel Corp.--Mitel, Inc., Herndon, VA; *Int'l*, pg. 870
Millard, John, Gen. Mgr.--Atkinson Industries, Inc., Pittsburg, KS; *U.S. Public*, pg. 159
Millard, Ken C., Pres.--Artistcare Pty. Ltd., Brookvale, Australia; *Int'l*, pg. 460
Millard, Mark, V.P.--C.I.S. Co. of Alabama, Guntersville, AL; *U.S. Private*, pg. 223
Miller de Lombera, Martha, V.P. & Gen. Mgr.-Health & Beauty Care Prods.-U.K. & Ireland--Procter & Gamble (Health & Beauty Care) Limited, Egham, United Kingdom; *U.S. Public*, pg. 1332
Miller-Smith, Susan J., Pres.--Merisel Canada, Concord, Canada; *U.S. Public*, pg. 1096
Miller, A.J., Sec.--L-N Safety Glass, SA de CV, Mexicali, Mexico; *Int'l*, pg. 1056
Miller, Al, V.P.--FlightSafety Services Corporation, Littleton, CO; *U.S. Public*, pg. 218
Miller, Alan B., Chm. Bd. & Chief Exec. Officer--Universal Health Realty Income Trust, King of Prussia, PA; *U.S. Public*, pg. 1697
Miller, Allan, Pres.--MacGregor Golf Australia pty. Ltd., Mulgrave, Australia; *Int'l*, pg. 73
Miller, Barry, Pres. & Chief Exec. Officer--Precision Printing & Packaging, Clarksville, TN; *U.S. Public*, pg. 115
Miller, Barry, Pres.--Firestone Tire & Rubber Company of New Zealand Limited, Auckland, New Zealand; *Int'l*, pg. 214
Miller, Barry, V.P.--La Cross, Farmingdale, NY; *U.S. Public*, pg. 494
Miller, Ben, Plant Mgr.--Sweetheart Cup Company Inc., Manchester, NH; *U.S. Private*, pg. 1058
Miller, Ben, Plant Mgr.--Sweetheart Cup Company Inc., Somerville, MA; *U.S. Private*, pg. 1058
Miller, Bernard, Gen. Mgr.--H&K America Inc., Saint Louis, MO; *Int'l*, pg. 737
Miller, Bill, Gen. Mgr.--Symons Corporation, Centralia, IL; *U.S. Private*, pg. 932
Miller, Bob, Branch Mgr.--Union-Transport Corporation-Tulsa Office, Tulsa, OK; *U.S. Private*, pg. 1120
Miller, Brian, Pres. & Chief Exec. Officer--Willis Corroon Corp. of Wash. D.C., Bethesda, MD; *Int'l*, pg. 1507
Miller, C.Q., Chm. Bd. & Chief Exec. Officer--Raytheon Engineers & Constructors, Inc., Englewood, CO; *U.S. Public*, pg. 1366
Miller, C.W., Pres.--ICI Explosives, West Prestonburg, KY; *Int'l*, pg. 664
Miller, Caroline, Editor-In-Chief--New York Magazine, New York, NY; *U.S. Public*, pg. 1328
Miller, Charles, Gen. Mgr.--Rock-Tenn, Dothan, AL; *U.S. Public*, pg. 1397
Miller, Charles C., III, Pres.--BellSouth International, Inc., Atlanta, GA; *U.S. Public*, pg. 208
Miller, Charles Q., Chm. Bd. & Chief Exec. Officer--Raytheon Engineers & Constructors International, Inc., Lexington, MA; *U.S. Public*, pg. 1366
Miller, Charles Q., Chief Exec. Officer--Raytheon Engineers & Constructors International, Philadelphia, PA; *U.S. Public*, pg. 1366
Miller, Charlie, Pres.--Otis Specialty Papers, Jay, ME; *Int'l*, pg. 1107
Miller, Chris, Pres.--Planet Earth Products, Carlsbad, CA; *U.S. Public*, pg. 940
Miller, Christopher, Gen. Mgr.--Arrow/Schweber Electronics, Rochester, NY; *U.S. Public*, pg. 134
Miller, Chuck, Pres.--Garrett Airline Services Division, Phoenix, AZ; *U.S. Public*, pg. 50
Miller, Chuck, Pres.--AlliedSignal Commercial Avionics Systems, Redmond, WA; *U.S. Public*, pg. 50
Miller, D., Chief Exec. Officer--Zurich Pacific Insurance Pty. Ltd., Port Moresby, Papua New Guinea; *Int'l*, pg. 1532
Miller, D. K., Pres.--Commodore National Life, Macon, GA; *U.S. Public*, pg. 282
Miller, D.K., Pres.--CNL/Resource Marketing Corp., Macon, GA; *U.S. Public*, pg. 282
Miller, D.K., Pres.--Cherokee National Life Insurance Co., Macon, GA; *U.S. Public*, pg. 282
Miller, Dale A., Pres. & Chief Exec. Officer--Sandoz Agro, Inc., Des Plaines, IL; *Int'l*, pg. 974
Miller, Dan, V.P. & Gen. Mgr.--Yosemite Express Co., Lathrop, CA; *U.S. Private*, pg. 968
Miller, Dane A., Ph.D., Pres. & Chief Exec. Officer--Biomet, Inc., Warsaw, IN; *U.S. Public*, pg. 231
Miller, Daniel S., Pres.--Alemite Corporation, Charlotte, NC; *Int'l*, pg. 127
Miller, David, Pres. & Chief Exec. Officer--Lensclean, Inc., Buzzards Bay, MA; *U.S. Private*, pg. 162
Miller, David, Pres.--Brenton Engineering Company, Alexandria, MN; *Int'l*, pg. 395

Miller, David, V.P. & Gen. Mgr.--The General Publishing Group, Reading, MA; *Int'l*, pg. 1026
Miller, David, Div. Mgr.--Wyle Electronics-Seattle, Redmond, WA; *Int'l*, pg. 1458
Miller, David, Mng. Dir.--State Street Global Advisors (U.K.) Limited, London, United Kingdom; *U.S. Public*, pg. 1513
Miller, David J., Chief Oper. Officer-Providian Direct Insurance--AEGON USA, Inc., Louisville, KY; *Int'l*, pg. 26
Miller, David J., Pres.--The Testor Corporation, Rockford, IL; *U.S. Public*, pg. 1358
Miller, David P., Chm. Bd.--The Universal Steel Co., Cleveland, OH; *U.S. Private*, pg. 256
Miller, Dean, Chief Oper. Officer--Bang & Olufsen of America, Inc., Mount Prospect, IL; *Int'l*, pg. 146
Miller, Dick, Pres. & Dir.-Transport--Auction Transport Inc., Lees Summit, MO; *U.S. Public*, pg. 1648
Miller, Douglas J., V.P.--Chase Global Funds Service Company, Boston, MA; *U.S. Public*, pg. 338
Miller, Duane E., Jr., Mgr.-Branch--Piper Jaffray Inc., Storm Lake, IA; *U.S. Public*, pg. 1302
Miller, Duane E., Jr., Mgr.-Branch--Piper Jaffray Inc., Spencer, IA; *U.S. Public*, pg. 1303
Miller, Duane L., V.P.--International Division, Fort Collins, CO; *U.S. Public*, pg. 1776
Miller, Edgar, Mgr.--Rocco Feeds, Inc., Harrisonburg, VA; *U.S. Private*, pg. 937
Miller, Francine, Pres.-Housing--Central Florida Div., Clearwater, FL; *U.S. Public*, pg. 1682
Miller, Fred, Pres.--121 S.W. Salmon St. Corp., Portland, OR; *U.S. Public*, pg. 585
Miller, G.O, Regional Dir.--Laporte Industries (Singapore) Pte Limited, Bangkok, Thailand; *Int'l*, pg. 803
Miller, G.O., Gen. Mgr.--Laporte Industries (Singapore) Pte Limited, Singapore, Singapore; *Int'l*, pg. 803
Miller, Gary, Plant Mgr.--Silgan Containers, La Porte, IN; *U.S. Public*, pg. 1473
Miller, Gary W., Pres.--Protective Insurance Company, Indianapolis, IN; *U.S. Public*, pg. 169
Miller, Gary W., Pres.--Sagamore Insurance Company, Indianapolis, IN; *U.S. Public*, pg. 169
Miller, Gary W., Pres.--B & L Insurance, Ltd., Hamilton, Bermuda; *U.S. Public*, pg. 169
Miller, Gene, Gen. Mgr.--PEC Moark, Poplar Bluff, MO; *U.S.* Private, pg. 871
Miller, George, District Mgr.--Circle Freight International USA, Windsor, CT; *U.S. Public*, pg. 371
Miller, Glen, Regional V.P.--CAP Gemini America (Dayton Branch), Dayton, OH; *Int'l*, pg. 263
Miller, Glenn, Mgr.-Northeast Region--Circle Frieght International USA, East Boston, MA; *U.S. Public*, pg. 371
Miller, Glenn, Reg. V.P.--Max Gruenhut International Inc. USA, East Boston, MA; *U.S. Public*, pg. 372
Miller, H.C.W., Mng. Dir.--De La Rue Identity Systems Limited, Basingstoke, United Kingdom; *Int'l*, pg. 387
Miller, H.E., Pres.--ARBCO Electronics, Van Nuys, CA; *Int'l*, pg. 664
Miller, Harold E., Div. Pres.--Winn-Dixie Montgomery, Inc., Montgomery, AL; *U.S. Public*, pg. 1771
Miller, Heidi G., Pres.--Offshore Equities, Inc., New York, NY; *U.S. Public*, pg. 338
Miller, Heidi G., Pres.--The Andean Fund, Inc., New York, NY; *U.S. Public*, pg. 338
Miller, J., Pres.--Sharp Corporation of New Zealand Ltd., Mangere, New Zealand; *Int'l*, pg. 1229
Miller, Jack, Mgr.-Mfg.--Systems Bio Industries, Langhorne, PA; *Int'l*, pg. 445
Miller, James D., Pres.--Magnetics, Butler, PA; *U.S. Private*, pg. 1020
Miller, James K., Pres.-Roadmaster Leisure Inc.--Roadmaster/Brunswick, Olney, IL; *U.S. Public*, pg. 265
Miller, James L., Pres. & Chief Exec. Officer--JP Foodservice Distributors, Inc., Columbia, MD; *U.S. Public*, pg. 918
Miller, James L., Chm. Bd. & Chief Exec. Officer--U.S. Food Service, Wilkes-Barre, PA; *U.S. Public*, pg. 918
Miller, James R., V.P. & Gen. Mgr.--Joy/Green Fan Division, New Philadelphia, OH; *U.S. Public*, pg. 789
Miller, Jeff, Mgr.-Mktg. N.A.--Numetrix Inc., Norwalk, CT; *Int'l*, pg. 990
Miller, Jeff, Plant Mgr.--American Natl. Can Co., Saint Paul, MN; *Int'l*, pg. 1029
Miller, Jeffrey A., Pres.--CAE Division, San Jose, CA; *U.S. Public*, pg. 290
Miller, Jerry K., Pres.--Sunwest Bank of Rio Arriba, N.A., Espanola, NM; *U.S. Public*, pg. 1165
Miller, Jim, Gen. Mgr.--Jannock Steel Fabricating, Inc., Springdale, AR; *Int'l*, pg. 699
Miller, John, Pres.--Brim Healthcare, Portland, OR; *U.S. Private*, pg. 168
Miller, John, Gen. Mgr.--Roof Tile Manufacturing Co., Corona, CA; *U.S. Public*, pg. 905
Miller, John C., Pres.--Miller Finance Corp., Saint Nazianz, WI; *U.S. Private*, pg. 748
Miller, John C., Pres., Chief Exec. Officer & Chief Oper. Officer--Badger Farm Systems, Inc., Saint Nazianz, WI; *U.S. Private*, pg. 748
Miller, John R. Jr., Chm. Bd.--Peoples National Bank of Central Pennsylvania, State College, PA; *U.S. Public*, pg. 1222 .
Miller, John S., V.P.--Technology Group, Pittsburgh, PA; *U.S. Public*, pg. 748
Miller, John T., Pres. & Chief Exec. Officer--Pacific Generation Company, Portland, OR; *U.S. Public*, pg. 1252
Miller, John, III, V.P. & Grp. Publr.--Home Magazine Publishing Corp., New York, NY; *Int'l*, pg. 795
Miller, Jon, Pres. & Chief Exec. Officer--USA Broadcasting, New York, NY; *U.S. Public*, pg. 1686
Miller, Jonathan, V.P.--Georex Inc., Houston, TX; *Int'l*, pg. 241
Miller, Joseph P., Pres. & Chief Exec. Officer--Citizens Bank of Jasper, Jasper, IN; *U.S. Public*, pg. 280
Miller, K.E., Pres.--Lockheed Support Systems, Inc., Arlington, TX; *U.S. Public*, pg. 1009
Miller, Lawrence R., Sr. Exec. Dir.--AON Advisors, Inc., Chicago, IL; *U.S. Public*, pg. 117
Miller, Leonard, Chm. Bd.--H. Miller & Sons, Inc., Boca Raton, FL; *U.S. Public*, pg. 989
Miller, Lester, Chief Oper. Officer--Chicago AutoWerks, Inc., Chicago, IL; *U.S. Private*, pg. 1030
Miller, Luke, Gen. Mgr.--CMC-North Augusta, North Augusta, SC; *U.S. Public*, pg. 412
Miller, Lynn, Pres.--City Machine & Wheel Co., Stow, OH; *U.S. Private*, pg. 299
Miller, M., Vice Chm.--National Yarn Crafts, New York, NY; *U.S. Private*, pg. 787
Miller, Mark J., Chief Oper. Officer & Exec. V.P.--Atlantic City Showboat, Atlantic City, NJ; *U.S. Public*, pg. 1469
Miller, Michael, V.P.--Piedmont Div., Atlanta, GA; *U.S. Public*, pg. 732
Miller, Michael A., Pres. & Chief Exec. Officer--Firestone Financial, Newton, MA; *U.S. Public*, pg. 1660
Miller, Michael J., Pres.--Wm. H. McGee & Co., Inc., New York, NY; *U.S. Public*, pg. 1231
Miller, Mickey, Pres.--Flowers Baking Co. of Thomasville, Inc., Thomasville, GA; *U.S. Public*, pg. 657
Miller, Mont, Pres.--Club Car, Inc., Martinez, GA; *U.S. Public*, pg. 877
Miller, P. Dan, Pres.--Whirlpool do Brazil S.A., Sao Paulo, Brazil; *U.S. Public*, pg. 1765
Miller, Paul, Pres.--Litton Marine Systems, Charlottesville, VA; *U.S. Public*, pg. 1003
Miller, Phil, Pres.--Prentice Hall Humanities & Social Sciences, Upper Saddle River, NJ; *U.S. Private*, pg. 778
Miller, R.A., Pres.--J.E. Morgan Knitting Mills Inc., Tamaqua, PA; *Int'l*, pg. 386
Miller, R.E., Gen. Mgr.--Western Filter, Commerce City, CO; *U.S. Public*, pg. 1234
Miller, Richard J., Pres.--Old Reliable Casualty Co., Webster Groves, MO; *U.S. Public*, pg. 1374
Miller, Robert, Pres.--Career Blazers of White Plains, Inc., White Plains, NY; *U.S. Private*, pg. 209
Miller, Robert, Pres.--Northeast Environmental Services, Inc., Canastota, NY; *U.S. Public*, pg. 546
Miller, Robert, Pres.--Environmental Services of America-IN, Inc., South Bend, IN; *U.S. Public*, pg. 546
Miller, Robert, Pres.--Environmental Services of America-MO, Inc., Scott City, MO; *U.S. Public*, pg. 546
Miller, Robert C., Chief Oper. Officer--Bowhead Equipment Company, Seattle, WA; *U.S. Private*, pg. 683
Miller, Robert G., Pres. & Chief Exec. Officer--Smith's Food & Drug Centers, Inc., Salt Lake City, UT; *U.S. Public*, pg. 1103
Miller, Robert G., Pres.--Fred Meyer Stores, Portland, OR; *U.S. Public*, pg. 1103
Miller, Rod, Pres.--American Consolidation Services Ltd., Oakland, CA; *Int'l*, pg. 912
Miller, Ronald, Plant. Super.--The Ohio Mattress Company Licensing & Components Group, Colorado Springs, CO; *U.S. Private*, pg. 979
Miller, Ronald D., Pres.--A.G. Industries Inc., Cleveland, OH; *U.S. Public*, pg. 78
Miller, Russell W., Pres.--Zions Insurance Agency, Inc., Salt Lake City, UT; *U.S. Public*, pg. 1793
Miller, Russell W., Pres.--Zions Life Insurance Co., Salt Lake City, UT; *U.S. Public*, pg. 1793
Miller, S.C., Plant Mgr.--Household Products, Houston, TX; *U.S. Public*, pg. 387
Miller, Samuel V., Pres.--American Medical Security Holdings, Inc., Green Bay, WI; *U.S. Public*, pg. 1692
Miller, Sanford, Chm. & Chief Exec. Officer--Budget Rent A Car Corporation, Lisle, IL; *U.S. Private*, pg. 178
Miller, Scott F., Pres.--Miller Transporters, Inc., Jackson, MS; *U.S. Private*, pg. 329
Miller, Sharon, Media Asst.--Western International Media Corporation, Palm Springs, CA; *U.S. Private*, pg. 1167
Miller, Sherman E., Plant Mgr.--Industrial Bag Division - Kansas City Plant, Kansas City, MO; *U.S. Public*, pg. 1521
Miller, Stephen, Chief Exec. Officer--Pumpex Inc., Lebanon, NJ; *Int'l*, pg. 270
Miller, Steven, Chief Exec. Officer--Resort Condominiums International, Indianapolis, IN; *U.S. Public*, pg. 322
Miller, Steven, Chief Exec. Officer--Miller Personnel, Inc., North Brunswick, NJ; *U.S. Private*, pg. 748
Miller, Steven, Chief Exec. Officer--Miller Temporaries, Inc., North Brunswick, NJ; *U.S. Private*, pg. 748
Miller, Steven, Chief Exec. Officer--Miller Scientific, Inc., North Brunswick, NJ; *U.S. Private*, pg. 748
Miller, Tom, Gen. Mgr.--Norand Mobile Systems Div., Cedar Rapids, IA; *U.S. Public*, pg. 1699
Miller, Tom D., Pres.--Preferred Products, Inc., Eden Prairie, MN; *U.S. Public*, pg. 1541
Miller, Tony, Pres.--Sterling Electronics, San Jose, CA; *U.S. Public*, pg. 1051
Miller, W. Keith, Pres.--Nobel/Sysco Food Services Co.-Albequerque, Albuquerque, NM; *U.S. Public*, pg. 1551
Miller, W.A., Pres. & Mng. Dir.--Amoco Chemical (Europe) S.A., Geneva, Switzerland; *U.S. Public*, pg. 103
Miller, W.A., Pres.--Amoco Deutschland GmbH, Gronau, Germany; *U.S. Public*, pg. 103
Miller, W.A., Mng. Dir.--Amoco Chemical (UK) Ltd., London, United Kingdom; *U.S. Public*, pg. 103
Miller, Walter, Mgr.--Sandvik Process Systems, Inc., Totowa, NJ; *Int'l*, pg. 1185
Miller, Wayne, Pres.--Century Supply Corp., Madison Heights, MI; *U.S. Public*, pg. 1389
Miller, William, Chm. Bd.--Accor UK, London, United Kingdom; *Int'l*, pg. 21
Miller, Woody, Pres.-Plastics Div.--Edison Plastics Co., McAlester, OK; *U.S. Private*, pg. 1179
Millet, Hubert, Pres.--Seagram Global Brands, Paris, France; *Int'l*, pg. 1217
Millet, Jorge, Pres.--AGA S.A., Montevideo, Uruguay; *Int'l*, pg. 13
Millet, Rich, Mgr.-Opers.--Woodward-Clyde, Denver, CO; *U.S. Public*, pg. 1656
Millet, Ronald A., Gen. Mgr.--Deseret Book Co., Salt Lake City, UT; *U.S. Private*, pg. 327
Milligan, Bruce, Pres. & Chief Exec. Officer--Republic Financial Services, Inc., Dallas, TX; *Int'l*, pg. 346
Milligan, Bruce R., Pres.--Republic Underwriters Insurance Co., Dallas, TX; *Int'l*, pg. 346
Milligan, Bruce R., Pres.--Republic-Vanguard Life Insurance Co., Dallas, TX; *Int'l*, pg. 346
Milligan, Bruce R., Pres. & Chief Exec. Officer--Republic Diversified Services, Inc., Dallas, TX; *Int'l*, pg. 346
Milligan, Bruce R., Pres.--Southern Insurance Co., Dallas, TX; *Int'l*, pg. 346
Milligan, Bruce R., Pres.--Republic Financial Services, Inc., Dallas, TX; *Int'l*, pg. 346
Milligan, Bruce R., Pres.--Southern Underwriters Insurance Company, Dallas, TX; *Int'l*, pg. 346
Milligan, Bruce R., Pres.--Republic Fire & Casualty Insurance Company, Dallas, TX; *Int'l*, pg. 346
Milligan, Bruce R., Pres.--Republic Group No. Two, Dallas, TX; *Int'l*, pg. 346
Milligan, Bruce R., Pres.--Eagle General Agency, Dallas, TX; *Int'l*, pg. 346
Milligan, Bruce R., Pres.--Allied Premium Finance, Dallas, TX; *Int'l*, pg. 346
Milligan, Dee, Pres.--ProEquities, Inc., Birmingham, AL; *U.S.* Public, pg. 1336
Milligan, Jay I., Pres.--Sysco Food Services of St. Louis, Inc., Saint Charles, MO; *U.S. Public*, pg. 1552
Milligan, Patrick M., Pres. & Chief Exec. Officer--Willis Corroon Corp. of Northern Ohio, Dublin, OH; *Int'l*, pg. 1506
Millikan, Doug, Plant Mgr.--Square D Company, Monroe, NC; *Int'l*, pg. 1208
Millikan, Robert J., G.M.--Port Hudson Pulp Mill, Zachary, LA; *U.S. Public*, pg. 737
Milliken, C.F., V.P. & Gen. Mgr.--McNally Pittsburg Mfg. Corp., Wellston, OH; *Int'l*, pg. 1326
Millilkin, Lynn, Plant Mgr.--Du Pont Electronics Information Storage Division, Circleville, OH; *U.S. Public*, pg. 531
Milling, Sture, Chief Oper. Officer--Nordic Forestry Equipment AB, Partille, Sweden; *Int'l*, pg. 439
Milliron, Tim, Chief Oper. Officer--Allright Roanoke Parking, Inc., Roanoke, VA; *U.S. Private*, pg. 43
Millman, James R., Chm. & Chief Exec. Officer--Millsport, Stamford, CT; *U.S. Public*, pg. 1224
Millot, Noel, Mng. Dir.--Eldon France, Saint Ouen, France; *Int'l*, pg. 436
Mills Jr., Sam, Sr. V.P. & Chief Mgr.-Western Region--Westpac Banking Corporation (Los Angeles Branch), Los Angeles, CA; *Int'l*, pg. 1496
Mills, Andy, Chief Exec. Officer--Thomson Financial Services, Inc., Boston, MA; *U.S. Public*, pg. 1600
Mills, Cadman Atta, Resident Rep.--The World Bank, Dakar, Senegal; *U.S. Private*, pg. 1190
Mills, Charles, Pres.--Medcrest Div., Mundelein, IL; *U.S. Private*, pg. 728
Mills, Douglas W., Exec. V.P.--U.S. & Canadian Food Products, Chicago, IL; *U.S. Public*, pg. 1347
Mills, Glenn, Chief Oper. Officer--Union-Transport (Aust) Pty Ltd, Tullamarine, Australia; *U.S. Private*, pg. 1120
Mills, Howard C., Pres. & Chief Exec. Officer--Halifax Engineering, Inc., Alexandria, VA; *U.S. Public*, pg. 775
Mills, Howard C., Pres. & Chief Exec. Officer--Halifax Technical Services, Alexandria, VA; *U.S. Public*, pg. 775
Mills, James, Gen. Mgr.--ICIS LOR-Asia/Pacific, Singapore, Singapore; *Int'l*, pg. 1094
Mills, James L., Pres.--Caterpillar Financial Nordic Services A.B., Danderyd, Sweden; *U.S. Public*, pg. 315
Mills, Melvin, Pres.--Anderson Electrical Sales, Salt Lake City, UT; *Int'l*, pg. 736
Mills, P. Gerald, Pres.--Jacobson Stores Realty Company, Jackson, MI; *U.S. Public*, pg. 922
Mills, P. Gerald, Pres.--Jacobson Credit Corporation, Jackson, MI; *U.S. Public*, pg. 922
Mills, R.D., Pres.--Amax Research & Development Inc., Englewood, CO; *U.S. Public*, pg. 470
Mills, Robert E., Mng. Dir.--JLG Industries (United Kingdom) Limited, Cumbernauld, United Kingdom; *U.S. Public*, pg. 918
Mills, Robert G., Pres.--Martin-Brower of Canada, Ltd., Mississauga, Canada; *Int'l*, pg. 376
Mills, Russell, Pres. & Publisher--The Ottawa Citizen, Ottawa, Canada; *Int'l*, pg. 631
Mills, Walter C., Pres.--Sysco Food Services of Indianapolis, Inc., Indianapolis, IN; *U.S. Public*, pg. 1551
Mills, Warren T., Pres.--MicroAge Solutions, Inc. (MAS), Kansas City, MO; *U.S. Public*, pg. 1105
Millstein, Jack H., Jr., Pres.--Lightcraft, Jeannette, PA; *U.S Private*, pg. 749
Millstein, Jack, Jr., Pres.--JHJ Realty, Youngwood, PA; *U.S. Private*, pg. 749
Millstein, Jack, Jr., Pres.--Cherry Creek Golf, Youngwood, PA; *U.S. Private*, pg. 749
Millstein, Steven A., Pres.--Westar Security, Topeka, KS; *U.S. Public*, pg. 1760
Millweard, Tom, Exec. V.P. & Mng. Dir.--Ackerman McQueen, Inc., Irving, TX; *U.S. Private*, pg. 13
Milne, David, Chief Exec. Officer--Willis Corroon Risk Consulting Limited, London, United Kingdom; *Int'l*, pg. 1503
Milne, David S., Jr., Pres. & Chief Exec. Officer--Gas Energy Inc., Brooklyn, NY; *U.S. Public*, pg. 296
Milne, G., Chief Exec. Officer--Milk Products Holdings (Europe) Ltd., Reigate, United Kingdom; *Int'l*, pg. 923
Milne, Ian, V.P.-Canadian Contracting Opers.--Grinnell Canada Ltd., Mississauga, Canada; *U.S. Public*, pg. 1651
Milne, Philip, Pres. & Chief Exec. Officer--Travelers Express Company, Inc., Saint Louis Park, MN; *U.S. Public*, pg. 1718
Milner, Andrew Blakey, Gen. Mgr.--Bundy South Africa, King Williams Town, South Africa; *Int'l*, pg. 1341
Milner, D.A., Mng. Dir.--Castell Safety International Limited, London, United Kingdom; *Int'l*, pg. 589

Milner, Kenneth C., Gen. Mgr.--Kee Services, Warren, MI; *U.S. Public*, pg. 1054
Milner, Kenneth C., Gen. Mgr.--Kee Cutters, Warren, MI; *U.S. Public*, pg. 1054
Milner, S.A., Pres.--Chieftain Development Co. Ltd., Edmonton, Canada; *Int'l*, pg. 49
Milner, S.A., Pres. & Chief Oper. Officer--Chieftain International (U.S.) Inc., Edmonton, Canada; *Int'l*, pg. 284
Milone, Michael D., Chief Revenue Officer--Heinz Pet Products Company, Newport, KY; *U.S. Public*, pg. 806
Milonski, Donna, Chief Oper. Officer--Royal Copenhagen Porcelain Corporation, New York, NY; *Int'l*, pg. 1134
Milovich, Mitch, Pres.--Baker Material Handling Corp., Summerville, SC; *Int'l*, pg. 810
Milowitz, Billy, Pres.--Balson-Hercules Ltd., New York, NY; *Int'l*, pg. 326
Milstein, Alexander, Mng. Dir.--TBWA Dusseldorf GmbH, Dusseldorf, Germany; *U.S. Private*, pg. 1063
Min, Jae-Hong, Chm. Bd. & Chief Exec. Officer--Samsung Asia Headquarters, Singapore, Singapore; *Int'l*, pg. 1183
Minagawa, Takashi, Mng. Dir.--NLI Properties UK Limited, London, United Kingdom; *Int'l*, pg. 936
Minakawa, Atsushi, Chief Oper. Officer--Tosoh Hellas A.I.C., Thessaloniki, Greece; *Int'l*, pg. 1408
Minami, Junichi, Chief Oper. Officer--Nissho Iwai do Brasil S.A., Sao Paulo, Brazil; *Int'l*, pg. 948
Minami, Wayne K., Pres. & Chief Exec. Officer--American Savings Bank, F.S.B., Honolulu, HI; *U.S. Public*, pg. 800
Minassian, Michael, Mng. Dir.--Costain Middle East, Dubai, United Arab Emirates; *Int'l*, pg. 337
Minato, Shungo, Chm. & Mng. Dir.--Pioneer Electronic (Europe) NV, Melsele, Belgium; *Int'l*, pg. 1058
Minato, Yuji, Chief Representative--The Sumitomo Bank, Ltd.-Tehran Representative Office, Tehran, Iran; *Int'l*, pg. 1310
Minaud, Pierre, Chief Oper. Officer--Jet Chef, Le Bourget, France; *Int'l*, pg. 560
Minchk, Frederick, Pres. & Chief Oper. Officer--National Loss Control Service Corp., Long Grove, IL; *U.S. Private, pg. 614*
Minear, David, Vice Chm. & Grp. Chief Exec.-Melbourne--Y&R Mattingly, Richmond, Australia; *U.S. Private*, pg. 325
Minear, Kenny, Pres.--John Wieland Homes of Tenessee, Inc., Franklin, TN; *U.S. Private*, pg. 1175
Mineart, Paul, Pres.--Firestone Building Products Company, Carmel, IN; *Int'l*, pg. 214
Minelli, J., Chief Oper. Officer--Bristolipe Division, Bristol, IN; *Int'l*, pg. 618
Miner, Brian, Pres.--Reliance Steel Fabricators Limited, Tilbury, Canada; *Int'l*, pg. 75
Miner, Brian, Pres.--Superior Steel Acquisition Corporation, Cheshire, CT; *Int'l*, pg. 75
Miner, Earl, Gen. Mgr.--Chris-Craft Industrial Products, Inc., Mono-Sol Div., Gary, IN; *U.S. Public*, pg. 351
Miner, M. Bruce, Chief Oper. Officer--Brown Brothers Harriman Trust Co. of Florida, Naples, FL; *U.S. Private*, pg. 173
Miner, Steve, V.P.-Retail Div.--Market Development Inc., Salt Lake City, UT; *U.S. Private*, pg. 90
Miner, Wally, Plant Mgr.--TDK Electronics, Huntsville, Huntsville, AL; *Int'l*, pg. 1336
Minerva, Daniel O., Co-Pres. & Co-Chief Exec. Officer--Eastbridge Capital Inc., New York, NY; *Int'l*, pg. 933
Minerva, Vito P., Pres.--Tecom Industries, Inc., Chatsworth, CA; *U.S. Public*, pg. 1563
Mines, S., Branch Mgr--M&N Valve, Long Beach, CA; *Int'l*, pg. 1449
Ming, Liu Chee, Dir.--Jardine Fleming Securities Limited, Central, Hong Kong; *Int'l*, pg. 494
Mingarro, C., Gen. Mgr.--Wellcome Farmaceutica SA, Madrid, Spain; *Int'l*, pg. 553
Mingay, Robert, V.P.-British Columbia--GPC Government Policy Consultants (Vancouver), Vancouver, Canada; *U.S. Public*, pg. 1225
Minigh, Howard L., Ph.D., Pres.--Cyanamid Agricultural Products Division, Parsippany, NJ; *U.S. Public*, pg. 79
Minkhorst, Robert, Pres. & Chief Exec. Officer--Philips Consumer Electronics, Knoxville, TN; *Int'l*, pg. 1054
Minkhorst, Robert, Pres.--Philips Lighting, Somerset, NJ; *Int'l*, pg. 1055
Minkin, Gustav, Mng. Dir.--Nearby Eggs, Inc., Spring Grove, PA; *U.S. Public*, pg. 1529
Minkin, Gustave, Pres.--Sun City Egg Marketing, Inc., Fort Lauderdale, FL; *U.S. Public*, pg. 1529
Minkman, Wim, Mng. Dir.--Kimberly-Clark Benelux Operations B.V., Veenendaal, Netherlands; *U.S. Public*, pg. 959
Minkoff, Michael R., Pres.--WF Corroon Canada Inc., Montreal, Canada; *Int'l*, pg. 1502
Minneci, E., Gen. Mgr.--Moog Italiana (SRL), Malnate, Italy; *U.S. Public*, pg. 1128
Minner, Tom, Mng. Dir.--GNB Technologies, Atlanta, GA; *Int'l*, pg. 1021
Minnick, James E., Pres.--Morgan Grenfell Capital Management Incorporated, New York, NY; *Int'l*, pg. 405
Mino, Michael G., Gen. Mgr.--Branson Plastic Joining, Henrietta, NY; *U.S. Public*, pg. 574
Mino, Santiago, Mgr. Gen.--Lubricantes Del Sur, S.A. (LUBRISUR), Madrid, Spain; *Int'l*, pg. 323
Minodier, S., Pres.--Van Leer Italia SpA, Milan, Italy; *Int'l*, pg. 1147
Minor, David J., Mng. Dir.--Black Warrior Transmission Corp., Brookwood, AL; *U.S. Public*, pg. 1485
Minor, Michael L., Pres.--First Insurance Agency, Inc., Mount Vernon, WA; *U.S. Public*, pg. 1740
Minor, Roger, Pres.--Boeing North America, Space Systems Division, Downey, CA; *U.S. Public*, pg. 241
Minott, L.O., Mng. Dir.--MB Jamaica Limited, Kingston, Jamaica; *Int'l*, pg. 267
Minotto, Gene J., Pres. & Chief Exec. Officer--Basic American Medical Products, Inc., Atlanta, GA; *U.S. Public*, pg. 758
Minowa, Ikuzo, Mng. Dir.--Mazda Austria GmbH, Klagenfurt, Austria; *Int'l*, pg. 849
Minter, Paul, Mng. Dir.--Trion Ltd., Andover, United Kingdom; *U.S. Public*, pg. 1639
Minton, Cliff, Dir.--Lift Tech International, Muskegon, MI; *U.S. Public*, pg. 406
Minty, C.J., Deputy Chm. & Chief Exec. Officer--Henry Ansbacher Holding PLC, London, United Kingdom; *Int'l*, pg. 487
Mintz, Robert, Pres.--Kvaerner FSSL Inc., Sugar Land, TX; *Int'l*, pg. 770
Minutoli, Robert, Sr. V.P.-New Bus.--New Business, Columbia, MD; *U.S. Public*, pg. 1407
Minutolo, Frank, Pres.--Konica Medical Corporation, Wayne, NJ; *Int'l*, pg. 749
Miquel, Jean Pierre, Pres. & Chief Exec. Officer--Greyhound Leisure Services, Inc., Miami, FL; *U.S. Public*, pg. 1718
Miqueles, Luis Ernesto, Gen. Mgr.--Codelco-Asia, Singapore, Singapore; *Int'l*, pg. 303
Mir, Arshad A., Sr. V.P. & Gen. Mgr.--Habib Bank Ltd., London, United Kingdom; *Int'l*, pg. 585
Mir, Javier, Mng. Dir.--Gallina Blanca Purina, Barcelona, Spain; *U.S. Private*, pg. 159
Mir, Javier, Mng. Dir.--Gallina Blanca Purina, Barcelona, Spain; *U.S. Public*, pg. 1360
Mir, Pedro, Gen. Mgr.--Cosmhogar, S.A., Rubi, Spain; *U.S. Public*, pg. 1508
Mira, Elias, Mng. Dir.--Quaker Chemical, S.A., Barcelona, Spain; *U.S. Public*, pg. 1347
Mira, Fahad I., Chief Oper. Officer--Arabian Elevator & Escalator Co. Ltd. (AREECO), Jeddah, Saudi Arabia; *Int'l*, pg. 748
Mirab, Hamid, Dir.--Integrated Systems, Inc., Ltd., Welwyn Garden City, United Kingdom; *U.S. Public*, pg. 886
Mirabaud, Bertrand, Mng. Dir.--Lagon, Puteaux, France; *Int'l*, pg. 601
Miranda, Alfredo, Chief Oper. Officer--Pharos de Costa Rica S.A., Alajuela, Costa Rica; *Int'l*, pg. 1290
Miranda, Frank, Plant Mgr.--Block Plant, Baton Rouge, LA; *U.S. Public*, pg. 936
Miranda, Gordon, Plant Mgr.--Block Plant, Port Neches, TX; *U.S. Public*, pg. 936
Miranda, Richard, Chief Exec. Officer--ORIX Auto Finance (India) Limited, Mumbai, India; *Int'l*, pg. 1009
Mirani, C.H., Chm.--Sakura Capital India, Limited, Mumbai, India; *Int'l*, pg. 1180
Mirante, Arthur J., II, Pres. & Chief Exec. Officer--Cushman & Wakefield, Inc., New York, NY; *Int'l*, pg. 873
Miras, Abel, Mng. Dir.--Dart Argentina S.A., Buenos Aires, Argentina; *U.S. Public*, pg. 1322
Miravda, Carlos, Mgr.-Fin.--Johnson & Johnson de Chile S.A., Santiago, Chile; *U.S. Public*, pg. 930
Mirchandani, Rajesh, Dir.--Dun & Bradstreet (India) Pvt. Ltd., Mumbai, India; *U.S. Public*, pg. 536
Mirner, Kevin, Pres.--Harcros Chemicals Inc., Kansas City, KS; *Int'l*, pg. 598
Miron, Steven, Mng. Dir.--John Wiley & Sons (Asia) Pte. Ltd., Singapore; *U.S. Public*, pg. 1768
Mirossevich, Luciano, Gen. Mgr.--Elscint Italia S.r.L., Milan, Italy; *Int'l*, pg. 450
Mirow, Dr., Chief Oper. Officer--BK Ladenburg GmbH, Ladenburg, Germany; *Int'l*, pg. 626
Mirsky, B.S., Pres.--Bard Urological Div., Covington, GA; *U.S. Public*, pg. 189
Mis'hal, M. S., Pres.--Qatar Steel Co. Ltd., Umm Said, Qatar; *Int'l*, pg. 741
Misasi, Enrico, Pres.--Olivetti do Brasil S.A., Sao Paulo, Brazil; *Int'l*, pg. 1003
Misawa, Osamu, Branch Manager--Minebea Co., Ltd. - Hong Kong Branch, Kowloon, Hong Kong; *Int'l*, pg. 869
Mischinski, Paul, Pres. & Chief Exec. Officer-Bali Brand--Bali Company, Winston Salem, NC; *U.S. Public*, pg. 1433
Misdanitis, Kostas, Chief Exec.--Novo Nordisk Maroc, Casablanca, Morocco; *Int'l*, pg. 988
Mise, Yoshinari, Pres.--CPC Japan, Ltd., Tokyo, Japan; *U.S. Public*, pg. 447
Misek, Miroslav, Plant Mgr.--Bundy s.r.o, Mlada Boleslav, Czech Republic; *Int'l*, pg. 1342
Misener, James, Sr. V.P. & Gen. Mgr.--Newcourt Financial USA, Inc., Indianapolis, IN; *Int'l*, pg. 924
Mishari, H. E. Sheikh Hassan, Chm.--Banque Indosuez, Jeddah, Saudi Arabia; *Int'l*, pg. 315
Mishkind, William, Pres.--Pak-Sher Co., Kilgore, TX; *U.S. Private*, pg. 1062
Misiak, Greg, Pres.-Laser Systems--Laser Systems, Apopka, FL; *U.S. Public*, pg. 1002
Misiak, Tom, Pres.--The Falk Corporation, Milwaukee, WI; *U.S. Public*, pg. 1534
Misitano, Anthony, Pres. & Chief Exec. Officer--Continental Medical Systems, Inc., Mechanicsburg, PA; *U.S. Public*, pg. 839
Miskowski, Lee R., V.P. & Gen. Mgr.--Lincoln-Mercury Division, Detroit, MI; *U.S. Public*, pg. 662
Mislow, Robert, Admin.--Greenery Extended Care Center at Cheshire, Cheshire, CT; *U.S. Public*, pg. 836
Misra, Mohan, Dr., Pres.--Global Solar Energy, Tucson, AZ; *U.S. Public*, pg. 1670
Misra, Rajendra, Pres.--Tekelec-India Pvt. Ltd., Bangalore, India; *U.S. Public*, pg. 1566
Missaglia, Marcello, Rep.--Banco di Napoli-Brussels, Brussels, Belgium; *Int'l*, pg. 140
Mistry, Vino, Gen. Mgr.--Serca Food Service-Hickeson Div., Weston, Canada; *Int'l*, pg. 1012
Misumi, Yoshio, Pres. & Chief Exec. Officer--Pioneer/ Eclipse Corp., Sparta, NC; *Int'l*, pg. 71
Misunas, Kathy, Chief Exec.--Reed Travel Group, Dunstable, United Kingdom; *Int'l*, pg. 1097
Misunas, Kathy, Chief Exec. Officer--Reed Travel Group, Secaucus, NJ; *Int'l*, pg. 1097
Misunas, William, Exec. V.P.-Americas--Utell International-Secaucus, Secaucus, NJ; *Int'l*, pg. 1098
Mitani, Toru, Gen. Mgr.--Los Angeles Agency, Los Angeles, CA; *Int'l*, pg. 816
Mitch, David S., V.P. & Gen. Mgr.--Copperweld Bimetallics Products Co., Fayetteville, TN; *Int'l*, pg. 662
Mitchel, Bud, Pres.--HomeAdd Financial Corporation, Greenville, SC; *U.S. Public*, pg. 1358
Mitchel, J. A., Gen. Mgr.--Elastimold Co., Hackettstown, NJ; *U.S. Public*, pg. 1598
Mitchell, Allen, Reg. Mgr.--Port Charlotte, Port Charlotte, FL; *U.S. Public*, pg. 144
Mitchell, Andrew, Chief Exec. Officer--Miller Patterson Aldred Mitchell, London, United Kingdom; *U.S. Private*, pg. 1152
Mitchell, Bill, Gen. Mgr.--Ike's, Memphis, TN; *U.S. Public*, pg. 653
Mitchell, Bob, Gen. Mgr.--William's Bakery, Eugene, OR; *U.S. Private*, pg. 1124
Mitchell, Bradford W., Chm. Bd.--Harleysville Mutual Insurance, Harleysville, PA; *U.S. Public*, pg. 787
Mitchell, Brian, Mgr.--Willis Corroon (Private) Limited, Harare, Zimbabwe; *Int'l*, pg. 1509
Mitchell, Charles E., Pres.--Basic American Wood Products, Toccoa, GA; *U.S. Public*, pg. 404
Mitchell, Chris, Gen. Mgr.--Midwest Rubber Co., Barberton, OH; *U.S. Private*, pg. 56
Mitchell, Clement, Pres. & Chief Exec. Officer--FICON Corporation, Woodbridge, VA; *U.S. Public*, pg. 84
Mitchell, Curtis P., V.P.-Western Region--Wall Street Deli, Inc., Englewood, CO; *U.S. Public*, pg. 1734
Mitchell, Edson V., Pres.--Merrill Lynch Capital Services, Inc., New York, NY; *U.S. Public*, pg. 1097
Mitchell, Fred, V.P. & Gen. Mgr.--Boeing Fabrication Division, Auburn, WA; *U.S. Public*, pg. 240
Mitchell, G.E., Mng. Dir.--Bundaberg Sugar Company, Brisbane, Australia; *Int'l*, pg. 1357
Mitchell, George, Dir.--Stewart & Stevenson (U.K.) Limited, Houston, TX; *U.S. Public*, pg. 1518
Mitchell, Guy, Mgr.--Crinum Mine, Emerald, Australia; *Int'l*, pg. 224
Mitchell, Herb, Plant Mgr.--L.B. Foster Company, Bedford, PA; *U.S. Public*, pg. 676
Mitchell, Herbert, Plant Mgr.--L.B. Foster Company-Bedford Plant, Bedford, PA; *U.S. Public*, pg. 676
Mitchell, J. Tony, Pres.--Buchanan Construction Products, Inc., Hackettstown, NJ; *U.S. Private*, pg. 557
Mitchell, James, Chm. Bd.--IDS Certificate Company, Minneapolis, MN; *U.S. Public*, pg. 73
Mitchell, James L., Pres.--Norris, Tulsa, OK; *U.S. Public*, pg. 521
Mitchell, James P., Pres.--Patent Construction Systems, Paramus, NJ; *U.S. Public*, pg. 793
Mitchell, James R., Mng. Dir.--Janssen-Cilag Pty. Ltd., Lane Cove, Australia; *U.S. Public*, pg. 929
Mitchell, Jim, Dir.--BCT, Inc., Boise, ID; *U.S. Public*, pg. 243
Mitchell, John, Mng. Dir.--Avana Bakeries Ltd., Cardiff, United Kingdom; *Int'l*, pg. 1396
Mitchell, K.N., Gen. Mgr.--Harvest Products Pty. Ltd., Blacktown, Australia; *Int'l*, pg. 682
Mitchell, Kenneth, Pres.--Argo Instruments Inc., Winchester, VA; *Int'l*, pg. 839
Mitchell, Martin, Gen. Mgr.--Flowmatrix Corporation, Las Vegas, NV; *U.S. Public*, pg. 874
Mitchell, Michael A., Pres.--Textron Automotive Company, Troy, MI; *U.S. Public*, pg. 1590
Mitchell, Michael R., Pres.--Farah U.S.A., Inc., El Paso, TX; *U.S. Public*, pg. 613
Mitchell, Mike, Pres.--Aunt Fanny's Bakery, Atlanta, GA; *U.S. Public*, pg. 657
Mitchell, N. Andrew, Pres.--LifeStyle Contract Furnishings, Inc., High Point, NC; *U.S. Private*, pg. 431
Mitchell, P.H., Pres.--Tetra Plastics, Chesterfield, MO; *U.S. Public*, pg. 1184
Mitchell, Paul D., Pres.--McNeil Consumer Products Company, Guelph, Canada; *U.S. Public*, pg. 931
Mitchell, Peter M., V.P.-Opers. & Industrial Products--Vigoro Industries, Southeast Division, Savannah, GA; *U.S. Public*, pg. 856
Mitchell, Robert, Pres.--Teledyne Ryan Aeronautical, San Diego, CA; *U.S. Public*, pg. 43
Mitchell, Robert, Sr. V.P. & Mgr.--Imperial Real Estate Ventures, Costa Mesa, CA; *U.S. Public*, pg. 872
Mitchell, Shay, Gen. Mgr.--Aer Lingus, Hounslow, United Kingdom; *Int'l*, pg. 28
Mitchell, T. Scott, Pres.--Moore Data Management Services Div., Saint Louis Park, MN; *Int'l*, pg. 890
Mitchell, Thomas, Pres.--Mountain Valley Spring Company, Hot Springs National Park, AR; *U.S. Private*, pg. 963
Mitchell, W. Thomas, Chief Oper. Officer--Genencor International, Inc., Rochester, NY; *Int'l*, pg. 349
Mitchell, Warren I., Pres.--Southern California Gas Co., Los Angeles, CA; *U.S. Public*, pg. 1249
Mitchell, Warren I., Pres.--EcoTrans OEM Transportation, Los Angeles, CA; *U.S. Public*, pg. 1249
Mitchelson, C. S., Mng. Dir.--Cascade (U.K.) Ltd., Cramlington, United Kingdom; *U.S. Public*, pg. 311
Mitchem, Marian, Mgr.--General Employment Enterprises, Inc., Riverside, CA; *U.S. Public*, pg. 714
Mithcell, N. Andrew, Pres.--Intro Europe, Inc., High Point, NC; *U.S. Private*, pg. 431
Mitilier, T.J., Pres.--Imperial Casualty & Indemnity Co., Omaha, NE; *U.S. Public*, pg. 103
Mitnick, J.I., V.P. & Gen. Mgr.--Turner Construction Co., Pittsburgh, PA; *U.S. Public*, pg. 1645
Mitra, Tapan, Mng. Dir.--Indian Aluminium Co. Ltd., Calcutta, India; *Int'l*, pg. 51
Mitro, Robert F., Sr. V.P. & Gen. Mgr.--PictureTel Corporation-World Headquarters, Danvers, MA; *U.S. Public*, pg. 1295
Mitsuda, T., Chm.--Sharp Electronics (Europe) GmbH, Hamburg, Germany; *Int'l*, pg. 1230
Mitsui, Masahiko, Pres.--Dai-Ichi Kangyo Bank (Deutschland) AG, Frankfurt/Main, Germany; *Int'l*, pg. 362
Mitsuya, Joiche, Chief Oper. Officer--Nippon MacDermid K.K., Yokohama, Japan; *U.S. Public*, pg. 1030

Mitsuyasu, Chikatomo, Chief Oper. Officer--Oki Electric Cable Co., Ltd., Kanagawa, Japan; *Int'l*, pg. 999
Mittag, Michael T., Chief Exec. Officer--Electrovert, Grand Prairie, TX; *Int'l*, pg. 328
Mittal, Subodh, Exec. Dir.--Southern Region, Madras, India; *Int'l*, pg. 673
Mitte, Roy, Chm. Bd., Pres. & Chief Exec. Officer--InternContinental Life Corp., Austin, TX; *U.S. Public*, pg. 622
Mittelsteadt, Bernard A., Pres.--Orr-Schelen-Mayeron & Assoc., Inc., Minneapolis, MN; *U.S. Public*, pg. 1341
Mitter, Dr. Gerhard, Sr. Mng. Dir.--VOEST-ALPINE STAHL Donawitz Ges.m.b.H., Leoben, Austria; *Int'l*, pg. 1470
Mitzner, Don, Pres.--Group W Satellite Communications, Stamford, CT; *U.S. Public*, pg. 275
Miu, Bernard, Mng. Dir.--Union Carbide Asia Ltd., Kowloon, Hong Kong; *U.S. Public*, pg. 1667
Miura, Mamoru, Chm. & Rep. Dir.--Tokyu Agency Inc., Tokyo, Japan; *Int'l*, pg. 1394
Miura, N., Pres.--Morinaga Nutritional Foods Europe S.A., Brussels, Belgium; *Int'l*, pg. 895
Miura, N. Brian, Pres.--Pentax Canada Inc., Mississauga, Canada; *Int'l*, pg. 85
Miura, Shozo, Pres.--Yamaichi France S.A., Paris, France; *Int'l*, pg. 1517
Miura, Takashi, Exec. V.P.--International Public Relations Co. Ltd., Tokyo, Japan; *Int'l*, pg. 1227
Miura, Yasuhide, Acting Mgr.--Kintetsu Intermodal Inc., San Ysidro, CA; *Int'l*, pg. 735
Miura, Yuichi, Chm. Bd.--A&T Corporation, Tokyo, Japan; *Int'l*, pg. 1393
Miwa, Kazunari, Chief Rep.--The Sakura Bank - Yangon Representative Office, Yangon, Myanmar; *Int'l*, pg. 1180
Miwa, Yuichiro, Chief Representative--Frankfurt Representative Office, Frankfurt/Main, Germany; *Int'l*, pg. 702
Miyagawa, Kazuya, Chief Oper. Officer--Honda Clio Shin Tokyo Co., Ltd., Tokyo, Japan; *Int'l*, pg. 634
Miyagawa, Masahiro, Pres.--Dun & Bradstreet Japan Ltd., Tokyo, Japan; *U.S. Public*, pg. 536
Miyagi, Kohtaro, Chm. Bd.--Canon Marketing Services Pte. Ltd., Singapore, Singapore; *Int'l*, pg. 263
Miyagoshi, Takeshi, Pres.--Kawasaki Heavy Industries (U.S.A.), Inc., New York, NY; *Int'l*, pg. 725
Miyahara, M., Exec. V.P. & Gen. Mgr.--Asahi Glass America, Inc., New York, NY; *Int'l*, pg. 84
Miyahara, Yoshihiko, Pres.-Japanese Div.--Nordson K.K., Tokyo, Japan; *U.S. Public*, pg. 1189
Miyaji, Toshio, Chief Oper. Officer--Toyota Deutschland GmbH, Cologne, Germany; *Int'l*, pg. 1413
Miyajima, Yoshinori, Gen. Mgr.--The Sumitomo Bank, Ltd.- Kowloon Branch, Kowloon, Hong Kong; *Int'l*, pg. 1309
Miyakawa, Kazuo, Chm.--Dentsu Europe Ltd.-London, London, United Kingdom; *Int'l*, pg. 393
Miyakawa, Kazuo, Area Dir.--Area Headquarters-EUROPE & MIDDLE EAST, London, United Kingdom; *Int'l*, pg. 393
Miyakawa, Kazuto, Pres.--Hakuhodo Australia Pty. Ltd., Sydney, Australia; *Int'l*, pg. 588
Miyakawa, Kazuya, Chief Oper. Officer--Honda Trading Corp., Tokyo, Japan; *Int'l*, pg. 634
Miyakawa, Y., Pres.--Datastream International (Japan) KK, Tokyo, Japan; *U.S. Public*, pg. 1326
Miyakawa, Yasutsugu, Pres.--Super Channel Joint Enterprise, Tokyo, Japan; *Int'l*, pg. 588
Miyake, Shojiro, Pres.--Honda Motor Europe Ltd., London, United Kingdom; *Int'l*, pg. 635
Miyake, T., Chief Oper. Officer--Scholl Japan Limited, Tokyo, Japan; *Int'l*, pg. 1210
Miyamoto, Hideki, Mng. Dir.--Sakura Finance Australia Limited, Sydney, Australia; *Int'l*, pg. 1180
Miyamoto, Hiroshi, Vice Chm.--The Siam Sanwa Industrial Credit Co., Ltd., Bangkok, Thailand; *Int'l*, pg. 1190
Miyamoto, Masanori, Pres.--NMB Electro Precision Inc., Miyagi, Japan; *Int'l*, pg. 868
Miyamoto, Susumu, Pres.--Mitsui & Co. (Canada) Ltd., Toronto, Canada; *Int'l*, pg. 880
Miyamura, Satoru, Dir.--The World Bank, Tokyo, Japan; *U.S. Private*, pg. 1189
Miyanaga, Kazuhori, Mng. Dir. & Gen. Mgr.--Takugin International (Asia) Ltd., Hong Kong, Hong Kong; *Int'l*, pg. 627
Miyanaga, Kazunori, Gen. Mgr.--The Hokkaido Takushoku Bank, Ltd.-Los Angeles Agency, Los Angeles, CA; *Int'l*, pg. 627
Miyanaga, Kazunori, Joint Gen. Mgr.--The Hokkaido Takushoku Bank, Ltd. (Hong Kong), Hong Kong, Hong Kong; *Int'l*, pg. 627
Miyaoka, Hideki, Pres.--Toto Kiki (H.K.) Ltd., Wan Chai, Hong Kong; *Int'l*, pg. 1410
Miyasaka, Juichiro, Chief Oper. Officer--Kyowa Hakko-West Coast Office, Newport Beach, CA; *Int'l*, pg. 778
Miyasaka, Katsuro, Pres.--Shin-Etsu Polymer Co. Ltd., Tokyo, Japan; *Int'l*, pg. 1234
Miyata, Nagayoshi, Chm.--Daiwa Europe (Deutschland) GmbH, Frankfurt/Main, Germany; *Int'l*, pg. 375
Miyata, Yoshihiko, Mng. Dir.--DKB Asia Limited, Central, Hong Kong; *Int'l*, pg. 361
Miyato, Toshiyuki, Gen. Mgr.--Bank of Yokohama London, London, United Kingdom; *Int'l*, pg. 159
Miyauchi, Tetsuzo, Mng. Dir.--Siam NEC Co., Ltd., Chon Buri, Thailand; *Int'l*, pg. 1239
Miyazaki, Yasufumi, Gen. Mgr.--Fuji Bank, Taipei Branch, Taipei, Taiwan; *Int'l*, pg. 520
Miyazawa, Hisao, Chief Rep.--Vienna Representative Office, Vienna, Austria; *Int'l*, pg. 520
Miyazu, Akira, Pres.--Matsushita Industrial de Baja California, S.A., Tijuana, Mexico; *Int'l*, pg. 847
Miyoshi, Ryuhei, Pres.--Thai Sakura Finance & Securities Co., Ltd., Bangkok, Thailand; *Int'l*, pg. 677
Mizanin, Michael, Sec. & Treas.--Graycor International Inc., Homewood, IL; *U.S. Private*, pg. 472
Mize, E. Gail, Exec. V.P.--Astec, Inc., Chattanooga, TN; *U.S. Public*, pg. 141
Mize, John, Jr., Pres. & Chief Exec. Officer--Blish-Mize Co., Atchison, KS; *U.S. Private*, pg. 335
Mizel, Bernard H., Chm. Bd. & Pres.--ABI Management, Inc., San Francisco, CA; *U.S. Public*, pg. 74
Mizele, Mary, Admin.--Hillhaven Convalescent Center Raleigh, Raleigh, NC; *U.S. Public*, pg. 1713
Mizobuchi, Yasuo, Mng. Dir.--Sumitomo International Finance Australia Limited, Sydney, Australia; *Int'l*, pg. 1310
Mizoguchi, Nobuyoshi, Gen. Mgr.--D International Inc., Seattle, WA; *Int'l*, pg. 364
Mizoguchi, Shiro, Pres.--Beijing Descente Co., Ltd., Beijing, China; *Int'l*, pg. 396
Mizomoto, Mark, Pres.--Universal Fasteners Inc., Lawrenceburg, KY; *Int'l*, pg. 1515
Mizukami, Tokugoro, Chief Opr. Officer--Hitachi Cable, Ltd., Tokyo, Japan; *Int'l*, pg. 621
Mizuma, Yuichi, Mgr.-Fin., Opers. & Production--McGraw-Hill Publishing Co.-Japan Ltd., Tokyo, Japan; *U.S. Public*, pg. 1072
Mizuno, Hiroshi, Pres.--Mizuno Handy Harman, Ltd., Tokyo, Japan; *U.S. Public*, pg. 780
Mizuno, Kosuke, Mng. Dir.--Hakuhodo Inc., Hiroshima, Japan; *Int'l*, pg. 587
Mizuno, Masato, Dir.--Mizuno (UK) Ltd., Wokingham, United Kingdom; *Int'l*, pg. 885
Mizuno, Takashi, Mng. Dir.--NEC Deutschland GmbH, Ismaning, Germany; *Int'l*, pg. 901
Mizuno, Y., Pres.--Tokuyama America Inc., San Mateo, CA; *Int'l*, pg. 1394
Mizusawa, Masatake, Pres.--Komatsu Asia & Pacific Pte. Ltd., Jurong, Singapore; *Int'l*, pg. 744
Mizushima, Shigeru, Pres.--Hoxan America Incorporated, Piscataway, NJ; *Int'l*, pg. 363
Mizutani, H., Chief Oper. Officer--Sanko-Stevens Chemical, Inc., Tokyo, Japan; *U.S. Public*, pg. 1466
Mizutani, Satoshi, Chief Oper. Officer--Comdisco Japan Inc., Osaka, Japan; *U.S. Public*, pg. 408
Mizutani, Takeo, Gen. Mgr.--H.B. Fuller Japan Co. Ltd., Hamamatsu, Japan; *U.S. Public*, pg. 687
Mizutani, Yoshihiro, Gen. Mgr.--Asahi Bank Singapore Branch, Singapore, Singapore; *Int'l*, pg. 82
Mizutari, Shunicki, Sr. V.P.--Mitsui Foods Export, Burlingame, CA; *Int'l*, pg. 879
Mjorndal, Ake, Chief Oper. Officer--Agro Barter United AB, Stockholm, Sweden; *Int'l*, pg. 708
Mladucky, Gene, Gen. Mgr.--Newly Weds Foods, Inc., Springdale, AR; *U.S. Private*, pg. 797
Mlnarik, Robert F., Pres. & Chief Exec. Officer--MACtac Morgan Adhesive Company, Stow, OH; *U.S. Public*, pg. 210
Mng. Dir..D., Admin.--Westlake Medical Center, Westlake Village, CA; *U.S. Public*, pg. 1697
Mnookin, Donald H., Gen. Mgr.--Corrugated Container Div.-Kansas City Plant, Liberty, MO; *U.S. Public*, pg. 1520
Mo, Kwoen Soon, Pres.--Ssangyong Australia Pty., Ltd., Sydney, Australia; *Int'l*, pg. 1291
Moak, Richard, Plant Mgr.--Industrial Bag Division - Arcadia Plant, Arcadia, LA; *U.S. Public*, pg. 1521
Moakley, Michael, Chm.--Philips Medical Systems North America Company, Shelton, CT; *Int'l*, pg. 1055
Moakley, Thomas J., Pres.--Graphic Instruments, East Greenwich, RI; *U.S. Public*, pg. 481
Moar, Jim, Pres. & Gen. Mgr.--DataCard Equipment, Minnetonka, MN; *U.S. Private*, pg. 312
Moberg, Per, Mng. Dir.--Emil Moestue as, Oslo, Norway; *Int'l*, pg. 460
Mobley, Dewey, Pres.--Amador Central Railroad Company, Jackson, CA; *U.S. Public*, pg. 736
Mobley, Dewey L., V.P.--Western Wood Prods. Mfg. Div., Portland, OR; *U.S. Public*, pg. 736
Mobley, Gary, Mgr.--Wilson Service Center, Wilson, NC; *U.S. Private*, pg. 214
Mochel, John, Pres.--5 Rubber Corporation, Kittanning, PA; *U.S. Public*, pg. 1504
Mochizuki, Yoshito, Pres.--American Isuzu Motors Inc., Whittier, CA; *Int'l*, pg. 692
Mock, Brian, Pres.--Mock Resources, Inc., Irvine, CA; *U.S. Private*, pg. 1175
Mockley, B.A., Pres.--Canal Refining Co., Tulsa, OK; *U.S. Private*, pg. 71
Mockley, B.A., Pres.--Cove Petroleum, Tulsa, OK; *U.S. Private*, pg. 71
Modaff, Ken, Gen. Mgr.--Acacia Technologies, Lisle, IL; *U.S. Public*, pg. 420
Model, John, Mng. Dir.--Kerry Ingredients UK Ltd., Aylesbury, United Kingdom; *Int'l*, pg. 732
Model, S. David, Dir.-Opers., North America--Airfoil Technologies International LLC, Cincinnati, OH; *U.S. Public*, pg. 1569
Moden, John, Mng. Dir.--Margetts Foods Limited, Tenbury, United Kingdom; *Int'l*, pg. 732
Modena, Goffred O., Pres.--Forem S.p.A., Milan, Italy; *U.S. Public*, pg. 46
Modjeski, R., Pres.-Scholl Sls.--Scholl U.S.A., Memphis, TN; *U.S. Public*, pg. 1438
Modjeski, R., Pres.--Plough U.S.A., Memphis, TN; *U.S. Public*, pg. 1438
Modlinski, Dan, Div. Mgr.--Transilwrap Company, Inc., Northlake, IL; *U.S. Private*, pg. 1097
Mody, N.R., Vice. Chm.--Tata Inc., New York, NY; *Int'l*, pg. 1356
Modzelewski, John F., Sr. Partner, Exec. V.P. & Gen. Mgr.--Fleishman-Hillard, Inc., Chicago, IL; *U.S. Private*, pg. 411
Moebius, Gordon, Dir.-Corp. Devel.--American Trans Air Execujet, Inc., Indianapolis, IN; *U.S. Public*, pg. 106
Moeckel, Merle, Product Mgr.--Amboy Specialty Foods, Dixon, IL; *U.S. Public*, pg. 490
Moeda, Antonio, Gen. Mgr.--Shell de Cabo Verde, Ilha do Sal, Cape Verde; *Int'l*, pg. 1137
Moehle, Walter, Mgr.--Micros Systems Deutschland, GmbH, Willich, Germany; *U.S. Public*, pg. 1107
Moehring, Edwin, Gen. Mgr.--NuArc Southeastern Div., Atlanta, GA; *U.S. Private*, pg. 809
Moehring, Hartmut, Dr., Pres. & Chief Oper. Officer--BASF Australia Ltd., Melbourne, Australia; *Int'l*, pg. 105
Moeller, John, Pres.--Simmons Juvenile Products Co., Inc., New London, WI; *U.S. Private*, pg. 1001
Moeller, Paul R., Pres.--Hercon Environmental Corporation, York, PA; *U.S. Public*, pg. 802
Moeller, Sverker, Pres.--Kvaerner Korea Ltd., Choryang, Korea; *Int'l*, pg. 767
Moeller, Sverker, Pres.--Kvaerner Korea Ltd., Pusan, Korea; *Int'l*, pg. 772
Moellering, John, Exec. V.P.--UNC Aviation Services, Inc., Annapolis, MD; *U.S. Public*, pg. 710
Moelling, Lother, Mng. Dir.--Thermon Deutschland GmbH, Burbach, Germany; *U.S. Private*, pg. 1081
Moen, Arne, Mng. Dir.--Shell of Stjoerdal, Stjoerdal, Norway; *Int'l*, pg. 1139
Moen, John, Gen. Mgr.--KEBC-AM, Oklahoma City, OK; *U.S. Public*, pg. 384
Moen, John, Gen. Mgr.--KTST-FM, Oklahoma City, OK; *U.S. Public*, pg. 384
Moenich, Glenn, Pres.--Forest City Commercial Construction Company, Inc., Cleveland, OH; *U.S. Public*, pg. 668
Moerck, Rudi E., V.P. & Gen. Mgr.--Salsbury Chemicals, Inc., Charles City, IA; *U.S. Public*, pg. 297
Moere, B.W.V., Mng. Dir.--Taylor Woodrow Services Ltd., Southall, United Kingdom; *Int'l*, pg. 1359
Moerne, Tor, Mng. Dir.--Maritime Protection A/S, Kristiansand, Norway; *U.S. Public*, pg. 1125
Moersch, Kevin P., Pres. & Chief Exec. Officer--MFS Network Technologies, Inc., Omaha, NE; *U.S. Public*, pg. 1779
Moffett, Ken, Chief Oper. Officer--Bay Park, Inc., Oakland, CA; *U.S. Private*, pg. 43
Moffitt, Christopher J., Grp. Dir.--Diamond Technology Partners, Chicago, IL; *U.S. Public*, pg. 1424
Mogan, Jim, Pres.--Olga Div., Bridgeport, CT; *U.S. Public*, pg. 1738
Moger, Stan, Pres.--SFM Entertainment, New York, NY; *U.S. Private*, pg. 957
Mogg, Jim, Pres.--Duke Energy Field Services, Inc., Denver, CO; *U.S. Public*, pg. 534
Mogi, Takemi, Chief Oper. Officer--Nippon Oil (Australia) Pty. Limited, Sydney, Australia; *Int'l*, pg. 937
Mogi, Yoshifumi, Pres.--TOHO America International Inc., New York, NY; *Int'l*, pg. 1390
Mogler, John G., Pres.--McLean Midwest, Champlin, MN; *U.S. Public*, pg. 1791
Moguol, Christiou, Chief Oper. Officer--Banque Generale du Luxembourg S.A., Milan, Italy; *Int'l*, pg. 162
Mohacsi, Bela, Gen. Mgr.--Cad Server Ltd., Budapest, Hungary; *U.S. Public*, pg. 1031
Mohally, Bryan, Mng. Dir.--Janssen Pharmaceutical Limited, Little Island, Ireland; *U.S. Public*, pg. 930
Mohamed, Noor Zulia, Dir.--Tourism Malaysia - Milan Office, Milan, Italy; *Int'l*, pg. 833
Mohamed, Syed Tamin, Reg. Dir.--Sime Darby Berhad Malaysia Region, Kuala Lumpur, Malaysia; *Int'l*, pg. 1250
Mohammed, A. Bin, Mng. Dir.--Tiram Kimia, Kuala Lumpur, Malaysia; *Int'l*, pg. 1140
Mohan, D.M., Pres.--The Alton & Southern Railway Co., Saint Louis, MO; *U.S. Public*, pg. 1668
Mohan, Madireddi C., V.P. & Gen. Mgr.-Portugal--Procter & Gamble Portugal, Matosinhos, Portugal; *U.S. Public*, pg. 1332
Mohan, Vishnu, Country Mgr.--Standard Chartered Bank Ghana Ltd., Accra, Ghana; *Int'l*, pg. 1294
Mohd, Idros, Dir.--Tourism Malaysia - Frankfurt Office, Frankfurt/Main, Germany; *Int'l*, pg. 833
Mohen, Frank, Mgr.-Office--Woodward-Clyde, Saint Leonards, Australia; *U.S. Public*, pg. 1658
Mohl, A.M., Gen. Mgr.--ANZ Managed Investments Limited, Sydney, Australia; *Int'l*, pg. 98
Mohlar, Perry, G.M.--Gillette Industries, Ltd., Isleworth, United Kingdom; *U.S. Public*, pg. 745
Mohme, David, Chief Oper. Officer--Directory Distributing Associates, Inc., Scarborough, Canada; *U.S. Private*, pg. 334
Mohr, David G., Pres.--ITC Flavor & Seasoning Div., Elyria, OH; *U.S. Public*, pg. 459
Mohr, H.J., Mng. Dir.--Rhein-Chemie Rheinau GmbH, Mannheim, Germany; *Int'l*, pg. 174
Mohr, Larry, Pres.--The Weitz Company, Inc., Phoenix, AZ; *U.S. Private*, pg. 1161
Mohri, Hiroshi, Terminal Mgr.--Kintetsu World Express Inc., Seatac, WA; *Int'l*, pg. 735
Mohri, K., Mng. Dir.--Bally Japan Ltd., Osaka, Japan; *Int'l*, pg. 997
Moir, Wayne, V.P. & Gen. Mgr.--Quebecor Printing PE&E, Etobicoke, Canada; *Int'l*, pg. 1077
Moisio, Jouko, V.P.--Valmet Corporation Service Development, Jyvaskyla, Finland; *Int'l*, pg. 1449
Moisio, Teemu, Mgr.--Honkalahti Sawmill and Planing Mill, Joutseno, Finland; *Int'l*, pg. 456
Moisset, Jacques, Chief Oper. Officer--CXR SA, Abondant, France; *U.S. Public*, pg. 1108
Moitra, Arun, Gen. Mgr.--Bitopi Advertising Ltd., Dhaka, Bangladesh; *U.S. Private*, pg. 184
Mojo, Francisco, Chief Oper. Officer--Pharmacia & Upjohn S.A., Barcelona, Spain; *Int'l*, pg. 1050
Mok, C.W., Gen. Mgr.--Standard Motor Products Hong Kong Limited, Sha Tin, Hong Kong; *U.S. Public*, pg. 1503
Mok, Julian, Gen. Mgr.--Spartus (HK) Ltd., Kowloon, Hong Kong; *Int'l*, pg. 595
Mokhtari, Shawn, Pres.--National Educational International Corp., Irvine, CA; *U.S. Public*, pg. 784
Mokley, Jack, Office Mgr.--Korn/Ferry International, Los Angeles, CA; *U.S. Private*, pg. 633
Moksnes, Jan, Pres.--Norwegian Contractors A/S, Stabekk, Norway; *Int'l*, pg. 42
Moksnes, Knut, Pres.--Aquatic Animal Health, Oslo, Norway; *U.S. Public*, pg. 58

Molan, John C., Mng. Dir.--McCormick (UK) Plc., Haddenham, United Kingdom; *U.S. Public*, pg. 1067
Molari, Russell E., Pres.--Scientific Systems Division, Redwood City, CA; *U.S. Public*, pg. 1516
Molenaar, J.C., Gen. Mgr.--Senior Engineering TIFT GmbH, Boenningstedt, Germany; *Int'l*, pg. 1223
Molenaar, Kelly, Pres.--Concept Manufacturing Company, Inc., Plainwell, MI; *U.S. Private*, pg. 548
Molenar, Nico, Mng. Dir.--Computer Task Group Europe B.V., Amsterdam, Netherlands; *U.S. Public*, pg. 423
Moles, Robert T., Pres. & Chief Exec. Officer--Century 21 Real Estate Corp., Parsippany, NJ; *U.S. Public*, pg. 321
Moletto, Roberto, Mng. Dir.--Miller Europa S.p.A., Milan, Italy; *U.S. Public*, pg. 869
Molin, Per, Chief Oper. Officer--Avesta AB, Stockholm, Sweden; *Int'l*, pg. 708
Molina, Alfonso, Mgr.--Grupo Termoindustrial ECA, S.A. de C.V., Santa Clara, Mexico; *U.S. Private*, pg. 361
Molina, Antonio Castro, Pres.--Grupo Carpenter S.A. de C.V., Tlalnepantla, Mexico; *U.S. Public*, pg. 308
Molina, Antonio Pareja, Vice Pres.--ENHER - E.N. Hidroelectrica Del Ribagorzana, S.A., Barcelona, Spain; *Int'l*, pg. 1224
Molina, Oscar, Plant Mgr.--AlliedSignal Automotive Ltda., Sao Paulo, Brazil; *U.S. Public*, pg. 52
Molinari, Gianluigi, Mng. Dir.--SIELTE, S.p.A., Rome, Italy; *Int'l*, pg. 1370
Molinari, Mike, Mgr.-Opers.--UNC Accessory Services-New York, Bay Shore, NY; *U.S. Public*, pg. 710
Molinari, Philip, Pres.--The Arrow Shirt Company, New York, NY; *Int'l*, pg. 194
Molineus, Hasso A., Resident Rep.--The World Bank, Tashkent, Uzbekistan; *U.S. Private*, pg. 1190
Moliterno, L.J., Pres.--Ajax Magnethermic Canada Ltd., Ajax, Canada; *Int'l*, pg. 113
Molitor, Robert F., Pres.--Zone VI Studios, Inc., Newfane, VT; *U.S. Private*, pg. 202
Molkenthin, Achim, Mng. Dir.--ARIDO Abdichtungs-Gesellschaft, Berlin, Germany; *Int'l*, pg. 423
Moll, Hector Perez, Gen. Mgr.--Laboratorios Bristol de Venezuela, S.A., Caracas, Venezuela; *U.S. Public*, pg. 256
Moll, Klaus, Pres.--Babcock-BSH AG, Bad Hersfeld, Germany; *Int'l*, pg. 399
Moll, Ted, Pres.--Aircap Industries Corp., Verona, MS; *U.S. Private*, pg. 688
Mollard, Peter, Pres.--Lafarge Materials, Toronto, Canada; *Int'l*, pg. 789
Moller-Christensen, Hans, Mng. Dir.--Nykredit Bank A/S, Copenhagen, Denmark; *Int'l*, pg. 993
Moller, Bernard, Pres.--Mackintosh of New England, Co., New York, NY; *U.S. Public*, pg. 233
Moller, Gerhard, Mng. Dir.--David, Munich, Germany; *U.S. Public*, pg. 787
Mollison, Ric B., Mng. Dir.--Elders Limited, Adelaide, Australia; *Int'l*, pg. 500
Mollison, Richard, Acting Mng. Dir.--K-C do Brasil Ltda., Sao Paulo, Brazil; *U.S. Public*, pg. 959
Molloy, B. Ann, Gen. Mgr.--Canterbury Hotel, Washington, DC; *U.S. Private*, pg. 1067
Molloy, Charles D., Exec. V.P.--Angelica Image Apparel, Saint Louis, MO; *U.S. Public*, pg. 113
Molloy, Peter, Pres.--MJB Rice Company, Union City, CA; *Int'l*, pg. 917
Molman, D., Pres.--Admedia bv, Amstelveen, Netherlands; *Int'l*, pg. 1445
Moloney, David, Mng. Dir.--Gelman Ireland Ltd., Dublin, Ireland; *U.S. Public*, pg. 1253
Moloney, Sharon, V.P. & Gen. Mgr.--WPMI-TV, Mobile, AL; *U.S. Public*, pg. 385
Moloney, Tom, Chief Exec. Officer--EMAP Consumer Magazines, London, United Kingdom; *Int'l*, pg. 451
Molstad, Bjorn, Chief Oper. Officer--Electrolux Constructor A/S, Oslo, Norway; *Int'l*, pg. 443
Molta, Guillermo, Mng. Dir.--Johnson & Johnson del Ecuador S.A., Guayaquil, Ecuador; *U.S. Public*, pg. 930
Molteni, Renzo, Chief Fin. Officer--Olivetti Corporation of Japan, Tokyo, Japan; *Int'l*, pg. 1003
Moltz, J.E., Chm., Pres., Chief Exec. Officer--C.J. Lawrence, Morgan Grenfell Inc., New York, NY; *Int'l*, pg. 405
Molvar, Allen E., Pres.--Handy & Harman Electronic Materials Corp., North Attleboro, MA; *U.S. Public*, pg. 780
Molvidson, Richard, Pres.--AROS Fondkommission AB, Stockholm, Sweden; *Int'l*, pg. 7
Molyneux, Greg, Mgr.-Intl. Sls., Middle East--Royal Skandia Life Assurance Ltd., Nicosia, Cyprus; *Int'l*, pg. 1257
Molyneux, Michael, Pres.--Cytec Fiberite Inc., Tempe, AZ; *U.S. Public*, pg. 471
Molyneux, Richard A., Chm. Bd., Pres. & Chief Exec. Officer--Key Bank of Maine, Portland, ME; *U.S. Public*, pg. 954
Momoi, Katsuo, Mng. Dir.--Hakuhodo Inc., Matsuyama, Japan; *Int'l*, pg. 587
Momoi, Katsuo, Mng. Dir.--Hakuhodo Inc., Okinawa, Japan; *Int'l*, pg. 587
Momose, Nabuo, Area Dir.--Area Headquarters-THE AMERICAS, New York, NY; *Int'l*, pg. 393
Momose, Nobuo, Chm. & Pres.--Dentsu USA Inc.-New York, New York, NY; *Int'l*, pg. 393
Momot, David E., Pres. & Chief Exec. Officer--G.E. Lighting Ltd., Enfield, United Kingdom; *U.S. Public*, pg. 713
Monaco, Joseph, Chief Oper. Officer--Dover Chemical Corp., Dover, OH; *U.S. Private*, pg. 553
Monaco, Ricardo, Chief Oper. Officer--Tefal Italia S.p.A., Milan, Italy; *Int'l*, pg. 568
Monaghan, A.S., Mgr.--Vancouver Island Stevedoring Co. Ltd., Nanaimo, Canada; *Int'l*, pg. 828
Monaghan, David G., Jr., V.P.-Fin.--GTE Government Systems Corporation, Needham, MA; *U.S. Public*, pg. 696
Monaghan, Nancy, Pres. & Publr.--Public Opinion, Chambersburg, PA; *U.S. Public*, pg. 700
Monahan, David, Gen. Mgr.--Kredietbank London Branch, London, United Kingdom; *Int'l*, pg. 760
Monahan, John, Mng. Dir.--Triumph Releasing Corporation - New England Territory, Boston, MA; *Int'l*, pg. 1282
Monahan, Michael T., Pres. & Chief Oper. Officer--Comerica Bank Michigan, Detroit, MI; *U.S. Public*, pg. 409
Monahan, Tom, Publr.--ACBJ Business Publications, Inc., Louisville, KY; *U.S. Private*, pg. 19
Monarca, Giulio Cesare, Dir.--Banca d'America e d'Italia S.p.a. (Livorno), Livorno, Italy; *Int'l*, pg. 403
Monastear, Chris, Chief Exec. Officer--Polyphase Instruments Co., Fort Washington, PA; *U.S. Public*, pg. 1315
Monastra, Richard, Chief Oper. Officer--Chicago Boat Yard, Inc., Chicago, IL; *U.S. Private*, pg. 194
Monauni, Christopher K., Pres.--Baker-CAC, Inc., Houston, TX; *U.S. Public*, pg. 166
Monbaron, Maurice, Mng. Dir.--Credit Lyonnais Suisse SA, Geneva, Switzerland; *Int'l*, pg. 344
Monchaux, Philippe, Chief Oper. Officer--Societe de Transmissions Automatiques, Barlin, France; *Int'l*, pg. 1102
Monchein, Robert F., Pres.--Forest City Land Group, Cleveland, OH; *U.S. Public*, pg. 668
Monchein, Robert F., Pres.--Sunrise Development Co., Cleveland, OH; *U.S. Public*, pg. 669
Monckton, Rosamond, Pres.--Tiffany & Co., London, United Kingdom; *U.S. Public*, pg. 1609
Moncrief, Lee E., Chm. Bd., Pres. & Chief Exec. Officer--SouthTrust Bank, Shoals, Florence, AL; *U.S. Public*, pg. 1492
Monday, John, Pres. & Gen. Mgr.--Multi Metals Div., Louisville, KY; *U.S. Public*, pg. 575
Mondoux, A.W., Pres.--Heron Industries Limited, Waterloo, Canada; *Int'l*, pg. 1150
Mondragon, Naomi, Admin.--Southwest Senior Care Center, Las Vegas, NM; *U.S. Public*, pg. 838
Mondville, M. Wayne, V.P.-Comml. Real Estate Services--Royal LePage - British Columbia Office, Vancouver, Canada; *Int'l*, pg. 1143
Monerris, Antonio, Chief Oper. Officer--Ceras Alex S.A., Madrid, Spain; *Int'l*, pg. 611
Monerris, Antonio, Partner & Mgr.--Vinizius/Young & Rubicam, S.A., Barcelona, Spain; *U.S. Private*, pg. 1199
Moneti, Gino, Gen. Mgr.--AlliedSignal Automotive Italia S.p.A., Crema, Italy; *U.S. Public*, pg. 53
Money, Kent, Pres.--Zion's Securities Corp., Salt Lake City, UT; *U.S. Private*, pg. 327
Monfort, Bryan, Gen. Mgr.--Lawry's The Prime Rib, Beverly Hills, CA; *U.S. Private*, pg. 654
Monge, Dimitri, Pres. & Chief Oper. Officer--Airtex Products, Fairfield, IL; *U.S. Private*, pg. 1113
Mongechazarria, Eduardo, Sls. Mgr.--Otis Mexicana, S.A., Reynosa, Mexico; *U.S. Public*, pg. 777
Monger, Stephen, Chm. Bd., Pres. & Chief Exec. Officer--Regions Bank/Huntsville, Huntsville, AL; *U.S. Public*, pg. 1372
Mongiello, James, Pres.--Larse Corporation, Santa Clara, CA; *Int'l*, pg. 710
Monie, Alain, Mng. Dir.--AlliedSignal Aerospace Service Corporation, Tokyo, Japan; *U.S. Public*, pg. 52
Monikan, John, Pres.--Liberty House, Inc., Honolulu, HI; *U.S. Private*, pg. 578
Monikan, John, Pres.--Liberty House, Honolulu, HI; *U.S. Private*, pg. 578
Monis, Tony, Pres.--Stusser Electric Company, Seattle, WA; *U.S. Private*, pg. 265
Monjardin, Sergio Lopez, Gen. Mgr.--PAXAR De Mexico, S.A. de C.V., Mexico, Mexico; *U.S. Public*, pg. 1266
Monk, Albert C., III, Pres. & Chief Exec. Officer--DIMON, International, Inc., Farmville, NC; *U.S. Public*, pg. 510
Monk, B., Mng. Dir.--Ashley & Rock Ltd., Ulverston, United Kingdom; *Int'l*, pg. 1511
Monk, Douglas R., Pres.--William L. Bonnell Co., Inc., Newnan, GA; *U.S. Public*, pg. 1634
Monker, Josephine, Chief Exec. Officer--Elsevier Opleidingen BV, Zwijndrecht, Netherlands; *Int'l*, pg. 1094
Monker, Josephine, Chief Exec. Officer--Koninklijke PBNA BV, Arnhem, Netherlands; *Int'l*, pg. 1100
Monker, Josephine, Chief Exec. Officer--CBBM BV, Zwijndrecht, Netherlands; *Int'l*, pg. 1100
Monker, Josephine, Chief Exec. Officer--Nederlands Studiecentrum, Vlaardingen, Netherlands; *Int'l*, pg. 1100
Monks, Harlan, V.P. & Gen. Mgr.--Durant Electronics, Inc., Durant, OK; *U.S. Private*, pg. 1047
Monks, Jeff, Gen. Mgr.--Dowty Tecmold, Marsa, Malta; *Int'l*, pg. 1338
Monks, Paul D., Pres.--NBD Securities, Inc., Detroit, MI; *U.S. Public*, pg. 628
Monneraud, Yves, Distr. Mgr.--Milchem Gabon S.A.R.L., Port Gentil, Gabon; *U.S. Public*, pg. 167
Monnier, Jacques, Chm. & Mng. Dir.--Groupe Usine Nouvelle, Paris, France; *Int'l*, pg. 239
Monnier, Nicolas, Pres. & Mng. Dir.--Alice, Paris, France; *U.S. Private*, pg. 678
Monohan, J.J., Mng. Dir.--Amoco Chemicals Pty. Ltd., Liverpool, Australia; *U.S. Public*, pg. 102
Monohan, Kevin, Plant Mgr.--Baldor Electric Company, Woodinville, WA; *U.S. Public*, pg. 169
Monopoli, Bill, Pres. & Publr.--The Times Herald Co., Port Huron, MI; *U.S. Public*, pg. 701
Monre, W.C., Gen. Mgr.--Wyeth Laboratuvarlari A.S., Istanbul, Turkey; *U.S. Public*, pg. 82
Monribot, Joel, Pres.--Kaufman and Broad Maisons Individuelles, Paris, France; *U.S. Public*, pg. 945
Monroe, Debbie, V.P.-Landmark Communications--Careerweb, Norfolk, VA; *U.S. Private*, pg. 647
Monroe, Gordon, V.P.--Mead Packaging Proprietary Ltd., Sydney, Australia; *U.S. Public*, pg. 1077
Monroe, James J., V.P. & Gen. Mgr.--Fox Valley Steel & Wire Co., Hortonville, WI; *U.S. Public*, pg. 956
Monroe, Stuart, Mng. Dir.--EuroChem Division, Liverpool, United Kingdom; *U.S. Public*, pg. 166
Monroy, Olga T., V.P.-Fin. & Admin.--Leo Burnett Publicidade, Ltda., Sao Paulo, Brazil; *U.S. Private*, pg. 185
Monseu, Andre, Mng. Dir.--Aluminium Europe S.A., En Abrege: "Aleurope S.A.", Ghlin, Belgium; *U.S. Public*, pg. 1386
Monshouwer, G., Gen. Mgr.--De La Rue Systems BV, Vianen, Netherlands; *Int'l*, pg. 387
Monson, Edward, Plant Mgr.--Huls America Inc., Cincinnati, OH; *Int'l*, pg. 1455
Monsour, Michael, Pres.--Market Place Print, Inc., Pittsburgh, PA; *U.S. Private*, pg. 701
Monsu, Phillipe, Gen. Mgr.--Dynetcom GmbH, Friedrichsdorf, Germany; *Int'l*, pg. 425
Mont, Stuart, Pres.--Recoton Canada Ltd., Markham, Canada; *U.S. Public*, pg. 1369
Montador, Paul, Pres.--Johnson & Johnson Medical Products Inc., Peterborough, Canada; *U.S. Public*, pg. 931
Montag, Alfred, Gen. Mgr.--Cross Huller, Fraser, MI; *Int'l*, pg. 1389
Montagne, Jean, Mng. Dir.--Kleber Reifen und Technische Gummiwaren AG, Saint Ingbert, Germany; *Int'l*, pg. 322
Montague, L. D., V.P. & Gen. Mgr.--Missile Systems Division, Sunnyvale, CA; *U.S. Public*, pg. 1009
Montalbano, Anthony, Pres.--Mortgage Guarantee & Title Co., Providence, RI; *U.S. Public*, pg. 626
Montanaro, David M., Pres.--NEC Business Communication Systems (East), Inc., East Syracuse, NY; *Int'l*, pg. 900
Montaner, Fernando, Chief Oper. Officer--BHF-Bank Representative Office, Mexico, Mexico; *Int'l*, pg. 120
Montealegis, Maria, Pres.--Caribbean Foreign Trade Corporation, Miami, FL; *Int'l*, pg. 279
Monteiro, Antonio Vieira, Chm. Bd.--Banco Luso Espanol S.A., Madrid, Spain; *Int'l*, pg. 251
Monteiro, Joe, Mng. Dir.--Loctite Co. de Mexico, S.A. de C.V., Mexico, Mexico; *Int'l*, pg. 611
Monteiro, R., Mgr.--Verbatim do Amazonas Industrial Ltd., Manaus, Brazil; *U.S. Public*, pg. 552
Montella, Luigi, Chief Exec. Officer--Sirti, Milan, Italy; *Int'l*, pg. 1362
Montellini, Giancarlo, Mng. Dir.--Diavia S.p.A., Molinella, Italy; *U.S. Public*, pg. 1691
Montenegro, Cesar, Mng. Dir.--Sulzer de Venezuala S.A., Caracas, Venezuela; *Int'l*, pg. 1306
Montermini, Giuseppe, Mng. Dir.--Repres. Off. Intern. Trade Center, Moscow, Russia; *Int'l*, pg. 1004
Montero, Fernan, Chm. & Chief Exec. Officer-Europe--Young & Rubicam Holdings Ltd., London, United Kingdom; *U.S. Private*, pg. 1199
Montero, Santiago, Editor--Floor Covering Weekly, Garden City, NY; *U.S. Private*, pg. 516
Montesinos, K., Pres.--Square D Company Andina S.A., Quito, Ecuador; *Int'l*, pg. 1209
Montez, Victor, Branch Mgr.--Jaco Electronics, Yorba Linda, CA; *U.S. Public*, pg. 920
Montezemolo, Gianni, Sr. Exec. V.P.-Europe--Johnson Wax S.p.A., Milan, Italy; *U.S. Private*, pg. 593
Montfort, Frank W., Pres.--WPI Transportation, Inc., Pasadena, TX; *U.S. Public*, pg. 71
Montfort, Frank W., Pres.--WPI Waste Carriers, Inc., Houston, TX; *U.S. Public*, pg. 71
Montfort, Richard L., Pres. & Chief Oper. Officer--ConAgra Red Meat Companies, Greeley, CO; *U.S. Public*, pg. 427
Montgomery, B.K., Mng. Dir.--GKN Wheels, Telford, United Kingdom; *Int'l*, pg. 535
Montgomery, B.K., Mng. Dir.--GKN Wheels Nagbol A/S, Lunderskov, Denmark; *Int'l*, pg. 535
Montgomery, David, Gen. Mgr.--Barton's of Lepanto, Lepanto, AR; *U.S. Private*, pg. 119
Montgomery, George, Pres. & Chief Exec. Officer--Taylor Made Golf Co. Inc., Carlsbad, CA; *Int'l*, pg. 1181
Montgomery, Jeffrey A., Chief Oper. Officer & Exec. V.P.--Washington Square Securities, Minneapolis, MN; *U.S. Public*, pg. 1376
Montgomery, Mike, Sr. V.P.--Law Companies Group, Atlanta, GA; *U.S. Private*, pg. 653
Montgomery, R., Chief Exec. Officer--Trench Electric, Montreal, Canada; *Int'l*, pg. 113
Montgomery, Roberta, Chief Oper. Officer--The Tearoom in Utica Square, Inc., Tulsa, OK; *U.S. Public*, pg. 808
Montgomery, Scott, Pres.--Technicomp, Inc., Cleveland, OH; *U.S. Public*, pg. 260
Montgoris, William J., Chief Oper. Officer--Bear, Stearns & Co. Inc., New York, New York, NY; *U.S. Public*, pg. 198
Monthan, Erkki, Mng. Dir.--Merita Bank Ltd.-Tallinn Branch, Tallinn, Estonia; *Int'l*, pg. 859
Monti, Peter C., Pres.--Land Span Inc., Norcross, GA; *U.S. Private*, pg. 1153
Montiegel, James, Pres.--Stride Rite Children's Group, Inc.-Retail Div., Lexington, MA; *U.S. Public*, pg. 1525
Montrone, Paul M., Chm. Bd., Pres. & Chief Exec. Officer--Fisher Scientific International, Hampton, NH; *U.S. Private*, pg. 658
Montuori, Mario, Mng. Dir.--Johnson & Johnson Taiwan Ltd., Taipei, Taiwan; *U.S. Public*, pg. 931
Monus, Mark, Gen. Mgr.--Orwell Plant, Orwell, OH; *U.S. Private*, pg. 1044
Monza, Roberto, Dir. Gen.--BAI Factoring S.p.A., Milan, Italy; *Int'l*, pg. 403
Monzini, C., Mng. Dir.--Pignone France S.a.r.l., Paris, France; *Int'l*, pg. 991
Mooberry, D.D., Grp. V.P.--Du Pont Medical Products, Wilmington, DE; *U.S. Public*, pg. 531
Moodie, George, Divisional Dir.--N.G. Bailey & Co. Ltd.-Aberdeen Branch, Aberdeen, United Kingdom; *Int'l*, pg. 132
Moodie, Richard, Chief Oper. Officer--Kraftmaid Cabinetry, Inc., Middlefield, OH; *U.S. Public*, pg. 1053
Moodie, Richard, Chief Oper. Officer--Kraftmaid Trucking, Inc., Middlefield, OH; *U.S. Public*, pg. 1053
Moody, Bill, Pres.--Coast Fed Services, Chatsworth, CA; *U.S. Public*, pg. 389

Moody, Dan, V.P. & Gen. Mgr.--Perfect Circle Products Div., Richmond, IN; *U.S. Public*, pg. 479
Moody, Dan, Plant Superintendant--General Shale Products Corp., Somerset, VA; *Int'l*, pg. 844
Moody, Jeffrey A., Pres. & Chief Concept Officer--Kentucky Fried Chicken Corporation (KFC), Louisville, KY; *U.S. Public*, pg. 1636
Moody, Marilyn J., Pres.--Ikon Office Solutions-North California, Sacramento, CA; *U.S. Public*, pg. 863
Moody, Richard S., Regional Pres.--First Tennessee Bank - Franklin, Franklin, TN; *U.S. Public*, pg. 639
Moody, Ross R., Chm. Bd.--NWL Financial, Inc., Austin, TX; *U.S. Public*, pg. 1161
Moody, Ross R., Chm. Bd. & Chief Exec. Officer--NWL Services, Inc., Austin, TX; *U.S. Public*, pg. 1161
Moog, G., Plant Mgr.--Wissembourg Factory, Wissembourg, France; *Int'l*, pg. 894
Mookerjee, C.K., Chief Oper. Officer--MSA India Limited, Calcutta, India; *U.S. Public*, pg. 1115
Moon, Alan C., Pres.--TransAlta Enterprises Corporation, Calgary, Canada; *Int'l*, pg. 1416
Moon, Craig, Publr.--Tennessean Newspapers, Inc., Nashville, TN; *U.S. Public*, pg. 701
Moon, Don, Pres.--Tandy Leather Co., Fort Worth, TX; *U.S. Public*, pg. 1561
Moon, H.U., Pres.--Electronic Systems Packaging Corp., Rancho Dominguez, CA; *U.S. Private*, pg. 370
Moon, J.L., Pres.--American Chrome & Chemicals, Inc., Corpus Christi, TX; *Int'l*, pg. 598
Moon, Scott, Mng. Dir.--Service Motor Co., Stevens Point, WI; *U.S. Private*, pg. 986
Moon, W.T., V.P. & Gen. Mgr.--Tennessee Div., Lebanon, TN; *Int'l*, pg. 1243
Moon, Yong-dal, Chief Rep.--The Export-Import Bank of Korea, Jakarta, Indonesia; *Int'l*, pg. 467
Moonen, R.T.M., Mgr.--ING Bank Antwerp, Mortsel, Belgium; *Int'l*, pg. 649
Mooney, Michael M., Pres. & Chief Exec. Officer--Key Bank of Idaho, Boise, ID; *U.S. Public*, pg. 954
Mooney, Paul, Chief Oper. Officer--Novo Nordisk Pharmaceuticals Ltd., Dublin, Ireland; *Int'l*, pg. 988
Mooney, Robert W., Exec. V.P.--Tower Group International, New York, NY; *U.S. Public*, pg. 1071
Mooney, Stuart A., Pres. & Chief Oper. Officer--Vernon Rentals & Leasing Inc., Toronto, Canada; *Int'l*, pg. 559
Mooney, Tim, Chief Exec. Officer--HIH America, Irvine, CA; *U.S. Private*, pg. 153
Moonves, Leslie, Pres. & Exec. V.P.-CBS--CBS Entertainment, Los Angeles, CA; *U.S. Public*, pg. 274
Moor, Chris, Gen. Mgr.--BHP Steel Building Products (Thailand) Ltd., Pathum Thani, Thailand; *Int'l*, pg. 226
Moor, Vic, Mgr.--Australian Guarantee Corporation Limited - A.C.T., Canberra, Australia; *Int'l*, pg. 1496
Mooratoff, George, Mng. Dir.--Paramount Pictures (Australia) Pty. Ltd., Sydney, Australia; *U.S. Private*, pg. 777
Moore, Alan, Pres.--Dahlberg Sciences, Ltd., Kitchener, Canada; *U.S. Public*, pg. 194
Moore, Ann S., Pres.--People, New York, NY; *U.S. Public*, pg. 1613
Moore, B.F., Pres.--Meggitt USA, Inc., Manchester, NH; *Int'l*, pg. 853
Moore, B.L., Pres. & Chief Exec. Officer--Chep USA, Orlando, FL; *Int'l*, pg. 211
Moore, Bob, Chief Oper. Officer--Atlas Roofing Corp., Ardmore, OK; *U.S. Private*, pg. 96
Moore, Bob, Div. Reg. Mgr.--BHP Wire Products, Five Dock, Australia; *Int'l*, pg. 226
Moore, Bob, V.P.--Publix Super Markets, Inc., Atlanta, GA; *U.S. Private*, pg. 894
Moore, Brad, Pres.--Signboard Hill Productions, Kansas City, MO; *U.S. Private*, pg. 496
Moore, Bruce, Branch Mgr.--Devoe & Raynolds, Salt Lake City, UT; *Int'l*, pg. 663
Moore, Charles, Mng. Dir.--Jardine Fleming Australia Limited, Sydney, Australia; *Int'l*, pg. 494
Moore, Chester W., Pres.--Enkel Corporation, Rockford, IL; *U.S. Public*, pg. 170
Moore, Christopher S., Mng. Dir.--Rigby-Maryland (Stainless) Ltd., Liversedge, United Kingdom; *U.S. Public*, pg. 780
Moore, Cleon E., Chm. Bd.--The Citizens Bank of Cochran, Cochran, GA; *U.S. Public*, pg. 1549
Moore, Colin, Editor--Southern Outdoors Magazine, Montgomery, AL; *U.S. Private*, pg. 106
Moore, Dan, Mgr.-Natl. Accts.--Sole Control, Evanston, IL; *U.S. Public*, pg. 1369
Moore, Dan, Chief Exec. Officer--SEE Technologies Inc., Fremont, CA; *U.S. Public*, pg. 1421
Moore, Dave, Chief Oper. Officer--Women's Clothing Division, New York, NY; *U.S. Private*, pg. 998
Moore, Dave, Reg. Mgr.--M/D Totco Instrumentation, Aberdeen, United Kingdom; *U.S. Public*, pg. 1709
Moore, David, Plant Mgr.--Liberty-Penn Div., Jamesville, NC; *Int'l*, pg. 340
Moore, David, Pres.--Kelley Atlantic, LTD, Ajax, Canada; *U.S. Private*, pg. 613
Moore, Don, Plant Mgr.--Hydro Conduit Corp., Baltimore, MD; *Int'l*, pg. 245
Moore, Don, Gen. Mgr.--NBS Card Services, Mississauga, Canada; *Int'l*, pg. 898
Moore, E. Keith, Resident V.P.--Southeastern Regional Office, Alpharetta, GA; *U.S. Private*, pg. 224
Moore, Ed, Gen. Mgr.--Poe & Brown of Florida, Kissimmee, FL; *U.S. Public*, pg. 1312
Moore, Frank, Pres. & Gen. Mgr.--Indiana Broadcasting Co. (WANE), Fort Wayne, IN; *U.S. Public*, pg. 11
Moore, Frank J., Mgr.--Lower Bucks Cablevision, Inc., Levittown, PA; *U.S. Public*, pg. 1611
Moore, G.W. Pete, Admin.--Guardian Care of Gastonia, Gastonia, NC; *U.S. Public*, pg. 1712
Moore, Gary, Plant Mgr.--Firestone Building Products Company-Kingstree Plant, Kingstree, SC; *Int'l*, pg. 214
Moore, Herbert B., Pres.--Blackman Uhler Chemical Co., Augusta, GA; *U.S. Public*, pg. 1548
Moore, Herbert B., Jr., Pres.--Blackman Uhler Chemical Co., Spartanburg, SC; *U.S. Public*, pg. 1548
Moore, Ivan R., Jr., Pres.--Sysco Food Services-San Antonio, Inc., San Antonio, TX; *U.S. Public*, pg. 1552
Moore, J. Douglas, V.P.--EDO Industrial Products Division, Salt Lake City, UT; *U.S. Public*, pg. 542
Moore, J.T., Gen. Mgr.--Mount Vernon Mills, Inc., Woodruff, Woodruff, SC; *U.S. Private*, pg. 835
Moore, Jack, Pres.--Union Underwear Co., Inc., Bowling Green, KY; *U.S. Public*, pg. 686
Moore, Jack R., Pres.--Aichelin-Stalh, Inc., Lees Summit, MO; *U.S. Private*, pg. 1029
Moore, James, Mng. Dir.--Morphy Richards Appliances, Mexborough, United Kingdom; *Int'l*, pg. 554
Moore, James E., V.P. & Mgr.--California State Bank-Brea, Brea, CA; *U.S. Public*, pg. 294
Moore, James H., Pres.--Falconbridge U.S. Inc., Pittsburgh, PA; *Int'l*, pg. 434
Moore, James L., Pres.--Case Advertising, Inc., Charlotte, NC; *U.S. Public*, pg. 391
Moore, Jane, Mgr.-Acctg.--PrimeEnergy Management Corporation, Stamford, CT; *U.S. Public*, pg. 1329
Moore, John, Pres.--Continental Homes of Dallas, L.P., Grapevine, TX; *U.S. Public*, pg. 441
Moore, John, Pres.--Moore Electric Supply, Inc., Charlotte, NC; *U.S. Public*, pg. 847
Moore, John, Office Mgr.--Stone & Webster Engineering, Miami, FL; *U.S. Public*, pg. 1519
Moore, John A., Pres.--Sun Alliance USA, Inc., New York, NY; *Int'l*, pg. 1131
Moore, John R., Pres. & Chief Exec. Officer--Midas-International Corp., Chicago, IL; *U.S. Public*, pg. 1766
Moore, Joseph D., Sr. V.P.-Devel. & Fin.--Hospital Development Co., Nashville, TN; *U.S. Public*, pg. 405
Moore, K.A., Pres.--Dallas Terminal Railway and Union Depot Co., San Francisco, CA; *U.S. Public*, pg. 1668
Moore, K.A., Pres.--The Ogden Union Railway and Depot Co., Ogden, UT; *U.S. Public*, pg. 1668
Moore, K.A., Pres.--Portland Traction Co., Portland, OR; *U.S. Public*, pg. 1668
Moore, Kenneth O., Pres.--American West Trading Co., Dresden, TN; *U.S. Public*, pg. 1073
Moore, Kevin, Chief Fin. Officer--Softride, Inc., Bellingham, WA; *U.S. Private*, pg. 44
Moore, Lonnie, Warden--Correctional Treatment Facility, Washington, DC; *U.S. Public*, pg. 450
Moore, M.T., Chm. Bd.--Pickands Mather & Co. International, Wynard, Australia; *U.S. Public*, pg. 386
Moore, Mackey, Pres.--First Tennessee Bank National Association Mississippi, Southaven, MS; *U.S. Public*, pg. 639
Moore, Marieta J., Admin.--Twin Pines Healthcare, Santa Paula, CA; *U.S. Public*, pg. 1715
Moore, Marilyn A., Pres.--Team Rehab, Inc., Saint Louis, MO; *U.S. Public*, pg. 1373
Moore, Max L., V.P. & Mgr.--First Oklahoma Bank & Trust Company of Edmond, Edmond, OK; *U.S. Public*, pg. 174
Moore, Nancy Jackie, Admin.--Maywood Acres Healthcare, Oxnard, CA; *U.S. Public*, pg. 1714
Moore, Niel, Gen. Mgr.--CFP Foods, Saskatoon, Canada; *Int'l*, pg. 1195
Moore, Nigel, Mgr.--Sullivan Systems Div., Fort Lee, NJ; *Int'l*, pg. 1379
Moore, Oswald F., Pres.--Colina Insurance Company Limited, Nassau, Bahamas; *U.S. Public*, pg. 363
Moore, P.A., Mng. Dir--Hong Kong Telecom CSL Limited, Taikoo Shing, Hong Kong; *Int'l*, pg. 247
Moore, P.E., Chief Oper. Officer--Kidde Fire Protection Ltd., Northolt, United Kingdom; *Int'l*, pg. 1499
Moore, R.H., Chief Exec. Officer--Optim Electronics Corporation, Germantown, MD; *Int'l*, pg. 208
Moore, R.L., Gen. Mgr.--Onan Corporation, Huntsville, AL; *U.S. Public*, pg. 468
Moore, R.L., Gen. Mgr.--ING Mercantile Mutual Bank, Sydney, Australia; *Int'l*, pg. 650
Moore, Richard, Mgr.--Sadtler Research Laboratories, Philadelphia, PA; *U.S. Public*, pg. 230
Moore, Richard L., Pres. & Chief Exec. Officer--Kingswood Interactive, Ardmore, PA; *U.S. Private*, pg. 622
Moore, Robert, Mgr.--Carolina Steel-Greenville Plant, Greenville, SC; *U.S. Private*, pg. 214
Moore, Roger, Chief Oper. Officer--Novo Nordisk Pharma Ltd., Tokyo, Japan; *Int'l*, pg. 988
Moore, Ronald L., Pres.--Intermountain Bankshares of Colorado, Inc., Denver, CO; *U.S. Public*, pg. 173
Moore, Simon, V.P.--Snowden Rubber Industries, Oshawa, Canada; *Int'l*, pg. 1423
Moore, Stephen, Mng. Dir.--FoxVideo Limited, London, United Kingdom; *Int'l*, pg. 926
Moore, Stephen, Dir.--Showplatronics (M) Sdn. Bhd., Johor Baharu, Malaysia; *Int'l*, pg. 1237
Moore, Stuart, Gen. Mgr.--Symbol Technologies Canada Inc., Mississauga, Canada; *U.S. Public*, pg. 1546
Moore, T.E., Gen. Mgr.--Walbridge Coatings, Inc., Walbridge, OH; *U.S. Public*, pg. 879
Moore, Terry, Pres.--Englewood Community Hospital, Inc., Englewood, FL; *U.S. Public*, pg. 404
Moore, Thomas A., V.P. & Gen. Mgr.--Procter & Gamble Health & Personal Care Div., Cincinnati, OH; *U.S. Public*, pg. 1331
Moore, Thomas Ira, Mgr.-Sls.--Klockner-Moeller, Novi, MI; *Int'l*, pg. 736
Moore, Thomas R., Pres.--Chevron Shipping Co., San Francisco, CA; *U.S. Public*, pg. 348
Moore, W. Booker, III, Pres.--The Tallahassee State Bank, Tallahassee, FL; *U.S. Public*, pg. 1549
Moore, W. Kent, Pres.--Reynolds Metals Company-Troutdale, Troutdale, OR; *U.S. Public*, pg. 1386
Moore, Wayne, Gen. Mgr.--Rexam Custom, Matthews, NC; *Int'l*, pg. 1106
Moore, William, Mng. Dir.--SMC International U.K. 7392, London, United Kingdom; *U.S. Public*, pg. 1717
Moore, William H., Pres.--ALLTEL Distribution, Inc., Dallas, TX; *U.S. Public*, pg. 55
Moore, William P., Pres.--Steelcraft Manufacturing Company, Cincinnati, OH; *U.S. Public*, pg. 877
Moorehead, Tom, Plant Superintendant--General Shale Products Corp., Mooresville, IN; *Int'l*, pg. 844
Moorehouse, Scott, Mgr.-Office--Woodward-Clyde, San Diego, CA; *U.S. Public*, pg. 1657
Moorhouse, Carl L., Plant Mgr.--Carson Plant, Carson, CA; *U.S. Public*, pg. 1348
Moorhouse, D.G., Chief Exec.--John Brown - Engineering & Construction Sector, London, United Kingdom; *Int'l*, pg. 772
Moorhouse, Jim, Chief Exec. Officer--Expamet Building Products, Hartlepool, United Kingdom; *Int'l*, pg. 467
Moorman, Dr. Gunter, Mng. Dir.--Uniferm GmbH & Co., Werne, Germany; *Int'l*, pg. 1143
Moos, Frank, Pres.--Collegeville Advertising, Norristown, PA; *U.S. Public*, pg. 1422
Moose, John, Pres.--Collins & Aikman Products Co., Roxboro, NC; *U.S. Public*, pg. 399
Mooslin, Michael D., Pres.--Color Me Mine, Inc., Van Nuys, CA; *U.S. Public*, pg. 966
Mooty, Charles W., Pres.--D.Q.F., Inc., Minneapolis, MN; *U.S. Public*, pg. 220
Moquist, Ron, Chief Oper. Officer--Glasstite, Inc., Dunnell, MN; *U.S. Public*, pg. 1361
Moquist, Ronald M., Pres.--Beta Raven Inc., Bridgeton, MO; *U.S. Public*, pg. 1361
Mora, Francisco, J., Gen. Mgr.--Kodak Venezuela, S.A., Caracas, Venezuela; *U.S. Public*, pg. 555
Mora, Jose, Mng. Dir.--Janssen Farmaceutica, S.A. de C.V., Mexico, Mexico; *U.S. Public*, pg. 929
Mora, Roberto, Fin. Controller--F.I.A.P. SpA, Turate, Italy; *U.S. Public*, pg. 5
Morabet, Ali, Mgr.-Saudi Arabia--Raychem Saudi Arabia Limited, Riyadh, Saudi Arabia; *U.S. Public*, pg. 1363
Morabito, Guiseppe, Chief Oper. Officer--Krauss-Maffei Chemiomeccanica S.r.l., Milan, Italy; *Int'l*, pg. 836
Moraes, Eduardo, Pres.--Bundy Latin America, Sao Paulo, Brazil; *Int'l*, pg. 1342
Moraes, J.D., Mgr.--Kelsey Bay Div., Sayward, Canada; *Int'l, pg. 828*
Morais, Douglas H., Dr., Pres.--California Microwave, Inc.-Wireless Products Grp., Sunnyvale, CA; *U.S. Public*, pg. 293
Morales, A., Mng. Dir.--Bondioli y Pavesi Iberica S.A., Zaragoza, Spain; *Int'l*, pg. 201
Morales, Jules C., Jr., Chief Oper. Officer--Allright New Orleans, Inc., New Orleans, LA; *U.S. Private*, pg. 43
Morales, Santiago, Gen. Mgr.--Oral-B Laboratories S.A. de C.V., Mexico, Mexico; *U.S. Public*, pg. 745
Morales, Vicky, Country Mgr.--Grace Central America, Guatemala, Guatemala; *U.S. Public*, pg. 755
Moralez, Abelardo, Pres. & Chief Exec. Officer--Banca Serfin, S.A., New York Agency, New York, NY; *Int'l*, pg. 137
Moramarco, Jon, Pres.--The Wine Alliance, Healdsburg, CA; *Int'l*, pg. 63
Moran, Bill, Pres.--Save-A-Lot, Inc., Saint Louis, MO; *U.S. Public*, pg. 1541
Moran, Charles E., Pres.--CA-1 Services, Buffalo, NY; *U.S. Private*, pg. 322
Moran, Charles E., Pres.--National Education Training Group, Naperville, IL; *U.S. Public*, pg. 784
Moran, Chuck, Pres.--NETG Holding, Inc., Irvine, CA; *U.S. Public*, pg. 784
Moran, David E., Jr., Mgr.--General Employment Enterprises, Inc., San Francisco, CA; *U.S. Public*, pg. 714
Moran, E.A., Pres.--Public Service Resources Corporation, Newark, NJ; *U.S. Public*, pg. 1340
Moran, E.A., Pres.--Enterprise Group Development Corporation, Newark, NJ; *U.S. Public*, pg. 1340
Moran, Harry J., V.P.--Consumer Products Div., Hartsville, SC; *U.S. Public*, pg. 1486
Moran, Manuel a., Chief Oper. Officer--Aerolineas Argentinas, Buenos Aires, Argentina; *Int'l*, pg. 575
Moran, Mike, Pres. & Gen. Mgr.--KGAN-TV, Cedar Rapids, IA; *U.S. Private*, pg. 439
Moran, Robert, Chm. Bd.--Sears de Mexico, Mexico, Mexico; *Int'l*, pg. 573
Moran, Thomas J., Pres. & Chief Exec. Officer--American Life Insurance Company of New York, New York, NY; *U.S. Private*, pg. 769
Moran, William M., Jr., Pres. & Chief Exec. Officer--Moran Foods, Inc./Save-A-Lot Ltd., Saint Louis, MO; *U.S. Public*, pg. 1541
Morani, Giorgio, Mgr.--Sandvik Hard Materials, Milan, Italy; *Int'l*, pg. 1186
Moraza, Don, Gen. Mgr.--Pilmico, Cebu, Philippines; *Int'l*, pg. 411
Morbey, R.I., Chm. Bd.--E & D Taylor (Insurance Brokers) Limited, Greenford, United Kingdom; *Int'l*, pg. 1358
Morbey, R.I., Chm. Bd.--Taylor Insurance Brokers Limited, Southall, United Kingdom; *Int'l*, pg. 1358
Morcillo, D. Francisco Mochon, Pres.--Telefonia y Finanzas, S.A. (Telfisa), Madrid, Spain; *Int'l*, pg. 1372
Morcom, W. Russ, V.P. & G.M.--Semiconductor Products Division, Melbourne, FL; *U.S. Public*, pg. 792
Mordt, Per J., Chief Oper. Officer--Jobu A/S, Drobak, Norway; *Int'l*, pg. 443
More, Alvaro, Gen. Mgr.--MADD Agency, Montevideo, Uruguay; *U.S. Private*, pg. 1200
More, Avery, Chm. Bd. & V.P.--Computer City, Fort Worth, TX; *U.S. Public*, pg. 1560
More, R.P., V.P. & Gen. Mgr.--Lacey Mfg. Co., Bridgeport, CT; *Int'l*, pg. 468
Moreau, C.P., Pres.--Texaco Puerto Rico, Inc., San Juan, PR; *U.S. Public*, pg. 1583
Moreau, P., Sr. V.P. & Gen. Mgr. Quebec--Publicite McKim Ltee., Montreal, Canada; *U.S. Private*, pg. 104
Moreels, Genevieve, Gen. Mgr.--Forbo Decor S.A., Braine-l'Alleud, Belgium; *Int'l*, pg. 497

Morehead, Jim, Mgr.--American Econo-Therm, Tulsa, OK; *U.S. Private*, pg. 858

Moreira Lima, Carlos Alberto, Jr., Mgr.--SLC S.A. Industria e Comercio, Porto Alegre, Brazil; *U.S. Public*, pg. 493

Moreira, Eduardo Henry, Chief Oper. Officer--Axel Johnson do Brasil Ind. E. Com. Ltda., Sao Paulo, Brazil; *Int'l*, pg. 711

Morel, Bernard, Chm.--Jet Tours, Ivry-sur-Seine, France; *Int'l*, pg. 560

Morel, Bernard, Chief Oper. Officer--Go Voyages, Paris, France; *Int'l*, pg. 560

Morel, Bernard, Reg. Mgr.-USA--Air France (U.S. Region), New York, NY; *Int'l*, pg. 561

Morel, Patrick, Country Mgr.--Berlitz France S.A., Paris, France; *U.S. Public*, pg. 222

Moreland, D.R., Mng. Dir.--De La Rue Systems (Latin America), Miami, FL; *Int'l*, pg. 387

Morell, Klaus, Sls. Dir.-Kraft Paper--Wisaforest Deutschland GmbH, Altenstadt, Germany; *Int'l*, pg. 1429

Morella, Bob, Plant Mgr.--Commercial Intertech Corp., Kings Mountain, NC; *U.S. Public*, pg. 411

Morelli, Antonio, Rep.--Cariplo (Athens), Athens, Greece; *Int'l*, pg. 275

Morelli, B., Chief Oper. Officer--Sibeka, Brussels, Belgium; *Int'l*, pg. 1442

Morelli, C.R., Pres.--Charleston Tool Services, Charleston, SC; *U.S. Public*, pg. 468

Moren, John G., Pres.--Parsons Construction Services, Inc., Houston, TX; *U.S. Private*, pg. 842

Moreno, Alfonso, Gen. Mgr.--Cutter Beechcraft, El Paso, TX; *U.S. Private*, pg. 299

Moreno, Alonso, Gen. Mgr.--Santander Merchant, S.A., Santiago, Chile; *Int'l*, pg. 144

Moreno, David J., V.P. & Gen. Mgr.--Wabash Fibre Box Company-Fort Wayne Plant, Fort Wayne, IN; *U.S. Private*, pg. 1170

Moreno, Frutos, Mng. Dir.-Madrid--TBWA Madrid, S.A., Madrid, Spain; *U.S. Private*, pg. 1063

Moreno, J., Gen. Mgr.--ADT Prosegur, Lisbon, Portugal; *U.S. Public*, pg. 1649

Moreno, Miguel, Gen. Mgr.--Notifier Espana S.A., Barcelona, Spain; *U.S. Public*, pg. 1307

Morentz, Jake, Pres.--B&G Electronics, Fort Lauderdale, FL; *Int'l*, pg. 1462

Moresby, Port, Mng. Dir.--Australia & New Zealand Banking Group (PNG) Limited, Port Moresby, Papua New Guinea; *Int'l*, pg. 100

Moret, Dr. Mark, Chm. & Chief Exec. Officer--Sandoz International Ltd., Basel, Switzerland; *Int'l*, pg. 972

Moret, Jean, Dir.--Angenieux, Saint-Heand, France; *Int'l*, pg. 1381

Moreton, John, Chief Exec. Officer--Sun Healthcare Group International Ltd., Windsor, United Kingdom; *U.S. Public*, pg. 1531

Moreton, Paul, Mng. Dir.--Coopers Payen Ltd., Slough, United Kingdom; *Int'l*, pg. 1334

Moretti, Enver, Reg. Mgr.-Middle East--AEI Italy, Milan, Italy; *U.S. Public*, pg. 30

Moretti, Fabio, Gen. Mgr.--Nokia Mobile Phones (Korea) Ltd., Seoul, Korea; *Int'l*, pg. 952

Moretto, Anthony, Mgr.--CAP Gemini America (Philadelphia Branch), Bala Cynwyd, PA; *Int'l*, pg. 264

Morgan, Bernard W., Chief Oper. Officer--Instron Pty. Ltd., Bayswater, Australia; *U.S. Public*, pg. 883

Morgan, Braxton, Pres.--PEPCON Systems, Inc., Las Vegas, NV; *U.S. Public*, pg. 88

Morgan, Calvert, Chm. Bd. & Pres.--Del-Vest Inc., Wilmington, DE; *U.S. Public*, pg. 1243

Morgan, Calvert A., Chm. Bd. & Pres.--Bank of Delaware, Wilmington, DE; *U.S. Public*, pg. 1243

Morgan, Calvert A., Jr., Chm. Bd., Pres. & Chief Oper. Officer--PNC Bank, Delaware, Wilmington, DE; *U.S. Public*, pg. 1243

Morgan, Colin J., Pres.--Helene Curtis International, Chicago, IL; *Int'l*, pg. 1434

Morgan, D., Gen. Mgr.--Australia & New Zealand Banking Group Limited Hong Kong, Central, Hong Kong; *Int'l*, pg. 99

Morgan, D.F., Mgr.-Sls.--Moore Products Co. (Italia) S.r.l., Milan, Italy; *U.S. Public*, pg. 1129

Morgan, GAry, Reg. Mgr.--Green Tree Acceptance, Inc., Broomfield, CO; *U.S. Public*, pg. 762

Morgan, Gwyn, Pres.--AEC Oil & Gas, Calgary, Canada; *Int'l*, pg. 48

Morgan, I., Sr. Repr.--Jardine Pacific Ltd Regional Representative Office, Jakarta, Indonesia; *Int'l*, pg. 705

Morgan, J.H., Mng. Dir.--Coral Racing Ltd., Barking, United Kingdom; *Int'l*, pg. 170

Morgan, J.M., Chm. Bd.--Comfort Financieringen Nederland BV, Houten, Netherlands; *Int'l*, pg. 911

Morgan, J.M., Pres.-Shell Oil Prods.--Shell Oil Company, Houston, TX; *Int'l*, pg. 1136

Morgan, Jack, Admin.--Kannapolis Rest Home, Inc., Kannapolis, NC; *U.S. Public*, pg. 1714

Morgan, James H., Pres. & Chief Exec. Officer--Interstate/Johnson Lane Corporation, Charlotte, NC; *U.S. Public*, pg. 910

Morgan, Jerry, Pres.--Sargent and Greenleaf, Nicholasville, KY; *U.S. Private*, pg. 981

Morgan, Jim, Pres.--Hanel Lumber Co., Inc., Hood River, OR; *U.S. Private*, pg. 538

Morgan, Joseph, Pres.--Pasta Central, Atlanta, GA; *U.S. Public*, pg. 236

Morgan, Marc C., V.P. & Gen. Mgr.--WSB, Inc., Atlanta, GA; *U.S. Private*, pg. 282

Morgan, Mary, Publr.--Time Inc. Health, New York, NY; *U.S. Public*, pg. 1613

Morgan, Mike, Gen. Mgr.--Omicron Proprietary Ltd., Tullamarine, Australia; *U.S. Public*, pg. 756

Morgan, N.B., Gen. Mgr.--CHEMCENTRAL/Tulsa, Tulsa, OK; *U.S. Private*, pg. 232

Morgan, Nathan J., Pres.--Zions Investment Securities, Inc., Salt Lake City, UT; *U.S. Public*, pg. 1793

Morgan, Owen, Gen. Mgr.--Warner-Jenkinson Canada, Kingston, Canada; *U.S. Public*, pg. 1696

Morgan, Paul, Mng. Dir.--Jamaica Match Holding Ltd., Kingston, Jamaica; *U.S. Private*, pg. 127

Morgan, Paul G., Pres.--Sysco Food Services of Oklahoma, Inc., Norman, OK; *U.S. Public*, pg. 1552

Morgan, R.W., Mgr.--Public Service Company of Oklahoma-Northern Div., Bartlesville, OK; *U.S. Public*, pg. 324

Morgan, Robert A., Mng. Dir.--Wallace & Tiernan, Tonbridge, United Kingdom; *Int'l*, pg. 1444

Morgan, Robert B., Pres.--Cincinnati Insurance Co., Fairfield, OH; *U.S. Public*, pg. 368

Morgan, Robert B., Pres.--Cincinnati Indemnity Company, Fairfield, OH; *U.S. Public*, pg. 368

Morgan, Robert W., Pres.--Environmental Health Strategies, Menlo Park, CA; *U.S. Public*, pg. 609

Morgan, Roger L., Pres.--HomeAmerican Mortgage Corp., Denver, CO; *U.S. Public*, pg. 1025

Morgan, Ron, Plant Mgr.--The Ohio Mattress Company Licensing & Componets Group, Rensselaer, IN; *U.S. Private*, pg. 979

Morgan, Stephen, Pres.--EUA Citizens Conservation Services, Inc., Lowell, MA; *U.S. Public*, pg. 549

Morgan, Stephen W., Chief Fin. Officer & V.P.--Aquapore Moisture Systems, Inc., Phoenix, AZ; *Int'l*, pg. 1066

Morgan, Thomas E., Pres.--Western Reserve Life Assurance Co. of Ohio, Largo, FL; *Int'l*, pg. 27

Morgan, Thomas J., Pres.--Sysco Food Services of Idaho, Inc., Boise, ID; *U.S. Public*, pg. 1551

Morgan, W. Brett, Pres. & Chief Exec. Officer--Regions Bank/Enterprise, Enterprise, AL; *U.S. Public*, pg. 1372

Morgan, William T., Pres.--Fiduciary Trust Co. of New Hampshire, Kansas City, MO; *U.S. Public*, pg. 1623

Morgan, William T., Pres.--Waddell and Reed, Inc., Shawnee Mission, KS; *U.S. Public*, pg. 1623

Morgan, William T., Pres.--W & R Insurance Agency, Inc. of Wyoming, Inc., Kansas City, MO; *U.S. Public*, pg. 1623

Morganthall, Fred J., II, Pres.--Harris Teeter, Inc., Charlotte, NC; *U.S. Public*, pg. 1412

Morgels, G., Sec.--Flachglas AG, Furth, Germany; *Int'l*, pg. 1056

Morgen, Ivan, Chief Oper. Officer--IMR Finance S.A., Chatou, France; *U.S. Public*, pg. 1284

Morgues, Henrique, Reg. Dir. S. Asia--AlliedSignal Aerospace Service Corporation, Singapore, Singapore; *U.S. Public*, pg. 52

Mori, Kazid Kazitaka, Pres.--SPS/Unbrako K.K., Tokyo, Japan; *U.S. Public*, pg. 1420

Mori, Ken, Gen. Mgr.--Dentsu Europe-Brussels, Brussels, Belgium; *Int'l*, pg. 393

Mori, Shoichiro, Gen. Mgr.--Ashikaga Bank-New York Branch, New York, NY; *Int'l*, pg. 88

Mori, T., Gen. Mgr.--Candela K.K., Tokyo, Japan; *U.S. Public*, pg. 301

Mori, Takashi, Pres.--Unikis Japan Co. Ltd., Osaka, Japan; *Int'l*, pg. 1432

Moriarty, Daniel, Warden--Torrance County Detention Facility, Estancia, NM; *U.S. Public*, pg. 451

Moriarty, Thomas, Gen. Mgr.--Moog Ltd., Cork, Ireland; *U.S. Public*, pg. 1128

Moricoli, Daniel J., Pres.--Grey Directory Marketing Inc., Chicago, IL; *U.S. Public*, pg. 764

Moriga, Etsuo, Mgr.--Tokio Marine Management Inc. - Chicago, Chicago, IL; *Int'l*, pg. 1392

Morikawa, Shigeru, Chief Oper. Officer--Makita (U.K.) LTD., Milton Keynes, United Kingdom; *Int'l*, pg. 832

Morimoto, Kiyofumi, Pres.--Nissan Motor (Schweiz) AG, Urdorf, Switzerland; *Int'l*, pg. 945

Morimoto, N., Mng. Dir.--ITT Flygt Ltd., Tokyo, Japan; *U.S. Public*, pg. 860

Morimoto, Nobuhiro, Pres.--Bloomington-Normal Seating Company, Normal, IL; *Int'l*, pg. 830

Morimoto, T., Chief Oper. Officer--The Furukawa Battery Co., Ltd., Yokohama, Japan; *Int'l*, pg. 530

Morin, Eliane, Chief Oper. Officer--Framatome Connectors France, Versailles, France; *Int'l*, pg. 503

Morin, Jacques, V.P. & Gen. Mgr.--MDF La Baie Inc., La Baie, Canada; *Int'l*, pg. 1432

Morin, K.R., Chief Oper. Officer--Shanks & McEwan (Northern) Ltd, Coatbridge, United Kingdom; *Int'l*, pg. 1228

Morin, L., Pres.--La Brasserie Labatt Limitee, La Salle, Canada; *Int'l*, pg. 679

Morin, Michael K., Pres.--Comsearch, Inc., Reston, VA; *U.S. Public*, pg. 46

Morin, Patrick, Pres.--Halterm Container Terminal, Halifax, Canada; *Int'l*, pg. 924

Morin, Robert E., Pres.--Keystone Morin, Inc., Pelham, AL; *U.S. Public*, pg. 1650

Morin, Ronald, Gen. Mgr.--Beauport Plant St. Lawrence Cement, Quebec, Canada; *Int'l*, pg. 629

Morinaga, Masamoto, Pres.--The Bank of Tokyo-Mitsubishi (Panama Branch), Panama, Panama; *Int'l*, pg. 158

Morine, H. Donald, Pres.--Allegheny Development Corp., Pittsburgh, PA; *U.S. Public*, pg. 474

Morine, H. Donald, Pres.--Property Ventures, Ltd., Pittsburgh, PA; *U.S. Public*, pg. 474

Moring, David A., Contact--Chemical Bank (Guernsey) Limited, Saint Peter Port, United Kingdom; *U.S. Public*, pg. 341

Morino, Shoichi, Gen. Mgr.--Nippon Credit Bank Ltd.-Grand Cayman, Georgetown, Cayman Islands; *Int'l*, pg. 933

Morishige, Naoki, Deputy Chief Exec. & Chief Gen. Mgr.--IBJ Australia Bank Limited, Melbourne, Australia; *Int'l*, pg. 676

Morishige, Toru, Vice Chm. & Mng. Dir.--PanAgora Asset Managment, Inc., Boston, MA; *Int'l*, pg. 935

Morishige, Toru, Vice Chm. & Mng. Dir.--PanAgora Asset Managment, Inc., Boston, MA; *U.S. Public*, pg. 987

Morishita, Itsuo, Dir. & Gen. Mgr.--Fukuoka Branch Office, Fukuoka, Japan; *Int'l*, pg. 1491

Morison, Stephen G., Pres.--Chancellor Asset Corporation, Boston, MA; *U.S. Public*, pg. 335

Morison, Stephen G., Pres.--Chancellor DataComm, Inc., Boston, MA; *U.S. Public*, pg. 335

Morison, Stephen G., Pres.--Chancellor Management Corporation, Boston, MA; *U.S. Public*, pg. 335

Morita, M., Pres.--Sony Service Co., Park Ridge, NJ; *Int'l*, pg. 1281

Morita, Masaaki, Vice Chm. & Chief Exec. Officer--Sony U.S.A., New York, NY; *Int'l*, pg. 1281

Morita, S., Gen. Mgr.--Marubeni American Corporation, Seattle Branch, Seattle, WA; *Int'l*, pg. 845

Morita, Shunichi, Chief Rep.--The Hokkaido Takushoku Bank, Ltd. (Jakarta), Jakarta, Indonesia; *Int'l*, pg. 627

Morito, Kazukiyo, Chm. & Mng. Dir.--Mitsui & Co. (Middle East) E.C., Manama, Bahrain; *Int'l*, pg. 882

Moritz, Donald I., Chm. Bd.--Equitech Division, Pittsburgh, PA; *U.S. Public*, pg. 590

Moritz, Francis, Mng. Dir.--Ilco Unican (U.K.) Ltd., London, United Kingdom; *Int'l*, pg. 1432

Moritz, Francis, Mng. Dir.--Ilco Unican France S.A., Courbevoie, France; *Int'l*, pg. 1432

Moriura, Keiji, Gen. Mgr.--International Division (Nara), Nara, Japan; *Int'l*, pg. 905

Mork, Bjorn, Pres.--Gyproc Gipsplatefabrikk A/S, Fredrikstad, Norway; *Int'l*, pg. 1200

Mork, Lothar, V.P. & Gen. Mgr.--Seagate Technology (Singapore) Pte. Ltd., Singapore, Singapore; *U.S. Public*, pg. 1450

Morl, D., Chief Oper. Officer--Rhenania Umschlag und Lagerei GmbH, Wesel, Germany; *Int'l*, pg. 1034

Morlacchi, Pierre-Andre, Mng. Dir.--Driver-Harris Italiana, S.p.A., Milan, Italy; *Int'l*, pg. 723

Morlan, Robert, Pres. & Chief Exec. Officer--BankAmerica Insurance Group, San Diego, CA; *U.S. Public*, pg. 181

Morley, Michael, Deputy Chm. & Pres.-New York--Edelman Worldwide, Inc., New York, NY; *U.S. Private*, pg. 362

Morley, S., Mng. Dir.--Getinge AB Japan, Tokyo, Japan; *Int'l*, pg. 551

Mormarco, Jon, Pres.--Callaway Vineyard & Winery, Temecula, CA; *Int'l*, pg. 63

Morns, R.R., Mng. Dir.--Chemoxy International plc, Middlesbrough, United Kingdom; *Int'l*, pg. 88

Moro, Ramon, Chief Exec. Officer--Woodlines Shipping Limited, Hamilton, Bermuda; *Int'l*, pg. 683

Moro, Vincenzo, V.P.--Aerimpianti S.p.A., Milan, Italy; *Int'l*, pg. 653

Moroney, Pat, Pres.--Continental Homes of Miami, Miami, FL; *U.S. Public*, pg. 441

Morooka, Yasukazu, Pres.--Sumitomo Metal U.S.A. Corp., Chicago, IL; *Int'l*, pg. 1316

Moros, N.P., Pres.--Cyprus Amax Coal Sales Corporation, Milford, OH; *U.S. Public*, pg. 471

Morosov, Stanislas, Gen. Mgr.--CCF Uzbekistan, Tashkent, Uzbekistan; *Int'l*, pg. 342

Morotomi, Masa, Chief Representative--Toyo Seikan Kaisha, Ltd. (U.S.A.), Chicago, IL; *Int'l*, pg. 1411

Morr, Hector Perez, Pres.--Mead Johnson de Venezuela, S.A., Caracas, Venezuela; *U.S. Public*, pg. 256

Morrell, Andres F., Pres.--Velco, Caparra Heights, PR; *U.S. Public*, pg. 176

Morrell, Andy, Pres.--Popular Leasing & Rental, Inc., San Juan, PR; *U.S. Public*, pg. 176

Morrell, D., Chief Oper. Officer--East Maui Irrigation Co., Ltd., Paia, HI; *U.S. Public*, pg. 39

Morreo, Phillip A., Pres. & Chief Exec. Officer--Emergi-Lite, Inc., Westbrook, CT; *Int'l*, pg. 725

Morrill, Robert J., Pres.--Microwave Radio Communications, Chelmsford, MA; *U.S. Public*, pg. 294

Morris, Alan R., V.P. & Publisher--Chemical Engineering, New York, NY; *U.S. Public*, pg. 1071

Morris, Brian, Chief Oper. Officer--AVX Ltd., Aldershot, United Kingdom; *Int'l*, pg. 776

Morris, Brian, Reg. Dir.--SMS-Washington, D.C., Herndon, VA; *U.S. Public*, pg. 1463

Morris, Brian R., Chief Exec. Officer & Chm. Bd.-WF Corroon Limited--WF Corroon-United Kingdom & International, London, United Kingdom; *Int'l*, pg. 1501

Morris, C., Jr., Pres.--Wolverine Pipe Line Co., Dallas, TX; *U.S. Public*, pg. 1584

Morris, Carl, Pres. & Chief Exec. Officer--McCain Foods (Japan) Limited, Tokyo, Japan; *Int'l*, pg. 850

Morris, Chuck, Pres. & Publr.--Commercial-News, Danville, IL; *U.S. Public*, pg. 700

Morris, Dan, Plant Mgr.--Hydro Conduit Corp., Tallahassee, FL; *Int'l*, pg. 246

Morris, David, Chm. & Chief Exec. Officer--DMB&B/Weekes Morris Osborn, Ultimo, Australia; *U.S. Private*, pg. 304

Morris, Doug, V.P.-Opers.--Datamarine International Australia Pty., Ltd., Artarmon, Australia; *U.S. Public*, pg. 487

Morris, Doug, Gen. Mgr.--Peterson Spring-Windsor Plant, Windsor, Canada; *U.S. Private*, pg. 857

Morris, Edie, Controller--Glen Oaks Hospital, Greenville, TX; *U.S. Public*, pg. 1697

Morris, Edna K., Pres.--Quincy Family Steak House, Spartanburg, SC; *U.S. Public*, pg. 23

Morris, Gil, Pres.--Hilti Inc., Tulsa, OK; *Int'l*, pg. 620

Morris, Gill, Mng. Dir.--GPC Connect (London), London, United Kingdom; *U.S. Public*, pg. 1225

Morris, Ginny, Pres. & Gen. Mgr.--KSTP-FM, Inc., Saint Paul, MN; *U.S. Private*, pg. 544

Morris, Grant, V.P.--Central Div., Columbus, OH; *U.S. Public*, pg. 732

Morris, J., Gen. Mgr.-Airport Services, N.E. U.S.A.--Air Canada, New York, NY; *Int'l*, pg. 36

Morris, James, Publr.--Managing Automation, New York, NY; *U.S. Private*, pg. 1082

Morris, James T., Pres. & Chief Exec. Officer--IWC Resources Corporation, Indianapolis, IN; *U.S. Public*, pg. 1185

Morris, James T., Chm. Bd. & Pres.--Harbour Water Corporation, Indianapolis, IN; *U.S. Public*, pg. 1185

Morris, Jerry, Plant Mgr.--Lane Graphics Products Div., Phoenix, AZ; *U.S. Public*, pg. 707

Morris, Jim, Mng. Dir.--Harris Lanier Australia, Sydney, Australia; *U.S. Public*, pg. 791
Morris, John, Gen. Mgr.--Impact Furniture Co. Inc., Hildebran, NC; *U.S. Public*, pg. 193
Morris, John R., Pres.--CCG Corp., Camden, SC; *U.S. Public*, pg. 267
Morris, Kathryn J., V.P.-H.R.--Amurcon Equities, Southfield, MI; *U.S. Private*, pg. 69
Morris, L.O., III, Chief Oper. Officer--Mylon C. Jacobs Supply Co., Broken Arrow, OK; *U.S. Private*, pg. 963
Morris, R.H, Mng. Dir.--Beazer Homes (Bridgwater) Limited, Bridgwater, United Kingdom; *Int'l*, pg. 182
Morris, R.R., Mng. Dir.--Dawmec Limited, Southampton, United Kingdom; *Int'l*, pg. 88
Morris, Ray, Mng. Dir.--Conwed Plastics/N.V. S.A., Heverlee, Belgium; *U.S. Public*, pg. 990
Morris, Richard G., Div. V.P.--Construction & Home Improvement Markets Division, Saint Paul, MN; *U.S. Public*, pg. 1605
Morris, Robert, Pres. & Chief Exec. Officer--City National Bank, Hastings, NE; *U.S. Public*, pg. 629
Morris, Stephen B., Pres.--The Arbitron Company, New York, NY; *U.S. Public*, pg. 331
Morris, T., Gen. Mgr.--Gan National Insurance Co., New York, NY; *Int'l*, pg. 564
Morris, Timothy J., Pres. & Chief Exec. Officer--The Portfolio Group, Inc., New York, NY; *U.S. Public*, pg. 338
Morris, Virginia, Pres. & Gen. Mgr.--KSTP-AM, Inc., Maplewood, MN; *U.S. Private*, pg. 544
Morris, W. S., IV, Pres.--Southeastern Newspapers Corporation, Augusta, GA; *U.S. Private*, pg. 996
Morris, W. S., 111, Pres.--Athens Newspapers, Inc., Augusta, GA; *U.S. Private*, pg. 996
Morris, W.S., 111, Chm. Bd. & Chief Exec. Officer--Southeastern Newspapers Corporation, Augusta, GA; *U.S. Private*, pg. 996
Morris, Walter K., Pres.--Gannett Fleming Investment Corporation, Harrisburg, PA; *U.S. Private*, pg. 439
Morris, William S., III, Chm. Bd. & Chief Exec. Officer--Stauffer Communications, Inc., Augusta, GA; *U.S. Private*, pg. 995
Morris, William S., IV, Pres.--Stauffer Communications, Inc., Augusta, GA; *U.S. Private*, pg. 995
Morris, William, IV, Pres.--Morris Communications Corporation, Augusta, GA; *U.S. Private*, pg. 995
Morrison, A.G., Chm.--Dairy Farm Management Services Limited, Causeway Bay, Hong Kong; *Int'l*, pg. 703
Morrison, A.G., Mng. Dir.--Mandarin Oriental Hotel Group Limited, Causeway Bay, Hong Kong; *Int'l*, pg. 704
Morrison, Bill, Pres.--Supermarket Insurance Agency, Inc., Shawnee Mission, KS; *U.S. Private*, pg. 93
Morrison, Bill, Pres.--Benchmark Insurance Company, Shawnee Mission, KS; *U.S. Private*, pg. 93
Morrison, Bob, Pres.--AGRA Foundations Limited, Edmonton, Canada; *Int'l*, pg. 30
Morrison, Colin, Chm. Bd.--EMAP Business Communications Division, London, United Kingdom; *Int'l*, *pg. 451*
Morrison, Colin, Chm. Bd.--EMAP Business Information/EMAP Heighway, London, United Kingdom; *Int'l*, pg. 451
Morrison, Craig, Pres.--Van Leer Containers, Inc., Alsip, IL; *Int'l*, pg. 1146
Morrison, Dale, Pres.--Campbell Sales, Dallas, TX; *U.S. Public*, pg. 299
Morrison, David, V.P.-Europe--Oral-B Laboratories Limited, Aylesbury, United Kingdom; *U.S. Public*, pg. 745
Morrison, David G., Pres. & Chief Exec. Officer--Brewster Transport Co. Ltd., Banff, Canada; *U.S. Public*, pg. 1719
Morrison, Dennis R., Pres. & Chief Exec. Officer--Norwest Bank Illinois, N.A., Galesburg, IL; *U.S. Public*, pg. 1202
Morrison, Dolphus, Pres.--SMI Steel, Inc., Birmingham, AL; *U.S. Public*, pg. 412
Morrison, Donald, Gen. Mgr. & Treas.--Eureka Manufacturing Co., Inc., Norton, MA; *U.S. Private*, pg. 916
Morrison, Garry W., Pres.--Textile Products Div., New Bedford, MA; *U.S. Public*, pg. 217
Morrison, Gregory, Mgr.-Sls.--Lindenmeyr Munroe, Mansfield, MA; *U.S. Private*, pg. 224
Morrison, J.A., Mng. Dir.--Minebea Electronics (UK) Ltd., Glasgow, United Kingdom; *Int'l*, pg. 868
Morrison, James, Gen. Mgr.--Buckhorn Canada Ltd., Brampton, Canada; *U.S. Public*, pg. 1143
Morrison, Jerry, V.P.--College & New Products Group, Austin, TX; *U.S. Private*, pg. 258
Morrison, Jerry L., Pres. & Chief Oper. Officer--BRC Holdings, Dallas, TX; *U.S. Public*, pg. 163
Morrison, Jimmy, Pres. & Chief Exec. Officer--Siemens Transportation Systems, Inc., Iselin, NJ; *Int'l*, pg. 1246
Morrison, Jobe B., V.P. & Gen. Mgr.--Miami Mill, Dayton, OH; *Int'l*, pg. 434
Morrison, John A., Pres.--Nordion International Inc., Kanata, Canada; *Int'l*, pg. 827
Morrison, Karolyn, Chief Oper. Officer--Long Beach Community Hospital, Long Beach, CA; *U.S. Private*, pg. 1118
Morrison, Nathan, Gen. Mgr.--Commercial Products Inc., Laurinburg, NC; *Int'l*, pg. 166
Morrison, Reggie, Gen. Mgr.--AM Entertainment, New York, NY; *U.S. Private*, pg. 38
Morrison, Richard, Pres.--Allegro MicroSystems Inc., Worcester, MA; *Int'l*, pg. 1188
Morrison, Richard G., Gen. Mgr.--Eli Lilly do Brasil Limitada, Sao Paulo, Brazil; *U.S. Public*, pg. 993
Morrison, Robert P., Pres.--Roots Division, Connersville, IN; *U.S. Public*, pg. 528
Morrison, Robert S., Chm. & Chief Exec. Officer--Kraft Foods, Inc., Northfield, IL; *U.S. Public*, pg. 1287
Morrison, Robert S., Chm. Bd. & Chief Exec. Officer--Kraft Foods Inc., Rye Brook, NY; *U.S. Public*, pg. 1288
Morrison, Ronald C., Pres. & Gen. Mgr.--Kodak Canada Inc., Toronto, Canada; *U.S. Public*, pg. 553
Morrison, Ronald J., Plant Mgr.--Washington Plant, Washington, IN; *U.S. Public*, pg. 1620
Morrison, Scott, Pres. & Chief Exec. Officer--Commercial Testing & Engineering Co., Lombard, IL; *Int'l*, pg. 1153
Morrison, T. Truxtun, Chm. Bd.--ConAgra International, Omaha, NE; *U.S. Public*, pg. 426
Morrison, William, Chm. Bd., Pres. & Chief Exec. Officer--Northern Trust Bank of Florida, N.A., Miami, FL; *U.S. Public*, pg. 1196
Morrissey, Annie, Reg. Dir.-Brazil, Bolivia & Guyana--Utell International-Brazil, Sao Paulo, Brazil; *Int'l*, pg. 1098
Morrissey, Tim, Pres.--KFSM-TV, Fort Smith, AR; *U.S. Public*, pg. 1174
Morrissey, William, Gen. Mgr.--Helicoid Gauge Div., Watertown, CT; *Int'l*, pg. 473
Morron, Jaume, Mgr.--Duni Iberica S.L., Tarragona, Spain; *Int'l*, pg. 421
Morrow, Charles B., Pres.--Fannie May Candy Shops, Inc., Chicago, IL; *U.S. Private*, pg. 598
Morrow, David, V.P.-Sls.--Magnolia Division, Columbus, MS; *U.S. Private*, pg. 964
Morrow, Robert N., Mng. Dir.--Industrias Purina, S.A. de C.V., Mexico, Mexico; *U.S. Public*, pg. 1360
Morrow, Suzanne B., Pres.--HSN Insurance, Inc., Saint Petersburg, FL; *U.S. Public*, pg. 1685
Morrow, William K., Mgr.--Voest-Alpine Services and Technologies Corp.-Romulus, Romulus, MI; *Int'l*, pg. 1471
Morschbach, Marcel, Dr., Dir. Gen.--Bayerische Vereinsbank AG, Milan, Italy; *Int'l*, pg. 180
Morse, Alan, Pres.--Research Institute of America, New York, NY; *U.S. Public*, pg. 1602
Morse, Clint, Pres.--Apex Computer Co., Redmond, WA; *U.S. Public*, pg. 332
Morse, Gordon, Branch Mgr.--Bear Stearns & Co. Inc., Atlanta, Atlanta, GA; *U.S. Public*, pg. 198
Morse, Howard L., Pres. & Chief Oper. Officer--Acurex Environmental Corp., Mountain View, CA; *Int'l*, pg. 607
Morse, Roger, Chief Fin. Officer--TLC Group, Inc., Zeeland, MI; *U.S. Public*, pg. 352
Morse, Sanford M., Exec. Editor--BNA Legal Services Div., Washington, DC; *U.S. Private*, pg. 182
Mortensen, Christian, Pres.--Mejeriernes Maelkedisponeringsselskab A.m.b.a, Viby, Denmark; *Int'l*, *pg. 826*
Mortensen, Davis K., Exec. V.P.-Building Products--Georgia-Pacific Building Products Division, Atlanta, GA; *U.S. Public*, pg. 735
Mortensen, H., Mng. Dir.--AB Starla-Werken, Vittaryd, Sweden; *U.S. Public*, pg. 1580
Mortensen, H., Mng. Dir.--Lydex A/S, Middelfart, Denmark; *U.S. Public*, pg. 1580
Mortensen, Jorgen, Mng. Dir.--Nordsten, Skive, Denmark; *Int'l*, pg. 1386
Mortensen, Peter, Chm.--First National Bank of Pennsylvania, Hermitage, PA; *U.S. Public*, pg. 607
Mortensen, Peter, Chm.--Regency Finance Company, Hermitage, PA; *U.S. Public*, pg. 607
Mortensen, Peter, Chief Oper. Officer--Penn-Ohio Life Insurance Company, Phoenix, AZ; *U.S. Public*, pg. 607
Mortensen, R.E., Pres.--Merchants Despatch Transp. Co., Plymouth Meeting, PA; *U.S. Public*, pg. 432
Mortier, Denis, Chm. Bd.--Saint Dominique Participations, Paris, France; *Int'l*, pg. 344
Mortimer, Anthony, Chief Oper. Officer--Goethe Management Ltd., Saint Peter Port, United Kingdom; *Int'l*, pg. 162
Mortimer, Jim, Pres.& Gen. Mgr.--Deseret News, Salt Lake City, UT; *U.S. Private*, pg. 327
Mortine, Neil R., Exec. V.P., Pub. Rels. Dir. & Investor Rels. Dir.--Lord, Sullivan & Yoder Public Relations, Columbus, OH; *U.S. Private*, pg. 676
Morton, A., Mng. Dir.--Davy International, Poole, United Kingdom; *Int'l*, pg. 773
Morton, B. Carole, Pres.--Information Management Division, Woodland Hills, CA; *U.S. Public*, pg. 1516
Morton, David L., Pres. & Chief Exec. Officer--The Quaker Oats Co. of Canada Ltd., Peterborough, Canada; *U.S. Public*, pg. 1348
Morton, Dennis K., Chief Oper. Officer--NationsBank of Texas National Life Insurance Co., Dallas, TX; *U.S. Public*, pg. 1163
Morton, Kenneth S., V.P.--Martin Marietta Technical Support Services, Cherry Hill, NJ; *U.S. Public*, pg. 1007
Morton, Larry, Gen. Mgr.--GATX Logistics, Inc.-Georgia (Norpack), Doraville, GA; *U.S. Public*, pg. 691
Morton, Larry T., Pres. & Chief Oper. Officer--Stocker Resources, Inc., Los Angeles, CA; *U.S. Public*, pg. 1308
Morton, Mark, Pres.--Bowmar Technologies, Fort Wayne, IN; *U.S. Public*, pg. 248
Morton, Robert H., Pres. & Rep. Dir.--Janssen-Cilag K.K., Tokyo, Japan; *U.S. Public*, pg. 929
Morton, T.R., Pres.--PACCAR Financial Corp., Bellevue, WA; *U.S. Public*, pg. 1247
Mortusewicz, Romuald, Mng. Dir.--Schmitt & Weitz Baustoffwerke GmbH & Co. KG, Kleinostheim, Germany; *Int'l*, pg. 606
Mortvedt, Odd, Chief Oper. Officer--A/S Norlett, Askim, Norway; *Int'l*, pg. 443
Moscato, Guglielmo, Pres.--AGIP SpA, Milan, Italy; *Int'l*, pg. 428
Mosch, James G., V.P. & Gen. Mgr.--Dentsply Ash, York, PA; *U.S. Public*, pg. 499
Moscheni, Claude, Dir.-Novotel--Societe Internationale des Hotels Novotel, Evry, France; *Int'l*, pg. 21
Moscogiuri, G., Mng. Dir.--Pignone Engineering Ltd., London, United Kingdom; *Int'l*, pg. 991
Moscon, Antonio, V.P.--Sulzer Brasil S.A., Sao Paulo, Brazil; *Int'l*, pg. 1305
Moscon, Antonio, Mng. Dir.--Fundinox Ltda., Sao Paulo, Brazil; *Int'l*, pg. 1305
Moseby, Wayne, Pres.--Plateau Forest Products, Inc., Bend, OR; *U.S. Public*, pg. 669
Mosel, Ed, V.P.--Pollak-Switching, Canton, MA; *U.S. Private*, *pg. 1045*
Moseley, David, Mng. Dir.--Ferro Corporation (Australia) Pty. Ltd., Melbourne, Australia; *U.S. Public*, pg. 619
Moseley, T., Mng. Dir.--Ascom Timeplex Australia Pty. Ltd., Sydney, Australia; *Int'l*, pg. 87
Moser, Dr. C., Chief Oper. Officer--Gruner + Jahr (Espana) Distribuidora S.A., Madrid, Spain; *Int'l*, pg. 190
Moser, Geoffrey L., Publr.--The Times Herald, Norristown, PA; *U.S. Public*, pg. 935
Moser, Harry, Pres.--Charmilles Technologies Corp., Lincolnshire, IL; *Int'l*, pg. 489
Moser, Marcelo Adolfo, Mgr.--Banco do Brasil S.A.-Chicago, Chicago, IL; *Int'l*, pg. 141
Moser, Peter, Mng. Dir.--Sulzer Friotherm Ltd., Winterthur, Switzerland; *Int'l*, pg. 1306
Moser, Rainer, Pres.--Pfaff American Sales Corp., Paramus, NJ; *Int'l*, pg. 1046
Moser, Roger R., Mgr.--Oakman Telephone Company, Oakman, AL; *U.S. Public*, pg. 1571
Moses, Chuck, Plant Mgr.--Conaire Div., Dayton, OH; *Int'l*, pg. 1398
Moses, Willy, Pres.--AlliedSignal Air Transport Avionics, Fort Lauderdale, FL; *U.S. Public*, pg. 50
Mosgrove, Harry, Pres.--Copper Mountain Resort, Frisco, CO; *Int'l*, pg. 685
Moshe, Celes, Pres.--Netwiz Ltd., Haifa, Israel; *Int'l*, pg. 645
Mosher, Howard, Pres.--Rolls-Royce Motor Cars Incorporated, Lyndhurst, NJ; *Int'l*, pg. 1467
Mosher, James, Pres.--Scotia Trawler Equipment Limited, Lunenburg, Canada; *Int'l*, pg. 909
Mosher, Oren A., Pres.--Eagle Packaging Group, Oakland, CA; *U.S. Private*, pg. 832
Mosher, Paul F., Pres.--Kelco Div., Okmulgee, OK; *U.S. Public*, pg. 1125
Mosimann, Philip, Mng. Dir.--Sulzer Thermatec Ltd., Winterthur, Switzerland; *Int'l*, pg. 1307
Mosle, Robin, V.P.--The Village of Cross Keys, Inc., Baltimore, MD; *U.S. Public*, pg. 1409
Mosley, David, V.P.--Gerber Canada, Mississauga, Canada; *Int'l*, pg. 973
Moss, Bryan C., Vice Chm.--Gulfstream Aerospace Corporation, Savannah, GA; *U.S. Private*, pg. 419
Moss, Cruse W., Chm. Bd. & Chief Exec. Officer--ASIA flxible Automotive Tech. Corp., Ann Arbor, MI; *U.S. Private*, pg. 444
Moss, H. V., Chief Oper. Officer--Featherlite Building Products Operation, Austin, TX; *U.S. Public*, pg. 936
Moss, J. W., Pres.--Patterson Services, Inc., Houma, LA; *U.S. Public*, pg. 1356
Moss, J. W., Pres.--Patterson Truck Line, Inc., Houma, LA; *U.S. Public*, pg. 1356
Moss, Jay, Pres.--Kaufman and Broad of Nevada, Inc., Las Vegas, NV; *U.S. Public*, pg. 945
Moss, Larry, Plant Mgr.--Block Plant, Amarillo, TX; *U.S. Public*, pg. 936
Moss, Michael C., Pres. & Chief Oper. Officer--Atlas Automotive, Inc., Albany, GA; *U.S. Private*, pg. 444
Moss, Perry, Gen. Mgr.--Reclamation Div. (Kansas City), Kansas City, KS; *Int'l*, pg. 1270
Moss, Tony, Pres.--American Fine Foods, Inc., Payette, ID; *U.S. Public*, pg. 349
Moss, William, Pres.--Unichem, Houston, TX; *U.S. Public*, pg. 161
Mossberg, Anders, Mng. Dir.--S-E-Banken Forsakring, Stockholm, Sweden; *Int'l*, pg. 1259
Mosser, Thomas W., Pres.--Avatar Vacation Resorts, Inc., Coral Gables, FL; *U.S. Public*, pg. 151
Mosseri, Marco, Chief Oper. Officer--Nordica S.r.l., Milan, Italy; *Int'l*, pg. 35
Mosshart, Donald, V.P.--Limbach Holdings, Inc., Pittsburgh, PA; *Int'l*, pg. 321
Mosson, Harriet C., Pres.--Liz Claiborne Dress Division, New York, NY; *U.S. Public*, pg. 1006
Mossotto, Cesare, Gen. Mgr.--Cselt, Turin, Italy; *Int'l*, pg. 1362
Mosteller, David E., Pres.--The Frymaster Corp., Shreveport, LA; *Int'l*, pg. 188
Mostert, Adam, Mgr.-Mktg. & Logistics--Sasol Fertilizers, Randburg, South Africa; *Int'l*, pg. 1196
Mostonen, Jussi, Mng. Dir.--Merita Fund Management Ltd., Helsinki, Finland; *Int'l*, pg. 859
Mostrom, Joel, Pres.--Delmarva Properties, Inc., West Point, VA; *U.S. Public*, pg. 347
Mota-Velasco, German Larrea, Chm. & Pres.--Grupo Mexico S.A. de C.V., Mexico, Mexico; *U.S. Public*, pg. 138
Mota, Fernando, Pres.--AGA S.A., Rio de Janeiro, Brazil; *Int'l*, pg. 13
Motet, Andre, Pres.--Nucletudes, Les Ulis, France; *Int'l*, pg. 29
Motherway, Thomas J., Pres.--Boeing Capital Corp., Long Beach, CA; *U.S. Public*, pg. 240
Motherway, Thomas J., Pres. & Chief Fin. Officer--Boeing Realty Corporation, Long Beach, CA; *U.S. Public*, pg. 241
Mothes, Jean, Chief Oper. Officer--Societe Chantilly, Saint Remy-les-Chevreuse, France; *Int'l*, pg. 919
Moticha, John, V.P.-Opers.--The Orvis Company, Roanoke, VA; *U.S. Private*, pg. 820
Motl, Lionel T., V.P. & Gen. Mgr.--Baycoat Limited, Hamilton, Canada; *Int'l*, pg. 1299
Motley, Lyle, Pres. & Chief Exec. Officer--Miami Div., Hialeah, FL; *U.S. Public*, pg. 1148
Motlik, Axel, Mng. Dir.--Korn/Ferry International, Frankfurt/Main, Germany; *U.S. Private*, pg. 633
Motohashi, Takashi, Gen. Mgr.--Daiwa Bank-International Treasury Division, Tokyo, Japan; *Int'l*, pg. 373
Motohashi, Toshiro, Pres.--Dai-Ichi Kangyo Bank (Canada), Toronto, Canada; *Int'l*, pg. 362
Motomatsu, Yukuto, Chief Exec. Officer--Ascom Hasler (Japan) Ltd., Tokyo, Japan; *Int'l*, pg. 87
Motonti, Frank, Pres.--Co-Jac Finishers, Inc., West Orange, NJ; *U.S. Private*, pg. 120
Motoshige, Eiichi, Pres.--Kajima Development Corp., Monterey Park, CA; *Int'l*, pg. 722

Motraghi, Mahyar, Pres.--Nokia Display Products Inc., Sausalito, CA; *Int'l*, pg. 954
Mott, Frederick B., Jr., Pres. & Publr.--The State-Record Company, Columbia, SC; *U.S. Public*, pg. 964
Mott, Mikael, Mgr.--Sandvik (Schweiz) AG, Zurich, Switzerland; *Int'l*, pg. 1187
Mott, Rodney, V.P. & Gen. Mgr.--Nucor Steel-Arkansas, Blytheville, AR; *U.S. Public*, pg. 1205
Mott, Tony, Dir.-Publicity--Bantam Paperbacks UK, London, United Kingdom; *Int'l*, pg. 191
Motta, James, Chief Exec. Officer--Arvida, Boca Raton, FL; *U.S. Private*, pg. 578
Motter, Carl J., Jr., Pres.--Bedford Associates, Inc., Johnstown, PA; *U.S. Public*, pg. 164
Mottern, K. Neil, Jr., Pres.--Triumph Air Repair, Phoenix, AZ; *U.S. Public*, pg. 1640
Mottershead, Derek, Mng. Dir.--Bang & Olufsen United Kingdom Ltd., Wokingham, United Kingdom; *Int'l*, pg. 146
Mottino, Piergiacomo, Chief Fin. Officer--Olivetti Malaysia Sdn Bhd, Kuala Lumpur, Malaysia; *Int'l*, pg. 1003
Mottola, John T., Pres.--Gibraltar Casualty Co., Newark, NJ; *U.S. Private*, pg. 892
Mottola, Kathy, Mgr.--Quest Diagnostic, Edison, NJ; *U.S. Public*, pg. 1351
Mottola, Kathy, Lab Mgr.--Quest Diagnostic-Holmdel, Holmdel, NJ; *U.S. Public*, pg. 1351
Mottram, J., Mng. Dir.--Simon Access (U.K.) Ltd., Gloucester, United Kingdom; *Int'l*, pg. 1251
Motzkin, Barry, V.P. & Asst. Treas.--Kingston Oil Supply Corp., Port Ewen, NY; *U.S. Public*, pg. 741
Moudarres, Louaye, Mgr.--EG & G Instruments Division, Evry, France; *U.S. Public*, pg. 544
Moudarri, Soubhi, Mng. Dir.--Farouk Advertising, Jeddah, Saudi Arabia; *U.S. Private*, pg. 304
Mougeot, Robert F., Chm. Bd. & Pres.--HEI Investment Corp., Honolulu, HI; *U.S. Public*, pg. 800
Mougeot, Robert F., Chief Oper. Officer & Chief Fin. Officer--HEI Diversified, Inc., Honolulu, HI; *U.S. Public*, pg. 800
Moulds, Richard, Gen. Mgr.--Videoserver Connections, Burlington, MA; *U.S. Public*, pg. 1720
Moulierac, Olivier, Creative Dir.--EURO RSCG Institutionnel, Levallois-Perret, France; *Int'l*, pg. 600
Moult, William, Pres. & Chief Exec. Officer--ASI Market Research, Inc., Stamford, CT; *U.S. Private*, pg. 554
Moulton, E., Chief Oper. Officer--Signal Capital Corporation, Danvers, MA; *U.S. Public*, pg. 115
Moum, Ingebrigt, Pres.--Kvaerner Engineering A/S, Lysaker, Norway; *Int'l*, pg. 766
Mounsey, J.B., Sr. V.P.-Investments--Manulife International Investment Office, London, United Kingdom; *Int'l*, pg. 841
Mounsey, Joseph, Chm. Bd. & Mng. Dir.--The Manufacturers Life Insurance Company (UK) Limited, Stevenage, United Kingdom; *Int'l*, pg. 841
Mount, Don, V.P.-Jeff. Div.--Wyandot, Inc., Jeffersonville, IN; *U.S. Private*, pg. 1193
Mount, John M., Pres. & Chief Exec. Officer--Service America Systems, Inc., Deerfield Beach, FL; *U.S. Public*, pg. 344
Mountcastle, Thomas L., Pres.--Halifax Technology Services Company, Richmond, VA; *U.S. Public*, pg. 775
Mourad, Henry, Pres.--CXR Telcom Corporation, Fremont, CA; *U.S. Public*, pg. 1108
Mousley, Janet, V.P.--Software Plus Inc., Durham, NC; *U.S. Private*, pg. 1012
Moussu, Gerard, Pres.--Bensons, Paris, France; *Int'l*, pg. 460
Mouton, E., Chief Exec. Officer--WAGO Contact SARL, Roissy Charles de Gaulle, France; *Int'l*, pg. 209
Mouyas, Dennis, Reg. Mgr.--SMS-New York, New York, NY; *U.S. Public*, pg. 1463
Mowatt, Bruce, Branch Mgr.--Queensland Branch, Acacia Ridge, Australia; *Int'l*, pg. 226
Mowatt, George, Pres.--Kvaerner H&G Offshore Ltd, Croydon, United Kingdom; *Int'l*, pg. 771
Mowatt, Thomas, Pres. & Chief Oper. Officer--Champion Laboratories, Inc., Albion, IL; *U.S. Private*, pg. 1113
Mowatt, Thomas, Chief Oper. Officer--Luber-Finer, Europe, N.V./S.A., Antwerp, Belgium; *U.S. Private*, pg. 1113
Mowday, Graeme, Gen. Mgr.--Goldsack Harris Thompson Advertising, Wellington, New Zealand; *U.S. Private*, pg. 184
Mowder, John P., Pres.--Dixon Industries, Inc., Coffeyville, KS; *U.S. Public*, pg. 238
Mowers, Rob, Gen. Mgr.--Southern California Auto Auction, Fontana, CA; *U.S. Private*, pg. 282
Mowery, Richard, Mgr.--General Employment Enterprises, Raleigh, NC; *U.S. Public*, pg. 714
Mowitz, Hakan, Pres.--ICA Meny Foretagen AB, Bromma, Sweden; *Int'l*, pg. 643
Mowris, Bob, Exec. V.P.--Accudyne Corporation, Janesville, WI; *U.S. Public*, pg. 47
Mowry, Ron, Mgr.-Sls.--Weatherford US Inc., Grand Junction, CO; *U.S. Public*, pg. 1750
Moxley, J., Gen. Mgr.--Kodak (Near East) Inc., Athens, Greece; *U.S. Public*, pg. 554
Moya Ferrera, Fernando, Mng. Dir.--Comunica Leo Burnett Panama, S.A., Panama, Panama; *U.S. Private*, pg. 184
Moyan, Francois, Pres. & Chief Exec. Officer--Companhia Siderurgica Belgo-Mineira, Belo Horizonte, Brazil; *Int'l*, pg. 79
Moyd, Jim, Plant Mgr.--Eufaula Plant, Eufaula, AL; *U.S. Public*, pg. 444
Moye, Larry, Gen. Mgr.--Poe & Brown of Florida, Leesburg, FL; *U.S. Public*, pg. 1312
Moyen, Francois, Pres.--B.M.B. Belgo-Mineira Bekaert Artefatos de Arame Ltda., Vespasiano, Brazil; *Int'l*, pg. 184
Moyer, Bill, Plant Mgr.--Mossberg Industries, Hubbard Division, Garrett, IN; *U.S. Private*, pg. 764
Moyer, Dennis, Reg. Gen. Mgr.--Carrier Ontario, Rexdale, Canada; *U.S. Public*, pg. 1691
Moyer, Kevin, Pres.-Capital Markets Group--Dana Commercial Credit Corp. (Ohio), Toledo, OH; *U.S. Public*, pg. 479
Moyes, Jerry, Pres.--Swift Leasing Co., Phoenix, AZ; *U.S. Public*, pg. 1543
Moylan, James E., Chm. Bd.--Citrus Corp., Houston, TX; *U.S. Public*, pg. 585
Moylan, Tom, Mgr.--Sandvik Steel Canada, Arnprior, Canada; *Int'l*, pg. 1188
Moynan, John, Pres.--Financial Collection Agencies, Inc., Phoenix, AZ; *Int'l*, pg. 471
Moynan, John, Pres.--Financial Collection Agencies, Hato Rey, PR; *Int'l*, pg. 471
Moynan, John, Pres.--Financial Collection Agencies of Pennsylvania Inc, Wayne, PA; *Int'l*, pg. 471
Moynan, John H., Pres.--Financial Collection Agencies (UK) Limited, London, United Kingdom; *Int'l*, pg. 471
Moynan, John H., Pres.--FCA Holdings, Inc., Wayne, PA; *Int'l*, pg. 471
Moynan, John H., Pres.--Financial Collection Agencies (1990) Inc., Mobile, AL; *Int'l*, pg. 471
Moynan, John H., Pres.--Financial Collection Agencies (1990) Inc., Cohoes, NY; *Int'l*, pg. 471
Moynan, John H., Pres.--Financial Collection Agencies (1990) Inc., Scotch Plains, NJ; *Int'l*, pg. 471
Moynan, John H., Pres.--Financial Collection Agencies (1990) Inc., Boston, MA; *Int'l*, pg. 471
Moynan, John H., Pres.--Financial Collection Agencies (1990) Inc., Lombard, IL; *Int'l*, pg. 471
Moynan, John H., Pres.--Financial Collection Agencies (1990) Inc., Houston, TX; *Int'l*, pg. 471
Moynan, John H., Pres.--Financial Collection Agencies (1990) Inc., Milwaukee, WI; *Int'l*, pg. 471
Moynan, John H., Pres.--Financial Collection Agencies (1990) Inc., Richmond, VA; *Int'l*, pg. 471
Moynan, John H., Pres.--Financial Collection Agencies (1990) Inc., San Diego, CA; *Int'l*, pg. 471
Moynan, John H., Pres.--Financial Collection Agencies, Manchester, United Kingdom; *Int'l*, pg. 471
Moynan, John H., Pres.--Structured Financial Capital Inc., Wayne, PA; *Int'l*, pg. 471
Moynan, John H., Pres.--Recon Consultants, Inc., Wayne, PA; *Int'l*, pg. 471
Moysey, Warren, Pres. & Chief Exec. Officer--Aetna Canada Holdings Ltd., Toronto, Canada; *U.S. Public*, pg. 27
Mozilo, Angelo R., Pres. & Chief Exec. Officer--Countrywide Funding Corporation, Pasadena, CA; *U.S. Public*, pg. 453
Mozley, Anthony, Mng. Dir.--Robert Fleming Italia SpA, Milan, Italy; *Int'l*, pg. 494
Mozota, J., Mgr.--Nalco de Venezuela, C.A., Caracas, Venezuela; *U.S. Public*, pg. 1150
Mpofu, S.G., Mng. Dir.--Longman Zimbabwe (Pte) Ltd., Harare, Zimbabwe; *Int'l*, pg. 1026
Mraz, Kenneth J., Gen. Mgr.--Corrugated Container Div.-Charlotte Plant, Charlotte, NC; *U.S. Public*, pg. 1520
Mroue, Mike, Division Mgr.--Horizon Technology Group - Romulus Division, Romulus, MI; *U.S. Private*, pg. 539
Mroz, Leo B., Chief Oper. Officer--Akerlund & Rausing GmbH, Hamburg, Germany; *Int'l*, pg. 33
Mu, Ruisheng, Gen. Mgr.--Bank of China, New York, NY; *Int'l*, pg. 152
Muasher, N., Company Head--SKF Intertrade S.A. Amman, Amman, Jordan; *Int'l*, pg. 1158
Muchatuta, Victor, Chief Exec.--Southampton Assurance Company of Zimbabwe Limited, Harare, Zimbabwe; *Int'l*, pg. 77
Muchnick, Alberto, First V.P.--RNBNY Branch Office-Santiago, Santiago, Chile; *U.S. Public*, pg. 1381
Muck, Henry, Mng. Dir.--ComAlloy International Company, Nashville, TN; *U.S. Public*, pg. 1441
Muck, Henry, Gen. Mgr.--Com Alloy International Company, Akron, OH; *U.S. Public*, pg. 1441
Muckle, Rick L., V.P.--Standard Commercial Tobacco Co. of Canada Ltd., Tillsonburg, Canada; *U.S. Public*, pg. 1502
Muckleroy, M.C., Pres.--Camco Products & Services Company, Houston, TX; *U.S. Public*, pg. 298
Muczko, John, V.P. & Gen. Mgr.--GKI Electronic Enclosure Division-Orlando, Orlando, FL; *U.S. Public*, pg. 717
Muczko, John, V.P.--GKI Electronic Enclosure Division-Johnstown, Johnstown, PA; *U.S. Public*, pg. 717
Mudd, Larry, V.P.-McBee Opers.--A.O. Smith Water Products Company, McBee, SC; *U.S. Public*, pg. 1477
Mudge, Fred, Plant Mgr.--Square D Co., Schiller Park, IL; *Int'l*, pg. 1208
Mudrak, Ota, Pres.--Mann Filtr Jipap s.r.o., Okrisky, Czech Republic; *Int'l*, pg. 484
Muehlhausen, E.W., Mgr.-Opers.--Belarus Machinery, Inc., Milwaukee, WI; *Int'l*, pg. 101
Mueller, Alfred K., Div. Mgr.--Interstate Brick Company, West Jordan, UT; *U.S. Private*, pg. 830
Mueller, B.J., Mgr.--General Employment Enterprises, Inc., Torrance, CA; *U.S. Public*, pg. 714
Mueller, Bob, V.P. & Reg. Mgr.--Circle Freight International USA, Bensenville, IL; *U.S. Public*, pg. 371
Mueller, Charles W., Pres. & Chief Exec. Officer--AmerenUE, Saint Louis, MO; *U.S. Public*, pg. 66
Mueller, Donald D., Pres.--Mapelli Brothers Company, Greeley, CO; *U.S. Public*, pg. 427
Mueller, Eberhard, Gen. Mgr. & Head Chef--Lutece, New York, NY; *U.S. Public*, pg. 130
Mueller, Ed, Pres. & Chief Exec. Officer--Pacific Bell, San Ramon, CA; *U.S. Public*, pg. 1416
Mueller, Ed, Pres. & Chief Exec. Officer--Pacific Bell, San Francisco, CA; *U.S. Public*, pg. 1416
Mueller, Fred, Gen. Mgr.--AlliedSignal Aerospace Canada, Aeromarine, Richmond, Canada; *U.S. Public*, pg. 53
Mueller, Fred, Pres.--Card Technology Corp., Paramus, NJ; *Int'l*, pg. 898
Mueller, Hans Gunter, Prof. Dr., Chm.--Mannesmann Demag Fordertechnik AG, Wetter, Germany; *Int'l*, pg. 837
Mueller, Heinz, Mng. Dir.--Industrial Acoustics Company GmbH, Niederkruchten, Germany; *U.S. Public*, pg. 875
Mueller, Jack J., Pres. & Chief Exec. Officer--Cincinnati Bell Directory Inc., Cincinnati, OH; *U.S. Public*, pg. 367
Mueller, James, Pres.--The Hall Chemical Company, Wickliffe, OH; *U.S. Private*, pg. 461
Mueller, John J., Div. V.P.--Packaging Systems Division, Saint Paul, MN; *U.S. Public*, pg. 1605
Mueller, Kurt, Dr., Pres.--Kvaerner Pulping AG, Zurich, Switzerland; *Int'l*, pg. 768
Mueller, Kurt, Dr., Pres.--Kamyr Holding AG, Zurich, Switzerland; *Int'l*, pg. 770
Mueller, Larry, Pres.--ABB Process Analytics, Lewisburg, WV; *Int'l*, pg. 5
Mueller, Martin R., Pres.--Information Technology Division, Bellevue, NE; *U.S. Public*, pg. 1516
Mueller, Paula, V.P. & Sec.--Dualite Sales & Service, Inc., Williamsburg, OH; *U.S. Private*, pg. 344
Mueller, Rand, Pres.--Tessco Group, Inc., Georgetown, TX; *U.S. Public*, pg. 394
Mueller, Rand, Pres.--Code Alarm Security Systems, Madison Heights, MI; *U.S. Public*, pg. 394
Mueller, Richard G., Mng. Dir.--Toro-Wheel Horse, South Bend, IN; *U.S. Public*, pg. 1624
Mueller, Robert, Pres.--Lockheed Martin Electro-Optical Systems, Pasadena, CA; *U.S. Public*, pg. 1008
Mueller, Robert W., Pres. & Chief Exec. Officer--Victoria Financial Corporation, Cleveland, OH; *U.S. Public*, pg. 1660
Mueller, Robert W., Pres. & Chief Exec. Officer--Victoria Fire & Casualty, Cleveland, OH; *U.S. Public*, pg. 1660
Mueller, Steve C., Gen. Mgr.--Round Mountain Gold Corporation, Round Mountain, NV; *U.S. Public*, pg. 562
Mueller, Wolfgang, Gen. Mgr.--Encore Computer GmbH, Dusseldorf, Germany; *U.S. Public*, pg. 580
Muffler, Thomas, Pres.--Allo Pro GmbH, Gelsenkirchen, Germany; *Int'l*, pg. 1307
Muftuoglu, Zeki, Chief Oper. Officer--Cignasa Sigorta A.S., Istanbul, Turkey; *U.S. Public*, pg. 363
Muftuoglu, Zeki, Chief Oper. Officer--Cignasa Sigorta A.S., Istanbul, Turkey; *Int'l*, pg. 1167
Mugiri, Dr. E.M., Mng. Dir.--Longman Kenya Ltd., Nairobi, Kenya; *Int'l*, pg. 1027
Mugler, Thierry, Chief Exec. Officer--Mugler Triumvirat, Paris, France; *Int'l*, pg. 295
Mugnai, Franco, Chm. Bd.--Italfid Italiana Fiduciaria S.p.A., Milan, Italy; *Int'l*, pg. 138
Muhlbradt, Karl, Chief Oper. Officer--MacGREGOR (ESP) S.A., Las Arenas, Spain; *Int'l*, pg. 670
Muhle, Rudolf, Mng. Dir.--Dyckerhoff & Widmann AG Sucursal Buenos Aires, Buenos Aires, Argentina; *Int'l*, pg. 424
Muhleisen, M., Gen. Mgr.--Kodak AG, Stuttgart, Germany; *U.S. Public*, pg. 552
Muhlenkamp, Ben J., Pres.--Red Wing Co. Inc., Fredonia, NY; *Int'l*, pg. 1398
Muhr, E., Gen. Mgr.--Branson (Europa) B.V., Soest, Netherlands; *U.S. Public*, pg. 576
Muir, Dave, Mgr.--Eclipse Combustion, Inc., Lake Stevens, WA; *U.S. Private*, pg. 360
Muir, Edward D., Chm. & Chief Exec. Officer--Rapidforms, Inc., Thorofare, NJ; *U.S. Public*, pg. 1171
Muir, Sam, Dir.--Ervin Amasteel Uk. LP, Tipton, United Kingdom; *U.S. Private*, pg. 382
Muis, Leo, Pres.--Perstorp Nederland B.V., Oud-Beijerland, Netherlands; *Int'l*, pg. 1038
Mujagic, Christophe, Mng. Dir.--Chargeurs Wool, Paris, France; *Int'l*, pg. 280
Mukoyama, S., Pres.--Nippon Light Metal Co. Ltd., Tokyo, Japan; *Int'l*, pg. 52
Mulak, Tom, Asst. V.P. & Fulfillment Dir.--Human Sciences Press, Inc., New York, NY; *U.S. Public*, pg. 1311
Mulally, Alan R., Pres.--Boeing Defense & Space Group, Kent, WA; *U.S. Public*, pg. 240
Mulcahy, J. Clifford, Publisher--Business Marketing, Chicago, IL; *U.S. Private*, pg. 285
Mulcahy, Joseph L., V.P.--Methode Electronics Inc.-East, Willingboro, NJ; *U.S. Public*, pg. 1101
Mulcahy, Richard T., V.P. & Div. Mgr.--Ragnar Benson, Inc., Monroeville, PA; *U.S. Private*, pg. 99
Mulder, Dave, Gen. Mgr.--Sun Microsystems of Canada-Edmonton, Edmonton, Canada; *U.S. Public*, pg. 1532
Mulder, Michel F.J., Mgr.--Barenbrug U.K. Ltd., Bury Saint Edmunds, United Kingdom; *Int'l*, pg. 167
Mulder, N., Mng. Dir.--Dynadro bv, s Hertogenbosch, Netherlands; *Int'l*, pg. 681
Mulders, Hans, Mgr.--Sandvik Process Systems B.V., Raamsdonksveer, Netherlands; *Int'l*, pg. 1186
Muldoon, Patricia, Pres.--Star States Development Co., Wilmington, DE; *U.S. Public*, pg. 1729
Muldoon, Thomas W., V.P. & Gen. Mgr.-Services Sector--GTE Government Systems Corporation, Needham, MA; *U.S. Public*, pg. 696
Muldowney, P., Pres. & Chief Exec. Officer--Morgan Chemical Products Inc., Tucker, GA; *Int'l*, pg. 892
Mulhall, John, Mgr.-Opers./Canada--Cooper Industries (Canada) Inc., Barrie, Canada; *U.S. Public*, pg. 444
Mulhaupt, F., Pres.--NFPA Research Foundation, Quincy, MA; *U.S. Private*, pg. 783
Mulhench, Kevin, Chief Exec. Officer--Lambert Smith Hampton, Belfast, United Kingdom; *Int'l*, pg. 797
Mulhern, Malcolm, Chief Oper. Officer--Frionor (Thailand) Ltd., Bangkok, Thailand; *Int'l*, pg. 516
Mulholland, Michael, Chief Exec. Officer--Sungard Recovery Services Group, Wayne, PA; *U.S. Public*, pg. 1535
Mulholland, Paul, Chief Oper. Officer--Chemrock Corporation, Jacksonville, FL; *U.S. Private*, pg. 903
Mulholland, R. J., Pres.--Durr Industries, Inc., Plymouth, MI; *Int'l*, pg. 421
Mulholland, Ross, Mgr.--BHP Fastener Products, Altona, Australia; *Int'l*, pg. 226
Mulkey, Terry, Pres.--Sunrise Mobility Products Division, Longmont, CO; *U.S. Public*, pg. 1536
Mullagh, Michael, Pres. & Chief Exec. Officer--Whisper Communications, Sunnyvale, CA; *U.S. Public*, pg. 1425

Mulle, Rogerio Dalle, Gen. Mgr.--Acos Villares Plant - Pindamonhangaba, Pindamonhangaba, Brazil; *Int'l*, pg. 23
Mullen, Dennis M., Pres. & Chief Exec. Officer--Agrilink Foods, Inc., Rochester, NY; *U.S. Private*, pg. 887
Mullen, Ivan D., Pres.--Fleming Foods of Alabama, Inc., Geneva, AL; *U.S. Public*, pg. 653
Mullen, John, Pres.--Financial Indemnity, Burbank, CA; *U.S. Public*, pg. 1694
Mullen, Paul B., Pres. & Chief Exec. Officer--GES Exposition Services, Inc., Las Vegas, NV; *U.S. Public*, pg. 1718
Muller-Bunz, Manfred, Mng. Dir.--Wuestenrot Grundstuecksverwertungs-GmbH, Ludwigsburg, Germany; *Int'l*, pg. 1514
Muller-Eschenbach, Peter, Chm. Bd.--Krupp Widia GmbH, Essen, Germany; *Int'l*, pg. 510
Muller, Bernard, Chm. Bd.--Compagnie Bancaire, Paris, France; *Int'l*, pg. 319
Muller, Daniel, Pres.--Ohio Alloy Steels Corporation, Youngstown, OH; *U.S. Public*, pg. 1617
Muller, Ed, Chief Oper. Officer--TrefilARBED Grembergen S.A., Grembergen, Belgium; *Int'l*, pg. 80
Muller, Eduard, Mng. Dir.--Salzgitter Oberflachentechnik GmbH, Salzgitter, Germany; *Int'l*, pg. 1308
Muller, Edward R., Pres. & Chief Exec. Officer--Edison Mission Energy, Irvine, CA; *U.S. Public*, pg. 564
Muller, F.C.L., Pres.--Scholastic-Canada, Ltd., Richmond Hill, Canada; *U.S. Public*, pg. 1440
Muller, Gary, Gen. Mgr.--Sterling Electronics, Phoenix, AZ; *U.S. Public*, pg. 1051
Muller, H., Pres. & Chief Exec. Officer--Voith Sulzer Papiertechnik GmbH, Heidenheim, Germany; *Int'l*, pg. 1307
Muller, Hans, Mng. Dir.--Sulzer Papertec GmbH, Krefeld, Germany; *Int'l*, pg. 1305
Muller, Heinz, Mng. Dir.--Bang & Olufsen AG, Bassersdorf, Switzerland; *Int'l*, pg. 146
Muller, Heinz, Sr. V.P.--Voest-Alpine Industries, Inc.-Continuous Casting, New York, NY; *Int'l*, pg. 1470
Muller, Henry, Chm.--Coop Winterthur, Winterthur, Switzerland; *Int'l*, pg. 329
Muller, Hermann, Mng. Dir.--Sulzer Korea Ltd., Seoul, Korea; *Int'l*, pg. 1306
Muller, Jurgen, Mng. Dir.--Dynacast Deutschland GmbH, Braunlingen, Germany; *Int'l*, pg. 300
Muller, Karl, Mng. Dir.--Dun & Bradstreet Norge AS, Oslo, Norway; *U.S. Public*, pg. 536
Muller, Klaus H.F., Mng. Dir.--Dresdner Bank AG, Manama, Bahrain; *Int'l*, pg. 419
Muller, Kurt, Pres.--Parker Hannifin GmbH/Pradifa Packing Division, Bietigheim-Bissingen, Germany; *U.S. Public*, pg. 1262
Muller, Kurt, Grp. Pres.--Parker Hannifin GmbH, O-Ring Div. Europe, Pleidelsheim, Germany; *U.S. Public*, pg. 1263
Muller, L., Mng. Dir.--GKN Remanufacturing GmbH, Offenbach/Main, Germany; *Int'l*, pg. 536
Muller, Louise, Admin.--Hillhaven Convalescent Hospital Sherwood, Sacramento, CA; *U.S. Public*, pg. 1713
Muller, Louise, Admin.--Saylor Lane Convalescent Hospital, Sacramento, CA; *U.S. Public*, pg. 1714
Muller, M.K., Mgr.--Schweizerischer Bankverein, Saint Gallen, Switzerland; *Int'l*, pg. 1329
Muller, Norbert, Chief Exec. Officer--Thuringia Versicherung AG, Munich, Germany; *Int'l*, pg. 15
Muller, P.B., Pres.--Peabody Engineering Corp., Stamford, CT; *Int'l*, pg. 1065
Muller, Reidar, Chief Oper. Officer--Nordisk Elektra AB, Malmo, Sweden; *Int'l*, pg. 709
Muller, Wolfgang, Mng. Dir.--Wallace & Tiernan GmbH, Guenzberg, Germany; *U.S. Public*, pg. 61
Mullet, Geoff, Chief Oper. Officer--AB Pharos Marine Pte. Ltd., Singapore, Singapore; *Int'l*, pg. 1290
Mullican, Mark, Pres.--First Maryland Brokerage Corporation, Baltimore, MD; *Int'l*, pg. 64
Mullican, Mark, Pres.--First Maryland Annuities Agency Corporation, Baltimore, MD; *Int'l*, pg. 64
Mullick, G., Exec. Dir.--Western Region, Mumbai, India; *Int'l*, pg. 673
Mulligan, Gerald T., Pres. & Chief Exec. Officer--First Mutual of Boston, Boston, MA; *U.S. Public*, pg. 184
Mulligan, John, Reg. Dir.--Willis Corroon Midlands Limited, Leicester, United Kingdom; *Int'l*, pg. 1502
Mulligan, Michael J., Exec. V.P.--Berlitz Publishing Company Inc., New York, NY; *U.S. Public*, pg. 221
Mulligan, Michael J., Exec. V.P.--Berlitz Translation Services, Inc., New York, NY; *U.S. Public*, pg. 221
Mullin, L., Pres.--BFC Utilities, Scarborough, Canada; *Int'l*, pg. 118
Mullin, L., Pres.--Cliffside Utility Contractors, Scarborough, Canada; *Int'l*, pg. 118
Mullinax, Larry, Pres.--Ed Mullinax Ford, Inc., Amherst, OH; *U.S. Public*, pg. 1379
Mullinex, Melton "Bill" W., Jr., Admin.--Piedmont Nursing Center, Inc., Albemarle, NC; *U.S. Public*, pg. 1714
Mullins, Ken, Mng. Dir.--Damart, Bingley, United Kingdom; *Int'l*, pg. 376
Mullins, Sandra, Gen. Mgr.--Converse Land Title Company, Douglas, WY; *U.S. Public*, pg. 625
Mullis, Jr., H. John, Pres. & Chief Exec. Officer--Washburn Graphics, Inc., Charlotte, NC; *U.S. Public*, pg. 291
Mulqueen, Tom, Plant Mgr.--Abbott Laboratories Ltd.-Mfg., Montreal, Canada; *U.S. Public*, pg. 14
Multer, Karl, Gen. Mgr.--Dun & Bradstreet Danmark A/S, Copenhagen, Denmark; *U.S. Public*, pg. 536
Mulvany, Ken G., Gen. Mgr.--Avery Label Ltd., Dublin, Ireland; *U.S. Public*, pg. 153
Mulvey, Neil, Gen. Mgr.--EA Engineering, Science & Technology, Inc., Berkeley Heights, NJ; *U.S. Public*, pg. 541
Mulvey, S., Mng. Dir.--Kvaerner Process Systems Inc., Calgary, Canada; *Int'l*, pg. 768
Mulvihill, Maureen, Branch Mgr.--Downey Savings & Loan Association, F.A., Newport Beach, CA; *U.S. Public*, pg. 526
Mulyana, Anthony, Mgr.--P.T. Crown Cork & Seal Indonesia, Jakarta, Indonesia; *U.S. Public*, pg. 464
Muma, Leslie M., Vice Chm., Pres. & Chief Oper. Officer--Fiserv, Inc., Brookfield, WI; *U.S. Public*, pg. 647
Mumanyi, Charles, Dir.--TAC The Advertising Company Limited, Nairobi, Kenya; *U.S. Private*, pg. 389
Mumford, Richard, Mng. Dir.--Stansand Limited, London, United Kingdom; *Int'l*, pg. 1377
Mumm, Robert, V.P.-Sls.--Wilton Tool Corp., Schiller Park, IL; *U.S. Private*, pg. 1181
Mummert, Jim, Reg. Dir.--AlliedSignal Aerospace Service Corporation, Athens, Greece; *U.S. Public*, pg. 52
Munch, Hans, Sls. Dir.--Intervascular GmbH, Bensheim, Germany; *U.S. Public*, pg. 488
Munck, Gabriel, Pres.--YLA, Inc., Benicia, CA; *Int'l*, pg. 1037
Munda, Alfredo, Gen. Mgr.--Gillette de Venezuela S.A., Caracas, Venezuela; *U.S. Public*, pg. 744
Mundell, D.E., Chm.--ORIX USA Corporation-San Francisco, San Francisco, CA; *Int'l*, pg. 1009
Mundt, G. Henry, III, Pres. & Chief Exec. Officer--MasterCard International-Cirrus Brand, Purchase, NY; *U.S. Private*, pg. 714
Mundy, Roy W., II, Pres.--Kentucky-American Water Co., Lexington, KY; *U.S. Public*, pg. 95
Muneshigo, Okira, Pres.--Mitsui Sugar Co., Ltd., Tokyo, Japan; *Int'l*, pg. 878
Mungall, J.N., Gen. Mgr.--Rocol/Molybond Laboratories Division, Smithfield, Australia; *Int'l*, pg. 895
Munger, Charles T., Chm. Bd.--Wesco Financial Corporation, Pasadena, CA; *U.S. Public*, pg. 217
Mungo, Frank, Chief Exec. Officer--Bryant Mungo Division, Lansing, IL; *U.S. Private*, pg. 1075
Muniz, Cris, Asst. Gen. Mgr. & Mgr.-Matls.--IEC Edinburg, Texas, Edinburg, TX; *U.S. Public*, pg. 855
Munn, Edward, Pres.--MNC Mortgage Corporation, Baltimore, MD; *U.S. Public*, pg. 639
Munnich, Walter, Pres.--A. Friedrich Flender AG, Bocholt, Germany; *Int'l*, pg. 400
Munnich, Walter, Chm.--Flender Ishibashi Co. Ltd., Fukuoka, Japan; *Int'l*, pg. 400
Munnikhuysen, David, Gen. Mgr.--Ohio Auto Auction, Columbus, OH; *U.S. Private*, pg. 283
Munoz, Frank, Dir.--Ryerson de Mexico, San Nicolas, Mexico; *Int'l*, pg. 66
Munoz, Luis, Chief Oper. Officer--Specia Colombia, Bogota, Colombia; *Int'l*, pg. 1114
Munoz, Raul, Pres.--Du Pont (New Zealand) Ltd., Auckland, New Zealand; *U.S. Public*, pg. 533
Munoz, T.G., Gen. Mgr.--ING Bank Sofia, Sofia, Bulgaria; *Int'l*, pg. 649
Munro, Angus, Representative--Kvaerner Professional Services Ltd., Nesbru, Norway; *Int'l*, pg. 767
Munro, Jose E Martinez, Pres.--Dynapac S.A., Madrid, Spain; *Int'l*, pg. 1420
Munro, Richard, Mng. Dir.--Hanimex (NZ) Limited, Albany, New Zealand; *Int'l*, pg. 1116
Munro, Robert J., Exec. V.P. & Gen. Mgr.--Motor Coach Industries Ltd., Winnipeg, Canada; *Int'l*, pg. 326
Munroe, Gerry A., Gen. Mgr.--John O. Butler Company (Canada), Guelph, Canada; *Int'l*, pg. 1320
Munson, Edward, Jr., Pres. & Gen. Mgr.--WAVY-Television, Inc., Portsmouth, VA; *U.S. Public*, pg. 11
Munson, Gary A., V.P.-Sls.--Crown Cork & Seal, Western Div., La Mirada, CA; *U.S. Public*, pg. 463
Munson, Rick, Gen. Mgr.--Beveridge Paper Co., Indianapolis, IN; *U.S. Private*, pg. 1000
Munson, Robin, Investment Mgr.--Financial Opportunities, Inc., Enfield, CT; *U.S. Public*, pg. 477
Munt, D., Mng. Dir.--Ferrymasters Limited, Altrincham, United Kingdom; *Int'l*, pg. 1033
Muntjewerf, A.K., Mng. Dir.--Analytisch Biochemisch Laboratorium B.V., Assen, Netherlands; *Int'l*, pg. 991
Munz, Klaus Martin, Mng. Dir.--TOBETON, Societe Togolaise de Beton, S.A., Lome, Togo; *Int'l*, pg. 425
Munzel, Friedrich, Mng. Dir.--PROREMA An-und Vermietungsgesellschaft mbH, Hamburg, Germany; *Int'l*, pg. 423
Murad, Humayun, Mng. Dir.--ORIX Leasing Pakistan Limited, Karachi, Pakistan; *Int'l*, pg. 1010
Murai, Hiroshi, Gen. Mgr.--Kyodo Advertising Co., Ltd., Osaka, Japan; *Int'l*, pg. 776
Murai, Masaru, Chm.--Compaq Computer Japan KK, Tokyo, Japan; *U.S. Public*, pg. 418
Murakami, Akira, Gen. Mgr.--New Oji Paper Co., Ltd., Seattle, WA; *Int'l*, pg. 998
Murakami, Koji, Pres.--Kyodo TDI Limited Company, Tokyo, Japan; *U.S. Public*, pg. 1219
Murakami, Kunio, Mng. Dir.--Yamaichi International (Middle East) E.C., Manama, Bahrain; *Int'l*, pg. 1518
Murakami, Mamoru, Gen. Mgr.--Universal Studios Music KK, Tokyo, Japan; *Int'l*, pg. 1217
Murakami, Tomio, Pres.--Laboratorios Miquel, S.A., Barcelona, Spain; *Int'l*, pg. 1014
Murakami, Yasufumi, Chief Oper. Officer--Makita Do Brasil Ferramentas Eletricas LTDA., Sao Bernardo do Campo, Brazil; *Int'l*, pg. 832
Muramatsa, Tadashi, Mgr.-Terminal--Yokohama Terminal, Yokohama, Japan; *U.S. Public*, pg. 693
Muranushi, H.D., Chief Oper. Officer--A & A Japan Ltd., Tokyo, Japan; *U.S. Public*, pg. 1561
Muraoka, Noboru, Mng. Dir.--Hanimex Vivitar Japan K.K., Tokyo, Japan; *Int'l*, pg. 1061
Muraoka, Sadao, Chief Rep.--Long-Term Credit Bank of Japan, Limited, Dallas, TX; *Int'l*, pg. 816
Murase, Yasuhisa, Pres.--Tokai Bank (Deutschland) GmbH, Frankfurt/Main, Germany; *Int'l*, pg. 1391
Murata, Mike, Mgr.-Chicago Office--Noritake Co., Inc.-Electronics Division, Arlington Heights, IL; *Int'l*, pg. 959
Murata, Minotu, Mgr.-Boston Office--Noritake Co., Inc.-Electronics Div., Boston, Burlington, MA; *Int'l*, pg. 959
Murata, Taketo, Pres.--ConAgra Grocery Products Packaging Company, Omaha, NE; *U.S. Public*, pg. 428
Murayama, Satoshi, Gen. Mgr.--The Sakura Bank - Seoul Branch, Seoul, Korea; *Int'l*, pg. 1179
Murchek, John, Mng. Dir.--Commercial Hydraulics Kontak Ltd., Grantham, United Kingdom; *U.S. Public*, pg. 411
Murchison, Bruce K., Pres. & Chief Exec. Officer--Celeron Corporation, Bakersfield, CA; *U.S. Public*, pg. 753
Murdoch, Drew, Mng. Dir.--Vishay Components (U.K.) Ltd., Sunderland, United Kingdom; *U.S. Public*, pg. 1722
Murdoch, Drew, Mng. Dir.--Vishay Components U.K. Ltd., Wymondham, United Kingdom; *U.S. Public*, pg. 1722
Murdoch, Keith Rupert, Chm. Bd.--The New York Post, New York, NY; *Int'l*, pg. 927
Murdock, Bill, Pres. & Gen. Mgr.--KSL-TV, Salt Lake City, UT; *U.S. Private*, pg. 327
Murdock, David H., Chm. Bd. & Pres.--PHC Holdings, Inc., Los Angeles, CA; *U.S. Private*, pg. 831
Murga, Rogelio M., Chief Oper. Officer--EEI-TOEI Animation Corporation, Manila, Philippines; *Int'l*, pg. 426
Murillo, Enrique J., Pres. & Gen. Mgr.--General Electric de Mexico, S.A. de C.V., Mexico, Mexico; *U.S. Public*, pg. 713
Murillo, Jose I., Dr., Pres.--Filtros Mann S.A., Zaragoza, Spain; *Int'l*, pg. 484
Murillo, Victor M., Mgr.--Banco Nacional de Mexico, London, United Kingdom; *Int'l*, pg. 574
Murney, Gary, Plant Mgr.--Water Technologies Group, Seneca Falls, NY; *U.S. Public*, pg. 861
Murphy, Andy, V.P.--Fox Net, Los Angeles, CA; *Int'l*, pg. 926
Murphy, Bill, Branch Mgr.--BSA Advertising, Inc., Boston, MA; *U.S. Private*, pg. 108
Murphy, Bob, Plant Mgr.--Amarillo Plant, Amarillo, TX; *U.S. Public*, pg. 444
Murphy, Brad, Pres.--CUNA Mortgage Corporation, Madison, WI; *U.S. Private*, pg. 296
Murphy, Brian A., Pres.--Empresa Guatemaltica CIGNA de Seguros, Sociedad Anonima, Guatemala, Guatemala; *U.S. Public*, pg. 364
Murphy, Charles O., Chm. Bd., Pres. & Chief Exec. Officer--SouthTrust Bank, Suncoast, Sarasota, FL; *U.S. Public*, pg. 1492
Murphy, Christopher J., III, Pres.--1st Source Capital Corporation, South Bend, IN; *U.S. Public*, pg. 638
Murphy, David G., Pres.--Mill Maple Properties, Inc., Seattle, WA; *U.S. Public*, pg. 1742
Murphy, David G., Pres.--North American Acceptance Corporation, Seattle, WA; *U.S. Public*, pg. 1742
Murphy, David G., Pres.--Preston Properties of California, Inc., Seattle, WA; *U.S. Public*, pg. 1742
Murphy, David G., Pres.--Preston Properties Texas, Inc., Seattle, WA; *U.S. Public*, pg. 1742
Murphy, Donald, Pres.--IAC Industries, Brea, CA; *U.S. Private*, pg. 553
Murphy, E., Gen. Mgr.--ITW Heistrap GmbH, Heidenau, Germany; *U.S. Public*, pg. 868
Murphy, E., Gen. Mgr.--Signode, Swansea, United Kingdom; *U.S. Public*, pg. 869
Murphy, Edward, Pres.--PWS-Kent Publishing Co., Boston, MA; *U.S. Public*, pg. 1600
Murphy, Enda, Chief Mgr.--Bank of Ireland Trust Services, Dublin, Ireland; *Int'l*, pg. 152
Murphy, Fred, Pres. & Chief Oper. Officer--Fishercast, Peterborough, Canada; *Int'l*, pg. 491
Murphy, Fred, Pres. & Chief Oper. Officer--Fishertech, Peterborough, Canada; *Int'l*, pg. 491
Murphy, George, Gen. Mgr.--North Star Print Group Inc., Milwaukee, WI; *U.S. Private*, pg. 601
Murphy, George E., Pres.--Jupiter Energy Corp., Chicago, IL; *U.S. Private*, pg. 602
Murphy, Gordon L., Pres.--INA Life Insurance Company of New York, New York, NY; *U.S. Public*, pg. 362
Murphy, Helen, Mgr.--Utell International-Ireland, Dublin, Ireland; *Int'l*, pg. 1098
Murphy, James, Pres. & Mng. Dir.--Provident Securities & Investment Company, Cincinnati, OH; *U.S. Public*, pg. 1338
Murphy, James, Pres. & Chief Exec. Officer--Willis Corroon Corp. of Los Angeles, Glendale, CA; *Int'l*, pg. 1506
Murphy, James J., Pres. & Chief Oper. Officer--Entech, Inc., Butte, MT; *U.S. Public*, pg. 1127
Murphy, James Timmerman, Pres.--Dun & Bradstreet Poland SP. Z.O.O., Warsaw, Poland; *U.S. Public*, pg. 536
Murphy, Jeanne M., V.P.--Willis Corroon Financial Services Corp., Milwaukee, WI; *Int'l*, pg. 1507
Murphy, John, Jr., Chm.--First Trust National Association, Saint Paul, MN; *U.S. Public*, pg. 1681
Murphy, Joseph M., Pres. & Sec.--838 Investment Group, Inc., Wilmington, DE; *U.S. Public*, pg. 1729
Murphy, Kay, V.P. & Mgr.--City of Industry Office, City of Industry, CA; *U.S. Public*, pg. 381
Murphy, Lee, V.P.-Sls.--Kent Feeds Inc., Muscatine, IA; *U.S. Private*, pg. 1134
Murphy, Linda, Admin.--Hudson Elms Nursing Home, Hudson, OH; *U.S. Public*, pg. 838
Murphy, M., Mng. Dir.--G.E. Lighting Limited, Mitcham, United Kingdom; *U.S. Public*, pg. 713
Murphy, Mark A., Plant Mgr.--Bundy Corporation, Russell Schmidt Tool Plant, Chesterfield, MI; *Int'l*, pg. 1341
Murphy, Michael, Fleet Dir.--AlliedSignal Transportation Inc., South Bend, IN; *U.S. Public*, pg. 51
Murphy, Michael, Pres.--M&M/Mars, Hackettstown, NJ; *U.S. Private*, pg. 707
Murphy, Michael, V.P.--Kvaerner EnviroPower, Inc., Coeur D'Alene, ID; *Int'l*, pg. 770
Murphy, Michael, Pres.--Hilb, Rogal and Hamilton Company of Baltimore, Baltimore, MD; *U.S. Public*, pg. 827
Murphy, Michael, Mng. Dir.--Shandwick Asia Pacific, Central, Hong Kong; *Int'l*, pg. 1227
Murphy, Michael, Chief Exec.--Shandwick Hong Kong Ltd., Central, Hong Kong; *Int'l*, pg. 1227
Murphy, Mike, Gen. Mgr.--WLIT-FM, Chicago, IL; *U.S. Private*, pg. 779

Murphy, Noel, Pres.--Camp Healthcare, Jackson, MI; *Int'l*, pg. 1425
Murphy, Patrick F., Pres. & Chief Exec. Officer--AGA Gas, Inc., Independence, OH; *Int'l*, pg. 13
Murphy, Paul F., Gen. Mgr.--Lincoln Canada Limited, Mississauga, Canada; *U.S. Public*, pg. 1274
Murphy, Pernell, Gen. Mgr.--Metz Baking Co., Roseville, MN; *U.S. Private*, pg. 1022
Murphy, Peter F., Pres.--Bard Vascular Systems Div., Billerica, MA; *U.S. Public*, pg. 189
Murphy, Peter J., Chief Oper. Officer--Flexible Circuit Products Division, Methuen, MA; *U.S. Public*, pg. 1264
Murphy, R.W., Pres.--Amoco Development Company, Chicago, IL; *U.S. Public*, pg. 103
Murphy, Richard J., Gen. Mgr.--BPA International - Chicago, Chicago, IL; *U.S. Private*, pg. 107
Murphy, Robert J., Pres.--Merv Griffin Enterprises, Beverly Hills, CA; *Int'l*, pg. 1282
Murphy, Ronan M., Mng. Dir.--Bank of Ireland International Finance Limited, Dublin, Ireland; *Int'l*, pg. 152
Murphy, Steve, V.P. & Gen. Mgr.--AgCast, West Des Moines, IA; *U.S. Public*, pg. 484
Murphy, Susan, Sr. V.P. & Gen. Mgr.--Ramada Express, Laughlin, NV; *U.S. Public*, pg. 158
Murphy, Thomas F., Account Mgr.--Bank of Montreal - Mexico, Mexico, Mexico; *Int'l*, pg. 155
Murphy, Thomas P., V.P.--Suntel Corp., Earth City, MO; *Int'l*, pg. 814
Murphy, Tony, Mgr.--Woodward Governor (U.K.) Ltd., Reading, United Kingdom; *U.S. Public*, pg. 1777
Murray, Alexander B., Chm. Bd.--Ford Credit Funding plc, Brentwood, United Kingdom; *U.S. Public*, pg. 665
Murray, Allen E., Chm. Bd., Pres. & Chief Exec. Officer--Mobil Oil Corporation, Fairfax, VA; *U.S. Public*, pg. 1118
Murray, Bill, Mgr.--Palm Harbor Homes, Siler City, NC; *U.S. Public*, pg. 1255
Murray, Bobby R., Gen. Mgr.--W.H. King Drug Co., Raleigh, NC; *U.S. Public*, pg. 214
Murray, C.M.R., Mgr.--Horizon Aluminium Prods. Ltd., Auckland, New Zealand; *Int'l*, pg. 51
Murray, Colin, Mgr.--Kerr-McGee China Petroleum Ltd., Beijing, China; *U.S. Public*, pg. 952
Murray, Crandell, V.P. & Gen. Mgr.--La-Z-Boy Canada Ltd., Waterloo, Canada; *U.S. Public*, pg. 973
Murray, D.C., V.P.--Household Products Co., Oakland, CA; *U.S. Public*, pg. 387
Murray, David R., Pres.--Service & Industrial Sector, Roswell, GA; *U.S. Public*, pg. 958
Murray, E.R., Pres.--Texas-New Mexico Pipe Line Co., Houston, TX; *U.S. Public*, pg. 1584
Murray, Frederick W., Exec. V.P.--SouthTrust Leasing, Inc., Birmingham, AL; *U.S. Public*, pg. 1492
Murray, Frederick W., Jr., Exec. V.P.--SouthTrust Insurance Agency, Inc., Birmingham, AL; *U.S. Public*, pg. 1492
Murray, Frederick W., Jr., Exec. V.P.--SouthTrust Life Insurance Co., Birmingham, AL; *U.S. Public*, pg. 1492
Murray, Graeme, Pres.--Colgate-Palmolive Canada Inc., Toronto, Canada; *U.S. Public*, pg. 398
Murray, Graeme, V.P. & Gen. Mgr.--Colgate-Palmolive Pty. Ltd., Sydney, Australia; *U.S. Public*, pg. 399
Murray, J.F., Mng. Dir.--Nepal Grindlays Bank Limited, Kathmandu, Nepal; *Int'l*, pg. 100
Murray, James E., Chief Fin. Officer--Humana Medical Plan Inc.-Jacksonville, Jacksonville, FL; *U.S. Public*, pg. 848
Murray, Jerry, Plant Supvr.--Fairway District Production Office, Poynor, TX; *U.S. Private*, pg. 548
Murray, Jim, Pres.--Alumitech, Somerset, KY; *U.S. Private*, pg. 513
Murray, John, Gen. Mgr.--Canadian Forest Products Ltd., Englewood Logging Division, Woss, Canada; *Int'l*, pg. 260
Murray, John, Mgr.--John Crane Saudi Arabia Ltd., Al-Khobar, Saudi Arabia; *Int'l*, pg. 1339
Murray, Lee, Gen. Mgr.--Automotive Distribution Sales Div., Maumee, OH; *U.S. Public*, pg. 479
Murray, Lee A., Pres.--CADAM Inc., Burbank, CA; *U.S. Public*, pg. 896
Murray, Michael J., Chm. Bd.--Continental Partners Group, Inc., Chicago, IL; *U.S. Public*, pg. 181
Murray, Moira J., V.P.--St. Paul Service, Inc., Franklin Park, IL; *U.S. Public*, pg. 1428
Murray, Moira J., V.P.--Annuity Network Inc., Franklin Park, IL; *U.S. Public*, pg. 1428
Murray, Niall, Gen. Mgr.--Kredietbank Dublin Branch, Dublin, Ireland; *Int'l*, pg. 760
Murray, Richard C., Pres.--Wacoal America Inc., New York, NY; *Int'l*, pg. 1484
Murray, S.P., Mng. Dir.--Boots Opticians, Nottingham, United Kingdom; *Int'l*, pg. 202
Murray, T., Pres.--Tyton Hellermann Canada Incorporated, Markham, Canada; *Int'l*, pg. 209
Murray, Tom, Gen. Mgr.--Elixir Industries, Sacramento, CA; *U.S. Private*, pg. 371
Murray, William J., Grp. V.P.--Cyanamid Agricultural Products Division, Parsippany, NJ; *U.S. Public*, pg. 79
Murray, William T., Publr.--The Register Citizen, Torrington, CT; *U.S. Public*, pg. 935
Murray, William Tom, V.P. & Acting Chief Exec. Officer--NationsBank of Pulaski County, Richland, MO; *U.S. Public*, pg. 1164
Murrell, Butch, Gen. Mgr.--Barton's of Dumas, Dumas, AR; *U.S. Private*, pg. 119
Murrell, Charles, Exec. V.P.--SouthTrust Data Services, Inc., Birmingham, AL; *U.S. Public*, pg. 1492
Murrell, Paul, V.P. & Gen. Mgr.--Penn Locomotive Gear, Louisville, KY; *Int'l*, pg. 281
Murrell, R., Pres. & Chief Exec. Officer--Birdsall, Inc., Riviera Beach, FL; *U.S. Public*, pg. 1182
Murrer, Thomas, Pres.--Renold, Inc., Westfield, NY; *Int'l*, pg. 1104
Murrin, P., Mng. Dir.--Andrew AG, Bachenbulach, Switzerland; *U.S. Public*, pg. 113
Murrin, P., Mng. Dir.--Andrew Antennas, Lochgelly, United Kingdom; *U.S. Public*, pg. 113
Murry, Albert B., Chm. Bd., Pres. & Chief Exec. Officer--Keystone Heritage Group, Inc., Lebanon, PA; *U.S. Public*, pg. 687
Murry, Jim, Reg. Acct. Dir.--RP alpha/Dallas, Irving, TX; *U.S. Private*, pg. 950
Murtagh, Laurence M., Mng. Dir.--NEC Semiconductors Ireland Limited, Ballivor, Ireland; *Int'l*, pg. 900
Murtha, Bob, Plant Mgr.--Donaldson Co., Inc., Oelwein, IA; *U.S. Public*, pg. 517
Murton, Rodney, Mng. Dir.--Perkin-Elmer Ltd., Beaconsfield, United Kingdom; *U.S. Public*, pg. 1279
Musa, Edson Vaz, Chief Oper. Officer--Rhodia S.A., Sao Paulo, Brazil; *Int'l*, pg. 1112
Musacchio, Joe, Mgr.-Reg.--Volt Technical Services-East, New York, NY; *U.S. Public*, pg. 1724
Musalem, Alberto Roque, Resident Rep.--The World Bank, Sofia, Bulgaria; *U.S. Private*, pg. 1189
Musarra, Kathy, Branch Mgr.--Valley National Bank, Chester, NJ; *U.S. Public*, pg. 1706
Muscalino, T.L., Pres.-Home Furnishings Mktg.--Dan River Inc.-Home Furnishings & Related Prods., Div. I, Danville, VA; *U.S. Public*, pg. 479
Muse, H.S., Jr., Mgr.--Tencarva Machinery Co., Greensboro, NC; *U.S. Private*, pg. 1076
Muse, Scott, Pres.--Progress Lighting, Spartanburg, SC; *U.S. Public*, pg. 1684
Muselik, Milos, Dir.-Fin.--IPC Corporation spol.s.r.o, Zlin, Czech Republic; *Int'l*, pg. 651
Musey, Dr. Gerd, Mng. Dir.--Rank Xerox AG, Zurich, Switzerland; *U.S. Public*, pg. 1785
Mushkin, Albert S., Chief Oper. Officer--Master Trouser/ Master Apparel/ Botany 500 Slacks Ltd., New York, NY; *U.S. Private*, pg. 713
Mushovic, Tom, Gen. Mgr.--AFSC Signature Flight Support, Anchorage, AK; *Int'l*, pg. 700
Musi, Giovanni, Gen. Mgr.--Banco di Sicilia, Paris, France; *Int'l*, pg. 140
Musil, Ronald J., Pres.--Banta Book Group, Menasha, WI; *U.S. Public*, pg. 188
Musilli, Charles A., Pres.--Selective Technical Administrative Services, Inc., Branchville, NJ; *U.S. Public*, pg. 1456
Mussallem, James, Gen. Mgr.--American Bank Note Company, Bedford Park, IL; *U.S. Public*, pg. 68
Musselwhite, Jimmie, Mgr.-Opers. Div.--Southland Corp.-British Columbia Division, Burnaby, Canada; *Int'l*, pg. 694
Mussenden, Felix, Exec. V.P. & Gen. Mgr.--Universal Studios Music Australia, Sydney, Australia; *Int'l*, pg. 1216
Mustafa, Sherad, Branch Mgr.--Downey Savings & Loan Association, F.A., Norwalk, CA; *U.S. Public*, pg. 526
Mustain, William G., Chm. Bd., Pres. & Chief Exec. Officer--American Phone Centers, Inc., Charlottesville, VA; *U.S. Public*, pg. 407
Mustain, William G., Chm. Bd., Pres. & Chief Exec. Officer--Comdial Telecommunications International, Inc., Charlottesville, VA; *U.S. Public*, pg. 407
Mustapha, Mohd Affendi Hj, Exec. Dir.--Kuala Lumpur Golf & Country Club Berhad, Kuala Lumpur, Malaysia; *Int'l*, pg. 1250
Muston, Michael J., Pres.--Mycogen Seeds, Saint Paul, MN; *U.S. Public*, pg. 1142
Musu, Rumengan, Pres. & Chief Exec. Officer--P.T. International Nickel Indonesia, Jakarta, Indonesia; *Int'l*, pg. 947
Muta, Koichi, Pres.--ORIX Securities Co., Ltd., Tokyo, Japan; *Int'l*, pg. 1009
Mutasa, L.C., Gen. Mgr.--Kodak (Zimbabwe) Ltd., Harare, Zimbabwe; *U.S. Public*, pg. 555
Mutch, Duncan, Plant Mgr.--Crown Cork Company S.A. (Pty.) Ltd., Bellville, South Africa; *U.S. Public*, pg. 464
Mutch, R.E., Pres.--Curtiss-Wright Flight Systems, Inc., Fairfield, NJ; *U.S. Public*, pg. 469
Mutch, Richard, Mgr.--Ker Monolithics, Leeds, United Kingdom; *Int'l*, pg. 789
Mutchler, E. Michael, V.P. & Group Exec.--GM Powertrain Group, Pontiac, MI; *U.S. Public*, pg. 719
Mutchler, E. Michael, V.P. & Grp. Exec.--North American Passenger Car Platforms, Detroit, MI; *U.S. Public*, pg. 719
Mutchler, E. Michael, V.P. & Grp. Exec.--Chevrolet, Pontiac, GM of Canada Group, Warren, MI; *U.S. Public*, pg. 720
Muth, Steve, Sls.--North Hills Signal Processing, Glen Cove, NY; *U.S. Public*, pg. 1317
Mutikainen, Matti, Chief Oper. Officer--Oy Liesimyynti-Spisforsaljning AB, Helsinki, Finland; *Int'l*, pg. 441
Mutton, Nick, V.P. & Gen. Mgr.--The Ritz-Carlton, Chicago, IL; *Int'l*, pg. 502
Muttupulle, E.C.S.R., Mng. Dir.--Lanka ORIX Leasing Company Limited, Rajagirya, Sri Lanka; *Int'l*, pg. 1009
Mutz, Gregory T., Chm. Bd.--Amli Realty, Inc., Chicago, IL; *U.S. Public*, pg. 169
Muundrell, P., Chm. Bd.--Chemtronics Inc., Kennesaw, GA; *Int'l*, pg. 892
Muzzio, Carlos, Gen. Mgr.--Varig Brazilian Airlines, New York, NY; *Int'l*, pg. 1451
Muzzolon, N., Mgr.--Unitecta Italiana SpA, Milan, Italy; *Int'l*, pg. 1501
Mwangi, G.M., Chief Exec. Officer--Blackwood Hodge (Kenya) Ltd., Nairobi, Kenya; *Int'l*, pg. 231
Myatt, Charles, Regional Pres.--First Tennessee Bank - Murfreesboro, Murfreesboro, TN; *U.S. Public*, pg. 639
Mybry, Seth, Sr. V.P.-Radio Div.--Telemobitel, Haninge, Sweden; *Int'l*, pg. 1373
Myers, B., Mng. Dir.--Trafalgar House Construction Ltd., Croydon, United Kingdom; *Int'l*, pg. 773
Myers, Chuck, Pres. & Chief Exec. Officer--Country Kitchen International, Inc., Madison, WI; *U.S. Private*, pg. 624
Myers, Cynthia, Administrator--Casa Arena Blanca, Alamogordo, NM; *U.S. Public*, pg. 838
Myers, Daniel, Gen. Mgr.--Procter & Gamble Inc., Grande Prairie, Canada; *U.S. Public*, pg. 1332
Myers, Frank, Gen. Mgr.--Container Div. (Chicago), Bridgeview, IL; *Int'l*, pg. 1269
Myers, Frank E., Pres.--WestEx, Inc., Phoenix, AZ; *U.S. Public*, pg. 1788
Myers, Gary F., Pres.--Shadowood Golf Inc., Seymour, IN; *U.S. Private*, pg. 629
Myers, Jay E., Chm. Bd. & Chief Exec. Officer--United Southwest Bank, Washington, IN; *U.S. Public*, pg. 1217
Myers, John A., Pres. & Chief Exec. Officer--AIG Aviation, Inc., Atlanta, GA; *U.S. Public*, pg. 85
Myers, Kevin, Warden--South Central Correctional Center, Clifton, TN; *U.S. Public*, pg. 451
Myers, R., Pres.--United Sciences Inc., Gibsonia, PA; *Int'l*, pg. 208
Myers, Robert L., Chief Oper. Officer & Exec. V.P.--Priority Healthcare Corporation, Altamonte Springs, FL; *U.S. Public*, pg. 229
Myers, Shannon, Media Dir.--Western International Media Corporation, Kansas City, MO; *U.S. Private*, pg. 1167
Myers, Tom, Plant Mgr.--Industrial Bag Division - Los Angeles Plant, Los Angeles, CA; *U.S. Public*, pg. 1521
Myers, Wayne, Pres.--Spicer Axle Div., Fort Wayne, IN; *U.S. Public*, pg. 479
Mygind, Hans Ole, Pres.--MD Foods Italia S.r.l., Lomazzo, Italy; *Int'l*, pg. 826
Myhre, Oyvind, Pres.--Kvaerner Thune A/S, Hamar, Norway; *Int'l*, pg. 769
Myklestu, Hans Fredrik, Gen. Mgr.--Cimbenin S.A., Cotonou, Benin; *Int'l*, pg. 1201
Myles, George, Region Mgr.--Weatherford Oil Tool Middle East Ltd., Dubai, United Arab Emirates; *U.S. Public*, pg. 1750
Myrin, Cail-Goran, Chief Oper. Officer--Siemens-Elema AB, Solna, Sweden; *Int'l*, pg. 1247
Myrup, Niels Chr., Mng. Dir.--FLS Data A/S, Valby, Denmark; *Int'l*, pg. 476
Myrvold, Pal, Pres.--Kvaerner Mesna A/S, Lillehammer, Norway; *Int'l*, pg. 769
Myslenski, Jack, Pres.--Fluid Connectors Group, Cleveland, OH; *U.S. Public*, pg. 1260
Mysliwiec, Jerome Anthony, Dir.--Motorola Malaysia Sdn. Bhd., Penang, Malaysia; *U.S. Public*, pg. 1140
Naab, D., V.P. & Gen. Mgr.--Simicon Div., Holland, MI; *Int'l*, pg. 1243
Nabais, Antonio Maia, Dir.--Generale Bank - Porto, Porto, Portugal; *Int'l*, pg. 547
Nabakowski, John, Gen. Mgr.--GATX Logistics, Inc.-Illinois, Normal, IL; *U.S. Public*, pg. 691
Nabaw, Steve, Gen. Mgr.--Woody's, New York, NY; *U.S. Public*, pg. 130
Naber, S.S., Pres.--Lucas Aerospace Power Transmission, Utica, NY; *Int'l*, pg. 820
Nabers, Drayton, Jr., Pres.--Protective Life Insurance Co., Birmingham, AL; *U.S. Public*, pg. 1336
Nabeshima, Katsumi, Mng. Dir.--OMRON Business Systems Singapore Private Limited, Singapore, Singapore; *Int'l*, pg. 1005
Nabeshima, Yoshika, Chief Oper. Officer--OKI Systems (Deutschland) GmbH, Dusseldorf, Germany; *Int'l*, pg. 1000
Nabetani, N., Pres.--Nissho Propane Sekiyu Corp., Sapporo, Japan; *Int'l*, pg. 947
Nabielsky, Gabriel, Mng. Dir.--American Textil, S.A. de C.V., Santa Clara, Mexico; *U.S. Public*, pg. 769
Nabuurs, P.J.J.G., Chief Exec. Officer--OCE-Belgium N.V./ S.A., Brussels, Belgium; *Int'l*, pg. 994
Naccarati, David C., Pres.--Phelps Dodge Tyrone, Tyrone, NM; *U.S. Public*, pg. 1287
Naccarato, Vincent, Pres.--Rowoco, Woodridge, IL; *U.S. Private*, pg. 1182
Nachman, G., Pres.--Metal Improvement Co., Paramus, NJ; *U.S. Public*, pg. 469
Nachmoni, Z., V.P. & Gen. Mgr.--Electronics Group (IAI), Yehuda, Israel; *Int'l*, pg. 690
Nachtigal, Arie, Gen. Mgr.--Amerford Intl. Ltd., Tel Aviv, Israel; *Int'l*, pg. 1388
Nachury, Jean-Louis, Chief Opr. Officer--C.O.F.E.C., Levallois-Perret, France; *Int'l*, pg. 792
Nada, S., Pres.--Shimadzu Oceania Pty. Ltd., Rydalmere, Australia; *Int'l*, pg. 1232
Nadal, Domingo, Mng. Dir.--Velcro Europe S.A., Argentona, Spain; *Int'l*, pg. 1462
Nadal, Domingo, Acting Gen. Mgr.--Systems De Fermeture S.A., Valnor, France; *Int'l*, pg. 1462
Nadal, Domingo, Mng. Dir.--Velcro Italia S.R.L., Milan, Italy; *Int'l*, pg. 1462
Nadal, Pablo, Mng. Dir.--TMP Worldwide, Inc., Madrid, Spain; *U.S. Private*, pg. 1065
Nadasdy, Laszlo, Rep.--DG Bank-Budapest, Budapest, Hungary; *Int'l*, pg. 352
Nadeau, Jacques, Gen. Mgr.--Joliette Plant St. Lawrence Cement, Joliette, Canada; *Int'l*, pg. 629
Nadeau, T.J., Pres.--Sorevco Inc., Coteau du Lac, Canada; *Int'l*, pg. 414
Nadel, Herbert, Pres. & Chief Exec. Officer--Nadel Architects, PC Nevada, Las Vegas, NV; *U.S. Private*, pg. 773
Nadel, Roger, V.P. & Gen. Mgr.--KFWB Radio, Los Angeles, CA; *U.S. Public*, pg. 274
Nader, Jesus, Chief Oper. Officer--Itapeva, Itapeva, Brazil; *Int'l*, pg. 677
Nadig, Gerald G., Pres.--Pre Finish Metals Inc., Elk Grove Village, IL; *U.S. Public*, pg. 1057
Nadj, Luke, Mng. Dir.--World's Finest Chocolate Australia Pty. Ltd., Stanmore, Australia; *U.S. Private*, pg. 1191
Nadolski, Keith, Pres.--Beech Holdings, Inc., Wichita, KS; *U.S. Public*, pg. 1365
Naegeli, John P., Mng. Dir.--Sulzer Pumps Ltd., Winterthur, Switzerland; *Int'l*, pg. 1306
Naesset, Per-Ole, Chief Oper. Officer--Perstorp Components, Kitchener, Canada; *Int'l*, pg. 1040
Naeve, Don, Plant Mgr.--The Lamson & Sessions Co., Clinton, IA; *U.S. Public*, pg. 976
Naeve, Ingemar, Mng. Dir.--Ericsson Sistemas Avanzados S.A., Madrid, Spain; *Int'l*, pg. 1367
Nafilyan, Guy, Pres.--Kaufman and Broad Developpement, Paris, France; *U.S. Public*, pg. 945

Nafilyan, Guy, Pres.--Kaufman and Broad Renovations, Paris, France; *U.S. Public*, pg. 945
Nafilyon, Guy, Pres.--Bati-Service, Paris, France; *U.S. Public*, pg. 945
Nag, Tore, Branch Mgr.--Christiania Bank-New York Branch, New York, NY; *Int'l*, pg. 289
Nagafuchi, Hideo, Pres.--Nissan Motor Nederland B.V., Lisse, Netherlands; *Int'l*, pg. 945
Nagai, Hidetake, Chief Oper. Officer--Joyama Kaihatsu Ltd., Hoi-gun, Japan; *Int'l*, pg. 831
Nagai, Joji, Gen. Mgr.--Asahi Bank (Schweiz) AG, Zurich, Switzerland; *Int'l*, pg. 83
Nagai, Kazuo, Pres.--Toyo Tire (U.S.A.) Corporation, Cypress, CA; *Int'l*, pg. 1411
Nagai, S., Pres.--Sharp Electronics (Taiwan) Co., Ltd., Kaohsiung, Taiwan; *Int'l*, pg. 1230
Nagai, Shusai, Gen. Mgr.--The Industrial Bank of Japan, Limited (Los Angeles Agency), Los Angeles, CA; *Int'l*, pg. 674
Nagai, Tatsuo, Mng. Dir.--Suzuki Marina, Hamanako, Co., Ltd., Shizuoka, Japan; *Int'l*, pg. 1323
Nagai, Yasunori, Chm.--IBJ Merchant Bank (Singapore) Limited, Singapore, Singapore; *Int'l*, pg. 676
Nagai, Yasushi, Pres.--NLI International Canada Inc., Toronto, Canada; *Int'l*, pg. 936
Nagakura, Delegues Katsumi, Admin.--The Bank of Tokyo-Mitsubishi (Luxombourg) S.A., Luxembourg, Luxembourg; *Int'l*, pg. 158
Nagakura, Masatada, Pres.--Ikeda Bussan Co., Ltd., Ayase, Japan; *Int'l*, pg. 944
Nagai, Toshizasu, Pres.--Union Carbide Japan K.K., Tokyo, Japan; *U.S. Public*, pg. 1667
Nagami, Tohru, Pres.--Toho Kagaku Kenkyusho Co., Ltd., Tokyo, Japan; *U.S. Public*, pg. 540
Nagamine, Mitsuru, Pres.--Civil Engineering Instrument Center, Kanagawa, Japan; *Int'l*, pg. 868
Nagamine, Toshio, Terminal Mgr.--Kintetsu World Express Inc., New York, NY; *Int'l*, pg. 734
Nagano, Shinobu, Gen. Mgr.--Nippo Corporation, Europe Branch, Amsterdam, Netherlands; *Int'l*, pg. 932
Nagano, Shunichi, Gen. Mgr.--Dicalite Orient Co. Ltd., Tokyo, Japan; *U.S. Private*, pg. 903
Naganoma, Kazuhiko, Pres.--ORIX Capital Corporation, Tokyo, Japan; *Int'l*, pg. 1008
Nagao, Wayne K., Sr. V.P. & Dir.-Facilities--Jefferies & Company, Inc., Los Angeles, CA; *U.S. Public*, pg. 925
Nagaoka, Hiroshi, Pres.--LEC, Inc., Tokyo, Japan; *Int'l*, pg. 929
Nagarkatti, Dr. Jai, Pres.--Aldrich Chemical Co., Inc., Milwaukee, WI; *U.S. Public*, pg. 1471
Nagarwadia, A.R., Pres. & Chief Oper. Officer--Ingersoll-Rand (India) Private Ltd., Mumbai, India; *U.S. Public*, pg. 878
Nagasaka, Kunihiko, Pres.--Aomori Hakuhodo Inc., Aomori, Japan; *Int'l*, pg. 587
Nagasaki, Komaki, Chief Exec.--Sumitomo Finance (Asia) Limited, Central, Hong Kong; *Int'l*, pg. 1310
Nagasawa, Fujio, Chief Exec.--Takenaka Civil Engineering & Construction Co., Ltd., Tokyo, Japan; *Int'l*, pg. 1351
Nagase, Naoki, Pres.--Yamaha-Olin Metal Corporation, Shizuoka, Japan; *U.S. Public*, pg. 1220
Nagashima, Takayoshi, Chief Rep.--The Sakura Bank - Mexico Representative Office, Mexico, Mexico; *Int'l*, pg. 1180
Nagata, Hiroshi, Dir.--Showpla Brasil Ltd., Manaus, Brazil; *Int'l*, pg. 1237
Nagata, Isao, Dir & Gen Mgr--Sumitomo Trust & Banking Co., Tokyo, Japan; *Int'l*, pg. 1318
Nagata, Masahisa, Vice Chm. & Gen. Mgr.--South China International Leasing Company Limited, Shenzhen, China; *Int'l*, pg. 627
Nagata, Takehiko, Chief Oper. Officer--Taiko Electric Work, Ltd., Tokyo, Japan; *Int'l*, pg. 999
Nagata, Teruyuki, Mng. Dir.--Kintetsu World Express (Taiwan), Inc., Taipei, Taiwan; *Int'l*, pg. 735
Nagataki, Masahiko, Mng. Dir. & Gen. Mgr.--Sumitomo Trust & Banking (Luxembourg) S.A., Luxembourg, Luxembourg; *Int'l*, pg. 1318
Nagatomi, Sadamu, Dir.--Taiwan Takenaka Co., Ltd., Taipei, Taiwan; *Int'l*, pg. 1351
Nagatomi, Sadamu, Dir.--Taiwan Takenaka Engineering Co., Ltd., Taipei, Taiwan; *Int'l*, pg. 1351
Nagaya, Shumei, V.P.--Kokusai Electric Co., Ltd. America, Lake Success, NY; *Int'l*, pg. 743
Nagayama, Toru, Pres.--Haseko (Hawaii) Inc., Honolulu, HI; *Int'l*, pg. 600
Nagayama, Toru, Pres.--Haseko Realty Inc., Honolulu, HI; *Int'l*, pg. 600
Nagayasu, Hideo, Chief Representative--Mexico Representative Office, Mexico, Mexico; *Int'l*, pg. 520
Nagazumi, Tsutomu, Gen. Mgr.--The Bank of Tokyo-Mitsubishi (Holland) N.V., Amsterdam, Netherlands; *Int'l*, pg. 158
Nagel, Bruce, Pres.--Cole-Layer-Trumble Company (CLT), Dayton, OH; *U.S. Private*, pg. 317
Nagel, Bruce, Pres.--Landisc Systems, Dayton, OH; *U.S. Private*, pg. 317
Nagel, C. M., Mng. Dir.--Rainsfords Metal Products Pty. Limited, Lonsdale, Australia; *Int'l*, pg. 217
Nagel, H. Robert, Pres.--PHH Mortgage Services Corporation, Mount Laurel, NJ; *U.S. Public*, pg. 321
Nagel, John, Pres. & Chief Exec. Officer--North American Financial Corp., Minneapolis, MN; *U.S. Private*, pg. 212
Nagel, John R., Pres.--Carlson Leasing, Inc., Minneapolis, MN; *U.S. Private*, pg. 212
Nagel, Kevin, Chm. Bd., Pres. & Chief Exec. Officer--EBP Life Insurnace Co., Minneapolis, MN; *U.S. Public*, pg. 635
Nagel, Manifred, Chief Oper. Officer--Siemens Schieiz AG, Zurich, Switzerland; *Int'l*, pg. 1248
Nagel, Richard, Pres.--Sax Arts & Crafts, Inc., New Berlin, WI; *U.S. Public*, pg. 1687
Nagelstad, Bjorn, Mng. Dir.--Jotun Thailand Ltd., Bangkok, Thailand; *Int'l*, pg. 715
Nagin, C. Ray, V.P. & Gen. Mgr.--Cox Communications-Jefferson Parish Office, Harahan, LA; *U.S. Public*, pg. 455
Nagin, C. Ray, V.P. & Gen. Mgr.--Cox Communications-New Orleans, New Orleans, LA; *U.S. Public*, pg. 455
Nagl, B., Chief Oper. Officer--Twin Disc (South Africa) (Pty.) Ltd., Johannesburg, South Africa; *U.S. Public*, pg. 1647
Nagle, Paul R., Jr., Mng. Dir.--Parsons Brinckerhoff Ltd., London, United Kingdom; *U.S. Private*, pg. 841
Nagle, William B., V.P.--Georgia-Pacific Mid-Continent Wood Prods. Mfg. Div., Crossett, AR; *U.S. Public*, pg. 735
Nagor, Abdul Shukor, Div. Dir.--Sime Darby Commodity Trading & Plantations Division, Petaling Jaya, Malaysia; *Int'l*, pg. 1250
Nagor, Abdul Shukor, Div. Dir.--Plantations Division, Petaling Jaya, Malaysia; *Int'l*, pg. 1250
Nagorniak, John J., Chm., Pres. & Chief Exec. Officer--Franklin Portfolio Associates Trust, Boston, MA; *U.S. Public*, pg. 1085
Nagorsen, Tony, V.P.-Sls.--Penske Performance, Inc., Detroit, MI; *U.S. Private*, pg. 850
Nagura, Toshiyasu, Chief Rep.--Asahi Bank Kuala Lumpur Representative Office, Kuala Lumpur, Malaysia; *Int'l*, pg. 83
Nagy, Bill, Mgr.--Shepler's Houston West, Houston, TX; *U.S. Public*, pg. 413
Nahal, Gary, Pres.--Fedders International, Inc., Liberty Corner, NJ; *U.S. Public*, pg. 614
Nahas, A.P., Gen. Mgr.--Kodak (Near East), Inc., Dubai, United Arab Emirates; *U.S. Public*, pg. 554
Nahas, Andre, Area Bus. Mgr.--Kodak Pakistan Ltd., Karachi, Pakistan; *U.S. Public*, pg. 554
Nahas, Mostafa El, Chief Oper. Officer--Marryat & Scott Egypt-S.A., Cairo, Egypt; *Int'l*, pg. 748
Nahmias, Joseph R., Mng. Dir.--Productos Quaker, S.A., Cali, Colombia; *U.S. Public*, pg. 1348
Nahmias, Joseph R., Mng. Dir.--Productos Quaker, C.A., Caracas, Venezuela; *U.S. Public*, pg. 1348
Nail, E. S., Pres. & Mng. Dir.--Tenneco Oil & Minerals of Australia, Inc., Brisbane, Australia; *U.S. Public*, pg. 1580
Nail, James M., Chm. Bd. & Pres.--Canadian Road Credit Company, Limited, Oakville, Canada; *U.S. Public*, pg. 665
Naim, Andre, Comml. Dir.--Intervascular, S.A., La Ciotat, France; *U.S. Public*, pg. 488
Naines, Tony, V.P. & Gen. Mgr.--Cableware Technology Div., Naples, FL; *U.S. Private*, pg. 675
Naito, Sasumu, Pres. & Chief Oper. Officer--Rinnai America Corp., La Grange, GA; *Int'l*, pg. 1118
Najera, Manuel, Admin.--Seven Oaks Care Center, Bonham, TX; *U.S. Public*, pg. 839
Nakada, Kusuo, Chief Oper. Officer--Hitachi Electronics Engineering Co., Ltd., Tokyo, Japan; *Int'l*, pg. 621
Nakagaki, T., Pres.--Hokuriku (Malaysia), Sdn. Bhd., Shah Alam, Malaysia; *Int'l*, pg. 628
Nakagawa, Itaru, Pres.--Tabuchi Electric Company of America, Cordova, TN; *Int'l*, pg. 1346
Nakagawa, Kazutsugu, Chm. Bd.--Tokyo-Mitsubishi International (Singapore) Ltd., Singapore, Singapore; *Int'l*, pg. 158
Nakagawa, Norio, Dir.--Showa Plastics (Shenzhen) Co. Ltd., Shenzhen, China; *Int'l*, pg. 1237
Nakagawa, Osamu, Dir.--Willis Corroon Japan Limited, Glendale, CA; *Int'l*, pg. 1509
Nakagawa, Teruyuki, Mng. Dir.--Showpla International Pte. Ltd., Singapore, Singapore; *Int'l*, pg. 1237
Nakagawa, Toru, Chief Rep.--Toray Industries, Inc.-Europe Office, London, United Kingdom; *Int'l*, pg. 1400
Nakagome, Chihiro, Pres.--Mitsubishi Materials, New York, NY; *Int'l*, pg. 875
Nakahara, Yoh, Gen. Mgr.--The Industrial Bank of Japan, Limited (San Francisco), San Francisco, CA; *Int'l*, pg. 674
Nakai, Ken-ichiro, Chief Oper. Officer--Makita (China) Co., Ltd., Jiangyin, China; *Int'l*, pg. 832
Nakai, Nobukazu, Mng. Dir.--Kintetsu World Express (U.K.) Ltd., Slough, United Kingdom; *Int'l*, pg. 735
Nakajima, Eiichiro, Dir.--P.T. Hutama-Takenaka Corporation Indonesia, Jakarta, Indonesia; *Int'l*, pg. 1351
Nakajima, Hideo, Gen. Mgr.--Fuji Bank, Los Angeles, Los Angeles, CA; *Int'l*, pg. 520
Nakajima, Katsuro, Pres.--General Ceramics, Inc., Haskell, NJ; *Int'l*, pg. 1394
Nakajima, Nobutada, Chief Oper. Officer--Kuwano Electrical Instruments Co., Ltd., Kawasaki, Japan; *Int'l*, pg. 999
Nakajima, Seiji, Chief Rep.--Beijing Representative Office, Beijing, China; *Int'l*, pg. 520
Nakajima, Shigeo, Pres.--Sumikin Bussan International (HK) Ltd., Kowloon, Hong Kong; *Int'l*, pg. 1308
Nakajima, Yoji, Pres.--Yoshitomi-Astra Ltd., Osaka, Japan; *Int'l*, pg. 94
Nakakubo, T., Chief Oper. Officer--Shinko Telecommunications Construction Co., Ltd., Tokyo, Japan; *Int'l*, pg. 530
Nakamachi, Ikuo, Chief Rep.--Bangkok Representative Office, Bangkok, Thailand; *Int'l*, pg. 520
Nakamura, Pres.--UBE Machinery, Inc., Ann Arbor, MI; *Int'l*, pg. 1427
Nakamura, Isao, Pres.--Nihon Kyoei Securities Co. Ltd., Tokyo, Japan; *Int'l*, pg. 702
Nakamura, Katsumi, Pres.--NLI Properties Central, Inc., Chicago, IL; *Int'l*, pg. 935
Nakamura, M., Pres.--Y.K.K. (U.S.A.) Inc., Macon, GA; *Int'l*, pg. 1515
Nakamura, Masaharie, Chm. & Pres.--Tokio Marine Management Inc., New York, NY; *Int'l*, pg. 1392
Nakamura, Masaru, Pres.--Mitsubishi Electric Industrial Control, Mount Prospect, IL; *Int'l*, pg. 872
Nakamura, Nobuhiko, Pres.--Kawasaki Motoren GmbH, Friedrichsdorf, Germany; *Int'l*, pg. 726
Nakamura, Nori, Pres.--Hakuhodo Foods Services Co., Ltd., Tokyo, Japan; *Int'l*, pg. 588
Nakamura, Tadashi, Pres.--Nanto Estate Co., Ltd., Osaka, Japan; *Int'l*, pg. 905
Nakamura, Taizo, Mng. Dir.--Ancra Japan, Yokohama, Japan; *U.S. Private*, pg. 71
Nakamura, Takaaki, Chief Oper. Officer--Daiko Pacific International Advertising Co., Beijing, China; *Int'l*, pg. 366
Nakamura, Takaki, Pres.--Hakuhodo France S.A., Boulogne-Billancourt, France; *Int'l*, pg. 588
Nakamura, Takami, Pres.--Haseko Livenet Inc., Tokyo, Japan; *Int'l*, pg. 600
Nakamura, Toshio, Mng. Dir.--NEC Semiconductors (UK) Limited, Livingston, United Kingdom; *Int'l*, pg. 900
Nakamura, Toshiya, Mng. Dir.--NLI International France S.A., Paris, France; *Int'l*, pg. 936
Nakamura, Yoshiharu, Mng. Dir.--Sakura Finanz (Deutschland) GmbH, Dusseldorf, Germany; *Int'l*, pg. 1180
Nakane, Tsuyoshi, Pres.--United-Asatsu International Ltd., Taipei, Taiwan; *Int'l*, pg. 86
Nakano, H., Pres.--Nakano Foods, Burlingame, CA; *Int'l*, pg. 883
Nakano, Hiroshi, Mng. Dir. & Gen. Mgr.--Sumitomo Trust Finance (Australia) Limited, Sydney, Australia; *Int'l*, pg. 1318
Nakano, Junichi, Pres.--Nomura Real Estate Development Co., Ltd., Tokyo, Japan; *Int'l*, pg. 956
Nakano, Keisuke, Terminal Mgr.--Kintetsu Intermodal Inc., Irving, TX; *Int'l*, pg. 735
Nakano, Keisuke, Terminal Mgr.--Kintetsu World Express Inc., Irving, TX; *Int'l*, pg. 735
Nakano, Moriyoshi, Pres.--Yokohama Aeroquip KK, Tokyo, Japan; *Int'l*, pg. 1521
Nakano, Mutsuo, Chief Oper. Officer--The Sumitomo Bank, Ltd.-Cairo Representative Office, Cairo, Egypt; *Int'l*, pg. 1309
Nakano, Shigeru, Gen. Mgr.--Industriebank von Japan (Deutschland) Aktiengesellschaft, Dusseldorf, Germany; *Int'l*, pg. 676
Nakano, T., Pres.--Sharp (Philippines) Corporation, Manila, Philippines; *Int'l*, pg. 1230
Nakano, Tomohiko, Chief Oper. Officer--Honda Engineering Co., Ltd., Sasayama, Japan; *Int'l*, pg. 634
Nakao, Nick, Gen. Mgr.--MMC Electronics America Inc., Rolling Meadows, IL; *Int'l*, pg. 875
Nakao, Tsuyoshi, Corp. Sec.--CAPCO U.S.A., Inc., Elk Grove Village, IL; *Int'l*, pg. 278
Nakashima, Akira, Gen. Mgr.-Fin. Div.--PT. Satomo Indovyl Polymer, Jakarta, Indonesia; *Int'l*, pg. 1408
Nakasnishi, T., Mng. Dir.--Nippon Kaiji Kyokai, Fort Lee, NJ; *Int'l*, pg. 934
Nakasone, Robert C., Pres.--Toys "R" Us United States, Paramus, NJ; *U.S. Public*, pg. 1626
Nakasuji, Shunsuke, Pres.--DKB Data Services (USA) Inc., Jersey City, NJ; *Int'l*, pg. 360
Nakata, H., Pres.--NIK Metal Corp., Osaka, Japan; *Int'l*, pg. 946
Nakata, Shun, Gen. Mgr.--Hills Colgate Japan Ltd., Tokyo, Japan; *U.S. Public*, pg. 399
Nakatani, Kanetake, Pres.--Komatsu Shantui Construction Machinery Co., Ltd., Shandong, China; *Int'l*, pg. 744
Nakatsugawa, Koji, Pres.--Earth Development (S) Pte. Ltd., Singapore, Singapore; *Int'l*, pg. 741
Nakav, Koji, Gen. Mgr.--Airbus Industrie Tokyo, Tokyo, Japan; *Int'l*, pg. 39
Nakawishi, Masahiko, Gen. Mgr.--Sakura Bank - Houston Agency, Houston, TX; *Int'l*, pg. 1179
Nakayama, Takeshi, Pres.--Toshiba Dalian Co. Ltd., Dalian, China; *Int'l*, pg. 1406
Nakayama, Teruo, Sr. V.P.--Nitto Denko America, Inc., Fremont, CA; *Int'l*, pg. 950
Nakayama, Y., Chm. Bd.--Dunlop Tire Corporation, Buffalo, NY; *Int'l*, pg. 1317
Nakazawa, Masatake, Chief Oper. Officer--Nippon Vishay K.K., Tokyo, Japan; *U.S. Public*, pg. 1722
Nalin, B., Mgr.--Parker Hannifin SpA, Milan, Italy; *U.S. Public*, pg. 1263
Nallathambi, Anand, Pres.--First American Appraisal Services, San Diego, CA; *U.S. Public*, pg. 625
Nalls, Billy E., Pres.--The Citizens Bank of Cochran, Cochran, GA; *U.S. Public*, pg. 1549
Nam, Chung-hyun, Pres.--Daewoo Engineering Company, Seoul, Korea; *Int'l*, pg. 357
Nam, Hyon Min, Mng. Dir.--Korea Orix Lease and Finance Limited, Hong Kong, Hong Kong; *Int'l*, pg. 1009
Nam, Sohn Choong, Pres.--Ssangyong International Ltd., Monrovia, Liberia; *Int'l*, pg. 1292
Nambiar, P.G., Mng. Dir.--Bowthorpe Thermometrics (India) Pvt. Ltd., Bangalore, India; *Int'l*, pg. 208
Nambu, Koichi, Chief Oper. Officer--Toyota Motor Thailand Co., Ltd., Samutprakan, Thailand; *Int'l*, pg. 1414
Namekawa, Fumiaki, Chief Oper. Officer--The Tokio Marine International Fund (Luxembourg) S.A., Luxembourg, Luxembourg; *Int'l*, pg. 1393
Namekawa, Fumiaki, Chief Oper. Officer--Tokio Marine International Fund (Bahama) Company Limited, Nassau, Bahamas; *Int'l*, pg. 1393
Namiki, Hisao, Exec. Dir.--ORIX Corporate Finance Limited, London, United Kingdom; *Int'l*, pg. 1009
Namiot, Milton, Pres. & Chief Exec. Officer--Deering Ice Cream, Inc., Portland, ME; *U.S. Private*, pg. 403
Namitome, Norio, Mng. Dir. & Gen. Mgr.--The Sumitomo Trust & Banking Co., Ltd., Hong Kong, Hong Kong; *Int'l*, pg. 1318
Nammari, Kelly M., Grp. V.P. & Gen. Mgr.--Pre Finish Metals Incorporated, Elk Grove Village, IL; *U.S. Public*, pg. 1056
Namokel, S., Mng. Dir.--Gebr. Becker Sportanlagenbau GmbH, Taunusstein, Germany; *Int'l*, pg. 608
Namsatien, Thanit, Gen. Mgr.--AlliedSignal Laminate Systems Thailand Co., Ltd., Bangkok, Thailand; *U.S. Public*, pg. 53
Nan, Tan Soo, Chm.--DBS Asia Capital Ltd., Central, Hong Kong; *Int'l*, pg. 351
Nancarrow, John, State Mgr.--National Mutual South Australia, Adelaide, Australia; *Int'l*, pg. 908

Nance, Larry, Mgr.--Commercial Metals Company, Canutillo, TX; *U.S. Public*, pg. 413
Nance, Larry, Plant Mgr.--Switchcraft de Mexico, S.A., Tijuana, Mexico; *U.S. Public*, pg. 1366
Nanda, Arun, Chm. Bd. & Mng. Dir.--Rediffusion-DY&R Pvt. Ltd., Mumbai, India; *U.S. Private*, pg. 326
Nania, Enrico, Gen. Mgr.--Renishaw Latino Americana Ltda., Sao Paulo, Brazil; *Int'l*, pg. 1103
Nankani, Gobind T., Dir.--Banco Mundial, Brasilia, Brazil; *U.S. Private*, pg. 1189
Nanner, Mark, Gen. Mgr.--National Fleet & Lease, Mississauga, Canada; *U.S. Public*, pg. 354
Nanri, M., Mng. Dir.--Sharp-Roxy Electronics Corporation (M) Sdn. Bhd., Batu Pahat, Malaysia; *Int'l*, pg. 1230
Nantel, Gilles, Pres.--CAE ScreenPlates Inc., Lennoxville, Canada; *Int'l*, pg. 237
Nantell, William, Pres.--ASI Technology, Colorado Springs, CO; *U.S. Public*, pg. 110
Nanto, Katsuyuki, Terminal Mgr.--Kintetsu World Express Inc., Elk Grove Village, IL; *Int'l*, pg. 735
Napel, Ten, Chief Exec. Officer--President Frito-Lay Corp., Tai-nan, Taiwan; *Int'l*, pg. 1069
Napier, John Boyd, Gen. Mgr.--Zimmer New Zealand Limited, Auckland, New Zealand; *U.S. Public*, pg. 257
Napier, Robert H., Pres.--NationsBank Realty Services Corp., Nashville, TN; *U.S. Public*, pg. 1164
Napoli, Daniel T., Chm. Bd.--Merrill Lynch Government Securities, Inc., New York, NY; *U.S. Public*, pg. 1097
Naprstek, K., Pres.--ICI Performance Products, Wilmington, DE; *Int'l*, pg. 664
Naqvi, Saiyid T., Pres. & Chief Exec. Officer--PNC Mortgage Corporation of America, Vernon Hills, IL; *U.S. Public*, pg. 1243
Nara, Hiroshi, Rep.--The Kyoei Mutual Fire & Marine Insurance Company, Hong Kong Representative Office, Hong Kong, Hong Kong; *Int'l*, pg. 777
Naranjo, Ramon, Mgr. -Opers.--Etiquetas Internacionales, Inc., Santo Domingo, Dominican Republic; *Int'l*, pg. 132
Narayanan, R., Mgr.-Fin. & Co. Sec.--Castrol Singapore Pte. Ltd., Singapore, Singapore; *Int'l*, pg. 236
Nardelli, Robert L., Pres. & Chief Exec. Officer--G.E. Power Systems, Schenectady, NY; *U.S. Public*, pg. 711
Nardi, Ronald G., Pres.--General Motors Egypt S.A.E., Cairo, Egypt; *Int'l*, pg. 692
Nardi, Ronald G., Pres.--General Motors Egypt S.A.E., Cairo, Egypt; *U.S. Public*, pg. 724
Nardone, John, Mng. Dir., Media Dir. & Res. Dir.--Modem Media New York, New York, NY; *U.S. Public*, pg. 1641
Nardulli, Ettore, Pres. & Chief Oper. Officer--Black Dot Graphics, Inc., Crystal Lake, IL; *U.S. Public*, pg. 503
Nardulli, Ettore G., Pres.--Typo-Graphics, Inc., Orlando, FL; *U.S. Public*, pg. 503
Nardulli, Ettore G., Pres.--Taproot Interactive, Inc., Chicago, IL; *U.S. Public*, pg. 503
Nargi, E. L., Pres.--Saft America Inc., Valdosta, GA; *Int'l*, pg. 55
Narhi, Antti, Pres.--Outokumpu Steel Oy, Tornio, Finland; *Int'l*, pg. 1018
Narihiro, Yasundobu, Pres. & Chief Exec. Officer--D.F. Stauffer Biscuit Co., York, PA; *Int'l*, pg. 855
Narita, Akhito, Pres.--Symantec K.K., Tokyo, Japan; *U.S. Public*, pg. 1545
Narita, Fujiaki, Pres.--Narita Giken Co., Ltd., Amagasaki, Japan; *Int'l*, pg. 1125
Narita, Ryuhei, Pres.--Nissan Research & Development Corp., Farmington Hills, MI; *Int'l*, pg. 945
Narita, Yosuke, Pres.--Kawasaki Heavy Industries (H.K.) Ltd., Central, Hong Kong; *Int'l*, pg. 726
Narlinger, Dennis, Pres.--Shugart Corp., Upland, CA; *U.S. Private*, pg. 997
Narlis, Anthony, Gen. Mgr.--Circle Freight International Greece S.A., Athens, Greece; *U.S. Public*, pg. 372
Narman, Borje, Chief Oper. Officer--Electrolux Commercial Refrigeration AB, Arvika, Sweden; *Int'l*, pg. 438
Narozniak, Y., Rep.--Gan Incendie Accidents Hong Kong, Central, Hong Kong; *Int'l*, pg. 564
Narsey, Chittu B., Mng. Dir.--Khimline Pumps Limited, Thane, India; *Int'l*, pg. 1305
Narsh, Paula, Mgr.--Peterson Builders, Inc.-Ingleside Div., Ingleside, TX; *U.S. Private*, pg. 857
Narushima, Makiyo, Gen. Mgr.--The Sakura Bank - Paris Branch, Paris, France; *Int'l*, pg. 1179
Narvinger, Anders, Pres.--ABB HV Switchgear AB, Ludvika, Sweden; *Int'l*, pg. 7
Narwani, Dru, Country Mgr.--Standard Chartered Bank (Thailand), Bangkok, Thailand; *Int'l*, pg. 1296
Nash, Alan W., Mng. Dir.--Carter-Wallace (Australia) Pty. Limited, Frenchs Forest, Australia; *U.S. Public*, pg. 310
Nash, Craig M., Chief Exec. Officer--Interval International Inc., Miami, FL; *U.S. Public*, pg. 320
Nash, Gaynor, Mgr.-Opers.--InterLake Papers, Inc., Kimberly, WI; *U.S. Public*, pg. 436
Nash, Merrill L., Pres.--Symons Corporation, Pasadena, CA; *U.S. Private*, pg. 932
Nash, Richard A., Pres.--SunTrust Insurance Company, Atlanta, GA; *U.S. Public*, pg. 1538
Nash, William A., Mgr.--Scott & Stringfellow, Inc., Roanoke, VA; *U.S. Public*, pg. 1446
Nashif, Ziad Y., Mng. Dir.--General Motors Turkiye Limited Sirketi, Izmir, Turkey; *U.S. Public*, pg. 723
Nasholm, Goran, Mgr.--Jirva AB, Huddinge, Sweden; *Int'l*, pg. 1422
Nasi, John R., Pres. & Chief Exec. Officer--Transportation Manufacturing Corporation, Roswell, NM; *Int'l*, pg. 326
Nasky, Thomas G., Exec. V.P.-Sls. & Mktg.--Dualite Sales & Service, Inc., Williamsburg, OH; *U.S. Private*, pg. 344
Nasland, Kurt, Mng. Dir.--Lubrizol Scandinavia AB, Danderyd, Sweden; *U.S. Public*, pg. 1017
Nason, Charles T., Pres. & Chief Exec. Officer--Acacia Financial Corporation, Bethesda, MD; *U.S. Private*, pg. 11
Nason, Charles T., Pres. & Chief Exec. Officer--Acacia National Life Ins. Co., Bethesda, MD; *U.S. Private*, pg. 11
Nason, James, Pres.--Empress Foods Ltd., Vancouver, Canada; *U.S. Public*, pg. 1426
Nason, Tucker, Pres. & Chief Exec. Officer--Burbank Aircraft Supply Inc., Sun Valley, CA; *U.S. Public*, pg. 187
Nason, Tucker, Pres. & Chief Exec. Officer--Harco, El Segundo, CA; *U.S. Public*, pg. 187
Nass, Howard, Sr. V.P., Exec. Dir.-Brdcst. Devel.--TN Entertainment, New York, NY; *U.S. Public*, pg. 1641
Nass, Ken, Mgr.-Office--Woodward-Clyde, Omaha, NE; *U.S.* Public, pg. 1656
Nassar, J.A., Dir. Pres.--Autolatina Financiadora S.A.-Credito, Financiamento e Investimentos, Sao Paulo, Brazil; *U.S. Public*, pg. 665
Nassar, J.A., Pres.--Consorcio Nacional Ford Ltda., Rio de Janeiro, Brazil; *U.S. Public*, pg. 665
Nassauer, G., Mng. Dir.--Elektrowerk Weisweiler GmbH, Eschweiler, Germany; *U.S. Private*, pg. 735
Nasser, Jacques A., Pres.--Ford North American Automotive Operation, Dearborn, MI; *U.S. Public*, pg. 662
Nasu, A., Pres.--Mita Copystar America Inc., Fairfield, NJ; *Int'l*, pg. 870
Natale, Jim L., Pres.--Corporate Marketing and Services, Murray Hill, NJ; *U.S. Public*, pg. 189
Natale, Mike, V.P. & Gen. Mgr.--Dillard, A ResourceNet International Company, Norfolk, VA; *U.S. Public*, pg. 902
Natalicci, Giulio, Gen. Mgr.--Banca Monte dei Paschi di Siena, New York, NY; *Int'l*, pg. 136
Nathan, Jean-Jacques, Chm.--Fernand Nathan, Paris, France; *Int'l*, pg. 240
Nathan, John, Gen. Mgr.--Glass Plant, Rogers, AR; *U.S. Private*, pg. 486
Nathikanchanalab, Thirasakdi, Mng. Dir.--SCT Co., Ltd., Bangkok, Thailand; *Int'l*, pg. 1238
Nation, Douglas P. C., Mng. Dir.--Bear, Stearns International Limited, London, United Kingdom; *U.S. Public*, pg. 198
Nativ, Arie, Sec.--Ma'berot Hayarden Limited, Haifa, Israel; *Int'l*, pg. 691
Natoli, Joseph, Pres.--The Miami Herald, Miami, FL; *U.S. Public*, pg. 964
Natori, Tadaaki, Pres.--Japan Securities Agents, Ltd., Tokyo, Japan; *Int'l*, pg. 702
Nattier, Robert, Chief Oper. Officer, Chief Fin. Officer & Gen. Mgr.--Lubrication Consultants, L.L.C., Moundridge, KS; *U.S. Private*, pg. 743
Nattier, Robert, Mng. Partner--Haven Commodities LLC, Moundridge, KS; *U.S. Private*, pg. 743
Nattore, Mac, Pres.--Regal Japan Co. Ltd., Nagoya, Japan; *U.S. Private*, pg. 917
Nauert, Robert F., Pres.--Network Air Medical Systems, Inc., Rockford, IL; *U.S. Public*, pg. 433
Naukkarinen, Tyrki, Chief Oper. Officer--Plastilon, Willich, Germany; *Int'l*, pg. 915
Nauleau, Heidi, Pres.--Aarque Steel Corporation, Jamestown, NY; *U.S. Private*, pg. 9
Nauleau, Heidi, Pres.--Aarque Management Corp., Jamestown, NY; *U.S. Private*, pg. 9
Nauman, Ralph, Pres.--Wah Chang, Albany, OR; *U.S. Public*, pg. 44
Naumanen, Lasse, Chief Oper. Officer--Oy Electrolux Ab-ASAB, Helsinki, Finland; *Int'l*, pg. 441
Naumann, Hans R.E., Gen. Mgr.-Metering--Landis & Staefa Inc., Lafayette, IN; *Int'l*, pg. 800
Naumann, Michael, Pres.--Henry Holt & Co. Publishing, New York, NY; *Int'l*, pg. 1479
Nausler, R. Terry, Pres.--Coors Distributing Co., Golden, CO; *U.S. Public*, pg. 445
Nautsheim, Friedrich, Dr., Chm.--Fichtel & Sachs AG, Schweinfurt, Germany; *Int'l*, pg. 835
Navarro, Jose Luis, Gen. Mgr.-Health & Beauty Care--Procter & Gamble Espana S.A., Madrid, Spain; *U.S. Public*, pg. 1332
Navarro, Juan Francisco, Gen. Mgr.--Amway Chile, Santiago, Chile; *U.S. Private*, pg. 69
Navarro, Larry A., Chief Oper. Officer--C.E.T. Robertshaw, Paris, France; *Int'l*, pg. 1244
Navarro, Tirso, Gen. Mgr.--Dun & Bradstreet S.A., Madrid, Spain; *U.S. Public*, pg. 537
Navas-Pinzon, Jorge, Gen. Mgr.--CCF Bogota, Bogota, Colombia,; *Int'l*, pg. 342
Navi, Menashe, Mng. Dir.--Autologic Information International Ltd., Ramat Gan, Israel; *U.S. Public*, pg. 1724
Navotna, Hanna, Dir.--Berlitz Schools of Languages Czechoslovakia Spol.sr.o, Prague, Czech Republic; *U.S. Public*, pg. 222
Nawab, Y., Mng. Dir.--Mackinnon Mackenzie & Co. of Pakistan (Private) Ltd., Karachi, Pakistan; *Int'l*, pg. 1035
Nawolsky, Russ, Dir.-Opers.--Hunt Oil Canadian Division Office, Calgary, Canada; *U.S. Private*, pg. 549
Nawrocki, Christopher, Pres.--Benchmark Electronics, Inc.-Winona Division, Winona, MN; *U.S. Public*, pg. 211
Nayar, N.K., Chm. Bd.--IRD Mechanalysis (India) Limited, Mumbai, India; *U.S. Public*, pg. 790
Naylor, Keith E., Prod. Mgr.--Duni Ltd., Runcorn, United Kingdom; *Int'l*, pg. 421
Naylor, Nick, V.P. & Gen. Mgr.--Simon Marketing, Ltd., London, United Kingdom; *U.S. Private*, pg. 1001
Nazarathy, Moshe, Mgr.--Harmonic Lightwaves (Israel) Ltd., Pardis Hana, Israel; *U.S. Public*, pg. 788
Ndahakwaje, Libere, Dir. & Gen. Mgr.--Banque Commerciale du Burundi Sarl, Bujumbura, Burundi; *Int'l*, pg. 148
Neal, George E., Exec. V.P.-Investment Opers.--Manulife Financial, Toronto, Canada; *Int'l*, pg. 840
Neal, Henry, Pres. & Gen. Mgr.--BHP Hawaii, Inc., Honolulu, HI; *Int'l*, pg. 225
Neal, Howard E., V.P. & Gen. Mgr.--KFI, Inc., Los Angeles, CA; *U.S. Private*, pg. 282
Neal, John, Mng. Dir.--Sorbus Europe, Ltd., Hampton, United Kingdom; *U.S. Public*, pg. 204
Neal, Loyd, Pres.--Hilb, Rogal and Hamilton Company of Corpus Christi, Corpus Christi, TX; *U.S. Public*, pg. 827
Neal, Philip M., Grp. V.P.--Materials Group North America, Painesville, OH; *U.S. Public*, pg. 153
Neal, Robert F., Sr. V.P.-Opers.--The Southern New England Telephone Company, New Haven, CT; *U.S. Public*, pg. 1491
Neal, Stanley L., V.P. & Div. Mgr.--Bindley Western, Indianapolis Division, Indianapolis, IN; *U.S. Public*, pg. 228
Neal, Thomas, Jr., Gen. Mgr.--Cove Shoe Company, Martinsburg, PA; *U.S. Public*, pg. 217
Neal, William, Chief Exec. Officer--Elite Information Systems, Inc., New York, NY; *U.S. Public*, pg. 258
Neal, William, Chief Exec. Officer--Elite Information Systems, Inc., London, United Kingdom; *U.S. Public*, pg. 258
Neale, Gary L., Chm.--NIPSCO Exploration Co., Inc., Hammond, IN; *U.S. Public*, pg. 1185
Neale, Gary L., Pres.--NIPSCO Fuel Company, Inc., Hammond, IN; *U.S. Public*, pg. 1185
Neale, Gary L., Pres.--NIPSCO Energy Services, Inc., Hammond, IN; *U.S. Public*, pg. 1185
Neale, Gary L., Pres.--NI-TEX, Inc., Hammond, IN; *U.S. Public*, pg. 1185
Neals, Gary L., Chm.--Shore Line Shops, Inc., Hammond, IN; *U.S. Public*, pg. 1185
Neame, John, Mng. Dir.--EMAP Enterprise Events, Purley, United Kingdom; *Int'l*, pg. 451
Neapole, Robert, Chief Oper. Officer--Kamtech Inc., Glens Falls, NY; *Int'l*, pg. 34
Near, Earl, Pres.--Dominion Stores, Etobicoke, Canada; *Int'l*, pg. 1375
Near, Wm., Pres. & Chief Exec. Officer--The Cedar Point Bridge Co., Sandusky, OH; *U.S. Public*, pg. 319
Nearing, R., Pres.--Nyacol Products, Inc., Ashland, MA; *U.S.* Private, pg. 827
Neary, Tom, Plant Mgr.--Ash Grove Cement Plant, Louisville, NE; *U.S. Private*, pg. 88
Nebel, J., Gen. Mgr.--Kolana S.A., Callao, Peru; *U.S. Public*, pg. 81
Nebot, B., Gen. Mgr.--AMP Espanola, S. A., Barcelona, Spain; *U.S. Public*, pg. 8
Nebot, B., Gen. Mgr.--AMP Portugal, Lda., Lisbon, Portugal; *U.S. Public*, pg. 9
Necchi-Ghiri, Toni, Mgr.--EG & G S.p.A. Instruments Division, Milan, Italy; *U.S. Public*, pg. 544
Nechiporchik, John D., Pres.--Automobile Specialty Co., Southgate, MI; *U.S. Private*, pg. 8
Neckermann, Bill, Gen. Mgr.--Maintenance, Inc., Wooster, OH; *Int'l*, pg. 1068
Nectoux, Georges, Chm. & Chief Exec. Officer--Ricard, Marseilles, France; *Int'l*, pg. 566
Ned, Phyllis, V.P. & Gen. Mgr.--KETV, Omaha, NE; *U.S. Public*, pg. 1343
Nederlof, Gerhard, Pres.--C-Cor Europe, B.V., Almere, Netherlands; *U.S. Public*, pg. 272
Nedley, R.E., Pres.--St. Joe Forest Products Company, Port Saint Joe, FL; *U.S. Public*, pg. 1427
Nedwin, Glenn E., Chief Oper. Officer--Novo Nordisk Biotech, Inc., Davis, CA; *Int'l*, pg. 987
Nee, Billy, Mgr.--Kintetsu Intermodal (Taiwan), Inc., Taipei, Taiwan; *Int'l*, pg. 735
Needham, Rick, Pres.--Circle Seal Controls, Inc., Corona, CA; *U.S. Public*, pg. 1746
Needlemann, Elliott, Pres.--GP Taurio, Inc., Alexandria, VA; *U.S. Public*, pg. 694
Neel, M.L., Pres.--Bellsouth China, Inc., Beijing, China; *U.S. Public*, pg. 208
Neel, Thomas H., Pres.--ADS Environmental Services Inc., Huntsville, AL; *Int'l*, pg. 709
Neeley, Harvey, Mgr.--Consolidated Electric Supply, Inc., Orlando, FL; *Int'l*, pg. 1107
Neely, A., Mng. Dir.--Borden Foods (Pty) Ltd., Bronfontein, South Africa; *U.S. Private*, pg. 159
Neely, Alan, Office Mgr.--Korn/Ferry International, Atlanta, GA; *U.S. Public*, pg. 633
Neely, Alan, Regional Mgr.--Korn/Ferry International, Dallas, TX; *U.S. Private*, pg. 633
Neely, David B., Pres.--Lynden Transport, Inc., Kent, WA; *U.S. Private*, pg. 684
Neely, Denny, Gen. Mgr.--Surplus Warehouse-Alexandria, Alexandria, LA; *U.S. Private*, pg. 119
Neer, Edward A., Jr., Pres. & Chief Exec. Officer--MLT Vacations, Inc., Minnetonka, MN; *U.S. Public*, pg. 1200
Neervoort, A.F., Dir.--Hoogovens Staalverwerking en Handel BV, Bloemendaal, Netherlands; *Int'l*, pg. 754
Neervoort, A.F., Mng. Dir.--Hoogovens Buizen B.V., Oosterhout, Netherlands; *Int'l*, pg. 754
Neese, Jimmie, Pres.--Lee Construction Co., Charlotte, NC; *U.S. Private*, pg. 782
Neeser, Craig, Mgr.--Custom Processing Division, Richmond, Canada; *Int'l*, pg. 828
Neeson, Cheryl Pirello, Pres.--Banta Integrated Media, Boston, MA; *U.S. Public*, pg. 188
Neeve, James B., Mgr.-Sls.--Amcast Industrial Ltd., Burlington, Canada; *U.S. Public*, pg. 63
Neff, Charles C., Gen. Mgr.--Cigna Healthplan of North Louisiana, Shreveport, LA; *U.S. Public*, pg. 360
Neff, David, Pres.--CWT Farms International, Gainesville, GA; *Int'l*, pg. 202
Neff, Deborah J., Pres.--Becton Dickinson Immunocytometry Systems, San Jose, CA; *U.S. Public*, pg. 199
Neff, Phillip R., Pres. & Chief Exec. Officer--Willis Corroon Corp. of Kansas, Wichita, KS; *Int'l*, pg. 1506
Neffgen, Alfred V., Pres.--Jones Management Services, Inc., Charlotte, NC; *Int'l*, pg. 633
Negre, Jean-Luc, Pres.--Baccarat, Inc., Edison, NJ; *Int'l*, pg. 132
Negri, Robert, V.P.-Fin.--Hayes-Albion, Jackson, MI; *U.S. Public*, pg. 796
Nehrer, Hans, Dir.-Austrian Opers.--Pioneer Saaten AG, Parndorf, Austria; *U.S. Public*, pg. 1299
Neighbors, Thomas H., Pres. & Chief Oper. Officer--SAIC, Mc Lean, VA; *U.S. Private*, pg. 976

Neill, Donald M., Pres. & Chief Exec. Officer--Lufkin National Bank, Lufkin, TX; *U.S. Public*, pg. 630
Neill, Doug, Pres.--Business Information Group, Rockford, IL; *U.S. Public*, pg. 433
Neill, R.A., Pres. & Chief Oper. Officer--Orenda Aerospace Corporation, Mississauga, Canada; *Int'l*, pg. 829
Neill, Richard A., Pres.--Orenda (Canada), Mississauga, Canada; *Int'l*, pg. 604
Neill, Thomas, Plant Mgr.--Bundy Corporation, Hillsdale Plant, Hillsdale, MI; *Int'l*, pg. 1340
Neill, Tom, Plant Mgr.--Bundy Corporation, Coldwater Plant, Coldwater, MI; *Int'l*, pg. 1340
Neill, William J., Publisher & Chief Exec. Officer--The Ottawa Sun, Ottawa, Canada; *Int'l*, pg. 1320
Neilsen, Bernie, Gen. Mgr.--Hub City, Inc., Aberdeen, SD; *U.S. Public*, pg. 1371
Neilson, James R., Pres.--Thompson Division, Golden Valley, MN; *U.S. Public*, pg. 1683
Neilson, Kenneth T., Chm. Bd. & Chief Exec. Officer--Lafayette American Bank, Union City, NJ; *U.S. Public*, pg. 845
Neira, Sergio, Chief Exec.--KONE Elevadores, S.A., Madrid, Spain; *Int'l*, pg. 747
Neirynck, J., Chief Oper. Officer--Amylum N.V., Aalst, Belgium; *Int'l*, pg. 1357
Neiva, Edmilson, Chief Oper. Officer--Rhone-Poulenc de Mexico S.A. de C.V., Mexico, Mexico; *Int'l*, pg. 1112
Neiva, Edmilson, Mng. Dir.--Rhone-Poulenc de Mexico S.A. de C.V., Mexico, Mexico; *Int'l*, pg. 1113
Nekman, Donald, Chm., Partner & Chief Fin. Officer--EURO RSCG, Copenhagen, Copenhagen, Denmark; *Int'l*, pg. 602
Nekvasil, Jiri, Chm.--Obalex, A.S., Znojmo, Czech Republic; *U.S. Public*, pg. 440
Nelander, D., Dr., Mgr.-Mfg.--Kodak Limited, Harrow, United Kingdom; *U.S. Public*, pg. 553
Nelis, Jan, Dir.--Alpha Credit, Brussels, Belgium; *Int'l*, pg. 546
Nelissen, R.J., Chm. Bd.--Amsterdam-Rotterdam Bank N.V., Amsterdam, Netherlands; *Int'l*, pg. 9
Nelissen, Willy, Mng. Dir.--Delaware Computing Zwevegem, Zwevegem, Belgium; *Int'l*, pg. 183
Nelligan, Michael T., Pres.--Western Aggregates, Inc., Boulder, CO; *Int'l*, pg. 672
Nello, Hugues, Mng.Dir.--Mitchell Sports SA, Marignier, France; *U.S. Public*, pg. 933
Nellul, Frederic, Mng. Dir.--Credit Lyonnais Capital Markets plc, London, United Kingdom; *Int'l*, pg. 344
Nelson, Barry E., Pres. & Chief Exec. Officer--Cincinnati Bell Long Distance Inc., Cincinnati, OH; *U.S. Public*, pg. 367
Nelson, Bruce, Pres.--BT-U.S.A., Inc., Buffalo Grove, IL; *Int'l*, pg. 756
Nelson, Charles E., Chm. Bd., Pres. & Chief Exec. Officer--Liberty Bancorp, Inc., Oklahoma City, OK; *U.S. Public*, pg. 174
Nelson, Craig H., V.P.--Consumer Products Div., San Francisco, CA; *U.S. Public*, pg. 1318
Nelson, Curt, Pres.--Continental Homes of Denver, Englewood, CO; *U.S. Public*, pg. 441
Nelson, David, Gen. Mgr.--Lakeview Resort & Conference Center, Morgantown, WV; *U.S. Public*, pg. 1537
Nelson, David, Gen. Mgr.--Euro-Suites, Morgantown, WV; *U.S. Public*, pg. 1537
Nelson, Dennis, Mgr.--Woodward Cable TV, Inc., Woodward, OK; *U.S. Public*, pg. 1611
Nelson, Dennis H., Mgr.-Branch--Piper Jaffray Inc., Topeka, KS; *U.S. Public*, pg. 1301
Nelson, Dennis H., Mgr.-Branch--Piper Jaffray Inc., Hiawatha, KS; *U.S. Public*, pg. 1303
Nelson, Donald E., Pres.--Metro-North Commuter Railroad Company, New York, NY; *U.S. Private*, pg. 739
Nelson, Douglas, Plant Mgr.--Hill's Pet Products, Bowling Green, OH; *U.S. Public*, pg. 397
Nelson, Eric B., Pres.--Energy Pacific, Los Angeles, CA; *U.S. Public*, pg. 584
Nelson, Eric B., Pres.--Pacific Interstate Company, Los Angeles, CA; *U.S. Public*, pg. 1249
Nelson, Eric B., Pres.--Pacific Lighting Gas Development Co., Los Angeles, CA; *U.S. Public*, pg. 1249
Nelson, Eric B., Pres.--Pacific Western Resources Co., Los Angeles, CA; *U.S. Public*, pg. 1249
Nelson, Eric B., Pres.--Pacific Synthetic Fuel Company, Los Angeles, CA; *U.S. Public*, pg. 1249
Nelson, Eric B., Pres.--Pacific Interstate Offshore Company, Los Angeles, CA; *U.S. Public*, pg. 1249
Nelson, Eric B., Pres.--Pacific Interstate Transmission Company, Los Angeles, CA; *U.S. Public*, pg. 1249
Nelson, Eric B., Pres.--Pacific Interstate Mojave Company, Los Angeles, CA; *U.S. Public*, pg. 1249
Nelson, Eric B., Pres.--Pacific Interstate Transmission Company (Arctic), Los Angeles, CA; *U.S. Public*, pg. 1249
Nelson, Eric B., Pres.--Energy Pacific, Los Angeles, CA; *U.S. Public*, pg. 1249
Nelson, Frederick, Pres.--Kaiser Cement Corporation, Pleasanton, CA; *Int'l*, pg. 593
Nelson, Gregory N., Pres.--Seadrift Pipeline Corp., Danbury, CT; *U.S. Public*, pg. 1667
Nelson, Gregory N., Pres.--Ucar Pipeline, Inc., Danbury, CT; *U.S. Public*, pg. 1667
Nelson, H. Donald, Pres. & Chief Exec. Officer--United States Cellular Corporation, Chicago, IL; *U.S. Public*, pg. 1572
Nelson, Helen, Mgr.-Office--Jani King of Minnesota, Inc., Minneapolis, MN; *U.S. Private*, pg. 582
Nelson, J. R., Chief Oper. Officer--Den norske Bank, New York Branch, New York, NY; *Int'l*, pg. 392
Nelson, Jeffrey D., Pres.--Nationwide Acceptance, Arlington, TX; *U.S. Private*, pg. 917
Nelson, Jerry R., Pres.--ConAgra Turkey Company, El Dorado, AR; *U.S. Public*, pg. 427
Nelson, Jim, Dir.-Sls. & Mktg.--Ederer Cranes, Seattle, WA; *U.S. Private*, pg. 363
Nelson, Jim, Pres. & Chief Exec. Officer--Southern Progress Corporation, Birmingham, AL; *U.S. Public*, pg. 1613
Nelson, Jim, Pres. & Chief Exec. Officer--Time Publishing Ventures, Inc., Los Angeles, CA; *U.S. Public*, pg. 1613
Nelson, John, Mgr.--Bergen Brunswig Medical Corporation, Orlando, FL; *U.S. Public*, pg. 214
Nelson, John, Plant Mgr.--TDK Electronics, Detroit, Livonia, MI; *Int'l*, pg. 1336
Nelson, Karl, Dir.--Postal Commemorative Society Collection, Norwalk, CT; *U.S. Private*, pg. 685
Nelson, Ken, V.P. & Gen. Mgr.--Dayton Rogers of Texas, Arlington, TX; *U.S. Private*, pg. 318
Nelson, King, Pres.--Dade Behring, Miami, FL; *U.S. Private*, pg. 110
Nelson, L. Scott, Chm. Bd., Pres. & Chief Exec. Officer--First Security Bank of Utah, N.A., Salt Lake City, UT; *U.S. Public*, pg. 637
Nelson, M.C., Pres. & Chief Exec. Officer--Radisson Hotel Corporation, Minneapolis, MN; *U.S. Private*, pg. 212
Nelson, Marla, Gen. Mgr.--Hayes Microcomputer Products Ltd., Fleet, United Kingdom; *U.S. Public*, pg. 801
Nelson, Mary Jo, Pres.-Yellow Pages Div.--Ruppman National Yellow Pages Service Inc., Peoria, IL; *U.S. Private*, pg. 952
Nelson, Mike, Pres.--Group Insurance of Colorado, Denver, CO; *U.S. Private*, pg. 484
Nelson, P.T., Chief Oper. Officer--Kidde-Graviner Australia Pty. Limited, Mordialloc, Australia; *Int'l*, pg. 1500
Nelson, Pat, Plant Mgr.--Up-Right Work Platforms Division, Selma, CA; *U.S. Private*, pg. 1128
Nelson, Ray, Mng. Dir.--Laboratory Supply Company, Des Moines, IA; *U.S. Private*, pg. 642
Nelson, Robert, Pres. & V.P.--Avondale Mills Yarn Div., Sylacauga, AL; *U.S. Private*, pg. 103
Nelson, Robert, Sr. V.P. & Gen. Mgr.--Tamarron Division, Durango, CO; *U.S. Private*, pg. 1036
Nelson, Rodney R., Pres.--First American Bank N.A., Crookston, MN; *U.S. Private*, pg. 167
Nelson, Roger, V.P. & Gen. Mgr.--Clow Valve Div., Oskaloosa, IA; *U.S. Private*, pg. 725
Nelson, Ronald, Chief Oper. Officer--Colman OEM, Inc., Crystal Lake, IL; *Int'l*, pg. 1242
Nelson, Ronald D., Mgr.--Mid-State Telephone Co., New London, MN; *U.S. Public*, pg. 1571
Nelson, Ronald G., Pres. & Chief Exec. Officer--MCI Acceptance Corp., Phoenix, AZ; *Int'l*, pg. 326
Nelson, S. Pat, Plant Mgr.--Harvester Division, Selma, CA; *U.S. Private*, pg. 1128
Nelson, Steve, Pres.--Taylor Rental, East Butler, PA; *U.S. Private*, pg. 1108
Nelson, Susan L., Asst. Sec.--Investment Technology Group, Inc., New York, NY; *U.S. Public*, pg. 924
Nelson, Tom, Chm. & Creative Dir.--Ammirati & Puris Ltd./Toronto, Toronto, Canada; *U.S. Private*, pg. 67
Nelson, W. Peterson, Chm.--Nelson, Benson & Zellmer, Inc., Denver, CO; *U.S. Public*, pg. 1673
Nelson, Wendell, V.P. & Gen. Mgr.--General Implement Distributors, Salt Lake City, UT; *U.S. Private*, pg. 84
Nelson, William, Dir.-Personnel--Kikkoman Foods, Inc., Walworth, WI; *Int'l*, pg. 733
Nelson, William C., Chm. Bd. & Pres.--NationsBank of Kansas City, Kansas City, MO; *U.S. Public*, pg. 1164
Nemchinov, Alexander, Gen. Mgr.--Kvaerner Masa-Yards Inc., Moscow, Moscow, Russia; *Int'l*, pg. 771
Neme, Nilo, V.P. & Regional Representative--NationsBank (Brazil) Branch, Rio de Janeiro, Brazil; *U.S. Public*, pg. 1166
Nemenz, Howard, Gen. Mgr.--WSJS, Winston Salem, NC; *U.S. Public*, pg. 385
Nemenz, Howard, Gen. Mgr.--WTQR, Winston Salem, NC; *U.S. Public*, pg. 385
Nemenz, Howard, Gen. Mgr.--WXRA, Winston Salem, NC; *U.S. Public*, pg. 385
Nemling, Ingomar, Sr. V.P.--Voest-Alpine Steel Corp.-Forgings & Castings, New York, NY; *Int'l*, pg. 1471
Nenonen, Matti, V.P.--Kirkniemi Paper Mills, Kirkniemi, Finland; *Int'l*, pg. 863
Nentwick, Thomas, Gen. Mgr.--Alumax Extrusions, Inc., Hernando, MS; *U.S. Public*, pg. 59
Nenzen, Henrik P., Chm. Bd.--Ford Vagnskadegaranti AB, Stockholm, Sweden; *U.S. Public*, pg. 666
Neporadny, John, Gen. Mgr.--Continental Electric, Trussville, AL; *U.S. Private*, pg. 692
Nepote, Mario, Mng. Dir.--SKF Multitec, Cascina, Italy; *Int'l*, pg. 1159
Nerbonne, Robert A., Pres.--Pitco Frialator Inc., Bow, NH; *U.S. Public*, pg. 1065
Neri, Thomas, Publr.--Pioneer Press Newspapers Inc., Glenview, IL; *Int'l*, pg. 632
Nerlet, N., Mng. Dir.--Credit Lyonnais Espana SA, Madrid, Spain; *Int'l*, pg. 344
Nes, Robert, Gen. Mgr.--Nielsen Norge, Oslo, Norway; *U.S. Public*, pg. 1184
Nesbit, Tom, Sls. Representative--PENCO-Alambama, Birmingham, AL; *Int'l*, pg. 1508
Nesbitt, A., Gen. Mgr.--G.D. Holmes Limited, Immingham Dock, United Kingdom; *Int'l*, pg. 802
Nesbitt, G. Alan, Pres. & Gen. Mgr.--KABC-TV, Century City, CA; *U.S. Public*, pg. 512
Neslund, Scott, Intl. Media Dir.--Leo Burnett Kyodo Co. Ltd., Tokyo, Japan; *U.S. Private*, pg. 185
Ness, Duane, Pres.--Tower Electronics, Inc., Fridley, MN; *U.S. Public*, pg. 20
Nessis, Moshe, Gen. Mgr.--Geller Nessis/DMB&B Tel Aviv, Tel Aviv, Israel; *U.S. Private*, pg. 304
Nesta, Vincenzo, Pres.--Pittway Tecnologica S.p.A., Trieste, Italy; *U.S. Public*, pg. 1307
Nestoras, Fotios P., Mng. Dir.--Bristol Hellas A.E.B.E., Athens, Greece; *U.S. Public*, pg. 255
Nestrick, Dwight, Chief Exec. Officer--Citizens Bank of Kentucky, Madisonville, KY; *U.S. Public*, pg. 280
Nestrick, Dwight L., Pres. & Chief Exec. Officer--Citizens Bank of Kentucky, Henderson, KY; *U.S. Public*, pg. 280
Netherland, Joseph H., Gen. Mgr.--FMC Energy & Transportation Equipment Group, Houston, TX; *U.S. Public*, pg. 605
Netherton, Pete, Chief Fin. Officer--Spartanburg Steel Products, Spartanburg, SC; *U.S. Private*, pg. 300
Neto, Antonio Campos, Gen. Mgr.--Colgate-Palmolive, Inc., Montevideo, Uruguay; *U.S. Public*, pg. 398
Neto, Carlos, Plant Mgr.--Bundy SA - Sucursal Portugesa, Vendas, Portugal; *Int'l*, pg. 1341
Neto, Jose Ferreira, Pres.--Banco Internacional de Credito S.A., Lisbon, Portugal; *Int'l*, pg. 142
Netolicka, Robert, V.P.--Johnson Controls World Services Inc., Cape Canaveral, FL; *U.S. Public*, pg. 932
Netols, Pat, Gen. Mgr.--Process Color Plate, Chicago, IL; *U.S. Public*, pg. 1437
Nett, Merle, V.P.--Richco Structures, Haven, WI; *U.S. Private*, pg. 929
Netter, Edward, Chm. Bd. & Chief Exec. Officer--Independence Holding Company, Stamford, CT; *U.S. Private*, pg. 446
Netting, Kelvin, Mng. Dir.--The Great Australian Pie Company Pty. Ltd., Labrador, Australia; *Int'l*, pg. 1074
Nettles, Mike, Mgr.-Plant--Beech-Nut Nutrition Corporation, Canajoharie, NY; *U.S. Public*, pg. 1359
Nettles, Mike, Mgr.-Plant--Beech-Nut Nutrition Corporation, Fort Plain, NY; *U.S. Public*, pg. 1359
Neu, Christian, Dr., Gen. Dir.--ELVIA Leben, Geneva, Switzerland; *Int'l*, pg. 60
Neu, Gunter, Co-Chief Oper. Officer--Saarberg-Fernwaerme GmbH, Saarbruecken, Germany; *Int'l*, pg. 1166
Neu, Gunter, Co-Chief Oper. Officer--FernwaermeVerbund Saar GmbH, Voelklingen, Germany; *Int'l*, pg. 1167
Neu, Gunter, Co-Chief Oper. Officer--GVT Gesellschaft fuer Versorgungstechnik mbH, Saarbruecken, Germany; *Int'l*, pg. 1167
Neu, Robert, Dir.-Air Inter, North America--Air France, New York, NY; *Int'l*, pg. 560
Neubauer, Friedrich, Mng. Dir.--ISS Marischka spol.s.r.o., Bratislava, Slovakia; *Int'l*, pg. 657
Neubayer, Joseph, Pres.--Aramark Correctional Services, Oak Brook, IL; *U.S. Private*, pg. 79
Neuberger, Hans, Chief Oper. Officer--Pfaff-Pegasus of U.S.A., Suwanee, GA; *Int'l*, pg. 1046
Neubert, Dick, Mgr.-Mktg.--Duro-Test Intl. Corp., Fairfield, NJ; *U.S. Private*, pg. 349
Neuchterlien, Dave, Pres.--ENPAC, Eastlake, OH; *U.S. Public*, pg. 592
Neudorfer, M., Gen. Mgr.--Barclays Discount Bank Ltd., Tel Aviv, Israel; *Int'l*, pg. 166
Neuenschwander, D.V., Mgr.--Swiss Bank Corporation, Santiago, Chile; *Int'l*, pg. 1330
Neugarten, Maks, Chief Oper. Officer--Novo Nordisk A/S, Warsaw, Poland; *Int'l*, pg. 989
Neuhaeuser, Guenther, Dir.--Krupp Hoesch Berufsbildung GmbH, Dortmund, Germany; *Int'l*, pg. 512
Neuhas, Alfred W., Mgr.--Commerzbank AG Representative Office-Warsaw, Warsaw, Poland; *Int'l*, pg. 312
Neuhaus, Christofer A., Chief Oper. Officer--Granges Metall Gmbh, Frankfurt/Main, Germany; *Int'l*, pg. 442
Neukirchen, Kajo, Dr., Chm. Bd.--FAG Bearings Corporation, Danbury, CT; *Int'l*, pg. 469
Neuman, David A., Pres.--Walt Disney Network Television, Burbank, CA; *U.S. Public*, pg. 511
Neuman, Deanne, Exec. Editor--BNA Health Care Information Division, Washington, DC; *U.S. Private*, pg. 182
Neuman, Deanne E., Exec. Editor--BNA Employment Relations Information Div., Washington, DC; *U.S. Private*, pg. 182
Neuman, Lest, V.P. & Gen. Mgr.--AMICO-West Distr. Center, Fontana, CA; *U.S. Private*, pg. 30
Neuman, Russell H., Gen. Mgr.--Atlas Alchem Plastics, Inc., Paulding, OH; *U.S. Public*, pg. 1496
Neumann-Spallart, Dr. Dieter, Chief Oper. Officer--Mead Coated Board Europe Kartonvertriebs-A.G., Vienna, Austria; *U.S. Public*, pg. 1076
Neumann, E., Mgr.--Lindberg Heat Treating Co., Saint Louis, MO; *U.S. Public*, pg. 999
Neumann, Gunter, Mng. Dir.--Waggonbau Bruninghaus GmbH, Schwerte, Germany; *Int'l*, pg. 509
Neumann, Hans Joergen, Reg. Mng. Dir.--Berendsen PMC A/S, Ski, Norway; *Int'l*, pg. 1285
Neumann, Hans Jorgen, Acting Chief Exec. Officer--Berendsen PMC AB, Stockholm, Sweden; *Int'l*, pg. 1285
Neumann, Klas, Pres.--Kvaerner Ships Equipment GmbH After Sales Service, Hamburg, Germany; *Int'l*, pg. 768
Neumeyer, Dean C., Pres.--Herider Farms, Inc., Camden, NJ; *U.S. Public*, pg. 299
Neuschel, Robert F., V.P. & Gen. Mgr.--Lane Graphics Products Div., Phoenix, AZ; *U.S. Public*, pg. 707
Neuschwander, H., Chief Oper. Officer--Schering (Schweiz) AG, Schlieren, Switzerland; *Int'l*, pg. 1204
Neuschwander, Rolf, Mgr.--John Crane (Switzerland) AG, Bottmingen, Switzerland; *Int'l*, pg. 1339
Neuss, Wolfgang, Mng. Dir.--Bertrand Faure Sitztechnik GmbH & Co. KG, Bad Abbach, Germany; *Int'l*, pg. 193
Neustadt, Marc A., Admin.--Walden House Healthcare, Concord, MA; *U.S. Public*, pg. 1715
Neuvile, Patrick Martin, Pres. & Chief Exec. Officer--Calberson Overseas, Roissy, France; *Int'l*, pg. 549
Neuwirth, Frank, Pres.--Span-Track, Jackson, NJ; *U.S. Private*, pg. 1117
Nevala, Jouko, Reg. Mgr.--Det Norske Veritas, Helsingfors, Finland; *Int'l*, pg. 397
Neve, J., Mng. Dir.--Oki Systems (Holland) B.V., Hoofddorp, Netherlands; *Int'l*, pg. 1000
Neville, Gordon, Mgr.-Natl. Sls.--Containerboard Div., Memphis, TN; *U.S. Public*, pg. 901
Neville, N.J., Pres.--Schlumberger Oilfield Services, Houston, TX; *U.S. Public*, pg. 1439
Nevin, Bob, Pres.--Wilmer Service Line, Dayton, OH; *U.S. Public*, pg. 1385
Nevin, John J., Pres. & Chief Exec. Officer--Broadcast Electronics, Inc., Quincy, IL; *U.S. Private*, pg. 531

Nevin, John M., Pres. & Chief Exec. Officer--Broadcast Programming, Seattle, WA; *U.S. Private*, pg. 531

Nevin, Robert C., Pres.--Reynolds and Reynolds-Business Forms Division, Dayton, OH; *U.S. Public*, pg. 1385

Nevler, Leona, V.P. & Editor-in-Chief--Fawcett Books, New York, NY; *U.S. Private*, pg. 21

New, R.F., Chm. Bd.--Ets. Marshall S.A., Gonesse, France; *Int'l*, pg. 891

Newall, J.E., Sr. V.P.-Agricultural Products--Du Pont Agricultural Products, Wilmington, DE; *U.S. Public*, pg. 531

Newball, Rafael E., Gen. Mgr.--Johnson & Johnson Panama S.A., Panama, Panama; *U.S. Public*, pg. 931

Newberry, William E., Pres.--Channel Industries, Inc., Santa Barbara, CA; *U.S. Private*, pg. 228

Newblom, Len, Gen. Mgr.--Drivetrain Service Div., Holland, OH; *U.S. Public*, pg. 479

Newcomb, Jonathan, Pres. & Chief Exec. Officer--Simon & Schuster, New York, NY; *U.S. Private*, pg. 777

Newcomb, Verne W., Gen. Counsel--Cascade Corporation, Troutdale, OR; *U.S. Public*, pg. 310

Newcombe-Dierl, Lisa, Pres.--Terra Tech Labs, Inc., Santa Ana, CA; *U.S. Public*, pg. 1594

Newcomer, David W., Pres.--Funeral Security Plans, Inc., Kansas City, MO; *U.S. Private*, pg. 796

Newell, Charles D., Jr., Regional Pres.--First Tennessee Bank - Jackson, Jackson, TN; *U.S. Public*, pg. 639

Newell, Eugene D., Mgr.--Wolverine Telephone Company, Millington, MI; *U.S. Public*, pg. 1572

Newell, James, Mgr.--Fargo Glass & Paint Co., Billings, MT; *U.S. Private*, pg. 393

Newell, James, Pres.--Cummins Komatsu Engine Company, Seymour, IN; *U.S. Public*, pg. 468

Newell, James, Pres.--Cummins Komatsu Engine Company, Seymour, IN; *Int'l*, pg. 744

Newell, P., Gen. Mgr.--Illawarra Newspaper Holdings Pty. Limited, Wollongong, Australia; *Int'l*, pg. 477

Newell, William, Pres. & Chief Fin. Officer--Noll Printing Corporation, Huntington, IN; *U.S. Private*, pg. 821

Newham, D.H., Mng. Dir.--A.C. Labs (Pty.) Ltd., Sebenza, South Africa; *U.S. Public*, pg. 38

Newhouse, John E., II, Publisher--The Palatka Daily News, Inc., Palatka, FL; *U.S. Public*, pg. 1175

Newhouse, Richard, Chief Oper. Officer--Comp-Aire Systems Inc., Grand Rapids, MI; *Int'l*, pg. 126

Newland, Tom D., Pres.--The East Ohio Gas Co., Cleveland, OH; *U.S. Public*, pg. 435

Newlin, Steven, Pres.--Nalco Europe, Leiden, Netherlands; *U.S. Public*, pg. 1151

Newman, A.R., Pres.--ALLTEL South Carolina, Inc., Lexington, SC; *U.S. Public*, pg. 56

Newman, Alan, Dir.--Metro Brick Company Pty. Limited, Perth, Australia; *Int'l*, pg. 216

Newman, Bill, Gen. Mgr.--Quaker Industries, Antioch, IL; *U.S. Public*, pg. 1259

Newman, Craig, Chief Officer--Callahan Enterprises, Westfield, IN; *Int'l*, pg. 566

Newman, Don, V.P. & Gen. Mgr.--Massey's, Lynchburg, VA; *U.S. Private*, pg. 284

Newman, Francine M., Pres.--Cigna Re Corporation, Bloomfield, CT; *U.S. Public*, pg. 360

Newman, Francine M., Pres.--Disability Claim Services, Inc., Bloomfield, CT; *U.S. Public*, pg. 362

Newman, G. Robert, Pres.--Fairmont Tamper, West Columbia, SC; *U.S. Public*, pg. 793

Newman, Gordon, Pres.--Rotorex Company, Inc., Walkersville, MD; *U.S. Public*, pg. 615

Newman, Janice, Controller--Quebecor Printing Haughton, Scarborough, Canada; *Int'l*, pg. 1077

Newman, Jim, Chief Oper. Officer--Dynacast, Seneca, SC; *Int'l*, pg. 300

Newman, Judy, Dir.--The Trumpet Club, New York, NY; *Int'l*, *pg. 191*

Newman, Maurice, Chm.--Bain & Company Limited, Sydney, Australia; *Int'l*, pg. 406

Newman, Paula, Asst. V.P. & Branch Mgr.--Pacific Crest Investment & Loan (San Diego Branch), San Diego, CA; *U.S. Public*, pg. 1249

Newman, R., Pres.--UTLAS International, Overland Park, KS; *U.S. Public*, pg. 1600

Newman, R. Donald, V.P.-Opers.--Bowater Newsprint Division, Calhoun, TN; *U.S. Public*, pg. 248

Newman, Richard, Plant Mgr.--Rhone-Poulenc Specialty Chemicals Div., Marietta, GA; *Int'l*, pg. 1110

Newman, Roland H., Pres.--Universal Shoe Mfg. Co., Lynchburg, VA; *U.S. Private*, pg. 284

Newman, Sherrill, Plant Mgr.--Pirelli Cable, Power Cable Div., Abbeville, SC; *Int'l*, pg. 1059

Newman, Stephen H., Chm. Bd. & Chief Exec. Officer--Underwriters Reinsurance, Woodland Hills, CA; *U.S. Public*, pg. 42

Newman, Tom, Gen. Mgr.--Quality Casting Company, Waukesha, WI; *U.S. Private*, pg. 741

Newmann, Heinz, Chief Oper. Officer--Decision Data, Heppenheim, Germany; *Int'l*, pg. 645

Newton, Charles D., Plant Mgr.--Ash Grove Lime Plant, Springfield, MO; *U.S. Private*, pg. 88

Newton, D.V., Pres. & Chief Oper. Officer--Canada Life Casualty Insurance Company, Etobicoke, Canada; *Int'l*, pg. 254

Newton, David, Mgr.-Opers.--Magnesium Elektron, Twickenham, United Kingdom; *Int'l*, pg. 51

Newton, David, Chief Oper. Officer--Rhone-Poulenc Australia Holdings Pty. Ltd., Melbourne, Australia; *Int'l*, pg. 1112

Newton, Gary, Pres.--Manac Solutions, Montreal, Canada; *U.S. Private*, pg. 872

Newton, James, Pres.--Conrail Direct, Plymouth Meeting, PA; *U.S. Public*, pg. 432

Newton, John T., Chm. & Chief Exec. Officer--KU Capital Corporation, Lexington, KY; *U.S. Public*, pg. 941

Newton, Keith, Reg. Plng. Dir.--Young & Rubicam Australia/New Zealand, Sydney, Australia; *U.S. Private*, pg. 1198

Newton, Michael, Gen. Mgr.--Vulcan Brunswick Bowling Pin Company, Cincinnati, OH; *U.S. Public*, pg. 266

Newton, Miller, Chief Oper. Officer--TMP Worldwide/Interactive Division, Framingham, MA; *U.S. Private*, pg. 1065

Newton, Paul, Dr., Gen. Mgr.--The MacNeal-Schwendler Co. Ltd., Walton-on-Thames, United Kingdom; *U.S. Public*, pg. 1032

Newton, Schaloj, V.P. & Mng. Dir.--Allergan K.K., Tokyo, Japan; *U.S. Public*, pg. 46

Newton, Steven T., Pres. & Gen. Mgr.--Occidental De Colombia, Inc., Bogota, Colombia; *U.S. Public*, pg. 1210

Ney, Carlos, Chief Oper. Officer--Hughes Tool Company S.A., Bogota, Colombia; *U.S. Public*, pg. 167

Ney, Joseph, Pres.--Grocers and Merchants Insurance, Inc., Covina, CA; *U.S. Private*, pg. 227

Ney, Joseph, Pres.--Grocers & Merchants Management Co., Covina, CA; *U.S. Private*, pg. 227

Ney, K.P., Deputy Chm.--Century Employers Life Assurance Company Limited, London, United Kingdom; *Int'l*, pg. 685

Neyret, Michelle, Mgr.--Cray Research France S.A., Paris, France; *U.S. Public*, pg. 1474

Neyssen, John, Plant Mgr.--Twin City Die Castings Co., Watertown, SD; *U.S. Private*, pg. 1111

Neyts, Freddy, Pres.--Radio Contact, Brussels, Belgium; *Int'l*, pg. 561

Nezen, H., Chm. Bd.--Ford Credit AB, Stockholm, Sweden; *U.S. Public*, pg. 666

Nezin, Gerard, Chief Oper. Officer--ITMI, Boulogne-Billancourt, France; *Int'l*, pg. 263

Ng, Andrew S.O., Mng. Dir.--Sylva Industries Limited, Kwai Chung, Hong Kong; *Int'l*, pg. 537

Ng, Andy, Gen. Mgr.--Hayes Microcomputer Products, Inc., North Point, Hong Kong; *U.S. Public*, pg. 801

Ng, Anita, Reg. V.P.-North Asia--Mentholatum Co. (Hong Kong) Ltd., Sha Tin, Hong Kong; *Int'l*, pg. 1126

Ng, B., Chief Rep.--ING Insurance International, Guangzhou, China; *Int'l*, pg. 650

Ng, Chai Seng, Mgr.--Nalco Pacific, Jurong, Singapore; *U.S. Public*, pg. 1151

Ng, D., Mgr.--P.T. Nalco Perkasa, Jakarta, Indonesia; *U.S. Public*, pg. 1151

Ng, Daniel, V.P.--McDonald's Restaurants (Hong Kong) Ltd., Hong Kong, Hong Kong; *U.S. Public*, pg. 1069

Ng, James, Mng. Dir.--First Pacific Bank, Hong Kong, Hong Kong; *Int'l*, pg. 487

Ng, K.K., Pres.--Respironics (HK), Ltd., Kowloon, Hong Kong; *U.S. Public*, pg. 1383

Ng, Patrick, Gen. Mgr.--IPC Corporation (Australia) Pty Ltd., Botany, Australia; *Int'l*, pg. 651

Ng, Richard, Dir.-Europe & Reg. Dir.-France--Singapore Tourist Promotion Board - Paris, Paris, France; *Int'l*, pg. 1254

Ng, Valerie, Gen. Mgr.-Western Australia--Singapore Tourist Promotion Board - Perth, Perth, Australia; *Int'l*, pg. 1254

Ng, Watson, Gen. Mgr.--Watlow Singapore Pte. Ltd., Singapore, Singapore; *U.S. Private*, pg. 1154

Ngah, Mohd Izam, Dir.--MTPB - East Coast Region, Kuala Terengganu, Malaysia; *Int'l*, pg. 833

Ngai, Boris, Pres.--MacGregor Golf Hong Kong Ltd., Hong Kong, Hong Kong; *Int'l*, pg. 73

Ngai, Q., Dep. Gen. Mgr.--ING Trust (Hong Kong), Central, Hong Kong; *Int'l*, pg. 650

Ngarn, Tan Kok, Gen. Mgr.--Dresdner (South East Asia) Ltd., Singapore, Singapore; *Int'l*, pg. 419

Ngiam, David, Mng. Dir.--Corex Technology (S) Pte Ltd., Singapore, Singapore; *Int'l*, pg. 651

Nguyen, C.D., Pres. & Treas.--Esso Trading Company of Abu Dhabi, Saint Georges, Bermuda; *U.S. Public*, pg. 602

Nguyen, C.D., Pres. & Treas.--Mediterranean Standard Oil Co., Saint Georges, Bermuda; *U.S. Public*, pg. 602

Nguyen, Robert, Mgr.--BHP Steel Building Products Vanuatu, Port Vila, Vanuatu; *Int'l*, pg. 227

Ni, David, Gen. Mgr.--BFCE China, Shanghai, China; *Int'l*, pg. 161

Ni, Robert, Gen. Mgr.--Shakespeare (Hong Kong) Ltd., Kowloon, Hong Kong; *U.S. Public*, pg. 940

Nicandros, Constantine S., Pres. & Chief Exec. Officer--Conoco Inc., Houston, TX; *U.S. Public*, pg. 531

Niccolls, Philip, Dr., Mng. Dir.--Battenfeld Gloenco Extrusion Systems Ltd., Droitwich, United Kingdom; *Int'l*, pg. 825

Niccum, Thomas E., Div. V.P.--Industrial Mineral Products Division, Saint Paul, MN; *U.S. Public*, pg. 1605

Nice, Peter, Chief Oper. Officer--Chase Bank NV, Amsterdam, Netherlands; *U.S. Public*, pg. 339

Nice, Roy, Gen. Mgr.--Esselte S.A., Madrid, Spain; *Int'l*, pg. 461

Nichol, David A., Chm., Pres & Chief Exec. Officer--Destination Products International, Inc., Toronto, Canada; *Int'l*, pg. 338

Nicholas, David, Mng. Dir.--Harmo Industries, Ltd., Birmingham, United Kingdom; *U.S. Public*, pg. 1579

Nicholls, Michael, Chief Oper. Officer--Swedish Royal Refrigeration Ltd., Watford, United Kingdom; *Int'l*, pg. 444

Nichols, Calvin, Mng. Dir.--Laboratory Supply Company, Winston Salem, NC; *U.S. Private*, pg. 642

Nichols, Cathy, Chm. Bd. & Chief Exec. Officer--Universal Studios Recreation Services Group, Universal City, CA; *Int'l*, pg. 1216

Nichols, Fred R., Chm. Bd., Pres. & Chief Exec. Officer--TCA Management Company, Tyler, TX; *U.S. Public*, pg. 1553

Nichols, G.A., Dir. Gen.--Westminster Insurance Agencies Limited, London, United Kingdom; *Int'l*, pg. 565

Nichols, George Q., Pres.--National Publishing Co., Philadelphia, PA; *U.S. Public*, pg. 453

Nichols, Gregory L., CPA, Chief Fin. Officer--Giffels Associates Inc., Phoenix, AZ; *U.S. Private*, pg. 452

Nichols, James J., V.P.--Kelso-Burnett Rockford Branch, Rockford, IL; *U.S. Private*, pg. 613

Nichols, James M., Pres.--NationsBank of Nevada, Nevada, MO; *U.S. Public*, pg. 1164

Nichols, Joe, Mgr.--Harley Valve & Instrument, Norfolk, VA; *U.S. Public*, pg. 880

Nichols, Mark, Mgr.-Station--KSNC, Great Bend, KS; *U.S. Public*, pg. 984

Nichols, Max T., Pres.--Zions Credit Corporation, Salt Lake City, UT; *U.S. Public*, pg. 1793

Nichols, Peter, Pres.--Allied Colloids Inc., Suffolk, VA; *Int'l*, pg. 62

Nichols, Robert, Office Mgr.--Alpha Industries, USA, Ltd., Marlow, United Kingdom; *U.S. Public*, pg. 57

Nichols, Ron, Chief Oper. Officer--Countrywide Services Corp., Chesterfield, MO; *U.S. Private*, pg. 789

Nichols, Sam, V.P.-Cellular & Mktg.--Telecommunications Div., Fort Worth, TX; *Int'l*, pg. 1433

Nicholson, Frank, Mng. Dir.--Vaux Breweries Ltd., Sunderland, United Kingdom; *Int'l*, pg. 1454

Nicholson, Gary D., Pres. & Chief Exec. Officer--Camco International Inc., Houston, TX; *U.S. Public*, pg. 298

Nicholson, Jim, Mgr.--Lapham-Hickey Steel Corp., Saint Louis, MO; *U.S. Private*, pg. 651

Nicholson, L. Dale, Pres. & Chief Oper. Officer--KATV, LLC, Little Rock, AR; *U.S. Private*, pg. 854

Nicholson, Michael J., Pres.--Western Medical Services Inc., Walnut Creek, CA; *U.S. Public*, pg. 1760

Nicholson, Rod, Mng. Dir.--Danbrand Products Australasia, Te Papapa, New Zealand; *U.S. Public*, pg. 904

Nicholson, Thomas J., Pres. & Chief Exec. Officer--Central Bank of Monroe, Monroe, LA; *U.S. Public*, pg. 629

Nichter, Mark S., Pres.--ProSoft International Co., Inc., Colorado Springs, CO; *U.S. Public*, pg. 441

Nick, John W., Pres.--Dresdner-NY Inc., New York, NY; *Int'l*, pg. 418

Nickel, Albert G., Pres. & Chief Oper. Officer--Lyons Lavey Nickel Swift, Inc., New York, NY; *U.S. Public*, pg. 1224

Nickel, J.R., Mgr.--Monarch Homes Inc., Stafford, TX; *Int'l*, pg. 1510

Nickell, Bob, Pres.--Tucker-Rocky Distributing, Irving, TX; *U.S. Private*, pg. 639

Nickinello, Lou, Pres.--Ackerley Communications of Massachusetts, Stoneham, MA; *U.S. Public*, pg. 15

Nicklasson, Martin, Pres.--Astra Hassle AB, Molndal, Sweden; *Int'l*, pg. 93

Nickle, John, Gen. Mgr.--Tractor Machining Co., Mesa, AZ; *U.S. Private*, pg. 375

Nicklous, Michael, Mng. Dir.--MAINCO Elevator Services Co., Long Island City, NY; *Int'l*, pg. 656

Nickly, John, Pres. & Chief Exec. Officer--Regence Life & Health Insurance Co., Portland, OR; *U.S. Private*, pg. 918

Nickson, K.B., Mng. Dir.--Tenneco-Walker (U.K.) Limited, Burnley, United Kingdom; *U.S. Public*, pg. 1580

Nickson, Lord, Chm. Bd.--Clydesdale Bank PLC, Glasgow, United Kingdom; *Int'l*, pg. 906

Niclasson, Bjorn, Mng. Dir.--Stroms Bruk, Stromsnabruk, Sweden; *Int'l*, pg. 886

Nicod, Jean-Francois, Mgr.-Office--Woodward-Clyde, Lausanne, Switzerland; *U.S. Public*, pg. 1657

Nicol, A. M., Pres.--Laing Construction Services, New Canaan, CT; *Int'l*, pg. 797

Nicolai, G.C.A., Chm. Bd.--Karbon Grafit Sanayi A.S., Istanbul, Turkey; *Int'l*, pg. 891

Nicolai, Willi, Mng. Dir.--Battenfeld Schweiz AG, Volketswil, Sweden; *Int'l*, pg. 826

Nicolaides, John, Gen. Mgr.--Colgate-Palmolive (Zambia) Ltd., Ndola, Zambia; *U.S. Public*, pg. 399

Nicolaidis, Alain, Chief Oper. Officer--Matra Datavision S.A., Paris, France; *Int'l*, pg. 793

Nicolaidus, Gregory C., Pres.--Convesco Vehicle Sales GmbH, Russelsheim, Germany; *U.S. Public*, pg. 724

Nicolas, Jean Louis, Pres & Chief Exec. Officer--Lafarge PlatresInternational, Sorges, France; *Int'l*, pg. 789

Nicolau, Emilio, Gen. Mgr.--Nordson Iberica S.A., Valencia, Spain; *U.S. Public*, pg. 1189

Nicolau, Emilio, Gen. Mgr.--Nordson Portugal Equipamento Industrial, Lda., Maia, Portugal; *U.S. Public*, pg. 1189

Nicolaus, Peter, Chief Oper. Officer--Electrolux Industrier A/S, Oslo, Norway; *Int'l*, pg. 443

Nicolet, Georges, Chm.--ECIA-Equipments Et Composants Pour L'industrie Automobile, Audincourt, France; *Int'l*, pg. 1021

Nicoletti, Arthur A., Pres.--Texaco Trading & Transportation Inc., Denver, CO; *U.S. Public*, pg. 1583

Nicoletti, William, Chief Officer--Dolisos, Las Vegas, NV; *Int'l*, pg. 566

Nicolicchia, Teresa, Branch Mgr.--Valley National Bank, Budd Lake, NJ; *U.S. Public*, pg. 1706

Nicolier, D., Rep.--Swiss Bank Corporation, Bogota, Colombia; *Int'l*, pg. 1330

Nicolosi, V., Mng. Dir.--Silvani Antincendi SpA, Milan, Italy; *Int'l*, pg. 1500

Nicolson, Ivo Neville, Mng. Dir.--J.I. Case (Australia) Pty., Ltd., Northmead, Australia; *U.S. Public*, pg. 1579

Nicosia, Joseph A., Pres. & Chief Exec. Officer--GATX Logistics, Inc., Jacksonville, FL; *U.S. Public*, pg. 691

Nider, Raimondo, Mng. Dir.--Korn/Ferry International, Milan, Italy; *U.S. Private*, pg. 633

Niebel, Volker, Mng. Dir.--SECON GmbH, Dransfeld, Germany; *Int'l*, pg. 669

Niederer, Claus M., Gen. Mgr.--Migrol Cooperative Society, Zurich, Switzerland; *Int'l*, pg. 866

Niedergang, Claude, Pres.--SCPA, Mulhouse, France; *Int'l*, pg. 459

Niederhagemann, P.D., V.P. & Gen. Mgr.--Ferguson Machine Co. S.A., Braine-le-Chateau, Belgium; *U.S. Public*, pg. 457

Nieland, Theo, Dir.-Indus. Bus. Devel.--McCormick Ingredients Europe, Inc., Bloemendaal, Netherlands; *U.S. Public*, pg. 1067

Nield, D.A., Chm. Bd.--Canada Life Assurance (Ireland) Ltd., Blackrock, Ireland; *Int'l*, pg. 255

Nielsen, B., Mgr.--THORN EMI Danmark A/S, Hvidovre, Denmark; *Int'l*, pg. 428

Nielsen, Bruce, Exec. V.P.--Rodenstock Precision Optics, Inc., Rockford, IL; *Int'l*, pg. 1007

Nielsen, Gary R., Pres. & Gen. Mgr.--WOKR-TV, Rochester, NY; *U.S. Private*, pg. 439

Nielsen, Greg, Dir.-Opers.--Bausch & Lomb Personal Products Division-SC, Greenville, SC; *U.S. Public*, pg. 194

Nielsen, Helge, Chief Oper. Officer--Molnlycke S.A. Health Care, Brussels, Belgium; *Int'l*, pg. 1326

Nielsen, James N., Mgr.--Maid-O-Mist, Chicago, IL; *U.S. Private*, pg. 1053

Nielsen, K., Gen. Mgr.--Oki Systems (Danmark) A.S., Vallensbaek, Denmark; *Int'l*, pg. 1000

Nielsen, Kaj, Mng. Dir.--Ericsson Network Engineering Ltd., London, United Kingdom; *Int'l*, pg. 1367

Nielsen, Lars Poppelgaard, Pres.--Danisco Flexible, Horsens, Denmark; *Int'l*, pg. 378

Nielsen, Mogens, Pres.--Gyproc A/S, Kalundborg, Denmark; *Int'l*, pg. 1200

Nielsen, N. Giverson, Admin. Dir.--The Borden Co. A/S, Esbjerg, Denmark; *U.S. Private*, pg. 159

Nielsen, Peggy, Personal Lines Underwriter--Service General South, Metairie, LA; *U.S. Private*, pg. 609

Nielsen, Soeren, Chief Oper. Officer--Georg Jensen Silversmithy Ltd., Copenhagen, Denmark; *Int'l*, pg. 1134

Nielsen, Ulrik, Gen. Mgr.--Life Technologies A/S, Roskilde, Denmark; *U.S. Public*, pg. 505

Nielsen, Valther, Mgr.--Trans-American Steamship Agency, San Francisco, CA; *Int'l*, pg. 1418

Nielsen, Viggo, Pres.--O.G. Hoyer Inc., Lake Geneva, WI; *Int'l*, pg. 1378

Nielson, Erik, Chief Oper. Officer--Nyborg Vas kerimaskiner A/S, Tommerup, Denmark; *Int'l*, pg. 441

Niem, Eddie, Gen. Mgr.--Hawley & Hazel Chemical Co., (Hong Kong) Ltd., Aberdeen, Hong Kong; *U.S. Public*, pg. 399

Niemann, H.C., Chief Exec. Officer--Paul Hellermann GmbH, Pinneberg, Germany; *Int'l*, pg. 209

Niemi, Steve, Pres.--TSI Mason Laboratories, Worcester, MA; *U.S. Public*, pg. 733

Niemi, Timo J., Pres.--PT. Valmet Indonesia, Pondok Gede, Indonesia; *Int'l*, pg. 1448

Nieminen, Markku, Sawmill Mgr.--Uimaharju Sawmill, Uimaharju, Finland; *Int'l*, pg. 456

Nienstedt, Heinz-Werner, Dr., Mng. Dir.--Verlagsgruppe Handelsblatt GmbH, Dusseldorf, Germany; *Int'l*, pg. 1479

Nierman, Bob, Chief Oper. Officer--Metaphase Technology, Inc., Arden Hills, MN; *U.S. Public*, pg. 1525

Niesen, G. S., Mng. Dir.--CIBC Jamaica Ltd., Kingston, Jamaica; *Int'l*, pg. 258

Niesen, Jon Sivert, Pres.--Kvaerner Eureka A/S, Tranby, Lier, Norway; *Int'l*, pg. 766

Nieto, Enrique, Pres.--Asesores Publicitarios, S.A., San Jose, Costa Rica; *U.S. Private*, pg. 1200

Nieto, F., Reg. Dir.--EMI Odeon Chilena SA, Santiago, Chile; *Int'l*, pg. 427

Nieto, Fernando, Chief Exec. Officer--Grupo Barro Testa, Madrid, Spain; *Int'l*, pg. 1377

Niewenhuizen, Hermann, Chm. Bd.--Cigna Life Insurance Company of Europe S.A.-N.V., Brussels, Belgium; *U.S. Public*, pg. 364

Nigbor, Robert, Pres.--Agbabian Associates, Inc., Pasadena, CA; *Int'l*, pg. 1019

Nightingale, A.J.L., Mng. Dir.--Jardine Pacific Ltd., Quarry Bay, Hong Kong; *Int'l*, pg. 704

Nightingale, A.J.L., Joint Mng. Dir.--Jardine International Motor Holdings Ltd., Hong Kong, Hong Kong; *Int'l*, pg. 705

Nightingale, John A., Pres.--Rio Algom Limited, Elliot Lake, Canada; *Int'l*, pg. 1118

Nightingale, R., Gen. Mgr.--ITW Devcon, Wellingborough, United Kingdom; *U.S. Public*, pg. 868

Nignucci, Bernard, Gen. Mgr.--Credit Lyonnais Hong-Kong, Central, Hong Kong; *Int'l*, pg. 344

Nigro, Tony, Mng. Dir.--Cellphone Sales Ltd., Auckland, New Zealand; *Int'l*, pg. 1365

Nihlmark, Eric, Chief Oper. Officer--Fastighetsaktiebolaget Hufvudstaden, Goteborg, Sweden; *Int'l*, pg. 478

Nii, Takaharu, Chief Oper. Officer--Makita Gulf FZE, Dubai, United Arab Emirates; *Int'l*, pg. 832

Niileksela, Martti, Mng. Dir.--AB SANI-Maskiner, Malmo, Sweden; *U.S. Public*, pg. 444

Niino, Kenjiro, Mng. Dir.--Florasynth-Lautier K.K., Tokyo, Japan; *Int'l*, pg. 173

Nijboer, Willem, V.P. & Reg. Mgr.--Bank of America NT&SA, Amsterdam, Netherlands; *U.S. Public*, pg. 182

Nijdam, Freek, Pres.--Atlas Copco ACT, Wilrijk, Belgium; *Int'l*, pg. 96

Nijland, H.J., Mgr.--Parker Hannifin B.V., Oldenzaal, Netherlands; *U.S. Public*, pg. 1263

Nijssen, Wilhelmus J.J., Gen. Dir.--Northrup King y Compania, S.A. de C.V., Guadalajara, Mexico; *Int'l*, pg. 983

Nijweide, R.J., Gen. Mgr.--Koudijs-Wouda Voeders B.V., s Hertogenbosch, Netherlands; *Int'l*, pg. 555

Nikazmerad, Nick, Pres.--Nukem, Inc., Stamford, CT; *Int'l*, pg. 1081

Nikkanen, Armas O., Gen. Mgr.--Oy Tulenkestavaat Tiliet, A.B., Helsinki, Finland; *U.S. Private*, pg. 904

Nikkila, Kalevi, Pres.--Outokumpu Technology Oy, Espoo, Finland; *Int'l*, pg. 1017

Niklasson, Sten, Mng. Dir.--Neste Sverige AB, Stockholm, Sweden; *Int'l*, pg. 915

Nikopoulos, George, Mng. Dir.--Producta-TBWA, Athens, Greece; *U.S. Private*, pg. 1062

Nikulski, Heinz, Mng. Dir.--Harman Deutschland GmbH, Heilbronn, Germany; *U.S. Public*, pg. 787

Nileansson, Olle, Pres.--NCC Building - Karlstad, Karlstad, Sweden; *Int'l*, pg. 898

Niles, Nicholas H., Pres. & Chief Exec. Officer--The Sporting News Publishing Company, Saint Louis, MO; *U.S. Public*, pg. 1616

Niles, Robert, Pres.--American Cablevision of Kansas City, Inc., Kansas City, MO; *U.S. Public*, pg. 1610

Niles, Terry, Pres.--Gage Adistra Corp., Plymouth, MI; *U.S. Private*, pg. 437

Nilsen, Brad, Gen. Mgr.--KNXV-TV, Phoenix, AZ; *U.S. Public*, pg. 1448

Nilsen, F. O., Chm. Bd.--OCE-Danmark AS, Copenhagen, Denmark; *Int'l*, pg. 994

Nilsen, Leif E., Mng. Dir.--Lincoln Norweld AS, Stavern, Norway; *U.S. Public*, pg. 997

Nilson, Sten-Olau, Pres.--Kvaerner Installasjon, Agotnes Division, Agotnes, Norway; *Int'l*, pg. 769

Nilsson, B., Mng. Dir.--Consilium Bulk - Babcock Atlanta Inc., Doraville, GA; *Int'l*, pg. 131

Nilsson, Bengt, Pres.--MRC Bearings, Jamestown, NY; *Int'l*, pg. 1157

Nilsson, Carl-Erik, Chief Oper. Officer--Saab Deutschland GmbH, Frankfurt/Main, Germany; *Int'l*, pg. 687

Nilsson, Gunnar, Chief Oper. Officer--Molnlycke AB Feminine Hygiene Products, Molnlycke, Sweden; *Int'l*, pg. 1326

Nilsson, Ingemar, Chief Officer--Obs! Stormarknaden AB, Stockholm, Sweden; *Int'l*, pg. 718

Nilsson, Karl-Erik, Mgr.--Savsjo Falgar AB, Savsjo, Sweden; *Int'l*, pg. 1422

Nilsson, Kjell, Mng. Dir.--Ericsson Telekom GmbH, Neu-Isenburg, Germany; *Int'l*, pg. 1368

Nilsson, Kjell, Mgr.--Boliden Mineral AB, Boliden, Sweden; *Int'l*, pg. 1422

Nilsson, Lars Olof, Pres.--ABB Traction AB, Vasteras, Sweden; *Int'l*, pg. 7

Nilsson, LaRS-Erik, Country Mgr.--CCS Deskpro Computer AB, Kista, Sweden; *U.S. Public*, pg. 418

Nilsson, Lars-Ivar, Chief Oper. Officer--Fabriken Odin AB, Nykoping, Sweden; *Int'l*, pg. 1378

Nilsson, Leif, Pres.--Armaturteknik i Osby AB, Osby, Sweden; *Int'l*, pg. 1323

Nilsson, N.O., Mng. Dir.--GKN Nordiska Kardan AB, Amal, Sweden; *Int'l*, pg. 536

Nilsson, Nils Lennart, Bus. Area Mgr.--Cardo Railway AB, Malmo, Sweden; *Int'l*, pg. 271

Nilsson, R., Mng. Dir.--Laporte Kemwood AB, Helsingborg, Sweden; *Int'l*, pg. 803

Nilsson, Sven-Bertil, Mgr.--Skapafors Paper Mill, Bengtsfors, Sweden; *Int'l*, pg. 421

Nilsson, Tommy, Gen. Mgr.--Viking Metallurgical Corporation, Verdi, NV; *Int'l*, pg. 488

Nilsson, Tommy, Pres.--NCC Invest, Solna, Sweden; *Int'l*, pg. 899

Nilsson, Torbjorn, Pres.--Precon AB, Falkenberg, Sweden; *Int'l*, pg. 1199

Nilstoft, Clas, Pres.--Rexam Closures, Evansville, IN; *Int'l*, pg. 1106

Nimnicht, Terry L., Pres.--Cigna Healthcare of Washington, Inc., Seattle, WA; *U.S. Public*, pg. 360

Nims, C.W., Pres.--Branson Ultrasonics, Danbury, CT; *U.S. Public*, pg. 574

Nims, Charles W., Pres.--Branson Ultrasonics Corp. - Precision Cleaning Div., Danbury, CT; *U.S. Public*, pg. 574

Nink, Trevor, Chief Oper. Officer--KONE Elevators (Australia) Pty. Ltd., Alexandria, Australia; *Int'l*, pg. 748

Ninomiya, Shoichi, Pres.--PFU Limited, Ishikawa Pref., Japan; *Int'l*, pg. 526

Nirode, Del, V.P. & Gen. Mgr.--Southeastern Wisconsin Products Co., Inc., Milwaukee, WI; *U.S. Public*, pg. 299

Nisbet, Brooke, Branch Mgr.--Financial Collection Agencies, Edinburgh, United Kingdom; *Int'l*, pg. 471

Nisbet, W. Olin, III, Chm. Bd.--Sterling Capital Management Company, Charlotte, NC; *U.S. Public*, pg. 1674

Nisbit, Michael M., Pres. & Chief Exec. Officer--AFCO Credit Corp., New York, NY; *U.S. Public*, pg. 1085

Nisenbaum, Michael, V.P. & Gen. Mgr.--Tsubaki, Inc. - Engineering Chain Div., Sandusky, OH; *Int'l*, pg. 1425

Nishi, Hideki, Chief Oper. Officer--Kyowa Hakko Kogyo Co., Ltd., Shanghai, China; *Int'l*, pg. 778

Nishi, Kyosuke, Gen. Mgr.--Asahi Advertising Inc., Yokohama, Japan; *Int'l*, pg. 81

Nishida, Akinori, Chief Rep.--The Hokkaido Takushoku Bank, Ltd. (Bangkok), Bangkok, Thailand; *Int'l*, pg. 627

Nishida, Atsutoshi, Pres.--Toshiba America Information Systems, Inc., Irvine, CA; *Int'l*, pg. 1405

Nishiguchi, Hiroshi, Chief Oper. Officer--Makita (Taiwan) LTD., Taipei, Taiwan; *Int'l*, pg. 832

Nishiguchi, Yoshihiro, Gen. Mgr.--The Sumitomo Bank, Ltd.-Milan Branch, Milan, Italy; *Int'l*, pg. 1309

Nishihama, K., Pres.--Archer Pipe & Tube Co., Inc., Torrance, CA; *Int'l*, pg. 845

Nishihara, M., Chief Oper. Officer--Nippon Express Canada Ltd., Brampton, Canada; *Int'l*, pg. 934

Nishihara, Masayuki, Gen. Mgr.--Eagle-Picher Far East, Inc., Nagoya, Japan; *U.S. Private*, pg. 355

Nishikata, M.N., Pres.--Emerson Japan, Ltd., Tokyo, Japan; *U.S. Public*, pg. 576

Nishikata, M.N., Pres.-Emerson Japan--Aichi-Emerson Electric Co., Nagoya, Japan; *U.S. Public*, pg. 578

Nishikawa, Katsuhiro, Pres.--Thai Toray Textile Mills Public Company Limited, Bangkok, Thailand; *Int'l*, pg. 1400

Nishikawa, Yoshifumi, Pres.--The Sumitomo Bank, LTD.-Tokyo, Tokyo, Japan; *Int'l*, pg. 1308

Nishikiori, Shinichi, Mng. Dir.--Sumitomo Finance (Dublin) Limited, Dublin, Ireland; *Int'l*, pg. 1310

Nishimiya, Yutaka, Chief Oper. Officer--Japan Servo Co., Ltd., Tokyo, Japan; *Int'l*, pg. 622

Nishimoto, Bunpei, Chief Opr. Officer--Hitachi Construction Machinery Co., Ltd., Tokyo, Japan; *Int'l*, pg. 621

Nishimoto, K., Office Chief--Man Nen Sha, Inc., Hiroshima, Japan; *Int'l*, pg. 834

Nishimoto, Masayoshi, Gen. Mgr.--The Sumitomo Bank, Ltd.-Brussels Branch, Brussels, Belgium; *Int'l*, pg. 1309

Nishimoto, Masayoshi, Chief Rep.--The Sumitomo Bank, Ltd.-Amsterdam Representative Office, Amsterdam, Netherlands; *Int'l*, pg. 1309

Nishimura, F., Pres.--Sumitomo Canada Ltd., Toronto, Canada; *Int'l*, pg. 1312

Nishimura, Kanji, Pres.--Wuxi Sanwa Garment Materials Co., Ltd., Wuxi, China; *Int'l*, pg. 579

Nishimura, S., Sec./Treas.--Kansai Paint (America), Inc., Fort Lee, NJ; *Int'l*, pg. 723

Nishino, Shinichi, Pres.--Asahi Bank (Deutschland) GmbH, Frankfurt/Main, Germany; *Int'l*, pg. 83

Nishio, Masaharu, Pres. & Chief Exec. Officer--Muratech America, Inc., Plano, TX; *Int'l*, pg. 897

Nishioka, F., Pres.--Man Nen Sha Agency, Inc., Kyoto, Japan; *Int'l*, pg. 834

Nishioka, Hiroshi, Chief Oper. Officer--Hitachi Lighting, Ltd., Ryugasaki, Japan; *Int'l*, pg. 621

Nishioka, Ikuo, Pres.--Intel Japan, Tokyo, Japan; *U.S. Public*, pg. 887

Nishioka, Nobumi, Pres.--Hakuhodo Lintas, Tokyo, Japan; *Int'l*, pg. 587

Nishitani, Takeo, Pres. & Chief Exec. Officer--International Public Relations Co. Ltd., Tokyo, Japan; *Int'l*, pg. 1227

Nishiyama, Isao, Pres.--BTM Leasing & Finance, Inc., New York, NY; *Int'l*, pg. 157

Nishiyama, Masaharu, Pres.--Nippon Dome Structures Co., Ltd., Tokyo, Japan; *Int'l*, pg. 763

Nishiyama, Toshio, Mng. Dir.--The Bank of Tokyo-Mitsubishi (Australia) Ltd., Sydney, Australia; *Int'l*, pg. 158

Nishiyama, Yasuji, Dir.--Showpla (Delhi) Private Limited, Ghaziabad, India; *Int'l*, pg. 1237

Nissan, I., Gen. Mgr.--MBT Division/Electronics Group, Yehuda, Israel; *Int'l*, pg. 690

Nissen-Sollie, Jan, Mng. Dir.--Beaumont-Bennett A/S, Sandefjord, Norway; *Int'l*, pg. 714

Nissen, D.I., Gen. Mgr.--Commonwealth Bank of Australia-Queensland, Brisbane, Australia; *Int'l*, pg. 313

Nissen, Dietmar, Dr., Pres. & Chief Oper. Officer--BASF Japan Ltd., Tokyo, Japan; *Int'l*, pg. 106

Nissen, E. Jagd, Mng. Dir.--ITT Flygt A/S, Glostrup, Denmark; *U.S. Public*, pg. 860

Nissen, Ejvind Jagd, Mng. Dir.--ITT Flygt A/S, Oslo, Norway; *U.S. Public*, pg. 860

Nitschke, Albrecht, Exec. V.P.-European Opers.--Nielsen Design GmbH, Rheda-Wiedenbruck, Germany; *Int'l*, pg. 462

Nitta, Koji, Pres.--Tomen (U.K.) Plc., London, United Kingdom; *Int'l*, pg. 1395

Nitta, Toyoharu, Pres.--Quaker State Japan Co., Ltd., Tokyo, Japan; *U.S. Public*, pg. 1348

Nittmann, Susan, Mngmt. Supvr.--Louis London Advertising & Sales Promotion, Raleigh, NC; *U.S. Private*, pg. 674

Nitu, Marian, Gen. Mgr.--Atalanta (U.K.) Ltd., London, United Kingdom; *U.S. Private*, pg. 94

Nitzgen, Ralph, Mgr.--Commerzbank AG Representative Office-Bahrain, Manama, Bahrain; *Int'l*, pg. 311

Niven, Vernon, Gen. Mgr.--Zapata Haynie Corp., Abbeville, LA; *U.S. Public*, pg. 1790

Niwa, Norio, Pres. & Chief Exec. Officer--Epson America Inc., Torrance, CA; *Int'l*, pg. 1219

Nix, Charlie, V.P.-Wichita Opers.--Smith Fiberglass Products, Inc., Wichita, KS; *U.S. Public*, pg. 1477

Nix, W.S., Pres.--Lumonics Inc., Kanata, Canada; *Int'l*, pg. 1314

Nixon, B., Mng. Dir.--Fletcher Homes Limited, Auckland, New Zealand; *Int'l*, pg. 495

Nixon, Ralph E., Joint Mng. Dir.--Liberty Distributors Inc., Boston, MA; *U.S. Private*, pg. 666

Nixon, Ray, Pres.--Certified Bakers, Wichita, KS; *U.S. Public*, pg. 653

Nixon, Robert E., Pres.--John Deere Insurance Company, Moline, IL; *U.S. Public*, pg. 492

Nizam, Ike, Chief Oper. Officer--Master Distributors, Santa Monica, CA; *U.S. Private*, pg. 714

Nkojo, Gedion B., Resident Rep.--The World Bank, Lusaka, Zambia; *U.S. Private*, pg. 1190

No'Man, Samir, Gen. Mgr.--Mantech Computer & Education Aids, Al-Khobar, Saudi Arabia; *Int'l*, pg. 502

Noack, Jorg, Mng. Dir.--Nortrans Speditionsgesellschaft mbH, Dorpen, Germany; *Int'l*, pg. 1430

Noakes, Brian, Mng. Dir.--Oneida Silversmiths, U.K., Ruislip, United Kingdom; *U.S. Public*, pg. 1226

Noakes, M., Chm.--Hamworthy Engineering Limited, Poole, United Kingdom; *Int'l*, pg. 1065

Noakes, William, Mng. Dir.--IRCON, Ltd., Swanley, United Kingdom; *Int'l*, pg. 1209

Noar, Stephen, Chm. & Mng. Dir.--Denplan Limited, Winchester, United Kingdom; *Int'l*, pg. 1020

Noble, A.W., Pres. & Mng. Dir.--F.E. Myers (Canada) Ltd./Ltee., Kitchener, Canada; *U.S. Public*, pg. 1274

Noble, Bruce A., Country Mgr.--Pillsbury U.K. Ltd., Uxbridge, United Kingdom; *Int'l*, pg. 411

Noble, Howard, Chief Oper. Officer--NIFE Power Systems Ltd., Aycliffe, United Kingdom; *Int'l*, pg. 53

Noble, K.D., Pres.--Hoover Canada Inc., Burlington, Canada; *U.S. Public*, pg. 1065

Noble, Larry G., Pres.--Allen Milk Co., Columbus, OH; *U.S. Public*, pg. 977

Noble, Michael C., Mng. Dir.--Fleet Investment Services, Providence, RI; *U.S. Public*, pg. 650

Noble, Patrick A., Mng. Dir.--Firstar Export Credit Limited, Milwaukee, WI; *U.S. Public*, pg. 643

Noble, Peter, Mgr.--Kvaerner Masa Marine Inc., Vancouver, Canada; *Int'l*, pg. 771

Noble, Robert B., Chm. & Chief Exec. Officer--Noble & Associates/Chicago, Chicago, IL; *U.S. Private*, pg. 800

Noble, Robert B., Pres. & Chief Exec. Officer--Noble & Associates Promotion Group, Springfield, MO; *U.S. Private*, pg. 800

Nobles, John, Chief Oper. Officer--Black & Veatch Pritchard, Inc., Overland Park, KS; *U.S. Private*, pg. 146

Nobles, Robert, Pres.--Renaissance Publishing Co., Inc., Auburn, IN; *Int'l*, pg. 185

Noblitt, James P., V.P. & Gen. Mgr.--Missiles & Space Division, Huntsville, AL; *U.S. Public*, pg. 241

Nobrega, Vincent P., Plant Mgr.--The Lamson & Sessions Co., Nazareth, PA; *U.S. Public*, pg. 976

Nobuta, Kazuhiro, Joint Mng. Dir.--Dentsu Europe-Dusseldorf, Dusseldorf, Germany; *Int'l*, pg. 393

Nocair, R.G., Gen. Mgr.--Diesel ReCon Charleston, Charleston, SC; *U.S. Public*, pg. 468
Noce, Vincent J., Pres.--Roush Products Co., Inc., Cedar Rapids, IA; *Int'l*, pg. 411
Nocera, Michael J., Pres.--NYLIFE Equity Inc., New York, NY; *U.S. Private*, pg. 795
Nocera, Michael J., Pres.--NYLIFE Realty Inc., New York, NY; *U.S. Private*, pg. 795
Nocera, Michael J., Pres.--NYLIFE Depositary Corporation, New York, NY; *U.S. Private*, pg. 795
Nochimovski, David, Mgr.--Bank Leumi le-Israel B.M., Beverly Hills, CA; *Int'l*, pg. 150
Nock, John, Plant Mgr.--American Natl. Can Co., Kent, WA; *Int'l*, pg. 1029
Nocker, Gerald, Gen. Mgr.--Colgate-Palmolive Ltd., Boksburg, South Africa; *U.S. Public*, pg. 398
Nockles, N.P., Chief Exec. Officer--Blackwood Hodge (Australia) Pty. Ltd., Parramatta, Australia; *Int'l*, pg. 231
Nocman, Samir, Gen. Mgr.--Computer Div., Dammam, Saudi Arabia; *Int'l*, pg. 501
Noda, Hideki, Pres.--Sakura Dellsher, Inc., Chicago, IL; *Int'l*, *pg. 1179*
Noda, Ricardo S., V.P.-Opers.--Sensormatic Do Brazil Electronica Ltda., Santo Andre, Brazil; *U.S. Public*, pg. 1457
Noda, Yoshiteru, Mgr.--NPR of America Inc., Cerritos, CA; *Int'l*, pg. 938
Noe, Greg, Pres. & Chief Exec. Officer--Pilliod Furniture, Greensboro, NC; *U.S. Public*, pg. 974
Noel, Dennis, Pres.--NASTECH Corp., Bennington, VT; *Int'l*, *pg. 903*
Noel, Gerard, Acting Pres.--Great Lakes Confectionery, Cleveland, OH; *Int'l*, pg. 865
Noel, Michael, Chief Fin. Officer & Sr. V.P.--The Mission Group, Irvine, CA; *U.S. Public*, pg. 564
Noel, Rob, Pres.--Practice Patterns Science, Maryland Heights, MO; *U.S. Public*, pg. 601
Noel, Ronald R., Pres.--Newport Steel Corporation, Newport, KY; *U.S. Public*, pg. 1147
Noel, Tony, Chm.--Spanish Executive Information Services (SEIS), Madrid, Spain; *U.S. Private*, pg. 617
Noellenburg, Arno, Mgr.--Commerzbank Sao Paulo Servicos Ltda. Representative Office, Sao Paulo, Brazil; *Int'l*, pg. 312
Noelting, Jean, Pres. & Chief Exec. Officer--Parmalat Canada Ltd., Etobicoke, Canada; *Int'l*, pg. 1023
Noens, Benny, V.P.-European Sls. & Mng. Dir.-Metrologic GmbH--Metrologic Instruments GmbH, Munich, Germany; *U.S. Public*, pg. 1102
Noer, John A., Chm., Pres. & Chief Exec. Officer--Northern States Power Co. (Wis.), Eau Claire, WI; *U.S. Public*, pg. 1195
Nofsinger, William M., Pres.--Nofsinger, Inc., Kansas City, MO; *U.S. Private*, pg. 187
Nofziger, Marvin, Gen. Mgr.--ATAPCO Globe-Weis/Fresno, Fresno, CA; *U.S. Private*, pg. 64
Nogami, Keiji, Pres.--Toyota Tsusho Corporation, Nagoya, Japan; *Int'l*, pg. 1412
Nogi, Laurie, Gen. Mgr.--Shin-Etsu Polymer America, Inc., Union City, CA; *Int'l*, pg. 1234
Noglows, William P., V.P. & Gen. Mgr.-Global Opers.--Cabo-Sil Div. Cabot Corp., Tuscola, IL; *U.S. Public*, pg. 289
Noguchi, K., Pres.--Sharp Electronics France S.A., Roissy, France; *Int'l*, pg. 1230
Noguchi, Masao, Mng. Dir.--Nippon Kayaku Pharmaceutical Div., Tokyo, Japan; *Int'l*, pg. 934
Noguchi, Morikazu, Sr. V.P. & Gen. Mgr.--Chicago Branch Office, Chicago, IL; *Int'l*, pg. 935
Noguchi, Yoshio, Dir.--JEOL (U.S.A.), Inc., Palo Alto, CA; *Int'l*, pg. 697
Nogueira, Artur M., Chief Oper. Officer & V.P.--Sapropur, S.A.R.L., Lisbon, Portugal; *U.S. Public*, pg. 429
Nogueira, Jose Carlos A., Gen. Mgr.-Mfg.--Acos Villares Sao Caetano Plant, Sao Caetano do Sul, Brazil; *Int'l*, pg. 23
Nogues, Claude, Mng. Dir.--Acuson S.A.R.L., Les Ulis, France; *U.S. Public*, pg. 18
Noha, Edward, Chm. Bd.--CNA Financial Corp., Chicago, IL; *U.S. Public*, pg. 1010
Nohr, Karl, Gen. Mgr.--Forbo Helmitin GmbH, Pirmasens, Germany; *Int'l*, pg. 497
Noiret, Yves, Chm. Bd. & Chief Exec. Officer--Eternit Industries, Vernouillet, France; *Int'l*, pg. 430
Nojima, Paul, Pres.--Bandai America, Inc., Cypress, CA; *Int'l*, pg. 145
Nokes, Robert L., Pres. & Chief Exec. Officer--Key Trust Company of the Northwest, Seattle, WA; *U.S. Public*, pg. 954
Nokes, Robert L., Pres.--SAFECO Trust Company, Seattle, WA; *U.S. Public*, pg. 1423
Nolan, C.J., Pres.--Xerox Medical Systems, Monrovia, CA; *U.S. Public*, pg. 1784
Nolan, Cary J., Pres. & Chief Exec. Officer--Picker International, Inc., Cleveland, OH; *Int'l*, pg. 545
Nolan, David, Pres.--Comdisco Continuity Services, Rosemont, IL; *U.S. Public*, pg. 408
Nolan, Edwin J., Chm. Bd. & Mng. Dir.--Henry Ford & Son, Limited, Cork, Ireland; *U.S. Public*, pg. 665
Nolan, John G., Pres.--National School Bus Service, Barrington, IL; *Int'l*, pg. 1213
Nolan, Peter, Mng. Dir.--Incentive International Finance, Dublin, Ireland; *Int'l*, pg. 669
Nolan, Robert, Gen. Mgr.--Alumax Extrusions, Inc., Yankton, SD; *U.S. Public*, pg. 59
Nolan, Robert, Pres.--Interop, Inc., Mountain View, CA; *U.S. Public*, pg. 1600
Nolan, Tim, Gen. Mgr.--Byron's, Inc., Gallatin, TN; *U.S. Private*, pg. 928
Nolasco, Antonio, Gen. Mgr.--R.P. Scherer do Brasil Encapsulacoes Ltda., Sorocaba, Brazil; *U.S. Public*, pg. 1438
Nolen, James S., Pres.--J.S. Nolen & Associates, Houston, TX; *U.S. Public*, pg. 1004
Nolen, Lawrence D., Pres.--Security Reinsurance Co., Farmington, CT; *U.S. Public*, pg. 1231
Nolf, David M., Sec.--Integrated Performance Decisions, North Stonington, CT; *U.S. Public*, pg. 110
Nolin, Jerry, V.P. & Gen. Mgr.--Poli-Twine Canada (Calgary), Calgary, Canada; *Int'l*, pg. 1362
Nolin, Richard G., Chief Oper. Officer--Ahlstrom Kamyr Services Inc., Pell City, AL; *Int'l*, pg. 34
Noll, Gregory P., Pres. & Chief Exec. Officer--The Provident Bank of Kentucky, Cincinnati, OH; *U.S. Public*, pg. 1338
Noll, Rich, Chief Exec. Officer--Sara Lee Sock Company, High Point, NC; *U.S. Public*, pg. 1434
Nolte, Tim, Plant Mgr.--Mangum Mfg. Co. of Missouri, Inc., Kansas City, MO; *U.S. Public*, pg. 46
Noma, Sawako, Pres.--Kodansha International Ltd, Tokyo, Japan; *Int'l*, pg. 742
Nomiyama, Hiroshi, Pres.--Asatsu (Deutschland) GmbH, Trebur, Germany; *Int'l*, pg. 86
Nomoto, Yukiyoshi, Chief Oper. Officer--Noritake Service Center -Table Top Div., Cincinnati, Cincinnati, OH; *Int'l*, pg. 959
Nomura, Kaoru, Mng. Dir.--Brother Industries (Ireland) Ltd., Drogheda, Ireland; *Int'l*, pg. 229
Nomura, Katsuyoshi, Chief Rep.--The Industrial Bank of Japan, Limited (Guangzhou), Guangzhou, China; *Int'l*, pg. 675
Nomura, Kenji, Pres.--The Yasuda Fire & Marine Insurance Co. of America, New York, NY; *Int'l*, pg. 1519
Nomura, M., Pres.--Premier Edible Oils Corp., Portland, OR; *Int'l*, pg. 872
Nomura, Y., Pres.--Toshiba Thailand Co., Ltd., Bangkok, Thailand; *Int'l*, pg. 1407
Nong, Gu, Plant Mgr.--Nanjing Owens Corning XPS Foam Co. Ltd., Jiangsu, China; *U.S. Public*, pg. 1237
Nonnsen, U., Mng. Dir.--NRG Office Systems GmbH, Hannover, Germany; *Int'l*, pg. 1116
Nonwood, Ken, Plant Mgr.--Houston Galvanizing Div., Houston, TX; *U.S. Public*, pg. 159
Noojin, Tom, Pres.--Hickory Venture Capital Corporation, Huntsville, AL; *U.S. Public*, pg. 639
Noojin, Tom, Pres.--Hickory Capital Corporation, Huntsville, AL; *U.S. Public*, pg. 639
Noomen, Lowell, Div. Mgr.--Morgantown Machine Anderson Mavor, Rock Springs, WY; *Int'l*, pg. 280
Noon, R.E., Dir. & Gen. Mgr.--Britax (P.M.G.) Limited, Bridlington, United Kingdom; *Int'l*, pg. 216
Noonan, Al, Plant Mgr.--Ion Beam Systems Division, Austin, TX; *U.S. Public*, pg. 557
Noonan, Bill, Pres.--Gaynes Engineering Co., Franklin Park, IL; *U.S. Private*, pg. 801
Noonan, Bill, Pres.--L.A.B. Equipment, Skaneateles, NY; *U.S. Private*, pg. 801
Noonan, Edward J., Pres. & Chief Exec. Officer--American Re Corporation, Princeton, NJ; *Int'l*, pg. 897
Noonan, Edward J., Pres. & Chief Exec. Officer--American Re-Insurance Company, Princeton, NJ; *Int'l*, pg. 897
Noonan, Frank R., Pres.--The Reuben H. Donnelley Corporation, Purchase, NY; *U.S. Public*, pg. 535
Noonan, John M., V.P. & Gen. Mgr.--Construction Products Div., Richmond, VA; *U.S. Public*, pg. 1386
Noor, M., Gen. Mgr.--Kreasindo Advertising & Marketing Consultants, Jakarta, Indonesia; *U.S. Private*, pg. 184
Noorderviiet, Philip, Dir.--Noordervliet & Winninghoff/Leo Burnett B.V., Amsterdam, Netherlands; *U.S. Private*, pg. 186
Noordin, Azizan, Dir.--Tourism Malaysia - Seoul Office, Seoul, Korea; *Int'l*, pg. 833
Noorduyn, A., Pres.--Erven Lucas Bols S.A., Buenos Aires, Argentina; *Int'l*, pg. 751
Noordwijk, John, Pres.--Atlas Copco Comptec Inc., Voorheesville, NY; *Int'l*, pg. 96
Nooteboom, Gijs, Pres. & Gen. Mgr.--Polarcup Benelux B.V., Groenlo, Netherlands; *Int'l*, pg. 638
Nopanen, Markku, Mgr.--Summa Mills, Hamina, Finland; *Int'l*, pg. 457
Nora, George, Mng. Dir.--Scanpoint Technology A/S, Brondby, Denmark; *U.S. Public*, pg. 466
Noramsky, J.M., Pres.--Coastwise Trading Company, Inc., Chicago, IL; *U.S. Public*, pg. 103
Norberg, Lars, Pres.--Jonsereds Godsskydd AB, Partille, Sweden; *Int'l*, pg. 439
Norbury, R. L., Chm. Bd.--NatWest Wood MacKenzie & Co Limited, London, United Kingdom; *Int'l*, pg. 911
Norby, Verner, Chief Oper. Officer--LKM Group A/S, Kolding, Denmark; *Int'l*, pg. 1379
Nordahl, Rolf, Mng. Dir.--SKF (Schweiz), Schwerzenbach, Switzerland; *Int'l*, pg. 1159
Nordblad, Tony, Mng. Dir.--SINSER (Luxembourg) Sarl, Luxembourg, Luxembourg; *Int'l*, pg. 1258
Norder, Scott, Mng. Dir.--Inso Chicago Corporation, Chicago, IL; *U.S. Public*, pg. 882
Nordgren, Torsten, Mng. Dir.--SKF Bearing Ind. (Malaysia) Sdn. Bhd., Nilai, Malaysia; *Int'l*, pg. 1158
Nordin, Ronald H., Pres. & Chief Exec. Officer--SQA, Inc., Burlington, MA; *U.S. Public*, pg. 1361
Nordin, Staffan, Gen. Mgr.--Atlas Copco Compressor International, Wilrijk, Belgium; *Int'l*, pg. 96
Nordin, Stig, Mng. Dir.--Industriforvaltnings AB Kinnevik, Stockholm, Sweden; *Int'l*, pg. 759
Nordkild, Peter, Chief Oper. Officer--Novo Nordisk Pharma Gesellschaft mbH, Vienna, Austria; *Int'l*, pg. 988
Nordlander, Lars, Mgr.--AB Varanmo Gummifabrik, Varanmo, Sweden; *Int'l*, pg. 1422
Nordling, Lars, Chief Fin. Officer--Euroc Beton AB, Vaxjo, Sweden; *Int'l*, pg. 1199
Nordloh, Gary L., Pres. & Chief Exec. Officer--Entrada Industries, Inc., Salt Lake City, UT; *U.S. Public*, pg. 1352
Nordloh, Gary L., Pres. & Chief Exec. Officer--Celsius Energy Company, Salt Lake City, UT; *U.S. Public*, pg. 1352
Nordloh, Gary L., Pres. & Chief Exec. Officer--Universal Resources Corporation, Salt Lake City, UT; *U.S. Public*, pg. 1352
Nordman, Carl G., Pres.--Oy AGA Ab, Espoo, Finland; *Int'l*, pg. 13
Nordquist, Lars-Anders, Mgr.--AB Sandvik Rock Tools, Sandviken, Sweden; *Int'l*, pg. 1185
Nordqvist, Hans, Chief Oper. Officer--A. Ahlstrom Corporation, Noormarkku, Finland; *Int'l*, pg. 32
Nordqvist, O., Gen. Mgr.--Wellpharma Oy, Espoo, Finland; *Int'l*, pg. 553
Nordstrom, David, V.P.--Amana-Nordstrom Motel Co., Amana, IA; *U.S. Private*, pg. 48
Nordstrom, Jean, Pres.--ABB Motores S.A., Saint Quirze del Valles, Spain; *Int'l*, pg. 8
Nordstrom, Ken, Plant Mgr.--Cincinnati Thermal Spray South, Rocky Point, NC; *U.S. Private*, pg. 240
Nordstrom, Lars, Pres.--AB Novum, Helsingborg, Sweden; *Int'l*, pg. 678
Nordstrom, Leif, Chief Oper. Officer--Ahlstromforetagen Svenska AB-Matfors Core Plant, Matfors, Sweden; *Int'l*, pg. 33
Nordwall, Anders, Chief Oper. Officer--MacGREGOR Cranes AB, Ornskoldsvik, Sweden; *Int'l*, pg. 670
Norell, Jan-Erik, Mng. Dir.--Alfa-Laval Separation AB, Tumba, Sweden; *Int'l*, pg. 1378
Norgren, H.V., V.P. & Gen. Mgr.--Bouygues Offshore USA, Walnut Creek, CA; *Int'l*, pg. 206
Norin, Mats, Chief Oper. Officer--KONE Elevator (H.K.) Ltd., Kowloon, Hong Kong; *Int'l*, pg. 747
Norlander, John, Pres.--National Hotel Corp., Minneapolis, MN; *U.S. Private*, pg. 212
Norling, Jim, Pres.--Motorola Ltd., Slough, United Kingdom; *U.S. Public*, pg. 1140
Norman, H., Crumpton, V.P.-Sls. & Mktg.--H.H. Robertson Burford Plant, Hamilton, Canada; *U.S. Public*, pg. 1394
Norman, Hugh, Pres. & Gen. Mgr.--B.C. Chemicals Limited, Prince George, Canada; *Int'l*, pg. 260
Norman, Jim, Plant Mgr.--Block Plant, Dallas, TX; *U.S. Public*, pg. 936
Norman, Joseph J., Mng. Dir.--Ferro Metal & Chemical Corporation Ltd., Reading, United Kingdom; *U.S. Private*, *pg. 861*
Norman, Tom, V.P. & Gen. Mgr.--Continental Carbon Company, Houston, TX; *Int'l*, pg. 286
Norman, William L., Pres.--Norman Enterprises, Inc., Burbank, CA; *U.S. Public*, pg. 1292
Normandin, James, Publr.--The Haverhill Gazette, Haverhill, MA; *U.S. Public*, pg. 1343
Normandin, M., Pres.--O.B. Allan Jewellers, Montreal, Canada; *Int'l*, pg. 197
Normark, Didrik, Pres.--AB Elektrokoppar, Helsingborg, Sweden; *Int'l*, pg. 7
Norpecc, Kurt, Mgr.-Plant--Nestle Chocolate & Confections Company, Salinas, CA; *Int'l*, pg. 917
Norrey, Ronald W., Pres.--Woodhead Canada Ltd., Mississauga, Canada; *U.S. Public*, pg. 1776
Norrey, Ronald W., Mng. Dir.--AKAPP Electro Industries B.V., Barneveld, Netherlands; *U.S. Public*, pg. 1776
Norris, Adrian J., Assoc. Dir.--WF Corroon-Reading, Reading, United Kingdom; *Int'l*, pg. 1502
Norris, Brad, Pres.--Deerfield Manufacturing Co., Inc., Mason, OH; *U.S. Private*, pg. 1044
Norris, Charles H., Jr., Pres.--Resolite, Zelienople, PA; *U.S. Public*, pg. 1676
Norris, Don, Gen. Mgr.--Gigante Verte S.A., Irapuato, Mexico; *Int'l*, pg. 409
Norris, Don, Mgr.--Southern Agricultural Insecticides, Hendersonville, NC; *U.S. Private*, pg. 1015
Norris, Edward D., Pres.--Monitor Liability Managers, Inc., Rolling Meadows, IL; *U.S. Public*, pg. 215
Norris, Frank W., Jr., Pres.--Badger Crane Co., Winona, MN; *U.S. Private*, pg. 102
Norris, Graham, Mng. Dir.--Allianz Cornhill Insurance (Far East) Ltd., Hong Kong, Hong Kong; *Int'l*, pg. 59
Norris, H. Sidney, Mng. Dir.--Inter-Globe Security Services Ltd., Glasgow, United Kingdom; *Int'l*, pg. 593
Norris, J. Edward, Jr., Pres.--First State Bank and Trust Company, Valdosta, GA; *U.S. Public*, pg. 1549
Norris, J.C., Pres. & Chief Exec. Officer--Turner Foods Corporation, Punta Gorda, FL; *U.S. Public*, pg. 608
Norris, John F., Jr., Pres.--Duke Engineering & Services, Inc., Charlotte, NC; *U.S. Public*, pg. 534
Norris, Ken, Plant Mgr.--Hydraulics Div., Spencer, IA; *U.S. Public*, pg. 557
Norris, Paul J., Pres.--Fluorine Products Div., Morristown, NJ; *U.S. Public*, pg. 50
Norris, Ray, Gen. Mgr.--Custom Concrete, Markham, Canada; *Int'l*, pg. 629
Norris, Roy, Mng. Dir.--Kalmar Kockum Ltd., Peterborough, United Kingdom; *Int'l*, pg. 1421
Norris, Roy H., III, Pres.--Raytheon Corporate Jets, Inc., Hatfield, United Kingdom; *U.S. Public*, pg. 1366
Norris, T.C., Pres.--The Spring Grove Water Co., Spring Grove, PA; *U.S. Public*, pg. 746
Norris, Tom, Mgr.--Newport Timber, Riceboro, GA; *U.S. Private*, pg. 573
Norrish, Paul, Chief Oper. Officer--Dusenbery Europe Ltd., Bedford, United Kingdom; *U.S. Private*, pg. 350
Norrman, Ulf, Pres.--Skanska Capital AB, Danderyd, Sweden; *Int'l*, pg. 1260
Norstrom, Goran, Chief Oper. Officer--SIA Lustgarden AB, Landskrona, Sweden; *Int'l*, pg. 439
North, Gary, Chief Oper. Officer--Matson Terminals, Inc., San Francisco, CA; *U.S. Public*, pg. 40
North, Patrick, V.P. & Gen. Mgr.--KPHO-TV, Phoenix, AZ; *U.S. Public*, pg. 1094
North, Richard, Mng. Dir.--Stream International Limited, Feltham, United Kingdom; *U.S. Public*, pg. 518
Northacker, Gene, Pres.--CPC Latin America Corn Refining Division, Englewood Cliffs, NJ; *U.S. Public*, pg. 448
Northcutt, Douglas B., V.P.-Information Srvcs.--Hospital Data Processing, Fort Myers, FL; *U.S. Public*, pg. 405
Northrup, Ed, Pres.--Dynacor Div., Mundelein, IL; *U.S. Private*, pg. 728
Northrup, Jack J., Mgr.--Mt. Vernon Telephone Co., Verona, WI; *U.S. Public*, pg. 1571

Northsea, Michel, Gen. Mgr.--Riverland News, Dunnellon, FL; *U.S. Private*, pg. 648
Norton, Ceil, District Mgr.--Rathbone, King & Seeley Insurance Services, Fresno, CA; *U.S. Private*, pg. 610
Norton, D.A., Mng. Dir.--Jonas Woodhead Limited, Leeds, United Kingdom; *Int'l*, pg. 268
Norton, David W., Chm. & Chief Exec. Officer--Dresser-Rand Co., Corning, NY; *U.S. Public*, pg. 529
Norton, Denise M., V.P.--Cushman & Wakefield, Atlanta Office, Atlanta, GA; *Int'l*, pg. 873
Norton, Donn H., Pres.--Bellemead Development Corp., Roseland, NJ; *U.S. Public*, pg. 355
Norton, Edward, Chief Oper. Officer--Williamhouse of California, Inc., City of Industry, CA; *U.S. Public*, pg. 89
Norton, Gerald R., Pres.--DeVlieg-Bullard Tooling Systems Division, Frankenmuth, MI; *U.S. Public*, pg. 502
Norton, J.H.L., Chm. Bd.--Morgan Grenfell (Cayman) Limited, Georgetown, Cayman Islands; *Int'l*, pg. 406
Norton, James, Mng. Dir.--Barber & Colman Ltd., Sale, United Kingdom; *Int'l*, pg. 1243
Norton, James J., Pres.--Washington Specialty Metals, Buffalo Grove, IL; *U.S. Public*, pg. 1020
Norton, Jeffrey P., Pres.--Liberty National Bank of Northern Kentucky, Erlanger, KY; *U.S. Public*, pg. 173
Norton, Lawrence J., Pres.--Modern Equipment Rentals Inc., Wilmington, DE; *U.S. Private*, pg. 754
Norton, M., Regional Chm.--Barratt Northern, Newcastle upon Tyne, United Kingdom; *Int'l*, pg. 168
Norton, Paul, Pres.--Stemco Truck Products Division, Longview, TX; *U.S. Public*, pg. 402
Norton, Peter R.E., Chief Oper. Officer & Mng. Dir.--Sasol Chemicals Europe Limited, Solihull, United Kingdom; *Int'l*, pg. 1196
Norton, Richard, Pres.--Aero Manufacturing, Inc., Syracuse, IN; *U.S. Public*, pg. 1602
Norton, Richard, Pres.--Dutchmen Fold Down Camper Division, Syracuse, IN; *U.S. Public*, pg. 1602
Norton, Richard E., Mng. Dir.--INLAN-Industria de Componentes Mecanicos, S.A., Ponte de Sor, Portugal; *U.S. Public*, pg. 723
Norvang, Karl Johan Norvang, Mgr.--Radiometer Analytical S.A., Villeurbanne, France; *Int'l*, pg. 1084
Norwood, Joe D., Gen. Mgr.--Cannon Military/Aerospace, Santa Ana, CA; *U.S. Public*, pg. 859
Nosbusch, Keith D., Sr. V.P.--Control & Information Group, Mequon, WI; *U.S. Public*, pg. 1397
Nosch, Elmer, Gen. Mgr.--Schwermetall Halbzeugwerk GmbH & Co. KG, Stolberg, Germany; *U.S. Public*, pg. 1220
Nose, Kensaku, Pres.--Beijing Office, Beijing, China; *Int'l*, pg. 578
Noskes, E., Mgr.--Algemene Bank Nederland (Schweiz) Basle, Basel, Switzerland; *Int'l*, pg. 12
Noso, Shunji, Pres.--Teijin America, Inc., New York, NY; *Int'l*, pg. 1362
Nosworthy, John R., Mng. Dir.--MEM Ltd. 500V, Birmingham, United Kingdom; *Int'l*, pg. 390
Noteware, James D., Pres. & Chief Exec. Officer--MAXXAM Property Company, Houston, TX; *U.S. Public*, pg. 1062
Nothstine, David E., Pres.--Boeing Services, Inc., Khamis Mushayt, Saudi Arabia; *U.S. Public*, pg. 242
Noumi, Kimikazu, Gen. Mgr.--The Norinchukin Bank, New York, NY; *Int'l*, pg. 958
Nousiainen, Markku, Resident Mgr.--Savonlinna Mill, Savonlinna, Finland; *Int'l*, pg. 1429
Novacek, P., Chief Oper. Officer--Scholl Spol sro, Prague, Czech Republic; *Int'l*, pg. 1210
Novak, Francais E., Pres.--Walbar Turbine Components Division, Peabody, MA; *U.S. Public*, pg. 402
Novak, John, Pres.--Fordyce Concrete Co., Inc., Shawnee Mission, KS; *U.S. Private*, pg. 88
Novak, John, Pres.--Union Quarries, Inc., Shawnee Mission, KS; *U.S. Private*, pg. 88
Novak, John V., Mgr.--CAP Gemini America (Chicago Commercial Branch), Westchester, IL; *Int'l*, pg. 263
Novak, Ron, Branch Mgr.--EIS, Inc., Tampa, FL; *U.S. Private*, pg. 368
Novasic, Nicholas J., Chief Fin. Officer--Charleston Containers Shops Inc., Charleston, SC; *Int'l*, pg. 1214
Novich, Neil S., Pres. & Chief Exec. Officer--Ryerson Tull, Chicago, IL; *U.S. Public*, pg. 879
Novik, Jay A., Mng. Dir.--Swiss Re Atrium Corporation, New York, NY; *Int'l*, pg. 1333
Novo, C.R., Pres.--John Wyeth Laboratories S.A., Buenos Aires, Argentina; *U.S. Public*, pg. 82
Novotny, William, Chief Oper. Officer--Ransome Lift, Bensalem, PA; *U.S. Private*, pg. 453
Nowacki, Adriana, Contact--Quest Diagnostic, Rochester, NY; *U.S. Public*, pg. 1351
Nowak, Helmut, Pres.--Astra Portuguesa Lda., Lisbon, Portugal; *Int'l*, pg. 94
Nowak, Joseph, Pres.--MascoTech Industrial Components, Inc., Northville, MI; *U.S. Public*, pg. 1055
Nowak, Larry, Chief Exec. Officer--American Church, Youngstown, OH; *U.S. Private*, pg. 60
Nowak, Larry, Chief Exec. Officer--American Church, Richmond, VA; *U.S. Private*, pg. 60
Nowak, Lynne C., Plant Mgr.--Longview Fibre Co. Central Container Div., Minneapolis, MN; *U.S. Public*, pg. 1014
Nowinski, Dr. Robert C., Pres.--Genetic Systems Corporation, Seattle, WA; *Int'l*, pg. 445
Nowley, William T., Pres.--Fidus Instrument Corp., Richmond, VA; *Int'l*, pg. 233
Noy, Ze'ev, Gen. Mgr.--Analog Devices Ltd., Ra'ananna, Israel; *U.S. Public*, pg. 108
Noyce, Jeffrey P., Pres.--Chicago West Pullman Financial Corporation, Cincinnati, OH; *U.S. Private*, pg. 236
Noyes, James W., Chm. Bd.--Willis Corroon Corp. of Penn., Radnor, PA; *Int'l*, pg. 1507
Noyes, K., Gen. Mgr.--Universal Transport Operations Pty. Ltd., Brisbane, Australia; *Int'l*, pg. 827
Noyes, Kent, Plant Mgr.--Hydro Conduit Corp., Tulsa, OK; *Int'l*, pg. 245
Nozaki, Kohei, V.P. & Treas.--Nichirei Foods, Seattle, WA; *Int'l*, pg. 928
Nozko, Henry W., Jr., Pres.--Geremia Electric Co., Inc., New Britain, CT; *U.S. Public*, pg. 16
Nuccio, Patrick, Gen. Mgr.--Elkay Plastics Co., Inc., Stock Service Center, Carrollton, TX; *U.S. Private*, pg. 372
Nuckles, Craig, Mng. Dir.--Two Rivers Psychiatric Hospital, Kansas City, MO; *U.S. Public*, pg. 1697
Nuckols, Jim, Mng. Dir.--Hill-Rom/Le Couviour S.A., Pluvigner, France; *U.S. Public*, pg. 828
Nuckols, William M., Pres. & Chief Exec. Officer--Pass & Seymour/Legrand, Syracuse, NY; *Int'l*, pg. 806
Nudelman, Phillip, Pres.--Kaiser Permanente, Northwest Division, Portland, OR; *U.S. Private*, pg. 605
Nudson, Steven B., Pres.--SuperValu, Inc.-Andover Div, Andover, MA; *U.S. Public*, pg. 1540
Nuga, Ed, Editor--Rubber & Plastics News, Akron, OH; *U.S. Private*, pg. 285
Nugent, Frank, Mng. Dir.--Dowty Aerospace, Wolverhampton, Wolverhampton, United Kingdom; *Int'l*, pg. 1337
Nugent, Jeffrey, Pres.-Worldwide--Neutrogena Corporation, Los Angeles, CA; *U.S. Public*, pg. 928
Nugent, John H., Chm. Bd.--AT&T Datatek Inc., Dallas, TX; *U.S. Public*, pg. 10
Nugent, R. A., Div. Mgr.--Gillies Inc., Braeside, Canada; *Int'l*, pg. 19
Nuhn, A., Chief Oper. Officer--Oy Richardson-Vicks A.B., Helsinki, Finland; *U.S. Public*, pg. 1332
Nuhn, Adriaan, Chief Oper. Officer--Richardson-Vicks AB, Stockholm, Sweden; *U.S. Public*, pg. 1333
Nui, Theo, Sls. Dir.--Omni Films International, Heithuizen, Netherlands; *U.S. Public*, pg. 916
Null, Joseph, Branch Mgr.--Broughton Foods Company, Clarksburg, WV; *U.S. Public*, pg. 260
Nulle, Henner, Mng. Dir.--INCA Presswood Pallets, Ltd., Dover, OH; *Int'l*, pg. 678
Nulman, Richard, Pres.--Pace Advertising, New York, NY; *Int'l*, pg. 1483
Nulty, George, V.P.-Pur.--Campbell's Fresh, Inc., Blandon, PA; *U.S. Public*, pg. 299
Numaguchi, Kikuo, Gen. Mgr.--Ashikaga Bank-Treasury Division, Tokyo, Japan; *Int'l*, pg. 88
Numann, Guy, Pres.--TVT, Cambridge, United Kingdom; *U.S. Public*, pg. 791
Numeg, Luis Carlos, Mng. Dir.--Kellogg Company of South Africa (Proprietary) Limited, Springs, South Africa; *U.S. Public*, pg. 947
Numrich, Dieter, Mng. Dir.--BFR GmbH, Berlin, Germany; *Int'l*, pg. 657
Nune, David, Pres.--Alpine American, Natick, MA; *Int'l*, pg. 635
Nunes, Geoffrey, Mgr.--Millipore GmbH, Eschborn, Germany; *U.S. Public*, pg. 1113
Nunes, Richard V., Pres. & Chief Oper. Officer--UniCARE Insurance Company, Irvine, CA; *U.S. Private*, pg. 152
Nunez, Augustin, Chief Oper. Officer--Armstrong Amortiguadores S.A., Gijon, Spain; *Int'l*, pg. 265
Nunez, Elsa, Chief Fin. Officer--Johnson & Johnson Medical Caribbean, Caguas, PR; *U.S. Public*, pg. 928
Nunez, Jerry, Reg. Opers. Mgr.--Production Operators, Inc. (Lafayette Office), Lafayette, LA; *U.S. Public*, pg. 298
Nunez, Juan Luis Ruiz, Pres.--Santa Barbara Empresa Nacional de Industrias Militares, S.A., Madrid, Spain; *Int'l*, pg. 1224
Nunez, Leopoldo Quintero, Pres.--Superenvases Envalic C.A., Caracas, Venezuela; *U.S. Public*, pg. 1387
Nunez, Rafael A., V.P. & Gen. Mgr.-Venezuela--Procter & Gamble de Venezuela C.A., Caracas, Venezuela; *U.S. Public*, pg. 1332
Nunn, Chris, Gen. Mgr.--Hunter Plastics Ltd., London, United Kingdom; *Int'l*, pg. 430
Nunn, Donnie, Gen. Mgr.--San Antonio Learning Center, San Antonio, TX; *U.S. Public*, pg. 219
Nunn, Mike, Gen. Mgr.--Servitex, Inc., Greensboro, NC; *U.S. Private*, pg. 782
Nunn, R., Mng. Dir.--Air UK Engineering Ltd., Stansted, United Kingdom; *Int'l*, pg. 39
Nunn, Raymond, Supvr.--Oakland Division, Oakland, ME; *U.S. Public*, pg. 438
Nunn, Raymond, Supvr.--Skowhegan Division, Skowhegan, ME; *U.S. Public*, pg. 438
Nunn, Raymond, Superintendent--Hartland Division, Skowhegan, ME; *U.S. Public*, pg. 438
Nunn, Robert, Mng. Dir.--Air UK Engineering, Norfolk, United Kingdom; *Int'l*, pg. 39
Nunneley, Luke, Mng. Dir.--Fleming Canada Partners Inc., Toronto, Canada; *Int'l*, pg. 493
Nunnelly, Walter S., III, Pres.--Sysco Food Services of Arkansas, Inc., Little Rock, AR; *U.S. Public*, pg. 1551
Nurettin, Zorlu, Svc. Supvr.--Weatherford Oil Tool Middle East Ltd., Ankara, Turkey; *U.S. Public*, pg. 1750
Nurse, Larry, Pres.--Warehouse Concepts, Inc., West Sacramento, CA; *U.S. Private*, pg. 908
Nurtaugh, Philip F., Pres.--IBC Vehicles Ltd., Luton, United Kingdom; *Int'l*, pg. 693
Nurtrich, M., Chief Oper. Officer--Isover S.A., Lausanne, Switzerland; *Int'l*, pg. 1176
Nusbaum, William, Pres. & Publr.--Green Bay Press-Gazette, Green Bay, WI; *U.S. Public*, pg. 700
Nuse, Wilhelm, Mgr.--Commerzbank AG-Prague Branch, Prague, Czech Republic; *Int'l*, pg. 311
Nussbaum, V.M., Pres.--Home Division, Greensboro, NC; *U.S. Private*, pg. 1016
Nussbaum, V.M., Pres.--Institutional Division, Greensboro, NC; *U.S. Private*, pg. 1016
Nusser, H.J., Mgr.--Noma Tooling Enterprises, Scarborough, Canada; *Int'l*, pg. 955
Nutile, F., Fin. Controller--AEP/Borden S.A., Baudour, Belgium; *U.S. Public*, pg. 5
Nuttall, Allan, Mng. Dir.--Denver Equipment Pty., Ltd., Artarmon, Australia; *Int'l*, pg. 1326
Nutter, K.M., Dr., Gen. Mgr.--Morgan Matroc Limited Rugby Division, Rugby, United Kingdom; *Int'l*, pg. 893
Nutter, Richard F., Chief Oper. Officer--Washington Service Bureau, Inc., Washington, DC; *Int'l*, pg. 1513
Nutting, Ronald G., Pres.--OMNI Products, Inc., McHenry, IL; *U.S. Private*, pg. 816
Nuzzaci, Edward, Pres.--Sandvik Steel Co., Scranton, PA; *Int'l*, pg. 1185
Nuzzo, Anthony G., Pres.--Chase Manhattan Bank Delaware, Wilmington, DE; *U.S. Public*, pg. 338
Nuzzo, Sal J., Pres. & Gen. Mgr.--Intercontinental Mfg. Co., Garland, TX; *U.S. Private*, pg. 313
Nyberg, Ake, Mgr.--Sandvik de Mexico S.A. de C.V., Mexico, Mexico; *Int'l*, pg. 1188
Nyberg, D.A., Pres.--Tesoro Marine Services, Houston, TX; *U.S. Public*, pg. 1582
Nyberg, Lars, Pres.--GG Ws Gross, Karlstad, Sweden; *Int'l*, pg. 359
Nyberg, Olavi, Mng. Dir.--Neopac Oy, Tampere, Finland; *Int'l*, pg. 863
Nybom, Lars-Goran, Chief Oper. Officer--Ahlstrom Machinery AB-Sawmill Machinery, Stockholm, Sweden; *Int'l*, pg. 35
Nybondas, Mats, Mng. Dir.--Dun & Bradstreet Finland Oy., Espoo, Finland; *U.S. Public*, pg. 536
Nydegger, Peter, Chm. Bd.--Swissair Associated Companies Ltd., Zurich, Switzerland; *Int'l*, pg. 1334
Nye, Dick, V.P.-Eagle Ice Cream--Eagle Ice Cream Div., Cleveland, OH; *U.S. Private*, pg. 451
Nye, Erle, Pres.--Texas Utilities Fuel Co., Dallas, TX; *U.S. Public*, pg. 1588
Nye, Erle, Pres.--Texas Utilities Mining Co., Dallas, TX; *U.S. Public*, pg. 1588
Nye, Erle, Chm. Bd. & Chief Exec. Officer--TU Electric, Dallas, TX; *U.S. Public*, pg. 1588
Nye, Erle, Chm. Bd. & Chief Exec. Officer--Texas Utilities Communications Inc., Dallas, TX; *U.S. Public*, pg. 1588
Nye, Erle, Chm. Bd. & Chief Exec. Officer--Texas Utilities Properties Inc., Dallas, TX; *U.S. Public*, pg. 1588
Nye, John, Gen. Mgr.--ITW Spit Fixings, Crawley, United Kingdom; *U.S. Public*, pg. 869
Nye, Willard, Mgr.--Stephen Gould of Illinois, Inc., Schaumburg, IL; *U.S. Private*, pg. 467
Nygaard, Arne, Mng. Dir.--DYWIDAG Systems Norge A/S, Hagan, Norway; *Int'l*, pg. 424
Nygaard, Paul, Gen. Mgr.--Rohr Industries, Foley Plant, Foley, AL; *U.S. Public*, pg. 751
Nygaard, Ulrich, Pres.--Heidelberg Finishing Systems, Dayton, OH; *Int'l*, pg. 604
Nygard, Tor, Gen. Mgr.--Ghacem, Ltd., Accra, Ghana; *Int'l*, pg. 1201
Nygard, Tor, Gen. Mgr.--Ghana Cement Co. Ltd., Accra, Ghana; *Int'l*, pg. 1201
Nygren, Hans, Dir.-Mktg.--SKF Transmission AB, Jonkoping, Sweden; *Int'l*, pg. 1157
Nygren, R., Reg. Dir.--EMI Svenska AB, Solna, Sweden; *Int'l*, pg. 427
Nyhof, Leo, Gen. Mgr.--Cherry Australia Pty. Ltd., Oakleigh, Australia; *U.S. Public*, pg. 346
Nyland, Bob, Pres.--Outdoor Services, New York, NY; *U.S. Private*, pg. 1166
Nyland, Robert, Pres.--Outdoor Services, Chicago, IL; *U.S. Private*, pg. 1166
Nyls, Maurice, Dir. Gen.--Brodard et Taupin, La Fleche, France; *Int'l*, pg. 792
Nyman, Lars-Erik, Mng. Dir.--Mactec AB, Kristianstad, Sweden; *U.S. Public*, pg. 860
Nyman, Svante, Chm.--ITT Flygt AB, Solna, Sweden; *U.S. Public*, pg. 860
Nyquist, Mats, Reg. Pres.--Melitta AB, Handen, Sweden; *Int'l*, pg. 857
Nyqvist, Lisa, Chief Exec. Officer--AB Sukab Representative Office, Harare, Zimbabwe; *Int'l*, pg. 712
Nys, P.H., Mgr.-Opers.--Belgian Fuelling and Services Company, Zaventem, Belgium; *Int'l*, pg. 1168
Nystrom, J., Gen. Mgr.--Kodak Oy, Vantaa, Finland; *U.S. Public*, pg. 554
Nystrom, Jon A., Chm., Pres. & Chief Exec. Officer--First Virginia Bank-Commonwealth, Williamsburg, VA; *U.S. Public*, pg. 641
Nystrom, Lars-Erik, Pres.--Aseri Tellis AS, Aseri, Estonia; *Int'l*, pg. 1200
Nystrom, Lars-Erik, Pres.--Optimix AS, Aravete, Estonia; *Int'l*, pg. 1200
Nystrom, Lennart, Mng. Dir.--SKF Portugal Rolamentos, Lda., Amadora, Portugal; *Int'l*, pg. 1159
Nystrom, Ulf, Chief Oper. Officer--ICA Kort AB, Stockholm, Sweden; *Int'l*, pg. 643
Nzeribe, May, Mng. Dir.--Sunrise Marketing Communications Ltd., Lagos, Nigeria; *U.S. Private*, pg. 305
O' Mahony, Jack, Pres.--Howmedica, Inc., Rutherford, NJ; *U.S. Public*, pg. 1282
O'Boyle, Tom, V.P.-Opers.--Eaton Corporation, Truck Components Operations-North America, Galesburg, MI; *U.S. Public*, pg. 557
O'Boyle, Tom, V.P.-Opers.--Truck Parts Division, Galesburg, MI; *U.S. Public*, pg. 558
O'Brien, A.M., Gen. Mgr.--Starch Australia, Gladesville, Australia; *Int'l*, pg. 555
O'Brien, C., Dir.--Baring Brothers Burrows & Co. Ltd., Sydney, Australia; *Int'l*, pg. 648
O'Brien, Charles G., V.P. & Gen. Mgr.--Meriam Instrument, Cleveland, OH; *U.S. Public*, pg. 218
O'Brien, Chris, Dir.-Sls.--Sensormatic New Zealand Ltd., Auckland, New Zealand; *U.S. Public*, pg. 1458
O'Brien, Daniel R., Pres. & Chief Exec. Officer--Beneficial Insurance Group, Inc., Peapack, NJ; *U.S. Public*, pg. 211
O'Brien, Daniel R., Pres. & Chief Exec. Officer--The Central National Life Insurance Co. of Omaha, Inc., Peapack, NJ; *U.S. Public*, pg. 211
O'Brien, David L., Pres. & Gen. Mgr.--Hapco/American Div., Abingdon, VA; *U.S. Private*, pg. 351
O'Brien, Ed, Mgr.--Stephen Gould of Carolina, Inc., Morrisville, NC; *U.S. Private*, pg. 467
O'Brien, G.R., Pres.--Cigna Employee Benefits Services, Inc., Bloomfield, CT; *U.S. Public*, pg. 358

O'Brien, G.R., Chm. Bd.--Cigna Healthcare, Inc., Bloomfield, CT; *U.S. Public*, pg. 359
O'Brien, G.R., Chm. Bd.--Cigna Life Insurance Company, Bloomfield, CT; *U.S. Public*, pg. 361
O'Brien, Gerry B., Chm.--Enfield Holdings Ltd., Bulawayo, Zimbabwe; *Int'l*, pg. 390
O'Brien, J.F., Pres.--Portec Ltd., Lachine, Canada; *U.S. Public*, pg. 1318
O'Brien, James, Pres.--Valvoline Company, Lexington, KY; *U.S. Public*, pg. 139
O'Brien, James B., Pres.--Jones Intercable, Inc., Englewood, CO; *U.S. Private*, pg. 597
O'Brien, Jimmy, Mgr.--GGK Dublin, Dublin, Ireland; *Int'l*, pg. 1335
O'Brien, John, Plant Mgr.--Maywood Division, Maywood, NJ; *U.S. Public*, pg. 1514
O'Brien, John, Pres.--Spectra-Physics Scanning Systems Inc., Eugene, OR; *U.S. Public*, pg. 1594
O'Brien, John D., Pres.--Borg-Warner Protective Services Corporation, Parsippany, NJ; *U.S. Public*, pg. 245
O'Brien, John P., Pres.--Fleet Securities, Inc., New York, NY; *U.S. Public*, pg. 650
O'Brien, L., Gen. Mgr.--American Alloy Castings Company, Bixby, OK; *U.S. Private*, pg. 55
O'Brien, M.E., Gen. Mgr.--Turner Construction Company, San Jose, CA; *U.S. Public*, pg. 1645
O'Brien, M.V., Chm.--Getty Petroleum Ireland, Ltd., White Plains, NY; *U.S. Public*, pg. 1583
O'Brien, Mark, Area Mgr.--Lifetime Assurance Co. Limited, Slough, United Kingdom; *Int'l*, pg. 153
O'Brien, Mark J., Pres.--Pulte Southeast Division, Tampa, FL; *U.S. Public*, pg. 1345
O'Brien, Michael J., Chief Exec. Officer--Salick Health Care, Inc., Los Angeles, CA; *Int'l*, pg. 1524
O'Brien, Mike, Mgr.--Raynor Distribution Center, Lincoln Park, NJ; *U.S. Private*, pg. 912
O'Brien, Morgan, Pres.--BEI Graphics, Boulder, CO; *U.S. Private*, pg. 796
O'Brien, Patrick J., Pres.--A & M Products, Danbury, CT; *U.S. Public*, pg. 627
O'Brien, R. Michael, Pres.--GMAC Mortgage Corporation, Horsham, PA; *U.S. Public*, pg. 720
O'Brien, Richard T., Pres.--PacifiCorp Group Holdings Company, Portland, OR; *U.S. Public*, pg. 1251
O'Brien, Richard T., Sr. V.P.--Utah Power & Light, Salt Lake City, UT; *U.S. Public*, pg. 1251
O'Brien, Robert J., Asst. V.P.--IBP-Storm Lake, Storm Lake, IA; *U.S. Public*, pg. 852
O'Brien, Thomas, Pres.--WWF Paper Corporation - Midwest, Elk Grove Village, IL; *U.S. Private*, pg. 1145
O'Brien, Thomas H., Chm. Bd.--PNC Bancorp Inc., Wilmington, DE; *U.S. Public*, pg. 1243
O'Brien, Tom, Gen. Mgr.--Capstone Electronics Div., Raleigh, NC; *U.S. Public*, pg. 134
O'Brien, Tom, Mgr.-Plant--Nestle Chocolate & Confections Company, Fulton, NY; *Int'l*, pg. 917
O'Brien, Vincent, Chm. Bd. & Mng. Dir.--Texaco (Ireland) Ltd., Dublin, Ireland; *U.S. Public*, pg. 1584
O'Brien, Wilbur D., Pres.--ERA Aviation, Inc., Anchorage, AK; *U.S. Public*, pg. 1410
O'Brien, William, Pres.--Converter Power, Inc., Ipswich, MA; *U.S. Public*, pg. 856
O'Byrne, Arnold J., Mng. Dir.--General Motors Distribution Ireland Ltd., Dublin, Ireland; *U.S. Public*, pg. 722
O'Callaghan, Tim, Mng. Dir.--Standex (Ireland) Ltd., Mountmellick, Ireland; *U.S. Public*, pg. 1508
O'Colmain, Diarmuid, Mng. Dir.--Ericsson Systems Expertise Ltd., Athlone, Ireland; *Int'l*, pg. 1367
O'Colmaine, Peter, Gen. Mgr.--Four Seasons Resorts, Kihei, HI; *Int'l*, pg. 502
O'Connell, Dan, Mng. Dir.--Shandwick USA, New York, NY; *Int'l*, pg. 1227
O'Connell, Francis M., Chief Fin. Officer--Innovir Laboratories, Inc., New York, NY; *U.S. Public*, pg. 1702
O'Connell, G.M., Pres. & Chief Oper. Officer--TN Technologies Inc., Westport, CT; *U.S. Public*, pg. 1641
O'Connell, Howard J., Pres.--Stanley Design-Build, Inc., Muscatine, IA; *U.S. Private*, pg. 1033
O'Connell, Robert J., V.P. & Gen. Mgr.--Air Express Intl. Agency, Inc., Darien, CT; *U.S. Public*, pg. 30
O'Connell, Thomas C., Mng. Dir.--Johnson & Johnson (Ireland) Ltd., Dublin, Ireland; *U.S. Public*, pg. 930
O'Conner, Richard, Publr.--Incentive, New York, NY; *Int'l*, pg. 1446
O'Connor, B.P., Chm. Bd.--Dorbyl Structural Engineering (Pty) Ltd., Germiston, South Africa; *Int'l*, pg. 416
O'Connor, Bernard, Chief Oper. Officer--KONE Wood Ltd., Nepean, Canada; *Int'l*, pg. 14
O'Connor, Bernard P., Mng. Dir.--Zimmer Australia Pty. Limited, Frenchs Forest, Australia; *U.S. Public*, pg. 256
O'Connor, Bill, Gen. Mgr.--Mitel Far East Ltd., Wan Chai, Hong Kong; *Int'l*, pg. 870
O'Connor, Bill, Gen. Mgr.--Tianchi-Mitel Telecommunications Corporation, Tianjin, China; *Int'l*, pg. 870
O'Connor, C. Kelly, Pres.--Rio Algom Exploration, Inc., Toronto, Canada; *Int'l*, pg. 1118
O'Connor, Gerald A., Gen. Mgr.--Molinos Modernos, S.A., Guatemala, Guatemala; *Int'l*, pg. 411
O'Connor, James J., Chm. Bd. & Pres.--Commonwealth Research Corp., Chicago, IL; *U.S. Public*, pg. 1664
O'Connor, James J., Chm. Bd.--Cotter Corp., Lakewood, CO; *U.S. Public*, pg. 1664
O'Connor, James J., Chm. Bd. & Pres.--Edison Development Canada, Inc., Chicago, IL; *U.S. Public*, pg. 1664
O'Connor, John, Chief Exec. Officer & Exec. Gen. Mgr.--BHP Petroleum, Melbourne, Australia; *Int'l*, pg. 224
O'Connor, John, Pres.--Day & Zimmerman Infrastructure, Inc., Philadelphia, PA; *U.S. Private*, pg. 317
O'Connor, Kevin, Chief Exec. Officer--Ord O'Connor Grieve Limited, Wellington, New Zealand; *Int'l*, pg. 1497
O'Connor, Laurence P., Chm. Bd., Pres. & Chief Exec. Officer--Unigard Indemnity Co., Bellevue, WA; *Int'l*, pg. 345
O'Connor, Michael J., Gen. Mgr.--Dufferin Aggregates, Concord, Canada; *Int'l*, pg. 628
O'Connor, Michael R., Pres.--Peak Oilfield Services Company, Anchorage, AK; *U.S. Public*, pg. 1149
O'Connor, Paul J., Office Mgr.--Roy F. Weston of New York, New York, NY; *U.S. Public*, pg. 1761
O'Connor, R.G., Mng. Dir.--Tip Top Ice Cream Co. Limited, Auckland, New Zealand; *Int'l*, pg. 1040
O'Connor, Thomas P., Exec. V.P.-Bed Fashions--Home Furnishings Segment, Fort Mill, SC; *U.S. Public*, pg. 1500
O'Connor, William, Pres.--Merrill Lynch Specialists Inc., New York, NY; *U.S. Public*, pg. 1098
O'Connor, William E., Pres.--Waukesha Engine Division, Waukesha, WI; *U.S. Public*, pg. 528
O'Dea, Kelly, Pres.-Worldwide Client Service-New York & London--Ogilvy & Mather Worldwide, Inc., New York, NY; *Int'l*, pg. 1483
O'Dea, Patrick, Pres. & Chief Oper. Officer--Mother's Cake & Cookie Co., Oakland, CA; *U.S. Private*, pg. 1022
O'Dell, Charles, Pres.--Marriott Management Services (MMS), Washington, DC; *U.S. Public*, pg. 1048
O'Dell, Lawrence, Gen. Mgr.--Armstrong-Hunt, Inc., Milton, FL; *U.S. Private*, pg. 83
O'Dell, Nancy, Sr. V.P. & Branch Mgr.--California State Bank-Arcadia, Arcadia, CA; *U.S. Public*, pg. 294
O'Dell, W.W., Pres.-Liebert Corp.--Liebert Corporation, Columbus, OH; *U.S. Public*, pg. 573
O'Donnel, Mike, Pres.--Richheimer Food, Moonachie, NJ; *U.S. Private*, pg. 1158
O'Donnell, Clem, Gen. Mgr.--Filtration Systems Division, Angola, NY; *U.S. Public*, pg. 126
O'Donnell, J., Mng. Dir.--AIB International Financial Services Ltd, Dublin, Ireland; *Int'l*, pg. 64
O'Donnell, J., Mng. Dir.--AIB Corporate Finance Ltd., Dublin, Ireland; *Int'l*, pg. 64
O'Donnell, Jack, Pres.--Aircraft Bearing Corp., Los Angeles, CA; *U.S. Public*, pg. 187
O'Donnell, Jim, Sec.--ITW Limited, Windsor, United Kingdom; *U.S. Public*, pg. 868
O'Donnell, P.A., Pres.--Strand Lighting Inc., Rancho Dominguez, CA; *Int'l*, pg. 1087
O'Donnell, Thomas H., Pres.--Sunrise Medical Mobility Products, Fresno, CA; *U.S. Public*, pg. 1536
O'Donnell, Tim, Pres.--Olathe Daily News, Olathe, KS; *U.S. Private*, pg. 613
O'Donnell, W.F., Mng. Dir.--Diesel ReCon UK, Cumbernauld, United Kingdom; *U.S. Public*, pg. 469
O'Driscoll, Donnach, Chm.--Country 103.5, London, United Kingdom; *Int'l*, pg. 561
O'Farrell, Dean, Chm. Bd. & Chief Exec. Officer--SouthTrust Bank of Huntsville, Huntsville, AL; *U.S. Public*, pg. 1492
O'Fill, R.J., Div. V.P.--Ameron Protective Linings Division, Brea, CA; *U.S. Public*, pg. 99
O'Flaherty, Tom, Mng. Dir.--Luxo Lamp Corporation, Port Chester, NY; *Int'l*, pg. 821
O'Flanagan, Sean, Mgr.-Communications--BNP Capital Finance Limited - Ireland, Dublin, Ireland; *Int'l*, pg. 163
O'Floinn, Ruairi, Mng. Dir.--Lifetime Assurance Co. Limited, Dublin, Ireland; *Int'l*, pg. 152
O'Flynn, Patrick S., Chm., Pres. & Chief Exec. Officer--Interstate National Corp., Chicago, IL; *Int'l*, pg. 59
O'Flynn, Patrick S., Pres.--Interstate National Corp., Chicago, IL; *Int'l*, pg. 59
O'Gara, Gabriel, Dir.--Chemical Fabrics Limited, Kilrush, Ireland; *U.S. Public*, pg. 344
O'Gorman, Jeremiah J., Gen. Mgr.--Vickers Systems Ltd., Pakuranga, New Zealand; *U.S. Public*, pg. 25
O'Gorman, P.J., Gen. Mgr.--Kodak Philippines Ltd., Manila, Philippines; *U.S. Public*, pg. 554
O'Gorman, Patrick, Gen. Mgr.--Kodak (Singapore) Pte. Limited, Singapore, Singapore; *U.S. Public*, pg. 554
O'Gorman, Timothy, Exec. V.P.--ABN AMRO Chicago Corp Financial Services, Chicago, IL; *Int'l*, pg. 10
O'Grady, G., Gen. Mgr.--Aer Lingus, Brussels, Belgium; *Int'l*, pg. 28
O'Grady, John, Gen. Mgr.--Merck Sharp & Dohme (New Zealand) Ltd., Wiri, New Zealand; *U.S. Public*, pg. 1092
O'Grady, John F., Exec. Dir.--Elder's Finance Group, Melbourne, Australia; *Int'l*, pg. 500
O'Grady, V.J., V.P. & Gen. Mgr.--Silica Catalysts & Adsorbents Business, Valley Forge, PA; *U.S. Private*, pg. 827
O'Grady, V.J., V.P. & Gen. Mgr.--Inorganic Colloids Business, Valley Forge, PA; *U.S. Private*, pg. 827
O'Halleran, Michael D., Pres. & Chief Oper. Officer--Alexander & Alexander Services Inc., New York, NY; *U.S. Public*, pg. 117
O'Halloran, Colm, Plant Mgr.--Rorer Ireland, Ltd., Nenagh, Ireland; *Int'l*, pg. 1112
O'Halloran, Martin, Pres.--ISS Cleaning Services Group, Inc., New York, NY; *Int'l*, pg. 656
O'Halloran, Terry, Pres.--Titus Products Div., Richardson, TX; *Int'l*, pg. 1398
O'Hanlon, Michael A., Pres. & Chief Oper. Officer--DVI Business Credit, Inc., Newport Beach, CA; *U.S. Public*, pg. 476
O'Hanlon, Michael M., Pres.--Merrill Lynch Credit Corporation, Jacksonville, FL; *U.S. Public*, pg. 1098
O'Hara, Mike, Gen. Mgr.--Olympic Steel - Connecticut Division, Milford, CT; *U.S. Public*, pg. 1221
O'Hare, Dean R., Chm. & Pres.--Federal Insurance Co., Warren, NJ; *U.S. Public*, pg. 355
O'Hare, Dean R., Chm. & Pres.--Vigilant Insurance Co., New York, NY; *U.S. Public*, pg. 355
O'Hare, Richard, Pres.--Todd-AO Video Services, Hollywood, CA; *U.S. Public*, pg. 1619
O'Horo, Daniel J., Gen. Mgr.--EMPIRE Hydraulic Service, Mesa, AZ; *U.S. Private*, pg. 374
O'Horo, Jim, Gen. Mgr.--Grand Rapids Plant - Stone Packaging Corp., Grand Rapids, MI; *U.S. Public*, pg. 1521
O'Keefe, Bob, V.P.--BancTec Payment Systems, Saint Petersburg, FL; *U.S. Public*, pg. 177
O'Keefe, James, Chief Exec. Officer--Aetna Realty Investors, Inc., Hartford, CT; *U.S. Public*, pg. 26
O'Keefe, Shan, Pres.--Windsor Airmotive, East Granby, CT; *U.S. Public*, pg. 190
O'Keefe, Tim, Chief Oper. Officer--Rangen Aquaculture Research, Buhl, ID; *U.S. Private*, pg. 909
O'Keeffe, K.J., Pres.--Regent-Sheffield Ltd., New Hyde Park, NY; *Int'l*, pg. 852
O'Keeffe, Martin, Gen. Mgr.--North DeKalb Cable T.V. Company, Chamblee, GA; *U.S. Public*, pg. 1448
O'Keeffe, Whitney, Chm. Bd. & Chief Exec. Officer--SunTrust Bank, Treasure Coast, N.A., Fort Pierce, FL; *U.S. Public*, pg. 1538
O'Keeffe, William, Pres.--Safety And Fire Technology, Inc., San Francisco, CA; *U.S. Private*, pg. 813
O'Kelly, Sean T., Reg. Dir.--Sime Darby Philipinas, Inc., Manila, Philippines; *Int'l*, pg. 1251
O'Leary, Daniel J., Chief Oper. Officer--Stupp Corporation, Baton Rouge, LA; *U.S. Private*, pg. 1048
O'Leary, Edward T., Pres. & Chief Exec. Officer--First Security Bank of New Mexico, Albuquerque, NM; *U.S. Public*, pg. 637
O'Leary, John, Pres.--Forwest Inc., Houston, TX; *Int'l*, pg. 496
O'Leary, John C., V.P. & Gen. Mgr.--Bristol-Myers Oncology Division, Evansville, IN; *U.S. Public*, pg. 254
O'Leary, R.J., Chmn. & Pres.--PMT of the Southwest, Inc., Burlingame, CA; *U.S. Public*, pg. 1668
O'Lenick, Tony, Pres.--Lambent Technologies Inc., Norcross, GA; *U.S. Private*, pg. 858
O'Loughlin, Michael, Mng. Dir.--Normalair-Garrett Ltd., Yeovil, United Kingdom; *U.S. Public*, pg. 54
O'Malley, Michael, Pres.--Mickey & Company, New York, NY; *U.S. Public*, pg. 519
O'Malley, Wiliam, Pres.--Point Marine, Inc., New Orleans, LA; *U.S. Public*, pg. 1608
O'Malley, William, Pres.--Pental Insurance Co., Ltd., New Orleans, LA; *U.S. Public*, pg. 1608
O'Malley, William, Pres.--Tidewater Marine, Inc., Amelia, LA; *U.S. Public*, pg. 1608
O'Malley, William, Pres.--Tidewater Marine International, Inc., New Orleans, LA; *U.S. Public*, pg. 1608
O'Malley, William, Pres.--Tidewater Marine Western, Inc., New Orleans, LA; *U.S. Public*, pg. 1608
O'Malley, William, Pres.--Tidewater Offshore Services, Inc., New Orleans, LA; *U.S. Public*, pg. 1608
O'Malley, William, Pres.--Seafarer Boat Corporation, New Orleans, LA; *U.S. Public*, pg. 1608
O'Malley, William C., Pres. & Chief Oper. Officer--Tidewater Marine Service, Inc., New Orleans, LA; *U.S. Public*, pg. 1608
O'Malley, William M., Pres.--Twenty Grand Offshore, New Orleans, LA; *U.S. Public*, pg. 1608
O'Meara, John, Pres.--Hemostatix, Cherry Hill, NJ; *U.S. Private*, pg. 1073
O'Meara, John, Pres.--Sonex, Cherry Hill, NJ; *U.S. Private*, pg. 1073
O'Meara, John M., Chm. Bd. & Chief Exec. Officer--First Midwest Bank, N.A., Itasca, IL; *U.S. Public*, pg. 636
O'Meara, Peter, Gen. Mgr.--Lexmark Australia, Frenchs Forest, Australia; *U.S. Public*, pg. 991
O'Neal, Bob H., Dir.--Stewart & Stevenson (U.K.) Limited, Houston, TX; *U.S. Public*, pg. 1518
O'Neal, Gary, V.P. & Gen. Mgr.--Central Plains Steel Co., Wichita, KS; *U.S. Private*, pg. 824
O'Neal, J.T., Gen. Mgr.--Pacific Industrial Furnace Division, Redford, MI; *U.S. Public*, pg. 502
O'Neil, Antoine, Pres. & Chief Oper. Officer--Foster Wheeler France S.A., Paris, France; *U.S. Public*, pg. 677
O'Neil, Brian E., Pres. & Chief Exec. Officer--Northwest Pipeline Corp., Salt Lake City, UT; *U.S. Public*, pg. 1769
O'Neil, Bruce P., Chm. Bd. & Chief Exec. Officer--Willis Corroon Corp. of Illinois, Chicago, IL; *Int'l*, pg. 1506
O'Neil, Daniel J., Pres.-U.S. Soup--Campbell Soup (Texas) Inc., Paris, TX; *U.S. Public*, pg. 299
O'Neil, R.S., Mgr.-Office--DeLeuw, Cather & Company, Jacksonville, FL; *U.S. Private*, pg. 841
O'Neil, R.S., V.P.--DeLeuw Cather & Co., Engineering Div., Buffalo, NY; *U.S. Private*, pg. 841
O'Neil, R.S., Pres.--DeLeuw Cather & Co., Fairfax, VA; *U.S. Private*, pg. 841
O'Neil, R.S., Pres.--DeLeuw, Cather International Ltd., Abu Dhabi, United Arab Emirates; *U.S. Private*, pg. 842
O'Neil, Robert, Pres.--DeLeuw, Cather & Company, Washington, DC; *U.S. Private*, pg. 841
O'Neil, W.E., Chm. Bd.--W.E. O'Neil Construction Company, Chicago, IL; *U.S. Private*, pg. 817
O'Neil, William J., Chm. Bd. & Pres.--O'Neil Data Systems, Inc., Los Angeles, CA; *U.S. Private*, pg. 817
O'Neill, Brian, Pres. & Chief Exec. Officer--Williams Natural Gas Company, Tulsa, OK; *U.S. Public*, pg. 1769
O'Neill, Colam, Mgr.--Allergan Pharmaceuticals (Ireland) Ltd., Inc., Westport, Ireland; *U.S. Public*, pg. 46
O'Neill, Dan, Pres.--Star-Kist Foods Inc., Newport, KY; *U.S. Public*, pg. 805
O'Neill, Dan, Pres.--Star-Kist Foods, Inc., Newport, KY; *U.S. Public*, pg. 806
O'Neill, Donald F., Chm. Bd. & Chief Exec. Officer--Perfecseal Company, Philadelphia, PA; *U.S. Public*, pg. 210
O'Neill, Leo C., Pres. & Chief Ratings Officer--Standard & Poor's Ratings Services, New York, NY; *U.S. Public*, pg. 1071
O'Neill, P. M., Plant Mgr.--Beaumont Petrochemical Plant, Beaumont, TX; *U.S. Public*, pg. 1118
O'Neill, Paul T., V.P. & Gen. Mgr.--The Bank of Bermuda Limited-Hong Kong Branch, Central, Hong Kong; *Int'l*, pg. 151

O'Neill, Paul T., Pres.--NER Holdings, Inc., Stamford, CT; *U.S. Private*, pg. 502
O'Neill, Richard J., Grp. V.P.--Elizabethtown Gas Co., Union, NJ; *U.S. Public*, pg. 1147
O'Neill, Robert B., V.P., Gen. Counsel & Sec.--Capitol Industries-EMI Inc., Hollywood, CA; *Int'l*, pg. 427
O'Neill, William, Mng. Editor--The Sun, London, United Kingdom; *Int'l*, pg. 927
O'Reilly, Charles L., Jr., Pres.--Thomas K. Dyer, Inc., Lexington, MA; *U.S. Private*, pg. 492
O'Reilly, David, Pres.--Hi/LO Automotive, Inc., Houston, TX; *U.S. Public*, pg. 1230
O'Reilly, David E., Chief Exec. Officer--Ozark Automotive Distributors, Inc., Springfield, MO; *U.S. Public*, pg. 1230
O'Reilly, David E., Chief Exec. Officer--Greene County Realty Company, Springfield, MO; *U.S. Public*, pg. 1230
O'Reilly, John P.H., Mng. Dir.--H.J. Heinz Company (Ireland) Limited, Blackrock, Ireland; *U.S. Public*, pg. 806
O'Reilly, Knowlton J., Pres.--Oxford Separates, New York, NY; *U.S. Public*, pg. 1239
O'Reilly, P.J., Mng. Dir.--AIB International Consultants Ltd., Dublin, Ireland; *Int'l*, pg. 64
O'Riley, Kelly, Gen. Mgr.--Circle Freight International USA, Grand Rapids, MI; *U.S. Public*, pg. 371
O'Rourke, Chuck, Pres.--First American Title Insurance Co. of Oregon, Portland, OR; *U.S. Public*, pg. 626
O'Rourke, James, Pres.--Nameplate, Hillsborough, NC; *U.S. Private*, pg. 595
O'Rourke, John, V.P. & Mgr.--First American Title Co. of Bellingham, Bellingham, WA; *U.S. Public*, pg. 625
O'Rourke, John, V.P.-Sls.--Custom Brands Div., Cumberland, MD; *U.S. Public*, pg. 753
O'Rourke, Louise, V.P.--Douglas Elliman-Jane Hayes, Inc., Locust Valley, NY; *U.S. Private*, pg. 341
O'Rourke, Terry, Chief Oper. Officer--Tredit Tire & Wheel Co., Elkhart, IN; *U.S. Private*, pg. 300
O'Sallon, Thomas, Pres.--Boeing Aerospace & Electronics, Inc., Plano, TX; *U.S. Public*, pg. 240
O'Shaughnessy, Gerald, Pres.--Lario Enterprises, Inc., Wichita, KS; *U.S. Private*, pg. 651
O'Shaughnessy, R.F., Pres. & Chief Exec. Officer--Pacific Northern Gas Ltd., Vancouver, Canada; *Int'l*, pg. 1492
O'Shea, Bill, Pres.--Lucent Technologies, Business Communications Systems Div., Basking Ridge, NJ; *U.S. Public*, pg. 1017
O'Shea, Jeri J., V.P. & Mgr.--City National Bank - Sunset-Doheny Office, Los Angeles, CA; *U.S. Public*, pg. 381
O'Shea, Michael, Gen. Mgr.--KJR-FM, Seattle, WA; *U.S. Private*, pg. 792
O'Shea, Terry, Chief Oper. Officer--Ahlstrom Process Equipment Inc., Appleton, WI; *Int'l*, pg. 34
O'Sullivan, Alexander W., Mng. Dir.--Befab-Safeland, Ltd., Shannon, Ireland; *U.S. Private*, pg. 313
O'Sullivan, Grant, Gen. Mgr.--New Zealand Fibre Glass Company-Imported Products Division, Auckland, New Zealand; *U.S. Public*, pg. 904
O'Sullivan, Kilian, Representative--NationsBank (France), Paris, France; *U.S. Public*, pg. 1166
O'Sullivan, Michael, Plant Mgr.--Waterford Plant, Waterford, Ireland; *U.S. Public*, pg. 673
O'Toole, M., Pres.--Simon Aerials Inc., Milwaukee, WI; *Int'l*, pg. 1252
O'Toole, Richard, V.P. & Gen. Mgr.--Metron Steel, Chicago, IL; *Int'l*, pg. 572
O'Toole, Timothy S., Chm. Bd. & Chief Exec. Officer--Patient Care, Inc., West Orange, NJ; *U.S. Public*, pg. 344
O'Toole, Timothy T., Pres.--The St. Lawrence & Adirondack Railway Co., Philadelphia, PA; *U.S. Public*, pg. 432
Oak, A.D., Pres.--TECO Finance, Inc., Tampa, FL; *U.S. Public*, pg. 1565
Oak, A.D., Pres.--TECO Investments, Inc., Tampa, FL; *U.S. Public*, pg. 1565
Oak, Frank, Mgr.--Titex Tools Ltd., Birmingham, United Kingdom; *Int'l*, pg. 1187
Oakes, Alan J., Pres.--Macmillan General Reference USA, New York, NY; *U.S. Private*, pg. 777
Oakes, Bruce, Mgr.--Morgan Europe, Sheffield, United Kingdom; *U.S. Private*, pg. 761
Oakley, Robert, Mng. Dir.--Sunsites Limited, Knutsford, United Kingdom; *Int'l*, pg. 465
Oakley, T., Dir. & Gen. Mgr.--Moore Paragon Central Africa Limited, Harare, Zimbabwe; *Int'l*, pg. 890
Oaks, J.G., Pres.--CRC Properties, Inc., Philadelphia, PA; *U.S. Public*, pg. 432
Oatman, Peter, Gen. Mgr.--EUA Cogenex West, Boulder, CO; *U.S. Public*, pg. 549
Oba, Akira, Chief Oper. Officer--Nishimatsu - Corpro Construction (M) Sdn. Bhd., Kuala Lumpur, Malaysia; *Int'l*, pg. 943
Obara, S., Pres.--Olin Japan, Inc., Tokyo, Japan; *U.S. Public*, pg. 1220
Obaya, Lilia, Branch Mgr.--Downey Savings & Loan Association, F.A., Dana Point, CA; *U.S. Public*, pg. 526
Obendorfer, B.J., Mgr.--Ballast Nedam International B.V.-Philippine Branch, Manila, Philippines; *Int'l*, pg. 134
Ober, D.G., Chief Oper. Officer--Adams Express Co., Baltimore, MD; *U.S. Public*, pg. 1280
Oberg, George, Chief Fin. Officer & V.P.--Costain Coal Inc., Lexington, KY; *Int'l*, pg. 337
Oberg, S., Exec. V.P.--Ro-Search, Inc., Hazelwood, NC; *U.S. Public*, pg. 1752
Oberholser, Steve, Division Mgr.--Higgins San Diego Operations, San Diego, CA; *U.S. Private*, pg. 527
Oberlanda, James D., Pres.--ESCOD Industries, Morrisville, NC; *U.S. Public*, pg. 881
Oberling, Jim, V.P.-Sls.--Hayes Brake, Mequon, WI; *U.S. Private*, pg. 299
Oberly, K.E., Pres.--Fluid Conservation Systems Inc., Milford, OH; *Int'l*, pg. 590
Oberman, Allan, Pres.--Best Foods Canada, Inc., Etobicoke, Canada; *U.S. Public*, pg. 224
Obermayer, William G., Pres.--Sprint North Supply, New Century, KS; *U.S. Public*, pg. 1501
Obermeyer, James R., Pres.--Geo-Con, Inc., Denver, CO; *U.S. Public*, pg. 1657
Obermueller, G., Chief Exec. Officer--Bramac Dachsysteme International GmbH, Pochlarn, Austria; *Int'l*, pg. 1092
Oberstein, Maurice L., Chm.--Phonogram Ltd., London, United Kingdom; *Int'l*, pg. 1053
Obert, Mark J., Pres. & Chief Oper. Officer--ASIA flxible Automotive Tech. Corp., Ann Arbor, MI; *U.S. Private*, pg. 444
Obletter, P., Chief Exec. Officer--Braas Italia S.p.A., Bolzano, Italy; *Int'l*, pg. 1092
Obletz, Kenneth, V.P. & Gen. Mgr.--Lindenmeyr Munroe, Melville, NY; *U.S. Private*, pg. 224
Obokata, H., Pres.--Cosmo Oil of U.S.A. Inc., New York, NY; *Int'l*, pg. 335
Obregon, Rafael, Mng. Dir.--Kellogg de Mexico S.A. de C.V., Queretaro, Mexico; *U.S. Public*, pg. 948
Obreiter, William, Vice Pres.--Chicopee Inc., Dayton, NJ; *Int'l*, pg. 113
Obrer, M. Estaban, Chief Oper. Officer--Agrolaser S.A., Madrid, Spain; *Int'l*, pg. 1289
Ocampo, Oscar L., Pres.--Gulf Asia International Corporation, Manila, Philippines; *Int'l*, pg. 426
Occhipinti, Umberto, Chm. Bd. & Mng. Dir.--Assiprogetti S.p.A., Milan, Italy; *Int'l*, pg. 138
Ochiltree, Stuart A., Pres. & Chief Exec. Officer, Direct Sls. Grp.--Avon Products, Inc., New York, NY; *U.S. Public*, pg. 156
Ochinski, Walt, Mgr.--Glasteel Tennessee, Inc., Collierville, TN; *U.S. Private*, pg. 45
Ochs, Charlie, V.P. & Gen. Mgr.--WMZQ-AM/FM, Washington, DC; *U.S. Private*, pg. 779
Ochs, Ronald K., Chm. Bd. & Chief Exec. Officer--M & I Bank of Janesville, Janesville, WI; *U.S. Public*, pg. 1050
Ochsendorf, Udo, Plant Mgr.--Bundy Systemwerk, Gifhorn, Germany; *Int'l*, pg. 1342
Ochtrup, Robert, V.P.--Chicago Tube & Iron Company of Minnesota, Saint Paul, MN; *U.S. Private*, pg. 235
Ocrant, Andrew M., Mng. Dir.--Sheldon Good & Company Auctions NE, New York, NY; *U.S. Private*, pg. 464
Ocskay, A., Chief Oper. Officer--SAIA AG, Murten, Switzerland; *Int'l*, pg. 1500
Ocskay, A.Z., Mgr.--Burgess-SAIA Hong Kong Limited, Chai Wan, Hong Kong; *Int'l*, pg. 1500
Ocskay, Andreas, Dir.--ABB Maschinenfabrik Meyer AG, Deitingen, Switzerland; *Int'l*, pg. 1
Oda, Hajime, Gen. Mgr.--The Bank of Tokyo-Mitsubishi, Ltd. (Los Angeles Branch), Los Angeles, CA; *Int'l*, pg. 157
Oda, Kanji, Exec. V.P.--Toshiba America Consumer Products Manufacturing Div., Lebanon, TN; *Int'l*, pg. 1405
Oda, Yasuyuki, Chief Exec.--KONE Japan Co. Ltd., Tokyo, Japan; *Int'l*, pg. 747
Odawara, Yoshiki, Pres.--Fuji Bank (Schweiz) AG, Zurich, Switzerland; *Int'l*, pg. 521
Oddaker, Oddbjorn, Pres.--J.L. Tiedemanns Tobaksfabrik, Oslo, Norway; *Int'l*, pg. 1390
Odden, Eddy, Mng. Dir.--Leo Burnett/Connaghan & May (QLD.) Pty. Ltd., Milton, Australia; *U.S. Private*, pg. 185
Odeen, Phillip, Pres. & Chief Exec. Officer--BDM International, Inc., Mc Lean, VA; *U.S. Public*, pg. 1558
Odeishi, Tsunehiro, Mng. Dir.--Cascade (Japan) Ltd., Osaka, Japan; *U.S. Public*, pg. 311
Odell, Peter J., Mng. Dir.--Cherry Electrical Products, Ltd., Harpenden, United Kingdom; *U.S. Public*, pg. 346
Odenmark, Nils-Erik, Pres.--Dynapac Heavy Equipment AB, Karlskrona, Sweden; *Int'l*, pg. 1420
Odenram, Gunnar, Chief Oper. Officer--Progress-Elektrogerate Mauz & Pfeiffer GmbH & Co., Nurtingen, Germany; *Int'l*, pg. 442
Odermatt, Ernst, Chief Exec. Officer--Oerlikon-Contraves AG, Zurich, Switzerland; *Int'l*, pg. 998
Odet, Jean Francois, Chief Oper. Officer--France St.-Yorre, Saint Yorre, France; *Int'l*, pg. 919
Odgers, E.T., Mng. Dir.--Amalgamated Beverage Industries, Wendywood, South Africa; *Int'l*, pg. 1286
Odienne, Roger, Chm. Bd.--Societe Anonyme Mediterraneene de Salaisons, Biot, France; *U.S. Public*, pg. 429
Odio, Carlos E., Pres.--Gumaco Industria E Comercio Ltda., Sao Paulo, Brazil; *U.S. Public*, pg. 705
Odiotti, Massie, V.P. & Gen. Mgr.--Sun Chemical General Printing Inc., Northlake, IL; *Int'l*, pg. 370
Odom, F.A., Pres. & Chief Exec. Officer--United States National Bank, Galveston, TX; *U.S. Public*, pg. 467
Odom, Howard, Pres. & Chief Exec. Officer--Ortronics, Inc., Pawcatuck, CT; *Int'l*, pg. 806
Odom, William E., Chm. Bd.--The American Road Insurance Company, Dearborn, MI; *U.S. Public*, pg. 664
Odsberg, Hans, Mng. Dir.--Ovako Couplings AB, Hofors, Sweden; *Int'l*, pg. 1157
Odum, John, Pres.--Six Flags St. Louis, Eureka, MO; *U.S. Public*, pg. 1612
Odum, Kathleen O'Neil, Pres.--GTE Northwest Incorporated, Irving, TX; *U.S. Public*, pg. 697
Oe, Seiichi, Chief Rep.--Dai-Ichi Kangyo Bank, Ltd.-Bahrain, Manama, Bahrain; *Int'l*, pg. 361
Oean, Kirk, Pres.--Norwest Bank Minnesota Southwest, N.A., Marshall, MN; *U.S. Public*, pg. 1202
Oehrlein, F.R., V.P. & Gen. Mgr.-S.E. Asia Opers.--McDermott Southeast Asia Pty. Ltd., Singapore, Singapore; *U.S. Public*, pg. 1068
Oellrich, Ganto, Chief Oper. Officer--Advanced Micro Devices GmbH, Stuttgart, Germany; *U.S. Public*, pg. 21
Oelrich, H., Chief Oper. Officer--Volkswagen Intl. Finance N.V., Amsterdam, Netherlands; *Int'l*, pg. 1475
Oelze, J. Phillip, Mgr.-Branch--Piper Jaffray Inc., Scottsdale, AZ; *U.S. Public*, pg. 1301
Oertley, Karen, Publisher--Amusement Business, Nashville, TN; *Int'l*, pg. 1446
Oeschsle, Walter, Pres.--Oechsle International Advisors L.P., Boston, MA; *Int'l*, pg. 418
Oesorisa, Roberto, Gen. Mgr.--Perretti, New York, NY; *U.S. Public*, pg. 130
Oess, George, Pres.--Cadaco, Chicago, IL; *U.S. Private*, pg. 910
Oestlien, Bredo, Pres.-Seagram Asia Pacific/Global Duty Free Div.--Joseph E. Seagram & Sons, Inc., New York, NY; *Int'l*, pg. 1215
Oestlund, Hans, Mng. Dir.--A.C. Nielsen Company AB, Malmo, Sweden; *U.S. Public*, pg. 1183
Oeter, Heinz, Mng. Dir.--Krupp Stahlbau Berlin GmbH & Co. KG, Berlin, Germany; *Int'l*, pg. 508
Offen, Robert, Chief Exec. Officer--Mediapolis, London, United Kingdom; *Int'l*, pg. 853
Offeney, Rolf, Gen. Mgr.--Ernst Siegling GmbH & Co., Hannover, Germany; *Int'l*, pg. 497
Offergeld, Egon, Pres.--VITS Maschinenbau GmbH, Lagenfeld, Germany; *Int'l*, pg. 399
Offor, Ian, Chief Exec. Officer--Royal Scottish Assurance plc, Edinburgh, United Kingdom; *Int'l*, pg. 1132
Offord, Matthew, Gen. Mgr.--Bose Australia, Parramatta, Australia; *U.S. Private*, pg. 161
Offringa, C., Mng. Dir.--Combined Terminals Amsterdam V.O.F., Amsterdam, Netherlands; *Int'l*, pg. 1144
Offutt, Carl, V.P.--Whirlpool Corp., Evansville Div., Evansville, IN; *U.S. Public*, pg. 1765
Ofuku, Mamoru, Pres.--International Learning Systems (Japan) Ltd., Tokyo, Japan; *U.S. Public*, pg. 222
Ofverberg, Mats, Pres.--Aydin Corporation West, San Jose, CA; *U.S. Public*, pg. 158
Ofverholm, Ivan, Chief Oper. Officer--Saab Space AB, Goteborg, Sweden; *Int'l*, pg. 687
Ogando, Ray, Plant Mgr.--Setco, Inc. Cranbury Plant, Cranbury, NJ; *U.S. Public*, pg. 1067
Ogard, Bjorn, Bus. Area Mgr.--Euroc Trade AB, Malmo, Sweden; *Int'l*, pg. 1199
Ogasawara, Toshiaki, Chm. Bd. & Pres.--Simmons Co. Ltd., Zama, Japan; *Int'l*, pg. 929
Ogata, Keith, Pres., Chief Exec. Officer & Treas.--National Education Credit Corporation, Irvine, CA; *U.S. Public*, pg. 784
Ogawa, Harunobu, Mng. Dir.--NEC Hong Kong Limited, Kowloon, Hong Kong; *Int'l*, pg. 900
Ogawa, J., Chief Rep. Officer--The Kansai Electric Power Co. - New York Office, New York, NY; *Int'l*, pg. 723
Ogawa, K., Gen. Mgr.--Mitsui & Co. (U.S.A.), Inc., Lexington, KY; *Int'l*, pg. 879
Ogawa, Katsuro, Pres.--P.T. Lautan Otsuka Chemical, Jakarta, Indonesia; *Int'l*, pg. 1014
Ogawa, Ken, Dir.--Takenaka (U.S.A.) Corporation, San Francisco Office, San Francisco, CA; *Int'l*, pg. 1351
Ogawa, Kosaburo, Gen. Mgr.--SNK America, Inc., Elk Grove Village, IL; *Int'l*, pg. 1234
Ogawa, Masahira, Pres.--Heinz Japan Ltd., Tokyo, Japan; *U.S. Public*, pg. 806
Ogawa, Michitsugu, Gen. Mgr.--Ozeki Sake (U.S.A.) Inc., Hollister, CA; *Int'l*, pg. 1019
Ogawa, Seiichi, Mng. Dir.--Sanwa Australia Limited, Sydney, Australia; *Int'l*, pg. 1190
Ogawa, Tadahiko, Chm. Bd.--Tokai Financial Services, Inc., Berwyn, PA; *Int'l*, pg. 1391
Ogawa, Tetsuo, Gen. Mgr.--Nippon Credit Bank Ltd.-Hong Kong, Hong Kong, Hong Kong; *Int'l*, pg. 933
Ogawa, Yoshinori, Chief Rep.--Dai-Ichi Kangyo Bank, Ltd.-Melbourne, Melbourne, Australia; *Int'l*, pg. 361
Ogawa, Yoshinori, Chief Rep.--Dai-Ichi Kangyo Bank, Ltd.-Sydney, Sydney, Australia; *Int'l*, pg. 361
Ogawara, Akihiro, Pres.--Earth Environmental Sanitary Service Co., Ltd., Osaka, Japan; *Int'l*, pg. 1013
Ogawara, Tai, Exec. Dir.--Dentsu Young & Rubicam Inc. (Tokyo), Tokyo, Japan; *U.S. Private*, pg. 325
Ogden, Bill, Mgr.-Bus. Devel.--Dun & Bradstreet Do Brasil Ltda, Sao Paulo, Brazil; *U.S. Public*, pg. 536
Ogden, John C., Pres. & Chief Exec. Officer--Suncor Development Company, Phoenix, AZ; *U.S. Public*, pg. 1298
Ogden, Roger, Pres. & Gen. Mgr.-KCNC-TV--National Broadcasting Co., Inc., New York, NY; *U.S. Public*, pg. 712
Oggel, L.A., Chief Oper. Officer--Makro International AG, Chur, Switzerland; *Int'l*, pg. 1155
Ogier, Michael O., Pres. & Chief Exec. Officer--Pioneer Concrete of America, Houston, TX; *Int'l*, pg. 1058
Ogihara, Shinpei, Chief Oper. Officer--Oki Electronics (Singapore) Pte Ltd., Singapore, Singapore; *Int'l*, pg. 1000
Ogilvie, Gael, Mgr.-Opers.--Woodward-Clyde International, North Point, Hong Kong; *U.S. Public*, pg. 1658
Ogilvie, James A., Pres. & Chief Exec. Officer--M & I Bank, Ashland, WI; *U.S. Public*, pg. 1050
Ogilvie, R. M., Pres.--Toromont CAT, Concord, Canada; *Int'l*, pg. 1400
Ogino, Hitoshi, Pres.--Toshiba Medical do Brasil Ltda., Vila Olimpia, Brazil; *Int'l*, pg. 1407
Ogino, Kent, Pres.--California Woodfiber Corp., West Sacramento, CA; *Int'l*, pg. 845
Oglesby, George Thomas, Jr., V.P.--Keystone & Childs, Inc., Elberton, GA; *U.S. Public*, pg. 1396
Oglesby, George Thomas, Jr., V.P.--C & K Tracking, Inc., Elberton, GA; *U.S. Public*, pg. 1396
Oglesby, W., Mng Dir.--Enraf Inc., Houston, TX; *Int'l*, pg. 389
Ogolw, Jmhor J., Chief Oper. Officer--Mediterranean Fertilizer Industries Company, Ankara, Turkey; *Int'l*, pg. 766
Ogram, David, Gen. Mgr.--AMS Management Systems UK Ltd, London, United Kingdom; *U.S. Public*, pg. 87
Ogris, K., Pres.--Thunder Bay Terminals Ltd., Thunder Bay, Canada; *Int'l*, pg. 1150
Ogrizek, Michel, Pres.-Europe--Edelman-Rouet France, Paris, France; *U.S. Private*, pg. 363
Ogura, Izumi, Gen. Mgr.--Dresdner Bank AG, Tokyo, Japan; *Int'l*, pg. 419
Ogura, J., Chief Oper. Officer--Furukawa Electric Co., Ltd. London, London, United Kingdom; *Int'l*, pg. 530

Oguz, Turgut, Gen. Mgr.--I-Bimsa Uluslararasi Is Bilgi Veyonetim Sistemleri A.S., Istanbul, Turkey; *U.S. Public*, pg. 898

Oguz, Turgut, Gen. Mgr.--I-Bimsa Uluslararasi Is Bilgi Veyonetim Sistemleri A.S., Istanbul, Turkey; *Int'l*, pg. 1167

Oh Kwon, Dong, Representative--West Company of Korea Limited, Seoul, Korea; *U.S. Public*, pg. 1756

Oh, Dong-Hwee, Pres.--Ssangyong Research Institute, Seoul, Korea; *Int'l*, pg. 1292

Oh, Kum-je, Chief Rep.--The Export-Import Bank of Korea, Santiago, Chile; *Int'l*, pg. 467

Ohama, Fumio, Pres.--Unitika America Corp., New York, NY; *Int'l*, pg. 1444

Ohara, Mark, Admin.--Indian Meadows Nursing Center, Overland Park, KS; *U.S. Public*, pg. 837

Ohashi, Hitoshi, Pres.--Toshiba America Consumer Products, Inc., Wayne, NJ; *Int'l*, pg. 1405

Ohashi, M., Pres.--ITW Dynatec KK, Tokyo, Japan; *U.S. Public*, pg. 868

Ohayon, G., Mng. Dir.--Pathe Marconi EMI SA, Boulogne-Billancourt, France; *Int'l*, pg. 427

Ohazama, Takashi, Mng. Dir.--Mitsui Trust Finance (Hong Kong) Ltd., Central, Hong Kong; *Int'l*, pg. 883

Ohgawara, T., Mng. Dir.--Sharp Electronics (Thailand) Ltd., Kaohsiung, Thailand; *Int'l*, pg. 1230

Ohgusu, Hironobu, Pres.--Cognex K.K., Tokyo, Japan; *U.S. Public*, pg. 394

Ohinouye, Tsuneo, Chm. & Chief Exec. Officer--Diamond Star Motors, Normal, IL; *Int'l*, pg. 875

Ohiwa, Toshiaki, Pres.--Falconbridge (Japan) Ltd., Tokyo, Japan; *Int'l*, pg. 434

Ohki, Satoru, Vice Chm. & Dir.--Leasing Andino S.A., Santiago, Chile; *Int'l*, pg. 1009

Ohkubo, K., Chief Oper. Officer--Riken Electric Wire Co., Ltd., Tokyo, Japan; *Int'l*, pg. 530

Ohlhues, Robert D., Pres. & Chief Oper. Officer--Associated Commercial Mortgage, Inc., Green Bay, WI; *U.S. Public*, pg. 140

Ohling, Jannes C., Mng. Dir. & V.P.--GATX Financial Services GmbH, Frankfurt/Main, Germany; *U.S. Public*, pg. 691

Ohls, Bengt, Chief Oper. Officer--Oy Electrolux Ab, Helsinki, Finland; *Int'l*, pg. 441

Ohlson, Johnny, Mng. Dir.--Griffin Bacal Ltd., London, United Kingdom; *U.S. Private*, pg. 480

Ohlson, Karl Olof, Pres.--Stora Financial Services, Stockholm, Sweden; *Int'l*, pg. 1303

Ohlson, L., Mng. Dir.--Oki Systems (Sweden) AB, Spangenas, Sweden; *Int'l*, pg. 1000

Ohlsson, Bjorn W., Gen. Mgr.--ESAB Representative Office, Beijing, China; *Int'l*, pg. 282

Ohlsson, Kenneth, Chm. Reg. Bd.--ICA Handlarna Vast AB, Kungalv, Sweden; *Int'l*, pg. 643

Ohlsson, Kenth, Mng. Dir.--Sodra Skogagarna, Vaxjo, Sweden; *Int'l*, pg. 1275

Ohlsson, Magnus, Mng. Dir.--Handelsbanken Liv, Stockholm, Sweden; *Int'l*, pg. 1327

Ohm, John, V.P.-Opers.--Kankakee, IL Steel Division, Bourbonnais, IL; *U.S. Public*, pg. 232

Ohmae, S., Chief Oper. Officer--Bangkok Telecom Co., Ltd. (BTC), Bangkok, Thailand; *Int'l*, pg. 531

Ohman, Kyle, Gen. Mgr.--Atlanta Auto Auction, Inc., Red Oak, GA; *U.S. Private*, pg. 282

Ohman, Kyle, Gen. Mgr.--Colorado Auction Services Corporation, Commerce City, CO; *U.S. Private*, pg. 282

Ohmura, Nobuaki, Pres. & Chief Oper. Officer--Daiwa Securities America Inc., New York, NY; *Int'l*, pg. 375

Ohmura, Nobuaki, Gen. Mgr.--Daiwa Securities America Inc.-Chicago, Chicago, IL; *Int'l*, pg. 375

Ohmura, Nobuaki, Pres.--Daiwa Securities Canada Limited, Toronto, Canada; *Int'l*, pg. 376

Ohnesorge, Joachim, Chief Oper. Officer--Schering Espana S. A., Madrid, Spain; *Int'l*, pg. 1204

Ohnishi, Kenichi, Pres.--Nissho Iwai Korea Corporation, Seoul, Korea; *Int'l*, pg. 948

Ohnishi, Osamu, Gen. Mgr.--Nippon Credit Bank Ltd.-Singapore, Singapore, Singapore; *Int'l*, pg. 933

Ohno, Kaname, Pres.--Okabe Company, Inc., Vernon Hills, IL; *Int'l*, pg. 999

Ohno, Mitsumasa, Gen. Mgr.--Moog Japan Ltd., Hiratsuka, Japan; *U.S. Public*, pg. 1128

Ohno, Mitsumasa, Gen. Mgr.--Moog Korea, Kyonggi-do, Korea; *U.S. Public*, pg. 1128

Ohnuki, Toru, V.P. & Gen. Mgr.--Japan International Enterprises, Inc., Tokyo, Japan; *Int'l*, pg. 1282

Ohnuki, Yoshiaki, Chm.--Mitsui & Co. International (Europe) B.V., Amsterdam, Netherlands; *Int'l*, pg. 880

Ohta, Hitoshi, Gen. Mgr.--Wakayama Branch Office, Wakayama, Japan; *Int'l*, pg. 1491

Ohta, N., Gen. Mgr.--Asahi Optical (International) Ltd., Tsuen Wan, Hong Kong; *Int'l*, pg. 85

Ohta, Nobuoki, Dir.--Sony Engineering & Manufacturing of America, San Diego, CA; *Int'l*, pg. 1284

Ohta, T., Mgr.--Kodak Japan Ltd.-Technical Center, Yokohama, Japan; *U.S. Public*, pg. 552

Ohtagaki, Itaru, Chief Oper. Officer--Disco Hi-Tec (Singapore) Pte, Ltd., Singapore, Singapore; *Int'l*, pg. 413

Ohtani, Masamichi, Chief Investment Officer--Chase Trust Bank, Tokyo, Japan; *U.S. Public*, pg. 341

Ohtani, Yukio, Chief Exec. Officer & Mng. Dir.--Japan Airlines American Region, New York, NY; *Int'l*, pg. 700

Ohtsuka, T., Mng. Dir.--OMRON Electronics Hong Kong, Ltd., Kowloon, Hong Kong; *Int'l*, pg. 1006

Ohuchi, H., Mng. Dir.--Sharp Electronics (Singapore) Pte. Ltd., Singapore, Singapore; *Int'l*, pg. 1230

Ohwada, Takeshi, Pres.--TDK Corporation of America, Mount Prospect, IL; *Int'l*, pg. 1336

Ohyama, Rei, Chm. Bd.--Taiyo Life Realty of America, Inc., New York, NY; *Int'l*, pg. 1349

Ohyama, Rei, Chm. Bd.--Taiyo Life International (U.K.), Ltd., London, United Kingdom; *Int'l*, pg. 1349

Ohyama, Rei, Chm. Bd.--Taiyo Life International (H.K.), Ltd., Central, Hong Kong; *Int'l*, pg. 1349

Oike, Osamu, Pres.--DKB Financial Products (Hong Kong) Limited, Central, Hong Kong; *Int'l*, pg. 361

Oischinger, Karl H., Intl. Mgr.--AMETEK G.m.b.H., Wiesbaden, Germany; *U.S. Public*, pg. 100

Ojala, Harri, Div. Mgr.--Montgomery Elevator Controls Division, Commerce, TX; *Int'l*, pg. 746

Ojala, Harri, Div. Mgr.--Montgomery Elevator Division, Mc Kinney, TX; *Int'l*, pg. 746

Ojala, Harri, Chief Oper. Officer--KONE Aufzugwerke, Hannover, Germany; *Int'l*, pg. 747

Ojala, Risto, Mng. Dir.--Kemira Pigments B.V., Rozenburg, Netherlands; *Int'l*, pg. 729

Ojanen, Asko, Pres.--Outokumpu Base Metals Oy, Espoo, Finland; *Int'l*, pg. 1016

Ojanpaa, Paave, Pres.--Schauman Wood Oy, Lahti, Finland; *Int'l*, pg. 1430

Ojefors, Lars, Chief Oper. Officer--AxTrade Scandinavia AB, Stockholm, Sweden; *Int'l*, pg. 708

Ojima, Sakae, Branch Mgr.--Dayton Progress of Japan, Tokyo, Japan; *U.S. Public*, pg. 617

Ojiro, T., Gen. Mgr.--ITW Industry Co., Ltd., Tokyo, Japan; *U.S. Public*, pg. 868

Oka, Koji, Pres.--Nomura Tourist Bureau, Inc., Tokyo, Japan; *Int'l*, pg. 956

Okabe, Kunihiko, Gen. Mgr.--Dai-Ichi Kangyo Bank, Ltd.-Shanghai, Shanghai, China; *Int'l*, pg. 361

Okada, Katsuposhi, Gen. Mgr.--Takashimaya New York, Inc., New York, NY; *Int'l*, pg. 1350

Okada, Kazuhiro, Pres.--P.T. Asian Development Securities, Jakarta, Indonesia; *Int'l*, pg. 1517

Okada, Kimikatsu, Mng. Dir.--Hakuhodo Inc., Sendai, Japan; *Int'l*, pg. 587

Okada, Mark, Terminal Mgr.--Kintetsu World Express Inc., Mississauga, Canada; *Int'l*, pg. 735

Okada, Motoi, Mng. Dir.--Universal (U.K.) Limited, London, United Kingdom; *Int'l*, pg. 1444

Okada, Ryozo, Advisor--Commerce International Merchant Bankers Berhad, Kuala Lumpur, Malaysia; *Int'l*, pg. 1190

Okada, S., Chm. Bd.--Mitsubishi Foods (MC), Inc., San Diego, CA; *Int'l*, pg. 872

Okada, Takeshi, Chief Oper. Officer, Dir.-Sls.--Takagi Chokoku Co., Ltd.-Hamamatsu Factory, Hamamatsu, Japan; *Int'l*, pg. 1349

Okada, Takuya, Chm. Bd. & Chief Exec. Officer--JUSCO Co., Ltd., Chiba, Japan; *Int'l*, pg. 28

Okado, Hiroshi, Pres.--P.T. Komatsu Indonesia Tbk, Jakarta, Indonesia; *Int'l*, pg. 744

Okagaki, Sam, Pres. & Chief Exec. Officer--Amano Cincinnati, Inc., Roseland, NJ; *Int'l*, pg. 70

Okagawa, Hideki, Pres.--Shanghai Yin Tong Trust Co., Ltd., Shanghai, China; *Int'l*, pg. 1010

Okamoto, Hiroshi, Chief Oper. Officer--Makita (Australia) Pty. Ltd., Sydney, Australia; *Int'l*, pg. 831

Okamoto, Isao, Mng. Dir.--NEC Australia Pty. Ltd., Glen Waverley, Australia; *Int'l*, pg. 901

Okamoto, Kazuhiko, Mng. Dir.--Bang & Olufsen of Japan Ltd., Tokyo, Japan; *Int'l*, pg. 146

Okamoto, Masahiro, Pres.--Asatsu Europe B.V., Hoofddorp, Netherlands; *Int'l*, pg. 86

Okamoto, Shiyo, Chief Oper. Officer--Nippon Oil Exploration U.K. Limited, London, United Kingdom; *Int'l*, pg. 937

Okamoto, Y., Gen. Mgr.--Signode Kabushiki Kaisha, Kobe, Japan; *U.S. Public*, pg. 869

Okane, James, Admin.--Nutmeg Pavilion Healthcare, New London, CT; *U.S. Public*, pg. 1714

Okano, Jun, Chief Exec. Officer & Mng. Dir.--Nikko Europe Plc, London, United Kingdom; *Int'l*, pg. 930

Okano, Yoshiaki, Pres. Dir.--P.T. Daiwa Perdania Bank, Jakarta, Indonesia; *Int'l*, pg. 374

Okawa, Shuji, Pres.--Hakuhodo U.K. Ltd., London, United Kingdom; *Int'l*, pg. 588

Okawara, Taisuke, Gen. Mgr.--Letraset Japan Ltd., Tokyo, Japan; *Int'l*, pg. 462

Okayama, Morio, Pres.--Sumitomo Life America, Inc., New York, NY; *Int'l*, pg. 1315

Okazaki, Hyoichi, Chief Oper. Officer--Japan Cargo Co., Ltd., Matsuyama, Japan; *Int'l*, pg. 1262

Oken, Brian, Pres.--Holga Inc., Van Nuys, CA; *U.S. Public*, pg. 772

Oki, Katsutoshi, Sr. V.P. & Gen. Mgr.--Los Angeles Branch Office, Los Angeles, CA; *Int'l*, pg. 935

Oki, Susumu, Gen. Mgr.--The Bank of Tokyo-Mitsubishi, Ltd. (Seoul Central Branch), Seoul, Korea; *Int'l*, pg. 158

Okimoto, Takashi, Gen. Mgr.--The Sakura Bank - Brussels Branch, Brussels, Belgium; *Int'l*, pg. 1179

Okochi, Hiroshi, Mgr.--Ampex Japan Limited, Tokyo, Japan; *U.S. Public*, pg. 104

Okon, Theodore A., Pres.--Medical Marketing Group, Inc., Southport, CT; *U.S. Public*, pg. 1091

Okonkwo, Chief G.C., Mng. Dir.--Savannah Bank of Nigeria Ltd., Lagos, Nigeria; *U.S. Public*, pg. 183

Okresek, Willi, Chief Oper. Officer--Bran & Luebbe G.m.b.H., Salzburg, Austria; *Int'l*, pg. 1379

Oksanen, Jouni, Mng. Dir.--K-Maatalousyhtiot Oy, Vantaa, Finland; *Int'l*, pg. 732

Okubo, H., Gen. Mgr.--Shoko Chukin Bank, New York, NY; *Int'l*, pg. 1236

Okubo, Tadashi, Gen. Mgr.--Nichifu America, Inc., Elk Grove Village, IL; *Int'l*, pg. 927

Okuda, Isao, Chief Exec.--Asahi Facility Management Inc., Tokyo, Japan; *Int'l*, pg. 1351

Okuda, K., Pres.--Sharp International Finance (U.K.) PLC., Watford, United Kingdom; *Int'l*, pg. 1230

Okuda, Keiichiro, Gen. Mgr.--The Industrial Bank of Japan Limited (Zurich), Zurich, Switzerland; *Int'l*, pg. 675

Okuda, Minoru, Pres.--Otsuka Ohmi Ceramics Co., Ltd., Osaka, Japan; *Int'l*, pg. 1013

Okuda, Takehiko, Pres.--Wuxi Okuda Garment Co. Ltd., Wuxi, China; *Int'l*, pg. 579

Okuda, Y., Pres.--AP Techno Glass Company, Elizabethtown, KY; *Int'l*, pg. 84

Okudaira, Takamochi, Pres.--Tokai Credit Corporation, Pasadena, CA; *Int'l*, pg. 1391

Okuma, Syuzo, Chief Oper. Officer--Taiwan Nisseki Co., Ltd., Kao-hsiung, Taiwan; *Int'l*, pg. 937

Okumura, Ariyoshi, Pres. & Chief Exec. Officer--IBJ NW Asset Management Co., Ltd., Tokyo, Japan; *Int'l*, pg. 1485

Okumura, Masaya, Pres.--Toshiba International Corporation, Utility Division, San Francisco, CA; *Int'l*, pg. 1405

Okuno, Kazuo, Mng. Dir.--NEC Semiconductors (Malaysia) Sdn. Berhad, Kuala Langat, Malaysia; *Int'l*, pg. 900

Okuto, Taku, Mng. Dir.--NEC (UK) Ltd., London, United Kingdom; *Int'l*, pg. 901

Okuzawa, Yasufumi, Mgr.--Settsu USA, San Francisco, CA; *Int'l*, pg. 1225

Oland, Thomas E., Chm. Bd.--R&D Systems Inc., Minneapolis, MN; *U.S. Public*, pg. 1564

Olankun, Sitthichai, Mng. Dir.--Astra (Thai) Ltd., Bangkok, Thailand; *Int'l*, pg. 94

Olave, Jose Ignacio, Gen. Mgr.--Rodamientos USA SA, Bilbao, Spain; *Int'l*, pg. 212

Olave, Roberto, Pres. & Gen. Mgr.--Baccardi-Martini Uruguay S.A., Montevideo, Uruguay; *U.S. Private*, pg. 109

Olbers, Klaus, Pres.--Intervet America, Inc., Millsboro, DE; *Int'l*, pg. 48

Olbert, Kurt, Rep.--Bayerische Landesbank Girozentrale, Prague, Czech Republic; *Int'l*, pg. 177

Olbrich, F., Chief Exec. Officer--Ziegelwerke Gleinstatten GmbH & Co. KG, Gleinstatten, Austria; *Int'l*, pg. 1092

Oldenburg, Wayne C., Owner--Lake Shore, Inc., Kingsford, MI; *U.S. Private*, pg. 814

Olderheim, Vegard, Plant Mgr.--Elkem Mangan Sauda, Sauda, Norway; *Int'l*, pg. 447

Oldham, Frank, Mng. Dir.--CD Products (UK) Ltd., London, United Kingdom; *U.S. Public*, pg. 276

Oldham, Laurance W., Sr. V.P.-Oper. & Marketing--Southern Hospitality Corporation, Nashville, TN; *U.S. Public*, pg. 488

Oldsey, William, Pres.--Prentice Hall Business Publishing, Upper Saddle River, NJ; *U.S. Private*, pg. 778

Olen, Carl, Gen. Mgr.--Capstone Electronics Div., Itasca, IL; *U.S. Public*, pg. 134

Oler, R. Wayne, Chief Oper. Officer--Addison-Wesley Higher Education, Reading, MA; *Int'l*, pg. 1026

Oles, David, Pres.--NC Builders Inc., Wilmington, DE; *U.S. Private*, pg. 775

Oletti, Mark, V.P. & Gen. Mgr.--Keystone Fasteners, Springdale, AR; *U.S. Public*, pg. 956

Olevson, Ken, Gen. Mgr.--Sermatech Klock, Manchester, CT; *U.S. Public*, pg. 1570

Olffers, Harmut, Mgr.--Southern Branch, Eutingen im Gau, Germany; *Int'l*, pg. 401

Olgac, Kemal, Gen. Mgr.--Sark Hayat Sigorta T.A.S, Istanbul, Turkey; *Int'l*, pg. 61

Olgesby, W., Dir.--Enraf-Nonius Tank Inventory Systems Inc., Stafford, TX; *Int'l*, pg. 389

Olguin, Jose, Mgr.-Regional--Alimak Elevator Company, Webster, TX; *U.S. Private*, pg. 34

Olholm, Svend, Mng. Dir.--GN Ejendomme, Copenhagen, Denmark; *Int'l*, pg. 537

Oliana, P.L., Pres.--Orion SpA., Colfosco di Susegana, Italy; *Int'l*, pg. 1432

Oliel, Claude, Pres.--Colorado, Boulogne, France; *Int'l*, pg. 601

Olieman, F.J., Mng. Dir.--CSM Suiker BV, Diemen, Netherlands; *Int'l*, pg. 243

Oligny, Vance, Chief Oper. Officer--Caddock Network Division, Riverside, CA; *U.S. Private*, pg. 198

Oligny, Vance, Chief Oper. Officer--Resistor Division, Riverside, CA; *U.S. Private*, pg. 198

Olin, John, V.P. & Gen. Mgr.--Banta Direct Marketing Group, Chanhassen, MN; *U.S. Public*, pg. 188

Olin, Kent O., Pres.--Affiliated First Colorado Lease Company, Denver, CO; *U.S. Public*, pg. 173

Oliva, Carlos, Gen. Mgr.--Whitehall Laboratories, Guaynabo, PR; *U.S. Public*, pg. 81

Oliva, Jean-Pierre, Pres.--Nordlys SA, Bailleul, France; *Int'l*, pg. 415

Oliveira, Jose N., Reg. Mgr.--Det Norske Veritas Portugal, Lda., Lisbon, Portugal; *Int'l*, pg. 398

Oliver, Aloysius J., Pres. & Treas.--CFC Data Corp., Midland, MI; *U.S. Public*, pg. 345

Oliver, David R., Pres.--F-P Electronics, Mississauga, Canada; *U.S. Public*, pg. 1045

Oliver, E. Victor, Pres.--SHL Computer Innovations, Brampton, Canada; *Int'l*, pg. 1154

Oliver, Gene, Pres. & Chief Exec. Officer--SouthTrust Bank, West Florida, Saint Petersburg, FL; *U.S. Public*, pg. 1492

Oliver, James E., Chief Oper. Officer--Wheat First Butcher Singer, Inc., Richmond, VA; *U.S. Public*, pg. 640

Oliver, Jr., John T., Chm. Bd.--First National Bank, Jasper, AL; *U.S. Public*, pg. 1549

Oliver, Juan Tesoro, Pres.--AHM ALTOS HORNOS DEL MEDITERRANEO, S.A., Sagunto, Spain; *Int'l*, pg. 1223

Oliver, L.S., Mng. Dir.--Whitbread Pub Partnerships, Luton, United Kingdom; *Int'l*, pg. 1498

Oliver, Marilynn, Pres. & Chief Oper. Officer--Countrywide Agency, Inc., Pasadena, CA; *U.S. Public*, pg. 452

Oliver, Michael J., Mgr.--Commerzbank AG (East Asia) Ltd., Hong Kong, Hong Kong; *Int'l*, pg. 311

Oliver, Paul, Pres.--Grand Metropolitan Foodservice Inc., Minneapolis, MN; *Int'l*, pg. 408

Oliver, Robert, Sec.--Datascope Medical Co., Ltd., Cambridge, United Kingdom; *U.S. Public*, pg. 488

Oliver, Robert, Mng. Dir.--Datascope SARL, Creteil, France; *U.S. Public*, pg. 488

Oliver, Robert W., Pres.--Tesoro Exploration & Production Co., San Antonio, TX; *U.S. Public*, pg. 1582

Oliveras, R.P., Chm. Bd.--Lucas Automotive SA, Spain, Barcelona, Spain; *Int'l*, pg. 820

Oliveras, Ramon Pinto, Pres.--CESA - Compania Espanola de Sistemas Aeronauticos, S.A., Getafe, Spain; *Int'l*, pg. 1224

Oliveres, Michel, Pres.--Dumez-Jaya Sdn Bhd, Kuala Lumpur, Malaysia; *Int'l*, pg. 823
Olivieri, Ian, Pres.--NS Komatsu Pty., Ltd., Fairfield, Australia; *Int'l*, pg. 745
Olivieri, Peter, Pres.--Olivieri Foods, Vancouver, Canada; *Int'l*, pg. 841
Olk, Hans, Chief Exec. Officer--Harpen Transport AG, Duisburg, Germany; *Int'l*, pg. 597
Ollari, Frank J., Pres.--NYLIFE Funding Inc., Wilmington, DE; *U.S. Private*, pg. 795
Olle, Antonio, Gen. Mgr.--BBL Sucursal de Barcelona, Barcelona, Spain; *Int'l*, pg. 148
Ollen, Richard A., Pres.--GEICO Investment Services Co., Washington, DC; *U.S. Public*, pg. 220
Oller, C.R., Gen. Mgr.--A.C. Nielsen (Argentina) S.A., Buenos Aires, Argentina; *U.S. Public*, pg. 1183
Oller, Lynn, Gen. Mgr.--Hiland Dairy Company, Springfield, MO; *U.S. Private*, pg. 879
Ollivier-Lamarque, Florence, Mng. Dir.--Flik Flak, Itingen, Switzerland; *Int'l*, pg. 1160
Ollivier-Lamarque, Florence, Mng. Dir.--SMH Belgium SA, Brussels, Belgium; *Int'l*, pg. 1161
Ollus, Yngve, Mng. Dir.--Oy LM Ericsson Ab, Jorvas, Finland; *Int'l*, pg. 1368
Olmos, Harold, Chief of Bureau--The Associated Press de Venezuela, S.A., Caracas, Venezuela; *U.S. Private*, pg. 92
Olofsson, Bengt, Pres.--NCC Sundsvall, Sundsvall, Sweden; *Int'l*, pg. 899
Olofsson, Gunnar, Pres.--Strabruken AB, Sollentuna, Sweden; *Int'l*, pg. 899
Olsea, Lawrence T., Pres.--Cowles Syndicate, Inc., New York, NY; *U.S. Private*, pg. 518
Olsen, Arne-Erik, Pres.--Brodrene Dahl A/S, Oslo, Norway; *Int'l*, pg. 359
Olsen, Arthur L., Pres.--Polk City Directory Div., Detroit, MI; *U.S. Private*, pg. 874
Olsen, B., Dir.-B.O.M.--Brother International Maskinaktieselskab A/S, Ishoj, Denmark; *Int'l*, pg. 229
Olsen, Bruce, Pres.--AMCAN Specialty Steels, New Brunswick, NJ; *U.S. Public*, pg. 308
Olsen, C. Elwynn, Mgr.-Branch--Piper Jaffray Inc., Salt Lake City, UT; *U.S. Public*, pg. 1302
Olsen, Dan, Gen. Mgr.--Stanfast, Inc., Dayton, OH; *U.S. Public*, pg. 1505
Olsen, John, Chief Exec. Officer--Cunard Line Ltd., New York, NY; *Int'l*, pg. 773
Olsen, Kenneth, Chief Oper. Officer--Regency Thermographers of Mass., Inc., Boston, MA; *U.S. Public*, *pg. 89*
Olsen, Richard J., Pres.--Candela Skin Care Centers, Inc., Boston, MA; *U.S. Public*, pg. 300
Olsen, Terje, Mng. Dir.--Multiass Assicurazioni S.p.A., Milan, Italy; *Int'l*, pg. 1256
Olsen, Terje, Mng. Dir.--Uniass Assicurazioni S.p.A., Rome, Italy; *Int'l*, pg. 1256
Olsen, Torben, Pres.--MD Foods Deutschland GmbH, Dusseldorf, Germany; *Int'l*, pg. 826
Olson, Archie, Pres.--Juno, Inc., Plymouth, MN; *U.S. Private*, *pg. 290*
Olson, B.L., Pres.--Salem Furnace Co., Carnegie, PA; *U.S. Private*, pg. 961
Olson, B.L., Pres.--Salem Erectors, Carnegie, PA; *U.S. Private*, pg. 961
Olson, Barclay, Pres.--Greenlee Textron, Rockford, IL; *U.S. Public*, pg. 1589
Olson, Bruce J., Pres.--Marcus Theatres Corp., Milwaukee, WI; *U.S. Public*, pg. 1044
Olson, Dale E., Pres.--Citizens Insurance of Evansville, Evansville, IN; *U.S. Public*, pg. 280
Olson, Eric, Pres.--Brougher Agency, Inc., Indianapolis, IN; *Int'l*, pg. 464
Olson, Gary, Chm.--Norwest Bank South Dakota, N.A., Sioux Falls, SD; *U.S. Public*, pg. 1203
Olson, Gene, Gen. Mgr.--Arrow/Schweber Electronics, Lenexa, KS; *U.S. Public*, pg. 134
Olson, Gene, Gen. Mgr.--Arrow/Schweber Electronics, Saint Louis, MO; *U.S. Public*, pg. 134
Olson, Gregory J., V.P.--Bindley Western, Southeastern Division, Orlando, FL; *U.S. Public*, pg. 228
Olson, James, Plant Mgr.--Power Distribution Division, Milwaukee, WI; *U.S. Public*, pg. 557
Olson, Kurt, Client Services Dir.--SFM/Los Angeles, Los Angeles, CA; *U.S. Private*, pg. 957
Olson, Lennart, Pres.--Kockums Computer Systems AB, Malmo, Sweden; *Int'l*, pg. 277
Olson, Lon, Gen. Mgr.--Plastics Div., Sioux Falls, SD; *U.S. Public*, pg. 1361
Olson, Matt, Product Mgr.--Faultless Nutting, Watertown, SD; *Int'l*, pg. 473
Olson, Paul, Pres.--Commerce Services Group, Dublin, OH; *U.S. Public*, pg. 1516
Olson, Steven C., Pres.--Mercantile Bank of Washington County, N.A., Washington, IA; *U.S. Public*, pg. 1088
Olson, Thor, Pres.--Ziff Information Services, Medford, MA; *Int'l*, pg. 1276
Olson, Tom, Pres. & Chief Exec. Officer--Katz Media Group, Inc., New York, NY; *U.S. Public*, pg. 335
Olson, Torbjorn, Mng. Dir.--Kamyr Engineering AB, Karlstad, Sweden; *Int'l*, pg. 771
Olsson, Arne O., Gen. Mgr.--ITT Flygt N.V./S.A., Zaventem, Belgium; *U.S. Public*, pg. 860
Olsson, Bjoern, Mng. Dir.--DIAX Telekomm A/S, Struer, Denmark; *Int'l*, pg. 1365
Olsson, Bo, Pres.--Volvo Penta do Brasil-Industria Comercio de Motores Ltda., Rio de Janeiro, Brazil; *Int'l*, pg. 1477
Olsson, Carl-Axel, Gen. Mgr.--Handelsbanken Helsinki, Helsinki, Finland; *Int'l*, pg. 1327
Olsson, Carsten, Mgr.--Kemira Kemi AB, Helsingborg, Sweden; *Int'l*, pg. 728
Olsson, Hans-Olof, Pres.--Stockholm Regional Office, Kista, Sweden; *Int'l*, pg. 899
Olsson, Ingemar, Chm. Bd. & Pres.--Swedish Match do Brasil S/A, Rio de Janeiro, Brazil; *Int'l*, pg. 1328
Olsson, Leif, Chief Oper. Officer--ICA Ekonomibyra AB, Vasteras, Sweden; *Int'l*, pg. 643
Olsson, Mats, Pres.--AB Custodia, Stockholm, Sweden; *Int'l*, *pg. 272*
Olsson, Olov, Pres.--Swedish Motor Assemblies Sdn. Bhd., Shah Alam, Malaysia; *Int'l*, pg. 1477
Olsson, Roger, Gen. Mgr.--Siegling Svenska A.B., Kallered, Sweden; *Int'l*, pg. 498
Olsson, Sven-Erik, Pres.--Kvaerner Pulping Pte. Ltd., San Centre, Singapore; *Int'l*, pg. 768
Olsson, Wilmar, Chief Oper. Officer--Ahlstromforetagen Svenska AB-Eljo, Bastad, Sweden; *Int'l*, pg. 33
Olsten, Lars, Fin. Dir.--Andren & Werne Leo Burnett AB, Stockholm, Sweden; *U.S. Private*, pg. 184
Olszewski, John, Chief Oper. Officer--Matra Datavision U.S.A., Woburn, MA; *Int'l*, pg. 795
Oltrogge, Raymond E., Div. Mgr.--Montana Power Billings Div., Billings, MT; *U.S. Public*, pg. 1126
Olvey, Daniel R., Pres. & Chief Exec. Officer--Bay West Paper Corp. Towel & Tissue Div., Middletown, OH; *U.S. Public*, pg. 1747
Oman, Larry, V.P.-Opers.--Eaton Corporation, Engine Components Division, Marshall, MI; *U.S. Public*, pg. 556
Oman, Mark C., Pres. & Chief Exec. Officer--Norwest Mortgage, Inc., Des Moines, IA; *U.S. Public*, pg. 1202
Omano, Julio Gavito, Pres.--Barreras Hijos De J. Barreras, S.A., Vigo, Spain; *Int'l*, pg. 1223
Omar, Fayez S., Resident Rep.--The World Bank, Addis Ababa, Ethiopia; *U.S. Private*, pg. 1189
Omari, Dunstan A., Chm.--East African Cables Ltd., Nairobi, Kenya; *Int'l*, pg. 390
Omata, Konoshin, Chief Oper. Officer--Yamako Electric Manufacture Co., Ltd., Tokyo, Japan; *Int'l*, pg. 999
Omi, Okinari, Chief Oper. Officer--Kyowa Electric Wire Co., Ltd., Osaka, Japan; *Int'l*, pg. 530
Omichi, Hidetaka, Chief Rep.--The Industrial Bank of Japan, Limited (Seoul), Seoul, Korea; *Int'l*, pg. 675
Omiya, Tadashu, Mng. Dir.--Fuji Bank (Luxembourg) S.A., Luxembourg, Luxembourg; *Int'l*, pg. 521
Omlie, Blake J., Mgr.-Branch--Piper, Jaffray & Hopwood Incorporated, London, London, United Kingdom; *U.S. Public*, pg. 1303
Omote, Koji, Chief Oper. Officer--Makita Mexico, S.A. De C.V., Mexico, Mexico; *Int'l*, pg. 832
Omreng, Bjorn H., Pres.--Kvaerner Hydro Power, Inc., Stamford, CT; *Int'l*, pg. 770
Omreng, Bjorn H., Pres.--Kvaerner Energy Development, Inc., Stamford, CT; *Int'l*, pg. 770
Omreng, Bjorn H., Pres.--Kvaerner Inc., New York, NY; *Int'l*, *pg. 770*
Omstedt, Per, Chief Oper. Officer--Pharmacia & Upjohn Biotech K.K., Tokyo, Japan; *Int'l*, pg. 1048
Omura, Matt, Gen. Mgr.--NPR of America Inc., Farmington, MI; *Int'l*, pg. 938
Onestinghel, Diego, Mng. Dir.--ESI Stampa Medica Srl, Milan, Italy; *Int'l*, pg. 1099
Ong, Andrew, Mng. Dir.--ESAB Singapore Pte. Ltd., Singapore, Singapore; *Int'l*, pg. 282
Ong, Egil, Chief Oper. Officer--COBE Laboratories, Inc., Singapore, Singapore; *Int'l*, pg. 667
Ong, G., Chief Oper. Officer--The Kendall Co.-Singapore Representative Office, Singapore, Singapore; *U.S. Public*, pg. 1647
Ongyert, Werner, V.P.--MTS Systems GmbH, Berlin, Germany; *U.S. Public*, pg. 1029
Onishi, Gen. Mgr.--NSK-RHP Deutschland G.m.b.h., Ratingen, Germany; *Int'l*, pg. 904
Onishi, R., Gen. Mgr.-NSH--Fujitsu Ten Corp. of America, Torrance, CA; *Int'l*, pg. 526
Onishi, Susumu, Pres.--Excerpta Medica Limited-Japan, Tokyo, Japan; *Int'l*, pg. 1099
Onn, D., Pres.--Israel Aircraft Industries International Inc., New York, NY; *Int'l*, pg. 690
Ono, Fujio, Pres.--NKK America Inc., New York, NY; *Int'l*, pg. 902
Ono, Keiichiro, Pres.--Yokogawa-Kitz-Valtek Corp. (Y-K-V), Tokyo, Japan; *U.S. Public*, pg. 659
Ono, Kozo, Chief Exec. & Mng. Dir.--Yamaichi Bank (U.K.) Plc, London, United Kingdom; *Int'l*, pg. 1517
Ono, Masatoshi, Chm. Bd. & Chief Exec. Officer--Bridgestone/Firestone, Inc., Nashville, TN; *Int'l*, pg. 213
Ono, Naoto, Pres.--Prentice Hall Regents Japan, Inc., Tokyo, Japan; *U.S. Private*, pg. 778
Ono, Noriyasu, Chief Rep.--Dai-Ichi Kangyo Bank, Ltd.-Brussels, Brussels, Belgium; *Int'l*, pg. 361
Ono, S., Mng. Dir.--Toshiba Sales and Services Sdn. Bhd., Petaling Jaya, Malaysia; *Int'l*, pg. 1407
Ono, Takashi, Mng. Dir.--Nippon Express (U.K.), Ltd., Hounslow, United Kingdom; *Int'l*, pg. 934
Ono, Tor, Pres.--Taisei America Corp., New York, NY; *Int'l*, pg. 1347
Ono, Toshihiko, Pres.--NS Invest, Inc., New York, NY; *Int'l*, pg. 940
Ono, Yoshio, Mng. Dir.--ORIX Europe Limited, London, United Kingdom; *Int'l*, pg. 1009
Onodera, J., Pres.--Toko America, Inc., Mount Prospect, IL; *Int'l*, pg. 1393
Onofrio, P., Chief Exec. Officer--Ficut S.p.A., Milan, Italy; *Int'l*, pg. 994
Onopa, Ronald F., Pres.--Port City Electrical Supply, Inc., Orlando, FL; *U.S. Public*, pg. 847
Onoura, Akira, Chief Rep.--The Meiji Life Insurance Company Sao Paulo Office, Sao Paulo, Brazil; *Int'l*, pg. 854
Onstead, R. Randall, Jr., Pres.--Randalls Warehouse Corporation, Houston, TX; *U.S. Private*, pg. 909
Ontoso, Isabel, Gen. Mgr.--Conquest Europe, Madrid, Spain; *Int'l*, pg. 1483
Ontsuka, Zenichiro, Mng. Dir.--Morioka Hakuhodo Inc., Morioka, Japan; *Int'l*, pg. 588
Onuma, Tetsuo, Gen. Mgr.--Asahi Bank London Branch, London, United Kingdom; *Int'l*, pg. 82
Ooi, Kim Hoe, Gen. Mgr.--Hua Yan Bundy Tubing Corporation, Qinhuangdao, China; *Int'l*, pg. 1341
Oomens, W.H., Mng. Dir.--Nutricia Export B.V., Zoetermeer, Netherlands; *Int'l*, pg. 991
Ooms, Roger, Dir. Gen.--Stafford-Miller Continental, N.V. S.A., Geel, Belgium; *U.S. Public*, pg. 237
Ooms, Wil., Chief Exec.--Carrefour Nederland B.V., Rotterdam, Netherlands; *Int'l*, pg. 273
Oord, W.R., Mng. Dir.--Damco Maritime International B.V., Rotterdam, Netherlands; *Int'l*, pg. 1144
Oostenwall, Jan, Pres.--Techni-Therm Inc., Cornwall, Canada; *Int'l*, pg. 416
Oosterbaan, Henk, Gen. Mgr.--Forbo Bonaparte B.V., Goirle, Netherlands; *Int'l*, pg. 497
Oosterbroek, Jan, Dir.--NVS Salland Verzekeringen N.V., Amsterdam, Netherlands; *Int'l*, pg. 61
Oosterman, Ben, Gen. Mgr.--Reclamation Div. (San Jose), San Jose, CA; *Int'l*, pg. 1271
Oosterveld, J.L., Dir. Gen.--Zuivelonderneming De Vijfheerenlanden B.V., Leerdam, Netherlands; *Int'l*, pg. 751
Opalewski, Vincent J., Pres.--Printing Developments, Inc., Racine, WI; *U.S. Public*, pg. 707
Opdahl, Torgeir, Mng. Dir.--Saga Petroleum ASA - Libya, Tripoli, Libya; *Int'l*, pg. 1169
Openshaw, David, Mng. Dir.--ISS Servisystem Ltd., London, United Kingdom; *Int'l*, pg. 657
Openshaw, David, Mng. Dir.--ISS Airport Services Ltd., Hounslow, United Kingdom; *Int'l*, pg. 657
Ophey, Lothar, Dr. Ing., Pres.--Traub Drehmaschinen GmbH, Reichenbach, Germany; *Int'l*, pg. 1419
Oplinger, A.J., V.P. & Gen. Mgr.--The Glatfelter Pulp Wood Co., Spring Grove, PA; *U.S. Public*, pg. 746
Oplinger, Randy, Pres.--NRL Financial Corp., Kansas City, KS; *U.S. Private*, pg. 1066
Oppedahl, John E., Publr. & Chief Exec. Officer--Phoenix Newspapers, Inc., Phoenix, AZ; *U.S. Public*, pg. 326
Oppedal, Kjell, Pres.--ABB Trallfa Robot A/S, Bryne, Norway; *Int'l*, pg. 8
Oppel, Hans, Gen. Mgr.--Forbo Contel Handelsgesellschaft mbH, Vienna, Austria; *Int'l*, pg. 497
Oppenheim, Eytan, Chm. Bd.--Elscint Central & Eastern Europe, Vienna, Austria; *Int'l*, pg. 450
Oppenheim, Richard, Gen. Mgr.--CPC Foods (Ireland) Ltd., Dublin, Ireland; *U.S. Public*, pg. 225
Oppenheim, Richard, Gen. Mgr.--CPC (United Kingdom) Ltd., Esher, United Kingdom; *U.S. Public*, pg. 225
Oppenheimer, Nicholas, Deputy Chm.--De Beers Centenary AG, Lucerne, Switzerland; *Int'l*, pg. 77
Opperhauser, Scott S., V.P.--Trace Laboratories East, Linthicum Heights, MD; *U.S. Public*, pg. 1101
Opperman, Bruce, Gen. Mgr.--Lima Communications Corp., Lima, OH; *U.S. Private*, pg. 147
Oppliger, Gerald T., Pres.--Lockheed Space Operations Co., Titusville, FL; *U.S. Public*, pg. 1009
Orban, G. Steven, Pres.--Perini Building Co., Inc.-Eastern U.S. Division, Framingham, MA; *U.S. Public*, pg. 1278
Orban, J., Pres.--Distribution Control Systems, Inc. (DCS), Hazelwood, MO; *U.S. Public*, pg. 546
Orban, Peter, Mng. Dir.--Young & Rubicam Hungary, Budapest, Hungary; *U.S. Private*, pg. 1199
Orbanek, George, Publisher--Grand Junction Newspapers, Inc., Grand Junction, CO; *U.S. Private*, pg. 281
Orbanke, Jens, Mgr.--Sandvik Italia S.p.A., Milan, Italy; *Int'l*, pg. 1186
Orbeck, Ulf, Mng. Dir.--Bold, Oslo, Norway; *U.S. Private*, pg. 678
Orchard, Joe, Chief Oper. Officer--Saab-Scania Finance Ltd, Marlow, United Kingdom; *Int'l*, pg. 688
Orchard, William, Chief Oper. Officer--KONE Lifts Ltd., Hounslow, United Kingdom; *Int'l*, pg. 747
Ord, Kent, Sr. V.P. & Mng. Dir.--FUTUREWORKS, Seattle, WA; *U.S. Private*, pg. 385
Order, Philip, Gen. Mgr.--Lockheed Martin-Fairchild, Yonkers, NY; *U.S. Public*, pg. 1008
Ordre, Michael, Pres. & Gen. Mgr.--New York Revenue Automation, New York, NY; *U.S. Public*, pg. 466
Oreel, N.F., Gen. Mgr.--Radio Holland Group Hong Kong, Kwai Chung, Hong Kong; *Int'l*, pg. 1152
Orelli, Corrado, Gen. Mgr.--Swifloor SA, Giubiasco, Switzerland; *Int'l*, pg. 497
Orfinger, Alex, Publr.--American City Business Journals, Inc., Dallas, TX; *U.S. Private*, pg. 19
Orfinik, Michael H., Pres.--Melnor Inc., Winchester, VA; *U.S. Public*, pg. 1234
Orgera, George, Pres.--Hubbard Communications, Saint Petersburg, FL; *U.S. Private*, pg. 544
Orgera, George, Pres.--F & F Productions, Inc., Saint Petersburg, FL; *U.S. Private*, pg. 544
Orgera, George, Pres.--Diamond P Sports, Saint Petersburg, FL; *U.S. Private*, pg. 544
Orgoni, Aurelio, V.P.--Keystone Vanessa S.r.l., Piacenza, Italy; *U.S. Public*, pg. 1650
Orito, M., Gen. Mgr.--Hanwa American Corp., Saint Louis, MO; *Int'l*, pg. 595
Orito, Yusuke, Pres.--Toray Deutschland GmbH, Frankfurt/Main, Germany; *Int'l*, pg. 1400
Orlandini, Andrea, Pres.--Nikko Italia Societa Di Intermediazione Mobilare S.p.A., Milan, Italy; *Int'l*, pg. 931
Orlando, John, Plant Mgr.--Saint Louis Plant, Saint Louis, MO; *U.S. Public*, pg. 443
Orlans, Eric, Gen. Mgr.--Gent Local Head Office, Gent, Belgium; *Int'l*, pg. 147
Orlik, Simon, Chief Oper. Officer--Akerlund & Rausing Ltd., Leicester, United Kingdom; *Int'l*, pg. 33
Orlin, Peter, Chief Oper. Officer--Krauss-Maffei Verfahrenstechnik GmbH, Munich, Germany; *Int'l*, pg. 836
Orloff, Malcolm, Dr., Chief Exec. Officer--Moore & Munger Marketing Inc., Shelton, CT; *Int'l*, pg. 1197
Orlowski, Henry, Pres. & Chief Exec. Officer--Emtec Products Corporation, Coldwater, MI; *U.S. Public*, pg. 968
Orme, A.C., Mng. Dir.--AAH Retail Pharmacy Limited, Hook, United Kingdom; *Int'l*, pg. 591

Ormond, R., Unit Mgr.--Rockware Plastics Ltd., Kingston upon Thames, United Kingdom; *Int'l*, pg. 124
Ormston, J.J., Chief Oper. Officer--Babcock Jenkins Ltd., Retford, United Kingdom; *Int'l*, pg. 472
Ornaghi, Paulo Roberto, Mgr.--Kodak Brasileira C.I.L., Recife, Brazil; *U.S. Public*, pg. 552
Orndorff, Ronald D., Chm. Bd. & Chief Exec. Officer--M & I First National Leasing Corp., Milwaukee, WI; *U.S. Public, pg. 1051*
Ornstein, Mike, Mgr.--CAP Gemini America (New York Banking & Insurance), New York, NY; *Int'l*, pg. 264
Orodeckis, Edward J., Pres.--Marketdyne International, Inc., Philadelphia, PA; *U.S. Public*, pg. 366
Orozco, Francisco G., Gen. Mgr.--Springs de Mexico, S.A. de C.V., Mexico, Mexico; *U.S. Public*, pg. 1500
Orr, Andy, British Columbia Dir.--GPC Government Policy Consultants (Victoria), Victoria, Canada; *U.S. Public*, pg. 1225
Orr, C.K., Pres.--Cancarb Gas Services Limited, Calgary, Canada; *Int'l*, pg. 1417
Orr, Charles L., Pres. & Chief Exec. Officer--Shaklee Corporation, San Francisco, CA; *Int'l*, pg. 1518
Orr, David, Pres. & Chief Exec. Officer--Alcatel Telecom, Richardson, TX; *Int'l*, pg. 55
Orr, Don, Gen. Mgr.--Barton's of Monette, Monette, AR; *U.S. Private*, pg. 119
Orr, Francis, Gen. Mgr.--Barton's of Trumann, Trumann, AR; *U.S. Private*, pg. 119
Orr, James, Mng. Dir.--HLA Envirosciences Pty. Ltd., Pymble, Australia; *U.S. Public*, pg. 785
Orr, James E., Gen. Mgr.--Kansas City Auto Auction, Kansas City, MO; *U.S. Private*, pg. 282
Orr, James F. III, Pres.--UNUM Holding Company, Portland, ME; *U.S. Public*, pg. 1699
Orr, James F. III, Pres.--UNUM Development Corp., Portland, ME; *U.S. Public*, pg. 1699
Orr, James F., III, Chm. Bd. & Chief Exec. Officer--Colonial Life & Accident Insurance Co., Columbia, SC; *U.S. Public*, pg. 1699
Orr, James F., III, Chm. Bd.--Continental National Life Insurance Co., Piscataway, NJ; *U.S. Public*, pg. 1700
Orr, James F., III, Chm. Bd.--Continental International Life Insurance Co., Piscataway, NJ; *U.S. Public*, pg. 1700
Orr, Leit, Publisher--The Daily News, Truro, Canada; *Int'l*, pg. 631
Orr, Leith, Acting Publisher--The Evening News, New Glasgow, Canada; *Int'l*, pg. 631
Orr, M.N., Pres.--Thermic Refractories Inc., Girard, IL; *Int'l*, pg. 894
Orr, Michael P., Pres.--John Deere Capital Corporation, Reno, NV; *U.S. Public*, pg. 492
Orr, Michael P., Pres.--Farm Plan Corporation, Madison, WI; *U.S. Public*, pg. 492
Orr, Michael P., Pres.--Deere Credit, Inc., Moline, IL; *U.S. Public*, pg. 492
Orr, Michael P., Pres.--John Deere Credit Company, Moline, IL; *U.S. Public*, pg. 492
Orr, Ron, Pres. & Gen. Mgr.--Molded Fiber Glass Co., Ashtabula, OH; *U.S. Private*, pg. 756
Orr, W. Gregory, Pres.--Campbell Wells Corporation, Lafayette, LA; *U.S. Public*, pg. 1686
Orrgren, Kenneth, Pres.--NCC Building, Goteborg, Sweden; *Int'l*, pg. 898
Orrgren, Kenneth, Pres.--NCC HUS, Goteborg, Sweden; *Int'l*, pg. 899
Orrico, Eugene, Chm. Bd.--Beef Distributors, Inc., Renton, WA; *U.S. Private*, pg. 611
Orrorne, Greg, Mgr.-Natl. Sls.--DeVilbiss Ransburg Industrial Coating Equipment, Maumee, OH; *U.S. Public*, pg. 865
Orsini, Tom T., Pres.--ALLTEL Finance Corporation, Little Rock, AR; *U.S. Public*, pg. 55
Orsini, Tom T., Pres.--ALLTEL Services, Inc., Little Rock, AR; *U.S. Public*, pg. 56
Orstrom, Hans, Chief Oper. Officer--Pharmacia & Upjohn Nederland B.V., Woerden, Netherlands; *Int'l*, pg. 1050
Ortega, Eduardo, Chief Oper. Officer--Balmanta S.A., Guayaquil, Ecuador; *U.S. Public*, pg. 172
Ortega, Eduardo, Chief Oper. Officer--Compania Ecuatoriana de Balsa S.A., Guayaquil, Ecuador; *U.S. Public*, pg. 172
Ortega, Eduardo, Chief Oper. Officer--Maderas Secas C.A. (Maseca), Guayaquil, Ecuador; *U.S. Public*, pg. 172
Ortega, Eduardo, Chief Oper. Officer--Productos del Pacifico S.A., Guayaquil, Ecuador; *U.S. Public*, pg. 172
Ortega, Frances, Mgr.-Office--Jani King of San Antonio, Inc., San Antonio, TX; *U.S. Private*, pg. 582
Ortega, H., Chief Oper. Officer--Kendall de Mexico S.A. de D.V., Mexico, Mexico; *U.S. Public*, pg. 1648
Ortega, Mr., Dir. gen.--Eyelet Iberica, S.A., Madrid, Spain; *U.S. Public*, pg. 464
Ortelli, Ugo, Mgr.-Italy--Medtronic Italia S.p.A., Milan, Italy; *U.S. Public*, pg. 1084
Orten, Arnfinn, Pres.--Kvaerner Oil & Gas Services, Aberdeen, United Kingdom; *Int'l*, pg. 768
Orten, Arnfinn, Gen. Mgr.--Kvaerner Rosenberg A/S Kvaerner Egersund, Egersund, Norway; *Int'l*, pg. 769
Ortgies, Reinhard, Chief Oper. Officer--Anacomp (Japan) Ltd., Tokyo, Japan; *U.S. Public*, pg. 107
Orth, Charles W., Pres.--Unimark Plastics Company, Greer, SC; *U.S. Public*, pg. 57
Orth, Frederick, Mgr.--Autologic Information International, Inc., Ivry-sur-Seine, France; *U.S. Public*, pg. 1724
Orth, Hermann, Gen. Mgr.--Dorries GmbH, Dueren, Germany; *Int'l*, pg. 1473
Orth, William, Plant Mgr.--Hershey Chocolate U.S.A., Hazleton, PA; *U.S. Public*, pg. 812
Ortiz Monasterio, Jose Ramon, Gen. Mgr.--Eurocermex N.V., Brussels, Belgium; *U.S. Public*, pg. 115
Ortiz, Adrian E., Pres.--Universal Insurance Co., San Juan, PR; *U.S. Public*, pg. 962
Ortiz, E., Chief Oper. Officer--A.I. Ocean S.A., Buenos Aires, Argentina; *Int'l*, pg. 14
Ortiz, Edgar, Pres.--Halliburton Energy Services, Houston, TX; *U.S. Public*, pg. 776
Ortiz, Edwin, Chief Oper. Officer--El Conquistador Development Corp., Trujillo Alto, PR; *U.S. Public*, pg. 988
Ortiz, Juan Hilario, Pres.--Chr. Hansen de Mexico, S.A. de CV, Mexico, Mexico; *Int'l*, pg. 289
Ortiz, Luis, Mng. Dir.--Pharmacia & Upjohn Compania Limitada, Santiago, Chile; *Int'l*, pg. 1049
Ortiz, R., Gen. Mgr.--Vivagel, Vitry-sur-Seine, France; *Int'l*, pg. 380
Ortiz, Rudolph T., Pres.--Thermo Process Systems Inc./Cal-Doran Metallurgical, Inc., Los Angeles, CA; *U.S. Public*, pg. 1594
Ortlund, Jan, Chief Oper. Officer--Frigoscandia Food Process Systems AB, Bangkok, Thailand; *U.S. Public*, pg. 606
Ortolina, Emilio, Gen. Mgr.--Braun Italia, S.r.l., Milan, Italy; *U.S. Public*, pg. 744
Ortwein, Hank, Pres.--Allegheny Rail Products, Pittsburgh, PA; *U.S. Public*, pg. 676
Orvati, Werner, Dir.--LGT Treuhand Aktiengesellschaft, Vaduz, Liechtenstein; *Int'l*, pg. 809
Orza, Vincent F., Jr., Chm. Bd., Pres. & Chief Exec. Officer--Pepperoni Grill, Oklahoma City, OK; *U.S. Public*, pg. 555
Orzechowski, Robert, Branch Mgr.--Klockner-Moeller, Cerritos, CA; *Int'l*, pg. 736
Osaka, Toshiharu, Gen. Mgr.--Fuji Bank, Dalian Branch, Dalian, China; *Int'l*, pg. 520
Osatananda, Prasan, Chm.--EURO RSCG Partnership, Bangkok, Thailand; *Int'l*, pg. 602
Osawa, Akira, Pres. & Chief Exec. Officer--Nikko Hotels International-USA, New York, NY; *Int'l*, pg. 700
Osawa, Mikio, Pres.--Nikkei News Bulletin, Inc., Tokyo, Japan; *Int'l*, pg. 929
Osberg, James, Gen. Mgr.--ITW Southern Gage Co., Erin, TN; *U.S. Public*, pg. 867
Osborn, Kenny, Gen. Mgr.--Golden Gate Auto Auction Inc., Fremont, CA; *U.S. Public*, pg. 1649
Osborn, W., Chief Exec. Officer--Blackwood Hodge (Zambia) Ltd., Kitwe, Zambia; *Int'l*, pg. 231
Osborne, Bob, Mng. Dir.--Heinemann Educational Publishing, Oxford, United Kingdom; *Int'l*, pg. 1094
Osborne, Bruce F., Pres.--Harris Bank Winnetka N.A., Winnetka, IL; *Int'l*, pg. 154
Osborne, Burl, Publisher & Editor--The Dallas Morning News, Inc., Dallas, TX; *U.S. Public*, pg. 209
Osborne, Ed, Pres.--AMI Industries F.S.C., Inc., Charlotte Amalie, VI; *U.S. Public*, pg. 401
Osborne, J., Mng. Dir.--Longman Penguin Japan Co. ltd., Tokyo, Japan; *Int'l*, pg. 1025
Osborne, Joe C., Pres.--The Variable Annuity Marketing Co., Houston, TX; *U.S. Public*, pg. 76
Osborne, Peter, Mng. Dir.--Haymarket Exhibitions Ltd., London, United Kingdom; *Int'l*, pg. 114
Osborne, Roger, Pres.--Work 'n Gear, Hyde Park, MA; *U.S. Public*, pg. 168
Osborne, Thomas C., Chief Exec. Officer--ICI Paints, Cleveland, OH; *Int'l*, pg. 664
Osborne, Tom, Pres.--Grow Group, Inc., Cleveland, OH; *Int'l*, pg. 663
Osburn, Kathy, Branch Mgr.--Downey Savings & Loan Association, F.A., Hesperia, CA; *U.S. Public*, pg. 527
Osculati, Gianemilio, Admin. Dir. Gen.--Banca d'America e d'Italia S.p.A., Milan, Italy; *Int'l*, pg. 403
Ose, Stan, Gen. Mgr.--Electronic Internconnect Systems Inc., South Hadley, MA; *Int'l*, pg. 955
Osegueda, J.W., Gen. Mgr.--CHEMCENTRAL/Pittsburgh, Coraopolis, PA; *U.S. Private*, pg. 232
Oses, L., Gen. Mgr.--Purac Bioquimica S.A., Montmelo, Spain; *Int'l*, pg. 244
Osher, John, Pres.--Cap Toys, Inc., Bedford, OH; *U.S. Public*, pg. 797
Oshima, Terry, Pres.--Kyotaru USA, Hawthorne, CA; *Int'l*, pg. 778
Oshima, Toshiyuki, Mng. Dir.--Dai-Ichi Kangyo Bank (Luxembourg) S.A., Luxembourg, Luxembourg; *Int'l*, pg. 362
Oshimo, Masahi, Chief Rep.--Asahi Bank Bombay Representative Office, Mumbai, India; *Int'l*, pg. 83
Oshio, Takashi, Pres.--Rock of Ages Asia Corp., Osaka, Japan; *U.S. Public*, pg. 1396
Oshio, Yukihiko, Pres.--Dynapac Kenki KK, Kawaguchi, Japan; *Int'l*, pg. 1420
Osias, Barry, Mgr.--Stephen Gould Paper Co., Inc., Whippany, NJ; *U.S. Private*, pg. 468
Osler, Randy W., Pres.--Carrier Markets, Overland Park, KS; *U.S. Public*, pg. 1500
Oslos, Kyle, Reg. V.P.-Central--GATX Contract Carriers, Inc., Normal, IL; *U.S. Public*, pg. 691
Osman, Borhanuddin, Mng. Partner & Mng. Dir.--Paragon Communications Sdn. Bhd. (Kuala Lumpur), Kuala Lumpur, Malaysia; *U.S. Private*, pg. 325
Osman, Osman Mohamed, Mgmt.--MISR DYWIDAG, Cairo, Egypt; *Int'l*, pg. 425
Osman, Peter M., Mng. Dir.--Gibson Greetings International Limited, Telford, United Kingdom; *U.S. Public*, pg. 742
Osman, Wayne, Mng. Dir.--Dexion Ltd.-Storage Div., Hemel Hempstead, United Kingdom; *U.S. Public*, pg. 893
Osmars, Dave, Gen. Mgr.--Royal Insurance Ottawa Regional Centre, Ottawa, Canada; *Int'l*, pg. 1131
Osmer, Robert H., Pres.--Devoe Coatings Co., Louisville, KY; *Int'l*, pg. 663
Osmun, Robert, Pres.--Kyocera Industrial Ceramics Corp., Vancouver, WA; *Int'l*, pg. 776
Osorio, Atillo E., Pres.--Carbozulia, S.A., Maracaibo, Venezuela; *Int'l*, pg. 1045
Osorio, Martin, Media Dir.--Leo Burnett Chile, Santiago, Chile; *U.S. Private*, pg. 185
Osorio, Omar, Plant Dir.--Wang de Mexico, S.A. de C.V., Mexico, Mexico; *U.S. Public*, pg. 1737
Osos, Alan, Prod. Mgr.--Specialty Products Group, Niles, MI; *U.S. Public*, pg. 1160
Ossard, Remy, Mng. Dir.--CPM & Compagnie, Boulogne-Billancourt, France; *Int'l*, pg. 116
Ossenbuhl, B., Mng. Dir.--OMRON Electronics GmbH, Hilden, Germany; *Int'l*, pg. 1006
Osslund, Lisa, Branch Mgr.--Downey Savings & Loan Association, F.A., Escondido, CA; *U.S. Public*, pg. 526
Osso, Carlos, Div. Mgr.--Keystone do Brasil Ltda., Sao Paulo, Brazil; *U.S. Public*, pg. 1650
Ostberg, Cliffert, Chief Oper. Officer--Ahlstromforetagen Svenska AB-Norrkoping Core Plant, Norrkoping, Sweden; *Int'l*, pg. 33
Ostby, Ragnar, Gen. Mgr.--Kvaerner Fish Process Technology a.s - Kvaerner Kulde, Lier, Norway; *Int'l*, pg. 768
Ostendorf, Danny, Mng. Dir.--Norvista B.V., Amsterdam, Netherlands; *Int'l*, pg. 486
Ostendorf, R.E., Pres.--TRI-GLAS, Daleville, AL; *U.S. Private*, pg. 848
Ostenrieder, Karl, Mng. Dir.--Deutsche Bank AG (Buenos Aires), Buenos Aires, Argentina; *Int'l*, pg. 404
Ostenson, Gunnar, Pres.--Skanska Oresund AB, Malmo, Sweden; *Int'l*, pg. 1261
Oster, Wolfgang, M.D., V.P.-Intl. Clinical Research--USB Pharma Ltd., Watford, United Kingdom; *U.S. Public*, pg. 1681
Ostergren, Greg V., Pres. & Chief Exec. Officer--American National Property & Casualty Co., Springfield, MO; *U.S. Public*, pg. 87
Ostergren, Greg V., Pres.--American National Insurance Service Co., Springfield, MO; *U.S. Public*, pg. 88
Ostergren, Gustaf, Chief Oper. Officer--Electrolux GmbH, Berlin, Germany; *Int'l*, pg. 442
Ostergren, Hakan, Gen. Mgr.--Ground Support Division, Ostersund, Sweden; *Int'l*, pg. 277
Osterlund, Kaj, Pres.--Oy Lining AB, Vantaa, Finland; *Int'l*, pg. 678
Osterlund, Kaj, Pres.--YTM Industrial Oy, Vantaa, Finland; *Int'l*, pg. 678
Osterman, David, Reg. Mgr.--Cumberland Cove, Monterey, TN; *U.S. Public*, pg. 144
Osterman, James S., Pres.--Blount, Inc. Oregon Cutting Systems Division, Portland, OR; *U.S. Public*, pg. 238
Osterman, James S., Pres.--Blount Europe, S.A., Nivelles, Belgium; *U.S. Public*, pg. 238
Osterman, James S., Pres.--Omark Properties, Inc., Portland, OR; *U.S. Public*, pg. 239
Osterman, James S., Pres.--Blount Japan Inc., Tokyo, Japan; *U.S. Public*, pg. 239
Osterman, James S., Pres.--Blount Holdings Ltd., Guelph, Canada; *U.S. Public*, pg. 239
Osterman, James S., Pres.--Blount Canada Ltd., Guelph, Canada; *U.S. Public*, pg. 239
Ostermyer, D., Pres.--DST Securities, Inc., Kansas City, MO; *U.S. Public*, pg. 943
Osterwind, Michael, Sr. Mng. Dir.--Deutsche Bank AG (Stuttgart), Stuttgart, Germany; *Int'l*, pg. 402
Ostin, Gunnar, Pres.--Silja Line AB, Stockholm, Sweden; *Int'l*, pg. 899
Ostli, J., Mng. Dir.--EMI Norsk A/S, Oslo, Norway; *Int'l*, pg. 427
Ostling, Leif, Gen. Mgr.-Scania Div.--Scania Division, Sodertalje, Sweden; *Int'l*, pg. 687
Ostlund, Bert, Mng. Dir.--Celbi SA, Figueira da Foz, Portugal; *Int'l*, pg. 1303
Ostlund, Gothe, Pres.--AB Wibe, Mora, Sweden; *Int'l*, pg. 678
Ostlund, Kurt, Pres.--Procordia Food AB, Malmo, Sweden; *Int'l*, pg. 1011
Ostlund, Torbjorn, Mng. Dir.--Reemtsma International Praha spol. s.r.o., Prague, Czech Republic; *Int'l*, pg. 1101
Ostmeier, Konrad, Mng. Dir.--Solvitol Limited, Birtley, United Kingdom; *Int'l*, pg. 858
Ostrander, Paul J., Gen. Mgr.--Dufferin Construction, Oakville, Canada; *Int'l*, pg. 628
Ostransky, Martin, V.P.-Construction & Svcs.--Industrial & Construction Products Div., Valley, NE; *U.S. Public*, pg. 1707
Ostrom, Bjorn, Branch Mgr.--Christiania Bank-Singapore Branch, Singapore, Singapore; *Int'l*, pg. 289
Ostrom, Bjorn, Mng. Dir.--Christiania Bank Luxembourg S.A., Luxembourg, Luxembourg; *Int'l*, pg. 289
Ostroski, Dick, Pres.--Wayne Home Equipment Div., Fort Wayne, IN; *U.S. Public*, pg. 218
Ostroski, Gerald B., Pres.--Synertec, Incorporated, Duluth, MN; *U.S. Public*, pg. 1116
Ostrovsky, Steven N., Chief Exec. Officer--VTA Management Services, Inc., Brooklyn, NY; *U.S. Public*, pg. 839
Ostrow, Joel, Pres.--Plej's Linen Supermarket, Rock Hill, SC; *U.S. Private*, pg. 821
Ostrowski, Ron, V.P. & Asst. Gen. Mgr.--777 Program, Everett, WA; *U.S. Public*, pg. 240
Ostruszka, Wayne D., Branch Mgr.--CAP Gemini America (Milwaukee Branch), Milwaukee, WI; *Int'l*, pg. 264
Osugi, Masami, Mng. Dir.--Asahi Investment Australia Ltd., Sydney, Australia; *Int'l*, pg. 85
Osugi, Masami, Mng. Dir.--Asahi Property Australia Pty. Ltd., Sydney, Australia; *Int'l*, pg. 85
Oswald, Eduard, Gen. Mgr.--Erste Bank - London Branch, London, United Kingdom; *Int'l*, pg. 459
Oswald, Fred, Mgr.-Admin. Services--AM General Corporation, Livonia, MI; *U.S. Private*, pg. 922
Oswald, John H., Pres.--The Riverside Publishing Co., Chicago, IL; *U.S. Public*, pg. 841
Oswald, Robert, Chm., Pres. & Chief Exec. Officer--Robert Bosch Corporation, Broadview, IL; *Int'l*, pg. 204
Oswald, Robert, Pres.--Bosch Automotive Group, Farmington, MI; *Int'l*, pg. 204
Oswald, Robert, Pres.--Bosch Braking Systems-North America, South Bend, IN; *Int'l*, pg. 204
Oswaldson, Rolf, Pres.--Kvaerner Eureka Gaevle AB, Gavle, Sweden; *Int'l*, pg. 767
Oswaldson, Rolf, Pres.--Kvaerner Pulp Equipment AB, Gavle, Sweden; *Int'l*, pg. 768
Oswalt, W.D., Branch Mgr.--Zellerbach Division, Spokane, WA; *U.S. Public*, pg. 1075

Ota, Pres.--Nintendo of Europe GmbH, Germany; *Int'l*, pg. 932
Ota, Hiroaki, Rep.--The Sakura Bank - Melbourne Representative Office, Melbourne, Australia; *Int'l*, pg. 1180
Ota, Mitsunori, Chief Rep.--Bahrain Representative Office, Manama, Bahrain; *Int'l*, pg. 1485
Ota, Noboru, Pres.--Tsuchiya Mfg. Co., Ltd., Tokyo, Japan; *Int'l*, pg. 944
Ota, Tetsuo, Pres.--Quick Corp., Tokyo, Japan; *Int'l*, pg. 929
Ota, Yoshiaki, Mng. Dir.--I.M.I.B.J. S.p.A., Rome, Italy; *Int'l*, pg. 676
Otake, Akira, Dir.--Thai Takenaka International Ltd., Bangkok, Thailand; *Int'l*, pg. 1352
Otamura-Kester, Judith K., Asst. Sec.--Investment Technology Group, Inc., New York, NY; *U.S. Public*, pg. 924
Otamura-Kester, Judith K., Sr. V.P., Asst. Gen. Counsel & Asst. Sec.--Jefferies & Company, Inc., Los Angeles, CA; *U.S. Public*, pg. 925
Otani, Akiyoshi, Gen. Mgr.--Daiwa Bank-London, London, United Kingdom; *Int'l*, pg. 373
Otani, Akiyoshi, Chm. Bd.--Daiwa Bank (Schweiz) AG, Zurich, Switzerland; *Int'l*, pg. 373
Otani, Takashi, Dir.--Showpla (Thailand) Co. Ltd., Tambol, Thailand; *Int'l*, pg. 1237
Otegui, I., Mng. Dir.--GKN Forjas de Precision de Legazpia SA, Legazpia, Spain; *Int'l*, pg. 536
Oteiza, Mariano, Gen. Mgr.--Wackenhut Internation (Panama), S.A., Panama, Panama; *U.S. Public*, pg. 1731
Otero, Gerardo, Mgr.--Broad National Bank-North Newark, Newark, NJ; *U.S. Public*, pg. 258
Otobe, Masayuki, Gen. Mgr.--The Hokkaido Takushoku Bank, Ltd. (London), London, United Kingdom; *Int'l*, pg. 627
Ots, Tony, Pres.--Raypak, Inc., Westlake Village, CA; *Int'l*, pg. 1022
Otsu, Takuro, Chief Oper. Officer--Hitachi Heating Appliances Co., Ltd., Kashiwa, Japan; *Int'l*, pg. 621
Otsubo, Kozo, Gen. Mgr.--The Sumitomo Bank, Ltd.-Mumbai Branch, Mumbai, India; *Int'l*, pg. 1309
Otsuka, Akihiko, Pres.--Otsuka Foods Co., Ltd., Osaka, Japan; *Int'l*, pg. 1013
Otsuka, Isao, Pres.--Otsuka Science Co., Ltd., Aichi, Japan; *Int'l*, pg. 1013
Otsuka, Masatomi, Pres.--Earth Chemical Co., Ltd., Tokyo, Japan; *Int'l*, pg. 1013
Otsuka, Masatomi, Pres.--Earth Biochemical Co., Ltd., Tokyo, Japan; *Int'l*, pg. 1013
Otsuka, Masatomi, Chm. Bd.--ARS Chemical (Thailand) Co., Ltd., Bangkok, Thailand; *Int'l*, pg. 1014
Otsuka, Masayuki, Gen. Mgr.--The Industrial Bank of Japan, Limited (Madrid Branch), Madrid, Spain; *Int'l*, pg. 675
Otsuka, Masayuki, Chm.--IBJ Espana, Madrid, Spain; *Int'l*, pg. 676
Otsuka, S., Gen. Mgr.--Hanwa American Corp., Houston, TX; *Int'l*, pg. 595
Otsuka, Yuya, Pres.--Otsuka Beverage Co., Ltd., Tokyo, Japan; *Int'l*, pg. 1013
Otsuki, Hiroshi, Chm. Bd.--Yamaichi Bank (Deutschland) GmbH, Frankfurt/Main, Germany; *Int'l*, pg. 1517
Otsuki, Yuji, Gen. Mgr.--The Mitsui Trust and Banking Company - Hong Kong, Central, Hong Kong; *Int'l*, pg. 883
Ott, Alan W., Chm. Bd.--Chemical Bank Bay Area, Bay City, MI; *U.S. Public*, pg. 345
Ott, H.H., Dir.--Unichema-Chemie B.V., Gouda, Netherlands; *Int'l*, pg. 1438
Ott, Thomas L., Pres.--Palisades Energy Services, Pearl River, NY; *U.S. Public*, pg. 1229
Ottaviani, Joe, V.P. & Gen. Mgr.--A-Z Terminal Corporation, Crosby, TX; *U.S. Private*, pg. 1014
Ottaway, James H., Jr., Chm., Pres. & Chief Exec. Officer--Ottaway Newspapers, Inc., Campbell Hall, NY; *U.S. Public*, pg. 525
Otten, Leslie, Pres.--Sunday River, Bethel, ME; *U.S. Private, pg. 62*
Otten, Winfred, Gen. Mgr.--Nordson Walcom B.V., Udenhout, Netherlands; *U.S. Public*, pg. 1189
Ottensmeyer, David J., Chm. Bd.--Lovelace Health Systems, Inc., Albuquerque, NM; *U.S. Public*, pg. 360
Otterbeck, Lars, Chief Oper. Officer--Axel Johnson Chemicals AB, Malmo, Sweden; *Int'l*, pg. 708
Otterbeck, Lars, Pres.--Dagab Snabbgross AB, Solna, Sweden; *Int'l*, pg. 708
Otterbeck, Lennart, Mng. Dir.--Soderhamns Verkstader AB, Soderhamn, Sweden; *Int'l*, pg. 1421
Otterson, G. L., Chief Oper. Officer--John Deere Engine Works, Waterloo, IA; *U.S. Public*, pg. 492
Ottesen, Gunvald, Pres.--Aker Elektro a.s., Sagvag, Norway; *Int'l*, pg. 41
Ottey, Trevor F., Mng. Dir.--Colgate-Palmolive Co. (Jamaica) Ltd., Kingston, Jamaica; *U.S. Public*, pg. 398
Ottinger, William C., V.P.--Willis Corroon Corp. of Penn., Bethlehem, PA; *Int'l*, pg. 1506
Ottink, G., Chief Exec. Officer--Hoogovens Handel BV, Amsterdam, Netherlands; *Int'l*, pg. 754
Ottman, Steve, V.P.-Opers.--Tucchetti, Phoenix, AZ; *U.S. Private*, pg. 661
Ottman, Steve, V.P.-Opers.--Tucci Benucch, Bloomington, MN; *U.S. Private*, pg. 661
Ottman, Steve, V.P.-Opers.--Food Life, Chicago, IL; *U.S. Private*, pg. 661
Ottman, Steve, V.P.-Opers.--Tucci Benucch, Seattle, WA; *U.S. Private*, pg. 661
Ottman, Steve, V.P.-Opers.--Twin City Diner, Bloomington, MN; *U.S. Private*, pg. 662
Ottmann, Steve, V.P.-Opers.--Scoozi, Chicago, IL; *U.S. Private*, pg. 661
Otto, Bruce, Gen. Mgr.--Banta Global Turnkey, Plover, WI; *U.S. Public*, pg. 188
Otto, D., Mng. Dir.--Bally Moda SA, Madrid, Spain; *Int'l*, pg. 997
Otto, Frank W., Gen. Mgr.--EDO Marine & Aircraft Systems, College Point, NY; *U.S. Public*, pg. 542
Otto, Joachim, Pres.--AB Carlsson & Moller, Helsingborg, Sweden; *Int'l*, pg. 678
Otto, Joachim, Pres.--Linatex A/S, Vallensbaek, Denmark; *Int'l*, pg. 678
Otto, Lyn, Contact--Quest Diagnostic, Liverpool, NY; *U.S. Public*, pg. 1351
Otto, Ulrich, Chm.--Trischler und Partner GmbH, Darmstadt, Germany; *Int'l*, pg. 608
Ottosson, David, Chm. Reg. Bd.--ICA Handlarna Ost AB, Arsta, Sweden; *Int'l*, pg. 642
Oudshoorn, R.H., drs, Mgr.--Vredestein Banden B.V., Enschede, Netherlands; *Int'l*, pg. 1481
Ouedraogo, Gaspart, Pres.--Banque Internationale du Burkina (BIB), Ouagadougou, Burkina Faso; *Int'l*, pg. 548
Ouellet, J., Mgr.--SBC Portfolio Management (Canada) Inc., Toronto, Canada; *Int'l*, pg. 1332
Ouimet, Pierre-Andre, Pres.--E-Z-EM Canada Inc., Anjou, Canada; *U.S. Public*, pg. 540
Oung, F.Y., Dir.--Exploration & Production Research Center, Miao-li, Taiwan; *Int'l*, pg. 286
Ouroda, Frantisek, Mgr.--Commenda C.R. s.r.o., Prague, Czech Republic; *Int'l*, pg. 1501
Oussoren, Reinout G., V.P.--SF Air Filtration AG, Klus, Switzerland; *U.S. Public*, pg. 161
Oussov, Anatoli, Company Head--SKF Moscow, Moscow, Russia; *Int'l*, pg. 1159
Outman, Susan, Pres.--BSA Advertising, Inc., Englewood, CO; *U.S. Private*, pg. 108
Ouvry, D.J.D., Gen. Mgr.--Laboratorios Wellcome de Portugal Lda, Lisbon, Portugal; *Int'l*, pg. 553
Ouwehand, Hans, Chief Oper. Officer & Mng. Dir.--Littelfuse B.V., Utrecht, Netherlands; *U.S. Public*, pg. 1001
Ouzts, Michael, Pres.--Greenlee Lighting Inc., Carrollton, TX; *U.S. Public*, pg. 971
Overdevest, M.P.H., Mgr.--Bellast Nedam Caribbean N.V., Willemstad, Netherlands Antilles; *Int'l*, pg. 134
Overheau, Gerald A., V.P. & Gen. Mgr.--Vista Lighting, Santa Ana, CA; *Int'l*, pg. 821
Overholt, Harold S., Jr., Chm., Pres. & Chief Exec. Officer--Dreyfus Investment Services Corp., Pittsburgh, PA; *U.S. Public*, pg. 1085
Overholtzer, Durand, Pres.--Wood Colony Millworks, Modesto, CA; *U.S. Private*, pg. 823
Overlie, Ola, Pres.--Moxy Trucks AS, Elnesvagen, Norway; *Int'l*, pg. 745
Overman, Mary Jayne, Pres.--Public Storage Properties, Glendale, CA; *U.S. Public*, pg. 1341
Overocker, H.L., Chief Oper. Officer--Frazee Industries Inc., San Diego, CA; *Int'l*, pg. 1501
Overstrom, Gunnar S., Chm. Bd.--Fleet National Bank, Providence, RI; *U.S. Public*, pg. 649
Overton, Martin, Chief Oper. Officer--Custom Food Products Inc., Alsip, IL; *U.S. Private*, pg. 481
Overwater, W.T., Gen. Mgr.--Lorlea Architectural Systems Division, London, Canada; *Int'l*, pg. 698
Ow, K.C., Gen. Mgr.--S.C. Johnson & Son Pte. Limited, Singapore, Singapore; *U.S. Private*, pg. 593
Owada, Goro, Gen. Mgr.--ORIX Commodities Singapore Pte Limited, Singapore, Singapore; *Int'l*, pg. 1009
Owada, Kiyoharu, Pres.--Nissan Canada Inc., Mississauga, Canada; *Int'l*, pg. 945
Owada, Nobuyuki, Mng. Dir.--Cosmo Securities (Europe) Limited, London, United Kingdom; *Int'l*, pg. 335
Owen, A., Gen. Mgr.--Hercules Chemicals Investments Pty. Ltd., Melbourne, Australia; *U.S. Public*, pg. 811
Owen, D., Mng. Dir.--Crompton Lighting Ltd., Doncaster, United Kingdom; *Int'l*, pg. 124
Owen, D.L., Chief Oper. Officer--Babcock Moxey Div., Johannesburg, South Africa; *Int'l*, pg. 474
Owen, David, Mng. Dir.--The Gates Rubber Company Ltd., Dumfries, United Kingdom; *Int'l*, pg. 1397
Owen, David H., Mng. Dir.--Morse Controls Ltd., Basildon, United Kingdom; *U.S. Public*, pg. 857
Owen, Dr. Robert, V.P.-Technology Devel.--Thomas A. Edison Technical Center, Franksville, WI; *U.S. Public*, pg. 443
Owen, E.H., Pres.--Parish Water Company, Inc., Baton Rouge, LA; *U.S. Private*, pg. 123
Owen, E.H., Pres.--Ascension Water Co., Baton Rouge, LA; *U.S. Private*, pg. 123
Owen, H. Lee, Pres.--Farmers Bank & Trust Co., Madisonville, KY; *U.S. Public*, pg. 1217
Owen, Jay L., Pres.--Harris Trust Company of Florida, West Palm Beach, FL; *Int'l*, pg. 155
Owen, Jim, Div. Mgr.--Godwins Limited, Birmingham, United Kingdom; *U.S. Public*, pg. 119
Owen, Jim, V.P.-Fin. & Admin.--Gradco (USA), Inc., Irvine, CA; *U.S. Public*, pg. 757
Owen, Joseph L., Mgr.--Scott & Stringfellow, Inc., Kinston, NC; *U.S. Public*, pg. 1446
Owen, Joseph L., Mgr.--Scott & Stringfellow, Inc., Wilmington, NC; *U.S. Public*, pg. 1446
Owen, Judy, Chm. Bd.--Norwest Bank Nebraska, N.A., Omaha, NE; *U.S. Public*, pg. 1202
Owen, Mark, Pres., Chief Exec. Officer & Gen. Mgr.--Aero Corporation, Lake City, FL; *U.S. Public*, pg. 1766
Owen, Michael C., Mgr.--Scott & Stringfellow, Inc., Winston Salem, NC; *U.S. Public*, pg. 1446
Owen, Nicholas, Mng. Dir.--Robert Fleming (Isle of Man) Limited, Douglas, United Kingdom; *Int'l*, pg. 493
Owen, Richard F., Pres.--Central Plains Steel Co., Kansas City, KS; *U.S. Private*, pg. 824
Owen, Richard S., Pres.--Lamons Metal Gasket Co., Houston, TX; *U.S. Public*, pg. 1054
Owen, Robert E., Pres. & Mng. Dir.--Paxton & Vierling, Omaha, NE; *U.S. Private*, pg. 824
Owens, Bruce, Mgr.--Surplus Warehouse-Temple, Temple, TX; *U.S. Private*, pg. 120
Owens, Byron, Chm. Bd.--Vesture Corporation, Asheboro, NC; *U.S. Public*, pg. 192
Owens, Cliff, V.P. & Gen. Mgr.--Medtronics Inc., Parker, CO; *U.S. Public*, pg. 1083
Owens, Gene S., Mgr.--Williston Telephone Co., Williston, SC; *U.S. Public*, pg. 1572
Owens, James G., Pres.--Controlled Power (CPC), Canton, OH; *Int'l*, pg. 74
Owens, Janis A., Branch Mgr.--The Commercial Bank-Gomer Banking Center, Gomer, OH; *U.S. Public*, pg. 410
Owens, Jerry D., Sr. V.P.-Central Opers.--Robert E. McKee, Inc., Los Angeles, CA; *U.S. Public*, pg. 921
Owens, John, Pres.--The Clarinda Company, Clarinda, IA; *U.S. Private*, pg. 206
Owens, Michael L., Chief Oper. Officer, Sr. V.P. & Treas.--Monumental General Insurance Company, Baltimore, MD; *Int'l*, pg. 27
Owens, Patricia, Chm. Bd.--Options and Choices, Inc., Cheyenne, WY; *U.S. Public*, pg. 1699
Owens, Phil, Pres. & Chief Oper. Officer--Top-Seal Corp., Phoenix, AZ; *U.S. Private*, pg. 1071
Owens, Russell L., Mgr.--Struers Ltd., Glasgow, United Kingdom; *Int'l*, pg. 1084
Owens, Ted A., Grp. V.P.--Inland Container-Containerboard Division, Indianapolis, IN; *U.S. Public*, pg. 1575
Owings, Frank, Mgr.--Tri-State Mack Inc., Little Rock, AR; *U.S. Private*, pg. 1101
Owings, J. Thomas, V.P.--InnoServ Technologies, Inc., Arlington, TX; *U.S. Public*, pg. 880
Ownes, David, Pres.--Asia Minerals Corp., Vancouver, Canada; *U.S. Public*, pg. 1411
Owre, Erik Lokke, Plant Mgr.--Elkem Aluminium Mosjoen, Mosjoeen, Norway; *Int'l*, pg. 447
Owusu, Phillip, (Resident Rep.)--Banco Mundial, Luanda, Angola; *U.S. Private*, pg. 1189
Oxley, Alan R., Gen. Mgr.--Forbo Australia Pty. Ltd., Sydney, Australia; *Int'l*, pg. 497
Oya, Saburo, Gen. Mgr.--Fluke, Inc., Tokyo, Japan; *U.S. Public*, pg. 659
Oyama, Masahiro, Chm. Bd.--Daiwa Overseas Finance Ltd., Central, Hong Kong; *Int'l*, pg. 373
Oyama, Masahiro, Gen. Mgr.--Daiwa Bank-Hong Kong, Central, Hong Kong; *Int'l*, pg. 373
Ozaki, Hideo, Mng. Dir.--NEC Technologies Hong Kong Limited, Sha Tin, Hong Kong; *Int'l*, pg. 900
Ozaki, Kazumasa, Mng. Dir.--McCormick-Lion Ltd., Tokyo, Japan; *U.S. Public*, pg. 1067
Ozawa, H., Reg. Mgr.-Northeast Asia Region--Lord Far East, Inc., Tokyo, Japan; *U.S. Private*, pg. 676
Ozawa, Shigeki, Chief Oper. Officer--Hitachi Denshi, Ltd., Tokyo, Japan; *Int'l*, pg. 621
Ozawa, Yoshio, Pres.--Hakuhodo Creative & Development, Inc., Tokyo, Japan; *Int'l*, pg. 588
Ozbirn, W.P., Pres.--Hobbs Corporation, Springfield, IL; *Int'l, pg. 127*
Ozbun, David, Pres.--Citizens Banc Leasing, Louisville, KY; *U.S. Public*, pg. 280
Ozcelik, Vejdi, Pres.--Akcansa, Istanbul, Turkey; *Int'l*, pg. 605
Ozeki, H., Mng. Dir.--SEIKO Deutschland GmbH, Dusseldorf, Germany; *Int'l*, pg. 1218
Ozeki, Hiroshi, Pres.--Mazda Research & Development of North America, Inc., Irvine, CA; *Int'l*, pg. 849
Ozer, Marty, Pres.--Katz National Television, New York, NY; *U.S. Public*, pg. 335
Ozgowicz, Mike, Plant Mgr.--Farr Company, Corcoran, CA; *U.S. Public*, pg. 614
Ozsen, Sefik, Gen. Mgr.--Reed Travel Group-Germany, Dusseldorf, Germany; *Int'l*, pg. 1097
Ozveren, Bulend, Chief Exec. Officer--Penajans DMB&B Ticaret, Istanbul, Turkey; *U.S. Private*, pg. 305
Paalman, G.J., Chief Oper. Officer & Mng. Dir.--Ter Huurne, Buurse, Netherlands; *Int'l*, pg. 749
Paarish, Lee, Pres.--Digital Communications of America, Inc., Oklahoma City, OK; *U.S. Private*, pg. 872
Paasikivi, Henry, Mng. Dir.--Sako Oy, Riihimaki, Finland; *Int'l*, pg. 954
Paasikivi, Henry, Pres.--Sako Ltd., Riihimaki, Finland; *Int'l*, pg. 1449
Paass, K., Pres.--BIAO Togo, Lome, Togo; *Int'l*, pg. 547
Pabbruwe, H.A., Mng. Dir.--Wolters Kluwer Law and Taxation, Deventer, Netherlands; *Int'l*, pg. 1513
Pabbruwe, H.A., Pres.--Kluwer Academic Publishers, Norwell, MA; *Int'l*, pg. 1513
Pabers, Ron J., V.P.-Instrumentation--Gems Sensors, Plainville, CT; *U.S. Public*, pg. 481
Pabon, Julio E., Gen. Mgr.--Dunkin' Donuts Venezuela, Caracas, Venezuela; *Int'l*, pg. 63
Pabst, Robert D., Pres. & Grp. Exec.--E.V. International, Inc., Buchanan, MI; *U.S. Private*, pg. 479
Paccino, M.P., Gen. Mgr.--Baring Private Equity Partners, Paris, France; *Int'l*, pg. 648
Pace, H.D., Mng. Dir.--Compania Hulera Goodyear-Oxo Sociedad Anonima, Mexico, Mexico; *U.S. Public*, pg. 753
Pace, William F., Chief Oper. Officer--Eastern Elevator Limited, Halifax, Canada; *Int'l*, pg. 747
Pacella, Jerry, Natl. Sls. Mgr.--Computer Products Div., Fair Lawn, NJ; *Int'l*, pg. 622
Pacelli, James A., Pres.--GFI-Genfare, Elk Grove Village, IL; *U.S. Public*, pg. 727
Pache, Eugene P., Gen. Mgr.--Label Products Div., Omaha, NE; *U.S. Public*, pg. 1152
Pacheco, C., Chief Oper. Officer--Tintas Robbialac S.A., Sacavem, Portugal; *Int'l*, pg. 1501
Pachl, Rudy, Pres.--Barry Callebaut, Saint Albans, VT; *Int'l*, pg. 252
Pacholder, Sylvia A., Pres.--Wedco Technology, Bloomsbury, NJ; *U.S. Public*, pg. 854
Pachoud, J.Y., Chief Oper. Officer--Skis Dynastar S.A., Salindres, France; *Int'l*, pg. 1127
Pacinda, George, Gen. Mgr.--Pittsburgh Tube Co.-Monroe Div., Monroe, NY; *U.S. Private*, pg. 868
Pacinda, Mark G., Mng. Dir.--Arby's Canada Inc., Mississauga, Canada; *U.S. Public*, pg. 1635
Pacini, Pierluigi, Dr., Gen. Mgr.--Forbo Resilienti S.r.l., Milan, Italy; *Int'l*, pg. 498
Paciocco, Paul, V.P. & Gen. Mgr.--Hilton Works, Hamilton, Canada; *Int'l*, pg. 1299

Pacitti, Peter, Mng. Dir.--Rank Video Services Ltd., Brentford, United Kingdom; *Int'l*, pg. 1087
Packalen, Kristian, Chief Oper. Officer & Mng. Dir.--Copap, Paris, France; *Int'l*, pg. 457
Packard, Craig, Plant Mgr.--TFX Marine, Hagerstown, MD; *U.S. Public*, pg. 1570
Packard, Dennis, Mng. Dir.--Brooktree Asia Pacific, Singapore, Singapore; *U.S. Public*, pg. 1398
Packer, Clyde, Pres.--USA Vacuum Ind. Inc. LLC, Saint James, MO; *U.S. Private*, pg. 1067
Packer, Daniel F., Pres.--Entergy New Orleans, Inc., New Orleans, LA; *U.S. Public*, pg. 586
Packer, John, Mng. Dir.--Texas Granite Corp., Marble Falls, TX; *U.S. Private*, pg. 251
Packer, Robert, Mgr.--Jefferson City Plant, Jefferson City, TN; *Int'l*, pg. 1055
Packham, Sue, Gen. Mgr.--TMP Worldwide Pty Ltd., Parramatta, Australia; *Int'l*, pg. 1342
Packham, William D., Pres.--Midland Walwyn Capital Inc., Toronto, Canada; *Int'l*, pg. 865
Pacton, Gregory, Gen. Mgr.--Joslyn Manufacturing Co.-Hardware Div., Chicago, IL; *U.S. Public*, pg. 481
Pacynski, Stefan, Mgr.--Woodward Governor Poland Sp.z.o.o., Warsaw, Poland; *U.S. Public*, pg. 1777
Padden, Preston, Pres.--ABC Television Network Group, New York, NY; *U.S. Public*, pg. 511
Paddington, Paul, Gen. Mgr.--Medtronic Bio-Medicus, Eden Prairie, MN; *U.S. Public*, pg. 1083
Paddock, James S., Chief Oper. Officer--Titanium Industries, Fairfield, NJ; *Int'l*, pg. 34
Paddock, James S., Pres. & Chief Exec. Officer--Titanium Industries, Inc., Morristown, NJ; *U.S. Public*, pg. 43
Padewer, Harvey, Pres.--Aquila Energy Corp., Omaha, NE; *U.S. Public*, pg. 1701
Padget-Parker, Carolyn, Admin.--Guardian Care of Kenansville, Kenansville, NC; *U.S. Public*, pg. 1712
Padgett, Carrol, Admin.--Guardian Care of Scotland Neck, Scotland Neck, NC; *U.S. Public*, pg. 1713
Padilla, Teodoro, Gen. Mgr.--Banco Santander, Manila, Philippines; *Int'l*, pg. 144
Padley, John, Gen. Mgr.--AMP Ireland Limited, Dublin, Ireland; *U.S. Public*, pg. 9
Padley, Ted, Pres.--TK Gray, Minneapolis, MN; *U.S. Public*, pg. 1329
Paek, K.W., Gen. Mgr.--Nalco Korea Co., Ltd., Seoul, Korea; *U.S. Public*, pg. 1151
Paes-Braga, Ruy, Gen. Mgr.--Four Seasons Hotel, Vancouver, Canada; *Int'l*, pg. 502
Paetzold, David, Pres. & Chief Exec. Officer--SouthTrust Bank, Southwest Florida, Fort Myers, FL; *U.S. Public*, pg. 1492
Paez, R., Plant Mgr.--Foamex, San Bernardino, CA; *U.S. Private*, pg. 1094
Paffenholz, Heinz-Peter, Pres.--CEAG Sicherheitstechnik GmbH, Soest, Germany; *U.S. Public*, pg. 444
Pagan, Earl, Plant Mgr.--Ivex Packaging Corporation-Visalia, Visalia, CA; *U.S. Public*, pg. 915
Paganelli, Luciano, Mng. Dir.--Olivetti Colombiana S.A., Bogota, Colombia; *Int'l*, pg. 1003
Pagano, Paul, V.P.-Sls.--Fairfield Harbour, New Bern, NC; *U.S. Public*, pg. 610
Page, Douglas F., Pres.--United Missouri Leasing Corporation, Kansas City, MO; *U.S. Public*, pg. 1655
Page, Fred, Pres.--ConAgra Grain Companies, Minneapolis, MN; *U.S. Public*, pg. 426
Page, George P., Gen. Mgr.--Elco Construction Products Division, Rockford, IL; *U.S. Public*, pg. 1590
Page, Jim, Plant Mgr.--Franklin Plant, Belden Division, Franklin, NC; *U.S. Public*, pg. 201
Page, Lew, Pres.--Paumier Company Inc., Canton, OH; *U.S. Private*, pg. 300
Page, M.J., Gen. Mgr.--Laporte (Thailand) Ltd., Bangkok, Thailand; *Int'l*, pg. 803
Page, Wayne, Gen. Mgr.--Tandy Signs, Arlington, TX; *U.S. Public*, pg. 1560
Pagels, George, Pres.--Baumgarten Stamp Co., Baltimore, MD; *U.S. Private*, pg. 58
Pagendarm, W., Mgr.--Natco Limited Partnership, Oak Brook, IL; *Int'l*, pg. 134
Pagendarm, William F., V.P. & Mgr.--North American Trailing Co., Oak Brook, IL; *U.S. Private*, pg. 474
Pages, James A., Pres.--VicWest Steel Division North American Building Products, Oakville, Canada; *Int'l*, pg. 698
Pages, Maury, Pres.--Pepsi-Cola Central, Itasca, IL; *U.S. Public*, pg. 1277
Pagett, J. A., Mng. Dir.--A.C. Hatrick Chemicals Pty. Limited, Botany, Australia; *U.S. Public*, pg. 811
Pagidas, M., Gen. Mgr.--S.C. Johnson & Son (Hellas) E.P.E., Athens, Greece; *U.S. Private*, pg. 593
Pagneaux, Bernard, Mng. Dir.--Viking Direct S.A.R.L., Paris, France; *U.S. Public*, pg. 1721
Pahl, Jeff, Gen. Mgr.--America's Beverage Co., Irving, TX; *U.S. Public*, pg. 967
Pahwa, Lalit K., Pres.--Webb India Ltd., Bangalore, India; *U.S. Private*, pg. 1157
Pai, David, Chm. Bd. & Pres.--Foster Wheeler Development Corp., Livingston, NJ; *U.S. Public*, pg. 676
Paicu, G.N., Pres.--Frontec Corporation, Edmonton, Canada; *Int'l*, pg. 95
Paidas, George P., Pres. & Chief Exec. Officer--The Old Phoenix National Bank of Medina, Medina, OH; *U.S. Public*, pg. 646
Paige, Dick, V.P.-Product Devel.--PIERS, New York, NY; *Int'l*, pg. 1026
Pailleret, Pierre, Chief Oper. Officer--Orly Air Traiteur, Wissous, France; *Int'l*, pg. 560
Painchaud, Francois, Chief Exec. Officer--Nouveler, Montreal, Canada; *Int'l*, pg. 640
Paine, Andrew J., Jr., Pres.--NBD Bank (Indiana), Indianapolis, IN; *U.S. Public*, pg. 628
Painter, Adrian, Mng. Dir.--Kvaerner EnviroPower Ltd., London, United Kingdom; *Int'l*, pg. 767
Painter, Carl, Chm. Bd. & Chief Exec. Officer--BICC Cables Corporation, West Nyack, NY; *Int'l*, pg. 120
Painter, Jeff, Gen. Mgr.--Hardel Builders Center, Olympia, WA; *U.S. Private*, pg. 501
Painter, Jeff, Gen. Mgr.--Hardel Builders Center, Centralia, WA; *U.S. Private*, pg. 501
Painter, Richard, Pres.--Prudential Commercial Insurance Co., Holmdel, NJ; *U.S. Private*, pg. 892
Paisley, Peter W., Sr., Pres.--CCL Custom Manufacturing, Toronto, Canada; *Int'l*, pg. 239
Paisley, Wes, Pres.--Dearborn Fabricating & Engineering Co., Detroit, MI; *Int'l*, pg. 1397
Paisley, Wes, Pres.--Mid-West Conveyor Co., Inc., Kansas City, KS; *Int'l*, pg. 1398
Paisner, Bruce L., Pres.--Hearst Entertainment, New York, NY; *U.S. Private*, pg. 516
Pajak, Stanislaw, Pres.--Pol Krusz S.A., Warsaw, Poland; *Int'l*, pg. 1200
Pajakowski, Mark, Gen. Mgr.--Michigan Tube Co., Eau Claire, MI; *U.S. Private*, pg. 533
Pajares, Ramon, Reg. V.P. & Gen. Mgr.--Inn On The Park, London, United Kingdom; *Int'l*, pg. 502
Pajoharju, Tapio, Pres.--Leaf Poland Sp.z.o.o, Legionowo, Poland; *Int'l*, pg. 638
Pakebusch, Joachim, Mng. Dir.--Emsland-Raisio Chemie GmbH, Hamburg, Germany; *Int'l*, pg. 1086
Pakkala, Juhani, Pres.--Valmet Inc., Charlotte, NC; *Int'l*, pg. 1448
Palach, Randal, Pres.--Signode Canada, Scarborough, Canada; *U.S. Public*, pg. 869
Palacio, Jose Ignacio, Office Dir.--DMB&B Bilbao, Bilbao, Spain; *U.S. Private*, pg. 303
Palacios, Emilia, Chief Officer--Villares Corporation of America, Dayton, NJ; *Int'l*, pg. 23
Palacios, Ulrich, Plant Mgr.--L.B. Foster Company-Seneca Yard, Seneca, IL; *U.S. Public*, pg. 676
Palantoni, F., Gen. Mgr.--Griffins Foods Ltd., Auckland, New Zealand; *Int'l*, pg. 381
Palanuwech, Akom, Chief Oper. Officer--Griffith Laboratories Limited, Samutprakan, Thailand; *U.S. Private*, pg. 481
Palavidis, Manos, Vice Chm., Mng. Dir., Creative Dir. & New Bus. Contact--EURO RSCG, Maroussi, Greece; *Int'l*, pg. 602
Palazzo, Richard, Pres.--Con-Way Central Express, Inc., Ann Arbor, MI; *U.S. Public*, pg. 281
Paled, Uzi, Mgr.--Tel-Ad Jerusalem Studio Ltd., Jerusalem, Israel; *Int'l*, pg. 644
Palenske, Grant, Gen. Mgr.--Ultra Industries, Inc., Monterey Park, CA; *U.S. Private*, pg. 692
Palensky, Frederic J., Div. V.P.--Dental Products Division, Saint Paul, MN; *U.S. Public*, pg. 1605
Palesny, Michael, Pres.--Charleston Industries, Charleston, MS; *U.S. Private*, pg. 856
Palfy, Jozsef, Gen. Mgr.--CCF Hungary, Budapest, Hungary; *Int'l*, pg. 342
Palijchook, Sergej O., Mng. Dir.--Reemtsma Ukraine, Kiev, Ukraine; *Int'l*, pg. 1101
Palk, Eun Hak, Pres. & Chief Exec. Officer--California Cho Hung Bank, Los Angeles, CA; *Int'l*, pg. 287
Palko, Lorri, Pres.--Dorsey Trailers, Inc., Elba, AL; *U.S. Public*, pg. 520
Pall, G., Pres. & Gen. Mgr.--Eonic Inc., Detroit, MI; *U.S. Public*, pg. 1176
Palladino, Marco, Chm. & Mng. Dir.--Hydrocarbons International Holding Co., Zurich, Switzerland; *Int'l*, pg. 429
Pallak, Hal, Pres.--Harte Hanks Shoppers, Redwood City, CA; *U.S. Public*, pg. 794
Palm, John, Pres.--Gannett New Media, Arlington, VA; *U.S. Public*, pg. 699
Palm, Lars, Pres.--NCC Building, Sundsvall, Sweden; *Int'l*, pg. 898
Palm, M.D., Chief Exec. Officer--Centre Reinsurance (Bermuda) Ltd., Hamilton, Bermuda; *Int'l*, pg. 1531
Palm, Stanley D., Mng. Dir.--Crisson Securities NV, Willemstad, Netherlands Antilles; *Int'l*, pg. 1115
Palma, Alvaro, Chief Oper. Officer--Laboratories Griffith de Mexico, S.A. de C.V., Monterrey, Mexico; *U.S. Private*, pg. 482
Palma, Gian Franco, Gen. Mgr.--Polaroid Italia S.A.R.L., Arisate, Italy; *U.S. Public*, pg. 1314
Palmano, B., Gen. Mgr.--Australian AMP Pty. Limited, Castle Hill, Australia; *U.S. Public*, pg. 9
Palmberg, Dr. Paul W., Gen. Mgr.--Perkin Elmer Physical Electronics Div., Eden Prairie, MN; *U.S. Public*, pg. 1279
Palmblad, Ulf, Pres.--Skanska Data AB, Danderyd, Sweden; *Int'l*, pg. 1260
Palmborg, Christen, Pres.--Interdental AB, Stockholm, Sweden; *Int'l*, pg. 708
Palmborg, Christen, Chief Oper. Officer--Axel Johnson Dental AB, Upplands Vasby, Sweden; *Int'l*, pg. 709
Palme, Gunnar, Pres.--Atlas Copco Industrial Tools & Equipment, Stockholm, Sweden; *Int'l*, pg. 96
Palmen, Rolf, Mgr.--Sandvik South East Asia Ltd., Jurong, Singapore; *Int'l*, pg. 1187
Palmer, C.R., Pres.--Rowan Drilling Co., Inc. Western Div., Odessa, TX; *U.S. Public*, pg. 1410
Palmer, C.R., Pres.--Rowandrill, Inc., Houston, TX; *U.S. Public*, pg. 1410
Palmer, C.R., Pres.--RDC Marine, Inc., Houston, TX; *U.S. Public*, pg. 1410
Palmer, Carl H., Mgr.--Hartland & St. Albans Telephone Co., Hartland, ME; *U.S. Public*, pg. 1572
Palmer, Dan M., Chief Exec. Officer--Concord National Bank, Inc., Memphis, TN; *U.S. Public*, pg. 429
Palmer, Dave, Branch Mgr.--Burns & Wilcox - Aurora Office, Aurora, CO; *U.S. Private*, pg. 609
Palmer, David, Pres.--F.T. Publications Inc., New York, NY; *Int'l*, pg. 1026
Palmer, Donna, Contact--Quest Diagnostic-Geneseo, Geneseo, NY; *U.S. Public*, pg. 1351
Palmer, Duncan, Gen. Mgr.--P.T. Jaya Mandarin Agung, Jakarta, Indonesia; *Int'l*, pg. 704
Palmer, Edward, Pres.--Howden Sirocco, Inc., Hyde Park, MA; *Int'l*, pg. 636
Palmer, Fay, Office Mgr.--Meadowbrook Co., Spelter, WV; *U.S. Private*, pg. 331
Palmer, G.C.A., Chief Oper. Officer--Richardson-Vicks S.A., Madrid, Spain; *U.S. Public*, pg. 1333
Palmer, Gary G., V.P.--Martin Marietta International, Inc., Canberra, Australia; *U.S. Public*, pg. 1010
Palmer, Gary G., Gen. Mgr.--Martin Marietta International, Inc., Riyadh, Saudi Arabia; *U.S. Public*, pg. 1010
Palmer, George R., Pres.--Photon Systems Ltd., Calgary, Canada; *U.S. Public*, pg. 1563
Palmer, Glenn S., Pres.--Liz Claiborne Collection Division, New York, NY; *U.S. Public*, pg. 1006
Palmer, Heather, Division Mgr.--Horizon Technology Group - Taylor Division, Taylor, MI; *U.S. Private*, pg. 539
Palmer, Jack, Mgr.--Duferco Steel Inc., New York, NY; *U.S. Private*, pg. 345
Palmer, Jim, V.P.-Sls.--Shorewood Packaging of California, Inc., Hollywood, CA; *U.S. Public*, pg. 1468
Palmer, Jon, Chief Exec. Officer--Wellspring Resources, LLC, Jacksonville, FL; *U.S. Private*, pg. 1154
Palmer, Jon, Chief Exec. Officer--Wellspring Resources, LLC, Jacksonville, FL; *U.S. Public*, pg. 1513
Palmer, Jonathan J., Chief Exec. Officer--Barnett Technologies, Inc., Jacksonville, FL; *U.S. Public*, pg. 1162
Palmer, Mike, Pres.--Tech Group Phoenix, Inc., Tempe, AZ; *U.S. Private*, pg. 1071
Palmer, N., Mng. Dir.--NRG Group Limited, Northampton, United Kingdom; *Int'l*, pg. 1114
Palmer, N. J., Mng. Dir.--Gestetner (Ireland) Limited, Dublin, Ireland; *Int'l*, pg. 1115
Palmer, R. Jay, Pres.--Old Kent Financial Life Insurance Company, Grand Rapids, MI; *U.S. Public*, pg. 1217
Palmer, Reginald, Mgr.--West Penobscot Telegraph & Telephone Co., Corinna, ME; *U.S. Public*, pg. 1572
Palmer, Robert, Gen. Mgr.--The Orchid Center, Arcadia, FL; *U.S. Private*, pg. 1050
Palmer, Roger, Pres.--Colloid Environmental Technologies Company (CETCO), Arlington Heights, IL; *U.S. Public*, pg. 64
Palmer, Ron, Pres. & Chief Exec. Officer--Business Air, Grosse Ile, MI; *U.S. Private*, pg. 539
Palmer, Ron, Chm. Bd.--Horizon Technology Group LLC, Taylor, MI; *U.S. Private*, pg. 539
Palmer, Sam, Mng. Dir.--Cellex Manufacturing, Inc., London, Canada; *U.S. Private*, pg. 1080
Palmer, Vince, Gen. Mgr.--Frank Paxton Lumber Company, Cincinnati, OH; *U.S. Private*, pg. 585
Palmer, W. Raymond, Gen. Mgr.--ITT Flygt Ltd., Dublin, Ireland; *U.S. Public*, pg. 860
Palmer, Walter Jr., Plant Mgr.--Glass Plant, Corsicana, TX; *U.S. Private*, pg. 486
Palmer, William, Pres.--Pall Power Generation Division, Greenvale, NY; *U.S. Public*, pg. 1254
Palmer, William C., Pres.--Pall Process Filtration Company, Greenvale, NY; *U.S. Public*, pg. 1254
Palmgren, George, Dir.-Fin.--Whirlpool do Brazil S.A., Sao Paulo, Brazil; *U.S. Public*, pg. 1765
Palmieri, Frank, Pres.--The Media & Marketing Group, Cherry Hill, NJ; *U.S. Private*, pg. 902
Palmieri, Giustino, Chief Admin. Officer--Triumph Adler (U.K.) Ltd., Colchester, United Kingdom; *Int'l*, pg. 1004
Palmisano, Joseph A., Acting Chief Oper. Officer--Fleet Bank, Boston, MA; *U.S. Public*, pg. 649
Palmisano, Robert J., V.P.--Bausch & Lomb Eyewear Division-TX, San Antonio, TX; *U.S. Public*, pg. 194
Palmisano, Robert J., V.P.--Bausch & Lomb Eyewear Division-MD, Oakland, MD; *U.S. Public*, pg. 194
Palmtag, R., Gen. Mgr.--Minserco, Inc., South Milwaukee, WI; *U.S. Private*, pg. 177
Palo, James F., Pres.--Universal Foods Corp.-Dehydrated Products Div., Turlock, CA; *U.S. Public*, pg. 1696
Palo, James F., Pres.--Rogers Foods, Turlock, CA; *U.S. Public*, pg. 1696
Palo, Neil, Exec. V.P.--McNeil Specialty Products Company, New Brunswick, NJ; *U.S. Public*, pg. 928
Paloma, Ray, Div. Mgr.--Wyle Electronics-Phoenix, Phoenix, AZ; *Int'l*, pg. 1457
Palonen, Gary L., Chief Exec. Officer--Veda Systems, Incorporated, California, MD; *U.S. Private*, pg. 1136
Paloniemi, Ilpo, Chief Oper. Officer--KONE Wood Oy, Hollola, Finland; *Int'l*, pg. 14
Palovaara, Pekka, Pres.--Valmet Ges.m.b.H., Vienna, Austria; *Int'l*, pg. 1448
Palovaara, Pekka, Pres.--Valmet Vertrieb Gmbh, Pfungstadt, Germany; *Int'l*, pg. 1448
Palovaara, Pekka, Pres.--Valmet Service GmbH, Pfungstadt, Germany; *Int'l*, pg. 1449
Palsho, Dorothea Coccoli, Pres.--Dow Jones Interactive, Princeton, NJ; *U.S. Public*, pg. 524
Palsho, Dorothea Coccoli, Pres.--Dow Jones Interactive Publishing, Princeton, NJ; *U.S. Public*, pg. 524
Palsson, Bengt, Chief Oper. Officer--Perstorp Analytical Tecator AB, Hoganas, Sweden; *Int'l*, pg. 1040
Paluck, Robert J., Chief Exec. Officer--Convex Technology Center - Hewlett-Packard, Richardson, TX; *U.S. Public*, pg. 815
Palus, Andrew, Mgr.--EG & G Instruments Applied Research, Oak Ridge, TN; *U.S. Public*, pg. 543
Palusci, P., Mng. Dir.--Goodyear Italiana S.p.A., Rome, Italy; *U.S. Public*, pg. 753
Paluska, Stephen M., Treas. & Dir.--Dav-El Services, Inc., Long Island City, NY; *U.S. Private*, pg. 314
Pamplin, R.B., Jr., Dr., Chm. Bd. & Chief Exec. Officer--Mount Vernon Mills, Inc., Greenville, SC; *U.S. Private*, pg. 835
Pamplin, R.B., Jr., Dr., Pres. & Chief Exec. Officer--K.F. Jacobson Co., Portland, OR; *U.S. Private*, pg. 836
Pan, Peter, Dr., Pres.--Thiele Engineering, Minneapolis, MN; *U.S. Private*, pg. 118
Panacek, Radomir, Liaison Officer--Adverta, Prague, Czech Republic; *U.S. Private*, pg. 1152

Panacio, Dominic, Pres.--Lockheed Martin Training & Technical Services, Horsham, PA; U.S. Public, pg. 1009
Panagopulos, D., Pres.--Theo Davies Marine Agencies, Inc., Honolulu, HI; Int'l, pg. 704
Panas, Louis, Pres.--Ottawa River Steel Co., Toledo, OH; U.S. Public, pg. 1095
Pando, Robert T., Chm. Bd. & Pres.--Lynch Machinery, Inc., Bainbridge, GA; U.S. Public, pg. 1022
Pandza, Hubert, Representative--Deutsche Bank AG (Moscow), Moscow, Russia; Int'l, pg. 404
Pandzich, M.J., V.P. & Gen. Mgr.--Copco Steel Co., Livonia, MI; Int'l, pg. 1150
Panettiere, John M., Pres. & Chief Exec. Officer--Blount, Inc., Montgomery, AL; U.S. Public, pg. 238
Panettiere, John M., Chm. Bd.--Frederick Manufacturing Corporation, Kansas City, MO; U.S. Public, pg. 238
Panettiere, John M., Pres.--4520 Corp., Inc., Montgomery, AL; U.S. Public, pg. 239
Pang, C.M., V.P. & Country Mgr.--Bank of America NT&SA, Beijing, China; U.S. Public, pg. 182
Pang, Peter, Gen. Mgr.--Xi'An System Sensor Electronics, Ltd., Xian, China; U.S. Public, pg. 1307
Pang, Thomas, V.P.-Central U.S.--Singapore Tourist Promotion Board - Chicago, Chicago, IL; Int'l, pg. 1254
Pangan, E.S., Exec. V.P. & Gen. Mgr.--Philippines Dairy Products Corp., Manila, Philippines; Int'l, pg. 923
Pangestu, Prajogo, Chm. Bd.--United Pulp & Paper Company Limited, Jurong, Singapore; Int'l, pg. 1444
Panis, Jean, Mng. Dir.--Marcam Belgium N.V., Zaventem, Belgium; U.S. Public, pg. 1043
Panis, Jean, Gen. Dir.--Marcam Nederland B.V., Best, Netherlands; U.S. Public, pg. 1043
Panitzki, Alexander, Sr. Mng. Dir.--Deutsche Bank-Kreditbank AG (Leipzig), Leipzig, Germany; Int'l, pg. 402
Pankakoski, Isto, Mng. Dir.--Nokia Mobile Phones UK Sales Ltd., Godmanchester, United Kingdom; Int'l, pg. 952
Pankamaa, Heikki, Chief Oper. Officer--Ahlstrom Kauttua Ltd., Kauttua, Finland; Int'l, pg. 35
Pankau, G.M., Chief Exec. Officer--Centronic Inc., Thousand Oaks, CA; Int'l, pg. 892
Panko, Bill, Reg. Acct. Dir.--RP alpha/Chicago, Arlington Heights, IL; U.S. Private, pg. 950
Pannekoek, Ton, Country Mgr.--Compaq Computer B.V., Gouda, Netherlands; U.S. Public, pg. 418
Pannetier, Claude, Pres.--Execorp., Paris, France; Int'l, pg. 29
Panno, Phil, Administrator--Boardman Community Care Center, Youngstown, OH; U.S. Public, pg. 838
Panoff, Oleg, Mgr.--EURO RSCG Media, Moscow, Russia; Int'l, pg. 603
Panopoulos, George J., Mng. Dir.--Cartellas S.A., Athens, Greece; U.S. Public, pg. 672
Panozzo, Larry L., Pres.--Banta Publications Group, Hinsdale, IL; U.S. Public, pg. 188
Panse, Horst, Mgr.--Aro GmbH, Ratingen, Germany; U.S. Public, pg. 877
Pantel, Richard, V.P.--Gefinor U.S.A., Inc., New York, NY; Int'l, pg. 542
Pantoja, Francisco Botia, Pres.--Central Termica Litoral de Almeria A.I.E., Carboneras, Spain; Int'l, pg. 1224
Panton, Ian, Pres.--Ross Breeders, Inc., Elkmont, AL; Int'l, pg. 619
Panton, Keith S., Dr., Pres.--Alcan Jamaica Co., Manchester, Jamaica; Int'l, pg. 51
Panyeko, Stephen H., Pres. & Chief Exec. Officer--United Jersey Leasing Company, Princeton, NJ; U.S. Public, pg. 1528
Panyeko, Stephen H., Pres. & Chief Exec. Officer--United Jersey Venture Capital, Inc., Princeton, NJ; U.S. Public, pg. 1528
Panyko, Stephen, V.P. & Gen. Mgr.--Rockwell Switching Systems Div., Wood Dale, IL; U.S. Public, pg. 1398
Panzarini, Rinaldo, Dir.--Banca d'America e d'Italia S.p.A. (Verona), Verona, Italy; Int'l, pg. 403
Panzer, John, Resident Representative--Banco Mundial, Quito, Ecuador; U.S. Private, pg. 1189
Panzetti, Maurizio, Chief Oper. Officer--Griffith Laboratories Italia S.r.l., Rome, Italy; U.S. Private, pg. 481
Paolino, Richard F., V.P. & Gen. Mgr.--Measuring Systems Division, North Kingstown, RI; U.S. Public, pg. 260
Paone, Tom, Gen. Mgr.--Arrow/Schweber Electronics, Lake Mary, FL; U.S. Public, pg. 134
Paonessa, Gregorio, Gen. Mgr.--Aerimpianti S.p.A., Milan, Italy; Int'l, pg. 653
Paosio, P., Sec.--Pilkington Lahden Lasitehdas Oy, Lahti, Finland; Int'l, pg. 1056
Papa, Ralph J., Reg. Pres. & Chief Exec. Officer--Mellon Bank, N.A.-Central Region, State College, PA; U.S. Public, pg. 1085
Papadia, Enzo, Pres.--Gedy Iberica, Barcelona, Spain; Int'l, pg. 542
Papaila, Ted, V.P.-Mktg.--Commercial Communications Div., Fort Worth, TX; Int'l, pg. 1433
Papanier, George, Chief Oper. Officer--Resorts Casino Hotel, Atlantic City, NJ; U.S. Public, pg. 1531
Papao, A., Pres.--Merck Sharp y Dohme Espana S.A., Barcelona, Spain; U.S. Public, pg. 1092
Papas, Mirka Giacoletto, V.P.--Ketchum Public Relations, SRL, Milan, Italy; U.S. Private, pg. 617
Papas, Peter B., V.P. & Gen. Mgr.--Countermeasures Div., Nashua, NH; U.S. Public, pg. 1008
Papasan, Larry, Pres.--Smith & Nephew Orthopedics, Memphis, TN; Int'l, pg. 1263
Papazoglou, Anastasios, Chief Oper. Officer--MacGREGOR (GRC) E.P.E., Piraeus, Greece; Int'l, pg. 670
Papciak, Wally, Chief Oper. Officer--Quality Education Data (QED), Denver, CO; U.S. Private, pg. 858
Pape, Dieter, Chief Oper. Officer--Volkswagen Leasing S.A. de C.V., Puebla, Mexico; Int'l, pg. 1475
Pape, John J., Pres.--NorLease, Inc., Chicago, IL; U.S. Public, pg. 1196
Papesh, Ron, Pres.--Meco USA Inc., Rock Hill, SC; Int'l, pg. 1064
Papesh, Ronald, Pres.--Meco Metal Finishing USA Inc., Rock Hill, SC; Int'l, pg. 1064
Papesh, William G., Pres.--Murphey Favre Securities Services, Inc., Spokane, WA; U.S. Public, pg. 1742
Papetti, Arthur, Chief Exec. Officer--Papetti Hygrade Egg Products, Elizabeth, NJ; U.S. Public, pg. 1104
Papillaud, Pierre, Chm. Bd.--Crystal Geyser Roxane Water L.P., Olancha, CA; Int'l, pg. 1013
Papillon, Michel, Pres.--Sunrise Medical Canada Inc., Concord, Canada; U.S. Public, pg. 1536
Papillou, Paul, Pres.--Borden France S.A., Paris, France; U.S. Private, pg. 159
Papineau, William, Pres.--West Agro, Inc., Kansas City, MO; Int'l, pg. 1379
Paplowski, Gunter, Mng. Dir.--LBS Immobilien GmbH Berlin, Berlin, Germany; Int'l, pg. 160
Pappalardo, Frank S., Pres.--TRI-S Incorporated, Ellington, CT; U.S. Public, pg. 546
Pappalardo, Tom, Mgr.--Lason Information Management, Detroit, MI; U.S. Public, pg. 979
Pappas, M.M., Pres.--Blazer Financial Services, Cordova, TN; U.S. Public, pg. 1741
Pappas, Michael M., Pres.--Great Western Consumer Finance Group, Tampa, FL; U.S. Public, pg. 1741
Pappas, Michael M., Pres.--Consumer Finance Group, Tampa, FL; U.S. Public, pg. 1741
Pappas, Tim, Pres.--Keyes Investments, Miami, FL; U.S. Private, pg. 618
Papson, Hardy, Pres.--PT BHP Steel Indonesia, Cilegon, Indonesia; Int'l, pg. 227
Paquette, Dick, Pres.--Air Midwest, Inc., Wichita, KS; U.S. Public, pg. 1099
Paquette, J. F., Jr., Chm.--Eastern Pennsylvania Development Co., Philadelphia, PA; U.S. Public, pg. 1268
Paquette, J.F., Jr., Chm. Bd.--Adwin Equipment Co., Philadelphia, PA; U.S. Public, pg. 1268
Paquette, Steve, Gen. Mgr.--Groundwater Technology Government Services, Inc., Westchester, PA; U.S. Public, pg. 660
Paquin, Claude, Gen. Mgr.--Midland Bank S.A., Paris, France; Int'l, pg. 580
Para, Dick, Gen. Mgr.--Poe & Brown of Florida, Sarasota, FL; U.S. Public, pg. 1312
Paradissiotis, Chris, Pres.--Coastal Stock Co., Ltd., Hamilton, Bermuda; U.S. Public, pg. 390
Paradissiotis, Chris, Pres.--Holborn Oil Trading Ltd., Hamilton, Bermuda; U.S. Public, pg. 390
Paraszcaka, John, Pres.--Yates Investment Casting Wax Inc., Chicago, IL; Int'l, pg. 234
Parato, Vito J., V.P. & Gen. Mgr.--U.S. Gauge, Sellersville, PA; U.S. Public, pg. 100
Parazzo, Gabriele, Gen. Mgr.--Fischer & Porter Italiana S.p.A., Genoa, Italy; Int'l, pg. 449
Parba, D., Mgr.--Plywood Plastics, Inc., Rochester, NY; U.S. Private, pg. 873
Pardo, Alberto, Chief Oper. Officer--Boart Longyear S.A. de C.V., Mexico, Mexico; Int'l, pg. 76
Pardoak, Adolfo, Mng. Dir.--Gestetner Chile S.A., Santiago, Chile; Int'l, pg. 1115
Pardridge, Donald, Plant. Mgr.--Sycamore Plant, Sycamore, IL; U.S. Public, pg. 444
Pardus, Donald G., Chm. Bd.--EUA Service Corporation, West Bridgewater, MA; U.S. Public, pg. 549
Pare, Jean, Pres.--Magazines Maclean Hunter Quebec, Montreal, Canada; Int'l, pg. 1123
Paredes, Carlos, Exec. Dir.--Onena Bolsas de Papel, S.A., Pamplona, Spain; U.S. Public, pg. 440
Paredes, Jaime, Chief Oper. Officer--Skandia Seguros De Vida S.A., Bogota, Colombia; Int'l, pg. 1258
Paredes, Lombardo, Pres.--CIED Centro Internacional de Educacion y Desarrollo, Caracas, Venezuela; Int'l, pg. 1045
Paredes, Marco, Jr., Chief Oper. Officer--Pennsylvania Parking, Inc., Philadelphia, PA; U.S. Private, pg. 43
Parello, A. Richard, V.P.--Land Instruments International, Inc., Bristol, PA; Int'l, pg. 798
Parent, Calvin L., Pres.--Ross Roy Communications Canada, Limited, Windsor, Canada; U.S. Private, pg. 946
Parent, Jocelyn, Mgr.-Area Sls.--Sensormatic Canada, Inc., Ville Saint Laurent, Canada; U.S. Public, pg. 1457
Parfitt, Steven, Plant Mgr.--Donaldson Filter Components Ltd., Kingston-upon-Hull, United Kingdom; U.S. Public, pg. 517
Parham, Don, Gen. Mgr.--Surplus Warehouse-Jackson, Jackson, MS; U.S. Private, pg. 119
Parham, W.E., Chief Oper. Officer--K.R. Edwards Leaf Tobacco Co., Inc., Smithfield, NC; U.S. Public, pg. 1694
Pariani, Ron, Pres.--Outokumpu Wenmec, Inc., Lithia Springs, GA; Int'l, pg. 1017
Parigot de Souza, Cid V., Chm. Bd.--Nordesclor S.A., Recife, Brazil; U.S. Public, pg. 1219
Parikh, H.N., Mgr.--Morton Chemical Div., Elk Grove Village, IL; U.S. Public, pg. 1135
Pariot, S., V.P. & Gen. Mgr.--Martel Catala et Cie, Selestat, France; U.S. Public, pg. 37
Paris, P., Gen. Mgr.--Barings (France), Paris, France; Int'l, pg. 648
Paris, Raymond, V.P. & Gen. Mgr.--Healthcare Services Division, Melville, NY; U.S. Public, pg. 946
Paris, William C., Jr., Chief Oper. Officer--EMCON Associates, Fresno, CA; U.S. Public, pg. 571
Parise, Thomas C., Pres.--Inter-Tel Integrated Systems, Inc., Chandler, AZ; U.S. Public, pg. 888
Parise, Thomas C., Pres.--Inter-Tel Equipment UK, Ltd., Wellingborough, United Kingdom; U.S. Public, pg. 888
Parish, Robert G., Dr., Mng. Dir.--Scientific Software-Intercomp (U.K.) Limited, Egham, United Kingdom; U.S. Public, pg. 1444
Parish, Thomas, Pres.--Norwest Properties, Inc., Minneapolis, MN; U.S. Public, pg. 1202
Parivar, Ken, Mgr.-Opers.--Fontana, Fontana, CA; U.S. Public, pg. 730
Park, Bill, Chief Oper. Officer--Curtis Mathes Corporation, Dallas, TX; U.S. Public, pg. 1057
Park, Bong S., Pres.--Tokyo Printing Ink Corporation U.S.A, Rancho Dominguez, CA; Int'l, pg. 1394
Park, C. W., Mgr.-Tech. Sls.--ANGUS Korea, Daechi-Dong, Korea; U.S. Private, pg. 75
Park, Chris, Dir.-Dayton Hudson Foundation--Dayton Hudson Corporation, Minneapolis, MN; U.S. Public, pg. 489
Park, Chung-Il, Pres.--Bum-A Petroleum Co., Ltd., Seoul, Korea; Int'l, pg. 1292
Park, D.S., Gen. Mgr.--Hanjin Co., Ltd., Long Beach, CA; Int'l, pg. 592
Park, Frederick B., Pres.--Tenneco Uranium, Inc., Houston, TX; U.S. Public, pg. 1579
Park, George, Publisher--Finger Lakes Printing Company, Geneva, NY; U.S. Private, pg. 559
Park, Howard R., Jr., Chm. Bd.--Commercial Bank and Trust Company of Troup County, La Grange, GA; U.S. Public, pg. 1549
Park, J.C., V.P.--Genus Korea, Ltd., Seoul, Korea; U.S. Public, pg. 733
Park, Je Hwa, Gen. Mgr.--Janssen Korea, Ltd., Seoul, Korea; U.S. Public, pg. 929
Park, Jong Soo, Chief Oper. Officer--Daewoo Bank (Hungary) Ltd., Budapest, Hungary; Int'l, pg. 359
Park, Joon-chang, Pres.--Goldstar Electric Co. Ltd., Seoul, Korea; Int'l, pg. 779
Park, Kyung Yong, Gen. Mgr.--Cho Hung Bank, Osaka Branch, Osaka, Japan; Int'l, pg. 288
Park, M.S., Pres.--Hyundai Corp., U.S.A., Bensenville, IL; Int'l, pg. 641
Park, Matthew, Mng. Dir.--Inso Corporation, Ltd., London, United Kingdom; U.S. Public, pg. 882
Park, Roy, Gen. Mgr.--Moog Australia Pty. Ltd., Mulgrave, Australia; U.S. Public, pg. 1127
Park, Seung-Ki, Pres.--Dongseong Express Tourists Co., Ltd., Busan, Korea; Int'l, pg. 1292
Park, Ung-Suh, Pres.--Samsung Petrochemical Co. Ltd., Seoul, Korea; U.S. Public, pg. 102
Parke, Raymond, Mng. Dir.--Thrige-Scott Ltd., Belfast, United Kingdom; Int'l, pg. 1387
Parke, Robert N., Treas.--SPF Insurance Agency, Franklin Park, IL; U.S. Public, pg. 1428
Parke, Robert N., V.P. & Treas.--EFS/San Diego Service Corporation, Chicago, IL; U.S. Public, pg. 1428
Parker, Bruce, Pres.--Smith & Nephew Casting, Inc., Charlotte, NC; Int'l, pg. 1263
Parker, Carlton, Gen. Mgr.--Sanderson Computers Hong Kong Ltd., Causeway Bay, Hong Kong; Int'l, pg. 1185
Parker, Carlton, G.M.--Sanderson Computers Pte. Ltd., Singapore, Singapore; Int'l, pg. 1185
Parker, Daniel, Pres.--Surface Technology Business, East Windsor, CT; U.S. Public, pg. 582
Parker, Dave, Mgr.-Fin.--W.R. Grace & Co. of Canada Ltd., Grace Construction Products, Ajax, Canada; U.S. Public, pg. 755
Parker, Don, Pres. & Chief Oper. Officer--Farr Filtration, Ltd., Birmingham, United Kingdom; U.S. Public, pg. 614
Parker, Eric, Gen. Mgr.--ITW Shakeproof/Specialty Products, Elgin, IL; U.S. Public, pg. 867
Parker, G., Mgr.-Sls.--Olin Corporation N.Z. Limited, Manukau, New Zealand; U.S. Public, pg. 1220
Parker, Gary, Pres.--Lindsay Transportation Inc., Lindsay, NE; U.S. Public, pg. 1000
Parker, Giles, V.P.-Sls.--All Star Gas Co.-Region XI, Lebanon, MO; U.S. Private, pg. 35
Parker, Guy, Mng. Dir.--K-Tron Great Britain, Ltd., Oldham, United Kingdom; U.S. Public, pg. 938
Parker, H. Stewart, Pres.--Targeted Genetics Corp., Seattle, WA; U.S. Public, pg. 871
Parker, J., Chief Oper. Officer--Lloyds Bank Finance (Isle of Man) Ltd., Douglas, United Kingdom; Int'l, pg. 813
Parker, JoAnn, Chm. Bd.--Omniflight Helicopters, Inc., Dallas, TX; U.S. Private, pg. 817
Parker, Jonathan, Mng. Dir.--Osprey, London, United Kingdom; Int'l, pg. 1093
Parker, Lewis, Chief Oper. Officer--Covance Laboratories, Vienna, VA; U.S. Public, pg. 454
Parker, Michael, Grp. Sr. V.P.--Southwest Loan Administration, Dallas, TX; U.S. Public, pg. 650
Parker, Michael, Div. Mgr.--VicWest Steel Supply, Cambridge, Canada; Int'l, pg. 698
Parker, Michael, Pres.--Trader Joe's Co., South Pasadena, CA; U.S. Private, pg. 1067
Parker, Michael D., Pres.--Dow Chemical North America, Midland, MI; U.S. Public, pg. 522
Parker, Michael R., Sr. V.P.--Willis Faber North America, Inc.-Connecticut, Stamford, CT; Int'l, pg. 1503
Parker, Nancy, Pres.--Winchell's Donut Houses, L.P., Santa Ana, CA; Int'l, pg. 1230
Parker, Nancy J., Pres.--Sportservice Corporation, Buffalo, NY; U.S. Private, pg. 322
Parker, Neil, Pres.--Thomas & Betts Ltd., Iberville, Canada; U.S. Public, pg. 1598
Parker, Richard, Pres.--ADMC Inc, Temple, TX; U.S. Private, pg. 86
Parker, Richard E., Jr., Pres.--XLM Company, Mount Pleasant, IA; U.S. Public, pg. 772
Parker, Robert A., Pres. & Chief Exec. Officer--Regions Bank/Stephens County, Toccoa, GA; U.S. Public, pg. 1373
Parker, Robert S., Pres.--Berol Inc., Bellwood, IL; U.S. Public, pg. 1177
Parker, Ron, Pres.--DG Trim Products Div., Charlotte, NC; U.S. Private, pg. 560
Parker, Ron, Pres.--MGM Brakes Div., Charlotte, NC; U.S. Private, pg. 560
Parker, Wendell W., Chief Oper. Officer--GAI Consultants-NC, Inc., Raleigh, NC; U.S. Private, pg. 434
Parkerson, Eugene, Pres.--Power Purchasing, Inc., Exton, PA; U.S. Private, pg. 233
Parkes, Bruce W., Chm. Bd.--Ford Fleet Financing Limited, Brentwood, United Kingdom; U.S. Public, pg. 666

Parkes, R., Gen. Mgr.--Cookson Matthey Ceramics, West Chester, PA; *Int'l*, pg. 714
Parkes, Rose L., Chief Exec. Officer--Surgecenter of Palo Alto, Palo Alto, CA; *U.S. Public*, pg. 1716
Parkin, Ray, Pres.--Componenta International Marketing (F.E.) Pte. Ltd., Singapore, Singapore; *Int'l*, pg. 1421
Parkinson, Kirk, Publr.--The Daily Herald, Provo, UT; *U.S. Public*, pg. 1343
Parkinson, Nigel, Pres.--Kvaerner de Mexico, S.A. de C.V., Mexico, Mexico; *Int'l*, pg. 767
Parkinson, Ron, V.P. & Mng. Dir.--J.W. Messner, Inc., Pittsburgh, PA; *U.S. Private*, pg. 734
Parkinson, Sheri Fogg, V.P.--Naturally You, Jacksonville Beach, FL; *U.S. Private*, pg. 1015
Parks, Bill, Pres.--Pioneer Hi-Bred Limited, Chatham, Canada; *U.S. Public*, pg. 1299
Parks, Brian, Dir.--Kemira Coatings Ltd., Haverhill, United Kingdom; *Int'l*, pg. 729
Parks, Clyde, Gen. Mgr.--Today's Kids, Booneville, AR; *U.S. Private*, pg. 1020
Parks, Gordon, Mng. Dir.--Roteq Services Sdn. Bhd., Terengganu, Malaysia; *Int'l*, pg. 1305
Parks, Paul W., Pres. & Chief Exec. Officer--Mercantile Mortgage Corp., Baltimore, MD; *U.S. Public*, pg. 1089
Parks, Ralph T., Pres. & Chief Exec. Officer--FootAction USA, Irving, TX; *U.S. Public*, pg. 661
Parks, S., V.P.-Printing (Southwest Area)--Zellerbach Division, Norwalk, CA; *U.S. Public*, pg. 1076
Parks, S.B., V.P.-Printing (Southwest Area)--Zellerbach Division, National City, CA; *U.S. Public*, pg. 1076
Parks, S.B., V.P.-Printing (Southwest Area)--Zellerbach Division, Las Vegas, NV; *U.S. Public*, pg. 1076
Parlman, Robert M., Gen. Mgr. & V.P.--Zeeland Chemicals, Inc., Zeeland, MI; *U.S. Public*, pg. 297
Parlog, John, III, Pres.--Valmark Industries, Inc., Fremont, CA; *U.S. Private*, pg. 598
Parman, Michael J., Publisher--The Press Democrat, Santa Rosa, CA; *U.S. Public*, pg. 1175
Parmar, J., Mng. Dir.--Linread Automotive, Hockley, United Kingdom; *Int'l*, pg. 851
Parmelee, Harold J., Pres.--Turner Development Corporation, New York, NY; *U.S. Public*, pg. 1646
Parmentier, A., Mng. Dir.--Imtech Projects Zuit B.V., Roermond, Netherlands; *Int'l*, pg. 681
Parmentier, Guy-Francis, Mng. Dir.--AlliedSignal Laminate Systems S.A., Les Ulis, France; *U.S. Public*, pg. 53
Parmigiano, John M., Gen. Mgr. & Mng. Dir.--Unocal Netherlands, Hague, Netherlands; *U.S. Public*, pg. 1698
Parod, Richard W., Pres.--Irritol System, Riverside, CA; *U.S. Public*, pg. 1624
Parodi, Donald, Pres.--Setco, Inc., Anaheim, CA; *U.S. Public*, pg. 1066
Parola, Olli, Pres. & Chief Exec. Officer--United Paper Mills Ltd., Valkeakoski, Finland; *Int'l*, pg. 1429
Parque, Ronald D., Pres.--Mrs. Cubbison's Foods, Inc., Montebello, CA; *U.S. Public*, pg. 909
Parr, G.T., Mng. Dir.--Pontin's Limited, Chorley, United Kingdom; *Int'l*, pg. 1211
Parr, Paul, Pres.--Quebecor Litho Plus, Willowdale, Canada; *Int'l*, pg. 1076
Parra, Alirio, Mng. Dir.--Petroleos de Venezuela UK, S.A., London, United Kingdom; *Int'l*, pg. 1046
Parra, Jose V., Mgr.--Acesita Sandvik Tubos Inox S.A., Sao Paulo, Brazil; *Int'l*, pg. 1187
Parra, Jose V., Mgr.--Sandvik do Brasil S.A., Sao Paulo, Brazil; *Int'l*, pg. 1188
Parra, Luis Guillermo, Pres. & Chief Oper. Officer--BASF Quimica Colombiana S.A., Bogota, Colombia; *Int'l*, pg. 107
Parrilla, Jose A., Mng. Dir.--SKF Productos Industriales S.A., Barcelona, Spain; *Int'l*, pg. 1159
Parrillo, Gillian M., Pres.--Systems Management Group, Plano, TX; *U.S. Public*, pg. 1516
Parrish, Henry N., Pres.--Chicago West Pullman Heavy Industries, Cincinnati, OH; *U.S. Private*, pg. 236
Parrish, James, Chief Oper. Officer--Innovative South, Nashville, TN; *U.S. Private*, pg. 565
Parrish, Mike, V.P. & Gen. Mgr.--Nucor Steel-Texas, Jewett, TX; *U.S. Public*, pg. 1205
Parrish, O. B., Pres.--Searle Chemicals, Inc., Chicago, IL; *U.S. Public*, pg. 1125
Parrish, Ronald K., Pres.--Elastomer Seals - North America, Morton Grove, IL; *Int'l*, pg. 1338
Parrish, S., Mng. Dir.--British Sterilizer Ltd., Mansfield, United Kingdom; *Int'l*, pg. 551
Parrish, S., Mng. Dir.--The Sterilizing Equipment Co. Ltd., Mansfield, United Kingdom; *Int'l*, pg. 552
Parrish, Stanton C., Pres.--Harbor Financial Services, Spokane, WA; *U.S. Public*, pg. 1516
Parrish, Tom, Pres.--Champion Home Builders Co., Auburn Hills, MI; *U.S. Public*, pg. 332
Parrotti, Thomas, Chief Oper. Officer--Multiple Parking Services, Inc., Binghamton, NY; *U.S. Private*, pg. 43
Parry, Dave, Gen. Mgr.--ITW Devcon Industrial, Danvers, MA; *U.S. Public*, pg. 866
Parry, David, Mng. Dir.--British Aerospace Defence Limited (Royal Ordnance), Chorley, United Kingdom; *Int'l*, pg. 217
Parsigian, Jeffrey, Exec. V.P.--Pulte Homes of Michigan, Royal Oak, MI; *U.S. Public*, pg. 1344
Parsons, Aaron, Publisher--The Daily World, Opelousas, LA; *U.S. Public*, pg. 1175
Parsons, Brad, Div. V.P.--Owens & Minor Medical/Surgical Division, Richmond, VA; *U.S. Public*, pg. 1236
Parsons, Brad, Div. V.P.--Owens & Minor, Inc, Norfolk, VA; *U.S. Public*, pg. 1236
Parsons, Colin J., Pres.--The Heronhill Corporation, Sugar Land, TX; *Int'l*, pg. 1359
Parsons, Gary M., Chief Exec. Officer--MCImetro, Vienna, VA; *U.S. Public*, pg. 1024
Parsons, Joe, Pres.--Albrecht Inc., Akron, OH; *U.S. Private*, pg. 32
Parsons, M., Gen. Mgr.-Sls.--Germantown (USA) Co., Broomall, PA; *Int'l*, pg. 555
Parsons, Peter, Mng. Dir.--Park Lane Tobacco Company Ltd., Maidenhead, United Kingdom; *Int'l*, pg. 1101
Parsons, Terry, Pres.--GSW Water Heating Company, Fergus, Canada; *Int'l*, pg. 538
Parsson, Par-Ivan, Mng. Dir.--Svenska Handelsbanken Frankfurt/Main, Frankfurt, Germany; *Int'l*, pg. 1327
Partain, C. Raymond, Pres.--Metric Constructors, Inc., Charlotte, NC; *Int'l*, pg. 633
Parten, R.B., Pres.--Lockheed Engineering & Sciences Co., Inc., Houston, TX; *U.S. Public*, pg. 1009
Partenheimer, Robert H., Pres.--CBC-U.S.A Inc., Chicago, IL; *U.S. Public*, pg. 337
Parthasarathy, Ravi, Mng. Dir.--Infrastructure Leasing & Financial Services Limited, Mumbai, India; *Int'l*, pg. 1009
Partin, Wayne, Pres.-Nestle Frozen Food Co.--Nestle Frozen/Refrigerated Food Co., Solon, OH; *Int'l*, pg. 918
Partington, Robert J., Mgr.--Producto Diemakers Supplies Ltd., Downsview, Canada; *U.S. Private*, pg. 889
Partio, Pasi, Mng. Dir.--Finnewos Aqua Oy, Turku, Finland; *Int'l*, pg. 349
Parton, Albert, Administrator--Horizon Village Nursing & Rehabilitation, Warren, OH; *U.S. Public*, pg. 838
Parton, Glenn, Gen. Mgr.--Isomedix Operations Inc., Libertyville, IL; *U.S. Public*, pg. 1515
Partridge, Keith J., Chief Exec. Officer & Mng. Dir.--Carlton Paper Corp. Ltd., Johannesburg, South Africa; *U.S. Public*, pg. 959
Parupia, M.A., Pres.--First American Title Co. of St. Lucie County, Inc., Port Saint Lucie, FL; *U.S. Public*, pg. 625
Parzybok, Tim, V.P. & Gen. Mgr.--Subaru of America Western, Inc., Portland, OR; *Int'l*, pg. 523
Pasanen, Raimo, Mgr.-Mill--Lappeenranta Mills, Lappeenranta, Finland; *Int'l*, pg. 1429
Paschall, Charles C., Pres. & Chief Admin. Officer--First Virginia Bank-Clinch Valley, Richlands, VA; *U.S. Public*, pg. 641
Paschall, John, Pres.--Williams Advanced Materials, Inc., Buffalo, NY; *U.S. Public*, pg. 266
Pascoe, F. Michael, V.P. & Gen. Mgr.-Americas Region--Newbridge Networks Corporation, Kanata, Canada; *Int'l*, pg. 924
Pash, G.K., Pres.--Invesco Inc., Boston, MA; *Int'l*, pg. 685
Pashin, Yuri, Gen. Mgr.--Young & Rubicam/Sovero, Moscow, Russia; *U.S. Private*, pg. 1199
Paskal, Joseph, Pres.--Magnasync Moviola Corporation, Hollywood, CA; *U.S. Private*, pg. 576
Paskin, Kenneth G., Pres.--James Bliss & Co., Inc., Edison, NJ; *U.S. Public*, pg. 1756
Paskins, I., Chief Exec. Officer--OCE (U.K.) Finance Limited, Loughton, United Kingdom; *Int'l*, pg. 995
Pasley, Drucilla, Pres.--Firstar Community Investment Corp., Milwaukee, WI; *U.S. Public*, pg. 643
Pasquale, Vincent J., Pres.--Intercraft Company, Taylor, TX; *U.S. Public*, pg. 1177
Pasquale, Vincent J., Pres.--Decorel Incorporated, Taylor, TX; *U.S. Public*, pg. 1177
Pasquali, Tarcisio, Gen. Mgr.--Bontex Italia S.R.L., Verona, Italy; *U.S. Public*, pg. 734
Pasquarelli, Anthony P., Pres.--Becton Dickinson Laboratory Products-Europe, Meylan, France; *U.S. Public*, pg. 200
Pasquinelli, Nino, Mng. Dir.--Pibiviesse SpA (PBVS), Nerviano, Italy; *U.S. Public*, pg. 1747
Passaglia, Paolo, Chief Oper. Officer--Gambro Sales AB, Trieste, Italy; *Int'l*, pg. 668
Passardi, L., Mng. Dir.--Bank Aufina, Brugg, Switzerland; *Int'l*, pg. 1439
Passemard, Thierry, Mng. Dir.--ALS Tonic, Bordeaux, France; *Int'l*, pg. 116
Passeri, David, Pres.--AlliedSignal Communications Systems, Baltimore, MD; *U.S. Public*, pg. 50
Passman, Jan, Chief Oper. Officer--Mayfran Limburg, B.V., Landgraaf, Netherlands; *Int'l*, pg. 1398
Passmore, Glen, Jr., Gen. Mgr.--Tarco of Texas, Inc., Belton, TX; *U.S. Private*, pg. 1069
Passow, Harry D., Pres.--St. Louis Division, Saint Louis, MO; *U.S. Public*, pg. 509
Passy, David S., Pres.--American Guarantee Insurance Company, Raleigh, NC; *U.S. Public*, pg. 629
Passy, David S., Pres.--Triangle Life Insurance, Raleigh, NC; *U.S. Public*, pg. 629
Pastena, James R., Pres.--Electro-Biology, Inc., Guaynabo, PR; *U.S. Public*, pg. 231
Pastena, Jim, Pres.--EBI Medical Systems, Inc., Parsippany, NJ; *U.S. Public*, pg. 231
Paster, R.D., Pres.--Boeing North America, Autonetics Electronics Sys Div., El Paso, TX; *U.S. Public*, pg. 241
Paster, Robert D., Pres.--Boeing North America, Autonetics Electronic Systems Division, Anaheim, CA; *U.S. Public*, pg. 241
Pasternak, James A., Mgr.--Central Florida Pipeline Corp., Tampa, FL; *U.S. Public*, pg. 692
Pasternak, James A., Mgr.-CRPL & SWFPL--Southwest Florida Pipeline Corp., Tampa, FL; *U.S. Public*, pg. 692
Pasternak, Y., Mng. Dir.--Charles River WIGA G.m.b.H., Sulzfeld, Germany; *U.S. Public*, pg. 195
Pastor, Art, Pres.--Admiral Equipment Co., Akron, OH; *U.S. Public*, pg. 522
Pastor, Christian, Administrator--Ferro France-Eurostar, Fosses, France; *U.S. Public*, pg. 619
Pastor, Josefa Martinez, Chm. Bd.--Envases Valencianos, S.A., Valencia, Spain; *U.S. Public*, pg. 1386
Pastore, Dalton, Chief Exec. Officer--Carillo, Pastore EURO RSCG, Sao Paulo, Brazil; *Int'l*, pg. 603
Pastorini, Massimo, Chief Oper. Officer--Chem-Plast S.p.A., Milan, Italy; *Int'l*, pg. 611
Pastowski, Heinz, Mgr.--Kredietbank-Bankverein AG, Dusseldorf, Germany; *Int'l*, pg. 761
Pastucha, Stephen J., Plant Mfg. Mgr.--Micromatic Operations (Swannanoa Plant), Swannanoa, NC; *U.S. Public*, pg. 1590
Patai, Mihaly, Dr., Mng. Dir.--Hungaria Biztosito Rt., Budapest, Hungary; *Int'l*, pg. 60
Patakos, G.N., Gen. Mgr.--Algemene Bank Nederland (Piraeus), Piraeus, Greece; *Int'l*, pg. 12
Pataky, Nicolas, Pres.--P.T. Bristol-Myers Indonesia, Jakarta, Indonesia; *U.S. Public*, pg. 255
Pate, F. Wayne, Pres. & Treas.--Golden Flake Snack Foods, Inc., Birmingham, AL; *U.S. Public*, pg. 750
Pate, James L., Pres.--Pennzoil Products Co., Houston, TX; *U.S. Public*, pg. 1272
Pate, Mike, Pres. & Publr.--Tallahassee Democrat, Inc., Tallahassee, FL; *U.S. Public*, pg. 964
Pate, R. Carter, Pres.--Plastics Manufacturing Company, Dallas, TX; *U.S. Public*, pg. 1530
Patek, Jim W., Mng. Dir.--Fletcher Challenge Petroleum Limited, Wellington, New Zealand; *Int'l*, pg. 495
Patek, Paul, Pres.-Fisher Scientific Company/Res. Div.--Fisher Scientific Company, Pittsburgh, PA; *U.S. Private*, pg. 658
Patel, Ash, V.P. & Branch Mgr.--California State Bank-Alhambra, Alhambra, CA; *U.S. Public*, pg. 294
Patel, Ganpat, Pres.--Cherokee International LLC, Tustin, CA; *U.S. Private*, pg. 233
Patel, Mayur, Chief Oper. Officer--Novo Nordisk A/S, Nairobi, Kenya; *Int'l*, pg. 987
Patel, Rohit, Acting Pres.--BNA Communications, Inc., Rockville, MD; *U.S. Private*, pg. 182
Paterakis, Andreas, Mng. Dir.--Wackenhut Security (Hellas), Ltd., Athens, Greece; *U.S. Public*, pg. 1732
Paterson, Ford, Dir.--Willis Corroon Scotland Limited, Edinburgh, United Kingdom; *Int'l*, pg. 1503
Paterson, Keith J., Exec. V.P.--Icore International Inc., Sunnyvale, CA; *Int'l*, pg. 1268
Paterson, Norman, Mng. Dir.--Royal Bank Insurance Consultants Ltd., Glasgow, United Kingdom; *Int'l*, pg. 1132
Paterson, Russell F., Mng. Dir.--Lactos Pty. Ltd., Burnie, Australia; *Int'l*, pg. 201
Paterson, Susan M., Gen. Mgr.--Wiremakers Limited, Auckland, New Zealand; *Int'l*, pg. 495
Patey, Richard, Mgr.--Girpi, Saint Cloud, France; *Int'l*, pg. 430
Patin, Gabriel, Pres.--Sakata Seed America, Inc., Morgan Hill, CA; *Int'l*, pg. 1178
Patinella, John, Pres. & Chief Exec. Officer--Homestead Publishing, Bel Air, MD; *U.S. Public*, pg. 1616
Patino, C., Gen. Mgr.--Coutts & Co (Uruguay) s.a., Montevideo, Uruguay; *Int'l*, pg. 911
Paton, J.H., Mng. Dir.--P&O European Transport Services Ltd., Altrincham, United Kingdom; *Int'l*, pg. 1033
Paton, John, Publisher & Chief Exec. Officer--The London Free Press, London, Canada; *Int'l*, pg. 1320
Paton, William V., Gen. Mgr. & Dir.--Dexter Nonwovens Division, Chirnside, United Kingdom; *U.S. Public*, pg. 505
Patradhilok, Prasert, Mng. Dir.--IFCT Finance & Securities Co., Ltd., Bangkok, Thailand; *Int'l*, pg. 677
Patrian, Ermand, Plant Mgr.--Outboard Marine Motors de Amazonia Ltd., Manaus, Brazil; *U.S. Private*, pg. 479
Patrician, Robert A., Pres.--Rockwell Heavy Vehicle Suspension Systems Company, Inc., Troy, MI; *U.S. Public*, pg. 1096
Patrick, Carl, Plant Mgr.--Duraco Products Inc. of South Carolina, Union, SC; *U.S. Private*, pg. 348
Patrick, D.W., Chief Oper. Officer--Lynden Air Freight, Inc., Seattle, WA; *U.S. Private*, pg. 683
Patrick, D.W., Chief Oper. Officer--Lynden Forwarding, Inc., Seattle, WA; *U.S. Private*, pg. 684
Patrick, Dave, Pres.--Arrow Industries, Inc., Carrollton, TX; *U.S. Public*, pg. 426
Patrick, David N., Pres.--The Stone Building Company, Providence, RI; *U.S. Private*, pg. 334
Patrick, Donald N., V.P. & Gen. Mgr.--Dillard, A ResourceNet International Company, Augusta, GA; *U.S. Public*, pg. 902
Patrick, Michael, Gen. Mgr.--Frontier Communication of Lamar County, Inc., Millport, AL; *U.S. Public*, pg. 683
Patrick, Michael, Gen. Mgr.--Frontier Communications of Alabama, Inc., Monroeville, AL; *U.S. Public*, pg. 683
Patrick, R.J., Pres.--MATAC Cargo Ltd., Mirabel, Canada; *Int'l*, pg. 36
Patrick, Ralph L., Chief Oper. Officer--Cincinnati Industrial Machinery Div., Cincinnati, OH; *U.S. Private*, pg. 355
Patrick, Tom, V.P.--Wheeling Corrugating Co., Wheeling, WV; *U.S. Public*, pg. 1727
Patrick, Wayne T., Publisher--Rock Hill Herald, Rock Hill, SC; *U.S. Public*, pg. 1066
Patriquin, P., Plant Mgr.--Sierra Cast Inc., Carson City, NV; *U.S. Public*, pg. 1782
Patron, Ann, Pres.--Frank Smythson Inc., New York, NY; *Int'l*, pg. 707
Patten, Joseph P., Pres.--LeFebure Corp., Cedar Rapids, IA; *Int'l*, pg. 387
Patten, Tom, Pres.--Patten-Beers Constructors, Nashville, TN; *Int'l*, pg. 1261
Patterson, A. Glenn, Pres. & Chief Oper. Officer--Patterson Drilling Co., Snyder, TX; *U.S. Public*, pg. 1265
Patterson, Bill, V.P.--Reputation Management, Columbus, OH; *U.S. Private*, pg. 492
Patterson, Bill, Chief Exec. Officer--Lansdown Conquest, London, United Kingdom; *Int'l*, pg. 1482
Patterson, Cliff, Gen. Mgr.--Lakeland Auto Auction, Lakeland, FL; *U.S. Private*, pg. 282
Patterson, Colin, Mgr.-Customs--Circle International (N.Z.) Ltd., Auckland, New Zealand; *U.S. Public*, pg. 373
Patterson, Dave, Pres. & Chief Oper. Officer--Kemper National Services, Plantation, FL; *U.S. Private*, pg. 614
Patterson, Dave, Mgr.--Texas Polymer Services, Inc., Orange, TX; *U.S. Public*, pg. 1441
Patterson, Dave, Plant Mgr.--Ringier America, Corinth Division, Corinth, MS; *U.S. Public*, pg. 1778
Patterson, Diana G., Dir.--Women's Sports and Event Marketing, New York, NY; *Int'l*, pg. 190
Patterson, Dick, V.P.-Mktg.--Aerospace Products, Inc., Wilmington, MA; *U.S. Public*, pg. 100
Patterson, James, Mng. Dir.--Humbrol Limited, Kingston-upon-Hull, United Kingdom; *U.S. Private*, pg. 159
Patterson, James E., Mng. Editor--Times On-Line Services, Inc., Morris Plains, NJ; *U.S. Public*, pg. 1174

Patterson, James E., Dir.--The New York Times Index, New York, NY; *U.S. Public*, pg. 1174
Patterson, John R., Pres.--TLC Group, Inc., Zeeland, MI; *U.S. Public*, pg. 352
Patterson, Joseph H., Grp. Pres.--Hoechst Celanese Film & Fiber Intermediates Group, Charlotte, NC; *Int'l*, pg. 626
Patterson, Keith, Mgr.--Doubleday New Zealand Ltd., Auckland, New Zealand; *Int'l*, pg. 192
Patterson, Kent E., Pres.--ERM-EnviroClean, Exton, PA; *U.S. Private*, pg. 379
Patterson, L., Pres.--Menardi-Criswell, Trenton, SC; *Int'l*, pg. 636
Patterson, Laurie, Mng. Dir.--Ancra Australia Pty. Ltd., Springvale, Australia; *U.S. Private*, pg. 71
Patterson, Mike, Gen. Mgr.--Letraset UK, London, United Kingdom; *Int'l*, pg. 462
Patterson, Pat, Plant Superintendent--Morgantown Machine Anderson Mavor, New Philadelphia, OH; *Int'l*, pg. 281
Patterson, Ray, Pres.--Bell & Howell Ltd., Woodbridge, Canada; *U.S. Public*, pg. 201
Patterson, Rick, Dir.-Opers.--Watson Bowman Acme Corp., Amherst, NY; *U.S. Private*, pg. 505
Patterson, Robert G., Pres.--Baseline Financial Services, Inc., New York, NY; *U.S. Public*, pg. 1325
Patterson, Steve, Gen. Mgr.--WARQ, Columbia, SC; *U.S. Public*, pg. 384
Patterson, Steve, Gen. Mgr.--WWDM, Columbia, SC; *U.S. Public*, pg. 385
Patterson, Steve, Pres.--Leisure Arts, Inc., Little Rock, AR; *U.S. Public*, pg. 1613
Patterson, Susan, Publr. & Editor--The Union-Recorder, Milledgeville, GA; *U.S. Private*, pg. 259
Patterson, Tom, Pres.--TXEN, Birmingham, AL; *U.S. Public*, pg. 1182
Pattillo, Bob, Pres. & Chief Exec. Officer--Shop 'n Save Warehouse Foods, Inc., Kirkwood, MO; *U.S. Public*, pg. 1541
Pattinson, John, Mng. Dir.--Dresdner Australia Ltd., Sydney, Australia; *Int'l*, pg. 419
Pattinson, Michael, Pres.--Teca Corporation, Pleasantville, NY; *Int'l*, pg. 1468
Pattinson, Mick, Chm. Bd.--Barratt American Inc., Carlsbad, CA; *Int'l*, pg. 168
Pattis, Mark R., Pres. & Chief Exec. Officer--NTC/Contemporary Publishing Group, Lincolnwood, IL; *U.S. Public*, pg. 1635
Pattison, David, Pres.--Perstorp Analytical Inc., Silver Spring, MD; *Int'l*, pg. 1039
Pattison, Dr. J. C., Mng. Dir.--CIBC Limited, London, United Kingdom; *Int'l*, pg. 257
Patton, Jim, Managing Partner--Infrastructure Business, Kansas City, MO; *U.S. Private*, pg. 146
Patton, John, Reg. Mgr.--SMS-Los Angeles, Seal Beach, CA; *U.S. Public*, pg. 1463
Patton, John, Reg. Mgr.--SMS-San Francisco, Pleasanton, CA; *U.S. Public*, pg. 1463
Patton, Mike, V.P.--Houston Division, Katy, TX; *U.S. Public*, pg. 38
Patton, R., Mgr.-Winery--Andres Wines (Alberta) Ltd., Calgary, Canada; *Int'l*, pg. 76
Patz, Klaus, Gen. Mgr.--Landesgirokasse Bank, Frankfurt/Main, Germany; *Int'l*, pg. 800
Patzewitz, Sigfried, Mgr.--Gould Instrument Systems GmbH, Lilienthal, Germany; *U.S. Public*, pg. 1592
Pauelka, Jim, Gen. Mgr.-Consumer Div.--Lunalite, Inc., Mound, MN; *U.S. Public*, pg. 1624
Paufique, Jean-Pierre, Chief Oper. Officer--ELYO Corp., Nanterre, France; *Int'l*, pg. 823
Paul, A.S., Pres.--Bard Access Systems, Salt Lake City, UT; *U.S. Public*, pg. 189
Paul, Ben E., Pres.--OEA Aerospace, Inc., Fairfield, CA; *U.S. Public*, pg. 1207
Paul, Cathy, Mgr.-Opers.--General Magnaplate Canada, Ajax, Canada; *U.S. Public*, pg. 717
Paul, Charles S., Pres.-MCA Enterprises, Inc. & Exec. V.P.--Universal Studios, Inc., Universal City, CA; *Int'l*, pg. 1215
Paul, David, Dir.--Willis Corroon Construction Risks Limited, Kingston upon Thames, United Kingdom; *Int'l*, pg. 1502
Paul, Dr. Gerald, Mng. Dir.--Draloric Electronic GmbH, Selb, Germany; *U.S. Public*, pg. 1722
Paul, Eric, Sr. V.P.-Opers.--Mozzarella's Restaurants, Mobile, AL; *U.S. Public*, pg. 1412
Paul, G., Chief Exec. Officer--Thomson Regional Newspapers Ltd., Watford, United Kingdom; *U.S. Public*, pg. 1601
Paul, Guilles, V.P.--Bombardier Corporation, Benton, IL; *Int'l*, pg. 200
Paul, J.M., Dir.-Food--Pauls plc, Ipswich, United Kingdom; *Int'l*, pg. 598
Paul, Jacques, Chief Exec. Officer--Societe pour le Perfectionnement des Materiels et Equipements Aerospatiaux SA (SOPEMEA), Velizy-Villacoublay, France; *Int'l*, pg. 1165
Paul, John D., Pres.--Old Kent Bank-Grand Traverse, Traverse City, MI; *U.S. Public*, pg. 1216
Paul, Kathryn, Sr. V.P. & Reg. Mgr.--Kaiser Permanente, Rocky Mountain Division, Denver, CO; *U.S. Private*, pg. 605
Paul, L.M., Pres.--Standard Alloys & Manufacturing, Port Arthur, TX; *U.S. Private*, pg. 153
Paul, Lee, Pres.--Tape & Label Engineering, Saint Petersburg, FL; *U.S. Private*, pg. 1157
Paul, Louise, Gen. Mgr.--Bayerische Landesbank - Labuan Branch, Labuan, Malaysia; *Int'l*, pg. 176
Paul, M., Joint Chief Exec.--Caparo Industries Plc., Birchills, United Kingdom; *Int'l*, pg. 265
Paul, Marina, Reg. Acct. Mgr.--Utell International-Canada, Markham, Canada; *Int'l*, pg. 1098
Paul, Peter M., Mng. Dir.--Camford Engineering PLC, Letchworth, United Kingdom; *Int'l*, pg. 507
Paul, Richard, V.P. & Gen. Mgr.--Coltec Peabody Division, Peabody, MA; *U.S. Public*, pg. 402
Paul, Roger, Pres.--VSK Group, Harelbeke, Belgium; *U.S. Public*, pg. 49
Paul, Swraj, Chm.--Caparo Industries Plc, Walsall, United Kingdom; *Int'l*, pg. 264
Paul, Thomas A., Pres. & Chief Exec. Officer--International Thomson Publishing Limited, London, United Kingdom; *U.S. Public*, pg. 1600
Paule, Steven R., V.P. & Gen. Mgr.--Fiske Brothers Refining, Toledo Div., Toledo, OH; *U.S. Private*, pg. 409
Pauletich, Richard P., Pres.--First American Title Guaranty Co., Oakland, CA; *U.S. Public*, pg. 625
Pauli, Charles G., Pres.--Day-Glo Color Corp., Cleveland, OH; *U.S. Public*, pg. 1357
Pauli, Charles G., Pres.--Kop-Coat, Pittsburgh, PA; *U.S. Public*, pg. 1357
Pauli, H.G., Chief Exec. Officer--Grupo Siemens S.A. de C.V., Mexico, Mexico; *Int'l*, pg. 1247
Paulin, Thomas, Mgr.--J.W. Andersson Maskin AB, Kiruna, Sweden; *Int'l*, pg. 1422
Pauling, Kenneth D., Pres.--Lee Ranch Coal Company, Grants, NM; *Int'l*, pg. 594
Paulits, Fanny, V.P. & Mgr.--The Chinese American Bank, New York, NY; *Int'l*, pg. 683
Paulk, E. Wayne, Plant Mgr.--Statesboro Plant, Statesboro, GA; *U.S. Public*, pg. 444
Paulk, Wayne, Plant Mgr.--Cooper Tools, Statesboro, GA; *U.S. Public*, pg. 444
Paulokangas, Ray, Gen. Mgr.--Milgray/Western Canada, Burnaby, Canada; *U.S. Public*, pg. 207
Pauls, William E., Pres.--Denver Technological Center, Englewood, CO; *Int'l*, pg. 1035
Paulsen, Christian, Pres.--Diatom Verktoj A/S, Hvidovre, Denmark; *Int'l*, pg. 678
Paulson, Bruce, Pres.--King Company, Owatonna, MN; *U.S. Public*, pg. 1676
Paulson, Larry M., Mng. Dir.--Nokia Products Corporation, Melbourne, FL; *Int'l*, pg. 952
Paulson, Richard L., V.P.--Northwest Paper Div., Cloquet, MN; *U.S. Public*, pg. 1318
Paulus, C., V.P. & Gen. Mgr.-Augat Europe--Augat Automotive GmbH, Troisdorf, Germany; *U.S. Public*, pg. 1598
Paulus, S., Chief Fin. Officer--S.A. Olivetti Belgium N.V., Brussels, Belgium; *Int'l*, pg. 1003
Paumen, William C., Opers. Officer--Citizens Security Mutual Insurance, Red Wing, MN; *U.S. Public*, pg. 1095
Pausch, J., Pres.--Marshall Labs Inc., Hopkins, MN; *U.S. Public*, pg. 531
Pautler, William L., Mgr.-Branch--Piper Jaffray Inc., Green Valley, AZ; *U.S. Public*, pg. 1301
Pauvert, Henri, Gen. Mgr.--Wang France S.A., Charenton-le-Pont, France; *U.S. Public*, pg. 1738
Pauwels, Chris, Plant Mgr.--Bekaert Corporation, Van Buren, AR; *Int'l*, pg. 184
Pavao, James S., Pres.--Whaling Manufacturing Company, Inc., Fall River, MA; *U.S. Private*, pg. 1170
Pavek, Peter, Chief Oper. Officer--Gensym, Uppsala, Sweden; *U.S. Public*, pg. 731
Pavero, Richard J., Pres.--Kayeness, Inc., Morgantown, PA; *U.S. Private*, pg. 138
Pavese, John R., Mng. Dir.--Olin Pte., Ltd., Singapore, Singapore, Singapore; *U.S. Public*, pg. 1220
Pavesic, R., Branch Mgr.--A.M. Castle & Co., San Diego, CA; *U.S. Public*, pg. 313
Pavey, Allan, Mng. Dir.--Farah Manufacturing (U.K.) Limited, Crawley, United Kingdom; *U.S. Public*, pg. 613
Pavilla, Adrian, Chief Exec. Officer--Jetro Cash & Carry, Long Beach, CA; *U.S. Private*, pg. 587
Pavlak, Gary, Gen. Mgr.--Footquarters, New York, NY; *U.S. Public*, pg. 1777
Pavlosky, Stephen, Pres.--General Dynamics, Pittsfield, MA; *U.S. Public*, pg. 1006
Pavlov, Sergei, Liaison Officer--E/B/D/Interpartners - Moscow GmbH, Moscow, Russia; *U.S. Private*, pg. 1152
Pavlowski, Sylvain, Mng. Dir.--VMark Software, Ltd., Bologna, Italy; *U.S. Public*, pg. 129
Pawley, D.K., Gen. Mgr.-Advance Mfg. Opers.--Outer Drive Manufacturing Technical Center, Detroit, MI; *U.S. Public*, pg. 353
Pawlick, W.F., Exec. V.P. & Gen. Mgr.--GKN Drivetech Inc., Walled Lake, MI; *Int'l*, pg. 535
Pawlish, Andrew, Mng. Dir.--Woodward Governor Asia-Pacific Pte. Ltd., Singapore, Singapore; *U.S. Public*, pg. 1776
Pawlisz, Rennie, V.P. & Credit Mgr.--Bancard Div., Redondo Beach, CA; *U.S. Public*, pg. 871
Pawluk, Victor H. T., Chief Oper. Officer--Brian Controls Division, Edmonton, Canada; *Int'l*, pg. 711
Pawsey, E.J.B., Chief Oper. Officer--Hart, Fenton & Co. Ltd., Portsmouth, United Kingdom; *Int'l*, pg. 1214
Paxton, Brad, V.P. & Gen. Mgr.--Kodak Printer Products Div., Rochester, NY; *U.S. Public*, pg. 555
Paxton, Gary, Pres. & Chief Exec. Officer--Dollar Rent A Car, Tulsa, OK; *U.S. Public*, pg. 354
Paxton, Johnnie, District Sls. Mgr.-West Coast--Aero Peru, Los Angeles, CA; *U.S. Private*, pg. 24
Paxton, Michael J., Pres. & Chief Exec. Officer--The Haagen-Dazs Company Inc., Minneapolis, MN; *Int'l*, pg. 411
Payer, Jacques, Mng. Dir.--MET S.A., Massy, Finland; *Int'l*, pg. 1369
Payne, D., Mng. Dir.--Kemet Electronics SA, Geneva, Switzerland; *U.S. Public*, pg. 949
Payne, D.D., Exec. V.P.--Harcros Chemicals Inc., Merrimack, NH; *Int'l*, pg. 598
Payne, David, Mng. Dir.--Payne Stracey Ltd. (direct marketing), London, United Kingdom; *U.S. Private*, pg. 1152
Payne, David L., Chm. Bd., Pres. & Chief Exec. Officer--Westamerica Bank, San Rafael, CA; *U.S. Public*, pg. 1756
Payne, Derek, Commercial Mgr.-Europe--VARI-FORM, Telford, United Kingdom; *Int'l*, pg. 1341
Payne, Donald, Chm. Bd. & Chief Exec. Officer--Willis Corroon Americas, Nashville, TN; *Int'l*, pg. 1505
Payne, Gary, Div. Mgr.--Century Telephone of Central Louisiana, Inc., Jena, LA; *U.S. Public*, pg. 329
Payne, Helen, Gen. Mgr.--Frontier Communications of Breezewood, Inc., Breezewood, PA; *U.S. Public*, pg. 683
Payne, Helen, Gen. Mgr.--Frontier Communications-Oswayo River, Inc., Shinglehouse, PA; *U.S. Public*, pg. 684
Payne, James L., Chief Oper. Officer--Helmerich & Payne Properties, Inc., Tulsa, OK; *U.S. Public*, pg. 808
Payne, James L., Chief Oper. Officer--Space Center, Inc., Tulsa, OK; *U.S. Public*, pg. 808
Payne, James L., Chief Oper. Officer--Utica Square Shopping Center, Inc., Tulsa, OK; *U.S. Public*, pg. 808
Payne, John, Grp. V.P.--Logic Division, Santa Clara, CA; *U.S. Public*, pg. 884
Payne, M.W., V.P. & Gen. Mgr.--Roan Resources LTD, Calgary, Canada; *U.S. Public*, pg. 1127
Payne, Mickey, V.P.-Canada--Altana Exploration Company, Calgary, Canada; *U.S. Public*, pg. 1127
Payne, Robert, Mng. Dir.-Europe--Bytex DataCom Ltd., Hammondsworth, United Kingdom; *U.S. Public*, pg. 1522
Payne, Ted L., Gen. Mgr.--Punchcraft Company, Warren, MI; *U.S. Public*, pg. 1054
Paynter, Douglas G., Mgr.--Asotin Telephone Co., Asotin, WA; *U.S. Public*, pg. 1571
Paynter, Stacey, Chief Oper. Officer-San Francisco, Exec. V.P. & Dir.--EvansGroup, Salt Lake City, UT; *U.S. Private*, pg. 385
Paysen, Lueder, Chief Oper. Officer--BMW Bank GmbH, Munich, Germany; *Int'l*, pg. 177
Payson, Brian, Acting Pres.--AI/FOCS, Inc., Franklin, MA; *U.S. Public*, pg. 1776
Payton, Earl E., Chief Fin. Officer--Great American Oak, Inc., Chino, CA; *U.S. Private*, pg. 280
Payton, Earl E., Pres., Chief Exec. Officer & Chief Fin. Officer--Cowden Metal-San Jose, San Jose, CA; *U.S. Private*, pg. 280
Payton, Roger E., Pres. & Chief Exec. Officer--Merchants Home Delivery Service Inc., Oxnard, CA; *Int'l*, pg. 901
Payton, Stanford L., Chm., Chief Exec. Officer & Pres.--Liberty National Bank of Owensboro, Owensboro, KY; *U.S. Public*, pg. 173
Pazos, Guillermo, Pres.--Bridgestone/Firestone do Brasil Industria e Commercio Ltda, Sao Paulo, Brazil; *Int'l*, pg. 214
Peabody, Betty Sue, Pres.--Citicorp Savings, A Federal Savings & Loan Assn., Oakland, CA; *U.S. Public*, pg. 378
Peabody, George, Pres.--Southwest Power Products, Tucson, AZ; *U.S. Public*, pg. 1670
Peach, A.D., Pres.--AGRA Shawmont Limited, Saint John, Canada; *Int'l*, pg. 30
Peach, Les, Mgr.-Sls.--PENCO-Illinois, Aurora, IL; *Int'l*, pg. 1508
Peacock, Campbell, Mgr.-Country--Colgate Palmolive AB, Stockholm, Sweden; *U.S. Public*, pg. 398
Peacock, Gary, Chief Exec. Officer--Barnett Bank of Southwest Georgia, Columbus, GA; *U.S. Public*, pg. 1162
Peacock, John H., Gen. Mgr.--Corrugated Container Div.-Tyler Plant, Tyler, TX; *U.S. Public*, pg. 1521
Peacock, Lorey, Reg. Mgr.--Green Tree Acceptance of Louisiana, Inc., Baton Rouge, LA; *U.S. Public*, pg. 762
Peacock, Richard, Pres.--PVS-Nolwood Chemicals, Inc., Detroit, MI; *U.S. Private*, pg. 828
Peak, J., Mng. Dir.--Westminster Contractors Ltd., Wirral, United Kingdom; *Int'l*, pg. 135
Peak, Paul E., Pres. & Chief Exec. Officer--The Forest Hill State Bank, Bel Air, MD; *U.S. Public*, pg. 1089
Peake, David, Chm.--BNP UK Holdings Ltd., London, United Kingdom; *Int'l*, pg. 164
Peano, Alberto, Mng. Dir.--Logicasiel SpA, Bologna, Italy; *Int'l*, pg. 815
Pearce, B.D., Chief Oper. Officer--Larch-Lap Limited, Hartlebury, United Kingdom; *Int'l*, pg. 925
Pearce, C. Alan, Gen. Mgr.--Soabar Marking Systems Ltd., Whetstone, United Kingdom; *U.S. Public*, pg. 154
Pearce, C.J., Mgr.--Tencarva Machinery Co., Chattanooga, TN; *U.S. Private*, pg. 1075
Pearce, David, Gen. Mgr. & Editor--Mount Vernon Democrat, Mount Vernon, IN; *U.S. Private*, pg. 648
Pearce, David C., Mng. Dir.--Brite Voice Systems Group, Ltd., Cheadle, United Kingdom; *U.S. Public*, pg. 257
Pearce, Doug, Gen. Mgr.--Leo Burnett/Connaghan & May (VIC.) Pty. Ltd., Melbourne, Australia; *U.S. Private*, pg. 185
Pearce, Earl R., Pres.--Weston Resources, Toronto, Canada; *Int'l*, pg. 1495
Pearce, John, Chief Exec. Officer--Healthsource Georgia, Atlanta, GA; *U.S. Public*, pg. 360
Pearce, Ronald, Reg. V.P.-Japan--Nippon Vicks K.K., Osaka, Japan; *U.S. Public*, pg. 1331
Pearce, T.H., Chief Exec.--Da Gama Textile Company, East London, South Africa; *Int'l*, pg. 1287
Pearce, Vernon, Dir.-UK Opers.--Lawson Products Ltd., Bristol, United Kingdom; *U.S. Public*, pg. 980
Pearce, W. McFall, Pres. & Chief Exec. Officer--PYA/Monarch, Inc., Greenville, SC; *U.S. Public*, pg. 1433
Pearce, Walter, Pres. & Chief Fin. Officer--KCI Communications, Inc, Mc Lean, VA; *U.S. Private*, pg. 784
Peard, B., Mfg. Dir.--Rockware Plastics Ltd., Norwich, United Kingdom; *Int'l*, pg. 124
Pearl, Jeff, Factory Supervisor--Earl Scheib Automotive Paint Finishes, Inc., Springfield, MO; *U.S. Public*, pg. 1437
Pearlman, Herbert M., Chm. Bd.--Unapix Entertainment Inc., New York, NY; *U.S. Public*, pg. 1664
Pearlman, Jack, Pres.--Atlite Lighting Equip, Inc., Maspeth, NY; *U.S. Public*, pg. 443
Pears, D.G., Pres.--Midwest Pipeline Contractors Ltd., Edmonton, Canada; *Int'l*, pg. 31
Pears, D.G., Pres.--Midwest Management (1987) Limited, Edmonton, Canada; *Int'l*, pg. 31
Pearse, David W., Gen. Mgr.--Isomedix Corporation (Canada), Whitby, Canada; *U.S. Public*, pg. 1515

Pearson, Allan, Mng. Dir.--Thermon U.K. (Ltd.), Washington, United Kingdom; *U.S. Private*, pg. 1081
Pearson, Brian, Pres.--Allied Colloids (Asia) Ltd., Wan Chai, Hong Kong; *Int'l*, pg. 62
Pearson, C., Pres. & Chief Exec. Officer--PNC Bank, Camp Hill, PA; *U.S. Public*, pg. 1243
Pearson, D., Mgr.--Rockware Glass Ltd.-Headlands Factory, Knottingley, United Kingdom; *Int'l*, pg. 124
Pearson, Earl, Sr. V.P. & Gen. Mgr.--Gould Electronics (Canada) Ltd., Shawmut Div., Toronto, Canada; *U.S. Public*, pg. 1592
Pearson, Fiona, Mng. Dir.--The Flight Data Company Ltd., West Drayton, United Kingdom; *Int'l*, pg. 207
Pearson, G., Mng. Dir.--BTR Nylex Limited, Mentone, Australia; *Int'l*, pg. 129
Pearson, G.C., Branch Mgr.--Zellerbach Division, Honolulu, HI; *U.S. Public*, pg. 1076
Pearson, Jim, Pres.--Aurora Metals Division L.P.C., Montgomery, IL; *U.S. Private*, pg. 529
Pearson, Martin J., Pres.--Reader's Digest European Systems Group, Limited, Swindon, United Kingdom; *U.S. Public*, pg. 1368
Pearson, Neal, Chief Oper. Officer--Enway Inc., Clackamas, OR; *Int'l*, pg. 1262
Pearson, Patrick, V.P. & Mgr.--City National Bank - South Bay Regional Office, Torrance, CA; *U.S. Public*, pg. 381
Pearson, Robert, Pres.--Dover Corporation (Canada) Ltd.-Industrial Div., Strathroy, Canada; *U.S. Public*, pg. 522
Pearson, Vern Nil, Mgr.--Blount Industrial de Correntes Ltda., Curitiba, Brazil; *U.S. Public*, pg. 239
Peart, M.F.B., Mng. Dir.--Barclays Bank of Sierra Leone Ltd., Freetown, Sierra Leone; *Int'l*, pg. 165
Peary, Stephen, Pres.--Transportation Equipment Indemnity Co. Ltd., San Francisco, CA; *U.S. Public*, pg. 1242
Peattie, Allan E., Pres. & Chief Oper. Officer--Southeastern Development Company, Port Huron, MI; *U.S. Public*, pg. 1489
Peavy, S. Land, Pres.--American-Amicable Life Insurance Company of Texas, Waco, TX; *U.S. Public*, pg. 1271
Peavy, S. Lanny, Pres.--Pioneer Security Life Ins. Co., Waco, TX; *U.S. Public*, pg. 1271
Pecas, Serge, Controller--Films Paramount S.A., Paris, France; *U.S. Private*, pg. 777
Pecchioli, Roberto, Chief Oper. Officer--KONE Ascensori S.p.A., Milan, Italy; *Int'l*, pg. 747
Pecchioli, Roberto, Chief Oper. Officer--KONE Italia S.p.A., Milan, Italy; *Int'l*, pg. 747
Pechar, Ed, Chief Oper. Officer--Tennessee Dickel Distilling Co., Tullahoma, TN; *Int'l*, pg. 412
Pechota, Gary, Pres.--Kapco Division, Bath, PA; *U.S. Public*, *pg. 741*
Pechota, Gary L., Chm. & Chief Exec. Officer--Giant Cement Company, Harleyville, SC; *U.S. Public*, pg. 741
Pechter, Richard H., Chief Exec. Officer--Pershing Division, Jersey City, NJ; *U.S. Public*, pg. 589
Pechtl, Hans, Mng. Dir.--Sun Electric Austria G.m.b.H., Vienna, Austria; *U.S. Public*, pg. 1481
Peck, J. Richard, Chief Oper. Officer--Slant-Fin, Ltd./Ltee, Mississauga, Canada; *U.S. Private*, pg. 1005
Peckham, Layne, Mgr.--Stewart Smith West, Inc., Phoenix, AZ; *Int'l*, pg. 1508
Peckham, Neil, Mng. Dir.--Skycell Communications Private Limited, Madras, India; *U.S. Public*, pg. 209
Pedder, A.E., Chief Oper. Officer--Tioxide Europe Limited, Billingham, United Kingdom; *Int'l*, pg. 663
Peddie, Richard, Gen. Mgr.--Bright's & Martin's Foods, Niagara Falls, Canada; *Int'l*, pg. 411
Peden, George, Mng. Dir.--The Ballantyne Cashmere Company Ltd, Innerleithen, United Kingdom; *Int'l*, pg. 385
Peden, Sue, Pub. Rels. Coord.--Leo Burnett/Connaghan & May (VIC.) Pty. Ltd., Melbourne, Australia; *U.S. Private*, pg. 185
Pederneschi, Fabio, Gen. Mgr.--Gleason Milano, Milan, Italy; *U.S. Public*, pg. 746
Pedersen, Arne, Mng. Dir.--ISS Sverige AB, Stockholm, Sweden; *Int'l*, pg. 656
Pedersen, Birger, Chief Oper. Officer--Ferrosan AB, Malmo, Sweden; *Int'l*, pg. 989
Pedersen, Bjarne Lynge, Chief Oper. Officer--KONE Elevator A/S, Copenhagen, Denmark; *Int'l*, pg. 747
Pedersen, Caryn, Mgr.--Gensym Corporation, Midwestern Regional Office, Elk Grove Village, IL; *U.S. Public*, pg. 731
Pedersen, Chris, Gen. Mgr.--Colgate-Palmolive (Hellas) S.A., Piraeus, Greece; *U.S. Public*, pg. 398
Pedersen, Einar, Mng. Dir.--TTS International AS, Oslo, Norway; *Int'l*, pg. 283
Pedersen, Gordon M., Pres.--Affiliated Banks Building Co., Denver, CO; *U.S. Public*, pg. 173
Pedersen, Jens Bang, Pres.--MD Foods USA Inc., Springfield, NJ; *Int'l*, pg. 826
Pedersen, Jens Lind, Chief Exec.--Novo Nordisk de Mexico S.A. de C.V., Mexico, Mexico; *Int'l*, pg. 989
Pedersen, Jetre W., Pres.--MD Foods Espana, Gava, Spain; *Int'l*, pg. 826
Pedersen, Kaj, Mng. Dir.--Shell of Aalborg, Noerresundby, Denmark; *Int'l*, pg. 1138
Pedersen, Kaj Juul, Mng. Dir.--LM Ericsson A/S, Brondby, Denmark; *Int'l*, pg. 1368
Pedersen, Kjeld Lercke, Mng. Dir.--HyperVision A/S, Skovlunde, Denmark; *Int'l*, pg. 146
Pedersen, Mogens C., Chief Oper. Officer--Ferrosan Healthcare Ltd., Byfleet, United Kingdom; *Int'l*, pg. 989
Pedersen, Niels Ulrich, Pres.--MD Foods Caltsoyias Hellas S.A., Athens, Greece; *Int'l*, pg. 826
Pedersen, P. M., Mng. Dir.--Albright & Wilson Denmark AS, Glostrup, Denmark; *Int'l*, pg. 49
Pedersen, Per Martin, Pres.--Kato Kraner Norge A/S, Honefoss, Norway; *Int'l*, pg. 1420
Pedersen, Svein A.A., Mng. Dir.--Opel Norge AS, Skedsmokorset, Norway; *U.S. Public*, pg. 723
Pedersen, Wyona, Gen. Mgr.--Zippo Manufacturing Company of Canada Limited, Niagara Falls, Canada; *U.S. Private*, pg. 1207
Pederson, Dennis A., Pres.--COUNTEC Recycling Systems Division, Des Moines, IA; *U.S. Public*, pg. 1318
Pedicch, Vittorio, Mng. Dir.--Jotun Brignola S.p.A., Muggia, Italy; *Int'l*, pg. 715
Pedini, Dennis J., Dir. & Chief Exec. Officer--East Asia Aetna Insurance Group, Taikoo Shing, Hong Kong; *U.S. Public*, pg. 27
Pedoussant, Bernard, Pres.--Logo of the Americas, Fort Lauderdale, FL; *Int'l*, pg. 462
Pedrazzo, Giovanni, Gen. Mgr.--Lincoln Electric Italia SRL, Genoa, Italy; *U.S. Public*, pg. 997
Pedrini, Egidio Enrico, Pres.--Aerimpianti S.p.A., Milan, Italy; *Int'l*, pg. 653
Pedroli, John, Pres. & Chief Oper. Officer--Screen Graphics, Inc., Memphis, TN; *U.S. Public*, pg. 1486
Peebler, Robert P., Pres. & Chief Exec. Officer--Landmark Graphics Corporation, Houston, TX; *U.S. Public*, pg. 776
Peek, E.J.A., Gen. Mgr.--Cacao de Zaan B.V., Koog aan de Zaan, Netherlands; *U.S. Public*, pg. 128
Peek, H.L., V.P.--Mount Vernon Mills, Inc., Riegel Textile Div. (Trion), Trion, GA; *U.S. Private*, pg. 835
Peek, Phil, Mng. Dir.--Timloc Building Products Ltd., Goole, United Kingdom; *Int'l*, pg. 467
Peel, William W., Gen. Dir.--General Motors Canada Diesel Div., London, Canada; *U.S. Public*, pg. 722
Peeler, John R., Pres. & Chief Exec. Officer--Telecommunications Techniques Corp., Germantown, MD; *U.S. Public*, pg. 539
Peerbhoy, Bunty, Chm. Bd., Chief Exec. Officer & Mng. Dir.--MAA Communications Bozell, Bangalore, India; *U.S. Public*, pg. 1642
Peers, Antony, Chm.--Seaforth Maritime Limited, Aberdeen, United Kingdom; *U.S. Public*, pg. 776
Peeters, Paul, Dir. General--Banque Atlantique Cote D'Ivoire (BACI), Abidjan, Cote d'Ivoire; *Int'l*, pg. 547
Peeters, Peter, Mng. Dir.--Marsh Company M.C.S.A., Bellevue, Switzerland; *U.S. Private*, pg. 708
Pefanis, Harry N., Pres.--Plains Marketing & Transportation, Houston, TX; *U.S. Public*, pg. 1308
Pegg, F.R., Vice Chm.--Volumatic Limited, Coventry, United Kingdom; *Int'l*, pg. 590
Pegler, Donald H., Jr., Chm.--Pegler-Sysco Food Services Co., Lincoln, NE; *U.S. Public*, pg. 1550
Pehrsson, Lars-Olof, Pres.--Dynapac Construction Equipment Ltd., Reading, United Kingdom; *Int'l*, pg. 1420
Pei, B.Y., Gen. Mgr.--Kaohsiung Refinery, Kao-hsiung, Taiwan; *Int'l*, pg. 286
Pei, Tian Wen, Pres.--Guangdong Otsuka Pharmaceutical Co., Ltd., Guangdong, China; *Int'l*, pg. 1014
Peigner, D., Gen. Mgr.--Gan Pacifique Vie, Noumea, New Caledonia; *Int'l*, pg. 564
Peigner, D., Gen. Rep.--Gan Pacifique Iard, Noumea, New Caledonia; *Int'l*, pg. 564
Peinhardt, Curt, Mgr.-Division--Haleyville Drapery Manufacturing Division, Lakeland, FL; *U.S. Public*, pg. 491
Peirce, Roger, Pres.--CES/Card Establishment Services Inc., Melville, NY; *U.S. Public*, pg. 631
Peitzmeier, N., Mng. Dir.--Kidde-Deugra GmbH, Ratingen, Germany; *Int'l*, pg. 1500
Peladeau, Erik, Chm. Bd. & Chief Exec. Officer--Quebecor Multimedia Inc., Montreal, Canada; *Int'l*, pg. 1076
Peladeau, Michel, Mgr.--Anixter Quebec City, Vanier, Canada; *U.S. Public*, pg. 116
Pelaez, Edgar, Area Mgr.--Milchem Western Hemisphere Inc., Bogota, Colombia; *U.S. Public*, pg. 167
Pelagio, Greg, Gen. Mgr.--Royston Laboratories, Pittsburgh, PA; *U.S. Public*, pg. 337
Peleckis, Anthony J., Gen. Mgr.--BEAU Interconnect Systems, Gilford, NH; *U.S. Public*, pg. 157
Peled, Benjamin, Gen. Mgr.--Elscint Ltd., Haifa, Israel; *Int'l*, pg. 644
Peled, Zvi, Pres. & Chief Exec. Officer--Bogen Communications, Inc., Ramsey, NJ; *U.S. Public*, pg. 739
Pelerman, Brian, Management Consultant--Aloette Cosmetics (Australasia) Pty. Ltd., Carrum Downs, Australia; *U.S. Public*, pg. 57
Pelfry, Jerry, Chief Oper. Officer--Flowers Baking Co. of Gadsden, Inc., Gadsden, AL; *U.S. Public*, pg. 657
Pelham, Reg, Pres.--Day & Zimmermann Services, Greenville, SC; *U.S. Private*, pg. 317
Pelisson, Gilles, Dir.-Novotel Opers.--Societe Internationale des Hotels Novotel, Evry, France; *Int'l*, pg. 21
Pelka, Lawrence J., Exec. V.P.--Associates Commercial Equipment Div., Dallas, TX; *U.S. Public*, pg. 663
Pelkonen, Markku, Resident Mgr.--Viiala Mill, Viiala, Finland; *Int'l*, pg. 1429
Pelkonen, Paavo, Mng. Dir.--KONE Middle East GIBCA Ltd., Dubai, United Arab Emirates; *Int'l*, pg. 747
Pelland, Michel, V.P. & Gen. Mgr.--Cott Corporation - North Central Region, Maryland Heights, MO; *Int'l*, pg. 337
Pellandini, Edoardo, Gen. Mgr.--Riseria Taverne S.A., Taverne, Switzerland; *Int'l*, pg. 866
Pelle, Jean Claude, Pres.--GSM, Poissy, France; *Int'l*, pg. 292
Pellegrini, Benjamin J., Pres. & Chief Exec. Officer--Day & Zimmermann LLC, Philadelphia, PA; *U.S. Private*, pg. 317
Pellegrini, M., Sls. Mgr.--OCG Microelectronic Materials S.r.l., Milan, Italy; *U.S. Public*, pg. 1220
Pellegrino, Anthony, Chm. Bd.--LORAD Corporation, Danbury, CT; *U.S. Public*, pg. 1595
Pellegrino, J., Mgr.--Lindberg Heat Treating Co., Solon, OH; *U.S. Public*, pg. 999
Pellenberg, Charles, Pres.--American Down & Textile Company, La Crosse, WI; *U.S. Public*, pg. 782
Pellenberg, Charles, Pres.--Company Store Holdings, Inc., La Crosse, WI; *U.S. Public*, pg. 782
Peller, John P., Pres.--Boeing North America, Systems Development Center, Seal Beach, CA; *U.S. Public*, pg. 241
Pellerin, Jean-Luc, Div. Mgr.--Wayagamack Div., Trois-Rivieres, Canada; *Int'l*, pg. 20
Pellerito, Thomas J., Pres.--Richmond American Homes of Virginia, Inc., Fairfax, VA; *U.S. Public*, pg. 1025
Pelletier, Martin P., V.P.-Opers.--Cascades, Inc., Kingsey Falls, Canada; *Int'l*, pg. 273
Pelletier, Philippe, Reg. Mgr.--Air France (Mid Atlantic Region), Washington, DC; *Int'l*, pg. 560
Pellett, S., Mng. Dir.--Avnet VSI Electronics (N.Z.) Ltd., Auckland, New Zealand; *U.S. Public*, pg. 155
Pellisier, P., Chief Oper. Officer--BV Hepworth-NGI, Belfeld, Netherlands; *Int'l*, pg. 615
Pellisier, P., Chief Oper. Officer--Keramik-Rohr Vertriebs-und Beratungs GmbH, Dusseldorf, Germany; *Int'l*, pg. 615
Pelster, K.H., Gen. Mgr.--Picker International GmbH, Munich, Germany; *Int'l*, pg. 545
Pelstring, Bart, Pres.--Dialysis Corporation of America, Hialeah, FL; *U.S. Public*, pg. 1080
Pelstring, Bart, Pres.--Dialysis Service of Florida, Fort Walton Beach, FL; *U.S. Public*, pg. 1080
Pelto, K., Plant Mgr.--Square D Co., Oshkosh, WI; *Int'l*, pg. 1208
Pelzel, R.G., Pres. & Treas.--Viking Freight System, Inc., San Jose, CA; *U.S. Public*, pg. 604
Pelzl, Peter, Gen. Mgr.--Gema Volstatic Industrial Powder Systems (Switzerland), Saint Gallen, Switzerland; *U.S. Public*, pg. 868
Pemberton, Brian B., Pres.--UNR-Rohn Div., Peoria, IL; *U.S. Public*, pg. 1404
Pena, Eduardo, Mgr.--Cyanamid de Columbia SA, Bogota, Colombia; *U.S. Public*, pg. 80
Pena, Jose, Consumer Opers. Gen. Mgr.--Frutera Colombiana S.A., Bogota, Colombia; *U.S. Public*, pg. 447
Penafiel, Jesus, Pres.--Serpo Onena S.A., Munguia, Spain; *Int'l*, pg. 1200
Penalvar, Adrian, Gen. Mgr.--Vickers Systems S.A., Barcelona, Spain; *U.S. Public*, pg. 25
Penbeek, Ruud Slie, Co. Mgr.--Best Foods Saudi Arabia Co. Ltd., Jeddah, Saudi Arabia; *U.S. Public*, pg. 225
Pence, John W., Pres.--HSN Mail Order, Inc., Saint Petersburg, FL; *U.S. Public*, pg. 1685
Pencer, Gary, V.P. & Gen. Mgr.--Bessey Juice Inc., Ville Saint Laurent, Canada; *Int'l*, pg. 337
Penchuk, Katherine, Chief Oper. Officer--American International Group-Moscow Representative Office, Moscow, Russia; *U.S. Public*, pg. 85
Pendergast, Michael, Chief Oper. Officer--Weatherby Locums Inc., Fort Lauderdale, FL; *U.S. Private*, pg. 1155
Pendergrass, J., Chief Fin. Officer--Lucas NovaSensor Inc., Fremont, CA; *Int'l*, pg. 820
Pendergrass, Jane C., Admin.--Rockingham Nursing Center, Madison, NC; *U.S. Public*, pg. 1714
Pendlebury, David, V.P. & Gen. Mgr.--AlliedSignal Amorphous Metals, Parsippany, NJ; *U.S. Public*, pg. 51
Pendleton, Alexander, Chm. Bd. & Chief Exec. Officer--Ken Tool, Akron, OH; *U.S. Private*, pg. 1050
Pendleton, Arthur L., Chief Oper. Officer--Bluefield Gas Company, Bluefield, WV; *U.S. Public*, pg. 1393
Pendleton, Chris J., Gen. Mgr.--Pacific Steel Ltd., Auckland, New Zealand; *Int'l*, pg. 495
Pendleton, Mark J., Pres.--Kitchell Contractors, Inc. of Arizona, Phoenix, AZ; *U.S. Private*, pg. 624
Pendleton, Terry, Sr. V.P.-Sls.--Trois-Rivieres Mill, Trois-Rivieres, Canada; *Int'l*, pg. 761
Penedo, Dilio Sergio, Pres.--Embratel-Empresa Brasiliera de Telecomunicagoes S.A., Rio de Janeiro, Brazil; *Int'l*, pg. 1362
Pengilly, Lloyd, Mng. Dir.--Fleming Martin Inc., New York, NY; *Int'l*, pg. 493
Penha, Manuel, Mng. Dir.--SKF Latintrade, Inc., Panama, Panama; *Int'l*, pg. 1159
Penick, James, Gen. Mgr.--Nupar, Claremore, OK; *U.S. Public*, pg. 169
Penido, Jose Luciano, Pres.--Samarco Mineracao SA, Belo Horizonte, Brazil; *Int'l*, pg. 224
Penland, James J., Pres. & Chief Exec. Officer--Regions Bank/Winchester, Winchester, TN; *U.S. Public*, pg. 1373
Penley, Joseph H., Plant Mgr.--General Tire Div., Barnesville, GA; *Int'l*, pg. 327
Penman, Ian, Mng. Dir.--CCA Systems, Pty. Ltd., Pyrmont, Australia; *U.S. Public*, pg. 418
Penman, Ian, Country Mgr.--Compaq Computer New Zealand LTd., Auckland, New Zealand; *U.S. Public*, pg. 418
Penn, Anthony, V.P. & Gen. Mgr.--Western American Manufacturing, Inc., San Diego, CA; *U.S. Public*, pg. 1749
Penn, Austin, Chief Oper. Officer--Ahlstrom Machinery Ltd., Bury, United Kingdom; *Int'l*, pg. 35
Penn, Les, Pres.--Flowers Specialty Foods of Montgomery, Inc., Montgomery, AL; *U.S. Public*, pg. 657
Penn, Michael, V.P.-Machining & Assembly Opers.--Lufkin Industries, Machinery Div., Lufkin, TX; *U.S. Public*, pg. 1019
Penn, Tony, Pres.--Western American Manufacturing, Inc., San Diego, CA; *U.S. Public*, pg. 1749
Pennel, Emile, Plant Mgr.--Sodipan Biessard, Biesles, France; *U.S. Public*, pg. 673
Penneman, Stanley, Gen. Mgr.--Federal Parts, Dallas, TX; *U.S. Public*, pg. 1503
Penner, Donald, Pres.--Dynalectric Company, Mc Lean, VA; *U.S. Public*, pg. 571
Pennesi, Giovanni, Mng. Dir.-Picture Tube Div.--BMG Ariola Music Ltda., Sao Paulo, Brazil; *Int'l*, pg. 192
Pennesse, Michael, Pres.--Infu-Tech, Englewood Cliffs, NJ; *U.S. Public*, pg. 440
Pennifold, Trevor R., Gen. Mgr.--BHP Refractories Pty Ltd., Mayfield, Australia; *Int'l*, pg. 227
Penniman, Lynn, Mgr.-Office--Woodward-Clyde, Raleigh, NC; *U.S. Public*, pg. 1656
Pennings, Harry, Chm. Bd.--OCE-U.S.A., Itasca, IL; *Int'l*, pg. 994

Penninx, E.G.M., Chm. Bd.--VNU Dagbladengroep B.V., Nijmegen, Netherlands; *Int'l*, pg. 1445
Pennise, Ron, Dir.-Opers.--Nice Pak Products, Inc., Mooresville, IN; *U.S. Private*, pg. 798
Penny, M.W., Mng. Dir.--Redland Roof Tiles Ltd., Reigate, United Kingdom; *Int'l*, pg. 1091
Penny, Mike, Mgr.-Opers.--Homeshield Fabricated Products, Naperville, IL; *U.S. Public*, pg. 1350
Penny, Philip L., Pres.--Cowles Enthusiast Media, Inc., Stamford, CT; *U.S. Private*, pg. 281
Penny, Scott, Gen. Mgr.--Poe & Brown of Florida, Jacksonville, FL; *U.S. Public*, pg. 1312
Pennycook, Roger A., V.P.-Power Transmission Grp.--Boston Gear, Quincy, MA; *U.S. Public*, pg. 857
Penta, David Della, Pres.--Sani-Tech Inc., Lafayette, NJ; *U.S. Public*, pg. 1545
Pentikainen, Markku, Mng. Dir.--Pakenso Oy, Lahti, Finland; *Int'l*, pg. 456
Pentland, Lawrence, Exec. V.P.--Cott Corporation - North East Division, Toronto, Canada; *Int'l*, pg. 337
Penton, D.M., Chm. Bd.--Wimpey Group Services Ltd., London, United Kingdom; *Int'l*, pg. 1510
Penwarden, Gavin, Mng. Dir.--Atlantic Service Co. (U.K.) Ltd., Newport, United Kingdom; *U.S. Public*, pg. 165
Penzhorn, B.E., Chief Exec. Officer--Rotek Industries (Pty) Ltd, Cleveland, South Africa; *Int'l*, pg. 459
Peonski, Edward, Pres.--AirTronics Co., Elgin, IL; *U.S. Public*, pg. 944
Pepe, Franco, Mgr.--Micro-Controle Italia Srl, Milan, Italy; *U.S. Public*, pg. 1179
Pepe, Michael, Grp. Publisher--Money, New York, NY; *U.S. Public*, pg. 1613
Pepin, Marcel, Pres.--The Imperial Life Assurance Co., Toronto, Canada; *Int'l*, pg. 396
Pepino, G.J., Pres. & Gen. Mgr.--PACCAR International, Kirkland, WA; *U.S. Public*, pg. 1246
Pepper, J. E., Pres.--Procter & Gamble Distr. Co., Cincinnati, OH; *U.S. Public*, pg. 1331
Pepper, J. E., Pres.--D H Food Co., Cincinnati, OH; *U.S. Public*, pg. 1331
Pepper, J. Stanley, Pres.--Pepper Construction Co., Chicago, IL; *U.S. Private*, pg. 851
Pepper, J. Stanley, Pres.--Pepper Construction Company, Irvine, CA; *U.S. Private*, pg. 851
Pepper, J.E., Chief Oper. Officer--Hines-Park Foods, Inc., Cincinnati, OH; *U.S. Public*, pg. 1331
Pepper, J.E., Pres.--Procter & Gamble Mfg. Co., Cincinnati, OH; *U.S. Public*, pg. 1331
Pepper, Ken, Mng. Dir.--ISS Food Hygiene Ltd., Birmingham, United Kingdom; *Int'l*, pg. 657
Pepper, Ken, Mng. Dir.--ISS Cleaning Services Ltd., Aylesbury, United Kingdom; *Int'l*, pg. 657
Pepper, M., Mng. Dir.--Toshiba Cambridge Research Centre Ltd., Cambridge, United Kingdom; *Int'l*, pg. 1406
Pepper, M. J., Pres.--Allied Thread Co. Inc., Manila, Philippines; *Int'l*, pg. 299
Pepper, Samuel J., Publisher--The Yuma Daily Sun, Yuma, AZ; *U.S. Public*, pg. 1601
Peppercorn, J.E., Pres.--Chevron Chemical Co., San Ramon, CA; *U.S. Public*, pg. 348
Peppers, Richard, Mng. Dir.--Black & Decker (Overseas) A.G., Vaduz, Liechtenstein; *U.S. Public*, pg. 234
Pera, Jaime, Mgr.-Mktg.--Sensormatic E.C., S.A., Madrid, Spain; *U.S. Public*, pg. 1457
Peraino, Roy T., Chm. Bd.--Midlantic Bank, N.A., Edison, NJ; *U.S. Public*, pg. 1242
Peralta, Cornelio T., Chm. Bd. & Pres.--Kimberly-Clark Philippines Inc., Manila, Philippines; *U.S. Public*, pg. 959
Peranginangin, P., Gen. Mgr.--Union Carbide Indonesia PT, Jakarta, Indonesia; *U.S. Public*, pg. 1667
Peranteau, Paul, Chief Oper. Officer--John Benjamins North America Inc, Philadelphia, PA; *Int'l*, pg. 187
Peraux, Francois, Dir.-Admin.--Alpha Contact, Brussels, Belgium; *Int'l*, pg. 546
Percelay, David, Pres. & Chief Exec. Officer--Scripps Howard Productions, Santa Monica, CA; *U.S. Public*, pg. 1448
Percriaux, P., Chief Oper. Officer--Twin Disc Intl., S.A., Nivelles, Belgium; *U.S. Public*, pg. 1647
Percy, Keith E., Chief Exec. Officer--UBS Asset Management (UK) Ltd., London, United Kingdom; *Int'l*, pg. 1440
Perdigao, Mark A., Pres.--BNY Brokerage, Inc., New York, NY; *U.S. Public*, pg. 178
Peregrina, Daniel, Dir.--Tiffany & Co. Watch Center S.A., Morges, Switzerland; *U.S. Public*, pg. 1609
Pereira, Antonio Alvaro, Mgr.--Santos Branch, Santos, Brazil; *Int'l*, pg. 139
Pereira, J.F., Bus. Unit Mgr.--Van Leer Elpack A.E.B.E., Mandra-Attikis, Greece; *Int'l*, pg. 1146
Pereira, Joe, Gen. Mgr.--Circle International, Mendota Heights, MN; *U.S. Public*, pg. 371
Pereira, Maria J., Mng. Dir.--Brown Brothers Harriman (Hong Kong) Ltd., Central, Hong Kong; *U.S. Private*, pg. 173
Pereira, Ronaldo A.G., Mng. Dir.--Champion Papel e Celulose, S.A., Sao Paulo, Brazil; *U.S. Public*, pg. 334
Pereira, Rui, Mng. Dir.--Barro Marketing & Publicidade, Lisbon, Portugal; *Int'l*, pg. 1377
Pereles, Richard S., Pres.--Cato Oil & Grease Co., Oklahoma City, OK; *Int'l*, pg. 1045
Perera, J.E.D., Chief Exec. Officer--Blackwood Hodge (Ceylon) Ltd., Colombo, Sri Lanka; *Int'l*, pg. 231
Peretz, S., Dir.--IAI-Europe-EAT-European Advanced Technologies S.A., Paris, France; *Int'l*, pg. 690
Perez Lizaur, Jose Ignacio, Chief Oper. Officer--Wal-Mart Holding Co., Mexico, Mexico; *Int'l*, pg. 241
Perez Lizaur, Jose Ignacio, Chief Oper. Officer--Wal-Mart Holding Co., Mexico, Mexico; *U.S. Public*, pg. 1733
Perez-Aucar, Manuel A., Gen. Mgr.--Acme/Chaston Puerto Rico, Carolina, PR; *U.S. Public*, pg. 694
Perez-Labarta, Salvador, Chief Exec. Officer--NeoCom Publicidade, Alges, Portugal; *U.S. Private*, pg. 678
Perez, Alana S., Pres. & Chief Exec. Officer--OFC/DMB&B Bucharest, Bucharest, Romania; *U.S. Private*, pg. 305
Perez, Angel Alvarez, Pres. & Chief Exec. Officer--First Federal Finance Corporation, Santurce, PR; *U.S. Public*, pg. 644
Perez, Angel Alvarez, Pres. & Chief Exec. Officer--First Leasing & Rental Corporation, Toa Baja, PR; *U.S. Public*, pg. 644
Perez, C.M. Criado, Chief Oper. Officer--Makro Taiwan Ltd., Taipei, Taiwan; *Int'l*, pg. 1156
Perez, Dr. German, Gen. Mgr.--Hibriven Hibridos Venezolanos S.A., Valencia, Venezuela; *U.S. Public*, pg. 1299
Perez, Emilio, Mgr.-Fin. & Admin.--Sensormatic E.C., S.A., Madrid, Spain; *U.S. Public*, pg. 1457
Perez, Hector, Mng. Dir.--Ericsson de Colombia S.A., Bogota, Colombia; *Int'l*, pg. 1366
Perez, Hugo, Chief Oper. Officer--Sistemas NIFE S.A. de C.V., Mexico, Mexico; *Int'l*, pg. 54
Perez, J.L., Mng. Dir.--Vilter Export Corp., Milwaukee, WI; *U.S. Private*, pg. 1141
Perez, Jean-Yves, Pres.--Woodward-Clyde Group, Inc., Denver, CO; *U.S. Public*, pg. 1655
Perez, Jean-Yves, Pres.--Woodward-Constructors, Denver, CO; *U.S. Public*, pg. 1657
Perez, Jose, Division Mgr.--Higgins San Fernando Valley Operations, Pacoima, CA; *U.S. Private*, pg. 527
Perez, Jose A., Chief Fin. Officer--OFC/DMB&B Bucharest, Bucharest, Romania; *U.S. Private*, pg. 305
Perez, L., Gen. Mgr.--ING Bank Quito, Quito, Ecuador; *Int'l*, pg. 649
Perez, Louis, Exec. Editor--The Ledger, Lakeland, FL; *U.S. Public*, pg. 1175
Perez, Ruben, V.P.--Vitt Media-New Media, New York, NY; *U.S. Private*, pg. 1142
Perez, Rudy, Chief Oper. Officer--7-UP/RC of Harlingen, Harlingen, TX; *U.S. Private*, pg. 470
Perez, Thomas N., Chief Exec. Officer--Willis Corroon, Inc., Seattle, WA; *Int'l*, pg. 1507
Perfect, S., Pres.--BFC Civil, Scarborough, Canada; *Int'l*, pg. 118
Perfect, S., Pres.--The Foundation Company, Scarborough, Canada; *Int'l*, pg. 118
Pergande, Wil F., Chief Oper. Officer & V.P.--Vaponics Inc., Rockland, MA; *U.S. Public*, pg. 1234
Periard, Ronal W., Pres., Chief Exec. Officer & Sec. of the Bd.--Central National Bank of Mattoon, Mattoon, IL; *U.S. Public*, pg. 643
Perie, Jean-Claude, Mng. Dir.--Etablissement de Merignac, Merignac, France; *Int'l*, pg. 383
Perieres, J., Chief Oper. Officer--Guigues S.A., Aix-en-Provence, France; *Int'l*, pg. 1361
Perinne, Bernard, Pres.--K-D Manitou, Inc., Waco, TX; *Int'l*, pg. 834
Perino, Larry, Reclamation Mgr.--Sunnyside Gold Corporation, Silverton, CO; *U.S. Public*, pg. 562
Perkett, Charles R., Pres.--CSC Logic, Inc., Dallas, TX; *U.S. Public*, pg. 422
Perkins, Brian D., Pres.--McNeil Consumer Products Company, Fort Washington, PA; *U.S. Public*, pg. 928
Perkins, D.G., Pres.--Micro Motion Inc., Boulder, CO; *U.S. Public*, pg. 574
Perkins, D.W., Pres.--Johnson Matthey Refining, Inc., Salt Lake City, UT; *Int'l*, pg. 713
Perkins, David, Gen. Mgr.--Froude Consine Inc., Livonia, MI; *Int'l*, pg. 473
Perkins, J.O., Pres. & Corp. Exec. Officer--Equifax Insurance Services Inc., Atlanta, GA; *U.S. Public*, pg. 588
Perkins, Jeff, Pres.--First American Title Insurance Agency of Yavapai, Inc., Prescott, AZ; *U.S. Public*, pg. 626
Perkins, John J., Pres.--Western Environmental Contracting, Inc., Los Angeles, CA; *U.S. Public*, pg. 296
Perkins, John J., Pres.--Western Thermal Soils Co., Los Angeles, CA; *U.S. Public*, pg. 296
Perkins, Kenneth A., Pres.--Gemaire Distributors, Inc., Deerfield Beach, FL; *U.S. Public*, pg. 1746
Perkins, Kevin, Pres. & Chief Exec. Officer--CFI Pty., Ltd., Los Angeles, CA; *U.S. Public*, pg. 1475
Perkins, Minor, Co-Mgr.--Investment Banking Div., Memphis, TN; *U.S. Public*, pg. 1131
Perkins, R.A., Gen. Mgr.--Commonwealth Bank of Australia-New South Wales, Sydney, Australia; *Int'l*, pg. 312
Perkins, Ralph L., V.P.--Corning International Corporation, Corning, NY; *U.S. Public*, pg. 448
Perkins, Steve, Branch Mgr.--Downey Savings & Loan Association, F.A., Rancho Santa Margarita, CA; *U.S. Public*, pg. 526
Perkins, Steve, Pres.--Communications Software Division, Irving, TX; *U.S. Public*, pg. 1516
Perkowsky, Rudi, V.P. & Country Mgr.--Bank of America NT&SA, Frankfurt, Germany; *U.S. Public*, pg. 182
Perlis, Morris, Pres. & Chief Exec. Officer--Stadtlander Drug Company, Inc., Pittsburgh, PA; *Int'l*, pg. 338
Perlis, Morris, Pres. & Chief Exec. Officer--Health Management, Inc., Ronkonkoma, NY; *Int'l*, pg. 338
Perliski, Frank, Pres.--Taylor Publishing Co., Dallas, TX; *U.S. Public*, pg. 881
Perlman, George H., Gen. Mgr.--Martin Marietta International, Inc., Beijing, China; *U.S. Public*, pg. 1009
Perlman, Peter, Mng. Dir.--Haworth Thailand Company Ltd., Bangkok, Thailand; *U.S. Private*, pg. 512
Perlman, Uriel, Branch Mgr.--Union-Transport Corporation-Baltimore Office, Baltimore, MD; *U.S. Private*, pg. 1119
Perlman, Uriel, Branch Mgr.--Union-Transport Corporation-Washington, DC Office, Sterling, VA; *U.S. Private*, pg. 1120
Perlmuter, Michael, Pres.--Perlmuter Printing Company, Cleveland, OH; *Int'l*, pg. 1177
Perlov, S.A., Gen. Mgr.--Kvaerner Hymac, Moscow Office, Mitischtehi, Russia; *Int'l*, pg. 770
Pernstich, K., Chief Oper. Officer--Siemens Ltd., Mumbai, India; *Int'l*, pg. 1247
Peroni, Roger, Pres.--Parmalat USA Corporation, Teaneck, NJ; *Int'l*, pg. 1023
Perozzi, Donald J., Pres.--BellSouth Advertising & Publishing Corp., Atlanta, GA; *U.S. Public*, pg. 208
Perrault, Paul, Pres.--Chittenden Bank, Burlington, VT; *U.S. Public*, pg. 351
Perrazzo, M., Mng. Dir.--SBS SIM S.p.A., Milan, Italy; *Int'l*, pg. 1331
Perre, Len, Pres.--Hanovia Colight, Union, NJ; *Int'l*, pg. 17
Perreault, Fernand, Pres.--Cadev, Montreal, Canada; *Int'l*, pg. 249
Perreault, Fernand, Pres. & Chief Oper. Officer--SITQ Immobilier, Montreal, Canada; *Int'l*, pg. 249
Perreault, Robert, Pres. & Chief Exec. Officer--Air Alliance, Sainte-Foy, Canada; *Int'l*, pg. 36
Perrelli, Gary M., V.P. & Gen. Mgr.--Cox Communications-Rhode Island, Cranston, RI; *U.S. Public*, pg. 455
Perrett, J.G., Pres.--KTI Gas Processors Ltd., Richmond, United Kingdom; *Int'l*, pg. 837
Perrett, T. Robert, Pres.--Aesculap, Inc., South San Francisco, CA; *Int'l*, pg. 29
Perric, D.W., Mng. Dir.--Beazer Homes (Glaston) Limited, Cumbernauld, United Kingdom; *Int'l*, pg. 182
Perriello, James J., Pres.--Logicon Syscon Services, Inc., Falls Church, VA; *U.S. Public*, pg. 1199
Perrin, C., Chm. Bd.--Bail Equipement, Paris, France; *Int'l*, pg. 563
Perrin, Hubert, Pres.--Usines Dehousse SA, Pau, France; *Int'l*, pg. 1166
Perrin, John D., V.P. & Gen. Mgr.--Dillard, A ResourceNet International Company, Richmond, VA; *U.S. Public*, pg. 902
Perrin, Keith, Gen. Mgr.--Handy & Harman of Canada Ltd., Rexdale, Canada; *U.S. Public*, pg. 780
Perrin, Robert, Mng. Dir.--Kollmorgan Artus, Avrille, France; *U.S. Public*, pg. 966
Perritt, D., Pres.--D'Allairds, Montreal, Canada; *Int'l*, pg. 843
Perron, Allen A., Pres. & Treas.--Tellus, Inc., Bellevue, WA; *U.S. Public*, pg. 1342
Perrone, L., Pres.--Branson International Plasma Corp., Hayward, CA; *U.S. Public*, pg. 574
Perrone, Michael M., Pres. & Chief Oper. Officer--Fields Financial Services, Inc., Bryan, TX; *U.S. Public*, pg. 942
Perrot, Eric, Gen. Mgr.--Mapa, Levallois-Perret, France; *Int'l*, pg. 1409
Perrot, Gerard, Pres.--Valois of America, Inc., Greenwich, CT; *U.S. Public*, pg. 125
Perrotta, Richard, Plant Mgr.--Tennessee Tubebending Inc., Knoxville, TN; *U.S. Private*, pg. 762
Perrotto, Larry J., Pres. & Chief Exec. Officer--American Publishing Management Services Inc., West Frankfort, IL; *Int'l*, pg. 632
Perry, A.W., Pres. & Chief Exec. Officer--Trunkline LNG Co., Houston, TX; *U.S. Public*, pg. 535
Perry, Arlin R., Pres.--Gear Products Inc., Tulsa, OK; *U.S. Public*, pg. 238
Perry, Barry W., Grp. V.P. & Gen. Mgr.--Pigments & Additives, Iselin, NJ; *U.S. Public*, pg. 582
Perry, Cal, Gen. Mgr.--Elkay Plastics Co., Inc., Stock Service Center, Seattle, WA; *U.S. Private*, pg. 372
Perry, Cal, Gen. Mgr.--Elkay Plastics Co., Inc., Stock Service Center, Hayward, CA; *U.S. Private*, pg. 372
Perry, Christopher J., Pres.--Continental Illinois Venture Corp., Chicago, IL; *U.S. Public*, pg. 181
Perry, D.F., Gen. Mgr.--Long Manufacturing Ltd.-Aftermarket Division, Burlington, Canada; *Int'l*, pg. 815
Perry, David, Pres.--Shiny Entertainment Inc., Laguna Beach, CA; *U.S. Private*, pg. 573
Perry, Ed, Div. Mgr.--Pressure Products Div., Dallas, TX; *U.S. Public*, pg. 1268
Perry, George, Pres. & Chief Exec. Officer--Siemens Automotive Corporation, Auburn Hills, MI; *Int'l*, pg. 1245
Perry, Jack, Chief Oper. Officer--Panduit Canada Ltd., Markham, Canada; *U.S. Private*, pg. 836
Perry, James M., Pres.--Connecticut-American Water Co., Greenwich, CT; *U.S. Public*, pg. 95
Perry, James M., Pres.--Massachusetts Capital Resources Company, Hingham, MA; *U.S. Public*, pg. 95
Perry, James R., Pres. & Chief Exec. Officer--Dillingham Construction Pacific, Ltd., Honolulu, HI; *U.S. Private*, pg. 333
Perry, James R., Pres. & Chief Exec. Officer--Hawaiian Dredging & Construction Company, Honolulu, HI; *U.S. Private*, pg. 333
Perry, John, Gen. Mgr.--Victaulic Fire Safety Company LLC, Easton, PA; *U.S. Private*, pg. 1138
Perry, Larry, Gen. Mgr.--Alro Group, Perrysburg, Perrysburg, OH; *U.S. Private*, pg. 46
Perry, M. Dunham, Jr., Pres.--Flo-Line Filters, Inc., Amarillo, TX; *U.S. Private*, pg. 855
Perry, M. Dunham, Jr., Pres.--United Filters, Inc., Amarillo, TX; *U.S. Private*, pg. 855
Perry, Michael W., Chief Oper. Officer & Exec. V.P.--Countrywide Asset Management Corporation, Pasadena, CA; *U.S. Public*, pg. 452
Perry, Michael W., Pres. & Chief Exec. Officer--Indimac, Inc., Pasadena, CA; *U.S. Public*, pg. 857
Perry, Michael W., Chm.--Warehouse Lending Corporation of America, Pasadena, CA; *U.S. Public*, pg. 857
Perry, Michael W., Chm.--Construction Lending Corporation of America-Builder Division, Pasadena, CA; *U.S. Public*, pg. 857
Perry, Michael W., Pres.--Indimac Mortgage Obligations, Inc., Pasadena, CA; *U.S. Public*, pg. 858
Perry, Michael W., Pres.--Indimac Mortgage Obligations, II, Inc., Pasadena, CA; *U.S. Public*, pg. 858
Perry, N., Gen. Mgr.--ING Baring Securities Argentina, Buenos Aires, Argentina; *Int'l*, pg. 649
Perry, R., Chief Exec.--EMI Records (UK), London, United Kingdom; *Int'l*, pg. 427
Perry, Richard, Pres.-Intl. Division--Waverly International, Baltimore, MD; *U.S. Public*, pg. 1748
Perry, Robert, Pres.--Hydro-Mill Co., Chatsworth, CA; *U.S. Public*, pg. 1640

Perry, Roger, Mng. Dir.--Brotherton Chemicals Ltd., Wakefield, United Kingdom; *U.S. Public*, pg. 356
Perry, Stephen C., Pres.--Leucadia Inc. Manufacturing Division, Lincolnton, NC; *U.S. Public*, pg. 990
Perry, Wes, Pres.--BF Goodrich Avionic Systems, Inc., Grand Rapids, MI; *U.S. Public*, pg. 751
Persason, Lars, Chief Oper. Officer--Geodimeter Gmbh, Weiterstadt, Germany; *Int'l*, pg. 1290
Perschetz, Arthur D., Pres.--Commercial Marketing Systems, Charlotte, NC; *Int'l*, pg. 1131
Persichini, Dominic, Pres.--Air Gage Company, Livonia, MI; *U.S. Public*, pg. 1676
Persico, Gennaro, Gen. Mgr.--Handelsfinanz-CCF Bank, Geneva, Switzerland; *Int'l*, pg. 343
Persico, Yvon, Pres.--Bataan Optical Inc., Manila, Philippines; *Int'l*, pg. 462
Persinger, Mick, Plant Mgr.--Penford Food Ingredients Company, Richland, WA; *U.S. Public*, pg. 1269
Persinko, Ken, Admin.--Great Barrington Healthcare, Great Barrington, MA; *U.S. Public*, pg. 1712
Person, Nancy, Admin.--San Jacinto Manor, Deer Park, TX; *U.S. Public*, pg. 839
Persson, B., Chief Exec. Officer--Zanda AB, Sennan, Sweden; *Int'l*, pg. 1092
Persson, B., Chief Exec. Officer--Zanda A/S, Slemmestad, Norway; *Int'l*, pg. 1092
Persson, Bo, Pres. & Reg. Mgr.--ASEA S.A. de C.V., Tlalnepantla, Mexico; *Int'l*, pg. 8
Persson, Christer, Chm.--Aero Systems Engineering Inc., Saint Paul, MN; *Int'l*, pg. 276
Persson, Erik, Pres.--Hilleshog AB, Landskrona, Sweden; *Int'l*, pg. 982
Persson, Ingemar, Chief Oper. Officer--AB Formverktyg, Hagersten, Sweden; *Int'l*, pg. 439
Persson, Lars, Pres.--Abetong America Inc., Voorhees, NJ; *Int'l*, pg. 1199
Persson, Lars, Chief Oper. Officer--Geodimeter Handels Gesmbh, Vienna, Austria; *Int'l*, pg. 1290
Persson, Mai, Chief Oper. Officer--Medical Rubber AB, Horby, Sweden; *Int'l*, pg. 1036
Persson, Neils-Ereik, Gen. Mgr.--Handelsbanken Copenhangen, Copenhagen, Denmark; *Int'l*, pg. 1327
Persson, Per-Ingemar, Pres.--Skanska Syd, Malmo, Sweden; *Int'l*, pg. 1260
Persson, Ulf, Chief Oper. Officer--Electrolux Thailand Co. Ltd., Bangkok, Thailand; *Int'l*, pg. 444
Persson, Ulf, Chief Oper. Officer--Axel Johnson Resources AB, Moscow, Russia; *Int'l*, pg. 712
Persson, Unger, Pres.--NCC Building - Vaxjo, Vaxjo, Sweden; *Int'l*, pg. 899
Perti, Dan, Gen. Mgr.--Data National, Chantilly, VA; *U.S. Public*, pg. 1724
Perticone, Giacomo, Chief Exec. Officer & Gen. Mgr.-Palermo--Banco di Sicilia, New York, NY; *Int'l*, pg. 140
Pertsch, Eric W., V.P. Fin. & Admin.--Universal Studios Canada Ltd., Willowdale, Canada; *Int'l*, pg. 1216
Perugini, Mario, Gen. Mgr.--BFCE Milan, Milan, Italy; *Int'l*, pg. 161
Pervola, John, Chief Oper. Officer--Lamco J.V. Operating Co., Monrovia, Liberia; *Int'l*, pg. 443
Perwaiz, Muhammad, V.P. & Chief Mgr.--Habib Bank Ltd., Port Louis, Mauritius; *Int'l*, pg. 584
Pesa, Frank, Dir.--Takenaka (U.S.A.) Corporation, Honolulu Office, Honolulu, HI; *Int'l*, pg. 1351
Pesatori, Enrico, Pres.--Tandem Computers Inc., Cupertino, CA; *U.S. Public*, pg. 417
Pesce, Giovanni, Dir. Gen.--BAI Gest S.p.A., Milan, Italy; *Int'l*, pg. 403
Peschiera, Jorge, Chief Oper. Officer--H.B. Fuller Peru, Lima, Peru; *U.S. Public*, pg. 687
Pesci, Robert, Pres.-Packaging Prods. Div.--Sealed Air Packaging Products Division, Saddle Brook, NJ; *U.S. Public*, pg. 1451
Pescod, T., Gen. Mgr.--Kodak Panama Limited, Panama, Panama; *U.S. Public*, pg. 554
Peshkin, J.R., Pres.--Taylor Woodrow Homes Florida Inc., Sarasota, FL; *Int'l*, pg. 1359
Peskin, Kenneth G., Pres.--Sea Ranger Products, Edison, NJ; *U.S. Public*, pg. 1756
Pesola, Simo, Chief Oper. Officer--Enso AG, Pfaffikon, Switzerland; *Int'l*, pg. 457
Pesquie-Nikitine, Isabelle, Chm. Bd.--P.N.B., S.A., Suresnes, France; *U.S. Public*, pg. 1604
Pessl, Harald, Mng. Dir.--Battenfeld Automatisierungstechnik Ges.m.b.H., Kottingbrunn, Austria; *Int'l*, pg. 825
Petenusso de Lima, Luiz Antonio, Mgr.--Novo Hamburgo Branch, Novo Hamburgo, Brazil; *Int'l*, pg. 139
Peter, Adrian, Pres. & Chief Exec. Officer--Siemens Nixdorf Information Systems Inc., Burlington, MA; *Int'l*, pg. 1245
Peter, Alfred, Pres.--Elma Electronic Ltd., Wetzikon, Switzerland; *Int'l*, pg. 1305
Peter, Hans Rudolf, Plng. Dir.--Analog Devices SA, Dubendorf, Switzerland; *U.S. Public*, pg. 108
Peter, Jean D., Pres.--Union Carbide do Brasil S/A, Sao Paulo, Brazil; *U.S. Public*, pg. 1667
Peter, Jean D., Chm. Bd.--Union Carbide South Africa (Pty.) Ltd., Johannesburg, South Africa; *U.S. Public*, pg. 1667
Peterman, Charles, Dir.-Research & Devel.--Hydril Technology Center, Houston, TX; *U.S. Private*, pg. 551
Peterman, Darjes, Chief Exec. Officer--BM Mannheim Beteiligungen GmbH, Mannheim, Germany; *Int'l*, pg. 331
Peters, Brian, Mng. Dir.--Rolled Alloys Ltd., Wetherby, United Kingdom; *U.S. Private*, pg. 941
Peters, Claude, Chief Oper. Officer--Frigoriferi di Tavazzano s.p.a., Tavazzano, Italy; *U.S. Public*, pg. 606
Peters, D.F., Chief Oper. Officer--Mohawk Furniture, Inc., Broadalbin, NY; *U.S. Private*, pg. 443
Peters, Daniel L., Pres.--Nycomed Amersham, Princeton, NJ; *Int'l*, pg. 993
Peters, Earl W., Pres. & Chief Exec. Officer--Farmers Bank & Trust Co., Henderson, KY; *U.S. Public*, pg. 1217
Peters, Frederick C., III, Pres.--1st Main Line Bank, Saint Davids, PA; *U.S. Public*, pg. 1159
Peters, Geoffrey, Gen. Dir.--Willis Corroon France SA, Paris, France; *Int'l*, pg. 1509
Peters, George B., Jr., Supvr.--Camden/Rockland Division, Rockport, ME; *U.S. Public*, pg. 438
Peters, Hans-Martin, Country Mgr.--Berlitz Thailand Ltd., Bangkok, Thailand; *U.S. Public*, pg. 222
Peters, Harold, Plant Mgr.--Gem Southeast, Inc., Toccoa, GA; *U.S. Private*, pg. 443
Peters, Horst, Mng. Dir.--ESAB-Hancock GmbH, Karben, Germany; *Int'l*, pg. 282
Peters, J.E., Pres.--Delmar Photographic and Printing Company, Charlotte, NC; *U.S. Private*, pg. 268
Peters, J.E., Pres.--Delmar Studios, Charlotte, NC; *U.S. Private*, pg. 268
Peters, James R., Pres.--Worldwide Paper Factors Inc., Portland, OR; *Int'l*, pg. 72
Peters, Jay, Pres.--Horizon International, Etobicoke, Canada; *Int'l*, pg. 1012
Peters, Joe, ChieF Oper. Officer--Neste Resins B.V., Delfzijl, Netherlands; *Int'l*, pg. 915
Peters, John, Mng. Dir.--Young & Rubicam Adelaide Pty. Ltd., Dulwich, Australia; *U.S. Private*, pg. 1198
Peters, John H., Pres.--Ikon Office Solutions-Nashville, Nashville, TN; *U.S. Public*, pg. 863
Peters, John L., Plant Mgr.--Hydro Conduit Corp., Hagerstown, MD; *Int'l*, pg. 246
Peters, Jon, Co-Chief Exec. Officer--The Guber Peters Entertainment Company, Los Angeles, CA; *Int'l*, pg. 1283
Peters, Karl Heinz, Chief Oper. Officer--Auto-trol Technology GmbH, Dusseldorf, Germany; *U.S. Public*, pg. 148
Peters, M.E., Pres.--Marathon Ashland Pile Line LLC, Findlay, OH; *U.S. Public*, pg. 1662
Peters, Mark, Gen. Mgr.--Accord Controls, Inc., Cincinnati, OH; *U.S. Public*, pg. 658
Peters, Philip M., Pres.--France Compressor Products Division, Newtown, PA; *U.S. Public*, pg. 402
Peters, Rick, Gen. Mgr.--International Carolina Glass Corp., Rock Hill, SC; *U.S. Public*, pg. 895
Peters, Robert, Chm. Bd.--Gibraltar Corp. of America, New York, NY; *U.S. Public*, pg. 1528
Peters, Samuel L., Pres.--Uforma Shelby Business Forms, Shelby, OH; *U.S. Private*, pg. 740
Peters, Samuel L., Pres.--Specialty Envelope, Cincinnati, OH; *U.S. Private*, pg. 740
Peters, W., Chief Exec. Officer--Swiss Bank Corporation, Central, Hong Kong; *Int'l*, pg. 1330
Peters, William D., Gen. Mgr.--Wyle Laboratories-Western Operations, Norco, CA; *U.S. Private*, pg. 1193
Petersen, Allen, Chm. Bd. & Chief Exec. Officer--American Tool Companies, Inc., Lincoln, NE; *U.S. Private*, pg. 63
Petersen, Bruce, Div. Dir.--PPD Pharmaco (Analytical Laboratory), Richmond, VA; *U.S. Public*, pg. 1285
Petersen, C., Pres.--Minebea Electronics Mexico S.A. de C.V., Nogales, Mexico; *Int'l*, pg. 868
Petersen, Donald K., V.P.-Meridian Business Systems--Northern Telecom - National Repair & Distribution Center, Nashville, TN; *Int'l*, pg. 970
Petersen, Ib, Gen. Mgr.--Siegling Danmark A/S, Brondby, Denmark; *Int'l*, pg. 498
Petersen, Joel, Plant Mgr.--Cylinder Div., Atlanta, GA; *U.S. Public*, pg. 1261
Petersen, John V., Chief Oper. Officer--Alfa-Laval Zeta A/S, Roedovre, Denmark; *Int'l*, pg. 1379
Petersen, K.L., Gen. Mgr.--ING Bank Beirut, Beirut, Lebanon; *Int'l*, pg. 648
Petersen, Mike, Pres. & Chief Oper. Officer--Baker's Supermarkets, Inc., Omaha, NE; *U.S. Public*, pg. 652
Petersen, Peter, Mng. Dir.--Swatch Telecom AG, Bienne, Switzerland; *Int'l*, pg. 1161
Petersen, Peter, Mng. Dir.--Swatch S.A., Bienne, Switzerland; *Int'l*, pg. 1161
Petersen, Peter, Mng. Dir.--SMH Japan KK, Tokyo, Japan; *Int'l*, pg. 1161
Petersen, Peter, Mng. Dir.--SMH (Korea) Ltd., Seoul, Korea; *Int'l*, pg. 1161
Petersen, Rich, Reg. Sls. Mgr.--Aromat New England Sales Office, Marlborough, MA; *Int'l*, pg. 848
Petersen, Robert A., Mgr.-Branch--Piper Jaffray Inc., Tacoma, WA; *U.S. Public*, pg. 1301
Peterson, Arthur M., Pres.--Kampgrounds of America (Canada) Ltd., Brampton, Canada; *U.S. Private*, pg. 603
Peterson, Borje, Pres.--ETP Transmission AB, Linkoping, Sweden; *Int'l*, pg. 678
Peterson, Charles D., Plant Mgr.--Ash Grove Cement-Western Region Cement Plant, Clancy, MT; *U.S. Private*, pg. 88
Peterson, David H., Chm. Bd., Pres. & Chief Exec. Officer--NRG Energy, Inc., Minneapolis, MN; *U.S. Public*, pg. 1195
Peterson, Dennis E., Pres.--Oil-Dri Transportation Co., Ochlocknee, GA; *U.S. Public*, pg. 1215
Peterson, Diane, Pres.--First Deposit National Bank, Tilton, NH; *U.S. Public*, pg. 1338
Peterson, E. Mitchell, Pres.--LaBarge Mirrors, Inc., Holland, MI; *U.S. Private*, pg. 432
Peterson, Gerald H., Pres.--Ford Communications, Inc., Dearborn, MI; *U.S. Public*, pg. 664
Peterson, Howard, Plant Mgr.--The Coleman Company, Lake City, SC; *U.S. Private*, pg. 691
Peterson, Howard, Pres.--MNX Trucking, Inc., Saint Joseph, MO; *U.S. Public*, pg. 1046
Peterson, James, Gen. Mgr.--Frontier Communications of Iowa, Inc., Fort Dodge, IA; *U.S. Public*, pg. 683
Peterson, John, Pres. & Chief Oper. Officer--Warren Electric Telecommunications-Utilities Company, Houston, TX; *U.S. Private*, pg. 1151
Peterson, John C., V.P.--Foothills Trader, Inc., Collinsville, CT; *U.S. Public*, pg. 934
Peterson, John C., Pres.-New England Newspaper Grp.--The Advertiser, Branford, CT; *U.S. Public*, pg. 934
Peterson, John E., Gen. Mgr.--Colony Printing & Labeling, Eaton, IN; *U.S. Public*, pg. 976
Peterson, Jon, V.P. & Gen. Mgr.--Cott Corporation - Pacific Central Region, Burlingame, CA; *Int'l*, pg. 338
Peterson, Kelly, Country Mgr.-Malaysia & Singapore--Cerner Singapore Pte Ltd., Singapore, Singapore; *U.S. Public*, pg. 331
Peterson, Kris, Gen. Mgr.--Peterson Spring-Packaging & Distribution, Three Rivers, MI; *U.S. Private*, pg. 857
Peterson, Loren B., Pres.--Bowne of Los Angeles, Inc., Los Angeles, CA; *U.S. Public*, pg. 249
Peterson, Norman A., Pres. & Chief Exec. Officer--Willis Corroon Corp. of Wisconsin, Milwaukee, WI; *Int'l*, pg. 1507
Peterson, O. James, III, Pres. & Chief Exec. Officer--Dominion Capital, Inc., Richmond, VA; *U.S. Public*, pg. 516
Peterson, Phil, Mgr.--Vegas Electric Supply, Las Vegas, NV; *U.S. Private*, pg. 265
Peterson, Phil, Admin.--Birchwood Terrace Healthcare, Burlington, VT; *U.S. Public*, pg. 1712
Peterson, R.B., Chm. & Chief Exec. Officer--Imperial Oil Limited, Toronto, Canada; *U.S. Public*, pg. 602
Peterson, Randall J., Pres. & Chief Oper. Officer--Associated Bank Green Bay, Green Bay, WI; *U.S. Public*, pg. 141
Peterson, Richard, Mng. Dir.--The Lincoln Electric Company (Asia Pacific) Pte. Ltd., Singapore, Singapore; *U.S. Public*, pg. 996
Peterson, Robert, Gen. Mgr.--Jordan's Foods-Colchester Division, Colchester, VT; *U.S. Private*, pg. 599
Peterson, Ron, Mgr.--Alliant Techsystems-Magna, Magna, UT; *U.S. Public*, pg. 47
Peterson, Ronald, V.P.-Western Reg.--W. Braun Co., Sun Valley, CA; *U.S. Private*, pg. 166
Peterson, Ronald, Pres. & Chief Exec. Officer--Blue Coral Systems, Tucson, AZ; *U.S. Public*, pg. 1348
Peterson, Stacy, Sr. V.P.--Western Marketing-Los Angeles Region, Sherman Oaks, CA; *U.S. Public*, pg. 650
Petersson, Conny, Pres.--Ventim AB, Kalmar, Sweden; *Int'l*, pg. 678
Petit, Henri, Chief Oper. Officer--Consumer Imaging Division, Rochester, NY; *U.S. Public*, pg. 555
Petit, Henri, Chm. Bd.--Ecole de Pilotage Amaury de la Grange, Merville, France; *Int'l*, pg. 560
Petit, L.J.J.M., Mng. Dir.--Van Swaay Toegangstechniek bv, Capelle aan den Ijssel, Netherlands; *Int'l*, pg. 680
Petit, Marc, Chief Oper. Officer--SFIC, Nanterre, France; *Int'l*, pg. 1176
Petitgas, Philippe, Gen. Mgr.--BFCE Hong Kong, Wan Chai, Hong Kong; *Int'l*, pg. 161
Petitjean, Guy, Mgr.--Barenbrug France SA, Collegien, France; *Int'l*, pg. 167
Petitt, Richard G., Pres.--Conseco Life of New York, Orangeburg, NY; *U.S. Public*, pg. 433
Petitt, Richard G., Chm. Bd. & Pres.--Colonial Penn Life Insurance Company, Philadelphia, PA; *U.S. Public*, pg. 433
Petitt, Richard G., Chm. Bd. & Pres.--Empire Insurance Group, New York, NY; *U.S. Public*, pg. 990
Petoyan, Galen, Pres.--SCS Field Services, Inc., Long Beach, CA; *U.S. Private*, pg. 956
Petrak, Michael R., Exec. V.P. & Gen. Mgr.--The Kansas City Star Company, Kansas City, MO; *U.S. Public*, pg. 964
Petratsas, Peter P., Pres.--Robinson-Ransbottom Pottery Company, Roseville, OH; *U.S. Private*, pg. 169
Petrauskas, Helen O., V.P.--Ford Environmental & Safety Engineering Staff, Dearborn, MI; *U.S. Public*, pg. 663
Petrenko, Jim, Pres.--ITW Irathane, Hibbing, MN; *U.S. Public*, pg. 866
Petrie, Ed, Pres.--Ackerley Airport Advertising, New York, NY; *U.S. Public*, pg. 15
Petrie, William, Mng. Dir.--Brush Electrical Machines Ltd., Loughborough, United Kingdom; *Int'l*, pg. 124
Petrie, William, Pres.--Hendrickson International, Woodridge, IL; *U.S. Private*, pg. 155
Petro, Francis J., Pres.--Inco Alloys International, Inc., Huntington, WV; *Int'l*, pg. 672
Petro, P. Paul, Pres.--Plexco/Spirolite, Norcross, GA; *U.S. Public*, pg. 348
Petroff, Victor, Gen. Mgr.--Precision Interconnect, Portland, OR; *U.S. Public*, pg. 8
Petronio, Nick, Chief Oper. Officer--Pool Company (Texas), Inc., Houston, TX; *U.S. Public*, pg. 1316
Petrotta, Frank, Branch Mgr.--Downey Savings & Loan Association, F.A., Fountain Valley, CA; *U.S. Public*, pg. 526
Petrou, David, Pres. & Chief Oper. Officer-Eisner Petrou & Assoc. Pub. Rels.--Eisner & Associates, Inc., Baltimore, MD; *U.S. Private*, pg. 366
Petrou, David, Pres. & Chief Oper. Officer--Eisner, Petrou & Associates, Inc., Baltimore, MD; *U.S. Private*, pg. 366
Petrowski, J. H., Pres.--CNG Power Services Corporation, Pittsburgh, PA; *U.S. Public*, pg. 435
Petrowski, Joseph H., Pres.--CNG Energy Services Corporation, Pittsburgh, PA; *U.S. Public*, pg. 435
Petroz, Herve, Chm.--Minoterie Coop Rivaz, Puidoux, Switzerland; *Int'l*, pg. 330
Petruzzi, Robert J., Chief Oper. Officer--Arnold Transportation Services, Camp Hill, PA; *U.S. Public*, pg. 132
Petry, Ulrich, Mng. Dir.--Ketchum Advertising GmbH, Frankfurt, Germany; *U.S. Private*, pg. 617
Petshler, Jan, Pres.--NCC Building - Umea, Umea, Sweden; *Int'l*, pg. 898
Petta, Valerie, Regional Mgr.--Brookfield Homes-Eastern Region, North York, Canada; *Int'l*, pg. 228
Pettengill, Robert S., Pres.--Motors Trading Corporation, Detroit, MI; *U.S. Public*, pg. 721
Pettersen, Knut, Chief Representative--Kvaerner Hydro Power, Beijing Representative Office, Beijing, China; *Int'l*, pg. 767
Petterson, John S., Pres.--Tiffany & Co. ICT, Inc., New York, NY; *U.S. Public*, pg. 1609

Pettersson, Folke, Mng. Dir.--Kvaerner Pulping Oy, Helsinki, Finland; Int'l, pg. 768
Pettersson, Folke, Pres.--Kamyr Oy, Helsinki, Finland; Int'l, pg. 771
Pettersson, Goran, Chief Oper. Officer--Pharmacia & Upjohn Ltd., Milton Keynes, United Kingdom; Int'l, pg. 1050
Pettersson, Hans, Mng. Dir.--MoDo Paper AB, Ornskoldsvik, Sweden; Int'l, pg. 886
Pettersson, Kjell, Mng. Dir.--Pitney Bowes Svenska Aktiebolag, Solna, Sweden; U.S. Public, pg. 1304
Pettersson, Lars, Pres.--Tretorn Forsaljnings AB, Helsingborg, Sweden; Int'l, pg. 1072
Pettersson, Lars, Mgr.--AB Sandvik Coromant, Sandviken, Sweden; Int'l, pg. 1185
Pettersson, Lennart, Pres.--Nybro Smide, Nybro, Sweden; Int'l, pg. 1421
Pettersson, Rolf, Mng. Dir.--Rammer Svenska AB, Sodertalje, Sweden; Int'l, pg. 1352
Pettersson, Torbjorn, Pres.--Stora Billerud AB, Skoghall, Sweden; Int'l, pg. 1302
Petteson, Bengt, Chief Oper. Officer--SCA Nordliner AB, Obbola, Sweden; Int'l, pg. 1326
Pettesson, Leif, Pres.--NCC Vaxjo, Vaxjo, Sweden; Int'l, pg. 899
Pettiette, Patrick L., Exec. V.P.-Intl.--Heavy Civil Construction, Boise, ID; U.S. Public, pg. 1134
Pettigrew, Al, Plant Mgr.--OMC El Paso, El Paso, TX; U.S. Private, pg. 478
Pettigrew, Ed A., Mgr.--Area 3, Fruitland, NM; Int'l, pg. 224
Pettigrew, Richard, Mgr.--Inspectorate (Suisse) S.A., Prilly, Switzerland; Int'l, pg. 679
Pettine, Antonio Luis, Mng. Dir.--KONE Ascensores S.A., Buenos Aires, Argentina; Int'l, pg. 747
Pettine, William, Pres.--Dutchmen Manufacturing, Inc., Goshen, IN; U.S. Public, pg. 1602
Pettine, William, Pres.--Thor Indiana, Inc., Bristol, IN; U.S. Public, pg. 1602
Pettipher, John R., Chm. Bd.--Ford Financial Services Inc., Dearborn, MI; U.S. Public, pg. 663
Pettit, Peter, Pres.--M & H Financial Corp., Memphis, TN; U.S. Public, pg. 653
Pettit, T. Christopher, Pres.--Lehman Commercial Paper Inc., New York, NY; U.S. Public, pg. 987
Pettit, Wallace, Pres.--Polka Dot Dairy/Tom Thumb Food Markets, Hastings, MN; U.S. Private, pg. 874
Petty, D. B., Property Mgr.--Tubac Valley Water Company, Inc., Stamford, CT; U.S. Public, pg. 380
Petty, George S., Chm. Bd. & Chief Exec. Officer--Alcell Technologies Inc., Newcastle, Canada; Int'l, pg. 1104
Petty, Herschel, Plant Mgr.--L.B. Foster Company-Parkersburg Plant, Washington, WV; U.S. Public, pg. 676
Petty, James R., Pres.--U.S. Home Mortgage Corporation, Clearwater, FL; U.S. Public, pg. 1683
Petty, Mark, Pres.--Industrial Drives Div., Radford, VA; U.S. Public, pg. 965
Petty, R.B., Chm. Bd., Pres. & Chief Exec. Officer--SouthTrust Bank, Montgomery, Montgomery, AL; U.S. Public, pg. 1491
Petzinger, Gerd, Div. Dir.--Herberts-O'Brien Inc., Houston, TX; Int'l, pg. 626
Peudopin, Daniel, V.P.-Cargo, USA--Air France, New York, NY; Int'l, pg. 560
Peuiere, Y., Mng. Dir.--Ascom Elsydel SA, Paris, France; Int'l, pg. 87
Pew, R.A., Pres.--Helios Capital Corporation, Philadelphia, PA; U.S. Public, pg. 1530
Peyrelongue, Guy, Pres. & Chief Exec. Officer--Cosmair, Inc., New York, NY; Int'l, pg. 818
Peyser, C. Alan, Pres.--Cable & Wireless of North America, Inc., Vienna, VA; Int'l, pg. 247
Peyser, D., Mgr.--Harris Metals-Arrow Acme Co., Webster City, IA; U.S. Public, pg. 999
Pezzi, Daniel, Gen. Mgr.--Young & Rubicam Damaris, C. por A., Santo Domingo, Dominican Republic; U.S. Private, pg. 1200
Pezzolo, Donald E., Chm. Bd. & Co-Chief Exec. Officer--Diablo Research Corporation, Sunnyvale, CA; U.S. Public, pg. 1424
Pfaff, Edward, Chm. & Chief Exec. Officer--Condor Tool & Die, Inc., Cleveland, OH; U.S. Private, pg. 71
Pfaff, Edward, Chm. Bd.--Anchor Metal Processing, Cleveland, OH; U.S. Private, pg. 71
Pfaffeneder, Gottfried, Gen. Mgr.--Siegling Iberica S.A., Montcada, Spain; Int'l, pg. 498
Pfau, Reinhard, Gen. Mgr.--Sanit, Eisenberg, Germany; Int'l, pg. 430
Pfeffer, Joseph, Mng. Dir.--RAFI GmbH & Co. Elektrotechnische Spezialfabrik, Berge, Germany; Int'l, pg. 516
Pfeifer, David, Pres.--Gamma One, Inc., North Haven, CT; U.S. Public, pg. 228
Pfeifer, Ray, Chief Exec. Officer--Cascade Controls, Inc., Tempe, AZ; U.S. Private, pg. 1060
Pfeifer, Richard J., Grp. V.P. Opers.-Refrigerator Prods.--Frigidaire Home Products-Refrigerator Products, Greenville, MI; Int'l, pg. 440
Pfeiffer, Michael, Pres. & Chief Exec. Officer--Aircraft of Canada Ltd., Calgary, Canada; U.S. Public, pg. 1365
Pfeiffer, Paul, Dir.-Admin.--Brasilux S.A., Luxembourg, Luxembourg; Int'l, pg. 79
Pfeiffer, Phyllis, Pres. & Publr.--California Newspapers, Inc., Novato, CA; U.S. Public, pg. 700
Pfeifle, D., Dr., Mng. Dir.--Robert Bosch GmbH, Hildesheim, Germany; Int'l, pg. 204
Pfeifle, Dr., Mng. Dir.--Blaupunkt-Werke GmbH, Hildesheim, Germany; Int'l, pg. 203
Pfeil, H.K., Gen. Mgr.--OMRON Electronics Ges.m.b.H., Vienna, Austria; Int'l, pg. 1006
Pfeil, Hans-Jurgen, Chief Oper. Officer--Ceresit GmbH, Dusseldorf, Germany; Int'l, pg. 609
Pfeil, Hans-Jurgen, Chief Oper. Officer--Henkel Bautechnik GmbH, Dusseldorf, Germany; Int'l, pg. 609
Pfeil, Roy, Dir.--Easton Press Books, Norwalk, CT; U.S. Private, pg. 685
Pfendt, Glenn, Mgr.--A.O. Smith Water Products Division, Florence, KY; U.S. Public, pg. 1477
Pfennig, Richard, Pres.--PSA Airlines, Inc., Vandalia, OH; U.S. Public, pg. 1680
Pfister, Jacques, Pres. & Chief Exec. Officer--Orangina France, Aix-en-Provence, France; Int'l, pg. 566
Pfister, Jean-Pierre, Gen. Mgr.--Limmatdruck AG, Spreitenbach, Switzerland; Int'l, pg. 865
Pfister, Karl A., Pres.--MPI International, Inc., Rochester Hills, MI; Int'l, pg. 737
Pfister, Leon, Mgr.--Jasper Laminates, Jasper, IN; U.S. Public, pg. 957
Pfitzer, W., Dr., Mng. Dir.--Ascom GCT GmbH & Co., Kerpen, Germany; Int'l, pg. 87
Pfluger, Urs N., Chief Oper. Officer--Novo Nordisk Pharma AG, Kusnacht, Switzerland; Int'l, pg. 988
Phair, James J., Chief Oper. Officer--Tokio Re Corporation, New York, NY; Int'l, pg. 1392
Phaneuf, Gene, Mgr.-Opers.--Electronics Division, Bloomfield, CT; Int'l, pg. 388
Phansalkar, Ashok, Mng. Dir.--Semcon Electronics Pvt. Ltd., Mumbai, India; U.S. Public, pg. 1107
Pharris, Walter, Pres. & Chief Exec. Officer--Fairfield Industries, Inc., Houston, TX; U.S. Private, pg. 391
Phelizon, Jean Francois, Chief Oper. Officer--SPAFI, Courbevoie, France; Int'l, pg. 1177
Phelps, H.T.H.M., Chm. Bd.--Beeton Rumford Ltd., London, United Kingdom; Int'l, pg. 1032
Phelps, R.D., Pres.--Alcoa Properties, Inc., Burlington, VT; U.S. Public, pg. 61
Phelps, Richard J., Pres.--Superior Brands, Inc., Quincy, MA; Int'l, pg. 917
Phelps, William, Pres.--Buffalo Air Handling, Amherst, VA; U.S. Public, pg. 103
Pheng, Lim Chwee, Rep.--Sanpaolo-Bangkok Representative Office, Bangkok, Thailand; Int'l, pg. 691
Pherigo, William L., Pres. & Chief Exec. Officer--The National Bank of South Carolina, Sumter, SC; U.S. Public, pg. 1549
Phikas, Aristomenis D., Pres.--Hansen Hellas Abee, Thessaloniki, Greece; Int'l, pg. 289
Philco, O., Mng. Dir.--Gestetner S.A., San Isidro, Peru; Int'l, pg. 1115
Philip, Craig, Chief Oper. Officer & Sr. V.P.--Ingram Barge Company, Nashville, TN; U.S. Private, pg. 563
Philip, Robert W., Pres.--Proler International Corp., Portland, OR; U.S. Public, pg. 1440
Philipon, Jean, Pres.--Flender-Graffenstaden S.A., Illkirch-Graffenstaden, France; Int'l, pg. 400
Philipp, Grant, V.P. & Gen. Mgr.--Morgardshammar Inc., Charlotte, NC; Int'l, pg. 378
Philippen, L., Mng. Dir.--Ballast Nedam Bouwmaterieel B.V., Almere, Netherlands; Int'l, pg. 133
Philips, Frank, Div. Head--Leslie Fay II, New York, NY; U.S. Public, pg. 989
Philips, George, Pres.--Primedia Inc., Mahwah, NJ; U.S. Public, pg. 1328
Philipson, David, Mng. Dir.--AB Reportagebild, Stockholm, Sweden; Int'l, pg. 29
Phillipo, B.L., Dr., Mng. Dir.--Davy International, Stockton on Tees, United Kingdom; Int'l, pg. 773
Phillips, Andrew, Mng. Dir.--Hayes Microcomputer Products Ltd., Sydney, Australia; U.S. Public, pg. 801
Phillips, Bert T., Pres. & Gen. Mgr.--Topeka Group, Incorporated, Duluth, MN; U.S. Public, pg. 1116
Phillips, Bert T., Chm. & Chief Exec. Officer--Heater Utilities, Incorporated, Cary, NC; U.S. Public, pg. 1116
Phillips, Bert T., Pres. & Chm.--Lehigh Utilities Inc., Apopka, FL; U.S. Public, pg. 1116
Phillips, Bill, Area Superintendent--Midkiff Gas Plant, Midkiff, TX; U.S. Public, pg. 1759
Phillips, Bill, Area Superintendent--Perkins/Bronte Plant, Silver, TX; U.S. Public, pg. 1759
Phillips, Byron, Gen. Mgr.--Olympia Park Hotel, Park City, UT; U.S. Public, pg. 1537
Phillips, C.J., Pres.--Alcatel Cable Systems Group, Claremont, NC; Int'l, pg. 55
Phillips, Cody H., Pres.--Delta Life Corporation, Memphis, TN; U.S. Private, pg. 59
Phillips, Dallas, Mgr.-Plant--Servitex, Inc., Danville, VA; U.S. Private, pg. 782
Phillips, Daniel J., Gen. Mgr.--Partridge Meats, Inc., Cincinnati, OH; U.S. Public, pg. 75
Phillips, Dave, Chm. Bd. & Chief Exec. Officer--CCC Information Services, Chicago, IL; U.S. Private, pg. 562
Phillips, David, Gen. Dir.--P.T. CSSL Indonesia, Jakarta, Indonesia; U.S. Public, pg. 1043
Phillips, David, Pres.--Alcolac Ltd., Valleyfield, Canada; Int'l, pg. 1113
Phillips, Don, Chief Oper. Officer--Oldelft Corp. of America, Columbia, MD; Int'l, pg. 389
Phillips, Donald C., Pres. & Chief Exec. Officer--Bank of Coweta, Newnan, GA; U.S. Public, pg. 1549
Phillips, Douglas S., Pres.--Trusco Capital Management, Atlanta, GA; U.S. Public, pg. 1538
Phillips, Dr. Fletcher, Pres.--Santa Barbara Research Center, Goleta, CA; U.S. Public, pg. 1365
Phillips, Ernie, Chm. Bd.--First American Title Co. of New Mexico, Albuquerque, NM; U.S. Public, pg. 625
Phillips, H.A., Pres.--Rio Grande Land Co., Denver, CO; U.S. Public, pg. 1668
Phillips, J. Russell, Pres. & Chief Exec. Officer--Shurflo Pump Manufacturing Co., Santa Ana, CA; U.S. Public, pg. 1767
Phillips, Jim, Dir.-Oper.--Armor Bond Building Products, Inc., Sardis, MS; Int'l, pg. 699
Phillips, Jim, Plant Mgr.--American Natl. Can Co., Shelbyville, TN; Int'l, pg. 1029
Phillips, Jimmy E., Pres.--Southern Life and Health Insurance Company, Birmingham, AL; U.S. Private, pg. 447
Phillips, John, V.P.--Cable & Wireless (N.Y.) Inc., New York, NY; Int'l, pg. 247
Phillips, John H., Acting Pres. & Chief Exec. Officer--Cadmus, Sandston, VA; U.S. Public, pg. 290
Phillips, Kenneth, Dir.-Opers.--CPS Credit Corp., Elmhurst, IL; U.S. Public, pg. 309
Phillips, Lynn, Gen. Mgr.--Retail Services, Memphis, TN; U.S. Public, pg. 653
Phillips, Mike, Gen. Mgr.--Republic Automotive Parts Sales, Inc., Marquette, MI; U.S. Public, pg. 1378
Phillips, Mike, Editor--Bremerton Sun, Bremerton, WA; U.S. Public, pg. 1447
Phillips, N., Pres.--Autolatina, Sao Paulo, Brazil; Int'l, pg. 1474
Phillips, P.J., Exec. V.P., Asst. Gen. Mgr. & Branch Mgr.--Lloyds Bank Plc., New York, NY; Int'l, pg. 813
Phillips, R., Chief Exec. Officer--Ascom Timeplex, Woodcliff Lake, NJ; Int'l, pg. 86
Phillips, Randall, V.P.-Oper. & Gen. Mgr.--Eaton Corporation Automotive Controls Division, Carol Stream, IL; U.S. Public, pg. 557
Phillips, Ron, Chm. Bd.--Lever Brothers Co., New York, NY; Int'l, pg. 1435
Phillips, Scott, Gen. Mgr.--PSI Repair Services, Inc., Livonia, MI; U.S. Private, pg. 862
Phillips, Thomas, Pres.--Groen, A Dover Industries Co., Elk Grove Village, IL; U.S. Public, pg. 521
Phillips, Wayne, V.P. & Gen. Mgr.--KIMN AM & KYGO FM, Denver, CO; U.S. Public, pg. 926
Phillips, William, Pres.--World Book, Inc., Columbus, OH; U.S. Public, pg. 218
Phillips, William, Dir.--Budd Technical Center, Auburn Hills, MI; Int'l, pg. 1388
Phillips, William G., Pres.--Abrams Properties, Inc., Atlanta, GA; U.S. Public, pg. 14
Phillis, Collin, Gen. Mgr.--TMP Worldwide Pty Ltd., Leederville, Australia; Int'l, pg. 1342
Philpot, Gerald, Pres.--Lagerquist Corporation, Minneapolis, MN; U.S. Public, pg. 521
Philpot, T.A., Mng. Dir.--Cementation Piling & Foundations Limited, Rickmansworth, United Kingdom; Int'l, pg. 772
Philpott, D.K., Prod. Mgr.--MB-Clarke Ltd., Peterborough, United Kingdom; Int'l, pg. 386
Phinney, E.E., Chm. Bd., Pres. & Chief Exec. Officer--SouthTrust Bank of Central Florida, Deland, FL; U.S. Public, pg. 1492
Phinney, Loring, Gen. Mgr.--Optimum Public Relations (Vancouver) Inc., Vancouver, Canada; Int'l, pg. 336
Phippen, Michael K., Pres.--Western Light Industrial Services, Walnut Creek, CA; U.S. Public, pg. 1760
Phipps, Allen, Pres. & Chief Exec. Officer--SRI Consulting, Menlo Park, CA; U.S. Private, pg. 958
Phipps, R.J., Mng. Dir., Europe--Hubbell, Ltd., Kempston, United Kingdom; U.S. Public, pg. 845
Phiri, D.A.R., Chm.--Stanbic Bank Zambia, Lusaka, Zambia; Int'l, pg. 1294
Phornpraphа, Phornpong, Pres.--Siam Kabaya Co., Ltd., Samutprakan, Thailand; Int'l, pg. 727
Phornprapha, Phornthep, Pres.--Bangkok Komatsu Co., Ltd., Chon Buri, Thailand; Int'l, pg. 745
Phreat, J.B., Mgr.-Plant--Identification Systems, Searcy, AR; U.S. Public, pg. 1059
Phulpin, Francois, Chm.--CAP Sesa Industrie, Paris, France; Int'l, pg. 263
Phutrakul, Viroj, Chm.--Lever Brothers (Thailand) Ltd., Bangkok, Thailand; Int'l, pg. 1437
Piana, Michael R., Gen. Mgr.--Wolf's Head Oil Company, Houston, TX; U.S. Public, pg. 1273
Piancastelli, Paolo, Mng. Dir.--Allo Pro Italia s.r.l., Milan, Italy; Int'l, pg. 1307
Piano, Toni, Plant Mgr.--San Giorgio Macaroni, Lebanon, PA; U.S. Public, pg. 812
Piattoli, Roberto, Pres.--Snamprogetti S.p.A., Milan, Italy; Int'l, pg. 429
Piattoli, Roberto, Chm. & Mng. Dir.--Snamprogetti International S.A., Geneva, Switzerland; Int'l, pg. 429
Piay, R., Mng. Dir.--EMI Capitol de Mexico SA de CV, Mexico, Mexico; Int'l, pg. 427
Piazza, John, Chief Exec. Officer--Sara Lee Hosiery, Winston Salem, NC; U.S. Public, pg. 1434
Picado, Romulo, Chief Exec.--Productos de Concreto S.A., San Jose, Costa Rica; Int'l, pg. 629
Picard, K.J., Chief Fin. Officer--Oil Drilling & Exploration Limited, Sydney, Australia; Int'l, pg. 101
Picard, Patrick, Chief Oper. Officer--Technip Anlagenbau GmbH, Dusseldorf, Germany; Int'l, pg. 1361
Picari, Giuseppe, Gen. Dir.--Sanpaolo Bank (Austria) A.G., Vienna, Austria; Int'l, pg. 692
Picchi, Giordano, Mng. Dir.--Ademco-Italia S.p.A., Milan, Italy; U.S. Public, pg. 1307
Piccione, James J., Pres.--Dale Foods, Melrose Park, IL; U.S. Private, pg. 301
Piccione, James J., Pres.--Gage Food Products Company, Melrose Park, IL; U.S. Private, pg. 301
Piccolo, C.A. Lance, Chief Exec. Officer--Caremark International Inc, Northbrook, IL; U.S. Public, pg. 1082
Pichan, William W., Pres.--T & N Industries, Inc., Ann Arbor, MI; Int'l, pg. 1334
Piche, A.W., V.P.--Trimac Transportation-Western Division, Calgary, Canada; Int'l, pg. 1424
Piche, M., Chief Oper. Officer--Detrey Dentsply S.A., Bois-Colombes, France; U.S. Public, pg. 500
Pichery, Pierre, Mgr.--AlliedSignal Aerospace Service Corporation, Blagnac, France; U.S. Public, pg. 52
Pichl, Helmut, Gen. Dir.--Radex Austria, A.G., Radenthein, Austria; U.S. Private, pg. 904
Pichler, Christoph, Mng. Dir.--ESAB Ges.m.b.H, Vienna, Austria; Int'l, pg. 282
Pichler, Christoph, Mng. Dir.--Nederman Ges.m.b.H., Vienna, Austria; Int'l, pg. 283
Pichon, Gilles, Mng. Dir.--Ericsson Composants S.A., Guyancourt, France; Int'l, pg. 1366
Pichotta, Nicholas, Pres.--CooperSurgical Inc., Shelton, CT; U.S. Public, pg. 442

Pickard, Mark, Gen. Mgr.--Infra Ready Products Ltd., Saskatoon, Canada; *Int'l*, pg. 1195

Pickel, K.P., Mgr.--Swiss Bank Corporation, Sao Paulo, Brazil; *Int'l*, pg. 1330

Pickell, Barry, Gen. Mgr.--Hussey Seating Co. (Canada) Ltd., Mississauga, Canada; *U.S. Private*, pg. 550

Pickell, Ira S., Chm. Bd. & Chief Exec. Officer--The Bon Marche, Inc., Seattle, WA; *U.S. Public*, pg. 617

Pickell, L.A., Pres.--Commercial Interior Builders, Inc., Jessup, MD; *U.S. Public*, pg. 913

Picken, Findlay, Mng. Dir.--National Tyre Service Ltd., Stockport, United Kingdom; *Int'l*, pg. 328

Pickens, J.Q., Gen. Mgr.--Superior Dairies, Inc., Austin, TX; *U.S. Private*, pg. 158

Pickens, Steve A., Pres.--Nocona Boot Co., Nocona, TX; *U.S. Public*, pg. 937

Pickens, William S., Jr., Sls. Mgr.--Sackner-South Div., Verona, MS; *U.S. Public*, pg. 924

Picker, Arnd, Chief Oper. Officer--Cordes & Co. GmbH, Porta Westfalica, Germany; *Int'l*, pg. 609

Pickerill, P.J., Pres.--MSA Canada, Inc., North York, Canada; *U.S. Public*, pg. 1114

Pickering, Ken, Pres.--Minera Escondida Limitada, Santiago, Chile; *Int'l*, pg. 227

Pickersgill, J.B., Mng. Dir.--Top Rank Limited, Maidenhead, United Kingdom; *Int'l*, pg. 1087

Pickert, Richard W., Chief Fin. Officer--Fairview Printing, Lantana, FL; *U.S. Public*, pg. 87

Pickett, Leonard, Pres.--Crosman Airguns, East Bloomfield, NY; *U.S. Private*, pg. 291

Pickett, Michael H., Pres. & Publisher--Harcourt Brace & Company Farm Publications Inc., Orlando, FL; *U.S. Public*, pg. 783

Pickle, Kirby, Pres.--MFS Intelenet Companies, San Ramon, CA; *U.S. Public*, pg. 1779

Pickle, Kirby G., Pres. & Chief Exec. Officer--MFS Intelenet Companies, Jersey City, NJ; *U.S. Public*, pg. 1779

Pickle, Penny, R.N., Admin.--The Care Group of Texas, Inc., Dallas, TX; *U.S. Public*, pg. 305

Pickles, G.M., Dir. & Gen. Mgr.--H&C Cereales S.A., Montdidier, France; *Int'l*, pg. 752

Pickles, R., Mng. Dir.--Verosol Australia Pty.Ltd., Kingsgrove, Australia; *Int'l*, pg. 198

Pickrell, Floyd, Pres.--Sybron Dental Specialties, Inc., Glendora, CA; *U.S. Public*, pg. 1545

Picks, Rolf, Mng. Dir.--ISS Servisystem GmbH, Frankfurt, Germany; *Int'l*, pg. 657

Picot, Claude, Chief Oper. Officer--Saint-Gobain Desjonqueres, Courbevoie, France; *Int'l*, pg. 1171

Picot, Jim, Pres.--Axel Johnson Corp. (Australia) AB, Reservoir, Australia; *Int'l*, pg. 710

Pidal, I. Munoz, Gen. Mgr.--ABN, Sucursal en Espana (Madrid), Madrid, Spain; *Int'l*, pg. 11

Piechocki, Duane B., Pres.--Pall East Hills Manufacturing Corp., Greenvale, NY; *U.S. Public*, pg. 1254

Piedrahita, J. M., Representative--Morgan Grenfell (Colombia), Bogota, Colombia; *Int'l*, pg. 405

Piegari, Thomas, Gen. Mgr.--Poe & Brown of New Jersey, Clark, NJ; *U.S. Public*, pg. 1312

Piekkari, Timo, Chief Oper. Officer--Oy Esmi Ab, Espoo, Finland; *Int'l*, pg. 32

Pielsticker, James E., Chief Oper. Officer--Johnson Gear, Lincoln, NE; *U.S. Private*, pg. 85

Pieper, Roel, Pres. & Chief Exec. Officer--UB Networks, Santa Clara, CA; *Int'l*, pg. 924

Piepponen, Pekka, Pres.--Enso International, Inc., Stamford, CT; *Int'l*, pg. 457

pier, Arne, Pres.--Malmo Regional Office, Malmo, Sweden; *Int'l*, pg. 899

Pieraccioni, Gianni, Mng. Dir.--Johnson & Johnson S.p.A., Rome, Italy; *U.S. Public*, pg. 931

Pierami, Ed, V.P. & Gen. Mgr.--Yardley of London, Inc., Memphis, TN; *Int'l*, pg. 819

Pieranunzi, Richard, Pres.-U.S. Opers.--SGS-Thomson Microelectronics, Inc., Carrollton, TX; *Int'l*, pg. 1153

Pierburg, B., Mng. Dir.--GKN Gelenkwellenwerk Mosel GmbH, Mosel, Germany; *Int'l*, pg. 535

Pierburg, B., Mng. Dir.--Lohr & Bromkamp GmbH, Offenbach/Main, Germany; *Int'l*, pg. 536

Pierburg, B., Mng. Dir.--GKN Gelenkwellenwerk Kiel GmbH, Kiel, Germany; *Int'l*, pg. 536

Pierce, David, Resident Rep.--The World Bank, Almaty, Kazakhstan; *U.S. Private*, pg. 1189

Pierce, Garland, Pres.--Toyota Lift, Inc., Santee, CA; *Int'l*, pg. 1412

Pierce, J.L., Pres. & Chief Exec. Officer--Mid-Continent Casualty Company, Tulsa, OK; *U.S. Public*, pg. 75

Pierce, James B., Mgr.--Scott & Stringfellow, Inc., Williamsburg, VA; *U.S. Public*, pg. 1445

Pierce, James H., Gen. Mgr.--Corrugated Container Div.-Jackson Plant, Jackson, MS; *U.S. Public*, pg. 1520

Pierce, Robert W., Pres. & Chief Exec. Officer--Beneficial National Bank, Wilmington, DE; *U.S. Public*, pg. 211

Pierce, Ronnie, Gen. Mgr.--Barton's of Walnut Ridge, Walnut Ridge, AR; *U.S. Private*, pg. 119

Pierce, Scott, Mgr.--MascoTech Sintered Components, Inc., Ridgway, PA; *U.S. Public*, pg. 1055

Piergallini, Alfred A., Pres.--Gerber Products Company of Puerto Rico, Inc., Carolina, PR; *Int'l*, pg. 973

Piergallini, Alfred A., Pres.--Productos Gerber de Centroamerica, S.A., San Jose, Costa Rica; *Int'l*, pg. 973

Pieroni, Peter, Mng. Dir.--SPS Technologies Ltd., Coventry, United Kingdom; *U.S. Public*, pg. 1420

Pieros, Larry, Pres. & Chief Exec. Officer--Armor All Products Group, Oakland, CA; *U.S. Public*, pg. 387

Pierre, Henri, Pres.--Georg Fischer NV-SA, Brussels, Belgium; *Int'l*, pg. 489

Pierry, Joseph, Gen. Mgr.--AlliedSignal Guidance Systems Div., Boyne City, MI; *U.S. Public*, pg. 50

Pierson, Jerry, Exec. V.P. & Gen. Mgr.--Lanier Worldwide, Inc.-European Division, Brussels, Belgium; *U.S. Public*, pg. 791

Pierson, N.L., Pres.--Yadkin, Inc., Badin, NC; *U.S. Public*, pg. 61

Pieschacon, Camilo, Mng. Dir.--Intercaser S.A. de Seguros y Reaseguros, Madrid, Spain; *Int'l*, pg. 1256

Pieters, G. M., Chief Oper. Officer--Eij Imtech NV, Antwerp, Belgium; *Int'l*, pg. 681

Pieters, Robert W., Pres.--Federated Bank, S.S.B., Wauwatosa, WI; *U.S. Public*, pg. 643

Pietersen, William G., Pres.--The Seagram Beverage Group, New York, NY; *Int'l*, pg. 1217

Pietila, Hannu, Sr. V.P. & Bus. Unit Exec.--Valmet Automation Inc.-Control Systems, Tampere, Finland; *Int'l*, pg. 1449

Pietrafetta, Philip, Reg. Mgr.--WWF Paper Corp.-New England, Franklin, MA; *U.S. Private*, pg. 1145

Pietramala, Anthony, Pres. & Chief Oper. Officer--Pro-Pastries Inc., Mississauga, Canada; *U.S. Public*, pg. 806

Pietramala, Anthony, Pres. & Chief Oper. Officer--Heinz Bakery Products, Mississauga, Canada; *U.S. Public*, pg. 806

Pietrini, Andrew G., Chief Oper. Officer--UIS Export Corporation, New York, NY; *U.S. Private*, pg. 1113

Pietroforte, Martin, V.P.--Republic National Bank of New York (Gibraltar) Ltd., Gibraltar, Gibraltar; *U.S. Public*, pg. 1381

Pietroski, Joseph J., Sr. V.P. & Gen. Counsel--Manulife Financial, Toronto, Canada; *Int'l*, pg. 840

Pietsch, Theo, Chief Rep.--Westpac Banking Corporation-Germany, Frankfurt/Main, Germany; *Int'l*, pg. 1497

Pietzsch, L., Mng. Dir.--Ascom Hasler GmbH, Olching, Germany; *Int'l*, pg. 87

Pifer, Jay S., Pres.--West Penn Power Co., Greensburg, PA; *U.S. Public*, pg. 42

Pigaiani, Walter, Chief Oper. Officer--Land Instruments Srl, Milan, Italy; *Int'l*, pg. 798

Pigault, Christian, Gen. Mgr.--Analog Devices S.A., Antony, France; *U.S. Public*, pg. 108

Piggot, K.J., Mng. Dir.--Do It All, Dudley, United Kingdom; *Int'l*, pg. 203

Piggott, K.S., Mng. Dir.--Childrens World, Nottingham, United Kingdom; *Int'l*, pg. 1304

Piggott, Keith, Chief Oper. Officer--Amari Plastics Plc, Weybridge, United Kingdom; *Int'l*, pg. 554

Piggott, Raymond, V.P.-European Mktg.--Dataproducts International Ltd., Egham, United Kingdom; *Int'l*, pg. 621

Pihl, Christer, Chief Oper. Officer--Ahlstrom Glassfibre Ltd.-Karhula Plant, Karhula, Finland; *Int'l*, pg. 32

Pihlgren, Roger, Chief Oper. Officer--AB Profila, Norrkoping, Sweden; *Int'l*, pg. 1377

Piironen, Raimo, Mng. Dir.--Tikkurila Oy, Vantaa, Finland; *Int'l*, pg. 729

Pijpera, W.R.C., Gen. Mgr.--ING Bank Hong Kong, Central, Hong Kong; *Int'l*, pg. 649

Pijpers, W.R.C., Gen. Mgr.--ING Capital Markets (Hong Kong), Central, Hong Kong; *Int'l*, pg. 650

Pike, Andrew, Pres.--Ellis & Watts Div., Batavia, OH; *U.S. Public*, pg. 286

Pike, Christopher W., V.P. & Gen. Mgr.--Harrisburg Television, Inc, Harrisburg, PA; *U.S. Private*, pg. 854

Pike, Gregory, Pres. & Chief Exec. Officer--First County Bank, Chardon, OH; *U.S. Public*, pg. 607

Pike, John, Pres.--The Northern Trust Company-Canadian Representative Office, Toronto, Canada; *U.S. Public*, pg. 1197

Pike, John W., Chief Oper. Officer--Bethlehem Intl. Sales Corp., Easton, PA; *U.S. Public*, pg. 226

Pike, Randy, Pres.--Pike Industries Inc., Tilton, NH; *Int'l*, pg. 242

Piker, Ahmet, Gen. Mgr.--Brisa Bridgestone Sabanci Lastik Sanayi Ve Ticaret A.S., Istanbul, Turkey; *Int'l*, pg. 213

Pikering, John, II, Chief Oper. Officer & Mng. Dir.--Brown Brothers Harriman Trustee Services (Ireland) Limited, Dublin, Ireland; *U.S. Private*, pg. 173

Pilato, Jean Paul, Chief Oper. Officer--MacDermid France S.A., Evry, France; *U.S. Public*, pg. 1030

Pilch, Raymond, Pres.--Blackmer Pump/Dover Resources Co, Grand Rapids, MI; *U.S. Public*, pg. 521

Pilcher, Dave, Pres. & Chief Exec. Officer--Interform Corporation, Bridgeville, PA; *U.S. Public*, pg. 333

Pileski, Rob, Div. Mgr.--Mid-West Div., Waukegan, IL; *U.S. Public*, pg. 70

Piletti, Dominic, Pres.--Thomas & Betts Electronics Division, Memphis, TN; *U.S. Public*, pg. 1597

Pilger, Dale R., Mng. Dir.--General Motors Kenya Ltd., Nairobi, Kenya; *U.S. Public*, pg. 724

Pilgrim, G. A., Mng. Dir.--The South China Morning Post, Limited, Quarry Bay, Hong Kong; *Int'l*, pg. 925

Piliguian, Tro, Pres.-O&M NY--Ogilvy & Mather Worldwide, Inc., New York, NY; *Int'l*, pg. 1483

Pilka, Karl, Chief Oper. Officer--A. Ahlstrom Ges.m.b.H., Wels, Austria; *Int'l*, pg. 34

Pilkington, J.D., Chief Oper. Officer--Fuller-F.L. Smidth (Pacific) Pty. Ltd., Greenwich, Australia; *Int'l*, pg. 475

Pillard, L.G., Pres.--A.E. Staley Manufacturing Co., Decatur, IL; *Int'l*, pg. 1356

Pillaud, Max, Chief Oper. Officer--Rhone-Poulenc S.A., Algiers, Algeria; *Int'l*, pg. 1113

Pillow, George, Pres.--NAFCO National Floor Company, Florence, AL; *Int'l*, pg. 415

Pilus, Azizan M., Mng. Dir.--Sapura-Nokia Telecommunications Sdn. Bhd., Kuala Lumpur, Malaysia; *Int'l*, pg. 954

Pim, Ken, Pres.--Channel Products, Inc., Chesterland, OH; *U.S. Private*, pg. 228

Pin, Chua, Gen. Mgr.--PT BNP Lippo Utama Leasing, Jakarta, Indonesia; *Int'l*, pg. 164

Pinaud, Jean-Rene, Mgr.--EG & G Sealol-Callisto S.A., Coignieres, France; *U.S. Public*, pg. 544

Pinault, G., Pres. & Dir. General--Brossette BTI SA, Lyon, France; *Int'l*, pg. 1511

Pinciotti, James V., Pres.--King of Prussia - General Merchandise Div., Oaks, PA; *U.S. Public*, pg. 653

Pincon, Jean-Francois, Representatve--Banque Indosuez, Cairo, Egypt; *Int'l*, pg. 315

Pincus, Robert P., Pres. & Chief Exec. Officer--NationsBank Metro, Washington, DC; *U.S. Public*, pg. 1162

Pinder, M., Chief Exec.--National Australia Life, London, United Kingdom; *Int'l*, pg. 906

Pine, William R., Gen. Mgr.--Caraloe, Inc., Irving, TX; *U.S. Public*, pg. 309

Pinera, Angel, Gen. Mgr.--Alberto-Culver (P.R.), Inc., Hato Rey, PR; *U.S. Public*, pg. 38

Pineros, Ignacio, Chief Oper. Officer--La Federal Compania de Seguros, S.A., Bogota, Colombia; *U.S. Public*, pg. 355

Ping, Stephen Chou, Chief Oper. Officer--Rhone-Poulenc Singapore Pte. Ltd., Singapore, Singapore; *Int'l*, pg. 1114

Ping, Tan Fong, Reg. Mgr.-Non-Life--Skandia International Insurance Co., Singapore, Singapore; *Int'l*, pg. 1258

Pingkalavan, Banthoeng, Mgr.-Chemicals--Chemicals Div., Bangkok, Thailand; *Int'l*, pg. 1140

Pinheiro, J.M., Pres.--PruServicos Participacoes, S.A., c/o Prudential Atlantic Companhia Brasileira de Seguros, Sao Paulo, Brazil; *U.S. Private*, pg. 893

Pink, A.I.H., Pres.--ICI Advanced Materials, Wilmington, DE; *Int'l*, pg. 663

Pink, Alan, Chief Exec. Officer--Zeneca Agrochemicals and Seeds, Maidstone, United Kingdom; *Int'l*, pg. 1524

Pink, Krut, Mng. Dir.--Lincoln Smitweld GmbH, Erkrath, Germany; *U.S. Public*, pg. 997

Pinker, Lamont T., Pres. & Chief Oper. Officer--Gateway Communications, Johnson City, NY; *U.S. Private*, pg. 693

Pinkerton, John H., Pres.--Lomak Production Company, Hartville, OH; *U.S. Public*, pg. 1012

Pinkerton, John H., Pres. & Chief Exec. Officer--Lomak Operating Company, Hartville, OH; *U.S. Public*, pg. 1012

Pinkley, Robert, Dir.--Relm Demand Side Management Systems, Indianapolis, IN; *U.S. Public*, pg. 1376

Pinkney, Thomas S., Plant Mgr.--Kohler Ltd., Armstrong, Canada; *U.S. Private*, pg. 631

Pinkow, Werner, Mng. Dir.--Krupp Hoesch Informationsverarbeitung GmbH, Dortmund, Germany; *Int'l*, pg. 512

Pinnegar, Tim, Media Dir.--Leo Burnett Pte. Ltd., Singapore, Singapore; *U.S. Private*, pg. 185

Pinneker, R.V., Pres. & Chief Exec. Officer--Security Pacific Services Corporation, San Diego, CA; *U.S. Public*, pg. 182

Pinner, D.K., Div. Pres.--Fort Wayne Specialty Alloys Div., Fort Wayne, IN; *Int'l*, pg. 1263

Pinney, R.E., Mng. Dir.--National Australia Group (UK) Limited, Glasgow, United Kingdom; *Int'l*, pg. 906

Pinnow, Dieter, Rep.--DG Bank-Moscow, Moscow, Russia; *Int'l*, pg. 352

Pinnow, Werner, Pres.--Hapag-Lloyd (America), Inc., Piscataway, NJ; *Int'l*, pg. 596

Pino, Tony, Pres.--National Group Life Insurance Company, Rockford, IL; *U.S. Public*, pg. 433

Pinochet, Gabriel, Gen. Mgr.--Ruedas de Aluminio C.A. "Rualca", Valencia, Venezuela; *U.S. Public*, pg. 1387

Pinomaa, Juha, Mng. Dir.--Nokia Mobile Phones, S.E.A. Pte. Ltd., Singapore, Singapore; *Int'l*, pg. 952

Pinon, Christian, Pres.--Alcatel Telspace, Nanterre, France; *Int'l*, pg. 56

Pinsent, P.D., Chief Oper. Officer--Babcock Argentina S.A., Buenos Aires, Argentina; *Int'l*, pg. 473

Pinsley, Sol, Chief Oper. Officer--Saratoga Industries, Saratoga Springs, NY; *U.S. Public*, pg. 592

Pintens, E.A., Gen. Mgr.--Monsanto B.V., Hague, Netherlands; *U.S. Public*, pg. 1125

Pinter, Douglas F., Pres.--Merrill Corporation, San Francisco, CA; *U.S. Public*, pg. 1097

Pinti, John A., Pres.--Berwick Industries, Inc., Berwick, PA; *U.S. Public*, pg. 284

Pinto, Joao Costa, Chief Exec.--Banco de Comercio E Industria, S.A., Lisbon, Portugal; *Int'l*, pg. 144

Pinto, Jose Miguel, Gen. Mgr.--The Clorox Co. of Puerto Rico, Caguas, PR; *U.S. Public*, pg. 387

Pinto, Richard C., Pres.--Excellon Automation Co., Torrance, CA; *U.S. Public*, pg. 594

Pintos, Daniel Edgardo, Country Mgr.--Det Norske Veritas, Buenos Aires, Argentina; *Int'l*, pg. 396

Pinzino, Thomas F., Pres. & Chief Exec. Officer--Sunnyland Refining Co., Inc., Birmingham, AL; *U.S. Private*, pg. 607

Pion, Jean Francois, Exec. Dir.--Siplast S.A., Paris, France; *Int'l*, pg. 659

Pioppi, N. William, Pres.--Russell Harrington Cutlery Inc., Southbridge, MA; *U.S. Private*, pg. 551

Piotrowski, Dick, Mgr.--A.T.I. Tools, Inc., Escondido, CA; *U.S. Public*, pg. 1480

Piouro, Mario, Chief Exec. Officer--SPF Promotio Sim SPA, Milan, Italy; *Int'l*, pg. 341

Pipitone, Guy L., Div. Mgr.--Ohio Edison Co.-Akron Div., Akron, OH; *U.S. Public*, pg. 645

Pippas, T., Gen. Mgr.--A.C. Nielsen Hellas Ltd., Kallithea, Greece; *U.S. Public*, pg. 1183

Pippin, M. Lenny, Chief Oper. Officer--Albert Fisher North America, Dallas, TX; *Int'l*, pg. 491

Pippin, Ronald H., Chm. Bd., Pres. & Chief Exec. Officer--SouthTrust Bank of Bay Minette, Bay Minette, AL; *U.S. Public*, pg. 1492

Piquard, A., Mng. Dir.--SNC GEC Composants et Cie, Asnieres-sur-Seine, France; *Int'l*, pg. 546

Piquette, Thomas, Mgr.--EG & G Sealol Eagle, Warwick, RI; *U.S. Public*, pg. 544

Piras, Guy, Dir.--Etablissement de Biarritz, Biarritz, France; *Int'l*, pg. 383

Pirchl, Helmut, Exec. V.P.--Sulzer Ruti Group, Bern, Switzerland; *Int'l*, pg. 1307

Pirchl, Helmut, Mng. Dir.--Sulzer Ruti Limited, Ruthi, Switzerland; *Int'l*, pg. 1307

Pirel, Louis, Chm. & Chief Exec. Officer--Minniti, Noumea, New Caledonia; *Int'l*, pg. 823

Pirella, Emanuele, Pres. & Mng. Dir.--Pirella Gottsche Lowe, Milan, Italy; *U.S. Private*, pg. 678

Pires, Ernani, Pres. & Chief Exec. Officer--SGS International Certification Services, Inc., Rutherford, NJ; *Int'l*, pg. 1153

Pires, V.M. Couto, Dir.--AlliedSignal Automotive Portugal Ltda., Abrantes, Portugal; *U.S. Public*, pg. 53

Pirie, Glen, Gen. Mgr.--American Consumer Products, Solon, OH; *U.S. Private*, pg. 1142

Pirie, Robert S, Chm. Bd.--Rothchild Asset Management Inc., New York, NY; *U.S. Private*, pg. 947

Pirisi, Istvan, Chief Oper. Officer--AGA Gaz Kft., Budapest, Hungary; *Int'l*, pg. 13

Pirklbauer, Harald E., Dir.-Pur.--Voest-Alpine International Corp.-Purchasing Service, New York, NY; *Int'l*, pg. 1471

Pirkner, Gabor, Mng. Dir.--Gebruder Sulzer Gesellschqaft mbH, Anlagen- und Gebaudetechnik, Vienna, Austria; *Int'l*, pg. 1306

Pirkner, Gabor, Chief Exec.--Sulzer Infra Anlagen- und Gebaudetechnik Gesellschaft m.b.H, Vienna, Austria; *Int'l*, pg. 1306

Pirner, Hans G., Mgr.--Commerzbank AG Representative Office-Beirut, Beirut, Lebanon; *Int'l*, pg. 311

Pirnie, Douglas D., Jr., Sr. V.P.-Sls. & Mktg.--IMG, New York, NY; *U.S. Private*, pg. 555

Pirogovsky, Joseph, Pres.--Advance Thermal Corp., Bensenville, IL; *U.S. Private*, pg. 1096

Pironnet, J.M., Chm.--AGIP Praha Ltd., Prague, Czech Republic; *Int'l*, pg. 428

Pirotte, Myriam, Branch Mgr.--Elsevier SA, Senningerberg, Luxembourg; *Int'l*, pg. 1093

Pirrone, Gaetano, V.P.--American Tractebel Corporation, New York, NY; *Int'l*, pg. 1415

Pirscher, Carl, Pres.--Commercial Design Architects/HEPY, Mountlake Terrace, WA; *U.S. Private*, pg. 503

Pirtle, Ronald M., Gen. Mgr.--Delphi Harrison Thermal Systems, Lockport, NY; *U.S. Public*, pg. 719

Pisani, Claudio, V.P. & Mng. Dir.--Cyanamid Italia S.p.A, Catania, Italy; *U.S. Public*, pg. 81

Pisani, Gerald V., Pres.--Pollak Division, Boston, MA; *U.S. Private*, pg. 1045

Pisano, Michel, Exec. Mgr.--UTE, Buenos Aires, Argentina; *Int'l*, pg. 824

Pischetsrieder, Bernd, Chm. Bd.--Rover Group Limited, Birmingham, United Kingdom; *Int'l*, pg. 178

Pishkur, Walter J., Pres.--Consumers Ohio Water Company, Boardman, OH; *U.S. Public*, pg. 438

Pistilli, Frederick M., Pres.--Westclox, Norcross, GA; *U.S. Private*, pg. 445

Pistilli, Frederick M., Chm. & Chief Exec. Officer--Seth Thomas, Norcross, GA; *U.S. Private*, pg. 445

Pitcher, Desmond, Sir, Chm.--North West Water Limited, Warrington, United Kingdom; *Int'l*, pg. 1444

Pitcher, N.J., Chief Oper. Officer--Armstrong Electra Ltd., London, United Kingdom; *Int'l*, pg. 796

Pitcher, T.M., V.P.--The Bank of Nova Scotia, Boston, MA; *Int'l*, pg. 156

Pitchford, Charles, Exec. V.P. & Gen. Mgr.--Voltec, McMurray, PA; *U.S. Private*, pg. 968

Pitchford, Terry L., Exec. V.P.-Distr. Div.--Rolland Inc., Distribution Division, Mississauga, Canada; *Int'l*, pg. 273

Pithey, Roy, Chm. Bd.--Aquachlor (Proprietary) Limited, Kempton Park, South Africa; *U.S. Public*, pg. 1219

Pitkanen, Risto, Mng. Dir.--Grako OY, Helsinki, Finland; *U.S. Public*, pg. 78

Pitkowsky, Murray, Pres.--Bioplex Medical B.V., Vaals, Netherlands; *U.S. Public*, pg. 487

Pitkowsky, Murray, Pres.--Datascope FSC, Ltd., Paramus, NJ; *U.S. Public*, pg. 487

Pitkowsky, Murray, Pres.--Datascope Holding Corp., Paramus, NJ; *U.S. Public*, pg. 487

Pitkowsky, Murray, Chief Oper. Officer--Datascope Investment Corp., Paramus, NJ; *U.S. Public*, pg. 487

Pitkowsky, Murray, Pres.--Datascope B.V., Hoevelaken, Netherlands; *U.S. Public*, pg. 488

Pitkowsky, Murray, Gen. Mgr.--Datascope GmbH, Bensheim, Germany; *U.S. Public*, pg. 488

Pitman, C.J., Pres. & Gen. Mgr.--Amoco Egypt Oil Company, Maadi, Egypt; *U.S. Public*, pg. 102

Pitman, G.R., Pres.--Chevron Overseas Petroleum Limited, Hamilton, Bermuda; *U.S. Public*, pg. 348

Pitman, M.D., Mng. Dir.--Analytical Development Company Limited, Hoddesdon, United Kingdom; *Int'l*, pg. 589

Pitney, Garwin, V.P. & Gen. Mgr.--Radar Companies, Inc., Dalton, MA; *U.S. Public*, pg. 789

Pitou, Augustus, III, Pres.--K2 Bike, Woonsocket, RI; *U.S. Public*, pg. 940

Pitsch, Karl-Heinz, Chm. Bd., Pres. & Chief Exec. Officer--The Wella Corporation, Montvale, NJ; *Int'l*, pg. 1489

Pitsch, L.H., Pres.--CPM, Nashua, NH; *U.S. Public*, pg. 705

Pitsch, Larry, V.P.--Pulp Machinery Division, Crawfordsville, IN; *U.S. Public*, pg. 705

Pitschel, Ernest O., Exec. V.P.--Cebu Mining Operation, Cebu, Philippines; *Int'l*, pg. 95

Pitt, David, Pres.--Kvaerner AM Ltd., United Kingdom; *Int'l*, pg. 767

Pitt, David, Mng. Dir.--Kvaerner Engineering (UK) Ltd., Slough, United Kingdom; *Int'l*, pg. 772

Pitt, John J., Pres. & Gen. Mgr.--Canada Brick Div., Streetsville, Canada; *Int'l*, pg. 698

Pittas, J., Chm. Bd.--Laporte Inc., Princeton, NJ; *Int'l*, pg. 802

Pittman, Jerry, Pres.--Cameo Window Furnishings, New York, NY; *U.S. Private*, pg. 1094

Pittman, John A., Pres. & Gen. Mgr.--RTP, Pompano Beach, FL; *U.S. Public*, pg. 422

Pittman, Larry, Pres.--InterAmerican-Star Group, Los Angeles, CA; *Int'l*, pg. 1529

Pittman, Robert W., Pres. & Chief Exec. Officer--Time Warner Enterprises, New York, NY; *U.S. Public*, pg. 1611

Pitts, Bob, Sr. V.P. & Div. Dir.--PENCO-Ohio, Worthington, OH; *Int'l*, pg. 1508

Pitts, Ken, Gen. Mgr.--Pacific Elevators Limited, Vancouver, Canada; *Int'l*, pg. 1195

Pitts, Kevin, Branch Mgr.--Klockner-Moeller, Kennesaw, GA; *Int'l*, pg. 736

Pitz, Peter E., Pres. & Publr.--The Wichita Eagle and Beacon Publishing Co., Inc., Wichita, KS; *U.S. Public*, pg. 964

Piutado, Pedro Donado, Gen. Mgr.--Arrow Iberia, S.A., Madrid, Spain; *U.S. Public*, pg. 135

Pivnev, Gennadj, District Mgr.--ZAO Russia, Moscow, Russia; *Int'l*, pg. 638

Piyavidhaijakarn, Apichat, Mng. Dir.--Beiersdorf (Thailand) Co. Ltd., Bangkok, Thailand; *Int'l*, pg. 183

Pizarek, Richard A., Chief Oper. Officer--Bosch Braking Systems-North America, Gallatin, TN; *Int'l*, pg. 204

Pizio, Ernie, Reg. V.P.--Ruppman Marketing Technologies, Inc., West Paterson, NJ; *U.S. Private*, pg. 952

Pizzimenti, Robert, Chief Oper. Officer--Ericsson Paging Systems Inc., Greenwich, CT; *Int'l*, pg. 1365

Pla Vila, Agustin, Mng. Dir.--3i Iberia de Inversiones Industriales SA, Barcelona, Spain; *Int'l*, pg. 1386

Pla, Fermin, V.P.--Stanhome S.A., Barcelona, Spain; *U.S. Public*, pg. 1508

Place, Penny, Administrator--Lynwood Manor, Adrian, MI; *U.S. Public*, pg. 837

Plack, James, Chief Oper. Officer--Human Affairs International Inc., Sandy, UT; *U.S. Public*, pg. 1036

Plaisance, Daryl, Mgr.--Martin's Uniforms Div.- New Orleans, Kenner, LA; *U.S. Public*, pg. 1539

Plaisted, Wes, V.P.--Northern Division, Phillipsburg, NJ; *U.S. Public*, pg. 438

Plakopitas, A., Mgr.--Baring Hellenic Ventures S.A., Athens, Greece; *Int'l*, pg. 648

Plana, Eduardo, Chm. Bd. & Chief Exec. Officer--EURO RSCG, Madrid, Spain; *Int'l*, pg. 602

Planchon, Eric, Mng. Dir.--Rhone-Poulenc Vietnam, Ho Chi Minh City, Vietnam; *Int'l*, pg. 1114

Plancon, Christophe, Mgr.--Babyliss. SA, Montrouge, France; *U.S. Private*, pg. 261

Planes, John J., Chief Exec. Officer--Planes Moving & Storage Company Of Columbus, Columbus, OH; *U.S. Private*, pg. 869

Plank, F., Mng. Dir.--Ascom Austria Ges.mbH, Vienna, Austria; *Int'l*, pg. 86

Plank, Ken, Plant Mgr.--Jon Donaire Desserts, Inc., Santa Fe Springs, CA; *U.S. Public*, pg. 1527

Plank, Raymond, Chm. Bd. & Chief Exec. Officer--NAGASCO, Inc., Houston, TX; *U.S. Public*, pg. 119

Plant, George E., Pres.--Bardon (England) Ltd., Leicester, United Kingdom; *Int'l*, pg. 166

Plant, J.C., Mng. Dir.--Lucas Electrical and Electronic Systems, Shirley, United Kingdom; *Int'l*, pg. 819

Plante, N.R., Div. Pres.--Sorel Forge Inc., Sorel, Canada; *Int'l*, pg. 1262

Plasencia, Santiago Fernandez, Vice Pres.--Electra de Viesgo, S.A., Santander, Spain; *Int'l*, pg. 1224

Plasman, Christian G., Pres.--Baker Knapp & Tubbs Inc., Grand Rapids, MI; *U.S. Private*, pg. 630

Plate, Dick, Pres.--Atlas Copco Compressor Canada, Dorval, Canada; *Int'l*, pg. 96

Platen, F., Chief Oper. Officer--Acco Platen GmbH, Weilmunster, Germany; *Int'l*, pg. 473

Plato, James N., Pres.--United Presidential Life Insurance Co., Carmel, IN; *U.S. Public*, pg. 434

Platt, George, Pres. & Chief Exec. Officer--InteCom, Dallas, TX; *Int'l*, pg. 794

Platt, Marc, Pres.--Tri-Star Pictures, Inc., Culver City, CA; *Int'l*, pg. 1282

Platt, Richard, Refinery Mgr.--Frontier Refining, Inc., Cheyenne, WY; *U.S. Public*, pg. 1732

Platt, Stuart F., Pres.--Data Systems Group, Santa Clara, CA; *U.S. Public*, pg. 474

Platz, Jens Lykke, Chief Exec. Officer--Novo Nordisk Ferment Ltd., Dittingen, Switzerland; *Int'l*, pg. 989

Platz, Mark, Mgr.-Sls.--Gulf State Specialties, Inc., South Houston, TX; *U.S. Private*, pg. 487

Platzer, W., Mng. Dir.--Quaker Chemical B.V., Uithoorn, Netherlands; *U.S. Public*, pg. 1346

Plaul, Hans-Ulrich, Dr., Chm.--Buderus AG, Wetzlar, Germany; *Int'l*, pg. 861

Playford, Alyson, Gen. Mgr.-Sls. & Mktg./Northern Europe--Utell International-United Kingdom, Sutton, United Kingdom; *Int'l*, pg. 1098

Pleau, M.H., Pres.--P.S.I. Division, Ellington, CT; *U.S. Private*, pg. 832

Plenier, Jacques, Chm. Bd.--Avions de Transport Regional - ATR, Blagnac, France; *Int'l*, pg. 654

Plenter, J., Mgr.--Radio Holland Group Head Office-Houston, Houston, TX; *Int'l*, pg. 1152

Plesha, Dennis, Pres.--Tyton Corporation, Milwaukee, WI; *Int'l*, pg. 208

Pless, Bob, V.P. & Gen. Mgr.--Davco Div., Thomasville, GA; *U.S. Public*, pg. 1682

Plever, Roland, Mgr.-Plant--Sucrerie D'aulnois-Sous-Laon, Aulnois-sous-Laon, France; *Int'l*, pg. 549

Plevisani, Claudio, Dir. Gen.--LLoyd Adratico Espana, Madrid, Spain; *Int'l*, pg. 60

Pliessnig, Herbert, Gen. Mgr.--The Pierre, New York, NY; *Int'l*, pg. 502

Plimpton, T.E., Gen. Mgr.--Peterbilt Motors Co., Denton, TX; *U.S. Public*, pg. 1247

Plisky, Clarence, Gen. Mgr.--Pettibone Tiffin Parts, Tiffin, OH; *U.S. Private*, pg. 860

Plocinik, Tom, Pres.--Trico Products Corporation, Buffalo, NY; *Int'l*, pg. 1397

Plomgren, E., Mng. Dir.--Rank Leisure Machine Services Ltd., Maidenhead, United Kingdom; *Int'l*, pg. 1087

Plonskier, Irving, Media Dir.--Young & Rubicam Latam (Miami), Miami, FL; *U.S. Private*, pg. 1198

Plonzke, Klaus C., Chief Exec. Officer--CSC Ploenzke, Kliedrich, Germany; *U.S. Public*, pg. 423

Plossu, Philippe, Mng. Dir.--Ancra International Sarl, Saint Quentin, France; *U.S. Private*, pg. 71

Plotica, Philip G., Pres.--ESAB Welding & Cutting Products, Hanover, PA; *Int'l*, pg. 281

Plotrowicz, Scott, Admin.--Silverbrook Manor, Niles, MI; *U.S. Public*, pg. 837

Plotzeneder, Thomas, Client Service Dir.--GGK Occidental Holding AG, Vienna, Austria; *Int'l*, pg. 1335

Plouffe, Dan, Pres.--Firstcom Marketing Inc., Toronto, Canada; *U.S. Private*, pg. 1200

Plouffe, David H., Pres.--Policy Management Systems Canada, Ltd., Islington, Canada; *U.S. Public*, pg. 1315

Plugge, Nico, Mng. Dir.--Simco (Nederland) B.V., Lochem, Netherlands; *U.S. Public*, pg. 869

Plum, Larry R., Pres.--Cincinnati Casualty Co., Fairfield, OH; *U.S. Public*, pg. 368

Plumb, H.E.B., Mng Dir--Davy International, Sheffield, United Kingdom; *Int'l*, pg. 773

Plumbe, Colin, Mng. Dir.--Todd & Duncan Ltd., Kinross, United Kingdom; *Int'l*, pg. 385

Plumbe, Colin, Mng. Dir.--Laidlaw & Fairgrieve Ltd, Selkirk, United Kingdom; *Int'l*, pg. 385

Plumer, Hans-Joachim, Gen. Mgr.--ITW Befestigungssysteme, Iserlohn, Germany; *U.S. Public*, pg. 868

Plumeri, Joseph J., II, Chm. & Chief Exec. Officer--Primerica Financial Services, Duluth, GA; *U.S. Public*, pg. 1633

Plummer, Gale L., Gen. Mgr.--EMPIRE Power Systems, Phoenix, AZ; *U.S. Private*, pg. 375

Plummer, Kevin J., Pres.--Wynn's Australia, Pty. Limited, Frenchs Forest, Australia; *U.S. Public*, pg. 1782

Plummer, Lord, Chm. Bd.--Century Employers Life Assurance Company Limited, London, United Kingdom; *Int'l*, pg. 685

Plummer, Tom, Branch Mgr.--Skandia America Reinsurance Corp., Chicago Branch Office, Chicago, IL; *Int'l*, pg. 1257

Plunk, Kenneth W., Chm. Bd. & Chief Acctg. Officer--Union Planters Bank, Memphis, TN; *U.S. Public*, pg. 1669

Plunk, Stephen D., Pres. & Chief Credit Officer--Liberty Bank & Trust Company of Tulsa, Tulsa, OK; *U.S. Public*, pg. 174

Plunkert, Jerry, Gen. Mgr.--Stanfast, Inc., Baltimore, MD; *U.S. Public*, pg. 1505

Plunkett, Thomas P., Pres.--TPS Technologies Inc., Apopka, FL; *U.S. Public*, pg. 1594

Plunkett, Tom, Pres.--Thermo Process Systems Inc./ Holcroft, Livonia, MI; *U.S. Public*, pg. 1594

Plust, H.G., Chief Oper. Officer--Deutsche Automobilgesellschaft mbH, Esslingen am Neckar, Germany; *Int'l*, pg. 1473

Pluvinage, Jacques, Chief Oper. Officer--Hospal-Gambro Limitee, Saint Leonard, Canada; *Int'l*, pg. 668

Plyler, James C., Jr., Pres.--USCO, Incorporated, Monroe, NC; *U.S. Public*, pg. 847

Poage, Roy L., Pres.--DeKalb Swine Breeders, Inc., De Kalb, IL; *U.S. Public*, pg. 493

Poch, Gerlad A., Co-Chm. Bd., Pres., Chief Exec. Officer & Sec.--AmeriData Technologies, Inc., Stamford, CT; *U.S. Public*, pg. 711

Poddar, Saroj, Mng. Dir.--Caristrap India, Calcutta, India; *Int'l*, pg. 272

Podewils, Robert, Chief Oper. Officer--ICC Trading, Inc., New York, NY; *U.S. Private*, pg. 553

Podolny, William, V.P. & Gen. Mgr.--Fuel Cell Operations, South Windsor, CT; *U.S. Public*, pg. 1690

Podowski, Charles, Pres.--Advanta Insurance Companies, Horsham, PA; *U.S. Public*, pg. 22

Podowski, Charles H., Pres.--Advanta Business Services, Voorhees, NJ; *U.S. Public*, pg. 22

Podowski, Charles H., Chm. Bd.--INA Life Insurance Co., Ltd., Tokyo, Japan; *U.S. Public*, pg. 362

Podsiadlo, Rick, Chief Oper. Officer--Novo Nordisk Canada, Inc., Mississauga, Canada; *Int'l*, pg. 988

Poe, Finley, Gen. Sls. Mgr.-West--Tokheim Investment Corp., Houston, TX; *U.S. Public*, pg. 1620

Poe, George, Gen. Mgr.--Republic Automotive Parts Sales, Inc., Tacoma, WA; *U.S. Public*, pg. 1378

Poe, John, V.P. & Gen. Mgr.--Ragland Manufacturing Company Inc., Houston, TX; *U.S. Public*, pg. 895

Poe, Keith, Pres.--Chrome Crankshaft Company, Bell Gardens, CA; *U.S. Public*, pg. 1710

Poe, Keith, Pres.--Chrome Crankshaft of Illinois, Chicago, IL; *U.S. Public*, pg. 1710

Poe, Keith, Pres.--Prime Manufacturing Company, Oak Creek, WI; *U.S. Public*, pg. 1711

Poe, Thomas R., Pres. & Chief Exec. Officer--National City Commercial Finance, Inc., Cleveland, OH; *U.S. Public*, pg. 1154

Poe, William, V.P. & Grp. Exec.--Space Systems Group, Clearwater, FL; *U.S. Public*, pg. 834

Poehlsen, Heinz, Gen. Mgr.--Deutsche Bank AG (Kuala Lumpur), Kuala Lumpur, Malaysia; *Int'l*, pg. 404

Poehner, Michael, Pres. & Chief Exec. Officer--DMR Group, Inc., Montreal, Canada; *Int'l*, pg. 527

Poehnlein, David, Mgr.--Tenney Telephone Co., Alma, WI; *U.S. Public*, pg. 1572

Poelck, W.J., Pres. UE&C-Catalytic--Raytheon Engineers & Constructors, Inc., Englewood, CO; *U.S. Public*, pg. 1366

Poelker, John S., Chm. Bd. & Chief Exec. Officer--Fleet Finance, Inc., Atlanta, GA; *U.S. Public*, pg. 650

Poer, Bryard, Chief Oper. Officer & Exec. V.P.--First American Field Services, Lakewood, NJ; *U.S. Public*, pg. 625

Poeschko, Kurt, Mng. Dir.--Det Norske Veritas, Zurich, Switzerland; *Int'l*, pg. 397

Poeschko, Kurt, Mng. Dir.--Det Norske Veritas, Vienna, Austria; *Int'l*, pg. 397

Poeter, Hans Josef, Mng. Dir.--Hoesch Bausysteme GmbH, Vienna, Austria; *Int'l*, pg. 508

Poetker, Bernard, Pres.--Dukane Canada Ltd., Kitchener, Canada; *U.S. Private*, pg. 346

Pofcher, Paul, Gen. Mgr.--Rowenta (USA), Inc., Medford, MA; *Int'l*, pg. 569

Poggemann, Gerd, Chief Oper. Officer--Babcock Industrierohrleitungsbau GmbH, Leverkusen, Germany; *Int'l*, pg. 399

Poggi, A. Robert, Chm. Bd.--Willis Corroon Corp. of Western Michigan, Grand Rapids, MI; *Int'l*, pg. 1507

Poggi, Jean Charles, Pres.--Pyroindustrie S.A., Les Mureaux, France; *U.S. Public*, pg. 1207

Pogorilic, Sani, Chief Oper. Officer--Novo Nordisk A/S, Zagreb, Croatia; *Int'l*, pg. 987

Pohjanheimo, Jikka, Chief Oper. Officer--Neste Chemicals Holding Inc., Houston, TX; *Int'l*, pg. 913

Pohl, Bruno, Mng. Dir.--Anacomp, GmbH, Wiesbaden, Germany; *U.S. Public*, pg. 107
Pohl, David, Chief Oper. Officer--Dentsply (Australia) Pty. Ltd., Abbotsford, Australia; *U.S. Public*, pg. 499
Pohl, Gunther, Mng. Dir.--Tesa Leitz GmbH, Freiburg, Germany; *U.S. Public*, pg. 260
Pohl, Susan, District Mgr.--Circle Freight International USA, Wilder, KY; *U.S. Public*, pg. 371
Pohl, Susan P., Branch Mgr.--Max Gruenhut International Inc. USA, Wilder, KY; *U.S. Public*, pg. 372
Pohl, Werner, Dr., Gen. Mgr.--MacNeal-Schwendler GmbH, Munich, Germany; *U.S. Public*, pg. 1032
Pohlabel, Steven, Mgr.-Terminal--Kintetsu World Express Inc., Cudahy, WI; *Int'l*, pg. 734
Pohlman, Stephen C., Rep. Dir. & Gen. Mgr.--Westvaco Asia, K.K., Tokyo, Japan; *U.S. Public*, pg. 1762
Pohly, Pamela, Admin.--Bayview Hospital, Corpus Christi, TX; *U.S. Public*, pg. 404
Poiesz, J.W.J., Mgr.--Ballast Nedam International (Malaysia) Sdn. Bhd., Kuala Lumpur, Malaysia; *Int'l*, pg. 134
Pointon, J. B., Mng. Dir.--MacMillan Bloedel Pulp & Paper Sales Ltd., Twickenham, United Kingdom; *Int'l*, pg. 829
Pointson, Maurice, Pres.--New England Centerless Grinding, West Hartford, CT; *Int'l*, pg. 391
Poiree, Alain, Chm.--FCA!BMZ Paris, Suresnes, France; *Int'l*, pg. 469
Poirer, Andre, Chief Oper. Officer--MTS Testing Systems Canada Ltd., Mississauga, Canada; *U.S. Public*, pg. 1029
Poirier, Robert, Gen. Mgr.--Industrial Division, Granby, Canada; *Int'l*, pg. 32
Poirier, Victor L., Pres., Chief Exec. & Oper. Officer--Thermo Cardiosystems Inc., Woburn, MA; *U.S. Public*, pg. 1592
Poirot, Jean, Gen. Mgr.--S.I.S., Besancon, France; *Int'l*, pg. 569
Poissant, Alice, Plant Mgr.--Regina Seed Processors Ltd., Richardson, Canada; *Int'l*, pg. 1195
Poist, William G., Pres.--COM/Energy Acushnet Realty, Cambridge, MA; *U.S. Public*, pg. 414
Poist, William G., Chief Oper. Officer--COM/Energy Freetown Realty, Cambridge, MA; *U.S. Public*, pg. 414
Pokorney, E.Wayne, Pres.--Avesta Sheffield Plate Inc., New Castle, IN; *Int'l*, pg. 221
Pokorny, Gerald E., Pres.--Electron Devices Div., San Carlos, CA; *U.S. Public*, pg. 1003
Pokou, Yao, Resident Rep.--The World Bank, N'djamena, Chad; *U.S. Private*, pg. 1189
Polacco, Alessandro, Rep.--Cariplo (Tokyo), Tokyo, Japan; *Int'l*, pg. 275
Polak, David A., Mng. Dir.--NWQ Investment Managaement Company, Los Angeles, CA; *U.S. Public*, pg. 1673
Polak, Hal, Pres.--Potpourri (Harte-Hanks Northern California CDM, Inc.), Santa Clara, CA; *U.S. Public*, pg. 794
Polan, Jesse N., Pres.--Federal APD, Inc., Farmington, MI; *U.S. Public*, pg. 616
Poland, William F., Pres. & Chief Exec. Officer--Willis Corroon Corp. of California, San Francisco, CA; *Int'l*, pg. 1505
Polestra, Frank M., Pres.--Pioneer Capital Corporation, Boston, MA; *U.S. Public*, pg. 1298
Polestra, Frank M., Pres.--Pioneer SBIC Corp., Boston, MA; *U.S. Public*, pg. 1298
Polgar, Marina, Chief Exec. Officer & Creative Dir.--Equipe, Milan, Italy; *Int'l*, pg. 602
Policy, Al, Plant Mgr.--Firestone Agricultural Tire Company-Des Moines, Des Moines, IA; *Int'l*, pg. 214
Polifka, James R., Gen. Mgr.--Loctite Puerto Rico, Inc., Sabana Grande, PR; *Int'l*, pg. 611
Poline, J.C., Pres.--U.B.R., Vincennes, France; *Int'l*, pg. 565
Poliner, Randall, Chm. Bd.--First American Flood Data Services, Austin, TX; *U.S. Public*, pg. 625
Politis, Donald A., Pres.--Global Special Risks Insurance Services California, San Francisco, CA; *Int'l*, pg. 1503
Polito, Antonio, Pres.-Corp. Office--Rizzoli International Publications, Inc., New York, NY; *Int'l*, pg. 1078
Politova, Vicky, Exec. Dir.--Leo Burnett Advertising, Sofia, Bulgaria; *U.S. Private*, pg. 184
Polk, L. Douglas, Div. Pres.--Thomas & Howard Co., Newberry, SC; *U.S. Private*, pg. 1082
Polkki, Voitto, Group Mgr.--Forest Operations Division, Imatra, Finland; *Int'l*, pg. 455
Polkow, Gary A., Pres.--Douglas-Randall, Inc., Pawcatuck, CT; *U.S. Public*, pg. 1341
Polkowski, Andrzej, Gen. Mgr.--Nordson Polska Sp.z.o.o., Warsaw, Poland; *U.S. Public*, pg. 1189
Poll, Lawrence, Div. Mgr.--North Carolina Gas Service, Reidsville, NC; *U.S. Public*, pg. 1148
Pollack, John, V. Chm.--Andy Johns Fashions, Inc., New York, NY; *U.S. Public*, pg. 233
Pollack, Thomas, Exec. V.P. & Chm.-Universal Studios Motion Picture Grp.--Universal Studios, Inc., Universal City, CA; *Int'l*, pg. 1215
Pollaert, Ted, Pres.--Lurgi Corporation, Paramus, NJ; *Int'l*, pg. 861
Pollak, Lee, Pres.--Philip Morris Management Corp., New York, NY; *U.S. Public*, pg. 1289
Pollak, Martin, Chm. Bd.--General Physics Corporation, Columbia, MD; *U.S. Public*, pg. 694
Pollanen, Pekka, Mng. Dir.--Pankakoski Boards Oy Ltd., Pankakoski, Finland; *Int'l*, pg. 456
Pollard Carl F., Chief Oper. Officer--Galen of Mississippi, Inc., Louisville, KY; *U.S. Public*, pg. 404
Pollard, Carl F., Chief Oper. Officer--Galen BH, Inc., Shreveport, LA; *U.S. Public*, pg. 404
Pollard, Donald R., Ph.D., Pres.--Louisiana Reference Laboratory, Baton Rouge, LA; *Int'l*, pg. 1265
Pollari, Kristiina, Mng. Dir.--Johnson & Johnson KFT, Budapest, Hungary; *U.S. Public*, pg. 930
Polledro, Pierluigi, Mng. Dir.--Italgestra s.r.L., Milan, Italy; *Int'l*, pg. 550
Pollick, Richard R., V.P.-Intl. Equip.--International Equipment, Bloomington, MN; *U.S. Public*, pg. 1624
Pollock, Dan, Gen. Mgr.--Market Direct, Valley View, OH; *Int'l*, pg. 1177
Pollock, David M., Mng. Dir.--Hyster Europe Ltd., Basingstoke, United Kingdom; *U.S. Public*, pg. 1149
Pollock, J. Mandry, S., Mng. Dirs.--Raysil Gowns Ltd., London, United Kingdom; *Int'l*, pg. 300
Pollock, John G., Pres.--ServiceMaster Business & Industry Group, Downers Grove, IL; *U.S. Public*, pg. 1462
Pollock, John R., Pres. & Chief Exec. Officer--General Casualty Company of Wisconsin, Sun Prairie, WI; *Int'l*, pg. 345
Pollock, Kenneth L., Chm. Bd.--PG Energy, Inc., Wilkes-Barre, PA; *U.S. Public*, pg. 1271
Pollock, Lawrence J., Pres.--Capital Cities/ABC Owned Television Stations, Philadelphia, PA; *U.S. Public*, pg. 512
Pollock, R. W., Pres.--Halliburton Services, Ltd., Calgary, Canada; *U.S. Public*, pg. 777
Pollock, Robert B., Pres. & Chief Exec. Officer--Fortis Benefits Insurance Company, Kansas City, MO; *Int'l*, pg. 499
Pollock, William I., Pres.--Atlas Alloys, Etobicoke, Canada; *Int'l*, pg. 1118
Pollux, P.M.J., Chief Exec. Officer--OCE-Czech-Republic s.r.o., Prague, Czech Republic; *Int'l*, pg. 994
Polly, Debbie, Gen. Mgr. & Editor--Larue County Herald News, Hodgenville, KY; *U.S. Private*, pg. 648
Polman, Paul, Mng. Dir.--Procter & Gamble Ltd., Newcastle upon Tyne, United Kingdom; *U.S. Public*, pg. 1332
Polson, Dick, Chief Oper. Officer--Environmental Control Inc., Santa Fe, NM; *U.S. Public*, pg. 49
Polychronopoulos, Ioannis, Dir. Gen.--Macedonian Airlines, Athens, Greece; *Int'l*, pg. 1004
Poma, G., Mgr.--Algemene Bank Nederland (Svizzera), Chiasso, Switzerland; *Int'l*, pg. 12
Pomante, Louis, Mgr.-Opers.--Allegro MicroSystems Inc., Willow Grove, PA; *Int'l*, pg. 1188
Pombo Concha, Jose V., Partner--Korn/Ferry International, Bogota, Colombia; *U.S. Private*, pg. 633
Pomerantz, Howard K., Pres.--Franklin-Burlington Plastics, Conshohocken, PA; *U.S. Public*, pg. 1496
Pomerleau, Bob, Dir.-Opers.--Conmed Andover Medical, Inc., Haverhill, MA; *U.S. Public*, pg. 431
Pomeroy, Cynthia, Pres.--First American Title Guaranty Agency of Cheyenne, Cheyenne, WY; *U.S. Public*, pg. 625
Pomeroy, Jeffrey C., Pres.--HNTB Design & Build, Irvine, CA; *U.S. Private*, pg. 492
Pomeroy, John E., Pres.--Dover Technologies, Binghamton, NY; *U.S. Public*, pg. 521
Pommeranz, Winifried, Reg. Pres.--Eul & Gunther GmbH & Co KG, Emmerich, Germany; *Int'l*, pg. 857
Pompe, H., Gen. Mgr.--A.B. Dick Holland B.V., Demeern, Netherlands; *U.S. Private*, pg. 791
Pompei, Don-Pierre, Gen. Mgr.--IPC Corporation (France) S.A., Ivry-sur-Seine, France; *Int'l*, pg. 651
Pomphrett, W. George, Mng. Dir.--Celebration Arts Group Limited, Corby, United Kingdom; *U.S. Public*, pg. 78
Pond, Debbie, Pres.--Adecco Employment Services, Redwood City, CA; *Int'l*, pg. 24
Pond, P. Michael, Pres.--Caterpillar Investment Management Ltd., Peoria, IL; *U.S. Public*, pg. 316
Ponds, Annette, Mgr.-Office--Woodward-Clyde, Austin, TX; *U.S. Public*, pg. 1656
Ponds, Annette, Mgr.-Office--Woodward-Clyde, San Antonio, TX; *U.S. Public*, pg. 1657
Ponik, Wayne, V.P.--Teradyne Semiconductor Test Division, Agoura Hills, CA; *U.S. Public*, pg. 1581
Ponman, Steve, Chief Exec.--KPI Elevators, Inc., Makati, Philippines; *Int'l*, pg. 747
Ponroy, Thibault, Mng. Dir.--Johnson & Johnson AG, Spreitenbach, Switzerland; *U.S. Public*, pg. 930
Pons-Torres, Enrique Hernandez, Pres. & Chief Oper. Officer--McCormick de Mexico, S.A. de C.V., Mexico, Mexico; *U.S. Public*, pg. 1067
Pons, Ramon, Mng. Dir.--Lincoln KD S.A., Barcelona, Spain; *U.S. Public*, pg. 997
Pontano, Benjamin A., Dr., Pres.--COMSAT Laboratories, Clarksburg, MD; *U.S. Public*, pg. 424
Pontarelli, Thomas, Pres.--Washington National Insurance Co., Carmel, IN; *U.S. Public*, pg. 434
Ponte, Leonard P., Pres. & Chief Exec. Officer--LaSalle Bank of Lisle, Lisle, IL; *Int'l*, pg. 10
Pontes, Jose Paulo, Country Mgr.--Det Norske Veritas, Mexico, Mexico; *Int'l*, pg. 397
Pontiakas, George, Gen. Mgr. & Managing Dir.--Wavetek Corp., San Diego, CA; *U.S. Private*, pg. 1155
Pontier, Roland, Controller & Deputy Mng. Dir.--MacGREGOR (FRA) S.A., Marseilles, France; *Int'l*, pg. 670
Pontillo, Ralph, Div. Mgr.--Ringier America, New Berlin Division, New Berlin, WI; *U.S. Public*, pg. 1778
Pontin, Paul, Mng. Dir.--Universal Calibration Laboratories Ltd., Romsey, United Kingdom; *Int'l*, pg. 390
Pontremoli, R., Mng. Dir.--La Previdente S.p.A., Milan, Italy; *Int'l*, pg. 784
Pontual, Felipe, Gen. Mgr.--Uniao de Bancos Brasileiros (Unibanco) (Brazil), New York, NY; *Int'l*, pg. 1431
Ponzellini, Alberto, Admin. Del.--Castelli S.p.A., Bologna, Italy; *U.S. Private*, pg. 512
Pool, Daniel F., Pres.--Cosco Fire Protection Inc., Gardena, CA; *U.S. Public*, pg. 1795
Pool, J.A., Mng. Dir.--Pandrol International Limited, Addlestone, United Kingdom; *Int'l*, pg. 280
Poole, Bill, Gen. Mgr.--Madison, Inc., Tulsa, OK; *U.S. Private*, pg. 428
Poole, J. William, Gen. Mgr.--Radio Stations WFLS FM & WYSK-AM-FM, Fredericksburg, VA; *U.S. Private*, pg. 425
Poole, James, Unit Mgr.--Niachlor, Niagara Falls, NY; *U.S. Public*, pg. 1219
Poole, Rich, Dir.-Mktg.--Dykem Company, Saint Louis, MO; *U.S. Public*, pg. 866
Poole, Richard, Mng. Dir.--K-Tron Germany, Soder Division, Gelnhausen, Germany; *U.S. Public*, pg. 938
Poole, Tony, Mng. Dir.--Dowty O Rings & Actuation Polymers, Qormi, Malta; *Int'l*, pg. 1338
Poolman, Craig, Gen. Mgr.--Chief Industries - Agri/Industrial Products Div., Grand Island, NE; *U.S. Private*, pg. 236
Poon, Patrick, Gen. Mgr.--Aetna Life Insurance Co. of America (ALICA), Taipei, Taiwan; *U.S. Public*, pg. 27
Poonawalla, Lila, Chief Oper. Officer--Alfa-Laval India Ltd, Mumbai, India; *Int'l*, pg. 1380
Poore, Jeffrey, Dr., Pres.--CompHealth, Inc., Salt Lake City, UT; *U.S. Public*, pg. 839
Pope, Carter D., Pres.--Atlanta Blueprint Company, Atlanta, GA; *U.S. Public*, pg. 1735
Pope, Gene, Gen. Mgr.--Action Commodities Corporation, Loganville, GA; *U.S. Private*, pg. 1076
Pope, Jeffrey, Mng. Dir.--Malayan Cement Berhad, Kuala Lumpur, Malaysia; *Int'l*, pg. 198
Pope, Jim, Pres.--Atlantic States Bank, Norcross, GA; *U.S. Public*, pg. 629
Pope, John R., Pres.--Williams Printing Company, Atlanta, GA; *U.S. Public*, pg. 1736
Pope, Larry D.J., Pres.-Engrng. & Construction--Brown & Root Inc., Alhambra, CA; *U.S. Public*, pg. 775
Pope, Lawrence D.J., Pres.--Brown & Root Petroleum and Chemicals, Houston, TX; *U.S. Public*, pg. 775
Pope, M. Dean, Pres.--DMD, Woodlands, TX; *U.S. Public*, pg. 528
Pope, Mark C., IV, Pres. & Chief Oper. Officer--Graphic Industries, Inc., Atlanta, GA; *U.S. Public*, pg. 1735
Pope, Michael, Pres.--Control Dynamics Division, Huntsville, AL; *U.S. Private*, pg. 106
Pope, R.L., Pres.--H C Products Co., Princeville, IL; *U.S. Public*, pg. 61
Pope, Randall, Pres.--Prudential Agricultural Credit, Inc., Newark, NJ; *U.S. Private*, pg. 892
Pope, W.A., Pres.--NZU, Inc., Albuquerque, NM; *U.S. Public*, pg. 1172
Pope, William A., Pres.--NZ Development Corporation, Phoenix, AZ; *U.S. Public*, pg. 1172
Pope, William A., Pres.--NZ Properties, Inc., Phoenix, AZ; *U.S. Public*, pg. 1172
Popeell, Judy, Dir.-Opers.--Reliable/Bethea Power Products Inc., Pelham, AL; *U.S. Private*, pg. 692
Popenko, Oleg, Mng. Dir.--DMB&B LLC/Kiev, Kiev, Ukraine; *U.S. Private*, pg. 304
Popescu, Anca, Chief Oper. Officer--Novo Nordisk A/S, Bucharest, Romania; *Int'l*, pg. 988
Popik, Carlos, Pres.--Monsanto Argentina S.A.I.C., Buenos Aires, Argentina; *U.S. Public*, pg. 1125
Popoff, Frank, Pres.--Dow Credit Corporation, Midland, MI; *U.S. Public*, pg. 522
Popp, Karl, Reg. Pres.--Melitta Bentz & Co, Egerkingen, Switzerland; *Int'l*, pg. 857
Popp, Karl, Reg. Pres.--Melitta-Gesellschaft MbH & Co KG, Salzburg, Austria; *Int'l*, pg. 857
Poppe, Dave, Plant Mgr.--Schlegel Oklahoma, Inc., Frederick, OK; *Int'l*, pg. 128
Poppe, Gene, Pres.--Mercantile Bank of Mount Ayr, Mount Ayr, IA; *U.S. Public*, pg. 1088
Poppe, Rick, Pres.--Weitz-Cohen Construction Co., Denver, CO; *U.S. Private*, pg. 1161
Poppele, K., Mgr.-Sales & Mktg.--Carbone of America, Parsippany, NJ; *Int'l*, pg. 1028
Poppell, Larry, Mng. Dir.--National Distributing Co., Inc., Augusta, GA; *U.S. Private*, pg. 781
Poppen, Bob, Gen. Mgr.--Spiralkote, Orlando, FL; *U.S. Private*, pg. 411
Popplewell, Richard, Mng. Dir.--National Utility Service Ltd., Croydon, United Kingdom; *U.S. Private*, pg. 787
Popwell, Lynda W., Pres.--Carolina Eastman Co., Columbia, SC; *U.S. Public*, pg. 550
Poran, Rafi, Pres.--Adanet Communications, Or Yehud, Israel; *Int'l*, pg. 645
Porcaro, Rob, Gen. Mgr.--Robertson Leo Burnett Pty. Ltd., Adelaide, Australia; *U.S. Private*, pg. 186
Porche, Larry, Mgr.-Opers.--Aqua Power Marine Products Div., New Orleans, LA; *U.S. Public*, pg. 857
Porco, Dominick, Pres.--News America Publishing Inc., New York, NY; *Int'l*, pg. 925
Porelius, Sven, Chief Oper. Officer--Molnlycke Tissue AB, Goteborg, Sweden; *Int'l*, pg. 1326
Poremsky, Claire, Gen. Mgr.--Toledo Precision Machining Div., Perrysburg, OH; *U.S. Public*, pg. 353
Porer, Al, Pres.--Missouri Portland Cement Holding, Davenport, IA; *Int'l*, pg. 788
Porras, Carlos, Mgr.--Commercial Metals Company, Clute, TX; *U.S. Public*, pg. 413
Porras, Peter, Admin.--Valley Grande Manor, Brownsville, TX; *U.S. Public*, pg. 839
Porrett, James, Gen. Mgr.--Lawler's, Inc., Rochester, MN; *U.S. Public*, pg. 1537
Porrone, Roberto, Mng. Dir.-Torino--Armando Testa S.p.A, Rome, Italy; *Int'l*, pg. 1377
Porsch, Reinhard, Country Mgr.--Compaq Computer GmbH, Vienna, Austria; *U.S. Public*, pg. 418
Porsche, C. F., Chief Oper. Officer--Karosseriewerk Porsche GmbH, Stuttgart, Germany; *Int'l*, pg. 1063
Port, George, Exec. V.P.--Video Treasures, Troy, MI; *U.S. Public*, pg. 780
Portal, Claude, Chief Oper. Officer--Alfa-Laval S.A., Les Clayes-sous-Bois, France; *Int'l*, pg. 1379
Portale, Carl, Publisher--Mirabella, New York, NY; *Int'l*, pg. 795
Portelance, M., Pres.--Labatt Breweries of Canada - Prairie Region, Edmonton, Canada; *Int'l*, pg. 679
Portell, David, Gen. Mgr.--Arena Auto Auction Inc., Bolingbrook, IL; *U.S. Public*, pg. 1648
Porten, Norbert W., Co-Chief Oper Officer--BHF & IKB Immobilien-Leasing GmbH, Dusseldorf, Germany; *Int'l*, pg. 645
Porter, A.E., Acting Gen. Mgr.--Detrex Equipment Div., Bowling Green, KY; *U.S. Public*, pg. 501
Porter, Colin, Gen. Mgr.--Vaughn-Harmon Ltd., Ware, United Kingdom; *U.S. Public*, pg. 788

Porter, Edward L., Pres.--Output Technologies SRI Group, Inc., Kansas City, MO; *U.S. Public*, pg. 944
Porter, G., Site Services Mgr.--R & J Garroway Limited, Glasgow, United Kingdom; *Int'l*, pg. 802
Porter, H., Gen. Mgr.--SHL Division/Commercial Aircraft Group, Israel; *Int'l*, pg. 690
Porter, Ivan, Pres. & Chief Exec. Officer--Canron Inc., Rexdale, Canada; *Int'l*, pg. 695
Porter, James, Mng. Dir.--Hunt Lascaris/TBWA Durban, Westville, South Africa; *U.S. Private*, pg. 1062
Porter, L.E., Chief Exec. Officer--Mount Vernon Mills, Inc., Riegel Textile Div. (Alto), Alto, GA; *U.S. Private*, pg. 835
Porter, M. McNeil, Pres. & Chief Exec. Officer--CSX Intermodal, Inc., Hunt Valley, MD; *U.S. Public*, pg. 284
Porter, Michael, Reg. Media Dir.--Young & Rubicam Australia/New Zealand, Sydney, Australia; *U.S. Private*, pg. 1198
Porter, Mike, Pres.--First American Bank Valley, Grand Forks, ND; *U.S. Private*, pg. 167
Porter, Norbert W., Chief Oper. Officer--BHF & IKB Immobilien-Leasing GmbH, Dusseldorf, Germany; *Int'l*, pg. 119
Porter, R.B., Plant Mgr.--Laporte Absorbents (Baulking) Limited, Faringdon, United Kingdom; *Int'l*, pg. 802
Porter, Richard A., Pres.--Lamb-Weston, Inc., Kennewick, WA; *U.S. Public*, pg. 427
Porter, Richard M., Pres.--Queens Properties, Charlotte, NC; *Int'l*, pg. 633
Porter, Tracey, Gen. Mgr.--Southern Post Company-Texas, San Marcos, TX; *U.S. Public*, pg. 412
Porter, William, Pres.--McMullen/Argus Publishers, Placentia, CA; *U.S. Public*, pg. 1328
Porter, William, Pres.--Argus Publishers, Placentia, CA; *U.S. Public*, pg. 1328
Portera, Vito S., Chm. Bd.--Republic International Bank of New York, Miami, FL; *U.S. Public*, pg. 1380
Porteret, Jacques, Program Sls. Mgr.--Columbia Pictures Television, Paris, France; *Int'l*, pg. 1282
Portillo Acuna, Bernardo, Chm. Bd.--Domicilio Conocido Hercules, Ciudad Camargo, Mexico; *Int'l*, pg. 572
Portillo, Bernardo, Chief Oper. Officer--Minera del Norte, Chihuahua, Mexico; *Int'l*, pg. 66
Portman, Robert G., Pres.--Carlton Cards Division, Cleveland, OH; *U.S. Public*, pg. 78
Portman, Robert G., Pres. & Chief Exec. Officer--Chocoamerican Inc., Cleveland, OH; *Int'l*, pg. 865
Portmann, Shawn, Gen. Mgr.--WCKT, Fort Myers, FL; *U.S. Public*, pg. 384
Portno, A.D., Chm. Bd.--Britvic Soft Drinks Ltd., Chelmsford, United Kingdom; *Int'l*, pg. 170
Portno, A.D., Chm. Bd.--Bass International Brewers, Birmingham, United Kingdom; *Int'l*, pg. 170
Portno, A.D., Chm. Bd.--Britvic Soft Drinks Ltd., Chelmsford, United Kingdom; *Int'l*, pg. 1499
Portnoj, Joel, Pres.--Polarcup Finland, Hameenlinna, Finland; *Int'l*, pg. 638
Porzio, D.K., Pres.--Marley Electric Heating Company, Bennettsville, SC; *U.S. Public*, pg. 1676
Posek, David J., V.P.--Martin Marietta Space & Aeronautics Services, Hyattsville, MD; *U.S. Public*, pg. 1007
Posey, Richard E., Pres. & Chief Exec. Officer--Hamilton Beach/Proctor-Silex, Inc., Glen Allen, VA; *U.S. Public*, pg. 1149
Poskiparta, Risto, Gen. Mgr.--Nokia Representative Office, Jakarta, Indonesia; *Int'l*, pg. 953
Posner, Gerald D., Pres.--Electronic Measurements, Inc., Neptune, NJ; *U.S. Private*, pg. 138
Post, Dan, Pres.--Charter Group, Inc., Dallas, TX; *Int'l*, pg. 1257
Post, Gary, Pres. & Chief Oper. Officer--Muskegon Construction Company, Muskegon, MI; *U.S. Private*, pg. 824
Post, I., Plant Dir.--Keebler Co./Grand Rapids Bakery, Grand Rapids, MI; *U.S. Public*, pg. 657
Post, William, Pres.--Levy Restaurants, Chicago, IL; *U.S. Private*, pg. 664
Postel, Alan, Mgr.--American Iron & Metal Co., Dallas, TX; *U.S. Public*, pg. 413
Postell, Jim, Brick Superintendant--General Shale Products Corp., Kingsport, TN; *Int'l*, pg. 843
Postelwait, Larry L., Div. Pres.--The Crosby Group Inc., Tulsa, OK; *Int'l*, pg. 473
Posten, William, Dir.-Mktg.--Turner Construction Company, Richmond, VA; *U.S. Public*, pg. 1646
Postewait, Jerry, Pres.--Mercantile Insurance Services, Inc., Saint Louis, MO; *U.S. Public*, pg. 1088
Postiglione, Mike, Gen. Mgr.--Advocate Services, Inc., Butler, PA; *U.S. Private*, pg. 1108
Postl, James, Pres.--Hostess Frito-Lay Co., Mississauga, Canada; *U.S. Public*, pg. 1277
Poston, Tom, Plant Mgr.--Acme Brick Co., Malvern, AR; *U.S. Public*, pg. 936
Postwaite, Jerry, Pres.--Mississippi Valley Life Insurance Company, Saint Louis, MO; *U.S. Public*, pg. 1087
Poth, Greg, Exec. V.P.--Magna Bank, Carbondale Region, Carbondale, IL; *U.S. Public*, pg. 1037
Potier, Eric, Gen. Mgr.--Shandwick S.A. Infopublic N.V., Brussels, Belgium; *Int'l*, pg. 1228
Pottecher, Antoine, Gen. Mgr.--ITW Gunther, Fontaine-les-Luxeuil, France; *U.S. Public*, pg. 868
Potteiger, Jim, Area Superintendent--Edgewood Plant, Edgewood, TX; *U.S. Public*, pg. 1759
Potter, D., Chief Oper. Officer--British Fermentation Products Ltd., Felixstowe, United Kingdom; *Int'l*, pg. 1143
Potter, David, Chm. Bd.--Guinness Yokohama Leasing Limited, London, United Kingdom; *Int'l*, pg. 159
Potter, Keenan, Gen. Mgr.--Flow Asia, Hsin-chu, Taiwan; *U.S. Public*, pg. 656
Potter, Keith, Pres.--Leaver Mushrooms Co. Limited, Campbellville, Canada; *U.S. Public*, pg. 428
Potter, Mr., Chm.--Jagenberg Papier Technik GmbH, Neuss, Germany; *Int'l*, pg. 1108
Potter, N.R., Pres. & Chief Exec. Officer--Fleet Call of Utah, Inc., Salt Lake City, UT; *U.S. Public*, pg. 1180
Potter, Walter R., Resident V.P.--National Surety Corporation, Chicago, IL; *Int'l*, pg. 59
Potthast, Ulrich, Chief Exec. Officer--VEBA Kraftwerke Ruhr AG, Gelsenkirchen, Germany; *Int'l*, pg. 1460
Potthoff, G.A., Pres.--Systems & Electronics Inc., Saint Louis, MO; *U.S. Public*, pg. 547
Pottier, J., Chief Oper. Officer--Buss Waeschle Sarl, Saint Denis, France; *Int'l*, pg. 490
Potts, Charles F., Pres.--APAC Holdings, Inc., Atlanta, GA; *U.S. Public*, pg. 139
Potts, Christopher George, V.P.-Admin.--Combined Insurance Company of Ireland Ltd., Dublin, Ireland; *U.S. Public*, pg. 118
Potts, Daniel T., Gen. Mgr.--Containerboard & Paper Div.-Florence Mill, Florence, SC; *U.S. Public*, pg. 1520
Potts, Dennis, Gen. Mgr.--The Southland Corporation, Willow Grove, PA; *Int'l*, pg. 694
Potts, Fred T., Gen. Mgr.--Richmond Converters, Inc., Laurel Hill, NC; *Int'l*, pg. 1059
Potts, Gary, Chief Exec. Officer--Maxoptix Corp., Fremont, CA; *Int'l*, pg. 762
Potts, Gorden D., Pres.--Chemap, Inc., South Plainfield, NJ; *Int'l*, pg. 1378
Potts, Larry W., Plant Mgr.--Amcast Automotive-Richmond Plant, Richmond, IN; *U.S. Public*, pg. 63
Potts, Robert H., Pres.--Bonnet Resources Corp., Dallas, TX; *U.S. Public*, pg. 175
Potts, Tom, Plant Mgr.--Baldor Electric Company, Westville, OK; *U.S. Public*, pg. 169
Potts, W.J., Jr., V.P. & Gen. Mgr.-Res. & Opers.--Union Camp Kraft Paper & Board Div., Savannah, GA; *U.S. Public*, pg. 1666
Potts, William, Pres.--Precor, Inc., Bothell, WA; *U.S. Public*, pg. 1322
Poublon, Alain, Mng. Dir.--Union-Transport N.V. S.A., B-1931, Belgium; *U.S. Private*, pg. 1120
Pouillot, Didier, Country Mgr.--Autodesk S.a.r.L., Saint Maurice, France; *U.S. Public*, pg. 150
Poulars, Bernard, Mng. Dir.--Wynn's France, S.A., Courbevoie, France; *U.S. Public*, pg. 1783
Poulin, Claude, Mng. Dir.--Tarif Media S.A., Paris, France; *Int'l*, pg. 451
Poulin, Gerald C., Pres.--The Union Water-Power Co., Lewiston, ME; *U.S. Public*, pg. 325
Pouliot, Adrien D., Chm. Bd.--CF Cable TV Inc., Montreal, Canada; *Int'l*, pg. 240
Pouliot, Adrien D., Chm. Bd.--Reseau de Television Quatre Saisons Inc., Montreal, Canada; *Int'l*, pg. 241
Pouliot, Adrien D., Chm. Bd. & Chief Exec. Officer--Laurentien Cable TV Inc., Montreal, Canada; *Int'l*, pg. 241
Pouliot, Adrien D., Chm. Bd. & Chief Exec. Officer--Northern Cable Holdings Ltd., Montreal, Canada; *Int'l*, pg. 241
Pouliot, Paul T., Pres.--CFX Mortgage, Inc., Keene, NH; *U.S. Public*, pg. 278
Poulsen, Jans Peter, Pres.--MD Foods Norge A/S, Oslo, Norway; *Int'l*, pg. 826
Poulsen, Larry D., Pres.--Republic Powdered Metals, Inc., Medina, OH; *U.S. Public*, pg. 1357
Poulsen, Preben E., Chief Oper. Officer--FeF Chemicals A/S, Koge, Denmark; *Int'l*, pg. 987
Poulsen, Svend, Chief Oper. Officer--Nordfoil Odense Flexible A.p.S., Odense, Denmark; *Int'l*, pg. 441
Poulson, Larry, Pres.--Haartz-Mason, Inc., Watertown, MA; *U.S. Public*, pg. 1358
Poulson, S., Mgr.--G.W. Sprinkler Gmbh, Koblenz, Germany; *Int'l*, pg. 1500
Poulson, S., Mng. Dir.--G.W. Sprinkler A/S, Glamsbjerg, Denmark; *Int'l*, pg. 1500
Poulter, Donald, Pres.--ConferTech Canada Inc., Etobicoke, Canada; *U.S. Public*, pg. 683
Poulter, Mike, Mng. Dir.--ISS Contract Cleaning Services (South), Bracknell, United Kingdom; *Int'l*, pg. 657
Poulton, Ted, Pres.--Old Kent Bank of Grand Haven, Grand Haven, MI; *U.S. Public*, pg. 1217
Pound, Mike, Mng. Dir.--Ohmeda Medical Engineering, Norcross, GA; *Int'l*, pg. 121
Pound, Walter, Pres.--Anzon Inc., Philadelphia, PA; *Int'l*, pg. 328
Pountney, Jack J., Pres.--Proctor Silex Canada, Inc., Scarborough, Canada; *U.S. Public*, pg. 1150
Pountney, Rhydian, Gen. Mgr.--Renishaw (Hong Kong) Ltd., Kowloon Bay, Hong Kong; *Int'l*, pg. 1103
Poupon, P., Dir.--NatWest Sellier SA, Paris, France; *Int'l*, pg. 911
Poure, Timothy O., Chief Oper. Officer--General Alum - New England, Searsport, ME; *U.S. Private*, pg. 443
Poussot, Bernard, Pres.--Whitehall-Robins International, Inc., Madison, NJ; *U.S. Public*, pg. 80
Poussot, Bernard, Pres.--Wyeth-Ayerst International, Inc., Radnor, PA; *U.S. Public*, pg. 80
Poutanen, Heikki, Pres.--Millar Elevator Industries, Inc., Holland, OH; *Int'l*, pg. 1205
Poutanen, Matti, Chief Oper. Officer--Norlatex Oy, Kulloo, Finland; *Int'l*, pg. 913
Pouvaret, Ir. B., Mng. Dir.--BSL Industries S.A., Thiais, France; *Int'l*, pg. 1134
Pouyat, Alain, Chief Exec. Officer--E.P.I., Villeneuve-le-Roi, France; *Int'l*, pg. 206
Pouyet, Jean, Pres.--Volvo Vehicules Industriels France S.A., Chaville, France; *Int'l*, pg. 1478
Povey, Michael A., V.P. & Gen. Mgr.--Semtech Ltd., Glenrothes, United Kingdom; *U.S. Public*, pg. 1456
Pow, Albert, Pres.--Kaufman and Broad Inland Empire, Anaheim, CA; *U.S. Public*, pg. 945
Powch, George, Pres. & Chief Exec. Officer--Champlain Cable Corp., Colchester, VT; *Int'l*, pg. 637
Powdrill, Bob, Pres.--ConAgra Dairy & Food Oils, Omaha, NE; *U.S. Public*, pg. 427
Powell, Alan, Pres.--Danisco Pack Ltd., Altrincham, United Kingdom; *Int'l*, pg. 378
Powell, Bob, Area Foreman--Talisman Energy Inc., Edson, Canada; *Int'l*, pg. 1352
Powell, Brian, Mng. Dir.--Hepworth Home Products Limited, Belper, United Kingdom; *Int'l*, pg. 615
Powell, C.P., Chief Oper. Officer--Air Products World Trade, Inc. c/o Chase Trade, Inc., Charlotte Amalie, VI; *U.S. Public*, pg. 31
Powell, D.T., Mng. Dir.--Barlow Information Systems (Pty) Ltd., Rivonia, South Africa; *Int'l*, pg. 167
Powell, David, Gen. Mgr.--Eclipse Combustion Ltd., Droitwich, United Kingdom; *U.S. Private*, pg. 361
Powell, David W., Div. V.P.--Stationery & Office Supplies, Saint Paul, MN; *U.S. Public*, pg. 1605
Powell, Dean, Mgr.-Opers.--General Marble Corporation, Hornell, NY; *U.S. Public*, pg. 990
Powell, Dick, Gen. Mgr.--Lawry's The Prime Rib, Las Vegas, NV; *U.S. Private*, pg. 654
Powell, Earl W., Chm. Bd.--Biscayne Apparel, Inc., Miami, FL; *U.S. Public*, pg. 233
Powell, Ed, V.P.--White Electrical Construction Co., Jacksonville, FL; *U.S. Private*, pg. 1172
Powell, Hank, Gen. Mgr.--Nytron Inductors, Florence, SC; *U.S. Public*, pg. 1722
Powell, J.A., Chm.--Global Travel Computer Holdings Ltd., Toronto, Canada; *Int'l*, pg. 36
Powell, John, Pres. & Chief Oper. Officer--P. Lawson Travel, Ltd., Islington, Canada; *U.S. Private*, pg. 212
Powell, John A., V.P.--Harper Mechanical Corporation, Sanford, FL; *Int'l*, pg. 322
Powell, John A., Pres.--American Travellers Corporation, Bensalem, PA; *U.S. Public*, pg. 433
Powell, John A., Pres.--United General Life Insurance, Bensalem, PA; *U.S. Public*, pg. 433
Powell, Kendall, Pres.--Big 'G' Div., Minneapolis, MN; *U.S. Public*, pg. 718
Powell, Kent D., Pres.--Ames Co., Inc., Woodland, CA; *U.S. Public*, pg. 1746
Powell, Laurie, Mgr.--Radiometer Pacific Ltd., Auckland, New Zealand; *Int'l*, pg. 1084
Powell, Michael, Chief Oper. Officer--MacGREGOR (CHN) Ltd., Shanghai, China; *Int'l*, pg. 670
Powell, Michael, Mng. Dir.--MacGREGOR (HKG), Ltd., Kowloon, Hong Kong; *Int'l*, pg. 671
Powell, Michael, Chief Oper. Officer--MacGREGOR (Kor) Ltd., Pusan, Korea; *Int'l*, pg. 671
Powell, Norman, Pres.--SGS Control Services Inc., Edison, NJ; *Int'l*, pg. 1153
Powell, Rob, Mng.--ENVIRON International Corporation-Emeryville, Emeryville, CA; *U.S. Public*, pg. 1285
Powell, Robert S., Jr., Pres.--DKM Properties Corporation, Lawrenceville, NJ; *U.S. Private*, pg. 351
Powell, Rod, Pres.--Fujitsu Systems of America, Inc., La Jolla, CA; *Int'l*, pg. 526
Powell, Susan F., Chief Oper. Officer--Investors Insurance Corp., Jacksonville, FL; *U.S. Public*, pg. 912
Powell, Thomas A., V.P. & Gen. Mgr.--Acco Systems Div., Warren, MI; *Int'l*, pg. 472
Powell, Tom, Pres.--Directional Furniture, High Point, NC; *U.S. Private*, pg. 193
Powell, Tom, Pres.--Thor West, Ontario, CA; *U.S. Public*, pg. 1602
Powell, Tom, Pres.--Thor California, Inc., Moreno Valley, CA; *U.S. Public*, pg. 1602
Powell, William, Pres. & Chief Exec. Officer--Union Planters Bank of Alabama, Decatur, AL; *U.S. Public*, pg. 1669
Power, Alan, Pres.--Decoma International Inc., Concord, Canada; *Int'l*, pg. 829
Power, Ernest, Pres.--Atlas Copco Rental Inc., Fairfield, NJ; *Int'l*, pg. 96
Power, Maurice, Mgr.-Sls.--Fasson Ireland Ltd., Dublin, Ireland; *U.S. Public*, pg. 154
Power, Michael J., Mgr.--Det Norske Veritas, Guayaquil, Ecuador; *Int'l*, pg. 396
Power, P., Mgr.-Res.--Marathon Petroleum Indonesia, Ltd., Jakarta, Indonesia; *U.S. Public*, pg. 1662
Power, William, Chm. Bd., Pres. & Chief Exec. Officer-Canada--Young & Rubicam Ltd., Toronto, Canada; *U.S. Private*, pg. 1200
Powers, Dan, Plant Mgr.--Chock Full O' Nuts Coffee Company, Hialeah, FL; *U.S. Public*, pg. 351
Powers, Joe D., Chm. Bd. & Chief Exec. Officer--Merchants National Bank, Fort Smith, AR; *U.S. Public*, pg. 501
Powers, John R., Pres.--Central Products Company, Inc., Menasha, WI; *U.S. Public*, pg. 1022
Powers, Paul, Branch Mgr.--Zellerbach Division, Memphis, TN; *U.S. Public*, pg. 1075
Powers, Roy, V.P. & Mng. Dir.--Western International Media Corporation, Reno, NV; *U.S. Private*, pg. 1167
Powers, Timothy L., Chief Fin. Officer--Quest Staffing, Atlanta, GA; *U.S. Public*, pg. 45
Powers, William, Pres.--Star Gas Corporation, Stamford, CT; *U.S. Public*, pg. 1281
Powers, William F., V.P.--Ford Research Staff, Dearborn, MI; *U.S. Public*, pg. 664
Pownall, J.R., Div. Pres.--Winn-Dixie Atlanta, Inc., Atlanta, GA; *U.S. Public*, pg. 1771
Poyet, P., Mgr.--Societe de Banque Suisse, Lausanne, Switzerland; *Int'l*, pg. 1329
Poynei, Allian H., Mng. Dir.--Aqualon (UK) Limited, Warrington, United Kingdom; *U.S. Public*, pg. 810
Poyner, William K., Pres.--Hansen Corporation, Princeton, IN; *Int'l*, pg. 868
Poynter, James J., Chief Exec. Officer--GN Nettest Fiber Optic Division, Utica, NY; *Int'l*, pg. 536
Poynter, Lou Ann, Chm. Bd. & Chief Exec. Officer--UPB of Southern Mississippi, Hattiesburg, MS; *U.S. Public*, pg. 1669
Poythress, James H., Pres.--Foster Mortgage Corporation, Fort Worth, TX; *U.S. Public*, pg. 1675
Pozetto, Jacques, Pres.--Ciments Francais Data Processing Center, Guerville, France; *Int'l*, pg. 292
Prabhu, Prabha, Gen. Mgr.--Madison DMB&B Advertising, Mumbai, India; *U.S. Private*, pg. 305

Prache, Gerard, Pres. & Gen. Dir.--Bayerische Vereinsbank S.A. (BV France), Paris, France; *Int'l*, pg. 181
Pradas, Francisco, Pres.--Intevep, S.A., Los Taques, Venezuela; *Int'l*, pg. 1045
Prade, Hugo C., Representative--UBS Representative Office, Buenos Aires, Argentina; *Int'l*, pg. 1441
Praet, Yvan, Chief Exec. Officer--S.A. Dirame, Brussels, Belgium; *Int'l*, pg. 710
Prahl, Ulf, Mng. Dir.--Gurtec GmbH & Co., KG, Schoppenstedt, Germany; *Int'l*, pg. 1353
Prakobkit, Preecha, Gen. Mgr.--Amway (Thailand) Limited, Bangkok, Thailand; *U.S. Private*, pg. 70
Pralehunhangsit, Adisorn, Mng. Dir.--The Nawaloha Industry Co., Ltd., Sara Buri, Thailand; *Int'l*, pg. 1238
Pralong, Pierre, Dist. Mgr.--Milchem France S.A.R.L., Bayonne, France; *U.S. Public*, pg. 167
Pranckun, John, Pres.--World Tableware, Inc., Dallas, TX; *Int'l*, pg. 1056
Prandner, Eckart, V.P.--Sulzer-Escher Wyss GmbH, Lindau, Germany; *Int'l*, pg. 1307
Prang, Joseph, Pres.--Systems Design Division, San Jose, CA; *U.S. Public*, pg. 290
Prasad, Suresh, Pres.--Ellesmere Britannia Ltd., Georgetown, Cayman Islands; *Int'l*, pg. 31
Prasnikar, Wilhelm, Gen. Mgr.--Nordson GmbH (Austria), Schwechat, Austria; *U.S. Public*, pg. 1189
Prasser, Gary P., Pres.--Joslyn Manufacturing Co., Chicago, IL; *U.S. Public*, pg. 481
Prat, Eduardo, Mng. Dir.--ESAB Iberica S.A., Alcobendas, Spain; *Int'l*, pg. 282
Prater, Steve, Mgr.-Opers.--Moore's Food Service Products, Fort Atkinson, WI; *U.S. Public*, pg. 805
Prather, Dawn, Branch Mgr.--Downey Savings & Loan Association, F.A., Sun City, CA; *U.S. Public*, pg. 527
Pratoomsuvarw, Arthit, Mng. Dir.--The Siam Pipe Products Co., Ltd., Bangkok, Thailand; *Int'l*, pg. 1238
Pratoomsuvaw, Arthit, Mng. Dir.--The Siam Fibre-Cement Co., Ltd., Bangkok, Thailand; *Int'l*, pg. 1238
Pratt, Arthur T., Pres.--Seneca Foods-Kennett Division, Kennett Square, PA; *U.S. Public*, pg. 1457
Pratt, Brian, Pres.--ARB, Inc.-Building Division, Lake Forest, CA; *U.S. Private*, pg. 7
Pratt, Bruce, Pres. & Gen. Mgr.--Jostens Sportswear, Overland Park, KS; *U.S. Public*, pg. 686
Pratt, Elizabeth, Admin.--Horizon Specialty Hospital - Kansas City, Overland Park, KS; *U.S. Public*, pg. 837
Pratt, Joel, Pres.--Arthrotek, Inc., Ontario, CA; *U.S. Public*, pg. 231
Pratt, Michael G., Pres. & Chief Exec. Officer--Coats & Clark Inc., Greenville, SC; *Int'l*, pg. 300
Pratt, R.B.A., Mng. Dir.--Federated-Blaikie Ltd., Sandton, South Africa; *Int'l*, pg. 167
Pratt, Randy, V.P. & Gen. Mgr.--KSAS-TV, Wichita, KS; *U.S. Public*, pg. 384
Pratt, Steve, Pres.--Proprietory Products Group, Portland, OR; *U.S. Private*, pg. 383
Praw, Albert Z., Pres.--Kaufman and Broad-Antelope Valley Regional Office, Palmdale, CA; *U.S. Public*, pg. 945
Pray, Bill, Pres.--Barnett Inc., Jacksonville, FL; *U.S. Public*, pg. 1749
Preas, Ed, Gen. Mgr.--Trico Industries, Inc., Greenville, TX; *U.S. Public*, pg. 1247
Prebble, Andy, Country Mgr.--Standard Chartered Bank, London, United Kingdom; *Int'l*, pg. 1294
Preble, Tom, V.P. & Gen. Mgr.--Quebecor Printing Glen Burnie, Glen Burnie, MD; *Int'l*, pg. 1076
Precht, Dave, Editor--Bassmaster Magazine, Montgomery, AL; *U.S. Private*, pg. 105
Preckert, B.E., Chief Oper. Officer--Hughes Tool Company of Australia Limited, Melville, Australia; *U.S. Public*, pg. 167
Preda, Dan, Warehouse Supvr.--Circle Freight International USA, Inglewood, CA; *U.S. Public*, pg. 371
Preddy, Fred A., Pres.--Hammary Furniture Co., Lenoir, NC; *U.S. Public*, pg. 973
Predpall, Daniel, Mgr.-Opers.--Woodward-Clyde, Wayne, NJ; *U.S. Public*, pg. 1657
Preece, Scott, V.P.--Waremart Inc., Salem, OR; *U.S. Private*, pg. 1150
Pregulman, John, Pres.--Sisken Steel, Chattanooga, TN; *U.S. Public*, pg. 1375
Preis, Herwig, Pres.--Select Communications, GmbH, Koblenz, Koblenz, Germany; *U.S. Private*, pg. 982
Preising, D. L., Mgr.-Plant--Akzo Salt Inc., Akron, OH; *Int'l*, pg. 48
Preisler, Michael, Gen. Mgr.--Societe Miniere de Bougrine S.A., Bougrine, Tunisia; *Int'l*, pg. 862
Premuroso, Ron, Acting Mng. Dir.--Sensormatic Australia Pty Limited, Sydney, Australia; *U.S. Public*, pg. 1457
Premuroso, Ronald F., V.P.-Asia/Pacific Opers.--Sensormatic Asia/Pacific, Singapore, Singapore; *U.S. Public*, pg. 1457
Prenard, Al, Pres. & Gen. Mgr.--Boral Gypsum Inc., Nashville, AR; *Int'l*, pg. 203
Prenat, A., Pres.--Toshiba Systems (France) S.A., Puteaux, France; *Int'l*, pg. 1407
Prendergast, G. Joseph, Chm. Bd.--Wachovia Bank of South Carolina, Columbia, SC; *U.S. Public*, pg. 1730
Prendergast, James, Pres.--Accurate Forming Div., Hamburg, NJ; *U.S. Public*, pg. 1647
Prendergast, Thomas J., Chief Exec. Officer & Exec. V.P.--R.P. Scherer Korea Limited, Seoul, Korea; *U.S. Public*, pg. 1438
Prendergast, Vic, Pres.--Shaklee Canada Inc., Burlington, Canada; *Int'l*, pg. 1518
Prescott, James, Pres.--Alumax Mill Products, Inc., Morris, IL; *U.S. Public*, pg. 59
Preskey, G., Reg. Dir.-CIS--John Brown/Davy International, Moscow, Russia; *Int'l*, pg. 772
Presley, Eric, Pres.--PPC, Inc., Cherryville, NC; *U.S. Public*, pg. 1168
Presley, R. Michael, Pres.--Liberty National GroupCare, Inc., Birmingham, AL; *U.S. Public*, pg. 1623
Press, Peter, Gen. Mgr.--Viacom Intl. Pty. Ltd., Sydney, Australia; *U.S. Private*, pg. 779
Pressley, George, Pres. & Chief Oper. Officer--Lapp Insulator Company, Le Roy, NY; *U.S. Private*, pg. 473
Pressley, George, Plant Mgr.--Square D Co., Clearwater, FL; *Int'l*, pg. 1208
Pressley, James M., Div. Pres.--Oxford Collection, New York, NY; *U.S. Public*, pg. 1239
Pressman, Thane, Pres.--Labatt U.S.A., Darien, CT; *Int'l*, pg. 679
Pressouyre, Gerard, Chm. Bd.--Seb S.A., Selongey, France; *Int'l*, pg. 569
Preston, Bernard, Dir.--Rolls-Royce Motor Cars UK Operations, Crewe, United Kingdom; *Int'l*, pg. 1467
Preston, Collin, Mng. Dir.--Bradstock Insurance Brokers Limited, Glasgow, United Kingdom; *Int'l*, pg. 210
Preston, George V., V.P. & Gen. Mgr.--Thomas Lighting-C&I Indoor Divison, Tupelo, MS; *U.S. Public*, pg. 1599
Preston, John, Media Partner--TN Media, Cremore, Australia; *U.S. Public*, pg. 1641
Preston, John M., Ph.D., Chm. Bd. & Pres.--Merial Ltd., London, United Kingdom; *U.S. Public*, pg. 1092
Preston, John M., Ph.D., Chm. Bd. & Pres.--Merial Ltd., London, United Kingdom; *Int'l*, pg. 1110
Preston, Marietta P., Admin.--Windsor Health Care Center, Louisville, KY; *U.S. Public*, pg. 1715
Preston, P.S., Pres. & Chief Exec. Officer--McDonald's Hamburgers Limited, London, United Kingdom; *U.S. Public*, pg. 1069
Preston, Robert, Pres.--NM Funds Management (North America) Inc., New York, NY; *Int'l*, pg. 908
Preston, Sara Jane, Pres. & Chief Exec. Officer--NationsBank of Charleston, Charleston, IL; *U.S. Public*, pg. 1164
Prestwood, Thomas A., Jr., V.P. & Gen. Mgr.-Myrtle Beach Opers.--Vanguard Cellular Systems of South Carolina, Inc., Myrtle Beach, SC; *U.S. Public*, pg. 1708
Pretorius, Johan G., Chief Exec.--Anglo-Alpha Ltd., Sandton, South Africa; *Int'l*, pg. 629
Pretorius, Karei, Chief Oper. Officer--Sasolchem, Rosebank, South Africa; *Int'l*, pg. 1196
Pretortus, Uys, Gen. Mgr.--Hyde Pharmaceuticals (Pty.) Ltd., East London, South Africa; *Int'l*, pg. 1126
Pretot, Claude, Pres.--Societe Monsanto S.A., Neuilly-sur-Seine, France; *U.S. Public*, pg. 1126
Prevost, Jean-Michel, Chief Oper. Officer--Plastilon France S.A., Sotteville, France; *Int'l*, pg. 915
Prevost, John, Mgr.--Hercules Inc.-Kalamazoo, Kalamazoo, MI; *U.S. Public*, pg. 810
Price, Bill, Mgr.--Semi-Custom Products Div., Sunnyvale, CA; *Int'l*, pg. 1054
Price, Bob, Mgr.-Division--Hawthorne Power Systems, San Diego, CA; *U.S. Private*, pg. 513
Price, Dawn, Admin.--Missouri River Manor, Great Falls, MT; *U.S. Public*, pg. 837
Price, Derek, Pres.--Fisher & Ludlow, Burlington, Canada; *Int'l*, pg. 598
Price, Don, Supervisor-Warehouse--GATX Logistics, Inc.-Washington, Seattle, WA; *U.S. Public*, pg. 692
Price, Donald, Pres.--Shawver Price, Inc., Kansas City, MO; *U.S. Private*, pg. 511
Price, E.P., Pres.--Chevron Shale Oil Co., Englewood, CO; *U.S. Public*, pg. 348
Price, Eric, Pres.--John Wieland Homes of North Carolina, Inc., Charlotte, NC; *U.S. Private*, pg. 1175
Price, Frank, Pres.--Universal City Studios (DISC), Inc., Universal City, CA; *Int'l*, pg. 1216
Price, G., Mgr.--Morton Salt Division, Salt Lake City, UT; *U.S. Public*, pg. 1135
Price, Hank, Pres. & Gen. Mgr.--KARE-TV, Minneapolis, MN; *U.S. Public*, pg. 702
Price, Janet L., Mgr.-Risk Mngmt.--Grocery Supply of El Paso, El Paso, TX; *U.S. Private*, pg. 436
Price, Jeffrey D., Pres.--Price Woods, Inc., Mesa, AZ; *U.S. Private*, pg. 1187
Price, John, Mng. Dir.--Willenhall Steel Stockholders Ltd., Rowley Regis, United Kingdom; *Int'l*, pg. 79
Price, John, Mng. Dir.--Howard E. Perry & Co. Ltd., Willenhall, United Kingdom; *Int'l*, pg. 79
Price, John, Mng. Dir.--Hughes & Spencer Steel Ltd., Stourbridge, United Kingdom; *Int'l*, pg. 79
Price, John, Gen. Mgr.--Chief Industries - Buildings Div., Grand Island, NE; *U.S. Private*, pg. 236
Price, Michael, Pres.--Esix, Atlanta, GA; *U.S. Private*, pg. 565
Price, O.H., Gen. Mgr.--Nippon Wellcome KK, Osaka, Japan; *Int'l*, pg. 553
Price, O.H., Reg. Gen. Mgr.--Amersham K.K., Tokyo, Japan; *Int'l*, pg. 993
Price, Peter, Mktg. Mgr.-Industrial Sector--Square D Company Australia Pty. Limited, Preston, Australia; *Int'l*, pg. 1209
Price, R., Pres--Innotech Aviation Industries Ltd., Dorval, Canada; *Int'l*, pg. 36
Price, Raymond, Mgr.--Universal Telephone Southwest-Arizona, Keams Canyon, AZ; *U.S. Public*, pg. 330
Price, Robert V., Pres. & Chief Exec. Officer--CECOS International, Inc., Buffalo, NY; *U.S. Public*, pg. 264
Price, Rodney, Exec. Dir.--Brierley Investments Ltd., London, United Kingdom; *Int'l*, pg. 215
Price, Ronald, Plant Mgr.--Huls America Inc., Mountain Top, PA; *Int'l*, pg. 1455
Price, Steven S., Pres.--AlliedSignal, Automotive Aftermarket, Rumford, RI; *U.S. Public*, pg. 51
Price, Timothy F., Pres.-MCI Bus. Markets--MCI Telecommunications Corp., Washington, DC; *U.S. Public*, pg. 1024
Price, Timothy R., Chm. Bd.--Trilon Financial Corp., Toronto, Canada; *Int'l*, pg. 434
Prichard, Mathew, Chief Oper. Officer--Booker Entertainment, London, United Kingdom; *Int'l*, pg. 202
Priddle, R., Reg. Mgr.--Air France (U.S. Pacific Region), Los Angeles, CA; *Int'l*, pg. 561
Pridemore, Stephen, Pres.--Bright of America, Inc., Summersville, WV; *U.S. Public*, pg. 223
Priegel, Richard V., Pres.--Abrams Fixture Corporation, Atlanta, GA; *U.S. Public*, pg. 14
Priem, Ted, Pres.--NV-Mannor, Saint Croix Falls, WI; *U.S. Private*, pg. 800
Priem, Windle B., Vice Chm. & Pres.-N. America--Korn/Ferry International, New York, NY; *U.S. Private*, pg. 633
Priest, Donald, Project Engr.--Harry O. Hefter-Associates, Inc., Chicago, IL; *U.S. Private*, pg. 492
Priestley, Guy T., Pres.--Automatic Power, Inc., Houston, TX; *Int'l*, pg. 1289
Prieszol, Jozsef, Chief Exec.--Holderbank Ungarn GmbH, Budapest, Hungary; *Int'l*, pg. 629
Prieto, Pablo, Pres.--Menasco Aerospace Ltd., Oakville, Canada; *U.S. Public*, pg. 402
Prigent, Loic, Plant Mgr.--Neutrogena Provence SARL, Toulon, France; *U.S. Public*, pg. 928
Prijatel, John, Pres.--Farmland MissChem, Ltd., Port of Spain, Trinidad & Tobago; *U.S. Public*, pg. 1117
Prikryl, J. K., Gen. Mgr.--Stelwire Ltd., Hamilton, Canada; *Int'l*, pg. 1299
Primer, Jonathan, Pres.--Dermal Management Sys., Mundelein, IL; *U.S. Private*, pg. 728
Primura, Ichiro, Rep.--The Industrial Bank of Japan (Kuala Lumpur), Kuala Lumpur, Malaysia; *Int'l*, pg. 675
Prince, Bob, V.P. & Gen. Mgr.--New Castle Corp., Las Vegas, NV; *U.S. Public*, pg. 375
Prince, Gary J., Pres.--Stroehmann Bakeries, L.C., Horsham, PA; *Int'l*, pg. 1495
Prince, Richard, Mng. Dir.--Plasma-Technik Ltd., Newport, United Kingdom; *Int'l*, pg. 1308
Prince, Robert, Chief Oper. Officer--General Technical Services, Inc., Columbia, MD; *U.S. Public*, pg. 695
Prince, Robert E., Pres., Chief Exec. Officer--Duratek Corporation, Columbia, MD; *U.S. Public*, pg. 694
Pringels, Philippe, Mng. Dir.--Equator, Brussels, Belgium; *Int'l*, pg. 602
Pringle, D.L., Pres.--Special Products Div., Hazelwood, MO; *U.S. Public*, pg. 575
Pringle, Hamish, Chief Exec. Officer--K Advertising, London, United Kingdom; *U.S. Public*, pg. 1422
Pringle, Homer, Pres.--Haney Seed Co., Twin Falls, ID; *U.S. Public*, pg. 428
Pringle, Ian, Mng. Dir.--Pitman Publishing Ltd., London, United Kingdom; *Int'l*, pg. 1025
Pringle, Ken, Mng. Dir.--The Tetley Group Limited, Greenford, United Kingdom; *Int'l*, pg. 1377
Pringuet, M., Dir. & Gen. Mgr.--Britax (Geco) S.A., Vulaines-sur-Seine, France; *Int'l*, pg. 216
Pringuet, Pierre, Chm. & Chief Exec. Officer--PR Europe, Paris, France; *Int'l*, pg. 566
Prinsen, W., Pres.--ING (U.S.) Financial Services kk, New York, NY; *Int'l*, pg. 648
Prinsloo, Tammy, Mgr.-Reservations & Admin./South Africa--Utell International-South Africa, Johannesburg, South Africa; *Int'l*, pg. 1099
Prinsze, Fritz, Plant Mgr.--Fasson Producten Verkoopmaatshappij B.V., Hazerwovde, Netherlands; *U.S. Public*, pg. 154
Prior, David, Pres.--Codar Technology Inc., Longmont, CO; *U.S. Public*, pg. 1144
Prior, Dennis, Gen. Mgr.--Novilon Ltd., Watford, United Kingdom; *Int'l*, pg. 498
Prior, Eileen, Dir.--Shandwick Scotland Ltd., Edinburgh, United Kingdom; *Int'l*, pg. 1226
Prior, F. Joseph, Pres.--CorTec Company, Washington Court House, OH; *U.S. Public*, pg. 456
Prior, M., Mng. Dir.--Hosokawa Micron Ltd., Runcorn, United Kingdom; *Int'l*, pg. 636
Prischak, Bob, Gen. Mgr.--Triangle Tool Co., Erie, PA; *U.S. Private*, pg. 870
Prischak, Robert, Gen. Mgr.--Pioneer Tool & Mold, Inc., Erie, PA; *U.S. Private*, pg. 870
Pritchard, Beth, Pres.--Bath & Body Works, Reynoldsburg, OH; *U.S. Public*, pg. 995
Pritchard, David, V.P. & Gen. Mgr.--Banks Environmental Service Technologies, Inc., Duluth, GA; *U.S. Private*, pg. 114
Pritchard, Donald, Plant Mgr.--Shelly Bros., Inc., Souderton, PA; *U.S. Private*, pg. 163
Pritchard, James, Mgr.-Div.--Aramark Sports & Entertainment Services Inc., New Orleans, LA; *U.S. Private*, pg. 79
Pritchard, K., Mgr.--M&N Valve, Compton, CA; *Int'l*, pg. 1449
Pritchard, Lionel, Mng. Dir.--Jotun Decorative Coatings Ltd., Milton Keynes, United Kingdom; *Int'l*, pg. 715
Pritchard, Marc S., Pres.--Procter & Gamble Cosmetics Co., Hunt Valley, MD; *U.S. Public*, pg. 1330
Pritchard, O.J., Gen. Mgr.--Wellcome Biofarma SA, Porrino, Spain; *Int'l*, pg. 553
Pritchard, P., Chief Oper. Officer--Alfa-Laval Cheddar Systems Ltd., Yeovil, United Kingdom; *Int'l*, pg. 1380
Pritchett, Greg, Gen. Mgr.--Mechanical Seal Division, Los Alamitos, CA; *U.S. Public*, pg. 689
Pritchett, Pete, Gen. Mgr.--Lyntone Belts, Edmond, OK; *U.S. Private*, pg. 442
Pritts, G. Robert, Pres.--Carmun International, San Antonio, TX; *Int'l*, pg. 646
Pritzker, Penny, Pres.--Classic Residence by Hyatt, Chicago, IL; *U.S. Private*, pg. 551
Pritzky, Doug, Gen. Mgr.--Griffin Industries, Inc., Ellenwood, GA; *U.S. Private*, pg. 481
Proano, Stephan, Chief Exec. Officer & Chief Oper. Officer--Punto Aparte Publicidad, S.A., Panama, Panama; *U.S. Private*, pg. 305
Probert, Charles, Mgr.-Opers.--Instrument Specialties Europe Ltd., East Kilbride, United Kingdom; *U.S. Private*, pg. 565
Probert, Tim, Pres.--Eimco Process Equipment Co., Salt Lake City, UT; *U.S. Public*, pg. 166
Probert, Timothy J., Pres.--Baker Hughes INTEQ, Houston, TX; *U.S. Public*, pg. 166

Probolus, John X., Pres.--Rollins Hudig Hall of Massachusetts, Inc., Boston, MA; *U.S. Public*, pg. 117
Probst, Urs, Mng. Dir.--Metawa-Tray B.V., Tiel, Netherlands; *Int'l*, pg. 1307
Probstfield, J. S., Dir.--Sunkist Growers, Inc.-Western Division, Visalia, CA; *U.S. Private*, pg. 1052
Prochaska, Bernard, Gen. Mgr.--CSD, Vandenberg AFB, Vandenberg AFB, CA; *U.S. Public*, pg. 1690
Procopio, Dimple, V.P.--Gates/Arrow Commercial Systems Div., Dublin, OH; *U.S. Public*, pg. 133
Procopio, Frank, Pres.--Mohawk Commercial Carpet, Atlanta, GA; *U.S. Public*, pg. 1121
Procopio, Frank, Pres.--Karastan Bigelow Commercial, Atlanta, GA; *U.S. Public*, pg. 1121
Procopio, Vince, Gen. Mgr.--MTI Systems Div., Beachwood, OH; *U.S. Public*, pg. 135
Proctor, Arno, Gen. Mgr.--ITW Mima, Inc., Boca Raton, FL; *U.S. Public*, pg. 866
Proctor, David F., Sr. V.P. & Country Mgr.--Bank of America NT&SA, Bangkok, Thailand; *U.S. Public*, pg. 182
Proctor, Dean, Jr., Pres.--N.W. Ayer & Partners Chicago, Chicago, IL; *U.S. Private*, pg. 104
Proctor, Dominic, Exec. V.P., CEO-JWT/London & Area Dir.-UK & Ireland--J. Walter Thompson Company, New York, NY; *Int'l*, pg. 1483
Proctor, Gordon, Pres.--CHR Industries, Inc., New Haven, CT; *U.S. Public*, pg. 689
Proctor, Michael, V.P.-Fin. & Corp. Sec.--Battle Mountain Canada Ltd., Toronto, Canada; *U.S. Public*, pg. 193
Proctor, Richard, Pres.--Cruising Equipment Company, Seattle, WA; *U.S. Public*, pg. 1705
Proczak, Bernie, Mgr.--IBP-Perry, Perry, IA; *U.S. Public*, pg. 852
Proffitt, John, V.P. & Gen. Mgr.--KMGH-TV, Denver, CO; *U.S. Public*, pg. 1070
Proffitt, John, Gen. Mgr.--Desert Turbine Services, Inc., Farmington, NM; *U.S. Public*, pg. 1099
Prohorenko, Nikolaj, Mng. Dir.--Reemtsma Kiew Tyutyunova Fabrika, Kiev, Ukraine; *Int'l*, pg. 1101
Prommesberger, Adolf, Chief Oper. Officer--BMW Motorsport GmbH, Munich, Germany; *Int'l*, pg. 177
Prompsy, Jean-Jacques, Chief Oper. Officer--Sita, Paris, France; *Int'l*, pg. 824
Proper, Donald, Gen. Mgr.--Plastek Industries, Inc., Erie, PA; *U.S. Private*, pg. 870
Prosiewicz, Richard, Pres.--Western Power Products, Inc., Hood River, OR; *U.S. Public*, pg. 444
Prosser, I.M.G., Chm. Bd.--Bass Investments PLC, London, United Kingdom; *Int'l*, pg. 170
Prosser, P.J., Chief Oper. Officer--Legal & General Assurance Society Limited, London, United Kingdom; *Int'l*, pg. 805
Prosser, P.J., Chief Oper. Officer--Legal & General Finance Plc, London, United Kingdom; *Int'l*, pg. 805
Prostor, Jeffrey J., Pres.--Brookfield Homes-Orange County, Santa Ana, CA; *Int'l*, pg. 228
Protaschik, Aleksei, Dir.--Amerpap East Ltd., Saint Petersburg, Russia; *Int'l*, pg. 863
Proto, Frank W., Pres.--Alberta Oil Sands Pipeline Ltd., Calgary, Canada; *Int'l*, pg. 48
Protopapadakis, I., Mgr.--ING Barings Greece EPE, Athens, Greece; *Int'l*, pg. 650
Prou, Michael, Pres.--Roussel Corporation, Montvale, NJ; *Int'l*, pg. 625
Proudfoot, Collin, Mgr.--Specialty Filaments Ltd., Durham, United Kingdom; *U.S. Private*, pg. 77
Proudfoot, Garry, Pres. & Gen. Mgr.--Web Press Graphics Ltd., Port Coquitlam, Canada; *Int'l*, pg. 1077
Prough, Stephen W., Pres.--Western Consumer Services, Inc., Irvine, CA; *U.S. Public*, pg. 1757
Prout, Steven, L., Pres.--Southern Gage Inc., Erin, TN; *U.S. Private*, pg. 45
Provance, Jason, Gen. Mgr.--Shanghai Agmet Electro-Science Laboratory, Ltd, Shanghai, China; *U.S. Private*, pg. 369
Provanzano, Salvatore, Pres.--Process Automation, Pompano Beach, FL; *U.S. Public*, pg. 422
Provau, Mike, Gen. Mgr.--Sun Chemical Company, Inc., Arcadia, FL; *U.S. Private*, pg. 1050
Provenzano, Giana, Gen. Mgr.--ATC Cablevision of San Marino, Inc., South Pasadena, CA; *U.S. Public*, pg. 1610
Provenzano, Giana, Mgr.--ATC Cablevision of South Pasadena, Inc., South Pasadena, CA; *U.S. Public*, pg. 1610
Provo, Jay, Chief Oper. Officer--Fremont Premium Finance Corp., Santa Monica, CA; *U.S. Public*, pg. 681
Provost, Normand, Pres.--Capital d'Amerique CDPQ, Montreal, Canada; *Int'l*, pg. 249
Pruden, Peter D., III, Pres.--Smithfield Division, Smithfield, VA; *U.S. Public*, pg. 1479
Prudhomme, Patrick R., Exec. V.P. & Gen. Mgr.--Piccadilly Restaurants, Inc., Baton Rouge, LA; *U.S. Public*, pg. 1294
Pruitt, Peter T., Chm. Bd.--Risk Science International Inc., Fairfax, VA; *U.S. Public*, pg. 117
Prum Jr., P., Chief Exec. Officer--Zurich-Anglo Seguradora S.A., Sao Paulo, Brazil; *Int'l*, pg. 1532
Pruniefas, Francois, Dir.-Clinical Devel. & Services--PPD Pharmaco Intl., Gentilly, France; *U.S. Public*, pg. 1285
Prusakiewicz, Andrzej, Mgr.--ITT Flygt Sp.z.o.o., Warsaw, Poland; *U.S. Public*, pg. 860
Prusator, Rick, Gen. Mgr.--WTVQ-TV (ABC) Channel 36, Lexington, KY; *U.S. Public*, pg. 1078
Prusiewicz, Richard, Pres.--Kearney Company, Tucker, GA; *U.S. Public*, pg. 444
Pruskowski, Joseph J., V.P.--InterConnections, Inc., Bellevue, WA; *U.S. Public*, pg. 579
Prutzman, P. Edward, Pres., Chief Oper. Officer & V.P.--Sunbank Joslyn, Inc., Paso Robles, CA; *U.S. Public*, pg. 482
Pry, Jim, Pres.--Standard Products (Canada) Ltd., Stratford, Canada; *U.S. Public*, pg. 1505
Pryde, John, Pres.--General Coach, Hensall, Canada; *U.S. Public*, pg. 1602
Pryor, Karen, Exec. Mgr.--Image By Design, Niles, IL; *U.S. Private*, pg. 310
Pryor, Robert, Pres.--Poe & Brown of Texas, Houston, TX; *U.S. Public*, pg. 1312
Pryor, William G., Pres.--Van Dorn Demag Corporation, Strongsville, OH; *Int'l*, pg. 837
Pryzby, Stanley J., Dir.--Martin Marietta Fleet Combat System Services, Arlington, VA; *U.S. Public*, pg. 1007
Psomas, Tim, Pres.--Psomas Associates, Salt Lake City, UT; *U.S. Private*, pg. 893
Puantin, Jean, Exec. Officer-Brazil--Carrefour Commercio e Industria, Sao Paulo, Brazil; *Int'l*, pg. 272
Pucci, Giorgio, V.P. & Gen. Mgr.--Dun & Bradstreet Kosmos Spa, Milan, Italy; *U.S. Public*, pg. 536
Pucci, Giovanni, Mng. Dir.--Pucci Sulzer, Zurich, Switzerland; *Int'l*, pg. 1377
Pucci, Mark, Pres. & Chief Exec. Officer--Walker Group/CNI Inc., New York, NY; *Int'l*, pg. 1483
Pucell, Jim, Pres.--Jetcom, Cincinnati, OH; *U.S. Public*, pg. 1329
Puckavich, Dennis, Reg. Mgr.--Oriental Motor U.S.A. Corp, Parsippany, NJ; *Int'l*, pg. 1008
Puckett, Frank, Jr., Pres.--Abilene Reporter News, Abilene, TX; *U.S. Public*, pg. 793
Puckett, Linton B., Chm. Bd.--Willis Corroon Corp. of South Carolina, Greenville, SC; *Int'l*, pg. 1507
Puckett, Page, Admin.--Western Care Nursing Home No. 439, Helena, MT; *U.S. Public*, pg. 1715
Pudles, Stephen, Pres.--Tanon Express, West Long Branch, NJ; *U.S. Public*, pg. 541
Puel, Henri Paul, Dir.--AIR Training Center, Toulouse, France; *Int'l*, pg. 29
Puel, Henri-Paul, Chief Exec. Officer--Avions de Transport Regional - ATR, Blagnac, France; *Int'l*, pg. 654
Puente, E. A., Pres. & Chief Exec. Officer--Tree of Life, Inc., Saint Augustine, FL; *Int'l*, pg. 752
Puerner, John, Pres. & Chief Exec. Officer--Orlando Sentinel Communications, Orlando, FL; *U.S. Public*, pg. 1636
Puetz, J.D., Pres.--Great Lakes Biochemical Co., Inc., Milwaukee, WI; *Int'l*, pg. 802
Puffer, Dennis B., Plant Mgr.--Miller Brewing Company, Trenton, OH; *U.S. Public*, pg. 1289
Puft, J., Gen. Mgr.--Armco Inc.-Mansfield Operations, Mansfield, OH; *U.S. Public*, pg. 131
Puget, Lionel, Pres.--Axson France, Paris, France; *Int'l*, pg. 103
Pugh, A.V., Exec. Gen. Mgr.-Europe--Mount Isa Holdings (UK) Ltd., Maidstone, United Kingdom; *Int'l*, pg. 827
Pugh, George, Mgr.--Red Wing Shoe Vasque Div., Red Wing, MN; *U.S. Private*, pg. 915
Pugh, Gordon, Reg. Mng. Dir.--Willis Corroon South Limited, Maidstone, United Kingdom; *Int'l*, pg. 1503
Pugh, Graham, Mng. Dir.--Ferranti Air Systems Ltd., Manchester, United Kingdom; *Int'l*, pg. 384
Pugh, J. Randolph, Chief Oper. Officer--Willis Corroon Corp. of San Diego, San Diego, CA; *Int'l*, pg. 1507
Pugh, M.J., Mng. Dir.--Thomas De La Rue and Company Limited, Basingstoke, United Kingdom; *Int'l*, pg. 386
Pugh, Robert J., V.P.-Midwest Region--Analysts International, Midwest Region, Saint Louis, MO; *U.S. Public*, pg. 110
Pugh, Ron, Div. Mgr.--Wyle Electronics-Dallas, Richardson, TX; *Int'l*, pg. 1457
Pugsley, Tom F., Gen. Mgr.--Falconbridge Chile S.A., Santiago, Chile; *Int'l*, pg. 434
Puhakka, H., Mng. Dir.--Oy EMI Finland AB, Helsinki, Finland; *Int'l*, pg. 427
Puig Del Campo, Javier, Gen. Mgr.--Edelman Espana S.A., Madrid, Spain; *U.S. Private*, pg. 363
Puig, Juan Echevarria, Pres.--Nissan Motor Iberica S.A., Barcelona, Spain; *Int'l*, pg. 945
Puig, Mariano, Pres.--Paco Rabanne Parfums, Neuilly-sur-Seine, France; *Int'l*, pg. 1073
Puignero, Josep Ricart i, Mng. Dir.--Elsevier Prensa SA, Barcelona, Spain; *Int'l*, pg. 1100
Puirk-Russo, Paula, Gen. Mgr./Australia & New Zealand--Utell International-Australia, Chatswood, Australia; *Int'l*, pg. 1098
Pujol, J.M., Chief Oper. Officer--Pujol Y Tarrago S.A., Barcelona, Spain; *Int'l*, pg. 474
Pulam, Dr. Taweesak, Gen. Mgr.--Pioneer Overseas Corporation (Thailand), Ltd., Sara Buri, Thailand; *U.S. Public*, pg. 1299
Pulgar, Juan J., Pres. & Chief Exec. Officer--BITOR America Corp., Boca Raton, FL; *Int'l*, pg. 1045
Pullen, M.E., Pres.--Interbath of Canada Ltd., Mississauga, Canada; *U.S. Private*, pg. 566
Pulli, Juhani, Chief Oper. Officer--Borealis Polymers Oy, Porvoo, Finland; *Int'l*, pg. 913
Pun, Patrick, Gen. Mgr.--Dentsply Dental (Tianjin) Co., Ltd., Teda, China; *U.S. Public*, pg. 499
Pundt, Jeffrey L., Pres.--Landstar Inway, Inc., Rockford, IL; *U.S. Public*, pg. 978
Puno, Tong S., Joint Chief Exec. Officer--SPA/FCB, Manila, Philippines; *U.S. Private*, pg. 389
Punoose, Salil, Chm. Bd. & Mng. Dir.--Corn Products Co. (India) Ltd., Mumbai, India; *U.S. Public*, pg. 224
Puntil, Ronald M., Pres. & Chief Oper. Officer--Grubb & Ellis Management Services, Inc., Northbrook, IL; *U.S. Public*, pg. 767
Puolamaki, Kalevi, V.P. & Gen. Mgr.--Valmet Inc., Hudson Falls Division, Hudson Falls, NY; *Int'l*, pg. 1449
Puputti, Mari, Chief Oper. Officer--Ahlstrom Glassfibre Ltd.-Mikkeli Plant, Mikkeli, Finland; *Int'l*, pg. 32
Purainen, H., Mng. Dir.--Guilin-Nokia Telecom Ltd., Guilin, China; *Int'l*, pg. 954
Purcell, Henry, Reg. V.P.--Subaru of America, Inc., Savage, MD; *Int'l*, pg. 523
Purcell, Joan, Gen. Mgr.--WROC, Inc., Rochester, NY; *U.S. Private*, pg. 389
Purcell, Joseph, Pres. & Treas.--Bell Atlantic Financial Services, Wilmington, DE; *U.S. Public*, pg. 202
Purcell, Pat, Publisher & Pres.--The Boston Herald, Boston, MA; *Int'l*, pg. 926
Purcell, Woody, Reg. V.P.--Subaru of America Southeast Region, Austell, GA; *Int'l*, pg. 523
Purdin, James S., Pres.--Sterling Plastics Co., Madison, WI; *U.S. Public*, pg. 1178
Purdue, Shawn W., Pres.--New North Media Inc., Saint John, Canada; *Int'l*, pg. 230
Puri, K., Mng. Dir.--Metal Box India Limited, Calcutta, India; *Int'l*, pg. 267
Purkiss, D., Chief Exec. Officer--Turegum Insurance Company, London, United Kingdom; *Int'l*, pg. 1530
Purkiss, D., Chief Exec. Officer--Zurich Re (UK) Limited, London, United Kingdom; *Int'l*, pg. 1532
Purlow, Ari, Pres.--Armin Plastics Division, Jersey City, NJ; *U.S. Public*, pg. 1647
Purmort, F.W., Jr., Pres.--All America Insurance Company, Van Wert, OH; *U.S. Private*, pg. 224
Purmort, F.W., Jr., Pres.--Cafco, Van Wert, OH; *U.S. Private*, pg. 224
Purnell, John H., Chm. Bd. & Chief Exec. Officer--Anheuser-Busch International, Inc., Saint Louis, MO; *U.S. Public*, pg. 114
Pursell, Tate, Pres.--American Metal Products, Olive Branch, MS; *U.S. Public*, pg. 1053
Purser, Marion, Mng. Dir.--Lambert Smith Hampton, Athens, Greece; *Int'l*, pg. 797
Purser, Rick, Plant Mgr.--Household Products, Tampa, FL; *U.S. Public*, pg. 387
Pursiainen, Alpo, Chief Oper. Officer--A/O Ahlstrom, Saint Petersburg, Russia; *Int'l*, pg. 34
Purtell, Patrick, Gen. Mgr.--McLaughlin Mine, Lower Lake, CA; *U.S. Public*, pg. 833
Purtinen, Olli, Mng. Dir.--Ifi OY, Kerava, Finland; *Int'l*, pg. 501
Purtz, James H., Gen. Mgr.--Stark Regional Division, Massillon, OH; *U.S. Public*, pg. 439
Purves, W., Chm. Bd.--The British Bank of The Middle East, Saint Helier, United Kingdom; *Int'l*, pg. 579
Pusateri, Paul, Gen. Mgr.--Four Seasons Clift Hotel, San Francisco, CA; *Int'l*, pg. 502
Pussinen, Petri, Mgr.--Kotka Sawmill and Planing Mill, Kotka, Finland; *Int'l*, pg. 456
Putnam, David C., Pres.--TBV, Inc., Westborough, MA; *U.S. Private*, pg. 1138
Putnam, J. Stephen, Pres.--Robert Thomas Securities, Inc., Saint Petersburg, FL; *U.S. Public*, pg. 923
Putnins, John, Gen. Mgr.--John Crane Canada, Inc., Hamilton, Canada; *Int'l*, pg. 1339
Puton, Roland, Pres.--Rolex Industries, Inc., New York, NY; *Int'l*, pg. 1126
Putrino, Cary P., V.P. & Mng. Exec.--Northern Trust Bank of Florida, N.A., Venice, FL; *U.S. Public*, pg. 1196
Putter, Johannes, Mng. Dir.--Wynn Oil (South Africa)(Pty.)Ltd., Sandton, South Africa; *U.S. Public*, pg. 1783
Puymartin, Jacques, Chief Oper. Officer--Quillet S.A., Levallois-Perret, France; *Int'l*, pg. 793
Puyol, A., Gen. Mgr.--SASIB Railway Iberica S.A., Madrid, Spain; *Int'l*, pg. 1195
Pyatt, Michael, V.P.-Corn Prods. & Pres.-Casco--Casco Inc., Etobicoke, Canada; *U.S. Public*, pg. 448
Pych, Lawrence J., Pres.--SAFECO Administrative Services, Inc., Milwaukee, WI; *U.S. Public*, pg. 1423
Pye, Roderick D., Project Mgr.--Meikle Mine Project, Elko, NV; *Int'l*, pg. 169
Pyle, Byron, Chm. Bd.--Valley National Bank of Cortez, Cortez, CO; *U.S. Public*, pg. 1793
Pyle, Gary, Plant Mgr.--General Tire Div., Mayfield, KY; *Int'l*, pg. 327
Pyle, Paul, Mgr.--General Employment Enterprises, Newark, CA; *U.S. Public*, pg. 714
Pyle, Robyn, Mng. Dir.--NWW Properties Limited, Risley, United Kingdom; *Int'l*, pg. 1444
Pyne, J., Mgr.--Lindberg Heat Treating Co., Lansing, MI; *U.S. Public*, pg. 999
Pyne, J.H., Pres.--Dixie Carriers, Inc., Houston, TX; *U.S. Public*, pg. 962
Pyne, J.H., Chief Oper. Officer--Dixie Bulk Transport, Inc., Houston, TX; *U.S. Public*, pg. 962
Pyritz, Bernd, Mgr.-Opers.--Titan Germany GmbH, Holle, Germany; *U.S. Public*, pg. 1619
Pyson, R.S., Pres.--Penn Central Communications Corp., Philadelphia, PA; *U.S. Public*, pg. 432
Pytel, W., Mng. Dir.--Nokia Telecommunications Sp.z.o.o., Warsaw, Poland; *Int'l*, pg. 954
Pyvis, Richard, Gen. Mgr.--Westpac Banking Corp. - Japan, Tokyo, Japan; *Int'l*, pg. 1497
Qadri, A.I., V.P. & Chief Mgr.--Habib Bank Ltd., Male, Maldives; *Int'l*, pg. 584
Qanbar, Mohamed, Mgmt.--Qanbar Dywidag Precast Concrete Ltd., Jubail, Saudi Arabia; *Int'l*, pg. 425
Qoi, Stephen, Gen. Mgr.--Zimmer Pte Ltd., Singapore, Singapore; *U.S. Public*, pg. 257
Quackenbush, Lee, Chief Oper. Officer--Instructional Fair, Inc., Grand Rapids, MI; *U.S. Private*, pg. 288
Qualey, Allen R., Chief Oper. Officer--1st Source Leasing, South Bend, IN; *U.S. Public*, pg. 638
Qualls, Jim, Mgr.--Dan River Spindale Inc., Spindale, NC; *U.S. Public*, pg. 479
Qualls, Mark, Gen. Mgr.--Barton's of Stuttgart, Stuttgart, AR; *U.S. Private*, pg. 119
Quamme, Jack O., Pres.--Dayco Rubber Products Co., Miamisburg, OH; *U.S. Public*, pg. 1045
Quang, Trung Pham, Gen. Mgr.--ING Bank Hanoi, Hanoi, Vietnam; *Int'l*, pg. 649
Quang, Trung Pham, Gen. Mgr.--ING Bank Ho Chi Minh City, Ho Chi Minh City, Vietnam; *Int'l*, pg. 649
Quarles, Ron, V.P.--Ennis Business Forms Tenn Inc., Knoxville, TN; *U.S. Public*, pg. 583
Quarry, John, Chief Exec. Officer--International Marketing & Promotions, London, London, United Kingdom; *U.S. Private*, pg. 304

Quasey, Jim, Plant Mgr.--Respironics, Inc., Murrysville, PA; *U.S. Public*, pg. 1383
Quasman, E. Robert, Dir.-Res.--Legg Mason Wood Walker, Incorporated, Baltimore, MD; *U.S. Public*, pg. 985
Quay, Missy, Pres.--Risk Management Solutions, Inc., Waltham, MA; *U.S. Private*, pg. 489
Queenan, J.P., Pres.--Blackhawk Collision Repair Inc., Waukesha, WI; *U.S. Public*, pg. 805
Quek, N.K., V.P. & Gen. Mgr.--SCI (Thailand) Ltd., Pathum Thani, Thailand; *U.S. Public*, pg. 1417
Quek, Yong H., V.P. & Gen. Mgr.-Beauty Care Prods.-Canada--Procter & Gamble Inc., North York, Canada; *U.S. Public*, pg. 1331
Quell, Ron, Pres.--The Bentley-Harris Manufacturing Co., Lionville, PA; *Int'l*, pg. 1334
Quercioli, Gerardo, Branch Mgr.--Banco di Napoli-Hong Kong, Central, Hong Kong; *Int'l*, pg. 140
Querfeld, Kurt, Dir.--Nordsee Deutsche Hochseefischerei G.m.b.H., Bremerhaven, Germany; *Int'l*, pg. 1438
Query, Howard, Publisher--Globe-Gazette, Mason City, IA; *U.S. Public*, pg. 983
Quesada, Eric, Gen. Mgr.--Amway Costa Rica, San Jose, Costa Rica; *U.S. Private*, pg. 69
Quesadacespedes, J.C., Gen. Mgr.--Salt Lake City Airline Learning Center, Salt Lake City, UT; *U.S. Public*, pg. 219
Questa, Koldo Ruiloba, Mng. Dir.--Lubriner (Lubricates Del Nervion, S.A.), Bilbao, Spain; *Int'l*, pg. 323
Questo, Silk, Gen. Mgr.--Palmer Jarvis Advertising, Victoria, Canada; *Int'l*, pg. 1022
Questrocy, Jean, Chief Oper. Officer--Siemens S.A., Saint-Gilles, Belgium; *Int'l*, pg. 1248
Quevedo, Benito Cantalapiedra, Pres.--Banco Santander Puerto Rico, Hato Rey, PR; *Int'l*, pg. 143
Quezada, Lionel, Mgr.--Nalco Productos Quimicos de Chile S.A., Santiago, Chile; *U.S. Public*, pg. 1151
Quick, Bruce, Chief Oper. Officer--Fiserv (ASPAC), Pte. Ltd., Singapore, Singapore; *U.S. Public*, pg. 647
Quick, Christopher C., Pres.--JJC Specialist Corp., New York, NY; *U.S. Public*, pg. 650
Quick, Donald A., Pres.--Huntington Tile, Inc., Pomona, CA; *U.S. Private*, pg. 831
Quick, Leslie C., III, Pres. & Chief Oper. Officer--U.S. Clearing Corp., New York, NY; *U.S. Public*, pg. 650
Quick, Peter, Pres.--Quick & Reilly, Inc., New York, NY; *U.S. Public*, pg. 650
Quick, Ray, Mgr.-Office--Woodward-Clyde, Little Rock, AR; *U.S. Public*, pg. 1656
Quick, T., Mgr.-Bus. Unit--TOC, Rochester Hills, MI; *Int'l*, pg. 815
Quick, Thomas C., Pres. & Chief Oper. Officer--The Quick & Reilly Group Inc., Palm Beach, FL; *U.S. Public*, pg. 650
Quierin, A., Chief Oper. Officer--VW-Wohnungs Gesellschaft mbH, Wolfsburg, Germany; *Int'l*, pg. 1474
Quigg, Thomas, Pres.--Overseas Assets Holdings Inc., San Francisco, CA; *U.S. Public*, pg. 181
Quigley, E. James, Pres.--First Colorado Bankshares Insurance Co., Denver, CO; *U.S. Public*, pg. 173
Quigley, G. L., Pres.-European Opers.--Moore Products Co. B.V., Ridderkerk, Netherlands; *U.S. Public*, pg. 1129
Quigley, G.L., Pres.-European Opers.--Moore Products Co. (U.K.) Ltd., Yeovil, United Kingdom; *U.S. Public*, pg. 1129
Quigley, Greg, District Mgr.--Circle International, College Park, GA; *U.S. Public*, pg. 371
Quigley, James, Gen. Mgr.--Color Div., Cleveland, OH; *U.S. Public*, pg. 619
Quillen, Joan, Pres.--JC Penney National Bank, Harrington, DE; *U.S. Public*, pg. 917
Quimby, Ed, V.P.--Turner Construction Co., Philadelphia, PA; *U.S. Public*, pg. 1645
Quin, Alan, Natl. Mgr.--Dun & Bradstreet (New Zealand) Ltd., Auckland, New Zealand; *U.S. Public*, pg. 536
Quin, B., Plant Mgr.--Hoeganaes Corp., Watsontown, PA; *U.S. Public*, pg. 893
Quin, David, Mng. Dir.--Emery Expedite!, Overland Park, KS; *U.S. Public*, pg. 281
Quinlan, B.E., Mng. Dir.--Powerflex, Waltham Cross, United Kingdom; *Int'l*, pg. 1221
Quinlan, John M., Pres.--Massachusetts Casualty Insurance Company, Boston, MA; *Int'l*, pg. 1319
Quinlan, Pat, Mgr.--Century Telephone, Region I, Alexandria, LA; *U.S. Public*, pg. 329
Quinlan, Peter, Sec.--QPI Financial Services, Dublin, Ireland; *Int'l*, pg. 1078
Quinn, Conor, Joint Mng. Dir.--Quinn McDonnell Pattison DMB&B Dublin, Dublin, Ireland; *U.S. Private*, pg. 305
Quinn, Dan, Pres.--Pentek Corporation, Indianapolis, IN; *U.S. Private*, pg. 352
Quinn, Dan, Pres.--Corpak Inc., Wheeling, IL; *U.S. Public*, pg. 1592
Quinn, Donal M., Gen. Mgr.--Mallinckrodt Medical GmbH, Hennef, Germany; *U.S. Public*, pg. 1040
Quinn, Edward, V.P. & Gen. Mgr.--KGTV, San Diego, CA; *U.S. Public*, pg. 1070
Quinn, James E., Pres.--Tiffany & Co. Mexico, S.A. de C.V., Mexico, Mexico; *U.S. Public*, pg. 1609
Quinn, M.F., Pres.--National Silicates Ltd., Etobicoke, Canada; *U.S. Private*, pg. 827
Quinn, Michael, V.P. & Gen. Mgr.--Akzo Nobel Coatings Inc., Columbus, OH; *Int'l*, pg. 48
Quinn, Michael, Pres.--Western Design Corporation, Irvine, CA; *Int'l*, pg. 636
Quinn, Michael A., Pres.--Affiliated Banks Service Co., Thornton, CO; *U.S. Public*, pg. 173
Quinn, N., Mng. Dir.--Apollo Fire Detectors Limited, Havant, United Kingdom; *Int'l*, pg. 589
Quinn, Paul, V.P. & Gen. Mgr.--WGAL-TV, Lancaster, PA; *U.S. Public*, pg. 1344
Quinn, Peter, Mng. Dir.--Mentor Investment Group, Richmond, VA; *U.S. Public*, pg. 640
Quinn, Robert, Div. Mgr.--Montana Power Helena Div., Helena, MT; *U.S. Public*, pg. 1126
Quinn, Thomas, Pres.--Continental Cement Co. Inc., Margate, FL; *Int'l*, pg. 1201
Quinn, Thomas H., Chm. Bd.--Welcome Home, Inc., Wilmington, NC; *U.S. Private*, pg. 598
Quinn, Tony, Pres.--LEP Profit International, Inc., Marietta, GA; *U.S. Private*, pg. 571
Quinn, W.P., Gen. Mgr.--Kodak Taiwan Limited, Taipei, Taiwan; *U.S. Public*, pg. 555
Quinn, William F., Pres.--AMR Investment Services, Inc., Dallas-Fort Worth Airport, TX; *U.S. Public*, pg. 9
Quinnell, Bruce, Pres.--Walden Book Company, Ann Arbor, MI; *U.S. Public*, pg. 245
Quinoa, Jose, Chief Oper. Officer--Tefal Espana SA, Barcelona, Spain; *Int'l*, pg. 568
Quinones, Hector, Pres.--Pueblo International, Inc.-P.R. Div., Carolina, PR; *U.S. Private*, pg. 894
Quinoz, Luis, Dr., Gen. Mgr.--Dentsply Mexico, S.A. de C.V., Mexico, Mexico; *U.S. Public*, pg. 499
Quint, Manfred, Pres.--Mann & Hummel Hydromation GmbH, Ludwigsburg, Germany; *Int'l*, pg. 484
Quintana, Duane, Western Reg. Dir.--Utell International-Los Angeles, Los Angeles, CA; *Int'l*, pg. 1098
Quintanal, J., Mng. Dir.--AEGON-Union Aseguradora, S.A. de Seguros y Reasequros, Madrid, Spain; *Int'l*, pg. 28
Quintero, Leopoldo, Dir.--Reciclajes Envalic, C.A., Valencia, Venezuela; *U.S. Public*, pg. 1387
Quintero, Ramon Mantellini, Pres.--Deltaven S.A., Caracas, Venezuela; *Int'l*, pg. 1045
Quinton, Gregory L., Gen. Mgr.--Crouse-Hinds Molded Products, La Grange, NC; *U.S. Public*, pg. 444
Quiring, Ernst, Representative--Union Bank of Switzerland, Taipei Branch, Taipei, Taiwan; *Int'l*, pg. 1441
Quirion, Gerard P., Chief Oper. Officer--Novo Nordisk A/S, Budapest, Hungary; *Int'l*, pg. 988
Quirk, Peter R., Pres. & Chief Exec. Officer--Walk, Haydel & Associates, Inc., New Orleans, LA; *Int'l*, pg. 624
Quirk, William, Pres. & Chief Exec. Officer--Horsehead Resource Development Company, Inc., Palmerton, PA; *U.S. Private*, pg. 540
Quirke, Mike, Mng. Dir.--Costain Construction Limited, Maidenhead, United Kingdom; *Int'l*, pg. 336
Quirke, Mike, Mng. Dir.-Construction & Management Div.--Costain Building & Civil Engineering Limited, Maidenhead, United Kingdom; *Int'l*, pg. 336
Quiroz, Arturo, Gen. Mgr.--Fasson de Mexico, S.A., Mexico, Mexico; *U.S. Public*, pg. 154
Quist, Chad, Pres.--Information Products, Inc., Holland, MI; *U.S. Public*, pg. 519
Quist, S.J., Dir.--Cosmoferm B.V., Delft, Netherlands; *Int'l*, pg. 1143
Ra, Jim, Chief Oper. Officer--Scholastic Inc. Information Center, Lyndhurst, NJ; *U.S. Public*, pg. 1440
Raad, Ramzi, Chief Oper. Officer & V.P.-Reg. Opers.--Intermarkets U.A.E., Dubai, United Arab Emirates; *Int'l*, pg. 680
Raaijmakeb, Raoul, Chief Oper. Officer--COBE International Ltd, Zaventem, Belgium; *Int'l*, pg. 667
Raaijmakeb, Raoul, Chief Oper. Officer--COBE Laboratories Europe N.V., Veenendaal, Netherlands; *Int'l*, pg. 667
Raanes, Chris, Mgr.--EG & G Optoelectronics Reticon, Sunnyvale, CA; *U.S. Public*, pg. 543
Raasch, Jochen, Mng. Dir.--OPTIMALGRUND Bautragergesellschaft mbH, Munich, Germany; *Int'l*, pg. 423
Raat, Jan, Chief Fin. Officer--ARA/BDDP, Rotterdam, Netherlands; *Int'l*, pg. 117
Rabaut, Thomas W., Pres. & Chief Exec. Officer--United Defense L.P., Arlington, VA; *U.S. Private*, pg. 213
Rabbi, Luigi, Mng. Dir.--Olivetti Supplies, Inc., Middletown, PA; *Int'l*, pg. 1002
Rabbidge, Charles, Mgr.-Sls. & Mktg.--Scania USA Inc., Orange, CT; *Int'l*, pg. 687
Rabeling, F.J., Gen. Mgr.--Van Melle Latin America NV, Curacao, Netherlands Antilles; *Int'l*, pg. 1451
Rabeyroux, Rickel, Pres.--Scori Holding, Montigny-le-Bretonneux, France; *Int'l*, pg. 292
Rabin, Neville, Natl Sls. Mgr.--Analog Devices Ltd., Walton-on-Thames, United Kingdom; *U.S. Public*, pg. 108
Rabinowicz, Daniel, Exec. V.P.--Cossette Communication-Marketing (Montreal) Inc., Montreal, Canada; *Int'l*, pg. 336
Rabiu, Alhaji I., Chm.--Stanbic Merchant Bank Nigeria Limited, Lagos, Nigeria; *Int'l*, pg. 1294
Rabizzoni, Antonio, Chief Oper. Officer--Perstorp SpA-Div. Compounds, Castellanza, Italy; *Int'l*, pg. 1037
Rabold, Robert E.H., Pres. & Chief Exec. Officer--MICO Insurance Company, Columbus, OH; *U.S. Private*, pg. 764
Raborn, Eugene, Gen. Mgr.--R.J. Brown America, Inc., Houston, TX; *Int'l*, pg. 766
Rabuck, Robert, Pres.--Pathway Bellows, Inc., Oak Ridge, TN; *U.S. Public*, pg. 521
Raburn, Don, Chm. Bd.--Sanden International (U.S.A.), Inc., Wylie, TX; *Int'l*, pg. 1184
Rabut, Jean-Eudes, Chief Exec. Officer--Air Charter, Rungis, France; *Int'l*, pg. 560
Rachels, G.K., Mgr.-Sls./Southeast Reg.--Industrial Maintenance Corp., Charlotte, NC; *U.S. Public*, pg. 562
Rachiatore, Tom, Plant Mgr.--Silgan Containers, Fairport, NY; *U.S. Public*, pg. 1473
Rachke, Tim, Plant Mgr.--Rexam Medical Packaging, Inc., Mundelein, IL; *Int'l*, pg. 1106
Racicot, Francois, Mgr.--Dayton Superior Canada Ltd., Montreal, Canada; *U.S. Private*, pg. 932
Rack, Alec, Pres.--New Progress, Arthur, IL; *U.S. Private*, pg. 1066
Rackoff, W.H., Pres.--American Shear Knive Co., Homestead, PA; *U.S. Private*, pg. 89
Raclin, Ernestine M., Chm. Bd.--1st Source Bank Consolidated, South Bend, IN; *U.S. Public*, pg. 638
Racz, Janos, Chief Oper. & Quality Officer--Aeroplex of Central Europe Ltd., Budapest, Hungary; *Int'l*, pg. 834
Racz, Janos, Chief Oper. & Quality Officer--Aeroplex of Central Europe Ltd., Budapest, Hungary; *U.S. Public*, pg. 1006
Raczkiewicz, Maciej, Pres.--Epstein Engineering Export, Ltd., Chicago, IL; *U.S. Private*, pg. 379
Raczkiewicz, Maciej A., Pres. & Chief Oper. Officer--Epstein Engineering Export (Warsaw), Ltd., Warsaw, Poland; *U.S. Private*, pg. 379
Radau, Gene, Dir.-Corp. Communications--Ford, Bacon & Davis Companies Inc., Duluth, GA; *Int'l*, pg. 401
Radcliff, Barry, Gen. Mgr.--Meenan Oil/Young Supply Co., Upper Darby, PA; *U.S. Private*, pg. 729
Radcliffe, Frederick R., Jr., Pres.--The Flexaust Co., Amesbury, MA; *U.S. Public*, pg. 394
Radcliffe, Frederick R., Jr., Pres.--The Flexaust Co., Warsaw, IN; *U.S. Public*, pg. 394
Radcliffe, M.F., Mng. Dir.--Brush Transformers Ltd., Loughborough, United Kingdom; *Int'l*, pg. 124
Raddi, William J., Chief Tech. Officer, Sr. V.P. & Gen. Mgr.-Small Systems Group, Raleigh, NC; *Int'l*, pg. 126
Rademacher, Jeni, Sr. Sls. Representative--PENCO-Wisconsin, Racine, WI; *Int'l*, pg. 1508
Rademacher, Johannes, Dr., Chief Oper. Officer--EMG Eisen-und Metallgusswerk GmbH, Waldkrainburg, Germany; *Int'l*, pg. 400
Rademaker, Richard J., Mng. Dir.--Trinc Company, Bryan, OH; *U.S. Public*, pg. 1214
Rader, Donald, Pres.--Los Angeles Smoking & Curing Company, Los Angeles, CA; *U.S. Private*, pg. 810
Rader, John, Gen. Mgr.--Gai's Northwest Bakeries, Seattle, WA; *U.S. Private*, pg. 1124
Rader, Monte, Plant Mgr.--The Ohio Mattress Company Licensing & Components Group, Delano, PA; *U.S. Private*, pg. 979
Radford, Daniel, Chief Exec. Officer--Editions Jean-Claude Lattes, Paris, France; *Int'l*, pg. 794
Radford, David, Chirf Oper. Officer--COBE Laboratories Pty Ltd.-Melbourne, Blackburn, Australia; *Int'l*, pg. 667
Radford, David, Chief Oper. Officer--COBE Laboratories Pty Ltd.-Sydney, Frenchs Forest, Australia; *Int'l*, pg. 667
Radice, Frank, Chm. Bd. & Chief Exec. Officer--Garland Commercial Industries, Inc., Freeland, PA; *Int'l*, pg. 188
Radin, W., Gen. Mgr.--Kenner Parker (H.K.) Ltd., Kowloon, Hong Kong; *U.S. Public*, pg. 797
Radkovic, M., Rep.--ING Bank Liberec, Liberec, Czech Republic; *Int'l*, pg. 649
Radlein, John, G.M.--Arlington, Ltd., Portarlington, Ireland; *U.S. Public*, pg. 156
Radler, F. David, Publisher--Chicago Sun Times, Chicago, IL; *Int'l*, pg. 632
Radmacher, Ric, Gen. Mgr.--GATX Logistics, Inc.-Illinois, Bedford Park, IL; *U.S. Public*, pg. 691
Radmer, Joachim, Mng. Dir.--Spektrum Fachverlage GmbH, Stuttgart, Germany; *Int'l*, pg. 1478
Radmer, Joachim, Mng. Dir.--Gustav Fischer Verlag GmbH & Co. KG, Stuttgart, Germany; *Int'l*, pg. 1478
Rado, Gary, V.P. & Mgr.--Texas Instruments Consumer Products Div., Dallas, TX; *U.S. Public*, pg. 1586
Radtke, H. Helmut, Pres. & Chief Exec. Officer--Melitta U.S.A., Inc., Clearwater, FL; *Int'l*, pg. 857
Radtke, Linda, Pres.--Intech Technology Corporation, Broadview, IL; *Int'l*, pg. 490
Radu, Diana, Liaison Officer--Monopoly International S.A., Bucharest, Romania; *U.S. Private*, pg. 1152
Rae, John Maitland, Chief Oper. Officer--BHF-Bank Representative Office, Sao Paulo, Brazil; *Int'l*, pg. 120
Raettig, R., Chief Oper. Officer--Dentsply GmbH, Dreieichenhain, Germany; *U.S. Public*, pg. 499
Rafalat, Andrew, Mgr.--Pizza Hut (USSR), Moscow, Russia; *U.S. Public*, pg. 1637
Raff, Beryl, Chief Oper. Officer & Exec. V.P.--Zale Corporation, Irving, TX; *U.S. Public*, pg. 1789
Raff, K. Newton, Regional Pres.--First Tennessee Bank - Johnson City, Johnson City, TN; *U.S. Public*, pg. 639
Raffauf, Friedrich, Gen. Mgr.--Flachform Stahl GmbH, Schwerte, Germany; *Int'l*, pg. 79
Raffenaud, James P., Pres.--Old Kent Bank-Southeast, Trenton, MI; *U.S. Public*, pg. 1217
Raffenbeul, Joel W., Pres.--SuperValu, Inc.-Ohio Valley Div., Xenia, OH; *U.S. Public*, pg. 1540
Rafferty, Don, Pres.--Time Warner Cable Liberty Division, Ferndale, NY; *U.S. Public*, pg. 1611
Rafferty, James J., Jr., Pres.--Advanced Metallurgy, Inc., Export, PA; *U.S. Public*, pg. 1564
Rafferty, James J., Jr., Pres.--AMI Gibson, Inc., Luquillo, PR; *U.S. Public*, pg. 1564
Rafferty, S.J., Treas.--NGE Enterprises, Inc., Binghamton, NY; *U.S. Public*, pg. 1173
Raffetto, J.A., Rep.--Cariplo (Los Angeles), San Francisco, CA; *Int'l*, pg. 275
Raffety, A.T., Chief Oper. Officer--Whipp & Bourne Ltd., Rochdale, United Kingdom; *Int'l*, pg. 473
Raffo, A.J., Pres.--CMI Industries, Inc., Elkin, NC; *U.S. Private*, pg. 195
Rafter, Steve, Plant Mgr.--Hunt Valley Plant, Hunt Valley, MD; *U.S. Public*, pg. 1066
Rafter, Tracy R., Publr.--Taunton Daily Gazette, Taunton, MA; *U.S. Public*, pg. 935
Raftery, Joseph P., Chm. Bd. & Chief Exec. Officer--Bank of America Business Credit, San Diego, CA; *U.S. Public*, pg. 180
Ragazzi, A.R., Dir. & Gen. Mgr.--Monroe Auto Pecas S.A., Sao Paulo, Brazil; *U.S. Public*, pg. 1580
Raggett, Marty, Plant Mgr.--Ash Grove Cement Plant, Forman, AR; *U.S. Private*, pg. 88
Ragheb, Tarek M., Gen. Mgr.--Martin Marietta International, Inc., Riyadh, Saudi Arabia; *U.S. Public*, pg. 1010
Ragland, John C., Chm., Pres. & Chief Exec. Officer--Liberty National Bank and Trust Company of Indiana, New Albany, IN; *U.S. Public*, pg. 173
Ragland, Ron, Pres.--RF Microsystems, San Diego, CA; *U.S. Public*, pg. 1376
Ragna, Bengt, Pres.--Svenska Handelsbanken, New York, New York, NY; *Int'l*, pg. 1327

Ragosta, Guy, Mng. Dir.-N. America Captive Mngmt. Opers.--Willis Corroon Management (Vermont) Ltd., Burlington, VT; *Int'l*, pg. 1505
Rahal, Robert, Pres.--Financial Trust Corp, Carlisle, PA; *U.S. Public*, pg. 956
Rahamno-Mossavar, Bijan, Pres.--Apache International, Inc., Houston, TX; *U.S. Public*, pg. 119
Rahe, Martin E., Sr. V.P. & Gen. Mgr.--Deutsche Bank AG (Chicago Branch), Chicago, IL; *Int'l*, pg. 403
Rahill, Richard E., Pres.--Corning Enterprises Inc., Corning, NY; *U.S. Public*, pg. 448
Rahilly, Alan, Pres.--Tarmac Virginia, Inc., Norfolk, VA; *Int'l*, pg. 1356
Rahim, Zahid, Country Mgr.--Standard Chartered Bank (Pakistan), Karachi, Pakistan; *Int'l*, pg. 1295
Rahman, Habibur, Chm.--Lever Brothers Pakistan Ltd., Karachi, Pakistan; *Int'l*, pg. 1437
Rahman, S.H., Chief Exec. Officer--Blackwood Hodge (Bangladesh) Ltd., Dhaka, Bangladesh; *Int'l*, pg. 231
Rahn, Noel P., Chief Exec. Officer--Investment Advisers, Inc., Minneapolis, MN; *Int'l*, pg. 813
Rahr, George, Gen. Mgr.--NUS-South Africa, Rosebank, South Africa; *U.S. Private*, pg. 787
Rahusen, Dave, Reg. Mgr.--Oriental Motor U.S.A. Corp., Peachtree City, GA; *Int'l*, pg. 1008
Rai, Heikichi, Mng. Dir.--Nissan Motor Co. (Australia) Pty. Ltd., Dandenong, Australia; *Int'l*, pg. 945
Raidl, Klaus, Dr., Chm.--Bohler Uddeholm AG, Vienna, Austria; *Int'l*, pg. 1471
Raiger, Walter, Gen. Mgr.--Analog Devices HDLSGESMBH, Vienna, Austria; *U.S. Public*, pg. 108
Raikkonen, Antti, Mng. Dir.--Nokia Telecommunications (Singapore) Pte. Ltd., Singapore, Singapore; *Int'l*, pg. 954
Railey, Steve, Plant Mgr.--Ropak Southwest Inc., Mansfield, TX; *Int'l*, pg. 812
Railton, Denis, Branch Office Mgr.--Dumez GTM, Manila, Philippines; *Int'l*, pg. 823
Raimann, H., Mgr.-Adv.--Getranke-Dienst AG, Dietikon, Switzerland; *Int'l*, pg. 479
Raimondo, Orlando, Pres. & Chief Exec. Officer--Pirelli Cable Corporation, Florham Park, NJ; *Int'l*, pg. 1059
Raina, Ishan, Mgr.--EURO RSCG-Bombay, Mumbai, India; *Int'l*, pg. 602
Raines, Johnny, Pres.--Simpson County Bank, Franklin, KY; *U.S. Public*, pg. 1669
Raines, Larry R., V.P.-Mfg. Prod.--Manitowoc Debanking Technology, Memphis, TN; *U.S. Private*, pg. 518
Rainey, Jack G., Pres. & Chief Exec. Officer--Regions Bank/Troy, Troy, AL; *U.S. Public*, pg. 1373
Rainoldi, Joseph C., Chm. Bd.--Rainoldi, Kerzner & Radcliffe, San Francisco, CA; *U.S. Public*, pg. 1224
Rains, R. E., Gen. Mgr.--Taber Metals, Inc., Russellville, AR; *U.S. Private*, pg. 1068
Rainville, Donald, Pres. & Chief Oper. Officer--Universal Dynamics, Inc., Woodbridge, VA; *Int'l*, pg. 484
Rainville, William, Pres.--Thermo Fibertek, Inc., Waltham, MA; *U.S. Public*, pg. 1593
Rainville, William A., Pres.--Thermo Electron Wisconsin, Inc., Kaukauna, WI; *U.S. Public*, pg. 1593
Rainwater, Gary L., Pres. & Chief Exec. Officer--AmerenCIPS, Springfield, IL; *U.S. Public*, pg. 65
Rais Saman, Mohd, Dir.--Tourism Malaysia - Johannesburg Office, Johannesburg, South Africa; *Int'l*, pg. 833
Raison, Philippe, Chief Oper. Officer--Club Mediterranee (Bureau Suisse) S.A., Geneva, Switzerland; *Int'l*, pg. 298
Raissig, Peter, Mng. Dir.--Impuls Direct, Kusnacht, Switzerland; *Int'l*, pg. 666
Raithelhuber, Christopher, Dir.--Wirtschafs-und Privatbank, Zurich, Switzerland; *Int'l*, pg. 181
Raitis, Teppo, Chief Oper. Officer--KONE Elevators, BU 2, Hyvinkaa, Finland; *Int'l*, pg. 746
Raj, Gopi, Gen. Mgr.--Janssen-Cilag, Dubai, United Arab Emirates; *U.S. Public*, pg. 929
Rajagopalan, T.R., Mng. Dir.--Metal Box Trinidad Limited, Port of Spain, Trinidad & Tobago; *Int'l*, pg. 267
Rajala, Ari, Chief Oper. Officer--Neste Oil Poland Ltd., Warsaw, Poland; *Int'l*, pg. 915
Rajas, Raul, Gen. Dir.--Braun de Mexico y Compania de C.V., Mexico, Mexico; *U.S. Public*, pg. 744
Rajendran, R., Mgr.--Dunearn Distribution Services Private Limited, Singapore, Singapore; *Int'l*, pg. 1250
Rajeswaran, Francesca, Gen. Mgr.--Bank Brussels Lambert, Dubai Representative Office, Dubai, United Arab Emirates; *Int'l*, pg. 148
Rajtmajer, Bojan, Mng. Dir.--ISS Servisystem d.o.o., Maribor, Slovenia; *Int'l*, pg. 657
Raju, G. J., Chief Oper. Officer--ACC-Babcock Ltd., Mumbai, India; *Int'l*, pg. 474
Rakestraw, John, Sr. V.P. & Gen. Mgr.--Cattle Feeding Div., Boulder, CO; *U.S. Private*, pg. 268
Rakich, Robert T., Pres. & Chief Exec. Officer--Desjardins Laurentian Life Assurance, Wayne, PA; *Int'l*, pg. 396
Rakocy, Terry J., Pres.--Consumers Illinois Water Co., Kankakee, IL; *U.S. Public*, pg. 438
Rakstang, Robert, Pres.--Hanna Corporation, Chicago, IL; *U.S. Private*, pg. 231
Raleigh, W.J., Pres.--CMI Industries, Inc., New York, NY; *U.S. Private*, pg. 195
Ralph, Doug, Mgr.--Morgantown Machine, Helper, UT; *Int'l*, pg. 281
Ralston, E., V.P. & Gen. Mgr.--Babcock & Wilcox International, Cambridge, Canada; *U.S. Public*, pg. 1068
Ralston, Troy, Dir.--Keller Graduate School of Management, Oak Brook, IL; *U.S. Public*, pg. 504
Ramacher, W.G.Y., Chief Exec. Officer--Advanced Metal Forming CV, Zwolle, Netherlands; *Int'l*, pg. 753
Ramaekers, Larry, Pres. & Chief Oper. Officer--Color Tile, Inc., Fort Worth, TX; *Int'l*, pg. 686
Ramael, Francois, Mng. Dir.--Black & Decker (Belgium) N.V., Brussels, Belgium; *U.S. Public*, pg. 234
Ramage, Dick, V.P. & Gen. Mgr.--Carnation Products Div., Glendale, CA; *Int'l*, pg. 916
Ramagnano, Michael, Field Service Engineer--AlliedSignal Airline Services, Allied Signal Aerospace Canada, Etobicoke, Canada; *U.S. Public*, pg. 53
Ramaker, David B., Pres. & Chief Exec. Officer--Chemical Bank & Trust Company, Midland, MI; *U.S. Public*, pg. 345
Ramakrishnan, K., Chief Exec. Officer & Chief Mgr.--State Bank of India, New York, NY; *Int'l*, pg. 1297
Ramamurthi, T.S., Gen. Mgr.--Circle Freight International India Pvt. Ltd., Madras, India; *U.S. Public*, pg. 372
Raman, R.K., V.P.--India Photographic Company Limited, Madras, India; *U.S. Public*, pg. 552
Ramasco, Carlo, Liaison Officer--Studio Piu, Milan, Italy; *U.S. Private*, pg. 1152
Ramat, Charles S., Pres.--Members Only By Europe Craft, New York, NY; *U.S. Public*, pg. 129
Rambaud, Yves, Vice Chm. & Pres.--Eramet-SLN, Paris, France; *Int'l*, pg. 661
Rambo, Bill, Pres.--MacDuff Underwriters, Daytona Beach, FL; *U.S. Public*, pg. 1312
Rambo, Chuck, Plant Mgr.--American Natl. Can Co., Neenah, WI; *Int'l*, pg. 1029
Rambo, Kathleen, Admin.--Hillhaven Convalescent Center Memphis, Memphis, TN; *U.S. Public*, pg. 1713
Ramdant, Denzil, V.P. & Gen. Mgr.--Peterson Spring-Greenville Plant, Greenville, IL; *U.S. Private*, pg. 857
Ramenason, Gaston, Chm.--BMOI, Antananarivo, Madagascar; *Int'l*, pg. 163
Ramey, Sidney M., Pres.--Peoples Abstract Co., Des Moines, IA; *U.S. Public*, pg. 626
Ramian, Artoun, Pres.--Weatherford Enterra Business Development Group, Ltd., London, United Kingdom; *U.S. Public*, pg. 1750
Ramierz, Mario, Pres.--Circuit City Southern Div., Atlanta, GA; *U.S. Public*, pg. 374
Ramirez-Isava, Daniel, Pres. & Chief Exec. Officer--BITOR Europe, Brentford, United Kingdom; *Int'l*, pg. 1046
Ramirez, Alfonso, Gen. Mgr.--Puerto Rico Container Co., Bayamon, PR; *U.S. Public*, pg. 1666
Ramirez, Eddie, Pres.--Palmaven, S.A., Caracas, Venezuela; *Int'l*, pg. 1045
Ramirez, Ernesto, Chief Exec. Officer--Asland do Brasil Ltda., Sao Paulo, Brazil; *Int'l*, pg. 790
Ramirez, J.I., Gen. Mgr.--CE Sonora S.A. de C.V., Sonora, Mexico; *U.S. Public*, pg. 468
Ramirez, Jorge, Mng. Dir.--Bank of Boston, Montevideo, Uruguay; *U.S. Public*, pg. 184
Ramirez, Rodolfo, Gen. Mgr.--Credit Commercial de France, Mexico, Mexico; *Int'l*, pg. 343
Ramiro, Angel Juan Simon, Pres.--ENSA - Equipos Nucleares, S.A., Madrid, Spain; *Int'l*, pg. 1224
Ramis, Hy, Pres.--Big Foot Cattle Co., Harvard, IL; *U.S. Private*, pg. 1140
Ramke, Raymond, Gen. Mgr.--Bank of Tonga, Nuku'alofa, Tonga; *U.S. Public*, pg. 1248
Ramlow, Don, Pres.--Matheson Gas Products, Inc., Secaucus, NJ; *Int'l*, pg. 938
Rammell, George, Pres.--Transdyn Controls, Inc., Concord, CA; *U.S. Public*, pg. 1319
Ramon, J.S., Gen. Mgr.--Trinova Divisao Vickers System, Sao Paulo, Brazil; *U.S. Public*, pg. 25
Ramon, John, Dir. Pres.--Trinova do Brazil S.A.-Divisao Aeroquip, Rio de Janeiro, Brazil; *U.S. Public*, pg. 25
Ramos, Antonio C., Pres.--Georgia Stone Industries, Inc., Elberton, GA; *U.S. Private*, pg. 793
Ramos, Fabio, V.P.--Porta Systems S.A. de C.V., Matamoros, Mexico; *U.S. Public*, pg. 1317
Ramos, Hector R., V.P. & Gen. Mgr.--Fleishman-Hillard Caribbean, Old San Juan, PR; *U.S. Private*, pg. 411
Ramos, Joseph M., Pres. & Gen. Mgr.--Rubbermaid Commercial Products Inc., Winchester, VA; *U.S. Public*, pg. 1411
Ramos, Manuel E., Gen. Mgr.--W.R. Grace (Philippines) Inc., Pasay, Philippines; *U.S. Public*, pg. 756
Ramos, Simone, Rep.--Singapore Tourist Promotion Board - Sao Paulo, Sao Paulo, Brazil; *Int'l*, pg. 1254
Ramp, William, Gen. Mgr.--Revlon Manufacturing Facilities, Jacksonville, FL; *U.S. Private*, pg. 690
Rampata, Walter, V.P. & Gen. Mgr.--Becton Dickinson Primary Care Diagnostics, Sparks, MD; *U.S. Public*, pg. 199
Rampelberg, Victor H., V.P. & Gen. Mgr.--Decorative Films Division, Schererville, IN; *U.S. Public*, pg. 153
Rampey, Charles A., Jr., Pres.--SCANA Energy Marketing Inc., Columbia, SC; *U.S. Public*, pg. 1436
Rampon, Richard E., Pres.--BTR Precision Die Casting, Inc., Russellville, KY; *Int'l*, pg. 127
Rampton, Christopher, Dir.--Jardine Fleming Limited, Central, Hong Kong; *Int'l*, pg. 494
Rams, Joachim, Mng. Dir.--Ludwig Metrologie, SA, Fontenay-sous-Bois, France; *U.S. Public*, pg. 260
Ramsay, David B., Pres. & Chief Exec. Officer--SunTrust Bank, Tallahassee, N.A., Tallahassee, FL; *U.S. Public*, pg. 1538
Ramsay, Dennis A., Pres.--Bristol Laboratories (Philippines), Inc., Manila, Philippines; *U.S. Public*, pg. 255
Ramsay, Dennis A., Gen. Mgr.--Mead Johnson Philippines, Inc., Manila, Philippines; *U.S. Public*, pg. 256
Ramsden-Wood, Garry, Pres.-North Canadian Mktg.--North Canadian Marketing, Calgary, Canada; *Int'l*, pg. 434
Ramseier, U., Mng. Dir.--Ascom Systec AG, Magenwil, Switzerland; *Int'l*, pg. 86
Ramsey, Chuck, Pres.--Dayton Tire Company-Oklahoma City, Oklahoma City, OK; *Int'l*, pg. 214
Ramsey, Chuck, Pres.--Firestone Agricultural Tire Company, Des Moines, IA; *Int'l*, pg. 214
Ramsey, Dave, Pres.--Morgan Keegan Mortgage Company, Inc., Memphis, TN; *U.S. Public*, pg. 1131
Ramsey, J.H., Gen. Mgr.--Alloy Ring Service, Carmel, IN; *U.S. Public*, pg. 780
Ramsey, Michael, Gen. Mgr.--Soje/Lonsdale Advertising Inc, Saint Michael, Barbados; *U.S. Public*, pg. 1422
Ramsey, V.B., Pres.--AVEX Electronics, Inc., Huntsville, AL; *U.S. Private*, pg. 545
Ramseyer, J.P., Mgr.--Societe de Banque Suisse, Sion, Switzerland; *Int'l*, pg. 1329
Ramstorf, Rolf, Pres.--Altana, Inc., Melville, NY; *Int'l*, pg. 66
Ramthor, Wolfgang, Gen. Mgr.--Bank of Boston, Frankfurt/Main, Germany; *U.S. Public*, pg. 184
Ramvall, Per, Pres.--ABB Asea Brown Boveri Ltd., Zurich, Switzerland; *Int'l*, pg. 8
Rana, Dr. Saverio, Chief Opr. Officer--Alfa Romeo Avio S.p.A., Naples, Italy; *Int'l*, pg. 481
Ranalli, A., Plant Mgr.--Treitler-Owens, Inc., Washington, NJ; *U.S. Public*, pg. 1238
Rance, Robin, Pres.--Walbar Inc., Peabody, MA; *U.S. Public*, pg. 402
Rancke, Hans-Herbert, Mng. Dir.--Det Norske Veritas, Hamburg, Germany; *Int'l*, pg. 397
Rand, A. Barry, Pres.--Xerox U.S. Marketing Group, Rochester, NY; *U.S. Public*, pg. 1784
Rand, D., Gen. Mgr.--Steelweld U.K., Witney, United Kingdom; *Int'l*, pg. 71
Randall, Dale, Mgr.--Pace Industries, Inc., Harrison, AR; *U.S. Public*, pg. 986
Randall, John, Mng. Dir.--Emhart International Ltd., Oadby, United Kingdom; *U.S. Public*, pg. 233
Randall, Robert, V.P. & Gen. Mgr.--New Jersey Transit Rail Operations, Newark, NJ; *U.S. Private*, pg. 794
Rander, Robert H., Pres.--APV Baker Inc., Food Machinery Div., Goldsboro, NC; *Int'l*, pg. 1240
Randi, Salvatore, Chief Exec. Officer--Italtel, Milan, Italy; *Int'l*, pg. 1363
Randjelovic, John, V.P. & Gen. Mgr.--Pierce Manufacturing, Inc., Appleton, WI; *U.S. Public*, pg. 1233
Randle, Bruce, Mng. Dir.--A.C. Nielsen Pty., Ltd., Sydney, Australia; *U.S. Public*, pg. 1184
Randol, Mark A., Pres.-Shopping Center Division--Forest City Commercial Mngmt. Div., Cleveland, OH; *U.S. Public*, pg. 668
Randolph, Diane, Office Mgr.--Professional Travel Inc., Calhoun, GA; *U.S. Private*, pg. 408
Randolph, Jackson H., Chm. Bd.--Cinergy Investments, Inc., Indianapolis, IN; *U.S. Public*, pg. 369
Randolph, Jackson H., Chm. Bd., Pres. & Chief Exec. Officer--Lawrenceburg Gas Co., Cincinnati, OH; *U.S. Public*, pg. 369
Randolph, Jackson H., Chm. Bd.--Cinergy Corp., Cincinnati, OH; *U.S. Public*, pg. 369
Randolph, Tony, Pres.--Integral Corp., Dallas, TX; *U.S. Private*, pg. 1019
Rands, Gordon, Gen. Mgr.--Langs Cold Storage Div., Hamilton, Canada; *Int'l*, pg. 1012
Ranebo, Mats, Mng. Dir.--Sodra AG, Basel, Switzerland; *Int'l*, pg. 1276
Range, Rolf, Chief Oper. Officer--Bruckner Grundbau GmbH, Essen, Germany; *Int'l*, pg. 623
Ranki, Jorma, Dir.--Kemi Mills, Kemi, Finland; *Int'l*, pg. 863
Ranki, Kari, Mng. Dir.--Partita Ltd., Helsinki, Finland; *Int'l*, pg. 859
Rankin, D. Jeffrey, Pres.--TECO Transport & Trade Corp., Tampa, FL; *U.S. Public*, pg. 1565
Rankin, Jack, Operations Mgr.-Pig Products--Pigging Products, Tulsa, OK; *U.S. Private*, pg. 1180
Rankin, Les, Chief Oper. Officer--AgPro Grain, Winnipeg, Canada; *Int'l*, pg. 1195
Rankin, Samuel, Dir.--American Mathematical Society Washington Office, Washington, DC; *U.S. Private*, pg. 59
Rankin, Sheldon, Pres.--J&H Marsh & McLennan Ltd., Toronto, Canada; *U.S. Public*, pg. 1049
Rankin, Tom, Pres.--Multi-Line Cans, Inc., Dade City, FL; *U.S. Private*, pg. 682
Rankin, William J., Div. Pres.--Logistics Management, Inc., Manchester, CT; *U.S. Public*, pg. 1021
Rankin, William J., Div. Pres.--Lydall & Foulds Div., Manchester, CT; *U.S. Public*, pg. 1021
Ransdell, Thomas R., Pres.--Vulcan Materials Company-Southwest Div., San Antonio, TX; *U.S. Public*, pg. 1726
Ransdell, Thomas R., Pres.--Vulcan Gulf Coast Materials, Inc., Birmingham, AL; *U.S. Public*, pg. 1726
Ransom, Calvin L., Pres.--United Technologies Microelectronics Center, Colorado Springs, CO; *U.S. Public*, pg. 1690
Ransom, Marshall, Pres.--Hunt-Wesson Foodservice Division, Fullerton, CA; *U.S. Public*, pg. 428
Ranson, Richard C., Pres.--Crescent Resources, Inc., Charlotte, NC; *U.S. Public*, pg. 534
Rantala, Esko, Mng. Dir.--LK Products Oy, Kempele, Finland; *Int'l*, pg. 952
Rantala, Tapio, V.P.--Valmet Corporation Foundry, Jyvaskyla, Finland; *Int'l*, pg. 1448
Rantanen, Juha, Chief Oper. Officer--Borealis Holding A/S, Lyngby, Denmark; *Int'l*, pg. 914
Ranza, Renato, Gen. Mgr.--UBS Representative Office Ltd., Tehran, Iran; *Int'l*, pg. 1441
Ranzini, Lorenzo, Mgr.--Banco Di Napoli International S.A., Luxembourg, Luxembourg; *Int'l*, pg. 140
Rao, Dan, Pres.--Chadwick's of Boston, West Bridgewater, MA; *U.S. Public*, pg. 996
Rao, J. Rameshwar, Chm. Bd.--Orient Longman Ltd., Hyderabad, India; *Int'l*, pg. 1026
Rao, M., Area Rep./BGE--BGE-NH 8 Project, Jaipur, India; *Int'l*, pg. 823
Rapciewicz, Edward A., V.P.--Central Division, Hamilton, NJ; *U.S. Public*, pg. 438
Raper, Bryant, V.P.-Sls.--Greensboro Sales, Greensboro, NC; *U.S. Public*, pg. 611
Raper, Harold E., Gen. Mgr.--AlliedSignal Guidance & Control Systems, Mishawaka, IN; *U.S. Public*, pg. 50
Raper, Wiley, Pres.--General Merchandise Distributors, Inc., Dallas, TX; *U.S. Public*, pg. 653
Rapisarda, F., Mng. Dir.--Societa Assicuratrice Industriale Spa (SAI), Turin, Italy; *Int'l*, pg. 565
Rapoport, M., Pres.--Friden Alcatel, Hayward, CA; *Int'l*, pg. 55
Rapp, C., Pres.--Carborundum Abrasives North America, High Point, NC; *Int'l*, pg. 1174

Rapp, John, Chief Oper. Officer--Hawkeye Leasing Corporation, West Des Moines, IA; *U.S. Public*, pg. 1087
Rapp, John B., Exec. V.P.--First of America Trust Company, Kalamazoo, MI; *U.S. Public*, pg. 637
Rapp, Kenneth M., Pres. & Chief Oper. Officer--DynaMark, Inc., Saint Paul, MN; *U.S. Public*, pg. 610
Rapp, Mattias, Chief Exec. Officer--Straits Petroleum Limited, London, United Kingdom; *Int'l*, pg. 712
Rapp, Richard T., Pres.--National Economic Research Associates (NERA), White Plains, NY; *U.S. Public*, pg. 1049
Rappaport, Claude, Chief Oper. Officer--American Bearing Division, Inc., Oklahoma City, OK; *U.S. Public*, pg. 970
Rarick, Mide, Branch Mgr.--National Mine Service Company, Price Div., Price, UT; *Int'l*, pg. 281
Ras, Jaap, Mng. Dir.--Jotun Polymer B.V., Stellendam, Netherlands; *Int'l*, pg. 714
Rascoe, David S., Pres. & Chief Oper. Officer--Thermal Industries, Inc., Pittsburgh, PA; *U.S. Private*, pg. 490
Rasdal, Dan, Chm. Bd. & Chief Exec. Officer--Linfinity Microelectronics Inc., Garden Grove, CA; *U.S. Public*, pg. 1547
Rash, J. Dennis, Pres.--NationsBank Community Development Corp., Charlotte, NC; *U.S. Public*, pg. 1165
Rasheed, Aslam, Mng. Dir.--Euroconsult Pakistan, Lahore, Pakistan; *Int'l*, pg. 606
Rashkow, Ronald, Pres.--A-OK Delaware Inc., Schaumburg, IL; *Int'l*, pg. 533
Raskin, Fred C., Pres.--Midland Enterprises Inc., Cincinnati, OH; *U.S. Public*, pg. 549
Raskob, Horst, Dir.--Von Roll Eisen & Stahlgiesserei AG, Bienne, Switzerland; *Int'l*, pg. 1480
Rasmus, Ralf, Chief Oper. Officer--Aluma Metalli, Vantaa, Finland; *Int'l*, pg. 441
Rasmusen, Poul Steen, Pres.--Leca Portugal Argilas Expandidas S.A., Avelar, Portugal; *Int'l*, pg. 1200
Rasmussen, Alfredo Leontic, Pres.--Wackenhut Chile, S.A., Santiago, Chile; *U.S. Public*, pg. 1731
Rasmussen, Claes, Mng. Dir.--TBWA Copenhagen, Copenhagen, Denmark; *U.S. Private*, pg. 1063
Rasmussen, Gerald, Mgr.--Bonduel Telephone Co., Bonduel, WI; *U.S. Public*, pg. 1571
Rasmussen, Gerald A., Mgr.--Scandinavia Telephone Co., Iola, WI; *U.S. Public*, pg. 1571
Rasmussen, Hans-Henrik, Mng. Dir.--Young & Rubicam Copenhagen, Copenhagen, Denmark; *U.S. Private*, pg. 1199
Rasmussen, Karen, Chief Oper. Officer--A/S Akerlund & Rausing, Roedovre, Denmark; *Int'l*, pg. 33
Rasmussen, Louis C., Mng. Dir.--A.O. Smith Electric Motors (Ireland) Ltd., Bray, Ireland; *U.S. Public*, pg. 1477
Rasmussen, Robert, Mng. Dir.--Scan-Ad Odense A/S, Odense, Denmark; *Int'l*, pg. 1198
Rasmusson, Trond, Gen. Mgr.--Ciments du Togo, S.A., Lome, Togo; *Int'l*, pg. 1201
Rasor, John F., V.P.--Georgia-Pacific Eastern Wood Products Manufacturing Div., Atlanta, GA; *U.S. Public*, pg. 735
Rasp, Bob, Pres.--Teledyne Laars, Moorpark, CA; *U.S. Public*, pg. 43
Rasp, Robert, Pres.--Teledyne Laars/Jandy Products, Novato, CA; *U.S. Public*, pg. 43
Raspino, Louis A., Jr., Chm. Bd.--LL&E Yemen, Ltd., Hamilton, Bermuda; *U.S. Public*, pg. 269
Rasquin, W., Mgr.--Vision Centers, Brussels, Belgium; *Int'l*, pg. 533
Rasti, Svein, Chief Oper. Officer--Nobel Elektronikk A/S, Oslo, Norway; *Int'l*, pg. 1290
Ratanawichiew, Pakdee, Mng. Dir.--Thai CRT Co., Ltd., Ban Si Racha, Thailand; *Int'l*, pg. 1238
Ratcliff, Bob, Acting Gen. Mgr.--SNE Enterprises, Inc., Mosinee, WI; *U.S. Public*, pg. 1193
Ratcliff, Keith, Pres.--AGRA Plastics Inc., Mississauga, Canada; *Int'l*, pg. 30
Ratcliffe, Anthony, Gen. Mgr.--National Mutual New Zealand, Wellington, New Zealand; *Int'l*, pg. 908
Rath, F.E., Jr., Chm. Bd., Pres. & Chief Exec. Officer--Today's Kids, Booneville, AR; *U.S. Private*, pg. 1020
Rath, Gunter, Gen. Mgr.--C.H. Knorr Nahrungsmittelfabrik, Ges. mb H., Wels, Austria; *U.S. Public*, pg. 225
Rath, John, Pres.--Insurance Administration Center., Inc., Tampa, FL; *U.S. Public*, pg. 1312
Rathbone, Jim, Mng. Dir.--Sensormatic CamEra Ltd., Warwick, United Kingdom; *U.S. Public*, pg. 1457
Rathbun, John, Pres.--Venture Packaging, Inc., Charlotte, NC; *U.S. Private*, pg. 138
Rathemacher, Carl P., Pres.--Modern Handling Equipment of N.J., Inc., Edison, NJ; *U.S. Private*, pg. 755
Rathgeb, Karl-Helmut, Gen. Mgr.--Landesgirokasse Bank, New York, NY; *Int'l*, pg. 800
Rathgeber, Frank, Pres.--SMC International, S.A., Velizy-Villacoublay, France; *U.S. Public*, pg. 1717
Rathke, Dieter B., Pres.--Philipp Holzmann USA, Ltd., Charlotte, NC; *Int'l*, pg. 633
Rathke, Tom, Dir.-Admin.--Vesta Dial Forsikring A/S, Oslo, Norway; *Int'l*, pg. 1257
Rathke, Tom, Dir.-Admin.--DIAL Forsikring A/S, Oslo, Norway; *Int'l*, pg. 1257
Rathnam, Michael S.V., Resident Rep.--The World Bank, Bishek, Kyrgyzstan; *U.S. Private*, pg. 1190
Ratia, Heikki, Chief Oper. Officer--Plastilon Oy, Imatra, Finland; *Int'l*, pg. 913
Ratia, Lauri, Pres.--Lohja Rudus Oy AG, Helsinki, Finland; *Int'l*, pg. 1200
Ratkus, Ted, Sr. V.P.-Sls.--Shorewood Packaging Corporation of Virginia-Williamsburg Operations, Newport News, VA; *U.S. Public*, pg. 1468
Ratliff, Joseph, Dir.-Distribution--KYB Corp. of America, Cypress, CA; *Int'l*, pg. 727
Ratna, A.K., V.P.-Northern Region--India Photographic Company Limited, New Delhi, India; *U.S. Public*, pg. 552
Ratner, Albert B., Pres.--Forest City Credit Corporation, Cleveland, OH; *U.S. Public*, pg. 668
Ratner, Brian J., Pres.--Tower City Development, Inc., Cleveland, OH; *U.S. Public*, pg. 669
Ratner, James A., Pres. & Chief Exec. Officer--Forest City Commercial Construction Company, Inc., Cleveland, OH; *U.S. Public*, pg. 668
Ratner, James A., Pres. & Chief Exec. Officer--Forest City Rental Properties Corporation, Cleveland, OH; *U.S. Public*, pg. 668
Ratner, Ronald A., Pres. & Chief Exec. Officer--Forest City Residential Development Inc., Cleveland, OH; *U.S. Public*, pg. 669
Ratosi, E., Chm.--Dunastyr Polystyr. Manufacturing Co. Ltd., Budapest, Hungary; *Int'l*, pg. 429
Ratton, Jean Pierre, Chief Exec.--Industria Nacional de Cemento S.A., San Jose, Costa Rica; *Int'l*, pg. 630
Raty, Anssi, Mng. Dir.--Nokia Mobile Phones Manufacturing (USA) Ltd., Fort Worth, TX; *Int'l*, pg. 952
Ratz, William, Vice Chm. & Mng. Dir.-Willis Corroon Construction Div.--Willis Corroon Marine & Energy, Houston, TX; *Int'l*, pg. 1508
Ratz, William H., Reg. Construction Mng. Dir.--Willis Corroon Corp. of Texas, Houston, TX; *Int'l*, pg. 1507
Rau, Jerome E., Pres. & Chief Exec. Officer--Minuteman International, Inc., Addison, IL; *Int'l*, pg. 587
Rau, John, Pres. & Chief Exec. Officer--ABN/LaSalle North America Inc., Chicago, IL; *Int'l*, pg. 11
Rau, John, Pres. & Chief Exec. Officer--Chicago Title Insurance Co., Chicago, IL; *U.S. Public*, pg. 42
Rau, Lou, Pres.--NRCTSC, Atlanta, GA; *U.S. Public*, pg. 1182
Rau, Nelly Maria, Res. Dir.--Leo Burnett Co. Inc., Buenos Aires, Argentina; *U.S. Private*, pg. 185
Rau, Robert H., Pres. & Chief Exec. Officer--Rohr, Inc., Chula Vista, CA; *U.S. Public*, pg. 751
Rauber, Hans, Pres.--Corona Engineering Corporation, Lithonia, GA; *U.S. Public*, pg. 1761
Rauch, Ben, Mng. Dir.--Korn/Ferry International, Tokyo, Japan; *U.S. Private*, pg. 633
Rauch, Don, Pres.--M & C Specialties (Ireland) Limited, Athlone, Ireland; *U.S. Private*, pg. 684
Rauchle, Craig, Pres.--Inter-Tel DataComm, Inc., Phoenix, AZ; *U.S. Public*, pg. 888
Rauchle, Craig W., Pres.--Inter-Tel Technologies, Inc., Phoenix, AZ; *U.S. Public*, pg. 888
Rauchle, Craig W., Pres.--Southwest Telephone Systems, Inc., Phoenix, AZ; *U.S. Public*, pg. 888
Rauchwerger, Cristina, Country Mgr.--Utell International-Switzerland, Zurich, Switzerland; *Int'l*, pg. 1099
Raudi, Salvatore, Chm.--Telsi Ltd., London, United Kingdom; *Int'l*, pg. 1248
Rauenhorst, Neil, Pres.--Normandale Properties, Tampa, FL; *U.S. Private*, pg. 818
Raugust, T., Pres.--Autocon Industries Inc., Saint Paul, MN; *Int'l*, pg. 1026
Rauh-Hain, Rolf, Mng. Dir.--Dicaser S.A. de C.V., Mexico, Mexico; *U.S. Private*, pg. 903
Rauh, Steve, Gen. Mgr.--Frontier Communications of DePue, Inc., Depue, IL; *U.S. Public*, pg. 683
Raukko, Raimo, Mng. Dir.--Mykora Oy, Kiukainen, Finland; *Int'l*, pg. 728
Raul, Figueroa Jose, Reg. Mgr.--Monsanto de Costa Rica, S.A., San Jose, Costa Rica; *U.S. Public*, pg. 1125
Raull, Jorge, Mgr.--Banco Nacional de Mexico, Houston, TX; *Int'l*, pg. 574
Raum, Wolfgang, Country Mgr.--BMC Software GmbH, Frankfurt/Main, Germany; *U.S. Public*, pg. 162
Raunchle, Craig W., Pres.--Inter-Tel Midwest, Inc., Phoenix, AZ; *U.S. Public*, pg. 888
Rauscher, Sigfried, Mng. Dir.--Munters GmbH, Hamburg, Germany; *Int'l*, pg. 669
Rautamaki, Kari, Mgr.--CAE ScreenPlates-Finland, Varkaus, Finland; *Int'l*, pg. 238
Rautenberg, Sven P., Pres.--Wallbergs Fabriks Aktiebolag, Halmstad, Sweden; *U.S. Public*, pg. 37
Rautiainen, Ismo, Pres.--Roxon Oy, Hollola, Finland; *Int'l*, pg. 1353
Ravailhe, Serge, Dir.-Novotel Opers.--Societe Internationale des Hotels Novotel, Evry, France; *Int'l*, pg. 21
Raveggi, Ferdinando, Mng. Dir.--SIELTE Padana S.p.A., Turin, Italy; *Int'l*, pg. 1370
Raven, Charles H., Pres.--Hanson Investment Management Company, San Rafael, CA; *U.S. Public*, pg. 1673
Raven, Gregory, Pres.--Hills Department Store Company, Canton, MA; *U.S. Public*, pg. 828
Ravenstein, Kurt, Admin.--Cherry Creek Village Nursing Center, Wichita, KS; *U.S. Public*, pg. 837
Ravenswood, Cecil, Gen. Mgr.--Wigwam Resort, Litchfield Park, AZ; *Int'l*, pg. 721
Ravera, Philippe, Mng. Dir.--Neste Chimie France S.N.C., Silic, France; *Int'l*, pg. 914
Ravert, Scott, Asst. Branch Mgr.--McNeilus Companies, Morgantown, PA; *U.S. Private*, pg. 725
Ravesloot, Hugo, Dir. & Gen. Mgr.--Alcan Tubes, Redditch, United Kingdom; *Int'l*, pg. 51
Ravettino, Jorge, Gen. Mgr.--Peruana de Seguridad y Vigilancia, S.A. (Pesevisa), Lima, Peru; *U.S. Public*, pg. 1731
Ravin, Richard M., Chm. Bd., Pres. & Chief Exec. Officer--Combined Insurance Company of America, Chicago, IL; *U.S. Public*, pg. 118
Raviola, Giuliano, Mng. Dir.--Olivetti Advanced Technology Center, Inc., Cupertino, CA; *Int'l*, pg. 1002
Raviv, Gabriel Dr., Pres.--Bio-Logic Systems Corporation Ltd., Haifa, Israel; *U.S. Public*, pg. 230
Rawe, Martin C., Assoc. Dir.--WF Corroon-Global Support Unit, Thatcham, United Kingdom; *Int'l*, pg. 1502
Rawle, R.H., V.P. & Gen. Mgr.--Fabrication & Offshore Operations, Morgan City, LA; *U.S. Public*, pg. 1068
Rawlings, C.F., Chief Oper. Officer--Twin Disc (Pacific) Pty. Ltd., Albury, Australia; *U.S. Public*, pg. 1647
Rawlings, Dolores, Pres.--Crown Central Petroleum Foundation, Baltimore, MD; *U.S. Public*, pg. 462
Rawlings, Kyle, Chief Oper. Officer--Monitor Labs, Inc., Englewood, CO; *Int'l*, pg. 208
Rawlings, Michael S., Pres. & Chief Concept Officer--Pizza Hut, Inc., Dallas, TX; *U.S. Public*, pg. 1636
Rawls, Benjamin M., Pres.--Versar Risk Management, Inc., Springfield, VA; *U.S. Public*, pg. 1717
Rawls, Dennis E., Mgr.-Mdsg.--Noland Air Conditioning/Refrigeration Div., Newport News, VA; *U.S. Public*, pg. 1187
Rawls, Robert, Gen. Mgr.--Uniwood Div., Statesville, NC; *U.S. Public*, pg. 903
Ray, Clarence L., Jr., Pres.--Duke/Fluor Daniel, Charlotte, NC; *U.S. Public*, pg. 535
Ray, David, Exec. V.P. & Chief Oper. Officer--Husman Snack Foods, Co., Cincinnati, OH; *U.S. Private*, pg. 887
Ray, Don, Gen. Mgr.--WSAZ-TV, Huntington, WV; *U.S. Public*, pg. 984
Ray, J.W., Chief Exec. Officer--Pillar Electrical plc, London, United Kingdom; *Int'l*, pg. 267
Ray, John, Gen. Mgr.--Southwestern Graphite Co., Burnet, TX; *U.S. Public*, pg. 515
Ray, John, Pres. & Gen. Mgr.--WJHG-TV, Inc., Channel 7, Panama City, FL; *U.S. Public*, pg. 759
Ray, Russell L., Jr., Pres. & Chief Exec. Officer--World Airways, Inc., Herndon, VA; *U.S. Public*, pg. 1780
Ray, Shannon, Asst. V.P. & Branch Mgr.--Pacific Crest Investment & Loan (Encino Branch), Encino, CA; *U.S. Public*, pg. 1249
Ray, Terry, Pres.--American Color, Phoenix, AZ; *U.S. Public*, pg. 1133
Ray, William H, Jr., Exec. V.P. & Treas.--Torchmark Investment Advisory Company, Inc., Birmingham, AL; *U.S. Public*, pg. 1623
Rayburn, James, V.P.--The Walt Disney Company (Canada), Etobicoke, Canada; *U.S. Public*, pg. 514
Rayburn, Wayne, Pres.--Olen Corporation, Columbus, OH; *U.S. Private*, pg. 631
Rayden, Michael, Pres.--Limited, Too, Columbus, OH; *U.S. Public*, pg. 996
Raye, Eleanor T., Pres.--AMGRO, Inc., Worcester, MA; *U.S. Public*, pg. 54
Raymo, W. J., Property Mgr.--Sun City Sewer Company, Stamford, CT; *U.S. Public*, pg. 380
Raymo, W. J., Property Mgr.--Sun City West Utilities Company, Stamford, CT; *U.S. Public*, pg. 380
Raymond, Allan, Mng. V.P.--Korn/Ferry International, Minneapolis, MN; *U.S. Private*, pg. 633
Raymond, Howard W., Asst. to the Chm.--Stevens Security Systems, Paris, France; *U.S. Public*, pg. 1517
Raymond, Jeffrey, Mgr.--Badger Telecam, Inc., Neillsville, WI; *U.S. Public*, pg. 1571
Raymond, L. John, Pres.--Crestar Insurance Agency Incorporated, Richmond, VA; *U.S. Public*, pg. 458
Raymond, Paul, Mng. Dir.--Sulzer (UK) Ltd., Farnborough, United Kingdom; *Int'l*, pg. 1307
Raymond, Walter, Pres.--Heinkel Filtering Systems Inc., Bridgeport, NJ; *Int'l*, pg. 609
Raynal, Pierre, Mng. Dir.--SARMA, Saint Vallier, France; *Int'l*, pg. 1158
Rayner, Marcus J., Dir.--Weatherall Green & Smith (New York) Inc., New York, NY; *Int'l*, pg. 1488
Rayner, Tom, Chief Exec. Officer--Expanded Metal Industrial, Hartlepool, United Kingdom; *Int'l*, pg. 467
Rayner, Tom, Chief Exec. Officer--Industrial Building Components Ltd., Hartlepool, United Kingdom; *Int'l*, pg. 467
Raynor, Stephen K., Sr. V.P. & Chief Oper. Officer--Urban Group, Toronto, Canada; *Int'l*, pg. 253
Raza, Syed Ali, Sr. V.P. & Country Mgr.--Bank of America NT&SA, Karachi, Pakistan; *U.S. Public*, pg. 182
Razaq, Mohammad Abdul, Mng. Dir.--General Motors Italia, S.p.A., Rome, Italy; *U.S. Public*, pg. 722
Raziel, A., Gen. Mgr.--Flight Operations/BEDEK Aviation Group, Israel; *Int'l*, pg. 690
Razzano, Mike, Mgr.--Associated Wholesale Electric Co., La Mirada, CA; *U.S. Private*, pg. 92
Rdissi, Ali, Mgr.--Eastern American Energy Corp., Indiana, PA; *U.S. Private*, pg. 357
Re, Louis, Dir.-Media--Doubleday Book Club, Garden City, NY; *Int'l*, pg. 191
Read, Harold T., Exec. V.P. & Chief Oper. Officer--Value Line Securities, Inc., New York, NY; *U.S. Private*, pg. 137
Read, Robert A., Pres. & Chief Oper. Officer--NBD Banking Company, North, Chesterton, IN; *U.S. Public*, pg. 628
Read, Rosalie, Country Mgr.--Berlitz Schools of Languages Ltd., London, United Kingdom; *U.S. Public*, pg. 222
Readal, Tom, V.P.-Export Sls.--Penreco, Karns City, PA; *U.S. Public*, pg. 1273
Reade, J., Gen. Mgr.--Square D Co., Central Distribution Ctr., Memphis, TN; *Int'l*, pg. 1208
Reader, Dave, Chief Oper. Officer--D & H Tool and Die, East Sparta, OH; *U.S. Private*, pg. 1124
Reader, Norman, Mng. Dir.--Ancra Canada, Scarborough, Canada; *U.S. Private*, pg. 71
Reading, Andrew, Pres.--Micro Processor Systems, Inc., Sterling Heights, MI; *U.S. Public*, pg. 558
Reading, Anthony, Chm. Bd.--Smith & Wesson Corp., Springfield, MA; *Int'l*, pg. 1397
Reading, Anthony, Chm. Bd.--Tomkins Corporation, Dayton, OH; *Int'l*, pg. 1397
Ready, Jack, Mgr.-Opers.--Titan Tire Corporation of TN, Clinton, TN; *U.S. Public*, pg. 1618
Ready, Jim, Chief Tech. Officer--Microtec Division, San Jose, CA; *U.S. Public*, pg. 1086
Ready, Robert J., Pres.--Abolite Lighting Inc., Cincinnati, OH; *U.S. Public*, pg. 971
Reagan, Charles, Pres.--Patterson-Kelley Company, Tulsa, OK; *U.S. Public*, pg. 793
Reagan, J. B., V.P. & Gen. Mgr.--Research & Development Division, Palo Alto, CA; *U.S. Public*, pg. 1009
Reagan, Jerry, V.P., Reg. Dir. & Div. Mgr.--Wyle Electronics-Santa Clara, Santa Clara, CA; *Int'l*, pg. 1458
Reagan, Mark, Chm. Bd. & Chief Exec. Officer--Willis Corroon Construction Division, Nashville, TN; *Int'l*, pg. 1504

Realf, E.R., Gen. Mgr.--NUS International Pty. Ltd., Sydney, Australia; *U.S. Private*, pg. 787
Ream, L., Opers. Mgr.--Armco Inc. - Dover Operations, Dover, OH; *U.S. Public*, pg. 131
Ream, Norman B., Jr., Chm. Bd.--Greenbrier Valley National Bank, Lewisburg, WV; *U.S. Public*, pg. 836
Rearden, Daniel, Pres.--Bass Retail Div., South Portland, ME; *U.S. Public*, pg. 1291
Reardon, Daniel R., Pres.--G.H. Bass & Co., South Portland, ME; *U.S. Public*, pg. 1291
Reardon, John, V.P. & Controller--The Goldhirsh Group, New York, NY; *U.S. Private*, pg. 461
Reardon, John, V.P. & Gen. Mgr.--KTLA, Inc., Los Angeles, CA; *U.S. Public*, pg. 1636
Reardon, Leonard, Chief Oper. Officer--Worldwide Leasing, Troy, OH; *U.S. Public*, pg. 866
Reardon, Thomas J., Pres. & Chief Oper. Officer--C.H. Patrick & Co., Inc., Greenville, SC; *U.S. Public*, pg. 751
Reasoner, Robert R., Pres.--Hilleshog Mono-Hy Inc., Longmont, CO; *Int'l*, pg. 973
Reasor, Robert A., Pres. & Chief Exec. Officer--Security Bank & Trust Co., Mount Carmel, IL; *U.S. Public*, pg. 1217
Reattig, Randolph, Mng. Dir.--Bristol-Myers G.m.b.H., Neu-Isenburg, Germany; *U.S. Public*, pg. 255
Reaves, Dennis, Pres. & Chief Oper. Officer--Penn-Daniels, Inc., Quincy, IL; *U.S. Public*, pg. 1467
Rebeau, Kim, V.P.-Opers.--Lason, Inc., Madison Heights, MI; *U.S. Public*, pg. 979
Rebello, Monica Amaral, Gen. Mgr.--Salles/DMB&B Publicidade S.A., Brasilia, Brazil; *U.S. Private*, pg. 305
Reber, Stephen A., Pres.--Macbeth Div., New Windsor, NY; *U.S. Public*, pg. 965
Rebich, Robert, Jr., Pres.--Daedal Division, Harrison City, PA; *U.S. Public*, pg. 1259
Rebmann, Bruce, Chief Oper. Officer--Platinum Technology - Santa Barbara Laboratory, Goleta, CA; *U.S. Public*, pg. 1309
Rebne, Bjorn, Mng. Dir.--Vel-Vask Tekstil Service A/S, Oslo, Norway; *Int'l*, pg. 1286
Rebolledo, Rogelio, Pres.--Sabritas S.A. de C.V., Mexico, Mexico; *U.S. Public*, pg. 1278
Recabarren, Alberto, Gen. Mgr.--Fate do Brasil Ltda., Sao Paulo, Brazil; *Int'l*, pg. 478
Recayte, Daniel, V.P.--Shiseido France S.A., Paris, France; *Int'l*, pg. 1235
Rech, Werner, Dr., Mgr.--EG & G Heimann Opto. Gmbh, Wiesbaden, Germany; *U.S. Public*, pg. 544
Rechmann, Karl-Heinz, Chief Oper. Officer--Kloeckner-Wilhelmsburger GmbH, Geesthacht, Germany; *Int'l*, pg. 737
Recio Pando, Jose F., Mgr.--AB Sandvik International, Havana, Cuba; *Int'l*, pg. 1188
Reckert, J., Mng. Dir.--Bally-Biver S.a.r.l., Luxembourg, Luxembourg; *Int'l*, pg. 997
Reckert, Ullrich, Pres.--Henkel Canada Ltd., Mississauga, Canada; *Int'l*, pg. 612
Reckinger, Dennis, Pres.--Midwest Rubber, Deckerville, MI; *U.S. Public*, pg. 1176
Reckinger, Robert, V.P. & Mng. Dir.--Banque de Luxembourg, Luxembourg, Luxembourg; *Int'l*, pg. 406
Recnik, Ivan, Mgr.--Schiess-Metalna Gmbh, Maribor, Slovenia; *Int'l*, pg. 860
Recoder, Jose-Ignacio, Chief Oper. Officer--Boart Longyear S.A., Madrid, Spain; *Int'l*, pg. 76
Recorbet, Andre-Yves, Dir.--Oy Berlitz AB, Helsinki, Finland; *U.S. Public*, pg. 221
Recoussine, Jean-Louis, Chief Oper. Officer--Bank Brussels Lambert, New York Branch, New York, NY; *Int'l*, pg. 147
Reddekopp, Joe, Gen. Mgr.--Nashua Photo Limited, Saskatoon, Canada; *U.S. Public*, pg. 1152
Redden, Randolph, Admin.--Cloverleaf Healthcare, Hemet, CA; *U.S. Public*, pg. 1712
Redder, Don, Gen. Mgr.--Goshen County Abstract & Title, Torrington, WY; *U.S. Public*, pg. 626
Redding, A., Gen. Mgr.--Fletcher Wood Panels Limited, Auckland, New Zealand; *Int'l*, pg. 495
Redding, Mark, V.P. & Gen. Mgr.--J & L Fiber Services, Inc., Waukesha, WI; *U.S. Public*, pg. 789
Redding, P.S., Exec. V.P. & Chief Oper. Officer--Document Management Division, Dayton, OH; *U.S. Public*, pg. 1505
Reddington, Martha, V.P. & Dir.-Special Markets--Consumer Group Special Markets, New York, NY; *U.S. Private*, pg. 777
Reddington, Tom, Plant Mgr.--Northwestern Steel & Wire Company-Kentucky, A Delaware Corp., Sterling, IL; *U.S. Public*, pg. 1201
Reddrop, Colin, Pres.--Astra Charnwood, Leicester, United Kingdom; *Int'l*, pg. 93
Reddy, James M., Pres.--Pluess-Staufer (California), Inc., Lucerne Valley, CA; *Int'l*, pg. 1061
Reddy, Vishu, Gen. Mgr.--Electrostatic Technology, Inc., Branford, CT; *U.S. Public*, pg. 1189
Reder, Jim, Pres.--Atlas Foundry & Machine Co., Tacoma, WA; *U.S. Private*, pg. 1063
Redfield, John, V.P.--Great Lakes Filter, Detroit, MI; *U.S. Private*, pg. 13
Rediker, Dennis, Pres.--ECC International Inc., Atlanta, GA; *Int'l*, pg. 455
Redington, Mike B., Pres.--M/A/R/C Marketing and Research Counselors, Inc., Irving, TX; *U.S. Public*, pg. 1023
Redman, Allen, Mng. Dir.--Donaldson Australasia (Pty.) Ltd., Wyong, Australia; *U.S. Public*, pg. 517
Redman, Chuck, Pres.--Calavo Foods, Inc., Santa Ana, CA; *U.S. Private*, pg. 199
Redman, Franz, Mng. Dir.--Julius Meinl Grosshandels-Ges.m.b.H., Vienna, Austria; *Int'l*, pg. 856
Redman, John, Chief Oper. Officer--Electrolux Group, Luton, United Kingdom; *Int'l*, pg. 444
Redman, John, Chief Oper. Officer--Lamberts Healthcare Ltd., Tunbridge Wells, United Kingdom; *Int'l*, pg. 989
Redman, Pat, V.P.--Professional Information Managment, Southfield, MI; *U.S. Private*, pg. 982
Redman, Peter, Pres.--Cessna Finance Corp., Wichita, KS; *U.S. Public*, pg. 1589
Redmon, John W., Pres.--Brown & Root Power & Mfg., Houston, TX; *U.S. Public*, pg. 775
Redmond, Donald P., Pres. & Chief Exec. Officer--Integon National Insurance Co., Winston Salem, NC; *U.S. Public*, pg. 720
Redmond, Donald P., Pres. & Chief Exec. Officer--Integon Indemnity Corporation, Winston Salem, NC; *U.S. Public*, pg. 720
Redmond, Donald P., Pres. & Chief exec. Officer--Integon General Insurance Corporation, Winston Salem, NC; *U.S.* Public, pg. 720
Redmond, Donald P., Pres. & Chief Exec. Officer--New South Insurance Company, Winston Salem, NC; *U.S. Public*, pg. 720
Redmond, Donald P., Pres. & Chief Exec. Officer--Integon Specialty Insurance Company, Winston Salem, NC; *U.S. Public*, pg. 720
Redmond, Donald P., Pres. & Chief Exec. Officer--Integon Preferred Insurance Company, Winston Salem, NC; *U.S. Public*, pg. 720
Redmond, Donald P., Pres. & Chief Exec. Officer--Integon Casualty Insurance Company, Winston Salem, NC; *U.S. Public*, pg. 720
Redmond, Donald P., Pres.--National General Insurance Co., Earth City, MO; *U.S. Public*, pg. 721
Redmond, Wesley, Admin.--Sable Care Center, Aurora, CO; *U.S. Public*, pg. 836
Redondi, Attilio, Mng. Dir.--Dega S.r.l., Mori, Italy; *U.S. Public*, pg. 807
Redpath, Alan, Pres.-MMS Intl.--McGraw-Hill Financial Information Services Group, New York, NY; *U.S. Public*, pg. 1071
Redstone, Sumner M., Chm. Bd.--Viacom International Inc., New York, NY; *U.S. Private*, pg. 778
Reeb, Bill, Pres.--Ralph Wilson Plastics Co., Temple, TX; *U.S. Public*, pg. 1322
Reeb, H.B., Pres.--NRI Schools, Washington, DC; *U.S. Public*, pg. 1071
Reeb, Harold, V.P. & Gen. Mgr.--McGraw-Hill Continuing Education Center, Washington, DC; *U.S. Public*, pg. 1070
Reeb, William, Pres. & Chief Exec. Officer--Wilsonart International, Inc., Temple, TX; *U.S. Public*, pg. 1322
Reece, Bill, Chief Exec. Officer--HealthGate Data Corp., Malden, MA; *U.S. Public*, pg. 1182
Reece, Coy, Dir.--Hydril Rubber Opers., Humble, TX; *U.S. Private*, pg. 551
Reece, Paris G., III, Pres.--Financial Asset Management Corporation, Denver, CO; *U.S. Public*, pg. 1025
Reece, Randy, Mgr.--Weatherford US Inc., Riverton, WY; *U.S. Public*, pg. 1750
Reed, Andrew M., Ph.D., Pres.--PolyMedica Wound Care Company, Golden, CO; *U.S. Public*, pg. 1315
Reed, Brian D., Mng. Dir.--The Illinois Lock Co. Div., Wheeling, IL; *U.S. Public*, pg. 548
Reed, C.W., Pres.--Martin-Yale Industries, Inc., Wabash, IN; *U.S. Public*, pg. 591
Reed, Dale C., Div. Mgr.--Soladyne Division, San Diego, CA; *U.S. Public*, pg. 1097
Reed, Gail, Gen. Mgr.--Walker Lumber & Supply, Inc., Woodland, PA; *U.S. Private*, pg. 502
Reed, H. Thomas, Pres. & Gen. Mgr.--Penford Products Co., Cedar Rapids, IA; *U.S. Public*, pg. 1269
Reed, Jackie L., Pres. & Chief Exec. Officer--Regions Bank/Heard County, Franklin, GA; *U.S. Public*, pg. 1372
Reed, James R., Pres.--SeaquistPerfect Dispensing, Cary, IL; *U.S. Public*, pg. 125
Reed, John, Mgr.-Area Sls.--Gensym Corporation, Philadelphia Area Office, Trevose, PA; *U.S. Public*, pg. 731
Reed, John, Mng. Dir.--H.R. Williams Inc., Kansas City, MO; *U.S. Private*, pg. 1078
Reed, Kenneth R., Pres.--The Boeing Company Canada Ltd., Toronto, Canada; *U.S. Public*, pg. 242
Reed, Mark, Pres.--In Focus Services, Inc., Wilsonville, OR; *U.S. Public*, pg. 873
Reed, Martin, Dr., Chief Exec. Officer--Logica, Inc., Lexington, MA; *Int'l*, pg. 814
Reed, Mike, Mgr.--CoMet Steel, Inc., Dallas, TX; *U.S. Public*, pg. 412
Reed, Richard, Mng. Dir.--Brother International Corporation (Ireland) Ltd., Dublin, Ireland; *Int'l*, pg. 229
Reed, Robert N., Pres.--Reed Brothers Inc., Buhl, ID; *U.S. Private*, pg. 916
Reed, Sam, Chief Exec. Officer--Sunshine Biscuits, Inc., Woodbridge, NJ; *U.S. Private*, pg. 434
Reed, Sam, Pres. & Chief Exec. Officer--Keebler Company, Elmhurst, IL; *U.S. Public*, pg. 657
Reed, Sam, Chief Exec. Officer--Sunshine Biscuits, Inc., Woodbridge, NJ; *U.S. Public*, pg. 657
Reed, W., Pres.--North Safety Products, Safety Equipment Division, Cranston, RI; *Int'l*, pg. 1243
Reed, W.L., Pres.--North Safety Products, Hand Protection Division, Charleston, SC; *Int'l*, pg. 1243
Reed, W.L., Pres.--North Safety Products, Health Care Division, Rockford, IL; *Int'l*, pg. 1243
Reed, Warren, Pres.--WNEP-TV, Scranton, PA; *U.S. Public*, pg. 1174
Reed, William, Publ.--Better Homes and Gardens Wood Magazine, Des Moines, IA; *U.S. Public*, pg. 1094
Reed, William R., Jr., Chm. Bd., Pres. & Chief Exec. Officer--NBC Bank, FSB (Belzoni), Belzoni, MS; *U.S. Public*, pg. 1155
Reeder, D. Scott, Pres.--Daytronic Corporation, Miamisburg, OH; *Int'l*, pg. 126
Reeg-Muller, Angela, Chief Oper. Officer--EMS Kurierpost GmbH, Bonn, Germany; *Int'l*, pg. 407
Reehling, Ronald E., Pres.--Circle Business Credit, Inc., Indianapolis, IN; *U.S. Public*, pg. 1785
Rees, A.W., Pres.--Central California Traction Co., San Francisco, CA; *U.S. Public*, pg. 1668
Rees, David, V.P.--Bank of America NT&SA, Moscow, Russia; *U.S. Public*, pg. 182
Rees, P., Gen. Mgr.-U.K. Dental Opers.--CERAMCO Ltd., Weybridge, United Kingdom; *U.S. Public*, pg. 499
Reese, David, Pres.-Plastics Div.--Edison Plastics Div., South Plainfield, NJ; *U.S. Private*, pg. 1179
Reese, Howard, Gen. Mgr.--Levy Home Entertainment, Hillside, IL; *U.S. Private*, pg. 664
Reese, K. W., Chm. Bd. & Pres.--Tenneco Domestic International Sales Corp., Houston, TX; *U.S. Public*, pg. 1578
Reese, K. W., Chm. Bd.--Tenneco Financial Services, Inc., Houston, TX; *U.S. Public*, pg. 1578
Reese, K. W., Pres.--TCI International Sales Corp., Houston, TX; *U.S. Public*, pg. 1578
Reese, Richard B., Pres. & Chief Exec. Officer--JBB Worldwide, Inc., Deerfield, IL; *U.S. Public*, pg. 675
Reese, Richard B., Pres.--Bourbon Warehouse Receipts, Inc., Deerfield, IL; *U.S. Public*, pg. 675
Reese, Richard B., Pres.--Wood Terminal Company, Northbrook, IL; *U.S. Public*, pg. 675
Reese, Ulf, Pres.--Handelsbanken Finans, Stockholm, Sweden; *Int'l*, pg. 1327
Reese, William, Pres.--Spartywood Products, Inc., Spartanburg, PA; *U.S. Private*, pg. 983
Reeser, Alvin L., Exec. V.P. & Gen. Mgr.--United Space Boosters, Inc., Huntsville, AL; *U.S. Public*, pg. 1690
Reeser, J. R., Mgr.--DWF of Gaylord, Gaylord, MI; *U.S. Private*, pg. 326
Reeve, Roger, Chief Oper. Officer--Drayton Control (Engineering) Limited, West Drayton, United Kingdom; *Int'l*, pg. 1241
Reeve, Stan, Gen. Mgr.--ITW Waterbury Buckle, Waterbury, CT; *U.S. Public*, pg. 867
Reeves, Donna, Pres. & Chief Oper. Officer--Frontier Cellular, Rochester, NY; *U.S. Public*, pg. 683
Reeves, Doug, V.P. & Gen. Mgr.--Gage Marketing Group-West Coast, Newport Beach, CA; *U.S. Private*, pg. 437
Reeves, Graham, Chief Oper. Officer--Frionor (England) Ltd., Grimsby, United Kingdom; *Int'l*, pg. 516
Reeves, Jean, Chm. Bd., Pres. & Chief Exec. Officer--NationsBank/Hickman County, Centerville, TN; *U.S. Public*, pg. 1163
Reeves, Jenner, Mng. Dir.--Costain Oil, Gas & Process Limited Pipeline & Offshore Division, Wirral, United Kingdom; *Int'l*, pg. 336
Reeves, Marjorie, Mgr.--S.Two Systems, Inc., Atlanta, GA; *U.S. Public*, pg. 1524
Reeves, Mike, Gen. Mgr.--MTS Systems Ltd. (UK), Gloucester, United Kingdom; *U.S. Public*, pg. 1029
Reeves, Stuart, Exec. V.P.--EDS, Government Systems Group, Bethesda, MD; *U.S. Public*, pg. 570
Reeves, Thomas P., Mng. Dir.--Merisel Europe, Brentford, United Kingdom; *U.S. Public*, pg. 1096
Reeves, Thomas P., Acting Gen. Mgr.--Merisel France, Paris, France; *U.S. Public*, pg. 1096
Reeves, William, Mng. Dir.--USF Ltd., Meir, United Kingdom; *U.S. Public*, pg. 61
Regal, Robert J., Pres. & Chief Exec. Officer--Universal-Rundle Corp., New Castle, PA; *U.S. Public*, pg. 1193
Regan-Smith, Maureen, Publr.--The Denver Business Journal, LLC, Denver, CO; *U.S. Private*, pg. 19
Regan, Bob, Pres.--Air Systems Ltd., Brampton, Canada; *Int'l*, pg. 1398
Regan, Dennis, Pres.--Camp America, Greenwich, CT; *U.S. Private*, pg. 57
Regan, Dennis, Chief Fin. Officer--Leo Burnett Limited, London, United Kingdom; *U.S. Private*, pg. 185
Regan, Rob W., Mgr.--Moura Mine, Moura, Australia; *Int'l*, pg. 224
Regener, Otto, Mng. Dir.--Deutsche Bank Finance N.V., Curacao, Netherlands Antilles; *Int'l*, pg. 405
Regensburger, Klaus, Dr., Chief Oper. Officer--Chemie Linz UK Ltd., Richmond, United Kingdom; *Int'l*, pg. 356
Regnier, Francois, Mng. Dir.--The Brand Company, Boulogne, France; *Int'l*, pg. 116
Regulinski, Stephan G., Pres.--United Cogen, Inc., San Francisco, CA; *U.S. Public*, pg. 1653
Reherman, R.G., Chm. Bd. & Chief Exec. Officer--Energy Systems Group, Inc., Evansville, IN; *U.S. Public*, pg. 1471
Reherman, R.G., Chm. Bd., Pres. & Chief Exec. Officer--ComSource, Inc., Evansville, IN; *U.S. Public*, pg. 1471
Reherman, Ronald G., Chm. Bd., Pres. & Chief Exec. Officer--Southern Indiana Gas & Electric Co., Evansville, IN; *U.S. Public*, pg. 1471
Rehkopf, Ward, Plant Mgr.--Engine Components Div., Belmond, IA; *U.S. Public*, pg. 556
Rehmann, Larry J., Gen. Mgr.--John Crane Marine USA, Buffalo Grove, IL; *Int'l*, pg. 1339
Rehn, Jan-Peter, Mng. Dir.--Merita Bank Luxembourg S.A., Luxembourg, Luxembourg; *Int'l*, pg. 859
Rehn, Peter F., Mng. Dir.--CSC Australia, Saint Leonards, Australia; *U.S. Public*, pg. 423
Rehnberg, Jan, Chief Oper. Officer--Gambro S.A., Colombes, France; *Int'l*, pg. 668
Rehnman, Lars, Pres.--NCC Building - Jonkoping, Jonkoping, Sweden; *Int'l*, pg. 898
Reich, Charles, Div. V.P.--Occupational Health & Environmental Safety Division, Saint Paul, MN; *U.S. Public*, pg. 1605
Reich, Heinz, Gen. Mgr.--Resopal GmbH, Gross-Umstadt, Germany; *U.S. Public*, pg. 1322
Reichardt, Peter, V.P.--EMI Music Publishing, London, United Kingdom; *Int'l*, pg. 427
Reichel, Michael M., Mng. Dir.--Commerzbank AG-Beijing Representative Office, Beijing, China; *Int'l*, pg. 311
Reichel, Norris, V.P. & Gen. Mgr.--WOFL-TV, Lake Mary, FL; *U.S. Public*, pg. 1094
Reichelt, Ferdinand H., Pres.--Fireside Thrift, Newark, CA; *U.S. Public*, pg. 1694
Reicher, Michael, Pres.--UDL Laboratories, Inc., Rockford, IL; *U.S. Public*, pg. 1143

Reichert, Charles M., Pres. & Gen. Mgr.--BNI Coal, Ltd., Bismarck, ND; *U.S. Public,* pg. 1116
Reichert, Lothar, Chief Oper. Officer & Exec. V.P.--Porta Holdings Inc., Clearwater, FL; *Int'l,* pg. 857
Reichman, Bob, Editor--Sumter County Times, Bushnell, FL; *U.S. Private,* pg. 648
Reid, Alan A., Chief Oper. Officer--Foster's China, Central, Hong Kong; *Int'l,* pg. 501
Reid, Andrew, Pres.--Andy Johns Fashions, Inc., New York, NY; *U.S. Public,* pg. 233
Reid, Anthony, Mng. Dir.--Lincoln Smitweld Belgium NV, Drogenbos, Belgium; *U.S. Public,* pg. 997
Reid, Anthony, Mng. Dir.--Lincoln Smitweld BV, Nijmegen, Netherlands; *U.S. Public,* pg. 997
Reid, Bob, Mgr.-Division--Haleyville Manufacturing Of Elkhart, Elkhart, IN; *U.S. Public,* pg. 491
Reid, Charles, Pres.--United Guaranty Corp., Greensboro, NC; *U.S. Public,* pg. 84
Reid, Charles, Mng. Dir.--Baker Div., Hartselle, AL, *U.S. Public,* pg. 1486
Reid, Dave, Gen. Mgr.--KCBA-TV, Salinas, CA; *U.S. Public,* pg. 16
Reid, Dave, V.P. & Gen. Mgr.--Milcare, Inc., Zeeland, MI; *U.S. Public,* pg. 1112
Reid, David, Pres.--Medscreen Limited, London, United Kingdom; *U.S. Public,* pg. 1286
Reid, David, Gen. Mgr.--Stanfast, Inc., Buena Park, CA; *U.S. Public,* pg. 1505
Reid, David P., V.P. & Gen. Mgr.--KVOS Television Corp., Bellingham, WA; *U.S. Public,* pg. 16
Reid, Hugh J., Pres. & Gen. Mgr.--Hazelwood Farms Bakeries, Inc., Atlanta, GA; *U.S. Public,* pg. 1541
Reid, I.M., Chief Exec. Officer--Redland Aggregates Ltd., Groby, United Kingdom; *Int'l,* pg. 1090
Reid, I.M., Chief Exec. Officer--Redland Readymix Ltd., Groby, United Kingdom; *Int'l,* pg. 1091
Reid, J., Pres.--Ranco Inc., Plain City, OH; *Int'l,* pg. 1243
Reid, J.L., Gen Mgr.--Automotive Division, Geelong, Australia; *Int'l,* pg. 1057
Reid, Jack P., Chief Oper. Officer--Navajo Corp., Artesia, NM; *U.S. Public,* pg. 830
Reid, John, Gen. Mgr.--Colgate-Palmolive Ltd., Guildford, United Kingdom; *U.S. Public,* pg. 398
Reid, John W., Exec. V.P. & Chief Fin. Officer--Ranco North America, Plain City, OH; *Int'l,* pg. 1243
Reid, M. Bagley, Pres. & Chief Exec. Officer--Scott & Stringfellow Capital Management, Inc., Richmond, VA; *U.S. Public,* pg. 1445
Reid, P.A., Mng. Dir.--Baker Perkins (NZ) Limited, Auckland, New Zealand; *Int'l,* pg. 1240
Reid, Peter, Pres.--Titan Steel Corp., Baltimore, MD; *U.S. Private,* pg. 1089
Reid, Robert, Pres.--Iroquois Gas Transmission System, Shelton, CT; *Int'l,* pg. 1417
Reid, Robert, Pres.--Iroquois Gas Transmission System, Shelton, CT; *U.S. Public,* pg. 1787
Reid, Steve, Plant Mgr.--Crane Deming Pumps, Salem, OH; *U.S. Public,* pg. 457
Reid, W., Mng. Dir.--Brown Brothers & Company Ltd., Edinburgh, United Kingdom; *Int'l,* pg. 1466
Reid, William P., Pres. & Chief Exec. Officer--GSE Living Technology, Inc., Houston, TX; *U.S. Public,* pg. 770
Reid, William T., Pres.--G.I. Trucking Co., La Mirada, CA; *U.S. Public,* pg. 131
Reidenouer, John, Gen. Mgr.--Durand Inc., Philadelphia, PA; *U.S. Private,* pg. 638
Reidy, Carolyn K., Pres. & Publisher--Simon & Schuster Trade Division, New York, NY; *U.S. Private,* pg. 777
Reidy, Carolyn K., Pres. & Publisher--Simon & Schuster, New York, NY; *U.S. Private,* pg. 778
Reidy, Martin, Pres. & Chief Oper. Officer--R/GA Interactive, New York, NY; *U.S. Public,* pg. 1641
Reidy, Maureen, Pres.--Miss Universe, L.P., Los Angeles, CA; *U.S. Private,* pg. 1108
Reifer, Charles, Pres.--Louis Hand Div., New York, NY; *U.S. Private,* pg. 1094
Reifer, Charles, Pres.--Savoy Drapery Div., New York, NY; *U.S. Private,* pg. 1094
Reifert, Lothar, Pres.--Caterpillar Leasing GmbH (Ismaning), Ismaning, Germany; *U.S. Public,* pg. 315
Reiff, A., Mgr.--Hevea B.V., Raalte, Netherlands; *Int'l,* pg. 1481
Reiff, Craig, Corp. V.P.--Medi-Vac/Airlife Respiratory Care, McGaw Park, IL; *U.S. Public,* pg. 44
Reigh, Thomas E., Pres.--AlliedSignal-Jidosha Kiki Corporation, Gallatin, TN; *U.S. Public,* pg. 51
Reigle, Jeffrey A., Pres.--Regal Ware, Inc., Jacksonville, AR; *U.S. Private,* pg. 917
Reigrod, R.H., Pres.--Brother International de Mexico, S.A. de C.V., Mexico, Mexico; *Int'l,* pg. 229
Reihl, Lance, Pres.--PML Securities Co., Newark, DE; *U.S. Private,* pg. 892
Reihm, Homer D., Pres.--ILC Dover, Inc., Frederica, DE; *U.S. Private,* pg. 555
Reijonen, Petri, Mng. Dir.--Nokia Telecommunications Kft, Budapest, Hungary; *Int'l,* pg. 953
Reijrink, Jaco, Sr. Country Officer--Banque de Suez Nederland NV, Amsterdam, Netherlands; *Int'l,* pg. 314
Reijula, Peter, Pres.--McCain Citrus Inc., Oak Brook, IL; *Int'l,* pg. 850
Reike, Paul, Pres.--Outboard Marine Corp. of Canada Ltd., Peterborough, Canada; *U.S. Private,* pg. 478
Reiland, Nicholas, Chief Exec. Officer--Healthsource Arkansas, Inc., Little Rock, AR; *U.S. Public,* pg. 360
Reilly, Edward T., Pres. & Chief Oper. Officer--McGraw-Hill Broadcasting Co., Inc., New York, NY; *U.S. Public,* pg. 1070
Reilly, J.P. Jr., V.P. & Gen. Mgr.--Rhone-Poulenc, Chemical Division, Monmouth Junction, NJ; *Int'l,* pg. 1109
Reilly, Joseph M., Mgr.-Mfg. & Services--CAP Gemini America (Minneapolis Branch), Edina, MN; *Int'l,* pg. 264
Reilly, Lawrence J., Pres.--Granite State Electric Co., Lebanon, NH; *U.S. Public,* pg. 1171
Reilly, Lawrence J., Pres.--Massachusetts Electric Co., Westborough, MA; *U.S. Public,* pg. 1171
Reilly, Michael, Pres.--Old Ben Coal Co., Fairview Heights, IL; *U.S. Public,* pg. 1790
Reilly, Michael, Pres.--Franklin Coal, Fairview Heights, IL; *U.S. Public,* pg. 1790
Reilly, Michael F., V.P. & Plant Mgr.--Schilling Plant, Salinas, CA; *U.S. Public,* pg. 1066
Reilly, N.A., Mng. Dir.--De La Rue Smurfit Limited, Bray, Ireland; *Int'l,* pg. 386
Reilly, Paul V., Pres.--American Mail-Well Envelope, Englewood, CO; *U.S. Public,* pg. 1038
Reilly, Robert E., Pres.--Coclisa S.A. de C.V., Juarez, Mexico; *U.S. Public,* pg. 665
Reimerdes, Carl, Pres.--Fenton Hill American Limited, Valley Stream, NY; *Int'l,* pg. 103
Reimerdes, Carl, Pres.--The Sports Section Inc., Chicago, IL; *Int'l,* pg. 103
Reimers, E., Mgr.--Aluminum Norf GmbH, Neuss, Germany; *Int'l,* pg. 51
Reimers, Ernst, Mng. Dir.--Dresdner Bank AG, Johannesburg, South Africa; *Int'l,* pg. 419
Reimers, Svend, Gen. Mgr.--Analog Devices APS, Herlev, Denmark; *U.S. Public,* pg. 108
Reimers, T.E., Chief Oper. Officer & Exec. V.P.--Mitsubishi Fuso Truck of America, Inc., Bridgeport, NJ; *Int'l,* pg. 875
Reinarts, Thomas M., Chief Exec. Officer--Keller & Gannon, San Francisco, CA; *U.S. Private,* pg. 626
Reinbold, Dan, Office Mgr.--Heat Bath Park Metallurgical Products, Detroit, MI; *U.S. Private,* pg. 518
Reinbolt, Lynn C., Gen. Mgr.--Road Systems, Inc, Searcy, AR; *U.S. Public,* pg. 281
Reinders, Constant, Country Mgr.--Berlitz Schools of Languages B.V., Amsterdam, Netherlands; *U.S. Public,* pg. 222
Reinecke, Chris, Dr., Gen. Mgr.--Sasol Technology (Pty) Ltd., Sasolburg, South Africa; *Int'l,* pg. 1197
Reinecke, Ebbe, Mng. Dir.--Esselte A/S, Frederiksberg, Denmark; *Int'l,* pg. 460
Reinemund, Steven S., Chm. Bd. & Chief Exec. Officer--Frito-Lay Company, Plano, TX; *U.S. Public,* pg. 1277
Reiner, Arthur E., Chief Exec. Officer--Finlay Fine Jewelry Corporation, New York, NY; *U.S. Public,* pg. 624
Reinert, Jerry, Pres.--First National Bank of Springdale, Springdale, AZ; *U.S. Public,* pg. 639
Reines, Jose, Pres.--Fujitsu Business Communication Systems, Anaheim, CA; *Int'l,* pg. 526
Reines, Lewis, Pres.--W.B. Saunders Company, Philadelphia, PA; *U.S. Public,* pg. 784
Reinhard, Martin, Gen. Mgr.--Frontier Communications of Canton, Inc., Canton, PA; *U.S. Public,* pg. 683
Reinhard, Martin, Gen. Mgr.--Frontier Communications of New York, Inc., Monroe, NY; *U.S. Public,* pg. 684
Reinhardt, A., Chief Oper. Officer--Van Melle Brasil Ltda., Jundiai, Brazil; *Int'l,* pg. 1451
Reinhardt, Mary, V.P.-Sls.--Fairfield Williamsburg, Williamsburg, VA; *U.S. Public,* pg. 611
Reinhart, David C., V.P. & Gen. Mgr.--WFLA-AM, Tampa, FL; *U.S. Public,* pg. 922
Reinhart, David C., V.P. & Gen. Mgr.--WFLZ-FM, Tampa, FL; *U.S. Public,* pg. 922
Reinhart, Larry, Gen. Mgr.--Pneumatic Div., Richland, MI; *U.S. Public,* pg. 1259
Reinhold, Immo, Mgr.--EG & G Berthold (HQ), Bad Wilbad, Germany; *U.S. Public,* pg. 544
Reinisch, H., Mng. Dir.--EMI Austria GesmbH, Vienna, Austria; *Int'l,* pg. 427
Reinke, Jerome, Pres. & Chief Exec. Officer--Hoskins Mfg. Co., Detroit, MI; *U.S. Private,* pg. 83
Reinke, Jerome, Pres.--Hoskins Thermal Systems, Inc., Detroit, MI; *U.S. Private,* pg. 83
Reinke, Winfried, Co-Chief Oper. Officer--Luxembourg Branch, Luxembourg, Luxembourg; *Int'l,* pg. 645
Reinke, Winfried, Co-Chief Oper. Officer--IKB International, Luxembourg, Luxembourg; *Int'l,* pg. 646
Reinmann, Hartwig, Dr., Mgr.--Gotek GmbH, Frankfurt/Main, Germany; *Int'l,* pg. 861
Reinmuller, Gert H., Mng. Dir.--Creditanstalt a.s., Prague, Czech Republic; *Int'l,* pg. 348
Reins, Ralph E., Pres.--AlliedSignal Inc., AlliedSignal Automotive, Southfield, MI; *U.S. Public,* pg. 51
Reinskou, Svein, Mng. Dir.--Neste Kjemi A/S, Larvik, Norway; *Int'l,* pg. 915
Reis, A. Bethencourt, Mgr.--AEGON-Union Aseguradora, S.A. de Seguros y Reaseguros, Lisbon, Portugal; *Int'l,* pg. 28
Reis, Frederico Batalha, Mng. Dir.--A.S. Companhia Portuguesa de Seguros, Lisbon, Portugal; *Int'l,* pg. 784
Reis, Lucia, Mgr.--Broad National Bank-Bayway, Elizabeth, NJ; *U.S. Public,* pg. 257
Reis, Tony R., Mng. Dir.--IBM Switzerland, Zurich, Switzerland; *U.S. Public,* pg. 897
Reischl, Rudolf-Markus, Mng. Dir.--RTL 2, Grunwald, Germany; *Int'l,* pg. 562
Reischmann, Mark S., Reg. Dir.--Piper Jaffray Inc., Denver, CO; *U.S. Public,* pg. 1301
Reiser, H., Gen. Mgr.--Georg A. Brenner Arzneimittel-Fabrik GmbH, Alpirsbach, Germany; *U.S. Public,* pg. 80
Reisgen, Valentin, Gen. Mgr.--The West Company Hispania, S.A., Alcala de Henares, Spain; *U.S. Public,* pg. 1756
Reising, Jim, V.P.--Nightingale-Conant Recording & Tape Duplicating Div., Niles, IL; *U.S. Private,* pg. 799
Reisinger, Bob, Gen. Mgr.--Arrow/Schweber Electronics, Centerville, OH; *U.S. Public,* pg. 133
Reisner, John A., Pres.--Chemical Bank West, Cadillac, MI; *U.S. Public,* pg. 345
Reiss, Jacques, Pres.--Sanofi Canada, Mississauga, Canada; *Int'l,* pg. 445
Reiss, Richard, Pres.--Eagle Asset Management, Inc., Saint Petersburg, FL; *U.S. Public,* pg. 923
Reist, M.V., Pres.--Howe Monenco Inc., Thunder Bay, Canada; *Int'l,* pg. 31
Reitan, Bernt, Sr. V.P.--Elkem Aluminium ANS, Oslo, Norway; *Int'l,* pg. 446
Reitan, David, Reg. Mgr.-Sls.--PENCO-Nebraska, Omaha, NE; *Int'l,* pg. 1508
Reiter, Erich, Pres.--Villeroy & Boch (USA) Inc., Pine Brook, NJ; *Int'l,* pg. 1468
Reiter, G., Gen. Mgr.-After Market Dist. Europe--Timken Europa GmbH, Haan, Germany; *U.S. Public,* pg. 1618
Reiter, Klaus-Dieter, Rep.--DG Bank-Milan, Milan, Italy; *Int'l, pg. 352*
Reith, James N., Pres. & Chief Exec. Officer--Jennie-O Foods, Inc., Willmar, MN; *U.S. Public,* pg. 840
Reitman, Jeremy H., Pres.--Reitmans Inc., Montreal, Canada; *Int'l,* pg. 1102
Reitsema, Keith, Mng. Dir.--DMR Gruppe GmbH, Eschborn, Germany; *Int'l,* pg. 528
Reives, Louis, Pres.--Versatech Engineering, Lexington, KY; *U.S. Private,* pg. 712
Reizer, Michael, Pres.--Bredero-Shaw, Slough, United Kingdom; *U.S. Public,* pg. 529
Rejto, T., Gen. Mgr.--ING Bank Hungary, Budapest, Hungary; *Int'l,* pg. 649
Rejto, T., Gen. Mgr.--ING Bank Budapest, Budapest, Hungary; *Int'l,* pg. 649
Rekik, S., Mgr.-Fin.--Compagnie de Faisceaux Tunisian International S.A., Tunis, Tunisia; *U.S. Public,* pg. 723
Relam, Dennis, Mgr.-Branch--TIE Systems Arizona, Tempe, AZ; *U.S. Private,* pg. 1085
Relander, Krister, Mng. Dir.--ESAB Oy, Helsinki, Finland; *Int'l,* pg. 282
Relen, Daniel, Mng. Dir.--Construtora Dumez-GTM Ltda, Santo Amaro, Brazil; *Int'l,* pg. 823
Rellis, G., Chief Exec. Officer--OCE-Ireland Ltd., Dublin, Ireland; *Int'l,* pg. 994
Remack, Bob, Pres.--revolution, inc., Kansas City, MO; *U.S. Private,* pg. 1131
Rembold, Wilson K., V.P. & Gen Mgr.--Judd's, Inc., Strasburg, VA; *U.S. Private,* pg. 855
Rembutsu, Katsuhari, Chm. & Pres.--Daiwa Securities Trust Company, Jersey City, NJ; *Int'l,* pg. 375
Remes, P., Mng. Dir.--Nutricia France S.A., Paris, France; *Int'l,* pg. 992
Remick, James C., Pres.--Timpte, Inc., Council Bluffs, IA; *U.S. Private,* pg. 1088
Remish, Joe, Mgr.-Mfg.--Pittsburgh Tube Monaca Div., Monaca, PA; *U.S. Private,* pg. 868
Remmerbach, Jurgen, Dr., Chm. Bd.--Krupp Hoesch Verbarbeitung, Dortmund, Germany; *Int'l,* pg. 508
Remnanat, R.J., Chief Representative--Jardine Pacific Vietnam, Hanoi, Vietnam; *Int'l,* pg. 705
Remsing, Dennis, Exec. V.P. & Gen. Mgr.--RP alpha, Santa Monica, CA; *U.S. Private,* pg. 950
Remund, Rene, Pres.--Lambert Smith Hampton, Tampa, FL; *Int'l,* pg. 797
Remy, Jesus Matos, Gen. Mgr.--El Sol Compania de Seguros Generales, Lima, Peru; *Int'l,* pg. 61
Remy, Maurice, Chief Oper. Officer--Nortel France S.A., Saint Georges, France; *Int'l,* pg. 793
Ren, Q.J., Pres.--Shanghai Ebara Engineering and Services Co., Ltd., Shanghai, China; *Int'l,* pg. 432
Renafort, Michael, Mng. Dir.--AlliedSignal General Aviation Avionics, Singapore, Singapore; *U.S. Public,* pg. 52
Renaga, Jose'llorens, Chm.--Unidad Hermetica S.A., Saint Quirze del Valles, Spain; *Int'l,* pg. 443
Renard, Antoine, Pres.--Freinrail S.A., Reims, France; *Int'l,* pg. 738
Renard, Thomas, Pres.--Foley Martens Company, Minneapolis, MN; *U.S. Private,* pg. 416
Renaud, Anthony, V.P. & Gen. Mgr.--WBT AM & WBCY FM, Charlotte, NC; *U.S. Public,* pg. 926
Renaud, Ken, Dir.-Mktg.--Eaton Corp., Aerospace & Commercial Controls Div., Costa Mesa, CA; *U.S. Public,* pg. 557
Renaud, Ronald, Pres.--Flashmedia Advertising Inc., Outremont, Canada; *Int'l,* pg. 1076
Rendic, Jerko, Pres.--Rendic International, Miami, FL; *U.S. Private,* pg. 413
Rene, Jean-Guy, Chief Exec. Officer--Societe d'energie de la Baie James, Montreal, Canada; *Int'l,* pg. 640
Renerd, L., Mng. Dir.--S.C. Recherche et Developpement du Groupe Cockerill Sambre R.D.C.S., Ougree, Belgium; *Int'l,* pg. 301
Renfro, Linda R., Program V.P.--Martin Marietta Software Services, Baltimore, MD; *U.S. Public,* pg. 1007
Rengstedt, Arne, Pres.--Perstorp Compounds Inc., Florence, MA; *Int'l,* pg. 1037
Renirie, Lex, V.P. & Gen. Mgr.--Bakken Research Center B.V., Maastricht, Netherlands; *U.S. Public,* pg. 1083
Renken, Eva, Gen. Mgr.--Bank of Montreal - Germany, Frankfurt/Main, Germany; *Int'l,* pg. 155
Renna, Aurelio, Mng. Dir.--Erifin Servizi Finanziari S.p.A., Rome, Italy; *Int'l,* pg. 1368
Renner, John F., Pres.--Fidelity Oil Co., Bismarck, ND; *U.S. Public,* pg. 1025
Renner, John F., Pres.--Fidelity Oil Holdings, Inc., Bismarck, ND; *U.S. Public,* pg. 1025
Renner, L., Mgr.--Schweizerischer Bankverein, Lucerne, Switzerland; *Int'l,* pg. 1329
Renner, Lowell, Mgr.-Opers.--Masoneilan North American Operations, Houston, TX; *U.S. Public,* pg. 528
Renner, Reinhard, Chief Exec. Officer & Bus. Devel/Information--MHI Partners Werbeagentur GMBH, Starnberg, Germany; *U.S. Public,* pg. 1422
Rennie, Alex, Gen. Mgr.--Canadian Fabricated Products, Stratford, Canada; *U.S. Public,* pg. 354
Rennie, Stephen, Chief Exec. Officer--Glynwed Consumer & Construction Products Ltd., Royal Leamington Spa, United Kingdom; *Int'l,* pg. 554
Rennirt, Jim, Plant Mgr.--Transmission Div., Kings Mountain, NC; *U.S. Public,* pg. 556
Renollet, Lewis R., Pres. & Chief Exec. Officer--The Citizens Savings Bank Company, Pemberville, OH; *U.S. Public,* pg. 1412

Renouard, Edward J., V.P. & Gen. Mgr.--Everett Division, Everett, WA; *U.S. Public*, pg. 240
Renreard, Dominique, Chm.--Total Norge AS, Oslo, Norway; *Int'l*, pg. 1409
Rensi, Edward H., Pres. & Chief Exec. Officer--McDonald's U.S.A., Oak Brook, IL; *U.S. Public*, pg. 1069
Rensinghoff, Stefan, Chief Oper. Officer--Hong Kong Representative Office, Hong Kong, Hong Kong; *Int'l*, pg. 645
Rentas, Carlos, Gen. Mgr.--Sensormatic del Caribe, Isla Verde, PR; *U.S. Public*, pg. 1457
Rentenbach, T. M., Pres. & Chief Exec. Officer--Rentenbach Constructors Incorporated, Knoxville, TN; *U.S. Private*, pg. 923
Renteria, Efrain, Plant Mgr.--Raychem Technologias, S.A. DE C.V., Tijuana, Mexico; *U.S. Public*, pg. 1363
Renton, Douglas, Plant Mgr.--Cobourg Plant, Cobourg, Canada; *U.S. Public*, pg. 201
Renton, Steve, V.P. & Gen. Mgr.--Harris Ranch Restaurant, Coalinga, CA; *U.S. Private*, pg. 506
Renvall, Alf, Pres.--Valmet-Raisio Oy, Raisio, Finland; *Int'l*, pg. 1448
Renwick, Robin, Sir, Chm. Bd.--Fluor Daniel Limited, Camberley, United Kingdom; *U.S. Public*, pg. 660
Renzi, R., Chief Oper. Officer & Mng. Dir.--Yale Security Products S.p.A. (Italy), Aprilia, Italy; *Int'l*, pg. 1499
Renzulli, Michael H., Pres.--Sally Beauty Company, Inc., Denton, TX; *U.S. Public*, pg. 38
Reol, Jean, Mng. Dir.--Fenwick Kalmar SA, Cergy-Pontoise, France; *Int'l*, pg. 1421
Repass, Thomas, V.P.--Rottlund Homes of Indiana, Inc., Indianapolis, IN; *U.S. Public*, pg. 1406
Replane, Chuck, V.P.-Sls.--Automotive Products, Elkhart, IN; *U.S. Public*, pg. 285
Replogle, Robert P., V.P. & Dir.--International Sales Division, Harleysville, PA; *U.S. Public*, pg. 1100
Replogle, Robert P., V.P. & Dir.--Mefiag Division, Harleysville, PA; *U.S. Public*, pg. 1100
Repman, Jim, Pres.--Onoda Northwest, Inc., Seattle, WA; *Int'l*, pg. 284
Requien, Francois, Co-Mgr.--Euro RSCG Ensemble, Lyon, France; *Int'l*, pg. 600
Requillart, Alain, Gen. Mgr.--Forbo Sarlino SA, Reims, France; *Int'l*, pg. 498
Resca, Mario, Mng. Dir.--McDonald's Italia S.r.l., Milan, Italy; *U.S. Public*, pg. 1069
Reschke, Wilfried A., Mgr.--Commerzbank AG-Copenhagen Representative Office, Copenhagen, Denmark; *Int'l*, pg. 311
Reseigh, Christopher, Pres.--Parsons Brinckerhoff Construction Services, Inc., Herndon, VA; *U.S. Private*, pg. 841
Resell, John, Div. Mgr.--Oliver Rubber Co., Asheboro, NC; *U.S. Public*, pg. 1504
Resende, Itamar, Pres.--Metallurg do Brazil Ltda., Sao Paulo, Brazil; *U.S. Private*, pg. 735
Resende, Marco Antonio, Gen. Mgr.--Acos Villares Plant - Mogi das Cruz, Sao Paulo, Brazil; *Int'l*, pg. 23
Reshef, Ron, Rep. for Panama--Bank Hapoalim (Panama City), Panama, Panama; *Int'l*, pg. 150
Resmini, Fabrizio, Mgr.--Master Tools S.p.A., Rovereto, Italy; *Int'l*, pg. 1186
Resmini, Fabrizio, Mgr.--Dormer Tools S.p.A., Milan, Italy; *Int'l*, pg. 1186
Resnick, Jack, Pres. & Chief Exec. Officer--Transkrit Corporation, Roanoke, VA; *U.S. Private*, pg. 782
Ressler, Azarya, Sr. V.P. & Mgr.--Bank Hapoalim (Chicago), Chicago, IL; *Int'l*, pg. 149
Rester, James C., Pres.--Sime Darby Commodities Inc., Destin, FL; *Int'l*, pg. 1250
Rester, James M., Pres.--Sandestin Resort Inc., Destin, FL; *Int'l*, pg. 1250
Resto, Edwin, Mgr.--W. Braun Distribution Center, Summit, IL; *U.S. Private*, pg. 166
Restrepo, Adriana, Reg. Dir.-Andean Region--Utell International-Colombia, Bogota, Colombia; *Int'l*, pg. 1098
Restrepo, Joe, Opers. Mgr.--TMP Worldwide/Direct Marketing Services, Miami, FL; *U.S. Private*, pg. 1064
Restuccia, Bernard S., Pres.--Ford Motor Dealership Facilities Co., Dearborn, MI; *U.S. Public*, pg. 664
Restuccia, Eduardo, Mng. Dir.--Compania Ericsson S.A.C.I., Buenos Aires, Argentina; *Int'l*, pg. 1365
Resweber, Louis J., Pres. & Chief Exec. Officer--Network Acquisition Corp., Baton Rouge, LA; *U.S. Public*, pg. 1169
Reszler, Akos, Chief Oper. Officer--Recognita, Budapest, Hungary; *U.S. Public*, pg. 291
Retamozo, Juan, Mgr.--Sandvik del Peru S.A., Lima, Peru; *Int'l*, pg. 1188
Retelle, John P., Pres.--PAR Government Systems Corporation, New Hartford, NY; *U.S. Public*, pg. 1256
Rettinger, Dale G., Pres.--PDC Securities, Inc., Bridgeport, WV; *U.S. Public*, pg. 1280
Rettke, Wayne, Mng. Dir.--Mosler Counter Systems Div., Buffalo, NY; *U.S. Private*, pg. 763
Retzler, K.E., V.P.--Carlson Acquisition Group, Minneapolis, MN; *U.S. Private*, pg. 212
Reuflinger, Paul, Pres.--Sobelair S.A., Brussels, Belgium; *Int'l*, pg. 1168
Reum, James L., Pres.--LPI Corporation, Hollywood, FL; *U.S. Public*, pg. 804
Reum, James L., Pres.--Aircraft Technology, Inc., Hollywood, FL; *U.S. Public*, pg. 804
Reuning, J., Chm. Bd. & Gen. Dir.--Otis GmbH, Berlin, Germany; *U.S. Public*, pg. 1690
Reuter, Bernard, Pres.--Villeroy & Boch Tableware, Ltd., Princeton, NJ; *Int'l*, pg. 1468
Reuter, Carol, Pres.--New York Life Foundation, New York, NY; *U.S. Private*, pg. 795
Reuter, Charles, Plant Mgr.--Acme Brick Co., Jamestown, LA; *U.S. Public*, pg. 936
Reuter, D., Mng. Dir.--Shell Research Ltd., London, United Kingdom; *Int'l*, pg. 1139
Reuter, Edzard, Dr., Chm.--Berliner Bank AG, Berlin, Germany; *Int'l*, pg. 159
Reuter, Gerald N., First V.P.--NBD Leasing, Inc., Indianapolis, IN; *U.S. Public*, pg. 628
Reuter, William J., Chm. Bd., Pres. & Chief Exec. Officer--Farmers and Merchants Bank and Trust, Hagerstown, MD; *U.S. Public*, pg. 1542
Reuter, William J., Pres.--Susquehanna Bancshares South, Inc., Lititz, PA; *U.S. Public*, pg. 1543
Reuterskiold, Clas, Pres.--Inductus/Industrial Operations, Stockholm, Sweden; *Int'l*, pg. 678
Reutlinger, Paul, Chm. Bd.--Delta Air Transport N.V., Deurne, Belgium; *Int'l*, pg. 1168
Reuven, Y., Chief Oper. Officer--BL Jersey Ltd, Saint Helier, United Kingdom; *Int'l*, pg. 150
Reuveni, Moshe, Mng. Dir.--Reuveni Pridan Advertising Agency Ltd., Tel Aviv, Israel; *U.S. Private*, pg. 186
Revely, Thomas, III, Pres. & Chief Exec. Officer--Cincinnati Bell Supply Company, Cincinnati, OH; *U.S. Public*, pg. 367
Revington, George, Pres.--Universal Furniture Industries, Inc., High Point, NC; *U.S. Private*, pg. 432
Revis, William T., Gen. Mgr.--Avent, S.A. de C.V., Nogales, Mexico; *U.S. Public*, pg. 959
Revoir, P.J., Mng. Dir.--Red Carnation Gums Ltd., London, United Kingdom; *Int'l*, pg. 1034
Rew, H.B. Jr., Pres. & Chief Exec. Officer--Farmers & Merchants Bank-Eastern Shore, Onley, VA; *U.S. Public*, pg. 1089
Rewey, Robert L., V.P.--Ford Sales Operations, Dearborn, MI; *U.S. Public*, pg. 662
Rex, Scot, Mgr.-Plant--Sugar Creek Packing Co., Washington Court House, OH; *U.S. Private*, pg. 1049
Rexach, Eduardo Serra, Pres.--Peugeot Talbot Espana, Madrid, Spain; *Int'l*, pg. 1021
Rey-Baltar, Cesareo, Dir.--Generale Bank - Banco Belga, Valencia, Spain; *Int'l*, pg. 547
Rey, Alfonso, Chief Exec. Officer--Milk Products Holdings (Latin America) Ltd., Fort Lauderdale, FL; *Int'l*, pg. 923
Rey, Yves, Mng. Dir.--McCain Sunnyland Belgium, Turnhout, Belgium; *Int'l*, pg. 850
Reyenger, Rick, Pres.--Carl A. Lowe Industries, Inc., Lebanon, MO; *U.S. Private*, pg. 478
Reyenger, Rick, Plant Mgr.--Hydra-Sports Corporation, Nashville, TN; *U.S. Private*, pg. 478
Reyenger, Rick, Pres.--Sea Nymph Inc., Lebanon, MO; *U.S. Private*, pg. 478
Reyland, N., Dir.-Admin.--Captive Management Company SA (Captima), Luxembourg, Luxembourg; *Int'l*, pg. 548
Reymond, Antoine, Mgr.--Partner Relations, Europe, Voisins-le-Bretonneux, France; *U.S. Public*, pg. 1032
Reynier, Jean, Chief Oper. Officer--Rhone-Poulenc Italia SpA, Milan, Italy; *Int'l*, pg. 1113
Reynold, Randolph, Dir.--Sayanal, Moscow, Russia; *U.S. Public*, pg. 1387
Reynolds, Brian T., Pres.--Correctional Foodservices Management, Palm Beach Gardens, FL; *U.S. Public*, pg. 1731
Reynolds, C., Mng. Dir.--Forward Insurance Brokers Limited, Birmingham, United Kingdom; *Int'l*, pg. 216
Reynolds, David, Gen. Mgr.--Living Color Div., Glen Cove, NY; *U.S. Public*, pg. 730
Reynolds, David, Admin.--Golden Plains Care Center, Hutchinson, KS; *U.S. Public*, pg. 837
Reynolds, Donald W., Mgr.--Delta County Tele-Comm, Inc., Paonia, CO; *U.S. Public*, pg. 1571
Reynolds, Edgar L., Pres.--Bellsouth Wireless, Inc., Atlanta, GA; *U.S. Public*, pg. 208
Reynolds, Glenn, Chief Oper. Officer--Prior Remanufacturers, Inc., Garland, TX; *U.S. Private*, pg. 300
Reynolds, J.J., Div. V.P.--Ameron Pole Products & Systems, Fillmore, CA; *U.S. Public*, pg. 99
Reynolds, James G., Pres.--Gray & Company, Forest Grove, OR; *U.S. Private*, pg. 876
Reynolds, Joseph, Chief Oper. Officer--Delmar Publishers Inc., Albany, NY; *U.S. Public*, pg. 1600
Reynolds, Joseph C., Pres.--Carolina First Mortgage Company, Columbia, SC; *U.S. Public*, pg. 306
Reynolds, M., Mgr.--Kodak Limited, Glasgow, United Kingdom; *U.S. Public*, pg. 553
Reynolds, Mary Ann, Admin.--Majestic Pines Care Center, Hayward, CA; *U.S. Private*, pg. 733
Reynolds, Mike, Mng. Dir.--BellSouth New Zealand, Auckland, New Zealand; *U.S. Public*, pg. 208
Reynolds, Mike, Mgr.--Sun Valley Cablevision, Inc., Ketchum, ID; *U.S. Public*, pg. 1553
Reynolds, Pat, Branch Mgr.--Eby-Brown Co., Aurora, IL; *U.S. Private*, pg. 359
Reynolds, R.J., Pres.--Jaguar Canada Inc., Bramalea, Canada; *U.S. Public*, pg. 667
Reynolds, Randolph N., Pres.--Alumino Reynolds de Venezuela, S.A., Maracay, Venezuela; *U.S. Public*, pg. 1386
Reynolds, Robert, Plant Mgr.--Rhone-Poulenc Specialty Plastics Div., Lakewood, NJ; *Int'l*, pg. 1110
Reynolds, Ron, Gen. Mgr.--INCA Presswood Pallets, Ltd., Sardis, MS; *Int'l*, pg. 678
Reynolds, S.L., Pres.--Porth Plastic Co., Des Plaines, IL; *Int'l*, pg. 233
Reynolds, Stephen A., V.P. & Gen. Mgr.-Beet Sugar Opers.--Holly Sugar Corporation, Sugar Land, TX; *U.S. Public*, pg. 872
Reynolds, Stephen D., Admin.--Hillhaven Rehabilitation Convalescent Center, Asheville, Asheville, NC; *U.S. Public*, pg. 1714
Reynolds, Steve, Plant Mgr.--Baldor Electric Company, Ozark, AR; *U.S. Public*, pg. 169
Reynolds, Terri, Admin.--Gulfport Convalescent Center Manor, Gulfport, MS; *U.S. Public*, pg. 1713
Reynolds, Tom, Gen. Mgr.--Jannock Steel Fabricating, Inc., Spokane, WA; *Int'l*, pg. 699
Reynoldson, Peter, Mng. Dir.-Australia--Cooper Tools Pty. Ltd., Albury, Australia; *U.S. Public*, pg. 445
Reynoldson, Ray, Mng. Dir.--Quality Heat Treatment, Bayswater, Australia; *U.S. Public*, pg. 530
Reyonds, Darlene, V.P.--Westmark Mortgage Corporation, Costa Mesa, CA; *U.S. Public*, pg. 1761
Reznik, Maurice, Pres.--Warner's, Bridgeport, CT; *U.S. Public*, pg. 1738
Rhaleb, Nourdin, Gen. Mgr.--Cinemapresse Agence Conseil en Communication, Casablanca, Morocco; *U.S. Private*, pg. 1198
Rhea, Jim, Chief Oper. Officer--Hudson General Corp., Des Plaines, IL; *U.S. Public*, pg. 845
Rheaume, Ghislain, Branch Mgr.--Financial Collection Agencies, Sainte-Foy, Canada; *Int'l*, pg. 470
Rhee, Kwang-in, Chief Rep.--The Export-Import Bank of Korea, New York, NY; *Int'l*, pg. 467
Rhee, Seong, Chief Oper. Officer--Bosch Braking Systems-North America, Engineering Center, Troy, MI; *Int'l*, pg. 205
Rhein-Knudsen, Claus, Rep.--Christiania Bank-Copenhagen Representative Office, Copenhagen, Denmark; *Int'l*, pg. 289
Rhein, Barry, V.P.-Opers.--Johnson & Johnson Asia Pacific, Singapore, Singapore; *U.S. Public*, pg. 930
Rhind, Jerry S., Gen. Mgr.--Alumax Extrusions, Inc., Plant City, FL; *U.S. Public*, pg. 59
Rhoads, Ross H., Gen. Mgr.--Powertrain Div., Hagerstown, MD; *Int'l*, pg. 1103
Rhode, Oscar, Pres.--Bayer Japan Ltd., Tokyo, Japan; *Int'l*, pg. 174
Rhodenizer, Wayne, Pres. & Gen. Mgr.--Brockhouse Canada Limited, Bramalea, Canada; *Int'l*, pg. 426
Rhodes, Barry, Chief Oper. Officer--Turner Machine Company, Salem, OH; *U.S. Private*, pg. 368
Rhodes, Calvin, Pres.--Flowers Baking Co. of Opelika, Inc., Opelika, AL; *U.S. Public*, pg. 657
Rhodes, Dee Dee, V.P.--AmSouth Mortgage Co., Birmingham, AL; *U.S. Public*, pg. 105
Rhodes, George, Pres.--SACOM, Inc., Frederick, MD; *U.S. Private*, pg. 956
Rhodes, J., Reg. Mgr.--Manulife Financial - Phoenix, Phoenix, AZ; *Int'l*, pg. 841
Rhodes, J.S., Mng. Dir.--Superform Metals, Blackpool, United Kingdom; *Int'l*, pg. 52
Rhodes, James T., Pres. & Chief Exec. Officer--Virginia Electric and Power Company, Richmond, VA; *U.S. Public*, pg. 516
Rhodes, Mark, Dir.--Willis Corroon Credit Limited, Birmingham, United Kingdom; *Int'l*, pg. 1502
Rhodes, Peter, Mng. Dir.--Reed MIDEM Organisation-UK, London, United Kingdom; *Int'l*, pg. 1096
Rhodes, Richard G., Pres. & Chief Exec. Officer--Regions Bank/Dalton/Cartersville/Chattanooga, Dalton, GA; *U.S. Public*, pg. 1372
Rhonehouse, Robert, Pres.--ABB CEAG Power Supplies Inc., Palm Coast, FL; *Int'l*, pg. 4
Rhulen, Harry W., Pres.--Frontier Pacific Insurance Company, La Jolla, CA; *U.S. Public*, pg. 685
Rhulen, Walter A., Pres.--Frontier Insurance Company, Rock Hill, NY; *U.S. Public*, pg. 685
Rhune, Ron, Div. Mgr.--Wyle Electronics-Austin, Austin, TX; *Int'l*, pg. 1457
Riahi, Brahim Ben, Pres. Dir. Gen.--Societe Tunisienne d'Assurances et de Reassurances, Tunis, Tunisia; *Int'l*, pg. 61
Rialp, E.A., Gen. Mgr.--S.C. Johnson & Son, Inc., Manila, Philippines; *U.S. Private*, pg. 593
Rian, G., Gen. Mgr.--Kodak Norge A/S, Kolbotn, Norway; *U.S. Public*, pg. 554
Ribalta, Juan, Chief Oper. Officer--Commercial Henkel S.A. (Cohesa), Barcelona, Spain; *Int'l*, pg. 611
Ribarchik, Andy, V.P.--United Insurance Company of America, Schiller Park, IL; *U.S. Public*, pg. 1694
Ribas, Iraja B., Pres.--Kvaerner Pulping Ltda., Curitiba, Brazil; *Int'l*, pg. 768
Ribas, Iraja B., Pres.--Gotaverken Energy do Brasil, Rio de Janeiro, Brazil; *Int'l*, pg. 771
Ribas, Juan, Gen. Mgr.--Braun Espanola, S.A., Llobregat, Spain; *U.S. Public*, pg. 744
Ribaut, Gerard, Chief Oper. Officer--MTS Systems France (Marne la Vallee), Marne la Vallee, France; *U.S. Public*, pg. 1029
Ribbers, Rob, Dir. Gen.--Generale Bank - Maastricht, Maastricht, Netherlands; *Int'l*, pg. 547
Ribeiro, Francisco Flavio P., Mgr.--Manaus Branch, Manaus, Brazil; *Int'l*, pg. 139
Ribes, Jean-Martial, Mng. Dir.--Ketchum Public Relations/Paris, Levallois-Perret, France; *U.S. Private*, pg. 617
Ribich, Lewis J., Pres.--Ramsey Technology, Inc., Minneapolis, MN; *U.S. Public*, pg. 1592
Ribolla, Luigi, Pres.--Heinz Plasmon Dietetci Alimentari S.p.A., Milan, Italy; *U.S. Public*, pg. 806
Ribolla, Luigi, Chm. Bd.--PLADA S.p.A., Milan, Italy; *U.S. Public*, pg. 807
Ribosa, Pedre, Mgr.--Mead Sistemas Embalaje S.A., Barcelona, Spain; *U.S. Public*, pg. 1077
Ricard, Michael, V.P. & Gen. Mgr.--Shutters, Inc., Hebron, IL; *U.S. Public*, pg. 832
Riccardi, Richard G., Pres.--Motion Control Systems Division, San Diego, CA; *U.S. Public*, pg. 157
Ricci, Mario, Mng. Dir.--S.I.A., S.p.A., Milan, Italy; *Int'l*, pg. 170
Ricciardi, Joe, Pres.--Detectors, Inc., Graham, TX; *U.S. Private*, pg. 727
Ricco, Enzo, Chief Oper. Officer--Shiseido Cosmetici (Italia) S.p.A., Milan, Italy; *Int'l*, pg. 1235
Ricco, Gary, Pres.--Farley Candy Company, Chicago, IL; *U.S. Private*, pg. 397
Ricco, William, Pres.--Oxford Health Centers, Norwalk, CT; *U.S. Public*, pg. 1239
Riccobono, Joseph, Pres.--Institutional Brokers Estimate System Inc. (IBIS), New York, NY; *U.S. Public*, pg. 1325
Rice, Bill, Gen. Mgr.--Stretch Film, Matthews, NC; *U.S. Public*, pg. 5

Rice, C.J., Mng. Dir.--Butler's Warehousing & Distribution Ltd., Greenford, United Kingdom; *Int'l*, pg. 1033
Rice, C.J., Asst. Mng. Dir.--P&O European Transport Services Ltd., Altrincham, United Kingdom; *Int'l*, pg. 1033
Rice, Charles A., Pres. & Chief Exec. Officer--Dey Laboratories Inc., Napa, CA; *Int'l*, pg. 812
Rice, Charles E., Chm. & Chief Exec. Officer--Barnett Banks, Inc., Jacksonville, FL; *U.S. Public*, pg. 1162
Rice, Frederick A., Pres.--Jordan's Foods-Bangor Division, Bangor, ME; *U.S. Private*, pg. 599
Rice, J. Craig, Pres.--Brenco, Inc., Petersburg, VA; *U.S. Public*, pg. 1710
Rice, J. Craig, Pres.--Quality Bearing Service of Nevada, Inc., Sparks, NV; *U.S. Public*, pg. 1711
Rice, James, V.P.--Northern California Division, Rocklin, CA; *U.S. Public*, pg. 38
Rice, James, Gen. Mgr.--Barton's of Lake Village, Lake Village, AR; *U.S. Private*, pg. 119
Rice, John, Pres.--Team Edition Apparel, Inc., Bradenton, FL; *U.S. Public*, pg. 1777
Rice, John D., Pres.--ADM Food Oils, Decatur, IL; *U.S. Public*, pg. 128
Rice, Karen Lee, Gen. Mgr.--KGUN-TV, Tucson, AZ; *U.S. Public*, pg. 983
Rice, Kevin, State Mgr.--National Mutual Western Australia, Perth, Australia; *Int'l*, pg. 908
Rice, L.A., Gen. Mgr.--PD Terminals (Pty) Limited, Durban, South Africa; *Int'l*, pg. 1065
Rice, Michael D., Pres.--AON Specialty Group, Inc., Chicago, IL; *U.S. Public*, pg. 117
Rice, Paddi, Gen. Mgr.--Nordson (Malaysia) Sdn. Bhd., Shah Alam, Malaysia; *U.S. Public*, pg. 1189
Rice, Rex, Gen. Mgr.--Inter-Continental and Forum Hotels, Chicago, IL; *Int'l*, pg. 1178
Rice, Roger, Gen. Mgr.--Jeff Wyler Chevrolet, Inc., Batavia, OH; *U.S. Private*, pg. 1193
Rice, Steve, Pres.--NAI Systems Division, Columbia, MD; *U.S. Public*, pg. 1144
Rice, T. G., Pres. & Chief Oper. Officer--Lykes Pasco Inc., Dade City, FL; *U.S. Private*, pg. 682
Rice, Thomas, Pres. & Publr.--Alton Telegraph, Alton, IL; *U.S. Public*, pg. 934
Rice, Thomas E., Pres. & Chief Exec. Officer--Suburban Newspapers of Greater St. Louis, Saint Louis, MO; *U.S. Public*, pg. 935
Rice, Thomas G., Pres. & Chief Exec. Officer--MedaSonics, Inc., Fremont, CA; *Int'l*, pg. 1225
Rich, Alan, Chm. Bd.--Elite Information Systems, Inc., Los Angeles, CA; *U.S. Public*, pg. 258
Rich, Francis P., Pres.--Action Tire, Candia, NH; *U.S. Private*, pg. 15
Rich, Francis P., Jr., Pres.--AC Leasing Corporation, Candia, NH; *U.S. Private*, pg. 15
Rich, Francis P., Jr., Pres.--Action Supply, Candia, NH; *U.S.* Private, pg. 15
Rich, Francis P., Jr., Pres.--JJJ Realty Trust, Candia, NH; *U.S. Private*, pg. 15
Rich, Gord W., V.P. & Gen. Mgr.--Lake Erie Steel Company Ltd., Nanticoke, Canada; *Int'l*, pg. 1299
Rich, Kim, Gen. Mgr. & Editor--Spencer Magnet, Taylorsville, KY; *U.S. Private*, pg. 648
Rich, Malcolm, Pres. & Chief Oper. Officer--AirKaman of Jacksonville, Inc., Jacksonville, FL; *U.S. Public*, pg. 942
Rich, Michael, Pres.--Tenax Corporation, Danbury, CT; *Int'l*, pg. 193
Rich, Simon B., Jr., Chm. Bd.--Louis Dreyfus Natural Gas Corp., Oklahoma City, OK; *U.S. Private*, pg. 342
Rich, Tim, Gen. Mgr.--SmithKline Beecham Clinical Laboratories, Seattle, WA; *Int'l*, pg. 1265
Rich, Wayne, Pres. & Chief Oper. Officer--Myo-Tech Electronics, Americus, GA; *U.S. Public*, pg. 244
Richard, Albert J., Gen. Mgr.--Gillette Bosphorus Sanayi A.S., Istanbul, Turkey; *U.S. Public*, pg. 744
Richard, Marcel, Chief Oper. Officer--Compagnie Francaise de Boissons Gazeuses, Paris, France; *Int'l*, pg. 918
Richard, Oliver G., III, Chm. Bd., Pres. & Chief Exec. Officer--Columbia Gas System Service Corp., Wilmington, DE; *U.S. Public*, pg. 403
Richardi, Ralph, Pres. & Chief Oper. Officer--Simmons American Eagle Airlines, Dallas-Fort Worth Airport, TX; *U.S. Public*, pg. 10
Richardi, Ralph L., Pres.--Simmons Airlines, Chicago, IL; *U.S. Public*, pg. 9
Richards, A.G., Chief Exec. Officer--ReadyMix Muscat LLC & Premix LLC, Muscat, Oman; *Int'l*, pg. 1092
Richards, Andrew, Mng. Dir.--3i Germany, Frankfurt/Main, Germany; *Int'l*, pg. 1386
Richards, B., Branch Mgr.--Senior Tift-Prospect, Prospect, Australia; *Int'l*, pg. 1223
Richards, Bruce, Mng. Dir.--Benton Plastics, Inc., Clinton, TN; *U.S. Public*, pg. 537
Richards, David L., Chief Exec. Officer & Mng. Dir.--Warwick International Ltd., Flintshire, United Kingdom; *U.S. Public*, pg. 1459
Richards, Doug, Gen. Mgr.-N.E. Region--Flowserve Duriron Canada, Woodbridge, Canada; *U.S. Public*, pg. 659
Richards, Gilbert, Chm. Bd.--Richards Industries Metalworking Group, Cincinnati, OH; *U.S. Private*, pg. 929
Richards, Gilbert, Chm. Bd.--Richards Industries Valve Group, Cincinnati, OH; *U.S. Private*, pg. 929
Richards, Glen R., Pres.--Oregon Culvert Co., Inc., Tualatin, OR; *U.S. Public*, pg. 1305
Richards, Jack, V.P.-Tour Opers.--Amber Tours, Inc., Indianapolis, IN; *U.S. Public*, pg. 106
Richards, Jack, V.P.-Tour Opers.--Amber Travel, Inc., Indianapolis, IN; *U.S. Public*, pg. 106
Richards, Jack, V.P.-Tour Opers.--Ambassadair Travel Club, Inc., Indianapolis, IN; *U.S. Public*, pg. 106
Richards, Jim, Mng. Dir.--Quebecor Integrated Media, Fife, WA; *Int'l*, pg. 1076
Richards, Mark, Mng. Dir.--Meta Farm, Des Moines, IA; *U.S.* Private, pg. 1104
Richards, Michael, Mng. Dir.--Durkopp Adler (UK) Ltd., Rugby, United Kingdom; *Int'l*, pg. 469
Richards, Mike, Dir.-Disk Drive Prod. Sioux Falls Opers.--Hutchinson Technology Inc., Sioux Falls, Sioux Falls, SD; *U.S. Public*, pg. 851
Richards, Paul A., V.P. & Gen. Mgr.--Miramichi Pulp & Paper Inc., Newcastle, Canada; *Int'l*, pg. 1104
Richards, Peter C., Pres.--Connecticut General Benefit Payments, Inc., Bloomfield, CT; *U.S. Public*, pg. 360
Richards, Peter C., Pres.--LINA Benefit Payments, Inc., Bloomfield, CT; *U.S. Public*, pg. 362
Richards, Rick, V.P.--Kvaerner Energy USA, Milford, OH; *Int'l*, pg. 770
Richardson, Ann, Pres.--Hospitality Procurement Division, Minneapolis, MN; *U.S. Private*, pg. 212
Richardson, B. Phil, Exec. V.P.-Opers.--Alfa Financial Corporation, Montgomery, AL; *U.S. Public*, pg. 40
Richardson, Bill, Pres.--Bird Products Corporation, Palm Springs, CA; *U.S. Public*, pg. 1591
Richardson, D.B., Pres.--Shell Development Co., Houston, TX; *Int'l*, pg. 1136
Richardson, Dave, Chief Oper. Officer & V.P.--Schlosser Casting Company, Redmond, OR; *U.S. Private*, pg. 970
Richardson, David J., Mng. Dir.--Engineered Seals, Tewkesbury, United Kingdom; *Int'l*, pg. 1338
Richardson, David W., Div. Mgr.--Composite Materials Div., Rogers, CT; *U.S. Public*, pg. 1402
Richardson, Donald E., Plant Mgr.--Martin Marietta Assembly Services, Americus, GA; *U.S. Public*, pg. 1007
Richardson, Eskil, Gen. Mgr.--Abetong Miljo AB, Vaxjo, Sweden; *Int'l*, pg. 1199
Richardson, F D, Exec. Dir.--WF Corroon-Thatcham, Thatcham, United Kingdom,; *Int'l*, pg. 1502
Richardson, Gail, Chm. Bd.--Educational Management Group, Scottsdale, AZ; *U.S. Private*, pg. 778
Richardson, Jim, Branch Mgr.--Union-Transport Corporation-Chicago Office, Elk Grove Village, IL; *U.S. Private*, pg. 1119
Richardson, John, Pres.--Kearney-National Canada Ltd., Saint Leonard, Canada; *U.S. Private*, pg. 351
Richardson, John, V.P. & Gen. Mgr.--Logica Inc., Toronto, Canada; *Int'l*, pg. 814
Richardson, John, Exec. V.P.--Willis Corroon International/ Americas, Nashville, TN; *Int'l*, pg. 1508
Richardson, Joseph H., Pres. & Chief Exec. Officer--Florida Power Corporation, Saint Petersburg, FL; *U.S. Public*, pg. 655
Richardson, Kenneth, Pres.--Foster Wheeler Zack, Inc., Clinton, NJ; *U.S. Public*, pg. 677
Richardson, Les, Mng. Dir.--Flexitallic Ltd, Cleckheaton, United Kingdom; *U.S. Private*, pg. 413
Richardson, Maurice M., Pres.--Sonoco Engraph, Inc., Atlanta, GA; *U.S. Public*, pg. 1486
Richardson, Michael C., Pres.--Air Land Forwarders, Inc., Jacksonville, FL; *U.S. Private*, pg. 1049
Richardson, Michael J., Pres. & Chief Exec. Officer--ADT Automotive, Inc., Nashville, TN; *U.S. Public*, pg. 1648
Richardson, Paul, Exec. V.P.--Cott Corporation International Operations, Burlingame, CA; *Int'l*, pg. 338
Richardson, Peter, Mng. Dir.--Battenfeld UK Ltd., High Wycombe, United Kingdom; *Int'l*, pg. 826
Richardson, R. Fred, Pres.--Crown Life Investment Management Company (CLIMCO), Toronto, Canada; *Int'l*, pg. 468
Richardson, R.M., Plant Mgr.--The Kingsford Products Co., Springfield, OR; *U.S. Public*, pg. 387
Richardson, Robert, Pres. & Publisher--The Sault Star Ltd., Sault Sainte Marie, Canada; *Int'l*, pg. 631
Richardson, Rodney, Chief Exec. Officer--Roth SA, Mions, France; *Int'l*, pg. 467
Richardson, Ronald, Dir.-Admin.--Eurolease, Brussels, Belgium; *Int'l*, pg. 547
Richardson, T.H., Mng. Dir.--Nordiskafilt AB, Halmstad, Sweden; *U.S. Public*, pg. 37
Richardson, Tommy, District Superintendent--Midland Production District Office, Midland, TX; *U.S. Private*, pg. 548
Richardson, Tony, Pres.--Networks and Peripherals Ltd., Huntingdon, United Kingdom; *Int'l*, pg. 645
Richardson, Tony, Pres.--Decision Data U.K. Ltd., Huntingdon, United Kingdom; *Int'l*, pg. 645
Richardson, William S., Pres. & Chief Exec. Officer--Dow Hickam Pharmaceuticals Inc., Sugar Land, TX; *U.S. Public*, pg. 1143
Richel, Victor M., Grp. V.P.--Elizabethtown Gas Co., Union, NJ; *U.S. Public*, pg. 1147
Richer, Alvin, Owner--Vickers Truck Equipment, Salt Lake City, UT; *U.S. Private*, pg. 84
Richer, Jurgen, Dr., Pres.--Ullstein GmbH, Berlin, Germany; *Int'l*, pg. 102
Richey, Alvan (Al), Pres.--A & S Building Systems, Inc., Caryville, TN; *U.S. Public*, pg. 1146
Richings, Michael, Pres. & Chief Exec. Officer--Granges, Inc., Denver, CO; *U.S. Public*, pg. 1723
Richings, Mike, Pres.--Sociedad Industrial Minera Yamin Ltda., Denver, CO; *U.S. Public*, pg. 1723
Richmond, C. F., Mng. Dir.--Canadian Imperial Bank of Commerce Trust Co. (Bahamas) Limited, Nassau, Bahamas; *Int'l*, pg. 257
Richmond, D. A. B., Mng. Dir.--MB Tanzania Limited, Dar es Salaam, Tanzania; *Int'l*, pg. 267
Richmond, George R., Pres. & Chief Oper. Officer--Jim Walter Resources, Inc., Brookwood, AL; *U.S. Public*, pg. 1737
Richmond, Jane, Mng. Dir.--SKF Specialty Products, Bethlehem, PA; *Int'l*, pg. 1157
Richmond, John A., Sr. V.P. & Gen. Mgr.--Beet Sugar Opers.--Holly Sugar Corporation, Sugar Land, TX; *U.S. Public*, pg. 872
Richmond, Kim F., Chief Oper. Officer--Center for Comprehensive Examinations, Hapeville, GA; *U.S. Public*, pg. 1715
Richmond, Thomas M., Div. V.P. & Gen. Mgr.--Vacuum Metalizing Div., Thomaston, CT; *U.S. Public*, pg. 463
Richomme, Yannick, Pres.--Alfa Laval Separation Inc., Warminster, PA; *Int'l*, pg. 1378
Richter, August J., V, Pres.--Richter-Schroeder Company, Inc., Milwaukee, WI; *U.S. Public*, pg. 1051
Richter, E., Mgr.--Albright & Wilson GmbH (Austria), Vienna, Austria; *Int'l*, pg. 49
Richter, George, Pres.--Consolidated Converting Co., Whittier, CA; *U.S. Public*, pg. 466
Richter, H.I.H., Gen. Mgr.--Portals Packaging Tapes, Manchester, United Kingdom; *Int'l*, pg. 386
Richter, Ken, Area V.P.--Avon Manufacturing Lab., Springdale, OH; *U.S. Public*, pg. 156
Richter, Kurt, Sls. Mgr.--Luxtronic Maschinen GmbH, Wermelskirchen, Germany; *Int'l*, pg. 993
Richter, Michael, Mng. Dir.--Young & Rubicam GmbH, Frankfurt/Main, Germany; *U.S. Private*, pg. 1199
Richter, Rick, Pres. & Publisher--Simon & Schuster Children's Publishing, New York, NY; *U.S. Private*, pg. 777
Richter, W., Gen. Mgr.--ING Lease Deutschland, Hamburg, Germany; *Int'l*, pg. 650
Richter, W., Gen. Mgr.--ING Lease, Hamburg, Germany; *Int'l*, pg. 650
Rickard, Keith G., Pres.--Storage Management Division, Rancho Cordova, CA; *U.S. Public*, pg. 1516
Ricker, Charles W., Jr., Pres. & Reg. Mgr.--Troy Telephone Co., Inc., Kendrick, ID; *U.S. Public*, pg. 1572
Ricker, Fred, Pres.--Thorobred Containers Incorporated, Louisville, KY; *U.S. Private*, pg. 567
Ricketts, Joseph, V.P.--Specialty Metal Products Division, Wallingford, CT; *U.S. Public*, pg. 100
Rickey, Mark J., Pres.--Auto Insurance Solutions Inc., Cleveland, OH; *U.S. Public*, pg. 1334
Ricknoland, L.F., Pres.--Whitmire Micro-gen Research Laboratories Inc., Saint Louis, MO; *U.S. Private*, pg. 592
Ricks, Blair C., Div. Mgr.--Montana Power Great Falls Div., Great Falls, MT; *U.S. Public*, pg. 1126
Ricks, R. Roydon, Pres. & Chief Oper. Officer--Trans-Apparel Group, Michigan City, IN; *U.S. Public*, pg. 796
Ricksater, Ted, Chief Oper. Officer--Nortec Electronics AB, Solna, Sweden; *Int'l*, pg. 709
Rickson, Kenneth M., Pres. & Chief Oper. Officer--MML Investors Services, Inc., Springfield, MA; *U.S. Private*, pg. 712
Ricky, Roger, V.P.--Transportation Electronics Division, El Paso, TX; *U.S. Private*, pg. 1045
Rico, C., Pres.--Productora de Alcoholes Hidratados, C.A. (PRALCA), Caracas, Venezuela; *U.S. Public*, pg. 1220
Rico, Daniel, Chief Oper. Officer--Rahns Specialty Metals, Inc., Collegeville, PA; *Int'l*, pg. 572
Rico, Emilio, Chief Oper. Officer--NIFE Espana S.A., Madrid, Spain; *Int'l*, pg. 53
Ricoma, Juan, Gen. Mgr.--Kemira Iberica S.A., Barcelona, Spain; *Int'l*, pg. 728
Ricoy, Luis Dans, Pres.--CACESA - Compania Auxiliar Al Cargo Expres, S.A., Coslada, Spain; *Int'l*, pg. 1224
Riddell, A.J., Pres.--Canadian Timken Ltd., Saint Thomas, Canada; *U.S. Public*, pg. 1617
Riddell, Glenn, Pres.--Laurel Steel, Burlington, Canada; *Int'l*, *pg. 598*
Riddell, Peter, Mgr.-Office--Woodward-Clyde, Auckland, New Zealand; *U.S. Public*, pg. 1657
Riddell, Tim, Chm.--Sedgwick Oakwood Underwriting Agents Limited, London, United Kingdom; *Int'l*, pg. 1218
Ridder, Peter, Chm. & Publr.--The Knight Publishing Co., Charlotte, NC; *U.S. Public*, pg. 964
Ridder, Peter, Publr.--The Charlotte Observer, Charlotte, NC; *U.S. Public*, pg. 964
Ridderstad, Frederik, Chief Oper. Officer--Auto-Products AB, Bromma, Sweden; *Int'l*, pg. 708
Riddle, Norman, Chief Exec.--Capital House Investment Management Limited, London, United Kingdom; *Int'l*, pg. 1132
Riddle, Ron, Admin.--Silas Creek Manor, Winston Salem, NC; *U.S. Public*, pg. 1714
Riddle, Stephen, Pres.--Asbury Louisiana, Inc., De Quincy, LA; *U.S. Private*, pg. 87
Rideau, Charles, Pres. & Gen. Mgr.--First American Title Insurance Agency of Pinal, Casa Grande, AZ; *U.S. Public*, pg. 626
Ridenout, L.C., Gen. Mgr.--Container Div. (Springfield), Springfield, MO; *Int'l*, pg. 1270
Ridge, David, Dir. Opers.--AlliedSignal Aerospace Systems & Equipment, Eatontown, NJ; *U.S. Public*, pg. 50
Ridge, G.O., Chief Oper. Officer--WD-40 Company (Australia), Epping, Australia; *U.S. Public*, pg. 1726
Ridge, Roy, Pres.--Allied Broadcast Equipment, Canada, Ltd., Richmond Hill, Canada; *U.S. Public*, pg. 791
Ridgeway, Paul, Pres.--Easterday Janitorial Supply Co., San Francisco, CA; *U.S. Public*, pg. 2
Ridgeway, Paul, Mgr.--Southern Electric Supply Co., Inc., Decatur, AL; *Int'l*, pg. 1107
Ridgley, Robert L., Pres.--NNG Financial Corporation, Portland, OR; *U.S. Public*, pg. 1200
Ridgwell, Phil, Dr., Bus. Mgr.--African Amines (Pty) Ltd., Bryanston, South Africa; *Int'l*, pg. 1196
Riding, Bob, Chief Exec.--RoyScot Finance Group plc, Croydon, United Kingdom; *Int'l*, pg. 1132
Ridler, A.H., V.P. & Gen. Mgr.--Kaydon Ring & Seal, Inc., Baltimore, MD; *U.S. Public*, pg. 946
Ridler, Peter, Chief Exec. Officer--Savia S.A., Bielsko-Biala, Poland; *Int'l*, pg. 1376
Ridling, Jim L., Pres. & Chief Exec. Officer--Southern Guaranty Insurance Companies, Montgomery, AL; *Int'l*, pg. 346
Ridout, Derek M., Pres.--Silcorp Limited, Scarborough, Canada; *Int'l*, pg. 1249
Ridsdale, B.P., Chief Exec. Officer--Zurich Life Assurance Company Limited, Portsmouth, United Kingdom; *Int'l*, pg. 1532
Riebau, R. R., Exec. V.P. & Gen. Mgr.--Components Div., Racine, WI; *U.S. Public*, pg. 311
Riebau, Robert R., Pres.--Pryor Foundry, Inc., Pryor, OK; *U.S. Public*, pg. 312

Rieben, W. P., Pres.--GE Fanuc Automation Europe S.A., Echternach, Luxembourg; *Int'l*, pg. 478

Rieber, John, Grp. Pres.--Lee's Famous Recipe Restaurant, Nashville, TN; *U.S. Private*, pg. 906

Rieck, Tim, Pres.--Pies, Inc., Chaska, MN; *U.S. Public*, pg. 658

Riedel, Ricardo, Gen. Mgr.--Rorer do Brasil Quimica E. Farmaceutica Ltda., Sao Paulo, Brazil; *Int'l*, pg. 1111

Riedel, Steven C., Acting Pres.--PCC Specialty Products, Inc., Worcester, MA; *U.S. Public*, pg. 1321

Riederer, Walter, Member of Mngmt.--VOEST-ALPINE Krems Ges.m.b.H., Krems, Austria; *Int'l*, pg. 1470

Riedl, S., Western Service Center Mgr.--Square D Co., Bakersfield, CA; *Int'l*, pg. 1208

Rieger, A.L., Mgr.--Nalco Argentina S.A., Buenos Aires, Argentina; *U.S. Public*, pg. 1150

Riemenschneider, Friedhelm, Speaker--August Bilstein GmbH & Co. KG, Ennepetal, Germany; *Int'l*, pg. 507

Riepe, Wolfgang, Mng. Dir.--KEBE Ersatzteile GmbH, Rosbach, Germany; *Int'l*, pg. 283

Riera, J.L., Gen. Mgr.--MSA Espanola, S.A., Barcelona, Spain; *U.S. Public*, pg. 1115

Ries, Mike, Pres.--Metal Treating, Inc., Milwaukee, WI; *U.S. Public*, pg. 1592

Rieson, Dean A., Pres. & Chief Exec. Officer--Carlson Real Estate Company, Minnetonka, MN; *U.S. Private*, pg. 212

Riess, J.M., Chief Exec. Officer--The Gates Corporation, Denver, CO; *Int'l*, pg. 1396

Riess, John M., Pres. & Chief Oper. Officer--The Gates Rubber Company, Denver, CO; *Int'l*, pg. 1396

Riet, N.C., Mgr.--Radio-Holland AV Systems Group, Amsterdam, Netherlands; *Int'l*, pg. 1151

Rietberg, P.L., Mng. Dir.--P. Van Leeuwen Jr's Buizenhandel B.V., Zwijndrecht, Netherlands; *Int'l*, pg. 1449

Rietveld, K., Mng. Dir.--Lancer Holland BV, Wamel, Netherlands; *Int'l*, pg. 552

Rieves, Glenn, Plant Mgr.--Cloud Corporation, Skokie, IL; *U.S. Private*, pg. 247

Rifakes, George P., Pres.--Cotter Corp., Lakewood, CO; *U.S. Public*, pg. 1664

Rife, Carson J., Gen. Mgr.--Basin Creek Mine, Helena, MT; *U.S. Public*, pg. 1269

Rifenbergh, James, Pres. & Chief Exec. Officer--Brown Printing Co., Inc., Waseca, MN; *Int'l*, pg. 190

Rigal, Gilles, Country Mgr.--BMC Software France, Saint Cloud, France; *U.S. Public*, pg. 162

Rigano, Louis J., Pres.--Appraisal Services, Inc., Milwaukee, WI; *U.S. Public*, pg. 141

Rigaud, Jacques, Chief Exec. Officer--RTL, Paris, France; *Int'l*, pg. 561

Rigaud, Patricia, Gen. Mgr.--Select Communications, Paris, Paris, France; *U.S. Private*, pg. 982

Rigberg, Allen, Chief Exec. Officer--Just Toys, New York, NY; *U.S. Private*, pg. 903

Rigby, J.S., Mng. Dir.--Stafford-Miller Limited, Welwyn Garden City, United Kingdom; *U.S. Public*, pg. 237

Rigby, Peter J., Mng. Dir.--Handy & Harman (Europe) Ltd., Harrogate, United Kingdom; *U.S. Public*, pg. 780

Rigg, Thomas, Mgr.-Terminal--Galena Park Terminal, Galena Park, TX; *U.S. Public*, pg. 692

Riggins, Jim, Pres.--UPB of Southwest Missouri, Springfield, MO; *U.S. Public*, pg. 1669

Riggio, Joseph, Pres.--Holmes Protection of New Jersey, Inc., Edison, NJ; *U.S. Public*, pg. 1649

Riggs, Daniel, Pres.--Somerset Steel, Stoystown, PA; *U.S. Private*, pg. 930

Riggs, George, Publr.--Contra Costa Newspapers, Inc., Walnut Creek, CA; *U.S. Public*, pg. 964

Riggs, George, Publr.--Ledger Dispatch, Antioch, CA; *U.S. Public*, pg. 964

Riggs, George, Publr.--Contra Costa Times, Walnut Creek, CA; *U.S. Public*, pg. 964

Riggs, George, Publr.--Valley Times, Pleasanton, CA; *U.S. Public*, pg. 964

Riggs, George, Publr.--West County Times, Richmond, CA; *U.S. Public*, pg. 964

Riggs, Sidney W., Chm. Bd., Sec. & Treas.--Somerset Welding & Steel, Inc., Somerset, PA; *U.S. Private*, pg. 930

Rigney, Bob, Pres. & Chief Exec. Officer--Liberty National Bank of Shelbyville, Shelbyville, KY; *U.S. Public*, pg. 173

Rigoulot, Pierre, Chief Exec. Officer--Beaud-Challes-Solap S.A., Rumilly, France; *Int'l*, pg. 430

Rigsby, James H., Jr., Pres. & Chief Exec. Officer--Allied Bank of Georgia, Thomson, GA; *U.S. Public*, pg. 1373

Riha, William E., Dr., Pres.--Seagram's Corp. Research and Development, White Plains, NY; *Int'l*, pg. 1217

Riihinen, Kalevi, Mng. Dir.--Savon Sellu Oy, Kuopio, Finland; *Int'l*, pg. 863

Riihinen, Tapio, Gen. Mgr.--Leaf Russia, Saint Petersburg, Russia; *Int'l*, pg. 638

Rijnberg, Witte L., Chief Oper. Officer--Novo Nordisk A/S, Vienna, Austria; *Int'l*, pg. 987

Rijos, John, Pres.--Lane Hospitality, Inc., Northbrook, IL; *U.S. Private*, pg. 650

Rijsdijk, F.B., Mng. Dir.--Capax Electrische Apparatenfabriek B.V., Eindhoven, Netherlands; *U.S. Public*, pg. 576

Rikli, Eduard, Mng. Dir.--Sulzer Turbo Ltd., Zurich, Switzerland; *Int'l*, pg. 1305

Riley, Ann A., Pres.--Clayton Reinsurance, Ltd., Webster Groves, MO; *U.S. Public*, pg. 1374

Riley, David K., Vice Chm. & Chief Exec. Officer--Community First Bank & Trust, Celina, OH; *U.S. Public*, pg. 633

Riley, Dennis, Pres.--Faraday, Inc., Tecumseh, MI; *Int'l*, pg. 1246

Riley, Dennis, Mgr.-Office--Woodward-Clyde, Petaling Jaya, Malaysia; *U.S. Public*, pg. 1657

Riley, F., District Mgr.--A.M. Castle & Co., Cleveland, OH; *U.S. Public*, pg. 313

Riley, Frank, Supervisor--GATX Logistics, Inc.-California (Public), Mira Loma, CA; *U.S. Public*, pg. 691

Riley, Gerry, Pres. & Publisher--Chronicle-Tribune, Marion, IN; *U.S. Public*, pg. 700

Riley, H. Patrick, Pres.--CNG Producing Co., New Orleans, LA; *U.S. Public*, pg. 435

Riley, Jan, Gen. Mgr.--Shoshone Title Insurance & Abstract Company, Cody, WY; *U.S. Public*, pg. 626

Riley, Kevin, Reg. Mgr.--The C.P. Hall Company, Torrance, CA; *U.S. Private*, pg. 495

Riley, Lisa, Mgr.--Triad Personnel Services, Reading, MA; *U.S. Public*, pg. 715

Riley, Malcolm W., Publr. & Dir.-Editorial--Plastics Technology, New York, NY; *Int'l*, pg. 1446

Riley, Michael, Exec. V.P.--Bank Marketing Association, Washington, DC; *U.S. Private*, pg. 51

Riley, Patrick D., Pres.--BankAmerica Sutter Mortgage Corporation, Phoenix, AZ; *U.S. Public*, pg. 181

Riley, Peter, Mng. Dir.--Beazer Homes (Redditch) Limited, Sudley, United Kingdom; *Int'l*, pg. 182

Riley, Robert E., Chief Exec. Officer--Mandarin Oriental International Limited, Hamilton, Bermuda; *Int'l*, pg. 704

Riley, Stephen J., Mng. Dir.--Swiss Reinsurance Company UK Ltd., London, United Kingdom; *Int'l*, pg. 1333

Riley, T. J., Pres.--Aero Tech Manufacturing Inc., North Salt Lake, UT; *Int'l*, pg. 1400

Riley, T.J., Pres.-Aero Tech Mfg. Inc--Toromont Industries Ltd., Concord, Canada; *Int'l*, pg. 1400

Riley, Tom, Pres.--Riley Natural Gas, Bridgeport, WV; *U.S. Public*, pg. 1281

Riley, Tom, Gen. Mgr.--Poe & Brown of Florida, Fort Lauderdale, FL; *U.S. Public*, pg. 1312

Riley, William W., Pres.--ABC Transportation Co., Eufaula, AL; *U.S. Public*, pg. 69

Rimbey, Robert A., Pres. & Chief Exec. Officer--Reeves Bank, Beaver Falls, PA; *U.S. Public*, pg. 607

Rimbo, Bruce, Pres.--Sunflower Racing Inc., Kansas City, KS; *U.S. Public*, pg. 831

Rimpot, G.L., Chief Oper. Officer--De Lage Landen Leasing S.A., Paris, France; *Int'l*, pg. 1082

Rimstidt, Joseph R., V.P.--Liquid Packaging Div., Memphis, TN; *U.S. Public*, pg. 903

Rinaldi, Anthony J., Pres. & Corp. V.P.--Tredegar Film Products, Richmond, VA; *U.S. Public*, pg. 1634

Rinaldi, Vincent, Pres.--Information Leasing Corporation, Cincinnati, OH; *U.S. Public*, pg. 1338

Rincon, Antonio Fernandez, Pres.--Mead Johnson Ecuador, S.A., Guayaquil, Ecuador; *U.S. Public*, pg. 256

Rincon, Esther, Gen. Mgr.--DISEL (Diseno e Ingenieria de Sistemas Electronicos S.A.), Madrid, Spain; *U.S. Public*, pg. 1032

Rinder, Jerry, V.P. & Gen. Mgr.--Victorinox, Shelton, CT; *U.S. Public*, pg. 1544

Rinehart, Jerry, Pres.--Maytag International, Inc., Chicago, IL; *U.S. Public*, pg. 1065

Rinella, Thomas J., Sr. V.P.--Community Finance Corporation, Chicago, IL; *U.S. Public*, pg. 1428

Riner, Preston, Reg. V.P.--Comverse Network Systems, Marietta, GA; *U.S. Public*, pg. 425

Rines, John R., Gen. Mgr.--Motors Holding Division, Detroit, MI; *U.S. Public*, pg. 721

Ring, Carrol, Chief Oper. Officer--Rogers Cable TV-Cornwall, Cornwall, Canada; *Int'l*, pg. 1122

Ringberg, A., Mgr.--Frankfurter Munzhandlung GmbH, Frankfurt/Main, Germany; *Int'l*, pg. 1330

Ringer, John M., Pres.--Foley-PLP Company, Rochester, NY; *U.S. Private*, pg. 416

Ringle, C.K., Plant Mgr.--Firestone Synthetic Rubber & Latex Company-Orange, Orange, TX; *Int'l*, pg. 214

Ringler, Dominique, Gen. Mgr. & Client Services Dir.--TBWA Belgium, Brussels, Belgium; *U.S. Private*, pg. 1063

Ringo, Philip J., Pres. & Chief Exec. Officer--Chemical Leaman Tank Lines, Inc., Exton, PA; *U.S. Private*, pg. 233

Ringross, D.W., Dir.-Malt--Pauls plc, Ipswich, United Kingdom; *Int'l*, pg. 598

Ringwood, James, Natl. Sls. Mgr.--Professional Industrial Sales, Fair Lawn, NJ; *Int'l*, pg. 622

Rini, Charles A. Sr., Pres.--Rini-Rego Supermarkets, Inc., Cleveland, OH; *U.S. Private*, pg. 451

Rink, Peter, Gen. Mgr.--Signode B.V., Hoofddorp, Netherlands; *U.S. Public*, pg. 869

Rink, Peter, Gen. Mgr.--Signode Belgium, Zaventem, Belgium; *U.S. Public*, pg. 869

Rinker, Michael, Chm. Bd.--Avesta Sheffield East, Inc., Baltimore, MD; *Int'l*, pg. 221

Rinker, Michael R., Pres.--Avesta Sheffield, Inc., Schaumburg, IL; *Int'l*, pg. 221

Rinker, Thomas L., Pres.--Kvaerner EnviroPower Inc., Owings Mills, MD; *Int'l*, pg. 770

Rinnankoski, Jarmo, Pres.--AGA Venezolana C.A., Caracas, Venezuela; *Int'l*, pg. 14

Rinsch, Charles E., Chm. Bd. & Pres.--Argonaut Co., Menlo Park, CA; *U.S. Public*, pg. 129

Rinta, Jorma, Chief Oper. Officer--Neste Resins Corporation, Mississauga, Canada; *Int'l*, pg. 915

Rintala, J., Mng. Dir.--Ascom Fintel OY, Vantaa, Finland; *Int'l*, pg. 87

Rinus, U., Mng. Dir.--Ascom Tateco GmbH, Frankfurt, Germany; *Int'l*, pg. 87

Riond, N., Chief Oper. Officer--Francaise De Mecanique, Haisnes, France; *Int'l*, pg. 1021

Riordan, James J., Pres.--Mann & Hummel Filter Technology Inc., Greensboro, NC; *Int'l*, pg. 484

Riordan, John F., Chm. Bd., Pres. & Chief Exec. Officer--MidCon Texas Pipeline Operator, Inc., Houston, TX; *U.S. Public*, pg. 1210

Riordan, Rip, Chief Oper. Officer & Exec. V.P.--Clear Channel Television, Inc., Minneapolis, MN; *U.S. Public*, pg. 383

Riordan, Steven, Pres.--GNWC Wire, Cable & Network Products, Downers Grove, IL; *U.S. Private*, pg. 259

Riordan, Thomas, Pres.--Service Solution, Warren, MI; *U.S. Public*, pg. 1421

Riordan, Thomas J., Gen. Mgr.--USNR, Langley, Canada; *Int'l*, pg. 604

Rios, Alfredo, Gen. Mgr.--Olin Quimica, S.A. de C.V., Mexico, Mexico; *U.S. Public*, pg. 1220

Rios, Carlos, Mng. Dir.--McGraw-Hill/Interamericana de Mexico, S.A. de CV, Mexico, Mexico; *U.S. Public*, pg. 1072

Rios, Francisco Emilio, Dr., Pres.--Filtros Mann S.A., Buenos Aires, Argentina; *Int'l*, pg. 484

Rios, Victor N., Pres. & Gen. Mgr.--ITT Gilfillan, Van Nuys, CA; *U.S. Public*, pg. 859

Ripley, Richard L., Pres.--South Trust Bank of Georgia, Atlanta, GA; *U.S. Public*, pg. 1492

Rippe, Stephen N., Pres. & Chief Exec. Officer--Nevada National Bancorporation, Las Vegas, NV; *U.S. Public*, pg. 181

Rippy, James P., Pres.--Jefferson-Pilot Property Insurance Company, Greensboro, NC; *U.S. Public*, pg. 926

Risberg, Per, Pres.--Saab-Scania Combitech, Jonkoping, Sweden; *Int'l*, pg. 686

Risch, F.A., Pres.--Ancon Insurance Company, Inc., Irving, TX; *U.S. Public*, pg. 601

Riseman, Milton, Pres.--Advanta Mortgage Corp. USA, Fort Washington, PA; *U.S. Public*, pg. 22

Risinger, James A., Pres. & Chief Exec. Officer--Old National Bank, Evansville, IN; *U.S. Public*, pg. 1217

Risinger, Philip, Div. Mgr.--Oliver Rubber Co., Paris, TX; *U.S. Public*, pg. 1504

Risk, John T., Pres.--Keystone Group Inc., Indianapolis, IN; *U.S. Private*, pg. 981

Rislakki, Jaakko, Pres.--UPM Pack, Valkeakoski, Finland; *Int'l*, pg. 1430

Risley, Gary, Pres.--Mesa Airlines Pilot Development, Inc., Farmington, NM; *U.S. Public*, pg. 1099

Rislov, Gerald, Pres.--Dakota Case Inc., Philip, SD; *U.S. Private*, pg. 636

Risoldi, G., Gen. Mgr.--Feed Additives Division, Atlanta, GA; *Int'l*, pg. 1109

Risse, Jacques, Chief Oper. Officer--Sodeva, Paris, France; *Int'l*, pg. 557

Risso, M.A., Pres.--Jannock Vinyl Group, Pittsburgh, PA; *Int'l*, pg. 699

Ristau, Harry, Gen. Mgr.--General Slicing/Red Goat Disposers, Murfreesboro, TN; *U.S. Public*, pg. 1506

Rister, Frank, Pres.--Wyatt Field Service Co., Houston, TX; *U.S. Private*, pg. 801

Risto, Jikka, Chief Oper. Officer--AS Traffic Service, Tallinn, Estonia; *Int'l*, pg. 915

Ristola, Pentti, Chief Oper. Officer--OY Ferrosan AB, Espoo, Finland; *Int'l*, pg. 989

Riswick, Erik, Pres.--Ready Bake Foods Inc., Mississauga, Canada; *Int'l*, pg. 1495

Ritch, Dave, Dir.--Willis Corroon Property & Casualty Programs Div., Nashville, TN; *Int'l*, pg. 1508

Ritch, Dave, Dir.--PENCO-Tennessee, Nashville, TN; *Int'l*, pg. 1508

Ritchey, Jimmy, Pres.--Anderson Hickey, Inc., Henderson, TX; *U.S. Private*, pg. 512

Ritchie, Bill, Mgr.-Opers.--Boston Gear, Charlotte, NC; *U.S. Public*, pg. 857

Ritchie, David R., Chm. Bd., Pres. & Chief Exec. Officer--Farmers Bank of Maryland, Annapolis, MD; *U.S. Public*, pg. 641

Ritchie, Howard F., Jr., V.P. & Gen. Mgr.--WISN-TV, Milwaukee, WI; *U.S. Private*, pg. 516

Ritchie, J.M., Mng. Dir.--Lancaster plc, Colchester, United Kingdom; *Int'l*, pg. 705

Ritchie, Malcom, Chief Exec. Officer & Mng. Dir.--H.J. Heinz Company, Limited, Hayes, United Kingdom; *U.S. Public*, pg. 806

Ritchie, Miles M., Mng. Dir.--Jardine Insurance Brokers Ltd., Hong Kong, Hong Kong; *Int'l*, pg. 705

Ritchie, Paul E., Div. Pres.--Lydall Composite Materials, Hoosick Falls, NY; *U.S. Public*, pg. 1021

Ritchie, Peter, Chm. & Chief Exec. Officer--McDonald's System of Australia Ltd., Thornleigh, Australia; *U.S. Public*, pg. 1069

Ritenour, Perry N., Sr. V.P.--International Banking Div., Los Angeles, CA; *U.S. Public*, pg. 872

Rithmoeller, Edward R., Mgr.--Designed & Engineered Systems, Syosset, NY; *U.S. Public*, pg. 6

Ritt, Hans, Gen. Mgr.--Swiss Shipping and Neptune AG, Basel, Switzerland; *Int'l*, pg. 866

Rittenberg, Sheldon M., Pres.--Cabletel Communications Inc., Markham, Canada; *Int'l*, pg. 17

Rittenhouse, Ann N., Exec. Dir.--Recovery Inn of Menlo Park, Menlo Park, CA; *U.S. Public*, pg. 1715

Ritter, Bob, Editor--Gannett News Service, Inc., Arlington, VA; *U.S. Public*, pg. 700

Ritter, Christian, Exec. V.P. & Gen. Mgr.--Landesbank Hessen-Thuringen Girozentrale New York Branch, New York, NY; *Int'l*, pg. 799

Ritter, Don, Gen. Mgr.--Mexia Fabricators, Inc., Wortham, TX; *U.S. Public*, pg. 424

Ritter, Douglas, Chief Oper. Officer--C.R.H International, Inc., Canton, MA; *U.S. Public*, pg. 828

Ritter, Joseph M., Pres. & Treas.--Jefferson-Pilot Title Insurance Co., Greensboro, NC; *U.S. Public*, pg. 926

Ritter, Kurt, Pres.--SAS International Hotels A/S, Brussels, Belgium; *Int'l*, pg. 1202

Ritter, Martin L., Pres.--Ritter Sysco Food Service, Inc., Jersey City, NJ; *U.S. Public*, pg. 1550

Ritter, R.A., Pres.--The Pipelines of Puerto Rico, Inc., San Juan, PR; *U.S. Public*, pg. 1584

Ritter, Richard, Pres.--Refineria Texaco de Honduras, S.A., San Pedro Sula, Honduras; *U.S. Public*, pg. 1584

Ritter, Susan, V.P. & Branch Mgr.--Fort Myers Branch Office, Fort Myers, FL; *U.S. Public*, pg. 1683

Ritterling, Curtis D., Chm. Bd. & Pres.--NationsBank of Marshall, Marshall, MO; *U.S. Public*, pg. 1164

Rittichier, David L., Pres.--Alcoa Composites, Inc., Monrovia, CA; *U.S. Public*, pg. 60

Rittler, Charlotte, Chief Oper. Officer--Ahlstrom Papiervertrieb GmbH, Munich, Germany; *Int'l*, pg. 35

Rittmanic, Mark, Pres.--Trase-Miller, Oak Brook, IL; *U.S. Private*, pg. 688

Ritto, M., Mng. Dir.--EMI-Medley, Copenhagen, Denmark; *Int'l*, pg. 427
Rittwage, William R., Chm. Bd., Pres. & Chief Exec. Officer--California Offset Printers, Inc., Glendale, CA; *U.S. Private*, pg. 196
Ritvala, Kai, Pres.--Valmet (SEA) Pte Ltd. Paper Machinery Division, Singapore, Singapore; *Int'l*, pg. 1448
Ritz, Robert J., Pres.--Pure Solutions, Phoenix, AZ; *U.S. Public*, pg. 912
Rivalta, Danilo, Country Mgr.--BMC Software Srl, Milan, Italy; *U.S. Public*, pg. 163
Rivard, Dick, Publr.--The Newport Daily Express, Newport, VT; *U.S. Public*, pg. 1343
Rivarola, Cristina, Mng. Dir.--BNP (Uruguay) SA, Montevideo, Uruguay; *Int'l*, pg. 164
Rivellini, Carlo, Mng. Dir.--Jotun Itoc S.r.l., San Polo di Piave, Italy; *Int'l*, pg. 716
Rivera, Edwardo, Chief Oper. Officer--Marvin de Mexico, S.A. de C.V., Queretaro, Mexico; *U.S. Public*, pg. 137
Rivera, Joaquin Echenique, Gerente Gen.--Allianz Compania de Seguros S.A., Santiago, Chile; *Int'l*, pg. 59
Rivera, Jose, Pres.--Staff/DMB&B, Santo Domingo, Dominican Republic; *U.S. Private*, pg. 305
Rivera, Melchor, Gen. Mgr.--Dentsply Philippines, Manila, Philippines; *U.S. Public*, pg. 500
Rivera, R, Gen. Mgr.--Thomas De La Rue (Singapore) Pte. Limited, Singapore, Singapore; *Int'l*, pg. 386
Rivera, Regulo, Gen. Mgr.--Banco de la Provincia de Buenos Aires, New York, NY; *Int'l*, pg. 140
Rivera, Richard, Pres. & Chief Exec. Officer--TGI Friday's, Inc., Addison, TX; *U.S. Private*, pg. 212
Rivers, Ronald D., Pres.--Vigoro Industries, Inc., Washington Court House, OH; *U.S. Public*, pg. 856
Rivers, W.A., Branch Mgr.--Zellerbach Division, Birmingham, AL; *U.S. Public*, pg. 1075
Riverso, Renato, Dir. Gen.--IBM Europe, S.A., Puteaux, France; *U.S. Public*, pg. 897
Rivet, Julien, Plant Mgr.--Fasson France S.a.r.L., Jarrie, France; *U.S. Public*, pg. 154
Rivette, Glen, Gen. Mgr.--Baton Rouge Machine Works Inc., Baton Rouge, LA; *Int'l*, pg. 1489
Rivier, Andre, Gen. Mgr.--StorageTek France, S.A., Buc, France; *U.S. Public*, pg. 1523
Riviera, Gus, Gen. Mgr.--KNOGO Caribe, Inc., Cidra, PR; *U.S. Public*, pg. 1458
Riviere, Charles J., Dir. Gen.--SRA Europe, S.A., Suresnes, France; *U.S. Private*, pg. 958
Rivkin, Elliott R., Pres.--Amram's Distributing, Ltd., Etobicoke, Canada; *U.S. Public*, pg. 223
Rivlin, Joe, Pres.--Chicago Laser Systems, Des Plaines, IL; *U.S. Public*, pg. 569
Rivrud, Svein, Mgr.--Kvaerner Ships Equipment a.s Tranby, Lier, Norway; *Int'l*, pg. 770
Rizkaller, Fernando, Pres.--Oster de Venezuela S.A., Caracas, Venezuela; *U.S. Public*, pg. 1533
Rizzini, Elizabetta, Acting Dir.--Washington Language Center, Turin, Italy; *U.S. Public*, pg. 222
Rizzo, Michael, Pres.--United Distillers USA, Inc., Stamford, CT; *Int'l*, pg. 412
Roach, Alfred J., Chm. Bd.--TII Electronics, Inc., Copiague, NY; *U.S. Public*, pg. 1556
Roach, Cathy, Gen. Mgr.--Ancillary Products--Mother's Bookshelf, Des Moines, IA; *U.S. Private*, pg. 1056
Roach, J., Pres.--Tandy International Electronics, Inc., Fort Worth, TX; *U.S. Public*, pg. 1560
Roach, John H., Jr., Chm.--CBC-U.S.A Inc., Chicago, IL; *U.S. Public*, pg. 337
Roach, Paul, Gen. Mgr.--Enco-Knoxville, Knoxville, TN; *U.S. Private*, pg. 375
Roach, Timothy, Chm. Bd.--TII-Ditel, Hickory, NC; *U.S. Public*, pg. 1556
Roach, Timothy J., Pres. & Chief Exec. Officer--Intercom Systems, Inc., Copiague, NY; *U.S. Public*, pg. 1556
Roake, Andrew, Chief Exec.--Welbilt Corporation, Stamford, CT; *Int'l*, pg. 188
Roan, Lynn, Mgr.-Division--Haleyville Manufacturing, Goshen, IN; *U.S. Public*, pg. 491
Roan, Mike, Div. Mgr.--Gladwin Machine Products Div., Gladwin, MI; *U.S. Public*, pg. 1475
Roark, Janet, Mgr.--Downey Savings & Loan Association, F.A., Cudahy, CA; *U.S. Public*, pg. 527
Roath, S.D., Pres.--Longs Drug Stores California, Inc., Walnut Creek, CA; *U.S. Public*, pg. 1013
Roave, Robert C., Pres. & Chief Exec. Officer--The Riggs National Bank of Virginia, Merrifield, VA; *U.S. Public*, pg. 1390
Rob, Joseph M., Chm. Bd. & Chief Exec. Officer--Equity Services, Inc., Montpelier, VT; *U.S. Private*, pg. 785
Roba, Paul, Dir. & Gen. Mgr.--Artisan Electronics Corporation, Parsippany, NJ; *Int'l*, pg. 892
RoBards, Richard, Publr. & Editor--Central Kentucky News-Journal, Campbellsville, KY; *U.S. Private*, pg. 648
Robb, Paul, Chief Oper. Officer--Duck Head Apparel, Winder, GA; *U.S. Public*, pg. 498
Robb, Peters J., Pres.--Bank of Boston International, New York, NY; *U.S. Public*, pg. 184
Robberds, Peter H., Mgr.--Sheet & Coil Products New South Wales, Port Kembla, Australia; *Int'l*, pg. 227
Robbie, D. W., Mng. Dir.--CIBC (Hong Kong) Limited, Hong Kong, Hong Kong; *Int'l*, pg. 257
Robbins, Bruce E., Pres. & Chief Exec. Officer--PNC Bank, N.A., Pittsburgh, PA; *U.S. Public*, pg. 1243
Robbins, Charles L., Jr., Pres. & Chief Exec. Officer--Tri-City Bank and Trust Company, Blountville, TN; *U.S. Public*, pg. 642
Robbins, Charles R., V.P.-Pur. & Div. Mgr.--Higgins Lumber Purchasing, Union City, CA; *U.S. Private*, pg. 527
Robbins, Charles R., V.P.-Pur.--Higgins Sacramento/Purch, Rancho Cordova, CA; *U.S. Private*, pg. 527
Robbins, Dave, Plant Mgr.--Sealy Mattress Company - Lexington, Lexington, NC; *U.S. Private*, pg. 979
Robbins, Douglas R., V.P.--Clarke Container Company, Inc., Jamestown, NY; *U.S. Public*, pg. 1045
Robbins, G.F., Mng. Dir.--Dywidag-Systems (U.K.) Ltd., Southam, United Kingdom; *Int'l*, pg. 425
Robbins, George W., Pres.--SCM Glidco Organic, Jacksonville, FL; *Int'l*, pg. 594
Robbins, Jerry, Gen. Mgr.--M & E Manufacturing Co., Laconia, NH; *U.S. Private*, pg. 870
Robbins, Marty, Pres.--Valtek Controls, Ltd., Edmonton, Canada; *U.S. Public*, pg. 659
Robbins, Patrick, V.P.--Bandag Inc. of S.A. (Pty.) Ltd., Germiston, South Africa; *U.S. Public*, pg. 178
Robbins, Patrick, V.P.--Bandag New Zealand Ltd., Auckland, New Zealand; *U.S. Public*, pg. 178
Robbins, Robert, Pres.--Yellow Book of New Jersey, Paramus, NJ; *U.S. Private*, pg. 767
Robbins, Steve, Gen. Mgr.--Amway de Panama S.A., El Dorado, Panama; *U.S. Private*, pg. 69
Robbins, Steve, Gen. Mgr.--Amway Argentina, Inc., Buenos Aires, Argentina; *U.S. Private*, pg. 69
Robbins, Steve M., Mgr.--Science and Engineering Lancaster Office, Lancaster, CA; *U.S. Public*, pg. 1597
Robelow, Harold, V.P. & Gen. Mgr.--Marion 100, Inc., Marion, IL; *U.S. Private*, pg. 708
Roberge, Bernard, Mng. Dir.--Fibro Friction, Anjou, Canada; *U.S. Public*, pg. 1503
Roberge, Genest, Gen. Mgr.--Uniboard Canada Inc.-LDI Division, Lac des Iles, Canada; *Int'l*, pg. 1431
Roberge, Jean-Guy, Reg. V.P.--Imprimerie Quebecor Lebonfon, Val d'Or, Canada; *Int'l*, pg. 1077
Roberson, Ricky, Mgr.--General Employment Enterprises, Inc., Atlanta, GA; *U.S. Public*, pg. 714
Robert, Carlos, Gen. Mgr.--Sensormatic Electronics Corp. de Puerto Rico, Aguadilla, PR; *U.S. Public*, pg. 1457
Robert, Donald A., Pres.--First American CREDCO, San Diego, CA; *U.S. Public*, pg. 625
Robert, Jean-Pierre, Pres.--Chryso, Montrouge, France; *Int'l*, pg. 789
Robert, Pierre, Gen. Mgr.--Fine Cheese Division, Montreal, Canada; *Int'l*, pg. 32
Robert, Stephen, Chm. Bd.--Oppenheimer Capital, New York, NY; *Int'l*, pg. 257
Roberts, Alex, Pres.--Programmed Composites, Inc., Anaheim, CA; *U.S. Private*, pg. 882
Roberts, Bert C., Jr., Chm. Bd. & Chief Exec. Officer--MCI Telecommunications Corp., Washington, DC; *U.S. Public*, pg. 1024
Roberts, Bob, Mng. Dir.--Albany International Pty., Ltd., Gosford, Australia; *U.S. Public*, pg. 37
Roberts, Brian, Gen. Mgr.--Howard, Napa, CA; *Int'l*, pg. 1387
Roberts, Budd, Pres. & Chief Oper. Officer--American Automobile Insurance Co., Creve Coeur, MO; *Int'l*, pg. 59
Roberts, C. Frank, Pres.-Broadcast Grp.--The New York Times Company Broadcasting Group, Memphis, TN; *U.S. Public*, pg. 1173
Roberts, C. Frank, Pres.--The New York Times Broadcasting Service, Inc., Memphis, TN; *U.S. Public*, pg. 1173
Roberts, Carter, Pres.--INS Investigations Bureau, Inc., Parsippany, NJ; *Int'l*, pg. 1153
Roberts, Dan, Mgr.--Genus KK, Yokohama, Japan; *U.S. Public*, pg. 733
Roberts, Dave, Gen. Mgr.--Standco Oilfield Products Div., Houston, TX; *U.S. Private*, pg. 1032
Roberts, David, Fin. Dir.--Leo Burnett Co., S.r.l., Milan, Italy; *U.S. Private*, pg. 185
Roberts, David, Mng. Dir.--SKF Kenya Ltd., Nairobi, Kenya; *Int'l*, pg. 1159
Roberts, David A., Pres.--International Div., AM International, Mount Prospect, IL; *U.S. Public*, pg. 1141
Roberts, David J., Chm. Bd., Pres. & Chief Exec. Officer--Foster Wheeler Real Estate Development Corp., Clinton, NJ; *U.S. Public*, pg. 677
Roberts, David O., Publisher--Spartanburg Herald-Journal, Spartanburg, SC; *U.S. Public*, pg. 1175
Roberts, Dennis, Gen. Mgr.--Buckhorn Rubber Products Inc., Hannibal, MO; *U.S. Public*, pg. 1143
Roberts, Denny, Mgr.--W.C. Caye & Co., Jacksonville, FL; *U.S. Private*, pg. 220
Roberts, Donald R., Gen. Mgr.--PCS Potash - New Brunswick, Sussex, Canada; *Int'l*, pg. 1064
Roberts, Doreen, V.P. & Gen. Mgr.--Outdoor Systems, Inc.-New York, Los Angeles, CA; *U.S. Public*, pg. 1235
Roberts, Edward, Gen. Mgr.--Heath Spring Company LTD, Redditch, United Kingdom; *U.S. Private*, pg. 857
Roberts, Frank F., Jr., Mgr.--Hesco Supply Co., Inc., New York, NY; *U.S. Private*, pg. 518
Roberts, Fritz, Mgr.-Division--Gould Paper Corporatioin-Baltimore/Washington, Laurel, MD; *U.S. Private*, pg. 467
Roberts, G. Wayne, Mgr.--Grove Hill Telephone Co., Grove Hill, AL; *U.S. Public*, pg. 1571
Roberts, Gary, Gen. Mgr.--Greenstone Roberts Advertising, Melville, NY; *U.S. Public*, pg. 763
Roberts, George, Partner--Kohlberg Kravis Roberts, Menlo Park, CA; *U.S. Private*, pg. 629
Roberts, George H., Pres.--Reliance Reinsurance Corp., Philadelphia, PA; *U.S. Public*, pg. 1374
Roberts, Gregory B. G., V.P. & Gen. Mgr.--L3 Communications, Camden, NJ; *U.S. Private*, pg. 638
Roberts, Hugh C., Pres.--ESIS International, Inc., Philadelphia, PA; *U.S. Public*, pg. 366
Roberts, James, Gen. Mgr.--General Latex & Chemical Corporation (Georgia), Dalton, GA; *U.S. Private*, pg. 444
Roberts, John, Chm. Bd. & Pres.--Busch Entertainment Corp., Clayton, MO; *U.S. Public*, pg. 114
Roberts, Keith, V.P. & Reg. Mgr.--Riedel-Smith Environmental Services, Portland, OR; *U.S. Public*, pg. 1478
Roberts, Keith C., Sr. V.P., Exec. V.P.-Riedel Environmental Services Inc.--Smith Technologies Corp., Portland, OR; *U.S. Public*, pg. 1478
Roberts, Ken, Chm. Bd. & Pres.--Lippincott & Margulies, Inc., New York, NY; *U.S. Public*, pg. 1048
Roberts, Kenneth, Gen. Mgr.--Camrose Pipe Company, Camrose, Canada; *U.S. Public*, pg. 1230
Roberts, Kenny, Pres.--SouthTrust Bank, Russell County, Phenix City, AL; *U.S. Public*, pg. 1492
Roberts, Kevin, Acct. Dir.--Lally, McFarland & Pantello, Toronto, Canada; *Int'l*, pg. 603
Roberts, M. Gary, Pres.--Vanguard Bank & Trust Company, Valparaiso, FL; *U.S. Public*, pg. 1549
Roberts, Nigel, Gen. Mgr.--Marina Bay Hotel Private Limited, Singapore, Singapore; *Int'l*, pg. 704
Roberts, Norman, Gen. Mgr.--Gillette (Japan) Inc., Tokyo, Japan; *U.S. Public*, pg. 745
Roberts, Paul, Mng. Dir.--Kammer Vannes S.A.R.L., Cergy-Pontoise, France; *U.S. Public*, pg. 659
Roberts, R., Chief Oper. Officer--Babcock Bristol Africa Div., Johannesburg, South Africa; *Int'l*, pg. 474
Roberts, Ralph, V.P.--WAVE, Malvern, PA; *U.S. Public*, pg. 1780
Roberts, Ralph L., Owner & Pres.--R & L Carriers, Wilmington, OH; *U.S. Private*, pg. 441
Roberts, Richard J., Gen. Mgr.--Stone Packaging Systems, Inc., Orlando, FL; *U.S. Public*, pg. 1521
Roberts, Richard S., Pres.--Guilford Mills (Fibers), Fuquay Varina, NC; *U.S. Public*, pg. 769
Roberts, Rick, Plant Mgr.--Baldor Electric Company, Saint Louis, MO; *U.S. Public*, pg. 169
Roberts, Rod, Chm. Bd.--Willis Corroon North Limited, Liverpool, United Kingdom; *Int'l*, pg. 1502
Roberts, Ross H., V.P. & Gen. Mgr.--Ford Division, Detroit, MI; *U.S. Public*, pg. 662
Roberts, Roy S., Gen. Mgr.--Pontiac-GMC Truck Division, Pontiac, MI; *U.S. Public*, pg. 720
Roberts, Seth, Chief Exec. Officer--Total Holdings (Australia) Pty. Ltd., Sydney, Australia; *Int'l*, pg. 1409
Roberts, Victor, Mng. Dir.--Eurofoil Ltd., Blaenavon, United Kingdom; *U.S. Public*, pg. 868
Roberts, W.F., Jr., Chief Oper. Officer--Hughes Tool Company Limited, Belfast, United Kingdom; *U.S. Public*, pg. 167
Roberts, Wade, Pres.--Hale Products Inc., Conshohocken, PA; *U.S. Public*, pg. 862
Roberts, Wilfred A., Territorial Mgr.--Grace Argentina S.A., Buenos Aires, Argentina; *U.S. Public*, pg. 755
Roberts, William, Pres.--Brooks/Cole Publishing Co., Pacific Grove, CA; *U.S. Public*, pg. 1600
Roberts, William Ted, Pres. & Chief Exec. Officer--SouthTrust Bank of Elba, Elba, AL; *U.S. Public*, pg. 1492
Robertshaw, G.T., Mgr.-Plant--Longview Fiber Co. Eastern Container Div., Amsterdam, NY; *U.S. Public*, pg. 1014
Robertson, Andrew, Mng. Dir.--Robertson Leo Burnett Pty. Ltd., Adelaide, Australia; *U.S. Private*, pg. 186
Robertson, Arthur, Mgr.--Westpac Banking Corp. - Solomon Islands, Honiara, Solomon Islands; *Int'l*, pg. 1497
Robertson, Chuck, Chief Exec. Officer--VeriBest Inc., Boulder, CO; *U.S. Public*, pg. 891
Robertson, Clive A.M., Mng. Dir.--MEM Ltd. 250 V, Oldham, United Kingdom; *Int'l*, pg. 390
Robertson, D. James, Reg. Mgr.--Falconbridge Explorations, Winnipeg, Canada; *Int'l*, pg. 433
Robertson, D. Page, Pres.--Monaco Coach Corporation, Coburg, OR; *U.S. Public*, pg. 1123
Robertson, Dan, Mgr.-Customer Service--AMICO-Houston Distr. Center, Houston, TX; *U.S. Private*, pg. 30
Robertson, Dan M., Pres.--Berkley Risk Managers, Somerset, NJ; *U.S. Public*, pg. 215
Robertson, David, Sr. V.P. & Gen. Mgr.-U.S.A.--Royal Bank of Canada, New York, NY; *Int'l*, pg. 1131
Robertson, Diana, Dir.--Robertson Leo Burnett Pty. Ltd., Adelaide, Australia; *U.S. Private*, pg. 186
Robertson, F., Pres.--O.O.M. Onderlinge Verzekering-Maatschappij U.A, Hague, Netherlands; *Int'l*, pg. 26
Robertson, F., Pres.--O.O.M. Onderlinge Molestverzekering-Maatschappij U.A., Hague, Netherlands; *Int'l*, pg. 26
Robertson, Gerald, Pres.--Great Lakes Castings Corporation, Ludington, MI; *U.S. Private*, pg. 169
Robertson, Guy, Reg. Dir.-Fin.--Colliers Jardine Holdings Ltd., Hong Kong, Hong Kong; *Int'l*, pg. 705
Robertson, Hal, Chief Oper. Officer--Hagglunds Drives Inc., Stoney Creek, Canada; *Int'l*, pg. 670
Robertson, Hans, Chief Oper. Officer--Saab Training Systems AB, Huskvarna, Sweden; *Int'l*, pg. 687
Robertson, J.A., Chief Exec.--Smurfit Corrugated (UK) Limited, Hatfield, United Kingdom; *Int'l*, pg. 1271
Robertson, James C., Pres.--Consumers Life Insurance Company, Camp Hill, PA; *U.S. Public*, pg. 438
Robertson, Jim, Area V.P.-WAll-Asia/Pacific--Wyeth Australia Pty. Ltd., Baulkham Hills, Australia; *U.S. Public*, pg. 82
Robertson, Jim, Plant Mgr.--New Castle Chassis Systems Div., New Castle, IN; *U.S. Public*, pg. 353
Robertson, Joseph E., Jr., Pres.--The Ore & Chemical Corp., New York, NY; *Int'l*, pg. 862
Robertson, M., Gen. Mgr.--Blackwell Scientific Publications (Australia) Pty. Ltd., Carlton Hill, Australia; *Int'l*, pg. 197
Robertson, N., Mng. Dir.--Dixons Stores Group (Far East) Limited, Hong Kong, Hong Kong; *Int'l*, pg. 414
Robertson, P.J., Sr. V.P.-Alberta Div.--Bank of Montreal - Calgary, Calgary, Canada; *Int'l*, pg. 153
Robertson, Peter, Pres.--Chevron U.S.A. Inc., San Francisco, CA; *U.S. Public*, pg. 348
Robertson, Peter, Mng. Dir.--Iggesund Converters Ltd., Milton Keynes, United Kingdom; *Int'l*, pg. 886
Robertson, Robert A., Gen. Mgr.--Turbine Engine Components Textron, Danvers, MA; *U.S. Public*, pg. 1588
Robertson, Ron, Chief Exec. Officer--Savant Instruments Inc., Farmingdale, NY; *U.S. Public*, pg. 1595
Robertson, Timothy B., Chm. Bd. & Pres.--MTM Enterprises, Inc., Studio City, CA; *Int'l*, pg. 927
Robertson, V.O., III, V.P. & Gen. Mgr.--Dillard, A ResourceNet International Company, Columbia, SC; *U.S. Public*, pg. 902
Robertson, Walt, Pres.--Maxwell Federal Division, San Diego, CA; *U.S. Public*, pg. 1062

Robertson, Walter, Pres.--Maxwell Technologies-Federal Division, San Diego, CA; *U.S. Public*, pg. 1062
Robertson, William W., Chm.--Beverage-Air Co., Spartanburg, SC; *U.S. Public*, pg. 1496
Robeys, Paul, Mng.--N.V. Vectur S.A., Brussels, Belgium; *U.S. Private*, pg. 1129
Robillard, Jacques, Plant Mgr.--Y & S Candies Plant, Montreal, Canada; *U.S. Public*, pg. 812
Robillard, Robert, Plant Mgr.--Eaton Corp. Div., Athens, AL; *U.S. Public*, pg. 556
Robillard, Tom, Pres.--Mercado Gas Services, Austin, TX; *U.S. Public*, pg. 1491
Robin, Arnold M., Pres.--Syndicated Office Systems, Inc., Orange, CA; *U.S. Public*, pg. 1577
Robinet, Bernard, Mng. Dir.--BNP-Dresdner Bank (Polska) S.A., Warsaw, Poland; *Int'l*, pg. 418
Robinette, Gary, Pres.--Erb Lumber, Inc., Birmingham, MI; *Int'l*, pg. 1512
Robinette, Judy, Publisher--Sebring News-Sun, Avon Park, FL; *U.S. Public*, pg. 1175
Robins, John, Pres. & Gen. Mgr.--SMI Joist Florida, Starke, FL; *U.S. Public*, pg. 412
Robins, John, Pres.--SMI Joist South Carolina, West Columbia, SC; *U.S. Public*, pg. 412
Robins, John, Pres. & Gen. Mgr.--SMI Joist Company, Hope, AR; *U.S. Public*, pg. 413
Robins, John, Pres.--SMI Joist Nevada, Fallon, NV; *U.S. Public*, pg. 413
Robinson, Bill, Pres. & Chief Exec. Officer--Pacific Mutual Distributors, Newport Beach, CA; *U.S. Private*, pg. 831
Robinson, Bill, Mgr.--Metrologic South Central Region, Plano, TX; *U.S. Public*, pg. 1102
Robinson, Brian D., Mng. Dir.--Quality Bakers Australia Ltd., Eastwood, Australia; *Int'l*, pg. 555
Robinson, Charles, Pres.--Atlas Copco Tools Inc., Farmington Hills, MI; *Int'l*, pg. 96
Robinson, Chris J., Mng. Dir.--Russ Berrie (U.K.) Limited, Chandlers Ford, United Kingdom; *U.S. Public*, pg. 223
Robinson, Christopher, Principal Officer--CUNA Mutual Group-Jamaica, Kingston, Jamaica; *U.S. Private*, pg. 297
Robinson, D.R., Gen. Mgr.--Fleetguard International Corporation, Quimper, France; *U.S. Public*, pg. 469
Robinson, David, Regional Mgr.--Deutsche Bank AG (Manchester), Manchester, United Kingdom; *Int'l*, pg. 404
Robinson, David, Gen. Mgr.--Nielsen UK, London, United Kingdom; *Int'l*, pg. 462
Robinson, David, Pres.--SunGard Investment Systems Inc., Hinsdale, IL; *U.S. Public*, pg. 1535
Robinson, David L., Pres. & Chief Exec. Officer--Bank of Lake County, N.A., Lakeport, CA; *U.S. Public*, pg. 1756
Robinson, E.A., Pres.--Exxon Asset Management Company, Irving, TX; *U.S. Public*, pg. 601
Robinson, Edward R., Chief Oper. Officer--Snowmax Technologies, Rochester, NY; *U.S. Public*, pg. 551
Robinson, Floyd, Pres.--NationsCredit Commercial Corporation, Cleveland, OH; *U.S. Public*, pg. 1165
Robinson, Francis Alastair Lavie, Chm. Bd.--Barclays Financial Services Co. Ltd., London, United Kingdom; *Int'l*, pg. 164
Robinson, G. D., Chm. Bd. & Pres.--Kellogg Sales Company, Battle Creek, MI; *U.S. Public*, pg. 947
Robinson, G.W., Mng. Dir.--Tata Timken Limited, Jamshedpur, India; *U.S. Public*, pg. 1617
Robinson, Gary J., Pres. & Chief Oper. Officer-Columbia Gas of PA & MD--Columbia Gas Distribution Companies, Columbus, OH; *U.S. Public*, pg. 402
Robinson, Gary J., Pres. & Chief Exec. Officer--Columbia Gas of Maryland, Inc., Columbus, OH; *U.S. Public*, pg. 403
Robinson, Gary J., Pres. & Chief Exec. Officer--Columbia Gas of Pennsylvania, Inc., Columbus, OH; *U.S. Public*, pg. 403
Robinson, Gary R., V.P. & Gen. Mgr.--WEWS-TV, Cleveland, OH; *U.S. Public*, pg. 1448
Robinson, Greg, Mng. Dir.--Holiday RV Superstores, Inc., Greer, SC; *U.S. Public*, pg. 829
Robinson, J. Douglas, Pres.--Utica National Life Insurance Company, Utica, NY; *U.S. Private*, pg. 1130
Robinson, J.E., Gen. Mgr.--Hunter Douglas Pleated Shade Corp., Gastonia, NC; *Int'l*, pg. 639
Robinson, J.W., Chief Exec. Officer--Butler Metal Products, Cambridge, Canada; *Int'l*, pg. 113
Robinson, James A., Pres.--Fairchild Dornier USA, San Antonio, TX; *U.S. Private*, pg. 391
Robinson, James M., Pres. & Gen. Mgr.-WRQX-FM--WMAL, Inc., Washington, DC; *U.S. Public*, pg. 512
Robinson, James M., Pres. & Gen. Mgr.--WRQX-FM, Washington, DC; *U.S. Public*, pg. 512
Robinson, Jeff, Gen. Mgr.--Bucksport Division, Bucksport, ME; *U.S. Public*, pg. 438
Robinson, Joe, Gen. Mgr.--Unisource, Wichita, KS; *U.S. Public*, pg. 1671
Robinson, Julie, Gen. Mgr.--Jefferson Smurfit Label, Saint Charles, IL; *Int'l*, pg. 1270
Robinson, Kenneth, V.P. & Mng. Dir.--BankAmerica Trust Co. (Jersey) Ltd., Saint Helier, United Kingdom; *U.S. Public*, pg. 183
Robinson, Kevin, Pres.--Shorrock Military Systems Inc., Hanover, MD; *Int'l*, pg. 1286
Robinson, P.N.O., Mng. Dir.--Fortis (U.K.) Limited, Eastleigh, United Kingdom; *Int'l*, pg. 499
Robinson, Patricia, Pres.--Mead School & Office Products, Dayton, OH; *U.S. Public*, pg. 1074
Robinson, R., Exec. Dir.--TNT New Zealand Limited, Auckland, New Zealand; *Int'l*, pg. 1343
Robinson, R. David, V.P. & Gen. Mgr.--Canadian Locker Co., Ltd., Scarborough, Canada; *U.S. Public*, pg. 86
Robinson, Ralph A., Pres.--Weston Bakeries Limited, Etobicoke, Canada; *Int'l*, pg. 1495
Robinson, Richard A., Pres.--Tenneco Credit Corp., Houston, TX; *U.S. Public*, pg. 1578
Robinson, Robert J., Mng. Dir.--Otis Elevator Co. Pty. Ltd., Bankstown, Australia; *U.S. Public*, pg. 1691
Robinson, Roland J., Sr. V.P.--Southeast Loan Administration, Charlotte, NC; *U.S. Public*, pg. 649
Robinson, Ronald, Pres.--Anderson Power Products Div., Sterling, MA; *U.S. Private*, pg. 528
Robinson, Ronald, Pres.--Carbolon Division, Sterling, MA; *U.S. Private*, pg. 528
Robinson, S., Branch Mgr.--Zellerbach Division, Tulsa, OK; *U.S. Public*, pg. 1075
Robinson, S., Chief Oper. Officer--De Lage Landen Factors Ltd., Tunbridge Wells, United Kingdom; *Int'l*, pg. 1082
Robinson, S. Craig, Chm. Bd., Pres. & Chief Exec. Officer--SouthTrust Bank, Covington County, Opp, AL; *U.S. Public*, pg. 1491
Robinson, S. J., Mng. Dir.--John Menzies Retail, Edinburgh, United Kingdom; *Int'l*, pg. 707
Robinson, Steve, Div. Mgr.--Spartanburg Div., Spartanburg, SC; *U.S. Public*, pg. 1504
Robinson, Steven J., Branch Mgr.--Zellerbach Division, Oklahoma City, OK; *U.S. Public*, pg. 1076
Robinson, Susan, V.P.-Fin.--Warnaco Inc.-Menswear Div., New York, NY; *U.S. Public*, pg. 1738
Robinson, Thomas C., Grp. Pres.--Technology Management Group, Falls Church, VA; *U.S. Public*, pg. 423
Robinson, Thomas C., Acting Pres.--Integrated Business Services, Falls Church, VA; *U.S. Public*, pg. 423
Robinson, Tim, Gen. Mgr.--Heil West, Inc., Dixon, CA; *U.S. Public*, pg. 521
Robinson, Tracy, V.P. & Local Brdcst. Dir.--Quantum Media International, Inc., Los Angeles, CA; *U.S. Private*, pg. 899
Robinson, William, Pres.--Cyborg Systems of Canada, Cornwall, Canada; *U.S. Private*, pg. 299
Robinson, William, Pres.--Reed & Barton Housewares, Taunton, MA; *U.S. Private*, pg. 916
Robinson, William B., Pres.--Fortis Long Term Care, Milwaukee, WI; *Int'l*, pg. 499
Robinson, William B., Chm. & Chief Exec. Officer--AdultCare, Inc., Deerfield Beach, FL; *Int'l*, pg. 499
Robison, A.N., Pres. & Chief Exec. Officer--Motorways (1980) Limited, Winnipeg, Canada; *Int'l*, pg. 1150
Robison, Dave, Gen. Mgr.--Republic Automotive Parts Sales, Inc., Davenport, IA; *U.S. Public*, pg. 1378
Robison, James, Exec. Editor--Newspaper Enterprise Association, New York, NY; *U.S. Public*, pg. 1448
Robison, Kevin, Pres. & Chief Oper. Officer--Quanta SecurSystems, Inc., Hanover, MD; *U.S. Public*, pg. 420
Robison, Paul, Reg. Mgr.--Green Tree Acceptance, Inc., Smyrna, GA; *U.S. Public*, pg. 762
Robles, Fernando Lezama, V.P. & Gen. Mgr.--Avon Cosmetics, S.A. de C.V., Mexico, Mexico; *U.S. Public*, pg. 156
Robles, Luis, Gen. Mgr.--Industrias de Maiz y Alimentos S.A., Santiago, Chile; *U.S. Public*, pg. 447
Robles, Michael L., Acct. Mgr.--EMPIRE Machinery - Kingman, Kingman, AZ; *U.S. Private*, pg. 375
Robroeks, Huub, Gen. Mgr.--Muva Greetings B.V., Heerlen, Netherlands; *U.S. Public*, pg. 78
Robson, Brian, Mgr.--Speedwing Consulting, London, United Kingdom; *Int'l*, pg. 219
Robson, H.B.E., Pres. & Dir.--P.T. Jardine Insurance Brokers Indonesia, Jakarta, Indonesia; *Int'l*, pg. 705
Robson, I.D., Mng. Dir.--De La Rue Card Technology Limited, Tewkesbury, United Kingdom; *Int'l*, pg. 387
Robson, Joyce, Mgr.-Employee Benefits--WF Corroon-Alberta, Edmonton, Canada; *Int'l*, pg. 1502
Robuste, Fidias, Exec. V.P. & Mng. Dir.--Molinos Nacionales, C.A. (Venezuela), Caracas, Venezuela; *U.S. Public*, pg. 901
Roby, Don, Mgr.--Westco Food Service, Las Vegas, NV; *Int'l*, pg. 244
Roby, Philip B., Pres. & Chief Exec. Officer--NBD Banking Company, Northeast, Fort Wayne, IN; *U.S. Public*, pg. 628
Roca, J., Mgr.-Factory--De La Rue Lerchundi Personalizacion SA, Badalona, Spain; *Int'l*, pg. 386
Roccaforte, J., Pres. & Chief Exec. Officer--Thomas Pipe & Steel, Inc., Baton Rouge, LA; *U.S. Private*, pg. 508
Rocco, Anthony, V.P. & Plant Mgr.--Grist Mill Company, Danville, IL; *U.S. Public*, pg. 766
Rocen, Gunno, Mgr.--Horda Packingsindustri AB, Rydaholm, Sweden; *Int'l*, pg. 1422
Roch, Ronald, Pres.--Morgan Matroc Inc.-Electro Ceramics Division, Bedford, OH; *Int'l*, pg. 893
Rochat, Constant, Sr. Representative--UBS Representative Office, Sao Paulo, Brazil; *Int'l*, pg. 1441
Roche, B., Mng. Dir.--Boyers & Co. Limited, Dublin, Ireland; *Int'l*, pg. 81
Roche, D'Arcy, Pres.--Raylan, Palo Alto, CA; *U.S. Public*, pg. 8
Roche, David H., Pres. & Chief Oper. Officer--Michigan Sugar Company, Saginaw, MI; *U.S. Public*, pg. 873
Roche, David H., Pres. & Chief Exec. Officer--Great Lakes Sugar Company, Fremont, OH; *U.S. Public*, pg. 873
Roche, David H., Pres.--Savannah Foods Industrial, Inc., Savannah, GA; *U.S. Public*, pg. 873
Roche, Frank, Mng. Dir.--Dataproducts Ltd., Reading, United Kingdom; *Int'l*, pg. 621
Roche, Geoffrey B., Pres. & Creative Dir.--Roche Macaulay & Partners, Toronto, Canada; *U.S. Private*, pg. 678
Roche, James G., V.P.--Electronic Sensors & Systems Division, Linthicum Heights, MD; *U.S. Public*, pg. 1198
Roche, P., Mng. Dir.--AG Stanley Limited, Holmes Chapel, United Kingdom; *Int'l*, pg. 202
Rocher, M., Dir.--Baars France SA, Mulhouse, France; *Int'l*, pg. 752
Rochfort, H.J., Pres.--Alcan (Bermuda) Ltd., Hamilton, Bermuda; *Int'l*, pg. 50
Rocholl, Klaus, Chief Oper. Officer--Agrarchemikalien Munchen GmbH., Munich, Germany; *Int'l*, pg. 356
Rochussen, P. N., Pres.--Metallurg (Canada) Limited, Mississauga, Canada; *U.S. Private*, pg. 735
Rock, John D., V.P. & Gen. Mgr.--Oldsmobile Div. General Motors Corp., Lansing, MI; *U.S. Public*, pg. 720
Rock, Kenneth, Pres.--Wheaton Glass Products, Millville, NJ; *Int'l*, pg. 67
Rock, Kenneth A., Branch Mgr.--Titeflex Industrial Americas, Oceanside, CA; *Int'l*, pg. 1340
Rocker, Kirk B., Pres. & Chief Exec. Officer--Bank of Millen, Millen, GA; *U.S. Public*, pg. 1371
Rocktaschel, Christian, Dr., Mng. Dir.--Martinswerk GmbH fur chemische und metallurgische Produktion, Bergheim, Germany; *Int'l*, pg. 69
Rockwood, Frederick W., Pres. & Chief Exec. Officer--The Forethought Group, Inc., Batesville, IN; *U.S. Public*, pg. 828
Rockwood, Richard R., Pres.--A. Biederman, Inc., Glendale, CA; *U.S. Public*, pg. 1640
Rod, Raymond, Pres.--Bensons International Systems Inc., Clifton, NJ; *Int'l*, pg. 460
Rodatz, Wolfrom, Chief Oper. Officer--Bio-Rad Laboratories, GmbH, Munich, Germany; *U.S. Public*, pg. 230
Roddey, Sidney, Pres.--The State Printing Company, Inc., Columbia, SC; *U.S. Public*, pg. 1736
Roddey, W. David, Chm. Bd. & Chief Exec. Officer--NationsBank/Memphis, Memphis, TN; *U.S. Public*, pg. 1163
Roddik, Bent, Mng. Dir.--SKF Danmark A/S, Brondby, Denmark; *Int'l*, pg. 1158
Rode, G., Mgr.--Amersham Sweden AB, Solna, Sweden; *Int'l*, pg. 993
Rodemoyer, William, Chief Oper. Officer--Vesuvius U.S.A., Champaign, IL; *Int'l*, pg. 329
Roder, Ronald E., Pres.--Firstar Information Services Corporation, Milwaukee, WI; *U.S. Public*, pg. 643
Rodgers, A.T., Pres. & Chief Exec. Officer--Celtite Inc., Georgetown, KY; *Int'l*, pg. 234
Rodgers, Bow, Pres.--PowerTV, Inc., Cupertino, CA; *U.S. Public*, pg. 1443
Rodgers, Bruce W., Exec. V.P.-Opers.--Newbridge Networks Corporation, Kanata, Canada; *Int'l*, pg. 924
Rodgers, Franklyn L., Pres.--Warner Publisher Services, Inc., New York, NY; *U.S. Public*, pg. 1614
Rodgers, Gordon, Gen. Mgr.--IPC Corporation (UK) Ltd., Nelson, United Kingdom; *Int'l*, pg. 651
Rodgers, Lisa, Mgr.-Natl. Sls.--Irma Shorell, Inc., Lynchburg, VA; *U.S. Private*, pg. 1101
Rodgers, Paul V., Gen. Mgr.--Orange County Metal Works, Orange, CA; *U.S. Public*, pg. 411
Rodgers, Ronald W., Pres. & Chief Oper. Officer--Tri Tech Laboratories, Inc., Lynchburg, VA; *U.S. Private*, pg. 1101
Rodia, Robert, Pres.--People's Securities Incorporated, Bridgeport, CT; *U.S. Public*, pg. 1274
Rodiles, Betsy, Acct. Supvr.--Heil-Brice Retail Advertising, Inc., Phoenix, AZ; *U.S. Private*, pg. 519
Rodin, Marshall E., Pres.--Bagcraft Corporation of America, Midwest Div., Baxter Springs, KS; *U.S. Public*, pg. 136
Rodman, Michael W., Pres.--NBD Neighborhood Revitalization Corp., Indianapolis, IN; *U.S. Public*, pg. 628
Rodocanachi, Emmanuel, Chm. Bd.--Financiere Saint Dominique, Paris, France; *Int'l*, pg. 344
Rodrigue, Myron, Pres.--Aker Gulf Marine, Ingleside, TX; *Int'l*, pg. 42
Rodrigues, Dilton G., Gen. Mgr.--Petrocoque S.A., Sao Paulo, Brazil; *Int'l*, pg. 52
Rodrigues, Sunil, Gen. Mgr.--IPC Interactive Pte Ltd., Singapore, Singapore; *Int'l*, pg. 651
Rodriguez L., Miguel, Mgr.-Mfg.--Grace Quimica Cia. Ltda., Santiago, Chile; *U.S. Public*, pg. 756
Rodriguez Lopes, B., Gen. Mgr.--Interservicios y Tecnologia S.A., Barcelona, Barcelona, Spain; *Int'l*, pg. 681
Rodriguez Marquez, Jorge H., V.P.-Corp. Communication--Bacardi Services (North America) Corp., Coral Gables, FL; *Int'l*, pg. 131
Rodriguez, Beth, Chief Oper. Officer--Northridge Hospital-Sherman Way Campus, Van Nuys, CA; *U.S. Private*, pg. 1118
Rodriguez, Carlos, Exec. Gen. Mgr.--Aviaco, Madrid, Spain; *Int'l*, pg. 574
Rodriguez, Edgardo, V.P. & Gen. Mgr.--B & C Bottlers Corp., Cayey, PR; *Int'l*, pg. 131
Rodriguez, Godofredo R., Pres. & Mng. Dir.--Johnson & Johnson Medical (Philippines), Inc., Manila, Philippines; *U.S. Public*, pg. 931
Rodriguez, Hector, Dir.-Medical--Century Dialysis Corporation, Los Angeles, CA; *Int'l*, pg. 1525
Rodriguez, Ing. Roberto P., Chief Oper. Officer--Cydsa S.A. Fibers Div., Garza Garcia, Mexico; *Int'l*, pg. 246
Rodriguez, Jessica, Pres.--Travel Channel-Latin America, Miami, FL; *U.S. Private*, pg. 647
Rodriguez, Jorge, Gen. Mgr.--American Church, Tucson, AZ; *U.S. Private*, pg. 60
Rodriguez, Jorge, Chief Exec. Officer-Miami--Young & Rubicam Latam (Miami), Miami, FL; *U.S. Private*, pg. 1198
Rodriguez, Jose, Pres.--Asea Brown Boveri S.A., Caracas, Venezuela; *Int'l*, pg. 8
Rodriguez, Juan, Pres.--OTRASA, Buenos Aires, Argentina; *Int'l*, pg. 1515
Rodriguez, Juan, Pres.--Petroleos Transandinos YPF S.A., Santiago, Chile; *Int'l*, pg. 1515
Rodriguez, Luis, Plant Mgr.--Medtronic Med Rel, Inc., Humacao, PR; *U.S. Public*, pg. 1083
Rodriguez, M., Chief Exec. Officer--Great Brands of Europe, Stamford, CT; *Int'l*, pg. 381
Rodriguez, M. A., Chief Oper. Officer--Construcciones Radio Electro Mecanicas S.A., Barcelona, Spain; *Int'l*, pg. 265
Rodriguez, Manuel, Plant Mgr.--Barry of Laredo, Laredo, TX; *U.S. Public*, pg. 192
Rodriguez, Pedro, Plant Mgr.--Florida Lime Corp., San Juan, PR; *U.S. Public*, pg. 1342
Rodriguez, R., Plant Mgr.--Foamex, Conyers, GA; *U.S. Private*, pg. 1094
Rodriguez, Rodd, Pres.--The Rodd Group, New York, NY; *U.S. Public*, pg. 1224
Rodriguez, Ruben O., Pres.--Boston Overseas Financial Corporation S.A., Buenos Aires, Argentina; *U.S. Public*, pg. 185

Rodriguez, Sarah, Office Admin.--Mitsubishi Heavy Industries America, Inc. (MHIA), New York, NY; *Int'l*, pg. 874
Rodriquez, Segundo, Mgr.--Arapiles, S.A., Madrid, Spain; *Int'l*, pg. 1447
Rodriquez, Ulpiano, Gen. Mgr.--Gillette Espanola, S.A., Madrid, Spain; *U.S. Public*, pg. 744
Rodriquez, Hector, M.D., Dir.-Medical--USHAWL, Inc., Los Angeles, CA; *Int'l*, pg. 1525
Rodriquez, Jose R., Chief Oper. Officer--First Brands Puerto Rico, Hato Rey, PR; *U.S. Public*, pg. 627
Rodriquez, Joseph, Dir.--Whittaker Communications, Inc., Beaverton, OR; *U.S. Public*, pg. 1767
Rodriquez, M., Gen. Mgr.--Cummins S.A. de C.V., San Luis Potosi, Mexico; *U.S. Public*, pg. 469
Rodriquez, Marco Antonio, Controller--Leo Burnett Comunica S.A., Guatemala, Guatemala; *U.S. Private*, pg. 185
Rodriquez, P., Chief Oper. Officer--Kendall S.A., Panama, Panama; *U.S. Public*, pg. 1648
Roe, David H., Pres. & Chief Exec. Officer--Bankers Security Life Insurance Society, Woodbury, NY; *U.S. Public*, pg. 1375
Roe, Robert, Publr.--American City Business Journals of Florida, Inc., Orlando, FL; *U.S. Private*, pg. 19
Roebben, Peter, Rep.--Kredietbank Oficina de Representacion, Madrid, Spain; *Int'l*, pg. 760
Roeber, Bill, Mgr.--Dynasonics, Naperville, IL; *U.S. Private*, pg. 906
Roebuck, P.T., Mng. Dir.--Cow & Gate Nutricia Ltd., Trowbridge, United Kingdom; *Int'l*, pg. 991
Roebuck, Tim, Pres.--Britrail Travel International Inc., New York, NY; *Int'l*, pg. 1165
Roed, Erling, Gen. Mgr.--Kvaerner Eiendom a.s, Ostfold Moss Division, Moss, Norway; *Int'l*, pg. 766
Roeder, Marc, Mng. Dir.--Protek Synthes S.A., Etupes, France; *Int'l*, pg. 1307
Roedy, William, Mng. Dir.--MTV Europe, London, United Kingdom; *U.S. Private*, pg. 779
Roelofs, Roger, Gen. Mgr.--Penn Champ, East Butler, PA; *U.S. Private*, pg. 145
Roels, Andre, Rep.--Allianz Versicherungs-AG, Antwerp, Belgium; *Int'l*, pg. 61
Roemer, Mike, Reg. V.P.--Central Region, Dallas, TX; *Int'l*, pg. 694
Roennau, Albert, Gen. Mgr--ITW ATECO GmbH, Norderstedt, Germany; *U.S. Public*, pg. 868
Roeser, Gerhard, Gen. Mgr.--Karsdorfer Zement Beteiligungs GmbH, Karsdorf, Germany; *Int'l*, pg. 789
Roeser, Robert R., Pres. & Chief Exec. Officer--Elo TouchSystems, Inc., Fremont, CA; *U.S. Public*, pg. 1362
Roesler, Gerd, Mng. Dir.--Gambro Medizintechnik GmbH, Planegg, Germany; *Int'l*, pg. 668
Roesler, Gerd, Chief Oper. Officer--MTN Medizintechnik Neubrandenburg GmbH I.G., Neubrandenburg, Germany; *Int'l*, pg. 669
Roetering, Ric, Mng. Dir.--Tedak AB, Eskilstuna, Sweden; *Int'l*, pg. 281
Roether, Kim, Mng. Dir.--Derby Cycle Werke GmbH, Cloppenburg, Germany; *Int'l*, pg. 394
Rof, Juan Sancho, Pres.--Repsol Comercial de Productos Petroliferos, S.A., Madrid, Spain; *Int'l*, pg. 1104
Rogan, David, Mng. Dir.--Alliance Paper Group PLC, Manchester, United Kingdom; *Int'l*, pg. 863
Rogan, Owen F., Pres.--Ikon Office Solutions (British Columbia), Vancouver, Canada; *U.S. Public*, pg. 864
Rogan, T.B., Chief Oper. Officer--Frank R. MacNeill & Son, Inc., Miami, FL; *Int'l*, pg. 705
Rogatko, Michael, Chief Exec. Officer--Gerber Polska, Warsaw, Poland; *Int'l*, pg. 973
Roger, Maurice, Mng. Dir.--Parfums Christian Dior, Paris, France; *Int'l*, pg. 781
Roger, Serge, Chm. Bd. & Pres.--Elscint France S.A., Bagnolet, France; *Int'l*, pg. 450
Rogers, Billy E., V.P.-Vending Opers.--Old Fashion Food, Austell, GA; *U.S. Private*, pg. 814
Rogers, Brooks, Prod. Mgr.--Seratronics, Inc., Lexington, MA; *Int'l*, pg. 505
Rogers, Charles G., Pres.--BellSouth Products, Inc., Roanoke, VA; *U.S. Public*, pg. 209
Rogers, D.W., Chm. Bd.--Woodside Petroleum Ltd., Melbourne, Australia; *Int'l*, pg. 1137
Rogers, Dave, Gen. Mgr.--Quebecor Imaging (Alphatext), Richmond Hill, Canada; *Int'l*, pg. 1077
Rogers, Douglas D., Mgr.--Piper Jaffray Inc., Rapid City, SD; *U.S. Public*, pg. 1302
Rogers, Edward S., Chief Exec. Officer--Rogers Cable Systems, Etobicoke, Canada; *Int'l*, pg. 1123
Rogers, Gary L., Pres. & Chief Exec. Officer--G.E. Plastics, Pittsfield, MA; *U.S. Public*, pg. 710
Rogers, James H., Pres.--Quebec Street Investments, Inc., Bloomfield, CT; *U.S. Public*, pg. 361
Rogers, James M., Pres.--Hercules Korea Chemical Co. Ltd., Seoul, Korea; *U.S. Public*, pg. 811
Rogers, John A., Chief Oper. Officer--Ingram & Bell Inc., Don Mills, Canada; *Int'l*, pg. 826
Rogers, Lynn R., V.P. & Gen. Mgr.--Georg Fischer Amasteel S.A., Schaffhausen, Switzerland; *U.S. Private*, pg. 382
Rogers, M. M., Pres.--Lippincott-Raven Publishing, New York, NY; *Int'l*, pg. 1513
Rogers, M.C., Chief Exec. Officer--Moore Formularios Limitada, Bauru, Brazil; *Int'l*, pg. 889
Rogers, Ray, Pres.--Innovative Membrane Systems, Inc., Norwood, MA; *U.S. Public*, pg. 1320
Rogers, Stephen C., Pres. & Chief Exec. Officer--SouthTrust Bank, Selma, Selma, AL; *U.S. Public*, pg. 1492
Rogers, Steve, Pres.--Cerplex Mass, Inc., Lawrence, MA; *U.S. Public*, pg. 332
Rogers, Steve, Gen. Mgr.--Weatherford, Houston, TX; *U.S. Public*, pg. 1749
Rogers, Ted, Pres.--Rogers Cable TV-Vancouver, Burnaby, Canada; *Int'l*, pg. 1122
Rogers, Terry W., Pres.--Fleming Foods West, Salt Lake City, UT; *U.S. Public*, pg. 653
Rogers, Tracy, V.P.-Pur.--Montoi Mattel Toys, Laredo, TX; *U.S. Public*, pg. 1058
Rogers, Walter D., Jr., Pres.--Current Technology, Inc., Irving, TX; *U.S. Public*, pg. 480
Rogers, William, Gen. Mgr.--Teleflex Electrical Systems, Sarasota, FL; *U.S. Public*, pg. 1569
Rogers, Yandell, Jr., Pres., Chief Exec. Officer & Gen. Counsel--YRJ Corporation, Houston, TX; *U.S. Private*, pg. 1176
Rogers, Yandell, Jr., Pres.--Ridgway's, Inc., Houston, TX; *U.S. Private*, pg. 1176
Rogers, Yandell, Jr., Pres.--US Reprographics, Inc., Philadelphia, PA; *U.S. Private*, pg. 1176
Rogerson, Andrew P., ResidentRep.--World Bank, London, United Kingdom; *U.S. Private*, pg. 1189
Rogerson, Garry, V.P. & Gen. Mgr.--Chromatography Systems, Walnut Creek, CA; *U.S. Public*, pg. 1710
Rogerson, Leif, Mng. Dir.--Alfa-Laval Agri International AB, Tumba, Sweden; *Int'l*, pg. 1377
Rogerson, William D., Pres.--De-Sta-Co, A Dover Resources Co., Troy, MI; *U.S. Public*, pg. 521
Rogersson, Leif, Pres.--Alfa Laval AB, Lund, Sweden; *Int'l*, pg. 1378
Roggemans, Albert, Gen. Mgr.--Charleroi Local Head Office, Charleroi, Belgium; *Int'l*, pg. 147
Rogier, James L., Gen. Mgr.--Container Div. (Humboldt), Humboldt, TN; *Int'l*, pg. 1269
Rogow, S.M., Dir.--Coates Chemie Compounds (Pty.) Ltd., Cape Town, South Africa; *Int'l*, pg. 1410
Rogren, Rolf, Dir. & Gen. Mgr.--Crown Cork Co. (Scandinavia) A/S, Tastrup, Denmark; *U.S. Public*, pg. 464
Rogy, Bernard, Mng. Dir.--Creusot-Loire Industrie, Puteaux, France; *Int'l*, pg. 571
Rohde, Ellen, Pres.--Vanity Fair, New York, NY; *U.S. Public*, *pg. 1702*
Rohde, Wolfgang, Mgr.--Commerzbank AG (South East Asia) Ltd., Singapore, Singapore; *Int'l*, pg. 311
Rohdin, Lars, Pres.--Lars Jonsson AB, Malmo, Sweden; *Int'l*, pg. 922
Rohfritch, John W., Sr., Chm. Bd.--Cigna Healthcare of Illinois, Inc., Des Plaines, IL; *U.S. Public*, pg. 359
Rohfritch, John W., Sr., Pres.--Cigna Healthcare of Kansas City/Missouri, Inc., Wichita, KS; *U.S. Public*, pg. 359
Rohfritch, John W., Sr., Pres.--Cigna Healthcare of St. Louis, Inc., Saint Louis, MO; *U.S. Public*, pg. 360
Rohkamm, Eckhard, Dr., Pres.--Thyssen Industrie Aktiengesellschaft, Bad-Wuertt, Germany; *Int'l*, pg. 1387
Rohle, Michael, Chief Exec. Officer-DMB&B-Germany--DMB&B Frankfurt, Frankfurt/Main, Germany; *U.S. Private*, pg. 303
Rohle, Michael, Mng. Dir. & Chief Exec. Officer-Frankfurt--DMB&B Hamburg, Hamburg, Germany; *U.S. Private*, pg. 303
Rohle, Michael, Chief Exec. Officer (Out of Frankfurt)--DMB&B Dusseldorf, Dusseldorf, Germany; *U.S. Private*, pg. 303
Rohleder, Claus, Dr., Chief Oper. Officer--Boehringer Ingelheim, Ingelheim, Germany; *Int'l*, pg. 199
Rohleder, Michael J., Pres. & Chief Exec. Officer--Wyle Electronics, Irvine, CA; *Int'l*, pg. 1457
Rohlfs, Ray, V.P. & Gen. Mgr.--U.S. Brick, Inc., Grand Prairie, TX; *Int'l*, pg. 699
Rohlke, Gary, Dir.-Mktg.--Wandel & Goltermann Inc., Research Triangle Park, NC; *Int'l*, pg. 1486
Rohloff, P., Chief Oper. Officer--V.A.G. Vertriebszentrum Weser-EMS GmbH U Co. KG, Bremen, Germany; *Int'l*, pg. 1474
Rohm, Keith, Mng. Dir.--Service Motor Co., Seymour, WI; *U.S. Private*, pg. 986
Rohne, Cal, Gen. Mgr.--Premdor Mouldings Inc., Concord, Canada; *Int'l*, pg. 1067
Rohner, Peter, Chief Exec. Officer--Kulling & Partner Identity, Zurich, Switzerland; *U.S. Private*, pg. 1199
Rohr, James E., Pres.--PNC International Bank, Pittsburgh, PA; *U.S. Public*, pg. 1243
Rohrback, Frank, V.P. & Gen. Mgr.--ARC Propulsion Division, Camden, AR; *U.S. Public*, pg. 1458
Rohrbaiser, Markus, Gen. Mgr.--UBS Securities LLC, New York, NY; *Int'l*, pg. 1440
Rohrer, David W., Chief Oper. Officer--Rohrer Corporation, Buford, GA; *U.S. Private*, pg. 940
Rohrer, Dr. Bernt W., Gen. Mgr.--Europaische Hypothekenbank der Deutschen Bank, Luxembourg, Luxembourg; *Int'l*, pg. 405
Rohrs, Chris, Gen. Mgr.--Post-Newsweek Stations, Connecticut, Inc., Hartford, CT; *U.S. Public*, pg. 1743
Rohrs, Jack, Gen. Mgr.--Hanover Foods Corp., Clayton, DE; *U.S. Private*, pg. 499
Rohrs, John, Jr., V.P.-Syndication, Midwestern Region--Columbia Tri-Star Television Distribution - Chicago Office, Chicago, IL; *Int'l*, pg. 1282
Rohs, Thomas W., Chm. Bd. & Chief Exec. Officer--American Modern Home Insurance Group, Amelia, OH; *U.S. Public*, pg. 1110
Rohs, Thomas W., Pres.--American Family Home Insurance Co., Amelia, OH; *U.S. Public*, pg. 1110
Rohs, Thomas W., Pres.--American Modern Home Insurance Co., Amelia, OH; *U.S. Public*, pg. 1110
Rohs, Thomas W., Pres.--Main Life Insurance Co., Amelia, OH; *U.S. Public*, pg. 1111
Rohweder, Thomas, V.P.--Aanekoski Board Mill, Aanekoski, Finland; *Int'l*, pg. 863
Rojanasena, Paitoon, Pres.--M.E. Otsuka Co., Ltd., Bangkok, Thailand; *Int'l*, pg. 1014
Rojas, J.V., Pres.--Chevron Petroleum Company of Colombia, Bogota, Colombia; *U.S. Public*, pg. 348
Rojas, Luis F., Dr., Partner In Charge--GEO- Ambiental Consultores Cia Ltda., Chile; *U.S. Private*, pg. 434
Rojas, Matias, Gen. Mgr.--Duratec, Santiago, Chile; *Int'l*, pg. 430
Rojas, Raul, Gen. Mgr.--Esselte de Mexico, S.A. de C.V., Mexico, Mexico; *Int'l*, pg. 461
Rojel, Anja, Gen. Mgr.--Scancem Service AB, Malmo, Sweden; *Int'l*, pg. 1200
Rokhvarg, Alex, Pres.--Advanced Conversion Products, Cedar Knolls, NJ; *U.S. Private*, pg. 1097
Rokkum, Tor, Chief Oper. Officer--Kvaerner Installasjon, Kristiansund Division, Kristiansand, Norway; *Int'l*, pg. 769
Rolano, Luciano, Chm. & Pres.--Iveco Trucks Of North America Inc., Bensalem, PA; *Int'l*, pg. 484
Rolenberg, Greg, Chief Exec. Officer--Express Scripts Vision, Earth City, MO; *U.S. Public*, pg. 601
Rolfes, Ken, V.P.-Oper.--Graphic Controls Industrial, Buffalo, NY; *U.S. Private*, pg. 471
Rolfsen, Erik Rolf, Mng. Dir.--Total Norge AS, Oslo, Norway; *Int'l*, pg. 1409
Rolla, Stephen J., Pres.--3kon Office Solutions-Upstate New York, Rochester, NY; *U.S. Public*, pg. 864
Rolland, Alain, Pres.--Jelmoli AG, Zurich, Switzerland; *Int'l*, pg. 705
Rolland, Jan, Mng. Dir., Chief Exec. Officer--Clarion I.M.P. A/S, Oslo, Norway; *U.S. Private*, pg. 303
Rolland, Lucien, Chm. Bd.--Select Robinson Inc., Portland, ME; *Int'l*, pg. 274
Roller, Donald E., Pres. & Chief Exec. Officer--United States Gypsum Co., Chicago, IL; *U.S. Public*, pg. 1660
Roller, Jochen, Gen. Mgr.--Bayerische Hypotheken-und Wechsel-Bank AG (Hong Kong), Central, Hong Kong; *Int'l*, pg. 176
Rollings, James, V.P. & Gen. Mgr.--Peterson Spring-Commonwealth Plant, Worcester, MA; *U.S. Private*, pg. 857
Rollins, Kenneth J., Pres.--Quincy Compressor Division Coltec Industries, Quincy, IL; *U.S. Public*, pg. 402
Rollio, M., Sales Mgr.--Aqualon Italia S.p.A., Castel Maggiore, Italy; *U.S. Public*, pg. 810
Rollo, Leonardo, Pres.--Metalac S.A. Industria e Comercio, Sorocaba, Brazil; *U.S. Public*, pg. 1420
Rolph, P. R., Chief Oper. Officer--Metier Management Systems, Hayes, United Kingdom; *U.S. Public*, pg. 1010
Rolshoven, Rachele, Dir.--Yoh Health Care Services, Van Nuys, CA; *U.S. Private*, pg. 317
Roman, Gladys, Mgr.--Charlio's, New York, NY; *U.S. Private*, pg. 786
Roman, Juan, Gen. Mgr.--Sonoco Colombiana S.A., Cali, Colombia; *U.S. Public*, pg. 1487
Roman, Paul, Pres.--Rollins Protective Services, Atlanta, GA; *U.S. Public*, pg. 1404
Roman, Stanley R., Pres.--Air Products of Puerto Rico, Inc., Allentown, PA; *U.S. Public*, pg. 31
Roman, William S., Pres.--Parsons Brinckerhoff Energy Services Inc., New York, NY; *U.S. Private*, pg. 841
Romanchych, Vladimir E., Pres.--Hop-In Michigan, Inc., Ann Arbor, MI; *Int'l*, pg. 1249
Romandetti, John A., Pres.--Denny's, Inc., Spartanburg, SC; *U.S. Public*, pg. 23
Romanese, Gino, V.P.-Residential Real Estate Services--Royal LePage - British Columbia Office, Surrey, Canada; *Int'l*, pg. 1143
Romaniuk, Don, Pres.--TELUS Advertising Services, Calgary, Canada; *Int'l*, pg. 1374
Romano, Donald, Chief Exec. Officer--Heritage Air Systems, Inc., Deer Park, NY; *U.S. Public*, pg. 572
Romano, Giuseppe, Dir.--Banca d'America e d'Italia S.p.A. (Napoli), Naples, Italy; *Int'l*, pg. 403
Romano, James R., Pres.--Bel-Air Patrol, Santa Monica, CA; *U.S. Public*, pg. 245
Romano, Marco, Gen. Mgr.--Augat SRL, Milan, Italy; *U.S. Public*, pg. 1598
Romano, Perry, V.P. & Gen. Mgr.--Quality Lighting, Inc., Franklin Park, IL; *Int'l*, pg. 821
Romano, Rene, Mng. Dir.--Cerca, Paris, France; *Int'l*, pg. 503
Romanos, Jack, Pres.--Simon & Schuster Consumer Group, New York, NY; *U.S. Private*, pg. 777
Romanow, Marc, Publr.--The Bristol Press, Bristol, CT; *U.S. Public*, pg. 934
Romanow, Marc, Publr.--Imprint Newpapers, Bristol, CT; *U.S. Public*, pg. 935
Romanow, Marc, Publr.--The Herald, New Britain, CT; *U.S. Public*, pg. 935
Romanowski, Thomas S., Pres. & Chief Exec. Officer--CILCORP Ventures Inc., Peoria, IL; *U.S. Public*, pg. 367
Romanu, Nellie, Office Mgr.--E & E Steel, Inc., Los Angeles, CA; *U.S. Private*, pg. 941
Rombouts, F., Chm.--Campina N.V./S.A., Aalst, Belgium; *Int'l*, pg. 254
Rombouts, Rene, Gen. Mgr.-Europe--A. Schulman AG, Zurich, Switzerland; *U.S. Public*, pg. 1441
Rombouts, Rene, Mng. Dir.--N.V.A. Schulman Plastics, S.A., Bornem, Belgium; *U.S. Public*, pg. 1441
Rombouts, Renee, Mng. Dir.--A. Schulman S.A., Paris, France; *U.S. Public*, pg. 1441
Romeo, Charles, Exec. V.P.--EFS Service Corporation, Chicago, IL; *U.S. Public*, pg. 1428
Romeo, Charles, Exec. V.P.--Custom Source Realty Corporation, Saint Charles, IL; *U.S. Public*, pg. 1429
Romeo, Charles J., 1st V.P. & Gen. Mgr.--St. Paul Financial Development Corp., West Chicago, IL; *U.S. Public*, pg. 1429
Romer, Ciro B., Mgr.--Banque de Suez Nederland International N.V., Curacao, Netherlands Antilles; *Int'l*, pg. 314
Romer, Gordon, Pres.--Solion, Westwood, MA; *U.S. Public*, pg. 1293
Romero Garces, Jose Luis, Gen. Mgr.--CEPSA U.K., Ltd., Luton, United Kingdom; *Int'l*, pg. 323
Romero, D. German Ramajo, Chief Exec. Officer--Compania Telefonos Chile (C.T.C.), Santiago, Chile; *Int'l*, pg. 1373
Romero, Eduardo, Gen. Mgr.--Coppermol S.A., Buenos Aires, Argentina; *Int'l*, pg. 303
Romero, Rogelio, Mgr.--Grupo Termoindustrial ECA, S.A. de C.V., Mexico, Mexico; *U.S. Private*, pg. 361

Romeu, Mike E., Pres.--Automax Finance, Santurce, PR; *U.S. Public*, pg. 644
Romijn, R., Mgr.--Ballast Nedam International B.V., Kowloon, Hong Kong; *Int'l*, pg. 134
Romijn, R., Area Mgr.--Ballast Nedam Dredging (HK) Branch, Kowloon, Hong Kong; *Int'l*, pg. 134
Rominiecki, Ronald R., Pres. & Chief Oper. Officer--National Propane Corp., Cedar Rapids, IA; *U.S. Public*, pg. 1635
Rommrath, Herbert G., Pres. & Rep. Dir.--G.E. Plastics Pacific Ltd., Singapore, Singapore; *U.S. Public*, pg. 713
Romoff, H. M., Chief Oper. Officer--Canada Maritime Limited, London, United Kingdom; *Int'l*, pg. 259
Romoren, Bente-Lill B., Chief Oper. Officer--Novo Nordisk Pharma A/S, Rud, Norway; *Int'l*, pg. 988
Rompala, Richard M., Pres. & Chief Exec. Officer--Valspar Paints, Minneapolis, MN; *U.S. Public*, pg. 1707
Romzek, Pat, Reg. Mgr.--SMS-Ann Arbor, Novi, MI; *U.S. Public*, pg. 1463
Ronaghan, John, Mng. Dir.--Ericsson Treasury Ireland Ltd., Dun Laoghaire, Ireland; *Int'l*, pg. 1368
Ronahan, Donald F., Pres.--ManuLife (Singapore) Pte. Ltd., Singapore, Singapore; *Int'l*, pg. 841
Ronald, Mark, Pres.--GEC-Marconi Hazeltine Corporation, Greenlawn, NY; *Int'l*, pg. 544
Ronan, Chris, Media Dir.--Von Broembsen Marson Leo Burnett/Harare, Harare, Zimbabwe; *U.S. Private*, pg. 186
Ronan, Joel, Pres.--Amano Pioneer Credit Corp., Woodbridge, VA; *Int'l*, pg. 71
Ronca, M.V., Pres.--Domain Energy Ventures Corporation, Houston, TX; *U.S. Public*, pg. 516
Ronca, M.V., Pres.--Domain Energy Production Corporation, Houston, TX; *U.S. Public*, pg. 516
Ronca, M.V., Pres.--Domain Energy International Corporation, Houston, TX; *U.S. Public*, pg. 516
Ronca, M.V., Pres.--Domain Energy Finance Corporation, Houston, TX; *U.S. Public*, pg. 516
Roncarty, Ron, Plant Mgr.--The Clinipad Corp., Norwich, CT; *U.S. Private*, pg. 247
Roncelli, G., Gen. Mgr.--Keithley Instruments SRL, Milan, Italy; *U.S. Public*, pg. 947
Rondelli, Lucio, Mng. Dir.--Credito Italiano, Milan, Italy; *Int'l*, pg. 652
Rondou, Stephan, Pres.--Martin Mathys, NV, Zelem, Belgium; *U.S. Public*, pg. 1358
Ronel, Samuel H., Ph.D., Pres. & Chief Exec. Officer--Interferon Sciences, Inc., New Brunswick, NJ; *U.S. Public*, pg. 694
Ronen, David, Gen. Mgr.--Astronautics C.A. Ltd., Bnei-Brak, Israel; *U.S. Private*, pg. 93
Roney, M.J., Mng. Dir.--Companhia Goodyear do Brasil Produtos de Borracha, Sao Paulo, Brazil; *U.S. Public*, pg. 753
Rong, Yang Qing, Dir.--Chang Cheng-Takenaka Construction Co., Ltd., Beijing, China; *Int'l*, pg. 1351
Ronk, G. E., V.P. & Grp. Exec.--Electrical Controls Sector, Stamford, CT; *U.S. Public*, pg. 726
Ronkko, Tuomo, Sector Pres.--Ahlstrom Machinery, Helsinki, Finland; *Int'l*, pg. 33
Ronner, Jim, V.P. & Gen. Mgr.--Vulcraft Div., Saint Joe, IN; *U.S. Public*, pg. 1206
Ronner, Oskar K., Pres. & Chief Exec. Officer--Electrowatt Ltd., Zurich, Switzerland; *Int'l*, pg. 1246
Ronnie, Leonard H., Chm. Bd.--International Paper Realty Corp., Park Ridge, NJ; *U.S. Public*, pg. 904
Ronsberg, Kare Bergsvein, Mng. Dir.--Det Norske Veritas, Aberdeen, United Kingdom; *Int'l*, pg. 397
Ronzani, Nario, Mng. Dir.--Monarimport S.p.A., Villanova di Castenaso, Italy; *Int'l*, pg. 295
Rood, Terrence, Gen. Mgr.--B & L Plastics Inc., Rockford, MI; *U.S. Public*, pg. 867
Roof, William M., Chm. Bd.-Clintock Ltd.--Clintock Limited, Dublin, Ireland; *U.S. Public*, pg. 262
Rook, Lennart, Mng. Dir.--Willis Faber Gothia AB, Goteborg, Sweden; *Int'l*, pg. 1510
Rooke, Kevin C., Pres. & Gen. Mgr.--Pathfinder Div., Canon City, CO; *U.S. Public*, pg. 1318
Rooks, Richard, Branch Mgr.--Circle Freight International USA, Phoenix, AZ; *U.S. Public*, pg. 371
Rooney, Gerry, Sr. V.P.-Opers.--Joy Mining Machinery, Warrendale, PA; *U.S. Public*, pg. 790
Rooney, John E., Pres.--Ameritech Consumer Services, Hoffman Estates, IL; *U.S. Public*, pg. 98
Rooney, L.F., III, Chm. Bd. & Chief Exec. Officer--Manhattan Construction Company, Tulsa, OK; *U.S. Private*, pg. 943
Rooney, Michael, Publisher--Outdoor Life, New York, NY; *U.S. Public*, pg. 1617
Rooney, Phillip B., Chm. Bd. & Dir.--Rust International Inc., Birmingham, AL; *U.S. Public*, pg. 1366
Rooniy, Brian, Gen. Mgr.--U.S. Filters Control Systems, Saint Paul, MN; *U.S. Public*, pg. 61
Roos, A. G., Dir.--Mautner Markhof International GmbH, Vienna, Austria; *Int'l*, pg. 753
Roos, G., Pres.--ALZ N.V., Genk, Belgium; *Int'l*, pg. 79
Roos, Henrik, V.P. & Gen. Mgr.--Dentsply Gendex Division, Des Plaines, IL; *U.S. Public*, pg. 499
Roos, J.F.D., Pres.--Georg Fischer N.V., Epe, Netherlands; *Int'l*, pg. 489
Roos, Larry, V.P. & Plant Mgr.--Nucor Steel-Indiana, Crawfordsville, IN; *U.S. Public*, pg. 1205
Roosen, Humphrey, Branch Mgr.--Union-Transport Corporation-Los Angeles, Lawndale, CA; *U.S. Private*, pg. 1119
Roosen, M., Gen. Mgr.--3M/ECC Europa BV, Amersfoort, Netherlands; *Int'l*, pg. 209
Roost, Ueli, Chief Exec. Officer--Cerasiv GmbH, Plochingen, Germany; *Int'l*, pg. 861
Root, Douglas W., Chief Oper. Officer & Exec. V.P.--Successful Money Management Seminars, Inc., Tualatin, OR; *U.S. Public*, pg. 1376
Root, Jack B., Pres.--Successful Money Management Seminars, Inc., Tualatin, OR; *U.S. Public*, pg. 1376
Rope, R.E., Pres.--Taylor Woodrow Homes California Limited, Laguna Hills, CA; *Int'l*, pg. 1359
Roper, Helen, Pres. & Gen. Mgr.--American International Management Co. (Barbados) Ltd., Bridgetown, Barbados; *U.S. Public*, pg. 85
Roper, Mary Lynn, V.P. & Gen. Mgr.--KOAT-TV, Albuquerque, NM; *U.S. Public*, pg. 1344
Roper, R.E., Plant Mgr.--Ropak West, La Mirada, CA; *Int'l*, pg. 812
Roper, Rich, Mgr.-Div.--Aramark Services, Rosemont Horizon, Rosemont, IL; *U.S. Private*, pg. 79
Roppa, R., District Mgr.--A.M. Castle & Co., Cincinnati, OH; *U.S. Public*, pg. 313
Roque, Emilio, Pres.--Tefal Rowenta Portugal, Lisbon, Portugal; *Int'l*, pg. 568
Roquelpo, Bruno, Chm. Bd. & Mng. Dir.--Campbell Distillers Limited, Brentford, United Kingdom; *Int'l*, pg. 567
Roquette, Jerome, Mng. Dir.--Nickel, Marcq-en-Baroeul, France; *Int'l*, pg. 116
Rorai, Joe, Gen. Mgr.--CCTF, Mississauga, Canada; *Int'l*, pg. 453
Rorie, Greg, Gen. Mgr.--Reclamation Div. (Evansville), Evansville, IN; *Int'l*, pg. 1270
Rorke, Kevin C., Pres. & Gen. Mgr.--Flomaster Div., Canon City, CO; *U.S. Public*, pg. 1318
Ros, Alberto P., Gen. Mgr.--Security Plastics West, Inc., McAllen, TX; *U.S. Private*, pg. 981
Rosa, Jack, Pres.--Electroid Corp., Springfield, NJ; *U.S. Private*, pg. 1131
Rosa, Nick E., Pres. & Mng. Dir.--Nutrasweet Europe, Zug, Switzerland; *U.S. Public*, pg. 1126
Rosa, Ronald L., V.P. & G.M.--Cannon Equipment Co., Cannon Falls, MN; *Int'l*, pg. 646
Rosamilia, Richard, Pres.--Amboy Aggregates, South Amboy, NJ; *U.S. Private*, pg. 474
Rosch, Klaus W., Chief Oper. Officer & Mng. Dir.--Bausparkasse Gemeinschaft der Freunde Wuestenrot gem.GmbH, Ludwigsburg, Germany; *Int'l*, pg. 1514
Roscoe, Michael R., Pres. & Chief Exec. Officer--Distribution Services, Inc., Lantana, FL; *U.S. Public*, pg. 87
Rose, Albert F., Pres.--Atlantic Wholesalers Ltd., Sackville, Canada; *Int'l*, pg. 1495
Rose, Bill, Mng. Dir.--Noble Drilling (West Africa) Ltd., Lagos, Nigeria; *U.S. Public*, pg. 1187
Rose, Bill, Area Mgr.--Noble Drilling (U.K.) Ltd., Aberdeen, United Kingdom; *U.S. Public*, pg. 1187
Rose, Dan, Pres.--DuCoa L.P., Highland, IL; *U.S. Private*, pg. 301
Rose, Dave, Mgr.--Anixter-Birmingham, Birmingham, United Kingdom; *U.S. Public*, pg. 116
Rose, David, Chief Oper. Officer--Sonotron Holding AG, Zug, Switzerland; *Int'l*, pg. 644
Rose, Gib, Pres.--Chelsea Group, Wyandotte, MI; *U.S. Private*, pg. 539
Rose, Graham, Dir.-European Frit Opers.--Ferro (Great Britain) Limited, Wolverhampton, United Kingdom; *U.S. Public*, pg. 619
Rose, Jim, Gen. Mgr.--John Crane Singapore Pte. Ltd., Singapore, Singapore; *Int'l*, pg. 1339
Rose, Joe A., Exec. V.P.--Information Services Division, Atlanta, GA; *U.S. Public*, pg. 1156
Rose, John, V.P. & Gen. Mgr.--KCTV, Fairway, KS; *U.S. Public*, pg. 1094
Rose, Ken, Mng. Dir.--Ross & Catherall Ceramics Limited, Derby, United Kingdom; *Int'l*, pg. 1467
Rose, Lynn, Pres.--Chemol Co., Inc., Greensboro, NC; *U.S. Private*, pg. 999
Rose, Merritt S., Jr., V.P. & Gen. Mgr.--WFTV, Inc., Orlando, FL; *U.S. Private*, pg. 282
Rose, Michael, Chief Oper. Officer--MacDermid Australia Branch, Revesby, Australia; *U.S. Public*, pg. 1030
Rose, Michel, Pres.--Orsan, Paris, France; *Int'l*, pg. 791
Rose, P.M., Mng. Dir.--Butterley Brick Ltd., Ripley, United Kingdom; *Int'l*, pg. 592
Rose, Paul E., Pres.--Promotion Information Management (PIM), Chicago, IL; *U.S. Private*, pg. 649
Rose, Peter, Mgr.--RGB Stainless Ltd., Birmingham, United Kingdom; *Int'l*, pg. 1186
Rose, Porter B., Chm. Bd. & Pres.--Liberty Investment Group, Inc., Greenville, SC; *U.S. Public*, pg. 992
Rose, Richard J., Pres.--Sysco Food Services of Cleveland, Inc., Bedford, OH; *U.S. Public*, pg. 1551
Rose, Robert E., Pres. & Chief Exec. Officer--Diamond Offshore Drilling, Inc., Houston, TX; *U.S. Public*, pg. 1011
Rose, Ron, Gen. Mgr.--Elixir Industries, Leola, PA; *U.S. Private*, pg. 371
Rose, Sidney, Chief Oper. Officer--Allright Florida, Inc., Tampa, FL; *U.S. Private*, pg. 42
Rosell, Hans, Chief Oper. Officer--DataCard Sweden AB, Stockholm, Sweden; *U.S. Private*, pg. 313
Rosen, B., Chief Oper. Officer--AVX Israel Ltd., Jerusalem, Israel; *Int'l*, pg. 776
Rosen, Elaine D., Pres.--First UNUM Life Insurance Company, Tarrytown, NY; *U.S. Public*, pg. 1699
Rosen, Gerald, Dir.-Medical--Comprehensive Cancer Centers, Los Angeles, CA; *Int'l*, pg. 1525
Rosen, Harry, Chm. Bd. & Chief Exec. Officer--Harry Rosen Inc., Toronto, Canada; *Int'l*, pg. 425
Rosen, Jack, Pres.--Plus Mark, Inc., Cleveland, OH; *U.S. Public*, pg. 78
Rosen, Jack, Pres.--CompreMedx, Inc., Englewood Cliffs, NJ; *U.S. Public*, pg. 440
Rosen, Kenneth, Gen. Mgr.--International Window-Arizona, Inc., Phoenix, AZ; *U.S. Public*, pg. 895
Rosen, Lewis, Admin.--Embassy House Healthcare, Brockton, MA; *U.S. Public*, pg. 1712
Rosen, Sven, Chief Oper. Officer--Alfa-Laval South East Asia Pty Ltd., Singapore, Singapore; *Int'l*, pg. 1380
Rosenauer, James, Pres.--Paradata Financial Systems, Chesterfield, MO; *U.S. Public*, pg. 1778
Rosenband, Phillip, Pres.--Morgan Marshall Industries, Inc., Chicago Heights, IL; *U.S. Private*, pg. 904
Rosenberg, C.T., Chief Exec. Officer--Bowthorpe-Hellermann (Pty.) Ltd., Johannesburg, South Africa; *Int'l*, pg. 208
Rosenberg, Claude N., Jr., Sr. Principal--RCM Capital Management, San Francisco, CA; *Int'l*, pg. 418
Rosenberg, Dennis, Div. Mgr.--Rogers Cable TV-Toronto Div., Don Mills, Canada; *Int'l*, pg. 1122
Rosenberg, H.A., Pres.--Crown Gold, Inc., Baltimore, MD; *U.S. Public*, pg. 462
Rosenberg, H.A., Jr., Pres.--Crown Central Pipe Line Co., Bellaire, TX; *U.S. Public*, pg. 462
Rosenberg, H.A., Jr., Chm.--Crown Central Holding Corp., Baltimore, MD; *U.S. Public*, pg. 462
Rosenberg, Henry A., Jr., Chm. Bd.--Crown Nigeria, Inc., Baltimore, MD; *U.S. Public*, pg. 462
Rosenberg, Howard, Gen. Mgr.--Lawson Products, Inc., Norcross, GA; *U.S. Public*, pg. 980
Rosenberg, Kenneth M., Chm. Bd.--Pharmavite Corporation, Mission Hills, CA; *Int'l*, pg. 1013
Rosenberg, Richard, Chm. Bd.--Bank of America NT&SA, San Francisco, CA; *U.S. Public*, pg. 180
Rosenberg, Robert, Pres. & Chief Exec. Officer--Baskin-Robbins Incorporated, Glendale, CA; *Int'l*, pg. 63
Rosenberg, Robert, Chm. Bd.--Mister Donut of America, Inc., Randolph, MA; *Int'l*, pg. 63
Rosenberg, Robert C., Pres.--Grenadier Realty Corp., New York, NY; *U.S. Private*, pg. 1035
Rosenberg, Steven, Pres.--Home Box Office International, Inc., New York, NY; *U.S. Public*, pg. 1612
Rosenberg, Willy, Gen. Mgr.--Nordson Andina Limitada, Envigado, Colombia; *U.S. Public*, pg. 1189
Rosenberger, John, V.P.--Conwed Plastics, Minneapolis, MN; *U.S. Public*, pg. 990
Rosenberger, Raymond, Gen. Mgr.--Arrow Hart Wiring Devices, Syracuse, NY; *U.S. Public*, pg. 444
Rosenblum, Barry, Gen. Mgr.--American Cablevision of Brooklyn, Inc., Flushing, NY; *U.S. Public*, pg. 1610
Rosenblum, Barry, Gen. Mgr.--American Cablevision of Queens, Inc., Woodside, NY; *U.S. Public*, pg. 1610
Rosenblum, Lewis, Chief Exec. Officer--Forma Scientific Inc., Marietta, OH; *U.S. Public*, pg. 1595
Rosencrance, Jim, Plant Mgr.--OMC Spruce Pine, Spruce Pine, NC; *U.S. Private*, pg. 478
Rosenfeld, Arthur, Pres.--Maxwell Macmillan Professional & Business Reference Publishing, Englewood Cliffs, NJ; *U.S. Public*, pg. 1602
Rosenfeld, Irene, Pres.--Kraft Canada Inc., Don Mills, Canada; *U.S. Public*, pg. 1288
Rosenfeld, Robert, Chief Fin. Officer--Barton Associates, West Orange, NJ; *U.S. Private*, pg. 120
Rosenfeld, Robert, Chief Fin. Officer--Lakeside Enterprises, Inc., West Orange, NJ; *U.S. Private*, pg. 120
Rosenfield, Richard, Pres.--California Pizza Kitchen Inc., Los Angeles, CA; *U.S. Public*, pg. 1277
Rosengard, Folke, Country Mgr.--Nokia Telecommunications Belgium, Diegem, Belgium; *Int'l*, pg. 953
Rosengren, U., Pres.--Rubsteel AB, Perstorp, Sweden; *Int'l*, pg. 1146
Rosenkilde, Palle, Chief Oper. Officer--Electrolux-Wascator A/S, Roedovre, Denmark; *Int'l*, pg. 441
Rosenshine, Allen, Chm. Bd., Chief Exec. Officer & Dir.--BBDO Worldwide Inc., New York, NY; *U.S. Public*, pg. 1223
Rosenthal, Cliff, Exec. Dir.--National Federation of Community Development Credit Unions, New York, NY; *U.S. Private*, pg. 288
Rosenthal, Dan, Pres.--DSL Service Co., Newport Beach, CA; *U.S. Public*, pg. 527
Rosenthal, Mark, Admin.--Rehabilitation Institute of Oklahoma, Oklahoma City, OK; *U.S. Public*, pg. 1714
Rosenthal, Philip, Chm. Bd.--Rosenthal U.S.A. Limited, Carlstadt, NJ; *Int'l*, pg. 1127
Rosenthal, Reuben, Pres. & Chief Exec. Officer--Quala Systems, Inc., Exton, PA; *U.S. Private*, pg. 233
Rosenthal, Reuben, Pres.--EnviroPower, Exton, PA; *U.S. Private*, pg. 233
Rosenzweig, Richard S., Pres.--Playboy Shows, Inc., Los Angeles, CA; *U.S. Public*, pg. 1310
Rosetti, Richard, Pres.--Impulse Productions, Inc., Beverly Hills, CA; *U.S. Public*, pg. 1310
Rosevear, Kenneth A., Pres. & Chief Oper. Officer--MGM Grand Development, Inc., Las Vegas, NV; *U.S. Public*, pg. 1027
Rosewall, Ray, Pres.--Harmon Industries-Riverside, Riverside, CA; *U.S. Public*, pg. 788
Rosewall, Ray, Pres.--Harmon Industries-Grain Valley, Grain Valley, MO; *U.S. Public*, pg. 788
Rosey, R., Pres.--Ebara Solar, Inc., Large, PA; *Int'l*, pg. 432
Rosholm, Peter, Pres.--Kvaerner Ships Equipment AB, Goteborg, Sweden; *Int'l*, pg. 768
Rosian, Butch, Plant Mgr.--Retail Bag Division - Phoenix, Phoenix, AZ; *U.S. Public*, pg. 1521
Rosica, Gabriel, Chief Oper. Officer--Bailey Controls Company, Wickliffe, OH; *Int'l*, pg. 654
Rosica, Giorgio Maria, Gen. Mgr.--Cariplo Hong Kong, Wan Chai, Hong Kong; *Int'l*, pg. 275
Rosier, William G., Pres. & Chief Exec. Officer--McLane Company, Inc., Temple, TX; *U.S. Public*, pg. 1733
Rosing, Wayne E., Pres.--Sun Microsystems Laboratories, Inc., Mountain View, CA; *U.S. Public*, pg. 1531
Rosini, Carlo, Gen. Mgr.--Partenavia Construzioni Aeronautiche, Naples, Italy; *Int'l*, pg. 653
Rosinski, Norman, Pres. & Publr.--Star Publications, Chicago Heights, IL; *Int'l*, pg. 632
Roskowski, Nicholas, Chief Exec. Officer--Enskilda S.A., Paris, France; *Int'l*, pg. 1259
Roskoz, J.H., Pres.--Somerset Railroad Corp., Ithaca, NY; *U.S. Public*, pg. 1173
Roslan, Udo, Franchise Mgr.--Johnson & Johnson Medical GmbH, Norderstedt, Germany; *U.S. Public*, pg. 931
Rosner, Carl H., Pres.--Field Effects, Inc., Acton, MA; *U.S. Public*, pg. 893

Rosner, Carl H., Chm. Bd.--Intermagnetics General (Europe) Limited, Oxford, United Kingdom; U.S. Public, pg. 894
Rosner, Carl H., Chm. Bd.--APD Cryogenics, Aldermaston, United Kingdom; U.S. Public, pg. 894
Rosner, Carl H., Pres.--Intercool Energy Corporation, Latham, NY; U.S. Public, pg. 894
Rosner, Itschak, Plant Mgr.--Rhone-Poulenc Alcolac, Baltimore, MD; Int'l, pg. 1110
Ross, A.F., Mng. Dir.--Wellcome Ireland Ltd., Dublin, Ireland; Int'l, pg. 553
Ross, Alistair, Gen. Mgr.-Smelter Opers.--Phelps Dodge Hidalgo, Playas, NM; U.S. Public, pg. 1287
Ross, Cameron M., Pres.--Westminster Homes of North Carolina, Inc., Greensboro, NC; U.S. Public, pg. 1741
Ross, Charles, Plant Mgr.--AlliedSignal Filters & Spark Plugs, Fostoria, OH; U.S. Public, pg. 51
Ross, Chet S., Mng. Dir.--Process Instrumentation, Manchester, United Kingdom; Int'l, pg. 1444
Ross, Colin, Dr., Mng. Dir.--Noise & Vibration Systems, Cambridge, United Kingdom; Int'l, pg. 1431
Ross, David, Gen. Mgr.--WBGG-FM, Miami, FL; U.S. Public, pg. 384
Ross, David, Gen. Mgr.--WHYI-FM, Fort Lauderdale, FL; U.S. Public, pg. 385
Ross, Donald F., Pres.--Communications Data Services, Inc., Des Moines, IA; U.S. Private, pg. 517
Ross, Donald G., Exec. V.P.--SPF Insurance Agency, Franklin Park, IL; U.S. Public, pg. 1428
Ross, Eddie, V.P. & Gen. Mgr.--Domtar Forest Products, Montreal, Canada; Int'l, pg. 416
Ross, Ernie, V.P. & Gen. Mgr.--Puritan-Bennett Aero Systems Co., Lenexa, KS; U.S. Public, pg. 1040
Ross, Frank, Sr., Chm. Bd. & Chief Oper. Officer--HRH Construction Corp., New York, NY; U.S. Private, pg. 1035
Ross, Gary, Pres.--On Cue, Inc., Minnetonka, MN; U.S. Public, pg. 1142
Ross, George C., Chm.--Primerica Bank, Wilmington, DE; U.S. Public, pg. 1633
Ross, Gordon, Mng. Dir.--Merisel U.K., Brentford, United Kingdom; U.S. Public, pg. 1096
Ross, John, Branch Mgr.--Klockner-Moeller Corp., Garfield Heights, OH; Int'l, pg. 736
Ross, John, Controller--Imaging Services, Leominster, MA; Int'l, pg. 1076
Ross, Joseph E., Exec. V.P.--Baker Engineering, Inc., Chicago, IL; U.S. Public, pg. 168
Ross, M., Mng. Dir.--MB Central Africa Limited, Harare, Zimbabwe; Int'l, pg. 267
Ross, Mike, V.P. & Reg. Mgr.--Bergen Brunswig Medical Corporation, Denver, CO; U.S. Public, pg. 214
Ross, Mike, Pres.--UPB of Missouri, Saint Louis, MO; U.S. Public, pg. 1669
Ross, Norman, Opers. Mgr.--BHP Rail Products, Squamish, Canada; Int'l, pg. 226
Ross, Phillip, President--Sun Micro Stamping Inc., Clearwater, FL; U.S. Public, pg. 1531
Ross, R. Michael, V.P.--U.S. Container Div., Memphis, TN; U.S. Public, pg. 903
Ross, R.D., Pres.--Ross Technology, Inc., Austin, TX; Int'l, pg. 526
Ross, Richard, Pres.--DRS Photronics, Inc., Oakland, NJ; U.S. Public, pg. 474
Ross, Richard, Pres.--Volvo Truck North America Inc., Milton, Canada; Int'l, pg. 1477
Ross, Robert, Gen. Mgr.--Corrugated Container Div.-Buffalo Plant, North Tonawanda, NY; U.S. Public, pg. 1520
Ross, Robert M., Pres.--Pennsylvania-American Water Co., Hershey, PA; U.S. Public, pg. 95
Ross, Ronald R., Pres.--Systems Engineering Div., Falls Church, VA; U.S. Public, pg. 423
Ross, Scott B., Pres.--MCI Systemhouse, Atlanta, GA; U.S. Public, pg. 1024
Ross, Scott B., Pres.--MCI Business Markets, Atlanta, GA; U.S. Public, pg. 1024
Ross, Steve, Pres.--The Van Heusen Group of Companies, New York, NY; U.S. Public, pg. 1291
Ross, Stuart B., Chm., Pres. & Chief Exec. Officer--Xerox Financial Services Inc., Stamford, CT; U.S. Public, pg. 1784
Ross, Stuart B., Chm. Bd.--Xerox Credit Corporation, Stamford, CT; U.S. Public, pg. 1785
Ross, Theresa, Branch Mgr.--Downey Savings & Loan Association, F.A., Lancaster, CA; U.S. Public, pg. 526
Ross, William, V.P. & Gen. Mgr.--WGNO Inc., New Orleans, LA; U.S. Public, pg. 1636
Rossell, Jordi Vidal, Mgr. Gen.--CEDIPSA, Barcelona, Spain; Int'l, pg. 323
Rossen, Fredric K., Pres. & Chief Exec. Officer--Gerber Garment Technology, Inc., Tolland, CT; U.S. Public, pg. 740
Rosshirt, Gerry, Plant Mgr.--Ringier America, Senatobia Division, Senatobia, MS; U.S. Public, pg. 1778
Rossi, Carl, Pres.--Rodenstock USA, Inc., Danbury, CT; Int'l, pg. 1007
Rossi, G., Chm.--AGIP Deutschland AG, Munich, Germany; Int'l, pg. 428
Rossi, G., Chm.--AGIP (Suisse) S.A., Lausanne, Switzerland; Int'l, pg. 428
Rossi, John, Refinery Mgr.--Marcus Hook, PA Refinery, Marcus Hook, PA; U.S. Public, pg. 1530
Rossi, John, Refinery Mgr.--Point Breeze Refinery, Philadelphia, PA; U.S. Public, pg. 1530
Rossi, L., Chief Exec. Officer--EL. BO. MEC. Thermalloy Srl., Bologna, Italy; Int'l, pg. 209
Rossi, M., Rep.--Cariplo (Moscow), Moscow, Russia; Int'l, pg. 275
Rossi, Mario, Chief Oper. Officer--Argos Companhia de Seguros, Sao Paulo, Brazil; U.S. Public, pg. 355
Rossi, Mark A., Pres.--Merrill Corporation, Los Angeles, CA; U.S. Public, pg. 1097
Rossi, Michael, Pres.--BA Ventures, Inc., San Francisco, CA; U.S. Public, pg. 180
Rossi, Pedro, Gen. Mgr.--Sensormatic E.C., S.A., Madrid, Spain; U.S. Public, pg. 1457
Rossi, Piergiorgio, Chief Fin. Officer--Olivetti Hong Kong Ltd., Causeway Bay, Hong Kong; Int'l, pg. 1003
Rossi, R.A.S., Mng. Dir.--TNT Traco S.p.A., Turin, Italy; Int'l, pg. 1343
Rossi, Randall C., Chief Oper. Officer--Scotsman Ice Systems, Vernon Hills, IL; U.S. Public, pg. 1445
Rossi, Ronald J., Pres.--The Gillette Company, Gillette Grooming Products, USA, Boston, MA; U.S. Public, pg. 744
Rossi, T., Gen. Dir.--Laboratoires Prosalud S.A., Lima, Peru; U.S. Public, pg. 1092
Rossier, Jean-Claude, Gen. Mgr.--Mifroma S.A., Ursy, Switzerland; Int'l, pg. 866
Rossignolo, G.M., Chm.--Zanussi Componenti Plastica S.p.A., Oderzo, Italy; Int'l, pg. 442
Rossignolo, G.M., Chm.--Zanussi Elettrodomestici S.p.A., Pordenone, Italy; Int'l, pg. 442
Rossing, J., Dir.--HWZ, Hollandsche Wegenbouw Zanen B.V., Utrecht, Netherlands; Int'l, pg. 630
Rossini, Ronald, Sr. Mktg. Officer--Northeast Marketing-Philadelphia Business Center, Philadelphia, PA; U.S. Public, pg. 649
Rossiter, Paul, Mng. Dir.--Lynwood Scientific Developments Limited, Farnham, United Kingdom; U.S. Public, pg. 1144
Rossle, M.W., Chief Oper. Officer--Babcock Claudius Peters Div., Johannesburg, South Africa; Int'l, pg. 474
Rossman, Ray, Pres.--World Fuel Services of FL, Miami Springs, FL; U.S. Public, pg. 906
Rossman, William J., Pres. & Chief Exec. Officer--Mid-State Bank, Altoona, PA; U.S. Public, pg. 956
Rossner, Jeff, Pres.--KDFW, Dallas, TX; Int'l, pg. 926
Rosso, C.M., Mng. Dir.--Ferro Enamel Argentina, S.A., Buenos Aires, Argentina; U.S. Public, pg. 619
Rosso, Claudio, Gen. Mgr.--CPC Italia S.p.A., Milan, Italy; U.S. Public, pg. 225
Rost, M.W., Gen. Mgr.--CHEMCENTRAL/Cincinnati, Hamilton, OH; U.S. Private, pg. 232
Rost, R.D., Branch Mgr.--Zellerbach Division, Saint Louis, MO; U.S. Public, pg. 1075
Roswall, Lars, Mng. Dir.--UPM-Kymmene Deutschland GmbH, Hamburg, Germany; Int'l, pg. 1430
Roszkowski, Leszek, Chief Oper. Officer--Gambro Poland sp. z.o.o., Warsaw, Poland; Int'l, pg. 668
Rotelle, John F., Chm.--Rotelle, Inc., West Point, PA; U.S. Public, pg. 1389
Rotem, D., Gen. Mgr.--TAMAM Division/Electronics Group, Israel; Int'l, pg. 690
Rotenstreich, Jon W., Pres. & Chief Exec. Officer--United Investors Management Company, Kansas City, MO; U.S. Public, pg. 1623
Roterstreich, Jon W., Pres.--TMK/United Oil Management Company, Birmingham, AL; U.S. Public, pg. 1623
Roth, Alan, Plant Mgr.--RAYOVAC Corporation, Appleton, WI; U.S. Private, pg. 912
Roth, Clarence, Chirf Exec. Officer--Prince Rupert Grain Ltd., Vancouver, Canada; Int'l, pg. 1195
Roth, John A., Pres. & Chief Exec. Officer--MICOM Communications Corp., Simi Valley, CA; Int'l, pg. 969
Roth, Michael JC, Pres. & Chief Exec. Officer--USAA Investment Management Co., San Antonio, TX; U.S. Private, pg. 1114
Roth, Pat, V.P.--Circle International, Wilder, KY; U.S. Public, pg. 371
Roth, Steven, Chief Exec. Officer--Alexander's, Inc., Saddle Brook, NJ; U.S. Public, pg. 1725
Roth, Steven I., Pres.--ADI (Ademco Distribution, Inc.), Syosset, NY; U.S. Public, pg. 1306
Roth, W.R., Chief Oper. Officer--San Jose Water Company, San Jose, CA; U.S. Public, pg. 1418
Rothacker, Hartmut, Dr., Chief Oper. Officer--BHF-BANK International S.A., Luxembourg, Luxembourg; Int'l, pg. 119
Rothbaum, Michael, Pres. & Chief Exec. Officer--The Harwood Companies, Inc., Fort Lauderdale, FL; U.S. Public, pg. 1433
Rothbloom, Steven R., Chm. & Pres.--Harris Trust Company of New York, New York, NY; Int'l, pg. 155
Rothbloom, Steven R., Pres.--Bank of Montreal Trust Company (C.I.) Ltd., Saint Helier, United Kingdom; Int'l, pg. 155
Rothbrook, David, Mng. Dir.--Emerson Electric Indus. Controls Ltd., Swindon, United Kingdom; U.S. Public, pg. 576
Rothe, Patrick, Mng. V.P.--Poe & Brown of North Carolina, Charlotte, NC; U.S. Public, pg. 1312
Rother, Douglas C., Pres.--Jefferson-Pilot Data Services, Inc., Memphis, TN; U.S. Public, pg. 925
Rothgerber, John S., Gen. Mgr.--DMI Furniture, Inc., Ferdinand, IN; U.S. Public, pg. 473
Rothlaender, K. H., Chief Oper. Officer--Volkswagen Comercial S.A. de C.V., Puebla, Mexico; Int'l, pg. 1475
Rothmuller, Claudio, Mng. Dir.--Editora Campus Ltda., Rio de Janeiro, Brazil; Int'l, pg. 1100
Roths, Jim, Mgr.-Mktg.--Telex Communication Div., Lincoln, NE; U.S. Private, pg. 1074
Rothschild, Stanford Z., Jr., Pres.--Rothschild/Pell, Rudman & Co., Inc., Baltimore, MD; U.S. Public, pg. 1674
Rothstein, Bob, Mgr.--Atlantic Paper Group, Lyndhurst, NJ; U.S. Private, pg. 467
Rothweiler, Hans-Joset, Pres.--AGA-CRYO GmbH, Hamburg, Germany; Int'l, pg. 13
Rothwell, John, Mng. Dir.--Tonka Corp. Pty. Ltd., Rhodes, Australia; U.S. Public, pg. 798
Rotiroti, Joe, Mgr.--Ampex Data Systems Corporation, West Chester, PA; U.S. Public, pg. 104
Rottier, A., Chief Oper. Officer--Gist-Brocades France S.A., Seclin, France; Int'l, pg. 1143
Rottier, A.H.M., Mng. Dir.--Gist-Brocades France S.A., Seclin, France; Int'l, pg. 1142
Rouet-Grandclement, Marie, Gen. Mgr.--Edelman-Rouet France, Paris, France; U.S. Private, pg. 363
Rough, Greg, Deputy Mng. Dir.--Wyeth Australia Pty. Ltd., Baulkham Hills, Australia; U.S. Public, pg. 82
Roukens, Ph., Mgr.--Club SA, Brussels, Belgium; Int'l, pg. 533
Rouleau, Mark, Pres. & Chief Exec. Officer--Associated Hosts, Inc., Indianapolis, IN; Int'l, pg. 215
Rouleau, R.A., Pres.--Crows Nest Resources Limited, Calgary, Canada; Int'l, pg. 1138
Round Turner, Sheena, Chief Exec. Officer--MCL, Nairobi, Kenya; U.S. Public, pg. 1422
Rouse, Julie B., V.P. & Acct. Dir.--Grizzard (Sales Office), Madison, NJ; U.S. Private, pg. 482
Rouse, Mike, Mng. Dir.--British Aerospace Defence Limited (Systems & Services), Preston, United Kingdom; Int'l, pg. 217
Roush, Richard K., Pres. & Gen. Mgr.--Georgie Boy Manufacturing, Inc., Edwardsburg, MI; U.S. Public, pg. 388
Rousse, David E., V.P. & Gen. Mgr.--Office Products Division, Brattleboro, VT; U.S. Public, pg. 620
Rousseau, Andre, Pres. & Chief Exec. Officer--Les Editions CEC Inc., Ville d'Anjou, Canada; Int'l, pg. 794
Roussel, Alain, Mgr.--Sandvik Aciers S.N.C., Orleans, France; Int'l, pg. 1186
Roussel, Bernard, Pres.--SK Hand Tool Corp., Chicago, IL; Int'l, pg. 570
Roussel, Claude, Gen. Mgr.--2MA Centre S.a.r.l., Lassay-les-Chateaux, France; Int'l, pg. 498
Roussel, Claude, Gen. Mgr.--Forbo 2MA SA, Lassay-les-Chateaux, France; Int'l, pg. 498
Roussel, Guilaine, Mgr.-Office--Woodward-Clyde, Oakland, CA; U.S. Public, pg. 1656
Roussell, Richard, Pres.--Union Drilling Division, Buckhannon, WV; U.S. Public, pg. 590
Rousset, Alain, Chief Fin. Officer-Europe (London)--Young & Rubicam Holdings Ltd., London, United Kingdom; U.S. Private, pg. 1199
Rousset, Jean-Louis, Exec. Mgr.--Dumez Caledonia, Noumea, New Caledonia; Int'l, pg. 823
Rousset, Jean-Louis, Exec. Mgr.--Societe des Emulsions du Pacifique, Noumea, New Caledonia; Int'l, pg. 824
Roussie, Olivier, Pres.--Royal S.A.R.L., Corbehem, France; Int'l, pg. 1449
Roussin, Richard, Gen. Mgr.--Uniboard Division Mont Laurier, Mont Laurier, Canada; Int'l, pg. 1431
Rousso, Raul Yafe, Mng. Dir. & Client Service--Nucleo Publicidad, Montevideo, Uruguay; U.S. Private, pg. 186
Routh-Karki, Rowena, Grp. Dir.--Young & Rubicam Finland Oy, Helsinki, Finland; U.S. Private, pg. 1199
Routhier, Bernard, V.P.-Mfg.--Trois-Rivieres Mill, Trois-Rivieres, Canada; Int'l, pg. 761
Routhier, Bernard, Grp. V.P.--Ville LaSalle Plant, La Salle, Canada; Int'l, pg. 761
Roux, A., Pres.--Societe de Banque Suisse (Monaco), Monte Carlo, Monaco; Int'l, pg. 1331
Rouxel, Jean, Mng. Dir.--Compagnie de Construction Mecanique Sulzer, Mantes-la-Jolie, France; Int'l, pg. 1305
Rovira, Mario, Mng. Dir.--SAEL, Barcelona, Spain; Int'l, pg. 657
Rovolis, Anthony, Pres.--Food Carrier, Inc., Port Wentworth, GA; U.S. Public, pg. 872
Row, Ajay, Sr. Gen. Mgr.--Rediffusion-Dentsu, Young & Rubicam (Bangalore), Bangalore, India; U.S. Private, pg. 326
Rowan, Roddy, Regional Pres.--BB&T of South Carolina, Greenville, SC; U.S. Public, pg. 160
Rowan, Roman E., V.P.-Western Region--Analysts International, Western Region, San Francisco, CA; U.S. Public, pg. 110
Rowden, Dorinda, V.P.--Software Security, Inc., Darien, CT; U.S. Public, pg. 1359
Rowe, I., Chief Exec. Officer--Blackwood Hodge (Botswana) (Pty.) Ltd., Gaborone, Botswana; Int'l, pg. 231
Rowe, James W., Pres. & Chief Exec. Officer--Defense Credit Union Council, Washington, DC; U.S. Private, pg. 288
Rowe, Michael, Mgr.--EG & G Defense Materials Division, Tooele, UT; U.S. Public, pg. 543
Rowe, W.G., Controller--Ames Taping Tool Systems Co., Duluth, GA; U.S. Private, pg. 103
Rowe, William J., Publr., Pres. & Chief Exec. Officer--The Advocate, Stamford, CT; U.S. Public, pg. 1616
Rowe, William J., Pres., Chief Exec. Officer & Publr.--Greenwich Times, Greenwich, CT; U.S. Public, pg. 1616
Rowell, Donald, Pres. & Gen. Mgr.--Sensenich Wood Propeller Co., Inc., Lanham, MD; U.S. Private, pg. 861
Rowell, Lester John, Jr., Pres.--Provident Mutual Life & Annuity Company of America, Berwyn, PA; U.S. Private, pg. 892
Rowen, Alan, Pres.--Transbulk, Inc., Strongsville, OH; U.S. Private, pg. 782
Rowen, Harold C., Pres. & Chief Exec. Officer--Kinney Shoe Corporation, New York, NY; U.S. Public, pg. 1777
Rowen, Irving, Gen. Mgr.--Alro Specialty Metals, Menomonee Falls, Menomonee Falls, WI; U.S. Private, pg. 46
Rowland, Colin C., Mng. Dir.--Logica UK Ltd., London, United Kingdom; Int'l, pg. 814
Rowland, Dennie, Pres.--First American Title Insurance Co. of Texas, Inc., Houston, TX; U.S. Public, pg. 626
Rowland, Lawrence, Chm., Pres. & Chief Exec. Officer--Lincoln National Administrative Services Corp., Fort Wayne, IN; U.S. Public, pg. 998
Rowland, Lawrence, Chief Oper. Officer--Lincoln National Management Services, Inc., Fort Wayne, IN; U.S. Public, pg. 998
Rowland, Lawrence, Chm. Bd. & Chief Exec. Officer--Lincoln National Reinsurance Company (Bermuda) Limited, Fort Wayne, IN; U.S. Public, pg. 998
Rowland, Lawrence, Chm. & Chief Exec. Officer--Lincoln National Structured Settlement, Inc., Fort Wayne, IN; U.S. Public, pg. 998

Rowland, Lawrence, Chm. & Chief Exec. Officer--Old Fort Insurance Co., Ltd. (Bermuda), Hamilton, Bermuda; *U.S. Public*, pg. 998
Rowland, Thomas H., Pres.-Home Div.--Home Products Group, Danbury, CT; *U.S. Public*, pg. 627
Rowland, Thomas H., Pres.--Himolene Corp., Danbury, CT; *U.S. Public*, pg. 627
Rowley, Don G., Publr.--The Arizona Daily Sun, Flagstaff, AZ; *U.S. Public*, pg. 1343
Rowley, Howard H., V.P. & Gen. Mgr.--Dover Flour Mills, Cambridge, Canada; *Int'l*, pg. 417
Rowley, Ivan R., Pres. & Chief Exec. Officer--Astra USA, Inc., Westborough, MA; *Int'l*, pg. 93
Rowley, Thomas H., Pres.--Continental Divide Insurance Co., Englewood, CO; *U.S. Public*, pg. 221
Rowling, Robert B., Chm. Bd.--Omni Hotels, Irving, TX; *U.S. Private*, pg. 1065
Rownak, John J., Jr., Chief Oper. Officer--Citizens Bank of Northwest Arkansas, Fayetteville, AR; *U.S. Public*, pg. 163
Roy, Dennis, Gen. Mgr.--Oto-Sonic, Inc., Chicago, IL; *U.S. Private*, pg. 132
Roy, Dominique, Mgr.-Plant--Sucrerie D'Etrepagny, D'Etrepagny, France; *Int'l*, pg. 549
Roy, Don, Plant Mgr.--Hydro Conduit Corp., Kansas City, MO; *Int'l*, pg. 245
Roy, George W., Plant Mgr.--Moirs Plant, Dartmouth, Canada; *U.S. Public*, pg. 812
Roy, J.P., Gen. Mgr.--Augat S.A., Fresnes, France; *U.S. Public*, pg. 1598
Roy, J.S., Mgr.-Sls.--American Centrifugal, Birmingham, AL; *U.S. Private*, pg. 52
Roy, K.J., Vice Chm.--Palmer Environmental Limited, Cwmbran, United Kingdom; *Int'l*, pg. 589
Roy, Mike, Dir.-Sls. & Mktg.--Kohler Ltd., Etobicoke, Canada; *U.S. Private*, pg. 631
Roy, Pierre-Andre, Pres. & Chief Oper. Officer--Bombardier Capital Group, Colchester, VT; *Int'l*, pg. 200
Roy, Rob, V.P.-Client Service--Total Research Corporation, Chicago, IL; *U.S. Public*, pg. 1625
Roy, Sidhartha, V.P.--Rediffusion-Dentsu, Young & Rubicam (New Delhi), New Delhi, India; *U.S. Private*, pg. 326
Roy, William A., Area V.P.--Avon Sales & Distribution Branch, Pasadena, CA; *U.S. Public*, pg. 156
Roy, Xavier, Chief Exec.--Reed MIDEM Organisation S.A., Paris, France; *Int'l*, pg. 1097
Royal, M.J., Chief Exec. Officer--Davy McKee Engenharia S/A, Sao Paulo, Brazil; *Int'l*, pg. 775
Royall, Butch, Gen. Mgr.--Lauderdale-Miami Auto Auction Inc., Davie, FL; *U.S. Public*, pg. 1649
Royce, Rodney, Partner--Intermedia Capital Partners IV, L.P., San Francisco, CA; *U.S. Private*, pg. 222
Roycroft, John E., V.P.-Sls.--Crown Cork & Seal, Central Div., Alsip, IL; *U.S. Public*, pg. 463
Royer, Rick, Dir.-Sls.--Frontier Communications of New England, Burlington, VT; *U.S. Public*, pg. 684
Royer, William G., Mgr.-Branch--Piper Jaffray Inc., Billings, MT; *U.S. Public*, pg. 1301
Royle, John, V.P.-Europe--Hampshire Chemical Ltd., London, United Kingdom; *U.S. Private*, pg. 498
Royse, John N., Chm. Bd.--Merchants National Bank, Terre Haute, IN; *U.S. Public*, pg. 1217
Royston, Samantha, Mng. Dir.--Lynne Franks Ltd., London, United Kingdom; *Int'l*, pg. 117
Rozeboom, Henk, Pres.--Componenta Benelux B.V., Coevorden, Netherlands; *Int'l*, pg. 1421
Rozell, David, Gen. Mgr.--Ennis-Texas Tag, Wolfe City, TX; *U.S. Public*, pg. 583
Rozenboom, V., Mgr.-Branch--Piper, Jaffray & Hopwood, Inc., Oskaloosa, IA; *U.S. Public*, pg. 1300
Rozenbroek, Lex, Mng. Dir.--International Equipment News Europe NV, Brussels, Belgium; *Int'l*, pg. 1099
Rozentsvit, Analolij, Chief Oper. Officer--Ahlstrom Representation in Moscow, Moscow, Russia; *Int'l*, pg. 33
Rozier, Charlie, Mgr.--Raybro Electric Supplies, Tampa, FL; *U.S. Private*, pg. 265
Rozman, Robert, Pres.--Diehl Machines, Wabash, IN; *U.S. Public*, pg. 944
Roznoy, B.A., Mgr.-Sls.--Morgan Matroc Inc.-East Coast Sales Division, Scotch Plains, NJ; *Int'l*, pg. 893
Ruane, James J., Mng. Dir.--Bank of Ireland Corporate Banking, Dublin, Ireland; *Int'l*, pg. 152
Ruane, Vincent J., Div. V.P.--Traffic Control Materials Division, Saint Paul, MN; *U.S. Public*, pg. 1605
Ruas, Maria, Mgr.--Broad National Bank-Prudential Plaza, Newark, NJ; *U.S. Public*, pg. 258
Rubel, Matt, Pres.--The Princess Marcella Borghese, Inc., New York, NY; *U.S. Private*, pg. 690
Rubel, Matt, Pres.--Popular Club Plan, Garfield, NJ; *U.S. Private*, pg. 1078
Rubens, J., Mgr.--CW Rent Belgium N.V., Zaventem, Belgium; *Int'l*, pg. 648
Rubenstein, Dave, Pres.--Disc Manufacturing Cinram, Huntsville, AL; *Int'l*, pg. 293
Rubenstein, Richard, V.P.--Norman Levy Associates, Inc., Alameda, CA; *U.S. Private*, pg. 664
Ruberg, Werner, Chm. Bd. & Chief Exec. Officer--Owens-Corning Eternit Rohre GmbH, Aachen, Germany; *U.S. Public*, pg. 1237
Rubertone, Donna, Pres.--AmVestors Acquisition Subsidiary, Inc., Topeka, KS; *U.S. Private*, pg. 59
Rubiani Yanho, Jose, Gen. Mgr.--Mass Publicidad S.R.L., Asuncion, Paraguay; *U.S. Private*, pg. 186
Rubiani Yanho, Pascual, Mng. Dir.--Mass Publicidad S.R.L., Asuncion, Paraguay; *U.S. Private*, pg. 186
Rubilar, Carlos, Gen. Mgr.--Andina Division, Los Andes, Chile; *Int'l*, pg. 302
Rubin, Bonnie Snyder, V.P. & Mgr.--City National Bank - Wilshire/Westwood Regional Office, Los Angeles, CA; *U.S. Public*, pg. 381
Rubin, Joseph H., Pres.--Abrams Construction, Inc., Atlanta, GA; *U.S. Public*, pg. 14
Rubin, Lewis, Chief Oper. Officer--X-L-CO, Inc., Boston, MA; *U.S. Public*, pg. 1787
Rubin, Lewis, Pres. & Chief Oper. Officer--XTRA, Inc., Portland, ME; *U.S. Public*, pg. 1787
Rubin, Lewis, Chief Oper. Officer--XTRA-Intermodal Division, Liberty, MO; *U.S. Public*, pg. 1787
Rubin, Richard, Pres.--Christiansburg Garment Co. Inc., New York, NY; *U.S. Public*, pg. 520
Rubin, Seymour, Pres.--RFI Corp., Bay Shore, NY; *U.S. Public*, pg. 494
Rubin, Stephen, Pres. & Publisher--Doubleday Publishing Company, New York, NY; *Int'l*, pg. 191
Rubinelli, Marco, Gen. Mgr.--ITW Italia S.p.A., Turin, Italy; *U.S. Public*, pg. 868
Rubinfeld, Gerri, Pres.--Texfi Blends Division, Rocky Mount, NC; *U.S. Public*, pg. 1588
Rubino, Mary Ann, V.P.--Ampersand, Chatsworth, CA; *U.S. Public*, pg. 1369
Rubinoff, R., Gen. Mgr.--Hunter Douglas Verticals, Fort Lauderdale, FL; *Int'l*, pg. 639
Rubmall, M., Mng. Dir.--Ashby & Horner Ltd., Harrow, United Kingdom; *Int'l*, pg. 1032
Ruboczky, Tamas, Chief Oper. Officer--Akerlund & Rausing, Budapest, Hungary; *Int'l*, pg. 33
Rubow, W. Steven, Pres.--Kingston Marketing Co., Skokie, IL; *U.S. Private*, pg. 1091
Rubow, W. Steven, Pres.--World Brands Inc., Skokie, IL; *U.S. Private*, pg. 1091
Rubright, James A., Pres.--Southern Natural Gas Company, Birmingham, AL; *U.S. Public*, pg. 1485
Ruby, James, Sr. V.P.--Dayco Rubber Industrial Sales Division, Miamisburg, OH; *U.S. Public*, pg. 1045
Ruby, John H., Gen. Mgr.--Westcoast Cellufibre, Vancouver, Canada; *Int'l*, pg. 261
Ruceretta, Vince, Admin.--Alta Vista Healthcare, Arlington, CA; *U.S. Public*, pg. 1711
Ruch, W. Dow, Gen. Mgr.--Brite Vue Glass Systems, Visalia, CA; *U.S. Public*, pg. 60
Ruchjaibun, Parames, Pres.--Dentsu Young & Rubicam Ltd. (Bangkok), Bangkok, Thailand; *U.S. Private*, pg. 325
Ruckert, Jurg, Chm.--Reismuhle Brunnen AG, Brunnen, Switzerland; *Int'l*, pg. 330
Rucki, George, Mgr.-Aircraft Prods.--Champion Ignition Products-Weatherly Facility, Weatherly, PA; *U.S. Public*, pg. 443
Ruckmar, J., Chief Exec. Officer--Zurich Insurance (Malaysia) Sdn. Bhd., Kuala Lumpur, Malaysia; *Int'l*, pg. 1532
Rucks, William W., III, Chm. Bd.--The First National Bank of Lafayette, Lafayette, LA; *U.S. Public*, pg. 630
Ruda, Kevin, Pres. & Chief Exec. Officer--Beatrice Cheese Co., Waukesha, WI; *U.S. Public*, pg. 426
Rudd, S. Wheeler, V.P. & Gen. Mgr.--WTOL-TV, Toledo, OH; *U.S. Public*, pg. 992
Ruddock, A., Gen. Mgr.--Giddings & Lewis Ltd, Prescot, United Kingdom; *Int'l*, pg. 1389
Ruddock, John H., Gen. Mgr.--Forbo Scanachrome Ltd., Skelmersdale, United Kingdom; *Int'l*, pg. 498
Ruddy, John H., Mng. Dir.--Bermuda Trust Executors (Jersey) Limited, Saint Helier, United Kingdom; *Int'l*, pg. 151
Ruden, Bengt, Chief Oper. Officer--SCA Emballage AB, Varnamo, Sweden; *Int'l*, pg. 1326
Rudis, Jim, Pres. & Chief Exec. Officer--Overhill Farms, Inc., Culver City, CA; *U.S. Public*, pg. 1315
Rudisiler, Walter R., Pres.--Sysco Food Services-Jacksonville, Jacksonville, FL; *U.S. Public*, pg. 1551
Rudloff, Dr., Chief Oper. Officer--Praemix Wirkstoff GmbH, Mannheim, Germany; *Int'l*, pg. 331
Rudloff, Jean, Chief Exec. Officer--Jallatte S.A., Saint Hippolyte-du-Fort, France; *Int'l*, pg. 430
Rudman, Edward I., Chm. Bd. & Pres.--Pell, Rudman & Company, Boston, MA; *U.S. Public*, pg. 1673
Rudnay, Janos, Dr., Gen. Mgr.--Reemtsma Hungary Kereskedelmi Kft., Budapest, Hungary; *Int'l*, pg. 1101
Rudnicki, E.H., Pres.--First Church Financing Corporation, West Bend, WI; *U.S. Public*, pg. 1792
Rudolf, M., Chief Oper. Officer--Danzas AG, Basel, Switzerland; *Int'l*, pg. 382
Rudolph, Scott, Pres.--The Hudson Corporation, Bohemia, NY; *U.S. Public*, pg. 1166
Rudolph, Scott, Pres.--Vitamin World, Bohemia, NY; *U.S. Public*, pg. 1166
Rudrum, Malcolm, Pres.--Benelux Division, Brussels, Belgium; *U.S. Public*, pg. 423
Rueb, Guenther, Pres.--American Zettler Inc., Aliso Viejo, CA; *Int'l*, pg. 1528
Ruebel, M., Chief Oper. Officer--E. Scheurich Pharmwerk GmbH, Appenweier, Germany; *U.S. Public*, pg. 82
Ruecker, Bruce G., Pres.--First American Bank Metro, South Saint Paul, MN; *U.S. Private*, pg. 167
Rueckert, R. Kim, Gen. Mgr.--Sacramento Cable, Sacramento, CA; *U.S. Public*, pg. 1448
Ruede, Karl-Heinz, Dir.--Von Roll Machinery & Handling Systems, Delemont, Switzerland; *Int'l*, pg. 1480
Ruegg, Fred, Pres.--ELMA Electronic Inc., Fremont, CA; *Int'l*, pg. 1305
Ruela, J., Mng. Dir.--Jotun-Tinco Tintas Maritimas Lda., Almada, Portugal; *Int'l*, pg. 716
Ruelle, Mark A., Chm. Bd. & Pres.--Westar Energy, Topeka, KS; *U.S. Public*, pg. 1759
Ruelle, Patrick, V.P.--Rottlund Homes of Iowa, Inc., Urbandale, IA; *U.S. Public*, pg. 1406
Ruesch, E., Mng. Dir.--Hyposwiss (Swiss Mortgage & Commercial Bank), Zurich, Switzerland; *Int'l*, pg. 1440
Rufer, Walter, Gen. Mgr.--Kodak Ireland Limited, Dun Laoghaire, Ireland; *U.S. Public*, pg. 553
Ruff, Ross, G.M.--Avon Cosmetics Ltd., Pakuranga, New Zealand; *U.S. Public*, pg. 156
Ruffin, Nicholas C., Mgr.--Scott & Stringfellow, Inc., Vienna, VA; *U.S. Public*, pg. 1446
Ruffini, Jeanne, Admin.--Kimberly Manor Nursing and Convalescent Home, Rock Springs, WY; *U.S. Public*, pg. 1714
Ruffino, Tommy, Warden--West Tennessee Detention Facility, Mason, TN; *U.S. Public*, pg. 451
Ruffner, M. G., Refinery Mgr.--Toledo, OH Refinery, Toledo, OH; *U.S. Public*, pg. 1530
Ruffner, M. G., Refinery Mgr.--Tulsa, OK Refinery, Tulsa, OK; *U.S. Public*, pg. 1530
Ruffold, Renee, Mgr.--Image By Design, Niles, IL; *U.S. Private*, pg. 310
Ruffolo, Mick, Division Mgr.--Horizon Technology Group - Link Tool & Mfg. Div., Taylor, MI; *U.S. Private*, pg. 539
Ruffolo, Ugo, Chief Exec. Officer & Dir. Gen.--Banca Fideuran S.p.A., Rome, Italy; *Int'l*, pg. 692
Rugaber, Walter, Pres. & Publr.--The Roanoke Times, Roanoke, VA; *U.S. Private*, pg. 649
Ruge, K., Chief Oper. Officer--Manitec Consulting AG, Emmen, Switzerland; *Int'l*, pg. 1205
Rugg, Jerry, Dir.--AlliedSignal Controls & Accessories, Tucson, AZ; *U.S. Public*, pg. 50
Rugg, Noel, Mng. Dir.--Carlson Marketing Group (Aust.) Pty. Limited, Edgecliff, Australia; *U.S. Private*, pg. 212
Ruggeri, Carol, Pres.--HiChem Diagnostics, Inc., Brea, CA; *Int'l*, pg. 436
Ruggeri, Salvatore, Pres.--Energy Valve Division, Houston, TX; *U.S. Public*, pg. 528
Ruggirello, John R., Pres.--AES Enterprise, Arlington, VA; *U.S. Public*, pg. 5
Ruggles, Harvey, Mng. Dir.--DYWIDAG Systems International, USA, Inc., Columbus, OH; *Int'l*, pg. 424
Rugrugotska, Mary, Controller--Chicago Consolidated, Madison, WI; *U.S. Private*, pg. 533
Ruhl, Douglas L., Pres.--Lexco Petroleum, Oklahoma City, OK; *U.S. Public*, pg. 174
Ruhno, R., Pres.--PQ Australia Pty., Ltd., Dandenong, Australia; *U.S. Private*, pg. 827
Ruhno, R.A., Gen. Mgr.--Hollow Spheres Business, Valley Forge, PA; *U.S. Private*, pg. 827
Ruigrok, Aadrianis, Mng. Dir.--Societe Anonyme Formica (France), Paris, France; *Int'l*, pg. 130
Ruikka, Seppo, Mng. Dir.--Finnsugar Bioproducts, Helsinki, Finland; *Int'l*, pg. 349
Ruiz Nicoli, Pedro, Chm. & Chief Exec. Officer--Ruiz Nicoli Group, Madrid, Spain; *Int'l*, pg. 603
Ruiz, Fernando, Gen. Mgr.--Semillas Pioneer Chile Ltda., Santiago, Chile; *U.S. Public*, pg. 1299
Ruiz, Filho, Antonio, Pres.--AHP do Brasil, Sao Paulo, Brazil; *U.S. Public*, pg. 80
Ruiz, Joaquin, Gen. Mgr.--Bristol-Myers de Mexico, S.A. de C.V., Mexico, Mexico; *U.S. Public*, pg. 255
Ruiz, Victor, Gen. Mgr.--Esselte Pendaflex, Buena Park, CA; *Int'l*, pg. 460
Rukajarvi, Mauri, Pres.--Oulun Kumitehdas Oy, Oulu, Finland; *Int'l*, pg. 1449
Rukeyser, S., Chm. Bd., Chief Exec. Officer & Editor-in-Chief--Whittle Communications L.P., Knoxville, TN; *U.S. Public*, pg. 1614
Rullo, Fred, Pres.--ABB Combustion Engineering Systems, Windsor, CT; *Int'l*, pg. 3
Rumack, B.H., M.D., Pres.--Micromedex, Inc., Denver, CO; *U.S. Public*, pg. 1601
Rumball, David, Mgr.--Norman J. Hurll & Co., Sydney, Australia; *U.S. Private*, pg. 361
Rumball, M., Mng. Dir.--Ashby & Horner Furnishings Ltd., London, United Kingdom; *Int'l*, pg. 1032
Rumble, Clint, Pres. & Gen. Mgr.--Viking Recreational Vehicles, Inc., Centreville, MI; *U.S. Public*, pg. 388
Rumble, R.M., Pres. & Chief Exec. Officer--MediVators, Inc., Eagan, MN; *U.S. Public*, pg. 301
Rumbley, Charles T., Pres.--Kellwood Lingerie/Active Group, Summit, MS; *U.S. Public*, pg. 948
Rumgay, Ian, International Mktg. Dir.--Shandwick International Plc, London, United Kingdom; *Int'l*, pg. 1226
Rummage, Paula, Pres.--Stratos Boat Company, Ltd., Old Hickory, TN; *U.S. Private*, pg. 478
Rummage, Paula, Pres.--Hydra-Sports Corporation, Nashville, TN; *U.S. Private*, pg. 478
Rummel, Eric F., Pres.--Laurel Bank, Johnstown, PA; *U.S. Public*, pg. 164
Rummel, Grant D., Pres.--Moore-O-Matic, Inc., Waupaca, WI; *U.S. Public*, pg. 1193
Rummel, Peter S., Chm. Bd.--Walt Disney Imagineering, Glendale, CA; *U.S. Public*, pg. 513
Rumpf, G. S., Mng. Dir.--Transworld (Australia) Pty. Ltd., Melbourne, Australia; *Int'l*, pg. 191
Rumsey, Stephen C., Gen. Mgr.--Industria Mexicana de Fotocopiadoras, S.A. de C.V., Tijuana, Mexico; *U.S. Public*, pg. 554
Rumsey, Terry, Pres.--Carlson Marketing Group Ltd., Islington, Canada; *U.S. Private*, pg. 212
Runciman, A. James, Mng. Dir.--Donhad Armco Pty. Ltd., Bassendean, Australia; *Int'l*, pg. 391
Rund, Charles, Gen. Mgr.--Multibanco Internacional de Investimentos S.A. Sao Paulo Head Office, Sao Paulo, Brazil; *U.S. Public*, pg. 183
Rundshaug, Hans, Gen. Mgr.--Kvaerner Fjellstrand Shipping A/S, Bergen, Norway; *Int'l*, pg. 768
Rune, Gunnar, Pres.--NVS Nordiska Varme Sana AB, Malmo, Sweden; *Int'l*, pg. 899
Runk, Lee, Pres.--MascoTech Forming Technologies, Royal Oak, MI; *U.S. Public*, pg. 1055
Runkle, Don, V.P. & Gen. Mgr.--Delphi Energy & Engine Management Systems, Flint, MI; *U.S. Public*, pg. 719
Runyan, Bruce, Plant Mgr.--Baldor Electric Company, Plymouth, MN; *U.S. Public*, pg. 169
Runyan, K.W., Pres.--Ida-West Energy Company, Boise, ID; *U.S. Public*, pg. 862
Runyan, Prudence, Gen. Mgr.--C & J Clark Direct Marketing Division, Kennett Square, PA; *Int'l*, pg. 297
Ruocco, Stefano, Pres.--Italian Aerospace Industries, Arlington, VA; *Int'l*, pg. 654
Ruotsalainen, Pirjo, Mng. Dir.--Unitas Congres Center Ltd., Helsinki, Finland; *Int'l*, pg. 859
Rupel, Robert A., Pres.--Bank of Pennsylvania, Reading, PA; *Int'l*, pg. 64
Rupert, David J., Pres.--Pitney Bowes Business Supplies & Services, Stamford, CT; *U.S. Public*, pg. 1303

Rupkey, Kevin P., Pres.--Warrantech Consumer Product Services, Inc., Euless, TX; *U.S. Public*, pg. 1740
Ruppel, Ferdinand A., Jr., Pres. & Chief Exec. Officer--Westminster Bank & Trust Co. of Carroll County, Westminster, MD; *U.S. Public*, pg. 1089
Rupprecht, Gerhard, Chm.--Allianz Lebensversicherungs-AG, Stuttgart, Germany; *Int'l*, pg. 58
Rurka, David, Mng. Dir.--Toys "R" Us (UK) Ltd., Maidenhead, United Kingdom; *U.S. Public*, pg. 1626
Rurka, James E., Pres.--Cetus Oncology, Emeryville, CA; *U.S. Public*, pg. 350
Rus, Jan, Mng. Dir.--ZwitserLeven, Amsterdam, Netherlands; *Int'l*, pg. 1332
Rusbridge, Michael, Chm. Bd.--Reed Exhibition Companies-Europe, Paris, France; *Int'l*, pg. 1096
Rusbridge, Michael, Chm. & Chief Exec. Officer--Reed Exhibition Companies, Richmond, United Kingdom; *Int'l*, pg. 1096
Rusch, Bruce R., Acting V.P.--Measurement & Control Division, Peabody, MA; *U.S. Public*, pg. 109
Rusch, Bruce R., Pres.--SKY Computers, Inc., Chelmsford, MA; *U.S. Public*, pg. 109
Rusch, Freeland, Chm. Bd. & Chief Exec. Officer--M & I Merchants Bank, Rhinelander, WI; *U.S. Public*, pg. 1050
Rusch, Reiner, Gen. Mgr.--Deutsche Bank AG (Hong Kong), Central, Hong Kong; *Int'l*, pg. 404
Rush, Al, Pres.--Universal Studios Television Ltd., Universal City, CA; *Int'l*, pg. 1216
Rush, Cliff, V.P.-Baby Care Sales--Gerber Products Division-Baby Care, Reedsburg, WI; *Int'l*, pg. 973
Rush, Frank W., Pres.--Carolina Pump & Supply Corp., Charlotte, NC; *U.S. Public*, pg. 846
Rush, Gerald L., Chm. Bd. & Pres.--NBD Mortgage Corporation, Indianapolis, IN; *U.S. Public*, pg. 628
Rush, Kenneth, Gen. Mgr.--Sellersburg Stone Company, Inc., Sellersburg, IN; *U.S. Private*, pg. 459
Rush, Richard, Interm Pres.--Pacificare of Ohio, Cincinnati, OH; *U.S. Public*, pg. 1251
Rush, William J., Publr.--Elm City Newspaper, Milford, CT; *U.S. Public*, pg. 934
Rush, William J., Chief Exec. Officer & Publr.--New Haven Register, Inc., New Haven, CT; *U.S. Public*, pg. 935
Rush, William J., Publr.--Shore Line Newspaper, Guilford, CT; *U.S. Public*, pg. 935
Rushing, Jeff, Mgr.--Pace Industries Inc., Neosho, MO; *U.S. Public*, pg. 986
Rushing, R.G., V.P. & G.M.--Hubbell Plastics, Inc., Newtown, CT; *U.S. Public*, pg. 844
Rushworth, James L., Pres.--WCI International Company, Pittsburgh, PA; *Int'l*, pg. 440
Rusie, James, Reg. Pres.--Citizens Bank of Central Indiana-Bloomington Region, Bloomington, IN; *U.S. Public*, pg. 280
Rusinek, Chet, Regional Mgr.--CAP Gemini America (Washington D.C. Branch), Vienna, VA; *Int'l*, pg. 264
Ruska, Harry, V.P.-Opers.--Anchor Hocking, Monaca, PA; *U.S. Public*, pg. 1177
Ruskoski, Eric, Pres.--Seaquist Closures, Mukwonago, WI; *U.S. Public*, pg. 125
Rusling, Con, Pres.--Sheshunoff Information Services, Inc., Austin, TX; *U.S. Public*, pg. 1601
Ruspi, Stefania, Acting Dir.--World Languages SrL, Rome, Italy; *U.S. Public*, pg. 222
Russ, Jim, Chief Exec. Officer--Bardon USA Inc., Greenbelt, MD; *Int'l*, pg. 166
Russ, Jim, Pres.--Rockville Crushed Stone, Inc., Rockville, MD; *Int'l*, pg. 166
Russ, Jim, Pres.--Millville Quarry Inc., Millville, WV; *Int'l*, pg. 166
Russ, Mike, Gen. Mgr.--Sterling Electronics, Richmond, VA; *U.S. Public*, pg. 1051
Russeil, Jacques, Pres.--Lafarge Refractaires Monolithiques, Montrouge, France; *Int'l*, pg. 789
Russel, Terence A., Pres. & Chief Exec. Officer--Morgan Drive Away, Inc., Elkhart, IN; *U.S. Public*, pg. 1022
Russel, 220590 035, Jr., Div. Pres.--Renown Steel, Agincourt, Canada; *Int'l*, pg. 1262
Russell, B.B., Bus. Mgr.--Equipment Division, Bowling Green, KY; *U.S. Public*, pg. 502
Russell, B.R., Mng. Dir.--Albright & Wilson (Australia) Limited, Melbourne, Australia; *Int'l*, pg. 49
Russell, Debbie, Personal Lines Underwrter--Service General East, Charlotte, NC; *U.S. Private*, pg. 609
Russell, Donald G., Chm. Bd. & Chief Exec. Officer--Sonat Exploration Company, Houston, TX; *U.S. Public*, pg. 1485
Russell, Doug, Factory Supt.--Amalgamated Sugar Co., Nyssa, OR; *U.S. Private*, pg. 48
Russell, Edwin F., Pres.--Newhouse Newspapers Metro-Suburbia, Inc., New York, NY; *U.S. Private*, pg. 20
Russell, Gene, V.P. & Gen. Mgr.--Dillard, A ResourceNet International Company, Knoxville, TN; *U.S. Public*, pg. 902
Russell, George F., Jr., Chm.--Frank Russell Securities, Inc., Tacoma, WA; *U.S. Private*, pg. 952
Russell, George F., Jr., Chm.--Frank Russell Trust Co., Tacoma, WA; *U.S. Private*, pg. 952
Russell, James B., V.P. & Gen. Mgr.--Semtech Corpus Christi, Corpus Christi, TX; *U.S. Public*, pg. 1456
Russell, Jinee, Rep.--Singapore Tourist Promotion Board - Bangkok, Bangkok, Thailand; *Int'l*, pg. 1254
Russell, John, Chm. Bd.--Days Inns of America, Inc., Parsippany, NJ; *U.S. Public*, pg. 321
Russell, John, Chm. Bd.--Knights Franchise Systems, Inc., Parsippany, NJ; *U.S. Public*, pg. 321
Russell, John, Dir.--Bain & Company (Securities) Ltd., London, United Kingdom; *Int'l*, pg. 406
Russell, John, Mng. Dir.--Costar UK Ltd., High Wycombe, United Kingdom; *U.S. Public*, pg. 448
Russell, Leon, Gen. Mgr.--American Institutional Foods, Chattanooga, TN; *U.S. Private*, pg. 6
Russell, Mark R., Chief Oper. Officer--Hospital Group of America, Wayne, PA; *U.S. Public*, pg. 442
Russell, Pete, Gen. Mgr.--Arrow/Schweber Electronics, Plymouth, MI; *U.S. Public*, pg. 133
Russell, Richard, Chief Oper. Officer--General Chemical (Soda Ash) Partners, Parsippany, NJ; *Int'l*, pg. 1407
Russell, Richard R., Pres.--General Chemical Corporation, Parsippany, NJ; *U.S. Public*, pg. 707
Russell, Roy, Dir.-Opers.--DRS Technical Services, Chesapeake, VA; *U.S. Public*, pg. 474
Russell, S.G., Mng. Dir.--Boots The Chemists, Nottingham, United Kingdom; *Int'l*, pg. 203
Russell, William H., Pres.--MainStreet Trust Company, N.A., Martinsville, VA; *U.S. Public*, pg. 1039
Russell, Wilson A. Jr., Pres.--Automated Products, Inc. (Leader Systems, Inc.), Marietta, GA; *U.S. Public*, pg. 1659
Russo, Allain, Pres.--Geoffrey Beene Retail, Bridgewater, NJ; *U.S. Public*, pg. 1291
Russo, Frank B., Pres. & Chief Oper. Officer--Dorne & Margolin, Inc., Bohemia, NY; *U.S. Public*, pg. 1675
Russo, Jerry, Mgr.--Midland Color Company, Kansas City, MO; *Int'l*, pg. 1311
Russo, Joseph, Pres.--Henkel Adhesives Corporation, Hayward, CA; *Int'l*, pg. 610
Russo, Nick, Gen. Mgr.--E.C.D. Inc., North Brunswick, NJ; *U.S. Private*, pg. 353
Russo, Rich, Gen. Mgr.--Tesoro Northstore Company, Anchorage, AK; *U.S. Public*, pg. 1582
Russo, Richard A., Pres.--Tidewater Utilities, Inc., Odessa, DE; *U.S. Public*, pg. 1110
Russo, Richard A., Pres.--White Marsh Environmental Systems, Inc., Odessa, DE; *U.S. Public*, pg. 1110
Russo, Richard A., Pres.--Public Water Supply Company, Millsboro, DE; *U.S. Public*, pg. 1110
Russo, Robert, Exec. V.P. & Gen. Mgr.--Madison Square Garden Center Inc., New York, NY; *U.S. Public*, pg. 288
Russo, Robert, Pres.--National Technical Services, Norcross, GA; *U.S. Public*, pg. 1523
Russo, Thomas, Pres. & Chief Exec. Officer--Fyrnetics, Inc., Roselle, IL; *Int'l*, pg. 1499
Russo, Thomas J., Pres.--Miami Subs USA, Inc., Fort Lauderdale, FL; *U.S. Public*, pg. 1103
Russo, Tony, Tech. Mgr.--Kendall Therapy Center, Ltd., Miami, FL; *U.S. Public*, pg. 405
Russolo, Paolo, Mng. Dir.--Profarmaco Nobel S.r.l., Milan, Italy; *U.S. Public*, pg. 297
Rustichelli, Gian Paolo, Pres.--Collitex Srl, Ancarano, Italy; *U.S. Public*, pg. 1266
Rutan, Elbert L., Pres.--Scaled Composites, Inc., Mojave, CA; *U.S. Public*, pg. 1782
Ruth, Burl W., Chief Oper. Officer-Concrete Products--Louisiana Industries Div., Alexandria, LA; *U.S. Public*, pg. 1585
Ruth, George, Pres.--Sunwest Bank of Roswell, N.A., Roswell, NM; *U.S. Public*, pg. 1165
Rutherford, Frank N., Grp. Pres.--Elf Atochem Organic Peroxides Plant, Buffalo, NY; *Int'l*, pg. 446
Rutherford, G., Branch Mgr.--Senior Tift-Western Australia, Myaree, Australia; *Int'l*, pg. 1223
Rutherford, L., Reg. Dir.--EMI (Hong Kong) Ltd., Kowloon, Hong Kong; *Int'l*, pg. 427
Rutherfurd, John, Pres.--Moody's Investors Service, Inc., New York, NY; *U.S. Public*, pg. 536
Rutila, D.N., Gen. Mgr.--Diesel ReCon, El Paso, TX; *U.S. Public*, pg. 468
Rutkowski, Dennis, Pres.--Asian PVS Chemical Co., Ltd., Chachoengsao, Thailand; *U.S. Private*, pg. 828
Rutkowski, Joseph A., V.P. & Gen. Mgr.--Nucor Steel-South Carolina, Darlington, SC; *U.S. Public*, pg. 1205
Rutkowski, M., District Mgr.--A.M. Castle & Co., Wauwatosa, WI; *U.S. Public*, pg. 313
Rutkowski, Zbigniew, Mgr.--Barenbrug Polska Sp. z.o.o., Poznan, Poland; *Int'l*, pg. 167
Rutledge, A. Bradley, Pres. & Chief Exec. Officer--Regions Bank/Pickens County, Jasper, GA; *U.S. Public*, pg. 1372
Rutledge, Art, Mgr.-Transportation--The Apache Railway Company, Snowflake, AZ; *U.S. Public*, pg. 1521
Rutledge, Ronald, Pres.--Vistawall Architectural Products, Terrell, TX; *U.S. Public*, pg. 271
Rutt, T., Chief Oper. Officer--Molto GmbH, Lohnberg, Germany; *Int'l*, pg. 1501
Rutten, J.W.M., Mgr.--Honig Merkartikelen B.V., Nijmegen, Netherlands; *Int'l*, pg. 244
Rutter, H. Richard, Pres.--The GMR Group, Fort Washington, PA; *U.S. Public*, pg. 1224
Rutter, John P., Chief Oper. Officer--SIA (UK) Ltd., London, United Kingdom; *Int'l*, pg. 444
Rutter, Lee, Mng. Dir.--Torin Limited, Swindon, United Kingdom; *Int'l*, pg. 1267
Ruttkay, Michal, Mng. Dir.--Creo/Young & Rubicam, Bratislava, Slovakia; *U.S. Private*, pg. 1199
Ruud, Olav, Mng. Dir.--Gunnebo A/S, Oslo, Norway; *Int'l*, pg. 578
Ruusunen, Kari, Pres.--Kvaerner Masa-Yards Inc., Piikkio Works, Piikkio, Finland; *Int'l*, pg. 771
Ruutu, Hanno, Chief Oper. Officer--Neste Kide Oy, Espoo, Finland; *Int'l*, pg. 913
Ruvo, A.W., Gen. Mgr.--Union Camp Folding Carton Div., Clifton, NJ; *U.S. Public*, pg. 1666
Ruxton, S., Branch Mgr.--Zellerbach Division, Hartford City, IN; *U.S. Public*, pg. 1075
Ruyak, Francis, Pres.--Constitution Reinsurance Corporation, New York, NY; *Int'l*, pg. 467
Ruys, Anthony, Gen. Mgr.--Compania Colombiana de Grasas "Cogra-Lever" S.A., Bogota, Colombia; *Int'l*, pg. 1436
Ryall, James, Gen. Mgr.--Pesaka Jardine Fleming Sdn. Bhd., Kuala Lumpur, Malaysia; *Int'l*, pg. 494
Ryan, Babs, Mng. Dir.--Waring & LaRosa Direct, New York, NY; *U.S. Private*, pg. 1150
Ryan, Bill, Pres.--Price/Palmer Wireless Corp., Fort Myers, FL; *U.S. Public*, pg. 1324
Ryan, Bruce E., Pres.--FMC-Crosby Valve, Inc., Wrentham, MA; *U.S. Public*, pg. 605
Ryan, Conall E., Pres.--Houghton Mifflin Interactive Corp., Somerville, MA; *U.S. Public*, pg. 841
Ryan, Daniel B., III, Sr. V.P.--Willis Faber North America, Inc.-Illinois, Chicago, IL; *Int'l*, pg. 1503
Ryan, Dave, Dir.-United Kingdom--Raychem Ltd., Wiltshire, United Kingdom; *U.S. Public*, pg. 1362
Ryan, Dennis, V.P. & Chief Oper. Officer--Comprehensive Benefits Service Co., Inc., Exton, PA; *U.S. Public*, pg. 635
Ryan, Eamon, Pres.--Lexmark Canada Inc., Markham, Canada; *U.S. Public*, pg. 991
Ryan, Ed, Gen. Mgr.--Sonee Heat Treating, Phoenix, AZ; *U.S. Private*, pg. 608
Ryan, Ed, Gen. Mgr.--Karsten Engineering Corp., Phoenix, AZ; *U.S. Private*, pg. 608
Ryan, Edward T., Jr., Pres. & Gen. Mgr.--Talley Defense Systems, Inc., Mesa, AZ; *U.S. Public*, pg. 308
Ryan, Edwin, Gen. Counsel & Sec.--Tomkins Industries Inc., Dayton, OH; *Int'l*, pg. 1397
Ryan, F.D., Pres.--The Clinton Oil Company, Columbus, OH; *U.S. Public*, pg. 585
Ryan, F.D., Pres.--Clinton Gas Marketing, Columbus, OH; *U.S. Public*, pg. 585
Ryan, F.M., Pres. & Chief Oper. Officer--Canada Life Investment Management Limited, Toronto, Canada; *Int'l*, pg. 255
Ryan, Francis J., Pres.--Ryan Construction Company Of Minnesota, Hibbing, MN; *U.S. Private*, pg. 953
Ryan, Frank, Pres.--Ethicon, Inc., Somerville, NJ; *U.S. Public*, pg. 928
Ryan, George, Gen. Mgr.--Rohr, Incorporated-HTA Aerostructures, Inc., San Marcos, TX; *U.S. Public*, pg. 751
Ryan, Irene, Mng. Dir.--SINSER (Ireland) Ltd., Dublin, Ireland; *Int'l*, pg. 1258
Ryan, J., Mgr.--Daher Golden Eagle - Dallas, Double Oak, TX; *U.S. Public*, pg. 749
Ryan, J. Stuart, Mng. Dir.--AES Transpower, Singapore, Singapore; *U.S. Public*, pg. 5
Ryan, J.R., Pres.--Dussek Campbell, Inc., Skokie, IL; *Int'l*, pg. 234
Ryan, James P., Chief Oper. Officer--Stevens Point Brewery, Stevens Point, WI; *U.S. Public*, pg. 300
Ryan, James R., Pres.--Ryan Construction Company, Minneapolis, MN; *U.S. Private*, pg. 953
Ryan, Janet, Publisher--MacUser, Foster City, CA; *Int'l*, pg. 1276
Ryan, John J., Chief Oper. Officer--Seaway Shopping Centers, Inc., Garden City, NY; *U.S. Private*, pg. 229
Ryan, John J., Pres. & Chief Oper. Officer--Charan Realty Group, Garden City, NY; *U.S. Private*, pg. 229
Ryan, Kevin, Pres. & Chief Exec. Officer--Wesley-Jessen, Des Plaines, IL; *U.S. Private*, pg. 111
Ryan, Mark, Mgr.--IBP-Denison, Denison, IA; *U.S. Public*, pg. 852
Ryan, Mark, Pres.--Pub/Data, Inc., Cicero, IL; *Int'l*, pg. 1076
Ryan, Mark, Chief Fin. Officer--WDZL Channel 39, Hollywood, FL; *U.S. Public*, pg. 1636
Ryan, Mary Lou, Sls. Rep.--Acuson Canada, Ltd., Oakville, Canada; *U.S. Public*, pg. 18
Ryan, N.J., Mng. Dir.--Longman Cheshire Pty. Ltd., Melbourne, Australia; *Int'l*, pg. 1025
Ryan, Patrick G., Chm. & Chief Exec. Officer--AON Risk Services Inc. of Illinois, Chicago, IL; *U.S. Public*, pg. 117
Ryan, Patrick M.A., Chief Exec. Officer--Bank of Ireland International Services Limited, Dublin, Ireland; *Int'l*, pg. 152
Ryan, Richard, Pres.--MarketPulse, Framingham, MA; *U.S. Private*, pg. 260
Ryan, Robert, V.P. & Gen. Mgr.-Pulp Div.-British Columbia--Weyerhaeuser Canada Ltd., Kamloops, Canada; *U.S. Public*, pg. 1764
Ryan, Robert W., Pres.--Wally Findlay Galleries, Inc., Palm Beach, FL; *U.S. Private*, pg. 405
Ryan, Robert W., Pres.--Wally Findlay Galleries, Inc., New York, NY; *U.S. Private*, pg. 405
Ryan, Shamus, Mgr.--Anixter Leeds, Leeds, United Kingdom; *U.S. Public*, pg. 115
Ryan, Susan, V.P.--Customer Development Corporation, Huntington Beach, CA; *U.S. Private*, pg. 298
Ryan, T.A., Chm. & Chief Exec. Officer--GPA Group PLC, Shannon, Ireland; *Int'l*, pg. 37
Ryan, Tom, Pres.-Design Services Grp.--Design Services Group, Eden Prairie, MN; *U.S. Public*, pg. 1541
Ryan, Warren, Mgr.-Australia--Medtronic Australasia Pty. Ltd., Northbridge, Australia; *U.S. Public*, pg. 1083
Ryan, Wayne, Gen. Mgr.--Tristar Industries Ltd., Delta, Canada; *Int'l*, pg. 1473
Rybak, Jim, Mgr.-Plant--Manufacturing Plant, Waukegan, IL; *U.S. Private*, pg. 235
Ryckebosch, Etienne, Chief Oper. Officer--Schleicher & Schuell N.V. S.A., Gent, Belgium; *Int'l*, pg. 1206
Ryckevorsel, T.C.A.M., Gen. Mgr.--ABN Management Services A.G., Vaduz, Liechtenstein; *Int'l*, pg. 11
Rydell, William P., Pres.--Mellon Equity Associates Corp., Pittsburgh, PA; *U.S. Public*, pg. 1085
Ryden, D. Ray, Pres.-Located in Boise, ID--Minnesota, Dakota & Western Railway Co., International Falls, MN; *U.S. Public*, pg. 243
Ryden, Nils, Chief Oper. Officer--Alfa-Laval Equipamentos Ltda., Sao Paulo, Brazil; *Int'l*, pg. 1379
Ryder, David, Mgr.--Uddeholm Corporation, Cleveland, OH; *Int'l*, pg. 1472
Ryder, John, Pres. & Chief Oper. Officer-Retail--Metro/Basics, Baltimore, MD; *U.S. Public*, pg. 1388
Ryder, Michael, Chief Exec. Officer--Lambert Smith Hampton, Glasgow, United Kingdom; *Int'l*, pg. 797
Rydholm, Ralph W., Chief Exec. Officer--EURO RSCG Tatham, Chicago, IL; *Int'l*, pg. 601
Rydin, Anders, Chm. Bd.--Ford Motor Co. Aktiebolag, Stockholm, Sweden; *U.S. Public*, pg. 666
Rydin, Claes, Mng. Dir.--Jac Jacobsen AB, Molndal, Sweden; *Int'l*, pg. 821

Rydin, Craig, Pres.--Godiva Chocolatier, Inc., New York, NY; *U.S. Public*, pg. 299
Ryers, samuel, Owner--W & S Distributors, Inc., Bayamon, PR; *Int'l*, pg. 132
Ryker, Gary E., Pres. & Chief Exec. Officer--Union Switch & Signal Inc., Pittsburgh, PA; *Int'l*, pg. 77
Ryland, C.M., Mng. Dir.--Hawker Pacific Pty. Ltd., Yagoona, Australia; *Int'l*, pg. 128
Rylander, Goran, Pres.--Swedbank (Luxembourg) S.A., Luxembourg, Luxembourg; *Int'l*, pg. 1328
Ryley, Dennis, Pres.--Mid-Valley Oil Company, Inc., New Windsor, NY; *U.S. Private*, pg. 1151
Ryley, James S., Pres.--Cupertino Electric, Inc., Sunnyvale, CA; *U.S. Private*, pg. 1060
Rymar, Eugene J., Plant Mgr.--Hydra-matic Division, Strasbourg, France; *U.S. Public*, pg. 725
Rypien, John M., Pres.--O.J. Pipelines Corp., Nisku, Canada; *Int'l*, pg. 996
Rysman, Andre, Mng. Dir. & Creative Dir.--TBWA Belgium, Brussels, Belgium; *U.S. Private*, pg. 1063
Ryzman, Zvi, Pres. & Chief Exec. Officer--Andrea International, City of Commerce, CA; *U.S. Private*, pg. 57
Ryzman, Zvi, Pres. & Chief Exec. Officer--SuperNail, City of Commerce, CA; *U.S. Private*, pg. 57
Ryzman, Zvi, Pres. & Chief Exec. Officer--Ardell International, Inc., City of Industry, CA; *U.S. Private*, pg. 57
Saalbach, Horst, Pres.--Festo Corporation, Hauppauge, NY; *Int'l*, pg. 480
Saar, Rein, Chief Oper. Officer--Alfa-Laval Pty Ltd., Sydney, Australia; *Int'l*, pg. 1379
Saari, Lauri, Mng. Dir.--Wisapak Mertens GmbH, Julich, Germany; *Int'l*, pg. 1430
Saari, Timo, Mng. Dir.--OFA Oy Ab, Jokioinen, Finland; *Int'l*, pg. 578
Saarikangas, Martin, Pres.--Kvaerner Masa-Yards Inc., Helsinki New Shipyard, Helsinki, Finland; *Int'l*, pg. 771
Saarikoski, Erkki, Mng. Dir.--Nokia Telecommunications S.A., La Moraleja-Alcogendas, Spain; *Int'l*, pg. 954
Saarinen, Vesa, Gen. Mgr.--Esselte Meto, Helsinki, Finland; *Int'l*, pg. 461
Saarnak, Peeter, Div. Mgr.--Munksjoe Forpackningar AB, Nybro, Sweden; *Int'l*, pg. 1423
Saarnio, Markku, Mgr.--Varkaus Sawmill, Varkaus, Finland; *Int'l*, pg. 456
Saastamoinen, Ahti, Mng. Dir.--Puhos-Board Oy, Puhos, Finland; *Int'l*, pg. 1428
Saavedra, Jorge, Chief Oper. Officer--Banco Santander Puerto Rico, New York Branch, New York, NY; *Int'l*, pg. 143
Saba, George K., Pres.--Nation's Care, Inc., Farmington, CT; *U.S. Public*, pg. 1231
Sabala, Ronald, Mgr.-Sls.--Perma-Pipe Div., Niles, IL; *U.S. Public*, pg. 1026
Sabala, Tracy R., Publr.--Northeast Publishing, Inc.-The Herald News, Fall River, MA; *U.S. Public*, pg. 935
Sabaq, Tsuyoshi, Chm.--Toyota Auto Body Co., Ltd., Kariya City, Japan; *Int'l*, pg. 1412
Sabatacakis, Petros K., Chm. Bd.--Chase Manhattan Mortgage Corporation, Worthington, OH; *U.S. Public*, pg. 338
Sabate, Joan, Gen. Mgr.--Standex International S.A., Barcelona, Spain; *U.S. Public*, pg. 1507
Sabbag, Allen, Pres.--Better Homes and Gardens Real Estate Service, Des Moines, IA; *U.S. Public*, pg. 1094
Sabbagh, Paul, V.P. & Gen. Mgr.--IMI Cornelius Brasil, Rio de Janeiro, Brazil; *Int'l*, pg. 646
Sabbe, Filip, Gen. Mgr.--Banque Bruxelles Lambert (Suisse)-Basel, Basel, Switzerland; *Int'l*, pg. 148
Saber, Markram, Mng. Dir.--Circle Freight International (Saudi Arabia) Ltd., Jeddah, Saudi Arabia; *U.S. Public*, pg. 373
Sabin, Dan, Pres.--Iowa Northern Railroad, Greene, IA; *U.S. Private*, pg. 575
Sabin, Julia, Plant Mgr.--H.B. DeViney Co., New Bethlehem, PA; *U.S. Public*, pg. 1480
Sabol, Thomas A., Pres.--Englekirk & Sabol, Inc., Los Angeles, CA; *U.S. Private*, pg. 377
Sabounchi, Farid, Pres.--Aetrium-FSA, Grand Prairie, TX; *U.S. Public*, pg. 27
Sac, Jean-Claude, Country Mgr.--Nokia France S.A., Romainville, France; *Int'l*, pg. 954
Sacchi, Beppe, Pres.--Officine Aeronavali Venezia S.p.A., Tesero, Italy; *Int'l*, pg. 653
Sacerdote, Manuel, Reg. Mgr.--Bank of Boston, Buenos Aires, Argentina; *U.S. Public*, pg. 184
Sacerdote, Vittorio, Mng. Dir.--Dynisco S.r.L., Milan, Italy; *U.S. Private*, pg. 139
Sachdev, G.K., Mng. Dir.--Quaker Chemical India Ltd., Calcutta, India; *U.S. Public*, pg. 1346
Sachs, Stuart A., Pres.--NationsBank Capital Management Corporation, Richmond, VA; *U.S. Public*, pg. 1163
Sachse, Robert G., Pres.--Mapco Natural Gas Liquids Inc., Tulsa, OK; *U.S. Public*, pg. 1042
Sachtjen, Barry, Branch Mgr.--Zellerbach Division, Lanham, MD; *U.S. Public*, pg. 1075
Sack, Han, Pres.--Latrobe Special Products Div., Latrobe, PA; *U.S. Public*, pg. 1617
Sackett, David, Chief Oper. Officer & Exec. V.P.--PAID Prescriptions, Inc., Fair Lawn, NJ; *U.S. Public*, pg. 1091
Sackett, Neil, Pres.--Carter-Jones Lumber Co., Kent, OH; *U.S. Private*, pg. 217
Sackmann, Thomas F., Pres.--Action Mortgage Company, Spokane, WA; *U.S. Public*, pg. 1516
Sacknoft, Philip, Chm. Bd.--Angiographic Devices, Littleton, MA; *U.S. Public*, pg. 1596
Sacks, Ann, Pres.--Ann Sacks Tile & Stone, Inc., Portland, OR; *U.S. Private*, pg. 630
Sada, Armando Garza, Pres.--Sigma Alimentos, S.A. de C.V., Garza Garcia, Mexico; *Int'l*, pg. 56
Sada, Pablo Gonzalez, Pres.--Vitro, Sociedad Anonima - Chemical, Fibers & Mining, Garza Garcia, Mexico; *Int'l*, pg. 1469
Sada, Tomas Gonzalez, Chief Exec. Officer--Grupo Cydsa, S.A. de C.V., Garza Garcia, Mexico; *Int'l*, pg. 246
Sada, Tomas Gonzalez, Pres.--Vitromatic, S.A. de C.V., Garza Garcia, Mexico; *Int'l*, pg. 1469
Sada, Tomas Gonzalez, Pres.--Vitromatic, S.A. de C.V., Garza Garcia, Mexico; *U.S. Public*, pg. 1765
Sadakata, M., Mng. Dir.--Toshiba International Finance (Netherlands) B.V., Haarlem, Netherlands; *Int'l*, pg. 1406
Sadler, David G., Pres.--Rowe International, Inc., Grand Rapids, MI; *U.S. Private*, pg. 904
Sadler, Robert L., Pres. & Chief Exec. Officer--Old Kent Bank, Grand Rapids, MI; *U.S. Public*, pg. 1216
Sadlon, Richard, V.P. & Gen. Mgr.--National Book Distributors, Troy, MI; *U.S. Public*, pg. 780
Sadlowski, L.J., Div. Pres.--Winn-Dixie Texas, Inc., Fort Worth, TX; *U.S. Public*, pg. 1772
Sadove, Stephen I., Pres.--Clairol, Inc., Stamford, CT; *U.S. Public*, pg. 254
Sadowski, Rick, Pres. & Publr.--Saint Paul Pioneer Press Division, Saint Paul, MN; *U.S. Public*, pg. 964
Sadrossasatzadeh, S.M., Pres.--Monenco Iran, Tehran, Iran; *Int'l*, pg. 31
Saeger, John H., V.P.--Pennsylvania Power & Light Company-Lancaster Div., Lancaster, PA; *U.S. Public*, pg. 1244
Saegesser, Paul, Dir.-Mktg.--Nordson Schweiz AG, Munchenstein, Switzerland; *U.S. Public*, pg. 1189
Saegesser, Weiner, Mng. Dir.--Bose AG, Gelterkinden, Switzerland; *U.S. Private*, pg. 160
Saegusa, Masato, Pres.--Actus Corporation, Tokyo, Japan; *Int'l*, pg. 868
Saeki, Takehiko, Pres.--Kawasaki Motors Manufacturing Corp., U.S.A., Lincoln, NE; *Int'l*, pg. 725
Saeki, Y., Mng. Dir.--Sharp-Roxy Sales & Service Company (M) sdn. Bhd., Petaling Jaya, Malaysia; *Int'l*, pg. 1230
Saeki, Y., Mng. Dir.--Sharp-Roxy Appliances Corp. (M) Sdn. Bhd., Petaling Jaya, Malaysia; *Int'l*, pg. 1230
Saenc, Alfredo, Pres.--Banco Espanol de Credito SA, Madrid, Spain; *Int'l*, pg. 143
Saeng-Xuto, Chaisak, Mng. Dir.--The Siam Pulp and Paper Co., Ltd., Bangkok, Thailand; *Int'l*, pg. 1238
Saenz, Fernando Gonzales, Asst. Dir.--Ryerson de Mexico/West Division, Zapopan, Mexico; *Int'l*, pg. 66
Saeranie, Shan, Pres.--Harper-Wyman Co., Aurora, IL; *U.S. Public*, pg. 1209
Saether, R., Mng. Dir.--OMRON Electronics Norway A/S, Oslo, Norway; *Int'l*, pg. 1006
Saez, Engle, Pres.--Sperry Top-Sider, Inc., Cambridge, MA; *U.S. Public*, pg. 1525
Saez, Felipe, Chief Resident Mission--Banco Mundial, Bogota, Colombia; *U.S. Private*, pg. 1189
Saez, Manuel, Chief Oper. Officer--Alfa-Laval S.A., Madrid, Spain; *Int'l*, pg. 1380
Saez, Miguel Angel, Gen. Mgr.--Graficas Monte Alban, S.A., Queretaro, Mexico; *Int'l*, pg. 1078
Sagami, Yosuke, Gen. Mgr.--Hysol Japan Limited, Yokohama, Japan; *U.S. Public*, pg. 505
Sagar, P., Chief Oper. Officer--Tata-Yodogawa Ltd., Jamshedpur, India; *Int'l*, pg. 949
Sagar, Ravi, Mgr.--Arms Communications P. Ltd., Mumbai, India; *U.S. Public*, pg. 1642
Sagawa, Masahiro, Chief Rep.--Yangon Representative Office, Yangon, Myanmar; *Int'l*, pg. 521
Sagawa, Nobuo, Pres.--The Meijiseimei Insurance Agency of New York, Inc., New York, NY; *Int'l*, pg. 854
Sagawa, Wesley S., Pres.--Capstone Electronics Corp., Aurora, CO; *U.S. Public*, pg. 134
Sage, T.W., Plant Mgr.--Atlas Inc., Fostoria, OH; *U.S. Public*, pg. 468
Sagedahl, Christian, Gen. Mgr.--Kamyr Chile S A C el, Santiago, Chile; *Int'l*, pg. 771
Sager, Esther, Mng. Dir.--Pendia Pension Fund Services, Zurich, Switzerland; *Int'l*, pg. 1332
Sager, John R., Gen. Mgr.--Nortel Australia Pty. Limited, Chatswood, Australia; *Int'l*, pg. 970
Sager, Richard B., Plant Mgr.--Gilmour Hose Company, Excelsior Springs, MO; *U.S. Public*, pg. 575
Sagert, Charles, Pres.--INX International, Arden Hills, MN; *Int'l*, pg. 1311
Saggers, Geoffrey R., Sr. V.P.--Cigna Worldwide Insurance Company, Wilmington, DE; *U.S. Public*, pg. 365
Saggers, Geoffrey R., Pres.--Cigna Compania de Seguros de Vida (Chile) S.A., Santiago, Chile; *U.S. Public*, pg. 364
Saha, Dr. M.L., Chief Oper. Officer--Saha Woodall-Duckham (Private) Limited, Calcutta, India; *Int'l*, pg. 472
Saha, Saibal K., Mng. Dir.--P.T. Johnson & Johnson Indonesia, Jakarta, Indonesia; *U.S. Public*, pg. 930
Sahara, Toshio, Gen. Mgr.--Dai-Ichi Kangyo Bank, Ltd.-Panama, Panama, Panama; *Int'l*, pg. 360
Sahene, James M., Pres.--TCBY Systems, Inc., Little Rock, AR; *U.S. Public*, pg. 1554
Sahi, K.R., Pres. & Chief Exec. Officer--Consolidated Fastfrate, Toronto, Canada; *Int'l*, pg. 1150
Sahleen, Brad, Gen. Mgr.--Milgray/Utah, Inc., Murray, UT; *U.S. Public*, pg. 207
Sahlsten, Carl, Pres.--Carrabba's Italian Grill, Inc., Tampa, FL; *U.S. Public*, pg. 1235
Sahm, Volker, Pres.--American Sahm Corporation, Greenville, SC; *Int'l*, pg. 1169
Said, Mohammed Haji, Dato, Mng. Dir.--Sime UEP Properties Berhad, Petaling Jaya, Malaysia; *Int'l*, pg. 1250
Said, Perves, Mng. Dir.--Johnson & Johnson Pakistan (Private) Ltd., Karachi, Pakistan; *U.S. Public*, pg. 931
Said, Zulkifly, Dir.--MTPB - Northern Region, Penang, Malaysia; *Int'l*, pg. 833
Sailing, Dave, Gen. Mgr.--Zalk Joseph Fabrications, Inc., Stoughton, WI; *U.S. Private*, pg. 860
Saillant, J., Pres.--Stihl Eastern Canada Ltd., Vanier, Canada; *Int'l*, pg. 1301
Sain, Sanjiv, Chief Oper. Officer--Hagglunds Hydraulic Drives (India) Pvt. Ltd., Pune, India; *Int'l*, pg. 670
Saine, Into, Mgr.--Enso Cartonboards Oy Ltd., Anjalankoski, Finland; *Int'l*, pg. 456
Sainiemi, Jukka, Chief Oper. Officer--Ahlstrom Machinery Fiber Line, Karhula, Finland; *Int'l*, pg. 33
Sainio, Veikko, Chief Oper. Officer--KONE Lifts a.s., Prague, Czech Republic; *Int'l*, pg. 747
Saint Ouen, Marc, Mng. Dir.--EURO RSCG Institutionnel, Levallois-Perret, France; *Int'l*, pg. 600
Saint-Jacques, Madeleine, Chm.--Saint Jacques Vallee Young & Rubicam, Inc., Montreal, Canada; *U.S. Private*, pg. 1200
Saintherant, Patrice, Mgr.-Plant--Sucrerie de Roye, Roye, France; *Int'l*, pg. 549
Sainz de la Pena, Rolando, Mng. Dir.--Vitruvio-Leo Burnett, Madrid, Spain; *U.S. Private*, pg. 186
Saiontz, Steven J., Pres.--Lennar Financial Services, Inc., Miami, FL; *U.S. Public*, pg. 988
Sais, Joe, Chief Fin. Officer--Consolidated Paper Co., Bronx, NY; *U.S. Private*, pg. 838
Saishoji, Toshimasa, Pres.--Singapore Kobe Private Limited, Jurong, Singapore; *Int'l*, pg. 741
Saito, A., Chief Oper. Officer--Andrew International Corporation, Tokyo, Japan; *U.S. Public*, pg. 113
Saito, Akira, Pres.--International In-Flight Catering Co. Ltd., Honolulu, HI; *Int'l*, pg. 700
Saito, Atsushi, Pres.--Nomura Human Resources Development Co., Ltd., Tokyo, Japan; *Int'l*, pg. 955
Saito, Hiroshi, Gen. Mgr.--Dai-Ichi Kangyo Bank, Ltd.-Bangkok, Bangkok, Thailand; *Int'l*, pg. 361
Saito, Hiroshi, Dir.--Thai Investment & Securities Co. Ltd., Bangkok, Thailand; *Int'l*, pg. 362
Saito, Hiroyuki, Chief Exec. Officer--Novo Nordisk Bioindustry Ltd, Chiba, Japan; *Int'l*, pg. 989
Saito, Jiro, Chief Rep.--Ho Chi Minh Representative Office, Ho Chi Minh City, Vietnam; *Int'l*, pg. 520
Saito, Joichi, Chm. Bd. & Chief Exec. Officer--Central Pacific Bank, Honolulu, HI; *U.S. Public*, pg. 283
Saito, Joichi, Chm. Bd.--CPB Properties, Inc., Honolulu, HI; *U.S. Public*, pg. 283
Saito, Kaneyoshi, Sr. Rep.--Nippon Credit Bank Ltd.-Seoul, Seoul, Korea; *Int'l*, pg. 933
Saito, Keishiro, Pres.--Toray Europe Ltd., London, United Kingdom; *Int'l*, pg. 1400
Saito, M., Mgr.--Ballast Nedam International B.V., Tokyo, Japan; *Int'l*, pg. 134
Saito, M., Representative--Ballast Nedam Dredging, Tokyo, Japan; *Int'l*, pg. 134
Saito, Masanobu, Chief Rep.--Asahi Bank Manila Representative Office, Makati, Philippines; *Int'l*, pg. 83
Saito, Naotake, Pres.--Eastern Harbour Crossing Co., Ltd., Hong Kong, Hong Kong; *Int'l*, pg. 764
Saito, Naotake, Pres.--New Hong Kong Tunnel Co., Ltd., Hong Kong, Hong Kong; *Int'l*, pg. 764
Saito, Shinichiro, Deputy Pres.--P.T. Inter-Pacific Bank, Jakarta, Indonesia; *Int'l*, pg. 1190
Saito, Sumio, Gen. Mgr.--The Sumitomo Bank, Ltd.-Shanghai Branch, Shanghai, China; *Int'l*, pg. 1309
Saito, T., Dir.--SEIKO Hong Kong Ltd., Hong Kong, Hong Kong; *Int'l*, pg. 1218
Saito, Takeshi, Pres.--NLI Properties West, Inc., Los Angeles, CA; *Int'l*, pg. 935
Saito, Teru, Dir.-Mfg.--Clarion Manufacturing Corp. of America, Walton, KY; *Int'l*, pg. 296
Saito, Toshio, Pres.--ZEXEL Illinois Inc., Decatur, IL; *Int'l*, pg. 1528
Saito, Yoshito, Gen. Mgr.--The Daishi Bank, Ltd., New York, NY; *Int'l*, pg. 373
Saitoh, Harehisa, Mgr.--Nippon Lincoln Electric K.K., Tokyo, Japan; *U.S. Public*, pg. 997
Saiz, F., Gen. Mgr.--Kellogg Espana, S.A., Tarragona, Spain; *U.S. Public*, pg. 948
Saizu, Masaki, Chief Representative--Guangzhou Representative Office, Guangzhou, China; *Int'l*, pg. 520
Sajjavudh, Niphon, Mng. Dir--Batey Ads Thailand, Bangkok, Thailand; *Int'l*, pg. 117
Sakaguchi, Kiyofumi, Pres.--The Prudential Life Insurance Company, Ltd., Tokyo, Japan; *U.S. Private*, pg. 893
Sakai, Akihiko, Chief Oper. Officer--The Kyoei Annuity Home Co., Ltd., Tokyo, Japan; *Int'l*, pg. 776
Sakai, H., Pres.--Sunrack Oyodo Co., Ltd., Izumi-Otsu, Japan; *Int'l*, pg. 947
Sakai, Hideki, Pres.--Hirose Cherry Precision Company Ltd., Kawasaki, Japan; *U.S. Public*, pg. 346
Sakai, Hiroto, Pres.--Sumitomo Bank (Deutschland) GmbH, Frankfurt/Main, Germany; *Int'l*, pg. 1310
Sakai, Kiyofumi, Chief Rep.--Dai-ichi Kangyo Bank, Ltd.-Houston, Houston, TX; *Int'l*, pg. 359
Sakai, Kosaku, Chm. Bd.--LTCB Trust Company, New York, NY; *Int'l*, pg. 816
Sakai, Masaharu, Chief Oper. Officer--Kyowa Hakko (H.K.) Co., Ltd., Causeway Bay, Hong Kong; *Int'l*, pg. 778
Sakai, Tadamasa, Pres.--Seoul Office, Seoul, Korea; *Int'l*, pg. 578
Sakai, Tsutomu, Dir.--Asahi Advertising Inc., Sapporo, Japan; *Int'l*, pg. 81
Sakai, Yukio, Mng. Dir.--Tokai Australia Finance Corporation Limited, Sydney, Australia; *Int'l*, pg. 1391
Sakakibara, Isamu, Mng. Dir.--Daiwa Securities Australia Limited-Head Office, Melbourne, Australia; *Int'l*, pg. 375
Sakami, Tomio, Chief Oper. Officer--Kabushiki Kaisha TMK, Toyohashi, Japan; *Int'l*, pg. 831
Sakane, Masahiro, Pres.--Komatsu America Corp., Lincolnshire, IL; *Int'l*, pg. 744
Sakas, Gedas A., Pres.--Northern Telecom Canada Limited, Brampton, Canada; *Int'l*, pg. 969
Sakata, Fumihiko, Chief Rep.--Sydney Representative Office, Sydney, Australia; *Int'l*, pg. 520
Sakata, Fumihiko, Chief Rep.--Melbourne Representative Office, Melbourne, Australia; *Int'l*, pg. 520
Sakata, Haruo, Pres.--Gunsan Exportadora e Importadora Ltda., Sao Paulo, Brazil; *Int'l*, pg. 579
Sakata, Yoichi, Joint Gen. Mgr.--Fuji Bank, Labuan Office, Labuan, Malaysia; *Int'l*, pg. 520

Sakayama, Larry K., Pres.--TEC Cellular, Melbourne, FL; *U.S. Public*, pg. 1430
Sakelaris, John, Div. Mgr.--Transilwrap Company, Inc., Dallas, TX; *U.S. Private*, pg. 1097
Sakellaridis, Fotis, Mng. Dir.--Janssen/Cilag S.A.C.I., Athens, Greece; *U.S. Public*, pg. 929
Saker, Joseph J., Pres.--Shop Rite of Malverne, Inc., Freehold, NJ; *U.S. Public*, pg. 661
Saker, Joseph J., Pres.--New Linden Price Rite, Inc., Freehold, NJ; *U.S. Public*, pg. 661
Saker, Joseph J., Pres.--Regal Drugs, Inc., Freehold, NJ; *U.S. Public*, pg. 661
Sakhuja, Ravinder, Pres.--Tecogen Inc., Waltham, MA; *U.S. Public*, pg. 1592
Sakihama, Richard, Pres.--Plumbing Specialties & Supplies, Inc., Honolulu, HI; *Int'l*, pg. 1512
Sakisaka, Yuji, Chief Rep.--The Meiji Life Insurance Company Beijing Office, Beijing, China; *Int'l*, pg. 854
Sakko, Jorma, Mng. Dir.--Zeofinn Oy, Hamina, Finland; *U.S. Private*, pg. 545
Sakonju, T., Pres.--Nissho Iwai Nonferrous Metals Corp., Tokyo, Japan; *Int'l*, pg. 947
Sakr, Omar, V.P. & Country Mgr.--Financiera Bamerical S.A., Panama, Panama; *U.S. Public*, pg. 183
Sakuda, Tadashi, Pres.--Medtronic Japan Co., Ltd., Hokkaido, Japan; *U.S. Public*, pg. 1084
Sakuma, K., Chm. & Pres.--Otto Sumisho Inc., Tokyo, Japan; *Int'l*, pg. 1015
Sakuma, Shihei, Chief Gen. Mgr.--IBJ Australia Bank Limited, Perth, Australia; *Int'l*, pg. 676
Sakuma, Shuhei, Chief Rep.--The Industrial Bank of Japan, Limited (Panama), Panama, Panama; *Int'l*, pg. 675
Sakuma, Toshi, Gen. Mgr.--Yamaha Corp. of America, Sporting Goods Div., Buena Park, CA; *Int'l*, pg. 1516
Sakuma, Yuichi, Gen. Mgr.--Toyo Trust & Banking (Schweiz) AG, Zurich, Switzerland; *Int'l*, pg. 1411
Sakumah, Hajime, Pres.--Shin Caterpillar Mitsubishi Ltd., Yokohama, Japan; *U.S. Public*, pg. 317
Sakumah, Hajime, Pres.--Shin Caterpillar Mitsubishi Ltd., Yokohama, Japan; *Int'l*, pg. 873
Sakura, Sumioshi, Gen. Mgr.--Bose K.K., Tokyo, Japan; *U.S. Private*, pg. 161
Sakurai, Hiroyuki, Chief Rep.--New Delhi Representative Office, New Delhi, India; *Int'l*, pg. 520
Sakurai, Kenichi, Pres. & Chief Exec. Officer--Sanwa Bank Canada, Toronto, Canada; *Int'l*, pg. 1190
Sakurai, Shoji, Pres.--Daiwa Securities Bank (Switzerland) Head Office, Zurich, Switzerland; *Int'l*, pg. 376
Sakurai, Shoji, Gen. Mgr.--Daiwa Securities Bank-Geneva Branch, Geneva, Switzerland; *Int'l*, pg. 376
Sakurai, Shoji, Gen. Mgr.--Daiwa Securities Bank Switzerland-Lugano, Lugano, Switzerland; *Int'l*, pg. 376
Sakurai, T., Mng. Dir.--Metallurg (Far East) Limited, Tokyo, Japan; *U.S. Private*, pg. 735
Saladino, Joe, Mng. Dir.--Triumph Releasing Corporation - Mid-Atlantic Territory, Philadelphia, PA; *Int'l*, pg. 1282
Salamone, Anthony A., Pres.--Ke-Master, Dover, DE; *U.S. Private*, pg. 1053
Salard, Mike, Mgr.--Southern Electric Supply Co., Inc., Leesville, LA; *Int'l*, pg. 1108
Salard, Wayne, Mgr.--Southern Electric Supply Co., Inc., Alexandria, LA; *Int'l*, pg. 1108
Salas, Anthony, Gen. Mgr.--Chemwest Corp., Miami, FL; *Int'l*, pg. 332
Salas, E., Mgr.--Swiss Bank Corporation, Guayaquil, Ecuador; *Int'l*, pg. 1330
Salathe, Willy, Mng. Dir.--Asulab S.A., Biel, Switzerland; *Int'l*, pg. 1160
Salathe, Willy, Mng. Dir.--Comadur S.A., Le Locle, Switzerland; *Int'l*, pg. 1161
Salathe, Willy, Mng. Dir.--Lasag AG, Thun, Switzerland; *Int'l*, *pg. 1161*
Salathe, Willy, Mng. Dir.--Omega Electronics SA, Bienne, Switzerland; *Int'l*, pg. 1161
Salathe, Willy, Mng. Dir.--Oscilloquartz SA, Neuchatel, Switzerland; *Int'l*, pg. 1161
Salawi, Gabriel E., Advisor--Union Bank of Switzerland, Beirut, Lebanon; *Int'l*, pg. 1441
Salazar, Ceci, Admin.--Valle Norte Caring Center, Albuquerque, NM; *U.S. Public*, pg. 838
Salcedo, Gabriel, Chief Oper. Officer--CTD de Mexico, S.A., Colonia, Mexico; *U.S. Public*, pg. 950
Salcedo, Gabriel, Chief Oper. Officer--Herramientas Cleveland, S.A., Colonia, Mexico; *U.S. Public*, pg. 950
Salchli, Peter, Pres.--Volvo Trucks (Schweiz) AG, Lyss, Switzerland; *Int'l*, pg. 1478
Saldanha, Conrda, Exec. Dir.--Rediffusion-DY&R Pvt. Ltd., Mumbai, India; *U.S. Private*, pg. 326
Saldarelli, Tom, Pres.--Paragon, Lagrangeville, NY; *U.S. Public*, pg. 593
Salden, D.M., Pres.--Buss Waeschle Ltd., Stockport, United Kingdom; *Int'l*, pg. 490
Salegard, Jarl, Pres.--Ballast Vast AB, Goteborg, Sweden; *Int'l*, pg. 899
Saleh Al Jarbou, Abdulaziz, Dr., Pres.--Bondstrand, Ltd., Dammam, Saudi Arabia; *U.S. Public*, pg. 99
Salehi, Nasser, Chief Acct. Officer--Kredietbank-Bankverein AG, Berlin, Germany; *Int'l*, pg. 761
Salem, A.A., Grp. Mng. Dir.--Liberty Retail Limited, London, United Kingdom; *Int'l*, pg. 807
Salem, Irfan, V.P. & Gen. Mgr.--Lotus International Div., Cambridge, MA; *U.S. Public*, pg. 896
Salembier, Valerie, Publr.--Esquire, New York, NY; *U.S. Private*, pg. 517
Salerno, Robert, Pres. & Chief Oper. Officer--Avis Rent A Car System, Inc., Garden City, NY; *U.S. Public*, pg. 321
Sales, Jeff, Mgr.--KOLD-TV, Tucson, AZ; *U.S. Private*, pg. 912
Salessy, Georges, Pres.--APSYS (Aerospatiale Protection Systemes), Mantes-la-Jolie, France; *Int'l*, pg. 29
Salhany, Lucie, Pres.--Fox Broadcasting Company (FBC), Beverly Hills, CA; *Int'l*, pg. 926
Salhus, Vicki, Mgr.-Opers.--Akzo Nobel Coatings Inc., Birmingham, AL; *Int'l*, pg. 48
Saliba, Antonio Carlos, Exec. V.P. & Gen. Mgr.--Janssen Cilag Brazil, Sao Paulo, Brazil; *U.S. Public*, pg. 929
Salicetti, Arturo Casado, Pres.--Leo Burnett Venezuela, C.A., Caracas, Venezuela; *U.S. Private*, pg. 186
Salierno, Joseph, Gen. Mgr.--Avon Manufacturing Lab., Suffern, NY; *U.S. Public*, pg. 156
Salinas, Alfonso, Plant Mgr.--Kaydon S.A. de C.V., Guadalupe, Mexico; *U.S. Public*, pg. 946
Salines, Felis, Chief Oper. Officer--Dalworth Concrete Products, Inc., San Antonio, TX; *U.S. Private*, pg. 417
Salini, Lou, Pres. & Gen. Mgr.--Outdoor Systems, Inc.-St. Louis, Saint Louis, MO; *U.S. Public*, pg. 1235
Sall, Robert, Gen. Mgr.--Gleason Works Ltd., Plymouth, United Kingdom; *U.S. Public*, pg. 746
Sallam, Aly, Mgr.-Egypt--Raychem Egypt Ltd., Cairo, Egypt; *U.S. Public*, pg. 1362
Sallee, Darrell F., Group Gen. Mgr.--UTA Holland Plant, Holland, MI; *U.S. Public*, pg. 1691
Salles, Lywal, Pres.--Chase Bank of Maryland, Baltimore, MD; *U.S. Public*, pg. 338
Salles, Paulo, Pres.-DMB&B Americas--Salles/DMB&B Publicidade S.A., Sao Paulo, Brazil; *U.S. Private*, pg. 305
Salles, Pierre Michel, Chief Oper. Officer--Axel Johnson S.A., Paris, France; *Int'l*, pg. 712
Salley, John, Plant Mgr.--ITW Finishing Systems & Products, Jackson, TN; *U.S. Public*, pg. 866
Sallin, Lars-Erik, Pres.--Machinery East, Linkoping, Sweden; *Int'l*, pg. 899
Sallis, Richard, Pres.--Playmates Toys Inc., Costa Mesa, CA; *Int'l*, pg. 1060
Sallitt, Norman, V.P. & Gen. Mgr.--Harte-Hanks Direct Marketing/Pennsylvania, Forty Fort, PA; *U.S. Public*, pg. 794
Sallmen, Bengt, Pres.--Perstorp Polyols Inc., Toledo, OH; *Int'l*, pg. 1038
Salm, R.G., Mng. Dir.--Coats Bell, Arthur, Canada; *Int'l*, pg. 300
Salman, Steven L., Pres.--KMA Insurance Agency, Inc., Louisville, KY; *U.S. Private*, pg. 741
Salman, Steven L., Pres.--KMIC Investment Company, Louisville, KY; *U.S. Private*, pg. 741
Salminen, Risto, Dir.--Kemira Fibres Oy, Valkeakoski, Finland; *Int'l*, pg. 728
Salmon, J.D., Mng. Dir.--Crosfield Electronics Limited, Hemel Hempstead, United Kingdom; *U.S. Public*, pg. 532
Salmon, Leslie, Branch Mgr.--BSA Advertising, Inc., Los Angeles, CA; *U.S. Private*, pg. 108
Salmon, S.P., Gen. Mgr.--Commercial Seating Division, Starkville, MS; *U.S. Public*, pg. 654
Salmoon, Gary, Chief Fin. Officer--Acorn Computers Ltd., Cambridge, United Kingdom; *Int'l*, pg. 1002
Salo, J., Pres.--Nokia Telecommunications Inc., Roanoke, TX; *Int'l*, pg. 953
Salo, Jyrki, Mgr.-VS PCS 1900--Nokia Telecommunications, Espoo, Finland; *Int'l*, pg. 952
Salonen, Jarmo, V.P.--Aanekoski Art Paper Mill, Aanekoski, Finland; *Int'l*, pg. 863
Salonen, Jarmo, V.P.--Kangas Paper Mill, Jyvaskyla, Finland; *Int'l*, pg. 863
Salsamendi, Gonzalo, Gen. Mgr.--Wackenhut Paraguay S.R.L., Asuncion, Paraguay; *U.S. Public*, pg. 1732
Salsano, Onorio, Plant Mgr.--Cartiera Del Tirreno Mill, Cava de Tirreni, Italy; *U.S. Public*, pg. 673
Salsbery, Phil, Pres.--Dekko Automotive Technologies Iowa Assemblies Div., Osceola, IA; *U.S. Private*, pg. 484
Salstrom, Steve, Gen. Mgr.--Regency Thermographics of Washington, Inc., Tacoma, WA; *U.S. Public*, pg. 89
Salt, David, Gen. Mgr.--ITW Finishing Systems & Products Pty. Ltd., Milperra, Australia; *U.S. Public*, pg. 868
Salter, Graham, Mng. Dir.--West Footscray Engineering Works Pty. Ltd., Footscray, Australia; *Int'l*, pg. 392
Salter, Kevin, Sr. V.P.-N.J. Opers.--Willis Corroon Corp. of New Jersey, Morris Plains, NJ; *Int'l*, pg. 1506
Salterstrom, Per, Chief Oper. Officer--Electrolux-Wascator S.A., Paris, France; *Int'l*, pg. 441
Saltman, G. H., Mng. Dir.--Hunter Douglas Holdings Ltd., Rydalmere, Australia; *Int'l*, pg. 640
Salvador, Aldo, Mng. Dir.--Rhone-Poulenc Chine, Beijing, China; *Int'l*, pg. 1112
Salvador, Diosdado C., Jr., Mng. Dir.--Johnson & Johnson (Thailand) Ltd., Bangkok, Thailand; *U.S. Public*, pg. 931
Salvati, Sandro, Dr., Pres.--Lloyd Adriatico S.p.A, Trieste, Italy; *Int'l*, pg. 60
Salvatori, Romano, Pres.--Nations Energy Corporation, Tucson, AZ; *U.S. Public*, pg. 1670
Salveson, Raymond J., Dir.--AlliedSignal China Inc., AlliedSignal Aerospace Services Corporation, Beijing, China; *U.S. Public*, pg. 52
Salvo, A.W. Romay, Pres.--Alcan Aluminio del Uruguay S.A., Montevideo, Uruguay; *Int'l*, pg. 50
Salyard, Dan, Plant Mgr.--RAYOVAC Corporation, Portage, WI; *U.S. Private*, pg. 912
Salzano, Joe, Pres.--Amerex Men's, New York, NY; *U.S. Private*, pg. 49
Salzberger, Lee R., Pres. & Gen. Mgr.--WVEC-TV, Inc., Norfolk, VA; *U.S. Public*, pg. 209
Samama, Laurent, Gen. Mgr.--Nokia Telecommunications, Romainville, France; *Int'l*, pg. 953
Samaniego, Ventura, Exec. V.P.--Sealaska Timber Corporation, Ketchikan, AK; *U.S. Private*, pg. 978
Sambol, David, Pres. & Chief Exec. Officer--Countrywide Servicing Exchange, Pasadena, CA; *U.S. Public*, pg. 453
Sambol, David, Pres. & Chief Exec. Officer--Countrywide Capital Markets, Inc., Pasadena, CA; *U.S. Public*, pg. 453
Sambonet, Sergio, Mng. Dir.--3i Italy, Milan, Italy; *Int'l*, pg. 1386
Sambrook, Gordon, Chm. Bd.--British Steel General Steels Division, London, United Kingdom; *Int'l*, pg. 220
Sambrowsky, Joe, Pres.--Seltec Selective Technology Inc., Dallas, TX; *Int'l*, pg. 1528
Sambur, Marvin R., Pres. & Gen. Mgr.--ITT Aerospace/Communications Div., Fort Wayne, IN; *U.S. Public*, pg. 859
Samburg, Mike, Warden--Elizabeth Detention Center, Elizabeth, NJ; *U.S. Public*, pg. 450
Samela, Leonard V., Pres.--Greenwald Industries, Inc., Brooklyn, NY; *U.S. Public*, pg. 1341
Samford, John S.P., Pres.--Liberty National Auto Club, Inc., Birmingham, AL; *U.S. Public*, pg. 1623
Samide, Michael R., Pres.--Titan Wheel Corporation, Walcott, IA; *U.S. Public*, pg. 1618
Samide, Mike, Pres.--Hi Tech Division, Peterborough, NH; *Int'l*, pg. 868
Samilian, Mike, Div. Mgr.--Speedling Incorporated Sun City Nursery Division, Sun City, FL; *U.S. Private*, pg. 1024
Samilian, Mike, Div. Mgr.--Speedling Incorporated Bushnell Division, Bushnell, FL; *U.S. Private*, pg. 1024
Samji, Z.H.H., Pres.--Confederation Trust Company, Toronto, Canada; *Int'l*, pg. 326
Samlowski, Martin, Chief Oper. Officer--Henkel Australia Pty. Ltd., Kilsyth, Australia; *Int'l*, pg. 611
Sammet, W., Mng. Dir.--B.F. Goodrich Chemical Deutschland GmbH, Neuss, Germany; *U.S. Public*, pg. 752
Sammons, Bill, V.P.--Aaron Rents Convention Furnishings, Atlanta, GA; *U.S. Public*, pg. 12
Sammons, Bob, Pres.--Piper Impact, Inc., New Albany, MS; *U.S. Public*, pg. 1349
Sammons, Sammy, Gen. Mgr.--Nearby Eggs, Inc., Jarratt, VA; *U.S. Public*, pg. 1529
Sampedro, A., Mng. Dir.--GKN Indugasa SA, Vigo, Spain; *Int'l*, pg. 536
Sampei, Takehisa, Gen. Mgr.--Chiba Bank, Ltd.-London Branch, London, United Kingdom; *Int'l*, pg. 283
Samper, J. Phillip, Pres.--Sun Microsystems Computer Corporation, Mountain View, CA; *U.S. Public*, pg. 1531
Samphantarak, Dr. Krisda, Gen. Mgr.--Pioneer Hi-Bred (Thailand) Co. Ltd., Bangkok, Thailand; *U.S. Public*, pg. 1299
Sample, Bill, Grp. V.P.-Case Goods--The HON Co., Williamsport Plant, Williamsport, PA; *U.S. Public*, pg. 772
Samplik, Jaroslav, Mng. Dir.--Cokoladovny, Prague, Czech Republic; *Int'l*, pg. 381
Sampson, C.J., Mng. Dir.--Lloyds Bank Insurance Services Ltd., Haywards Heath, United Kingdom; *Int'l*, pg. 813
Sampson, Curtis A., Chm., Pres. & Chief Exec. Officer--Suttle Caribe, Inc., Humacao, PR; *U.S. Public*, pg. 415
Sampson, Curtis A., Pres.--Suttle Costa Rica S.A., Alajuela, Costa Rica; *U.S. Public*, pg. 416
Sampson, Scott B., Pres.--Coast Business Credit, Los Angeles, CA; *U.S. Public*, pg. 872
Samren, Ivar, Pres.--SAS Service Partner A/S, Copenhagen, Denmark; *Int'l*, pg. 1202
Sams, Larry, Gen. Mgr.--Mobile-Tech Corp., Hutchinson, KS; *U.S. Public*, pg. 400
Sams, Rusty, Pres.--Transdyne General Corporation, Spartanburg, SC; *U.S. Private*, pg. 298
Samsonas, Lui, Pres. & Mgr.--First American Title Co. of Hawaii, Inc., Honolulu, HI; *U.S. Public*, pg. 625
Samstad, Odd, Mng. Dir.--AGA Progas A/S, Oslo, Norway; *Int'l*, pg. 13
Samuel-Lajeunesse, Denis, Pres.--Lyonnaise de Banque, Lyon, France; *Int'l*, pg. 565
Samuel, Andre, Pres.--Total Italiana Srl., Milan, Italy; *Int'l*, pg. 1409
Samuel, Derrick, Gen. Mgr.--Colgate-Palmolive Ltd., Petone, New Zealand; *U.S. Public*, pg. 398
Samuel, Kitty, Chief Oper. Officer--Lynden Financial Services, Inc., Seattle, WA; *U.S. Private*, pg. 684
Samuel, Steven M., Mgr.--RCI Riley Construction, Inc., Worcester, MA; *Int'l*, pg. 401
Samuel, Theodore J., Chm. Bd. & Chief Exec. Officer--Niagara Portfolio Management Corporation, Dallas, TX; *U.S. Public*, pg. 955
Samuel, Werner E., Mgr.--Commerzbank AG-Canada Representative Office, Toronto, Canada; *Int'l*, pg. 311
Samuels, Bill, Jr., Pres.--Maker's Mark Distillery, Inc., Louisville, KY; *Int'l*, pg. 63
Samuels, Leslie E., Gen. Mgr.--WQIK-AM, Jacksonville, FL; *U.S. Public*, pg. 923
Samuels, Leslie E., V.P. & Gen. Mgr.--WQIK-FM, Jacksonville, FL; *U.S. Public*, pg. 923
Samuels, Mitchell, Pres.--Electri-Cord Manufacturing Co., Westfield, PA; *U.S. Public*, pg. 990
Samuelson, Larry, V.P.--Mountain Div., Denver, CO; *U.S. Public*, pg. 732
Samuelsson, Bengt, Chief Oper. Officer--Fokab AB, Stockholm, Sweden; *Int'l*, pg. 708
Samuelsson, Bertil, Pres.--Besam AB, Landskrona, Sweden; *Int'l*, pg. 678
Samuelsson, Gustav, Chief Oper. Officer--Excorim AB, Lund, Sweden; *Int'l*, pg. 667
Samuelsson, Tore, Mng. Dir.--S-E-Banken Luxembourg S.A., Luxembourg, Luxembourg; *Int'l*, pg. 1259
San Antonio, Randall, V.P.--Warrantech Direct, Inc., Euless, TX; *U.S. Public*, pg. 1740
San Jose, Emilio, Dir. Gen.--Eurovida S.A. (Allianz-RAS/Banco Popular), Madrid, Spain; *Int'l*, pg. 60
San Juan, T., Gen. Mgr.--BSN Vidrio Espana, Madrid, Spain; *Int'l*, pg. 381
San Martin, Pia, Res. Dir.--Leo Burnett Chile, Santiago, Chile; *U.S. Private*, pg. 185
San, Lim Kim, Chm. Bd.--Singapore Press Holdings Ltd., Singapore, Singapore; *Int'l*, pg. 1253
Sananvatananont, Preecha, Pres.--Reed Exhibition Companies-Thailand, Nonthaburi, Thailand; *Int'l*, pg. 1097
Sanborn, Robert B., Pres.--Security Insurance Co. (U.K.) Ltd., Farmington, CT; *U.S. Public*, pg. 1231
Sancerres, Guy, Mng. Dir.--BNP Bank N.V., Amsterdam, Netherlands; *Int'l*, pg. 163
Sanchez Lugo, Manuel, Pres.--Avantel, S.A., Mexico, Mexico; *Int'l*, pg. 574
Sanchez-Incera, Bernardo, Mng. Dir.--Banca Jover, Barcelona, Spain; *Int'l*, pg. 344
Sanchez-Llaca, Juan, Pres.--The Vagabond Inns, San Diego, CA; *U.S. Private*, pg. 558

Sanchez, Carlos, Gen. Mgr.--Kodak Dominicana, Santo Domingo, Dominican Republic; *U.S. Public*, pg. 553
Sanchez, Ernesto, Exec. V.P.--Hylsa S.A.-North Plant, Apodaca, Mexico; *Int'l*, pg. 56
Sanchez, Evagio, Chief Oper. Officer--Sol Melia America, Miami, FL; *Int'l*, pg. 1277
Sanchez, Frank, Pres.--Sanchez Computer Associates, Malvern, PA; *U.S. Public*, pg. 1425
Sanchez, Gregorio Gonzalez-Irun, Pres.--CARBOEX - Sociedad Espanola de Carbon Exterior, S.A., Madrid, Spain; *Int'l*, pg. 1224
Sanchez, Jorge, Gen. Mgr.--Banco Santander, Caracas, Venezuela; *Int'l*, pg. 144
Sanchez, Jorge Herrera, Gen. Mgr.--Rivas & Herrera C./ Young & Rubicam, Quito, Ecuador; *U.S. Private*, pg. 1200
Sanchez, Jose, Country Mgr.--Escuelas de Idiomas Berlitz de Espana, S.A., Madrid, Spain; *U.S. Public*, pg. 222
Sanchez, Michael, Chief Oper. Officer--Allright Parking Virginia, Inc., Richmond, VA; *U.S. Private*, pg. 43
Sanchez, Michael A., Chm. Bd.--Sanchez Computer Associates, Malvern, PA; *U.S. Public*, pg. 1425
Sanchez, Rene, Mng. Dir.--COBE Renal Care, Inc., Tijuana, Mexico; *Int'l*, pg. 667
Sanchez, Salvador, Chm. & Pres.--Refineria Panama S.A., Panama, Panama; *U.S. Public*, pg. 1584
Sand, Mel, V.P. & Gen. Mgr.--Dayton Rogers of New York, Rochester, NY; *U.S. Private*, pg. 318
Sand, Robert, Gen. Mgr.--Auburn Div., Auburn, AL; *U.S. Public*, pg. 575
Sandahl, B.W., Plant Mgr.--Rantoul Products Textron Inc., Rantoul, IL; *U.S. Public*, pg. 1589
Sandahl, Christer, Pres.--Scandinavian Leisure Group A.B., Stockholm, Sweden; *Int'l*, pg. 39
Sandahl, Ingemar, Mgr.--Network Systems AB, Partille, Sweden; *U.S. Public*, pg. 1522
Sandberg, Bob, Pres.-Automotive/Industrial--Sackner Products, Grand Rapids, MI; *U.S. Public*, pg. 924
Sandberg, Glenn, Pres.--Formax, Inc., Mokena, IL; *Int'l*, pg. 1378
Sandberg, Jhr. J.A.G., Gen. Mgr.--Algemene Bank Nederland (Suisse), S.A., Zurich, Switzerland; *Int'l*, pg. 12
Sandberg, Ray, Pres.--LaFarge Concrete Products, Toronto, Canada; *Int'l*, pg. 789
Sandberg, Roger, Pres.--Trencor, Inc., Grand Prairie, TX; *U.S. Public*, pg. 141
Sandelin, Martin, V.P.-Investor Rels.--NE-Products Oy, Oulu, Finland; *Int'l*, pg. 952
Sandelin, Tor-Erik, Chief Oper. Officer--KONE Elevators Finland, Helsinki, Finland; *Int'l*, pg. 746
Sandell, Richard D., Mgr.-Terminal--GATX Terminals Corp.-San Pedro, San Pedro, CA; *U.S. Public*, pg. 692
Sandeoni, Raffaele, Mgr.-Sls. & Mktg.--Vickers Systems, Milan, Italy; *U.S. Public*, pg. 25
Sander, Gert, Chief Oper. Officer--KONE Sander Aufzug GmbH, Berlin, Germany; *Int'l*, pg. 748
Sanderford, Robin E., Pres.--Gayfers, Montgomery, AL; *U.S. Public*, pg. 1090
Sanderlin, Gerald, V.P. & Gen. Mgr.--Cook Manley, Houston, TX; *U.S. Public*, pg. 521
Sanders, Charles, Gen. Mgr.--Georgia Dealers Auto Auction, Atlanta, GA; *U.S. Private*, pg. 282
Sanders, Charles J., III, Chief Oper. Officer & V.P.--Ingram Materials Co., Nashville, TN; *U.S. Private*, pg. 563
Sanders, Charles N., Gen. Mgr.--Bishop Brothers Auto Auction, Atlanta, GA; *U.S. Private*, pg. 282
Sanders, David B., Sr. Sls. Representative--Steel Products Div., Anniston, AL; *U.S. Private*, pg. 213
Sanders, Dean L., Pres. & Chief Exec. Officer--Sam's Clubs Div., Bentonville, AR; *U.S. Public*, pg. 1733
Sanders, Derek, Branch Dir.--N.G. Bailey & Co. Ltd.-Edinburgh Branch, Edinburgh, United Kingdom; *Int'l*, pg. 132
Sanders, Don, Principal--Credit & Risk Management Associates, Baltimore, MD; *U.S. Public*, pg. 610
Sanders, Gary, Pres.-Nuclear Opers.--Wackenhut Nuclear Services, Coral Gables, FL; *U.S. Public*, pg. 1731
Sanders, H.B., Plant Mgr.--Hydro Conduit Corp, Chattanooga, TN; *Int'l*, pg. 245
Sanders, J., Div. Mgr.--Campina Melkunie International Division, Veghel, Netherlands; *Int'l*, pg. 254
Sanders, K. J., Mng. Dir.--Texas Instruments Limited, Bedford, United Kingdom; *U.S. Public*, pg. 1586
Sanders, Katharine W., M.D., Medical Dir.--Conyers, Conyers, GA; *U.S. Public*, pg. 1715
Sanders, Ken, V.P. & Gen. Mgr.--National Mine Service Company, Distribution Div., Carnegie, PA; *Int'l*, pg. 281
Sanders, Max, Pres.--Pico-Matic Inc., Evanston, IL; *U.S. Private*, pg. 813
Sanders, Max, Chm. Bd.--Memcor Truohm, Huntington, IN; *U.S. Private*, pg. 813
Sanders, R.G., Pres. & Gen. Mgr.--Black Warrior Transmission Corp., Brookwood, AL; *U.S. Public*, pg. 1485
Sanders, R.G., Pres. & Gen. Mgr.--Black Warrior Methane Corp., Brookwood, AL; *U.S. Public*, pg. 1737
Sanders, R.G., Pres. & Gen. Mgr.--Black Warrior Transmission Corp., Brookwood, AL; *U.S. Public*, pg. 1737
Sanders, Robert, Gen. Mgr.--ITW Ramset/Red Head, Wood Dale, IL; *U.S. Public*, pg. 867
Sanders, Tracy, Office Mgr.--Fleishman-Hillard, Inc., Dallas, TX; *U.S. Private*, pg. 411
Sanders, Travis, Gen. Mgr.-Aviation Mktg.--PS Trading, Inc., Dallas, TX; *U.S. Public*, pg. 1245
Sanders, V. William, Pres.--Sirach Capital Management, Inc., Seattle, WA; *U.S. Public*, pg. 1674
Sanders, Walther, Gen. Mgr.--Letraset AG, Glattbrugg, Switzerland; *Int'l*, pg. 461
Sanderson, Allen, Pres.--Texas Bank N.A., Mc Kinney, TX; *U.S. Public*, pg. 626
Sanderson, Bryan, Chief Exec. Officer--BP Chemicals Ltd., London, United Kingdom; *Int'l*, pg. 220
Sanderson, Eric G., Gen. Mgr.--Rogers CFTR-AM, Toronto, Canada; *Int'l*, pg. 1123
Sanderson, Jr., Robert C., Pres. & Chief Exec. Officer--Citizens Bank Of Connecticut, New London, CT; *Int'l*, pg. 1132
Sanderson, L. Donald, Pres.--Falconbridge International Ltd., Christchurch, Barbados; *Int'l*, pg. 434
Sanderson, Len, Pres.-Eisner/Sanderson Public Affairs--Eisner & Associates, Inc., Baltimore, MD; *U.S. Private*, pg. 366
Sanderson, Michael, Pres. & Chief Exec. Officer--Instinet Corporation, New York, NY; *Int'l*, pg. 1106
Sanderson, Sandra, Pres.--Sani-Med, Columbus, MS; *U.S. Private*, pg. 964
Sanderson, Sandra, Pres.--Manufactured Home, Columbus, MS; *U.S. Private*, pg. 964
Sanderson, Sandra B., Chief Exec. Officer--Beneke, Columbus, MS; *U.S. Private*, pg. 964
Sandford, John, Gen. Mgr.--Dutch Mill Baking Company, Wyckoff, NJ; *U.S. Public*, pg. 1561
Sandfort, Maurice R., Pres.--NationsBank of West Plains, West Plains, MO; *U.S. Public*, pg. 1165
Sandherr, James, Rep.-Sls.--Mock Seed Company, Pittsburgh, PA; *U.S. Private*, pg. 981
Sandhu, Narindar, Dir.--Shandwick Sdn. Bhd., Kuala Lumpur, Malaysia; *Int'l*, pg. 1228
Sandilands, Peter, Reg. Mgr.--Check Point Software Technologies (Australia) Ltd., Baulkham Hills, Australia; *U.S. Public*, pg. 342
Sandkuyl, A., Chief Exec. Officer--Zurich Levensverzekering-Maatschappij, Hague, Netherlands; *Int'l*, pg. 1529
Sandkuyl, A., Chief Exec. Officer--Zurich Verzekeringen, Leidschendam, Netherlands; *Int'l*, pg. 1531
Sandkuyl, A., Chief Exec. Officer--Zurich International (Nederland) N.V., Leidschendam, Netherlands; *Int'l*, pg. 1532
Sandlin, David, Pres.--Flight International Aviation, Inc., Newport News, VA; *U.S. Public*, pg. 654
Sandlin, David E., Pres.--Flight International, Inc., Newport News, VA; *U.S. Public*, pg. 654
Sandman, Edward L., Pres.--Northwest Alloys, Inc., Addy, WA; *U.S. Public*, pg. 61
Sandmark, Stig, Mng. Dir.--Constel S.A., Burgos, Spain; *Int'l*, pg. 1365
Sandmark, Stig, Mng. Dir.--Telefonaktiebolaget LM Ericsson Libya Branch, Tripoli, Libya; *Int'l*, pg. 1370
Sandors, Charles, Pres.--Volunteer Leather Co., Nashville, TN; *U.S. Public*, pg. 728
Sandoz, David, Mng. Dir.--Newport Instruments Canada Corp., Mississauga, Canada; *U.S. Public*, pg. 1179
Sandquist, Hans, Mng. Dir.--Roxon AB, Orebro, Sweden; *Int'l*, pg. 1353
Sandrias, Agnes, Sr. Mng. Consultant--DRI Europe (U.K.) Ltd., London, United Kingdom; *U.S. Public*, pg. 1072
Sandridge, Michael, Plant Mgr.--Idaho Potato Opers., Shelley, ID; *Int'l*, pg. 411
Sands, Dick, Mng. Dir.--CMC (UK) Limited, Egham, United Kingdom; *U.S. Public*, pg. 414
Sands, Graeme, Mng. Dir.--Barrie Knitwear, Hawick, United Kingdom; *Int'l*, pg. 385
Sands, Jay, Mgr.-Eastern Div.--Columbia Pictures Eastern Division, New York, NY; *Int'l*, pg. 1281
Sands, Richard, Pres.--Manaschewitz Wine Company, Canandaigua, NY; *U.S. Public*, pg. 300
Sandsten, Ragnar, Mng. Dir.--RM Industrial Group A/S, Ballerup, Denmark; *Int'l*, pg. 476
Sandstrom, Anders, Mng. Dir.--Kalmar LMV East Asia Pte. Ltd., Singapore, Singapore; *Int'l*, pg. 1421
Sandstrom, Anton, Pres.--AB Svensk Leca, Linkoping, Sweden; *Int'l*, pg. 1200
Sandstrom, Anton, Pres.--Fibo ExClay Eesti AS, Parnu, Estonia; *Int'l*, pg. 1200
Sandusky, Donald L., V.P. & Gen. Mgr.--Jervis B. Webb Worldwide Co., Farmington Hills, MI; *U.S. Private*, pg. 1156
Sandvik, Terrence P., Pres.--FBS Information Services Corporation, Saint Paul, MN; *U.S. Public*, pg. 1681
SanFilippo, Michael, Pres.--Ragazzis, Inc., Raleigh, NC; *U.S. Private*, pg. 575
Sanford-Amandes, Janet C., Publr.--Visalia Times-Delta, Visalia, CA; *U.S. Public*, pg. 702
Sanford, J., Pres. & Chief Oper. Officer--Rolls-Royce Inc., Reston, VA; *Int'l*, pg. 1127
Sanford, John, Chm. Bd.--Structural Steel Products Division, Houston, TX; *U.S. Public*, pg. 1639
Sanford, Joseph P., Pres.--Mellon First Business Bank, Los Angeles, CA; *U.S. Public*, pg. 1085
Sanford, Mark, Gen. Mgr.--Cook/Sarasota Moving Systems Inc., Bradenton, FL; *U.S. Private*, pg. 273
Sanford, Robert A., Mng. Dir.--Brown Brothers Harriman Trust Co. (Cayman) Ltd., Georgetown, Cayman Islands,; *U.S. Private*, pg. 173
Sang, Li Ha, Oper. Mgr.--QST Far East Limited, Teun Mun, Hong Kong; *U.S. Private*, pg. 897
Sangalli, Steve, Gen. Mgr.--Peterson Spring-CIMA Plant, Three Rivers, MI; *U.S. Private*, pg. 857
Sangsten, H.L., Chief Exec. Officer-Europe--Tioxide Group Limited, London, United Kingdom; *Int'l*, pg. 663
Sangster, Brian, Pres. & Chief Oper. Officer--Lakehead Pipe Line Co., Inc., Superior, WI; *Int'l*, pg. 652
Sangster, George, V.P.-Sales & Mktg.--Varco (U.K.) Ltd. Drilling Systems, Montrose, United Kingdom; *U.S. Public*, pg. 1709
Sangster, Peter, Chief Oper. Officer--SCA Packaging Ltd., Packet Boat House, Uxbridge, United Kingdom; *Int'l*, pg. 1326
Sanjuan, Ricardo Medem, Pres. & Mng. Dir.--John Deere Iberica S.A., Madrid, Spain; *U.S. Public*, pg. 493
Sankarakrishnan, A., Chief Oper. Officer--KONE Elevator India Ltd., Madras, India; *Int'l*, pg. 748
Sann, Ted, Co-Chief Oper. Officer-New York & Dir.--BBDO Worldwide Inc., New York, NY; *U.S. Public*, pg. 1223
Sanna, Gavino, Pres.--Gavino Sanna Associati, Milan, Italy; *U.S. Private*, pg. 304
Sannders, V., Mng. Dir.--Oki Systems (Ireland) Ltd., Dublin, Ireland; *Int'l*, pg. 1000
Sannholm, Krister, Chief Oper. Officer--Ahlstrom Machinery Recovery Boilers & Heat Engineering, Helsinki, Finland; *Int'l*, pg. 33
Sannholm, Krister, Chief Oper. Officer--Ahlstrom Machinery Recovery Boilers & Heat Engineering, Varkaus, Finland; *Int'l*, pg. 33
Sano, H., Chief Oper. Officer--Soundesign Corporation Japan Ltd., Tokyo, Japan; *U.S. Private*, pg. 956
Sano, Hiroshi, Pres.--Toshiba Electromex, S.A. de C.V., Zaragoza, Mexico; *Int'l*, pg. 1406
Sano, Shoji, Pres.--GSI (Beijing) Hosiery Co., Ltd., Beijing, China; *Int'l*, pg. 579
Sansome, Frank, Mng. Dir.--Barringer Instruments-U.K., Ltd., Crawley, United Kingdom; *U.S. Public*, pg. 192
Sansone, Luigi, Branch Mgr.--Banco di Napoli-London, London, United Kingdom; *Int'l*, pg. 140
Sansone, Victor J., Pres. & Gen. Mgr.-KSCS-FM--WBAP-KSCS Radio, Inc., Arlington, TX; *U.S. Public*, pg. 512
Sansores, Oscar, Gen. Mgr.--Cia. Minera Constelacion S.A. de C.V., Guadalajara, Mexico; *Int'l*, pg. 308
Sansousi, Ray, Pres.--Schneider Automation, Inc., North Andover, MA; *Int'l*, pg. 1208
Sant, Stephen R., Pres. & Chief Exec. Officer--First Western Bank, National Association, New Castle, PA; *U.S. Public*, pg. 642
Santacrose, Mark F., Pres.--Bagcraft Corporation of America, Chicago, IL; *U.S. Public*, pg. 136
Santamarina, Agustin V., Pres.--John Deere S.A. de C.V., Monterrey, Mexico; *U.S. Public*, pg. 493
Santamarina, R., Chief Exec. Officer--Zurich Compania de Seguros, Buenos Aires, Argentina; *Int'l*, pg. 1531
Santamarina, R., Chief Exec. Officer--Iguazu Compania de Seguros, Buenos Aires, Argentina; *Int'l*, pg. 1531
Santamarina, R., Chief Oper. Officer--Zurich Iguazu Compania de Seguros de Retiro S.A., Buenos Aires, Argentina; *Int'l*, pg. 1532
Santambrogio, Lino, Mng. Dir.--S.p.A. Italiana Laboratori Bouty (Italy), Milan, Italy; *U.S. Public*, pg. 310
Santana, F., Mgr.--Kodak S.A., Las Palmas, Spain; *U.S. Public*, pg. 554
Santella, Jim, Dir.-Pharmacy Services--Direct Script, Edison, NJ; *U.S. Public*, pg. 1239
Santelle, Jeannie, Branch Mgr.--Downey Savings & Loan Association, F.A., Rolling Hills Estates, CA; *U.S. Public*, pg. 527
Santhanam, T. S., Chm.--Brakes India Ltd., Padi, India; *Int'l*, *pg. 820*
Santhidej, S., Chief Exec. Officer--OCE (Thailand) Ltd., Bangkok, Thailand; *Int'l*, pg. 995
Santi, G., Chief Fin. Officer--Olivetti A/B, Upplands Vasby, Sweden; *Int'l*, pg. 1003
Santiago, Carlos Castillo, Pres.--Dixon Ticonderoga Company de Mexico, S.A. de C.V., Tlalnepantla, Mexico; *U.S. Public*, pg. 515
Santiago, Francis, Pres.--Carter-Wallace, S.A., Mexico, Mexico; *U.S. Public*, pg. 310
Santiago, Jimmy F., Joint Chief Exec. Officer--SPA/FCB, Manila, Philippines; *U.S. Private*, pg. 389
Santiago, Manuel, Plant Mgr.--Medtronic Puerto Rico, Inc., Villalba, PR; *U.S. Public*, pg. 1083
Santilli, H., Gen. Mgr.--Kolynos SAIC, Buenos Aires, Argentina; *U.S. Public*, pg. 81
Santilli, Horacio, Gen. Mgr.--Whitehall Laboratorios S.A., Buenos Aires, Argentina; *U.S. Public*, pg. 82
Santin, Vitalino, Gen. Mgr.--Banco do Brasil S.A.-Uruguay, Montevideo, Uruguay; *Int'l*, pg. 141
Santis, Joyce, Dir.--Magellan Health Services, Inc., Macon, GA; *U.S. Public*, pg. 1036
Santogatta, Mike, Gen. Mgr.--Highland Manufacturing, Waterbury, CT; *U.S. Public*, pg. 866
Santonocito, Joseph A., Admin.--Andrew House Healthcare, New Britain, CT; *U.S. Public*, pg. 1711
Santorelli, Thomas, Pres.--Hertz Claim Management, Park Ridge, NJ; *U.S. Public*, pg. 664
Santorelli, Vincent, Pres.--Victor O. Schinnerer & Co., Ltd., Chevy Chase, MD; *U.S. Public*, pg. 1049
Santori, Jim, Publisher--La Crosse Tribune, La Crosse, WI; *U.S. Public*, pg. 983
Santoriello, Peter A., Pres.--Dreyfus Brokerage Services, Inc., New York, NY; *U.S. Public*, pg. 1085
Santos Filho, Celio V., Mng. Dir.--Papel de Imprensa, S.A., Sao Paulo, Brazil; *Int'l*, pg. 495
Santos, Antonio, Gen. Mgr.--Circle Freight International (Portugal) Ltda., Lisbon, Portugal; *U.S. Public*, pg. 373
Santos, Arturo, Pres. & Dir.--Companhia Adriatica de Seguros Gerais, Sao Paulo, Brazil; *Int'l*, pg. 61
Santos, David, Mng. Dir.--UPM-Kymmene Papel Lda., Lisbon, Portugal; *Int'l*, pg. 1430
Santos, Enrique, Chief Rep.--Grupo Santander, Johannesburg, South Africa; *Int'l*, pg. 144
Santos, Everaldo N., Pres. & Chief Exec. Officer--Alcan Empreendimentos Ltda., Sao Paulo, Brazil; *Int'l*, pg. 50
Santos, Henrique M., Jr., Gen. Mgr.--Forbo Pergol Revestimentos SA, Porto, Portugal; *Int'l*, pg. 498
Santos, Joseph M., Pres.--MBC Leasing, Baltimore, MD; *U.S. Public*, pg. 1089
Santos, Norton Seng Antunes, Mgr.--Banco do Brasil S.A.-Beijing Representative Office, Beijing, China; *Int'l*, pg. 142
Santos, Rafael, Gen. Mgr.--Colgate-Palmolive (Hong Kong) Ltd., Causeway Bay, Hong Kong; *U.S. Public*, pg. 398
Santos, Tom, Plant Mgr.--Anchor Fasteners, Cleveland, OH; *U.S. Public*, pg. 865
Santowski, Jerome G., Pres.--Broan Mfg. Co., Inc., Hartford, WI; *U.S. Public*, pg. 1193
Santoyo, Juancois, Chief Exec. Officer-Spain--Centros Commerciales Pryca, Madrid, Spain; *Int'l*, pg. 273
Sanz, Albino, Mgr.--Medelec Espana S.A., Madrid, Spain; *Int'l*, pg. 1467

Sanz, Juan, Pres.--Opel Espana, Zaragoza, Spain; *U.S. Public*, pg. 724
Sanz, Liberto, Mng. Dir.--SKF do Brasil Ltda., Guarulhos, Brazil; *Int'l*, pg. 1158
Sanzone, Vincent P., Pres.--Tecot Electric Supply Company, New Castle, DE; *U.S. Private*, pg. 951
Sapan, Joshua, Pres. & Chief Oper. Officer--Rainbow Programming Holdings, Inc., Woodbury, NY; *U.S. Public*, pg. 288
Saperstein, Jan, Gen. Mgr.--Savin Credit Corporation, Stamford, CT; *Int'l*, pg. 1114
Saponja, Walter, Pres. & Chief Oper. Officer--TransAlta Utilities, Calgary, Canada; *Int'l*, pg. 1416
Sapos, Mary Ann, Pres. & Chief Exec. Officer--Hutchins/Young & Rubicam, Rochester, NY; *U.S. Private*, pg. 1197
Sapp, Walter W., Pres.--Tenneco Phosphate, Inc., Houston, TX; *U.S. Public*, pg. 1578
Sappenfield, Buck, Pres.--Limited Real Estate, Columbus, OH; *U.S. Public*, pg. 995
Sappenfield, Richard W., Pres.--DeVlieg-Bullard Services Group, Rockford, IL; *U.S. Public*, pg. 502
Saquier, Julio, Dr., Pres.--La Nacion S.A., Buenos Aires, Argentina; *Int'l*, pg. 785
Sar, G.K., Gen. Mgr.--India Photographic Company Limited, Mumbai, India; *U.S. Public*, pg. 552
Sara-aho, Sirpa, Mng. Dir.--Merita Bank Ltd. - Moscow Representative Office, Moscow, Russia; *Int'l*, pg. 859
Saracini, Dr. Giuseppe, Dir.--Fiat Auto S.p.A., Milan, Italy; *Int'l*, pg. 481
Sarakitprija, Wirapich, Mgr.-Thailand--Raychem Thai Limited, Bangkok, Thailand; *U.S. Public*, pg. 1363
Saralegui, Xavier, Pres.--Galavision, New York, NY; *U.S. Private*, pg. 230
Sarancha, Rick, Facility Mgr.--Pro Shop (Los Angeles, CA), City of Industry, CA; *U.S. Public*, pg. 861
Saras, Ted, Gen. Mgr.--Sterling Electronics, Schaumburg, IL; *U.S. Public*, pg. 1051
Sarasin, K., Chm. Bd. & Mng. Dir.--Jardine Matheson (Thailand) Ltd., Bangkok, Thailand; *Int'l*, pg. 705
Saravia, Hector, Plant Superintendent--San Cristobal Mill & Plant, San Salvador, El Salvador; *U.S. Public*, pg. 410
Sarazin, Pierre, Gen. Mgr.--Pioneer France Mais S.A., Toulouse, France; *U.S. Public*, pg. 1299
Sarb, Jack, Div. Mgr.--Westborn Service Center, Inc., Dearborn, MI; *U.S. Public*, pg. 1505
Sarb, John, V.P. & Dir.-Logistics--Union Trucking Co., Dearborn, MI; *U.S. Public*, pg. 1505
Sardi, Gino, Mng. Dir.--Bundy Mexico SA, Tultitlan, Mexico; *Int'l*, pg. 1342
Sardina, Eduardo M., Pres.--Bacardi Service Corp., (North America), Coral Gables, FL; *Int'l*, pg. 131
Sareeduddin, Mohommad, Mgr.-Mfg.--NOVO Products, Ocala, FL; *U.S. Public*, pg. 1055
Saren, Jane, Mng. Dir.--GPC Market Access Scotland, Edinburgh, United Kingdom; *U.S. Public*, pg. 1225
Sares, Pekks, Chief Oper. Officer--Ahlstrom Machinery (Asia-Pacific) Pte Ltd., Singapore, Singapore; *Int'l*, pg. 35
Saresky, Ed, Gen. Mgr.--Outdoor Systems, Inc.-New York, Rochester, NY; *U.S. Public*, pg. 1235
Sargent, David, Mng. Dir.--Access Equipment Ltd., Newport, United Kingdom; *U.S. Private*, pg. 1128
Sargent, David K., Mng. Dir.--John Rusling Ltd., Newport, United Kingdom; *U.S. Private*, pg. 1128
Sargent, Henry B., Pres. & Chief Exec. Officer--El Dorado Investment Company, Phoenix, AZ; *U.S. Public*, pg. 1298
Sargent, John, Pres. & Chief Exec. Officer--DK Publishing, New York, NY; *Int'l*, pg. 417
Sargent, Joseph D., Pres.--The Guardian Insurance & Annuity Co. (GIAC), New York, NY; *U.S. Private*, pg. 486
Sargent, Leroy J., Gen. Mgr.--Gorman-Rupp Industries Div., Bellville, OH; *U.S. Public*, pg. 754
Sargent, Richard M., Jr., Dir.--The Chubb Institute, Parsippany, NJ; *U.S. Public*, pg. 355
Sargent, Steve, Mgr.--Genesys Combustion, Warwick, NY; *U.S. Private*, pg. 360
Sari, Mark, Gen. Mgr.--U.S. Broach & Machine Company, Sumter, SC; *U.S. Private*, pg. 102
Sarimento, Manuel E., V.P.-Trust--Trust Div., Hato Rey, PR; *U.S. Public*, pg. 176
Sarkes, H. Jay, Chm. Bd., Pres. & Chief Exec. Officer--Fleet Bank, N.A., Jersey City, NJ; *U.S. Public*, pg. 649
Sarkie, Robert M., Pres.--Entertainment Publications, Inc., Troy, MI; *U.S. Public*, pg. 320
Sarkiewicz-Hirszson, Olga, Chief Oper. Officer--Ferrosan International A/S, Warsaw, Poland; *Int'l*, pg. 989
Sarkisian, Norman, Pres.--Smyth Manufacturing Company, Bloomfield, CT; *U.S. Private*, pg. 126
Sarknas, F.J., Mgr.--Matthews Intl. Trading Corp., Pittsburgh, PA; *U.S. Public*, pg. 1060
Sarles, H. Jay, Chm. Bd.--Fleet Mortgage Group, Inc., Columbia, SC; *U.S. Public*, pg. 650
Sarmiento, H., Gen. Mgr.--AMP S.A. Argentina, Buenos Aires, Argentina; *U.S. Public*, pg. 9
Sarner, Gary, Pres.--TLC, Milwaukee, WI; *U.S. Public*, pg. 352
Sarney, George, Chief Oper. Officer--The Foxboro Company, Foxboro, MA; *Int'l*, pg. 1243
Sarnoff, William, Chm. Bd.--Time Warner Trade Publishing, New York, NY; *U.S. Public*, pg. 1614
Sarrat, Fernand B., Pres. & Chief Exec. Officer--Cylink Corp., Sunnyvale, CA; *U.S. Public*, pg. 1306
Sarrazin, Jochen, Pres.--Vorwerk USA Inc., Altamonte Springs, FL; *Int'l*, pg. 1481
Sarris, Lazaros, Reg. Mgr.--Det Norske Veritas, Manama, Bahrain; *Int'l*, pg. 398
Sarto, Gabriella, Gen. Mgr.-Opers.--Utell International-Italy, Milan, Italy; *Int'l*, pg. 1098
Sartore, Eugene, Gen. Mgr.--Alro Specialty Metals, Villa Park, Villa Park, IL; *U.S. Private*, pg. 46
Sartuche, Janis, Admin.--Occupational Health Associates-North, Fresno, CA; *U.S. Public*, pg. 1715
Sartuche, Janis, Admin.--Occupational Health Associates-South, Fresno, CA; *U.S. Public*, pg. 1715
Sarver, Roger, Pres.--Insurance Conformation Services, Cleveland, OH; *U.S. Public*, pg. 1334
Sarwanich-Charoen, Saeng, Gen. Mgr.--Kimberly-Clark Thailand Ltd., Bangkok, Thailand; *U.S. Public*, pg. 959
Sarwar Ali, S.M., Chm. Bd. & Mng. Dir.--Parke-Davis & Company, Limited, Karachi, Pakistan; *U.S. Public*, pg. 1739
Sarzotti, Giovanni, V.P.--Meteor Construzioni Aeronautiche ed Elettroniche S.p.A., Rome, Italy; *Int'l*, pg. 653
Sas, Chris, Dir.--HBM, Hollandsche Beton Maatschappij bv, Rijswijk, Netherlands; *Int'l*, pg. 630
Sas, John A., Chief Oper. Officer--Brian Controls Division, Sainte-Foy, Canada; *Int'l*, pg. 711
Sas, Wim, Gen. Mgr.--Sun Electric Belgium N.V., Deurne, Belgium; *U.S. Public*, pg. 1481
Sasaki, K., Mng. Dir.--Sharp-Roxy (Hong Kong) Ltd., Hong Kong, Hong Kong; *Int'l*, pg. 1230
Sasaki, Masaaki, Pres.--Kokusai Electric Co., Ltd. America, San Jose, CA; *Int'l*, pg. 743
Sasaki, Masanao, Mng. Dir.--NLI Insurance Services (Europe) Limited, London, United Kingdom; *Int'l*, pg. 936
Sasaki, Masato, Mgr.--Minebea Co., Ltd. - Shanghai Office, Shanghai, China; *Int'l*, pg. 869
Sasaki, Robert K., Chief Oper. Officer--A & B Development Co. (California), Honolulu, HI; *U.S. Public*, pg. 39
Sasaki, Shiro, Chief Rep.--Daiwa Bank-Madrid, Madrid, Spain; *Int'l*, pg. 373
Sasaki, T., Pres.--Ebara (Thailand) Limited, Bangkok, Thailand; *Int'l*, pg. 432
Sasaki, T., Pres.--Nissho Iwai Delica Corp., Kawasaki, Japan; *Int'l*, pg. 946
Sasaki, Takeshi, Pres.--NHK International Corp., Livonia, MI; *Int'l*, pg. 902
Sasaki, Yasuo, Pres.--Kobe International (S) Co., Pte. Ltd., Singapore, Singapore; *Int'l*, pg. 741
Sasamoto, Masaki, Chief Oper. Officer--The Wuphoon Insurance Company Limited, Singapore, Singapore; *Int'l*, pg. 1393
Sase, Yoichiro, Exec. V.P.--Dai-ichi Life Insurance Agency (U.S.A.), Inc.-Los Angeles, Los Angeles, CA; *Int'l*, pg. 362
Sashida, Seiichi, Pres.--Shaklee Japan K.K., Tokyo, Japan; *Int'l*, pg. 1518
Sass, John, Gen. Mgr.--Barton's of McGehee, McGehee, AR; *U.S. Private*, pg. 119
Sass, T.J., Plant Mgr.--Peterbilt Motors Co., Denton, TX; *U.S. Public*, pg. 1247
Sassano, Carl, Pres.--Polymer Technology Corporation, Wilmington, MA; *U.S. Public*, pg. 195
Sassen, J., Gen. Mgr.--Van Leeuwen Pipe and Tube (Thailand) Ltd., Sri Racha, Thailand; *Int'l*, pg. 1450
Sasser, Clyde M., Pres.--ConAgra Broiler Co., Omaha, NE; *U.S. Public*, pg. 427
Sasso, Christian, Mng. Dir.--Etablissement d'Istres, Istres, France; *Int'l*, pg. 383
Sasso, John, Pres. & Chief Exec. Officer--Fire Burglary Instruments, Inc., Syosset, NY; *U.S. Public*, pg. 1306
Sasso, Richard, Pres.--Celebrity Cruises, Inc., Miami, FL; *U.S. Public*, pg. 1410
Sassoon, David, Mgr.--NYLIFE Care, New York, NY; *U.S. Private*, pg. 795
Satake, Akio, Pres.--Nihon-Pall Ltd., Tokyo, Japan; *U.S. Public*, pg. 1254
Sathirangkul, Jarunee, Mng. Dir.--Korn/Ferry International, Bangkok, Thailand; *U.S. Private*, pg. 633
Sato, Akinari, Pres.--Amano Korea Corporation, Seoul, Korea; *Int'l*, pg. 71
Sato, H., Pres.--MacMillan Bloedel K. K., Tokyo, Japan; *Int'l*, pg. 829
Sato, Hideshi, Pres. Dir--P.T. Dai Nippon Printing Indonesia, Jakarta, Indonesia; *Int'l*, pg. 363
Sato, Isao, Chm. Bd.--Showa Products Co., Ltd., Osaka, Japan; *U.S. Public*, pg. 1487
Sato, Kazuhiro, Gen. Mgr.--Fuji Bank, Milan Branch, Milan, Italy; *Int'l*, pg. 520
Sato, Kozo, Pres.--Rohm Corporation, San Jose, CA; *Int'l*, pg. 1125
Sato, Kozo, Pres.--Rohm U.S.A., Inc., San Jose, CA; *Int'l*, pg. 1125
Sato, M., Pres.--Kobe Steel U.S.A. Inc. (New York), New York, NY; *Int'l*, pg. 740
Sato, M., Gen. Mgr.--ITW Devcon Japan, Osaka, Japan; *U.S. Public*, pg. 868
Sato, Masaaki, Chief Oper. Officer--NASAM International, Incorporated, South San Francisco, CA; *U.S. Public*, pg. 187
Sato, Mitsusuke, Chm. & Chief Exec. Officer--Tien Wah Press (Pte.) Ltd., Singapore, Singapore; *Int'l*, pg. 363
Sato, Norifumi, Chief Representative--Madrid Representative Office, Madrid, Spain; *Int'l*, pg. 1517
Sato, Norimasa, Mng. Dir.--Japan Cosmo Securities (Hong Kong) Limited, Hong Kong, Hong Kong; *Int'l*, pg. 335
Sato, Shigenori, Pres.--Nissho Iwai del Ecuador S.A., Quito, Ecuador; *Int'l*, pg. 948
Sato, Shuko, Pres.--Shimura Kako Company, Ltd., Tokyo, Japan; *Int'l*, pg. 673
Sato, Takahisa, Pres.--ORIX Taiwan Corporation, Taipei, Taiwan; *Int'l*, pg. 1010
Sato, Takayoshi, Pres.--San-J Intl. Inc., Richmond, VA; *Int'l*, pg. 1183
Sato, Tatsuo, Mng. Dir.--Toshiba Information Systems (U.K.) Ltd., Weybridge, United Kingdom; *Int'l*, pg. 1406
Sato, Tomoyasu, Chief Oper. Officer--Kyowa Hakko Kogyo Co., Ltd., Dusseldorf, Germany; *Int'l*, pg. 778
Sato, Toshihiko, Chief Rep. & Gen. Rep.-Malaysia--The Sakura Bank - Kuala Lumpur Representative Office, Kuala Lumpur, Malaysia; *Int'l*, pg. 1180
Sato, Tsuguo, Pres.--Tokyu Agency International/DMB&B Japan, Tokyo, Japan; *U.S. Private*, pg. 305
Sato, Yasuhiko, Pres.--Heraeus Shin-Etsu America Inc., Camas, WA; *Int'l*, pg. 616
Sato, Yukio, Pres.--Yamaichi Bank (Switzerland), Zurich, Switzerland; *Int'l*, pg. 1517
Satoh, Hiroshi, Pres.--Tri Petch Isuzu Sales Co., Ltd., Bangkok, Thailand; *Int'l*, pg. 693
Satoh, Yoichi, Chief Oper. Officer--Nissho Iwai (Nigeria) Ltd., Victoria Island, Nigeria; *Int'l*, pg. 948
Sattanathan, Siddhartha, Country Mgr.-India--Utell International-India, New Delhi, India; *Int'l*, pg. 1098
Satterfield, James, Pres.--United Capitol Insurance Company, Atlanta, GA; *U.S. Public*, pg. 685
Satterfield, Jay, Pres.--American Cablevision of Indianapolis, Inc., Indianapolis, IN; *U.S. Public*, pg. 1610
Satterfield, Jay, Pres.--Indiana Digital Access, Indianapolis, IN; *U.S. Public*, pg. 1610
Sauber, Peter, Gen. Mgr.--National Auto Dealers Exchange, Bordentown, NJ; *U.S. Private*, pg. 282
Saubert, Walter, Chm. Bd.--American Red Ball Transit Co. Inc., Indianapolis, IN; *U.S. Private*, pg. 97
Saucier, Steve, V.P.--Sealright Mfg. West, Inc., De Soto, KS; *U.S. Public*, pg. 1452
Sauebrey, Dennis, Gen. Mgr.--Engineered Systems Inc., Livonia, MI; *U.S. Private*, pg. 862
Sauer, Mark, Pres.--Pittsburgh Pirates, Pittsburgh, PA; *U.S. Private*, pg. 867
Sauer, Wulf, Chief Oper. Officer--Rhone-Poulenc Oy, Helsinki, Finland; *Int'l*, pg. 1113
Sauerbrey, Dennis, Gen. Mgr.--Mountain Optech Inc., Boulder, CO; *U.S. Private*, pg. 862
Sauerbrey, Dennis, Gen. Mgr.--Clyde Corporation, Livonia, MI; *U.S. Private*, pg. 862
Sauers, Laurence C., Pres. & Chief Exec. Officer--Meier Metal Service Centers, Inc., Hazel Park, MI; *U.S. Public*, pg. 1100
Sauey, Craig L., Pres. & Chief Exec. Officer--Flambeau Corporation, Baraboo, WI; *U.S. Private*, pg. 409
Sauey, Eric W., Pres. & Chief Oper. Officer--Seats Incorporated, Reedsburg, WI; *U.S. Private*, pg. 410
Sauey, Jason, Pres.--Duncan Toys Company, Middlefield, OH; *U.S. Private*, pg. 409
Sauey, Jason, Pres.--Flambeau Airmold Corporation, Roanoke Rapids, NC; *U.S. Private*, pg. 409
Sauey, Jason C., Pres. & Chief Oper. Officer--Flambeau Products Corp., Middlefield, OH; *U.S. Private*, pg. 409
Saugman, Peter, Pres.--Blackwell Scientific Publications, Inc., Cambridge, MA; *Int'l*, pg. 197
Saukko, Pirjo, Mng. Dir.--Oy Helsingen Huuttokauppakamari, Helsinki, Finland; *Int'l*, pg. 859
Saukko, Ronald E., V.P. & Gen. Mgr.--Centec Roll Corporation, Bethlehem, PA; *U.S. Private*, pg. 839
Saul, B. Francis, II, Chief Opr. Officer--B.F. Saul Advisory Co., Chevy Chase, MD; *U.S. Public*, pg. 1435
Saul, John, Pres.--Emcee Cellular, Inc., Wilmington, DE; *U.S. Public*, pg. 571
Saul, Neil, Pres.--Empire Industries, Inc., Tarboro, NC; *U.S. Public*, pg. 579
Saul, Robin, Publisher--Carroll County Times, Westminster, MD; *U.S. Private*, pg. 648
Sauline, Albert J., Gen. Mgr.--Struthers Division, Struthers, OH; *U.S. Public*, pg. 439
Saunders, A. M., Mng. Dir.--A.C. Nielsen of Ireland, Ltd., Dublin, Ireland; *U.S. Public*, pg. 1183
Saunders, Chip, Pres. & Dir.-Dell Computer K.K.--Dell Computer Japan, Kanagawa, Japan; *U.S. Public*, pg. 496
Saunders, David, Gen. Mgr.--Intro Marketing Limited, Doncaster, United Kingdom; *Int'l*, pg. 858
Saunders, Donald E., Pres.--DuBois Chemicals, Cincinnati, OH; *Int'l*, pg. 1437
Saunders, Herbert W., Pres.--American Appraisal Canada, Inc., Toronto, Canada; *U.S. Private*, pg. 50
Saunders, J.O., Chm. Bd.--Taywood Homes Ltd., Feltham, United Kingdom; *Int'l*, pg. 1359
Saunders, Joe, Pres. & Chief Exec. Officer--Household Bank, N.A., Salinas, CA; *U.S. Public*, pg. 842
Saunders, John, Deputy Mng. Dir.--Willis Corroon North Limited, Newcastle upon Tyne, United Kingdom; *Int'l*, pg. 1503
Saunders, John F., Mng. Dir.--Fleishman-Hillard Saunders Limited, Dublin, Ireland; *U.S. Private*, pg. 411
Saunders, Ray, Gen. Mgr.--Chief Industries Inc.- Fabrication Div., Grand Island, NE; *U.S. Private*, pg. 236
Saunders, Robert F., Pres.--Amleco Leasing Limited, Stellarton, Canada; *Int'l*, pg. 454
Saunders, Scott, N. American Sls. Mgr.--Edison Fuse Gear, Des Peres, MO; *U.S. Public*, pg. 443
Saunderson, Billy, Dir.--Bank of Ireland Credit Card Centre, Dublin, Ireland; *Int'l*, pg. 152
Saunderson, R. Ian, Dr., Laboratory Dir.--Springborn Testing & Research (UK) Ltd., Reading, United Kingdom; *U.S. Private*, pg. 1027
Saur, Klaus, Dr., Mng. Dir.--K.G. Saur, Munich, Germany; *Int'l*, pg. 1099
Saurel, Paul, Chief Exec.--Banco Santander (Suisse), S.A., Geneva, Switzerland; *Int'l*, pg. 144
Saurel, Paul L., Gen. Mgr.--Banco Santander-Suiza, Geneva, Switzerland; *Int'l*, pg. 143
Saurez, Louis, V.P.-Opers.--Kenyon Industries, Inc., Kenyon, RI; *U.S. Public*, pg. 778
Sautter, Remy, Pres. & Chief Exec. Officer--CLT-UFA, Luxembourg, Luxembourg; *Int'l*, pg. 561
Sautter, Remy, Chm.--CLT UK Radio, London, United Kingdom; *Int'l*, pg. 561
Sauvage, Alex, Mng. Dir.--Banque Bruxelles Lambert France Succursale de Lille, Lille, France; *Int'l*, pg. 148
Sauvanet, Guy, Chief Exec. Officer--Nigbel Merchant Bank (Nigeria) Ltd., Lagos, Nigeria; *Int'l*, pg. 548
Saux, Juan, Pres.--Park Advertising & Direct Marketing, Lima, Peru; *U.S. Private*, pg. 389
Savage, G.P., Chief Exec. Officer--Northern Bank Limited, Belfast, United Kingdom; *Int'l*, pg. 906
Savage, Jean, Plant Mgr.--Tube Fittings Div., Lewisburg, OH; *U.S. Public*, pg. 1261
Savage, Michael, Mgr.-Branch--Air Conditioning Co. Inc., Rancho Cordova, CA; *U.S. Private*, pg. 28
Savage, Ron, Gen. Mgr.--UNC Aerostructures-Washington, Everett, WA; *U.S. Public*, pg. 710

Savaglio, Ernesto, Mng. Dir.--Savaglio TBWA & Associados S.A., Buenos Aires, Argentina; *U.S. Private*, pg. 1063
Savard, Claude, V.P., Gen. Mgr.--Vachon Division, Montreal, Canada; *Int'l*, pg. 348
Savarese, Stephen, Reg. V.P.--Union-Transport Corporation-Boston, Revere, MA; *U.S. Private*, pg. 1119
Savas, Bulent, Gen. Mgr.--Beksa Celik Kord Sanayi ve Ticaret A.S., Istanbul, Turkey; *Int'l*, pg. 185
Saviano, James P., Pres.--CSC Consulting Group, Waltham, MA; *U.S. Public*, pg. 422
Saviano, James P., Acting Pres.--Consulting & Systems Integration, Waltham, MA; *U.S. Public*, pg. 422
Savich, J.R., Mgr.-Prod. Engrng.--Ericson Packard Electric Componentes S.A., Sao Jose dos Campos, Brazil; *U.S. Public*, pg. 724
Saville, Ian, Exec. V.P.--Cossette Communication-Marketing (Toronto) Inc., Toronto, Canada; *Int'l*, pg. 336
Saville, Ian, Exec. V.P.--Promotion Blitz Inc., Toronto, Canada; *Int'l*, pg. 336
Savitz, Maxine, Dir.--AlliedSignal Ceramic Components, Torrance, CA; *U.S. Public*, pg. 50
Savitz, S. Alan, M.D., Pres.--PacifiCare Behavioral Health, Laguna Hills, CA; *U.S. Public*, pg. 1251
Savonen, Lasse, Pres.--Suomen Astra Oy, Masaby, Finland; *Int'l*, pg. 94
Savonet, H., Chief Oper. Officer--Pum Inox, Charleroi, Belgium; *Int'l*, pg. 301
Savorgnan, Luciano, Mgr.--Nalcomex S.A. de C.V., Mexico, Mexico; *U.S. Public*, pg. 1151
Sawa, Yasuhiro, Pres.--Dentsu Hokkaido, Sapporo, Japan; *Int'l*, pg. 393
Sawachi, Terry, Pres. & Mng. Dir.--Kulicke & Soffa (Japan), Ltd., Tokyo, Japan; *U.S. Public*, pg. 969
Sawada, Etsusaburo, Gen. Mgr. & Personnel--Train Kogyo Co., Ltd., Tokyo, Japan; *Int'l*, pg. 759
Sawada, T., Pres.--K.K. Kodak Information Systems (KKKIS), Tokyo, Japan; *U.S. Public*, pg. 552
Sawada, T., Pres.--Kodak Imagica K.K. (KI), Tokyo, Japan; *U.S. Public*, pg. 555
Sawada, Yoshihiro, Gen. Mgr.--Fuji Bank, Paris Branch, Paris, France; *Int'l*, pg. 520
Sawamura, Haruo, Pres.--Mitsui Toatsu Chemicals, Inc., Tokyo, Japan; *Int'l*, pg. 877
Sawayama, Hiroshi, Mgr.--Central-European International Bank Ltd. (CIB), Budapest, Hungary; *Int'l*, pg. 181
Sawicki, Michael, Reg. Mgr.--Kredietbank Atlanta Branch, Atlanta, GA; *Int'l*, pg. 760
Sawran, William R., Pres.--Ashland Services Company, Lexington, KY; *U.S. Public*, pg. 139
Sawyer, Buz, Mng. Dir.--Wieden & Kennedy-Amsterdam, Amsterdam, Netherlands; *U.S. Private*, pg. 1175
Sawyer, Dan, Reg. V.P.--Subaru Western Region, Irvine, CA; *Int'l*, pg. 523
Sawyer, Gary, Plant Mgr.--Hydro Conduit Corp., Tampa, FL; *Int'l*, pg. 246
Sawyer, Hugh, Pres.--National Linen & Uniform Service, Atlanta, GA; *U.S. Public*, pg. 1160
Sawyer, J.E., Pres. & Acting Gen. Mgr.--Boeing Canada Technology Ltd., Winnipeg Division, Winnipeg, Canada; *U.S. Public*, pg. 242
Sawyer, James E., Pres.--Boeing Canada Technology Ltd., Arnprior Division, Arnprior, Canada; *U.S. Public*, pg. 242
Sawyer, John, Pres.--Penhall Co., Anaheim, CA; *U.S. Private*, pg. 849
Sawyer, Lamar, Mgr.-Sls.--PENCO-Texas, San Antonio, TX; *Int'l*, pg. 1508
Sawyer, Richard A., Pres.--Acadia Insurance Company, Westbrook, ME; *U.S. Public*, pg. 215
Sawyer, Ron, Publisher--The Tuscaloosa News, Tuscaloosa, AL; *U.S. Public*, pg. 1175
Sawyer, Sherri, Gen. Mgr.--WEGR, Memphis, TN; *U.S. Public*, pg. 384
Sawyer, Sherri, Gen. Mgr.--WREC, Memphis, TN; *U.S. Public*, pg. 385
Sawyer, Sherri, Gen. Mgr.--WRXQ, Memphis, TN; *U.S. Public*, pg. 385
Saxena, Ravindra, Representative--Butterworths India, New Delhi, India; *Int'l*, pg. 1095
Saxton, Robert L., Pres.--APT Coin Machines, Inc., Las Vegas, NV; *U.S. Public*, pg. 47
Saxton, Tom, Sr. V.P.--Hayes-Dana Service Parts Div., Beamsville, Canada; *U.S. Public*, pg. 480
Sayag, A., Mng. Dir.--Stirn Industries S.A., Joigny, France; *Int'l*, pg. 552
Sayag, Alain, Mng. Dir.--Lequeux S.A., Dourdan, France; *Int'l*, pg. 552
Sayah, Jon, Gen. Mgr.--Diamond Forecast, Elgin, IL; *U.S. Public*, pg. 730
Sayers, Neil, Gen. Mgr.--Marlette Homes, Inc., Lewistown, PA; *U.S. Public*, pg. 1442
Sayers, Neil B., V.P. & Gen. Mgr.--All American Homes of North Carolina, Inc., Rutherfordton, NC; *U.S. Public*, pg. 388
Sayers, W.J., Chief Oper. Officer--Elstree Computing Ltd., Borehamwood, United Kingdom; *Int'l*, pg. 796
Sayeski, Peter F., Pres.--SRA McGraw Hill, Worthington, OH; *U.S. Public*, pg. 1070
Sayles, Vernon, Sr. Trust Officer--Key Trust Company of Alaska, Anchorage, AK; *U.S. Public*, pg. 954
Sayre, Keith, Branch Mgr.--Broughton Foods Company, Charleston, WV; *U.S. Public*, pg. 260
Sazerac, Daniele, Branch Mgr.--Livingston International Freight, Roissy Charles de Gaulle, France; *U.S. Public*, pg. 373
Sbarro, Mario, Pres.--Sbarro of Roosevelt Field Inc., Commack, NY; *U.S. Public*, pg. 1436
Scaffide, Bill, V.P. & Gen. Mgr.--WKYC-TV, Cleveland, OH; *U.S. Public*, pg. 702
Scaife, Henry A., Sec. & Dir.-Legal Affairs--Ford Credit Australia Limited, Melbourne, Australia; *U.S. Public*, pg. 665
Scaillet, C., Chief Oper. Officer--Swish Benelux NV/SA, Aarschot, Belgium; *Int'l*, pg. 925
Scalea, Claiton, Dir.--Houghton Brazil LTDA., Sao Paulo, Brazil; *U.S. Private*, pg. 541
Scales, P., Gen. Mgr.--Baring (Isle of Man), Douglas, United Kingdom; *Int'l*, pg. 648
Scales, Robert, Mng. Dir.--Dynamec, Walton, KY; *Int'l*, pg. 193
Scaletta, Tony, Gen. Mgr.--Best Western Ogden Park Hotel, Ogden, UT; *U.S. Public*, pg. 1537
Scalf, Tom, Plant Mgr.--Donaldson Co., Inc., Dixon, IL; *U.S. Public*, pg. 517
Scandellari, Pier Luigi, Mng. Dir.--Sirmac Officine Meccaniche SpA, Bologna, Italy; *U.S. Public*, pg. 1619
Scangas, Angelo N., Vice Chm.--Richdale Dairy Stores, Inc., Lynn, MA; *U.S. Private*, pg. 969
Scanlan, Harry, Pres. & Gen. Mgr.--Fowler Tools of Canada, Kitchener, Canada; *U.S. Private*, pg. 422
Scanlon, James D., Gen. Mgr.--Martin Marietta Control Systems, Johnson City, NY; *U.S. Public*, pg. 1006
Scanlon, Ray, Gen. Mgr.--ABC Rail Cogifer Industries, Cincinnati, OH; *U.S. Public*, pg. 2
Scanlon, Ray, Gen. Mgr.--Cogifer SA, Croissy-sur-Seine, France; *Int'l*, pg. 386
Scanlon, Taylor F., V.P.-North America--Compass Design Automation Inc., San Jose, CA; *U.S. Public*, pg. 1703
Scannavino, Frank, Pres.--Clinton Machinery and Supply, Miami, FL; *U.S. Private*, pg. 1177
Scannel, Herb, Pres.--Nickelodeon/Nick At Nite, New York, NY; *U.S. Private*, pg. 779
Scarborough, Dean A., V.P. & Gen. Mgr.--Fasson Roll Div., Painesville, OH; *U.S. Public*, pg. 153
Scarbrough, John, V.P. & Gen. Mgr.--Ceco Building Systems-Southern Region, Columbus, MS; *U.S. Private*, pg. 221
Scardaci, Leslie, Controller--AVA Leasing Service Company, Atlanta, GA; *U.S. Private*, pg. 8
Scardina, Frank J., Pres.-West Region-Ryland Homes--M.J. Brock & Sons, Inc., Woodland Hills, CA; *U.S. Public*, pg. 1414
Scarisbrick, Kenneth, Pres.--International Forest Seed Company, Odenville, AL; *Int'l*, pg. 973
Scarlini, Giovanni, Mng. Dir.--Speedline S.p.A., Viano, Italy; *U.S. Public*, pg. 63
Scarpa, Lawrence P., First V.P.--Jefferies & Company, Inc., Los Angeles, CA; *U.S. Public*, pg. 925
Scattoloni, T.J., V.P.--Morton Chemical Powder Coatings, Reading, PA; *U.S. Public*, pg. 1135
Scelly, Richard M., Chief Oper. Officer--Electrolux Ltd., Wellington, New Zealand; *Int'l*, pg. 443
Scenna, Enzo, Branch Mgr.--Financial Collection Agencies, Montreal, Canada; *Int'l*, pg. 470
Scerbo, R.W., Gen. Mgr.--Bristol-Myers (Malaysia) Sdn. Bhd., Petaling Jaya, Malaysia; *U.S. Public*, pg. 255
Schaad, E.F., Dr., Chm.--HandelsBank NatWest, Zurich, Switzerland; *Int'l*, pg. 911
Schaaf, Donald, Plant Mgr.--U.S. Can Company, Jerseyville, IL; *U.S. Public*, pg. 1681
Schaaf, Jacob, Mgr.--ITW Devcon Ateco GmbH, Hochberg, Germany; *U.S. Public*, pg. 868
Schaaf, R., Dr., Pres.--Kinetics Technology International GmbH, Hamburg, Germany; *Int'l*, pg. 836
Schaap, Gerald, Gen. Mgr.--Eland-Brandt, B.V., Amsterdam, Netherlands; *U.S. Public*, pg. 895
Schaap, J. C., Pres.--A.O. Smith Harvestore Products, Inc., De Kalb, IL; *U.S. Public*, pg. 1477
Schaap, Mandelon, Mng. Partner--Noordervliet & Winninghoff/Leo Burnett B.V., Amsterdam, Netherlands; *U.S. Private*, pg. 186
Schabos, M., Mng. Dir.--Steelweld Division Zweigniederlassung Bonn der Ambac B.V., Saint Augustin, Germany; *Int'l*, pg. 71
Schack, Jim, Pres.--Utility Vault Co., Inc., Auburn, WA; *Int'l*, pg. 242
Schade, Albrecht, Co-Chief Oper. Officer--North Rhine Westphalia Branch, Dusseldorf, Germany; *Int'l*, pg. 645
Schaefer, Barry G., Abrasive Plants Mgr.--Micromatic Operations (Angola Plant), Angola, IN; *U.S. Public*, pg. 1589
Schaefer, Dr. Jens-Peter, Chm. Bd.--Lurgi AG, Frankfurt/Main, Germany; *Int'l*, pg. 861
Schaefer, George A., Jr., Pres. & Chief Oper. Officer--The Fifth Third Bank, Cincinnati, OH; *U.S. Public*, pg. 621
Schaefer, George A., Jr., Pres.--Fountain Square Management Co., Cincinnati, OH; *U.S. Public*, pg. 622
Schaefer, H.G., Plant Mgr.--Longview Fibre Co. Central Container Div., Cedar Rapids, IA; *U.S. Public*, pg. 1014
Schaefer, Jerry, Mgr.--Heritage Hills, Santa Claus, IN; *U.S. Public*, pg. 957
Schaefer, Joy, Pres.--WFS Financial, Inc., Irvine, CA; *U.S. Public*, pg. 1757
Schaefer, R., Mgr.--Swiss Bank Corporation, Los Angeles, CA; *Int'l*, pg. 1329
Schaefer, Richard, Chief Oper. Officer--Strober Long Island Building Materials Centers, Inc., Valley Stream, NY; *U.S. Private*, pg. 403
Schaefer, Wolfgang, Gen. Mgr.--Watlow Electric Mfg. Co. GmbH, Kronau, Germany; *U.S. Private*, pg. 1153
Schaefer, Wolfgang, Gen. Mgr.--Watlow France S.A.R.L., Cergy-Pontoise, France; *U.S. Private*, pg. 1154
Schaefers, Herbert, Gen. Mgr.--Total Walther Feuerschutz GmbH, Cologne, Germany; *U.S. Public*, pg. 1651
Schaeffer, Milo, Pres.--The BOC Group Inc. (Delaware), Murray Hill, NJ; *Int'l*, pg. 121
Schaeffer, Scott, Pres.--Plibrico Sales & Service, Inc., Chicago, IL; *U.S. Private*, pg. 872
Schaeffer, Scott F., Sr. V.P.-Real Estate & Pres.-Resource Properties, Inc.--Resource America, Inc., Philadelphia, PA; *U.S. Public*, pg. 1382
Schaele, Nicholas V., Gen. Mgr.--Ford Motor Company S.A. de C.V., (Mexico), Mexico, Mexico; *U.S. Public*, pg. 666
Schaenman, Philip, Pres.--TriData Inc., Arlington, VA; *U.S. Private*, pg. 1061
Schafer, Anton F., Pres.--UMB Columbine National Bank, Denver, CO; *U.S. Public*, pg. 1654
Schafer, C.J., Pres.--Lockheed Martin Tactical Defense Systems (Akron), Akron, OH; *U.S. Public*, pg. 1009
Schafer, D., Mgr.--Parker Fluid Verbindungstelle GmbH, Mucke, Germany; *U.S. Public*, pg. 1260
Schafer, Jack, Plant Mgr.--OMC Andrews, Andrews, NC; *U.S. Private*, pg. 478
Schafer, Todd, Gen. Mgr.--Frontier Communications-Lakeshore, Inc., Cecil, WI; *U.S. Public*, pg. 683
Schafer, Todd, Gen. Mgr.--Frontier Communications-St. Croix, Inc., New Richmond, WI; *U.S. Public*, pg. 684
Schafer, Todd, Gen. Mgr.--Frontier Communications of Wisconsin, Inc., Clintonville, WI; *U.S. Public*, pg. 684
Schafer, Ulrich, Gen. Mgr.--Esselte GmbH, Hannover, Germany; *Int'l*, pg. 461
Schafer, Ulrich, Gen. Mgr.--Letraset Deutschland GmbH, Frankfurt/Main, Germany; *Int'l*, pg. 461
Schafer, Volker, Mng. Dir.--Atlet Flurforderzeuge GmbH, Willich, Germany; *Int'l*, pg. 97
Schaff, Paula, Gen. Mgr.--Aftermarket Production Div., Maumee, OH; *U.S. Public*, pg. 479
Schaffer, Jamie H., V.P. & Treas.--AID Finance, Des Moines, IA; *U.S. Private*, pg. 39
Schaffer, Manfred, Dir.--Voest-Alpine International Corp.-Tumco Project Office, Dallas, TX; *Int'l*, pg. 1471
Schafflutzel, Urs, Gen. Mgr.--Baumann Springs USA, Inc., Pineville, NC; *Int'l*, pg. 171
Schaffner, Reinhard, Mng. Dir.--Newport Instruments AG, Schlieren, Switzerland; *U.S. Public*, pg. 1179
Schaffter, B., Gen. Mgr.--John Deere Ottumwa Works, Ottumwa, IA; *U.S. Public*, pg. 492
Schaick, Peter, Gen. Mgr.--CDR International NU/SA, Zaventem, Belgium; *U.S. Private*, pg. 413
Schakel, Matthew, Admin.--Heritage Care Center, Shelby, OH; *U.S. Public*, pg. 838
Schakenraad, Jos, Gen. Mgr.--Bensons International Systems BV, Utrecht, Netherlands; *Int'l*, pg. 460
Schalk, Donald F., Pres.--Agway Retail Services, Syracuse, NY; *U.S. Private*, pg. 27
Schalkamp, Toni, Mng. Dir.--Bose GmbH, Friedrichsdorf, Germany; *U.S. Private*, pg. 161
Schalke, P., Chief Oper. Officer--Babcock Duiker B.V., Kwintsheul, Netherlands; *Int'l*, pg. 472
Schaller, Herman, Ph.D., Pres.--Haarmann & Reimer Food Ingredients Div., Elkhart, IN; *Int'l*, pg. 173
Schaller, Ph., Mgr.--Societe de Banque Suisse, Fribourg, Switzerland; *Int'l*, pg. 1329
Schallner, Jay, Gen. Mgr.--CMI Weighing Equipment Division, Oklahoma City, OK; *U.S. Public*, pg. 279
Schalte, David, Mgr.--Stephen Gould of Michigan, Inc., Farmington Hills, MI; *U.S. Private*, pg. 467
Schank, John W., Pres.--Spirit Energy 76, Sugar Land, TX; *U.S. Public*, pg. 1698
Schano, Peter, Mgr.--Radiometer K.K., Tokyo, Japan; *Int'l*, pg. 1084
Schantz, Gary J., V.P. & Gen. Mgr.--Fasson Pty. Ltd., Elizabeth, Australia; *U.S. Public*, pg. 154
Schantz, Mark P., Gen. Mgr.-Learning Horizons--American Greetings Corporation, Cleveland, OH; *U.S. Public*, pg. 77
Schappel, Martin, Mgr.-Admin.--Florida Residential Treatment Centers, Inc., West Palm Beach, FL; *U.S. Public*, pg. 1035
Schara, Charles G., Pres.--Criterion Life Insurance Co., Washington, DC; *U.S. Public*, pg. 219
Scharfenberger, Joseph, Pres.--Chase Auto Finance Corporation, New Hyde Park, NY; *U.S. Public*, pg. 337
Scharfstein, Larry S., Pres.--Southwest Equity Life Insurance Co., Phoenix, AZ; *Int'l*, pg. 27
Scharin, Ulf, Mng. Dir.--MoDo Merchants AB, Stockholm, Sweden; *Int'l*, pg. 886
Scharlau, Charles E., Chm. Bd. & Pres.--SEECO, Inc., Fayetteville, AR; *U.S. Public*, pg. 1494
Scharlau, Charles E., Chm. Bd.--Southwestern Energy Pipeline Company, Fayetteville, AR; *U.S. Public*, pg. 1494
Scharlau, Charles E., Chm. Bd. & Pres.--Southwestern Energy Production Co., Houston, TX; *U.S. Public*, pg. 1494
Scharlau, Charles E., Chm. Bd. & Pres.--Arkansas Western Pipeline Company, Fayetteville, AR; *U.S. Public*, pg. 1494
Scharp, Anders, Chief Oper. Officer--Electrolux Svenska Forsaljnings AB, Stockholm, Sweden; *Int'l*, pg. 439
Scharrer, Raymond H., Asst. Mgr.-Europe--Cominco Resources Europe N.V., Saint-Stevens-Woluwe, Belgium; *Int'l*, pg. 308
Schary, Donald, Pres.--National Aerosol Products Co., Los Angeles, CA; *Int'l*, pg. 663
Schatteman, S., Pres. & Chief Exec. Officer--PNC Bank, Ohio National Assoc., Fort Mitchell, KY; *U.S. Public*, pg. 1243
Schatteman, S., Pres. & Chief Exec. Officer--PNC Bank, Northern Kentucky, Union, KY; *U.S. Public*, pg. 1243
Schattmeier, K., Pres.--Credit de la Bourse S.A., Paris, France; *Int'l*, pg. 1330
Schatz, E.R., Plant Mgr.--Longview Fibre Co. Western Container Div., Yakima, WA; *U.S. Public*, pg. 1014
Schatz, H.J., Chief Oper. Officer--Groupe SEB Polska, Warsaw, Poland; *Int'l*, pg. 568
Schatz, H.J., Chief Oper. Officer--Groupe SEB Hungary, Budapest, Hungary; *Int'l*, pg. 568
Schatz, H.J., Chief Oper. Officer--Groupe SEB Slovensko, Bratislava, Slovakia; *Int'l*, pg. 568
Schatz, H.J., Chief Oper. Officer--Groupe SEB CR, Prague, Czech Republic; *Int'l*, pg. 568
Schatz, H.J., Chief Oper. Officer--Tefal Deutschland GmbH, Walluf, Germany; *Int'l*, pg. 569
Schau Felberger, Jurg, Pres.--Georg Fischer Real Estate Services Ltd., Schaffhausen, Switzerland; *Int'l*, pg. 490
Schaub, Charles, Pres.--K & L Microwave Div., Salisbury, MD; *U.S. Public*, pg. 521
Schaub, Rodolfo, Mng. Dir.--Fabrimetal S.A., Santiago, Chile; *Int'l*, pg. 748

Schauer, Dietmar, V.P.-European Sls. Opers.--Bourns Benelux B.V., Voorburg, Netherlands; *U.S. Private*, pg. 161

Schauer, Dietmar, V.P.-Sls.--Bourns, GmbH, Stuttgart, Germany; *U.S. Private*, pg. 161

Schauer, Dietmar, V.P.-Sls--Bourns Electronics, Ltd., Dunfermline, United Kingdom; *U.S. Private*, pg. 161

Schauer, Dietmar, V.P.-Sls.--Bourns-Ohmic S.A., Paris, France; *U.S. Private*, pg. 161

Schauert, William J, Dir.-Tech.--Olivetti Systems & Networks, Hinsdale, IL; *Int'l*, pg. 1002

Schauman, Tom, Chief Exec. Officer--LIC Care Oy, Vantaa, Finland; *Int'l*, pg. 551

Schaupp, Herbert, Mng. Dir.--VOEST-ALPINE STAHL Judenburg Ges.m.b.H., Judenburg, Austria; *Int'l*, pg. 1470

Schauw, Hubert, Gen. Mgr.--Forbo Tapijt N.V., Deurne, Belgium; *Int'l*, pg. 498

Schauw, Hubert, Gen. Mgr.--Intertuft S.a.r.l., Aubervilliers, France; *Int'l*, pg. 498

Schawk, David A., Pres.--Schawkgraphics, Des Plaines, IL; *U.S. Public*, pg. 1437

Schebeczek, Helmut, Chief Oper. Officer--VOEST-ALPINE Rohstoffhandel Ges.m.b.H., Vienna, Austria; *Int'l*, pg. 1470

Scheben, William J., Jr., Chm. & Chief Exec. Officer--Liberty National Bank of Northern Kentucky, Erlanger, KY; *U.S. Public*, pg. 173

Scheck, Raimund, Mng. Dir.--STYRIA Federn Ges.m.b.H., Judenburg, Austria; *Int'l*, pg. 1470

Schecter, William H., Pres.--National City Capital Corp., Cleveland, OH; *U.S. Public*, pg. 1154

Schecter, William H., Pres.--National City Venture Corp., Cleveland, OH; *U.S. Public*, pg. 1154

Scheel, D., Gen. Mgr.--Dieter Scheel GmbH, Kehl, Germany; *Int'l*, pg. 759

Scheerer, William J., Pres.--Harmon Industries-Jacksonville, Jacksonville, FL; *U.S. Public*, pg. 788

Scheerlinck, Rik, Mng. Dir.--Kredietbank-Bankverein AG, Bremen, Germany; *Int'l*, pg. 761

Scheese, John, Mgr.--Eclipse Combustion, Inc., Pennington, NJ; *U.S. Private*, pg. 360

Scheessele, John R., Chief Exec. Officer--Wheeling-Pittsburgh Steel Corporation, Wheeling, WV; *U.S. Public*, pg. 1727

Scheetz, Tom, Pres.--Appleton Mills, Appleton, WI; *Int'l*, pg. 1473

Schefer, Hans-Peter, Gen. Mgr.--Medtronic (Schweiz) AG, Dubendorf, Switzerland; *U.S. Public*, pg. 1084

Scheffer, B.J.de Hoop, Gen. Mgr.--ABN (Luxembourg) S.A., Luxembourg, Luxembourg; *Int'l*, pg. 11

Scheffer, H.C., Dir.--Gist-Brocades International BV, Delft, Netherlands; *Int'l*, pg. 1142

Scheffer, H.C., Chm. Bd.--Gist-Brocades, Inc., Wilmington, DE; *Int'l*, pg. 1143

Scheffer, Jeffrey R., Pres.--American Drew, Greensboro, NC; *U.S. Public*, pg. 974

Scheffler, Gustavo, Chief Exec.-Latin America--Skandia S.A., Mexico, Mexico; *Int'l*, pg. 1256

Schehr, Robert, V.P. & Mng. Dir.--National Distributing Co., Inc., Pensacola, FL; *U.S. Private*, pg. 781

Scheidecker, Russ, Plant Mgr.--Elizabethtown Plant, Elizabethtown, KY; *U.S. Public*, pg. 443

Scheidegger, Rene, Gen. Mgr.--Conserves Estavayer S.A., Estavayer le Lac, Switzerland; *Int'l*, pg. 865

Scheidel, Irmgard, Mng. Dir.--Johnson & Johnson G.m.b.H., Hallein, Austria; *U.S. Public*, pg. 930

Scheidt, Ronald C., Mgr.-Property & Casualty S.W. Reg.--Willis Corroon Administrative Services Corporation, San Diego, CA; *Int'l*, pg. 1504

Scheile, N.V., Mng. Dir.--Ford Motor Compania Commercial, S.A. de C.V., Mexico, Mexico; *U.S. Public*, pg. 666

Schein, Alan, Pres.--Tele-Quote Corporation, Petaluma, CA; *Int'l*, pg. 28

Schein, Richard, Pres.--Habits, Inc., New York, NY; *U.S. Private*, pg. 968

Schein, Wilford, Pres.--Henry Birks Jewelers, Inc., Minneapolis, MN; *Int'l*, pg. 197

Scheinman, Tom, Pres.--New York Financial Corp., New York, NY; *U.S. Private*, pg. 993

Scheinman, Tom, Pres. & Chief Exec. Officer--Unimax Corp., New York, NY; *U.S. Private*, pg. 993

Scheivelbein, John J., V.P. & Gen. Mgr.--Mosinee Converted Products, Columbus, WI; *U.S. Public*, pg. 1747

Schelhorn, Fred B., Pres.--Mistal, Inc., Evanston, IL; *U.S. Public*, pg. 1579

Schell, Dana, Gen. Mgr.--Exabyte Scotland Limited, Larbert, United Kingdom; *U.S. Public*, pg. 597

Schelle, Rolf, Pres.--Filterwerk Mann & Hummel GmbH, Marklkofen, Germany; *Int'l*, pg. 484

Schellenberg, E., Pres.--Trane Co. of Canada, Toronto, Canada; *U.S. Public*, pg. 92

Schellenberger, Jean, Chm. Bd. & Chief Exec. Officer--Chantiers Modernes, Pessac, France; *Int'l*, pg. 823

Schellenger, Norman D., V.P. & Gen. Mgr.--Wyeth-Ayerst, Radnor, PA; *U.S. Public*, pg. 80

Scheller, David, Pres.--Coach Label, Evansville, IN; *U.S. Private*, pg. 387

Schellevis, P.R., V.P.--PolyGram International Ltd., London, United Kingdom; *Int'l*, pg. 1053

Schelling, P., Chief Exec. Officer--P.T. Zurich Insurance Indonesia, Jakarta, Indonesia; *Int'l*, pg. 1532

Schellpfeffer, H. Manfred, V.P. & Gen. Mgr.--Specialty Lighting, Shelby, NC; *Int'l*, pg. 821

Scheman, Mart, Pres.--Tyco Playtime Inc., New York, NY; *U.S. Public*, pg. 1058

Scheman, Martin, Chm. Bd. & Chief Exec. Officer--Tyco Preschool, New York, NY; *U.S. Public*, pg. 1058

Schemenaur, James, Chief Exec.--BWI Inex Vision Systems, Clearwater, FL; *Int'l*, pg. 130

Schemmer, Neil, Pres. & Chief Exec. Officer--Security National Bank & Trust Co. of Norman, Norman, OK; *U.S. Public*, pg. 630

Schenfeld, Larry, Sr. V.P.--U.S. Yellow Pages, San Francisco, CA; *U.S. Private*, pg. 1168

Schenian, Dale, Pres.--McClain Easy Pack, Galion, OH; *U.S. Public*, pg. 1065

Schenk, Douglas, Pres. & Chief Exec. Officer--Maui Pineapple Co., Ltd., Kahului, HI; *U.S. Public*, pg. 1060

Schenk, James M., Pres.--BellSouth Financial Services Corporation, Atlanta, GA; *U.S. Public*, pg. 209

Schenk, P.E., Jr., Pres.--Rymer Meat Inc., Chicago, IL; *U.S. Public*, pg. 1414

Schenker, R., Mgr.--Schweizerischer Bankverein, Zurich, Switzerland; *Int'l*, pg. 1329

Schennet, G., Chief Exec. Officer--OCE Osterreich Ges.m.b.H., Vienna, Austria; *Int'l*, pg. 995

Schepler, Charles, Exec. V.P. & Chief Oper. Officer--Manhattan National Life Insurance Company, Cincinnati, OH; *U.S. Public*, pg. 434

Schepman, Roeland R., Gen. Mgr.--Daiwa Europe Limited - Amsterdam, Amsterdam, Netherlands; *Int'l*, pg. 375

Scherb, Michael P., Pres.--Sherwood & James Advertising, Inc., Wayne, NJ; *U.S. Public*, pg. 1666

Schere, Jim, Pres.--L3 Communications Randtron Systems, Menlo Park, CA; *U.S. Private*, pg. 639

Scherer, Bob, V.P. & Gen. Mgr.--WAMZ-FM, Louisville, KY; *U.S. Public*, pg. 384

Scherer, C. D., Pres.--Rockwell PMC/Baker Perkins, Schaumburg, IL; *Int'l*, pg. 1240

Scherer, John, Pres. & Owner--Berlin Glove Company Ltd., Berlin, WI; *U.S. Private*, pg. 136

Scherer, John, Pres. & Owner--Mid-Western, Berlin, WI; *U.S. Private*, pg. 136

Scherer, Karl, Pres.--Intrafin S.A., Zug, Switzerland; *U.S. Public*, pg. 256

Scherer, Michael F., Pres. & Gen. Mgr.--Outdoor Systems, Inc.-Colorado, Denver, CO; *U.S. Public*, pg. 1235

Scherer, Michael J., Pres.--Starcraft Automotive Group, Inc., Goshen, IN; *U.S. Public*, pg. 1511

Scherer, Paul, Mng. Dir. & Chief Exec. Officer--Transworld Publishers Ltd., London, United Kingdom; *Int'l*, pg. 191

Scherer, Robert R., V.P. & Gen. Mgr.--WHAS-AM, Louisville, KY; *U.S. Public*, pg. 385

Scherini, Robert, Mng. Dir.--Johnson & Johnson Medical Pty. Ltd., Sydney, Australia; *U.S. Public*, pg. 931

Schermer, Dave, Reg. V.P.--Ruppman Marketing Technologies, Inc., Dallas, TX; *U.S. Private*, pg. 952

Scherr, Patrick, Mng. Dir.--ARIOS SA, Orleans, France; *Int'l*, pg. 607

Scherr, Ted, Pres. & Gen. Mgr.--Dakota Drug, Inc., Minot, ND; *U.S. Private*, pg. 308

Scherrer, Felix, Dir.--Protek Group, Munsingen, Switzerland; *Int'l*, pg. 1307

Scherrer, Jack L., V.P. & Gen. Mgr.--Logicon Geodynamics Eastern Division, Fairfax, VA; *U.S. Public*, pg. 1199

Scherrer, Urs, Exec. V.P.--Sulzer-Winterthur Group, Winterthur, Switzerland; *Int'l*, pg. 1307

Scherrer, Urs, Mng. Dir.--Sulzer Wintec Ltd., Winterthur, Switzerland; *Int'l*, pg. 1307

Scherrer, Urs, Mng. Dir.--Gebruder Sulzer Holding GmbH, Filderstadt, Germany; *Int'l*, pg. 1308

Scherrer, Willard H., Jr., Sr. V.P.-Transportation Systems--Emery Worldwide Airlines, Vandalia, OH; *U.S. Public*, pg. 281

Scherrer, Williard H., Jr., Chief Oper. Officer & Sr. V.P.--Emery Customs Brokers, Cleveland, OH; *U.S. Public*, pg. 281

Scherzer, D. J., Pres. & Chief Exec. Officer--NMI Corporation, Dallas, TX; *Int'l*, pg. 900

Scherzinger, Otto J., Mng. Dir.--Bear, Stearns & Co. Inc., Geneva, Geneva, Switzerland; *U.S. Public*, pg. 198

Schettino, Francisco Jose, Pres. & Dir.--Mineracao Rio do Norte S.A., Rio de Janeiro, Brazil; *Int'l*, pg. 52

Scheuing, Eckart, Pres.--Robert Bosch Inc., Mississauga, Canada; *Int'l*, pg. 205

Scheurer, Charles B., V.P.-Human Resources & Corp. Services--InterBold, Canton, OH; *U.S. Public*, pg. 506

Schexnaydre, Ronald J., Chief Exec. Officer--Hilb, Rogal and Hamilton Company of Louisiana, Metairie, LA; *U.S. Public*, pg. 827

Scheytt, Edward, V.P. & Gen. Mgr.--Furon Fluorglas Products, Hoosick Falls, NY; *U.S. Public*, pg. 689

Schiano, Tony, Pres. & Chief Oper. Officer--Edwards Super Food Stores, Carlisle, PA; *Int'l*, pg. 749

Schiavoni, Vince, Pres.--Duraloy Technologies, Scottdale, PA; *U.S. Private*, pg. 839

Schiavoni, Vince, Pres.--Electro Alloys, Elyria, OH; *U.S. Private*, pg. 839

Schiber, Gunter, Exec. V.P.--MAN GHH Corp., Pittsburgh, PA; *Int'l*, pg. 824

Schick, Rick, Gen. Mgr.--Trelleborg YSH, Inc.-Sandusky Division, Sandusky, MI; *Int'l*, pg. 1422

Schicker, P., Mng. Dir.--Schaffner-Behrend AG, Unterengstringen, Switzerland; *Int'l*, pg. 536

Schiebe, Jeffrey E., V.P. & Gen. Mgr.-Asia Pacific/Americas--PictureTel Japan KK, Tokyo, Japan; *U.S. Public*, pg. 1295

Schiebe, Jeffrey E., V.P. & Gen. Mgr.--PictureTel International Corp.-Asia Pacific/Americas Headquarters, Danvers, MA; *U.S. Public*, pg. 1295

Schiefer, D., Chief Exec. Officer--Braas Schweiz AG, Villmergen, Switzerland; *Int'l*, pg. 1092

Schiefler, Roger, Chm. Bd.--Capital Concept & Engineering, Wyoming, MI; *U.S. Private*, pg. 1060

Schiefler, Roger, Chm. Bd.--Q-Check Systems, Wyoming, MI; *U.S. Private*, pg. 1060

Schiefler, Roger, Chm. Bd.--Dielink, Grand Rapids, MI; *U.S. Private*, pg. 1060

Schieldrip, Frank, Unit Mgr.--Weatherford Norge, A/S, Stavanger, Norway; *U.S. Public*, pg. 1750

Schiele, C. B., Pres.--H-C Industries, Inc., Crawfordsville, IN; *U.S. Public*, pg. 60

Schiele, Dave, Mgr.--Bond Plastic Div., Upper Sandusky, OH; *U.S. Public*, pg. 1000

Schiele, David A., Div. Mgr.--Lake Erie East Division, Geneva, OH; *U.S. Public*, pg. 438

Schielke, Henry R., Pres.--Cigna Bond Services, Inc., Philadelphia, PA; *U.S. Public*, pg. 362

Schieman, L. Richard, Chief Oper. Officer--Hughes-Peters, Inc., Columbus, OH; *U.S. Private*, pg. 547

Schieren, Dr. Wolfgang, Chm. Bd.--Aquila Beteiligungsgesellschaft mbH, Munich, Germany; *Int'l*, pg. 58

Schiesser, J., Communications Mgr.--Eaton Corporation, Specialties Division, Troy, MI; *U.S. Public*, pg. 557

Schievelbein, Albert, Plant Mgr.--Southern Post Company-Utah, Brigham City, UT; *U.S. Public*, pg. 412

Schiever, David, Pres.--Wyse Direct, Cleveland, OH; *U.S. Private*, pg. 1194

Schiff, Kalman, Branch Mgr.--Bank Hapoalim (Manchester), Manchester, United Kingdom; *Int'l*, pg. 149

Schiff, Marsha, Dir.--Polaroid Education Program, New York, NY; *U.S. Public*, pg. 1314

Schiffer, Paul J., V.P.--Beachwood Place, Inc., Beachwood, OH; *U.S. Public*, pg. 1408

Schildt, Hannu, Mng. Dir.--Kaukas Oy, Lappeenranta, Finland; *Int'l*, pg. 1428

Schildt, Ron, Mgr.-Opers.--Titan Wheel Corporatio Of Illinois, Quincy, IL; *U.S. Public*, pg. 1618

Schile, Wayne E., Publisher--The Billings Gazette, Billings, MT; *U.S. Public*, pg. 983

Schilit, Steve, Pres.--E. Rabinowe & Company, Inc., Newington, CT; *U.S. Public*, pg. 694

Schiller, Harvey W., Pres.--Turner Sports, Inc., Atlanta, GA; *U.S. Public*, pg. 1615

Schiller, Jo Anne, Pres.--Everyday Learning/Creative Publications Group, Chicago, IL; *U.S. Public*, pg. 1635

Schilling, Theodor, Pres.--Knurr-Interplast GmbH, Bremen, Germany; *Int'l*, pg. 739

Schilt, Christian R., Pres.--Harte-Hanks Community Newspapers, Inc., Plano, TX; *U.S. Public*, pg. 793

Schilt, Paul U., Exec. V.P.--Switzerland Cheese Association, Inc., Valley Cottage, NY; *Int'l*, pg. 1211

Schimek, Gary, Sr. V.P.-Gen. Mgr.--Redi-Serve Foods, Fort Atkinson, WI; *U.S. Private*, pg. 817

Schimmelbusch, Heinz, Dr., Chm.--Metallgesellschaft Industrie AG, Dusseldorf, Germany; *Int'l*, pg. 861

Schimmelpenninck, Rutger J., Mng. Dir.--British Land Investments N.V., Amsterdam, Netherlands; *Int'l*, pg. 219

Schimpf, Georges, Gen. Mgr.--Wilson Color, Cergy-Pontoise, France; *U.S. Public*, pg. 781

Schinasi, Leo, Plant Mgr.--Huls America Inc., Pleasanton, CA; *Int'l*, pg. 1455

Schindele, Henry A., V.P. & Reg. Treas.--Toronto Dominion Japan, Tokyo, Japan; *Int'l*, pg. 1401

Schindler, Paul R., Sr. V.P.--AlliedSignal International, Inc., Central, Hong Kong; *U.S. Public*, pg. 52

Schindler, Ralph J., Jr., Chief Oper. Officer--Chicago Fire Brick of Delaware, Inc., Chicago, IL; *U.S. Private*, pg. 194

Schini, Thomas W., Chief Oper. Officer--First Federal Savings Bank La Crosse-Madison, La Crosse, WI; *U.S. Public*, pg. 632

Schipp, Mark, Gen. Mgr.--BHP Steel Building Products (B) Sdn Bhd, Berakas, Brunei Darussalam; *Int'l*, pg. 226

Schipper, A.J., Mng. Dir.--Van Leeuwen Pipe and Tube (Far East) Pte. Ltd., Singapore, Singapore; *Int'l*, pg. 1450

Schipper, G.A.J., Chief Oper. Officer--De Lage Landen Factors SpA, Turin, Italy; *Int'l*, pg. 1082

Schipper, R., Dir.--Zuiderhout B.V., Nieuw-Vennep, Netherlands; *Int'l*, pg. 751

Schira, Claudio, Gen. Mgr.--Forbo-Giubiasco SA, Giubiasco, Switzerland; *Int'l*, pg. 497

Schirado, Luis R., Pres. & Chief Exec. Officer--Siemens S.A., Buenos Aires, Argentina; *Int'l*, pg. 1248

Schirck, Ted, Plant Mgr.--Medtronic Milaca, Inc., Milaca, MN; *U.S. Public*, pg. 1083

Schirinzi, Marco, Mgr.--Sandvik Saws and Tools, Milan, Italy; *Int'l*, pg. 1187

Schirmboeck, G., Gen. Mgr.--Kodak Gessellschaft m.b.H., Vienna, Austria; *U.S. Public*, pg. 553

Schirmer, Andreas, Mng. Dir.--Bauverlag GmbH, Walluf, Germany; *Int'l*, pg. 451

Schirmer, D.A., Pres.--Abitibi-Consolidated Paper Sales Corporation, Greenwich, CT; *Int'l*, pg. 20

Schischek, W., Chief Oper. Officer--Maschinenfabrik KBA Modling AG, Enzersdorf, Austria; *Int'l*, pg. 742

Schjerven, Robert E., Pres. & Chief Oper. Officer--Lennox Industries Inc., Richardson, TX; *U.S. Private*, pg. 659

Schjetlein, Ivar O., Pres.--Kvaerner Concrete Construction a.s., Lysaker, Norway; *Int'l*, pg. 766

Schjetlein, Ivar O., Pres.--Kvaerner Concrete Construction a.s., Hovik, Norway; *Int'l*, pg. 766

Schjolberg, Martin, Gen. Mgr.--Eastern Bulkcem Co. Ltd., Port Harcourt, Nigeria; *Int'l*, pg. 1201

Schlackman, Neil, M.D., Pres.--U.S. Quality Algorithms, Inc., Blue Bell, PA; *U.S. Public*, pg. 27

Schlagenhauf, Paul, Pres.--Siva Truck Leasing Inc., Milwaukee, WI; *U.S. Private*, pg. 110

Schlanser, Joseph, Chief Oper. Officer--EMS-Ohio, Solon, OH; *U.S. Public*, pg. 565

Schlansky, Norman, Chief Oper. Officer--SunGard Shareholder Systems Inc., San Mateo, CA; *U.S. Public*, pg. 1535

Schlapfer, H., Mgr.--EMI Records (Interton) AG, Baar, Switzerland; *Int'l*, pg. 427

Schlapfer, Kurt, Chief Oper. Officer--Electrolux AG, Zurich, Switzerland; *Int'l*, pg. 443

Schlatter, D.A., Chief Oper. Officer--Abros, Inc., Toledo, OH; *U.S. Private*, pg. 86

Schlatter, Emil, Dir.--Von Roll AG Departement Stahlprodukte, Gerlafingen, Switzerland; *Int'l*, pg. 1480

Schlatter, Hans R., Chm. Bd. & Pres.--H.A. Schlatter AG, Schlieren, Switzerland; *Int'l*, pg. 1205

Schleckser, Jim, Pres.--General Eastern Instruments Corporation, Woburn, MA; *U.S. Private*, pg. 528

Schlegel, David M., Pres.--Envirco Corporation, Albuquerque, NM; *U.S. Public*, pg. 1639

Schlegel, G., Chief Exec. Officer--Ascom Infrasys AG, Solothurn, Switzerland; *Int'l*, pg. 86

Schlegel, J., Dir.-Pur.--Turco Products Division, Long Beach, CA; *Int'l*, pg. 446
Schlegel, James, Dir.-Pur.--Turco Products Division, Westminster, CA; *Int'l*, pg. 446
Schlegelmilch, Rick, V.P.--Customer Development Corporation, Framingham, MA; *U.S. Private*, pg. 298
Schleider, James, V.P.--System Service Division, Tullahoma, TN; *U.S. Public*, pg. 466
Schlein, Dov C., Pres. & Chief Oper. Officer--Republic National Bank of New York, New York, NY; *U.S. Public*, pg. 1380
Schleisman, Mark, Plant Mgr.--Vogel Popcorn Company, Hamburg, IA; *U.S. Public*, pg. 427
Schleisman, Steve A., Pres.--American International Underwriters Corp., New York, NY; *U.S. Public*, pg. 85
Schlemper, Klaus, Mng. Dir.--PDA International/Germany, Munich, Germany; *U.S. Public*, pg. 1031
Schlepphege, Werner, Mng. Dir.--Schnurpfeil Bohr-GmbH, Munich, Germany; *Int'l*, pg. 423
Schlesinger, Bent-Axel, Chief Oper. Officer--Autogerma S.p.A., Verona, Italy; *Int'l*, pg. 1474
Schlesinger, William, Branch Mgr.--Holmes Protection Group, Inc., New York, NY; *U.S. Public*, pg. 1649
Schlessman, Paul M., V.P. & Gen. Mgr.--Alpha Wire Company, Elizabeth, NJ; *U.S. Public*, pg. 201
Schleyer, Robert J., Pres.--United Casualty Insurance Company of America, Chicago, IL; *U.S. Public*, pg. 1694
Schleyer, Robert J., Pres.--United Insurance Company of America, Schiller Park, IL; *U.S. Public*, pg. 1694
Schleyer, William T., Pres.--MediaOne, Boston, MA; *U.S. Public*, pg. 1688
Schlichfting, H., Reg. Pres.--Melitta Hong Kong Ltd., Hong Kong, Hong Kong; *Int'l*, pg. 857
Schlicht, Robert A., Pres. & Chief Oper. Officer--M & I Madison Bank, Madison, WI; *U.S. Public*, pg. 1050
Schlichtenberger, Fritz, Mng. Dir.--Nira Deutschland Zweigniederlassung der Nira International B.V., Frankfurt/Main, Germany; *Int'l*, pg. 1369
Schlichting, Hartmut, Reg. Pres.--Melitta Catering Pty. Ltd., Crows Nest, Australia; *Int'l*, pg. 857
Schlichting, Hatmut, Mng. Dir.--Melitta Pacific Ltd., Hong Kong, Hong Kong; *Int'l*, pg. 857
Schllig, Christian, Publisher--Coward-McCann, Inc., New York, NY; *Int'l*, pg. 1027
Schlosser, Carl, Pres.--Salant Childrens Apparel Group, New York, NY; *U.S. Public*, pg. 1429
Schlosser, Gerhard, Mgr.--Sandvik Process Systems Ges.m.b.H., Vienna, Austria; *Int'l*, pg. 1187
Schlosser, Tom, Gen. Mgr.--Quik Park Inc., Washington, DC; *U.S. Private*, pg. 898
Schlosser, Woflgang, Chief Oper. Officer--Perstorp Analytical GmbH, Rodgau, Germany; *Int'l*, pg. 1039
Schlouppe, F., Gen. Mgr.--Cadillac Plastic France S.A., Paris, France; *U.S. Public*, pg. 781
Schlue, Carl-Hans, Mng. Dir.--BNP-Dresdner Bank (Rossija), Saint Petersburg, Russia; *Int'l*, pg. 418
Schlumberger, P., Mng. Dir.--Oki (France) sarl, L'Hay-les-Roses, France; *Int'l*, pg. 1000
Schlumpf, G., Mng. Dir.--Contraves Advanced Devices, Sdn. Bhd., Melaka, Malaysia; *Int'l*, pg. 998
Schluter, Andreas S., Pres.--Deutsche Babcock Industrie und Systemtechnik AG, Oberhausen, Germany; *Int'l*, pg. 399
Schlyter, Goren, Mng. Dir.--Ericsson Business Communications NV/SA, Brussels, Belgium; *Int'l*, pg. 1366
Schmale, P., Dir.--Gelderlander Fleischwaren GmbH, Emmerich, Germany; *Int'l*, pg. 752
Schmalz, Brian F., Pres.--Creations Aromatiques, Inc., Englewood Cliffs, NJ; *Int'l*, pg. 173
Schmatz, Linda, Bureau Chief--Bridge, Overland Park, KS; *U.S. Private*, pg. 1162
Schmbert, William C, Pres.--Kitchell Development Company, Phoenix, AZ; *U.S. Private*, pg. 624
Schmedding, Gary N., Pres.--New Mexico Broadcasting Co., Albuquerque, NM; *U.S. Public*, pg. 984
Schmeling, Bernd, Gen. Mgr.--Bendix Deutschland G.m.b.H., Neunkirchen, Germany; *U.S. Public*, pg. 54
Schmelzel, Randy, Chief Oper. Officer--River Ranch - Northeast, Buffalo, NY; *Int'l*, pg. 491
Schmelzer, Henry L.P., Pres.--TNE Investment Services Corp., Boston, MA; *U.S. Private*, pg. 737
Schmelzer, Henry L.P., Pres.--New England Securities Corp., Boston, MA; *U.S. Private*, pg. 738
Schmergel, G., Pres.--Genetics Institute, Inc., Andover, MA; *U.S. Public*, pg. 80
Schmick, John E., Gen. Mgr.--Boeing Electronics, Inc., Seattle, WA; *U.S. Public*, pg. 240
Schmid, Alfons, Dr., Chief Oper. Officer--NOBIS Societe des Banques Privees, Luxembourg, Luxembourg; *Int'l*, pg. 119
Schmid, C., Chief Exec. Officer--Ascom Zeag, Spreitenbach, Switzerland; *Int'l*, pg. 86
Schmid, Charles, Pres.--E.F. MacDonald Motivation Div., Minneapolis, MN; *U.S. Private*, pg. 212
Schmid, Charles W., Pres.--Carlson Marketing Group, Inc., Minneapolis, MN; *U.S. Private*, pg. 212
Schmid, Charles W., Pres. & Chief Oper. Officer--Carlson Travel Group, Inc., Minneapolis, MN; *U.S. Private*, pg. 212
Schmid, George R., V.P.--The Willowbrook Corp., Wayne, NJ; *U.S. Public*, pg. 1408
Schmid, Hans, Mng. Dir.--GGK Wien Werbeagentur GmbH, Vienna, Austria; *Int'l*, pg. 1336
Schmid, Herbert, Chief Oper. Officer--Alpargatas Santista Textil S.A., Sao Paulo, Brazil; *Int'l*, pg. 1193
Schmid, Jakob, Mng. Dir.--Texas Instruments (Switzerland) AG, Dietikon, Switzerland; *U.S. Public*, pg. 1586
Schmid, John, Chief Oper. Officer--Allright Parking of Austin, Inc., Austin, TX; *U.S. Private*, pg. 43
Schmid, Jorg, Gen. Mgr.--Cold Storage Warehouse AG St. Margrethen, Saint Margrethen, Austria; *Int'l*, pg. 866
Schmid, Jorg, Gen. Mgr.--Migros Distribution Center Neuendorf AG, Neuendorf, Switzerland; *Int'l*, pg. 866
Schmid, Karl, Mng. Dir.--Hobart AG, Zurich, Switzerland; *U.S. Public*, pg. 1322
Schmid, Karl, Dr., Chm. Bd.--Krupp Koppers GmbH, Essen, Germany; *Int'l*, pg. 511
Schmid, Max, Chief Oper. Officer--Frionor AG, Basel, Switzerland; *Int'l*, pg. 516
Schmid, Rudolf, Pres.--Productora de Papeles S.A. (PROPAL), Cali, Colombia; *U.S. Public*, pg. 906
Schmid, Walter A., Gen. Mgr.--Forbo Industrieprodukte Ges.m.b.H., Steyr, Austria; *Int'l*, pg. 497
Schmidbauer, Friedrich, Chief Oper. Officer--Krauss-Maffei Versicherungsdienst GmbH, Munich, Germany; *Int'l*, pg. 836
Schmidhammer, Florian, Pres. & Gen. Mgr.--Medal Distributing Co., Sharon, PA; *U.S. Public*, pg. 1748
Schmidt-Kallesoe, Per, Mgr.-Prod.--Neopac A/S, Naestved, Denmark; *Int'l*, pg. 864
Schmidt, Arnold, Pres.--Bay Insulation, Green Bay, WI; *U.S. Private*, pg. 124
Schmidt, Arthur W., III, Chief Oper. Officer--Hit Promotional Products Inc., Largo, FL; *U.S. Private*, pg. 277
Schmidt, Bjarne Th., Pres.--a.s. Norsk Leca, Oslo, Norway; *Int'l*, pg. 1200
Schmidt, Charles, Dir.--AlliedSignal Computer-Aided Engineering Center, Teterboro, NJ; *U.S. Public*, pg. 50
Schmidt, Dan, Chief Oper. Officer--Allright New York Parking, Inc., Rochester, NY; *U.S. Private*, pg. 43
Schmidt, Dave, Gen. Mgr.--Alro Group, Jackson, Jackson, MI; *U.S. Private*, pg. 46
Schmidt, Dietrich, Pres.--Petoseed Co., Saticoy, CA; *U.S. Private*, pg. 188
Schmidt, E. Frank, Chm. Bd. & Chief Exec. Officer--SouthTrust Bank of Mobile, Mobile, AL; *U.S. Public*, pg. 1492
Schmidt, Eric E., Pres.--Sun Technology Business, Mountain View, CA; *U.S. Public*, pg. 1531
Schmidt, Fred A., Mgr.--Piper Jaffray Inc., Bismarck, ND; *U.S. Public*, pg. 1301
Schmidt, G. Gerry, Chm. Bd. & Pres.--Spectrum Razor Tools, Costa Mesa, CA; *U.S. Private*, pg. 831
Schmidt, Gary, Gen. Mgr.--First American Title Guaranty Agency of Carbon County, Rawlins, WY; *U.S. Public*, pg. 625
Schmidt, Hans, Mng. Dir.--GGK Vienna, Vienna, Austria; *Int'l*, pg. 1336
Schmidt, Hans A., Pres.--Centre Foundry & Machine Co., Wheeling, WV; *U.S. Private*, pg. 351
Schmidt, Hans Dieter, Dir.-Mktg.--McDonald's Deutschland Inc., Frankfurt/Main, Germany; *U.S. Public*, pg. 1069
Schmidt, J. Stephen, Pres.--American Commonwealth Management Services Company, Inc., Hershey, PA; *U.S. Public*, pg. 95
Schmidt, James L., Gen. Mgr.--McAlpin's, Cincinnati, OH; *U.S. Public*, pg. 1090
Schmidt, Jo, Mgr.-Pub. Rels.--Schwarz Pharma Inc., Mequon, WI; *Int'l*, pg. 1211
Schmidt, John, Pres.--Fers Personal Financial Services, L.L.C., Chicago, IL; *U.S. Private*, pg. 428
Schmidt, John, Pres.--Essex, L.L.C., Chicago, IL; *U.S. Private*, pg. 428
Schmidt, Jurgen, Gen. Mgr.--Max Grunhut GmbH, Bremen, Germany; *Int'l*, pg. 1033
Schmidt, Mark, Reg Dir.--Reed Business Information-China, Beijing, China; *Int'l*, pg. 1094
Schmidt, Oscar, Dir. General--Metropolitan Life Seguros de Vida, S.A., Buenos Aires, Argentina; *U.S. Private*, pg. 738
Schmidt, Peter, Pres.--Klockner Stadler Hurter, Ltd., Montreal, Canada; *Int'l*, pg. 1081
Schmidt, Peter, Chief Oper. Officer--TOSOH Europe, Wertheim, Germany; *Int'l*, pg. 1408
Schmidt, Peter G., Chief Exec. Officer--Marco Seattle, Inc., Seattle, WA; *U.S. Private*, pg. 703
Schmidt, Pierre, Pres.--Bongard, Holtzheim, France; *Int'l*, pg. 570
Schmidt, Pierre, Mng. Dir.--N.V. Olin Europe S.A., Brussels, Belgium; *U.S. Public*, pg. 1220
Schmidt, Pierre C., Dir.--N.V. Olin Hunt Specialty Products, Saint-Niklaas, Belgium; *U.S. Public*, pg. 1220
Schmidt, Pierre C., Dir.--N.V. Olin Hunt Trading, Saint-Niklaas, Belgium; *U.S. Public*, pg. 1220
Schmidt, Richard K., Chief Exec. Officer--IEA, Inc., Research Triangle Park, NC; *U.S. Public*, pg. 126
Schmidt, Richard K., Chm. Bd.--Aquarion Management Services, Bridgeport, CT; *U.S. Public*, pg. 126
Schmidt, Rob T., Pres.--Canadian American Railroad Company, Bangor, ME; *U.S. Private*, pg. 575
Schmidt, Robert, Pres. & Chief Exec. Officer--M & I Mid-State Bank, Stevens Point, WI; *U.S. Public*, pg. 1050
Schmidt, Robert H., Pres.--Dreyfus Service Corp., New York, NY; *U.S. Public*, pg. 1085
Schmidt, Ronald, Gen. Mgr.--ITW Basic Switch Products, Chicago, IL; *U.S. Public*, pg. 866
Schmidt, Skip, Gen. Mgr.--GCI Dallas, Inc/GCI Texas, Inc, Dallas, TX; *U.S. Private*, pg. 470
Schmidt, Uwe, Pres. & Chief Exec. Officer--Olympic Continental Resources, LLC, Pepper Pike, OH; *U.S. Public*, pg. 1221
Schmidt, V., Fin. Controller--F.I.A.P. Deutschland GmbH, Rems, Germany; *U.S. Public*, pg. 5
Schmidt, W. P., Chief Oper. Officer--V.A.G. Financement S.A., Villers-Cotterets, France; *Int'l*, pg. 1475
Schmidt, William, Pres.--WWF Paper Corporation - West (California), City of Industry, CA; *U.S. Private*, pg. 1145
Schmidt, Wolfgang, Mgr.--GGK Communications, Dusseldorf, Germany; *Int'l*, pg. 1335
Schmit, J., Gen. Mgr.--Boeing Louisiana, Inc., Lake Charles, LA; *U.S. Public*, pg. 242
Schmits, Reinhardt, Chief Officer--Generale Bank & Co., Essen, Germany; *Int'l*, pg. 548
Schmitt, Andrew, Pres.--Christensen Products, Salt Lake City, UT; *U.S. Public*, pg. 981
Schmitt, Helmut, Mng. Dir.--Merisel Germany, Munich, Germany; *U.S. Public*, pg. 1096
Schmitt, Helmut, Mng. Dir.--Merisel Austria, Vienna, Austria; *U.S. Public*, pg. 1096
Schmitt, Mike, Pres.--Richards Industries Metalworking Group, Cincinnati, OH; *U.S. Private*, pg. 929
Schmitt, Rolf, Co-Chief Oper. Officer--Winschermann Sued GmbH, Karlsruhe, Germany; *Int'l*, pg. 1167
Schmitz-le-Hanne, Arno, Gen. Mgr.--Formica Vertriebs GmbH, Cologne, Germany; *Int'l*, pg. 130
Schmitz, Bobby, System Superintendent--Hilight Gas Plant, Gillette, WY; *U.S. Public*, pg. 1759
Schmitz, Bobby, System Supervisor--Kitty Gas Plant, Gillette, WY; *U.S. Public*, pg. 1759
Schmitz, Bobby, System Supervisor--Newcastle Gas Plant, Newcastle, WY; *U.S. Public*, pg. 1759
Schmitz, Bobby, System Superintendent--Reno Junction Isomerization Unit, Gillette, WY; *U.S. Public*, pg. 1759
Schmitz, James G., Asst. V.P.--IBP-Waterloo, Waterloo, IA; *U.S. Public*, pg. 852
Schmitz, Michael J., Chm. Bd.--RE Services, Inc., Milwaukee, WI; *U.S. Public*, pg. 643
Schmitz, P., Chief Oper. Officer--Schlatter Benelux B.V., Breda, Netherlands; *Int'l*, pg. 1206
Schmitz, Peter, Pres.--Cantex Corp., Schenectady, NY; *Int'l*, pg. 113
Schmitz, Werner, Pres.--Deutz Corporation, Norcross, GA; *Int'l*, pg. 408
Schmoecker, Erwin, Base Leader--Weatherford Norge, A/S, Floro, Norway; *U.S. Public*, pg. 1750
Schmoyer, Ron, Mng. Dir.--ISS Landscape Management Services, Inc., Tampa, FL; *Int'l*, pg. 656
Schmuelling, Eugen, Dir.--Unichema Chemie G.m.b.H., Emmerich, Germany; *Int'l*, pg. 1438
Schnack, Uwe, Chief Oper. Officer--TSC Shannock Corporation, Calgary, Canada; *Int'l*, pg. 1343
Schnack, Uwe, Chief Oper. Officer--TSC Shannock Corporation, Don Mills, Canada; *Int'l*, pg. 1343
Schnaider, David, Div. Head--Ziff-Davis Interactive, New York, NY; *Int'l*, pg. 1276
Schnee, J. E., Chief Oper. Officer--Air Pollution Control, Somerville, NJ; *U.S. Public*, pg. 29
Schneerson, Boris, Pres.--Frigoscandia Food Process Systems S.A., Paris, France; *U.S. Public*, pg. 607
Schneider, Achim, Mng. Dir.--Georg Fischer Pty Ltd., Oakleigh, Australia; *Int'l*, pg. 488
Schneider, Andreas, Mgr.-Office--Woodward-Clyde, Wuppertal, Germany; *U.S. Public*, pg. 1658
Schneider, D., Chief Oper. Officer--Busch-Jaeger Ludenscheider Metallwerk GmbH, Ludenscheid, Germany; *Int'l*, pg. 1427
Schneider, Dana, Plant Mgr.--Haarman & Reimer Aroma Chemicals, Goose Creek, SC; *Int'l*, pg. 173
Schneider, Dr. Fred, Dir.--Bayerische Immobilien-Leasing GmbH, Munich, Germany; *Int'l*, pg. 179
Schneider, Erich, Chief Oper. Officer--Oerlikon-Contraves AG, Zurich, Switzerland; *Int'l*, pg. 998
Schneider, Ernst, Chm. Bd.--PSA International S.A., Geneva, Switzerland; *Int'l*, pg. 1021
Schneider, Francis, Pres.--GTL Truck Lines, Inc., Norfolk, NE; *U.S. Public*, pg. 1152
Schneider, Franz, Gen. Mgr.--Besan-Besin Sanayi ve Ticaret A.S., Sisli, Turkey; *U.S. Public*, pg. 224
Schneider, Heinz, Mng. Dir.--Lamb AG, Wettingen, Switzerland; *U.S. Private*, pg. 378
Schneider, Howard M., Pres.--BT Securities Corp., New York, NY; *U.S. Public*, pg. 185
Schneider, Marv, Pres.--Duralam, Inc., Appleton, WI; *U.S. Private*, pg. 966
Schneider, Norbert, Pres.--The Fuller Brush Company, Great Bend, KS; *U.S. Public*, pg. 282
Schneider, P., Chief Oper. Officer--Volkswagen Leasing Anlagen GmbH, Braunschweig, Germany; *Int'l*, pg. 1474
Schneider, Roger, Chief Oper. Officer--Allright Cal. Inc., Los Angeles, CA; *U.S. Private*, pg. 42
Schneider, Ronald E., Chm. Bd., Pres. & Chief Exec. Officer--First National Bank in Cleburne, Cleburne, TX; *U.S. Public*, pg. 633
Schneider, Stan, Mgr.--Stephen Gould of Pennsylvania Corp., Marlton, NJ; *U.S. Private*, pg. 467
Schneider, Steven L., Pres.--LEI Extras, Inc., Tulsa, OK; *U.S. Public*, pg. 1016
Schneider, Steven L., Pres.--Lowrance Canada, Mississauga, Canada; *U.S. Public*, pg. 1016
Schneider, Steven L., Pres.--Lowrance Australia, Brookvale, Australia; *U.S. Public*, pg. 1016
Schneider, Steven L., Pres.--Disclosure Incorporated, Bethesda, MD; *U.S. Public*, pg. 1325
Schneider, T., Gen. Mgr.--OMC Milwaukee, Milwaukee, WI; *U.S. Private*, pg. 478
Schneider, Tom, Chief Oper. Officer--Allright Long Beach Parking, Long Beach, CA; *U.S. Private*, pg. 42
Schneider, Tom, Refinery Mgr.--Total Petroleum, Inc., Alma, MI; *U.S. Public*, pg. 1663
Schneiders, M.M., Gen. Mgr.--ING Bank Caracas, Caracas, Venezuela; *Int'l*, pg. 649
Schnell, Lloyd J., Pres.--Imasco Finance L.L.C., Wilmington, DE; *Int'l*, pg. 112
Schnelle, H., Chief Oper. Officer--V.A.G. Marketing Management Institut GmbH, Braunschweig, Germany; *Int'l*, pg. 1473
Schneller, Robert J., Mgr.--Scott & Stringfellow, Inc., Charlottesville, VA; *U.S. Public*, pg. 1446
Schneringer, Al, Sr. V.P.--Air Conditioning Co., Inc., San Diego, CA; *U.S. Private*, pg. 28
Schniepp, Don, Gen. Mgr.--Unitog Company, Saint Charles, MO; *U.S. Public*, pg. 1693
Schniering, H.J., Chief Oper. Officer--De Lage Landen Leasing GmbH, Dusseldorf, Germany; *Int'l*, pg. 1082
Schnur, Louis S., Pres.--Cornell Manufacturing Company, Orangeburg, NY; *U.S. Private*, pg. 602
Schober, Alois, Mng. Dir.--Young & Rubicam GmbH, Vienna, Austria; *U.S. Private*, pg. 1199
Schoch, Stan, Gen. Mgr.--PSI International, El Paso, TX; *U.S. Public*, pg. 1522

Schochet, Barry, Gen. Mgr.--Tenet HealthSystem Hospitals, Inc., Dallas, TX; *U.S. Public*, pg. 1577

Schocke, Dave, Pres.--Custom Product Div., Grand Island, NE; *U.S. Private*, pg. 236

Schocke, David, V.P. & Gen. Mgr.--Custom Products Division, Grand Island, NE; *U.S. Private*, pg. 236

Schockemoehl, Gene F., Pres.--Braden Manufacturing Co., Tulsa, OK; *U.S. Public*, pg. 924

Schoder, Alphonse, Gen. Mgr.--Galvalange S.a.r.l., Dudelange, Luxembourg; *Int'l*, pg. 79

Schoeffler, Pierre, Mng. Dir.--Handelsbanken Markets France S.A., Paris, France; *Int'l*, pg. 1328

Schoeller, Monika, Pres.--S. Fischer Verlag GmbH, Frankfurt/Main, Germany; *Int'l*, pg. 1478

Schoen, Fred, Pres.--Spartanburg Steel Products, Spartanburg, SC; *U.S. Private*, pg. 300

Schoen, Mel, Mng. Dir.--TBWA Hamburg GmbH, Hamburg, Germany; *U.S. Private*, pg. 1063

Schoen, Rich, Mgr.--SmithKline Diagnostics, Palo Alto, CA; *U.S. Public*, pg. 199

Schoenberg, Lester L., Chm. Bd. & Pres.--NYLIFE Insurance Company of Arizona, Scottsdale, AZ; *U.S. Private*, pg. 795

Schoenenberger, Tullio, Gen. Mgr.--Abbott Laboratories S.A., Geneva, Switzerland; *U.S. Public*, pg. 14

Schoenke, Richard W., Pres.--Firstar Corporation of Minnesota, Milwaukee, WI; *U.S. Public*, pg. 643

Schoenke, Richard W., Pres.--Firstar Bank of Minnesota, Bloomington, MN; *U.S. Public*, pg. 643

Schoenleber, Wilfred, Mng. Dir.--Elefanten-Schuh GmbH, Kleve, Germany; *Int'l*, pg. 505

Schoenwitz, Frank, Pres. & Chief Exec. Officer--Weldun International, Inc., Bridgman, MI; *Int'l*, pg. 205

Schoettert, J., Pres.--J & F Steel Corporation, Chicago, IL; *Int'l*, pg. 79

Schoffer, Andreas, Dir.--Ord Minnett Group Limited, Frankfurt/Main, Germany; *Int'l*, pg. 1497

Schofield, Jonathan M., Chm. Bd. & Chief Exec. Officer--Airbus Industrie of North America, Inc., Herndon, VA; *Int'l*, pg. 39

Schofield, Philip W., Gen. Mgr.--Fiber Optic Products Division, Chicago, IL; *U.S. Public*, pg. 1101

Scholfield, Paul, Gen. Mgr.-Power Systems--G.E. Canada Power Systems, Lachine, Canada; *U.S. Public*, pg. 713

Scholl, Klaus, Mgr.--Gunther & Co. GmbH, Frankfurt/Main, Germany; *Int'l*, pg. 1186

Schollmaier, E.H., Pres. & Chief Exec. Officer--Alcon Surgical, Fort Worth, TX; *Int'l*, pg. 916

Schollmaier, Edgar H., Chm. Bd., Pres. & Chief Exec. Officer--Alcon Laboratories, Inc., Fort Worth, TX; *Int'l*, pg. 916

Scholten, J., Chm. Bd.--Tijdschriften Uitgevers Maatschappij, Antwerp, Belgium; *Int'l*, pg. 1447

Scholten, J., Chm. Bd.--Editions Francophones Belges sa (EFB), Brussels, Belgium; *Int'l*, pg. 1447

Scholtens, Michael J., Pres.--ABB C-E Services, Windsor, CT; *Int'l*, pg. 3

Scholtz, Ed, Pres. & Chief Exec. Officer--The Murray Ohio Mfg. Co., Brentwood, TN; *Int'l*, pg. 1397

Scholz, Jane, Editor--KRT News & Information Services, Washington, DC; *U.S. Public*, pg. 965

Schomaker, Hans-Peter, Pres.--Reckitt & Colman S.A., Massy, France; *Int'l*, pg. 1090

Schomberg, P., Gen. Mgr.--Alemite GmbH, Haan, Germany; *Int'l*, pg. 127

Schomer, Fred K., Chm. Bd.--Gerber Life Insurance Co., White Plains, NY; *Int'l*, pg. 973

Schonberg, Alan R., Pres.--Management Recruiters International, Inc., Cleveland, OH; *U.S. Public*, pg. 277

Schonberg, Gunnar, Chief Rep.--The Sumitomo Bank, Ltd.-Stockholm Representative Office, Stockholm, Sweden; *Int'l*, pg. 1310

Schonberger, Alfred, Pres.--Clermont Specialty Managers, Ltd., Hackensack, NJ; *U.S. Public*, pg. 215

Schonbrodt, Robert, Dir.--Alpha Credit, Brussels, Belgium; *Int'l*, pg. 546

Schonenberger, Herr, Mng. Dir.--Burgmann do Brasil, Campinas, Brazil; *Int'l*, pg. 233

Schonheyder, Jan, Chief Oper. Officer--Norwesco A/S, Skare, Norway; *Int'l*, pg. 33

Schonhoff, Richard, Pres.--The Northern Trust Company, Chicago, IL; *U.S. Public*, pg. 1197

Schonhoff, Richard, Pres.--The Northern Trust Company, Schaumburg, IL; *U.S. Public*, pg. 1197

Schoning, Joachim, Mng. Dir.--Norddeutsche Hypotheken und Wechselbank AG, Hamburg, Germany; *Int'l*, pg. 418

Schonleber, Peter, Oper. Officer--Rhenania Transport GmbH, Heilbronn, Germany; *Int'l*, pg. 1033

Schonmeier, Manfred, Pres. & Chief Exec. Officer--F.W. Woolworth GmbH Co. (Germany), Frankfurt/Main, Germany; *U.S. Public*, pg. 1778

Schonwald, Bernd, Dr., Speaker--Werner & Pfleiderer GmbH, Stuttgart, Germany; *Int'l*, pg. 510

Schoolcraft, Joseph, Div. Mgr.--Yokohama Tire Corp., Houston, TX; *Int'l*, pg. 1521

Schoon, Sven-Erik, Mng. Dir.--Hagglunds Lidan AB, Lidkoping, Sweden; *Int'l*, pg. 670

Schoonmaker, Tim, Mng. Dir.--EMAP Radio, London, United Kingdom; *Int'l*, pg. 451

Schoonyoung, Frank, Pres. & Gen. Mgr.-Industrial Yeast North America--Fleischmann's Yeast, Fenton, MO; *Int'l*, pg. 237

Schoonyoung, Frank, Pres.--Crompton & Knowles Ingredient Technology Corp., Mahwah, NJ; *U.S. Public*, pg. 459

Schopback, Allen, Chief Oper. Officer--QC, Inc., Southampton, PA; *U.S. Private*, pg. 646

Schops, Gerhard, Chm. & Mng. Dir.--EURO RSCG, Dusseldorf, Germany; *Int'l*, pg. 602

Schork, Harold G., Pres. & Chief Exec. Officer--NationsBank of Quincy, Quincy, IL; *U.S. Public*, pg. 1164

Schorling, Thomas, Pres.--EG & G Astrophysics, Long Beach, CA; *U.S. Public*, pg. 543

Schornack, Paul, Pres.--Snappy Air Distribution Products, Detroit Lakes, MN; *U.S. Public*, pg. 1506

Schorner, Jochen, Dr., Chm.--Flender-ATB-Loher Systemtechnik GmbH, Rott, Germany; *Int'l*, pg. 400

Schorr, Howell S., Pres.--First Choice, Deer Park, NY; *U.S. Public*, pg. 978

Schorr, Marc D., Pres.--Treasure Island, Corp., Las Vegas, NV; *U.S. Public*, pg. 1117

Schossleitner, Dieter, Gen. Mng. Dir.--Maschinenfabrik Andritz AG, Graz, Austria; *Int'l*, pg. 14

Schossmann, Wolfgang, Mng. Dir.-Sls.--ESAB GmbH, Solingen, Germany; *Int'l*, pg. 282

Schott, Lyle W., V.P. & Mgr.-Opers.--Herberts-O'Brien Inc., Houston, TX; *Int'l*, pg. 626

Schottenstein, Saul, Pres.--Kroehler Furniture Manufacturing Company, Inc., Hickory, NC; *U.S. Private*, pg. 972

Schottland, Peter, Pres.--American Packaging Corporation, Rochester, NY; *U.S. Private*, pg. 60

Schottler, Hans-Peter, Pres.--Kohler Interconsult, Feldkirchen, Germany; *Int'l*, pg. 1420

Schottler, Karl, Gen. Mgr.--Signode Bernpak GmbH, Remscheid, Germany; *U.S. Public*, pg. 869

Schou, Christian, Chief Oper. Officer--Ferrosan Norge AS, Osteras, Norway; *Int'l*, pg. 989

Schou, Hans Didrik, Pres.--Kvaerner Hilnor a.s., Oslo, Norway; *Int'l*, pg. 769

Schouela, Allan, Pres.--Republic National Bank of New York (Canada), Montreal, Canada; *U.S. Public*, pg. 1381

Schouler, Tom, Gen. Mgr.--Sterling Electronics, Irvine, CA; *U.S. Public*, pg. 1051

Schoultz, Richard E., Pres.--Autron Incorporated, Holyoke, MA; *Int'l*, pg. 845

Schouten, A., Dir.--De Globe BV, Belfeld, Netherlands; *Int'l*, pg. 753

Schouwenburg, P., Chief Exec. Officer--Redland Dakprodukten B.V., Montfoort, Netherlands; *Int'l*, pg. 1093

Schowe, Carlton P., Pres.--IMI Systems Inc., Melville, NY; *U.S. Public*, pg. 1221

Schrader, Bob, Pres.--TACTech, Inc., Yorba Linda, CA; *U.S. Public*, pg. 1792

Schrader, Charles C., Gen. Mgr.--Leitchfield Div., Leitchfield, KY; *U.S. Public*, pg. 575

Schrader, Ernst, Mng. Dir.--Spraying Systems Deutschland GmbH, Hamburg, Germany; *U.S. Private*, pg. 1027

Schrader, Herbert, V.P.--Gould Electronics GmbH Foil Division, Eichstetten, Germany; *U.S. Public*, pg. 1592

Schrader, James, Plant Mgr.--Formica Corp., Cincinnati, OH; *Int'l*, pg. 129

Schrader, James, Sr. V.P.--Pacific Combining Corp., Los Angeles, CA; *U.S. Public*, pg. 802

Schrader, Thomas F., Pres. & Chief Exec. Officer--Wisconsin Gas Company, Milwaukee, WI; *U.S. Public*, pg. 1767

Schram, John R., Pres.--Simon & Schuster Elementary Division, Parsippany, NJ; *U.S. Private*, pg. 778

Schram, Ron, Pres.--Johnson Industries, Elgin, IL; *U.S. Private*, pg. 543

Schramek, Gregory A., Pres.-Northeast Region--ALLTEL Pennsylvania, Inc., Kittanning, PA; *U.S. Public*, pg. 56

Schramek, Gregory A., Reg. Pres.--Brookville Telephone Company, Brookville, PA; *U.S. Public*, pg. 56

Schramek, Gregory A., Pres.--Alltel Pennsylvania, Inc., Export, PA; *U.S. Public*, pg. 56

Schramek, Gregory A., Pres.--Mountain State Telephone Co., Masontown, WV; *U.S. Public*, pg. 380

Schramm, David J., Mng. Dir.--Packard Electric Ireland Limited, Dublin, Ireland; *U.S. Public*, pg. 723

Schrandt, Brian, V.P.--Detroit Gasket, Charlotte, NC; *U.S. Private*, pg. 560

Schratz, Theodore, Chief Oper. Officer--Caisse Hypothecaire du Luxembourg, Luxembourg, Luxembourg; *Int'l*, pg. 162

Schraufnagel, Harland, Pres.--Abbyland Pork Rack, Curtiss, WI; *U.S. Private*, pg. 10

Schraufnagel, Neil, Plant Mgr.--Bush Brothers & Company Plant, Dandridge, TN; *U.S. Private*, pg. 189

Schraufnalez, Harland, Pres.--Abbyland Illinois, Inc., Chicago, IL; *U.S. Private*, pg. 10

Schraum, Diane, Dir.-Nursing--Premier Tropic Staffing, Inc., Fort Myers, FL; *U.S. Public*, pg. 405

Schreer, Peter, Pres.-Philip Morris/Brazil--Philip Morris International Inc., Rye Brook, NY; *U.S. Public*, pg. 1289

Schreiber, Bill, Gen. Mgr.--Land O' Lakes, Carlisle, PA; *U.S. Private*, pg. 646

Schreim, Yousef, Company Head--SKF Intertrade Rep. Office, Dubai, United Arab Emirates; *Int'l*, pg. 1158

Schreiner, Claude, Gen. Mgr.--Produits Roche S.A., Neuilly-sur-Seine, France; *Int'l*, pg. 1121

Schreiner, Richard, Pres.--Fluid Regulators Co., Painesville, OH; *U.S. Public*, pg. 594

Schremp, John, Pres.--Firestone Synthetic Rubber & Latex Co., Akron, OH; *Int'l*, pg. 214

Schreuder, P.R.L., Mng. Dir.--Traditional Beer Investments, Sloane Park, South Africa; *Int'l*, pg. 1287

Schrewe, Klaus, Dir.--Correcta GmbH, Bad Wildungen, Germany; *Int'l*, pg. 172

Schriber, M.G., Dir.-Admin.--Du Pont de Nemours International S.A., Geneva, Switzerland; *U.S. Public*, pg. 532

Schrieber, H., Chief Oper. Officer--SAIA-Burgess GmbH, Dresden, Germany; *Int'l*, pg. 1501

Schrier, Eric, Pres. & Chief Exec. Officer--Time Inc. Health, San Francisco, CA; *U.S. Public*, pg. 1613

Schriever, Fred M., Chm. & Pres.--RCG International Inc., New York, NY; *U.S. Public*, pg. 1374

Schriever, Fred M., Pres.--RCC/Moody-Tottrup, New York, NY; *U.S. Public*, pg. 1374

Schrimpf, William, Pres.--Hartford-Wood River Terminal, Hartford, IL; *U.S. Private*, pg. 864

Schriner, Frank, Regional Pres.--First Tennessee Bank - Chattanooga, Chattanooga, TN; *U.S. Public*, pg. 639

Schroder, Johan, Mgr.--Radiometer (UK) Ltd., Crawley, United Kingdom; *Int'l*, pg. 1084

Schroder, Manfred F., Pres. & Chief Exec. Officer--VAW of America, Inc., Phoenix, AZ; *Int'l*, pg. 1466

Schroder, Ulrich, Plant Mgr.--Dexter GmbH, Garching, Germany; *U.S. Public*, pg. 505

Schroeder, Connie L., Personal Lines Underwriter--Service General Southeast, Tampa, FL; *U.S. Private*, pg. 609

Schroeder, Frank C., Pres.--First Maryland Intl. Banking Corp., York, PA; *Int'l*, pg. 64

Schroeder, H., Reg. Dir.--Max Gruenhut, GmbH & Co., Hamburg, Germany; *U.S. Public*, pg. 373

Schroeder, J.M., Pres.--Martinair Holland, Amsterdam, Netherlands; *Int'l*, pg. 719

Schroeder, Manfred F., Pres. & Chief Exec. Officer--VAW of America, Inc., Ellenville, NY; *Int'l*, pg. 1466

Schroeder, Manfred F., Pres. & Chief Exec. Officer--VAW of America, Inc., Saint Augustine, FL; *Int'l*, pg. 1466

Schroeder, Poul, Pres.--Finagrain, Cie Commerciale Agricole et Financiere S.A., Geneva, Switzerland; *U.S. Private*, pg. 268

Schroeder, Ronald A., Pres.--EPCO, Inc., Fremont, OH; *Int'l*, pg. 773

Schroeder, Vern, Pres.--Sanwa Leasing Corp., Troy, MI; *Int'l*, pg. 1189

Schroepfer, Mark T., Pres.--Lincoln Industrial, Saint Louis, MO; *U.S. Public*, pg. 1273

Schroers, William P., Pres.--Polytech Netting Industries, Orillia, Canada; *Int'l*, pg. 1362

Schroeter, Heimar, Chief Exec. Officer--Michael Conrad & Leo Burnett GmbH, Frankfurt/Main, Germany; *U.S. Private*, pg. 184

Schroiff, Gunter, Gen. Mgr.--AlliedSignal Bromsbelag GmbH, Hamburg, Germany; *U.S. Public*, pg. 52

Schroppe, J. Thomas, Pres.--Foster Wheeler Martinez, Martinez, CA; *U.S. Public*, pg. 677

Schropshire, Lewis, Pres.--Holiday Inn, Athens, GA; *U.S. Private*, pg. 134

Schrott, Franz, Gen. Mgr.--Dresdner (South East Asia) Ltd., Singapore, Singapore; *Int'l*, pg. 419

Schrushy, Richard, Pres. & Chief Exec. Officer--Healthsouth Corporation, Sunnyvale, CA; *U.S. Public*, pg. 803

Schrutt, Norman S., Pres. & Gen. Mgr.--WKHX-AM/WKHX-FM, Atlanta, GA; *U.S. Public*, pg. 512

Schryber, Mark, Pres.--Star Furniture Company, Houston, TX; *U.S. Public*, pg. 221

Schub, Barry A., Pres.--UAM Retirement Plan Services, Inc., New York, NY; *U.S. Public*, pg. 1674

Schube, Greg, Pres. & Chief Exec. Officer--Dualite Sales & Service, Inc., Williamsburg, OH; *U.S. Private*, pg. 344

Schubert, Clayton, Pres--Clarklift of North Dakota, West Fargo, ND; *U.S. Private*, pg. 244

Schubert, Holger, Dr., Mgr.--Didier-Anlagentechnik Holding GmbH, Wiesbaden, Germany; *Int'l*, pg. 1464

Schuch, Michael E., V.P. & Gen. Mgr.--WWWB-TV, Tampa, FL; *U.S. Private*, pg. 516

Schuchart, John A., Pres.--Centennial Energy Holdings, Inc., Bismarck, ND; *U.S. Public*, pg. 1025

Schuck, Timothy B., Exec. V.P. & Chief Oper. Officer--Barclays American/Mortgage Corp., Charlotte, NC; *Int'l*, pg. 165

Schue, G.K., Pres.--Great Lakes Chemical (Europe) Ltd., Frauenfeld, Switzerland; *U.S. Public*, pg. 760

Schuele, Alban W., V.P. & Pres.--Hoechst Specialty Products Group, Somerville, NJ; *Int'l*, pg. 625

Schueller, R.W., Pres.--Kemlite Company, Joliet, IL; *U.S. Public*, pg. 457

Schuerch, Hans Rudolph, Mng. Dir.--Sulzermedica Japan K.K., Tokyo, Japan; *Int'l*, pg. 1307

Schues, W., Chief Oper. Officer--The Tokio Marine & Fire Insurance Company (U.K.) Limited, Hamburg, Germany; *Int'l*, pg. 1393

Schuessler, James, Gen. Mgr.--WLUK-TV, Green Bay, WI; *U.S. Public*, pg. 1685

Schuette, Marvin, Chm. Bd., Pres., Chief Exec. Officer & Chief Oper. Officer--Sterling Building Systems, Inc., Rothschild, WI; *U.S. Private*, pg. 1154

Schugens, Siegfried, Chief Oper. Officer--Columbia Cosmetics GmbH, Berlin, Germany; *Int'l*, pg. 609

Schuh, Dale R., Pres.--Sentry Life Insurance Co., Stevens Point, WI; *U.S. Private*, pg. 985

Schuit, A., Pres.--Van Leer Flexibles, Inc., Houston, TX; *Int'l*, pg. 1146

Schuit, Bram, Pres.--ALK Benelux BV, Groningen, Netherlands; *Int'l*, pg. 288

Schul, R.J., Pres.--Alco Controls Div., Maryland Heights, MO; *U.S. Public*, pg. 572

Schulein, S., Chief Exec. Officer--Oce-Credit Corporation, Purchase, NY; *Int'l*, pg. 994

Schuler, C., Chief Oper. Officer--Zurich Compagnie d'assurances sur la vie, Luxembourg, Luxembourg; *Int'l*, pg. 1529

Schuler, C., Chief Exec. Officer--Zurich Compagnie d'Assurances, Luxembourg, Luxembourg; *Int'l*, pg. 1531

Schuler, C., Chief Exec. Officer--Zurich International Services (Luxembourg) S.A., Luxembourg, Luxembourg; *Int'l*, pg. 1532

Schuler, E., Rep.--Swiss Bank Corporation, Tokyo, Japan; *Int'l*, pg. 1330

Schuler, Joe, V.P. & Gen. Mgr.--Smart Cards & Systems, Minnetonka, MN; *U.S. Private*, pg. 312

Schull, Daniel S., Pres. & Chief Exec. Officer--First Security Insurance, Inc., Salt Lake City, UT; *U.S. Public*, pg. 638

Schull, Daniel S., Pres. & Chief Exec. Officer--First Security Life Ins. Co. of Arizona, Salt Lake City, UT; *U.S. Public*, pg. 638

Schuller tot Peursum, P.C., Gen. Mgr.--ING (BVI) Trust, Road Town, Virgin Islands (British); *Int'l*, pg. 650

Schulman, Paul M., Pres.--Paul Schulman Co., New York, NY; *Int'l*, pg. 117

Schulman, S.L., Dr., Pres.--De La Rue Faraday, Chantilly, VA; *Int'l*, pg. 387

Schulman, Sharon E., Pres.--Consumers New Jersey Water Company, Hamilton, NJ; *U.S. Public*, pg. 438

Schulman, Sharon E., Pres.--Consumers New Hampshire Water Co., Londonderry, NH; *U.S. Public*, pg. 438

Schulmeyer, Gerhard, Chief Oper. Officer--Siemens-Nixdorf Informationssysteme AG, Paderborn, Germany; *Int'l*, pg. 1245
Schult, Robert W., Pres. & Chief Oper. Officer--Nestle USA, Glendale, CA; *Int'l*, pg. 916
Schulte-Hillen, Gerd Dr., Chm.-Exec. Bd. & Chief Exec. Officer--Gruner + Jahr AG & Co., Hamburg, Germany; *Int'l*, pg. 190
Schulte-Noelle, Henning, Dr., Chm. Bd.-Mngmt.--Allianz Aktiengesellschaft, Munich, Germany; *Int'l*, pg. 58
Schulte, Darrell J., Pres. & Chief Exec. Officer--Colorado Business Bank of Littleton, N.A., Littleton, CO; *U.S. Private*, pg. 255
Schulte, G., Mng. Dir.--Georg Fischer Automobilguss GmbH, Singen, Germany; *Int'l*, pg. 488
Schulte, Joseph, Gen. Mgr.--Capitol Hardware, Inc., Niles, MI; *U.S. Private*, pg. 904
Schulte, Manfred, Rep.--Generale Bank & Co., Dusseldorf, Germany; *Int'l*, pg. 548
Schultz, Diana, Mgr.--Rittenhouse Paper Co., Park Ridge, IL; *U.S. Private*, pg. 933
Schultz, Dr. Peter, Pres.--Heraeus Amersil Inc., Duluth, GA; *Int'l*, pg. 616
Schultz, Edgard, Mng. Dir.--Acuson Pty. Ltd., Epping, Australia; *U.S. Public*, pg. 18
Schultz, Erik, Chief Oper. Officer--SAPA A/S, Grena, Denmark; *Int'l*, pg. 441
Schultz, Gary, Plant Supvr.--Gilster Mary Lee Corp., Momence, IL; *U.S. Private*, pg. 455
Schultz, Harvey, Pres.--AMREP Solutions, Inc., New York, NY; *U.S. Public*, pg. 104
Schultz, James, Chief Exec. Officer--PREPLINK, Cleveland, OH; *U.S. Private*, pg. 475
Schultz, James R., Pres.--GL Direct, Avon Lake, OH; *U.S. Private*, pg. 475
Schultz, Joel, Distr. Ctr. Mgr.--E.J. Brach, Inc., Morrow, GA; *U.S. Private*, pg. 163
Schultz, Kevin, Chief Oper. Officer--Hoffer's Glass Fab, Schofield, WI; *U.S. Private*, pg. 239
Schultz, Martin, Mng. Dir.--Munters Euroform GmbH, Aachen, Germany; *Int'l*, pg. 669
Schultz, Mylo, V.P. & Gen. Mgr.--LeFebure, Area North, Bensenville, IL; *Int'l*, pg. 387
Schultz, P., Dir.--Euryza Reis GmbH, Hamburg, Germany; *Int'l*, pg. 244
Schultz, R., Dir.-Res.--OCG Microelectronic Materials AG, Basel, Switzerland; *Int'l*, pg. 973
Schultz, R., Dir.-Res.--OCG Microelectronic Materials AG, Basel, Switzerland; *U.S. Public*, pg. 1220
Schultz, Raymond E., Pres. & Chief Exec. Officer--Hampton Inns, Inc., Memphis, TN; *U.S. Public*, pg. 1335
Schultz, Tom, Plant Mgr.--National Frozen Foods Corporation - Moses Lake, Moses Lake, WA; *U.S. Private*, pg. 783
Schulweis, Melvin, Pres.--Judel Products Corp., Elmsford, NY; *U.S. Public*, pg. 1609
Schulz, David W., Pres.--M & I Investment Management Corp., Milwaukee, WI; *U.S. Public*, pg. 1051
Schulz, Ekkehard, Dr., Pres.--Thyssen Stahl AG, Duisburg, Germany; *Int'l*, pg. 1388
Schulz, H., Admin. Mgr.--Ferro Industrial Products Ltd., Oakville, Canada; *U.S. Public*, pg. 619
Schulz, Hans, Mng. Dir.--Balzers Verschleissschutz GmbH, Bingen, Germany; *Int'l*, pg. 997
Schulz, Herman, Pres.--Dallas Aerospace, Inc., Carrollton, TX; *U.S. Public*, pg. 187
Schulz, John, Pres.--Rogerson Aircraft Systems, Irvine, CA; *U.S. Private*, pg. 940
Schulz, Jurgen W., Mng. Dir.--Sulzer Weise GmbH, Bruchsal, Germany; *Int'l*, pg. 1306
Schulze, Horst, Pres. & Chief Oper. Officer--The Ritz-Carlton Hotel Company LLC, Atlanta, GA; *U.S. Private*, pg. 594
Schulze, Horst H., Pres. & Chief Oper. Officer-The Ritz-Carlton Hotel Company--Marriott International, Inc., Washington, DC; *U.S. Public*, pg. 1047
Schulze, Jeurgen H., Gen. Mgr.--Lonza-Werke GmbH, Waldshut, Germany; *Int'l*, pg. 67
Schulze, Klaus Dieter, Chief Oper. Officer--Frigoscandia Food Process Systems GmbH, Lintorf, Germany; *U.S. Public*, pg. 606
Schulze, Peter, Dr., V.P.--Bayport Specialty Polymers & Waxes Division, Pasadena, TX; *Int'l*, pg. 624
Schulzezur Wiersch, Ulrich, Sr. V.P. & Mng. Dir.--Pharm-Allergan GmbH, Ettlingen, Germany; *U.S. Public*, pg. 46
Schumacher, C., Chief Exec. Officer--Baumberger-Getranke AG, Langenthal, Switzerland; *Int'l*, pg. 479
Schumacher, Hans H., Pres. & Chief Exec. Officer--Voest-Alpine International Corporation, New York, NY; *Int'l*, pg. 1470
Schumacher, Heidi, Rep.--CMC International (S.E. Asia) Pte. Ltd., Beijing, China; *U.S. Public*, pg. 413
Schumacher, Heidi, Gen. Mgr.--Cometals China, Inc., Beijing, China; *U.S. Public*, pg. 414
Schumacher, Juergen, Pres.--Dole Latin America, San Jose, Costa Rica; *U.S. Public*, pg. 515
Schumaker, Norbert, Exec. V.P.--McGraw-Hill Publications Services Group, New York, NY; *U.S. Public*, pg. 1071
Schumaker, Tom, Publr.--Keynoter Publishing Company, Inc., Marathon, FL; *U.S. Public*, pg. 964
Schumann, Bill, V.P. & Gen. Mgr.--FMC Corp., Agricultural Products Group, Philadelphia, PA; *U.S. Public*, pg. 605
Schummacher, Jean-Philippe, Gen. Mgr.--Allen Automotive International (France) S.A.R.L., Boulogne, France; *U.S. Public*, pg. 1
Schunmann, William C., V.P.--Rogers Japan Inc., Tokyo, Japan; *U.S. Public*, pg. 1403
Schunter, Roland, Chief Oper. Officer--Floordress Reinigungsgerate GmbH, Lorch, Germany; *Int'l*, pg. 609
Schupp, Gerhard, Chief Oper. Officer--Krauss-Maffei Automationstechnik GmbH, Munich, Germany; *Int'l*, pg. 836
Schupphaus, Herbert, Pres.--Eickhoff Corporation, Pittsburgh, PA; *Int'l*, pg. 542
Schurer, H., Chief Oper. Officer--Charmilles Deutschland Maschinen Ges. mbH, Fellbach, Germany; *Int'l*, pg. 489
Schurmann, Maximilian, Mng. Dir.--Dresdner Bank AG, Taipei, Taiwan; *Int'l*, pg. 419
Schurmann, P.R., Gen. Mgr.--Maerz Ofenbau AG, Zurich, Switzerland; *U.S. Private*, pg. 904
Schuster, Richard S., Pres.--NIC Components Corp., Amityville, NY; *U.S. Public*, pg. 1205
Schuster, Werner, Pres.--Schuster & Partner, Neuss, Germany; *Int'l*, pg. 394
Schuster, Wes, Pres.--Tecomet-Albuquerque, Albuquerque, NM; *U.S. Public*, pg. 1592
Schuster, Wesley, Chief Oper. Officer--Tecomet Inc., Wilmington, MA; *U.S. Public*, pg. 1591
Schuster, Wesley, Pres.--Tecomet-Tempe, Tempe, AZ; *U.S. Public*, pg. 1592
Schuster, Wesley, Pres.--Tecomet Inc., Wilmington, MA; *U.S. Public*, pg. 1592
Schutte, Herbert T., Pres.--Danis Heavy Construction Co., Dayton, OH; *U.S. Private*, pg. 310
Schutz, Charles J., V.P. & Gen. Mgr.--Waukesha Cherry-Burrell, Jeffersontown, KY; *U.S. Public*, pg. 1677
Schutz, Gerhard, Mng. Dir.--Sulzer Chemtech AG, Winterthur, Switzerland; *Int'l*, pg. 1307
Schutz, Gustav, Gen. Mgr.--Polaroid GmbH, Offenbach/Main, Germany; *U.S. Public*, pg. 1314
Schutz, Hans-Josef, Pres.--Pfeiffer of America, Inc., Princeton, NJ; *U.S. Public*, pg. 125
Schutz, Hubert, Gen. Mgr.--Forbo Glawo GmbH, Wermelskirchen, Germany; *Int'l*, pg. 497
Schutz, P.R., Mng. Dir.--Wyeth (Ireland) Limited, Limerick, Ireland; *U.S. Public*, pg. 82
Schutze, Peter, Pres.--Componenta International Deutschland GmbH, Ratingen, Germany; *Int'l*, pg. 1421
Schwab, Anthony, Pres. & Chief Exec. Officer--Sprayway, Inc., Addison, IL; *U.S. Private*, pg. 462
Schwab, Frederick J., Pres. & Chief Exec. Officer--Porsche Cars North America, Inc., Reno, NV; *Int'l*, pg. 1063
Schwab, Peter, Pres. & Chief Oper. Officer--The Foothill Group, Inc., Los Angeles, CA; *U.S. Public*, pg. 1201
Schwab, Shelly, Pres.--Universal Studios TV, Universal City, CA; *Int'l*, pg. 1215
Schwab, Stephen, Grp. V.P.--Engineered Systems Group, Jackson, MI; *U.S. Public*, pg. 24
Schwab, W., Gen. Mgr.--MSD Sharp & Dohme GmbH, Munich, Germany; *U.S. Public*, pg. 1092
Schwach, Gary, Pres. & Gen. Mgr.--AAR Cadillac Manufacturing Div., Cadillac, MI; *U.S. Public*, pg. 1
Schwade, Hans, Pres. & Chief Exec. Officer--Bergemann USA, Inc., Atlanta, GA; *Int'l*, pg. 401
Schwager, John L., Pres. & Chief Exec. Officer--Alamco, Inc., Charleston, WV; *U.S. Public*, pg. 403
Schwager, John L., Pres.--Alamco-Delaware, Inc., Wilmington, DE; *U.S. Public*, pg. 403
Schwaller, Jim, Pres.--Guzzler Manufacturing, Inc., Birmingham, AL; *U.S. Public*, pg. 616
Schwallie, Ambrose, Pres.--Westinghouse Savannah River Co., Aiken, SC; *U.S. Public*, pg. 273
Schwamm, P., Gen. Mgr.--American Drug Corporation, Tokyo, Japan; *U.S. Public*, pg. 80
Schwamm, P., Gen. Mgr.--A.H. Robins International Company, Tokyo, Japan; *U.S. Public*, pg. 82
Schwander, Beat, Gen. Mgr.--Optigal S.A., Lausanne, Switzerland; *Int'l*, pg. 866
Schwanz, Don, Pres.--Space & Aviation Control, Phoenix, AZ; *U.S. Public*, pg. 834
Schwarczer, Etienne, Mng. Dir.--Hidepito, Budapest, Hungary; *Int'l*, pg. 823
Schwardt, Peter, Pres.--LEP International Inc., Etobicoke, Canada; *U.S. Private*, pg. 571
Schwartkopf, Hermann, Gen. Mgr.--Life Sciences-Meissner & Wurst, Stuttgart, Germany; *U.S. Private*, pg. 317
Schwartz, Alain, First V.P.--RNBNY Representative Office-Mexico, Mexico, Mexico; *U.S. Public*, pg. 1381
Schwartz, Alan, Chief Fin. Officer & V.P.--Valleyfair, Shakopee, MN; *U.S. Public*, pg. 319
Schwartz, Alfred, Chief Oper. Officer--Bio-Rad Clinical Div., Hercules, CA; *U.S. Public*, pg. 230
Schwartz, Bruce J., Pres.--Sysco Food Services of Los Angeles, Inc., Walnut, CA; *U.S. Public*, pg. 1551
Schwartz, Craig, Pres.--American Steel LLC, Portland, OR; *U.S. Public*, pg. 1375
Schwartz, Dennis, Pres. & Chief Exec. Officer--Valley American Bank, South Bend, IN; *U.S. Public*, pg. 674
Schwartz, Diane, Pres.--The Manufacturers Life Insurance Company of Michigan, Toronto, Canada; *Int'l*, pg. 840
Schwartz, E. Ernest, Grp. V.P. & Gen. Mgr.--Aircraft Products Company, Delray Beach, FL; *U.S. Public*, pg. 159
Schwartz, Fred W., Pres.--Leviton Mfg. Co., Inc., Little Neck, NY; *U.S. Private*, pg. 663
Schwartz, H.G., Jr., Chm. Bd. & Pres.--Sverdrup Environmental Inc., Maryland Heights, MO; *U.S. Private*, pg. 1057
Schwartz, H.G., Jr., Dr., Pres.--Sverdrup Civil, Inc., Maryland Heights, MO; *U.S. Private*, pg. 1057
Schwartz, H.L. III, Publr.--Capitol City Publishing Co., Inc.-The Trentonian, Trenton, NJ; *U.S. Public*, pg. 934
Schwartz, Irwin, Pres. & Chief Exec. Officer--Gibraltar Corp. of America, New York, NY; *U.S. Public*, pg. 1528
Schwartz, Jeanne M., Pres.--The Remembrance Institute, Atlanta, GA; *Int'l*, pg. 499
Schwartz, Joel A., Pres.--Benihana International, Inc., Miami, FL; *U.S. Public*, pg. 212
Schwartz, John, Gen. Mgr.--SmithKline Beecham Clinical Laboratories, Schaumburg, IL; *Int'l*, pg. 1265
Schwartz, Leaonard, Pres.--VGF Corporation, Lake Success, NY; *U.S. Public*, pg. 15
Schwartz, Mark, V.P.-Opers.--Hypermart USA, Bentonville, AR; *U.S. Public*, pg. 1733
Schwartz, Mordecai, Pres.--AIC Holdings, Inc., Philadelphia, PA; *U.S. Public*, pg. 362
Schwartz, Paul H., Pres.--Indeco, Inc., Bettendorf, IA; *U.S. Private*, pg. 591
Schwartz, Randy S., Pres.--Process & Industrial Division-S.E., Charlotte, NC; *U.S. Private*, pg. 317
Schwartz, Robin, Pres.--Pioneer Direct Corporation, Rockford, IL; *U.S. Public*, pg. 433
Schwartz, Stanley, Chief Opr. Officer--Techniform Corp., Oklahoma City, OK; *U.S. Public*, pg. 971
Schwartz, Stewart, Gen. Mgr.--KMSP Television, Inc., Eden Prairie, MN; *U.S. Public*, pg. 352
Schwarz, Dennis, Div. Mgr.--Oregon Division, Portland, OR; *U.S. Public*, pg. 38
Schwarz, Hans Rudolf, Chief Oper. Officer--SAB NIFE (Suisse) S.A., Neuendorf, Switzerland; *Int'l*, pg. 54
Schwarz, James R., Pres. & Gen. Mgr.--Viking Formed Products, Middlebury, IN; *U.S. Public*, pg. 388
Schwarz, Kent, Area Mgr.--P.T. Milchem Indonesia, Jakarta, Indonesia; *U.S. Public*, pg. 167
Schwarz, M., Corp. Sec.--Noorderviiet & Winninghoff/Leo Burnett B.V., Amsterdam, Netherlands; *U.S. Private*, pg. 186
Schwarzbeck, Sandra, Reg. Mgr.--U.S. Yellow Pages, Chicago, IL; *U.S. Private*, pg. 1167
Schwarzenbach, Robert, Chief Fin. Officer--Baltec Maschinenbau AG, Pfaffikon, Switzerland; *Int'l*, pg. 479
Schwecke, Fred, Pres.--Relm Communications, Inc., Melbourne, FL; *U.S. Public*, pg. 1376
Schweickart, Klaus, Chm.--BYK Gulden-Lomberg GmbH, Konstanz, Germany; *Int'l*, pg. 66
Schweinhage, P., Mng. Dir.--Deminex UK Oil and Gas Ltd., London, United Kingdom; *Int'l*, pg. 1461
Schweitzer, Frank, Mgr.--Sandvik Belzer GmbH, Wuppertal, Germany; *Int'l*, pg. 1186
Schweitzer, Mike, Exec. V.P. & Mng. Dir.--Western International Media Corporation, Orlando, FL; *U.S. Private*, pg. 1167
Schweizer, Richard, Gen. Mgr.--ACS Mistermesh, Houston, TX; *U.S. Private*, pg. 4
Schwendimann, Carlo, Mng. Dir.--Del Bosco & C.S.R.L., Milan, Italy; *Int'l*, pg. 303
Schwenger, Bruce, Pres.--Bank of Montreal Investor Services Limited, Toronto, Canada; *Int'l*, pg. 153
Schwenk, G. Timothy, Mgr.--General Employment Enterprises, Inc., Columbus, OH; *U.S. Public*, pg. 714
Schwenk, Oscar J., Mng. Dir.--Pilatus Flugzeugwerke AG, Stans, Switzerland; *Int'l*, pg. 998
Schwensen, Jurgen, Chief Oper. Officer--Akerlund & Rausing Verpackung GmbH, Hamburg, Germany; *Int'l*, pg. 33
Schwesig, Norman L., Pres.--Maritz Performance Improvement Company, Fenton, MO; *U.S. Private*, pg. 704
Schwindling, Jean-Jacques, Mng. Dir.--SKF (Ho Chi Minh City), Ho Chi Minh City, Vietnam; *Int'l*, pg. 1158
Schwinghammer, P., Chief Exec. Officer--Wiler Aktienbrauerei, Wil, Switzerland; *Int'l*, pg. 479
Schwitter, Oswald, Gen. Mgr.--Sensormatic AG, Cham, Switzerland; *U.S. Public*, pg. 1457
Schwitzer, Allen, Pres.--Integral Marketing, Inc., Lanham, MD; *U.S. Public*, pg. 883
Schwizer, Arthur, Mng. Dir.--Sulzer Medical Technology Ltd., Winterthur, Switzerland; *Int'l*, pg. 1307
Schwob, Richard, Gen. Mgr.--Lorain Products, Lorain, OH; *U.S. Private*, pg. 921
Schwob, Richard, Gen. Mgr.--RELTEC Systems, Bedford, TX; *U.S. Private*, pg. 921
Schwob, Richard, Gen. Mgr.--Reltec, Inc., Warrenville, IL; *U.S. Private*, pg. 921
Schyler, Jerry, Pres.--ARCO Dubai, Incorporated, Dubai, United Arab Emirates; *U.S. Public*, pg. 144
Scibilia, Phillip, Pres.--Appleton & Lange, Norwalk, CT; *U.S. Private*, pg. 778
Scidenberger, Phil, Pres. & Gen. Mgr.--Southern Post South Carolina, West Columbia, SC; *U.S. Public*, pg. 413
Scifres, Donald R., Pres.--Spectra Diode Laboratories, San Jose, CA; *U.S. Public*, pg. 1785
Scipio del Campo, Andrew H., Pres. & Chief Exec. Officer--Scotia Discount Brokerage Inc., Toronto, Canada; *Int'l*, pg. 155
Scirea, Giovanni, Mng. Dir.--AMETEK Italia, Milan, Italy; *U.S. Public*, pg. 100
Sciuto, John J., Pres. & Chief Exec. Officer--Comptek Federal Systems, Inc., Buffalo, NY; *U.S. Public*, pg. 419
Scmalkamp, Tony, Gen. Mgr.--Bose B.V., Edam, Netherlands; *U.S. Private*, pg. 161
Scobey, Mike, Pres. & Publr.--Wausau Daily Herald, Wausau, WI; *U.S. Public*, pg. 700
Scoble, T.J., Dir.--KEG Restaurants U.S., Inc., Wilmington, DE; *Int'l*, pg. 1499
Scoby, Gloria, V.P. & Publisher--Crain's Chicago Business, Chicago, IL; *U.S. Private*, pg. 285
Scodari, Joseph C., Exec. V.P.-Pharmaceutical Div.--Centocor Pharmaceutical Division, Malvern, PA; *U.S. Public*, pg. 323
Scoggins, Don W., Pres.--Texas Eastman Co., Longview, TX; *U.S. Public*, pg. 550
Scohy, Jim, Resident Mgr.--Port Huron Mill, Port Huron, MI; *U.S. Public*, pg. 465
Scola, Mariano, Exec. V.P. & Gen. Mgr.--Banco Santander Trust & Banking Corporation (Bahamas) Ltd., Nassau, Bahamas; *Int'l*, pg. 143
Scolan, Daniel, Pres.--Information et Technologies, Paris, France; *Int'l*, pg. 239
Scollard, W.E., V.P.--Ford Manufacturing Operations, Dearborn, MI; *U.S. Public*, pg. 662
Scollen, Donald, Plant Mgr.--Mitchell Corporation, Clare Div., Clare, MI; *U.S. Private*, pg. 753
Scolnick, Edward M., M.D., Pres.--Merck Research Laboratories, Rahway, NJ; *U.S. Public*, pg. 1091
Scornavacca, Art, Gen. Mgr.--Microsemi PPC, Inc., Riviera Beach, FL; *U.S. Public*, pg. 1107
Scorsone, L.V., Pres.--Engineered Construction Division, Woodlands, TX; *U.S. Public*, pg. 1304
Scotchbrook, Godfrey E., Chm.--Scotchbrook Communications Ltd., Wan Chai, Hong Kong; *U.S. Private*, pg. 411

Scotland, Nick J., Mng. Dir.--Jotun-Henry Clark Ltd., London, United Kingdom; *Int'l*, pg. 715
Scott, A. Nathan, Mng. Dir.--Velsicol Eesti A.S., Tallinn, Estonia; *U.S. Private*, pg. 1135
Scott, Billy, Pres.--Allright Sierra Parking Inc., Las Vegas, NV; *U.S. Private*, pg. 43
Scott, Carl E., Pres.--Tele-Trip Company, Omaha, NE; *U.S. Private*, pg. 770
Scott, Charles R., Pres.--Computrol, Inc., Boise, ID; *U.S. Private*, pg. 83
Scott, Chuck, Gen. Mgr.--Sermatech Southwest, Sugar Land, TX; *U.S. Public*, pg. 1570
Scott, Crellin, Gen. Mgr.--Black Pine Mine, Burley, ID; *U.S. Public*, pg. 1269
Scott, David, Pres.--Huval Bakery, Inc., Lafayette, LA; *U.S. Public*, pg. 657
Scott, David Maxwell, Mng. Dir.--Matthew Gloag & Son Limited, Perth, United Kingdom; *Int'l*, pg. 619
Scott, Derek, Pres.--Fosbel, Inc., Berea, OH; *Int'l*, pg. 234
Scott, Des I., Mng. Dir.--JA/MONT Ireland Ltd., Dublin, Ireland; *U.S. Public*, pg. 673
Scott, Gary R., V.P. & Gen. Mgr.--737/757 Programs, Renton, WA; *U.S. Public*, pg. 240
Scott, Geoff, Grp. Chief Exec. Officer--Frontline- Distribution Division, Peterborough, United Kingdom; *Int'l*, pg. 451
Scott, J.B., Chief Exec. Officer--Zurich Life Insurance Company of America, Schaumburg, IL; *Int'l*, pg. 1530
Scott, J.D., Chm. Bd.-ScottPolar Corp.--Toromont Industries Ltd., Concord, Canada; *Int'l*, pg. 1400
Scott, J.D., Chm. Bd.--ScottPolar Corporation, Twin Falls, ID; *Int'l*, pg. 1400
Scott, J.E., Mng. Dir.--New Tech Coatings Ltd., Preston, United Kingdom; *Int'l*, pg. 124
Scott, Jack, Pres.--AGRA Vadeko Inc., Oakville, Canada; *Int'l*, pg. 30
Scott, Jack, Pres.--Hydrometrics, Inc., Helena, MT; *U.S. Public*, pg. 138
Scott, James, Pres.--Locknetics Security Engineering, Forestville, CT; *U.S. Private*, pg. 507
Scott, Jim, Gen. Mgr.--Fort Worth Auto Auction, Fort Worth, TX; *U.S. Private*, pg. 283
Scott, Joe L., Pres.--Charlotte Community Hospital, Indianapolis, IN; *U.S. Public*, pg. 404
Scott, Joe L., Pres.--Rehabilitative Health Services, Inc., Indianapolis, IN; *U.S. Public*, pg. 405
Scott, John, Pres.--N-Lynx Andrew, Simi Valley, CA; *U.S. Public*, pg. 112
Scott, John A., Chief Oper. Officer--Philadelphia Investment Corporation of Delaware, Wilmington, DE; *U.S. Public*, pg. 357
Scott, John S., Chm. & Chief Exec. Officer--XL Vision Inc., Sebastian, FL; *U.S. Public*, pg. 1424
Scott, Keith, Gen. Mgr.--Thermo Electron (Canada), Saint Leonard, Canada; *U.S. Public*, pg. 1596
Scott, Ken, Mng. Dir.--Hamptons Residential, Bristol, United Kingdom; *Int'l*, pg. 216
Scott, Lisa, V.P. & Gen. Mgr.--Eastern News Distributors, Inc., New York, NY; *U.S. Private*, pg. 517
Scott, M., Branch Mgr.--Van Leeuwen Pipe & Tube Corp., Tampa, FL; *Int'l*, pg. 1450
Scott, Mark, Gen. Mgr.--Allegan County Cablevision Inc., Allegan, MI; *U.S. Public*, pg. 287
Scott, Marlene, Pres.--Ingram Periodicals Inc., La Vergne, TN; *U.S. Private*, pg. 563
Scott, Marvin, V.P. & Gen. Mgr.--Van Leeuwen Pipe & Tube of the Southeast, Inc., Tampa, FL; *Int'l*, pg. 1450
Scott, Michael J., Pres. & Gen. Mgr.--International Correspondence Schools Canadian Ltd., Montreal, Canada; *U.S. Public*, pg. 784
Scott, Michael S., Mng. Dir.--Tees Storage Company Limited, Middlesbrough, United Kingdom; *U.S. Public*, pg. 693
Scott, P.B., Plant Mgr.--Curtis 1000, Inc., Mason City, IA; *U.S. Public*, pg. 70
Scott, R. Dale, Pres. & Gen. Mgr.--Glacier Park, Inc., Phoenix, AZ; *U.S. Public*, pg. 1718
Scott, R.M., Mng. Dir.--MSA (Britain) Limited, Coatbridge, United Kingdom; *U.S. Public*, pg. 1114
Scott, Randall, Pres.--Meadowlark, Inc., Englewood, CO; *U.S. Public*, pg. 471
Scott, Randall J., Pres.--Amax Coal Company, Keensburg, IL; *U.S. Public*, pg. 470
Scott, Randall J., Pres.--Ayrshire Land Company, Sullivan, IN; *U.S. Public*, pg. 471
Scott, Randall J., Pres.--Beech Coal Company, Bicknell, IN; *U.S. Public*, pg. 471
Scott, Robert M., Pres.--Integrated Marketing Services, Omaha, NE; *U.S. Public*, pg. 631
Scott, Robert W., Plant Mgr.--Axle and Brake Div., Humboldt, TN; *U.S. Public*, pg. 556
Scott, Roland, Pres.--Burtco Metal Systems, Westminster Station, VT; *U.S. Private*, pg. 188
Scott, Ronald H., Pres.--Midwest Carbide Corporation, Keokuk, IA; *U.S. Public*, pg. 33
Scott, Ronald H., Pres.--Nitrous Oxide Corp. (Donora), Keokuk, IA; *U.S. Public*, pg. 33
Scott, S.C., Pres.--Corn Products North America Div., Argo, IL; *U.S. Public*, pg. 448
Scott, S.R., Pres.--Waverley Mineral Corporation, Bala Cynwyd, PA; *Int'l*, pg. 803
Scott, Terence M., V.P.--Sulzer Infra (UK), Farnborough, United Kingdom; *Int'l*, pg. 1306
Scott, Thomas, Pres.--Publisher Resources Inc., La Vergne, TN; *U.S. Private*, pg. 563
Scott, Tom W., Pres.--Commerce General Corporation, Memphis, TN; *U.S. Public*, pg. 1155
Scott, William J., Sr., Pres.--Joy Environmental Technologies, Inc., Houston, TX; *U.S. Public*, pg. 789
Scotten, Tom, Pres.--Bechtel Power Corporation, Gaithersburg, MD; *U.S. Private*, pg. 128
Scotti, Anthony J., Chm. Bd.--Scotti Brothers Entertainment Industries, Santa Monica, CA; *U.S. Public*, pg. 41
Scotti, Gavin A., Chm. & Chief Exec. Officer--Klemtner Advertising Inc., New York, NY; *U.S. Public*, pg. 1422
Scougall, Christopher, Assoc. Dir.--National Australia Bank/GATX, Sydney, Australia; *U.S. Public*, pg. 691
Scovic, Peter, Pres.--Ronningen-Petter Div., Portage, MI; *U.S. Public*, pg. 521
Scowcroft, B., Branch Mgr.--Senior Tift-Victoria, Sunshine, Australia; *Int'l*, pg. 1223
Scozzie, James A., Dr., Pres.--Ricera Inc., Painesville, OH; *Int'l*, pg. 689
Scribner, Coy J., Pres.--Metric Systems Corp., Fort Walton Beach, FL; *U.S. Public*, pg. 1563
Scrimshaw, J. Eric, Mng. Dir.--United Kingdom Plant, Loughborough, United Kingdom; *U.S. Public*, pg. 443
Scripps, Charles E, Jr., Gen. Mgr.--The Courier Journal, Jupiter, FL; *U.S. Public*, pg. 1447
Scriven, J., Pres.--Teshmont Consultants Inc., Winnipeg, Canada; *Int'l*, pg. 31
Scrivener, M.J., V.P. & Gen. Mgr.--K.W. Power Source, Skokie, IL; *Int'l*, pg. 127
Scriver, Gerald H., Pres. & Chief Exec. Officer--Westpeak Investment Advisors, Inc., Boulder, CO; *U.S. Private*, pg. 738
Scrofano, Robert, Pres.--AlliedSignal Ocean Systems, Sylmar, CA; *U.S. Public*, pg. 50
Scruby, Dale, Gen. Mgr.--Western Automotive Rebuilders, Saskatoon, Canada; *Int'l*, pg. 23
Scruggs, H.E., Jr., Chm. Bd.--American Investment Bank, NA, Salt Lake City, UT; *U.S. Public*, pg. 990
Scruggs, Mike, Pres.--Larson Boats, Little Falls, MN; *U.S. Private*, pg. 447
Scruggs, Mike, Pres.--Glastron Boats, Little Falls, MN; *U.S. Private*, pg. 447
Scrutton, Simon, Gen. Mgr.--Letraset Ashford, Ashford, United Kingdom; *Int'l*, pg. 461
Scull, Douglas, Mgr.-Plant--Chardon Electrical Components, Inc., Greeneville, TN; *U.S. Private*, pg. 229
Scull, Jorge, Chief Exec. Officer--EURO RSCG-Venezuela, Caracas, Venezuela; *Int'l*, pg. 603
Sculley, Robert F., Pres.--Tarmac Florida, Deerfield Beach, FL; *Int'l*, pg. 1355
Scullion, Bob, Mng. Dir.--Blackwood Brothers Ltd, Kilmarnock, United Kingdom; *Int'l*, pg. 385
Scully, Dennis, Pres.--Cordley Temprite, Oak Brook, IL; *U.S.* Private, pg. 372
Scully, James A., Jr., Pres.-PMKK Japan--Philip Morris International Inc., Rye Brook, NY; *U.S. Public*, pg. 1289
Scurati, Eng., Pres.--Immobiliare Metanopoli S.p.A., Milan, Italy; *Int'l*, pg. 428
Scussel, Jon, Gen. Mgr.--Tyco Backplanes, Stafford Springs, CT; *U.S. Public*, pg. 1648
Seabolt, Stephen J., Pres. & Chief Exec. Officer--Sunset Publishing Corporation, Menlo Park, CA; *U.S. Public*, pg. 1613
Seaborn, John, Mng. Dir.--Kimberly-Clark, Quebec, Hull, Canada; *U.S. Public*, pg. 959
Seabridge, G., Chief Oper. Officer--Cornercroft Engineering Limited, Coventry, United Kingdom; *Int'l*, pg. 265
Seabrook, Francis G., Chief Exec. Officer--Barnett Mortgage Company, Jacksonville, FL; *U.S. Public*, pg. 1162
Seabrook, Graeme, Mng. Dir.--The Dairy Farm Company, Limited, Causeway Bay, Hong Kong; *Int'l*, pg. 703
Seagrave, Richard A., V.P.-Mfg.--Construction Equipment Div., Racine, WI; *U.S. Public*, pg. 311
Seagraves, Harold E., Pres.--H.E.S. International, Inc., Kansas City, KS; *U.S. Public*, pg. 1209
Seah, Michael S.I., Gen. Mgr.--Wang Computers (Pte.) Limited, Singapore, Singapore; *U.S. Public*, pg. 1737
Seal, Brad, Gen. Mgr.--Jannock Steel Fabricating, Inc., Grapevine, TX; *Int'l*, pg. 699
Seale, Kenneth R., Mgr.--Calnev Pipeline Company, Las Vegas, NV; *U.S. Public*, pg. 692
Seale, Lloyd, Chief Oper. Officer--Electrolux Ltd., Saint Michael, Barbados; *Int'l*, pg. 441
Seales, G., Opers. Mgr.--Albany International/Monofilament Plant, Homer, NY; *U.S. Public*, pg. 37
Seaman, Irwin, Pres.--AIM Electronics Corporation, Sunrise, FL; *U.S. Private*, pg. 598
Seaman, James D., Pres.--King Fisher, Inc., Montevallo, AL; *U.S. Private*, pg. 979
Seaman, John T., Jr., V.P.-Opers.--Hickman, Williams & Company of Kentucky, Chicago, IL; *U.S. Private*, pg. 525
Seaman, Ronald G., Gen. Mgr.--Freeport Division, Freeport, ME; *U.S. Public*, pg. 438
Seamans, Thomas J., Pres.--Beemak Plastics, Gardena, CA; *U.S. Private*, pg. 598
Seamer, R.C., Dir. & Principal Mgr.--Lloyds Bank (Americas) Ltd., Nassau, Bahamas; *Int'l*, pg. 813
Searle, H.T., Div. Mng. Dir.--Detergents Division, Albright & Wilson Limited, Whitehaven, United Kingdom; *Int'l*, pg. 49
Searle, Jennifer, Admin.--Greenery Extended Care Center, Worcester, MA; *U.S. Public*, pg. 837
Searle, Kevin, Dist. Mgr.--Flowserve Duriron Canada Inc., London, Canada; *U.S. Public*, pg. 659
Searle, P.M., Chief Oper. Officer--Volkswagen of South Africa (Pty.) Ltd., Uitenhage, South Africa; *Int'l*, pg. 1475
Sears, Buford, V.P. & Reg. Representative--NationsBank (United Kingdom) Branch, London, United Kingdom; *U.S.* Public, pg. 1166
Sears, Mike, Pres.--McDonnell Aircraft & Missile Systems Div., Berkeley, MO; *U.S. Public*, pg. 241
Seath, M., Pres.--Whitehall-Robins Inc., Mississauga, Canada; *U.S. Public*, pg. 82
Seaton, Charles E., Pres.--IMC Agribusiness, Collinsville, IL; *U.S. Public*, pg. 856
Seats, John H., Sr. V.P.--F & E Community Developers of Florida, Inc., Fort Myers, FL; *U.S. Public*, pg. 404
Seaward, Michael, Exec. V.P.--Rio Minerales, San Jose, Costa Rica; *Int'l*, pg. 1498
Seay, Austin, Mng. Dir.--Tidex (Malaysia) Sdn. Bhd., New Orleans, LA; *U.S. Public*, pg. 1608
Sebastian, Dainel P., Pres.--Matthew Warren Inc., Logansport, IN; *U.S. Private*, pg. 500
Sebastian, Jerry G., Chm. Bd., Pres. & Chief Exec. Officer--United Missouri Bank of Monett, Monett, MO; *U.S. Public*, pg. 1655
Sebra, Joseph W., V.P.-Pharmaceutical Opers.--Sandoz Pharmaceuticals Corp., East Hanover, NJ; *Int'l*, pg. 974
Sebring, Joseph B., Pres. & Chief Oper. Officer--John Morrell & Co., Cincinnati, OH; *U.S. Public*, pg. 1479
Secades, Jose Bourkaib, Mng. Dir.--CC Banque Belgique, Brussels, Belgium; *Int'l*, pg. 144
Seccombe, R.J., V.P.--Automated Production Systems Div., Farmington, MI; *U.S. Public*, pg. 877
Sechovec, Bobbie, Admin.--Heritage Manor Plano, Plano, TX; *U.S. Public*, pg. 839
Seck, Wee Tai, Chief Oper. Officer--Neste Petroleum (Singapore) PTE. Ltd., Singapore, Singapore; *Int'l*, pg. 915
Secker, Alan, Chief Oper. Officer--TOSOH Europe B.V., Cheadle, United Kingdom; *Int'l*, pg. 1408
Secrest, Lynn T., Gen. Mgr.--Strobic Air Corp., Harleysville, PA; *U.S. Public*, pg. 1100
Secrist, Rich, Jr., Exec. V.P.--The George E. Failing Company, Enid, OK; *U.S. Private*, pg. 153
Sedgewick, James L., Pres.--United Investors Life Insurance Co., Birmingham, AL; *U.S. Public*, pg. 1623
Sedgwick, Katherine, Gen. Mgr. & Editor--Port Hope Evening Guide, Port Hope, Canada; *Int'l*, pg. 631
Sedlmeier, M.E., Pres. & Chief Exec. Officer--Ziegler Leasing Corp., West Bend, WI; *U.S. Public*, pg. 1792
See, Johnson, Mng. Dir.--KONE Elevator Pte. Ltd., Singapore, Singapore; *Int'l*, pg. 747
Seeber, Gerald R., Pres.--Agway Insurance Co., Syracuse, NY; *U.S. Private*, pg. 27
Seehawer, Garry C., Mgr.-Div.--Candlewick Division, Poplar Grove, IL; *U.S. Public*, pg. 438
Seehawer, Garry C., Mgr.-Div.--Oak Run Utilities, Galesburg, IL; *U.S. Public*, pg. 438
Seeker, Steven, Gen. Mgr., Distr. Switchgear--South Milwaukee Plant, South Milwaukee, WI; *U.S. Public*, pg. 443
Seekins, Michael, Gen. Mgr.--Dead River Transport, Bangor, ME; *U.S. Private*, pg. 318
Seeley, Donald L., Pres. & Chief Exec. Officer--The Alexander Consulting Group Inc., Lyndhurst, NJ; *U.S. Public*, pg. 117
Seely, Mike, Chief Oper. Officer--COBE de Mexico, S.A. de C.V., Mexico, Mexico; *Int'l*, pg. 667
Seemann, Wilhelm, Dr., Gen. Mgr.--BYK Gulden, S.A. de C.V., Mexico, Mexico; *Int'l*, pg. 66
Seeseke, Norbert, Chief Oper. Officer--MacGREGOR (DEU) GmbH, Hamburg, Germany; *Int'l*, pg. 670
Seetti, Franco, Mng. Dir.--Sperlari, S.R.L., Milan, Italy; *U.S. Public*, pg. 812
Seewar, Nicholas, Gen. Mgr.--Mount Nelson Hotel Ltd., Cape Town, South Africa; *Int'l*, pg. 1214
Sefcik, J.A., Mng. Dir.--Packard CTA Pty. Ltd., Ararat, Australia; *U.S. Public*, pg. 723
Sefiani, Robyn, Pres.-Asia/Pacific--Daniel J. Edelman Pty. Ltd., Sydney, Australia; *U.S. Private*, pg. 363
Sefiani, Robyn, Pres.-Asia Pacific--Daniel J. Edelman Pty. Ltd., Melbourne, Australia; *U.S. Private*, pg. 363
Seftali, Semih, Chief Oper. Officer--Tefal Istanbul, Istanbul, Turkey; *Int'l*, pg. 568
Sefton, Paul H., Gen. Mgr.--John Crane Sigma a.s., Lutin, Czech Republic; *Int'l*, pg. 1339
Segal, Dennis, Dr., Mng. Dir.--Milupa Ltd., Uxbridge, United Kingdom; *Int'l*, pg. 991
Segal, Mike, Gen. Mgr.--MatrixOne, Inc., Shelton, CT; *U.S. Private*, pg. 18
Segal, Myron, Chm. Bd., Pres. & Chief Exec. Officer--Premier Mill Corp., Reading, PA; *U.S. Private*, pg. 881
Segal, Myron, Chm. Bd., Pres. & Chief Exec. Officer--Integrated Press Systems, Reading, PA; *U.S. Private*, pg. 881
Segal, R.L., Pres.--Canada Dry Division, Downsview, Canada; *Int'l*, pg. 248
Segal, Richard, Mng. Dir.--Odeon Cinemas Ltd., Maidenhead, United Kingdom; *Int'l*, pg. 1086
Segal, Sam, Gen. Mgr.--Hampshire Hotel, Washington, DC; *U.S. Private*, pg. 1067
Segale, John, Sr. V.P. & Gen. Mgr.--Fleishman-Hillard, Inc., Sacramento, CA; *U.S. Private*, pg. 411
Segawa, Shuichi, Pres.--NLI Properties, New York, NY; *Int'l, pg. 935*
Segee, Thomas A., Pres.--Fleetwood Credit Corp., Yorba Linda, CA; *U.S. Public*, pg. 663
Segersteen, Christer, Vice Chm.--Sodra Skogagarna, Vaxjo, Sweden; *Int'l*, pg. 1275
Segonds, Daniel, Pres.--SocKalb G.I.E. France, Rodez, France; *U.S. Public*, pg. 493
Segovia, Carlos G., Pres.--Vitro, Sociedad Anonima - Capital Goods, Garza Garcia, Mexico; *Int'l*, pg. 1469
Segui, Jean, Pres.--Sextant Avionique, Meudon, France; *Int'l*, pg. 29
Seguin, Andre, Chief Oper. Officer--Societe des Eaux Minerales de Thonon-Les-Bains, Thonon-les-Bains, France; *Int'l*, pg. 919
Seguin, Daniel, Gen. Mgr.--Panneaux Vicply Inc., Saint-Laurent, Canada; *Int'l*, pg. 1432
Seguin, J-M, Mng. Dir.--Ascom Monetel SA, Guilherand-Granges, France; *Int'l*, pg. 87
Seguin, Ken, Gen. Mgr. & Publisher--The Sudbury Star, Sudbury, Canada; *Int'l*, pg. 631
Segura, Eclilberto L., Chief Of Mission--World Bank, Kiev, Ukraine; *U.S. Private*, pg. 1189
Segura, Gerardo, Pres.--Mary Kay Cosmetics, S.A., Buenos Aires, Argentina; *U.S. Private*, pg. 711
Segura, Jose, Mng. Dir.--Lurgi Espanola S.A., Madrid, Spain; *Int'l*, pg. 861
Segura, Odon Rodrigo, Branch Mgr.--Banco di Napoli-Barcelona, Barcelona, Spain; *Int'l*, pg. 140
Segura, Ricardo, Mgr.--Radiometer Espana S.A., Madrid, Spain; *Int'l*, pg. 1084
Sehring, Louis J., Pres.--Harris Bank Batavia, N.A., Batavia, IL; *Int'l*, pg. 154

Seibel, John, Reg. Acct. Dir.--RP alpha/Chicago, Arlington Heights, IL; *U.S. Private*, pg. 950
Seibel, Ron, Exec. V.P. & Chief Oper. Officer--Preferred Health Network, Long Beach, CA; *U.S. Public*, pg. 678
Seibert, Fred, Pres.--HB Entertainment Co., Los Angeles, CA; *U.S. Public*, pg. 1615
Seibert, Kurt, Gen. Mgr.--Computer Associates International, Inc., Islandia, NY; *U.S. Public*, pg. 420
Seibert, Kurt, Gen. Mgr.--MK Group, Islandia, NY; *U.S. Public*, pg. 420
Seidel, Alex, Gen. Mgr.--CPC Foods A.S., Prague, Czech Republic; *U.S. Public*, pg. 225
Seidel, R. J., V.P.--Petreco Baker Hughes Company, Houston, TX; *U.S. Public*, pg. 166
Seidenberg, Otto, Pres. & Chief Exec. Officer--Hoffer's Inc., Schofield, WI; *U.S. Private*, pg. 239
Seidenberg, Phil, Pres. & Gen. Mgr.--SMI Steel-Arkansas, Magnolia, AR; *U.S. Public*, pg. 413
Seidenberger, Phil, Pres.--Southern Post Company, Magnolia, AR; *U.S. Public*, pg. 412
Seidensticker, Nils, Chm. Bd.--Durriesscharmann, AG, Dusseldorf, Germany; *Int'l*, pg. 860
Seidl, Hans Helmut, Asst. V.P.--Bankers Trust New York Corporation, Frankfurt/Main, Germany; *U.S. Public*, pg. 186
Seidl, Maximilian R., Gen. Mgr.--Soabar G.m.b.H., Eching, Germany; *U.S. Public*, pg. 154
Seidler, James F., Pres.--Clayton Reinsurance, Ltd., Hamilton, Bermuda,; *U.S. Public*, pg. 1374
Seidner, Lester D., Gen. Mgr.--Valley Bell Dairy Co., Charleston, WV; *U.S. Private*, pg. 158
Seifert, Jurgen, Chief Oper. Officer--Schering Wien Ges.m.b.H., Vienna, Austria; *Int'l*, pg. 1204
Seiler, Hans, Pres.--Astra Pharmaceutica AG, Dietikon, Switzerland; *Int'l*, pg. 94
Seiler, Ingrid, Mng. Dir.--Kaolin-Und Tonwerke Seilitz-Lothain GmbH, Mehren, Germany; *Int'l*, pg. 1488
Seiler, J.F., Mgr.--Swiss Bank Corporation, Rio de Janeiro, Brazil; *Int'l*, pg. 1330
Seimer, Arnold B., Pres.--Automatic Timing & Controls, Lancaster, PA; *U.S. Private*, pg. 327
Seino, H., Pres.--Mitsukoshi (U.S.A.) Inc., New York, NY; *Int'l*, pg. 883
Seino, Hidetoshi, Chief Rep.--Mitsui Trust & Banking Company, Limited, Chicago, IL; *Int'l*, pg. 883
Seinsheimer, J. Fellman, III, Pres. & Chief Exec. Officer--American Indemnity Company, Galveston, TX; *U.S. Public*, pg. 83
Seinsheimer, J.F., III, Pres. & Chief Exec. Officer--Texas General Indemnity Co., Galveston, TX; *U.S. Public*, pg. 83
Seipel, S.S., V.P.--ABN-AMRO Trust Company (Virgin Islands), Saint Thomas, VI; *Int'l*, pg. 11
Seiple, William, Gen. Mgr.--Frontier Communications-Lakewood, Inc, Barnesville, PA; *U.S. Public*, pg. 683
Seipp, Philip J., Pres.--Sysco Food Services of Minnesota, Inc., Saint Paul, MN; *U.S. Public*, pg. 1551
Seitchik, Jay, Pres.--The Whitaker Corporation, Wilmington, DE; *U.S. Public*, pg. 8
Seitei, Lesedi, Mgr.--Heinemann Educational Botswana, Gaborone, Botswana; *Int'l*, pg. 1094
Seitle, Rolf, V.P.--Transdyn Controls, Inc., Concord, CA; *U.S. Public*, pg. 1319
Seitz, Anthony J., Pres.--ConAgra Retail Companies, Omaha, NE; *U.S. Public*, pg. 426
Seitz, William E., Pres. & Chief Exec. Officer--Raymond Engineering, Middletown, CT; *U.S. Public*, pg. 942
Sejovia, Jaime Rodriguez, Chief Oper. Officer--Cydsa S.A. Treament Div., Garza Garcia, Mexico; *Int'l*, pg. 246
Sekeres, Charles E., Pres. & Chief Exec. Officer--Diet Center Worldwide, Inc., Akron, OH; *U.S. Private*, pg. 864
Sekeres, William, Chm. Bd.--ITT Cannon Sealectro, New Britain, CT; *U.S. Public*, pg. 859
Seki, Akiyoshi, Pres.--P.T. Surya Toto Indonesia, Jakarta, Indonesia; *Int'l*, pg. 1410
Seki, Akiyoshi, Pres.--Totokiki (Malaysia) Sdn.Bhd., Seremban, Malaysia; *Int'l*, pg. 1410
Seki, Harumitsu, Gen Mgr--The Sumitomo Bank, Ltd.-Houston Agency, Houston, TX; *Int'l*, pg. 1309
Seki, Masami, Mng. Dir. & Gen. Mgr.--Asahi Bank (Nederland) N.V., Amsterdam, Netherlands; *Int'l*, pg. 83
Seki, S., Pres.--Aisin U.S.A. Mfg. Inc., Seymour, IN; *Int'l*, pg. 39
Seki, T., Pres. & Gen. Mgr.--Wyeth (Japan) Corporation, Tokyo, Japan; *U.S. Public*, pg. 82
Seki, Toshio, Pres.--JTB Air Cargo Inc., Tokyo, Japan; *U.S. Private*, pg. 1120
Sekido, Tsuneaki, Chief Rep.--Daiwa Bank-Ho Chi Minh City, Ho Chi Minh City, Vietnam; *Int'l*, pg. 373
Sekiguchi, Masumi, Mng. Dir.--Wako Merchant Bank (Singapore) Limited, Singapore, Singapore; *Int'l*, pg. 1485
Sekiguchi, Tsuneo, Vice Chm.--Kuo Hua Inc., Taipei, Taiwan; *Int'l*, pg. 394
Sekine, Dan, Gen. Mgr.--St. Clement Vineyards, Saint Helena, CA; *Int'l*, pg. 1193
Sekine, Hideo, Pres.--Anritsu Elektronik GmbH, Dusseldorf, Germany; *Int'l*, pg. 77
Sekine, Masaji, Pres.--Mitrans Corporation, New York, NY; *Int'l*, pg. 874
Seko, Akira, Pres. & Chief Exec. Officer--ORIX USA Corporation-New York, New York, NY; *Int'l*, pg. 1009
Selbekk, Bjorn, Chief Oper. Officer--Ahlstrom Machinery AB, Stockholm, Sweden; *Int'l*, pg. 34
Selby, Alan, Chief Exec. Officer--Mando Marketing Limited, Aylesbury, United Kingdom; *Int'l*, pg. 1482
Selby, Dane, Gen. Mgr.--Kansas Gas Supply, Pratt, KS; *U.S. Public*, pg. 1146
Selden, Paul, Pres.--Atlantic Hardware & Supply Co., New York, NY; *U.S. Public*, pg. 400
Selders, F., Mng. Dir.--Electro West B.V., Honselersdijk, Netherlands; *Int'l*, pg. 1133
Sele, J., Chief Exec. Officer--Zurich Versicherungs-Gesellschaft, Vaduz, Liechtenstein; *Int'l*, pg. 1531
Seley, Peter S., Pres.--Advanco Constructors, Inc., Upland, CA; *U.S. Public*, pg. 1795
Seley, Peter S., Pres.--Gary Concrete Products Inc., Augusta, GA; *U.S. Public*, pg. 1795
Selhagen, Leif, Chief Oper. Officer--NAPS Sweden AB, Skarholmen, Sweden; *Int'l*, pg. 913
Selig, Jeff, Pres.--Capitol City Steel Co., Buda, TX; *U.S. Public*, pg. 413
Selig, Marvin, Chm. Bd. & Chief Exec. Officer-CMC Steel Grp.--Structural Metals, Inc., Seguin, TX; *U.S. Public*, pg. 412
Selig, Tom, Pres. & Chief Oper. Officer--BLH Electronics, Inc., Canton, MA; *Int'l*, pg. 1289
Seligman, Irving, Chief Oper. Officer--Seligman & Assocs. of Michigan, Southfield, MI; *U.S. Private*, pg. 982
Seligman, Scott J., Pres.--Mid-States Mortgage Corp., Southfield, MI; *U.S. Private*, pg. 982
Selingant, R., Area Mgr.--Compagnie Africaine de Geophysique, Rabat, Morocco; *Int'l*, pg. 241
Selis, John L., V.P.-Iron Ore--Eveleth Mines, Eveleth, MN; *U.S. Public*, pg. 1213
Selkerki, Wayne, Reg. Mgr.--Green Tree Acceptance of Alabama, Inc., Montgomery, AL; *U.S. Public*, pg. 762
Selkowe, Pete, Publisher--The Journal Times, Racine, WI; *U.S. Public*, pg. 983
Selky, John L., Pres.--I/N Tek, New Carlisle, IN; *U.S. Public*, pg. 879
Selky, John L., Pres.--I/N Kote, New Carlisle, IN; *U.S. Public*, pg. 879
Selky, John L., Pres.--I/N Tek, New Carlisle, IN; *Int'l*, pg. 940
Sell, Vicki, Dir.-Pur.--Koss Classics Ltd., Milwaukee, WI; *U.S. Public*, pg. 966
Sellag, Bjorn, Pres.--Norcem Industrier, Oslo, Norway; *Int'l*, pg. 42
Selland, Howard M., Pres.--Aeroquip Corporation, Maumee, OH; *U.S. Public*, pg. 24
Sellars, R.C., Dir.--Beringer Division, Marblehead, MA; *Int'l*, pg. 774
Sellers, Lawrence R., Pres.--The Huntington Service Company, Columbus, OH; *U.S. Public*, pg. 850
Sellers, Robert, Pres.--Berlinger Div., Marblehead, MA; *Int'l*, pg. 773
Sellers, Robert, Plant Mgr.--Interlake Material Handling, Sumter, SC; *U.S. Public*, pg. 893
Sellier, Eric, Mng. Dir.--Groupe ESAB S.A., Cergy-Pontoise, France; *Int'l*, pg. 283
Sellman, Michael B., Pres. & Chief Exec. Officer--Maine Yankee, Brunswick, ME; *U.S. Public*, pg. 325
Sells, James, Pres. & Chief Oper. Officer--Matson Intermodal System, Inc., San Francisco, CA; *U.S. Public*, pg. 40
Sells, Mayford, Plant Mgr.--Samson Apparel Corp., Washington, NC; *U.S. Public*, pg. 779
Sells, Roger B., Mgr.-Sls.--Fasson Norge A/S, Fjellhamar, Norway; *U.S. Public*, pg. 154
Selman, Gabriel Alma, Pres.--Wackenhut Dominicana, S.A., Santo Domingo, Dominican Republic; *U.S. Public*, pg. 1731
Selmeci, Gabor, Country Mgr.--Dun & Bradstreet Hungaria Kft., Budapest, Hungary; *U.S. Public*, pg. 536
Selmer, B., Mng. Dir.--GKN Glaenzer Cardan SA, Poissy, France; *Int'l*, pg. 536
Selvey, Anthony R., Pres.--Taylor & Francis Philadelphia, Bristol, PA; *Int'l*, pg. 1358
Selvey, Anthony R., Pres.--Taylor & Francis, Washington, DC; *Int'l*, pg. 1358
Selzer, Frank, Chief Oper. Officer--Dipl.-Ing Selzer Aufzuge GmbH, Berlin, Germany; *Int'l*, pg. 747
Selzer, Steve, Pres.--NTS, Fort Worth, TX; *U.S. Public*, pg. 631
Semans, Bruce, Gen. Mgr.--Dielectric Laboratories, Cazenovia, NY; *U.S. Public*, pg. 521
Semel, Terry S., Co-Chm. Bd., Pres. & Chief Oper. Officer--Warner Bros. Studios, Inc., Burbank, CA; *U.S. Public*, pg. 1611
Semerena, Jose Luis Alberro, Dr., Dir.--Pemex Gas y Petroquimica Basica, Mexico, Mexico; *Int'l*, pg. 1046
Seminel, Maurice, Plant Mgr.--Sotteville Plant, Sotteville-les-Rouen, France; *U.S. Public*, pg. 673
Semmler, Steve, Pres.--Corken, Inc., Oklahoma City, OK; *U.S. Public*, pg. 862
Semonart, Michel, Mng. Dir.--BN Division, Saint-Michiels, Belgium; *Int'l*, pg. 200
Semrod, T. Joseph, Chm. Bd., Pres. & Chief Exec. Officer--United Jersey Bank, Hackensack, NJ; *U.S. Public*, pg. 1528
Sen, Satish, Mng. Dir., Bus. Devel. & Information--ALM & Company, Stockholm, Sweden; *U.S. Public*, pg. 1422
Senchuk, William, Gen. Mgr.--Davies Molding Co., Carol Stream, IL; *U.S. Private*, pg. 859
Sendler, Israel, Mng. Dir.--Orbotech Pacific Ltd., Wan Chai, Hong Kong; *Int'l*, pg. 1007
Sendlmeier, Helmut, Chief Exec. Officer--TBWA Dusseldorf GmbH, Dusseldorf, Germany; *U.S. Private*, pg. 1063
Senecal, Normand, Pres.--Patterson Dental Canada Inc., Montreal, Canada; *U.S. Public*, pg. 1265
Seneker, Stanley A., Chm. Bd.--Ford Holdings Inc., Dearborn, MI; *U.S. Public*, pg. 663
Senft, Paul, Publr.--The Daily Chronicle, De Kalb, IL; *U.S. Public*, pg. 1343
Seng Wah, Chui, Dir.-Australia & New Zealand--Singapore Tourist Promotion Board - Sydney, Sydney, Australia; *Int'l*, pg. 1254
Seng, Ong Poh, Dr., Chief Exec. Officer--Milk Products Holdings (SEA), Singapore, Singapore; *Int'l*, pg. 923
Seng, Ph., Chief Oper. Officer--Societe Internationale d'Ingenierie et de Maintenance S.A. (2IM), Rueil-Malmaison, France; *Int'l*, pg. 1361
Seng, Poh Beng, Dir.--TNT Logistics Asia Pte Ltd., Singapore, Singapore; *Int'l*, pg. 1343
Seng, S.E., Mng. Dir.--Associated Pan Malaysia Cement Sdn. Berhad, Kuala Lumpur, Malaysia; *Int'l*, pg. 198
Seng, Soon Boon, Mng. Dir.--Baymont Malaysia SDN BHD, Kuala Lumpur, Malaysia; *Int'l*, pg. 31
Seng, Soon Boon, Mng. Dir.--Baymont Technologies (PTE) Ltd., Singapore, Singapore; *Int'l*, pg. 31
Seng, Yeo Loy, Gen. Mgr.--Tradewinds Pte. Ltd., Singapore, Singapore; *Int'l*, pg. 1374
Senger, Donna, V.P. & Branch Mgr--Burns & Wilcox-St. Louis Office, Saint Louis, MO; *U.S. Private*, pg. 610
Sengstack, Lynn, V.P.--Shawnee Press, Inc., Delaware Water Gap, PA; *U.S. Private*, pg. 768
Senie, Kevin, Pres. & Chief Exec. Officer--The Travel Channel, Atlanta, GA; *U.S. Private*, pg. 647
Senior, Robert, Pres.--Richard E. Thibaut, Inc., Newark, NJ; *U.S. Public*, pg. 1358
Senior, Robert, Pres.--Wm. Zinsser & Co., Inc., Somerset, NJ; *U.S. Public*, pg. 1358
Senior, Robert, Pres.--Bradshaw-Praeger Co., Chicago, IL; *U.S. Public*, pg. 1358
Senior, Robert, Pres.--Mantrose Bradshaw Zinsser Group, Westport, CT; *U.S. Public*, pg. 1358
Senior, Walter, Chm. & Chief Exec. Officer--Famous Players Inc., Toronto, Canada; *U.S. Private*, pg. 779
Senn, Dr. John, Pres.--Courtaulds Performance Films Inc., Martinsville, VA; *Int'l*, pg. 339
Senn, Felix, Chief Oper. Officer--Schleicher & Schuell AG, Riehen, Switzerland; *Int'l*, pg. 1206
Senn, Ricardo, Mgr.--Utell International-Chile, Santiago, Chile; *Int'l*, pg. 1098
Sennett, Morton W., Pres.--Eskay Screw Corporation, Wood Dale, IL; *U.S. Public*, pg. 1054
Senoh, Hirobumi, Pres.--Sogei Inc., Tokyo, Japan; *Int'l*, pg. 1277
Senov, P.A., Chief Oper. Officer--General Paint Ltd., Vancouver, Canada; *Int'l*, pg. 1501
Sensor, Edward E., Pres. & Chief Exec. Officer--Banknorth Mortgage Company, Brattleboro, VT; *U.S. Public*, pg. 187
Senstrom, Dave, Gen. Mgr.--Turner Construction Company, Costa Mesa, CA; *U.S. Public*, pg. 1645
Sentell, Greg, Reg. Sls. Mgr.--Varco BJ Oil Tools, Jurong, Singapore; *U.S. Public*, pg. 1709
Sentell, John, Gen. Mgr.--Madison Industries Inc. of Arizona, Phoenix, AZ; *U.S. Private*, pg. 428
Sentuna, C., Mng. Dir.--Bilar Bilgi Araclari Ticaret A.S., Istanbul, Turkey; *Int'l*, pg. 1115
Seo, Byung Soo, Country Mgr.--BMC Software Korea Ltd., Seoul, Korea; *U.S. Public*, pg. 163
Seo, K.Y., Chief Oper. Officer--Ahlstrom Korea Co., Ltd.-Hyun Poon Mill, Seoul, Korea; *Int'l*, pg. 35
Seo, Kim Yong, Pres.--Ssangyong Information & Communication Corporation, Seoul, Korea; *Int'l*, pg. 1292
Seo, O.S., Chief Rep.--Bank Brussels Lambert-Seoul Representative Office, Seoul, Korea; *Int'l*, pg. 148
Seow, A.G., Gen. Mgr.--Laporte Chemicals (Malaysia) Sdn Bhd, Petaling Jaya, Malaysia; *Int'l*, pg. 803
Sepeta, Donald W., Gen. Mgr.--Richards Micro-Tool, Inc., Plymouth, MA; *U.S. Public*, pg. 1054
Seppa, Veijo, Gen. Mgr.--Nokia Mobile Phones (Mexico) S.A. de C.V., Puebla, Mexico; *Int'l*, pg. 952
Sepulvado, Johnnie V., Gen. Mgr.--Atlas Alchem Plastics, Inc., Wichita, KS; *U.S. Public*, pg. 1495
Sepulvado, Johnnie W., Gen. Mgr.--Atlas-Alchem Plastics-Minnesota, Mankato, MN; *U.S. Public*, pg. 1496
Sepulvado, Johnnie W., Gen. Mgr.--Atlas-Alchem Plastics-Missouri, Cape Girardeau, MO; *U.S. Public*, pg. 1496
Sepulvado, Johnnie W., Gen. Mgr.--Atlas-Alchem Plastics-Texas, Arlington, TX; *U.S. Public*, pg. 1496
Sepulveda, Joaquin Guzman, Exec. V.P.--Hylsa S.A.-Tubular Division, San Nicolas, Mexico; *Int'l*, pg. 56
Serada, Syuji, Pres.--Nissho Iwai New Zealand Limited, Auckland, New Zealand; *Int'l*, pg. 948
Serafini, Claudio, Chief Exec. Officer & Mng. Dir.--Heinz Food Service S.r.l., Commessaggio, Italy; *U.S. Public*, pg. 806
Serafini, Claudio, Mng. Dir.--AIAL (Arimpex S.r.l. Industrie Alimentari), Commessaggio, Italy; *U.S. Public*, pg. 807
Seramur, John C., Pres., Chief Exec. Officer & Chief Oper. Officer--First Financial Corporation, Stevens Point, WI; *U.S. Public*, pg. 140
Sereci, Mark, Pres.--Kinemetrics, Inc., Pasadena, CA; *Int'l*, pg. 1019
Seren, Levent, Repr.--Kredietbank Representative Office (Ankara), Ankara, Turkey; *Int'l*, pg. 760
Sereny, John T., Vice Chm.--Green Forest Lumber Corporation, Toronto, Canada; *Int'l*, pg. 828
Sergeant, Craig C., Chm. Bd., Pres. & Chief Exec. Officer--Cornerstone Construction & Materials, Inc., Neptune, NJ; *Int'l*, pg. 593
Sergeant, K., Mng. Dir.--Vent-Axia Ltd., Crawley, United Kingdom; *Int'l*, pg. 1267
Serin, Bernard, Pres.--Edgcomb Metals, Bensalem, PA; *Int'l*, pg. 572
Serirak, Tavisale, Mng. Dir.--The Siam Construction Steel Co., Ltd., Bangkok, Thailand; *Int'l*, pg. 1238
Serna, Ricardo, Pres.--Janssen Farmaceutica, S.A. de C.V., Mexico, Mexico; *U.S. Public*, pg. 929
Sernik, Kleber Antonio, Gen. Mgr.-Mfg.--Acos Villares Sao Caetano Plant, Sao Caetano do Sul, Brazil; *Int'l*, pg. 23
Serodio, Ademar, Gen. Mgr.--Cosmeticos Avon, S.A.C.I., Buenos Aires, Argentina; *U.S. Public*, pg. 156
Serra, B., Chief Oper. Officer--BFF Italia Srl, Milan, Italy; *Int'l*, pg. 798
Serra, J., Chief Exec. Officer--Blackwood Hodge (Angola) Ltda., Luanda, Angola; *Int'l*, pg. 231
Serra, Luiz, Gen. Mgr.--Banco Itau S.A., New York, NY; *Int'l*, pg. 142
Serra, Matthew D., Chm. & Chief Exec. Officer--Stern's, Paramus, NJ; *U.S. Public*, pg. 618
Serra, Rick, Chief Oper. Officer--Multiple Parking Services, Inc., Buffalo, NY; *U.S. Private*, pg. 43
Serralunga, G., Gen. Mgr.--Star S.p.A., Milan, Italy; *Int'l*, pg. 380
Serrance, W.S., Gen. Mgr.--Du Pont Taiwan Limited, Taipei, Taiwan; *U.S. Public*, pg. 533

Serrano, A. Garcia, Mgr.--Van Leeuwen Tubos Espana S.A.E., Seville, Spain; *Int'l*, pg. 1450
Serrano, Isidoro, Pres. & Regional Dir.--Leo Burnett Comunica S.A., Guatemala, Guatemala; *U.S. Private*, pg. 185
Serrat, Jordi, Liaison Officer--Slogan Publicidad, Barcelona, Spain; *U.S. Private*, pg. 1152
Serre, Pierre, Pres.--Unibeton, Saint Denis, France; *Int'l*, pg. 292
Serrell, Roy, Mgr.--Wing Industries Northeastern, Manchester, CT; *U.S. Private*, pg. 1183
Serrone, H. James, Gen. Mgr.--Torotel Products, Inc., Grandview, MO; *U.S. Public*, pg. 1624
Serton, Ken, Branch Mgr.--CAP Gemini America (Seattle Branch), Seattle, WA; *Int'l*, pg. 264
Sertthin, Somsook, Gen. Mgr.--AMP Thailand, Bangkok, Thailand; *U.S. Public*, pg. 9
Servaes, Jeroen, Gen. Mgr.--Topps Brasil Ltda., Sao Paulo, Brazil; *U.S. Public*, pg. 1622
Servedio, D.M., Pres.--STV Incorporated, New York, NY; *U.S. Public*, pg. 1421
Servedro, D., Pres.--STV International, New York, NY; *U.S. Public*, pg. 1421
Servedro, D.M., Pres.--STV Construction Services, Douglassville, PA; *U.S. Public*, pg. 1421
Servin, Larry, Mng. Dir.--Scancem Fastigheter AB, Malmo, Sweden; *Int'l*, pg. 1200
Sesma, Jose Miguel, Gen. Mgr.--Calseg S.A., Artajona, Spain; *Int'l*, pg. 430
Sessegolo, A., Chm.--Zanussi Grandi Impianti S.p.A., Pordenone, Italy; *Int'l*, pg. 442
Sessegolo, A., Chm.--Zanussi Vending S.p.A., Valbrembo, Italy; *Int'l*, pg. 442
Sessoms, Bob D., Pres.--Associates International Management Company, Dallas, TX; *U.S. Public*, pg. 663
Sestito, Frank A., Pres.--S&S-Hartwell Co., Inc., Portsmouth, NH; *Int'l*, pg. 710
Sesto, Dominic, Exec. V.P.--Personal Finance Co., Olympia Fields, IL; *U.S. Private*, pg. 750
Seta, Y., Pres.--Japan Marine Technologies Ltd., Tokyo, Japan; *Int'l*, pg. 1339
Setiawan, Putu, Pres. & Dir.--P.T. Asuransi Allianz Aken Life, Jakarta, Indonesia; *Int'l*, pg. 60
Setola, Michael, Pres.--Obion Company, Inc., New York, NY; *U.S. Public*, pg. 1429
Settepassi, Cesare, Pres.--Tiffany-Faraone, S.p.A. (Milan), Milan, Italy; *U.S. Public*, pg. 1609
Settlage, Randy, Pres.--AGRA Foundations Inc., Everett, WA; *Int'l*, pg. 31
Settle, Larry, Pres.--Krupp Gerlach Company, Danville, IL; *Int'l*, pg. 508
Settle, Larry L., Mgr.--Turbine Engine Components Textron, Cleveland, OH; *U.S. Public*, pg. 1589
Setzer, David, Gen. Mgr.--Park Newspapers of Marion, Inc., Marion, NC; *U.S. Public*, pg. 1078
Setzer, David, Gen. Mgr.--McDowell News, Marion, NC; *U.S. Public*, pg. 1078
Seul, Roland, Dr., Chm.--Gradmann & Holler & GmbH, Stuttgart, Germany; *U.S. Public*, pg. 1049
Severin, Eric, Pres.--Poggenpohl Mobelwerke GmbH, Herford, Germany,; *Int'l*, pg. 1261
Sevier, Helen, Chief Oper. Officer--Fishing Tackle Retailer, Montgomery, AL; *U.S. Private*, pg. 105
Sevier, Helen, Chief Oper. Officer--Bassmaster Magazine, Montgomery, AL; *U.S. Private*, pg. 105
Sevier, Helen, Chief Oper. Officer--Southern Outdoors Magazine, Montgomery, AL; *U.S. Private*, pg. 106
Sevilla, Benjamin C., Pres.--Bank of Boston of the Philippines, Manila, Philippines; *U.S. Public*, pg. 184
Sevilla, Fernando Monzonilla, Dir.--Pemex Refinacion, Mexico, Mexico; *Int'l*, pg. 1046
Sevin, R.A., Div. Pres.--Winn-Dixie Stores, Inc.-Tampa Div., Tampa, FL; *U.S. Public*, pg. 1771
Sevo, Vince, Mgr.--Anixter Toronto, Mississauga, Canada; *U.S. Public*, pg. 116
Sewaki, Nobuhiro, Chief Oper. Officer--Tokio Marine South-East Servicing Company Limited, Bangkok, Thailand; *Int'l*, pg. 1393
Sewing, Rainer, Mgr.-Sales & Mktg.--Amicon G.m.b.H., Witten, Germany; *U.S. Public*, pg. 1113
Sexton, Ed, Plant Mgr.--Elkem-American Carbide Company (Pryor), Pryor, OK; *U.S. Public*, pg. 33
Sexton, G. Len, Pres.--Synovus Securities, Inc., Columbus, GA; *U.S. Public*, pg. 1550
Sexton, Ken, Mgr.--Triad Personnel Services, Schaumburg, IL; *U.S. Public*, pg. 715
Sexton, Marvin E., Pres.--Montgomery Tank Lines, Inc., Plant City, FL; *U.S. Public*, pg. 1028
Sexton, Michael, Pres.--Central Maine Newspapers, Augusta, ME; *U.S. Private*, pg. 439
Sexton, Ray, Chief Oper. Officer--Flowers Baking Co. of Morristown, Morristown, TN; *U.S. Public*, pg. 657
Seya, Hiromichi, Pres.--Asahi-Olin Ltd., Tokyo, Japan; *U.S. Public*, pg. 1219
Seyadi, Yousef A., Exec. V.P.--Medical Supplies Division, Dammam, Saudi Arabia; *Int'l*, pg. 502
Seydi, Idris, Pres.--Societe Generale de Banques Au Senegal, Dakar, Senegal; *Int'l*, pg. 548
Seymour, James C., Chief Oper. Officer--Prattville Progress, Prattville, AL; *U.S. Public*, pg. 699
Seymour, John P., Mgr.-Office--Woodward-Clyde, Livonia, MI; *U.S. Public*, pg. 1656
Sfeir-Younis, Alfredo, Special Rep. To The U.N.--The World Bank Mission to the United Nations, New York, NY; *U.S. Private*, pg. 1189
Sfura, R., Controller--Hunter Douglas Metals, Homewood, IL; *Int'l*, pg. 639
Sghibartz, Chris, Mng. Dir.--Jotun Polymer (UK) Ltd., Mitcham, United Kingdom; *Int'l*, pg. 714
Shaari, Abdul Rahman b., Dir.--Tourism Malaysia - Paris Office, Paris, France; *Int'l*, pg. 833
Shackelford, B.K., Gen. Mgr.--Triad Chemical, Donaldsonville, LA; *U.S. Public*, pg. 1117
Shackleford, B.K., V.P. & Complex Mgr.--Triad Nitrogen, Inc., Donaldsonville, LA; *U.S. Public*, pg. 1117
Shackleford, J.J., Pres.--TECO Coal Corp., Tampa, FL; *U.S. Public*, pg. 1565
Shackleton, Nick, Pres.--World Trade Center, Tampa, FL; *Int'l*, pg. 1359
Shackouls, Bobby S., Chm. Bd., Pres. & Chief Exec. Officer--The Louisiana Land and Exploration Company, New Orleans, LA; *U.S. Public*, pg. 269
Shad, Doug, Gen. Mgr.--Nucor Iron Carbide, Port of Spain, Trinidad & Tobago; *U.S. Public*, pg. 1206
Shadbolt, Derek, Mgr.-Sls., So. Central--Singapore Airlines Ltd., Houston, TX; *Int'l*, pg. 1374
Shady, Joseph J., Pres.--Chrysler Realty Corp., Troy, MI; *U.S. Public*, pg. 354
Shaefer, W.N., Pres.--LASMO America Inc., Houston, TX; *Int'l*, pg. 804
Shafer, Thomas B., Program V.P.--Martin Marietta EPA National Computer Center, Research Triangle Park, NC; *U.S. Public*, pg. 1007
Shaff, Gerald, Pres.--Custom Products Corporation, North Haven, CT; *U.S. Public*, pg. 244
Shaffer, Charles P., Sr. V.P. & Gen. Mgr.-Soft Home, Hard Lines & Cosmetics Divisions--Elder-Beerman Stores Div., Dayton, OH; *U.S. Private*, pg. 395
Shaffer, Robert W., Gen. Mgr.--Nature's Sunshine Products of Canada, Ltd., Orangeville, Canada; *U.S. Public*, pg. 1167
Shaffner, Ted L., Gen. Mgr.--Kennedy Space Center Operations, Cape Canaveral, FL; *U.S. Public*, pg. 1597
Shaftman, Frederick A., Chief Exec. Officer--BellSouth Communication Systems, Inc., Roanoke, VA; *U.S. Public*, *pg. 209*
Shaftman, Frederick K., Pres.--BellSouth Network Solutions, Inc., Atlanta, GA; *U.S. Public*, pg. 209
Shafto, Robert A., Pres. & Chief Exec. Officer--The New England, Boston, MA; *U.S. Private*, pg. 737
Shafto, Robert A., Pres.--New England Life Insurance Co, Boston, MA; *U.S. Private*, pg. 738
Shah, Hasmukh, V.P.--Azonix Inc., Billerica, MA; *U.S. Public*, pg. 457
Shah, Nitin, Dir.-Indian Subcontinent--Medtronic International, Ltd., Baroda, India; *U.S. Public*, pg. 1083
Shah, Sanjay, Chm. Bd.--Precision Fasteners Ltd., Thane, India; *U.S. Public*, pg. 1420
Shahabi, Donna, Mgr.--Jefferies & Company, Inc., Jersey City, NJ; *U.S. Public*, pg. 925
Shahan, Bill, Branch Mgr.--Downey Savings & Loan Association, F.A., San Diego, CA; *U.S. Public*, pg. 527
Shaheen, G.L., Mng. Dir.--Caterpillar Overseas S.A., Geneva, Switzerland; *U.S. Public*, pg. 316
Shaheen, Gabriel, Mng. Dir.--Lincoln Assurance Limited, Uxbridge, United Kingdom; *U.S. Public*, pg. 998
Shaheen, Gabriel, Mng. Dir.--Lincoln National (UK) plc, Oxbridge, United Kingdom; *U.S. Public*, pg. 998
Shaheen, Gabriel L., Pres.--Lincoln National Health & Casualty Insurance Co., Fort Wayne, IN; *U.S. Public*, pg. 998
Shaheen, Gabriel L., Pres. & Chief Exec. Officer--Lincoln National Reinsurance Company (Barbados) Limited, Fort Wayne, IN; *U.S. Public*, pg. 998
Shaheen, George T., Mng. Partner--Andersen Consulting, Palo Alto, CA; *U.S. Private*, pg. 72
Shaheen, John, Chm. Bd.--Sunrise Carpet Ind. Inc., Dalton, GA; *U.S. Private*, pg. 1190
Shaheen, John, Chm. Bd.--White-Crest Dorsett Inc., Dalton, GA; *U.S. Private*, pg. 1190
Shahidi, Kambiz, Resident Rep.--Generale Bank, Tehran, Iran; *Int'l*, pg. 547
Shahmoon, Elisha, Gen. Mgr.--Motorola Israel Information Systems Ltd., Ramat Gan, Israel; *U.S. Public*, pg. 1139
Shahmoon, Elisha, Gen. Mgr.--Motorola Semiconductor Israel Ltd., Ramat Gan, Israel; *U.S. Public*, pg. 1140
Shaikh, Abdul H., ResidentRep.--The World Bank Resident Mission, Riyadh, Saudi Arabia; *U.S. Private*, pg. 1190
Shailer, Barry L., Sr. V.P.-Europe & Mng. Dir.--B of B (Europe) Limited, London, United Kingdom; *Int'l*, pg. 151
Shain, Joseph, Pres.--SCP Direct Inc., New York, NY; *U.S. Public*, pg. 1224
Shake, Edward E., Chief Exec. Officer--Hamilton Lamp Corp., North Kansas City, MO; *U.S. Public*, pg. 1354
Shaker, Anthony I., Pres.--Building Technologies Engineering, Boston, MA; *U.S. Private*, pg. 376
Shaker, Anthony I., Pres.--Balco, Inc., Boston, MA; *U.S. Private*, pg. 376
Shakespeare, David, Natl. Mgr.--Juno Lighting Ltd., Mississauga, Canada; *U.S. Public*, pg. 935
Shalack, Theodore J., Pres. & Chief Exec. Officer--MONY Credit Corporation, New York, NY; *U.S. Private*, pg. 769
Shalem, Y., Gen. Mgr.--Shikma, Petah Tiqwa, Israel; *Int'l*, pg. 75
Shalev, S., Gen. Mgr.--Engines Division/BEDEK Aviation Group, Israel; *Int'l*, pg. 690
Shalit, E., Mr., Rep.-Montreal--Bank Hapoalim B.M., Montreal, Canada; *Int'l*, pg. 149
Shallcross, James, Gen. Mgr.--General Nutrition Franchising, Inc., Pittsburgh, PA; *U.S. Public*, pg. 725
Shamir, Moshe, Pres.--Vishay Israel Ltd., Holon, Israel; *U.S. Public*, pg. 1722
Shamlock, Daniel P., Chief Oper. Officer--Brian Controls Division, Winnipeg, Canada; *Int'l*, pg. 711
Shamsaei, Marcus, Chief Fin. Officer--Rainbow Technologies, GmbH, Unterschleissheim, Germany; *U.S. Public*, pg. 1359
Shanahan, Pat, Mng. Dir.--Tellabs Ltd., Shannon, Ireland; *U.S. Public*, pg. 1573
Shaner, William, Pres. & Chief Oper. Officer--Laneco, Inc., Easton, PA; *U.S. Public*, pg. 1541
Shaner, William, Jr., Pres.--SuperValu, Inc.-Maryland Div., Williamsport, MD; *U.S. Public*, pg. 1540
Shank, David, Pres.--G.P. Putnam Sons, New York, NY; *Int'l*, pg. 1215
Shank, Gloria, Pres. & Gen. Mgr.--CCS, Holland, OH; *U.S. Private*, pg. 147
Shank, Jeremy, Lab Mgr.--Quest Diagnostic-Albany, Albany, NY; *U.S. Public*, pg. 1351
Shank, Jeremy, Lab Mgr.--Quest Diagnostic-Delmar, Delmar, NY; *U.S. Public*, pg. 1351
Shankland, Bruce, Mng. Dir.--Amway (Europe) Ltd., Hemel Hempstead, United Kingdom; *U.S. Private*, pg. 69
Shankland, Bruce, Reg. Mgr.--Amway Nederland Ltd., Tiel, Netherlands; *U.S. Private*, pg. 70
Shanley, F.S., Sr. Partner--Riada & Co., Dublin, Ireland; *Int'l*, pg. 12
Shannon, Dave, Mng. Dir.-Sls. & Mktg.--Toyota Motor Distributors (Ireland) Ltd., Dublin, Ireland; *Int'l*, pg. 1413
Shannon, Michael G., Pres.--Gayfers, Mobile, AL; *U.S. Public*, pg. 1090
Shannon, Michael G., Pres.--J.B. White, Columbia, SC; *U.S. Public*, pg. 1090
Shannon, Michael G., Pres.--Maison Blanche, Inc., Baton Rouge, LA; *U.S. Public*, pg. 1090
Shannon, Mike, V.P. & Gen. Mgr.--WRFY-FM, Reading, PA; *U.S. Public*, pg. 385
Shannon, Rex B., Chm. Bd., Pres. & Chief Exec. Officer--Allianz Life Insurance Co., Dallas, TX; *Int'l*, pg. 58
Shannon, Ronald J., V.P.-Sls.--Guinness Southern Division, Newport Beach, CA; *Int'l*, pg. 412
Shannon, Rosamond Pickering, Pres.--Douglas Elliman Pickering Assoc., Inc., Greenwich, CT; *U.S. Private*, pg. 341
Shannon, Timothy F., Pres.--Bradner Smith & Co., Chicago, IL; *U.S. Private*, pg. 164
Shapira, A., Gen. Mgr.--Hogla-Kimberly Ltd., Petah Tiqwa, Israel; *Int'l*, pg. 75
Shapira, A., Gen. Mgr.--Hogla-Kimberly Ltd., Petah Tiqwa, Israel; *U.S. Public*, pg. 959
Shapira, Menachem, Chief Oper. Officer--ECI Telecom (UK) Limited, Basingstoke, United Kingdom; *Int'l*, pg. 644
Shapiro, Bernard J., Pres. & Chief Exec. & Oper. Officer--Familian Pipe Inc., Van Nuys, CA; *Int'l*, pg. 1512
Shapiro, David J., Pres.--Familian Pipe & Supply Co., Van Nuys, CA; *Int'l*, pg. 1512
Shapiro, Harry, Pres.--Strick Lease, Inc., Fairless Hills, PA; *U.S. Public*, pg. 1787
Shapiro, Howard, V.P. & Asst. Sec.--Playboy Clubs International, Inc., Chicago, IL; *U.S. Public*, pg. 1310
Shapiro, Isaac, Partner--Skadden, Arps, Slate, Meagher & Flom LLP, Paris, France; *U.S. Private*, pg. 1005
Shapiro, Marc J., Chm. Bd., Pres. & Chief Exec. Officer--Texas Commerce Bank, Houston, TX; *U.S. Public*, pg. 339
Shapiro, Mark R., Pres.--Golden Grain Company, Pleasanton, CA; *U.S. Public*, pg. 1348
Shapiro, Martin C., Pres.--M.S. Chambers Engraving Group, Baltic, CT; *U.S. Private*, pg. 351
Shapiro, R.H., Grp. Pres.--Raytheon Support Systems, Long Beach, CA; *U.S. Public*, pg. 1364
Shapiro, Selwyn, Grp. Gen. Mgr.-Fin. & Admin.--Leo Burnett/Connaghan & May Pty. Ltd., Sydney, Australia; *U.S. Private*, pg. 185
Shapiro, Thomas J., Pres.--Wayne Steel, Inc., Wooster, OH; *U.S. Public*, pg. 1101
Shapon, Mike, Pres.--Fers Technology Group, L.L.C., Chicago, IL; *U.S. Private*, pg. 428
Sharef, Dr. U., Chief Oper. Officer--Siemens S.A., Bogota, Colombia; *Int'l*, pg. 1248
Sharef, M., Chief Oper. Officer--Siemens S.A., Caracas, Venezuela; *Int'l*, pg. 1248
Sharer, Charles, Gen. Mgr.--Industrial Packaging Div. (Franklin), Franklin, KY; *Int'l*, pg. 1270
Sharkey, Charles, Plant Mgr.--Wooster Magikoter West Division, Reno, NV; *U.S. Private*, pg. 1188
Sharkey, David K., Mgr.--Victaulic Tool Company, Easton, PA; *U.S. Private*, pg. 1138
Sharko, John L., Dir.-N.A.--Italian Line, South Plainfield, NJ; *Int'l*, pg. 653
Sharma, Arvin, Mgr.-Opers.--Bonhomme, New York, NY; *U.S. Private*, pg. 909
Sharman, G.C., Gen. Mgr.--UMC Industries, Ltd., Lytham Saint Anne's, United Kingdom; *U.S. Public*, pg. 457
Sharp-Smith, Duncan, Dir.--SadCo Ltd., Southampton, United Kingdom; *U.S. Private*, pg. 589
Sharp, Ben H., Dir.-Res.--Wyle Laboratories-Eastern Operations, Arlington, VA; *U.S. Private*, pg. 1193
Sharp, Bill, Pres.--Katin, Costa Mesa, CA; *U.S. Public*, pg. 940
Sharp, Brad, Pres.--Interchange Software Division, Dublin, OH; *U.S. Public*, pg. 1516
Sharp, Charles, Chm. Bd., Pres. & Chief Exec. Officer--Clinton State Bank, Clinton, AR; *U.S. Public*, pg. 630
Sharp, Dabney L., Pres.--Suburban Propane Group, Inc., Sumter, SC; *U.S. Public*, pg. 1436
Sharp, David L., Pres.--Wedgestone Automotive Corp., Irwindale, CA; *U.S. Public*, pg. 1751
Sharp, David L., Pres.--Fey Mfg. Co., Inc., Irwindale, CA; *U.S. Public*, pg. 1751
Sharp, F., Mng. Dir.--Endevco UK Ltd., Royston, United Kingdom; *Int'l*, pg. 853
Sharp, Jim, V.P. & Gen. Mgr.--Road Machinery Division, Shippensburg, PA; *U.S. Public*, pg. 876
Sharp, Larry, Gen. Mgr.--ITW Chronomatic, Chicago, IL; *U.S. Public*, pg. 866
Sharp, Merle, Gen. Mgr.--Gregg Foods of Portland, Inc., Portland, OR; *U.S. Private*, pg. 158
Sharp, Michael, Pres.--Unbrako Div., Jenkintown, PA; *U.S. Public*, pg. 1420
Sharp, Michael M., Pres.--NationsBank Futures Corporation, Richmond, VA; *U.S. Public*, pg. 1163
Sharp, Patrick E., Chm. Bd.--Transcon Insurance Ltd., Hamilton, Bermuda; *U.S. Public*, pg. 667
Sharp, W.R., Pres.--Adams Resources Exploration Corp., Houston, TX; *U.S. Public*, pg. 19
Sharpe, Anthony, Mng. Dir.-Wackenhut U.K.--Wackenhut U.K., Ltd., London, United Kingdom; *U.S. Public*, pg. 1732
Sharpe, Charles, Admin.--Guardian Care of Burgaw, Burgaw, NC; *U.S. Public*, pg. 1712

Sharpe, Gary, Pres.--Delphax Systems, Randolph, MA; *U.S. Public*, pg. 153
Sharpe, Guy, Mgr.--Southern Electric Supply Co., Inc., Vicksburg, MS; *Int'l*, pg. 1108
Sharpe, J., Mng. Dir.--IDenticam Systems Ltd., Markham, Canada; *U.S. Private*, pg. 557
Sharpe, John T., Chm.--American Health and Life Insurance Co., Fort Worth, TX; *U.S. Public*, pg. 1633
Sharpe, Ray, Pres.--Alpha Metals, Inc., Jersey City, NJ; *Int'l, pg. 328*
Sharpe, Robert, Gen. Mgr.--CMC-Lexington, Lexington, SC; *U.S. Public*, pg. 412
Sharratt, B.J., Mng. Dir.--Dunlop Automotive Composites (UK) Limited, United Kingdom; *U.S. Public*, pg. 665
Shato, M., Pres.--Cosmo Securities (America) Inc., New York, NY; *Int'l*, pg. 335
Shattuck, Mayo A., III, Pres. & Chief Oper. Officer--BT Alex. Brown Inc., Baltimore, MD; *U.S. Public*, pg. 185
Shaughnessy, Jack, Pres.--Boston Security Counsellors, Inc., Boston, MA; *U.S. Public*, pg. 23
Shaughnessy, Jack, Pres.--Dilks Stamp Co., Philadelphia, PA; *U.S. Private*, pg. 58
Shaughnessy, Jack, Pres.--Quaker City Stamp Co., Philadelphia, PA; *U.S. Private*, pg. 59
Shaughnessy, Kevin, Pres.--CCW Stamp Co., Cherry Hill, NJ; *U.S. Private*, pg. 58
Shaughnessy, William J., Pres. & Chief Exec. Officer--Wilbur Chocolate Co., Inc., Lititz, PA; *U.S. Private*, pg. 210
Shaukat, Al-Saud, Mgr.--Computer & Electronic Division, Dammam, Saudi Arabia; *Int'l*, pg. 501
Shaum, Blaine, Reg. Gen. Mgr.--Societe Generale, Los Angeles, CA; *Int'l*, pg. 1273
Shaver, Paul, Mgr.--EG & G Optoelectronics-St. Louis, Saint Louis, MO; *U.S. Public*, pg. 543
Shaver, William G., Pres.--Airborne Systems Integration Division, Baltimore, MD; *U.S. Public*, pg. 293
Shaver, William G., Pres.--Airborne Systems Integration Division, Belcamp, MD; *U.S. Public*, pg. 293
Shaw, Bill, Chief Oper. Officer--Turner Reciprocal Advertising Corporation, Atlanta, GA; *U.S. Public*, pg. 1615
Shaw, Bill, Pres.--Turner Omni Venture, Inc., Atlanta, GA; *U.S. Public*, pg. 1615
Shaw, Bruce C., Exec. V.P. & Gen. Mgr.--Bay Shipbuilding Co., Sturgeon Bay, WI; *U.S. Public*, pg. 1041
Shaw, Bruce C., Exec. V.P.--Toledo Shiprepair Company, Toledo, OH; *U.S. Public*, pg. 1041
Shaw, Colin, Pres.--AMS Management Systems Canada Inc., Ottawa, Canada; *U.S. Public*, pg. 86
Shaw, Craig W., Pres.--Perini Building Co., Inc. Western U.S. Division, Phoenix, AZ; *U.S. Public*, pg. 1278
Shaw, D. R., Mng. Dir.--NatWest Ventures Limited, London, United Kingdom; *Int'l*, pg. 910
Shaw, D.G., Mng. Dir.--GKN Sheepbridge Stokes Ltd., Chesterfield, United Kingdom; *Int'l*, pg. 535
Shaw, D.W., Pres.--Means Industries, Inc., Saginaw, MI; *U.S. Public*, pg. 1711
Shaw, David, Pres.--Standard Arrow Ltd., Winnipeg, Canada; *Int'l*, pg. 127
Shaw, David, Pres.--Delta V Technologies, Inc., Tucson, AZ; *U.S. Public*, pg. 1324
Shaw, David A., Pres.--Secure Communications Division, Chantilly, VA; *U.S. Public*, pg. 717
Shaw, Evelyn, Gen. Mgr.--Payson Texas, Inc., Dallas, TX; *U.S. Private*, pg. 844
Shaw, Frank, Admin.--Mountain Towers Healthcare, Cheyenne, WY; *U.S. Public*, pg. 1714
Shaw, G., Mng. Dir.--Arnold Wragg (Bolts & Nuts) Ltd., Stannington, United Kingdom; *Int'l*, pg. 586
Shaw, H., Mng. Dir.--Ascom Timeplex SA, Brussels, Belgium; *Int'l*, pg. 87
Shaw, Henry D., Pres.--John Hancock Variable Life Insurance Co., Boston, MA; *U.S. Private*, pg. 590
Shaw, J.P., Mng. Dir.--Senior Davis Derby, Derby, United Kingdom; *Int'l*, pg. 1220
Shaw, James C., Pres.--Spirol Ind. Ltd., Windsor, Canada; *U.S. Private*, pg. 1026
Shaw, James C., Pres.--Spirol West, Corona, CA; *U.S. Private*, pg. 1026
Shaw, James C., Pres.--Spirol International Corp., Cuyahoga Falls, OH; *U.S. Private*, pg. 1026
Shaw, James E., V.P. & Gen. Mgr.--Graphics Systems Division, Merrillville, IN; *U.S. Public*, pg. 153
Shaw, James R., Jr., Pres. & Chief Exec. Officer--Regions Bank/Jackson County, Jefferson, GA; *U.S. Public*, pg. 1372
Shaw, Jeff, Pres.--Dean Foods Vegetable Company, Green Bay, WI; *U.S. Public*, pg. 490
Shaw, John, Mng. Dir.--OIP, Paris, France; *Int'l*, pg. 1097
Shaw, John C., Jr., Exec. V.P. & Asst. Mgr.-Natl. Sls.--Jefferies & Company, Inc., Los Angeles, CA; *U.S. Public, pg. 925*
Shaw, John C., Jr., Asst. Mgr.-Natl. Sls.--Jefferies & Company, Inc., Boston, MA; *U.S. Public*, pg. 925
Shaw, M.M., Pres.--Atco Gas Services Ltd., Calgary, Canada; *Int'l*, pg. 95
Shaw, Mike, Mgr., No. Sea Area--Milchem Drilling Fluids Limited, Aberdeen, United Kingdom; *U.S. Public*, pg. 167
Shaw, Nicholas Byam, Pres.--Grove's Dictionaries of Music Inc., New York, NY; *Int'l*, pg. 1479
Shaw, Philip, Mng. Dir.--Butterworth-Heinemann Limited, Oxford, United Kingdom; *Int'l*, pg. 1094
Shaw, Ray, Gen. Mgr.--North Castle Design, Stamford, CT; *U.S. Private*, pg. 804
Shaw, Ray, V.P. & Gen. Mgr.--Nuclear Magnetic Resonance Instruments, Palo Alto, CA; *U.S. Public*, pg. 1710
Shaw, Richard, Pres.--Jones Apparel Group, Inc. Canada, Downsview, Canada; *U.S. Public*, pg. 933
Shaw, Robert, Div. Mgr.--Rogers Cable TV-Hamilton, Hamilton, Canada; *Int'l*, pg. 1122
Shaw, Ronald G., Pres. & Chief Oper. Officer--The Pilot Pen Corp. of America, Trumbull, CT; *Int'l*, pg. 1057
Shaw, Thomas S., Pres.--Delmarva Capital Investments, Inc., Wilmington, DE; *U.S. Public*, pg. 431
Shaw, William, Pres.--National American Corporation, Gautier, MS; *U.S. Public*, pg. 1688
Shawley, W.C., Pres.--Tate & Lyle Inc., Wilmington, DE; *Int'l*, pg. 1357
Shay, Jerry, Pres.--KME Kabelmetal America Inc., Oak Brook, IL; *Int'l*, pg. 719
Shay, Kevin, Pres.--Componenta International Inc., Bridgeport, CT; *Int'l*, pg. 1421
Shayne, Alan, Pres.--Warner Bros. Television, Inc., Burbank, CA; *U.S. Public*, pg. 1611
Shayne, P., Gen. Mgr.--Five Crowns, Corona Del Mar, CA; *U.S. Private*, pg. 654
Shea, Andrew J., Pres.--Sico North America Inc., Minneapolis, MN; *U.S. Private*, pg. 997
Shea, Charlie, Chief Exec. Officer--The Fifth Third Bank of Northeastern Ohio, Cleveland, OH; *U.S. Public*, pg. 621
Shea, Christina L., Pres.--Betty Crocker Products, Minneapolis, MN; *U.S. Public*, pg. 718
Shea, Daniel R., Pres.--Kingsley Machine Co., Downers Grove, IL; *U.S. Public*, pg. 866
Shea, James, Plant Mgr.--Ash Grove Cement Plant, Chanute, KS; *U.S. Private*, pg. 88
Shea, John, Refinery Mgr.--Yabucoa, PR Refinery, Yabucoa, PR; *U.S. Public*, pg. 1530
Shea, Kevin C., Gen. Mgr.--Retail Application Systems & Services, Atlanta, GA; *U.S. Public*, pg. 1156
Shea, Michael D., Pres. & Chief Oper. Officer--Defiance Precision Products, Inc., Defiance, OH; *U.S. Public*, pg. 493
Shea, Terry J., Gen. Mgr.--Buckeye Container, Wooster, OH; *U.S. Private*, pg. 177
Shead, Ken, Gen. Mgr.--Justrite Mfg. Co., Mattoon, IL; *U.S. Public*, pg. 617
Sheaff, Kenneth D., Mgr.-Opers.--Delroyd Worm Gear, Trenton, NJ; *U.S. Public*, pg. 857
Sheaffer, James W., Chm., Mng. Dir.--AMS Management Systems Deutschland GmbH, Frankfurt, Germany; *U.S. Public*, pg. 87
Sheaffer, James W., Chm., Mng. Dir.--AMS Management Systems Europe, SA, NV, Brussels, Belgium; *U.S. Public, pg. 87*
Shealy, T.W., Pres.--Springs Industries, Bedding Division, Charlotte, NC; *U.S. Public*, pg. 1500
Sheard, C.K., Pres.--Northwestern Utilities Limited, Edmonton, Canada; *Int'l*, pg. 95
Sheard, Mark, Mng. Dir.--Percheron Properties, Sunderland, United Kingdom; *Int'l*, pg. 1454
Shearer, Gary, Gen. Mgr.--Tyco Engineered Systems, Manchester, CT; *U.S. Public*, pg. 1648
Shearer, Gary E., Gen. Mgr.--North American Printed Circuit Div., Stafford, CT; *U.S. Public*, pg. 1648
Shearer, Jeffrey, Chief Oper. Officer & Publisher--Saturday Night Magazine Limited, Toronto, Canada; *Int'l*, pg. 631
Sheargold, Glenn, Branch Sls. Mgr.--Kohler Australia, Wetherill Park, Australia; *U.S. Private*, pg. 631
Shears, William H., V.P. & Gen. Mgr.--Jamestown Perforators Inc., Jamestown, NY; *U.S. Public*, pg. 617
Sheavaleau, Dennis, Pres.--Ameda AG, Hunenberg, Switzerland; *U.S. Private*, pg. 535
Sheed, James C., Chief Exec. Officer--Hastings Deering (Australia) Limited, Archerfield, Australia; *Int'l*, pg. 1250
Sheehan, A., Grp. Mng. Dir.--ANI Aurora Plc, Sheffield, United Kingdom; *Int'l*, pg. 101
Sheehan, Kevin, Gen. Mgr.--Dynacraft, Louisville, KY; *U.S. Public*, pg. 1246
Sheehan, Mary L., Asst. Mgr.-Branch--Piper Jaffray Inc., Menlo Park, CA; *U.S. Public*, pg. 1301
Sheehy, Pres.--Denver Thomas, Inc., Birmingham, AL; *Int'l*, pg. 1325
Sheehy, Robert J., Pres. & Chief Exec. Officer--United HealthCare of Ohio, Inc., Columbus, OH; *U.S. Public*, pg. 1678
Sheehy, Terry, Media Svcs.--Leo Burnett Company Ltd., Toronto, Canada; *U.S. Private*, pg. 185
Sheeny, Thomas D., Pres.--Signal Knitwear, Chattanooga, TN; *U.S. Public*, pg. 1472
Sheets, James, Branch Mgr.--Union-Transport Corporation-Oklahoma City Office, Oklahoma City, OK; *U.S. Private*, pg. 1120
Sheff, Michael, Grp. Sr. V.P. & Mktg. Mgr.--Southwest Marketing-Dallas Business Center, Dallas, TX; *U.S. Public*, pg. 650
Sheffel, Wallace, Pres.--MFG Union City Operations, Union City, PA; *U.S. Private*, pg. 756
Sheffield, Bob, Plant Mgr.--Square D Oxford Plant, Oxford, OH; *Int'l*, pg. 1208
Sheffler, Tom, Pres.--L3 Communications Conic Div., San Diego, CA; *U.S. Private*, pg. 638
Sheffy, F., V.P. & Gen. Mgr.--Johnson Matthey Pharmaceuticals Materials, Deptford, NJ; *Int'l*, pg. 713
Shehan, David M., Mgr.--Piper, Jaffray & Hopwood, Inc., Omaha, NE; *U.S. Public*, pg. 1300
Shei, Johnson, Mng. Dir.--Seika Electric Co., Euclid, OH; *Int'l*, pg. 1218
Shei, Kurt, Dir.-Mfg.--Essex Specialty Products, Auburn Hills, MI; *U.S. Public*, pg. 523
Sheikh, Jawed Igbal, Asst. V.P. & Mgr.--Habib Bank Ltd., Mahe, Seychelles; *Int'l*, pg. 584
Sheikh, Zaryab, V.P.-Opers.--Harper Freight International, Southall, United Kingdom; *U.S. Public*, pg. 373
Sheith, Nipun, Mng. Dir.--Battenfeld India Ltd., Gujarat, India; *Int'l*, pg. 825
Shek, Clara, Mng. Dir.--Edelman Worldwide (Hong Kong) Limited, Causeway Bay, Hong Kong; *U.S. Private*, pg. 363
Sheldon, Jim, Pres.--Holiday Rambler, Wakarusa, IN; *U.S. Public*, pg. 1123
Sheldon, Noble, V.P. & Gen. Mgr.--Androck Products/ Newell Bulldog, Watford, Canada; *U.S. Public*, pg. 1178
Sheley, G. Michael, Chief Exec. Officer--National Health Plans, Modesto, CA; *U.S. Public*, pg. 1577
Shell, Owen G., Jr., Pres. & Chief Exec. Officer--Nationsbank/Tennessee, Nashville, TN; *U.S. Public*, pg. 1163
Shelly, David, Mgr.-Europe--Ideal Tape-Belgium, Ronse, Belgium; *U.S. Public*, pg. 69
Shelly, Ronald, Pres.--Solectron Texas, Austin, TX; *U.S. Public*, pg. 1483
Shelton, Darold E., Pres. & Chief Exec. Officer--United Missouri Bank of Cass County, Peculiar, MO; *U.S. Public*, pg. 1655
Shelton, Gene, Chm. Bd. & Pres.--Sunclipse, Inc., Buena Park, CA; *Int'l*, pg. 72
Shelton, Kevin, Pres.--P&H Transportation, North Haverhill, NH; *U.S. Private*, pg. 164
Shelton, Paul, Pres.--Ameri-Co Carriers, Inc., Scottsbluff, NE; *U.S. Public*, pg. 63
Shelton, Paul, Pres.--Nationwide Freight Services, Inc., Scottsbluff, NE; *U.S. Public*, pg. 64
Shelton, Richard E., Sr. V.P.--Allen-Bradley Global Sales & Support Group, Milwaukee, WI; *U.S. Public*, pg. 1397
Shelton, Roger, Plant Mgr.--Acme Brick Co., Millsap, TX; *U.S. Public*, pg. 936
Shelton, Stanley W., Sr. V.P. & Gen. Mgr.--State Street Bank-London Branch, London, United Kingdom; *U.S. Public*, pg. 1513
Shelvey, M.J., Gen. Mgr.--Morgan Matroc Limited Park Royal Division, Sandy, United Kingdom; *Int'l*, pg. 893
Shen, Andrew, Mgr.-Sls.--China Airlines Ltd., Washington, DC; *Int'l*, pg. 285
Shen, Frank H.L., Mng. Dir.--Raw Materials Ltd., Taipei, Taiwan; *Int'l*, pg. 303
Shen, Vivian, Rep.--Jardine Fleming Securities Ltd. Services, Shanghai, China; *Int'l*, pg. 494
Shenfield, Martin A.F., Chief Exec. Officer--Ki Pacific Asset Management, London, United Kingdom; *U.S. Public*, pg. 1674
Shenkenburg, W.J., Pres. & Chief Exec. Officer--M & I Bank of Racine, Racine, WI; *U.S. Public*, pg. 1050
Shenloogian, William, Mng. Dir.--Gunnebo Fastening Corporation, Lonoke, AR; *Int'l*, pg. 578
Shepard, Allan, Pres.--Tri State Steel Construction, Strongsville, OH; *U.S. Private*, pg. 782
Shepard, Donald J., Chm. Bd., Pres. & Chief Exec. Officer--AEGON USA, Inc., Baltimore, MD; *Int'l*, pg. 26
Shepard, Robert, Plant Mgr.--McInnes Rolled Rings, Erie, PA; *U.S. Private*, pg. 722
Shepard, Susan, Admin.--Bryant Nursing Center, Edmond, OK; *U.S. Public*, pg. 839
Shepard, Terry, Pres.--St. Jude Medical Division, Saint Paul, MN; *U.S. Public*, pg. 1428
Shepard, Victor, Pres.--Computer Design Inc., Grand Rapids, MI; *U.S. Private*, pg. 465
Sheperd, Martin, Chief Oper. Officer--KONE Elevators (Australia) Pty. Ltd., Newton, New Zealand; *Int'l*, pg. 747
Shepherd, Donald R., Chm. Bd.--Loomis, Sayles & Co., Boston, MA; *U.S. Private*, pg. 737
Shepherd, J.M., Gen. Mgr.--S.C. Johnson & Son de Venezuela, C.A., Caracas, Venezuela; *U.S. Private*, pg. 593
Shepherd, N., Mng. Dir.--Gestetner Australasia Limited, Brookvale, Australia; *Int'l*, pg. 1115
Shepherd, Peter, Dr., Mng. Dir.--Elsevier Science SA, Lausanne, Switzerland; *Int'l*, pg. 1100
Shepherd, William, Chief Exec.--Reed Educational and Professional Publishing, Oxford, United Kingdom; *Int'l*, pg. 1094
Sheppard-Jones, John, Mng. Dir.--Manitowoc Europe Ltd., Northampton, United Kingdom; *U.S. Public*, pg. 1041
Sheppard, David, Mgr.--New South Wales Branch, Mayfield, Australia; *Int'l*, pg. 226
Sheppard, David M., Chm. & Chief Exec. Officer--Fleet Services Corp., Providence, RI; *U.S. Public*, pg. 650
Sheppard, Robert, Chief Oper. Officer--Krauss-Maffei (U.K.) Ltd., Warrington, United Kingdom; *Int'l*, pg. 836
Sheppard, Scott, Publr.--Southern Living, Inc., Birmingham, AL; *U.S. Public*, pg. 1613
Sheppard, T., Mng. Dir.--Computasia Limited, Taikoo Shing, Hong Kong; *Int'l*, pg. 247
Sher-Khan, Nabi, Regional Head--National Bank of Pakistan, New York, NY; *Int'l*, pg. 908
Sher, Phil, Admin.--Blueberry Hill Healthcare, Beverly, MA; *U.S. Public*, pg. 1712
Sherberg, Ellen, Publr.--St. Louis Business Journal Corp., Saint Louis, MO; *U.S. Private*, pg. 20
Sheridan, J. Martin, Area Mgr.--Cablevision of Raleigh, Inc., Raleigh, NC; *U.S. Public*, pg. 1610
Sheridan, Kevin, Pres.--KIC, Ltd., Hamilton, Bermuda; *Int'l*, pg. 594
Sheridan, Phillip R., Pres.--West Instruments, Brighton, United Kingdom; *U.S. Public*, pg. 1045
Sheridan, Richard, Pres.--Printing Service Incorporated, Madison Heights, MI; *U.S. Public*, pg. 1736
Sheridan, Susan, Mng. Dir.--SCT, Rochester, NY; *U.S. Public*, pg. 1552
Sheridan, Terrance, V.P.--Keithley Instruments Inc.-Radiation Measurements Div., Cleveland, OH; *U.S. Public*, pg. 946
Sheridan, Wayne M., Pres.--Fischbach & Moore, Inc., New York, NY; *U.S. Public*, pg. 84
Sherin, L., Chief Exec. Officer--Zurich International Services (Ireland) Limited, Dublin, Ireland; *Int'l*, pg. 1532
Sherling, George L., Pres. & Chief Exec. Officer--Compass Bank Dallas, Richardson, TX; *U.S. Public*, pg. 419
Sherlock, Gary, Pres. & Publr.--Gannett Suburban Newspapers, White Plains, NY; *U.S. Public*, pg. 700
Sherman, Bob, Mgr.--Gould Southern, Norcross, GA; *U.S. Private*, pg. 467
Sherman, Brooks F., Pres.--Selkirk HVAC, Dallas, TX; *U.S. Public*, pg. 1795
Sherman, Chad, Opers. Mgr.--Chemrich, Inc., Lafayette, LA; *Int'l*, pg. 49
Sherman, Christopher R., Pres.--Pacific Enterprises International, Los Angeles, CA; *U.S. Public*, pg. 1249
Sherman, Floyd, Chm. Bd. & Chief Exec. Officer-Triangle Pacific--Bruce Hardwood Floors, Dallas, TX; *U.S. Public*, pg. 1634

Sherman, Jeff, Chief Oper. Officer--Ransome Engine, Bensalem, PA; *U.S. Private*, pg. 453
Sherman, L.J., Pres. & Chief Oper. Officer--A.Y. McDonald Mfg. Co., Dubuque, IA; *U.S. Private*, pg. 721
Sherman, L.J., Pres. & Chief Oper. Officer--A.Y.M. Inc., Albia, IA; *U.S. Private*, pg. 721
Sherman, Lawrence F., Pres.--MONY Securities Corp., New York, NY; *U.S. Private*, pg. 769
Sherman, Malcolm L., Chief Exec. Officer--Ekco Housewares, Inc., Franklin Park, IL; *U.S. Public*, pg. 566
Sherman, Malcolm L., Pres.--Ekco Cleaning, Inc., Franklin Park, IL; *U.S. Public*, pg. 566
Sherman, Malcolm L., Chm. Bd. & Chief Exec. Officer--Ekco International, Inc., Nashua, NH; *U.S. Public*, pg. 566
Sherman, R., Dir.-Opers.--Bausch & Lomb Ireland Limited, Waterford, Ireland; *U.S. Public*, pg. 195
Sherman, R. Keith, Pres.--Caterpillar Risk Management Services Ltd., Peoria, IL; *U.S. Public*, pg. 316
Sherman, Robert E., Pres. & Chief Oper. Officer--RSI International, Ltd., Rochester, United Kingdom; *U.S. Public*, pg. 424
Sherman, Selina, Dir.--Boam Produce (Overseas) Ltd., Camden, NJ; *U.S. Private*, pg. 689
Sherman, Stanley, Pres. & Chief Exec. Officer--Ciba Specialty Chemicals, Tarrytown, NY; *Int'l*, pg. 291
Sherman, Thomas W., Pres.--Bay State Energy Development, Inc., Westborough, MA; *U.S. Public*, pg. 197
Sherman, Thomas W., V.P.--Bay State Gas Company, Westborough, MA; *U.S. Public*, pg. 197
Shernit, Bill, Pres.--Quality Systems Inc., Mc Lean, VA; *U.S. Public*, pg. 1627
Sherrier, John T., Plant Mgr.--Bundy Corporation, Ashley Plant, Ashley, IN; *Int'l*, pg. 1340
Sherriff, Anthony G., Mng. Dir.--Perfect Pizza Ltd., Chertsey, United Kingdom; *Int'l*, pg. 1213
Sherrill, Bobby, Mgr.--Southern Agricultural Insecticides, Boone, NC; *U.S. Private*, pg. 1015
Sherrill, Carolyn H., Admin.--Wesleyan Nursing Home, Inc., Charlotte, NC; *U.S. Public*, pg. 1715
Sherry, James, Pres.--Interealty Corporation, Vienna, VA; *U.S. Private*, pg. 797
Sherwell, Enrique, Gen. Mgr.--Topps Mexico, S.A. de C.V., Mexico, Mexico; *U.S. Public*, pg. 1622
Sherwin, Ted, Pres.--Harte-Hanks Direct Marketing Cincinnati, Cincinnati, OH; *U.S. Public*, pg. 794
Sherwood, James B., Chm. Bd. & Chief Exec. Officer--Orient-Express Hotels Inc., New York, NY; *Int'l*, pg. 1213
Sherwood, Simon, Chief Exec. Officer--B.B.H. Asia Pacific, Singapore, Singapore; *Int'l*, pg. 169
Sheth, A.P., Chief Oper. Officer--Amol Dicalite Ltd., Ahmedabad, India; *U.S. Private*, pg. 903
Sheth, Nipun, Mng. Dir.--Battenfeld India Ltd., Mumbai, India; *Int'l*, pg. 825
Shetter, Thaine, Publr.--Ravalli Republic, Hamilton, MT; *U.S. Public*, pg. 1343
Shettle, John F., Sr., Pres.--MEDEX Assistance Corporation, Timonium, MD; *U.S. Public*, pg. 152
Shettle, John F., Sr., Pres.--Brooks-Shettle Co., Timonium, MD; *U.S. Public*, pg. 152
Shetty, Ajit, Dr., Exec. V.P.--Janssen Pharmaceutica N.V., Beersel, Belgium; *U.S. Public*, pg. 930
Shevlin, John A.B., Mng. Dir.--JLG Industries (Australia) Pty. Limited, Port MacQuarie, Australia; *U.S. Public*, pg. 918
Shibata, Keisuke, Pres.--Glaverbel S.A., Brussels, Belgium; *Int'l*, pg. 85
Shibata, M., Pres.--Mitsubishi Monsanto Chemical Co., Tokyo, Japan; *U.S. Public*, pg. 1125
Shibata, Naoshige, Mng. Dir.--Nippon Life (Deutschland) GmbH, Frankfurt/Main, Germany; *Int'l*, pg. 936
Shibata, Ren, Pres.--Yokogawa Corporation of America, Newnan, GA; *Int'l*, pg. 1521
Shibata, Shinichi, Pres. Dir.--P.T. Indonesia Dai-Ichi Kangyo Bank, Jakarta, Indonesia; *Int'l*, pg. 362
Shibata, T., Mng. Dir.--Anritsu Europe Ltd., Luton, United Kingdom; *Int'l*, pg. 77
Shibatsuchi, Kazuhiro, Gen. Mgr.--Asahi Bank New York Branch, New York, NY; *Int'l*, pg. 82
Shibley, Rod, Plant Mgr.--AlliedSignal Canada Inc., Automotive Aftermarket, Mississauga, Canada; *U.S. Public*, pg. 52
Shibusawa, Yoshitaka, Exec. V.P. & Gen Mgr.--Nippon Steel U.S.A., Inc., Los Angeles, CA; *Int'l*, pg. 940
Shibuya, K., Pres.--Sharp Corporation (Taiwan), Taipei, Taiwan; *Int'l*, pg. 1229
Shibuya, Kameo, Pres.--Nippon Express U.S.A. Inc., New York, NY; *Int'l*, pg. 934
Shibuya, Naoaki, Pres.--CPB Properties, Inc., Honolulu, HI; *U.S. Public*, pg. 283
Shichiri, Tadashi, Gen. Mgr.--Shimex Ltd., Tokyo, Japan; *Int'l*, pg. 303
Shida, Ryohei, Mng. Dir.--Marubeni Plasma Technik Co. Ltd., Tokyo, Japan; *Int'l*, pg. 1307
Shiel, James G., Pres.--Berkley Dean & Company, Inc., Greenwich, CT; *U.S. Public*, pg. 216
Shields, Daniel, Gen. Mgr.--Schult Homes Corporation, Milton, PA; *U.S. Public*, pg. 1442
Shields, John, Chm. Bd. & Chief Exec. Officer--Trader Joe's Co., South Pasadena, CA; *U.S. Private*, pg. 1067
Shields, John, Publr.--Santa Maria Times, Santa Maria, CA; *U.S. Public*, pg. 1343
Shier, Barry, Pres. & Chief Exec. Officer--GNLV, Corp., Las Vegas, NV; *U.S. Public*, pg. 1117
Shiever, Don, Gen. Mgr.--Trelleborg YSH, Inc.-Carmi Division, Carmi, IL; *Int'l*, pg. 1422
Shifo, Tom, Pres.--The Ingersoll Milling Machine Co., Rockford, IL; *U.S. Private*, pg. 562
Shifris, O., Gen. Mgr.--MATA (Helicopters) Division/Military Aircraft Group, Jerusalem, Israel; *Int'l*, pg. 690
Shigemitsu, Hirouyuki, V.P. & Gen. Mgr.--Lotte U.S.A., Inc., Battle Creek, MI; *Int'l*, pg. 819
Shigeta, Hiroaki, Pres.--Nippon Roche K.K., Tokyo, Japan; *Int'l*, pg. 1121
Shigeta, Hiroshi, Gen. Mgr.--The Sakura Bank - Shanghai Branch, Shanghai, China; *Int'l*, pg. 1179
Shigeta, Toyohiko, Pres.--Nova Promotion Group Inc., Hackensack, NJ; *Int'l*, pg. 393
Shih, Chang Tai, Reg. Dir.-Americas-USA--China Airlines Ltd., Los Angeles, CA; *Int'l*, pg. 284
Shih, T.M., Exec. V.P.--Fubon Insurance Co. Ltd., Taipei, Taiwan; *Int'l*, pg. 60
Shiina, Hiromi, Gen. Mgr.--Kyodo Advertising Co., Ltd., Utsunomiya, Japan; *Int'l*, pg. 776
Shikata, Hirofumi, Dir. & Gen. Mgr.--Hiroshima Branch Office, Hiroshima, Japan; *Int'l*, pg. 1491
Shikato, Teruo, Pres.--Mizuno Finance Netherlands B.V., Amsterdam, Netherlands; *Int'l*, pg. 885
Shilander, Robert G., Div. Mgr.--Townsend & Bottum, Inc., Ann Arbor, MI; *U.S. Private*, pg. 146
Shill, Barry, V.P.-Branch Mgr.--Dallas Branch, Dallas, TX; *U.S. Public*, pg. 1683
Shillestad, John G., Chm. Bd., Pres. & Chief Oper. Officer--Columbian Life Insurance Company, Binghamton, NY; *U.S. Private*, pg. 256
Shillima, Don, Pres.--Kalitta Flying Service, Ypsilanti, MI; *U.S. Private*, pg. 57
Shilling, W.E., Mng. Dir.--Monteith Travel Services LTD, London, United Kingdom; *Int'l*, pg. 1510
Shim, Jae Hyung, Pres.--Rohm Electronics (Tianjin) Co., Ltd., Tianjin, China; *Int'l*, pg. 1125
Shim, Jae Jin, Pres.--Rohm Electronics Korea Corporation, Seoul, Korea; *Int'l*, pg. 1125
Shim, Jang Sop, Pres.--Rohm Korea Corporation, Seoul, Korea; *Int'l*, pg. 1125
Shim, Young-Cheol, Pres.--Ssangyong Resources Development Co., Ltd., Tonghae, Korea; *Int'l*, pg. 1291
Shima, K., VP & Gen Mgr-Pulp & Paper Div--MacMillan Bloedel K. K., Tokyo, Japan; *Int'l*, pg. 829
Shima, Koshi, Sr. V.P.--Shima American Corp., Carol Stream, IL; *Int'l*, pg. 1232
Shimacu, Takeshi, Pres.--Kirin USA, Inc., New York, NY; *Int'l*, pg. 736
Shimada, Kunio, Pres.--Komatsu Changlin Construction Machinery Corp., Jiangsu, China; *Int'l*, pg. 745
Shimada, Shigeyoshi, Chief Oper. Officer--The Sumitomo Bank, Ltd.-Dalian Representative Office, Dalian, China; *Int'l*, pg. 1309
Shimada, Takayuki, Gen. Mgr.--Daiwa Bank-Singapore, Singapore, Singapore; *Int'l*, pg. 373
Shimada, Toshisaka, Mgr.--Japan Oxygen, Inc., Torrance, CA; *Int'l*, pg. 938
Shimamoto, Toshihiko, Terminal Mgr.--Kintetsu World Express Inc., Miami, FL; *Int'l*, pg. 735
Shimamura, Kimizo, Mng. Dir. & Gen. Mgr.--The Industrial Bank of Japan, Limited (London Branch), London, United Kingdom; *Int'l*, pg. 675
Shimano, Yoshizo, Pres.--Shimano American Corporation, Irvine, CA; *Int'l*, pg. 1232
Shimaya, Noriaki, Mng. Dir. & Gen. Mgr.--Yokohama Asia Limited, Central, Hong Kong; *Int'l*, pg. 159
Shimaya, Yutaka, Chief Rep.--The Industrial Bank of Japan, Limited (Bahrain), Manama, Bahrain; *Int'l*, pg. 675
Shimazoe, Kazuhiro, Pres.--Sumitomo Life Insurance Agency America, Inc., New York, NY; *Int'l*, pg. 1315
Shimazu, Hitoshi, Chief Rep.--Kuroda Precision Industries, Chicago, IL; *Int'l*, pg. 764
Shimazu, Toshio, Gen. Mgr.--Yamaha Motor do Brasil Ltda., Convica, Brazil; *Int'l*, pg. 1516
Shimizu, Ikyo, Pres.--Honda Canada Inc., Scarborough, Canada; *Int'l*, pg. 635
Shimizu, Kenji, V.P.--Candela Europe, Eindhoven, Netherlands; *U.S. Public*, pg. 300
Shimizu, Kenji, V.P.--Candela Singapore, Singapore, Singapore; *U.S. Public*, pg. 301
Shimizu, Kuniyasu, Dir.--Takenaka do Brasil Construtora Ltda., Sao Paulo, Brazil; *Int'l*, pg. 1351
Shimizu, Ryo, Rep. Dir.--Sunkist Pacific, Ltd., Tokyo, Japan; *U.S. Private*, pg. 1053
Shimizu, Tamotsu, Mng. Dir. & Gen. Mgr.--Imaging Business Grp., Nagoya, Japan; *Int'l*, pg. 229
Shimizu, Taruhiko, Sr. V.P. & Gen. Mgr.--Sumitomo Corporation of America, Seattle, WA; *Int'l*, pg. 1312
Shimizu, Yusuke, Pres.--Ismac, Inc., Calhoun, GA; *Int'l*, pg. 744
Shimmin, Maxine, Mng. Dir.--Dixons Finance Plc, London, United Kingdom; *Int'l*, pg. 414
Shimoda, H., Pres.--Toshoku America, Inc., New York, NY; *Int'l*, pg. 1407
Shimoda, Kazutoshi, Gen. Mgr.--Sumitomo Trust & Banking (Switzerland) Limited, Zurich, Switzerland; *Int'l*, pg. 1318
Shimoda, Kouichi, Pres.--GSI Europe-Import & Export GmbH, Dusseldorf, Germany; *Int'l*, pg. 579
Shimoda, Tadashi, Joint Gen. Mgr.--Dai-Ichi Kangyo Bank, Ltd.-Madrid, Madrid, Spain; *Int'l*, pg. 360
Shimokawa, Tokiji, Pres.--Kintetsu Intermodal (U.S.A.), Inc., Carson, CA; *Int'l*, pg. 735
Shimokawa, Tomohiro, Pres.--Sanyo Energy (U.S.A.) Corporation, San Diego, CA; *Int'l*, pg. 1191
Shimomura, C., Gen. Mgr.--Marubeni America Corporation, Atlanta Office, Atlanta, GA; *Int'l*, pg. 844
Shimomura, Ryoichi, Mng. Dir.--Kyowa Hakko Industry (Singapore) Pte. Ltd., Singapore, Singapore; *Int'l*, pg. 778
Shimoyama, Sumio, Chief Oper. Officer--Skandia Life Insurance Co. (Japan) Ltd., Tokyo, Japan; *Int'l*, pg. 1258
Shimoyama, Yasuo, Chief Representative--The Bank of Tokyo-Mitsubishi, Ltd. (Shanghai Branch), Shanghai, China; *Int'l*, pg. 158
Shimp, Steven C., Chief Oper. Officer--Owen-Ames-Kimball Co., Fort Myers, FL; *U.S. Private*, pg. 824
Shimpi, Prakash A., Mng. Dir.--Swiss Re Financial Products, New York, NY; *Int'l*, pg. 1333
Shimura, Sumiya, Gen. Mgr.--Sophisticated Products Div., Tokyo, Japan; *Int'l*, pg. 934
Shimura, Toshiaki, Chief Rep.--Kuala Lumpur Representative Office, Kuala Lumpur, Malaysia; *Int'l*, pg. 520
Shin, S.S., Dir.--Daewoo International America Corp. - Santa Clara, Santa Clara, CA; *Int'l*, pg. 357
Shinall, Wilton, Sr. Mktg. Officer--Northeast Marketing Div., Harrisburg, PA; *U.S. Private*, pg. 296
Shindo, Mitsusaburo, Pres.--Amada Engineering & Service Co., Inc., La Mirada, CA; *Int'l*, pg. 70
Shine, Gretchen, V.P. & Gen. Mgr.--Cox Communications-Roanoke, Roanoke, VA; *U.S. Public*, pg. 455
Shine, T.K., Pres. & Chief Exec. Officer--Logo 7, Inc., Indianapolis, IN; *U.S. Public*, pg. 1644
Shing, Tan Tock, Dir. & Gen. Mgr.--Crown Cork of Malaysia SDN BHD, Johor Baharu, Malaysia; *U.S. Public*, pg. 465
Shingyoji, Shintaro, Pres.--Hitachi Koki U.S.A. Ltd., Norcross, GA; *Int'l*, pg. 620
Shinju, M., Chief Oper. Officer--Daido International Inc., New York, NY; *Int'l*, pg. 364
Shinkawa, Rodney R., Pres.--First Federal Savings & Loan of America, Honolulu, HI; *U.S. Public*, pg. 1248
Shinneman, Frank, V.P.--Quality Metals, Orangeburg, NY; *Int'l*, pg. 1283
Shinoda, Takao, Sr. Rep.--Bayerische Landesbank Girozentrale, Tokyo, Japan; *Int'l*, pg. 177
Shinoda, Yasuo, Gen. Mgr.--The Sumitomo Bank, Ltd.-Madrid Branch, Madrid, Spain; *Int'l*, pg. 1309
Shinoda, Yasuo, Gen. Mgr.--The Sumitomo Bank, Ltd.-Barcelona Branch, Barcelona, Spain; *Int'l*, pg. 1309
Shinohara, Akira, Pres.--Denki Kagaku Kogyo Kabushiki Kaisha, Tokyo, Japan; *Int'l*, pg. 877
Shinohara, H., Mng. Dir.--NOF Jotun Co. Ltd., Tokyo, Japan; *Int'l*, pg. 716
Shinohara, M., Pres.--MSP Steel Works Ltd., Singapore, Singapore; *Int'l*, pg. 948
Shinohara, Tadashi, Reg. Dir.--Dentsu Hong Kong Office, Central, Hong Kong; *Int'l*, pg. 393
Shinomiya, K., Chief Oper. Officer--Okumura Metals Co., Ltd., Osaka, Japan; *Int'l*, pg. 530
Shinozuka, Koji, Gen. Mgr.--Dai-Ichi Kangyo Bank, Ltd.-Milan, Milan, Italy; *Int'l*, pg. 360
Shinya, K., Pres.--Toshiba Display Devices (Thailand) Co., Ltd., Pathum Thani, Thailand; *Int'l*, pg. 1406
Shiojima, Tadashi, Branch Mgr.--Daiwa Securities (Taipei), Taipei, Taiwan; *Int'l*, pg. 376
Shiomi, Hiromasa, Chief Oper. Officer--Disco Hi-tec Europe GmbH, Pliening, Germany; *Int'l*, pg. 413
Shiota, Robert, Pres.--Richmond American Homes of California, Inc., Irvine, CA; *U.S. Public*, pg. 1025
Shiplet, J.L., Pres.--PACCAR Leasing Corporation, Bellevue, WA; *U.S. Public*, pg. 1247
Shipley, Ken, Div. Mgr.--Wyle Electronics-Denver, Thornton, CO; *Int'l*, pg. 1457
Shipley, Richard C., Pres.--Shipley Co., LLC, Marlborough, MA; *U.S. Public*, pg. 1403
Shipman, Mark L., Pres.--Coco's & Carrows Restaurants, Irvine, CA; *U.S. Public*, pg. 23
Shipmon, Frederick S., III, Pres.--Drake Construction Company, Portland, OR; *U.S. Private*, pg. 347
Shipp, Barry, Pres.--Parman Lubricants, Nashville, TN; *U.S. Private*, pg. 840
Shipp, Robbie, Pres.--Rembrandt Photo Services, City of Commerce, CA; *U.S. Private*, pg. 222
Shirai, Tadahiro, Pres.--Nissan Europe N.V., Amsterdam, Netherlands; *Int'l*, pg. 945
Shiraishi, Shinobu, Pres.--ORIX Life Insurance Corporation, Tokyo, Japan; *Int'l*, pg. 1009
Shiraishi, Yutaka, Pres.--ORIX Interior Corporation, Osaka, Japan; *Int'l*, pg. 1008
Shirakawa, Junya, Gen. Mgr.--Milton Roy (Japan) Ltd., Tokyo, Japan; *U.S. Public*, pg. 1534
Shiraki, Tak, V.P. & Gen. Mgr.--Panasonic Factory Automation Co., Elgin, IL; *Int'l*, pg. 847
Shiratani, Suiji, Pres.--Sanki Engineering Co., Ltd., Tokyo, Japan; *Int'l*, pg. 877
Shircliff, J.D., Pres.--Onan Power Electronics, Saint Peter, MN; *U.S. Public*, pg. 468
Shirley, Ben, Dir.-Small Appliances--KitchenAid Co., Saint Joseph, MI; *U.S. Public*, pg. 1765
Shirley, George S., Chm. Bd. & Pres.--AmSouth of Tuscaloosa, Tuscaloosa, AL; *U.S. Public*, pg. 105
Shirouza, Osamu, Chief Oper. Officer--TM Claims Service, Inc., New York, NY; *Int'l*, pg. 1392
Shirvanian, Kosti, Chief Oper. Officer--Western Waste Industries, Inc. of Florida, Orlando, FL; *U.S. Public*, pg. 1686
Shitoto, Hideo, Mng. Dir.--Intermedics Japan K.K., Tokyo, Japan; *Int'l*, pg. 1307
Shivakumar, Jayasankar, Country Dir.--The World Bank, Bangkok, Thailand; *U.S. Private*, pg. 1189
Shivers, Ronald W., Pres.--Dee Zee Mfg., Inc., Des Moines, IA; *U.S. Public*, pg. 976
Shivery, Charles W., Pres.--Constellation Power, Inc., Baltimore, MD; *U.S. Public*, pg. 172
Shkedi, S., Gen. Mgr.--Aircraft Division/BEDEK Aviation Group, Israel; *Int'l*, pg. 690
Shlappig, Arnold, Exec. V.P. & Gen. Mgr.--Bayerische Hypotheken-und Wechsel-Bank Aktiengesellschaft New York Branch, New York, NY; *Int'l*, pg. 176
Shmuely, M., Mng. Dir.--Elta Electronics Industries, Ltd., Ashdod, Israel; *Int'l*, pg. 690
Shoaff, Gary, Gen. Mgr.--Sermatech Middle Atlantic, Limerick, PA; *U.S. Public*, pg. 1570
Shoda, Mitsuteru, Pres.--Wateree Textile Corp., Lugoff, SC; *Int'l*, pg. 845
Shoemake, John, Branch Mgr.--Jaco Electronics, Inc., Austin, TX; *U.S. Public*, pg. 921
Shoemake, Marvin D., Pres.--SatCom Technologies Division, Duluth, GA; *U.S. Public*, pg. 424
Shoemaker, Richard A., Pres. & Chief Exec. Officer--First Virginia Bank-Franklin County, Rocky Mount, VA; *U.S. Public*, pg. 641
Shoemaker, Steven J., Mgr.--Minneapolis Milling, Minneapolis, MN; *U.S. Public*, pg. 128
Shoen, E.J. "Joe", Pres.--U-Haul International, Inc., Phoenix, AZ; *U.S. Private*, pg. 49

Shoffner, John P., Pres.--Dura-Line Corp., Middlesboro, KY; *U.S. Private*, pg. 598
Shogan, Edward N., Pres.--Springfield Division, New York, NY; *U.S. Public*, pg. 1500
Shoh, Koichi, Pres.--Japan Visual-Soft Network Co., Tokyo, Japan; *Int'l*, pg. 588
Shoham, Y., Pres. & Chief Exec. Officer--Onyx Interactive Multimedia Ltd., Tel Aviv, Israel; *Int'l*, pg. 1007
Shoji, Tsuyoshi, Pres.--Yamaichi International (Canada) Limited/Limitee, Montreal, Canada; *Int'l*, pg. 1517
Shokrgozar, Hamid, Pres.--White Microelectronics, Phoenix, AZ; *U.S. Public*, pg. 248
Sholder, Jason, Pres.--Datascope Cardiac Assist Division, Fairfield, NJ; *U.S. Public*, pg. 487
Shom, Emery, Mgr.-Fin. & Admin.--Sensormatic Hong Kong Limited, Kowloon, Hong Kong; *U.S. Public*, pg. 1458
Shon, M., Pres.--Bohlin Instruments Inc., Cranbury, NJ; *Int'l, pg. 208*
Shon, Mark S., Pres. & Chief Exec. Officer--E-C Apparatus Corp., Saint Petersburg, FL; *U.S. Public*, pg. 1595
Shoniker, James E., Pres.--Bank of Boston Canada, Toronto, Canada; *U.S. Public*, pg. 184
Shoniker, James E., Pres.--Boston Factors of Canada, Inc., Montreal, Canada; *U.S. Public*, pg. 185
Shono, Ryosaku, Gen. Dir.--CSO Division/CSK, Tokyo, Japan; *U.S. Public*, pg. 1043
Shonov, Georgi, Mng. Dir.--KONE Representative Office, Moscow, Russia; *Int'l*, pg. 747
Shonsey, Ed, Pres. & Chief Exec. Officer--Northrup King Co., Golden Valley, MN; *Int'l*, pg. 974
Shook, Arlin, Branch Mgr.--RHG Corpus Christi, Corpus Christi, TX; *Int'l*, pg. 1151
Shordone, Frank, Pres.--Tia's Tex-Mex Restaurants, Mobile, AL; *U.S. Public*, pg. 1412
Shore-Dundas, Debra, Div. V.P.--Trade Products, Lynnwood, WA; *U.S. Public*, pg. 1526
Short, James L., Chm. & Pres.--NationsBank Mountain Grove, Mountain Grove, MO; *U.S. Public*, pg. 1164
Short, Lloyd J., Pres.--Macmillan Digital USA, Indianapolis, IN; *U.S. Private*, pg. 777
Short, Richard, V.P.--Fullerton Div., Fullerton, CA; *U.S. Public*, pg. 1161
Short, Richard, V.P. & Mgr.-Sls.--NTS-Los Angeles Division, Los Angeles, CA; *U.S. Public*, pg. 1161
Shorter, Maurice J., Pres.--Thermo Electron Ltd., Southwater, United Kingdom; *U.S. Public*, pg. 1596
Shorter, Maurice T., Pres.--Eberline Instrument Company Ltd., Southwater, United Kingdom; *U.S. Public*, pg. 1596
Shorts, Gary K., Publisher & Chief Exec. Officer--The Morning Call, Allentown, PA; *U.S. Public*, pg. 1616
Shotton, Jim, Pres.--Denver Autometrics, Boulder, CO; *Int'l*, pg. 1325
Shotton, John, V.P.--Consolidation Coal Co., Rend Lake Mine, Sesser, IL; *U.S. Public*, pg. 531
Shotts, David A., Pres.--Frisby P.M.C. Incorporated, Elk Grove Village, IL; *U.S. Public*, pg. 894
Shoulders, Barry W., Pres. & Chief Exec. Officer--BWI Kartridg Pak, Davenport, IA; *Int'l*, pg. 130
Shoultz, Jim, Gen. Mgr.--Colgate-Palmolive A/S, Glostrup, Denmark; *U.S. Public*, pg. 398
Shoup, Allan C., Pres.--International Wine & Spirits Ltd., Greenwich, CT; *U.S. Public*, pg. 1661
Shoup, Allen C., Pres. & Chief Exec. Officer--Stimson Lane Ltd., Woodinville, WA; *U.S. Public*, pg. 1661
Shouse, H.T., Chm., Pres. & Chief Exec. Officer--Morganfield National Bank, Morganfield, KY; *U.S. Public, pg. 1217*
Shovlin, Robert J., Pres.--Pennsylvania Mines Corp., Ebensburg, PA; *U.S. Public*, pg. 1244
Showalter, Neil D., Pres.--Cassco Ice & Cold Storage, Inc., Harrisonburg, VA; *U.S. Public*, pg. 1727
Showers, Paula, Plant Mgr.--Benzonia Manufacturing, Benzonia, MI; *U.S. Private*, pg. 753
Shrachan, I.C., Chm. Bd.--RTZ Pillar Ltd., London, United Kingdom; *Int'l*, pg. 267
Shrader, James, Publisher--The Times Reporter, New Philadelphia, OH; *U.S. Public*, pg. 935
Shrader, Joseph M., Chief Exec. Officer--Urban Retail Properties, Inc., Chicago, IL; *U.S. Public*, pg. 1700
Shrawder, J.E., Pres. & Chief Oper. Officer--Elrick & Lavidge, Inc., Chicago, IL; *U.S. Public*, pg. 588
Shrem, Charles J., Pres.--Commonwealth Metal, Englewood Cliffs, NJ; *U.S. Public*, pg. 412
Shrimpton, Stephen, Sr. V.P.-Mktg. & Sls. Europe--Warner Music International (Europe) Ltd., London, United Kingdom; *U.S. Public*, pg. 1615
Shrode, Dick, Pres.--Baldwin Filters, Kearney, NE; *U.S. Public*, pg. 381
Shroeder, Vern, Chief Oper. Officer--The Marvel Group, Inc., Chicago, IL; *U.S. Public*, pg. 1053
Shroff, Avanti C., Sr. V.P.--Iffland Kavanagh Waterbury, PLLC, New York, NY; *U.S. Private*, pg. 364
Shroyer, J., Pres.--Sharp Digital Information Products, Inc., Irvine, CA; *Int'l*, pg. 1229
Shroyer, J., Pres.--Sharp Flat Display Manufacturing Company, Camas, WA; *Int'l*, pg. 1229
Shroyer, Jon A., Pres.--Sharp Microelectronics Technology, Inc., Camas, WA; *Int'l*, pg. 1229
Shtayyeh, Munther, V.P.-Opers.--Anco Products, Michigan City, IN; *U.S. Public*, pg. 442
Shua, Ken, Pres.--Accucare Div., Mundelein, IL; *U.S. Private*, pg. 728
Shubin, Lewis, Pres.--Sope Creek, Marietta, GA; *U.S. Public*, pg. 1539
Shubrook, J., Sls. Mgr.--International Paint Eastern Div., Union, NJ; *Int'l*, pg. 339
Shucet, Phillip, Pres.--Baker Environmental, Inc., Coraopolis, PA; *U.S. Public*, pg. 168
Shuey, John H., Pres.--Amcast Industrial Ltd., Burlington, Canada; *U.S. Public*, pg. 63
Shufeldt, R. Charles, Chief Exec. Officer--SunTrust Securities, Inc., Atlanta, GA; *U.S. Public*, pg. 1538
Shugars, Curtis E., Dir.-Eastern Reg.--GAI Construction Services, Inc., King of Prussia, PA; *U.S. Private*, pg. 434
Shugars, Curtis E., Mgr.-Eastern Reg.--GAI Consultants, Inc., King of Prussia, PA; *U.S. Private*, pg. 434
Shugh, Jim, Gen. Mgr.--Comdisco Technical Services, Inc., Schaumburg, IL; *U.S. Public*, pg. 408
Shugimoto, Masashi, Gen. Mgr.--Mitsui & Co. (U.S.A.), Inc., Chicago, IL; *Int'l*, pg. 879
Shugrue, J. Edward, Pres.--Triumph Releasing Corporation, Los Angeles, CA; *Int'l*, pg. 1282
Shukla, Hari, Mng. Dir.--MISR Pioneer Seed Co. S.A.E., Cairo, Egypt; *U.S. Public*, pg. 1299
Shuler, Tom, Pres.--Insignia Residential Group, Greenville, SC; *U.S. Public*, pg. 881
Shull, Denise, Chief Oper. Officer--Associated Claims Management, Inc. of California, Rancho Cordova, CA; *U.S. Public*, pg. 678
Shull, Noel J., Exec. V.P.--United Missouri Capital Corporation, Kansas City, MO; *U.S. Public*, pg. 1655
Shulstein, R., Gen. Mgr.--Tambour Limited, Acre, Israel; *Int'l*, pg. 644
Shulte-Ratz, Elke, Mgr.-Opers.--Herbalife International Deutschland GmbH, Weiterstadt, Germany; *U.S. Public*, pg. 809
Shultz, Ed, Pres.--Shannon Properties, Charlotte, NC; *U.S. Public*, pg. 480
Shultz, Ed, Pres.--Diamond Financial Holdings, Inc., Toledo, OH; *U.S. Public*, pg. 480
Shultz, Preston, Gen. Mgr.--Burton Electrical Engineering, El Segundo, CA; *U.S. Private*, pg. 1193
Shum, P. Lui Po, Mng. Dir.--Damco Maritime (HK) Ltd., Hong Kong, Hong Kong; *Int'l*, pg. 1144
Shumacher, Norbert, Sr. V.P.-Publication Services--Modern Plastics, New York, NY; *U.S. Public*, pg. 1071
Shumsky, Mike, Pres.--Sonic Restaurants, Inc., Oklahoma City, OK; *U.S. Public*, pg. 1485
Shupe, John, Pres.--TWC of Florida, Incorporated, Saint Petersburg, FL; *U.S. Public*, pg. 1755
Shurman, John, Pres.--Beverage Canners International Corp., Miami, FL; *U.S. Private*, pg. 106
Shurman, John, Pres.--Naturalle Springs, Inc., Greeneville, TN; *U.S. Private*, pg. 106
Shurville, Ian, Chief Oper. Officer--Perstorp Pharma Ltd. Wound Care Division, Basingstoke, United Kingdom; *Int'l*, pg. 1037
Shuster, Dan, Gen. Mgr.--Amway de Espana, S.A., Barcelona, Spain; *U.S. Private*, pg. 69
Shuster, Dan, Reg. Dir.--Amway (U.K.) Limited, Milton Keynes, United Kingdom; *U.S. Private*, pg. 70
Shuttleworth, R., Mng. Dir.--WBB Devon Clays Ltd., Newton Abbot, United Kingdom; *Int'l*, pg. 1487
Shutz, Paul, Pres. & Gen. Mgr.--Pure Carbon Company, Saint Marys, PA; *Int'l*, pg. 891
Shymko, H., Pres.--BetzDearborn Inc., Mississauga, Canada; *U.S. Public*, pg. 227
Shyu, Jiin Ming, Chief Oper. Officer--Far Eastern Electric Industry Co., Ltd., Taipei, Taiwan; *Int'l*, pg. 1000
Siabane, Carlo, Gen. Mgr.--Banca Monte Paschi Belgio, Brussels, Belgium; *Int'l*, pg. 147
Sibois, Jean Bernard, Mng. Dir.--Bureau Rhone-Poulenc, Cairo, Egypt; *Int'l*, pg. 1112
Sibrain, Nicolas, Mgr.--San Cristobal Mill & Plant, San Salvador, El Salvador; *U.S. Public*, pg. 410
Siciliano, Arthur A., Ph.D., Pres.--PolyMedica Pharmaceuticals (U.S.A.), Inc., Woburn, MA; *U.S. Public*, pg. 1315
Siddens, Ernest G., Pres.--Union Electric Steel N.V., Tessenderlo, Belgium; *U.S. Public*, pg. 104
Siddens, Larry, Pres.--Reeves Brothers Inc., New York, NY; *U.S. Private*, pg. 507
Siddens, Larry, Pres.--Finished Goods Div., New York, NY; *U.S. Private*, pg. 507
Sidebottom, Kevin, Mgr.-Mktg.--Cerner Arabia Ltd., Riyadh, Saudi Arabia; *U.S. Public*, pg. 331
Sider, John H., V.P.--Network Buss Division, Rolling Meadows, IL; *U.S. Public*, pg. 1101
Sideris, Julien, Mng. Dir.--Compania Ericsson S.A., Lima, Peru; *Int'l*, pg. 1365
Sidersky, Jean Pierre, Pres.--Mead Johnson S.A., Paris, France; *U.S. Public*, pg. 256
Sides, James R., Chm. & Chief Exec. Officer--Atlantic Research Corporation, Gainesville, VA; *U.S. Public*, pg. 1458
Sides, June, Admin.--Knollwood Hall, Winston Salem, NC; *U.S. Public*, pg. 1714
Sidgmore, John, Pres. & Chief Oper. Officer--MFS WorldCom, Inc., Omaha, NE; *U.S. Public*, pg. 1779
Sidgmore, John W., Chief Exec. Officer--UUNET Technologies, Inc., Fairfax, VA; *U.S. Public*, pg. 1779
Sidlik, Thomas W., Chm. Bd., V.P. & Gen. Mgr.-Small Car Opers.--Chrysler Financial Corporation, Southfield, MI; *U.S. Public*, pg. 354
Sidoff, Bjorn, Mng. Dir.--SKF Korea Ltd., Pusan, Korea; *Int'l, pg. 1159*
Sidoova, Zdenka, Rep.--Generale Bank, Prague, Czech Republic; *Int'l*, pg. 547
Sidor, Marek, Pres.--LOT Polish Airlines SA, New York, NY; *Int'l*, pg. 1062
Sidwell, Martin, Gen. Mgr.--DunsGate, New York, NY; *U.S. Public*, pg. 535
Siebel, Ronald, Pres.--J.E. Siebel & Sons Company Inc., Chicago, IL; *Int'l*, pg. 1110
Siebelink, Dr. Dernardus M.A., Dir.--Van den Bergh en Jurgens B.V., Rotterdam, Netherlands; *Int'l*, pg. 1439
Sieben, Tony, Mng. Dir.--ISS Contract Cleaning Services (North), Middleton, United Kingdom; *Int'l*, pg. 657
Sieber, Karl, Mng. Dir.--Mikronwerk GmbH, Aschaffenburg, Germany; *Int'l*, pg. 1157
Siebers, Michael A., Gen. Mgr.--Oregon City Div., Oregon City, OR; *Int'l*, pg. 1269
Siebert, Wolfgang, Co-Chief Oper. Officer--Saarberg Handel GmbH, Saarbruecken, Germany; *Int'l*, pg. 1167
Siedsma, Paul, Plant Mgr.--The Kingsford Products Co., Parsons, WV; *U.S. Public*, pg. 387
Sieg, Frank, Gen. Mgr.--International Extrusion Corporation-Texas, Waxahachie, TX; *U.S. Public*, pg. 895
Siegel, Brad, Pres.--Turner Network Television, Inc., Atlanta, GA; *U.S. Public*, pg. 1615
Siegel, Clifford A., Chief Exec. Officer--Jefferies International Limited, London, United Kingdom; *U.S. Public*, pg. 925
Siegel, David N., Pres.--Continental Express, Houston, TX; *U.S. Public*, pg. 439
Siegel, E.M., Pres.--Wirth Ltd., Montreal, Canada; *Int'l*, pg. 1150
Siegel, Fred, Pres.--Secretly Yours Inc., Harrison, NJ; *U.S. Private*, pg. 565
Siegel, John, Pres.--KBHK Television, Inc., San Francisco, CA; *U.S. Public*, pg. 352
Siegel, John T., Mng. Dir.--Thompson, Siegel & Walmsley, Inc., Richmond, VA; *U.S. Public*, pg. 1674
Siegel, L. Pendleton, Pres.--Clearwater Commodity Corp., San Francisco, CA; *U.S. Public*, pg. 1318
Siegel, Mo, Chief Exec. Officer--Celestial Beverages, Inc., Boulder, CO; *U.S. Public*, pg. 320
Siegel, Mo, Chief Exec. Officer--Tea Direct, Boulder, CO; *U.S. Public*, pg. 320
Siegel, Randy, Partner, Exec. V.P. & Gen. Mgr.--Fleishman-Hillard, Inc., Atlanta, GA; *U.S. Private*, pg. 411
Siegel, Robert, Mgr.--Plastic Suppliers Inc., Fullerton, CA; *U.S. Private*, pg. 871
Siegel, Stuart N., Pres. & Mng. Dir.--Sotheby's International Realty, New York, NY; *U.S. Public*, pg. 1487
Siegele, Stephen, Pres.--ADCS, Inc., Austin, TX; *U.S. Public*, pg. 12
Siegendorf, Bill, Gen. Mgr.--SMI Georgia Rebar, Lawrenceville, GA; *U.S. Public*, pg. 412
Siegers, R., Mng. Dir.--Faxion B.V., Amsterdam, Netherlands; *Int'l*, pg. 1144
Siegert, Heinz, Mng. Dir.--Verlag Kremayr und Scheriau, Vienna, Austria; *Int'l*, pg. 192
Sieghart, Josef J., Pres.--Voest-Alpine Industries, Inc., New York, NY; *Int'l*, pg. 1470
Siegle, H.R., Mng. Dir.--Whitbread Property, Luton, United Kingdom; *Int'l*, pg. 1498
Siegmund, Ernst, Mng. Dir.--VOEST-ALPINE Austria Draht Ges.m.b.H., Bruck, Austria; *Int'l*, pg. 1470
Siegrist, Fred, Mng. Dir.--Swiss Life Portfolio Management, Zurich, Switzerland; *Int'l*, pg. 1332
Siegrist, Terrence, Pres.--Maxwell Technologies-Information Systems Division, San Diego, CA; *U.S. Public*, pg. 1062
Siegrist, Terry, Pres.--Information Systems Division, San Diego, CA; *U.S. Public*, pg. 1062
Sieja, L. J., Pres. & Gen. Mgr.--Portec, Inc., Shipping Systems Div., Oak Brook, IL; *U.S. Public*, pg. 1318
Siek, Robert D., V.P.-Federal Programs--Jacobs Engineering Group Inc., Denver, CO; *U.S. Public*, pg. 921
Sielck, Rainer, Dr., Pres.--AdvoCard Rechtsschutzversichereng AG, Hamburg, Germany; *Int'l*, pg. 15
Siemer, G.H., Gen. Mgr.--Flexsteel Division, New Paris, IN; *U.S. Public*, pg. 654
Siemers, Jerry E., Gen. Mgr.--Boeing Petroleum Services, Inc., New Orleans, LA; *U.S. Public*, pg. 242
Siems, Volker, Pres.--Freudenberg Building Systems Inc., Lawrence, MA; *Int'l*, pg. 506
Sier, F.H.J., Dir.--Brother International (Nederland) B.V., Amstelveen, Netherlands; *Int'l*, pg. 229
Sierra, Juan Carlos, Mng. Dir.--Ediciones Larousse Colombiana Ltda., Bogota, Colombia; *Int'l*, pg. 240
Sierwald, Kevin H., Gen. Mgr.--Durco Process Equipment Ltd., Milton Keynes, United Kingdom; *U.S. Public*, pg. 659
Siesto, Edoardo Dello, Gen. Mgr.--Meteor Construzioni Aeronautiche ed Elettroniche S.p.A., Rome, Italy; *Int'l*, pg. 653
Sievers, C.H., Sr. V.P. & Mgr.-Branch--ABN AMRO Bank, N.V. (Seattle), Seattle, WA; *Int'l*, pg. 10
Sievers, F., Chief Oper. Officer--WESER-EMS Vertriebsgesellschaft mbH, Bremen, Germany; *Int'l*, pg. 1474
Sigar, Edward, Gen. Mgr.--Tankstore Pte Ltd., Singapore, Singapore; *U.S. Public*, pg. 693
Sigg, Dr. Hans-Peter, Pres.--Sandoz Technology Ltd., Basel, Switzerland; *Int'l*, pg. 972
Sigler, Michael W., Mgr.-Plant--The Flexaust Co., Warsaw, IN; *U.S. Public*, pg. 394
Sigley, Timothy D., Pres.--Plastic Packaging Company, Muncie, IN; *U.S. Public*, pg. 57
Sigmai, Gordon H., Jr., Exec. V.P. & Gen. Mgr.-Strategic Defense Systems--Strategic Defense Systems, Washington, DC; *U.S. Public*, pg. 1690
Sigman, Robert, Chief Exec. Officer--Republic Entertainment, Inc., Los Angeles, CA; *U.S. Private*, pg. 776
Sigman, Stan, Pres. & Chief Exec. Officer--Southwestern Bell Mobile Systems, Inc., Dallas, TX; *U.S. Public*, pg. 1415
Sigmon, Bill, Gen. Mgr.--Bassett Motion Division, Saltillo, MS; *U.S. Public*, pg. 193
Sigmund, Ralph, Dir. Gen.--L'Oreal Parfumerie, Brussels, Belgium; *Int'l*, pg. 819
Signare, John, Plant Mgr.--Tulip Corp., Niagara Falls Div., Niagara Falls, NY; *U.S. Private*, pg. 1109
Signorelli, Ivan, Pres.--American Flange & Manufacturing Co. Inc., Carol Stream, IL; *Int'l*, pg. 1146
Signorelli, Pat, Dir.-Adv.--Hunt-Wesson Consumer Advertising Div., Fullerton, CA; *U.S. Public*, pg. 428
Sigurdson, Barry, Area Mgr.--Heffley Creek Division, Kamloops, Canada; *Int'l*, pg. 1395
Sigurdsson, Jon, Mng. Dir.--Icelandic Alloys, Akranes, Iceland; *Int'l*, pg. 448
Sigward, M.F., Branch Mgr.--Zellerbach Division, Atlanta, GA; *U.S. Public*, pg. 1075
Sijbesma, F., Mng. Dir.--Food Specialties Division, Delft, Netherlands; *Int'l*, pg. 1142
Silander, Harald, Mng. Dir.--BTL Sweden AB, Goteborg, Sweden; *Int'l*, pg. 123
Silavanich, Thanarak, Pres.--Siam Mariwasa Toto, Inc., Manila, Philippines; *Int'l*, pg. 1410

Silberfeld, Jacques, Mng. Dir.--ISS Net Inter S.A., Pantin, France; *Int'l*, pg. 657
Silberman, Anna, Exec. Dir.--Health Education Center Inc., Pittsburgh, PA; *U.S. Private*, pg. 529
Silberman, Simon, Mng. Dir.--Zircotube, Paris, France; *Int'l*, pg. 503
Silbermayr, Franz, Dr., Gen. Mgr.--J.M. Voith AG, Saint Polten, Austria; *Int'l*, pg. 1473
Silcott, Jack, Pres.--Hancock Manufacturing, Toronto, OH; *U.S. Private*, pg. 299
Silen, Jouko, Mgr.--Inkeroinen Sawmill, Anjalankoski, Finland; *Int'l*, pg. 456
Siler, Ron, Pres.--West Kentucky Division, Sturgis, KY; *Int'l*, pg. 337
Silingsby, B., Mgr.--Rockware Glass Ltd.-Wheatley Factory, Doncaster, United Kingdom; *Int'l*, pg. 124
Silk, Bert, Pres. & Div. Mgr.--Bisceglia Brothers Wine Co., Madera, CA; *U.S. Public*, pg. 300
Sill, Harold, V.P. & Gen. Mgr.--Thorn Apple Valley-Carolina Division, Holly Ridge, NC; *U.S. Public*, pg. 1603
Sillantaka, Erkki, Mng. Dir.--VV-Auto Oy, Helsinki, Finland; *Int'l*, pg. 732
Sillard, Benoit, Chief Exec. Officer--Fun Radio, Neuilly-sur-Seine, France; *Int'l*, pg. 561
Silva-Flores, Magda, Branch Mgr.--Downey Savings & Loan Association, F.A., San Bruno, CA; *U.S. Public*, pg. 527
Silva, C.F., Gen. Mgr.--S.C. Johnson & Son Colombiana S.A., Bogota, Colombia; *U.S. Private*, pg. 593
Silva, Carlos Eduardo Konder Lins E., Dir.--Latas De Aluminio, S/A-LATASA, Rio de Janeiro, Brazil; *U.S. Public*, pg. 1387
Silva, Cesar, Chief Oper. Officer--Gambro Lda., Parede, Portugal; *Int'l*, pg. 668
Silva, Cesar Ocampa, Gen. Mgr.--Inmobiliaria Wackenhut, S.A. de C.V., Mexico, Mexico; *U.S. Public*, pg. 1731
Silva, Claudio A., Sup. Dir.--Gillette da Amazonia S/A, Manaus, Brazil; *U.S. Public*, pg. 744
Silva, F.R., Pres.--Nestle Puerto Rico, Inc., Catano, PR; *Int'l*, pg. 917
Silva, Gil, Pres.--J.A. Sexauer, Inc., Scarsdale, NY; *U.S. Private*, pg. 352
Silva, Jose Lizano, Gen. Mgr.--Distribuidora de Manufacturas Centro-Americanas, S.A., San Jose, Costa Rica; *U.S. Public*, pg. 959
Silva, Mauro A., Plant Mgr.--TI Brazil Industria E Comerico Ltda., Curitiba, Brazil; *Int'l*, pg. 1342
Silva, William L., Exec. V.P.--Maytag Aircraft Corp., Colorado Springs, CO; *U.S. Public*, pg. 1093
Silvas, Lee, Pres.--McPherson's America, Inc., New Hyde Park, NY; *Int'l*, pg. 852
Silver, Cary, Gen. Mgr.--Office Depot, Detroit, MI; *U.S. Public*, pg. 1212
Silver, Casey, Chm. Bd.--Universal Pictures, Universal City, CA; *Int'l*, pg. 1216
Silver, J.A.R., Representative--Morgan Grenfell (Venezuela), Caracas, Venezuela; *Int'l*, pg. 406
Silver, J.F., Pres.--Clipper Abrasives Inc., Niagara Falls, NY; *Int'l*, pg. 1174
Silver, Jerry, Gen. Mgr.--West Palm Beach Auto Auction, Inc., West Palm Beach, FL; *U.S. Public*, pg. 1649
Silvere, Jean, Pres. & Gen. Dir.--Alcatel France, Paris, France; *Int'l*, pg. 55
Silverman, Henry, Chief Exec. Officer--Owned Television Stations, New York, NY; *U.S. Private*, pg. 148
Silverman, Howard B., Pres.--Illinois Banc One Insurance Services, Inc., Evanston, IL; *U.S. Public*, pg. 174
Silverman, Jay N., Pres.--Seitel Geophysical, Inc. dba Eagle Geophysical, Inc., Houston, TX; *U.S. Public*, pg. 1454
Silverman, Joel, Acting Chief Exec. Officer--Galyan's Trading Co., Plainfield, IN; *U.S. Public*, pg. 995
Silverman, Mark, Publr. & Editor--The Detroit News, Detroit, MI; *U.S. Public*, pg. 700
Silvertooth, Jerry, Pres.--Hausted, Medina, OH; *U.S. Private*, *pg. 1001*
Silvey, James M., Pres.--Silvey Corporation, Columbia, MO; *Int'l*, pg. 543
Silvi, Claudio, Dir. Gen.--Alfa Romeo Espana, Madrid, Spain; *Int'l*, pg. 481
Sim, George A., V.P. & Gen. Mgr.--Delta/Cyklop Strapping, Charlotte, NC; *U.S. Public*, pg. 865
Simal, Joao, Mng. Dir.-Sls.--Sensormatic Lda., Lisbon, Portugal; *U.S. Public*, pg. 1458
Simard, Jean Francois, Pres. & Gen. Mgr.--Lumec, Inc., Boisbriand, Canada; *U.S. Public*, pg. 1599
Simard, Jean Marc, Gen. Mgr.--Groupe Beton Quebec, Quebec, Canada; *Int'l*, pg. 629
Simcox, John P., Gen. Mgr.--Tank Division, Fremont, OH; *U.S. Public*, pg. 345
Simi, Louis W., Jr., Exec. V.P.--Atrium Companies, Inc., Irving, TX; *U.S. Private*, pg. 98
Simic, Zeljko, District Mgr.--Det Norske Veritas, Rijeka, Croatia; *Int'l*, pg. 397
Simiyu, Mathias, Gen. Mgr.--Kodak (Kenya) Limited, Nairobi, Kenya; *U.S. Public*, pg. 553
Simkins, D., Mng. Dir.--GKN Driveline Ltd., Sutton Coldfield, United Kingdom; *Int'l*, pg. 534
Simkins, Robert, Pres.--Pall Industrial Hydraulics Corp., Glen Cove, NY; *U.S. Public*, pg. 1254
Simkins, Robert, Pres.--Pall Mobile Aftermarket Division, Glen Cove, NY; *U.S. Public*, pg. 1254
Simkins, Robert, Pres.--Pall Well Technology Company, Glen Cove, NY; *U.S. Public*, pg. 1254
Simko, John S., Pres.--Minera Sunshine Del Peru, S.A., Lima, Peru; *U.S. Public*, pg. 1536
Simko, Robert, V.P.--Sealright Mfg. Fulton, Inc., Fulton, NY; *U.S. Public*, pg. 1452
Simmerman, Gary F., Reg. Pres.--Summit Bank, Bethlehem, PA; *U.S. Public*, pg. 1528
Simmons, Bill, Chief Oper. Officer--Gulf Coast Division, Holiday, FL; *U.S. Public*, pg. 656
Simmons, Bob, Publisher--Rubber & Plastics News, Akron, OH; *U.S. Private*, pg. 285
Simmons, Bob, Dir.-Publ.--Tire Business, Akron, OH; *U.S. Private*, pg. 285
Simmons, Bob, Gen. Mgr.--Tru-Test Mfg. Co., Cary, IL; *U.S. Private*, pg. 1108
Simmons, Christopher J., Pres.--U.S. Filter, Lowell, MA; *U.S. Public*, pg. 1682
Simmons, Gary F., Pres.--Healthtex, Greensboro, NC; *U.S. Public*, pg. 1702
Simmons, George M., Pres.--First Chemical Corp., Pascagoula, MS; *U.S. Public*, pg. 344
Simmons, Harold, Pres.--Rothenberger USA, Inc., Monterey Park, CA; *Int'l*, pg. 1129
Simmons, Harris H., Chm. Bd.--Zions First National Bank, Salt Lake City, UT; *U.S. Public*, pg. 1793
Simmons, Jack, V.P. & Central Div. Mgr.--TriStar Pictures Central Division, Des Plaines, IL; *Int'l*, pg. 1283
Simmons, James, Mgr.-Plant--Schnadig Corp., Cornelia, GA; *U.S. Private*, pg. 971
Simmons, James P., Pres.--The Weitz Company, Inc., Des Moines, IA; *U.S. Private*, pg. 1161
Simmons, John, Pres.--Hoosier Insurance Company, Indianapolis, IN; *Int'l*, pg. 346
Simmons, L.E., Chm. Bd.--Tuboscope Incorporated, Houston, TX; *U.S. Public*, pg. 1643
Simmons, Richard, Gen. Mgr.--Toccoa Div., Toccoa, GA; *U.S. Public*, pg. 575
Simmons, Richard E., III, Pres. & Chief Exec. Officer--Hilb, Rogal and Hamilton Company of Alabama, Inc., Birmingham, AL; *U.S. Public*, pg. 827
Simmons, Ron, Gen. Mgr.--Esselte Pendaflex, Syracuse, NY; *Int'l*, pg. 460
Simmons, Ronald J., Pres.--Waterloo Furniture Components Limited, Kitchener, Canada; *U.S. Private*, pg. 270
Simmons, Roy W., Chm. Bd.--Nevada State Bank, Las Vegas, NV; *U.S. Public*, pg. 1793
Simms, Derrick, Chief Exec. Officer-Bldg. Materials--Brooklyns Limited, Wareham, United Kingdom; *Int'l*, pg. 1355
Simms, Douglas D., Chm. Bd.--F. C. Banks, Omaha, NE; *U.S. Private*, pg. 398
Simms, Steven E., Pres.-Professional Tools Div.--Danaher Tool Group, Lancaster, PA; *U.S. Public*, pg. 480
Simms, Steven E., Acting Pres.--Hennessy Industries, Inc., La Vergne, TN; *U.S. Public*, pg. 481
Simoes, Ana, Fin. Dir.--Cineponto/Leo Burnett Publicidade Lda., Lisbon, Portugal; *U.S. Private*, pg. 184
Simoes, Joao, Pres.--Kvaerner do Brasil Ltda, Rio de Janeiro, Brazil; *Int'l*, pg. 767
Simoes, Joao, Pres.--Kvaerner Ships Equipment Ltda., Rio de Janeiro, Brazil; *Int'l*, pg. 768
Simon, Alan, Chm. Bd. & Chief Exec. Officer--Omaha Steaks Food Service, Omaha, NE; *U.S. Private*, pg. 816
Simon, Edward, Pres.--Tho-Ro Products, Inc., Carlstadt, NJ; *U.S. Private*, pg. 354
Simon, Ernest M., Pres., Chief Exec. & Oper. Officer--Plaid Enterprises Inc., Norcross, GA; *U.S. Private*, pg. 352
Simon, Frederick J., Pres.--Gourmet Foods Div., Omaha, NE; *U.S. Private*, pg. 816
Simon, Harvey J., V.P. & Gen. Mgr.--Chesterfield Division, Lancaster, SC; *U.S. Public*, pg. 1500
Simon, J.S., Pres. & Mng. Dir.--Esso Italiana S.p.A., Rome, Italy; *U.S. Public*, pg. 602
Simon, James B., Grp. V.P.--Giddings & Lewis Automation Technology, Fond Du Lac, WI; *Int'l*, pg. 1389
Simon, James E., Mng. Dir.--Aetna Universal Insurance SDN. BHD., Kuala Lumpur, Malaysia; *U.S. Public*, pg. 27
Simon, Jonathon, Pres.--Fleming Capital Management, New York, NY; *Int'l*, pg. 493
Simon, Ludwig, Chief Oper. Officer--Transit Kuhlhausgesellschaft mbH (TKG), Emmerich, Germany; *U.S. Public*, pg. 607
Simon, Mark I., V.P.--Books Management, Inc., Montgomeryville, PA; *U.S. Public*, pg. 491
Simon, Perry, Exec. V.P.-West Coast Opers.--Viacom Productions Inc., Universal City, CA; *U.S. Private*, pg. 779
Simon, Robert, Admin. Dir.--Time-Life International S.A., Paris, France; *U.S. Public*, pg. 1615
Simon, Robert, Chief Oper. Officer--Time-Life International S.r.L., Milan, Italy; *U.S. Public*, pg. 1615
Simon, Susie, Grp. V.P.--TMP Worldwide, Inc., Memphis, TN; *U.S. Private*, pg. 1064
Simonato, Gaston, Mng. Dir.--Lhomme S.A., Pont-sur-Yonne, France; *U.S. Public*, pg. 1487
Simonds, Brian, Mgr.-Sls.--Kingsbury Machining Center, Div., Keene, NH; *U.S. Private*, pg. 622
Simone, Ginny, Sr. V.P. & Mng. Dir.--The Mercury Group, Alexandria, VA; *U.S. Private*, pg. 13
Simonel, Charlie, Admin.--Southern Oaks Health Care Center, Saint Cloud, FL; *U.S. Public*, pg. 837
Simonet, Jacques, Dir.-Europe Opers.--Delco Moraine NDH Division, Gennevilliers, France; *U.S. Public*, pg. 724
Simonetti, Donna, Lab Mgr.--Quest Diagnostic-Harrisburg, Harrisburg, PA; *U.S. Public*, pg. 1351
Simonetti, Sergio, Pres.--Ansaldo Industria S.p.A., Genoa, Italy; *Int'l*, pg. 653
Simoni, Franis, Chief Oper. Officer--Electric Furnace France S.A.R.L., Garches, France; *U.S. Private*, pg. 368
Simonic, Bojan, Dir. Gen.--Tobacna Ljubljana d.o.o., Ljubljana, Slovenia; *Int'l*, pg. 1101
Simonin, Dominique, Mng. Partner & Chief Edec. Officer-Europe--Conquest Europe S.A.R.L., Neuilly-sur-Seine, France; *Int'l*, pg. 1484
Simonin, Dominique, Mng. Partner-Europe--Conquest Europe, Turin, Italy; *Int'l*, pg. 1484
Simonis, Jerry, Mng. Dir.--Pierre Balmain, Saint Imier, Switzerland; *Int'l*, pg. 1160
Simonis, Jerry, Mng. Dir.--Columna S.A., Lausanne, Switzerland; *Int'l*, pg. 1160
Simonis, Peter, Chm. Bd.--British American Offshore Limited, London, United Kingdom; *U.S. Public*, pg. 1410
Simonnet, Jacques, Mng. Dir--General Motors France, Gennevilliers, France; *U.S. Public*, pg. 724
Simons, Cyril, Mng. Dir.--Universal Studios Music Ltd., London, United Kingdom; *Int'l*, pg. 1217
Simons, John, Gen. Mgr.--Alro Group, Detroit, Detroit, MI; *U.S. Private*, pg. 46
Simons, John, Gen. Mgr.--Alro Specialty Metals, Redford, Redford Township, MI; *U.S. Private*, pg. 46
Simons, Paul, Chm. Bd.--Woolworths Limited, Yennora, Australia; *Int'l*, pg. 676
Simons, Raymond B., Gen. Mgr.--Methode Technical Components, Chicago Ridge, IL; *U.S. Public*, pg. 1101
Simons, Richard, Pres.--Northeast Properties, Inc., Boston, MA; *U.S. Public*, pg. 559
Simonson, Karl D., Pres.--Ontario Foods, Inc., Albion, NY; *U.S. Public*, pg. 728
Simonson, Robert D., Mgr.--Piper Jaffray Inc., Missoula, MT; *U.S. Public*, pg. 1302
Simonsson, Bengt-Roland, Chm. Reg. Bd.--ICA Handlarna Sydost AB, Vaxjo, Sweden; *Int'l*, pg. 643
Simonsson, Clase, Chief Oper. Officer--SAPA Aluminium Profile GmbH, Dusseldorf, Germany; *Int'l*, pg. 442
Simpkins, Clint, Pres.--Belmont Dyers Company, Belmont, NC; *U.S. Private*, pg. 732
Simpson, Barrie, Pres.--Warren Industries, Inc., Lafayette, IN; *U.S. Private*, pg. 945
Simpson, Becky, Mng. Dir.--Shandwick USA, Louisville, KY; *Int'l*, pg. 1227
Simpson, Bruce D., Pres. & Chief Exec. Officer--Lucent Netcare Messaging Services, Dallas, TX; *U.S. Public*, pg. 1018
Simpson, Bruce W., Pres. & Chief Oper. Officer--Nova Gas Transmission Ltd., Calgary, Canada; *Int'l*, pg. 971
Simpson, David W., Pres.--Westmoreland Resources, Inc., Billings, MT; *U.S. Public*, pg. 1761
Simpson, Harry R., Sr. V.P.-Life Company--American States Life Insurance Co., Indianapolis, IN; *U.S. Public*, pg. 997
Simpson, J.H., Chief Oper. Officer--Den norske Bank AS, Singapore Branch, Singapore, Singapore; *Int'l*, pg. 392
Simpson, Jack, Chief Oper. Officer--Advance Seed Company, Fulton, KY; *Int'l*, pg. 566
Simpson, Jim, Resident V.P.--Fireman's Fund Insurance Co. of Iowa, Bettendorf, IA; *Int'l*, pg. 59
Simpson, John, Mng. Dir.--Sigmaform Australia, Mount Ommaney, Australia; *U.S. Public*, pg. 1363
Simpson, L., Pres.--Standco Canada, Ltd., Woodbridge, Canada; *U.S. Public*, pg. 1420
Simpson, L.G., Pres.--Arkansas & Memphis Railway Bridge and Terminal Co., San Francisco, CA; *U.S. Public*, pg. 1668
Simpson, L.S., V.P. & Gen. Mgr.--Stelco USA, Inc., Troy, MI; *Int'l*, pg. 1300
Simpson, Lee, V.P.-Mfg. & Opers.--Capitol Records, Inc., Jacksonville, IL; *Int'l*, pg. 428
Simpson, Mark E., Pres.--Portsmouth Savings Bank, Portsmouth, NH; *U.S. Public*, pg. 278
Simpson, Murray S., Jr., V.P.--Super Concrete Corp., Washington, DC; *Int'l*, pg. 166
Simpson, N.T., Dir. & Principal Mgr.--Lloyds Bank International Ltd., Nassau, Bahamas; *Int'l*, pg. 813
Simpson, R. Bruce, Pres.--Roberts Express, Inc., Akron, OH; *U.S. Public*, pg. 604
Simpson, Robert, Gen. Mgr.--Louisiana Pacific Western Div., Samoa, CA; *U.S. Public*, pg. 1015
Simpson, Robert L., Pres. & Chief Exec. Officer--The Eastville Bank, Eastville, VA; *U.S. Public*, pg. 1089
Simpson, Sam, Pres. & Chief Exec. Officer--Cable Car Beverage Corporation, Denver, CO; *U.S. Public*, pg. 1635
Simpson, William, V.P. & Gen. Mgr.--Dynaray Incorporated, Waltham, MA; *Int'l*, pg. 725
Simpson, William A., Pres. & Chief Exec. Officer--All American Life Insurance Co., Chicago, IL; *U.S. Public*, pg. 77
Sims-Brown, Priscilla, Pres.--Lincoln Financial Advisors, Fort Wayne, IN; *U.S. Public*, pg. 998
Sims-Williams, Boyd, V.P.--Howe AGRA Limited, Ottawa, Canada; *Int'l*, pg. 31
Sims, Douglas D., Pres. & Chief Exec. Officer--CoBank, Englewood, CO; *U.S. Private*, pg. 398
Sims, Douglas D., Chm. Bd.--Farm Credit Council Services, Fargo, ND; *U.S. Private*, pg. 398
Sims, Douglas D., Chm. Bd.--Farm Credit Council Services, Grand Forks, ND; *U.S. Private*, pg. 398
Sims, James K., Pres. & Chief Exec. Officer--Cambridge Technology Partners, Cambridge, MA; *U.S. Public*, pg. 1424
Sims, Jerry L., Pres. & Treas.--Hilb, Rogal and Hamilton Company of Houston, Houston, TX; *U.S. Public*, pg. 827
Sims, Paul, Pres.--Houston Division, Houston, TX; *U.S. Public*, pg. 1683
Sims, Richard, Pres.--Tranzonic Industrial Textiles Division, Highland Heights, OH; *U.S. Public*, pg. 1632
Sims, T. Pinckney, Exec. V.P. & Gen. Mgr.--Kleinert's, Inc., of Alabama, Elba, AL; *U.S. Private*, pg. 625
Sims, William J., Pres.--Zenith Sales Co. Div., Glenview, IL; *U.S. Public*, pg. 1790
Sims, Willis D., Pres. & Chief Exec. Officer--SunTrust Bank, South Georgia, N.A., Albany, GA; *U.S. Public*, pg. 1538
Sinay, Debbie, Gen. Mgr.--WPRI-TV, East Providence, RI; *U.S. Private*, pg. 385
Sinclair, Bruce, Pres.--Dell Computer Corporation, North York, Canada; *U.S. Public*, pg. 496
Sinclair, Christopher A., Pres. & Chief Exec. Officer--PepsiCo Foods & Beverages International, Somers, NY; *U.S. Public*, pg. 1277
Sinclair, D., Pres.--Noma-International, Inc., Itasca, IL; *Int'l*, pg. 955
Sinclair, Desmond W., Pres.--Siltin Industries, Inc., Hillside, NJ; *U.S. Private*, pg. 320
Sinclair, Eoin, Gen. Mgr.--NIIB Group Limited, Bangor, Ireland; *Int'l*, pg. 152
Sinclair, Mark, Mgr.--AHI Roll-A-Door, East Tamaki, New Zealand; *U.S. Public*, pg. 904
Sinclair, Ray, Branch Mgr.--Zellerbach Division, Sparks, NV; *U.S. Public*, pg. 1076
Sinclair, Robert M., Pres.--Sinclair Paint Co., Los Angeles, CA; *Int'l*, pg. 663

Sinclair, William R., Dir.-Fin. & Admin.--Eli Lilly S.A., Geneva, Switzerland; *U.S. Public*, pg. 994
Sinden, Roy, Pres.--Ready-Lite Mfg. Ltd., Victoria, Canada; *Int'l*, pg. 725
Sinder, Tom, Mgr.--Grand Prairie Co-op, Inc., Philo, IL; *U.S. Private*, pg. 469
Sinder, Tom, Mgr.--Grand Prairie Co-op, Inc., Sidney, IL; *U.S. Private*, pg. 469
Sinders, John W., Jr., Mng. Dir.--Jefferies & Company, Inc., Los Angeles, CA; *U.S. Public*, pg. 925
Sines, James V., Pres.--United Aviation Fuels Corp., Elk Grove Village, IL; *U.S. Public*, pg. 1653
Sinfield, A.F., Mgr.-Southern--HFC Trust & Savings Ltd., Bracknell, United Kingdom; *U.S. Public*, pg. 842
Sing, Foo Sei, Mng. Dir.--Albright & Wilson (Marchon) Pte. Limited, Singapore, Singapore; *Int'l*, pg. 49
Sing, Young Kuan, Office Mgr.--Korn/Ferry International, Singapore, Singapore; *U.S. Private*, pg. 633
Singer, H.L., Pres.--Powers Process Controls, Skokie, IL; *U.S. Public*, pg. 457
Singer, Karl, Pres.--Ryan Insurance Group, Inc., Chicago, IL; *U.S. Public*, pg. 118
Singer, Karl, Pres.--Karl Singer Companies, Inc., Chicago, IL; *U.S. Public*, pg. 118
Singer, Marty, Pres.--Safco Technologies, Inc., Chicago, IL; *U.S. Public*, pg. 1430
Singerman, A., Pres.--Artistic Brass Div., South Gate, CA; *U.S. Public*, pg. 1054
Singh, D., Local Rep.--CGG Pan India Ltd., New Delhi, India; *Int'l*, pg. 241
Singh, J.G., Gen. Mgr.--RTI Laboratories Division, Livonia, MI; *U.S. Public*, pg. 502
Singh, Karmjit, Chief Exec. Officer & Gen. Mgr.--SATS Apron Services Pte., Ltd., Singapore, Singapore; *Int'l*, pg. 1374
Singh, Renu Daulet, Gen. Mgr.--Trikona Services Ltd., New Delhi, India; *Int'l*, pg. 303
Singhoff, F. Scott, Representative--NationsBank (Japan), Tokyo, Japan; *U.S. Public*, pg. 1166
Singleton, J.S., Chief Oper. Officer--Bristol-Babcock Ltd., Croydon, United Kingdom; *Int'l*, pg. 474
Singleton, Trevor, Gen. Mgr.--Frigidaire Home Products, Mc Rae, GA; *Int'l*, pg. 440
Singleton, William Dean, Vice Chm., Pres. & Chief Exec. Officer--Garden State Newspapers, Inc., Denver, CO; *U.S. Private*, pg. 727
Singson, Creddie, Gen. Mgr.--Elan Pharma Philippines, Inc., Manila, Philippines; *Int'l*, pg. 436
Sink, David, Admin.--Village Care Center, Galion, OH; *U.S. Public*, pg. 838
Sink, Joe S. Jr., Publisher--The Dispatch Publishing Company, Inc., Lexington, NC; *U.S. Public*, pg. 1175
Sinke, Huib W., Mng. Dir.--Heidemij Realisatie BV, Arnhem, Netherlands; *Int'l*, pg. 607
Sinke, Huib W., Mng. Dir.--Heidemij Realisatie Lelystad BV, Arnhem, Netherlands; *Int'l*, pg. 607
Sinkinson, E., Mgr.-Mktg.--Military Book Club, Garden City, NY; *Int'l*, pg. 191
Sinn, Rebecca, Gen. Mgr.--Loews New York, New York, NY; *U.S. Public*, pg. 1011
Sinnott, Dan, Dir.-Sls.--Turner Construction Co., Detroit, MI; *U.S. Public*, pg. 1645
Sinsigalli, Gerald, Pres.--Food Service Division, Wilbraham, MA; *U.S. Public*, pg. 682
Sipahi, Galip, Mng. Dir.--Ardem Pisiriciler Ve Isitici San. A.S., Istanbul, Turkey; *Int'l*, pg. 741
Sipe, H., Pres.--Boral Concrete Products Inc., Rialto, CA; *Int'l*, pg. 203
Sipe, James, Pres.--Planning Corporation of America, Saint Petersburg, FL; *U.S. Public*, pg. 923
Sipe, K.L., Pres.--Boral Resources Inc., Pomona, CA; *Int'l*, pg. 203
Sipf, Eric, Pres.--Pacificare of Colorado, Englewood, CO; *U.S. Public*, pg. 1251
Sipila, Yrjo, Dir.--Kemira Chemicals Oy, Helsinki, Finland; *Int'l*, pg. 728
Sipko, Dale, Reg. Mgr.--Green Tree Acceptance of Ohio, Inc., Reynoldsburg, OH; *U.S. Public*, pg. 762
Sipling, Philip J., Pres.--Martin Marietta Magnesia Specialties, Inc., Raleigh, NC; *U.S. Public*, pg. 1007
Sipos, Donald J., Pres.--SL Surface Technology, Inc., Camden, NJ; *U.S. Public*, pg. 1419
Sipowicz, Laura D., Banking & Fin. Svcs. Officer--Troy Savings Bank-Quaker Road, Queensbury, NY; *U.S. Private*, pg. 1106
Siquiera, Valdir, Mng. Dir.--V&S Comunicacoes, Rio de Janeiro, Brazil; *U.S. Private*, pg. 1200
Siraci, Serdar, Pres.--Danko Gida Ticaret A.S., Istanbul, Turkey; *Int'l*, pg. 288
Siracusano, Bruno, Gen. Mgr.--Meda SIM Bipiemme S.p.A., Milan, Italy; *Int'l*, pg. 137
Sire, Philippe, Mng. Dir.--Dumez-GTM Cambodge, Phnom Penh, Kampuchea; *Int'l*, pg. 823
Siregar, B., Resident Mgr.--Deminex Indonesia, Jakarta, Indonesia; *Int'l*, pg. 1461
Siresee, Swai, Office Mgr.--Prakit/FCB, Vientiane, Laos; *U.S. Private*, pg. 389
Sirianni, John, Mgr.-Branch--Piper Jaffray Inc., Eau Claire, WI; *U.S. Public*, pg. 1301
Sirianni, John F., Gen. Mgr.--American Auto Auction, Inc., North Dighton, MA; *U.S. Private*, pg. 282
Siridhara, Dhanit, Mng. Dir.--Siam Cement Industrial Land Co., Ltd., Nong Khae, Thailand; *Int'l*, pg. 1238
Sirisantana, Vanich, Mng. Dir.--The Thai Wanaphan Co., Ltd., Samutprakan, Thailand; *Int'l*, pg. 1239
Sirjord, Jerry, Gen. Mgr.--Crow River Industries Incorporated, Plymouth, MN; *U.S. Public*, pg. 1040
Sirois, Robert J., Pres.--CCL Label, Inc., Shelton, CT; *Int'l*, pg. 238
Sirotek, Jonathan, V.P.--Illinois Auto Electric Midwest Engine Warehouse Div., Elmhurst, IL; *U.S. Private*, pg. 558
Sirou, Jean, Pres.--Componenta International France S.A., Gennevilliers, France; *Int'l*, pg. 1421
Sirrs, Dick, Div. Mgr.--Accord Contract Services, Garden Grove, CA; *Int'l*, pg. 1458
Sisco, Dennis G., Chm. Bd.--Dataquest Incorporated, San Jose, CA; *U.S. Public*, pg. 535
Sisco, Dennis G., Pres.--D & B Enterprises inc, Wilton, CT; *U.S. Public*, pg. 535
Sison III, Leopoldo S., Pres.--BMC Forestry Corporation, Baguio, Philippines; *Int'l*, pg. 186
Sistiaga, Jose Maria, Mgr.--ATECSA, Madrid, Spain; *Int'l*, pg. 424
Sisto, John, Pres.--Horizons Consulting Inc., Parsippany, NJ; *U.S. Public*, pg. 421
Sit, Terence L.K., Dir. & Gen. Mgr.--Jardine Shipping Agencies (Hong Kong) Ltd., Quarry Bay, Hong Kong; *Int'l*, pg. 704
Sitek, Petr, Dr., Chief Oper. Officer--Barum Continental spol. s.r.o., Otrokovice, Czech Republic; *Int'l*, pg. 327
Sites, James E., Pres.--PacifiCorp Trans, Inc., Portland, OR; *U.S. Public*, pg. 1252
Sitt, Robert, Mng. Dir.--Mase Westpac Hong Kong Limited, Central, Hong Kong; *Int'l*, pg. 1497
Sittason, Charles R., Chm. Bd. & Chief Exec. Officer--Regions Bank/Tuscaloosa, Tuscaloosa, AL; *U.S. Public*, pg. 1373
Sivan, Y., Representative--Bank Hapoalim (Sao Paulo), Sao Paulo, Brazil; *Int'l*, pg. 150
Sivey, Paul, Mng. Dir.-Intl. Div.--Costain Building & Civil Engineering Limited, Maidenhead, United Kingdom; *Int'l*, pg. 336
Sivey, Paul, Mng. Dir.--Costain Marine International Limited, Maidenhead, United Kingdom; *Int'l*, pg. 336
Sivitz, William, Pres.--Wallpapers-To-Go, Houston, TX; *U.S. Private*, pg. 1175
Six, Pierre, Dir.--Standard Wool France, SA, Tourcoing, France; *U.S. Public*, pg. 1502
Sixel, Jerome, Pres.--Master Products Mfg. Co., Los Angeles, CA; *Int'l*, pg. 340
Sjoberg, Alf, Pres.--Industriventilation Produkt AB, Vaxjo, Sweden; *Int'l*, pg. 1260
Sjoberg, Bjorn, Chief Officer--KF Fastigheter AB, Stockholm, Sweden; *Int'l*, pg. 718
Sjoberg, Gertz, Dir.--Helly-Hansen AB, Spanga, Sweden; *Int'l*, pg. 1010
Sjoberg, Jan, Mng. Dir.--Ericsson Sielte-International S.p.A., Rome, Italy; *Int'l*, pg. 1367
Sjoberg, Per, Chief Oper. Officer--Perstorp Pharma AB, Lund, Sweden; *Int'l*, pg. 1036
Sjoberg, Per-Olof, Chief Oper. Officer--Husqvarna AB, Huskvarna, Sweden; *Int'l*, pg. 439
Sjoblom, Per, Chief Oper. Officer--Molnlycke AB Consumer Products, Goteborg, Sweden; *Int'l*, pg. 1326
Sjoblom, S., Mng. Dir.--Ascom Energy Systems AB, Vaxjo, Sweden; *Int'l*, pg. 87
Sjoegren, Stig, Mng. Dir.--Bicapa-Bjoernklaeder AB, Hisings Backa, Sweden; *Int'l*, pg. 1285
Sjogren, Bengt-Ake, Chief Oper. Officer--Nobel Elektronik AB, Karlskoga, Sweden; *Int'l*, pg. 1289
Sjogren, Hans, Pres.--Esselte Europe, London, United Kingdom; *Int'l*, pg. 460
Sjokvist, Goran, Pres.--LBI Luftbehandling AB, Karlstad, Sweden; *Int'l*, pg. 1261
Sjolander, Gunnar, Chief Oper. Officer--Granges Essem Iberica S.A., Madrid, Spain; *Int'l*, pg. 443
Sjolin, Christer, Pres.--Stora Power AB, Falun, Sweden; *Int'l*, pg. 1303
Sjolund, Erik, Mng. Dir.--Iggesund Paperboard AB, Iggesund, Sweden; *Int'l*, pg. 886
Sjosledt, Jan, Pres.--Skanska International Building AB, Malmo, Sweden; *Int'l*, pg. 1260
Sjostedt, Haus, Chief Oper. Officer--Electrolux Mecatronik AB, Malmo, Sweden; *Int'l*, pg. 438
Sjostedt, Lennart, Chief Oper. Officer & Exec. V.P.--SAB WABCO N.V., Zaventem, Belgium; *Int'l*, pg. 271
Sjursen, Egil H., Dir.-Admin.--Vesta Forvaltning AS, Bergen, Norway,; *Int'l*, pg. 1258
Skaar, Odd, Gen. Mgr.--Hydro Aluminium Ardal Verk, Ovre Ardal, Norway; *Int'l*, pg. 959
Skagen, Jim, Pres.--CGF Sign, Inc., Denver, CO; *U.S. Private*, pg. 194
Skaggs, Don L., Exec. V.P. & Gen. Mgr.--Skaggs Telecommunications Services, Inc., Murray, UT; *U.S. Public*, pg. 93
Skaggs, Robert C., Jr., Pres. & Chief Exec. Officer--Columbia Gas of Kentucky, Inc., Columbus, OH; *U.S. Public*, pg. 403
Skaggs, Robert C., Jr., Pres. & Chief Exec. Officer--Columbia Gas of Ohio, Inc., Columbus, OH; *U.S. Public*, pg. 403
Skandrani, N., Chm.--Groupe des Assurances de Tunisie (GAT), Tunis, Tunisia; *Int'l*, pg. 565
Skaperdas, Wes, Gen. Mgr.--Phipps & Bird, Richmond, VA; *U.S. Public*, pg. 1073
Skard, Per, Mng. Dir.--NFT Ericsson Communications ANS, Billingstad, Norway; *Int'l*, pg. 1369
Skarupa, Tony, Chief Fin. Officer & V.P.--National Journal Group, Washington, DC; *U.S. Private*, pg. 785
Skeeles, Charles, Mng. Dir.--Shandwick China, Beijing, China; *Int'l*, pg. 1227
Skelley, John, Pres.--Valley Seed Co., Casa Grande, AZ; *U.S. Private*, pg. 82
Skellie, J., Plant Mgr.--Albany Engineered Systems, Stone Mountain, GA; *U.S. Public*, pg. 1593
Skelly, Jim, Chief Exec. Officer--Thermalloy, Inc., Farmers Branch, TX; *Int'l*, pg. 208
Skelton, Charles W., II, Mgr.--Communications Corp. of Indiana, Roachdale, IN; *U.S. Public*, pg. 1571
Skelton, John, Exec. Dir.--Albany International Research Co., Mansfield, MA; *U.S. Public*, pg. 36
Skelton, Raymond E., Pres. & Chief Oper. Officer--NBD Banking Company, Southwest, Jeffersonville, IN; *U.S. Public*, pg. 628
Skelton, Thomas A., Chief Oper. Officer--Manugistics Inc., Rockville, MD; *U.S. Public*, pg. 1042
Skene, Bill, Div. Mgr.--BJ Process & Pipeline Services Ltd., Aberdeen, United Kingdom; *U.S. Public*, pg. 161
Skeoch, Gordon D., Area V.P.--Avon Sales & Distribution Branch, Morton Grove, IL; *U.S. Public*, pg. 156
Skeppner, Ake, Mng. Dir.--Thule International S.A., Brussels, Belgium; *Int'l*, pg. 436
Skeppner, Hans, Mng. Dir.--Eldon International S.A., Brussels, Belgium; *Int'l*, pg. 436
Skerl, Damir, Pres.--Western Atlas Logging Services, Houston, TX; *U.S. Public*, pg. 1757
Skidmore, A. Allan, Vice Chm.--Glentel Inc., Burnaby, Canada; *Int'l*, pg. 1336
Skidmore, Thomas E., Chm. Bd., Pres. & Chief Exec. Officer--Glentel Inc., Burnaby, Canada; *Int'l*, pg. 1336
Skierczynska-Rocca, Katarzyna, Mng. Dir.--R.F.R./ARIP, Warsaw, Poland; *Int'l*, pg. 1377
Skiff, Tom, Pres.--Amex Life Assurance Co., San Rafael, CA; *U.S. Public*, pg. 712
Skiles, ALlan, Pres.--Tolk, Inc., Fairfax, VA; *U.S. Private*, pg. 329
Skiles, Judy, Mgr.--DWF of Saint Louis, Inc., Saint Louis, MO; *U.S. Private*, pg. 326
Skillested, John G., Pres.--Washington National Life Insurance Co. of New York, New York, NY; *U.S. Private*, pg. 256
Skilton, Harry I., Pres. & Chief Exec. Officer--American Meter Company, Horsham, PA; *Int'l*, pg. 1149
Skinner, C. Mickey, Vice Chm.--Hershey Pasta and Grocery Group, Hershey, PA; *U.S. Public*, pg. 812
Skinner, Claire C., Pres. & Gen. Mgr.--Coachmen Recreational Vehicle Company, Middlebury, IN; *U.S. Public*, pg. 388
Skinner, Greg, Plant Mgr.--Liqui-Box Corp., Lake Wales, FL; *U.S. Public*, pg. 1001
Skinner, J.J.H., Mng. Dir.--Cerebos Australia Limited, Seven Hills, Australia; *Int'l*, pg. 1322
Skinner, John, Pres.--North American Van Lines Canada Ltd., Oshawa, Canada; *U.S. Public*, pg. 1192
Skinner, John, Pres.--Jeweler's Financial Service, Inc., Irving, TX; *U.S. Public*, pg. 1789
Skinner, R.G., Mng. Dir.--Barclays Bank of Swaziland Ltd., Mbabane, Swaziland; *Int'l*, pg. 165
Skinner, Robert C., Jr., Div. Pres.--Oxford Shirts, New York, NY; *U.S. Public*, pg. 1239
Skinner, Ronald, Gen. Mgr.--Polaroid Canada Inc., Etobicoke, Canada; *U.S. Public*, pg. 1314
Skipper, John, V.P.-Magazine Publishing--Disney Publishing Group, Burbank, CA; *U.S. Public*, pg. 511
Skipper, John, V.P. of Magazines--Discover, New York, NY; *U.S. Public*, pg. 513
Skirbekk, Arne, Mng. Dir.--Kalmar Kockum A/S, Oslo, Norway; *Int'l*, pg. 1421
Skjelbred, Gunnar, Pres.--Kvaerner Gibralter Ltd., Gibraltar, Gibraltar; *Int'l*, pg. 772
Skjellvik, Birger, Pres.--Volvo Norge A/S, Kolbotn, Norway; *Int'l*, pg. 1477
Skjolberg, Einar Martin, Plant Mgr.--Elkem Thamshavn, Orkanger, Norway; *Int'l*, pg. 448
Skladal, Gerhard, Mng. Dir.--Ericsson Redes S.A., Madrid, Spain; *Int'l*, pg. 1367
Skoda, Dan, Pres.--Marshall Field, Chicago, IL; *U.S. Public*, pg. 489
Skoda, Mark, Pres.--TNT Logistics North America, Linthicum Heights, MD; *Int'l*, pg. 1343
Skoghall, Daniel, Pres.--Drott AB, Goteborg, Sweden; *Int'l*, pg. 1260
Skoglund, Bjorn, Mng. Dir. & Chief Fin. Officer--W.R. Grace AB, Helsingborg, Sweden; *U.S. Public*, pg. 755
Skoglund, Bjorn, Mng. Dir.--W.R. Grace A/S, Herlev, Denmark; *U.S. Public*, pg. 755
Skoglund, Bjorn, Mng. Dir.--Grace (Sweden) AB, Helsingborg, Sweden; *U.S. Public*, pg. 756
Skoglund, Palmer L., Gen. Mgr.--Akzo Nobel Fibers, Inc., Asheville, NC; *Int'l*, pg. 48
Skogman, Gunnar, Pres.--Symbicom AB, Umea, Sweden; *Int'l*, pg. 93
Skogsberg, Lennart, Pres.--NCC Goteburg, Goteborg, Sweden; *Int'l*, pg. 899
Skogsborg, Christer, Gen. Mgr.--Saab Aircraft Division, Linkoping, Sweden; *Int'l*, pg. 686
Skolas, J., Pres.--Thorn EMI Inc., Wilmington, DE; *Int'l*, pg. 427
Skold, Bjorn, Mgr.--AB Sandvik Service, Sandviken, Sweden; *Int'l*, pg. 1185
Skold, Carl, Chief Fin. Officer--CAP Programmator, Bromma, Sweden; *Int'l*, pg. 264
Skold, Leif, Chief Oper. Officer--Autoliv GmbH, Elmshorn, Germany; *Int'l*, pg. 442
Skolds, John L., Pres.--SCANA Resources, Inc., Columbia, SC; *U.S. Public*, pg. 1436
Skomorowski, Christopher R., Div. Pres.--Lydall Westex, Hamptonville, NC; *U.S. Public*, pg. 1021
Skondras, A.P., Chm. Bd. & Mng. Dir.--Texaco Greek Petroleum Company S.A., Psychiko, Greece; *U.S. Public*, pg. 1584
Skoog, K., Mgr.--Parker Hannifin (Sweden) AB, Spanga, Sweden; *U.S. Public*, pg. 1263
Skoog, Lars-Olof, Mgr.--Sandvik Chomutov, Chomutov, Czech Republic; *Int'l*, pg. 1186
Skoog, Olle, Mgr.--Delsbo Factory, Delsbo, Sweden; *Int'l*, pg. 421
Skornicki, Eli, Pres.--Cometals, New York, NY; *U.S. Public*, pg. 412
Skott, Preben, Mng. Dir.--Novo Nordisk Pharmaceuticals Pty. Ltd., North Rocks, Australia; *Int'l*, pg. 988
Skoufalos, Jim, Mgr.--HI Products Inc., Sinking Spring, PA; *U.S. Private*, pg. 533
Skough, Jan, Pres. & Chief Oper. Officer--Skandia U.S. Holding Corporation, New York, NY; *Int'l*, pg. 1257
Skouveroe, J. Fritzhof, Pres.--Stolt Sea Farm A/S, Oslo, Norway; *Int'l*, pg. 1302
Skov, Kurt, Mng. Dir.--Howard Maschinenfabrik GmbH, Michelstadt, Germany; *Int'l*, pg. 1387

Skovmose, A.R., Mng. Dir.--Bank of Commerce Trinidad and Tobago Limited, Port of Spain, Trinidad & Tobago; Int'l, pg. 257
Skrabec, Louis E., Pres.--Chace Precision Metals, Inc., Reidsville, NC; U.S. Public, pg. 1564
Skrenes, Larry D., Pres.--TDS Computing Services, Inc., Madison, WI; U.S. Public, pg. 1572
Skrypek, John, Pres.--Sequa Can Machinery, East Rutherford, NJ; U.S. Public, pg. 1458
Skull, J.R., Gen. Mgr.--Westeel Agricultural Products Division, Winnipeg, Canada; Int'l, pg. 698
Skutt, Thomas J., Chm. Bd.--United of Omaha Life Insurance Company, Omaha, NE; U.S. Private, pg. 770
Skweres, Mark, Pres.--Evans Environmental & Geological Science and Management Inc., Miami, FL; U.S. Public, pg. 563
Slack, Les, Gen. Mgr.--ST Piping, Inc., Torrance, CA; U.S. Public, pg. 1460
Slack, Michael L., Pres.--Zin-Plas Corporation, Comstock Park, MI; U.S. Public, pg. 1258
Slack, Mike, Pres.--Grand Rapids Die Casting Corp., Grand Rapids, MI; U.S. Public, pg. 1258
Slack, Mike, Pres.--Grand Rapids Die Casting Corp., Walker, MI; U.S. Public, pg. 1258
Slade, Len, Pres.--SuperValu, Inc.-Hazelwood Div., Hazelwood, MO; U.S. Public, pg. 1540
Slade, Leonard J., Pres.--SuperValu, Inc.-St. Louis Div., Hazelwood, MO; U.S. Public, pg. 1541
Sladek, Keith, Pres.--Lyon Metal Products, Inc., Montgomery, IL; U.S. Private, pg. 638
Sladnick, Clifford M., V.P. & Sec.--EFS/San Diego Service Corporation, Chicago, IL; U.S. Public, pg. 1428
Slagel, R.C., Gen. Mgr.-Works--Union Camp Chemicals, Durham, United Kingdom; U.S. Public, pg. 1666
Slaggs, Doug, Mgr.-Sls.--L.B. Foster Company, Slidell, LA; U.S. Public, pg. 676
Slagle, Fred, V.P.-Sls.--Cincinnati Sales, Mason, OH; U.S. Public, pg. 611
Slaine, Mason, Chief Exec. Officer--Securities Data Company, Inc., Newark, NJ; U.S. Public, pg. 1600
Slaine, Mason P., Pres. & Chief Exec. Officer--Thomson Financial Services, Stamford, CT; U.S. Public, pg. 1601
Slama, Thomas G., Pres. & Chief Exec. Officer--National Infusion Services, Inc., Indianapolis, IN; U.S. Public, pg. 229
Slamecka, Thomas A., Pres. & Chief Oper. Officer--ConAgra Poultry Company, El Dorado, AR; U.S. Public, pg. 427
Slanina, Glenda, Branch Mgr.--Downey Savings & Loan Association, F.A., Claremont, CA; U.S. Public, pg. 526
Slatcher, David, Mng. Dir.--Shearings Limited, Wigan, United Kingdom; Int'l, pg. 1087
Slater, Charles H., Pres.--Boeing Middle East Limited, Riyadh, Saudi Arabia; U.S. Public, pg. 242
Slater, Chuck, Chief Exec. Officer--Healthsource North Texas, Inc., Fort Worth, TX; U.S. Public, pg. 360
Slater, Donald, Pres.--Totino's/Wellston, Wellston, OH; Int'l, pg. 411
Slater, J.S., Sr. Mgr.--The Royal Bank of Scotland plc, Piraeus, Greece; Int'l, pg. 1133
Slater, James K., Chief Exec. Officer--Barnett Banks Services Insurance, Inc., Jacksonville, FL; U.S. Public, pg. 1162
Slater, John, Pres.--ARCO Coal Company, Denver, CO; U.S. Public, pg. 144
Slater, John E., Sr. V.P. & Publisher--Electrical World, New York, NY; U.S. Public, pg. 1071
Slater, John J., Sr. V.P. & Publisher--Power, New York, NY; U.S. Public, pg. 1071
Slater, Larry, Plant Mgr.--Fabrication Plant/Custom Products, Shamokin, PA; U.S. Public, pg. 1177
Slater, Mark, Gen. Mgr.--Northland Sports Inc., Minot, ND; U.S. Private, pg. 1026
Slater, Martin, Mng. Dir.--Noesis/The Corporate Company, Milan, Italy; Int'l, pg. 117
Slater, P.J.H., Mng. Dir.--Piher International Ltd., Swindon, United Kingdom; Int'l, pg. 853
Slater, R., Pres.--Leesona, Heywood, United Kingdom,; Int'l, pg. 774
Slater, R.W., Dir.--David Whitehead & Sons Ltd., Burnley, United Kingdom; Int'l, pg. 818
Slater, Ross, Pres.--Leesona Corp., Burlington, NC; Int'l, pg. 774
Slater, Stuart M., Chief Rep.--Manchester Representative Office, Manchester, United Kingdom; Int'l, pg. 520
Slator, Mark, V.P.--Mustang Industrial Equipment Co., Houston, TX; U.S. Private, pg. 769
Slattery, Anne, Chm. Bd.--Fleet Bank, F.S.B., Boca Raton, FL; U.S. Public, pg. 649
Slaughter, Jerome, Plant Mgr.--Samson Manufacturing Corp., Wilson, NC; U.S. Public, pg. 779
Slaughter, Mike, Exec. Editor--The Courier, Houma, LA; U.S. Public, pg. 1175
Slaughterback, Fred, Pres.--Slautterback Corp., Sand City, CA; U.S. Public, pg. 1188
Slavich, A., Mgr.-Plant--Fourco Glass Co., Bridgeport, WV; Int'l, pg. 84
Slavin, Joe, Grp. V.P.--TMP Worldwide, Inc., Hoboken, NJ; U.S. Private, pg. 1064
Slavinsky, Jack, Gen. Mgr.--GE Capital/IT Solutions, South Plainfield, NJ; U.S. Public, pg. 711
Slawek, Joseph, Mgr.--EG & G Optoelectronics Montgomeryville, Montgomeryville, PA; U.S. Public, pg. 543
Slaybaugh, Jon, Pres.--Namco Controls GmbH, Herzhorn, Germany; U.S. Public, pg. 482
Slayden, Anthony W., V.P.--UCG Energy Corporation, Brentwood, TN; U.S. Public, pg. 146
Sleepeck, Michael, Pres.--Dixonweb Printing Company, Dixon, IL; U.S. Private, pg. 1005
Sleewuwenhoek, Hans, Pres. & Chief Exec. Officer--Tactyl Technologies, Inc., Vista, CA; U.S. Public, pg. 1425
Slehofer, Gerald, Pres.--Aydin Molded Devices Div., Rancho Dominguez, CA; U.S. Public, pg. 158
Sleice, John, Gen. Mgr.--Volunteer Engineering, Inc., Manchester, TN; U.S. Private, pg. 315
Sleigh, Ron, Pres. & Chief Exec. Officer--UPB of North Central Tennessee, Erin, TN; U.S. Public, pg. 1669
Slemko, Sam, Pres.--Core Laboratories-Canada Ltd., Calgary, Canada; U.S. Public, pg. 1004
Sletsjoe, Kjell, Mng. Dir.--Jotun (Malaysia) Sdn. Bhd., Shah Alam, Malaysia; Int'l, pg. 715
Sleurs, L., Chief Oper. Officer--Liebig Benelux NV, Schoten, Belgium; Int'l, pg. 380
Slevin, John, Plant Mgr.--CIBA-GEIGY Pharmaceutical Production, Suffern, NY; Int'l, pg. 973
Slim, Andrew, Reg. Mgr.--Kredietbank Manchester Branch, Manchester, United Kingdom; Int'l, pg. 760
Slingerland, H., Mng. Dir.--Toshiba Medical Systems Europe B.V., Zoetermeer, Netherlands; Int'l, pg. 1407
Sloan, Don, Gen. Mgr.--Sericol Inc., Kansas City, KS; Int'l, pg. 235
Sloan, J. David, V.P. & Mng. Dir.--Toronto Dominion-Hong Kong Branch, Hong Kong, Hong Kong; Int'l, pg. 1401
Sloan, L. Lawrence, Exec. V.P.--Price Stern Sloan Inc., Los Angeles, CA; Int'l, pg. 1215
Sloan, Michael, Dir.-Sls. & Mktg.--Blistex Limited, Mississauga, Canada; U.S. Private, pg. 149
Sloane, Larry, Pres.--Questron Div., Los Angeles, CA; Int'l, pg. 1215
Sloane, W.A., Jr., Div. V.P.--Steel Fabrication Div., Fontana, CA; U.S. Public, pg. 99
Slobig, R.J., Gen. Mgr.--Emerson Motor Company, Sturgeon Bay, WI; U.S. Public, pg. 573
Slocum, Frank H., Pres.--Raybestos Aftermarket Products Co., Crawfordsville, IN; U.S. Public, pg. 1363
Slocum, G.F., Pres.--Detector Electronics Corporation, Minneapolis, MN; Int'l, pg. 1500
Slocum, George D., Pres.--General Electric (USA) Consumer Electronics (Pte) Ltd., Singapore, Singapore; U.S. Public, pg. 714
Slocum, Ronald A., Chm. & Pres.--Bank of America Idaho, Boise, ID; U.S. Public, pg. 180
Slocumb, Frank G., Pres.--Harris Bank Naperville, Naperville, IL; Int'l, pg. 154
Slogrove, Richard, Pres.--Memorex Telex Canada Inc., Markham, Canada; Int'l, pg. 857
Slosberg, D., Gen. Mgr.--Hunter Douglas Architectural Products Inc., Duluth, GA; Int'l, pg. 639
Slosberg, Karl, Sr. Bus. Devel. Officer--Northeast Marketing-Cleveland Business Center, Cleveland, OH; U.S. Public, pg. 649
Slosberg, Lee R., Pres.--Crown America Life Insurance Company, Alexandria, VA; Int'l, pg. 468
Slosek, Patrick F., V.P. & Gen. Mgr.--Dollinger/Technolab, Stanley, NC; U.S. Public, pg. 1676
Slosson, Peter, V.P.-Opers.--Pneumatic Scale-Akron, Akron, OH; U.S. Private, pg. 118
Slotkin, Todd J., Leveraged Capital Div. Exec.--Citicorp Venture Capital Ltd., New York, NY; U.S. Public, pg. 377
Slotte, Karsten, Mng. Dir.--Vaasamills Ltd., Helsinki, Finland; Int'l, pg. 349
Slowikowska, Grazyna, Dir.--Berlitz-Polska Limited Liability Company, Warsaw, Poland; U.S. Public, pg. 222
Slupek, Chris, Chief Oper. Officer--Futaba Corporation of America, Farmington, MI; Int'l, pg. 531
Slusarchuk, William A., Pres. & Chief Exec. Officer--AGRA Earth & Environmental Limited, Calgary, Canada; Int'l, pg. 30
Slusser, Daniel E., V.P., Sr. V.P. & Gen. Mgr.-Universal City--Universal Studios, Inc., Universal City, CA; Int'l, pg. 1215
Slusser, Sarah, Mng. Dir.--AES Aurora, Arlington, VA; U.S. Public, pg. 5
Sluszka, Peter, Pres.--Steinman, Boynton, Gronquist & Birdsall Inc., New York, NY; U.S. Private, pg. 842
Sluyter, Erik, V.P.-Mfg.--Circon Video Div., Santa Barbara, CA; U.S. Public, pg. 373
Sly, P.J., Pres.--Air Comfort Products Div., Hazelwood, MO; U.S. Public, pg. 572
Sly, P.J., Pres.--Ridge Tool Co., Elyria, OH; U.S. Public, pg. 574
SLy, P.J., Pres.--Western Forge Div., Colorado Springs, CO; U.S. Public, pg. 575
Smaal, F.J., Mgr.--Van Leeuwen Tubes SA, Port-de-Bouc, France; Int'l, pg. 1450
Smack, James W., Pres.--Vulcan Materials Company-Mideast Div., Winston Salem, NC; U.S. Public, pg. 1725
Smaga, Andy, Mng. Dir.--Bose S.A.R.L., Saint Germain-en-Laye, France; U.S. Private, pg. 161
Smale, Leo, Mng. Dir.--Comtest Limited, Wokingham, United Kingdom; U.S. Public, pg. 1596
Small, A., Chief Exec. Officer--Zurich Australian Insurance Limited, Sydney, Australia; Int'l, pg. 1531
Small, A., Chief Exec. Officer--Zurich Australian Life Insurance Limited, Sydney, Australia; Int'l, pg. 1531
Small, A. Francis, Mgr.-Devel.--Tranzrail Limited, Willington, New Zealand; U.S. Public, pg. 1773
Small, Herman, Pres.--Flowers Baking Co. of Fountain Inn, Inc., Fountain Inn, SC; U.S. Public, pg. 657
Small, Peter, Area Sls. Mgr.--Analog Devices Ltd., Livingston, United Kingdom; U.S. Public, pg. 108
Small, William R., V.P. & Mgr.--Westvaco Corporation-Consumer Packaging Div., Richmond, VA; U.S. Public, pg. 1762
Smalley, Gary, Pres.--Dayton Parts, Inc., Harrisburg, PA; U.S. Public, pg. 919
Smalley, Randall S., Pres. & Chief Exec. Officer--Cruise America, Inc., Mesa, AZ; U.S. Private, pg. 178
Smalley, Robert A., Jr., Pres. & V.P.-Sls.--American Land Cruisers, Mesa, AZ; U.S. Private, pg. 178
Smalling, Rich, Pres.--American Innovations, Ltd., Austin, TX; U.S. Private, pg. 491
Smallwood, David E., V.P. & Gen. Mgr.--A.H. Robins Manufacturing Co., Barceloneta, PR; U.S. Public, pg. 80
Smallwood, Robert, Pres.--Allied Colloids Chemicals (Far East) Pte. Ltd., Singapore, Singapore; Int'l, pg. 62
Smans, Ludo, Mng. Dir.--GEDAS NV, Deurne, Belgium; Int'l, pg. 608
Smart, Craig, Gen. Mgr.--Ferguson Limited, Enfield, United Kingdom; Int'l, pg. 1384
Smart, Jeff, Gen. Mgr.--Barton's of Malden, Malden, MO; U.S. Private, pg. 119
Smart, John, Sr. V.P. & Mng. Dir.--Interbrand Schechter, San Francisco, CA; U.S. Public, pg. 1224
Smart, Larry, Mng. Dir.--Kolmar (Aust.) Pty Ltd., Hornsby, Australia; Int'l, pg. 239
Smart, P.D., Chief Oper. Officer--Ensign-Bickford, Bromhof, South Africa; Int'l, pg. 1196
Smee, Raymond, Gen. Mgr.--Stafford-Miller Ltd., Padstow, Australia; U.S. Public, pg. 237
Smejikel, David, Admin.--Sun Valley Health Care Center, Harlingen, TX; U.S. Public, pg. 839
Smelas, William A., Exec. V.P. of HRD & Acting Pres.--Zinc Corporation of America, Monaca, PA; U.S. Private, pg. 540
Smelser, Emmett, Pres. & Publr.--Palladium Publishing Corp., Richmond, IN; U.S. Public, pg. 701
Smelser, Jack, Plant Mgr.--Y & S Candies, Farmington, NM; U.S. Public, pg. 812
Smerling, Robert F., Pres.--Reading Entertainment Inc., Philadelphia, PA; U.S. Public, pg. 456
Smetana, J.C., Dir.--American International Managers Ltd., Dublin, Ireland; U.S. Public, pg. 85
Smets, J., Chief Oper. Officer--Babcock Services (Belgium), Grace-Hollogne, Belgium; Int'l, pg. 474
Smets, Raymond J., II, Pres.--BellSouth Applied Technologies, Inc., Atlanta, GA; U.S. Public, pg. 209
Smeulders, A.A.F.H., Mng. Dir.--Sugro B.V., Zaltbommel, Netherlands; Int'l, pg. 991
Smiledge, Peter, Reg. Mgr.--SMS-Kansas City, Shawnee Mission, KS; U.S. Public, pg. 1463
Smiley, Alan M., Pres.--General Wig Manufacturers, Inc., Hialeah, FL; U.S. Private, pg. 690
Smit, H., Dir.--Rheinische Presshefe - und Spirtwerke GmbH, Monheim, Germany; Int'l, pg. 1143
Smit, J., Media Dir.--Noordervliet & Winninghoff/Leo Burnett B.V., Amsterdam, Netherlands; U.S. Private, pg. 186
Smit, Jack, Pres.--Miracle Feeds Inc., London, Canada; U.S. Private, pg. 432
Smith-Cox, Peter, Dir.-Fin.--Jardine Securicor Ltd., Kowloon, Hong Kong; Int'l, pg. 705
Smith-Everhard, Suzee, Dir.-Programming--Arizona Sports Programming Network, Phoenix, AZ; U.S. Public, pg. 455
Smith, A. E., Chief Oper. Officer & V.P.--Piedmont Mechanical, Inc., La Grange, GA; U.S. Private, pg. 865
Smith, A. Martin, Chief Oper. Officer--Bermead Insurance Company Ltd., Hamilton, Bermuda; U.S. Public, pg. 1076
Smith, A.J.C., Chm. Bd.--J&H Marsh & McLennan, Inc., New York, NY; U.S. Public, pg. 1049
Smith, A.K., Mng. Dir.--Babcock Rosyth Defence Limited, Rosyth, United Kingdom; Int'l, pg. 131
Smith, A.R., Dir.-Opers.--Charles River U.K., Ltd., Margate, United Kingdom; U.S. Public, pg. 195
Smith, A.W., Pres.--Smith Data Processing Div., Spartanburg, SC; U.S. Private, pg. 1008
Smith, Al, Gen. Mgr.--Triple S Plastics Tooling & Technology Centre, Vicksburg, MI; U.S. Public, pg. 1640
Smith, Alan, Sls. Mgr.--BMC Software, Limited, Camberley, United Kingdom; U.S. Public, pg. 163
Smith, Alan, Mng. Dir.--Jardine Fleming Holdings Ltd., Central, Hong Kong; Int'l, pg. 494
Smith, Alan, Sec.--Aston Martin Finance Limited, Newport Pagnell, United Kingdom; U.S. Public, pg. 665
Smith, Alan, Sec.--Aston Martin Sales Limited, United Kingdom; U.S. Public, pg. 665
Smith, Alan, Mng. Dir.--Reed Publishing (NZ) Ltd., Birkenhead, New Zealand; Int'l, pg. 1094
Smith, Allen D., Pres.--First Citizens Investor Services, Inc., Raleigh, NC; U.S. Public, pg. 629
Smith, Anderson, Regional Pres.--First Tennessee Bank - Morristown, Morristown, TN; U.S. Public, pg. 639
Smith, Andrew, Chm.--Sedgwick Limited, Melbourne, Australia; Int'l, pg. 1218
Smith, Arthur McWilliam, Chm. Bd.--Air Express International (S.A.) (Pty), Ltd., Boksburg, South Africa; U.S. Public, pg. 30
Smith, Arvin H., Pres.--Thermo Instrument Systems Inc., Waltham, MA; U.S. Public, pg. 1593
Smith, Barbara, Partner & Gen. Mgr.--B. Smith's, New York, NY; U.S. Public, pg. 130
Smith, Barbara A., Pres. & Chief Exec. Officer--United Missouri Bank N.A., Brookfield, MO; U.S. Public, pg. 1654
Smith, Bert, V.P.-Southwest Region--Hudson Aviation Services Inc., Houston, TX; U.S. Public, pg. 845
Smith, Betty, V.P. & Publr.--Baxter County Newspapers, Inc., Mountain Home, AR; U.S. Public, pg. 699
Smith, Bill, Plant Mgr.--Hydro Conduit Corp., Castroville, TX; Int'l, pg. 246
Smith, Bill, Gen. Mgr.--Metz Baking Co., Chicago, IL; U.S. Private, pg. 1022
Smith, Bill, Gen. Mgr.--Total Mexicana, Tultitlan, Mexico; U.S. Public, pg. 1651
Smith, Billie, Publr.--Aberdeen News Company, Aberdeen, SD; U.S. Public, pg. 963
Smith, Bob, Chief Oper. Officer--MacDermid Singapore Pte. Ltd., Singapore, Singapore; U.S. Public, pg. 1030
Smith, Bob, Mng. Dir.--Cosworth Castings Ltd., Worcester, United Kingdom; Int'l, pg. 1467
Smith, Brad, Pres.--South Valley National Bank, Gilroy, CA; U.S. Public, pg. 1248
Smith, Brian, Mgr.--ServiceMaster AG, Zurich, Switzerland; U.S. Public, pg. 1462
Smith, Brian McQueen, Chief Oper. Officer--AGEMA Infrared Systems Ltd., Leighton Buzzard, United Kingdom; Int'l, pg. 1289
Smith, Bruton, Pres.--Texas Motor Speedway, Fort Worth, TX; U.S. Public, pg. 1498
Smith, Bruton, Chm. Bd.--Sears Point Raceway, Sonoma, CA; U.S. Public, pg. 1498

Smith, Buz, V.P.-Opers.--Home Depot Canada, Scarborough, Canada; *U.S. Public*, pg. 832
Smith, C., Chief Exec. Officer--Mte-TURCK Ltd., Leigh-on-Sea, United Kingdom; *Int'l*, pg. 449
Smith, C. Harrison, V.P. & Agent--Bancomer New York Agency, New York, NY; *Int'l*, pg. 145
Smith, C.A., Gen. Mgr.--Container Div. (Lexington), Lexington, KY; *Int'l*, pg. 1270
Smith, C.J., Mng. Dir.--Chemviron Specialty Chemicals, Overijse, Belgium; *U.S. Public*, pg. 1091
Smith, C.M., Mng. Dir.--Chemviron Specialty Chemicals, Huddersfield, United Kingdom; *U.S. Public*, pg. 1091
Smith, Carlos W., Pres.--Florida Favorite Fertilizer, Lakeland, FL; *Int'l*, pg. 1064
Smith, Chris, Gen. Mgr.--R.J. Brown & Associates (UK) Limited, Slough, United Kingdom; *Int'l*, pg. 772
Smith, Chris, Mgr.-Opers.--J & J Register Div., El Paso, TX; *Int'l*, pg. 1397
Smith, Clifton L., Pres. & Chief Exec. Officer--Corning Asahi Video Products Company, Corning, NY; *Int'l*, pg. 84
Smith, Clifton L., Pres. & Chief Exec. Officer--Corning Asahi Video Products Company, Corning, NY; *U.S. Public*, pg. 449
Smith, Colin, Chief Exec. Officer--Safeway Stores plc, Hayes, United Kingdom; *Int'l*, pg. 1169
Smith, Cort O., Mgr.-Sls.--PENCO-Utah, Sandy, UT; *Int'l*, pg. 1508
Smith, Craig, Chm. Bd., Pres. & Chief Exec. Officer--Hereford State Bank, Hereford, TX; *U.S. Public*, pg. 633
Smith, Craig, Chm. Bd.--Allomatic Products Company, Sullivan, IN; *U.S. Public*, pg. 1363
Smith, Cullen F., Pres. & Chief Exec. Officer--Bergen Brunswig Medical Corporation, Orange, CA; *U.S. Public*, pg. 214
Smith, D. L., Pres.--Kimmel Motz Refrigeration Corp., Los Angeles, CA; *Int'l*, pg. 1400
Smith, D.C., Chief Oper. Officer & Mng. Dir.--Hammerite Products Limited, Prudhoe, United Kingdom; *Int'l*, pg. 1501
Smith, D.L., Pres.-Kimmel-Motz Refrigeration Corp.--Toromont Industries Ltd., Concord, Canada; *Int'l*, pg. 1400
Smith, D.M., Mgr.--Lindberg Heat Treating Co., Worcester, MA; *U.S. Public*, pg. 999
Smith, Darren, Admin.--Carson Convalescent Center, Carson City, NV; *U.S. Public*, pg. 837
Smith, Daryl C., Gen. Mgr. & Publisher--The Observer (Sarnia), Sarnia, Canada; *Int'l*, pg. 631
Smith, David, Pres. & Chief Exec. Officer--American Eurocopter Corp., Grand Prairie, TX; *Int'l*, pg. 29
Smith, David, Chief Exec. Officer--Healthsource Indiana, Indianapolis, IN; *U.S. Public*, pg. 360
Smith, David, Chief Exec. Officer--Healthsource Kentucky, Louisville, KY; *U.S. Public*, pg. 360
Smith, David, Mgr.--Hercules Inc.-Brunswick, Brunswick, GA; *U.S. Public*, pg. 810
Smith, David, Admin.--San Juan Manor, Farmington, NM; *U.S. Public*, pg. 838
Smith, David, Mng. Dir.--Chartham Papers, Canterbury, United Kingdom; *Int'l*, pg. 1107
Smith, David D., Chief Fin. Officer--Material Handling Equipment Division, Oak Creek, WI; *U.S. Public*, pg. 788
Smith, David J., Mng. Dir.--Citibank (Zaire) S.A.R.L., Kinshasa, Congo; *U.S. Public*, pg. 379
Smith, David J., Pres. & Chief Exec. Officer--First Security Bank of Nevada, Las Vegas, NV; *U.S. Public*, pg. 637
Smith, David M., Pres.--Fortis Sales, Milwaukee, WI; *Int'l*, pg. 499
Smith, Dean, V.P. & Gen. Mgr.--Envirex Inc., Waukesha, WI; *U.S. Public*, pg. 61
Smith, Dennis A., Pres.--Crawford & Company International, Inc., London, United Kingdom; *U.S. Public*, pg. 458
Smith, Dennis C., Pres. & Chief Exec. Officer--Foster Wheeler Arabia, Ltd., Clinton, NJ; *U.S. Public*, pg. 677
Smith, Derek, Mng. Dir.--Hong Kong Air Terminal Services Ltd., Kowloon, Hong Kong; *Int'l*, pg. 705
Smith, Don, Div. Mgr.--Tamarack Homes Div., Weiser, ID; *U.S. Public*, pg. 332
Smith, Donald A., Gen. Mgr.--Dufferin-Custom Concrete Group, Concord, Canada; *Int'l*, pg. 628
Smith, Donald G., V.P. & Gen. Mgr.--Sky Courier, Reston, VA; *U.S. Public*, pg. 33
Smith, Doug, Gen. Mgr.--Ecusta Australia Pty. Limited, Sydney, Australia; *U.S. Public*, pg. 746
Smith, Doug, Administrator--Nalco Canada Inc., Burlington, Canada; *U.S. Public*, pg. 1150
Smith, Doug C., Pres.--MD Foods Canada Inc., Brampton, Canada; *Int'l*, pg. 826
Smith, Douglas A., Chm. & Chief Exec. Officer--Borden Foods Corporation, Columbus, OH; *U.S. Private*, pg. 157
Smith, E. Warren, Jr., Pres. & Chief Exec. Officer--Regions Bank/Middle Tennessee, Nashville, TN; *U.S. Public*, pg. 1372
Smith, E.T., Grp. V.P.--International Group, Hayes, United Kingdom; *U.S. Public*, pg. 24
Smith, Ed, Mgr.-Plant--Nestle Beverage Company, Garden City Park, NY; *Int'l*, pg. 918
Smith, Ed., Pres.--Veedol (Canada) Ltd., Toronto, Canada; *Int'l*, pg. 236
Smith, Elwood, Pres. & Chief Oper. Officer--Hayes Axle, Inc., Seminole, OK; *U.S. Private*, pg. 299
Smith, Erik, Chief Exec. Officer--AxTrade Scandinavia A/S, Oslo, Norway; *Int'l*, pg. 710
Smith, F., Mng. Dir.--United Biscuits Asia Pacific, West Drayton, United Kingdom; *Int'l*, pg. 1442
Smith, F.P., V.P.--Industrial Chemicals Div., Cincinnati, OH; *U.S. Public*, pg. 1330
Smith, Frank P., V.P. & Gen. Mgr.--Boeing Aerospace Operations, Cocoa Beach, FL; *U.S. Public*, pg. 241
Smith, Frank P., V.P. & Gen. Mgr.--Boeing Technical Operations, Inc., Cocoa Beach, FL; *U.S. Public*, pg. 242
Smith, G. Edward, Pres.--Gai-Tronics Corporation, Mohnton, PA; *U.S. Public*, pg. 1430
Smith, Gary, Mgr.--BHP Trading Inc., Houston, TX; *Int'l*, pg. 226
Smith, Gary Dr., Gen. Mgr.--SmithKline Beecham Clinical Laboratories, Dallas, TX; *Int'l*, pg. 1265
Smith, Gary J., V.P. & Gen. Mgr.--Consol of Kentucky, Inc., Lambric, KY; *U.S. Public*, pg. 531
Smith, Gary K., Pres.--American Uniform Co., Cleveland, TN; *U.S. Private*, pg. 1039
Smith, Ge. E., Pres.--BHP Coated Steel Corp., Rancho Cucamonga, CA; *Int'l*, pg. 226
Smith, Geoffrey F., Mng. Dir.-UK & N. America--Messier-Dowty Ltd., Gloucester, United Kingdom; *Int'l*, pg. 1340
Smith, Geoffrey F., Mng. Dir.-UK & N. America--Messier-Dowty Inc., Toronto, Ajax, Canada; *Int'l*, pg. 1340
Smith, Geoffrey F., Mng. Dir.-UK & N. America--Messier-Dowty Electronics, Peterborough, Canada; *Int'l*, pg. 1340
Smith, Geoffrey F., Mng. Dir.-UK & N. America--Messier-Dowty Inc., Montreal, Saint-Janvier, Canada; *Int'l*, pg. 1340
Smith, George, Pres.--Dixie Synthetic Yarn Group, Gastonia, NC; *U.S. Public*, pg. 514
Smith, George, Pres.--Drumheller Bag & Supply, Valdosta, GA; *U.S. Private*, pg. 802
Smith, George, Gen. Mgr.--Hermiston Foods, Inc., Hermiston, OR; *U.S. Private*, pg. 802
Smith, George, Pres.--Universal Studios Videodisc, Inc., Universal City, CA; *Int'l*, pg. 1216
Smith, George J., Pres. & Chief Exec. Officer--Arrow Group Industries, Inc., Wayne, NJ; *U.S. Private*, pg. 477
Smith, Gilbert P., Pres.--Helene Curtis North America, Chicago, IL; *Int'l*, pg. 1434
Smith, Glen E., Gen. Mgr.--Larsan Manufacturing Co., Newark, OH; *U.S. Public*, pg. 575
Smith, Glenn, Plant Mgr.--Wolverine Technologies Inc., Grinnell, IA; *Int'l*, pg. 1171
Smith, Glenn C., Pres.--United Parcel Service of Canada, Mississauga, Canada; *U.S. Private*, pg. 1123
Smith, Gordon, Gen. Mgr.--WAGO Limited, Rugby, United Kingdom; *Int'l*, pg. 209
Smith, Gordon, Gen. Dir.--Marcam Australia Pty., Ltd., Melbourne, Australia; *U.S. Public*, pg. 1043
Smith, Graham, Gen. Mgr.--TMP Worldwide Pty Ltd., Adelaide, Australia; *Int'l*, pg. 1342
Smith, Guy W., Pres.--United Health, Inc., Milwaukee, WI; *Int'l*, pg. 468
Smith, H.B., II, Pres.--Leica Inc., Deerfield, IL; *Int'l*, pg. 806
Smith, Harold, Plant Mgr.--OMC Burnsville, Burnsville, NC; *U.S. Private*, pg. 478
Smith, Harold, V.P. & Gen. Mgr.--McRae Graphics, Inc., Mount Gilead, NC; *U.S. Public*, pg. 1074
Smith, Harold L., Chm. Bd.--Hilb, Rogal and Hamilton Company of Gainesville, Georgia, Gainesville, GA; *U.S. Public*, pg. 827
Smith, Harry E., V.P. & Gen. Mgr.--Webb-Triax Company, Chardon, OH; *U.S. Private*, pg. 1157
Smith, Harvey, Resident Dir.--Valley Manor Apartments, Tucson, AZ; *U.S. Public*, pg. 1715
Smith, Haywood C., Pres.--Arjay Equipment Corporation, Winston Salem, NC; *U.S. Public*, pg. 1355
Smith, Henrydale, Jr., Pres.--Smith Premium Services, Spartanburg, SC; *U.S. Private*, pg. 1008
Smith, Hudson, Gen. Mgr.--SIFCO Forge Group, Cleveland, OH; *U.S. Public*, pg. 1471
Smith, Ian, Mgr.--Westpac Banking Corp. - Vanuatu, Port Vila, Vanuatu; *Int'l*, pg. 1497
Smith, Ian, Mng. Dir.--Lunn Poly Ltd., Royal Leamington Spa, United Kingdom; *U.S. Public*, pg. 1601
Smith, III, Roscoe L., Publisher--Architectural Record, New York, NY; *U.S. Public*, pg. 1070
Smith, J. Albert, Jr., Pres.--Bank One, Mortgage Company, New Berlin, WI; *U.S. Public*, pg. 174
Smith, J. Albert, Jr., Pres.--Banc One Mortgage Corporation, Indianapolis, IN; *U.S. Public*, pg. 175
Smith, J. D., Gen. Mgr.--Coca-Cola Bottling Co. Consolidated of Arden, Arden, NC; *U.S. Public*, pg. 391
Smith, J. K., Pres.--NGE Enterprises, Inc., Binghamton, NY; *U.S. Public*, pg. 1173
Smith, J. R., Mgr.-Zone--Santa Fe Intl. Services Inc., Jakarta, Indonesia; *Int'l*, pg. 766
Smith, J.E., Chief Exec. Officer--Waters Coal Company, Andalusia, AL; *U.S. Private*, pg. 30
Smith, J.E., Chief Exec. Officer--United Energy Corporation, Andalusia, AL; *U.S. Private*, pg. 30
Smith, J.E., Chief Exec. Officer--Lakeside Coal Company, Andalusia, AL; *U.S. Private*, pg. 30
Smith, J.E., Chief Exec. Officer--Andalusia & Conecuh Railroad, Inc., Andalusia, AL; *U.S. Private*, pg. 30
Smith, J.G., Dir.--Barton Engineering Ltd., Walsall, United Kingdom; *Int'l*, pg. 264
Smith, J.J., Pres.--Dominion Stores, Inc., Martinsville, VA; *U.S. Public*, pg. 1644
Smith, J.K., Mng. Dir.--Wolters Kluwer Academic Publishers, Dordrecht, Netherlands; *Int'l*, pg. 1512
Smith, J.R., Mgr.--Tencarva Machinery Co., Johnson City, TN; *U.S. Private*, pg. 1076
Smith, J.R., Chm. Bd. & Mng. Dir.--Taywood Engineering Ltd., Southall, United Kingdom; *Int'l*, pg. 1359
Smith, J.T., V.P.--Tencarva Machinery Co., Chesapeake, VA; *U.S. Private*, pg. 1076
Smith, Jack, Pres. & Chief Exec. Officer--Pharmacists Public Relations Bureau, New York, NY; *U.S. Private*, pg. 295
Smith, James, Pres. & Chief Oper. Officer--ConAgra Prepared Food Companies, Omaha, NE; *U.S. Public*, pg. 427
Smith, James C., Chm. Bd., Pres. & Chief Exec. Officer--Webster Bank, Waterbury, CT; *U.S. Public*, pg. 1751
Smith, James Craven, Mng. Dir.--Hugh Baird & Sons Limited, Witham, United Kingdom; *U.S. Public*, pg. 428
Smith, James E., V.P. & Gen. Mgr.--UAD Laboratories, Jackson, MS; *U.S. Public*, pg. 670
Smith, James P., Publisher--Buford Gazette, Beaufort, SC; *U.S. Public*, pg. 1065
Smith, James P., Publisher--Hilton Head Island Packet, Hilton Head Island, SC; *U.S. Public*, pg. 1065
Smith, James T., Pres.--ConAgra Frozen Food Company, Omaha, NE; *U.S. Public*, pg. 427
Smith, James T., Pres.--ConAgra Frozen Foods, Council Bluffs, IA; *U.S. Public*, pg. 427
Smith, James T., Jr., Pres.--Service Assets Corp., Newport Beach, CA; *U.S. Private*, pg. 171
Smith, Jay R., Pres.--Cox Newspapers, Inc., Atlanta, GA; *U.S. Private*, pg. 281
Smith, Jeff, Mgr.-Facility/Line--Cutter Deer Valley, Phoenix, AZ; *U.S. Private*, pg. 299
Smith, Jeffrey, Mng. Dir.--Woodward-Clyde, Richmond, Australia; *U.S. Public*, pg. 1657
Smith, Jeffrey M., Pres.--Churchill Downs Management Co., Louisville, KY; *U.S. Public*, pg. 356
Smith, Jerry, Mgr.--Carolina Steel-Salem Plant, Winston Salem, NC; *U.S. Private*, pg. 214
Smith, Jerry, Gen. Mgr.--Lone Star Division, Texarkana, TX; *U.S. Private*, pg. 317
Smith, Jim, V.P. & Gen. Mgr.--KMOD-FM, Tulsa, OK; *U.S. Public*, pg. 384
Smith, Jim, Plant Mgr.--L.B. Foster Company-Doraville Yard/Fabrication Shop, Norcross, GA; *U.S. Public*, pg. 676
Smith, Jim, Plant Mgr.--Cylinder Div., Santa Fe Springs, CA; *U.S. Public*, pg. 1261
Smith, Jim, V.P.-Women's Mfg.--Frolic Footwear Div., Jonesboro, AR; *U.S. Public*, pg. 1775
Smith, Jimmy, Div. Mgr.--Atlantic Homes Div., Henry, TN; *U.S. Public*, pg. 332
Smith, Joan, Admin.--Guardian Care of Walnut Cove, Walnut Cove, NC; *U.S. Public*, pg. 1713
Smith, Joe, Pres.--Warner-Lambert Worldwide Shaving Products Group, Milford, CT; *U.S. Public*, pg. 1739
Smith, John, Representative Dir.--Aetna Investment Management (Japan), K.K., Tokyo, Japan; *U.S. Public*, pg. 27
Smith, John, Gen. Mgr.--Breed UK Limited, Carlisle, United Kingdom; *U.S. Public*, pg. 251
Smith, John, Chief Oper. Officer--MacGREGOR (AUS) Pty. Ltd., Balmain, Australia; *Int'l*, pg. 670
Smith, John, Dir. & Gen. Mgr.--Inco Alloys Limited, Hereford, United Kingdom; *Int'l*, pg. 672
Smith, John F., V.P. & Gen. Mgr.--Cadillac Motor Car Division, Warren, MI; *U.S. Public*, pg. 720
Smith, John F., Pres.--PerSeptive Biosystems, Inc., Framingham, MA; *U.S. Public*, pg. 1279
Smith, John M., Pres.--Association Management Corp., Rockford, IL; *U.S. Public*, pg. 433
Smith, John M., Pres.--Guardian Investor Services Corp., New York, NY; *U.S. Private*, pg. 486
Smith, John W., Pres.--PM Terminals, Inc., Richmond, VA; *U.S. Private*, pg. 859
Smith, John W., Pres.--PM Transport, Inc., Roanoke, VA; *U.S. Private*, pg. 859
Smith, Joseph, Pres.--Air Products Group, York, PA; *U.S. Public*, pg. 1789
Smith, Joseph S., V.P. & Gen. Mgr.--Telephonics Command Systems Div., Farmingdale, NY; *U.S. Public*, pg. 558
Smith, June, Exec. V.P.--Houghton Mifflin College Div., Boston, MA; *U.S. Public*, pg. 841
Smith, Justin L., Pres.--Seymour Smith & Son, Oakville, CT; *U.S. Public*, pg. 575
Smith, K., Chief Oper. Officer--Van Leeuwen Pipe and Tube Eastern Australia Pty. Ltd., Charlestown, Australia; *Int'l*, pg. 1450
Smith, Keith, V.P.--Kollman Div., Orange, VA; *U.S. Public*, pg. 575
Smith, Ken, Gen. Mgr.--Amway Do Brasil LTDA., Sao Paulo, Brazil; *U.S. Private*, pg. 69
Smith, Ken, Chief Exec. Officer--SSP Pumps Ltd., Eastbourne, United Kingdom; *Int'l*, pg. 1380
Smith, Kenneth G., V.P. & Gen. Mgr.--Moog GmbH, Boblingen, Germany; *U.S. Public*, pg. 1128
Smith, Larry, Mgr.-Credit--U.S. Amada, Buena Park, CA; *Int'l*, pg. 70
Smith, Larry, Gen. Mgr.--Bellsouth Israel, Inc. (CellCom Israel Ltd.), Herzliyya, Israel; *U.S. Public*, pg. 208
Smith, Larry, Gen. Mgr.--Cady Lifters, Tonawanda, NY; *U.S.* Public, pg. 405
Smith, Larry, Gen. Mgr.--Conco, Tonawanda, NY; *U.S. Public*, pg. 405
Smith, Laurance B., V.P. & Gen. Mgr.--Resortes y Productos Metalicos-Mexico City Plant, Mexico, Mexico; *U.S. Private*, pg. 857
Smith, Laurance B., V.P. & Gen. Mgr.--Resortes y Productos Metalicos-Queretaro Plant, Queretaro, Mexico; *U.S. Private*, pg. 857
Smith, Louis W., Pres.--Kansas City Div., Kansas City, MO; *U.S. Public*, pg. 50
Smith, Lowndes A., Pres. & Chief Oper. Officer--Hartford Life Insurance Co., Hartford, CT; *U.S. Public*, pg. 795
Smith, Lynn, V.P.--Delta Faucet of Canada, London, Canada; *U.S. Public*, pg. 1053
Smith, M., Mng. Dir.--CSP Pacific, Auckland, New Zealand; *Int'l*, pg. 495
Smith, M., Chief Oper. Officer--Van Leeuwen Tubes Ltd., Testwood, United Kingdom; *Int'l*, pg. 1450
Smith, M.A., V.P. & Gen. Mgr.--Business and Commuter Aviation Systems Division, Phoenix, AZ; *U.S. Public*, pg. 834
Smith, M.J., Vice Chm.--Smith Flow Control Limited, Witham, United Kingdom; *Int'l*, pg. 590
Smith, M.J., Mng. Dir.--Alex Lawrie Factors Ltd., Banbury, United Kingdom; *Int'l*, pg. 813
Smith, M.J., Gen. Mgr.--Zellerbach Division, Boise, ID; *U.S. Public*, pg. 1075
Smith, Malachy, Reg. Mgr.--Wang Netherland B.V., Culemborg, Netherlands; *U.S. Public*, pg. 1738
Smith, Malcolm, Pres.--W.R. Grace (Hong Kong) Ltd., Quarry Bay, Hong Kong; *U.S. Public*, pg. 756
Smith, Marc C., Pres.--Crestar Mortgage Corporation, Richmond, VA; *U.S. Public*, pg. 458

Smith, Mark, Pres. & Chief Exec.Officer--Stewart Smith East, Inc., New York, NY; *Int'l*, pg. 1508

Smith, Mark L., Office Mgr.--Korn/Ferry International, Boston, MA; *U.S. Private*, pg. 633

Smith, Mary, Exec. Dir.--Hillcrest Health Care, Inc., Boise, ID; *U.S. Public*, pg. 1713

Smith, Mary, V.P.--Volt Temporary Services, Orange, CA; *U.S. Public*, pg. 1724

Smith, Matthew R., Branch Mgr.--Burns & Wilcox - Springfield Office, Springfield, MO; *U.S. Private*, pg. 610

Smith, Michael A., Pres.--Martin Marietta Astro Space, Princeton, NJ; *U.S. Public*, pg. 1007

Smith, Michael B., Sr. V.P.--Turner Construction Co., Miami, FL; *U.S. Public*, pg. 1645

Smith, Michael J., V.P. & Gen. Mgr.--Avery Intl. Adhesive Prods., Ltd., Marlow, United Kingdom; *U.S. Public*, pg. 153

Smith, Michael P., Gen. Mgr.--Pipeline Induction Heat Limited, Burnley, United Kingdom; *U.S. Public*, pg. 1750

Smith, Michael R., Gen. Mgr.-Peruvian Exploration & Devel.--Barrick Gold Peru S.A., Lima, Peru; *Int'l*, pg. 169

Smith, Mike, Mgr.--Anixter Aberdeen, Aberdeen, United Kingdom; *U.S. Public*, pg. 116

Smith, Mike, Gen. Mgr.--Surplus Warehouse-Paris, Paris, TX; *U.S. Private*, pg. 120

Smith, Mike, Chief Exec. Officer & V.P.--Reedspectrum, Holden, MA; *Int'l*, pg. 624

Smith, Mitchel, Gen. Mgr.--Barton's of Paragould, Paragould, AR; *U.S. Private*, pg. 119

Smith, N.A., Pres.--Predelivery Service Corporation, Dearborn, MI; *U.S. Public*, pg. 664

Smith, N.R., Mng. Dir.--Senior Conflow, Nottingham, United Kingdom; *Int'l*, pg. 1220

Smith, Ned A., Pres. & Chief Exec. Officer--American Steamship Company, Williamsville, NY; *U.S. Public*, pg. 690

Smith, Neil C., Mng. Dir.--Bell-IRH Industries Pty. Ltd., Lidcombe, Australia; *Int'l*, pg. 391

Smith, Norman, Mng. Dir.--Instron International Ltd., Offenbach/Main, Germany; *U.S. Public*, pg. 883

Smith, Norman, Mng. Dir.--Amsler Otto Wolpert Werke GmbH, Ludwigshafen, Germany; *U.S. Public*, pg. 883

Smith, Norman E., Chm. Bd.--North American Metals Distribution Group, Coon Rapids, MN; *Int'l*, pg. 1118

Smith, O. Bruton, Chm. Bd.--Atlanta Motor Speedway, Hampton, GA; *U.S. Public*, pg. 1498

Smith, O. Darwin, Pres.--NationsBank Properties, Inc., Charlotte, NC; *U.S. Public*, pg. 1165

Smith, O. Darwin, Pres.--NationsBank Plaza Charlotte, Inc., Charlotte, NC; *U.S. Public*, pg. 1165

Smith, P. Nicholson, Chm. Bd. & Mng. Dir.--AEGON Insurance Company (UK) Limited, London, United Kingdom; *Int'l*, pg. 28

Smith, P.E., Mng. Dir.--Morgan Grenfell (Jersey, C.I.) Limited, Saint Helier, United Kingdom; *Int'l*, pg. 406

Smith, P.S., Pres.--AMI, Crawley, United Kingdom; *Int'l*, pg. 707

Smith, P.S., Pres.--Concorde Express, Bedford, United Kingdom; *Int'l*, pg. 707

Smith, Pamela, Pres.--Steco, Enid, OK; *U.S. Private*, pg. 153

Smith, Patrick J., Pres.--Western Towing Company, Channelview, TX; *U.S. Public*, pg. 961

Smith, Paul, Mng. Dir.--Beazer Homes (Colchester) Limited, Witham, United Kingdom; *Int'l*, pg. 182

Smith, Paul, Pres.--Circle International, Alexandria, VA; *U.S. Public*, pg. 372

Smith, Paul B., Pres.--Boeing North America, Rocketdyne Division, Canoga Park, CA; *U.S. Public*, pg. 241

Smith, Paul K., Mng. Dir.--LeaRonal UK Ltd., Buxton, United Kingdom; *U.S. Public*, pg. 982

Smith, Peter, Mng. Dir.--Marconi Instruments Ltd., Saint Albans, United Kingdom; *Int'l*, pg. 544

Smith, Phil, V.P. & Gen. Mgr.--Pitney Bowes of Canada Ltd.-Leasing Div., Mississauga, Canada; *U.S. Public*, pg. 1304

Smith, Philip, Pres.--AGEMA Infrared Systems, Inc., Secaucus, NJ; *Int'l*, pg. 1289

Smith, Pillip N., Pres.--Vista Insurance Services, Inc., Lake Buena Vista, FL; *U.S. Public*, pg. 514

Smith, R. Keith, Mgr.--Scott & Stringfellow, Inc., Martinsville, VA; *U.S. Public*, pg. 1446

Smith, R.A., Pres.--BSL Engineering Limited, Manchester, United Kingdom; *Int'l*, pg. 212

Smith, R.J., Gen. Mgr.--Pocono Fabricators, East Stroudsburg, PA; *U.S. Public*, pg. 793

Smith, R.J., Chie Oper. Officer--Rabobank Guernsey Ltd., Saint Peter Port, United Kingdom; *Int'l*, pg. 1082

Smith, R.L., Pres.--Eastman Kodak (Japan) Ltd., Tokyo, Japan; *U.S. Public*, pg. 552

Smith, Randall E., Pres. & Chief Exec. Officer--Regions Bank/Talladega County, Talladega, AL; *U.S. Public*, pg. 1373

Smith, Raymond, Pres.--Andover Bank NH, Salem, NH; *U.S. Public*, pg. 112

Smith, Reed R., Pres.--Bowne of Atlanta, Inc., Atlanta, GA; *U.S. Public*, pg. 248

Smith, Richard, V.P.--LFE Traffic Control, Clinton, MA; *U.S. Public*, pg. 1045

Smith, Richard A., Chm. Bd.--Coldwell Banker Real Estate Corporation, Parsippany, NJ; *U.S. Public*, pg. 321

Smith, Richard M., Pres. & Editor-in-Chief--Newsweek, Inc., New York, NY; *U.S. Public*, pg. 1743

Smith, Richard P., Pres.--Empire Livestock Marketing Inc., Syracuse, NY; *U.S. Private*, pg. 308

Smith, Rick, V.P.--BancTec, Inc.-Los Angeles, Orinda, CA; *U.S. Public*, pg. 177

Smith, Rick, Pres.--Meridian Inc., Spring Lake, MI; *U.S. Public*, pg. 1112

Smith, Robert, V.P. & Gen. Mgr.--Avery Dennison Corporation Label Group, Ontario, CA; *U.S. Public*, pg. 153

Smith, Robert, Mgr.--W.C. Caye & Co., Columbus, GA; *U.S. Private*, pg. 220

Smith, Robert, V.P. & Gen. Mgr.--Bell Packaging Corporation-Menominee Div., Menominee, MI; *Int'l*, pg. 1066

Smith, Robert, Base Mgr.--Mercury Air Center, Ontario, CA; *U.S. Public*, pg. 1093

Smith, Robert A., Exec. V.P.-Consumer Fin.--Oakwood Acceptance Corp., Greensboro, NC; *U.S. Public*, pg. 1209

Smith, Robert D., V.P. & Gen. Mgr.--Business Systems Division, Azusa, CA; *U.S. Public*, pg. 153

Smith, Robert E., Chief Oper. Officer--Essex Polytech, Inc., Sausalito, CA; *U.S. Public*, pg. 523

Smith, Robert J., Pres.--Hunt Foreign Investment Corp., West Paterson, NJ; *U.S. Public*, pg. 1219

Smith, Robert R., Chief Oper. Officer--SpeedFam Limited, Hinckley, United Kingdom; *U.S. Public*, pg. 1498

Smith, Robert R., Mng. Dir.--SpeedFam GmbH, Ingelfingen, Germany; *U.S. Public*, pg. 1498

Smith, Rockford, Asst. V.P.-Computer Sls. Div.--The Computer Patch of Joplin, Joplin, MO; *U.S. Private*, pg. 995

Smith, Rockford E., Asst. V.P.-Computer Sls. Div.--Stauffer Media Systems, Inc., Joplin, MO; *U.S. Private*, pg. 995

Smith, Roger F., Pres.--Citizens First Bank, Rome, GA; *U.S. Public*, pg. 1549

Smith, Roger G., Pres.--Cigna Seguradora S.A., Rio de Janeiro, Brazil; *U.S. Public*, pg. 363

Smith, Roland C., Pres.--Triarc Restaurant Group, Fort Lauderdale, FL; *U.S. Public*, pg. 1635

Smith, Ron, Chief Oper. Officer--Granges Automotive (UK) Ltd., Manchester, United Kingdom; *Int'l*, pg. 444

Smith, Ron, Plant Mgr.--Glass Plant, Carleton, MI; *U.S. Private*, pg. 486

Smith, Ron, Chief Oper. Officer--Morgantown Plastics Company, Morgantown, KY; *U.S. Public*, pg. 1054

Smith, Ron E., Mgr.-Property & Casualty Claims--Willis Corroon Administrative Services Corporation, Dallas, TX; *Int'l*, pg. 1505

Smith, Ronald, V.P. & Gen. Mgr.--Westchester Plastics, Nesquehoning, PA; *U.S. Public*, pg. 100

Smith, Ronald C., Pres.--Firstar Leasing Corporation, Milwaukee, WI; *U.S. Public*, pg. 643

Smith, Ronald D., Chief Oper. Officer--Gamco Products Co., Henderson, KY; *U.S. Public*, pg. 1053

Smith, Ronald E., Pres. & Publr.--GuestInformant, Inc., Woodland Hills, CA; *U.S. Public*, pg. 11

Smith, Ronald W., V.P. & Gen. Mgr.--Haveg Div., Wilmington, DE; *U.S. Public*, pg. 100

Smith, Rosemary, Mng. Dir.--Mardev, London, United Kingdom; *Int'l*, pg. 1094

Smith, S., Chief Exec. Officer--Zurich Insurance Company, Toronto, Canada; *Int'l*, pg. 1531

Smith, S., Chief Exec. Officer--Zurich Indemnity Company of Canada, Toronto, Canada; *Int'l*, pg. 1531

Smith, S. Troy, Pres. & Chief Oper. Officer--Luker Inc., Augusta, GA; *U.S. Private*, pg. 459

Smith, S.B., Pres. & Chief Exec. Officer--Ph. Orth Co., Oak Creek, WI; *Int'l*, pg. 244

Smith, S.J., Pres.--Louisville Ladder Div., Louisville, KY; *U.S. Public*, pg. 574

Smith, Samuel J., III, Pres.--WACO Chemical Company, Sandersville, GA; *U.S. Private*, pg. 1081

Smith, Scott, Chief Exec. Officer--KBA-Motter Corp., York, PA; *Int'l*, pg. 742

Smith, Scott, Pres. & Publr.--Chicago Tribune Co., Chicago, IL; *U.S. Public*, pg. 1635

Smith, Stan, District Superintendent--Casper Wyoming Production District Office, Casper, WY; *U.S. Private*, pg. 548

Smith, Stephen F., Pres.--Sysco Food Services of Central Florida, Inc., Ocoee, FL; *U.S. Public*, pg. 1551

Smith, Steve, Div. Mgr.--Century Telephone of Mountain Home, Mountain Home, AR; *U.S. Public*, pg. 330

Smith, Steve, Pres. & Chief Exec. Officer--UPB of Central Arkansas NA, Clinton, AR; *U.S. Public*, pg. 1669

Smith, Steve, Pres.--Bank of Commerce, Woodbury, TN; *U.S. Public*, pg. 1669

Smith, Steven J., Mgr.-Property & Casualty Claims--Willis Corroon Administrative Services Corporation, Livonia, MI; *Int'l*, pg. 1504

Smith, Ted, Pres.--Honeywell Asia Pacific Inc., Wan Chai, Hong Kong; *U.S. Public*, pg. 834

Smith, Terry, Mgr.-Airfreight--Circle Freight International USA, Vandalia, OH; *U.S. Public*, pg. 371

Smith, Thad, III, Pres.--Brown & Root Civil, Houston, TX; *U.S. Public*, pg. 775

Smith, Thad, III, Pres.--Brown & Root Environmental, Houston, TX; *U.S. Public*, pg. 775

Smith, Theodore B., Chm. Bd. & Pres.--HITCO, Westbury, NY; *U.S. Private*, pg. 509

Smith, Theodore B., Chm. Bd.--Cantrock Realty Corp., Hicksville, NY; *U.S. Private*, pg. 509

Smith, Thomas J., Pres. & Chief Exec. Officer--Coats North America, Charlotte, NC; *Int'l*, pg. 300

Smith, Thomas L., Pres.--Yellow Services, Inc., Overland Park, KS; *U.S. Public*, pg. 1788

Smith, Tim, Mng. Dir.--Kitchens of Sara Lee-United Kingdom, Bridlington, United Kingdom; *U.S. Public*, pg. 1434

Smith, Tom, Mgr.--Westco Products/Intermountain, Salt Lake City, UT; *Int'l*, pg. 244

Smith, Tom E., V.P.--Edwards & Kelcey Construction, Inc., Morristown, NJ; *U.S. Private*, pg. 364

Smith, W. Heard, Pres.--Caro Knit (Jefferson Plant), Jefferson, SC; *U.S. Public*, pg. 514

Smith, W. J., Chm. Bd.--MRM Properties, Inc., Charlotte, NC; *U.S. Public*, pg. 1163

Smith, W. J., Chm. Bd.--MAR, Inc., Charlotte, NC; *U.S. Public*, pg. 1163

Smith, W. Jack, Pres.--Wausau Underwriters Insurance Co., Wausau, WI; *U.S. Private*, pg. 789

Smith, W. Norman, Pres.--Astec, Inc., Chattanooga, TN; *U.S. Public*, pg. 141

Smith, W.H., Mgr.--Morton Chemical Div., Stamford, CT; *U.S. Public*, pg. 1135

Smith, W.L., Sr. V.P.-Opers.--Frito-Lay Company, Plano, TX; *U.S. Public*, pg. 1277

Smith, W.O., Pres.--Arkansas Valley Distributing, Tulsa, OK; *U.S. Private*, pg. 494

Smith, W.T., Pres.--Flexible Technologies Inc., Abbeville, SC; *Int'l*, pg. 1267

Smith, Walter, Mgr.--Plastic Suppliers Inc., Chicago Heights, IL; *U.S. Private*, pg. 871

Smith, Warren, Pres.--Morton International, Ltd., Ajax, Canada; *U.S. Public*, pg. 1136

Smith, Wayne, Pres.--GenCorp Vehicle Sealing Div., Batesville, AR; *U.S. Public*, pg. 706

Smith, Wayne, Mgr.--Tri-State Mack Inc., Meridian, MS; *U.S. Private*, pg. 1101

Smith, Wayne, Mgr.-Office--Woodward-Clyde, Overland Park, KS; *U.S. Public*, pg. 1656

Smith, Wayne A., Pres.--GenCorp Vehicle Sealing Div., Evansville, IN; *U.S. Public*, pg. 706

Smith, Wayne A., Pres.--GenCorp Vehicle Sealing Div., Fort Smith, AR; *U.S. Public*, pg. 706

Smith, Wayne T., Chief Oper. Officer--Galen Hospital Illinois, Inc., Louisville, KY; *U.S. Public*, pg. 404

Smith, William, V.P. & Mng. Dir.--Crown Cork Coordination Center N.V., Deurne, Belgium; *U.S. Public*, pg. 464

Smith, William, Branch Mgr.--Downey Savings & Loan Association, F.A., Sacramento, CA; *U.S. Public*, pg. 526

Smith, William H., Jr., Pres.--Pioneering Services Corporation, Boston, MA; *U.S. Public*, pg. 1298

Smith, William J., Pres. & Chief Exec. Officer--Scotia Investment Management Ltd., Toronto, Canada; *Int'l*, pg. 155

Smith, William K., Gen. Mgr.--Westvaco Hong Kong, Ltd., Hong Kong, Hong Kong; *U.S. Public*, pg. 1763

Smith, William N., Gen. Mgr.--New Zealand Fibre Glass, Penrose, New Zealand; *U.S. Public*, pg. 904

Smith, William T., Pres.--Flexible Technologies Inc., La Mirada, CA; *Int'l*, pg. 1267

Smith, William W., Pres.--Pacific Electro-Dynamics, Inc., Redmond, WA; *U.S. Public*, pg. 1219

Smith, William W., Pres.--Primex Technologies, Inc., Primex Aerospace, Redmond, WA; *U.S. Public*, pg. 1329

Smith, Winthrop H., Jr., Chm. Bd.--Merrill Lynch International, Inc., New York, NY; *U.S. Public*, pg. 1098

Smithers, Joe, Admin.--Horizon Specialty Hospital, Edmond, OK; *U.S. Public*, pg. 839

Smithies, David, Pres.--Waldbaum's Supermarkets, Inc., Central Islip, NY; *Int'l*, pg. 1375

Smithies, James, Chief Exec. Officer--Lambert Smith Hampton, Leeds, United Kingdom; *Int'l*, pg. 797

Smithlin, Michael, Pres.--Dorr-Oliver Incorporated, Milford, CT; *Int'l*, pg. 839

Smithson, John W., Chm. Bd., Pres. & Chief Exec. Officer--PMA Reinsurance Corporation, Philadelphia, PA; *U.S. Public*, pg. 1272

Smithyman, M.J., Chm.--Dorbyl Automotive Products (Pty) Ltd., Bedfordview, South Africa; *Int'l*, pg. 416

Smits, J. C., Mng. Dir.--Baukje Beheer bv, Rijssen, Netherlands; *Int'l*, pg. 243

Smits, Paul, Mng. Dir.--Delta Group Australia Pty. Ltd., Melbourne, Australia; *Int'l*, pg. 391

Smitt, W.H. Sillevis, Chief Oper. Officer--Rabobank (Schweiz) AG, Zurich, Switzerland; *Int'l*, pg. 1082

Smiy, P.R., Chief Exec. Officer--New Elliott Corporation, Jeannette, PA; *Int'l*, pg. 432

Smoak, Van, Mgr.--Southern Electric Supply Co., Inc., Gainesville, FL; *Int'l*, pg. 1107

Smoler, Robert, Pres.--Oxford Health Insurance, Inc., Norwalk, CT; *U.S. Public*, pg. 1239

Smolinski, Bob, Pres.--Modular Power Systems, Hackettstown, NJ; *U.S. Private*, pg. 1097

Smollar, Marvin, Pres. & Chief Oper. Officer--CLR Corporation, Tarboro, NC; *U.S. Public*, pg. 579

Smollor, Marvin, Gen. Mgr.--Caldwell Button Company, Tarboro, NC; *U.S. Public*, pg. 579

Smothers, Ted, Gen. Mgr.--Alumax Extrusions, Inc., West Chicago, IL; *U.S. Public*, pg. 59

Smrekar, Thomas J., Pres.--The Prescott & Northwestern Railroad Co., Warren, AR; *U.S. Public*, pg. 1318

Smrekar, Thomas J., Pres.--St. Maries River Railroad, Lewiston, ID; *U.S. Public*, pg. 1318

Smrekar, Thomas J., Pres.--Warren & Saline River Railroad Co., Warren, AR; *U.S. Public*, pg. 1318

Smurfit, M.W.J., Chm.--Jefferson Smurfit Corporation, Saint Louis, MO; *Int'l*, pg. 1269

Smurthwaite, Tricia, Mgr.--Du Pont Canada-Burnaby, Burnaby, Canada; *U.S. Public*, pg. 532

Smuts, J., Mng. Dir.--Babcock Tripplejay, Johannesburg, South Africa; *Int'l*, pg. 131

Smyth, Francis J., Mng. Dir.--First Rate Bureau de Change Limited, Dublin, Ireland; *Int'l*, pg. 152

Smyth, George C., Chm. Bd. & Pres.--Bell-Northern Research Ltd., Nepean, Canada; *Int'l*, pg. 116

Smyth, Norm, Mgr.--Westpac Banking Corp. - Cook Islands, Avarua, Cook Islands; *Int'l*, pg. 1497

Smyth, Richard N., Chief Oper. Officer--Parkson Corporator, Dorval, Canada; *Int'l*, pg. 711

Smythe, Geoff, Opers. Mgr.--Fiat Auto (UK) Ltd., London, United Kingdom; *Int'l*, pg. 483

Smythe, Hugh, Pres.--Blackcomb Skiing Enterprises Ltd., Whistler, Canada; *Int'l*, pg. 685

Smythe, Jim, Gen. Mgr.--Texas Hobby Auto Auction, Houston, TX; *U.S. Private*, pg. 283

Smythe, John, Chm.--Smythe Dorward Lambert, London, United Kingdom; *U.S. Public*, pg. 1225

Snape, David W., Mng. Dir.--Home Automation Group Ltd., Chippenham, United Kingdom; *Int'l*, pg. 390

Snapp, M.L., Jr., V.P. & Gen. Mgr.--Masonite Corporation, Chicago, IL; *U.S. Public*, pg. 904

Snare, Anders, Mng. Dir.--Telefonaktiebolaget LM Ericsson Technical Office Kuwait, Safat, Kuwait; *Int'l*, pg. 1370

Snarr, Sharon, Mgr.--Downey Savings & Loan Association, F.A., San Jose, CA; *U.S. Public*, pg. 527

Snead, Michael J., Pres. & Chief Exec. Officer--Carolina Casualty Insurance Company, Jacksonville, FL; *U.S. Public*, pg. 216
Snead, Michael J., Chm. Bd.--Great Divide Insurance Company, Scottsdale, AZ; *U.S. Public*, pg. 216
Snedaker, Dianne, Pres.--Ketchum Advertising/San Francisco, San Francisco, CA; *U.S. Private*, pg. 616
Sneddon, Paul, Pres. & Chief Exec. Officer--H.J. Heinz Co. of Canada Ltd., North York, Canada; *U.S. Public*, pg. 806
Sneddon, Paul, Pres. & Chief Exec. Officer--Omstead Foods Limited, Wheatley, Canada; *U.S. Public*, pg. 806
Sneed, Paula, Pres.--Food Service Prods. Div., White Plains, NY; *U.S. Public*, pg. 1287
Sneep, Folkert, Chief Exec. Officer (Northern Europe)--McCain Foods Holland B.V. (The Netherlands), Hoofddorp, Netherlands; *Int'l*, pg. 850
Snejbjerg, Per, Gen. Mgr.--Polarcup Germany, Alf, Germany; *Int'l*, pg. 638
Snell, D., Reg. Mng. Dir.--EMI Music Australia, Cremorne, Australia; *Int'l*, pg. 427
Snell, James, Pres. & Chief Oper. Officer--Shield Healthcare Centers, Valencia, CA; *Int'l*, pg. 740
Snell, Riley, V.P. & Gen. Mgr.-Cable & Entertainment--GCI Cable, Inc., Anchorage, AK; *U.S. Public*, pg. 708
Snelling, Mark H., Pres.--Shelburne Husky Div., Shelburne, VT; *U.S. Private*, pg. 991
Snethlage, Constantijn, Mng. Dir.--PDA International/ Netherlands, Gouda, Netherlands; *U.S. Public*, pg. 1031
Snider, Carol, Sr. V.P.-Atlantic Provinces Div.--Bank of Montreal - Halifax, Halifax, Canada; *Int'l*, pg. 153
Snider, Richard C., Mktg. Communications Coord.--Armament Systems Div., Minneapolis, MN; *U.S. Private*, pg. 213
Snider, Stephen A., Pres.--Tidewater Compression Service, Inc., Houston, TX; *U.S. Public*, pg. 1608
Sniegowski, Bob, Pres. & Gen. Mgr.--Jesco Company, Bloomington, MN; *U.S. Private*, pg. 590
Sniekers, Niek, Chief Oper. Officer--Novo Nordisk Farma B.V., Alphen aan den Rijn, Netherlands; *Int'l*, pg. 988
Snijders, J.M.G., Gen. Mgr.--Van Melle Export B.V., Breda, Netherlands; *Int'l*, pg. 1451
Snodgrass, Rick H., Pres.--Richmond American Homes, Inc., Tucson, AZ; *U.S. Public*, pg. 1025
Snoek, Bert, Mktg. Mgr.--Grace B.V., Capelle aan den Ijssel, Netherlands; *U.S. Public*, pg. 755
Snoep, P.P., Chm.--Drankenhandel De Graafschap B.V., Doetinchem, Netherlands; *Int'l*, pg. 559
Snook, William L., Pres. & Gen. Mgr.--Shasta Industries, Middlebury, IN; *U.S. Public*, pg. 388
Snook, William L., Pres. & Gen. Mgr.--Travelmaster Recreational Vehicles, Middlebury, IN; *U.S. Public*, pg. 388
Snow, David, Pres.--Applied Automation Inc., Bartlesville, OK; *Int'l*, pg. 835
Snow, David P., Jr., Pres.--Oxford Health Plans (PA), Inc., Philadelphia, PA; *U.S. Public*, pg. 1239
Snow, John, Pres.--Strippit, Inc., Akron, NY; *U.S. Public*, pg. 862
Snow, John J., Pres. & Chief Exec. Officer--First NH Investment Services Corporation, Manchester, NH; *Int'l*, pg. 153
Snow, John T., Pres.--Hilb, Rogal and Hamilton Company of Tampa Bay, Inc., Tampa, FL; *U.S. Public*, pg. 827
Snow, Mark, Mng. Dir.--River Crest Hospital, San Angelo, TX; *U.S. Public*, pg. 1697
Snow, Nick, Gen. Mgr.--Nashville Auto Auction Inc., Nashville, TN; *U.S. Public*, pg. 1649
Snow, Robert M., Pres.--Chandler Evans Control Systems Division, West Hartford, CT; *U.S. Public*, pg. 401
Snowball, Michael, Pres.--Mead Containerboard, Atlanta, GA; *U.S. Public*, pg. 1074
Snowball, Michael, Pres.--Mead Coated Board, Atlanta, GA; *U.S. Public*, pg. 1074
Snowden, Gerald W., Pres.--McCormick Canada, Ltd., London, Canada; *U.S. Public*, pg. 1067
Snowden, Joseph I., Pres.--Cannon-Muskegon Corp., Muskegon, MI; *U.S. Public*, pg. 1420
Snowdon, David J., Mng. Dir.--London Brick Company Ltd., Bedford, United Kingdom; *Int'l*, pg. 593
Snuttjer, Dave, Mgr.-Sls.--Mid Res Service Div., Niles, IL; *U.S. Public*, pg. 1026
Snyder, Bill, Pres.--CSR Florida, West Palm Beach, FL; *Int'l, pg. 245*
Snyder, Bill, Chief Exec. Officer--Rinker Materials Corp., West Palm Beach, FL; *Int'l*, pg. 246
Snyder, C.A., V.P.--J.M. Huber, Solem Div., Norcross, GA; *U.S. Private*, pg. 545
Snyder, Charles H., Pres.--American Equipment Company, Inc., Greenville, NC; *U.S. Public*, pg. 660
Snyder, Christopher, Pres. & Gen. Mgr.--Huffy Bicycle Company, Celina, OH; *U.S. Public*, pg. 846
Snyder, Dave, Editor--Crain's Chicago Business, Chicago, IL; *U.S. Private*, pg. 285
Snyder, Duke, Div. Mgr.--Morgantown Machine Anderson Mavor, Nashville, IL; *Int'l*, pg. 280
Snyder, Gary, Admin.--Heritage Hillhaven Nursing Home, Vancouver, WA; *U.S. Public*, pg. 1713
Snyder, Greg, Pres.--New Jersey Div., Freehold, NJ; *U.S. Public*, pg. 1683
Snyder, II, H.A., Mgr.-Mdsg.--Noland Plumbing/Heating Div., Newport News, VA; *U.S. Public*, pg. 1187
Snyder, John, Pres.--The Ajax Manufacturing Company, Cleveland, OH; *U.S. Public*, pg. 1258
Snyder, Kenneth E., Pres.--Colgate-Palmolive Co., Institutional Products Div., Tenafly, NJ; *U.S. Public*, pg. 397
Snyder, Lynn E., Pres. & Chief Exec. Officer--Churubusco State Bank, Churubusco, IN; *U.S. Public*, pg. 674
Snyder, Paul, Gen. Mgr.--Scot Laboratories, Chagrin Falls, OH; *U.S. Public*, pg. 218
Snyder, Randy, Gen. Mgr.--Champs, New York, NY; *U.S. Public*, pg. 1777
Snyder, Richard G., Pres. & Chief Exec. Officer--Reflectone, Inc., Tampa, FL; *Int'l*, pg. 218
Snyder, Robert, Chm. Bd.--Lynch Telephone Corporation II, Greenwich, CT; *U.S. Public*, pg. 1022
Snyder, Ross, Pres.--Group Life & Health Insurance Company, Richardson, TX; *U.S. Private*, pg. 152
Snyder, Steven E., Pres. & Chief Oper. Officer--AFSA Data Corp., Long Beach, CA; *U.S. Public*, pg. 649
Snyder, Thomas J., Pres. & Chief Oper. Officer--Delco Remy America, Inc., Anderson, IN; *U.S. Public*, pg. 495
Snyder, Troy, Admin.--Imperial Skilled Care Center, Warren, OH; *U.S. Public*, pg. 838
Snyder, Walter E., Pres.--American Empire Surplus Lines Insurance Company, Cincinnati, OH; *U.S. Public*, pg. 74
Snyders, Richard A., Pres. & Chief Exec. Officer--Van Deventer & Hoch, Glendale, CA; *U.S. Public*, pg. 339
Snyman, Frik, Mgr.--Sasol Fuel Oil, Alrode, South Africa; *Int'l*, pg. 1197
So, Alan, Natl. Sls. Mgr.--NextLevel Systems (Hong Kong), Hong Kong, Hong Kong; *U.S. Public*, pg. 716
So, Byung-Hwa, Gen. Mgr.--Ssangyong Eng. & Const. (M) Sdn. Bhd., Keluang, Malaysia; *Int'l*, pg. 1292
Soady, William C., Pres.--Universal Film Exchanges, Inc., New York, NY; *Int'l*, pg. 1216
Soady, William C., Pres.-Domestic Distr.--TriStar Pictures, Culver City, CA; *Int'l*, pg. 1283
Soares, Antonio, Sls. & Mktg. Mgr.--Whitehall Portugal, Lisbon, Portugal; *U.S. Public*, pg. 81
Soares, Ciro, Pres.-Bundy Mercosur--TI Brazil Industria E Comerico Ltda., Sao Jose dos Campos, Brazil; *Int'l*, pg. 1342
Soares, Ciro, Pres.-Mercosur--Bundy Argentina SA, Victoria, Argentina; *Int'l*, pg. 1342
Soares, Ednaldo, Mgr.--Banco do Brasil S.A.-Rome, Rome, Italy; *Int'l*, pg. 141
Soares, Jose Roha, Chief Oper. Officer--MacGREGOR (PRT) Lda., Almada, Portugal; *Int'l*, pg. 671
Sobaleski, Dave, Mgr.-Sls.--Montgomery Division, Detroit, MI; *Int'l*, pg. 518
Soberg, Otto, Pres.--Kvaerner Warnow Werft GmbH, Rostock, Germany; *Int'l*, pg. 772
Sobey, David F., Chm. Bd.--Sobey Inc., Stellarton, Canada; *Int'l*, pg. 454
Sobey, Paul D., Pres.--Atlantic Shopping Centres Limited, Stellarton, Canada; *Int'l*, pg. 454
Soble, David S., Pres. & Chief Exec. Officer--Interstate Steel Co. Inc., Des Plaines, IL; *Int'l*, pg. 572
Sobol, Yehiel, Pres. & Chief Exec. Officer--Kao Infosystems Canada, Inc., Arnprior, Canada; *Int'l*, pg. 717
Sobolik, Rolfe, Mng. Dir.--Donaldson Far East Ltd., Tsuen Wan, Hong Kong; *U.S. Public*, pg. 517
Sobottka, Evelin, Mng. Dir.--Lausitzer Rundschau Verlag und Druckerei GmbH, Cottbus, Germany; *Int'l*, pg. 1478
Socha, Vladimir, Mng. Dir.--American Appraisal, Ltd., Prague, Czech Republic; *U.S. Private*, pg. 50
Soda, Junichi, Pres.--Osaka Chain & Machinery, Ltd., Osaka, Japan; *Int'l*, pg. 740
Sodaro, Don, Pres.--The Accor Group, Inc., Corona Del Mar, CA; *Int'l*, pg. 21
Soderberg, Dick, Pres.--Hassle Lakemedel AB, Molndal, Sweden; *Int'l*, pg. 93
Soderberg, Gunnar, Mgr.--Sigma AB, Orebro, Sweden; *Int'l*, pg. 1422
Soderberg, Jan, Mgr.--Broderna Edstrand AB, Malmo, Sweden; *Int'l*, pg. 1422
Soderberg, Lars, Chief Oper. Officer--HAB Mercator, Stockholm, Sweden; *Int'l*, pg. 708
Soderholm, Hardy, Chief Oper. Officer--California Hardware Company, Ontario, CA; *U.S. Private*, pg. 335
Soderi, Caterina, V.P.--Bank of America NT&SA, Caracas, Venezuela; *U.S. Public*, pg. 182
Soderlind, Sara, Reservations. Mgr.--Utell International-Sweden, Stockholm, Sweden; *Int'l*, pg. 1099
Soderlund, Bo, Mgr.--Sandvik Rock Tools Ltd., Nuneaton, United Kingdom; *Int'l*, pg. 1187
Soderlund, Tony, Pres.--Kvaerner Generator AB, Partille, Sweden; *Int'l*, pg. 767
Soderquist, Craig, Pres.--Artel Utah Scientific, Inc., Salt Lake City, UT; *U.S. Private*, pg. 86
Soderstrom, Anders O., Chief Info. Officer--American Skandia Information Services & Tecnology Corp., Shelton, CT; *Int'l*, pg. 1257
Soderstrom, Baltzar, Pres.--Indra AB, Helsingborg, Sweden; *Int'l*, pg. 920
Soderstrom, Bjorn, Mng. Dir.--Enso (Holland) B.V., Amsterdam, Netherlands; *Int'l*, pg. 457
Soderstrom, Bjorn, Mng. Dir.--Fins Verkoopkantoor, Amsterdam, Netherlands; *Int'l*, pg. 458
Soderstrom, Martti, Chief Oper. Officer--Oy Kationi Ab, Lapua, Finland; *Int'l*, pg. 1085
Sodeyama, Hiroshi, Chief Rep.--Bank of Yokohama Seoul, Seoul, Korea; *Int'l*, pg. 159
Sodeyama, Humitaka, Pres.--Toray Industries (H.K.) Ltd., Kowloon, Hong Kong; *Int'l*, pg. 1400
Sodhi, Ajit, Pres. & Chief Oper. Officer--Securiplex Inc., Dorval, Canada; *Int'l*, pg. 1162
Soegiharto, Soebagio, Mng. Dir.--P.T. Burgmann Indonesia, Bekasi, Indonesia; *Int'l*, pg. 233
Soejima, Naoki, Chief Oper. Officer--The Taiyo Mutual Life Insurance Co., London, United Kingdom; *Int'l*, pg. 1349
Soell, Susan, Admin.--Hillhaven Wichita, Wichita, KS; *U.S. Public*, pg. 1714
Soemardi, Langgeng, Pres.--P.T. Otsuka Jaya Indah, Jakarta, Indonesia; *Int'l*, pg. 1014
Soerjoesing, Georg D., Mng. Dir.--Ilaco Suriname NV, Paramaribo, Suriname; *Int'l*, pg. 606
Soeseke, Norbert, Mng. Dir.--MacGREGOR Conver GmbH, Bremen, Germany; *Int'l*, pg. 670
Soetanto, Didi, Chief Oper. Officer--PT Kes Sinar Mas Securities, Jakarta, Indonesia; *Int'l*, pg. 733
Soeters, Martin, Chief Oper. Officer--Novo Nordisk Pharmaceutique S.A., Boulogne-Billancourt, France; *Int'l, pg. 988*
Soffi, Paolo, Pres.--Charmilles Technologies (Italia) Srl., Milan, Italy; *Int'l*, pg. 489
Sofue, M., Chm.--Fuji-Hunt Electronics Technology Co., Ltd., Tokyo, Japan; *U.S. Public*, pg. 1219
Soga, Hiromu, Pres.--Eidesign Technologies, Inc., Mountain View, CA; *Int'l*, pg. 940
Sognini, Tony, Branch Mgr.--Jaco Electronics, Inc., Tewksbury, MA; *U.S. Public*, pg. 921
Soh, C.C., Gen. Mgr.--Laporte (Malaysia) Sdn Bhd, Pasir Panjang, Malaysia; *Int'l*, pg. 803
Soh, S., Gen. Mgr.--Gerrard Signode Pte. Ltd., Jurong, Singapore; *U.S. Public*, pg. 868
Sohl, Egon, Mgr.--Foodane A/S, Struer, Denmark; *Int'l*, pg. 1464
Sohm, Woo-Heon, Pres.--Ssangyong Investment Management Co., Ltd., Seoul, Korea; *Int'l*, pg. 1292
Sohmer, Paul, Dr., Pres.--Nellcor Puritan Bennett Incorporated, Pleasanton, CA; *U.S. Public*, pg. 1039
Soiron, H.H., Chm. Bd.--Ford Credit S.A., Zurich, Switzerland; *U.S. Public*, pg. 666
Sokol, Brian, Pres.--Blue Coral/Slick 50, Cleveland, OH; *U.S. Public*, pg. 1348
Sokol, Larry, Gen. Mgr.--Alloys International, Baytown, TX; *U.S. Public*, pg. 865
Sokolik, Samuel, Natl. Mgr.--Lemo U.S.A. Inc., Santa Rosa, CA; *Int'l*, pg. 806
Sokolow, Stephen, Pres. & Chief of Opers.-Canada--Manufacture Leviton du Canada, Pointe-Claire, Canada; *U.S. Private*, pg. 663
Sola, Fernando, Mng. Dir --Nederman Iberica S.A., Madrid, Spain; *Int'l*, pg. 283
Sola, Joan, Mng Dir.--Shandwick Barcelona, Barcelona, Spain; *Int'l*, pg. 1227
Solari, Roger, Dir.-Opers.--Arianespace Kourou, Kourou, French Guiana; *Int'l*, pg. 81
Solberg, Elizabeth T., Sr. Partner, Exec. V.P. & Gen. Mgr.--Fleishman-Hillard, Inc., Kansas City, MO; *U.S. Private*, pg. 411
Solberg, Knut, Mgr.-Bus. Area.--Det Norske Veritas, Gdansk, Poland; *Int'l*, pg. 396
Solberg, R.A., Chm.--Texaco Indonesia Corp., White Plains, NY; *U.S. Public*, pg. 1583
Solberg, R.A., Chm.--Texaco Overseas Petroleum Co., White Plains, NY; *U.S. Public*, pg. 1583
Solberg, R.A., Chm. Bd.--Texaco Natuna Inc., Jakarta, Indonesia; *U.S. Public*, pg. 1584
Solberg, Robert A., Chm. Bd.--Saudi Arabian Texaco Inc., White Plains, NY; *U.S. Public*, pg. 1583
Solberg, Wallace C., V.P. & Gen. Mgr.--Aircraft Division, Hawthorne, CA; *U.S. Public*, pg. 1198
Soldateli, Ilarioo, Pres.--Fiat Automisveis S.A., Sao Paulo, Brazil; *Int'l*, pg. 483
Soldo, Nick, Mgr.--SMP II, L.P., Chandler, AZ; *U.S. Public*, pg. 1537
Solender, T. Jeff, V.P.-Devel. & Plng.--Grey Asia Pacific, Quarry Bay, Hong Kong; *U.S. Public*, pg. 765
Soler, Arthur, Pres.--Cadbury Chocolate Canada, Inc., Toronto, Canada; *Int'l*, pg. 248
Soler, Miguel Alemany, Mgr. Gen.--Resinas Sinteticas, S.A. (RESISA), Barcelona, Spain; *Int'l*, pg. 323
Solgen, Paul, Gen. Mgr.--Waldo Bros. Company, South Windsor, CT; *U.S. Private*, pg. 1147
Solheim, Ola, Pres.--Igloo Pool, Oslo, Norway; *Int'l*, pg. 766
Soliday, W.E., Gen. Mgr.--Fluid Recycling Services Company, L.L.C., Livonia, MI; *U.S. Public*, pg. 1346
Soliman, Mohamed Aly, Chm. Bd. & Mng. Dir.--Egyptian Aluminium Products Company, Cairo, Egypt; *U.S. Public*, pg. 1386
Solito, Michele, Dir.--Verdichter Oe. G.m.b.H., Fuerstenfeld, Austria; *Int'l*, pg. 443
Solla, Jose Luis, Pres.--Hispano Olivetti Office, Barcelona, Spain; *Int'l*, pg. 1003
Sollenberger, Samuel K., Chm. Bd.--The Metropolitan Savings Bank of Ohio, Youngstown, OH; *U.S. Public*, pg. 608
Sollit, Jan, Pres.--Vingmed Sound A/S, Horten, Norway; *Int'l*, pg. 644
Solofrio, Jerry, Gen. Mgr.--Kent Paper Co., Inc., Bloomfield, NJ; *U.S. Public*, pg. 89
Solombrino, Scott, Pres.--Dav-El West, Hawthorne, CA; *U.S. Private*, pg. 314
Solombrino, Scott, Pres.--Dav-El Washington DC Inc., Long Island City, NY; *U.S. Private*, pg. 314
Solomon, Andrew, Chief Oper. Officer--Ahlstrom South Africa (Pty) Ltd., Benoni, South Africa; *Int'l*, pg. 35
Solomon, Bart, Gen. Mgr.--Products Research & Chemical Corp. Manufacturing Facilities Div., Mojave, CA; *Int'l*, pg. 339
Solomon, H. Bryce, Pres.--Blue Ridge Finance Co., Inc., Greenville, SC; *U.S. Public*, pg. 306
Solomon, Harry, Chm.--Hillsdown Ltd., Spalding, United Kingdom; *Int'l*, pg. 619
Solomon, Harvey, Pres.--Sag Harbor, New York, NY; *U.S. Public*, pg. 948
Solomon, Howard, Pres.--Inwood Laboratories, Inc., Inwood, NY; *U.S. Public*, pg. 670
Solomon, Howard, Pres.--Forest Pharmaceuticals, Inc., Maryland Heights, MO; *U.S. Public*, pg. 670
Solomon, James E., Pres.--Analog Division, San Jose, CA; *U.S. Public*, pg. 290
Solomon, Steve, V.P. & Gen. Mgr.--Fuji Computer Media Div., Elmsford, NY; *Int'l*, pg. 524
Solomons, Alan, Chief Exec. Officer--Lambert Smith Hampton, Manchester, United Kingdom; *Int'l*, pg. 797
Solomonson, F., Chief Oper. Officer--Marathon Petroleum Netherlands, Ltd., Dordrecht, Netherlands; *U.S. Public*, pg. 1662
Soltermann, Bernhard, Mng. Dir.--Comteco S.A., Bogota, Colombia; *Int'l*, pg. 1306
Soltis, Bruce L., Pres.--Arrow-Sysco Food Services, Inc., Harahan, LA; *U.S. Public*, pg. 1551
Solvano, Oyvind, Gen. Mgr.--Power-Packer U.S., Butler, WI; *U.S. Public*, pg. 124

Solvberg, Kjell, Mgr.--Viking Mjoendalen A/S, Mjoendalen, Norway; *Int'l*, pg. 1423

Solveson, C., Dir.-Perfex Indus. Prods.--Senior Engineering Co.-Milwaukee, Milwaukee, WI; *Int'l*, pg. 1222

Solyom, Laszlo, Chief Exec.--Zementwerke Labatlan GmbH, Labatlan, Hungary; *Int'l*, pg. 629

Soma, Jack, Pres.--Otari Corporation, Foster City, CA; *Int'l*, pg. 1013

Soma, Ramesh, Mng. Dir.-Australia--W.R. Grace Australia Ltd., Fawkner, Australia; *U.S. Public*, pg. 755

Soman, S., Mgng. Dir.--Autofield Engineers Private Ltd., Pune, India; *U.S. Public*, pg. 469

Someno, Tomoji, Pres.--HY Marketing Inc., Taipei, Taiwan; *Int'l*, pg. 588

Somers, Doug, V.P.-Network & Service Mngmnt. Systems--Newbridge Networks Corporation, Kanata, Canada; *Int'l*, pg. 924

Somers, John W., Sr. V.P. & Branch Mgr.--DG Bank-Atlanta Branch, Atlanta, GA; *Int'l*, pg. 352

Somers, Raymond, Mgr.--Livingston International Freight Belgium, Antwerp, Belgium; *U.S. Public*, pg. 373

Somervaille, R.D., Deputy Chm.--P&O Australia Ltd., Sydney, Australia; *Int'l*, pg. 1035

Somerville, Brent, Mng. Dir.--Datastream International (Hong Kong) Limited, Central, Hong Kong; *U.S. Public*, pg. 1326

Somerville, Ervin W., Pres. & Chief Exec. Officer--M & I Central Bank & Trust, Marshfield, WI; *U.S. Public*, pg. 1050

Somerville, Leo, Pres.--Renishaw Inc., Schaumburg, IL; *Int'l*, *pg. 1103*

Somezawa, Yoshiyasu, Mng. Dir.--Oki Europe Ltd., Hounslow, United Kingdom; *Int'l*, pg. 1000

Sominski, Dlotr, Chief Oper. Officer--Akerlund & Rausing, Warsaw, Poland; *Int'l*, pg. 33

Somm, Mr., Pres.--Asea Brown Boveri AG, Baden, Switzerland; *Int'l*, pg. 1

Sommer, A., Dir.--NatWest Securities GmbH, Munich, Germany; *Int'l*, pg. 911

Sommer, Adrian, Partner--A & N Leasing, Dale, WI; *U.S. Private*, pg. 986

Sommer, Holger F., Gen Mgr--Dresdner Bank AG, Madrid, Spain; *Int'l*, pg. 419

Sommer, James, Gen. Mgr.--Molded Fiber Glass/West, Adelanto, CA; *U.S. Private*, pg. 756

Sommer, James, Partner--A & N Leasing, Dale, WI; *U.S. Private*, pg. 986

Sommer, John, Pres.--Mid Continent Market Center, Topeka, KS; *U.S. Public*, pg. 1759

Sommer, Nila, Partner--A & N Leasing, Dale, WI; *U.S. Private*, pg. 986

Sommer, Roger, Pres.--Earthgrains Co., Carrollton, TX; *U.S. Public*, pg. 547

Sommer, Ron, Pres. & Chief Oper. Officer--Sony Electronics, Park Ridge, NJ; *Int'l*, pg. 1281

Sommer, Scott, Gen. Mgr.--Crown Products, Indianapolis, IN; *U.S. Private*, pg. 1014

Sommer, Sue, Mng. Dir.--IVTx, Maryland Heights, MO; *U.S. Public*, pg. 601

Sommerer, Peter, Pres. & Chief Oper. Officer--Newbridge Networks Corporation, Kanata, Canada; *Int'l*, pg. 924

Sommerfeld, S., Plant Mgr.--Square D Co.- Control Products Hqtrs., Knightdale, NC; *Int'l*, pg. 1208

Sommerfelt, Christian, Gen. Mgr.--Sierra Leone Cement Corp. Ltd., Freetown, Sierra Leone; *Int'l*, pg. 1201

Sommers, Bill, Pres. & Gen. Mgr.--KLOS-FM Radio, Inc., Los Angeles, CA; *U.S. Public*, pg. 512

Sommers, James B., Pres.--NationsBank Trust, Atlanta, GA; *U.S. Public*, pg. 1165

Sommers, Scott, Gen. Mgr.--Freeway Rockford, Rockford, IL; *U.S. Private*, pg. 426

Sommerville, Paul, Mgr.-Office--Woodward-Clyde, Pasadena, CA; *U.S. Public*, pg. 1656

Son, J.G., Gen. Mgr.--Daewoo International America Corp. - Chicago, Arlington Heights, IL; *Int'l*, pg. 357

Sonamai, Khun Kitti, Exec. Chm.--Clays & Minerals (Thailand) Ltd., Pathum Thani, Thailand; *Int'l*, pg. 1488

Soncini, M., Exec. V.P.--Pignone Inc., New York, NY; *Int'l*, pg. 991

Sondenbroe, Peter, Gen. Mgr.--Elkem Danmark a/s, Vedbaek, Denmark; *Int'l*, pg. 447

Sonderegger, P., Plant Mgr.--Swissmetal Plant Boillat, Reconvilier, Switzerland; *Int'l*, pg. 1427

Sonderegger, Paul, Chief Oper. Officer--Swissmetal Deutschland Handelsgesellschaft mbH, Schwenningen, Germany; *Int'l*, pg. 1427

Sondergaard, Lars, Mng. Dir.--ISS Catering A/S, Copenhagen, Denmark; *Int'l*, pg. 656

Sondgereth, Gary, V.P.--PMI, Ames, IA; *U.S. Private*, pg. 1089

Sonego, Ronald A., Pres.--Surftran Division, Madison Heights, MI; *Int'l*, pg. 204

Song, Bo-Soon, Chm. Bd. & Chief Exec. Officer--Samsung Electronics North America Inc., Ridgefield Park, NJ; *Int'l*, *pg. 1183*

Song, K.R., Pres.--Samsung Electronics America, Inc., Ridgefield Park, NJ; *Int'l*, pg. 1183

Song, Kyung Sup, Gen. Mgr.--Cho Hung Bank, Singapore Branch, Singapore, Singapore; *Int'l*, pg. 288

Songer, James, V.P.--Esco International, Portland, OR; *U.S. Private*, pg. 383

Songer, Tom, Gen. Mgr.--Murray Turbomachinery Corporation, Burlington, IA; *U.S. Private*, pg. 1110

Songin, Margaret, Mgr.-Mktg.--Clinicare Systems, Inc., Orchard Park, NY; *U.S. Private*, pg. 442

Sonjanic, Diana, Mgr.--Utell International-Peru, Lima, Peru; *Int'l*, pg. 1098

Sonne, Kim, V.P. & Country Mgr.--Berlitz International Danmark A/S, Copenhagen, Denmark; *U.S. Public*, pg. 222

Sonnenberg, Ronni, Div. Head--Ziff-Davis Business Media Group, New York, NY; *Int'l*, pg. 1276

Sonnenberg, Willie B., Chm. Bd. & Exec. Creative Dir.--Sonnenberg Murphy Leo Burnett, Sunninghill, South Africa; *U.S. Private*, pg. 186

Sonner, Harvey, Pres.--Lightalarms Electronics Corporation, Baldwin, NY; *Int'l*, pg. 725

Sonntag, A.D., Dr., Chief Oper. Officer--Rabobank Deutschland AG, Frankfurt/Main, Germany; *Int'l*, pg. 1082

Sonntag, Heinz, Mng. Dir.--Elco Eurpoe GmbH, Betzdorf, Germany; *U.S. Public*, pg. 1590

Sonobe, Takashi, Pres. & Chief Exec. Officer--Mitsubishi Motor Sales of America, Inc., Cypress, CA; *Int'l*, pg. 875

Soo, A.H., Mng. Dir.--Nan Shan Life Insurance Company, Ltd., Taipei, Taiwan; *U.S. Public*, pg. 85

Soo, Han. Seung, Chm. Bd.--Korea Otsuka Pharmaceutical Co., Ltd., Seoul, Korea; *Int'l*, pg. 1014

Soon, Lee Meng, Pres.--PT Bank DBS Buana, Jakarta, Indonesia; *Int'l*, pg. 350

Soon, Soh Kim, Chm.--DBS Investment Research Pte. Ltd., Singapore, Singapore; *Int'l*, pg. 350

Soon, Soh Kim, Chm.--DBS Factors Pte. Ltd., Singapore, Singapore; *Int'l*, pg. 350

Soon, Soh Kim, Chm.--DBS Securities Singapore Pte. Ltd., Singapore, Singapore; *Int'l*, pg. 351

Soon, Soh Kim, Chm.--DBS Securities Holding Pte. Ltd., Singapore, Singapore; *Int'l*, pg. 351

Soon, Soh Kim, Chm.--DBS Securities Nominees Pte. Ltd., Singapore, Singapore; *Int'l*, pg. 351

Soon, Soh Kim, Chm.--DBS Futures Hong Kong Ltd., Queensway, Hong Kong; *Int'l*, pg. 351

Soon, Soh Kim, Chm.--DBS Securities Hong Kong Ltd., Queensway, Hong Kong; *Int'l*, pg. 351

Soon, Soh Kim, Chm.--DBS Securities Malaysia Pte Ltd., Singapore, Singapore; *Int'l*, pg. 351

Soon, Soh Kim, Chm.--DBS Securities UK Ltd., London, United Kingdom; *Int'l*, pg. 351

Soong, Leo, Pres.--Crystal Geyser Water Company, Calistoga, CA; *Int'l*, pg. 1013

Soong, Ronnie, Mng. Dir.--Galco International Toys, N.V., Kowloon, Hong Kong; *U.S. Public*, pg. 698

Soous, C., Mng. Dir.--VCST Industrial Products N.V., Saint Truiden, Belgium; *Int'l*, pg. 1134

Sorano, Edgar, Plant Mgr.--TI Brazil Industria E Comerico Ltda., Pindamonhangaba, Brazil; *Int'l*, pg. 1342

Soranson, Robyn, Mng. Dir.--Aetna Capital Management Investment Limited, London, United Kingdom; *U.S. Public*, pg. 27

Sordo, Fabio, Mng. Dir.--Siagarage S.p.A., Milan, Italy; *Int'l*, pg. 170

Sorel, Bernard, Mng. Dir.--Bombardier Eurorail, Brussels, Belgium; *Int'l*, pg. 200

Sorensen, Berner C., Gen. Mgr.--Wormald International (Scandinavia) A/S, Odense, Denmark; *U.S. Public*, pg. 1651

Sorensen, Johan, Mgr.--Sandvik GmbH, Dusseldorf, Germany; *Int'l*, pg. 1186

Sorensen, Marina Hother, Mng. Dir.--ISS University Hotel, Holte, Denmark; *Int'l*, pg. 656

Sorensen, O.P., Gen. Mgr.--Nordisk Case A/S, Roskilde, Denmark; *U.S. Public*, pg. 1580

Sorensen, Olaf Bredahl, Chief Oper. Officer--Electrolux Constructor, Hvidovre, Denmark; *Int'l*, pg. 441

Sorensen, Ove, Statutory Dir.--Reynolds Aluminium Holland B.V., Harderwijk, Netherlands; *U.S. Public*, pg. 1387

Sorensen, Robert C., Pres.--Duro-Test Intl. Corp., Fairfield, NJ; *U.S. Private*, pg. 349

Sorensen, Tor Magne, Pres.--Aker Base a.s., Tananger, Norway; *Int'l*, pg. 41

Sorensen, Vagn, Chief Opr. Officer--Granges Danmark A/S, Glostrup, Denmark; *Int'l*, pg. 441

Sorenson, John, Pres. & Chief Exec. Officer--Rogers N.K. Seed Co., Boise, ID; *Int'l*, pg. 974

Sorenson, Robert, Pres.--Optimage Interactive Services Co., Des Moines, IA; *Int'l*, pg. 1054

Sorenson, S., Mng. Dir.--Nutricia Danmark A/S, Copenhagen, Denmark; *Int'l*, pg. 992

Sorenson, Sonja, Pres. & Publr.--St. Cloud Daily Times, Inc., Saint Cloud, MN; *U.S. Public*, pg. 701

Sorg, Denise K., Controller--Energy Dynamics Division, Chandler, AZ; *U.S. Public*, pg. 1250

Soriano, Jose Manuel, Country Mgr.--Retail Brands SA, Madrid, Spain; *Int'l*, pg. 338

Sorme, Kjell, Mng. Dir.--LM Ericsson Pty. Ltd., Broadmeadows, Australia; *Int'l*, pg. 1369

Soro, Christopher, Gen. Mgr.--Allen & Hoshall, Knoxville, TN; *U.S. Private*, pg. 36

Soroka, Robert H., Chm.--Robinsons-May, North Hollywood, CA; *U.S. Public*, pg. 1064

Sorrell, C.S., Pres. & Chief Exec. Officer--Calvert Group, Ltd., Bethesda, MD; *U.S. Private*, pg. 11

Sorrell, Martin, Chief Exec. Officer--WPP Group USA Inc., New York, NY; *Int'l*, pg. 1483

Sorrent, M., Chief Oper. Officer--S.A. Entreprise de Travaux et de Constructions ENTRACON, Mont-Saint Guibert, Belgium; *Int'l*, pg. 301

Sorsa, Pekka, Pres.--Xyrofin (UK) Ltd., Redhill, United Kingdom; *Int'l*, pg. 350

Sorvik, Airrd Ihge, Plant Mgr.--Meraker Naeringspark, Koppera, Norway; *Int'l*, pg. 448

Sosman, Herbert, Pres.--Wallace Laboratories, Cranbury, NJ; *U.S. Public*, pg. 310

Sosrosukarto, Budiardjo, Pres.--PT Hokuriku United Forging Industries, Bekasi, Indonesia; *Int'l*, pg. 745

Sossi, Adriano, Chief Oper. Officer--Geotronics Italia S.P.A., Vimercate, Italy; *Int'l*, pg. 1290

Sossong, A.T., Pres.--Wilmore Coal Company, Windber, PA; *U.S. Private*, pg. 138

Sossong, A.T., Pres.--Reitz Coal Company, Windber, PA; *U.S. Private*, pg. 139

Sotelino, Gabino, V.P.-Opers.--Cafe Ba-Ba-Reeba, Chicago, IL; *U.S. Private*, pg. 661

Sotelino, Gabino, V.P.-Opers.--Ambria, Chicago, IL; *U.S. Private*, pg. 661

Sotelino, Gabino, V.P.-Opers.--Un Grand Cafe', Chicago, IL; *U.S. Private*, pg. 662

Sotir, Gary, V.P. & Gen. Mgr.--Topeka Television, Corp., Topeka, KS; *U.S. Public*, pg. 984

Soto, D. Gernam Ancochea, Pres.--Telefonica Internacional De Espana S.A., Madrid, Spain; *Int'l*, pg. 1372

Soto, Elena, Pres.--Katz Hispanic Media, New York, NY; *U.S. Public*, pg. 335

Soto, Hiroo, Pres.--Bank of Tokyo-Mitsubishi Ltd., Paris Branch, Paris, France; *Int'l*, pg. 158

Soto, J., Mng. Dir.--Goodyear de Chile S.A.I.C., Santiago, Chile; *U.S. Public*, pg. 753

Soto, R., Mgr.-Opers. & Reg. Fin. Controller-Central America--Formularios Moore de Guatemala, S.A., Guatemala, Guatemala; *Int'l*, pg. 889

Sotoca, Jose Luis, Mng. Dir.--Janssen-Cilag, Madrid, Spain; *U.S. Public*, pg. 929

Sotomayor, Bernardo, V.P. & Gen. Mgr.--Iconovex Corporation, Bloomington, MN; *U.S. Public*, pg. 880

Sotomi, Teppei, Mng. Dir.--Kobelco Middle East (E.C.), Manama, Bahrain; *Int'l*, pg. 741

Soubestre, Francis, Mng. Dir.--SKF Equipements S.n.c., Montigny-le-Bretonneux, France; *Int'l*, pg. 1158

Soudain, Thierry Huot, Mgr.-Plant--Ateliers Sucre Liquide et Conditionnement-Laboratoire de Recherche de Nassandres, Nassandres, France; *Int'l*, pg. 549

Souden, Dean, Pres.--Kal Grafx, Kentwood, MI; *U.S. Private*, pg. 387

Souden, Dean, Pres.--Sterling Color Process, Kentwood, MI; *U.S. Private*, pg. 387

Sougy, J., Chm. Bd.--Tecminemet, Trappes, France; *Int'l*, pg. 662

Soukris, Dimitri, Chief Oper. Officer--Novo Nordisk A/S, Cairo, Egypt; *Int'l*, pg. 988

Soukup, Mark A., Pres. & Chief Exec. Officer--The State Bank and Trust Company, Defiance, OH; *U.S. Public*, pg. 1413

Soulatt, Nicole, Gen. Mgr.-Mktg.--Estee Lauder SNC, Paris, France; *U.S. Public*, pg. 594

Soule, C., Dir. Gen.--Societe Generale de Banques en Guinee, Conakry, Papua New Guinea; *Int'l*, pg. 548

Soule, Charles E., Pres. & Chief Exec. Officer--The Paul Revere Corporation, Worcester, MA; *U.S. Public*, pg. 1338

Soule, Michael, Plant Mgr.--Dowty Automotive Gaskets, Milford Haven, United Kingdom; *Int'l*, pg. 1338

Soules, A.A., Mng. Dir.--Kohler de Mexico, S.A. de C.V., Mexico, Mexico; *U.S. Private*, pg. 631

Soulie, R., Chm. Bd.--Minemet Australia Pty. Ltd., Sydney, Australia; *Int'l*, pg. 661

Soultanian, Sarkis, Pres.--National Utility Service (Canada) Ltd., North York, Canada; *U.S. Private*, pg. 787

Soussan, Andre, Mng. Dir.--Rhone-Poulenc Afrique Centrale, Douala, Cameroon; *Int'l*, pg. 1112

South, Gord, Gen. Mgr.--DeVilbiss Compressor Products, Barrie, Canada; *U.S. Public*, pg. 867

Southall, Tom, Gen. Mgr.--ITW Brand Merchandising, Wood Dale, IL; *U.S. Public*, pg. 866

Southard, Donald, Pres.--Datascope Patient Monitoring Division, Paramus, NJ; *U.S. Public*, pg. 487

Souther, G. Parks, Pres.--Parkson Corporation, Fort Lauderdale, FL; *Int'l*, pg. 710

Southern, D., Chief Exec. Officer--Bowthorpe Australia Pty. Ltd., Sydney, Australia; *Int'l*, pg. 208

Southern, William, Pres.--Mason Electric Co., San Fernando, CA; *U.S. Public*, pg. 594

Southwick, Stephen W., Sec.--IES Investments Inc., Cedar Rapids, IA; *U.S. Public*, pg. 855

Southworth, Paul, Mng. Dir.--Avon Cosmetics Ltd., Northampton, United Kingdom; *U.S. Public*, pg. 156

Southworth, Richard A., V.P. & Gen. Mgr.--Spectrum Control, Connecting Devices Div., Erie, PA; *U.S. Public*, pg. 1497

Southworth, Richard A., V.P. & Gen. Mgr.--Spectrum Control, Filter Products Group, Fairview, PA; *U.S. Public*, *pg. 1497*

Souviron, J.P., Pres. & Dir. Gen.--Morgan Grenfell France S.A., Paris, France; *Int'l*, pg. 406

Souviron, Philippe, Chief Oper. Officer--Bankers Trust New York Corporation, Paris, France; *U.S. Public*, pg. 186

Souza, Alan, Pres.--Zenith Construction Co, Inc., Merriam, KS; *U.S. Private*, pg. 585

Sovey, William P., Pres.--Newell Operating Company, Freeport, IL; *U.S. Public*, pg. 1177

Soviero, J.C., Chm. Bd.--Union Carbide (Europe) S.A., Meyrin, Switzerland; *U.S. Public*, pg. 1667

Sovonet, M., Chief Oper. Officer--S.A. Proprete, Assainissement, Gestion de l'Environnement P.A.G.E., Charleroi, Belgium; *Int'l*, pg. 301

Sowan, Raja, Reg. Media Dir.--Radius Leo Burnett, Dubai, United Arab Emirates; *U.S. Private*, pg. 186

Soyak, Necip, Pres. & Chief Exec. Officer--Chicago Pneumatic Tool Company, Rock Hill, SC; *Int'l*, pg. 96

Spaans, M.G., Chief Oper. Officer--B.V. Machinefabriek Spaans, Hoofddorp, Netherlands; *Int'l*, pg. 472

Spackman, C.J., Mng. Dir.--Bovis Construction Group, Harrow, United Kingdom; *Int'l*, pg. 1032

Spackman, G. Lawrence, Pres.-Gas Mktg. Grp.--TransCanada Energy Ltd., Calgary, Canada; *Int'l*, pg. 1417

Spada, B., Admin. Mgr.--Diffucap-Eurand S.A., Stabio, Switzerland; *U.S. Public*, pg. 81

Spada, Vito, Branch Mgr.--Banco di Napoli-New York, New York, NY; *Int'l*, pg. 140

Spadaro, Romano, Mng. Dir.--ISS Hasco Management AG, Oberentfelden, Switzerland; *Int'l*, pg. 657

Spaetz, Kenneth, Pres.--Performance Contracting, Inc., Charlotte, NC; *U.S. Private*, pg. 853

Spagnolo, A., Chief Oper. Officer--Danone S.p.A., Milan, Italy; *Int'l*, pg. 379

Spahr, Bradley W., Pres.--HR Textron, Valencia, CA; *U.S. Public*, pg. 1589

Spahr, Jeff, Gen. Mgr.--Day Industries, Hudson, MI; *U.S. Private*, pg. 878

Spain, A.J., Chm. Bd.--National Irish Bank Limited, Dublin, Ireland; *Int'l*, pg. 906
Spalatin, George, Chief Oper. Officer--MacGREGOR (HRV) d o o, Rijeka, Croatia; *Int'l*, pg. 671
Spalding, Brian, Mgr.--Sandvik Process Systems Canada Ltd., Guelph, Canada; *Int'l*, pg. 1188
Spalding, Daniel L., Pres.--Powercor Australia Limited, Southbank, Australia; *U.S. Public*, pg. 1252
Spalding, Edgar S., Admin. Mgr.--Inversiones Ina Limitada, Santiago, Chile; *U.S. Public*, pg. 364
Spalla, Frank, Pres. & Chief Exec. Officer--Ajax Magnethermic Corp., Warren, OH; *Int'l*, pg. 113
Spalla, Linda, Pres.--WHNT-TV, Huntsville, AL; *U.S. Public*, pg. 1174
Spalletti, F., Dr., Chief Oper. Officer--Eurogenetics Italia SRL, Turin, Italy; *Int'l*, pg. 1408
Spalteholz, Bianca, Gen. Mgr.Sls. & Mktg./Germany, Austria & Central/Eastern Europe--Utell International-Germany, Frankfurt, Germany; *Int'l*, pg. 1098
Spaminato, James, Pres.--Asher Candy Company, New Hyde Park, NY; *U.S. Public*, pg. 1052
Span, Jeff, Mgr.-Plant--Pittsburgh Tube Darlington Div., Darlington, PA; *U.S. Private*, pg. 868
Spandet, Terry L., Pres.--Central Rubber Company, Belvidere, IL; *U.S. Public*, pg. 1776
Spandet, Terry L., Pres.--Daniel Woodhead Company, Northbrook, IL; *U.S. Public*, pg. 1776
Spangler, C.D., Jr., Chm. Bd.--National Gypsum Company, Charlotte, NC; *Int'l*, pg. 790
Spangler, Dale, Admin.--Baltic Country Manor, Baltic, OH; *U.S. Public*, pg. 838
Spangler, David L., Chm. Bd., Pres. & Chief Exec. Officer--First National Bank of Huntington, Huntington, IN; *U.S. Public*, pg. 674
Spangler, Dean, V.P. & Gen. Mgr.--Boren Clay Products Company, Pleasant Garden, NC; *Int'l*, pg. 699
Spanholtz, Charlotte, Gen. Mgr.--DMB&B Beijing, Beijing, China; *U.S. Private*, pg. 303
Spanier, H.M., Branch Mgr.--Van Leeuwen Pipe & Tube Corp., South Holland, IL; *Int'l*, pg. 1450
Spannring, Dr. Gernot, Mng. Dir.--DSI DYWIDAG-Systems International GmbH, Aschheim, Germany; *Int'l*, pg. 423
Spano, Lori, V.P.-Sls.--Outdoor Systems, Inc. Sales, New York, NY; *U.S. Public*, pg. 1235
Sparagon, Louise L., Office Mgr.--The Ohio Art Co., New York, NY; *U.S. Public*, pg. 1214
Spargo, Mark, Gen. Mgr.--Snavely Forest Products, Inc., Dallas, TX; *U.S. Private*, pg. 1010
Sparkes, Geoff, Pres. & Dir. Gen.--Dowty SA, Le Bourget, France; *Int'l*, pg. 1338
Sparks, Jack B., Jr., Pres.--Lamb Grays Harbor Co, Hoquiam, WA; *U.S. Private*, pg. 378
Sparks, K.W., Chm. Bd.--Lucas Automotive GmbH, Koblenz, Germany; *Int'l*, pg. 820
Sparks, Robert P., Chief Oper. Officer--Allright Birmingham, Inc., Birmingham, AL; *U.S. Private*, pg. 42
Sparks, Robert P., Pres.--JPS Automotive L.P., Greenville, SC; *U.S. Private*, pg. 1095
Sparks, Sam, Admin.--Torrey Pines Care Center, Las Vegas, NV; *U.S. Public*, pg. 1715
Sparks, W. Alvon, Chm. Bd. & Pres.--Resolute Management Corporation, Stamford, CT; *U.S. Public*, pg. 220
Sparrow, Karen, Admin.--Guardian Care of Zebulon, Zebulon, NC; *U.S. Public*, pg. 1713
Sparvero, Robert P., Pres.--Ford International Export Sales (Asia-Pacific Region) Incorporated, Dearborn, MI; *U.S. Public*, pg. 664
Sparvero, Robert P., Chm. Bd. & Pres.--Ford Direct Markets, Incorporated, Dearborn, MI; *U.S. Public*, pg. 664
Spatz, D.D., Chm. Bd. & Chief Exec. Officer--Autotrol Corporation, Milwaukee, WI; *U.S. Public*, pg. 1234
Spatz, Edward C., Pres.--Security/DBS Division, Dallas, TX; *U.S. Public*, pg. 528
Spatz, Neal, Div. V.P.--AMP Distributor Marketing Div., Harrisburg, PA; *U.S. Public*, pg. 7
Spatz, William, Pres.--Spatz & Co. Development, Northbrook, IL; *U.S. Private*, pg. 1021
Spatz, William, Pres.--Spatz Centers, Inc., Northbrook, IL; *U.S. Private*, pg. 1021
Spatz, William, Pres.--S & C Maintenance Corp., Northbrook, IL; *U.S. Private*, pg. 1021
Spaul, Michael, V.P. & Gen. Mgr.--Communicolor Division, Newark, OH; *U.S. Public*, pg. 1505
Spaulding, Dek, Mgr.--Furman Wholesale Lumber Branch, Atlanta, GA; *U.S. Private*, pg. 431
Spaulding, Peter C., Pres.--Wilton Tool Div., Palatine, IL; *U.S. Private*, pg. 1181
Spaulding, Peter C., V.P. & Gen. Mgr.--Barber-Colman Company, Rockford, IL; *Int'l*, pg. 1242
Speak, Patricia, Admin.--Greenery Rehabilitation & Skilled Nursing Center, Canonsburg, PA; *U.S. Public*, pg. 839
Speaks, Roy, V.P. & Gen. Mgr.--Shelter Products Group-Western Div., Cucamonga, CA; *Int'l*, pg. 1398
Spearing, Robert, Pres.--Telos Information Systems, Pasadena, CA; *U.S. Public*, pg. 1573
Spears, Alexander, Chm. Bd. & Chief Exec. Officer--Lorillard Tobacco Company, Greensboro, NC; *U.S. Public*, pg. 1011
Spears, Harold, Pres.--Floyd Theatres, Inc., Lakeland, FL; *U.S. Public*, pg. 1056
Spears, Richard F., Pres.--Landmark Specialty Publications, Inc., Norfolk, VA; *U.S. Private*, pg. 649
Spears, William E., Pres.--Tupperware U.S., Inc., Orlando, FL; *U.S. Public*, pg. 1644
Specht, Rex, Area Superintendent--Chaney Dell Plant, Ringwood, OK; *U.S. Public*, pg. 1759
Speciale, Phil, Dir.-Mktg.--AT&T Language Line Services, Monterey, CA; *U.S. Public*, pg. 11
Spee, Hans, Chief Oper. Officer--Gambro B.V., Breda, Netherlands; *Int'l*, pg. 667
Speetzen, B.L., Freeman--General Electric Railcar Repair Services Corp., Chicago, IL; *U.S. Public*, pg. 712
Speetzen, Robert W., Pres.--General Electric Capital Railcar Services, Chicago, IL; *U.S. Public*, pg. 712
Spegele, John A., Pres.--APG Lime Corp., New Braunfels, TX; *U.S. Public*, pg. 761
Spegele, John A., Pres.--APG Lime Corp., Ripplemead, VA; *U.S. Public*, pg. 761
Spegele, John A., Pres.--A.P.G. Lime Corp., Roanoke, VA; *U.S. Public*, pg. 761
Speheger, Kent, Mng. Dir.--DYWIDAG Systems International, USA, Inc., Florissant, MO; *Int'l*, pg. 424
Speice, Byron, Pres.--Diamond Chain Company, Indianapolis, IN; *U.S. Private*, pg. 68
Speier, Melvin H., V.P.--Voest-Alpine Steel Corp.-Rolled Steel Products, New York, NY; *Int'l*, pg. 1471
Speirs, Loin, Mng. Dir.--Fisons A/S, Soeborg, Denmark; *Int'l*, pg. 1111
Speiser, Robert D., Pres.--Hercon Laboratories Corp., New York, NY; *U.S. Public*, pg. 802
Speiser, Robert D., Pres.--Transderm Laboratories Corporation, New York, NY; *U.S. Public*, pg. 802
Speizer, Mark A., Chief Exec. Officer--Pinnacle Data Corporation, San Bruno, CA; *U.S. Public*, pg. 1158
Speld, R., Gen. Mgr.--North Sea Ferries Ltd., Kingston-upon-Hull, United Kingdom; *Int'l*, pg. 1035
Speld, R.E., Mng. Dir.--Noordzee Veerdiensten B.V., Rotterdam, Netherlands; *Int'l*, pg. 1145
Spelde, Wiecher, Chief Oper. Officer--NIFE B.V., Haarlem, Netherlands; *Int'l*, pg. 53
Spelling, Aaron, Chm. Bd. & Chief Exec. Officer--Spelling Television, Los Angeles, CA; *U.S. Private*, pg. 776
Spellings, George E., Pres.-Gen. Precision Tool & Die Division--General Precision Tool & Die Division, Muscle Shoals, AL; *U.S. Public*, pg. 986
Spelta, Andrea, Mng. Dir.--Inamed S.R.L., Verona, Italy; *U.S. Public*, pg. 874
Speltz, Steve, Pres.--MPH Industries, Riverside, MI; *U.S. Public*, pg. 726
Spence, Bill, Pres.--Engineered Carbons Inc., Borger, TX; *U.S. Private*, pg. 65
Spence, Bob, V.P. & Gen. Mgr.--Dillard Paper Co. of Orlando, Orlando, FL; *U.S. Public*, pg. 902
Spence, Charles A., V.P. & Publisher--Midland Reporter-Telegram, Midland, TX; *U.S. Private*, pg. 517
Spence, Douglas, Mgr.-Opers.--Distex Ind. Inc., Milton, Canada; *U.S. Public*, pg. 560
Spence, John C., Pres.--Avco Insurance Services/Balboa Life & Casualty, Irvine, CA; *U.S. Public*, pg. 1589
Spence, Philip, Pres.--Pulse Sciences, Inc., San Leandro, CA; *U.S. Public*, pg. 1618
Spence, Will B., Pres. & Chief Exec. Officer--South Carolina National Corporation, Columbia, SC; *U.S. Public*, pg. 1730
Spence, Will B., Pres. & Chief Exec. Officer--Wachovia Bank of South Carolina, N.A., Columbia, SC; *U.S. Public*, *pg. 1730*
Spenceley, Chris, Field Supvr.--Weatherford Inc.-Thailand, Songkhla, Thailand; *U.S. Public*, pg. 1750
Spencer, Allan F., Exec. Dir.--NAAO Production Purchasing, Dearborn, MI; *U.S. Public*, pg. 662
Spencer, Curt, Plant Mgr.--Hydro Conduit Corp., Fort Smith, AR; *Int'l*, pg. 245
Spencer, David, Div. Pres.--Grocery Supply Company-San Antonio, San Antonio, TX; *U.S. Private*, pg. 436
Spencer, Howard, Regional Mgr.--Westpac Banking Corp. - French Polynesia, Papeete, French Polynesia; *Int'l*, pg. 1497
Spencer, Kade, Mgr.--Purolator Products Co., Tulsa, OK; *U.S. Public*, pg. 1045
Spencer, P., Pres.--Merck Sharp & Dohme B.V., Brussels, Belgium; *U.S. Public*, pg. 1092
Spencer, Rodney, Pres.--Surlean Meat Co., San Antonio, TX; *U.S. Private*, pg. 660
Spencer, W.E., Vice Chm., Pres. & Chief Exec. Officer--ANR Production Co., Houston, TX; *U.S. Public*, pg. 389
Spencer, William, Dir.-Media & Tech.--Ginn Division, Needham, MA; *U.S. Private*, pg. 778
Spencer, William J., V.P.--Xerox Corporate Research Group, Stamford, CT; *U.S. Public*, pg. 1784
Spender, Geoff, Chief Mgr.--Westpac Banking Corp. - Hong Kong, Hong Kong, Hong Kong; *Int'l*, pg. 1497
Spendiff, Joe E., Unit Director Washington Satellite--Bundy U.K. Ltd., Washington, United Kingdom; *Int'l*, pg. 1341
Sperber, Perry, Chm. Bd. & Pres.--Metal Fab Corporation, Ormond Beach, FL; *U.S. Public*, pg. 658
Sperling, John G., Chm. Bd.--Institute for Professional Development, Phoenix, AZ; *U.S. Public*, pg. 120
Sperling, Michael, Chief Oper. Officer--BOCM Silcock (N.I.) Ltd., Hannover, Germany; *Int'l*, pg. 440
Spero, J.N., Pres.--Baldwin International, Inc., Solon, OH; *Int'l*, pg. 1150
Sperry, Bill, Chm. Bd.--Costain Building & Civil Engineering Limited, Maidenhead, United Kingdom; *Int'l*, pg. 336
Sperry, Bill, Mng. Dir.--Costain South East Asia, Wan Chai, Hong Kong; *Int'l*, pg. 337
Spesert, Len, Pres.--Hazelnut Growers of Oregon, Cornelius, OR; *U.S. Private*, pg. 1051
Speyer, W. Kip, Pres.--Leisegang Medical, Inc., Boca Raton, FL; *U.S. Public*, pg. 698
Spice, Reginald, Chief Oper. Officer--SCA Euroliner U.K., Aylesford, United Kingdom; *Int'l*, pg. 1326
Spicehandler, Jonathan R., M.D., Pres.--Schering-Plough Research Institute, Kenilworth, NJ; *U.S. Public*, pg. 1438
Spicer, Anthony J., Dir.-Sls.--International Div., El Monte, CA; *U.S. Private*, pg. 245
Spicer, Roger, Mng. Dir.--Puritan Maid Ltd., Aylesbury, United Kingdom; *Int'l*, pg. 210
Spicher, Edgar, Chm.--Coop Broye-Fribourg-Moleson, Givisiez, Switzerland; *Int'l*, pg. 329
Spickschen, Thorlef, Mng. Dir.--Knoll AG, Ludwigshafen, Germany; *Int'l*, pg. 104
Spidalette, Lou, Pres.--LINC Medical Imaging, Newport Beach, CA; *U.S. Public*, pg. 996
Spiedel, Ben, IV, V.P. & Gen. Mgr.--Silver City Casino, Las Vegas, NV; *U.S. Public*, pg. 375
Spiedel, Ben, IV, V.P. & Gen. Mgr.--Slots-A-Fun, Inc., Las Vegas, NV; *U.S. Public*, pg. 375
Spiegel, Arthur H., III, Pres.--CSC Healthcare Group, New York, NY; *U.S. Public*, pg. 423
Spiegel, Franz, Mng. Dir.--Franz Spiegel Buch GmbH, Ulm, Germany; *Int'l*, pg. 1478
Spiegel, Steven, Chm.--Lehman Brothers International Limited, New York, NY; *U.S. Public*, pg. 987
Spiegel, Tamio, Pres.--Noma Intl. Inc., Newburgh, NY; *Int'l*, pg. 955
Spiekerman, Tom, Pres.--TBWA/H NETH-work, Amstelveen, Netherlands; *Int'l*, pg. 589
Spielman, Jeff, Pres.--SIMS Portex Inc., Keene, NH; *Int'l*, pg. 1268
Spielvogel, Andrew, Pres.--SuperValu, Inc.-Maine Div., Portland, ME; *U.S. Public*, pg. 1540
Spielvogel, Andrew R., V.P. & Gen. Mgr.--SuperValu, Inc.-Maine Div., Presque Isle, ME; *U.S. Public*, pg. 1540
Spiers, David, Dr., Mng. Dir.--Dynacast International Limited, Alcester, United Kingdom; *Int'l*, pg. 299
Spiers, Gary A., V.P.--Idaho Division, Boise, ID; *U.S. Public*, pg. 38
Spiess, W.H., Mng. Dir.--Saudi-Swiss Bank, Geneva, Switzerland; *Int'l*, pg. 1440
Spiewack, D., Mgr.--Protimeter Zweigniederlassung der Bowthorpe GmbH, Cologne, Germany; *Int'l*, pg. 209
Spiewak, Michael, Chm. Bd. & Chief Exec. Officer--TSE Leasing Co., New York, NY; *U.S. Private*, pg. 1025
Spiewak, Michael, Chm. Bd. & Chief Exec. Officer--Trade Show Enterprises, New York, NY; *U.S. Private*, pg. 1025
Spiewak, Michael, Chm. Bd. & Chief Exec. Officer--Trappings Co., New York, NY; *U.S. Private*, pg. 1025
Spigner, Ray, V.P.-Sls.--St. Louis Sales, Chesterfield, MO; *U.S. Public*, pg. 611
Spiker, T. Scott, Pres.--IFG Asset Management Services, Inc., Minneapolis, MN; *U.S. Public*, pg. 476
Spikesman, Roger, Mng. Dir.--WWF Paper Sales U.K., Ltd., Leatherhead, United Kingdom; *U.S. Private*, pg. 1145
Spiller, Ben M., Pres. & Chief Oper. Officer--Southern Pilot Insurance Company, Greensboro, NC; *Int'l*, pg. 346
Spillers, R.C., Pres.--Arkansas Eastman Co., Batesville, AR; *U.S. Public*, pg. 550
Spillmann, Hans Rudolf, Gen. Mgr.--Chocolat Frey AG, Buchs, Switzerland; *Int'l*, pg. 865
Spillmann, Werner, Chief Oper. Officer--Omnitechnic GmbH, Hannover, Germany; *Int'l*, pg. 610
Spillyards, Thomas W., Pres. & Chief Exec. Officer--NationsBank of Pine Bluff, Pine Bluff, AR; *U.S. Public*, pg. 1164
Spina, Jay, Gen. Mgr.--Corrugated Container Div.-Westfield Plant, Westfield, MA; *U.S. Public*, pg. 1521
Spindler, G.R., Pres.--Cyprus Amax Coal Co., Englewood, CO; *U.S. Public*, pg. 470
Spinelli, Carol, Pres.--Beldoch Popper Division, New York, NY; *U.S. Public*, pg. 520
Spinelli, Lawrence M., Pres.--Binswanger Realty Group-Midwest, Chicago, IL; *U.S. Private*, pg. 144
Spinetti, Alberto, Mng. Dir.--Valmet-Rotomec S.p.A., San Giorgio, Italy; *Int'l*, pg. 1449
Spinetto, H. Bosoni, Gen. Mgr.--ING Insurance Seguros de Vida, Buenos Aires, Argentina; *Int'l*, pg. 650
Spinetto, Hugo Bosoni, Pres.--Cigna Salud Isapre S.A., Santiago, Chile; *U.S. Public*, pg. 364
Spinner, Ernest, Gen. Mgr.--Arizona Chemical Div., Panama City, FL; *U.S. Public*, pg. 901
Spinner, J.M., Pres.--Mount Vernon Mills, Inc., Riegel Consumer Products Div., Johnston, SC; *U.S. Private*, pg. 835
Spinner, J.M., Pres.--Mount Vernon Mills, Inc., Consumer Products Div. (McCormick), McCormick, SC; *U.S. Private*, *pg. 835*
Spira, James C., Grp. Dir.--Diamond Technology Partners, Chicago, IL; *U.S. Public*, pg. 1424
Spiteri, Joe, Mgr.--Barrick Gold, Milton, Canada; *Int'l*, pg. 169
Spitler, Kenneth F., Pres.--Sysco Food Services of Houston, Inc., Houston, TX; *U.S. Public*, pg. 1551
Spitz, Ray, Plant Mgr.--AVX Raleigh Plant, Raleigh, NC; *Int'l*, pg. 775
Spitzer, Kirk, Pres.--Alfa Laval Thermal Inc., Richmond, VA; *Int'l*, pg. 1378
Spitzer, Louis, Chief Fin. Officer--WTIC, Hartford, CT; *U.S. Public*, pg. 1636
Spitznagel, John T., Pres. & Chief Oper. Officer--Roberts Laboratories, Inc., Eatontown, NJ; *U.S. Public*, pg. 1393
Spitznagel, John T., Pres. & Chief Exec. Officer--Monmouth Pharmaceutical, Ltd., Guildford, United Kingdom; *U.S. Public*, pg. 1394
Spitznagel, John T., Pres. & Chief Exec. Officer--Roberts Pharmaceutical of Canada, Oakville, Canada; *U.S. Public*, pg. 1394
Splane, H., Gen. Mgr.--Johnson Matthey Noble Metals Business Unit, Royston, United Kingdom; *Int'l*, pg. 713
Spoelder, Johan, Mng. Dir.--Dow Plastics Development AG, Taegerwilen, Switzerland; *U.S. Public*, pg. 524
Spolane, Ronald S., Chm. Bd., Pres. & Chief Exec. Officer--Sterling Electronics Corporation, Houston, TX; *U.S. Public*, pg. 1051
Sponseller, Gene B., Pres.--Warsaw Orthopedic Inc., Winona Lake, IN; *U.S. Public*, pg. 1482
Sponyoe, John V., Pres.--Lockheed Martin Federal Systems-Owego, Owego, NY; *U.S. Public*, pg. 1008
Spooner, Robert M., Chief Oper. Officer--General Trade Associates, Atlanta, GA; *U.S. Private*, pg. 448
Spore, Eric, V.P.-Mktg.--Alpha Olefins North America Inc., Houston, TX; *Int'l*, pg. 1196
Spore, Keith, Pres.--Milwaukee Journal Sentinel, Milwaukee, WI; *U.S. Private*, pg. 601
Sportello, Larry, Gen. Mgr.--Engraph Machine Group, Mount Laurel, NJ; *U.S. Public*, pg. 1486
Sprague, W.W., III, Pres.--Everglades Sugar Refinery, Inc., Clewiston, FL; *U.S. Public*, pg. 873

Sprague, William W., III, Pres. & Chief Exec. Officer--Savannah Foods & Industries, Inc., Savannah, GA; *U.S. Public*, pg. 872

Spranger, Erhard L., Mng. Dir.--General Motors de Portugal, Sociedade Anonima, Lisbon, Portugal; *U.S. Public*, pg. 722

Spratt, Q., Mng. Dir.--Hepworth Building Products International, Stocksbridge, United Kingdom; *Int'l*, pg. 615

Spratt, William, Pres.--Court Galvanizing Limited, Guelph, Canada; *Int'l*, pg. 698

Spreenberg, Robert, V.P.--Midwesco Mechanical Energy, Niles, IL; *U.S. Public*, pg. 1026

Spreeuw, ir. E., Gen. Mgr.--The MacNeal-Schwendler Co. B.V., Gouda, Netherlands; *U.S. Public*, pg. 1032

Sprengel, Paul, Mgr.--Kleber Industrie GmbH, Mettmann, Germany; *Int'l*, pg. 322

Sprengers, Frank, V.P. & Gen. Mgr.--Medtronic B.V., Kerkrade, Netherlands; *U.S. Public*, pg. 1083

Spriggs, Tony, Gen. Mgr.--Falcon-Anaheim, Anaheim, CA; *U.S. Public*, pg. 611

Sprimont, Roger, Pres.--Kvaerner Mandal A/S, Mandal, Norway; *Int'l*, pg. 769

Spring, Stevie, Agency Dir.-Y&R London--Young & Rubicam Holdings Ltd., London, United Kingdom; *U.S. Private*, pg. 1199

Springer, Allen G., Pres.--Rammer Inc., Baltimore, MD; *Int'l*, pg. 1352

Springer, Douglas D., Pres.--Columbia Services, Inc., Seattle, WA; *U.S. Public*, pg. 1742

Springer, Douglas D., Pres.--Murphey Favre, Inc., Seattle, WA; *U.S. Public*, pg. 1742

Springer, Douglas D., Pres.--Washington Mutual Life Insurance Services, Inc., Seattle, WA; *U.S. Public*, pg. 1742

Springer, George, Pres.--Universal Blueprint Paper Co., Fort Worth, TX; *U.S. Private*, pg. 1176

Springer, J. Darryl, Pres.--Major Smith Inc., New Holland, PA; *Int'l*, pg. 201

Springer, Joe, Mng. Dir.--Buckbee-Mears Europe GmbH, Mullheim-Baden, Germany; *U.S. Public*, pg. 162

Springer, Sylvia, Pres.--Axel Johnson Ore & Metals, Inc., Exton, PA; *Int'l*, pg. 710

Springer, William C., Pres.-Heinz North America--Heinz U.S.A. Div., Pittsburgh, PA; *U.S. Public*, pg. 805

Springfield, Gary, Gen. Mgr.--EDO Ceramics, Salt Lake City, UT; *U.S. Public*, pg. 542

Springman, Paul W., Pres. & Chief Oper. Officer--Shand, Morahan & Co., Inc., Evanston, IL; *U.S. Public*, pg. 1046

Springman, Robert, V.P.-CHB--Dulles Airport Office, Washington, DC; *U.S. Public*, pg. 749

Sproat, Brian, Ph.D., Dir.-Res.--Innovir GmbH, Rosdorf, Germany; *U.S. Public*, pg. 1703

Sproat, Charles, Gen. Mgr.-Opers.--Leaf Ireland Ltd., Kilcock, Ireland; *Int'l*, pg. 638

Spronck, Paul, Gen. Mgr.--Nordson European Distribution B.V., Maastricht, Netherlands; *U.S. Public*, pg. 1189

Spruell, J.R., Chief Exec. Officer--GKN Bound Brook Ltd., Lichfield, United Kingdom; *Int'l*, pg. 534

Spruell, J.R., Chief Exec.--GKN Powder Metallurgy Division, Lichfield, United Kingdom; *Int'l*, pg. 534

Spruijt, Herman P., Chm. Bd. & Chief Exec. Officer--Elsevier Science (International), Amsterdam, Netherlands; *Int'l*, pg. 1099

Spruill, John, Chm. Bd.--Alcon Surgical, Fort Worth, TX; *Int'l*, pg. 916

Spruit, G.M.J.M., Mng. Dir.--Geesink B.V., Emmeloord, Netherlands; *Int'l*, pg. 1066

Spruit, Hans, Reg. Mgr.-Europe--qad.europe b.v., Hoofddorp, Netherlands; *U.S. Public*, pg. 1345

Spruit, Hans, Reg. Mgr. Europe--qad.ab, Sollentuna, Sweden; *U.S. Public*, pg. 1345

Spruit, Hans, Reg. Mgr.-Europe--qad.germany GmbH, Neu-Isenburg, Germany; *U.S. Public*, pg. 1345

Spruit, Hans, Reg. Mgr.-Europe--qad.united kingdom ltd., Leatherhead, United Kingdom; *U.S. Public*, pg. 1345

Spruit, Hans, Reg. Mgr.--qad.france eurl, Noisy-le-Grand, France; *U.S. Public*, pg. 1345

Sprull, Larry, V.P.--Orkin Plantscaping, Atlanta, GA; *U.S. Public*, pg. 1405

Spungin, Lawrence D., V.P. & Pres.-Universal Studios Devel.--Universal Studios, Inc., Universal City, CA; *Int'l*, pg. 1215

Spur, G., Chief Oper. Officer--VW-Gesellschaft fur Technische Datanverarbeitungssysteme mbH, Berlin, Germany; *Int'l*, pg. 1474

Spurgin, Ralph, Pres.--Alliance Data Systems, Columbus, OH; *U.S. Public*, pg. 995

Spurr, Ronald M., Mgr.-Bus.--Ventura County Star-Free Press, Ventura, CA; *U.S. Public*, pg. 1448

Sqali, Omar, Chm.--Klem EURO RSCG, Casablanca, Morocco; *Int'l*, pg. 603

Squadere, Ron, Supervisor-Property & Casualty Claims--Willis Corroon Administrative Services Corporation, Albany, NY; *Int'l*, pg. 1505

Squbini, Luciano, Pres.--Saipem S.p.A., Milan, Italy; *Int'l*, pg. 428

Squeri, Charles, Chm. Bd. & Chief Exec. Officer--Squeri Foodservice, Cincinnati, OH; *U.S. Public*, pg. 918

Squicciarini, Arthur M., Pres.--Dimetrics, Inc., Davidson, NC; *U.S. Public*, pg. 308

Squier-Dow, Mae H., Pres.--ACC TeleCom, Rochester, NY; *U.S. Public*, pg. 3

Squier, David L., Pres. & Chief Exec. Officer--Howmet Corporation, Greenwich, CT; *U.S. Private*, pg. 213

Squier, David L., Pres. & Chief Exec. Officer--Howmet Corporation, Greenwich, CT; *U.S. Public*, pg. 1597

Srednicki, Richard, Pres. & Chief Exec. Officer--AT&T Universal Card Services Corp., Jacksonville, FL; *U.S. Public*, pg. 11

Sreesankar, R., Mgr.--Baring Asset Management (India), Mumbai, India; *Int'l*, pg. 648

Sret, Albert, Pres.--Mueller's Muehle GmbH, Gelsenkirchen, Germany; *Int'l*, pg. 896

Sriffin, C. N., Gen. Mgr.--Kodak Mexicana SA de C.V., Mexico, Mexico; *U.S. Public*, pg. 554

Srinivasan, M., Mng. Dir.--Vickers Systems International Ltd., Mumbai, India; *U.S. Public*, pg. 25

Sroufe, Parker, Pres.--Esca Corporation, Bellevue, WA; *Int'l*, pg. 53

Srrickland, David M., Chief Exec. Officer--Barnett Investments Inc., Jacksonville, FL; *U.S. Public*, pg. 1162

St. Amour, Andre, Pres. & Chief Oper. Officer--National Reinsurance Company of Canada, Toronto, Canada; *U.S. Private*, pg. 443

St. Amour, Sam, V.P. & Gen. Mgr.--Electro-Tec Corp., Blacksburg, VA; *U.S. Public*, pg. 946

St. Jacques, R. J., Chief Exec. Officer--ING America Life, Chicago, IL; *Int'l*, pg. 647

St. Jean, Rick, Area Foreman--Talisman Energy Inc., Lac La Biche, Canada; *Int'l*, pg. 1352

St. John, John, Pres.--Baldwin Stobb San Bernardino, San Bernardino, CA; *U.S. Public*, pg. 170

St. John, Mike, V.P.-Sls.--All Star Gas Co.-Region XIV, Lebanon, MO; *U.S. Private*, pg. 36

St. Johnson, Sir Kerry, Chm. Bd.--P&O Bulk Carriers Ltd. (Bermuda), London, United Kingdom; *Int'l*, pg. 1033

St. Louis, Paul, Pres.--BPCO, Dorval, Canada; *Int'l*, pg. 453

St. Mark, Carole F., Chief Oper. Officer--Ameriscribe Corporation, New York, NY; *U.S. Public*, pg. 1303

St. Onge, John, V.P.--Mall St. Matthews Corporation, Louisville, KY; *U.S. Public*, pg. 1408

St. Onge, John, V.P. & Gen. Mgr.--Rouse Service (Canada) Limited, Etobicoke, Canada; *U.S. Public*, pg. 1409

St. Pierre, Hugues, V.P.-Admin. & Fin.--Quebec-Telephone, Rimouski, Canada; *U.S. Public*, pg. 697

St. Romain, Frank, Chief Exec. Officer--SCP Pool Corporation, Covington, LA; *U.S. Private*, pg. 249

Staab, Robert J., Pres.--Candle-Lite, A Lancaster Colony Co., Cincinnati, OH; *U.S. Public*, pg. 976

Staab, Robert J., Pres.--Indiana Glass Company, Sapulpa, OK; *U.S. Public*, pg. 977

Staaf, G., Gen. Mgr.--Rewo Chemische Werke GmbH, Steinau, Germany; *U.S. Public*, pg. 1774

Staaf, Ove, Mng. Dir.--Skandia Marine Insurance Company (UK) Ltd., London, United Kingdom; *Int'l*, pg. 1257

Staal, A.J., Chm.--ING (U.S.) Capital Holdings, New York, NY; *Int'l*, pg. 648

Staal, M. F., Chief Oper. Officer--Croner Publications, Ltd., Kingston upon Thames, United Kingdom; *Int'l*, pg. 1514

Staaterman, Robyn, Pres.--CT Corporation System, New York, NY; *Int'l*, pg. 1513

Stabell-Johansen, Tore, Managing Dir.--Viking Fottoy A.S., Oslo, Norway; *Int'l*, pg. 1011

Stabosz, Thomas F., V.P. & Gen. Mgr.--Joslyn Power Products Corporation, Alsip, IL; *U.S. Public*, pg. 482

Stabosz, Tom, Plant Mgr.--Olean Plant, Olean, NY; *U.S. Public*, pg. 443

Stacey, Craig, Branch Mgr.--Jaco Electronics, Inc., Eden Prairie, MN; *U.S. Public*, pg. 921

Stacey, David, Dir.--Royal Insurance Service Co. (Isle of Man) Ltd., Douglas, United Kingdom; *Int'l*, pg. 1130

Stacey, Ronald L., Exec. V.P.--Western Group, Sherman Oaks, CA; *U.S. Public*, pg. 650

Stach, Manfred, Dr., Gen. Mgr.--Deutsche Unilever Gmbh, Hamburg, Germany; *Int'l*, pg. 1436

Stach, Phil, Gen. Mgr.--Servitex, Inc., Virginia Beach, VA; *U.S. Private*, pg. 782

Stachelek, Norman, Admin.--Mountain View Healthcare, Windsor, CT; *U.S. Public*, pg. 1714

Stachofsky, Bob, V.P.--Inland Empire Division, Spokane, WA; *U.S. Public*, pg. 38

Stachowiak, Paul A., AIA, Pres.--Giffels Hoyem Basso, Inc., Troy, MI; *U.S. Private*, pg. 452

Stachura, Robert D., V.P. & Exec. Mgr.--Douglas & Lomason Company, Red Oak, IA; *Int'l*, pg. 830

Stachura, Robert D., V.P.-Mfg. & Exec. Mgr.--Douglas & Lomason Company, Columbus, NE; *Int'l*, pg. 830

Stachura, Robert D., V.P. & Exec. Mgr.--Douglas & Lomason Company, Troy, MO; *Int'l*, pg. 830

Stachura, Robert D., V.P. & Exec. Mgr.--Douglas & Lomason Company, Excelsior Springs, MO; *Int'l*, pg. 830

Stack, Chuck, Admin.--Hillhaven Highland House, Highland, CA; *U.S. Public*, pg. 1713

Stack, Jackie, Gen. Mgr.--Edelman Worldwide China, Guangzhou, China; *U.S. Private*, pg. 363

Stack, Robert B., Pres.--Xerox Financial Services Life Insurance Co., Oak Brook Terrace, IL; *U.S. Public*, pg. 1785

Stackhouse, William, District Mgr.--Circle Freight International USA, Kansas City, MO; *U.S. Public*, pg. 371

Stackler, Olivier, Chief Oper. Officer--Electrolux & Cie SNC, Cergy-Pontoise, France; *Int'l*, pg. 441

Stacy, Mike, Plant Superintendant--General Shale Products Corp., Marion, VA; *Int'l*, pg. 844

Stacy, T.D., Chm. Bd. & Pres.--Amoco Canada Resources Ltd., Calgary, Canada; *U.S. Public*, pg. 103

Stade, Gabi, Mgr.-Country--Colgate-Palmolive AG, Zurich, Switzerland; *U.S. Public*, pg. 398

Stade, Myra, Admin.--Las Vegas Convalescent Center, Las Vegas, NV; *U.S. Public*, pg. 1714

Stade, Yngve, Pres.--Kamyr AB, Karlstad, Sweden; *Int'l*, pg. 771

Stade, Yngve, Pres.--Stora Corporate Research, Falun, Sweden; *Int'l*, pg. 1303

Stadler, Gerald, Pres.--National Pipe Line Co., Escanaba, MI; *U.S. Public*, pg. 1259

Stadler, Gerard A., Pres.--Ohio Crankshaft Div., Cleveland, OH; *U.S. Public*, pg. 1258

Stadler, Werner, Mng. Dir.--Corning GmbH, Wiesbaden, Germany; *U.S. Public*, pg. 449

Staebler, Tom, Pres.--Special Editions, Ltd., Chicago, IL; *U.S. Public*, pg. 1310

Staecker, Detlev, Exec. V.P. & Gen. Mgr.--Deutsche Bank AG (New York Branch), New York, NY; *Int'l*, pg. 403

Staes, Charles W., Pres.--Sysco Food Services Chicago, Inc., Des Plaines, IL; *U.S. Public*, pg. 1551

Staff, Joel V., Pres.--Baker Hughes Drilling Technologies, Houston, TX; *U.S. Public*, pg. 166

Staffa, Donald J., Pres.--Accelerated Claims Processing, Inc., New York, NY; *U.S. Public*, pg. 802

Staffa, Donald J., Chm. Bd. & Pres.--Quality Medical Adjudication, Inc., Rancho Cordova, CA; *U.S. Public*, pg. 802

Stafford-Deitsch, Andrew, Chief Oper. Officer--J. Rothschild Wolfensohn & Co., London, United Kingdom; *Int'l*, pg. 1178

Stafford, A.J., Chief Oper. Officer--Cuprinol Limited, Frome, United Kingdom; *Int'l*, pg. 1501

Stafford, Gerry S., Pres. & Chief Exec. Officer--Commercial Union of Canada Holdings Ltd, Toronto, Canada; *Int'l*, pg. 308

Stafford, Gerry S., Pres. & Chief Exec. Officer--Commercial Union Assurance Company of Canada, Toronto, Canada; *Int'l*, pg. 308

Stafford, Raymond, Chief Oper. Officer--Tosara Group, Dublin, Ireland; *U.S. Public*, pg. 670

Stafford, Robert G., Pres.--Telsmith, Inc., Mequon, WI; *U.S. Public*, pg. 141

Stage, Jon D., Gen. Mgr.--Plastic Colorants Division, Stryker, OH; *U.S. Public*, pg. 619

Stagg, Rosemary, Mng. Dir.--Longman Paul Ltd., Takapuna, New Zealand; *Int'l*, pg. 1025

Stahelin, T., Chief Oper. Officer--HOLAD Holding & Administration AG, Basel, Switzerland; *Int'l*, pg. 1475

Stahl, Jack, Pres.--Coca-Cola USA, Atlanta, GA; *U.S. Public*, pg. 392

Stahl, Keith L., Gen. Mgr.--Strandflex Division, Oriskany, NY; *U.S. Public*, pg. 780

Stahl, Sigfried, G.M.--Newport Electronics GmbH, Deckenpfronn, Germany; *U.S. Private*, pg. 816

Stahlman, Paul, Reg. V.P.-Sls.--All Star Gas Co.-Region III, Lebanon, MO; *U.S. Private*, pg. 35

Stahlschmidt, Bengt, Chief Oper. Officer--QMS International GmbH, Munich, Germany; *U.S. Public*, pg. 1346

Stahmann, D., Chief Oper. Officer--Hoogovens Aluminium Huttenwerk GmbH, Voerde, Germany; *Int'l*, pg. 755

Stahr, E., Mng. Dir.--NTO, Hannover, Germany; *Int'l*, pg. 1145

Stahura, John, Pres.--Vanner, Inc., Hilliard, OH; *Int'l*, pg. 449

Staiano, Edward F., Pres.--Motorola General Systems Group, Schaumburg, IL; *U.S. Public*, pg. 1137

Stainforth, Daniel E., Mng. Dir.--General Motors Luxembourg Operations S.A., Bascharage, Luxembourg; *U.S. Public*, pg. 723

Stair, Charles W., Chm. Bd.--ServiceMaster Diversified Health Services, Inc., Memphis, TN; *U.S. Public*, pg. 1462

Stair, G.M., Div. Mgr.--Ohio Edison Co. Western Div., Sandusky, OH; *U.S. Public*, pg. 645

Stait-Gardner, Zane, Pres.--ManuLife (International) P & C Ltd., Hamilton, Bermuda; *Int'l*, pg. 841

Stajkowski, Michael, Plant Mgr.--Bundy Corporation, Cartersville Plant, Cartersville, GA; *Int'l*, pg. 1340

Stajkowski, Ronald F., Pres. & Chief Exec. Officer--Beverly Trust Company, Oak Lawn, IL; *U.S. Public*, pg. 227

Stak, Gregory, Natl. Sls. Mgr.--R.H. Forschner Division, Shelton, CT; *U.S. Public*, pg. 1544

Staker, Thomas, Sr. V.P.-Opers.--Big O Tires Incorporated, Englewood, CO; *U.S. Public*, pg. 1553

Stakey, Richard C., Pres.--Pulte Colorado Division, Aurora, CO; *U.S. Public*, pg. 1344

Stakkestad, Hand K., Gen. Mgr.--Kvaerner Eureka, Bryne Division, Bryne, Norway; *Int'l*, pg. 767

Stalberg, Carl-Eric, Pres.--JM Byggnads och Fastighets AB, Stockholm, Sweden; *Int'l*, pg. 1260

Stalem, Sverre, Mgr.--Permipipe Titanium A/S (PTI), Glomfjord, Norway; *U.S. Public*, pg. 1662

Staley, George R., Pres.--Toys "R" Us International, Paramus, NJ; *U.S. Public*, pg. 1626

Stalkamp, William J., Chm. Bd. & Chief Exec. Officer--Mellon PSFS, Philadelphia, PA; *U.S. Public*, pg. 1085

Stallard, Hubert R., Pres. & Chief Exec. Officer--Bell Atlantic-VA, Richmond, VA; *U.S. Public*, pg. 203

Stallkamp, James, Pres.--Bankers Trust (Delaware), Wilmington, DE; *U.S. Public*, pg. 185

Stallman, Keith, Pres.--SAIC, Sacramento, CA; *U.S. Private*, pg. 976

Stallman, Kenneth, V.P. & Mgr.--Texas Bank N.A., Houston, TX; *U.S. Public*, pg. 626

Stalmans, F. R., Mng. Dir.--N.V. Red Band S.A., Turnhout, Belgium; *Int'l*, pg. 245

Stalstrom, Yngve, Chief Oper. Officer--Gambro A/S, Horten, Norway; *Int'l*, pg. 667

Stalvey, Rupert A., Pres.--First Southeast Insurance Agency, Conway, SC; *U.S. Public*, pg. 634

Stamatiade, Pericles P., Grp. Chm.--Johnson & Johnson Hellas S.A., Athens, Greece; *U.S. Public*, pg. 930

Stamford, Christopher, Rep.--Sanpaolo-Stockholm Representative Office, Stockholm, Sweden; *Int'l*, pg. 692

Stamm, James, Pres.-Specialized Transportation Grp.--Atlas Specialized Transportation, Evansville, IN; *U.S. Private*, pg. 97

Stamm, Peter, Co.-Chief Oper. Officer--Kohle-Kontor-Saar GmbH, Saarbruecken, Germany; *Int'l*, pg. 1167

Stammer, Geo, Mng. Dir.--SKF de Mexico, S.A. de C.V., Mexico, Mexico; *Int'l*, pg. 1158

Stamp, P., Gen. Mgr.--Parker Hannifin (U.K.) Ltd. Instrumentation Products Div., Barnstaple, United Kingdom; *U.S. Public*, pg. 1264

Stamp, Philip B., Pres.-Fluid Connectors--Parker Hannifin Corporation, Hemel Hempstead, United Kingdom; *U.S. Public*, pg. 1263

Stampe, Dieter, Dir.--Tetra-Pak Romont SA, Romont, Switzerland; *Int'l*, pg. 1380

Stamper, Bradlee F., Pres.--The Fifth Third Bank of Northern Kentucky, Florence, KY; *U.S. Public*, pg. 621

Stamper, Gordon, Mgr.-Sls.--PENCO-Pennsylvania, Harrisburg, PA; *Int'l*, pg. 1508

Stamper, Jerry L., Pres.--L3 Communications Telemetry & Instrumentation Div., San Diego, CA; *U.S. Private*, pg. 639
Stancil, Dave, V.P.-Natl. Sls.--U.S. Divers, Santa Ana, CA; *U.S. Private*, pg. 1125
Standaert, Randall, Mgr.-Sls.--PENCO-Wyoming, Worland, WY; *Int'l*, pg. 1508
Standish, C., Chief Exec. Officer--SBC Australia Limited, Sydney, Australia; *Int'l*, pg. 1330
Standring, G.B., Mng. Dir.--Three Quays Marine Services Ltd., London, United Kingdom; *Int'l*, pg. 1035
Stanes, P.J.D., Chm. Bd.--Feltrax International, Inc., Auckland, New Zealand; *Int'l*, pg. 130
Stanford, Mike, Gen. Mgr.--Hano Document Printers, Inc., Mount Olive, IL; *U.S. Public*, pg. 1686
Stang, Olav, Pres.--Nokia Mobile Phones Japan K.K., Tokyo, Japan; *Int'l*, pg. 952
Stangel, Michael, V.P.--Professional Div., Melrose Park, IL; *U.S. Public*, pg. 37
Stanghellini, M., Sls. Mgr.-Europe--OCG Microelectronic Materials N.V., Saint-Niklaas, Belgium; *U.S. Public*, pg. 1220
Stangl, Jim, V.P.--Wilsey Foods, Inc., Saint Joseph, MO; *Int'l*, pg. 879
Stangoe, I., Area Mgr.--TML Metrology Centre for Scotland, Glasgow, United Kingdom; *U.S. Public*, pg. 260
Stanhope, Phillip, Dir.-Corp. Commun.--Titan Wheel Corporation, Walcott, IA; *U.S. Public*, pg. 1618
Stanlake, Robert C., Pres.--Westshore Terminals Ltd., Delta, Canada; *Int'l*, pg. 1491
Stanley, A. Jack, Chm. Bd. & Chief Exec. Officer--The M.W. Kellogg Company, Houston, TX; *U.S. Public*, pg. 528
Stanley, Colin, Plant Mgr.--Weber Marking Systems Canada ltd., Mississauga, Canada; *U.S. Private*, pg. 1157
Stanley, Jeffrey L., Mgr.--Home Telephone Co. of Pittsboro, Inc., Pittsboro, IN; *U.S. Public*, pg. 1571
Stanley, Philip, Chief Oper. Officer--Opp Micolas Mills Inc., Opp, AL; *U.S. Public*, pg. 933
Stanley, Ron, Sr. V.P. & Gen. Mgr.--Royal Bank of Canada, London, United Kingdom; *Int'l*, pg. 1131
Stanley, Ronald G., Pres.--Landstar Express America, Inc., Charlotte, NC; *U.S. Public*, pg. 978
Stanley, Winford E., Chm. Bd.--First Bank of Stuart, Stuart, VA; *U.S. Public*, pg. 1039
Stansfeld, A., Mng. Dir.--Pilatus Britten-Norman Ltd., Bembridge, United Kingdom; *Int'l*, pg. 998
Stanton, David T., Pres.--Beverly National Bank, Wilmington, IL; *U.S. Public*, pg. 227
Stanton, F. Ronald, V.P. & Gen Mgr.-Sls. & Mktg.--Allen & Hanburys, Research Triangle Park, NC; *Int'l*, pg. 552
Stanton, Peter M., Pres.--Intercomp Resource Development & Engineering (Canada) Ltd., Calgary, Canada; *U.S. Public*, pg. 1444
Stanton, W., Mgr.-Mktg.--Truck Parts Division, Galesburg, MI; *U.S. Public*, pg. 558
Stanulonis, John, Gen. Mgr.--The Humphrey Chemical Company, Inc., North Haven, CT; *U.S. Public*, pg. 297
Stanulonis, John, Gen. Mgr.--Heico Chemicals, Inc., Delaware Water Gap, PA; *U.S. Public*, pg. 297
Stanutz, Nicholas G., Pres.--The Huntington Acceptance Company, Pittsburgh, PA; *U.S. Public*, pg. 850
Stanway, W., Chm. & Grp. Mng. Dir.--London & Edinburgh Insurance Group Limited, Worthing, United Kingdom; *U.S. Public*, pg. 795
Stanziale, Ronald C., Chief Fin. Officer & Sr. V.P.--Willis Faber North America, Inc.-New York, New York, NY; *Int'l*, pg. 1503
Stanzione, Dan, Pres.--Lucent Technologies, Network Systems Div., Warren, NJ; *U.S. Public*, pg. 1017
Stanzione, Daniel C., Pres.--Bell Labs, Murray Hill, NJ; *U.S. Public*, pg. 1018
Staple, Edmund W., Pres.--Cherry Textron, Santa Ana, CA; *U.S. Public*, pg. 1589
Staples, Brian, Mng. Dir.--Tarmac Construction Limited, Wolverhampton, United Kingdom; *Int'l*, pg. 1355
Stapleton, Gregory, Pres.--OEM Group, Martinsville, IN; *U.S. Public*, pg. 787
Stapleton, H., Mng. Dir.--Sea Oil Homco Ltd., Aberdeen, United Kingdom; *Int'l*, pg. 1034
Stapleton, Nigel, Chm.--Reed International P.L.C., London, United Kingdom; *Int'l*, pg. 1093
Stapleton, Nigel, Chm. & Pres.--Reed Elsevier Inc., New York, NY; *Int'l*, pg. 1095
Stapleton, Nigel, Chm.--Reed Technology and Information Services Inc., Horsham, PA; *Int'l*, pg. 1096
Stapleton, Nigel, Chm.--LEXIS-NEXIS, Miamisburg, OH; *Int'l*, *pg. 1096*
Stapor, Ed, Mng. Dir.--Lally, McFarland & Pantello, Toronto, Canada; *Int'l*, pg. 603
Stapor, Edward, Mng. Dir. & V.P.--Lally, McFarland & Pantello Advertising Canada Ltd., Montreal, Canada; *Int'l*, pg. 603
Stappen, P., Mgr.--ING Bank Frankfurt, Frankfurt/Main, Germany; *Int'l*, pg. 649
Stara, Friedrich, Pres. & Chief Exec. Officer--Henkel Austria Group, Vienna, Austria; *Int'l*, pg. 611
Starcher, David L., Pres. & Gen. Mgr.--Magna Division, Elizabethtown, KY; *U.S. Public*, pg. 575
Starck, Henri, Chief Exec. Officer--Thomainfor, Velizy-Villacoublay, France; *Int'l*, pg. 1383
Stark, Arnold, V.P. & G.M.--Freudenberg Nonwovens Inc., Cornwall, Canada; *Int'l*, pg. 506
Stark, David, Pres. & Gen. Mgr.--Datatrol Transaction Terminals, Minnetonka, MN; *U.S. Private*, pg. 312
Stark, Jack, Plant Mgr.--VARI-FORM, Strathroy, Canada; *Int'l*, pg. 1341
Stark, Peter, Pres.--Motoren-Werke Mannheim AG, Mannheim, Germany; *Int'l*, pg. 408
Stark, Robert, Chief Exec. Officer--San Gabriel Valley Medical Center, San Gabriel, CA; *U.S. Private*, pg. 1118
Stark, Walter, Mgr.-Norelco Razor Div.--Razor Div., Stamford, CT; *Int'l*, pg. 1054
Starke, Linda, Gen. Mgr.--Central States Multiplex, Dewey, OK; *U.S. Private*, pg. 16
Starke, Peter J., Mng. Dir.--Elektro Metall Export Gmbh, Ingolstadt, Germany; *U.S. Private*, pg. 313
Starke, W.M., Pres.--Invesco Capital Management, Atlanta, GA; *Int'l*, pg. 685
Starkey, A.R., Chm. Bd.--L.A. Rumbold Limited, Camberley, United Kingdom; *Int'l*, pg. 216
Starkey, Jack, Gen. Mgr.--Reeves Rubber, Albertville, AL; *Int'l*, pg. 127
Starkey, Tim, Pres.--Komag Material Technology Inc., Santa Rosa, CA; *U.S. Public*, pg. 966
Starks, Daniel J., Chief Exec. Officer--Daig Corporation, Minnetonka, MN; *U.S. Public*, pg. 1428
Starling, D.M., Mng. Dir.--Kmart Far East Ltd., Hong Kong, Hong Kong; *U.S. Public*, pg. 963
Starling, H. Ray, Pres.--HEI Power Corp., Honolulu, HI; *U.S. Public*, pg. 800
Starnes, Billy, Pres.--Gold Lance, Inc., Houston, TX; *U.S. Public*, pg. 1625
Starnes, J., Exec. V.P. & Gen. Mgr.--Equifax Government & Special Services, Washington, DC; *U.S. Public*, pg. 588
Starnini, Dr. Giorgio, Mng. Dir. & Gen. Mgr.--SPICA S.p.A., Livorno, Italy; *Int'l*, pg. 481
Starr, Bill E., Exec. V.P.--Transportation Division, Chicago, IL; *U.S. Public*, pg. 663
Starr, F. B., Pres.--Thomasville Furniture Industries, Inc., Thomasville, NC; *U.S. Public*, pg. 688
Starr, T., Chief Exec. Officer--Bowthorpe EMP Limited, Brighton, United Kingdom; *Int'l*, pg. 207
Stas, J., Mng. Dir.--Morgan Thermal Ceramics GmbH, Wiesbaden, Germany; *Int'l*, pg. 894
Stasiak, Ernestd, Mng. Dir.--Gestetner Colombia S.A., Bogota, Colombia; *Int'l*, pg. 1115
Staskelunas, David, Gen. Mgr.--Tranter Inc.-Edgefield Div., Edgefield, SC; *U.S. Public*, pg. 522
Statham, Allan D., Mgr.-Works--Detrick Refractory Fibers, Inc., Ellisville, MS; *U.S. Public*, pg. 761
Statler, Benjamin, Sr. V.P.--Consolidated Coal Co., Moundsville, WV; *U.S. Public*, pg. 531
Statler, Benjamin, Sr. V.P.-Mining--Consolidation Coal Co.-Eastern Region, Washington, PA; *U.S. Public*, pg. 531
Statler, Gerard, Pres.--Cleveland City Forge, Cleveland, OH; *U.S. Public*, pg. 1258
Staton, B. Gene, Pres. & Chief Exec. Officer--Morrilton Security Bank, N.A., Morrilton, AR; *U.S. Public*, pg. 630
Staton, Mark, Gen. Mgr.-UK & Ireland--Polarcup United Kingdom Ltd., Portadown, United Kingdom; *Int'l*, pg. 638
Staton, Mark, Gen. Mgr.-UK & Ireland--Polarcup United Kingdom Ltd., Gosport, United Kingdom; *Int'l*, pg. 639
Staubell, Paul, Pres.--Taugbol & Overland A/S, Oslo, Norway; *Int'l*, pg. 42
Stauber, Ed, Chief Oper. Officer--Bio-Rad Laboratories Pty. Limited, Regents Park, Australia; *U.S. Public*, pg. 230
Stauffer, Clay W., Publr.--The Holland Sentinel, Holland, MI; *U.S. Private*, pg. 995
Stauffer, Heinrich, Mng. Dir.--Sulzer Sistemas e Instalaciones (Chile) S.A., Santiago, Chile; *Int'l*, pg. 1306
Stauffer, Tom, Pres.--Renaissance International Hotels, Cleveland, OH; *U.S. Public*, pg. 1048
Stauffer, Tom, Pres.--Ramada International Hotels & Resorts, Cleveland, OH; *U.S. Public*, pg. 1048
Stauffer, William H., Publr.--The Ardmore Daily Ardmoreite, Ardmore, OK; *U.S. Private*, pg. 995
Stauner, James P., Corp. V.P.--V. Mueller, Deerfield, IL; *U.S. Public*, pg. 44
Staunton, Paddy, Dir.-Fin.--BCB Beverages Limited, Ringaskiddy, Ireland; *Int'l*, pg. 338
Stavbli, O., Chief Oper. Officer--Viscosuisse S.A., Emmen, Switzerland; *Int'l*, pg. 1114
Stavinoha, Rayburn F., Pres.--Sentry Polymers, Inc., Freeport, TX; *U.S. Public*, pg. 1357
Stavish, T.M., Pres.--Akzo Electronics Materials Co., Colorado Springs, CO; *Int'l*, pg. 48
Stavley, Robert E., Pres.--Omni Business Systems, Inc., Melbourne, FL; *U.S. Public*, pg. 864
Stavropoulos, William S., Pres. & Chief Exec. Officer--Essex Chemical Corporation, Clifton, NJ; *U.S. Public*, pg. 523
Stawarer, Mike, Mgr.--Anixter Calgary, Calgary, Canada; *U.S. Public*, pg. 115
Stawasz, Cherie, Pres. & Partner--Stawasz & Partners/Health Care Communications, New York, NY; *U.S. Private*, pg. 599
Stawecki, John, Mgr.--Stewart Smith East, Inc., Farmington, CT; *Int'l*, pg. 1508
Steadman, John H., Pres.--Norandal U.S.A., Newport, AR; *Int'l*, pg. 434
Steagall, Allan J., Pres.--Nevada Cement Co., Fernley, NV; *U.S. Public*, pg. 323
Steagall, Allan J., Pres.--Mountain Cement Company, Laramie, WY; *U.S. Public*, pg. 323
Stearley, Doug, Chief Exec. Officer--Industrial Custom Products L.L.C., Minneapolis, MN; *U.S. Private*, pg. 352
Stearley, Doug, Chief Exec. Officer--We Vac Plastics, Elkhart, IN; *U.S. Private*, pg. 352
Stearns, Clive, Chief Exec. Officer--John Crane Polymer Division, Abingdon, United Kingdom; *Int'l*, pg. 1338
Stearns, F. Cole, V.P.-Project Devel.--Marketing & Project Development, Erie, PA; *U.S. Public*, pg. 1794
Stearns, Richard E., Pres.--Lenox Products Group, Lawrenceville, NJ; *U.S. Public*, pg. 261
Stebbing, H.D.C., Mng. Dir.--Lloyds Bank Commercial Properties Ltd., London, United Kingdom; *Int'l*, pg. 813
Stebenne, Roger, Mgr.-Opers.--Smith Valve Corporation, Whitinsville, MA; *U.S. Public*, pg. 1651
Stec, Bob, Pres.--Stetson Hat Co., Saint Joseph, MO; *U.S. Private*, pg. 510
Stecher, Harry, Pres.--Sears Portrait Studios, Saint Louis, MO; *U.S. Public*, pg. 283
Stecher, Harry, Pres.--CPI Corp., Brampton, Canada; *U.S. Public*, pg. 283
Stecher, W., Mng. Dir.--Georg Fischer Verkehrstechnik GmbH, Singen, Germany; *Int'l*, pg. 488
Steck, Brian J., Chm. Bd. & Chief Exec. Officer--The Nesbitt Thomson Corporation Limited, Toronto, Canada; *Int'l*, pg. 153
Steck, Joachim, Dr., Mng. Dir.--Metallbank GmbH, Frankfurt/Main, Germany; *Int'l*, pg. 861
Steckel, Curt, Chief Fin. Officer--Hayes Brake, Mequon, WI; *U.S. Private*, pg. 299
Steckel, Marie Monique, Pres.--France Telecom Inc., New York, NY; *Int'l*, pg. 504
Steckel, Peter, Div. Mgr.--Mitsui Foods, Inc., Western Div., Burlingame, CA; *Int'l*, pg. 879
Stecko, Paul T., Pres. & Chief Exec. Officer--Tenneco Packaging, Evanston, IL; *U.S. Public*, pg. 1579
Steed, Frank, Pres.--American Tourister, Inc., Warren, RI; *U.S. Public*, pg. 1430
Steed, J., Mng. Dir.--Riley Advertising (Bristol) Ltd., Bristol, United Kingdom; *Int'l*, pg. 1117
Steedman, Ralph B., Pres.--Moore Business Forms & Systems Ltd., Mississauga, Canada; *Int'l*, pg. 889
Steegh, H.P.R., Mgr.--CMV Crediet Maatschappij Venlo N.V. Steegh Assurantien B.V., Venlo, Netherlands; *Int'l*, pg. 9
Steegmans, Jos, Gen. Mgr.--E.S.P. Europese Staalprefabricatie N.V., Geel, Belgium; *Int'l*, pg. 79
Steel, K.W., Chm.--Morgan Grenfell Australia Ltd., Sydney, Australia; *Int'l*, pg. 406
Steel, R. D., Gen. Mgr.--Australian Mutual Provident Society, Wan Chai, Hong Kong; *Int'l*, pg. 100
Steele, A.L., Chief Oper. Officer--Makro Self Service Wholesalers Ltd., Manchester, United Kingdom; *Int'l*, pg. 1156
Steele, Denny, Pres.--Inteplex, Orange, CA; *U.S. Public*, pg. 215
Steele, Don, Chief Oper. Officer--River Ranch - Southwest, Dallas, TX; *Int'l*, pg. 491
Steele, G.W., Chief Oper. Officer--Huwood Electric Ltd., Newcastle upon Tyne, United Kingdom; *Int'l*, pg. 473
Steele, Gary, V.P.-Sls.--Loctite Canada Inc., Mississauga, Canada; *Int'l*, pg. 611
Steele, George, Mgr.--Furman Wholesale Lumber Branch, Stafford, TX; *U.S. Private*, pg. 431
Steele, Graham, Mng. Dir.--Superdrug Stores PLC, Croydon, United Kingdom; *Int'l*, pg. 734
Steele, J.R., Chm. Bd.--P&O European Transport Services Ltd., Altrincham, United Kingdom; *Int'l*, pg. 1033
Steele, Michael A., Sr. V.P. & Gen. Mgr.--Destination Products International, Inc., Toronto, Canada; *Int'l*, pg. 338
Steele, Randall, Mng. Dir.--ISS Southern Management Company, Chattanooga, TN; *Int'l*, pg. 656
Steele, Ray, Gen. Mgr.--The Fresno Bee, Fresno, CA; *U.S. Public*, pg. 1065
Steele, Steve, Gen. Mgr.--Hamilton Beach-Proctor Silex, Washington, NC; *U.S. Public*, pg. 1149
Steele, William, Pres.--Banc One Building Management Corporation, Milwaukee, WI; *U.S. Public*, pg. 173
Steen, Arvid, Plant Mgr.--Elkem Rana, Mo, Norway; *Int'l*, pg. 447
Steen, Erik, Chief Oper. Officer--Novo Nordisk Comercio de Produtos Farmaceuticos, Lda, Rio de Mouro, Portugal; *Int'l*, pg. 988
Steen, Thomas, Pres.--Cybus Capital Markets, Des Moines, IA; *U.S. Private*, pg. 769
Steenbeke, Francis, V.P.--Veeco GmbH, Munich, Germany; *U.S. Public*, pg. 1711
Steenbeke, Francis, V.P.--Veeco Instruments Ltd., Watford, United Kingdom; *U.S. Public*, pg. 1711
Steenbeke, Francis, V.P.--Nihon Veeco K.K., Tokyo, Japan; *U.S. Public*, pg. 1711
Steenbeke, Francis, V.P.--Veeco S.A., Dourdan, France; *U.S. Public*, pg. 1711
Steenbergen, James, Pres., Chief Exec. Officer & Chief Fin. Officer--AMATI Communications Corp., San Jose, CA; *U.S. Public*, pg. 1585
Steenhagen, James, V.P. & Gen. Mgr.--APV Chemical Machinery, Inc., Process Systems Div., Saginaw, MI; *Int'l*, pg. 1240
Steenkist, Piet, Pres.--CCMP N.V., Antwerp, Belgium; *Int'l*, pg. 678
Steenkist, Piet, Pres.--Hitma BV, Uithoorn, Netherlands; *Int'l*, pg. 678
Steer, Andrew, Country Dir.--The World Bank, Hanoi, Vietnam; *U.S. Private*, pg. 1190
Steer, Brian L., Pres.--Zimmer International, S.A., Brussels, Belgium; *U.S. Public*, pg. 257
Steeskov, Poul, Mng. Dir.--Danisco Foods, Copenhagen, Denmark; *Int'l*, pg. 378
Steetskamp, B., Div. Mgr.--Mona, Woerden, Netherlands; *Int'l*, pg. 254
Stefanelli, Joseph, Pres.--Amex Commodities Corporation, New York, NY; *U.S. Private*, pg. 62
Stefanov, Mark A., V.P.--United Eastern Coal Sales Corp., Indiana, PA; *U.S. Public*, pg. 1395
Steffen, Cennert, Chief Oper. Officer--B. Johanssons Pappersforadling AB, Lodose, Sweden; *Int'l*, pg. 439
Steffen, Raoul, Gen. Mgr.--Tektronix GmbH, Cologne, Germany; *U.S. Public*, pg. 1567
Steffens, Gretchen, Pres.-Pub. Rels. & Sls. Promo.--Key Communications, Inc., San Juan, PR; *U.S. Private*, pg. 318
Steffens, Gunter Z., Gen. Mgr.--Dresdner Bank AG, London, United Kingdom; *Int'l*, pg. 419
Steffensen, Mads, Mng. Dir.--Scan Care A/S, Copenhagen, Denmark; *Int'l*, pg. 656
Steffler, H. Peter, Pres.--Finora Company, Inc., Englewood, CO; *U.S. Private*, pg. 802
Stege, Hans Joerg, Gen. Mgr.--Siegling Mexico S.A. de C.V., Tlalnepantla, Mexico; *Int'l*, pg. 498
Stegemiller, David C., Pres.--Cast Products, Jackson, MI; *U.S. Public*, pg. 796
Stegman, Don, Div. Mgr.--Oliver Rubber Co., Athens, GA; *U.S. Public*, pg. 1504
Steib, J. Nicholas, Mng. Dir.--GGK Barcelona, Barcelona, Spain; *Int'l*, pg. 1335
Steiger, Elmar, Chief Oper. Officer--Clarins GmbH, Starnberg, Germany; *Int'l*, pg. 295
Steiger, John, Mgr.--AMICO-Lakeland, Lakeland, FL; *U.S. Private*, pg. 30

Steilhack, Kurt, Gen. Mgr.--Four Seasons Hotel, Los Angeles, CA; *Int'l*, pg. 502

Steimer, Robert J., Pres.--Nestle Capital Corporation, Stamford, CT; *Int'l*, pg. 916

Steimers, Gerald, Pres.--Pioneer Claim Management, Inc., Rock Hill, NY; *U.S. Public*, pg. 685

Stein, Arnold, Pres.--McColls Dairy, Redding, CA; *U.S. Private*, pg. 294

Stein, C.L., Sr. V.P.--Palm Beach Div.-Florida Public Utilites, West Palm Beach, FL; *U.S. Public*, pg. 655

Stein, Howard, Pres.--Howard Carpet Mills, Inc., Eton, GA; *U.S. Public*, pg. 1464

Stein, James C., Pres. & Chief Oper. Officer--Fluor Daniel Inc., Irvine, CA; *U.S. Public*, pg. 660

Stein, Jay S., V.P. & Chm.-Universal Studios Recreation Services Grp.--Universal Studios, Inc., Universal City, CA; *Int'l*, pg. 1215

Stein, Michael, Pres.--Electro-Science Deutschland, Munich, Germany; *U.S. Private*, pg. 369

Stein, N.M., Gen. Mgr.--GKN Sankey Industrial Products, Telford, United Kingdom; *Int'l*, pg. 535

Stein, Steven B., Chief Oper. Officer--Allied Security Inc., Minneapolis, MN; *U.S. Private*, pg. 40

Steinbach, Dieter, Gen. Mgr.--ITW Signode System GmbH, Dinslaken, Germany; *U.S. Public*, pg. 869

Steinbach, R., Mng. Dir.--Wm. H. Muller & Co. Bremen/Hamburg, Hamburg, Germany; *Int'l*, pg. 682

Steinbacher, Horst, Pres.--HALI-Buromobel Vertriebs GesmbH, Vienna, Austria; *Int'l*, pg. 589

Steinbeck, Greg, Gen. Mgr.--Blackhawk, Cedar Falls, IA; *U.S. Public*, pg. 1176

Steinbecker, Terry F., Pres.--SJLP Inc., Saint Joseph, MO; *U.S. Public*, pg. 1427

Steinberg, Dennis P., Pres.--TPC Corporation, Houston, TX; *U.S. Public*, pg. 1252

Steinberg, Howard, Pres.--Ply-Gem Manufacturing, Haddon Heights, NJ; *U.S. Public*, pg. 1193

Steinberg, Lawrence, Pres. & Chief Exec. Officer--Modern Publishing, New York, NY; *U.S. Private*, pg. 1120

Steinberg, Michael, Chm. Bd.--Macy's West, San Francisco, CA; *U.S. Public*, pg. 618

Steinberg, Phil, Chm. Bd.--Crest Steel Corp., Carson, CA; *Int'l*, pg. 845

Steinberg, Robert M., Chm. Bd. & Chief Exec. Officer--Reliance Insurance Company, Philadelphia, PA; *U.S. Public*, pg. 1374

Steinberg, S.L., Pres.--Carboline Co., Saint Louis, MO; *U.S. Public*, pg. 1357

Steinberg, Sue, V.P.-Television Devel.--Barris Productions, Inc., Los Angeles, CA; *Int'l*, pg. 1283

Steinberg, Terri, Mgr.-Sls.-Midwest--Singapore Airlines Ltd., Chicago, IL; *Int'l*, pg. 1374

Steinberger, David, Pres.--HarperCollins Adult Trade Division, New York, NY; *Int'l*, pg. 926

Steinberger, David, Pres.--Basic Books, Inc., New York, NY; *Int'l*, pg. 927

Steinei, D., Chief Exec. Officer--Agrippina Ruckversicherung Aktiengesellschaft, Cologne, Germany; *Int'l*, pg. 1531

Steiner, Bob, IV, Pres. & Chief Exec. Officer--Regions Bank/Lee County, Auburn, AL; *U.S. Public*, pg. 1372

Steiner, D., Chief Oper. Officer--Turegum Insurance Company, Zurich, Switzerland; *Int'l*, pg. 1529

Steiner, Erwin, Pres.--American Suessen, Charlotte, NC; *Int'l*, pg. 1290

Steiner, Jeffrey, Pres.--Fairchild Aerospace Fasteners Division, Chantilly, VA; *U.S. Public*, pg. 610

Steiner, John E., Pres.--MagneTek Lighting Products Group, Nashville, TN; *U.S. Public*, pg. 1037

Steiner, Peter, Mng. Dir.--UPM-Kymmene Italia S.r.L., Milan, Italy; *Int'l*, pg. 1430

Steiner, Robert, Mgr. Reg. Sls.--JEOL (U.S.A.), Inc., Rosemont, IL; *Int'l*, pg. 697

Steiness, Harald, Pres.--NorBetong a.s, Oslo, Norway; *Int'l*, pg. 1199

Steinfeld, Richard, Dr., Gen. Mgr.--Scientific Imaging Systems, New Haven, CT; *U.S. Public*, pg. 550

Steingrover, Werner, CO-Chief Oper. Officer--North Rhine Westphalia Branch, Dusseldorf, Germany; *Int'l*, pg. 645

Steinhart, Arthur F., Pres.--Andy Johns MacKintosh, New York, NY; *U.S. Public*, pg. 233

Steinhoff, Klaus, Gen. Mgr.--Union-Transport Do Brasil Ltda, Sao Paulo, Brazil; *U.S. Private*, pg. 1120

Steinitz, Paul S., Pres.-Asia/Pacific--Moore Products Co. (S) Pte. Ltd., Singapore, Singapore; *U.S. Public*, pg. 1129

Steinmann, W., Chief Oper. Officer--Volkswagen Bank GmbH, Braunschweig, Germany; *Int'l*, pg. 1474

Steinmetz, K.A., Chief Oper. Officer--Deutsche FATA GmbH, Wiesbaden, Germany; *Int'l*, pg. 474

Steinmetz, Mark S., Pres. & Gen. Mgr.--KQRS-AM/FM, Minneapolis, MN; *U.S. Public*, pg. 512

Steinmo, Harald, Gen. Mgr.--Kvaerner Kimek a.s, Murmansk Office, Murmansk, Russia; *Int'l*, pg. 772

Steinnes, Harald, Pres.--Aker Betong a.s., Oslo, Norway; *Int'l*, pg. 42

Steinway, Robert C., Pres.--U.S. Marine Division, Arlington, WA; *U.S. Public*, pg. 266

Stejskal, Andreas, Country Mgr.--BMC Software GmbH, Vienna, Austria; *U.S. Public*, pg. 162

Stell, Louis E., Pres. & Chief Exec. Officer--First National Bank of Conway, Conway, AR; *U.S. Public*, pg. 630

Stella, Eng., Mng. Dir.--Fiorentina Gas S.p.A., Florence, Italy; *Int'l*, pg. 428

Stella, Gianni, Chm.--Enichem International Holdings B.V., Amsterdam, Netherlands; *Int'l*, pg. 429

Stellman, Richard G., Pres.--The Pace Consultants, Inc., Houston, TX; *U.S. Public*, pg. 921

Steltenkamp, R. Stephen, Pres.--Matrix Building Co., Inc., Covington, KY; *U.S. Private*, pg. 694

Stelter, John, Gen. Mgr.--United States Aluminum Corp.-Illinois, Bedford Park, IL; *U.S. Public*, pg. 895

Stemmler, Robert, Winemaker & Co-Owner--Robert Stemmler Winery, Sonoma, CA; *Int'l*, pg. 1083

Stenberg, James R., V.P. & Gen. Mgr.--Elco Consumer Products Corp., Rockford, IL; *U.S. Public*, pg. 1590

Stenberg, Olle, Chief Oper. Officer--Axel Johnson & Co. (SEA) Pte. Ltd., Singapore, Singapore; *Int'l*, pg. 711

Stenbit, John P., Acting Exec. V.P. & Gen. Mgr.--TRW Systems Integration Group, Fairfax, VA; *U.S. Public*, pg. 1558

Stenersen, Sverre, Pres.--ASEA Skandia A/S, Oslo, Norway; *Int'l*, pg. 7

Stenger, Richard T., Publr.--The Daily Local News, West Chester, PA; *U.S. Public*, pg. 934

Stening, Peter, Reg. Devel. Dir.-North Asia--EURO RSCG Partnership, Quarry Bay, Hong Kong; *Int'l*, pg. 602

Stenius, Robert, Pres.--Kvaerner Masa-Yards Inc., Turku New Shipyard, Turku, Finland; *Int'l*, pg. 771

Stennett, P., Chm. Bd.--Redland Technologies Ltd., Crawley, United Kingdom; *Int'l*, pg. 1091

Stenovich, Michael, Gen. Mgr.--Gregg Foods of Garden Grove, Inc., Garden Grove, CA; *U.S. Private*, pg. 158

Stenram, Robert, Mgr.--Swedbank, Tokyo, Japan; *Int'l*, pg. 1328

Stensland, John G., Pres.--Merrill Corporation, Chicago, IL; *U.S. Public*, pg. 1097

Stensrud, Lorry J., Pres.--Cova Financial Services Life Insurance Co., Oak Brook Terrace, IL; *U.S. Private*, pg. 443

Stenzel, James, Pres.--Adra Systems, Inc., Chelmsford, MA; *U.S. Private*, pg. 18

Stenzler, Rochelle, Pres.--PharmaPlus Drugmarts Limited, Mississauga, Canada; *Int'l*, pg. 1012

Stepan, Walter, Pres. & Chief Exec. Officer--Bacou U.S.A., Inc., Smithfield, RI; *Int'l*, pg. 132

Stephan, Don, Plant Mgr.--Champion Ignition Products-Dumas Plant, Dumas, AR; *U.S. Public*, pg. 443

Stephan, Said, Fin. Dir.--H&C, Leo Burnett, Beirut, Lebanon; *U.S. Private*, pg. 184

Stephanites, Conrad R., Pres.--SuperValu, Inc.-Pittsburgh Div., New Stanton, PA; *U.S. Public*, pg. 1540

Stephans, Linda, V.P. & Mng. Exec.--Winnetka Financial Center, Winnetka, IL; *U.S. Public*, pg. 1197

Stephen, Barry, Pres.--Kitchen Fair, Jacksonville, AR; *U.S. Private*, pg. 917

Stephen, Randall, Pres.--Circuit City Northeast Division, Richmond, VA; *U.S. Public*, pg. 374

Stephens, Anthony K., Pres. & Chief Exec. Officer--Morguard Investments Limited, Toronto, Toronto, Canada; *U.S. Private*, pg. 738

Stephens, Arthur E., Pres.--Brown & Root Services Corporation, Houston, TX; *U.S. Public*, pg. 775

Stephens, Cedric E., Chm.--Industrial Finance Corporation Limited, Kingston, Jamaica; *Int'l*, pg. 156

Stephens, Cedric E., Chm.--International Insurance Brokers Limited, Kingston, Jamaica; *Int'l*, pg. 156

Stephens, David, Pres.--Mercantile Bank of Tipton, Tipton, IA; *U.S. Public*, pg. 1088

Stephens, Derwood M., Exec. V.P.--Rolled Alloys/Atek Metals Division, Cincinnati, OH; *U.S. Private*, pg. 941

Stephens, Earl, Mgr.--Furman Wholesale Lumber Branch, Memphis, TN; *U.S. Private*, pg. 431

Stephens, Frank, Pres.--Specialty Brands, San Francisco, CA; *Int'l*, pg. 237

Stephens, Gerald D., Chm. Bd.--RLI Insurance Company, Peoria, IL; *U.S. Public*, pg. 1356

Stephens, Gerald D., Chm. Bd.--Mt. Hawley Insurance Company, Peoria, IL; *U.S. Public*, pg. 1356

Stephens, Howard, Mgr.-District--W. Braun Co., Norwalk, CT; *U.S. Private*, pg. 166

Stephens, J.T., Pres. & Chief Exec. Officer--Ebsco Investment Services, Inc., Birmingham, AL; *U.S. Private*, pg. 359

Stephens, J.T., Pres. & Chief Exec. Officer--Ebsco Graphics, Oklahoma City, OK; *U.S. Private*, pg. 359

Stephens, J.T., Pres. & Chief Exec. Officer--Plastics Research & Development Co., Fort Smith, AR; *U.S. Private*, pg. 359

Stephens, J.T., Pres. & Chief Exec. Officer--H. Wilson Company, South Holland, IL; *U.S. Private*, pg. 359

Stephens, J.T., Pres. & Chief Exec. Officer--Luxor, Waukegan, IL; *U.S. Private*, pg. 359

Stephens, Ken, Branch Mgr.--Financial Collection Agencies, Vancouver, Canada; *Int'l*, pg. 470

Stephens, Lindsay, Mng. Dir.--Howard Pacific Ltd., Palmerston North, New Zealand; *Int'l*, pg. 1387

Stephens, Lindsay, Mng. Dir.--Howard Australia Pty. Ltd., Seven Hills, Australia; *Int'l*, pg. 1387

Stephens, Lindsay, Mng. Dir.--Howard Engineering Ltd., Palmerston North, New Zealand; *Int'l*, pg. 1387

Stephens, Lindsay, Mng. Dir.--Howard Rotavator Co., Palmerston North, New Zealand; *Int'l*, pg. 1387

Stephens, Lindsay, Mng. Dir.--Howard Machinery (Pty.) Ltd., Howick, South Africa; *Int'l*, pg. 1387

Stephens, Mike, District Mgr.--Circle International, Grapevine, TX; *U.S. Public*, pg. 371

Stephens, Philip, Chief Oper. Officer-Surety & Sr. V.P.--SAFECO Property & Casualty Insurance Companies, Seattle, WA; *U.S. Public*, pg. 1423

Stephens, Richard D., V.P. & Gen. Mgr.--Boeing North America, Tactical Systems Division, Duluth, GA; *U.S. Public*, pg. 241

Stephens, Shane, V.P.-Warehousing--Staple Cotton Cooperative Association/Itta Bena, Greenwood, MS; *U.S. Private*, pg. 1033

Stephenson, Arthur G., V.P. & Gen. Mgr.--Oceaneering Space Systems, Houston, TX; *U.S. Public*, pg. 1211

Stephenson, L.C., Deputy Mng. Dir.--P&O European Ferries Ltd., Dover, United Kingdom; *Int'l*, pg. 1033

Stephenson, R. B., Pres. & Chief Exec. Officer--Siemens Power Corp., Milwaukee, WI; *Int'l*, pg. 1246

Stephenson, Robert, Mgr.--CaroHome LLC, Raleigh, NC; *U.S. Public*, pg. 307

Stepien, Ronald W., Chm. Bd. & Chief Exec. Officer--MidAmerican Capital Company, Des Moines, IA; *U.S. Public*, pg. 1109

Steptoe, John, Mng. Dir.--PG Technology, Ltd., Mitcham, United Kingdom; *U.S. Public*, pg. 424

Ster, Brian, Pres.--Zimmer Spain S.A., Barcelona, Spain; *U.S. Public*, pg. 257

Sterba, Hans D., Co-Chief Oper. Officer--IKB Consult GmbH, Dusseldorf, Germany; *Int'l*, pg. 645

Sterk, Fred, Dir.--Sun Electric Nederland, B.V. (SEN) Varodo B.V. (VRD), Amsterdam, Netherlands; *U.S. Public*, pg. 1481

Sterlin, Larry O., Pres.--Asia-Pacific Operations, Singapore, Singapore; *U.S. Public*, pg. 1795

Sterling, Cheryl, Chief Oper. Officer--Ralph Lauren Womenswear Co., L.P., New York, NY; *U.S. Private*, pg. 875

Sterling, G.S., Opers. Dir.--The Barden Corp., (U.K.) Ltd., Plymouth, United Kingdom; *Int'l*, pg. 468

Stern, Arnold, Pres.--Jarchem Specialty Chemical Division, Newark, NJ; *U.S. Private*, pg. 583

Stern, Arthur P., Pres.--Advanced Products & Systems Corp., Torrance, CA; *U.S. Public*, pg. 1365

Stern, Doug, Pres. & Chief Exec. Officer--United Media, New York, NY; *U.S. Public*, pg. 1448

Stern, Ernest, Pres.--Thomson Components, Totowa, NJ; *Int'l*, pg. 1384

Stern, Michael, Pres. & Chief Exec. Officer--Huntington Clothiers, Inc., Columbus, OH; *U.S. Private*, pg. 490

Stern, Michael, Pres.--Custom Shop Shirtmakers Inc., New York, NY; *U.S. Private*, pg. 490

Stern, Michael, Pres.--Morley Shirt Company, Franklin, NJ; *U.S. Private*, pg. 490

Stern, Paul, Dr., Chm. Bd., Pres. & Chief Exec. Officer--BNR, Inc., Research Triangle Park, NC; *Int'l*, pg. 969

Sternberg, Seymour, Pres.--New York Life & Health Insurance Company, Wilmington, DE; *U.S. Private*, pg. 795

Sternberg, Seymour, Pres.--NYLIFE Inc., New York, NY; *U.S. Private*, pg. 795

Sterner, Al G., Chm. & Chief Exec. Officer--M & I Bank of Delavan, Delavan, WI; *U.S. Public*, pg. 1050

Sterner, Eddie, Chief Oper. Officer--Scansped Group, Goteborg, Sweden; *Int'l*, pg. 123

Sterns, Reggie, V.P. & Div. Mgr.--Orlando Paving Company, Winter Park, FL; *U.S. Private*, pg. 544

Sterry, Don, Mgr.-Gen. Office--National Distributors, Vernon, CA; *U.S. Private*, pg. 781

Stertzer, Donald R., V.P. & Chief Oper. Officer--Scholastic Inc. National Distribution Center, Jefferson City, MO; *U.S. Public*, pg. 1440

Stes, Anne, Mgr.--Utell International-Benelux, Hilversum, Netherlands; *Int'l*, pg. 1098

Steuck, Gary R., Pres.--Lands' End Japan, K.K., Yokohama, Japan; *U.S. Public*, pg. 978

Stevanin, Gilbert, Chief Oper. Officer--Club Mediterranee Italia S.p.A., Rome, Italy; *Int'l*, pg. 298

Steven, Douglas, Pres.--Wayne Chemical Corporation, Milwaukee, WI; *Int'l*, pg. 599

Steven, I.L., Chief Oper. Officer--Babcock Power-Production Div., Renfrew, United Kingdom; *Int'l*, pg. 472

Stevens, Bruce A., Pres.--Boston Piano Company, Long Island City, NY; *U.S. Public*, pg. 1514

Stevens, Butch, Branch Mgr.--Continental Eagle Visalia, CA, Visalia, CA; *U.S. Private*, pg. 267

Stevens, Clark, Pres.--Mesa Airlines, Inc., Farmington, NM; *U.S. Public*, pg. 1099

Stevens, Derek, Pres. & Chief Exec. Officer--Ajax Metal Processing, Detroit, MI; *U.S. Private*, pg. 250

Stevens, Derek, Pres.--Direct Tool Inc., Roseville, MI; *U.S. Private*, pg. 250

Stevens, Donna, Chief Exec. Officer--Outpatient Surgery Center of Coral Springs, Coral Springs, FL; *U.S. Public*, pg. 405

Stevens, F.W., Pres.--Valmont Financial Corporation, Omaha, NE; *U.S. Public*, pg. 335

Stevens, F.W., Pres.--Valmont Indemnity Co. Ltd., Omaha, NE; *U.S. Public*, pg. 335

Stevens, Frank P., V.P.--Professional/First Travelcorp, Dalton, GA; *U.S. Private*, pg. 408

Stevens, Greg, Publr.--The World, Coos Bay, OR; *U.S. Public*, pg. 1343

Stevens, John, Chief Oper. Officer--EUA Service Corporation, West Bridgewater, MA; *U.S. Public*, pg. 549

Stevens, John M., Pres.--The Gunlocke Company, Wayland, NY; *U.S. Public*, pg. 772

Stevens, John R., Pres.--EUA Bioten, Inc., Boston, MA; *U.S. Public*, pg. 549

Stevens, K.V., Mng. Dir.--Senior Australia Limited, Smithfield, Australia; *Int'l*, pg. 1222

Stevens, Kenneth A., Pres. & Gen. Mgr.--Pirelli Tri-State Inc., Redding, CA; *Int'l*, pg. 1059

Stevens, Linda, Mgr.--New Hermes Inc.-West Coast, Garden Grove, CA; *U.S. Private*, pg. 794

Stevens, Lord, of Ludgate, Chm. Bd.--Express Newspapers plc, London, United Kingdom; *Int'l*, pg. 1443

Stevens, Mike, Branch Mgr.--Saunders Oil Co., Inc., Norfolk, VA; *U.S. Private*, pg. 968

Stevens, Peter, Jr., V.P. & Gen. Mgr.--Hirose Electric (U.S.A.), Inc., Simi Valley, CA; *Int'l*, pg. 620

Stevens, Rich, Chief Exec. Officer--Medical Advances Inc., Milwaukee, WI; *U.S. Public*, pg. 894

Stevens, Richard D., Gen. Mgr.--Country Skillet Catfish Co., Isola, MS; *U.S. Public*, pg. 428

Stevens, Ronald, Pres.--C.J. Rush Inc., Scarborough, Canada; *Int'l*, pg. 395

Stevens, Tim, Mgr.--General Employment Enterprises, Inc., Orange, CA; *U.S. Public*, pg. 714

Stevens, William J., Chm. Bd. & Pres.--Motion Industries, Inc., Irondale, AL; *U.S. Public*, pg. 732

Stevenson, A.C.M., Chief Oper. Officer--Babcock Welding Products Limited, Renfrew, United Kingdom; *Int'l*, pg. 472

Stevenson, E.W., Pres.--AmSouth Bank N.A., Huntsville, AL; *U.S. Public*, pg. 105

Stevenson, George, Gen. Mgr.--Gould Electronics Ltd., Circuit Protection, Thornhill, United Kingdom; *U.S. Public*, *pg. 1592*

Stevenson, J. Alan, Mng. Dir.--Multi-Arc (U.K.) Ltd., Durham, United Kingdom; *Int'l*, pg. 1198
Stevenson, Jim, Mgr.--Sandvik International, Kranj, Slovenia; *Int'l*, pg. 1186
Stevenson, John L., Pres.--J.I. Case Credit Corp., Racine, WI; *U.S. Public*, pg. 312
Stevenson, Michael, Chief Oper. Officer--SCA Recycling Maybank, Aylesford, United Kingdom; *Int'l*, pg. 1327
Stevenson, Mike, Dir.-Facilities--Sony Microelectronics, San Antonio, TX; *Int'l*, pg. 1284
Stevenson, P.D., Mng. Dir.--Martex Investments (Pty) Ltd, Gaborone, Botswana; *Int'l*, pg. 167
Stevenson, Paul, Gen. Mgr.--Wavetek Limited, Norwich, United Kingdom; *U.S. Private*, pg. 1155
Stevenson, R.A., Pres.--Moulinex Canada Ltd., Richmond Hill, Canada; *Int'l*, pg. 896
Stever, Bob, Mng. Dir.--ENV Services, Inc., King of Prussia, PA; *U.S. Public*, pg. 517
Steward, H.L., Chm. Bd.--LL&E Colombia, Inc., New Orleans, LA; *U.S. Public*, pg. 269
Steward, H.L., Chm. Bd. & Pres.--Inexco Oil Company, New Orleans, LA; *U.S. Public*, pg. 269
Steward, Jerry N., Grp. V.P.--Poultry Group, Atlanta, GA; *U.S. Private*, pg. 459
Steward, Ken, Pres.--Canadelle, Inc., Montreal, Canada; *U.S. Public*, pg. 1434
Stewart B., Gen. Mgr.--Alpo Pet Foods, Arden Hills, MN; *Int'l*, pg. 917
Stewart Warner, J. D., Pres.--Stewart Warner Instruments Corporation, El Paso, TX; *U.S. Private*, pg. 1043
Stewart, A.G., Rep.--Swiss Bank Corporation, Edinburgh, United Kingdom; *Int'l*, pg. 1330
Stewart, B.D., Pres.--The Thompson's Company, Memphis, TN; *U.S. Public*, pg. 1466
Stewart, Barry D., Exec. V.P.--Suncor Exploration & Production Group, Calgary, Canada; *Int'l*, pg. 1320
Stewart, Dave, Area Foreman--Talisman Energy Inc., Chetwynd, Canada; *Int'l*, pg. 1352
Stewart, David B., Pres. & Chief Exec. Officer--The UCS Group, Toronto, Canada; *Int'l*, pg. 792
Stewart, David T., Pres.--Loblaw Supermarkets Inc., North York, Canada; *Int'l*, pg. 1495
Stewart, Donald J., Gen. Mgr.--World Book Finance, Inc., Chicago, IL; *U.S. Public*, pg. 218
Stewart, Edward, Admin.--Greenery Extended Care Center at Danvers, Danvers, MA; *U.S. Public*, pg. 836
Stewart, Eric, Mng. Dir.--Kvaerner Computing & Consultancy Ltd., Gateshead, United Kingdom; *Int'l*, pg. 771
Stewart, Eric W., Pres.--Kvaerner Computing & Consultancy Ltd., Gateshead, United Kingdom; *Int'l*, pg. 767
Stewart, Evelyn, Admin.--Horizon Specialty Hospital - El Paso, El Paso, TX; *U.S. Public*, pg. 839
Stewart, George, Mgr.--Curtis 1000, Inc., Cincinnati, OH; *U.S. Public*, pg. 70
Stewart, Gordon W., Pres.--HHH, Inc., Wilmington, DE; *U.S. Public*, pg. 847
Stewart, Gordon W., Pres.--HSI Corp., Wilmington, DE; *U.S. Public*, pg. 847
Stewart, Harrison, V.P. & Gen. Mgr.--Dillard, A ResourceNet International Company, Greensboro, NC; *U.S. Public*, pg. 902
Stewart, Harvey, Plant Mgr.--Liv-A-Snaps, Inc., Saint Paul, MN; *Int'l*, pg. 917
Stewart, J. Michael, Pres.--Texas Microsystems Inc., Houston, TX; *U.S. Public*, pg. 1586
Stewart, J.W., Pres.--BJ-Titan Services Company (Partnership), Houston, TX; *U.S. Public*, pg. 166
Stewart, James, Pres.--Devon Capital Corp., Levittown, NY; *U.S. Public*, pg. 400
Stewart, James, Div. V.P.--Dayton Superior Corp., Santa Fe Springs, CA; *U.S. Private*, pg. 932
Stewart, James, Gen. Mgr.--Stackpole Limited, Toronto, Canada; *U.S. Private*, pg. 1028
Stewart, James G., V.P. & Gen. Mgr.--Milne & Craighead Customs Brokers, Inc., Calgary, Canada; *U.S. Public*, pg. 435
Stewart, James T., Pres. & Chief Exec. Officer--CRSS Capital, Inc., Houston, TX; *Int'l*, pg. 1415
Stewart, James W., Pres.--Southern Mortgage Associates, Inc., Levittown, NY; *U.S. Public*, pg. 400
Stewart, Joe J., Pres.-Govt. Grp.--Babcock & Wilcox Co., Barberton, OH; *U.S. Public*, pg. 1068
Stewart, John, Pres.--Duff-Norton, Charlotte, NC; *U.S. Public*, pg. 406
Stewart, John, Pres.--Intercontinental Corporation, Indianapolis, IN; *Int'l*, pg. 464
Stewart, John M., Mng. Partner--Coscan Stewart Limited Partnership, Irvine, CA; *Int'l*, pg. 228
Stewart, John M., Pres.--Raytheon Canada Limited, Waterloo, Canada; *U.S. Public*, pg. 1366
Stewart, Juanita, Pres.--First American Abstract & Title Co., Tulsa, OK; *U.S. Public*, pg. 625
Stewart, K.M., Mgr.--Lindberg Heat Treating Co., Rochester, NY; *U.S. Public*, pg. 999
Stewart, K.W., Mng. Dir.--Comalco Smelting, Melbourne, Australia; *Int'l*, pg. 307
Stewart, L.H., Plant Mgr.--Bryan Metals, Inc., Bryan, OH; *U.S. Public*, pg. 1219
Stewart, Larry H., Pres.--Bridgeport Brass Corporation, Indianapolis, IN; *U.S. Public*, pg. 1219
Stewart, Patrick K., Pres.--ConAgra Consumer Direct, Inc., Santa Ana, CA; *U.S. Public*, pg. 426
Stewart, Paul B., Pres.--Unisource (S.E. Regional Office), Jacksonville, FL; *U.S. Public*, pg. 1671
Stewart, Peter, Gen. Mgr.--EG & G Rotron, Woodstock, NY; *U.S. Public*, pg. 543
Stewart, R. Gord, V.P. & Gen. Mgr.--Sonco Steel Tube Div., Ferrum Inc., Brampton, Canada; *Int'l*, pg. 699
Stewart, Randolph, V.P. & Gen. Mgr.--Harris Air Systems Company, Saint Paul, MN; *U.S. Private*, pg. 505
Stewart, Richard, Pres. & Chief Exec. Officer--S&S Energy Products, Houston, TX; *U.S. Public*, pg. 711
Stewart, Richard, Pres.--Brown Machine, Beaverton, MI; *Int'l*, pg. 774
Stewart, Richard R., Chief Oper. Officer--Composite Thread Protectors, Inc., Houston, TX; *U.S. Private*, pg. 963
Stewart, Richard R., Pres.--Stewart & Stevenson International, Inc., Houston, TX; *U.S. Public*, pg. 1517
Stewart, Richard R., Pres.--Cypress Acquisition, Inc., Houston, TX; *U.S. Public*, pg. 1517
Stewart, Ronald L., Pres.--Doehler-Jarvis, Inc., Toledo, OH; *U.S. Public*, pg. 796
Stewart, T. David, Plant. Mgr.--Lumberton Plant, Lumberton, MS; *U.S. Public*, pg. 443
Stewart, Tony, V.P.-Opers.--Harvard Interiors Manufacturing Co., Saint Louis, MO; *U.S. Public*, pg. 796
Stewart, W.W., Chm. Bd.--AEGON Financial Services Group (UK) Ltd., London, United Kingdom; *Int'l*, pg. 28
Stewart, William, Gen. Mgr.--Food Oils Corporation, Carlstadt, NJ; *U.S. Private*, pg. 1103
Steyn, Peet, Mng. Dir.--Sasol Petroleum International (Pty) Ltd., Rosebank, South Africa; *Int'l*, pg. 1197
Stiba, Beverly, Pres.--Ikon Office Solutions, Waco, TX; *U.S. Public*, pg. 863
Stibich, Ron, Pres. & Chief Exec. Officer--Fibre Glass-Evercoat Company, Cincinnati, OH; *U.S. Public*, pg. 866
Stich, Andrew C., Pres. & Chief Exec. Officer--Robert Scott/David Brooks, Dedham, MA; *U.S. Public*, pg. 948
Stich, Mike, Pres.--Manning Truck Modification, Louisville, KY; *U.S. Private*, pg. 700
Stichbury, Peter, Chief Oper. Officer--Carter Holt Harvey Roofing USA, Inc., Houston, TX; *U.S. Public*, pg. 905
Stichter, Bruce L., Pres.--Hewitt Soap Co., Dayton, OH; *U.S. Private*, pg. 597
Stichter, Dennis, Gen. Mgr.--Supreme MidAtlantic Corporation, Jonestown, PA; *U.S. Public*, pg. 1542
Stickles, David, Pres.--G2 Advertising, Huntington Beach, CA; *U.S. Public*, pg. 764
Stickman, Robert, Branch Mgr.--Sharp Electronics Corporation, Carson, CA; *Int'l*, pg. 1229
Stidham, Richard W., V.P. & Gen. Mgr.--Soabar Graphics Division, Greensboro, NC; *U.S. Public*, pg. 153
Stiehl, Gaston, Chief Oper. Officer--Henkel Cosmetic GmbH, Dusseldorf, Germany; *Int'l*, pg. 609
Stieler, Eric, Pres.--Danske Landmaend K/S, Copenhagen, Denmark; *Int'l*, pg. 826
Stier, Mary, Pres. & Publr.--Rockford Newspapers, Inc., Rockford, IL; *U.S. Public*, pg. 701
Stier, Robert H., Jr., V.P.-Program Management--Program Management, Boston, MA; *U.S. Public*, pg. 744
Stiff, P. Enoch, Pres. & Chief Exec. Officer--OmniQuip International, Inc., Port Washington, WI; *U.S. Private*, pg. 500
Stiff, Robert, Editor--The Dispatch, Lexington, NC; *U.S. Public*, pg. 1175
Stigson, Bjorn, Pres.--Flakt AB, Stockholm, Sweden; *Int'l*, pg. 7
Stiles, David, Gen. Mgr.--Surplus Warehouse-Seagoville, Seagoville, TX; *U.S. Private*, pg. 120
Stiles, David, Site Mgr.--Chem Fab Corporation, North Bennington, VT; *U.S. Public*, pg. 344
Stiles, G. E. R., Sr. V.P.--A.H. Robins-Finance Division, Richmond, VA; *U.S. Public*, pg. 80
Stiles, Mark W., Pres.--Trinity Construction Products, Dallas, TX; *U.S. Public*, pg. 1639
Stiles, Robert, Pres.--Gelson's Markets, Encino, CA; *U.S. Public*, pg. 129
Stiles, Robert F., Pres.--Production Oil Tools, Irving, TX; *U.S. Public*, pg. 547
Still, Julian, Gen. Mgr.--Kemira Color N.V., Heist-op-den-Berg, Belgium; *Int'l*, pg. 729
Stiller, Bernd, Mng. Dir.--Dexion GmbH, Laubach, Germany; *U.S. Public*, pg. 893
Stimpert, M.A., Chief Exec. Officer & Exec. V.P.--Golden Peanut Company, Alpharetta, GA; *U.S. Private*, pg. 459
Stine, Richard, Chief Oper. Officer--Kamtech Inc., Roswell, GA; *Int'l*, pg. 34
Stinson, Kenneth E., Chm. Bd.--Kiewit Construction Group, Inc., Omaha, NE; *U.S. Private*, pg. 619
Stinson, Mark, Pres.--The Hamilton Communications Group, Chicago, IL; *U.S. Private*, pg. 497
Stinson, Paul, Mng. Dir.--AES Silk Road, Richmond, United Kingdom; *U.S. Public*, pg. 5
Stirling, Douglas S., Pres.--Rollins Hudig Hall of Oregon, Inc., Portland, OR; *U.S. Public*, pg. 117
Stirling, Lewis W., Pres.--Stirling Properties, Inc., New Orleans, LA; *U.S. Private*, pg. 715
Stirling, Lynne, Ph.D., V.P.-RAQA--Diamedix Corporation, Miami, FL; *U.S. Public*, pg. 914
Stirnimann, D., Mgr.--Swiss Bank Corporation, Miami, FL; *Int'l*, pg. 1329
Stirnimann, Kurt, Mng. Dir.--Charmilles Technologies SA, Meyrin, Switzerland; *Int'l*, pg. 489
Stites, Peter M., Chief Oper. Officer--Rock Products Div., Vancouver, Canada; *Int'l*, pg. 628
Stitzer, Todd, Pres. & Chief Exec. Officer--Dr Pepper/Seven Up No. America, Dallas, TX; *Int'l*, pg. 248
Stix, Helmut, Mgr.--Sandvik in Austria Ges.m.b.H., Vienna, Austria; *Int'l*, pg. 1186
Stjarnesund, Rolf, Chief Oper. Officer--Geotronics S.A., Madrid, Spain; *Int'l*, pg. 1290
Stjernvall, Henrik, Mng. Dir.--S.A. Enso N.V. Enso West, Antwerp, Belgium; *Int'l*, pg. 457
Stobaugh, James F., Chm. & Chief Exec. Officer--NationsBank of Northwest Arkansas, Fayetteville, AR; *U.S. Public*, pg. 1164
Stock, Timothy F., Pres.--Ford International Services, Inc., Dearborn, MI; *U.S. Public*, pg. 664
Stockdale, Mark, Plng.--Leo Burnett Limited, London, United Kingdom; *U.S. Private*, pg. 185
Stockdale, William, Chief Exec. Officer & Mng. Dir.--HSB Engineering Insurance Limited, London, United Kingdom; *U.S. Public*, pg. 795
Stockel, Richard F., Dr., Chief Oper. Officer--Tosoh USA, Inc.-New Jersey Office, Bound Brook, NJ; *Int'l*, pg. 1407
Stockel, Volker, Sr. V.P.--Bayerische Landesbank - Hong Kong Branch, Central, Hong Kong; *Int'l*, pg. 176
Stocker, John, Gen. Mgr.--Weetabix of Canada (Mfg.) Limited, Thornhill, Canada; *Int'l*, pg. 1488
Stockholm, G., Chief Exec. Officer--Zurich Livsforsikring, Copenhagen, Denmark; *Int'l*, pg. 1530
Stockley, P., Mng. Dir.--Balzers Ltd., Milton Keynes, United Kingdom; *Int'l*, pg. 997
Stockli, O., Mgr.--Schweizerischer Bankverein, Basel, Switzerland; *Int'l*, pg. 1329
Stocklin, Peter, Gen. Dir.--ELVIA Reiseversicherungen, Zurich, Switzerland; *Int'l*, pg. 60
Stockmann, Doris, Mng. Dir.--Academic Bookstore, Helsinki, Finland; *Int'l*, pg. 1301
Stocko, George, Gen. Mgr.--SASIB Beverage & Food N.A., Inc., Charleston, SC; *Int'l*, pg. 1194
Stockton, Dale L., Pres.--Empire Foundry, Tulsa, OK; *U.S. Public*, pg. 457
Stoddard, Brandon, Pres.--ABC Productions, Century City, CA; *U.S. Public*, pg. 511
Stoddard, Brandon, Pres.--Empty Chair Productions, Inc., Los Angeles, CA; *U.S. Public*, pg. 511
Stoddard, Brandon, Pres. & Chief Oper. Officer--JBS Productions Holding Company, Inc., New York, NY; *U.S. Public*, pg. 511
Stoddard, Randy, Pres.--First National Insurance Co. of America, Seattle, WA; *U.S. Public*, pg. 1423
Stoddard, Randy, Pres.--SAFECO Insurance Co. of America, Seattle, WA; *U.S. Public*, pg. 1423
Stoddard, Randy, Pres.--SAFECO Lloyds Insurance Co., Richardson, TX; *U.S. Public*, pg. 1423
Stoddard, Richard C., Pres.--Healthcare Staffing Solutions, Inc., Lowell, MA; *U.S. Public*, pg. 1373
Stoddard, W. Randall, Pres.--SAFECO Property & Casualty Insurance Companies, Seattle, WA; *U.S. Public*, pg. 1423
Stoddart, Mike, Division Mgr.--Horizon Technology Group - Tiffin Division, Tiffin, OH; *U.S. Private*, pg. 539
Stoe, Jaques, Pres.--Varilux Corporation, Foster City, CA; *Int'l*, pg. 462
Stoecklein, Robert L., Pres.--NationsBank of Boonville, Boonville, MO; *U.S. Public*, pg. 1164
Stoecklin, George A., Pres.--Huntco Nevada, Inc., Las Vegas, NV; *U.S. Public*, pg. 849
Stoesser, Dieter, Area Sls.--Analog Devices GMBH - Technisches Buero Suedwest, Karlsruhe, Germany; *U.S. Public*, pg. 108
Stohler, Jerry D., V.P. & Gen. Mgr.--Indiana Tube Corp., Evansville, IN; *U.S. Public*, pg. 780
Stoimenov, Ivan, Mng. Dir.--SKF Sofia, Sofia, Bulgaria; *Int'l*, pg. 1159
Stoke, Woody, Reg. Mgr.--SMS-Charlotte, Charlotte, NC; *U.S. Public*, pg. 1463
Stokes, Gary, Pres. & Chief Exec. Officer--WVTM-TV, Inc., Birmingham, AL; *U.S. Public*, pg. 712
Stokes, James, Opers. Mgr.-Greenville Plants--Nicholson, Greenville, MS; *U.S. Public*, pg. 444
Stokes, James, Pres.--Quorum Health Resources, Inc., Brentwood, TN; *U.S. Public*, pg. 1354
Stokes, Melvin, Mgr.--Southern Electric Supply Co., Inc., Baton Rouge, LA; *Int'l*, pg. 1108
Stokes, Patrick T., Pres.--Anheuser-Busch, Inc., Saint Louis, MO; *U.S. Public*, pg. 114
Stokes, R. B., Pres. & Chief Exec. Officer--Trans Mountain Oil Pipe Line Corp., Vancouver, Canada; *Int'l*, pg. 114
Stokes, W.J., Jr., Pres.--LEXIS Document Services, Springfield, IL; *Int'l*, pg. 1096
Stokes, Warren, Pres.--Heart Interface Corporation, Kent, WA; *U.S. Public*, pg. 1705
Stokholm, G., Chief Exec. Officer--Zurich Forsikring, Copenhagen, Denmark; *Int'l*, pg. 1531
Stokoe, Jamie, Chief Oper. Officer--Gambro Pty Ltd., Baulkham Hills, Australia; *Int'l*, pg. 668
Stokoe, Jamie, Chief Oper. Officer--Gambro Pty Ltd., Auckland, New Zealand; *Int'l*, pg. 668
Stokoe, Jamie, Chief Oper. Officer--Gambro Pty. Ltd., Kenmore, Australia; *Int'l*, pg. 668
Stokol, John E., Mng. Dir.--Union Carbide Austria GmbH, Vienna, Austria; *U.S. Public*, pg. 1667
Stokol, John E., Mng. Dir.--Union Carbide Benelux NV, Antwerp, Belgium; *U.S. Public*, pg. 1667
Stolberg, Al, Chief Exec. Officer--Metrosonics Inc., Rochester, NY; *Int'l*, pg. 208
Stolker, G. H., Mng. Dir.--Konijn Baggertechniek BV, Hoorn, Netherlands; *Int'l*, pg. 607
Stoll, Charles, Jr., Mgr.-Property & Casualty Claims--Willis Corroon Administrative Services Corporation, Aurora, IL; *Int'l*, pg. 1504
Stoll, John, Pres.--Lepel Corporation, Edgewood, NY; *U.S. Private*, pg. 560
Stoll, Raymond E., Ph.D., Dir.-Toxicology & Pathology--Sandoz Research Institute, East Hanover, NJ; *Int'l*, pg. 974
Stoll, Roger G., Ph.D., Chief Exec. Officer--Ohmeda, Inc., Liberty Corner, NJ; *Int'l*, pg. 121
Stoller, Janet, Asst. Branch Mgr.--Burns & Wilcox - Chicago Office, Chicago, IL; *U.S. Private*, pg. 609
Stoller, Lester, Mgr.--Fabrication Plant/Custom Products, Middlebury, IN; *U.S. Public*, pg. 1177
Stollery, H.J., Chief Exec. Officer--TNT North America and Canada Inc., Mississauga, Canada; *Int'l*, pg. 1343
Stolnack, Thomas, Chief Oper. Officer--Hudson Aviation Services Inc., California, Los Angeles, CA; *U.S. Public*, pg. 845
Stolte, Sandra L., Pres., Chief Exec. Officer & Sec.--Central Bank, Fairview Heights, IL; *U.S. Public*, pg. 643
Stoltz, Ove, Pres.--Asea Brown Boveri Industrie B.V., Apeldoorn, Netherlands; *Int'l*, pg. 8
Stolz, Philip M., V.P. & Gen. Mgr.--WBAL-TV, Baltimore, MD; *U.S. Private*, pg. 516
Stolze, Harald, Dir.--KS Winston Ltd., Maidenhead, United Kingdom; *Int'l*, pg. 861
Stolzenberg, Rick, V.P. & Gen. Mgr.--Reciprocating/Rotary Air Compressor Accessory Div., Davidson, NC; *U.S. Public*, pg. 876

Stommen, Jeffery, Gen. Mgr.--Frontier Communications-Lakeside, Inc., Champaign, IL; *U.S. Public*, pg. 683
Stommen, Jeffery, Gen. Mgr.--Frontier Communications of Illinois, Inc., Champaign, IL; *U.S. Public*, pg. 683
Stommen, Jeffery, V.P. & Gen. Mgr.--Frontier Communications of Michigan, Inc., Jackson, MI; *U.S. Public*, pg. 683
Stommen, Jeffery, Gen. Mgr.--Frontier Communications of Mt. Pulaski, Inc., Mount Pulaski, IL; *U.S. Public*, pg. 684
Stommen, Jeffery, Gen. Mgr.--Frontier Communications-Prairie Inc., Champaign, IL; *U.S. Public*, pg. 684
Stommen, Jeffrey, Gen. Mgr.--Frontier Communications-Midland, Inc., Champaign, IL; *U.S. Public*, pg. 683
Stone, Alan, Div. Mgr.--Wyle Electronics-Houston, Houston, TX; *Int'l*, pg. 1457
Stone, Bill, Office Mgr.--ENVIRON Corporation, Princeton, NJ; *U.S. Public*, pg. 1285
Stone, Craig, Pres.--WK Mfg. Company, Arnold, MO; *U.S. Private*, pg. 603
Stone, Daniel, Pres. & Chief Exec. Officer--Testcom, Inc., Albany, NY; *Int'l*, pg. 1154
Stone, David J., Pres.--La Franco Penn Life Compania De Segures De Vida S.A., Buenos Aires, Argentina; *U.S. Public*, pg. 1271
Stone, Don, Chief Oper. Officer--Cole Hall Lumber Co., Pelham, AL; *U.S. Private*, pg. 680
Stone, Gary V., Pres.--Milprint Inc., Oshkosh, WI; *U.S. Public*, pg. 210
Stone, Gregory J., V.P. & Gen. Mgr.--Georgia Television Company, Atlanta, GA; *U.S. Private*, pg. 282
Stone, Gregory L., Pres.--Carquest Canada Ltd., London, Canada; *U.S. Private*, pg. 445
Stone, Jack, Plant Mgr.--The Jefferson Division, Jefferson, IA; *U.S. Public*, pg. 349
Stone, John H., Gen. Mgr.-Pacific Islands Div.--Westpac Banking Corporation-Pacific Islands Div., Suva, Fiji; *Int'l*, pg. 1497
Stone, Ken, Publr.--Grant County News, Williamstown, KY; *U.S. Private*, pg. 648
Stone, Michael E., Plant Mgr.--UTA Niles Plant, Niles, MI; *U.S. Public*, pg. 1691
Stone, Patrick F., Pres.--Fidelity National Title Insurance Company, Irvine, CA; *U.S. Public*, pg. 620
Stone, Patrick F., Pres.--Fidelity National Title Insurance Company of Pennsylvania, Hialeah, FL; *U.S. Public*, pg. 621
Stone, Pete, Reg. V.P.--Arrow/Schweber Electronics, Carrollton, TX; *U.S. Public*, pg. 134
Stone, Pete, Reg. V.P.--Arrow/Schweber Electronics, Tulsa, OK; *U.S. Public*, pg. 134
Stone, Richard, Pres. & Publr.--The Times, Shreveport, LA; *U.S. Public*, pg. 700
Stone, Robert, Mgr.--EG & G Missouri Metals, Saint Louis, MO; *U.S. Public*, pg. 544
Stone, Robert M., Chm. Bd. & Pres.--J. A. Jones Applied Research Co., Charlotte, NC; *Int'l*, pg. 633
Stone, Ron, Sr. Mktg. Officer--Western Marketing Div., Pomona, CA; *U.S. Private*, pg. 296
Stone, Shirley, Mgr.--DWF of Norfolk, Norfolk, VA; *U.S. Private*, pg. 326
Stone, Steve, Plant Mgr.--South Bend Plant, South Bend, IN; *U.S. Public*, pg. 1066
Stonehocker, James, Plant Mgr.--Frito-Lay Inc., Beloit, WI; *U.S. Public*, pg. 1277
Stonehouse, Stephen G., Pres.--Pacific Indemnity Co., Los Angeles, CA; *U.S. Public*, pg. 355
Stonehouse, Stephen G., Pres.--Texas Pacific Indemnity Co., Dallas, TX; *U.S. Public*, pg. 355
Stoneman, Gordon C., Exec. V.P., Reg. Mgr. & Branch Mgr.-Toronto--Willis Corroon Melling Inc., Toronto, Canada; *Int'l*, pg. 1509
Stoner, David, Gen. Mgr.--Princeville Canning Co., Princeville, IL; *U.S. Public*, pg. 349
Stoner, John M., Pres.--True Temper Hardware Company, Camp Hill, PA; *U.S. Public*, pg. 846
Stoner, Richard B. Jr., Pres.--Holset Engineering Co. Ltd., Huddersfield, United Kingdom; *U.S. Public*, pg. 469
Stonier, Brian, Exec. Chm.--The Macmillan Co. of Australia Pty. Ltd., Melbourne, Australia; *Int'l*, pg. 1480
Stoopin, George, Gen. Mgr.--Westpac Banking Corporation-New Zealand, Wellington, New Zealand; *Int'l*, pg. 1497
Stoops, John C., Pres.--Wiegand Industrial-Chromalox, Pittsburgh, PA; *U.S. Public*, pg. 573
Stoppenbrink, G. H., Pres.--Kuehne & Nagel International Ltd., Mississauga, Canada; *Int'l*, pg. 763
Storch, Wendy, Exec. V.P. & Mng. Dir.--Promotion House, San Francisco, CA; *U.S. Private*, pg. 1166
Storck, Dr. Ekkehard, Dir. Gen.--Deutsche Bank Luxembourg S.A., Luxembourg, Luxembourg; *Int'l*, pg. 405
Storck, Friedrich, Dr., Chm. Bd.--Hoesch Siegerlandwerke GmbH, Siegen, Germany; *Int'l*, pg. 508
Storck, Friedrich, Dr., Chm. Bd.--Ross Industrie- und Fassadenbau GmbH, Wilnsdorf, Germany; *Int'l*, pg. 509
Storen, Robert S., Pres.--Perini Building Company-Central U.S. Division, Southfield, MI; *U.S. Public*, pg. 1278
Storiko, Adolf, Gen. Mgr.--Saar-Industrie, GmbH, Cologne, Germany; *U.S. Public*, pg. 666
Storiko, Adolf, Mgr.--Ford-Versorgungs-Und Unterstutzungseinrichtung GmbH, Cologne, Germany; *U.S. Public*, pg. 666
Stork, Donald A., Pres.--Advanswers Media/Programming, Saint Louis, MO; *Int'l*, pg. 117
Stork, Sven, Chief Oper. Officer--Electrolux, Siegen, Germany; *Int'l*, pg. 442
Storkaas, Frode, Mng. Dir.--ISS Darenas a.s., Oslo, Norway; *Int'l*, pg. 656
Storm, Colin, Mng. Dir.--Guinness Ireland (Holdings) Ltd., Dublin, Ireland; *Int'l*, pg. 412
Storm, Martin, Gen. Mgr.--DDF Dental Depotet Flex A/S, Glostrup, Denmark; *Int'l*, pg. 710
Storm, O.J., Chm.--Brother Norge A.S., Oslo, Norway; *Int'l*, pg. 230
Storm, Philip B., Pres.--American Sunroof Company, Southgate, MI; *U.S. Private*, pg. 8
Stormer, Barry, Chief Oper. Officer--RAV Construction Company, Akron, OH; *U.S. Private*, pg. 586
Storozum, Ted, Pres.--Dominion Industrial Fabrics Company, Montreal, Canada; *Int'l*, pg. 415
Story, Edward T., Pres. & Chief Exec. Officer--SOCO International, Inc., Houston, TX; *U.S. Public*, pg. 1482
Stotlar, Douglas W., V.P. & Gen. Mgr.--Con-Way NOW, Ann Arbor, MI; *U.S. Public*, pg. 281
Stotmeister, Kevin, Pres.--Sign Division, Oak Brook, IL; *U.S. Public*, pg. 617
Stott, James, Chief Oper. Officer--Kramer International, Inc., Milwaukee, WI; *U.S. Public*, pg. 142
Stott, James, Chief Oper. Officer--Quaker Alloy, Inc., Myerstown, PA; *U.S. Public*, pg. 142
Stott, Jim, Chief Oper. Officer--Pennsylvania Steel Foundry & Machine Company, Hamburg, PA; *U.S. Public*, pg. 142
Stott, Leslie D., Pres.--Automotive Division, Grow Group, Inc., Troy, MI; *Int'l*, pg. 663
Stott, W.L.B., Chm.--Isle of Man Bank Limited, Douglas, United Kingdom; *Int'l*, pg. 910
Stotts, Dale, Pres.--Dallas/Fort Worth Div., Dallas, TX; *U.S. Public*, pg. 1682
Stouber, Randy M., First V.P.--Jefferies & Company, Inc., Los Angeles, CA; *U.S. Public*, pg. 925
Stoudt, M., Pres.--Edicon Systems, Rochester, NY; *U.S. Public*, pg. 551
Stough, Bill, Pres. & Gen. Mgr.--WGME-TV, Portland, ME; *U.S. Private*, pg. 439
Stoughton, Richard H., Pres.--Charleston Financial Services, Inc., Charleston, SC; *U.S. Public*, pg. 634
Stoughton, W. Vickery, Pres.--SmithKline Beecham Clinical Laboratories, Nashville, TN; *Int'l*, pg. 1265
Stout, Charles, Publisher--Ocala Star-Banner Corporation, Ocala, FL; *U.S. Public*, pg. 1175
Stout, E. L., Jr., Pres.--Acme Brick Co., Fort Worth, TX; *U.S. Public*, pg. 936
Stout, Gary, Pres. & Chief Exec. Officer--Gannett Offset, Springfield, VA; *U.S. Public*, pg. 699
Stout, Harry, Pres.--Fidelity & Guaranty Life Insurance Co., Baltimore, MD; *U.S. Public*, pg. 1659
Stout, Harry Lee, Pres.--KCS Energy Marketing Inc., Edison, NJ; *U.S. Public*, pg. 938
Stout, Harry Lee, Pres.--Enercop Gas Marketing, Houston, TX; *U.S. Public*, pg. 938
Stout, Harry Lee, Pres.--KCS Energy Marketing, Inc., Houston, TX; *U.S. Public*, pg. 939
Stout, Harry Lee, Pres.--KCS Pipeline Systems, Inc., Houston, TX; *U.S. Public*, pg. 939
Stout, Harry Lee, Pres.--KCS Michigan Resources, Inc., Houston, TX; *U.S. Public*, pg. 939
Stout, Harry Lee, Pres.--KCS Energy Services, Inc., Houston, TX; *U.S. Public*, pg. 939
Stout, Jay, Plant Mgr.--Condiment Plant, Hunt Valley, MD; *U.S. Public*, pg. 1066
Stout, Mike, Pres.--Thor America, Middleburg, PA; *U.S. Public*, pg. 1602
Stout, Quenten, Plant Mgr.--CTS Corp., Connector Products, Baldwin, WI; *U.S. Public*, pg. 285
Stout, Stephen, Chief Exec.--Butterworths British and Irish Legal, London, United Kingdom; *Int'l*, pg. 1095
Stoutjesdijk, Hans, Mng. Dir.--Thermon Europe B.V., Pijnacker, Netherlands; *U.S. Private*, pg. 1081
Stoutjesdijk, P. G., Mng. Dir.--PURAC Group, Gorcum, Netherlands; *Int'l*, pg. 244
Stoveken, Bill, Plant Mgr.--Household Products Co., Cleveland, OH; *U.S. Public*, pg. 387
Stovel, William, Mgr.--Hi-Pro Animal Health, Friona, TX; *U.S. Private*, pg. 429
Stover, B.H., Pres.--Anadarko Algeria Corporation, Houston, TX; *U.S. Public*, pg. 107
Stover, Matthew J., Pres. & Chief Exec. Officer--Bell Atlantic Yellow Pages, Middleton, MA; *U.S. Public*, pg. 203
Stover, W. Robert, Chm. Bd. & Chief Exec. Officer--Western Permanent Services Agency, Inc., Walnut Creek, CA; *U.S. Public*, pg. 1760
Stover, W. Robert, Chm. Bd. & Chief Exec. Officer--Western Staff Services (USA), Inc., Walnut Creek, CA; *U.S. Public*, pg. 1760
Stoversten, Oscar, Chief Oper. Officer--Husqvarna A/S, Oslo, Norway; *Int'l*, pg. 443
Stow, M., Gen. Mgr.--De La Rue Systems SA, Mane-la-Vallee, France; *Int'l*, pg. 387
Stoyanov, Milan, Pres.--Forest City Trading Group, Inc., Portland, OR; *U.S. Public*, pg. 669
Stoychev, Kancho, Mng. Dir.--Champions, Sofia, Bulgaria; *U.S. Private*, pg. 1199
Stoycos, A.V., Pres.--Specialty Products and Insulation Company, Lancaster, PA; *U.S. Public*, pg. 913
Stoycos, A.V., Pres.--Boatwright Insulation Company, Inc., Raleigh, NC; *U.S. Public*, pg. 913
Stoyle, Nudia, Gen. Mgr.--Edelman Worldwide China, Shanghai, China; *U.S. Private*, pg. 363
Straat, H.C., Pres.--Uitgeversmaatschappij De Limburger bv, Maastricht, Netherlands; *Int'l*, pg. 1445
Straathof, Jacques, Chief Oper. Officer--Neste Chemicals Benelux Holding B.V., Breda, Netherlands; *Int'l*, pg. 914
Stracka, James J., Pres.--Zahorik Co., Inc., Pasadena, CA; *Int'l*, pg. 28
Strading, P. ap G, Pres.--NatWest International Trust Corporation (Europe) Limited, Douglas, United Kingdom; *Int'l*, pg. 911
Stradling, Derek, Mgr.--Sandvik Hard Materials Ltd., Coventry, United Kingdom; *Int'l*, pg. 1186
Stradling, Rod, Pres.--BOC Coating Technology, Fairfield, CA; *Int'l*, pg. 121
Straeter, Terry A., Dr., Pres.--GDE Systems, Inc., San Diego, CA; *U.S. Public*, pg. 1627
Strahan, Dorman L., Pres.--Marine Systems, Inc.-Gulf Coast, Houma, LA; *U.S. Public*, pg. 961
Strahm, Peter, Mng. Dir.--Novelair-Sifrag AG, Zurich, Switzerland; *Int'l*, pg. 1306
Straka, Mark, Pres.--Southern California Air Gas, Gardena, CA; *U.S. Public*, pg. 33
Straka, Mark, Pres.--Southern California Air Gas, Lakewood, CA; *U.S. Public*, pg. 33
Stramaglia, M.P., Chief Exec. Officer--Zurich Life Insurance Co. of Canada, Willowdale, Canada; *Int'l*, pg. 1532
Stranaland, David, Pres.--Dan-Co Bakery, Inc., Forest Park, GA; *U.S. Public*, pg. 657
Strand, Edward E., Pres.--Unisource, Appleton, WI; *U.S. Public*, pg. 1671
Strand, James W., Pres.--Prairie Communications, Inc., Lincoln, NE; *U.S. Public*, pg. 41
Strand, Lars, Pres.--Optiroc A.S., Varde, Denmark; *Int'l*, pg. 1200
Strand, Ragnar, Pres.--Kvaerner Eiendom a.s, Oslo, Norway; *Int'l*, pg. 766
Strand, Steve, Chief Oper. Officer--Major Pharmaceuticals, San Diego, CA; *U.S. Private*, pg. 475
Strandlarsen, Freddy, Mng. Dir.--Anco Trae A/S, Herlev, Denmark; *Int'l*, pg. 1429
Strange, Bob, Pres.--Commercial Cold Storage, Inc., Atlanta, GA; *U.S. Public*, pg. 1519
Strange, Bruce, Chief Oper. Officer--Frionor Australia Pty. Ltd., Melbourne, Australia; *Int'l*, pg. 516
Strano, Paul V., Pres.--Strano Syscco Foodservice Limited, Peterborough, Canada; *U.S. Public*, pg. 1552
Straschnoy, Dario, Pres.--Young & Rubicam de Buenos Aires, Buenos Aires, Argentina; *U.S. Private*, pg. 1200
Strassburg, C.E., Division Mgr.--Indiana Division, Carmel, IN; *Int'l*, pg. 518
Strassburger, Chris, V.P.-Printing (Intermountain Area)--Zellerbach Division, Denver, CO; *U.S. Public*, pg. 1075
Strasser, Alain, Pres.--N.V. Biscuits Delacre S.A., Vilvoorde, Belgium; *U.S. Public*, pg. 300
Strassle, Walter, Mng. Dir.--Union Bank of Switzerland (Panama) Inc., Panama, Panama; *Int'l*, pg. 1441
Strassler, Hans-Rudolf, Pres. & Chief Oper. Officer--Forbo International SA, Eglisau, Switzerland; *Int'l*, pg. 497
Strath, A., Mng. Dir.--Compugraphics International Limited, Glenrothes, United Kingdom; *Int'l*, pg. 802
Strathdee, S., Mng. Dir.--Tate & Lyle International, London, United Kingdom; *Int'l*, pg. 1356
Stratton, G., Mgr.--Daher Golden Eagle - San Francisco, South San Francisco, CA; *U.S. Public*, pg. 749
Stratton, Richard, Pres.--Nabors Drilling USA, Inc., Houston, TX; *U.S. Public*, pg. 1149
Stratton, Thomas W., Pres.--Partel Research Corp., Melbourne, FL; *Int'l*, pg. 27
Stratton, Tony, Chief Exec. Officer--CPM International, Thame, United Kingdom; *U.S. Public*, pg. 1225
Stratviet, Leif, Mgr.--Frionor-Produkter A/S, Rud, Norway; *Int'l*, pg. 516
Straub, Michael, Mgr.--Rhone-Poulenc Rorer, Oak Forest, IL; *Int'l*, pg. 1111
Straub, P.J., V.P. & Gen. Mgr.--Bliss, Hastings, MI; *U.S. Private*, pg. 196
Straube, D.R., Chief Fin. Officer--Raytheon Systems Mississippi, Forest, MS; *U.S. Public*, pg. 1365
Strausbaugh, Robert L., Vice Chm., Pres. & Chief Exec. Officer--Spring Grove National Bank, Spring Grove, PA; *U.S. Public*, pg. 1542
Strauser, Randy, Plant Mgr.--Firestone Building Products Company-Prescott, Prescott, AR; *Int'l*, pg. 214
Strauss, C. B., Chm.--Standard Bank London Limited, London, United Kingdom; *Int'l*, pg. 1294
Strauss, David, Chm. Bd.--Sedgwick Noble Lowndes Group Limited, Croydon, United Kingdom; *Int'l*, pg. 1218
Strauss, David, Chm.--Sedgwick Noble Lowndes Limited, Melbourne, Australia; *Int'l*, pg. 1218
Strauss, Gary J., Pres.--Ikon Office Solutions-St. Louis, Saint Louis, MO; *U.S. Public*, pg. 864
Strauss, Gerhard, Pres.--Danfoss Electronic Drives, Rockford, IL; *Int'l*, pg. 377
Strauss, John, V.P. & Gen. Mgr.--Audible/Visible & Waterflow Division, Saint Charles, IL; *U.S. Public*, pg. 1306
Strauss, Jurgen, Mng. Dir.--Schweizerische Rentenanstalt, Munich, Germany; *Int'l*, pg. 1332
Strauss, Phil, Pres.--Multiplex Technology, Inc., Brea, CA; *U.S. Public*, pg. 1705
Strauss, Philip E., Jr., Exec. V.P.--Central Group, Chicago, IL; *U.S. Public*, pg. 649
Strauss, Stanley, Vice Pres. & Gen. Mgr.--Hallmark Educational Products Div., Easton, PA; *U.S. Private*, pg. 496
Stravitz, Russell, Chm.--Rich's/Lazarus/Goldsmith's, Atlanta, GA; *U.S. Public*, pg. 618
Straw, David, Gen. Mgr.--TEC Fab Div., Richmond, IN; *U.S. Private*, pg. 868
Strawn, Dave, Div. Mgr.--ConAgra Broiler Co., Dalton, GA; *U.S. Public*, pg. 427
Strawn, Steve, V.P.-Sls.--City Club of Charlotte, Fort Mill, SC; *U.S. Public*, pg. 610
Strawson, Robert, Gen. Mgr.--Serca Food Service-Fitzsimmons Div., Thunder Bay, Canada; *Int'l*, pg. 1012
Streatfeild, D.A., Mng. Dir.--Christie, Manson & Woods Limited, London, United Kingdom; *Int'l*, pg. 290
Strebel, Max, Pres. & Chief Exec. Officer--Union Bank of Switzerland (Canada), Toronto, Canada; *Int'l*, pg. 1441
Street, James E., Chm. Bd. & Chief Exec. Officer--United Missouri Bank of Springfield, Springfield, MO; *U.S. Public*, pg. 1655
Street, John M, Pres.--Ikon Office Solutions-Richmond, Richmond, VA; *U.S. Public*, pg. 864
Street, Peter C.R., Mng. Dir.--Roe Lee Paper Chemicals Co. Ltd., Blackburn, United Kingdom; *Int'l*, pg. 1086
Streff, Darrell, Pres.--Feterl Mfg. Co., Salem, SD; *U.S. Public*, pg. 1676
Streiff, Christina, Pres.-Paper Div.--Pont-a-Mousson SA, Nancy, France; *Int'l*, pg. 1176
Streitender, J.L., Mgr.--Hanna Insurance Services Division, Cleveland, OH; *U.S. Public*, pg. 781
Strelecki, Clem, Gen. Mgr.--Elixir Industries, Vancouver, WA; *U.S. Private*, pg. 371

Strellner, Leland R., Pres.--K-T Corp., Shelbyville, IN; *U.S. Public*, pg. 1640
Strenger, Christian, Mng. Dir.--Deutsche Bank Capital Corporation, New York, NY; *Int'l*, pg. 403
Streppel, J.B.M., Chm. Bd.--Labouchere N.V., Amsterdam, Netherlands; *Int'l*, pg. 26
Streule, Roland, Mng. Dir.--Rado Uhren AG, Lengnau, Switzerland; *Int'l*, pg. 1160
Streule, Roland, Mng. Dir.--SMH (U.S.) Inc., Weehawken, NJ; *Int'l*, pg. 1161
Streur, Harold, Chm. Bd.--Castex Incorporated, Holland, MI; *U.S. Public*, pg. 1577
Strey, Kurt, Mng. Dir.--Fishery Foods GmbH, Cuxhaven, Germany; *Int'l*, pg. 492
Strick, Karl H., V.P. & Gen. Mgr.--Air Systems Div., Birmingham, AL; *U.S. Public*, pg. 1794
Strickland, J.E., Chm. Bd.--The Hongkong and Shanghai Banking Corporation Limited (HongkongBank), Central, Hong Kong; *Int'l*, pg. 583
Strickland, James, Admin.--Hillhaven-Sunnybrook Convalescent Center, Raleigh, NC; *U.S. Public*, pg. 1714
Strickland, Joe C., Pres.--Amoco Foam Products Co., Atlanta, GA; *U.S. Public*, pg. 102
Strickland, Robert, Chm. Bd. & Chief Exec. Officer--Trust Company Of Georgia, Atlanta, GA; *U.S. Public*, pg. 1538
Strickland, Robert W., V.P.-Opers.--Holly Sugar Corporation, Sugar Land, TX; *U.S. Public*, pg. 872
Strickland, Terry D., Pres. & Mgr.--First American Title Co. of Mendocino County, Ukiah, CA; *U.S. Public*, pg. 625
Strickler, Mark, Pres.--Rocco Building Supplies Inc., Harrisonburg, VA; *U.S. Private*, pg. 937
Strickler, Peter, Chief Exec. Officer--Holderchem Ltd., Zurich, Switzerland; *Int'l*, pg. 628
Strickler, Twig, Chm. Bd.--Shady Brook Farms, Dayton, VA; *U.S. Private*, pg. 937
Strid, Bertil, Mng. Dir.--Ericsson Network Constructions AB, Stockholm, Sweden; *Int'l*, pg. 1363
Striegler, Kenneth, Pres.--Chr. Hansen Industria e Comercio Ltda., Sao Paulo, Brazil; *Int'l*, pg. 289
Strigl, Dennis F., Pres. & Chief Exec. Officer--Bell Atlantic Mobile, Bedminster, NJ; *U.S. Public*, pg. 202
Strijbos, Marc, Gen. Mgr.--Life Technologies SARL, Cergy-Pontoise, France; *U.S. Public*, pg. 505
Stringfellow, R.J., Mng. Dir.--Southern Sun Hotel Holdings Limited, Sandton, South Africa; *Int'l*, pg. 1287
Stringfellow, R.S., Mng. Dir.--OK Bazaars (1929) Ltd., Germiston, South Africa; *Int'l*, pg. 1287
Stringle, Stan, Chief Exec. Officer--Omega Environmental Inc., Richmond, VA; *U.S. Public*, pg. 1222
Strittmatter, Hermann, Pres.--TBWA/GGK, Zurich, Switzerland; *U.S. Private*, pg. 1063
Strode, Jim, V.P.-Mfg.--Williams Scotsman Group, Inc., Santa Fe Springs, CA; *U.S. Private*, pg. 977
Stroebel, Piet, Mng. Dir.--Sasol Two Div., Secunda, South Africa; *Int'l*, pg. 1197
Stroetszel, Klaus, Chief Oper. Officer--Fricke GmbH & Co. KG, Greven, Germany; *Int'l*, pg. 719
Stroh, B. Gregory, Pres.-Package--Packaging Business, Milford, OH; *U.S. Public*, pg. 671
Stroh, B. Gregory, Pres.--Folding Carton Group, Milford, OH; *U.S. Public*, pg. 671
Strolz, Albin, Reg. Dir.--ITT Flygt Kft, Budaors, Hungary; *U.S. Public*, pg. 860
Strom, Arne, Pres.--Frigoscandia Food Process Systems Ltd., Hoddesdon, United Kingdom; *U.S. Public*, pg. 607
Strom, D., Mktg. & Sls. Mgr.--Microsi, Phoenix, AZ; *Int'l*, pg. 1234
Strom, Milton G., Partner--Skadden, Arps, Slate, Meagher & Flom LLP, Toronto, Canada; *U.S. Private*, pg. 1005
Strom, Richard, Pres.--Pulte Houston Division, Houston, TX; *U.S. Public*, pg. 1344
Strom, Richard L., Pres.--Pulte Dallas Division, Irving, TX; *U.S. Public*, pg. 1344
Strom, Stephen, Pres.--Home Computer Software Div., Troy, MI; *U.S. Public*, pg. 779
Strom, Vesa Svart, Mng. Dir.--Berendsen Components OY, Vantaa, Finland; *Int'l*, pg. 1284
Strombos, Nick, Pres.--Alpha Coatings, Livonia, MI; *U.S. Private*, pg. 1152
Stromquist, Dag, Pres.--EKA Nobel AB, Surte, Sweden; *Int'l*, pg. 48
Stromsoe, Erik, Pres.--Kvaerner Chile S.A., Santiago, Chile; *Int'l*, pg. 767
Strong, James, Gen. Mgr.--SmithKline Beecham Clinical Laboratories, San Antonio, TX; *Int'l*, pg. 1265
Strong, Joseph M., V.P. & Gen. Mgr.--Dillard, A ResourceNet International Company, Birmingham, AL; *U.S. Public*, pg. 902
Strong, Joseph M., V.P. & Gen. Mgr.--Dillard, A ResourceNet International Company, Montgomery, AL; *U.S. Public*, pg. 902
Strong, Peter R., Pres. & Chief Exec. Officer--Buehler, Limited, Lake Bluff, IL; *U.S. Public*, pg. 574
Strong, Robert F., II, Pres. & Chief Oper. Officer--Longview National Bank, Longview, TX; *U.S. Public*, pg. 630
Strong, Robert T., Pres.--NEFA Corporation, Southampton, PA; *U.S. Public*, pg. 1326
Strong, W.B., Mgr.--Tencarva Machinery Co., Memphis, TN; *U.S. Private*, pg. 1075
Stroobants, Roger, Mgr.--GGK Brussels, Brussels, Belgium; *Int'l*, pg. 1335
Stroom, Eric C., Opers. Mgr.--Amcast Automotive-Gas City Plant, Gas City, IN; *U.S. Public*, pg. 63
Strotham, Wendy J., Exec. V.P.--Houghton Mifflin Trade & Reference Div., Boston, MA; *U.S. Public*, pg. 841
Strotmann, Michael, Plant Mgr.--Donaldson Gesellschaft m.b.H., Dulmen, Germany; *U.S. Public*, pg. 517
Stroud, Garry, Pres.--Copeland Canada, Ltd., Brantford, Canada; *U.S. Public*, pg. 576
Stroud, Steve, Pres.--Mercantile Investment & Trust Services, Des Moines, IA; *U.S. Public*, pg. 1088
Stroud, Walter, Pres.--Olympic Manufacturing Co., Wilkesboro, NC; *U.S. Private*, pg. 200
Stroud, Wayne, Gen. Mgr.--Dallas Auto Auction Inc., Dallas, TX; *U.S. Public*, pg. 1648
Stroupe, David, Chief Oper. Officer & V.P.--Green Mountain Propane Gas Co., Burlington, VT; *U.S. Public*, pg. 761
Strouse, Scott, Plant Mgr.--L.B. Foster Company-Newport Plant, Newport, KY; *U.S. Public*, pg. 676
Strub, Peter, Co-Owner & Chief Fin. Officer--Eurad RSCG, Zurich, Switzerland; *Int'l*, pg. 602
Strubi, Vera, Chief Oper. Officer--Thierry Mugler Parfums, Neuilly-sur-Seine, France; *Int'l*, pg. 295
Struck, H.J., Chief Oper. Officer--Volkswagen of Nigeria Ltd., Lagos, Nigeria; *Int'l*, pg. 1475
Strulovici, Christian, Chm. Bd.--Cofassur Vie, Paris, France; *Int'l*, pg. 564
Strumbos, Nick, Pres.--Alpha Bolt Company, Madison Heights, MI; *U.S. Private*, pg. 1152
Strumwasser, Barry, Pres.--Baker Norton Pharmaceuticals, Inc., Miami, FL; *U.S. Public*, pg. 914
Strunce, D. G., Gen. Mgr. & Exec. V.P.--Eurand International S.p.A., Milan, Italy; *U.S. Public*, pg. 81
Strunck, Gunther, Mng. Dir.--Woelm Pharma GmbH & Co., Eschwege, Germany; *Int'l*, pg. 1112
Struthers, Jim, Interim Publisher--Medicine Hat News, Medicine Hat, Canada; *Int'l*, pg. 631
Strutton, Larry D., Pres. & Chief Exec. Officer--Rocky Mountain News, Denver, CO; *U.S. Public*, pg. 1448
Strutz, George A., Pres.--Clopay Corporation, Cincinnati, OH; *U.S. Public*, pg. 766
Strutz, Richard, Pres.--National Bank of Alaska, Anchorage, AK; *U.S. Public*, pg. 1153
Struz, J., Gen. Mgr.--ING Bank Prague, Prague, Czech Republic; *Int'l*, pg. 649
Stry, David W., Gen. Mgr.--Building Materials Distribution Div., Overland Park, KS; *U.S. Public*, pg. 901
Strydom, C.H., Mng. Dir.--J.I. Case South Africa (Pty.) Ltd., Isando, South Africa; *U.S. Public*, pg. 1580
Stryker, D., Pres.--MB Paper, Seattle, WA; *Int'l*, pg. 829
Stuart, Arthur, Pres.--Bridgestone/Firestone Original Equipment Tire Sales Company, Southfield, MI; *Int'l*, pg. 213
Stuart, D.L., Gen. Mgr.--ING (London) Futures & Options, London, United Kingdom; *Int'l*, pg. 650
Stuart, Douglas, Mng. Dir.--Spar Aerospace (U.K.) Limited, Hayes, United Kingdom; *Int'l*, pg. 1288
Stuart, Ian, Pres.--Mead Johnson Nutritionals, Evansville, IN; *U.S. Public*, pg. 255
Stuart, James, III, Chm. Bd.--First Commerce Investors, Lincoln, NE; *U.S. Public*, pg. 629
Stuart, Tom, Gen. Mgr.--Ransomes Inc., Johnson Creek, WI; *Int'l*, pg. 1088
Stuart, William, Mgr.--Service Telephone Co., Inc., Fair Bluff, NC; *U.S. Public*, pg. 1572
Stuart, William M., Pres.--Charles S. Lewis & Co., Inc., Saint Louis, MO; *Int'l*, pg. 1489
Stubblefield, Mitch, Div. Mgr.--Universal Telephone Co. of Colorado, Pagosa Springs, CO; *U.S. Public*, pg. 330
Stubbs, J. A., Mgr.--Nassau Terminals, Fernandina Beach, FL; *Int'l*, pg. 758
Stubbs, Robert W., Pres. & Chief Exec. Officer--Bell Atlantic Capital Corporation, Paramus, NJ; *U.S. Public*, pg. 202
Stubbs, Stoney M., Jr., Pres.--AM Can, Dallas, TX; *U.S. Public*, pg. 685
Stuber, Dr. Fred, Mng. Dir.--Tesa, S.A., Renens, Switzerland; *U.S. Public*, pg. 260
Stuckalov, V. D., Mng. Dir.--AMT, Moscow, Russia; *Int'l*, pg. 954
Stucke, Ken, Reg. Mgr.--Brock Exploration Corporation, New Orleans, LA; *U.S. Public*, pg. 953
Stuckey, Buddy S., Chief Oper. Officer--Flint & Walling Industries, Inc., Kendallville, IN; *U.S. Public*, pg. 1053
Stuckey, James C., Jr., Chief Oper. Officer--Wholesale Wood Products, Dothan, AL; *U.S. Private*, pg. 680
Stucki, Hans-Rudolf, Dr., Chm. Bd.--Blue Ridge Insurance Co., Simsbury, CT; *Int'l*, pg. 345
Studener, Wolfgang, Mng. Dir.--Battenfeld Extrusionstechnik GmbH, Bad Oeynhausen, Germany; *Int'l*, pg. 825
Studer, Don, Chief Oper. Officer--Allright Parking Minnesota, Inc., Minneapolis, MN; *U.S. Private*, pg. 43
Stuelpe, G. Walter, Jr., Pres. & Chief Exec. Officer--Apcoa, Inc., Cleveland, OH; *U.S. Private*, pg. 533
Stuenkel, Mark H., Pres. & Chief Exec. Officer--Southern California Bank, Newport Beach, CA; *U.S. Public*, pg. 1758
Stuenkel, Wayne E., Pres.--American Foundation Life Insurance Company, Birmingham, AL; *U.S. Public*, pg. 1336
Stueve, John, Pres.--Alta Dena Inc., City of Industry, CA; *Int'l*, pg. 201
Stukenberg, Bob, Mgr.--SunRidge Hotel & Conference Center, Bullhead City, AZ; *U.S. Private*, pg. 673
Stulemeijer, C.A.J., Chief Oper. Officer--Breemars Assurantien B.V., Breda, Netherlands; *Int'l*, pg. 1133
Stulik, Miroslav, Mgr.-Sls.--PENCO-Washington, Tukwila, WA; *Int'l*, pg. 1508
Stultz, B.M., Pres.--FPC, Inc., Hollywood, CA; *U.S. Public*, pg. 551
Stum, Ed, Mgr.-Sls.--PENCO-Oklahoma, Oklahoma City, OK; *Int'l*, pg. 1508
Stumpf, John, Chm.--Norwest Bank Texas, N.A., Lubbock, TX; *U.S. Public*, pg. 1203
Stuntz, Mayo S., Jr., Pres.--Compuserve Interactive Services, Inc., Columbus, OH; *U.S. Public*, pg. 66
Stuntz, William, Pres.--Dranetz-BMI, Edison, NJ; *U.S. Private*, pg. 1144
Stupetzky, Andreas, Mng. Dir.--ISS Servisystem GesmbH, Vienna, Austria; *Int'l*, pg. 657
Stupnik, Manfred, Chief Oper. Officer--Gamma-f Corporation, Torrance, CA; *U.S. Public*, pg. 1718
Stupple, George, Gen. Mgr.--BHP Steel Building Products India, New Delhi, India; *Int'l*, pg. 226
Sturdevant, Truman, V.P.--Smurfit Newsprint Corporation, Oregon City, OR; *Int'l*, pg. 1271
Sturdivant, John E., Gen. Mgr.--Music City News, Nashville, TN; *U.S. Public*, pg. 701
Sturdivant, Walter, Gen. Mgr.--WQDR, Raleigh, NC; *U.S. Private*, pg. 298
Sturegard, Claes, Mng. Dir.--SKF Eurotrade AB, Goteborg, Sweden; *Int'l*, pg. 1157
Sturiale, Thomas, Pres. & Chief Exec. Officer--Neles-Jamesbury Corp., Worcester, MA; *Int'l*, pg. 1428
Sturken, Craig, Grp. V.P.-Michigan--Farmer Jack Supermarkets, Detroit, MI; *Int'l*, pg. 1375
Sturkenboom, Wim, Fin. Dir.--Noordervliet & Winninghoff/Leo Burnett B.V., Amsterdam, Netherlands; *U.S. Private*, pg. 186
Sturm, Gerhard, Mng. Dir.--Wilhelm Weber GmbH, Pfungstadt, Germany; *U.S. Private*, pg. 160
Sturm, William L., Grp. V.P. & Gen. Mgr.--Chemical Catalysts, Iselin, NJ; *U.S. Public*, pg. 582
Sturmfels, Dipl.-Ing. Juergen, Chief Oper. Officer--Streif AG, Vettelschoss, Germany; *Int'l*, pg. 623
Sturn, Wolfgang J., Dr., Pres.--Florasynth Inc., Teterboro, NJ; *Int'l*, pg. 173
Sturrock, Ian, Mng. Dir.--Willis Corroon Scotland Limited, Dundee, United Kingdom; *Int'l*, pg. 1503
Sturrock, Wilma, Pres.--Ridge Vineyards Inc., Cupertino, CA; *Int'l*, pg. 1013
Sturrus, Anthony, Chief Oper. Officer--Baldwin Hardware Corporation, Reading, PA; *U.S. Public*, pg. 1053
Sturrus, Tony, Chief Oper. Officer--Baldwin Hardware Service Corporation, Reading, PA; *U.S. Public*, pg. 1053
Sturt, Trevor H., Mng. Dir.--Thermal Processing Group Ltd., Exhall, United Kingdom; *Int'l*, pg. 1338
Stutler, Robert, Plant Mgr.--Sturm, Ruger & Co., Inc., Prescott, AZ; *U.S. Public*, pg. 1526
Stutvoet, William, Gen. Mgr. & Controller--Thompack B.V., Apeldoorn, Netherlands; *U.S. Public*, pg. 5
Stutz, Hermann, Mng. Dir.--Joseph Dawson AG, Zug, Switzerland; *Int'l*, pg. 386
Styles, Edie, Branch Mgr.--Downey Savings & Loan Association, F.A., Yucca Valley, CA; *U.S. Public*, pg. 527
Styrlind, Kenneth A., Pres. & Chief Exec. Officer--Witcher Construction Company, Eden Prairie, MN; *U.S. Private*, pg. 347
Styrvold, Knut, Pres.--Erling Sande A/S, Oslo, Norway; *Int'l*, pg. 1390
Stys, Ray, Gen. Mgr.--Cableco, Los Angeles, CA; *U.S. Private*, pg. 215
Su, Kim Kye, Gen. Mgr.--Watlow Korea, Seoul, Korea; *U.S. Private*, pg. 1154
Su, P.P., Exec. V.P.--Interworld Enterprises Ltd., Taipei, Taiwan; *Int'l*, pg. 594
Suarez, Alfonso Fuertes, Pres.--Iber-Swiss Catering, S.A., Madrid, Spain; *Int'l*, pg. 1225
Suarez, Gonzalez, Pres.--Suarez & Clavera/DMB&B, Montevideo, Uruguay; *U.S. Private*, pg. 305
Suarez, Jesus, Mng. Dir.--UPM-Kymmene Papel S.A., Madrid, Spain; *Int'l*, pg. 1430
Suaudeau, Yves, Mng. Dir.--Editions Edouard Privat SA, Toulouse, France; *Int'l*, pg. 239
Subia, Robert, Chm., Pres. & Chief Exec. Officer--Micron Custom Manufacturing Services, Inc., Nampa, ID; *U.S. Public*, pg. 1105
Subijana, Pedro Sagues, Pres.--Infoleasing SAF, S.A., Madrid, Spain; *Int'l*, pg. 1225
Sublett, Gregg, Plant Mgr.--Acme Brick Co., Denton, TX; *U.S. Public*, pg. 936
Subphon, Siri, Mng. Dir.--Anju Jewelry Limited, Kowloon, Hong Kong; *U.S. Public*, pg. 1625
Subra, Daniel, Dir. General--Banque Dupuy de Parceval, Sete, France; *Int'l*, pg. 548
Subrahmanyam, N., Dir.--Tata McGraw-Hill Publishing Co., Private Limited, New Delhi, India; *U.S. Public*, pg. 1072
Subramanian, K.S., Gen. Mgr.--John Crane Engineered Sealing Systems Ltd., Madras, India; *Int'l*, pg. 1339
Sucaldito, Enrique L., Pres.--Equipment Engineers Inc., Manila, Philippines; *Int'l*, pg. 426
Sucaldito, Enrique L., Chief Oper. Officer--EEI Power Corp., Manila, Philippines; *Int'l*, pg. 426
Sucher, D., Mgr.-Sls.--Zellerbach Division, Knoxville, TN; *U.S. Public*, pg. 1075
Suchomel, Jim, Gen. Mgr.--U.S. Filter/Arrowhead Inc., Rockford, IL; *U.S. Public*, pg. 1682
Suchordt, Volkert, Chief Oper. Officer--Busch-Jaeger Ludenscheider Metallwerk GmbH, Ludenscheid, Germany; *Int'l*, pg. 1427
Suda, Nokio, Mng. Dir.--Nikko Bank (Deutschland) GmbH, Frankfurt/Main, Germany; *Int'l*, pg. 930
Sudderth, Grant, Gen. Mgr.--Henkel Corporation Minerals Industry Div., Tucson, AZ; *Int'l*, pg. 610
Sudderth, John, Pres.--Dowell Schlumberger Canada Inc., Calgary, Canada; *U.S. Public*, pg. 1439
Sudderth, Robert J., Jr., Chm. & Chief Exec. Officer--SunTrust Bank, Chattanooga, N.A., Chattanooga, TN; *U.S. Public*, pg. 1538
Suder, John M., V.P. & Gen. Mgr.--KWGN Inc., Englewood, CO; *U.S. Public*, pg. 1636
Sudiran, Lahuree bin, Mng. Dir.--W.R. Grace (Malaysia) Sdn. Bhd., Pahang, Malaysia; *U.S. Public*, pg. 756
Sudmeier, John, Publisher--RCR Publications, Denver, CO; *U.S. Private*, pg. 285
Sudo, Kazuyoshi, Dir.-Admin.--Chugai Boyeki (America) Corp., Commack, NY; *Int'l*, pg. 290
Sudo, Masamichi, Chief Oper. Officer--Daikyo Seiko Co., Ltd., Tokyo, Japan; *U.S. Public*, pg. 1756
Sudo, Paul, Sr. Exec. V.P.--Chugai Boyeki (America) Corp., New York, NY; *Int'l*, pg. 290
Suduck, Robert, Pres.--Posterloid Corporation, Long Island City, NY; *U.S. Public*, pg. 1315
Suehiro, S., Pres.--Taiyo Chemical Industry Co., Ltd., Osaka, Japan; *Int'l*, pg. 947
Suen, Susanna, Controller--Kulicke & Soffa (Asia), Ltd., Kowloon, Hong Kong; *U.S. Public*, pg. 969
Suenaga, Isshi, Pres.--Mitsui Engineering & Shipbuilding Co., Ltd., Tokyo, Japan; *Int'l*, pg. 878
Suerth, Hank, Pres.--Infinity Systems, Inc., Chatsworth, CA; *U.S. Public*, pg. 787

Suess, Tom, Gen. Mgr.--Lebus Manufacturing Co., Longview, TX; *Int'l*, pg. 473
Suetans, Regine, Office Mgr.--DRI Europe, Inc., Brussels, Belgium; *U.S. Public*, pg. 1072
Suetsugu, Hiroshi, Pres. & Chief Exec. Officer--Nippon Steel U.S.A., Inc., New York, NY; *Int'l*, pg. 939
Suga, Yasuro, Pres.--Konica Canada Inc., Mississauga, Canada; *Int'l*, pg. 749
Sugar, David E., V.P. & Sec.--NGL American Life, Menasha, WI; *U.S. Private*, pg. 784
Sugata, M., Pres.--Instron Japan Co. Ltd., Tokyo, Japan; *U.S. Public*, pg. 883
Suggett, A., Dr., Mng. Dir.--Smith & Nephew Research Ltd., York, United Kingdom; *Int'l*, pg. 1263
Suggitt, N.S.W., Mng. Dir.--Olin Australia Limited, Geelong, Australia; *U.S. Public*, pg. 1220
Suggitt, N.W.S., Chm. Bd. & Pres.--Olin Far East, Limited, Stamford, CT; *U.S. Public*, pg. 1219
Suggitt, N.W.S., Mng. Dir.--Olin Australia Limited, Saint Leonards, Australia; *U.S. Public*, pg. 1220
Sugimoto, M., Pres.--Toyobo America Inc., New York, NY; *Int'l*, pg. 1411
Sugimoto, Tsuyoshi, Gen. Mgr.--The Yokohama Rubber Co., Ltd., Seattle, WA; *Int'l*, pg. 1521
Sugimoto, Yasuo, Mng. Dir. & Gen. Mgr.-Prod. Plng. & Mngmt. Div.--Fuji Heavy Industries, Ltd., Automobile Div., Oita, Japan; *Int'l*, pg. 522
Sugimura, Kenjiro, Mng. Dir.--Toyo Trust International Limited, London, United Kingdom; *Int'l*, pg. 1411
Sugino, Seechi, Sr. Rep.--Nippon Credit Bank Ltd.-Beijing, Beijing, China; *Int'l*, pg. 933
Sugita, Kojo, Vice Chm.--Alfa Romeo e Nissan Autoveicoli S.p.A., Naples, Italy; *Int'l*, pg. 481
Sugita, Satoshi, Exec. V.P.--Prap Japan, Inc., Tokyo, Japan; *U.S. Private*, pg. 617
Sugita, Yoshihiko, Chief Rep.--The Sumitomo Bank, Ltd.-Yangon Representative Office, Yangon, Myanmar; *Int'l*, pg. 1310
Sugiura, Hiroaki, Pres.--Toyota Motor Corporation, Detroit Branch, Southfield, MI; *Int'l*, pg. 1412
Sugiura, Toshiro, Mng. Dir.--Asahi Finance (U.K.) Ltd., London, United Kingdom; *Int'l*, pg. 83
Sugiuro, Tatsuya, Chm.--Mitsubishi Electric Sales America, Cypress, CA; *Int'l*, pg. 872
Sugiyama, Kunio, Joint Gen. Mgr.--Dai-Ichi Kangyo Bank, Ltd.-Milan, Milan, Italy; *Int'l*, pg. 360
Sugiyama, Mineo, Pres.--NEC Industries, Inc., New York, NY; *Int'l*, pg. 900
Sugiyama, Mineo, Pres. & Chief Exec. Officer--NEC America, Inc., Melville, NY; *Int'l*, pg. 900
Sugiyama, Mineo, Pres.--NEC USA, Inc., Melville, NY; *Int'l*, pg. 900
Sugiyama, Takaji, Chief Rep.--Dai-Ichi Kangyo Bank, Ltd.-Guangzhou, Guangzhou, China; *Int'l*, pg. 361
Sugo, Kazuo, Pres.--Sakura Bank (Schweiz) AG, Zurich, Switzerland; *Int'l*, pg. 1180
Suguri, S., Pres.--Aromat Canada Inc., Etobicoke, Canada; *Int'l*, pg. 848
Suhonen, Kauko, Gen. Mgr.--Koltek Oy, Vantaa, Finland; *Int'l*, pg. 1379
Suhonen, Olli, Mng. Dir.--Nokia Switching Systems, Saint Petersburg, Russia; *Int'l*, pg. 954
Suidal, Cathy, Gen. Mgr.--Devils Lake Journal, Devils Lake, ND; *U.S. Public*, pg. 1078
Suijkerbuijk, D.P., Mng. Dir.--Nedlloyd Road Cargo Division, Dusseldorf, Germany; *Int'l*, pg. 1145
Suijkerbuijk, D.P., Mng. Dir.--Nedlloyd Unitras, Dusseldorf, Germany; *Int'l*, pg. 1145
Suijkerbuijk, D.P., Mng. Dir.--Nedlloyd Road Cargo FTL, Moerdijk, Netherlands; *Int'l*, pg. 1145
Suila, Keijo, Pres. & Chief Exec. Officer--Leaf Group B.V., Espoo, Finland,; *Int'l*, pg. 638
Suisman, Gary, Pres. & Publr.--Lansing State Journal, Lansing, MI; *U.S. Public*, pg. 701
Suitirong, Pramon, Chm. Bd.--Thai Kabaya Industries Co., Ltd., Chon Buri, Thailand; *Int'l*, pg. 727
Suk, S.K., Pres.--Varian Korea Ltd., Kyonggi-do, Korea; *U.S. Public*, pg. 1710
Suk, Yeun H., Dir.--Hyosung America, Inc., Cerritos, CA; *Int'l*, pg. 641
Sukarna, Agus, Pres. & Dir.--P.T. Bank Merincorp, Jakarta, Indonesia; *Int'l*, pg. 1310
Sukawaty, Andrew, Chief Exec. Officer--Sprint PCS, Kansas City, MO; *U.S. Public*, pg. 1501
Sukolski, P., Chief Oper. Officer--McKechnie Pacific, Chatswood, Australia; *Int'l*, pg. 852
Sukosky, Jane, Regional V.P.--BSA Advertising, Inc., Chicago, IL; *U.S. Private*, pg. 108
Sulaiman, Nor Aznan, Dir.--Tourism Malaysia - Vancouver Office, Vancouver, Canada; *Int'l*, pg. 833
Sulak, Johann, Mgr.--Sandvik Magyarorzagon KFT, Budapest, Hungary; *Int'l*, pg. 1186
Sulentic, Thomas, Pres.-Special Mkts. Div.--Danaher Tool Group, Lancaster, PA; *U.S. Public*, pg. 480
Sulger, Martin, Pres. & Chief Exec. Officer--Siemens Pakistan Engineering Co. Ltd., Karachi, Pakistan; *Int'l*, pg. 1247
Sullam, Ronaldo, Pres.--Air Products Europe, Inc., Allentown, PA; *U.S. Public*, pg. 30
Sullam, Ronaldo, Chief Oper. Officer--S.E. Carburos Metalicos S.A., Barcelona, Spain; *U.S. Public*, pg. 32
Sullivan, Bill, Chief Oper. Officer & Exec. V.P.--Optical Radiation Corporation, Azusa, CA; *U.S. Public*, pg. 160
Sullivan, Ceil, Mgr.-Dist. Sls.--Singapore Airlines Ltd., Washington, DC; *Int'l*, pg. 1374
Sullivan, Charles, Pres.--Cargill Salt, Newark, CA; *U.S. Private*, pg. 210
Sullivan, Dan T., Pres.--Burlington Madison Yarn, Greensboro, NC; *U.S. Public*, pg. 268
Sullivan, Dennis, Branch Mgr.--Zellerbach Division, Hillside, IL; *U.S. Public*, pg. 1075
Sullivan, Donald H., Pres.--Cigna Conference Facilities, Inc., Philadelphia, PA; *U.S. Public*, pg. 358
Sullivan, J., Pres.--Columbia Scientific Industries Corporation, Austin, TX; *Int'l*, pg. 1500
Sullivan, James C., Pres.--Dixie Insurance Company, Birmingham, AL; *U.S. Public*, pg. 75
Sullivan, John, Chief Oper. Officer--Lifetouch National School Studios Inc., Chesapeake, VA; *U.S. Private*, pg. 667
Sullivan, John, Admin.--Columbia House Healthcare, Columbia, MO; *U.S. Public*, pg. 1712
Sullivan, John B., Pres. & Chief Exec. Officer--Willis Corroon Corp. of Illinois, Chicago, IL; *Int'l*, pg. 1506
Sullivan, John Fox, Chm., Pres., Chief Exec. Officer & Publr.--National Journal Group, Washington, DC; *U.S. Private*, pg. 785
Sullivan, John J., Pres.--Carlton Cards, Ltd., Toronto, Canada; *U.S. Public*, pg. 78
Sullivan, K.T., Gen. Mgr.--Allen Taylor & Co. Limited, Wetherill Park, Australia; *Int'l*, pg. 203
Sullivan, Kevin, Sr. Bus. Devel. Officer--Northeast Marketing-St. Louis Business Center, Saint Louis, MO; *U.S. Public*, pg. 649
Sullivan, Kurt, V.P. & Gen. Mgr.--Circus Circus-Las Vegas Hotel & Casino, Las Vegas, NV; *U.S. Public*, pg. 375
Sullivan, Lee, Pres.--Freudenberg Spunweb Co., Durham, NC; *Int'l*, pg. 505
Sullivan, Michael, V.P.--Sulpaco West, Appleton, WI; *U.S. Private*, pg. 1050
Sullivan, Michael P., Pres.--Karmelkorn Shoppes, Minneapolis, MN; *U.S. Public*, pg. 220
Sullivan, Pat, Pres. & Chief Exec. Officer--Citizens Bank of Kentucky, Shively, KY; *U.S. Public*, pg. 280
Sullivan, Richard, Sr. Partner, Exec. V.P. & Gen. Mgr.--Fleishman-Hillard, Inc., Washington, DC; *U.S. Private*, pg. 411
Sullivan, Robert, Pres. & Gen. Mgr.--WUSA-TV, Washington, DC; *U.S. Public*, pg. 702
Sullivan, Stephen, Pres. & Chief Oper. Officer--Ling Electronics Inc., Anaheim, CA; *U.S. Public*, pg. 1077
Sullivan, Stephen W., Publisher--Corpus Christi Caller-Times, Corpus Christi, TX; *U.S. Public*, pg. 793
Sullivan, T., Pres.--Switching Systems International, Placentia, CA; *Int'l*, pg. 208
Sullivan, Tim, Pres.--Connectware, Inc. LLC, Fort Washington, PA; *U.S. Public*, pg. 8
Sullivan, Vincent P., Pres.--Serco Company, Dallas, TX; *U.S. Public*, pg. 1676
Sullivent, Wendell, Plant Mgr.--AEP Industries, Inc., Waxahachie, TX; *U.S. Public*, pg. 5
Sulman, David, V.P.--Teradyne Industrial/Consumer Division, Boston, MA; *U.S. Public*, pg. 1581
Sulzberger, Arthur Ochs, Chm. Bd. & Chief Exec. Officer--The New York Times, New York, NY; *U.S. Public*, pg. 1174
Sulzberger, Arthur, Jr., Publisher--New York Times Newspaper Group, New York, NY; *U.S. Public*, pg. 1174
Sulzer, H., Chief Oper. Officer--Jeumont-Schneider of America, Stratford, CT; *Int'l*, pg. 706
Sulzmann, Bernard S., Mgr.--Al-Futtaim Willis Faber (Private) Ltd., Dubai, United Arab Emirates; *Int'l*, pg. 1509
Sum, Y.C., Mng. Dir.--Amersham Far East Trading Limited, Sha Tin, Hong Kong; *Int'l*, pg. 993
Sumi, Yoshihiko, Chief Rep.--The Sakura Bank - Jakarta Representative Office, Jakarta, Indonesia; *Int'l*, pg. 1179
Sumikawa, Kunio, Pres.--Toshiba America Medical Systems, Inc., Tustin, CA; *Int'l*, pg. 1405
Sumino, Eiji, Gen. Mgr.--The Sumitomo Bank, Ltd.-Chicago Branch, Chicago, IL; *Int'l*, pg. 1308
Sumino, Jack, Pres.--CIE America, Inc., Irvine, CA; *Int'l*, pg. 694
Sumio, Shinsuke, Gen. Mgr.--The Sumitomo Bank, Ltd.-Yangpu Branch, Hainai, China; *Int'l*, pg. 1309
Sumitomo, Yasuji, Mng. Dir.--Sumitomo Financial Futures (Singapore) pte. Ltd., Singapore, Singapore; *Int'l*, pg. 1310
Sumiya, Takashi, Pres.--Sumikin Bussan International (Korea) Co., Ltd., Seoul, Korea; *Int'l*, pg. 1308
Sumiyoshi, Toru, Chief Rep.--The Industrial Bank of Japan, Limited (Jakarta), Jakarta, Indonesia; *Int'l*, pg. 675
Summe, Greg, Pres.--AlliedSignal Commercial Avionic Systems, Olathe, KS; *U.S. Public*, pg. 50
Summer, Robert, Pres.--B.M.G. Records, New York, NY; *Int'l*, pg. 1383
Summers, Aaron, Plant Mgr.--Ventura Foods, Albert Lea, MN; *U.S. Private*, pg. 508
Summers, Al, V.P. & Gen. Mgr.--Minera Hecla S.A. de CV, Hermosillo, Mexico; *U.S. Public*, pg. 804
Summers, R., Chm. Bd.--Home Brewery plc, Nottingham, United Kingdom; *Int'l*, pg. 1211
Sumner, Bill, Gen. Mgr.--Raymond Transportation Corporation, Greene, NY; *Int'l*, pg. 123
Sumner, Jessie, Plant Mgr.--National Spinning Co., Beulaville, NC; *U.S. Private*, pg. 787
Sumpter, Jerry, Pres.--The Akro Corporation, Canton, OH; *U.S. Public*, pg. 399
Sun Lee, Peter Iai, Branch Mgr.--Mead Coated Board (Malaysia) Sdn. Bhd., Port Kelang, Malaysia; *U.S. Public*, pg. 1076
Sun, Lee Young, Pres.--Namkwang Engineering & Construction Co., Ltd., Seoul, Korea; *Int'l*, pg. 1291
Sun, Wayne, Gen. Mgr.--Union-Transport Ltd, Beijing, China; *U.S. Private*, pg. 1120
Sunago, Toyoyuki, Gen. Mgr.--Long-Term Credit Bank of Japan, Ltd. - Paris Branch, Paris, France; *Int'l*, pg. 816
Sunayama, Hiroyasu, Pres.--World Fashion Hosiery Inc., Kowloon, Hong Kong; *Int'l*, pg. 579
Sund, Ake, Pres.--VingCard Systems Inc., Dallas, TX; *Int'l*, pg. 18
Sund, Kenneth, Mgr.--Sandvik Coromant U.K., Birmingham, United Kingdom; *Int'l*, pg. 1186
Sundaran, S. K., Mng. Dir.--Glaxo Wellcome Singapore Pte. Ltd., Singapore, Singapore; *Int'l*, pg. 553
Sundblad, Erik, Mng. Dir.--Neste Cellplast AB, Norrtalje, Sweden; *Int'l*, pg. 914
Sundby, Ake, Mgr.--Sandvik Belzer Produktion GmbH, Wuppertal, Germany; *Int'l*, pg. 1186
Sundby, Paul, Pres.--International Tank, Inc, Kansas City, KS; *U.S. Private*, pg. 1066
Sundeen, Alan, Gen. Mgr.--ITW Plastiglide Ltd. of Canada/ ITW Fastex, Concord, Canada; *U.S. Public*, pg. 869
Sunderaj, N., V.P.-N.W. U.S./San Francisco--Singapore Airlines Ltd., San Francisco, CA; *Int'l*, pg. 1374
Sunderland, Charles T., Pres.--Cedar Creek Properties Inc., Olathe, KS; *U.S. Private*, pg. 88
Sunderland, David K., Pres.--Gates Land Co., Colorado Springs, CO; *U.S. Private*, pg. 249
Sunderland, Lee, Pres. & Chief Exec. Officer--Cliftex, New Bedford, MA; *U.S. Public*, pg. 1777
Sunderland, Lee A., Pres. & Chief Exec. Officer--The Richman Brothers Co., Fall River, MA; *U.S. Public*, pg. 1777
Sunderland, Trevor, V.P. & Mng. Dir.--BankAmerica Trust & Banking Corp. (Bahamas) Ltd., Nassau, Bahamas; *U.S. Public*, pg. 183
Sundgren, Donald E., Pres.--Watkins Engineers & Constructors, Inc., Tallahassee, FL; *U.S. Private*, pg. 333
Sundh, Kenneth V., Mgr.--Sandvik Ltd., Birmingham, United Kingdom; *Int'l*, pg. 1186
Sundin, Christer, Mng. Dir.--Ornskoldsviks Mekaniska Verkstad (OMV), Ornskoldsvik, Sweden; *Int'l*, pg. 221
Sundman, Donald, Pres.--Mystic Stamp Company, Camden, NY; *U.S. Private*, pg. 671
Sundquist, Harry, Chief Oper. Officer--Kaukas Pulp Mill, Lappeenranta, Finland; *Int'l*, pg. 1428
Sundstedt, John E., Mgr.--Woodward Governor (Japan) Ltd., Chiba, Japan; *U.S. Public*, pg. 1777
Sundstrom, Hakan, Chief Oper. Officer--Scania Osterreich Ges.m.b.H., Brunn am Gebirge, Austria; *Int'l*, pg. 687
Sundstrom, Harold, Gen. Mgr.--Soplacas Lda, Parede, Portugal; *Int'l*, pg. 1199
Sundstrom, Peter, Mgr.--ITW Fixlock AB, Goteborg, Sweden; *U.S. Public*, pg. 868
Sundstrom, Rolf, Mng. Dir.--Motala Hissar A.B., Motala, Sweden; *Int'l*, pg. 748
Sundt, Jan, Mgr.--Jan Sundt AS, Oslo, Norway; *Int'l*, pg. 731
Sundvik, Carl, Mng. Dir.--S-E-Banken BoLan AB, Stockholm, Sweden; *Int'l*, pg. 1259
Sunelli, Kari, Mgr.-Access Systems--Nokia Telecommunications, Espoo, Finland; *Int'l*, pg. 952
Sunemo, Lars, Mgr.--Ahlsell El AB, Spangenas, Sweden; *Int'l*, pg. 1422
Sung, Kihong, Chm.--Kolon-Met Life Insurance Company Limited, Seoul, Korea; *U.S. Private*, pg. 738
Sung, T.Y., Dr., Mng. Dir.--SangAm Communications Co., Ltd., Seoul, Korea; *U.S. Public*, pg. 765
Sunityo, Elvia, Rep.--Generale Bank, Jakarta, Indonesia; *Int'l*, pg. 547
Sunley, Robert J., Pres.--NETG Limited, London, United Kingdom; *U.S. Public*, pg. 784
Sunley, Roy, Pres.--NETG Applied Learning GmbH, Dusseldorf, Germany; *U.S. Public*, pg. 784
Sunley, Roy, Pres.--NETG Applied Learning GmbH, Vienna, Austria; *U.S. Public*, pg. 784
Sunley, Roy, Pres.--A.S.I. (Computer Training) Netherlands B.V., Amsterdam, Netherlands; *U.S. Public*, pg. 784
Suntayodom, Thanan, Pres.--Thai Otsuka Pharmaceutical Co., Ltd., Bangkok, Thailand; *Int'l*, pg. 1014
Suntola, Tuomo, Chief Oper. Officer--Mikrokemia Oy, Espoo, Finland; *Int'l*, pg. 913
Suokas, Matti, Pres.--Finnsugar Ltd., Kantvik, Finland; *Int'l*, pg. 349
Suominen, Hanna, Pres.--Nokia Industrial Electronics, Salo, Finland; *Int'l*, pg. 951
Suominen, Jukka, Pres.--SILJA OY Ab, Helsinki, Finland; *Int'l*, pg. 899
Suplick, Michael, Mng. Dir.--Total Research Corporation, Minneapolis, MN; *U.S. Public*, pg. 1625
Surakka, Tapani, Chief Oper. Officer--Akerlund & Rausing Oy, Anjalankoski, Finland; *Int'l*, pg. 32
Surane, James, Pres.--Vermont American Tool Group, Lincolnton, NC; *U.S. Public*, pg. 575
Surber, H.U., Mgr.--Swiss Bank Corporation, San Francisco, CA; *Int'l*, pg. 1329
Surbranche, Michel, Co-Mgr.--EURO RSCG Quartet, Annecy, France; *Int'l*, pg. 601
Surdell, Daniel, Pres.--Orent GraphicArts, Inc., Omaha, NE; *U.S. Public*, pg. 503
Surdell, Daniel L., Pres.--Meridian Retail, Inc., Troy, MI; *U.S. Public*, pg. 503
Surenkok, Gunay, Gen. Mgr.--Det Norske Veritas, Istanbul, Turkey; *Int'l*, pg. 397
Surface, R. C., Mng. Dir.--Pearl Group Plc, Peterborough, United Kingdom; *Int'l*, pg. 100
Surgey, P.M., Mng. Dir.--Plascon (Pty) Ltd., Johannesburg, South Africa; *Int'l*, pg. 167
Suriyasat, Korn, Pres.--Thai Toshiba Electric Industries Co., Ltd., Bangkok, Thailand; *Int'l*, pg. 1406
Surmanek, Jim, Sr. V.P. & Gen. Mgr.--Carat ICG, Chicago, IL; *U.S. Private*, pg. 207
Surpin, Jo, Pres.--MEDIQ Management Services, Inc., Pennsauken, NJ; *U.S. Public*, pg. 1081
Surpin, Jo, Pres.--MEDIQ Diagnostic Centers, Pennsauken, NJ; *U.S. Public*, pg. 1081
Suryawinata, S., Rep.--Van Leeuwen Pipe and Tube (Far East) Pte. Ltd., Jakarta, Indonesia; *Int'l*, pg. 1450
Susanto, F.X., Representative--CUNA Mutual Group-Indonesia, Jakarta, Indonesia; *U.S. Private*, pg. 297
Susnak, Joe, Gen. Mgr.--Lafayette Steel, Detroit, MI; *U.S. Public*, pg. 1221
Susor, Robert, Pres.--Genuine Parts Ltd., Calgary, Canada; *U.S. Public*, pg. 732
Sussex, David, Gen. Mgr.--Wynn Oil (U.K.) Limited, Reading, United Kingdom; *U.S. Public*, pg. 1783
Sussler, Rafi, Representative & Mgr.--Hapoalim (Latin America) S.A., Montevideo, Uruguay; *Int'l*, pg. 150
Sussler, Rafi, Mgr.--Hapoalim (Latin America) S.A., Punta del Este, Uruguay; *Int'l*, pg. 150

Sussman, Leslie I., V.P.--Wellman Nonwovens Div., City of Commerce, CA; U.S. Public, pg. 1753
Sussmeier, Hansruedi, Chief Oper. Officer--Perstorp Vertriebs AG, Cham, Switzerland; Int'l, pg. 1039
Susuki, Konen, Pres.--Ford Motor Company (Japan) Ltd., Tokyo, Japan; U.S. Public, pg. 666
Susuki, N., Sr. V.P. & Gen. Mgr.--Nikko Securities Co., Los Angeles, Los Angeles, CA; Int'l, pg. 930
Sutcliff Almada, E.L., Chief Oper. Officer--Aluplast S.A. de C.V., Morelos, Mexico; U.S. Public, pg. 1756
Sutcliff Almada, E.L., Chief Oper. Officer--The West Company Mexico, SA.de C.V., Mexico, Mexico; U.S. Public, pg. 1756
Sutcliffe, Chuck, Acting Pres.--Tempress, Santa Clara, CA; U.S. Public, pg. 727
Sutcliffe, Chuck, Acting Pres.--General Signal Thinfilm Company, Fremont, CA; U.S. Public, pg. 727
Sutcliffe, T., Dir. & Gen. Mgr.--Weiser (U.K.) Ltd., Peterlee, United Kingdom; U.S. Public, pg. 1055
Sutenbach, Paul, Gen. Mgr.--ITW Produx, Cleveland, OH; U.S. Public, pg. 867
Suter, B.H., V.P. & Gen. Mgr.--Stone & Webster Management Consultants, Inc., New York, NY; U.S. Public, pg. 1519
Suter, Hans Jorg, Gen. Mgr.--Forbo Immob SA, Eglisau, Switzerland; Int'l, pg. 497
Suter, P., Mgr.-Bus. Unit--Long Manufacturing Ltd., Mississauga, Canada; Int'l, pg. 815
Suter, Peter, Mgr.--AB Mataki, Malmo, Sweden; Int'l, pg. 1422
Suter, Ulrich H., Exec. V.P.--Alusuisse-Lonza America Inc., New York, NY; Int'l, pg. 67
Suthapong, W., Mgr.--Nalco Chemical Co. (Thailand) Ltd., Bangkok, Thailand; U.S. Public, pg. 1150
Suther, Kurtis W., Asst. V.P.--IBP-Amarillo, Amarillo, TX; U.S. Public, pg. 852
Sutherland, Allan, Pres.--Roberts Systems, Inc., Charlotte, NC; Int'l, pg. 395
Sutherland, George, Sr. V.P.--BHP International Ltd., Honolulu, HI; Int'l, pg. 225
Sutherland, Hamish, Gen. Mgr.-Mktg.--Quality Bakers New Zealand Ltd., Auckland, New Zealand; Int'l, pg. 556
Sutherland, James, Dist. Mgr.--Plains Petroleum Operating Company, Midland, TX; U.S. Public, pg. 191
Sutherland, Jim, Chief Oper. Officer--Adalet Div., Cleveland, OH; U.S. Public, pg. 217
Sutherland, Joe, Mng. Dir.--GN Nettest, Datacom Division, Markham, Canada; Int'l, pg. 537
Sutherland, M., Gen. Mgr.--TMP Worldwide Pty Ltd., Hobart, Australia; Int'l, pg. 1342
Sutherland, Sandy, Chief Oper. Officer--Ahlstrom Machinery Canada Inc., Annacis Island, Canada; Int'l, pg. 35
Sutherland, T.F., Mng. Dir.--Trico Pty. Ltd., Springvale, Australia; Int'l, pg. 1397
Sutherlin, James, Pres.--HSB Reliability Technologies, Hartford, CT; U.S. Public, pg. 795
Suthons, D., Dr., Chief Gen. Mgr.--Holter Group, Essen, Germany; Int'l, pg. 101
Sutley, John R., Pres.--Nalco/Exxon Energy Chemicals, L.P., Sugar Land, TX; U.S. Public, pg. 1150
Sutter, C.L., Chm. Bd.--East Rand Gold and Uranium Mining, Johannesburg, South Africa; Int'l, pg. 77
Suttler, Goodloe, Gen. Mgr.--Analog Devices Semiconductor, Wilmington, MA; U.S. Public, pg. 108
Suttles, Tim, Gen. Mgr--Elixir Industries, Reidsville, NC; U.S. Private, pg. 371
Suttner, James, Plant Mgr.--Sargento Foods Inc., Hilbert, WI; U.S. Private, pg. 966
Sutton, Alan, Plant Mgr.--Cambridge Industries - Woodstock, Woodstock, Canada; U.S. Private, pg. 202
Sutton, Charles I., Chief Oper. Officer--Allright Baton Rouge, Inc., Baton Rouge, LA; U.S. Private, pg. 42
Sutton, Don, Gen. Mgr.--Amway of New Zealand Limited, Auckland, New Zealand; U.S. Private, pg. 70
Sutton, Dorset, Gen. Mgr.--Colgate-Palmolive (Eastern) Pte. Ltd., Singapore, Singapore; U.S. Public, pg. 398
Sutton, Dorsett, Gen. Mgr.--Colgate-Palmolive (Malaysia) Sdn. Bhd., Petaling Jaya, Malaysia; U.S. Public, pg. 398
Sutton, Harry, Gen. Mgr.--Eclipse Combustion, Montreal, Canada; U.S. Private, pg. 361
Sutton, James, Pres.--Sky Bros. Inc., Altoona, PA; U.S. Public, pg. 918
Sutton, Kelso F., Pres. & Chief Exec. Officer--The Time Inc. Book Company, New York, NY; U.S. Public, pg. 1613
Sutton, Lester E., Pres.--Ingram Barge Company, Nashville, TN; U.S. Private, pg. 563
Sutton, Martyn, Chief Oper. Officer--Griffith Laboratories Limited, Derby, United Kingdom; U.S. Private, pg. 481
Sutton, Mike, Country Mgr.--Autodesk Ltd., Guildford, United Kingdom; U.S. Public, pg. 149
Sutton, Mike, Gen. Dir.-MAPICS--Marcam France, Paris, France; U.S. Public, pg. 1043
Sutton, Pamela, New Bus.--Leo Burnett/Connaghan & May (VIC.) Pty. Ltd., Melbourne, Australia; U.S. Private, pg. 185
Sutton, R.C., Mng. Dir.--Jardine Matheson (Australia) Ltd., Sydney, Australia; Int'l, pg. 705
Sutton, Terrye, Chief Fin. Officer--Letraset Canada Ltd., Markham, Canada; Int'l, pg. 461
Suurkuusk, Ants, Pres.--Myresjo AB, Vetlanda, Sweden; Int'l, pg. 1260
Suvanamaf, Chalermkiat, Gen. Mgr.--Thai Airways Intl. Ltd.-U.S. Office, El Segundo, CA; Int'l, pg. 1381
Suwa, M., Pres.--Funai Corporation, Teterboro, NJ; Int'l, pg. 530
Suwak, Lawrence M., Pres.--H.L. Yoh Group LLC, Philadelphia, PA; U.S. Private, pg. 317
Suwyn, M.A., Grp. V.P.--Du Pont Imaging Systems, Wilmington, DE; U.S. Public, pg. 531
Suykens, Cathy, Repr.--Kredietbank Representative Office (Milan), Milan, Italy; Int'l, pg. 760
Suzuki, A., V.P.-Intl. Div.--Harman Japan, Tokyo, Japan; U.S. Public, pg. 787
Suzuki, A., Managing Dir.--SEIKO UK Limited, Maidenhead, United Kingdom; Int'l, pg. 1218
Suzuki, Akio, Pres.--Shinko Electric Co., Ltd., Tokyo, Japan; Int'l, pg. 740
Suzuki, Gen, Mng. Dir.--NLI International Hong Kong Limited, Central, Hong Kong; Int'l, pg. 936
Suzuki, George, Pres.--Pasco U.S.A., Inc., Mechanicsburg, PA; Int'l, pg. 1024
Suzuki, Goro, Pres.--Nagoya Mitsukoshi, Ltd., Nagoya, Japan; Int'l, pg. 883
Suzuki, H., Pres.--Nihon Seiko Co. Ltd., Tokyo, Japan; Int'l, pg. 947
Suzuki, Hidehiko, Pres.--Kawasaki Motors N.V., Vianen, Netherlands; Int'l, pg. 726
Suzuki, Hideo, Pres.--Makita Canada Inc., Whitby, Canada; Int'l, pg. 832
Suzuki, Hiroo, Chief Oper. Officer--Kyowa Hakko Do Brasil Ltda., Sao Paulo, Brazil; Int'l, pg. 778
Suzuki, Hiroshi, Mng. Dir.--BTM Finance and Securities (Thailand) Ltd., Bangkok, Thailand; Int'l, pg. 157
Suzuki, Hitoshi, Pres.--Meijiseimei International France S.A., Paris, France; Int'l, pg. 854
Suzuki, Itaro, Chm. & Mng. Dir.--Mitsui & Co. (Australia) Ltd., Sydney, Australia; Int'l, pg. 880
Suzuki, Kaneo, Chm. Bd.--NEC Europe Ltd., London, United Kingdom; Int'l, pg. 900
Suzuki, Kokichi, Chief Oper. Officer--Toyota del Peru S.A., Lima, Peru; Int'l, pg. 1414
Suzuki, Masahiro, Chief Rep.--The Sumitomo Bank, Ltd.-Johannesburg Representative Office, Sandton, South Africa; Int'l, pg. 1310
Suzuki, Masatoshi, Chief Oper. Officer--Suzuka Circuitland Co., Ltd., Suzuka, Japan; Int'l, pg. 634
Suzuki, Nobuo, Gen. Mgr.--Asahi Bank Chicago Branch, Chicago, IL; Int'l, pg. 82
Suzuki, Noriyuki, Dir.--Yamaichi Trust & Bank, Ltd., Tokyo, Japan; Int'l, pg. 1517
Suzuki, Noriyuki, Chm. Bd.--Yamaichi International (H.K.) Ltd., Central, Hong Kong; Int'l, pg. 1518
Suzuki, Ryo, Pres.--NS Sales Inc., Chicago, IL; Int'l, pg. 940
Suzuki, S., Exec. Dir.-Lumber--MacMillan Bloedel K. K., Tokyo, Japan; Int'l, pg. 829
Suzuki, Sadao, Chief Oper. Officer--Berjaya General Insurance Sdn. Bhd., Kuala Lumpur, Malaysia; Int'l, pg. 1392
Suzuki, Sadao, Chief Oper. Officer--The Tokio Marine Management (Australia) Pty. Ltd., Sydney, Australia; Int'l, pg. 1393
Suzuki, Seiichiro, Gen. Mgr.--Dai-Ichi Kangyo Bank, Ltd.-Singapore, Singapore, Singapore; Int'l, pg. 361
Suzuki, Shigero, Pres. & V.P.-Japan Opers.--Tekelec, Ltd., Tokyo, Japan; U.S. Public, pg. 1566
Suzuki, Tadao, Pres.--Matsushita Seiko Co., Ltd., Osaka, Japan; Int'l, pg. 846
Suzuki, Takashi, Pres.--Nikkei Business Publications Inc., Tokyo, Japan; Int'l, pg. 929
Suzuki, Takeo, Dir. & Gen. Mgr.--Daiwa Bank International Business Division-Head Office, Osaka, Japan; Int'l, pg. 373
Suzuki, Tamon, Pres.--Showa Aluminum Corp. of America, Mount Sterling, OH; Int'l, pg. 1236
Suzuki, Tatsuro, Mng. Dir.--Tokai Financial Futures (Singapore) Pte. Ltd., Singapore, Singapore; Int'l, pg. 1391
Suzuki, Toshifumi, Pres. & Representative Dir.--Seven-Eleven Japan Co., Ltd., Tokyo, Japan; Int'l, pg. 693
Suzuki, Toshio, V.P.-Resident DIr.--Blount Japan Inc., Tokyo, Japan; U.S. Public, pg. 239
Suzuki, Y., Gen. Mgr.--Marubeni America Corporation, Nashville Office, Nashville, TN; Int'l, pg. 845
Suzuki, Yoichiro, Mng. Dir.--National Mutual Funds Management (Japan) Limited, Tokyo, Japan; Int'l, pg. 909
Suzuki, Yoshiya, Chief Rep.--Sao Paulo Representative Office, Sao Paulo, Brazil; Int'l, pg. 520
Suzuki, Yuji, Chm.--The Industrial Bank of Japan Trust Company, New York, NY; Int'l, pg. 675
Suzumasa, Hirokazu, Pres.--Rohm Electronics Taiwan Co., Ltd., Taipei, Taiwan; Int'l, pg. 1125
Svanberg, Torben, Pres.--Sonofon, Horsholm, Denmark; Int'l, pg. 537
Svare, Tore Ivar, Mng. Dir.--Optiroc AS, Skare, Norway; Int'l, pg. 1200
Svatek, Dennis, Pres.--Discovery Plastics, Inc., Albany, OR; U.S. Private, pg. 904
Svedberg, Tord, Pres.--Astra Production Chemicals AB, Sodertalje, Sweden; Int'l, pg. 93
Svedberg, William, Mng. Dir.--Ericsson Business Communications A/S, Nesbru, Norway; Int'l, pg. 1366
Svedin, Bjorn, Chief Oper. Officer--Ahlstrom Machinery AB-Fiber Processes, Stockholm, Sweden; Int'l, pg. 34
Svellentrop, Steve, Pres.--ARCO British Limited, Guildford, United Kingdom; U.S. Public, pg. 144
Svenang, Goran, Pres.--Hansa Industrial Insurance N.V., Rotterdam, Netherlands; Int'l, pg. 1425
Svendsen-Tune, Rene, Mng. Dir.--Nokia Telecommunications A/S, Tastrup, Denmark; Int'l, pg. 953
Svendsen, Erik, Pres.--Bohler-Uddeholm Corp., Rolling Meadows, IL; Int'l, pg. 1471
Svendsen, Jan, Mgr.--Kvaerner Ships Equipment a.s, Kvaerner Moss, Moss, Norway; Int'l, pg. 770
Svendsen, Kjell Reier, Gen. Mgr.--El-Mohandes Jotun Egypt, Cairo, Egypt; Int'l, pg. 715
Svendsson, Sven, Mng. Dir.--Kvaerner Gotfab AB, Goteborg, Sweden; Int'l, pg. 767
Svennson, Nils-Ake, Mgr.--Trelleborgdack AB, Trelleborg, Sweden; Int'l, pg. 1422
Svensen, Tore, Gen. Mgr.--Tektronix Norge A/S, Oslo, Norway; U.S. Public, pg. 1568
Svenson, Lars, Pres.--Axel Johnson Lab System AB, Solna, Sweden; Int'l, pg. 709
Svensson, Arne, Pres.--Dynapac AB, Sollentuna, Sweden; Int'l, pg. 1420
Svensson, Bengt, Pres.--ASEA Truck AB, Harnosand, Sweden; Int'l, pg. 7
Svensson, Carl Axel, Chief Oper. Officer--NIFE Corporation, Scarborough, Canada; Int'l, pg. 54
Svensson, Christer, Mgr.--Shenyang ITT Flygt Jinbei Pump Co., Ltd., Shenyang, China; U.S. Public, pg. 860
Svensson, Christer, Mng. Dir.--Kalmar Lagab AB, Laholm, Sweden; Int'l, pg. 1421
Svensson, Dag, Pres.--NCC Building, Malmo, Sweden; Int'l, pg. 898
Svensson, Gouran, Pres.--NCC Anlaggring, Stockholm, Sweden; Int'l, pg. 899
Svensson, Jan, Dir.--Dial Forsikring A/S, Copenhagen, Denmark; Int'l, pg. 1257
Svensson, Nils-Erik, Chief Exec.--Sulzer Metco (Norden) AB, Stockholm, Sweden; Int'l, pg. 1308
Svensson, Ragnar, Mng. Dir.--Johnson & Johnson AB, Sollentuna, Sweden; U.S. Public, pg. 930
Svensson, Rune, Pres.--Volvo Transport Corporation, Goteborg, Sweden; Int'l, pg. 1476
Sverdrupsen, Leif, Mng. Dir.--Nederman A/S, Oslo, Norway; Int'l, pg. 283
Svet, Frank A., V.P. & Gen. Mgr.--Test and Colibration Instruments, Largo, FL; U.S. Public, pg. 100
Svetlana, Frolova, Gen. Mgr.--Utell International-Russia, Moscow, Russia; Int'l, pg. 1099
Swadey, Robert J., Chm. Bd.--Midland Title Security, Inc., Cleveland, OH; U.S. Public, pg. 626
Swaerd, S., Pres. & Chief Exec. Officer--Siemens AB, Stockholm, Sweden; Int'l, pg. 1247
Swaffar, Jim, Plant Mgr.--Dayton Superior Corp., Parker, AZ; U.S. Private, pg. 932
Swafford, Larry, Pres.--Lykes Meat Group, Plant City, FL; U.S. Public, pg. 1479
Swager, Richard E., Chm. Bd. & Chief Exec. Officer--Reinsurance Alternatives, Inc., Minneapolis, MN; Int'l, pg. 1503
Swahn, Hans, Pres.--Esselte Meto International GmbH, Heppenheim, Germany; Int'l, pg. 461
Swahn, Hans, Chief Exec.--Esselte Meto, Heppenheim, Germany; Int'l, pg. 461
Swaile, William C., Pres.--ALLTEL New York, Inc., Jamestown, NY; U.S. Public, pg. 56
Swain, Bob, Gen. Mgr.--Shady Maple Farms Ltd., La Guadeloupe, Canada; U.S. Public, pg. 806
Swain, Don, V.P.-Fin. & Corp. Treas.--Parthenon Insurance Co., Nashville, TN; U.S. Public, pg. 405
Swain, E.P., Jr., Pres.--Port Townsend Paper Corporation, Bainbridge Island, WA; Int'l, pg. 586
Swain, G. Joseph, Pres.--Chemical Bank North, Grayling, MI; U.S. Public, pg. 345
Swain, Hugh J., Pres.--Andrew Antenna Co. Ltd., Whitby, Canada; U.S. Public, pg. 113
Swain, James, Mng. Dir.--Elsag Bailey Pty Limited, Regents Park, Australia; Int'l, pg. 449
Swain, Randy, Pres.--Ackerley Communications of the Northwest-Seattle, Seattle, WA; U.S. Public, pg. 15
Swain, Terrence P., Pres.--Derlan Inc./Phoenix Facility, Phoenix, AZ; Int'l, pg. 395
Swain, William R., Publisher--Springfield Newspapers, Inc., Springfield, OH; U.S. Private, pg. 281
Swallow, Dr. David, Pres.--Rhone Poulenc Performance Resins & Coatings Division, London, United Kingdom; Int'l, pg. 1113
Swan, Doug, Gen. Mgr.--Reclamation Div. (Tacoma), Tacoma, WA; Int'l, pg. 1271
Swanhaus, John G., Sr. V.P. & Gen. Mgr.--PepsiCo Wines & Spirits International, Purchase, NY; U.S. Public, pg. 1277
Swank, Charles, Pres.--Florida Pneumatic Mfg. Corp., Jupiter, FL; U.S. Public, pg. 1240
Swank, Donald, Gen. Mgr.--Schult Homes Corporation, Middlebury, IN; U.S. Public, pg. 1442
Swanky, Olie E., Pres. & Chief Exec. Officer--Bell Atlantic Systems Leasing International, Inc., Phoenix, AZ; U.S. Public, pg. 203
Swanson, Dave, Gen. Mgr.--Illinois Bldg. Div., Forest Park, IL; U.S. Private, pg. 10
Swanson, Dennis D., Pres.--ABC Sports, Inc., New York, NY; U.S. Public, pg. 511
Swanson, Dennis D., Pres. & Chief Oper. Officer--ABC Sports Holding Company, Inc., New York, NY; U.S. Public, pg. 511
Swanson, Edward B., Pres. & Chief Exec. Officer--Independent Bank-South Michigan, Leslie, MI; U.S. Public, pg. 874
Swanson, Robert, Pres.--R & R Plastics, Swanton, OH; U.S. Private, pg. 431
Swanson, Robert H., V.P. & Gen. Mgr.--Countermeasures & Combat Systems Division, Austin, TX; U.S. Public, pg. 1627
Swanson, Robert R., Jr., Pres.--Bankston Nissan in Irving, Inc., Irving, TX; U.S. Public, pg. 1379
Swanson, S. Keith, Pres.--Joslyn Electronic Systems Corporation, Goleta, CA; U.S. Public, pg. 481
Swanson, William H., Exec. V.P. & Gen. Mgr.--Raytheon Electronics Systems, Marlborough, MA; U.S. Public, pg. 1364
Swanson, William H., Sr. V.P. & Gen. Mgr.--Raytheon Electronics Systems, Bedford, MA; U.S. Public, pg. 1364
Swanstrom, Kenneth A., Pres.--PEM Intl. Ltd., Doncaster, United Kingdom; U.S. Public, pg. 1270
Swarbrick, Ronald, Mgr.--EG & G Canada, Ltd. Optoelectronics, Vaudreuil, Canada; U.S. Public, pg. 544
Swart, Wayne R., Pres.--Eldorado Division, Eldorado, IL; U.S. Private, pg. 948
Swart, Wayne R., Pres.--Roundy's, Evansville, IN; U.S. Private, pg. 948
Swartwout, Robert L., Pres.--New Mexico Utilities, Inc., Albuquerque, NM; U.S. Public, pg. 1494
Swartz, D. Bruce, Pres.--L3 Communications Narda-Microwave West Div., Folsom, CA; U.S. Private, pg. 638
Swartz, Diane, Pres.--The Manufacturers Life Insurance Company of America, Toronto, Canada; Int'l, pg. 840

Swaw, Joe, Gen. Mgr.--GATX Logistics, Inc.-Texas (Public), Arlington, TX; *U.S. Public*, pg. 692
Swayne, S., Mng. Dir.--Eurodis Bytech Electronics Limited, Basingstoke, United Kingdom; *Int'l*, pg. 1247
Swayne, William, Pres.--Holmatro, Inc., Glen Burnie, MD; *Int'l*, pg. 632
Swearingen, James J., Pres.--Unisource (West Region), Renton, WA; *U.S. Public*, pg. 1671
Swearingen, R., Chief Oper. Officer--Southern Division, Saint Louis, MO; *Int'l*, pg. 518
Sweatman, Sharon, Pres.--United Missouri Brokerage Services, Kansas City, MO; *U.S. Public*, pg. 1655
Sweatt, Blaine, II, Pres.--Bahama Breeze, Orlando, FL; *U.S.* Public, pg. 484
Sweatt, J.D., Gen. Mgr.--CHEMCENTRAL/Dallas, Dallas, TX; *U.S. Private*, pg. 232
Sweeney, Anne, Pres.--The Disney Channel, Burbank, CA; *U.S. Public*, pg. 513
Sweeney, B.M., Chief Oper. Officer--Siemens Ltd., Dublin, Ireland; *Int'l*, pg. 1247
Sweeney, Dennis, Pres.--Prudential Service Co., Louisville, KY; *U.S. Private*, pg. 893
Sweeney, Dennis, Gen. Mgr.--Microsemi RF Products, Inc., Montgomeryville, PA; *U.S. Public*, pg. 1107
Sweeney, Jacob E., Jr., Pres.--Jake Sweeney Jeep Eagle, Inc., Cincinnati, OH; *U.S. Private*, pg. 1058
Sweeney, Joan M., Pres. & Chief Oper. Officer--Allied Capital Advisors, Inc., Washington, DC; *U.S. Public*, pg. 47
Sweeney, Mary S., Pres. & Dir.-Adv.--Jake Sweeney Auto Leasing, Inc., Cincinnati, OH; *U.S. Private*, pg. 1058
Sweeney, Paul L., Pres. & Chief Oper. Officer--John Hancock Property and Casualty Holding Co., Boston, MA; *U.S. Private*, pg. 590
Sweeney, Paul L., Pres.--John Hancock Insurance Company of Bermuda Ltd., Hamilton, Bermuda; *U.S. Private*, pg. 590
Sweet, H. Randolph, Chief Oper. Officer--EMCON Northwest, Inc., Portland, OR; *U.S. Public*, pg. 571
Sweet, H. Randolph, Chief Oper. Officer--EMCON Northwest, Inc., Bothell, WA; *U.S. Public*, pg. 571
Sweet, H. Randolph, Chief Oper. Officer--Columbia Analytical Services, Inc., Kelso, WA; *U.S. Public*, pg. 571
Sweet, Sheff, Gen. Mgr.--Liqui-Box Corp., Ashland, OH; *U.S. Public*, pg. 1000
Sweet, William, Gen. Mgr.--Republic Automotive Parts Sales, Inc., Latham, NY; *U.S. Public*, pg. 1378
Sweetman, Walter J., Pres.--Basalt Precast Division, Napa, CA; *U.S. Private*, pg. 333
Sweetnam, James M., Pres.--Holset Engineering Company Ltd., Madison, IN; *U.S. Public*, pg. 468
Sweigart, Donald, Sr. V.P.--Burnham Hydronics Div., Lancaster, PA; *U.S. Public*, pg. 270
Sweitzer, Michael, Gen. Mgr.--Tyrone Division, Tyrone, PA; *U.S. Public*, pg. 349
Sweney, Liz, Pres.--Cricket Lane, West Bridgewater, MA; *U.S. Public*, pg. 948
Swenson, Alan, Factory Supt.--Amalgamated Sugar Co., Paul, ID; *U.S. Private*, pg. 48
Swenson, G., V.P. & Gen. Mgr.--Kellems Div., Stonington, CT; *U.S. Public*, pg. 844
Swenson, James W., Pres.--LGS Financial Services, Inc., Harvey, LA; *U.S. Public*, pg. 380
Swenson, James W., Pres.--LGS Pipeline, Inc., Harvey, LA; *U.S. Public*, pg. 380
Swenson, K.F., Pres.--Esso Eastern Inc., Houston, TX; *U.S. Public*, pg. 601
Swenson, K.F., Pres.--Exxon Yemen Inc., Houston, TX; *U.S.* Public, pg. 601
Swenson, P., Pres.--Kona Corporation, Gloucester, MA; *U.S. Private*, pg. 138
Swenson, R.L., Pres.-Plastics Div.--Edison Plastics Co., Newport News, VA; *U.S. Private*, pg. 1179
Swenson, Robert L., Pres.--Frankel Metal Company, Detroit, MI; *U.S. Private*, pg. 735
Swenson, Scott, Gen. Mgr.--Advertiser, Coralville, IA; *U.S. Private*, pg. 442
Swerdlow, Steve, Sr. Mng. Officer--CB Commercial Real Estate Group, New York, New York, NY; *U.S. Public*, pg. 273
Swertseger, K.W., Gen. Mgr.--HISPAN Corp., Decatur, AL; *U.S. Public*, pg. 810
Swetland, Lawrence, Plant Mgr.--Surfactant Dept. Plant, Bordentown, NJ; *U.S. Public*, pg. 1514
Swetman, G.D., Chm. Bd.--British & Soviet International Carbon Limited, Windsor, United Kingdom; *Int'l*, pg. 894
Swetnam, Paul, Pres.--Aeroflex Lintek Corp., Powell, OH; *U.S. Public*, pg. 24
Swider, Frank, Mgr.--Southern Electric Supply Co., Inc., Oxford, MS; *Int'l*, pg. 1108
Swiderski, Richard B., V.P.--La-Z-Boy Arkansas, Siloam Springs, AR; *U.S. Public*, pg. 973
Swidorski, Tom, Plant Mgr.--Lexington Plant, Lexington, KY; *U.S. Public*, pg. 671
Swift, Collin, Mgr.-Plant--Nestle Beverage Company, Sunbury, OH; *Int'l*, pg. 918
Swift, Mathew D., Pres.--Developers Investors, Inc., Columbus, GA; *U.S. Private*, pg. 164
Swift, Steve, Area Foreman--Talisman Energy Inc., Chauvin, Canada; *Int'l*, pg. 1352
Swigert, J. L., Mgr.--Morton Chemical Div., Woodstock, IL; *U.S. Public*, pg. 1135
Swildens, P.J.M., Gen. Mgr.--AEP/Borden B.V., Apeldoorn, Netherlands; *U.S. Public*, pg. 5
Swimm, Ken, Pres.--Martin Marietta Management & Data Systems, Philadelphia, PA; *U.S. Public*, pg. 1007
Swindell, John T., Pres.--Merrill Corporation, Westfield, NJ; *U.S. Public*, pg. 1097
Swindell, John T., Pres.--Merrill Corporation, New York, NY; *U.S. Public*, pg. 1097
Swindells, William, Exec. V.P.--Northeast Group, Glastonbury, CT; *U.S. Public*, pg. 649
Swindle, Larry, Chief Oper. Officer--NationsBank of Kennett, Kennett, MO; *U.S. Public*, pg. 1165
Swindler, Fred, Pres.--Kelsar, S.A., Tijuana, Mexico; *U.S. Public*, pg. 81
Swineford, Gail, Branch Mgr.--Wachovia Bank, Richmond, VA; *U.S. Public*, pg. 1730
Swinimer, William A., Chm. Bd. & Chief Exec. Officer--Uniplast Industries, Inc., Orillia, Canada; *Int'l*, pg. 1424
Swink, Gary, Pres. & Gen. Mgr.--Simco, Hatfield, PA; *U.S. Public*, pg. 865
Swinsky, Morton, Pres. & Chief Exec. Officer--Fuji Securities Inc.-New York, New York, NY; *Int'l*, pg. 519
Swinton, Michael H., Plant Mgr.--Rapidsyn Div., Racine, WI; *U.S. Public*, pg. 90
Swisher, Bill, Chief Oper. Officer--Oklahoma City Division, Oklahoma City, OK; *U.S. Public*, pg. 279
Swithenbank, Thomas, Pres.--Harte-Hanks Data Technologies, Billerica, MA; *U.S. Public*, pg. 794
Switzer, L.R.K., Mng. Dir.--Carter Holt Harvey Building Products Group Limited, Auckland, New Zealand; *U.S. Public*, pg. 904
Swoboda, Ralph, Pres.--CUNA Service Group, Inc., Madison, WI; *U.S. Private*, pg. 288
Sy, Jane, Pres. & Treas.--Christian Mutual Life Insurance Co., Houston, TX; *U.S. Private*, pg. 225
Sy, Victor, Mng. Dir.--Shanghai McCormick Seasoning & Foodstuffs Company, Limited, Shanghai, China; *U.S. Public*, pg. 1067
Sy, Victor K., Pres.--McCormick Thailand, Inc., Bangkok, Thailand; *U.S. Public*, pg. 1067
Sycamore, Allan, Chief Oper. Officer--Ahlstrom ANZ Pty Ltd., Melbourne, Australia; *Int'l*, pg. 34
Sychta, P., Mng. Dir.--Ascom Timeplex Ltd., Slough, United Kingdom; *Int'l*, pg. 87
Sydell, Jack, Dir. Gen.--OfficeMax De Mexico, Mexico, Mexico; *U.S. Public*, pg. 1212
Sydow, Hans, Pres., Acct. Supvr.--Hall & Cederquist, Inc., New York, NY; *U.S. Private*, pg. 1197
Sygel, Kristoffler, Mng. Dir.--Data General GmbH, Schwalbach, Germany; *U.S. Public*, pg. 486
Sykes, Greg, Pres.--Seitz Foods Inc., Saint Joseph, MO; *U.S. Public*, pg. 1434
Sykes, Guy R., Pres.--Eastern Shore Markets, Inc., Norfolk, VA; *U.S. Private*, pg. 203
Sykes, Malcolm, V.P. & Gen. Mgr.--U.S. Brick, Inc.-Michigan Division, Corunna, MI; *Int'l*, pg. 699
Sykes, Ronald, V.P. & Gen. Mgr.--Polycold Systems International, Inc., San Rafael, CA; *U.S. Public*, pg. 894
Syltevik, Kristin, Mng. Dir.--Miller/Shandwick Communications Ltd., London, United Kingdom; *Int'l*, pg. 1226
Sylvan, Ulf, Mng. Dir. & Grp. Chief Exec. UK--Svenska Handelsbanken London, London, United Kingdom; *Int'l*, pg. 1327
Sylvester, C., Chief Oper. Officer--Barbados Dairy Industries Ltd., Saint Michael, Barbados; *Int'l*, pg. 923
Sylvester, Richard, V.P.--Customline Div., Linden, NJ; *Int'l*, pg. 53
Syme, Tom, Pres. & Chief Exec. Officer--Air Ontario, London, Canada; *Int'l*, pg. 36
Symes, John, Pres.--MGM Worldwide Television, Group., Santa Monica, CA; *U.S. Public*, pg. 1102
Symes, Peter, Mng. Dir.--Yorkshire Guernsey, Saint Peter Port, United Kingdom; *Int'l*, pg. 1522
Synder, Dana, Pres.--Best Insurors, Inc., Tampa, FL; *U.S. Public*, pg. 1736
Synder, Robert, Gen. Mgr.--Air-Dry Corporation of America, Moorpark, CA; *U.S. Public*, pg. 481
Synnersten, Kenneth, Pres.--ABB Plast AB, Pitea, Sweden; *Int'l*, pg. 7
Syphard, David W., Pres.--CRSS International, Inc., Houston, TX; *U.S. Public*, pg. 922
Syre, Jim, Gen. Mgr.--Barton's of Weiner, Weiner, AR; *U.S. Private*, pg. 119
Syrjamaki, Maxine, Chief Fin. Officer & Exec. V.P.--Jefferies & Company, Inc., Los Angeles, CA; *U.S. Public*, pg. 925
Syslak, Hulda, Country Mgr.--BMC Software A/S, Ballerup, Denmark; *U.S. Public*, pg. 162
Syvanen, Veikko, Mng. Dir.--Hobby Hall, Helsinki, Finland; *Int'l*, pg. 1301
Syversen, Gunnar, Chief Oper. Officer--TA Control System A/S, Oslo, Norway; *Int'l*, pg. 670
Syverson, David B., Chief Exec. Officer--Dave Syverson Truck Center, Inc., Rochester, MN; *U.S. Private*, pg. 1061
Syvertsen, Edwin T., Jr., Pres.--Rolero Omega Operations, Cleveland, OH; *U.S. Public*, pg. 443
Szabo, Frank, Pres.--Diversified Stainless Steel of Canada, Downsview, Canada; *U.S. Public*, pg. 308
Szabo, Klara, Liaison Officer--E/B/D-Interpartners Budapest KFT, Budapest, Hungary; *U.S. Private*, pg. 1152
Szabo, Stephen, Mng. Dir.--Valmet Paper Machinery (UK) Ltd., Purley, United Kingdom; *Int'l*, pg. 1448
Szalla, John, Terminal Mgr.--Carson Terminal, Carson, CA; *U.S. Public*, pg. 692
Szallai, John, Mgr.--Los Angeles Harbor Terminal, San Pedro, CA; *U.S. Public*, pg. 692
Szczeblowski, Thomas, Plant Mgr.--Surfactant Dept. Plant, Anaheim, CA; *U.S. Public*, pg. 1514
Sze, Andy, Pres.--Caro Trans Intl., Lemont, IL; *U.S. Public*, pg. 130
Sze, Joseph, Mgr.-China--Singapore Tourist Promotion Board - Shanghai, Shanghai, China; *Int'l*, pg. 1254
Szep, Suzanna, Office Mgr.--Sensormatic kfi, Budapest, Hungary; *U.S. Public*, pg. 1458
Szescila, Andrew J., Pres.--Hughes Christensen Co., Salt Lake City, UT; *U.S. Public*, pg. 166
Szescila, Andy, Pres.--Hughes Christensen, Houston, TX; *U.S. Public*, pg. 166
Szeto, Henry, Chief Oper. Officer--Griffith Laboratories (H.K.) Ltd., Sha Tin, Hong Kong; *U.S. Private*, pg. 481
Szippl, Dave, Plant Mgr.--Wagner Manufacturing, Sidney, OH; *U.S. Private*, pg. 1146
Szmanski, Chester, Pres.--Unilever Research & Development Co., Edgewater, NJ; *Int'l*, pg. 1436
Szmulewitz, Armend, Chief Exec. Officer--Rexall Inc. Consumer Products Div., Boca Raton, FL; *U.S. Public*, pg. 1384
Szokol, George, Dr., Mng. Dir.-Sls.--ESAB KFT, Budapest, Hungary; *Int'l*, pg. 282
Szomjassy, Michael A., Pres.--OHM International, Inc., Findlay, OH; *U.S. Public*, pg. 1208
Szuchman, Mark, Mng. Dir.--MGR Sports, Wilton, CT; *U.S. Public*, pg. 1641
Szuhy, Lawrence G., Gen. Mgr.--OEM Div., Hope, AR; *U.S. Public*, pg. 335
Szuhy, Lawrence G., Gen. Mgr.--Champion Parts (Canada) Ltd., Concord, Canada; *U.S. Public*, pg. 335
Szulik, Matthew, Pres.-N. American Opers.--Sapiens USA, Inc., Durham, NC; *Int'l*, pg. 1193
Szuluk, C.W., Chm. Bd. & Pres.--Ford Electronics Manufacturing Corporation, Markham, Canada; *U.S. Public*, pg. 665
Szuluk, Charles W., Pres.--Altec Electronica de Chihuahua S. A. de C. V., Chihuahua, Mexico; *U.S. Public*, pg. 665
Szydlowski, T., Chief Exec. Officer--ISI Norgen, Inc., Fraser, MI; *Int'l*, pg. 646
Szymanski, Conrad, Pres.--Beall's Dept. Stores, Bradenton, FL; *U.S. Private*, pg. 126
T'Joens, Frans, Mng. Dir.--Bekaert International Trade, Zwevegem, Belgium; *Int'l*, pg. 183
Taafe, Willie, Pres. & Chief Exec. Officer--Knapp Shoes Inc., Penn Yan, NY; *U.S. Private*, pg. 401
Tabata, Hideki, Pres.--Sumitomo Life Realty (N.Y.), Inc., New York, NY; *Int'l*, pg. 1315
Tabata, Nobuyuki, Pres.--Amano Cleantech Malaysia Sdn. Bhd., Petaling Jaya, Malaysia; *Int'l*, pg. 71
Tabayashi, Kozo, Honorary Chm.--LTCB Asia Limted, Hong Kong, Hong Kong; *Int'l*, pg. 816
Tablak, Jeff, Pres., Chief Exec. Officer & Co-Founder--Nextron, San Jose, CA; *U.S. Public*, pg. 1424
Tabor, Hollis, Pres. & Gen. Mgr.--Norris Screen & Mfg., Inc., Princeton, WV; *U.S. Private*, pg. 370
Tabor, Lindy, Pres.--Tabor Machine Co., Bluefield, WV; *U.S. Private*, pg. 371
Tabrett, Ian, Mng. Dir.--Reed Business Information Pty. Limited, Chatswood, Australia; *Int'l*, pg. 1094
Tabuchi, Susumu, Sr. V.P. & Gen. Mgr.--Sumitomo Corporation of America, Los Angeles, CA; *Int'l*, pg. 1312
Tachikawa, Achira, Pres.--Tetsudo Sharyo Kogyo Co., Ltd., Tokyo, Japan; *Int'l*, pg. 764
Tachikawa, Nohuhiko, Mng. Dir.--Mitsui Trust International Ltd., London, United Kingdom; *Int'l*, pg. 883
Tackett, Wayne, Mgr.--Huntsville Space Operations, Huntsville, AL; *U.S. Public*, pg. 1597
Tackey, Ron, Plant Mgr.--Edmonton Plant, Edmonton, Canada; *U.S. Public*, pg. 672
Tacl, M., Gen. Mgr.--Nationale-Nederlanden Zivotni Pojist'ovna, Prague, Czech Republic; *Int'l*, pg. 651
Tadano, Hiroshi, Gen. Mgr.--S.B. Merchant Bank (Singapore) Limited, Singapore, Singapore; *Int'l*, pg. 1309
Tadashi, S., Pres.--Bausch & Lomb Japan Co., Ltd., Tokyo, Japan; *U.S. Public*, pg. 195
Tadmor, Dov, Chief Oper. Officer--Discount Investment Corporation Ltd., Tel Aviv, Israel; *Int'l*, pg. 644
Tadokoro, M., Gen. Mgr.--JCB International Credit Card Co., Ltd.-USA, San Francisco, CA; *Int'l*, pg. 696
Taeymans, Jules, Dir.--Van Leer Belgium BV, Lier, Belgium; *Int'l*, pg. 1146
Taffer, Mike, Pres.--Stilwell Foods, Inc., Stilwell, OK; *U.S. Public*, pg. 658
Taffy, Paul J., Mng. Dir.--Kimberly-Clark Malaysia Sendirian Berhad, Petaling Jaya, Malaysia; *U.S. Public*, pg. 960
Taft, Rick, Gen. Mgr.--Textile Care Services, Inc., Salt Lake City, UT; *U.S. Public*, pg. 1537
Taga, Junichiro, Pres.--Ibiden Co., Ltd., Gifu, Japan; *Int'l*, pg. 878
Tagawa, Craig K., Chief Exec. Officer--GK Financing, LLC, San Francisco, CA; *U.S. Public*, pg. 91
Taggart, D., Gen. Mgr.--Aer Lingus, Amsterdam, Netherlands; *Int'l*, pg. 28
Taggart, David, Pres.--CTB/McGraw Hill, Monterey, CA; *U.S. Public*, pg. 1070
Taggart, J.K., Pres.--TECO Diversified, Inc., Tampa, FL; *U.S. Public*, pg. 1565
Taggart, R., Pres.--Pringle of Scotland, New York, NY; *Int'l*, pg. 386
Tagle, G., Gen. Mgr.--ING Bank Santiago de Chile, Santiago, Chile; *Int'l*, pg. 649
Tagle, G., Gen. Mgr.--ING Compania de Inversiones y Servicios Ltda., Santiago, Chile; *Int'l*, pg. 650
Tagliaferri, Chicco, Mng. Dir.--Shandwick Rome Srl, Rome, Italy; *Int'l*, pg. 1228
Tagliaferro, John, Pres.--IDB WorldCom, New York, NY; *U.S. Public*, pg. 1779
Taglio, J.P., Pres.--Morrison Homes, Pleasant Hill, CA; *Int'l*, pg. 1510
Taguchi, Fumio, Mng. Dir.--Brother Office Equipment S.p.A., Milan, Italy; *Int'l*, pg. 230
Taguchi, Tadao, Chm. & Chief Exec. Officer--Toshiba America Inc., New York, NY; *Int'l*, pg. 1405
Tahany, M. Peter, Chm.--Sheller-Clifford Ltd., Birmingham, United Kingdom; *U.S. Public*, pg. 1691
Tahara, Masao, Chief Oper. Officer--Makita Power Tools (H.K.) LTD., Sha Tin, Hong Kong; *Int'l*, pg. 832
Tahch, Cary, V.P.-Opers.--Jacobs Engineering Group Inc., Baton Rouge, LA; *U.S. Public*, pg. 921
Tahhel, Staffen, Mgr.--Boliden WP-Contech AB, Stockholm, Sweden; *Int'l*, pg. 1422
Tahtinen, Kari, Pres.--Imatra Steel Oy Ab, Helsinki, Finland; *Int'l*, pg. 863
Tahvanainen, Olli-Matti, Mng. Dir.--Metsa-Serla Tissue GmbH, Dusseldorf, Germany; *Int'l*, pg. 864
Tai, Chi-Shen, Asst. V.P. & Rep.--The International Commercial Bank of China, Manama, Bahrain; *Int'l*, pg. 683

Tai, Chi-Shen, Asst. V.P. & Rep.--The International Commercial Bank of China, Jeddah, Saudi Arabia; *Int'l*, pg. 683
Tai, Hidenori, Mng. Dir. & Gen. Mgr.--Takugin Finance International Ltd., London, United Kingdom; *Int'l*, pg. 627
Taiana, Erich, Mng. Dir.--Sulzer Energy Consulting Inc., Winterthur, Switzerland; *Int'l*, pg. 1306
Taida, H., Mng. Dir.--Marubeni U.K. Plc., London, United Kingdom; *Int'l*, pg. 845
Tait, David C., Pres.--MBC Realty, Inc., Baltimore, MD; *U.S. Public*, pg. 1089
Tait, Thomas J., V.P. & Mng. Dir.--Thomas Tait & Sons, Ltd., Montvale, NJ; *U.S. Public*, pg. 904
Tajika, Toshihiko, Chief Rep.--Asahi Bank Sao Paulo Representative Office, Sao Paulo, Brazil; *Int'l*, pg. 83
Tajima, K., Pres.--Buss (Japan) Ltd., Tokyo, Japan; *Int'l*, pg. 490
Tajiri, Akira, Area Dir.-China--Dentsu East Japan Inc., Tokyo, Japan; *Int'l*, pg. 393
Tajiri, Akira, Area Dir.--Area Headquarters-CHINA, Tokyo, Japan; *Int'l*, pg. 393
Takacs, L., Mng. Dir.--EGIS-Nutricia Kft, Budapest, Hungary; *Int'l*, pg. 991
Takada, H., Pres.Dir.--NSK-RHP UK Limited, Ruddington, United Kingdom; *Int'l*, pg. 904
Takada, Hiromichi, Gen. Mgr.--Chiba Bank, Ltd.-Los Angeles Agency, Los Angeles, CA; *Int'l*, pg. 283
Takada, M., Chief Rep. Officer--The Kansai Electric Power Co. - Paris Office, Paris, France; *Int'l*, pg. 723
Takada, Norifumi, Chief Rep.--Frankfurt Representative Office, Frankfurt/Main, Germany; *Int'l*, pg. 816
Takada, O, Pres.--Kobe Alumina Associates (Australia) Pty. Ltd., Perth, Australia; *Int'l*, pg. 741
Takada, Yoichi, Pres.--Dai-ichi Life International (Canada), Inc., Toronto, Canada; *Int'l*, pg. 362
Takafuku, M., Pres.--Sharp Electronics (Svenska) AB, Skarholmen, Sweden; *Int'l*, pg. 1230
Takagaki, Katsusuke, Pres.--Tong Shing Inc., Taipei, Taiwan; *Int'l*, pg. 1400
Takagi, Kiyoshi, Gen. Mgr.--Dai-Ichi Kangyo Bank Nederland N.V., Amsterdam, Netherlands; *Int'l*, pg. 362
Takagi, Matt, Mgr.--Hitachi Power Tools U.S.A. Ltd., Chatsworth, CA; *Int'l*, pg. 620
Takagi, Noboru, Chief Rep.--Dai-Ichi Kangyo Bank, Ltd.-Jakarta, Jakarta, Indonesia; *Int'l*, pg. 361
Takagi, Shigeru, Chief Oper. Officer--Honda Australia Pty., Ltd., Tullamarine, Australia; *Int'l*, pg. 635
Takagi, Shigeru, Pres.--MEC USA, Inc., Wilmington, DE; *Int'l*, pg. 873
Takagi, Shinichi, Pres.--Consumer Video Products Co., Park Ridge, NJ; *Int'l*, pg. 1281
Takagi, T., Pres.--Mikuni Shoko Corp., Tokyo, Japan; *Int'l*, pg. 867
Takahashi, Akio, Gen. Mgr.--Fuji Bank, Shanghai Branch, Shanghai, China; *Int'l*, pg. 520
Takahashi, Akio, Chief Oper. Officer--Nagano Oki Electric Co., Ltd., Nagano, Japan; *Int'l*, pg. 999
Takahashi, Eiichi, Mng. Dir. & Gen. Mgr.--Chuo Trust & Banking Company (Europe) S.A., Brussels, Belgium; *Int'l*, *pg. 291*
Takahashi, Hiroshi, Pres.--Citizen America Corp., Santa Monica, CA; *Int'l*, pg. 294
Takahashi, Hitoshi, Sr. V.P.--The Korea Industrial Leasing Co., Ltd., Seoul, Korea; *Int'l*, pg. 933
Takahashi, Ikuo, Pres.--IDD Co., LTD., Tokyo, Japan; *Int'l*, pg. 1125
Takahashi, Katsuya, Pres.--NSK do Brasil Industria e Comercio de Rolamentos Ltda., Bela Vista, Brazil; *Int'l*, pg. 904
Takahashi, Ken, Gen. Mgr.--Mitsui Trust & Banking Company, Limited, Los Angeles, CA; *Int'l*, pg. 883
Takahashi, Ken, Gen. Mgr.--The Mitsui Trust and Banking Company - Los Angeles, Los Angeles, CA; *Int'l*, pg. 883
Takahashi, Kenichi, Chief Representative--The Bank of Tokyo-Mitsubishi, Ltd. (San Francisco Branch), San Francisco, CA; *Int'l*, pg. 157
Takahashi, Kenichiro, Div. Head--JDAC, Tokyo, Japan; *U.S. Private*, pg. 1065
Takahashi, Masa, Gen. Mgr.--Tokyo Gas, Los Angeles, CA; *Int'l*, pg. 1394
Takahashi, Masayoshi, Chief Rep.--Asahi Bank Jakarta Representative Office, Jakarta, Indonesia; *Int'l*, pg. 83
Takahashi, Masayoshi, Mng. Dir.--Mitsui Trust Bank (Europe) S.A., Brussels, Belgium; *Int'l*, pg. 883
Takahashi, N., Mng. Dir.--Ebara Engineering (Malaysia) Sdn. Bhd., Kuala Lumpur, Malaysia; *Int'l*, pg. 432
Takahashi, Shigemitsu, Terminal Mgr.--Kintetsu Intermodal Inc., Miami, FL; *Int'l*, pg. 735
Takahashi, Takeshi, Gen. Mgr.--Fuji Bank, Chicago Branch, Chicago, IL; *Int'l*, pg. 519
Takahashi, Teruo, Gen. Mgr.--Dai-Ichi Kangyo Bank, Ltd.-Chicago, Chicago, IL; *Int'l*, pg. 359
Takahashi, Yuzuru, Sr. Rep.--Nippon Credit Bank Ltd.-Bahrain, Manama, Bahrain; *Int'l*, pg. 933
Takahira, Manabu, Gen. Mgr.--T.K.G. International Corp., Macon, GA; *Int'l*, pg. 1349
Takai, Keiji, Pres.--Kawasaki Rail Car, Inc., Yonkers, NY; *Int'l*, pg. 725
Takaki, V.I., Mng. Dir.--OMRON Eletronika Do Brasil Ltda., Sao Paulo, Brazil; *Int'l*, pg. 1006
Takakura, Yoichi, Chief Rep.--The Sumitomo Bank, Ltd.-Shenyang Representative Office, Shenyang, China; *Int'l*, pg. 1310
Takamori, Kotaro, Pres.--China Orient Leasing Co., Ltd., Beijing, China; *Int'l*, pg. 1009
Takano, Masahiro, Deputy Chm.--Guinness Mahon Holdings Plc, London, United Kingdom; *Int'l*, pg. 159
Takano, Masayoshi, Mgr. & Controller--Hitachi-Borden Chemical Products, Inc., Tokyo, Japan; *U.S. Public*, pg. 5
Takano, Masayoshi, Mgr. & Controller--Hitachi-Borden Chemical Products, Inc., Tokyo, Japan; *Int'l*, pg. 622
Takano, Takehito, Gen. Mgr.--Nippon Credit (Schweiz) AG, Zurich, Switzerland; *Int'l*, pg. 933
Takanose, Takaaki, Chief Oper. Officer--Hagglunds Drives Ltd, Yokohama, Japan; *Int'l*, pg. 670
Takanose, Takaaki, Chief Oper. Officer--Hagglunds Ltd. Dept. Drives, Yokohama, Japan; *Int'l*, pg. 670
Takashi, Sanefuji, Pres.--Companhia Brasileira de Estireno, Sao Paulo, Brazil; *U.S. Public*, pg. 1125
Takashi, Toshishige, Pres.--Yamamoto Mfg. (USA) Inc., San Jose, CA; *Int'l*, pg. 295
Takavitz, F.J., Pres.--Exel Logistics North America, Westerville, OH; *Int'l*, pg. 901
Takawira, I.G., Mng. Dir.--Barclays Bank of Zimbabwe Ltd., Harare, Zimbabwe; *Int'l*, pg. 165
Takayama, Naoki, Mng. Dir.--Korea-Japan Finance Company Limted (KJF), Central, Hong Kong; *Int'l*, pg. 816
Takayanagi, Akira, Chief Oper. Officer--Hitachi Telecom Technologies Co., Ltd., Kouriyama-shi, Japan; *Int'l*, pg. 622
Takayasu, Tsunao, Chief Oper. Officer--Hanoi Resident Representative Office, Hanoi, Vietnam; *Int'l*, pg. 942
Takebayashi, T., Sr. Exec. Dir.--Toppan Moore Company Ltd., Tokyo, Japan; *Int'l*, pg. 890
Takebyshi, Shogo, Pres.--Mitsui Petrochemical Industries, Ltd., Tokyo, Japan; *Int'l*, pg. 877
Takechi, Sueharu, Pres.--O.S. Engines Mfg. Co., Ltd., Osaka, Japan; *Int'l*, pg. 531
Takeda, Kenzo, Pres.--Haseko Urban Co., Ltd., Tokyo, Japan; *Int'l*, pg. 600
Takeda, Masatoshi, Pres.--STB Corporate Development, Inc., Houston, TX; *Int'l*, pg. 1317
Takeda, S., Pres.--Toshiba Consumer Products (Thailand) Co., Ltd., Pathum Thani, Thailand; *Int'l*, pg. 1406
Takeda, Shozo, Pres.--Hosho America Inc., Seattle, WA; *Int'l*, pg. 733
Takeda, T., Pres.--Nalco Japan Co., Ltd., Tokyo, Japan; *U.S. Public*, pg. 1151
Takehara, Junji, Gen. Mgr.--The Hokuriku Bank, Ltd.-Hong Kong, Central, Hong Kong; *Int'l*, pg. 627
Takehisa, T., Pres.--Nissho Electronics Corp., Tokyo, Japan; *Int'l*, pg. 946
Takei, Arata, Exec. V.P.--Nikko Securities Co., Los Angeles, Los Angeles, CA; *Int'l*, pg. 930
Takei, M., Pres.--Nissho Iwai Petroleum Corp., Osaka, Japan; *Int'l*, pg. 947
Takekawa, Neil M., Pres.--Island Air, Honolulu, HI; *U.S. Private*, pg. 44
Takekoshi, Mr., Mng. Dir.--Fuji Photo Film (U.K.), Ltd., London, United Kingdom; *Int'l*, pg. 524
Takemura, Yashihiro, Sr. V.P. & Gen. Mgr.--Sumitomo Corporation of America, Chicago, IL; *Int'l*, pg. 1312
Takenaka, Hiroshi, Branch Mgr.--Yamaichi International (America) Inc.-Los Angeles Branch, Los Angeles, CA; *Int'l*, pg. 1517
Takenaka, Shuichi, Pres.--P.T. Bank LTCB Central Asia, Jakarta, Indonesia; *Int'l*, pg. 816
Takenaka, Toichi, Chief Exec.--Takenaka Real Estate Development Co., Ltd., Tokyo, Japan; *Int'l*, pg. 1351
Takens, R.J., Mng. Dir.--Audisio Industrie Alumentari SRL, Fossano, Italy; *Int'l*, pg. 244
Takeo, Tsunemi, Dir.--PT Showpla Indo, Bekasi, Indonesia; *Int'l*, pg. 1237
Takeshita, Tatsuo, Gen. Mgr.--Pioneer Hi-Bred Japan Co. Ltd., Tokyo, Japan; *U.S. Public*, pg. 1299
Takeuchi, Haruo, Pres.--Pasco-Certeza Computer Mapping Corporation, Manila, Philippines; *Int'l*, pg. 1024
Takeuchi, M., Mng. Dir. & Gen. Mgr.--CM Human Services Co. Ltd., Kanagawa, Japan; *U.S. Public*, pg. 317
Takeuchi, Masakazu, Pres. & Chief Exec. Officer--Gradco (Japan), Ltd., Tokyo, Japan; *U.S. Public*, pg. 757
Takeuchi, Minoru, Pres.--Shinko Engineering Co., Ltd., Ogaki, Japan; *Int'l*, pg. 740
Takeuchi, Toshio, Pres.--Bank of Tokyo-Mitsubishi (Deutschland) AG, Frankfurt/Main, Germany; *Int'l*, pg. 158
Takeuchi, Yorio, Pres.--Toshiba Electronics Taiwan Corp., Taipei, Taiwan; *Int'l*, pg. 1406
Takeyama, Hajime, Mng. Dir.--Nippon Express (Deutschland) GmbH, Monchengladbach, Germany; *Int'l*, *pg. 934*
Taki, Masatoshi, Mng. Dir.--Nippon Express Tours (Europe) Ltd., London, United Kingdom; *Int'l*, pg. 934
Takiguchi, Toshirou, Gen. Mgr.--The Sakura Bank - Mumbai Branch, Mumbai, India; *Int'l*, pg. 1179
Takiguichi, Shoji, Pres. & Chief Exec. Officer--Ipanema Shoe Corporation, New York, NY; *Int'l*, pg. 1312
Takis, Avio, Mng. Dir.--Estravel, Tallinn, Estonia; *Int'l*, pg. 486
Takiuchi, Toshio, Chief Rep. Officer--Kanebo, Ltd., New York, NY; *Int'l*, pg. 722
Tako, Tony, Pres.--Pabco Metals Corporation, Houston, TX; *U.S. Private*, pg. 449
Takubo, Tadashi, Pres.--Nomura Investor Relations Co., Ltd., Tokyo, Japan; *Int'l*, pg. 956
Takumi, Masaaki, Chief Oper. Officer--Industrial Resins (Malaysia) Sdn. Bhd.-Johor Baharu Plant, Johor Baharu, Malaysia; *Int'l*, pg. 1408
Talagrand, Noel, Pres.--Facom, Morangis, France; *Int'l*, pg. 570
Talbert, J. Michael, Pres. & Chief Oper. Officer--Lone Star Energy Co., Dallas, TX; *U.S. Public*, pg. 1587
Talbert, Tom, Pres.--SWENCO-Western, Inc., Denver, CO; *U.S. Public*, pg. 1543
Talbert, William, Pres.--JacksonLea, Conover, NC; *U.S. Public*, pg. 924
Talbot, Deborah, Pres.--Chase U.S. Consumer Services, New York, NY; *U.S. Public*, pg. 338
Talbot, Jocelyn, Telesales Dir.--TMP Worldwide/Interactive Division, Framingham, MA; *U.S. Private*, pg. 1065
Talbot, John, Pres.--Epstein Civil Engineering, Inc., Chicago, IL; *U.S. Private*, pg. 379
Talbot, Randall H., Pres.--Talbot Financial Corporation, Albuquerque, NM; *U.S. Public*, pg. 1423
Talbot, Terry, Reg. Mgr.--SMS-Chicago, Rolling Meadows, IL; *U.S. Public*, pg. 1463
Talbot, Todd, Pres.--Alsons Corporation, Hillsdale, MI; *U.S. Public*, pg. 1053
Talbott, Mark, Project Mgr.-Bridge Div.--Calumet Construction Corporation-South Bend Division, South Bend, IN; *U.S. Private*, pg. 202
Talboys, Richard, Dir.--Willis Corroon Credit Limited, Kingston upon Thames, United Kingdom; *Int'l*, pg. 1502
Taldu, Gilles, Gen. Mgr.--Thomson Sintra ASM, Sophia Antipolis, France; *Int'l*, pg. 1383
Talen, Edward J., Pres.--Clover Insurance Agency, Inc., Ontario, CA; *U.S. Public*, pg. 826
Taljaard, D.L.M., Pres. & Chief Exec. Officer--London & Leeds (USA) Corporation, New York, NY; *Int'l*, pg. 788
Talkington, Larry D., Pres.--Challenge Industries, Bryan, OH; *Int'l*, pg. 438
Tall, Craig E., Pres.--First Columbia Escrow, Inc., Seattle, WA; *U.S. Public*, pg. 1742
Tallec, Jean-Paul, Chief Exec. Officer & Dir.--Jimten, Alicante, Germany; *Int'l*, pg. 430
Tallett, W.K., Pres.--Mauna Kea Agribusiness Co., Inc., Papaikou, HI; *U.S. Private*, pg. 190
Talley, John V., Jr., Pres.--Penwest Pharm. Co., Patterson, NY; *U.S. Public*, pg. 1269
Talley, S.G., Gen. Mgr.--Quaker Chemical Environmental Products Division, Conroe, TX; *U.S. Public*, pg. 1346
Talley, W.F., Pres.--Smiths Industries Aerospace & Defense Systems Inc.-Florham Park Operation, Florham Park, NJ; *Int'l*, pg. 1268
Tallman, Cliff, Publisher--Sailing World, Newport, RI; *U.S. Public*, pg. 1174
Tallman, Cliff, Publisher--Cruising World, Newport, RI; *U.S. Public*, pg. 1174
Tallman, Steven C., Pres.--Quinton Instrument Company, Bothell, WA; *U.S. Public*, pg. 80
Talu, Turhan, Gen. Mgr.--Philip Morris Sabanci Pazalarma Ve Satis A.S., Istanbul, Turkey; *Int'l*, pg. 1168
Talu, Turhan, Gen. Mgr.--Philip Morris Sabanci Pazalarma Ve Satis A.S., Istanbul, Turkey; *U.S. Public*, pg. 1290
Tam, Kevin, Div. Mgr.--Hawthorne Lift Systems, Escondido, CA; *U.S. Private*, pg. 513
Tam, Simon, Mgr.--Fischer Imaging China, Beijing, China; *U.S. Public*, pg. 647
Tamaki, Tatsuji, Gen. Mgr.--Fuji Bank, Mumbai Branch, Mumbai, India; *Int'l*, pg. 520
Tamamoto, Tahmon, Pres.--Subaru-Isuzu Automotive, Inc., Lafayette, IN; *Int'l*, pg. 523
Tamaoki, Yuzo, Sr. Rep.--Nippon Credit Bank Ltd.-Paris, Paris, France; *Int'l*, pg. 933
Tamaroff, Marvin, Pres.--Tamaroff Leasing Co., Southfield, MI; *U.S. Private*, pg. 1067
Tamaru, Akira, Chief Rep.--Tianjin Representative Office, Tianjin, China; *Int'l*, pg. 520
Tamaru, K., Pres.--NSK-RHP Europe Limited, Ruddington, United Kingdom; *Int'l*, pg. 904
Tamayo, Jesus, Mng. Dir.--Productos Asfalticos, S.A. (PROAS), Madrid, Spain; *Int'l*, pg. 323
Tambakeras, Marcos, Pres.--Honeywell, Inc., Fort Washington, PA; *U.S. Public*, pg. 834
Tambakeras, Markos I., Pres.--Industrial Automation & Control Division, Phoenix, AZ; *U.S. Public*, pg. 833
Tamberlane, John, Pres.--Republic Bank for Savings, New York, NY; *U.S. Public*, pg. 1380
Tamblyn, Michael, Mng. Dir.--WD-40 Company Ltd., Milton Keynes, United Kingdom; *U.S. Public*, pg. 1726
Tamburini, Guido, Sls. Mgr.--Durco Europe S.R.L., Costa di Mezzate, Italy; *U.S. Public*, pg. 659
Tamigniaux, Rene, Mng. Dir.--Group Fabricom S.A., Brussels, Belgium; *Int'l*, pg. 1415
Tamm, Per, Company Head--Ovako Stahl GmbH, Erkrath, Germany; *Int'l*, pg. 1157
Tamminen, Markku, Pres.--Auto-Bon Oy, Vantaa, Finland; *Int'l*, pg. 72
Tamura, Hiroshi, Gen. Mgr.--Showa Denko America, Inc., San Mateo, CA; *Int'l*, pg. 1237
Tamura, Kimichi, Pres.--Kansei Corp., Omiya, Japan; *Int'l*, pg. 944
Tan, A.K., Chief Oper. Officer--KONE Elevator (M) Sdn. Bhd., Kuala Lumpur, Malaysia; *Int'l*, pg. 747
Tan, Chen T., Mng. Dir.--Plasma Technik Coating Systems S.E.A. PTE Ltd., Singapore, Singapore; *Int'l*, pg. 1307
Tan, Cheng T., Mng. Dir.--Sulzer Metco (Singapore) PTE Ltd., Singapore, Singapore; *Int'l*, pg. 1308
Tan, Daniel, Chief Rep.--Bank Brussels Lambert-Bangkok Representative Office, Bangkok, Thailand; *Int'l*, pg. 148
Tan, Heather, Gen. Mgr.--Tektronix Hong Kong Ltd., Wan Chai, Hong Kong; *U.S. Public*, pg. 1567
Tan, Irene, Mgr.--American Biltrite Far East, Inc., Singapore, Singapore; *U.S. Public*, pg. 69
Tan, J.C., Gen. Mgr.--AMP Tools (India) Pvt. Ltd., Cochin, India; *U.S. Public*, pg. 9
Tan, J.C., Gen. Mgr.--AMP Phillippines Inc., Manila, Philippines; *U.S. Public*, pg. 9
Tan, Jonathan, Mng. Dir.--Keystone Southeast Asia Pty. Ltd., Jurong, Singapore; *U.S. Public*, pg. 1650
Tan, K.B., Mng. Dir.--Bally Singapore (Pte) Ltd., Singapore, Singapore; *Int'l*, pg. 997
Tan, Lilian, Gen. Mgr.--Benmark Pte. Ltd., Singapore, Singapore; *Int'l*, pg. 187
Tan, Raymond, Gen. Mgr.--W.R. Grace (Singapore) Pte. Ltd., Singapore, Singapore; *U.S. Public*, pg. 756
Tan, Ricky, Reg. Mgr.--M/S Fischbein Packaging (Singapore) Pte. Ltd., Singapore, Singapore; *U.S. Private*, *pg. 103*
Tan, S.C., Mng. Dir.--MSA S.E. Asia Pte. Ltd., Singapore, Singapore; *U.S. Public*, pg. 1115
Tan, T.G., Gen. Mgr.--Kimberly-Clark Far East Pte. Ltd., Singapore, Singapore; *U.S. Public*, pg. 959
Tanabe, Kuninori, Pres. & Chief Exec. Officer--Fuji Bank Canada, Toronto, Canada; *Int'l*, pg. 521
Tanahashi, K., Pres.--Alloy Tool Steel Inc., Santa Fe Springs, CA; *Int'l*, pg. 947
Tanaka, H., Gen. Mgr.--Marubeni America Corporation, Chicago Branch, Chicago, IL; *Int'l*, pg. 844

Tanaka, Haruhiko, Pres.--Japan Information Processing Service Co. Ltd., Tokyo, Japan; *Int'l*, pg. 702
Tanaka, Hideo, Pres.--Kawasaki Motors Netherlands N.V., Hoofddorp, Netherlands; *Int'l*, pg. 726
Tanaka, Hisayuki, Representative--Dai-Ichi Kangyo Bank, Ltd.-Toronto, Toronto, Canada; *Int'l*, pg. 361
Tanaka, Hitokuni, Chief Oper. Officer--Hong Kong Architectural Project Office, Tsim Tsa Tsui, Hong Kong; *Int'l*, pg. 942
Tanaka, I., Pres.--Nissho Iwai (Shanghai) Corporation, Shanghai, China; *Int'l*, pg. 948
Tanaka, Jiro, Chief Rep.--Asahi Bank San Francisco Representative Office, San Francisco, CA; *Int'l*, pg. 82
Tanaka, Junichiro, Pres.--Mitsui Real Estate Development Co., Ltd., Tokyo, Japan; *Int'l*, pg. 878
Tanaka, Kenji, Pres.--Asahi Bank of California, Los Angeles, CA; *Int'l*, pg. 82
Tanaka, Koji, Pres.--Nikko Espana Sociedad de Valores, S.A., Madrid, Spain; *Int'l*, pg. 930
Tanaka, Masuo, Pres.--Fujitsu Computer Products of America, Inc., San Jose, CA; *Int'l*, pg. 526
Tanaka, Nobuo, Pres.--GSI Trading Hong Kong Limited, Kowloon, Hong Kong; *Int'l*, pg. 579
Tanaka, P.H., Pres.--GKN Japan Ltd., Osaka, Japan; *Int'l*, pg. 536
Tanaka, S., Gen. Mgr.--The Yokohama Rubber Co., Ltd., Schaumburg, IL; *Int'l*, pg. 1521
Tanaka, Stuart, Pres.--Hokuriku U.S.A. Co., Ltd., Huntsville, AL; *Int'l*, pg. 628
Tanaka, T., Pres.--Astro Business Solutions, Inc., Gardena, CA; *Int'l*, pg. 262
Tanaka, T., Pres.--Racet Computes Limited, Brea, CA; *Int'l*, pg. 740
Tanaka, T., Gen. Mgr.--Marubeni America Corporation, Washington Office, Washington, DC; *Int'l*, pg. 845
Tanaka, Takayasu, Mng. Dir.--DKB International Public Limited Company, London, United Kingdom; *Int'l*, pg. 361
Tanaka, Yasuo, Office Mgr.--Kintetsu World Express Inc., Minneapolis, MN; *Int'l*, pg. 734
Tanaka, Yoichi, Mng. Dir.--Kintetsu World Express (H.K.) Ltd., Kowloon, Hong Kong; *Int'l*, pg. 735
Tanaka, Yoichi, Chief Oper. Officer--Oki Electronics (Hong Kong) Ltd., Kowloon, Hong Kong; *Int'l*, pg. 1000
Tananbaum, Andrew, Pres.--Century Data Services, Inc., New York, NY; *U.S. Private*, pg. 226
Tandarich, S.T., Pres.--LI Service Company, Coatesville, PA; *U.S. Public*, pg. 1020
Tandberg, Truls, Admin. Dir.--Titania A/S, Hague, Netherlands; *U.S. Private*, pg. 271
Tang, Don F., V.P. & Gen. Mgr.--Space Systems Division, Sunnyvale, CA; *U.S. Public*, pg. 1009
Tang, Henry, Sr. V.P. & Dir.-Investment Services--Jefferies & Company, Inc., Los Angeles, CA; *U.S. Public*, pg. 925
Tang, Hsien-Jen, Sr. V.P. & Gen. Mgr.--The International Commercial Bank of China, Los Angeles, CA; *Int'l*, pg. 683
Tang, Joe, Mng. Dir.--Solectron Technology Sdn. Bhd, Penang, Malaysia; *U.S. Public*, pg. 1483
Tang, Joe, Gen. Mgr.--Toys "R" US Lifung (Hong Kong) Ltd., Hong Kong, Hong Kong; *U.S. Public*, pg. 1626
Tang, Kenneth Y., Dr., Pres.--Thermolase, San Diego, CA; *U.S. Public*, pg. 1595
Tang, Kevin, Gen. Mgr.--Leaf China, Wuxi, China; *Int'l*, pg. 638
Tang, N.C., Sls. Dir.--Pan Malaysia Cement Works (Singapore) Pte. Ltd., Singapore, Singapore; *Int'l*, pg. 198
Tang, Quinly, Pub. Rels. Dir.--Leo Burnett Worldwide Asia/ Pacific Hdqtrs., Hong Kong, Hong Kong; *U.S. Private*, pg. 186
Tang, Simon, Gen. Mgr.--Elscint (Asia Pacific) Ltd., Wan Chai, Hong Kong; *Int'l*, pg. 450
Tang, Thomas, Representative--CUNA Mutual Group-Taiwan, Tai-chung, Taiwan; *U.S. Private*, pg. 297
Tang, Thomas, Mng. Dir.--Dataproducts (Hong Kong), Ltd., Kowloon, Hong Kong; *Int'l*, pg. 621
Tang, V., Chief Exec. Officer--Sanshui Redland Building Materials Co. Ltd., Guangzhou, China; *Int'l*, pg. 1093
Tangel, Frank, Chief Oper. Officer & Facilities Mgr.--Contadina Dalla Casa Buitoni, Glendale, CA; *Int'l*, pg. 916
Tangen, I., Mng. Dir.--Deminex Norge AS, Oslo, Norway; *Int'l*, pg. 1461
Tangen, Kjell, Branch Mgr.--Christiania Bank-London Branch, London, United Kingdom; *Int'l*, pg. 289
Tanguay, Gilles, Pres.--Filpac, Inc., Terrebonne, Canada; *Int'l*, pg. 233
Tanguy, Andre, Mng. Dir.--Jotun France S.A., Neuilly-sur-Seine, France; *Int'l*, pg. 715
Tangye, Richard, Gen. Mgr.--Jardine, Matheson & Co., Ltd., Taipei, Taiwan; *Int'l*, pg. 704
Tanhuanpaa, Kalle, Pres.--Leaf Finland, Turku, Finland; *Int'l*, pg. 638
Tani, Michio, Mng. Dir.--Fuji Capital Markets (HK) Limited, Central, Hong Kong; *Int'l*, pg. 521
Tanigawa, A., Pres.--Tokyo Calpis Beverages Co., Ltd., Tokyo, Japan; *Int'l*, pg. 253
Tanigawa, H., Mng. Dir.--Sharp-Roxy Sales (Singapore) Pte. Ltd., Singapore, Singapore; *Int'l*, pg. 1230
Tanigawa, Toru, Chief Representative--The Japan Development Bank-Los Angeles Representative Office, Los Angeles, CA; *Int'l*, pg. 701
Taniguchi, Tsukasa, Branch Mgr.--Wako Securities (America), Inc., Los Angeles, CA; *Int'l*, pg. 1485
Tanii, Akio, Pres.--Matsushita Industrial Equip. Co., Ltd., Kadoma, Japan; *Int'l*, pg. 846
Tanimoto, Michiharu, Pres.--Kawasaki Robotics (U.S.A.), Inc., Farmington, MI; *Int'l*, pg. 725
Tanimoto, Sadao, Pres.--UBE Industries (America) Inc., New York, NY; *Int'l*, pg. 1427
Tanimoto, Tonomi, Pres.--Thai Kobe Welding Co., Ltd., Samutprakan, Thailand; *Int'l*, pg. 741
Tanishima, H., Pres.--Ebara - Elliott Service (Taiwan) Co., Ltd., Tai-chung, Taiwan; *Int'l*, pg. 432
Taniuchi, Sonny, V.P.--Consumer Products Group, Ramsey, NJ; *Int'l*, pg. 869
Taniuchi, Yoichi, Chief Oper. Officer--Okazaki Golf Club KK, Okazaki, Japan; *Int'l*, pg. 1362
Taniyama, Yasuro, Pres. & Chief Oper. Officer--Suntory International Corp., New York, NY; *Int'l*, pg. 1321
Tanizaki, Yoshiharu, Pres.--BetzDearborn K.K., Tokyo, Japan; *U.S. Public*, pg. 227
Tank, V., Chief Exec. Officer--Shaoxing Redland Building Materials Co., Inc., Shaoxing, China; *Int'l*, pg. 1093
Tankha, Ashok, Mgr.--Commerzbank AG-Mambai (Bombay), Mumbai, India; *Int'l*, pg. 311
Tanksley, Jeff, Warehouse Mgr.--Pace Industries, Inc., Columbus, GA; *U.S. Public*, pg. 986
Tanler, Ronald F., Pres.--Lord & Taylor, New York, NY; *U.S.* Public, pg. 1064
Tannehill, Joseph K., Pres.--Stock Equipment Co., Chagrin Falls, OH; *U.S. Public*, pg. 727
Tannenberg, Dieter E.A., Pres. & Chief Exec. Officer--Bell & Howell Document Management Products Company, Chicago, IL; *U.S. Public*, pg. 201
Tanner, Lance, Plant Mgr.--CMC-Cayce, Cayce, SC; *U.S. Public*, pg. 412
Tanner, M.G., Gen. Mgr.--Westpac Banking Corp. - Tuvalu, Funafuti, Tuvalu; *Int'l*, pg. 1497
Tanner, Mark, Gen. Mgr.--Dexter, U.K. Ltd., Slough, United Kingdom; *U.S. Public*, pg. 505
Tanner, Marshall, Plant Mgr.-Oxford--Tread Rubber Plant, Oxford, NC; *U.S. Public*, pg. 177
Tanner, Mike, Plant Mgr.--Bundy Corporation, Sabina Plant, Sabina, OH; *Int'l*, pg. 1341
Tanner, Mike, Plant Mgr.--Bundy Corporation, Washington Court House Plant, Washington Court House, OH; *Int'l*, pg. 1341
Tanner, Ray, Chm. Bd. & Chief Exec. Officer--Volunteer Bank, Jackson, TN; *U.S. Public*, pg. 176
Tanner, Ronald F., Pres.--Great Vacations International, Sedona, AZ; *U.S. Public*, pg. 1172
Tanner, Roy, Pres.--Control Laser Corporation, Orlando, FL; *U.S. Public*, pg. 599
Tanner, Ted, V.P.-Devel.--Catellus Development Corporation, Los Angeles, CA; *U.S. Public*, pg. 315
Tanner, Travis, Pres.--Walt Disney Travel Co., Inc., Anaheim, CA; *U.S. Public*, pg. 513
Tanner, Van G., Pres.--HRH Insurance Services of the Coachella Valley, Inc., Palm Desert, CA; *U.S. Public*, pg. 826
Tannion, K., Mng. Dir.--John Wyeth & Brother (N.Z.) Ltd., Auckland, New Zealand; *U.S. Public*, pg. 82
Tannus, Gabriel, Pres.--Astra Quimica e Farmaceutica Ltda., Sao Paulo, Brazil; *Int'l*, pg. 94
Tanoue, Katsuyasu, Mng. Dir.--Home Electronics Co., Ltd., Bangkok, Thailand; *Int'l*, pg. 1239
Tansley, P. George, Mng. Dir.--Linread North Bridge, Wigston, United Kingdom; *Int'l*, pg. 852
Tanssens, G., Mng. Dir.--EMI Music Publishing (Belgium) SA, Brussels, Belgium; *Int'l*, pg. 427
Tant, John, Gen. Mgr.--Barton's of Kennett, Kennett, MO; *U.S. Private*, pg. 119
Tantangelo, Domenico, Gen. Mgr.--Aermacchi S.p.A., Varese, Italy; *Int'l*, pg. 653
Tantivejesak, Pisuth, Mgr.--Svenska Thailand Ltd., Bangkok, Thailand; *Int'l*, pg. 1187
Tanton, Russell, Plant Mgr.--M.A. Hanna Rubber Compounding, Santa Fe Springs, CA; *U.S. Public*, pg. 781
Tanuma, Hidehisa, Pres.--Nomura Business Services Co., Ltd., Tokyo, Japan; *Int'l*, pg. 956
Tanzer, David, Pres.--Channel One Communications, New York, NY; *U.S. Public*, pg. 1328
Tao, Harold L., Pres. & Chief Exec. Officer--International Commercial Bank of Cathay, Toronto, Canada; *Int'l*, pg. 684
Tao, Richard, Pres.--May Design & Construction Co., Saint Louis, MO; *U.S. Public*, pg. 1064
Taparia, Pramod, Chief Oper. Officer--Frigoscandia Winner Food Process Systems Pvt Ltd, Indore, India; *U.S. Public*, pg. 607
Tapazio, Bob, V.P. & Gen. Mgr.--R.H. Forschner Division, Shelton, CT; *U.S. Public*, pg. 1544
Tapella, Gary I., Pres. & Chief Exec. Officer--Rheem Manufacturing Co., New York, NY; *Int'l*, pg. 1022
Tapia, Nicholas, Mng. Dir. & Chief Oper. Officer--Foster Wheeler Energia, S.A., Madrid, Spain; *U.S. Public*, pg. 677
Tapken, Jane, V.P.--Jani King of Dallas, Carrollton, TX; *U.S.* Private, pg. 582
Tapper, Bo, Chief Oper. Officer--Neste Gas AB, Sundsvall, Sweden; *Int'l*, pg. 915
Tappertzhofen, Werner, Chm.--Flender Getriebewerk Penig GmbH, Penig, Germany; *Int'l*, pg. 400
Tappmeir, Jochen, Chief Oper. Officer--Jung-Pumpen GmbH, Steinhagen, Germany; *U.S. Public*, pg. 1054
Taps, Johann, Mgr.--Sandvik Kosta GmbH, Renningen, Germany; *Int'l*, pg. 1186
Taps, Johann, Mgr.--Sandvik Process Systems GmbH, Fellbach, Germany; *Int'l*, pg. 1187
Tarajana, Rick M, Pres.--Pala Interstate, Baton Rouge, LA; *U.S. Private*, pg. 834
Taranova, Frank, V.P.--RCI Travel, Indianapolis, IN; *U.S. Public*, pg. 322
Taranto, Joseph, Pres.--Transatlantic Reinsurance Co., New York, NY; *U.S. Public*, pg. 84
Taranto, Joseph, Pres.--Putnam Reinsurance Co., New York, NY; *U.S. Public*, pg. 84
Taranto, Joseph V., Chm. Bd.--Everest National Insurance Co., Liberty Corner, NJ; *U.S. Public*, pg. 597
Taranto, Joseph V., Chm. Bd.--Everest Reinsurance, Ltd., London, United Kingdom; *U.S. Public*, pg. 597
Taranto, Ken, Gen. Mgr.--CHR Division, New Haven, CT; *U.S. Public*, pg. 689
Taranto, Ken, Gen. Mgr.--CHR Division, Rolling Meadows, IL; *U.S. Public*, pg. 689
Tarantolo, Paul, Chief Oper. Officer--Texas Metal Fabricating, Houston, TX; *U.S. Public*, pg. 1639
Tarapaski, Bill, V.P.--Siplast Canada Inc., Burnaby, Canada; *Int'l*, pg. 659
Tarapasky, Gordon, Mgmt.--DYWIDAG-Systems International Far East, Ltd., Hong Kong, Hong Kong; *Int'l*, pg. 424
Taras, Nick K., Pres.--Robert Orr-Sysco Food Services Co., Nashville, TN; *U.S. Public*, pg. 1551
Tarasevich, D.J., Pres.--Tuscaloosa Steel Corp., Tuscaloosa, AL; *Int'l*, pg. 221
Tarbert, Jeff, Mgr.--Colorado Springs Cablevision, Inc., Colorado Springs, CO; *U.S. Public*, pg. 1610
Tarbox, Glenn S., Pres.--Harza Engineering Company of California, Oakland, CA; *U.S. Private*, pg. 509
Tarbuck, G., Mng. Dir.--Portec (U.K.) Ltd., Wrexham, United Kingdom; *U.S. Public*, pg. 1318
Tardio, Thomas A., Pres. & Chief Exec. Officer--Rogers & Cowan, Inc., Century City, CA; *Int'l*, pg. 1227
Tardio, Vicente, Gen. Mgr.--Cresa Aseguradora y Reaseguradora Iberica S.A., Barcelona, Spain; *Int'l*, pg. 61
Tarello, John A., Pres.--Analogic Foreign Sales Corp., Saint Thomas, VI; *U.S. Public*, pg. 109
Tarleton, Cullie M., Sr. V.P. & Gen. Mgr.--WBTV/WBT-AM & FM, Charlotte, NC; *U.S. Public*, pg. 926
Tarng, Karen, Mng. Dir./Partner--EURO RSCG Partnership, Taipei, Taiwan; *Int'l*, pg. 602
Tarongi, Jose Ignacio Gracia, Pres.--SODIAR - Sociedad Para el Desarrollo Industrial de Aragon, S.A., Zaragoza, Spain; *Int'l*, pg. 1225
Taronick, Felix, Pres.--Kay Home Products, Inc., Cleveland, OH; *U.S. Public*, pg. 1258
Tarorick, Felix, Pres.--Marshallan Industries, Cleveland, OH; *U.S. Public*, pg. 1259
Tarpey, James W., Pres.--Clove Development Corp., Pearl River, NY; *U.S. Public*, pg. 1229
Tarpey, James W., Pres.--O & R Development, Inc., Pearl River, NY; *U.S. Public*, pg. 1229
Tarpley, W.D., Pres.--HRR Enterprises, Inc., Chicago, IL; *U.S. Private*, pg. 607
Tarquin, Donald, Pres.--Sargent Controls, Tucson, AZ; *U.S. Public*, pg. 521
Tarr, Steve, Gen. Mgr.--Perfection Automotive Products Corporation, Goshen, IN; *U.S. Public*, pg. 1577
Tarrach, R. Raymond, Pres. & Chief Exec. Officer--The Chestertown Bank of Maryland, Chestertown, MD; *U.S. Public*, pg. 1088
Tarrio, Jose, Mgr.-Teriminal--Bilbao Terminal, Vizcaya, Spain; *U.S. Public*, pg. 693
Tartaglione, Nicholas L., Pres.--Akemi Plastics Inc., Eaton Rapids, MI; *U.S. Public*, pg. 1061
Tarvainen, Matti, Pres.--Outokumpu Mintec Canada Ltd., Mississauga, Canada; *Int'l*, pg. 1017
Tarver, David, Pres.--Telecom Analysis Systems, Eatontown, NJ; *Int'l*, pg. 208
Tasaki, T., Mng. Dir.--Hexcel, Far East, Tokyo, Japan; *U.S. Public*, pg. 824
Taschner, Terry, Pres.--BIEC International Inc., Bethlehem, PA; *Int'l*, pg. 226
Tase, D., Pres.--Wienerschnitzel, Newport Beach, CA; *U.S. Private*, pg. 437
Tashie, Joe, Pres. & Chief Oper. Officer--Hardin's Bakery, Inc., Tuscaloosa, AL; *U.S. Public*, pg. 657
Tashiro, Masaaki, Pres. & Chief Exec. Officer--ORIX Real Estate Equities, Inc., Chicago, IL; *Int'l*, pg. 1009
Tashiro, Shunji, Pres. & Chief Exec. Officer--NEC Systems Laboratory, Inc., San Jose, CA; *Int'l*, pg. 900
Tashiro, Takao, Pres.--Tokai Securities, Inc., New York, NY; *Int'l*, pg. 1391
Tashiro, Yutaka, Chief Rep.--The Industrial Bank of Japan, Limited (Washington), Washington, DC; *Int'l*, pg. 674
Tasker, J.L.G., Dir. & Mgr.--Crown Cork Company Zimbabwe (1958) (PVT), Ltd., Harare, Zimbabwe; *U.S. Public*, pg. 464
Taskey, Ron, V.P.-Sls.--Fairfield Plantation, Villa Rica, GA; *U.S. Public*, pg. 611
Taskey, Ron, V.P.-Sls.--Atlanta Sales, Duluth, GA; *U.S. Public*, pg. 611
Tassara, L., Ing., Chief Oper. Officer--Silectron SPA, Bologna, Italy; *Int'l*, pg. 287
Tassini, Carlo, Gen. Mgr. & Mng. Dir.--Wyeth S.p.A., Rome, Italy; *U.S. Public*, pg. 82
Tasui, T., Mng. Dir.--Toshiba Singapore Pte., Ltd., Singapore, Singapore; *Int'l*, pg. 1407
Tatarczyk, C., Mgr.--Daher Golden Eagle - Phoenix, Phoenix, AZ; *U.S. Public*, pg. 749
Tate, Carey K., Pres.--Rea Construction Co., Charlotte, NC; *Int'l*, pg. 633
Tate, George, Pres.--Eclipse-Dungs Controls, L.P., Roseville, MN; *U.S. Private*, pg. 360
Tate, Henry, Gen. Mgr.--HSN Telecommunications, Inc., Chicago, IL; *U.S. Public*, pg. 1685
Tate, J.C.H., Chm. Bd.--Confederation Pension Investment Management Limited, Stevenage, United Kingdom; *Int'l*, pg. 1319
Tate, Joe, Plant Mgr.--Concord Fabrics Inc., Milledgeville, GA; *U.S. Public*, pg. 429
Tate, Larry K., Pres.--American Telecommunications Corporation, Charlottesville, VA; *U.S. Public*, pg. 407
Tate, Mark A., Pres.--Equitable Pipeline Company, Pittsburgh, PA; *U.S. Public*, pg. 590
Tate, Mark K., Pres.--Louisiana Intrastate Gas Corporation, Houston, TX; *U.S. Public*, pg. 590
Tate, Richard D., Mng. Dir.--Agmet Ltd., Reading, United Kingdom; *U.S. Private*, pg. 369
Tate, Sidney B., Chm. Bd., Pres. & Chief Exec. Officer--First Union National Bank of South Carolina, Greenville, SC; *U.S. Public*, pg. 640
Tatebayashi, Makoto, Chief Rep.--Toronto Representative Office, Toronto, Canada; *Int'l*, pg. 816

Tateiwa, Kazuyoshi, Pres.--P.T. Tokai Lippo Bank, Jakarta, Indonesia; *Int'l*, pg. 1391
Tatelski, Gero, Exec. V.P.-Sls.--Keystone Valve (Europa) B.V., Breda, Netherlands; *U.S. Public*, pg. 1650
Tatesi, Fumio, Pres.--Omron Canada, Inc., Scarborough, Canada; *Int'l*, pg. 1005
Tatman, J. Russell, Mgr.-Opers.--Woodward-Clyde, Wilmington, DE; *U.S. Public*, pg. 1657
Tatman, Richard J., V.P.--Magic Circle Manufacturing Div., Coffeyville, KS; *U.S. Private*, pg. 13
Tatro, Deborah A., Pres.--United Insurance Corporation of America, Milwaukee, WI; *U.S. Public*, pg. 1694
Tatsch, Michael G., Pres. & Chief Exec. Officer--Chromium Corp., Dallas, TX; *U.S. Public*, pg. 568
Tatsumi, Takahiko, Gen. Mgr.--Hakuhodo Deutschland GmbH, Hamburg, Germany; *Int'l*, pg. 588
Tatsuta, Shoichi, Pres.--Dai-ichi Life Insurance Agency (U.S.A.) Inc., New York, NY; *Int'l*, pg. 362
Tatsuta, Yoshio, Mgr.-L.A. Office--Noritake Co., Inc.-Electronics Div., Los Angeles Branch, Compton, CA; *Int'l*, pg. 959
Tatsuya, Mike, Pres.--Oriental Motor U.S.A. Corp., Torrance, CA; *Int'l*, pg. 1008
Tatt, Oh Teik, Div. Dir.--Tractors Malaysia Berhad, Petaling Jaya, Malaysia; *Int'l*, pg. 1250
Tattersal, Alan, Chief Oper. Officer--Inventory Management Corp., Columbia, MD; *U.S. Public*, pg. 694
Tattersall, Alan, Acting Pres.--Power Management Associates, Inc., Columbia, MD; *U.S. Public*, pg. 695
Tattum, George, Controller--AEP Industries Australia Pty. Ltd., Kirrawee, Australia; *U.S. Public*, pg. 5
Tatum, Robert D., V.P. & Gen. Mgr.--Davis Process Div., Tallevast, FL; *U.S. Public*, pg. 1682
Tatum, W.S., Mgr.--Tencarva Machinery Co., Richmond, VA; *U.S. Private*, pg. 1076
Taub, Stephen, Pres. & Chief Oper. Officer--Mafco Worldwide Corp., Camden, NJ; *U.S. Private*, pg. 690
Taule, Egil, Pres.--Titech-Autosort, Oslo, Norway; *Int'l*, pg. 1390
Taunton, J.T., Jr., Pres.--Russell Corp., Fabrics Div., Alexander City, AL; *U.S. Public*, pg. 1413
Tavakolli, P., Gen. Mgr.--Elbar B.V., Lomm, Netherlands; *Int'l*, pg. 673
Tavares Coloneze, Jorge Wiz, Gen. Mgr.--Banco do Brasil S.A.-Venezuela, Caracas, Venezuela; *Int'l*, pg. 142
Tavel, Mark K., Pres. & Chief Investment Officer--Rothchild Asset Management Inc., New York, NY; *U.S. Private*, pg. 947
Tavenius, Tapio, Chief Oper. Officer--Raisio Group plc, Raisio, Finland; *Int'l*, pg. 1085
Taverrite, Gary, Mgr.--Gould Paper of Florida, Inc., Deerfield Beach, FL; *U.S. Private*, pg. 467
Tavertite, Gary, Mgr.--Stephen Gould of Puerto Rico, Inc., Condado, PR; *U.S. Private*, pg. 468
Tawarada, Tadashi, Mng. Dir.--Kemira-Ube Ltd., Tokyo, Japan; *Int'l*, pg. 728
Tawengwa, S. C., Chm. Bd.--Rio Tinto Zimbabwe Limited, Harare, Zimbabwe; *Int'l*, pg. 1119
Tawfik, David A., Pres.--AlliedSignal Guidance & Control Systems, Teterboro, NJ; *U.S. Public*, pg. 50
Tay, Alan, Mgr.--Hutchinson Technology Asia, Singapore, Singapore; *U.S. Public*, pg. 851
Tay, Chee Khiam, Chief Oper. Officer--Knurr-Spectra (S.E.A.) Pte. Ltd., Singapore, Singapore; *Int'l*, pg. 739
Tay, Clement C.H., Mng. Dir.--Scotiatrust (Asia) Limited, Hong Kong, Hong Kong; *Int'l*, pg. 156
Tay, James, Gen. Mgr.--Bensons Metal Products Pte. Ltd., Singapore, Singapore; *Int'l*, pg. 460
Tayer, Everest, Gen. Mgr.--Calavo Foods de Mexico, S.A. de C.V., Mexicali, Mexico; *U.S. Private*, pg. 200
Tayloe, R.W., V.P. & Mgr.--Tencarva Machinery Co., Wilmington, NC; *U.S. Private*, pg. 1076
Taylor, A., Pres.--AGRA Inc., Calgary, Canada; *Int'l*, pg. 30
Taylor, A., Pres.--Maxum Engineering Enterprises Ltd., Calgary, Canada; *Int'l*, pg. 31
Taylor, A. Edward, Pres.--Scotia Mortgage Corporation, Scarborough, Canada; *Int'l*, pg. 156
Taylor, Alan, Mng. Dir.--The Baxenden Chemical Co., Ltd., Accrington, United Kingdom; *U.S. Public*, pg. 1774
Taylor, Albert G., Mng. Dir.--Moore Business Forms de Mexico S.A. de C.V., Tlalnepantla, Mexico; *Int'l*, pg. 889
Taylor, Alex, Pres.--AGRA Inc., Oakville, Canada; *Int'l*, pg. 30
Taylor, Alexander, Pres.--Ellesmere Developments Ltd., Calgary, Canada; *Int'l*, pg. 31
Taylor, Anthony R., V.P. & Gen. Mgr.--Knape & Vogt Canada Inc., Etobicoke, Canada; *U.S. Public*, pg. 963
Taylor, Barry M., Exec. V.P.--Jefferies & Company, Inc., Los Angeles, CA; *U.S. Public*, pg. 925
Taylor, Ben, Sr. Mgr.--AM General Corporation, Mishawaka, IN; *U.S. Private*, pg. 922
Taylor, Benjamin B., Pres.--The Boston Globe, Boston, MA; *U.S. Public*, pg. 1175
Taylor, Bill, Pres.--Sunstrand Fluid Handling, Arvada, CO; *U.S. Public*, pg. 1534
Taylor, Bing, Sr. V.P.--International Div., New York, NY; *U.S. Public*, pg. 1440
Taylor, Bradley E., Pres.--AmericanAnglian Environmental Technologies, Inc., Voorhees, NJ; *U.S. Public*, pg. 95
Taylor, Brian, Mng. Dir.--Irish Biscuits (N.I.), Hillsborough, Ireland; *Int'l*, pg. 688
Taylor, Cal, V.P.-Sls.--Romeo Rim Inc., Romeo, MI; *U.S. Private*, pg. 300
Taylor, D.L., Mng. Dir.--AAH Pharmaceuticals Limited, Runcorn, United Kingdom; *Int'l*, pg. 591
Taylor, Daniel J., Chm. Bd.--Zee Medical, Inc., Irvine, CA; *U.S. Public*, pg. 1073
Taylor, David, Mng. Dir.-U.K.--Chembank Nominees Limited, London, United Kingdom; *U.S. Public*, pg. 341
Taylor, David, Pres.--Donnelly Electronics, Holly, MI; *U.S. Public*, pg. 519
Taylor, David, Gen. Mgr.--Moog Controls Corp., Baguio, Philippines; *U.S. Public*, pg. 1128
Taylor, David G., Mng. Dir.-U.K.--ChemBank Depository Nominees Ltd., London, United Kingdom; *U.S. Public*, pg. 341
Taylor, David N., Chief Exec. Officer--Glynwed Metal Services Ltd., Kingston, United Kingdom; *Int'l*, pg. 554
Taylor, David R., Pres. & Chief Exec. Officer--Centex Forcum-Lannom, Inc., Dyersburg, TN; *U.S. Public*, pg. 322
Taylor, David W., Mgr.--Perkinsville Telephone Co., Inc., Perkinsville, VT; *U.S. Public*, pg. 1571
Taylor, Diane C., Pres.--Artesian Wastewater Management Inc., Newark, DE; *U.S. Public*, pg. 135
Taylor, Floyd V., Pres.--Kansas Fire & Casualty Co., Topeka, KS; *U.S. Public*, pg. 221
Taylor, Frances, Exec. V.P. & Mng. Dir.--BA Asia Ltd., Hong Kong, Hong Kong; *U.S. Public*, pg. 182
Taylor, Frederick C., Mgr.--EG & G Frank Hill Associates, El Cajon, CA; *U.S. Public*, pg. 543
Taylor, G.W., Pres.--Racal Instruments, Inc., Irvine, CA; *Int'l*, pg. 1083
Taylor, Geoff, Pres.--Fischer & Porter (Canada) Ltd., Downsview, Canada; *Int'l*, pg. 449
Taylor, George H., Chief Oper. Officer--Wellsville Fire Brick Company, Wellsville, MO; *U.S. Private*, pg. 194
Taylor, Gerald H., Pres. & Chief Oper. Officer--MCI Telecommunications Corp., Washington, DC; *U.S. Public*, pg. 1024
Taylor, Gordon, Gen. Mgr.--St. Louis Sabreliner Learning Center, Saint Louis, MO; *U.S. Public*, pg. 219
Taylor, Graham, Exec. Pub. Dir.--EMAP Images, London, United Kingdom; *Int'l*, pg. 451
Taylor, Greg, Reg. Mgr.--SMS-Salt Lake City, Salt Lake City, UT; *U.S. Public*, pg. 1463
Taylor, Henry, Pres.--Thomas & Howard Co., Spartanburg, SC; *U.S. Private*, pg. 1082
Taylor, Jack, Pres.--Star Building Systems, Oklahoma City, OK; *U.S. Public*, pg. 1394
Taylor, James, Pres. & Chief Exec. Officer--Andros Service Inc., Hoenheim, France; *U.S. Private*, pg. 74
Taylor, James, Pres. & Chief Exec. Officer--Scitec Corporation, Kennewick, WA; *U.S. Private*, pg. 74
Taylor, James, Mng. Dir.--Colex International, Ltd., Leicester, United Kingdom; *U.S. Private*, pg. 796
Taylor, James R., V.P.-Chemical Div.--Georgia-Pacific Chemical Div., Atlanta, GA; *U.S. Public*, pg. 735
Taylor, Jeffrey W., Chm. Bd.--Cole Taylor Bank, Wheeling, IL; *U.S. Private*, pg. 1070
Taylor, Jim, Gen. Mgr.--The Windsor & Hantsport Railway Co. Ltd., Windsor, Canada; *U.S. Private*, pg. 575
Taylor, John, Mng. Dir.--Trebor Bassett Ltd., Maple Cross, United Kingdom; *Int'l*, pg. 248
Taylor, John, Pres. & Chief Exec. Officer--Ingram Entertainment Inc., La Vergne, TN; *U.S. Private*, pg. 563
Taylor, John, Pres.-Gaming & Entertainment--Dreamport, Inc., Boca Raton, FL; *U.S. Public*, pg. 767
Taylor, John, Mng. Dir.--Ultra Electronics Command & Control Systems, High Wycombe, United Kingdom; *Int'l*, pg. 1431
Taylor, John, Reg. Mng. Dir.--Willis Corroon South Limited, Cheltenham, United Kingdom; *Int'l*, pg. 1503
Taylor, John C.W., V.P.-Transmission--Northern Telecom - Transmission Div., Atlanta, GA; *Int'l*, pg. 970
Taylor, John L., Mng. Dir.--Manganese Metal Co. Pty. Ltd., Johannesburg, South Africa; *Int'l*, pg. 392
Taylor, John S., Country Mgr.--Standard Chartered Bank Cameroon S.A., Douala, Cameroon; *Int'l*, pg. 1294
Taylor, Judy, Gen. Mgr.--Mississippi Auto Auction Inc., Hattiesburg, MS; *U.S. Public*, pg. 1649
Taylor, K.H., Chm. & Chief Exec. Officer--Esso UK plc, London, United Kingdom; *U.S. Public*, pg. 602
Taylor, K.H., Chm. Bd. & Chief Exec. Officer--Esso Petroleum Company, Limited, London, United Kingdom; *U.S. Public*, pg. 602
Taylor, K.H., Chm. Bd. & Chief Exec. Officer--Esso Exploration and Production UK Limited, London, United Kingdom; *U.S. Public*, pg. 602
Taylor, Kathryn M., Branch Mgr.--Valley National Bank, Andover, NJ; *U.S. Public*, pg. 1706
Taylor, Kathy, Pres. & Gen. Mgr.--M & C Remco Tape Products Co., North Hollywood, CA; *U.S. Private*, pg. 684
Taylor, Keith, Chief Oper. Officer--MacGREGOR (GBR) Ltd., Whitley Bay, United Kingdom; *Int'l*, pg. 670
Taylor, Kenneth, Dr., Pres.--Syntex, Palo Alto, CA; *Int'l*, pg. 1120
Taylor, Lyndon C., Partner--Skadden, Arps, Slate, Meagher & Flom LLP, Houston, TX; *U.S. Private*, pg. 1004
Taylor, M.P., Pres.--The White Pass & Yukon Corp. Limited, Whitehorse, Canada; *Int'l*, pg. 1150
Taylor, Matthew A., Pres.--Cyro Industries, Rockaway, NJ; *Int'l*, pg. 1454
Taylor, Michael J., Pres.--SoilTech, Inc., Porter, IN; *U.S. Public*, pg. 1478
Taylor, Mike, Chief Oper. Officer--Textiles Morelos S.A. de C.V., Mexico, Mexico; *U.S. Public*, pg. 268
Taylor, Mike, V.P. & Gen. Mgr.--Kraft Food Ingredients Corp., Memphis, TN; *U.S. Public*, pg. 1288
Taylor, Mike, Mgr.--Weatherford, Nikiski, AK; *U.S. Public*, pg. 1749
Taylor, P.N., Mng. Dir.--Ascom Telecommunications Ltd., Cardiff, United Kingdom; *Int'l*, pg. 87
Taylor, Peggy, Gen. Mgr.--American Environmental Network, Inc., Columbia, MD; *U.S. Public*, pg. 1587
Taylor, Peter, Pres.--Y.P.F. Gas S.A., Buenos Aires, Argentina; *Int'l*, pg. 1515
Taylor, Peter J., Mng. Dir.--Opella Ltd., Hereford, United Kingdom; *Int'l*, pg. 391
Taylor, R., Mng. Dir.--St. Katharine by the Tower Limited, London, United Kingdom; *Int'l*, pg. 1358
Taylor, R. Edwards, V.P. & Asst. Dir.-Retail Leasing--Rouse Retail Leasing Div., Columbia, MD; *U.S. Public*, pg. 1407
Taylor, R. Eugene, Pres.--NationsBank Florida, Tampa, FL; *U.S. Public*, pg. 1162
Taylor, R. Frederick, Pres. & Chief Exec. Officer--The Huntington Mortgage Company, Columbus, OH; *U.S. Public*, pg. 850
Taylor, Richard, Gen. Mgr.--Forbo Invest Ltd., Saint Helier, United Kingdom; *Int'l*, pg. 497
Taylor, Robert, Gen. Mgr.--Milgray/Toronto, Inc., Mississauga, Canada; *U.S. Public*, pg. 207
Taylor, Robert, Gen. Mgr.--Milgray/Montreal, Pointe-Claire, Canada; *U.S. Public*, pg. 207
Taylor, Robert, Gen. Mgr.--International Extrusion Corp., Alhambra, CA; *U.S. Public*, pg. 895
Taylor, Robert, Dir.-Canadian Opers.--Puritan-Bennett Canada Ltd., Pickering, Canada; *U.S. Public*, pg. 1040
Taylor, Robert Y., Pres. & Chief Exec. Officer--NationsBank of Russellville, Russellville, AR; *U.S. Public*, pg. 1164
Taylor, Robin, Pres. & Chief Oper. Officer--Healthcare Prescription Services, Inc., Indianapolis, IN; *U.S. Public*, pg. 405
Taylor, Ronald, V.P. & Gen. Mgr.--Jervis B. Webb Company Ltd., Milton Keynes, United Kingdom; *U.S. Private*, pg. 1157
Taylor, Ronald L., Pres.--Becker CPA Review, Encino, CA; *U.S. Public*, pg. 504
Taylor, Steve, Pres.--Brim Health Care, Portland, OR; *U.S. Private*, pg. 168
Taylor, Steve, Regional Mgr.--Circle Freight International USA, College Park, GA; *U.S. Public*, pg. 371
Taylor, T.G., Pres.--Phillips Pipe Line Company, Bartlesville, OK; *U.S. Public*, pg. 1291
Taylor, Volney, Chm. Bd.--Dun & Bradstreet, Murray Hill, NJ; *U.S. Public*, pg. 535
Taylor, W. Brent, Pres.--Kaibab Metals, Inc., Phoenix, AZ; *U.S. Private*, pg. 605
Taylor, W. Luther, Chm. Bd. & Pres.--Bank of Pensacola, Pensacola, FL; *U.S. Public*, pg. 1549
Taylor, Walter J., Dir.-Intl Bus. Devel.--Best Foods Exports, Englewood Cliffs, NJ; *U.S. Public*, pg. 224
Taylor, William O., Publisher--Globe Newspaper Company, Boston, MA; *U.S. Public*, pg. 1175
Tazaki, Kaziaki, Chm. & Mng. Dir.--Brother U.K., Ltd., Manchester, United Kingdom; *Int'l*, pg. 230
Tazaki, Kazuaki, Pres.--Brother (Schweiz) A.G., Baden, Switzerland; *Int'l*, pg. 230
Tazaki, Kazuaki, Pres.--Brother Macchine Industriali S.R.L., Bologna, Italy; *Int'l*, pg. 230
Tazaki, Masamitsu, Mng. Dir.--Sakata Seed do Brasil Ltda., Sao Paulo, Brazil; *Int'l*, pg. 1178
Tazzioli, R., Gen. Mgr.-Sls.--SASIB Railway Electrification S.p.A., Rome, Italy; *Int'l*, pg. 1194
Tchang, K.T. Thomas, Pres.--Red Star Yeast & Products Div., Milwaukee, WI; *U.S. Public*, pg. 1695
Tchuruk, Serge, Chief Oper. Officer--Specialty Chemicals Div., Courbevoie, France; *Int'l*, pg. 1109
Teague, Jack, Gen. Mgr.--BIC Special Mkts. Div., Clearwater, FL; *Int'l*, pg. 1273
Teague, Larry, Gen. Mgr.--Alumax Extrusions, Inc., Catawba, NC; *U.S. Public*, pg. 59
Teague, Thomas L., Chief Oper. Officer--Salem Leasing Corp., Winston Salem, NC; *U.S. Private*, pg. 962
Teague, Thomas L., Chief Oper. Officer--Salem Carriers. Inc., Winston Salem, NC; *U.S. Private*, pg. 962
Tearprasert, Tada, Chief Exec. Officer--CPAC Roof Tile Co., Limited, Bangkok, Thailand; *Int'l*, pg. 1092
Tearprasert, Tada, Mng. Dir.--The CPAC Roof Tile Co., Ltd., Bangkok, Thailand; *Int'l*, pg. 1237
Tebaldi, Claudio, Dir.--Martin Merkel Italia s.r.l., Verona, Italy; *Int'l*, pg. 860
Tebbenkamp, Bob, Chief Oper. Officer--T&W Disposal Co., Concordia, MO; *U.S. Public*, pg. 49
Tebbutt, Anthony, Pres.--Whitby, Inc., Richmond, VA; *Int'l*, pg. 1427
Tebbutt, Barry L., Pres.--The Northern Trust International Banking Corporation, New York, NY; *U.S. Public*, pg. 1197
Techar, Frank, Dir.--Bank of Montreal - Houston, Houston, TX; *Int'l*, pg. 154
Techasupatkul, Pramote, Mng. Dir.--Siam Yamato Steel Co., Ltd., Bangkok, Thailand; *Int'l*, pg. 1238
Teck, Kwek Chye, Mng. Dir.--ORIX Leasing Singapore Limited, Singapore, Singapore; *Int'l*, pg. 1010
Teck, Tan Seong, Chief Oper. Officer--Clarins SDN BHD, Kuala Lumpur, Malaysia; *Int'l*, pg. 295
Tecocoatzi, Javier, Mgr.--Tork Electro Sistemas S.A. de C.V., Mexico, Mexico; *U.S. Private*, pg. 1092
Teder, Ando, Sr. V.P.-Opers.--Dick Clark Restaurants, Inc., Burbank, CA; *U.S. Public*, pg. 382
Tedesco, Colette, Chief Oper. Officer--Georg Jensen S.A.R.L., Paris, France; *Int'l*, pg. 1134
Tedesco, Sue, Publisher--St. Louis Daily Record, Saint Louis, MO; *U.S. Public*, pg. 513
Tedesco, Sue, Publisher--St. Louis Countian, Clayton, MO; *U.S. Public*, pg. 513
Tedstrom, Kenneth, V.P.--Dale Electronics Resistor Network, El Paso, TX; *U.S. Public*, pg. 1722
Tee, Albert, Area Mgr.--Griffith Laboratories Pte. Ltd., Singapore, Singapore; *U.S. Private*, pg. 481
Tee, T.S., Mng. Dir.--Toshiba Data Dynamics Pte. Ltd., Singapore, Singapore; *Int'l*, pg. 1406
Teeling, William, Pres.--Dynapac Norden AB, Jarfalla, Sweden; *Int'l*, pg. 1420
Teensma, Jan, Pres.--ALLTEL Kentucky, Inc., Shepherdsville, KY; *U.S. Public*, pg. 56
Teerikangas, Reima, Chief Oper. Officer--AS Eesti AGA, Tallinn, Estonia; *Int'l*, pg. 14
Teeters, Bruce W., Chief Fin. Officer--Lake Placid Groves, Lake Placid, FL; *U.S. Public*, pg. 437
Teeters, Bruce W., Pres.--Indigo Group Inc., Daytona Beach, FL; *U.S. Public*, pg. 437
Teets, Peter B., Pres.--Martin Marietta Space Group, Bethesda, MD; *U.S. Public*, pg. 1007
Tegarden, William H., Chm. Bd., Pres. & Chief Exec. Officer--Citizens Bank of Central Indiana-Orleans Region, Orleans, IN; *U.S. Public*, pg. 280

Tegeder, Volker, Mng. Dir.--Livingston Services GmbH, Darmstadt, Germany; *Int'l*, pg. 212
Tegner, Charles, Gen. Mgr.--Forbo Parquet SA, Joinville-le-Pont, France; *Int'l*, pg. 498
Teh, Ivan, Gen. Mgr.--Polarcup Singapore Pte. Ltd., Singapore, Singapore; *Int'l*, pg. 639
Teich, Dan, Chief Oper. Officer--Ransomes-Cushman-Ryan, Lincoln, NE; *Int'l*, pg. 1088
Teichert, Fred, Chief Oper. Officer--Teichert Land Co., Sacramento, CA; *U.S. Private*, pg. 1073
Teik, Tan Boon, Chm. Bd.--Singapore Petroleum Company Ltd., Singapore, Singapore; *U.S. Public*, pg. 102
Teissier, Serge, Chm. Bd.--Minemet-France, Paris, France; *Int'l*, pg. 661
Tejada, Ramiro, Mng. Dir.--MSA del Peru S.A., Lima, Peru; *U.S. Public*, pg. 1115
Tejima, Masao, Gen. Mgr.--Adobe Systems Co. Limited, Tokyo, Japan; *U.S. Public*, pg. 20
Tekker, Peter, Pres.--Gates Canada Inc., Brantford, Canada; *Int'l*, pg. 1396
Tekrony, Ken, Gen. Mgr.--Engineered Films Div., Flexible Films Dept., Sioux Falls, SD; *U.S. Public*, pg. 1361
Telechea, Julio, Pres.--Servired YPF S.A., Buenos Aires, Argentina; *Int'l*, pg. 1515
Telfer, George, Pres.--Nodeco, Ltd., Aberdeen, United Kingdom; *U.S. Public*, pg. 1750
Telford, Ian, Gen. Mgr.--Hayes Microcomputer Products (Canada) Ltd., Waterloo, Canada; *U.S. Public*, pg. 801
Tellechea, Julio, Pres.--O.P.E.S.S.A., Buenos Aires, Argentina; *Int'l*, pg. 1515
Teller, Alvin M., V.P. & Chm.-MCA Music Entertainment Grp.--Universal Studios, Inc., Universal City, CA; *Int'l*, pg. 1215
Tello, Jim, Gen. Mgr.--System Sensor de Mexico S.S. de C.V., Chihuahua, Mexico; *U.S. Public*, pg. 1307
Tellor, Michael D., Pres.--Rust-Oleum Corporation, Vernon Hills, IL; *U.S. Public*, pg. 1358
Telnack, John J., V.P.--Ford Design Staff, Dearborn, MI; *U.S. Public*, pg. 663
Telnack, John J., Chm. Bd.--Ghia, Inc., Dearborn, MI; *U.S. Public*, pg. 664
Telnack, John J., Chm. Bd. & Pres.--Ghia, S.p.A., Turin, Italy; *U.S. Public*, pg. 666
Telo, M., Chief Oper. Officer--Axios, Ltda., Sao Paulo, Brazil; *U.S. Public*, pg. 1577
Temiyasathit, Pipat, Dir.-Thailand--North West Water (Thailand), Bangkok, Thailand; *Int'l*, pg. 1444
Temkin, Victor, Pres.--Universal Studios Publishing Group, Universal City, CA; *Int'l*, pg. 1215
Temme, Wilmar, Co-Mng. Dir.--Blefa GmbH, Kreuztal, Germany; *Int'l*, pg. 508
Tempaku, Itoh, Mng. Dir.--Hakuhodo Inc., Shizuoka, Japan; *Int'l*, pg. 587
Tempest, Brian, Pres.--Medeva Pharmaceuticals, Rochester, NY; *Int'l*, pg. 852
Templar, B.S., Mng. Dir.--Transfleet Services Limited, Coventry, United Kingdom; *Int'l*, pg. 911
Temple, David J., Pres. & Chief Exec. Officer--Canplas Industries Ltd., Barrie, Canada; *Int'l*, pg. 430
Temple, Frederick Thomas, Chief-Res. Mission--The World Bank, Ankara, Turkey; *U.S. Private*, pg. 1190
Temple, J. A., Chief Oper. Officer--GEC South Africa (Pty) Ltd., Knights, South Africa; *Int'l*, pg. 546
Temple, Ron, V.P. & Gen. Mgr.--Spicer Europe, Wolverhampton, United Kingdom; *U.S. Public*, pg. 480
Temple, Steve, Pres.--CAE Ransohoff Inc., Cincinnati, OH; *Int'l*, pg. 237
Temple, Thomas C., Pres.--U.S. Oil & Refining Co., Tacoma, WA; *U.S. Private*, pg. 1086
Temple, William N., Pres.--Hamer Properties, Inc., Tampa, FL; *U.S. Public*, pg. 1736
Temple, William N., Pres.--J.W. Walter, Inc., Tampa, FL; *U.S. Public*, pg. 1736
Temple, William N., Pres.--United Land Corp., Birmingham, AL; *U.S. Public*, pg. 1736
Templeman, Brad, Gen. Mgr.--ITW Finishing Systems & Products-North America, Maumee, OH; *U.S. Public*, pg. 866
Templer, Phil, Mgr.--Westpac Banking Corp. - Niue, Alofi, Cook Islands; *Int'l*, pg. 1497
Templeton, David R., V.P. & Gen. Mgr.--Virsan S.A. de C.V., Sonora, Mexico; *U.S. Public*, pg. 1721
Templeton, James E., V.P.--Walsh Industrial & Commercial Group, Trumbull, CT; *U.S. Public*, pg. 143
Temporiti, John J., Pres.--Mayflower Transit, Inc., Fenton, MO; *U.S. Private*, pg. 1117
Ten Berge, Hans, Mng. Dir.--Kemira Agro Rozenburg B.V., Vondelingenplaat, Netherlands; *Int'l*, pg. 729
ten Bosch, H.W., Gen. Mgr.--ING Bank Eurasia, Moscow, Russia; *Int'l*, pg. 649
ten Tije, J.A., Chief Oper. Officer--Pneu Uniroyal Englebert S.A., Herstal, Belgium; *Int'l*, pg. 327
Tendler, Lance, Pres.--Com Corp Factors, Inc., Van Nuys, CA; *U.S. Private*, pg. 615
Tendler, Lance, Pres.--Stanleigh International, Inc., Van Nuys, CA; *U.S. Private*, pg. 615
Teneback, Anders, Company Head--Ovako Ajax, Inc., York, SC; *Int'l*, pg. 1157
Tener, Will, Pres.--Fluidtec Engineer Products, Greensboro, NC; *U.S. Public*, pg. 401
Teng, Michael, Mng. Dir.--The West Company Singapore Pty. Ltd., Singapore, Singapore; *U.S. Public*, pg. 1756
Teng, Teh Peng, Chief Exec. Officer--Scholl (Malaysia) SDN Bhd., Petaling Jaya, Malaysia; *Int'l*, pg. 1210
Tengroth, Bengt, Pres.--Eriksbergs Forvaltnings AB, Goteborg, Sweden; *Int'l*, pg. 277
Tenland, Will, Sr., Mng. Officer--CB Commercial Real Estate Group Central Division, Houston, TX; *U.S. Public*, pg. 272
Tennant, James R., Chm. Bd. & Chief Exec. Officer--Home Products International, Inc., Chicago, IL; *U.S. Public*, pg. 832
Tennby, Kjell, Pres.--AB Kranlyft, Goteborg, Sweden; *Int'l*, pg. 1420
Tenneson, P., Chm. & Chief Exec. Officer--Herstal S.A., Herstal, Belgium; *Int'l*, pg. 617
Tenney, Robert N., Pres. & Chief Exec. Officer--Fremont Financial Corporation, Santa Monica, CA; *U.S. Public*, pg. 681
Tenney, Russ L., V.P.-Intl. Opers.--California Energy International, Ltd., Jakarta, Indonesia; *U.S. Public*, pg. 292
Tennille, Bob, V.P. & Gen. Mgr.--Dillard Paper Co. of Jacksonville, Jacksonville, FL; *U.S. Public*, pg. 902
Tennille, Bob, V.P. & Gen. Mgr.--Dillard, A ResourceNet International Company, Jacksonville, FL; *U.S. Public*, pg. 902
Tennison, Raymond P., Gen. Mgr.--Simpson Tacoma Kraft Co., Tacoma, WA; *U.S. Private*, pg. 1003
Tensil, Toar, Mgr.--Deutsche Bank AG (Surabaya), Surabaya, Indonesia; *Int'l*, pg. 405
Tensing, Ben, Gen. Mgr.-Furniture--Precision, Chicago, IL; *U.S. Private*, pg. 581
Tensing, Ben, Gen. Mgr.-Furniture--ABCO, Florence, AL; *U.S. Private*, pg. 581
Teo, Alfred, Pres.--Beta Plastics, Carlstadt, NJ; *U.S. Private*, pg. 45
Teo, Alfred, Pres.--Omega Plastics, Lyndhurst, NJ; *U.S. Private*, pg. 45
Teo, Colin, Gen. Mgr.-Taiwan--Singapore Tourist Promotion Board - Taipei, Taipei, Taiwan; *Int'l*, pg. 1254
Teo, Paul, Mng. Dir.--SKF Vehicle Parts Asia (Pte) Ltd., Singapore, Singapore; *Int'l*, pg. 1159
Teo, Ronnie, Chm.--DBS Asset Management (United States) Pte. Ltd., Singapore, Singapore; *Int'l*, pg. 350
Teo, S., Chief Exec. Officer--Zurich Insurance (Singapore) Pte. Ltd., Singapore, Singapore; *Int'l*, pg. 1532
Teoh, Teng Pang, Gen. Mgr.--Vickers Systems Pte. Ltd., Singapore, Singapore; *U.S. Public*, pg. 25
Tepavich, Nick, Gen. Mgr.--Argo Terminal Co., Bedford Park, IL; *U.S. Private*, pg. 435
Tepper, Michael, Chief Oper. Officer--Allright Parking of Milwaukee, Inc., Milwaukee, WI; *U.S. Private*, pg. 43
Tepper, Mike, Mng. Dir.--LSB Europa Ltd., Milan, Italy; *U.S. Public*, pg. 971
Tequi, Marc, Gen. Mgr.--BFCE Vietnam, Hanoi, Vietnam; *Int'l*, pg. 161
Terajima, Masahide, Pres.--Hakuhodo Deutschland GmbH, Dusseldorf, Germany; *Int'l*, pg. 588
Teran, Antonio, Opers. Mgr.--Herbalife International Espana, S.A., Madrid, Spain; *U.S. Public*, pg. 809
Teran, Antonio, Opers. Mgr.--Herbalife International, S.A.-Portugal, Lisbon, Portugal; *U.S. Public*, pg. 809
Terao, Koichi, Pres.--NEC Technologies Philippines, Inc., Cebu, Philippines; *Int'l*, pg. 900
Terao, Koichi, Pres.--NEC Technologies (Thailand) Co., Ltd., Pathum Thani, Thailand; *Int'l*, pg. 900
Terao, Masahide, Pres.--Sanwa Bank (Schweiz) AG, Zurich, Switzerland; *Int'l*, pg. 1190
Terao, Masahisa, Pres.--Taisei Rotec Corp., Tokyo, Japan; *Int'l*, pg. 1347
Terao, Munekazu, Pres.--Wako Securities (America), Inc., New York, NY; *Int'l*, pg. 1485
Terasawa, H., Pres.--Eisai U.S.A., Inc., Teaneck, NJ; *Int'l*, pg. 435
Terasawa, Tsuyoshi, Pres.--Kawasho International (U.S.A.) Inc., Fort Lee, NJ; *Int'l*, pg. 726
Terashima, Ikuo, Pres.--Tokai Bank Canada, Toronto, Canada; *Int'l*, pg. 1391
Terashima, Toru, Mng. Dir.--The Industrial Bank of Japan (Luxembourg) S.A., Luxembourg, Luxembourg; *Int'l*, pg. 676
Terebenin, Andrei, Country Gen. Mgr.--Dun & Bradstreet CIS, Moscow, Russia; *U.S. Public*, pg. 536
Terek, Ted S., Pres.--SuperValu, Inc.-Milton Div., Milton, WV; *U.S. Public*, pg. 1540
Terhune, Michael, Pres.--Wells Fargo Alarm Services, Inc., King of Prussia, PA; *U.S. Public*, pg. 246
Terhune, Stanley B., V.P.--Pine Tree Castings Div., Newport, NH; *U.S. Public*, pg. 1526
Terling, Ove, Chief Oper. Officer--AB Pharos Marine, Vastra Frolunda, Sweden; *Int'l*, pg. 1289
Termini, Deanne, Pres.--Belden Associates, Dallas, TX; *Int'l*, pg. 1447
Terni, S.P., Jr., Pres.--Compania Minera Disputada de Las Condes S.S., Santiago, Chile; *U.S. Public*, pg. 601
Ternus, Gary S., Pres.--Dunn Nutratech, Dunn, NC; *U.S. Public*, pg. 128
Ternus, Gary S., Pres.--Nutratech Animal Health, Douglas, GA; *U.S. Public*, pg. 128
Ternus, John, Plant Mgr.--Industrial Wire Products, Rancho Cucamonga, CA; *U.S. Private*, pg. 561
Terracciano, Suzanne, Exec. Dir.--Howell Medical Center, Norcross, GA; *U.S. Public*, pg. 1715
Terradas, Rosendo, Pres.--Bridgestone/Firestone Venezolana, C.A., Valencia, Venezuela; *Int'l*, pg. 214
Terrazone, Claude, Dir.--Avions Div., Paris, France; *Int'l*, pg. 29
Terrell, Andy, Mgr.-Reg. Sls.--Burgmann Seals America, Inc., Conyers, GA; *Int'l*, pg. 233
Terrell, Bruce, Mgr.-Texas Distribution Grp.--McAllen Pipe & Supply Div., McAllen, TX; *U.S. Public*, pg. 1682
Terrell, Bud, Pres.--New America Financial, Inc., Dallas, TX; *U.S. Public*, pg. 644
Terrell, Douglas E., V.P.-Opers.--McQuick's Oilube, Inc., Muncie, IN; *U.S. Public*, pg. 1348
Terrell, James R., Pres. & Chief Oper. Officer-TV Stations--Gaylord Broadcasting Co., Nashville, TN; *U.S. Public*, pg. 704
Terrell, William P., Pres. & Gen. Mgr.--Cadmus Financial, Charlotte, NC; *U.S. Public*, pg. 291
Terreri, David, V.P.-Opers.--Canstar Apparel Inc., Swanton, VT; *U.S. Public*, pg. 1184
Terrien, Jean Francois, Pres. & Chief Exec. Officer--Neyrpic Framatome Mecanique (NFM), Paris, France; *Int'l*, pg. 503
Terrill, Bill, Plant Mgr.--Industrial Bag Division - New Philadelphia Plant, New Philadelphia, OH; *U.S. Public*, pg. 1521
Terry, Anna L., Asst. Treas. & Branch Mgr.--Valley National Bank, Blairstown, NJ; *U.S. Public*, pg. 1706
Terry, Bruce, Pres. & Chief Exec. Officer--Mayfran International, Inc., Cleveland, OH; *Int'l*, pg. 1397
Terry, Dennis, Gen. Mgr.--Cable/Cisco, Sacramento, CA; *U.S. Private*, pg. 215
Terry, Glen C., Pres. & Chief Exec. Officer--Napa Valley Bank, Napa, CA; *U.S. Public*, pg. 1756
Terry, James W., Jr., Pres.--Carolina First Bank, Greenville, SC; *U.S. Public*, pg. 306
Terry, Mark, Pres.--JBL Professional, Northridge, CA; *U.S. Public*, pg. 787
Terry, Peter, Gen. Mgr.--Polaroid Australia Pty. Ltd., Sydney, Australia; *U.S. Public*, pg. 1314
Terry, Richard E., Chm. Bd. & Chief Exec. Officer--North Shore Gas Co., Waukegan, IL; *U.S. Public*, pg. 1275
Terry, Richard E., Chm. Bd. & Chief Exec. Officer--Peoples District Energy Corporation, Chicago, IL; *U.S. Public*, pg. 1275
Terry, Richard E., Chm. Bd. & Chief Exec. Officer--Peoples Energy Services Corporation, Chicago, IL; *U.S. Public*, pg. 1275
Terry, Richard E., Chm. Bd. & Chief Exec. Officer--Peoples NGV Corp., Chicago, IL; *U.S. Public*, pg. 1275
Tertenik, Pete, Mgr.-Natl. Sls.--Flambeau Products-Columbus, Columbus, IN; *U.S. Private*, pg. 410
Tertzakian, G., Pres.--Terochem Laboratories Limited a/k/a Raylo Chemicals, Edmonton, Canada; *Int'l*, pg. 803
Teruya, Wayne, Pres.--Times Super Market Ltd., Honolulu, HI; *U.S. Private*, pg. 1078
Tervel, Javier, Pres. & Gen. Mgr.--Colgate-Palmolive, S.A. De C.V., Mexico, Mexico; *U.S. Public*, pg. 399
Terzic, Branko, Pres., Chief Exec./Oper. Officer--Yankee Energy Financial Services Company, Meriden, CT; *U.S. Public*, pg. 1787
Teshinsky, Fred, Plant Mgr.--P.H.I. Division, City of Industry, CA; *U.S. Private*, pg. 1109
Teshoian, Nishan, Chm. Bd.--Anderson, Greenwood & Co., Stafford, TX; *U.S. Public*, pg. 1650
Teshoian, Nishan, Pres.--Keystone International Holdings Corp., Houston, TX; *U.S. Public*, pg. 1650
Tessier, Edward J., Pres. & Chief Exec. Officer--Amerifoods Snacks, York, PA; *U.S. Private*, pg. 65
Tessier, Edward J., Pres. & Chief Exec. Officer--Bon Ton Foods, Inc., York, PA; *U.S. Private*, pg. 65
Tessier, Sylvain, Gen. Mgr.--Impact Recherche, Quebec, Canada; *Int'l*, pg. 336
Tessitore, Gary L., Exec. V.P. & Gen. Mgr.--Agricultural Equipment Div., J.I. Case, Racine, WI; *U.S. Public*, pg. 311
Testa, Roberto, Mng. Dir.--The West Company Argentina S.A., Buenos Aires, Argentina; *U.S. Public*, pg. 1755
Testen, Christer, Pres.--Astra Pharmaceuticals Pty. Ltd., Sydney, Australia; *Int'l*, pg. 94
Tester, Stephen, Gen. Mgr.--Vickers Systems Pty., Ltd., Maribyrnong, Australia; *U.S. Public*, pg. 25
Testi, Prof. A., Dir.--Fiat Auto S.p.A., Milan, Italy; *Int'l*, pg. 481
Testoni, Helio, Gen. Mgr.--Banco do Brasil S.A.-Argentina, Buenos Aires, Argentina; *Int'l*, pg. 141
Testut, Michel, Pres.--EURO RSCG D 10, Perigueux, France; *Int'l*, pg. 600
Tetrault, Roger E., Pres.--General Dynamics Land Systems Div., Warren, MI; *U.S. Public*, pg. 709
Tetreault, A., Gen. Mgr.--ITT Flygt, Pointe-Claire, Canada; *U.S. Public*, pg. 860
Tetreault, Denis, Dir. Gen.--Imprimerie Quebecor St-Jean, Saint-Jean, Canada; *Int'l*, pg. 1077
Tetreault, Denis, Reg. V.P.--Imprimerie Quebecor St-Romuald, Saint-Romvald, Canada; *Int'l*, pg. 1077
Tettamanti, Walter, Opers. Mgr.--Vickers Polymotor, Casella, Italy; *U.S. Public*, pg. 25
Teunissen, T.H.M., Gen. Mgr.--AMEV V-A Ardanta, Enschede, Netherlands; *Int'l*, pg. 499
Tevebaugh, C.R., V.P. & Gen. Mgr.--Rhone-Poulenc Inc., Fine Inorganic Chemical Division, Monmouth Junction, NJ; *Int'l*, pg. 1110
Teves, Joseph A., Pres.--Distrigas Corp., Boston, MA; *U.S. Public*, pg. 289
Teves, Joseph A., Pres.--Distrigas of Massachusetts Corporation, Boston, MA; *U.S. Public*, pg. 289
Tews, Herb, Pres.--Precision Plastics, Crawfordsville, IN; *U.S. Private*, pg. 879
Tews, Herb, Pres.--Columbia Die Mold, Columbia City, IN; *U.S. Private*, pg. 879
Tezuka, Hiroyuki, Mng. Dir.--Siam Toyota Manufacturing Co., Ltd., Bangkok, Thailand; *Int'l*, pg. 1239
Thacher, Bruce, Acting Pres. & Chief Oper. Officer--Westec Security Inc., Irvine, CA; *Int'l*, pg. 1217
Thacker, Del, V.P. & Gen. Mgr.--Delmonico Foods, Louisville, KY; *U.S. Public*, pg. 812
Thacker, Ted, Pres.--Pylon Manufacturing Corp., Deerfield Beach, FL; *U.S. Public*, pg. 1055
Thacker, Ted, Pres.--Mr. Bracket, Deerfield Beach, FL; *U.S. Public*, pg. 1055
Thain, John, Co.-Chm.--Goldman Sachs International Limited, London, United Kingdom; *U.S. Private*, pg. 462
Thakur, S., Chief Mgr.--State Bank of India, Chicago, IL; *Int'l*, pg. 1297
Thalacker, Bruce A., Div. V.P.--Tape Manufacturing Division, Saint Paul, MN; *U.S. Public*, pg. 1605
Thalmaier, Gerald, Mng. Dir.--ISS Servisystem GesmbH, Graz, Austria; *Int'l*, pg. 657
Thalmann, Rudolf W., Representative--UBS Representative Office, Rio de Janeiro, Brazil; *Int'l*, pg. 1441
Tham, Yew Mun, District Mgr.--Det Norske Veritas, Taipei, Taiwan; *Int'l*, pg. 397
Thamarak, Chavalit, Mng. Dir.--Aggregate Supply Co., Ltd., Bangkok, Thailand; *Int'l*, pg. 1237
Thamasujarit, Wankeow, Admin. Mgr.--Utell International-Thailand, Bangkok, Thailand; *Int'l*, pg. 1099

Thames, George W., Gen. Mgr.--ConAgra Feed Co., Augusta, GA; *U.S. Public,* pg. 428
Thampi, P.M., Pres. & Chief Oper. Officer--BASF India Ltd., Mumbai, India; *Int'l,* pg. 106
Thanamsing, Hunsa, Creative Dir.--Dentsu Young & Rubicam Ltd. (Bangkok), Bangkok, Thailand; *U.S. Private,* pg. 325
Thanarugchok, C., Pres.--Asia Shinwa Engineering Co., Ltd., Bangkok, Thailand; *Int'l,* pg. 432
Thanh, Dinh Ba, Mgr.--Vietnam Advertising Co., Ho Chi Minh City, Vietnam; *Int'l,* pg. 602
Thanscheidt, Heinrich, Mng. Dir.--Ericsson Business Communications GmbH, Dusseldorf, Germany; *Int'l,* pg. 1366
Tharp, Walter L., Plant Mgr.--Salem Carpet Mills, Trenton, SC; *U.S. Public,* pg. 1464
Tharpe, Terry, Mgr.-Southern Div.--Columbia Pictures Southern Division, Duluth, GA; *Int'l,* pg. 1281
Thater, John, Mng. Dir.--EMAP Media, London, United Kingdom; *Int'l,* pg. 451
Thater, John, Mng. Dir.--EMAP Media Ltd., London, United Kingdom; *Int'l,* pg. 451
Thater, William C., Pres.--Security Equity Life Insurance Company, Armonk, NY; *U.S. Private,* pg. 443
Thayer, Grant E., Chief Oper. Officer--Presidio Exploration, Inc., Englewood, CO; *U.S. Public,* pg. 262
Thayer, James N., Chm. Bd., Pres. & Chief Exec. Officer--Gibraltar Savings, Simi Valley, CA; *U.S. Public,* pg. 181
Thayer, Raymond M., Jr., Pres.--Bank One Wisconsin Bankcard Corporation, Milwaukee, WI; *U.S. Public,* pg. 174
Thayer, T. D., Dir.--Mack Leasing System, Allentown, PA; *Int'l,* pg. 1102
Thean Seng, Douglas Russell Ooi, Mng. Dir.--Kim Eng Securities (Private) Limited, Singapore, Singapore; *Int'l,* pg. 733
Thede, Merv, Pres.--Alcoa Steamship Co., Inc., Pittsburgh, PA; *U.S. Public,* pg. 61
Theel, Mark, Pres.--Sterling Software Application Development Division, Plano, TX; *U.S. Public,* pg. 1516
Thein, Pierre, Pres.--TechnoARBED Luxembourg S.a.r.l., Luxembourg, Luxembourg; *Int'l,* pg. 80
Theis, Stuart H., V.P.--Marine Transportation, Cleveland, OH; *U.S. Public,* pg. 1213
Theiss, Michael, Gen. Mgr.--Braun Nederland B.V., Rijswijk, Netherlands; *U.S. Public,* pg. 744
Thelin, Claus, Pres. & Chief Exec. Officer--Essex Industries, New Haven, CT; *Int'l,* pg. 18
Thellier, Regis, Mgr.-Plant--Sucrerie D'Eppeville/Ham, D'Eppeville, France; *Int'l,* pg. 549
Then, J.L., Chief Oper. Officer--Kidde Technologies, Inc., Wilson, NC; *Int'l,* pg. 1500
Then, Joe, Mgr.--Kidde Technologies Inc. (Walter Kidde Aerospace), Wilson, NC; *Int'l,* pg. 1500
Theodosi, J.G., Chief Exec. Officer--Zurich Insurance Company, Athens, Greece; *Int'l,* pg. 1531
Theriault, Jim, Chief Oper. Officer--Hudson General Aviation Services Inc., Elmsdale, Canada; *U.S. Public,* pg. 846
Theriot, Alfred, Div. Mgr.--Atlas Steel & Wire, Harahan, LA; *U.S. Private,* pg. 65
Therkildsen, Erik, Chief Oper. Officer--Novo Nordisk A/S, Vouliagmeni, Greece; *Int'l,* pg. 988
Therson, Michael G., Gen. Mgr.--EDO Fiber Science, Salt Lake City, UT; *U.S. Public,* pg. 542
Thery, Marc, Chm.--Rowenta France S.A., Vernon, France; *Int'l,* pg. 569
Thery, Marianne, Mng. Dir.--Textuel, Paris, France; *Int'l,* pg. 116
Thery, Marianne, Mng. Dir.--Les Editions Textuel, Paris, France; *Int'l,* pg. 116
Theuer, Carsten, Mgr.--Commerzbank AG Representative Office-Minsk, Minsk, Belarus; *Int'l,* pg. 312
Theuns, Frank, Mgr.--Sydney Wire Mill, Five Dock, Australia; *Int'l,* pg. 226
Theurauf, Ingo, Pres. & Chief Exec. Officer--Preussag North America, Greenwich, CT; *Int'l,* pg. 1070
Thevenaz, Armand, Gen. Mgr.--Decolletage S.A. St.-Maurice, Saint Maurice, Switzerland; *U.S. Public,* pg. 9
Thevenot, Anthony, Gen. Mgr.--Norco Terminal, Norco, LA; *U.S. Public,* pg. 692
Theveny, Michel, Chief Exec. Officer--Credit Agricole (CNCA) London, London, United Kingdom; *Int'l,* pg. 341
Thewes, Joachim, Chief Oper. Officer--Land Infrarot GmbH, Leverkusen, Germany; *Int'l,* pg. 798
Thiagarajan, Arun, Pres.--ASEA Limited, Bangalore, India; *Int'l,* pg. 8
Thiam, R., Chief Oper. Officer--De Lage Landen Factors S.A., Paris, France; *Int'l,* pg. 1082
Thibadeau, Jim, Plant Mgr.--Liqui-Box Corp., Worthington, OH; *U.S. Public,* pg. 1001
Thibblin, Christer, Gen. Mgr.--AMP Finland OY, Helsinki, Finland; *U.S. Public,* pg. 8
Thibodeau, J.S. Robert, V.P. & Plant Mgr.--APD Cryogenics Inc., Allentown, PA; *U.S. Public,* pg. 894
Thidoloaux, Ricky, Chief Oper. Officer & Gen. Mgr.--Caro Produce & Institutional Foods, Houma, LA; *U.S. Public,* pg. 1278
Thiede, Gene G., Mgr.--Central State Telephone Co., Vesper, WI; *U.S. Public,* pg. 1571
Thiel, Peter, Mgr.--Commerzbank AG-Istanbul Representative Office, Istanbul, Turkey; *Int'l,* pg. 311
Thiel, Wilbert, Pres.--ABN AMRO Chicago Corporation, Chicago, IL; *Int'l,* pg. 10
Thiele, P.A., Pres. & Chief Exec. Officer--St. Paul Fire and Marine Insurance Co., Saint Paul, MN; *U.S. Public,* pg. 1429
Thiele, Rosemary, Administrator--Horizon Specialty Hospital - Las Vegas, Las Vegas, NV; *U.S. Public,* pg. 837
Thielemans, Daniel, Chief Exec. Officer--Generale Bank, New York, NY; *Int'l,* pg. 547
Thielemans, Leo, Pres.--Synerfi SA, Brussels, Belgium; *Int'l, pg. 547*
Thielen, Franz G., Dir.--Deutsche Bank AG (Strasbourg), Strasbourg, France; *Int'l,* pg. 405
Thielke, Russ, Gen. Mgr.--Big Stone Cheese Factory, Big Stone City, SD; *U.S. Private,* pg. 1040
Thieme, Otto, Chief Oper. Officer--A. Ahlstrom GmbH, Kirchheim, Germany; *Int'l,* pg. 34
Thier, Jay, Pres.--Charlie's Specialties Inc., Callery, PA; *U.S.* Private, pg. 191
Thilmoat, Bob, Mgr.--Woodward Governor Company (Australia), Kingsgrove, Australia; *U.S. Public,* pg. 1776
Thimm, Franz Mario, Dr., Dir. Gen.--Allianz RAS Tutela Guidiziaria S.p.A., Milan, Italy; *Int'l,* pg. 60
Thinbrant, Bill, Pres.--Tremix AB, Skarholmen, Sweden; *Int'l, pg. 1324*
Thipthorpe, Derek, Mng. Dir.--Florasynth Limited, Chalfont Saint Giles, United Kingdom; *Int'l,* pg. 173
Thiry, Kent J., Pres.--Viva Specialty Partners, San Mateo, CA; *U.S. Public,* pg. 1724
Thitipatana, Theera, Mgr.-Fin.--W.R. Grace (Thailand) Ltd., Samutprakan, Thailand; *U.S. Public,* pg. 756
Thodal-Ness, Einar, Chief Oper. Officer--S-E-Banken Custody Service, Stockholm, Sweden; *Int'l,* pg. 1259
Tholan, Kenneth M., Pres.--Team Industrial Services, Inc., Alvin, TX; *U.S. Public,* pg. 1562
Tholan, Kenneth M., Pres.--Pipe Repairs, Inc., Alvin, TX; *U.S. Public,* pg. 1562
Thom, Preston, Pres.--Comdisco Canada Ltd., Toronto, Canada; *U.S. Public,* pg. 408
Thoma, G. Stephan, Chm. Bd.--Merrill Lynch Business Financial Services Inc., Plainsboro, NJ; *U.S. Public,* pg. 1098
Thoma, Helmut, Dr., Mng. Dir.--RTL Television, Cologne, Germany; *Int'l,* pg. 561
Thoma, Ronald R., Pres.--Crown Cork & Seal Company, Inc.-Subsidiaries Division, Philadelphia, PA; *U.S. Public,* pg. 463
Thoma, Tim, Branch Mgr.--Union-Transport Corporation-Minneapolis Office, Minneapolis, MN; *U.S. Private,* pg. 1120
Thomann, Christoph, Mgr.-Opers.--Herbalife International France, S.A., Strasbourg, France; *U.S. Public,* pg. 809
Thomann, Christophe, Opers. Mgr.--Herbalife International-Czechoslovakia, Strasbourg, France; *U.S. Public,* pg. 809
Thomann, Michael, Pres. & Chief Exec. Officer--Brad Ragan, Inc., Charlotte, NC; *U.S. Public,* pg. 753
Thomas, Brantley D., Sr. V.P.--Westvaco Corporation-Kraft Div., Charleston, SC; *U.S. Public,* pg. 1762
Thomas, Bryan, Mng. Dir.--Houghton Vaughn plc, Birmingham, United Kingdom; *U.S. Private,* pg. 541
Thomas, C. Steven, V.P.--Mill Products Div., Richmond, VA; *U.S. Public,* pg. 1386
Thomas, C.W., Gen. Mgr.--Kodak Rahola, Inc., Santurce, PR; *U.S. Public,* pg. 551
Thomas, C.W., III, Pres.--Simcoe Leaf Tobacco Company, Ltd., Simcoe, Canada; *U.S. Public,* pg. 1695
Thomas, Charles, Pres.--Pepsi-Cola Bottling Co. of Long Island City, Long Island City, NY; *U.S. Public,* pg. 1276
Thomas, Christopher, Chief Exec. Officer--Lindustries Ltd., Stevenage, United Kingdom; *Int'l,* pg. 593
Thomas, Christopher R., Pres.--Sizzler USA, Inc., Los Angeles, CA; *U.S. Public,* pg. 1475
Thomas, D.H., Gen. Mgr.--LASMO Oil Pakistan Limited, Karachi, Pakistan; *Int'l,* pg. 804
Thomas, D.M., Chief Exec. Officer--Pizza Hut (UK) Ltd., Borehamwood, United Kingdom; *Int'l,* pg. 1499
Thomas, D.M., Chief Exec. Officer--Pizza Hut (UK) Ltd., Borehamwood, United Kingdom; *U.S. Public,* pg. 1637
Thomas, D.V., Dir. & Chief Mgr.--Lloyds Bank SA, Paris, France; *Int'l,* pg. 813
Thomas, Dave, Pres.--Alphabet Design Center, Cortland, OH; *U.S. Private,* pg. 1044
Thomas, Dave, Mgr.--Smucker Salinas Plant, Salinas, CA; *U.S. Public,* pg. 1480
Thomas, David, Mng. Dir.--ISS U.K. Ltd., Hounslow, United Kingdom; *Int'l,* pg. 657
Thomas, David, Supervisor-Property & Casualty Claims--Willis Corroon Administrative Services Corporation, Charlotte, NC; *Int'l,* pg. 1505
Thomas, David A., V.P.-Eastern Region--Wall Street Deli, Inc., Alexandria, VA; *U.S. Public,* pg. 1734
Thomas, David A., Jr., Pres. & Chief Exec. Officer--Citizens Commercial & Savings Bank, Flint, MI; *U.S. Public,* pg. 379
Thomas, David G., Pres.--EvansGroup, Salt Lake City, UT; *U.S. Private,* pg. 385
Thomas, David L., Reg. Pres.--ALLTEL Ohio, Inc., Newark, OH; *U.S. Public,* pg. 56
Thomas, David L., Pres.--Alltel Ohio, Inc., Elyria, OH; *U.S. Public,* pg. 56
Thomas, David L., Pres.--Alphabet Division, Warren, OH; *U.S. Private,* pg. 1044
Thomas, David M., Mng. Dir.--Whitbread Restaurants & Leisure, Luton, United Kingdom; *Int'l,* pg. 1498
Thomas, E.G., Mng. Dir.--Trico Ltd., Pontypool, United Kingdom; *Int'l,* pg. 1397
Thomas, Fran, Admin.--Pineville Health Care Center, Inc., Pineville, KY; *U.S. Public,* pg. 1714
Thomas, Frank, Pres.--Mile High Equipment Co., Denver, CO; *Int'l,* pg. 189
Thomas, G.L., Mng. Dir.--Barclays Bank of Uganda Ltd., Kampala, Uganda; *Int'l,* pg. 165
Thomas, George H., Chm.--Sysco Food Services, Cincinnati, OH; *U.S. Public,* pg. 1551
Thomas, Gerald W., Pres.--Investment Network, Inc., Franklin Park, IL; *U.S. Public,* pg. 1428
Thomas, Geryk, Unit Mgr.--Weatherford (Malaysia) Sdn. Bhd., Ehsan, Malaysia; *U.S. Public,* pg. 1750
Thomas, Geryk, Mng. Dir.--Weatherford Norge, A/S, Stavanger, Norway; *U.S. Public,* pg. 1750
Thomas, Glenn E., Corp. V. P. & Gen. Mgr.--Corporate Engineering, Louisville, KY; *U.S. Public,* pg. 575
Thomas, Gregory, Mgr.-Office--Woodward-Clyde, Totowa, NJ; *U.S. Public,* pg. 1656
Thomas, Ian R., Mgr.--Melbourne Laboratories, Mulgrave, Australia; *Int'l,* pg. 227
Thomas, J. Grover, Jr., Pres. & Chief Exec. Officer--United Family Life Insurance Co., Atlanta, GA; *Int'l,* pg. 499
Thomas, J.A., Chief Oper. Officer--Twin Disc (Far East) Ltd., Singapore, Singapore; *U.S. Public,* pg. 1646
Thomas, Jack, V.P. & Gen. Mgr.--Eastman Kodak Life Sciences Div., Rochester, NY; *U.S. Public,* pg. 551
Thomas, Jack, Publr.--Herald Voice, Hazard, KY; *U.S. Public,* pg. 1343
Thomas, Jerry, Mgr.-Sls.--PENCO-Missouri, Jefferson City, MO; *Int'l,* pg. 1508
Thomas, Joe, Mng. Dir.--Carlson Marketing Group (U.K.) Limited, Northampton, United Kingdom; *U.S. Private,* pg. 212
Thomas, John R., Mgr.-Opers.--EMPIRE Transport, Mesa, AZ; *U.S. Private,* pg. 375
Thomas, Karl, Exec. V.P.-Technical Grp.--Pratt & Whitney Technical Group, East Hartford, CT; *U.S. Public,* pg. 1690
Thomas, L.M., Chief Oper. Officer--Williams Fairey Engineering Ltd., Stockport, United Kingdom; *Int'l,* pg. 1500
Thomas, Larry, Pres.--Triton Engineering Services Company, Houston, TX; *U.S. Public,* pg. 1186
Thomas, Larry R., Pres.--MK Centennial, Arvada, CO; *U.S. Public,* pg. 1134
Thomas, Les, Pres.--Shea Homes Southern California, Brea, CA; *U.S. Private,* pg. 991
Thomas, Lowell, V.P.--Sea Containers Caribbean Inc., Miami, FL; *Int'l,* pg. 1214
Thomas, Mark, Pres. & Chief Exec. Officer--Standard Communications Corp., Torrance, CA; *Int'l,* pg. 841
Thomas, Martin, V.P.--Sulzer (UK) Pumps Ltd., Leeds, United Kingdom; *Int'l,* pg. 1306
Thomas, Michael S., Pres.--Vara Internatonal, Vero Beach, FL; *U.S. Public,* pg. 293
Thomas, Ogden, Pres.--ENSCO Marine Co., Broussard, LA; *U.S. Public,* pg. 585
Thomas, Peter G., Pres. & Mng. Dir.--Holden's Engine Products Overseas Corporation, Melbourne, Australia; *U.S. Public,* pg. 723
Thomas, R., Mng. Dir.--Scholl (UK) Ltd., London, United Kingdom; *U.S. Public,* pg. 1439
Thomas, R. B., Dir.--County NatWest Securities Australia Limited, Melbourne, Australia; *Int'l,* pg. 911
Thomas, R.J., Chief Oper. Officer--Armstrong York Pty., Ltd., Melbourne, Australia; *Int'l,* pg. 265
Thomas, Richard E., Pres.--COMSAT RSI, Inc., Sterling, VA; *U.S. Public,* pg. 424
Thomas, Robert, Dir.--Jardine Fleming Investment Management Limited, Central, Hong Kong; *Int'l,* pg. 494
Thomas, Robert, Gen. Mgr.--Weston Paper & Mfg. Co. Mill Div., Terre Haute, IN; *U.S. Private,* pg. 1170
Thomas, Roger, Mng. Dir.--Strategic Marketing Services London, London, United Kingdom; *U.S. Public,* pg. 1625
Thomas, Steve, Pres.--REPP Ltd. Big and Tall, Saint Louis, MO; *U.S. Public,* pg. 564
Thomas, Steve, Pres.--Kirsch, Sturgis, MI; *U.S. Public,* pg. 1176
Thomas, Tim, Gen. Mgr. & Pres.-Dixon Canada)--Dixon Ticonderoga Inc., Newmarket, Canada; *U.S. Public,* pg. 515
Thomas, Tobert M., Pres.--Satellite Networks Division, Sterling, VA; *U.S. Public,* pg. 424
Thomas, Tom, Pres.--Fort James Canada, Inc., Toronto, Canada; *U.S. Public,* pg. 672
Thomas, W.G., Chief Oper. Officer--Babcock Transformers Ltd., Bilston, United Kingdom; *Int'l,* pg. 472
Thomason, Bruce, Branch Mgr.--AFA New Jersey, Inc., New Brunswick, NJ; *U.S. Public,* pg. 6
Thomason, Bruce A., Mgr.--AFA Protective Systems, Inc., North Brunswick, NJ; *U.S. Public,* pg. 5
Thomason, Bruce A., Mgr.--AFA Protective Systems, Inc., Mount Laurel, NJ; *U.S. Public,* pg. 6
Thomason, Jim, V.P.-Mfg.--Selkirk Metalbestos, Dallas, TX; *U.S. Public,* pg. 1794
Thomason, Robert, Gen. Mgr.--Westreet Industries, Baltimore, MD; *U.S. Private,* pg. 1022
Thomke, Ernst, Dr., Chief Exec. Officer--Bally Management AG, Schonenwerd, Switzerland; *Int'l,* pg. 996
Thommessen, G., Chief Oper. Officer--Marathon Petroleum Company (Norway), Oslo, Norway; *U.S. Public,* pg. 1662
Thomopulos, Gregs G., Chm. Bd. & Pres.--Stanley Design-Build, Inc., Muscatine, IA; *U.S. Private,* pg. 1033
Thompson-Draper, Cheryl, Pres. & Chief Oper. Officer--Warren Electric Company, Houston, TX; *U.S. Private,* pg. 1151
Thompson, Al, Pres. & Chief Exec. Officer--Air BC, Richmond, Canada; *Int'l,* pg. 36
Thompson, Allan W., Pres.--Telecommunications Technology, Milpitas, CA; *U.S. Public,* pg. 727
Thompson, Benjamin J., Chief Operator--Erseco, Inc., Erving, MA; *U.S. Private,* pg. 382
Thompson, Bill, Pres.--Atkins Kroll Inc., Tamuning, GU; *Int'l, pg. 671*
Thompson, Bill, Dir.-Central Reg.--Custom Cheques of Canada, North York, Canada; *Int'l,* pg. 1077
Thompson, Brent, Pres.--API Katema Inc., Grand Prairie, TX; *U.S. Public,* pg. 90
Thompson, Bruce, Mgr.--Nalco Saudi Co. Ltd., Dammam, Saudi Arabia; *U.S. Public,* pg. 1151
Thompson, Bryan, Chief Oper. Officer--Custom Lumber Mfg. Co., Dothan, AL; *U.S. Private,* pg. 680
Thompson, C., V.P.-Sls.--Penny & Giles Aerospace Inc., Santa Monica, CA; *Int'l,* pg. 208
Thompson, C., V.P.-Sls.--Penny & Giles Aerospace Inc., Valley Center, KS; *Int'l,* pg. 208
Thompson, C. Simon, Chm.--R.J. Reynolds Finance S.A., Geneva, Switzerland; *U.S. Public,* pg. 1355
Thompson, Christopher, Sr. V.P. & Gen. Mgr.--Fleishman-Hillard France, Paris, France; *U.S. Private,* pg. 411
Thompson, D.S., Gen. Mgr.--Wellcome Kenya Ltd, Nairobi, Kenya; *Int'l,* pg. 553
Thompson, David, Pres.--Value City Furniture, Columbus, OH; *U.S. Private,* pg. 972

Thompson, David C., Pres. & Chief Oper. Officer--SEA, Inc., Mountlake Terrace, WA; *U.S. Public*, pg. 487
Thompson, E.J., Sec.--Nutmeg Insurance Limited, Hamilton, Bermuda; *U.S. Public*, pg. 1219
Thompson, Evan, Chief Oper. Officer--KCOP Television, Inc., Los Angeles, CA; *U.S. Public*, pg. 352
Thompson, Frank, Mng. Dir.--Insoleq Semafour, Newtownards, Ireland; *U.S. Private*, pg. 453
Thompson, G.W., Pres. & Gen. Mgr.--Kansas City Terminal Railway Co., Kansas City, MO; *U.S. Public*, pg. 1668
Thompson, Gary, Mgr.--Woolrich Store Co., Alliance, NE; *U.S. Private*, pg. 1188
Thompson, Gary, Gen. Mgr.--Golin/Harris Technologies, San Francisco, CA; *Int'l*, pg. 1227
Thompson, Gordon, Sr. V.P. & Branch Mgr.--California State Bank-Covina Main, Covina, CA; *U.S. Public*, pg. 294
Thompson, I.A., Chief Exec. Officer--Transco Railway Products Inc., Bucyrus, OH; *U.S. Private*, pg. 1096
Thompson, Iain, Mng. Dir.--Partnership Pacific Limited, Sydney, Australia; *Int'l*, pg. 1496
Thompson, J., Sr. V.P. & Mgr.-Branch--ABN AMRO Bank, N.V. (Los Angeles), Los Angeles, CA; *Int'l*, pg. 10
Thompson, J. Kenneth, Pres.--ARCO Alaska Inc., Anchorage, AK; *U.S. Public*, pg. 144
Thompson, J. Kenneth, Chief Oper. Officer--ARCO Transportation Alaska, Inc., Anchorage, AK; *U.S. Public*, pg. 144
Thompson, J. Stark, Dr., Pres. & Chief Exec. Officer--Life Technologies, Inc., Rockville, MD; *U.S. Public*, pg. 504
Thompson, J.C., V.P.--Morgan Matroc Inc.-Midwest Sales Division, Milwaukee, WI; *Int'l*, pg. 893
Thompson, J.D., Pres.--Southland Life Insurance Company, Atlanta, GA; *Int'l*, pg. 648
Thompson, James, Pres.--Newell Paper Co. of Columbus, Columbus, MS; *U.S. Private*, pg. 579
Thompson, James G., Pres.--Upland Resources, Inc., Keyser, WV; *U.S. Public*, pg. 1762
Thompson, James K., Plant Mgr.--UTA Thompson Plant, Thomson, GA; *U.S. Public*, pg. 1691
Thompson, James R., Pres.--Ikon Office Solutions (Atlantic), Halifax, Canada; *U.S. Public*, pg. 864
Thompson, James W., Chm. Bd.--NationsBank South Carolina Corporation, Columbia, SC; *U.S. Public*, pg. 1163
Thompson, James W., Chm. Bd.--NationsBank Futures Corp., Charlotte, NC; *U.S. Public*, pg. 1165
Thompson, James W., Pres. & Chief Exec. Officer--Vallen Safety Supply Company, Ltd., Markham, Canada; *U.S. Public*, pg. 1705
Thompson, Jeff, Gen. Mgr.--Eaton Corporation, Engineered Fasteners Division, Brunswick, OH; *U.S. Public*, pg. 556
Thompson, Jim, G.M.-Western--Western Pulp & Paper Div., Portland, OR; *U.S. Public*, pg. 736
Thompson, Jim, Gen. Mgr.--KMAZ, Las Cruces, NM; *U.S. Public*, pg. 983
Thompson, Jim, Gen. Mgr.--KRQE-TV, Albuquerque, NM; *U.S. Public*, pg. 984
Thompson, Jim, Pres. & Gen. Mgr.--The Sports Network (TSN), Willowdale, Canada; *Int'l*, pg. 1343
Thompson, John, Pres. & Chief Exec. Officer--Montreal Trustco, Montreal, Canada; *Int'l*, pg. 155
Thompson, John, Gen. Mgr.--ESAB Australia Pty. Ltd., Ermington, Australia; *Int'l*, pg. 282
Thompson, John, Chief Exec. Officer--Western Specialty Container, City of Industry, CA; *U.S. Private*, pg. 559
Thompson, John, Gen. Mgr.--Corrugated Container Div.-Atlanta (Lithonia) Plant, Lithonia, GA; *U.S. Public*, pg. 1520
Thompson, John B., Pres.--AC Rochester Overseas Corporation, Southampton, United Kingdom; *U.S. Public*, pg. 722
Thompson, John E., V.P. & Gen. Mgr.--Bergen Brunswig Medical Corporation (Durr Drug), Montgomery, AL; *U.S. Public*, pg. 214
Thompson, John P., Mgr.-Mktg. Communications--Packaging and Material Handling Equipment Div., Homer City, PA; *U.S. Public*, pg. 606
Thompson, John S., Pres. & Chief Exec.--BTR, Inc., Stamford, CT; *Int'l*, pg. 127
Thompson, John S., Pres.--BTR Paper Group, Wellesley Hills, MA; *Int'l*, pg. 127
Thompson, Keith, Pres.--Measurement Systems, Inc., Fairfield, CT; *Int'l*, pg. 1431
Thompson, Kevin, Gen. Mgr.--Randall County Feed Yard, Amarillo, TX; *U.S. Private*, pg. 429
Thompson, Larry, Gen. Mgr.--Hach Co., Ames, IA; *U.S. Public*, pg. 773
Thompson, Lisa, Media--Leo Burnett/Connaghan & May (VIC.) Pty. Ltd., Melbourne, Australia; *U.S. Private*, pg. 185
Thompson, Lori, Branch Mgr.--Downey Savings & Loan Association, F.A., Costa Mesa, CA; *U.S. Public*, pg. 526
Thompson, M.A., Chm.--Halifax Rack & Screw Cutting Co., Ltd., Brighouse, United Kingdom; *Int'l*, pg. 448
Thompson, Mark, Mgr.--Sandvik New Zealand Ltd., Pakuranga, New Zealand; *Int'l*, pg. 1187
Thompson, Matthew G., Mng. Dir.--Thompson, Siegel & Walmsley, Inc., Richmond, VA; *U.S. Public*, pg. 1674
Thompson, Mike, Gen. Mgr.--Taiyo Yuden (U.S.A.) Inc., Schaumburg, IL; *Int'l*, pg. 1349
Thompson, Noel, Gen. Mgr.--Newmarket Company, Millburn, NJ; *U.S. Private*, pg. 584
Thompson, Norman J., Sr. V.P.--Air New Zealand Ltd. (U.S.A.), El Segundo, CA; *Int'l*, pg. 38
Thompson, P.M., Pres.--Phillips Coal Company, Richardson, TX; *U.S. Public*, pg. 1291
Thompson, Paul, Pres.--Bou-Matic, Madison, WI; *U.S. Private*, pg. 301
Thompson, Paul, Chm. & Mng. Dir.--Sanderson Computer Services, Sheffield, United Kingdom; *Int'l*, pg. 1184
Thompson, Peter, Pres. & Chief Exec. Officer--Snack Ventures Europe, Zaventem, Belgium; *U.S. Public*, pg. 718
Thompson, Ray F., Pres.--Lake Investment Co., Phoenix, AZ; *U.S. Public*, pg. 1563
Thompson, Richard J., Regional Mgr.-Opers.--Brookfield Homes-Western Region, Calgary, Canada; *Int'l*, pg. 228
Thompson, Robert, Pres.--Thompson-McCully Asphalt Paving Co., Belleville, MI; *U.S. Private*, pg. 1083
Thompson, Robert E., Pres.--Old Kent Bank of St. Johns, Saint Johns, MI; *U.S. Public*, pg. 1217
Thompson, Samuel, Mgr.--Westvaco Pacific Pty. Ltd., Sydney, Australia; *U.S. Public*, pg. 1763
Thompson, T. L., Pres. & Chief Oper. Officer--MH Leasing International, New York, NY; *U.S. Public*, pg. 338
Thompson, T. Stephen, Pres. & Chief Exec. Officer--Immtech International, Inc., Evanston, IL; *U.S. Public*, pg. 459
Thompson, Terry W., Chm. Bd., Pres. & Chief Exec. Officer--State Bank of Standish, Standish, MI; *U.S. Public*, pg. 379
Thompson, Tim, Mgr.--Westco Products/Bay Area, Union City, CA; *Int'l*, pg. 244
Thompson, Timothy, Pres.--Furman Lumber Company Inc., Dallas, TX; *U.S. Private*, pg. 431
Thompson, Tom, Pres.--Circuit Works, Mundelein, IL; *U.S. Private*, pg. 669
Thompson, W., Pres.--David & Sons, Fresno, CA; *Int'l*, pg. 917
Thompson, Wayne, Chief Oper. Officer--Super Services Waste Management Inc., Flagstaff, AZ; *U.S. Public*, pg. 49
Thompson, Wayne, Chief Exec. Officer--Interprovincial Cooperative Limited (IPCO), Saskatoon, Canada; *Int'l*, pg. 1195
Thompson, William L., Mng. Dir.--General Motors New Zealand Ltd., Upper Hutt, New Zealand; *U.S. Public*, pg. 722
Thompson, William O., Jr., Mgr.-Branch--Piper Jaffray Inc., Casper, WY; *U.S. Public*, pg. 1302
Thompson, William R., Chm., Pres. & Chief Exec. Officer--SunTrust Bank, Augusta, N.A., Augusta, GA; *U.S. Public*, *pg. 1538*
Thoms, William H., Admin.--Greenbriar Terrace Healthcare, Nashua, NH; *U.S. Public*, pg. 1712
Thomsen, Buo, V.P. & Gen. Mgr.--Lincoln Steel, Lincoln, NE; *U.S. Private*, pg. 824
Thomsen, Craig F., Chm. Bd.--First American Title Co. of Utah, Salt Lake City, UT; *U.S. Public*, pg. 625
Thomsen, Kurt, Chief Exec. Officer--Novo Nordisk Bioindustrial SA, Caracas, Venezuela; *Int'l*, pg. 989
Thomsen, Ralf, Gen. Mgr.--OMRON Electronics Norway A/S, Oslo, Norway; *Int'l*, pg. 1006
Thomson, A.P.C., Chief Oper. Officer--Babcock Industrial & Electrical Products Ltd., Bilston, United Kingdom; *Int'l*, pg. 472
Thomson, Barry, Vice Chm.--Aluma Systems Corp., Toronto, Canada; *Int'l*, pg. 1423
Thomson, Barry P., Gen. Mgr.--Thomas Lighting-Canadian Division, Markham, Canada; *U.S. Public*, pg. 1599
Thomson, Donald, Pres.--Precision Arc Co., Bridgeport, CT; *U.S. Private*, pg. 1008
Thomson, George, Sls. Representative--Brian Controls Division, Nepean, Canada; *Int'l*, pg. 711
Thomson, James S., Pres.--CNG International Corp., Reston, VA; *U.S. Public*, pg. 435
Thomson, Jerry, V.P.-Refining--Citgo Petroleum, Lake Charles, LA; *Int'l*, pg. 1045
Thomson, Michael J., Pres. & Chief Exec. Officer--Community Energy Alternatives Incorporated, Ridgewood, NJ; *U.S. Public*, pg. 1340
Thomson, Robert H., Pres.--Special Erection Services, Inc., Cranford, NJ; *U.S. Private*, pg. 266
Thong, Tong Kam, Center Mgr. & Dir.--Veritas DGC INC, Kuching, Malaysia; *U.S. Private*, pg. 1137
Thons, Bodo, Dr., Mgr.--Commerzbank AG Representative Office-Novosibirsk, Novosibirsk, Russia; *Int'l*, pg. 312
Thonus, Bernard, Mng. Dir.--Creep, Boulogne, France; *U.S. Private*, pg. 1199
Thorboll, Werner, Gen. Mgr.--Letraset AS, Herlev, Denmark; *Int'l*, pg. 461
Thordin, Goran, Chief Oper. Officer--Saab Norge A/S, Etterstad, Norway; *Int'l*, pg. 688
Thorell, Jan, Gen. Mgr.--Wang Svenska AB, Solna, Sweden; *U.S. Public*, pg. 1738
Thoren, Per, Mng. Dir.--SKF Treasury Centre, Goteborg, Sweden; *Int'l*, pg. 1157
Thoresen, Guttorm, Pres.--GPA Plast A/S, Ski, Norway; *Int'l*, pg. 678
Thoresen, Odd Petter, Gen. Mgr.--Elkem Carbon, Kristiansand, Norway; *Int'l*, pg. 447
Thorn, Bill, Mgr.-Regional--Alimak Elevator Company, Santa Fe Springs, CA; *U.S. Private*, pg. 34
Thorn, Julia, Chm. & Chief Exec.--Paragon Communications (UK) Ltd., London, United Kingdom; *Int'l*, pg. 1226
Thornber, Clayton, Gen. Mgr.--Service Motor Co., Fond Du Lac, WI; *U.S. Private*, pg. 986
Thornberg, Betty, Admin.--Hillhaven Convalescent Center Birmingham, Birmingham, AL; *U.S. Public*, pg. 1713
Thornborough, Wayne D., Mng. Dir.--UBS Asset Management (New York) Inc., New York, NY; *Int'l*, pg. 1440
Thornburgh, Jeff, Pres.--Dekko Heating Technologies, Inc., Cromwell, IN; *U.S. Private*, pg. 484
Thornburgh, Jeff, Pres.--Dekko Heating Technologies, Inc., Afton, IA; *U.S. Private*, pg. 484
Thornburgh, Jeff, Pres.--Dekko Heating Technologies, Inc., North Webster, IN; *U.S. Private*, pg. 484
Thornburn, Roger, Pres.--Anritsu Wiltron, Morgan Hill, CA; *Int'l*, pg. 77
Thorne, Mark, Chief Fin. Officer & Chief Oper. Officer--Hill and Knowlton, Inc., New York, NY; *Int'l*, pg. 1483
Thorne, R. Ernest, Mgr.--Tennessee Telephone Company, Bruceton, TN; *U.S. Public*, pg. 1572
Thorne, Richard, Sr. V.P.-Airline Business--Reed Travel Publishing, Dunstable, United Kingdom; *Int'l*, pg. 1097
Thornell, Jack, Pres.--Lockheed Martin Command & Control Systems, Colorado Springs, CO; *U.S. Public*, pg. 1008
Thornhill, Glenn, Pres.--Sea Cliff Water Company, Sea Cliff, NY; *U.S. Public*, pg. 126
Thornley, Richard, European Mgng. Dir.-MP/OEM--RAYOVAC Limited, Maidstone, United Kingdom; *U.S. Private*, pg. 912
Thornley, Richard, European Mng. Dir.--RAYOVAC UK Limited, Washington, United Kingdom; *U.S. Private*, pg. 912
Thornley, Stoney, Plant Mgr.--Albany International/Press Fabrics Division, Saint Stephen, SC; *U.S. Public*, pg. 36
Thornquist, Torgill, Chief Oper. Officer--Datapoint Svenska AB, Stockholm, Sweden; *Int'l*, pg. 384
Thornton, Jim, Plant Mgr.--Bridgestone/Firestone Off Road Tire Company-Bloomington, Bloomington, IL; *Int'l*, pg. 213
Thornton, John, Co.-Chm.--Goldman Sachs International Limited, London, United Kingdom; *U.S. Private*, pg. 462
Thornton, Nelson, Dir.-Pur.--Shell West Exploration & Production Inc., Brandon, MS; *Int'l*, pg. 1142
Thornton, Richard C., Pres.--Thornton & Co. Ltd., London, United Kingdom; *Int'l*, pg. 420
Thornton, Tom, Plant Mgr.--United Cement Co., Artesia, MS; *Int'l*, pg. 628
Thornton, William C., Pres.--Union Standard Insurance Company, Irving, TX; *U.S. Public*, pg. 216
Thorogood, L.C, Mng. Dir.--MB Kenya Limited, Nairobi, Kenya; *Int'l*, pg. 267
Thorp, Albert, III, Pres.--Technitrol Investments, Inc., Wilmington, DE; *U.S. Public*, pg. 1564
Thorpe, Albert, III, Pres.--Technitrol International, Inc., Wilmington, DE; *U.S. Public*, pg. 1564
Thorpe, Donald E., Pres.--Hy Vee Weitz Construction, L.C., West Des Moines, IA; *U.S. Private*, pg. 1161
Thorpe, J., Gen. Mgr.--Kenner Parker (N.Z.) Ltd., Auckland, New Zealand; *U.S. Public*, pg. 798
Thorpe, P.E., Dr., Gen. Mgr.--Morgan Matroc Limited Anderman Division, West Molesey, United Kingdom; *Int'l*, *pg. 893*
Thorstensson, Ingemar, Pres.--Boxholms Skogar AB/Skanska Forestry Group, Boxholm, Sweden; *Int'l*, pg. 1260
Thorstensson, Robert, Pres.--Skanska Fastigheter Riks AB, Danderyd, Sweden; *Int'l*, pg. 1260
Thorud, Erik, Mng. Dir.--Western Staff Services, Sandvika, Norway; *U.S. Public*, pg. 1760
Thostesen, Eliot, Gen. Mgr.--Midwest Litho Arts, Des Plaines, IL; *U.S. Public*, pg. 1779
Thounard, Jean-Pierre, Mng. Dir.--Mather & Platt Wormald S.A., Trappes, France; *U.S. Public*, pg. 1650
Thouvenet, Luc, Chief Exec. Officer--Auda S.A., Saint Germain-Lembron, France; *Int'l*, pg. 430
Thrall, J. Jeffrey, Chm. Bd. & Chief Exec. Officer--Naz-Dar Company, Chicago, IL; *U.S. Private*, pg. 1084
Thrane, Thomas, Mng. Dir.--FRAM Europe A.B., Bandhagen, Sweden; *U.S. Public*, pg. 53
Thrash, J.E., Pres.--GAICO, Reading, PA; *U.S. Private*, pg. 841
Thrash, James E., Pres.--Parsons Power Group, Inc., Reading, PA; *U.S. Private*, pg. 841
Thrash, James E., Pres.--Gilbert/Commonwealth International, Inc., Louisville, TN; *U.S. Private*, pg. 841
Thrash, James E., Pres.--Parsons Main, Inc., Boston, MA; *U.S. Private*, pg. 842
Thrasher, Dan, V.P. & Gen. Mgr.--Edgewater Hotel Corp., Laughlin, NV; *U.S. Public*, pg. 375
Threston, Joseph T., V.P. & Gen. Mgr.--Martin Marietta Government Electronic Systems, Moorestown, NJ; *U.S. Public*, pg. 1007
Thrift, Bill, V.P.--Atlantic National Corporation, Charleston, SC; *U.S. Private*, pg. 512
Thrift, Bill, V.P.--Hawthorne ABE, Allentown, PA; *U.S. Private*, pg. 512
Throdahl, M. C., Gen. Mgr.--MCC Div., Saint Louis, MO; *U.S. Public*, pg. 1039
Thron, John E., Pres.--Programart France Incorporated, Clichy, France; *U.S. Private*, pg. 890
Thrower, Richard, Admin.--East Manor Medical Care Center, Sarasota, FL; *U.S. Public*, pg. 1712
Thrower, Richard, Admin.--Hillhaven Convalescent Center Sarasota, Sarasota, FL; *U.S. Public*, pg. 1713
Thue, Ernst, Mng. Dir.--Esselte A/S, Oslo, Norway; *Int'l*, pg. 460
Thue, Odd H., Gen. Mgr.--Polarcup Norway, Lierstranda, Norway; *Int'l*, pg. 638
Thull, Steve, V.P.-Sls.--Fairfield Pagosa, Pagosa Springs, CO; *U.S. Public*, pg. 611
Thuluri, Ram, Pres.--RamaTech LLC, Romulus, MI; *U.S. Private*, pg. 539
Thunander, Steve, V.P. & Gen. Mgr.--Joslyn Manufacturing Co.-Apparatus Div., Franklin Park, IL; *U.S. Public*, pg. 481
Thunander, Steven L., V.P. & Gen. Mgr.--Joslyn Manufacturing Co., Chicago, IL; *U.S. Public*, pg. 481
Thunbrant, Bill, Pres.--Mitrex AB, Skarholmen, Sweden; *Int'l*, *pg. 1420*
Thunell, Lars, Pres.--Trygg-Hansa Insurance Co. Ltd., Stockholm, Sweden; *Int'l*, pg. 1425
Thurber, Lynn C., Principal Officer--LaSalle Advisors Limited, Chicago, IL; *U.S. Public*, pg. 979
Thurber, Lynn C., Mng. Dir.--LaSalle Advisors Limited, Baltimore, MD; *U.S. Public*, pg. 979
Thurlow, M., Chief Opr. Officer--Triplejay (Pty) Ltd., Jet Park, South Africa; *Int'l*, pg. 474
Thurman, R.H., Exec. V.P. & Grp. Pres.--Rhone-Poulenc Rorer - U.S., Collegeville, PA; *Int'l*, pg. 1110
Thurman, Randy, Pres.--Rorer Puerto Rico Inc., Manati, PR; *Int'l*, pg. 1111
Thurman, Ron, Vice Adm., Pres.--CAE Electronics Inc.-New York, Leesburg, VA; *Int'l*, pg. 237
Thurman, Wayne, Plant Mgr.--Baldor Electric Company, Fort Mill, SC; *U.S. Public*, pg. 169

Thurnherr, Rolf, Joint Chief Exec. Officer--Eurodis Electron Group, Reigate, United Kingdom; *Int'l*, pg. 1247
Thurston, Barry, Pres.-Syndication--Columbia Tri-Star Television Distribution, Burbank, CA; *Int'l*, pg. 1282
Thym, Dr. Gunther A., Pres.--Lawson Mardon Flexible Packaging, Inc., Bellwood, IL; *Int'l*, pg. 67
Tian, F., Chief Exec. Officer--Zurich Insurance Company, Beijing, China; *Int'l*, pg. 1531
Tianchon, Robert C., Pres.--Westinghouse Motor Company, Round Rock, TX; *U.S. Public*, pg. 275
Tibbels, C., Pres.--Michelin Korea Tire Company Limited, Seoul, Korea; *Int'l*, pg. 322
Tiberski, Walt, V.P. & Gen. Mgr.--WERE, Cleveland, OH; *U.S. Public*, pg. 385
Tiburski, Walt, V.P. & Gen. Mgr.--WNCX, Cleveland, OH; *U.S. Public*, pg. 385
Tice, Dan, Gen. Mgr.--La-Z-Boy Midwest, Neosho, MO; *U.S. Public*, pg. 973
Tice, Gary L., Chm. Bd.--Customer Service Center of F.N.B., L.L.C., Naples, FL; *U.S. Public*, pg. 607
Tice, Gary L., Chm. Bd.--Southwest Banks, Inc., Naples, FL; *U.S. Public*, pg. 607
Tice, Gary L., Chm. Bd.--First National Bank of Naples, Naples, FL; *U.S. Public*, pg. 607
Tidball, Robert N., Pres.--Transportation Equipment Corporation, San Francisco, CA; *U.S. Public*, pg. 1241
Tidenberg, Veijo, Chief Oper Officer--Savo Procurement Area, Kuopio, Finland; *Int'l*, pg. 455
Tidik, Steve, Pres.--Dunbar Sales Inc., City of Commerce, CA; *U.S. Public*, pg. 1720
Tidmore, Ronald W., Pres.--Pepsi-Cola South, Dallas, TX; *U.S. Public*, pg. 1277
Tidstrom, Johnny, Mng. Dir.--Ovako Arvika AB, Arvika, Sweden; *Int'l*, pg. 1157
Tidwell, Jim, Pres.--Heritage Press, Inc., Dallas, TX; *U.S. Public*, pg. 1735
Tiede, Rodney M., V.P. & Gen. Mgr.--Instore Satellite Network/Business TV, Midvale, UT; *U.S. Public*, pg. 484
Tiedeman, Robert, V.P. & Mng. Dir.--Northern Trust Bank of California, N.A., Los Angeles, CA; *U.S. Public*, pg. 1196
Tieghi, Giorgio, 1st V.P. & Mgr.--Banca Commerciale Italiana, Chicago, IL; *Int'l*, pg. 652
Tieh, Jackson, Pres.--Integrity Life Insurance Company, Taipei, Taiwan; *Int'l*, pg. 908
Tiensuu, Lief, Mng. Dir.--KOPO AB, Haparanda, Sweden; *Int'l*, pg. 1353
Tierney, Brian P., Pres. & Chief Exec. Officer--Tierney & Partners, Philadelphia, PA; *U.S. Public*, pg. 1641
Tierney, Chuck, Gen. Mgr.--Domestic Uniform Rental, Richmond, VA; *U.S. Private*, pg. 338
Tierney, Kathy, Pres.--Smith & Hawken, Mill Valley, CA; *U.S. Public*, pg. 279
Tierney, Mike, Gen. Mgr.--KEBE, Seattle, WA; *U.S. Private*, pg. 792
Tierney, Richard E., Pres.--Interstate Electronics Corp., Anaheim, CA; *U.S. Public*, pg. 622
Tierno, Anthony F., V.P.-Opers.--MediaNews Group, Eastern Operations, Woodbury, NJ; *U.S. Private*, pg. 727
Tiestini, Luciano, Chief Oper. Officer--NIFE Italia S.p.A., Genoa, Italy; *Int'l*, pg. 54
Tietjen, Hugh, Pres.--Computer Intelligence, La Jolla, CA; *Int'l*, pg. 1276
Tietke, Heiko, Gen. Mgr.--Colgate-Palmolive A.B., Hamburg, Germany; *U.S. Public*, pg. 398
Tiffney, J., Gen. Mgr.--Abel Lemon & Bleakley, Silverwater, Australia; *Int'l*, pg. 803
Tiger, Francois, Pres. & Chief Exec. Officer-France--DMB&B Paris, Asnieres-sur-Seine, France; *U.S. Private*, pg. 304
Tigerstedt, Ulv, Gen. Mgr.--Det Norske Veritas, Piraeus, Greece; *Int'l*, pg. 397
Tiget, M., Mng. Dir.--Balzers S.A., Meudon, France; *Int'l*, pg. 997
Tight, Thomas N., Pres.--First Virginia Insurance Services, Inc., Falls Church, VA; *U.S. Public*, pg. 642
Tigler, Bjorn, Mng. Dir.--S-E-Banken Fastigheter AB, Stockholm, Sweden; *Int'l*, pg. 1259
Tiilila, Pekka, Mng. Dir.--Tehdaspuu Oy, Kouvola, Finland; *Int'l*, pg. 1429
Tikhomiroff, S., Chief Oper. Officer--Tefal et KV Saint Petersburg, Saint Petersburg, Russia; *Int'l*, pg. 568
Tikkakoski, Matti, Pres. & Chief Exec. Officer--Polarcup Group Headquarters, Espoo, Finland; *Int'l*, pg. 638
Tikkinen-Ari, Maritta, Area Mgr.--Schauman Wood Oy-Istanbul Office, Istanbul, Turkey; *Int'l*, pg. 1429
Tilbrook, A., Chief Oper. Officer--J.M. Clarke (Electrical Engineers) Limited, Leicester, United Kingdom; *Int'l*, pg. 448
Tilburn, S., Mng. Dir.--Costain Mining Limited, Woking, United Kingdom; *Int'l*, pg. 336
Tilghman, Richard H., Pres.--Pepper Environmental Technologies, Inc., Chicago, IL; *U.S. Private*, pg. 851
Tillberg, Bo, Chief Oper. Officer--Daekko Presenning Kompagni A/S, Bronshoj, Denmark; *Int'l*, pg. 441
Tille, Uwe, Site Mgr./Mng. Dir.--Grace Silica N.V., Puurs, Belgium; *U.S. Public*, pg. 756
Tillens, Jacques, Head-Intl. Factors--International Factors, Brussels, Belgium; *Int'l*, pg. 147
Tilley, C.R., Chm. & Chief Exec. Officer--Columbia Gas Distribution Companies, Columbus, OH; *U.S. Public*, pg. 402
Tilley, Harold W., Mng. Dir--BLE Capital Limited, Sydney, Australia; *Int'l*, pg. 1496
Tilley, Ralph W., Chm. Bd., Pres. & Chief Exec. Officer--Vevay Deposit Bank, Vevay, IN; *U.S. Public*, pg. 633
Tillisch, Christian F., Pres.--GN Netcom A/S, Copenhagen, Denmark; *Int'l*, pg. 537
Tillman, Stuart, Sr. Business Devel. Officer--Southwest Marketing-Houston, Houston, TX; *U.S. Public*, pg. 650
Tillmann, Wolfgang, Dr., Sr. Mng. Dir.--Deutsche Bank AG (Essen), Essen, Germany; *Int'l*, pg. 402
Tillmanns, Hanns Joachim, Co-Mng. Dir.--Krupp Hoesch Dienstleistigungen GmbH, Essen, Germany; *Int'l*, pg. 512
Tillon, M., Dir. Gen.--Interbrands NV, Brussels, Belgium; *Int'l*, pg. 752
Tilman, Jean Pierre, V.P.-Air Freight--Circle Ziegler S.A. Airfreight, Zaventem, Belgium; *U.S. Public*, pg. 373
Tilton, Glenn F., Chm. & Pres.--TRMI Holdings Inc., Houston, TX; *U.S. Public*, pg. 1583
Timberlake, John, Gen. Mgr.--Clearwater Phillies, Clearwater, FL; *U.S. Private*, pg. 861
Timberlake, Mark, Gen. Mgr.--Alro Group, Indianapolis, Indianapolis, IN; *U.S. Private*, pg. 46
Timbers, Michael J., Pres.--Information Handling Services, Englewood, CO; *Int'l*, pg. 1335
Timbers, Stephen B., Chm. & Chief Exec. Officer--Zurich Kemper Investments, Inc., Chicago, IL; *Int'l*, pg. 1530
Timblick, A.J., Branch Dir.--Barclays Bank PLC, Seoul, Korea; *Int'l*, pg. 165
Timerman, Bill, Gen. Mgr.--Texas Auto Auction Services, Inc., Houston, TX; *U.S. Private*, pg. 283
Timm, Christopher, Pres.--Environmental & Commercial Insurance, Columbus, OH; *U.S. Public*, pg. 684
Timm, Simon, Mng. Dir.--EMAP Finance & Freight Ltd., London, United Kingdom; *Int'l*, pg. 451
Timmer, Jim, Mgr.-Engrng. Opers.--Ivex Packaging Corporation-Engineering Group, Grant Park, IL; *U.S. Public*, pg. 915
Timmermann, Gernot, Mng. Dir.--Bang & Olufsen Ges. m.b.H., Vienna, Austria; *Int'l*, pg. 146
Timmermann, K.W., Dep. Chm. & Mng. Dir.--P&O Bulk Shipping Ltd., London, United Kingdom; *Int'l*, pg. 1033
Timmins, H. Chester, Div. V.P.--AMP Automotive/Consumer Div., Harrisburg, PA; *U.S. Public*, pg. 7
Timmins, Kelley, Pres.--Nautilus International, Independence, VA; *U.S. Public*, pg. 498
Timmins, L., Mgr.-Opers.--Wyman-Gordon Forgings, North Grafton, MA; *U.S. Public*, pg. 1782
Timmins, Robert, Dr., Pres.--Organon Teknika Corp., Durham, NC; *Int'l*, pg. 46
Timmons, Dick, Publr.--The Daily News, Rhinelander, WI; *U.S. Public*, pg. 1343
Timms, Peter, Pres.--Dialight Corporation, Manasquan, NJ; *Int'l*, pg. 1130
Timms, T., Mng. Dir.--Target Technology Ltd., Ashford, United Kingdom; *Int'l*, pg. 853
Tindberg, Gunnar, Pres.--Indutrade AB, Kista, Sweden; *Int'l*, pg. 678
Tindberg, Gunnar, Pres.--GA Lindberg AB, Kista, Sweden; *Int'l*, pg. 678
Ting, D.L., Gen. Mgr.--Life Insurance Company of Georgia, Taipei, Taiwan; *Int'l*, pg. 650
Ting, Michael, Gen. Mgr.--CPM/Pacific Private Ltd., Singapore, Singapore; *U.S. Public*, pg. 705
Tingley, Charles E., Pres. & Chief Exec. Officer--Transamerica Leasing Inc., Purchase, NY; *U.S. Public*, pg. 1630
Tingley, Kenneth E., Pres.--Tau-tron, Westford, MA; *U.S. Public*, pg. 727
Tingstad, G.R., Mgr.-Opers.--Eaton Corporation, Defense Valve and Actuator Division, El Segundo, CA; *U.S. Public*, pg. 556
Tinkler, David A., Mgr.-Terminal--Avonmouth Terminal, Avonmouth, United Kingdom; *U.S. Public*, pg. 692
Tinkoff, Don, Gen. Mgr.--Corrugated Container Div.-Teterboro Plant, Teterboro, NJ; *U.S. Public*, pg. 1520
Tinley, Lawton E., V.P. & Gen. Mgr.--Coachmen Recreational Vehicle Company of Georgia, Fitzgerald, GA; *U.S. Public*, pg. 388
Tinnell, J. R., Chief Oper. Officer--Sonoco Fibre Drum, Stamford, CT; *U.S. Public*, pg. 1486
Tino, J. Robert, Pres. & Chief Exec. Officer--Sandusky Plastics, Inc., Sandusky, OH; *U.S. Public*, pg. 586
Tinsley, Edward, Chm. Bd.--NBD Equipment Finance, Inc., Novi, MI; *U.S. Public*, pg. 628
Tintle, Myles, Pres.--Wilcom Products, Inc., Laconia, NH; *U.S. Public*, pg. 1144
Tiong, Choo Boon, Mng. Dir.--International Factors Leasing Pte Ltd., Singapore, Singapore; *Int'l*, pg. 684
Tippett, Ken, Chief Oper. Officer--Alaska Boat Co., Seattle, WA; *U.S. Private*, pg. 1150
Tipping, Keith, Mng. Dir.--Komatsu UK, Ltd., Chester, United Kingdom; *Int'l*, pg. 744
Tippy, D. Kent, Grp. V.P.--Soabar Products Group, Philadelphia, PA; *U.S. Public*, pg. 153
Tipton, Ron D., Pres. & Chief Exec. Officer--Montana-Dakota Utilities Co., Bismarck, ND; *U.S. Public*, pg. 1025
Tipton, Roy, Plant Mgr.--Acme Brick Co., Fort Smith, AR; *U.S. Public*, pg. 936
Tirebuck, Gordon, Gen. Mgr.--Bernardin of Canada, Ltd., Etobicoke, Canada; *U.S. Public*, pg. 56
Tirkkonen, Esa, Dir.--Kemira Agro Oy, Helsinki, Finland; *Int'l*, pg. 727
Tirney, Stephen G., Pres. & Chief Oper. Officer--PMA Reinsurance Corporation, Philadelphia, PA; *U.S. Public*, pg. 1272
Tirschtigel, Georg, Pres. & Gen. Mgr.--Cartonajes Union, S.A., Gandia, Spain; *U.S. Public*, pg. 1666
Tisch, Jonathan M., Pres. & Chief Exec. Officer--Loews Hotels, New York, NY; *U.S. Public*, pg. 1011
Tisdall, Mike, Chief Oper. Officer & Mng. Dir.--Sasol Chemicals Pacific Limited, Wan Chai, Hong Kong; *Int'l*, pg. 1196
Titcombe, D. C., Dir. & Mgr.--Coutts & Co (Bermuda) Limited, Hamilton, Bermuda; *Int'l*, pg. 911
Titley, R.J.W., Chm.--Sedgwick Limited, London, United Kingdom; *Int'l*, pg. 1218
Tittle, William, V.P.--Bergen Brunswig Medical Corporation, Chattanooga, TN; *U.S. Public*, pg. 214
Titus, Don, Pres.--Kewanee Boiler Manufacturing Company, Inc., Kewanee, IL; *U.S. Public*, pg. 270
Titus, Donald B., Pres.--New Yorker Boiler Co., Inc., Colmar, PA; *U.S. Public*, pg. 270
Titus, Greg, Dir.--Arnold Interactive, Boston, MA; *U.S. Private*, pg. 84
Titus, Harold, Gen. Mgr.--Stanfast, Inc., Norcross, GA; *U.S. Public*, pg. 1505
Titus, Tom, Mgr.--Gould Paper of Florida, Inc., Tampa, FL; *U.S. Private*, pg. 467
Titze, Eberhard, Gen. Mgr.--RWM-Rohrwerke Muldenstein GmbH, Muldenstein, Germany; *Int'l*, pg. 79
Tiwari, S.K., Mgr.--Van Leeuwen Pipe and Tube (Malaysia) SDN. BHD., Kuala Lumpur, Malaysia; *Int'l*, pg. 1450
Tizio, Michael, Gen. Mgr.--McHutchinson Div., Ridgefield, NJ; *Int'l*, pg. 973
Tizzio, Thomas R., Pres.--AIU Insurance Company, New York, NY; *U.S. Public*, pg. 84
Tizzio, Thomas R., Pres.--Birmingham Fire Insurance Co. of Pennsylvania, New York, NY; *U.S. Public*, pg. 84
Tizzio, Thomas R., Pres.--Insurance Company of the State of Pennsylvania, New York, NY; *U.S. Public*, pg. 84
Tjaden, Klaus, Mgr.--Commerzbank International, S.A., Luxembourg, Luxembourg; *Int'l*, pg. 311
Tjornemark, Bent, Mng. Dir.--Danisco Finance Plc, Dublin, Ireland; *Int'l*, pg. 378
Tkachuk, Bordan, Mng. Dir.--Viglen Limited, Alperton, United Kingdom; *Int'l*, pg. 1468
Tlustos, Pat, Pres.--Hills Materials Co., Rapid City, SD; *U.S. Private*, pg. 806
To, Raymond, Gen. Mgr.--Velcro Hong Kong Ltd., Hong Kong, Hong Kong; *Int'l*, pg. 1462
Toake, Yoshikazu, Pres.--Amano International Trading (Shanghai) Co. Ltd., Shanghai, China; *Int'l*, pg. 71
Toal, Mike, Pres.--ComPair LeRoi, Sidney, OH; *Int'l*, pg. 1242
Toal, Paul M., Pres.--Sysco Food Services of Dallas, Dallas, TX; *U.S. Public*, pg. 1551
Toale, Owen, Gen. Mgr.--Park Newspapers of Medina, Inc., Medina, NY; *U.S. Public*, pg. 1078
Toale, Owen, Gen. Mgr.--Medina Journal-Register, Medina, NY; *U.S. Public*, pg. 1079
Toalson, D.C., Pres.--Reading & Bates Development Co., Houston, TX; *U.S. Public*, pg. 1354
Tober, Lester V., Pres.--World Import Co., Saint Louis, MO; *U.S. Private*, pg. 1089
Tobey, Gene, Pres.--Intelligent Instrumentation Inc., Tucson, AZ; *U.S. Public*, pg. 270
Tobias, Kal, Pres.-DHL Canada--DHL International Express Ltd., Mississauga, Canada; *U.S. Private*, pg. 302
Tobin, Bernard, Mng. Dir.--Rolls-Royce Motor Cars International S.A., Saint Prex, Switzerland; *Int'l*, pg. 1467
Tobin, Jack, Gen. Mgr.--Greater Philadelphia/Wilmington, New Castle, DE; *U.S. Public*, pg. 218
Tobin, Paul, V.P.-System/Support Services--Wyle Laboratories-Eastern Operations, Hampton, VA; *U.S. Private*, pg. 1193
Tobisson, Olle, Chief Oper. Officer--Molnlycke AB New Markets Development, Molnlycke, Sweden; *Int'l*, pg. 1326
Tobler, Steve, Gen. Mgr.--BancTec (Australia) Pty. Limited, Sydney, Australia; *U.S. Public*, pg. 177
Tocci, Leonard J., Chief Exec. Officer--Tamor Corp., Leominster, MA; *U.S. Public*, pg. 832
Tocci, Mike, Gen. Mgr.--Hyundai Motor America Eastern Regional Office, Jamesburg, NJ; *Int'l*, pg. 641
Tochterman, Fred, V.P. & Gen. Mgr.--Lehigh Press ColorTronics, Elk Grove Village, IL; *U.S. Private*, pg. 659
Tochterman, Robert C., Mgr.-Sls.--Packaging and Material Handling Division, Chicago, IL; *U.S. Public*, pg. 606
Tockarshewsky, Joseph B., Chm. Bd., Pres. & Chief Exec. Officer--Bank of the Hudson, Poughkeepsie, NY; *U.S. Public*, pg. 1319
Toczek, Jozef, Rep.--Kredietbank Representative Office (Warsaw), Warsaw, Poland; *Int'l*, pg. 760
Tod, G. Robert, Pres. & Chief Exec. Officer--NordicTrack, Inc., Chaska, MN; *U.S. Public*, pg. 279
Toda, Kengo, Chm.--Nippondenso Co., Ltd., Kariya, Japan; *Int'l*, pg. 1412
Todaro, Ralph, Pres.--Pacific Library Tower, Los Angeles, CA; *U.S. Public*, pg. 1249
Todd, A. John, 111, Pres.--Todd Juice Products, Kalamazoo, MI; *U.S. Private*, pg. 1090
Todd, Barbara, Pres.--Orchids Etc., Milwaukie, OR; *Int'l*, pg. 1518
Todd, C.B., Pres.--Mylan Pharmaceuticals Inc., Morgantown, WV; *U.S. Public*, pg. 1143
Todd, Harold B., Jr., Sr. Trust Exec.--Institutional Trust & Investment Services, Cleveland, OH; *U.S. Public*, pg. 1154
Todd, Henry W., Pres.--Zink & Triest, Montgomeryville, PA; *U.S. Private*, pg. 1090
Todd, Paul, Jr., Pres.--Kalsec, Inc., Kalamazoo, MI; *U.S. Private*, pg. 606
Todd, S., Pres.--Rolls-Royce Industries Canada Inc., Lachine, Canada; *Int'l*, pg. 1127
Todd, Trish, Editor-in-Chief--Fireside Books, New York, NY; *U.S. Private*, pg. 777
Todd, William F., Chm. & Chief Exec. Officer--NationsBank of Franklin County, Benton, IL; *U.S. Public*, pg. 1164
Todd, William F., Chm. Bd.--NationsBank of Franklin County, Zeigler, IL; *U.S. Public*, pg. 1164
Todorova, Katherina, Liaison Officer--Interpartners Bulgaria, Sofia, Bulgaria; *U.S. Private*, pg. 1152
Toellner, Fritz, Pres.--Cardinal EG Saws Corp., Elk Grove Village, IL; *Int'l*, pg. 228
Toernblom, Olle, Chief Oper. Officer--H.B. Fuller Sverige AB, Frolunda, Sweden; *U.S. Public*, pg. 687
Toerpe, Robert, Pres.--Wisconsin Insurance Management, Inc., Waukesha, WI; *U.S. Public*, pg. 141
Toffier, Jean-Pierre, Gen. Mgr.--Francomet S.A., Paris, France; *Int'l*, pg. 303
Toft, Richard P., Chm. Bd.--Chicago Title & Trust Co., Chicago, IL; *U.S. Public*, pg. 42
Togashi, Kazuya, Gen. Mgr.--Siegling (Japan) Ltd., Yokohama, Japan; *Int'l*, pg. 498
Togni, A., Chief Credit Officer--Schweizerischer Bankverein, Basel, Switzerland; *Int'l*, pg. 1329
Togo, Y., Pres.--Toyota Motor Credit Corp., Torrance, CA; *Int'l*, pg. 1413
Tohga, Tom, Mgr.-Sls.--NAIS Products Sales Office, New Providence, NJ; *Int'l*, pg. 848

Tohyama, Tsutomu, Mng. Dir.--Brother Industries Technology (M) Sdn. Bhd., Johor Baharu, Malaysia; Int'l, pg. 229

Toiminen, Rainer, Pres.--Kvaerner Tamturbine Oy, Tammerfors, Finland; Int'l, pg. 772

Tointon, Bryan, Pres.--Phelps Tointon Millwork, Fort Collins, CO; U.S. Private, pg. 861

Toiviainen, Heimo, Mng. Dir.--Ahlstrom Aquaflow Ltd., Savonlinna, Finland; Int'l, pg. 34

Toivola, Olavi, Pres.--Nokian Paperi Oy, Nokia, Finland; U.S. Public, pg. 673

Toivonen, Hannu, Chief Oper. Officer--Kesoil Oy, Tampere, Finland; Int'l, pg. 913

Tojek, Gile, Pres.--Iochpe-Maxion Ohio, Inc., Cleveland, OH; Int'l, pg. 688

Tojo, Harry, Reg. Mgr.-Sls.--Taiyo Yuden (U.S.A) Inc., Vista, CA; Int'l, pg. 1349

Tokiwa, Toshiji, Mng. Dir. & Gen. Mgr.--Dai-Ichi Kangyo Bank, Ltd.-New York, New York, NY; Int'l, pg. 359

Tokiwa, Toshiji, Mng. Dir. & Gen. Mgr.--Dai-Ichi Kangyo Bank, Ltd-Cayman Island, Georgetown, Cayman Islands; Int'l, pg. 360

Tokoro, S., Chief Oper. Officer--Kanaflex do Brasil Industria de Plasticos Ltda., Butanta, Brazil; Int'l, pg. 948

Tokraks, Eugene V., Plant Mgr.--Image Technology Corporation, Chandler, AR; U.S. Public, pg. 1219

Tokunaga, Dr. Junzo, Chief Oper. Officer--Griffith Laboratories, K.K., Tokyo, Japan; U.S. Private, pg. 481

Tokura, Muneharu, Gen. Mgr.--Dentsu Shanghai Office, Shanghai, China; Int'l, pg. 393

Tokuzumi, Mario Masayoshi, Pres.--Rohm Electronics Brasil Ltda., Sao Paulo, Brazil; Int'l, pg. 1125

Tolan, Patrick J., Mng. Dir.--X.L. Europe Insurance, Dublin, Ireland; Int'l, pg. 467

Toland, Richard E., Pres.--KPL, Topeka, KS; U.S. Public, pg. 1759

Tolbert, William R., Ph.D., V.P.-Tech. Affairs--Chiron Corporation, Saint Louis, MO; U.S. Public, pg. 350

Toler, Karen, Branch Mgr.--Burns & Wilcox Ltd., Morehead City, NC; U.S. Private, pg. 609

Tolkowsky, Dan, Mng. Partner--Athena Venture Partners L.P., New York, NY; Int'l, pg. 644

Tollett, Leland, Pres. & Chief Oper. Officer--Tyson Export Sales, Inc., Springdale, AR; U.S. Public, pg. 1652

Tollison, Eugene, Mgr.-Personnel--Palmetto Spinning Corp., Laurens, SC; U.S. Public, pg. 1052

Tolson, Ray, Chief Oper. Officer--Pride Offshore, Inc., Houma, LA; U.S. Public, pg. 1325

Tolvaren, Sukari, Co. Dir.--CPC Foods Oy, Espoo, Finland; U.S. Public, pg. 225

Tolworthy, Thomas, V.P.--Scribner's Bookstores, New York, NY; U.S. Public, pg. 189

Toma, K., V.P. & Gen. Mgr.--JCB International Credit Card Co., Ltd.-USA, New York, NY; Int'l, pg. 696

Tomas, Conrado Torras, Dir.-General--Senalizacion y Accesorios Del Automovil Yorka, S.A., Barcelona, Spain; U.S. Public, pg. 724

Tomas, F. Garcia, Gen. Mgr.--Compania Radio Aerea Maritima Espanola, S.A., Madrid, Spain; Int'l, pg. 1152

Tomas, Jose Luis Martin, Chief Oper. Officer--Rhone-Poulenc Delegation Generale, Madrid, Spain; Int'l, pg. 1113

Tomasso, Donald C., Pres.--Manor Care, Inc., Gaithersburg, MD; U.S. Public, pg. 1041

Tomasso, Donald C., Chm. Bd. & Chief Exec. Officer--Vitalink Pharmacy Services, Inc., Naperville, IL; U.S. Public, pg. 1041

Tomaszewski, Romuald, Chief Oper. Officer--MacGREGOR (POL) Sp. z.o.o., Gdynia, Poland; Int'l, pg. 671

Tomblin, Fred, Pres.--Commonwealth Land Title Insurance Company, Philadelphia, PA; U.S. Public, pg. 1374

Tomcho, Joe, Plant Mgr.--Connor Corporation, Indianapolis, IN; U.S. Private, pg. 264

Tome, John, Chm. Bd. & Mng. Dir.--Ford Lusitana, Lisbon, Portugal; U.S. Public, pg. 666

Tomeski, George, Gen. Mgr.--DMB&B Beijing, Beijing, China; U.S. Private, pg. 303

Tomfeld, Robert, Plant Mgr.--Thermice Corporation, Muscatine, IA; U.S. Public, pg. 1341

Tomie, Shinji, Chief Oper. Officer--Toyota do Brasil S.A., Industria e Comercio, Sao Bernardo do Campo, Brazil; Int'l, pg. 1414

Tominaga, Takashi, Chief Oper. Officer--Tokio Marine Realty Co., Ltd., New York, NY; Int'l, pg. 1392

Tominaga, Takashi, Chief Oper. Officer--Tokio Marine Property Limited, London, United Kingdom; Int'l, pg. 1393

Tomine, Eizaburo, Chief Oper. Officer--T.K.K. Co., Ltd., Tokyo, Japan; Int'l, pg. 1362

Tominovich, A. Robert, Pres., Chief Exec. Officer & Compliance Officer--McGraw-Hill Securities Trading, Inc., New York, NY; U.S. Public, pg. 1071

Tomioka, Shigeki, Chief Rep.--Sakura Bank - Detroit Representative Office, Southfield, MI; Int'l, pg. 1179

Tomita, Hiroshi, Pres.--Citic Golden Tiger Group Co., Ltd., Beijing, China; Int'l, pg. 579

Tomita, Toshio, Chief Rep.--Daiwa Bank-Jakarta, Jakarta, Indonesia; Int'l, pg. 373

Tomita, Ushio, Pres.--Sampo Techno Construction Co., Ltd., Toyokawa, Japan; Int'l, pg. 764

Tomito, Kazuhiro, Pres.--Otsuka Tokyo Assay Laboratories Inc., Tokyo, Japan; Int'l, pg. 1013

Tomiyama, Joji, Export Terminal Mgr.--Kintetsu World Express Inc., Burlingame, CA; Int'l, pg. 735

Tomiyama, Shoichi, Mng. Dir.--Marubeni Corporation, Osaka, Japan; Int'l, pg. 844

Tomiyama, Tsuguo, Pres. & Chief Exec. Officer--DIC Trading (USA) Inc., Fort Lee, NJ; Int'l, pg. 369

Tomkinson, P., Mng. Dir.--Durham Chemicals Ltd., Chester le Street, United Kingdom; Int'l, pg. 598

Tomko, Thomas A., Sole Administrator--Alambrados Automotrices, S.A. de C.V., Mexico, Mexico; U.S. Public, pg. 721

Tomko, Thomas A., Sole Administrator--Ensamble de Cables y Componentes, S.A. de C.V., Mexico, Mexico; U.S. Public, pg. 721

Tomlinson, Janice M., Pres.--Chubb Insurance Co. of Canada, Toronto, Canada; U.S. Public, pg. 355

Tomlinson, Steve, Pres.--Union City Chair Co., Union City, PA; U.S. Private, pg. 170

Tomlinson, Thomas, Pres.--Aero Electronics Incorporated, Memphis, TN; U.S. Private, pg. 731

Tomlinson, Vince, Co-Pres.--Schroff, Straubenhardt, Germany; U.S. Public, pg. 1274

Tommasi, Enzio, Gen. Mgr.--Siegling Italia S.p.a., Paderno Dugnano, Italy; Int'l, pg. 498

Tommasini, Bernard, Mng. Dir. & V.P.--Kelly Services, Paris, France; U.S. Public, pg. 949

Tommolillo, Mary, Admin.--Sherwood Convalescent Hospital, Sacramento, CA; U.S. Public, pg. 1714

Tomono, Kenji, Chm. Bd.--Yamaichi International (Europe) Ltd., London, United Kingdom; Int'l, pg. 1518

Tomono, Norio, Pres.--Chiyoda Life Realty France S.A., Courbevoie, France; Int'l, pg. 287

Tomooka, Yuji, Chief Oper. Officer--Tokio Marine de Venezuela, C.A., Caracas, Venezuela; Int'l, pg. 1393

Tomozaki, Tokuya, Chief Oper. Officer--Toyota Finance Australia Ltd., Melbourne, Australia; Int'l, pg. 1414

Tompkins, J. Bruce, Exec. V.P.--Southdown Cement Group, Houston, TX; U.S. Public, pg. 1489

Tompkins, J. Richard, Pres.--Utility Service Affiliates, Inc., Iselin, NJ; U.S. Public, pg. 1110

Tompkins, Richard, Pres.--Diamond Electronics, Inc., Carroll, OH; U.S. Public, pg. 1663

Tompkins, Ronald E., Mng. Dir.--The Bank of Nova Scotia Trust Company (Cayman) Limited, Grand Cayman, Cayman Islands; Int'l, pg. 156

Tompsett, Peter A., V.P.-Admin.--James Walker Mfg. Co., Glenwood, IL; Int'l, pg. 1485

Toms, Nicholas R.H., Chm., Pres. & Chief Exec. Officer--Peak Technologies Group, Inc., New York, NY; Int'l, pg. 890

Tomsett, John, V.P. & Mng. Dir.--Shakespeare Company United Kingdom, Redditch, United Kingdom; U.S. Public, pg. 940

Tonachio, W., Gen. Mgr.--Buckhorn Material Handling Group Inc., Milford, OH; U.S. Public, pg. 1143

Tonaka, Kiichiro, Pres.--NCR-Japan Ltd., Toyko, Japan; U.S. Public, pg. 1146

Toney, James W., Pres.--TRI Realty, Inc., Houston, TX; U.S. Public, pg. 312

Toney, James W., Pres. & Gen. Mgr.--Tenneco Realty, Inc., Houston, TX; U.S. Public, pg. 1578

Tong Cuong, Eric, Co-Chief Exec. Officer--EURO RSCG Babinet, Erra, Tong Cuong, Levallois-Perret, France; Int'l, pg. 600

Tong, Anthony, Gen. Mgr.--Farah (Far East) Limited, Kowloon, Hong Kong; U.S. Public, pg. 613

Tong, Ophelia, Mng. Dir.--National Mutual Funds Management (Asia) Hong Kong, Hong Kong, Hong Kong; Int'l, pg. 909

Tonge, Charles R., Pres.--Harris Bank Barrington, N.A., Barrington, IL; Int'l, pg. 154

Tongson, Mario M., Pres.--Union Carbide Philippines (Far East) Inc., Manila, Philippines; U.S. Public, pg. 1667

Toni, Sergio, Chief Exec. Officer--Schleicher & Schuell Italia SRL, Milan, Italy; Int'l, pg. 1206

Tonin, Ivo C., Grp. Rep.--Australia & New Zealand Banking Group Limited Brazil, Rio de Janeiro, Brazil; Int'l, pg. 99

Tonkery, Daniel, Pres.--Readmore Publications Inc., New York, NY; Int'l, pg. 197

Tonkin, H.T., Gen. Mgr.--Jones Blair Co., Chattanooga, TN; U.S. Private, pg. 596

Tonkon, Ed, Pres. & Gen. Mgr.--Huffy Service First, Inc., Miamisburg, OH; U.S. Public, pg. 846

Tonkovich, Gene, Pres.--Guardian Products/Capital Wire, Highland Heights, KY; Int'l, pg. 1487

Tonn, Falko, Chief Oper. Officer--Krauss-Maffei Dienstleistung GmbH, Munich, Germany; Int'l, pg. 836

Tonning, Ken, Pres. & Gen. Mgr.--WTLV-TV, Jacksonville, FL; U.S. Public, pg. 702

Tonooka, Katsuhito, Gen. Mgr.--Los Angeles Agency, Los Angeles, CA; Int'l, pg. 1520

Tonseth, Erik, Pres. & Chief Exec. Officer--Kvaerner a.s, Oslo, Norway; Int'l, pg. 766

Toohey, Gerard E., Gen. Mgr.--General Valve, Fairfield, NJ; U.S. Public, pg. 1262

Toohey, John T., Pres.--Commerce & Industry Insurance Co., New York, NY; U.S. Public, pg. 84

Toole, Patrick A., Sr. V.P. & Gen. Mgr.--IBM Technology Products, White Plains, NY; U.S. Public, pg. 896

Toole, Timothy O., V.P.--Salem Carpet Mills, Santa Fe Springs, CA; U.S. Public, pg. 1464

Tooley, Roger, Pres.--Flowers Baking Co. of Jamestown, Inc., Jamestown, NC; U.S. Public, pg. 657

Toomey, Kevin, V.P. & Gen. Mgr.--Department/Specialty Division, Greensboro, NC; Int'l, pg. 576

Toonen, Erik, Dir.--Generale Bank - Utrecht, Utrecht, Netherlands; Int'l, pg. 547

Topffer, Anders, Mng. Dir.--Telefonaktiebolaget LM Ericsson Saudi Arabia, Riyadh, Saudi Arabia; Int'l, pg. 1370

Topolski, Patrick J., Chief Opr. Officer--BankAmerica Capital Corp., San Francisco, CA; U.S. Public, pg. 181

Topolski, Patrick J., Chief Opr. Officer--BankAmerica Capital Investments, Inc., San Francisco, CA; U.S. Public, pg. 181

Topp, Richard A., Pres. & Chief Exec. Officer--NYLIFE Securities Inc., New York, NY; U.S. Private, pg. 795

Topping, James G., Pres. & Gen. Mgr.--KGO Television, Inc., San Francisco, CA; U.S. Public, pg. 512

Toran, Alfonso, Mgr. Gen.--Condepols S.A., Madrid, Spain; Int'l, pg. 323

Toratake, Yuji, Dir. & Gen. Mgr.--Kanazawa Branch Office, Kanazawa, Japan; Int'l, pg. 1491

Torbett, Gary B., Mgr.--Oklahoma Communication Systems, Inc., Choctaw, OK; U.S. Public, pg. 1571

Torchin, Mimi, Editor-in-Chief--Soap Opera Weekly, New York, NY; U.S. Public, pg. 1328

Torcolini, Robert J., Pres.--Dynamet Inc., Washington, PA; U.S. Public, pg. 307

Tordai, Ferenc, Mng. Dir.--American Appraisal Hungary Co. Ltd., Budapest, Hungary; U.S. Private, pg. 50

Tordi, Robert F., Foundry Mgr. & Plant Mgr.--Dodge Division, Mishawaka, IN; U.S. Public, pg. 1398

Tordoir, P.P., Mng. Dir.--VNU Business Information Europe, Haarlem, Netherlands; Int'l, pg. 1445

Tores, D., Chief Oper. Officer--La Teledynamique S.A., Vaux-le-Penil, France; Int'l, pg. 474

Torfs, F., Mng. Dir.--Maritima Services, Rotterdam, Netherlands; Int'l, pg. 682

Torgersen, Hans Petter, Sr. V.P.--Kvaerner Earl and Wright, Inc., Houston, TX; Int'l, pg. 771

Torgersen, Helge, Pres.--Chr. Hansen AS, Oslo, Norway; Int'l, pg. 289

Toriello, Eduardo, Gen. Mgr.--ECO, Young & Rubicam S.A., Guatemala, Guatemala; U.S. Private, pg. 1200

Torigoye, Hiroshi, Pres.--Hydron Japan K.K., Tokyo, Japan; U.S. Public, pg. 695

Torii, Nobutoshi, Terminal Mgr.--Kintetsu World Express Inc., Elk Grove Village, IL; Int'l, pg. 734

Torii, Nobutoshi, Terminal Mgr.--Kintetsu Intermodal Inc., Elk Grove Village, IL; Int'l, pg. 735

Torikoe, Tatsuya, Gen. Mgr.--Dai-Ichi Kangyo Bank, Ltd.-Seoul, Seoul, Korea; Int'l, pg. 361

Torkilsen, Ernest, V.P. & Gen. Mgr.--Wilton Machinery Div., Palatine, IL; U.S. Private, pg. 1181

Tormey, Mark, V.P.-Opers.--Maggiano's Little Italy, Chicago, IL; U.S. Private, pg. 661

Tormey, Mark, V.P.-Opers.--Maggiano's Little Italy, Oak Brook, IL; U.S. Private, pg. 661

Torne, Alberto, Man. Dir.--Torne-Jotun S.A., Barcelona, Spain; Int'l, pg. 716

Tornell, Per, Mgr.--Sandvik Bahco Norden AB, Enkoping, Sweden; Int'l, pg. 1185

Torneus, Jan-Erik, Mng. Dir.--Svenska Blount AB, Varberg, Sweden; U.S. Public, pg. 239

Tornga, Mark, Admin.--Valley House Healthcare, Tucson, AZ; U.S. Public, pg. 1715

Tornquist, Ulf, Pres.--NCC Building, Orebro, Sweden; Int'l, pg. 898

Toro, Fernando, Gen. Mgr.--Bundy Venezolana C.A., Valencia, Venezuela; Int'l, pg. 1342

Toro, Jose, V.P. & Gen. Mgr.--Bumble Bee International Inc., Mayaguez, PR; U.S. Private, pg. 526

Toro, Luis Fernando, Pres.--Bundy Colombia S.A., Bogota, Colombia; Int'l, pg. 1342

Torok, R., Mng. Dir.--NRG Latin America S.A., Montevideo, Uruguay; Int'l, pg. 1116

Torok, R., Mng. Dir.--NRG South America S.A., Montevideo, Uruguay; Int'l, pg. 1116

Torok, Robert, Mng. Dir.--Gestetner Regional Services Inc. (USA), Coral Gables, FL; Int'l, pg. 1115

Torok, Steven, Exec. Dir.-Sls.--Chrysler/Plymouth Division, Detroit, MI; U.S. Public, pg. 353

Torrance, Anthony, Pres.--Data Rental/Sales, Division, Van Nuys, CA; U.S. Public, pg. 568

Torrence, Samuel L., V.P. & Mgr.--Westvaco Corporation-Chemical Div., Charleston, SC; U.S. Public, pg. 1762

Torres, Agnel, Mng. Dir.--Esselte S.A., Terrassa, Spain; Int'l, pg. 461

Torres, Alvaro, Gen. Mgr.--Janssen Farmaceutica S.A., Bogota, Colombia; U.S. Public, pg. 929

Torres, Esau, Gen. Mgr.--Littelfuse S.A. de C.V., Piedras Negras, Mexico; U.S. Public, pg. 1001

Torres, J.P., Asst. Division Mgr.--J.E. Higgins Lumber Company, San Ysidro, CA; U.S. Private, pg. 527

Torres, Laurent, Gen. Mgr.--Esselte Meto SNC, Saint Quentin-en-Yvelines, France; Int'l, pg. 461

Torres, Manuel, Mng. Dir.-Latin America--Bujias Champion de Mexico, S.A. de C.V., Mexico, Mexico; U.S. Public, pg. 444

Torri, Emilio, Pres.--Baltea, Ivrea, Italy; Int'l, pg. 1002

Torsher, Lennart, Mgr.--Ahlsell Kyl AB, Skarholmen, Sweden; Int'l, pg. 1422

Torti, Jose Luis, V.P.--Banco Nacional de Mexico, Tokyo, Japan; Int'l, pg. 574

Torton, Shay, Pres.--American Fine Wire Corp., Selma, AL; U.S. Public, pg. 969

Torum, Alf Richard, Pres.--Kvaerner Ships Equipment a.s Dubai Branch, Dubai, United Arab Emirates; Int'l, pg. 768

Torvund, Aage, Gen. Mgr.--OTD&C A/S (Offshore Technology Development & Consulting), Oslo, Norway; U.S. Public, pg. 1032

Tory, John H., Chief Oper. Officer-Media--Rogers Communications, Inc., Toronto, Canada; Int'l, pg. 1122

Tosato, A., Chief Oper. Officer--Swish Italiana Srl, Albignasego, Italy; Int'l, pg. 925

Tosi, J.S., V.P.--Middleton Aerospace Corporation, Middleton, MA; Int'l, pg. 829

Tostmann, Tom, Dr., Mng. Dir.--Tostmann & Domann, Frankfurt/Main, Germany; Int'l, pg. 1336

Toth, James, Gen. Mgr.--Schult Homes Corporation, Redwood Falls, MN; U.S. Public, pg. 1442

Toth, Joseph, Pres.--Allied Tool Products Inc., Milwaukee, WI; U.S. Public, pg. 617

Toth, R.E., Chm. Bd.--Montal (Insurance) Limited, Basingstoke, United Kingdom; U.S. Public, pg. 1126

Toth, Steve, Chief Oper. Officer--Visual Services Inc., Bloomfield Hills, MI; U.S. Public, pg. 1703

Tottlemire, Dan, Chief Oper. Officer--Ahlstrom Process Equipment Inc., Vancouver, WA; Int'l, pg. 34

Touchot, Yve, Mgr.--Kodak-Pathe, Marne la Vallee, France; U.S. Public, pg. 554

Touffu, Daniel, Gen. Mgr.--BFCE Los Angeles, Los Angeles, CA; Int'l, pg. 161

Tough, Steven D., Pres. & Chief Oper. Officer--Foundation Health Federal Services, Inc., Rancho Cordova, CA; U.S. Public, pg. 678

Touhy, Michael R., Chief Exec. Officer & Mng. Dir.--Tillinghast-Towers Penn, New York, NY; *U.S. Private*, pg. 1093
Toumanov, V.P., Rep.--ING Bank Vladivostok, Vladivostok, Russia; *Int'l*, pg. 649
Touri, Jeffrey C., Controller--Gantos, Inc., Grand Rapids, MI; *U.S. Public*, pg. 702
Tourigny, D., Mng. Dir.--S.F.T. Gongrand Freres, Paris, France; *U.S. Private*, pg. 1120
Tourikian, Lou, Gen. Mgr.--Courtaulds Aerospace, Mississauga, Canada; *Int'l*, pg. 339
Tourniaire, J.N., Chm. & Mng. Dir.--TIFT SA, Cergy-Pontoise, France; *Int'l*, pg. 1223
Tous, Francese, Pres.--Leaf Iberia S.A., Barcelona, Spain; *Int'l*, pg. 638
Toussaint, Claude, Chm. Bd.--Credit Foncier de Monaco, Monaco, Monaco; *Int'l*, pg. 314
Touw, Henk, Mng. Dir.--Donaldson Europe N.V., Leuven, Belgium; *U.S. Public*, pg. 517
Touw, Henk, Mng. Dir.--Donaldson Coordination Center, N.V., Leuven, Belgium; *U.S. Public*, pg. 517
Towar, Jeanne, Publisher--Detroit Monthly, Detroit, MI; *U.S. Private*, pg. 285
Towatari, H., Pres.--Sharp Corporation of Australia Pty. Ltd., Blacktown, Australia; *Int'l*, pg. 1229
Towers, J., Mng. Dir.--Riley Advertising (Norwich) Ltd., Norwich, United Kingdom; *Int'l*, pg. 1117
Towers, J., Mng. Dir.--Riley Advertising (Nottingham) Ltd., Nottingham, United Kingdom; *Int'l*, pg. 1117
Townes, Stephen, Pres.--SabreTech, Inc., Phoenix, AZ; *U.S. Private*, pg. 959
Townsend, Jackie, Plant Mgr.--Denise Lingerie, Johnson City, TN; *U.S. Private*, pg. 542
Townsend, Alair, Publisher--Crain's New York Business, New York, NY; *U.S. Private*, pg. 285
Townsend, Brent, Dir.-Mktg.--Ion Beam Systems Division, Austin, TX; *U.S. Public*, pg. 557
Townsend, Charles H., Grp. Pres.--Women's Magazines Group, New York, NY; *Int'l*, pg. 190
Townsend, Ernest W., Pres. & Chief Oper. Officer--Frank's Nursery & Crafts, Inc., Detroit, MI; *U.S. Public*, pg. 715
Townsend, Joe, Mgr.-Zone--Keydril Nigeria Limited, Lagos, Nigeria; *Int'l*, pg. 765
Townsend, K. N., Dir.--EMI Records (UK), Studios Div., London, United Kingdom; *Int'l*, pg. 427
Townsend, Merton L., Pres.--Chamberlain Manufacturing Corp., Elmhurst, IL; *U.S. Private*, pg. 344
Townsend, Thomas, Pres.--Kentucky Hydrocarbon Division, Langley, KY; *U.S. Public*, pg. 589
Townsend, William G., Sr. V.P. & Gen. Mgr.--St. Lawrence Cement, Ontario Division, Concord, Canada; *Int'l*, pg. 629
Townsley, Boyd T., V.P.-Property Mgr.--Kauai Electric Div., Kauai, HI; *U.S. Public*, pg. 380
Toy, Jack C., Pres.--SuperValu, Inc.-Fargo Div., Fargo, ND; *U.S. Public*, pg. 1540
Toyama, Makoto, Pres.--Konica Supplies Manufacturing U.S.A., Inc., Elkton, MD; *Int'l*, pg. 749
Toyama, Noriyuki, Pres.--Banyu Pharmaceutical Co. Ltd., Tokyo, Japan; *U.S. Public*, pg. 1091
Toyama, Yoji, Pres.--Mazda Motor of America, Inc., Irvine, CA; *Int'l*, pg. 849
Toyama, Yoji, Pres.--Mazda (North America), Inc., Irvine, CA; *Int'l*, pg. 849
Toyokawa, Hiroshi, Pres.--Okura & Co., Tokyo, Japan; *Int'l*, pg. 1001
Toyomaru, Koichi, Pres. & Chief Exec. Officer--Nippon Life Insurance Company of America, New York, NY; *Int'l*, pg. 935
Toyooka, Hirotaka, Mng. Dir.--Bingo Express Co., Ltd., Hiroshima, Japan; *Int'l*, pg. 934
Toyoshima, Makoto, Gen. Mgr.--Japan Energy (U.S.A.), Inc., New York, NY; *Int'l*, pg. 702
Traba, Anne W., V.P. & Mng. Exec.--Northern Trust Bank of Florida, N.A., Key Biscayne, FL; *U.S. Public*, pg. 1196
Trabanco, F. Valdes, Chief Exec. Officer--Industrias Transformadoras del Cemento Eternit SA, Madrid, Spain; *Int'l*, pg. 1092
Trabelski, Yitzhak, Mgr.--Bank Hapoalim (Switzerland) Ltd., Geneva, Switzerland; *Int'l*, pg. 150
Traboulsi, Jean, Mng. Dir. & Pub. Rels. Coord.--AMA Leo Burnett, Giza, Egypt; *U.S. Private*, pg. 184
Tracey, David H., Chief Oper. Officer--Glynwed Pipe Systems, Coleshill, United Kingdom; *Int'l*, pg. 554
Tracey, John, Dir.-Pub. Affairs--Procter & Gamble AG, Geneva, Switzerland; *U.S. Public*, pg. 1332
Tracey, R. Michael, Pres.--Kidde Systems, Inc., Baltimore, MD; *U.S. Public*, pg. 1341
TrachtenberG, Joseph M., Chief Exec. Officer--Victaulic International, Easton, PA; *U.S. Private*, pg. 1138
Tracy, R.J., Gen. Mgr.--ACI Standard, Steubenville, OH; *Int'l*, pg. 891
Tracy, Tom, Gen. Mgr.--Hatfield Auto Auction, Hatfield, PA; *U.S. Public*, pg. 1649
Trad, Raja, Chief Exec. Officer--H&C, Leo Burnett, Beirut, Lebanon; *U.S. Private*, pg. 184
Trad, Raja, Reg. Mng. Dir.--Radius Leo Burnett, Dubai, United Arab Emirates; *U.S. Private*, pg. 186
Tradup, Thomas R., Pres. & Gen. Mgr.--WLS, Inc., Chicago, IL; *U.S. Public*, pg. 512
Tradup, Thomas R., Pres. & Gen. Mgr.--WLS-FM Radio, Inc., Chicago, IL; *U.S. Public*, pg. 512
Trahan, Guy, Pres.--Imprimerie Quebecor Montreal, Montreal, Canada; *Int'l*, pg. 1077
Trahan, Patrick J., Pres. & Chief Exec. Officer--Rapides Bank & Trust Company of Alexandria, Alexandria, LA; *U.S. Public*, pg. 630
Trailes, Philip J., Pres.--Bunton Division, Louisville, KY; *U.S.* Public, pg. 1589
Train, Peter R., Resident Dir.--Foster Wheeler (Thailand) Limited, Chon Buri, Thailand; *U.S. Public*, pg. 677
Trainor, Donald, Gen. Mgr.--Stationery House, Inc., Hagerstown, MD; *U.S. Public*, pg. 89
Tralies, Philip, Pres.--Jacobsen Textron, Racine, WI; *U.S. Public*, pg. 1589
Trammer, Monte, Pres. & Publr.--The Saratogian, Saratoga Springs, NY; *U.S. Public*, pg. 700
Tran, Alan, Jr., Gen. Mgr.--Sterling Color Process, Kentwood, MI; *U.S. Private*, pg. 387
Tran, Henri, Pres.--PTDBS Securities Indonesia, Jakarta, Indonesia; *Int'l*, pg. 351
Tran, Ken, Gen. Mgr.--Nordson Pacific, Inc., Ho Chi Minh City, Vietnam; *U.S. Public*, pg. 1189
Trancu, Patrick, Rep.--Singapore Tourist Promotion Board - Milan, Milan, Italy; *Int'l*, pg. 1254
Trandum, William, Pres.--Pierce County Herald, Puyallup, WA; *U.S. Public*, pg. 1066
Trani, John M., Pres. & Chief Exec. Officer--G.E. Medical Systems, Milwaukee, WI; *U.S. Public*, pg. 710
Trankjaer, Ove, Mng. Dir.--Nilfisk-Gerni A/S, Randers, Denmark; *Int'l*, pg. 932
Trannoy, Marie-Bernard, Chief Oper. Officer--Laboratoire LaChartre S.A., Blois, France; *U.S. Public*, pg. 1331
Transou, Robert H., Exec. Dir.--Ford Body Engineering, Dearborn, MI; *U.S. Public*, pg. 662
Transou, Robert H., Pres.--Ford Ensite International Inc. (Canadian), Windsor, Canada; *U.S. Public*, pg. 665
Trapani, Kevin A., Pres.--The Redwoods Group, Morrisville, NC; *U.S. Private*, pg. 430
Traslosheros, A., Gen. Mgr.--A.C. Nielsen Co., Mexico, Mexico; *U.S. Public*, pg. 1183
Trate, Rick, Dir.-Central Asia--Carpenter Technology Corp. (Taiwan) Ltd., Taipei, Taiwan; *U.S. Public*, pg. 308
Trattler, Bruce, Pres.-Retail Div.--Etienne Aigner, New York, NY; *U.S. Private*, pg. 384
Trautwein, Wolfgang, Mng. Dir.--Dynex Technologies GmbH, Denkendorf, Germany; *U.S. Public*, pg. 1591
Travers, Mike, Gen. Mgr.--Letraset Export, Ashford, United Kingdom; *Int'l*, pg. 461
Travetto, Frank, Corp.--Earle M. Jorgensen Company/ Ontario, Mississauga, Canada; *U.S. Private*, pg. 600
Travis, Brian T., Mng. Dir.--Donald Brown (Brownall) Ltd., Manchester, United Kingdom; *Int'l*, pg. 390
Travis, Harry J., V.P. & Gen. Mgr.--National Specialty Services, Inc., Nashville, TN; *U.S. Public*, pg. 304
Travis, J.V., Branch Mgr.--Zellerbach Division, Indianapolis, IN; *U.S. Public*, pg. 1075
Travis, Joseph D., Chief Oper. Officer--Norwest Asia Limited, Central, Hong Kong; *U.S. Public*, pg. 1203
Travis, Ken, Plant Mgr.--Oxford Automotive, Howell Industries Div., Lapeer, MI; *U.S. Private*, pg. 825
Travis, Richard, Pres.--MB Manufacturing, Valparaiso, IN; *U.S. Private*, pg. 300
Trawick, Mike, Mgr.--White Electrical Construction Co., Mobile, AL; *U.S. Private*, pg. 1172
Trayling, Ivan, Mng. Dir.--Ericsson Defense Systems Pty. Ltd., Preston, Australia; *Int'l*, pg. 1366
Traylor, Alan, Pres.--Alnor Instrument Company, Skokie, IL; *U.S. Public*, pg. 1559
Traylor, Steve, Pres. & Chief Exec. Officer--Regions Bank/ Santa Rosa County, Pensacola, FL; *U.S. Public*, pg. 1372
Treacy, Edward, Exec. V.P. & Gen. Mgr.--Bank of Ireland (U.S.A.), New York, NY; *Int'l*, pg. 152
Treasure, C., Mng. Dir.--Buck & Hickman Limited, Sheffield, United Kingdom; *Int'l*, pg. 1032
Trebel, John, Pres. & Chief Exec. Officer--Waterloo Industries, Inc., Waterloo, IA; *U.S. Public*, pg. 675
Tredennick, Curtis, Pres.--North State Pyrophyllite, Greensboro, NC; *U.S. Private*, pg. 924
Treen, William Raymond, Dir. & Gen. Mgr.--Cornhill Insurance PLC, Guildford, United Kingdom; *Int'l*, pg. 60
Treen, William Raymond, Dir. & Chief Exec. Officer--Cornhill Insurance Plc, London, United Kingdom; *Int'l*, pg. 60
Treis, F. Edward, Chm. Bd. & Chief Exec. Officer--Arandell-Schmidt, Menomonee Falls, WI; *U.S. Private*, pg. 79
Tremblay, J., Mgr.--ABN AMRO Bank Canada (Montreal), Montreal, Canada; *Int'l*, pg. 11
Tremblay, John F., Pres.--The Bank of Mid-Jersey, Bordentown, NJ; *U.S. Public*, pg. 1528
Tremblay, Micheline, Pres.--Editions d'enseignements-religieux F.P.R. Inc., Montreal, Canada; *Int'l*, pg. 1077
Tremblay, Rene, Pres. & Chief Oper. Officer--Ivanhoe, Montreal, Canada; *Int'l*, pg. 249
Tremblay, Richard, Dir. Gen.--Imprimerie Quebecor L'Eclaireur, Beauceville, Canada; *Int'l*, pg. 1077
Tremmel, Klaus, Gen. Mgr.--Amway Gesellschaft M.B.H., Vienna, Austria; *U.S. Private*, pg. 70
Tremont, Dr. Edmund, Pres.--Novavax Inc., Rockville, MD; *U.S. Public*, pg. 855
Tremonti, Vince, Gen. Mgr.--Sterling Electronics, Westlake Village, CA; *U.S. Public*, pg. 1051
Trenary, John M., V.P.--Bausch & Lomb Oral Care Division, Tucker, GA; *U.S. Public*, pg. 194
Trepant, P., Mng. Dir.--Mobil Oil A/S Norge, Oslo, Norway; *U.S. Public*, pg. 1119
Trepat, Albert, Chief Exec. Officer-Barcelona--Grupo Barro Testa, Madrid, Spain; *Int'l*, pg. 1377
Tresaloni, Dave, Gen. Mgr.--Cutter Aviation, Austin, TX; *U.S. Private*, pg. 299
Treska, Clay, Gen. Mgr.--Olympic Steel - Southern Division, Greenville, SC; *U.S. Public*, pg. 1221
Tressler, Keith R., Mgr.--Mahanoy & Mahantongo Telephone Company, Herndon, PA; *U.S. Public*, pg. 1571
Trettin, Daniel R., Gen. Mgr.--Georgia-Pacific Port Edwards Operations, Port Edwards, WI; *U.S. Public*, pg. 736
Treu, Tiziano, Chm. Bd.--La Centrale Formazione S.r.l., Vicenza, Italy; *Int'l*, pg. 138
Treutler, Kurt, Mng. Dir.--Sulzer Chemtech GmbH, Butzbach, Germany; *Int'l*, pg. 1308
Trevino de la Garza, Jose A., V.P.--Northern Zone Office, Torreon, Mexico; *Int'l*, pg. 573
Trevino, Jose, Pres.--Mark Net World, Mequon, WI; *U.S. Private*, pg. 108
Trew, John, Dir.-Indonesia--North West Water Indonesia, Jakarta, Indonesia; *Int'l*, pg. 1444
Treweek, Timothy J., Pres.--Hilb, Rogal and Hamilton Company of Gainesville, Florida, Inc., Gainesville, FL; *U.S. Public*, pg. 827
Trewhella, Stephen W., Jr., V.P. & Gen. Mgr.--Glassmaster Controls Company, Inc., Kalamazoo, MI; *U.S. Public*, pg. 746
Triaire, Didier, Mng. Dir.--Check Technology France S.A., Lisses, France; *U.S. Public*, pg. 342
Triant, Deborah, Pres. & Chief Exec. Officer--Check Point Software Technologies Inc., Redwood City, CA; *U.S. Public*, pg. 342
Triantafillou, Panagiotis, Mng. Dir.--Dresdner Bank AG, Athens, Greece; *Int'l*, pg. 419
Trias, Carlos, Pres.--Laboratorio Astra Espana, S.A., Barcelona, Spain; *Int'l*, pg. 94
Tribe, G.B. H., Mng. Dir.--NatWest International Trust Corporation (Jersey) Limited, Saint Helier, United Kingdom; *Int'l*, pg. 911
Tribe, Graham D., Mng. Dir.--Hyster Australia Pty. Ltd., Milperra, Australia; *U.S. Public*, pg. 1149
Tribe, Lane, District Mgr.--Master Builders Inc., San Mateo, CA; *Int'l*, pg. 1465
Tribel, Philip, Pres.--Tipper Tie, Inc., Apex, NC; *U.S. Public*, pg. 520
Tribouillier, Jean-Pierre, Co-Mgr.--EURO RSCG Novation, Marseilles, France; *Int'l*, pg. 601
Tribouillier, Jean-Pierre, Co-Mgr.--EURO RSCG Novation, Villeneuve-Loubet, France; *Int'l*, pg. 601
Trice, Robert H., Pres.--The Boeing Company, London, United Kingdom; *U.S. Public*, pg. 242
Tricker, Brian, Chief Oper. Officer--Boart Longyear S.A., Trappes, France; *Int'l*, pg. 76
Trienekens, H., V.P.--J.L. de Ball of America Ltd. Apparel Div., New York, NY; *Int'l*, pg. 552
Trier, Clayton, Chief Exec. Officer--Corporate Express Delivery Systems, Houston, TX; *U.S. Public*, pg. 449
Trifonov, V.S., Mng. Dir.--Becema, Moscow, Russia; *Int'l*, pg. 1134
Trigano, Gilbert, Chief Oper. Officer--Trident Enterprise Ltd., Nassau, Bahamas; *Int'l*, pg. 298
Triggiani, L.V., Pres.--Amoco Technology Company, Naperville, IL; *U.S. Public*, pg. 103
Triglia, Massimo, Chief Oper. Officer--MacGREGOR (ITA) S.p.A., Genoa, Italy; *Int'l*, pg. 671
Trigo-Anez, D., Chief Oper. Officer--BHF-Bank Representative Office, Buenos Aires, Argentina; *Int'l*, pg. 120
Trigony, Nicholas D., Pres.--Cox Broadcasting Inc., Atlanta, GA; *U.S. Private*, pg. 281
Trigwell, James, Gen. Mgr.--Colgate-Palmolive (India) Ltd., Mumbai, India; *U.S. Public*, pg. 398
Trilli, Harvey J., Sr. V.P. & Gen. Mgr.-Engineering & Constrution--Davy Dravo Division, Pittsburgh, PA; *Int'l*, pg. 774
Trilsus, N., Dr., Mng. Dir.--GKN Componenti Firenze SpA, Campi Bisenzio, Italy; *Int'l*, pg. 536
Trimarche, Richard C., Pres.--Malone & Hyde, Inc.-Drug Distributors, Memphis, TN; *U.S. Public*, pg. 653
Trimble, Charles R., Pres.--TR Navigation Corporation, Austin, TX; *U.S. Public*, pg. 1638
Trimble, Mason H. III, Pres.--Fleming Foods West - Fresno Div., Fresno, CA; *U.S. Public*, pg. 653
Trimmer, Gordon, Mgr.--A. Schulman Canada Ltd., Saint Thomas, Canada; *U.S. Public*, pg. 1442
Trinder, Paul, Mng. Dir.--Emergi-Lite Safety Systems Ltd., Dewsbury, United Kingdom; *Int'l*, pg. 725
Trinkunas, Julius, Pres.--Lagoven, S.A., Caracas, Venezuela; *Int'l*, pg. 1045
Trip, D. Laman, Chm. Bd.--Postbank Retail Banking, Amsterdam, Netherlands; *Int'l*, pg. 647
Tripathi, M.L., Gen. Mgr.--Burns Philp Company of San Francisco, San Francisco, CA; *Int'l*, pg. 236
Tripathi, Praveen, Assoc. Reg. Dir.-Media & Strategic Plng.--Chaitra Leo Burnett Private Ltd., Mumbai, India; *U.S. Private*, pg. 184
Triplett, M. S., Works Mgr.--John Deere Davenport Works, Davenport, IA; *U.S. Public*, pg. 492
Tripp, B.B., Div. Pres.--Winn-Dixie Charlotte, Inc., Charlotte, NC; *U.S. Public*, pg. 1771
Tripp, Doug, Pres.--Pulte Tampa Division, Tampa, FL; *U.S. Public*, pg. 1345
Trippitelli, Gerald J., Pres.--Matlack (DE), Inc., Wilmington, DE; *U.S. Public*, pg. 1057
Triptree, Brian, Mng. Dir.--Tyco Toys (UK) Ltd., Marlow, United Kingdom; *U.S. Public*, pg. 1059
Trisdale, David, Plant Superintendant--General Shale Products Corp.-Sparta Concrete Div., Sparta, TN; *Int'l*, pg. 844
Trisel, Darren, Admin.--Fallon Convalescent Center, Fallon, NV; *U.S. Public*, pg. 837
Tristano, M.J., Mgr.--Harris Metals, Racine, WI; *U.S. Public*, pg. 999
Tritt, John R., Pres.--QA Products, Inc., Elk Grove Village, IL; *Int'l*, pg. 244
Trocme, J.P., Gen. Mgr.--ITW Finishing Systems & Products-Southern Europe, Valence, France; *U.S. Public*, *pg. 868*
Troeh, H., Mgr.--Alaskan Copper Companies, Portland, OR; *U.S. Private*, pg. 31
Trogen, Karl-Erling, Pres.--Volvo Truck Corporation, Goteborg, Sweden; *Int'l*, pg. 1477
Tromba, Ray, Gen Mgr.--Louisiana Downs, Bossier City, LA; *U.S. Private*, pg. 319
Trombetta, Frank, Pres.--Evanite Fiber Corp., Corvallis, OR; *U.S. Private*, pg. 535
Tromp, J. T., Mng. Dir.--R. & H. Systems B.V., Rotterdam, Netherlands; *Int'l*, pg. 680
Tronconi, Augusto, Chief Oper. Officer--Banque Bruxelles Lambert (Suisse)-Lugano, Lugano, Switzerland; *Int'l*, pg. 148
Troncoso, Ignacio, Mgr.-Chile--Raychem Industrial Y Comercial Limitada, Santiago, Chile; *U.S. Public*, pg. 1362

Trone, Ron, Gen. Mgr.--Southeastern Metal Processing, Winder, GA; *U.S. Public*, pg. 1221

Tropp, Joerg, Dr., Interactive Media--Michael Conrad & Leo Burnett GmbH, Frankfurt/Main, Germany; *U.S. Private*, pg. 184

Trosper, Thomas R., Asst. V.P.--IBP-Dakota City, Dakota City, NE; *U.S. Public*, pg. 852

Trotman, Alexander J., Chm. Bd.--Ford Leasing Development Co., Dearborn, MI; *U.S. Public*, pg. 664

Trotman, Chris, Mng. Dir.--SKF (U.K.) Ltd., Luton, United Kingdom; *Int'l*, pg. 1159

Trott, Helmut, Gen Mgr--Dresdner Bank AG, Central, Hong Kong; *Int'l*, pg. 419

Trotter, Glenn, Dir.-Opers.--Rema Bakeware, Salina, KS; *U.S. Public*, pg. 1177

Trotter, Lloyd G., Pres. & Chief Exec. Officer--G.E. Electric Distribution & Control Manufacturing, Plainville, CT; *U.S. Public*, pg. 710

Trotter, Mike, Pres.--Quintana Petroleum Services, Houston, TX; *U.S. Private*, pg. 901

Trotter, Mike, Pres.--Quintana Environmental Services, Inc., Houston, TX; *U.S. Private*, pg. 901

Trotter, Thomas W., Sr. V.P.--Wachovia Mortgage Co., Winston Salem, NC; *U.S. Public*, pg. 1731

Trotter, Tim, Chm. & Chief Exec. Officer--Ludgate Group Limited, London, United Kingdom; *U.S. Private*, pg. 1157

Trouche-Brugger, Frederic, Rep.--Banque Regionale du Nord, Lens, France; *Int'l*, pg. 548

Troughton, E., Dir.--NatWest Investment Management Asia Limited, Causeway Bay, Hong Kong; *Int'l*, pg. 911

Troupe, T.L., Pres.--SPACECON, Inc., New Castle, DE; *U.S. Public*, pg. 913

Troupe, Terry L., Pres.--MBC Agency, Inc., Baltimore, MD; *U.S. Public*, pg. 1089

Trouse, Wayne, Pres.--Hermes Electronics, Inc., Dartmouth, Canada; *Int'l*, pg. 1431

Troussel, Jean-Pierre, Mng. Dir.--Swiss Life (Belgium), Brussels, Belgium; *Int'l*, pg. 1332

Trout, Bill T., V.P.--Burnham Foundry Div., Zanesville, OH; *U.S. Public*, pg. 270

Troutaud, Michel, Mng. Dir.--Allied Domecq Spirits & Wine (UK) Ltd., Horsham, United Kingdom; *Int'l*, pg. 63

Troutman, Dave, Sr. V.P.-Southwestern Ontario Div.--Bank of Montreal - Kitchener, Kitchener, Canada; *Int'l*, pg. 153

Troutt, Don, Pres. & Gen. Mgr.--KKBQ-AM-FM, Houston, TX; *U.S. Public*, pg. 335

Trovaag, Knut, Mng. Dir.--Nordic Electronic Systems A/S, Billingstad, Norway; *Int'l*, pg. 1369

Trowman, Rick, Gen. Mgr.--Felsted Division, Holmesville, OH; *U.S. Public*, pg. 689

Troy, Ron, Branch Mgr.--Union-Transport Corporation-Cleveland Office, Middleburg, OH; *U.S. Private*, pg. 1119

Troyer, Kermit, Pres. & Chief Oper. Officer--Troyer Foods, Inc., Goshen, IN; *Int'l*, pg. 619

Troyes, F.X., Gen. Rep.--Gan Incendie Accidents Guadeloupe, Pointe-a-Pitre, Guadeloupe; *Int'l*, pg. 564

Troyes, F.X., Gen. Rep.--Gan Incendie Accidents Martinique, Fort-de-France, Martinique; *Int'l*, pg. 564

Troyes, F.X., Gen. Rep.--Gan Vie Guadeloupe, Pointe-a-Pitre, Guadeloupe; *Int'l*, pg. 565

Troyes, F.X., Gen. Rep.--Gan Vie Martinique, Fort-de-France, Martinique; *Int'l*, pg. 565

Trozzo, Samuel R., Chm. Bd. & Chief Exec. Officer--Rice, Hall, James & Associates, San Diego, CA; *U.S. Public*, pg. 1674

Trubisz, Anthony, Jr., Pres.--Columbia Energy Services Corporation, Pittsburgh, PA; *U.S. Public*, pg. 402

Trudeau, Robert, V.P. & Gen. Mgr.--Uni-Line Div., Corona, CA; *Int'l*, pg. 1243

Trudel, Michel, Pres. & Chief Exec. Officer--Inglis Limited, Mississauga, Canada; *U.S. Public*, pg. 1765

Truderung, H.W., Pres.--TELUS Mobility, Calgary, Canada; *Int'l*, pg. 1374

True, Dennis L., Property Mgr.--Citizens Utilities Company, Nogales, AZ; *U.S. Public*, pg. 380

True, Thmas, V.P.--Riverton Truckers, Inc., Clarksville, IN; *U.S. Private*, pg. 459

Trufant, Ridgeley, Gen. Mgr.--Beekman 1766 Tavern, Rhinebeck, NY; *U.S. Public*, pg. 130

Truitt, Roger E., Pres.--ARCO Products Co., Los Angeles, CA; *U.S. Public*, pg. 144

Trujillo, Andres, Chief Oper. Officer--Bank Brussels Lambert Sucursal en Espana, Madrid, Spain; *Int'l*, pg. 148

Truluck, Dave, Plant Mgr.--Oil-Dri (U.K.) Ltd., Wisbech, United Kingdom; *U.S. Public*, pg. 1215

Trumbull, George R., III, Pres.--Cigna Investment Group, Inc., Bloomfield, CT; *U.S. Public*, pg. 357

Truschel, Jack, Plant Mgr.--Circon ACMI, Norwalk, OH; *U.S. Public*, pg. 373

Trusler, Colin, Mng. Dir.-United Kingdom--Shandwick United Kingdom, London, United Kingdom; *Int'l*, pg. 1226

Trusler, Colin, Mng. Dir.-United Kingdom--Shandwick International Plc, London, United Kingdom; *Int'l*, pg. 1226

Trusler, Norm, Mgr.-Transmission Support--Peace River Transmission Co., Ltd., Surrey, Canada; *Int'l*, pg. 114

Trussler, Gary J., Pres.--ACCO Europe Plc, Peterborough, United Kingdom; *U.S. Public*, pg. 674

Trust, Martin, Pres.--Mast Industries, Andover, MA; *U.S. Public*, pg. 996

Truta, Joseph M., Pres.--Adams Express Co., Baltimore, MD; *U.S. Public*, pg. 1280

Truyens, Luc, Gen. Mgr.--Kortrijk Local Head Office, Kortrijk, Belgium; *Int'l*, pg. 147

Trybus, Tom, Sr. V.P.--Central Beauty Equipment, Belvidere, IL; *U.S. Private*, pg. 1008

Trygg, Steve, Chm. Bd.--Anderson & Lembke Inc., San Francisco, CA; *U.S. Private*, pg. 72

Tryon, Michael, Pres.--Harris Waste Mgmt. Group, Inc., Peachtree City, GA; *Int'l*, pg. 473

Tsafrir, Moshe, Gen. Mgr.-U.K. Branches--Bank Hapoalim B.M., London, United Kingdom; *Int'l*, pg. 149

Tsaggaris, Lex, Pres.--DQE Energy Services, Pittsburgh, PA; *U.S. Public*, pg. 474

Tsai, Chi-Ta, Asst. V.P. & Gen. Mgr.--The International Commercial Bank of China, Manila, Philippines; *Int'l*, pg. 683

Tsai, K.Y., Dir.--Refining & Manufacturing Research Center, Chiayi, Taiwan; *Int'l*, pg. 286

Tsai, M. S., Mgr.--Eclipse Combustion Taiwan Ltd., Taipei, Taiwan; *U.S. Private*, pg. 361

Tsai, Mar-Ling, Pres.--China Hi-Ment Corp., Kao-hsiung, Taiwan; *Int'l*, pg. 285

Tsai, R., Rep.--Van Leeuwen Pipe and Tube (Far East) Pte. Ltd., Taipei, Taiwan; *Int'l*, pg. 1450

Tsai, S.L., Gen. Mgr.--Taiwan Marketing & Transportation Div., Taipei, Taiwan; *Int'l*, pg. 286

Tsang, Chung Ming, Chief Exec.--Banco Santander, Beijing, China; *Int'l*, pg. 144

Tsangarakis, Miltiadis, Chief Exec. Officer--Olympic Aviation, Athens, Greece; *Int'l*, pg. 1004

Tschanz, L., Plant Mgr.--Square D Company, Milwaukee, WI; *Int'l*, pg. 1208

Tschorn, Erhardt, Chief Oper. Officer--Perrin GmbH, Nidderau, Germany; *Int'l*, pg. 1528

Tschudin, Jean-Charles, Pres.--R.P. Scherer (Europe) AG, Zug, Switzerland; *U.S. Public*, pg. 1438

Tschuor, B., Chief Exec. Officer--Alstadt Insurances, Zurich, Switzerland; *Int'l*, pg. 1529

Tse, B.M., Mng. Dir.--Wayfoong Credit Ltd., Wan Chai, Hong Kong; *Int'l*, pg. 584

Tse, Edmund, Pres. & Chief Exec. Officer--American International Assurance Co. Ltd., Hong Kong, Hong Kong; *U.S. Public*, pg. 85

Tseng, C.S., Gen. Mgr.--Foster Electric Co. (Taiwan), Ltd., Kao-hsiung, Taiwan; *Int'l*, pg. 500

Tsikirayi, Stanley, Country Mgr.--Standard Chartered Bank Sierra Leone Ltd., Freetown, Sierra Leone; *Int'l*, pg. 1295

Tskukimura, Ray R., Pres.--Aerotest Operations, Inc., San Ramon, CA; *U.S. Public*, pg. 1207

Tso, Bob, Mng. Dir.--Oxford Products International Ltd., Kwai Chung, Hong Kong; *U.S. Public*, pg. 1239

Tsou, Patrick, Gen. Mgr.--AMP Shanghai Connector, Ltd., Shanghai, China; *U.S. Public*, pg. 9

Tsuboi, T., Pres.--Gomiya USA, Inc., Elk Grove Village, IL; *Int'l*, pg. 531

Tsuboi, Takayori, Pres.--Mitsubishi Chemical America, Inc., White Plains, NY; *Int'l*, pg. 871

Tsubokawa, Norio, Pres. & Chief Exec. Officer--YKK Corporation of America, Lyndhurst, NJ; *Int'l*, pg. 1515

Tsubota, Toshiro, Gen. Mgr.--The Hokuriku Bank, Ltd.-New York, New York, NY; *Int'l*, pg. 627

Tsuchida, Ryoko, Gen. Mgr.--Printemps Ginza S.A., Paris, France; *Int'l*, pg. 364

Tsuchida, Toru, Pres.--Nomura Asset Management Co., Ltd., Tokyo, Japan; *Int'l*, pg. 955

Tsuchimoto, Masayuki, Pres.--NABCO Ltd., Kobe, Japan; *Int'l*, pg. 740

Tsuchiya, Daijiro, Gen. Mgr.--Sakura Bank - Los Angeles Agency, Los Angeles, CA; *Int'l*, pg. 1179

Tsuchiya, Toshiaki, Pres.--Aichi Machine Industry Co., Ltd., Nagoya, Japan; *Int'l*, pg. 943

Tsuda, Akitake, Mng. Dir.--NEC Electronics (Europe) GmbH, Dusseldorf, Germany; *Int'l*, pg. 901

Tsuda, K., Chief Oper. Officer--Furukawa Sangyo Kaisha, Ltd., Tokyo, Japan; *Int'l*, pg. 530

Tsuda, Kosuke, Pres.--Sumitomo Chemical (U.K.) plc, London, United Kingdom; *Int'l*, pg. 1312

Tsuda, M., Mng. Dir.--OMRON Asiapacific Pte. Ltd., Singapore, Singapore; *Int'l*, pg. 1005

Tsuda, Masahiro, Dir. & Gen. Mgr.--Daiwa Bank-International Division, Tokyo, Japan; *Int'l*, pg. 373

Tsue, Kakuichi, Pres.--Kvaerner Pulping KK, Tokyo, Japan; *Int'l*, pg. 768

Tsue, Kakuichi, Mng. Dir.--Kamyr KK, Tokyo, Japan; *Int'l*, pg. 771

Tsuge, Hirohumi, Chief Oper. Officer--Makita Werkzeug Gesellschaft m.b.H., Vienna, Austria; *Int'l*, pg. 832

Tsuge, Norihiko, Gen. Mgr. & Dir.--The Chuo Trust & Banking Co., Ltd., New York, NY; *Int'l*, pg. 291

Tsui, John K., Chm. Bd. & Chief Exec. Officer--First Hawaiian Leasing, Inc., Honolulu, HI; *U.S. Public*, pg. 635

Tsui, John K., Pres.--American Security Properties, Inc., Honolulu, HI; *U.S. Public*, pg. 635

Tsuji, Eiji, Dir.--Takenaka (U.S.A.) Corporation, Portland Office, Portland, OR; *Int'l*, pg. 1351

Tsuji, Masato, Technical Advisor--P.T. Private Development Finance Company of Indonesia, Jakarta, Indonesia; *Int'l*, pg. 933

Tsuji, Masayuki, Chief Rep.--The Hokuriku Bank, Ltd.-Frankfurt Representative Office, Frankfurt/Main, Germany; *Int'l*, pg. 627

Tsuji, Nobuo, Pres.--Nissho Iwai France S.A., Paris, France; *Int'l*, pg. 948

Tsujimoto, Hirokazu, Chief Oper. Officer & Exec. V.P.--Kintetsu World Express (U.S.A.), Inc., Roslyn Heights, NY; *Int'l*, pg. 734

Tsujimoto, Y., Pres.--Sharp Manufacturing France S.A., Soultz, France; *Int'l*, pg. 1230

Tsujino, Yuji, Gen. Mgr.--The Sakura Bank - Guangzhou Branch, Guangzhou, China; *Int'l*, pg. 1179

Tsujita, Koji, Pres.--Honda Power Equipment Manufacturing, Inc., Swepsonville, NC; *Int'l*, pg. 635

Tsukada, E., Pres.--Nissho Iwai Apparel Co., Ltd., Osaka, Japan; *Int'l*, pg. 946

Tsukada, E., Pres.--Nissho Iwai Fiber & Yarn Ltd., Osaka, Japan; *Int'l*, pg. 946

Tsukada, Yoshihiro, Mng. Dir.--Nippon Express (H.K.) Co., Ltd., Kowloon, Hong Kong; *Int'l*, pg. 934

Tsukahara, Kazuhiro, Pres.--Kirin USA, Inc., Los Angeles, CA; *Int'l*, pg. 736

Tsukahara, Kozo, Pres.--Nifast Corporation, Glendale Heights, IL; *Int'l*, pg. 947

Tsukakoshi, Noboru, Gen. Mgr.--Bank of Boston, Tokyo, Japan; *U.S. Public*, pg. 184

Tsukamoto, Eisuke, Pres.--Haseko Community Inc., Tokyo, Japan; *Int'l*, pg. 600

Tsukiji, Yoshinori, Pres. Dir.--P.T. ORIX Indonesia Finance, Jakarta, Indonesia; *Int'l*, pg. 1009

Tsukuda, Takayuki, Dir. & Gen. Mgr.--The Sumitomo Bank, Ltd.-London Branch, London, United Kingdom; *Int'l*, pg. 1309

Tsunoda, Ichiro, Pres.--Nomura Babcock & Brown Co., Ltd., Tokyo, Japan; *Int'l*, pg. 955

Tsuru, T., Pres.--Eagle Industry, Ltd., Tokyo, Japan; *U.S. Public*, pg. 544

Tsuruma, Mr. Takeshi, Mng. Dir.--Farah Japan Limited, Tokyo, Japan; *U.S. Public*, pg. 613

Tsuruta, Tetsuya, Gen. Mgr.--Minebea Technologies Pte. Ltd., Singapore, Singapore; *Int'l*, pg. 868

Tsurutani, Masatoshi, Pres.--Kawasaki Motors Corp., U.S.A., Irvine, CA; *Int'l*, pg. 725

Tsusaka, John, Sr. Exec. V.P.--MIC-USA Inc., New York, NY; *Int'l*, pg. 867

Tsutsui, Yasuo, Pres.--Otsuka Techno Co., Ltd., Tokushima, Japan; *Int'l*, pg. 1013

Tsutsumi, Seiji, Mng. Dir.--Sakura Finance Asia Ltd., Hong Kong, Hong Kong; *Int'l*, pg. 1180

Tsutsumi, Seiji, Mng. Dir.--Sakura Bank Hong Kong Trustee Limited, Hong Kong, Hong Kong; *Int'l*, pg. 1180

Tu, Charlene Tsen, V.P. & Mgr.--The Chinese American Bank, Flushing, NY; *Int'l*, pg. 683

Tu, Paul, Grp. Pres.--Universal (Hong Kong Teakwood), Singapore, Singapore; *U.S. Private*, pg. 432

Tubbs, Jim, Div. Mgr.--Otis Engineering International, Ciudad Ojeda, Venezuela; *U.S. Public*, pg. 777

Tubbs, Richard, Branch Mgr.--National Mine Service Company, Alabama Div., Birmingham, AL; *Int'l*, pg. 281

Tuchel, Charles, Pres.--Universal Flavors-U.S.A., Indianapolis, IN; *U.S. Public*, pg. 1696

Tuck, Curtis, Gen. Mgr.--Clovis Independent, Clovis, CA; *U.S. Public*, pg. 1065

Tuck, Richard, Pres.--G&H Products Corp., Kenosha, WI; *Int'l*, pg. 1378

Tuck, Tommy, Plant Mgr.--Baldor Electric Company, Fort Smith, AR; *U.S. Public*, pg. 169

Tuck, Tommy M., Plant Mgr.--Southwestern Die Casting, Inc., Fort Smith, AR; *U.S. Public*, pg. 169

Tuck, William M., Pres.--Crouse-Hinds, Syracuse, NY; *U.S. Public*, pg. 444

Tucker, Brian, Publisher/Editorial Dir.--Crain's Cleveland Business, Cleveland, OH; *U.S. Private*, pg. 285

Tucker, F. Byron, Pres.-Lighthouse Studios--Eisner & Associates, Inc., Baltimore, MD; *U.S. Private*, pg. 366

Tucker, G.H., Mng. Dir.--Barlow Handling (Pty) Ltd., Isando, South Africa; *Int'l*, pg. 167

Tucker, Gary, Mgr.-Opers.--Titan Wheel-Peoria, East Peoria, IL; *U.S. Public*, pg. 1619

Tucker, John L., Publr.--Shawnee News-Star, Shawnee, OK; *U.S. Private*, pg. 995

Tucker, M., Mng. Dir.--Autolease Fleets Limited, Birmingham, United Kingdom; *Int'l*, pg. 216

Tucker, Mark, Chief Exec.--Prudential Asia, Central, Hong Kong; *Int'l*, pg. 1073

Tucker, Michael, Mng. Dir.--Liebert Ltd., Marlow, United Kingdom; *U.S. Public*, pg. 577

Tucker, Patrick W., Mgr.--Scotiabank Jamaica Building Society, Kingston, Jamaica; *Int'l*, pg. 156

Tucker, Rusty, Gen. Mgr.--Action Oilfield Services, Inc., La Salle, CO; *U.S. Public*, pg. 1325

Tucker, Ruxton, Gen. Mgr.--General Power Systems, Inc., Irvine, CA; *U.S. Private*, pg. 260

Tucker, Sidney, Gen. Mgr.--Wichita Citation Learning Center, Wichita, KS; *U.S. Public*, pg. 219

Tucker, Terry L., Pres.--Gulfmark Energy Inc., Houston, TX; *U.S. Public*, pg. 19

Tucker, Thomas S., Jr., Pres. & Chief Oper. Officer--Associated Mortgage, Inc., De Pere, WI; *U.S. Public*, pg. 140

Tucker, Yvonne C., Branch Mgr.--Burns & Wilcox - Columbia Office, Columbia, MD; *U.S. Private*, pg. 609

Tuckman, Mitchell, Pres.--Math Associates, Amityville, NY; *U.S. Public*, pg. 717

Tudball, Mike, Exec. Dir.--Reed Elsevier (Singapore) PTE Limited, Singapore, Singapore; *Int'l*, pg. 1095

Tudela, Mary, Pres.--SecurityLink from Ameritech, Oak Brook, IL; *U.S. Public*, pg. 98

Tuer, Robert, Mng. Dir.--Haden Schweitzer Canada Inc., Toronto, Canada; *Int'l*, pg. 586

Tuerff, James R., Pres.--American General Property Insurance Company, Nashville, TN; *U.S. Public*, pg. 76

Tuerk-Ward, Doris L., Pres.--Standard Brokerage Services, Inc., Troy, MI; *Int'l*, pg. 11

Tuley, Tom, Pres. & Editor--The Evansville Courier, Evansville, IN; *U.S. Public*, pg. 1447

Tulin, John, Pres.--Crestline Div., Norwalk, CT; *U.S. Public*, pg. 1543

Tulk, R.H., Gen. Mgr.--Statim Finance Limited, Southampton, United Kingdom; *Int'l*, pg. 591

Tullgren, Phil, Reg. Mgr.--Green Tree Acceptance, Inc., Bedford, NH; *U.S. Public*, pg. 762

Tullis, Thomas, V.P. & Gen. Mgr.--Quinn Machine & Foundry, Boone, IA; *U.S. Private*, pg. 571

Tulloch, P. P., Mng. Dir.--CIBC Asia Limited, Singapore, Singapore; *Int'l*, pg. 257

Tuner, Wesley, Pres. & Publisher--Star-Telegram Newspaper, Inc., Fort Worth, TX; *U.S. Public*, pg. 964

Tung, Stephen, Gen. Mgr.--Leo Burnett Worldwide Asia/Pacific Hdqtrs., Hong Kong, Hong Kong; *U.S. Private*, pg. 186

Tunmire, Robert, Pres.--Mr. Appliance Corp., Waco, TX; *U.S. Public*, pg. 538

Tunney, David, Mng. Dir.--S.A. Dexion Redirack, Nivelles, Belgium; *U.S. Public*, pg. 893

Tunnicliffe, Paul, V.P. & Gen. Mgr.--Redland Ohio Inc., Woodville, OH; *Int'l*, pg. 1091

Tunnicliffe, Peter, Pres.--CDM Engineers & Constructors Inc., Cambridge, MA; *U.S. Private*, pg. 204

Tunno, Robert, Pres.--Breeze Industrial, Saltsburg, PA; *U.S. Public*, pg. 1632
Tunon, Ricardo Diaz, Mng. Dir.--Rhone-Poulenc Colombia Ltda., Bogota, Colombia; *Int'l*, pg. 1112
Tuominen, Kari, Mgr.-Sls.--Tako Carton Plant Ltd., Jarvenpaa, Finland; *Int'l*, pg. 863
Tuominen, Matti, Pres.--Rammer Oy, Lahti, Finland; *Int'l*, pg. 1352
Tuomola, Seppo, Mng. Dir.--FILARC Welding Industries B.V., Utrecht, Netherlands; *Int'l*, pg. 283
Tupker, A.C., Mng. Dir.--ABN-Amro Securities (U.K.) Ltd, London, United Kingdom; *Int'l*, pg. 12
Tupper, Wallace L., Pres.--Old Kent Bank of Hillsdale, Hillsdale, MI; *U.S. Public*, pg. 1217
Turano, Joseph A., III, Pres.--Co-Counsel, Inc., Houston, TX; *U.S. Public*, pg. 1221
Turcotte, Glen W., Pres.--Glit, Wrens, GA; *U.S. Public*, pg. 944
Turcsik, Peter, Mgr.-Quality Assurance--Georgette Klinger Laboratories, South Hackensack, NJ; *U.S. Private*, pg. 626
Turgeon, Marc, Chief Oper. Officer--T-Fal Canada Inc., Scarborough, Canada; *Int'l*, pg. 568
Turgeon, Robert, Pres.--TQM Pipeline Partnership, Montreal, Canada; *Int'l*, pg. 541
Turgeon, Robert, Pres.--Trans Quebec & Maritimes Pipeline, Montreal, Canada; *Int'l*, pg. 1417
Turic, Alice, Admin.--Village Square Nursing Center, Orwell, OH; *U.S. Public*, pg. 838
Turk, Gary, Reg. Mgr.--Riedel-Smith Environmental Services, Torrance, CA; *U.S. Public*, pg. 1478
Turk, Gary, District Mgr.--Riedel-Smith Environmental Services, Alameda, CA; *U.S. Public*, pg. 1478
Turkenkopf, Robert, Gen. Mgr.--Sterling Electronics, Parsippany, NJ; *U.S. Public*, pg. 1052
Turlay, Jean Claude, Pres.--Fromagerie des Chaumes S.A., Juarancon, France; *Int'l*, pg. 201
Turley, Douglas, Mgr.--Banco Nacional de Mexico, Los Angeles, CA; *Int'l*, pg. 574
Turley, Marv, Pres.--Farnsworth Homes, Mesa, AZ; *U.S. Private*, pg. 397
Turnbull, Charles E., Pres.--Polyken Technologies, Mansfield, MA; *U.S. Public*, pg. 1647
Turnbull, John, Reg. Sls. Mgr.--Esselte Meto, Mountain View, CA; *Int'l*, pg. 460
Turnbull, Paul, Chief Oper. Officer--Frigoscandia Food Process Systems Pty Ltd, Bankstown, Australia; *U.S. Public*, pg. 607
Turner, B.C., Chief Oper. Officer--Pillar Building Products ltd., London, United Kingdom; *Int'l*, pg. 267
Turner, Bob, V.P.--DoorCraft & Challenge, Plymouth, IN; *U.S. Private*, pg. 585
Turner, C. Phillip, V.P. & Gen. Mgr.--Large Aircraft Controls, Rockford, IL; *U.S. Public*, pg. 1776
Turner, Cal, Jr., Pres.--Dolgencorp, Inc., Scottsville, KY; *U.S. Public*, pg. 515
Turner, Clay, Sr. V.P. & Creative Dir.--Ackerman McQueen, Inc., Colorado Springs, CO; *U.S. Private*, pg. 13
Turner, Clay, Branch Mgr.--Circle International, Memphis, TN; *U.S. Public*, pg. 371
Turner, Cliff, Mng. Dir.--Kontite, U.K., Ltd., Bolton, United Kingdom; *U.S. Public*, pg. 780
Turner, D.R., Pres.--Berwind Railway Service Company, Hollidaysburg, PA; *U.S. Private*, pg. 139
Turner, Danny, Plant Mgr.--Baldor Electric Company, Columbus, MS; *U.S. Public*, pg. 169
Turner, David, Mng. Dir.--Barclays Property Holdings, London, United Kingdom; *Int'l*, pg. 165
Turner, Don, Pres.--ELE International, Inc./Soiltest, Lake Bluff, IL; *Int'l*, pg. 1287
Turner, E.B., Dir.-Admin.--BTR Nylex Limited, Melbourne, Australia; *Int'l*, pg. 128
Turner, E.M., Mng. Dir.--P&O Scottish Ferries Ltd., Aberdeen, United Kingdom; *Int'l*, pg. 1034
Turner, E.M., Chief Exec.--Appletiser South Africa (Pty) Ltd., Cramerview, South Africa; *Int'l*, pg. 1286
Turner, G.N., Gen. Mgr. & Div. V.P.-Asia, Pacific--NDC Tokyo Representative Office, Tokyo, Japan; *U.S. Public*, pg. 1156
Turner, J.A., V.P. & Gen. Mgr.--Turner Construction Co., Arlington, VA; *U.S. Public*, pg. 1645
Turner, J.G., Mng. Dir.--P&O Roadways Ltd., Ipswich, United Kingdom; *Int'l*, pg. 1034
Turner, James E., Pres.--General Dynamics Electric Boat, Groton, CT; *U.S. Public*, pg. 709
Turner, Jeffery L., V.P. & Gen. Mgr.--Wichita Division, Wichita, KS; *U.S. Public*, pg. 240
Turner, Jerry, Pres.--Avia, Irvine, CA; *U.S. Private*, pg. 62
Turner, Jimmy, Warden--Metro Davidson Co. DF, Nashville, TN; *U.S. Public*, pg. 450
Turner, Jimmy, Administrator--Davidson County Juvenile Detention Center, Nashville, TN; *U.S. Public*, pg. 450
Turner, Joe Ben, Chm. Bd., Pres. & Chief Exec. Officer--Willis Corroon Corp. of Knoxville, Knoxville, TN; *Int'l*, pg. 1506
Turner, John, Pres.--Bradley Specialty Retailing, Columbus, GA; *U.S. Private*, pg. 164
Turner, John D., Pres.--Copperweld Bimetallics Products Co., Fayetteville, TN; *Int'l*, pg. 662
Turner, John D., Pres.--Copperweld Tubing, Pittsburgh, PA; *Int'l*, pg. 662
Turner, John M., Pres.--RELA, Inc., Boulder, CO; *U.S. Public*, pg. 401
Turner, Kelly, Gen. Mgr.--G & H Castings Corporation, Slaton, TX; *U.S. Public*, pg. 861
Turner, Lee, Div. Mgr.--Winnsboro Div., Winnsboro, SC; *U.S. Public*, pg. 1504
Turner, M.J., Chm. Bd.--British Aerospace Regional Aircraft Limited, Middleton, United Kingdom; *Int'l*, pg. 218
Turner, M.W., Mng. Dir.--Lombard NatWest Commercial Services Limited, Feltham, United Kingdom; *Int'l*, pg. 910
Turner, Mark, Gen. Mgr.--Hitek Product Finishing, Inc., Chino, CA; *U.S. Private*, pg. 280
Turner, Martin, Dir.-Intl. Brewing--Stag Brewery, London, United Kingdom; *U.S. Public*, pg. 115
Turner, Marvin, Gen. Mgr.--Alamo Steel Company, Waco, TX; *U.S. Public*, pg. 412
Turner, Michael R., Chief Oper. Officer--Preferred Millwork, Inc., West Chicago, IL; *U.S. Private*, pg. 706
Turner, Mike J., Chm. Bd.--British Aerospace Regional Aircraft, Avro Intl. Aerospace Div., Woodford, United Kingdom; *Int'l*, pg. 218
Turner, Nancy D., Pres.--Turner/CAS Laboratories, Inc., Tucson, AZ; *U.S. Public*, pg. 571
Turner, Patrick, Chief Oper. Officer--Trinity Transportation, Inc., Dallas, TX; *U.S. Public*, pg. 1639
Turner, Philip, Pres.--Cluett, Peabody Canada Inc., Toronto, Canada; *Int'l*, pg. 194
Turner, R. E., Pres.--Turner Music Publishing, Inc., Atlanta, GA; *U.S. Public*, pg. 1615
Turner, R.E., Chm. Bd.--Atlanta Hawks, Inc., Atlanta, GA; *U.S. Public*, pg. 1614
Turner, R.E., Pres.--RET Corp., Atlanta, GA; *U.S. Public*, pg. 1615
Turner, R.E., Chm. Bd.--Turner Home Entertainment, Atlanta, GA; *U.S. Public*, pg. 1615
Turner, R.H.C., Mng. Dir.--Town & Country Bank Ltd., Perth, Australia; *Int'l*, pg. 98
Turner, Roger G., Mng. Dir.--United Gas Co. Ltd., London, United Kingdom; *U.S. Public*, pg. 1701
Turner, Ronald L., Pres. & Chief Exec. Officer--Computing Devices International, Bloomington, MN; *U.S. Public*, pg. 331
Turner, Wanda, Admin.--Heritage Park, Plano, TX; *U.S. Public*, pg. 839
Turner, Wilhelm, Gen. Mgr.--Ernst Siegling Beteiligungs GmbH, Hannover, Germany; *Int'l*, pg. 497
Turner, William, Pres.--AJD, Richmond, VA; *U.S. Private*, pg. 510
Turner, William I.M., Chm. Bd.--Proudfoot USA Company, West Palm Beach, FL; *Int'l*, pg. 1072
Turner, William I.M., Chm. Bd.--SNC-Lavalin Inc., Montreal, Canada; *Int'l*, pg. 1162
Turner, William K., Publr.--Hillsdale Daily News, Hillsdale, MI; *U.S. Private*, pg. 995
Turney, David L., Pres. & Gen. Mgr.-Aircraft Prods.--Luminator, Plano, TX; *U.S. Public*, pg. 1045
Turney, Duane, Pres.--Scope Beauty Ent., Inc., Whittier, CA; *U.S. Public*, pg. 1444
Turnlund, Steven L., Gen. Mgr.--Willamette Sales Co., Portland, OR; *U.S. Public*, pg. 281
Turnock, Philip H., Gen. Mgr.--AlliedSignal Fluid Systems, San Diego, CA; *U.S. Public*, pg. 51
Turpin, Ron, Gen. Mgr.--Barton's of West Memphis, West Memphis, AR; *U.S. Private*, pg. 119
Turra, Antonio, Chief Oper. Officer--Paper-Fin S.p.A., Schio, Italy; *Int'l*, pg. 35
Turrentine, Drake, Pres.--Saab Systems, Inc., Rochelle Park, NJ; *Int'l*, pg. 687
Turri, William, Pres.--The Case-Hoyt Corporation, Rochester, NY; *U.S. Private*, pg. 101
Turri, William, Pres.--Monroe Litho Inc., Rochester, NY; *U.S. Public*, pg. 1736
Turton, Tom, Mgr.-Office--Woodward-Clyde, Tampa, FL; *U.S. Public*, pg. 1657
Turturro, August B., Pres. & Chief Exec. Officer--Natkin Group, Inc., Englewood, CO; *U.S. Public*, pg. 84
Turvoll, Odd Rune, Gen. Mgr.--Kvaerner Hetland a.s, Bryne, Norway; *Int'l*, pg. 769
Tusinac, Edda, Mng. Dir.--Caere GmbH, Munich, Germany; *U.S. Public*, pg. 291
Tuthill, John B., Jr., Pres.--Merrill Corporation, Atlanta, GA; *U.S. Public*, pg. 1097
Tuthill, John B., Jr., Pres.--Merrill/Denver, Denver, CO; *U.S. Public*, pg. 1097
Tutt, Chris, Mgr.--EG & G GmbH Instruments Division, Munich, Germany; *U.S. Public*, pg. 544
Tuttle, Daniel J., Pres.--Keck Instruments, Inc., Williamston, MI; *U.S. Public*, pg. 367
Tuttle, John R., Chm. Bd., Pres. & Treas.--Micron Communications, Inc., Boise, ID; *U.S. Public*, pg. 1105
Tuxbury, William, Pres.--Fermont Div., Bridgeport, CT; *U.S. Public*, pg. 286
Tveit, Inge, Chief Oper. Officer--Esmi A/S, Skare, Norway; *Int'l*, pg. 33
Twa, C.O., Pres. & Chief Oper. Officer--Canadian Utilities Limited, Calgary, Canada; *Int'l*, pg. 95
Twa, Warren L., Pres.--Loffland Brothers de Venezuela, C.A., Caracas, Venezuela; *U.S. Public*, pg. 1149
Twedell, Steve, Gen. Mgr.--Brooks County Sausage, Quitman, GA; *U.S. Public*, pg. 1479
Twedell, Wayne C., Pres.--The JCM Group, Los Angeles, CA; *U.S. Private*, pg. 846
Tweedle, Michael, Dr., Pres.--Bracco Research, Inc., Princeton, NJ; *Int'l*, pg. 210
Twer, David, Pres. & Chief Exec. Officer--PanCanadian Petroleum Limited, Calgary, Canada; *Int'l*, pg. 259
Twigg, T. J., Chief Fin. Officer--Rolls-Royce Industrial & Marine Gas Turbines Ltd., Coventry, United Kingdom; *Int'l*, pg. 1127
Twinn, Doug C., Mgr.--Grays Terminal, Grays, United Kingdom; *U.S. Public*, pg. 693
Twyble, William J., Chm. Bd. & Chief Exec. Officer--The Lincoln Electric Co. Australia Pty. Ltd., Padstow, Australia; *U.S. Public*, pg. 996
Twyford, Walt, Director--Tridon Inc., Lawrenceburg, TN; *U.S. Public*, pg. 11
Tychsen, Ulf, Mng. Dir.--The West Company Holding, G.m.b.H, Eschweiler, Germany; *U.S. Public*, pg. 1756
Tychsen, Ulf C., Pres. & Chief Fin. Officer--The West Company Deutschland, Eschweiler, Germany; *U.S. Public*, pg. 1756
Tydd, C.B., Chief Oper. Officer--Fluidised Combustion Contractors Ltd., London, United Kingdom; *Int'l*, pg. 472
Tydemo, Bengt, Chief Oper. Officer--DAB Dental AB, Malmo, Sweden; *Int'l*, pg. 711
Tyksinski, Tom, Gen. Mgr.--Turner Construction Company, Denver, CO; *U.S. Public*, pg. 1645
Tyler, B., Esq., Mng. Dir.--Able Translations Limited, Baldock, United Kingdom; *U.S. Public*, pg. 221
Tyler, H.H., Pres. & Chief Exec. Officer--The Northern Trust Company, Lake Forest, IL; *U.S. Public*, pg. 1197
Tyler, H.H., Pres. & Chief Exec. Officer--The Northern Trust Company, Lake Bluff, IL; *U.S. Public*, pg. 1197
Tyler, Hugh D., V.P. & Gen. Mgr.--Virco-Conway Div., Conway, AR; *U.S. Public*, pg. 1721
Tyler, James, Pres.--El Dorado Tire Co., Troy, MI; *Int'l*, pg. 1312
Tyler, Tim, Gen. Mgr.--Marcam Asia-Pacific Pte., Ltd, Singapore, Singapore; *U.S. Public*, pg. 1043
Tyler, Warren, Pres.--COMBI Block, Inc., Columbus, OH; *Int'l*, pg. 1020
Tymn, Greg, Gen. Mgr.--Printer Operations-Storage Tek, Palm Bay, FL; *U.S. Public*, pg. 1523
Tynan, David, V.P. & Gen. Mgr.--KHTV-TV, Houston, TX; *U.S. Public*, pg. 1636
Tynell, Markku, Mng. Dir.--Amerpap Oy, Helsinki, Finland; *Int'l*, pg. 863
Tyree, Tom, Div. Mgr.--Champion Home Builders Co., York, NE; *U.S. Public*, pg. 332
Tyrell, Edwin, Dir.-Sales & Mktg.--IMI Cornelius Canada, Brampton, Canada; *Int'l*, pg. 646
Tyron, R.M., Dir.--SBC Warburg Futures & Options Ltd., London, United Kingdom; *Int'l*, pg. 1331
Tyrone, J.C., Pres.--Fine Paper Div., Chillicothe, OH; *U.S. Public*, pg. 1074
Tyska, Tom, Plant Mgr.--Electronic Products Division, Somerville, NJ; *Int'l*, pg. 626
Tysklind, P.O., Chief Oper. Officer--AxTrade LIC Medica S.A., Madrid, Spain; *Int'l*, pg. 710
Tyson, Ted, Pres.--Commercial Products, Inc., Monroe, NC; *U.S. Private*, pg. 331
Tyson, Ted, Pres.--Dickerson, Inc., Monroe, NC; *U.S. Private*, pg. 331
Tyson, Ted, Pres.--Dickerson Realty Corp., Monroe, NC; *U.S. Private*, pg. 331
Tyson, Ted, Pres. & Chief Oper. Officer--Dickerson Carolina, Inc., Monroe, NC; *U.S. Private*, pg. 331
Tyson, Timothy, V.P. & Gen. Mgr.--Glaxo Dermatology, Research Triangle Park, NC; *Int'l*, pg. 553
Tze, Ker Sin, Dr., Chm. Bd.--Superior Metal Printing Limited, Singapore, Singapore; *Int'l*, pg. 1322
Uber, R. Barry, Pres.--Production Equipment Group, Woodcliff Lake, NJ; *U.S. Public*, pg. 877
Ubieda, Julio, Gen. Mgr.--Stanhome Panamericana, C.A., Caracas, Venezuela; *U.S. Public*, pg. 1508
Ubilla, Hernan, Mng. Dir.--Skega Chilena S.A., Vina del Mar, Chile; *Int'l*, pg. 1323
Uby, Bjorn, Mng. Dir.--SKF Intertrade S.A., Brussels, Belgium; *Int'l*, pg. 1158
Uchida, E., V.P. & Gen. Mgr.--Nichimen America, Inc., Houston Branch, Houston, TX; *Int'l*, pg. 928
Uchida, Kosuke, Branch Mgr.--Noritake Co., Inc.-Table Top Div., Los Angeles, Compton, CA; *Int'l*, pg. 959
Uchida, Minoru, Pres.--Calsonic Mfg. Corp., Shelbyville, TN; *Int'l*, pg. 944
Uchida, Osamu, Chief Rep.--The Japan Development Bank-London Representative Office, London, United Kingdom; *Int'l*, pg. 702
Uchida, Shun, Chm. Bd.--Tuta Laboratories (Australia) Pty., Ltd., Lane Cove, Australia; *Int'l*, pg. 1014
Uchida, Shun, Chm. Bd.--Otsuka Pharmaceutical Australia Pty. Ltd., Pymble, Australia; *Int'l*, pg. 1014
Uchida, Soichiro, Mgr.--NOK EG & G Optoelectronics Corporation, Kanagawa, Japan; *U.S. Public*, pg. 544
Uchida, Y., Pres.--Sharp Precision Manufacturing (U.K.) Ltd., Wrexham, United Kingdom; *Int'l*, pg. 1230
Uchigasaki, Morikuni, Pres.--Sumitomo Bank (Schweiz) AG, Zurich, Switzerland; *Int'l*, pg. 1310
Uchino, Yoshio, Pres.--P.T. Bank Sakura Swadharma, Jakarta, Indonesia; *Int'l*, pg. 1180
Uchiyama, Etsuji, Chief Oper. Officer--Nittsu Kiko Unyu Co., Ltd., Sapporo, Japan; *Int'l*, pg. 934
Uchtenhagen, Lilian, Dr., Chm.--Coop Zurich, Zurich, Switzerland; *Int'l*, pg. 329
Ucros, Mario, V.P.--Bankers Trust New York Corporation, Bogota, Colombia; *U.S. Public*, pg. 186
Udden, Per, Mng. Dir.--Ericsson India Ltd., New Delhi, India; *Int'l*, pg. 1367
Udelhofen, Mark, V.P. & Gen. Mgr.--ITW Nexus, Wood Dale, IL; *U.S. Public*, pg. 866
Udell, Richard, Pres.--Harcourt Brace & Company Real Properties Corporation, Orlando, FL; *U.S. Public*, pg. 783
Uding, George E., Chm. Bd.--Cement Transit Co., Cleveland, OH; *U.S. Public*, pg. 1084
Uding, George E., V.P.--James H. Drew Corp., Indianapolis, IN; *U.S. Public*, pg. 1084
Uding, George E., Chm. Bd.--Canadian Cement Ltd., Owen Sound, Canada; *U.S. Public*, pg. 1084
Udvar-Hazy, Steven F., Pres. & Chief Exec. Officer--International Lease Finance Corporation, Los Angeles, CA; *U.S. Public*, pg. 85
Udvar-Hazy, Steven F., Pres.--Interlease Trading Corp., Beverly Hills, CA; *U.S. Public*, pg. 85
Uebelmesser, Robert, Mgr.--Cray Research GmbH, Munich, Germany; *U.S. Public*, pg. 1474
Ueberecken, N., Pres.--TradeARBED S.A., Luxembourg, Luxembourg; *Int'l*, pg. 79
Ueberecken, Nicolas, Chm.--AIT - Arbed International Trading S.A., Luxembourg, Luxembourg; *Int'l*, pg. 79
Ueda, Hiroyuki, Chief Representative--The Sumitomo Bank, Ltd.-Seattle Representative Office, Seattle, WA; *Int'l*, pg. 1309
Ueda, Masahiro, Mng. Dir.--Showa Denko Oita Works, Oita, Japan; *Int'l*, pg. 1236
Ueda, Masato, Gen. Mgr.--The Sumitomo Bank, Ltd.-Paris Branch, Paris, France; *Int'l*, pg. 1309
Ueda, N., Office Chief--Man Nen Sha, Inc., Fukuoka, Japan; *Int'l*, pg. 834

Ueda, Nobuo, Chief Rep.--The Meiji Life Insurance Company Seoul Office, Seoul, Korea; *Int'l*, pg. 854
Ueda, T., Pres.--Nippla Kasei Co., Ltd., Tokyo, Japan; *Int'l*, pg. 946
Ueda, Tatsuo, Gen. Mgr.--The Sumitomo Bank, Ltd.-Los Angeles Branch, Los Angeles, CA; *Int'l*, pg. 1308
Ueda, Yoshinori, Pres. Dir.--P.T. Sanwa-BRI Finance, Jakarta, Indonesia; *Int'l*, pg. 1190
Uehara, Mamoru, Gen. Mgr.--Dai-Ichi Kangyo Bank (Schweiz) AG, Zurich, Switzerland; *Int'l*, pg. 362
Uehara, N., Chief Oper. Officer--The Kyoei Life Insurance Co., Ltd.-London Office, London, United Kingdom; *Int'l*, pg. 777
Uehara, T., Chief Oper. Officer--P.T. Iron Wire Works Indonesia, Tangerang, Indonesia; *Int'l*, pg. 948
Uehara, Yoshihiro, Exec. Dir.--Daihatsu Malaysia Sdn. Bnd., Shah Alam, Malaysia; *Int'l*, pg. 365
Uehara, Yujio, Chief Rep.--Asahi Bank Fuzhou Representative Office, Fujian, China; *Int'l*, pg. 83
Ueki, Fumio, Chief Rep.--Ho Chi Minh City Representative Office, Ho Chi Minh City, Vietnam; *Int'l*, pg. 83
Uekita, Paulo, Dir.--Bradesco Leasing S.A. Arrendamento Mercantil, Sao Paulo, Brazil; *Int'l*, pg. 1009
Uelen, Robert, V.P. & Group Gen. Mgr.--Unisys Nederland N.V., Amsterdam, Netherlands; *U.S. Public*, pg. 1671
Uemura, Satoshi, Pres.--Nissan Shatai Co., Ltd., Hiratsuka, Japan; *Int'l*, pg. 944
Uemura, Yuji, Pres.--Subaru Research & Design, Inc., Garden Grove, CA; *Int'l*, pg. 523
Ueno, Akire, Gen. Mgr.--Juki Union Special, Inc.-California Office, Santa Fe Springs, CA; *Int'l*, pg. 716
Ueno, Hiroshi, Dir. & Gen. Mgr.--Mitsui Trust & Banking Company, Limited, New York, NY; *Int'l*, pg. 883
Ueno, Hiroshi, Gen. Mgr.--The Mitsui Trust and Banking Company - Cayman, Grand Cayman, Cayman Islands; *Int'l*, pg. 883
Ueno, Katsuji, Dir.--Showa Plastics (Jinan) Co. Ltd., Jinan, China; *Int'l*, pg. 1237
Ueno, Makoto, Pres.--Katsushiro Rome Corporation, Rome, GA; *Int'l*, pg. 744
Ueno, Mary, Mgr.-Sls.--Kintetsu Intermodal Inc., Carson, CA; *Int'l*, pg. 735
Ueno, Masahiro, Mgr.-Terminal--Kawasaki Terminal, Kawasaki, Japan; *U.S. Public*, pg. 693
Ueno, Shinzo, Pres. & Chief Exec. Officer--Dentsu, Sudler & Hennessey Inc., Tokyo, Japan; *U.S. Private*, pg. 325
Ueno, Takashi, Pres. & Chief Exec. Officer--Sakura Global Capital, Inc., New York, NY; *Int'l*, pg. 1179
Uesato, S., Gen. Mgr.--Marubeni America Corporation, Detroit Branch, Southfield, MI; *Int'l*, pg. 844
Ugglas, Erik af, Chief Oper. Officer--Euroclean AB, Atvidaberg, Sweden; *Int'l*, pg. 439
Ugolyn, Victor, Pres. & Chief Exec. Officer--The Enterprise Group, Atlanta, GA; *U.S. Private*, pg. 769
Uhlarik, Ken, Plant Mgr.--E.J. Brach, Inc., Sullivan, IL; *U.S. Private*, pg. 163
Uhley, David W., Chief Oper. Officer--FBC Finance Co., Torrance, CA; *U.S. Public*, pg. 613
Uhlig, Richard, V.P. & Gen. Mgr.--Acorn Custom Molding/ Cal Tube, Chino, CA; *U.S. Private*, pg. 14
Uhlir, Elizabeth, Terminal Mgr.--Kintetsu World Express Inc., San Diego, CA; *Int'l*, pg. 735
Uhrig, J.A., Chm. Bd.--CRA Limited, Melbourne, Australia; *Int'l*, pg. 1119
Uiari, Kipling, Gen. Mgr.--Port Moresby BHP Papua New Guinea, Port Moresby, Papua New Guinea; *Int'l*, pg. 228
Uihlein, Walter R., Pres. & Chief Exec. Officer--Acushnet Company, Fairhaven, MA; *U.S. Public*, pg. 675
Uihlein, Walter R., Pres.--Acushnet International Inc., Fairhaven, MA; *U.S. Public*, pg. 675
Uijterlinden, Jan, Country Mgr.--Skandia Insurance Company Ltd., Rotterdam, Netherlands; *Int'l*, pg. 1258
Ujikawa, Norikazu, Chief Rep.--Daiwa Bank-Kuala Lumpur, Kuala Lumpur, Malaysia; *Int'l*, pg. 373
Ukai, Yuhei, Dir. Gen.--NEC de Mexico, S.A. de C.V., Mexico, Mexico; *Int'l*, pg. 901
Ukegawa, Miromi, Exec. V.P.--Nikko Securities Co., Chicago, Chicago, IL; *Int'l*, pg. 930
Ula, Tanju, Gen. Mgr.--Dusa Endustriyel Iplik Sanayi Ve Ticaret A.S., Istanbul, Turkey; *U.S. Public*, pg. 533
Ula, Tanju, Gen. Mgr.--Dusa Endustriyel Iplik Sanayi Ve Ticaret A.S., Istanbul, Turkey; *Int'l*, pg. 1167
Ulasewicz, Eugenia, Sr. V.P. & Dir.-Stores, Midwest Region--Saks Fifth Avenue, New York, NY; *U.S. Public*, pg. 1429
Ulbrich, Fredrick C., Jr., Chm. Bd. & Chief Exec. Officer--Ulbrich Wire, Inc., North Haven, CT; *U.S. Private*, pg. 1115
Ulbrich, Jeffrey, Chief of Bureau--The Associated Press, Ltd., Toronto, Canada; *U.S. Private*, pg. 92
Ulch, Larry, Gen. Mgr.--The HON Co., Sulphur Springs Plant, Sulphur Springs, TX; *U.S. Public*, pg. 772
Ulewicz, William, Pres.--Casablanca Fan Company, Pomona, CA; *U.S. Private*, pg. 549
Ulin, Ulf, Mng. Dir.--AB S.A. des Roulements a Billes Suedois SKF, Tehran, Iran; *Int'l*, pg. 1158
Ullal, Shashi, Mng. Dir.--Modi Olivetti Ltd., New Delhi, India; *Int'l*, pg. 1003
Ullebo, Egil M., Managing Dir.--Borregaard Industries Limited, Sarpsborg, Norway; *Int'l*, pg. 1011
Ullmer, Marco L., Mgr.-Terminal--Portland Terminal, Portland, OR; *U.S. Public*, pg. 692
Ullrich, Gunter, Dr., Chm. Bd.-Mngmt.--Deutsche Versicherungs-AG, Berlin, Germany; *Int'l*, pg. 58
Ulmanen, Tomi, Pres.--Valmet Korea Inc., Seoul, Korea; *Int'l*, pg. 1448
Ulmen, James C., Mgr.--Piper Jaffray Inc., Pierre, SD; *U.S. Public*, pg. 1302
Ulmer, Mike, V.P. & Gen. Mgr.--Colorado Belle, Laughlin, NV; *U.S. Public*, pg. 375
Ulmer, William, Gen. Mgr.--Nestle Dairy Systems, Licensing Division, Columbus, OH; *Int'l*, pg. 918
Ulrich, Jake, Mng. Dir.--Accord Energy Ltd., Slough, United Kingdom; *Int'l*, pg. 279
Ulrich, Jerry, Pres.--Netwave Technologies, Inc., Pleasanton, CA; *U.S. Public*, pg. 1564
Ulrich, Marli, Mgr.--Blumenau Branch, Blumenau, Brazil; *Int'l*, pg. 139
Ulrich, Scott, Admin.--Parkway Pavilion Healthcare, Enfield, CT; *U.S. Public*, pg. 1714
Ulsh, Gordon, Pres.--Champion Ignition Products, Chesterfield, MO; *U.S. Public*, pg. 442
Um, Jusoo, Mgr.-Area Sls.--Hanguke Gensym, Seoul, Korea; *U.S. Public*, pg. 731
Umbach, William, Chief Oper. Officer--Strober New Jersey Building Supply Centers, Inc., Edison, NJ; *U.S. Private*, pg. 403
Umemoto, Kaoru, Mng. Dir.--Central Japan Railway Company-Tokyo Head Office, Tokyo, Japan; *Int'l*, pg. 279
Umemoto, Seiichi, Dir.--Shanghai Showa Plastics Co. Ltd., Shanghai, China; *Int'l*, pg. 1237
Umemura, Toshihide, Gen. Mgr.--The Hokkaido Takushoku Bank, Ltd., New York Branch, New York, NY; *Int'l*, pg. 626
Umer, S.M., Chief Oper. Officer--Blackwood Hodge (Pakistan) Ltd., Karachi, Pakistan; *Int'l*, pg. 231
Umino, Takao, Gen. Mgr.--The Sakura Bank - Hong Kong Branch, Central, Hong Kong; *Int'l*, pg. 1179
Umland, Klaus, Co-Chief Oper. Officer--IKB Leasing Berlin GmbH, Berlin, Germany; *Int'l*, pg. 645
Umland, Klaus, Co-Chief Oper. Officer--IKB Leasing GmbH, Hamburg, Germany; *Int'l*, pg. 645
Umphrey, Kirk A., Pres.--Quaker State Q-Lube, Inc., Salt Lake City, UT; *U.S. Public*, pg. 1348
Unander-Scharin, Bengt, Div. Mgr.--Aspa Bruk, Aspabruk, Sweden; *Int'l*, pg. 1423
Underdahl, Jerry, Reg. Mgr.--Green Tree Acceptance, Inc., Saint Paul, MN; *U.S. Public*, pg. 762
Underdahl, Jerry, Reg. Mgr.--Green Tree Acceptance, Inc., Appleton, WI; *U.S. Public*, pg. 762
Underhill, David, Gen. Mgr.--Tribune Regional Programming Inc., Oak Brook, IL; *U.S. Public*, pg. 1636
Underhill, Maurice, Dir.--Clydesdale Walton Co., Wolverhampton, United Kingdom; *Int'l*, pg. 265
Underwood, David, Controller--Teleflex Automotive, Hillsdale, MI; *U.S. Public*, pg. 1569
Underwood, Elaine, Mng. Dir.--J.A. Sharwood & Company Limited, Egham, United Kingdom; *Int'l*, pg. 1396
Underwood, Elaine, Mng. Dir.--RHM Grocery Ltd., Egham, United Kingdom; *Int'l*, pg. 1396
Underwood, Judy, Editor--Morgan County News, Wartburg, TN; *U.S. Private*, pg. 648
Underwood, Michael, Gen. Mgr.--ITW Engineered Polymers, Whetstone, United Kingdom; *U.S. Public*, pg. 868
Underwood, Randy, Mgr.--Cable & Wireless Communications Inc.-Texas, Dallas, TX; *Int'l*, pg. 247
Underwood, William S., Gen. Mgr.--Elkem Ltd. - Materials, High Wycombe, United Kingdom; *Int'l*, pg. 447
Unfried, Charles, Pres.--Mercantile Credit Corp., Baton Rouge, LA; *U.S. Public*, pg. 1090
Ungar, Manny, Gen. Mgr.--Queens Group North Carolina, Inc., Stanley, NC; *U.S. Private*, pg. 900
Unger, Edward, Div. Mgr.--Cape May Div., Cape May Court House, NJ; *U.S. Public*, pg. 1488
Unger, James J., Vice Chm.--ACF Industries, Inc., Saint Charles, MO; *U.S. Private*, pg. 556
Unger, Michael, Pres.--CAM Manufacturing, Inc., Cokato, MN; *U.S. Private*, pg. 293
Unger, Robert F., Pres.--Raytheon Marine, Manchester, NH; *U.S. Public*, pg. 1366
Ungerer, S.B., Pres.--Atlantic Southern Properties, Inc., Pleasantville, NJ; *U.S. Public*, pg. 430
Ungerer, S.B., Chief Exec. Officer--Atlantic Generation, Inc., Pleasantville, NJ; *U.S. Public*, pg. 430
Unickel, Jeffrey, Pres.--Sierra Craft, Inc., City of Industry, CA; *Int'l*, pg. 1512
Unneberg, Arild, Dir.-Production--Saga Petroleum ASA, Forus, Norway; *Int'l*, pg. 1169
Unno, Masayasu, Chief Exec.--Nippon Homes Co., Ltd., Tokyo, Japan; *Int'l*, pg. 1351
Uno, Sadao, Pres.--Rohm Mechatech Co., Ltd., Kyoto, Japan; *Int'l*, pg. 1125
Unoki, Hajime, Pres.--Aiwa Co., Ltd., Tokyo, Japan; *Int'l*, pg. 1280
Unroe, Brad, V.P. & Gen. Mgr.--Abelson-Taylor, Inc., Indianapolis, IN; *U.S. Private*, pg. 10
Unruh, Tim, Gen. Mgr.--Canfor U.S.A., Bellingham Division, Bellingham, WA; *Int'l*, pg. 260
Unto, Roine, Chief Oper. Officer--Ekotech, Paris, France; *Int'l*, pg. 1360
Unu, Takeo, Pres.--The Bank of Tokyo-Mitsubishi (Canada), Toronto, Canada; *Int'l*, pg. 158
Unum, Arnfinn, Gen. Mgr.--Kvaerner Process Systems A/S, Billingstad, Norway; *Int'l*, pg. 766
Unum, Arnfinn, Pres.--Kvaerner Process Systems a.s, Billingstad, Norway; *Int'l*, pg. 769
Upchurch, M., Pres.--Burns, Philp Inc., San Francisco, CA; *Int'l*, pg. 236
Upfill-Brown, S., Gen. Mgr.--International Paint Powder Coatings Div., Houston, TX; *Int'l*, pg. 339
Upfill-Brown, S., Pres.--Haltermann Ltd., Houston, TX; *Int'l*, pg. 590
Upland, Ted, Pres. & Chief Exec. Officer--CPI Prints Plus, Inc., Concord, CA; *U.S. Public*, pg. 283
Ura, Shinichi, Chief Rep.--Seoul Representative Office, Seoul, Korea; *Int'l*, pg. 1485
Uraisami, Kazuya, V.P.--Union Bank of Switzerland (Trust and Banking) Limited, Tokyo, Japan; *Int'l*, pg. 1441
Urakami, Akio, Dr., Chm. Bd. & Pres.--Ryobi Motor Products, Anderson, SC; *Int'l*, pg. 1151
Uranga Fernandez, Enrique, Gen. Dir.--Quimica S.A. de C.V., Mexico, Mexico; *Int'l*, pg. 614
Urbaetis, Frank, Gen. Mgr.--Universal Studios Mfg., Gloversville, NY; *Int'l*, pg. 1216
Urban, Michael, Pres.--Urban & Schwarzenberg GmbH, Munich, Germany; *U.S. Public*, pg. 1748
Urban, S.D., Pres.--Amoco Netherlands Petroleum Co., Hague, Netherlands; *U.S. Public*, pg. 102
Urban, Ulrich, Dir.--Babcock-Omnical-Industriekessel GmbH, Oberhausen, Germany; *Int'l*, pg. 398
Urbanavicius, Paulo, Exec. Dir.--Industria Aeronautica Neiva S.A., Botucatu, Brazil; *Int'l*, pg. 452
Urbanek, Michal, Chief Oper. Officer--Ferrosan International A/S, Prague, Czech Republic; *Int'l*, pg. 989
Urbanek, Ted, Pres.--National Crane, Waverly, NE; *Int'l*, pg. 593
Urbani, E., Gen. Mgr.--ABN Finanziaria S.p.A., Milan, Italy; *Int'l*, pg. 11
Urbanski, K., Mgr.--Business Management & Finance International Ltd., Katowice, Poland; *Int'l*, pg. 1332
Urbin, Dominique, Chief Oper. Officer--COBE S.A., Rungis, France; *Int'l*, pg. 667
Urch, James, Mgr.-Adv.--Telegraphics Printing, Granville, NY; *U.S. Private*, pg. 1074
Urdahl, Susan, Sr. Mgr.-Opers.--21st Vision, Taylor, MI; *U.S. Private*, pg. 539
Urdal, Alfredo Martinez, Chief Exec. Officer--Coca-Cola FEMSA, S.A. de CV, Mexico, Mexico; *Int'l*, pg. 496
Urdaneta, Luis, Pres.--Interven, S.A., Caracas, Venezuela; *Int'l*, pg. 1045
Uren, Jim, Gen. Mgr.--BancTec Service Corp., Dallas, TX; *U.S. Public*, pg. 177
Uriarte, Enrique, Mgr.--Eclipse Combustion S.A., Barcelona, Spain; *U.S. Private*, pg. 361
Uriarte, Jose R. Ubarrechena, Mgr.-Mill--Prat de Allo Mill, Allo, Spain; *U.S. Public*, pg. 673
Uribarri, Lawrence, Admin.--Ojai Manor, Ojai, CA; *U.S. Public*, pg. 1714
Uribe, Jaime, V.P. & Fin. Dir.--Leo Burnett Columbiana, S.A., Bogota, Colombia; *U.S. Private*, pg. 185
Urip, Sri, Pres.--Unilever Financierings Maatschappij B.V., Rotterdam, Netherlands; *Int'l*, pg. 1439
Urland, Robert S., Pres. & Chief Exec. Officer--Griffin Technology Incorporated, Farmington, NY; *U.S. Public*, pg. 506
Urquhart, Margaret, Pres.--Lowe's Food Stores, Inc., Winston Salem, NC; *U.S. Private*, pg. 657
Urquidi, J.C., Mng. Dir.--Laboratorios Wyeth-Whitehall Ltd., Sao Paulo, Brazil; *U.S. Public*, pg. 81
Urquiza, Fernando Correa, Pres.--The Boston Investment Group S.A., Buenos Aires, Argentina; *U.S. Public*, pg. 185
Urquiza, Fernando Correa, Pres.--Berkley International, S.A., Buenos Aires, Argentina; *U.S. Public*, pg. 216
Urrutia, Larry J., Plant Mgr.--Longview Fibre Co. Western Container Div., Twin Falls, ID; *U.S. Public*, pg. 1014
Ursin-Smith, Kjell, Mng. Dir.--Kvaerner a.s London Office, London, United Kingdom; *Int'l*, pg. 771
Urso, R., Chief Oper. Officer--Budd Plastics Design Center, Troy, MI; *Int'l*, pg. 1388
Urso, Richard J., Pres.--Plastic Products Div., Madison Heights, MI; *Int'l*, pg. 1388
Urso, Ross, Gen. Mgr.--GATX Logistics, Inc.-Florida (Honda), Jacksonville, FL; *U.S. Public*, pg. 691
Urtso, Leonard R., Pres.--A.L. Lee Corp., Lester, WV; *U.S. Private*, pg. 961
Urushisako, T., Chm. & Pres.--Sharp Electronics Corporation, Mahwah, NJ; *Int'l*, pg. 1228
Urwin, T., Mng. Dir.--GEC Plessey Semiconductors, Swindon, United Kingdom; *Int'l*, pg. 544
Urwin, Tom, V.P.-European Opers.--Analog Devices Marketing Ltd., Newbury, United Kingdom; *U.S. Public*, pg. 108
Ury, Claude, Pres.--Orlane Institut de Beaute, Paris, France; *Int'l*, pg. 1011
Usami, Moriaki, Pres.--BlueWave Inn Corporation, Tokyo, Japan; *Int'l*, pg. 1008
Usami, Tatsuo, Chief Rep.--The Sakura Bank - Sao Paulo Representative Office, Sao Paulo, Brazil; *Int'l*, pg. 1180
Usami, Toru, Pres.--Okayama Taiho Pharmaceutical Co., Ltd., Okayama, Japan; *Int'l*, pg. 1013
Uselton, J.C., Chm. Bd. & Pres.--Sverdrup Investments, Inc., Maryland Heights, MO; *U.S. Private*, pg. 1057
Usher, George, Chief Exec. Officer--Dextran Products Limited, Scarborough, Canada; *Int'l*, pg. 1063
Usher, Rodney L., Pres.--Pulsafeeder Inc., Rochester, NY; *U.S. Public*, pg. 862
Ushio, Eiji, Pres.--Kintetsu World Express (Deutschland) GmbH, Ratingen, Germany; *Int'l*, pg. 735
Usinger, Emil, Chief Oper. Officer--BluePoints Co., Inc., West Sayville, NY; *U.S. Public*, pg. 637
Usry, Ira P., Jr., Reg. Mgr.--Green Tree Acceptance, Inc., Columbia, SC; *U.S. Public*, pg. 762
Ussery, Dave, Pres. & Representative Dir.--Amway Korea, Ltd., Seoul, Korea; *U.S. Private*, pg. 70
Ussery, David, Gen. Mgr.--Amway Philippines, Makati, Philippines; *U.S. Private*, pg. 70
Ussery, Richard W., Chm. & Chief Exec. Officer--Total System Services, Inc., Columbus, GA; *U.S. Public*, pg. 1550
Ussher, Alberto H., Pres.--Camea S.A., Buenos Aires, Argentina; *Int'l*, pg. 51
Usui, Takashi, V.P. & Branch Mgr.--Dai-Ichi Kangyo Bank of California-Torrance, Torrance, CA; *Int'l*, pg. 360
Usui, Yutaro, Pres.--Usui Bundy Tubing Co. Ltd., Shizuoka, Japan; *Int'l*, pg. 1341
Utano, Toshihiro, Gen. Mgr.--The Daishi Bank, Ltd.-Tokyo, Tokyo, Japan; *Int'l*, pg. 372
Utaski, James R., Pres.--Johnson & Johnson Development Corporation, New Brunswick, NJ; *U.S. Public*, pg. 928
Utray, Jorge Fabra, Pres.--Red Electrica de Espana, S.A., Madrid, Spain; *Int'l*, pg. 1224
Utrialnen,, Juha, Mrg.--Gas Systems, Finland Oy, Helsinki, Finland; *U.S. Private*, pg. 361
Utset, George, V.P.--Latin American Representative Comdisco, Inc., Miami, FL; *U.S. Public*, pg. 408
Utter, Harry W., Gen. Mgr.--Logicon Geodynamics Services Corporation, Englewood, CO; *U.S. Public*, pg. 1199
Utton, Kurt, Mgr.--Northern Petroleum, Saint Johnsbury, VT; *U.S. Private*, pg. 164

Utz, C.K., Gen. Mgr.--Detrex Automation Div., Southfield, MI; *U.S. Public*, pg. 501
Utz, Gary W., Gen. Mgr.--Greenville Div., Greenville, NC; *U.S. Public*, pg. 575
Uurala-Corbion, Leena, Mng. Dir.--Norvista, Paris, France; *Int'l*, pg. 486
Uusimae, Pekka, Mng. Dir.--Nokia (Malaysia) Sdn. Bhd., Kuala Lumpur, Malaysia; *Int'l*, pg. 953
Uusitale, Tuure, Pres.--Finbow Oy, Nokia, Finland; *Int'l*, pg. 1449
Uvarova, Natalija V., Dir.--Berlitz Sovincenter, Moscow, Russia; *U.S. Public*, pg. 222
Uwatoko, Uzuhiko, Pres.--Toyo Engineering Corp., Tokyo, Japan; *Int'l*, pg. 878
Uyeda, Allen B., Pres. & Chief Exec. Officer--First Insurance Co. of Hawaii, Ltd., Honolulu, HI; *U.S. Public*, pg. 1011
Uyeda, Allen B., Pres. & Chief Exec. Officer--First Insurance Co. of Hawaii, Ltd., Honolulu, HI; *Int'l*, pg. 1392
Vaaraniemi, Markku, Sr. V.P. & Bus. Unit Exec.--Valmet Automation Kajaani Ltd., Kajaani, Finland; *Int'l*, pg. 1449
Vaatainn, Maria, Chief Oper. Officer--Valmet Trade Promotion Office, Saint Petersburg, Russia; *Int'l*, pg. 1449
Vaca, Bruce, Admin.--Dirksen House Healthcare, Springfield, IL; *U.S. Public*, pg. 1712
Vacca, Phil, Gen. Mgr.--Rohr Industries, Hagerstown Plant, Hagerstown, MD; *U.S. Public*, pg. 751
Vaccerelli, Vincent, Dir.-Mktg.--Leica, Inc., Depew, NY; *Int'l*, pg. 806
Vacher, Mike, Mng. Dir.--The Miller Group Limited (Telford), Telford, United Kingdom; *U.S. Public*, pg. 869
Vachon, Michel, Mill Mgr.--Papier Malette, Saint Leonard, Canada; *Int'l*, pg. 833
Vadas, James, Chief Oper. Officer--Schleicher & Schuell, Budapest, Hungary; *Int'l*, pg. 1206
Vaden, F. Rogers, Mgr.--Scott & Stringfellow, Inc., Lynchburg, VA; *U.S. Public*, pg. 1446
Vadseth, Per S., Gen. Mgr.--Kvaerner Fodema a.s., Valderoy, Norway; *Int'l*, pg. 769
Vagliasindi, Jug, Chief Oper. Officer--Osram Societa Riunite Osram-Edison-Clerici S.p.A., Milan, Italy; *Int'l*, pg. 1244
Vago, Paul M., First V.P.--Jefferies & Company, Inc., Los Angeles, CA; *U.S. Public*, pg. 925
Vagola, Anthony, Chief Oper. Officer--Elite Personalized Creations, Waynesboro, PA; *U.S. Public*, pg. 89
Vahlmann, Wilfried, Mng. Dir.--BASF S.A., Sao Bernardo do Campo, Brazil; *Int'l*, pg. 107
Vaidya, Rajiv, Mng. Dir.--Triton Communications, New Delhi, India; *Int'l*, pg. 118
Vaillancourt, Marcel, Exec. V.P. & Gen. Mgr.--B.A. Bank Note, Ottawa, Canada; *Int'l*, pg. 1077
Vainikka, Timo, Chief Exec. Officer--OAO Komsomolets, Kommunar, Russia; *Int'l*, pg. 864
Vainisi, James, Pres.--Torco Automotive Division, Wheaton, IL; *U.S. Private*, pg. 1092
Vainola, Toomas, Pres.--Rudus Eesti AS, Tallinn, Estonia; *Int'l*, pg. 1201
Vairo, Ricardo, Chief Exec. Officer--EURO RSCG Norton, Montevideo, Uruguay; *Int'l*, pg. 603
Vaisaren, A., V.P.--Nokia Mobile Phones, Inc., San Diego, CA; *Int'l*, pg. 952
Vaittinen, Kari, Chief Oper. Officer--Akerlund & Rausing Oy, Lieksa, Finland; *Int'l*, pg. 32
Vaiya, Farid, Pres.--Raleigh Industries of Canada Ltd., Oakville, Canada; *Int'l*, pg. 394
Valantasis, Gust, Pres.--Orlando Div., Winter Park, FL; *U.S. Public*, pg. 1683
Valbak, Ole, Chief Oper. Officer--Alfa-Laval Nirex Engineering A/S, Ballerup, Denmark; *Int'l*, pg. 1379
Valbona, Bruno M., Pres.--Waring Products, New Hartford, CT; *U.S. Public*, pg. 286
Valderama, Jorge, Chief Oper. Officer--Dentsply Argentina S.A.C.I., Buenos Aires, Argentina; *U.S. Public*, pg. 499
Valdes-Fauli, G., Dir.--Barclays Bank PLC, Miami, FL; *Int'l*, pg. 165
Valdimarsson, Magnus, Gen. Mgr.--Kvaerner Eureka Islandi, Reykjavik, Iceland; *Int'l*, pg. 767
Valdivieso, Gaston, Gen. Mgr.--Loctite Corp. Chile Ltda., Santiago, Chile; *Int'l*, pg. 611
Vale, Pedro Rogerio Seixas, Dir.-Admin.--Portugal Previdente Companhia de Seguros (RAS), Lisbon, Portugal; *Int'l*, pg. 61
Valelly, Stephen J., Pres.--Bank of Boston International, Miami, FL; *U.S. Public*, pg. 184
Valente, Helder Castro, Gen. Mgr.--Merloni Electrodomesticos Lda., Setubal, Portugal; *Int'l*, pg. 860
Valenti, Nick, Pres. & Chief Exec. Officer--Restaurant Associates Catering, New York, NY; *U.S. Private*, pg. 925
Valentin, P M., Chief Oper. Officer--Tecnologie Progetti Lavori Spa, Rome, Italy; *Int'l*, pg. 1361
Valentine, Chuck, Sr. V.P. & Grp. Acct. Dir.--Rubin Postaer & Associates, Santa Monica, CA; *U.S. Private*, pg. 950
Valentine, Dean, Pres. & Chief Exec. Officer--UPN-United Paramount Network, Los Angeles, CA; *U.S. Public*, pg. 352
Valentine, Dean, Pres. & Chief Exec. Officer--UPN-United Paramount Network, Los Angeles, CA; *U.S. Private*, pg. 777
Valentine, Desmond K., Reg. Gen. Mgr.-Caribbean--Moore Business Forms de Puerto Rico, S.A., Hato Rey, PR; *Int'l*, pg. 889
Valentine, Frank, Chief Oper. Officer--George Meller Ltd., London, United Kingdom; *Int'l*, pg. 712
Valentine, John, Dir.-Mktg.--Belden Wire & Cable Company, Richmond, IN; *U.S. Public*, pg. 201
Valentine, Robert J., Jr., Pres. & Gen. Mgr.--Kysor/Medallion, Spring Lake, MI; *U.S. Public*, pg. 968
Valentini, Mario, Mng. Dir. & National Dir.--ITW Fastex Italia, SpA, Turin, Italy; *U.S. Public*, pg. 868
Valentini, Robert M., Pres. & Chief Exec. Officer--Bell Atlantic-PA, Philadelphia, PA; *U.S. Public*, pg. 203
Valentino, Harry, Chief Oper. Officer--Sugardale Foods Inc., Canton, OH; *U.S. Private*, pg. 427
Valentino, Harry, Chief Oper. Officer--Superior's Brand Meats, Massillon, OH; *U.S. Private*, pg. 427
Valenzuela, Pablo, Mng. Dir.--Frederick & Valenzuela/TBWA, Santiago, Chile; *U.S. Private*, pg. 1062
Valenzuela, Robert, Pres.--Sun-Litho, Van Nuys, CA; *U.S. Private*, pg. 762
Valera, Jesus Montenez, Asst. Dir.--Ryerson de Mexico, Monclova Div., Monclova, Mexico; *Int'l*, pg. 66
Valerio, A., Mgr.--Van Leeuwen Pipe and Tube Corporation, Mexico, Mexico; *Int'l*, pg. 1450
Valerio, Dr. David, Chief Oper. Officer--Covance Research Products, Inc., Denver, PA; *U.S. Public*, pg. 454
Valeriote, Rick, Pres. & Chief Exec. Officer--Dowty Silcofab, Guelph, Canada; *Int'l*, pg. 1338
Valero, Guy, Dir. General Adjoint--Union Congolaise De Banques, Brazzaville, Congo; *Int'l*, pg. 548
Valero, Patricia, Controller--Prenatal, S.A., Barcelona, Spain; *Int'l*, pg. 1068
Valez, Luis, Chief Oper. Officer--Richardson-Vicks S.A. de C.V., Mexico, Mexico; *U.S. Public*, pg. 1333
Valk-Long, Lisa, Publisher--Time, New York, NY; *U.S. Public*, pg. 1613
Valkonen, Harri, Mng. Dir.--Merita Bank Ltd., Beijing Representative Office, Beijing, China; *Int'l*, pg. 859
Valkonen, Olavi, Resident Mgr.--Heinola Mill, Heinola, Finland; *Int'l*, pg. 1428
Valkonen, Olavi, Resident Mgr.--Lahti Mills, Lahti, Finland; *Int'l*, pg. 1429
Valla, Francois, Mng. Dir.--Credit Lyonnais, Chicago, IL; *Int'l*, pg. 344
Valle, Wilfredo, Chief Oper. Officer--Peerless Tube Co. of Puerto Rico, Inc., Humacao, PR; *U.S. Public*, pg. 1269
Vallee, Bruno, Chief Oper. Officer--CEGF, Paris, France; *U.S. Public*, pg. 606
Vallee, Louis-Eric, Pres. & Chief Exec. Officer--Saint Jacques Vallee Young & Rubicam, Inc., Montreal, Canada; *U.S. Private*, pg. 1200
Vallentin, Bo, Mgr.--GGK Copenhagen, Copenhagen, Denmark; *Int'l*, pg. 1335
Vallerand, Andre, Dir. Gen.--Imprimerie Quebecor Lasalle, La Salle, Canada; *Int'l*, pg. 1077
Valles, Gene, Pres.--Arts & Crafts Press, San Diego, CA; *U.S. Private*, pg. 268
Valles, Gene, Chm.--Rush Press, San Diego, CA; *U.S. Private*, pg. 268
Valles, Jose, Mng. Dir.--Jotun S.A.E., Barcelona, Spain; *Int'l*, *pg. 715*
Valletta, Horacio, Dir. Gen.--Salvat Editores Argentina, SA, Buenos Aires, Argentina; *Int'l*, pg. 796
Valley, R. Bruce, Chm. Bd., Pres. & Chief Exec. Officer--Piedmont Trust Bank, Martinsville, VA; *U.S. Public*, pg. 1039
Vallies, Pierre, Pres.--Sogerma-Socea, Merignac, France; *Int'l*, pg. 29
Vallinkoski, Ilkka, Mng. Dir.--Enso Trading Handelsgesellschaft mbH, Vienna, Austria; *Int'l*, pg. 457
Vallino, M. Cagna, Chief Oper. Officer--FATA Industrie S.A., Cergy-Pontoise, France; *Int'l*, pg. 474
Vallortigara, John, Mgr.--Business Management Personnel, Inc., Chicago, IL; *U.S. Public*, pg. 714
Valls, Juan, Controller--ITW Espana, S.A., Barcelona, Spain; *U.S. Public*, pg. 868
Valls, Juan, Mgr.--ITW Nexus Europe, Barcelona, Spain; *U.S. Public*, pg. 868
Vallstrom, Eero, Mgr.-New Radio Technologies--Nokia Telecommunications, Espoo, Finland; *Int'l*, pg. 952
Valmorisco Martin, Manuel, Chm. & Creative Dir.--GGK Madrid, Madrid, Spain; *Int'l*, pg. 1335
Valone, Arthur, Gen. Mgr.--Queens Group New Jersey, Inc., Edison, NJ; *U.S. Private*, pg. 900
Valotaire, J., Pres. & Chief Oper. Officer--Belair Insurance Company, Montreal, Canada; *Int'l*, pg. 648
Valovuo, Jouni, Dir.--Metpela Oy, Laitila, Finland; *Int'l*, pg. 729
Valve, Kari, Chief Oper. Officer--Ahlstrom Automation Oy, Varkaus, Finland; *Int'l*, pg. 34
Valverde, Jeff, Branch Mgr.--Financial Collection Agencies (1990) Inc., Las Vegas, NV; *Int'l*, pg. 471
Vamos, Istvan, Pres.--Advanced Forming Technology, Inc., Longmont, CO; *U.S. Public*, pg. 1320
Van Able, Justin, Laboratory Mgr.--Quest Diagnostic-Reading, Reading, PA; *U.S. Public*, pg. 1351
Van Agtmaal, J.G., Mng. Dir.--Balzers Process Systems Europe N.V., Maarssen, Netherlands; *Int'l*, pg. 997
Van Agtmaal, J.G., Mng. Dir.--S.A. Balzers N.V., Zaventem, Belgium; *Int'l*, pg. 998
Van Alsberg, Cecil, Pres.--Applied Films Corp., Boulder, CO; *U.S. Public*, pg. 519
Van Ameron, H.J., Dir.--Lever Brothers (Malaysia) Sdn. Bhd., Kuala Lumpur, Malaysia; *Int'l*, pg. 1437
van Apeloloum, H., Chief Exec. Officer--Hoogovens Staalverwerking en Handel BV, Bloemendaal, Netherlands; *Int'l*, pg. 754
van As, Eugene, Chm. Bd. & Chief Exec. Officer--S.D. Warren Co., Boston, MA; *Int'l*, pg. 1193
van As, J.P.Th., Chief Oper. Officer--De Lage Landen Leasing Ltd., Dublin, Ireland; *Int'l*, pg. 1082
van Aswegen, Eddy, Chief Oper. Officer--MacDermid S.A. (PTY) Ltd., Bramley, South Africa; *U.S. Public*, pg. 1030
van Baarsel, E.W., Dir.--HMI, Hollandsche Maatschappij Installatietechniek bv, Rijswijk, Netherlands; *Int'l*, pg. 630
Van Baren, Gise, Pres. & Gen. Mgr.--Hy-Alloy Steels Co., Chicago, IL; *U.S. Public*, pg. 313
Van Beck, Peter, Mng. Dir.--Schauman B.V., Bussum, Netherlands; *Int'l*, pg. 1429
Van Beek, Harry J. G., Pres.--Klockner Pentaplast of America, Inc., Gordonsville, VA; *Int'l*, pg. 737
Van Beek, Keith, Pres.--Toys "R" US (Canada) Ltd., Concord, Canada; *U.S. Public*, pg. 1626
Van Bell, Richard J., Pres.--John Deere Health Care, Inc., Moline, IL; *U.S. Public*, pg. 492
Van Beusekom, Roger D., Pres.--Norstan Financial Services, Inc., Maple Grove, MN; *U.S. Public*, pg. 1192
van Bijsterveld, F.J.S., Chief Oper. Officer--Rabobank Belgie, Antwerp Branch, Antwerp, Belgium; *Int'l*, pg. 1082
Van Bogan, R., Chm. Bd., Pres. & Chief Exec. Officer--SouthTrust Bank, Orlando, Orlando, FL; *U.S. Public*, pg. 1492
van Boven, P.R.P., Gen. Mgr.--Tiel Utrecht, Utrecht, Netherlands; *Int'l*, pg. 647
Van Brusselt, Roger, Mng. Dir.--Bundy Belgium SA, Wandre, Belgium; *Int'l*, pg. 1341
Van Bueren, Tom, Mgr.--Radiometer Nederland B.V., Zoetermeer, Netherlands; *Int'l*, pg. 1084
Van Buskirk, Chris, V.P. & Chief Oper. Officer--TNTI, Toronto, Canada; *U.S. Public*, pg. 1642
Van Bussel, J.W., Chief Oper. Officer--Kanterbrau S.A., Boulogne-Billancourt, France; *Int'l*, pg. 381
van Campen, Johannes A., Mng. Dir.--Van Campen Bending Technics B.V., Lelystad, Netherlands; *U.S. Public*, pg. 1387
van Cann, J.H., Chief Oper. Officer--VNU Verkoopgroep BV, De Meern, Netherlands; *Int'l*, pg. 1445
van Cann, J.H., Mng. Dir.--bv Aldipress, De Meern, Netherlands; *Int'l*, pg. 1445
Van Cleave, Robert C., Pres. & Chief Exec. Officer--Centex Construction Company, Dallas, TX; *U.S. Public*, pg. 322
van Dalen, M.J., Mng. Dir.--Wolters Kluwer Educational Activities, Groningen, Netherlands; *Int'l*, pg. 1513
van Dam, B., Mng. Dir.--Van Leeuwen Buizen Europa BV, Zwijndrecht, Netherlands; *Int'l*, pg. 1449
Van Dam, Gert, Gen. Mgr.--Keithley Instruments B.V., Amsterdam, Netherlands; *U.S. Public*, pg. 947
van Damme, Frank, Mng. Dir.--MoDo Papier Belgium, Kallo, Belgium; *Int'l*, pg. 886
van de Donck, Albert, Mng. Dir.--Henningsen Nederland B.V., Waalwijk, Netherlands; *Int'l*, pg. 1074
van de Geijn, P., Chm. Bd., Pres. & Chief Exec. Officer--AEGON Nederland N.V., Hague, Netherlands; *Int'l*, pg. 26
Van de Graaf, Adrian, Mgr.--CAE Vanguard, Ltd.-Manitoba, Winnipeg, Canada; *Int'l*, pg. 237
Van De Graat, Jacobus J., Chief Oper. Officer--Towers Perrin Reinsurance, Philadelphia, PA; *U.S. Private*, pg. 1093
Van de Mortel, C., Chief Oper. Officer--Marine Port Terminals Inc., Brunswick, GA; *Int'l*, pg. 758
van de Pas, K.H., Pres.--Uitgeversmaatschappij De Gelderlander bv, Nijmegen, Netherlands; *Int'l*, pg. 1445
Van de Put, Tony, Sub. Mgr.--Millipore B.V., Etten-Leur, Netherlands; *U.S. Public*, pg. 1113
van de Putte, E., Dir.--Seelow Kasewerke GmbH, Seelow, Germany; *Int'l*, pg. 753
van de Roemer, H.J., Mng. Dir.--KNSM-Kroonburgh B.V., Rotterdam, Netherlands; *Int'l*, pg. 1144
Van De Ryt, J.K., Gen. Mgr.--CHEMCENTRAL/Louisville, Louisville, KY; *U.S. Private*, pg. 232
Van De Walle, P.L.J., Chm. & Mng. Dir.--S.A. Texaco Petroleum N.V., Brussels, Belgium; *U.S. Public*, pg. 1584
Van de Walle, P.L.J., Chm. Bd.--Texaco Italiana SpA, Rome, Italy; *U.S. Public*, pg. 1584
van de Water, Peter, Gen. Dir.--Marcam European Support Centre, BV, Best, Netherlands; *U.S. Public*, pg. 1043
Van Dell, Ron, Mng. Dir.--Square D Company Europe, Walton-on-Thames, United Kingdom; *Int'l*, pg. 1209
van den Akker, Gerard J., Grp. V.P.--Fasson (Nederland) B.V., Leiden, Netherlands; *U.S. Public*, pg. 154
van den Beemt, C.M., Chief Oper. Officer--SAB Profiel B.V., Ijsselstein, Netherlands; *Int'l*, pg. 754
Van Den Berg, G., Chief Oper. Officer--Boart Longyear B.V., Etten-Leur, Netherlands; *Int'l*, pg. 76
Van den Bergh, Hugo, Mng. Dir.--Monti NV, Lier, Belgium; *Int'l*, pg. 462
Van den Bergh, Jan, Chief Exec. Officer-Strategy & Creation--Quattro DMB&B, Brussels, Brussels, Belgium; *U.S. Private*, pg. 305
Van den Borre, Jean-Marie, Office Mgr.--Korn/Ferry International, Amsterdam, Netherlands; *U.S. Private*, pg. 633
Van den Borre, Jean-Marie, Partner--Korn/Ferry International, Brussels, Belgium; *U.S. Private*, pg. 633
van den Bosch, Jos, Mng. Dir.--Multicom TBWA Advertising B.V., Eindhoven, Netherlands; *U.S. Private*, pg. 1062
Van den bossche, Jozef, Gen. Mgr.--Wynn's Belgium N.V., Saint-Niklaas, Belgium; *U.S. Public*, pg. 1782
van den Brink, J., Mng. Dir.--Ballast Nedam Grondstoffen B.V., Zaandam, Netherlands; *Int'l*, pg. 133
van den Broek, Theo, Chm.--ARA/BDDP, Rotterdam, Netherlands; *Int'l*, pg. 117
van den Eijkel, B., Gen. Mgr.--Graphic Lease, Amsterdam, Netherlands; *Int'l*, pg. 647
Van den Eynde, Alain, Mng. Dir. & Legal Dir.--Garbarski EURO RSCG, Brussels, Belgium; *Int'l*, pg. 603
van den Heuvel, J.J., Dir. Gen.--Duif Convenience Foods BV, Katwijk, Netherlands; *Int'l*, pg. 751
van den Hout, S.A., Dir.--HAM, Hollandsche Aanneming Maatschappij B.V., Rotterdam, Netherlands; *Int'l*, pg. 630
van den Hove, Ph., Chief Oper. Officer--Rabobank Belgie, Brussels Office, Brussels, Belgium; *Int'l*, pg. 1082
van den Hurk, G.J., Mng. Dir.--Handel und Finanz Warmond AG, Zug, Switzerland; *Int'l*, pg. 682
van den Plas, J.E.A., Gen. Mgr.--AMEV Ontwikkeling Maatschappij N.V., Utrecht, Netherlands; *Int'l*, pg. 499
van der Geer, C.H.M., Mgr.--Insurance Systems Nederland B.V., Hoofddorp, Netherlands; *Int'l*, pg. 26
Van Der Gucht, Bernard, Gen. Mgr.--Pacific Scientific S.A.R.L., Palaiseau, France; *U.S. Public*, pg. 1250
van der Ham, C.A.A., Gen. Mgr.--Algemene Bank Nederland, Kenya; *Int'l*, pg. 11
van der Hee, H.C., Mng. Dir.--Ascom Zarli BV, Zoeterwoude-Rijndijk, Netherlands; *Int'l*, pg. 87
van der Heijden, W.A.J.M., Chm. Bd.--FGH Bank N.V., Utrecht, Netherlands; *Int'l*, pg. 26
van der Helm, Frits C., Mng. Dir.--Schilperoort Beheer, B.V., Rotterdam, Netherlands; *Int'l*, pg. 1306

van der Hoek, J., Mng. Dir.--Nedlloyd Road Cargo International, Dusseldorf, Germany; *Int'l*, pg. 1145
van der Hoeven, Jans, Chief Oper. Officer--A. Johnson & Co. A/S, Offshore, Stavanger, Norway; *Int'l*, pg. 711
Van Der Hofstadt, Luc, Liaison Officer--Gelder Advertising, Brussels, Belgium; *U.S. Private*, pg. 1152
van der Jagt, J.J., Gen. Mgr.--De Boo Beheer B.V., Delft, Netherlands; *Int'l*, pg. 1200
Van Der Kamp, Jerry, Chief Exec. Officer & Exec. V.P.--Agri Financial Services Inc., West Des Moines, IA; *U.S. Private*, pg. 55
Van Der Kamp, Jerry, Chief Exec. Officer & Exec. V.P.--Agri Terminal Corporation, West Des Moines, IA; *U.S. Private*, *pg. 55*
Van Der Kamp, Jerry, Chief Exec. Officer & V.P.--Industrial & Transportation Equipment Co., West Des Moines, IA; *U.S. Private*, pg. 55
van der Kwaak, Joop N J, Mng. Dir.--SKF Multitec B.V., Amsterdam, Netherlands; *Int'l*, pg. 1159
van der Lande, M.R.B., Mng. Dir.--Lakatex B.V., Goor, Netherlands; *Int'l*, pg. 198
van der Lilij, Cees, Mng. Dir.--Tyco Toys (Benelux) N.V., Saint-Niklaas, Belgium; *U.S. Public*, pg. 1059
Van Der Linde, Keas Dean, Mng. Dir.--Elf Atochem Rotterdah B.V., Rotterdam, Netherlands; *Int'l*, pg. 446
van der Luft, R., Grp. V.P.--Du Pont International, Wilmington, DE; *U.S. Public*, pg. 531
van der Meer, A.C., Mng. Dir.--Tenneco Transicol B.V., Maastricht, Netherlands; *U.S. Public*, pg. 1580
van der Mersch, A., Gen. Mgr.--CW Lease Belgium, Aartselaar, Belgium; *Int'l*, pg. 648
van der Mespel, Peter, Gen. Mgr.--DG Bank-Hong Kong, Hong Kong, Hong Kong; *Int'l*, pg. 352
Van der Motten, Michael, Mng. Dir.--Battenfeld Belgium N.V., Aarschot, Belgium; *Int'l*, pg. 825
van der Pas, J.G.J., Dir.--Van Melle Nederland B.V., Breda, Netherlands; *Int'l*, pg. 1451
Van der Pas, John, Pres.--Lips USA Inc., Ocean Springs, MS; *Int'l*, pg. 812
Van der Plas, H., Chm.--Samas Universal Office Supplies, Utrecht, Netherlands; *Int'l*, pg. 707
van der Poll, Frank, Gen. Mgr.--Gandalf Systems Belgium, S.A., Brussels, Belgium; *Int'l*, pg. 541
van der Pool, Kees, Pres.-Components Grp.--Hathaway Motors & Instruments Division, Tulsa, OK; *U.S. Public*, pg. 799
van der Pool, Kees, Pres.--Computer Optical Products Inc., Chatsworth, CA; *U.S. Public*, pg. 799
van der Putten, G.J., Chief Oper. Officer--Makro Cash and Carry Poland Ltd. Sp. z.o.o., Warsaw, Poland; *Int'l*, pg. 1155
Van der Schaaf, Haite J., Chief Oper. Officer--H.B. Fuller Netherlands B.V., Amerongen, Netherlands; *U.S. Public*, pg. 687
Van Der Schee, Jack, Mng. Dir.--LB Rheinland Pfalz Finance B.V., Amsterdam, Netherlands; *Int'l*, pg. 799
van der Talen, A., Mng. Dir.--ABI Imtech NV, Tielrode, Belgium; *Int'l*, pg. 681
Van Der Tuuk, Terry, Vice Chm.--Graphic Technology, Inc., New Century, KS; *Int'l*, pg. 950
van der Vaart, Rob, Mng. Dir.--Inamed B.V., Breda, Netherlands; *U.S. Public*, pg. 874
van der Walt, H.B., Mng. Dir.--Barlows Equipment Manufacturing Co. SA, Boksburg, South Africa; *Int'l*, pg. 167
van der Walt, L., Chm.--The Lion Match Company Limited, Durban, South Africa; *Int'l*, pg. 1287
van der Wansem, Paul J., Pres.--BTU Engineering Corporation, North Billerica, MA; *U.S. Public*, pg. 164
van der Weijden, Job J.J., Mng. Dir.--Sulzer Keuls B.V., Heerlen, Netherlands; *Int'l*, pg. 1306
van der Westhuizen, Jannie, Mng. Dir.--Sasol Mining (Pty.) Ltd., Secunda, South Africa; *Int'l*, pg. 1197
van der Wiel, A.M.L., Dir. Gen.--Den Hertog B.V., Mepissant, Netherlands; *Int'l*, pg. 752
Van der Wouden, J., Gen. Mgr.--Schaap & Citroen, Hague, Netherlands; *Int'l*, pg. 1462
van der Zouwen, C., Mgr.-Monitronics--Radio-Holland Security Systems, Amsterdam, Netherlands; *Int'l*, pg. 1151
Van DerLee, Chuck, Pres. & Chief Exec. Officer--Rogers Entertainment Inc., Calgary, Canada; *Int'l*, pg. 1123
van Deventer, H. J., Gen. Mgr.--Albright & Wilson B.V., Brussels, Belgium; *Int'l*, pg. 49
van Deventur, Gregor, Mgr.--Sasol Akrylo, Secunda, South Africa; *Int'l*, pg. 1196
van Dijk, Dick A., Dir.--Grabowsky & Poort BV, Hague, Netherlands; *Int'l*, pg. 606
van Dijk, H., Mng. Dir.--Getinge-D.S.E. NV, Antwerp, Belgium; *Int'l*, pg. 551
van Dijk, H., Mng. Dir.--Getinge-D.S.E. BV, Rosmalen, Netherlands; *Int'l*, pg. 551
van Dijk, M., Mgr.--Bowthorpe BV, Rotterdam, Netherlands; *Int'l*, pg. 208
van Ditmarsch, J.J., Mgr.--Albank B.V., Amersfoort, Netherlands; *Int'l*, pg. 9
Van Domburg, C.S., Supervising Dir.--B.F. Goodrich Chemical Sales Co., B.V., Hague, Netherlands; *U.S. Public*, pg. 752
Van Donkelaar, Aart, V.P. & Gen. Mgr.--Wynn's-Precision (Canada) Ltd., Orillia, Canada; *U.S. Public*, pg. 1783
van Dooren, A.P.S., Chief Oper. Officer--Rabobank Trustmaatschappij, Curacao, Netherlands Antilles; *Int'l*, pg. 1082
Van Doorselaere, I., Pres.--Interbrew Netherlands, Breda, Netherlands; *Int'l*, pg. 679
van Dord, Hans, Mng. Dir.--Heidemij Advies BV, Arnhem, Netherlands; *Int'l*, pg. 607
van Driel, A.A.J., Chief Exec. Officer--OCE Nederlandse Verkoopmaatschappij B.V., s Hertogenbosch, Netherlands; *Int'l*, pg. 994
Van Duijvenvoorde, Harry, Gen. Mgr.--Amerford Intl. Nederland B.V., Amsterdam, Netherlands; *Int'l*, pg. 1388
van Duinen, Dan, Pres.--Jacuzzi Bros., Jacuzzi, Inc., Little Rock, AR; *U.S. Public*, pg. 1684
van Duinen, Jack, Mng. Dir.--Wrigley Ljubljana, Ltd., Ljubljana, Slovenia; *U.S. Public*, pg. 1781
Van Dusen, R.G., Pres.--Danbel Industries Inc., Toronto, Canada; *Int'l*, pg. 955
Van Dyck, Paul, V.P. & Mng. Dir.--Tyco Toys (Belgium) N.V., Saint-Niklaas, Belgium; *U.S. Public*, pg. 1059
Van Dyke, Don, Gen. Mgr.--BioImage Products, Ann Arbor, MI; *U.S. Public*, pg. 1112
Van Dyke, Ed, Pres.--True Temper Sports Division, Memphis, TN; *U.S. Public*, pg. 233
Van Dyke, R. Scott, Pres. & Chief Exec. Officer--Explorer Pipeline Co., Tulsa, OK; *U.S. Public*, pg. 1584
Van Dyke, Robert G., Pres.--Eagle Converting Inc., Lombard, IL; *U.S. Private*, pg. 165
van Eaghen, Henri, Chief Oper. Officer--Berghuizer-Enso Formaatfabriek B.V., Wapenveld, Netherlands; *Int'l*, pg. 458
Van Engeland, Maarten, Mng. Dir.--ISS Darenas International A/S, Nivaa, Denmark; *Int'l*, pg. 656
van Engeland, Maarten, Mng. Dir.--ISS Darenas AB, Sollentuna, Sweden; *Int'l*, pg. 656
Van Epps, Bill, Pres.--Chesapeake Bagel Bakery, Atlanta, GA; *U.S. Private*, pg. 5
Van Erden, Don, V.P.--ITW Corporate Technology, Glenview, IL; *U.S. Public*, pg. 866
van Esch, J.J.J.M., Chief Oper. Officer--Smith's Chewing Sweets Mij. B.V., Hornelaan, Netherlands; *Int'l*, pg. 1451
van Essen, G., Mgr.-Pub. Rels.--Ballast Nedam International B.V., Amstelveen, Netherlands; *Int'l*, pg. 133
van Etten, F.H., Gen. Mgr.--Interadvies (NNFD, Regiobank, NVB/Vola), Amsterdam, Netherlands; *Int'l*, pg. 647
van Etten, R., Pres.--Kvaerner Ships Equipment b.v., Ridderkerk, Netherlands; *Int'l*, pg. 768
van Etten, R., Pres.--Kvaerner Rotterdam bv, Ridderkerk, Netherlands; *Int'l*, pg. 772
Van Eyk, Gary, Gen. Mgr.--Kal Grafx Imaging, Battle Creek, MI; *U.S. Private*, pg. 387
van Eynde, Paul, Mng. Dir.--Brooktree Central Europe, Munich, Germany; *U.S. Public*, pg. 1398
Van Geiwen, J.H., V.P.--Small Tube Products Co., Inc., Altoona, PA; *U.S. Public*, pg. 1775
Van Gelder, Jerrie, Sr. V.P. & Reg. Dir.--Arnold Advertising, Minneapolis, MN; *U.S. Private*, pg. 84
Van Gelder, John, Pres.--Koch Engineering Co., Inc., Wichita, KS; *U.S. Private*, pg. 628
van Geuns, A., Mng. Dir.--Amaco B.V., Amstelveen, Schiphol, Netherlands; *Int'l*, pg. 682
van Gils, Rafael, Pres.--CPAC Europe N.V., Herentals, Belgium; *U.S. Public*, pg. 282
Van Ginckel, Leo, Mng. Dir.--Janssen/Cilag B.V., Tilburg, Netherlands; *U.S. Public*, pg. 929
Van Ginkel, Leo, Mng. Dir.--Taxandria Pharmaceutica B.V., Tilburg, Netherlands; *U.S. Public*, pg. 932
Van Gogh, Frank, Pres.--Rotoflow Corporation, Gardena, CA; *Int'l*, pg. 96
Van Gogh, Ger W.P., Mng. Dir.--Amersham Nederland BV, Das' Hertogenbosch, Netherlands; *Int'l*, pg. 993
Van Grinsven, Mark J., Jr., Sr. V.P.--The Northern Trust Co., London, United Kingdom; *U.S. Public*, pg. 1197
Van Grunsven, Bob, Pres.--Carver Boat Corp., Pulaski, WI; *U.S. Private*, pg. 447
van Hanja, Nicolas, Mgr.--Barenbrug Tourneur Recherches SA, Mas-Grenier, France; *Int'l*, pg. 167
van Hardeveld, J., Mgr.--Vredestein Fietsbanden B.V., Doetinchem, Netherlands; *Int'l*, pg. 1481
Van Hatten, Rich, Chief Oper. Officer--National Waste Services Inc., Chicago, IL; *U.S. Public*, pg. 49
Van Hattum, Andre M.J., Chm. Bd. of Mngmt.--Bridgewater Paper Limited, London, United Kingdom; *Int'l*, pg. 20
van Hedel, T.J.M., Mng. Dir.--Nutricia Nederland B.V., Zoetermeer, Netherlands; *Int'l*, pg. 991
van Heek, Jan, V.P. & G.M.--Genzyme B.V., Eemnes, Netherlands; *U.S. Public*, pg. 733
Van Heereveld, Guus, Dir.--H.J. Heinz GmbH, Cologne, Germany; *U.S. Public*, pg. 806
van Heerikhuizen, Egbert J., Gen. Mgr.--Siegling Nederland B.V., Wijk, Netherlands; *Int'l*, pg. 498
van Heerikhuizen, Egbert J., Gen. Mgr.--Te Hennepe LIN-PACK B.V., Dieren, Netherlands; *Int'l*, pg. 498
Van Helden, Bill, Gen. Mgr.--Camloc Fastener GmbH, Kelheim, Germany; *U.S. Public*, pg. 610
Van Helden, Pete J., V.P.--Florida Division, Maitland, FL; *U.S. Public*, pg. 38
Van Helsiden, John, Fin. Controller--Gestetner (Pty) Limited, Johannesburg, South Africa; *Int'l*, pg. 1115
van Helten, W.H., Chief Oper. Officer--Gebr. Verduijn's Suikerwerkenfabriek B. V., Breskens Kreek, Netherlands; *Int'l*, pg. 1451
van Heyst, C.J., Dir.--Bruil Specialistische Bouwtechnieken B.V., Soest, Netherlands; *Int'l*, pg. 134
Van Holle, Paul, Gen. Mgr.--Sikel N.V., Genk, Belgium; *Int'l*, *pg. 79*
Van Hook, Jim, Pres.--Brentwood Label Group, Brentwood, TN; *Int'l*, pg. 1529
Van Hoose, David, Dir. Gen.-Mexican Opers.--Avicola Pilgrim's Pride de Mexico, S.A. de C.V., Mexico, Mexico; *U.S. Public*, pg. 1296
Van Hoose, David, Pres.-Mexican Opers.--Alimentos Balanceados Pilgrim's Pride, Queretaro, Mexico; *U.S. Public*, pg. 1296
Van Horn, Koreen, Gen. Mgr.--AE Farms, Inc., Des Moines, IA; *U.S. Private*, pg. 72
Van Horn, L.R., Pres.--Ziegler Collateralized Securities, Inc., West Bend, WI; *U.S. Public*, pg. 1792
Van Horne, Jan F., V.P. & G.M., Health & Beauty Care Prods. Austria--Procter & Gamble Austria GmbH, Vienna, Austria; *U.S. Public*, pg. 1332
van Houten, Alfons, Chief Oper. Officer--SOCAMIC Ste. de Caoutchouc et de Produits Chimiques S.a.r.l., Bischwiller, France; *Int'l*, pg. 1167
van Houten, H.T.F., Chief Oper. Officer--Makro Cash & Carry Distribution (M) Sdn. Bhd., Shah Alam, Malaysia; *Int'l*, pg. 1155
van Houten, Rien, Gen. Mgr.--John Crane Marine-Lips, Drunen, Netherlands; *Int'l*, pg. 1339
Van Hulle, John V., Pres.--Cosan Chemical Corp., Carlstadt, NJ; *U.S. Public*, pg. 297
Van Hulle, John V., Pres.--CasChem Inc., Bayonne, NJ; *U.S. Public*, pg. 297
van Humalda Eysinga, F.W.B., Mng. Dir.--Wolters Kluwer Professional Training, Nyon, Switzerland; *Int'l*, pg. 1514
van Hyfte, Philippe, Mgr.--Bijhuis Antwerpen, Antwerp, Belgium; *Int'l*, pg. 312
Van Jacobsen, Harlan, Pres.--Panel Concepts, L.P., Santa Ana, CA; *U.S. Public*, pg. 1504
van Kaldekerken, Rolf, Gen. Mgr.--Viking Direct B.V.I.O., Venlo, Netherlands; *U.S. Public*, pg. 1721
van Kaldekerken, Rolf, Gen. Mgr.--Viking Direct Limited GmbH, Grossostheim, Germany; *U.S. Public*, pg. 1721
Van Keerberghen, Eric, Mng. Dir.--Coditel Brabant S.A., Brussels, Belgium; *Int'l*, pg. 1415
van Kempen, C.H., Mng. Dir.--Wolters Kluwer Australia, Sydney, Australia; *Int'l*, pg. 1513
Van Kerkhove, Jim, V.P.-Opers.--Salem Manufacturing Facility, Salem, OR; *Int'l*, pg. 875
van Keymeulen, J.P., Chief Oper. Officer--Rabobank Luxembourg S.A., Luxembourg, Luxembourg; *Int'l*, pg. 1082
Van Kleeck, Peter, Pres. & Chief Exec. Officer--Pawling Savings Bank, Pawling, NY; *U.S. Public*, pg. 1334
van Kuijerew, H., Mng. Dir.--EMI Music Holland BV, Heemstede, Netherlands; *Int'l*, pg. 427
van Laere, A., Chief Oper. Officer--Stelrad NV, Mechelen, Belgium; *Int'l*, pg. 268
Van Lanen, James L., Chm. & Chief Exec. Officer--ANR Venture Management Co., Houston, TX; *U.S. Public*, pg. 389
Van Lanen, James L., Pres.--Coastal States Energy Co., Salt Lake City, UT; *U.S. Public*, pg. 390
Van Lanen, James L., Chm. Bd. & Chief Exec. Officer--Coastal Power Production Company, Houston, TX; *U.S. Public*, pg. 390
van Leersum, A.M., Chm. Bd.--McCain Argentina SA, Buenos Aires, Argentina; *Int'l*, pg. 850
Van Leersum, J., Chief Oper. Officer--Alabastine Holland BV (Manufacturing), Ammerzoden, Netherlands; *Int'l*, pg. 1501
van Leeuwen, J.K., Chm. & Gen. Mgr.--Prumyslovy Penzijni Fond, a.s., Prague, Czech Republic; *Int'l*, pg. 651
Van Leeuwen, John E., Pres.--Trans Canada Credit Corporation, Etobicoke, Canada; *U.S. Public*, pg. 1202
van Leeuwen, Marianne, Mng. Dir.--Toeristiek BV, Pufmerend, Netherlands; *Int'l*, pg. 1099
van Lieshout, J.J.M., Mng. Dir.--Comfort Financieringen Nederland BV, Houten, Netherlands; *Int'l*, pg. 911
van Lith, P.J.M., Div. Mgr.--Campina Melkunie, Cheese Division, Tilburg, Netherlands; *Int'l*, pg. 254
Van Loan, Dave, Pres.--Everett/Charles Contact Products, Inc., Pomona, CA; *U.S. Private*, pg. 386
van Lokhorst, Wim, Chief Oper. Officer--Molnlycke Clinical Products AB, Goteborg, Sweden; *Int'l*, pg. 1326
van Loon, G.A., Mng. Dir.--N.V. Antradex Nutricia Americas, Willemstad, Netherlands Antilles; *Int'l*, pg. 991
Van Loue, Douglas, Plant Mgr.--GSH Corp., Snow Hill, NC; *U.S. Private*, pg. 466
van Luit, H., Mng. Dir.--EMI Compact Disc (Holland) BV, Uden, Netherlands; *Int'l*, pg. 427
van Lynden van Keppel , W.J.R. Baron, Chief Oper. Officer--Rabobank Asia Ltd., Singapore, Singapore; *Int'l*, pg. 1082
Van Lysebeth, Herman, Div. Mgr.--Rogers N.V., Gent, Belgium; *U.S. Public*, pg. 1403
Van Maanen, J.H., Chief Fin. Officer--Olivetti Nederland B.V., Leiden, Netherlands; *Int'l*, pg. 1003
Van Manen, Dick, Plant Mgr.--Canandaigua Plastics Div., Canandaigua, NY; *U.S. Private*, pg. 202
van Manen, R.O., Gen. Mgr.--Algemene Sein Industrie B.V., Utrecht, Netherlands; *Int'l*, pg. 1194
Van Marion, A.B., Gen. Mgr.--Wang Benelux S.A/N.V., Diegem, Belgium; *U.S. Public*, pg. 1737
van Meene, R.C., Mgr.-Pub. Rels.--Ballast Nedam Grond en Wegen B.V., Amstelveen, Netherlands; *Int'l*, pg. 133
Van Melle, I.L.G., Dir.--Van Melle International Trust B.V., Breda, Netherlands; *Int'l*, pg. 1451
van Melle, Marius, Pres. & Gen. Mgr.--Van Melle USA, Inc., Erlanger, KY; *Int'l*, pg. 1451
van Melsen, Henk, Mng. Dir.--Robinson Nugent (Europe) B.V., Eindhoven, Netherlands; *U.S. Public*, pg. 1395
Van Meter, Bill M., Pres. & Chief Oper. Officer--Energy Companies Of ONEOK, Tulsa, OK; *U.S. Public*, pg. 1226
Van Meter, John D., Pres.--Ashland Oil Intl. Ltd., London, United Kingdom; *U.S. Public*, pg. 139
Van Midden, J. M., Chief Oper. Officer--Electrolux Constructor B.V., Diemen, Netherlands; *Int'l*, pg. 443
Van Mierln, Jan, Mng. Dir.--McCain Foods Belgium N.V. (Belgium), Turnhout, Belgium; *Int'l*, pg. 850
van Mil, Chell, Sales--Formica Nederland B.V., Voorschoten, Netherlands; *Int'l*, pg. 129
van Moerbeke, Marc, Chief Oper. Officer--N.V. Griffith Laboratories S.A., Herentals, Belgium; *U.S. Private*, pg. 481
Van Mogh, Guy, Mng. Dir.--Bailey-Fischer & Porter B.V., Gorinchem, Netherlands; *Int'l*, pg. 449
van Mook, Brian, Gen. Mgr.--Oceaneering Intervention Engineering, Houston, TX; *U.S. Public*, pg. 1211
van Moorleghem, William, Chief Oper. Officer--Advanced Materials and Technologies N.V., Herk-de-Stad, Belgium; *Int'l*, pg. 1427
van Mourik, G., Mgr.--Holantse Bank-Uni, Istanbul, Turkey; *Int'l*, pg. 12
Van Nes, Irving, Chief Oper. Officer--Mead Verpakking B.V., Roosendaal, Netherlands; *U.S. Public*, pg. 1076
Van Ness, Kathy, Pres.-Swimwear/Taren--Cole of California, Los Angeles, CA; *U.S. Public*, pg. 148

van Nieuwburg, Pieter, Chief Oper. Officer--Ahlstrom Papier B.V., Wormerveer, Netherlands; *Int'l*, pg. 35
Van Noord, Robert K., Pres.-Fittings Group--Trinity-Structural Steel, Montgomery, AL; *U.S. Public*, pg. 1639
Van Nort, Peter S., Pres.--ABB Combustion Engineering Nuclear Power, Windsor, CT; *Int'l*, pg. 3
Van Oorde, Pim, Mgr.--Samna GmbH, Eschborn, Germany; *U.S. Public*, pg. 896
van Oostenrijk, Cornelis, Dr., Gen. Mgr.--Forbo Novilon produktiebedrijven bv, Coevorden, Netherlands; *Int'l*, pg. 497
Van Ord, Norman, Pres.--Blue Seal Feeds, Inc., Londonderry, NH; *U.S. Private*, pg. 1134
van Osnabrugge, Jan, Pres. & Chief Exec. Officer--Peerless Chain Company, Winona, MN; *U.S. Public*, pg. 1268
Van Ouytnel, Bart, Pres.--Structural Europe, Herentals, Belgium; *U.S. Public*, pg. 593
Van Overbeek, H.M.C., Gen. Mgr.--AMEV Beleggingsconsortium N.V., Utrecht, Netherlands; *Int'l*, pg. 499
van Pallandt, F., Mng. Dir.--KLM Cityhopper, Amsterdam, Netherlands; *Int'l*, pg. 719
Van Panhuys, Jan E., Representative--Banque International a Luxembourg S.A., New York, NY; *Int'l*, pg. 162
van Parys, Frederick, Pres. & Chief Exec. Officer--Pitney Bowes of Canada Ltd., Toronto, Canada; *U.S. Public*, pg. 1304
van Peer, E.F.M., Chief Oper. Officer--Makro Morocco S.A., Casablanca, Morocco; *Int'l*, pg. 1155
Van Pelt, Wim, Pres. & Chief Exec. Officer--Banner Pharmacaps, Inc., High Point, NC; *Int'l*, pg. 1272
Van Pelt, Wim, Pres.--Banner Pharmacaps Inc., High Point, NC; *Int'l*, pg. 1272
van Pottelberge, W., Chm.--De Vaderlandsche Insurance, Antwerp, Belgium; *Int'l*, pg. 648
van Prooijen, W., Mng. Dir.--Honig Foods-B.V., Koog aan de Zaan, Netherlands; *Int'l*, pg. 244
van Ream, J., Mgr.--ABN Trustcompany (Nederland) B.V., Amsterdam, Netherlands; *Int'l*, pg. 9
Van Reesema, N. H. Siewertsz, Chief Oper. Officer--Van Ommeren Shipping, Inc., Stamford, CT; *Int'l*, pg. 758
Van Remmen, Thomas, Pres. & Chief Oper. Officer--Andersen 2000 Inc., Peachtree City, GA; *U.S. Public*, pg. 462
Van Rensselaer, J.T., V.P. & Gen. Mgr.--American Pipe and Construction International, Bogota, Colombia; *U.S. Public*, pg. 99
van Riet, F.W., Mng. Dir.--Neddrill Nederland B.V., Rotterdam, Netherlands; *Int'l*, pg. 1144
van Riet, Frits, V.P.-Eastern Hemisphere--Noble Neddrill, Rotterdam, Netherlands; *U.S. Public*, pg. 1187
van Rijckevorsel, J.J.M., Mgr.--ABN Assurantie Holding B.V., Rotterdam, Netherlands; *Int'l*, pg. 9
Van Rijsseghem, Christine, Gen. Mgr.--Kredietbank S.A. France, Paris, France; *Int'l*, pg. 760
van Rikxoort, P.G., Mng. Dir.--Internatio Hout B.V., Dordrecht, Netherlands; *Int'l*, pg. 682
Van Rooy, Jean-Pierre, Pres.--Otis Elevator Company, Farmington, CT; *U.S. Public*, pg. 1690
van Rossem, Henk, Gen. Mgr.--Mallinckrodt Medical B.V., Petten, Netherlands; *U.S. Public*, pg. 1040
van Rossum, P.J.A., Mgr.--Sailtron B.V., Utrecht, Netherlands; *Int'l*, pg. 1151
Van Roy, Andre, Mng. Dir.--General Motors Continental, Antwerp, Belgium; *U.S. Public*, pg. 722
Van Ruth, Gary, Mng. Dir.--Loctite (Australia) Pty. Ltd., Caringbah, Australia; *Int'l*, pg. 611
van Ryckevorsel, T.C.A.M., Mgr.--ABN Trustcompany (Suisse) S.A., Geneva, Switzerland; *Int'l*, pg. 12
Van Sant, R.W., Pres.--Sponsor's Plan Asset Management, Inc., New Castle, DE; *U.S. Public*, pg. 1020
Van Schalk, Andy, Mgr.--Standard Flour Co., City of Commerce, CA; *Int'l*, pg. 244
van Schandevijl, Jean-Paul, Gen. Mgr.-EAM Region--T.D. Williamson (U.K.) Ltd., Swindon, United Kingdom; *U.S. Private*, pg. 1180
Van Schooten, Antoine, Mng. Dir.--Bregal, Bremer Galvanislerungs GmbH, Bremen, Germany; *Int'l*, pg. 79
Van Sickle, J., Sr. V.P.--Marquette Bank Rochester, Rochester, MN; *U.S. Private*, pg. 706
van Sijll, L.J., Works Dir.--Tonnema B.V., Sneek, Netherlands; *Int'l*, pg. 244
Van Skilling, D., Exec. V.P. & Gen. Mgr.--TRW Information Systems & Services, Orange, CA; *Int'l*, pg. 557
Van Slaars, Jonathan, Chief Oper. Officer & Exec. Dir.--HMO Texas, L.C., Houston, TX; *U.S. Public*, pg. 1470
van Soest, C.A.C., Mng. Dir.--Nettenbouw B.V., Amersfoort, Amersfoort, Netherlands; *Int'l*, pg. 681
Van Steen Kiste, P., Mng. Dir.--N.V. Acotech S.A., Zwevegem, Belgium; *Int'l*, pg. 183
van Stek, Hans, Mng. Dir.--BMC Software B.V., Nieuwegein, Netherlands; *U.S. Public*, pg. 162
van Straelen, Dominique, Mgr.--Sandvik Outillage S.N.C., Orleans, France; *Int'l*, pg. 1186
van Stratum, Pierre, Dir. Gen.--Boreas S.A. IARD, Antwerp, Belgium; *Int'l*, pg. 61
Van Strydonck, John, Chm. Bd. & Chief Exec. Officer--NAPP Systems Inc, San Marcos, CA; *U.S. Public*, pg. 984
Van Strydonck, John, Publisher--Rapid City Journal, Rapid City, SD; *U.S. Public*, pg. 984
van Stuijvenberg, Pieter A., Mng. Dir.--BMB Management Consulting for Development BV, Arnhem, Netherlands; *Int'l*, pg. 606
van Tienen, G. J., Gen Mgr--Lipton Tea Company Ltd., London, United Kingdom; *Int'l*, pg. 1434
van Till, G.B.E., Mgr.-General Staff Srvcs.--Chefaro International B.V., Oss, Netherlands; *Int'l*, pg. 44
van Tongeren, H., Mng. Dir.--Ballast Nedam Engineering B.V., Amstelveen, Netherlands; *Int'l*, pg. 133
van Tuil, Ton, Mng. Dir.--Kimball Systems BV, Terborg, Netherlands; *Int'l*, pg. 461
van Uitert, H.G., Mng. Dir.--Ballast Nedam Grond en Wegen Specialiteiten B.V., Leerdam, Netherlands; *Int'l*, pg. 133
van Uitert, H.G., Mng. Dir.--Ballast Nedam Petrol Stations, Rosmalen, Netherlands; *Int'l*, pg. 133
Van Varenberg, Andre, Dir.-Admin.--Thibaut - Colson - De Nef (TCD), Brussels, Belgium; *Int'l*, pg. 547
van Veen, C., Chm.--F van Lanschot Bankiers NV, s Hertogenbosch, Netherlands; *Int'l*, pg. 911
van Veen, M.C., Chm.-Mngmt. Bd.--Hoogovens Ijmuiden, Ijmuiden, Netherlands; *Int'l*, pg. 753
Van Velkinburgh, Stephen, Pres.--Penguin's Industries, Granada Hills, CA; *Int'l*, pg. 201
Van Vleet, W.B., Pres.--Health & Life Insurance Co. of America, Rockford, IL; *U.S. Public*, pg. 434
Van Vleet, W.B., Pres.--Union Benefit Life Insurance Co., Rockford, IL; *U.S. Public*, pg. 434
Van Vleet, William, Pres.--Manhattan National Life Insurance Company, Cincinnati, OH; *U.S. Public*, pg. 434
van Voorden, H., Pres.--Enraf B.V., Delft, Netherlands; *Int'l*, pg. 389
Van Voorhis, Larry W., Pres.--Quick 10, Raleigh, NC; *U.S. Private*, pg. 575
Van Voorst, Wim, Chief Oper. Officer--Everest & Jennings/ Graham-Field, Canada, Concord, Canada; *U.S. Public*, pg. 758
Van Vrecker, Hubert, Pres.--Asea Brown Boveri S.A., Zaventem, Belgium; *Int'l*, pg. 8
Van Vugt, Arie, Mgr.--Amway Belgium Co., Zaventem, Belgium; *U.S. Private*, pg. 69
van Vuuren, Jan, Chief Oper. Officer--Schering Agro B.V., Haren, Netherlands; *Int'l*, pg. 1203
Van Waes, D.J., Exec. V.P.--DSM Chemicals Rotterdam, Rotterdam, Netherlands; *Int'l*, pg. 353
van Weel, Patrick, Liaison Officer--Nijgh Interpartners, Rotterdam, Netherlands; *U.S. Private*, pg. 1152
van Wel, P.W., Chm. Bd.--Wolters Kluwer U.S., Riverwoods, IL; *Int'l*, pg. 1513
van Wel, P.W., Mng. Dir.--Wolters Kluwer U.K., Kingston upon Thames, United Kingdom; *Int'l*, pg. 1514
Van West, W.S., Pres.--Case France, S.A., Vierzon, France; *U.S. Public*, pg. 1579
van Wyk, Riaan, Mgr.--Sasol Carbo-Tar, Rosebank, South Africa; *Int'l*, pg. 1196
Van Wyk, T.J., Mng. Dir.--KLM/ERA Helicopters, Amsterdam, Netherlands; *Int'l*, pg. 719
van Zandbeek, Willem, Mng. Dir.--Van Zandbeek/The Corporate Company, Eindhoven, Netherlands; *Int'l*, pg. 118
Van Zandt, Russell, Pres.--Intervascular, S.A., La Ciotat, France; *U.S. Public*, pg. 488
Van Zant, David, Pres.--Sureco Inc., Fort Valley, GA; *U.S. Public*, pg. 1390
Van Zant, Norman, V.P. & Gen. Mgr.--Wynn's-Precision Fluid Sealing Div., Lynchburg, VA; *U.S. Public*, pg. 1783
Van Zele, Eric, Dir.-Belgium--Raychem N.V., Kessel-Lo, Belgium; *U.S. Public*, pg. 1362
Van Zeller, F., Mng. Dir.--Metal Portuguesa S.A., Vila Franca de Xira, Portugal; *U.S. Public*, pg. 619
Van Zliet, Peter, Pres.--Furness North America Inc., Houston, TX; *Int'l*, pg. 530
van Zutphen, Rik S.F., Mng. Dir.--Shandwick Van de Meeberg PR, Hague, Netherlands; *Int'l*, pg. 1227
Van Zyl, E.W., Deputy Chief Exec.--Delta S.A. (Pty.) Ltd., Sandown, South Africa; *Int'l*, pg. 392
Van, Michael D., Mgr.--Commercial Metals Company, Tampa, FL; *U.S. Public*, pg. 413
van't Hoff, R., Mng. Dir.--Amici, Houten, Netherlands; *Int'l*, pg. 750
van't Hooft, E., Pres.--Delft Instruments Defense BV, Delft, Netherlands; *Int'l*, pg. 388
van't Klooster, Gerard J.M., Mgr.--Barenbrug Research Wolfheze, Wolfheze, Netherlands; *Int'l*, pg. 166
van't Zelfde, W.C., Mng. Dir.--Van Leeuwen Stainless, Beesd, Netherlands; *Int'l*, pg. 1449
VanBenthuysen, Walter G., Chm. Bd. & Chief Exec. Officer--Hazelwood Farms Bakeries, Inc., Hazelwood, MO; *U.S. Public*, pg. 1541
Vanbever, Fernand, Gen. Mgr.--Institut de Reescompte et de Garantie, Brussels, Belgium; *Int'l*, pg. 147
Vanco, David, Pres.--Management Data Service, Elmhurst, IL; *U.S. Public*, pg. 1687
Vandaele, Herman, Mng. Dir.--Bekaert Coordinatiecentrum, Kortrijk, Belgium; *Int'l*, pg. 183
Vandagriff, Nick, Pres.--Holley Replacement Parts Division, Bowling Green, KY; *U.S. Public*, pg. 402
Vandam, Evan, Plant Mgr.--Sealy Mattress Company - Phoenix, Phoenix, AZ; *U.S. Private*, pg. 979
Vande Noorde, Edwin L., Sr. V.P. & Gen. Mgr.--Ball Aerospace Systems Division, Boulder, CO; *U.S. Public*, pg. 171
Vande Steeg, Nickolas W., Pres.--Seal Group, Irvine, CA; *U.S. Public*, pg. 1262
Vandedas, H., Gen. Mgr.--Van Melle Nederland Services B.V., Breda, Netherlands; *Int'l*, pg. 1451
Vanden Bulck, Werner, Chief Oper. Officer--Neste Shipping Benelux, N.V., Antwerp, Belgium; *Int'l*, pg. 915
Vandenberghe, Dirk, Gen. Mgr.--Decosteel N.V., Geel, Belgium; *Int'l*, pg. 79
Vandenberghe, Johan, Gen. Mgr.--Cofrafer S.A., Bonneuil-sur-Marne, France; *Int'l*, pg. 79
Vandenbroeck, W., Mng. Dir.--Amoco Fina N.V., Antwerp, Belgium; *U.S. Public*, pg. 102
Vandenbroucke, G., Gen. Mgr.--Runoto Belgium, Mechelen, Belgium; *Int'l*, pg. 651
Vander Helm, Gordon, Pres.--Sierra Spring Water Company, Sacramento, CA; *Int'l*, pg. 322
Vander Helm, P., Mgr.-Bus. Unit--Long Oil Coolers, Inc., Sheffield, PA; *Int'l*, pg. 815
Vander Heyden, William, Pres.--Badger Meter Industrial Div., Milwaukee, WI; *U.S. Public*, pg. 165
Vander Leegf, W., Pres.--Steelweld BV, Breda, Netherlands; *Int'l*, pg. 71
Vander Leegh, W., Pres.--Vimarc, Breda, Netherlands; *Int'l*, pg. 71
Vander Putten, A., V.P. & Gen. Mgr.--Micro-Tube Fabricators Inc., Middlesex, NJ; *U.S. Public*, pg. 780
Vanderlinden, Daniel, Chm.--Henrijean & Cie. S.A., Brussels, Belgium; *U.S. Public*, pg. 1049
Vandermeulen, E.S.J.B.M., Pres.--Nucletron BV, Veenendaal, Netherlands; *Int'l*, pg. 389
Vanderminden, Robert D., Pres. & Treas.--Mettowee Lumber & Plastic Co., Inc., Granville, NY; *U.S. Private*, pg. 1074
Vanderploeg, Mark, Branch Mgr.--Financial Collection Agencies, Toronto, Canada; *Int'l*, pg. 470
VanderPoll, Frank, Mng. Dir.--Gandalf Nederland B.V., Hoofddorp, Netherlands; *Int'l*, pg. 540
Vanderslice, John, Pres.--Aydin Vector Div., Newtown, PA; *U.S. Public*, pg. 158
Vanderslice, John, Mgr.--Plastic Suppliers, Inc., Mount Laurel, NJ; *U.S. Private*, pg. 871
Vanderzee, John B., Chm.--Young & Rubicam Detroit, Detroit, MI; *U.S. Private*, pg. 1198
Vandevoort, Gerald, V.P. & Gen. Mgr.--Military Avionics Division, Minneapolis, MN; *U.S. Public*, pg. 834
Vandiver, F. William, Jr., Pres.--NationsBank Overseas Corp., Charlotte, NC; *U.S. Public*, pg. 1165
Vanexan, Peter D., V.P.-Boise Cascade Office Products--Grand & Toy Limited, Don Mills, Canada; *U.S. Public*, pg. 243
Vangal, Ramesh, Mng. Dir.--Pepsi Foods Private Ltd., Channo, India; *U.S. Public*, pg. 1277
Vanghelder, Marc, Gen. Mgr.--EURO RSCG Est, Strasbourg, France; *Int'l*, pg. 600
Vanghelder, Marc, Gen. Mgr.--EURO RSCG Opinions, Issy-les-Moulineaux, France; *Int'l*, pg. 601
Vanghelder, Marc, Gen. Mgr.--EURO RSCG Est, Mulhouse, France; *Int'l*, pg. 601
VanGils, Tony, Gen. Mgr.--Gamko Holdings, Etten-Leur, Netherlands; *U.S. Public*, pg. 1497
vanGorp, H.A., Mng. Dir.--Logistic Services Division, Rotterdam, Netherlands; *Int'l*, pg. 1144
Vanhemelen, C., Gen. Mgr.--ING Lease Belgium, Aartselaar, Belgium; *Int'l*, pg. 650
Vanini, Luigi, V.P.-European Grp.--Loctite Italia S.p.A., Milan, Italy; *Int'l*, pg. 611
Vanlandingham, Donald W., Pres.--Ball Aerospace & Technologies Corp., Broomfield, CO; *U.S. Public*, pg. 171
VanLanen, Charles, Mgr.-Reg. Sls.--Interstate Steel Supply Co. of Maryland, Baltimore, MD; *U.S. Public*, pg. 1100
Vann, Bill, Plant Mgr.--Donaldson Co., Inc., Nicholasville, KY; *U.S. Public*, pg. 517
Vann, Les, V.P. & Mgr.-Station--WICD-TV, Champaign, IL; *U.S. Private*, pg. 439
Vanoverloop, Paul, Repr.--Kredietbank Representative Office (Prague), Prague, Czech Republic; *Int'l*, pg. 760
Vanson, Jean Claude, Gen. Mgr. & Dir.--Mobil Oil Abu Dhabi Inc., Abu Dhabi, United Arab Emirates; *U.S. Public*, pg. 1119
Vansten, Dan, Mgr.-Turkey--Raychem Elektro Yalitim Sistemleri Limited Sirkety, Istanbul, Turkey; *U.S. Public*, pg. 1362
Vanstone, Roger, V.P.--MSI Data International, European Hdqtrs., Brussels, Belgium; *U.S. Public*, pg. 1546
Vantillard, Alain, Chief Oper. Officer--Chemie Linz France S.A.R.L., Bezons, France; *Int'l*, pg. 356
Vanvliet, Robert, Gen. Mgr.--Van Melle Far East Ltd.-China Branch, Wan Chai, Hong Kong; *Int'l*, pg. 1451
VanWinkle, Gene, Gen. Mgr.--Omaha Auto Auction Inc., Omaha, NE; *U.S. Public*, pg. 1649
Vara, Francisco Javier Alvarez, Pres.--CASA - Construcciones Aeronauticas, S.A., Madrid, Spain; *Int'l*, pg. 1224
Varakian, Robert, Pres.--B.Via International Housewares, Inc., Franklin Park, IL; *U.S. Public*, pg. 566
Varanyananda, Vinai, Country Mgr.--Wang Thailand Ltd., Bangkok, Thailand; *U.S. Public*, pg. 1738
Vardanega, Roland, Chief Oper. Officer--Automobiles Peugeot S.A., Paris, France; *Int'l*, pg. 1020
Vardanega, Roland, Chm. Bd.--Peugeot-Citroen Moteurs (PCM), Nanterre, France; *Int'l*, pg. 1021
Vardeman, J. Rex, Pres.--Vertex Antennentechnik GmbH, Duisburg, Germany; *U.S. Public*, pg. 1718
Varesco, Ron, Gen. Mgr.--Cleveland Wood Products, Cleveland, OH; *U.S. Public*, pg. 217
Varga, C., Pres.--Freios Varga S/A, Limeira, Brazil; *Int'l*, pg. 820
Varga, George F., Pres. & Chief Exec. Officer--G.E. Tungstram Co., Vaciut, Hungary; *U.S. Public*, pg. 713
Varga, Steve, Pres.--Vitalaire Corporation, Walnut Creek, CA; *Int'l*, pg. 37
Varga, Steve T., Gen. Mgr.--Wabash Fibre Box Co.-Columbia, Columbia, TN; *U.S. Private*, pg. 1170
Vargas, B., Country Mgr.--ING Bank Bogota, Bogota, Colombia; *Int'l*, pg. 649
Vargas, B., Country Mgr.--ING Baring Securities (Andean Pact), Bogota, Colombia; *Int'l*, pg. 649
Vargas, Juan Carlos, Mgr.-Office--Woodward-Clyde de Mexico, S.A. de C.V., Coyoacan, Mexico; *U.S. Public*, pg. 1658
Vargas, Marisol, Chief Admin. Officer--Skandia Vida, S.A., Mexico, Mexico; *Int'l*, pg. 1258
Vargazon, Katja, Media Dir.--Votan Leo Burnett, Ljubljana, Slovenia; *U.S. Private*, pg. 186
Vargha, E., V.P. & Gen. Mgr.--New Stanton Div., Hillsboro, OH; *Int'l*, pg. 1243
Varholick, Joe, Pres.--Microdot/Recoil, Placentia, CA; *U.S. Public*, pg. 940
Varielles, Guy, Dir.--Essilor of America, Glen Head, NY; *Int'l*, pg. 462
Varis, Erkki, Mng. Dir.--Oy Metsa-Botnia AB, Espoo, Finland; *Int'l*, pg. 863
Varjabedian, H., Pres.--La Compagnie Foundation Limitee, Laval, Canada; *Int'l*, pg. 118
Varjas, Miguel A., Gen. Mgr.--AlliedSignal Materiaux de Friction S.A. Zona Franca, Barcelona, Spain; *U.S. Public*, pg. 54
Varju, Laszvo, Mng. Dir.--Malev Midwest Regional Office, Chicago, IL; *Int'l*, pg. 834

Varlet, Jean-Francois, Mng. Dir.--BNP Public Limited Co. (London), London, United Kingdom; *Int'l*, pg. 164
Varley, Brian, Mng. Dir.--Tyco Valves Limited, Manchester, United Kingdom; *U.S. Public*, pg. 1651
Varley, Christopher G., Mng. Dir.--Anheuser-Busch European Trade Ltd., London, United Kingdom; *U.S. Public*, pg. 115
Varley, S., Mng. Dir.--Powell Duffryn International Fuels Ltd., Harpenden, United Kingdom; *Int'l*, pg. 1065
Varn, Rex E., Pres.--Sonoco Ltd., Brantford, Canada; *U.S. Public*, pg. 1487
Varner, Larary, Pres.--Tyco, Spencer, NC; *U.S. Public*, pg. 1058
Varner, Ted, Pres. & Chief Oper. Officer--Convenience Stores Distributors, Richmond, IN; *U.S. Public*, pg. 1049
Varnum, Al, Mgr.-Opers.--JE Merit Constructors, Inc., Lakeland, FL; *U.S. Public*, pg. 921
Varriale, Sergio, Dir.--Banca d'America e d'Italia S.P.A. (Pescara), Pescara, Italy; *Int'l*, pg. 403
Vartanian, Vartan, Company Head--SKF Centr. Handlowo-Techn. Sp. z.o.o., Warsaw, Poland; *Int'l*, pg. 1158
Varvello, Pietro, Mng. Dir.--McGraw-Hill Libri Italia, S.r.l., Milan, Italy; *U.S. Public*, pg. 1072
Vasami, Ralph J., Pres.--Fiberlux, Inc., Purchase, NY; *U.S. Public*, pg. 1634
Vasan, K.N.K., Representative--Ballast Nedam Dredging, Mumbai, India; *Int'l*, pg. 134
Vasetti, M., Gen. Mgr.--AlliedSignal France SpA, Modugno, Italy; *U.S. Public*, pg. 54
Vashegyi, Gabor, Gen. Mgr.--KONE M-Lift Rt., Budapest, Hungary; *Int'l*, pg. 747
Vasilauskas, A., V.P. & Gen Mgr.--Southern Clay Products Inc., Gonzales, TX; *Int'l*, pg. 802
Vasiloff, C.P., Pres.-N.E. Asia--Tokyo Ryuki Seizo Co., Ltd., Yokohama, Japan; *U.S. Public*, pg. 878
Vasquez, Gloria, Branch Mgr.--Downey Savings & Loan Association, F.A., Campbell, CA; *U.S. Public*, pg. 527
Vasquez, Hector J., Gen. Mgr.--John Crane Colombia, Bogota, Colombia; *Int'l*, pg. 1340
Vass, David T., Pres.--Bondex Intl., Inc., Saint Louis, MO; *U.S. Public*, pg. 1357
Vassallo, John, Pres.--Dynapac Concrete Equipment AB, Ljungby, Sweden; *Int'l*, pg. 1420
Vasseur, Jacky, Dir. General--Banque Internationale pour L'Afrique en Guinee (BIAG), Conakry, Papua New Guinea; *Int'l*, pg. 548
Vasseva, Tanya, Fin.--Leo Burnett Advertising, Sofia, Bulgaria; *U.S. Private*, pg. 184
Vatanen, Leo, Mng. Dir.--Prospectus Ltd., Helsinki, Finland; *Int'l*, pg. 859
Vatanen, Matti, Mng. Dir.--Kesko Export Ltd., Helsinki, Finland; *Int'l*, pg. 732
Vaubel, Dirk, Dr., Pres.--Vaubel & Partners Ltd., Tokyo, Japan; *Int'l*, pg. 405
Vaughan-Johnson, Charles, Pres.--Bermuda Trust (Guernsey) Limited, Saint Peter Port, United Kingdom; *Int'l*, pg. 151
Vaughan, Brian, Pres.--Reuters America Inc., New York, NY; *Int'l*, pg. 1106
Vaughan, D.M., Mng. Dir.--Moygashel Ltd., Dungannon, United Kingdom; *Int'l*, pg. 798
Vaughan, David, Mng. Dir.--Rank Entertainment Limited, Maidenhead, United Kingdom; *Int'l*, pg. 1087
Vaughan, George C., Chief Oper. Officer--Alamo Forest Products, Inc., San Antonio, TX; *U.S. Private*, pg. 1135
Vaughan, I., Pres.--Van Leer Australia Pty. Ltd., Epping, Australia; *Int'l*, pg. 1146
Vaughan, J.H., V.P.--Gulf Telephone Co., Jacksonville, FL; *U.S. Public*, pg. 1427
Vaughan, J.H., V.P.--St. Joe Telephone & Telegraph Company, Jacksonville, FL; *U.S. Public*, pg. 1427
Vaughan, J.H., Pres.--St. Joe Communications, Inc., Port Saint Joe, FL; *U.S. Public*, pg. 1427
Vaughan, Jimmy, V.P. & Gen. Mgr.--Webb Electric Co., Farmington Hills, MI; *U.S. Private*, pg. 1156
Vaughan, P. J., Sec.--THORN EMI (Ireland) Limited, Tallaght, Ireland; *Int'l*, pg. 428
Vaughan, Stanley, Gen. Mgr.--Nashua Photo Products Div., Nashua, NH; *U.S. Public*, pg. 1152
Vaughan, Stanley, Gen. Mgr.--Nashua Photo Inc., Parkersburg, WV; *U.S. Public*, pg. 1152
Vaughn, Frank, Gen. Mgr.--General Prods. Div., Henderson, NC; *U.S. Public*, pg. 1272
Vaughn, J.H., Jr., Mgr.--Electrical Equipment Company, Augusta, GA; *U.S. Private*, pg. 368
Vaughn, Li, Branch Mgr.--Downey Savings & Loan Association, F.A., Encinitas, CA; *U.S. Public*, pg. 526
Vaughn, Martin, Pres.--American Brokerage Corporation, Hartford, CT; *U.S. Private*, pg. 863
Vaughn, Matt, V.P. & Gen. Mgr.--Cott Corporation - Pacific South West Region, San Bernardino, CA; *Int'l*, pg. 338
Vaughn, Millard V., Div. Mgr.--Camdel Metals Division, Camden-Wyoming, DE; *U.S. Public*, pg. 780
Vaughn, Ronald H., Pres.--Neapco, Inc., Pottstown, PA; *U.S. Private*, pg. 1113
Vaughn, Steve, Plant Mgr.--Hydro Conduit Corp., Wilson, NC; *Int'l*, pg. 246
Vaughn, T.J., Pres. & Gen. Mgr.--WAND Television, Inc., Decatur, IL; *U.S. Public*, pg. 11
Vaught, Randall, Publr.--The Casey County News, Liberty, KY; *U.S. Private*, pg. 648
Vaushn, Jim, Gen. Mgr.--FTZ Industries, Inc., Simpsonville, SC; *U.S. Private*, pg. 558
Vauthier, T., Pres.--Labatt Breweries British Columbia, New Westminster, Canada; *Int'l*, pg. 679
Vavra, John, Sr. V.P.-Sls. & Mktg.--Ascom Hasler Mailing Systems, Inc., Shelton, CT; *Int'l*, pg. 86
Vavrinek, Don, Gen. Mgr.--Little Nickel Want Ads, Lynnwood, WA; *U.S. Public*, pg. 983
Vayn, Patrick, Chief Oper. Officer--NIFE France S.A., Saint Cloud, France; *Int'l*, pg. 53
Vayrila, Juha, Pres.--Betomix AO, Saint Petersburg, Russia; *Int'l*, pg. 1200
Vayssie, Michel, Chief Oper. Officer--Banco Banque Nationale de Paris Brasil S/A, Sao Paulo, Brazil; *Int'l*, pg. 164
Vazquez, Edgardo N., Sr. V.P.--U.S. Operations Div., Hato Rey, PR; *U.S. Public*, pg. 176
Vazquez, Emilio, Branch Mgr.--Union-Transport Corporation-Tampa Office, Tampa, FL; *U.S. Private*, pg. 1120
Vazquez, J.R., Chief Oper. Officer--Construcciones Instalaciones Babcock S.A. de C.V., Polanco, Mexico; *Int'l*, pg. 474
Vazquez, Jose Luis, Chief Admin. Officer & Mng. Partner--Arthur Andersen, Chicago, IL; *U.S. Private*, pg. 72
Vazquez, Maria, Chief Oper. Officer--Banco Santander-Suiza, Geneva, Switzerland; *Int'l*, pg. 143
Vazzano, Thomas, Pres.--Welcome Wagon-Intl., Inc., Trumbull, CT; *U.S. Public*, pg. 321
Vdcoff, George J., Mng. Dir.--Ferrolegeringar AG, Dubendorf, Switzerland; *U.S. Private*, pg. 735
Veal, Brian, Pres.--Mirtone, Downsview, Canada; *U.S. Public*, pg. 727
Veale, Keith, Gen. Mgr.--Peyton Meats, El Paso, TX; *U.S. Public*, pg. 75
Veazey, Arthur E., Pres.--President Baking-Bishop Div., Cleveland, TN; *Int'l*, pg. 1069
Vecchia, George S., Pres.--New England Wholesale Drug Company, Brockton, MA; *U.S. Public*, pg. 229
Vecetta, Serge, Pres. & Chief Exec. Officer--Household Bank F.S.B., Newport Beach, CA; *U.S. Public*, pg. 842
Vecoli, C., Mgr.-Prod.--Scanalytics, Billerica, MA; *U.S. Public*, pg. 283
Vecten, Philippe, Chm. & Chief Exec. Officer--MDPA, Wittelsheim, France; *Int'l*, pg. 459
Vedelsby, P.O., Supvr.--Kodak & H-Color A/S, Korsor, Denmark; *U.S. Public*, pg. 552
Vedelsby, P.O., Supvr.--Kodak & H-Color A/S, Risskov, Denmark; *U.S. Public*, pg. 552
Vedo, Rene, Mng. Dir.--ISS Data A/S, Copenhagen, Denmark; *Int'l*, pg. 656
Vedo, Rene, Mng. Dir.--ISS Tele Response, Copenhagen, Denmark; *Int'l*, pg. 656
Vedoy, Arne W., Pres.--Kvaerner Singapore Pte Ltd, Singapore, Singapore; *Int'l*, pg. 768
Vedrenne, Arnaud, Chief Exec. Officer--Banque du Credit Agricole (Suisse) S.A., Geneva, Switzerland; *Int'l*, pg. 341
Veerman, Andre, Pres.--Leaf Germany, Hagen, Germany; *Int'l*, pg. 638
Veerman, Andre, Pres.--Leaf Holland B.V., Amsterdam, Netherlands; *Int'l*, pg. 638
Vega, Edward, V.P.-Consulting Svcs.--Financial Research Associates, Manchester, MO; *U.S. Private*, pg. 407
Vegel, Magne G., Chief Oper. Officer--NAPS Norway A/S, Oslo, Norway; *Int'l*, pg. 913
Veghte, Robert I., Pres. & Chief Exec. Officer--Wheaton Inc., Millville, NJ; *Int'l*, pg. 67
Vehara, Norio, Mng. Dir.--MIM Industries, Inc., Miamisburg, OH; *Int'l*, pg. 229
Vehmas, Jaakko-Pekka, Mng. Dir.--Finnish Rich Coffee Ltd., Vantaa, Finland; *Int'l*, pg. 732
Veilledent, Louis, Mng. Dir.--Eurafrican Bank (Tanzania) Ltd., Dar es Salaam, Tanzania; *Int'l*, pg. 548
Veilleux, Jacques, Chief Fin. Officer--Bromptonville Mill, Bromptonville, Canada; *Int'l*, pg. 761
Veillon, Jean, Pres.--Waterman S.A., Saint-Herblain, France; *U.S. Public*, pg. 745
Veirto, Heikki, Chief Oper. Officer--Nokia Plant, Nokia, Finland; *Int'l*, pg. 863
Veiser, Minika, Mgr.--Lexmark France, Paris, France; *U.S. Public*, pg. 991
Veit, David M., Pres.--Pearson, Inc., New York, NY; *Int'l*, pg. 1026
Veitengruber, Dieter, Mng. Dir.--A.C. Nielsen Co., GmbH, Frankfurt/Main, Germany; *U.S. Public*, pg. 1183
Veith, M.P., Chief Oper. Officer--Prometheus AG, Liestal, Switzerland; *Int'l*, pg. 443
Vela, Martin, Reg. Mgr.--Green Tree Acceptance, Inc., Jacksonville, FL; *U.S. Public*, pg. 762
Velarde, Francisco Javier Herrero, Pres.--Agra S.A., Lamiaco, Spain; *Int'l*, pg. 1436
Velasco, C., Mng. Dir.--Toshiba Medical Systems S.A., Madrid, Spain; *Int'l*, pg. 1407
Velasquez, Gary, Chief Oper. Officer & V.P.--Foundation Health PsychCare Services, Rancho Cordova, CA; *U.S. Public*, pg. 678
Veldkamp, Donald J., Pres.--Union Insurance Company, Lincoln, NE; *U.S. Public*, pg. 216
Velez, William, Mgr.--Automax Finance, Santurce, PR; *U.S. Public*, pg. 644
Vella, T., V.P.--Moore Products Co. (Canada), Inc., Brampton, Canada; *U.S. Public*, pg. 1129
Vellano, Vittorio, Chief Exec. Officer--Fiat USA Inc., New York, NY; *Int'l*, pg. 483
Vellucci, Vinnie, V.P.--Arrow/Schweber Electronics, Wilmington, MA; *U.S. Public*, pg. 133
Velly, Jean-Pierre, Mng. Dir.--Avnet Composants and Avnet Time, Chatillon, France; *U.S. Public*, pg. 155
Veloso, Hector, Gen. Mgr.--McCormick (Guangzhou) Food Company, Ltd., Guangzhou, China; *U.S. Public*, pg. 1067
Velot, Gerard, Priject Mgr.--JO DZ Int/Impregilo/Istaka Karya, Sumatera Barat, Indonesia; *Int'l*, pg. 823
Velthorst, H. W., Mng. Dir.--DYWIDAG-Systemen Nederland B.V., Zaltbommel, Netherlands; *Int'l*, pg. 424
Vendl, Charles J., Gen. Mgr.--Tuthill Pump Company of California, Concord, CA; *U.S. Private*, pg. 1111
Vendroux, Etienne, Chief Oper. Officer--Le Livre de Paris, Vanves, France; *Int'l*, pg. 792
Venetis, Petros, Chm. Bd.--Leo Burnett Athens, Athens, Greece; *U.S. Private*, pg. 184
Veneziale, Dominick, Act. Plant Mgr.--Silgan Containers, Evansville, IN; *U.S. Public*, pg. 1473
Vengroff, Harvey, Chief Exec. Officer--Vengroff Williams Realty Management, Centerport, NY; *U.S. Private*, pg. 1135
Venier, Gianmarco, Chm. Bd. & Mng. Dir.--Caboto International S.A., Lugano, Switzerland; *Int'l*, pg. 138
Venkatesh, B., Pres.--The Burke Institute, Covington, KY; *U.S. Private*, pg. 120
Venkateswaran, Ambi, Sr. V.P. & Country Mgr.--Bank of America NT&SA, New Delhi, India; *U.S. Public*, pg. 182
Venkateswaran, R., Resident Rep.--The World Bank, Kigali, Rwanda; *U.S. Private*, pg. 1190
Venneman, Henk, Mng. Dir.--ESTA B.V., Utrecht, Netherlands; *Int'l*, pg. 282
Venneman, Henk, Gen. Mgr.--Polarcup Sweden, Solna, Sweden; *Int'l*, pg. 639
Venold, Einar, Pres.--Det Norske Veritas Eiendom A/S, Hovik, Norway; *Int'l*, pg. 396
Venowa, Masahiro, Pres. & Mng. Dir.--Isuzu-General Motors Australia Ltd., Melbourne, Australia; *Int'l*, pg. 693
Venowa, Masahiro, Pres. & Mng. Dir.--Isuzu-General Motors Australia Ltd., Melbourne, Australia; *U.S. Public*, pg. 725
Venskys, Zigmundas, Chief Oper. Officer--AB Akerlund & Rausing, Litovskaya, Lithuania; *Int'l*, pg. 33
Ventosa, Martinet H., Sr. V.P. & Media Dir.--Hemisphere-Leo Burnett, Inc., Manila, Philippines; *U.S. Private*, pg. 184
Ventre, Marc, Pres. & Chief Exec. Officer--Fan Blade Associates, Inc., Wilmington, DE; *Int'l*, pg. 1166
Ventura, Jules C., Pres.--DCI Kids, New York, NY; *U.S. Private*, pg. 348
Venturi, Guiseppi, Exec. V.P.-US Opers.--G.D. Packaging Machinery Inc., Richmond, VA; *Int'l*, pg. 531
Venturini, Dario, Gen. Mgr.--Florasynth Italia S.R.L., Milan, Italy; *Int'l*, pg. 173
Venturini, Joseph L., Gen. Mgr.--Fasson Produtos Adesivos Ltda., Vinhedo, Brazil; *U.S. Public*, pg. 154
Venturini, Paolo, Mng. Dir.--Olivetti Argentina S.A.C. e I., Buenos Aires, Argentina; *Int'l*, pg. 1003
Verberk, W.M., Dir.--Interbeton B.V., Rijswijk, Netherlands; *Int'l*, pg. 630
VerBerkmoes, Krien III, Pres.--Bank One Wisconsin Investment Services Corporation, Milwaukee, WI; *U.S. Public*, pg. 174
Verbkel, Bert, Dir.-Mktg.--Eli Lilly Nederland B.V., Nieuwegein, Netherlands; *U.S. Public*, pg. 994
Vercoe, P.N., Dir.--MB Overseas Limited, Reading, United Kingdom; *Int'l*, pg. 267
Vercruysse, A., Mng. Dir.--DYWIBEL N.V., Herentals, Belgium; *Int'l*, pg. 424
Verdi, Nicholas, Pres.--Hudson United Bank-Cedar Grove, Cedar Grove, NJ; *U.S. Public*, pg. 845
Verdiani, Piero, Mng. Dir.--Ambrasoft International, Copenhagen, Denmark; *Int'l*, pg. 1002
Verdile, Louis, Mgr.-Sls.--PENCO-New York, Albany, NY; *Int'l*, pg. 1508
Verdon, Raymond J., Pres.--Nabisco Biscuit Company, East Hanover, NJ; *U.S. Public*, pg. 1355
Verdonk, Johannes P., Mng. Dir.--OPEL Nederland B.V., Sliedrecht, Netherlands; *U.S. Public*, pg. 723
Verduzio, L., Chm.--Zanussi Elettromeccanica S.p.A., Pordenone, Italy; *Int'l*, pg. 442
Verduzio, L., Chm.--Zanussi Metallurgica S.p.A., Maniago, Italy; *Int'l*, pg. 442
Verduzio, L., Chm.--IN.F.A. S.p.A., Aviano, Italy; *Int'l*, pg. 442
Verduzio, L., Chm.--Propria s.r.l., Pordenone, Italy; *Int'l*, pg. 442
Veret, Yves, Chm. Bd.--Matra Cap Systems, Velizy-Villacoublay, France; *Int'l*, pg. 792
Verey, Alan, Gen. Mgr.--Viking Office Products Pty. Ltd., North Rocks, Australia; *U.S. Public*, pg. 1721
Verey, David, Chief Exec. Officer--Lazard Brothers & Co. Ltd., London, United Kingdom; *Int'l*, pg. 1026
Verga, Nicoletta, Mng. Dir. & Media Dir.--Gariboldi Parisi Verga/Interad, Milan, Italy; *U.S. Private*, pg. 678
Vergani, Bruna, Media Dir.--Leo Burnett Co., S.r.l., Milan, Italy; *U.S. Private*, pg. 185
Vergara, Rodolfo L., Mng. Dir.--American Appraisal Thailand Ltd., Bangkok, Thailand; *U.S. Private*, pg. 50
Vergari, Marco, Mgr.--Hellerman Elettro Srl, Limena, Italy; *Int'l*, pg. 207
Vergeront, Thomas A., V.P. & Gen. Mgr.-Lake States Div.--Wausau-Mosinee Papers Specialty Papers Group, Rhinelander, WI; *U.S. Public*, pg. 1747
Verges, Henri, Pres.--Auxitrol S.A., Saint Cloud, France; *U.S. Public*, pg. 594
Vergnes, Bernard P., Pres.--Microsoft Europe, Paris, France; *U.S. Public*, pg. 1108
Vergon, James F., Chm. Bd.--CILCORP Investment Management Inc., Peoria, IL; *U.S. Public*, pg. 367
Vergona, A.B., Pres. & Gen. Mgr.--LVT, Rochester, NY; *U.S. Public*, pg. 551
Vergona, Albert, Chief Oper. Officer--Light Valve Technology, Rochester, NY; *U.S. Public*, pg. 551
Verhagen, C.H., V.P., Treas. & Sec.--AEGON Reinsurance Company of America, Short Hills, NJ; *Int'l*, pg. 26
Verhagen, C.H., V.P.-Tres. & Sec.--AEGON U.S. Holding Corp., Short Hills, NJ; *Int'l*, pg. 26
Verhagen, Cor H., Pres.--International Life Investors Insurance Company, New York, NY; *Int'l*, pg. 27
Verhagen, J.K., Pres. & Chief Oper. Officer--Compaction America, Kewanee, IL; *U.S. Public*, pg. 1676
Verhamme, M., Chief Oper. Officer--Danone, Brussels, Belgium; *Int'l*, pg. 379
Verheecke, C.M., Mng. Dir.--Premark Food Equipment Group Belgium, N.V., Zaventem, Belgium; *U.S. Public*, pg. 1323
Verhelst, L.A.P.A., Dir.--Exploitatiemaatschappij Leliegracht B.V., Nieuw-Vennep, Netherlands; *Int'l*, pg. 751
Verheul, Peet W.B., Mng. Dir.--IMd Micon BV, Barneveld, Netherlands; *Int'l*, pg. 607
Verhey, J., Mng. Dir.--Ascom EBS Elektronische Bank Systeme GmbH, Frickenhausen, Germany; *Int'l*, pg. 86
Verheye, Alain, Gen. Mgr.--Nairn Sol SA, Reims, France; *Int'l*, pg. 498
Verhoeven, George, Mgr.--Sandvik Benelux B.V., Schiedam, Netherlands; *Int'l*, pg. 1186

Verhoeven, Georges, Mgr.--Sandvik Benelux, Brussels, Belgium; *Int'l*, pg. 1186
Verhoeven, Joe, Gen. Mgr.--Rawlings Canada, Mississauga, Canada; *U.S. Public*, pg. 1362
Verhulst, David, Plant Mgr.--Dean Foods Vegetable Company, Cambria, WI; *U.S. Public*, pg. 490
Verjee, M., Gen. Mgr.--Signode Packaging Systems Limited, Nairobi, Kenya; *U.S. Public*, pg. 869
Verkade, F., Pres.--Van Leer (Malaysia) Sdn. Bhd., Petaling Jaya, Malaysia; *Int'l*, pg. 1147
Verkamp, Gilbert, Pres. & Chief Exec. Officer--Aristokraft, Inc., Jasper, IN; *U.S. Public*, pg. 675
Verlag, Orbis, Chier Oper. Officer-Munich--Mosaik Verlag, Munich, Germany; *Int'l*, pg. 190
Verlander, Chris A., Pres.--Florida Associated Services, Inc., Jacksonville, FL; *U.S. Public*, pg. 79
Verlodt, Gerrit, Gen. Mgr.--Limburg Local Head Office, Hasselt, Belgium; *Int'l*, pg. 147
Vermeer, J.B., Ph., V.P.-Intl.--Johnson & Johnson International, Sydney, Australia; *U.S. Public*, pg. 930
Vermeerbergen, Herman W., Mng. Dir.--General Motors Suisse S.A., Bienne, Switzerland; *U.S. Public*, pg. 723
Vermeeren, A.F.J., Chm. Bd.--Organon Pakistan (Private) Limited, Karachi, Pakistan; *Int'l*, pg. 45
Vermeeren, A.G., Pres.--Akzo Pharma Nederland B.V., Oss, Netherlands; *Int'l*, pg. 44
Vermeeren, A.G.J., Pres.--Akzo Pharma B.V., Oss, Netherlands; *Int'l*, pg. 44
Vermeulen, A.A., Gen. Mgr.--Nationale-Nederlanden Life, Milan, Italy; *Int'l*, pg. 651
Vermeylen, P. F., Chief Oper. Officer--Wanson Co. Ltd., Borehamwood, United Kingdom; *Int'l*, pg. 472
Vermille, Marc, Mng. Dir.--Banque Indosuez-South Africa, Johannesburg, South Africa; *Int'l*, pg. 314
Vermillion, Jim, Mgr.--Karchmer Iron & Metal Company, Springfield, MO; *U.S. Public*, pg. 413
Vernacchio, Pete, Gen. Mgr.--Arrow/Schweber Electronics, Marlton, NJ; *U.S. Public*, pg. 134
Vernegaard, Neils P., Pres.--H.H.U.K., Inc., Louisville, KY; *U.S. Public*, pg. 405
Vernerey, Jean-Jacques, Plant Mgr.--Delco Products Division, Evian-les-Bains, France; *U.S. Public*, pg. 724
Verni, Ralph F., Pres. & Chief Exec. Officer--New England Investment Associates, Boston, MA; *U.S. Private*, pg. 737
Verni, Ralph F., Chm. Bd., Pres. & Chief Exec. Officer--State Street Research & Management Company, Boston, MA; *U.S. Private*, pg. 738
Verni, Ralph F., Chm. Bd.--State Street Research Investment Services, Inc., Boston, MA; *U.S. Private*, pg. 738
Verni, Ralph F., Pres. & Chief Exec. Officer--New England Pension & Annuity Co., Boston, MA; *U.S. Private*, pg. 738
Vernick, Mitchell F., Pres. & Chief Exec. Officer--Transamerica Commercial Finance Corp., Inc., Chicago, IL; *U.S. Public*, pg. 1630
Vernikovsky, Zack, V.P.--Mercury Air Cargo, Los Angeles, CA; *U.S. Public*, pg. 1093
Vernizzi, Alberto, Mng. Dir.--Bipiemme-Gestione Polizze di Assicurazione S.p.A., Milan, Italy; *Int'l*, pg. 137
Vernon, W. Anthony, Pres.--Johnson & Johnson/Merck Consumer Pharmaceuticals Co., Whitehouse Station, NJ; *U.S. Public*, pg. 929
Verona, Dominic J., Pres.--National Marine, Inc., New Orleans, LA; *U.S. Private*, pg. 1135
Veronesi, Georgio, Mng. Dir.--Foster Wheeler Eastern Private Limited, Singapore, Singapore; *U.S. Public*, pg. 677
Veroni, Clive, Pres. & Chief Exec. Officer--Stringer Veroni Ketchum Advertising, Toronto, Canada; *U.S. Private*, pg. 617
Veronick, Donna, V.P. & Branch Mgr.--Clearwater Branch Office, Clearwater, FL; *U.S. Public*, pg. 1683
Verre, J., Pres. & Chief Exec. Officer--Esso Societe Anonyme Francaise, Rueil-Malmaison, France; *U.S. Public*, pg. 602
Verresa, A., Pres.--Brabants Nieuwsblad BV, Roosendaal, Netherlands; *Int'l*, pg. 1445
Verrier, Jose, V.P. & Gen. Mgr.--Imprimerie Quebecor Bromont, Bromont, Canada; *Int'l*, pg. 1077
Verrycken, R., Chief Oper. Officer--N.V. Polyfilla Products SA, Machelen, Belgium; *Int'l*, pg. 1501
Versavel, Erik, Chief Rep.--Bank Brussels Lambert - Jakarta Representative Office, Jakarta, Indonesia; *Int'l*, pg. 148
Verschoor, J., Chief Oper. Officer--Nedship Bank, Central, Hong Kong; *Int'l*, pg. 1082
Verschuren, P.T.M.M., Chief Oper. Officer--Peco Suikerwerken B.V., Breda, Netherlands; *Int'l*, pg. 1451
Versluijs, H., Dir.--Baars Marketing GmbH, Neuwied, Germany; *Int'l*, pg. 752
Versluys, F., Pres.--Delft Instruments Electro-Optics B.V., Delft, Netherlands; *Int'l*, pg. 389
Versluys, F., Pres.--OIP N.V., Oudenaarde, Belgium; *Int'l*, pg. 389
Versock, Gottfried, Pres.--Flender Corporation, Elgin, IL; *Int'l*, pg. 400
Verstraete, Claude, Mng. Dir.--A.C. Nielsen Co. (Belgium) S.A., Brussels, Belgium; *U.S. Public*, pg. 1183
Verstraete, Roy M., Pres.--Velcro Canada Inc., Brampton, Canada; *Int'l*, pg. 1462
Verver, R.W., Mng. Dir.--Verosol Nederland B.V., Enschede, Netherlands; *Int'l*, pg. 198
Verzijl, Willem I., Gen. Mgr.--Forbo Krommenie B.V., Krommenie, Netherlands; *Int'l*, pg. 497
Vesala, H., Mng. Dir.--Hellermann Finland, Vantaa, Finland; *Int'l*, pg. 209
Veskivali, Ain, Chief Oper. Officer--Balti Pakend, Tallinn, Estonia; *Int'l*, pg. 33
Vesstan, Kevin, Pres.--Indeck Energy Services, Inc., Buffalo Grove, IL; *U.S. Private*, pg. 559
Vest, Jerry, Pres.--Federal Savings Bank, Fort Smith, AR; *U.S. Private*, pg. 614
Vestal, David, Pres. & Chief Oper. Officer--Vestal Manufacturing, Sweetwater, TN; *U.S. Public*, pg. 1737
Vestergaard, Vagn, Chief Oper. Officer--Granges Metalock A/S, Copenhagen, Denmark; *Int'l*, pg. 441
Vesterinen, Eero, Mng. Dir.--K-linkki Oy, Helsinki, Finland; *Int'l*, pg. 732
Vetrano, Frank, Resident V.P.--Fireman's Fund Indemnity Corporation, Parsippany, NJ; *Int'l*, pg. 59
Vetri, George, Div. Mgr.--Rogers Cable TV-Mississauga Div., Mississauga, Canada; *Int'l*, pg. 1122
Vettier, Jean Paul, Pres.--Total Raffinage Distribution S.A., Levallois-Perret, France; *Int'l*, pg. 1409
Vettoretti, Daniel, Gen. Mgr.--Colgate-Palmolive Del Ecuador, S.A., Guayaquil, Ecuador; *U.S. Public*, pg. 398
Veyder, Frank, Gen. Mgr.--Banque Generale de Luxembourg, Hong Kong, Hong Kong; *Int'l*, pg. 548
Veyron, Pierre, Chief Exec. Officer & Dir.--Soparco, Conde-sur-Huisne, France; *Int'l*, pg. 430
Vezina, Jean, Dir.--Allied Research Corporation Limited, Vienna, VA; *U.S. Public*, pg. 49
Vezza, Richard J., Pres.--Gremac Inc., Hackensack, NJ; *U.S. Private*, pg. 693
Viaene, Hugo M., Pres.--China American Petrochemical Co., Ltd., Taipei, Taiwan; *U.S. Public*, pg. 102
Viang, H.J., Chief Oper. Officer--Van Leeuwen Pipe & Tube, Seoul, Korea; *Int'l*, pg. 1450
Viani, Steve, Mgr.-Opers.--Geo-Con, Inc., Rancho Cordova, CA; *U.S. Public*, pg. 1657
Viarengo, Robert P., Pres.--AlliedSignal Performance Materials, Morristown, NJ; *U.S. Public*, pg. 51
Viars, E. Leon, Pres.--Maremont Exhaust Systems Product Division, Loudon, TN; *U.S. Public*, pg. 137
Viars, E. Leon, Pres.--Gabriel Ride Control Products Division HQ, Brentwood, TN; *U.S. Public*, pg. 137
Viars, Leon, Pres.--Maremont Exhaust System Division, Loudon, TN; *U.S. Public*, pg. 137
Viatte, Jean-Claude, Mng. Dir.--Larousse (Suisse) SA, Geneva, Switzerland; *Int'l*, pg. 240
Viboolmeth, Nipon, Pres.--Siam City Credit Finance & Securities Co., Ltd., Bangkok, Thailand; *Int'l*, pg. 1239
Vicenc, Robert, Gen. Dir.--Marcam Spain, Barcelona, Spain; *U.S. Public*, pg. 1043
Vichich, William M., Chief Oper. Officer--Citizens Federal Bank, F.S.B., Dayton, OH; *U.S. Public*, pg. 376
Vicic, Joseph J., Pres.--Parker Hannifin Hong Kong Ltd., Fluid Handling Headquarters, Kwai Chung, Hong Kong; *U.S. Public*, pg. 1263
Vick, G. Etheridge, Mng. Dir.--CCA International, Inc., Nashville, TN; *U.S. Public*, pg. 451
Vickers, K.G., Pres. & Chief Exec. Officer--Courtaulds (Canada) Inc., Cornwall, Canada; *Int'l*, pg. 339
Vicky, B., Gen. Mgr.--Total Indonesie, Jakarta, Indonesia; *Int'l*, pg. 1409
Victory, S.P., Pres.--Hudson Engineering & Project Management Services, Houston, TX; *U.S. Public*, pg. 1068
Vidal, A., Chief Oper. Officer--Binks de Mexico, S.A. de S.V., Mexico, Mexico; *U.S. Public*, pg. 229
Vidal, Anthony, Pres.--Sycom Services Inc., Alexandria, VA; *U.S. Public*, pg. 773
Vidal, Christian, Mng. Dir.--Dumez Guyane, Kourou, French Guiana; *Int'l*, pg. 823
Vidal, M., Mng. Dir.--Alcantara, Lisbon, Portugal; *Int'l*, pg. 1357
Vidal, P., Pres.--Societe Nanceienne Varin-Bernier, Nancy, France; *Int'l*, pg. 565
Vidalenche, Gerard, Mng. Dir.--Investir Publications, Paris, France; *Int'l*, pg. 780
Vidan, Michael A., V.P.-Gypsum & Roofing--Georgia-Pacific Gypsum Div., Atlanta, GA; *U.S. Public*, pg. 735
Videler, Fre, Mng. Dir.--Bovil, Maastricht, Netherlands; *Int'l*, pg. 117
Videon, Spence, Chief Exec. Officer--Snowshoe Resort, Inc., Snowshoe, WV; *Int'l*, pg. 685
Vidil, Patrick, Dir.--GTM Guadeloupe, Petit Bourg, Guadeloupe; *Int'l*, pg. 823
Vieira, Carlos, Chief Oper. Officer--Lusotecna, Lisbon, Portugal; *Int'l*, pg. 1361
Vieira, Irving, Reg. Pres.--Melitta do Brasil Industria e Comercio Ltda., Sao Paulo, Brazil; *Int'l*, pg. 857
Vienne, Brigitte, Dir.--Societe de Reassurance des Risques Relatifs aux Applications Spatiales (S3R), Evry, France; *Int'l*, pg. 81
Vienneau, Henri P., Pres. & Gen. Mgr.--Mallinckrodt Canada, Inc., Pointe-Claire, Canada; *U.S. Public*, pg. 1040
Vierimaa, Johannes, Chief Oper. Officer--Ahlstrom Machinery Karhula Steel Foundry, Karhula, Finland; *Int'l*, pg. 33
Viering, Manfred, Pres.--Skanska Property GmbH, Hamburg, Germany; *Int'l*, pg. 1260
Viering, Peter, Co-Chief Oper. Officer--International Finance Division, Dusseldorf, Germany; *Int'l*, pg. 645
Vierkant, Eberhard, Mng. Dir.--Wilh. Schauman GmbH, Hamburg, Germany; *Int'l*, pg. 1429
Vietor, Sandy, Pres. & Chief Exec. Officer--Willis Corroon Marine & Energy, New York, NY; *Int'l*, pg. 1508
Viets, Victor, Mgr.-Office--Woodward-Clyde, Portland, OR; *U.S. Public*, pg. 1656
Viezzoli, Dr. F., Dir.--Fiat Auto S.p.A., Milan, Italy; *Int'l*, pg. 481
Vigeland, Pal, Plant Mgr.--Hydro Aluminium Holmestrand Rolling Mill, Holmestrand, Norway; *Int'l*, pg. 959
Viger, Pierre, Sr. V.P.-Quebec & the Maritimes Div.--Quebec & Maritimes Div. St. Lawrence Cement, Quebec, Canada; *Int'l*, pg. 629
Vigh, Donald A., Chief Oper. Officer & Exec. V.P.--Kimble Glass Inc., Vineland, NJ; *Int'l*, pg. 1464
Vigier, Marc Noel, Pres.--Editions du Moniteur, Paris, France; *Int'l*, pg. 239
Vigier, Marc-Noel, Pres.--Groupe L.S.A., Paris, France; *Int'l*, pg. 239
Vigil, Evelyn, Editor & Publshr.--Los Alamos Monitor, Los Alamos, NM; *U.S. Private*, pg. 648
Vigild, Peter, Mng. Dir.--Hydap S.A., Herblay, France; *Int'l*, pg. 1285
Vignau, P., Chm. Bd.--Chevron Chemical S.A., Neuilly-sur-Seine, France; *U.S. Public*, pg. 348
Vigo, Aig, Exec. Chm.--Heinemann Educational Nigeria Limited, Ibadan, Nigeria; *Int'l*, pg. 1094
Viise, Jaan, V.P.--United Missouri Trust Company of New York, New York, NY; *U.S. Public*, pg. 1655
Viitamo, Juhani, Mng. Dir.--Finnish Fibreboard Ltd., Heinola, Finland; *Int'l*, pg. 1428
Viitanen, Hannu, Gen. Mgr.--Merita Bank Ltd. London Branch, London, United Kingdom; *Int'l*, pg. 859
Vijil, Javier, Admin.--INAMEX S.A., Mexico, Mexico; *U.S. Public*, pg. 364
Viken, William, Gen. Mgr.--Union Cement Co., Ras al Khaimah, United Arab Emirates; *Int'l*, pg. 1201
Vikki, Kirsti, Chief Oper. Officer--Novo Nordisk A/S, Espoo, Finland; *Int'l*, pg. 987
Vila Cascals Sergio, Dir.--Generale Bank - Banco Belga, Barcelona, Spain; *Int'l*, pg. 547
Vila, Raul, Chief Oper. Officer--Puerto Rico Tourism Company, New York, NY; *U.S. Private*, pg. 894
Vilaitanarak, Vivat, Mng. Dir.--Synergie Tokyu DMB&B Ltd., Bangkok, Thailand; *U.S. Private*, pg. 305
Viland, Joseph, Pres.--Wabash Alloys Division, Wabash, IN; *U.S. Private*, pg. 264
Vilar-Andrade, Jaime Mario, Dr., Dir.--Pemex Petroquimica, Mexico, Mexico; *Int'l*, pg. 1046
Vilas, J.M., Gen. Mgr.--Knorr Portuguesa-Produtos Alimentares S.A., Lisbon, Portugal; *U.S. Public*, pg. 225
Vilas, Jose Maria, Pres.--CPC Spain, S.A., Barcelona, Spain; *U.S. Public*, pg. 225
Vilgrain, P., Chief Oper. Officer--Grande Semoulerie de L'Ouest a Gond-Pontouvre, Paris, France; *Int'l*, pg. 556
Viljanen, Seppo, Mng. Dir.--Oy Kalmar LMV, Pori, Finland; *Int'l*, pg. 1421
Vilkin, George, Pres.-Forest City Residential West, Inc.--Forest City Residential Development Inc., Cleveland, OH; *U.S. Public*, pg. 669
Villa-Massone, Gilbert, Chm. Bd. & Pres.--Gachot S.A., Montmorency, France; *U.S. Public*, pg. 1650
Villa, Aldo, Dir.--Banca d'America e d'Italia S.p.A. (Genoa), Genoa, Italy; *Int'l*, pg. 403
Villa, E., Mng. Dir.--Saunier Duval Italia Srl, Milan, Italy; *Int'l*, pg. 615
Villa, Emilio, Gen. Mgr.--Grace Italiana S.p.A., Milan, Italy; *U.S. Public*, pg. 756
Villa, F.J., Jr., Pres.--C & W Railway Co., Pueblo, CO; *U.S. Public*, pg. 1230
Villa, Rodolfo Martin, Pres.--Central Nuclear Vandellos II A.I.E., Barcelona, Spain; *Int'l*, pg. 1224
Villafane, Miguel A., Gen. Mgr.--Caribe Grolier, Inc., Santurce, PR; *Int'l*, pg. 794
Villafrance, Emanuele, Mng. Dir.--Jacuzzi Europe, S.p.A., Pordenone, Italy; *U.S. Public*, pg. 1684
Villalobos, Gloria, Admin.--Mountain View Place, El Paso, TX; *U.S. Public*, pg. 839
Villalobos, Oscar, Mgr.--Procermex Inc., San Antonio, TX; *U.S. Public*, pg. 115
Villani, Edmond D., Pres. & Chief Exec. Officer--Scudder Kemper Investments, Inc., New York, NY; *Int'l*, pg. 1530
Villante, Marcelo Oscar, Gen. Mgr.--John Crane Argentina, Buenos Aires, Argentina; *Int'l*, pg. 1339
Villanueva, Joaquin, Chief Exec.--Umar-Union Maritima Internacional S.A., Madrid, Spain; *Int'l*, pg. 629
Villar, Salvador, Pres. & Chief Exec. Officer--California Commerce Bank, Los Angeles, CA; *Int'l*, pg. 574
Villarejo, Juan Temboury, Pres.--ELECBRO - Termoelectrica del Ebro, S.A., Escatron, Spain; *Int'l*, pg. 1224
Villarino, C.R., Gen. Mgr.--Kodak Chilena S.A.F., Santiago, Chile; *U.S. Public*, pg. 553
Villarreal, J., Mng. Dir.--THORN, Madrid, Spain; *Int'l*, pg. 1386
Villarreal, Marcelino, Pres.--Vitro, Sociedad Anonima - Flat Glass Div., Garza Garcia, Mexico; *Int'l*, pg. 1469
Villegas, Jorge, Gen. Dir.-Communication Strategies--Graffiti/DMB&B, Buenos Aires, Argentina; *U.S. Private*, pg. 304
Villemejane, Michel, Chief Oper. Officer--Club Mediterranee S.A. Belge, Brussels, Belgium; *Int'l*, pg. 298
Villicana, Miguel, Gen. Mgr.--Chrysler de Mexico, Ramos Arizpe, Mexico; *U.S. Public*, pg. 354
Villijn, Fred, Gen. Mgr.--Medtronic Belgium, Strombeek-Bever, Belgium; *U.S. Public*, pg. 1083
Villneff, Larry T., Pres.--Ikon Office Solutions (Alberta), Calgary, Canada; *U.S. Public*, pg. 864
Villneff, Larry T., Pres.--Ikon Office Solutions, Edmonton, Canada; *U.S. Public*, pg. 864
Viloni, Eugenio, Chief Oper. Officer--Triton Columbia, Inc., Bogota, Colombia; *U.S. Public*, pg. 1640
Vilsmeier, Gerhart, Mng. Dir.--Heraeus Quarzglas GmbH, Hanau, Germany; *Int'l*, pg. 616
Vimercati, Piero Angelo, Chm. Bd.--La Centrale Consulenza S.p.A., Milan, Italy; *Int'l*, pg. 138
Vincent, Ben, V.P.--Wilsey Foods, Inc., Fort Worth, TX; *Int'l*, pg. 879
Vincent, D. Glenn, Pres.--Hilb, Rogal and Hamilton Company of Daytona Beach, Inc., Daytona Beach, FL; *U.S. Public*, pg. 827
Vincent, G., Chief Exec. Officer--P.T. Monier Indonesia, Jakarta, Indonesia; *Int'l*, pg. 1091
Vincent, Robin, Mng. Dir.--Clarins (UK) Ltd., London, United Kingdom; *Int'l*, pg. 295
Vincent, Thomas, Pres.--American Electric Co., Ltd., Honolulu, HI; *U.S. Public*, pg. 65
Vincent, William, Regional Mng. Dir.--Pier 1 Imports Canada, Ville Saint Laurent, Canada; *U.S. Public*, pg. 1295
Vinciarelli, Patrizio, Pres.--VLT Corporation, Andover, MA; *U.S. Public*, pg. 1719
Vinciarelli, Patrizio, Pres.--Vicor International, Andover, MA; *U.S. Public*, pg. 1719
Vincour, John, Exec. Editor--International Herald Tribune S.A., Neuilly-sur-Seine, France; *U.S. Public*, pg. 1176

Vinding, Joergen, Mng. Dir.--ISS Hospital Service A/S, Copenhagen, Denmark; *Int'l*, pg. 656
Vindum, J., Pres.--Core Research, Inc., Mountain View, CA; *U.S. Public*, pg. 1003
Vine-Lottt, Anthony K., Chm. Bd.--Barclays Bank Trust Co. Ltd., London, United Kingdom; *Int'l*, pg. 164
Viner, Anthony P., Pres.--Rogers CHFI-FM, Toronto, Canada; *Int'l*, pg. 1123
Viner, P.F., Mktg. Dir.--British-American Tobacco Co. (Singapore) Ltd., Singapore, Singapore; *Int'l*, pg. 111
Vines, Roger A.G., Sir, Chm. Bd.--Alcoa of Australia Limited, Melbourne, Australia; *U.S. Public*, pg. 62
Vingoe, John, Chm.--MTD Products Limited, Kitchener, Canada; *U.S. Private*, pg. 688
Vining, G.W., Pres.--Farmers New World Life Insurance Co., Mercer Island, WA; *Int'l*, pg. 110
Vinke, Nick, Pres.--Colgate Oral Pharmaceutical, Canton, MA; *U.S. Public*, pg. 397
Vinotti, Guiliano, Dir.--Olin Hunt Specialty Products S.r.l., Milan, Italy; *U.S. Public*, pg. 1220
Vinsonneau, M., Chief Exec. Officer--OCE-France S.A., Noisy-le-Grand, France; *Int'l*, pg. 994
Vinther, Jorgen Pilgaard, Mgr.-Sls.--Fibo ExClay Polska Sp.z.o.o., Szczecin, Poland; *Int'l*, pg. 1200
Vinuela, Jorge, Chief Oper. Officer--Esis International Asesorias Limitada, Santiago, Chile; *U.S. Public*, pg. 363
Viola, F., Pres.--Sharp Electronics (Italia) S.p.A., Milan, Italy; *Int'l*, pg. 1230
Violand, Basil, Pres.--Fleming Foods of Ohio, Inc., Massillon, OH; *U.S. Public*, pg. 653
Viort, Bernard, Chm. Bd.--Gie Amadeus France, Issy-les-Moulineaux, France; *Int'l*, pg. 560
Vipond, Mike, Pres.--USSI, Carter Lake, IA; *U.S. Public*, pg. 1629
Virata, Luis, Mng. Dir.--Exchange Capital Corporation, Manila, Philippines; *Int'l*, pg. 493
Virciglio, Paul, V.P. & Gen. Mgr.--WNEM-TV, Saginaw, MI; *U.S. Public*, pg. 1094
Virgilio, Abramo, Pres.--Bristol Europe S.p.A., Latina, Italy; *U.S. Public*, pg. 255
Virgilio, Abramo, Ph.D., Pres.--Bristol-Myers Research, Hillside, NJ; *U.S. Public*, pg. 254
Virley, Peter, Mng. Dir.--Scherer DDS Ltd., Swindon, United Kingdom; *U.S. Public*, pg. 1438
Virtanen, Jorma, Mgr.-Production--NUS Scandinavia AB, Stockholm, Sweden; *U.S. Private*, pg. 787
Virtue, Douglas A., V.P. & Gen. Mgr.--Virco-Torrance Division, Torrance, CA; *U.S. Public*, pg. 1721
Virtue, Glen, Mgr.-Plant--Nestle Beverage Company, Union City, CA; *Int'l*, pg. 917
Vis, S.F., Representative--Seoul Representative Office, Seoul, Korea; *Int'l*, pg. 651
Visagle, Unre v.B., Gen. Dir.--Marcam Southern Africa, Midrand, South Africa; *U.S. Public*, pg. 1043
Visca, Alessandro, Chief Oper. Officer--Ahlstrom Papeis Ltda., Louveira, Brazil; *Int'l*, pg. 35
Visciano, Amedeo, Dir.--Banca d'America e d'Italia S.p.A. (Bari), Bari, Italy; *Int'l*, pg. 403
Visconti, Gian Luca, Chief Oper. Officer--Rotta Farmaceutici, S.p.A., Milan, Italy; *Int'l*, pg. 1112
Viscusi, E., Chm.--AGIP Petroleum Co., Inc., Dover, DE; *Int'l*, pg. 428
Viseter, Sigurd, Pres.--Kvaerner Kleven Ulsteinvik A/S, Ulsteinvik, Norway; *Int'l*, pg. 769
Viseu, Guy, Mng. Dir.--Bertrand Faure Equipamentos para Automoveis SA, San Joao da Madeira, Portugal; *Int'l*, pg. 193
Visichio, Philip, Mgr.--Brambles Security Services Inc., Jamaica, NY; *Int'l*, pg. 211
Visscher, Frans, Mng. Dir.--Elsevier Science (The Netherlands), Amsterdam, Netherlands; *Int'l*, pg. 1099
Visscher, Frans, Mng. Dir.--Elsevier Science Limited, Kidlington, United Kingdom; *Int'l*, pg. 1100
Visser, A.G., Mng. Dir.--De Geillustreerde Pers/MC, Amsterdam, Netherlands; *Int'l*, pg. 1445
Visser, A.G., Mng. Dir.--De Geillustreerde Pers bv, Amsterdam, Netherlands; *Int'l*, pg. 1445
Visser, Frits, Mng. Dir.--Kemira Agro Pernis B.V., Rotterdam, Netherlands; *Int'l*, pg. 729
Visser, K.J., Dir. Gen.--Zuivelfabriek 'Salland' BV, Dalfsen, Netherlands; *Int'l*, pg. 752
Visser, Reinold, Mfg. Mgr.--Up-Right (Ireland) Ltd., Dublin, Ireland; *U.S. Private*, pg. 1128
Visser, Y., Mng. Dir.--Aannemingsbedrijf Van Oudbroekhuizen B.V., Nieuweglin, Nieuwegein, Netherlands; *Int'l*, pg. 681
Vitale, Alberto, Chm. Bd. & Chief Exec. Officer--Random House, Inc., New York, NY; *U.S. Private*, pg. 20
Vitale, Harold S., Sr. V.P.--Trillium Digital Division, San Jose, CA; *U.S. Public*, pg. 972
Vitale, Martin, Chief Oper. Officer--Twinco Trucking Co., Inc., Edison, NJ; *U.S. Private*, pg. 1111
Vitas, Ted, Mgr.--Stephen Gould of New England, Inc., Tewksbury, MA; *U.S. Private*, pg. 467
Vitito, Robert J., Chm. Bd.--Second National Bank of Saginaw, Saginaw, MI; *U.S. Public*, pg. 379
Vito, Dennis, Pres.--Day & Zimmermann Information Solutions, Wayne, PA; *U.S. Private*, pg. 317
Vittitow, J. Edward, Sr. V.P.--National City Leasing Corporation, Louisville, KY; *U.S. Public*, pg. 1154
Vittore, Ross F., Pres.--Great Northern Mortgage Company, Rolling Meadows, IL; *U.S. Public*, pg. 141
Vittorini, Carlo, Chm. Bd., Publisher, & Chief Exec. Officer--Parade Publications Inc., New York, NY; *U.S. Private*, pg. 20
Vittorini, Carlo, Chm. Bd., Publisher & Chief Exec. Officer--React Magazine, New York, NY; *U.S. Private*, pg. 20
Vitty, D., Mng. Dir.--Wellcome Nigeria Ltd, Lagos, Nigeria; *Int'l*, pg. 553
Vitulano, Lee, V.P. & Gen. Mgr.--Road Champs, Inc., West Caldwell, NJ; *U.S. Public*, pg. 923
Vivario, Michel, Mgr. & Sec.--Audiofina S.A., Luxembourg, Luxembourg; *Int'l*, pg. 561

Vives, Mauricio, Chief Exec. Officer--EURO RSCG Graffiti, Santiago, Chile; *Int'l*, pg. 603
Vivian, David J., Pres.--Rochester-Midland ICL, Omaha, NE; *U.S. Private*, pg. 937
Viviani, Gian-Carlo, Mng. Dir.--Dowty Polypac Spa, Livorno, Italy; *Int'l*, pg. 1338
Viviani, Massimo, Mng. Dir.--EMAP Publishing srl, Milan, Italy; *Int'l*, pg. 451
Viviano, Bill, Pres.--The Prince Co. of Michigan, Warren, MI; *U.S. Private*, pg. 158
Vivona, Bill, Pres.--Harrisburg Stamp Co., Harrisburg, PA; *U.S. Private*, pg. 59
Vizcaino, Carlos, Pres. & Mng. Dir.--Young & Rubicam, S.A. de C.V., Mexico, Mexico; *U.S. Private*, pg. 1200
Vizzini, Paul V., Chief Oper. Officer--Dennison Manufacturing Canada, Inc., Bowmanville, Canada; *U.S. Public*, pg. 153
Vladik, Jaroslav, Gen. Mgr.--Nordson CS, spol.s.r.o., Brno, Czech Republic; *U.S. Public*, pg. 1189
Vlasich, Bill, Pres.--Power Conversion, Inc., Elmwood Park, NJ; *Int'l*, pg. 127
Vlasman, O.A.M., Dir. Gen.--Oud Wijnkopers & Hustinx BV, Haarlem, Netherlands; *Int'l*, pg. 751
Vlcek, Don, Pres.--Domino's Pizza Distribution Corp., Ann Arbor, MI; *U.S. Private*, pg. 339
Vlewiez, William, Pres.--Casablanca Fan Co., Inc., Memphis, TN; *U.S. Private*, pg. 549
Vlielander, Alex, Gen. Mgr.--AAR Aviation Services U.K., Mitcham, United Kingdom; *U.S. Public*, pg. 1
Voelker, Phil, V.P.-Sls. & Mktg. (Western Region)--Northern Telecom Inc., Rochester, NY; *Int'l*, pg. 970
Voeller, Hans Joachim, Gen. Mgr.--Sequent GmbH, Ismaning, Germany; *U.S. Public*, pg. 1460
Voeste, Klaus, Representative--Allianz Shanghai Representative Office, Shanghai, China; *Int'l*, pg. 59
Vogel, A., Pres.--Alpine Aktiengesellschaft, Augsburg, Germany; *Int'l*, pg. 636
Vogel, Dieter H ., Dr., Pres.--Thyssen Handelsunion AG, Dusseldorf, Germany; *Int'l*, pg. 1388
Vogel, Edward P., V.P.--Ferre Export Corp., Valley Stream, NY; *U.S. Public*, pg. 1342
Vogel, George N., Pres.--McLean Engineering, Princeton Junction, NJ; *U.S. Public*, pg. 1791
Vogel, Hans, Mng. Dir.--Dresdner-ABD Securities Ltd., Central, Hong Kong; *Int'l*, pg. 419
Vogel, Manfred, Mng. Dir.--SKF Gleitlager GmbH, Puttlingen, Germany; *Int'l*, pg. 1158
Vogel, Michael, Gen. Mgr.--CCM Framlington Group Plc, London, United Kingdom; *Int'l*, pg. 342
Vogel, Michael J., Pres. & Chief Exec. Officer--Day-Timers of Canada, Limited, Niagara Falls, Canada; *U.S. Public*, pg. 674
Vogel, Peter H., Pres.--Zellerbach Division, Miamisburg, OH; *U.S. Public*, pg. 1074
Vogel, R.B., Mng. Dir.--Hoogovens Steel Strip Mill Products, Ijmuiden, Netherlands; *Int'l*, pg. 754
Vogel, Reener Nippert, Admin.--Productora de Cosmeticos S.A., Mexico, Mexico; *Int'l*, pg. 1490
Vogel, Richard, Dir--Datacolor AG, Zurich, Switzerland; *Int'l*, *pg. 213*
Vogel, Ronald B., Pres.--Great Western Malting Co., Vancouver, WA; *U.S. Public*, pg. 428
Vogelaar, D. M., Mgr. Dir.--NextLevel Systems (Australia), Chatswood, Australia; *U.S. Public*, pg. 716
Vogelezang, Eef, Mng. Dir.--Northprint B.V., Meppel, Netherlands; *Int'l*, pg. 1100
Vogels, Paul, Mng. Dir.--Gesellschaft fuer Markt- und Absatzforschung mbH, Ludwigsburg, Germany; *Int'l*, pg. 1514
Vogelsang, Gerd, Chief Oper. Officer--Precismeca-Montan Gesellschaft fur Fordertechnik mbH, Sulzbach, Germany; *Int'l*, pg. 399
Vogl, H., Gen. Mgr.--Western Operation, Gardena, CA; *U.S. Public*, pg. 1135
Vogler, Ibolya, Rep.--Bayerische Landesbank Girozentrale, Budapest, Hungary; *Int'l*, pg. 177
Vogt-Svendsen, J., Mng. Dir.--J.I. Case Norge A/S, Drammen, Norway; *U.S. Public*, pg. 1579
Vogt, Gunter, Mng. Dir.--Kammer Ventile GmbH, Essen, Germany; *U.S. Public*, pg. 659
Vogt, Hans, Mng. Dir.--Keystone G.m.b.H., Monchengladbach, Germany; *U.S. Public*, pg. 1650
Vogt, Harald, Commerzbank Delegate--Korea International Merchant Bank, Seoul, Korea; *Int'l*, pg. 312
Vogt, Harald, Mgr.--Commerzbank AG Representative Office-Seoul, Seoul, Korea; *Int'l*, pg. 312
Vogt, Valentin, Pres.--Sulzer Metco AG, Wohlen, Switzerland; *Int'l*, pg. 1307
Vogt, Vic, Mgr.--Shepler's Houston South, Houston, TX; *U.S. Public*, pg. 413
Vogtlander, Peter, Pres. & Chief Exec. Officer--Montell Polyolefins, Hoofddorp, Netherlands; *Int'l*, pg. 1136
Vohra, S., Gen. Mgr.--Howard Johnson, Washington, DC; *U.S. Private*, pg. 1067
Voigt, J.W., Chief Oper. Officer--Makro Autoservicio Mayorista, S.A., Madrid, Spain; *Int'l*, pg. 1155
Voigt, Jurgen-Peter, Chm. Bd.--Krupp Hoesch Informationsverarbeitung GmbH, Essen, Germany; *Int'l*, pg. 512
Voigt, K., Gen. Mgr.--AMP Norge A/S, Rud, Norway; *U.S. Public*, pg. 9
Voigtlander, Peter, Region Mgr.--Weatherford Oil Tool GmbH, Langenhagen, Germany; *U.S. Public*, pg. 1750
Vokes, A.R., Gen. Mgr.--Webb Heavy-Duty Roller Conveyor Systems, Harbor Springs, MI; *U.S. Private*, pg. 1156
Vokrouhlikova, Jirina, Chief Oper. Officer--Novo Nordisk A/S, Prague, Czech Republic; *Int'l*, pg. 987
Volanakis, George, Pres.--The Ertl Company, Inc, Dyersville, IA; *U.S. Public*, pg. 1684
Voldbeck, Henrick, Plant Mgr.--Ash Grove Cement-Western Region Cement Plant, Seattle, WA; *U.S. Private*, pg. 88
Vole, Jean Louis, Pres.--Vibratechniques STV, Saint Valery-en-Caux, France; *Int'l*, pg. 1420

Voliotis, D.J., Div. Mgr.--Snap-on Tools International, Ltd. (Middle East/Africa Division), Halandri, Greece; *U.S. Public*, pg. 1481
Volkenborn, Arnold, Pres.--Pequiven, S.A., Caracas, Venezuela; *Int'l*, pg. 1045
Volker, Cathy, Pres.--Hanes Hosiery, Inc., Winston Salem, NC; *U.S. Public*, pg. 1434
Volland, Hansjorg, Mng. Dir.--Volland Telemetry GmbH, Shaftlach, Germany; *Int'l*, pg. 209
Vollaro, John D., Pres. & Chief Exec. Officer--Signet Star Reinsurance Company, Florham Park, NJ; *U.S. Public*, pg. 216
Vollaro, John D., Pres. & Chief Exec. Officer--Signet Star Holdings, Inc., Stamford, CT; *U.S. Public*, pg. 216
Vollmar, Eric L., Pres.--Graphic Research, Inc., Chatsworth, CA; *U.S. Public*, pg. 1101
Vollmar, G.L., Pres. & Chief Oper. Officer--Walbro Automotive Corp., Auburn Hills, MI; *U.S. Public*, pg. 1733
Vollmer, Charles, V.P. & Resident Mgr.--St. Francisville Mill, Saint Francisville, LA; *U.S. Public*, pg. 466
Vollmer, Richard, Office Mgr.--Kintetsu World Express Inc., Erlanger, KY; *Int'l*, pg. 734
Volny, Peter I., Pres., Chief Exec. Officer & New Bus. Contact--Griffin Bacal Volny, Toronto, Canada; *U.S. Private*, pg. 480
Volonte, R., Mng. Dir.--Banca Cantrade Lugano SA, Lugano, Switzerland; *Int'l*, pg. 1439
Volpara, Paolo, Chief Exec. Officer--Markom/Leo Burnett A.S., Istanbul, Turkey; *U.S. Private*, pg. 186
Volpe, C.E., Chief Oper. Officer--Kemet Electronics Corporation, Simpsonville, SC; *U.S. Public*, pg. 949
Volpert, Pierre, Pres.--Worldwide Assistance Services Inc., Washington, DC; *Int'l*, pg. 90
Volpi, V., Mng. Dir.--Swiss Bank Corporation, Tokyo, Japan; *Int'l*, pg. 1330
Volpini, Jorge, Pres.--Banco de la Nacion Argentina, New York, NY; *Int'l*, pg. 140
Volstad, Conrad, Pres.--Merrill Lynch Derivative Products, Inc., New York, NY; *U.S. Public*, pg. 1097
von Armin, Bernd, Dr., Mng. Dir.--Deutsche Bank Berlin AG, Berlin, Germany; *Int'l*, pg. 402
von Blomberg, Peter, Chief Exec. Officer--Allianz Versicherungs-AG, Cologne, Germany; *Int'l*, pg. 58
von Braunmuhl, Hermann W., Dr., Chm.-Exec. Bd.--Delvag Luftfahrtversicherungs-AG, Cologne, Germany; *Int'l*, pg. 407
von Brockhausen, Joachim, Chief Oper. Officer--Frankfurt Consult GmbH, Frankfurt/Main, Germany; *Int'l*, pg. 119
von Broembsen, Tim, Mng. Dir.--Von Broembsen Marson Leo Burnett/Harare, Harare, Zimbabwe; *U.S. Private*, pg. 186
von Czernicki, Helen Muller, Mng. Dir.--Sodra Nederland B.V., Hague, Netherlands; *Int'l*, pg. 1276
von der Goltz, Bernhard Graf, Exec. V.P.--Plus Ultra, Compania Argentina de Seguros S.A., Buenos Aires, Argentina; *Int'l*, pg. 62
von der Osten, Christopher, Pres.--Kassbohrer North America, Gray, ME; *Int'l*, pg. 368
von der Porten, Bob, Pres.--Speedy Muffler King, Inc., Toronto, Canada; *U.S. Public*, pg. 1578
von der Weppen, Ernst, Co-Chief Oper. Officer--Kohlbecher & Co. GmbH, Voelklingen, Germany; *Int'l*, pg. 1166
von Essen, Michael, Chief Oper. Officer--Royal Copenhagen Antiques, Copenhagen, Denmark; *Int'l*, pg. 1134
von Fieandt, Henrik, Mng. Dir.--Industrial Bank of Finland Ltd., Helsinki, Finland; *Int'l*, pg. 859
Von Flaterm, Jon K., Gen. Mgr.--Brumko Magnetics, Elkhorn, NE; *U.S. Private*, pg. 696
von Foerster, Peter, Chief Exec. Officer--Nordcement AG, Hannover, Germany; *Int'l*, pg. 628
von Foerster, Peter, Chief Exec.--Alsen-Breitenburg Zement- un Kalwerke GmbH, Hamburg, Germany; *Int'l*, pg. 629
von Freyberg, Karl Ludwig Freiherr, Chm. Bd. of Mngmt.--Frankfurter Versicherungs-AG, Frankfurt/Main, Germany; *Int'l*, pg. 58
Von Groll, Hubertus, Pres.--Schering Mexicana SA, Mexico, Mexico; *Int'l*, pg. 1204
Von Hall, Birger, Pres.--Goteborg Regional Office, Goteborg, Sweden; *Int'l*, pg. 899
von Holtzbrinck, Dieter, Pres.--Zeitverlag Gerd Bucerius GmbH, Hamburg, Germany; *Int'l*, pg. 1479
von Hymmen, Dirk, Mng. Dir.--Reemtsma International GmbH - Russia, Moscow, Russia; *Int'l*, pg. 1101
von Kalm, Dr., Gen. Mgr.--Voith S.A. Maquinas e Equipamentos, Sao Paulo, Brazil; *Int'l*, pg. 1473
von Kanel, Walter, Mng. Dir.--Certina Gebr. Kurth AG, Grenchen, Switzerland; *Int'l*, pg. 1160
von Kantzow, Lars, Pres.--Perstorp Flooring, Raleigh, NC; *Int'l*, pg. 1039
von Kirchbach, Eckart, Pres.--Georg Fischer Gmbh, Albershausen, Germany; *Int'l*, pg. 489
Von Kleist-Retzow, Heinrich, Pres.--Sachtleben Chemie GmbH, Duisburg, Germany; *Int'l*, pg. 861
von Krempelhuber, Michael, Co-Chief Oper. Officer--Bavarian Branch, Munich, Germany; *Int'l*, pg. 645
von Laufenberg, Dr. Jurgen, Chief Oper. Officer--Gerhard Collardin GmbH, Herborn, Germany; *Int'l*, pg. 609
Von Le Fort, Baron, Pres.--Maxi-Papier Market GmbH, Hamburg, Germany; *U.S. Public*, pg. 1510
von Lobbecke, Peter, Pres.--AGA AG, Pratteln, Switzerland; *Int'l*, pg. 13
von Maack, Wolfgang, Sr. V.P.-Health Services--Manor Healthcare Corp., Gaithersburg, MD; *U.S. Public*, pg. 1041
von Malmborg, Bjorn, Mgr.--Sandvik Espanola S.A., Madrid, Spain; *Int'l*, pg. 1186
Von Memerty, Sandy, Chief Fin. Officer & Controller--Charter Medical of England Ltd., London, United Kingdom; *U.S. Public*, pg. 1036
von Oelreich, Jan, Chief Oper. Officer--Scania Deutschland GmbH, Koblenz, Germany; *Int'l*, pg. 687

Von Ostenbridge, Ron, Gen. Mgr.--K-Tron Electronics, Blackwood, NJ; *U.S. Public*, pg. 938
Von Paucker, H., Gen. Mgr.--Australia and New Zealand Banking Group Limited, New York, New York, NY; *Int'l*, pg. 98
von Pentz, H.D., Dr., Chief Exec. Officer & Mng. Dir.--Hoechst Australia Ltd., Melbourne, Australia; *Int'l*, pg. 626
Von Pichler, Cletus, Pres.--Demag Delaval Turbine, Trenton, NJ; *Int'l*, pg. 837
von Poser, Hilmar, Dr., Mng. Dir.--AVE Gesellschaft fur Horfunkbeteiligungen mbH, Hannover, Germany; *Int'l*, pg. 1478
von Prittwitz, H., Gen. Mgr.--Case Poclain GmbH & Co., Gross-Gerau, Germany; *U.S. Public*, pg. 1579
von Rosenberg Lipinsky, Hans H., Mgr.--Commerzbank AG-Budapest, Budapest, Hungary; *Int'l*, pg. 311
Von Roy, Eric, Gen. Mgr.--Tektronix N.V./S.A., Zaventem, Belgium; *U.S. Public*, pg. 1568
Von Roy, Joachim, Mng. Dir.--Squibb AG, Zurich, Switzerland; *U.S. Public*, pg. 256
von Sahr, Leo, Chief Oper. Officer--Leipzig Branch, Leipzig, Germany; *Int'l*, pg. 645
von Simson, D., Pres.--Societe de Banque Suisse S.A., Paris, France; *Int'l*, pg. 1331
von Sivers, Peter, Mng. Dir.--Skandia Investment Management Ltd., London, United Kingdom; *Int'l*, pg. 1258
von Sury, Adrian, District Sls. Mgr.--Intel Switzerland, Zurich, Switzerland; *U.S. Public*, pg. 887
von Sydow, Henrik, Chief Oper. Officer--Wilson Group, Goteborg, Sweden; *Int'l*, pg. 123
Von Thaden, Arthur G., Chief Opr. Officer--BankAmerica Realty Services, Inc., San Francisco, CA; *U.S. Public*, pg. 181
von Troil, Eric, Mng. Dir.--OY Willis Faber AB, Helsinki, Finland; *Int'l*, pg. 1510
von Wartenberg, Hans-Hartwig, Rep.--Representacion del Deutsche Bank AG (Caracas), Caracas, Venezuela; *Int'l*, pg. 405
von Wyss, Marc R., Pres. & Chief Exec. Officer--Dundee Cement Co., Dundee, MI; *Int'l*, pg. 628
von zer Muhlen, Bernt, Dir.--RTL Radio-Die Grossten Oldies, Luxembourg, Luxembourg; *Int'l*, pg. 561
von zur Muhlen, Bernt, Mng. Dir.--104.6 RTL, Berlin, Germany; *Int'l*, pg. 561
Vonderhaar, Douglas B., Gen. Mgr.--Automation Control, Fond Du Lac, WI; *Int'l*, pg. 1389
Vonnahme, Neil, Exec. V.P.--Rollins Logistics Inc., Wilmington, DE; *U.S. Public*, pg. 1405
Vooges, Phil, Chief Oper. Officer--Frigoscandia Transport B.V., Rotterdam, Netherlands; *U.S. Public*, pg. 607
Voorham, Fred, Chief Oper. Officer--MacGREGOR (NLD) B.V., Rotterdam, Netherlands; *Int'l*, pg. 671
Vooys, J., Pres.--Nederlandse Verzekerings Groep NV, Groningen, Netherlands; *Int'l*, pg. 26
Vora, Ravi, Chief Exec. Officer--Bundy India Ltd., Baroda, India; *Int'l*, pg. 1341
Vorderlondwehr, D.A., Dir.--Sunkist Growers, Inc.-Southern Division, Tucker, GA; *U.S. Private*, pg. 1052
Vorhoff, Stephanie, Sr. V.P.--HMS/Cincinnati, Cincinnati, OH; *U.S. Private*, pg. 492
Vornadoe, Susan C., Pres.--Applied Science Associates, Inc., Mc Lean, VA; *U.S. Public*, pg. 109
Vornanen, Sakari, Pres.--Sahkolahteenmaki Oy, Paimio, Finland; *Int'l*, pg. 8
Vos, Arend W.D., Pres.--PPG Industries Asia/Pacific Ltd., Tokyo, Japan; *U.S. Public*, pg. 1245
Vos, M.J., Mgr.-Mktg. & Sls.--Meneba Meel B.V., Rotterdam, Netherlands; *Int'l*, pg. 555
Vos, W.T.G., Mgr.-Marine Survey Equip.--Radio Holland Group-Survey Equip., Ijmuiden, Netherlands; *Int'l*, pg. 1151
Voscherau, Eggert, Pres. & Chief Exec. Officer--BASF Corporation, Mount Olive, NJ; *Int'l*, pg. 105
Voskuilen, Han, Mng. Dir.--Ancra Espana, Barcelona, Spain; *U.S. Private*, pg. 71
Vosloo, Andre, Mgr.--Butterworths South Africa, Cape Town, South Africa; *Int'l*, pg. 1095
Vosloo, Steve, Mgr.--Allianz Insurance of Namibia Ltd., Windhoek, Namibia; *Int'l*, pg. 59
Voss, Peter S., Chm. Bd. & Chief Exec. Officer--Security Pacific Hoare Govett (Holdings) Limited, London, United Kingdom; *U.S. Public*, pg. 183
Voss, Peter S., Chief Exec. Officer--Hoare Govett Limited, London, United Kingdom; *U.S. Public*, pg. 183
Voss, Peter S., Pres. & Chief Exec. Officer--New England Investment Companies, Inc., Boston, MA; *U.S. Private*, pg. 737
Voss, Peter S., Chm. Bd.--Reich & Tang, New York, NY; *U.S. Private*, pg. 737
Voss, Sarah, Admin.--Greenery Extended Care Center at Farmington, Farmington, MI; *U.S. Public*, pg. 837
Voss, William H., Mng. Dir.--Crown Can Hong Kong Ltd., Tai No, Hong Kong; *U.S. Public*, pg. 464
Voss, William H., Pres.--Crown Cork & Seal, Asia-Pacific Division, Singapore, Singapore; *U.S. Public*, pg. 464
Vosseller, Jim, Pres.--Everpure Inc., Westmont, IL; *U.S. Public*, pg. 467
Vosshenrich, Burkhard, Mng. Dir.--Dresdner (S.E. Asia) Ltd., Singapore, Singapore; *Int'l*, pg. 420
Votel, Richard H., Pres. & Chief Exec. Officer--First American Insurance Agencies, Inc., Saint Paul, MN; *U.S. Private*, pg. 167
Votze, Janet, Branch Mgr.--Circle International, East Boston, MA; *U.S. Public*, pg. 371
Voughn, Steve, Plant Mgr.--Hydro Conduit Corp., Thomasville, NC; *Int'l*, pg. 246
Voulgaris, Spyros, Fin. Dir.--Leo Burnett Athens, Athens, Greece; *U.S. Private*, pg. 184
Voutt, W.B., Gen. Mgr. & Chief Agent--The Hartford Fire Insurance Company, Willowdale, Canada; *U.S. Public*, pg. 794
Voutt, W.B., Pres.--The Great Eastern Insurance Company, Willowdale, Canada; *U.S. Public*, pg. 794
Voutt, W.B., Gen. Mgr. & Chief Agent in Canada--The Hartford Life Insurance Company, Willowdale, Canada; *U.S. Public*, pg. 794
Voutt, W.B., Pres.--London-Canada Insurance Company, Willowdale, Canada; *U.S. Public*, pg. 795
Vouvakis, Jim, Exec. V.P.--U.S. Yellow Pages, Los Angeles, CA; *U.S. Private*, pg. 1168
Vowell, J. Larry, Pres. & Chief Exec. Officer--Hussmann Corp., Bridgeton, MO; *U.S. Public*, pg. 1766
Voyles, Dennis L., V.P. & Branch Mgr.--California State Bank-Newport Beach, Newport Beach, CA; *U.S. Public*, pg. 294
Vraciu, Bob, Pres.--Vivra Health Advantage, Inc., Brentwood, TN; *U.S. Public*, pg. 1724
Vrancart, Al, Pres.--NBS Card Services, Inc., South Plainfield, NJ; *Int'l*, pg. 898
Vrancx, Daniel, Dir.-Novotel Opers.--Societe Internationale des Hotels Novotel, Evry, France; *Int'l*, pg. 21
Vranken, Luk, Mng. Dir.--N.V. Astra Pharmaceuticals S.A., Brussels, Belgium; *Int'l*, pg. 94
Vrba, John, Sr. V.P. & Mng. Dir.--Western International Media Corporation, Newport Beach, CA; *U.S. Private*, pg. 1167
Vrbanatz, Frank, Pres.--Villeroy & Boch Tableware, Ltd., Aurora, Canada; *Int'l*, pg. 1468
Vreeland, Elizabeth, Mgr.--Stewart Smith East, Inc., Cedar Knolls, NJ; *Int'l*, pg. 1508
Vreeman, G., Exec. V.P.--Purac America, Inc., Lincolnshire, IL; *Int'l*, pg. 244
Vreeswijk, Nico, Gen. Mgr.--Gamma Biologicals, B.V., Leiderdorp, Netherlands; *U.S. Public*, pg. 698
Vreewijk, M.E. Th., Gen. Mgr.--ADT Security Systems, Rotterdam, Netherlands; *U.S. Public*, pg. 1649
Vreezen, W.J., Mng. Dir.--Albro Bakkerijen Zwanenburg B.V., Gouda, Netherlands; *Int'l*, pg. 555
Vreezen, William Jan, Mng. Dir.--Etos bv, Zaandam, Netherlands; *Int'l*, pg. 749
Vreys, Frans, Chm.--Delimmo S.A., Brussels, Belgium; *Int'l*, pg. 463
Vriens, J.A., Mng. Dir.--Exploitatiemaatschappij Transportbeton B.V., Diemen, Netherlands; *Int'l*, pg. 134
Vriesenga, Jerry, Pres.--Dole Hawaii, Wahiawa, HI; *U.S. Public*, pg. 515
Vriesman, Wayne, Gen. Mgr.--WGN Radio, Chicago, IL; *U.S. Public*, pg. 1636
Vucekovic, P., Gen. Mgr.--Euralliance, Paris, France; *Int'l*, pg. 499
Vucins, Viesturs, Pres. & Chief Exec. Officer--Global One, Reston, VA; *U.S. Public*, pg. 1501
Vulysteke, D., Mgr.--Morton Salt Division, Manistee, MI; *U.S. Public*, pg. 1135
Vuori, Kari, Chief Oper. Officer--Nummela Plant, Nummela, Finland; *Int'l*, pg. 863
Vuoria, H., Mng. Dir.--Nutricia Fennica Oy, Turku, Finland; *Int'l*, pg. 992
Vuorialho, Kari, Gen. Mgr.--Salcomp Oy, Kemijarvi, Finland; *Int'l*, pg. 951
Vynne, James, Branch Dir.--N.G. Bailey & Co. Ltd.-Manchester Branch, Manchester, United Kingdom; *Int'l*, pg. 132
Waasdorp, Maarten, Gen. Mgr.--Forbo NL Holding B.V., Soest, Netherlands; *Int'l*, pg. 497
Waasdorp, Maarten, Gen. Mgr.--Corepro B.V., Coevorden, Netherlands; *Int'l*, pg. 497
Waasdorp, Maarten, Gen. Mgr.--Forbo s.r.o., Brno, Czech Republic; *Int'l*, pg. 498
Wachenhut, Richard R., Chm. Bd.--Wackenhut Resources, Inc., Palm Beach Gardens, FL; *U.S. Public*, pg. 1731
Wachner, Linda, Pres.--Authentic Fitness Corp. East Coast Region, New York, NY; *U.S. Public*, pg. 148
Wachob, Denny, Mgr.--INX International, Memphis, TN; *Int'l*, pg. 1311
Wachs, Hartmut, Chm.--Rowenta Werke, Offenbach/Main, Germany; *Int'l*, pg. 569
Wachtel, Mike, Chief Oper. Officer--Men's Wear, Oshkosh, WI; *U.S. Public*, pg. 1233
Wachtveitl, Kurt, Gen. Mgr.--The Oriental Hotel (Thailand) pcl, Bangkok, Thailand; *Int'l*, pg. 704
Wacker, Roger, Sr. V.P.--Union Bank of Switzerland, Los Angeles, CA; *Int'l*, pg. 1440
Wackman, Harold E., Country Dir.--The World Bank, Nairobi, Kenya; *U.S. Private*, pg. 1189
Wacznadze, David, Chief Oper. Officer--Safic Alcan & Cie S.A., Puteaux, France; *Int'l*, pg. 862
Wada, H., Mng. Dir.--ESL-Nippon Co. Ltd., Tokyo, Japan; *U.S. Private*, pg. 369
Wada, Hijime, Sr. V.P. & Dir.--Liberty Bank, Honolulu, HI; *Int'l*, pg. 1189
Wada, Horoyoshi, Pres. & Dir.--Tokio Marine Delaware Corporation, Dover, DE; *Int'l*, pg. 1392
Wada, Ken, Dir.--Takenaka (U.K.) Ltd., Cardiff, Cardiff, United Kingdom; *Int'l*, pg. 1352
Wada, Norio, Exec. V.P.-Mfg.--Bridgestone/Firestone Tire Manufacturing Operations, Nashville, TN; *Int'l*, pg. 213
Wada, O., Asst. Gen. Mgr.--Marubeni America Corporation, Boston Office, Burlington, MA; *Int'l*, pg. 844
Wada, Shigeakt, Pres.--Seiyo Food Systems, Ltd., Tokyo, Japan; *Int'l*, pg. 1178
Wada, Tadashi, Pres.--Shin-Etsu Handotai Co. Ltd., Tokyo, Japan; *Int'l*, pg. 1234
Wada, Takanobu, Sr. Mng. Dir.--Brother Industrial Sewing Machines Div., Nagoya, Japan; *Int'l*, pg. 229
Wada, Takao, Gen. Mgr.--The Bank of Tokyo-Mitsubishi, Ltd. (Singapore Branch), Singapore, Singapore; *Int'l*, pg. 158
Wada, Tomoyuki, Mgr.-Plant--Korea High Precision Co., Ltd., Seoul, Korea; *Int'l*, pg. 903
Waddell, William R., Pres.--Capital Resources of Virginia, Inc., Richmond, VA; *U.S. Private*, pg. 657
Waddington, Harold T., Pres.--Ganflec Corporation, Harrisburg, PA; *U.S. Private*, pg. 439
Waddington, Harold T., Pres.--Gannett Fleming Valuation and Rate Consultants, Inc., Harrisburg, PA; *U.S. Private*, pg. 439
Wade, Bill, Pres.--CR Services, Elgin, IL; *Int'l*, pg. 1157
Wade, Margaret, Publisher--The Bismarck Tribune, Bismarck, ND; *U.S. Public*, pg. 983
Wade, Martin, Pres.--Rowe Price-Fleming International Inc., London, United Kingdom; *Int'l*, pg. 493
Wade, Michael, Assoc. Publisher--Sports Afield, New York, NY; *U.S. Private*, pg. 517
Wade, Rod, Mng. Dir.--Talisman (Asia) Ltd., Jakarta, Indonesia; *Int'l*, pg. 1352
Wade, Ruth, Admin.--Ruidoso Care Center, Ruidoso, NM; *U.S. Public*, pg. 838
Wadensten, Ted S., Pres.--Vibco Vibration Products, Mississauga, Canada; *U.S. Private*, pg. 1138
Wadhwani, H.W., Pres.--Kinetics Technology India Ltd., New Delhi, India; *Int'l*, pg. 837
Wadia, Jim, Mng. Partner--Arthur Andersen, Chicago, IL; *U.S. Private*, pg. 72
Wadstein, Thomas, Pres.--Componenta Transport AB, Falkenberg, Sweden; *Int'l*, pg. 1420
Wadsten, Gary, V.P.-Sls.--Fairfield Myrtle Beach, Inc., North Myrtle Beach, SC; *U.S. Public*, pg. 611
Wadsworth, Joe, Gen. Mgr.--Oceaneering Technologies, Ventura, CA; *U.S. Public*, pg. 1211
Wadsworth, John S., Jr., Pres.--Morgan Stanley Japan Ltd., Tokyo, Japan; *U.S. Public*, pg. 1133
Wadsworth, Maurice A., Pres.--Gannett Fleming, Inc., Harrisburg, PA; *U.S. Private*, pg. 439
Wadsworth, Stanley, Pres. & Chief Exec. Officer--Golf Hosts, Inc., Palm Harbor, FL; *U.S. Private*, pg. 1036
Waelchli, Max, Actg. Dir.--Hamilton Bonaduz AG, Bonaduz, Switzerland; *U.S. Private*, pg. 497
Waern, Bo, Pres.--Asea Brown Boveri Inc., Manila, Philippines; *Int'l*, pg. 8
Wafer, Thomas J., Publr.--The Daily Breeze, Torrance, CA; *U.S. Private*, pg. 275
Wafer, Thomas J., Publr.--The News-Pilot, San Pedro, CA; *U.S. Private*, pg. 275
Wafer, Thomas J., Publr.--The Outlook, Santa Monica, CA; *U.S. Private*, pg. 275
Wagemans, A.T.J., Mng. Dir.--Montair Andersen B.V., Sevenum, Netherlands; *U.S. Public*, pg. 462
Wagener, Bert B., Chm.--Cigna Hospital of Los Angeles, Inc., Los Angeles, CA; *U.S. Public*, pg. 360
Wagener, Bert B., Jr., Pres.--Cigna Healthcare of California, Inc., Glendale, CA; *U.S. Public*, pg. 359
Wagener, Bert B., Jr., Pres.--Ross-Loos Health Plan of California, Glendale, CA; *U.S. Public*, pg. 359
Wagener, Bert B., Jr., Pres.--Ross Loos Hospital, Inc., Los Angeles, CA; *U.S. Public*, pg. 360
Wagenvoord, Rob G., Head of Employee Benefits--Willis Corroon Scheuer, Amsterdam, Netherlands; *Int'l*, pg. 1502
Wager, Richard K., V.P. & Publr.--Poughkeepsie Newspapers, Poughkeepsie, NY; *U.S. Public*, pg. 700
Waggerman, Eugene S., Chief Exec. Officer--Perkins-Goodwin Co. Inc., Stamford, CT; *Int'l*, pg. 586
Wagler, Paul, Sr. V.P. & Mgr.--ABN AMRO Bank Canada (Vancouver), Vancouver, Canada; *Int'l*, pg. 11
Wagman, Lee H., Pres.--TrizecHahn Centers Inc., San Diego, CA; *Int'l*, pg. 1425
Wagner, Bruce, Plant Mgr.--Cortland Plant, Cortland, NY; *U.S. Public*, pg. 444
Wagner, Dieter, Mng. Dir.--MMG Division, Goslar, Germany; *U.S. Public*, pg. 1227
Wagner, Dieter, Dr., Mng. Dir.--BASF Argentina S.A., Buenos Aires, Argentina; *Int'l*, pg. 105
Wagner, Earl, Plant Mgr.--Kellogg Convenience Food Plant, Hammonton, NJ; *U.S. Public*, pg. 947
Wagner, Ernst, Gen. Mgr.--Cadillac Plastic GmbH, Viernheim, Germany; *U.S. Public*, pg. 781
Wagner, Fernand, Chm. Bd.--Sidmar N.V., Gent, Belgium; *Int'l*, pg. 79
Wagner, George, Pres.--Worsham Sprinkler Company, Ashland, VA; *U.S. Private*, pg. 1191
Wagner, Gerald E., V.P.--Remote Services, Inc., Louisville, KY; *U.S. Public*, pg. 477
Wagner, Gerd, Opers. Mgr.--Reinshagen U.K., Coventry, United Kingdom; *U.S. Public*, pg. 723
Wagner, Hans, Mng. Dir.--Gunnebo GmbH, Wilnsdorf, Germany; *Int'l*, pg. 578
Wagner, James, V.P.-Opers.--Berlin-Gorham Operations, Berlin, NH; *U.S. Public*, pg. 465
Wagner, Ken, Pres.--Bretec Inc., Englewood, CO; *Int'l*, pg. 1352
Wagner, Knut, Gen. Mgr.--Research Cottrell, Europe, Somerville, NJ; *U.S. Public*, pg. 29
Wagner, N.P., Chm. Bd.--Southern Indiana Properties, Inc., Evansville, IN; *U.S. Public*, pg. 1471
Wagner, Norbert, Chief Oper. Officer--Sonauto S.A., Saint Ouen, France; *Int'l*, pg. 1063
Wagner, Reinhold, Pres.--Alcan Deutschland GmbH, Eschborn, Germany; *Int'l*, pg. 50
Wagner, Robert, V.P. & Mng. Exec.--Northern Trust Bank of Florida, N.A., Longboat Key, FL; *U.S. Public*, pg. 1197
Wagner, Rodger, Pres.--Big Horn Redi-Mix, Powell, WY; *U.S. Public*, pg. 1124
Wagner, Roger P., Pres. & Chief Oper. Officer--Trump's Marina Casino Resort, Atlantic City, NJ; *U.S. Private*, pg. 1108
Wagner, Thomas J., V.P. & Gen. Mgr.--Ford Parts and Service Div., Dearborn, MI; *U.S. Public*, pg. 662
Wagrodzki, Kezysztof, Chm. Bd.--WWT (Wytwornia Wyrobow Tytoniowych) S.A., Poznan, Poland; *Int'l*, pg. 1101
Waguespack, Raymond L., Pres.--Bancomm, Anaheim, CA; *U.S. Public*, pg. 488
Wah, David Yip Choong, Dir.--Takenaka Singapore Pte. Ltd., Singapore, Singapore; *Int'l*, pg. 1352
Wahedna, Javeed, Chm. & Creative Dir.--Wahedna/DMB&B, Karachi, Pakistan; *U.S. Private*, pg. 305

Wahila, Robert, Gen. Mgr.--Athletic Division, Endicott, NY; U.S. Public, pg. 1684

Wahila, Robert, Gen. Mgr.--Empire Division, Endicott, NY; U.S. Public, pg. 1684

Wahl, Andrew, Chief Exec. Officer--Intermark Corp., New York, NY; U.S. Public, pg. 771

Wahl, Ed, Chief Oper. Officer--Clark Oil Trading Company, Saint Louis, MO; U.S. Private, pg. 77

Wahl, J. H., Chm. Bd.--FABC (New York) Grp., New York, NY; Int'l, pg. 163

Wahl, Lothar, Pres. & Chief Oper. Officer--BOMAG, Boppard, Germany; U.S. Public, pg. 1677

Wahl, Nicholas P., Mgr.--Piper Jaffray Inc., Green Bay, WI; U.S. Public, pg. 1301

Wahlberg, Hakan, Pres.--Vipac Vibrator AB, Bromma, Sweden; Int'l, pg. 1420

Wahlberg, Lennart, Mgr.--Stifab Plat AB, Skelleftea, Sweden; Int'l, pg. 1422

Wahle, Elliott, Pres.--Braemar Apparel Inc., Toronto, Canada; Int'l, pg. 425

Wahlqvist, Lars, Mgr.--AB Sandvik Hard Materials, Stockholm, Sweden; Int'l, pg. 1185

Wahlroos, L.A., Mng. Dir.--UPM-Kymmene Far East Pte. Ltd., Singapore, Singapore; Int'l, pg. 1430

Wahrn, Mikael, Mng. Dir. & Gen. Mgr.--Merita Merchant Bank Singapore Ltd., Singapore, Singapore; Int'l, pg. 859

Wai, Semi Leung, Gen. Mgr.--Bermuda Trust (Western Samoa) Limited, Apia, Samoa; Int'l, pg. 151

Waid, Steve, Editor--Winston Cup Illustrated, Charlotte, NC; U.S. Private, pg. 20

Wain, J.I., Mng. Dir.--Barcrest Ltd., Ashton under Lyne, United Kingdom; Int'l, pg. 170

Wain, K.S., Mng. Dir.--Herr Voss Ltd., Derby, United Kingdom; U.S. Private, pg. 962

Wainerdi, Mary, Banking & Fin. Svcs. Officer--Troy Savings Bank-Clifton Park Hannaford Office, Clifton Park, NY; U.S. Private, pg. 1106

Waintraub, Lionel, Chief Oper. Officer--Proser, Creteil, France; Int'l, pg. 503

Wainwright, R., Chief Oper. Officer--Ancon CLC, Sheffield, United Kingdom; Int'l, pg. 925

Wait, Chuck, V.P. & Gen. Mgr.--Tetko Inc., Depew Operations, Lancaster, NY; U.S. Private, pg. 1078

Wait, John E., Pres.--Banc One-Newark, Newark, OH; U.S. Public, pg. 173

Waite, Paul, V.P.-Opers. (Ottawa)--Loeb Inc., Ottawa, Canada; Int'l, pg. 1073

Waite, Peter G., Pres.--PCC Airfoils, Inc., Beachwood, OH; U.S. Public, pg. 1320

Waite, William, Pres. & Chief Exec. Officer--Siemens Canada Ltd., Pointe-Claire, Canada; Int'l, pg. 1247

Waitkus, Bob, Mgr.-Office--Woodward-Clyde, Blue Bell, PA; U.S. Public, pg. 1656

Wakai, M., Representative--The Kyoei Life Insurance Co., Ltd.-Paris Office, Paris, France; Int'l, pg. 777

Wakamatsu, Shigeo, Gen. Mgr.--Mitsui Trust Bank (Switzerland) Ltd., Zurich, Switzerland; Int'l, pg. 883

Wakasa, K., Pres.--Shimadzu Precision Instruments, Inc., Torrance, CA; Int'l, pg. 1232

Wake, Matthew, Country Mgr.--Standard Chartered Bank (South Korea), Seoul, Korea; Int'l, pg. 1296

Wake, Richard, Pres.--Eby Brown Co., Ypsilanti, MI; U.S. Private, pg. 359

Wake, Richard, Co Pres.--Ohio Eby Brown, Springfield, OH; U.S. Private, pg. 359

Wake, Tom, Co. Pres.--Ohio Eby Brown, Springfield, OH; U.S. Private, pg. 359

Wakefield, Bill, V.P. & Gen. Mgr.--Marshall Erdman & Assoc., Inc., Atlanta, GA; U.S. Private, pg. 380

Wakefield, David A., Chm.--Priory Hospitals Group, London, United Kingdom; U.S. Public, pg. 1716

Wakefield, G.H.C., Chm. Bd.--Guy Carpenter & Co., Inc. New York, NY; U.S. Public, pg. 1048

Wakefield, Larry, Gen. Mgr.--Redding Record Searchlight, Redding, CA; U.S. Public, pg. 1448

Wakeley, M.J., Chm. Bd. & Chief Exec. Officer--Jardine Insurance Brokers Ltd., London, United Kingdom; Int'l, pg. 705

Wakelin, A., Mng. Dir.--Valor Ltd., Birmingham, United Kingdom; Int'l, pg. 925

Wakelin, Alan, Pres.--N.V. Allied Colloids Belgium S.A., Nivelles, Belgium; Int'l, pg. 62

Wakeling, James T., Sr. V.P.-Opers.--Knoll Intl., Inc., East Greenville, PA; U.S. Private, pg. 627

Wakeman, Martyn, Mng. Dir.--Sermatech (U.K.) Limited, Ripley, United Kingdom; U.S. Public, pg. 1570

Waki, Sueo, Mng. Dir.--Toshiba Electronics Scandinavia AB, Bromma, Sweden; Int'l, pg. 1406

Wakita, Masaharu, Gen. Mgr.--Kyodo Advertising Co., Ltd., Kanazawa, Japan; Int'l, pg. 776

Wakiya, Fumio, Chief Rep.--Dai-Ichi Kangyo Bank, Ltd.-Xiamen, Xiamen, China; Int'l, pg. 361

Wakley, James T., Pres.--Colonial Millwork, Inc., Beverly, WV; U.S. Private, pg. 706

Wakuyama, T., Pres.--SEIKO Canada Inc., Markham, Canada; Int'l, pg. 1218

Wakuyama, T., Pres.--SEIKO Time Corp., Mahwah, NJ; Int'l, pg. 1218

Wakuyama, Takashi, Pres.--SEIKO Corporation of America, Mahwah, NJ; Int'l, pg. 1218

Walastyan, Michael, Gen. Mgr.--Global TH, Budapest, Hungary; Int'l, pg. 1376

Walbridge, Timothy P., Sr. V.P. & Branch Mgr.--California State Bank-City of Industry, City of Industry, CA; U.S. Public, pg. 294

Walburn, H. Fred, Pres. & Chief Exec. Officer--Regions Bank/Sumter County, Livingston, AL; U.S. Public, pg. 1373

Walch, Philippe, Mng. Dir.--McDonald's Sistemas de Espana, Madrid, Spain; U.S. Public, pg. 1069

Walcher, Walter, Chief Oper. Officer--Porsche Italia S.p.A Padova, Padua, Italy; Int'l, pg. 1063

Walden, J.F., Pres.--Industrial Water Treatment Co., Houston, TX; Int'l, pg. 37

Walden, N. Russell, Pres.--Ridgewood Properties, Inc., Atlanta, GA; U.S. Public, pg. 1389

Walden, Philip, Pres.--Imperial Business Credit, San Diego, CA; U.S. Public, pg. 872

Waldenvik, A., Chief Exec. Officer--Zurich Forsakring, Stockholm, Sweden; Int'l, pg. 1531

Walder, D.G.T., Mgr.-Sls.--Fluid Connectors Group, Parker Hannifin (U.K.) Ltd., Derby, United Kingdom; U.S. Public, pg. 1261

Waldhof, Jens, Pres.--Rhodia A.G., Freiburg, Germany; Int'l, pg. 1112

Waldhof, Jens, Mng. Dir.--Rhone-Poulenc Rorer GmbH, Cologne, Germany; Int'l, pg. 1113

Waldron, C.H., Area Mgr.--Ballast Wiltshier Plc - South West Region, Clifton, United Kingdom; Int'l, pg. 135

Waldron, C.J., Mng. Dir.--Strand Lighting Limited, Isleworth, United Kingdom; Int'l, pg. 1087

Waldron, W. Daniel, Pres.--Elyria Savings & Trust National Bank, Elyria, OH; U.S. Public, pg. 646

Waldrop, Thomas E., Chm. Bd. & Pres.--Media General Cable of Fairfax County Inc., Chantilly, VA; U.S. Public, pg. 1078

Wale, N., Branch Mgr.--Senior Christchurch Limited, Christchurch, New Zealand; Int'l, pg. 1223

Walentiny, Richard, Gen. Mgr.--Sterling Electronics, Tulsa, OK; U.S. Public, pg. 1051

Waley-Cohen, Stephen, Bt, Sir, Chm. Bd.--Willis Faber & Dumas (Agencies) Limited, London, United Kingdom; Int'l, pg. 1503

Walgers, K., Gen. Mgr.--J.L. de Ball Canada Inc., Montreal, Canada; Int'l, pg. 552

Walicki, Robert R., Pres. & Chief Oper. Officer--Village Pantries, Inc., Indianapolis, IN; U.S. Public, pg. 1049

Waligiorski, Barbara, Gen. Mgr.--GATX Logistics, Inc.-Missouri, Saint Louis, MO; U.S. Public, pg. 691

Walkenhorst, Wilhelm, Mng. Dir.--Alcan Rorschach AG, Rorschach, Switzerland; Int'l, pg. 51

Walker, Bill, Gen. Mgr.--Central States Multiplex, Suwanee, GA; U.S. Private, pg. 16

Walker, Bill, Dir.-Sls. & Mktg.--Superior Machine Systems, Mason, OH; U.S. Private, pg. 1055

Walker, Brad, Chief Exec. Officer--Pretty Polly Limited, Sutton in Ashfield, United Kingdom; U.S. Public, pg. 1434

Walker, Clayton David, Mgr.-Property & Casualty Claims--Willis Corroon Administrative Services Corporation, Mobile, AL; Int'l, pg. 1504

Walker, Clint S., Chief Oper. Officer--ECW, Inc., Rio Linda, CA; U.S. Public, pg. 523

Walker, Cory, Exec. V.P.--Poe & Brown of California, San Francisco, CA; U.S. Public, pg. 1312

Walker, D.T., V.P. & Gen. Mgr.--Acheson Colloids Company, Port Huron, MI; U.S. Private, pg. 12

Walker, Doug, Mng. Dir.--Beazer Homes (Stockport) Limited, Stockport, United Kingdom; Int'l, pg. 182

Walker, Douglas A., Pres.--Chateau St. Jean Winery, Kenwood, CA; Int'l, pg. 1321

Walker, E. Dow, Sr. V.P.-Healthcare Concepts--Willis Faber North America, Inc.-Tennessee, Nashville, TN; Int'l, pg. 1504

Walker, Gary, Pres.--Contech Div. (Kalamazoo), Portage, MI; U.S. Public, pg. 1421

Walker, Geoff, Mng. Dir.--Milk Products Holdings (Middle East) EC, Manama, Bahrain; Int'l, pg. 923

Walker, Harry C., Pres.--Matterhorn Bank Programs, Inc., Timonium, MD; U.S. Public, pg. 152

Walker, I., Chief Exec. Officer--Redland Stone Products Co., San Antonio, TX; Int'l, pg. 1091

Walker, J.H.W., Mng. Dir.--Tate & Lyle Sugars, London, United Kingdom; Int'l, pg. 1356

Walker, Jack A., Pres.--Cubic Applications, Inc., Lacey, WA; U.S. Public, pg. 466

Walker, James, Fin.--Leo Burnett/Connaghan & May (QLD.) Pty. Ltd., Milton, Australia; U.S. Private, pg. 185

Walker, James, Pres.--Zemenick & Walker, Inc., Saint Louis, MO; U.S. Public, pg. 644

Walker, James A., Jr., Pres.--Kwickie/Flash Foods, Inc., Waycross, GA; U.S. Private, pg. 596

Walker, Jeffrey C., Pres.--Chase Equity Incorporated, New York, NY; U.S. Public, pg. 338

Walker, Jimmy L., Pres.--Kyber Coal Co., Kimper, KY; U.S. Private, pg. 138

Walker, Jimmy L., Pres.--Jesse Branch Coal Co., Kimper, KY; U.S. Private, pg. 139

Walker, K.D., Pres. & Chief Exec. Officer--Meineke Discount Muffler Shops, Inc., Charlotte, NC; Int'l, pg. 535

Walker, Kevin S., Pres.--Paine Supply of Jackson, Inc., Pearl, MS; U.S. Public, pg. 847

Walker, Kim, Chief Oper. Officer--Hudson General Aviation Services Inc., Richmond, Canada; U.S. Public, pg. 846

Walker, M.D., Chm. Bd.--Taysec Construction Limited, Accra, Ghana; Int'l, pg. 1359

Walker, Marv, Sr., Gen. Mgr.--Kettle River Gold Mine, Echo Bay Minerals, Republic, WA; U.S. Public, pg. 562

Walker, Merwyn, Gen. Mgr.--Mead Johnson Jamaica Ltd., Kingston, Jamaica; U.S. Public, pg. 256

Walker, Mike, Mgr.--Dormer Tools Ltd., Sheffield, United Kingdom; Int'l, pg. 1186

Walker, Norman, Pres.--Hasbro International, Inc., Springfield, MA; U.S. Public, pg. 797

Walker, R.A., Pres.--SPS Industrial Products Div., Cleveland, OH; U.S. Public, pg. 1420

Walker, R.D., Pres.--Centra Gas Ontario Inc., North York, Canada; Int'l, pg. 1492

Walker, Ron, Mngng. Dir.--Korn/Ferry International, Washington, DC; U.S. Private, pg. 633

Walker, Ron, Pres.--Captain D's Restaurant, Nashville, TN; U.S. Public, pg. 1467

Walker, Russ, Mng. Dir.--Cemac Commercial Interiors Ltd., Auckland, New Zealand; U.S. Public, pg. 905

Walker, Stephen D., Dir.--Earth Science Division, Arlington, TX; U.S. Private, pg. 53

Walker, Steven C., Pres. & Chief Exec. Officer--Commercial National Bank, Shreveport, LA; U.S. Public, pg. 500

Walker, Steven C., Pres. & Chief Exec. Officer--Cand Investments Inc., Shreveport, LA; U.S. Public, pg. 501

Walker, T. G., Chm.--S.H. Ward Inc., Sheffield, United Kingdom; Int'l, pg. 1454

Walker, Thomas K., Pres.--Amcast Automotive, Southfield, MI; U.S. Public, pg. 63

Walker, W. Lawrence, Publisher--San Antonio Express News, San Antonio, TX; U.S. Private, pg. 517

Walker, W.S., Grp. Pres. & Sr. V.P.--Ground Systems Group, Fullerton, CA; U.S. Public, pg. 1364

Walker, Walter, Mgr.--Bantam Book Canada Inc., Toronto, Canada; Int'l, pg. 191

Walker, Wayne, Exec. V.P.--Emco Distribution Group Western Region, Edmonton, Canada; Int'l, pg. 453

Walker, William W., Pres.--Minera Hispaniola, S.A., Santo Domingo, Dominican Republic; U.S. Public, pg. 302

Walklet, Preston N., Pres.--Banta Digital Group, Charlotte, NC; U.S. Public, pg. 188

Walklet, Preston N., Pres.--Banta Digital Group, Chanhassen, MN; U.S. Public, pg. 188

Walklet, Preston N., Pres.--Banta Digital Group, Needham, MA; U.S. Public, pg. 188

Walklet, Preston N., Pres.--Banta Digital Group, Chanhassen, MN; U.S. Public, pg. 188

Walkush, J.P., Pres.--SAIC Commercial Enterprises, Inc., San Diego, CA; U.S. Private, pg. 976

Wall, Burton, Chief Oper. Officer--G.Y. Industries, Inc., Chicago, IL; U.S. Public, pg. 89

Wall, C.J., Chief Exec. Officer--Vittinge Tegel AB, Morgongava, Sweden; Int'l, pg. 1092

Wall, Frank R., Pres. & Chief Exec. Officer--L & W Supply Corp., Chicago, IL; U.S. Public, pg. 1660

Wall, Furman G., Jr., Mgr.--Scott & Stringfellow, Inc., Chesapeake, VA; U.S. Public, pg. 1445

Wall, Furman G., Jr., Mgr.--Scott & Stringfellow, Inc., Virginia Beach, VA; U.S. Public, pg. 1445

Wall, Furman, Jr., Mgr.--Scott & Stringfellow, Inc., Norfolk, VA; U.S. Public, pg. 1446

Wall, James, Pres.--AMREP Southwest, Inc., Rio Rancho, NM; U.S. Public, pg. 104

Wall, James, Chief Oper. Officer--Eldorado at Santa Fe, Santa Fe, NM; U.S. Public, pg. 105

Wall, Kent, Pres.--Dockers Footwear, Nashville, TN; U.S. Public, pg. 728

Wall, Steven E., Pres. & Chief Oper. Officer--Society National Bank, Cleveland, OH; U.S. Public, pg. 954

Wallace, Alan, Pres.--J.G. Hook Enterprises, Inc., Burlington, NJ; U.S. Private, pg. 538

Wallace, Andy B., Mgr.--Cordex Exploration Co., Reno, NV; Int'l, pg. 1089

Wallace, Bryan, Pres.--SCANLAB Sdn. Bhd., Kuala Lumpur, Malaysia; Int'l, pg. 1390

Wallace, Dan B., V.P. & Gen. Mgr.--Logicon Operating Systems Division, Arlington, VA; U.S. Public, pg. 1199

Wallace, Jack, Plant Mgr.--Sealy-Stearns & Foster Bedding Co. - Atlanta, Conyers, GA; U.S. Private, pg. 979

Wallace, James E., Pres. & Chief Exec. Officer--Hamilton, Allen & Associates, Inc, Atlanta, GA; U.S. Public, pg. 1673

Wallace, Jane, Pres. & Gen. Mgr.--KXAN, Austin, TX; U.S. Public, pg. 11

Wallace, John, Mng. Dir.--Conran Octopus Limited, London, United Kingdom; Int'l, pg. 1093

Wallace, John D., Chm. Bd. & Chief Exec. Officer--New Jersey National Bank, Pennington, NJ; U.S. Public, pg. 447

Wallace, John L., Pres.--Aviall, Inc., Dallas, TX; U.S. Public, pg. 154

Wallace, Kevin, Pres. & Chief Exec. Officer--Thermo Separation Products, San Jose, CA; U.S. Public, pg. 1594

Wallace, Pat, Pres. & Gen. Mgr.-WMAQ-TV--National Broadcasting Co., Inc., New York, NY; U.S. Public, pg. 712

Wallace, Pat, Pres. & Gen. Mgr.--WCAU-TV, Philadelphia, PA; U.S. Public, pg. 712

Wallace, Ray, Pres.--Abbott Laboratories, Mountain View, CA; U.S. Public, pg. 13

Wallace, Robert, Pres. & Gen. Mgr.--Prudential Fund Management Canada Ltd., Scarborough, Canada; U.S. Private, pg. 893

Wallace, Steve, Chief Oper. Officer--Ahlstrom Process Equipment Inc., Pittsburgh, PA; Int'l, pg. 34

Wallace, W. Ray, Pres.--Trinity Difco, Findlay, OH; U.S. Public, pg. 1639

Wallace, Walker J., V.P.-Olestra--Olestra Div., Cincinnati, OH; U.S. Public, pg. 1330

Wallace, William F., Pres. & Chief Oper. Officer--Plains Petroleum Operating Co., Lakewood, CO; U.S. Public, pg. 191

Wallach, Don, Pres.--Micro Vesicular Systems, Inc., Nashua, NH; U.S. Public, pg. 855

Walle, Everette, V.P.--Heritage Merchandising Co., Inc., Colonial Heights, VA; U.S. Public, pg. 1272

Wallecamp, Maurits, Mng. Dir.--Banque Paribas Belgique, Brussels, Belgium; Int'l, pg. 319

Wallen, Fred, Plant Mgr.--American Natl. Can Co., Des Moines, IA; Int'l, pg. 1029

Waller, Art, Branch Mgr.--Burns & Wilcox - Columbus Office, Columbus, OH; U.S. Private, pg. 609

Waller, Michael E., Chief Exec. Officer & Publisher--The Hartford Courant Company, Hartford, CT; U.S. Public, pg. 1616

Waller, Peter C., Pres. & Chief Concept Officer--Taco Bell Corp., Irvine, CA; U.S. Public, pg. 1637

Wallers, Pascal, Dir.--Banque Regionale du Nord, Valenciennes, France; Int'l, pg. 548

Wallet, Barry, Gen. Mgr.--TMP Worldwide Pty Ltd., Griffith, Australia; Int'l, pg. 1342

Walley, W.J., Gen. Mgr.--S.C. Johnson & Son Pty. Ltd., Milsons Point, Australia; U.S. Private, pg. 593

Wallgren, Goran, Mng. Dir.--ESAB S.A. Industria e Comercio, Contagem, Brazil; Int'l, pg. 282

Wallgren, Per-Erik, Chief Oper. Officer--Neste Oy, Gas LPG International, Espoo, Finland; *Int'l*, pg. 913
Wallin, Richard E., Chief Oper. Officer--The Bank of New York, Madrid, Spain; *U.S. Public*, pg. 179
Wallin, Sixten, Pres.--Sektionsbyggarna AB, Anneberg, Sweden; *Int'l*, pg. 1260
Wallis, Charles T., Pres. & Chief Exec. Officer--Back Bay Advisors, Inc., Boston, MA; *U.S. Private*, pg. 737
Wallis, Edwardo, Chief Oper. Officer--La Federacion Compania de Seguros, C.A., Caracas, Venezuela; *U.S. Public*, pg. 355
Wallis, Graham, Pres.--Javelin Systems, Syosset, NY; *U.S. Public*, pg. 1306
Wallis, Lloyd, Pres.--Associated Concrete Products, Inc., Santa Ana, CA; *U.S. Private*, pg. 417
Wallis, Lloyd, Pres.--FlowSeal, Long Beach, CA; *U.S. Public*, pg. 457
Wallis, Lloyd, Pres.--Center Line, Tulsa, OK; *U.S. Public*, pg. 457
Wallner, Collette, V.P.-Mktg.--Associated Bank, National Association, Neenah, WI; *U.S. Public*, pg. 140
Wallner, M., Chief Exec. Officer--Schiedel Kaminwerke GmbH, Wartberg, Austria; *Int'l*, pg. 1092
Wallower, Richard, Mgr.-Property & Casualty Claims--Willis Corroon Administrative Services Corporation, Harrisburg, PA; *Int'l*, pg. 1505
Walls, James, Mgr.--Kassbohrer North America, Sparks, NV; *Int'l*, pg. 368
Wallunas, Don, Mgr.--Stephen Gould of California, Fremont, CA; *U.S. Private*, pg. 467
Wallwitz, Horst, Gen. Mgr.--Liberia Cement Corp., Monrovia, Liberia; *Int'l*, pg. 1201
Walnes, Jack R., Pres.--Varity Zecal, Churchville, NY; *Int'l*, pg. 820
Walpole, Peter R., Dir.--Royal Insurance Service Co. (Guernsey) Ltd., Saint Peter Port, United Kingdom; *Int'l*, pg. 1130
Walpole, R.H., Pres. & Chief Oper. Officer--Walbro Engine Management Corporation, Cass City, MI; *U.S. Public*, pg. 1733
Walrack, Rich, Pres.--Santee Dairies, Los Angeles, CA; *U.S. Public*, pg. 1349
Walrath, Marv, V.P. & Gen. Mgr.--Small Compressor Division, Davidson, NC; *U.S. Public*, pg. 876
Walravens, Dirk, Gen. Mgr.--N.V. Life Technologies SA, Merelbeke, Belgium; *U.S. Public*, pg. 505
Walsh, Bill, Base Mgr.--Mercury Air Center, Goleta, CA; *U.S. Public*, pg. 1093
Walsh, Bob, Plant Mgr.--Bridgestone/Firestone Tire Manufacturing Operations-Wilson, Wilson, NC; *Int'l*, pg. 213
Walsh, C. J., Mgr.--Embecon (New Zealand) Limited, Avondale, New Zealand; *Int'l*, pg. 982
Walsh, Daniel J., Pres.--Walsh Construction Co. of Illinois, Chicago, IL; *U.S. Private*, pg. 1148
Walsh, David, Gen. Mgr.--Relocation Consultants, Oak Brook, IL; *U.S. Public*, pg. 1635
Walsh, David P., Gen. Mgr.--Bagpak Div., Memphis, TN; *U.S. Public*, pg. 901
Walsh, G., Pres. & Chief Exec. Officer--Pratt & Whitney, Grand Prairie, TX; *U.S. Public*, pg. 1690
Walsh, G.F., Gen. Mgr.--Toplis Painters Limited, Nottingham, United Kingdom; *Int'l*, pg. 337
Walsh, Gerald R., V.P. & Gen. Mgr.--WFXT-TV, Needham, MA; *Int'l*, pg. 926
Walsh, J.E., Jr., Pres.--Friendswood Development Company, Houston, TX; *U.S. Public*, pg. 988
Walsh, James, Customer Service Ctr. Supvr.--Pirelli Cable, Power Div. Service Center, Colusa, CA; *Int'l*, pg. 1059
Walsh, John F., Pres.-Consumer Products Sector & Exec. V.P.--Warner-Lambert Consumer Healthcare, Morris Plains, NJ; *U.S. Public*, pg. 1739
Walsh, John F., Pres.--Warner-Lambert International Operations, Morris Plains, NJ; *U.S. Public*, pg. 1739
Walsh, John T., Pres.--Columbian Chemicals Company, Atlanta, GA; *U.S. Public*, pg. 1286
Walsh, Kevin F., Publisher--The Lorain Journal Company-The Morning Journal, Lorain, OH; *U.S. Public*, pg. 935
Walsh, L., Dr., Chm. Bd.--Dulmison Inc., Lawrenceville, GA; *Int'l*, pg. 893
Walsh, Lane, Chief Oper. Officer--Salem Carpet Mills, Dallas, TX; *U.S. Public*, pg. 1464
Walsh, Liam, V.P.-Opers.--Elan Pharma Ltd., Athlone, Ireland; *Int'l*, pg. 436
Walsh, Margaret A., Exec. Editor--The New York Times News Service, New York, NY; *U.S. Public*, pg. 1174
Walsh, Nicholas, Mng. Dir.--American International Underwriters (UK) Ltd., London, United Kingdom; *U.S. Public*, pg. 85
Walsh, Paul, Pres.--Wright Express Corporation, South Portland, ME; *U.S. Public*, pg. 321
Walsh, Robert, Gen. Mgr.--Tandy Wire & Cable, Fort Worth, TX; *U.S. Public*, pg. 1560
Walsh, Robert J., Pres.--Sprint Publishing & Advertising, Overland Park, KS; *U.S. Public*, pg. 1501
Walsh, Thomas L., Pres.--Energy Dynamics Division, Chandler, AZ; *U.S. Public*, pg. 1250
Walsh, William G. Jr., Pres.--Commonwealth Relocation Services, Inc., Philadelphia, PA; *U.S. Public*, pg. 1374
Walsh, William G. Jr., Pres.--CRS Financial Services, Inc., Ardmore, PA; *U.S. Public*, pg. 1374
Walshe, G., Chm.--Brother International (NZ) Limited, Petone, New Zealand; *Int'l*, pg. 229
Walston, Gary, Gen. Mgr.--Ohio Rod Products Company, Inc., Versailles, IN; *U.S. Private*, pg. 370
Walsworth, Gary D., Gen. Mgr.--Ikon Office Solutions-Jefferson City, Jefferson City, MO; *U.S. Public*, pg. 863
Walter, Christopher J., Gen. Mgr.--Productos Avon, S.A., Santo Domingo, Dominican Republic; *U.S. Public*, pg. 156
Walter, Frank, Pres. & Chief Exec. Officer--Bank One, Chicago, Chicago, IL; *U.S. Public*, pg. 173
Walter, Manfred, Chm. Bd. & Chief Exec. Officer--Traub-Hermle Corporation, Menomonee Falls, WI; *Int'l*, pg. 1419
Walter, Reinhard, Dr., Chm. Exec. Bd.--B.U.S. Berzelius Umwelt-Service GmbH, Frankfurt/Main, Germany; *Int'l*, pg. 860
Walter, Richard C., Chief Exec. Officer--Columbia House Music Club, New York, NY; *Int'l*, pg. 1281
Walter, Ronald, V.P. & Station Mgr.--WREG-TV, Memphis, TN; *U.S. Public*, pg. 1174
Walter, William R., Mgr.--Shiawassee Telephone Company, Perry, MI; *U.S. Public*, pg. 1572
Walterhouse, Kurt D., Plant Mgr.--Central States Can Co.-Composite Operations, Massillon, OH; *U.S. Public*, pg. 463
Walterich, Leo, Gen. Mgr.--ITW Woodworth, Ferndale, MI; *U.S. Public*, pg. 867
Walters, Alan H., Pres.--Deposit Guaranty Mortgage Co., Jackson, MS; *U.S. Public*, pg. 501
Walters, Alan H., Pres.--G & W Life Insurance Co., Jackson, MS; *U.S. Public*, pg. 501
Walters, Andy, District Mgr.--Marcon Shipping/A.N. Deringer, Valley Stream, NY; *U.S. Private*, pg. 326
Walters, Bruce, Pres.--AVM Inc., Marion, SC; *U.S. Public*, pg. 137
Walters, Eleanor, Mgr.--SanTran Inc., Columbus, MS; *U.S. Private*, pg. 964
Walters, J., Pres.--Mail Well Services Inc., Memphis, TN; *U.S. Public*, pg. 1328
Walters, Keith S., Plant Mgr.--UTA Sheridan Mfg. Plant, Wauseon, OH; *U.S. Public*, pg. 1691
Walters, Mark, Admin.--Heritage Western Hills, Fort Worth, TX; *U.S. Public*, pg. 839
Walters, Paul S., Chm. Bd. & Chief Exec. Officer--Sears Canada, Inc., Toronto, Canada; *U.S. Public*, pg. 1452
Walters, Thomas, Mgr.-Property & Casualty Claims--Willis Corroon Administrative Services Corporation, Radnor, PA; *Int'l*, pg. 1505
Walters, Thomas J., Pres.--Morton's of Chicago, Inc., Chicago, IL; *U.S. Public*, pg. 1136
Walther, Norbert H.H., Pres.--Demag Komatsu GmbH, Dusseldorf, Germany; *Int'l*, pg. 745
Walton, Anthony J., Gen. Mgr. & Exec. V.P.--Westpac Banking Corporation, New York, NY; *Int'l*, pg. 1496
Walton, James L., Pres.--Wal-Mart Properties, Inc., Bentonville, AR; *U.S. Public*, pg. 1733
Walton, Jonathan T., Pres.--NBD Financial Services of Michigan, Inc., Detroit, MI; *U.S. Public*, pg. 628
Walzak, Michael F.P., V.P. & Mng. Dir.--Toronto Dominion Australia Ltd., Melbourne, Australia; *Int'l*, pg. 1401
Wambolt, Ronald R., Chief Oper. Officer--Fluke International Corporation, Everett, WA; *U.S. Public*, pg. 659
Wamhoff, Richard H., Pres. & Chief Exec. Officer--Ore-Ida Foods, Inc., Boise, ID; *U.S. Public*, pg. 805
Wampler, Wesley, Publr.--Staunton Leader Publishing Co., Staunton, VA; *U.S. Public*, pg. 701
Wampler, William, Pres.--Clinch River Corp., Tazewell, VA; *U.S. Private*, pg. 370
Wamsley, H. Allen, V.P. & Publisher--Huron Daily Tribune, Bad Axe, MI; *U.S. Private*, pg. 517
Wamsley, Ted, Gen. Mgr.--American Door Company of Michigan, Inc., Walkerton, IN; *Int'l*, pg. 1067
Wan Kyuew, Kim, Mgr.--Union Corporation, Seoul, Korea; *U.S. Private*, pg. 361
Wan, John H.C., Mng. Dir.--Freight-Trans International Co., Ltd., Kwai Chung, Hong Kong; *Int'l*, pg. 704
Wandell, Ray, Gen. Mgr.--AMP de France, Pontoise, France; *U.S. Public*, pg. 8
Wanderon, Anton, Pres.--ERJ Insurance Group, Miami Springs, FL; *U.S. Public*, pg. 79
Wandmacher, Bill, V.P.--Mill Div., Saint Louis, MO; *Int'l*, pg. 1269
Wandmacher, W.N., V.P. & Gen. Mgr.--Jefferson Smurfit Corporation, Saint Louis, MO; *Int'l*, pg. 1270
Wanezaki, Kiichiro, Pres.--Snow Brand Food Co., Ltd., Tokyo, Japan; *Int'l*, pg. 1272
Wang, Benson, Gen. Mgr.--Formica Taiwan Corporation, Taipei, Taiwan; *Int'l*, pg. 130
Wang, C.W., Gen. Mgr.--Taoyuan Refinery, Tao-yuan, Taiwan; *Int'l*, pg. 286
Wang, Ch. C.T., Chief Exec. Officer--Malayan Overseas Insurance Corporation, Taipei, Taiwan; *Int'l*, pg. 1532
Wang, Chia-Nan, V.P. & Gen. Mgr.--The International Commercial Bank of China, Singapore, Singapore; *Int'l*, pg. 683
Wang, Gene, Gen. Mgr.--AGRA Construction (Wuhan China) Limited, Wuhan, China; *Int'l*, pg. 31
Wang, Joseph, Mgr.-Taiwan--Raychem Taiwan Limited, Taipei, Taiwan; *U.S. Public*, pg. 1363
Wang, Moo-Chung, Chief Oper. Officer--A & A International-Taipei Branch, Taipei, Taiwan; *U.S. Public*, pg. 1561
Wang, Richard, Gen. Mgr.--Metropolitan Insurance & Annuity Company, Taiwan Branch, Taipei, Taiwan; *U.S. Private*, pg. 738
Wang, W.N., Pres.--China Steel Global Trading Corporation, Kao-hsiung, Taiwan; *Int'l*, pg. 285
Wang, Wendall, Mgr.--Sandvik Taiwan Ltd., Taipei, Taiwan; *Int'l*, pg. 1187
Wang, Xiang Cheng, Dir.--Shanghai SPS Biao Wu Fastener Co. Ltd., Shanghai, China; *U.S. Public*, pg. 1420
Wang, Xuebing, Gen. Mgr.--Bank of China, New York, NY; *Int'l*, pg. 152
Wangaard, Clark, Pres.--Taylor Company, Rockton, IL; *U.S. Public*, pg. 1496
Wanglee, Suchin, Pres.--The Navakij Insurance Co., Ltd., Bangkok, Thailand; *Int'l*, pg. 61
Wangphongsawasd, Anant, Mng. Dir.--First Asia Securities Limited, Bangkok, Thailand; *Int'l*, pg. 485
Wani, S., Pres.--Tekmatex, Inc., Charlotte, NC; *Int'l*, pg. 845
Wanjui, J.B., Chm.--Stanbic Bank Kenya Limited, Nairobi, Kenya; *Int'l*, pg. 1293
Wann, Robert F.S., Pres.--Parker Brothers, Beverly, MA; *U.S. Public*, pg. 797
Wannamaker, Gerald, Chief Oper. Officer--R-4 KIT Mfg. Co., Mc Pherson, KS; *U.S. Public*, pg. 962
Wannamaker, W.F., V.P.--Tencarva Machinery Co., Columbia, SC; *U.S. Private*, pg. 1076
Wannborg, Anders, Chief Oper. Officer--Electrolux S.a.r.L., Vianden, Luxembourg; *Int'l*, pg. 443
Wanner, Paul, Mng. Dir.--SLM Immobilien AG, Winterthur, Switzerland; *Int'l*, pg. 1305
Wanner, Paul, Mng. Dir.--Sulzer Immobilien AG, Winterthur, Switzerland; *Int'l*, pg. 1306
Wanninger, Charles T., Pres. & Publr.--Press-Citizen Company, Inc., Iowa City, IA; *U.S. Public*, pg. 701
Wannop, Guy, Pres.--Walter Kidde Portable Equipment Inc., Mebane, NC; *Int'l*, pg. 1500
Wanson, Louis, Area Dir.--President Baking-Charlotte, Charlotte, NC; *Int'l*, pg. 1069
Wanttaja, Keith, Dir.-Opers.--The Toro Co., Shakopee, MN; *U.S. Public*, pg. 1624
Wanzenboeck, Franz, Gen. Mgr.--AMP Osterreich G.m.b.H., Vienna, Austria; *U.S. Public*, pg. 9
Waplan, Karl-Axel, Chief Oper. Officer--Axel Johnson Ore & Metals AB, Stockholm, Sweden; *Int'l*, pg. 709
Ward-Hall, G., Mng. Dir.--Fabrication Operations West, New Westminster, Canada; *Int'l*, pg. 695
Ward, Alan, Mgr.--Anixter Heston, Southall, United Kingdom; *U.S. Public*, pg. 116
Ward, Andrew, Acting Mng. Dir.--ANZ Banking Group (New Zealand) Ltd., Wellington, New Zealand; *Int'l*, pg. 98
Ward, Craig, Pres. & Sec.--LTB Ward Constructors, Inc., Houston, TX; *U.S. Private*, pg. 347
Ward, Craig G., Pres. & Chief Exec. Officer--LTB, Houston, TX; *U.S. Private*, pg. 668
Ward, Dave G., Sr., Pres.--Ground Water Associates, Inc., Bridgewater, NJ; *U.S. Private*, pg. 552
Ward, David, Pres.--American Rehability Services, Inc., Brentwood, TN; *U.S. Public*, pg. 1257
Ward, Don, Pres. & Gen. Mgr.--AAR Oklahoma, Oklahoma City, OK; *U.S. Public*, pg. 1
Ward, Doug, Gen. Mgr.--fp Label, Inc., Napa, CA; *U.S. Private*, pg. 411
Ward, F.E., Mgr.--Electrical Equipment Company, Laurinburg, NC; *U.S. Private*, pg. 368
Ward, Gayliss R., Chief Oper. Officer--Fiduciary Special Services, Inc., New York, NY; *U.S. Public*, pg. 621
Ward, Harold M., Dr., Chm. Bd.--Indian Rocks National Bank, Largo, FL; *U.S. Public*, pg. 608
Ward, Ian, Pres.--Berol Corp., Georgetown, KY; *U.S. Public*, pg. 1178
Ward, James, Pres.--Blue Circle Aggregates, Inc., Marietta, GA; *Int'l*, pg. 198
Ward, Jeff, Publisher & Exec. V.P.--Weight Watchers Magazine, Birmingham, AL; *U.S. Public*, pg. 1612
Ward, Jerry, V.P. & Dir.-Publ.--Better Homes and Gardens Special Interest Publications, Des Moines, IA; *U.S. Public*, pg. 1094
Ward, Jerry L., Pres.--Dresser Valve & Controls Div., Woodlands, TX; *U.S. Public*, pg. 528
Ward, John, Chm. Bd. & Chief Exec. Officer--American Express Bank Ltd., New York, NY; *U.S. Public*, pg. 73
Ward, John, Pres.--Leslie Fay Dress, New York, NY; *U.S. Public*, pg. 989
Ward, John, Gen. Mgr.--The Modesto Bee, Modesto, CA; *U.S. Public*, pg. 1065
Ward, Joseph J., Pres.-Book Grp.--Better Homes and Gardens Books, Des Moines, IA; *U.S. Public*, pg. 1094
Ward, L., Branch Mgr.--RHG San Francisco, Oakland, CA; *Int'l*, pg. 1151
Ward, Larry, Pres.--Breed Technologies, Sterling Heights, MI; *U.S. Public*, pg. 251
Ward, Liam, Gen. Mgr.--P.T. O'Donnell Griffin Indonesia, Jakarta, Indonesia; *U.S. Public*, pg. 1651
Ward, M. D., Chief Oper. Officer--Texas Clay Industries, Malakoff, TX; *U.S. Public*, pg. 1576
Ward, Milton H., Chm. Bd. & Chief Exec. Officer--Amax Gold Inc., Englewood, CO; *U.S. Public*, pg. 470
Ward, Nelson L., Gen. Mgr.--Government Communications Systems Division, Annapolis Junction, MD; *U.S. Public*, pg. 293
Ward, Peter, Chm. & Chief Exec. Officer--Rolls-Royce Motor Cars Limited, Crewe, United Kingdom; *Int'l*, pg. 1467
Ward, R. Howard, Pres. & Gen. Mgr.--Standard Cap & Seal, Norcross, GA; *U.S. Public*, pg. 1486
Ward, R. Howard, Pres.--Rixie Paper Products, Pottstown, PA; *U.S. Public*, pg. 1486
Ward, Richard, Pres.--Guaranty Asset Protection Services, Inc., West Hills, CA; *U.S. Public*, pg. 857
Ward, Robert, Pres.--United States Fleet Leasing, Inc., San Mateo, CA; *U.S. Public*, pg. 664
Ward, Rodman, Jr., Partner--Skadden, Arps, Slate, Meagher & Flom LLP, Wilmington, DE; *U.S. Private*, pg. 1004
Ward, S.M., Plant Mgr.--Spirolox Division, Saint Louis, MO; *U.S. Public*, pg. 946
Ward, Scott H., Pres. & Chief Fin. Officer--Whitman's Candies, Inc., Kansas City, MO; *U.S. Private*, pg. 953
Ward, Thomas S., Pres. & Chief Oper. Officer--Whitman's Candies, Inc., Kansas City, MO; *U.S. Private*, pg. 953
Ward, Tom, Plant Mgr.--RAYOVAC Corporation, Madison, WI; *U.S. Private*, pg. 912
Ward, V. A., Chm. Bd.--NatWest Futures Limited, London, United Kingdom; *Int'l*, pg. 910
Ward, William A., Pres. & Chief Exec. Officer--Allied International-American Eagle Trading Corp., Janesville, WI; *Int'l*, pg. 694
Wardeberg, George, Chm. Bd.--Sta-Rite Industries, Inc., Delavan, WI; *U.S. Public*, pg. 1767
Wardeberg, George, V.P.--Water Systems Group, Delavan, WI; *U.S. Public*, pg. 1767
Wardell, Keith, Gen. Mgr.--Equifax Consumer Direct, Washington, DC; *U.S. Public*, pg. 588
Warden, Robert P., Mng. Dir.--Logica UK Ltd., Cambridge, United Kingdom; *Int'l*, pg. 814

Wardlaw, Charles, V.P. & Gen. Mgr.--Shorewood Packaging Corporation of Georgia, La Grange, GA; *U.S. Public*, pg. 1468
Wardlaw, Craig M., Pres.--NationsBank Futures Corp., Charlotte, NC; *U.S. Public*, pg. 1165
Wardle, Stephen W., Div. Mgr.--Thermal Processing Group Ltd. (Sheffield), Sheffield, United Kingdom; *Int'l*, pg. 1338
Wardleworth, S., Mng. Dir.--Dunlite Power Generation Pty. Ltd., Hindmarsh, Australia; *U.S. Public*, pg. 469
Ware, Barry, Gen. Mgr.--Snyder Bakery, Spokane, WA; *U.S. Private*, pg. 1124
Ware, Bob, V.P. & Mng. Dir.--National Distributing Co., Inc., Atlanta, GA; *U.S. Private*, pg. 781
Ware, Carl, Pres.--Coca-Cola Southern Africa (Pty) Ltd., Johannesburg, South Africa; *U.S. Public*, pg. 392
Ware, James, Pres.--Durametallic Corp., Kalamazoo, MI; *U.S. Public*, pg. 658
Ware, Scott, Editor--The Albuquerque Tribune, Albuquerque, NM; *U.S. Public*, pg. 1447
Wareham, Peter, Mng. Dir.--Frontel Communications Services, London, United Kingdom; *U.S. Public*, pg. 684
Warendorf, Rip, Publisher--Snow Country Business, Trumbull, CT; *U.S. Public*, pg. 1174
Warenski, Alan, Gen. Mgr.--Standard Restaurant Equipment Co., Las Vegas, NV; *U.S. Private*, pg. 1031
Warfield, Ronald, Pres.--Country Investors Life Assurance Company, Bloomington, IL; *U.S. Private*, pg. 279
Warfield, Ronald, Pres.--Country Mutual Insurance Company, Bloomington, IL; *U.S. Private*, pg. 279
Warfield, Ronald, Pres.--Country Casualty Insurance Company, Bloomington, IL; *U.S. Private*, pg. 279
Warfield, Ronald, Pres.--Country Preferred Insurance Company, Bloomington, IL; *U.S. Private*, pg. 279
Warfield, Ronald, Pres.--CC Services, Bloomington, IL; *U.S. Private*, pg. 279
Wargo, Cindy, Pres.--North Coast Behavioral Research Group, Cleveland, OH; *U.S. Private*, pg. 1194
Warhover, Stephen, Pres.--The Gorton Group, Gloucester, MA; *Int'l*, pg. 1434
Warik, Olle, Pres.--NCC Building - Uppsala, Uppsala, Sweden; *Int'l*, pg. 899
Warkentin, Donald, Pres.--APT, Chicago, IL; *U.S. Public*, pg. 1570
Warland, P.G., Mng. Dir.--British European Associated Publishers Ltd., London, United Kingdom; *Int'l*, pg. 1445
Warlavmont, Mark, Gen. Mgr.--GCI Orange, Inc/GCI Orlando, Inc., Orlando, FL; *U.S. Private*, pg. 470
Warmels, Peter, Gen. Mgr.--Fieldfresh Farms Inc., Oakville, Canada; *Int'l*, pg. 1012
Warne, Greg, Admin. Plant Mgr.--Quad/West Pre-Press, Anaheim, CA; *U.S. Private*, pg. 898
Warne, Tom, Gen. Mgr.--Bloomfield Industries Canada Ltd., Mississauga, Canada; *U.S. Public*, pg. 1497
Warnegard, Per, Pres.--Fastighets AB Fundament/Real Estate Operations, Stockholm, Sweden; *Int'l*, pg. 678
Warneke, John, Plant Mgr.--CMI Load King Trailer Division, Elk Point, SD; *U.S. Public*, pg. 279
Warner, Fred, Pres.--Laubeck Corporation, Laubenstein Division, Ashland, PA; *U.S. Private*, pg. 653
Warner, Bob, Pres.--New England Correct Craft, Inc., Rochester, NH; *U.S. Private*, pg. 277
Warner, Greg, Mng. Dir.--A. Schulman, Inc., Hockessin, DE; *U.S. Public*, pg. 1441
Warner, J.M., Pres.--Hays Fluid Controls-Division of Romac Industries, Dallas, NC; *U.S. Private*, pg. 942
Warner, Jack, Pres.--Kerry Ingredients, Beloit, WI; *Int'l*, pg. 732
Warner, James A., Pres.-CBS Television Network--CBS Television Network, New York, NY; *U.S. Public*, pg. 274
Warner, Jamie, Sr. V.P.--Edelman Worldwide, Inc., Sacramento, CA; *U.S. Private*, pg. 362
Warner, John D., Pres.--Boeing Computer Services, Bellevue, WA; *U.S. Public*, pg. 240
Warner, John D., Pres.--Boeing Information & Support Services, Bellevue, WA; *U.S. Public*, pg. 241
Warner, Lee, V.P.--McGraw/Kokosing, Inc., Middletown, OH; *U.S. Private*, pg. 631
Warner, P.L., Joint Chm.--Bovis Urban Renewal Ltd., London, United Kingdom; *Int'l*, pg. 1032
Warner, Richard, Div. Mgr.--Higgins Sacramento Operations, Sacramento, CA; *U.S. Private*, pg. 527
Warner, Rick L., V.P.--Willis Corroon Financial Services Corp., Dallas, TX; *Int'l*, pg. 1507
Warner, Tim, Mgr.--Steel, Inc., Grand Junction, CO; *U.S. Private*, pg. 1038
Warner, Tom, Pres.--Woodhead Specialty Fabrics, Graniteville, SC; *U.S. Private*, pg. 103
Warnick, Miles, Mng. Dir.--Chesswood Produce Ltd., Thakeham, United Kingdom; *Int'l*, pg. 1396
Warosh, Del, Plant Mgr.--Eaton Corporation, Electric Drives Division, Kenosha, WI; *U.S. Public*, pg. 556
Warr, D.H., Chief Oper. Officer--Bristol Babcock Canada, Toronto, Canada; *Int'l*, pg. 473
Warrelmann, Veiko, Mgr.-Opers.--Woodward-Clyde International, Chemnitz, Germany; *U.S. Public*, pg. 1658
Warren, Anthony J., Exec. V.P. & Chief Oper. Officer--Illinois National Insurance Co., Manchester, NH; *U.S. Public*, pg. 84
Warren, Ben, Gen. Mgr.--Republic Automotive Parts Sales, Inc., Denver, CO; *U.S. Public*, pg. 1378
Warren, Billy W., Plant Mgr.--Wedco, Inc., Lovelady, TX; *U.S. Public*, pg. 854
Warren, Chris, Mgr.-Reg. Sls.--Robinson-Nugent Ltd., Basingstoke, United Kingdom; *U.S. Public*, pg. 1395
Warren, Delfin L., Mng. Dir.--P.T. Darya-Varia Laboratoria, Jakarta, Indonesia; *Int'l*, pg. 487
Warren, Donald G., Pres.--Suitt Construction Company, Inc., Greenville, SC; *U.S. Private*, pg. 106
Warren, Gary, District Mgr.--Weatherford Enterra U.S., L.P., Lafayette, LA; *U.S. Public*, pg. 1749
Warren, Gary, V.P. & Gen. Mgr.--Weatherford (U.K.) Ltd., Aberdeen, United Kingdom; *U.S. Public*, pg. 1750
Warren, Gary, V.P. & Gen. Mgr.--Weatherford (U.K.) Limited, Aberdeen, United Kingdom; *U.S. Public*, pg. 1750
Warren, James, Dir.--Columbia Medical Center Dallas Southwest, Dallas, TX; *U.S. Public*, pg. 404
Warren, Jorden, Partner & Gen. Mgr.--CKS Partners/San Francisco, San Francisco, CA; *U.S. Private*, pg. 195
Warren, Kathleen, Branch Mgr.--Valley National Bank, Belvidere, NJ; *U.S. Public*, pg. 1706
Warren, Leslie, Pres.--SmithKline Beecham Products Western Hemisphere Div., Intl., Clifton, NJ; *Int'l*, pg. 1264
Warren, Terry W., Pres. & Chief Exec. Officer--MedTrac, Inc., Nashville, TN; *Int'l*, pg. 1504
Warrenfeltz, Steven, Chief Exec. Officer--Old World Automotive Products, Northbrook, IL; *U.S. Private*, pg. 814
Warrick, Raymond E., Jr., Pres.--United Air Specialists, Inc., Cincinnati, OH; *U.S. Public*, pg. 382
Warrillow, James K., Pres.--Canadian Publishing, Toronto, Canada; *Int'l*, pg. 1123
Warrington, Gary L., Pres.--United Companies Life Insurance Co., Baton Rouge, LA; *U.S. Public*, pg. 1271
Warrington, Robert H., Pres.--Old Kent Mortgage Company, Grand Rapids, MI; *U.S. Public*, pg. 1216
Wartheimer, Zeen, Gen. Mgr.--Iscar Ltd., Nahariyya, Israel; *Int'l*, pg. 644
Wartiovaara, Tapio, Pres. & Chief Exec. Officer--W. Rosenlew Ltd., Helsinki, Finland; *Int'l*, pg. 1428
Warwick, M.F., V.P. & Sr. Dir.-Green Economizer--Senior Engineering Co.-Economiser Div., Union, NJ; *Int'l*, pg. 1222
Wascher, Uwe S., Sr. Mng. Dir.--G.E. Plastics Europe, Bergen-op-Zoom, Netherlands; *U.S. Public*, pg. 713
Waschl, Alfred, Chief Oper. Officer--Porsche Espana S.A., Madrid, Spain; *Int'l*, pg. 1063
Waseleski, John C., Pres.--Equipment Sales Co., Foxboro, MA; *U.S. Public*, pg. 594
Wasem, Robert, Mng. Dir.--F. Heusser AG, Zurich, Switzerland; *Int'l*, pg. 1306
Washburn, Dennis V., Pres.--Gannett Direct Marketing Services, Louisville, KY; *U.S. Public*, pg. 699
Washburn, Gina, Branch Mgr.--Troy Savings Bank-Glens Falls, Queensbury, NY; *U.S. Private*, pg. 1106
Washer, F. Gene, V.P. & Publr.--Leaf-Chronicle Co., Clarksville, TN; *U.S. Public*, pg. 699
Washington, James P., V.P. & Gen. Mgr.--Paltier Inc., Michigan City, IN; *U.S. Private*, pg. 638
Washington, R. Peter, Chm. Bd. & Chief Exec. Officer--Lyon Metal Products, Inc., Montgomery, IL; *U.S. Private*, pg. 638
Washio, T., Mng. Dir.--Toshiba International Finance (UK) plc, London, United Kingdom; *Int'l*, pg. 1406
Washizawa, Shigeru, Branch Mgr.--Yamaichi Bank-Geneva, Geneva, Switzerland; *Int'l*, pg. 1517
Wasilewski, Robert J., Reg. Mgr.-Latin America--Lord Industrial Ltda., Sao Paulo, Brazil; *U.S. Private*, pg. 676
Waskey, William C., Gen. Mgr.--Anvil Cases, Inc., City of Industry, CA; *U.S. Public*, pg. 1791
Wasmer, George F., Pres.--Lake Erie Screw Corporation, Cleveland, OH; *U.S. Public*, pg. 1054
Wasnac, Pete, Gen. Mgr.--Arrow/Schweber Electronics, Solon, OH; *U.S. Public*, pg. 133
Wason, S.K., V.P.--J.M. Huber, Chemicals Division, Havre De Grace, MD; *U.S. Private*, pg. 545
Waspi, Jeffrey L., Pres.--JLW Financial Management Systems, Inc., Merrillville, IN; *Int'l*, pg. 28
Wass, S.J., Pres.--Thomas De La Rue Inc., Chantilly, VA; *Int'l*, pg. 387
Wass, Tom, Chm. & Chief Exec. Officer--Tequila UK Ltd., London, United Kingdom; *Int'l*, pg. 118
Wassberg, C.W., Resident V.P.--Southwestern Regional Office, Irving, TX; *U.S. Private*, pg. 224
Wassberg, C.W., Attorney-in-Fact--CMI Lloyds, Irving, TX; *U.S. Private*, pg. 224
Wasserlein, John, Pres.--Fraser Papers, Inc., Stamford, CT; *Int'l*, pg. 434
Wasserman, Stephen, Pres. & Chief Exec. Officer--National Bank of Hastings, Hastings, MI; *U.S. Public*, pg. 633
Wassink, Bernard, Pres.--Plaxicon Company, City of Industry, CA; *Int'l*, pg. 1481
Wassler, Alfred R., Chief Oper. Officer--Gramercy Assets Corporation, New York, NY; *U.S. Public*, pg. 435
Wassman, Ernie, Pres. & Chief Exec. Officer--Tecmar Technologies, Inc., Longmont, CO; *Int'l*, pg. 1361
Wasson, James A., Pres.--Ransco Industries, Inc., Oxnard, CA; *U.S. Private*, pg. 327
Wasson, P. A. "Pat", Chief Oper. Officer--Central Florida Division, Orlando, FL; *U.S. Public*, pg. 656
Wasson, Ron, Pres.--KLT Telecom Inc., Kansas City, MO; *U.S. Public*, pg. 943
Wasson, Ronald, Pres.--KLT Inc., Kansas City, MO; *U.S. Public*, pg. 943
Wastell, Ernie, Mng. Dir.--Coats Cucirini S.p.A., Milan, Italy; *Int'l*, pg. 300
Wasterlid, Kurt, Mgr.--Mataki Heltackande Tak, Hoganas, Sweden; *Int'l*, pg. 1422
Wastl, Hubert, Mng. Dir.--Voest-Alpine Stahlrohr Kindberg Ges.m.b.H., Kindberg, Austria; *Int'l*, pg. 1470
Wat, E., Rep.--Kodak (China) Limited, Shanghai, China; *U.S. Public*, pg. 553
Watabe, Tsayoshi, Pres.--Penfabric Sdn. Berhad, Penang, Malaysia; *Int'l*, pg. 1400
Watanabe, Akinori, Chief Oper. Officer--Tohoku Oki Electric Co., Ltd., Fukushima, Japan; *Int'l*, pg. 999
Watanabe, August M., M.D., Pres.--Lilly Research Laboratories, Indianapolis, IN; *U.S. Public*, pg. 993
Watanabe, Gen, Pres.--Daiwa Bank Canada, Toronto, Canada; *Int'l*, pg. 373
Watanabe, H., Gen. Mgr.--MSC Japan Ltd., Tokyo, Japan; *U.S. Public*, pg. 1032
Watanabe, Hiromi, Pres.--Komatsu Changlin Foundry Corporation, Jiangsu, China; *Int'l*, pg. 745
Watanabe, Kohei, Mgr.--Hakuhodo Inc., Beijing, China; *Int'l*, pg. 588
Watanabe, Kohei, Mng. Dir.--Hakuhodo Inc., Hong Kong, Hong Kong; *Int'l*, pg. 588
Watanabe, Kuino, Mng. Dir.--Nippon Express (Singapore) Pte., Ltd., Singapore, Singapore; *Int'l*, pg. 934
Watanabe, Rokuro, Pres.--Takara Standard Co., Ltd., Osaka, Japan; *Int'l*, pg. 1349
Watanabe, Shinichi, Dir. & Treas.--Okaya (U.S.A.), Inc., Fort Lee, NJ; *Int'l*, pg. 999
Watanabe, Sizuo, Pres.--Toray Composites (America), Inc., Tacoma, WA; *Int'l*, pg. 1400
Watanabe, Sumio, Pres. & Representative of Dir.--Sumitomo-Yale Co., Ltd., Tokyo, Japan; *U.S. Public*, pg. 1150
Watanabe, Sumio, Pres. & Representative of Dir.--Sumitomo-Yale Co., Ltd., Tokyo, Japan; *Int'l*, pg. 1315
Watanabe, Susumu, Pres.--Nichiyu Koki Co., Ltd., Nagoya, Japan; *Int'l*, pg. 763
Watanabe, Tadashi, Pres.--Dentsu Espana S.A., Barcelona, Spain; *Int'l*, pg. 393
Watanabe, Takao, Pres.--Murata of America, Inc., Charlotte, NC; *Int'l*, pg. 897
Watanabe, Takashi, Pres.--Banque IBJ (France) S.A., Paris, France; *Int'l*, pg. 676
Watanabe, Takashi, Pres.--Rohm Electronics, Eastern Sales Div., Antioch, TN; *Int'l*, pg. 1125
Watanabe, Takashi, Pres.--Toshiba Hawaii, Inc., Honolulu, HI; *Int'l*, pg. 1405
Watanabe, Tomoyoshi, Chm.--Brother Corporation (Asia) Ltd., Kowloon, Hong Kong; *Int'l*, pg. 229
Watanabe, Tsukasa, Rep.--The Kyoei Mutual Fire & Marine Insurance Company, Sao Paulo, Brazil; *Int'l*, pg. 777
Watanabe, Yoshiaki, Pres.--TYK Refractories Co., Clairton, PA; *Int'l*, pg. 1345
Watanage, Takashi, Gen. Mgr.--The Industrial Bank of Japan, Limited (Paris Branch), Paris, France; *Int'l*, pg. 675
Watase, Kenji, Chief Oper. Officer--Asahi Electric Machinery Co., Ltd., Kawasaki, Japan; *Int'l*, pg. 530
Watchhorn, W.E., Pres. & Chief Exec. Officer--Federal Industries Industrial Group, Inc., Winnipeg, Canada; *Int'l*, pg. 1150
Watchus, Brian, Gen. Mgr.--Cascade (Canada) Inc., Mississauga, Canada; *U.S. Public*, pg. 311
Water, Barry, Mgr.-Plant--Golden Sun Feeds, Inc., Maquoketa, IA; *U.S. Private*, pg. 895
Waterbury, Jim, Gen. Mgr.--KWWL-TV, Waterloo, IA; *U.S. Private*, pg. 912
Waterfield, Patrick, Pres. & Chief Exec. Officer--Guerlain, Inc., New York, NY; *Int'l*, pg. 780
Waterhouse, David R., Mgr.--Bundy Tubing (New Zealand) Ltd., Auckland, New Zealand; *Int'l*, pg. 1341
Waterhouse, Rod, Mng. Dir.--Ilco Unican Australia (Pty.) Ltd., Willoughby, Australia; *Int'l*, pg. 1432
Waterman, Peter, Gen. Mgr.--Kenner Parker Europe, Maidenhead, United Kingdom; *U.S. Public*, pg. 797
Waters, Gary, V.P.--Marsam Pharmaceuticals, Cherry Hill, NJ; *U.S. Private*, pg. 969
Waters, John, Pres.--Frigidaire Home Products, Conway, AR; *Int'l*, pg. 439
Waters, Paul, Reg. Pres.--Citizens Bank, Gibson County Region, Princeton, IN; *U.S. Public*, pg. 281
Waters, Ron, Pres.--Rocco Farms, Harrisonburg, VA; *U.S. Private*, pg. 937
Waters, Ron, Pres.--Rocco Farm Foods, Inc., Edinburg, VA; *U.S. Private*, pg. 937
Waters, Scott, V.P.& Div. Mgr.--Bernard Johnson Young Inc., Bethesda, MD; *U.S. Private*, pg. 136
Waters, W. V., Pres.--Smith Fiberglass Products Inc., Little Rock, AR; *U.S. Public*, pg. 1477
Waters, Warner S., Jr., Chm., Pres. & Chief Exec. Officer--Mellon Bank (DE) National Association, Wilmington, DE; *U.S. Public*, pg. 1085
Waterschoot, Frank, Mng. Dir.--Circle Freight International (Canada) Ltd., Rexdale, Canada; *U.S. Public*, pg. 372
Waterworth, Frank, Gen. Mgr.--CiMatrix Ltd., Stourbridge, United Kingdom; *U.S. Public*, pg. 1395
Wathusing, Larry, Pres.--Dealers Truck Equipment, Louisville, KY; *U.S. Private*, pg. 700
Watkins, Benjamin L., III, Pres.--Specialty Fabrics Segment, Fort Mill, SC; *U.S. Public*, pg. 1500
Watkins, Benjamin L., III, Pres.--Retail & Specialty Fabrics, Rock Hill, SC; *U.S. Public*, pg. 1500
Watkins, D.H., Pres.--Amax Exploration, Inc., Englewood, CO; *U.S. Public*, pg. 470
Watkins, D.H., Pres.--Cyprus Exploration & Development Corporation, Englewood, CO; *U.S. Public*, pg. 471
Watkins, D.J., Sr. Island Mgr.--Lloyds Bank (Jersey) Ltd., Saint Helier, United Kingdom; *Int'l*, pg. 813
Watkins, Elizabeth, Admin.--Guardian Care of Roanoke Rapids, Roanoke Rapids, NC; *U.S. Public*, pg. 1713
Watkins, Greg, Pres.--Watkins Contracting, Inc., San Diego, CA; *U.S. Public*, pg. 1384
Watkins, J.F., Mng. Dir.--Salford Electrical Instruments Ltd., Heywood, United Kingdom; *Int'l*, pg. 545
Watkins, James D., Pres. & Chief Oper. Officer--ConAgra Diversified Products Companies, Omaha, NE; *U.S. Public*, pg. 426
Watkins, Jeff, Pres.--Watkins Manufacturing Corp./Hot Spring Portable Spas, Vista, CA; *U.S. Public*, pg. 1054
Watkins, John B., Pres.--Capital Cities/ABC National Television Sales, Inc., New York, NY; *U.S. Public*, pg. 511
Watkins, K.G., Gen. Mgr.--Rocco Quality Foods, Inc., Saint Pauls, NC; *U.S. Private*, pg. 937
Watkins, Lee, Chm. Bd. & Chief Exec. Officer--SouthTrust Bank of Marion County, Hamilton, AL; *U.S. Public*, pg. 1492
Watkins, Leo, Pres.--Servitex, Inc., Raleigh, NC; *U.S. Private*, pg. 781
Watkins, Neil, Pres.--Gulf States Manufacturers, Inc., Starkville, MS; *Int'l*, pg. 699

Watkins, Ralph L., Chm. Bd., Pres. & Chief Exec. Officer--SouthTrust Bank, Roanoke, Roanoke, AL; *U.S. Public*, pg. 1492
Watkins, Richard, Gen. Mgr.--GATX Logistics, Inc.-Utah, Clearfield, UT; *U.S. Public*, pg. 692
Watkins, Scott D., Pres. & Chief Exec. Officer--Access Corporation, Cincinnati, OH; *Int'l*, pg. 994
Watkins, Wendell K., Sr., Sr. V.P. & Chief Oper. Officer--Willis Corroon Corp. of South Carolina, Greenville, SC; *Int'l*, pg. 1507
Watson, A.E., Div. Mgr.--Metal Box plc., Food Packaging, Worcester, United Kingdom; *Int'l*, pg. 267
Watson, Alan E., Pres.--First Protective Insurance Group, Birmingham, AL; *U.S. Public*, pg. 1336
Watson, Alan E., Pres.--Protective Benefits Communications, Birmingham, AL; *U.S. Public*, pg. 1336
Watson, B., Mgr.--THORN EMI (Canada) Inc., Mississauga, Canada; *Int'l*, pg. 428
Watson, Bill, Mgr.--The Sacks Group, Solon, OH; *Int'l*, pg. 1107
Watson, Bob, Mng. Dir.--Iggesund Paperboard (Workington) Ltd., Workington, United Kingdom; *Int'l*, pg. 886
Watson, Brett, Admin.--Santa Paula Healthcare, Santa Paula, CA; *U.S. Public*, pg. 1714
Watson, C.C., Chief Oper. Officer--National-Oilwell/Dreco Europe LTD, London, United Kingdom; *U.S. Public*, pg. 1158
Watson, Charles E., Pres.--First Citizens Bank of Virginia Corporation, Roanoke, VA; *U.S. Public*, pg. 629
Watson, Christopher E., Pres.--Gulf Insurance Company, Irving, TX; *U.S. Public*, pg. 1633
Watson, D., Reg. Mng. Dir.--Ballast Wiltshier Plc - North East Region, Stockton on Tees, United Kingdom; *Int'l*, pg. 135
Watson, D.J., Reg. Mng. Dir.--Ballast Wiltshier Plc - North East Region, Gateshead, United Kingdom; *Int'l*, pg. 135
Watson, Dan E., Chm. Bd. & Pres.--Tenneco Asset Management Co., Houston, TX; *U.S. Public*, pg. 1578
Watson, Dan E., Chm. Bd. & Pres.--Tenneco Asset Planning Co., Houston, TX; *U.S. Public*, pg. 1578
Watson, Dan E., Chm. Bd. & Pres.--Tenneco Insurance Ventures, Houston, TX; *U.S. Public*, pg. 1578
Watson, David, Mng. Dir.--Donnelly Mirrors, Limited, Naas, Ireland; *U.S. Public*, pg. 519
Watson, David C., V.P.-Mfg.--Precision Industries Division, Malvern, AR; *U.S. Public*, pg. 986
Watson, David N., Pres.--Comcast Cellular Communications, Inc., Wayne, PA; *U.S. Public*, pg. 407
Watson, Donald B., Plant Mgr.--Luden's Inc., Reading, PA; *U.S. Public*, pg. 812
Watson, Donald K., Pres. & Chief Exec. Officer--Griffin Envelope, Inc., Seattle, WA; *U.S. Public*, pg. 1038
Watson, Donald K., Pres. & Chief Exec. Officer--Emerald Warehouse & Distribution Services, Seattle, WA; *U.S. Public*, pg. 1038
Watson, Donald R., Pres.--Associates Relocation Management Company, Inc., Dallas, TX; *U.S. Public*, pg. 663
Watson, Edward A., Pres.-Canadian Opers.--Dairy Queen Canada, Inc., Burlington, Canada; *U.S. Public*, pg. 220
Watson, G., Branch Mgr.--CEGP, Consulting Engineers Grabowsky & Poort), Nairobi, Kenya; *Int'l*, pg. 607
Watson, Gene, V.P.--GES Environmental, Inc., Richmond, VA; *U.S. Public*, pg. 1222
Watson, H., Mng. Dir.--Mirrlees Blackstone (Stockport) Ltd., Stockport, United Kingdom; *Int'l*, pg. 125
Watson, Harold, Pres. & Gen. Mgr.--Williams Detroit Diesel-Allison S.E., Inc., Atlanta, GA; *U.S. Private*, pg. 1179
Watson, Harold G., Pres.--Universal Propulsion Co., Inc., Phoenix, AZ; *U.S. Public*, pg. 308
Watson, J. Paul, Pres.--Brown & Sharpe Limited, Derby, United Kingdom; *U.S. Public*, pg. 260
Watson, J.J.H., Mng. Dir.--Boots Contract Manufacturing, Nottingham, United Kingdom; *Int'l*, pg. 202
Watson, J.S., Pres.--Chevron Canada Limited, Vancouver, Canada; *U.S. Public*, pg. 348
Watson, J.T., Gen. Mgr.--Nestle Singapore Pte. Ltd., Jurong, Singapore; *Int'l*, pg. 921
Watson, James F., Jr., Pres.--Thermo King Corporation, Minneapolis, MN; *U.S. Public*, pg. 877
Watson, James G., Pres.--Armtec, Guelph, Canada; *Int'l*, pg. 698
Watson, Jim, V.P.--Monenco AGRA Techmaster Ltd., Nicosia, Cyprus; *Int'l*, pg. 31
Watson, John, Pres.--Keeler Brass Company, Grand Rapids, MI; *Int'l*, pg. 473
Watson, John, Mng. Dir.--Daniel Industries Ltd., Falkirk, United Kingdom; *U.S. Public*, pg. 483
Watson, John, Chief Fin. Officer & Exec. V.P.--Rank America, Inc., Atlanta, GA; *Int'l* pg. 1087
Watson, John C., Chm. Bd., Pres. & Chief Exec. Officer--NACOLAH Holding Corp. Inc., Chicago, IL; *U.S. Private*, pg. 963
Watson, Leigh, V.P.--Young Poong Manulife, Seoul, Korea; *Int'l*, pg. 841
Watson, Lennete, Admin.--Hillhaven Convalescent Center Vancouver, Vancouver, WA; *U.S. Public*, pg. 1713
Watson, Lewis, Plant Mgr.--Justin Boot Company, Sarcoxie, MO; *U.S. Public*, pg. 937
Watson, Lisa, Reg. Acct. Mgr.--Utell International-San Francisco, San Francisco, CA; *Int'l*, pg. 1098
Watson, Moran, Mgr.-Opers.--Payne & Keller Company, Inc., Baton Rouge, LA; *U.S. Public*, pg. 921
Watson, N.J., Mng. Dir.--Beeton Rumford Ltd., London, United Kingdom; *Int'l*, pg. 1032
Watson, Peter D., Pres. & Chief Oper. Officer--Willis Corroon Melling Ltd., Edmonton, Canada; *Int'l*, pg. 1509
Watson, Ray, V.P. & Gen. Mgr.--KGET-TV, Bakersfield, CA; *U.S. Public*, pg. 16
Watson, Ronald D., Chm. Bd. & Chief Exec. Officer--Custodial Trust Company, Princeton, NJ; *U.S. Public*, pg. 198
Watson, Stephen, Pres. & Chief Exec. Officer--Gander Mountain Retail, Bloomington, MN; *U.S. Private*, pg. 534
Watson, T.D., Pres.--Kodak Korea Ltd., Seoul, Korea; *U.S. Public*, pg. 555
Watson, W. James, Pres.--General Motors Acceptance Corporation of Canada Limited, Toronto, Canada; *U.S. Public*, pg. 720
Watson, Weldon, Mgr.--Palm Harbor Homes, Sabina, OH; *U.S. Public*, pg. 1255
Watson, William B., Pres. & Chief Exec. Officer--SouthTrust Bank, Hartselle, Decatur, AL; *U.S. Public*, pg. 1491
Watt, Donald G., Chm. Bd.--The Watt Design Group Inc., Toronto, Canada; *Int'l*, pg. 338
Watt, Drew, Mng. Dir.--Woods of Perth, Perth, United Kingdom; *Int'l*, pg. 290
Watt, Gerard P., Gen. Mgr.--Howden Sirocco, Fluid Drive Department, Dearborn, MI; *Int'l*, pg. 636
Watt, Louise, Gen. Mgr.--TMP Worldwide Pty Ltd., Fortitude Valley, Australia; *Int'l*, pg. 1342
Watters, T.C.F., Plant Mgr.--Birfield Plant of GKN Hardy Spicer, Birmingham, United Kingdom; *Int'l*, pg. 534
Wattman, Kenneth E., Pres.--Kao Corporation of America (DE), Wilmington, DE; *Int'l*, pg. 717
Watts, Brian, Gen. Mgr.--Parker Hannifin (Australia) (Pty.) Ltd., Castle Hill, Australia; *U.S. Public*, pg. 1263
Watts, J., M.D., Chief Oper. Officer--Armitage Shanks Limited, Rugeley, United Kingdom; *Int'l*, pg. 197
Watts, Jon, Gen. Mgr.--National Band Three Ltd., Chelmsford, United Kingdom; *U.S. Public*, pg. 740
Watts, Michael, Pres.--Harman Interactive Group, San Jose, CA; *U.S. Public*, pg. 787
Watts, Robert, Reg. Sls. Mgr.--Thetford Corp., Warehouse Div., Elkhart, IN; *U.S. Private*, pg. 352
Watts, Robert, Pres. & Chief Exec. Officer--John Hancock Distributors, Inc., Boston, MA; *U.S. Private*, pg. 590
Watts, Robert G., Mng. Dir.--Swiss Re Australia Ltd., Melbourne, Australia; *Int'l*, pg. 1333
Watts, Ron, Pres.--Motion Industries (Canada), Inc., Lethbridge, Canada; *U.S. Public*, pg. 732
Watts, William, Pres. & Chief Exec. Officer--General Nutrition Products, Inc., Greenville, SC; *U.S. Public*, pg. 725
Wattz, Carl S., Pres. & Chief Exec. Officer--TBC Financial Services, Philadelphia, PA; *U.S. Public*, pg. 1561
Waugh, R.E., Exec. V.P.--The Bank of Nova Scotia, New York, NY; *Int'l*, pg. 156
Waugh, Whitney, V.P. & Gen. Mgr.--Chemrock Corporation, Nashville, TN; *U.S. Private*, pg. 903
Waumans, Frans, Sls. Mgr.--Wisapaper Benelux B.V., Antwerp, Belgium; *Int'l*, pg. 1430
Wauters, Jacques, Gen. Mgr.--Durco France S.A.R.L., Villeneuve d'Ascq, France; *U.S. Public*, pg. 659
Wawrzeniak, John, Gen. Mgr.--Beaird Industries, Inc., Shreveport, LA; *U.S. Public*, pg. 1639
Waxenberg, Alan M., Sr. V.P. & Publisher--Good Housekeeping, New York, NY; *U.S. Private*, pg. 517
Waxman, Armond, Co-Chief Exec. Officer--TWI International, Inc., Cleveland, OH; *U.S. Public*, pg. 1749
Waxman, Bert, V.P. & Gen. Mgr.--Film Div., Clark, NJ; *Int'l*, pg. 370
Waxman, Laurence, Pres.--Waxman Consumer Products Group, Bedford, OH; *U.S. Public*, pg. 1749
Waxman, Melvin, Chm. Bd. & Co-Chief Exec. Officer--WOC Inc., Bedford, OH; *U.S. Public*, pg. 1748
Way, Ron W., Pres.--Rentway Truck Leasing, Perrysburg, OH; *Int'l*, pg. 1424
Waybright, James M., Plant Mgr.--Steelcase, Inc./Athens Plant, Grand Rapids, MI; *U.S. Private*, pg. 1038
Wayne, Gregory W., Pres.--InteSys of California, Costa Mesa, CA; *U.S. Private*, pg. 574
Wayne, Norman M., Chm. Bd.--Cigna Run-Off Services, Inc., Philadelphia, PA; *U.S. Public*, pg. 365
Wayne, Norman M., Chm. Bd.--Cigna Reinsurance Company, Philadelphia, PA; *U.S. Public*, pg. 365
Wayne, Norman M., Chm. Bd.--Century Reinsurance Company, Philadelphia, PA; *U.S. Public*, pg. 365
Wayne, Robert, Plant Mgr.--Cheraw Plant, Cheraw, SC; *U.S. Public*, pg. 444
Wayworm, Russ, V.P.-Sls.--Robot Research, Inc., San Diego, CA; *U.S. Public*, pg. 1457
Weare, Norman E., Pres.--Carolina Metals, Inc., Barnwell, SC; *U.S. Public*, pg. 1511
Weatherall, Percy, Chief Exec. Officer--Hongkong Land Holdings Limited, Hamilton, Bermuda; *Int'l*, pg. 704
Weatherby, Jim, Pres.--Hart Forms & Services, Austin, TX; *U.S. Private*, pg. 507
Weathersby, Joe, Pres.--Texas Valley Div., McAllen, TX; *U.S. Public*, pg. 1683
Weathersby, Joe, Pres.--San Antonio Div., San Antonio, TX; *U.S. Public*, pg. 1683
Weatherston, Bob, Pres.--Hastings, Inc., Barrie, Canada; *U.S. Public*, pg. 798
Weatherstone, C., Gen. Mgr.--Collieries Division, Wollongong, Australia; *Int'l*, pg. 226
Weatherup, Craig, Chm. Bd. & Chief Exec. Officer--Pepsi-Cola Company, Somers, NY; *U.S. Public*, pg. 1277
Weaven, Jay, Mgr.-Plant--Nestle Frozen/Refrigerated Food Co., Springville, UT; *Int'l*, pg. 918
Weaver, Amy, Pres.--Emons Finance Corp., York, PA; *U.S. Public*, pg. 578
Weaver, Amy S., Pres., Treas. & Sec.--Emons Finance Corporation, Wilmington, DE; *U.S. Public*, pg. 578
Weaver, David, Mgr.--Southern Electric Supply Co., Inc., Vero Beach, FL; *Int'l*, pg. 1108
Weaver, David F., Pres.--Texas Bank N.A., Houston, TX; *U.S. Public*, pg. 626
Weaver, E.L., Pres.--Fusite Div., Cincinnati, OH; *U.S. Public*, pg. 573
Weaver, John C., V.P. & Grp. Pres.--Radar Systems Group, Los Angeles, CA; *U.S. Public*, pg. 1364
Weaver, Phil, Pres.--Eck Miller Transportation Corporation, Rockport, IN; *U.S. Public*, pg. 911
Weaver, R. Bradley, Pres. & Chief Exec. Officer--United Missouri Bank of Warrensburg, Warrensburg, MO; *U.S. Public*, pg. 1655
Weaver, W. Ross, Pres.--Pan-Alberta Gas Ltd., Calgary, Canada; *Int'l*, pg. 971
Weaver, W.S., Pres.--Puget Energy Inc., Bothell, WA; *U.S. Public*, pg. 1342
Weaver, William C., Pres.--Halliburton Energy Services, Carmel, IN; *U.S. Public*, pg. 776
Weavers, Jim, Chief Oper. Officer & V.P.--LSB Chemical Corp., Oklahoma City, OK; *U.S. Public*, pg. 971
Weaving, Rick, Pres.--Thomas Equipment Limited, Centreville, Canada; *Int'l*, pg. 850
Webb, Aubrey, V.P. & Publisher--Beaumont Enterprise, Beaumont, TX; *U.S. Private*, pg. 517
Webb, Barrie P., Chm. & Chief Exec. Officer--R.P. Scherer Holdings Pty. Ltd., Braeside, Australia; *U.S. Public*, pg. 1438
Webb, Carl, Pres. & Chief Oper. Officer--California Federal Bank, San Francisco, CA; *U.S. Private*, pg. 690
Webb, Carol A., Pres.--Ortho Biotech Inc., Raritan, NJ; *U.S. Public*, pg. 929
Webb, David, Pres.--Lever Brothers Household Products Div., New York, NY; *Int'l*, pg. 1436
Webb, Dennis, Mgr.--Bergen Brunswig Drug Company, Glen Allen, VA; *U.S. Public*, pg. 214
Webb, E. Lynn, Exec. V.P. & Treas.--Dualite Sales & Service, Inc., Williamsburg, OH; *U.S. Private*, pg. 344
Webb, Geoff, Mgr.--Brisbane Market Mill, Acacia Ridge, Australia; *Int'l*, pg. 227
Webb, Henry E., Jr., Pres.--Whiting Metals, Inc., Camden, SC; *U.S. Public*, pg. 1548
Webb, J.J., Pres. & Chief Exec. Officer--Atlantic Steel Industries, Inc., Atlanta, GA; *Int'l*, pg. 696
Webb, J.R., Pres.-Exxon Chemical Americas--Exxon Chemical Company, Houston, TX; *U.S. Public*, pg. 601
Webb, James R., Pres.--Uncle Ben's, Inc., Houston, TX; *U.S. Private*, pg. 707
Webb, Jeffrey G., Pres. & Chief Exec. Officer--Varsity Spirit Corporation, Memphis, TN; *U.S. Public*, pg. 1389
Webb, Jeffrey G., Pres.--Varsity Intropa, Memphis, TN; *U.S. Public*, pg. 1389
Webb, Jeffrey G., Pres.--Varsity USA, Memphis, TN; *U.S. Public*, pg. 1389
Webb, John, Reg. Mgr.--BHP Trading Inc., Pittsburgh, PA; *Int'l*, pg. 226
Webb, Jon, Mng. Dir.--NEXIS UK, London, United Kingdom; *Int'l*, pg. 1096
Webb, Lawrence, Gen. Mgr.--Shakespeare (Australia) Pty. Ltd., Bankstown, Australia; *U.S. Public*, pg. 940
Webb, Mike, Mng. Dir.--DMR Group Limited, West Drayton, United Kingdom; *Int'l*, pg. 528
Webb, Mitch, Mgr.--State Electric Supply Company, New Boston, OH; *U.S. Private*, pg. 1036
Webb, R.M., Chief Exec. Officer & Grp. Country Mgr.--Barclays Bank PLC, USA, New York, NY; *Int'l*, pg. 165
Webb, R.M.L., Chm.--Morgan Grenfell & Co. Limited, London, United Kingdom; *Int'l*, pg. 405
Webb, Tom, Chief Oper. Officer--Allright Parking Virginia, Inc., Lynchburg, VA; *U.S. Private*, pg. 43
Webb, Tom D., Mgr.--Texas Cold Finished Steel, Inc., Houston, TX; *U.S. Public*, pg. 412
Webb, V.R., Gen. Mgr.--Alcan Aluminium S.A., Geneva, Switzerland; *Int'l*, pg. 50
Webb, William H., Pres. & Chief Exec. Officer--Philip Morris International Inc., Rye Brook, NY; *U.S. Public*, pg. 1289
Webber, Andrew Lloyd, Exec. Dir.--The Really Useful Picture Company, London, United Kingdom; *Int'l*, pg. 1089
Webber, David L., Pres.--Harris Bank Roselle, Roselle, IL; *Int'l*, pg. 154
Webber, George, Chm.--Sprecher Energie AG, Oberentfelden, Switzerland; *Int'l*, pg. 55
Webber, George, Gen. Mgr.--Webber Gage Div., Cleveland, OH; *U.S. Public*, pg. 1511
Webber, Lee P., Chief Oper. Officer--Guam Publications, Inc., Agana, GU; *U.S. Public*, pg. 702
Webber, Lee P., Chief Oper. Officer--Pacific Media, Inc., Agana, GU; *U.S. Public*, pg. 702
Webels, H., Mng. Dir.--GKN Informatik GmbH, Rosrath, Germany; *Int'l*, pg. 536
Weber-Bemnet, Eduard, Gen. Mgr.--Daniel J. Edelman GmbH, Frankfurt/Main, Germany; *U.S. Private*, pg. 363
Weber, Andrew J., Pres. & Chief Exec. Officer--McKnight Medical Communications Company, Northfield, IL; *U.S. Public*, pg. 1601
Weber, Bruce, Plant Mgr.--Flavor Mfg. Center, Hunt Valley, MD; *U.S. Public*, pg. 1066
Weber, Curtis, Plant Mgr.--Macomb Plant, Macomb, IL; *U.S. Public*, pg. 443
Weber, Dan, V.P. & Gen. Mgr.--Welbilt Varimixer, Shreveport, LA; *Int'l*, pg. 189
Weber, Dennis K., Chief Oper. Officer--Wolverine Gasket & Manufacturing Co., Inkster, MI; *U.S. Private*, pg. 355
Weber, Dieter, Mgr.--GGK Paris, Levallois-Perret, France; *Int'l*, pg. 1335
Weber, Don, Pres.--Weber Plastics Co. Ltd., Waterloo, Canada; *U.S. Public*, pg. 987
Weber, Gerd, Dr., Chm. Bd.--Krupp Hoesch Maschinenbau GmbH, Essen, Germany; *Int'l*, pg. 509
Weber, H.R., Mgr.--Schweizerischer Bankverein Repräsentanz, Fribourg, Switzerland; *Int'l*, pg. 1330
Weber, Heinz, Chief Oper. Officer--Suedwestdeutsche Rohrleitungsbau GmbH, Frankfurt/Main, Germany; *Int'l*, pg. 623
Weber, Helene, Mng. Dir.--Bally (Schweiz) S.A., Zurich, Switzerland; *Int'l*, pg. 996
Weber, J., Pres.--Credit Industriel D'Alsace et de Lorraine, Strasbourg, France; *Int'l*, pg. 564
Weber, John, Pres.--Vickers, Incorporated, Maumee, OH; *U.S. Public*, pg. 24
Weber, Karl G., Mgr.--Kreditbank-Bankverein AG, Frankfurt, Germany; *Int'l*, pg. 761
Weber, O.G., Pres.--Foundation Nuclear Managers, Mississauga, Canada; *Int'l*, pg. 118
Weber, Owen, V.P. & Gen. Mgr.--KIKK AM/FM, Houston, TX; *U.S. Public*, pg. 274

Weber, Phil, Pres.--Abex Friction Products, Winchester, VA; *U.S. Public*, pg. 443

Weber, Richard, Pres. & Gen. Mgr.--TENERA Energy, LLC, San Francisco, CA; *U.S. Public*, pg. 1576

Weber, Robert, V.P.-Opers.--Manufacturing Division-Watches, Woodside, NY; *U.S. Public*, pg. 1010

Weber, Robert C., Pres.--United Consumer Financial Services Co., Westlake, OH; *U.S. Public*, pg. 218

Weber, Ronald A., Div. V.P.--Automotive Division, Saint Paul, MN; *U.S. Public*, pg. 1605

Weber, Thomas E., Jr., Pres. & Editor--Stuart News Company, Stuart, FL; *U.S. Public*, pg. 1448

Weber, William, Gen. Mgr.--Esco Industrial Service Center, Portland, OR; *U.S. Private*, pg. 383

Webster, B.O., Mgr.--Moose Jaw Plant, Moose Jaw, Canada; *U.S. Public*, pg. 387

Webster, Daniel, Mgr.--EG & G Instruments-Process Measurements/Chandler, Broken Arrow, OK; *U.S. Public, pg. 543*

Webster, David L., Pres.--Kinro, Inc., Arlington, TX; *U.S. Public*, pg. 529

Webster, David L., Pres.--Shoals Supply, Inc., Arlington, TX; *U.S. Public*, pg. 529

Webster, Donald R., Pres.--Perstorp Analytical Inc. Division NIRSystems, Silver Spring, MD; *Int'l*, pg. 1039

Webster, Eric T., V.P.-Europe/Africa Sls.--Santa Fe Braun (U.K.) Ltd., London, United Kingdom; *Int'l*, pg. 765

Webster, Gail S.T., Pres.--The Huntington Trust Company of Florida, N.A., Naples, FL; *U.S. Public*, pg. 850

Webster, Geoffrey, Pres.--Givaudan-Roure, Corporation-Fragrances Div., Teaneck, NJ; *Int'l*, pg. 1120

Webster, George K., Pres. & Chief Exec. Officer--Miltope Corporation, Montgomery, AL; *U.S. Public*, pg. 1114

Webster, J. L., Chief Oper. Officer--Dynacast, Yorktown Heights, NY; *Int'l*, pg. 300

Webster, Jackie, Admin.--Heritage Estates, Fort Worth, TX; *U.S. Public*, pg. 839

Webster, Michael, Mng. Dir.--D.W. Thorpe-Australia, Melbourne, Australia; *Int'l*, pg. 1095

Wechsler, Lawrence, Pres.--Bill Blass, Inc., New York, NY; *U.S. Private*, pg. 689

Wechsler, Lawrence, Pres.--Norell Perfumes, Inc., New York, NY; *U.S. Private*, pg. 690

Weck, M.J.F., Mng. Dir.--Ballast Nedam Telecom Infrastructures, Amstelveen, Netherlands; *Int'l*, pg. 133

Wedaman, David, Pres.--MNX Carriers, Inc., Saint Joseph, MO; *U.S. Public*, pg. 1046

Wedaman, David H., Pres.--Mark VII Transportation Company, Inc., Greenwood, IN; *U.S. Public*, pg. 1046

Wedding, I. J., Pres. Dir.--PT AMP Panin Life, Jakarta, Indonesia; *Int'l*, pg. 100

Weddle, J.R., Jr., Pres.--Gold Medal Insurance Co., Minneapolis, MN; *U.S. Public*, pg. 718

Wedemeyer, Carl, Gen. Mgr.--ARDCO/Traverse Lift, Houston, TX; *U.S. Private*, pg. 859

Wee, D., Mng. Dir.--EMI (Singapore) Pte Ltd., Singapore, Singapore; *Int'l*, pg. 427

Wee, Lian-Tek, Asst. Gen. Mgr.--Singapore Engine Overhaul Centre (Pte.) Ltd., Singapore, Singapore; *Int'l*, pg. 1374

Wee, Vincent, Chief Oper. Officer--Up-Right (Far East) Ltd., Singapore, Singapore; *U.S. Private*, pg. 1128

Weeden, Robert, Dir.-Opers.--Huls America Inc., Edison, NJ; *Int'l*, pg. 1455

Weekly, John W., Vice Chm. & Chief Exec. Officer--United of Omaha Life Insurance Company, Omaha, NE; *U.S. Private*, pg. 770

Weeks, Karen, Lab Mgr.--Quest Diagnostic-Greensburg, Greensburg, PA; *U.S. Public*, pg. 1351

Weeks, Karen, Laboratory Mgr.--Quest Diagnostic-Latrobe, Latrobe, PA; *U.S. Public*, pg. 1351

Weeks, L.W., Pres.--Ohio Star Forge Co., Warren, OH; *Int'l, pg. 364*

Weeks, Michael F., Pres.--Survey Research Associates, Baltimore, MD; *U.S. Private*, pg. 123

Weeks, R.E., Mng. Dir.--J.R. Phillips & Co., Ltd., Wokingham, United Kingdom; *Int'l*, pg. 1499

Weeks, Roland, Publisher--Sun Herald, Gulfport, MS; *U.S. Public*, pg. 964

Weeks, Roland, Jr., Publr.--Gulf Publishing Company, Inc., Biloxi, MS; *U.S. Public*, pg. 964

Weems, Lew, Regional Pres.--First Tennessee Bank - Knoxville, Knoxville, TN; *U.S. Public*, pg. 639

Wefer, Horst, Chief Oper. Officer--Electrolux-CR GmbH, Mosbach, Germany; *Int'l*, pg. 442

Weg, Kenneth E., Pres.--Bristol-Myers Squibb International, Princeton, NJ; *U.S. Public*, pg. 254

Wegelius, George, Reg. Mgr.--Schauman Wood Oy-Regional Office, Amman, Jordan; *Int'l*, pg. 1429

Wegener, William S., Pres.--ARCO Coal Australia, Inc., Brisbane, Australia; *U.S. Public*, pg. 144

Weger, Kris, Sr. V.P. & Gen Mgr.--Unistrut Corporation, Wayne, MI; *U.S. Public*, pg. 1651

Wegner, Arthur E., Chm. Bd., Chief Exec. Officer & Sr. V.P.--Raytheon Aircraft Company, Wichita, KS; *U.S. Public*, pg. 1365

Wegner, David A., Pres.--Seitel Gas & Energy Corp., Houston, TX; *U.S. Public*, pg. 1454

Wegner, Pamela J., Pres.--REAC, Inc., Madison, WI; *U.S. Public*, pg. 1728

Wehmeier, Heige H., Pres. & Chief Exec. Officer--Bayer Corporation, Pittsburgh, PA; *Int'l*, pg. 172

Wehmeier, Heige H., Pres. & Chief Exec. Officer--Bayer Corporation, Parsippany, NJ; *Int'l*, pg. 172

Wehmeier, Helge H., Pres. & Chief Exec. Officer--Bayer Corporation, Pittsburgh, PA; *Int'l*, pg. 172

Wehr, Heinz, Mgr.--Network Systems GmbH, Neuss, Germany; *U.S. Public*, pg. 1523

Wehrens, L.H., Gen. Mgr.--Winter-Bouts B.V., Venlo, Netherlands; *Int'l*, pg. 729

Wei, Chong Eng, Acting Pres.--IPC Peripherals, Inc., Fremont, CA; *Int'l*, pg. 651

Wei, Song, Chief Repr.--Kredietbank Shanghai Branch, Shanghai, China; *Int'l*, pg. 760

Wei, T.H., Pres.--Taiwan Otsuka Pharmaceutical Co., Ltd., Taipei, Taiwan; *Int'l*, pg. 1014

Weible, Glen, Gen. Mgr.--Canfor U.S.A. Corporation, Meridian, ID; *Int'l*, pg. 260

Weibler, Klaus P., Mng. Dir.--Gentex GmbH, Neckarsulm, Germany; *U.S. Public*, pg. 732

Weibley, Vance, Pres.--Carlisle Poultry & Egg Associates, Burgaw, NC; *U.S. Public*, pg. 1529

Weibye, Bjorn, Pres.--Det Norske Veritas Industry, Hovik, Norway; *Int'l*, pg. 396

Weich, Gerhard, Pres.--Pall Deutschland GmbH, Sprendlingen, Germany; *U.S. Public*, pg. 1254

Weich, Gerhard, Pres.--Pall Industrie-Hydraulik GmbH, Dreieichenhain, Germany; *U.S. Public*, pg. 1254

Weich, Gerhard, Pres.--Pall Filtrationstechnik GmbH, Dreieichenhain, Germany; *U.S. Public*, pg. 1254

Weicker, Jean-Claude, Gen. Mgr.--Liege Local Head Office, Liege, Belgium; *Int'l*, pg. 147

Weicker, Jean-Claude, Gen. Mgr.--Verviers Local Head Office, Verviers, Belgium; *Int'l*, pg. 147

Weida, G.R., Pres.--Penn Racquet Sports, Phoenix, AZ; *U.S. Public*, pg. 706

Weida, G.R., Pres.--Penn Racquet Sports, Mullingar, Ireland; *U.S. Public*, pg. 706

Weidemann, Poul, Chief Oper. Officer--Gambro Medicoteknik A/S, Vallensbaek, Denmark; *Int'l*, pg. 668

Weidner, H.D., Dr., Chm.--John Deere-Lanz Verwaltungs A.G., Mannheim, Germany; *U.S. Public*, pg. 493

Weigal, K.J., Gen. Mgr.--CHEMCENTRAL/Milwaukee, New Berlin, WI; *U.S. Private*, pg. 232

Weigand, Joe, Gen. Mgr.--Madison Industries, Los Angeles, CA; *U.S. Private*, pg. 428

Weigand, Martin, Dr., Dir.--Deutsche Bank AG (Mexico), Mexico, Mexico; *Int'l*, pg. 404

Weigle, Fred, Pres.--StacoEnergy Products Co., Dayton, OH; *U.S. Private*, pg. 260

Weigman, Craig A., Pres.--Ikon Office Solutions-Southern California, Irvine, CA; *U.S. Public*, pg. 864

Weihler, Tom, Gen. Mgr.--Frontier Communications of Orion, Inc., Orion, IL; *U.S. Public*, pg. 684

Weijun, Shen, Pres.--Sino-Sweed Pharmaceutical Corp Ltd., Wuxi, China; *Int'l*, pg. 94

Weil, Gerard, Chief Oper. Officer--Rhone-Poulenc Sverige AB, Stockholm, Sweden; *Int'l*, pg. 1114

Weiland, Bob, Div. V.P.--Defense Systems Div., Austin, TX; *U.S. Public*, pg. 1627

Weiler, Michael, Pres. & Chief Exec. Officer--Preferred Risk Life Insurance Co., West Des Moines, IA; *U.S. Private*, pg. 880

Weill, Fred, Pres.--Central Lewmar International, New York, NY; *U.S. Private*, pg. 223

Weinbaum, Shimon, Pres.--Maliline Ltd, Tel Aviv, Israel; *U.S. Private*, pg. 1120

Weinberg, A., Gen. Mgr.--Yavnir Trading Co. Ltd., Tel Aviv, Israel; *Int'l*, pg. 75

Weinberg, David L., Chief Exec. Officer--Nippon Credit International Limited, London, United Kingdom; *Int'l*, pg. 933

Weinberg, Mark, Sir, Chm.--J. Rothschild Assurance Holdings, Gloucester, United Kingdom; *Int'l*, pg. 1178

Weinberg, Ronald, Chm. Bd.--The S.K. Wellman Friction Products Co., Brook Park, OH; *U.S. Private*, pg. 511

Weinberg, Thomas A., Chief Oper. Officer-Los Angeles, Exec. V.P. & Dir.--EvansGroup, Salt Lake City, UT; *U.S. Private*, pg. 385

Weinberger, Caspar W., Chm. Bd.--Forbes Magazine Division, New York, NY; *U.S. Private*, pg. 417

Weinberger, Gerald, Mng. Dir.--A. Schulman GmbH, Kerpen, Germany; *U.S. Public*, pg. 1441

Weinbrenner, Horst, Dir.--Martin & Pagenstecher Rohstoffbet Riebe GmbH & Co. KG, Ruppach-Goldhausen, Germany; *Int'l*, pg. 1488

Weiner, Jeffrey R., Pres.--Design/Craft Fabric Corp., Niles, IL; *U.S. Public*, pg. 1357

Weiner, Leonard, V.P.--Bennett Brothers, Inc., Mahwah, NJ; *U.S. Private*, pg. 133

Weiner, Michael B., V.P.-Sales-Texas--Davenport Data Processors Inc., Dallas, TX; *U.S. Public*, pg. 181

Weiner, Mike, Gen. Mgr.--P/M Structural Parts Div., Columbus, OH; *U.S. Private*, pg. 619

Weiner, Susan, Sr. V.P.-Brand Mngmt.--Pearle Vision Express, Dallas, TX; *U.S. Public*, pg. 397

Weinhardt, J.W., Chief Oper. Officer--SJW Land Company, San Jose, CA; *U.S. Public*, pg. 1418

Weinhardt, W. John, Pres.--Fayetteville Tubular Products, Inc., Fayetteville, OH; *U.S. Public*, pg. 481

Weinhardt, W. John, Pres.--Fayette Tubular Products, Troy, MI; *U.S. Public*, pg. 481

Weinholtz, Mike, Chief Exec. Officer--CareerStaff Unlimited, Inc., Houston, TX; *U.S. Public*, pg. 1531

Weinholzer, Charles, Branch Mgr.--Midland Color Company, Milwaukee, WI; *Int'l*, pg. 1311

Weinhuff, Jeffry K., Exec. V.P. & Dir.-Corp. Fin.--Jefferies & Company, Inc., Los Angeles, CA; *U.S. Public*, pg. 925

Weinkauf, Thomas L., Mgr.--Piper Jaffray Inc., Wausau, WI; *U.S. Public*, pg. 1302

Weinlein, Jack, Gen. Mgr.--WBBB, Burlington, NC; *U.S. Private*, pg. 297

Weinlein, Jack, Gen. Mgr.--WPCM, Burlington, NC; *U.S. Private*, pg. 298

Weinreich, Harald, Chm. Bd.--Continental-Lensa S.A., Santiago, Chile; *U.S. Public*, pg. 1563

Weinryb, Gideon, Mng. Dir.--Aladdin Industries, Palaiseau, France; *U.S. Private*, pg. 31

Weins, Robert, Pres.--FACS Records Centre Inc., Vancouver, Canada; *Int'l*, pg. 1494

Weinseis, John, Pres.--Bowdens Media Monitoring Limited, Scarborough, Canada; *Int'l*, pg. 1124

Weinstein, Dr. Martin, Chm. & Chief Exec. Officer--Chromalloy Gas Turbine Corp., San Antonio, TX; *U.S. Public*, pg. 1458

Weinstein, Gary S., Chief Exec. Officer--ThermoTrex, San Diego, CA; *U.S. Public*, pg. 1595

Weinstein, Jeffrey A., Sec.--Ekco International Housewares, Ltd., Gwent, United Kingdom; *U.S. Public*, pg. 566

Weinstein, John, Pres.--Torre Lazur/Weber Healthcare Public Relations, Parsippany, NJ; *U.S. Private*, pg. 1157

Weinstein, Mark, Supvr.-Mktg.--BPA International - McLean, Mc Lean, VA; *U.S. Private*, pg. 107

Weinstein, Marty, Gen. Mgr.--Louisiana Community Bar & Grill, New York, NY; *U.S. Public*, pg. 130

Weir, Barry, Chief Gen. Mgr.--Steelmark-Eagle & Globe, Auburn, Australia; *Int'l*, pg. 100

Weir, Ben F., Jr., Publr.--The Independence Examiner, Independence, MO; *U.S. Private*, pg. 995

Weir, Ben F., Jr., Gen. Mgr.--Oak Grove Publications, Inc., Oak Grove, MO; *U.S. Private*, pg. 995

Weir, Brad, Mgr.--Kelso-Burnett Chicago Branch, Chicago, IL; *U.S. Private*, pg. 613

Weir, Greg, V.P. & Gen. Mgr.--PDI (Production.Design.Interactive), Houston, TX; *U.S. Private*, pg. 147

Weir, H.E., Chief Oper. Officer--Babcock Australia Holdings Ltd., Sydney, Australia; *Int'l*, pg. 474

Weirsoe, Steen, Pres.--Danisco Ingredients, Brabrand, Denmark; *Int'l*, pg. 378

Weis, Bernd, Principal--Conquest Europe, Frankfurt/Main, Germany; *Int'l*, pg. 1484

Weisberg, R.A., Pres.--Senior Engineering, Lyman, SC; *Int'l, pg. 1222*

Weise, Gerhard, Mng. Dir.--Teleindustria Ericsson, S.A. de C.V., Mexico, Mexico; *Int'l*, pg. 1371

Weisel, D., Gen. Mgr.--Amnir-Recycling Industries Ltd, Hadera, Israel; *Int'l*, pg. 75

Weisel, Tom, Chm. Bd. & Chief Exec. Officer--NationsBank Montgomery Securities LLC, San Francisco, CA; *U.S. Public*, pg. 1162

Weisenborn, W., Pres.--ING Futures & Options, Chicago, IL; *Int'l*, pg. 647

Weiser, Hans J., Mng. Dir.--Kabelwerke Reinshagen GmbH, Wuppertal, Germany; *U.S. Public*, pg. 723

Weiser, Hans J., Pres.--Unicables, S.A., Pamplona, Spain; *U.S. Public*, pg. 724

Weiser, Hans-Jurgen, Mng. Dir.--Packard Electric Europa Ges.m.b.H., Grosspetersdorf, Austria; *U.S. Public*, pg. 723

Weisheit, Alex, Gen. Mgr.--Indiana Fineblanking Division, Knox, IN; *Int'l*, pg. 737

Weisman, Adalbert, Mng. Dir.--Bran & Luebbe G.m.b.H., Norderstedt, Germany; *Int'l*, pg. 1379

Weismann, Bert, Mng. Dir.--SATTControl AB, Malmo, Sweden; *Int'l*, pg. 1378

Weismann, Frederick H., Pres. & Chief Oper. Officer--Hilco, Inc., Manchester, NH; *Int'l*, pg. 153

Weismantel, Lyle, Pres.--First American Bank Southwest, Marshall, MN; *U.S. Private*, pg. 167

Weiss, Allan J., Treas.--CAC Medical Centers, Inc., Coral Gables, FL; *U.S. Public*, pg. 1678

Weiss, Allan J., Treas.--United HealthCare of Texas, Inc., Austin, TX; *U.S. Public*, pg. 1678

Weiss, Gunther, Chief Oper. Officer--Weiss Scientific Glass Blowing Co., Inc., Portland, OR; *Int'l*, pg. 1408

Weiss, Gunther, Chief Oper. Officer--Weiss Glass Technologies, Inc., San Jose, CA; *Int'l*, pg. 1408

Weiss, Henning, Dir.--A/S Helly-Hansen, Brondby, Denmark; *Int'l*, pg. 1010

Weiss, James, Mng. Dir.--Triumph Releasing Corporation - Southwestern Territory, Dallas, TX; *Int'l*, pg. 1282

Weiss, Martin, Pres.--Weiss Money Management, Inc., Palm Beach Gardens, FL; *U.S. Private*, pg. 1160

Weiss, Martin, Pres.--Weiss Rating, Inc., Palm Beach Gardens, FL; *U.S. Private*, pg. 1160

Weiss, Martin, Pres.--Weiss Research, Inc., Palm Beach Gardens, FL; *U.S. Private*, pg. 1160

Weiss, Michael, Pres.--Express, Columbus, OH; *U.S. Public, pg. 995*

Weiss, Peter, Multinational Accts. & Opers. Dir.--Grey Daiko Advertising, Inc., Tokyo, Japan; *Int'l*, pg. 366

Weiss, Sam, Pres.--Howard Products, Pottsville, PA; *U.S. Private*, pg. 1124

Weiss, Wolfgang, Pres., Mgr. & Dir.--Mazda Austria GmbH, Klagenfurt, Austria; *Int'l*, pg. 849

Weissenborn, James A., Pres.--Pulte Financial Companies, Inc., Greenwood Village, CO; *U.S. Public*, pg. 1345

Weisser, Fredy, Acct. Dir.--GGK Zurich, Zurich, Switzerland; *Int'l*, pg. 1335

Weisshaar, Kenneth R., Pres.--Becton Dickinson Consumer Prods., Franklin Lakes, NJ; *U.S. Public*, pg. 199

Weisshaupt, Hp., Mgr.--Schweizerischer Bankverein, Basel, Switzerland; *Int'l*, pg. 1329

Weissman, Jerrold, Pres.--National-General Supply, Inc., Great Falls, MT; *U.S. Private*, pg. 1160

Weissman, Jerrold, Pres.--Northwest Fence Products Co., Great Falls, MT; *U.S. Private*, pg. 1160

Weitmann, H., Mgr.-Office--Kvaerner Brug (Deutschland) GmbH After Sales Service, Hamburg, Germany; *Int'l*, pg. 771

Weitz, Eric, Pres. & Chief Oper. Officer--Apparal America, Inc., New York, NY; *U.S. Public*, pg. 120

Weitz, Eric T., Pres. & Chief Exec. Officer--Robby Len Fashions, New York, NY; *U.S. Public*, pg. 121

Weitz, Robert, Pres.--Samuel Meisel & Company, Inc., Glen Burnie, MD; *Int'l*, pg. 103

Weitz, Robert, Pres.--Lipschutz Brothers Inc, Philadelphia, PA; *Int'l*, pg. 103

Weitz, Tom, Gen. Mgr.--Beal Mountain Mining Inc., Anaconda, MT; *U.S. Public*, pg. 1269

Weitze, Wolfgang, Dr., Chm.--Hypothekenbank in Hamburg AG, Hamburg, Germany; *Int'l*, pg. 418

Weitzel, John, Exec. V.P. & Mng. Dir.--J.W. Messner, Inc., Seattle, WA; *U.S. Private*, pg. 734

Welborn, Eugene, Plant Mgr.--Ryobi Motor Products, Pickens, SC; *Int'l*, pg. 1151

Welch, A., Plant Mgr.--Milchem Drilling Fluids Limited, Kingston-upon-Hull, United Kingdom; *U.S. Public*, pg. 167

Welch, Dean, Dr., V.P. & Gen. Mgr.--Solvay Animal Health, Inc., Charles City, IA; *Int'l*, pg. 1278
Welch, Patrick, Pres.--GNA Corp., Seattle, WA; *U.S. Public*, pg. 712
Welch, Patrick, Pres.--G.E. Capital Assurance, Seattle, WA; *U.S. Public*, pg. 712
Welch, Patrick E., Chm. Bd., Pres. & Chief Exec. Officer--The Life Insurance Co. of Virginia, Richmond, VA; *U.S. Public*, pg. 712
Welch, Robin, Chm. Bd.--NYLIFE Administration Corp., Austin, TX; *U.S. Private*, pg. 795
Welchman, Gary, Pres.--Klopman Fabrics Div., Greensboro, NC; *U.S. Public*, pg. 268
Weldert, Werner, Mng. Dir.--Ircon GMBH, Taunusstein, Germany; *Int'l*, pg. 1209
Weldon, Don, Mgr.--Massachusetts Steel Treating, Worcester, MA; *U.S. Private*, pg. 882
Weldon, N., Pres.--Adtech Inc., Honolulu, HI; *Int'l*, pg. 208
Welge, Wolfgang, Pres. & Chief Exec. Officer--Deutsche Bank AG (Canada), Toronto, Canada; *Int'l*, pg. 404
Welihan, Mike, Gen. Mgr.--Alro Group, Benton Harbor, Benton Harbor, MI; *U.S. Private*, pg. 46
Welk, R.E., Pres.--Sunset Railway Co., San Francisco, CA; *U.S. Public*, pg. 1668
Welka, Gene, Chm. Bd. & Chief Exec. Officer--Frozen Specialties, Inc., Archbold, OH; *U.S. Public*, pg. 378
Welland, Mark, Mgr.--Ampex Corporation, Cranford, NJ; *U.S. Public*, pg. 104
Wellauer, Thomas, Dr., Pres.-Corp. Exec. Bd. & Chief Exec. Officer--Winterthur Schweizerische Versicherungs Gesellschaft, Winterthur, Switzerland; *Int'l*, pg. 345
Wellborn, Robert H., Chief Oper. Officer--NationsBank of Texas National Ventures Group Inc., Dallas, TX; *U.S. Public*, pg. 1163
Wellborn, Samuel M., III, Pres.--Columbus Bank and Trust Company, Columbus, GA; *U.S. Public*, pg. 1549
Weller, F. Dale, Gen. Mgr.--Industrial Packaging Div. (Beardstown), Beardstown, IL; *Int'l*, pg. 1270
Weller, Jeffrey J., Pres.--Jerr-Dan Corporation, Greencastle, PA; *U.S. Public*, pg. 537
Welliver, L.C., V.P. & Gen. Mgr.--Solid State Electronics Center, Plymouth, MN; *U.S. Public*, pg. 834
Wellman, Thomas A., Chief Fin. Officer--A & B Properties, Inc., Honolulu, HI; *U.S. Public*, pg. 39
Wellman, Thomas A., Chief Fin. Officer--Kahului Trucking & Storage, Inc., Kahului, HI; *U.S. Public*, pg. 39
Wells, Alan, V.P.-Fin. & Investments--Midwest Capital Group, Des Moines, IA; *U.S. Public*, pg. 1109
Wells, Bill, Plant Mgr.--Tube Bend, Newington, CT; *U.S. Private*, pg. 693
Wells, Craig D., Publr.--The Bradenton Herald, Inc., Bradenton, FL; *U.S. Public*, pg. 964
Wells, Darrell F., V.P. & Gen. Mgr.--Cox Communications-Myrtle Beach, Myrtle Beach, SC; *U.S. Public*, pg. 455
Wells, H. Rickey, V.P.--K N Interstate Gas Transmission Co., Lakewood, CO; *U.S. Public*, pg. 937
Wells, Janene, Mgr.--DWF of Albuquerque, Albuquerque, NM; *U.S. Private*, pg. 326
Wells, John L., Mng. Dr.--SHL Systemhouse Nederland B.V., Hague, Netherlands; *Int'l*, pg. 1154
Wells, John R., Pres. & Chief Exec. Officer--Pandel, Inc., Cartersville, GA; *U.S. Public*, pg. 889
Wells, L.W., Pres.--Safecare Company, Seattle, WA; *U.S. Public*, pg. 1423
Wells, Mark, Chm. Bd. & Pres.--Case France S.A., Paris, France; *U.S. Public*, pg. 1579
Wells, Martha, Publisher--Ottumwa Courier, Ottumwa, IA; *U.S. Public*, pg. 984
Wells, Walter E., Pres.--Marlette Homes, Inc., Middlebury, IN; *U.S. Public*, pg. 1442
Wells, Wayne, V.P.--Western Div., Los Angeles, CA; *U.S. Public*, pg. 732
Wellsted, John M., V.P.--Porta Systems Limited, Coventry, United Kingdom; *U.S. Public*, pg. 1317
Welp, David, Pres.-Raytheon TI Systems & Sr. V.P.--Raytheon TI Systems, Lewisville, TX; *U.S. Public*, pg. 1365
Welp, David W., Gen. Mgr.--Sensors & Electronic Systems, El Segundo, CA; *U.S. Public*, pg. 1365
Welsch, J., Photofinishing Branch Mgr.--Kodak Fotoservice Gesellschaft m.b.H., Salzburg, Austria; *U.S. Public*, pg. 553
Welsey, Norman H., Pres. & Chief Exec. Officer--ACCO Canada Inc., Willowdale, Canada; *U.S. Public*, pg. 674
Welsh, D. O., Chief Oper. Officer--EPL Plant & Access, Saint Neots, United Kingdom; *Int'l*, pg. 796
Welsh, Dave, Mgr.--Newport Ltd., Newbury, United Kingdom; *U.S. Public*, pg. 1179
Welte, Hans-Jorng, Representative--UBS Representative Office, Bogota, Colombia; *Int'l*, pg. 1441
Welter, Bob, Pres.--Baldwin Steel Company, Jersey City, NJ; *U.S. Private*, pg. 345
Welti, W., Chief Exec. Officer--OMRON Electronics B.V., Hoofddorp, Netherlands; *Int'l*, pg. 1005
Welti, W., Mng. Dir.--OMRON Electronics AG, Steinhausen, Switzerland; *Int'l*, pg. 1005
Welton, Daniel L., Plant Mgr.--AC Rochester Division (Gennevilliers), Gennevilliers, France; *U.S. Public*, pg. 724
Welty, Rod, Pres.--Wal-Mart Shoe Div., Bentonville, AR; *U.S. Public*, pg. 1733
Weltz, Skip, Pres. & Chief Exec. Officer--Lafayette Precast, Fremont, CA; *U.S. Private*, pg. 1149
Wen, Danny, Mng. Dir.--Merita Bank Ltd., Beijing Representative Office, Beijing, China; *Int'l*, pg. 859
Wenaas, Eric P., Pres. & Chief Exec. Officer--Jacor, Inc., San Diego, CA; *U.S. Private*, pg. 584
Wenclawski, John P., Pres.--Stenograph Corporation, Mount Prospect, IL; *U.S. Private*, pg. 860
Wendel, Gary, Plant Mgr.--The HVR Company, Reno, NV; *U.S. Public*, pg. 387
Wendel, Joe, Gen. Mgr.--Witt Company, Muncie, IN; *U.S. Private*, pg. 1185
Wendel, Michael, Lab Mgr.--Quest Diagnostic-Binghamton, Binghamton, NY; *U.S. Public*, pg. 1351
Wendel, Michael, Lab. Mgr.--Quest Diagnostic-Vestal, Vestal, NY; *U.S. Public*, pg. 1352
Wendel, Mike, Lab Mgr.--Quest Diagnostic-Binghamton, Binghamton, NY; *U.S. Public*, pg. 1351
Wendel, Robert, Plant Mgr.--Dayton Superior Corp., Commerce City, CO; *U.S. Private*, pg. 932
Wendel, Tom, Pres. & Chief Exec. Officer--Bridge, Saint Louis, MO; *U.S. Private*, pg. 1162
Wendell, E.W., Pres. & Chief Exec. Officer--Gaylord Entertainment/Opryland USA, Nashville, TN; *U.S. Public*, pg. 704
Wendell, R., Mgr.-Communications--Telephonics Command Systems Div., Farmingdale, NY; *U.S. Public*, pg. 558
Wender, Herbert, Chm. Bd. & Chief Exec. Officer--Commonwealth Land Title Insurance Company, Philadelphia, PA; *U.S. Public*, pg. 1374
Wendland, Udo, Gen. Mgr.--Tchnoflow Tube-Systems GmbH, Fuldabruck, Germany; *Int'l*, pg. 1341
Wendle, Kevin, Pres. & Chief Oper. Officer--Quincy Jones Entertainment, Los Angeles, CA; *U.S. Public*, pg. 1611
Wendricks, Edward, Gen. Mgr.--Thyssen Haniel Logistics, Antwerp, Belgium; *Int'l*, pg. 1388
Wendt, Edward G., Jr., Vice Chm. & Chief Exec. Officer--Ethix Midlands, Dublin, OH; *U.S. Private*, pg. 795
Wendt, F. Otto, Dir.--Dresdner Bank Luxembourg S.A., Luxembourg, Luxembourg; *Int'l*, pg. 419
Wendt, Gary C., Chm., Pres. & Chief Exec. Officer--General Electric Capital Services, Inc., Stamford, CT; *U.S. Public*, pg. 711
Wenemmer, Manfred, Pres.--Freudenberg Nonwovens Limited Partnership, Chelmsford, MA; *Int'l*, pg. 505
Wenger, Carmon R., Pres.--Chore-Time/Brock International, Milford, IN; *U.S. Public*, pg. 285
Wenger, Robert, Mgr.--ENVIRON Corporation, Houston, TX; *U.S. Public*, pg. 1285
Wenger, Walter, Chm. Bd.--Coop Bern Oberland, Thun, Switzerland; *Int'l*, pg. 329
Wenino, Pam, Chief Fin. Officer--Tredit Tire & Wheel Co., Elkhart, IN; *U.S. Private*, pg. 300
Wenk-Woff, Kai, Pres.--NAPP Systems, San Marcos, CA; *U.S. Private*, pg. 875
Wennekes, W., Mgr.--Van Leeuwen Pipe and Tube Western Australia Pty. Ltd., Canning Vale, Australia; *Int'l*, pg. 1450
Wenner, Jann S., Editor-In-Chief--Us Magazine, New York, NY; *U.S. Private*, pg. 1162
Wennerstrom, Gosta, Mng. Dir.--Astra Tech AB, Molndal, Sweden; *Int'l*, pg. 93
Wennestrom, Claes, Chief Oper. Officer--Kuwait Swedish Cleaning Services Co. S.A.K., Safat, Kuwait; *Int'l*, pg. 443
Wenninger, Walter, Dr., Chm. Bd.--Bayer Corporation, Pittsburgh, PA; *Int'l*, pg. 172
Wenrich, Robert, Pres. & Chief Exec. Officer--Germantown (USA) Co., Broomall, PA; *Int'l*, pg. 555
Wensik, Roy E., Pres.--Pakhoed USA Inc., Houston, TX; *Int'l*, pg. 1147
Wenz, Axel, Gen. Mgr.--Nordson Deutschland GmbH, Erkrath, Germany; *U.S. Public*, pg. 1189
Werble, Cole, Pres.--FDC Reports Inc., Chevy Chase, MD; *Int'l*, pg. 1100
Werbrouck, Robert, Chief Oper. Officer--Kamyr Enterprises Inc., Saint-Laurent, Canada; *Int'l*, pg. 35
Werderman, John, Pres.--I-Bus Division, San Diego, CA; *U.S. Public*, pg. 1062
Werkendam, Simon, Mng. Partner--Bercum Boender Cardozo & Werkendam B.V., Amsterdam, Netherlands; *U.S. Private*, pg. 1198
Werkowski, Andrzej, Pres.--Optiroc Group Sp.z.o.o., Warsaw, Poland; *Int'l*, pg. 1200
Werlein, Gloria, Plant Mgr.--Moxness Products East Troy Division, East Troy, WI; *U.S. Public*, pg. 124
Werlich, Eugene, Pres.--Rocknel Fastener, Inc., Rockford, IL; *U.S. Public*, pg. 1590
Wermter, Volkmar, Mng. Dir.--TBWA Munich, Munich, Germany; *U.S. Private*, pg. 1063
Werne, Eric, Gen. Mgr.--UBS Representative Office Ltd., Abu Dhabi, United Arab Emirates; *Int'l*, pg. 1441
Werne, Hans, Mng. Dir.--Andren & Werne Leo Burnett AB, Stockholm, Sweden; *U.S. Private*, pg. 184
Werner Kuehn, Kurt, Chief Oper. Officer--Resart GmbH, Mainz, Germany; *Int'l*, pg. 104
Werner, Greg, Pres.--Gra-Gar Inc., Omaha, NE; *U.S. Public*, pg. 1755
Werner, Jack S., Chm., Pres. & Chief Exec. Officer--Second National Bank of Bay City, Bay City, MI; *U.S. Public*, pg. 379
Werner, John M., Pres.--Alimentos Heinz C.A., Caracas, Venezuela; *U.S. Public*, pg. 806
Werner, Peter, Mgr.--Commerzbank AG-Caracas Representative Office, Caracas, Venezuela; *Int'l*, pg. 311
Werner, Terry, Pres.--Tubular & Equipment Services, LLC (TES), Independence, KS; *U.S. Private*, pg. 162
Werner, Thomas H., Pres.--Harris Bank Hinsdale N.A., Hinsdale, IL; *Int'l*, pg. 154
Werner, Walter, Chm. Bd.--Krupp Mobilkrane GmbH, Wilhelmshaven, Germany; *Int'l*, pg. 510
Wernick, Eckart, Mng. Dir.--Protendidos DYWIDAG Ltda., Sao Paulo, Brazil; *Int'l*, pg. 425
Werny, Joe, Mgr.--Network Systems GmbH, Frankfurt/Main, Germany; *U.S. Public*, pg. 1523
Werny, Joe, Country Mgr.--Network Systems GmbH, Ismaning, Germany; *U.S. Public*, pg. 1523
Wernz, Logan F., Pres. & Gen. Mge.--Kysor/Warren, Conyers, GA; *U.S. Public*, pg. 1445
Wertheimer, Kim, V.P.-Gulf State Region--Circle International, Dallas-Fort Worth Airport, TX; *U.S. Public*, pg. 372
Wertman, Howard, Pres. & Chief Exec. Officer--Anthony and Sylvan Pools Corporation, Doylestown, PA; *U.S. Public*, pg. 593
Wertz, Harold E., Pres.--Custom Pipe & Coupling Co., Stanton, CA; *Int'l*, pg. 1512
Wesland, James, Plant Mgr.--Kendallville Plant, Kendallville, IN; *U.S. Public*, pg. 671
Wesley, Norman H., Chm. Bd. & Chief Exec. Officer--ACCO World Corporation, Lincolnshire, IL; *U.S. Public*, pg. 674
Wesley, Norman H., Chm. Bd. & Chief Exec. Officer--MasterBrand Industries, Inc., Lincolnshire, IL; *U.S. Public*, pg. 675
Wesner, R. F., Pres.--Kennedy Van Saun Corp., Danville, PA; *Int'l*, pg. 1326
Wesnitzer, Corey, V.P. & Gen. Mgr.--General Magnaplate Texas, Arlington, TX; *U.S. Public*, pg. 717
Wess, Sam, Pres.--United Metal Receptacle Corp., Pottsville, PA; *U.S. Private*, pg. 1124
Wessberg, Claes, Mng. Dir.--GCE, Malmo, Sweden; *Int'l*, pg. 14
Wessberg, Claes, Mng. Dir.--GCE-Gas Control Equipment AB, Malmo, Sweden; *Int'l*, pg. 281
Wessel-Aas, S., Chief Oper. Officer--Den norske Bank AS, London Branch, London, United Kingdom; *Int'l*, pg. 392
Wessel, James A., Pres.--Becton Dickinson Canada Inc., Mississauga, Canada; *U.S. Public*, pg. 200
Wessel, Jeffrey W., Chief Oper. Officer--Nippon Silica Glass USA, Inc., Bound Brook, NJ; *Int'l*, pg. 1407
Wessel, Onno, Partner--KKBR/Conquest, Amsterdam, Netherlands; *Int'l*, pg. 1484
Wessel, Robert L., Pres.--Peninsula Excess Insurance Brokers, Inc., Farmington, CT; *U.S. Public*, pg. 1231
Wesseldjk, J.A., Pres.--Akzo Coatings Nederland B.V., Sassenheim, Netherlands; *Int'l*, pg. 42
Wessels, Jerry, Sr. V.P. & Gen. Mgr.--Italia Advertising, Dallas, TX; *U.S. Private*, pg. 576
Wesser, Charles, Pres. & Chief Oper. Officer--Arden International Kitchens, Inc., Lakeville, MN; *U.S. Private*, pg. 972
Wesslau, Lars, Pres.--Forsakringsaktiebolaget Sirius, Stockholm, Sweden; *Int'l*, pg. 7
Wessling, Holger, Rep.--DG Bank - Shanghai, Shanghai, China; *Int'l*, pg. 352
Wesson, Steve, Pres. & Chief Exec. Officer--Citadel Holdings Corp., Los Angeles, CA; *U.S. Public*, pg. 456
Wesson, Steve, Pres.--Citadel Realty, Inc., Glendale, CA; *U.S. Public*, pg. 456
West, Armas O., Pres.--Valmet Canada Inc. - Enerdry, Thunder Bay, Canada; *Int'l*, pg. 1448
West, B. Kenneth, Pres.--Bankmont Financial Corp., New York, NY; *Int'l*, pg. 154
West, Bernard, Pres.--Rhone-Poulenc Canada, Ltd., Mississauga, Canada; *Int'l*, pg. 1112
West, Bob, Mng. Dir.--Scientific Atlantic Limited, Langley, United Kingdom; *U.S. Public*, pg. 1443
West, Charles, Pres.--MasterCraft Boat Company, Maryville, TN; *U.S. Private*, pg. 689
West, Donald, Pres. & Chief Exec. Officer--Total Petroleum Canada Ltd., Calgary, Canada; *Int'l*, pg. 1409
West, Donald T., Pres. & Chief Exec. Officer--Rigel Oil & Gas Ltd., Calgary, Canada; *Int'l*, pg. 1117
West, Donald T., Pres. & Chief Exec. Officer--Rigel Petroleum, Inc., Calgary, Canada; *Int'l*, pg. 1117
West, Donald T., Pres. & Chief Exec. Officer--Rigel Petroleum (NI) Limited, Calgary, Canada; *Int'l*, pg. 1117
West, Eileen, Pres.--Lanz, Inc., San Francisco, CA; *U.S. Private*, pg. 650
West, Eugene, Chief Oper. Officer--Alfa-Laval (N.Z.) Ltd., Hamilton, New Zealand; *Int'l*, pg. 1380
West, J., Mng. Dir.--Marlow Ropes Limited, Halisham, United Kingdom; *Int'l*, pg. 426
West, J. Thomas, Sr. V.P.-Advanced Systems Devel.--Data General Systems Development Division, Westborough, MA; *U.S. Public*, pg. 485
West, J.T., Pres.--Lockheed Finance Corporation, Burbank, CA; *U.S. Public*, pg. 1008
West, John C., Chm. Bd.--Consolidated American Insurance Co., Columbia, SC; *U.S. Public*, pg. 1454
West, John C., Chm. Bd.--Catawba Insurance Co., Columbia, SC; *U.S. Public*, pg. 1454
West, John C., Chm. Bd.--Investors National Life Insurance Co., Columbia, SC; *U.S. Public*, pg. 1454
West, John C., Chm. Bd.--Kentucky Insurance Co., Louisville, KY; *U.S. Public*, pg. 1454
West, John C., Chm. Bd.--Forest Lake Travel Service, Inc., Columbia, SC; *U.S. Public*, pg. 1454
West, Ken, Reg. Sls. Mgr.--Thetford Corp., Warehouse Div., Brea, CA; *U.S. Private*, pg. 352
West, L., Mng. Dir.--Britax Wingard Limited, Chichester, United Kingdom; *Int'l*, pg. 216
West, Maria Jose, Gen. Mgr.--Viceversa/Young & Rubicam, Montevideo, Uruguay; *U.S. Private*, pg. 1200
West, Mark, Pres.--Aerostar International, Sioux Falls, SD; *U.S. Public*, pg. 1361
West, Mike, Mgr.--John Crane Saudi Arabia Ltd., Al-Khobar, Saudi Arabia; *Int'l*, pg. 1339
West, Paul, Pres.--VL Bus Asia (Pte) Ltd., Singapore, Singapore; *Int'l*, pg. 1477
West, Peter, Pres.--Dieffenbacher North America, Windsor, Canada; *Int'l*, pg. 413
West, Randall E., Pres.--Automotive Carrier Div., Troy, MI; *U.S. Public*, pg. 1414
West, Randy D., Gen. Mgr.--ADM Milling Co., Plainview, TX; *U.S. Public*, pg. 128
West, Robert A., III, Pres.--Cigna Associates, Inc., Bloomfield, CT; *U.S. Public*, pg. 358
West, Robert A., III, Pres.--James P. Toner Company, Inc., Bloomfield, CT; *U.S. Public*, pg. 358
West, Ronald T., Mng. Dir.--Componentes Mecanicos de Matamoros S.A. de C.V., Mexico, Mexico; *U.S. Public*, pg. 721
West, Thomas L., Jr., Pres. & Chief Exec. Officer--The Variable Annuity Life Insurance Co., Houston, TX; *U.S. Public*, pg. 76
West, W. Michael, Pres. & Chief Oper. Officer--Octel Messaging Division, Milpitas, CA; *U.S. Public*, pg. 1017

West, Wayne, Pres.--Heritage Cutlery, Inc., Bolivar, NY; *U.S. Private*, pg. 940

West, William H., Dr., Chm. Bd.--Response Oncology, Inc., Memphis, TN; *U.S. Public*, pg. 1449

Westberg, Stefan, Gen. Mgr.--Abetong Teknik AB, Vaxjo, Sweden; *Int'l*, pg. 1199

Westbrook, G.R., Dir.--Eastman Kodak (Japan) Research & Devel. Ctr., Yokohama, Japan; *U.S. Public*, pg. 552

Westbury, A.J., Mng. Dir.--S & P Coil Products Limited, Leicester, United Kingdom; *Int'l*, pg. 590

Westbury, Ian, Mgr.--Trine Manufacturing Co., Turlock, CA; *U.S. Private*, pg. 558

Westcott, David J., Pres.--BA Mortgage & International Realty Corp., San Francisco, CA; *U.S. Public*, pg. 180

Westcott, David R., Mgr.-Branch--Piper Jaffray Inc., Portland, OR; *U.S. Public*, pg. 1303

Westendorf, William H., V.P. & Gen. Mgr.--Plastics Manufacturing Div., Mount Vernon, IN; *U.S. Public*, pg. 711

Wester, Anders, Pres., Creative Dir. & Art Dir.--Hall & Cederquist/Young & Rubicam, Stockholm, Sweden; *U.S.* Private, pg. 1198

Westerberg, Erik, Mng. Dir.--SKF (Zimbabwe) (Pvt.) Ltd., Harare, Zimbabwe; *Int'l*, pg. 1160

Westerberg, John R., Chm. Bd. & Chief Exec. Officer--Commercial Record Center, Elk Grove Village, IL; *U.S. Private*, pg. 1164

Westerberg, L.J., Pres.--The Creamette Co. of Canada Ltd., Winnipeg, Canada; *U.S. Private*, pg. 159

Westerberg, Lars, Pres. & Chief Exec. Officer--Granges AB, Stockholm, Sweden; *Int'l*, pg. 439

Westerdahl, Bernt, Pres.--Ballast Syd AB, Malmo, Sweden; *Int'l*, pg. 899

Westerdahl, Bertil, Pres.--Machinery South, Malmo, Sweden; *Int'l*, pg. 899

Westerholm, Goran, Mng. Dir.--Oy SKF AB, Espoo, Finland; *Int'l*, pg. 1158

Westerink, Jan, Pres.--Perstorp Analytical B.V, Oud-Beijerland, Netherlands; *Int'l*, pg. 1039

Westerlagen, H., Mng. Dir.--Center Parcs N.V., Rotterdam, Netherlands; *Int'l*, pg. 1212

Westerman, Gerhard, Co.-Chief Oper. Officer--Kohle-Kontor-Saar GmbH, Saarbruecken, Germany; *Int'l*, pg. 1167

Westermann, M.D., Pres.--Akzo Chemicals B.V., Amersfoort, Netherlands; *Int'l*, pg. 42

Westermann, Rainer, Mng. Dir.--Fleishman-Hillard Germany, Frankfurt/Main, Germany; *U.S. Private*, pg. 411

Westermann, Scott A., Mgr.--Piper Jaffray Inc., Mason City, IA; *U.S. Public*, pg. 1302

Westervoll, B., Mng. Dir.--Oki Systems (Norway) A/S, Skjetten, Norway; *Int'l*, pg. 1000

Westfall, Dick, Plant Mgr.--Teleflex Automotive, Lebanon, VA; *U.S. Public*, pg. 1569

Westfall, John, Pres.--Slates Brand, San Francisco, CA; *U.S. Private*, pg. 663

Westgate, David, Plant Mgr.--Bronson Specialties, Inc., Bronson, MI; *Int'l*, pg. 1277

Westhousing, Larry, Pres.--Manning Light Truck Equipment, Louisville, KY; *U.S. Private*, pg. 700

Westin, David, Pres.--American Broadcasting Companies, Inc., New York, NY; *U.S. Public*, pg. 511

Westinghouse, Tim A., Dir.-Fin.--The Dairy Farm Company, Limited, Causeway Bay, Hong Kong; *Int'l*, pg. 703

Westland, Jan, Mng. Dir.--Blount GmbH, Gartringen, Germany; *U.S. Public*, pg. 239

Westland, Jan C., Dir.-European Opers.--Blount Europe, S.A., Nivelles, Belgium; *U.S. Public*, pg. 238

Westlund, Mats, Gen. Mgr.--Analog Devices AB, Bromma, Sweden; *U.S. Public*, pg. 108

Westlund, Orjan, Company Head--Ovako La Foulerie S.A., Carignan, France; *Int'l*, pg. 1157

Westlund, Robert C., Mgr.--Piper Jaffray Inc., Des Moines, IA; *U.S. Public*, pg. 1301

Westman, D.A., Pres.--American Thermoplastics Corporation, Houston, TX; *U.S. Public*, pg. 1291

Westman, Inge, Pres.--ASEA Jumet S.A., Charleroi, Belgium; *Int'l*, pg. 7

Westman, Richard J., Pres.-Southwest Div./Houston--EJL Advertising/Houston, Houston, TX; *U.S. Private*, pg. 673

Westmoreland, J., Pres.--Chevron Land & Development Company, San Francisco, CA; *U.S. Public*, pg. 348

Westmoreland, J., Pres.--Huntington Beach Co., San Francisco, CA; *U.S. Public*, pg. 348

Weston, J.P., Chm. Bd.--British Aerospace Defence Limited (Military Aircraft), Preston, United Kingdom; *Int'l*, pg. 217

Weston, James A., V.P.-Opers.--Wolverine Leather Div., Rockford, MI; *U.S. Public*, pg. 1775

Weston, John, Pres.--Hansen Coupling Division, Berea, OH; *U.S. Private*, pg. 1110

Weston, Magaret, Pres.--The Portland Newspapers, Portland, ME; *U.S. Private*, pg. 439

Weston, Mike, Pres.--Manchester Plastics, Troy, MI; *U.S. Public*, pg. 399

Weston, R.C.M., Mng. Dir.--B.F. Goodrich Chemical (U.K.) Ltd., Hounslow, United Kingdom; *U.S. Public*, pg. 752

Weston, Roger, Pres.--GreatBanc Trust Company, Aurora, IL; *U.S. Public*, pg. 760

Weston, W.W., Chief Oper. Officer--Detrey Dentsply AG, Zurich, Switzerland; *U.S. Public*, pg. 500

Westover, Chris, Reg. Mgr.--Green Tree Acceptance, Inc., Sacramento, CA; *U.S. Public*, pg. 762

Westover, Tim, Pres.--Litton Systems Canada Ltd., Etobicoke, Canada; *U.S. Public*, pg. 1005

Westphal, Charles, Gen. Mgr.--Corrugated Container Div.-Philadephia-East Plant, Philadelphia, PA; *U.S. Public*, pg. 1520

Westphal, Hans, Pres.--Deutsche Babcock Borsig AG, Berlin, Germany; *Int'l*, pg. 399

Westra, G.R., Chief Exec. Officer--Cleanaway Limited, Brentwood, United Kingdom; *Int'l*, pg. 212

Westring, Peter, Chief Officer.--Grona Konsum Stockholm AB, Stockholm, Sweden; *Int'l*, pg. 718

Westrum, Thorbjoern, Mng. Dir.--Kaldnes Miljoteknologi A/S, Tonsberg, Norway; *Int'l*, pg. 965

Westwood, Ray, Chief Exec. Officer & Gen. Mgr.--Video Display Corporation Limited, Stratford-on-Avon, United Kingdom; *U.S. Public*, pg. 1720

Wetesnik, Bob, V.P. & Controller--Sea World of Texas, San Antonio, TX; *U.S. Public*, pg. 114

Wetherell, Carol, Supervisor-Property & Casualty Claims--Willis Corroon Administrative Services Corporation, Albuquerque, NM; *Int'l*, pg. 1505

Wetmore, Vernon E., Jr., Pres.--Sysco Food Services-Jamestown, Falconer, NY; *U.S. Public*, pg. 1551

Wetter, Rene, Chief Exec. Officer--Black & Decker (Switzerland) S.A., Delemont, Switzerland; *U.S. Public*, pg. 234

Wetterling, David, Mgr.-Service Corp.--Firstate Services, Inc., Hutchinson, MN; *U.S. Public*, pg. 608

Wetterquist, Per-Ake, Mng. Dir.--SKF Reinsurance Co. Ltd., Goteborg, Sweden; *Int'l*, pg. 1157

Wettle, Goran, Chief Oper. Officer--Perstorp S.A.-Div. Bakelite, Bezons, France; *Int'l*, pg. 1037

Wettstein, Jurg D., Gen. Mgr.--Repoxit SA, Winterthur, Switzerland; *Int'l*, pg. 497

Wetzel, D., Mng. Dir.--Societe de Banque Suisse (Luxembourg) S.A., Luxembourg, Luxembourg; *Int'l*, pg. 1331

Wetzel, Jerry, Gen. Mgr.--Slurry Pump Div., Ashland, PA; *U.S. Public*, pg. 860

Wetzel, William J., Pres.--Colloids Canada Inc., Saint Catharines, Canada; *Int'l*, pg. 1113

Wever, H.H., Chief Oper. Officer--Siemens S.A., Sao Paulo, Brazil; *Int'l*, pg. 1248

Wevers, Pierre Albert, Pres. & Chief Exec. Officer--Bigg's Hyper Shoppes Ohio, Inc., Milford, OH; *U.S. Public*, pg. 1541

Wexler, Steve, Pres.--Rolm Resale Systems, Maple Grove, MN; *U.S. Public*, pg. 1192

Wexner, Leslie H., Pres. & Chief Exec. Officer--Intimate Brands, Inc., Columbus, OH; *U.S. Public*, pg. 995

Wey, H., Dir.--Wessanen AG, Zug, Switzerland; *Int'l*, pg. 753

Weyerhaeuser, George, Jr, Pres. & Chief Exec. Officer--Weyerhaeuser Canada Ltd., Vancouver, Canada; *U.S. Public*, pg. 1764

Weyers, Larry L., Chm. Bd. & Chief Exec. Officer--Wisconsin Public Service Corporation, Green Bay, WI; *U.S. Public*, pg. 1728

Weyers, Larry L., Pres. & Chief Exec. Officer--WPS Power Development, Inc., Green Bay, WI; *U.S. Public*, pg. 1728

Weyers, Larry L., Pres. & Chief Exec. Officer--WPS Leasing, Inc., Green Bay, WI; *U.S. Public*, pg. 1728

Weyhausen, E., Chief Oper. Officer--BHF-Bank Liason Office, Melbourne, Australia; *Int'l*, pg. 120

Weymuller, Bruno, Chief Oper. Officer--Elf Petroland, s Gravenhage, Netherlands; *Int'l*, pg. 446

Weyner, David, Pres.--PolyGram Classics, Inc., New York, NY; *Int'l*, pg. 1052

Weyns, Tony, Mng. Dir.--N.V. Nira Communication Systems, Brussels, Belgium; *Int'l*, pg. 1369

Weyruch, Jean, Admin.--Adams House Healthcare, Torrington, CT; *U.S. Public*, pg. 1711

Wezner, Charles, Dist. Mgr.--Browning-Ferris Industries of Minnesota, Inc., Eden Prairie, MN; *U.S. Public*, pg. 263

Whalan, Brian E., Mng. Dir.--Halfords, Ltd., Redditch, United Kingdom; *Int'l*, pg. 203

Whalen, Geoffrey H., Chief Oper. Officer--Peugeot Motor Co. Plc, Coventry, United Kingdom; *Int'l*, pg. 1021

Whalen, Michael J., Pres. & Chief Exec. Officer--Old Kent Bank-Illinois, Elmhurst, IL; *U.S. Public*, pg. 1216

Whalen, Robert H., Pres.--Cigna Financial Futures, Inc., Bloomfield, CT; *U.S. Public*, pg. 357

Whalen, Wayne W., Partner--Skadden, Arps, Slate, Meagher & Flom (Illinois), Chicago, IL; *U.S. Private*, pg. 1004

Whaley, Edith K., V.P.--Carat ICG Retail/Co-op Div. of Carat ICG, Los Angeles, CA; *U.S. Private*, pg. 207

Whaley, Harry E., Pres.--Woodstream Corporation, Lititz, PA; *U.S. Public*, pg. 566

Whatley, Steve, Pres.--ALLTEL Alabama, Leeds, AL; *U.S. Public*, pg. 55

Wheat, James M., Pres.--Heritage Merchandising Co., Inc., Colonial Heights, VA; *U.S. Public*, pg. 1272

Wheat, James M., Pres.--Jiffy Lube International of Maryland, Inc., Houston, TX; *U.S. Public*, pg. 1272

Wheat, Jim, Acting Lab Mgr.--Quest Diagnostic-Rochester, Rochester, NY; *U.S. Public*, pg. 1351

Wheatcroft, K.M., Pres.--CRR Investments, Inc., Philadelphia, PA; *U.S. Public*, pg. 432

Wheatley, Jim, Gen. Mgr.--Harrisonburg Auto Auction, Harrisonburg, VA; *U.S. Private*, pg. 282

Wheatley, Joe, Mng. Dir.--AIB Securities Services Ltd., Dublin, Ireland; *Int'l*, pg. 64

Wheatley, John, Pres. & Chief Exec. Officer--Willis Corroon Corp. of Anchorage, Anchorage, AK; *Int'l*, pg. 1505

Wheaton, Scott, Pres.--Wheaton Scientific Products, Millville, NJ; *Int'l*, pg. 68

Wheeler, Charles, Pres.--Midcon Cables Co., Joplin, MO; *U.S. Public*, pg. 594

Wheeler, Dennis E., Pres.--Pinnacle Exploration, Inc., Coeur D'Alene, ID; *U.S. Public*, pg. 394

Wheeler, Dianne, Sales Dir.--Passport Books, Lincolnwood, IL; *U.S. Public*, pg. 1636

Wheeler, Earl F., V.P. & Gen. Mgr.--IBM Programming Systems, Purchase, NY; *U.S. Public*, pg. 895

Wheeler, Eric, Chief Fin. Officer--DeKalb Concrete Products, Inc., Eastonollee, GA; *U.S. Private*, pg. 417

Wheeler, H.A., Pres.--Charlotte Motor Speedway, Concord, NC; *U.S. Public*, pg. 1498

Wheeler, J. Wayne, Pres.--Quest International Flavors & Foods Inc., Owings Mills, MD; *Int'l*, pg. 1436

Wheeler, Jack, Pres.--Norel Paper Corporation, Little Ferry, NJ; *U.S. Public*, pg. 1671

Wheeler, Joe, Sr. V.P.--Forum Corporation of Canada, Ltd., Toronto, Canada; *U.S. Private*, pg. 420

Wheeler, John W., Pres. & Chief Exec. Officer--Security Pacific Housing Services, Inc., San Diego, CA; *U.S. Public*, pg. 182

Wheeler, Judith, Chief Oper. Officer--Cohoes Fashions, Inc., Cohoes, NY; *U.S. Public*, pg. 268

Wheeler, Ken, Controller--Container Div. (Wilson), Wilson, NC; *Int'l*, pg. 1270

Wheeler, Kim, V.P.--Honeywell-Measurex Management Systems Division (MSD), Cincinnati, OH; *U.S. Public*, pg. 833

Wheeler, Larry G., Pres.--Alpo Pet Foods, Inc., Allentown, PA; *Int'l*, pg. 917

Wheeler, Lorence, Pres.--Credit Union Benefits Services, Inc., Madison, WI; *U.S. Private*, pg. 288

Wheeler, Peter, Mgr.-Canadian Opers.--Ecusta Fibres Ltd., Winkler, Canada; *U.S. Public*, pg. 746

Wheeler, Richard, Pres.--Sony Communications Products Co., Park Ridge, NJ; *Int'l*, pg. 1281

Wheeler, Rob, Mng. Dir.--Gunnebo Mayor Ltd., Uckfield, United Kingdom; *Int'l*, pg. 578

Wheeler, Robert, V.P. & Gen. Mgr.--Niagara of Wisconsin Paper Corp., Niagara, WI; *U.S. Public*, pg. 436

Wheeler, Robert C., Pres. & Chief Exec. Officer--Hill's Pet Nutrition, Topeka, KS; *U.S. Public*, pg. 397

Wheeler, Robert L., Mgr.-Opers.--Niagara of Wisconsin, Niagara, WI; *U.S. Public*, pg. 436

Wheeler, Thomas M., Pres. & Chief Oper. Officer--Biltwell Company, Inc., Saint Louis, MO; *U.S. Public*, pg. 795

Wheeler, W.A., Pres.--Dowty Aerospace Yakima, Yakima, WA; *Int'l*, pg. 1337

Wheeler, Wendell, Pres.--Electronic Form Systems, Carrollton, TX; *U.S. Public*, pg. 1385

Wheeling, James R., Pres. & Chief Admin. Officer--First Virginia Bank-Southwest, Roanoke, VA; *U.S. Public*, pg. 642

Wheen, Ivan, Mng. Dir.-Strategic Plng.--Bankers Trust International (Asia) Ltd., Singapore, Singapore; *U.S. Public*, pg. 186

Whelan, J. Douglas, Pres.--Wyman-Gordon Forgings, North Grafton, MA; *U.S. Public*, pg. 1782

Whelan, J. Douglas, Pres.--Wyman-Gordon Forgings Inc, Houston, TX; *U.S. Public*, pg. 1782

Whelan, Michael D., Pres.--WSFS Credit Corp., Newark, DE; *U.S. Public*, pg. 1729

Whelen, J. Douglas, Pres.--Wyman-Gordon Forgings, Inc., Houston, TX; *U.S. Public*, pg. 1782

Whelpley, William J., Chief Fin. Officer, V.P. & Gen. Mgr.--BEI Defense Systems Company, Euless, TX; *U.S. Public, pg. 160*

Whicker, Edith S., Admin.--Willowbrook Care Center, Inc., Kernersville, NC; *U.S. Public*, pg. 1715

Whigham, John, Chief Exec. Officer--Dominion Television Rentals Limited, Manukau, New Zealand; *Int'l*, pg. 1386

Whigham, Ron, Pres.--Powerex Inc., Youngwood, PA; *Int'l*, pg. 873

Whipple, Dennis L., Pres.--ALLTEL Mobile Communications, Inc., Little Rock, AR; *U.S. Public*, pg. 56

Whipple, Donald E., Pres.--LSI Industries, Inc., Cincinnati, OH; *U.S. Public*, pg. 971

Whipple, Harry M., Pres. & Publr.--The Cincinnati Enquirer, Inc., Cincinnati, OH; *U.S. Public*, pg. 700

Whisler, J. Steven, Pres.--Phelps Dodge Mining Company, Phoenix, AZ; *U.S. Public*, pg. 1286

Whitaker-Sheppard, D., Mgr.-Opers.--Jacobs Engineering Group Inc., Arlington, VA; *U.S. Public*, pg. 921

Whitaker, Bill, Gen. Mgr.--Stamptech, Ann Arbor, MI; *U.S. Private*, pg. 692

Whitaker, C.J., Mng. Dir.--Sonnex Investments (Pty) Ltd, Windhoek, Namibia; *Int'l*, pg. 167

Whitaker, Sheila, Pres.--EDS of Canada Ltd., Whitby, Canada; *U.S. Public*, pg. 570

Whitaker, Terence M., Pres.--Teton Land Title Company, Jackson, WY; *U.S. Public*, pg. 626

Whitaker, Wharton P., Pres.--Eaton Vance Distributors, Inc., Boston, MA; *U.S. Public*, pg. 559

Whitbread, I., Mng. Dir.--Bally's Shoe Factories (Norwich) Ltd., Norwich, United Kingdom; *Int'l*, pg. 997

White, A. Thomas, Pres.--Dowty Aerospace Aviation Services, Sterling, VA; *Int'l*, pg. 1337

White, Alec, V.P. & Gen Mgr.--Northwest Aerospace Training Corporation, Eagan, MN; *U.S. Public*, pg. 1200

White, Anne, Admin.--Hillhaven Convalescent Center Madison, Madison, TN; *U.S. Public*, pg. 1713

White, Benedict V., Jr., Pres.--HSN Lifeway Health Products, Inc., Saint Petersburg, FL; *U.S. Public*, pg. 1685

White, Bill, Gen. Mgr.--Frontier Communications of Mississippi, Inc., Rienzi, MS; *U.S. Public*, pg. 684

White, Bob, Division Mgr.--Pacific Coast Laminating, Oxnard, CA; *U.S. Private*, pg. 528

White, Bob M., Pres.--Garvey International, Inc., Saint Charles, IL; *U.S. Private*, pg. 440

White, Bruce, Pres.--Pen-Stock, Inc., Sunnyvale, CA; *U.S. Public*, pg. 155

White, Bruce E., Exec. V.P. & Gen. Mgr.--Kemps Foods, Inc., Lancaster, PA; *Int'l*, pg. 752

White, Charles, Gen. Mgr.--Florida Auto Auction of Orlando, Inc., Ocoee, FL; *U.S. Private*, pg. 282

White, Charles F., Pres.--Unisource, Houston, TX; *U.S. Public*, pg. 1671

White, Charles T., V.P.--Rebuilding Div., Atlanta, GA; *U.S. Public*, pg. 732

White, Chauncey, Jr., Pres.--Joe D. Hughes, Inc., Houston, TX; *U.S. Public*, pg. 776

White, Craig, Pres.--Flowers Baking Co. of Miami, Inc., Miami, FL; *U.S. Public*, pg. 657

White, D. Sue, Mng. Dir.--River Oaks Hospital, New Orleans, LA; *U.S. Public*, pg. 1697

White, D.W., Chief Exec. Officer--Zurich Insurance Company, Portsmouth, United Kingdom; *Int'l*, pg. 1531

White, D.W., Chief Exec. Officer--Zurich International (UK) Limited, London, United Kingdom; *Int'l*, pg. 1532

White, David, Chief Exec.--Westpac Life Limited, Sydney, Australia; *Int'l*, pg. 1496

White, Don, Publr.--The Anderson News, Lawrenceburg, KY; *U.S. Private*, pg. 648
White, Don W., Pres.--Sunwest Bank of Grant County, Silver City, NM; *U.S. Public*, pg. 1165
White, Dr. R.L., Sr. Exec. V.P.--Bayer Corporation/Polymers Division, Pittsburgh, PA; *Int'l*, pg. 173
White, Emmett, Chief Oper. Officer--Louisiana Industries Div., New Orleans, LA; *U.S. Public*, pg. 1585
White, Eric, Area Mgr.--Varco (U.K.) Ltd. Oil Tools, Montrose, United Kingdom; *U.S. Public*, pg. 1709
White, Fred, Pres.--Upright, Lutz, FL; *U.S. Private*, pg. 1128
White, Gary, Mgr.--Gould Paper of Florida, Inc., Altamonte Springs, FL; *U.S. Private*, pg. 467
White, Gary F., Pres.--Rochester & Pittsburgh Coal Company (Canada) Ltd., Toronto, Canada; *U.S. Public*, pg. 1395
White, J. Turner, Pres.--KLT Energy Services Inc., Kansas City, MO; *U.S. Public*, pg. 943
White, J.B., Gen. Mgr.--GKN Squeezeform, Telford, United Kingdom; *Int'l*, pg. 534
White, J.D., Plant Mgr.--The Hidden Valley Ranch Co., Wheeling, IL; *U.S. Public*, pg. 387
White, J.D.F., Mng. Dir.--Quality Bakers New Zealand Ltd., Auckland, New Zealand; *Int'l*, pg. 556
White, J.R., Gen. Mgr.--Davco Services, Wetherill Park, Australia; *Int'l*, pg. 803
White, Jack, Pres.--Ovalstrapping Inc., Hoquiam, WA; *U.S. Private*, pg. 378
White, Jack E., Pres.--Plastex Extruders Inc., USA, Fort Payne, AL; *U.S. Private*, pg. 378
White, James, V.P. & Gen. Mgr.--Wajax Manufacturing Limited, Lachine, Canada; *Int'l*, pg. 1485
White, James, Pres.--360 Degrees Long Distance, Cary, NC; *U.S. Public*, pg. 1607
White, James, Gen. Mgr.--Suzhou Watts Valve Factory, Suzhou, China; *U.S. Public*, pg. 1747
White, James A., Pres.--Eclipse Combustion, Inc., Rockford, IL; *U.S. Private*, pg. 360
White, James E., Pres.--Bronto Skylift Oy AB, Tampere, Finland; *U.S. Public*, pg. 617
White, James E., Pres.--Sysco Food Services of Beaumont, Inc., Beaumont, TX; *U.S. Public*, pg. 1551
White, James O'Neal, V.P. & Branch Mgr.--Bergen Brunswig Medical Corporation, Meridian, MS; *U.S. Public, pg. 214*
White, James S., Pres.--Morrison Berkshire Inc., North Adams, MA; *U.S. Private*, pg. 762
White, Jimmy, Plant Mgr.--PAXAR Woven Labels, Canton, NC; *U.S. Public*, pg. 1266
White, John, Chief Oper. Officer--Integration and Systems Products Div., Rochester, NY; *U.S. Public*, pg. 555
White, John, Chief Oper. Officer--Kodak Software Systems Division, Rochester, NY; *U.S. Public*, pg. 555
White, John, Dir.-Opers.--The Lordsburg Mining Company, Melbourne, FL; *U.S. Public*, pg. 750
White, John, Div. Pres.--Thomas & Howard Co., Columbia, SC; *U.S. Private*, pg. 1082
White, John R., Dir.--White & Lewis, Sydney, Australia; *Int'l, pg. 1502*
White, Kay, V.P. & Branch Mgr.--Denver Branch Office, Englewood, CO; *U.S. Public*, pg. 1683
White, Kenneth, Pres.--Mrs. Smith's Bakeries of Pennsylvania, Inc., London, KY; *U.S. Public*, pg. 658
White, Linda, Branch Mgr.--Downey Savings & Loan Association, F.A., Mountain View, CA; *U.S. Public*, pg. 527
White, M., V.P.--EUA Cogenex Corporation, Lowell, MA; *U.S. Public*, pg. 549
White, Michael H., Chief Oper. Officer--Frommelt Industries, Dubuque, IA; *U.S. Private*, pg. 933
White, Murray, Gen. Mgr.--North Star/Norway, Norway, MI; *U.S. Private*, pg. 602
White, Nick, Exec. V.P.-Super Center Div.--Hypermart USA, Bentonville, AR; *U.S. Public*, pg. 1733
White, Norman B., Pres.--Pulte Georgia Division, Duluth, GA; *U.S. Public*, pg. 1344
White, O.J.G., Chief Exec. Officer--Redland Tile & Brick, Crumlin, United Kingdom; *Int'l*, pg. 1091
White, P.J., Pres.--Swiss Bank Corporation (Overseas) Ltd., Nassau, Bahamas; *Int'l*, pg. 1332
White, P.M., Chm.--Osman Textiles, Manchester, United Kingdom; *Int'l*, pg. 300
White, Patrick, Chief Exec. Officer--Courtaulds European Fibres, Coventry, United Kingdom; *Int'l*, pg. 339
White, Patrick J., Chief Oper. Officer--Berglen Distributors Limited, London, United Kingdom; *U.S. Public*, pg. 1055
White, Patrick J., Chief Oper. Officer--Berglen Group Limited, London, United Kingdom; *U.S. Public*, pg. 1055
White, R. G., Chief Oper. Officer--Froude Consine, Worcester, United Kingdom; *Int'l*, pg. 472
White, R.C., Chief Oper. Officer--Babcock FATA Ltd., Worcester, United Kingdom; *Int'l*, pg. 472
White, R.J., Pres.--Chevron TCI Inc., Houston, TX; *U.S. Public*, pg. 348
White, R.J., Pres.--Prairielands Energy Marketing, Inc., Bismarck, ND; *U.S. Public*, pg. 1025
White, R.S., Chief Oper. Officer--John Deere Des Moines Works, Ankeny, IA; *U.S. Public*, pg. 492
White, Ralph N., Pres.--Precision Controls Division, Richardson, TX; *U.S. Public*, pg. 424
White, Reed, Pres.--Dura Convertible Systems, Inc., Adrian, MI; *U.S. Public*, pg. 399
White, Richard, Chief Exec. Officer--Healthsource Maine, Inc., Freeport, ME; *U.S. Public*, pg. 360
White, Richard, Mng. Dir.--Goulds Pumps Singapore PTE, Ltd., Jurong, Singapore; *U.S. Public*, pg. 861
White, Richard, V.P.--MTS Japan Ltd. (Tokyo), Tokyo, Japan; *U.S. Public*, pg. 1029
White, Richard D., Pres. & Chief Exec. Officer--Regions Bank, Gainesville, GA; *U.S. Public*, pg. 1371
White, Rivhard L., Pres.--Bayer Corporation/Fibers, Organics & Rubber Division, Pittsburgh, PA; *Int'l*, pg. 172
White, Robert, Pres.--Breeze Eastern, Union, NJ; *U.S. Public*, pg. 1632
white, Robert A., Gen. Mgr.--Manufacturers Folding Carton, Inc., El Paso, TX; *U.S. Public*, pg. 1521
White, Robert P., Pres. & Chief Exec. Officer--Care America-Southern CA, Woodland Hills, CA; *U.S. Private*, pg. 153
White, Russell, Pres.--Elsevier Science Inc., New York, NY; *Int'l*, pg. 1100
White, Stephen, V.P.-Europe--McGraw-Hill Book Co. (U.K.) Ltd., Maidenhead, United Kingdom; *U.S. Public*, pg. 1072
White, Stephen E., Chief Exec. Officer--Metropolitan Life Holdings, Ltd., New York, NY; *U.S. Private*, pg. 737
White, Steve, Gen. Mgr.--Stone Container Corp.-Tupelo, Tupelo, MS; *U.S. Public*, pg. 1521
White, Steven, Chief Exec. Officer--Healthsource Tennessee, Inc., Brentwood, TN; *U.S. Public*, pg. 360
White, Timothy O., V.P. & Publisher--Albany Times Union, Albany, NY; *U.S. Private*, pg. 517
White, Tom, Chm. Bd. & Chief Exec. Officer--Enron Operations Corp., Houston, TX; *U.S. Public*, pg. 584
White, Tony L., Chm. Bd., Pres. & Chief Exec. Officer--Applied Biosystems, Foster City, CA; *U.S. Public*, pg. 1279
White, William, Pres.--Shoppers Food Warehouse, Lanham, MD; *U.S. Public*, pg. 484
White, William G., Pres.--Valley-Todeco, Inc., Sylmar, CA; *Int'l*, pg. 852
Whitehead, Alan, Mng. Dir.--Raisio Chemicals Canada Inc., Vancouver, Canada; *Int'l*, pg. 1086
Whitehead, Andrew G., Pres.--Silverman's Dental Supplies Inc., King of Prussia, PA; *Int'l*, pg. 710
Whitehead, David, Publr. & Editor--The Times Co., Marietta, OH; *U.S. Public*, pg. 700
Whitehead, Geoffrey, Chief Oper. Officer--Novo Nordisk Pharmaceuticals Ltd., Auckland, New Zealand; *Int'l*, pg. 988
Whitehead, H. Baird, Chief Oper. Officer--Franklin Brine Treatment Corporation, Houston, TX; *U.S. Public*, pg. 289
Whitehead, John, Gen. Mgr.--American Rigging & Supply, San Diego, CA; *U.S. Private*, pg. 215
Whitehead, Roger, Gen. Mgr.--Wang (UK) Limited, Isleworth, United Kingdom; *U.S. Public*, pg. 1738
Whitehead, Roger, Gen. Mgr.--Wang Ireland Limited, Dublin, Ireland; *U.S. Public*, pg. 1738
Whitehouse, Robert, Pres. & Chief Exec. Officer--AmTran Corporation, Conway, AR; *U.S. Public*, pg. 1167
Whitehouse, William L., Pres. & Chief Exec. Officer--Chelsea Moore Company, Loveland, OH; *U.S. Private*, pg. 1164
Whiteley, A.C., Mgr.-Sls.--Turner Construction Company, Raleigh, NC; *U.S. Public*, pg. 1646
Whiteley, Colin, Pres. & Dir.--Wormald Italiana S.P.A., Milan, Italy; *U.S. Public*, pg. 1651
Whiteley, Colin, Gen. Mgr.--Wormald Mather & Platt Espana S.A., Barcelona, Spain; *U.S. Public*, pg. 1651
Whitelock, T.K., Gen. Mgr.--CDM (Proprietary) Limited, Kimberley, South Africa; *Int'l*, pg. 77
Whitely, Elliott F., Div. Pres.--Lydall Technical Papers, Rochester, NH; *U.S. Public*, pg. 1021
Whiteman, Daniel E., Chief Oper. Officer--Walbridge Aldinger Company, Tampa, FL; *U.S. Private*, pg. 1147
Whiteman, John O., Pres.--EMPIRE Machinery, Mesa, AZ; *U.S. Private*, pg. 374
Whitener, Jerry, V.P. & Gen. Mgr.--KLRT-TV, Little Rock, AR; *U.S. Public*, pg. 384
Whitenight, Keith, Mgr.-Office--Woodward-Clyde, Gaithersburg, MD; *U.S. Public*, pg. 1656
Whitescarver, Olin D., V.P. & Gen. Mgr.--Unocal Geothermal of Indonesia Ltd., Jakarta, Indonesia; *U.S. Public*, pg. 1698
Whiteside, W.G., Pres.--Block Drug Co. (Canada) Ltd., Toronto, Canada; *U.S. Public*, pg. 237
Whitfield, Alan D., Pres.--Kamatics Corp., Bloomfield, CT; *U.S. Public*, pg. 942
Whitfield, Steven, Mng. Dir.--Eurocamp Independent Limited, Knutsford, United Kingdom; *Int'l*, pg. 465
Whitford, Peter D., Pres. & Chief Exec. Officer--Structure, Columbus, OH; *U.S. Public*, pg. 996
Whiting, Richard M., Pres.--Peabody COALSALES Company, Saint Louis, MO; *Int'l*, pg. 594
Whitley, Douglas L., Pres.--Ameritech, Chicago, IL; *U.S. Public*, pg. 97
Whitley, Edward A., Pres. & Chief Exec. Officer--Centex-Rodgers Construction Company, Nashville, TN; *U.S. Public*, pg. 322
Whitley, Ralph C., Pres.--CCH Computax Inc., Torrance, CA; *Int'l*, pg. 1513
Whitlock, C. William, Jr., Pres.--Old Kent Bank-Central, Owosso, MI; *U.S. Public*, pg. 1216
Whitlock, Sonny, Plant Mgr.--Salem Carpet Mills, Chickamauga, GA; *U.S. Public*, pg. 1464
Whitlow, Bill, Gen. Mgr.--Susquehanna Radio Corp., Virginia Beach, VA; *U.S. Private*, pg. 860
Whitlow, Don, Pres. & Chief Oper. Officer--Barbour Thread, Inc., Blue Mountain, AL; *Int'l*, pg. 618
Whitlow, Don, Pres.--Barbour Threads, Inc., Anniston, AL; *Int'l*, pg. 618
Whitlow, Jack, Gen. Mgr.--Frontier Communications of Indiana, Inc., Fairmount, IN; *U.S. Public*, pg. 683
Whitman, Peter M., Jr., Pres.--Dewey Square Investors Corporation, Boston, MA; *U.S. Public*, pg. 1673
Whitmarsh, Robert M., Pres. & Chief Exec. Officer--Willis Corroon Corp. of Portland, Portland, OR; *Int'l*, pg. 1507
Whitmer, Jack E., Pres.--McGraw-Hill Professional Publishing Group, New York, NY; *U.S. Public*, pg. 1070
Whitmire, J.L., Pres.--Phillips Alaska Natural Gas Corporation, Bellaire, TX; *U.S. Public*, pg. 1291
Whitmore, Donald E., Jr., Chief Fin. Officer & Exec. V.P.--The Eastern Company, Naugatuck, CT; *U.S. Public*, pg. 548
Whitmore, Garry R., Pres.--Tri-Lite Plastics South, Inc., Pell City, AL; *Int'l*, pg. 233
Whitmore, Tim, V.P. & Gen. Mgr.--BPI Inc., Salisbury Plant, Salisbury, NC; *U.S. Public*, pg. 772
Whitney, F. C., Plant Mgr.--Waterbury Companies, Inc., Biddeford, ME; *U.S. Public*, pg. 308
Whitney, Herb, Pres.--Citgo Pipeline Company, Tulsa, OK; *Int'l*, pg. 1045
Whitney, John, Chm. Bd.--The Really Useful Company, Inc., New York, NY; *Int'l*, pg. 1089
Whitney, Michael, Chm. Bd., Pres. & Chief Exec. Officer--Fleet Bank-NH, Nashua, NH; *U.S. Public*, pg. 649
Whitney, Michael C., Jr., Chm. Bd., Pres. & Chief Exec. Officer--Fleet Bank NH, Manchester, NH; *U.S. Public*, pg. 649
Whitney, Stephen, Mng. Dir.--Hussey Seating Systems (Europe) Ltd., Runcorn, United Kingdom; *U.S. Private*, pg. 550
Whiton, Jeffrey H., Pres.--Colorado Division, Englewood, CO; *U.S. Public*, pg. 1682
Whittaker, Barry, Gen. Mgr.--AMP of Canada Ltd., Markham, Canada; *U.S. Public*, pg. 9
Whittaker, Frank, Gen. Mgr.--The Sacramento Bee, Sacramento, CA; *U.S. Public*, pg. 1066
Whittaker, G., Mng. Dir.--Haden Engineering Pty, Rosebery, Australia; *Int'l*, pg. 586
Whittaker, J. Ronald, Gen. Mgr.--Stanfast, Inc., Peoria, IL; *U.S. Public*, pg. 1505
Whittall, S.B., Pres.--British Steel Canada Inc., Saint-Laurent, Canada; *Int'l*, pg. 222
Whittenberg, Bruce, Publisher--The Independent Record, Helena, MT; *U.S. Public*, pg. 983
Whittington, Marna, Partner--Miller, Anderson & Sherrerd, Conshohocken, PA; *U.S. Public*, pg. 1132
whittle, Don J., V.P. & Gen. Mgr.--Domtar Packaging Division, Malton, Canada; *Int'l*, pg. 416
Whittle, Ray, Gen. Mgr.--Barton's of Eudora, Eudora, AR; *U.S. Private*, pg. 119
Whitton, Barry, Mng. Dir.--Ademco-Sontrix (Australia) Pty. Ltd., Mortdale, Australia; *U.S. Public*, pg. 1307
Whitton, Barry, Gen. Mgr.--Ademco Australia Pty. Ltd., Parramatta, Australia; *U.S. Public*, pg. 1307
Whitworth, Don R., Publisher--Lakeland Ledger Publishing Corporation, Lakeland, FL; *U.S. Public*, pg. 1175
Whritenour, Robert, Pres.--Mueller Steam Specialty, Lumberton, NC; *U.S. Public*, pg. 1676
Whulan, J.B., Chm.--Gailey & Roberts Ltd., Nairobi, Kenya; *Int'l*, pg. 1437
Whyte, Hubert A.J., V.P.-MainStreet Access Products--Newbridge Networks Corporation, Kanata, Canada; *Int'l*, pg. 924
Whyte, Ralph, Sr. V.P.--Willis Corroon Aerospace of Canada Ltd., Vancouver, Canada; *Int'l*, pg. 1509
Wiatt, James, Pres.--International Creative Management, Inc., New York, NY; *U.S. Private*, pg. 554
Wibaux, Sylvaim, Chief Oper. Officer--Societe des Specialites Surgelees a Landevant, Paris, France; *Int'l*, pg. 556
Wiberg, Per, Chief Oper. Officer--ICA Specialvaror AB, Goteborg, Sweden; *Int'l*, pg. 643
Wible, Arthur E., Publr.--The Beacon-News, Aurora, IL; *U.S. Private*, pg. 275
Wible, Arthur E., Publr.--Daily Courier-News, Elgin, IL; *U.S. Private*, pg. 275
Wible, Arthur E., Publr.--Herald-News, Joliet, IL; *U.S. Private*, pg. 275
Wible, Arthur E., Publr.--The News-Sun, Waukegan, IL; *U.S.* Private, pg. 275
Wible, Steve, Mgr.-Plant--Terre Haute Plant, Terre Haute, IN; *U.S. Public*, pg. 716
Wichman, John, Pres.--Wenco Inc., San Dimas, CA; *U.S. Public*, pg. 1754
Wichmann, Egon, Reg. Mng. Dir.--Berendsen PMC GmbH, Dusseldorf, Germany; *Int'l*, pg. 1285
Wichtrich, John, Pres.--Rhone-Poulenc Specialty Chemicals Division, Cranbury, NJ; *Int'l*, pg. 1110
Wick, Michael A., Pres.-Color--Universal Flavors, Kearny, NJ; *U.S. Public*, pg. 1695
Wicker, Alain, Pres.--Fimagest, Paris, France; *Int'l*, pg. 548
Wickham, Lee, Chief Oper. Officer--Atcot Corp., Inc., Fresno, CA; *Int'l*, pg. 300
Wickland, John A., III, Pres.--Wickland Properties, Sacramento, CA; *U.S. Private*, pg. 1175
Wickland, Roy, Pres.--Wickland Oil Company, Inc., Sacramento, CA; *U.S. Private*, pg. 1175
Wickland, Roy, Pres.--Wickland International Asia, Ltd., Singapore, Singapore; *U.S. Private*, pg. 1175
Wickline, W. Rucker, Pres.--CDR Pigments & Dispersions, Elizabethtown, KY; *U.S. Private*, pg. 413
Wickman, Peter, V.P.-Opers.--Belden Wire & Cable Company, Richmond, IN; *U.S. Public*, pg. 201
Wickre, Gary L., Pres.--First American Bank West, Minot, ND; *U.S. Private*, pg. 167
Wickremasinghe, Anura, Rep.--HDF Securities PVT Limited, Colombo, Sri Lanka; *Int'l*, pg. 494
Wicks, Clyde, Pres. & Publisher--The Sun Times, Owen Sound, Canada; *Int'l*, pg. 631
Wickswat, George, V.P.--O.R.E. Subsidiary Corp., Schenectady, NY; *U.S. Public*, pg. 1643
Widdicombe, Elizabeth, Pres.--W.H. Freeman & Co., New York, NY; *Int'l*, pg. 1479
Widerstrom, Diane, V.P. & Acct. Dir.--Grizzard, Winter Park, FL; *U.S. Private*, pg. 482
Widham, Susan, Pres.--Beech-Nut Nutrition Corporation, Saint Louis, MO; *U.S. Public*, pg. 1359
Widick, Richard, Gen. Mgr.--Intertec Publishing, Chicago, IL; *U.S. Public*, pg. 1328
Widman, Philip, Chief Fin. Officer & Sr. V.P.--ABB Inc., Norwalk, CT; *Int'l*, pg. 3
Widmann, Jim, Gen. Mgr.--CMI Metro Pave, Cedar Falls, IA; *U.S. Public*, pg. 279
Widmann, Nancy C., Pres.--CBS Radio Div., New York, NY; *U.S. Public*, pg. 274
Widmer, Bruno, Pres.--Advico Young & Rubicam AG, Zurich, Switzerland; *U.S. Private*, pg. 1198
Widmer, Hans, Mng. Dir.--Vernicolor A.G., Gruningen, Switzerland; *U.S. Public*, pg. 505

Widmer, R., Mng. Dir.--MSA Switzerland Ltd., Bern, Switzerland; *U.S. Public*, pg. 1115

Widmer, Rolf, Pres.--Georg Fischer Treuhand A.G., Schaffhausen, Switzerland; *Int'l*, pg. 490

Widmer, Rudolf, Gen. Mgr.--Micarna S.A., Courtepin, Switzerland; *Int'l*, pg. 865

Widstrand, Thomas, Mng. Dir.--ESAB AB, Perstorp, Sweden; *Int'l*, pg. 281

Wiebe, Jack, Sls. Rep.-Ontario--Acuson Canada, Ltd., Oakville, Canada; *U.S. Public*, pg. 18

Wiedebush, N. Thomas, Dir.--First Trust Company of North Dakota, National Association, Fargo, ND; *U.S. Public*, pg. 1681

Wiedeler, Wolfgang, V.P. & Country Mgr.--Berlitz Schools of Languages GmbH, Frankfurt/Main, Germany; *U.S. Public*, pg. 222

Wiedeler, Wolfgang, V.P. & Country Mgr.--Berlitz Schools of Languages AG, Geneva, Switzerland; *U.S. Public*, pg. 222

Wiedeler, Wolfgang, V.P. & Country Mgr.--Berlitz Sprachschulen GmbH, Vienna, Austria; *U.S. Public*, pg. 222

Wiedemann, Joseph, Pres.--American Home Assurance Co., New York, NY; *U.S. Public*, pg. 84

Wiederkehr, Werner, Dir.--Dresdner Forfaitierungs Aktiengesellschaft, Zurich, Switzerland; *Int'l*, pg. 419

Wiedmann, Paul, Mgr.--Aluminum Norf GmbH, Neuss, Germany; *Int'l*, pg. 51

Wiegand, Dietmar, Gen. Mgr.--Forbo Erfurt GmbH, Erfurt, Germany; *Int'l*, pg. 497

Wiegand, Manfred, Mng. Dir.--Ericsson Paging Systems Zweigniederlassung Deutschland, Frankfurt/Main, Germany; *Int'l*, pg. 1367

Wiege, Gunter, Chief Oper. Officer--Electrolux Wascherei und Service GmbH, Wermelskirchen, Germany; *Int'l*, pg. 442

Wiegel, H. W., Gen. Mgr.--Winnsboro Assembly Division, Winnsboro, SC; *Int'l*, pg. 1103

Wiegel, Wim, Mng. Dir.--Circle Freight International (Holland) B.V., Hoofddorp, Netherlands; *U.S. Public*, pg. 372

Wieger, Garth, Pres. & Chief Exec. Officer--UDC Homes, Inc., Scottsdale, AZ; *U.S. Private*, pg. 5

Wieger, Garth, Pres.--Shea Homes Arizona, Scottsdale, AZ; *U.S. Private*, pg. 991

Wiehe, Marv, Gen. Mgr.--Marshall Erdman & Assoc., Inc., East Windsor, CT; *U.S. Private*, pg. 380

Wieland, Bernard, Pres.--Unarco Material, Springfield, TN; *U.S. Private*, pg. 922

Wieland, Eckart, Chm.--Flender-Himmelwerk GmbH, Tubingen, Germany; *Int'l*, pg. 400

Wieland, Gualterio, Pres. & Mng. Dir.--General Motors Colmotores, S.A., Bogota, Colombia; *U.S. Public*, pg. 722

Wieland, Homer, Div. V.P.--Analysis & Applied Research Div., Austin, TX; *U.S. Public*, pg. 1627

Wieland, John, Chief Oper. Officer--Residential Support Services, Inc., Atlanta, GA; *U.S. Private*, pg. 1175

Wieland, Nancy, V.P.--Paramus Park, Inc., Paramus, NJ; *U.S. Public*, pg. 1408

Wieland, Werner, Mng. Dir.--Reed Exhibition Companies-Austria, Salzburg, Austria; *Int'l*, pg. 1097

Wielgosz, John, Pres.--Metallurgical, Inc., Minneapolis, MN; *U.S. Public*, pg. 1594

Wieman, Marvin D., Gen. Mgr.--Electronic Systems Div., Sioux Falls, SD; *U.S. Public*, pg. 1361

Wiemer, Dierk, Gen. Mgr.--Aeroquip Sterling GmbH, Frankfurt/Main, Germany; *U.S. Public*, pg. 25

Wiend, W. David, V.P. & Gen. Mgr.--Sparton of Canada Ltd., London, Canada; *U.S. Public*, pg. 1496

Wiener, Elliot, Chief Oper. Officer--Levitt Corporation, Boca Raton, FL; *U.S. Private*, pg. 1035

Wiener, Louis, Chief Oper. Officer--Imperial Equities, Lynbrook, NY; *U.S. Private*, pg. 674

Wiens, D.L., Mgr.--Alloy Wire Belt Co., Modesto, CA; *U.S. Public*, pg. 999

Wiens, Mark, V.P. & Gen. Mgr.--Cott Corporation - Pacific North West Region (Calgary), Calgary, Canada; *Int'l*, pg. 337

Wienstein, David, Pres.--Concord House Division, New York, NY; *U.S. Public*, pg. 430

Wiernioci, Chris, Pres.--ABS Integrated Services, Houston, TX; *U.S. Private*, pg. 51

Wiersbe, Dale E., Jr., Pres. & Chief Oper. Officer--Inland Steel Products Company, East Chicago, IN; *U.S. Public*, pg. 889

Wierschem, Thomas M., Pres.--First American Bank, Breckenridge, MN; *U.S. Private*, pg. 167

Wiersema, P.L., Mgr.--Vredestein Icopro B.V., Renkum, Netherlands; *Int'l*, pg. 1481

Wiersma, Ken, Mgr.-Opers.--Circle Freight International USA, Grand Rapids, MI; *U.S. Public*, pg. 371

Wiersum, T., Pres.--BV Delft Electronic Products, Roden, Netherlands; *Int'l*, pg. 388

Wierzbicki, Jan, Mng. Dir.--WWT (Wytwornia Wyrobow Tytoniowych) S.A., Warsaw, Poland; *Int'l*, pg. 1101

Wiese-Hansen, Torre, Chm. Bd.--Air Products A/S-Gardner Cryogenics Div., Kristiansand, Norway; *U.S. Public*, pg. 31

Wiese, Fred, Mgr.-Opers.--Electronic Materials Division, San Diego, CA; *Int'l*, pg. 713

Wieseneck, Robert L., Pres.--SPS Payment Systems, Inc., Riverwoods, IL; *U.S. Public*, pg. 1132

Wiesner, Richard, Pres.--LifeScan, Inc., Milpitas, CA; *U.S. Public*, pg. 928

Wiessing, M.H., Gen. Mgr.--ING Bank Jakarta, Jakarta, Indonesia; *Int'l*, pg. 649

Wiewers, R.W., Pres.--Equifax Information Technology, Alpharetta, GA; *U.S. Public*, pg. 588

Wig, Jack, Mgr.--Voest-Alpine Services and Technologies Corp.-East Chicago, East Chicago, IN; *Int'l*, pg. 1471

Wigand, Art F., Pres. & Chief Exec. Officer--Cubic Communications, San Diego, CA; *U.S. Public*, pg. 466

Wigchers, Jr., Arthur W., Pres.--Towne Realty, Inc., Milwaukee, WI; *U.S. Private*, pg. 1206

Wigdale, J.B., Chm. Bd. & Chief Exec. Officer--M & I Marshall & Ilsley Bank, Milwaukee, WI; *U.S. Public*, pg. 1050

Wigdor, Lawrence A., Pres. & Chief Exec. Officer--Kronos, Inc., Houston, TX; *U.S. Private*, pg. 270

Wiggel, Theo, Pres.--Marine Power Australia, Pty. Ltd., Dandenong, Australia; *U.S. Public*, pg. 266

Wiggins, Ernie, Reg. Sls. Mgr.--Snyder Bakery, Yakima, WA; *U.S. Private*, pg. 1124

Wigginton, Eugene H., Pres.--Standard Publishing, Cincinnati, OH; *U.S. Public*, pg. 1506

Wiggishoff, Nic, Mgr.--Stewart Smith Southeast, Inc., Nashville, TN; *Int'l*, pg. 1508

Wight, Robin, Chm. Bd.--WCRS, London, United Kingdom; *Int'l*, pg. 603

Wigley, Bill, Gen. Mgr.--Vertical Products Div., City of Industry, CA; *U.S. Public*, pg. 861

Wiheking, W., Dr., Mng. Dir.--Claudius Peters AG, Buxtehude, Germany; *Int'l*, pg. 131

Wiig, Terje, Mng. Dir.--Korn/Ferry International, Oslo, Norway; *U.S. Private*, pg. 634

Wiik, Ingrid, Pres.--International Pharmaceuticals, Oslo, Norway; *U.S. Public*, pg. 58

Wijk, Goran, Mgr.--Sandvik (Pty.) Ltd., Benoni, South Africa; *Int'l*, pg. 1187

Wijk, Goran, Mgr.--Sandvik (Zambia) Ltd., Ndola, Zambia; *Int'l*, pg. 1187

Wijne, Jacques, Chief Oper. Officer--MacDermid Benelux B.V., Etten-Leur, Netherlands; *U.S. Public*, pg. 1030

Wijne, Jacques, Chief Oper. Officer--MacDermid GmbH, Bruchsal, Germany; *U.S. Public*, pg. 1030

Wijnen, Willem, Mng. Dir.--Hydrowa B.V., Eindhoven, Netherlands; *Int'l*, pg. 1285

Wijsmuller, J.B., Gen. Mgr.--ING Trust (Jersey), Saint Helier, United Kingdom; *Int'l*, pg. 650

Wikblom, Lennart, Chief Oper. Officer--Kohlswa Jernverk AB, Kolsva, Sweden; *Int'l*, pg. 439

Wikerson, Kenneth L., Chm.--Foley's, Houston, TX; *U.S. Public*, pg. 1063

Wiking, Wolf, Mng. Dir.--Scan-Ad Haderslev A/S, Haderslev, Denmark; *Int'l*, pg. 1198

Wiklund, Lars, Mgr.--AB Arv Anderson, Skelleftea, Sweden; *Int'l*, pg. 1422

Wikman, Bruno, Pres.--NCC Umea, Umea, Sweden; *Int'l*, pg. 899

Wikstrom, Goran, Pres.--ABB Service AB, Vasteras, Sweden; *Int'l*, pg. 7

Wikstrom, Lennart, Chief Oper. Officer--Mining Services Co. Minserco, Jeddah, Saudi Arabia; *Int'l*, pg. 443

Wikstrom, Soren, Mgr.--Sandvik Korea Ltd., Seoul, Korea; *Int'l*, pg. 1187

Wilander, T., Chm. Bd.--Edwards, Vastra Frolunda, Sweden; *Int'l*, pg. 661

Wilbers, J., Mng. Dir.--Mowe Teigwarenwerk GmbH, Waren, Germany; *Int'l*, pg. 244

Wilbourn, Brooks, Sls. Exec.--Circle International, Nashville, TN; *U.S. Public*, pg. 371

Wilbrett, Robert, Pres. & Chief Exec. Officer--Hilb, Rogal and Hamilton Company of Port Huron, Port Huron, MI; *U.S. Public*, pg. 827

Wilbrink, Louis, Pres.--Ravo International, Alkmaar, Netherlands; *U.S. Public*, pg. 617

Wilby, Bruce, Pres.--JPS Elastomerics Corp., Holyoke, MA; *U.S. Private*, pg. 578

Wilcott, Scott J., Pres.--CalMat Land Co., Los Angeles, CA; *U.S. Public*, pg. 295

Wilcott, Scott J., Pres.--Reliance Land Co., Los Angeles, CA; *U.S. Public*, pg. 296

Wilcox, Denis, Pres.--Mercantile Bank of Jasper County, Newton, IA; *U.S. Public*, pg. 1088

Wilcox, Diane, Gen. Mgr.--Mount Bachelor Village Corp., Bend, OR; *U.S. Private*, pg. 172

Wilcox, Fred, V.P.--Electric Utility Div., Kingston, PA; *U.S. Public*, pg. 1653

Wilcox, Jay, Pres.--Woodlore, Port Washington, WI; *U.S. Private*, pg. 37

Wilcox, Richard W. Jr., Pres.--Hilb, Rogal and Hamilton Company of Fort Lauderdale, Fort Lauderdale, FL; *U.S. Public*, pg. 827

Wilcox, Tina, Sr. V.P. & Creative Dir.--FAME, Minneapolis, MN; *U.S. Private*, pg. 710

Wilcoxson, J.C., Chm. Bd.--Cigna International Fund Managers (CI) Ltd., Saint Peter Port, United Kingdom; *U.S. Public*, pg. 364

Wild, J.N., Mng. Dir.--Park Cakes Ltd., Oldham, United Kingdom; *Int'l*, pg. 968

Wild, Keith, Mng. Dir.--Hedsorboard Ltd., Surbiton, United Kingdom; *Int'l*, pg. 864

Wilde, Norman T., Jr., Pres.--Janney Montgomery Scott Inc., Philadelphia, PA; *U.S. Private*, pg. 849

Wilde, Tim, Plant Mgr.--Elkay Manufacturing, Broadview, IL; *U.S. Private*, pg. 372

Wilder, Brian, Mng. Dir.--McGraw-Hill Book Co. Australia Pty. Ltd., Roseville, Australia; *U.S. Public*, pg. 1072

Wilder, Morris, V.P. & Gen. Mgr.--Ceco Building Systems-Eastern Region, Rocky Mount, NC; *U.S. Private*, pg. 221

Wildermuth, Gary, Div. Mgr.--Montgomery Elevator Parts Distribution Center, Moline, IL; *Int'l*, pg. 746

Wilding, R., Mng. Dir.--J.W. Spencer Engineering Ltd., Redhill, United Kingdom; *Int'l*, pg. 124

Wildish, P., Mng. Dir.--L.P. Foreman & Sons Ltd., Chelmsford, United Kingdom; *Int'l*, pg. 543

Wildman, John, Pres.--Cardio-Fitness Corporation, New York, NY; *U.S. Public*, pg. 806

Wildman, John A., Pres.--The Fitness Institute, Willowdale, Canada; *U.S. Public*, pg. 806

Wilensky, Stephen, Admin.--Hillhaven Convalescent Hospital Santa Ana, Santa Ana, CA; *U.S. Public*, pg. 1713

Wiles, Chip, Gen. Mgr.--National Frozen Foods Corporation - Burlington, Burlington, WA; *U.S. Private*, pg. 783

Wiley, Ed, Gen. Mgr.--Bowne Insurance Division, Secaucus, NJ; *U.S. Public*, pg. 248

Wiley, Ron, Pres.--Consumer Products Division, Englewood, NJ; *Int'l*, pg. 1489

Wiley, Steve, V.P. & Gen. Mgr.--Premdor Entry Systems, Dickson, TN; *Int'l*, pg. 1067

Wilfinger, Horst, Mng. Dir.--Austria III, Vienna, Austria; *U.S. Private*, pg. 1062

Wilhelm, Bernd, Mng. Dir.--Kellogg (Deutschland) Gesellschaft mit beschrankter Hartung (GmbH), Bremen, Germany; *U.S. Public*, pg. 948

Wilhelm, Jan, Dir.-Opers.--Grumman Ohio Corp., Worthington, OH; *U.S. Public*, pg. 1198

Wilhelm, Markus, Chief Exec.--BCA, London, United Kingdom; *Int'l*, pg. 192

Wilhelm, Paul J., Pres.--USS Kobe Steel, Lorain, OH; *Int'l*, pg. 741

Wilhelm, Paul J., Pres.--USS Kobe Steel, Lorain, OH; *U.S. Public*, pg. 1662

Wilhelm, Werner, Chief Oper. Officer--CWS International A.G., Glattbrugg, Switzerland; *Int'l*, pg. 592

Wilhelmsen, Elisabeth, Media Dir.--Leo Burnett A/S, Oslo, Norway; *U.S. Private*, pg. 184

Wilhelmsson, Ola, Pres.--AB Gustaf Kahr, Nybro, Sweden; *Int'l*, pg. 1260

Wilk, Cornelius, Pres.--Epipharm GmbH, Lienz, Austria; *Int'l*, pg. 288

Wilke, Manfred, Mng. Dir.--Novoferm GmbH, Rees, Germany; *Int'l*, pg. 509

Wilken, Dick, Mng. Dir.--Norta Timber B.V., Amsterdam, Netherlands; *Int'l*, pg. 458

Wilkens, Ian G., Pres. & Gen. Mgr.--Fischbein Co., Statesville, NC; *U.S. Private*, pg. 103

Wilkens, Roy A., Pres. & Chief Exec. Officer--LDDS WorldCom, Tulsa, OK; *U.S. Public*, pg. 1779

Wilkerson, Frank, Plant Mgr.--Alcoa Fujikura Inc., Shelbyville, KY; *U.S. Public*, pg. 61

Wilkerson, Jeffrey, Plant Mgr.--Bundy Corporation, Bloomington Plant, Normal, IL; *Int'l*, pg. 1340

Wilkes, Dave, Chief Oper. Officer--Southeast Region, Tampa, FL; *U.S. Private*, pg. 687

Wilkes, G. Steve, Chm. & Chief Exec. Officer--Regions Bank/Birmingham, Birmingham, AL; *U.S. Public*, pg. 1371

Wilkes, James E., Pres.--Ameritech, Detroit, MI; *U.S. Public*, pg. 97

Wilkes, Jamie, Plant Mgr.--Dygert Seating, Watkinsville, GA; *U.S. Public*, pg. 654

Wilkes, R.E., Mng. Dir.--Senior Phoenix RFS Limited, Bridgnorth, United Kingdom; *Int'l*, pg. 1221

Wilkie, Dennis F., Chm. Bd.--Ford Glass & Metal, Inc., Dearborn, MI; *U.S. Public*, pg. 664

Wilkie, Dennis Frank, Pres.--Autovidrio, S.A. de C.V., Juarez, Mexico; *U.S. Public*, pg. 665

Wilkins, C., Chief Oper. Officer--Filter Division, Parker Hannifin (U.K.) Ltd., Morley, United Kingdom; *U.S. Public*, pg. 1260

Wilkins, Morris B., Pres. & Chief Oper. Officer--Brookdale Resorts, Inc., Scotrun, PA; *U.S. Public*, pg. 1512

Wilkins, Morris B., Pres. & Chief Oper. Officer--Cove Haven, Inc., Lakeville, PA; *U.S. Public*, pg. 1512

Wilkins, Morris B., Pres. & Chief Oper. Officer--Paradise Stream, Inc., Mount Pocono, PA; *U.S. Public*, pg. 1512

Wilkins, Morris B., Pres. & Chief Oper. Officer--Pocono Palace, Inc., Marshalls Creek, PA; *U.S. Public*, pg. 1512

Wilkins, P.D., Pres.--Morganite Environmental Services Inc., Dunn, NC; *Int'l*, pg. 894

Wilkins, Robert, Mng. Dir.--Beazer Homes (Bedford) Limited, Bedford, United Kingdom; *Int'l*, pg. 182

Wilkinson, B. Andrew, Pres. & Chief Exec. Officer--Statex Petroleum, Inc., Dallas, TX; *U.S. Public*, pg. 1245

Wilkinson, C., Div. Mgr.--Pneumatic Div., Cannock, United Kingdom; *U.S. Public*, pg. 1264

Wilkinson, Frank S., Jr., Chief Exec. Officer--Paragon Reinsurance Risk Management Services, Inc., Minneapolis, MN; *U.S. Public*, pg. 236

Wilkinson, Frank S., Jr., Chm. Bd. & Chief Exec. Officer--E.W. Blanch Capital Risk Solutions, Inc., Minneapolis, MN; *U.S. Public*, pg. 236

Wilkinson, Jay, Pres.--Public Employees Benefit Services Corp., Columbus, OH; *U.S. Private*, pg. 789

Wilkinson, John, Mng. Dir.--Matthew Clark Brands, Bristol, United Kingdom; *Int'l*, pg. 848

Wilkinson, Jon, Chief Exec. Officer--Research International, London, United Kingdom; *Int'l*, pg. 1482

Wilkinson, William N., Pres.--Dover Corporation (Canada) Ltd.-Turnbull Elevator Div., Mississauga, Canada; *U.S. Public*, pg. 522

Wilkoc, A. Ronald, Counsel--Clupak, Inc., New York, NY; *U.S. Public*, pg. 1762

Wilkofsky, Roth, V.P. & Gen. Mgr.--Addison-Wesley Longman, New York, NY; *Int'l*, pg. 1026

Wilks, R.L., Mng. Dir.--Nissan Datsun Holdings Ltd., Auckland, New Zealand; *Int'l*, pg. 945

Wilkus, Richard, Pres.--ISI Insortex, Schaumburg, IL; *U.S. Public*, pg. 428

Will, Dennis, Gen. Mgr.--First American Title Guaranty Agency of Hot Springs County, Thermopolis, WY; *U.S. Public*, pg. 625

Will, J., Chief Oper. Officer--Sawhill Tubular Div., Sharon, PA; *U.S. Public*, pg. 131

Willamo, Matti, Mng. Dir.--Merita Customer Finance Ltd., Helsinki, Finland; *Int'l*, pg. 859

Willans, J.R.D., Chief Oper. Officer--Pillar Engineering Ltd., London, United Kingdom; *Int'l*, pg. 267

Willard, Eugene, Gen. Mgr.--Park Newspapers of Morganton, Inc., Morganton, NC; *U.S. Public*, pg. 1079

Willard, Eugene, Gen. Mgr.--Morganton News-Herald, Morganton, NC; *U.S. Public*, pg. 1079

Willard, Wynn, Pres.--Planters Company, East Hanover, NJ; *U.S. Public*, pg. 1355

Willasch, Dieter, Dr., Mng. Dir.--Spectris Messtechnik GmbH, Langen, Germany; *Int'l*, pg. 14

Willcock, Clarence, Mng. Dir.--Frialator International, Warrington, United Kingdom; *U.S. Public*, pg. 1065

Willcock, K.J., Mng. Dir.--Wajax (Australasia) Pty. Ltd., Thomastown, Australia; *Int'l*, pg. 1485
Willcox, James, Area V.P.--Avon Sales & Distribution Branch, Suwanee, GA; *U.S. Public*, pg. 156
Willcox, R., Plant Dir.--Keebler Co./Macon Bakery, Macon, GA; *U.S. Public*, pg. 657
Wille, Rod, Sr. V.P.-Regional Madages--Turner Construction Co., Chicago, IL; *U.S. Public*, pg. 1645
Willegems, Th., Chief Oper. Officer--SHV Makro, Utrecht, Netherlands; *Int'l*, pg. 1155
Willems, Bert, Pres.--Knurr NV Belgie, Kontich, Belgium; *Int'l*, pg. 739
Willems, Bert, Pres.--Knurr Nederland B.V., Breda, Netherlands; *Int'l*, pg. 739
Willemsen, A.J., Mng. Dir.--Ennia Caribe N.V., Willemstad, Netherlands Antilles; *Int'l*, pg. 28
Willemsen, J.C., Mgr.--Radio-Holland Group Middle East, Sharjah, United Arab Emirates; *Int'l*, pg. 1152
Willes, Mark, Publisher--Los Angeles Times, Los Angeles, CA; *U.S. Public*, pg. 1616
Willett, A., Reg. Mgr.--The Royal Bank of Scotland plc, Central, Hong Kong; *Int'l*, pg. 1133
Willett, Gary, Bus. Mgr.--Cerner Solutions Center -SNI Health Solutions Div., Luton, United Kingdom; *U.S. Public*, pg. 331
Willett, Steve, Gen. Mgr.--Container Div. (Dallas), Dallas, TX; *Int'l*, pg. 1269
Willey, Charles, Admin.--Park Manor Nursing & Convalescent Home, Rawlins, WY; *U.S. Public*, pg. 1714
Willey, Mark, Gen. Mgr.--Bayside Auto Auction of Tampa Inc., Tampa, FL; *U.S. Public*, pg. 1648
Willhdo, Tonya, Gen. Mgr.--Alro Group, Dayton, Dayton, OH; *U.S. Private*, pg. 46
William, Brian, Gen. Mgr.--Excelsior Hoteis E Investimentos Limitada, Macau, Macau; *Int'l*, pg. 704
Williams, Al, Mgr.-Outside Sls.--Jaco Electronics, Inc., San Jose, CA; *U.S. Public*, pg. 921
Williams, Andrew, Pres.--Cadmus Interactive, Tucker, GA; *U.S. Public*, pg. 291
Williams, Brian, Pres.--Dauman Displays, Inc., New York, NY; *U.S. Private*, pg. 268
Williams, C. Michael, V.P.--EG & G Technical Services Group, Rockville, MD; *U.S. Public*, pg. 544
Williams, Carole, Publr.--Business First of Columbus, Inc., Columbus, OH; *U.S. Private*, pg. 19
Williams, Cathy, Chief Oper. Officer--Dallas Global Travel, Dallas, TX; *U.S. Public*, pg. 478
Williams, Cecil R., Partner--Folmar & Associates, Mobile, AL; *U.S. Private*, pg. 417
Williams, Charles, Pres.--Addwest Minerals, Inc., Arvada, CO; *U.S. Private*, pg. 17
Williams, Clint O., Pres. & Chief Exec. Officer--Union Planters Bank of West Tennessee, Humboldt, TN; *U.S. Public*, pg. 1669
Williams, Colin J., Pres.--SCA Packaging, Zaventem, Belgium; *Int'l*, pg. 1326
Williams, Colin V.K., Pres. & Chief Exec. Officer--MFS International, Inc., Vienna, VA; *U.S. Public*, pg. 1779
Williams, Darlene, Admin.--Hillhaven Rehabilitation & Convalescent Hospital, Stockton, CA; *U.S. Public*, pg. 1713
Williams, David, V.P. & Gen. Mgr.--Matl. Systems Div.--Technical Materials, Inc., Lincoln, RI; *U.S. Public*, pg. 266
Williams, David, Plant Mgr.--Engelhard Corp.-Quincy Operations, Quincy, FL; *U.S. Public*, pg. 582
Williams, David, V.P. & Gen. Mgr.--Montek Div., Salt Lake City, UT; *U.S. Public*, pg. 1366
Williams, David A., Pres.--Royale Paint & Body, Garland, TX; *U.S. Private*, pg. 918
Williams, David D., Pres. & Chief Exec. Officer--Tribune Media Services, Inc., Chicago, IL; *U.S. Public*, pg. 1636
Williams, David J., Pres. & Chief Oper. Officer--Connaught Laboratories, Inc., Swiftwater, PA; *Int'l*, pg. 1109
Williams, David L., Pres.--WFS Clearing Services, Richmond, VA; *U.S. Public*, pg. 640
Williams, David M., Pres.--National Grocers Co. Ltd., Weston, Canada; *Int'l*, pg. 1495
Williams, Dean, Plant Mgr.--MacLean Esna, Pocahontas, AR; *U.S. Private*, pg. 692
Williams, Deb, Editor--Winston Cup Scene, Charlotte, NC; *U.S. Private*, pg. 20
Williams, Dennis, Pres.--Marquette Bank Rochester, Rochester, MN; *U.S. Private*, pg. 706
Williams, Derek, Mng. Dir.--K-Tron Asia Pacific Pte, Singapore, Singapore; *U.S. Public*, pg. 938
Williams, Derek, Chief Oper. Officer & Exec. V.P.--Pall Europe Ltd., Portsmouth, United Kingdom; *U.S. Public*, pg. 1254
williams, Derek, Chief Oper. Officer & Exec. V.P.--Pall Ilfracombe Ltd., Ilfracombe, United Kingdom; *U.S. Public*, *pg. 1254*
Williams, Derek, Chief Oper. Officer & Exec. V.P.--Pall Process Filtration Ltd., Portsmouth, United Kingdom; *U.S. Public*, pg. 1254
Williams, Don, Mgr.--Dixon Wearever Inc., Orwigsburg, PA; *U.S. Public*, pg. 515
Williams, Don, Admin.--University Nursing Center, Greenville, NC; *U.S. Public*, pg. 1715
Williams, Donald, Chm. Bd. & Chief Exec. Officer--First Banks, Inc., Sacramento, CA; *U.S. Public*, pg. 626
Williams, Douglas N., Pres.--UMB Bank of the West, N.A., Colorado Springs, CO; *U.S. Public*, pg. 1654
Williams, E. Wendell, Pres. & Chief Exec. Officer--United Missouri Bank Northland, Kansas City, MO; *U.S. Public*, pg. 1654
Williams, Edward, Pres. & Chief Oper. Officer--Galaxy Carpet Mills, Inc., Chatsworth, GA; *U.S. Public*, pg. 1121
Williams, Edward D., Pres.--Strategic Outsourcing Services Inc., Parsippany, NJ; *U.S. Public*, pg. 421
Williams, Elmer, Pres.--WWF Paper Corporation - Mid Atlantic, Annapolis, MD; *U.S. Private*, pg. 1145
Williams, F., Mgr.-Works--Wrexham Plant, Wrexham, United Kingdom; *U.S. Public*, pg. 672
Williams, Frank E., III, Chief Oper. Officer--Williams Equipment Corporation, Manassas, VA; *U.S. Public*, pg. 1770
Williams, Fred, Pres.--JC Penney Financial Services, Inc., Plano, TX; *U.S. Public*, pg. 917
Williams, Fred A., Pres.--JC Penney Reinsurance Company, Plano, TX; *U.S. Public*, pg. 917
Williams, G., Mng. Dir.--Enraf-Nonius Company (Ltd Pts), Bohemia, NY; *Int'l*, pg. 389
Williams, G., Mng. Dir.--Coutts & Co (Cayman) Limited, Grand Cayman, Cayman Islands; *Int'l*, pg. 911
Williams, G., Mng. Dir.--Toshiba Consumer Products (U.K.) Limited, Plymouth, United Kingdom; *Int'l*, pg. 1406
Williams, Geoff, Country Mgr.--Standard Chartered Bank (Bangladesh), Dhaka, Bangladesh; *Int'l*, pg. 1295
Williams, George C., Chm. Bd.--Allied Investment Corp., Washington, DC; *U.S. Public*, pg. 48
Williams, H. Arthur, Chief Oper. Officer--Williams Steel Erection Co., Inc., Falls Church, VA; *U.S. Public*, pg. 1770
Williams, H. Edward, Pres. & Chief Exec. Officer--Security Bank & Trust Co., Vincennes, IN; *U.S. Public*, pg. 1217
Williams, Harry E., V.P.--First Amtenn Life Insurance Company, Nashville, TN; *U.S. Public*, pg. 624
Williams, Helena, Gen. Mgr.--Metropolitan Suburban Bus Authority, Garden City, NY; *U.S. Private*, pg. 739
Williams, Henry, Plant Mgr.--Arrow Thompson Metals, North Hollywood, CA; *U.S. Private*, pg. 1083
Williams, Irving, Chief Oper. Officer--DC Division, Hartwood, VA; *U.S. Public*, pg. 1161
Williams, J., Plant Mgr.--Aztec Manufacturing (Waskom), Waskom, TX; *U.S. Public*, pg. 159
Williams, J.B., Chief Oper. Officer--Kinney Shoes (Australia), Ltd., Brisbane, Australia; *U.S. Public*, pg. 1778
Williams, J.T., Jr., Chief Oper. Officer--Capital Paving Co., Inc., Tallahassee, FL; *U.S. Public*, pg. 956
Williams, J.T., Jr., Chief Oper. Officer--Central Insurance Corp. of Tallahassee, Tallahassee, FL; *U.S. Public*, pg. 956
Williams, J.T., Jr., Chief Oper. Officer--Killearn Advisers, Inc., Tallahassee, FL; *U.S. Public*, pg. 956
Williams, J.T., Jr., Chief Oper. Officer--Killearn Apartment Management, Inc., Tallahassee, FL; *U.S. Public*, pg. 956
Williams, J.T., Jr., Chief Oper. Officer--Killearn Construction, Inc., Tallahassee, FL; *U.S. Public*, pg. 956
Williams, J.T., Jr., Chief Oper. Officer--Killearn Realty, Inc., Tallahassee, FL; *U.S. Public*, pg. 956
Williams, Jack, Gen. Mgr.--Hoover Hanes Company, Tallapoosa, GA; *U.S. Private*, pg. 56
Williams, Jack S., V.P. & Gen. Mgr.--Nichols-Homeshield Casting, Davenport, IA; *U.S. Public*, pg. 1350
Williams, James, Pres.--Great American Knitting Mills, New York, NY; *Int'l*, pg. 194
Williams, James, Pres.--BC-USA, New Holland, PA; *Int'l*, pg. 201
Williams, James, Chief Oper. Officer--Gauss Div., Sun Valley, CA; *U.S. Private*, pg. 479
Williams, James A., Pres.--San Francisco Reinsurance Co., Novato, CA; *Int'l*, pg. 59
Williams, Jeffrey W., Pres. & Chief Exec. Officer--American Security Group, Atlanta, GA; *Int'l*, pg. 499
Williams, Jerry, V.P. & Gen. Mgr.--Judd & Detweiler, Inc., Washington, DC; *U.S. Private*, pg. 855
Williams, Jim, Pres.--ALLTEL Oklahoma, Inc., Burns Flat, OK; *U.S. Public*, pg. 56
Williams, Jimmie D., Pres.--ALLTEL Missouri, Inc., Dixon, MO; *U.S. Public*, pg. 56
Williams, Jimmie D., Pres.--ALLTEL Texas, Inc., Nocona, TX; *U.S. Public*, pg. 56
Williams, Jimmie D., Pres.--ALLTEL Oklahoma, Inc., Poteau, OK; *U.S. Public*, pg. 56
Williams, Jobe, Puvlisher--Cape Breton Post, Sydney, Canada; *Int'l*, pg. 631
Williams, Joe, Mgr.-Reg. Sls.--MedTrac, Inc., Atlanta, GA; *Int'l*, pg. 1504
Williams, John, Mng. Dir.--Luxfer, Nottingham, United Kingdom; *Int'l*, pg. 51
Williams, John, Chief Exec. Officer--Lambert Smith Hampton, Maidenhead, United Kingdom; *Int'l*, pg. 797
Williams, John A., Pres. & Dir.--LL&E Algeria, Ltd., Hamilton, Bermuda; *U.S. Public*, pg. 269
Williams, John D., Jr., Pres.--Williams Crane & Rigging, Inc., Richmond, VA; *U.S. Private*, pg. 1178
Williams, John L., Gen. Dir.--Packard Electric Division Mexican Operations, Mexico, Mexico; *U.S. Public*, pg. 723
Williams, K.E.J., Mng. Dir.--GKN Computer Services Ltd., Warley, United Kingdom; *Int'l*, pg. 534
Williams, Kent, Pres.--Walter Lorenz Surgical, Inc., Jacksonville, FL; *U.S. Public*, pg. 231
Williams, L. Andy, Pres.--Bowne of Dallas, Inc., Dallas, TX; *U.S. Public*, pg. 249
Williams, L.D., Pres.--Post Acute Division, Houston, TX; *U.S.* Public, pg. 1256
Williams, Larry, Gen. Mgr.-Components--Component Operations, Warren, MI; *U.S. Public*, pg. 353
Williams, Lewis T., M.D., Ph.D, Pres.--Chiron Technologies, Emeryville, CA; *U.S. Public*, pg. 350
Williams, Linda, Admin.--Hillhaven Omaha, Omaha, NE; *U.S.* Public, pg. 1713
Williams, Malcom, Gen. Mgr.--Williams Advanced Materials, Inc., Buffalo, NY; *U.S. Public*, pg. 266
Williams, McGhee, Sr. V.P. & Gen. Mgr.--Burrell Communications Group, Inc., Atlanta, GA; *U.S. Private*, pg. 188
Williams, Mel, Mng. Dir.--British Airways Cargo, London, United Kingdom; *Int'l*, pg. 219
Williams, Mel, Pres.--Danzer Industries Inc., Hagerstown, MD; *U.S. Public*, pg. 747
Williams, Melvin T., Pres.--RD Manufacturing Corporation, Pleasantville, NY; *U.S. Public*, pg. 1367
Williams, Melvin T., Pres.--SMDDMS, Inc., Pleasantville, NY; *U.S. Public*, pg. 1368
Williams, Neil, Publr.--The Coalinga Record, Coalinga, CA; *U.S. Public*, pg. 1343
Williams, Neil, Publr.--The Avenal Progress, Avenal, CA; *U.S. Public*, pg. 1343
Williams, Neil, Publr.--The Twin Cities Times/Riverdale Free Press, Fresno, CA; *U.S. Public*, pg. 1343
Williams, Neil, Publr.--The Lemoore Advance, Lemoore, CA; *U.S. Public*, pg. 1343
Williams, Neil D., Publr.--The Hanford Sentinel, Hanford, CA; *U.S. Public*, pg. 1343
Williams, P.J., Mgr.--Armstrong Fastenings Ltd., Kingston-upon-Hull, United Kingdom; *Int'l*, pg. 265
Williams, P.T., Mng. Dir.--Brambles (U.K.) Ltd., Dorking, United Kingdom; *Int'l*, pg. 212
Williams, Peggy M., Pres. & Chief Exec. Officer--First State Bank, Greenville, KY; *U.S. Public*, pg. 1217
Williams, Peter, Pres.--Anacomp Magnetics, Inc., Atlanta, GA; *U.S. Public*, pg. 107
Williams, Philip A., Pres., Trust Officer & Sec. of the Bd.--Farmers and Merchants Bank of Carlinville, Carlinville, IL; *U.S. Public*, pg. 644
Williams, R., Mng. Dir.--Gestetner SA, Caracas, Venezuela; *Int'l*, pg. 1115
Williams, R.H., Mng. Dir.--P&O Shopping Centres Ltd., Manchester, United Kingdom; *Int'l*, pg. 1034
Williams, Rex, Gen. Mgr.--Sun Microsystems Australia Pty. Ltd.-Canberra, Turner, Australia; *U.S. Public*, pg. 1532
Williams, Richard, V.P.-Sls.--Fairfield Mountains, Lake Lure, NC; *U.S. Public*, pg. 610
Williams, Richard B., Pres.--TDW Trading, Inc., Tulsa, OK; *U.S. Private*, pg. 1180
Williams, Richard B., Pres. & Chief Oper. Officer--Lone Star Gas Co., Dallas, TX; *U.S. Public*, pg. 1587
Williams, Richard F., Pres. & Chief Exec. Officer--Fidelity & Deposit Company of Maryland, Baltimore, MD; *Int'l*, pg. 1530
Williams, Robert, Chief Fin. Officer--EDO Acoustic Products, Salt Lake City, UT; *U.S. Public*, pg. 542
Williams, Robert, Pres.--ITW Switches, Chicago, IL; *U.S. Public*, pg. 867
Williams, Robert, Mng. Dir.--Mills & Boon Ltd., Richmond, United Kingdom; *Int'l*, pg. 1402
Williams, Robert, Dir.-Data Div.--KNOGO Regional Office-Chicago, Villa Park, IL; *U.S. Public*, pg. 1458
Williams, Robert E., V.P. & Gen. Mgr.--Vacudyne Inc., Chicago Heights, IL; *U.S. Private*, pg. 46
Williams, Robert E., Pres.--Hunt-Wesson Grocery Sales Division, Fullerton, CA; *U.S. Public*, pg. 428
Williams, Robert S., V.P. & G.M.--ITW Fastex, Des Plaines, IL; *U.S. Public*, pg. 866
Williams, Roger, Mng. Dir.--TMC, Reading, United Kingdom; *Int'l*, pg. 1482
Williams, Roger P., Chief Oper. Officer--Nova Electric Mfg. Co., Bergenfield, NJ; *U.S. Public*, pg. 866
Williams, Ron, V.P. & Gen. Mgr.--Johnson Controls International, Inc., Milwaukee, WI; *U.S. Public*, pg. 932
Williams, Roy, Pres.--Keystone (Canada) Ltd., Burlington, Canada; *U.S. Public*, pg. 1650
Williams, S.B., Chm. Bd.--Williams-Rolls, Inc., Walled Lake, MI; *U.S. Private*, pg. 1178
Williams, S.F., Chief Oper. Officer--Algemene Bank Nederland, Birmingham, United Kingdom; *Int'l*, pg. 11
Williams, Serena, Sr. V.P. & Client Service Dir.--Fahlgren, Toledo, OH; *U.S. Private*, pg. 391
Williams, Sonny, Pres.--Fasco Industries, Inc., Southfield, MI; *Int'l*, pg. 125
Williams, Stan, Mgr.--Conway Import Co. Inc., San Jose, CA; *U.S. Private*, pg. 272
Williams, Stan, Pres.--Bach-Simpson Ltd., London, Canada; *U.S. Public*, pg. 944
Williams, Stephen J., Mgr.--Scott & Stringfellow, Inc., Richmond, VA; *U.S. Public*, pg. 1446
Williams, Stephen T., Gen. Mgr.--Hanover Lloyd's Insurance Company, Richardson, TX; *U.S. Public*, pg. 54
Williams, Steve, Gen. Mgr.--BNP Securities (Japan) Limited, Tokyo, Japan; *Int'l*, pg. 164
Williams, Steve, V.P.--Paramount Transmission Corp., Logan, OH; *U.S. Public*, pg. 1281
Williams, Terri, Dir.--Academic Year In America, Greenwich, CT; *U.S. Private*, pg. 56
Williams, Terry, Chief Oper. Officer--Ahlstrom Process Equipment Inc., Birmingham, AL; *Int'l*, pg. 34
Williams, Thomas, Pres.--Sidney Rich & Associates, Saint Louis, MO; *U.S. Public*, pg. 262
Williams, Thomas, Pres.--Horizon Initiatives, Wilmington, DE; *U.S. Public*, pg. 423
Williams, Thomas C., Chm. Bd. & Chief Exec. Officer--The Peoples Banking Company, Findlay, OH; *U.S. Public*, pg. 1413
Williams, Tim S., Pres. & Chief Exec. Officer--Regions Bank/Cherokee County, Centre, AL; *U.S. Public*, pg. 1372
Williams, Tom, Pres.--Universal Studios Florida, Orlando, FL; *Int'l*, pg. 1087
Williams, Tommy, Gen. Mgr.--Allison Corporation, Livingston, NJ; *U.S. Private*, pg. 41
Williams, Vance O., Pres.--Norwest Bank Wyoming, N.A., Casper, WY; *U.S. Public*, pg. 1202
Williams, Virginia, Admin.--Heritage Manor Canton, Canton, TX; *U.S. Public*, pg. 839
Williams, W. Earl, Reg. Mgr.--Green Tree Acceptance of Texas, Inc., San Antonio, TX; *U.S. Public*, pg. 762
Williams, W. H., Gen. Mgr.--A.C. Hatrick (N.Z.) Ltd., Parnell, New Zealand; *U.S. Public*, pg. 811
Williams, Warren L., Pres.--First American Bank, Brainerd, MN; *U.S. Private*, pg. 167
Williams, William D., Pres.--Phyxis Corporation, San Diego, CA; *U.S. Public*, pg. 305
Williams, William H., Pres.--Bear Creek Corporation, Medford, OR; *Int'l*, pg. 1518
Williams, Woody, V.P.-Sls.--Clayton-Marcus Company, Inc., Hickory, NC; *U.S. Public*, pg. 975
Williamson, Brad, Chief Oper. Officer--Cascadia Transport, Vancouver, WA; *U.S. Private*, pg. 683

Williamson, Dave, Mng. Dir.--NVR Building Products, Gaithersburg, MD; *U.S. Public*, pg. 1148
Williamson, Delbert L., V.P. & Gen. Mgr.--G.E. Industrial & Power Systems Sales, Fairfield, CT; *U.S. Public*, pg. 711
Williamson, Guy, Gen. Mgr.--Bristol-Myers Equible Canada Inc., Mississauga, Canada; *U.S. Public*, pg. 255
Williamson, I., Mgng. Dir.--Newage International Ltd., Stamford, United Kingdom; *U.S. Public*, pg. 469
Williamson, Max, Pres.--Scottsdale Insurance Company, Scottsdale, AZ; *U.S. Private*, pg. 789
Williamson, Peter H., Chief Exec. Officer--Foster's Brewing Group, Southbank, Australia; *Int'l*, pg. 501
Williamson, Richard B., Pres.--Williamson International Corp., Tulsa, OK; *U.S. Private*, pg. 1180
Williamson, Richard B., Pres.--TDW Building Corporation, Tulsa, OK; *U.S. Private*, pg. 1180
Williamson, Richard B., Pres.--TDW Foreign Sales Corp., Christiansted, VI; *U.S. Private*, pg. 1180
Williamson, Richard B., Pres.--TDW Delaware, Inc., Wilmington, DE; *U.S. Private*, pg. 1180
Williamson, T.G., Pres.--Autolatina Argentina S.A., Buenos Aires, Argentina; *U.S. Public*, pg. 667
Williamson, T.G., Pres.--Autolatina Argentina S.A., Buenos Aires, Argentina; *Int'l*, pg. 1475
Williamson, W.A., III, Branch Mgr.--Bergen Brunswig Medical Corporation, La Vergne, TN; *U.S. Public*, pg. 214
Williamsson, Anders, Chief Oper. Officer--Atos Medical AB, Horby, Sweden; *Int'l*, pg. 1036
Williford, John H., Pres. & Chief Exec. Officer--Menlo Logistics, Menlo Park, CA; *U.S. Public*, pg. 281
Williford, Robert, Pres.--American Health Consultants, Atlanta, GA; *U.S. Public*, pg. 1601
Williman, Hans, Gen. Mgr.--Four Seasons Hotels & Resorts, Don Mills, Canada; *Int'l*, pg. 502
Willingham, T.K., Pres.--Perfect Equipment Corp., La Vergne, TN; *U.S. Private*, pg. 138
Willis, Ian, Chm. Bd.--K.C.S.A. Holdings (Pty.) Ltd., Johannesburg, South Africa; *U.S. Public*, pg. 959
Willis, James S., Gen. Mgr.--Corrugated Container Div.-North Chicago Plant, North Chicago, IL; *U.S. Public*, pg. 1520
Willis, John, Pres.--Curlee Manufacturing Div., Houston, TX; *U.S. Public*, pg. 572
Willis, John, Gen. Mgr.--Domino Sugar Corporation-Chalmette, Chalmette, LA; *Int'l*, pg. 1356
Willis, John, Mgr.-Office--Woodward-Clyde, Tallahassee, FL; *U.S. Public*, pg. 1657
Willis, Larry H., Div. Pres.--Malone & Hyde, Inc.-Miami, Miami, FL; *U.S. Public*, pg. 653
Willis, Peter, Gen. Mgr.-Opers.--ITW Screen Process Specialist, Ltd., Plymouth, WI; *U.S. Public*, pg. 867
Willis, Ross W., Pres.--Rheem Air Conditioning Div., Fort Smith, AR; *Int'l*, pg. 1022
Willis, Thomas N., Pres.--Matco Tools, Stow, OH; *U.S. Public*, pg. 482
Willmann, James B., Exec. V.P.--XL Vision Inc., Sebastian, FL; *U.S. Public*, pg. 1424
Willott, Michael, Pres.--Adhesive Films, Santa Ana, CA; *U.S. Public*, pg. 165
Willoughby, Jed L., Mgr.-Branch--Piper Jaffray Inc., Waterloo, IA; *U.S. Public*, pg. 1302
Wills, D., Chief Oper. Officer--Babcock Metstep Div., Johannesburg, South Africa; *Int'l*, pg. 474
Wills, D., Gen. Mgr.--Baring Asset Management Inc., San Francisco, CA; *Int'l*, pg. 647
Wills, D.R., Mng. Dir.--W.D. & H.O. Wills (Australia) Ltd., Sydney, Australia; *Int'l*, pg. 112
Wills, John, V.P.--John Hancock Advisers International, Ltd., London, United Kingdom; *U.S. Private*, pg. 590
Wills, Joseph, Pres.--CIBA-GEIGY Canada Ltd., Mississauga, Canada; *Int'l*, pg. 976
Wills, Michael KR, Office Mgr.--Korn/Ferry International, Melbourne, Australia; *U.S. Private*, pg. 633
Wills, Travers H., Pres.--MCC Behavioral Care, Inc., Eden Prairie, MN; *U.S. Public*, pg. 362
Wills, Travers H., Pres. & Chief Exec. Officer--HealthWise of America, Nashville, TN; *U.S. Public*, pg. 1678
Wills, Travers H., Pres.--United HealthCare of Nevada, Inc., Las Vegas, NV; *U.S. Public*, pg. 1678
Willsie, Kevin, Plant Mgr/Plant II--Tread Rubber Plant, Muscatine, IA; *U.S. Public*, pg. 177
Willson, Dennis F., Mng. Dir.--Rorer, S.A., Madrid, Spain; *Int'l*, pg. 1112
Willson, Ricardo, Chief Exec. Officer--EURO RSCG Graffiti, Santiago, Chile; *Int'l*, pg. 603
Willson, Sam F., Pres.--Coscol Petroleum Corp., Houston, TX; *U.S. Public*, pg. 390
Wilmanski, Jose Luis, Chief Oper. Officer--Dresdner Bank AG, Barcelona, Spain; *Int'l*, pg. 419
Wilmarth, Carol, Mgr.--Frontier InfoServices, Rochester, NY; *U.S. Public*, pg. 684
Wilmers, John P., Pres. & Chief Exec. Officer--Ballantyne of Omaha, Inc., Omaha, NE; *Int'l*, pg. 17
Wilmes, J.P., Pres.--Charmilles Technologies (France) S.A., Palaiseau, France; *Int'l*, pg. 489
Wilmes, Jim, Plant Mgr.--Hydro Conduit Corp., Omaha, NE; *Int'l*, pg. 245
Wilms, Alfred, Chief Oper. Officer--Digital, Howald, Luxembourg; *U.S. Public*, pg. 507
Wilsenius, Bjorn-Ake, Mng. Dir.--Handelsbanken Oslo, Oslo, Norway; *Int'l*, pg. 1327
Wilsey, Alfred S., Jr., Pres.--Wilsey Bennett Real Estate Division, San Francisco, CA; *U.S. Private*, pg. 1180
Wilsey, Michael W., Pres.--Air Fresh Trucking, San Francisco, CA; *U.S. Private*, pg. 1180
Wilsford, Nancy, Administrator--Harbor View Care Center, Corpus Christi, TX; *U.S. Public*, pg. 839
Wilshire, Carol, Gen. Mgr.--Dentsu Burson Marsteller, Inc. Los Angeles Office, Los Angeles, CA; *Int'l*, pg. 393
Wilska, Kari-Pekka, Pres.--Nokia Inc., Irving, TX; *Int'l*, pg. 952
Wilska, Kimmo, Resident Mgr.--Kuopio Mill, Kuopio, Finland; *Int'l*, pg. 1429
Wilskey, Richard, Pres.--D.W. Close Company, Seattle, WA; *U.S. Public*, pg. 1029
Wilson, Alan, Pres.--Angelica Textile Services, Inc., Durham, NC; *U.S. Public*, pg. 113
Wilson, Alan A., Mng. Dir.--Royal Skandia Life Assurance Ltd., Douglas, United Kingdom; *Int'l*, pg. 1257
Wilson, Alan A., Mng. Dir.--Professional Life Assurance Co. Ltd., Southampton, United Kingdom; *Int'l*, pg. 1257
Wilson, Alan A., Gen. Mgr.--Skandia Life PEP Managers Ltd., Southampton, United Kingdom; *Int'l*, pg. 1258
Wilson, Anthony J., Chief Exec. Officer & Mng. Dir.--Guilford Europe, Ltd., Derby, United Kingdom; *U.S. Public*, pg. 769
Wilson, B., Pres.--Albany Port Railroad Co., Albany, NY; *U.S. Public*, pg. 432
Wilson, Barry, Pres.-Medtronic Europe, Middle East & Africa--Medtronic Europe S.A./N.V., Lausanne, Switzerland; *U.S. Public*, pg. 1083
Wilson, Bill, Warden--Bent Co. Colorado Correctional Facility, Las Animas, CO; *U.S. Public*, pg. 450
Wilson, C., District Mgr.--A.M. Castle & Co., Houston, TX; *U.S. Public*, pg. 313
Wilson, C. M., Mng. Dir.--Smiths Flour Mills Ltd., Nottingham, United Kingdom; *Int'l*, pg. 968
Wilson, C. Richard, Chm. Bd., Pres. & Chief Oper. Officer--Buckeye Pipe Line Company, L.P., Allentown, PA; *U.S. Public*, pg. 266
Wilson, C.J., Mng. Dir.--Vickers Precision Components, Crewe, United Kingdom; *Int'l*, pg. 1467
Wilson, Charles W., Pres. & Chief Exec. Officer--Shell Canada Ltd., Calgary, Canada; *Int'l*, pg. 1138
Wilson, Cheryl, Branch Mgr.--Downey Savings & Loan Association, F.A., Lake Forest, CA; *U.S. Public*, pg. 526
Wilson, D. Michael, V.P. & Gen. Mgr.--Wausau-Mosinee Papers Specialty Papers Group, Rhinelander, WI; *U.S. Public*, pg. 1747
Wilson, Dan, Gen. Mgr.--Velcro Laminates Inc., Manchester, NH; *Int'l*, pg. 1462
Wilson, David, Mgr.--Champion Spark Plug Co. (Aust.) Pty. Limited, Alexandria, Australia; *U.S. Public*, pg. 445
Wilson, David, Pres.--Ethyl Canada, Inc., Mississauga, Canada; *U.S. Public*, pg. 595
Wilson, David, Pres.--Milton Bradley Company, East Longmeadow, MA; *U.S. Public*, pg. 797
Wilson, David, Pres.--Rapid Mounting & Finishing, Union City, CA; *U.S. Private*, pg. 910
Wilson, David, Mng. Dir.--K-Tron Institute, Pitman, NJ; *U.S. Public*, pg. 938
Wilson, David W., Gen. Mgr.--Hurletron Inc., Danville, IL; *U.S. Private*, pg. 46
Wilson, Debbie, Mgr.--Fireman's Fund Insurance Co. of Ohio, Cincinnati, OH; *Int'l*, pg. 59
Wilson, Diane M., Chm. Bd. & Chief Exec. Officer--Trend Media, Atlanta, GA; *U.S. Public*, pg. 1634
Wilson, Don, Mng. Dir.--Totes Canada Ltd., Etobicoke, Canada; *U.S. Private*, pg. 111
Wilson, Don, Mng. Dir.-UK--Chase Netting (U.K.) Ltd., London, United Kingdom; *U.S. Public*, pg. 341
Wilson, Don, Chief Oper. Officer--Mid-South Manufacturing Co., Marked Tree, AR; *U.S. Private*, pg. 1113
Wilson, Dr. Iva M., Pres.--Philips Display Components, Ann Arbor, MI; *Int'l*, pg. 1055
Wilson, Ed, Pres.-CBS Enterprises & Eyemark Entertainment--CBS Enterprises Division, New York, NY; *U.S. Public*, pg. 274
Wilson, Ed, Plant Mgr.--Architectural Stone Quarry, Cedar Park, TX; *U.S. Public*, pg. 936
Wilson, Ed, Plant Mgr.--Precast Plant, Austin, TX; *U.S. Public*, pg. 937
Wilson, Faye, Chief Exec. Officer--Security Pacific Financial Services Inc., San Diego, CA; *U.S. Public*, pg. 181
Wilson, Fred, Pres.--Mercantile Bank of Onawa, Onawa, IA; *U.S. Public*, pg. 1088
Wilson, Frederick, Publisher--Pendulum, East Greenwich, RI; *U.S. Public*, pg. 935
Wilson, G., Pres.--Rantec Microwave and Electronics, Inc., Calabasas, CA; *U.S. Public*, pg. 546
Wilson, G. Larry, Pres.--Policy Management Systems International, Ltd., Columbia, SC; *U.S. Public*, pg. 1314
Wilson, Gary E., Pres.--Springs Canada, Ltd., Mississauga, Canada; *U.S. Public*, pg. 1500
Wilson, Glen W., Pres. & Chief Exec. Officer--AMCORE Trust Company, Rockford, IL; *U.S. Public*, pg. 65
Wilson, Gordon L., Gen. Mgr.--Chapleau Forest Products, Chapleau, Canada; *Int'l*, pg. 828
Wilson, H.G., Plant Mgr.--Quaker Chemical Corp., Detroit, MI; *U.S. Public*, pg. 1346
Wilson, Helen, Mgr.--General Employment Enterprises, Inc., San Diego, CA; *U.S. Public*, pg. 715
Wilson, Hosea E., Jr., Mgr.--Scott & Stringfellow, Inc., Danville, VA; *U.S. Public*, pg. 1446
Wilson, J.W., Pres. & Chief Exec. Officer--PCL Courier Holdings Inc., Mississauga, Canada; *Int'l*, pg. 36
Wilson, Jack, Pres.--SFA Datacomm Inc., Frederick, MD; *U.S. Private*, pg. 956
Wilson, Jack S., Mng. Dir.--The Hobart Manufacturing Co., Limited, London, United Kingdom; *U.S. Public*, pg. 1322
Wilson, James, Mng. Dir.--Callaway Golf (U.K.) Limited, Chessington, United Kingdom; *U.S. Public*, pg. 295
Wilson, James, Pres.--Kao Infosystems Canada Inc., Arnprior, Canada; *Int'l*, pg. 718
Wilson, James W., III, Pres.--Mason & Hanger Engineering Inc., Lexington, KY; *U.S. Private*, pg. 711
Wilson, Jay, Pres.e Mgr.--Cavalier Acceptance Corporation, Hamilton, AL; *U.S. Public*, pg. 318
Wilson, Jay, Pres.--Cavalier Insurance Agency, Inc., Hamilton, AL; *U.S. Public*, pg. 318
Wilson, Jeffrey R., Gen. Mgr.--Martin Marietta Regional Manufacturing Operation, Valley Forge, PA; *U.S. Public*, pg. 1007
Wilson, Jim, Mgr.-Plant--Duro Paper Bag Mfg. Co., Walton, KY; *U.S. Private*, pg. 349
Wilson, John, Pres.--Amtech Systems Corporation, Dallas, TX; *U.S. Public*, pg. 105
Wilson, John, Gen. Mgr.--Arrow/Schweber Electronics, Pine Brook, NJ; *U.S. Public*, pg. 134
Wilson, John, Mgr.--General Employment Enterprises, Dallas, TX; *U.S. Public*, pg. 714
Wilson, John, Gen. Mgr.--Nordson Canada Ltd., Markham, Canada; *U.S. Public*, pg. 1189
Wilson, John, Chm. Bd., Pres. & Chief Exec. Officer--SouthTrust Bank of Auburn, Auburn, AL; *U.S. Public*, pg. 1492
Wilson, John H., Pres. & Chief Exec. Officer--Hilb, Rogal and Hamilton Company of the District of Columbia, Rockville, MD; *U.S. Public*, pg. 827
Wilson, John J., Mgr.-Area Sls.--Gensym Corporation, Southeast Area Office, Tucker, GA; *U.S. Public*, pg. 731
Wilson, Jonathon D., Exec. V.P. & Gen. Mgr.-Convenience Foods Div.--Kellogg USA Convenience Foods Division, Battle Creek, MI; *U.S. Public*, pg. 947
Wilson, Jorge, Gen. Mgr.--Duro-Test de Mexico, S.A., Mexico, Mexico; *U.S. Private*, pg. 349
Wilson, Joseph E., Pres.--Old Republic Dealer Service Corporation, Chicago, IL; *U.S. Public*, pg. 1218
Wilson, K., Mng. Dir.--Eurodis Bytech OnBoard Limited, Basingstoke, United Kingdom; *Int'l*, pg. 1247
Wilson, Kate, Exec. Dir.--Macmillan Children's Books Limited, London, United Kingdom; *Int'l*, pg. 1479
Wilson, Keith, Gen. Mgr.--Spicer Trailer Products Div., Fort Wayne, IN; *U.S. Public*, pg. 479
Wilson, Keith H., Chief Oper. Officer--Alfa-Laval Ltd., Scarborough, Canada; *Int'l*, pg. 1379
Wilson, L., Mng. Dir.--The Caxton Group of Companies, Auckland, New Zealand; *U.S. Public*, pg. 905
Wilson, Lawrence, Chief Exec. Officer--Citadel Broadcasting Company, Greenbank, WA; *U.S. Private*, pg. 241
Wilson, Linda, Controller--Legacy Audio Inc., Springfield, IL; *U.S. Public*, pg. 45
Wilson, Linda, V.P.--Mid-America Credit Life Assurance Co., Oklahoma City, OK; *U.S. Public*, pg. 175
Wilson, Linda, V.P.--Mid-America Insurance Agency, Inc., Oklahoma City, OK; *U.S. Public*, pg. 175
Wilson, Linda, V.P.--Mid-America Leasing Corp., Oklahoma City, OK; *U.S. Public*, pg. 175
Wilson, M. Arthur, Pres.--Monarch Crown Corporation, New York, NY; *U.S. Public*, pg. 254
Wilson, M. Hamish, Chief Oper. Officer--Rhone-Poulenc Kenya Ltd., Nairobi, Kenya; *Int'l*, pg. 1113
Wilson, Marc, Pres. & Chief Exec. Officer--Safway Steel Products Inc., Waukesha, WI; *Int'l*, pg. 1389
Wilson, Mark, Sr. V.P. & Gen. Mgr.--Multimedia Security Service, Wichita, KS; *U.S. Public*, pg. 699
Wilson, Mark, Pres.--Ace Fastener, Rolling Meadows, IL; *U.S. Private*, pg. 845
Wilson, Max, Regional Mgr.--Westpac Banking Corp. - Fiji, Suva, Fiji; *Int'l*, pg. 1497
Wilson, Michael, Chief Oper. Officer--Hospal Ltd., Rugby, United Kingdom; *Int'l*, pg. 668
Wilson, Michael, Mgr.-Distr.--Weatherford US Inc., Evanston, WY; *U.S. Public*, pg. 1750
Wilson, Michael J., Mng. Dir.--Cyanamid of Great Britain Ltd., Gosport, United Kingdom; *U.S. Public*, pg. 81
Wilson, Peter, Gen. Mgr.--BHP Steel Building Products (Malaysia) Sdn Bhd, Shah Alam, Malaysia; *Int'l*, pg. 226
Wilson, Peter, Gen. Mgr.--Watlow Limited, Nottingham, United Kingdom; *U.S. Private*, pg. 1154
Wilson, R., Gen. Mgr.--ING Farm Finance, Byfleet, United Kingdom; *Int'l*, pg. 650
Wilson, R.B., Mng. Dir.--Jardine Matheson (Malaysia) Sdn Bhd, Kuala Lumpur, Malaysia; *Int'l*, pg. 705
Wilson, R.L., Mgr.--Morton Salt Division, New Iberia, LA; *U.S. Public*, pg. 1135
Wilson, R.M., Pres.--Simon United States Holdings Inc., Cincinnati, OH; *Int'l*, pg. 1252
Wilson, Richard, Div. Mgr.--Elkon Gas Service, Elkton, MD; *U.S. Public*, pg. 1148
Wilson, Richard, V.P. & Chief Exec. Officer--TNTI, Toronto, Canada; *U.S. Public*, pg. 1642
Wilson, Richard D., Plant Mgr.--Weber's Bread Bakeries, Kansas City, MO; *U.S. Public*, pg. 909
Wilson, Robert, Pres.--CSI Services, Knoxville, TN; *U.S. Public*, pg. 573
Wilson, Robert, Pres. & Chief Exec. Officer--Curtin & Pease/Peneco, Inc, Dunedin, FL; *U.S. Public*, pg. 1306
Wilson, Robert, Pres.--Feather Fine Services, Tampa, FL; *U.S. Public*, pg. 1306
Wilson, Ronald H., Sr. V.P.--U.S. Specialty Insurance Co., Saint Peters, MO; *U.S. Public*, pg. 152
Wilson, Ronald H., Pres.--Specialty Insurance Underwriters, Inc., Saint Peters, MO; *U.S. Public*, pg. 152
Wilson, Scott B., Pres.--Venture Resources, Inc., Houston, TX; *U.S. Public*, pg. 1519
Wilson, Stan, V.P.--APV Vent-Axia Inc., Wilmington, MA; *Int'l*, pg. 1241
Wilson, Steve, Gen. Mgr.--Hussey Plastics Co., Tyngsboro, MA; *U.S. Private*, pg. 550
Wilson, Steven A., Pres.--BASES Worldwide, Covington, KY; *U.S. Private*, pg. 120
Wilson, Terry, Plant Mgr.--The Coleman Company, Cedar City, UT; *U.S. Private*, pg. 691
Wilson, Thomas D., Chm. Bd., Pres. & Chief Exec. Officer--Helian Health Group, Inc., Monterey, CA; *U.S. Public*, pg. 1715
Wilson, Thomas D., Pres. & Chief Exec. Officer--Helian Health Group of Fresno, Inc., Monterey, CA; *U.S. Public*, pg. 1715
Wilson, Thomas D., Pres. & Chief Exec. Officer--Rehabilitative Back Center of Atlanta, Inc., Monterey, CA; *U.S. Public*, pg. 1715
Wilson, Thomas D., Pres. & Chief Exec. Officer--Helian Recovery Corp., Monterey, CA; *U.S. Public*, pg. 1715
Wilson, Thomas D., Pres. & Chief Exec. Officer--Helian ASC of Northridge, Inc., Monterey, CA; *U.S. Public*, pg. 1715
Wilson, Thomas E., Pres. & Chief Exec. Officer--NationsBank/Tri-Cities, Johnson City, TN; *U.S. Public*, pg. 1163

Wilson, Timothy L. Boyd, Pres.--J.P. Morgan Canada, Toronto, Canada; *U.S. Public*, pg. 1130
Wilson, Trudy, Branch Mgr.--Circle International, Lexington, KY; *U.S. Public*, pg. 371
Wilson, William, Pres.--Recognition Systems Inc., Campbell, CA; *U.S. Private*, pg. 507
Wilson, William H., Gen. Mgr.--Plastics Research & Development Co., Fort Smith, AR; *U.S. Private*, pg. 359
Wilson, William J., Pres.--Hawaiian Bitumuls & Paving Company, Honolulu, HI; *U.S. Private*, pg. 333
Wilson, William J., Chief Exec. Officer--Roper Starch Worldwide, Mamaroneck, NY; *U.S. Private*, pg. 944
Wilson, William M., Chm.--Alexander & Alexander Services (UK) Plc, London, United Kingdom; *U.S. Public*, pg. 118
Wilson, Wink, Gen. Mgr.--Rexam Flexible Packaging, Greensboro, NC; *Int'l*, pg. 1106
Wilt, Bill, Mgr.--J&L Tank, Rhome, TX; *U.S. Public*, pg. 521
Wilterink, Tom, Gen. Mgr.--Sackner-West Div., City of Commerce, CA; *U.S. Public*, pg. 924
Wilton, D., Gen. Mgr.--Southern Diesel Systems, Inc., Miami, FL; *U.S. Public*, pg. 1646
Wilton, Robert, Chm. Bd.--Bach-Simpson (UK) Ltd., Wadebridge, United Kingdom; *U.S. Public*, pg. 944
Wiltse, Jon, Gen. Mgr.--Northland Div., Watertown, NY; *U.S.* Public, pg. 218
Wiltshire, H.P., Pres.--J.H. Rayner (Mincing Lane) Limited, London, United Kingdom; *Int'l*, pg. 188
Wiltz, James W., Pres.--Patterson Dental Supply, Inc., Saint Paul, MN; *U.S. Public*, pg. 1265
Wilzig, Sherry, Chief Oper. Officer--Oil & Gas Operations, Oklahoma City, OK; *U.S. Public*, pg. 1770
Wimberly, Brooks, Mgr.--NationsBank of Texas National Bank Properties Inc., Dallas, TX; *U.S. Public*, pg. 1163
Wimberly, William, Branch Mgr.--CAP Gemini America (Dallas Branch), Dallas, TX; *Int'l*, pg. 263
Wimbish, Charles, Mgr.-Natl. Sls.--Weiman, Bassett, VA; *U.S. Public*, pg. 193
Wimer, Charles, Exec. V.P.--Fidelity National Title Insurance Company of New York, New York, NY; *U.S. Public*, pg. 620
Wims, Larry, Chief Oper. Officer--Regency Thermographers of Calif., Inc., Van Nuys, CA; *U.S. Public*, pg. 89
Win, Paul, Pres.--Enterprise Service Solutions, Carrollton, TX; *U.S. Public*, pg. 729
Winans, Leonard N., Pres.--LNW Networks, New Providence, NJ; *U.S. Public*, pg. 276
Winberg, Carl J., Mng. Dir.--Coastal States Petroleum (U.K.) Limited, London, United Kingdom; *U.S. Public*, pg. 391
Winblad, Mads, Mng. Dir.--Nokia Mobile Phones AB, Kista, Sweden; *Int'l*, pg. 952
Winblad, Mats, Mng. Dir.--Nokia Mobile Phones, Copenhagen, Denmark; *Int'l*, pg. 952
Winchester, George, Mgr.-Prod.--Dallas Plant, Irving, TX; *U.S. Public*, pg. 1066
Winchester, George, Mgr.-Opers.--Simpson Mfg. Div., Litchfield, MI; *U.S. Public*, pg. 1475
Winder, Nigel, Gen. Mgr.--Det Norske Veritas, London, United Kingdom; *Int'l*, pg. 397
Windfeldt, Gene, Pres. & Chief Exec. Officer--Kirby Company, Cleveland, OH; *U.S. Public*, pg. 217
Windham, Tim, Plant Mgr.--Household Products, Forest Park, GA; *U.S. Public*, pg. 387
Windhorst, C., Mgr.--Ballast Nedam Aruba N.V., Oranjestad, Aruba; *Int'l*, pg. 134
Windmill, D., Chief Oper. Officer--Marine Harvest McConnell, Edinburgh, United Kingdom; *Int'l*, pg. 202
Windmuller, David T., Pres.--Fluid Management, Inc., Wheeling, IL; *U.S. Public*, pg. 862
Windsor, James B., V.P. & Mgr.--Midwest National Bank of Midwest City, Midwest City, OK; *U.S. Public*, pg. 174
Windus, J. Preston, Pres. & Chief Fin. Officer--Comtech PST Corp., Melville, NY; *U.S. Public*, pg. 425
Winegar, Frank, Plant Mgr.--Square D Company, Lexington, KY; *Int'l*, pg. 1208
Winer, Jonathan H., Pres.--Mountain Energy, Inc., South Burlington, VT; *U.S. Public*, pg. 761
Winer, Jonathan H., Chief Oper. Officer & V.P.--Mountain Energy, Inc., South Burlington, VT; *U.S. Public*, pg. 761
Winfrey, A., District Mgr.--A.M. Castle & Co., Kansas City, MO; *U.S. Public*, pg. 313
Winfrey, A., Mgr.--A.M. Castle & Co., Wichita, KS; *U.S. Public*, pg. 313
Wing, Robert C., Pres.--NBD Bank FSB, Venice, FL; *U.S. Public*, pg. 628
Wing, Rodney, Mng. Dir.--Cirrus Logic International Ltd., Bridgetown, Barbados; *U.S. Public*, pg. 375
Wing, Sonnie, Mng. Dir.--SKF Plain Bearings, Winsted, CT; *Int'l*, pg. 1157
Wing, Sonnie, Pres.--SKF Mfg. Singapore (Pte.) Ltd., Singapore, Singapore; *Int'l*, pg. 1159
Wingar, Clive, Gen. Mgr.--Gelman Sciences, Ltd., Northampton, United Kingdom; *U.S. Public*, pg. 1253
Wingate, D.C.M., Dir. & Gen. Mgr.--Robert Hutchison Limited, Kirkcaldy, United Kingdom; *Int'l*, pg. 598
Winger, William, Chief Oper. Officer--Canada Alloy Castings, Ltd., Kitchener, Canada; *U.S. Public*, pg. 142
Wingett, Robert, V.P. & Publr.--Ohio Valley Publishing Co., Gallipolis, OH; *U.S. Public*, pg. 701
Wingett, Robert, V.P. & Publr.--Point Pleasant Register Co., Point Pleasant, WV; *U.S. Public*, pg. 701
Wingrove, Dennis, Pres.--Taisil Electronic Materials Corporation, Hsin-chu, Taiwan; *Int'l*, pg. 286
Winham, B.A., Deputy Chm.--P&O Property Developments Ltd., London, United Kingdom; *Int'l*, pg. 1034
Winiger, Rolf, Chm. Bd.--Balair/CTA Ltd., Geneva, Switzerland; *Int'l*, pg. 1333
Wink, Frank R., V.P. & Gen. Mgr.--Cox Communications-Lubbock, Lubbock, TX; *U.S. Public*, pg. 455
Winkel, T.L., Mng. Dir.--Marvelo B.V., Zaandam, Netherlands; *Int'l*, pg. 749
Winkel, Thomas R., V.P. & Pres.-Stryker Americas/Middle East--Stryker Corporation, Kalamazoo, MI; *U.S. Public*, pg. 1525
Winkleplech, Jake, Mgr.--Young Electric Signs Phoenix Div., Phoenix, AZ; *U.S. Private*, pg. 1201
Winkler, Paul, Pres.--Winkler Forming, Santa Fe Springs, CA; *U.S. Private*, pg. 827
Winkofske, Thomas, Pres.--LiphaTech, Inc., Milwaukee, WI; *Int'l*, pg. 812
Winland, Virgil, Grp. V.P.--Worthington Cylinder Corporation, Columbus, OH; *U.S. Public*, pg. 1780
Winlow, J.A., Mng. Dir.--Yorkshire Brick Company, Barnsley, United Kingdom; *Int'l*, pg. 591
Winnacott, Ronald, Fin.. Controller--AEP Canada, Inc., West Hill, Canada; *U.S. Public*, pg. 5
Winnemuller, Wim, Gen. Mgr.--Nordson Nederland B.V., Houten, Netherlands; *U.S. Public*, pg. 1189
Winner, Gregory T., Mgr.--Piper Jaffray Inc., Lincoln, NE; *U.S. Public*, pg. 1301
Winner, Tom, Brdcst. Buying Dir.--Wieden & Kennedy-New York, New York, NY; *U.S. Private*, pg. 1175
Winnick, Steve, Pres.--AlarmNet/Radscan, Syosset, NY; *U.S. Public*, pg. 1306
Winning, Don, Mng. Dir.--Reed Technology and Information Services (Europe), London, United Kingdom; *Int'l*, pg. 1096
Winninghoff, Albert C.M., Chm. & Chief Exec. Officer--Noordervliet & Winninghoff/Leo Burnett B.V., Amsterdam, Netherlands; *U.S. Private*, pg. 186
Winnowski, T.R., Chm. Bd., Pres. & Chief Exec. Officer--Key Bank of Oregon, Portland, OR; *U.S. Public*, pg. 954
Winset, George, Gen. Mgr.--A.C. Humko, Paris, IL; *Int'l*, pg. 92
Winslow, Dr. Robert, Pres.--Blood Cells, Inc., La Jolla, CA; *U.S. Public*, pg. 855
Winsnes, Arrita, Chief Oper. Officer--Akerlund & Rausing A/S, Drammen, Norway; *Int'l*, pg. 33
Winstead, Dwight, Pres.--Owen Health Care, Inc., Houston, TX; *U.S. Public*, pg. 304
Winston, Paul, Editor--Business Insurance, Chicago, IL; *U.S.* Private, pg. 285
Winter, Alison, Pres. & Chief Exec. Officer--Northern Trust Bank of California, N.A., Santa Barbara, CA; *U.S. Public*, *pg. 1196*
Winter, Alison, Pres. & Chief Exec. Officer--Northern Trust Bank of California, N.A., Los Angeles, CA; *U.S. Public*, pg. 1196
Winter, Alison, Pres. & Chief Exec. Officer--Northern Trust Bank of California, N.A., San Francisco, CA; *U.S. Public*, pg. 1196
Winter, Bob, Gen. Mgr.--Grand Island Contract Carriers & Brokerage, Inc., Grand Island, NE; *U.S. Private*, pg. 236
Winter, Frank D., Pres.--FirstMiss Steel, Inc., Hollsopple, PA; *U.S. Public*, pg. 344
Winter, Raymond F., Pres. & Chief Oper. Officer--BIC Corporation, Milford, CT; *Int'l*, pg. 1273
Winter, Tom, Pres.--Cardinal Systems, Fenton, MO; *Int'l*, pg. 1379
Winter, William, Pres.--Merrill Custom Communications, Minnetonka, MN; *U.S. Public*, pg. 1097
Winterhalder, Paul A., Pres.--Sysco Food Services of San Francisco, Inc., Fremont, CA; *U.S. Public*, pg. 1552
Wintermans, Jos, Pres. & Chief Exec. Officer--Canadian Tire Acceptance Ltd., Welland, Canada; *Int'l*, pg. 259
Winters, Bill, V.P. & Branch Mgr.--Burns & Wilcox - Daytona Beach Office, Daytona Beach, FL; *U.S. Private*, pg. 610
Winters, Christopher, Pres.--Beacon Container of PA, Montoursville, PA; *U.S. Private*, pg. 125
Winters, Henry, Pres.--British Steel, Inc., Schaumburg, IL; *Int'l*, pg. 221
Wintersteen, Gary, V.P. & Gen. Mgr.--Walbar of Arizona, Inc., Tempe, AZ; *U.S. Public*, pg. 402
Winterton, John, Gen. Mgr.--Milgray/Dallas, Inc., Dallas, TX; *U.S. Public*, pg. 206
Winther, Jorn, Chief Oper. Officer--Perstorp A/S Decorative Laminate, Tastrup, Denmark; *Int'l*, pg. 1038
Winton, William R., Reg. Dir.--Helian Occupational-South, Tucson, AZ; *U.S. Public*, pg. 1715
Winton, William R., Reg. Dir.--Helian Occupational-Central, Tucson, AZ; *U.S. Public*, pg. 1715
Winton, William R., Reg. Dir.--Helian Occupational-North, Tucson, AZ; *U.S. Public*, pg. 1715
Wintrode, Jim, Pres.--Six Flags Great America, Inc., Gurnee, IL; *U.S. Public*, pg. 1611
Wintsch, O., Pres. of the Bd.--Oerlikon Buhrle Immobilien AG, Zurich, Switzerland; *Int'l*, pg. 998
Wintzer, Heinrich S., Chief Oper. Officer--BHF Investment Management AG, Luxembourg, Luxembourg; *Int'l*, pg. 120
Wior, Mauricio, Gen. Mgr.--Compania De Radiocomunicaciones Moviles S.A., Buenos Aires, Argentina; *U.S. Public*, pg. 208
Wipfli, F., Chief Exec. Officer--Zurich Kosmos Versicherungen AG, Vienna, Austria; *Int'l*, pg. 1532
Wipperman, Klaus Peter, Mng. Dir.--EOC Normalien GmbH & Co. KG, Ludenscheid, Germany; *Int'l*, pg. 75
Wippermann, Klaus Peter, Mng. Dir.--EOC Formsystem GmbH, Mahlberg, Germany; *Int'l*, pg. 75
Wirdenius, Fredrik, Pres.--Skanska Fastigheter Stockholm AB, Danderyd, Sweden; *Int'l*, pg. 1260
Wirsen, Bo, Mng. Dir.--Alfa-Laval Food Engineering AB, Lund, Sweden; *Int'l*, pg. 1378
Wirsen, Lars-Erik, Pres.--ABB Cables AB, Stockholm, Sweden; *Int'l*, pg. 7
Wirt, Doug, Gen. Mgr.--Elixir Industries, Elkhart, IN; *U.S. Private*, pg. 371
Wirth, D.A., Mgr.--Tencarva Machinery Co., Roanoke, VA; *U.S. Private*, pg. 1076
Wirth, James T., Mgr.-Branch--Piper Jaffray Inc., Alexandria, MN; *U.S. Public*, pg. 1301
Wirth, Rolf H., Dir.--Deutsche Bank (Schweiz) AG (Zurich), Zurich, Switzerland; *Int'l*, pg. 405
Wirth, Thomas C., Pres.--Martin Marietta Manned Space Systems, New Orleans, LA; *U.S. Public*, pg. 1007
Wirz, D., Chief Exec. Officer--Zurich Pension Fund Consultants & Investments Mngmt. Ltd., Zurich, Switzerland; *Int'l*, pg. 1530
Wischek, A., Dir.-Pur.--Getranke-Dienst AG, Dietikon, Switzerland; *Int'l*, pg. 479
Wischhusen, Thomas, V.P. & Mng. Exec.--The Northern Trust Company, Schaumburg, IL; *U.S. Public*, pg. 1197
Wise, John, Pres.--South Charleston Stamping & Manufacturing, South Charleston, WV; *U.S. Private*, pg. 1030
Wise, Mark, Pres.--ANZ McCaughan Securities, New York, NY; *Int'l*, pg. 98
Wise, P.J.S., Chm. Bd.--NatWest Capital Markets Limited, London, United Kingdom; *Int'l*, pg. 910
Wise, Richard, Pres.--AT Acceptance Corporation, Cleveland, OH; *U.S. Public*, pg. 955
Wise, Richard, Pres.--AT Financial Corporation, Cleveland, OH; *U.S. Public*, pg. 955
Wise, Robert L., Pres. & Chief Oper. Officer--GPU Energy, Johnstown, PA; *U.S. Public*, pg. 695
Wise, Robert L., Pres.--GPU Generation Corporation, Johnstown, PA; *U.S. Public*, pg. 695
Wise, Sam, Pres.--Fischer Packing Co., Louisville, KY; *Int'l*, pg. 201
Wise, W., Mng. Dir.--Brother International Corporation do Brazil, Sao Paulo, Brazil; *Int'l*, pg. 229
Wiseman, I., Chief Oper. Officer--Bank Leumi (UK) PLC, Manchester, United Kingdom; *Int'l*, pg. 150
Wiseman, Mark B., Pres. & Chief Oper. Officer--NBD Banking Company, Jeffersonville, IN; *U.S. Public*, pg. 628
Wiseman, Michael L., Chief Fin. Officer--American Merchants Casualty Co., Columbus, OH; *U.S. Private*, pg. 764
Wiseman, Thomas R., Pres.--Braeburn Alloy Steel, Lower Burrell, PA; *U.S. Private*, pg. 193
Wiseman, Walter S., Pres.--Major Video Concepts, Inc., Indianapolis, IN; *U.S. Private*, pg. 639
Wishard, Jack A., V.P.--Procter & Gamble Productions, Inc., Los Angeles, CA; *U.S. Public*, pg. 1331
Wishart, Steven W., Pres. & Chief Exec. Officer--ReliaStar Investment Research, Inc., Minneapolis, MN; *U.S. Public*, *pg. 1376*
Wiskel, Dave, Mng. Dir.--Betrand Faure Components Ltd. - Vipond Plant, Mississauga, Canada; *Int'l*, pg. 193
Wislon, Alan, Pres.--Tubed Products, Inc., Easthampton, MA; *U.S. Public*, pg. 1066
Wismer, E.E., Pres.--Harvel Plastics, Inc., Easton, PA; *U.S. Public*, pg. 502
Wismer, Roland, Gen. Mgr.--Commercial Metals (International) AG, Zug, Switzerland; *U.S. Public*, pg. 414
Wisner, J.D., Pres.--The Gerstenslager Company, Wooster, OH; *U.S. Public*, pg. 1780
Wisneski, William J., Exec. V.P.--Houghton Mifflin School Division, Boston, MA; *U.S. Public*, pg. 841
Wissing, Lars, Mng. Dir.--Flavoring AB, Norrkoping, Sweden; *Int'l*, pg. 349
Wistrand, Torbjorn, Pres.--Skega AB, Ersmark, Sweden; *Int'l*, pg. 1323
Wiswall, John P., Sr. V.P. & Gen Mgr.--Cosmair, Inc., Ralph Lauren Fragrance Division, New York, NY; *Int'l*, pg. 818
Witcher, Bryce J., Mng. Dir.--Tasman Pulp & Paper Company Limited, Auckland, New Zealand; *Int'l*, pg. 495
Witches, Gary, Plant Mgr.--Tulip Corp., Milwaukee Div., Milwaukee, WI; *U.S. Private*, pg. 1109
Witherow, James B., Pres. & Chief Exec. Officer--Sunbelt National Mortgage Corporation, Dallas, TX; *U.S. Public*, pg. 639
Withers, Dan, Pres.--First Citizens Bank & Trust Company-White Sulphur Springs, White Sulphur Springs, WV; *U.S. Public*, pg. 629
Withers, Dan, Pres.--First Citizens Bank & Trust Company-West Virginia, Marlinton, WV; *U.S. Public*, pg. 629
Withers, Joan, Chief Exec. Officer--The Radio Network, Auckland, New Zealand; *U.S. Public*, pg. 386
Withers, Jonathan, Sls. V.P. & Branch Mgr.--BSA Advertising, Inc., San Diego, CA; *U.S. Private*, pg. 108
Withers, Vincent G., Pres. & Chief Exec. Officer--NewTel Enterprises Limited, Saint Johns, Canada; *Int'l*, pg. 115
Witherspoom, Jonathon, Publr. & Pres.--Piedmont Publishing Co., Inc., Winston Salem, NC; *U.S. Public*, pg. 1079
Witherspoon, Beth, Admin.--Harrodsburg Health Care, Harrodsburg, KY; *U.S. Public*, pg. 1713
Withka, Thomas F., Pres.--KCS Power Marketing, Inc., Edison, NJ; *U.S. Public*, pg. 939
Withrow, David, Pres., Chief Exec. Officer & Dir.-Sls.--FATA Production Machinery, Cleveland, OH; *Int'l*, pg. 474
Witkin, Kenneth, Exec. V.P.--Business Credit Div., Providence, RI; *U.S. Public*, pg. 650
Witmond, Paul, Gen. Mgr.--Colgate-Palmolive (Central America), Panama, Panama; *U.S. Public*, pg. 398
Witner, John, Mgr.--Dataforms, Inc., New Berlin, WI; *U.S. Public*, pg. 1385
Witowski, John, Pres.--Home Curtain Corporation, New York, NY; *U.S. Private*, pg. 536
Witschger, S.L., Chm. Bd., Pres. & Treas.--Paragon Resources, Inc., Albuquerque, NM; *U.S. Public*, pg. 1339
Witt, F. William, Grp. V.P.--Morse Controls, Hudson, OH; *U.S. Public*, pg. 857
Witt, Hilkka K., Asst. V.P.-Oil Country Tubular Goods--Voest-Alpine International Corp., Bellaire, TX; *Int'l*, pg. 1470
Witt, Mark, V.P.-Sls.--Fairfield Glade, Fairfield Glade, TN; *U.S. Public*, pg. 610
Witt, Paul, Mng. Dir.--Cheshire, Wood Dale, IL; *Int'l*, pg. 545
Witt, Ricardo, Mng. Dir.--Battenfeld-Pugliese Equipamentos Ltda., Osasco, Brazil; *Int'l*, pg. 825
Witt, Richard A., Pres. & Chief Exec. Officer--Mutual of Omaha Investor Services, Inc., Omaha, NE; *U.S. Private*, *pg. 770*
Witt, Tony, V.P.--Pioneer Express Inc., Indianapolis, IN; *Int'l*, *pg. 1469*
Wittau, Manfred, Pres. Dir.--P.T. Asuransi Allianz Utama Indonesia, Jakarta, Indonesia; *Int'l*, pg. 60
Witte, A., Mng. Dir.--EMI Music Publishing (Holland) B.V., Hilversum, Netherlands; *Int'l*, pg. 427

Witte, Steve, Gen. Mgr.--PEC Rio Grande Valley, McAllen, TX; *U.S. Private*, pg. 871
Wittering, Peter E., Chief Oper. Officer & Mng. Dir.--Sturmey-Archer Limited, Nottingham, United Kingdom; *Int'l*, pg. 394
Wittig, Detlef, Chief Oper. Officer--Volkswagen Audi Nippon K.K., Toyohashi, Japan; *Int'l*, pg. 1475
Wittler, Manfred, Div. V.P.- Strategies & Business Devel.-Europe--Data General Europe, Inc., Paris, France; *U.S. Public*, pg. 486
Wittlov, Arne, Pres.--Volvo Aero Corporation, Trollhattan, Sweden; *Int'l*, pg. 1476
Wittman, Peter, Pres.--WWF Paper Corporation - Mid Atlantic, Bridgeport, NJ; *U.S. Private*, pg. 1145
Wittman, T. Scott, Pres., Sec. & Treas.--Vantage Global Advisors, Inc., New York, NY; *U.S. Public*, pg. 998
Wittmann, Jens-Peter, Mng. Dir.--K-Tron Germany-Hasler Division, Lengerich, Germany; *U.S. Public*, pg. 938
Wittmer, Karen, Publisher--The Tribune, Mesa, AZ; *U.S. Public*, pg. 1601
Wittmer, Karen, Chief Exec. Officer-S.M.G.--The Yuma Daily Sun, Yuma, AZ; *U.S. Public*, pg. 1601
Wittstock, Ullrich, Mng. Dir.--Sachsen-Schwertransport GmbH, Dresden, Germany; *Int'l*, pg. 423
Witurawong, Vichai, Chief Oper. Officer--Kyowa Hakko (Thailand) Ltd., Bangkok, Thailand; *Int'l*, pg. 778
Witzleben, Charles K., Pres.--SUPERVALU International, Tacoma, WA; *U.S. Public*, pg. 1541
Wjunisky, Mauro, Gen. Mgr.--Produtos Medico Hospitalares Elscint Ltda., Sao Paulo, Brazil; *Int'l*, pg. 450
Wlaker, Nancy, Pres. & Chief Exec. Officer--Krames Communications, San Bruno, CA; *U.S. Public*, pg. 1616
Wnuk, Wade, Pres.--Norriseal Controls, Houston, TX; *U.S. Public*, pg. 521
Wobst, Frank, Chm.--The Huntington Trust Co., N.A., Columbus, OH; *U.S. Public*, pg. 850
Wock, John, V.P. & Gen. Mgr.--Paramount Tube, Fort Wayne, IN; *U.S. Private*, pg. 880
Woday, Jim, Gen. Mgr.--Northland Evergreens, Inc., West Olive, MI; *U.S. Private*, pg. 60
Wodzikci, Wojtek A., Mgr.-Exploration--Minera Cominco Bolivia Ltda., La Paz, Bolivia; *Int'l*, pg. 308
Woehler, Michael E., Pres.--Pharmacia & Upjohn Biotech Inc., Piscataway, NJ; *Int'l*, pg. 1047
Woelffer, Gale, Pres.--BRW Paper Co., Inc., Farmers Branch, TX; *U.S. Private*, pg. 467
Woertz, P.A., Pres.--Chevron International Trading Company-West Africa, Abidjan, Cote d'Ivoire; *U.S. Public*, pg. 348
Woest, J.J., Mng. Dir.--Tokheim So. Africa Ltd., Randburg, South Africa; *U.S. Public*, pg. 1620
Woeste, Bill, Pres.--Beech Isuzu, Cincinnati, OH; *U.S. Private*, pg. 129
Woeste, Bill, Pres.--Beechmont Chevrolet, Inc, Cincinnati, OH; *U.S. Private*, pg. 129
Woffard, J., Mng. Dir.--Gates Hydraulics Ltd., Huntingdon, United Kingdom; *Int'l*, pg. 1397
Woftus, B.M., Pres.--Coats Patons, Toronto, Canada; *Int'l*, pg. 300
Wogensen, Bertil, Mng. Dir.--Merita Bank Ltd., Warsaw Representative Office, Warsaw, Poland; *Int'l*, pg. 859
Wogstad, William O., V.P.--EFS/San Diego Service Corporation, Chicago, IL; *U.S. Public*, pg. 1428
Wohland, Helmut, Dr., Chm. Bd. & Pres.--Suspa Compart AG, Altdorf, Germany; *Int'l*, pg. 1322
Wohlens, Charles, Pres.--Garlock Valves & Industrial Plastics, Camden, NJ; *U.S. Public*, pg. 402
Wohlers, Birgit, Dir.--Takenaka Europe GmbH, Hamburg, Hamburg, Germany; *Int'l*, pg. 1351
Woit, Erik P., Chm.--Sea Containers America Inc., New York, NY; *Int'l*, pg. 1213
Woitkin, Philippe, Reg. Pres.--Ascona (Belgie) P.V.B.A., Saint-Niklaas, Belgium; *Int'l*, pg. 857
Wojciechowski, Timothy J., V.P. & Gen. Mgr.--Oglebay Norton Refractories & Minerals, Inc., Cleveland, OH; *U.S. Public*, pg. 1214
Wojcik, Paul N., Pres. & Chief Exec. Officer--BNA Books Div., Washington, DC; *U.S. Private*, pg. 181
Wojtyna, John P., Pres.--GAI Construction Monitoring Services, Inc., Monroeville, PA; *U.S. Private*, pg. 434
Wold, Casey R., Pres.--TrizecHahn Properties Inc., Chicago, IL; *Int'l*, pg. 1425
Wolf, Brian, Mgr.-Admin. & Mktg.--Basin Telecommunication, Inc., Bismarck, ND; *U.S. Private*, pg. 121
Wolf, Dallas, V.P.-Opers.--ISA Information Systems Services, Arlington, VA; *U.S. Private*, pg. 566
Wolf, Dennis C., Pres.--Composite Structures International, Inc., Dallas, TX; *U.S. Public*, pg. 1357
Wolf, Franz Josef, Mng. Dir.--Wolf-Ton GmbH & Co., Ltd., Ransbach-Baumbach, Germany; *Int'l*, pg. 1488
Wolf, Georg, Pres.--Knurr USA, Inc., Simi Valley, CA; *Int'l*, pg. 739
Wolf, Gregory H., Pres. & Chief Oper. Officer--Humana Health Chicago, Inc., Chicago, IL; *U.S. Public*, pg. 847
Wolf, Gregory H., Pres. & Chief Oper. Officer--Employers Health Insurance Company, Green Bay, WI; *U.S. Public*, pg. 847
Wolf, Gregory H., Pres. & Chief Oper. Officer--Humana Health Plan of Texas, Inc., San Antonio, TX; *U.S. Public*, pg. 848
Wolf, Gregory H., Pres. & Chief Oper. Officer--Humana Health Plan of Alabama, Inc., Montgomery, AL; *U.S. Public*, pg. 848
Wolf, Gregory H., Pres. & Chief Oper. Officer--Humana Wisconsin Health Organization Insurance Corporation, Milwaukee, WI; *U.S. Public*, pg. 848
Wolf, Gregory H., Pres. & Chief Oper. Officer--Network EPO, Inc., Milwaukee, WI; *U.S. Public*, pg. 848
Wolf, Gregory H., Pres.--Humana Wisconsin Health Organization Insurance Corporation, Milwaukee, WI; *U.S. Public*, pg. 848
Wolf, Hans Dieta, Dir.--Elida-Gibbs G.m.b.H., Hamburg, Germany; *Int'l*, pg. 1437
Wolf, Hans Peter, Gen. Mgr.--Zimmer Chirugie G.m.b.H., Roedermark, Germany; *U.S. Public*, pg. 256
Wolf, Jack D., Pres.--Targetbase Marketing, Irving, TX; *U.S. Public*, pg. 1023
Wolf, Kurt, Sr. V.P.-Intl. Opers., Europe--K2 Ski-Sport & Mode GmbH, Puchheim, Germany; *U.S. Public*, pg. 940
Wolf, Lloyd, V.P. & Gen. Mgr.--Davson Division, Itasca, IL; *U.S. Public*, pg. 1411
Wolf, Lorraine, Branch Mgr.--Downey Savings & Loan Association, F.A., Cerritos, CA; *U.S. Public*, pg. 526
Wolf, Peter, Chief Oper. Officer--DataCard Germany GmbH, Dusseldorf, Germany; *U.S. Private*, pg. 313
Wolf, Peter M., Chief Exec. Officer--Badische Tabakmanufaktur Roth-Handle GmbH, Lahr, Germany; *Int'l*, pg. 1101
Wolf, Richard L., Pres.--Trico Technologies Corporation, Brownsville, TX; *Int'l*, pg. 1397
Wolf, Rudolph C., Pres.--Barksdale, Inc., Los Angeles, CA; *U.S. Public*, pg. 457
Wolf, Wilhelm, Gen. Mgr.--Renishaw GmbH, Pliezhausen, Germany; *Int'l*, pg. 1103
Wolfe, Bertram, V.P. & Gen. Mgr.--G.E. Nuclear Energy, San Jose, CA; *U.S. Public*, pg. 711
Wolfe, Dale, Pres.--Accurate Forging Corp., Bristol, CT; *Int'l*, pg. 391
Wolfe, David, Gen. Mgr.--Enco-Jackson, Jackson, TN; *U.S. Private*, pg. 375
Wolfe, David, Gen. Mgr.--Enco-Memphis, Memphis, TN; *U.S. Private*, pg. 375
Wolfe, David G., Gen. Mgr.--Motorola Government Electronics Group, Scottsdale, AZ; *U.S. Public*, pg. 1137
Wolfe, F.C., Pres. & Chief Exec. Officer--NN Financial, Don Mills, Canada; *Int'l*, pg. 650
Wolfe, H. George, Pres.--Ney Dental International, Bloomfield, CT; *Int'l*, pg. 388
Wolfe, Herb, Pres. & Chief Exec. Officer--Atlantic City Showboat, Atlantic City, NJ; *U.S. Public*, pg. 1469
Wolfe, Jack, Pres.--AMCORE Bank, South Beloit, IL; *U.S. Public*, pg. 64
Wolfe, Jack A., Pres.--AMCORE Financial Life Insurance Company, Rockford, IL; *U.S. Public*, pg. 64
Wolfe, Jonathan, Pres. & Chief Oper. Officer--Oshawa Foods, Mississauga, Canada; *Int'l*, pg. 1012
Wolfe, Kate, Gen. Mgr.-Reservations--Utell International-Omaha, Omaha, NE; *Int'l*, pg. 1098
Wolfe, Richard, Chief Exec. Officer--Travel U.K., London, United Kingdom,; *U.S. Private*, pg. 647
Wolfe, Richard, Pres.--Codville Distributors, Winnipeg, Canada; *Int'l*, pg. 1012
Wolfe, Robert, Pres.--Aerojet, Sacramento, CA; *U.S. Public*, pg. 706
Wolfe, Robert, Pres.--Aerojet Azusa Operations, Azusa, CA; *U.S. Public*, pg. 706
Wolfe, Robert, Pres.--Aerojet, Rancho Cordova, CA; *U.S. Public*, pg. 706
Wolfe, Robert A., Pres.--Pratt & Whitney Commercial Engine Business, East Hartford, CT; *U.S. Public*, pg. 1690
Wolfe, Ron, Pres.--Sigma-Aldrich FS Corp., Saint Louis, MO; *U.S. Public*, pg. 1472
Wolfensberger, Gunter, Mng. Dir.--Rohm Electronics GmbH, Willich, Germany; *Int'l*, pg. 1125
Wolfer, Dale, Branch Mgr.--Circle Freight International USA, Portland, OR; *U.S. Public*, pg. 371
Wolfert, Frederick E., Pres. & Chief Exec. Officer--KeyCorp Leasing Ltd., Albany, NY; *U.S. Public*, pg. 954
Wolff, Christine, Mng. Dir.--WCI Umwelttechnik GmbH Frankfurt, Dreieich, Germany; *U.S. Public*, pg. 1657
Wolff, Cyril M., Mgr.--Piper Jaffray Inc., Appleton, WI; *U.S. Public*, pg. 1301
Wolff, Hans, Mng. Dir. & Chief Exec. Officer--Frese & Wolff Werbeagentur, Oldenburg, Germany; *U.S. Private*, pg. 304
Wolff, John, Mng. Dir.--CAB (Corporation for American Banking), Washington, DC; *U.S. Private*, pg. 51
Wolff, Odd Erling, Pres.--Kvaerner Kleven Leirvik A/S, Larvik, Norway; *Int'l*, pg. 769
Wolff, Richard, Mgr.-Branch--Graphic Systems, La Palma, CA; *U.S. Public*, pg. 1060
Wolfkeil, Bob, Pres.--Southwest Vacuum Devices, Inc., Stone Mountain, GA; *U.S. Public*, pg. 1720
Wolfs-Kokkeler, L.M., Mng. Dir.--Ballast Nedam Projectontwikkeling B.V., Rotterdam, Netherlands; *Int'l*, pg. 134
Wolfs, Hans, Div. Mgr.--Parker Ermeto GmbH, Wiener Neustadt, Austria; *U.S. Public*, pg. 1261
Wolfson, Bernardo, Pres.-Beverages, Latin America & Europe--Worldwide Quaker Beverages, Chicago, IL; *U.S. Public*, pg. 1347
Wolfson, Richard A., Pres.--U.S. Healthcare Dental Plan, Inc. (New Jersey), Blue Bell, PA; *U.S. Public*, pg. 26
Wolfson, Richard A., Pres.--U.S. Healthcare Dental Plan, Inc. (Delaware), Blue Bell, PA; *U.S. Public*, pg. 26
Wolfson, Richard A., Pres.--U.S. Healthcare Dental Plan, Inc. (Pennsylvania), Blue Bell, PA; *U.S. Public*, pg. 26
Wolk, Howard, Pres.--Valpey-Fisher Ultrasound Div., Hopkinton, MA; *U.S. Public*, pg. 1056
Wolk, Howard W., Pres.--Valpey-Fisher Frequency Control Div., Hopkinton, MA; *U.S. Public*, pg. 1056
Wolkenmuth, Edward F., Exec. V.P. & Gen. Mgr.--BASES Services & Durables Division, San Ramon, CA; *U.S. Private*, pg. 120
Wollaeger, Timothy J., Pres. & Chief Exec. Officer--Smith Laboratories, Inc., San Diego, CA; *U.S. Public*, pg. 405
Wollant, Doug, Gen. Mgr.--Grouse Creek Unit, Challis, ID; *U.S. Public*, pg. 804
Wollenberg, R.P., Pres.--Longfibre Ltd., Longview, WA; *U.S. Public*, pg. 1014
Wollenzien, Dennis H., Pres.--M & I Lake Country Bank, Hartland, WI; *U.S. Public*, pg. 1050
Woller, Robert, Mgr.-Property & Casualty Claims--Willis Corroon Administrative Services Corporation, Kent, WA; *Int'l*, pg. 1505
Wollersheim, Sepp, Chief Oper. Officer--Royal Copenhagen GmbH, Cologne, Germany; *Int'l*, pg. 1135
Wollschlager, Klaus, Dr., Chm.--Aral AG, Bochum, Germany; *Int'l*, pg. 1460
Wolpert, Mike, Pres.--Cardkey Systems, Inc., Simi Valley, CA; *U.S. Public*, pg. 105
Wolschlag, Richard, Gen. Mgr.--Container Strapping, Jacksonville, FL; *U.S. Public*, pg. 867
Wolter, Kurt, Mng. Dir.--Dresdner Bank AG, Mumbai, India; *Int'l*, pg. 419
Wolter, Robert A., Reg. Dir.--Piper Jaffray Inc., Phoenix, AZ; *U.S. Public*, pg. 1301
Wolters, Dennis, Pres.--Day International Printing Products Co., Dayton, OH; *U.S. Private*, pg. 56
Wolters, Erich J., Chief Oper. Officer--Ambulatory Resources, Inc., Atlanta, GA; *U.S. Public*, pg. 1033
Wolters, Kornel, Pres.--J.L. de Ball Canada Inc., Montreal, Canada; *Int'l*, pg. 552
Wolthvis, Dick, Plant Mgr.--Eaton Corporation, U.S. Engine Valve Corporation, Westminster, SC; *U.S. Public*, pg. 557
Woltz, William, Jr., Pres. & Chief Exec. Officer--Perry Mfg. Co., Mount Airy, NC; *U.S. Private*, pg. 834
Womack, J.E., Plant Mgr.--Longview Fibre Co. Western Container Div., Longview, WA; *U.S. Public*, pg. 1014
Womack, William L., Sr. V.P.--Perini Building Co., Inc. U.S. Heavy Division, Framingham, MA; *U.S. Public*, pg. 1278
Womble, B., Plant Mgr.--Sunbeam Mexicana S.A. de C.V., Tlalnepantla, Mexico; *U.S. Public*, pg. 1533
Womble, Charlie, Regional Pres.--First Tennessee Bank - Lebanon, Lebanon, TN; *U.S. Public*, pg. 639
Womelsdorf, L. Kenneth, Pres.--Custom Hoists, Inc., Hayesville, OH; *U.S. Public*, pg. 1506
Won-soo, Choi, Pres.--Astra Korea Ltd., Seoul, Korea; *Int'l*, pg. 94
Won, Frank, Gen. Mgr.--Wang Pacific Limited, Quarry Bay, Hong Kong; *U.S. Public*, pg. 1738
Won, Moon Sang, Pres. & Gen. Mgr--Cho Hung Bank of New York, New York, NY; *Int'l*, pg. 287
Won, Sohn Myung, Pres.--Ssangyong Motor Company, Seoul, Korea; *Int'l*, pg. 1292
Wong, Anthony C.M., Gen. Mgr.--Foshan Hua Nan Bundy Tubing Co Ltd., Guangdong, China; *Int'l*, pg. 1341
Wong, Audie, Gen. Mgr.--Amway Taiwan, Ltd., Taipei, Taiwan; *U.S. Private*, pg. 70
Wong, C.K., V.P.-Asia Pacific Opers.--Kollmorgen International Logistics, Singapore, Singapore; *U.S. Public*, pg. 966
Wong, C.M., Chm.--Toshiba Electronics Asia, Ltd., Kowloon, Hong Kong; *Int'l*, pg. 1406
Wong, Cheung Kee, Gen. Mgr.--Elkem Representative Office - Hong Kong, Hong Kong, Hong Kong; *Int'l*, pg. 447
Wong, Dennis, Mng. Dir.--Leo Burnett (China) Advertising Co., Ltd.-Guangzhou, Guangzhou, China; *U.S. Private*, pg. 184
Wong, Dennis, Mng. Dir.-Leo Burnett/Greater China--Leo Burnett Worldwide Asia/Pacific Hdqtrs., Hong Kong, Hong Kong; *U.S. Private*, pg. 186
Wong, E., Chief Rep.--Kodak (China) Limited, Beijing, China; *U.S. Public*, pg. 553
Wong, Harry, Mng. Dir.--Enso-Eurocan Hong Kong Ltd., Causeway Bay, Hong Kong; *Int'l*, pg. 457
Wong, Harry, Pres.--Dynapac Far East Ltd., Wan Chai, Hong Kong; *Int'l*, pg. 1420
Wong, James, Pres.--Allied Impex Corp., New York, NY; *U.S. Private*, pg. 6
Wong, James, Pres.--Interstate Photo Supply Corp., New York, NY; *U.S. Private*, pg. 6
Wong, James, Pres.--Soligor U.S.A., Inc., New York, NY; *U.S. Private*, pg. 6
Wong, John, Pres.--Aydin Controls Div., Fort Washington, PA; *U.S. Public*, pg. 158
Wong, Kenneth, Gen. Mgr.--Dentsu Young & Rubicam Sdn. Bhd. (Kuala Lumpur), Kuala Lumpur, Malaysia; *U.S. Private*, pg. 325
Wong, Kenneth, Sr. V.P. & Gen. Mgr.--Daiwa Bank-United Centre Branch, Hong Kong, Hong Kong; *Int'l*, pg. 374
Wong, Louis, Pres. & Exec. Creative Dir.--FCB/MegacoM, Guangzhou, China; *U.S. Private*, pg. 389
Wong, Peter B., Reg. Mgr.--AlliedSignal Chemicals, Kowloon, Hong Kong; *U.S. Public*, pg. 52
Wong, Philip, Mng. Dir.--Rising Paper Products Private Limited, Jurong, Singapore; *Int'l*, pg. 1251
Wong, Raymond, Representative--Allianz Guangzhou Representative Office, Guangzhou, China; *Int'l*, pg. 59
Wong, Raymond, Mgr.--BHP Steel Engineering Services Singapore Pte Ltd., Jurong, Singapore; *Int'l*, pg. 227
Wong, Robert, Mng. Dir.--Korn/Ferry International, Sao Paulo, Brazil; *U.S. Private*, pg. 633
Wong, Shu, Gen. Mgr.--The Mentholatum (Zhongsham) Pharmaceuticals Co., Ltd., Guangdong, China; *Int'l*, pg. 1126
Wong, V., Gen. Mgr.--Baring Asset Management (Australia) Ltd., Sydney, Australia; *Int'l*, pg. 648
Wong, William, Chief Fin. Officer--Bel Fuse Ltd., Kowloon, Hong Kong; *U.S. Public*, pg. 200
Wong, Yick Ping, Mgr.--Keppel FELS China Ltd., Wan Chai, Hong Kong; *Int'l*, pg. 731
Wongcharoew, Termsak, Mng. Dir.--Thai Engineering Products Co., Ltd., Bangkok, Thailand; *Int'l*, pg. 1238
Wongsupha, Somboon, V.P. & Gen. Mgr.--Dentsply (Thailand) Limited, Bangkok, Thailand; *U.S. Public*, pg. 500
Woo, Duck-Chang, Pres.--Ssangyong Cement Industrial Co., Ltd., Seoul, Korea; *Int'l*, pg. 1291
Wood, Alan, Chief Officer--Esselte Asia Pacific, Wan Chai, Hong Kong; *Int'l*, pg. 460
Wood, Andrew L., Chm. Bd. & Chief Exec. Officer--Burnham, Atlanta, GA; *Int'l*, pg. 686
Wood, Arthur M., Pres. & Chief Exec. Officer--Northern Trust Bank of Florida, N.A., Sarasota, FL; *U.S. Public*, pg. 1196
Wood, Brian, Mng. Dir.--PPP Lifetime plc, Stratford-on-Avon, United Kingdom; *Int'l*, pg. 1020

Wood, Bruce, Gen. Mgr.--ICI Explosives, Glen Morgan, WV; *Int'l*, pg. 664
Wood, Charles L., Pres.--United Insurance Company of America, Woodland Hills, CA; *U.S. Public*, pg. 1694
Wood, David, Pres. & Chief Exec. Officer--Harris Ranch Beef Co., Selma, CA; *U.S. Private*, pg. 505
Wood, David, Pres. & Chief Exec. Officer--First Security Bank of Wyoming, Rock Springs, WY; *U.S. Public*, pg. 637
Wood, David C., Chm. Bd. & Chief Exec. Officer--Norwest Financial, Inc., Des Moines, IA; *U.S. Public*, pg. 1202
Wood, David E., Chief Exec. Officer--Harris Feeding Co., Coalinga, CA; *U.S. Private*, pg. 505
Wood, David H., Pres.--AFIA Finance Corporation, Wilmington, DE; *U.S. Public*, pg. 363
Wood, Diane, Pres.--John Wiley & Sons, Canada, Ltd., Etobicoke, Canada; *U.S. Public*, pg. 1768
Wood, Dick, Chief Fin. Officer--Hamlin Steel Products, Akron, OH; *U.S. Private*, pg. 299
Wood, Fred, Mng. Dir.--A.B. Dick Company of Canada, Ltd., Rexdale, Canada; *U.S. Private*, pg. 791
Wood, J.J., Pres.--BMY-Wheeled Vehicles, Marysville, OH; *U.S. Public*, pg. 793
Wood, James F., Pres.-Power Generation Grp.--Babcock & Wilcox Co., Barberton, OH; *U.S. Public*, pg. 1068
Wood, Jeffrey, Mng. Dir.--La Amistad Residential Treatment Center, Maitland, FL; *U.S. Public*, pg. 1697
Wood, Joe T., Jr., Pres.--Hilb, Rogal and Hamilton Company of Gainesville, Georgia, Gainesville, GA; *U.S. Public*, pg. 827
Wood, John, Gen. Mgr.--Dowty Bonded Seals, Newtown, United Kingdom; *Int'l*, pg. 1338
Wood, John, Laboratory Mgr.--Quest Diagnostic-Olean, Olean, NY; *U.S. Public*, pg. 1351
Wood, John, Pres.--Thermedics Inc., Woburn, MA; *U.S. Public*, pg. 1592
Wood, Kenneth, Pres.--Barringer Instruments, Inc., Murray Hill, NJ; *U.S. Public*, pg. 192
Wood, Lynne, Mng. Dir.--Radio City, Liverpool, United Kingdom; *Int'l*, pg. 452
Wood, M.S., Mng. Dir.--Metal Box Nigeria Limited, Apapa, Nigeria; *Int'l*, pg. 267
Wood, Patricia A., Pres.--Leucadia Financial Corporation, Salt Lake City, UT; *U.S. Public*, pg. 990
Wood, Peggy, Admin.--Horizon Specialty Hospital - San Antonio, San Antonio, TX; *U.S. Public*, pg. 839
Wood, Peter J., Chief Exec. Officer--Direct Line Insurance plc, Croydon, United Kingdom; *Int'l*, pg. 1132
Wood, Robert C., Pres. & Chief Exec. Officer--Winterthur Reinsurance Corporation of America, New York, NY; *Int'l*, pg. 346
Wood, Robert J., Pres.--RJ Associates, Plymouth, MN; *U.S. Private*, pg. 932
Wood, Roger, Pres.--Soap Opera Magazine, Lantana, FL; *U.S. Public*, pg. 87
Wood, Roger, Pres.--Star Editorial, Inc., Lantana, FL; *U.S. Public*, pg. 87
Wood, Roger, Mng. Dir.--British Gas Services Ltd., Staines, United Kingdom; *Int'l*, pg. 279
Wood, Ron, Pres.--Dieffenbacher Toronto, Willowdale, Canada; *Int'l*, pg. 413
Wood, Stephen F., Pres. & Chief Exec. Officer--Constellation Energy Projects & Services, Inc., Baltimore, MD; *U.S. Public*, pg. 172
Wood, T., Chm. Bd. & Mng. Dir.--GKN Driveshafts Ltd., Walsall, United Kingdom; *Int'l*, pg. 534
Wood, Ted G., Pres.--Boehringer Mannheim Pharmaceuticals Corp., Rockville, MD; *Int'l*, pg. 331
Wood, Terry, Gen. Mgr.--WKKV-FM, Milwaukee, WI; *U.S. Public*, pg. 385
Wood, Terry, Gen. Mgr.--WLTI-FM, Southfield, MI; *U.S. Private*, pg. 779
Wood, Warren G., Pres.--Cabot Medical Corporation, Langhorne, PA; *U.S. Public*, pg. 373
Woodall, Bill, Pres.--Chicago Consolidated, Lemont, IL; *U.S.* Private, pg. 533
Woodard, Carl, Dir.-Mktg. Services--Hunt-Wesson Marketing Services Division, Fullerton, CA; *U.S. Public*, pg. 428
Woodard, Eugene, Pres. & Chief Exec. Officer--Hudson Life Reassurance Corporation, Shelton, CT; *Int'l*, pg. 1257
Woodard, James A., Pres.--Wabash Pioneer Container Division, Cedarburg, WI; *U.S. Private*, pg. 1170
Woodburn, Gerald R., V.P. & Gen. Mgr.--Handleman Company of Canada Ltd., Scarborough, Canada; *U.S. Public*, pg. 780
Woodbury, Michael, Gen.-Mgr.--Tecomet-Albuquerque, Albuquerque, NM; *U.S. Public*, pg. 1592
Woodcock, David, Gen. Mgr.--KTVX Television, Inc., Salt Lake City, UT; *U.S. Public*, pg. 352
Woodcroft, Richard, Mgr.--L.O. Jeffs Ltd., Ormskirk, United Kingdom; *Int'l*, pg. 542
Woodfine, J. M., Dr., Chief Exec. Officer--WBB Technology Ltd., Newton Abbot, United Kingdom; *Int'l*, pg. 1487
Woodford, Bill, Dir.-Sls. & Mktg.--Land O'Lakes Dairy Foods, Clear Lake, WI; *U.S. Private*, pg. 646
Woodford, Marcus, Gen. Mgr.--Kubota Tractor Corp., Suwanee, GA; *Int'l*, pg. 762
Woodford, Sandra, Gen. Mgr.--Holiday Inn Downtown, Rochester, MN; *U.S. Public*, pg. 1537
Woodger, Robert, V.P.--W. Braun Packaging, Canada Ltd., Markham, Canada; *U.S. Private*, pg. 166
Woodhead, David, Pres.--Dexter Magnetic Materials, Fremont, CA; *U.S. Public*, pg. 504
Woodhouse, Charles F., Pres. & Chief Exec. Officer--MariFarms, Inc., Woodbridge, NJ; *Int'l*, pg. 593
Woodhouse, J.C., Gen. Mgr.--ANZ Grindlays Bank plc Switzerland, Geneva, Switzerland; *Int'l*, pg. 99
Woodlan, Larry, Pres.--Burgess & Niple, Inc., Phoenix, AZ; *U.S. Private*, pg. 182
Woodland, Robert, Mng. Dir.--SHL Vision Solutions, Camberley, United Kingdom; *Int'l*, pg. 1154
Woodley, Donald, Country Mgr.--Compaq Canada, Inc., Richmond Hill, Canada; *U.S. Public*, pg. 418
Woodrich, Daniel I., Publr.--New England Newspapers, Inc.-The Times, Pawtucket, RI; *U.S. Public*, pg. 935
Woodrow, Ken, Pres.--Target Stores, Minneapolis, MN; *U.S.* Public, pg. 489
Woodruff, Norris, Pres.--Multilin, Markham, Canada; *U.S. Public*, pg. 713
Woods, Allan P., Pres. & Chief Exec. Officer--ChaseMellon Shareholder Services, L.L.C., Ridgefield, NJ; *U.S. Public*, *pg. 1085*
Woods, D., V.P.-Sls.-Western Canada--Andres Wines (B.C.) Ltd., Port Moody, Canada; *Int'l*, pg. 76
Woods, D., Chief Oper. Officer--Pall Mall Support Services Limited, London, United Kingdom; *Int'l*, pg. 385
Woods, Edward, Chief Exec. Officer--Westervelt Land Co., Tuscaloosa, AL; *U.S. Private*, pg. 488
Woods, Edward G., Chief Exec. Officer & Mng. Dir.--Kodak (Australasia) Pty. Ltd., Coburg, Australia; *U.S. Public*, pg. 552
Woods, G.A., Chief Oper. Officer--PACCAR Financial Services Ltd., Mississauga, Canada; *U.S. Public*, pg. 1247
Woods, G.D., Chief Exec. Officer--Algemene Bank Nederland (Ireland) Ltd., Dublin, Ireland; *Int'l*, pg. 12
Woods, H.J., Gen. Mgr.--J.I. Case Credit Corporation of Australia Pty. Limited, Northmead, Australia; *U.S. Public*, pg. 1579
Woods, Herb, Pres.--GMSI, Inc., Kanata, Canada; *U.S. Public*, pg. 740
Woods, I.R., Mgr.-Human Resources--Kodak Limited-Marketing Education Center, Hemel Hempstead, United Kingdom; *U.S. Public*, pg. 553
Woods, Ian, Publishing Mgr.--Elsevier Geo Abstracts, Norwich, United Kingdom; *Int'l*, pg. 1100
Woods, James R., Pres. Chief Oper. Officer--SunBank Capital Management, N.A., Orlando, FL; *U.S. Public*, pg. 1537
Woods, Jim, Dir.--Harris Broadcast Division, Richmond, IN; *U.S. Public*, pg. 791
Woods, John, Pres. & Chief Exec. Officer--Western Multiplex Corporation, Sunnyvale, CA; *U.S. Public*, pg. 747
Woods, John W., Chm. Bd., Pres. & Chief Exec. Officer--AmSouth Bank N.A., Birmingham, AL; *U.S. Public*, pg. 105
Woods, Katherine, Admin.--Heritage Gardens, Carrollton, TX; *U.S. Public*, pg. 839
Woods, Kenneth W., Chm. Bd.--Cigna Excess & Surplus Insurance Services, Inc. (CA), Los Angeles, CA; *U.S. Public*, pg. 362
Woods, Kenneth W., Chm. Bd.--Cravens, Dargan & Company, Pacific Coast, Philadelphia, PA; *U.S. Public*, pg. 365
Woods, Kenneth W., Chm. Bd.--American Adjustment Company, Inc., Irvine, CA; *U.S. Public*, pg. 365
Woods, Kenneth W., Chm. Bd.--Railroad Insurance Brokers, Inc., Los Angeles, CA; *U.S. Public*, pg. 366
Woods, Patrick, Mng. Dir.--Merisel Australia, Lane Cove, Australia; *U.S. Public*, pg. 1096
Woods, R.A., Pres.--ICI Agricultural Products, Wilmington, DE; *Int'l*, pg. 663
Woods, W.E., Pres.--Delhi Industries Inc., Delhi, Canada; *Int'l*, pg. 1150
Woodside, Kenith, Gen. Mgr.--Alro Group, Battle Creek, Battle Creek, MI; *U.S. Private*, pg. 46
Woodside, Richard L., Pres.--Boston International Data Services, Inc., Boston, MA; *U.S. Public*, pg. 184
Woodson, Kenneth, Pres. & Chief Exec. Officer--Louis Vuitton North America, Inc., New York, NY; *Int'l*, pg. 781
Woodward, Bob, Gen. Mgr.--GCI Lowell Inc/WZYZ F.M., Baltimore, MD; *U.S. Private*, pg. 470
Woodward, Bruce M., Pres.--Medalist Industries, Elk Grove Village, IL; *U.S. Public*, pg. 867
Woodward, Dave, Mgr.--Anixter Ottawa, Ottawa, Canada; *U.S. Public*, pg. 115
Woodward, Graham, Chief Oper. Officer--MSI Australia Pty. Ltd., Crows Nest, Australia; *U.S. Public*, pg. 1546
Woodward, Kirk P., Sr. Partner--Shared Services Division, Kansas City, MO; *U.S. Private*, pg. 146
Woodward, Ron, Pres.--Boeing Commercial Airplane Group, Renton, WA; *U.S. Public*, pg. 240
Woodwark, Chris, Dr., Exec. Chm.--Cosworth Engineering Ltd., Northampton, United Kingdom; *Int'l*, pg. 1466
Wook, Kim Dai, Pres.--Ssangyong Japan Corporation, Tokyo, Japan; *Int'l*, pg. 1291
Woolace, Larry A., V.P.--La-Z-Boy West, Redlands, CA; *U.S. Public*, pg. 973
Wooldridge, Nelson E., Pres.--Maytag Customer Service, Cleveland, TN; *U.S. Public*, pg. 1064
Woolf, Jack, Chm. Bd.--William L. Crow Construction Co., New York, NY; *Int'l*, pg. 633
Wools, Steve, Pres.--President Baking-Plantation, Lake Bluff, IL; *Int'l*, pg. 1069
Woolworth, Richard L., Chm. Bd.--HMO Oregon, Salem, OR; *U.S. Private*, pg. 918
Woomer, Pat, Gen. Mgr.--Corrugated Container Div.-Portland Plant, Portland, CT; *U.S. Public*, pg. 1520
Woosley, Don P., Pres.--Halliburton Environmental Technologies, Inc., Houston, TX; *U.S. Public*, pg. 776
Wooster, Michael G., Dir.-Opers.--John Crane EAA, Slough, United Kingdom; *Int'l*, pg. 1338
Worapongsathorn, W., Mgr.--Van Leeuwen Pipe and Tube Thailand Ltd., Bangkok, Thailand; *Int'l*, pg. 1450
Worch, R. C., Pres.--E.C. Ernst, Inc., Capital Heights, MD; *U.S. Private*, pg. 861
Work, H.K., Pres.--Elk Corp. of Alabama, Tuscaloosa, AL; *U.S. Public*, pg. 568
Work, H.K., Pres.--Elk Corporation of Texas, Ennis, TX; *U.S.* Public, pg. 568
Work, Harold K., Pres. & Chief Exec. Officer--Elk Corporation of Dallas, Dallas, TX; *U.S. Public*, pg. 568
Workman, Dave, Pres.--Audio King Corporation, Thornton, CO; *U.S. Public*, pg. 1662
World, Tore, Mng. Dir.--Kelley Bemanningslosninger, Oslo, Norway; *U.S. Public*, pg. 949
Worley, Morris T., V.P.-Opers.--Rayrock Mines, Inc., Winnemucca, NV; *Int'l*, pg. 1089
Worley, Richard, Partner--Miller, Anderson & Sherrerd, Conshohocken, PA; *U.S. Public*, pg. 1132
Worley, Rodney, Admin.--Wilson Convalescent Center, Wilson, NC; *U.S. Public*, pg. 1715
Wormington, S.L., Pres.--Tesoro Alaska Petroleum Company, Kenai, AK; *U.S. Public*, pg. 1582
Wormington, S.L., Pres.--Tesoro Alaska Pipeline Company, Anchorage, AK; *U.S. Public*, pg. 1582
Wormington, Steven, Pres.--Tesoro Alaska Petroleum Co., Anchorage, AK; *U.S. Public*, pg. 1582
Worner, Hartmut, Gen. Mgr.--James Burn International GmbH, Hamburg, Germany; *U.S. Public*, pg. 1507
Worner, Herbert, Chief Oper. Officer--Bosch-Siemens Hausgeraete GmbH, Munich, Germany; *Int'l*, pg. 204
Worner, Otto, V.P. & Gen. Mgr.--Carolina Shoe Company, Morganton, NC; *U.S. Public*, pg. 217
Worrall, Peter, V.P.-Chemical Engrng.--APV Crepaco, Inc., Dryer Div., North Attleboro, MA; *Int'l*, pg. 1240
Worrell, Chuck, Reg. V.P.--Subaru Southeast Region, West Palm Beach, FL; *Int'l*, pg. 523
Worrell, Deborah, Mgr.-Detroit--Detroit Division, Bloomfield Hills, MI; *U.S. Public*, pg. 1613
Worrell, W. Alan, Chm. Bd. & Chief Exec. Officer--Sterling Bank, Montgomery, AL; *U.S. Public*, pg. 1549
Wortberg, H.J., Mgr.--Aluminum Norf GmbH, Neuss, Germany; *Int'l*, pg. 51
Worth, Robert, Pres.--Norwest Bank Montana, N.A., Billings, MT; *U.S. Public*, pg. 1202
Worthen, John, Chief Oper. Officer--Simkins Carolina Folding Box Div., Landrum, SC; *U.S. Private*, pg. 1000
Worther, John, Gen. Mgr.--Simkins Carton Div.-Marietta, Marietta, GA; *U.S. Private*, pg. 1000
Worthington, Michael, Gen. Mgr.--Polypenco Canada Ltd., Guelph, Canada; *Int'l*, pg. 354
Worthy, Dennis B., Gen. Mgr.--Metro Milwaukee Auto Auction, Caledonia, WI; *U.S. Private*, pg. 282
Wortifek, Tim, V.P. & Gen. Mgr.--Stone Industrial, College Park, MD; *U.S. Private*, pg. 880
Wosepka, John T., Pres.--First American Bank, Alexandria, MN; *U.S. Private*, pg. 167
Wotan, Samuel, Chief Exec. Officer--KGV Lambert Smith Hampton, Bahau, Malaysia; *Int'l*, pg. 797
Wotring, Randall A., Mgr.--EG & G Washington Analytical Services Center, Rockville, MD; *U.S. Public*, pg. 543
Wotring, Randy, Mgr.--EG & G Technical Services of West Virginia, Morgantown, WV; *U.S. Public*, pg. 543
Woucters, Guido, Chief Oper. Officer--Brugge-Oostende Local Head Office, Brugge, Belgium; *Int'l*, pg. 147
Woulfe, Ronna, Gen. Mgr.--WIOD, Inc., Miami, FL; *U.S. Public*, pg. 385
Wouters, Bert, Mng. Dir.--Henningsen-Van den Burg, Waalwijk, Netherlands; *Int'l*, pg. 1074
Woxne, A.K., Mng. Dir.--Nutricia Nordica AB, Stockholm, Sweden; *Int'l*, pg. 992
Wozniak, D.R., Div. V.P.--Parmatech Corporation, Petaluma, CA; *U.S. Public*, pg. 307
Wozniak, Donald R., Pres.--Carpenter Special Products Corp., El Cajon, CA; *U.S. Public*, pg. 307
Woznica, Zbigniew, Gen. Mgr.--Polarcup Poland Sp. z.o.o., Siemianowice, Poland; *Int'l*, pg. 638
Wrafter, Adrian E., V.P. & Country Mgr.--Bank of America NT&SA, Dublin, Ireland; *U.S. Public*, pg. 182
Wraith, William, IV, Co-Pres.--Nomura Holding America, Inc., New York, NY; *Int'l*, pg. 956
Wrathall, David, Dir.--Willis Corroon Credit Limited, Leeds, United Kingdom; *Int'l*, pg. 1502
Wratschko, B., Sr. V.P.--Daher Golden Eagle - Los Angeles, El Segundo, CA; *U.S. Public*, pg. 749
Wratten, Thomas, Pres.--Principal Commercial Advisors, Inc., Overland Park, KS; *U.S. Private*, pg. 885
Wray, David B., Chm. Bd.--Sun Capital Advisers, Inc., Boston, MA; *Int'l*, pg. 1319
Wray, Dick, Exec. V.P., Chief Oper. Officer & Gen. Mgr.--J. Brown & Associates Minneapolis/St. Paul, Minneapolis, MN; *U.S. Public*, pg. 764
Wray, Fred H., Pres.--TN Media Inc., Chicago, IL; *U.S. Public*, pg. 1641
Wray, Ken, Owner--Global Moving & Storage, Inc., Irving, TX; *U.S. Private*, pg. 458
Wray, Tom, Pres. & Chief Exec. Officer--Farmers & Merchants Bank, Rogers, AR; *U.S. Public*, pg. 630
Wrede, Fabian, Chief Oper. Officer--Viking Fruit AB, Goteborg, Sweden; *Int'l*, pg. 643
Wrede, Harold F., Pres.--Battenfeld Gloucester Engineering Co., Inc., Gloucester, MA; *Int'l*, pg. 825
Wrederbrand, Torbjorn, Mng. Dir.--Ikea Svenska Forsaljnings AB, Almhult, Sweden; *Int'l*, pg. 660
Wren, Karl, Pres.--Rauland-Borg (Canada) Inc., Mississauga, Canada; *U.S. Private*, pg. 911
Wren, Mark, Gen. Mgr.--Preferred/Kahler Associates, Salt Lake City, UT; *U.S. Public*, pg. 1537
Wrench, Shirley, Branch Mgr.--Union-Transport Corporation-Atlanta, Forest Park, GA; *U.S. Private*, pg. 1119
Wrench, Shirley, Branch Mgr.--Union-Transport Corporation-Greenville/Spartanburg Office, Greer, SC; *U.S. Private*, pg. 1119
Wretas, Goran, Mgr.--Sandvik Ticaret Ltd. AS, Istanbul, Turkey; *Int'l*, pg. 1187
Wrigge, Hans-Christof, Gen. Mgr.--Hamburger Aluminium-Werk Gesellschaft Mit Beschrankter Haftung, Hamburg, Germany; *U.S. Public*, pg. 1387
Wright, A.D.B., Chm.--Stanbic Bank Uganda Limited, Kampala, Uganda; *Int'l*, pg. 1294
Wright, A.S., Chief Oper. Officer--PACCAR Australia Pty. Ltd., Bayswater, Australia; *U.S. Public*, pg. 1247
Wright, B.J., Gen. Mgr.--Commonwealth Development Bank, Sydney, Australia; *Int'l*, pg. 313
Wright, Bob, Plant Mgr.--Synflex Division, Kent, OH; *U.S. Public*, pg. 689
Wright, Charles, Mgr.--Horizon Technology Group - Jackson Division, Jackson, MI; *U.S. Private*, pg. 539

Wright, Charles R., Gen. Mgr.--Pirelli Armstrong Southeast Division, Madison, TN; *Int'l*, pg. 1058
Wright, Clyde A., Pres.--Cigna Healthcare of Arizona, Inc., Phoenix, AZ; *U.S. Public*, pg. 359
Wright, D.G., Pres.--Amoco Trinidad Oil Co., Port of Spain, Trinidad & Tobago; *U.S. Public*, pg. 103
Wright, D.J., Chief Exec. Officer--Blackwood Hodge (Sierra Leone) Ltd., Freetown, Sierra Leone; *Int'l*, pg. 231
Wright, D.J., Chief Exec. Officer--GKN Defence Ltd., Telford, United Kingdom; *Int'l*, pg. 534
Wright, David, Pres.-Sls. & Mktg. Div.--Duraliner U.S.A., Lapeer, MI; *U.S. Public*, pg. 537
Wright, David, Mng. Dir.--Camera House Limited, Auckland, New Zealand; *Int'l*, pg. 1115
Wright, David B., Pres. & Chief Exec. Officer--Amdahl Corporation, Sunnyvale, CA; *Int'l*, pg. 527
Wright, David B., European Gen. Mgr.--Amdahl International Management Services Limited (European Headquarters), Hartley Wintney, United Kingdom; *Int'l*, pg. 527
Wright, Derek, Chief Oper. Officer--Nyborg Engineering Ltd., Uxbridge, United Kingdom; *Int'l*, pg. 444
Wright, Frank, Pres.--American Colloid Company, Arlington Heights, IL; *U.S. Public*, pg. 63
Wright, Henry, Pres.--Schenectady Canada Ltd., Scarborough, Canada; *U.S. Private*, pg. 970
Wright, Ian, Chief Oper. Officer--Sandusky Limited, Glenrothes, United Kingdom; *U.S. Private*, pg. 965
Wright, Jack, Pres.--Pace Die Cast Products, Inc., Gardena, CA; *U.S. Public*, pg. 986
Wright, John, Pres.--Consolidated X-Ray Service Corporation, Dallas, TX; *Int'l*, pg. 337
Wright, John W., Pres.--Bercen Inc., Cranston, RI; *U.S. Private*, pg. 287
Wright, Kathleen, Branch Mgr.--Downey Savings & Loan Association, F.A., Victorville, CA; *U.S. Public*, pg. 527
Wright, Leon, Pres.--International Diverse Foods, Nashville, TN; *U.S. Private*, pg. 663
Wright, Leonard, Chief Oper. Officer--Penberthy Div., Saint Catharines, Canada; *Int'l*, pg. 711
Wright, Mark, Acct. Dir.--JWT/ARK Communications, Prague, Czech Republic; *Int'l*, pg. 1484
Wright, Mark H., Acting Pres. & Chief Exec. Officer--USAA Federal Savings Bank, San Antonio, TX; *U.S. Private*, pg. 1114
Wright, Norman, Mng. Dir.--Choice Publications Ltd, Peterborough, United Kingdom; *Int'l*, pg. 451
Wright, Norman, Mng. Dir.--EMAP Apex, Peterborough, United Kingdom; *Int'l*, pg. 451
Wright, P.J., Exec. Gen. Mgr.--Mount Isa Mines Ltd., Mount Isa, Australia; *Int'l*, pg. 827
Wright, Peter W., Pres.--Dowty Aerospace Turbine Engine Components Group, Mountain Top, PA; *Int'l*, pg. 1337
Wright, Phillip E., Chm. Bd. & Chief Exec. Officer--SunTrust Bank, North Florida, N.A., Jacksonville, FL; *U.S. Public*, pg. 1537
Wright, R., Gen. Mgr.--Australian Perlite, Banksmeadow, Australia; *Int'l*, pg. 803
Wright, R.E., Pres.--RE Wright Environmental, Inc., Middletown, PA; *U.S. Private*, pg. 976
Wright, Randy, Mgr.-Personnel--Quik N Tasty Foods, Belton, MO; *U.S. Private*, pg. 901
Wright, Raymond L., V.P. & Mng. Dir.--Frazer & Jones Div., Solvay, NY; *U.S. Public*, pg. 548
Wright, Robert C., Pres. & Chief Exec. Officer--National Broadcasting Co., Inc., New York, NY; *U.S. Public*, pg. 712
Wright, Robert F., Gen. Mgr.--ITT Pamona, Pomona, CA; *U.S. Public*, pg. 859
Wright, Robert S., Pres.--North America Foods, Minnetonka, MN; *U.S. Public*, pg. 901
Wright, Roy, Chief Exec. Officer--Columbia Medical Center-West, El Paso, TX; *U.S. Public*, pg. 404
Wright, Russell D., Pres. & Chief Oper. Officer--Commonwealth Energy System, Electric Division, Cambridge, MA; *U.S. Public*, pg. 414
Wright, Russell D., Pres. & Chief Oper. Officer--Commonwealth Electric Co., Cambridge, MA; *U.S. Public*, pg. 415
Wright, Sandra, Admin.--Sierra Convalescent Center, Carson City, NV; *U.S. Public*, pg. 837
Wright, Steve H., Pres.--SuperValu, Inc.-Desloge Div., Desloge, MO; *U.S. Public*, pg. 1540
Wright, T.K., Pres. & Chief Exec. Officer--NationsBank/Eastern, Oak Ridge, TN; *U.S. Public*, pg. 1163
Wright, Ted, Mng. Dir. & V.P.--The Cloister, Sea Island, GA; *U.S. Private*, pg. 978
Wright, Thomas, Pres.--Adidas (Canada) Ltd., Downsview, Canada; *Int'l*, pg. 24
Wright, Thomas C., Pres.--BMO Financial, Inc., Chicago, IL; *Int'l*, pg. 154
Wright, Thomas C., Chm. Bd. & Chief Exec. Officer--Wright Group Publishing, Inc., Bothell, WA; *U.S. Public*, pg. 1636
Wright, Thomas J., Pres.--PCS Phosphate - Raleigh, Raleigh, NC; *Int'l*, pg. 1064
Wright, Vernon, Gen. Mgr.--Lawry's The Prime Rib, Chicago, IL; *U.S. Private*, pg. 654
Wright, Warren, Gen. Mgr.--Cosmicar Lens Div., Englewood, CO; *Int'l*, pg. 85
Wright, William, Pres.--Barrier Films Corp., Sparks, NV; *U.S. Private*, pg. 1190
Wright, William M., Pres.--Hearst Book Group, New York, NY; *U.S. Private*, pg. 515
Wright, William S., Pres.--Lym-Tech Scientific, Chicopee, MA; *U.S. Private*, pg. 683
Wrighton, Brian, Gen. Mgr.--HBO & Company (UK) Limited, Buckinghamshire, United Kingdom; *U.S. Public*, pg. 770
Wrigley, James, Chief Exec. Officer--PAXAR Europe Ltd., Watford, United Kingdom; *U.S. Public*, pg. 1267
Wrigley, Julie A., Pres.--Four-Ten Corp., Chicago, IL; *U.S. Public*, pg. 1781
Wrobel, C.W., Gen. Mgr.--CHEMCENTRAL/Indianapolis, Indianapolis, IN; *U.S. Private*, pg. 232
Wrobel, Waledmar, Rep.--DG Bank-Warsaw, Warsaw, Poland; *Int'l*, pg. 352
Wroblewski, William, Pres.--Gates do Brasil Ind. e Com. Ltda., Sao Paulo, Brazil; *Int'l*, pg. 1396
Wroldsen, Alan, Gen. Mgr.--MTI Systems Div., Irvine, CA; *U.S. Public*, pg. 135
Wrona, Ted J., Pres.--Warrick Controls, Inc., Royal Oak, MI; *U.S. Public*, pg. 482
Wroten E.B., Gen. Mgr.--Grant Chemical Div., Zachary, LA; *U.S. Public*, pg. 618
Wu, C.H., Mgr.--Willis Corroon (Taiwan) Limited, Taipei, Taiwan; *Int'l*, pg. 1510
Wu, C.L., Chief Oper. Officer--Thermalloy Ltd., Kowloon, Hong Kong; *Int'l*, pg. 209
Wu, S.T., Gen. Mgr.--Maxim's Caterers Ltd., Central, Hong Kong; *Int'l*, pg. 704
Wu, T.H., Gen. Mgr.--Offshore & Overseas Petroleum Exploration Division, Taipei, Taiwan; *Int'l*, pg. 286
Wuerfel, Dr. Ing Helmut, Co-Chief Oper. Officer--GK Gesellschaft fuer Kohleverfluessigung mbH, Saarbruecken, Germany; *Int'l*, pg. 1166
Wuest, H., Chm. Bd.--Kamyn Industries (Tanzania) Ltd., Dar es Salaam, Tanzania; *Int'l*, pg. 948
Wuffli, P.A., Chief Fin. Officer--Schweizerischer Bankverein, Basel, Switzerland; *Int'l*, pg. 1329
Wuhrer, Wolfgang, Mngng. Dir.--Sulzer-Escher Wyss GmbH, Ravensburg, Germany; *Int'l*, pg. 1305
Wuhrer, Wolfgang, Mng. Dir.--Sulzer Hydro GmbH, Ravensburg, Germany; *Int'l*, pg. 1308
Wulff, Norm, V.P.--Ravenna Arsenal, Inc., Ravenna, OH; *U.S. Public*, pg. 1219
Wulkan, Samuel, Chief Oper. Officer--Cebrace, Sao Paulo, Brazil; *Int'l*, pg. 1177
Wullschleger, B., Mng. Dir.--Ascom Installationen AG, Bern, Switzerland; *Int'l*, pg. 86
Wulss, Harold Dr., Pres.--Henkel Chemical Specialties Div., Ambler, PA; *Int'l*, pg. 610
Wund, R.L., V.P. & Gen. Mgr.--Turner Construction Co., Los Angeles, CA; *U.S. Public*, pg. 1645
Wunn, Hermann, Chief Oper. Officer--Rhenania-Saar Speditions-GmbH, Saarbruecken, Germany; *Int'l*, pg. 1033
Wurmli, Hanspeter, Mng. Dir.--Junior Discount Service AG,, Dallenwil, Switzerland; *Int'l*, pg. 501
Wurth, Heiko, Gen. Mgr.--ITW Dynatec-Macon, Erkrath, Germany; *U.S. Public*, pg. 868
Wyatt, Alan, Chief Oper. Officer--Neste Gas Ltd., London, United Kingdom; *Int'l*, pg. 915
Wyatt, Eual, Gen. Mgr.--Hollywood Park Operating Company, Inglewood, CA; *U.S. Public*, pg. 831
Wyatt, Gene, Pres.--Firstbank, Texarkana, TX; *U.S. Public*, pg. 641
Wyatt, H.E., Chm. Bd.--Monsanto Canada, Inc., Mississauga, Canada; *U.S. Public*, pg. 1125
Wyatt, Kay, Admin.--Lake Haven Health Care Center, Benton, KY; *U.S. Public*, pg. 1714
Wyatt, O.S., Chm. Bd.--Coastal States Management Corp., Houston, TX; *U.S. Public*, pg. 390
Wyatt, O.S., Jr., Chm. Bd.--Coastal States Trading, Inc., Houston, TX; *U.S. Public*, pg. 390
Wyatt, Randy, V.P. & Reg. Mgr.--Aggregate Haulers Inc., Houston, TX; *Int'l*, pg. 1058
Wycherley, R., Mng. Dir.--Bally, Inc., New Rochelle, NY; *Int'l*, pg. 997
Wycoff, Paul L., Pres.--ITW Micro-Poise Division, Indianapolis, IN; *U.S. Public*, pg. 865
Wyda, A., Property Mgr.--Blue Mountain Consolidated Water Company, Stamford, CT; *U.S. Public*, pg. 379
Wyda, A., Property Mgr.--Lake Heritage Utilities, Inc., Stamford, CT; *U.S. Public*, pg. 380
Wyda, Al, Mgr.--Citizens Utilities Home Water Company, Royersford, PA; *U.S. Public*, pg. 380
Wyda, Al, Mgr.--Citizens Utilities Water Company of Pennsylvania, Wymissing, PA; *U.S. Public*, pg. 380
Wyder, Robert, V.P. & Gen. Mgr.--Volvo Automated Systems of North America, Sterling Heights, MI; *Int'l*, pg. 1477
Wyers, M.F.M, Gen. Mgr.--Algemene Bank Nederland (Athens), Athens, Greece; *Int'l*, pg. 12
Wykes, Clive, Sr. Officer--The Chase Manhattan Bank, N.A., Brussels, Belgium; *U.S. Public*, pg. 339
Wykoff, Richard L., Pres.--Imperial Nurseries Inc., Granby, CT; *U.S. Public*, pg. 707
Wylie, Duncan, Exec. Mng. Dir.--Banque Indosuez New Zealand Limited, Wellington, New Zealand; *Int'l*, pg. 315
Wylie, John, Pres.--Tech-Met Canada Ltd., Scarborough, Canada; *U.S. Public*, pg. 575
Wyman, Robert, Chm. Bd.--Suncor Inc., Calgary, Canada; *Int'l*, pg. 1320
Wymar, Uwe, Mgr.--EG & G GmbH Sealol, Mainz, Germany; *U.S. Public*, pg. 544
Wynia, G.D., Mng. Dir.--Begemann Rusland B.V., Bueda, Belgium; *Int'l*, pg. 1134
Wynkoop, Walter, Pres.--Jakson-A CHF Company, New York, NY; *U.S. Private*, pg. 1094
Wynn, Ed, Jr., Chief Oper. Officer--Allright Parking of Georgia, Atlanta, GA; *U.S. Private*, pg. 43
Wynn, John, Chief Oper. Officer--Allright Cincinnati, Inc., Cincinnati, OH; *U.S. Private*, pg. 42
Wynn, Kenneth R., Pres. & Chief Exec. Officer--Atlandia Design & Furnishings, Inc., Las Vegas, NV; *U.S. Public*, pg. 1116
Wynn, Ronnie, Pres.--Colonial Mortgage Company, Montgomery, AL; *U.S. Public*, pg. 400
Wynne, Cyndy, Sr. V.P.--Vitt Media-Corporate Trade, New York, NY; *U.S. Private*, pg. 1142
Wynne, George C., Pres.--Presque Isle Insurance Div., Erie, PA; *U.S. Public*, pg. 215
Wynne, John L., Pres. & Chief Exec. Officer--First Community Bank, Forest, VA; *U.S. Public*, pg. 1039
Wynne, Michael W., Pres.--Martin Marietta Astronautics Space Systems, Denver, CO; *U.S. Public*, pg. 1007
Wyrwa, Charles J., Sr. Mktg. Officer--Northeast Marketing-Boston Business Center, Boston, MA; *U.S. Public*, pg. 649
Wyskeil, Fred, Mng. Dir.--Bechtel Water Technology Ltd., Risley, United Kingdom; *U.S. Private*, pg. 128
Wyslych, P.L., Mng. Dir.--AAH Medical, Chesterfield, United Kingdom; *Int'l*, pg. 591
Wysock, David, Mgr.--General Employment Enterprises, Inc., Chicago, IL; *U.S. Public*, pg. 714
Wysocki, F.S., Gen. Mgr.--ACCPAC International, Santa Clara, CA; *U.S. Public*, pg. 420
Wyss, Nicolas K., Mng. Dir.--Brown Brothers Harriman Services AG, Zurich, Switzerland; *U.S. Private*, pg. 173
Wyvill, R.D., Pres.--The Elco Corp., Cleveland, OH; *U.S. Public*, pg. 502
Xairer, Jacob, Chief Oper. Officer--Tecplant Ingest, Barcelona, Spain; *Int'l*, pg. 1361
Xie, Jeffrey, Rep.--National Mutual Beijing, Beijing, China; *Int'l*, pg. 908
Xu, C., Deputy Rep.--Gan S.A. China, Beijing, China; *Int'l*, pg. 565
Yabe, Shigeo, Pres.--Wako Computer System Co., Ltd., Tokyo, Japan; *Int'l*, pg. 1485
Yablon, Leonard H., Pres.--Sangre de Cristos Ranches Inc., New York, NY; *U.S. Private*, pg. 418
Yabrudy, Grace M., Resident Rep.--The World Bank, Bamako, Mali; *U.S. Private*, pg. 1189
Yabuki, Koichiro, Pres.--Hakuhodo Advertising America Inc., New York, NY; *Int'l*, pg. 588
Yacoubian, Eddie, Gen. Dir.--Campbell Lee Computer Services Ltd., Falkirk, United Kingdom; *U.S. Public*, pg. 1043
Yado, Toshiaki, Gen. Mgr.--Fuji Bank, Shenzhen Branch, Shenzhen, China; *Int'l*, pg. 520
Yagaki, Norihiko, Chief Rep.--The Sumitomo Bank, Ltd.-Bahrain Representative Office, Manama, Bahrain; *Int'l*, pg. 1309
Yagaki, Norihiko, Mng. Dir. & Gen. Mgr.--Sumitomo Finance (Middle East) E.C., Manama, Bahrain; *Int'l*, pg. 1310
Yager, Leo, Pres.--Madison Furniture Industries, Canton, MS; *U.S. Public*, pg. 1465
Yagi, E., Chief Oper. Officer--Nissho Iwai Aerospace (America) Corp., New York, NY; *Int'l*, pg. 947
Yagi, Nobuhito, Gen. Mgr.--Dentsu Beijing Office, Beijing, China; *Int'l*, pg. 393
Yagi, Yoshihiko, Pres.--Marubeni International Electronics Corp., Santa Clara, CA; *Int'l*, pg. 845
Yago, N., Pres.--Ebara Technologies Inc., Sacramento, CA; *Int'l*, pg. 432
Yahn, C.H., Pres.--Leisure Life, Inc., Baxter, TN; *U.S. Public*, *pg. 34*
Yahn, Charles, Opers. Mgr.--Boston Gear, Louisburg, NC; *U.S. Public*, pg. 857
Yahnke, R.E., Gen. Mgr.--John Deere Company, Minneapolis, MN; *U.S. Public*, pg. 492
Yahr, Carol, Branch Mgr.--Zellerbach Division, Flint, MI; *U.S.* Public, pg. 1075
Yaji, Akio, Gen. Mgr.--Daiwa Bank-Seoul, Seoul, Korea; *Int'l*, *pg. 373*
Yakushiji, Hironasa, Gen. Mgr.--The Sumitomo Trust & Banking Co. (U.S.A.), New York, NY; *Int'l*, pg. 1317
Yalen, Gary, Pres.--Fortis Advisers, Inc., New York, NY; *Int'l*, pg. 499
Yamabe, Hiseo, Pres. & Chief Exec. Officer--Takeda America Inc., New York, NY; *Int'l*, pg. 1350
Yamada, Akira, Pres. Dir.--P.T. Dai-Ichi Kangyo Panin Leasing, Jakarta, Indonesia; *Int'l*, pg. 362
Yamada, Akira, Dir.--Daiko Advertising, Inc., Nagoya, Japan; *Int'l*, pg. 366
Yamada, Dr. Mikio, Mng. Dir.--Spraying Systems Co. Far East, Tokyo, Japan; *U.S. Private*, pg. 1027
Yamada, H., Sr. V.P. & Gen. Mgr.--Marubeni America Corporation, Portland Branch, Portland, OR; *Int'l*, pg. 845
Yamada, Hiroharu, Exec. V.P.--Mitsubishi Estate New York, Inc., New York, NY; *Int'l*, pg. 873
Yamada, Hiroki, Chief Rep.--The Industrial Bank of Japan, Limited (Chicago Branch), Chicago, IL; *Int'l*, pg. 674
Yamada, Koji, Mng. Dir.--DKB Merchant Bank (Singapore) Limited, Singapore, Singapore; *Int'l*, pg. 361
Yamada, Makoto, Representative Dir.--Zycad Japan K.K., Yokohama, Japan; *U.S. Public*, pg. 703
Yamada, Minoru, Mng. Dir.--Yamaichi Futures Pte. Ltd., Singapore, Singapore; *Int'l*, pg. 1517
Yamada, Naotomo, Pres.--Hakuhodo Malaysia Sdn. Bhd., Kuala Lumpur, Malaysia; *Int'l*, pg. 588
Yamada, Takatoshi, Chief Rep.--Sakura Bank - Lexington Representative Office, Lexington, KY; *Int'l*, pg. 1179
Yamada, Yasuhiro, Chm. Bd.--Josephine Cosmetics, Inc., Osaka, Japan; *Int'l*, pg. 1126
Yamada, Yukihiro, Pres.--Shiseido Company Ltd., Honolulu, HI; *Int'l*, pg. 1235
Yamagata, E., Pres. & Chief Exec. Officer--Yokohama Tire Corporation, Fullerton, CA; *Int'l*, pg. 1521
Yamagishi, Takayuki, Pres.--Minebea Electronics Co., Ltd., Shizuoka, Japan; *Int'l*, pg. 868
Yamaguchi, Hajime, Chm. Bd. & Pres.--Teac America, Inc., Montebello, CA; *Int'l*, pg. 1360
Yamaguchi, Haruki, Pres.--Yasuda Life America Capital Management, Ltd., New York, NY; *Int'l*, pg. 1520
Yamaguchi, Hiroshi, Pres.--Maxell Corp. Of America, Fair Lawn, NJ; *Int'l*, pg. 621
Yamaguchi, Ikuro, Chief Oper. Officer--Toyota Motor Corporation, Australia Ltd. (TMCA), Melbourne, Australia; *Int'l*, pg. 1414
Yamaguchi, Jinichi, Sr. Rep.--Nippon Credit Bank Ltd.-Sydney, Sydney, Australia; *Int'l*, pg. 933
Yamaguchi, Jinichi, Pres.--Nippon Credit Bank AG, Frankfurt/Main, Germany; *Int'l*, pg. 933
Yamaguchi, Koju, Pres.--Herman Miller Japan, Tokyo, Japan; *U.S. Public*, pg. 1112
Yamaguchi, Kunihiko, Mng. Dir.--Hakuhodo Inc., Nagoya, Japan; *Int'l*, pg. 587
Yamaguchi, Kunihiko, Mng. Dir.--Hakuhodo Inc., Kobe, Japan; *Int'l*, pg. 587

Yamaguchi, Masahiro, Chief Oper. Officer--Makita Manufacturing Europe LTD., Telford, United Kingdom; *Int'l*, pg. 832
Yamaguchi, Masao, Chief Oper. Officer--Waratoku Steel Co., Ltd., Saitama, Japan; *Int'l*, pg. 999
Yamaguchi, Satoshi, Pres.--Wako Finance Co., Ltd., Tokyo, Japan; *Int'l*, pg. 1485
Yamaguchi, Seiji, Pres.--Nanto Staff Service Co., Ltd., Nara, Japan; *Int'l*, pg. 906
Yamaguchi, T., Chief Oper. Officer--Shiseido Cosmetics (America) Ltd., Toronto, Canada; *Int'l*, pg. 1235
Yamaguchi, Takashi, Pres. & Chief Exec. Officer--Shiseido Cosmetics (America) Ltd., New York, NY; *Int'l*, pg. 1235
Yamaguchi, Takehiko, Mng. Dir.--Dai-ichi Life International (U.K.) Limited, London, United Kingdom; *Int'l*, pg. 362
Yamaguchi, Wataru, Mng. Dir.--Daiwa Securities (H.K.) Limited, Hong Kong, Hong Kong; *Int'l*, pg. 376
Yamaguchi, Yuzuru, Pres.--Kawasho International (Australia) Pty., Ltd., Sydney, Australia; *Int'l*, pg. 727
Yamaji, Teruhisa, Branch Mgr.--Daiwa Securities (Seoul), Seoul, Korea; *Int'l*, pg. 376
Yamakawa, Hiroshi, Gen. Mgr.--Showpla Vietnam Co. Ltd., Bien Hoa, Vietnam,; *Int'l*, pg. 1237
Yamakawa, Nobuyoshi, Pres.--Rohm Electronics Dalian Co., LTD., Dalian, China; *Int'l*, pg. 1125
Yamakawa, Yoji, Pres.--DNP (AMERICA), Inc., New York, NY; *Int'l*, pg. 363
Yamakoshi, Warren, Pres.--Nobart, Inc., Chicago, IL; *U.S. Public*, pg. 503
Yamamoto, H., Pres.--Morgan Grenfell International Asset Management Co. Ltd. (Tokyo), Tokyo, Japan; *Int'l*, pg. 406
Yamamoto, Hide, Export Terminal Mgr.--Kintetsu World Express Inc., Inwood, NY; *Int'l*, pg. 734
Yamamoto, Hiroki, Mng. Dir.--Nozaki America, Inc., Seattle Branch, Seattle, WA; *Int'l*, pg. 990
Yamamoto, Ikuo, Gen. Mgr.--Fuji Bank, Seoul Branch, Seoul, Korea; *Int'l*, pg. 520
Yamamoto, Junji, Gen. Mgr.--Kodak Brasileira C.I.L., Sao Jose dos Campos, Brazil; *U.S. Public*, pg. 553
Yamamoto, Kayunori, Pres. & Chief Exec. Officer--Pioneer Electronics (USA) Inc., Long Beach, CA; *Int'l*, pg. 1058
Yamamoto, Kensei, Chief Oper. Officer--The Tokio Marine & Fire Insurance Company (U.K.) Limited, Paris, France; *Int'l*, pg. 1392
Yamamoto, Kohei, Pres.--Rohm Apollo Electronics (Thailand) Co., Ltd., Pathum Thani, Thailand; *Int'l*, pg. 1125
Yamamoto, Kuni, V.P.--Genetics Institute Inc. of Japan, Tokyo, Japan; *U.S. Public*, pg. 80
Yamamoto, M., Pres.--American Yazaki Corp., Inc., Canton, MI; *Int'l*, pg. 1520
Yamamoto, Masakazu, Pres.--KHI (Dalian) Computer Technology Co., Ltd., Dalian, China; *Int'l*, pg. 726
Yamamoto, Minoru, Pres.--Nikko France S.A., Paris, France; *Int'l*, pg. 930
Yamamoto, Mitsuyoshi, Pres.--P.T. Easterntex, Jakarta, Indonesia; *Int'l*, pg. 1400
Yamamoto, Noriyuki, Mng. Dir.--Shougang NEC Electronics Co., Ltd., Beijing, China; *Int'l*, pg. 901
Yamamoto, Phil, Pres.--Aromat Corporation, New Providence, NJ; *Int'l*, pg. 847
Yamamoto, S., Gen. Mgr.--Marubeni America Corporation, Los Angeles Branch, Los Angeles, CA; *Int'l*, pg. 845
Yamamoto, Shoji, Mng. Dir.--Dai-ichi Life Insurance Agency Europe Limited, London, United Kingdom; *Int'l*, pg. 362
Yamamoto, Shuji, Mng. Dir.--NEC Electronics Taiwan Ltd., Taipei, Taiwan; *Int'l*, pg. 901
Yamamoto, T., Pres.--Optrex Glass, Plymouth, MI; *Int'l*, pg. 84
Yamamoto, T., Sr. V.P. & Gen. Mgr.--Marubeni America Corporation, San Francisco Branch, San Francisco, CA; *Int'l*, pg. 845
Yamamoto, T., Pres.--Optrex Glass, Plymouth, MI; *Int'l*, pg. 872
Yamamoto, T., V.P.-North American Mfg.--State College Operations, State College, PA; *Int'l*, pg. 897
Yamamoto, Toshinori, Chief Oper. Officer--Tosoh Europe B.V., Amsterdam, Netherlands; *Int'l*, pg. 1408
Yamamoto, Yoshihito, Chief Rep.--The Sumitomo Bank, Ltd.-Manila Representative Office, Manila, Philippines; *Int'l*, pg. 1310
Yamamoto, Yoshihito, Pres.--Sumigin Metro Investment Corp., Manila, Philippines; *Int'l*, pg. 1310
Yamamoto, Yukio, Pres. & Chief Exec. Officer--Aiwa America, Inc., Mahwah, NJ; *Int'l*, pg. 1280
Yamamura, Sam, Gen. Mgr.--Aisin World Corp.-Detroit, Plymouth, MI; *Int'l*, pg. 39
Yamamura, Shoichi, Vice Chm.--Beijing Dentsu Advertising Co., Ltd., Beijing, China; *Int'l*, pg. 393
Yaman, Antoine, Fin. Dir.--Targets-Leo Burnett Advertising, Jeddah, Saudi Arabia; *U.S. Private*, pg. 186
Yamana, Shinji, Chief Rep.--ORIX Maritime Corporation-Seoul Representative Office, Seoul, Korea; *Int'l*, pg. 1010
Yamanaka, Masayoshi, Pres.--NMB (USA) Inc., Chatsworth, CA; *Int'l*, pg. 868
Yamanami, Masanori, Mng. Dir. & Gen. Mgr.--Nikko Investment Banking (Middle East) E.C., Manama, Bahrain; *Int'l*, pg. 931
Yamanoi, Masatoshi, Pres.--Hakuho Communications, Inc., Taipei, Taiwan; *Int'l*, pg. 588
Yamanoto, Kohei, Pres.--Apollo Electronics Co., Ltd., Fukuoka, Japan; *Int'l*, pg. 1125
Yamaoka, Hironobu, Chm. Bd.--Titan Steel & Wire Co., Ltd., Surrey, Canada; *Int'l*, pg. 741
Yamaoka, Thomas, Mng. Dir.--Bonig & Yamaoka International Public Relations, Hamburg, Germany; *Int'l*, pg. 1210
Yamasaki, A., Pres.--Toshiba do Brasil S.A., Sao Bernardo do Campo, Brazil; *Int'l*, pg. 1406
Yamasaki, Terumasa, Gen. Mgr.--Fuji Bank, Atlanta, Atlanta, GA; *Int'l*, pg. 519
Yamashiro, Kenji, Mng. Dir.--NEC Electronics (UK) Limited, Milton Keynes, United Kingdom; *Int'l*, pg. 901
Yamashita, K. Thomas, V.P. & Gen. Mgr., Flavor Div.--Flavors Division, Branchburg, NJ; *Int'l*, pg. 174
Yamashita, Sumio, Mng. Dir.--Kintetsu World Express (Thailand) Co., Ltd., Bangkok, Thailand; *Int'l*, pg. 735
Yamashita, Toyohiko, Gen. Mgr. & Agent--Dai-Ichi Kangyo Bank, Ltd.-Los Angeles, Los Angeles, CA; *Int'l*, pg. 359
Yamashita, Toyohikou, Pres.--Dai-Ichi Kangyo Bank of California-Los Angeles, Los Angeles, CA; *Int'l*, pg. 360
Yamashita, Yoshio, Vice Chm.--Shuwa Investments Corp., Los Angeles, CA; *Int'l*, pg. 1237
Yamazaki, Hisao, Mng. Dir.--Nippon Express France, S.A., Roissy Charles de Gaulle, France; *Int'l*, pg. 934
Yamazaki, Katsuhiko, Pres.--Nikkei Visual Images, Inc., Tokyo, Japan; *Int'l*, pg. 929
Yamazaki, Nobuhisa, Chief Oper. Officer--Kyowa Hakko Kogyo Co., Ltd., Budapest, Hungary; *Int'l*, pg. 778
Yamazaki, Toshimori, Chief Representative--The Sumitomo Trust & Banking Co., Ltd., Beijing, China; *Int'l*, pg. 1318
Yamazawa, Tadahide, Pres.--Kyowa Takken Kaihatsu Co., Ltd., Tokyo, Japan; *Int'l*, pg. 763
Yamazoe, Akiteru, Chief Oper. Officer--Makita France S.A., Noisy-le-Grand, France; *Int'l*, pg. 832
Yammine, Riad N., Pres.--Speedway SuperAmerica LLC, Springfield, OH; *U.S. Public*, pg. 1662
Yamura, Akira, Dr., Exec. V.P.--Technical Service Center, San Jose, CA; *Int'l*, pg. 871
Yanagihara, Takahika, Pres.-U.S.--Takara Belmont U.S.A., Inc., New York, NY; *Int'l*, pg. 1349
Yanagihara, Takahiko, Pres.-U.S.--Koken Mfg. Co. Inc., Saint Louis, MO; *Int'l*, pg. 1349
Yanai, N., Pres.--Metalart Corporation, Kusatsu, Japan; *Int'l*, pg. 946
Yanai, Yural, Chm. Bd.--Elscint Espana S.A., Barcelona, Spain; *Int'l*, pg. 450
Yanaranop, Chollanat, Mng. Dir.--Thai Polyethylene Co., Ltd., Bangkok, Thailand; *Int'l*, pg. 1239
Yanes, Jorge, Plant Mgr.--Dart Industries Ltd., Harrow, United Kingdom; *U.S. Public*, pg. 1322
Yanet, Armando, Gen. Mgr.--Loctite de Colombia S.A., Bogota, Colombia; *Int'l*, pg. 611
Yang-Su, Chon, Representative--CUNA Mutual Group-Korea, Seoul, Korea; *U.S. Private*, pg. 297
Yang, Ann, Gen. Mgr.--Batey Ads Taiwan, Taipei, Taiwan; *Int'l*, pg. 117
Yang, Ben, Mgr.--LeaRonal (S.E. Asia) Ltd. Taiwan Branch, Tao-yuan, Taiwan,; *U.S. Public*, pg. 982
Yang, Michael, Gen. Mgr.--Shanghai Shared Data Network Co., Shanghai, China; *Int'l*, pg. 651
Yang, Samuel Y.C., Asst. V.P. & Gen. Mgr.--The International Commercial Bank of China, Subic Bay, Philippines; *Int'l*, pg. 683
Yaniko, David, Pres.--Allied Electronics Inc., Fort Worth, TX; *U.S. Public*, pg. 155
Yankowski, Carl, Pres.--Sundrop, Stamford, CT; *Int'l*, pg. 248
Yano, Makoto, Pres.--Kawasaki Loaders Manufacturing Corp., (U.S.A.), Newnan, GA; *Int'l*, pg. 725
Yano, Makoto, Chief Oper. Officer--Makita Korea Co., Ltd., Seoul, Korea; *Int'l*, pg. 832
Yano, Shinji, V.P.--Kobe Steel USA Inc. (Los Angeles), Los Angeles, CA; *Int'l*, pg. 740
Yano, Tamotsu, Pres.--Toray Industries (Singapore) Pte. Ltd., Singapore, Singapore; *Int'l*, pg. 1400
Yanuklis, John, Chief Oper. Officer--Strober King Building Supply Centers, Inc., Congers, NY; *U.S. Private*, pg. 403
Yao, David, Gen. Mgr.--China Airlines Ltd., New York, NY; *Int'l*, pg. 285
Yap-Azurin, Angelica, Mgr.--Deutsche Bank AG (Manila), Manila, Philippines; *Int'l*, pg. 404
Yap, Cyril M.F., Mng. Dir.--Jefferies Pacific Limited, Central, Hong Kong; *U.S. Public*, pg. 925
Yap, Peter, Mgr.-Singapore & Malaysia--Utell International-Singapore, Singapore, Singapore; *Int'l*, pg. 1099
Yapkowitz, Phil, Gen. Mgr.--Lake County Cablevision, Leesburg, FL; *U.S. Public*, pg. 1448
Yapp, G., Mng. Dir.--Nadella U.K. Limited, Coventry, United Kingdom; *U.S. Public*, pg. 878
Yaquimenko, Walter, Pres.--Kvaerner Eureka Espanola S.A., Madrid, Spain; *Int'l*, pg. 767
Yaquimenko, Walter, Pres.--Kvaerner Eureka Espanola S A, Villagarcia de Arosa, Spain; *Int'l*, pg. 767
Yarber, Danielle, V.P. & Gen. Mgr.--Dillard, A ResourceNet International Company, Salem, VA; *U.S. Public*, pg. 902
Yarbrough, Jerry A., Chm. Bd. & Chief Exec. Officer--Integrated Distributions, Inc., Little Rock, AR; *U.S. Public*, pg. 131
Yarbrough, John, V.P. & Div. Mgr.--Bindley Western, Mid-South Division, Atlanta, GA; *U.S. Public*, pg. 228
Yarbrough, Lee, Gen. Mgr.--Novo Nordisk BioChem, Inc., Franklinton, NC; *Int'l*, pg. 987
Yardy, Jim, Div. Mgr.--Rogers Cable TV-Brantford Div., Brantford, Canada; *Int'l*, pg. 1122
Yaremchuk, John D., Pres. & Chief Exec. Officer--First Virginia Bank-Maryland, Upper Marlboro, MD; *U.S. Public*, pg. 642
Yarom, Artzi, Chm. Bd.--Elscint GmbH, Wiesbaden, Germany; *Int'l*, pg. 450
Yasbrough, Wayne, Gen. Mgr.--Boomtown-Biloxi, Biloxi, MS; *U.S. Public*, pg. 831
Yashiki, Toyoji, Pres.--Honda of America Manufacturing, Inc., Marysville, OH; *Int'l*, pg. 635
Yashimatsu, Hitoshi, Gen. Rep.-Thailand--The Sakura Bank - Bangkok Branch, Bangkok, Thailand; *Int'l*, pg. 1179
Yasinsky, John B., Exec. V.P.--Westinghouse Power Systems Group, Pittsburgh, PA; *U.S. Public*, pg. 273
Yaskior, Adriana, Branch Mgr.--Union-Transport Corporation-San Juan Office, Guaynabo, PR; *U.S. Private*, pg. 1120
Yasment, Clement, Gen. Mgr.--Frontier Communications of AuSable Valley, Keeseville, NY; *U.S. Public*, pg. 683
Yasu, Kinji, Pres.--Stone Container Japan Company Limited, Tokyo, Japan; *U.S. Public*, pg. 1522
Yasuda, H., Chm. Bd.--Jardine Matheson K.K., Tokyo, Japan; *Int'l*, pg. 705
Yasuda, Isao, Pres.--Asahi Chemical Industry America, Inc., New York, NY; *Int'l*, pg. 84
Yasuda, Kazuo, Mng. Dir.--Mitsui Trust Futures (Singapore) Pte. Ltd., Singapore, Singapore; *Int'l*, pg. 883
Yasuda, Yufuka, Mng. Dir.--Paribas Capital Markets-Tokyo Branch, Tokyo, Japan; *Int'l*, pg. 321
Yasue, N., Pres.--Nissho Iwai Gas Co., Ltd., Tokyo, Japan; *Int'l*, pg. 946
Yasuhara, Jiro, Chief Oper. Officer--Lamma Power Station Project Office, Tsim Tsa Tsui, Hong Kong; *Int'l*, pg. 943
Yasuhara, Yoshio, Chief Rep.--Asahi Bank Shanghai Branch, Shanghai, China; *Int'l*, pg. 82
Yasui, Tomomasa, Dir.--Brother International G.m.b.H., Bad Vilbel, Germany; *Int'l*, pg. 229
Yasui, Tomomasa, Supvr. Bd.--Brother Internationale Industriemaschinen G.m.b.H., Emmerich, Germany; *Int'l*, pg. 230
Yasunda, M., Chief Oper. Officer--Furukawa Electric Co., Ltd. Australia, Sydney, Australia; *Int'l*, pg. 530
Yasutake, M., Mgr.--ITW Nifco Inc., Tokyo, Japan; *U.S. Public*, pg. 869
Yatabe, Makoto, Mng. Dir.--The Meijiseimei International Hong Kong, Ltd., Hong Kong, Hong Kong; *Int'l*, pg. 854
Yates, Arthur G., Banking & Fin. Svcs. Officer--Troy Savings Bank-Guilderland, Guilderland, NY; *U.S. Private*, pg. 1106
Yates, Charles, Admin.--Medicenter, Springfield, Springfield, MO; *U.S. Public*, pg. 1714
Yates, Chock, Mgr.--Commercial Metals Company, Galveston, TX; *U.S. Public*, pg. 412
Yates, Chock, Mgr.--Commercial Metals Co., Houston, TX; *U.S. Public*, pg. 413
Yates, Chock, Mgr.--Commercial Metals Company, Galveston, TX; *U.S. Public*, pg. 413
Yates, Cleon R., Pres.--Cryco Quartz, Inc., Austin, TX; *Int'l*, pg. 1408
Yates, Cleon R., Pres.--Cryco Twenty Two, Inc., Austin, TX; *Int'l*, pg. 1408
Yates, E.J., Chm. Bd. & Mng. Dir.--Kodak Limited, Hemel Hempstead, United Kingdom; *U.S. Public*, pg. 553
Yates, Edward S., III, Pres. & Chief Exec. Officer--First Virginia Bank-Blue Ridge, Staunton, VA; *U.S. Public*, pg. 641
Yates, G., Chief Opr. Officer--Hawke Cable Glands, Ashton under Lyne, United Kingdom; *Int'l*, pg. 851
Yates, Graham, Mng. Dir.--BHC Aerovox Ltd., Weymouth, United Kingdom; *U.S. Public*, pg. 26
Yates, Hal, Gen. Mgr.--Arrow/Schweber Electronics, Phoenix, AZ; *U.S. Public*, pg. 134
Yates, James R., Pres.--Aciers Francosteel Canada, Montreal, Canada; *Int'l*, pg. 572
Yates, John, Pres.--Butterworths Canada, Markham, Canada; *Int'l*, pg. 1095
Yates, Lauren, Editor--Trimble Banner Democrat, Bedford, KY; *U.S. Private*, pg. 648
Yates, Robert C., Chief Exec. Officer-Central Europe--Moore Ges.m.b.H., Vienna, Austria; *Int'l*, pg. 889
Yates, Tommie E., V.P. & Gen. Mgr.--American Trading & Production Corporation, Oil & Gas Div., Houston, TX; *U.S. Private*, pg. 64
Yato, Seizaburo, Chief Representative--The Sumitomo Trust & Banking Co., Ltd., Sydney, Australia; *Int'l*, pg. 1318
Yau, Sam, Chm. Bd.--ICS Learning Systems, Inc., Scranton, PA; *U.S. Public*, pg. 783
Yau, Sam, Chm. Bd. & Pres.--National Education Payroll Corp., Irvine, CA; *U.S. Public*, pg. 784
Yau, William, Gen. Mgr.--Signode Hong Kong Limited, Kowloon, Hong Kong; *U.S. Public*, pg. 869
Yavorsky, David, Pres.--First American Real Estate Tax Service, Inc., Irving, TX; *U.S. Public*, pg. 625
Yaw, Wee Cho, Chm. Bd.--Haw Par Brothers International Limited, Singapore, Singapore; *Int'l*, pg. 603
Yeadon, Richard, Pres.--Sasco/Valley Electric, Mountain View, CA; *U.S. Private*, pg. 967
Yeager, Robert, Pres. & Gen. Mgr.--Anchor Wire Corporation of Tennessee, Goodlettsville, TN; *U.S. Public*, pg. 1590
Yeagley, Albert, Mgr.--Orrville Plant, Orrville, OH; *U.S. Public*, pg. 1480
Yean, Liu Pao, Gen. Mgr.-Cargo--China Airlines Ltd., Los Angeles, CA; *Int'l*, pg. 285
Yearsley, Bob, Mng. Dir.--ISS Darenas Ltd., Sutton Coldfield, United Kingdom; *Int'l*, pg. 657
Yearsley, W.S., Chief Exec. Officer--Western Mobile Inc., Denver, CO; *Int'l*, pg. 1091
Yeary, C.M. Sam, Jr., V.P. & Publisher--Jasper News-Boy, Jasper, TX; *U.S. Private*, pg. 517
Yeates, Douglas T., Pres. & Chief Exec. Officer--Regions Bank/Habersham County, Cornelia, GA; *U.S. Public*, pg. 1372
Yeates, K., Gen. Mgr.--Chloride Power Electronics Inc., Caledonia, NY; *Int'l*, pg. 287
Yeboeh, S., Gen. Mgr.--Johnson's Wax Ltd., Accra, Ghana; *U.S. Private*, pg. 593
Yee, Lung Chia, Gen. Mgr.--China Airlines Ltd., Anchorage, AK; *Int'l*, pg. 285
Yeend, Dee B., Admin.--Hillhaven Convalescent Center Mobile, Mobile, AL; *U.S. Public*, pg. 1713
Yeh, Andy, Gen. Mgr.--Watlow Taiwan, Kao-hsiung, Taiwan; *U.S. Private*, pg. 1154
Yeh, Ch., Chief Exec. Officer--OCE (Taiwan) Ltd., Taipei, Taiwan; *Int'l*, pg. 995
Yeh, Tony, Mng. Dir.--FSQ Taiwan Co. Ltd., Taipei, Taiwan; *Int'l*, pg. 1157
Yelkencioglu, Teoman, Chief Oper. Officer--Linz Kimya Ticaret Ltd. Sirketi, Istanbul, Turkey; *Int'l*, pg. 356
Yellin, R. Dale, Pres.--SAFECO Select Insurance Services, Santa Ana, CA; *U.S. Public*, pg. 1423
Yelton, E. Jay, Pres.--JP Investment Management Co., Greensboro, NC; *U.S. Public*, pg. 925

Yelverton, William F., Chm. & Chief Exec. Officer--New York Life Worldwide Holding, Inc., New York, NY; *U.S. Private*, pg. 795
Yelverton, William F., Chm. Bd.--New York Life (U.K.) Limited, Telford, United Kingdom; *U.S. Private*, pg. 795
Yen, Anthony, Pres.--Adec Automation, Cleveland, OH; *U.S. Private*, pg. 17
Yen, Anthony, Pres.--Adaptive Electronics, Cleveland, OH; *U.S. Private*, pg. 17
Yeo, Dennis G., Chm. & Founder--Multigen Inc., San Jose, CA; *U.S. Public*, pg. 1425
Yeo, Harold, Mng. Dir.--DBS-Capital Trust Securities India Pvt. Ltd., New Delhi, India; *Int'l*, pg. 351
Yeo, Michael, Dir.--GATX Leasing (Pacific) LTD., Singapore, Singapore; *U.S. Public*, pg. 691
Yeo, Michael, Gen. Mgr.-China & Hong Kong--Singapore Tourist Promotion Board - Hong Kong, Wan Chai, Hong Kong; *Int'l*, pg. 1254
Yeo, Michael, Gen. Mgr.--Toys "R" Us-Metro (Singapore) Pte. Ltd., Singapore, Singapore; *U.S. Public*, pg. 1626
Yeo, Sharon, Reg. Dir.-CS Opers./Asia Reg.--Dun & Bradstreet Information Services (M) Sdn. Bhd., Kuala Lumpur, Malaysia; *U.S. Public*, pg. 536
Yeo, Sharon, Reg. Dir.--Dun & Bradstreet (Singapore) Pte. Ltd., Singapore, Singapore; *U.S. Public*, pg. 537
Yeo, Y.K., Gen. Mgr.--ITW Asia (Pte) Ltd., Singapore, Singapore; *U.S. Public*, pg. 868
Yeoh, Seng Aun, Gen. Mgr.--Colgate-Palmolive (Thailand) Ltd., Bangkok, Thailand; *U.S. Public*, pg. 399
Yeovil, Lord Peiton of, Pres.--British Alcan Aluminium plc, Gerrards Cross, United Kingdom; *Int'l*, pg. 51
Yeow, Ong Eng, Mng. Dir.--SKF Malaysia Sdn. Bhd., Kuala Lumpur, Malaysia; *Int'l*, pg. 1159
Yerant, Gene S., Chm. Bd. & Pres.--Transport Insurance Co., Dallas, TX; *U.S. Public*, pg. 75
Yerker, Eugene, Mgr.-Office--Harland Bartholomew & Associates Inc., Jacksonville, FL; *U.S. Private*, pg. 842
Yessin, Erhard, Chief Oper. Officer--Graham Transmissions Inc/Graham Gear Systems, Inc, Milwaukee, WI; *Int'l*, pg. 377
Yetman, Gary E., Chm. Bd.--Wagner Stott Clearing Corp., New York, NY; *U.S. Public*, pg. 1097
Yetter, Wayne, Chief Exec. Officer--Novartis Pharmaceuticals, East Hanover, NJ; *Int'l*, pg. 973
Yetter, Wayne P., Gen. Mgr.--Astra/Merck Group, Rahway, NJ; *U.S. Public*, pg. 1091
Yeung, Charles C.K., Dir.--Farah (Far East) Limited, Kowloon, Hong Kong; *U.S. Public*, pg. 613
Yeung, G., Regional Dir.--Kodak (Far East) Limited, North Point, Hong Kong; *U.S. Public*, pg. 553
Yeung, Lillienne, Dr., Mng. Dir.--Shanghai Johnson & Johnson Ltd., Shanghai, China; *U.S. Public*, pg. 932
Yew, Helen, Chief Oper. Officer--Royal Copenhagen (Hong Kong) Ltd., Hong Kong, Hong Kong; *Int'l*, pg. 1135
Yhouse, Paul A., Chief Exec. Officer--Holnam Inc., Dundee, MI; *Int'l*, pg. 628
Yi, Sang Won, Rep.--Cariplo (Seoul), Seoul, Korea; *Int'l*, pg. 275
Yiakas, Gus, Pres.--Wyle Laboratories-Western Operations, El Segundo, CA; *U.S. Private*, pg. 1193
Yildiz, Asim, Gen. Mgr.--AMP Elektrik-Elektronik, Istanbul, Turkey; *U.S. Public*, pg. 8
Ying, Hu Shao, Mgr.-District Sls.--China Airlines Ltd., Honolulu, HI; *Int'l*, pg. 285
Yip, Didi K., Mng. Dir.--MacMillan Bloedel (Asia) Limited, Hong Kong, Hong Kong; *Int'l*, pg. 829
Yip, G.C., Pres.--Adason Properties Limited, Toronto, Canada; *Int'l*, pg. 254
Yip, J.K., Reg. Dir.--Sime Singapore Limited, Singapore, Singapore; *Int'l*, pg. 1251
Yiu, Louis, Gen. Mgr.--Corex Technology (HK) Ltd., Kowloon, Hong Kong; *Int'l*, pg. 651
Yoba, Gerald, Pres.--Great Lakes-Eglinton, Bridgeport, MI; *U.S. Public*, pg. 1676
Yochum, Jerry, Pres.--Dover Diversified, Waukesha, WI; *U.S. Public*, pg. 521
Yocum, Dr. Ronald H., Pres. & Chief Exec. Officer--Millennium Petrochemicals, Inc., Cincinnati, OH; *Int'l*, pg. 594
Yoda, Osamu, Chief Oper. Officer--Kinseki, Ltd., Kawasaki, Japan; *Int'l*, pg. 999
Yoder, Edward, V.P.-Opers.--AlliedSignal Turbocharging & Truck Brake Systems, Torrance, CA; *U.S. Public*, pg. 51
Yoder, Edward L., Pres. & Chief Exec. Officer--Rurban Life Insurance Company, Defiance, OH; *U.S. Public*, pg. 1413
Yoder, Steve, Pres.--American Systems Technologies, Verona, WI; *U.S. Public*, pg. 2
Yoe, Robert H., III, Pres.--DeSoto Mills, Inc., Fort Payne, AL; *U.S. Public*, pg. 1413
Yogi, Dave, Mgr.-Office--Woodward-Clyde, Honolulu, HI; *U.S. Public*, pg. 1656
Yoguchi, Hiroshi, Chief Rep.--The Industrial Bank of Japan, Limited (Mexico), Mexico, Mexico; *Int'l*, pg. 675
Yoguelet, Clark, Admin.--Heritage Village, Richardson, TX; *U.S. Public*, pg. 839
Yoh, Karen B., Pres.--Barclay Travel Agency, Moorestown, NJ; *U.S. Private*, pg. 317
Yoh, Michael H., Pres.--Munitions Technology Division, Nash, TX; *U.S. Private*, pg. 317
Yohe, Frank, Chief Oper. Officer--MXL Industries, Inc., Lancaster, PA; *U.S. Public*, pg. 694
Yoho, Mendal L., Sr. V.P.--CNG Transmission Corporation, Clarksburg, WV; *U.S. Public*, pg. 435
Yokomizo, Michio, Chief Exec. Officer--Novo Nordisk Biochemicals KK, Hokkaido, Japan; *Int'l*, pg. 989
Yokotani, Hiroshi, Chief Oper. Officer--Daiko Advertising, Inc., Fukuoka, Japan; *Int'l*, pg. 366
Yokouchi, Akira, Pres.--Nissho Iwai Canada Ltd., Toronto, Canada; *Int'l*, pg. 948
Yokoyama, Masayuki, Pres.--KHI Europe Finance B.V., Amsterdam, Netherlands; *Int'l*, pg. 726
Yokoyama, Muneaki, Pres.--Hakuhodo Pro's, Inc., Tokyo, Japan; *Int'l*, pg. 588
Yokoyama, Ryoji, Pres.--Hitachi Chemical Co., Ltd., Tokyo, Japan; *Int'l*, pg. 621
Yoldi, E., Chief Fin. Officer--Lucas Girling S.A., Pamplona, Spain; *Int'l*, pg. 820
Yoldi, Emilio, Gen. Mgr.--Wang Espana, S.A., Madrid, Spain; *U.S. Public*, pg. 1737
Yomada, Susumu, Mgr.--Daido Hoxan Inc., Osaka, Japan; *Int'l*, pg. 363
Yomada, Takeshi, Chief Oper. Officer--Honda R&D North America, Inc., Torrance, CA; *Int'l*, pg. 634
Yon, S., Chief Exec. Officer--Holaday Industries, Inc., Eden Prairie, MN; *Int'l*, pg. 208
Yoneda, Kozo, Gen. Mgr.--The Sumitomo Bank, Ltd.-Bangkok International Banking Facility, Bangkok, Thailand; *Int'l*, pg. 1309
Yoneda, Kozo, Gen. Mgr.--P.I.B.F. Ayutthaya Branch, Ayutthaya, Thailand; *Int'l*, pg. 1310
Yoneda, Kozo, Gen. Mgr.--P.I.B.F. Chon Buri Branch, Chon Buri, Thailand; *Int'l*, pg. 1310
Yoneda, Takatomo, Chief Rep.--The Industrial Bank of Japan, Limited (Bangkok), Bangkok, Thailand; *Int'l*, pg. 675
Yonemitsu, Keiichi, Chief Oper. Officer--Nippon Oil (Asia) Pte. Ltd., Singapore, Singapore; *Int'l*, pg. 937
Yonetani, Nobuo, Chief Exec. Officer--Daiwa Europe Bank plc, London, United Kingdom; *Int'l*, pg. 375
Yoneyama, Minoru, Pres.--Yonex Corporation, Torrance, CA; *Int'l*, pg. 1522
Yonezawa, T., Pres.--Toshiba Semiconductor (Thailand) Co., Ltd., Pathum Thani, Thailand; *Int'l*, pg. 1407
Yong, Kim Ki, Mng. Dir.--Purina Korea Inc., Seoul, Korea; *U.S. Public*, pg. 1360
Yoo, B.Y., Gen. Mgr.--John Crane (Korea) Co., Ltd., Seoul, Korea; *Int'l*, pg. 1339
Yoo, Chong-Yul, Pres.--Hyosung Industries Co., Ltd., Seoul, Korea; *Int'l*, pg. 640
Yoo, K.B., Pres.--Daewoo International America Corp. - Ridgefield, Ridgefield Park, NJ; *Int'l*, pg. 357
Yoon, Leong Cheng, Dir.--Takenaka (Malaysia) Sdn. Bhd., Penang, Penang, Malaysia; *Int'l*, pg. 1351
Yoong, Y.L., Gen. Mgr.--AMP Singapore PTE. Ltd., Singapore, Singapore; *U.S. Public*, pg. 9
Yooprasert, Prin, Mgr.-Dist. Sls.--Thai Airways Intl. Ltd.-New York, New York, NY; *Int'l*, pg. 1381
Yorio, Ralph N., Pres.--Vibratech, Inc., Alden, NY; *U.S. Public*, pg. 862
York, D., Mng. Dir.--Ballast Phoenix Ltd., Bourne, United Kingdom; *Int'l*, pg. 133
York, Edward J., Branch Mgr.--Piper Jaffray Inc., Colorado Springs, CO; *U.S. Public*, pg. 1302
York, James, V.P.--The Bank of Nova Scotia, San Francisco, CA; *Int'l*, pg. 156
Yorke, Betsy, Gen. Mgr.--Admore Inc., Mount Clemens, MI; *U.S. Public*, pg. 583
Yorke, D., Mng. Dir.--Alexander Drew & Sons Ltd., Rochdale, United Kingdom; *Int'l*, pg. 798
Yorke, D., V.P.--Hybrid Products, Pearl River, NY; *Int'l*, pg. 1283
Yoshida, H., Mng. Dir.--Toshiba International (Europe) Ltd., Uxbridge, United Kingdom; *Int'l*, pg. 1406
Yoshida, Haruki, Pres.--The Wako Research Institute of Economics, Inc. (WRI), Tokyo, Japan; *Int'l*, pg. 1485
Yoshida, Hiromi, Pres.--SEIKO France S.A., Paris, France; *Int'l*, pg. 1218
Yoshida, Hitoshi, Mng. Dir.--The Meijiseimei International, London Ltd., London, United Kingdom; *Int'l*, pg. 854
Yoshida, Hitoshi, Mng. Dir.--The Meijiseimei Property U.K. Ltd., London, United Kingdom; *Int'l*, pg. 855
Yoshida, K., Pres.--Nissho Iwai Industrial Machinery Inc., Osaka, Japan; *Int'l*, pg. 946
Yoshida, Kanetaka, Pres. & Chief Exec. Officer--Union Bank of California, San Francisco, CA; *Int'l*, pg. 157
Yoshida, Katsumi, Pres.--Ricoh Electronics, Inc., Tustin, CA; *Int'l*, pg. 1114
Yoshida, Masaki, Pres.--Japan Associated Finance Co., Ltd., Tokyo, Japan; *Int'l*, pg. 955
Yoshida, Masamichi, Chief Rep.--The Sumitomo Bank, Ltd.-Beijing Representative Office, Beijing, China; *Int'l*, pg. 1309
Yoshida, Mitsunobu, Chief Oper. Officer--TM Management Services Limited, London, United Kingdom; *Int'l*, pg. 1392
Yoshida, Nobuyuki, Pres.--Kawasaki Heavy Industries GmbH, Dusseldorf, Germany; *Int'l*, pg. 726
Yoshida, Shu, Pres.--Kobelco Stewart Bolling Inc., Hudson, OH; *Int'l*, pg. 740
Yoshida, Susumu, Pres.--Sumitomo Chemical America, Inc., New York, NY; *Int'l*, pg. 1311
Yoshida, Tadashi, Chm. Bd.--NEC Industries (UK) Plc., London, United Kingdom; *Int'l*, pg. 900
Yoshida, Teruyaki, Gen. Mgr.--Toyo Trust Company of New York, New York, NY; *Int'l*, pg. 1411
Yoshida, Y., Mng. Dir.--Toshiba International Corporation Pty., Ltd., Lane Cove, Australia; *Int'l*, pg. 1406
Yoshida, Yoichi, Pres.--Chiba International Ltd., London, United Kingdom; *Int'l*, pg. 283
Yoshida, Youzou, Chief Oper. Officer--Honda Sogo Tatemono Co., Ltd., Tokyo, Japan; *Int'l*, pg. 634
Yoshida, Yutaka, Dir.--Dai Nippon Printing Co. (Singapore) Pte. Ltd., Singapore, Singapore; *Int'l*, pg. 363
Yoshihira, Soichi, Mng. Dir.--DKB Futures (Singapore) Pte Ltd., Singapore, Singapore; *Int'l*, pg. 361
Yoshihiro, Seiya, Sr. V.P.--Dentsu USA-Atlanta Office, Atlanta, GA; *Int'l*, pg. 393
Yoshikawa, Atsushi, Co-Pres.--Nomura Holding America, Inc., New York, NY; *Int'l*, pg. 956
Yoshikawa, Kazuo, V.P.--AlliedSignal Inc. Asia, Tokyo, Japan; *U.S. Public*, pg. 52
Yoshikawa, Masataka, Pres.--Bank of Tokyo-Mitsubishi Ltd. (Miami Agency), Coral Gables, FL; *Int'l*, pg. 157
Yoshikawa, Motoo, Chief Rep.--Toray Industries, Inc.-Beijing Office, Beijing, China; *Int'l*, pg. 1400
Yoshikawa, Togo, Gen. Mgr.--Showpla Hong Kong Ltd., Hong Kong, Hong Kong; *Int'l*, pg. 1237
Yoshimura, M., Gen. Mgr.--AMP (Japan), Ltd., Yokohama, Japan; *U.S. Public*, pg. 9
Yoshimura, Masayoshi, Mng. Dir.--Nanto Business Service Co., Ltd., Nara, Japan; *Int'l*, pg. 905
Yoshimura, Toru, Gen. Mgr.--Chiba Bank, Ltd.-Hong Kong Branch, Hong Kong, Hong Kong; *Int'l*, pg. 283
Yoshino, Akijiro, Chief Rep.--The Industrial Bank of Japan, Limited (Houston), Houston, TX; *Int'l*, pg. 674
Yoshino, Issei, Pres.--Nissan Mexicana, S.A. de C.V., Mexico, Mexico; *Int'l*, pg. 945
Yoshioka, Jim, Pres.--California Hospital Medical Center, Los Angeles, CA; *U.S. Private*, pg. 1118
Yoshioka, Mutsuo, Pres.--Kubota George Fischer Ltd., Osaka, Japan; *Int'l*, pg. 490
Yoshioka, Takaaki, Gen. Mgr.--The Bank of Tokyo-Mitsubishi, Ltd. (Madrid Branch), Madrid, Spain; *Int'l*, pg. 158
Yoshitaka, Inove, Gen. Mgr.--Tokico (USA) Inc., Berea, KY; *Int'l*, pg. 1391
Yoshitome, Yasuo, Pres., Mng. Dir.--Dentsu (Thailand) Ltd., Bangkok, Thailand; *Int'l*, pg. 394
Yoshizawa, Masashi, Chief Oper. Officer--Nippon Oil Exploration U.S.A. Limited, Houston, TX; *Int'l*, pg. 937
Yoshizumi, M., Mng. Dir.--ISK (Europe) S.A., Brussels, Belgium; *Int'l*, pg. 689
Yost, Carl, Pres.--Day & Zimmerman Construction Inc., Greenville, SC; *U.S. Private*, pg. 317
Yost, Daniel, Pres. & Gen. Mgr.-Metrocel Cellular Telephone Co., Dallas--LIN Cellular Group, Kirkland, WA; *U.S. Public*, pg. 11
Yotsumoto, Osamu, Pres.--Kawasaki Heavy Industries (Singapore) Pte. Ltd., Singapore, Singapore; *Int'l*, pg. 726
Youkhana, Arminak, Mgr.-Sls.--Kuwait Airways, Central USA, Arlington Heights, IL; *Int'l*, pg. 764
Youmans, Tammy, Chief Fin. Officer--Richard Hirschmann of America, Inc., Riverdale, NJ; *Int'l*, pg. 1108
Younes, Rami E., Pres. & Chief Exec. Officer--Advanced Monobloc Inc., Don Mills, Canada; *Int'l*, pg. 238
Young, Aubrey, Chm.--Liberty National Bank and Trust Company of Central Kentucky, Elizabethtown, KY; *U.S. Public*, pg. 173
Young, B.W., Gen. Mgr.--GF Food Services, Alexandria, Australia; *Int'l*, pg. 555
Young, Bob, Plant Mgr.--L.B. Foster Company-Langfield Yard, Houston, TX; *U.S. Public*, pg. 676
Young, C. Steve, Pres. & Chief Exec. Officer--MicroBilt Corporation, Atlanta, GA; *U.S. Public*, pg. 631
Young, C.H., Mng. Dir.--GEC Estates Department, London, United Kingdom; *Int'l*, pg. 544
Young, Christine, Branch Mgr.--Downey Savings & Loan Association, F.A., San Marcos, CA; *U.S. Public*, pg. 527
Young, Christine A., V.P. & Gen. Mgr.--Nexus Healthcare, Inc., Columbus, OH; *U.S. Public*, pg. 304
Young, Clifford, Jr., Pres.--Florida Heat Pump, Fort Lauderdale, FL; *U.S. Private*, pg. 506
Young, D. J., Div. Pres.--Melburn Truck Lines, Mississauga, Canada; *Int'l*, pg. 1262
Young, D.J., Mng. Dir.--Simon-Holder Ltd., Bury, United Kingdom; *Int'l*, pg. 1251
Young, Frederick C., Pres. & Chief Oper. Officer--Black Box Corporation of Pennsylvania, Lawrence, PA; *U.S. Public*, pg. 235
Young, George, Plant Mgr.--Salem Carpet Mills, Dalton, GA; *U.S. Public*, pg. 1464
Young, H.P., Chief Oper. Officer--Vascor, Ltd., Georgetown, KY; *Int'l*, pg. 912
Young, Harrison, Pres.--International Business Services, Inc., Vienna, VA; *U.S. Public*, pg. 406
Young, Harrison, Pres.--Decisions & Design, Inc., Vienna, VA; *U.S. Public*, pg. 406
Young, J., Mgr.--American Natl. Can Co., Graphic Arts Div., Bellwood, IL; *Int'l*, pg. 1029
Young, Jack, Chief Exec. Officer--Pocono Knits, Inc., Hazleton, PA; *U.S. Private*, pg. 1201
Young, Jayne, Pres. & Publr.--The Atlantic Advertising Sales, New York, NY; *U.S. Private*, pg. 95
Young, Jeff, Pres.--Lexington Furniture Industries, Lexington, NC; *U.S. Private*, pg. 432
Young, Jerry, Mgr.--Shorrock Security Ltd., Swindon, United Kingdom; *Int'l*, pg. 1285
Young, Jerry D., Pres.--Borden Foods Canada, Etobicoke, Canada; *U.S. Private*, pg. 159
Young, John, Chief Exec. Officer--Hewlett Packard Avondale, Wilmington, DE; *U.S. Public*, pg. 816
Young, John, Publisher--Today's Homeowner, New York, NY; *U.S. Public*, pg. 1617
Young, John C., Pres.--Universal Promotions, Inc., West Chester, PA; *U.S. Private*, pg. 707
Young, Kathy, Plant Mgr.--Baskin Robbins Production Facility, Peterborough, Canada; *Int'l*, pg. 63
Young, Lawrence J., Pres.--Angelica Image Apparel, Saint Louis, MO; *U.S. Public*, pg. 113
Young, Lawrence J., Pres.--Life Uniform & Shoe Shops, Saint Louis, MO; *U.S. Public*, pg. 113
Young, Lee In, Pres.--Top Mix Concrete, Singapore, Singapore; *Int'l*, pg. 1293
Young, Lee In, Pres.--Aeracom Technologies Pte. Ltd., Jurong, Singapore; *Int'l*, pg. 1293
Young, M.D., Chm.--Automotive Finance Limited, London, United Kingdom; *U.S. Public*, pg. 665
Young, Mary, Sec.--Liberty National Bank and Trust Company of Central Kentucky, Elizabethtown, KY; *U.S. Public*, pg. 173
Young, Michael, V.P. & Gen. Mgr.--Stanhome S.A., Puteaux, France; *U.S. Public*, pg. 1508
Young, Patricia, Pres.--Canadian Ad-Check Services Inc., Markham, Canada; *Int'l*, pg. 1124
Young, Phillip G., V.P. & Controller--Bergen Brunswig Medical Corporation, Montgomery, AL; *U.S. Public*, pg. 214
Young, R.J., Chm. Bd.--Harvey Plant Limited, Bedworth, United Kingdom; *Int'l*, pg. 910

Young, R.J., Chm. Bd.--Jaguar Cars Finance Limited, Coventry, United Kingdom; *Int'l*, pg. 910
Young, R.J., Chm. Bd.--Transfleet Services Limited, Coventry, United Kingdom; *Int'l*, pg. 911
Young, R.N., Pres.--Borden (U.K.) Ltd., Southampton, United Kingdom; *U.S. Private*, pg. 159
Young, Richard, Chief Fin. Officer--Banca March S.A., London, United Kingdom; *Int'l*, pg. 136
Young, Richard P., Pres.--Richard Young Office Products, Inc., Deerfield Beach, FL; *U.S. Public*, pg. 450
Young, Robert F., Publisher--Good Food Magazine, New York, NY; *Int'l*, pg. 925
Young, Robert F., Gen. Mgr.--Martin Marietta International, Inc., Tokyo, Japan; *U.S. Public*, pg. 1009
Young, Robert H., Pres.--C.V. Realty, Inc., Rutland, VT; *U.S. Public*, pg. 328
Young, Robert H., Pres. & Chief Exec. Officer--Connecticut Valley Electric Co., Inc., Rutland, VT; *U.S. Public*, pg. 328
Young, Robert H., Chm. Bd.--Vermont Yankee Nuclear Power Corp., Brattleboro, VT; *U.S. Public*, pg. 328
Young, Robert H., Pres. & Chief Exec. Officer--Smart Energy Services, Inc., Rutland, VT; *U.S. Public*, pg. 328
Young, Robert H., Pres.--Catamount Investment Corporation, Rutland, VT; *U.S. Public*, pg. 328
Young, Robert S., Pres.--Young Environmental Clean Up, Flint, MI; *U.S. Private*, pg. 1202
Young, Roger A., Pres.--Northern Utilities, Inc., Portsmouth, NH; *U.S. Public*, pg. 197
Young, Stan, Mgr.--Commercial Metals Co., Jacksonville, FL; *U.S. Public*, pg. 413
Young, Stephen, Mng. Dir.--Perry Equipment Ltd., Thetford, United Kingdom; *U.S. Private*, pg. 855
Young, Terry, Pres. & V.P.--Port City Press, Inc., Pikesville, MD; *U.S. Private*, pg. 855
Young, Thomas, Pres.--Finishmaster Inc., Muskegon, MI; *U.S. Private*, pg. 639
Young, Thomas J., Pres. & Chief Exec. Officer--BancIreland/First Financial Inc., Boston, MA; *Int'l*, pg. 152
Young, Tom, Pres.--Busse Brothers Inc., Randolph, WI; *U.S. Private*, pg. 866
Young, William, Plant Mgr.--Shredded Products Corp., Montvale, VA; *U.S. Public*, pg. 1392
Young, William B., Pres. & Chief Exec. Officer--The National Bank of Fredericksburg, Fredericksburg, VA; *U.S. Public*, *pg. 1089*
Young, William D., Sr., Pres. & Chief Exec. Officer--General Wholesale Company, Spartanburg, SC; *U.S. Private*, pg. 446
Youngblood, Henri, Pres.--World Trade Transport of Virginia, Sterling, VA; *U.S. Public*, pg. 749
Youngblood, James, Mgr.--Metclad S.A., Lannemezan, France; *U.S. Public*, pg. 1258
Youngblood, Ken, Regional Pres.--First Tennessee Bank - Maryville, Maryville, TN; *U.S. Public*, pg. 639
Youngblood, W. Dale, Mgr.--Fabrication Plant/Custom Products, Waco, TX; *U.S. Public*, pg. 1177
Younger, Geoffrey, Mng. Dir.--Thule Ltd., Bristol, United Kingdom; *Int'l*, pg. 436
Younger, Peter, Gen. Mgr.--Semiconductor Equipment Division, Beverly, MA; *U.S. Public*, pg. 557
Youngman, David, Chm. Bd.--Coates Brothers PLC, Saint Mary Cray, United Kingdom; *Int'l*, pg. 1409
Youngman, Frank W., Mng. Dir.--Delta Precision Ltd., Enfield, United Kingdom; *Int'l*, pg. 391
Yount, Bradley A., Pres. & Chief Exec. Officer--Specialty Filaments Inc., Andover, MA; *U.S. Private*, pg. 77
Yousen, Robert W., Gen. Mgr.--Technical Specialties Division, Fitchburg, MA; *U.S. Public*, pg. 620
Youssefzadeh, Emil, Pres.--Satellite Technical Management, Costa Mesa, CA; *Int'l*, pg. 1154
Yowell, C., Div. Mgr.--Tropar Mfg. Co., Inc., Ennis, TX; *U.S. Private*, pg. 1105
Ysewijn, Henri, Pres.--Airtec Division, Wilrijk, Belgium; *Int'l*, pg. 96
Yu, David, Mgr.-Sls.--Thai Airways Intl. Ltd.-Toronto, Toronto, Canada; *Int'l*, pg. 1381
Yu, Peter, Gen. Mgr.--Golden Donuts SBN. BHD., Kuala Lumpur, Malaysia; *Int'l*, pg. 63
Yuasa, Hisao, Chm. & Chief Exec. Officer--Ricoh Corporation, West Caldwell, NJ; *Int'l*, pg. 1114
Yuasa, Masakazu, Mng. Dir.--Hakuhodo Inc., Fukuoka, Japan; *Int'l*, pg. 587
Yuchengco, Y.S., Chief Exec. Officer--First Nationwide Assurance Corporation, Manila, Philippines; *Int'l*, pg. 1532
Yuchengco, Y.S., Chief Exec. Officer--Malayan Insurance Company, Inc., Manila, Philippines; *Int'l*, pg. 1532
Yuchengco, Y.S., Chief Exec. Officer--Malayan Zurich Insurance Company, Inc., Makati, Philippines; *Int'l*, pg. 1532
Yuen, Chow Yew, Mgr.--AMFELS Inc., Brownsville, TX; *Int'l*, *pg. 731*
Yuen, Jackson, Mgr.--Orion Research Far East Inc., Hong Kong, Hong Kong; *U.S. Public*, pg. 1592
Yuen, John A., Mng. Dir.--Johnson & Johnson Medical Hong Kong, Kowloon, Hong Kong; *U.S. Public*, pg. 931
Yuhjtman, Ephraim, Rep. for Argentina--Bank Hapoalim (Buenos Aires), Buenos Aires, Argentina; *Int'l*, pg. 149
Yui, Akira, Pres., Chief Oper. Officer--Dentsu Burson Marsteller, Inc., New York, NY; *Int'l*, pg. 393
Yui, Toshiaki, Gen. Mgr.--Beijing Dentsu Shanghai Branch (Dentsu Shanghai), Shanghai, China; *Int'l*, pg. 393
Yuill, Jeremy, Mng. Dir.--Arthur Hart Webbing, Somerset, United Kingdom; *Int'l*, pg. 215
Yuki, Hiroshi, Gen. Mgr.--Kanebo Cosmetics of Hawaii, Inc., Honolulu, HI; *Int'l*, pg. 722
Yun, Chu Keng, Chief Oper. Officer--Digiphonic Systems Pte. Ltd., Singapore, Singapore; *Int'l*, pg. 1000
Yun, David, Pres.--Scholastic Book Fairs, Inc., Lake Mary, FL; *U.S. Public*, pg. 1440
Yun, Kyu Soung, Gen. Mgr.--Cho Hung Bank, Tokyo Branch, Tokyo, Japan; *Int'l*, pg. 288
Yun, Lee Jae, Pres.--Kelim Toto Co., Ltd., Kyung Buk, Korea; *Int'l*, pg. 1410
Yun, Yeo Jik, Agent--Cho Hung Bank - San Francisco, San Francisco, CA; *Int'l*, pg. 287
Yundt, Jeffrey W., Pres.--NIPSCO Energy Trading Corporation, Inc., Hammond, IN; *U.S. Public*, pg. 1185
Yung, Kelvin SK, Rep.--Generale Belgian Bank, Guangzhou, China; *Int'l*, pg. 547
Yunkun, Chris, Pres. & Gen. Mgr.--Pettibone Michigan Div., Baraga, MI; *U.S. Private*, pg. 860
Yurch, George, Gen. Mgr.--Mako Compressors, Inc., Ocala, FL; *Int'l*, pg. 1243
Yurek, William L., Mgr.-SPD--Latrobe Special Products Div., Latrobe, PA; *U.S. Public*, pg. 1617
Yusa, Shigeyuki, Pres.--The Meijiseimei Insurance Services of California, Inc., San Francisco, CA; *Int'l*, pg. 854
Yusof, Nasura, Gen. Mgr. & Dir.--Solus Oceaneering (Malaysia) Sdn. Bhd., Kuala Lumpur, Malaysia; *U.S. Public*, pg. 1211
Yusuf, Yuhaini, Dir.--Tourism Malaysia - Stockholm Office, Stockholm, Sweden; *Int'l*, pg. 833
Yutaka, Masaru, Chm.--ORIX Alpha Corporation, Tokyo, Japan; *Int'l*, pg. 1008
Yuzawa, Noburu, Dir. & Gen. Mgr.--Fuji Heavy Industries, Ltd., Bus. Div., Isesaki, Japan; *Int'l*, pg. 523
Yuzon, Virgilio A., Chm.--Hemisphere-Leo Burnett, Inc., Manila, Philippines; *U.S. Private*, pg. 184
Yves, Fallouey, Chief Oper. Officer--Societe Mecanique Automobile de l'est, Hagondange, France; *Int'l*, pg. 1020
Yveviar, Gan Mar, Gen. Dir.--L'Oreal Belgilux SA, Brussels, Belgium; *Int'l*, pg. 819
Zabaski, Peter, Pres.--One Stop Supply, Inc., Nashville, TN; *U.S. Public*, pg. 847
Zabin, Burton A., V.P. & Gen. Mgr.--Life Science Group of Bio-Rad, Hercules, CA; *U.S. Public*, pg. 230
Zabriskie, John L., Pres.--Merck Manufacturing Div., Rahway, NJ; *U.S. Public*, pg. 1091
Zaccaglin, Victor, Chief Exec. Officer--West Coast Conversion Co., Inc., Los Angeles, CA; *U.S. Public*, pg. 296
Zacharias, J.D., Pres.--Celfortec Inc., Valleyfield, Canada; *Int'l*, pg. 698
Zachary, C. Ross, Jr., Pres.--Rigesa, Ltda., Sao Paulo, Brazil; *U.S. Public*, pg. 1762
Zachary, Norman, Mng. Dir.--Logica Technology Systems, Inc., Wellesley Hills, MA; *Int'l*, pg. 814
Zacky, Albert, Pres.--Integrated Grain & Milling, South El Monte, CA; *U.S. Private*, pg. 1203
Zacky, Robert, Pres.--Zacky Foods, South El Monte, CA; *U.S. Private*, pg. 1203
Zacky, Robert, Pres.--Stockton Further Processing, South El Monte, CA; *U.S. Private*, pg. 1203
Zacny, R.J., V.P. & Gen. Mgr.--Serv-Air, Inc., Greenville, TX; *U.S. Public*, pg. 1366
Zadel, William, Pres.--CIBA Corning Diagnostics Corp., Medfield, MA; *Int'l*, pg. 973
Zadig, Lennart, Chief Oper. Officer--AxTrade Dental AB, Solna, Sweden; *Int'l*, pg. 708
Zaeb, John, Dir.-Info. Systems & Services, Europe--AlliedSignal Europe N.V., Heverlee, Belgium; *U.S. Public*, *pg. 52*
Zaengerle, Rudolf, Pres.--Von Roll, Inc., Duluth, GA; *Int'l*, pg. 1480
Zafiropoulo, Arthur W., Pres.--Kayex Corp., Rochester, NY; *U.S. Public*, pg. 727
Zafra, Joaquim, Chief Oper. Officer--Gambro S.A., Madrid, Spain; *Int'l*, pg. 668
Zagar, Constance L., Pres.--Litton Precision Products International, Munich, Germany; *U.S. Public*, pg. 1004
Zagar, Constance L., Pres.-International Div.--Litton Precision Products (Switzerland), Zurich, Switzerland; *U.S. Public*, pg. 1004
Zagra, Cemal, Gen. Mgr.--Sark Sigorta T.A.S. (RAS), Istanbul, Turkey; *Int'l*, pg. 62
Zahid, Abdullah Md, Mgr.--Willis Faber (Malaysia) Sdn Bhd, Kuala Lumpur, Malaysia; *Int'l*, pg. 1510
Zahid, Mohammad, Chief Oper. Officer--National Bank of Pakistan, Chicago, IL; *Int'l*, pg. 908
Zahn, Randall, Pres.--Uniseal, Inc., Evansville, IN; *U.S. Private*, pg. 628
Zahn, Richard W., Pres.--Schering Laboratories, Kenilworth, NJ; *U.S. Public*, pg. 1438
Zahrt, Curtis, Gen. Mgr.--Nash Finch Co., Omaha, NE; *U.S. Public*, pg. 1152
Zaidi, S.K.A., Chief Oper. Officer--Novo Nordisk A/S, Karachi, Pakistan; *Int'l*, pg. 988
Zaidi, S.R.M., Exec. V.P. & Gen. Mgr.--Habib Bank Ltd., Nairobi, Kenya; *Int'l*, pg. 584
Zain, Tan S.A.A.B., Chm. Bd.--Teamwork Corporation Sdn Bhd, Kuala Lumpur, Malaysia; *Int'l*, pg. 1360
Zaine, Bo, Mng. Dir.--Telefonos Ericsson C.A., Quito, Ecuador; *Int'l*, pg. 1371
Zajak, Robert, Mng. Dir.--Mountaingate Engineering, Inc., Campbell, CA; *U.S. Public*, pg. 1188
Zajos, Ferenc, Chief Oper. Officer--Gambro kft, Budapest, Hungary; *Int'l*, pg. 667
Zak, Michael T., Pres.--BHA Company, Inc., Kansas City, MO; *U.S. Public*, pg. 161
Zak, Michael T., Pres.--PrecipTech, Inc., Kansas City, MO; *U.S. Public*, pg. 161
Zakahi, George, Branch Mgr.--Gasco, Inc., Lihue, HI; *Int'l*, pg. 225
Zakheim, Dov S., Dr., Chief Exec. Officer--SPC International Corp., Arlington, VA; *U.S. Private*, pg. 1061
Zaki, Galal, Pres.--Intermarkets Egypt, Cairo, Egypt; *Int'l*, pg. 680
Zaldariaggo, Ana, Gen. Mgr.--Gonzalez y Gonzalez, New York, NY; *U.S. Public*, pg. 130
Zalduondo, Carlos, V.P. & Mng. Dir.--Allergan-Lok Produtos, Farmaceuticos, Ltda., Sao Paulo, Brazil; *U.S. Public*, pg. 46
Zaleski, Stephen C., Pres.--New York Systems Exchange Corp., Melville, NY; *U.S. Private*, pg. 1060
Zalieckas, Joseph, Chief Oper. Officer--Beaut-Ease Corporation, Bedford Park, IL; *U.S. Private*, pg. 551
Zaliwski, Janusz, Mng. Dir.--American Appraisal Poland Sp. z.o.o., Warsaw, Poland; *U.S. Private*, pg. 50
Zaloker, Ante, Chief Oper. Officer--Novo Nordisk A/S, Ljubljana, Slovenia; *Int'l*, pg. 988
Zaloom, E. Anthony, Partner--Skadden, Arps, Slate, Meagher & Flom LLP, Beijing, China; *U.S. Private*, pg. 1004
Zaloom, E. Anthony, Partner--Skadden, Arps, Slate, Meagher & Flom, Tokyo, Japan; *U.S. Private*, pg. 1005
Zaloum, Marcel G., Pres.--Italia S.p.A., Milan, Italy; *U.S. Public*, pg. 912
Zalzal, Samir J., Pres. & Chief Exec. Officer--Ingersoll-Rand Canada, Inc., Kirkland, Canada; *U.S. Public*, pg. 878
Zambelli, Jean-Claude, Chief Oper. Officer--Matra Design Semiconductor Corp., Santa Clara, CA; *Int'l*, pg. 795
Zambrano, Marcelo, Chm.--Tolmex S.A. de C.V., Monterrey, Mexico; *Int'l*, pg. 278
Zamiar, George J., Gen. Mgr.--Notifier Network Technologies Company, Louisville, KY; *U.S. Public*, pg. 1306
Zamir, Zeev, Gen. Mgr.--MSI Engineering Software Ltd., Tel Aviv, Israel; *U.S. Public*, pg. 1032
Zamora, Louis, Mgr.--Universal Telephone Southwest-Pecos, Pecos, NM; *U.S. Public*, pg. 330
Zamora, M., Gen. Mgr.--De La Rue Lerchundi SA, Bilbao, Spain; *Int'l*, pg. 386
Zampa, Stefano, Commercial Mgr.--Whitehall Venezuela, Caracas, Venezuela; *U.S. Public*, pg. 81
Zampetis, Theodore K., Pres. & Chief Oper. Officer--The Standard Products Company, Dearborn, MI; *U.S. Public*, pg. 1504
Zanck, Charie A., Pres., Chief Exec. Officer & Dir.--AMCORE Bank N.A., Northwest, Woodstock, IL; *U.S. Public*, pg. 64
Zandee, D.W., Mng. Dir.--Placer Pacific Limited, Sydney, Australia; *Int'l*, pg. 1060
Zander, Edward J., Pres.--SunSoft, Mountain View, CA; *U.S. Public*, pg. 1531
Zanderigo, V., Rep.--Cariplo (Frankfurt A/M), Frankfurt/Main, Germany; *Int'l*, pg. 275
Zandman, Dr. Felix, Chief Opr. Officer--Vishay Resistor Products, Tustin, CA; *U.S. Public*, pg. 1722
Zandomenengo, Giacomo, Grp. Pres.-Latin America--Leo Burnett Worldwide, Latin American Hdqtrs., Coral Gables, FL; *U.S. Private*, pg. 184
Zangerle, E., Mng. Dir.--Bally Trading AG, Schonenwerd, Switzerland; *Int'l*, pg. 996
Zangerle, E., Mng. Dir.--Bally Schuhfabriken S.A., Schonenwerd, Switzerland; *Int'l*, pg. 996
Zangerle, Rudolf, Dir.--Von Roll AG Departement Umwelttechnik, Zurich, Switzerland; *Int'l*, pg. 1480
Zannini, Oscar, Acting Dir.--Multi Language Center SrL, Milan, Italy; *U.S. Public*, pg. 222
Zanowski, Greg, Sr. Mktg. Officer--Western Marketing Div., Southfield, MI; *U.S. Private*, pg. 296
Zanto, Lawrence, Asst. V.P.-Property & Casualty--Willis Corroon Administrative Services Corporation, Helena, MT; *Int'l*, pg. 1504
Zapevalova, Natalie, Dir. Gen.--Chudovo-RWS, Chudovo, Russia; *Int'l*, pg. 1429
Zapico, Antonio Rodriguez, Pres.--Ini Medioambiente, S.A., Madrid, Spain; *Int'l*, pg. 1225
Zappa, Robert J., Pres.--PolyMedica Healthcare, Inc., Golden, CO; *U.S. Public*, pg. 1315
Zappacosta, Pierre Luigi, Pres.--Logitech Inc., Fremont, CA; *Int'l*, pg. 815
Zaragoza, E.A., Chief Oper. Officer--P.T. Richardson-Vicks Indonesia, Jakarta, Indonesia; *U.S. Public*, pg. 1333
Zareh, M., V.P.--Sandwell Inc., Atlanta, GA; *Int'l*, pg. 1188
Zarges, Thomas H., Pres. & Chief Exec. Officer--Morrison Knudsen Corp.-Engineering & Construction, Cleveland, OH; *U.S. Public*, pg. 1134
Zarik, Trish, Branch Mgr.--Circle International, Romulus, MI; *U.S. Public*, pg. 371
Zarin, Larry, Pres.--Express Scripts Vision, Earth City, MO; *U.S. Public*, pg. 601
Zaro, Maria Isabel, V.P.-Media--Leo Burnett Venezuela, C.A., Caracas, Venezuela; *U.S. Private*, pg. 186
Zarowny, Wally, Mgr.-Aviation Bus. Centre--Shell Canada Products Ltd., Calgary, Canada; *Int'l*, pg. 1138
Zarrella, Ronald L., Pres.--Bausch & Lomb Inc., Rochester, NY; *U.S. Public*, pg. 194
Zarza, Jean-Michel, Mng. Dir.--Thrige Electric S.A., Nogent-sur-Seine, France; *Int'l*, pg. 1387
Zarza, Jean-Michel, Mng. Dir.--Electro Navale Moteurs SAS, Saint-Herblain, France; *Int'l*, pg. 1387
Zas, Seymour, V.P.-Mdsg.--Bennett Brothers, Inc., Mahwah, NJ; *U.S. Private*, pg. 133
Zauner, F., Gen. Mgr.--Hector & Co. A.B., Stockholm, Sweden; *U.S. Private*, pg. 904
Zauner, Marcel, Plant Mgr.--Eeklo Mill, Eeklo, Belgium; *U.S. Public*, pg. 673
Zavala, Moises Perez, Mng. Dir.--Prentice-Hall Hispanoamericana, S.A., Mexico, Mexico; *U.S. Private*, pg. 778
Zavaleta, Beatriz, Office Mgr.--Columbia Pictures International Television, Mexico, Mexico; *Int'l*, pg. 1282
Zavisa, John, V.P. & Gen. Mgr.--Procon Products, Murfreesboro, TN; *U.S. Public*, pg. 1506
Zaweski, Richard, Gen. Mgr.--Meenan LI Div., Wantagh, NY; *U.S. Private*, pg. 729
Zazulak, Jozef, Gen. Mgr.--McDonald's System of New Zealand Ltd., Freeman's Bay, New Zealand; *U.S. Public*, *pg. 1069*
Zazulia, Irwin, Pres. & Chief Exec. Officer--Hecht's, Arlington, VA; *U.S. Public*, pg. 1063
Zborovari, Kaitlin, Mng. Dir.--Korn/Ferry International, Budapest, Hungary; *U.S. Private*, pg. 633
Zchreiber, Kurt, Pres.--Nukem GmbH, Alzenau, Germany; *Int'l*, pg. 1081
Zdatny, Jay, Mgr.--White Rose Frozen Food, Garden City, NY; *U.S. Private*, pg. 330

Zeboulon, Paul, Mng. Dir.--Olivetti France S.A., Paris, France; *Int'l*, pg. 1003

Zebrowski, Edward, V.P.--EDO Washington Office, Arlington, VA; *U.S. Public*, pg. 542

Zecchini, Jim, Purchasing Director--Fairfield Purchasing & Design, Inc., Knoxville, TN; *U.S. Public*, pg. 611

Zech, Jochen, Dr., Chm. Bd.--Krupp Hoesch Immobilien GmbH, Essen, Germany; *Int'l*, pg. 512

Zechinati, James, Plant Mgr.--The Lamson & Sessions Co., Bowling Green, OH; *U.S. Public*, pg. 976

Zechnall, Dr., Mng. Dir.--MotoMeter AG, Leonberg, Germany; *Int'l*, pg. 204

Zeck, Fritz, Pres.--Cooper Lighting Division, Elk Grove Village, IL; *U.S. Public*, pg. 443

Zee, Jesse, Mng. Dir.--Smart Shirts Ltd., Kowloon, Hong Kong; *U.S. Public*, pg. 948

Zeen, Christie, Opers. Officer--California State Bank-Covina Downtown, Covina, CA; *U.S. Public*, pg. 294

Zegarski, Ronald, Chm. Bd.--System Sensor Division, Saint Charles, IL; *U.S. Public*, pg. 1306

Zeherlund, Bo, Mgr.--Sandvik K.K., Kobe, Japan; *Int'l*, pg. 1187

Zehnder, Mark E., Pres. & Gen. Mgr.--Gilmour Manufacturing Co., Somerset, PA; *U.S. Public*, pg. 575

Zeichner, Bernard, Pres. & Chief Exec. Officer--Contempo Casuals, Los Angeles, CA; *U.S. Public*, pg. 1763

Zeidler, Berniece, Admin.--Bowling Green Health Care Center, Bowling Green, KY; *U.S. Public*, pg. 1712

Zeiger, Robert, V.P. & Gen. Mgr.--Glaxo Pharmaceuticals, Research Triangle Park, NC; *Int'l*, pg. 552

Zeigler, Charles E., Chm. Bd.--PSNC Cardinal Pipeline Company, Gastonia, NC; *U.S. Public*, pg. 1340

Zeigler, Hans, Mng. Dir.--Logica GmbH, Frankfurt, Germany; *Int'l*, pg. 814

Zeikel, Arthur, Pres.--Merrill Lynch Investment Management, Inc., Plainsboro, NJ; *U.S. Public*, pg. 1098

Zeiler, R., Mng. Dir.--SIHI International AG, Zurich, Switzerland; *Int'l*, pg. 1156

Zeillmann, L., Pres.--Gaylord Chemical Corporation, Slidell, LA; *U.S. Public*, pg. 704

Zeitler, Klaus M., Pres. & Chief Exec. Officer--Metall Mining Corporation, Toronto, Canada; *Int'l*, pg. 862

Zeitlin, Bruce A., V.P.--IGC Advanced Superconductors, Inc., Waterbury, CT; *U.S. Public*, pg. 893

Zeitlin, Mark, Pres.--Insurance Automation Systems, Cleveland, OH; *U.S. Public*, pg. 1660

Zeitlyn, Jeremy, V.P.-South Pacific--AEI Australia Pty. Ltd., Alexandria, Australia; *U.S. Public*, pg. 30

Zeitoun, Raymond, Mng. Dir.--SMH do Brazil, Sao Paulo, Brazil; *Int'l*, pg. 1161

Zeitoun, Raymond, Chm. Bd.--SMH France S.A., Paris, France; *Int'l*, pg. 1161

Zeitoun, Raymond, Mng. Dir.--SMH Sweden AB, Stockholm, Sweden; *Int'l*, pg. 1161

Zeitoun, Raymond, Mng. Dir.--SMH Espana S.A., Madrid, Spain; *Int'l*, pg. 1161

Zelcer, Ami, Pres.--AAR Technical Service Center, Garden City, NY; *U.S. Public*, pg. 1

Zelenka, Elizabeth, Branch Mgr.--Downey Savings & Loan Association, F.A., Mission Viejo, CA; *U.S. Public*, pg. 526

Zell, Samuel, Chm. Bd.--First Capital Financial Corp., Troy, MI; *U.S. Private*, pg. 473

Zeller, Bernhard, Chief Oper. Officer--FEC Consult Ges. f. Management- und Beteiligungsberatung mbH, Frankfurt/Main, Germany; *Int'l*, pg. 799

Zeller, Herve, Pres.--Remy Amerique Inc., New York, NY; *Int'l*, pg. 1102

Zeller, M.M., Pres.--Powell Electrical Mfg. Co., Houston, TX; *U.S. Public*, pg. 1319

Zelms, Jeffrey L., Chief Exec. Officer--The Doe Run Company, Saint Louis, MO; *U.S. Private*, pg. 922

Zelnak, Stephen P., Jr., Pres.--Martin Marietta Aggregates, Raleigh, NC; *U.S. Public*, pg. 1007

Zelnak, Stephen P., Jr., Vice Chm., Pres. & Chief Exec. Officer--Martin Marietta Materials, Inc., Raleigh, NC; *U.S. Public*, pg. 1007

Zeloski, Richard P., Pres. & Chief Exec. Officer--First Signature Bank & Trust Co., Portsmouth, NH; *U.S. Private*, pg. 589

Zeman, John R., V.P. & Gen. Mgr.--Kodak Clinical Products Division, Rochester, NY; *U.S. Public*, pg. 551

Zemanek, Lewis, Plant Mgr.--GREFCO, Inc., Lompoc, CA; *U.S. Private*, pg. 903

Zemskij, Igor, Chief Oper. Officer--Frigoscandia Food Process Systems International AB, Moscow, Russia; *U.S. Public*, pg. 607

Zemsky, Howard, Pres.--Russer Foods, Buffalo, NY; *U.S. Private*, pg. 1204

Zenger, Gerold, Gen. Mgr.--Forbo Finanz SA, Eglisau, Switzerland; *Int'l*, pg. 497

Zenner, Albert, Gen. Mgr.--S.A. du Train Universel de Longwy, Longwy, France; *Int'l*, pg. 79

Zenner, Michael E., Pres.--DG Bank (Switzerland) Ltd., Zurich, Switzerland; *Int'l*, pg. 352

Zenner, Patrick J., Pres. & Chief Exec. Officer--Hoffmann-La Roche Inc., Nutley, NJ; *Int'l*, pg. 1120

Zept, Frank, Pres.--Zept Technologies, Clearwater, FL; *U.S. Private*, pg. 118

Zerenghi, Alberto, Dr., Gen. Mgr.--MSC (Italia) S.R.L., Rome, Italy; *U.S. Public*, pg. 1032

Zerfoss, David R., Pres.--Husqvarna Forest & Garden Products, Charlotte, NC; *Int'l*, pg. 440

Zermeno, Jorge Farrel, Pres.--Tokio Marine Compania de Seguros, S.A. de C.V., Mexico, Mexico; *Int'l*, pg. 1393

Zernhelt, Francis L., Pres.--Farnam Sealing Systems Division, Troy, MI; *U.S. Public*, pg. 401

Zetsche, Kurt, Pres.--Cascade Steel Rolling Mills, Inc., McMinnville, OR; *U.S. Public*, pg. 1440

Zetterlund, Bo, Chief Oper. Officer--Alfa-Laval Engineering K.K., Tokyo, Japan; *Int'l*, pg. 1380

Zetterstrom, Lars, Pres.--NCC Malmo, Malmo, Sweden; *Int'l*, pg. 899

Zewiske, D., Pres.--Phillips & Jacobs/South, Norcross, GA; *U.S. Public*, pg. 1329

Zhang, Jia-Ling, Mgr.--Bank of China, Los Angeles, CA; *Int'l*, pg. 152

Zhang, Thomas, Gen. Mgr.--IPC Information Technology (Beijing), Beijing, China; *Int'l*, pg. 651

Zheng, Sun Shu, Prof., Gen. Mgr.--Shenzhen CIC-Amersham Isotope Co Limited, Shenzhen, China; *Int'l*, pg. 993

Zhou, Leo Yi Feng, Chief Oper. Officer--Hagglunds China Ltd., Shanghai, China; *Int'l*, pg. 670

Zhou, Peter, Mgr.-Opers.--Shunde Donnelly Zhen Hua Automotive Systems Co. Ltd., Guangdong, China; *U.S. Public*, pg. 519

Zhubandykova, Leila A., Chief Exec.--Novo Nordisk A/S, Almaty, Kazakhstan; *Int'l*, pg. 987

Zibung, Andre, Mng. Dir.--Editor AG Multimedia und Design, Kusnacht, Switzerland; *Int'l*, pg. 666

Zic, Vincent, Lab Mgr.--Quest Diagnostic-Staten Island, Staten Island, NY; *U.S. Public*, pg. 1351

Zic, Vincent, Laboratory Mgr.--Quest Diagnostic-Staten Island, Staten Island, NY; *U.S. Public*, pg. 1352

Zick, John, Sr. V.P. & Gen. Mgr.--North American Grain Div., Chicago, IL; *U.S. Private*, pg. 268

Zieche, James, Distr. Mgr.--Browning-Ferris Industries of Ohio, Inc., Youngstown, OH; *U.S. Public*, pg. 264

Ziegenbein, Melvin, Jr., District Mgr.--Dallas/Ft. Worth District Office, Mesquite, TX; *U.S. Private*, pg. 150

Zieger, Claus, Pres.--Ondine Div., City of Industry, CA; *U.S. Private*, pg. 566

Ziegler, A., Chief Oper. Officer--Kidde Dexaero S.A., Antony, France; *Int'l*, pg. 1500

Ziegler, D., Pres.--Linatex Corporation of America, Gallatin, TN; *Int'l*, pg. 599

Ziegler, Dr. H.P., Dir.--Monaval Finanz AG, Zurich, Switzerland; *Int'l*, pg. 12

Ziegler, F., Mng. Dir.--Christie's (International) S.A., Rome, Italy; *Int'l*, pg. 290

Ziegler, H., Mng. Dir.--Alfred Ziegler Molkerei Schluctern GmbH & Co. KG, Schluctern, Germany; *Int'l*, pg. 992

Ziegler, Harold, Jr., Pres.--Youngstown Tire & Supply Company, Canton, OH; *U.S. Private*, pg. 1205

Ziegler, Ian G., Gen. Mgr.--Jotun Hellas Ltd., Piraeus, Greece; *Int'l*, pg. 715

Ziegler, Klaus, Chief Oper. Officer--Siemens Matsushita Components GmbH & Co. KG, Munich, Germany; *Int'l*, pg. 1245

Ziegler, O., Mng. Dir.--Georg Fischer Verkehrstechnik AG, Schaffhausen, Switzerland; *Int'l*, pg. 488

Ziegler, P.D., Pres. & Chief Exec. Officer--B.C. Ziegler & Co., West Bend, WI; *U.S. Public*, pg. 1792

Ziegler, R.D., Chm.--Ziegler Asset Management, Inc., West Bend, WI; *U.S. Public*, pg. 1792

Ziegler, Ralph, 1st. V.P. & Branch Mgr.--Union Bank of Switzerland, Tokyo Branch, Tokyo, Japan; *Int'l*, pg. 1440

Ziegler, Scott F., Chief Fin. Officer--St. Lawrence & Atlantic Railroad, York, PA; *U.S. Public*, pg. 578

Ziegler, Scott F., Chief Fin. Officer--Yorkrail Inc., York, PA; *U.S. Public*, pg. 579

Ziegler, Seeta, V.P.-Sls., Western Region--USA Network, Los Angeles, CA; *U.S. Public*, pg. 1686

Ziegler, Victor E., Exec. V.P.--Paco Pharmaceutical Services, Inc., Lakewood, NJ; *U.S. Public*, pg. 1755

Ziegler, Vince, Pres.--AGRA Land Surveys Ltd., Sherwood Park, Canada; *Int'l*, pg. 30

Zieky, Edward, Chief Oper. Officer--The General Building Supply Company, East Hartford, CT; *U.S. Private*, pg. 403

Zieky, Elliott, Chief Oper. Officer--The General Building Supply Company, East Hartford, CT; *U.S. Private*, pg. 403

Zielasko, Dave, Editor--Tire Business, Akron, OH; *U.S. Private*, pg. 285

Zielke, Frank, Gen. Mgr.--Liquid Air Corporation, Package Gases Div., Walnut Creek, CA; *Int'l*, pg. 37

Zielke, Jurgen, Gen. Mgr.--Cordis Medizinische Apparate GmbH, Haan, Germany; *U.S. Public*, pg. 928

Zielman, H. H., Chief Exec. Officer--OCE-Deutschland Leasing GmbH, Mulheim, Germany; *Int'l*, pg. 994

Ziemianski, Gordon, Mgr.--Knurlet Tool Co., Warren, MI; *U.S. Private*, pg. 608

Ziering, L.K., Pres.--ICI Specialties, Wilmington, DE; *Int'l*, pg. 664

Zieske, Paul, Gen. Mgr.--Rawal Engravers, Villa Park, IL; *U.S. Public*, pg. 1506

Zietlow, Rich, Branch Mgr.--Plover BLFC Branch, Plover, WI; *U.S. Private*, pg. 943

Zietz, Allen M., Sr. V.P. & Gen. Mgr.--Lucky Stores Northern California Division, San Leandro, CA; *U.S. Public*, pg. 93

Ziffzer, Stefan, Dr., Mng. Dir.--AV Euromedia Gesellschaft fur Audiovision mbH, Stuttgart, Germany; *Int'l*, pg. 1478

Zigmond, John, Pres.--Sula Supply, Chicago, IL; *U.S. Private*, pg. 1140

Zila, Faith, V.P. & Gen. Mgr.--WELI-AM, Hamden, CT; *U.S. Public*, pg. 384

Zila, Faith, V.P. & Gen. Mgr.--WKCI-FM, Hamden, CT; *U.S. Public*, pg. 385

Zilioli, G., Dr., Pres.--Buss S.r.l., Milan, Italy; *Int'l*, pg. 490

Zils, Joseph C., Pres. & Chief Fin. Officer--Flex Products, Inc., Santa Rosa, CA; *U.S. Public*, pg. 1227

Zima, Marvin W., Pres.--GenCorp Specialty Product Div., Mogadore, OH; *U.S. Public*, pg. 706

Zima, Marvin W., Pres.--GenCorp Specialty Product Div., Green Bay, WI; *U.S. Public*, pg. 706

Zimlich, Albert L., Chm. Bd.--Blue Grass Cooperage Co., Louisville, KY; *U.S. Public*, pg. 261

Zimlich, Albert L., Jr., Pres.--Jack Daniels Distillery, Lynchburg, TN; *U.S. Public*, pg. 261

Zimlich, Albert L., Jr., Pres.--Early Times Distillers Co., Louisville, KY; *U.S. Public*, pg. 261

Zimmer, Alan, Pres. & Chief Exec. Officer--Reeds Financial Services, Inc., Wilmington, NC; *U.S. Public*, pg. 1370

Zimmer, Frederik, Chief Oper. Officer--Soveper NV, Willemstad, Netherlands Antilles; *Int'l*, pg. 919

Zimmerman, Gary G., Pres.--SuperValu, Inc.-Minneapolis Div., Minneapolis, MN; *U.S. Public*, pg. 1540

Zimmerman, Howard, V.P.--Volt Technical Services-West, Orange, CA; *U.S. Public*, pg. 1724

Zimmerman, James, Pres.--Media General Broadcast Group, Inc., Tampa, FL; *U.S. Public*, pg. 1078

Zimmerman, James A., V.P. & Gen. Mgr.--Tampa Television, Inc., Tampa, FL; *U.S. Public*, pg. 1078

Zimmerman, Oscar, Pres.--Scotia Life Insurance Company, Toronto, Canada; *Int'l*, pg. 155

Zimmerman, Robert E., Pres.--Iowa Fidelity Life Insurance Co., Phoenix, AZ; *Int'l*, pg. 27

Zimmermann, Hans Peter, Gen. Mgr.--Forbo Murs SA, Marne la Vallee, France; *Int'l*, pg. 497

Zimmermann, Juergen, Pres.--Kontron Messtechnik GmbH, Eching, Germany; *Int'l*, pg. 177

Zimmermann, Waldemar, Chief Oper. Officer--Alfa-Laval Industriegesellschaft AB, Kloten, Switzerland; *Int'l*, pg. 1380

Zimpleman, Larry, Pres.--Principal Financial Advisors, Inc., Des Moines, IA; *U.S. Private*, pg. 885

Zingel, Rick, Gen. Mgr.--Siegling Canada Ltd., Mississauga, Canada; *Int'l*, pg. 498

Zink, Jeff, Publisher--Interiors, New York, NY; *Int'l*, pg. 1446

Zinkann, Karl-Heinz, Co-Mng. Dir.--Blefa GmbH, Kreuztal, Germany; *Int'l*, pg. 508

Zinnanti, Anthony, Mgr.-RSC--Klockner-Moeller, Stafford, TX; *Int'l*, pg. 736

Zinnenlauf, Martin, Chief Oper. Officer--Kabi Pharmacia & Upjohn AG, Dubendorf, Switzerland; *Int'l*, pg. 1049

Zino, Brian T., Pres.--Seligman Henderson Co., New York, NY; *Int'l*, pg. 609

Zino, Brian T., Pres.--Tri-Continental Corporation, New York, NY; *U.S. Private*, pg. 982

Zino, Brian T., Pres.--Seligman Henderson Co., New York, NY; *U.S. Private*, pg. 982

Ziolkowski, D.D., Gen. Mgr.--CHEMCENTRAL/Toledo, Toledo, OH; *U.S. Private*, pg. 232

Ziolkowski, David M., V.P.-Eastern Region--Hudson Aviation Services Inc., East Boston, MA; *U.S. Public*, pg. 845

Ziraldo, Donald, Pres.--InnisKillin Wines, Inc., Niagara on the Lake, Canada; *Int'l*, pg. 1468

Ziroli, Arnold M., Pres. & Chief Oper. Officer--Braun-Brumfield, Inc., Ann Arbor, MI; *U.S. Private*, pg. 993

Zirpoli, Lewis, Pres.--Selas Fluid Processing Corp., Blue Bell, PA; *Int'l*, pg. 811

Ziskin, Barry, Pres.--Z-Seven Fund, Inc., Mesa, AZ; *U.S. Public*, pg. 1789

Ziskind, D.M., Principal--STV/Silver & Ziskind, New York, NY; *U.S. Public*, pg. 1421

Ziter, Juliane, Admin.--Casa Maria Health Care Center, Roswell, NM; *U.S. Public*, pg. 838

Zito, Dan, Pres.--Gannett Media Technologies International, Cincinnati, OH; *U.S. Public*, pg. 699

Zitz, Jay T., Pres. & Chief Exec. Officer--Fort Wayne Newspaper Agency, Fort Wayne, IN; *U.S. Public*, pg. 964

Zitz, Jay T., Pres. & Chief Exec. Officer--Newspapers First, New York, NY; *U.S. Public*, pg. 964

Zitzmann, Dr. Michael, Pres. & Chief Exec. Officer--Deutsche Credit Corporation, Deerfield, IL; *Int'l*, pg. 403

Ziv, Zvi, Gen. Mgr.--Bank Hapoalim (Switzerland) Ltd., Zurich, Switzerland; *Int'l*, pg. 150

Ziven, A.B., Pres.--I. Bahcall Steel & Pipe Inc., Appleton, WI; *Int'l*, pg. 1150

Zlamany, Zdenek, Dir.--EXPOCHEM s.r.o., Prague, Czech Republic; *Int'l*, pg. 458

Zlotnik, Arnold, Chief Oper. Officer--Air-Scent International, Pittsburgh, PA; *U.S. Private*, pg. 1056

Zmijewski, Robert, Pres.--First Maryland Life Insurance Company, Baltimore, MD; *Int'l*, pg. 64

Zoccoli, Giovanni, Chm.--I.M.I.B.J. S.p.A., Rome, Italy; *Int'l*, pg. 676

Zoechbauer, Franz, Gen. Mgr.-North America--Austrian Airlines, Whitestone, NY; *Int'l*, pg. 101

Zoet, K., Works Dir.--Red Band, Roosendaal, Netherlands; *Int'l*, pg. 244

Zoffinger, George, Pres.--Value Property Trust, Woodland Hills, CA; *U.S. Public*, pg. 1707

Zoglio, Anthony, Plant Mgr.--Polymer & Surfactant Plant, Elwood, IL; *U.S. Public*, pg. 1514

Zoi, Charles L., Pres. & Chief Exec. Officer--Intertel, Inc., Houston, TX; *U.S. Public*, pg. 203

Zoll, P.Z., Mgr.--SBC Portfolio Management International Limited, London, United Kingdom; *Int'l*, pg. 1330

Zoller, H., Dir. & Gen. Mgr.--Britax Autozubehor GmbH, Ulm, Germany; *Int'l*, pg. 216

Zon Den, Lee, Reg. Mgr.--Circle Freight International Pte., Ltd., Singapore, Singapore; *U.S. Public*, pg. 373

Zonis, Irwin S., Pres. & Chief Exec. Officer--Essex Industrial Chemicals, Inc., Clifton, NJ; *U.S. Public*, pg. 523

Zook, J. Randolph, Pres.--Atlantic Envelope Co., Atlanta, GA; *U.S. Public*, pg. 1160

Zoratti, Michael, Mng. Dir.--ISS Securisystem GesmbH, Vienna, Austria; *Int'l*, pg. 1458

Zorich, B.M., V.P. & Gen. Mgr.--Flexonics OEM Products, Bartlett, IL; *Int'l*, pg. 1222

Zorich, Bruce M., Pres.--Huck International, Inc., Tucson, AZ; *U.S. Public*, pg. 1597

Zorn, Donald B., Pres.--Blount, Inc. Forestry & Industrial Equipment Division, Zebulon, NC; *U.S. Public*, pg. 238

Zorn, W.L., Gen. Mgr.--CHEMCENTRAL/Cleveland, Strongsville, OH; *U.S. Private*, pg. 232

Zottola, L., Mng. Dir.--MB Holdings S.p.A., Parma, Italy; *Int'l*, pg. 267

Zriny, Bob, Chief Exec. Officer--Whitney Corr-Pak International, Inc., East Brunswick, NJ; *U.S. Private*, pg. 249

Zriny, Robert, Pres. & Chief Exec. Officer--Retail Prods., Ocala, FL; *U.S. Public*, pg. 575

Zrno, John M., Pres. & Chief Exec. Officer--ALC Communications, Birmingham, MI; *U.S. Private*, pg. 556

Zschokke, A., Mng. Dir.--Bally (Italia) S.r.l., Florence, Italy; *Int'l*, pg. 997

zu Schweinsberg, Hauprecht F. Schenk, Chm. Bd.--Westdeutsches Assekuranz-Kontor GmbH, Essen, Germany; *Int'l*, pg. 512

Zuber, Kurt J., Gen. Mgr.--N.V. Kodak S.A., Vilvoorde, Belgium; *U.S. Public*, pg. 554

Zuber, Kurt J., Gen. Mgr.--Kodak Nederland B.V., Odijk, Netherlands; *U.S. Public*, pg. 554

Zuccarini, Ermenegildo, Chief Oper. Officer--Tipiel Colombia, Bogota, Colombia; *Int'l*, pg. 1361

Zuccotti, John E., Chm. Bd. & Chief Exec. Officer--World Financial Properties, Inc., New York, NY; *Int'l*, pg. 1004

Zucker, Jerry, Chm. & Pres.--The Intertech Group Inc., Charleston, SC; *Int'l*, pg. 113

Zuckerman, E., Gen. Mgr.--MALAT (Unmanned Air Vehicles) Division/Military Aircraft Group, Israel; *Int'l*, pg. 690

Zuckerman, Mitchell, Pres.--Sotheby's Financial Services, Inc., Reno, NV; *U.S. Public*, pg. 1487

Zueger, Ernest, Dr., Chief Exec. Officer--Sandoz Chemicals Ltd., Muttenz, Switzerland; *Int'l*, pg. 972

Zuendt, William, Pres.--Wells Fargo Bank, National Assn., San Francisco, CA; *U.S. Public*, pg. 1753

Zuern, David, Pres.--PNC Bank, Erie, PA; *U.S. Public*, pg. 1243

Zugel, F.J., Pres.--Wyman-Gordon Investment Castings, Inc., Groton, CT; *U.S. Public*, pg. 1782

Zugmeyer, Christian, Chief Oper. Officer--Granges Metallhandels-ges. GmbH, Waldegg, Austria; *Int'l*, pg. 440

Zuichur, Karen, Chief Oper. Officer--Autoshred Inc., Warrensburg, MO; *U.S. Public*, pg. 49

Zuil, Terrance, Gen. Mgr.--Howmet-Tempcraft, Inc., Cleveland, OH; *U.S. Private*, pg. 213

Zuke, S.H., Manager--Menzies Bay Division, Campbell River, Canada; *Int'l*, pg. 828

Zuker, R., Gen. Mgr.--Maman Division, Israel; *Int'l*, pg. 690

Zulauf, Dale, Pres.--Sunrise Healthcare Corporation, Newton, MA; *U.S. Public*, pg. 1531

Zulli, John, Jr., Pres.--Southwestern Reprographics Inc., Las Vegas, NV; *U.S. Private*, pg. 1176

Zullig, Weiner, Chief Oper. Officer--CAP Gemini Suisse, Geneva, Switzerland; *Int'l*, pg. 264

Zullo, Franco, Mng. Dir.--Olivetti Mexicana S.A., Mexico, Mexico; *Int'l*, pg. 1003

Zumann, Thomas, Gen. Mgr.--Webster Company, Inc., Racine, WI; *Int'l*, pg. 377

Zumba, John J., Pres.--Royal Foods Distributors, Inc., Woodbridge, NJ; *U.S. Public*, pg. 653

Zumbuhl, Marcel, Dr., Gen. Mgr.--Ex Libris AG, Dietikon, Switzerland; *Int'l*, pg. 865

Zumbusch, Patrick, Pres.--Global Atmospherics, Inc., Tucson, AZ; *Int'l*, pg. 1189

Zumino, Daniel, Sr. V.P. & Gen. Mgr.-Mktg. & Sls.--Courbevoie-Consumer Products Division, Courbevoie, France; *U.S. Public*, pg. 673

Zumpano, Ralph C., Sr., Mgr.--Leblanc Case Co., Elkhorn, WI; *U.S. Private*, pg. 657

Zumstein, Frank, Mgr.-Plant--Nestle Beverage Company, Ripon, CA; *Int'l*, pg. 918

Zunker, Richard E., Pres.--SAFECO Life and Health Insurance Companies, Redmond, WA; *U.S. Public*, pg. 1423

Zupnik, Shoshana, Rep.-Australia--Bank Hapoalim (Melbourne), Melbourne, Australia; *Int'l*, pg. 149

Zurcher, Steve, Pres.--Ammex Tax & Duty Free Shops, Ridgefield, CT; *Int'l*, pg. 103

Zurcher, Steve, Pres.--Ammex Tax & Duty Free Shops West, Inc., Ridgefield, CT; *Int'l*, pg. 103

Zurcher, Steven, Pres.--Ammex Warehouse Company, Inc., Ridgefield, CT; *Int'l*, pg. 103

Zurcher, Walter, Gen. Mgr.--Hotelplan International Travel Organization AG, Zurich, Switzerland; *Int'l*, pg. 865

Zureich, Herbert H., Pres.--Ameritech Audiotex Services Inc., Chicago, IL; *U.S. Public*, pg. 98

Zurilla, Tom, Pres. & Chief Exec. Officer--G B Stores, Columbus, OH; *U.S. Private*, pg. 972

Zurita, Guadalupe, Mgr.-Bus. Devel.--Arrow Internacional de Mexico S.A., Mexico, Mexico; *U.S. Public*, pg. 135

Zurlage, Greg, Pres.--American Health Packaging, Columbus, OH; *U.S. Public*, pg. 96

Zurlage, Gregory J., Reg. V.P. & Gen. Mgr.--AmeriSource-Columbus Div., Columbus, OH; *U.S. Public*, pg. 97

Zurmuhle, M.J., Gen. Mgr.--Glaxo Wellcome Belgium S.A., Brussels, Belgium; *Int'l*, pg. 553

Zweers, Jan, Mng. Dir.--ISS Food B.V., Leusden, Netherlands; *Int'l*, pg. 657

Zweifel, Bobby, V.P.-Sls.--Fairfield Flagstaff, Flagstaff, AZ; *U.S. Public*, pg. 611

Zweifel, Friedrich, Chief Oper. Officer--Volta Bregenz GmbH, Bregenz, Austria; *Int'l*, pg. 441

Zwieg, Grover, Gen. Mgr.--AMP Svenska AB, Jakobsberg, Sweden; *U.S. Public*, pg. 9

Zwirn, Randy H., Pres. & Gen. Mgr.--Westinghouse Power Generation, Orlando, FL; *U.S. Public*, pg. 273

Zybrycki, George, Pres.--Milwaukee Seasonings, Inc., Germantown, WI; *U.S. Public*, pg. 224

Zychick, Joel D., Pres. & Chief Exec. Officer--Getko Group Inc., Westbury, NY; *U.S. Public*, pg. 320

Zyke, J.C., Mng. Dir.--GKN Ribemont SARL, Ribemont, France; *Int'l*, pg. 536

Zypancic, Darryl, Gen. Mgr.--Quincy Design & Manufacturing, Quincy, IL; *U.S. Private*, pg. 176

CHIEF OPERATING OFFICER

Aaronson, Michael, Pres. & Chief Oper. Officer--Rag Shops, Inc., Hawthorne, NJ; *U.S. Public*, pg. 1358

Abada, Rami, Pres. & Chief Oper. Officer--Jennifer Convertibles Inc., Woodbury, NY; *U.S. Public*, pg. 926

Abbe, Charles J., Pres. & Chief Oper. Officer--Optical Coating Laboratory, Inc., Santa Rosa, CA; *U.S. Public*, pg. 1227

Abbott, Robert T., Chief Exec. & Chief Oper. Officer--NeoRx Corporation, Seattle, WA; *U.S. Private*, pg. 791

Abdalla, Gerald M., Pres. & Chief Oper. Officer--Croft Metals, Inc., McComb, MS; *U.S. Private*, pg. 290

Abel, Roger L., Pres. & Chief Oper. Officer--Occidental Oil & Gas Corporation, Bakersfield, CA; *U.S. Public*, pg. 1210

Abely, Joseph F., Pres. & Chief Oper. Officer--LoJack Corporation, Dedham, MA; *U.S. Public*, pg. 1012

Abramo, Joseph, Chief Oper. Officer--Eastman Worldwide, Buffalo, NY; *U.S. Private*, pg. 358

Abrams, Allan, Chm. Bd., Pres., Chief Exec. Officer & Chief Oper. Officer--Arrow Fastener Co., Inc., Saddle Brook, NJ; *U.S. Private*, pg. 85

Abrams, Donald L., Pres. & Chief Oper. Officer--Three D Departments, Inc., Costa Mesa, CA; *U.S. Public*, pg. 1604

Abrams, Jack, Chief Oper. Officer & Exec. V.P.--Nikon Inc., Melville, NY; *Int'l*, pg. 931

Abramson, David, Chief Oper. Officer & Exec. V.P.--Rapid Mounting & Finishing Co., Chicago, IL; *U.S. Private*, pg. 910

Accordino, Daniel T., Pres. & Chief Oper. Officer--Carrols Corporation, Syracuse, NY; *U.S. Private*, pg. 216

Ackerley, William N., Pres. & Chief Oper. Officer--The Ackerley Group, Seattle, WA; *U.S. Public*, pg. 15

Ackerman, Dennis, Mgr.-Pur.--Bel Fuse Inc., Jersey City, NJ; *U.S. Public*, pg. 200

Ackmann, Steven C., Pres. & Chief Oper. Officer--BT Financial Corporation, Johnstown, PA; *U.S. Public*, pg. 163

Adam, James V., Chief Oper. Officer--MGI PHARMA INC., Minneapolis, MN; *U.S. Public*, pg. 1026

Adams, Kirby C., Chief Oper. Officer & V.P.--Tremont Corporation, Denver, CO; *U.S. Private*, pg. 270

Adams, Robert A., Chief Oper. Officer & Exec. V.P.--American Annuity Group, Cincinnati, OH; *U.S. Public*, pg. 74

Adams, Robert E., Chief Oper. Officer & Exec. V.P.--Spencer Companies Inc., Huntsville, AL; *U.S. Private*, pg. 1024

Adamson, Jon, Chief Oper. Officers--GNB Technologies, Atlanta, GA; *Int'l*, pg. 1021

Adkins, William E., Chief Oper. Officer & Exec. V.P.--Hickory Hill Furniture Corporation, Valdese, NC; *U.S. Private*, pg. 808

Adler, Kevin, Pres. & Chief Oper. Officer--Cambridge Industries Inc., Madison Heights, MI; *U.S. Private*, pg. 202

Agadi, Harsha, Chief Oper. Officer--Little Caesar Enterprises, Inc., Detroit, MI; *U.S. Private*, pg. 671

Agathos, Louis, Chm. Bd., Pres. & Chief Exec. Officer--Belshaw Brothers, Inc., Seattle, WA; *Int'l*, pg. 188

Agler, Thomas S., Pres. & Chief Oper. Officer--Great Lakes Financial Resources, Inc., Matteson, IL; *U.S. Private*, pg. 474

Agnew, Patrick J., Pres. & Chief Oper. Officer--St. Paul Bancorp, Inc., Chicago, IL; *U.S. Public*, pg. 1428

Aguiar, Carlos Agusto, Chief Oper. Officer & Exec. V.P.--Aracruz Celulose S.A., Rio de Janeiro, Brazil; *Int'l*, pg. 78

Aguilar Romo, Marcos, Pres. & Chief Oper. Officer--Grupo Continental S.A., Tampico, Mexico; *Int'l*, pg. 573

Aguirre-Rojas, Ventura, Chief Oper. Officer--Novo Nordisk A/S, Mexico, Mexico; *Int'l*, pg. 988

Aguirre-Rojas, Ventura Lind, Chief Oper. Officer--Novo Nordisk de Mexico S.A. de C.V., Mexico, Mexico; *Int'l*, pg. 989

Ahern, John E., III, Pres. & Chief Oper. Officer--J.F. Ahern Co., Fond Du Lac, WI; *U.S. Private*, pg. 27

Ahlstrom, Morten, Chief Oper. Officer--Ahlstromforetagen Svenska AB, Stockholm, Sweden; *Int'l*, pg. 33

Ahmed, Iftikhar, Pres. & Chief Oper. Officer--The Singer Company, Hong Kong, Hong Kong; *Int'l*, pg. 1220

Airey, E., Chief Oper. Officer--John Laing Developments, Ltd., London, United Kingdom; *Int'l*, pg. 796

Akabane, Yoshitaka, Chief Oper. Officer--Brain Forum Co., Ltd., Tokyo, Japan; *Int'l*, pg. 1262

Akiba, Junjiro, Chief Oper. Officer--Chek Lap Kok Project Office, Tsim Tsa Tsui, Hong Kong; *Int'l*, pg. 942

Akin, Paul N., Grp. Pres. & Chief Oper. Officer--Inman Construction Corporation, Memphis, TN; *U.S. Private*, pg. 564

Al-Saleh, Faisal, Chief Oper. Officer--Arabian Plastic Manufacturing Company, Riyadh, Saudi Arabia; *Int'l*, pg. 489

Alberto, Pedinelli, Chief Oper. Officer--Candy Domestic Appliances Limited, Bromborough, United Kingdom; *Int'l*, pg. 260

Albertsen, David C., V.P.-Opers.--RK Mechanical, Inc., Denver, CO; *U.S. Private*, pg. 904

Albrecht, William, Pres.--Barry Controls, Brighton, MA; *U.S. Public*, pg. 124

Albright, Thomas E., Chief Oper. Officer--Essex Corporation, New York, NY; *U.S. Public*, pg. 320

Alcantara, Orlando, Chief Oper. Officer--KONE Ascensores C.A., Caracas, Venezuela; *Int'l*, pg. 747

Alcorn, Charles S., Pres., Chief Oper. Officer & Chief Fin. Officer--Donlee Technologies Inc., York, PA; *U.S. Private*, pg. 339

Aldeheim, Ian, Chief Oper. Officer--Medical Data Intelligence AB, Lund, Sweden; *Int'l*, pg. 667

Alekel, Dennis A., Chief Oper. Officer & Sr. V.P.--Lewis Homes Management Corp., Upland, CA; *U.S. Private*, pg. 665

Alexander, Anthony G.L., Chief Oper. Officer--Hanson PLC, London, United Kingdom; *Int'l*, pg. 592

Alexander, John, Chief Oper. Officer & Exec. V.P.-Admin./Opers.--Dugan Production Corp., Farmington, NM; *U.S. Private*, pg. 345

Alexander, Nick, Chief Oper. Officer--Pearson New Entertainment Europe, London, United Kingdom; *Int'l*, pg. 1026

Alexander, R., Chief Oper. Officer--Landmark Systems Corporation, Vienna, VA; *U.S. Private*, pg. 649

Alexander, Ron L., Chief Oper. Officer & Exec. V.P.--Willis Corroon Corp. of Knoxville, Knoxville, TN; *Int'l*, pg. 1506

Alkis, Halis, Chief Oper. Officer--Zima Corporation, Spartanburg, SC; *U.S. Private*, pg. 637

Allard, Michael E., Pres. & Chief Oper. Officer--Granite State Manufacturing Co., Manchester, NH; *U.S. Private*, pg. 36

Allen, D., Chief Oper. Officer--Dreamland Appliances Limited, Oldham, United Kingdom; *Int'l*, pg. 925

Allen, Patricia, Pres. & Chief Oper. Officer--Monticello Bank, Jacksonville, FL; *U.S. Private*, pg. 759

Allenberg, Howard, Chief Oper. Officer--BDO Seidman, LLP, Chicago, IL; *U.S. Private*, pg. 106

Alliman, Mike, Chief Oper. Officer--River Ranch - Orlando, Orlando, FL; *Int'l*, pg. 491

Allison, Bob, V.P.-Fin. & Admin.--Allison-Erwin Co. Inc., Charlotte, NC; *U.S. Private*, pg. 41

Allison, Herbert M., Jr., Pres. & Chief Oper. Officer--Merrill Lynch & Co., Inc., New York, NY; *U.S. Public*, pg. 1097

Almy, Richard E., Chief Oper. Officer & Exec. V.P.--Walter Industries, Inc., Tampa, FL; *U.S. Public*, pg. 1736

Alvesalo, Tapio, Chief Oper. Officer--NAPS International, Espoo, Finland; *Int'l*, pg. 913

Alyea, G. Mark, Pres. & Chief Oper. Officer--Alro Group, Jackson, MI; *U.S. Private*, pg. 45

Amato, Jay, Pres. & Chief Oper. Officer--Vanstar Corporation, Pleasanton, CA; *U.S. Public*, pg. 1708

Ambrosino, Allen, Pres. & Chief Oper. Officer--Database America Companies, Montvale, NJ; *U.S. Private*, pg. 312

Amellal, Ramdane, Chief Oper. Officer--Novo Nordisk A/S, Hydra, Algeria; *Int'l*, pg. 987

Ames, Mike, Chief Oper. Officer & Sr. V.P.--Inner Secrets, Inc., Harrison, NJ; *U.S. Private*, pg. 564

Amos, James H., Pres. & Chief Oper. Officer--Mail Boxes Etc., San Diego, CA; *U.S. Public*, pg. 1687

Amos, Stuart, Pres. & Chief Oper. Officer--Siebe plc, Windsor, United Kingdom; *Int'l*, pg. 1240

Amtmann, James S., Pres. & Chief Oper. Officer--First Alert, Inc., Aurora, IL; *U.S. Private*, pg. 406

Amy, Bill, Chief Oper. Officer--Process Systems, Inc. Construction Co., Memphis, TN; *U.S. Private*, pg. 888

Anastasiadis, Paul, Chief Oper. Officer--Cartonpack S.A., Corinth, Greece; *Int'l*, pg. 864

Ancira Elizondo, Manuel, Chief. Oper. Officer--Grupo Acerero del Norte S.A. de C.V. (GAN), Mexico, Mexico; *Int'l*, pg. 572

Andersen, Kaare, Chief Oper. Officer--Novo Nordisk A/S, Wan Chai, Hong Kong; *Int'l*, pg. 989

Andersen, Per, Chief Oper. Officer--Novo Nordisk Engineering A/S, Bagsvaerd, Denmark; *Int'l*, pg. 987

Andersen, Per, Chief Oper. Officer--Novo Nordisk A/S, Bagsvaerd, Denmark; *Int'l*, pg. 989

Anderson, Allen, Chief Opers. Officer--Imperial Litho & Dryography, Inc., Phoenix, AZ; *U.S. Private*, pg. 558

Anderson, Bradbury H., Pres. & Chief Oper. Officer--Best Buy Co., Inc., Eden Prairie, MN; *U.S. Public*, pg. 223

Anderson, Charles M., Pres. & Chief Oper. Officer--Stamler Corporation, Millersburg, KY; *U.S. Private*, pg. 814

Anderson, Conway M., Chief Oper. Officer--Young Automotive Group, Indianapolis, IN; *U.S. Private*, pg. 1095

Anderson, Curtis G., Pres. & Chief Oper. Officer--Kuhlman Corporation, Savannah, GA; *U.S. Public*, pg. 968

Anderson, Dana, Vice Chm. & Chief Oper. Officer--The Macerich Company, Santa Monica, CA; *U.S. Public*, pg. 1030

Anderson, Douglas P., Chief Oper. Officer--Darling International, Inc, Irving, TX; *U.S. Public*, pg. 484

Anderson, Girard F., Pres. & Chief Oper. Officer--TECO Energy, Inc., Tampa, FL; *U.S. Public*, pg. 1565

Anderson, Kent T., Chief Oper. Officer-Strategy & Devel.--American Stores Company, Salt Lake City, UT; *U.S. Public*, pg. 92

Anderson, Lavon N., Dr., Pres. & Chief Oper. Officer--Rexene Corporation, Dallas, TX; *U.S. Private*, pg. 549

Anderson, Michael J., Pres. & Chief Oper. Officer--The Andersons Incorporated, Maumee, OH; *U.S. Public*, pg. 111

Anderson, Paul M., Pres. & Chief Oper. Officer--Duke Energy Corporation, Charlotte, NC; *U.S. Public*, pg. 534

Anderson, Paul M., Pres. & Chief Oper. Officer--Duke Energy International, L.L.C., Houston, TX; *U.S. Public*, pg. 534

Anderson, Phelps, Chief Oper. Officer & Exec. V.P.--Hondo Oil & Gas Company, Roswell, NM; *Int'l*, pg. 818

Anderson, R.C., Chief Oper. Officer--Kidde International Protection Systems Pre. Ltd., Singapore, Singapore; *Int'l*, pg. 1500

Anderson, Robert W., Chief Oper. Officer--Lotte U.S.A., Inc., Battle Creek, MI; *Int'l*, pg. 819

Andersson, Sten, Chief Oper. Officer--KONE Hissar AB, Kista, Sweden; *Int'l*, pg. 747

Andino, Ralph, Exec. V.P.-Opers.--West Chemical Products, Inc., Princeton, NJ; *U.S. Private*, pg. 1158

Andrasick, James S., Pres. & Chief Oper. Officer--C. Brewer & Company, Limited, Honolulu, HI; *U.S. Private*, pg. 190

Andrea, John, Co.-Pres. & Chief Oper. Officer--Andrea Electronics Corporation, Long Island City, NY; *U.S. Public*, pg. 112

Andreen, Gunnar, Chief Oper. Officer & V.P.-Textile Svcs.--Sophus Berendsen A/S, Soeborg, Denmark; *Int'l*, pg. 1284

Andreozzi, Lou, Chief Oper. Officer--National Register Publishing, New Providence, NJ; *Int'l*, pg. 1096

Andreozzi, Lou, Chief Oper. Officer--Marquis Who's Who, New Providence, NJ; *Int'l*, pg. 1096

Andress, James N., Pres. & Chief Oper. Officer--Stern's, Paramus, NJ; *U.S. Public*, pg. 618

Andrews, Charles, Chief Oper. Officer & Exec. V.P.--Ripon Foods, Inc., Ripon, WI; *U.S. Private*, pg. 931

Andrews, Steven C., Chief Oper. Officer & Exec. V.P.--Integon Corporation, Winston Salem, NC; *U.S. Public*, pg. 719

Andrews, Steven C., Chief Oper. Officer--Integon National Insurance Co., Winston Salem, NC; *U.S. Public*, pg. 720

Andrews, Steven C., Chief Oper. Officer & Exec. V.P.--Integon Indemnity Corporation, Winston Salem, NC; *U.S. Public*, pg. 720

Andrews, Steven C., Chief Oper. Officer & Exec. V.P.--Integon General Insurance Corporation, Winston Salem, NC; *U.S. Public*, pg. 720

Andrews, Steven C., Chief Oper. Officer & Exec. V.P.--New South Insurance Company, Winston Salem, NC; *U.S. Public*, pg. 720

Andrews, Steven C., Chief Oper. Officer & Exec. V.P.--Integon Specialty Insurance Company, Winston Salem, NC; *U.S. Public*, pg. 720

Andrews, Steven C., Chief Oper. Officer & Exec. V.P.--Integon Preferred Insurance Company, Winston Salem, NC; *U.S. Public*, pg. 720

Andrews, Steven C., Chief Oper. Officer & Exec. V.P.--Integon Casualty Insurance Company, Winston Salem, NC; *U.S. Public*, pg. 720

Andringa, Mary, Pres. & Chief Oper. Officer--Vermeer Manufacturing Company, Pella, IA; *U.S. Private*, pg. 1137

Angelo, Ray, Pres.--Angelo Brothers Co., Philadelphia, PA; *U.S. Private*, pg. 74

Angermann, Bernd, Chief Oper. Officer--WABAG Leipzig GmbH Wassertechnische Anlagen, Markkleeberg, Germany; *Int'l*, pg. 399

Angiolini, Guido, Chief Oper. Officer--Compart SpA, Milan, Italy; *Int'l*, pg. 324

Annable, C.D., Pres. & Chief Oper. Officer--Canuck Engineering Inc., Calgary, Canada; *Int'l*, pg. 31

Annand, Peter, Chief Oper. Officer--Elscint Inc., Hackensack, NJ; *Int'l*, pg. 450

Answine, Emmanuel J., Sr. V.P.-Bus. Sys.--Southwest National Corporation, Greensburg, PA; *U.S. Public*, pg. 1493

Antonini, Richard L., Chm. Bd., Pres. & Chief Exec. Officer--Foremost Corporation of America, Caledonia, MI; *U.S. Public*, pg. 667

Anttomer, Risto, Chief Oper. Officer--Ahlstrom Alcore Ltd., Karhula, Finland; *Int'l*, pg. 33

Appenzeller, Bernd, Co-Chief Oper. Officer--Helaba Invest Kapitalanlagegesellschaft mbH, Frankfurt/Main, Germany; *Int'l*, pg. 799

Applegate, L. Thomas, Pres. & Chief Oper. Officer--Surgical Appliance Industries, Inc., Cincinnati, OH; *U.S. Private*, pg. 1056

Aquino, Humberto, Co-Chief Oper. Officer--Cott Corporation, Pointe-Claire, Canada; *Int'l*, pg. 337

Aquino, Jose, Chief Oper. Officer--Rums of Puerto Rico, New York, NY; *U.S. Private*, pg. 951

Arai, Atsumi, Chief Oper. Officer--Tesco Co., Ltd., Yamanashi, Japan; *Int'l*, pg. 1262

Archiszewski, Kasimar, Chief Oper. Officer--Speech Design, Munich, Germany; *U.S. Public*, pg. 740

Arduini, Giovanni, Chm. Bd., Pres., Chief Exec. & Oper. Officer--I.B.I.S.-S.p.A., Busseto, Italy; *Int'l*, pg. 642

Aretz, Gerhard, Worldwide Chief Oper. Officer--Select Communications, L.P., New York, NY; *U.S. Private*, pg. 982

Aritake, Masami, Chief Oper. Officer--Haseko Corp.-Kansai Office, Osaka, Japan; *Int'l*, pg. 600

Arlotta, John J., Chief Oper. Officer-Caremark Pharmaceuticals--Medpartners Inc., Birmingham, AL; *U.S. Public*, pg. 1082

Arlt, Marie Nastasi, Chief Oper. Officer--Analytic TSA Global Asset Management Inc., Los Angeles, CA; *U.S. Public*, pg. 1672

Armstrong, D.M., Chief Oper. Officer--Armstrong International, Inc., Three Rivers, MI; *U.S. Private*, pg. 83

Armstrong, Terry P., V.P. & Chief Oper. Officer--DAC International, Inc., Austin, TX; *U.S. Public*, pg. 187

Armstrong, Thomas R., Chief Oper. Officer & Exec. V.P.--Advent International, Boston, MA; *U.S. Private*, pg. 22

Arnold, Greg, Pres. & Chief Oper. Officer--Truman Arnold Companies, Texarkana, TX; *U.S. Private*, pg. 84

Arnold, Walter, Chief Oper. Officer--Banque Generale du Luxembourg (Suisse) SA, Zurich, Switzerland; *Int'l*, pg. 162

Arnstrup, Knud, Chief Oper. Officer--Novo Nordisk A/S, Beijing, China; *Int'l*, pg. 987

Arntzen, Jay, Chief Oper. Officer--FHE Services, Inc., Long Island City, NY; *Int'l*, pg. 746

Aron, Carl, Chief Oper. Officer Itron Inc., Spokane, WA; *U.S. Public*, pg. 914

Aronson, Louis V., II, Pres. & Chief Exec. Officer--Ronson Corporation, Somerset, NJ; *U.S. Public*, pg. 1405

Arpin, David, Pres. & Chief Oper. Officer--Paul Arpin Vanlines, Inc., West Warwick, RI; *U.S. Private*, pg. 85

Arrambide, Jesse, III, Chm. Bd. & Chief Oper. Officer--Pancho's Mexican Buffet, Inc., Fort Worth, TX; *U.S. Public*, pg. 1255

Arras, Richard K., Pres. & Chief Oper. Officer--Perkins Family Restaurants, Memphis, TN; *U.S. Private*, pg. 925

Arrleta, Felix, Chief Oper. Officer--New Ingenia SA, Boudry, Switzerland; *Int'l*, pg. 866

Arrowsmith, Peter D., Pres. & Chief Oper. Officer--Tetra Tech NUS, Inc., Gaithersburg, MD; *U.S. Public*, pg. 1582

Arsuaga, Michael, Chief Oper. Officer--Mercantile Bank, Brownsville, TX; *U.S. Private*, pg. 731

Artandi, George, Pres. & Chief Oper. Officer--Book of the Month Club, New York, NY; *U.S. Public*, pg. 1612

Arvin, Joseph L., Pres., Chief Oper. Officer & Chief Information Officer--Arrow Gear Company, Downers Grove, IL; *U.S. Private*, pg. 85

Asch, Michael A., Pres., Chief Oper. Officer, Chief Fin. Officer & Treas.--Rexx Environmental Corp., New York, NY; *U.S. Public*, pg. 1384

Aschinger, Chris, Chief Oper. Officer--Columbus Show Case Company, Columbus, OH; *U.S. Private*, pg. 257

Ash, David, Chief Oper. Officer--Sam Ash Music Corp., Hicksville, NY; *U.S. Private*, pg. 88

Ashe, Harol, Chief Oper. Officer--Pacific Capital Bancorp, Salinas, CA; *U.S. Public*, pg. 1247

Ashton, Craig, Chief Oper. Officer--T & S Brass & Bronze Works, Inc., Travelers Rest, SC; *U.S. Private*, pg. 1061

Askwyth, Diane, Chief Oper. Officer & Sr. V.P.--Willis Corroon Marine & Energy, New York, NY; *Int'l*, pg. 1508

Assandri, Franco, Chief Oper. Officer--Mikron SNC Nerviano, Nerviano, Italy; *Int'l*, pg. 867

Atte, Sidney Anuar, Chief Oper. Officer--BB-Tur-Viagens e Turismo, Brasilia, Brazil; *Int'l*, pg. 141

Attebery, Ray, V.P.-Opers.--Crowley, Milner & Company, Detroit, MI; *U.S. Public*, pg. 461

Augello, Mike, Pres. & Chief Oper. Officer--Reeves Southeastern Corporation, Tampa, FL; *U.S. Private*, pg. 916

Augustine, Peter, Chief Oper. Officer & Chief Fin. Officer--New Era Cap. Co., Derby, NY; *U.S. Private*, pg. 793

Aurichio, Joseph L., Pres. & Chief Oper. Officer--The Dyson-Kissner-Moran Corporation, New York, NY; *U.S. Private*, pg. 351

Aversenti, Candida C., Pres., Chief Oper. Officer & V.P.-Mktg.--General Magnaplate Corporation, Linden, NJ; *U.S. Public*, pg. 717

Aylsworth, John S., Chief Oper. Officer & Exec. Pres.--President Casinos, Inc., Saint Louis, MO; *U.S. Public*, pg. 1323

Ayres, James D., Pres. & Chief Oper. Officer--Harleysville Atlantic Insurance Company, Savannah, GA; *U.S. Public*, pg. 786

Ayres, Robert L., Chief Oper. Officer, Chief Fin. Officer & Exec. V.P.--Bush Industries Inc., Jamestown, NY; *U.S. Public*, pg. 270

Azizzadeh, R., Chief Oper. Officer--BHP-Bank Representative Office, Tehran, Iran; *Int'l*, pg. 120

Azoulay, Bernard, Pres. & Chief Exec. Officer--Elf Atochem North America, Inc., Philadelphia, PA; *Int'l*, pg. 445

Bacchiocchi, Alberto, Chief Oper. Officer--Sao Paulo Alpargatas S.A., Sao Paulo, Brazil; *Int'l*, pg. 1193

Bachus, Charles R., Pres. & Chief Oper. Officer--Southern Missouri Containers Inc., Springfield, MO; *U.S. Private*, pg. 1017

Bacon, David L., Pres. & Chief Oper. Officer--Schleicher & Schuell, Inc., Keene, NH; *Int'l*, pg. 1206

Bacon, Ernest, Chief Oper. Officer & Exec. V.P.--Community Health Systems, Inc., Brentwood, TN; *U.S. Private*, pg. 419

Baer, Larry, Chief Oper. Officer & Exec. V.P.--San Francisco Giants Baseball Club, San Francisco, CA; *U.S. Private*, pg. 964

Bagley, James W., Vice Chm. & Chief Oper. Office--Applied Materials, Inc., Santa Clara, CA; *U.S. Public*, pg. 123

Bagshawe, Anthony J., Chief Oper. Officer--Glynwed Metals Processing Ltd., Wednesbury, United Kingdom; *Int'l*, pg. 554

Bahnmuller, E., Chief Oper. Officer--Baumann GmbH, Lichtenstein, Germany; *Int'l*, pg. 171

Bahuet, Alan, Chief Oper. Officer--Club Mediterranee Australia Pty. Ltd., Sydney, Australia; *Int'l*, pg. 298

Bailey, Brian, Chief Oper. Officer--Akerlund & Rausing NA Inc., Duluth, GA; *Int'l*, pg. 33

Bailey, John, Chief Oper. Officer--Havens Steel Co., Kansas City, MO; *U.S. Private*, pg. 510

Bailey, John H., Chm. Bd., Pres., Chief Exec. & Chief Oper. Officer--The Climatic Corp., Columbia, SC; *U.S. Private*, pg. 246

Baillie, Aubrey W., Deputy Chm. & Chief Oper. Officer--The Nesbitt Thomson Corporation Limited, Toronto, Canada; *Int'l*, pg. 153

Baker, Dolph, Pres. & Chief Oper. Officer--Cal-Maine Foods, Inc., Jackson, MS; *U.S. Public*, pg. 292

Baker, G. Thomas, Pres., Chief Oper. Officer & Chief Fin. Officer--International Game Technology, Reno, NV; *U.S. Public*, pg. 900

Baker, M., Chief Oper. Officer--Penny & Giles Computer Products, Christchurch, United Kingdom; *Int'l*, pg. 207

Baker, Newell A., Jr., Exec. V.P. & Sec.--J.D. Streett & Co., Inc., Maryland Heights, MO; *U.S. Private*, pg. 1047

Baker, Paul M., Chief Exec. Officer--Great Financial Bank FSB, Louisville, KY; *U.S. Private*, pg. 473

Baker, Paul T., Chief Oper. Officer & Sr. V.P.--Indiana Gas Company, Inc., Indianapolis, IN; *U.S. Public*, pg. 875

Baker, Richard, Chief Oper. Officer--Tri Valley Growers, San Ramon, CA; *U.S. Private*, pg. 1101

Baker, Robert W., Chief Oper. Officer--AMR Corporation, Fort Worth, TX; *U.S. Public*, pg. 9

Bakke, Kjell, Chief Oper Officer--Ferrosan A/S, Soeborg, Denmark; *Int'l*, pg. 987

Baladjanian, Greg, Pres. & Chief Oper. Officer--Chromalloy Gas Turbine Corp., San Antonio, TX; *U.S. Public*, pg. 1458

Balakrishnan, C.V., Chief Oper. Officer & V.P.--British Trimmings Ltd., Stockport, United Kingdom; *U.S. Public*, pg. 434

Baldwin, Mike, Chief Oper. Officer--H & H Distributing Company, Inc., West Union, IA; *U.S. Private*, pg. 489

Balisteri, Tom, Chief Oper. Officer--Plastic Engineered Components Inc., Waukesha, WI; *U.S. Private*, pg. 870

Ball, John K., Pres. & Chief Oper. Officer--R.M. Shoemaker Co., West Conshohocken, PA; *U.S. Private*, pg. 996

Ball, Steven S., Chief Oper. Officer & Sr. V.P.--Williams Pipe Line Co., Tulsa, OK; *U.S. Public*, pg. 1769

Ballengee, J.H., Pres. & Chief Oper. Officer--Union Camp Corporation, Wayne, NJ; *U.S. Public*, pg. 1665

Ballinger, Dean, V.P.-Opers.--The H.T. Hackney Co., Knoxville, TN; *U.S. Private*, pg. 493

Ballou, Roger H., Pres. & Chief Oper. Officer--Alamo Rent-A-Car Inc., Fort Lauderdale, FL; *U.S. Public*, pg. 1379

Baltzer, Gregory L., Chief Oper. Officer--Precision Systems, Inc., Saint Petersburg, FL; *U.S. Public*, pg. 1321

Balucci, Dave, Chief Oper. Officer--MacDermid Taiwan Ltd., Hsin-chu, Taiwan; *U.S. Public*, pg. 1030

Bandreaux, Philip, Chief Oper. Officer--Ahlstrom Process Equipment Inc., Baton Rouge, LA; *Int'l*, pg. 34

Bankard, James, Pres. & Chief Oper. Officer--Home Juice Co., Melrose Park, IL; *U.S. Private*, pg. 537

Banzet, Serge, Pres. & Chief Oper. Officer--Peugeot Motors of America Inc., Little Falls, NJ; *Int'l*, pg. 1020

Barabino, C., Chief Oper. Officer--Saiwa, Genoa, Italy; *Int'l*, pg. 381

Barad, Jill, Chief Oper. Officer--Mattel Games/Puzzles, El Segundo, CA; *U.S. Public*, pg. 1058

Barber, Bruce, Pres. & Chief Oper. Officer--First National Bank, Palestine, Palestine, TX; *U.S. Public*, pg. 630

Barber, Mark M., Chief Oper. Officer--EAO Switch Corporation, Milford, CT; *Int'l*, pg. 444

Barber, W. Freeman, Chief Oper. Officer--ISC Futures Corporation, Charlotte, NC; *U.S. Public*, pg. 910

Barbosa, Wagner, Chief Oper. Officer--KONE Elevadores Ltda., Sao Jose dos Campos, Brazil; *Int'l*, pg. 747

Barbre, Erwin S., Chief Oper. Officer--Shepard's, Colorado Springs, CO; *Int'l*, pg. 1095

Barbre, Erwin S., Chief Oper. Officer--Shepard's, Colorado Springs, CO; *U.S. Public*, pg. 1616

Barker, Mike, Pres. & Chief Oper. Officer--InterVoice, Inc., Dallas, TX; *U.S. Public*, pg. 910

Barnes, Chris, Pres. & Chief Oper. Officer--Spectrulite Consortium, Inc., Madison, IL; *U.S. Private*, pg. 1024

Barnes, Pierre, Chief Oper. Officer & Exec. V.P.--Federation des caisses populaires Desjardins, Montreal, Canada; *Int'l*, pg. 479

Barnes, Richard A., Pres. & Chief Oper. Officer--Republic Fastener Products Corp., Great Falls, SC; *U.S. Private*, pg. 923

Barnes, Robert L., Pres. & Chief Oper. Officer--Knight Architects Engineers Planners, Inc., Chicago, IL; *U.S. Private*, pg. 626

Barnett, Thomas G., Pres. & Chief Oper. Officer--Marsh Company, Belleville, IL; *U.S. Private*, pg. 707

Barnhill, Al, Vice Chm. & Chief Oper. Officer-Blumenthal Mills--Blumenthal Print Works, Inc., New Orleans, LA; *U.S. Private*, pg. 153

Barnholt, Brandon, Exec. V.P.-Mktg. (St. Louis)--Clark Refining & Marketing Inc., Saint Louis, MO; *U.S. Private*, pg. 243

Barnum, Scott, Pres. & Chief Oper. Officer--Pete's Brewing Company, Palo Alto, CA; *U.S. Public*, pg. 1280

Baron, Bengt, Chief Oper. Officer--AB Frionor, Stockholm, Sweden; *Int'l*, pg. 516

Barr, David C., Chief Oper. Officer--Genesis Health Ventures, Inc., Kennett Square, PA; *U.S. Public*, pg. 728

Barr, David C., Chief Oper. Officer & Exec. V.P.--Genesis ElderCare, Philadelphia, PA; *U.S. Public*, pg. 728

Barr, Greg, Chief Oper. Officer & Exec. V.P.--Nob Hill General Store, Inc., Gilroy, CA; *U.S. Private*, pg. 799

Barr, John, Pres. & Chief Oper. Officer--Quaker State Corporation, Irving, TX; *U.S. Public*, pg. 1348

Barr, Michael R., Chief Oper. Officer & Exec. V.P.--Vencor, Inc., Louisville, KY; *U.S. Public*, pg. 1711

Barrett, Craig, Pres. & Chief Oper. Officer--Intel Corporation, Santa Clara, CA; *U.S. Public*, pg. 886

Barrett, David J., Chief Oper. Officer & Exec. V.P.--Hearst-Argyle Television Incorporated, New York, NY; *U.S. Private*, pg. 516

Barrington, Michael R., Vice Chm., Pres. & Chief Oper. Officer--AmeriCredit Corp., Fort Worth, TX; *U.S. Public*, pg. 96

Barron, Alan, Chief Oper. Officer--First Cash, Inc., Arlington, TX; *U.S. Public*, pg. 627

Barron, Eddie T., Chief Oper. Officer & V.P.--Utility Engineering Corporation, Amarillo, TX; *U.S. Public*, pg. 1170

Barron, Gary A., Chief Oper. Officer & Exec. V.P.--Southwest Airlines Co., Dallas, TX; *U.S. Public*, pg. 1493

Barry, Tom, Chm. Bd., Pres. & Chief Oper. Officer--Mighty Distributing System, Norcross, GA; *U.S. Private*, pg. 745

Bartell, George D., Pres. & Chief Oper. Officer--The Bartell Drug Company, Seattle, WA; *U.S. Private*, pg. 118

Bartels, Juergen, Pres. & Chief Oper. Officer--Carlson Hospitality Group, Inc., Minneapolis, MN; *U.S. Private*, pg. 212

Bartelt, Bruce, Chief Oper. Officer & Exec. V.P.--Rainfair, Inc., Racine, WI; *U.S. Private*, pg. 907

Bartelt, Kenneth H., Pres. & Chief Oper. Officer--PowderTech Corporation, Valparaiso, IN; *Int'l*, pg. 878

Bartlett, Robert A., Jr., Pres. & Chief Oper. Officer--The F.A. Bartlett Tree Expert Co., Stamford, CT; *U.S. Private*, pg. 119

Barton, Steven A., Chief Oper. Officer & Exec. V.P.--Benchmark Electronics Inc., Angleton, TX; *U.S. Public*, pg. 210

Bartram, N.F., Dir.-Opers.--Bernard Matthews PLC, Norwich, United Kingdom; *Int'l*, pg. 189

Basham, Robert T., Pres. & Chief Oper. Officer--Outback Steakhouse Inc., Tampa, FL; *U.S. Public*, pg. 1235

Basile, Joseph A., Chief Oper. Officer--Cable & Wireless Communications Inc., Vienna, VA; *Int'l*, pg. 247

Baskind, Barry, Pres., Chief Exec. Officer & Dir.-Cash Mngmt.--Mott's Holdings, Inc., Glastonbury, CT; *U.S. Private*, pg. 764

Basone, Michael, Chief Oper. & Info. Officer--Warrantech Corporation, Stamford, CT; *U.S. Public*, pg. 1740

Bass, Charles W., Chief Oper. Officer & Exec. V.P.--AGL Resources, Atlanta, GA; *U.S. Public*, pg. 6

Bateman, M. Joel, Chief Oper. Officer & V.P.--Cameron & Barkley Company, Charleston, SC; *U.S. Private*, pg. 203

Bates, Ernest A., M.D., Chm. Bd., Pres., Chief Exec. & Oper. Officer--American Shared Hospital Services, San Francisco, CA; *U.S. Public*, pg. 91

Batinovich, Andrew, Pres. & Chief Oper. Officer--Glenborough Realty Trust Incorporated, San Mateo, CA; *U.S. Public*, pg. 747

Battistello, Marc, Chief Oper. Officer--Medical Analysis Systems Inc., Camarillo, CA; *U.S. Private*, pg. 727

Battle, Fernando, Chief Opers./Retail Banking Officer& Exec. V.P.--Firstbank Puerto Rico, Santurce, PR; *U.S. Public*, pg. 644

Bauchiero, Frank E., Pres. & Chief Oper. Officer--Walbro Corporation, Cass City, MI; *U.S. Public*, pg. 1733

Bauchwitz, Barry, Chief Oper. Officer & Exec. V.P.--Account Specific Marketing, Inc. (ASM), Morristown, NJ; *U.S. Private*, pg. 345
Bauer, Theodore J., Pres. & Chief Oper. Officer--Medite Corporation, Medford, OR; *U.S. Private*, pg. 999
Baughman, Walter, III, Pres. & Chief Oper. Officer--Plastomer Corp., Livonia, MI; *U.S. Private*, pg. 872
Bauler, Beth, Chief Oper. Officer & Exec. V.P.--Alpha Omega Publications, Chandler, AZ; *U.S. Private*, pg. 168
Baum, Leonard M., Pres. & Chief Oper. Officer--Advanced Magnetics, Inc., Cambridge, MA; *U.S. Public*, pg. 20
Bauman, James J., Vice Chm. & Co-Chief Oper. Officer--Eastbridge Holdings Inc., New York, NY; *Int'l*, pg. 933
Baumann, Daniel E., Pres. & Chief Oper. Officer--Paddock Publications, Inc., Arlington Heights, IL; *U.S. Private*, pg. 833
Baumgarten, J.C., Chief Oper. Officer--Frequence Plus, Villepinte, France; *Int'l*, pg. 560
Baumgartner, Robert V., Chief Oper. Officer-Auto Glass--Apogee Enterprises, Inc., Minneapolis, MN; *U.S. Public*, pg. 120
Baxter, Brian, Chief Oper. Officer & V.P.--Equity Fire & Casualty Insurance Company, West Des Moines, IA; *U.S. Private*, pg. 881
Bays, F. Barry, Chief Oper. Officer & Sr. V.P.-Opers.--Xomed Surgical Products, Jacksonville, FL; *U.S. Public*, pg. 253
Bazet, James R., Pres., Chief Exec. Officer & Chief Oper. Officer--Cobra Electronics Corporation, Chicago, IL; *U.S. Public*, pg. 391
Bazzy, David, Pres. & Chief Oper. Officer--Kenwal Products Corp., Dearborn, MI; *U.S. Private*, pg. 615
Beach, William H., Chm. Bd., Pres., Chief Exec. & Oper. Officer--Beach Mold & Tool Inc., New Albany, IN; *U.S. Private*, pg. 125
Beadley, James, Pres. & Chief Oper. Officer--Koppel Steel Corp., Beaver Falls, PA; *U.S. Public*, pg. 1147
Beahm, Roger L., Pres., Chief Oper. Officer & New Bus. Contact--Coyne Beahm Inc., Colfax, NC; *U.S. Private*, pg. 283
Beal, Doris, Chief Oper. Officer--Entron Industries Limited Partnership, Forest Hills, NY; *U.S. Private*, pg. 378
Bearden, James, Exec. V.P., Gen. Mgr. & Chief Oper. Officer--Bush Hog Division, Selma, AL; *U.S. Public*, pg. 48
Beattie, William, Chief Oper. Officer--Northwest Parking Services Inc., Seattle, WA; *U.S. Private*, pg. 43
Beauchamp, Guy R., Pres. & Chief Oper. Officer-Cable TV--CFCF Inc., Montreal, Canada; *Int'l*, pg. 240
Beauchamp, Guy-R., Pres. & Chief Oper. Officer--Laurentien Cable TV Inc., Montreal, Canada; *Int'l*, pg. 241
Beauchamp, Guy-R., Pres. & Chief Oper. Officer--Northern Cable Holdings Ltd., Montreal, Canada; *Int'l*, pg. 241
Beaudin, Timothy, Sr. V.P.-Property Opers. & Indus. Devel.--Catellus Development Corporation, San Francisco, CA; *U.S. Public*, pg. 314
Beaudoin, Pierre, Pres. & Chief Oper. Officer--Bombardier Recreational Products, Montreal, Canada; *Int'l*, pg. 200
Beaumont, Mark, Chief Oper. Officer--Delta Apparel, Duluth, GA; *U.S. Public*, pg. 498
Bechmann, H., Chief Oper. Officer--Buss-SMS GmbH Verfahrenstechnik, Butzbach, Germany; *Int'l*, pg. 490
Beck, Arthur R., Pres. & Chief Oper. Officer--Precision Twist Drill Co., Crystal Lake, IL; *Int'l*, pg. 1185
Beck, Henry C., III, Chief Oper. Officer--HCBeck, Dallas, TX; *U.S. Private*, pg. 490
Becker, John A., Pres. & Chief Oper. Officer--Firstar Corporation, Milwaukee, WI; *U.S. Public*, pg. 642
Becker, John C., Pres., Chief Exec. Officer & Chief Oper. Officer--Axent Technologies, Rockville, MD; *U.S. Public*, pg. 157
Becker, Manfred, Co-Chief Oper. Officer--BHF & IKB Immobilien-Leasing GmbH, Dusseldorf, Germany; *Int'l*, pg. 645
Becker, Marc I., Chief Oper. Officer & Exec. V.P.--Network Long Distance, Inc., Baton Rouge, LA; *U.S. Public*, pg. 1169
Beckert, John A., Chief Oper. Officer & Exec. V.P.--Bristol Hotels & Resorts, Dallas, TX; *U.S. Public*, pg. 253
Becraft, F. Joseph, Vice Chm., Pres. & Chief Oper. Officer--Valero Marketing & Supply Company, San Antonio, TX; *U.S. Public*, pg. 1704
Becraft, F. Joseph, Vice Chm., Pres. & Chief Oper. Officer--Valero Refining Company, San Antonio, TX; *U.S. Public*, pg. 1704
Bednar, Barbara A., Chief Oper. Officer & V.P.--Total Renal Care, Berwyn, PA; *U.S. Public*, pg. 1625
Beecham, R. Thomas, Pres. & Chief Oper. Officer--Jernberg Industries, Inc., Chicago, IL; *U.S. Private*, pg. 586
Behler, Andrew D., Chief Oper. Officer--Blue Ridge Pressure Castings, Inc., Lehighton, PA; *U.S. Private*, pg. 153
Behrends, Frank, Chief Oper. Officer--BHF-Bank, Singapore, Singapore; *Int'l*, pg. 119
Bekes, Michael J., Chief Oper. Officer & V.P.--Badger Paper Mills, Inc., Peshtigo, WI; *U.S. Public*, pg. 165
Bekkers, John, Pres. & Chief Oper. Officer--Gold Kist, Inc., Atlanta, GA; *U.S. Private*, pg. 459
Belda, Alain, Pres. & Chief Oper. Officer--Aluminum Company of America, Pittsburgh, PA; *U.S. Public*, pg. 60
Bell, Wendell R., Chief Oper. Officer--Enerfab Inc., Cincinnati, OH; *U.S. Private*, pg. 376
Bell, William, Chief Oper. Officer & V.P.--Randall Stores, Inc., Mitchell, SD; *U.S. Private*, pg. 909
Bellini, Marco, Chief Oper. Officer--DeTrey/Dentsply S.r.l., Rome, Italy; *U.S. Public*, pg. 500
Bello, Paul S., Pres.& Chief Oper. Officer--Prism Integrated Sanitation Management, Inc., Miami, FL; *U.S. Private*, pg. 592
Bellow, H. Arthur, Chief Oper. Officer--Triangle Special Products, Livonia, MI; *U.S. Public*, pg. 147
Bellows, H. Arthur, Jr., Pres. & Chief Oper. Officer--Audits & Surveys Worldwide, New York, NY; *U.S. Public*, pg. 147
Belson, Ross A., Pres. & Chief Oper. Officer--General Datacomm Industries, Inc., Middlebury, CT; *U.S. Public*, pg. 708
Belusic, Lori, Chief Fin. Officer & Chief Oper. Officer--KPR, New York, NY; *U.S. Public*, pg. 1224
Belz, Martin S., Co-Pres. & Chief Oper. Officer--Belz Enterprises, Memphis, TN; *U.S. Private*, pg. 132
Belzer, Alan, Pres. & Chief Oper. Officer--AlliedSignal Inc., Morristown, NJ; *U.S. Public*, pg. 49
Belzer, Burton E., Chm. Bd., Chief Exec. Officer, Chief Fin. Officer & Treas.--TCI Aluminum, Gardena, CA; *U.S. Private*, pg. 1063
Belzer, John D., Pres. & Chief Oper. Officer--TCI Aluminum, Gardena, CA; *U.S. Private*, pg. 1063
Bement, Christian, Chief Oper. Officer & Exec. V.P.--Earl Scheib, Inc., Beverly Hills, CA; *U.S. Public*, pg. 1437
Benadiba, Mark, Co-Chief Oper. Officer--Cott Corporation, Pointe-Claire, Canada; *Int'l*, pg. 337
Bencsik, Doris D., Pres. & Chief Oper. Officer--Datapoint Corporation, San Antonio, TX; *Int'l*, pg. 384
Bencsik, Vilmos, Chief Oper. Officer--Malev Hungarian Airlines, Plc., Budapest, Hungary; *Int'l*, pg. 833
Benda, Victor C., Pres. & Chief Oper. Officer--Analysts International Corporation, Minneapolis, MN; *U.S. Public*, pg. 110
Bender, Robert L., Chm., Pres., Chief Exec. Officer & Chief Oper. Officer--Lord, Sullivan & Yoder Inc. Marketing Communications, Columbus, OH; *U.S. Private*, pg. 676
Benedetti, M., Chief Oper. Officer--Prodotti Baumann SpA, Cortine di Nave, Italy; *Int'l*, pg. 171
Bengston, John N., Chief Oper. Officer & Exec. V.P.--The Sands Regent, Reno, NV; *U.S. Public*, pg. 1431
Beni, John J., Pres. & Chief Oper. Officer--Parade Publications Inc., New York, NY; *U.S. Private*, pg. 20
Benjamin, Nash, Deputy Pres. & Chief Oper. Officer--F. J. Benjamin Holdings Ltd., Singapore, Singapore; *Int'l*, pg. 187
Bennett, Frank, Chief Oper. Officer, V.P. & Asst. Sec.--Camalloy, Incorporated, Washington, PA; *U.S. Private*, pg. 202
Bennett, Harold C., Pres.--Utility Trailer Manufacturing Co., City of Industry, CA; *U.S. Private*, pg. 1130
Bennett, James J., Chief Oper. Officer & V.P.--Bio-Rad Laboratories, Inc., Hercules, CA; *U.S. Public*, pg. 230
Bennett, James P., Pres. & Chief Oper. Officer--Healthsouth Corporation, Birmingham, AL; *U.S. Public*, pg. 803
Bennett, Michael, Chief Oper. Officer & Exec. V.P.--Terra Industries, Inc., Sioux City, IA; *U.S. Public*, pg. 1581
Bennett, Richard, Mgr.-Opers.--Ariel Corporation, Mount Vernon, OH; *U.S. Private*, pg. 81
Bennett, Stephen D., Pres. & Chief Exec. & Oper. Officer--Acme Metals Incorporated, Riverdale, IL; *U.S. Public*, pg. 16
Bennington, Jack, Chief Oper. Officer--Halex Div., Bedford, OH; *U.S. Public*, pg. 217
Benson, Jerry S., Jr., Pres. & Chief Oper. Officer--VTEL Corporation, Austin, TX; *U.S. Public*, pg. 1703
Benson, Thomas H., Exec. V.P. & Chief Oper. Officer-Atlanta Gas Light Company--AGL Resources, Atlanta, GA; *U.S. Public*, pg. 6
Benter, George H., Pres. & Chief Oper. Officer--City National Corporation, Beverly Hills, CA; *U.S. Public*, pg. 380
Berardi, John F., Chief Oper. Officer & Exec V.P.-Grain Bus.--Farmland Industries, Inc., Kansas City, MO; *U.S. Private*, pg. 395
Berenato, Joseph C., Pres., Chief Fin. Officer & Chief Oper. Officer--Ducommun Incorporated, Carson, CA; *U.S. Public*, pg. 533
Berend, Francis, Chief Oper. Officer--Interspiro Inc., Branford, CT; *Int'l*, pg. 1289
Berenfield, Greg, Mgr.-Opers.--Berenfield Containers, Inc., Mason, OH; *U.S. Private*, pg. 135
Berens, James R., Pres. & Chief Oper. Officer--Norwest Financial, Inc., Des Moines, IA; *U.S. Public*, pg. 1202
Beresford, Jan, Chief Oper. Officer--Meritcare, Inc., Sewickley, PA; *U.S. Private*, pg. 733
Berg, David, Chief Oper. Officer & Exec. V.P.-Sls.--PremiumWear, Inc., Minneapolis, MN; *U.S. Public*, pg. 1323
Bergeron, Robert, Chief Oper. Officer--Canadian Steel Foundries, Ltd., Montreal, Canada; *U.S. Public*, pg. 142
Bergler, Gerald, Chief Oper. Officer & Exec. V.P.--American Speedy Printing Centers, Inc., Troy, MI; *U.S. Private*, pg. 62
Bergman, Christer, Chief Oper. Officer--Avesta Information Systems AB, Vasteras, Sweden; *Int'l*, pg. 221
Bergonzi, Albert J., Pres. & Co-Chief Oper. Officer--HBOC, Atlanta, GA; *U.S. Public*, pg. 770
Bergstrom, Steve W., Pres. & Chief Oper. Officer--NGC Corporation, Houston, TX; *U.S. Public*, pg. 1146
Berk, Alexander, Pres. & Chief Oper. Officer--Barton Incorporated, Chicago, IL; *U.S. Public*, pg. 300
Berlan, Denis, Chief Oper. Officer & Exec. V.P.--Altera Corporation, San Jose, CA; *U.S. Public*, pg. 59
Berman, Stephen G., Chief Oper. Officer, Exec. V.P. & Sec.--JAKKS Pacific, Inc., Malibu, CA; *U.S. Public*, pg. 923
Bermudez, Irma, Chief Oper. Officer--American International Container, Inc., Miami, FL; *U.S. Private*, pg. 57
Bernacchi, James P., Chief Oper. Officer--Consorcio G. Grupo Dina, S.A. de C.V., Mexico, Mexico; *Int'l*, pg. 326
Bernacchi, James P., Chief Oper. Officer--Motor Coach Industries International, Inc., Phoenix, AZ; *Int'l*, pg. 326
Bernacchi, James P., Pres. & Chief Oper. Officer--Universal Coach Parts, Inc., Des Plaines, IL; *Int'l*, pg. 326
Bersett, Gerald W., Pres. & Chief Oper. Officer--Sturm, Ruger & Co., Inc., Southport, CT; *U.S. Public*, pg. 1526
Bertrand, Alain, Chief Oper. Officer--The Eurotunnel Group, London, United Kingdom; *Int'l*, pg. 466
Bertrand, J., Chief Oper. Officer--Polyfilla SA, La Courneuve, France; *Int'l*, pg. 1501
Bertsch, Don, Chief Oper. Officer--Intairdril Ltd., Quito, Ecuador; *U.S. Public*, pg. 1316
Best, Arthur C., Pres. & Chief Oper. Officer--C.B. Ragland Company, Nashville, TN; *U.S. Private*, pg. 907
Bethards, Brandon, Pres. & Chief Oper. Officer--Kvaerner Pulping Inc., Charlotte, NC; *Int'l*, pg. 770
Bethune, David R., Pres. & Chief Oper. Officer--IVAX Corporation, Miami, FL; *U.S. Public*, pg. 914
Betlem, Dick, Pres. & Chief Oper. Officer--Albemarle Corporation, Richmond, VA; *U.S. Public*, pg. 37
Beusse, Carlton G., Sr. V.P., Mng. Dir.-RMS, Exec. V.P. & Chief Oper. Officer-CRRUX--Willis Corroon Corp. of Wisconsin, Milwaukee, WI; *Int'l*, pg. 1507
Bever, Jay Andrew, Jr., Pres. & Chief Oper. Officer--B&B Corporate Holdings, Inc., Tampa, FL; *U.S. Private*, pg. 104
Biblowitz, Joshua, Pres. & Chief Oper. Officer--Masters, Inc., Westbury, NY; *U.S. Private*, pg. 714
Biciher, Gary R., Pres. & Chief Oper. Officer--Louis P. Ciminelli Construction Co. Inc., Buffalo, NY; *U.S. Private*, pg. 239
Bickes, Thomas, Pres. & Chief Oper. Officer--Staffing Solutions, Boulder, CO; *U.S. Private*, pg. 1028
Biddle, Willing L., Pres. & Chief Oper. Officer--Urstadt Biddle Properties, Inc., Greenwich, CT; *U.S. Public*, pg. 1700
Biedermann, Pierre, Chief Oper. Officer--Novo Nordisk Ferment AG, Athens, Greece; *Int'l*, pg. 989
Bigelow, Jonathan L., Chief Oper. Officer & Exec. V.P.--Cliggott Publishing, Greenwich, CT; *U.S. Private*, pg. 246
Biller, Leslie S., Pres. & Chief Oper. Officer--Norwest Corporation, Minneapolis, MN; *U.S. Public*, pg. 1201
Billian, Glenn, V.P.--Van Son Holland Ink Corp. of America, Mineola, NY; *U.S. Private*, pg. 1133
Billot, Thierry, Chief Oper. Officer--Pernod, Creteil, France; *Int'l*, pg. 566
Bin Mohd Ali, Mohd Yusoff, Chief Oper. Officer--Ke-Zan Securities Sdn Bhd, Penang, Malaysia; *Int'l*, pg. 733
Binder, Christian, Chief Oper. Officer--Steno Diabetes Center, Gentofte, Denmark; *Int'l*, pg. 987
Binder, Herbert R., Pres. & Chief Oper. Officer--Shoppers Drug Mart, Ltd., Toronto, Canada; *Int'l*, pg. 112
Binkley, Gregory R., Chief Oper. Officer & Exec. V.P.--The Sportsman's Guide, Inc., Saint Paul, MN; *U.S. Public*, pg. 1499
Binks, Simon, Chief Oper. Officer--Neste Exploration Ltd., London, United Kingdom; *Int'l*, pg. 915
Birch, Kjeld, Chief Oper. Officer--Novo Nordisk Farmaka Danmark A/S, Bagsvaerd, Denmark; *Int'l*, pg. 987
Birch, Viggo L., Chief Oper. Officer--Novo Nordisk Pharma S.A., Madrid, Spain; *Int'l*, pg. 988
Bird, Thomas, Pres. & Chief Oper. Officer--Nepera Inc., Harriman, NY; *U.S. Public*, pg. 297
Birdsall, Don, Mng. Officer--BVK/McDonald, Milwaukee, WI; *U.S. Private*, pg. 108
Birkenbeck, Heinz, Chief Oper. Officer--Akerlund & Rausing Verpackung GmbH, Hochheim, Germany; *Int'l*, pg. 33
Bisballe, Bruce, Pres. & Chief Oper. Officer--Manufacturers Products Company, Warren, MI; *U.S. Private*, pg. 701
Biscieglia, Charles, Chief Oper. Officer & Exec. V.P.--South Jersey Gas Co., Folsom, NJ; *U.S. Public*, pg. 1488
Bishop, Eugene D., Pres. & Chief Oper. Officer--California State Bank, West Covina, CA; *U.S. Public*, pg. 294
Bishop, Katherine, Pres. & Chief Oper. Officer--Lebanon Seaboard Corporation, Lebanon, PA; *U.S. Private*, pg. 656
Bishop, William L., Pres. & Chief Oper. Officer--The Western Group, Saint Louis, MO; *U.S. Private*, pg. 1165
Bisset, James L., Chief Oper. Officer--Fairways and Swinford (Travel) Ltd., London, United Kingdom; *Int'l*, pg. 1214
Bittner, Clarence J., Pres. & Chief Oper. Officer--Shook National Corporation, Dayton, OH; *U.S. Private*, pg. 996
Bittner, Gary W., Pres. & Chief Oper. Officer--Richfood, Inc., Mechanicsville, VA; *U.S. Public*, pg. 1389
Bixby, Walter E., III, Pres. & Chief Oper. Officer--Old American Insurance Co., Kansas City, MO; *U.S. Public*, pg. 943
Bjokdahl, Per, Chief Oper. Officer--TAC Control Pte. Ltd., Singapore, Singapore; *Int'l*, pg. 670
Black, Mike, Chief Oper. Officer--Kenneth Gordon IAG, Inc., New Orleans, LA; *U.S. Private*, pg. 581
Blackburn, Stephan P., Pres. & Chief Oper. Officer--United Missouri Bank of St. Louis, Saint Louis, MO; *U.S. Public*, pg. 1655
Blaikie, Peter M., Pres. & Chief Oper. Officer--Unican Security Systems Ltd., Montreal, Canada; *Int'l*, pg. 1432
Blair, Richard M., Chief Oper. Officer--Young-Phillips Sales Co., Clemmons, NC; *U.S. Private*, pg. 1201
Blakely, Sylvia, Chief Oper. Officer--Akerlund & Rausing Ltd., Bury, United Kingdom; *Int'l*, pg. 33
Blanco, Rafael, Esq., Pres., Chief Exec. & Oper. Officer--PonceBank, F.S.B., Ponce, PR; *U.S. Public*, pg. 1316
Blank, Arthur M., Pres., Chief Exec. Officer & Chief Oper. Officer--The Home Depot, Inc., Atlanta, GA; *U.S. Public*, pg. 831
Blank, Martin J., Chm. Bd., Chief Oper. Officer & Sec.--Automobile Protection Corporation-APCO, Atlanta, GA; *U.S. Public*, pg. 150
Blankenship, Truman, Pres., Chief Exec. Officer & Chief Oper. Officer--Berryman Products, Inc., Arlington, TX; *U.S. Private*, pg. 138
Blauer, Michael J., Chief Oper. Officer & V.P.--Blauer Manufacturing Co., Inc., Boston, MA; *U.S. Private*, pg. 149
Blease, Doug, Chief Oper. Officer & Exec. V.P.--D & W Food Centers, Inc., Grand Rapids, MI; *U.S. Private*, pg. 300
Blissenbach, Henry, Pres. & Chief Oper. Officer--Chronimed Inc., Minnetonka, MN; *U.S. Public*, pg. 352
Block, Thomas, Exec. V.P. & Chief Oper. Officer--Ingalls, Boston, MA; *U.S. Private*, pg. 562

Blohowiak, Bruce, Chief Oper. Officer, Sr. V.P. & Gen. Counsel--Metropolitan Mortgage & Securities Co., Inc., Spokane, WA; *U.S. Private*, pg. 738

Bloss, David, Pres. & Chief Oper. Officer--Watts Industries, Inc., North Andover, MA; *U.S. Public*, pg. 1746

Blossom, Rick L., Pres. & Chief Oper. Officer--First National Bank of Southwestern Ohio, Hamilton, OH; *U.S. Public*, pg. 633

Blott, Roger, Chief Oper. Officer--Millicom International Cellular SA, Bertrange, Luxembourg; *Int'l*, pg. 867

Blouch, Gerald B., Pres. & Chief Oper. Officer--Invacare Corporation, Elyria, OH; *U.S. Public*, pg. 911

Blue, David W., Pres. & Chief Oper. Officer--The O'Boise Corporation, Oak Brook, IL; *U.S. Private*, pg. 810

Blumenfeld, Peter, Pres. & Chief Oper. Officer--Sport Supply Group, Inc., Dallas, TX; *U.S. Public*, pg. 1499

Blumenthal, David, Chief Oper. Officer & Sr. V.P.--Lion Brand Yarn Co., New York, NY; *U.S. Private*, pg. 669

Boardman, Elaine, Pres. & Chief Oper. Officer--Patient Care, Inc., West Orange, NJ; *U.S. Public*, pg. 344

Bobis, Arthur H., Pres.-Metal Div.--RHC/Spacemaster Corporation, Melrose Park, IL; *U.S. Private*, pg. 904

Bobit, Ty F., Pres. & Chief Oper. Officer--Bobit Publishing Company, Torrance, CA; *U.S. Private*, pg. 154

Bodaken, Bruce, Pres. & Chief Oper. Officer--Blue Shield of California, San Francisco, CA; *U.S. Private*, pg. 153

Bodine, David, Chief Oper. Officer--Bodine Assembly and Test Systems, Bridgeport, CT; *U.S. Private*, pg. 154

Bodine, Jeffrey P., Exec. V.P.--Bodine Electric Company, Chicago, IL; *U.S. Private*, pg. 154

Bodine, Stanley A., Pres. & Chief Oper. Officer--Funco, Inc., Eden Prairie, MN; *U.S. Public*, pg. 688

Bodor, Paul W., Chief Oper. Officer, Sr. V.P. & Treas.--W & D Securities, Inc., Jersey City, NJ; *U.S. Public*, pg. 925

Boehm, Josef F., Pres. & Chief Oper. Officer--Alaska Industrial Hardware Inc., Anchorage, AK; *U.S. Private*, pg. 31

Boehm, Richard, Chief Oper. Officer--Outlook Foods, Inc., Oconomowoc, WI; *U.S. Public*, pg. 1235

Bohan, Daniel P., Chief Oper. Officer--Omega World Travel, Inc., Fairfax, VA; *U.S. Private*, pg. 816

Bohlig, James W., Chief Oper. Officer & Sr. V.P.--Casella Waste Systems, Inc., Rutland, VT; *U.S. Public*, pg. 312

Bohn, David G., Pres.--Preferred Utilities Manufacturing Corp., Danbury, CT; *U.S. Private*, pg. 881

Boiko, Alexander, Chief Oper. Officer--Novo Nordisk A/S, Kiev, Ukraine; *Int'l*, pg. 987

Boissonneault, Roger M., Pres. & Chief Oper. Officer--Warner-Chilcott Laboratories, Inc., Rockaway, NJ; *Int'l*, pg. 436

Bolger, Patrick K., Pres. & Chief Oper. Officer--TransTechnology Corporation, Liberty Corner, NJ; *U.S. Public*, pg. 1632

Bolger, Tom, Chief Oper. Officer & Exec. V.P.--EvansGroup, Dallas, TX; *U.S. Private*, pg. 385

Bolivar, Octavio, Sr. V.P.--Andover Bancorp, Inc., Andover, MA; *U.S. Public*, pg. 111

Bolza-Schunemann, Albrecht, Chief Oper. Officer--KBA-Planeta AG, Radebeul, Germany; *Int'l*, pg. 742

Bonacci, Eugene, Chief Oper. Officer--Matlack Systems, Inc., Wilmington, DE; *U.S. Public*, pg. 1057

Bonar, Brian, Chief Oper. Officer--Imaging Technologies Corp., San Diego, CA; *U.S. Public*, pg. 870

Bond, Glenn, Dir.-Opers.--Algoma Steel Inc., Sault Sainte Marie, Canada; *Int'l*, pg. 56

Bond, James H., Pres. & Chief Oper. Officer--Central Parking Corp., Nashville, TN; *U.S. Public*, pg. 326

Bond, Tom, Chief Oper. Officer--Mac Cosmetics, Toronto, Canada; *U.S. Public*, pg. 594

Bonham, Carol, Chief Oper. Officer & Exec. V.P.--Interpacific Investors Services, Seattle, WA; *U.S. Private*, pg. 572

Bonnelyche, Christina, Chief Oper. Officer--Georg Jensen Silver AB, Stockholm, Sweden; *Int'l*, pg. 1134

Bonner, Robert B., Chief Oper. Officer, Exec. V.P. & Sec.--First Federal Savings, East Hartford, CT; *U.S. Public*, pg. 632

Bonnet, Yves, Chief Oper. Officer & Exec. V.P.--SNECMA - Societe Nationale d'Etude et de Construction de Moteurs d'Aviation, Paris, France; *Int'l*, pg. 1165

Bonneville, Pamela M., V.P.-Admin.--Spirol International Corp., Danielson, CT; *U.S. Private*, pg. 1026

Boone, J. Christopher, Chief Oper. Officer--ISC Realty Corporation, Charlotte, NC; *U.S. Public*, pg. 910

Bores, Stephen J., Pres. & Chief Oper. Officer--Therma-Tru Corp., Maumee, OH; *U.S. Private*, pg. 1079

Borges, John P., Chief Oper. Officer & V.P.-Opers.--SmarTrunk Systems, Inc., Hayward, CA; *U.S. Private*, pg. 1006

Borghi, Richard, Chief Oper. Officer & Exec. V.P.--Advanced Accessories Systems, LLC., Sterling Heights, MI; *U.S. Private*, pg. 21

Borig, Klaus, Chief Oper. Officer--BHF-Bank, Singapore, Singapore; *Int'l*, pg. 119

Bork, William J., Pres. & Chief Oper. Officer--Penn National Gaming, Inc., Wyomissing, PA; *U.S. Public*, pg. 1270

Borland, Paul C., Pres. & Chief Oper. Officer--NS Group, Inc., Newport, KY; *U.S. Public*, pg. 1147

Boron, Gregory F., Chief Oper. Officer & Exec. V.P.--Boron LePore Group, Fair Lawn, NJ; *U.S. Public*, pg. 246

Boronow, Gordon C., Chief Oper. Officer--American Skandia Life Assurance Corporation, Shelton, CT; *Int'l*, pg. 1257

Borow, Leonard, Chief Oper. Officer & Exec. V.P.--Aeroflex Incorporated, Plainview, NY; *U.S. Public*, pg. 23

Borowsky, Ned S., Pres. & Chief Oper. Officer--North American Publishing Company, Philadelphia, PA; *U.S. Private*, pg. 803

Borrelli, Lou, Chief Oper. Officer & Exec. V.P.--Marcus Cable Company, L.P., Dallas, TX; *U.S. Private*, pg. 702

Borstad, Gerald E., Chief Oper. Officer--Willis Corroon Corp. of Anchorage, Anchorage, AK; *Int'l*, pg. 1505

Boscia, Oreste, Chief Oper. Officer--Windsor Quality Food Co., Ltd., Houston, TX; *U.S. Private*, pg. 1182

Bosman, C.F., Chief Oper. Officer--Dynartail bv, Zeist, Netherlands; *Int'l*, pg. 681

Bosmans, Luc, Chief Oper. Officer--S.A. Novo Nordisk Pharma NV, Brussels, Belgium; *Int'l*, pg. 988

Bostic, Sid A., Pres. & Chief Oper. Officer--FirstMerit Corporation, Akron, OH; *U.S. Public*, pg. 646

Boswell, E.F., Pres. & Chief Oper. Officer--Eddy Paper Company Limited, Ottawa, Canada; *Int'l*, pg. 1495

Boucard, A., Chief Oper. Officer--Renault Bisquit, Rouillac, France; *Int'l*, pg. 566

Bouchez, Jacques, Pres. & Chief Oper. Officer--The Crispin Company, Houston, TX; *U.S. Private*, pg. 290

Boughner, Robert L., Chief Oper. Officer & Exec. V.P.--Boyd Gaming Corporation, Las Vegas, NV; *U.S. Public*, pg. 249

Bourke, Anita Z., Chief Oper. Officer--Willis Corroon Corp. of Seattle, Seattle, WA; *Int'l*, pg. 1507

Bousquette, Kevin A., Chief Oper. Officer & Exec. V.P.--Sotheby's Holdings Inc., New York, NY; *U.S. Public*, pg. 1487

Bovaird, J.R., Chief Oper. Officer & Exec. V.P.--Bovaird Supply Co., Tulsa, OK; *U.S. Private*, pg. 162

Bovaird, W.J., Chm. Bd., Pres. & Chief Exec. Officer--Bovaird Supply Co., Tulsa, OK; *U.S. Private*, pg. 162

Bovender, Jack O., Jr., Pres. & Chief Oper. Officer--Columbia/HCA Healthcare Corporation, Nashville, TN; *U.S. Public*, pg. 403

Bovy, M., Chief Oper. Officer--S.A. P.A.G.E. Municipal, Liege, Belgium; *Int'l*, pg. 301

Bovy, M., Chief Oper. Officer--S.A. Legrain, Blehories, Belgium; *Int'l*, pg. 301

Bowden, Ashley E., Pres. & Chief Oper. Officer--QST Communications, Inc., Peoria, IL; *U.S. Public*, pg. 367

Bowe, James M., Chief Oper. Officer--Reedrill Inc., Denison, TX; *Int'l*, pg. 1325

Bowen, Lawrence H., Chief Oper. Officer--Weldotron Corporation, Piscataway, NJ; *U.S. Public*, pg. 1752

Bower, A. J., Chief Oper. Officer--Bridon Cordage Inc., Albert Lea, MN; *Int'l*, pg. 215

Bowers, John, Chief Oper. Officer--Marquette National Life Insurance Co., Dallas, TX; *U.S. Private*, pg. 1018

Bowles, Crandall C., Pres. & Chief Oper. Officer--Springs Industries, Inc., Fort Mill, SC; *U.S. Public*, pg. 1499

Bowman, Bruce, Sr. Dir.-Opers.--Ben & Jerry's Homemade Inc., South Burlington, VT; *U.S. Public*, pg. 210

Bowman, Robert A., Pres. & Chief Oper. Officer--ITT Corporation, New York, NY; *U.S. Public*, pg. 1512

Bowser, Lee H., Chief Oper. Officer--Insurer Physician Services Organization, Camp Hill, PA; *U.S. Private*, pg. 529

Box, Jerry W., Chief Oper. Officer & Exec. V.P.--Oryx Energy, Dallas, TX; *U.S. Public*, pg. 1232

Boyan, William L., Jr., Pres. & Chief Oper. Officer--John Hancock Mutual Life Insurance Company, Boston, MA; *U.S. Private*, pg. 589

Boyce, James, Chief Oper. Officer--InterDigital Communications Corp., King of Prussia, PA; *U.S. Public*, pg. 889

Boyce, Michael, Chief Oper. Officer--North American Salt Company, Overland Park, KS; *U.S. Private*, pg. 505

Boyd, Dan, Chief Oper. Officer--Boyle Engineering Corp., Newport Beach, CA; *U.S. Private*, pg. 163

Boyd, James R., Grp. Oper. Officer--APAC Holdings, Inc., Atlanta, GA; *U.S. Public*, pg. 139

Boyd, James R., Grp. Oper. Officer--Ashland Services Company, Lexington, KY; *U.S. Public*, pg. 139

Boyd, Ralph E., Pres. & Chief Oper. Officer--Cascade Natural Gas Corporation, Seattle, WA; *U.S. Public*, pg. 311

Boylan, Michael J., Vice Chm.-Publ.--American Media, Inc., Lake Worth, FL; *U.S. Public*, pg. 87

Bracken, Frank D., Pres. & Chief Oper. Officer--Haggar Corporation, Dallas, TX; *U.S. Public*, pg. 774

Bradley, Kevin B., Chief Oper. Officer & Controller--Taylor & Francis Philadelphia, Bristol, PA; *Int'l*, pg. 1358

Brady, Jack D., Chm. Bd., Pres. & Chief Exec. & Oper. Officer--Crown Andersen Inc., Peachtree City, GA; *U.S. Public*, pg. 462

Bragg, Paul A., Pres. & Chief Oper. Officer--Pride International, Inc., Houston, TX; *U.S. Public*, pg. 1324

Brahmstadt, Clifford A., V.P.-Mfg.--Bachman Company, Reading, PA; *U.S. Private*, pg. 109

Brait, Wolfgang, Chief Oper. Officer--Novo Nordisk A/S, Sofia, Bulgaria; *Int'l*, pg. 987

Bramble, David C., Pres. & Chief Oper. Officer--David A. Bramble, Inc., Chestertown, MD; *U.S. Private*, pg. 165

Brandenberg, Ernest A., Chief Oper. Officer--KONE Elevator GmbH, Baar, Switzerland; *Int'l*, pg. 748

Brannen, Charles A., V.P.--Overton Gear & Tool Corp., Addison, IL; *U.S. Private*, pg. 823

Bratton, Robert O., Chief Oper. Officer, Chief Fin. Officer & Exec. V.P.--First Charter Corporation, Concord, NC; *U.S. Public*, pg. 627

Braun, Donald L., Chief Oper. Officer, Exec. V.P. & Treas.--Hall Financial Group, Inc., Dallas, TX; *U.S. Private*, pg. 495

Braun, Hartmut, Chief Oper. Officer--Skandia Lebensversicherung AG, Berlin, Germany; *Int'l*, pg. 1258

Braun, Stanley, Pres., Chief Exec. Officer & Chief Oper. Officer--Pac Rim Holding Corporation, Woodland Hills, CA; *U.S. Public*, pg. 1246

Braun, Thomas, Chief Oper. Officer--Corporate Finance Magazine, New York, NY; *U.S. Private*, pg. 405

Bray, Michael E., H., Pres. & Chief Oper. Officer--Riley Consolidated, Inc., Worcester, MA; *Int'l*, pg. 401

Brazier, Robert G., Pres. & Chief Oper. Officer--Airborne Freight Corporation, Seattle, WA; *U.S. Public*, pg. 32

Brealey, Graham M., Chief Oper. Officer--British Building & Engineering Appliances Plc, Sandy, United Kingdom; *Int'l*, pg. 219

Brecht, Edwin, Co-Chief Oper. Officer--International Finance Division, Dusseldorf, Germany; *Int'l*, pg. 645

Breed, Johnnie Cordell, Pres. & Chief Oper. Officer--Breed Technologies, Inc., Lakeland, FL; *U.S. Public*, pg. 251

Breffort, Jean Claade, Chief Oper. Officer--Brasilit S.A., Sao Paulo, Brazil; *Int'l*, pg. 1171

Bregar, Raymond E., Exec. V.P.-Corp. Opers.--Semtech Corporation, Newbury Park, CA; *U.S. Public*, pg. 1456

Breisinger, James R., Chief Oper. Officer--Greenfield Industries Inc., Evans, GA; *U.S. Public*, pg. 950

Breitenbach, E. Allen, Dr., Chm. Bd. & Chief Exec. Officer--Scientific Software-Intercomp, Inc., Denver, CO; *U.S. Public*, pg. 1443

Brener, Micha, Chief Oper. Officer--Egged Israel Transport Cooperative Society Ltd., Tel Aviv, Israel; *Int'l*, pg. 435

Brennan, Robert J., Pres. & Chief Oper. Officer--American Institute for Foreign Study, Greenwich, CT; *U.S. Private*, pg. 56

Brenneman, Gregory D., Pres. & Chief Oper. Officer--Continental Airlines, Houston, TX; *U.S. Public*, pg. 439

Brenner, Harry, Chief Oper. Officer--Cumberland Farms, Inc., Canton, MA; *U.S. Private*, pg. 295

Brenner, Stephen, Chief Oper. Officer, Exec. V.P.-Bus. Affairs & Gen. Counsel--USA Networks, New York, NY; *U.S. Public*, pg. 1686

Breslawsky, Marc C., Pres. & Chief Oper. Officer--Pitney Bowes Inc., Stamford, CT; *U.S. Public*, pg. 1303

Brestovansky, Dennis, Chief Oper. Officer--ADCS, Inc., Austin, TX; *U.S. Public*, pg. 12

Brevenik, John R., Pres. & Chief Oper. Officer--Herberts-O'Brien Inc., Houston, TX; *Int'l*, pg. 626

Breyer, Robert, Pres. & Chief Oper. Officer--Alkeremes, Cambridge, MA; *U.S. Public*, pg. 41

Brian, Steven, Pres. & Chief Oper. Officer--Home Products International, Inc., Chicago, IL; *U.S. Public*, pg. 832

Brichant, Thierry, Chief Oper. Officer--Credit Mutuel, Paris, France; *Int'l*, pg. 344

Brick, Bill, Pres. & Chief Oper. Officer--Suiza Foods Corporation, Dallas, TX; *U.S. Public*, pg. 1526

Brick, Frank E., Pres., Chief Oper. Officer & Chief Exec. Officer--Telxon Corporation, Akron, OH; *U.S. Public*, pg. 1573

Brickel, Jack W., Pres., Chief Exec. & Chief Oper. Officer--BEC Inc., Richmond, MI; *U.S. Private*, pg. 106

Bricot, Michele, Chief Oper. Officer--G. Leblanc S.A., Boossey, France; *U.S. Private*, pg. 657

Brilliant, James, Chief Exec. Officer & Chief Oper. Officer--Sporto Corp., Boston, MA; *U.S. Private*, pg. 1026

Brindley, Thomas M., Chief Oper. Officer & Exec. V.P.--W.A. Roosevelt Co., La Crosse, WI; *U.S. Private*, pg. 943

Brining, David R., Pres., Chief Oper. & Chief Exec. Officer--Valley Forge Corporation, San Rafael, CA; *U.S. Public*, pg. 1705

Brink, Duane, Chief Oper. Officer--Brink Electric Construction Company, Rapid City, SD; *U.S. Private*, pg. 169

Brinkman, Lloyd D., Chm. Bd., Chief Exec. & Chief Oper. Officer--LDB Corporation, Kerrville, TX; *U.S. Private*, pg. 639

Brisbin, Thomas D., Chief Oper. Officer & Exec. V.P.--Tetra Tech, Inc., Pasadena, CA; *U.S. Public*, pg. 1582

Brix, Julian, Chief Oper. Officer--Georgia Transmission Corporation, Tucker, GA; *U.S. Private*, pg. 448

Brochu, Michael A., Pres. & Chief Oper. Officer--Sierra On-Line, Inc., Bellevue, WA; *U.S. Public*, pg. 321

Brockel, Detlef, Dr., Co-Chief Oper. Officer--IKB Consult GmbH, Dusseldorf, Germany; *Int'l*, pg. 645

Brognola, Michael J., Chief Oper. Officer & Exec. V.P.--Laidlaw Environmental Services, Inc., Columbia, SC; *U.S. Public*, pg. 975

Bronestine, Verne, Chief Oper. Officer--La Grange Foundry Inc., La Grange, MO; *U.S. Public*, pg. 142

Bronfman, Edgar, Jr., Pres. & Chief Exec. Officer--The Seagram Company Ltd., Montreal, Canada; *Int'l*, pg. 1214

Brooke, Will, Chief Oper. Officer & V.P.--Harbert Corporation, Birmingham, AL; *U.S. Private*, pg. 500

Brooks, Jean, Chief Oper. Officer & V.P.--ICG Media Consultants, Inc., Los Angeles, CA; *U.S. Private*, pg. 208

Broomfield, Michael W., Chief Oper. Officer--Giant Food Inc., Landover, MD; *U.S. Public*, pg. 741

Brosius, Andy, Pres., Chief Oper. Officer--Midwest Industries, Inc., Ida Grove, IA; *U.S. Private*, pg. 744

Brothers, John A., Grp. Oper. Officer--Ashland Chemical, Dublin, OH; *U.S. Public*, pg. 139

Brothers, John A., Grp. Oper. Officer--Valvoline Company, Lexington, KY; *U.S. Public*, pg. 139

Brothers, John A., Grp. Oper. Officer--Valvoline, Inc., Hernando, MS; *U.S. Public*, pg. 139

Brouilette, Alan, Chief Oper. Officer--Strombecker Chemtoy Division, Chicago, IL; *U.S. Private*, pg. 1047

Brouilette, Alan, Chief Oper. Officer--Tootsietoy Division, Chicago, IL; *U.S. Private*, pg. 1047

Brousseau, Gerald, Chief Oper. Officer & Chief Fin. Officer--Panneaux Malette-OSB Inc., Saint-Georges, Canada; *Int'l*, pg. 833

Brown, C.A., Chief Oper. Officer--Rechem International Ltd, Bourne, United Kingdom; *Int'l*, pg. 1228

Brown, Christopher A., Pres. & Chief Oper. Officer--Rotelle, Inc., West Point, PA; *U.S. Public*, pg. 1389

Brown, Colin, Chief Oper. Officer & Gen. Counsel--JM Family Enterprises Inc., Deerfield Beach, FL; *U.S. Private*, pg. 577

Brown, Craig, Vice Chm. & Chief Oper. Officer--The MacManus Group, Inc., New York, NY; *U.S. Private*, pg. 692

Brown, Donald, Pres. & Chief Oper. Officer--Slant/Fin Corporation, Greenvale, NY; *U.S. Private*, pg. 1005

Brown, Doug, Chief Oper. Officer & Sr. V.P.--Willis Corroon Corp. of Birmingham, Birmingham, AL; *Int'l*, pg. 1505

Brown, Glenn W., Jr., Chief Oper. Officer & Exec. V.P.--Sherman & Reilly, Inc., Chattanooga, TN; *U.S. Private*, pg. 993

Brown, James L., Chief Oper. Officer--Casino Aztar, Evansville, IN; *U.S. Public*, pg. 158

Brown, Michael, Pres. & Chief Oper. Officer--Litton Industries, Inc., Woodland Hills, CA; *U.S. Public*, pg. 1002
Brown, Michael S., Pres. & Chief Oper. Officer--Wometco Enterprises, Inc., Coral Gables, FL; *U.S. Private*, pg. 1186
Brown, Mike, Pres. & Chief Oper. Officer--City Meats & Provisions Co., Phoenix, AZ; *U.S. Private*, pg. 244
Brown, Mike, Chief Oper. Officer--Amecom Div., College Park, MD; *U.S. Public*, pg. 1002
Brown, Nicholas M., Jr., Pres. & Chief Oper. Officer--NAC Re Corp., Greenwich, CT; *U.S. Public*, pg. 1144
Brown, Paul, Chief Oper. Officer-Legal Information Services--LEXIS-NEXIS, Miamisburg, OH; *Int'l*, pg. 1096
Brown, Robert E., Pres. & Chief Oper. Officer--Bombardier Aerospace, Dorval, Canada; *Int'l*, pg. 200
Browning, D. Dale, Vice Chm. & Chief Oper. Officer--Colorado National Bankshares, Inc., Denver, CO; *U.S. Public*, pg. 1680
Browning, Peter C., Pres. & Chief Oper. Officer--Sonoco Products Company, Hartsville, SC; *U.S. Public*, pg. 1485
Brozman, Jack L., Chm. Bd., Pres. & Chief Exec. Officer--Concorde Career Colleges, Inc., Kansas City, MO; *U.S. Public*, pg. 430
Bruder, George A., Jr., Chief Oper. Officer & Sr. V.P.--DBT Online, Inc., Las Vegas, NV; *U.S. Public*, pg. 472
Brueck, Wolfgang, Co-Chief Oper. Officer--GK Gesellschaft fuer Kohleverfluessigung mbH, Saarbruecken, Germany; *Int'l*, pg. 1166
Brugman, H., Chief Oper. Officer--Van Rietschoten & Houwens Noord-West bv, Zaandam, Netherlands; *Int'l*, pg. 681
Bruhl, Hans-Hubert, Chief Exec. Officer--Harpen Transport AG, Duisburg, Germany; *Int'l*, pg. 597
Brunck, Robert, Chief Oper. Officer & Dir.-Gen.--Compagnie Generale de Geophysique, Massy, France; *Int'l*, pg. 241
Brunetti, Wayne H., Pres. & Chief Oper. Officer--New Century Energies, Inc., Denver, CO; *U.S. Public*, pg. 1170
Bryan, Anthony, Chief Oper. Officer--Novo Nordisk Bioindustrial Pty Ltd., North Rocks, Australia; *Int'l*, pg. 989
Bryan, G.R., Pres. & Chief Oper. Officer--Enserch Gas Co., Dallas, TX; *U.S. Public*, pg. 1587
Bryan, W. Lester, Pres. & Chief Oper. Officer--The Washington Water Power Company, Spokane, WA; *U.S. Public*, pg. 1744
Bryant, Carleton F., III, Chief Oper. Officer, Exec. V.P., Treas. & Sec.--Westerbeke Corporation, Avon, MA; *U.S. Public*, pg. 1757
Brzezinski, Francis, Pres. & Chief Oper. Officer--Wispark Corporation, Milwaukee, WI; *U.S. Public*, pg. 1773
Brzezinski, Francis, Pres. & Chief Oper. Officer--Wisvest Corporation, Milwaukee, WI; *U.S. Public*, pg. 1773
Brzuska, Wolfgang, Co-Chief Oper. Officer--IKB Leasing Berlin GmbH, Berlin, Germany; *Int'l*, pg. 645
Brzuska, Wolfgang, Co-Chief Oper. Officer--IKB Leasing GmbH, Hamburg, Germany; *Int'l*, pg. 645
Buades, Andres, Chief Oper. Officer--Sol Melia, Palma de Mallorca, Spain; *Int'l*, pg. 1277
Buchanan, Richard W., Chief Oper. Officer & Exec. V.P.-Corp. Asset & Fin.--First American Federal Savings Bank, Bristol, VA; *U.S. Public*, pg. 624
Buchholz, Mark, Chief Opers. Officer--Monrovia Nursery Co., Azusa, CA; *U.S. Private*, pg. 757
Buchsenschutz, Y., Chief Oper. Officer--Diepal-N.S.A., Villefranche-sur-Saone, France; *Int'l*, pg. 380
Buck, C.J., Chief Oper. Officer & Exec. V.P.--Buck Knives, Inc., El Cajon, CA; *U.S. Private*, pg. 177
Buck, Stephen, Chief Oper. Officer--Container Tooling Corporation, Neptune, NJ; *U.S. Public*, pg. 617
Buckley, John E., Chief Oper. Officer & Exec. V.P.--A.T. Cross Co., Lincoln, RI; *U.S. Public*, pg. 460
Buckley, Stephen R., V.P.-Opers. & Information Systems--RTG Furniture Corp., Seffner, FL; *U.S. Private*, pg. 905
Budde, Ken, Chief Fin. Officer, Chief Oper. Officer & V.P.--Arcade Inc., Chattanooga, TN; *U.S. Private*, pg. 79
Buddemeyer, David, Pres., Chief Exec. Officer & Chief Oper. Officer--Servico, Inc., West Palm Beach, FL; *U.S. Public*, pg. 1462
Budney, Albert J., Jr., Pres. & Chief Oper. Officer--Niagara Mohawk Power Corporation, Syracuse, NY; *U.S. Public*, pg. 1181
Buehler, Jay, Chief Oper. Officer & V.P.--ROHN Industries, Inc., Peoria, IL; *U.S. Public*, pg. 1404
Buell, Dick, Chief Oper. Officer & Exec. V.P.--Griffith Laboratories Worldwide, Inc., Alsip, IL; *U.S. Private*, pg. 481
Buerges, Ronald A., Chief Oper. Officer & Sr. Exec. V.P.--Magna Group, Inc., Saint Louis, MO; *U.S. Public*, pg. 1037
Buescher, James, Chief Oper. Officer--Idea Man, Inc., Los Angeles, CA; *U.S. Private*, pg. 557
Buffart, Roland, Head-BBL Waloon Region--BBL Walloon Region, Wavre, Belgium; *Int'l*, pg. 147
Buffington, Douglas A., Pres., Chief Oper. & Fin. Officer & Treas.--Square Two Golf Incorporated, Fairfield, NJ; *U.S.* Public, pg. 1501
Buhler, Michael O., Pres. & Chief Oper. Officer--Old Dominion Box Co., Inc., Madison Heights, VA; *U.S. Private*, pg. 814
Buicko, David M., Chief Oper. Officer--Galesi Group, Schenectady, NY; *U.S. Private*, pg. 437
Buicko, David M., Chief Oper. Officer & Exec. V.P.--Rotterdam Ventures Inc., Guilderland Center, NY; *U.S. Private*, pg. 437
Bukaty, Michael E., Pres. & Chief Oper. Officer--Latshaw Enterprises, Inc., Wichita, KS; *U.S. Public*, pg. 979
Bukovich, George, Chief Oper. Officer--Nobles Mfg. Inc., Saint Croix Falls, WI; *U.S. Private*, pg. 800
Buoniconti, Nicholas A., Vice Chm. & Chief Oper. Officer--Columbia Laboratories, Inc., Miami, FL; *U.S. Public*, pg. 405
Burdette, Lew, Chief Oper. Officer--Books-A-Million, Inc., Birmingham, AL; *U.S. Public*, pg. 244
Burenga, Kenneth L., Pres., Chief Exec. Officer & Chief Oper. Officer-Dow Jones Market--Dow Jones & Company, Inc., New York, NY; *U.S. Public*, pg. 524
Burg, H. Peter, Pres., Chief Oper. & Fin. Officer--FirstEnergy Corp., Akron, OH; *U.S. Public*, pg. 644
Burgo, Ray, Pres. & Chief Oper. Officer--Giant Eagle, Inc., Pittsburgh, PA; *U.S. Private*, pg. 450
Burkart, Clemens, Chief Oper. Officer--BHF-Bank Representative Office, Ho Chi Minh City, Vietnam; *Int'l*, pg. 120
Burke, James M., Chief Oper. Officer--Eateries, Inc., Oklahoma City, OK; *U.S. Public*, pg. 555
Burke, James M., Chief Oper. Officer--Pepperoni Grill, Oklahoma City, OK; *U.S. Public*, pg. 555
Burke, Jeffrey A., Pres. & Chief Oper. Officer--Osco Industries Inc., Portsmouth, OH; *U.S. Private*, pg. 820
Burke, Michael, V.P.-Opers.--Burke Engineering Company, South El Monte, CA; *U.S. Private*, pg. 183
Burkhardt, W., Chief Oper. Officer--BHF-Bank Representative Office, Paris, France; *Int'l*, pg. 120
Burkhead, R., Chief Oper. Officer--Marks Transfer & Storage, Cambridge, OH; *U.S. Private*, pg. 390
Burkhead, Scott, Pres., Chief Oper. Officer & New Bus. Contact--Rockett, Burkhead, Lewis & Winslow, Raleigh, NC; *U.S. Private*, pg. 938
Burks, Keith W., Chief Oper. Officer & Exec. V.P.--Bindley Western Industries, Inc., Indianapolis, IN; *U.S. Public*, pg. 228
Burnes, Kennett F., Pres. & Chief Oper. Officer--Cabot Corporation, Boston, MA; *U.S. Public*, pg. 288
Burnett, I. Malcolm, Chief Oper. Officer--Marine Midland Bank, Buffalo, NY; *Int'l*, pg. 581
Burnside, Mary M., Chief Oper. Officer--Novell Inc., San Jose, CA; *U.S. Public*, pg. 1203
Burrice, Robert N., Chief Oper. Officer & Exec. V.P.--Gateway Press, Inc., Louisville, KY; *U.S. Private*, pg. 441
Burris, Robert D., Pres. & Chief Oper. Officer--Burris Foods, Inc., Milford, DE; *U.S. Private*, pg. 188
Burriss, J.D., Chm. Bd., Pres. & Chief Exec. & Oper. Officer--The Alpha Corporation Of Tennessee, Collierville, TN; *U.S. Private*, pg. 44
Burroughs, James R., Pres. & Chief Oper. Officer--First Gray Line Corporation, Beverly Hills, CA; *U.S. Private*, pg. 407
Burroughs, Sarah, Pres. & Chief Oper. Officer--Burrell Communications Group Inc., Chicago, IL; *U.S. Private*, pg. 188
Burrows, Fred, Chief Oper. Officer--Malette Quebec, Inc., Montreal, Canada; *Int'l*, pg. 833
Burton, James, Chief Oper. Officer--Reading Tube Corp., Reading, PA; *U.S. Private*, pg. 202
Burzin, Klaus, Pres. & Chief Oper. Officer--Huls America Inc., Somerset, NJ; *Int'l*, pg. 1455
Busby, Jack W., Jr., Pres. & Chief Oper. Officer--Hancock Fabrics, Inc., Tupelo, MS; *U.S. Public*, pg. 779
Busch, Joseph F., Exec. V.P.--Ederer Inc., Seattle, WA; *U.S. Private*, pg. 363
Buser, Raoul C., Pres. & Chief Oper. Officer--Alcell Technologies Inc., Newcastle, Canada; *Int'l*, pg. 1104
Bush, Michael J., Chief Oper. Officer & Exec. V.P.--Movado Group, Inc., Lyndhurst, NJ; *U.S. Public*, pg. 1140
Bushee, Michael F., Chief Oper. Officer--Meditrust Corporation, Needham, MA; *U.S. Public*, pg. 1081
Bushwack, John R., Chief Oper. Officer--Valley National Gasses Inc., Wheeling, WV; *U.S. Private*, pg. 1132
Busin, Marco, Chief Oper. Officer--Biosol S.p.A., Sondalo, Italy; *Int'l*, pg. 667
Bussell, Gerald, V.P.-Opers.--Xomed Surgical Products, Jacksonville, FL; *U.S. Public*, pg. 253
Bustillo, Oscar, Jr., Chm. Bd., Pres. & Chief Exec. Officer--Republic National Bank of Miami, Miami, FL; *U.S. Private*, pg. 924
Busto, Richard, Pres. & Chief Oper. Officer--Gandalf Technologies Inc., Nepean, Canada; *Int'l*, pg. 540
Butcko, Joseph D., Chief Oper. Officer--Crescive Die & Tool, Inc., Saline, MI; *U.S. Private*, pg. 289
Butler, Norton L., Pres. & Chief Oper. Officer--Eastman House Of California, Inc., Burlington, IA; *U.S. Private*, pg. 238
Butler, Norton L., Pres. & Chief Oper. Officer--Eastman House Of Alabama, Inc., Burlington, IA; *U.S. Private*, pg. 238
Butler, Thomas R., Pres. & Chief Oper. Officer-Novus Services, Inc.--Dean Witter, Discover & Co., New York, NY; *U.S. Public*, pg. 1132
Butrus, Paul R., Chief Oper. Officer & Exec V.P.--Medical Assurance, Inc., Birmingham, AL; *U.S. Public*, pg. 1079
Butt, Mohammad Saeed, Chief Oper. Officer--National Bank of Pakistan, Karachi, Pakistan; *Int'l*, pg. 907
Buttler, Heinz, Chief Oper. Officer--MBA-KONE AG, Bassersdorf, Switzerland; *Int'l*, pg. 748
Butts, Steve, Chief Oper. Officer--Grandy's, Inc., Lewisville, TX; *U.S. Private*, pg. 61
Butz, Wayne D., Pres., Chief Oper. Officer & Actuary--Harleysville Life Insurance Co., Harleysville, PA; *U.S. Public*, pg. 787
Byland, Friedrich C., Chief Oper. Officer--Schweizer Verband der Raiffeisenbanken, Saint Gallen, Switzerland; *Int'l*, pg. 1211
Byrnes, Robert J., Pres. & Chief Oper. Officer--FFP Marketing Company, Inc., Fort Worth, TX; *U.S. Public*, pg. 604
Caccini, Gian Paolo, Vice Chm., Pres., Chief Exec. & Chief Oper. Officer--CertainTeed Corporation, Valley Forge, PA; *Int'l*, pg. 1170
Caffarone, Douglas P., Pres. & Chief Oper. Officer--Geyer-McAllister Publications, Inc., New York, NY; *U.S. Private*, *pg. 450*
Calabrese, Wayne H., Pres. & Chief Oper. Officer--Wackenhut Corrections Corporation, Palm Beach Gardens, FL; *U.S. Public*, pg. 1731
Calamari, Joseph, Pres. & Chief Oper. Officer--Marvel Entertainment Group, New York, NY; *U.S. Public*, pg. 1052
Caldwell, Donald R., Pres. & Chief Oper. Officer--Safeguard Scientifics, Inc., Wayne, PA; *U.S. Public*, pg. 1424
Calicchio, Doug, Chief Fin. Officer--Delcal Enterprises, Inc., New York, NY; *U.S. Private*, pg. 322
Call, Michael, Chief Oper. Officer--Maverik Country Stores, Inc., Salt Lake City, UT; *U.S. Private*, pg. 715
Callaghan, Frank, Chief Oper. Officer-Plastics Div.--Cookson Group plc, London, United Kingdom; *Int'l*, pg. 328
Callahan-Guion, Kathleen, Pres. & Chief Oper. Officer--E-Z Serve Corp., Houston, TX; *U.S. Public*, pg. 540
Callahan-Guion, Kathleen, Pres. & Chief Oper. Officer--E-Z Serve Convenience Stores, Inc., Houston, TX; *U.S. Public*, pg. 540
Callahan, Richard J., Pres. & Chief Oper. Officer--Greenwich Insurance Company, Greenwich, CT; *U.S. Public*, pg. 1144
Callahan, Richard J., Pres. & Chief Oper. Officer--Indian Harbor Insurance Company, Greenwich, CT; *U.S. Public*, *pg. 1144*
Calley, John, Pres. & Chief Oper. Officer--Sony Pictures Entertainment, Culver City, CA; *Int'l*, pg. 1281
Calvert, Horace A., Chief Oper. Officer & Exec. V.P.--Seitel, Inc., Houston, TX; *U.S. Public*, pg. 1454
Camba, Jose A., Chief Oper. Officer & Sr. V.P.--Banco Santander Puerto Rico, Hato Rey, PR; *Int'l*, pg. 143
Camerer, R. A., Chief Oper. Officer--BHF-Bank Representative Office, Rosebank, South Africa; *Int'l*, pg. 120
Cameron, John, Chief Oper. Officer--Jahn Foundry Corp., Springfield, MA; *U.S. Public*, pg. 142
Camino, Louis D., Pres. & Chief Oper. Officer--Rouge Steel Company, Dearborn, MI; *U.S. Public*, pg. 1406
Campagna, John, Chief Oper. Officer--Architectural Wall Systems, LLC, Edison, NJ; *U.S. Private*, pg. 403
Campanaro, Leonard A., Pres. & Chief Oper. Officer--Harsco Corporation, Camp Hill, PA; *U.S. Public*, pg. 792
Campbell, Dennis, Chief Oper. Officer & V.P.--Carl Weissman & Sons, Inc., Great Falls, MT; *U.S. Private*, pg. 1160
Campbell, Donald P., Chief Exec. Officer--Tokai Financial Services, Inc., Berwyn, PA; *Int'l*, pg. 1391
Campbell, John M., Chief Oper. Officer--E & A Industries, Inc., Indianapolis, IN; *U.S. Private*, pg. 352
Campbell, Peter J., Pres. & Chief Oper. Officer--Connaught Laboratories Limited, Willowdale, Canada; *Int'l*, pg. 1109
Camps, Steven, Chief Oper. Officer & Chief Fin. Officer--Interplay Productions, Inc., Irvine, CA; *U.S. Private*, pg. 572
Caneman, Monica, Chief Oper. Officer--Skandinaviska Enskilda Banken, Stockholm, Sweden; *Int'l*, pg. 1258
Canfield, William, V.P.-Opers.--Little Switzerland, Inc., Charlotte Amalie, VI; *U.S. Public*, pg. 1001
Canning, Simon, Pres. & Chief Oper. Officer--SBC Warburg Dillon Read, Stamford, CT; *Int'l*, pg. 1329
Canno, Jonathon S., Chm. Bd., Pres. & Chief Oper. Officer--Equitable Bag Company, Inc., Florence, KY; *U.S. Private*, pg. 380
Capps, Roger, Chief Oper. Officer & Sr. V.P.--Prairie Farms Dairy, Inc., Carlinville, IL; *U.S. Private*, pg. 878
Capursa, John, Chief Oper. Officer--Healthcare America, Inc., Austin, TX; *U.S. Private*, pg. 515
Carber, Gerald L., Chief Oper. Officer & V.P.--Embers Charcoal Company, Inc., Conway, SC; *U.S. Private*, pg. 373
Carendi, Jan R., Chief Oper. Officer--Skandia Leben Holding GmbH, Berlin, Germany; *Int'l*, pg. 1258
Carey, Al, Chief Oper. Officer--Frito-Lay Company, Plano, TX; *U.S. Public*, pg. 1277
Carey, Chase, Chief Oper. Officer--Fox, Inc., Los Angeles, CA; *Int'l*, pg. 926
Carey, Dave, Chief Oper. Officer--Carme' Cosmeceutical Sciences, Inc., Napa, CA; *U.S. Private*, pg. 213
Carey, Gene E., Pres. & Chief Oper. Officer--Spencer Gifts, Inc., Egg Harbor Township, NJ; *Int'l*, pg. 1216
Cargen, Bob, Mgr.-Opers.--Automotive Rentals, Inc. (ARI), Mount Laurel, NJ; *U.S. Private*, pg. 535
Cargiulo, Ralph J., Pres. & Chief Exec. Officer--The United States Life Ins. Co. In the City of New York, New York, NY; *U.S. Public*, pg. 77
Carleton, Larry, Chief Oper. Officer & Exec. V.P.--TCI West, Bellevue, WA; *U.S. Public*, pg. 1555
Carlisle, John C., Chief Oper. Officer & Exec. V.P.--Nabi, Boca Raton, FL; *U.S. Public*, pg. 1148
Carlson, Robert S., Chief Oper. Officer--HRH/Atlas Construction Inc., Stamford, CT; *U.S. Private*, pg. 1035
Carlson, Robert V., Chief Oper. Officer--Alternative Resources Corporation, Lincolnshire, IL; *U.S. Public*, pg. 59
Carlson, Scott, Pres. & Chief Oper. Officer--Westin, Inc., Omaha, NE; *U.S. Private*, pg. 1169
Carlson, Victor E., Pres., Chief Oper. Officer, Chief Exec. Officer--Foga Systems, Oxnard, CA; *Int'l*, pg. 496
Carlstrom, Errol, Pres. & Chief Oper. Officer--Sunrise Leasing Corporation, Golden Valley, MN; *U.S. Public*, pg. 1535
Carni, Giora, Chief Oper. Officer--Agis Industries Ltd., Bnei-Brak, Israel; *Int'l*, pg. 30
Carolan, Douglas, Chief Oper. Officer & Exec. V.P.--Associated Wholesale Grocers, Inc., Kansas City, KS; *U.S. Private*, pg. 93
Caron, Jean Pierre, Chief Oper. Officer--Frionor France SARL, Roissy Charles de Gaulle, France; *Int'l*, pg. 516
Carothers, W. Jay, Pres. & Chief Oper. Officer--Filene's Basement, Inc., Wellesley, MA; *U.S. Public*, pg. 622
Carp, Daniel A., Pres. & Chief Oper. Officer--Eastman Kodak Company, Rochester, NY; *U.S. Public*, pg. 550
Carrington, John, Chief Oper. Officer--Barrick Gold Corporation, Toronto, Canada; *Int'l*, pg. 168
Carrol, Charlie, Chief Oper. Officer--The G&C Foundry Company, Sandusky, OH; *U.S. Public*, pg. 142

Carrol, James Edward, Chief Oper. Officer & Grp. Gen. Mgr.--Computer Power Group Limited, Melbourne, Australia; *Int'l*, pg. 325

Carroll, Charles A., Pres. & Chief Oper. Officer--Rubbermaid Incorporated, Wooster, OH; *U.S. Public*, pg. 1411

Carroll, James E., Pres. & Chief Oper. Officer--Bradley Corporation, Menomonee Falls, WI; *U.S. Private*, pg. 164

Carroll, Lee S., Chief Oper. Officer-Liner Div.--Transportacion Maritima Mexicana S.A. de C.V., Mexico, Mexico; *Int'l*, pg. 1418

Carroll, Robert B., Chief Oper. Officer--Greenway Corporation, Jessup, MD; *U.S. Public*, pg. 1770

Carroll, Seamus, V.P.-Opers.--AFP Imaging Corporation, Elmsford, NY; *U.S. Public*, pg. 6

Carroll, Thomas, Pres. & Chief Exec. Officer--MEDIQ/PRN Life Support Services, Inc., Pennsauken, NJ; *U.S. Public*, *pg. 1081*

Carter, Charles A., Pres. & Chief Oper. Officer--MET Solutions, LLC, Raleigh, NC; *U.S. Public*, pg. 1642

Carter, J. Wesley, Pres. & Chief Oper. Officer--Extendicare Inc., Markham, Canada; *Int'l*, pg. 468

Carter, Joan, Pres., Chief Oper. Officer & Corp. Sec.--U.M. Holding Limited, Haddonfield, NJ; *U.S. Private*, pg. 1113

Carter, Thomas F., Jr., Pres. & Chief Oper. Officer--QST Environmental Inc., Peoria, IL; *U.S. Public*, pg. 367

Carus, M. Blouke, Chm. Bd., Chief Exec. Officer & Chief Oper. Officer--Carus Corporation, Peru, IL; *U.S. Private*, pg. 217

Caruso, Frank, Chief Oper. Officer & Exec. V.P.--Willis Corroon Corp. of Nashville, Nashville, TN; *Int'l*, pg. 1506

Caruso, Fred C., Chief Oper. Officer--Mercury Finance Co., Lake Forest, IL; *U.S. Public*, pg. 1093

Case, Stephen M., Chm. Bd., Pres, Chief Exec. & Oper. Officer--America Online Incorporated, Dulles, VA; *U.S. Public*, pg. 66

Casella, James, Chief Oper. Officer--International Data Group, Boston, MA; *U.S. Private*, pg. 569

Cassese, John J., Chm. Bd., Pres., Chief Oper. & Chief Exec. Officer--Computer Horizons Corp., Mountain Lakes, NJ; *U.S. Public*, pg. 421

Castaldo, Nicholas, Pres. & Chief Oper. Officer--Pollo Tropical, Inc., Miami, FL; *U.S. Public*, pg. 1315

Casty, Ronald G., Chm. Bd., Pres., Chief Exec. & Oper. Officer--Chelsea Industries, Inc., Peabody, MA; *U.S. Private*, pg. 231

Caswell, Hollis, Chief Oper. Officer--Advanced Energy Industry, Fort Collins, CO; *U.S. Public*, pg. 20

Cataldo, Robert J., Pres. & Chief Oper. Officer--Hostmark Management Group, Rolling Meadows, IL; *U.S. Private*, pg. 541

Cavaliere, Phyllis, Pres. & Chief Exec. Officer--Metropolitan Sunday Newspapers, Inc., New York, NY; *U.S. Private*, pg. 739

Cavallo, Ernest J., Pres. & Chief Oper. Officer--Triarc Beverage Group, White Plains, NY; *U.S. Public*, pg. 1635

Cavanagh, John, Chief Oper. Officer--Morse Diesel International, Inc., New York, NY; *U.S. Private*, pg. 762

Cavender, Art, Vice Chm. & Chief Oper. Officer--E-Z Bowz, Inc., Sevierville, TN; *U.S. Private*, pg. 352

Cavey, Gary L., Grp. Pres. & Chief Oper. Officer-Indus. Prods. Grp.--Valmont Industries, Inc., Valley, NE; *U.S. Public*, pg. 1706

Cavitt, Jerry, Pres. & Chief Oper. Officer--President Baking Company, Atlanta, GA; *Int'l*, pg. 1069

Ceccoli, Darryll M., Chief Oper. Officer--Manheim Auctions, Inc., Atlanta, GA; *U.S. Private*, pg. 282

Cei, Jay, Pres. & Chief Oper. Officer--Ulbrich Wire, Inc., North Haven, CT; *U.S. Private*, pg. 1115

Centaures, Marc, Chief Oper. Officer--Huhtamaki Finance B.V., Lausanne, Switzerland; *Int'l*, pg. 639

Chai, C.F., Chief Oper. Officer & Mng. Dir.--Littelfuse Fareast, PTE Ltd., Singapore, Singapore; *U.S. Public*, pg. 1001

Chaikin, Scott, Pres. & Chief Oper. Officer--Dix & Eaton Incorporated, Cleveland, OH; *U.S. Private*, pg. 336

Chalhoub, Joseph, Pres. & Chief Oper. Officer--Safety-Kleen Corp., Elgin, IL; *U.S. Public*, pg. 1425

Chambers, Russell K.J., Dir.-Opers.--Barlow Ltd., Sandton, South Africa; *Int'l*, pg. 167

Chamla, Alain, Chief Oper. Officer--CSR Pampryl, La Courneuve, France; *Int'l*, pg. 566

Champion, Michael J., Dr., Exec. V.P.-Opers.--Riverdale Chemical Co., Glenwood, IL; *U.S. Private*, pg. 934

Chan, P.K., Pres. & Chief Oper. Officer--Hayes Microcomputer Products, Inc., Norcross, GA; *U.S. Public*, *pg. 801*

Chance, Larry, Mgr.-Distr.--E.C. Barton & Company, Jonesboro, AR; *U.S. Private*, pg. 119

Chang, Paul, Chief Oper. Officer--Hagglunds Drives Ltd, Tsuen Wan, Hong Kong; *Int'l*, pg. 670

Chapman, Thomas F., Pres. & Chief Oper. Officer--Equifax Inc., Atlanta, GA; *U.S. Public*, pg. 588

Chapman, Wade, Chief Oper. Officer--Idaho Supreme Company, Firth, ID; *U.S. Private*, pg. 557

Charbonneau, Peter D., Pres. & Chief Oper. Officer--Newbridge Networks Corporation, Kanata, Canada; *Int'l*, pg. 923

Charland, Fran, Chief Oper. Officer & Treas.--The F. Dohmen Company, Germantown, WI; *U.S. Private*, pg. 338

Charlebois, Brian J., Chief Oper. Officer & Exec. V.P.--First International Bancorp, Inc., Hartford, CT; *U.S. Public*, pg. 635

Charlebois, Brian J., Chief Oper. Officer--First National Bank of New England, Hartford, CT; *U.S. Public*, pg. 636

Chase, M.R., Chief Oper. Officer--IPC Development Co., Dubuque, IA; *U.S. Public*, pg. 910

Chase, Michael R., Pres. & Chief Oper. Officer--Interstate Power Company, Dubuque, IA; *U.S. Public*, pg. 910

Chastain, Roger W., Pres. & Chief Oper. Officer--Mount Vernon Mills, Inc., Greenville, SC; *U.S. Private*, pg. 835

Chavez, Richard C., Chief Oper. Officer & Sr. V.P.-Asia--Costco Wholesale, Issaquah, WA; *U.S. Public*, pg. 451

Chavkin, Robert, Pres. & Chief Oper. Officer--Biddle Sawyer Corporation, New York, NY; *U.S. Private*, pg. 142

Chavoya, Rene Castro, Chief Oper. Officer--Grupo Simec, S.A. de C.V., Guadalajara, Mexico; *Int'l*, pg. 576

Chen, John S., Pres. & Chief Oper. Officer--Sybase, Inc., Emeryville, CA; *U.S. Public*, pg. 1544

Chen, John T., Chief Oper. Officer--Neste Shipping Canada Ltd., Toronto, Canada; *Int'l*, pg. 915

Chenault, Kenneth I., Pres. & Chief Oper. Officer--American Express Company, New York, NY; *U.S. Public*, pg. 73

Cheng Hai, Steven Chan, Chief Oper. Officer--Superior Metal Printing Limited, Singapore, Singapore; *Int'l*, pg. 1322

Cheong, K.P., Chief Oper. Officer--Hong Fok Land Pte. Ltd., Singapore, Singapore; *Int'l*, pg. 635

Cheong, K.P., Chief Oper. Officer--Yat Yuen Hong Company Limited, Singapore, Singapore; *Int'l*, pg. 635

Cherry, Jim, Pres. & Chief Oper. Officer--CAE Electronics, Ltd., Saint-Laurent, Canada; *Int'l*, pg. 237

Chesebro, Stephen D., Pres. & Chief Oper. Officer--Pennzoil Company, Houston, TX; *U.S. Public*, pg. 1272

Chesen, Edward, V.P. & Gen. Mgr.--J.H. Larson Electrical Company, Golden Valley, MN; *U.S. Private*, pg. 652

Cheshire, Michael J., Pres. & Chief Oper. Officer--Gerber Scientific, Inc., South Windsor, CT; *U.S. Public*, pg. 740

Chesonis, Arunas A., Pres. & Chief Oper. Officer--ACC Corp., Rochester, NY; *U.S. Public*, pg. 2

Chiarotti, John M., Chief Oper. Officer, Sec. & Gen. Mgr.--Amos-Hill Associates, Inc., Edinburgh, IN; *U.S. Private*, pg. 67

Childs, Julian, Chief Oper. Officer & Exec. V.P.--Dow Jones Markets, Jersey City, NJ; *U.S. Public*, pg. 525

Chilton, Nick, Pres. & Chief Oper. Officer--Wyandot Inc., Marion, OH; *U.S. Private*, pg. 1193

Chilvers, Anthony, Chief Oper. Officer--The West Company Group Limited, Saint Austell, United Kingdom; *U.S. Public*, pg. 1756

Cho, Yang-Ho, Pres. & Chief Oper. Officer--Korean Airlines Co., Ltd., Seoul, Korea; *Int'l*, pg. 758

Choe, Ng Kee, Deputy Pres. & Chief Oper. Officer--DBS Bank Ltd., Singapore, Singapore; *Int'l*, pg. 350

Chow, Shirley, Sr. V.P.-Admin. & Fin. & Corp. Sec.--Bachmann Industries, Inc., Philadelphia, PA; *U.S. Private*, *pg. 109*

Christensen, Carl E., Jr., Chief Oper. Officer & Chief Fin. Officer--Kreonite, Inc., Wichita, KS; *U.S. Private*, pg. 635

Christensen, Jorgen, Chief Oper. Officer--Novo Nordisk A/S, Kalundborg, Denmark; *Int'l*, pg. 987

Christensen, Thorkil K., Chief Oper. Officer--Novo Nordisk A/S, Singapore, Singapore; *Int'l*, pg. 987

Christenson, Clifford J., Chief Oper. Officer & Exec. V.P.--Wellman, Inc., Shrewsbury, NJ; *U.S. Public*, pg. 1752

Christopher, Eugene N., Chief Oper. Officer--TAD Resources International, Inc., Cambridge, MA; *U.S. Private*, pg. 1062

Chun-Hak, Ahn, Pres.--Korea Heavy Industries & Construction Co., Ltd., Seoul, Korea; *Int'l*, pg. 758

Church, Tom, Chief Oper. Officer--Fresh Western International, Salinas, CA; *Int'l*, pg. 491

Cibran, Bert, Pres. & Chief Oper. Officer--Ramsay Health Care, Inc., Coral Gables, FL; *U.S. Public*, pg. 1360

Ciepiel, Anthony M., Pres. & Chief Oper. Officer--Realty One, Cleveland, OH; *U.S. Private*, pg. 914

Cikacz, Michael, Chief Oper. Officer & Sr. V.P.--Healthcare Staffing Solutions, Inc., Lowell, MA; *U.S. Public*, pg. 1373

Ciraulo, Jerry, Chief Oper. Officer & Exec. V.P.--Carillon Importers, Ltd., Fort Lee, NJ; *Int'l*, pg. 409

Cirelli, Elio, Chief Oper. Officer--COBE Lab. Italia s.r.l., Felino, Italy; *Int'l*, pg. 667

Cirelli, Elio, Chief Oper. Officer--Hospal Dasco S.p.A., Medolla, Italy; *Int'l*, pg. 668

Cisneros, Henry, Pres. & Chief Oper. Officer--Univision Ltd. Partnership, New York, NY; *U.S. Private*, pg. 230

Clancy, Dick, Chief Oper. Officer--STAR Anchors & Fasteners, Mountainville, NY; *U.S. Private*, pg. 1033

Clanton, Fred, V.P.-Opers.--Colfax Envelope Corporation, Buffalo Grove, IL; *U.S. Private*, pg. 252

Clapp, David W., Chief Oper. Officer & Sr. V.P.--TrizecHahn Properties Inc., Chicago, IL; *Int'l*, pg. 1425

Clark, C.R.N., Chief Oper. Officer--Johnson Matthey Public Limited Company, London, United Kingdom; *Int'l*, pg. 713

Clark, David, Pres. & Chief Oper. Officer--WSMP, Inc., Claremont, NC; *U.S. Public*, pg. 1729

Clark, Harry V., Chief Oper. Officer--Frionor Asia Pacific Pte. Ltd., Singapore, Singapore; *Int'l*, pg. 516

Clark, Jeffrey, Chief Oper. Officer--TAC (UK) Ltd., Harpenden, United Kingdom; *Int'l*, pg. 670

Clark, John S., Chief Oper. Officer & V.P.--Snap-Tite, Inc., Erie, PA; *U.S. Private*, pg. 1010

Clark, Louis, Pres. & Chief Oper. Officer--The Clark Group, Mission, Canada; *Int'l*, pg. 296

Clark, Michael, Chief Oper. Officer & Sr. V.P.--Pegasus Gold Corporation, Spokane, WA; *U.S. Public*, pg. 1269

Clarke, C. Boyd, Pres. & Chief Oper. Officer--U.S. Bioscience, Inc., Conshohocken, PA; *U.S. Public*, pg. 1681

Clarke, Greg, Chief Oper. Officer--Cable & Wireless Communications plc, London, United Kingdom; *Int'l*, pg. 115

Clarke, Greg, Chief Oper. Officer--Cable & Wireless Communications plc, London, United Kingdom; *U.S. Public*, pg. 203

Clarke, Greg, Chief Oper. Officer--Cable & Wireless Communications plc, London, United Kingdom; *Int'l*, pg. 247

Clarke, Thomas E., Pres. & Chief Oper. Officer--Nike, Inc., Beaverton, OR; *U.S. Public*, pg. 1184

Clarkson, Alan, Chief Oper. Officer--Burns, Philp & Co., Camellia, Australia; *Int'l*, pg. 236

Clarkson, Colin, Chief Exec. Officer & V.P.-Mktg.--Lotus Cars USA, Inc., Lawrenceville, GA; *Int'l*, pg. 1071

Claudon, Ronald C., Sr., Pres. & Chief Oper. Officer--Valley Pontiac Buick GMC, Inc., Auburn, WA; *U.S. Private*, pg. 1132

Clayton, Joseph P., Pres. & Chief Oper. Officer--Frontier Corporation, Rochester, NY; *U.S. Public*, pg. 683

Clayton, Richard R., Pres. & Chief Oper. Officer--Eastern Enterprises, Weston, MA; *U.S. Public*, pg. 548

Cleary, J.V., Chief Oper. Officer--GMP Real Estate Corp., South Burlington, VT; *U.S. Public*, pg. 761

Clement, Rich, Chief Oper. Officer--Alimed, Inc., Dedham, MA; *U.S. Private*, pg. 34

Clemente, Chuck, Chief Oper. Officer & Exec. V.P.--Redgate Communications Corp., Vero Beach, FL; *U.S. Public*, pg. 66

Clements, Ronald L., Chief Exec. & Oper. Officer--Belden & Blake Corporation, Canton, OH; *U.S. Private*, pg. 1078

Clifford, James R., Pres. & Chief Oper. Officer--Sears Canada, Inc., Toronto, Canada; *U.S. Public*, pg. 1452

Cline, Bob L., Chief Oper. Officer--Custom Colorants, Inc., Dalton, GA; *U.S. Public*, pg. 1052

Cline, Jim, Chief Oper. Officer--Harris Broadcast Division, Richmond, IN; *U.S. Public*, pg. 791

Clooe, J. P., Chief Oper. Officer--S.A. Polytuil, Herstal, Belgium; *Int'l*, pg. 301

Close, Graham, Chief Oper. Officer--Aladdin Industries Pty. Ltd., Westgate, Australia; *U.S. Private*, pg. 31

Clowe, C. Thomas, Pres. & Chief Oper. Officer-Missouri Gas Energy--Southern Union Company, Austin, TX; *U.S. Public*, pg. 1491

Coatney, Michael, Sr. V.P. & Gen. Mgr.--Acme Truck Line, Inc., Harvey, LA; *U.S. Private*, pg. 14

Coburn, Al, Exec. V.P. & Chief Oper. Officer--Salem Sportswear, Hudson, NH; *U.S. Public*, pg. 686

Cocanougher, John, Chief Oper. Officer--Mack Printing Company, Easton, PA; *U.S. Private*, pg. 691

Cochran, James G., Chief Oper. Officer & Exec. V.P.--United Services Life Insurance Co., Arlington, VA; *U.S. Public*, pg. 1376

Cochrane, Len, Pres. & Chief Oper. Officer--The Family Channel Inc., Toronto, Canada; *Int'l*, pg. 1482

Cocquyt, Ronald A., Chief Oper. Officer & V.P.--Wilmorite, Inc., Rochester, NY; *U.S. Private*, pg. 1180

Coggin, James A., Pres. & Chief Oper. Officer--Proffitt's, Inc., Alcoa, TN; *U.S. Public*, pg. 1333

Cogman, Don V., Vice Chm., Chief Oper. Officer (New York)--Burson-Marsteller, New York, NY; *U.S. Private*, pg. 1197

Cohen, Alan H., Chief Oper. Officer, Exec. V.P. & Sec.--George Uhe Co., Inc., Paramus, NJ; *U.S. Private*, pg. 1115

Cohen, Bert, Chief Oper. Officer & Exec. V.P.--Worldvision Enterprises, New York, NY; *U.S. Private*, pg. 776

Colbert, Donald W., Pres. & Chief Oper. Officer--S & K Famous Brands, Inc., Glen Allen, VA; *U.S. Public*, pg. 1414

Colburn, David, Chief Oper. Officer--AP North American Aftermarket Division, Goldsboro, NC; *U.S. Private*, pg. 230

Cole, Chris, Chief Oper. Officer--Pinnacle Automation Inc., Saint Louis, MO; *U.S. Private*, pg. 866

Coleman, Richard J., Exec. V.P.--Florasynth Inc., Teterboro, NJ; *Int'l*, pg. 173

Colhag, Klas, Chief Oper. Officer--Hagglunds Drives Ltd, Singapore, Singapore; *Int'l*, pg. 670

Colianni, Albert J., Jr., Chief Oper. Officer--Marquette Bancshares Inc., Minneapolis, MN; *U.S. Private*, pg. 706

Collette, Patrick O., Chief Oper. Officer--ATIO Corporation USA, Inc., Hopkins, MN; *U.S. Public*, pg. 1716

Collin, Andre, Pres. & Chief Oper. Officer--Cadim, Montreal, Canada; *Int'l*, pg. 249

Collins, Arthur D., Jr., Pres. & Chief Oper. Officer--Medtronic, Inc., Minneapolis, MN; *U.S. Public*, pg. 1082

Collins, Don L., Chm. Bd., Pres., Chief Exec. & Oper. Officer--Collins Industries, Inc., Hutchinson, KS; *U.S. Public*, pg. 399

Collins, Jack, Chief Oper. Officer--Gulf States Steel, Inc., Gadsden, AL; *U.S. Private*, pg. 488

Colonna, Mark, Chief Oper. Officer-Mktg & Exec. V.P.--Colonna Bros., Inc., North Bergen, NJ; *U.S. Private*, pg. 254

Colson, Alfred, Chief Oper. Officer--Neste Chemicals Belgium N.V., Brussels, Belgium; *Int'l*, pg. 914

Commes, Thomas A., Pres. & Chief Oper. Officer--The Sherwin-Williams Company, Cleveland, OH; *U.S. Public*, pg. 1465

Comper, F. Anthony, Pres. & Chief Oper. Officer--Bank of Montreal, Toronto, Canada; *Int'l*, pg. 153

Compton, Harold, Chief Oper. Officer & Exec. V.P.--CompUSA, Dallas, TX; *U.S. Public*, pg. 420

Compton, Ned, Pres. & Chief Oper. Officer--Community First Bank & Trust, Celina, OH; *U.S. Public*, pg. 633

Congdon, David S., Pres. & Chief Oper. Officer--Old Dominion Freight Line, Inc., High Point, NC; *U.S. Public*, pg. 1216

Conlon, Timothy L., Pres. & Chief Oper. Officer--Berg Electronics, Saint Louis, MO; *U.S. Public*, pg. 212

Connelly, Gerald L., Chief Oper. Officer & V.P.--Robbins & Myers, Inc., Dayton, OH; *U.S. Public*, pg. 1393

Connelly, James G., III, Pres. & Chief Oper. Officer--Caremark International Inc, Northbrook, IL; *U.S. Public*, pg. 1082

Connor, Mark, Chief Oper. Officer--Ferrosan International A/S, Soeborg, Denmark; *Int'l*, pg. 987

Connor, Robert M., Chief Oper. Officer & Chief Fin. Officer--Amcel Corp., Watertown, MA; *U.S. Private*, pg. 48

Constalbe, Philip, Chief Oper. Officer--Wolverine Massachusetts Corporation, Merrimac, MA; *U.S. Private*, pg. 1186

Constantine, Simon, Chief Oper. Officer--Life Sciences International Plc, London, United Kingdom; *U.S. Public*, pg. 1594

Conti, Flavio, Chief Oper. Officer & Oper. Dir.--DPZ-Duailibi, Petit, Zaragoza, Propaganda S.A., Sao Paulo, Brazil; *Int'l*, pg. 352

Conway, Adrian, Dir.-Opers.--Cannon Rubber Ltd., London, United Kingdom; *Int'l*, pg. 261
Conway, James F., III, Chm. Bd., Pres., Chief Oper. & Exec. Officer--Courier Corporation, North Chelmsford, MA; *U.S. Public*, pg. 453
Conway, Ronald J., Chief Oper. Officer & Sr. V.P.-Opers.--Conrail, Inc., Philadelphia, PA; *U.S. Public*, pg. 431
Coogan, Keith R., Chief Oper. Officer & Exec. V.P.--Software Spectrum, Inc., Garland, TX; *U.S. Public*, pg. 1483
Cook, Greg, Pres. & Chief Oper. Officer--Cook Manufacturing Corporation, Duncan, OK; *U.S. Private*, pg. 272
Cook, John, Chief Oper. Officer & Exec. V.P.--Magruder Color Company, Inc., Elizabeth, NJ; *U.S. Private*, pg. 696
Cook, Stephen A., Chief Oper. Officer--Overland Transportation System, Inc., Indianapolis, IN; *Int'l*, pg. 1469
Cook, Thomas A., Pres. & Chief Oper. Officer--Healthcare Services Group, Inc., Huntingdon Valley, PA; *U.S. Public, pg. 803*
Cooke, A. Curts, Pres. & Chief Oper. Officer--Russ Berrie and Company, Inc., Oakland, NJ; *U.S. Public*, pg. 222
Coolidge, Awson, Chief Oper. Officer--Milton Roy Company, Ivyland, PA; *U.S. Public*, pg. 1534
Cooney, John M., Chief Oper. Officer--DiMark, Inc., Langhorne, PA; *U.S. Public*, pg. 793
Cooney, Robert J., Pres. & Chief Oper. Officer--X.L. Insurance Company, Ltd., Hamilton, Bermuda; *Int'l*, pg. 467
Cooper, Charles B., Pres. & Chief Oper. Officer--American Income Holding, Inc., Wilmington, DE; *U.S. Public*, pg. 1622
Cooper, Johnnie, Chief Oper. Officer--Victory Refrigeration Co. LC, Cherry Hill, NJ; *U.S. Private*, pg. 1139
Cooper, Larry, Chief Oper. Officer--Pool Insurance, Winnipeg, Canada; *Int'l*, pg. 1195
Cooper, Martyn L., Chief Oper. Officer--Tekgraf, Inc., Norcross, GA; *U.S. Private*, pg. 1073
Coots, Laurie, Chief Oper. Officer-Los Angeles--TBWA Chiat/Day Los Angeles, Venice, CA; *U.S. Private*, pg. 1062
Copeland, F.C., Pres. & Chief Exec. Officer--Citibank Canada, Toronto, Canada; *U.S. Public*, pg. 378
Coppola, Alfred C., Pres. & Chief Oper. Officer--The Okonite Company, Ramsey, NJ; *U.S. Private*, pg. 813
Corbo, V.J., Dr., Pres. & Chief Oper. Officer--Hercules Incorporated, Wilmington, DE; *U.S. Public*, pg. 809
Corcoran, John, Chief Oper. Officer & Exec. V.P.--FCB HealthCare, San Francisco, CA; *U.S. Public*, pg. 1641
Corder, Sidney V., Chief Oper. officer--ASI Technology, Colorado Springs, CO; *U.S. Public*, pg. 110
Cordes, Jeffrey D., Pres. & Chief Oper. Officer--Pillowtex Corporation, Dallas, TX; *U.S. Public*, pg. 1296
Cordes, Michael S., Chief Oper. Officer & Exec. V.P.--Mercantile Mortgage Corp., Baltimore, MD; *U.S. Public*, pg. 1089
Corey, Chase, Chief Oper. Officer--The News Corporation Limited, Sydney, Australia; *Int'l*, pg. 925
Corley, James W., Co-Chief Exec. Officer & Chief Oper. Officer--Dave & Buster's, Dallas, TX; *U.S. Public*, pg. 488
Corno, Marco, Chief Oper. Officer--Candy Iberica S.A., Barcelona, Spain; *Int'l*, pg. 260
Cornu, Jozef, Chief Oper. Officer--Alcatel Alsthom Compagnie Generale D'Electricite, Paris, France; *Int'l*, pg. 52
Corry, Edward K., Pres. & Chief Oper. Officer--Southeastern Financial Services, Inc., Port Huron, MI; *U.S. Public*, pg. 1489
Corry, Lawrence L., Chief Oper. Officer & Exec. V.P.--The Amalgamated Sugar Company LLC, Ogden, UT; *U.S. Private*, pg. 48
Corso, Vincent T., Grp. Pres. & Chief Oper. Officer-Irrigation & Coatings Grp.--Valmont Industries, Inc., Valley, NE; *U.S. Public*, pg. 1706
Corson, Keith D., Pres. & Chief Oper. Officer--Coachmen Industries, Inc., Elkhart, IN; *U.S. Public*, pg. 387
Corvin, Joe E., Pres. & Chief Oper. Officer--Oregon Steel Mills Inc., Portland, OR; *U.S. Public*, pg. 1230
Coss, Lawrence M., Chm. Bd., Pres. & Chief Exec. & Oper. Officer--Green Tree Financial Corporation, Saint Paul, MN; *U.S. Public*, pg. 761
Costa, Carlos, Chief Oper. Officer--BNP Factor - Portugal, Porto, Portugal; *Int'l*, pg. 163
Costa, Frank J., Pres. & Chief Oper. Officer--Active Voice Corporation, Seattle, WA; *U.S. Public*, pg. 17
Costa, Maurice, Chief Oper. Officer & V.P.--Business Insurance Corporation, Rancho Cordova, CA; *U.S. Public*, pg. 678
Costello, Craig T., Chief Oper. Officer & Exec. V.P.-Opers.--Weirton Steel Corporation, Weirton, WV; *U.S. Public*, pg. 1751
Costello, Robert L., Pres., Chief Exec. & Chief Oper. Officer--URS Greiner Engineering, Inc., Denver, CO; *U.S.* Public, pg. 1658
Cotherman, Scott, Pres. & Chief Oper. Officer--Corbett HealthConnect, A Frank J. Corbett, Inc., Company, Chicago, IL; *U.S. Public*, pg. 1223
Cothran, Roger, V.P.-Opers.--Coats North America, Charlotte, NC; *Int'l*, pg. 300
Cotros, Charles H., Chief Oper. Officer & Exec. V.P.--Sysco Corporation, Houston, TX; *U.S. Public*, pg. 1550
Cotton, M.W., Pres. & Chief Oper. Officer--Bergen Brunswig Medical Corporation, Montgomery, AL; *U.S. Public*, pg. 214
Cougher, Harry F., Chief Oper. Officer-Mining & Sr. V.P.--Sunshine Mining And Refining Company, Boise, ID; *U.S. Public*, pg. 1536
Coughlan, Bill, Chief Oper. Officer--Stewart Warner Corp. of Canada, Ltd., Belleville, Canada; *Int'l*, pg. 127
Coughlin, Michael, Pres. & Chief Oper. Officer--Brooks Beverage Management, Inc., Columbus, OH; *U.S. Private*, pg. 142
Cougill, Dan, Pres. & Chief Oper. Officer--Riddell Sports, Inc., New York, NY; *U.S. Public*, pg. 1389
Cougill, Dan, Pres. & Chief Oper. Officer--Riddell Sports, Inc., Chicago, IL; *U.S. Public*, pg. 1389
Couglin, T.C., Pres.--Riggs National Corporation, Washington, DC; *U.S. Public*, pg. 1389
Coulomb, Rene, Exec. V.P.--Lyonnaise des Eaux S.A., Nanterre, France; *Int'l*, pg. 822
Coulter, Robert, Pres. & Chief Oper. Officer--Shelby Williams Industries, Inc., Morristown, TN; *U.S. Public*, pg. 1464
Couri, Steven G., Chief Oper. Officer--Couristan Inc., Fort Lee, NJ; *U.S. Private*, pg. 279
Courtney, David W., Chief Oper. Officer & Exec. V.P.--CHEMCENTRAL Corporation, Bedford Park, IL; *U.S. Private*, pg. 231
Courville, Leon, Pres. & Chief Oper. Officer--National Bank of Canada, Montreal, Canada; *Int'l*, pg. 907
Cousens, Rod, Chief Oper. Officer--Acclaim Entertainment, Ltd, London, United Kingdom; *U.S. Public*, pg. 15
Coutry, Ezzat, Chief Oper. Officer & Exec. V.P.--La Quinta Inns, Inc., San Antonio, TX; *U.S. Public*, pg. 972
Coutu, Francois-Jean, Pres. & Chief Oper. Officer--The Jean Coutu Group (PJC) Inc., Longueuil, Canada; *Int'l*, pg. 340
Covington, Alec C., Exec. V.P. & Chief Oper. Officer-Wholesale Opers.--Richfood Holdings, Inc., Glen Allen, VA; *U.S. Public*, pg. 1388
Cowan, Malcolm, Chief Oper. Officer--Interphase Corporation, Dallas, TX; *U.S. Public*, pg. 908
Cowie, Bruce, Chief Oper. Officer & Exec. V.P.--Baton Broadcasting Incorporated, Scarborough, Canada; *Int'l*, pg. 170
Cowie, Bruce E., Pres. & Chief Oper. Officer-Broadcast Group--Electrohome Ltd., Kitchener, Canada; *Int'l*, pg. 438
Cox, Basil, Pres. & Chief Oper. Officer--Eat N Park Restaurants, Pittsburgh, PA; *U.S. Private*, pg. 358
Cox, Bill, Chief Oper. Officer--Blackeyed Pea Restaurants Inc., Scottsdale, AZ; *U.S. Public*, pg. 498
Cox, John E., Chief Oper. Officer & Exec. V.P.--Safeguard Health Enterprises, Inc., Anaheim, CA; *U.S. Public*, pg. 1424
Cox, Robert L., Chief Oper. Officer & Exec. V.P.--Tower Realty Trust, Inc., New York, NY; *U.S. Public*, pg. 1625
Cox, Sam, Chief Oper. Officer & Exec. V.P.--Goodwill Industries International, Bethesda, MD; *U.S. Private*, pg. 464
Cox, William G., Chief Oper. Officer--DenAmerica Corp., Scottsdale, AZ; *U.S. Public*, pg. 498
Crabtree, Richard, Pres.-Casualty & Property--Nationwide Mutual Insurance Co., Columbus, OH; *U.S. Private*, pg. 789
Crabtree, Richard D., Pres. & Chief Oper. Officer-P/C Company--Nationwide Insurance Enterprise, Columbus, OH; *U.S. Private*, pg. 788
Craig, Jim, Chief Oper. Officer & V.P.--United States Name Plate, Philadelphia, PA; *U.S. Private*, pg. 640
Craig, Walter M., Jr., Chief Oper. Officer & Exec. V.P.--Helm Resources Inc., Greenwich, CT; *U.S. Public*, pg. 808
Cramer, Dean, Chief Oper. Officer & Chief Information Officer--Precision Extrusions, Bensenville, IL; *U.S. Private*, pg. 879
Crandall, Robert M., Pres. & Chief Oper. Officer--Mentholatum Company, Buffalo, NY; *Int'l*, pg. 1126
Crawford, Edward, Chm. Bd., Pres & Chief Exec. & Oper. Officer--Park-Ohio Industries, Inc., Cleveland, OH; *U.S. Public*, pg. 1258
Crawford, Fred W., Jr., Chief Oper. Officer--Shepherd Construction Co., Inc., Atlanta, GA; *U.S. Private*, pg. 993
Crawford, John D., Chm. Bd., Chief Oper. Officer & Exec. V.P.--Network Long Distance, Inc., Baton Rouge, LA; *U.S. Public*, pg. 1169
Cree, Brian J., Chief Oper. Officer & Exec. V.P.--Patina Oil & Gas Corp., Denver, CO; *U.S. Public*, pg. 1264
Cremin, Robert W., Pres. & Chief Oper. Officer--Esterline Technologies Corporation, Bellevue, WA; *U.S. Public*, pg. 594
Crenshaw, Ed, Pres. & Chief Oper. Officer--Publix Supermarkets Inc., Lakeland, FL; *U.S. Private*, pg. 893
Crew, G.L., Chief Oper. Officer--Hong Kong Telecommunications Limited, Quarry Bay, Hong Kong; *Int'l*, pg. 247
Crim, Jack C., Pres. & Chief Oper. Officer--Talley Industries, Inc., Phoenix, AZ; *U.S. Public*, pg. 307
Crisman, Gene, Chief Oper. & Information Officer--Physician Sales & Services Inc., Beaumont, TX; *U.S. Public*, pg. 1294
Crist, Robert, Pres. & Chief Exec. & Chief Oper. Officer--American Recreation Centers, Inc., Sacramento, CA; *U.S. Public*, pg. 90
Croatti, Ronald D., Vice Chm., Pres. & Chief Exec. Officer--UniFirst Corporation, Wilmington, MA; *U.S. Public*, pg. 1665
Crombie, Christina, Chief Oper. Officer & Exec. V.P.--Talent Partners, Chicago, IL; *U.S. Private*, pg. 554
Cronin, Jim, Chief Oper. Officer & Exec. V.P.-Fin.--Ascent Entertainment Group, Inc., Denver, CO; *U.S. Public*, pg. 138
Crooke, Edward A., Pres. & Chief Oper. Officer--Baltimore Gas and Electric Company, Baltimore, MD; *U.S. Public*, pg. 172
Crosby, Samuel C., Chief Oper. Officer--Astre Corporate Group, Alexandria, VA; *U.S. Private*, pg. 93
Cross, Geoffrey, Pres. & Chief Oper. Officer--Petroferm Inc., Fernandina Beach, FL; *U.S. Private*, pg. 858
Crosser, Richard H., Pres. & Chief Oper. Officer--Crossmann Communities, Inc., Indianapolis, IN; *U.S. Public*, pg. 461
Crossley, Donald W., Chief Oper. Officer--Advance Packaging Corporation-Jackson Facility, Jackson, MI; *U.S. Private*, pg. 18
Crotty, Daniel W., Pres. & Chief Oper. Officer--Van Dyne-Crotty, Inc., Dayton, OH; *U.S. Private*, pg. 1132
Crous, A., Chief Oper. Officer & Mng. Dir.--Hammerite Productos Especiales, Barcelona, Spain; *Int'l*, pg. 1501
Crow, William, Pres. & Chief Oper. Officer--Friedman Industries, Inc., Houston, TX; *U.S. Public*, pg. 682
Crowell, Andrew, Chief Oper. Officer--Crowell, Weedon & Co., Los Angeles, CA; *U.S. Private*, pg. 291
Crowell, Steven H., Pres., Chief Oper. Officer, Chief Exec. Officer & Treas.--East Coast Steel, Inc., Claremont, NH; *U.S. Private*, pg. 356
Crowely, Ed, Chief Oper. Officer--Empire Steel Castings, Inc., Laureldale, PA; *U.S. Public*, pg. 142
Crowley, Joseph P., Pres. & Chief Oper. Officer--Philadelphia American Life Insurance Company, Houston, TX; *U.S. Public*, pg. 853
Crum, Lynn, Chief Oper. Officer--Simkins Carton Div.-Cleveland, Cleveland, OH; *U.S. Private*, pg. 1000
Cruwell, Bernd, Dr., Chief Oper. Officer--Hesse, Rhineland-Palatinate & Saar Branch, Frankfurt/Main, Germany; *Int'l*, pg. 645
Cubarsi, Rafael, Chief Oper. Officer--Vendo Iberia, S.A., Barcelona, Spain; *Int'l*, pg. 1184
Cuddihy, Robert V., Jr., Chief Oper. Officer, & Chief Fin. Officer--H.M.G. Worldwide Corp., New York, NY; *U.S. Public*, pg. 771
Cuddihy, Robert V., Jr., Chief Oper. Officer--Electronic Voting Systems, Inc., New York, NY; *U.S. Public*, pg. 771
Cuenin, James E., Jr., Exec. V.P.--Edwin B. Stimpson Company, Inc., Bayport, NY; *U.S. Private*, pg. 1043
Cuffaro, Joseph A., Jr., Chief Oper. Officer & Exec. V.P.--First American Appraisal Services, San Diego, CA; *U.S. Public*, pg. 625
Culberg, Paul, Chief Oper. Officer & Exec. V.P.--Columbia Tri-Star Home Video, Burbank, CA; *Int'l*, pg. 1282
Culich, Nick, Chief Oper. Officer--Union City Body Company, L.P., Union City, IN; *U.S. Private*, pg. 1118
Culver, Curt S., Pres. & Chief Oper. Officer--Mortgage Guaranty Insurance Corporation, Milwaukee, WI; *U.S. Public*, pg. 1026
Culver, Larry G., Chief Oper. & Fin. Officer & Exec. V.P.--CellPro, Incorporated, Bothell, WA; *U.S. Public*, pg. 320
Cumming, Alistair, Chief Oper. Officer--British Airways PLC, London, United Kingdom; *Int'l*, pg. 218
Cunningham, John P., Pres. & Chief Oper. Officer--International Aluminum Corporation, Monterey Park, CA; *U.S. Public*, pg. 894
Cunningham, Kathleen J., Chief Oper. Officer, Chief Fin. Officer & Sec.--NxTrend Technology, Inc., Colorado Springs, CO; *U.S. Private*, pg. 809
Cunningham, Milford B., Chief Oper. Officer & V.P.--Stahl Specialty Company, Kingsville, MO; *U.S. Private*, pg. 1029
Cunningham, Paul, Chief Oper. Officer--Proudfoot USA Company, West Palm Beach, FL; *Int'l*, pg. 1072
Curlander, Paul J., Dr., Pres. & Chief Oper. Officer--Lexmark International Group, Inc., Lexington, KY; *U.S. Public*, pg. 991
Curlander, Paul J., Dr., Pres. & Chief Oper. Officer--Lexmark International, Inc., Lexington, KY; *U.S. Public*, pg. 991
Curran, Timothy J., Exec. V.P. & Gen. Counsel--Curran Group, Inc., Crystal Lake, IL; *U.S. Private*, pg. 297
Currence, Anna, Pres. & Chief Oper. Officer--Crown Books Corporation, Landover, MD; *U.S. Public*, pg. 484
Currence, Richard M., Chief Oper. Officer--Tidewater Marine, Inc., Amelia, LA; *U.S. Public*, pg. 1608
Currence, Richard M., Chief Oper. Officer--Tidewater Marine Western, Inc., New Orleans, LA; *U.S. Public*, pg. 1608
Currence, Richard M., Chief Oper. Officer--Point Marine, Inc., New Orleans, LA; *U.S. Public*, pg. 1608
Currence, Richard M., Chief Oper. Officer--Tidewater Offshore Services, Inc., New Orleans, LA; *U.S. Public*, pg. 1608
Currence, Richard M., Chief Oper. Officer--Twenty Grand Offshore, New Orleans, LA; *U.S. Public*, pg. 1608
Currence, Richard M., Chief Oper. Officer--Seafarer Boat Corporation, New Orleans, LA; *U.S. Public*, pg. 1608
Curry, Edward J., Chief Oper. Officer & Exec. V.P.--Moore Products Co., Spring House, PA; *U.S. Public*, pg. 1128
Curry, Keys A., Jr., Pres. & Chief Oper. Officer--Destec Energy, Inc., Houston, TX; *U.S. Public*, pg. 1146
Curry, Kim Anderson, Chief Oper. Officer--K&M Associates, Providence, RI; *U.S. Public*, pg. 69
Curtas, William W., Chief Exec., Chief Oper. & Chief Fin. Officer & Exec. V.P.--Steego Corporation, West Palm Beach, FL; *Int'l*, pg. 216
Curtis, Paul F., Pres., Chief Oper. Officer & Treas.--L.N. Curtis & Sons, Oakland, CA; *U.S. Private*, pg. 297
Curtis, R., Sr. V.P.--Chickasha Cotton Oil Co., Chandler, AZ; *Int'l*, pg. 1395
Curtius, Michael D., Pres. & Chief Oper. Officer--Mercury General Corporation, Los Angeles, CA; *U.S. Public*, pg. 1093
Curvey, James C., Vice Chm. & Chief Oper. Officer--Fidelity Investments (FMR Corp.), Boston, MA; *U.S. Private*, pg. 402
Curwen, Richard, Chief Fin. Officer & Exec. V.P.--Appleton Papers Inc., Appleton, WI; *Int'l*, pg. 567
Cusumano, Gary M., Pres. & Chief Oper. Officer--The Newhall Land And Farming Company, Valencia, CA; *U.S.* Public, pg. 1178
Cutler, Alexander M., Pres. & Chief Oper. Officer--Eaton Corporation, Cleveland, OH; *U.S. Public*, pg. 555
Cyrenne, Roland O., Pres. & Chief Oper. Officer--Kruger Inc., Montreal, Canada; *Int'l*, pg. 761
Cyrenne, Roland O., Pres. & Chief Oper. Officer--Trois-Rivieres Mill, Trois-Rivieres, Canada; *Int'l*, pg. 761
Cyrenne, Roland O., Pres. & Chief Oper. Officer--Place Turcot Mill, Montreal, Canada; *Int'l*, pg. 761
Cyrenne, Roland O., Pres. & Chief Oper. Officer--Rexdale Plant, Rexdale, Canada; *Int'l*, pg. 761
Czyzyk, Joseph A., Pres. & Chief Oper. Officer--Mercury Air Group Inc., Los Angeles, CA; *U.S. Public*, pg. 1092

D'Alonzo, Thomas, M.D., Pres. & Chief Oper. Officer--Pharmaceutical Product Development, Inc., Wilmington, NC; *U.S. Public*, pg. 1285
D'Amour, Charles L., Chief Oper. Officer, Exec. V.P. & Sec.--Big Y Foods Inc., Springfield, MA; *U.S. Private*, pg. 143
D'Antuono, F.M., Chief Oper. Officer & Exec. V.P.--MidCon Corp., Lombard, IL; *U.S. Public*, pg. 1210
D'Aquino, Nuno A., Chief Oper. Officer--Carlton & United Breweries Ltd., Southbank, Australia; *Int'l*, pg. 500
Daenen, Victor, Chief Oper. Officer--KONE Luxembourg S.a.r.l., Strassen, Latvia; *Int'l*, pg. 747
Daggon, R.V., Chief Oper. Officer--Kidde Technologies Inc., Marlborough, MA; *Int'l*, pg. 1500
Dahl, Hans Ove, Mng. Dir.--Berendsen PMC A/S, Kokkedal, Denmark; *Int'l*, pg. 1284
Dahl, Richard J., Pres. & Chief Oper. Officer--Pacific Century Financial Corporation, Honolulu, HI; *U.S. Public*, pg. 1248
Dahlberg, Burton, Pres. & Chief Oper. Officer--Kraus-Anderson Incorporated, Minneapolis, MN; *U.S. Private*, pg. 635
Dahlberg, Burton F., Pres. & Chief Oper. Officer--Kraus-Anderson, Incorporated, Minneapolis, MN; *U.S. Private*, pg. 635
Dahlberg, Kenneth, Pres. & Chief Oper. Officer--Raytheon Systems Company, Arlington, VA; *U.S. Public*, pg. 1364
Dahlen, R. Daniel, Chief Oper. Officer & Exec. V.P.--Meldrum & Fewsmith Communications Inc., Cleveland, OH; *U.S. Private*, pg. 730
Dailey, Kenneth E., Gen. Mgr.--Seaman Timber Company, Inc., Montevallo, AL; *U.S. Private*, pg. 979
Dal Porto, James, Chief Oper. Officer & Exec. V.P.--I-Flow Corporation, Lake Forest, CA; *U.S. Public*, pg. 851
Daley, Charles D., Chief Oper. Officer & Exec. V.P.--QMS, Inc., Mobile, AL; *U.S. Public*, pg. 1346
Dalquist, H. David, III, Pres.--Northland Aluminum Products, Inc., Minneapolis, MN; *U.S. Private*, pg. 805
Dalton, Michael J., Pres. & Chief Oper. Officer--Unitil Corporation, Hampton, NH; *U.S. Public*, pg. 1692
Dalyai, Steve, Pres. & Chief Oper. Officer--QEI, Inc., Springfield, NJ; *U.S. Private*, pg. 897
Damico, Joseph F., Pres. & Chief Oper. Officer--Allegiance Healthcare Corp., McGaw Park, IL; *U.S. Public*, pg. 44
Damico, Joseph F., Pres. & Chief Oper. Officer--Allegiance Healthcare International, McGaw Park, IL; *U.S. Public*, pg. 45
Daniell, James, Pres. & Chief Oper. Officer--American Strip Steel Inc., Kearny, NJ; *U.S. Private*, pg. 62
Daniels, Lyndon R., Pres. & Chief Oper. Officer--Arch Communications Group, Inc., Westborough, MA; *U.S. Public*, pg. 127
Daoust, Paul R., Chief Oper. Officer & Exec. V.P.--Watson Wyatt Worldwide, Bethesda, MD; *U.S. Private*, pg. 1154
DaPra, Dennis, Pres. & Chief Oper. Officer--ACO Inc., Farmington Hills, MI; *U.S. Private*, pg. 3
Darby, Kenneth M., Pres. & Chief Exec. & Oper. Officer--Vicon Industries, Inc., Hauppauge, NY; *U.S. Public*, pg. 1719
Darby, Kenneth M., Chief Oper. Officer--Vicon Industries (U.K.) Ltd., Fareham, United Kingdom; *U.S. Public*, pg. 1719
Darche, Jean, Chief Oper. Officer--Eurolease Factor SA, Luxembourg, Luxembourg; *Int'l*, pg. 162
Darducci, Larry, Chief Oper. Officer--Molded Fiber Glass Co., Ashtabula, OH; *U.S. Private*, pg. 756
Darimont, M., Chief Oper. Officer--IC Imtech NV, Brussels, Belgium; *Int'l*, pg. 681
Darmos, Frank E., Chief Oper. Officer & Dir.-Opers.--Cramer Company, Old Saybrook, CT; *U.S. Public*, pg. 1238
Darnall, Ted, Chief Oper. Officer--Starwood Hotels & Resorts, Phoenix, AZ; *U.S. Public*, pg. 1512
Dartevelle, Jacques, Chief Oper. Officer--Akerlund & Rausing S.A.R.L., Paris, France; *Int'l*, pg. 33
Daures, Pierre, Chief Oper. Officer--Electricite de France, Paris, France; *Int'l*, pg. 437
David, Romeo S., Exec. V.P.--Philippine Airlines, Inc., Manila, Philippines; *Int'l*, pg. 1050
Davidson, Denis H., Pres. & Chief Exec. Officer--Clear Shield National, Inc., Wheeling, IL; *U.S. Public*, pg. 586
Davidson, Johnathan, Chief Oper. Officer--Generation Metals Corp., Hauppauge, NY; *U.S. Private*, pg. 446
Davidson, Lawrence J., Jr., Pres., Chief Exec.,Oper. & Fin. Officer--The Weathervane Retail Corp., New Britain, CT; *U.S. Private*, pg. 1156
Davidson, Mike, Chief Oper. Officer--Gemini Consulting, Morristown, NJ; *Int'l*, pg. 264
Davidson, Rick, Pres. & Chief Oper. Officer--O'Sullivan Industries Holdings, Lamar, MO; *U.S. Public*, pg. 1234
Davidson, William, Chm. Bd., Pres., Chief Exec. & Chief Oper. Officer--Guardian Industries Corp., Auburn Hills, MI; *U.S. Private*, pg. 485
Davies, Clive, Chief Oper. Officer & V.P.--Linear Technology Corp., Milpitas, CA; *U.S. Public*, pg. 1000
Davies, Gregory T.H., Pres. & Chief Oper. Officer--Westinghouse Air Brake Company, Wilmerding, PA; *U.S. Public*, pg. 1760
Davies, Tim, Chief Oper. Officer--National Information Services (NIS), Bethesda, MD; *Int'l*, pg. 1096
Davies, Tony, Dr., Chief Oper. Officer--Meggitt Petroleum Systems (UK), Blackburn, United Kingdom; *Int'l*, pg. 853
Davin, Thomas E., Chief Fin. Officer--Taco Bell Corp., Irvine, CA; *U.S. Public*, pg. 1637
Davis, Don H., Jr., Pres. & Chief Oper. Officer--Rockwell International Corporation, Costa Mesa, CA; *U.S. Public*, pg. 1397
Davis, James H., Chief Oper. Officer & Exec. V.P.--Quanex Corporation, Houston, TX; *U.S. Public*, pg. 1349
Davis, John L., Pres. & Chief Oper. Officer--The Wing Group, Woodlands, TX; *U.S. Public*, pg. 1760
Davis, Kenneth A., Pres., Chief Exec. Officer & Chief Oper. Officer--PharmHouse, Inc., New York, NY; *U.S. Public*, pg. 1286
Davis, Kim A., Pres. & Chief Oper. Officer--Gelman Sciences, Inc., Ann Arbor, MI; *U.S. Public*, pg. 1253
Davis, Nathaniel A., Chief Oper. Officer--MCImetro, Vienna, VA; *U.S. Public*, pg. 1024
Davis, Stephen A., Pres. & Chief Oper. Officer--American Saw & Mfg. Company, East Longmeadow, MA; *U.S. Private*, pg. 61
Davis, Terrence D., V.P.-Opers. & Indus. Sls.--North Carolina Natural Gas Corporation, Fayetteville, NC; *U.S. Public*, pg. 1194
Davis, Thomas, Chief Oper. Officer--Mannington Mills, Inc., Salem, NJ; *U.S. Private*, pg. 700
Davis, Wallace J., Chief Oper. Officer--Davis Wood Products, Inc., Hudson, NC; *U.S. Private*, pg. 315
Dawdy, Richard A., Pres. & Chief Oper. Officer--UMB First National Bank, Collinsville, IL; *U.S. Public*, pg. 1654
Dawson, Pete, Chm. Bd. & Chief Oper. Officer--Jacob Leinenkugel Brewing Co., Chippewa Falls, WI; *U.S. Public*, pg. 1289
Day-Harper, Melinda, Pres. & Chief Oper. Officer--Wise & Associates/S&W Technical Services, San Antonio, TX; *U.S. Public*, pg. 1161
Day, Larry, Pres. & Chief Oper. Officer--Monro Muffler/Brake, Inc., Rochester, NY; *U.S. Public*, pg. 1124
De Beeck, Jan Op, Chief Oper. Officer--Antwerp Local Head Office, Antwerp, Belgium; *Int'l*, pg. 147
De Benedetti, R., Chief Oper. Officer--SAIA-Burgess SRL, Milan, Italy; *Int'l*, pg. 1501
de Cars, Coqvelet, Chief Oper. Officer--ESPACE Expansion, Paris, France; *Int'l*, pg. 1431
de Castro, James, Pres. & Chief Oper. Officer--Chancellor Media Corporation, Irving, TX; *U.S. Public*, pg. 335
de David-Beauregard, Arnauld, Chief Oper. Officer & Mng. Dir.--Citroen Hispana S.A., Pontevedra, Spain; *Int'l*, pg. 1020
De Groote, Daniel, Chief Oper. Officer--Gralex S.A., Brussels, Belgium; *Int'l*, pg. 605
De Gryse, Bernard, Chief Oper. Officer--BBL Life, Brussels, Belgium; *Int'l*, pg. 147
De Gryse, Bernard, Chief Oper. Officer--BBL Insurance, Brussels, Belgium; *Int'l*, pg. 147
de Kruif, Dirk, Chief Oper. Officer--Elsevier Bedrijfinformatie B.V., Doetinchem, Netherlands; *Int'l*, pg. 1099
de la Houssaye, E. C., Chief Oper. Officer--Oce-van der Grinten N.V., Venlo, Netherlands; *Int'l*, pg. 993
de la Serre, Rene, Vice Chm. & Chief Oper. Officer--Credit Commercial de France, Paris, France; *Int'l*, pg. 341
de Maio, Mike, Pres. & Chief Oper. Officer--Lois/EJL Chicago, Chicago, IL; *U.S. Public*, pg. 1011
De Marle, Richard, Chief Oper. Officer--Kidde-Fenwal, Inc., Ashland, MA; *Int'l*, pg. 1500
de Oliveira, Evandro Lopes, Chief Oper. Officer--BBBI Banco de Investimento, Rio de Janeiro, Brazil; *Int'l*, pg. 141
De Vaucleroy, Jacques, Head-BBL/Central Region--BBL Central Region, Brussels, Belgium; *Int'l*, pg. 147
de Vink, Lodewijk J.R., Pres. & Chief Oper. Officer--Warner-Lambert Company, Morris Plains, NJ; *U.S. Public*, pg. 1738
De Vito, Robert A., Chm. Bd., Pres., Chief Exec. & Chief Oper. Officer--Cyber Systems, Inc., Anaheim, CA; *U.S. Private*, pg. 299
de Vries, S., Chief Oper. Officer--Imtech Projects Noord-Oost bv, Coevorden, Netherlands; *Int'l*, pg. 681
Deal, Steven C., Pres. & Chief Exec. Officer--Hilb, Rogal and Hamilton Company of Virginia, Glen Allen, VA; *U.S. Public*, pg. 827
Deasey, Stephen M., Pres. & Chief Oper. Officer--The Sygma Network, Inc.-Columbus Central Division, Columbus, OH; *U.S. Public*, pg. 1550
Decker, T.E., Pres. & Chief Oper. Officer--AC & S Inc., Lancaster, PA; *U.S. Public*, pg. 913
Decker, W. Patrick, Pres. & Chief Oper. Officer--Kronos Incorporated, Waltham, MA; *U.S. Public*, pg. 967
Decoster, Richard B., Chief Oper. Officer & Exec. V.P.--Willis Corroon Corp. of Missouri, Saint Louis, MO; *Int'l*, pg. 1506
Dedman, Robert H., Jr., Pres. & Chief Oper. Officer--Club Corporation International, Dallas, TX; *U.S. Private*, pg. 247
Dedoyard, Raoul, Head-BBL/Flemish Region--BBL Flemish Region, Antwerp, Belgium; *Int'l*, pg. 147
Deer, Andy, Chief Oper. Officer--Farnam Companies, Inc., Phoenix, AZ; *U.S. Private*, pg. 396
Deese, George, Pres. & Chief Oper. Officer-Flowers Bakeries, Inc.--Flowers Industries, Inc., Thomasville, GA; *U.S. Public*, pg. 656
Deferrari, Ronald S., Pres. & Chief Oper. Officer--Plasma-Therm, Inc., Saint Petersburg, FL; *U.S. Public*, pg. 1308
DeFuria, Richard, Chief Oper. Officer--Science & Engineering Associates, Albuquerque, NM; *U.S. Private*, pg. 975
DeHahn, Mary L., Partner & Chief Oper. Officer--Kupper Parker Communications Inc., Saint Louis, MO; *U.S. Private*, pg. 637
Dehmlow, Steven L., Pres., Chief Exec. & Chief Oper. Officer--GLS Corporation, Arlington Heights, IL; *U.S. Private*, pg. 435
Dekker, David, Chief Oper. Officer--Marcel Dekker, Inc., New York, NY; *U.S. Private*, pg. 321
Del Santo, Cesare, Chief Oper. Officer--Mikron Pavia s.r.l., Torre d'Isola, Italy; *Int'l*, pg. 867
Delany, Martin, Chief Oper. Officer--James Crean PLC, Dublin, Ireland; *Int'l*, pg. 340
Delgadillo, Joseph L., Pres. & Chief Oper. Officer--M & I Data Services, Inc., Brown Deer, WI; *U.S. Public*, pg. 1050
Delinikolov, Saso, Chief Oper. Officer--Novo Nordisk A/S, Skopje, Macedonia; *Int'l*, pg. 988
Della Noce, Joseph, Pres. & Chief Oper. Officer--Richfood Pennsylvania, Harrisburg, PA; *U.S. Public*, pg. 1389
Della Penta, David T., Pres. & Chief Exec. Officer--Nalge Company, Rochester, NY; *U.S. Public*, pg. 1545
Delmar, Jack, Pres. & Chief Oper. Officer--Brascan Brazil, Rio de Janeiro, Brazil; *Int'l*, pg. 435
DeLorenzo, David A., Pres. & Chief Oper. Officer--Dole Food Company, Inc., Westlake Village, CA; *U.S. Public*, pg. 515
Delva, Luc, Chief Oper. Officer--Bank Brussels Lambert (Singapore) Ltd., Singapore, Singapore; *Int'l*, pg. 148
Delvo, Jim, Chief Oper. Officer--Coors Ceramics Company, Golden, CO; *U.S. Public*, pg. 3
DelZotto, Elvio, Pres. & Chief Oper. Officer--Tridel Enterprises Inc., Downsview, Canada; *Int'l*, pg. 1423
DeMaio, Emanuel J., Chief Oper. Officer--Tel-Save Holdings, Inc., New Hope, PA; *U.S. Public*, pg. 1568
deMaio, Mike, Chief Oper. Officer & Exec. V.P.--Lois/USA Inc., New York, NY; *U.S. Public*, pg. 1011
Demarest, Clifford J., Chief Oper. Officer--Vester Corporation, Newtown Square, PA; *U.S. Private*, pg. 86
DeMaria, Roberto, Chief Oper. Officer--Elevadores Kone Sabiem S.A. de C.V., Mexico, Mexico; *Int'l*, pg. 747
DeMatteo, Daniel A., Pres. & Chief Oper. Officer--Babbage's Etc. LLC, Grapevine, TX; *U.S. Private*, pg. 108
Denardo, Donna, Pres. & Chief Oper. Officer--Vitalink Pharmacy Services, Inc., Naperville, IL; *U.S. Public*, pg. 1041
Denenberg, Robert, Chief Oper. Officer & V.P.--Adelphia Lamp & Shade Inc., Philadelphia, PA; *U.S. Private*, pg. 17
Denhardt, Gerry, Chief Oper. Officer & Exec. V.P.--Projects Unlimited, Inc., Dayton, OH; *U.S. Private*, pg. 890
Denison, Calvin, Pres. & Chief Oper. Officer--Divi Hotels, Inc., Chapel Hill, NC; *U.S. Private*, pg. 336
Denkwirth, Joachim, Chief Oper. Officer--Nema Warmetauscher GmbH, Netzschkau, Germany; *Int'l*, pg. 399
Denman, Gary, Chief Oper. Officer--GRC International, Inc., Vienna, VA; *U.S. Public*, pg. 695
Densmore, Marty D., Pres. & Chief Oper. Officer--Steelox Systems Inc., Mason, OH; *U.S. Private*, pg. 1038
Denter, Borje, Chief Oper. Officer--Skandia Leben AG, Zurich, Switzerland; *Int'l*, pg. 1258
Depke, Tom, Chief Oper. Officer--Petroleum Fuel & Terminal, Saint Louis, MO; *U.S. Private*, pg. 77
Derham Cato, John P., Vice Chm., Pres. & Chief Oper. Officer--The Cato Corporation, Charlotte, NC; *U.S. Public*, pg. 318
DeRosa, Patricia, Pres. & Chief Oper. Officer--AnnTaylor Stores Corporation, New York, NY; *U.S. Public*, pg. 116
DeRosa, Patricia, Pres. & Chief Oper. Officer--AnnTaylor, Inc., New York, NY; *U.S. Public*, pg. 116
Derry, Brian J., V.P.-Opers.--Brush Wellman Inc., Cleveland, OH; *U.S. Public*, pg. 266
Derry, James, Chief Oper. Officer--Brown Steel Div., Columbus, OH; *U.S. Private*, pg. 651
Derville, T., Chief Oper. Officer--Liebig Maille Amora, Dijon, France; *Int'l*, pg. 380
DeSanctis, Kevin, Chief Oper. Officer-N. America & Caribbean--Sun International Hotels Limited, Fort Lauderdale, FL; *U.S. Public*, pg. 1531
DeSantis, Dean, Chief Oper. Officer--Rexall Sundown Inc., Boca Raton, FL; *U.S. Public*, pg. 1384
Desmarais, Rene, Pres. & Chief Oper. Officer--CFCF 12, Montreal, Canada; *Int'l*, pg. 241
Desperak, Jack, Chm. Bd. & Chief Oper. Officer--New Age Intimates Inc., Long Island City, NY; *U.S. Private*, pg. 792
Despres, Germain L., Exec. V.P.--Danisco Ingredients USA, Inc., New Century, KS; *Int'l*, pg. 378
Detharding, Herbert, Chief Oper. Officer--Wintershall Gas GmbH, Kassel, Germany; *Int'l*, pg. 105
Devanna, Leonard R., Pres. & Chief Oper. Officer-COM/Energy Enterprises, Inc.--Commonwealth Energy System, Cambridge, MA; *U.S. Public*, pg. 414
Devanna, Leonard R., Pres. & Chief Oper. Officer--COM/Energy Resources Inc., Cambridge, MA; *U.S. Public*, pg. 414
Devanna, Leonard R., Pres. & Chief Oper. Officer--COM/Energy Enterprises, Cambridge, MA; *U.S. Public*, pg. 414
Devanny, Trace, Chief Oper. Officer & Pres.-ADAC Healthcare Info. Sys.--ADAC Laboratories Inc., Milpitas, CA; *U.S. Public*, pg. 3
DeVille, Paul, Pres., Chief Oper. Officer & Sec.--Persis Corporation, Honolulu, HI; *U.S. Private*, pg. 855
DeVink, Lodewink J.R., Pres. & Chief Oper. Officer-Warner-Lambert Co.--Warner-Lambert Consumer Healthcare, Morris Plains, NJ; *U.S. Public*, pg. 1739
Diamond, Chris, Pres., Chief Oper. Officer & Chief Exec. Officer--Haystack Ski Resort at Mount Snow, Wilmington, VT; *U.S. Private*, pg. 61
Diamond, Lawrence, Chm. Bd., Pres., Chief Exec. & Chief Oper. Officer & Dir.-Pur.--Triangle Marketing Corp., New York, NY; *U.S. Private*, pg. 1102
Diamond, Russell, Pres., Chief Oper. Officer & Dir.-Mktg. & Treas.--Snyder-Diamond, Santa Monica, CA; *U.S. Private*, pg. 1011
Diaz, Miguel, V.P.-Intl. Opers.--Duro-Test Corporation, Fairfield, NJ; *U.S. Private*, pg. 349
DiBui, William J., Pres., Chief Exec. Office & Chief Oper. Officer--Rumsey Electric Company, Conshohocken, PA; *U.S. Private*, pg. 951
Dicapua, Nicholas, Chief Oper. Officer, Chief Fin. Officer, V.P., Treas. & Sec.--Liberty Fabrics, Inc., New York, NY; *Int'l*, pg. 340
DiCerchio, Richard D., Chief Oper. Officer & Sr. Exec. V.P.--Costco Wholesale, Issaquah, WA; *U.S. Public*, pg. 451
Dickenson, J.T., Pres. & Chief Oper. Officer--Justin Industries, Inc., Fort Worth, TX; *U.S. Public*, pg. 936
Dickey, Boh A., Pres. & Chief Oper. Officer--SAFECO Corporation, Seattle, WA; *U.S. Public*, pg. 1423
Dickey, Joe W., Chief Oper. Officer--Tennessee Valley Authority, Knoxville, TN; *U.S. Public*, pg. 1580
Dickinson, Robert H., Pres. & Chief Oper. Officer - Carnival Cruise Lines--Carnival Corporation, Miami, FL; *U.S. Public*, pg. 306

Dickinson, Walter, Chief Oper. Officer--Walter Dickinson, Inc., Tampa, FL; *U.S. Private*, pg. 331
Dickson, Carol, Chief Oper. Officer--Brink's Home Security, Inc., Irving, TX; *U.S. Public*, pg. 1305
Dickson, John H., Pres. & Chief Oper. Officer--AllEnergy Marketing Company, L.L.C., Waltham, MA; *U.S. Public*, pg. 549
Diedrick, Curt, Chief Oper. Officer--Precision Parts Corp., Morristown, TN; *U.S. Private*, pg. 879
Diener, I. Howard, Pres. & Chief Oper. Officer--The Cosmetic Center Inc., Columbia, MD; *U.S. Private*, pg. 689
Dienes, John D., Pres. & Chief Oper. Officer--United Companies Financial Corporation, Baton Rouge, LA; *U.S. Public*, pg. 1675
Dieter, Mary Q., Chief Oper. Officer, Chief Fin. Officer & Exec. V.P.--Sonoma Valley Bank, Sonoma, CA; *U.S. Public*, pg. 1487
Dietz, George R., Sr. V.P.--Isomedix Inc., Whippany, NJ; *U.S. Public*, pg. 1515
Diez, Javier, Chief Oper. Officer--COBE Iberica S.A., Barcelona, Spain; *Int'l*, pg. 667
DiFeo, Samuel X., Jr., Pres. & Chief Oper. Officer--United Auto Group, Inc., New York, NY; *U.S. Private*, pg. 1095
Difilippo, Dominick, Chief Oper. Officer--MacLean Power Systems, Franklin Park, IL; *U.S. Private*, pg. 692
Diggs, Lawrence N., Chief Oper. Officer & Exec. V.P.--Willis Corroon Corp. of Michigan, Livonia, MI; *Int'l*, pg. 1506
DiLibero, Ramsey G., Chief Oper. Officer--Western Waste Industries, Torrance, CA; *U.S. Public*, pg. 1686
Dillard, William, II, Pres. & Chief Oper. Officer--Dillard's, Inc., Little Rock, AR; *U.S. Public*, pg. 509
Dille, Steven B., Pres. & Chief Oper. Officer--Scicom Data Services, Ltd., Minnetonka, MN; *U.S. Private*, pg. 975
Dillingham, William A., Pres. & Chief Oper. Officer--Aspen Imaging International, Inc., Cleveland, OH; *U.S. Public*, pg. 1339
Dillon, David B., Pres. & Chief Oper. Officer--The Kroger Co., Cincinnati, OH; *U.S. Public*, pg. 967
Dillon, George F., Pres. & Chief Oper. Officer--Nicholas Paper, Inc., Fitchburg, MA; *U.S. Private*, pg. 798
Dillon, John, Pres. & Chief Oper. Officer--Arbor Software Corporation, Sunnyvale, CA; *U.S. Public*, pg. 127
DiMaria, Peter, Chief Oper. Officer & Pres.--Accu-Time System, Ellington, CT; *U.S. Private*, pg. 11
DiMartino, Joseph S., Pres. & Chief Oper. Officer--The Dreyfus Corporation, New York, NY; *U.S. Public*, pg. 1085
DiMeola, Richard, Chief Oper. Officer & Exec. V.P.--Consolidated Cigar Corporation, Fort Lauderdale, FL; *U.S. Private*, pg. 690
Dimling, John A., Pres. & Chief Oper. Officer--Nielsen Media Research, New York, NY; *U.S. Public*, pg. 395
Dimon, James, Pres. & Chief Oper. Officer--Travelers Group, New York, NY; *U.S. Public*, pg. 1632
Dinetz, Steven, Chief Oper. Officer--Hicks, Muse, Tate & Furst Inc., Dallas, TX; *U.S. Private*, pg. 526
Dinger, Frank S., Chm. Bd. & Chief Oper. Officer--William H. Sadlier, Inc., New York, NY; *U.S. Public*, pg. 1422
Dinkel, Gene, Chief Oper. Officer & Exec. V.P.--Connector Manufacturing Company, Hamilton, OH; *U.S. Private*, pg. 264
Dinzole, John W., Pres. & Chief Oper. Officer--Devon Group, Inc., Stamford, CT; *U.S. Public*, pg. 503
Diogenes Pires, Jose Ernauton, Chief Oper. Officer--BB Administradora de Cartoes de Credito S.A., Brasilia, Brazil; *Int'l*, pg. 141
Dion, Philip J., Chm. Bd. & Chief Exec. Officer--Del Webb Corporation, Phoenix, AZ; *U.S. Public*, pg. 494
Dixon, Jim, Chief Oper. Officer--Ferodo Ltd., Stockport, United Kingdom; *Int'l*, pg. 1334
Doane, W. Allen, Chief Exec. Officer--A & B-Hawaii, Inc., Honolulu, HI; *U.S. Public*, pg. 39
Dockter, James E., Pres. & Chief Exec. Officer--PBD, Inc., Alpharetta, GA; *U.S. Private*, pg. 825
Dodic, Martin, Chief Oper. Officer--Novo Nordisk A/S, Bratislava, Slovakia; *Int'l*, pg. 987
Doellinger, Steve, Pres.--Don E. Williams Co., Rock Island, IL; *U.S. Private*, pg. 1177
Dolan, Janet M., Chief Oper. Officer--Tennant Company, Minneapolis, MN; *U.S. Public*, pg. 1577
Dolan, Michael, Chief Oper. Officer & Exec. V.P.--Smead Manufacturing Company, Hastings, MN; *U.S. Private*, pg. 1006
Donahue, Dennis, Pres. & Chief Exec. Officer & Chief Oper. Officer--The Will-Burt Company, Orrville, OH; *U.S. Private*, pg. 1177
Donahue, William L., Chm. Bd., Pres., Chief Exec. & Chief Oper. Officer--Dixon Paper Co., Denver, CO; *U.S. Public*, pg. 902
Donnelly, James C., Pres. & Chief. Exec. Officer--Sta-Rite Industries, Inc., Delavan, WI; *U.S. Public*, pg. 1767
Donnelly, John, Chief Oper. Officer--Cole-Haan, Yarmouth, ME; *U.S. Public*, pg. 1184
Donoso, Boris, Chief Oper. Officer--Novo Nordisk, Buenos Aires, Argentina; *Int'l*, pg. 987
Donovan, William, Chief Oper. Officer--Imperial Die Casting, Easley, SC; *U.S. Private*, pg. 903
Dooley, Kenneth J., Chief Oper. Officer--Holland Sweetener North America, Inc., Atlanta, GA; *Int'l*, pg. 1407
Doolittle, Dennis, Vice Chm. & Chief Oper. Officer--Autologic Information International, Inc., Thousand Oaks, CA; *U.S. Public*, pg. 1724
Doolittle, James H., Pres. & Chief Oper. Officer--Time Warner Cable, Stamford, CT; *U.S. Public*, pg. 1610
Dorfi, Klaus G., Pres. & Chief Oper. Officer--Atlantic Mutual Companies, New York, NY; *U.S. Private*, pg. 95
Dorman, John A., Pres. & Chief Oper. Officer--Broad National Bancorporation, Newark, NJ; *U.S. Public*, pg. 257
Dorsey, Jerry E., Chief Oper. Officer & Exec. V.P.--The West Company, Incorporated, Lionville, PA; *U.S. Public*, pg. 1755
Doubles, James E., Pres. & Chief Exec. Officer--TSI Incorporated, Shoreview, MN; *U.S. Public*, pg. 1559
Douce, Patrice, Pres. & Chief Oper. Officer--Sodexho S.A., Montigny-le-Bretonneux, France; *Int'l*, pg. 1274
Dougherty, Robert J., Jr., Pres. & Chief Oper. Officer--Enterprise Diversified Holdings Incorporated, Newark, NJ; *U.S. Public*, pg. 1340
Douglas, Gerry, Chief Oper. Officer--A.T. Clayton & Company, Inc., Greenwich, CT; *U.S. Private*, pg. 244
Dowd, Kevin P., Pres., Chief Exec. Officer & Chief Oper. Officer--Checkpoint Systems Inc., Thorofare, NJ; *U.S. Public*, pg. 343
Dowd, William, Pres. & Chief Oper. Officer--Fleming Companies, Inc., Oklahoma City, OK; *U.S. Public*, pg. 652
Downin, R.D., Chief Oper. Officer--Fireye, Inc., Derry, NH; *Int'l*, pg. 1500
Downing, Andrew J., Chief Oper. Officer & Exec. V.P.--Metro Information Services, Virginia Beach, VA; *U.S. Public*, pg. 1102
Doyle, Buzz, Pres. & Chief Oper. Officer--Furr's Supermarkets, Albuquerque, NM; *U.S. Private*, pg. 432
Doyle, J., Controller--Asahi Glass America, Inc., New York, NY; *Int'l*, pg. 84
Doyle, J. A., Chief Oper. Officer--Novo Nordisk Bioindustrie S.A., Nanterre, France; *Int'l*, pg. 989
Doyle, J. Aelred, Chief Oper. Officer--Novo Nordisk Bioindustrie SA, Europe, Nanterre, France; *Int'l*, pg. 989
Dozier, Michael, Pres. & Chief Oper. Officer--TIE/ Communications, Inc., Overland Park, KS; *U.S. Private*, pg. 1085
Drago, Joseph A., Pres. & Chief Oper. Officer--The Dartnell Corporation, Chicago, IL; *U.S. Private*, pg. 312
Drake, Ann M., Chief Exec. Officer--DSC Logistics, Inc., Des Plaines, IL; *U.S. Private*, pg. 306
Dreyfus-Cloarec, Claire, Chief Oper. Officer--Serese (Service de Restauration du Sud Est), Paris, France; *Int'l*, pg. 560
Driggers, Gary, Pres. & Chief Oper. Officer--Midcoast Aviation, Inc., Saint Louis, MO; *U.S. Private*, pg. 959
Drimal, Charles E., Jr., Pres., Chief Exec. Officer & Chief Oper. Officer--PrimeEnergy Corporation, Stamford, CT; *U.S. Public*, pg. 1328
Drosdick, John G., Pres. & Chief Oper. Officer--Sun Company, Inc., Philadelphia, PA; *U.S. Public*, pg. 1530
Drouillard, Charles, Exec. V.P. & Chief Oper. Officer--Maxwell Macmillan Professional & Business Reference Publishing, Englewood Cliffs, NJ; *U.S. Public*, pg. 1602
Drozeski, L.C., Jr., Pres. & Chief Oper. Officer--Bunzl Extrusion, Richmond, VA; *Int'l*, pg. 232
Drumm, Des, Chief Oper. Officer--C & C (Wholesale) Ltd., Tipperary, Ireland; *Int'l*, pg. 64
Dryburgh, Douglas T., Sr. V.P.-Sls. & Mktg.--Starter Corp., New Haven, CT; *U.S. Public*, pg. 1511
Dubnik, Steve M., Pres. & Chief Oper. Officer-ACC North America--ACC Corp., Rochester, NY; *U.S. Public*, pg. 2
Duchesne, Yvan, Chief Oper. Officer & Exec. V.P.-Fine Papers Div.--Rolland Inc., Saint-Jerome, Canada; *Int'l*, pg. 273
Dudek, John, Chief Oper. Officer & Exec. V.P.--Dudek & Bock Spring Manufacturing Company, Chicago, IL; *U.S. Private*, pg. 344
Dudley, James S., V.P. & Chief Oper. Officer-Pressure Cleaning & Agricul. Div.--Hypro Corporation, New Brighton, MN; *U.S. Public*, pg. 1767
Duesner, Walter, Chief Oper. Officer--Dornbirner Sparkasse, Dornbirn, Austria; *Int'l*, pg. 417
Duffy, Bill, Chief Oper. Officer & Exec. V.P.--Barnes & Noble Direct, Rockleigh, NJ; *U.S. Public*, pg. 189
Duffy, Bill, Chief Oper. Officer & Exec. V.P.--B. Dalton Bookseller, Inc., New York, NY; *U.S. Public*, pg. 189
Duffy, Kevin, Pres. & Chief Oper. Officer--Xyvision, Inc., Wakefield, MA; *U.S. Public*, pg. 1787
Duffy, Michael, Chief Oper. Officer--First USA Paymentech, Inc., Salem, NH; *U.S. Public*, pg. 174
Duffy, Rick, Pres. & Chief Oper. Officer--Creative Alliance, Inc., Louisville, KY; *U.S. Private*, pg. 287
Dumont, Arthur E., Chief Oper. Officer--Precision Drilling Corporation, Calgary, Canada; *Int'l*, pg. 1066
Dunavant, Leslie D., Pres. & Chief Oper. Officer-Claire's Boutiques--Claire's Stores Inc., Pembroke Pines, FL; *U.S. Public*, pg. 381
Dunham, Jamie, Chief Oper. Officer-Buntin Advertising, Inc. & Exec. V.P.--The Buntin Group, Nashville, TN; *U.S. Private*, pg. 181
Dunlap, Rex H., Pres. & Chief Oper. Officer--First Financial Building Corporation, Manchester, MO; *U.S. Private*, pg. 407
Dunleavy, Thomas J., Chief Oper. Officer & Sr. V.P.--Risdon Corporation, Naugatuck, CT; *U.S. Public*, pg. 463
Dunlop, W. Wayne, Chief Oper. Officer & V.P.--Barclay White Incorporated, Berwyn, PA; *U.S. Private*, pg. 115
Dunn, Gregory W., Chief Oper. Officer & Exec. V.P.--Regal Cinemas Inc., Knoxville, TN; *U.S. Public*, pg. 1371
Dunn, Howard L. Jr., Pres. & Chief Oper. Officer--Culp, Inc., High Point, NC; *U.S. Public*, pg. 467
Dunn, Jerry, Chief Oper. Officer, V.P. & Treas.--The Odom Corporation, Seattle, WA; *U.S. Private*, pg. 811
Dunn, Thomas R., Chm. & Chief Oper. Officer--M & I First American Bank, Wausau, WI; *U.S. Public*, pg. 1050
Durando, Ronald A., Chief Oper. Officer--Microphase Corporation, Norwalk, CT; *U.S. Private*, pg. 742
Durbec, Robert, Chief Oper. Officer & Dir.--Banque Nationale de Paris-Guyane, Cayenne, Guyana; *Int'l*, pg. 164
Duren, D. Ronald, Pres. & Chief Oper. Officer--Telecom Solutions, San Jose, CA; *U.S. Public*, pg. 1547
Durfee, J.Lang, V.P. & Sec.--Bethel Mills, Inc., Bethel, VT; *U.S. Private*, pg. 141
Durham, Paul, Chief Oper. Officer--Miller Meester Advertising Inc., Minneapolis, MN; *U.S. Private*, pg. 747
Durkin, William, Chief Oper. Officer--Amerford International Corporation, Atlanta, GA; *Int'l*, pg. 1388
Dussault, C., Pres. & Chief Oper. Officer--Le Groupe Commerce, Saint-Hyacinthe, Canada; *Int'l*, pg. 650
Dussek, Steven, Chief Oper. Officer & Sr. V.P.--Paging Network, Inc., Plano, TX; *U.S. Public*, pg. 1252
Dutriat, Philippe, Chief Oper. Officer--Schleicher & Schuell France SARL, Ecouviez, France; *Int'l*, pg. 1206
Dwyer, Robert, Chief Oper. Officer & Exec. V.P.--Industrial Coatings Group, Inc., Chicago, IL; *U.S. Private*, pg. 434
Dykstra, Gregg A., Chief Oper. Officer--Best Access Systems, Indianapolis, IN; *U.S. Public*, pg. 223
Dziubek, Paul, Chief Oper. Officer--Fuji Securities Inc.-Chicago, Chicago, IL; *Int'l*, pg. 519
Dziubek, Paul, Chief Oper. Officer--Fuji Securities Inc.-New York, New York, NY; *Int'l*, pg. 519
Eagle, John R., Pres. & Chief Oper. Officer--Eagle Lincoln Mercury Inc., Dallas, TX; *U.S. Private*, pg. 355
Earl, Robert M., Pres. & Chief Oper. Officer--Earl Construction Company, West Sacramento, CA; *U.S. Private*, pg. 1051
Earley, Anthony F., Jr., Pres. & Chief Oper. Officer--DTE Energy Company, Detroit, MI; *U.S. Public*, pg. 475
Easterly, David E., Pres. & Chief Oper. Officer--Cox Enterprises, Inc., Atlanta, GA; *U.S. Private*, pg. 281
Eastham, Dennis, Pres. & Chief Oper. Officer--Blau Marketing Technologies, Inc., Wilton, CT; *U.S. Private*, pg. 148
Eastwood, William, Chief Oper. Officer--Dexol, Torrance, CA; *U.S. Public*, pg. 1390
Ebert, Douglas, Pres. & Chief Exec. Officer--Michigan National Corporation, Farmington Hills, MI; *Int'l*, pg. 906
Ebert, Walter, Chief Oper. Officer--Thompson-Siegel GmbH, Dusseldorf, Germany; *Int'l*, pg. 610
Eby, James C., V.P.-Quality Assurance & Mfg.--Digital Sound Corporation, Carpinteria, CA; *U.S. Public*, pg. 508
Eckardt, Carl R., Pres. & Chief Oper. Officer--ISP Chemicals Inc., Calvert City, KY; *U.S. Public*, pg. 858
Eckardt, Carl R., Chief Oper. Officer--ISP Technologies Inc., Texas City, TX; *U.S. Public*, pg. 859
Ecker, H. Allen, Ph.D., Chief Oper. Officer & Sr. V.P.-Tech. Opers.--Scientific-Atlanta, Inc., Norcross, GA; *U.S. Public*, pg. 1443
Eckert, Carter, Chief Oper. Officer & V.P.-Bus. Devel.--Knoll Pharmaceutical Company, Whippany, NJ; *Int'l*, pg. 105
Edar, Itamar, Chief Oper. Officer & Mng. Dir.--IIS Intelligent Information Systems Ltd., Yokneam, Israel; *Int'l*, pg. 645
Edelman, Dan, Pres. & Chief Oper. Officer--The Bon Marche, Inc., Seattle, WA; *U.S. Public*, pg. 617
Edenfield, J Michael, Exec. V.P. & Chief Oper. Officer--ASI Properties, Inc., Atlanta, GA; *U.S. Public*, pg. 91
Edenfield, J. Michael, Chief Oper. Officer & Exec. V.P.--American Software, Inc., Atlanta, GA; *U.S. Public*, pg. 91
Edgar, Les, Chief Oper. Officer--Bullfrog Productions Ltd., Guildford, United Kingdom; *U.S. Public*, pg. 569
Edmeades, Michael, Chief Oper. Officer--WestWayne, Inc., Atlanta, GA; *U.S. Private*, pg. 1170
Edmondson, John, Chief Oper. Officer & Exec. V.P.--Duty Free International, Inc., Ridgefield, CT; *Int'l*, pg. 103
Edwards, William E., III, Pres. & Chief Oper. Officer--Cardinal Aluminum Co., Louisville, KY; *U.S. Private*, pg. 208
Edwardson, John A., Pres. & Chief Oper. Officer--UAL Corporation, Elk Grove Village, IL; *U.S. Public*, pg. 1652
Eertmans, Michel, Head-BBL/London Branch--Bank Brussels Lambert, London Branch, London, United Kingdom; *Int'l*, pg. 147
Egawa, Yasuhiro, Chief Oper. Officer--The Sri Muang Insurance Co., Ltd., Bangkok, Thailand; *Int'l*, pg. 1392
Eggensperger, Michael, Chief Oper. Officer--BHF-BANK (Switzerland) Ltd., Zurich, Switzerland; *Int'l*, pg. 119
Eggers, Harald, Chief Oper. Officer--Siemens Microelectronics Center GmbH & Co., Dresden, Germany; *Int'l*, pg. 1245
Eglinton, William M., Chief Oper. Officer & Exec. V.P.--Public Service Company of New Mexico, Albuquerque, NM; *U.S. Public*, pg. 1339
Egnew, J.C., Pres. & Chief Oper. Officer--Outdoor Venture Corp., Stearns, KY; *U.S. Private*, pg. 822
Ehrens, Gerald L., Chief Oper. Officer & Sr. V.P.-Corp. Devel.--Inamed Corporation, Las Vegas, NV; *U.S. Public*, *pg. 873*
Ehrlich, Klaus, Chief Oper. Officer--Novo Nordisk Pharma GmbH, Mainz, Germany; *Int'l*, pg. 988
Eich, Ken, Chief Oper. Officer--Davis Selected Advisors, L.P., Santa Fe, NM; *U.S. Private*, pg. 315
Eisenbach, Randall D., Chief Oper. Officer & Exec. V.P.--STB Systems, Inc., Richardson, TX; *U.S. Public*, pg. 1421
Eisenberg, Bernard, Chief Oper. Officer & V.P.--Glencraft Lingerie, Inc., New York, NY; *U.S. Private*, pg. 456
Eitel, Charles, Pres. & Chief Oper. Officer--Interface Inc., Atlanta, GA; *U.S. Public*, pg. 889
Ekaireb, Errol, Pres. & Chief Oper. Officer--Remec, Inc., San Diego, CA; *U.S. Public*, pg. 1376
Ekstrom, Kaj, Chief Oper. Officer--Hagglunds Drives Oy, Helsinki, Finland; *Int'l*, pg. 670
El-Din, M. Hussan, Chief Oper. Officer--Jotun Abu Dhabi (L.L.C.), Abu Dhabi, United Arab Emirates; *Int'l*, pg. 715
Elbert, Paul A., Exec. V.P. & Chief Oper. Officer-Natural Gas--Consumers Energy, Jackson, MI; *U.S. Public*, pg. 280
Elen, Robert, Pres. & Chief Oper. Officer--DavisElen Advertising, Inc., Los Angeles, CA; *U.S. Private*, pg. 316
Elgas, Devere L., Pres., Chief Exec. Officer & Chief Oper. Officer--Citizens Gas Fuel Company, Adrian, MI; *U.S. Public*, pg. 1025
Elizondo, Manuel Ancira, Chief Oper. Officer--Altos Hornos de Mexico, S.A., Monclova, Mexico; *Int'l*, pg. 66
Elkas, George, Pres. & Chief Oper. Officer--Flexi-Van Leasing, Inc., Kenilworth, NJ; *U.S. Private*, pg. 413
Elkins, Ken J., Sr. V.P.-Broadcasting Opers.--Pulitzer Publishing Company, Saint Louis, MO; *U.S. Public*, pg. 1343
Eller, Scott, Pres. & Chief Oper. Officer--Eller Media Company, Phoenix, AZ; *U.S. Public*, pg. 383

Ellerbrook, Niel, Pres. & Chief Oper. Officer--IEI Services, LLC, Indianapolis, IN; *U.S. Public*, pg. 875
Ellerbrook, Niel C., Pres. & Chief Oper. Officer--Indiana Energy, Inc., Indianapolis, IN; *U.S. Public*, pg. 874
Elliot, Chris, Chief Oper. Officer--Church's Chicken, Inc., Atlanta, GA; *U.S. Private*, pg. 5
Elliott, J. Mark, Pres. & Chief Oper. Officer--QST Enterprises Inc., Peoria, IL; *U.S. Public*, pg. 367
Elliott, Neal M., Chm. Bd., Pres. & Chief Exec. Officer--Horizon/CMS Healthcare Corporation, Albuquerque, NM; *U.S. Public*, pg. 836
Ellis, Gary L., Chief Oper. Officer & Exec. V.P.--United Bankshares, Inc., Parkersburg, WV; *U.S. Public*, pg. 1674
Ellstrom, Richard, V.P.-Opers.--Dearborn Gage Company, Garden City, MI; *U.S. Private*, pg. 319
Elsasser, J.T., V.P.-Bearings-Europe, Africa & West Asia--Timken France, Succursale de The Timken Co., Colmar, France; *U.S. Public*, pg. 1618
Emerson, Mark, Chief Oper. Officer--Max & Erma's Restaurants, Columbus, OH; *U.S. Public*, pg. 1060
Emerson, Richard B., Mng. Partner & Chief Oper. Officer, Divisions--Arnold Communications, Inc., Boston, MA; *U.S. Private*, pg. 83
Emery, Gerald R., Chief Oper. Officer--Concord Savings Bank, Concord, NH; *U.S. Public*, pg. 278
Emma, Edward C., Pres. & Chief Oper. Officer--Jockey International, Inc., Kenosha, WI; *U.S. Private*, pg. 588
Emmel, James, Chief Oper. Officer--Sentinel Technologies Inc., Downers Grove, IL; *U.S. Private*, pg. 984
Emmerling, John, Chm. Bd. & Chief Creative Officer--Emmerling Post, Inc., New York, NY; *U.S. Private*, pg. 374
Emrich, John A., Pres. & Chief Oper. Officer--Guilford Mills, Inc., Greensboro, NC; *U.S. Public*, pg. 768
Enderli, Yves, Exec. V.P. & Chief Oper. Officer--Basel Trading Company Ltd., Basel, Switzerland; *Int'l*, pg. 169
Endres, Jeff, Dir.-Opers.--Carl Zeiss Optical, Inc., Petersburg, VA; *Int'l*, pg. 1523
Engelke, Arno, Chief Oper. Officer--Gambro Dialysatoren GmbH & Co KG, Hechingen, Germany; *Int'l*, pg. 667
Engelkes, Donald J., V.P. & Gen. Mgr.--Country Life Insurance Company, Bloomington, IL; *U.S. Private*, pg. 278
Engelsman, Tom, Pres. & Chief Oper. Officer--Beloit Corporation, Beloit, WI; *U.S. Public*, pg. 789
English, John T., Pres. & Chief Oper. Officer--Florida Public Utilities Company, West Palm Beach, FL; *U.S. Public*, pg. 655
Enoki, Hiroshi, Chief Oper. Officer--Makita Corporation of America, Buford, GA; *Int'l*, pg. 831
Ensign, Michael, Chief Oper. Officer--Circus Circus - Las Vegas, Las Vegas, NV; *U.S. Public*, pg. 374
Ensign, Mike, Vice Chm. & Chief Oper. Officer--Circus Circus Hotel Casinos, Inc., Las Vegas, NV; *U.S. Public*, pg. 374
Epperly, Michael P., Sr. V.P.-Opers.--Buckeye Pipe Line Company, L.P., Allentown, PA; *U.S. Public*, pg. 266
Epstein, Glenn, Pres. & Chief Oper. Officer--Intermagnetics General Corporation, Latham, NY; *U.S. Public*, pg. 893
Erani, Albert, Chief Oper. Officer, Treas. & Sec.--A&E Stores, Inc., Teterboro, NJ; *U.S. Private*, pg. 1
Ernst, Markus M., Chief Oper. Officer & Exec. V.P.--Arbor Drugs, Inc., Troy, MI; *U.S. Public*, pg. 126
Eschbach, Alan R., Exec. V.P. & Chief Oper. Officer--Rheometric Scientific, Piscataway, NJ; *U.S. Public*, pg. 1387
Eskew, Carter, Chief Oper. Officer--BSMG Worldwide, New York, NY; *U.S. Public*, pg. 1642
Esmeyer, Hank, Chief Oper. Officer--Semitec, Inc., Santa Clara, CA; *U.S. Public*, pg. 969
Esposito, Joseph, Chief Oper. Officer & Exec. V.P.--Four Seasons Solar Products Corp., Holbrook, NY; *U.S. Private*, pg. 422
Ethier, James B., Pres. & Chief Oper. Officer--Bush Brothers & Company, Knoxville, TN; *U.S. Private*, pg. 189
Eureyecko, John, Pres. & Chief Oper. Officer--Piercing Pagoda, Inc., Bethlehem, PA; *U.S. Public*, pg. 1296
Evans, Andrew, Chief Oper. Officer--Leonard Lifts Ltd., London, United Kingdom; *Int'l*, pg. 748
Evans, Clarence, Chief Oper. Officer & Exec. V.P.-Personal Training & Devel.--The Mad Butcher, Inc., Pine Bluff, AR; *U.S. Private*, pg. 693
Evans, Gary, Exec. V.P. & Chief Oper Officer-Meats Grp.--Farmland Industries, Inc., Kansas City, MO; *U.S. Private*, *pg. 395*
Evans, Hywel, Chief Oper. Officer--Novo Nordisk Pharmaceuticals Ltd., Crawley, United Kingdom; *Int'l*, pg. 988
Evans, Michael, Chief Oper. Officer--Ferrosan Operations Ltd., Lewes, United Kingdom; *Int'l*, pg. 989
Evans, Michael L., Chief Oper. Officer--Ohio Casualty Corporation, Hamilton, OH; *U.S. Public*, pg. 1214
Evans, Morgan J., Pres. & Chief Oper. Officer--First Security Corporation, Salt Lake City, UT; *U.S. Public*, pg. 637
Evans, Philip B., Grp. V.P. & Sr. Oper. Officer-Americas--Avon Products, Inc., New York, NY; *U.S. Public*, pg. 156
Evans, Raymond, Chief Oper. Officer & Exec. V.P.--State Auto Life Insurance Company, Columbus, OH; *U.S. Public*, pg. 622
Evans, Richard, Chief Oper. Officer & Exec. V.P.--Gaylord Entertainment/Opryland USA, Nashville, TN; *U.S. Public*, *pg. 704*
Evans, Richard L., Chief Oper. Officer, Chief Fin. Officer, Exec. V.P. & Treas.--Reunion Industries, Inc., Stamford, CT; *U.S. Public*, pg. 1383
Evans, William F., Jr., Pres. & Chief Oper. Officer--Columbus Mills, Inc., Columbus, GA; *U.S. Private*, pg. 256
Everett, Donald S., Pres. & Chief Oper. Officer--Interstate Steel Supply Company, Philadelphia, PA; *U.S. Public*, pg. 1100
Everett, Michael S., Chief Oper. Officer--Wilkins-Rogers Incorporated, Ellicott City, MD; *U.S. Private*, pg. 1176
Everett, Rich, Chief Oper. Officer & Exec. V.P.--West Marine, Inc., Watsonville, CA; *U.S. Public*, pg. 1756
Ewald, Robert H., Chief Oper. Officer & Exec. V.P.-Computer Sys.--Silicon Graphics, Inc., Mountain View, CA; *U.S. Public*, pg. 1473
Ewing, Edward, Pres. & Chief Oper. Officer--Southwest Marine, Inc., San Diego, CA; *U.S. Private*, pg. 213
Ewing, Ron, Chief Fin. Officer, Chief Oper. Officer & Sec.--LVL Advertising, Palo Alto, CA; *U.S. Private*, pg. 640
Exum, James F., Jr., Pres. & Chief Oper. Officer--Krystal Company, Chattanooga, TN; *U.S. Private*, pg. 636
Fabiano, Anthony, Pres. & Chief Oper. Officer--Despatch Industries, Minneapolis, MN; *U.S. Private*, pg. 327
Fabick, Harry, Pres. & Chief Oper. Officer--John Fabick Tractor Company, Fenton, MO; *U.S. Private*, pg. 390
Fabre, Emmanuel, Chief Oper. Officer--NAPS France S.A., Lens, France; *Int'l*, pg. 913
Fabris, James, Chief Oper. Officer--Hurco Companies, Inc., Indianapolis, IN; *U.S. Public*, pg. 850
Fabrizzi, Vincent J., Pres. & Chief Oper. Officer--Paradigm Communications, Tampa, FL; *U.S. Private*, pg. 838
Fagerstrom, Thor, Chief Oper. Officer--Neste Air, Vantaa, Finland; *Int'l*, pg. 913
Fagerstrom, Thor, Chief Oper. Officer--Neste Aviation and Marine Sales, Espoo, Finland; *Int'l*, pg. 913
Faggioli, Douglas, Chief Oper. Officer--Nature's Sunshine Products, Inc., Provo, UT; *U.S. Public*, pg. 1166
Fain, John H., Chm. Bd., Pres., Chief Exec. Officer & Chief Oper. Officer--Metro Information Services, Virginia Beach, VA; *U.S. Public*, pg. 1102
Fairbanks, Walter, Grp. V.P.-Defense--Cubic Corporation, San Diego, CA; *U.S. Public*, pg. 466
Fairholm, Don, Chief Oper. Officer--Nurre Caxton, Sunrise, FL; *Int'l*, pg. 460
Falk, Lloyd, Pres., Chief Exec. Officer & Chief Oper. Officer--Fort Lock Corporation, River Grove, IL; *U.S. Private*, pg. 419
Famalette, James, Pres. & Chief Oper. Officer--Gottschalks Inc., Fresno, CA; *U.S. Public*, pg. 754
Fansler, Alan L., Chief Oper. Officer & Exec. V.P.--Quality Stores Inc., Muskegon, MI; *U.S. Private*, pg. 899
Farina, Gino, Chief Oper. Officer--Sabiem S.r.L., Bologna, Italy; *Int'l*, pg. 748
Farless, Luther, Chief Oper. Officer & V.P.--Leisure Technology, Inc., Atlanta, GA; *U.S. Private*, pg. 659
Farman, Richard D., Pres. & Chief Oper. Officer--Pacific Enterprises, Los Angeles, CA; *U.S. Public*, pg. 1249
Farmer, Roy F., Chm. Bd., Pres., Chief Exec. Officer & Chief Oper. Officer--Farmer Brothers Company, Torrance, CA; *U.S. Public*, pg. 613
Farmer, Scott D., Pres. & Chief Oper. Officer--Cintas Corporation, Mason, OH; *U.S. Public*, pg. 370
Farquhar, Peter, Mng. Dir.--Fleishman-Hillard Europe, London, United Kingdom; *U.S. Private*, pg. 411
Farrar, Clarence, Chief Oper. Officer & V.P.--JG Industries, Inc., Chicago, IL; *U.S. Public*, pg. 917
Farrell, Mary, Chief Oper. Officer & Exec. V.P.--Mintz & Hoke Inc., Avon, CT; *U.S. Private*, pg. 751
Farrell, Tana J., Chief Oper. Officer & Exec. V.P.--The Woodfin Suite Hotels, San Diego, CA; *U.S. Private*, pg. 1187
Farris, David J., Pres. & Chief Oper. Officer--Beneficial Corporation, Wilmington, DE; *U.S. Public*, pg. 211
Farris, G. Steven, Pres. & Chief Oper. Officer--Apache Corporation, Houston, TX; *U.S. Public*, pg. 119
Faulhaber, Alan M., Exec. V.P.--The F.D. Lawrence Electric Co., Cincinnati, OH; *U.S. Private*, pg. 654
Fawcett, Gerald A., Pres. & Chief Oper. Officer--Kaiser Ventures, Inc., Ontario, CA; *U.S. Public*, pg. 941
Fecan, Ivan, Pres. & Chief Oper. Officer--Baton Broadcasting Incorporated, Scarborough, Canada; *Int'l*, pg. 170
Feehan, Daniel R., Pres. & Chief Oper. Officer--Cash America International, Inc., Fort Worth, TX; *U.S. Public*, pg. 312
Feeley, Edmund, Pres. & Chief Oper. Officer--Fleer-Skybox International Inc., Mount Laurel, NJ; *U.S. Public*, pg. 1052
Feely, Pat, Pres. & Chief Oper. Officer--Radica USA Limited, Dallas, TX; *U.S. Private*, pg. 906
Fehrenbach, Dan, Pres. & Chief Exec. Officer--Citizens Bank of Western Indiana, Terre Haute, IN; *U.S. Public*, pg. 280
Feinstein, Martin D., Pres. & Chief Oper. Officer--Farmers Group, Inc., Los Angeles, CA; *Int'l*, pg. 110
Felber, Ronald, Pres., Chief Exec. & Chief Oper. Officer--Oakite Products, Inc., Berkeley Heights, NJ; *Int'l*, pg. 861
Feldenkreis, Oscar, Pres. & Chief Oper. Officer--Supreme International Corp., Miami, FL; *U.S. Public*, pg. 1542
Feller, Alan, Chief Oper. Officer, Chief Fin. Officer, Treas. & Sec.--G-III Apparel Group, Ltd., New York, NY; *U.S. Public*, pg. 690
Fellowes, James E., Pres. & Chief Oper. Officer--Fellowes Manufacturing Co., Itasca, IL; *U.S. Private*, pg. 400
Fellows, Eugene E., Chief Oper. Officer & V.P.-Opers.--SI/Baker, Inc., Easton, PA; *U.S. Public*, pg. 1418
Felsing, William D., Chief Oper. Officer & V.P.--PrimeCare Health Plan, Inc., Milwaukee, WI; *U.S. Public*, pg. 1678
Felsinger, Donald E., Pres. & Chief Oper. Officer--Enova Corp, San Diego, CA; *U.S. Public*, pg. 583
Feltenstein, Sidney, Chm. Bd., Chief Exec. Officer & Chief Oper. Officer--A&W Restaurants, Inc.-Carousel Div., Minneapolis, MN; *U.S. Private*, pg. 2
Ferber, Wolfgang, Chief Oper. Officer--Rhenania Schiffahrts-und Speditions-Gesellschaft mbH, Mannheim, Germany; *Int'l*, pg. 1033
Ferdinandtsen, G.R., Sr. Exec. V.P.--American National Insurance Company, Galveston, TX; *U.S. Public*, pg. 87
Ferguson, C. David, Chm. Bd., Pres., Chief Exec. & Chief Oper. Officer--Gould Electronics Inc., Eastlake, OH; *U.S. Public*, pg. 1591
Ferguson, Daryl A., Pres. & Chief Oper. Officer--Citizens Utilities Company, Stamford, CT; *U.S. Public*, pg. 379
Ferguson, Daryl A., Pres. & Chief Oper. Officer--Citizens Telecommunications, Stamford, CT; *U.S. Public*, pg. 380
Ferguson, Gerry, Pres., Chief Exec. Officer & Chief Oper. Officer--Binning's Building Products, Inc., Lexington, NC; *U.S. Public*, pg. 67
Ferguson, Ian, Chief Oper. Officer & Sr. V.P.--Parmalat Canada Ltd., Etobicoke, Canada; *Int'l*, pg. 1023
Ferguson, Lee, Pres. & Chief Oper. Officer--Bike Athletic Co., Knoxville, TN; *U.S. Private*, pg. 143
Ferguson, Sam, Pres., Chief Exec. & Chief Oper. Officer--Ferguson International, Inc., Dallas, TX; *U.S. Private*, pg. 401
Ferguson, Thomas, Pres. & Chief Oper. Officer--Mirro Company, Manitowoc, WI; *U.S. Public*, pg. 1177
Ferguson, Thomas A., Jr., Pres. & Chief Oper. Officer--Newell Co., Freeport, IL; *U.S. Public*, pg. 1176
Fermin, Mendizabal, Chief Oper. Officer--Mayc S.A., Berga, Spain; *Int'l*, pg. 260
Fernandez, Gonzalo, Exec. V.P.-Commercial Opers.--Pacific Crest Capital, Inc., Agoura Hills, CA; *U.S. Public*, pg. 1248
Fernandez, Jesus, Chief Exec. & Chief Oper. Officer--Tradicion Textil, S.A., Barcelona, Spain; *Int'l*, pg. 1416
Fernandez, Manuel, Exec. V.P. & Chief Oper. Officer-Worldwide Instruction--Berlitz International, Inc., Princeton, NJ; *U.S. Public*, pg. 221
Fernstrom, H. Allen, Chief Oper. Officer & Exec. V.P.--Marine Construction & Design Co., Seattle, WA; *U.S. Private*, pg. 703
Ferrari, Giannantonio, Pres. & Chief Oper. Officer--Honeywell Inc., Minneapolis, MN; *U.S. Public*, pg. 833
Ferre Rangel, Antonio L., Chief Oper. Officer--Ponce Cement Div., Ponce, PR; *U.S. Public*, pg. 1342
Fetrow, Chuck E., Chief Oper. Officer & V.P.--Service Supply Corporation, Harrisburg, PA; *U.S. Private*, pg. 1040
Fiedler, James J., Chief Exec. Officer--Coyote Network Systems, Inc., Westlake Village, CA; *U.S. Public*, pg. 455
Fiegehen, Allan G., Pres. & Chief Oper. Officer--Cubix Corporation, Carson City, NV; *U.S. Private*, pg. 294
Fields, Marvin G., Chief Oper. Officer & Sr. V.P.--Frisch's Restaurants, Inc., Cincinnati, OH; *U.S. Public*, pg. 682
Fields, Richard, Chief Oper. Officer--Cadet Manufacturing Company, Vancouver, WA; *U.S. Private*, pg. 198
Fierman, Daniel J., Chief Oper. Officer & Exec. V.P.--ANESCO, Kingston, PA; *U.S. Private*, pg. 74
Fillon, Oliver, Chief Oper. Officer--Hospal B.V., Uden, Netherlands; *Int'l*, pg. 668
Fillon, Oliver, Chief Oper. Officer--Hospal-COBE Renal N.V., Zaventem, Belgium; *Int'l*, pg. 668
Fimiano, Andrew, Chief Oper. Officer & V.P.--Southland Industries, Long Beach, CA; *U.S. Private*, pg. 1018
Fine, Alan, Chief Oper. Officer-Toy Biz Intl.--Toy Biz, Inc., New York, NY; *U.S. Public*, pg. 1625
Fine, Jay, Chief Oper. Officer & Exec. V.P.--Fort Lock Corporation, River Grove, IL; *U.S. Private*, pg. 419
Fine, Robert W., Pres. & Chief Oper. Officer--Transworld Home Healthcare, Inc., New York, NY; *U.S. Public*, pg. 1632
Fine, S.A., Pres. & Chief Oper. Officer--The Biltrite Corporation, Waltham, MA; *U.S. Private*, pg. 144
Fink, James W., Chief Oper. Officer & V.P.-Opers.--Dep Corporation, Rancho Dominguez, CA; *U.S. Public*, pg. 500
Finkelstein, David, Sr. Exec. V.P.--Century Business Credit Corporation, New York, NY; *U.S. Private*, pg. 225
Finlayson, Alan J., Chief Oper. Officer-USA--Bardon Group PLC, Solihull, United Kingdom; *Int'l*, pg. 166
Finley, C. Sue, V.P.-Opers. & Dir.-Sls.--Spartech Plastics, Portage, WI; *U.S. Public*, pg. 1496
Finn, L.P., Chief Exec. Officer & Chief Oper. Officer--Northern Rock PLC, Newcastle upon Tyne, United Kingdom; *Int'l*, pg. 968
Finnegan, Neal, Pres. & Chief Exec. Officer--UST Corporation, Boston, MA; *U.S. Public*, pg. 1660
Fiorito, Ricardo, Chm. Bd. & Chief Oper. Officer--Banco Quilmes, Buenos Aires, Argentina; *Int'l*, pg. 142
Firlotte, Charles V., Chief Oper. Officer & Sr. V.P.--BHC Company, Bridgeport, CT; *U.S. Public*, pg. 126
Fischer, Irving, Pres. & Chief Oper. Officer--Starrett HRH, New York, NY; *U.S. Private*, pg. 1035
Fischer, Mike, V.P.-Mfg.--Dorner Manufacturing Corp., Hartland, WI; *U.S. Private*, pg. 340
Fischer, Ulrich, Dr., Chief Oper. Officer--Industrie-Beteiligungs Gesellschaftmbh, Frankfurt/Main, Germany; *Int'l*, pg. 119
Fisher, Richard B., Pres. & Chief Oper. Officer--Morgan Stanley & Co. Incorporated, New York, NY; *U.S. Public*, pg. 1132
Fisher, Robert J., Chief Oper. Officer & Exec. V.P.--The Gap, Inc., San Francisco, CA; *U.S. Public*, pg. 702
Fisher, Vaughn C., Pres. & Chief Oper. Officer--Ingles Markets, Incorporated, Black Mountain, NC; *U.S. Public*, pg. 878
Fisk, Douglas R., Chief Oper. Officer & Exec. V.P.--Mustang Tractor & Equip. Co., Houston, TX; *U.S. Private*, pg. 768
Flakoll, Thomas J., Pres. & Chief Exec. & Oper. Officer--Technitrol, Inc., Trevose, PA; *U.S. Public*, pg. 1564
Flanagan, Patrick B., Chief Oper. Officer & Exec. V.P.--The Austin Company, Cleveland, OH; *U.S. Private*, pg. 99
Flanagan, Richard L., Pres. & Chief Oper. Officer-Borders--Borders Group, Inc., Ann Arbor, MI; *U.S. Public*, pg. 245
Flannery, Michael, Pres. & Chief Oper. Officer--Pope & Talbot, Inc., Portland, OR; *U.S. Public*, pg. 1316
Flatt, J. Bruce, Pres. & Chief Oper. Officer--Brookfield Properties Corporation, Toronto, Canada; *Int'l*, pg. 228
Flavio, Guacelli, Chief Oper. Officer--Groupe SEB Do Brasil, Sao Paulo, Brazil; *Int'l*, pg. 568
Flegenheimer, Roy A., Chief Oper. Officer, Treas. & Sec.--Employee Solutions, Inc., Phoenix, AZ; *U.S. Public*, pg. 579

Fleischhacker, Mark, Pres. & Chief Oper. Officer--Lake Region Manufacturing, Inc., Chaska, MN; *U.S. Private*, pg. 643
Fleischhacker, Mark, Chief Oper. Officer--Lake Region Medical, Inc., Pittsburgh, PA; *U.S. Private*, pg. 643
Fleming, Brian L., Pres. & Chief Oper. Officer--Santa Anita Enterprises, Inc., Arcadia, CA; *U.S. Public*, pg. 1081
Fleming, Eugene C., Chief Oper. Officer & Exec. V.P.--Quorum Health Group, Inc., Brentwood, TN; *U.S. Public*, pg. 1353
Fleming, Francis R., Pres. & Chief Oper. Officer--Chad Therapeutics, Chatsworth, CA; *U.S. Public*, pg. 332
Fleming, Kenneth, Pres. & Chief Oper. Officer--World Publishing Company, Tulsa, OK; *U.S. Private*, pg. 1190
Fletcher, David A., Pres. & Chief Oper. Officer--Deposition Technologies, Inc., San Diego, CA; *U.S. Public*, pg. 1056
Flicker, Warren, Pres. & Chief Oper. Officer--Homasote Company, Trenton, NJ; *U.S. Public*, pg. 831
Flickinger, William, Pres. & Chief Oper. Officer--HPM Corporation, Mount Gilead, OH; *U.S. Private*, pg. 492
Fligg, Loren L., Pres. & Chief Oper. Officer--Hawkeye Security Insurance Company, West Des Moines, IA; *Int'l*, *pg. 543*
Flint, Dennis, Chief Oper. Officer--Taylor Made Group, Inc., Gloversville, NY; *U.S. Private*, pg. 1070
Flippin, Pat, V.P. & Chief Oper. Officer--Kingsdown, Inc., Mebane, NC; *U.S. Private*, pg. 622
Flittie, John H., Vice Chm., Pres. & Chief Oper. Officer--ReliaStar Financial Corp., Minneapolis, MN; *U.S. Public*, pg. 1375
Flood, Doug, Chief Oper. Officer--Sportcraft Ltd., Mount Olive, NJ; *U.S. Private*, pg. 1026
Florsheim, Thomas W., Jr., Pres. & Chief Oper. Officer--Weyco Group, Inc., Milwaukee, WI; *U.S. Public*, pg. 1763
Floum, Bob, Chief Oper. Officer--Jumbo Sports Inc., Tampa, FL; *U.S. Public*, pg. 935
Flynn, James T., Pres. & Chief Oper. Officer--Long Island Lighting Company, Hicksville, NY; *U.S. Public*, pg. 1013
Flynn, Michael, Pres. & Chief Oper. Officer--Kimco Realty Corporation, New Hyde Park, NY; *U.S. Public*, pg. 960
Flynn, Patrick, Pres., Chief Exec. Officer, Chief Oper. Officer & Controller--Freeway Corporation, Cleveland, OH; *U.S. Private*, pg. 426
Flynn, Peter E., Exec. V.P. & Sec.--ENStar, Inc., Eden Prairie, MN; *U.S. Public*, pg. 585
Focht, Michael H., Sr., Pres. & Chief Oper. Officer--Tenet Healthcare Corporation, Santa Barbara, CA; *U.S. Public*, pg. 1576
Foerster, Jean-Paul, Chief Oper. Officer--Orient-Express Hotels Inc., New York, NY; *Int'l*, pg. 1213
Fogelstrom, Anders, Chief Oper. Officer--Geotronics S.A.R.L., Lagny, France; *Int'l*, pg. 1290
Foley, M.S., Chief Oper. Officer--Energizer Eveready Ltd., London, United Kingdom; *U.S. Public*, pg. 1360
Folger, Roger, Pres., Chief Exec. Officer & Chief Oper. Officer--Punch Press Products, Inc., Los Angeles, CA; *U.S. Private*, pg. 895
Folick, Jeffrey, Chief Oper. Officer & Exec. V.P.--PacifiCare Health Systems, Inc., Cypress, CA; *U.S. Public*, pg. 1250
Folz, Joseph L., Pres. & Chief Oper. Officer--Harleysville-Garden State Insurance Co., Marlton, NJ; *U.S. Public*, pg. 787
Fontanet, Xavier, Vice Chm. & Chief Oper. Officer--Essilor International Compagnie Generale d'Optique, Charenton-le-Pont, France; *Int'l*, pg. 462
Forbes, Jon, Chief Oper. Officer--Jensen Industries, Los Angeles, CA; *U.S. Public*, pg. 1193
Forbes, Timothy C., Chief Oper. Officer--Forbes, Inc., New York, NY; *U.S. Private*, pg. 417
Forbes, Timothy C., Pres. & Chief Oper. Officer--American Heritage Magazine, New York, NY; *U.S. Private*, pg. 417
Ford, Edsel B., II, Pres. & Chief Oper. Officer--Ford Motor Credit Company, Dearborn, MI; *U.S. Public*, pg. 663
Fordham, Michael, Chief Oper. Officer--Northumberland Group Ltd., Richmond, United Kingdom; *Int'l*, pg. 162
Fore, James R., Chm. Bd., Pres. & Chief Exec. & Oper. Officer--Communication Cable, Inc., Sanford, NC; *U.S. Public*, pg. 968
Foreman, Glen D., Chief Oper. Officer--Clearly Canadian Beverage Corp., Vancouver, Canada; *Int'l*, pg. 297
Forgione, Anthony, Chm. Bd. & Pres.--Boyer Candy Company Inc., Altoona, PA; *U.S. Private*, pg. 162
Formisano, Roger, Chief Oper. Officer--United Wisconsin Services, Inc., Milwaukee, WI; *U.S. Public*, pg. 1692
Forster, David, Chief Oper. Officer--Chipman-Union, Inc., Union Point, GA; *U.S. Private*, pg. 237
Forte, Gabriella, Chief Oper. Officer--Calvin Klein, Inc., New York, NY; *U.S. Private*, pg. 202
Fortun, Wayne M., Pres., Chief Exec. Officer & Chief Oper. Officer--Hutchinson Technology Inc., Hutchinson, MN; *U.S. Public*, pg. 850
Foster, Mark, Chief Oper. Officer--Medical Innovations Corp., Pocatello, ID; *U.S. Public*, pg. 171
Foster, Phillip B., Chief Oper. Officer & Sr. V.P.--Erving Paper Mills, Inc., Erving, MA; *U.S. Private*, pg. 382
Foster, W. David, Pres. & Chief Oper. Officer--C.H. Heist Corp., Clearwater, FL; *U.S. Public*, pg. 807
Foti, Samuel J., Pres. & Chief Oper. Officer--The Mutual Life Insurance Company of New York, New York, NY; *U.S. Private*, pg. 769
Fountain, Reginald M., Jr., Chm. Bd., Pres. & Chief Exec. & Oper. Officer--Fountain Powerboat Industries, Inc., Washington, NC; *U.S. Public*, pg. 678
Fouts, Ronnie L., Chief Oper. Officer & Sr. V.P.--Willis Corroon Corp. of Chattanooga, Chattanooga, TN; *Int'l*, pg. 1505
Fowden, J.S.G., Chief Oper. Officer--Bass Brewers Ltd., Burton on Trent, United Kingdom; *Int'l*, pg. 170
Fowler, George E., Pres. & Chief Oper. Officer--Hadron, Inc., Alexandria, VA; *U.S. Public*, pg. 773
Fowler, Peggy Y., Chief Oper. Officer & Exec. V.P.--Portland General Electric Co., Portland, OR; *U.S. Public*, pg. 584
Fowler, Robert E., Jr., Pres. & Chief Exec. & Oper. Officer--IMC Global, Bannockburn, IL; *U.S. Public*, pg. 856
Fox, Leslie B., Chief Oper. Officer & Exec. V.P.--Lexford Residential Trust, Columbus, OH; *U.S. Public*, pg. 991
Fox, Raymond A., Chief Oper. Officer, V.P. & Sec.--Active Electrical Supply Company, Chicago, IL; *U.S. Private*, pg. 15
Foxx, M.J., Chief Oper. Officer & Exec. V.P.--Handgards Inc., Northbrook, IL; *U.S. Private*, pg. 499
Fracassi, Philip, Chief Oper. Officer & Sr. V.P.--Philip Services Corp., Hamilton, Canada; *Int'l*, pg. 1050
Fradin, David W., Pres. & Chief Oper. Officer--IEC Electronics Corp., Newark, NY; *U.S. Public*, pg. 854
Franceschi, Vincent, Pres. & Chief Oper. Officer--Vectra Technologies, Inc., San Ramon, CA; *U.S. Public*, pg. 1711
Franco, Donna S., Pres. & Chief Oper. Officer--Melrose, Chatsworth, CA; *U.S. Public*, pg. 948
Francois, Georges, Chief Oper. Officer--Banque Generale du Luxembourg S.A., Metz, France; *Int'l*, pg. 162
Franey, Bart H., Pres. & Chief Oper. Officer Milcare--Milcare, Inc., Grandville, MI; *U.S. Public*, pg. 1112
Frank, H. Alan, Chm. Bd.--Union Industries, Inc., Providence, RI; *U.S. Private*, pg. 1119
Frank, Harley A., Pres. & Chief Oper. Officer--Union Industries, Inc., Providence, RI; *U.S. Private*, pg. 1119
Frank, Howard, Vice Chm. & Chief Oper. Officer--Carnival Corporation, Miami, FL; *U.S. Public*, pg. 306
Frank, Stephen E., Pres. & Chief Oper. Officer--Southern California Edison Company, Rosemead, CA; *U.S. Public*, pg. 564
Frank, Susan, Chief Oper. Officer & Exec. V.P.--Hanna-Barbera Productions, Inc., Hollywood, CA; *U.S. Public*, pg. 1614
Frankovic, Richard, Pres. & Chief Oper. Officer--The Rugby Group, Inc., Rockville Centre, NY; *Int'l*, pg. 625
Franks, J. Scott, Chief Oper. Officer & Exec. V.P.--Tierney & Partners, Philadelphia, PA; *U.S. Public*, pg. 1641
Franks, John R., Chief Oper. Officer & Sr. V.P.--Penn Central National Bank, Huntingdon, PA; *U.S. Public*, pg. 1222
Franz, G. Andrew, Chief Oper. Officer & Sr. V.P.-Opers./Pharmaceuticals--Jones Medical Industries Inc., Saint Louis, MO; *U.S. Public*, pg. 933
Fraser, Donald H., Chief Oper. Officer & Exec. V.P.--Farmers & Merchants Bank of Central California, Lodi, CA; *U.S. Private*, pg. 394
Frattaroli, Robert J., Pres. & Chief Oper. Officer--Pharmaceutical Marketing Services Inc., Phoenix, AZ; *U.S. Public*, pg. 1284
Frechette, Peter L., Pres. & Chief Exec. Officer--Patterson Dental Company, Saint Paul, MN; *U.S. Public*, pg. 1265
Freeman, Dick, Chief Oper. Officer--Pittsburgh Associates, Pittsburgh, PA; *U.S. Private*, pg. 867
Freeman, John, Chief Oper. Officer, V.P.-Sls. & Mktg.--Johnson & Quin, Inc., Niles, IL; *U.S. Private*, pg. 590
French, Ed, Pres. & Chief Oper. Officer--Heatcraft Inc., Grenada, MS; *U.S. Private*, pg. 659
French, Peter, Chief Oper. Officer & Exec. V.P.--Global Marketing Resources (GMR), New York, NY; *U.S. Private*, pg. 457
Frerker, Daved L., Chief Oper. Officer--PMR Corporation, San Diego, CA; *U.S. Public*, pg. 1242
Frescoln, L.D., Pres. & Chief Oper. Officer--Flint Ink Corp., Detroit, MI; *U.S. Private*, pg. 413
Fretz, Kent F., Chief Oper. Officer--The Pittman Company, Harleysville, PA; *U.S. Public*, pg. 1270
Frie, Leonard W., Chief Oper. Officer & Exec. V.P.--Total Renal Care Holdings, Inc., Torrance, CA; *U.S. Public*, pg. 1625
Frieder, Israel, Pres. & Chief Oper. Officer--Telematics Inc., Fort Lauderdale, FL; *Int'l*, pg. 643
Friedman, Eric D., Pres. & Chief Oper. Officer--The Grandoe Corp., Gloversville, NY; *U.S. Private*, pg. 469
Friedman, Norman E., Chief Oper. Officer & Exec. V.P.--Herbalife International of America, Inc., Century City, CA; *U.S. Public*, pg. 809
Friedman, Ron, Pres. & Chief Oper. Officer--Group 1 Software, Inc., Lanham, MD; *U.S. Public*, pg. 417
Friend, Norma J., Chief Oper. Officer & Exec. V.P.--Gianettino & Meredith Advertising, Short Hills, NJ; *U.S. Private*, pg. 450
Fristedt, Hans, Pres. & Chief Oper. Officer--American Trading and Production Corporation, Baltimore, MD; *U.S. Private*, pg. 63
Frith, Bud F., Chief Oper. Officer--MACE Products, Upland, CA; *U.S. Public*, pg. 1234
Fritschi, Alfred, Chief Oper. Officer--Gambro AG, Hunenberg, Switzerland; *Int'l*, pg. 667
Froemming, Herb, Pres. & Chief Oper. Officer--Brauns Fashions Corporation, Plymouth, MN; *U.S. Public*, pg. 251
Fronville, Louis, Chief Oper. Officer--Inter-Beton S.A., Brussels, Belgium; *Int'l*, pg. 605
Fruchtenbaum, Edward, Pres. & Chief Oper. Officer--American Greetings Corporation, Cleveland, OH; *U.S. Public*, pg. 77
Frump, J. Ronald, Pres. & Chief Oper. Officer--Vitality Foodservice, Inc., Zephyrhills, FL; *U.S. Private*, pg. 682
Fry, Jim, Pres. & Chief Oper. Officer--Tuscarora Yarns Inc., Mount Pleasant, NC; *U.S. Private*, pg. 1110
Fry, William N., IV, Exec. V.P. & Chief Oper. Officer-Floorcovering Grp.--The Dixie Group, Inc., Chattanooga, TN; *U.S. Public*, pg. 514
Fryling, Victor J., Pres. & Chief Oper. Officer--CMS Energy Corporation, Dearborn, MI; *U.S. Public*, pg. 279
Fuerst, John, Pres. & Chief Oper. Officer--Continental/Midland, Inc., Park Forest, IL; *U.S. Private*, pg. 268
Fukubayashi, Masami, Chief Oper. Officer--The Tokio Marine & Fire Insurance Company (U.K.) Limited, London, United Kingdom; *Int'l*, pg. 1392
Fukunaga, Eric S., Pres. & Chief Oper. Officer--Servco Pacific Inc., Honolulu, HI; *U.S. Private*, pg. 986
Fukushige, Y., Chief Oper. Officer--Littelfuse KK, Yokohama, Japan; *U.S. Public*, pg. 1001
Fulchino, Paul E., Pres. & Chief Oper. Officer--B/E Aerospace, Inc., Wellington, FL; *U.S. Public*, pg. 159
Fuller, Jeffrey L., Pres. & Chief Oper. Officer--Transcrypt International, Lincoln, NE; *U.S. Public*, pg. 1630
Fulwiler, Daniel, Chief Oper. Officer & V.P.--Wisconsin Label Corporation, Algoma, WI; *U.S. Private*, pg. 1184
Funke, Mark W., Exec. V.P. & Chief Oper. Officer-Oklahoma City--Bank of Oklahoma, N.A., Tulsa, OK; *U.S. Public*, pg. 163
Furman, Thomas D., Jr., Pres. & Chief Oper. Officer--Camp Dresser & McKee Inc., Cambridge, MA; *U.S. Private*, pg. 203
Furr, Randy W., Pres. & Chief Oper. Officer--Sanmina Corporation, San Jose, CA; *U.S. Public*, pg. 1431
Furu, Niels Christian, Chief Oper. Officer & Exec. V.P.--Olicom A/S, Lyngby, Denmark; *Int'l*, pg. 1001
Furubayashi, R., Dr., Chief Oper. Officer--Gemini Science, Inc., La Jolla, CA; *Int'l*, pg. 736
Fyfe, David, Pres. & Chief Oper. Officer--Thoro, Jacksonville, FL; *U.S. Private*, pg. 505
Gaber, Stephen, Chief Oper. Officer--Mesirow Financial, Chicago, IL; *U.S. Private*, pg. 733
Gabrys, Gerard, Pres. & Chief Oper. Officer--Guest Services, Inc., Fairfax, VA; *U.S. Private*, pg. 486
Gaddis, Leland L., Chief Oper. Officer--National Print Group, Inc., Chattanooga, TN; *U.S. Private*, pg. 785
Gaetz, Richard E., Pres. & Chief Oper. Officer--Vitran Corporation Inc., Toronto, Canada; *Int'l*, pg. 1469
Gage, Patrick, Dr., Pres. & Chief Oper. Officer--Genetics Institute, Inc., Cambridge, MA; *U.S. Public*, pg. 79
Gaines, Michael, Pres. & Chief Oper. Officer--Moore-Handley, Inc., Pelham, AL; *U.S. Public*, pg. 1128
Gaither, Hugh, Pres. & Chief Oper. Officer--Ridgeview, Inc., Newton, NC; *U.S. Private*, pg. 930
Gale, Andy, Pres. & Chief Oper. Officer--Landa, Inc., Portland, OR; *U.S. Private*, pg. 646
Gallagher, Bernard P., Pres. & Chief Oper. Officer--Century Communications Corp., New Canaan, CT; *U.S. Public*, pg. 329
Gallagher, Daniel, Chief Oper. Officer & Exec. V.P.--Southern Health Services, Inc., Richmond, VA; *U.S. Public*, pg. 454
Gallagher, Robert J., Pres. & Chief Oper. Officer--Acuson Corporation, Mountain View, CA; *U.S. Public*, pg. 18
Gallagher, Thomas C., Pres. & Chief Oper. Officer--Genuine Parts Company, Atlanta, GA; *U.S. Public*, pg. 732
Gallagher, Thomas J., Pres. & Chief Oper. Officer--Everest Reinsurance Holdings, Liberty Corner, NJ; *U.S. Public*, pg. 597
Gallagher, Thomas J., Pres. & Chief Oper. Officer--Everest Reinsurance Co., Liberty Corner, NJ; *U.S. Public*, pg. 597
Gallogly, James J., Pres. & Chief Oper. Officer--Sofamor Danek Group, Inc., Memphis, TN; *U.S. Public*, pg. 1482
Galloway, Bob, Chief Oper. Officer--Hubbard Petfood, Mankato, MN; *Int'l*, pg. 1116
Galvis, Christian, Co-Pres. & Chief Oper. Officer-Slipper Div.--R.G. Barry Corporation, Pickerington, OH; *U.S. Public*, pg. 192
Gamache, Brian, Pres. & Chief Oper. Officer--WHG Resorts & Casinos, Carolina, PR; *U.S. Public*, pg. 1265
Gambarara, Franco, Chief Oper. Officer--Mikron SpA Zingonia, Ciserano-Zingonia, Italy; *Int'l*, pg. 867
Gan, Yian Cheng, Chief Oper. Officer--Novo Nordisk Pharma (Taiwan) Ltd., Taipei, Taiwan; *Int'l*, pg. 988
Ganci, Paul J., Pres. & Chief Oper. Officer--Central Hudson Gas & Electric Corporation, Poughkeepsie, NY; *U.S. Public*, pg. 324
Gandy, James, V.P.-Opers.--Signtech USA, Ltd., San Antonio, TX; *U.S. Private*, pg. 999
Gangwal, Rakesh, Pres. & Chief Oper. Officer--US Airways Group, Inc., Arlington, VA; *U.S. Public*, pg. 1680
Gangwal, Rakesh, Pres. & Chief Oper. Officer--US Airways, Inc., Arlington, VA; *U.S. Public*, pg. 1680
Ganter, John, Chief Oper. Officer--Allen-Edmonds Shoe Corp., Port Washington, WI; *U.S. Private*, pg. 36
Garber, C. Stedman, Jr., Pres. & Chief Oper. Officer--Santa Fe International Corporation, Dallas, TX; *Int'l*, pg. 765
Garcia, German Gonzalez, Chief Oper. Officer--Hulleras Del Norte, S.A. (HUNOSA), Asturias, Spain; *Int'l*, pg. 639
Garcia, Jose Antonio, Pres. & Chief Oper. Officer--Philippine Airlines, Inc., Manila, Philippines; *Int'l*, pg. 1050
Garcia, Jose Antonio, Chief Oper. Officer--Philippine Airlines, Inc., San Francisco, CA; *Int'l*, pg. 1051
Garcia, Jose Luis, Chief Oper. & Exec. Officer--Agropecuaria de Guissona, S. Coop. Ltda., Guisona, Spain; *Int'l*, pg. 31
Garcia, Lazaro, Chief Oper. Officer & V.P.--Pollo Tropical, Inc., Miami, FL; *U.S. Public*, pg. 1315
Gard, Russell M., Vice Chm., Pres. & Chief Oper. Officer--American Pad and Paper Company, Dallas, TX; *U.S. Public*, pg. 88
Gardner, David E., Chief Oper. Officer--Nickles Bakery of Indiana Inc., Elkhart, IN; *U.S. Private*, pg. 799
Gardner, H. McIntyre, Pres. & Chief Oper. Officer--Helen of Troy Corporation, El Paso, TX; *U.S. Public*, pg. 807
Gardner, Jay K., Chief Oper. Officer & Sr. V.P.--Fort Wayne National Corporation, Fort Wayne, IN; *U.S. Public*, pg. 673
Gardner, Lee M., Pres. & Chief Oper. Officer--MascoTech, Inc., Taylor, MI; *U.S. Public*, pg. 1055
Gardner, Terri, Pres. & Chief Exec. Officer--Soft Sheen Products, Inc., Chicago, IL; *U.S. Private*, pg. 1012
Garlock, Randy, Pres. & Chief Oper. Officer--J.I. Kislak Inc., Hialeah, FL; *U.S. Private*, pg. 624
Garnier, Jean-Pierre, Chief Oper. Officer--SmithKline Beecham plc, Brentford, United Kingdom; *Int'l*, pg. 1264
Garnier, John-Pierre, Chief Oper. Officer--SmithKline Beecham Corporation, Philadelphia, PA; *Int'l*, pg. 1264
Garofalo, Richard, Pres. & Chief Oper. Officer--Health Acquisition Corp., Jamaica, NY; *U.S. Public*, pg. 1157

Garratt, Reginald G., Pres. & Chief Exec. Officer--Knowles Electronics, Inc., Itasca, IL; *U.S. Private*, pg. 627
Garufi, Michele, Chief Oper. Officer--Recordati-Elmu S.L., Madrid, Spain; *Int'l*, pg. 1090
Garvey, Michael, Pres. & Chief Oper. Officer--Moxness Products, Inc., Racine, WI; *U.S. Public*, pg. 124
Gaskin, G. Weber, Chief Oper. Officer & Exec. V.P.--Anheuser-Busch Recycling Corporation, Saint Louis, MO; *U.S. Public*, pg. 114
Gasper, Joseph G., Pres. & Chief Oper. Officer-Life Companies--Nationwide Insurance Enterprise, Columbus, OH; *U.S. Private*, pg. 788
Gates, Robert W., Jr., Pres. & Chief Oper. Officer--Horace Small Apparel Company, Nashville, TN; *Int'l*, pg. 635
Gathman, David D., Chief Oper. Officer--Integrated Systems Consulting Group, Wayne, PA; *U.S. Public*, pg. 1425
Gathright, Richard E., Pres. & Chief Oper. Officer--TransMontaigne Oil Company, Denver, CO; *U.S. Public*, pg. 1631
Gatti, R., Pres. & Chief Oper. Officer--IG Autotrim, Inc., Chicago, IL; *Int'l*, pg. 1117
Gattis, Jerry, Pres. & Chief Oper. Officer--Cagle's Inc., Atlanta, GA; *U.S. Public*, pg. 291
Gauld, Thomas K., Chief Oper. Officer--Canadian Tire Acceptance Ltd., Welland, Canada; *Int'l*, pg. 259
Gaulin, Jean, Vice Chm., Pres. & Chief Oper. Officer--Ultramar Diamond Shamrock Corporation, San Antonio, TX; *U.S. Public*, pg. 1663
Gault, Bob, Chief Oper. Officer & Exec. V.P.--Universal Studios Japan, Ltd., Tokyo, Japan; *Int'l*, pg. 1216
Gauthier, Henry E., Chm. Bd., Pres. & Chief Oper. Officer--Coherent, Inc., Santa Clara, CA; *U.S. Public*, pg. 395
Gavin, Mark A., CPA, Chief Oper. Officer & Exec. V.P.--CFX Bank, Keene, NH; *U.S. Public*, pg. 277
Gawlak, Kathryn, Sr. V.P.-Stores--Strawberries Inc., Milford, MA; *U.S. Private*, pg. 1046
Gawlik, Mark A., Pres. & Chief Oper. Officer--Play by Play Toys & Novelties, Inc., San Antonio, TX; *U.S. Public*, pg. 1309
Gebhardt, Scott W., Chief Oper. Officer--Enron Acess, Dublin, OH; *U.S. Public*, pg. 584
Geddes, James H., Pres. & Chief Oper. Officer--Barnett International/PAREXEL, Media, PA; *U.S. Public*, pg. 1258
Gehrlein, Edward J., Pres. & Chief Oper. Officer--Bedford Associates, Inc., Norwalk, CT; *Int'l*, pg. 219
Gehrs, Jonathan, Chief Oper. Officer--Pacific Foods, Inc., Kent, WA; *U.S. Private*, pg. 831
Geiger, James, Chief Oper. Officer--The Universal Steel Co., Cleveland, OH; *U.S. Private*, pg. 256
Geiger, James, Chief Oper. Officer--Universal Steel of Pennsylvania, Conshohocken, PA; *U.S. Private*, pg. 256
Gelardi, Ronald N., Chief Oper. Officer, Mng. Dir. & Sec.--Barr Brothers & Co., Inc., New York, NY; *U.S. Private*, pg. 117
Gelbmann, Christoph, Chief Oper. Officer--Skandia Leben AG, Vienna, Austria; *Int'l*, pg. 1258
Gensior, Eckehard, Co-Chief Oper. Officer--BHF & IKB Baumanagement GmbH, Dusseldorf, Germany; *Int'l*, pg. 645
Gentner, Roland, Pres. & Chief Oper. Officer--Sodak Gaming, Inc., Rapid City, SD; *U.S. Public*, pg. 1482
George, Bill, Pres. & Chief Oper. Officer--Groendyke Transports, Inc., Enid, OK; *U.S. Private*, pg. 483
George, Mary J., Pres. & Chief Oper. Officer--Bell Sports Corp., San Jose, CA; *U.S. Public*, pg. 207
George, Michael, Chief Oper. Officer--Sunstone Hotel Investors, Inc., San Clemente, CA; *U.S. Public*, pg. 1536
Geraghty, Richard, Chief Oper. Officer--Baccarat, Inc., Edison, NJ; *Int'l*, pg. 132
Gerard, Michel, Pres. & Chief Oper Officer--Cegelec, Levallois-Perret, France; *Int'l*, pg. 52
Gerber, Sam, Chief Oper. Officer--Alpha Shirt Co., Inc., Philadelphia, PA; *U.S. Private*, pg. 45
Gerchenson, Jeffery H., Pres. & Chief Oper. Officer--Alva/Amco Pharmacal Companies, Inc., Chicago, IL; *U.S. Private*, pg. 47
Gerdin, Russell A., Chm. Bd., Pres. Chief Exec. Officer, Chief Oper. Officer & Sec.--Heartland Express, Inc., Coralville, IA; *U.S. Public*, pg. 803
Gerhardsson, Peter, Chief Oper. Officer--Novo Nordisk Pharma AB, Malmo, Sweden; *Int'l*, pg. 988
Gerlach, John B., Jr., Pres., Chief Exec. Officer, Chief Oper. Officer & Sec.--Lancaster Colony Corporation, Columbus, OH; *U.S. Public*, pg. 976
German, Gary E., Chief Oper. Officer & Sr. V.P.--TVX Gold Inc., Toronto, Canada; *Int'l*, pg. 1345
Gernow, Per, Chief Oper. Officer--Novo Nordisk A/S, Santurce, PR; *Int'l*, pg. 987
Gersh, Joe, Chief Oper. Officer--New Vision Television, Atlanta, GA; *U.S. Private*, pg. 794
Gerstein, Harvey, V.P.--Miss Elaine Inc., Saint Louis, MO; *U.S. Private*, pg. 752
Geslin, Philippe, Pres. & Chief Oper. Officer--Compagnie de Suez, Paris, France; *Int'l*, pg. 313
Gestetner, G., Chief Oper. Officer & Mng. Dir.--Aqualisa Products Limited, Westerham, United Kingdom; *Int'l*, pg. 925
Gette, Anthony R., Pres., Chief Oper. Officer & Sec.--Mentor Corporation, Santa Barbara, CA; *U.S. Public*, pg. 1086
Gettler, Benjamin, Chief Oper. Officer--Vulcan Corporation, Clarksville, TN; *U.S. Public*, pg. 1725
Gewelb, Robert, Chief Oper. Officer & Exec. V.P.--Krasdale Foods Inc., White Plains, NY; *U.S. Private*, pg. 635
Ghergo, H. Jorge, Chief Oper. Officer--DeKalb Argentina, S.A., Buenos Aires, Argentina; *U.S. Public*, pg. 493
Gibbs, Frank, Pres. & Chief Oper. Officer--Ryan Herco Products Corp., Burbank, CA; *U.S. Private*, pg. 953
Gicquiaux, Yvon, Chief Oper. Officer--Novo Nordisk Ferment AG, Esentepe, Turkey; *Int'l*, pg. 988
Giedt, Ronel W., Pres. & Chief Oper. Officer--Juno Lighting, Inc., Des Plaines, IL; *U.S. Public*, pg. 935
Gielis, Laurent, Chief Oper. Officer--KONE Belgium S.A., Awans, Belgium; *Int'l*, pg. 747
Gilbane, Thomas F., Jr., Pres. & Chief Oper. Officer--Gilbane Building Company, Providence, RI; *U.S. Private*, pg. 452
Gilbert, Barry, Vice Chm. & Chief Oper. Officer--The Sharper Image, San Francisco, CA; *U.S. Public*, pg. 1464
Gilbert, John O., Pres. & Chief Oper. Officer--Aid Association for Lutherans, Appleton, WI; *U.S. Private*, pg. 27
Gilbert, Walter F., Chm. Bd., Pres., Chief Exec. Officer & Treas.--Semco Industries Inc., Stoughton, MA; *U.S. Private*, pg. 983
Gilbertson, Jay, Pres., Co-Chief Oper. Officer, Chief Fin. Officer, Treas. & Sec.--HBOC, Atlanta, GA; *U.S. Public*, pg. 770
Gilbertson, John, Chief Oper. Officer & Exec. V.P.--AVX Corporation, Myrtle Beach, SC; *Int'l*, pg. 775
Gilchrist, David, Jr., Pres. & Chief Oper. Officer--Varco-Pruden Buildings, Memphis, TN; *U.S. Public*, pg. 1677
Gill, James P., Chief Oper. Officer, Exec. V.P., Gen. Mgr. & Dir.-Mktg.--Jackson Hole Ski Resort, Teton Village, WY; *U.S. Private*, pg. 579
Gill, Thomas, Chief Oper. Officer & Chief Fin. Officer--FORE Systems, Inc., Warrendale, PA; *U.S. Public*, pg. 667
Gillis, Robert, Chief Oper. Officer & Exec. V.P.--Elopak, Inc., New Hudson, MI; *Int'l*, pg. 1390
Gilman, Bill, Pres. & Chief Oper. Officer--McLaughlin Manufacturing Company, Greenville, SC; *U.S. Private*, pg. 724
Gilmore, Michael, Chief Oper. Officer--Ferrero U.S.A., Inc., Somerset, NJ; *Int'l*, pg. 480
Gilroy, J.A., Chief Oper. Officer--LucasVarity plc, London, United Kingdom; *Int'l*, pg. 819
Gilroy, J.A., Pres. & Chief Oper. Officer--LucasVarity Inc., Buffalo, NY; *Int'l*, pg. 820
Gingerich, John C., Pres. & Chief Oper. Officer--Honeywell-Measurex Corporation, Cupertino, CA; *U.S. Public*, pg. 833
Ginsberg, Allan, Chief Oper. Officer--Empress Handbags, West New York, NJ; *U.S. Public*, pg. 920
Ginsberg, Ruediges, Chief Oper. Officer--BHF Trust Management Gesellschaft fur Vermoegensverwaltung mbH, Frankfurt/Main, Germany; *Int'l*, pg. 119
Ginsburg, Allan, Chief Oper. Officer--JLN, West New York, NJ; *U.S. Public*, pg. 920
Giraldin, James, Chief Oper. Officer & Sr. Exec. V.P.--FirstFed Financial Corp., Santa Monica, CA; *U.S. Public*, pg. 645
Giraldin, James, Chief Oper. Officer & Sr. Exec. V.P.--First Federal Bank of California, FSB, Santa Monica, CA; *U.S.* Public, pg. 646
Girouard, Marvin, Pres. & Chief Oper. Officer--Pier 1 Imports, Inc., Fort Worth, TX; *U.S. Public*, pg. 1295
Giroux, Donald K., Chief Oper. Officer--Harley Ellington Design, Southfield, MI; *U.S. Private*, pg. 503
Glankler, Frank, III, Chief Oper. Officer & Sr. V.P.--Forecast Group, Rancho Cucamonga, CA; *U.S. Private*, pg. 418
Glass, Alan, Chief Oper. Officer--Primedia Information Inc., Hightstown, NJ; *U.S. Public*, pg. 1328
Gleber, Carol, Chief Oper. Officer--Curative Health Services, East Setauket, NY; *U.S. Public*, pg. 469
Gleim, Michael L., Vice Chm. & Chief Oper. Officer--The Bon Ton Stores, Inc., York, PA; *U.S. Public*, pg. 244
Glendenning, Mark, Chief Oper. Officer--Inland Printing Co., Inc., La Crosse, WI; *U.S. Private*, pg. 564
Glenn, David W., Pres. & Chief Oper. Officer--Federal Home Loan Mortgage Corporation, Mc Lean, VA; *U.S. Public*, pg. 615
Glore, Jodie, Pres. & Chief Oper. Officer--Reliance Electric, Cleveland, OH; *U.S. Public*, pg. 1397
Glore, Jodie K., Sr. V.P. & Pres.-Rockwell Automation--Rockwell International Corporation, Costa Mesa, CA; *U.S. Public*, pg. 1397
Glosser, Roy J., Pres. & Chief Oper. Officer--American Locker Group, Inc., Jamestown, NY; *U.S. Public*, pg. 85
Glowacki, K.M., Chief Oper. Officer--Intertape Polymer Group, Green Bay, WI; *Int'l*, pg. 685
Gnath, Ulrich, Chief Oper. Officer--Helaba International Finance plc, Dublin, Ireland; *Int'l*, pg. 799
Gnath, Ulrich, Co-Chief Oper. Officer--Helaba Dublin-Landesbank International, Dublin, Ireland; *Int'l*, pg. 799
Gochnauer, Richard, Pres. & Chief Oper. Officer--Golden State Foods, Irvine, CA; *U.S. Private*, pg. 460
Godano, Giuseppe, Chief Oper. Officer--Italia Di Navigazione S.p.A., Genoa, Italy; *Int'l*, pg. 653
Goddard, David, Dir.-Opers.--Newmond PLC, Tamworth, United Kingdom; *Int'l*, pg. 924
Godel, D., Chief Oper. Officer--Schlatter do Brasil, Sao Bernardo do Campo, Brazil; *Int'l*, pg. 1206
Godshalk, Ernie, Chief Oper. Officer & Exec. V.P.--Prodigy Inc., White Plains, NY; *U.S. Private*, pg. 888
Godwin, Jerry H., Pres. & Chief Oper. Officer--Murphy Family Farms, Rose Hill, NC; *U.S. Private*, pg. 768
Goecke, Joseph M., Pres. & Chief Oper. Officer-Valmont Irrigation--Valmont Industries, Inc., Valley, NE; *U.S. Public*, pg. 1706
Goff, Neal, Chief Oper. Officer & Sr. V.P.--R.R. Bowker, New Providence, NJ; *Int'l*, pg. 1096
Gold, Stanley P., Pres.--Shamrock Holdings, Inc., Burbank, CA; *U.S. Private*, pg. 989
Goldberg, Howard, Pres. & Chief Oper. Officer--Lillian Vernon Corporation, New Rochelle, NY; *U.S. Public*, pg. 1716
Goldberg, Norman, Chief Oper. Officer & Exec. V.P.--Fortunoff, Uniondale, NY; *U.S. Private*, pg. 420
Golden, John, Exec. V.P.--Stephen Gould Paper Co., Inc., Whippany, NJ; *U.S. Private*, pg. 467
Goldman, Benjamin D., Pres. & Chief Oper. Officer--FPA Corporation, Bensalem, PA; *U.S. Public*, pg. 608
Golsen, Barry, Pres. & Chief Oper. Officer--Climatemaster Corp., Santa Monica, CA; *U.S. Public*, pg. 970
Golteus, Hans, Pres. & Chief Oper. Officer--Norwegian Cruise Line, Miami, FL; *U.S. Private*, pg. 808
Golub, Neil M., Pres. & Chief Oper. Officer--Golub Corporation, Schenectady, NY; *U.S. Private*, pg. 463
Gomez Gonzalez, Leopoldo, Chief Oper. Officer--Transportacion Maritima Mexicana S.A. de C.V., Mexico, Mexico; *Int'l*, pg. 1418
Gomez, Jose Federico, Chief Oper. Officer--La Rural del Paraguay S.A. , Paraguaya de Seguros, Asuncion, Paraguay; *Int'l*, pg. 1392
Gongaware, Donald F., Chief Oper. Officer & Exec. V.P.--Conseco Inc., Carmel, IN; *U.S. Public*, pg. 432
Gongaware, Donald F., Chief Oper. Officer--Bankers National Life Insurance Co., Carmel, IN; *U.S. Public*, pg. 433
Gongaware, Donald F., Chief Oper. Officer--National Fidelity Life Insurance Co., Carmel, IN; *U.S. Public*, pg. 433
Gongaware, Donald F., Chief Oper. Officer--Beneficial Standard Life Insurance Company, Carmel, IN; *U.S. Public*, pg. 433
Gongaware, Donald F., Chief Oper. Officer--Great American Reserve Insurance Company, Carmel, IN; *U.S. Public*, pg. 433
Gongaware, Donlad F., Chief Oper. Officer--Lincoln American Life Insurance Co., Carmel, IN; *U.S. Public*, pg. 433
Gonzalez, Angel Portilla, Chief Oper. Officer--Controladora Comercial Mexicana, S.A. de C.V., Mexico, Mexico; *Int'l*, pg. 328
Goocher, Robert L., Exec. V.P. & Chief Oper. Officer-AGL Resources Svcs. Company--AGL Resources, Atlanta, GA; *U.S. Public*, pg. 6
Good, Richard L., Pres. & Chief Oper. Officer--NTS Development Company, Louisville, KY; *U.S. Private*, pg. 772
Goodman, Wallace C., Chief Oper. Officer--Hilb, Rogal and Hamilton Company of Corpus Christi, Corpus Christi, TX; *U.S. Public*, pg. 827
Goodrich, Clifford C., Pres. & Chief Oper. Officer--Los Angeles Turf Club, Inc., Arcadia, CA; *U.S. Public*, pg. 1081
Goodspeed, Richard E., Pres. & Chief Oper. Officer--The Vons Companies, Inc., Arcadia, CA; *U.S. Public*, pg. 1426
Gordon, Ellen R., Pres. & Chief Oper. Officer--Tootsie Roll Industries, Inc., Chicago, IL; *U.S. Public*, pg. 1621
Gordon, Jerry A., Pres. & Chief Oper. Officer--Glacier Water Services Inc., Carlsbad, CA; *U.S. Public*, pg. 745
Gordon, Jerry A., Pres. & Chief Oper. Officer--GW Services, Inc., Carlsbad, CA; *U.S. Public*, pg. 745
Gordon, Jerry A., Chief Oper. Officer--Glacier Water Services, Inc., Carlsbad, CA; *U.S. Public*, pg. 745
Gorga, Lou, Chief Oper. Officer--Universal Standard Healthcare, Inc., Southfield, MI; *U.S. Public*, pg. 1697
Gorham, David L., Deputy Chief Oper. Officer & Sr. V.P.--The New York Times Company, New York, NY; *U.S. Public*, pg. 1173
Gorman, Kirk E., Pres., Chief Oper. & Fin. Officer--Universal Health Realty Income Trust, King of Prussia, PA; *U.S. Public*, pg. 1697
Gotliev, Meyer, Pres. & Chief Oper. Officer--The Samuel Goldwyn Company, Los Angeles, CA; *U.S. Private*, pg. 463
Gottdenker, Michael I., Pres. & Chief Oper. Officer--Commonwealth Telephone Enterprises, Inc., Dallas, PA; *U.S. Public*, pg. 415
Gottesman, Charles, Chief Oper. Officer & Exec. V.P.--Hyde Athletic Industries, Inc., Peabody, MA; *U.S. Public*, pg. 851
Gottwald, Thomas E., Pres. & Chief Oper. Officer--Ethyl Corporation, Richmond, VA; *U.S. Public*, pg. 595
Gough, Thomas L., Pres. & Chief Oper. Officer--Integral Systems, Inc., Lanham, MD; *U.S. Public*, pg. 883
Goulka, James E., Chief Oper. Officer--Encyclopaedia Britannica, Inc., Chicago, IL; *U.S. Private*, pg. 375
Grabbe, John, V.P.-Opers.--Producers Rice Mill Inc., Stuttgart, AR; *U.S. Private*, pg. 888
Graber, Don R., Pres. & Chief Oper. Officer--Huffy Corporation, Miamisburg, OH; *U.S. Public*, pg. 846
Grace, Kevin, Pres. & Chief Oper. Officer--Spring Engineers of Houston Ltd., Houston, TX; *U.S. Private*, pg. 956
Gradeen, Glenn D., Pres. & Chief Oper. Officer--Ocelot Energy Inc., Calgary, Canada; *Int'l*, pg. 996
Gradinger, William, Chief Oper. Officer--Golden Star Inc., Kansas City, MO; *U.S. Private*, pg. 460
Graeser, Christopher, Chief Oper. Officer--Paul Ecke Ranch, Encinitas, CA; *U.S. Private*, pg. 359
Graf, Rudy, Pres. & Chief Oper. Officer--Centennial Cellular Corp., New Canaan, CT; *U.S. Public*, pg. 329
Grafstein, Norman, Chief Oper. Officer & V.P.--North American Enclosures, Inc., Central Islip, NY; *U.S. Private*, pg. 803
Graham, Gordon, Pres., Chief Exec. Officer & Chief Oper. Officer--Bell Industries, Inc., El Segundo, CA; *U.S. Public*, *pg. 204*
Graham, Peter, Chief Oper. Officer & Exec. V.P.--Maxxim Medical, Inc., Clearwater, FL; *U.S. Public*, pg. 1063
Graham, Robert, Chief Oper. Officer--Aim Equity Funds, Inc., Houston, TX; *Int'l*, pg. 685
Graham, Vern W., District Gen. Mgr.--Canadian Pacific Railway, Minneapolis, MN; *Int'l*, pg. 259
Grainger, Tom, Chief Oper. Officer & Chief Fin. Officer--Weyerhaeuser Mortgage Company, Woodland Hills, CA; *U.S. Public*, pg. 1764
Grajeda, Mike, Chief Oper. Officer, Chief Fin. Officer & V.P.--Origin Systems, Inc., Austin, TX; *U.S. Public*, pg. 569
Granberry, William R., Pres. & Chief Oper. Officer--Tom Brown, Inc., Midland, TX; *U.S. Public*, pg. 262
Granberry, William R., Pres. & Chief Oper. Officer--Tom Brown, Inc., Englewood, CO; *U.S. Public*, pg. 262
Grand, Andre, Pres. & Chief Oper. Officer--Servirail, Paris, France; *Int'l*, pg. 560
Grange, James, Chief Oper. Officer--Chateau Communities, Inc., Englewood, CO; *U.S. Public*, pg. 341

Granger, Alain, Chief Oper. Officer--Hospal International Marketing, Lyon, France; *Int'l*, pg. 668
Granik, Russell, Chief Oper. Officer & Deputy Commissioner--National Basketball Association, New York, NY; *U.S. Private*, pg. 780
Grant, David S., Pres. & Chief Oper. Officer--Voyager Emblems, Inc., Sanborn, NY; *U.S. Private*, pg. 1143
Grant, Douglas M., Pres. & Chief Oper. Officer--Isco, Inc., Lincoln, NE; *U.S. Public*, pg. 913
Gravenhorst, Ted, Sr., Pres. & Chief Exec. Officer--John Boos & Company, Effingham, IL; *U.S. Private*, pg. 156
Gray, Bruce, Pres. & Chief Oper. Officer--Xicor, Inc., Milpitas, CA; *U.S. Public*, pg. 1785
Gray, C. Michael, Pres. & Chief Oper. Officer--Performance Food Group Company, Richmond, VA; *U.S. Public*, pg. 1278
Gray, James E., Pres. & Chief Oper. Officer--Macy's East, New York, NY; *U.S. Public*, pg. 618
Gray, Larry D., Chief Oper. Officer--American Oncology Resources, Inc., Houston, TX; *U.S. Public*, pg. 88
Gray, Stephen, Pres. & Chief Oper. Officer--McLeodUSA Incorporated, Cedar Rapids, IA; *U.S. Public*, pg. 1073
Gray, Tracey L., Pres. & Chief Oper. Officer--Elcotel, Inc., Sarasota, FL; *U.S. Public*, pg. 568
Gray, William, Chief Oper. Officer--American International Airways, Ypsilanti, MI; *U.S. Private*, pg. 57
Grayer, Jonathan, Pres. & Chief Oper. Officer--Kaplan Educational Centers Ltd., New York, NY; *U.S. Public*, pg. 1743
Grebow, Edward, Pres. & Chief Exec. Officer--Chyron Corp., Melville, NY; *Int'l*, pg. 1372
Greco, Thomas J., Chief Oper. Officer--Greenbull Inc., Louisville, KY; *U.S. Private*, pg. 477
Green, James R., Chief Fin. & Oper. Officer & Exec. V.P.--Bearden Lumber Company, Inc., Bearden, AR; *U.S. Private*, pg. 127
Green, John, Chief Oper. Officer--Mesa Airlines Pilot Development, Inc., Farmington, NM; *U.S. Public*, pg. 1099
Green, Jonathan, Chief Oper. Officer & V.P.-Fin.--Embedded Performance, Inc., Milpitas, CA; *U.S. Private*, pg. 373
Green, Louis R., Pres. & Chief Opers. Officer--Conestoga Wood Specialties Corp., East Earl, PA; *U.S. Private*, pg. 262
Green, Mike, Pres. & Chief Oper. Officer--InPower Inc., San Francisco, CA; *Int'l*, pg. 242
Green, Richard K., Pres. & Chief Oper. Officer--Blistex, Inc., Oak Brook, IL; *U.S. Private*, pg. 149
Green, Robert K., Pres. & Chief Oper. Officer--UtiliCorp United Inc., Kansas City, MO; *U.S. Public*, pg. 1700
Green, Terry G., V.P.-Opers.--Geupel DeMars, Inc., Indianapolis, IN; *U.S. Private*, pg. 449
Greenberg, Arthur, Chief Oper. Officer--SIFCO Selective Plating, Cleveland, OH; *U.S. Public*, pg. 1471
Greenberg, Arthur, Chief Oper. Officer--SIFCO Selective Plating, Monrovia, CA; *U.S. Public*, pg. 1471
Greenberg, Evan G., Pres. & Chief Oper. Officer--American International Group, Inc., New York, NY; *U.S. Public*, pg. 83
Greenblatt, Sherwin, Pres. & Chief Oper. Officer--Bose Corporation, Framingham, MA; *U.S. Private*, pg. 160
Greene, Judye, Chief Oper. Officer--Adair Greene Advertising, Atlanta, GA; *U.S. Private*, pg. 16
Greenhill, Robert D., Pres. & Chief Oper. Officer--Texas, New Mexico & Oklahoma Coaches, Inc., Lubbock, TX; *U.S. Public*, pg. 766
Greenwood, B., Chief Oper. Officer--Mikron (Birmingham) Ltd., Birmingham, United Kingdom; *Int'l*, pg. 867
Greer, Henry H., Pres., Chief Oper. Officer & Chief Fin. Officer--SEI Investments, Oaks, PA; *U.S. Public*, pg. 1417
Greer, John, Chief Oper. Officer, Exec. V.P. & New Bus. Contact--Cohn & Wells, San Francisco, CA; *Int'l*, pg. 601
Gregory, Ron, Chief Oper. Officer--International Correspondence Schools, Inc., Scranton, PA; *U.S. Public*, pg. 783
Gregory, Ronald, Chief Oper. Officer--ICS Learning Systems, Inc., Scranton, PA; *U.S. Public*, pg. 783
Gressel, Alan, Chm. Bd., Pres., Chief Exec. Officer & Chief Oper. Officer--Research Environmental Industries, Inc., Cleveland, OH; *U.S. Private*, pg. 924
Griffith, Glen, Chief Oper. & Information Officer & Sr. V.P.--Trammell Crow Company, Dallas, TX; *U.S. Public*, pg. 1628
Grigg, Richard R., Jr., Pres. & Chief Oper. Officer--Wisconsin Energy Corporation, Milwaukee, WI; *U.S. Public*, pg. 1773
Grigg, Richard R., Jr., Pres., Chief Oper. Officer & Chief Nuclear Officer--Wisconsin Electric Power Company, Milwaukee, WI; *U.S. Public*, pg. 1773
Griggs, Stephen P., Pres. & Chief Oper. Officer--RoTech Medical Corporation, Orlando, FL; *U.S. Public*, pg. 884
Grillo, Steven G., Pres., Chief Exec. Officer & Chief Oper. Officer--General Office Environments Inc., Rochelle Park, NJ; *U.S. Private*, pg. 445
Grimaldi, Joseph M., Principal & Chief Oper. Officer--Mullen Advertising, Inc., Wenham, MA; *U.S. Private*, pg. 766
Grindstaff, Kurt, Pres. & Chief Oper. Officer--Seven-Up Bottling Co. of St. Louis, Hazelwood, MO; *U.S. Private*, pg. 142
Gring, Clayton, Sr., Chief Oper. Officer & Sr. V.P.--Fairfield Communities, Inc., Little Rock, AR; *U.S. Public*, pg. 610
Grinstead, Steve R., Pres. & Chief Oper. Officer--Fresh America Corp., Dallas, TX; *U.S. Public*, pg. 681
Grize, William, Pres. & Chief Oper. Officer--The Stop & Shop Companies, Inc., Quincy, MA; *Int'l*, pg. 750
Grob, Christian, Chief Oper. Officer--SEB Asia, Kowloon, Hong Kong; *Int'l*, pg. 568
Groeninger, Robert, Chief Oper. Officer--Strober Bros., Inc. Building Supply Centers, Brooklyn, NY; *U.S. Private*, pg. 403
Groh, James H., Pres. & Chief Oper. Officer--Nu-Kote International, Dallas, TX; *U.S. Public*, pg. 1205
Gronberg, Per, Chief Oper. Officer--Neste Kemi Danmark A/S, Horsholm, Denmark; *Int'l*, pg. 915
Gronchi, Divo, Chief Exec. & Oper. Officers--Banca Monte dei Paschi di Siena S.p.A., Siena, Italy; *Int'l*, pg. 136
Gronda, Richard, Pres. & Chief Oper. Officer--Farrell Lines Incorporated, New York, NY; *U.S. Private*, pg. 397
Groom, John, Pres. & Chief Oper. Officer--Elan Corporation Plc, Dublin, Ireland; *Int'l*, pg. 435
Groom, John, Chief Oper. Officer--Players International, Inc., Atlantic City, NJ; *U.S. Public*, pg. 1310
Grow, David R., Chief Oper. & Fin. Officer & Exec. V.P.--Daw Technologies, Inc., Salt Lake City, UT; *U.S. Public*, pg. 489
Grow, Robert J., Pres. & Chief Oper. Officer--Geneva Steel, Vineyard, UT; *U.S. Public*, pg. 729
Growney, Robert L., Pres. & Chief Oper. Officer--Motorola, Inc., Schaumburg, IL; *U.S. Public*, pg. 1136
Grunewald, Fred, Pres. & Chief Oper. Officer--The Genie Company, Alliance, OH; *U.S. Private*, pg. 823
Grunewald, Fred S., Pres. & Chief Oper. Officer--Overhead Door Corporation, Dallas, TX; *U.S. Private*, pg. 822
Gruntker, Herbert Hans, Co-Chief Oper. Officer--Helaba Trust Beratungs-und Management Gesellschaft mbH, Frankfurt/Main, Germany; *Int'l*, pg. 799
Grvez, Nikki, Chief Oper. Officer--Lee Grocery Company, Everett, WA; *U.S. Private*, pg. 657
Guevara, Mario, Chief Oper. Officer--No Sabe Fallar S.A., Mexico, Mexico; *Int'l*, pg. 1273
Guezuraga, Robert M., Chief Oper. Officer & Exec. V.P.--Physio-Control Corporation, Redmond, WA; *U.S. Public*, pg. 1294
Guggenheimer, Ron, Chief Oper. Officer--Getko Group Inc., Westbury, NY; *U.S. Public*, pg. 320
Gugliemi, Peter, Chief Oper. Officer--Tellabs International, Inc., Bolingbrook, IL; *U.S. Public*, pg. 1573
Guinasso, Vic, Pres. & Chief Oper. Officer--DHL Worldwide Express, Redwood City, CA; *U.S. Private*, pg. 301
Guinasso, Vic A., Pres. & Chief Oper. Officer--DHL Airways, Inc., Redwood City, CA; *U.S. Private*, pg. 302
Gullaksen, Bjorn, Chief Oper. Officer, Gen. Mgr. & Mng. Dir.--SAS Park Royal Hotel, Lysaker, Norway; *Int'l*, pg. 1202
Gunnoe, Larry R., Pres. & Chief Oper. Officer--Idaho Power Company, Boise, ID; *U.S. Public*, pg. 861
Guntner, Christian R., Chief Oper. Officer & Exec. V.P.-Corp. Dev.--Publicker Industries Inc., Fairfield, CT; *U.S. Public*, pg. 1341
Guryan, George, Pres. & Chief Oper. Officer--The Excellence Group, Stamford, CT; *U.S. Private*, pg. 387
Gustafson, F. Edward, Chm. Bd., Pres. & Chief Exec. Officer--Envirodyne Industries, Inc., Oak Brook, IL; *U.S. Public*, pg. 586
Gustafson, James E., Pres. & Chief Oper. Officer--General Re Corporation, Stamford, CT; *U.S. Public*, pg. 725
Gustafson, Ronald R., Pres. & Chief Oper. Officer--Coast Packing Company, Vernon, CA; *U.S. Private*, pg. 248
Gustafsson, Mats, Chief Oper. Officer--Puma North America, Brockton, MA; *Int'l*, pg. 1072
Guter, Kur, Chief Oper. Officer--Granger Companies, Lansing, MI; *U.S. Private*, pg. 469
Gutterman, Arthur, Chm. Bd., Pres., Chief Exec. & Chief Oper. Officer--Jelmar Company, Lincolnwood, IL; *U.S. Private*, pg. 585
Guy, Thomas D., Sr. V.P.-Opers.--U.S. Surgical Corp., Norwalk, CT; *U.S. Public*, pg. 1687
Guzzetti, William L., Pres. & Chief Oper. Officer--Hallwood Energy Partners, L.P., Denver, CO; *U.S. Public*, pg. 778
Haapala, Jorma, Chief Oper. Officer--Neste Resins Oy, Hamina, Finland; *Int'l*, pg. 913
Haapavaara, Mikko, Chief Oper. Officer--Neste Singapore Holdings Pte. Ltd., Singapore, Singapore; *Int'l*, pg. 915
Haas, Kelley, Chief Oper. Officer & Sr. V.P.--MRA, An Integrated Marketing Communications Agency, Overland Park, KS; *U.S. Private*, pg. 687
Hach, Bruce J., Pres. & Chief Oper. Officer--Hach Company, Loveland, CO; *U.S. Public*, pg. 773
Hackenburg, P. Richard, Pres. & Chief Oper. Officer--Willis Corroon Advanced Risk Management Services, Nashville, TN; *Int'l*, pg. 1505
Hackett, Roger B., Chm. Bd., Pres., Chief Exec. & Chief Oper. Officer--Go-Video, Inc., Scottsdale, AZ; *U.S. Public*, pg. 748
Haeck, Lew, Chief Oper. Officer--Attwood Corporation, Lowell, MI; *U.S. Private*, pg. 1038
Hafez, Hassan M., Chief Oper. Officer--The Arab-Eastern Insurance Company Limited E.C., Manama, Bahrain; *Int'l, pg. 1392*
Haffey, John, Chief Oper. Officer & Exec. V.P./Energy & Telecommunications--Montana Power Company, Butte, MT; *U.S. Public*, pg. 1126
Hagan, Bernard F., Chief Oper. Officer & Exec. V.P.--Henkels & McCoy, Inc., Blue Bell, PA; *U.S. Private*, pg. 522
Hagen, Stein Erik, Chief Oper. Officer--Hakon Gruppen AS, Oslo, Norway; *Int'l*, pg. 643
Hager, R.L., Chief Oper. Officer & V.P.--IDenticard Systems, Inc., Lancaster, PA; *U.S. Private*, pg. 557
Haggar, Thomas, Chief Oper. Officer & Exec. V.P.--Premarc Corporation, Durand, MI; *U.S. Private*, pg. 881
Hahn, David L., Chief Oper. Officer & Exec. V.P.--Ogden Aviation Services, New York, NY; *U.S. Public*, pg. 1213
Hahn, Thomas M., Pres. & Chief Oper. Officer--Garden State Paper Co., Inc., Elmwood Park, NJ; *U.S. Public*, pg. 1078
Hahnloser, H. Georg, Chief Oper. Officer--Von Roll AG, Gerlafingen, Switzerland; *Int'l*, pg. 1480
Haire, Larry, Pres. & Chief Oper. Officer--Kilgore First National Bank, Kilgore, TX; *U.S. Public*, pg. 630
Haji, Hiroshi, Chief Oper. Officer--COBE Laboratories, K.K., Tokyo, Japan; *Int'l*, pg. 667
Halamuda, Jerry, Pres. & Chief Oper. Officer--Color Spot Nursery, Inc., Pleasant Hill, CA; *U.S. Private*, pg. 254
Halenke, Torsten, Chief Oper. Officer--BHF-Bank Representative Office, Madrid, Spain; *Int'l*, pg. 120
Haley, Thomas D., Pres. & Chief Oper. Officer--Centrex Corporation, Findlay, OH; *U.S. Private*, pg. 225
Hall, A. Stewart, Jr., Pres. & Chief Oper. Officer--Hughes Supply, Inc., Orlando, FL; *U.S. Public*, pg. 846
Hall, Jerry, Chief Oper. Officer & Exec. V.P.--Robert F. Driver Co., Inc., San Diego, CA; *U.S. Private*, pg. 343
Hall, Joseph C., Chief Oper. Officer & Sr. V.P.--Food Lion, Inc., Salisbury, NC; *Int'l*, pg. 463
Hall, Kurt C., Chief Fin. Officer & Exec. V.P.--United Artists Theatre Circuits Incorporated, Englewood, CO; *U.S. Private*, pg. 1120
Hall, Scott, Chief Oper. Officer & Exec. V.P.--Kragie/Newell, Des Moines, IA; *U.S. Private*, pg. 634
Hallam, Howard, Pres. & Chief Oper. Officer--Ben E. Keith Company, Fort Worth, TX; *U.S. Private*, pg. 611
Hallgren, Kenneth, Pres. & Chief Oper. Officer--Hurd Millwork Company, Inc., Medford, WI; *U.S. Private*, pg. 1113
Halper, Steven H., Chief Oper. Officer, Exec. V.P. & Sec.--Seaman Furniture Company, Inc., Woodbury, NY; *U.S. Public*, pg. 1452
Halpin, Philip, Chief Oper. Officer--National Irish Bank Limited, Dublin, Ireland; *Int'l*, pg. 906
Halstead, William B., Chief Oper. Officer--Halstead Industries, Inc., Greensboro, NC; *U.S. Private*, pg. 496
Halverson, Duane, Chief Oper. Officer & Exec. V.P.--Land O'Lakes, Inc., Arden Hills, MN; *U.S. Private*, pg. 645
Hama, Fudeji, Chief Oper. Officer--The Tokio (New York) Corporation, New York, NY; *Int'l*, pg. 1392
Hamershock, Larry, Chief Oper. Officer--Strober Building Supply Centers, Inc., Kingston, PA; *U.S. Private*, pg. 403
Hamilton, Charles W., Pres. & Chief Oper. Officer--Aristech Chemical Corporation, Pittsburgh, PA; *Int'l*, pg. 872
Hamilton, David L., Pres. & Chief Oper. Officer--George W. Auch Co., Pontiac, MI; *U.S. Private*, pg. 98
Hamilton, Victoria, Chief Oper. Officer & Exec. V.P.--General American Investors Company, Inc., New York, NY; *U.S. Public*, pg. 706
Hamm, Willi, Chief Oper. Officer & Exec. V.P.--Industra Service Corporation, New Westminster, Canada; *Int'l*, pg. 74
Hamm, Willi, Chief Oper. Officer--Industra Inc., Seattle, WA; *Int'l*, pg. 74
Hamm, Willi, Chief Oper. Officer--Industra Inc., Portland, OR; *Int'l*, pg. 74
Hamm, Willi, Chief Oper. Officer--Industra Inc., Greenville, SC; *Int'l*, pg. 74
Hammer, Kouhaila G., Chief Oper. Officer & Exec. V.P.--Ghafari Associates, Inc., Dearborn, MI; *U.S. Private*, pg. 450
Hammond, Craig, Pres., Chief Oper. Officer & Sec.--L. Perrigo Company, Allegan, MI; *U.S. Public*, pg. 1280
Hammond, Graham, Chief Oper. Officer--MacDermid New Zealand, Ltd., Auckland, New Zealand; *U.S. Public*, pg. 1030
Hammonds, Bruce L., Sr. Vice Chm. & Chief Oper. Officer--MBNA Corporation, Wilmington, DE; *U.S. Public*, pg. 1023
Hammonds, Bruce L., Sr. Vice Chm. & Chief Oper. Officer--MBNA America Bank N.A., Wilmington, DE; *U.S. Public*, pg. 1023
Hampson, David G., Pres. & Chief Oper. Officer--Willis Corroon Corp. of New Hampshire, Rochester, NH; *Int'l*, pg. 1506
Hana, Bob, Chief Oper. Officer--River Ranch - Los Angeles, Los Angeles, CA; *Int'l*, pg. 491
Hanajima, Kyozo, Chief Oper. Officer--The Tokio Marine & Fire Insurance Company (Singapore) Pte. Limited, Singapore, Singapore; *Int'l*, pg. 1392
Hanajima, Kyozo, Chief Oper. Officer--Tokio Management Services (Asia) Pte. Ltd., Singapore, Singapore; *Int'l*, pg. 1392
Hancock, Kevin, Chief Oper. Officer & Exec. V.P.--Hancock Lumber, Inc., Casco, ME; *U.S. Private*, pg. 498
Hancock, Phil, Chief Oper. Officer--Molded Fiber Glass Co., Union City, PA; *U.S. Private*, pg. 756
Handel-Nazzetti, H., Chief Oper. Officer--Hospal Med Tech GmbH, Nuremberg, Germany; *Int'l*, pg. 668
Hanik, Peter P., Pres. & Chief Oper. Officer--Millennium Petrochemicals Inc., Cincinnati, OH; *U.S. Public*, pg. 1111
Hanlin, Russell L., Pres., Chief Exec. & Chief Oper. Officer--Sunkist Growers, Inc., Sherman Oaks, CA; *U.S. Private*, pg. 1052
Hanlon, David P., Chief Oper. Officer & Exec. V.P.--Rio Hotel & Casino Inc., Las Vegas, NV; *U.S. Public*, pg. 1390
Hanlon, Jack, Pres. & Chief Oper. Officer--Gerber Plumbing Fixtures Corporation, Chicago, IL; *U.S. Private*, pg. 449
Hanlon, Jack, Pres. & Chief Oper. Officer--Kokomo Sanitary Pottery Corp., Kokomo, IN; *U.S. Private*, pg. 449
Hanna, William W., Pres. & Chief Oper. Officer--Koch Industries, Incorporated, Wichita, KS; *U.S. Private*, pg. 628
Hannigan, Andrew J., Chief Oper. Officer & Exec. V.P.--Centex Real Estate Corp./Centex Homes, Dallas, TX; *U.S. Public*, pg. 323
Hanratty, Derry Ker West, Exec. Dir.--McKechnie PLC, Walsall, United Kingdom; *Int'l*, pg. 851
Hansen, Frank J., Chief Oper. Officer & Sr. V.P.-Opers.--IDEX Corporation, Northbrook, IL; *U.S. Public*, pg. 862
Hanson, John Nils, Pres. & Chief Oper. Officer--Harnischfeger Industries, Inc., Saint Francis, WI; *U.S. Public*, pg. 788
Hanson, Lee J., Chief Oper. Officer--Roman, Inc., Roselle, IL; *U.S. Private*, pg. 942
Hanson, Leroy, Dr., Pres. & Chief Oper. Officer--Triple F, Inc., Des Moines, IA; *U.S. Private*, pg. 1104
Hara, Daiji, Chief Oper. Officer--America Latina Companhia de Seguros, Sao Paulo, Brazil; *Int'l*, pg. 1392
Haraldson, William, Chief Oper. Officer & Exec. V.P.-Mktg.--Rosauers Supermarkets, Inc., Spokane, WA; *U.S. Private*, pg. 944

Harcourt, R.M., Chief Oper. Officer--Angus Fire Armour Corp., Angier, NC; *Int'l*, pg. 1500

Harder, Michael, Chief Oper. Officer--Jordan's Meats, Portland, ME; *U.S. Private*, pg. 599

Hardin, Tom, Pres. & Chief Oper. Officer--Hub Group, Inc., Lombard, IL; *U.S. Public*, pg. 844

Hardman, Graham, Chief Oper. Officer--Neste (UK) Ltd., London, United Kingdom; *Int'l*, pg. 915

Hardy-Magerko, Maggie, Pres. & Chief Oper. Officer--84 Lumber Company, Eighty Four, PA; *U.S. Private*, pg. 366

Hardy, Thomas G., Pres. & Chief Oper. Officer--Trans Resources, Inc., New York, NY; *U.S. Private*, pg. 1096

Hare, Ronald, Pres. & Chief Oper. Officer--Petroleum Marketers, Inc., Roanoke, VA; *U.S. Private*, pg. 859

Harjuvaava, Heikki, Chief Oper. Officer--Ahlstrom Consumer Products Ltd., Helsinki, Finland; *Int'l*, pg. 32

Harlacher, Meredith I., Pres. & Chief Oper. Officer--Conectiv, Wilmington, DE; *U.S. Public*, pg. 430

Harmel, Paul, Pres. & Chief Oper. Officer--Lifetouch, Portrait Studios, Eden Prairie, MN; *U.S. Private*, pg. 667

Harmon, David E., Chm. Bd., Pres., Chief Exec. & Chief Oper. Officer--El Camino Resources, Ltd., Woodland Hills, CA; *U.S. Private*, pg. 366

Harp, Randy, Chief Oper. Officer & Chief Fin. Officer--Pre-Paid Legal Services, Inc., Ada, OK; *U.S. Public*, pg. 1320

Harper, Edwin L., Chief Exec. Officer--SyQuest Technology, Inc., Fremont, CA; *U.S. Public*, pg. 1550

Harper, Robert Y., Pres. & Chief Oper. Officer--Hopkinsville Milling Co., Hopkinsville, KY; *U.S. Private*, pg. 538

Harra, Robert V.A., Jr., Pres., Chief Oper. Officer & Treas.--Wilmington Trust Corporation, Wilmington, DE; *U.S. Public*, pg. 1770

Harrington, Richard J., Pres., Chief Exec. & Oper. Officer--The Thomson Corporation, Stamford, CT; *U.S. Public*, pg. 1599

Harris, Gerald, Chief Oper. Officer & Exec. V.P.--Charles Komar & Sons, Inc., New York, NY; *U.S. Private*, pg. 631

Harris, John, Pres. & Chief Oper. Officer--Harris Steel Group Inc., Willowdale, Canada; *Int'l*, pg. 597

Harris, Richard, Chief Oper. Officer--Emson, Inc., Bridgeport, CT; *U.S. Private*, pg. 375

Harrison, Bob, Chief Oper. Officer--International Center for Entrepreneurial Development, Inc., Cypress, TX; *U.S. Private*, pg. 568

Harrison, E. Hunter, Pres. & Chief Exec. Officer--Illinois Central Corporation, Chicago, IL; *U.S. Public*, pg. 864

Harrison, James M., Chief Fin. Officer, Exec. V.P., Treas. & Sec.--C.R. Gibson Co., Norwalk, CT; *U.S. Public*, pg. 1168

Harrison, Richard, Pres. & Chief Oper. Officer--Parametric Technology Corporation, Waltham, MA; *U.S. Public*, pg. 1257

Harrison, Roy J., Chief Oper. Officer--Tarmac plc, Wolverhampton, United Kingdom; *Int'l*, pg. 1355

Hart, Kenneth A., Pres., Chief Oper. Officer & Sec.--First Trust and Savings Bank of Taylorville, Taylorville, IL; *U.S. Public*, pg. 644

Hart, Robert J., Chief Oper. Officer--UCAR International Inc., Danbury, CT; *U.S. Public*, pg. 1662

Hart, Tom, Pres. & Chief Oper. Officer--The Crown Group, Inc., Warren, MI; *U.S. Private*, pg. 292

Hartlage, James A., Sr. V.P.-Tech. & Opers.--Stepan Company, Northfield, IL; *U.S. Public*, pg. 1514

Hartman, Carl C., Pres., Chief Exec. Officer & Chief Oper. Officer--Trinidad/Benham Corp., Denver, CO; *U.S. Private*, pg. 1103

Harvey, David E., Chm. Bd., Pres., Chief Oper. & Chief Exec. Officer--Rome Cable Corporation, Rome, NY; *U.S. Private*, pg. 942

Harvey, David R., Ph.D., Pres. & Chief Oper. Officer--Sigma-Aldrich Corporation, Saint Louis, MO; *U.S. Public*, pg. 1471

Harwood, Brett, Pres. & Chief Oper. Officer--Square Industries, Inc., Jersey City, NJ; *U.S. Public*, pg. 326

Hasch, J. Bruce, Pres. & Chief Oper. Officer--Peoples Energy Corporation, Chicago, IL; *U.S. Public*, pg. 1274

Hasch, J. Bruce, Pres. & Chief Oper. Officer--Peoples District Energy Corporation, Chicago, IL; *U.S. Public*, pg. 1275

Hasch, J. Bruce, Pres. & Chief Oper. Officer--Peoples Energy Services Corporation, Chicago, IL; *U.S. Public*, pg. 1275

Hasch, J. Bruce, Pres. & Chief Oper. Officer--Peoples NGV Corp., Chicago, IL; *U.S. Public*, pg. 1275

Haskamp, William, Chief Oper. Officer--Faribault Woolen Mill Co., Faribault, MN; *U.S. Private*, pg. 394

Haskell, Gregory W., Pres. & Chief Oper. Officer--XL Vision Inc., Sebastian, FL; *U.S. Public*, pg. 1424

Haslam, James A., III, Chief Exec. Officer & Chief Oper. Officer--Pilot Corporation, Knoxville, TN; *U.S. Private*, pg. 865

Hassan, Ahmad Sarkawi Mohd, Chief Oper. Officer--Pempena Consult Sdn. Bhd., Kuala Lumpur, Malaysia; *Int'l*, pg. 833

Hassinger, Norman M., Jr., Chm. Bd., Pres., Chief Exec. & Chief Oper. Officer--The Hassinger Companies Hoffman Homes, Arlington Heights, IL; *U.S. Private*, pg. 510

Hasten, Michael, Pres., Chief Exec. Officer & Chief Oper. Officer--Downey Designs International, Indianapolis, IN; *U.S. Private*, pg. 342

Hastings, Barry G., Pres. & Chief Oper. Officer--Northern Trust Corporation, Chicago, IL; *U.S. Public*, pg. 1195

Hatton, Robert, Chief Oper. Officer & V.P.--IDS Life Insurance Co. of New York, Albany, NY; *U.S. Public*, pg. 73

Hatziantoniou, Michalis, Chief Oper. Officer--Novo Nordisk Hellas Ltd., Athens, Greece; *Int'l*, pg. 988

Haugsland, Jack, Chief Oper. Officer--Greyhound Lines, Inc., Dallas, TX; *U.S. Public*, pg. 765

Haugsland, Jack W., Chief Oper. Officer & Exec. V.P.--Greyhound Lines, Inc., Dallas, TX; *U.S. Public*, pg. 765

Haugsvedt, Tore, Chief Oper. Officer--BNP Finans A/S - Norway, Oslo, Norway; *Int'l*, pg. 163

Haveson, Brian, Pres. & Chief Oper. Officer--Nutri/System Inc., Horsham, PA; *U.S. Private*, pg. 859

Hawk, Robert, Pres. & Chief Exec. Officer--Hale-Halsell Company, Tulsa, OK; *U.S. Private*, pg. 494

Hawken, Doug, Chief Oper. Officer--Karsten Manufacturing Corporation, Phoenix, AZ; *U.S. Private*, pg. 608

Hawks, Lawrence F., Pres. & Chief Oper. Officer--Marketing Communications, Lenexa, KS; *U.S. Public*, pg. 794

Hawks, Robert, Chief Oper. Officer--Ark-Mart, Tulsa, OK; *U.S. Private*, pg. 494

Hawley, Michael C., Pres. & Chief Oper. Officer--The Gillette Company, Boston, MA; *U.S. Public*, pg. 743

Hawn, Gates H., Chief Oper. Officer--Pershing Division, Jersey City, NJ; *U.S. Public*, pg. 589

Hawthorne, H. Robert, Chief Oper. Officer-Pillsbury--The Pillsbury Company, Minneapolis, MN; *Int'l*, pg. 411

Hayden, J. P., III, Chm. Bd. & Chief Oper. Officer--The Midland Company, Cincinnati, OH; *U.S. Public*, pg. 1110

Hayden, J. P., III, Pres. & Chief Oper. Officer--M/G Transportation Services, Inc., Amelia, OH; *U.S. Public*, pg. 1111

Hayko, Leonard J., Chief Oper. Officer & V.P.--Elkins-Sinn, Inc.-Lederle, Saint Davids, PA; *U.S. Public*, pg. 79

Hayson, Capt. C., Chief Oper. Officer--Air UK Ltd., Stansted, United Kingdom; *Int'l*, pg. 38

Hazard, Eric, Chief Oper. Officer--Campus Point Realty Corporation, San Diego, CA; *U.S. Private*, pg. 976

Heagney, W. Dennis, Pres. & Chief Oper. Officer--Transocean Offshore, Inc., Houston, TX; *U.S. Public*, pg. 1631

Healey, J., Chief Oper. Officer--Mosler Electronic Systems Div., Wayne, NJ; *U.S. Private*, pg. 763

Heath, Jim, Chief Oper. Officer & Sr. V.P.-Construction--Gulf States, Inc., Freeport, TX; *U.S. Private*, pg. 487

Hebenstreit, J.W., V.P.-Oper.--Laclede Steel Company, Saint Louis, MO; *U.S. Public*, pg. 974

Hebert, Lawrence I., Pres. & Chief Oper. Officer--Perpetual Corporation, Washington, DC; *U.S. Private*, pg. 854

Hecht, Allen D., Pres. & Chief Oper. Officer--Health Resources International, West Hartford, CT; *U.S. Private*, *pg. 514*

Heeter, William B., Pres. & Chief Oper. Officer--The Paper Factory of Wisconsin, Inc., Appleton, WI; *U.S. Public*, pg. 742

Heflebower, Jeffrey N., Pres. & Chief Exec. Officer--The Peoples Bank of Maryland, Denton, MD; *U.S. Public*, pg. 1089

Hegarty, David J., Pres. & Chief Oper. Officer--Health and Retirement Properties Trust, Newton, MA; *U.S. Public*, pg. 801

Hegarty, Michael, Pres. & Chief Oper. Officer--The Equitable Companies Incorporated, New York, NY; *U.S. Public*, pg. 588

Heider, James B., Pres. & Chief Oper. Officer--Gilman Paper Co., Saint Marys, GA; *U.S. Private*, pg. 454

Heilbronner, Heinrich, Vice Chm., Pres. & Chief Oper. Officer--Semikron International, GmbH & Co. KG, Nuremberg, Germany; *Int'l*, pg. 1220

Heiligbrodt, L. William, Pres. & Chief Oper. Officer--Service Corporation International, Houston, TX; *U.S. Public*, pg. 1460

Heim, Richard, Chief Oper. Officer--Modern Drop Forge Co., Blue Island, IL; *U.S. Private*, pg. 754

Heimbinder, Isaac, Pres., Co.-Chief Exec. Officer & Chief Oper. Officer--U.S. Home Corporation, Houston, TX; *U.S. Public*, pg. 1682

Hein, Eric P., Chief Oper. Officer & Dir.-Risk Mngmt.--Willis Corroon Corp. of Maryland, Hunt Valley, MD; *Int'l*, pg. 1506

Heine, Wolfgang, Chief Oper. Officer & Exec. V.P.--Voith Hydro, Inc., York, PA; *Int'l*, pg. 1473

Heinen, Thomas J., Pres. & Chief Oper. Officer--Heinen's Inc., Cleveland, OH; *U.S. Private*, pg. 519

Heinz, Terry J., Pres. & Chief Oper. Officer--Huntco Inc., Town and Country, MO; *U.S. Public*, pg. 849

Heinze, Peter R., Pres. & Chief Oper. Officer--International Specialty Products, Inc., Wayne, NJ; *U.S. Public*, pg. 858

Heise, Randy, V.P.-Underwriting--Saskatchewan Government Insurance, SGI, Regina, Canada; *Int'l*, pg. 1195

Heitman, Danny, Chief Oper. Officer--National Pipe Line Co., Escanaba, MI; *U.S. Public*, pg. 1259

Heitt, James D., Pres. & Chief Oper. Officer--Met-Coil Systems Corp., Cedar Rapids, IA; *U.S. Public*, pg. 1099

Helander, Mikko, Chief Oper. Officer--Valmet Corporation Calenders, Jarvenpaa, Finland; *Int'l*, pg. 1448

Helander, Veh-Pekka, Chief Oper. Officer--Neste Yrityspalvelu Oy, Espoo, Finland; *Int'l*, pg. 913

Held, Tomas, Chief Oper. Officer--BHF-Bank Representative Office, Bogota, Colombia; *Int'l*, pg. 120

Hellberg, C.E., Chief Oper. Officer--Creative Productions, Pittsburgh, PA; *U.S. Private*, pg. 288

Hellberg, Clifford W., Chm. Bd., Pres. & Chief Exec. Officer--Creative Productions, Pittsburgh, PA; *U.S. Private*, pg. 288

Heller, Fred, Chief Oper. Officer--Anedco, Inc., Houston, TX; *U.S. Public*, pg. 1016

Heller, Jeffrey M., Pres. & Chief Oper. Officer--Electronic Data Systems Corporation, Plano, TX; *U.S. Public*, pg. 569

Hellman, Peter S., Pres. & Chief Oper. Officer--TRW Inc., Cleveland, OH; *U.S. Public*, pg. 1558

Helmen, John R., Pres., Chief Exec. Officer & Chief Oper. Officer--Photo Control Corporation, Minneapolis, MN; *U.S. Public*, pg. 1292

Helmich, Karl W., Chief Oper. Officer--Sea Containers GmbH, Hamburg, Germany; *Int'l*, pg. 1214

Helms, Roger, Pres. & Chief Oper. Officer--The Arnold Palmer Golf Company, Ooltewah, TN; *U.S. Public*, pg. 132

Hembree, H. Lawson, IV, Pres. & Chief Oper. Officer--Merchants National Bank, Fort Smith, AR; *U.S. Public*, pg. 501

Henderson, Betty M., Chief Oper. Officer--Malibu Entertainment Worldwide, Dallas, TX; *U.S. Public*, pg. 1039

Henderson, David R., Chief Oper. Officer & Exec. V.P.--EEX Corporation, Houston, TX; *U.S. Public*, pg. 542

Henderson, Kirk, Chief Oper. Officer & Mng. Dir.--Great Pacific Enterprises Inc., Vancouver, Canada; *Int'l*, pg. 557

Hendricks, Larry, Chief Oper. Officer--Rainbow Rentals, Inc., Canfield, OH; *U.S. Private*, pg. 907

Hendrickson, Boyd W., Pres. & Chief Oper. Officer--Beverly Enterprises, Inc., Fort Smith, AR; *U.S. Public*, pg. 227

Henley, A. B., III, Chief Oper. Officer--Henley Paper Company, Greensboro, NC; *U.S. Private*, pg. 522

Hennessy, Mary R., Pres. & Chief Oper. Officer--TIG Holdings, Inc., New York, NY; *U.S. Public*, pg. 1555

Hennessy, Michael W., Chief Oper. Officer--Fannie May Candy Shops, Inc., Chicago, IL; *U.S. Private*, pg. 598

Henry, Roger P., Pres. & Chief Oper. Officer--Swingster Company, Kansas City, MO; *U.S. Private*, pg. 58

Hentges, Richard J., Pres. & Chief Oper. Officer--Foley-Belsaw Company, Minneapolis, MN; *U.S. Private*, pg. 416

Herail, Jacques, Chief Fin. Officer & Chief Oper. Officer--Havas Advertising, Levallois-Perret, France; *Int'l*, pg. 600

Herb, Ike, Chief Oper. Officer & Sr. V.P.--Hickory Farms, Inc., Maumee, OH; *U.S. Private*, pg. 525

Herberg, Richard, Chief Oper. Officer & V.P.-Mktg.--Bachman's, Inc., Minneapolis, MN; *U.S. Private*, pg. 109

Herbert, Richard K., Pres. & Chief Oper. Officer--Howell Corporation, Houston, TX; *U.S. Public*, pg. 843

Herbold, Robert J., Chief Oper. Officer & Exec. V.P.--Microsoft Corporation, Redmond, WA; *U.S. Public*, pg. 1107

Herdemian, Gregory, Chief Exec. Officer & Chief Oper. Officer--Empire Diamond Corporation, New York, NY; *U.S. Private*, pg. 374

Herdrich, William J., Pres. & Chief Exec. Officer--Poly-Seal Corporation, Baltimore, MD; *U.S. Private*, pg. 875

Herger, K., Chief Oper. officer--Mikron Machine Tool Asia Pte Ltd, Singapore, Singapore; *Int'l*, pg. 867

Herma, John F., Chief Oper. Officer, Exec. V.P. & Sec.--Kohl's Corporation, Menomonee Falls, WI; *U.S. Public*, pg. 965

Hermance, Frank S., Pres & Chief Oper. Officer--AMETEK, Inc., Paoli, PA; *U.S. Public*, pg. 99

Hermelin, Paul, Deputy Chief Oper. Officer--CAP Gemini S.A., Paris, France; *Int'l*, pg. 263

Hermesdorf, J., Chief Oper. Officer--Devro-Teepak, Inc., Westchester, IL; *Int'l*, pg. 408

Herndon, James L., Pres. & Chief Oper. Officer--Centex Construction Company, Dallas, TX; *U.S. Public*, pg. 322

Herndon, Vince, Pres. & Chief Oper. Officer--Holcomb & Hoke Mfg. Company, Inc., Indianapolis, IN; *U.S. Private*, pg. 533

Herr, Eric, Pres. & Chief Oper. Officer--Autodesk, Inc., San Rafael, CA; *U.S. Public*, pg. 148

Herres, Robert T., Chm. Bd., Chief Exec. & Chief Oper. Officer--USAA (United Services Automobile Association), San Antonio, TX; *U.S. Private*, pg. 1114

Herroff, Joe, Chief Oper. Officer--International Research & Evaluation, Eagan, MN; *U.S. Private*, pg. 571

Hertog, Roger, Pres. & Chief Oper. Officer--Sanford C. Bernstein & Co., Inc., New York, NY; *U.S. Private*, pg. 137

Hertz, Doug J., Pres. & Chief Oper. Officer--United Distributors, Inc., Smyrna, GA; *U.S. Private*, pg. 1121

Hertzke, Bruce D., Pres. & Chief Oper. Officer--Winnebago Industries, Inc., Forest City, IA; *U.S. Public*, pg. 1772

Hess, J. Daniel, Pres. & Chief Oper. Officer--Takatta Inc., Auburn Hills, MI; *U.S. Private*, pg. 528

Hess, Ronald G., Pres. & Chief Oper. Officer--W-B Supply Co., Pampa, TX; *U.S. Private*, pg. 1144

Hester, Philip L., Pres. & Chief Oper. Officer--Goldwell Cosmetics (USA) Inc., Linthicum Heights, MD; *Int'l*, pg. 718

Hetrick, C.N., Pres. & Chief Oper. Officer--Maxon Corporation, Muncie, IN; *U.S. Private*, pg. 716

Hewitt, William B., Pres. & Chief Oper. Officer--The Union Corporation, Greenwich, CT; *U.S. Public*, pg. 1667

Hickcox, W. Thomas, Pres. & Chief Oper. Officer--Continental Homes Holding Corp., Scottsdale, AZ; *U.S. Public*, pg. 440

Hickey, John R., Pres. & Chief Oper. Officer--Advantage Learning Systems, Inc., Wisconsin Rapids, WI; *U.S. Public*, pg. 22

Hickey, William V., Pres. & Chief Oper. Officer--Sealed Air Corporation, Saddle Brook, NJ; *U.S. Public*, pg. 1450

Hickingbotham, Herren C., Pres. & Chief Oper. Officer--TCBY Enterprises Inc., Little Rock, AR; *U.S. Public*, pg. 1553

Hide, Kelvin, Chief Oper. Officer & Dir-Comml.--Alliance UniChem PLC, Chessington, United Kingdom; *Int'l*, pg. 57

Hiemenz, Duane, Chief Oper. Officer & Exec. V.P.-Store Opers.--Michaels Stores, Inc., Irving, TX; *U.S. Public*, pg. 1104

Higashio, Takeshi, Pres. & Chief Fin. Officer--Haseko (California) Inc., Los Angeles, CA; *Int'l*, pg. 600

Higashio, Takeshi, Chief Oper. Officer--Haseko Realty (California), Inc., Los Angeles, CA; *Int'l*, pg. 600

Higby, Lawrence M., Pres. & Chief Oper. Officer--Apria Healthcare Group Inc., Costa Mesa, CA; *U.S. Public*, pg. 125

Higgins, Walter M., Chm. Bd., Pres. & Chief Exec. Officer--Sierra Pacific Resources, Reno, NV; *U.S. Public*, pg. 1470

High, Robert, Chief Oper. Officer--Kirshenbaum, Bond & Partners, New York, NY; *U.S. Private*, pg. 624

Highton, Keith David, Chief Oper. Officer & V.P.--Diasonics Credit Corporation, Santa Clara, CA; *Int'l*, pg. 644

Hightower, Sr., Neil H., Pres. & Chief Exec. Officer--Thomaston Mills, Inc., Thomaston, GA; *U.S. Public*, pg. 1599

Hilbert, William M., Sr., Pres. & Chief Oper. Officer--PHB Tool & Die, Girard, PA; *U.S. Private*, pg. 826
Hildebrand, W.R., Pres. & Chief Oper. Officer--Fiatallis North America, Inc., Carol Stream, IL; *Int'l*, pg. 483
Hilfinger, Bill, Chief Oper. Officer & V.P.--Central Goulet Supply, Manchester, NH; *U.S. Private*, pg. 469
Hilkert, Tom, Pres. & Chief Exec. Officer--MEG, Cambridge City, IN; *U.S. Private*, pg. 686
Hill, Joan, Chief Oper. Officer & V.P.-H.R.--Jami, Inc., Shawnee Mission, KS; *U.S. Private*, pg. 581
Hill, Lloyd L., Pres. & Chief Oper. Officer--Applebee's International, Inc., Overland Park, KS; *U.S. Public*, pg. 122
Hill, Malcolm, Chief Oper. Officer--MIC Technology Corporation, North Andover, MA; *U.S. Public*, pg. 24
Hill, Robert, Chief Oper. Officer & V.P.--Capital Plumbing & Heating Supply Co. Inc., Concord, NH; *U.S. Private*, pg. 469
Hill, Ted, Chief Oper. Officer & Sr. V.P.--KTI, Inc., Guttenberg, NJ; *U.S. Public*, pg. 939
Hiller, Manfred, Chief Oper. Officer--Neste Oel GmbH, Hamburg, Germany; *Int'l*, pg. 915
Hillukkala, Jukka, Chief Oper. Officer--Raisio Group plc, Vihanti, Finland; *Int'l*, pg. 1085
Hilpert, Dale W., Pres. & Chief Oper. Officer--Woolworth Corporation, New York, NY; *U.S. Public*, pg. 1777
Hilpert, Jochen, Chief Oper. Officer--LBS Immobilien GmbH, Frankfurt/Main, Germany; *Int'l*, pg. 799
Hinckley, Greg, Chief Oper. Officer, Chief Fin. Officer & Sr. V.P.--Mentor Graphics Corporation, Wilsonville, OR; *U.S. Public*, pg. 1086
Hinckley, James, Pres. & Chief Oper. Officer--Club Resorts Holding, Inc., Dallas, TX; *U.S. Private*, pg. 247
Hines, William A., Chief Oper. Officer & V.P.--Helian Health Group, Inc., Monterey, CA; *U.S. Public*, pg. 1715
Hinnant, Darrell, Chief Oper. Officer--Radiator Specialty Company, Charlotte, NC; *U.S. Private*, pg. 906
Hirano, Sadayoshi, Chief Oper. Officer--Makita Kft., Szekesfehervar, Hungary; *Int'l*, pg. 832
Hirata, Tadashi, Pres. & Chief Oper. Officer--Kyowa Hakko Kogyo Company, Ltd., Tokyo, Japan; *Int'l*, pg. 778
Hirsh, Lisa, Chief Oper. Officer--Accurate Box Co., Inc., Paterson, NJ; *U.S. Private*, pg. 11
Hirshman, Karl J., Pres. & Chief Oper. Officer--Doron Precision Systems, Inc., Binghamton, NY; *U.S. Private*, pg. 341
Hislop, Michael J., Pres. & Chief Oper. Officer--Il Fornaio America Corporation, Corte Madera, CA; *U.S. Public*, pg. 864
Hislop, Steven J., Chief Oper. Officer & Exec. V.P.--O'Charley's Inc., Nashville, TN; *U.S. Public*, pg. 1211
Hitpas, Terence A., Pres. & Chief Oper. Officer--Union Special Corp., Huntley, IL; *Int'l*, pg. 716
Hlavacek, James C., V.P.--Minerallac Co., Addison, IL; *U.S. Private*, pg. 750
Hlavacek, James H., Chief Oper. Officer & Exec. V.P.--Amtran, Inc., Indianapolis, IN; *U.S. Public*, pg. 106
Ho, Bernard, Chief Oper. Officer--Royal Copenhagen Singapore Pte. Ltd., Singapore, Singapore; *Int'l*, pg. 1135
Hoadley, Thomas C., Chief Oper. Officer & Exec. V.P.--Lanai Co., Ltd., Lanai City, HI; *U.S. Public*, pg. 313
Hoag, Frank E., Pres. & Chief Oper. Officer--Campbell-Ewald Advertising, Warren, MI; *U.S. Public*, pg. 908
Hobbs, Michael, Chief Oper. Officer--Hubbard Scientific, Chippewa Falls, WI; *U.S. Public*, pg. 71
Hobday, Charles W., Exec. V.P. & Gen. Mgr.--Lancaster Malleable Castings Company, Lancaster, PA; *U.S. Private*, pg. 645
Hochreiter, E. Joseph, Pres. & Chief Oper. Officer--Bailey, Fischer & Porter Company, Warminster, PA; *Int'l*, pg. 449
Hockemeyer, Rex, First V.P. & Dir.-IT--First Financial Bancorp, Hamilton, OH; *U.S. Public*, pg. 632
Hockenbrocht, David W., Pres. & Chief Oper. Officer--Sparton Corporation, Jackson, MI; *U.S. Public*, pg. 1496
Hodges, Ron, Pres. & Chief Oper. Officer--Volunteer Bank, Jackson, TN; *U.S. Public*, pg. 176
Hodgins, John A., Chief Oper. Officer & Sr. V.P.--Rigel Energy Corporation, Calgary, Canada; *Int'l*, pg. 1117
Hodgins, John A., Chief Oper. Officer--Rigel Oil & Gas Ltd., Calgary, Canada; *Int'l*, pg. 1117
Hodgins, John A., Chief Oper. Officer--Rigel Petroleum, Inc., Calgary, Canada; *Int'l*, pg. 1117
Hodgins, John A., Chief Oper. Officer--Rigel Petroleum (NI) Limited, Calgary, Canada; *Int'l*, pg. 1117
Hodgins, John A., Chief Oper. Officer--Rigel Petroleum UK Limited, Calgary, Canada; *Int'l*, pg. 1117
Hodgson, Thomas R., Pres. & Chief Oper. Officer--Abbott Laboratories, Abbott Park, IL; *U.S. Public*, pg. 12
Hoeg, Thomas E., Chief Oper. Officer--Amerisure Companies, Farmington Hills, MI; *U.S. Private*, pg. 65
Hoek, Hein, Chief Oper. Officer--NCT Singapore Pte. Ltd., Singapore, Singapore; *Int'l*, pg. 914
Hoel, Pat, Chief Oper. Officer & Exec. V.P.--Baltimore Stationery Co./Total Office, Baltimore, MD; *U.S. Private*, pg. 113
Hoeven, Pvander, Chief Oper. Officer--Vonk Systems, Coevorden, Netherlands; *Int'l*, pg. 681
Hoffman, Nito, Chief Oper. Officer--Bank Leumi (Luxembourg) S.A., Senningerberg, Luxembourg; *Int'l*, pg. 150
Hoffman, Richard R., Chief Oper. Officer & Exec. V.P.--Alamco, Inc., Charleston, WV; *U.S. Public*, pg. 403
Hoffmann, Peter, Chief Oper. Officer--Rhenania Schiffahrts- und Speditions-Gesellschaft mbH, Mannheim, Germany; *Int'l*, pg. 1033
Hofman, George W., Pres. & Chief Oper. Officer--Teleflex Automotive, Troy, MI; *U.S. Public*, pg. 1569
Hogan, John Anthony, Chief Oper. Officer--LASMO plc, London, United Kingdom; *Int'l*, pg. 803
Hogan, Paul, Chief Oper. Officer--Overseas Service Corporation, West Palm Beach, FL; *U.S. Private*, pg. 823
Hogan, William, Chief Oper. Officer--Nippon Silica Glass Europe Ltd., Stanley, United Kingdom; *Int'l*, pg. 1408
Hogarty, Charles J., Pres. & Chief Oper. Officer--Keystone Automotive Industries, Inc., Pomona, CA; *U.S. Public*, pg. 955
Hogenkamp, Timothy R., Pres. & Chief Oper. Officer--The Loewen Group, Inc., Burnaby, Canada; *Int'l*, pg. 814
Holaday, G.S., Chief Oper. Officer--Kauai Commercial Company, Inc., Puhi, HI; *U.S. Public*, pg. 39
Holahan, John M., Pres. & Chief Oper. Officer--Travel Ports of America Inc., Rochester, NY; *U.S. Public*, pg. 1632
Holbrook, Dick R., Pres. & Chief Oper. Officer--AFC Enterprises, Atlanta, GA; *U.S. Private*, pg. 5
Holcomb, Dennis, V.P. & Cashier--Valley Bank & Trust, Brighton, CO; *U.S. Private*, pg. 1132
Holcomb, Helen E., Chief Oper. Officer & First V.P.--Federal Reserve Bank of Dallas, Dallas, TX; *U.S. Private*, pg. 399
Holcombe, Hubert, Jr., Chief Oper. Officer & Exec. V.P.--Arrowhead Mills, Inc., Hereford, TX; *U.S. Private*, pg. 86
Holiday, Harry, Chief Oper. Officer--Owosso Corporation, King of Prussia, PA; *U.S. Public*, pg. 1238
Hollands, P.F.B., Chief Oper. Officer & Exec. V.P.--A&W Food Services of Canada Inc., North Vancouver, Canada; *Int'l*, pg. 1
Hollerscmid, Manfred, Chief Oper. Officer--Hospal Medizintechnische Produkte Ges.m.b.H, Vienna, Austria; *Int'l*, pg. 668
Holliger, Fredric L., Chief Oper. Officer & Exec. V.P.--Giant Industries Inc., Scottsdale, AZ; *U.S. Public*, pg. 741
Hollinger, Frederic L., Chief Oper. Officer & Exec. V.P.--Giant Industries Arizona, Inc., Scottsdale, AZ; *U.S. Public*, pg. 742
Holman, W.H., Jr., Chm. Bd., Chief Exec. & Oper. Officers--Jitney-Jungle Stores of America, Inc., Jackson, MS; *U.S.* Private, pg. 588
Holman, W.H., Jr., Chm. Bd., Chief Exec. & Chief Oper. Officer--Southern Jitney-Jungle, Inc., Jackson, MS; *U.S. Private*, pg. 588
Holman, W.H., Jr., Chm. Bd., Chief Exec. & Chief Oper. Officer--Jitney-Jungle Bakery, Inc., Jackson, MS; *U.S. Private*, pg. 588
Holsten, Joseph M., Chief Oper. Officer & Exec. V.P.--Waste Management, Inc., Oak Brook, IL; *U.S. Public*, pg. 1744
Holt, John A., Chief Oper. Officer--Holt Hosiery Mills, Inc., Burlington, NC; *U.S. Private*, pg. 536
Holthaus, Gerard E., Pres. & Chief Oper. Officer--Scotsman Holding Inc., Baltimore, MD; *U.S. Private*, pg. 976
Holthaus, Gerard E., Pres. & Chief Oper. Officer--Williams Scotsman, Inc., Baltimore, MD; *U.S. Private*, pg. 976
Holthaus, J.C.C., Chief Oper. Officer--Lips B.V., Drunen, Netherlands; *Int'l*, pg. 812
Holtzman, Seymour, Pres. & Chief Exec. Officer--Jewelcor Companies, Wilkes-Barre, PA; *U.S. Private*, pg. 587
Holzleithner, Klaus, Chief Oper. Officer--Agrolinz Melamin GmbH, Lienz, Austria; *Int'l*, pg. 356
Hondros, Paul J., Pres. & Chief Oper. Officer--Pilgram Baxter & Associates, Wayne, PA; *U.S. Public*, pg. 1673
Honeycutt, Marion A., Chief Oper. Officer& V.P.--Willis Corroon Corp. of South Carolina, Greenville, SC; *Int'l*, pg. 1507
Honeycutt, Robert, Chief Oper. Officer--Barra, Inc., Berkeley, CA; *U.S. Public*, pg. 191
Hong, Chng Hwee, Chief Oper. Officer--Haw Par Brothers International Limited, Singapore, Singapore; *Int'l*, pg. 603
Honse, Robert, Exec. V.P. & Chief Oper. Officer-Agriculture Input Bus.--Farmland Industries, Inc., Kansas City, MO; *U.S. Private*, pg. 395
Hoogenkamp, Derk A.J., Chief Oper. Officer--Hufvudstaden Nederland B.V., Amsterdam, Netherlands; *Int'l*, pg. 478
Hoogstraate, Walter, Chief Oper. Officer--Monterey Management B.V., Rotterdam, Netherlands; *Int'l*, pg. 162
Hopkins, Jerry W., Pres. & Chief Oper. Officer--Texas Refinery Corp., Fort Worth, TX; *U.S. Private*, pg. 1078
Hord, Noel, Pres. & Chief Oper. Officer--Nine West Group, Inc., Stamford, CT; *U.S. Public*, pg. 1185
Horii, H., Chief Oper. Officer--Miyata Industry Co., Ltd., Chigasaki, Japan; *Int'l*, pg. 884
Horiko, Yoshikazu, Chief Oper. Officer--Tosoh America, Inc., Atlanta, GA; *Int'l*, pg. 1407
Horiko, Yoshikazu, Chief Oper. Officer--Tosoh USA, Inc., Atlanta, GA; *Int'l*, pg. 1408
Horlacher, Werner, Chief Oper. Officer--Verin S.A., Berneck, Switzerland; *Int'l*, pg. 1322
Hornberger, Glenn, Pres. & Chief Oper. Officer--Mohawk Finishing Products, Inc., Amsterdam, NY; *U.S. Public*, pg. 1357
Horne, Jim, Pres. & Chief Oper. Officer--Ohmite Manufacturing Company, Skokie, IL; *U.S. Private*, pg. 813
Horne, William, Chief Oper. Officer--Einson Freeman Inc., Paramus, NJ; *Int'l*, pg. 1483
Horowitz, Edward D., Chief Oper. Officer--Citicorp, New York, NY; *U.S. Public*, pg. 376
Horsman, Raymond, Chief Oper. Officer & Exec. V.P.--MPS Corporation, Pittsburgh, PA; *U.S. Private*, pg. 687
Horstmann, Peter, Head-Trading & Intl. Network--Bank Brussels Lambert, Brussels, Belgium; *Int'l*, pg. 146
Horstmeyer, John, Pres. & Chief Oper. Officer--Independent Metals, Germantown, WI; *U.S. Private*, pg. 559
Horton, Adelaide, Pres. & Chief Oper. Officer--BDDP North America, Inc., New York, NY; *Int'l*, pg. 117
Horton, Donald R., Chm. Bd., Pres., Chief Exec. Officer & Chief Oper. Officer--D.R. Horton, Inc., Arlington, TX; *U.S.* Public, pg. 840
Horton, John, Chief Oper. Officer & V.P.--Heath Company, Benton Harbor, MI; *Int'l*, pg. 317
Hoshino, Hiroaki, Chief Oper. & Fin. Officer--Kajima U.S.A., Inc., New York, NY; *Int'l*, pg. 722
Houle, David C., Pres. & Chief Oper. Officer--IEA, Inc., Research Triangle Park, NC; *U.S. Public*, pg. 126
House, Don M., Pres. & Chief Oper. Officer--Venturian Corp., Hopkins, MN; *U.S. Public*, pg. 1716
Houston, William K., Chief Oper. Officer & Chief Fin. Officer--Georgia Tent & Awning Inc., Atlanta, GA; *U.S. Private*, pg. 448
Hovind, Knut, Chief Oper. Officer--KONE A/S, Oslo, Norway; *Int'l*, pg. 747
Hoving, Jan-Willem, Chief Oper. Officer--KONE Starlift B.V., Leidschendam, Netherlands; *Int'l*, pg. 748
Howard, Richard, Chief Oper. Officer--Tristar Corp., San Antonio, TX; *U.S. Public*, pg. 1640
Howard, William J., Chief Oper. Officer--Ultra Pac, Inc., Rogers, MN; *U.S. Public*, pg. 1662
Howell, William, Pres. & Chief Oper. Officer--Howell Instruments Inc., Fort Worth, TX; *U.S. Private*, pg. 543
Hower, Paul, Exec. V.P.-Opers.--Prime Hospitality Corp., Fairfield, NJ; *U.S. Public*, pg. 1326
Howlett, Brian, Chief Oper. Officer--COBE Laboratories Ltd., Gloucester, United Kingdom; *Int'l*, pg. 667
Hoyt, Carol A., V.P.-Opers.--Advance Packaging Corporation, Grand Rapids, MI; *U.S. Private*, pg. 18
Hoyt, Everette E., Pres. & Chief Oper. Officer--Black Hills Corporation, Rapid City, SD; *U.S. Public*, pg. 235
Hubbell, Richard A., Pres. & Chief Oper. Officer--RPC Incorporated, Atlanta, GA; *U.S. Public*, pg. 1356
Huber, Hans W., Chief Oper. Officer-Europe--Donnelly Corporation, Holland, MI; *U.S. Public*, pg. 519
Huber, John, Pres. & Chief Oper. Officer--Wynn's International, Inc., Orange, CA; *U.S. Public*, pg. 1782
Huber, K., Chief Oper. Officer--SAIA-Burgess Ges.mbH, Salzburg, Austria; *Int'l*, pg. 1501
Huberfield, David, Pres. & Chief Oper. Officer--Hunt Valve, Salem, OH; *U.S. Private*, pg. 549
Hubermeier, Juergen, Pres. & Chief Oper. Officer--Hexcel Corporation, Pleasanton, CA; *U.S. Public*, pg. 824
Hubner, C.E., Jr., Pres. & Chief Oper. Officer--Central/Shippee, Inc., Bloomingdale, NJ; *U.S. Private*, pg. 224
Huckvale, Robert W., Chief Fin. Officer--Landa, Inc., Portland, OR; *U.S. Private*, pg. 646
Hudgens, Jeri, Chief Oper. Officer & V.P.--Family Healthcare Services, Inc., Las Vegas, NV; *U.S. Public*, pg. 1469
Huffman, Neil, Pres. & Chief Oper. Officer--Neil Huffman Nissan Inc., Louisville, KY; *U.S. Private*, pg. 546
Hughes, G. Wilson, Exec. V.P. & Gen. Mgr.--General Communication, Inc., Anchorage, AK; *U.S. Public*, pg. 708
Hughes, Thomas, Chief Oper. Officer--V-Band Corporation, Elmsford, NY; *U.S. Public*, pg. 1701
Humenansky, Paul L., Chief Oper. Officer & Exec. V.P.--Platinum Technology, Inc., Oak Brook Terrace, IL; *U.S. Public*, pg. 1309
Humke, Ramon L., Pres. & Chief Oper. Officer--Indianapolis Power & Light Company, Indianapolis, IN; *U.S. Public*, pg. 913
Humphreys, Bob, Chief Oper. Officer--Stevcoknit Fabrics Company, Greer, SC; *U.S. Public*, pg. 498
Hunkin, J.S., Pres. & Chief Oper. officer--The CIBC Wood Gundy Corporation, Toronto, Canada; *Int'l*, pg. 256
Hunt, C.H., Chief Oper. Officer & Sr. V.P.- Co. Mngd. Htls. U S.--Holiday Inn Worldwide, Atlanta, GA; *Int'l*, pg. 170
Hunt, Robert C., Chm. Bd. & Chief Exec. Officer--The Hunt Corporation, Indianapolis, IN; *U.S. Private*, pg. 548
Hunt, Robert L., II, Pres. & Chief Oper. Officer--Coast Savings Financial, Inc., Los Angeles, CA; *U.S. Public*, pg. 388
Hunt, Ronald, V.P. & Chief Oper. Officer--Nationwide HMO, Inc., Columbus, OH; *U.S. Private*, pg. 789
Hunt, V. William, Pres. & Chief Oper. Officer--Arvin Industries, Inc., Columbus, IN; *U.S. Public*, pg. 136
Hunte, Henry F., Pres. & Chief Oper. Officer--Pre-Mix Concrete Co., San Diego, CA; *U.S. Private*, pg. 400
Hunter, John C., III, Pres. & Chief Oper. Officer--Solutia Inc., Saint Louis, MO; *U.S. Public*, pg. 1483
Hunter, R. Alan, Pres. & Chief Oper. Officer--The Stanley Works, New Britain, CT; *U.S. Public*, pg. 1508
Huntsman, Peter, Pres. & Chief Oper. Officer--Huntsman Corporation, Salt Lake City, UT; *U.S. Private*, pg. 549
Huntsman, Peter R., Pres. & Chief Oper. Officer--Huntsman Corporation, Salt Lake City, UT; *U.S. Private*, pg. 549
Hurst, Mike D., Pres. & Chief Oper. Officer--McCarthy Building Companies, Saint Louis, MO; *U.S. Private*, pg. 719
Hurt, Michael L., Pres. & Chief Oper. Officer--TB Wood's Corporation, Chambersburg, PA; *U.S. Public*, pg. 1562
Hurt, Randy, Chief Oper. Officer--Chemrock Corporation, Nashville, TN; *U.S. Private*, pg. 903
Hurt, Randy, Chief Oper. Officer--Chemrock Corporation, Lafayette, IN; *U.S. Private*, pg. 903
Hurt, Randy, Chief Oper. Officer--Chemrock Corporation, Thomaston, ME; *U.S. Private*, pg. 903
Huse, Mike, Chief Oper. Officer & Sr. V.P.--Quality Food Centers, Inc., Bellevue, WA; *U.S. Public*, pg. 1349
Huseman, Kenneth V., Chief Oper. Officer & Exec. V.P.--Key Energy Group Inc., East Brunswick, NJ; *U.S. Public*, pg. 953
Hussey, Timothy B., Pres. & Chief Exec. Officer--Hussey Corporation, North Berwick, ME; *U.S. Private*, pg. 550
Hutchens, Thomas D., Pres. & Chief Oper. Officer--JC Penney Company, Inc., Plano, TX; *U.S. Public*, pg. 916
Hutchins, P., Chief Oper. Officer--Chloride Power Electronics Inc., Burgaw, NC; *Int'l*, pg. 287
Huumonen, Jouka, Chief Oper. Officer--Neste Oy, Porvoo Refinery, Porvoo, Finland; *Int'l*, pg. 914
Hyatt, Donald, Exec. V.P.--Lifetime Doors Inc., Farmington, MI; *U.S. Private*, pg. 666
Hyde, W.R., Sr. Gen. Mgr.-Opers.--Standard Bank Investment Corporation Limited, Johannesburg, South Africa; *Int'l*, pg. 1293
Hyler, James B., Jr., Vice Chm. & Chief Oper. Officer--First Citizens Bank Shares, Inc., Raleigh, NC; *U.S. Public*, pg. 628
Hylland, R.R., Pres. & Chief Oper. Officer--Northwestern Growth Corp., Sioux Falls, SD; *U.S. Public*, pg. 1201
Ibarguen, Anthony A., Pres. & Chief Oper. Officer--Tech Data Corporation, Clearwater, FL; *U.S. Public*, pg. 1562

Ide, Joichi, Chief Oper. Officer--Red Robin International Inc., Irvine, CA; *Int'l*, pg. 1262

Idei, Nobuyuki, Pres. & Chief Oper. Officer--Sony Corporation, Tokyo, Japan; *Int'l*, pg. 1280

Iger, Robert A., Pres. & Chief Oper. Officer--ABC, Inc, New York, NY; *U.S. Public*, pg. 511

Iglesias, Leopoldo, Chief Oper. Officer--Binter Canarias, Las Palmas, Spain; *Int'l*, pg. 574

Ihamuotila, Jaako, Chief Oper. Officer--Neste Oy International Trading & Supply, Espoo, Finland; *Int'l*, pg. 913

Illig, Clifford W., Pres. & Chief Oper. Officer--Cerner Corporation, Kansas City, MO; *U.S. Public*, pg. 331

Imhoff, Herbert F., Jr., Pres., Chief Oper. Officer & Gen. Counsel--General Employment Enterprises, Inc., Oak Brook Terrace, IL; *U.S. Public*, pg. 714

Imperiale, Mark F., Pres., Chief Oper. Officer & Chief Fin. Officer--Data Broadcasting Corporation, Jackson, WY; *U.S. Public*, pg. 484

Imura, Hideaki, Chief Oper. Officer--Nishimatsu Construction Co., Ltd.-London Office, London, United Kingdom; *Int'l*, pg. 943

Inaba, Hirotsugu, Exec. Mng. Dir.--Nippo Corporation, Tokyo, Japan; *Int'l*, pg. 932

Ingman, Tom, Pres. & Chief Oper. Officer--Condor D.C. Power Supplies Inc., Oxnard, CA; *U.S. Public*, pg. 1419

Ingrassia, Paul, V.P., Exec. Editor & Chief Oper. Officer-Dow Jones News Services--Dow Jones & Company, Inc., New York, NY; *U.S. Public*, pg. 524

Ingrassia, Paul, Exec. Editor, V.P. & Chief Oper. Officer-News Services--AP-Dow Jones News Service, New York, NY; *U.S. Public*, pg. 524

Ingrassia, Paul, Exec. Editor, V.P. & Chief Oper. Officer-New Services--Dow Jones Financial News Services, Princeton, NJ; *U.S. Public*, pg. 524

Innella, Jim, Chief Oper. Officer--Aviation Sales Company, Miami, FL; *U.S. Public*, pg. 154

Inoue, Seijiro, Pres.--Toto Industries (Atlanta), Inc., Atlanta, GA; *Int'l*, pg. 1410

Iribe, P. Chrisman, Chief Oper. Officer & Exec. V.P.--U.S. Generating Company, Bethesda, MD; *U.S. Public*, pg. 1241

Irick, John E., Exec. V.P.--McBride and Associates, Inc., Albuquerque, NM; *U.S. Private*, pg. 719

Irisa, Junji, Chief Oper. Officer--Suita Institute, Osaka, Japan; *Int'l*, pg. 1019

Irish, Charles A., Sr. Exec. V.P.--The Whiting-Turner Contracting Co., Baltimore, MD; *U.S. Private*, pg. 1174

Irvine, George A., Pres. & Chief Oper. Officer--Airtite Contractors Inc., Chicago, IL; *U.S. Private*, pg. 29

Irvine, Richard H., Pres. & Chief Oper. Officer--Mikohn Gaming Corporation, Las Vegas, NV; *U.S. Public*, pg. 1111

Irwin, Phillip D., Chief Oper. Officer & Exec. V.P.--Ranger Oil Limited, Calgary, Canada; *Int'l*, pg. 1086

Irwin, Will, Pres. & Chief Oper. Officer--Labelon Corporation, Canandaigua, NY; *U.S. Private*, pg. 641

Isaacs, Robert C., Pres. & Chief Oper. Officer--CPAC, Inc., Leicester, NY; *U.S. Public*, pg. 282

Isaacs, Robert C., Chief Oper. Officer--The Fuller Brush Company, Great Bend, KS; *U.S. Public*, pg. 282

Isbell, A.B., Pres. & Chief Oper. Officer--Outdoor Communications, Inc., Corinth, MS; *U.S. Private*, pg. 822

Isemoto, Leslie, Pres. & Treas.--Isemoto Contracting Co. Ltd., Hilo, HI; *U.S. Private*, pg. 575

Isham, Lance, Pres. & Chief Oper. Officer--Polo/Ralph Lauren Corporation, New York, NY; *U.S. Private*, pg. 874

Ishii, Kikwichiro, Pres. & Chief Oper. Officer--Mikimoto (America) Co. Ltd., New York, NY; *Int'l*, pg. 866

Ishimaru, Yuichi, Chief Oper. Officer & Exec. V.P.--Marubeni America Corporation, New York, NY; *Int'l*, pg. 844

Isomura, Nobuaki, Chief Oper. Officer--Zimbabwe Project Office, Harare, Zimbabwe; *Int'l*, pg. 943

Israel, Robert L., Pres. & Chief Oper. Officer--Empire National Bank, Traverse City, MI; *U.S. Private*, pg. 374

Issler, James E., Pres. & Chief Oper. Officer--H.H. Brown Shoe Company, Inc., Greenwich, CT; *U.S. Public*, pg. 217

Itameri, Harry, Chief Oper. Officer--Novo Nordisk A/S, Moscow, Russia; *Int'l*, pg. 987

Itin, Thomas W., Chief Oper. Officer--Ajay Leisure Products, Inc., Delavan, WI; *U.S. Public*, pg. 34

Itoh, Yasutaka, Chief Oper. Officer--Bamiyan Co., Ltd., Tokyo, Japan; *Int'l*, pg. 1262

Iwama, Youichiro, Chief Oper. Officer--Tokio Marine Asset Management New York Co., Ltd., New York, NY; *Int'l*, pg. 1392

Iwasa, Yoshito, Sr. Mng. Dir--Sakata Seed Corporation, Yokohama, Japan; *Int'l*, pg. 1178

Jacamon, Jean-Paul, Vice Chm. & Chief Oper. Officer-Schneider Electric--Schneider S.A., Boulogne-Billancourt, France; *Int'l*, pg. 1207

Jacamon, Jean-Paul, Chief Oper. Officer--Schneider Electric S.A., Boulogne-Billancourt, France; *Int'l*, pg. 1207

Jackson, Marcus, Chief Oper. Officer & Exec. V.P.--Kansas City Power & Light Company, Kansas City, MO; *U.S. Public*, pg. 943

Jackson, Mary Anne, Chm. Bd., Pres., Chief Oper. & Chief Exec. Officer--My Own Meals, Inc., Deerfield, IL; *U.S. Private*, pg. 770

Jackson, Stanley H., Chief Oper. Officer & Sr. V.P.-Indus. Div.--Diversco, Inc., Spartanburg, SC; *U.S. Private*, pg. 336

Jackson, Wayne, Chief Oper. Officer--G.I. Joe's Inc., Wilsonville, OR; *U.S. Private*, pg. 435

Jacobellis, Luke, Chief Oper. Officer & V.P.--John Paul Mitchell Systems, Santa Clarita, CA; *U.S. Private*, pg. 753

Jacobs, Herman, Pres. & Chief Oper. Officer--Allou Health & Beauty Care, Inc., Brentwood, NY; *U.S. Public*, pg. 55

Jacobs, Jeffrey D., Pres. & Chief Oper. Officer--Harpo Entertainment Group, Chicago, IL; *U.S. Private*, pg. 504

Jacobs, P. Anthony, CFA, Pres. & Chief Oper. Officer--Seafield Capital Corporation, Kansas City, MO; *U.S. Public*, pg. 1449

Jacobsen, Earl D., Pres. & Chief Oper. Officer--Central Data Corporation, Champaign, IL; *U.S. Private*, pg. 223

Jacot, H. Dean, Exec. V.P. & Chief Oper. Officer--Bellaire Corporation, Dallas, TX; *U.S. Public*, pg. 1149

Jaeggi, Anton, Chief Oper. Officer--BHF-Bank Representative Office, Zurich, Switzerland; *Int'l*, pg. 120

Jager, Durk I., Pres. & Chief Oper. Officer--The Procter & Gamble Company, Cincinnati, OH; *U.S. Public*, pg. 1330

Jakowsky, Richard H., Pres., Chief Exec. Officer & Chief Oper. Officer--Anderson Electric, Inc., Springfield, IL; *U.S. Private*, pg. 72

Jaksa, E.A. Al, Jr., Chief Oper. Officer & Exec. V.P.--Landry's Seafood Restaurants Inc., Houston, TX; *U.S. Public*, pg. 977

Jamaluddin, Zaiton, Chief Oper. Officer--Novo Nordisk A/S, Petaling Jaya, Malaysia; *Int'l*, pg. 988

James, Kenneth T., Chief Oper. Officer & Exec. V.P.--Rauland-Borg Corporation, Skokie, IL; *U.S. Private*, pg. 911

Jamsen, Lauri, Chief Oper. Officer--Raision Lateksi Oy, Kaipiainen, Finland; *Int'l*, pg. 1085

Janikies, William N., Chief Oper. Officer--Jan-Co., Inc., Cranston, RI; *U.S. Private*, pg. 581

Janke, Robert F., Chief Oper. Officer--TosoHaas Company, Montgomeryville, PA; *U.S. Public*, pg. 1403

Janke, Robert F., Chief Oper. Officer--TosoHaas Company, Montgomeryville, PA; *Int'l*, pg. 1408

Janke, Robert F., Chief Oper. Officer--TosoHaas GmbH, Stuttgart, Germany; *Int'l*, pg. 1408

Jankovic, Paul, Pres., Chief Exec. & Chief Oper. Officer--GHM Industries, Inc., Worcester, MA; *U.S. Private*, pg. 435

Jannes, Zantero, Chief Oper. Officer--Gasum Oy, Espoo, Finland; *Int'l*, pg. 913

Janning, James C., Pres. & Chief Oper. Officer--Harbour Group Ltd., Saint Louis, MO; *U.S. Private*, pg. 500

Janssen, H. J., Chief Oper. Officer--Ferrosan Benelux B.V., Barneveld, Netherlands; *Int'l*, pg. 989

Janssen, Kent, Chief Oper. Officer & V.P.--Dakota Gasification Co., Bismarck, ND; *U.S. Private*, pg. 121

Janzen, George, Dr., Pres. & Chief Oper. Officer--Mineral San Sebastian S.A., San Salvador, El Salvador; *U.S. Public*, pg. 410

Jarchow, Jerry, Chief Oper. Officer & V.P.-Sls.--Kellermeyer Co., Toledo, OH; *U.S. Private*, pg. 612

Jarvinen, Tapio, Chief Oper. Officer--Latvian Traffic Service, Riga, Latvia; *Int'l*, pg. 914

Jarvinen, Teemu, Chief Oper. Officer--Melia Ltd., Raisio, Finland; *Int'l*, pg. 1085

Jarvis, J. Andrew, Pres. & Chief Oper. Officer--Ewing Cole Cherry Brott, Philadelphia, PA; *U.S. Private*, pg. 387

Jarvis, Ron, Pres. & Chief Oper. Officer--Technicolor, Inc., North Hollywood, CA; *Int'l*, pg. 272

Jaworski, Walter J., Chm. Bd., Chief Exec. Officer & Chief Oper. Officer--Miken Companies, Inc., Cheektowaga, NY; *U.S. Private*, pg. 745

Jean, Raymond A., Pres. & Chief Oper. Officer--Varlen Corporation, Naperville, IL; *U.S. Public*, pg. 1710

Jeffrey, S. Roy, Chief Oper. Officer--Westower Corporation, Vancouver, WA; *U.S. Public*, pg. 1762

Jeffs, Thomas H. II, Pres. & Chief Oper. Officer--NBD Bank (Michigan), Troy, MI; *U.S. Public*, pg. 628

Jelinek, W. Craig, Chief Oper. Officer & Exec. V.P.-N. Div.--Costco Wholesale, Issaquah, WA; *U.S. Public*, pg. 451

Jenkins, Joseph, M.D., Pres. & Chief Exec. Officer--Prime Medical Services, Inc., Austin, TX; *U.S. Public*, pg. 1327

Jenner, C.R., Pres. & Chief Oper. Officer--A.Y. McDonald Supply Co. Inc., Dubuque, IA; *U.S. Private*, pg. 721

Jennings, L. D., Chief Oper. Officer--Macmillan Distribution Ltd., Basingstoke, United Kingdom; *Int'l*, pg. 1479

Jensen, Bill, Chief Oper. Officer-Breckenridge--Vail Resorts, Inc., Vail, CO; *U.S. Public*, pg. 1704

Jensen, Dieter, Exec. V.P.-Prod.--Koenig & Bauer-Albert AG, Wurzburg, Germany; *Int'l*, pg. 742

Jensen, Henrik, Chief Oper. Officer--Novo Nordisk A/S, Levent, Turkey; *Int'l*, pg. 989

Jensen, John, Chief Oper. Officer & V.P.--Ringling Bros., Barnum & Bailey Combined Shows, Inc., Vienna, VA; *U.S. Private*, pg. 400

Jensen, Jorgen Mata, Chief Oper. Officer--Neste Thermisol A/S, Hedensted, Denmark; *Int'l*, pg. 915

Jensen, Robert K., Pres.--Fleischli Oil Company, Inc., Cheyenne, WY; *U.S. Private*, pg. 410

Jerney, Adam, Pres. & Chief Oper. Officer--ICN Pharmaceuticals, Inc., Costa Mesa, CA; *U.S. Public*, pg. 853

Jewett, Harvey, Chief Oper. Officer--Super 8 Motels, Inc., Aberdeen, SD; *U.S. Public*, pg. 322

Jezuit, Leslie J., Pres. & Chief Oper. Officer--Quixote Corporation, Chicago, IL; *U.S. Public*, pg. 1353

Jicinsky, Gerhard, Chief Oper. Officer--Novo Nordisk A/S, Vienna, Austria; *Int'l*, pg. 989

Jilek, John P., Pres. & Chief Oper. Officer--Lawter International, Inc., Kenosha, WI; *U.S. Public*, pg. 980

Joffe, Seymour, Pres. & Chief Oper. Officer--Porta Systems Corp., Syosset, NY; *U.S. Public*, pg. 1317

Johansson, Stig, Chief Oper. Officer--TA Control Oy, Vantaa, Finland; *Int'l*, pg. 670

Johns, John D., Pres. & Chief Oper. Officer--Protective Life Corporation, Birmingham, AL; *U.S. Public*, pg. 1336

Johnsen, Bent M., Chief Oper. Officer--Novo Nordisk A/S, Warsaw, Poland; *Int'l*, pg. 988

Johnson, Brian D., Vice Chm. & Chief Oper. Officer--Willis Corroon Americas, Nashville, TN; *Int'l*, pg. 1505

Johnson, Bruce, Pres. & Chief Oper. Officer--Richardson Electronics, Ltd., Lafox, IL; *U.S. Public*, pg. 1387

Johnson, Carl A., Pres., Chief Exec. & Chief Oper. Officer--The Berlin Steel Construction Company, Berlin, CT; *U.S. Private*, pg. 136

Johnson, Don, Chief Oper. Officer--Imperial Hotels, El Segundo, CA; *U.S. Private*, pg. 558

Johnson, Don, Chief Oper. Officer--The Vagabond Inns, San Diego, CA; *U.S. Private*, pg. 558

Johnson, Erick, Chief Oper. Officer & V.P.-Farming Div.--Harris Farms, Inc., Coalinga, CA; *U.S. Private*, pg. 505

Johnson, Harvey R., Chief Oper. Officer--Piedmont Metal Products, Inc., Bedford, VA; *U.S. Public*, pg. 1770

Johnson, Jarl P., Chief Oper. Officer--Coda Energy, Inc., Dallas, TX; *U.S. Public*, pg. 584

Johnson, Jim, Pres. & Chief Oper. Officer--The Apogee Companies, Inc., Lake Oswego, OR; *U.S. Private*, pg. 77

Johnson, Karen, Chief Oper. Officer--Bull, Inc., San Diego, CA; *U.S. Private*, pg. 976

Johnson, Leif, Chief Oper. Officer--Bauer Hiss AB, Frolunda, Sweden; *Int'l*, pg. 747

Johnson, Norman E., Pres. & Chief Oper. Officer--CLARCOR, Inc., Rockford, IL; *U.S. Public*, pg. 381

Johnson, Ralph W., Chief Oper. Officer--Turner International U.K. Ltd., London, United Kingdom; *U.S. Public*, pg. 1646

Johnson, Robert B., Chief Oper. Officer & Exec. V.P.--The Detroit Medical Center, Detroit, MI; *U.S. Private*, pg. 328

Johnson, Ronald, Pres. & Chief Oper. Officer--Hoogovens Aluminium Corp., Secaucus, NJ; *Int'l*, pg. 755

Johnson, Stephen, Chief Oper. Officer & Exec. V.P.--CFA Holding Company, Charlotte, MI; *U.S. Private*, pg. 194

Johnson, Stephen M., Chief Oper. Officer & Exec. V.P.--The Alpine Group, Inc., New York, NY; *U.S. Public*, pg. 58

Johnston, John C., Pres. & Chief Oper. Officer--Farr Company, El Segundo, CA; *U.S. Public*, pg. 613

Johnston, Thomas G., Pres. & Chief Oper. Officer--Alumax Inc., Atlanta, GA; *U.S. Public*, pg. 59

Johnston, William E., Jr., Pres. & Chief Oper. Officer--Morton International Inc., Chicago, IL; *U.S. Public*, pg. 1134

Jokelainen, Ari, Chief Oper. Officer--Exel Oy, Mantyharju, Finland; *Int'l*, pg. 913

Jokinen, Kari, Chief Oper. Officer--Raisio Group plc-Margarine, Raisio, Finland; *Int'l*, pg. 1085

Jonegard, Rolf, Chief Fin. Officer & Exec. V.P.--Svedala Industri AB, Malmo, Sweden; *Int'l*, pg. 1323

Jones, Carl E., Jr., Pres. & Chief Oper. Officer--Regions Financial Corporation, Birmingham, AL; *U.S. Public*, pg. 1371

Jones, Edward C., Pres. & Chief Oper. Officer--Jones Dairy Farm, Fort Atkinson, WI; *U.S. Private*, pg. 596

Jones, J.C., III, Chm. Bd.--Fuel South, Inc., Hazlehurst, GA; *U.S. Private*, pg. 596

Jones, James R., Pres. & Chief Oper. Officer--Dodson Group, Kansas City, MO; *U.S. Private*, pg. 338

Jones, Jerry D., Sr. V.P.-U.S. Opers.--The Minute Maid Company, Houston, TX; *U.S. Public*, pg. 392

Jones, L. Hollis, Pres. & Chief Oper. Officer--The Morning Star Group, Dallas, TX; *U.S. Public*, pg. 1527

Jones, Larry, Chief Oper. Officer--North American Recreation Products Company, Wichita, KS; *U.S. Private*, pg. 691

Jones, Miles E., Chief Oper. Officer & Sec.--Dawn Food Products, Inc., Jackson, MI; *U.S. Private*, pg. 316

Jones, Richard D., Pres. & Chief Oper. Officer--Centex Construction Products, Inc., Dallas, TX; *U.S. Public*, pg. 322

Jones, Rick, Chief Oper. Officer, Sr. V.P. & Gen. Mgr.-Mdse.--Tops Appliance City, Edison, NJ; *U.S. Public*, pg. 1622

Jones, Robert, Pres. & Chief Oper. Officer--Entex, Houston, TX; *U.S. Public*, pg. 843

Jones, Steve, Chief Oper. Officer--Sleepeezee Limited, London, United Kingdom; *Int'l*, pg. 1263

Jones, Thomas E., Jr., Chief Oper. & Chief Fin. Officer--Steadly Company, Carthage, MO; *U.S. Public*, pg. 986

Jonson, Jim, Pres. & Chief Oper. Officer--Gulfstream Aerospace Corporation, Savannah, GA; *U.S. Private*, pg. 419

Joos, David W., Exec. V.P. & Chief Oper. Officer-Electric--Consumers Energy, Jackson, MI; *U.S. Public*, pg. 280

Joos, Etienne, Chief Oper. Officer--Beamix-Bel S.A., Grimbergen, Belgium; *Int'l*, pg. 606

Jordan, Richard, Chief Oper. Officer--Atlas Lederer Co., Cleveland, OH; *U.S. Private*, pg. 256

Jordan, Richard, Chief Oper. Officer--Columbia Iron & Metal Co., Cleveland, OH; *U.S. Private*, pg. 256

Jordan, William M., Pres. & Chief Oper. Officer--Flowserve Corporation, Dayton, OH; *U.S. Public*, pg. 658

Jordan, William M., Pres. & Chief Oper. Officer--Flowserve Corporation, Long Beach, CA; *U.S. Public*, pg. 658

Jorndt, L. Daniel, Pres. & Chief Oper. Officer--Walgreen Co., Deerfield, IL; *U.S. Public*, pg. 1733

Joseph, Marcel P., Pres. & Chief Oper. Officer--Augat, Inc., Mansfield, MA; *U.S. Public*, pg. 1597

Joyce, Michael H., Pres. & Chief Oper. Officer--Twin Disc, Incorporated, Racine, WI; *U.S. Public*, pg. 1646

Judd, John, Chief Oper. Officer--Vibrametric, Hamden, CT; *U.S. Private*, pg. 622

Julian, Paul, Pres. & Chief Oper. Officer--General Medical Corp., Richmond, VA; *U.S. Public*, pg. 1073

Juliano, Mark, Pres. & Chief Oper. Officer--Boardwalk Regency Corporation, Atlantic City, NJ; *U.S. Public*, pg. 1512

Julius, George P., Jr., Pres. & Chief Oper. Officer--Beverage America, Inc., Holland, MI; *U.S. Private*, pg. 141

Juris, Brett, Chief Oper. Officer--Magnasync Moviola Corporation, Hollywood, CA; *U.S. Private*, pg. 576

Kaarnakari, Matti, Chief Oper. Officer--Neste Polyester S.A., Sauveterre, France; *Int'l*, pg. 915

Kaarnasaari, Jussi, Chief Oper. Officer--NCT Norden AB, Espoo, Finland; *Int'l*, pg. 913

Kafadar, C.B., Dr., Pres. & Chief Oper. Officer--OEA, Inc., Aurora, CO; *U.S. Public*, pg. 1206

Kafoure, Michael D., Pres. & Chief Oper. Officer--Interstate Bakeries Corporation, Kansas City, MO; *U.S. Public*, pg. 909

Kafoure, Michael D., Pres. & Chief Oper. Officer--Interstate Brands Corporation, Kansas City, MO; *U.S. Public*, pg. 909

Kahn, David, Pres.--Croscill, Inc., New York, NY; *U.S. Private*, pg. 290

Kahn, J. Alan, Chief Oper. Officer--Barnes & Noble Inc., New York, NY; *U.S. Public*, pg. 189

Kai, Masaru, Chief Oper. Officer--Nippon Oil (U.S.A.) Limited - New York Office, New York, NY; *Int'l*, pg. 937

Kain, Bruce E., Chief Oper. Officer--Pool Arabia, Ltd., Al-Khobar, Saudi Arabia; *U.S. Public*, pg. 1316

Kakures, Dennis C., Pres. & Chief Oper. Officer--McGrath RentCorp, Livermore, CA; *U.S. Public*, pg. 1069

Kalebic, Thomas V., Chief Oper. Officer & Exec. V.P.--Lane Industries, Inc., Northbrook, IL; *U.S. Private*, pg. 649

Kallet, Peter J., Pres. & Chief Oper. Officer--Oneida Ltd., Oneida, NY; *U.S. Public*, pg. 1225

Kalmet, J. John, Pres. & Chief Oper. Officer--Wheaton River Minerals Ltd., Toronto, Canada; *Int'l*, pg. 1498

Kaloyanides, James M., Pres. & Chief Oper. Officer--New England Coffee Company, Malden, MA; *U.S. Private*, pg. 792

Kaltenegger, Wolf-Dieter, Chief Oper. Officer--Frankfurt-Trust Investment GmbH, Frankfurt/Main, Germany; *Int'l*, pg. 119

Kaminski, Jerold, Pres. & Chief Oper. Officer--Northland Cranberries, Inc., Wisconsin Rapids, WI; *U.S. Public*, pg. 1197

Kaminski, Joseph J., Chief Oper. Officer--Middletown Oxygen Co., Inc., Allentown, PA; *U.S. Public*, pg. 31

Kaminsky, Kenneth, Chief Oper. Officer & Exec. V.P.--New Haven Savings Bank, New Haven, CT; *U.S. Private*, pg. 793

Kamminga, Peter, Chief Oper. Officer--Hermedico BV, Doesburg, Netherlands; *Int'l*, pg. 987

Kane, Douglas C., Chief Oper. Officer & Exec. V.P.--MDU Resources Group, Inc., Bismarck, ND; *U.S. Public*, pg. 1025

Kane, Gary A., Pres. & Chief Oper. Officer--J.G. Hook, Inc., New York, NY; *U.S. Private*, pg. 538

Kane, John C., Pres. & Chief Oper. Officer--Cardinal Health Inc., Dublin, OH; *U.S. Public*, pg. 304

Kaneto, Akinori, Chief Oper. Officer--P.T. Asuransi Tokio Marine Indonesia, Jakarta, Indonesia; *Int'l*, pg. 1392

Kanis, Spencer, Chief Oper. Officer & Chief Fin. Officer--Intercosmetics, Inc., New York, NY; *Int'l*, pg. 1489

Kantarian, Arlen, Chief Oper. Officer-Entertainment & Mktg.--Radio City Productions, New York, NY; *Int'l*, pg. 873

Kantor, Nathan, Pres. & Chief Oper. Officer--Winstar Communications, New York, NY; *U.S. Public*, pg. 1772

Kao, Lei Siu, Chief Oper. Officer--Banco Espirito Santo do Oriente SARL (Besor), Macau, Macau; *Int'l*, pg. 142

Kapella, Roger R., Pres. & Chief Oper. Officer--Patrick Cudahy Inc., Cudahy, WI; *U.S. Public*, pg. 1479

Kaplan, Ira, Chief Oper. Officer--EDO Corporation, New York, NY; *U.S. Public*, pg. 541

Kaplan, Philip, Pres. & Chief Oper. Officer--Loehmann's, Inc., Bronx, NY; *U.S. Public*, pg. 1010

Kappauf, Donald W., Chief Oper. Officer & Exec. V.P.--Digital Solutions, Inc., Somerset, NJ; *U.S. Public*, pg. 508

Kapur, Anil, Chief Oper. Officer--Novo Nordisk (India) Pvt Ltd, Bangalore, India; *Int'l*, pg. 988

Karchon, Dennis, Chief Oper. Officer & Controller--Engineering Service, Inc., Southfield, MI; *U.S. Private*, pg. 376

Kardos, Paul J., Pres., Chief Exec. Officer & Chief Oper. Officer--Horace Mann Educators Corporation, Springfield, IL; *U.S. Public*, pg. 835

Karg, Jack, Chief Oper. Officer & V.P.--White Cap Industries, Inc., Costa Mesa, CA; *U.S. Public*, pg. 1765

Karis, James M., Chief Oper. Officer--PAREXEL International Corporation, Waltham, MA; *U.S. Public*, pg. 1257

Kartarik, Mark, Chief Oper. Officer--Supercuts, Inc., San Francisco, CA; *U.S. Public*, pg. 1373

Karube, Kenji, Chief Oper. Officer--Makita U.S.A., Inc., La Mirada, CA; *Int'l*, pg. 831

Karvois, Paul J., Pres. & Chief Oper. Officer--Jevic Transportation, Inc., Delanco, NJ; *U.S. Public*, pg. 927

Kashgegian, Glen, Pres. & Chief Oper. Officer--Printed Circuit Corporation, Woburn, MA; *U.S. Private*, pg. 886

Kashmer, Bernard A., Chief Oper Officer & Exec. V.P.--Hull Corporation, Hatboro, PA; *U.S. Private*, pg. 547

Kasriel, Bernard, Vice Chm. & Chief Oper. Officer--Lafarge S.A., Paris, France; *Int'l*, pg. 788

Kassan, Michael E., Pres. & Chief Oper. Officer--Western International Media Corporation, Los Angeles, CA; *U.S. Private*, pg. 1165

Katayama, Hiroshi, Chief Oper. Officer--Nissho Iwai de Venezuela C.A., Caracas, Venezuela; *Int'l*, pg. 948

Katri, David E., Pres. & Chief Oper. Officer--Fluke Corporation, Everett, WA; *U.S. Public*, pg. 659

Katsarakes, George S., Chief Oper. Officer & Exec. V.P.--TII Industries, Inc., Copiague, NY; *U.S. Public*, pg. 1556

Katz, Stewart, Pres. & Chief Oper. Officer--Noodle Kidoodle Inc., Syosset, NY; *U.S. Public*, pg. 1188

Kauffman, Roger A., Chief Oper. Officer & Exec. V.P.--Hecla Mining Company, Coeur D'Alene, ID; *U.S. Public*, pg. 803

Kauffman, Will, Chief Oper. Officer & Sr. V.P.--Komag, Incorporated, San Jose, CA; *U.S. Public*, pg. 966

Kaufman, Jeffrey V., Chief Oper. Officer & Exec. V.P.--Wall Street Deli, Inc., Birmingham, AL; *U.S. Public*, pg. 1734

Kaufman, John S., Pres.-Koo Koo Roo USA--Koo Koo Roo, Inc., Los Angeles, CA; *U.S. Public*, pg. 966

Kaufmann, Joachim, Chief Exec. & Chief Oper. Officer--Feintool International Holding AG, Lyss, Switzerland; *Int'l*, pg. 479

Kawamori, Kiyoshi, Chief Oper. Officer--Makita, S.A., Madrid, Spain; *Int'l*, pg. 832

Kay, Tony, Chief Oper. Officer--Hagglunds Drives Ltd, York, United Kingdom; *Int'l*, pg. 670

Keane, Kevin T., Chief Oper. Officer--MOD-PAC CORP, Buffalo, NY; *U.S. Public*, pg. 142

Kearl, Greg, Chief Oper. Officer, Exec. V.P., Treas. & Sec.--Menley & James Laboratories, Inc., Horsham, PA; *U.S. Public*, pg. 1086

Kearns, Robert J., III, Chief Oper. Officer & Exec. V.P.-Fin.--Leasing Solutions, Inc., San Jose, CA; *U.S. Public*, pg. 982

Keatinge, Richard, Sr. V.P.-Oper. & Engrng.--Showtime Networks Inc., New York, NY; *U.S. Private*, pg. 779

Keckeis, Thomas M., V.P.-Opers.--Frank Messer & Sons Construction Co., Cincinnati, OH; *U.S. Private*, pg. 734

Keehbler, Nicholas, Chief Oper. Officer & Exec. V.P.--PennCorp Financial Group, Inc., New York, NY; *U.S. Public*, pg. 1271

Keen, Gerald S., V.P.-Opers.--Mobile Gas Service Corp., Mobile, AL; *U.S. Public*, pg. 1120

Keenan, John P., Chief Oper. Officer & Sr. V.P.--Bankers American Life Assurance Company, Pearl River, NY; *U.S. Public*, pg. 68

Keene, Howard, Chm. Bd., Pres.,Chief Exec. & Oper. Officer--Rawlings Sporting Goods Company, Fenton, MO; *U.S. Public*, pg. 1361

Keene, Joe, Chief Oper. Officer--Maxis, Walnut Creek, CA; *U.S. Public*, pg. 569

Keeney, Michael D., Pres. & Chief Oper. Officer--Walle Corporation, Harahan, LA; *U.S. Private*, pg. 1148

Keethler, Robert, Chief Oper. Officer & Gen. Mgr.--CMI Mobile, Inc., Milwaukee, WI; *U.S. Public*, pg. 1462

Kehlbeck, Fritz, Dr., Co-Chief Oper. Officer--BHF & IKB Baumanagement GmbH, Dusseldorf, Germany; *Int'l*, pg. 645

Kehoe, John M., Pres. & Chief Exec. Officer--Wheelabrator Technologies Inc., Hampton, NH; *U.S. Public*, pg. 1745

Kehoe, Vincent, Chief Oper. Officer--Bass International Brewers, Birmingham, United Kingdom; *Int'l*, pg. 170

Keller, James J., Chief Oper. Officer & Exec. V.P.--J.J. Keller & Associates, Inc., Neenah, WI; *U.S. Private*, pg. 612

Kelley, Peter H., Pres. & Chief Oper. Officer--Southern Union Company, Austin, TX; *U.S. Public*, pg. 1491

Kellogg, Tom N., Pres. & Chief Oper. Officer--General Reinsurance Corp., Stamford, CT; *U.S. Public*, pg. 725

Kelly, Brian, Pres., Chief. Oper. Officer & Sec.--Activision, Santa Monica, CA; *U.S. Public*, pg. 17

Kelly, Edmund F., Pres. & Chief Oper. Officer--Liberty Mutual Insurance Co., Boston, MA; *U.S. Private*, pg. 666

Kelly, J. Peter, Pres. & Chief Oper. Officer--The LTV Corporation, Cleveland, OH; *U.S. Public*, pg. 971

Kelly, Jack, Chief Oper. Officer & Sr. V.P.--Producto Machine Co. Ring Division, Jamestown, NY; *U.S. Private*, pg. 889

Kelly, John A., Chief Oper. Officer & Sr. V.P.--The Producto Machine Co., Bridgeport, CT; *U.S. Private*, pg. 889

Kelly, John F., Chm. Bd., Pres, Chief Exec. & Oper. Officer--Alaska Air Group, Inc., Seattle, WA; *U.S. Public*, pg. 35

Kelly, Raymond F., Chief Oper. Officer & Exec. V.P.--Baker Commodities, Inc., Los Angeles, CA; *U.S. Private*, pg. 111

Kelly, Thomas F., Chief Oper. Officer--Cirrus Logic, Inc., Fremont, CA; *U.S. Public*, pg. 375

Kelso, Joyce M., Chief Oper. Officer & Sr. V.P.--Concord EFS, Inc., Memphis, TN; *U.S. Public*, pg. 429

Kempinski, Chet, Chief Oper. Officer & Exec. V.P.--PHB Die Casting, Fairview, PA; *U.S. Private*, pg. 826

Kempinski, Chet, Chief Oper. Officer & Exec. V.P.--PHB Machining Division, Fairview, PA; *U.S. Private*, pg. 826

Kempinski, Chet, Chief Oper. Officer & Exec. V.P--PHB Tool & Die, Girard, PA; *U.S. Private*, pg. 826

Kempinski, Chet, Chief Oper. Officer & Exec. V.P.--PHB Plastic & Rubber Molding Division, Fairview, PA; *U.S. Private*, pg. 826

Kemsley, M.A., Chief Oper. Officer & Mng. Dir.--Yale Security Products (Hong Kong) Ltd., Causeway Bay, Hong Kong; *Int'l*, pg. 1499

Kendrick, Brian E., Vice Chm. & Chief Oper. Officer--Saks Fifth Avenue, New York, NY; *U.S. Public*, pg. 1429

Kenerleber, A.J., Pres. & Chief Oper. Officer--Video Display Corporation, Tucker, GA; *U.S. Public*, pg. 1720

Kennebeck, Alan W., Chief Oper. Officer--WM Trust Company, Seattle, WA; *U.S. Public*, pg. 1742

Kennedy, Bernard D., Pres. & Chief Oper. Officer--King Kullen Grocery Co., Inc., Westbury, NY; *U.S. Private*, pg. 621

Kennedy, John, Pres. & Chief Oper. Officer--Budget Group, Inc., Daytona Beach, FL; *U.S. Private*, pg. 178

Kennedy, John, Pres. & Chief Oper. Officer--Budget Rent A Car Corporation, Lisle, IL; *U.S. Private*, pg. 178

Kennedy, John C., Chm. Bd., Pres. & Chief Exec. Officer--Autocam Corporation, Grand Rapids, MI; *U.S. Public*, pg. 148

Kennedy, W.T., Sr. V.P. & Chief Oper. Officer-New Holland Inc.--New Holland Ltd., Brentford, United Kingdom; *Int'l*, pg. 484

Kenny, Jeff, Chief Oper. Officer--Superior Label Systems, Inc., Mason, OH; *U.S. Private*, pg. 1055

Kent, Conrad S., Chief Oper. Officer--Delamine B.V., Amersfoort, Netherlands; *Int'l*, pg. 1408

Kent, Conrad S., Chief Oper. Officer--Delamine B.V.-Delfzijl Plant, Delfzijl, Netherlands; *Int'l*, pg. 1408

Kent, Terrance, Chief Oper. Officer--Competitive Media Reporting, New York, NY; *Int'l*, pg. 1447

Kepple, John, Chief Oper. Officer--Allen Telecom Inc., Solon, OH; *U.S. Public*, pg. 45

Kerman, Richard, Pres. & Chief Oper. Officer--Steiner Electric Company, Elk Grove Village, IL; *U.S. Private*, pg. 1039

Kershaw, Michael P., Pres. & Chief Oper. Officer--Shirmax Retail Ltd., Montreal, Canada; *Int'l*, pg. 1235

Kerstetter, Bill, Chief Oper. Officer & Exec. V.P.--New World Entertainment, Inc., Los Angeles, CA; *Int'l*, pg. 926

Kersulis, Bernard J., Pres., Chief Exec. Officer & Chief Oper. Officer--Standun, Inc., Inglewood, CA; *U.S. Private*, pg. 1032

Kerzner, Jay J., Chief Oper. Officer & Exec. V.P.--Rainoldi, Kerzner & Radcliffe, San Francisco, CA; *U.S. Public*, pg. 1224

Kessel, Richard E., Chief Oper. Officer--Trigen Energy Corporation, White Plains, NY; *U.S. Public*, pg. 1637

Kessler, Edward, Chief Oper. Officer, V.P. & Gen. Mgr.--C & K Market, Inc., Brookings, OR; *U.S. Private*, pg. 191

Kewer, David B., Pres. & Chief Oper. Officer--Eskimo Pie Corporation, Richmond, VA; *U.S. Public*, pg. 592

Key, J. Douglas, Pres. & Chief Oper. Officer--Cabre Exploration Ltd., Calgary, Canada; *Int'l*, pg. 247

Kiblawi, Dan, Chief Oper. Officer--Horizon Technology Group LLC, Taylor, MI; *U.S. Private*, pg. 539

Kidner, Raymond L., Chief Oper. Officer--Tosoh SMD, Inc., Grove City, OH; *Int'l*, pg. 1407

Kiefer, David, Ph.D., Chief Oper. Officer--Diamedix Corporation, Miami, FL; *U.S. Public*, pg. 914

Kiely, W. Leo, III, Chief Oper. Officer--Adolph Coors Company, Golden, CO; *U.S. Public*, pg. 445

Kiely, W. Leo, III, Pres. & Chief Oper. Officer--Coors Brewing Company, Golden, CO; *U.S. Public*, pg. 445

Kikuchi, Koichi, Chief Oper. Officer--P.T. Standard Toyo Polymer-Merak Plant, Jawa, Indonesia; *Int'l*, pg. 1408

Kilgore, Gregory M., Pres. & Chief Oper. Officer--Track 'n Trail, El Dorado Hills, CA; *U.S. Public*, pg. 1626

Kilissanly, Peter E., Pres. & Chief Oper. Officer--Physician Corporation of America, Miami, FL; *U.S. Public*, pg. 1293

Killgallon, Martin L., II, Pres. & Chief Oper. Officer--The Ohio Art Company, Inc., Bryan, OH; *U.S. Public*, pg. 1214

Kim, Edward, Pres., Chief Oper. & Chief Exec. Officer--Pantech Construction Co., Lanham, MD; *U.S. Private*, pg. 837

Kim, K.H., Chief Oper. Officer & Exec. V.P.--Kodak Korea Ltd., Seoul, Korea; *U.S. Public*, pg. 555

Kim, Kyunghwa, Chief Oper. Officer--POSAM New York Office, New York, NY; *Int'l*, pg. 1062

Kim, S.T., Pres. & Chief Oper. Officer--AST Research Inc., Irvine, CA; *Int'l*, pg. 1181

Kimball, R. Jeffrey, Pres. & Chief Oper. Officer--L. Robert Kimball & Associates, Ebensburg, PA; *U.S. Private*, pg. 619

Kime, Donald, Chief Oper. Officer & Controller--TV Host Inc., Harrisburg, PA; *U.S. Private*, pg. 1066

Kimsey, William L., Deputy Chm. & Chief Oper. Officer--Ernst & Young, LLP, New York, NY; *U.S. Private*, pg. 381

Kindlund, Newton C., Chm. Bd., Pres., Chief Exec. & Chief Oper. Officer--Holiday RV Superstores, Inc., Orlando, FL; *U.S. Public*, pg. 829

Kindlund, Newton C., Chief Oper. Officer--Holiday RV Rental/Leasing, Inc., Orlando, FL; *U.S. Public*, pg. 829

King, Allen B., Pres. & Chief Oper. Officer--Universal Corporation, Richmond, VA; *U.S. Public*, pg. 1694

King, Gerry, Pres.-Catalog Fullfillment Svcs. & Chief Oper. Officer--LCS Industries, Inc., Clifton, NJ; *U.S. Public*, pg. 970

King, John H., Pres. & Chief Oper. Officer--HDS Services, Farmington Hills, MI; *U.S. Private*, pg. 490

King, Richard L., Pres. & Chief Oper. Officer--Albertson's, Inc., Boise, ID; *U.S. Public*, pg. 38

King, Robert, Pres. & Chief Oper. Officer--Corporate Express, Inc., Broomfield, CO; *U.S. Public*, pg. 449

King, Stephen M., Chief Oper. Officer & V.P.--TGI Friday's, Inc., Addison, TX; *U.S. Private*, pg. 212

King, Steve, Chief Oper. Officer--Zenith Media Services, Inc., New York, NY; *U.S. Private*, pg. 1204

Kingsbury, Art, Chief Oper. Officer--Billboard Magazine, New York, NY; *Int'l*, pg. 1446

Kinsel, Curt, Pres. & Chief Oper. Officer--Apple South, Inc., Madison, GA; *U.S. Public*, pg. 121

Kinsey, Gary S., Pres. & Chief Oper. Officer--Great Oaks Insurance Company, Dublin, OH; *U.S. Public*, pg. 786

Kinsley, P.H., Chm. Bd., Chief Exec. Officer & Chief Oper. Officer--Permark International (Pty.) Ltd., Johannesburg, South Africa; *Int'l*, pg. 1036

Kipp, Louis D., Chief Oper. Officer--Quipp, Inc., Hialeah, FL; *U.S. Public*, pg. 1353

Kirchner, Vinson E., Pres. & Chief Oper. Officer--Owens Country Sausage, Inc., Richardson, TX; *U.S. Public*, pg. 596

Kiremidjian, Fred, Sr. V.P. & Gen. Mgr.-Nuwave Grp.--Network Peripherals Inc., Milpitas, CA; *U.S. Public*, pg. 1169

Kirk, Mark, Pres., Chief Oper. Officer & Chief Fin. Officer--HMI Industries, Cleveland, OH; *U.S. Public*, pg. 771

Kirshner, Hal, Pres., Chief Oper. Officer, V.P. & Acting Dir.-Mktg.--LORAD Corporation, Danbury, CT; *U.S. Public*, pg. 1595

Kiser, Gerald L., Chief Oper. Officer & Exec. V.P.--La-Z-Boy Incorporated, Monroe, MI; *U.S. Public*, pg. 972

Kisting, Scott A., Chief Oper. Officer--Citizens Financial Group, Inc., Providence, RI; *Int'l*, pg. 1132

Kittrell, Charles J., Chief Oper. Officer & Exec. V.P.--Cornerstone Propane G.P. Inc., Watsonville, CA; *U.S. Public*, pg. 1201

Kiyohara, Eisuke, Chief Oper. Officer--Neste Chemicals (Japan) Co., Ltd., Tokyo, Japan; *Int'l*, pg. 914

Klein, Richard T. Jr., Pres. & Chief Oper. Officer--Klein Tools Inc., Skokie, IL; *U.S. Private*, pg. 625

Klein, Tom, Chief Oper. Officer--Novo Nordisk of North America, Inc., New York, NY; *Int'l*, pg. 987

Kleinbergen, J.J., Chief Oper. Officer--Zwjsen B.V., Hendrik-Ido-Ambacht, Netherlands; *Int'l*, pg. 754

Kleinman, Richard D., Pres. & Chief Oper. Officer--AFA Protective Systems, Inc., Syosset, NY; *U.S. Public*, pg. 5

Kleisner, Fred, Pres. & Chief Oper. Officer-Westin Hotel Co.--Westin Hotels & Resorts, Seattle, WA; *U.S. Public*, pg. 1512

Kliemann, Michael, Chief Oper. Officer--Gambro Vertriebsgesellschaft m.b.H., Vienna, Austria; *Int'l*, pg. 668

Kline, Richard D., Vice Chm., Pres. & Chief Oper. Officer.--Lehigh Portland Cement Company, Allentown, PA; *Int'l*, pg. 605

Kline, Rodger S., Chief Oper. Officer, Exec. V.P. & Treas.--Acxiom Corporation, Conway, AR; *U.S. Public*, pg. 18

Kloppenburg, Jerry, Mng. Officer--BVK/McDonald, Milwaukee, WI; *U.S. Private*, pg. 108

Klotzbuchen, Friedrich, Chief Oper. Officer--COBE Laboratories GmbH, Planegg, Germany; *Int'l*, pg. 667

Klowden, Michael L., Pres. & Chief Oper. Officer--Jefferies Group, Inc., Los Angeles, CA; *U.S. Public*, pg. 924

Klowden, Michael L., Pres. & Chief Oper. Officer--Jefferies & Company, Inc., Los Angeles, CA; *U.S. Public*, pg. 925

Kluth, Gerhard, Dr., Chief Oper. Officer--Siemens Finanzierungsgesellschaft fur Informationstechnik GmbH, Munich, Germany; *Int'l*, pg. 1245

Knackstedt, Walter, Chief Oper. Officer--Hagglunds Drives GmbH, Haan, Germany; *Int'l*, pg. 670

Knee, Kevin, Chief Oper. & Fin. Officer--Guthy-Renker Corp., Palm Desert, CA; *U.S. Private*, pg. 488

Kniberg, Alfred A., Pres. & Chief Oper. Officer--The Strouse, Adler Company, New Haven, CT; *U.S. Private*, pg. 1047

Knieling, Hermann, Chief Oper. Officer & Exec. V.P.--Airgas, Inc., Radnor, PA; *U.S. Public*, pg. 33

Knigiu, Neil, Pres. & Chief Oper. Officer--Movie Star, Inc., New York, NY; *U.S. Public*, pg. 1140

Knox, Fred, Chief Oper. Officer--Mercer Company, Sharon, PA; *U.S. Private*, pg. 256

Knox, Larry W., Chief Oper. Officer & V.P.--J.E. Higgins Lumber Co., Concord, CA; *U.S. Private*, pg. 527

Kobacker, Edward J., Chief Oper. Officer & Exec. V.P.--U.S. Timberlands Company, L.P., Klamath Falls, OR; *U.S. Public*, pg. 1688

Kobayashi, Toshiaki, Chief Oper. Officer--Gunze Sangyo (Kyoto), Kyoto, Japan; *Int'l*, pg. 578

Kobran, Mitch, Chief Oper. Officer & V.P.--Leonard Wholesale, Inc., Springfield, NJ; *U.S. Private*, pg. 660

Kobs, Duane, Chief Oper. Officer & Exec. V.P.--Quest Technologies, Inc., Oconomowoc, WI; *U.S. Private*, pg. 900

Koch, Craig R., Chief Oper. Officer--The Hertz Corporation, Park Ridge, NJ; *U.S. Public*, pg. 664

Koch, David, Chief Exec. & Chief Oper. Officer--Koch Engineering Company, Inc., Akron, OH; *U.S. Private*, pg. 628

Koch, Guenther, Co-Chief Oper. Officer--S-Beteiligungsgesellschaft Hessen- Thuringen mbH, Frankfurt/Main, Germany; *Int'l*, pg. 799

Koch, Peter, Pres. & Chief Oper. Officer--Plywood Plastics Inc., Buffalo, NY; *U.S. Private*, pg. 873

Koehrer, Ralph, Pres. & Chief Oper. Officer--Anacomp, Inc., Indianapolis, IN; *U.S. Public*, pg. 106

Koerber, Kathleen M., Chief Oper. Officer & Exec. V.P.--MBL Life Assurance Corporation, Newark, NJ; *U.S. Private*, pg. 685

Kohl, James F., Chief Oper. Officer--Furman Foods, Inc., Northumberland, PA; *U.S. Private*, pg. 431

Kohls, Bob, Chief Oper. Officer--The Kruse Company, Fairfield, OH; *U.S. Private*, pg. 636

Kohnhorst, E.E., Chief Oper. Officer & Exec. V.P.--Brown & Williamson Tobacco Corp., Louisville, KY; *Int'l*, pg. 111

Kohrt, Carl F., Exec. V.P. & Asst. Chief Oper. Officer--Eastman Kodak Company, Rochester, NY; *U.S. Public*, pg. 550

Kokheel, Marcel, Chief Oper. Officer--Ahold Vastgoed B.V., Zaandam, Netherlands; *Int'l*, pg. 749

Kolacki, Paul W., Chief Oper. Officer & Exec. V.P.--Hooper Holmes Corporation, Basking Ridge, NJ; *U.S. Public*, pg. 835

Kolber, George, Vice Chm & Chief Oper. Officer--American Eagles Outfitters Inc., Warrendale, PA; *U.S. Private*, pg. 53

Koller, H., Chief Oper. Officer--Manitec AG, Emmen, Switzerland; *Int'l*, pg. 1205

Kolonko, D., Chief Oper. Officer--SAIA-Burgess Electronics GmbH, Dreieichenhain, Germany; *Int'l*, pg. 1501

Kolson, Ronald J., Chief Oper. Officer & Exec. V.P.--Micros Systems Inc., Beltsville, MD; *U.S. Public*, pg. 1106

Kolsted, Darrell, Chief Oper. Officer & Exec. V.P.--Wick Building Systems, Mazomanie, WI; *U.S. Private*, pg. 1174

Komoto, Takahisa, Pres. & Chief Oper. Officer--Diamond Star Motors, Normal, IL; *Int'l*, pg. 875

Koncelik, David G., Pres. & Chief Exec. Officer--California & Hawaiian Sugar Company Inc., Crockett, CA; *U.S. Public*, pg. 39

Kone, Anne, Co-Chief Oper. Officer--Cofhylux SA, Luxembourg, Luxembourg; *Int'l*, pg. 162

Kono, Yasushi, Chief Oper. Officer--Nippon Oil (U.K.) Public Limited Company, London, United Kingdom; *Int'l*, pg. 937

Konrad, Hans-Martin, Chief Oper. Officer--BHF & IKB Asia Consult Ltd., Hong Kong, Hong Kong,; *Int'l*, pg. 646

Kopecek, Lubomir, Chief Oper. Officer--Gambro-Meopta S.R.O., Prerov, Czech Republic; *Int'l*, pg. 668

Kopko, Edward M., Chm. Bd., Pres., Chief Exec. & Chief Oper. Officer--Butler International, Inc., Montvale, NJ; *U.S. Public*, pg. 270

Koppel, P., Chief Oper. Officer--Baumann Spring Co. (S) Pte. Ltd., Singapore, Singapore; *Int'l*, pg. 171

Korell, Harold M., Exec. V.P.-Opers.--Southwestern Energy Company, Fayetteville, AR; *U.S. Public*, pg. 1494

Koridek, J., Chief Oper. Officer--ATT Network Sistems International, B.V., Hilversum, Netherlands; *Int'l*, pg. 1373

Korzilius, P.A.M., Chief Oper. Officer--Baumann Springs & Pressings (UK) Ltd., Sherborne, United Kingdom; *Int'l*, pg. 171

Kosht, Jon A., Pres., Chief Oper. Officer, Sec. & Treas.--Michigan Gas Company, Three Rivers, MI; *U.S. Public*, pg. 1489

Koss, Michael J., Pres., Chief Exec., Oper. & Fin. Officer--Koss Corporation, Milwaukee, WI; *U.S. Public*, pg. 966

Kotkamp, Ruediger, Dr., Pres. & Chief Oper. Officer--Rheinische Olefinwerke GmbH, Wesseling, Germany; *Int'l*, pg. 105

Kourad, Hans Martin, Chief Oper. Officer--BHF-Bank, Central, Hong Kong; *Int'l*, pg. 119

Kouzuma, Makoto, Chief Oper. Officer, Exec. V.P. & Gen. Mgr.--SpeedFam Co Ltd., Ayase, Japan; *U.S. Public*, pg. 1498

Kovel, Lee, Mng. Dir. & Chief Creative Officer--Kovel Kresser & Partners, Santa Monica, CA; *U.S. Private*, pg. 634

Kowaleski, Dianne, Chief Oper. Officer & Exec. V.P.--Jack Levy Associates, Chicago, IL; *U.S. Private*, pg. 664

Kowalski, Michael J., Pres. & Chief Oper. Officer--Tiffany & Co., New York, NY; *U.S. Public*, pg. 1608

Koyama, Koki, Chief Oper. Officer--Littelfuse do Brasil, Sao Paulo, Brazil; *U.S. Public*, pg. 1001

Kozak, Allan J., Pres. & Chief Oper. Officer--Digital Courier International Inc., Burnaby, Canada; *Int'l*, pg. 413

Koziol, Donald, Chief Oper. Officer & Exec. V.P.--AON Risk Services, Inc., Chicago, IL; *U.S. Public*, pg. 117

Kraeutler, John A., Pres. & Chief Oper. Officer--Meridian Diagnostics, Inc., Cincinnati, OH; *U.S. Public*, pg. 1094

Kramer, Earl, Pres., Chief Exec. & Chief Oper. Officer--Concord Fabrics Inc., New York, NY; *U.S. Public*, pg. 429

Kramer, Francis J., Pres. & Chief Oper. Officer--II-VI Incorporated, Saxonburg, PA; *U.S. Public*, pg. 1647

Krantz, Andrew, Chm. Bd., Pres. & Chief Oper. Officer--Eagle Iron Works, Des Moines, IA; *U.S. Private*, pg. 354

Krattenmaker, Kelly, Chief Oper. Officer & Exec. V.P.--E Prime, Inc., Denver, CO; *U.S. Public*, pg. 1170

Kravitz, Edward N., Pres. & Chief Oper. Officer--The Flxible Corp., Delaware, OH; *U.S. Private*, pg. 444

Krehbiel, John H., Jr., Pres. & Chief Oper. Officer--Molex Incorporated, Lisle, IL; *U.S. Public*, pg. 1121

Kreidel, Richard S., Pres. & Chief Oper. Officer--Adams Rite Manufacturing Co., City of Industry, CA; *U.S. Private*, pg. 17

Kreiter, Ned, Chief Oper. Officer, Treas. & Gen. Mgr.--Castcraft Industries, Inc., Skokie, IL; *U.S. Private*, pg. 219

Kretovic, Michael, Controller & Sec.--Don Alleson, Inc., Rochester, NY; *U.S. Private*, pg. 339

Krivkovich, Peter G., Pres. & Chief Oper. Officer--Cramer-Krasselt, Milwaukee, WI; *U.S. Private*, pg. 285

Kroese, John S., Jr., Chm. Bd. & Chief Oper. Officer--Gaffney-Kroese Electrical Supply Corp., Rahway, NJ; *U.S. Private*, pg. 437

Kronlof, Tom, Chief Oper. Officer--Raisio Svenska AB, Surte, Sweden; *Int'l*, pg. 1086

Krul, J.A., Pres. & Chief Oper. Officer--Hardings, Inc., Elmira, NY; *U.S. Private*, pg. 502

Krulik, Richard, Chm. Bd. & Chief Oper. Officer--United States Luggage Company, Hauppauge, NY; *U.S. Private*, pg. 1125

Krumholz, Stephen B., Chief Oper. Officer & Exec. V.P.--The Southland Corporation, Dallas, TX; *Int'l*, pg. 693

Krumwiede, James, Chm. Bd., Pres. & Chief Oper. Officer--C-Line Products, Inc., Des Plaines, IL; *U.S. Private*, pg. 192

Kruse, P., Dr., Chief Officer-Corp. Devel.--Kuehne & Nagel International AG, Schindellegi, Switzerland; *Int'l*, pg. 763

Kruse, Stuart A., Sr., Chief Oper. Officer--Kruse International, Auburn, IN; *U.S. Private*, pg. 636

Kruse, Thomas, Chief Oper. Officer--Berlin Branch, Berlin, Germany; *Int'l*, pg. 645

Kruy, Joseph F., Chm. Bd., Pres., Chief Exec. & Chief Oper. Officer--Cambex Corporation, Waltham, MA; *U.S. Public*, pg. 296

Krysiak, Bruce, Pres.--Dollar General Corporation, Nashville, TN; *U.S. Public*, pg. 515

Kucharik, John, Pres. & Chief Oper. Officer--Minnesota Valley Engineering/Cryogenic Association, Bloomington, MN; *U.S. Private*, pg. 751

Kudoh, Kiyohiko, Chief Oper. Officer--Finetech Co., Ltd., Tokyo, Japan; *Int'l*, pg. 1262

Kufeldt, James, Pres. & Chief Oper. Officer--Winn-Dixie Stores, Inc., Jacksonville, FL; *U.S. Public*, pg. 1771

Kuhl, H., Chief Oper. Officer--Burgess GmbH, Oldenburg, Germany; *Int'l*, pg. 1500

Kuhlmann, William, Pres., Chief Oper. & Exec. Officer--General Physics Corporation, Columbia, MD; *U.S. Public*, pg. 694

Kuhn, John, Chief Oper. Officer & Exec. V.P.--Heyman Corporation, Niles, IL; *U.S. Private*, pg. 524

Kuhn, Kelly L., Chief Oper. Officer & Sr. V.P.--Arrington Travel Center Inc., Chicago, IL; *U.S. Private*, pg. 85

Kuisma, Aimo, Chief Oper. Officer--Valmet Corporation Production, Jarvenpaa, Finland; *Int'l*, pg. 1448

Kujaiwen, John R., Chief Oper. Officer--Amite Foundry and Machine, Inc., Amite, LA; *U.S. Public*, pg. 142

Kujawa, John R., Chief Oper. Officer--Atchison/St. Joe Division, Atchison, KS; *U.S. Public*, pg. 142

Kulick, Cliff, Pres. & Chief Oper. Officer--Driv-Lok, Inc., Sycamore, IL; *U.S. Private*, pg. 343

Kullas, Robert H., Chm. Bd. & Chief Oper. Officer--Executive Risk, Inc., Simsbury, CT; *U.S. Public*, pg. 599

Kumar, Sanjay, Pres. & Chief Oper. Officer--Computer Associates International, Inc., Islandia, NY; *U.S. Public*, pg. 420

Kumar, Sanjay, Pres. & Chief Oper. Officer--Cheyenne, Roslyn Heights, NY; *U.S. Public*, pg. 420

Kumar, Sanjay, Pres. & Chief Oper. Officer--ACCPAC International, Santa Clara, CA; *U.S. Public*, pg. 420

Kumar, Sanjay, Pres. & Chief Oper. Officer--Acacia Technologies, Lisle, IL; *U.S. Public*, pg. 420

Kumar, Sanjay, Pres. & Chief Oper. Officer--NetHaven, Islandia, NY; *U.S. Public*, pg. 420

Kumar, Sanjay, Pres. & Chief Oper. Officer--Computer Associates International, Inc., Islandia, NY; *U.S. Public*, pg. 420

Kumar, Sanjay, Pres. & Chief Oper. Officer--MK Group, Islandia, NY; *U.S. Public*, pg. 420

Kummer, Glenn F., Chief Oper. Officer--Fleetwood Homes of Georgia, Inc. 651

Kunitomo, Hidehiro, Chief Oper. Officer--NEC Electronics (Germany) GmbH, Dusseldorf, Germany; *Int'l*, pg. 901

Kunkle, Gerald K., Pres. & Chief Oper. Officer--Dentsply International Inc., York, PA; *U.S. Public*, pg. 498

Kunz, Hansruedi, Chief Oper. Officer--Metallica SA, Crissier, Switzerland; *Int'l*, pg. 1427

Kunz, T., Chief Oper. Officer--Danone de Mexico, Mexico, Mexico; *Int'l*, pg. 379

Kunzig, Louis A., Chief Oper. Officer--Sciaky S.A., Vitry-sur-Seine, France; *Int'l*, pg. 1211

Kupillas, Conrad, V.P.--Northway Motorcar Corporation, Latham, NY; *U.S. Private*, pg. 806

Kurland, Stanford L., Pres. & Chief Oper. Officer--Countrywide Home Loans Inc., Pasadena, CA; *U.S. Public*, pg. 452

Kurland, Stanford L., Chief Oper. Officer & Sr. Mng. Dir.--Countrywide Funding Corporation, Pasadena, CA; *U.S. Public*, pg. 453

Kuronya, G., Chief Oper. Officer--WAGO Kontakttechnik Ges mbH, Vienna, Austria; *Int'l*, pg. 209

Kurtenbach, Aelred J., Chm. Bd., Pres., Chief Exec. & Oper. Officer--Daktronics, Inc., Brookings, SD; *U.S. Public*, pg. 478

Kurz, Mitch, Pres. & Chief Oper. Officer--Young & Rubicam Inc., New York, NY; *U.S. Private*, pg. 1196

Kwok, Joseph, Chief Oper. Officer--Neptune Orient Lines Ltd., Singapore, Singapore; *Int'l*, pg. 912

Kwon, T.Y., Chief Oper. Officer--Gambro Korea Co., Ltd, Seoul, Korea; *Int'l*, pg. 668

Kyle, David L., Pres. & Chief Oper. Officer--ONEOK Inc., Tulsa, OK; *U.S. Public*, pg. 1226

Kylmala, Jukka, Chief Oper. Officer--ZAO KONE Lifts, Moscow, Russia; *Int'l*, pg. 748

Kyuast, Bob, Chief Oper. Officer--Weldun International, Inc., Bridgman, MI; *Int'l*, pg. 205

La Grand, Kenneth, Exec. V.P.--Gentex Corporation, Zeeland, MI; *U.S. Public*, pg. 731

La Maina, Francis C., Pres. & Chief Oper. Officer--Dick Clark Productions, Inc., Burbank, CA; *U.S. Public*, pg. 382

La Rosa, Michael, Pres. & Chief Oper. Officer--La Rosa's, Inc., Cincinnati, OH; *U.S. Private*, pg. 640

Laalo-Ristila, Seija, Chief Oper. Officer--Valmet Trade Promotion Office, Moscow, Russia; *Int'l*, pg. 1449

LaBant, Robert, Pres. & Chief Oper. Officer--Candle Corporation, Santa Monica, CA; *U.S. Private*, pg. 204

Labrecque, Thomas G., Pres. & Chief Oper. Officer--The Chase Manhattan Corporation, New York, NY; *U.S. Public*, pg. 337

LaCava, Domenic J., Pres. & Chief Oper. Officer--PictureTel, Andover, MA; *U.S. Public*, pg. 1294

Lachaux, Michel, Chief Oper. Officer--Land Instruments Sarl, Bailly, France; *Int'l*, pg. 798

Lacour, F. D., Chief Oper. Officer--SPCI Societe de Produits Chimiques Industriels SA, Saint Denis, France; *Int'l*, pg. 682

Ladden, Paul, Chief Oper. Officer--Genzyme Diagnostics, Medix Biotech, San Carlos, CA; *U.S. Public*, pg. 733

Ladds, H.P., Jr., Pres. & Chief Exec. Officer--Columbus McKinnon Corp., Amherst, NY; *U.S. Public*, pg. 405

Ladell, Peter W., Chief Oper. Officer--Hoechst Marion Roussel, Inc., Bridgewater, NJ; *Int'l*, pg. 624

Ladell, Peter W., Chief Oper. Officer--Hoechst Marion Roussel AG, Frankfurt/Main, Germany; *Int'l*, pg. 624

Ladinig, U., Chief Oper. Officer--Molto Ges.m.b.H., Salzburg, Austria; *Int'l*, pg. 1501

Lae, Byung-Tae, Chief Oper. Officer & Exec. V.P.--Jaeneung Education Co., Ltd., Seoul, Korea; *Int'l*, pg. 697

Laferriere, Pierre, Pres. & Chief Oper. Officer--Teleglobe International Inc., Montreal, Canada; *Int'l*, pg. 1373

Laferriere, Richard, Pres. & Chief Oper. Officer--Coscient Group Inc., Montreal, Canada; *Int'l*, pg. 335

Lafont, Michel, Chief Oper. Officer--BMOI, Antananarivo, Madagascar; *Int'l*, pg. 163

Laforte, Pierre, Chief Oper. Officer--Ascenseurs Drolet KONE Inc., Quebec, Canada; *Int'l*, pg. 747

Laidlaw, W.S.H., Pres. & Chief Oper. Officer--Amerada Hess Corporation, New York, NY; *U.S. Public*, pg. 65

Laize, Georges, Chief Oper. Officer--Hospal Industrie S.A., Meyzieu, France; *Int'l*, pg. 668

Lal, Victor, Exec. V.P. & Chief Oper. Officer-New World Television--New World Entertainment, Inc., Los Angeles, CA; *Int'l*, pg. 926

Lalich, Sandra J., Chief Oper. Officer & Sr. Exec. V.P.--Willis Corroon Corp. of Illinois, Chicago, IL; *Int'l*, pg. 1506

Lalwani, P.J., Chief Oper. Officer, Chief Info. Officer, Controller & Sec.--Andrew Sports Club Inc., Secaucus, NJ; *U.S. Private*, pg. 73

Lamb, Ronald M., Pres. & Chief Oper. Officer--Casey's General Stores, Inc., Ankeny, IA; *U.S. Public*, pg. 312

Lamb, Steven G., Chief Oper. Officer & Exec. V.P.--Case Corporation, Racine, WI; *U.S. Public*, pg. 311

Lamb, William G., Sr. V.P. & Sr. Lending Officer--Elyria Savings & Trust National Bank, Elyria, OH; *U.S. Public*, pg. 646

Lambesis, Vicki, Vice Chm., Chief Fin. Officer & Chief Oper. Officer--Lambesis, Del Mar, CA; *U.S. Private*, pg. 644

Lamer, Gerald P., Pres., Chief Exec. & Chief Oper. Officer--Marine Travelift, Inc., Sturgeon Bay, WI; *U.S. Private*, pg. 703

Lamm, Lloyd H., Sr. V.P., Chief Oper. Officer & Sec.--The Metropolitan Savings Bank of Ohio, Youngstown, OH; *U.S. Public*, pg. 608

Lamont, Lee, Chief Oper. Officer--ICM Artists, Ltd., New York, NY; *U.S. Private*, pg. 554

Lampi, Steve, Pres. & Chief Oper. Officer--Bridgeman's Restaurants Inc., Minnetonka, MN; *U.S. Private*, pg. 167

Lampila, Jorma, Chief Oper. Officer--Neste Oy, Naantali Refinery, Naantali, Finland; *Int'l*, pg. 914

Lampinen, Kari, Chief Oper. Officer--Noptor Oy, Espoo, Finland; *Int'l*, pg. 913

Land, Thomas K., Chief Oper. Officer--Tempo Advertising, Inc., Las Vegas, NV; *U.S. Public*, pg. 1432

Landon, Richard, Pres. & Chief Oper. Officer--The Marley Cooling Tower Co., Overland Park, KS; *U.S. Public*, pg. 1676

Landwehr, Michael A., Chief Oper. Officer--American Republic Insurance Co., Des Moines, IA; *U.S. Private*, pg. 61

Lane, Clifford, Chm. Bd., Pres. & Chief Exec. & Chief Oper. Officer--ILC Industries, Inc., Bohemia, NY; *U.S. Private*, pg. 555

Lane, Raymond, Pres. & Chief Oper. Officer--Oracle Corporation, Redwood City, CA; *U.S. Public*, pg. 1227

Lane, Robert A., Pres. & Chief Oper. Officer--Sonat Exploration Company, Houston, TX; *U.S. Public*, pg. 1485

Lane, William, Chm. Bd. & Chief Exec. Officer--Atlas Electric Devices Co., Chicago, IL; *U.S. Private*, pg. 96

Lang, John D., Chief Oper. Officer--Epson America Inc., Torrance, CA; *Int'l*, pg. 1219

Lang, Jordan, Chief Oper. Officer--OfB Grundstuecksverwaltungs GmbH, Frankfurt/Main, Germany; *Int'l*, pg. 799

Lang, Jordan, Chief Oper. Officer--OfB Bauvermittlungs und Gewerbebau Gesellschaft mbH, Frankfurt/Main, Germany; *Int'l*, pg. 799

Lang, Jordan, Chief Oper. Officer--GKH Gesellschaft fuer Kommunalbau in Hessen mbH, Frankfurt/Main, Germany; *Int'l*, pg. 799

Langdon, John, Pres. & Chief Exec. Officer--CPC Baking Business, Bay Shore, NY; *U.S. Public*, pg. 224

Langer, Robert, Chief Oper. Officer--Universal International, Inc., New Hope, MN; *U.S. Public*, pg. 1697

Langerak, Hans, Chief Oper. Officer--Hagglunds Drives GmbH, Gorinchem, Netherlands; *Int'l*, pg. 670

Langford, Robert M., Chief Oper. Officer & Sr. Exec. V.P.--Shoney's, Inc., Nashville, TN; *U.S. Public*, pg. 1467

Langhammer, Fred H., Pres. & Chief Oper. Officer--Estee Lauder Companies Inc., New York, NY; *U.S. Public*, pg. 594

Langhan, Terri, Pres. & Chief Oper. Officer--First Strategic Group, Whittier, CA; *U.S. Public*, pg. 1157

Lanham, Joel, Pres. & Chief Oper. Officer--Rhodes, Inc., Atlanta, GA; *U.S. Public*, pg. 805

Lanier, Jean, Chief Oper. Officer--EULER, Paris, France; *Int'l*, pg. 463

Lanktree, Charles T., Pres., Chief Exec. Officer & Chief Oper. Officer--Eggland's Best, Inc., King of Prussia, PA; *U.S. Private*, pg. 366

Lapekas, Edward, Chief Oper. Officer-Beverage & Sr. Exec. V.P.--American National Can Company, Chicago, IL; *Int'l*, *pg. 1029*

Laphen, James A., Pres. & Chief Oper. Officer--Commercial Federal Corporation, Omaha, NE; *U.S. Public*, pg. 411

Lapid, A.B., Chief Oper. Officer--Pan-Malayan Insurance Corporation, Manila, Philippines; *Int'l*, pg. 1392

Lapin, Steven B., Pres. & Chief Oper. Officer--Independence Holding Company, Stamford, CT; *U.S. Private*, pg. 446

Lappin, Richard, Vice Chm. & Chief Oper. Officer--Fruit of the Loom, Inc., Chicago, IL; *U.S. Public*, pg. 685

Largen, Joseph, Pres. & Chief Oper. Officer--Brodart Company, Williamsport, PA; *U.S. Private*, pg. 170

LaRocca, Vincent, Chief Oper. Officer--Aqua Care Systems Inc., Coral Springs, FL; *U.S. Public*, pg. 126

LaRocco, J.L., Chief Oper. Officer--AquaMatic, Rockford, IL; *U.S. Public*, pg. 1234

Larsen, Joe, Chief Oper. Officer & Exec. V.P.--TrizecHahn Centers Inc., San Diego, CA; *Int'l*, pg. 1425

Larsen, Per Henrik, Chief Oper. Officer--Novo Nordisk (China) Biotechnology Co. Ltd., Tianjin, China; *Int'l*, pg. 989

Larsen, Steen, Chief Oper. Officer--Novo Nordisk A/S, Singapore, Singapore; *Int'l*, pg. 987

Larson, Ken, Pres. & Chief Oper. Officer--Polaris Industries, Inc., Minneapolis, MN; *U.S. Public*, pg. 1313

LaRue, David J., Chief Oper. Officer & Exec. V.P.--Forest City Commercial Construction Company, Inc., Cleveland, OH; *U.S. Public*, pg. 668

Latella, Robert N., Chief Oper. Officer & Exec. V.P.--Genesee Corporation, Rochester, NY; *U.S. Public*, pg. 728

Latham, Paul, Pres. & Chief Oper. Officer-SportsNation--Costco Wholesale, Issaquah, WA; *U.S. Public*, pg. 451

LaTorre, L. Donald, Pres. & Chief Oper. Officer--Engelhard Corporation, Iselin, NJ; *U.S. Public*, pg. 582

Lau, Joseph, Chief Oper. Officer & Sr. V.P.--IWI Holding Limited, Westmont, IL; *U.S. Public*, pg. 861

Laub, Steven A., Chief Oper. Officer & Sr. V.P.--Lattice Semiconductor Corporation, Hillsboro, OR; *U.S. Public*, pg. 979

Laubich, Arnold, Pres. & Chief Oper. Officer--New Plan Realty Trust, New York, NY; *U.S. Public*, pg. 1172

Laucirica, Louis, Pres., Chief Exec. Officer & Chief Oper. Officer--Norton Performance Plastics, Wayne, NJ; *Int'l*, pg. 1174

Lav, Tom, Chief Oper. Officer--Littelfuse HK Ltd., Kowloon, Hong Kong; *U.S. Public*, pg. 1001

Lawler, Jeff, Chief Oper. Officer--Orbex Inc., Circle Pines, MN; *U.S. Public*, pg. 238

Lawrence, Ralph, Pres. & Chief Oper. Officer--Hyde Manufacturing Co., Southbridge, MA; *U.S. Private*, pg. 551

Lawrie, Eugene G., Chief Oper. Officer--Phillips Service Industries, Inc., Livonia, MI; *U.S. Private*, pg. 862

Lawson, Clif, Chief Oper. Officer--P.A.M. Transport, Inc., Tontitown, AR; *U.S. Private*, pg. 825

Lawson, Thomas E., Mng. Partner & Chief Oper. Officer--Arnold Communications, Inc., Boston, MA; *U.S. Private*, pg. 83

Lawson, William J., Pres. & Chief Oper. Officer--American States Insurance Companies, Indianapolis, IN; *U.S. Public*, pg. 997

Lawton, G.E., Chief Oper. Officer--Nutone Canada Inc., Mississauga, Canada; *Int'l*, pg. 1499

Layton, Mark C., Pres., Chief Exec. & Oper. Officer--Daisytek International Corporation, Plano, TX; *U.S. Public*, pg. 477

Layton, Mark C., Pres., Chief Exec. & Oper. Officer--Daisytek (Canada) Inc., Toronto, Canada; *U.S. Public*, pg. 477

Layton, Mark C., Pres., Chief Exec. & Oper. Officer--Daisytek Latin America, Miami, FL; *U.S. Public*, pg. 477

Layton, Mark C., Pres., Chief Exec. & Oper. Officer--Daisytek De Mexico S.A. de C.V., Mexico, Mexico; *U.S. Public*, pg. 477

Layton, Mark C., Pres., Chief Exec. & Oper. Officer--Priority Fulfillment Services, Inc., Plano, TX; *U.S. Public*, pg. 477

Layton, Mark C., Pres., Chief Exec. & Oper. Officer--Daisytek Australia Pty. Ltd., Alexandria, Australia; *U.S. Public*, pg. 477

Lazarus, Franz E., Chief Oper. Officer & Exec. V.P.-Intl. Opers.--Costco Wholesale, Issaquah, WA; *U.S. Public*, pg. 451

Le Mouroux, Pierre, Co-Chief Oper. Officer--Forasol S.A., Velizy-Villacoublay, France; *Int'l*, pg. 496

Leafstedt, Douglas A., Chm. Bd. & Chief Exec. Officer--AFSA Data Corp., Long Beach, CA; *U.S. Public*, pg. 649

League, Deborah, Chief Oper. Officer--Stackig Advertising and Public Relations, Mc Lean, VA; *U.S. Private*, pg. 1028

Leasher, Randy S., Pres. & Chief Oper. Officer--Cassano's Inc., Dayton, OH; *U.S. Private*, pg. 218

Leath, Jerry L., Chief Oper. Officer & Exec. V.P.--Sabreliner Corporation, Saint Louis, MO; *U.S. Private*, pg. 959

Lebedev, Greg, Chief Oper. Officer & Exec. V.P.--Nation's Business, Washington, DC; *U.S. Private*, pg. 788

Leblanc, Jean-Yves, Pres. & Chief Oper. Officer--Transportation Equipment Group, Saint-Bruno, Canada; *Int'l*, pg. 200

LeBlanc, Robert D., Pres. & Chief Oper. Officer--Handy & Harman, New York, NY; *U.S. Public*, pg. 780

LeClair, Darryl A., Chm. Bd., Pres. & Chief Exec. Officer--Echelon International Corporation, Saint Petersburg, FL; *U.S. Public*, pg. 560

LeClair, Fred L., Chief Oper. Officer--E.B. Eddy Forest Products Ltd., Hull, Canada; *Int'l*, pg. 1495

Lederer, David, Chief Oper. Officer & Exec. V.P.--Detection Systems, Inc., Fairport, NY; *U.S. Public*, pg. 501

Lee, Alan, Mng. Dir.--Hillard Scotchbrook Communications Pte. Ltd., Singapore, Singapore; *U.S. Private*, pg. 411

Lee, Andrew, Chm. Bd., Pres. & Chief Oper. Officer--Daniel Caron Sportswear, New York, NY; *U.S. Private*, pg. 309

Lee, Carroll R., V.P.-Opers.--Bangor Hydro-Electric Company, Bangor, ME; *U.S. Public*, pg. 178

Lee, Charles R., Chm. Bd., Chief Exec. Officer & Chief Oper. Officer--GTE Corporation, Stamford, CT; *U.S. Public*, pg. 696

Lee, Chong-Won, Chief Oper. Officer--Novo Nordisk Pharma Korea Limited, Seoul, Korea; *Int'l*, pg. 988

Lee, Dan R., Chief Oper. Officer--Microtek Medical, Inc., Columbus, MS; *U.S. Public*, pg. 914

Lee, David, Chief Oper. Officer--Azon Corporation, Johnson City, NY; *U.S. Private*, pg. 104

Lee, Debra L., Pres. & Chief Oper. Officer--Black Entertainment Television Holdings Inc., Washington, DC; *U.S. Public*, pg. 235

Lee, Heehwan, Dr., Chief Oper. Officer & V.P.--National Micronetics, Inc., Kingston, NY; *Int'l*, pg. 1347

Lee, Jim, Pres. & Chief Oper. Officer--Furst-McNess Company, Freeport, IL; *U.S. Private*, pg. 432

Lee, Leighton, III, Chief Oper. Officer--Lee Products Ltd., Gerrards Cross, United Kingdom; *U.S. Private*, pg. 657

Leeds, Jeffrey, Pres. & Chief Oper. Officer--Elsinore Corporation, Las Vegas, NV; *U.S. Public*, pg. 570

Lefevre, Jacques, Vice Chm. & Chief Oper. Officer--Lafarge S.A., Paris, France; *Int'l*, pg. 788

Lefort, Christian, Chief Oper. Officer--Prudence Vie, S.A., Paris, France; *Int'l*, pg. 16

Legasey, Edward E., Chief Oper. Officer & Exec. V.P.--SRA International Inc., Arlington, VA; *U.S. Private*, pg. 957

Legg, Mark, Chief Oper. Officer--Vivitar Corporation, Newbury Park, CA; *Int'l*, pg. 1060

Lehmann, Richard J., Pres. & Chief Oper. Officer--Banc One Corporation, Columbus, OH; *U.S. Public*, pg. 172

Leifheit, Dennis, Chief Oper. Officer & Exec. V.P.--IHOP Corp., Glendale, CA; *U.S. Public*, pg. 862

Leifheit, Dennis, Chief Oper. Officer--International House of Pancakes, Inc., Glendale, CA; *U.S. Public*, pg. 862

Leininger, Mark E., Chief Oper. Officer--Software Publishing Corporation, Fairfield, NJ; *U.S. Public*, pg. 1483

Leite, Luiz, Chief Oper. Officer--Novo Nordisk Farmaceutica do Brasil Ltda., Sao Paulo, Brazil; *Int'l*, pg. 988

Lekach, Zalman, Pres. & Chief Oper. Officer--Parlux Fragrances Inc., Fort Lauderdale, FL; *U.S. Public*, pg. 1264

Lelikov, Konstantin, Chief Oper. Officer--Akerlund & Rausing, Saint Petersburg, Russia; *Int'l*, pg. 33

Lemay, Ronald T., Pres. & Chief Oper. Officer--Sprint Corporation, Westwood, KS; *U.S. Public*, pg. 1500

Lemman, Peter R., Pres.--North Coast Electric Company, Bellevue, WA; *U.S. Private*, pg. 804

Lemonnier, Jean-Pierre, Chief Oper. Officer--BNP (Mexico) SA, Mexico, Mexico; *Int'l*, pg. 164

Lenain, Philippe, Vice Chm. & Chief Oper. Officer--Danone Group, Paris, France; *Int'l*, pg. 379

Leonard, Robert, Chief Oper. Officer--FMS Management Systems, Inc., Miami, FL; *U.S. Private*, pg. 389

Leonard, Steven, Chief Oper. Officer--Circle International Group, Inc., San Francisco, CA; *U.S. Public*, pg. 370

Leonardo, John C., Jr., Chief Oper. Officer & Exec. V.P.--Texas Micro, Inc., Houston, TX; *U.S. Public*, pg. 1586

Lepage, Paul, Chief Oper. Officer--Vision Financial Corporation, Keene, NH; *U.S. Private*, pg. 1141

Lepeltier, Jean-Louis, Chief Oper. Officer--Orlando Wyndham, Devon Park, Australia; *Int'l*, pg. 567

Leppaaho, Rauli, Chief Oper. Officer--Turku Plant, Turku, Finland; *Int'l*, pg. 863

Lerch, John A., Chief Oper. Officer--Carrafiello, Diehl & Associates, Inc., Irvington, NY; *U.S. Private*, pg. 215

Lerner, Mark, Chief Oper. Officer--Go Jo Industries, Cuyahoga Falls, OH; *U.S. Private*, pg. 458

Leroux, Marc, Pres. & Chief Oper. Officer--Teleglobe World Mobility, Montreal, Canada; *Int'l*, pg. 1373

Lesar, David J., Pres. & Chief Oper. Officer--Halliburton Company, Dallas, TX; *U.S. Public*, pg. 775

Leser, Lawrence, Chief Oper. Officer--Scripps Howard Broadcasting, Cincinnati, OH; *U.S. Public*, pg. 1447

Lesley, Richard, Chief Oper. Officer & Exec. V.P.--Booth American, Detroit, MI; *U.S. Private*, pg. 156

Lesser, Richard, Chief Oper. Officer & Exec. V.P.--The TJX Companies, Inc., Framingham, MA; *U.S. Public*, pg. 1556

Lester, David W., Chief Oper. Officer & Sr. V.P.--Kentucky Medical Insurance Company (KMIC), Louisville, KY; *U.S. Private*, pg. 741

Lester, L.J., Pres. & Chief Oper. Officer--Man-Gill Chemical Company, Cleveland, OH; *U.S. Private*, pg. 699

Lester, W. Bernard, Pres. & Chief Oper. Officer--Alico, Inc., La Belle, FL; *U.S. Public*, pg. 41

Lestina, Jerry, Pres. & Chief Oper. Officer--Roundy's, Inc., Pewaukee, WI; *U.S. Private*, pg. 948

Letbetter, S., Pres. & Chief Oper. Officer--Houston Industries Incorporated, Houston, TX; *U.S. Public*, pg. 842

Letbetter, S., Pres. & Chief Oper. Officer--NorAm Energy Corp., Houston, TX; *U.S. Public*, pg. 843

Leu, Randall, Chief Oper. Officer--KONE Elevators C&N Products Corporation, Taipei, Taiwan; *Int'l*, pg. 747

Leung, Elsie, Chief Oper. & Fin. Officer--Gemstar International Group Limited, Pasadena, CA; *U.S. Public*, pg. 705

Leutenegger, Aldo, Chief Oper. Officer--Swissmetal Italia s.r.l., Milan, Italy; *Int'l*, pg. 1427

Levan, Steven, Chief Oper. Officer--Starving Students, Inc., Los Angeles, CA; *U.S. Private*, pg. 1035

Levin, Alan, M.D., Chief Oper. Officer--AmeriPath, Inc., Riviera Beach, FL; *U.S. Public*, pg. 96

Levin, Richard C., Chief Oper. Officer & V.P.-Plng.--Biospherics Incorporated, Beltsville, MD; *U.S. Public*, pg. 232

Levine, Elliot, Pres. & Chief Oper. Officer--Softmart, Inc., Downingtown, PA; *U.S. Private*, pg. 1012

Levine, Howard R., Pres. & Chief Oper. Officer--Family Dollar Stores, Inc., Matthews, NC; *U.S. Public*, pg. 612

Levine, Paul, Chief Oper. Officer, Exec. V.P. & Sec.--Hirsch International Corp., Hauppauge, NY; *U.S. Public*, pg. 829

Levine, Ralph, Pres. & Chief Oper. Officer--Carter-Wallace, Inc., New York, NY; *U.S. Public*, pg. 309

Levitt, Howard, Chief Oper. Officer--Tourneau Inc., New York, NY; *U.S. Private*, pg. 1093

Levy, Enrique, Pres. & Chief Oper. Officer--Caprius, Inc., Wilmington, MA; *U.S. Public*, pg. 303

Levy, Jeffrey M., Pres. & Chief Oper. Officer--EMCOR Group, Inc., Norwalk, CT; *U.S. Public*, pg. 571

Levy, Mark A., Pres. & Chief Oper. Officer--Oriole Homes Corp., Delray Beach, FL; *U.S. Public*, pg. 1230

Levy, Randall D., Chief Oper. Officer--Guaranty F.S.B., Dallas, TX; *U.S. Public*, pg. 1575

Levy, Robert, Pres., Chief Exec. Officer & Chief Oper. Officer--Norman Levy Associates, Inc., Southfield, MI; *U.S. Private*, pg. 664

Lew, Steven, Pres. & Chief Oper. Officer--Universal Studios Hollywood, Universal City, CA; *Int'l*, pg. 1216

Lewinter, Mel, Vice Chm. & Chief Oper. Officer--Universal Studios Music Entertainment Group, Universal City, CA; *Int'l*, pg. 1215

Lewis, Aylwin B., Chief Oper. Officer--Pizza Hut, Inc., Dallas, TX; *U.S. Public*, pg. 1636

Lewis, Jerry, Pres. & Chief Oper. Officer--Sterling Vision, Inc., East Meadow, NY; *U.S. Public*, pg. 1516

Lewis, Joseph E., Chief Oper. Officer & Sr. V.P.--Silcorp Limited, Scarborough, Canada; *Int'l*, pg. 1249

Lewis, R. Jack, Jr., Chief Oper. Officer--Lewis Bros. Bakeries (MO), Sikeston, MO; *U.S. Private*, pg. 665

Lewis, R. Jack, Jr., Pres., Chief Oper. & Exec. Officer--Hartford Bakery, Inc., Evansville, IN; *U.S. Private*, pg. 665

Lewis, R. Jack, Jr., Chief Oper. Officer--Bonnie Baking Co., La Porte, IN; *U.S. Private*, pg. 665

Lewis, R. Jack, Jr., Chief Oper. Officer--Lewis Bros. Bakeries, Nashville, TN; *U.S. Private*, pg. 665

Lewis, R.J., Jr., Chief Oper. Officer--Lewis Bros. Bakeries (TN), Murfreesboro, TN; *U.S. Private*, pg. 665

Lewis, R.J., Jr., Chief Oper. Officer--Lewis Vincennes, Inc., Vincennes, IN; *U.S. Private*, pg. 665

Lewis, R.J., Jr., Chief Oper. Officer--Chicago Baking Co., Chicago, IL; *U.S. Private*, pg. 665

Lewis, Russell T., Pres. & Chief Oper. Officer--The New York Times Company, New York, NY; *U.S. Public*, pg. 1173

Leyendecker, R.F., Pres. & Chief Oper. Officer--Northwestern Energy Corp., Huron, SD; *U.S. Public*, pg. 1201

Leyendecker, R.F., Pres. & Chief Oper. Officer--Nekota Resources Inc., Huron, SD; *U.S. Public*, pg. 1201

Lhota, William J., Pres. & Chief Oper. Officer--Kentucky Power Co., Ashland, KY; *U.S. Public*, pg. 72

Lhota, William J., Pres. & Chief Oper. Officer--Wheeling Power Company, Wheeling, WV; *U.S. Public*, pg. 73

Lichtenstein, Howard, Chief Oper. Officer--American Life Insurance Company of New York, New York, NY; *U.S. Private*, pg. 769

Liddell, W.K., Pres., Chief Exec. & Chief Oper. Officer--Irex Corporation, Lancaster, PA; *U.S. Public*, pg. 913

Liddy, Edward M., Pres. & Chief Oper. Officer--The Allstate Corporation, Northbrook, IL; *U.S. Public*, pg. 55

Lidow, Eric, Chm. Bd., Pres. & Chief Oper. Officer--International Rectifier Corporation, El Segundo, CA; *U.S. Public*, pg. 906

Liebergesell, Rolf K., Chm. Bd., Pres. & Chief Exec. Officer & Chief Oper. Officer--Farrel Corporation, Ansonia, CT; *U.S. Public*, pg. 614

Lienau, Robert, Jr., Pres.--Trend Offset Printing Services, Los Alamitos, CA; *U.S. Private*, pg. 1099
Lietz, Richard A., Chief Oper. Officer & Exec. V.P.--ANR Pipeline Co., Detroit, MI; *U.S. Public*, pg. 389
Lievense, Robert J., Pres. & Chief Oper. Officer--A.C. Nielsen, Stamford, CT; *U.S. Public*, pg. 1183
Light, L.L., Pres. & Chief Oper. Officer--L.B. Smith, Inc., Camp Hill, PA; *U.S. Private*, pg. 1009
Lightstone, Ronald, Chief Oper. Officer & Exec. V.P.--Spelling Television, Los Angeles, CA; *U.S. Private*, pg. 776
Liguori, James J., Pres. & Chief Oper. Officer--Morgan's Foods, Inc., Beachwood, OH; *U.S. Public*, pg. 1133
Lilley, David, Pres. & Chief Oper. Officer--Cytec Industries Inc., West Paterson, NJ; *U.S. Public*, pg. 471
Lilly, Peter B., Pres. & Chief Oper. Officer--Peabody Holding Company, Inc., Saint Louis, MO; *Int'l*, pg. 594
Lima, Helio, Pres. & Chief Oper. Officer--Citibank (Florida) N.A., Dania, FL; *U.S. Public*, pg. 377
Limato, John, Pres. & Chief Oper. Officer--J.T. Slocomb Company, South Glastonbury, CT; *U.S. Private*, pg. 1006
Limpuangthip, Chin, Chief Oper. Officer--Novo Nordisk Pharma (Thailand) Ltd., Bangkok, Thailand; *Int'l*, pg. 988
Lin, W.H., Chief Oper. Officer--Gambro Taiwan Ltd., Taipei, Taiwan; *Int'l*, pg. 668
Lincoln, John, Grp. V.P.-Revenue Collection--Cubic Corporation, San Diego, CA; *U.S. Public*, pg. 466
Lind, Geoffrey E., Chm Bd. & Chief Oper. Officer--UMB Bank Colorado, Colorado Springs, CO; *U.S. Public*, pg. 1654
Linda, Luca, Chief Oper. Officer--Conquest Europe S.A.R.L., Neuilly-sur-Seine, France; *Int'l*, pg. 1484
Lindahl, Agneta, Chief Oper. Officer--Scandinavian Heart Center AB, Goteborg, Sweden; *Int'l*, pg. 670
Lindahl, Herbert W., Pres. & Chief Oper. Officer--State Industries Inc., Ashland City, TN; *U.S. Private*, pg. 1036
Lindal, Douglas F., Pres. & Chief Oper. Officer--Lindal Cedar Homes, Inc., Seattle, WA; *U.S. Public*, pg. 998
Lindblad, Anders, Chief Oper. Officer & Mng. Dir.--Hagglunds Drives AB, Mellansel, Sweden; *Int'l*, pg. 670
Lindbloom, Paul M., Pres. & Chief Oper. Officer--Acrometal Companies, Inc., Plymouth, MN; *U.S. Private*, pg. 14
Lindell, Aulis, Chief Oper. Officer--Neste Liikennepalvelu Oy, Espoo, Finland; *Int'l*, pg. 913
Lindgren, James, Chief Oper. Officer & V.P.-Opers.--Micro-Met L Corp., Indianapolis, IN; *U.S. Private*, pg. 742
Lindner, Carl H., III, Pres. & Chief Oper. Officer--American Financial Group, Cincinnati, OH; *U.S. Public*, pg. 75
Lindsay, Mike, Chief Oper. Officer--STM Wireless, Inc., Irvine, CA; *U.S. Public*, pg. 1421
Linginfelter, William, Chief Oper. Officer-Branches--South Trust Bank of Georgia, Atlanta, GA; *U.S. Public*, pg. 1492
Link, Herbert, Chief Oper. Officer-Corp. Mfg.--Clariant International Ltd., Muttenz, Switzerland; *Int'l*, pg. 624
Linn, James W., Chief Oper. Officer & Exec. V.P.--Parker Drilling Company, Tulsa, OK; *U.S. Public*, pg. 1259
Lipman, Allan M., Jr., Pres. & Chief Exec. Officer--The Amalgamated Sugar Company LLC, Ogden, UT; *U.S. Private*, pg. 48
Liszewski, Barbara, Chief Oper. Officer, Treas.--Nurses Inc., Houston, TX; *Int'l*, pg. 1285
Littelfield, Ben, Chief Oper. Officer--Cinamerica Theatres, L.P., Encino, CA; *U.S. Private*, pg. 239
Little, Lewis R., Pres. & Chief Oper. Officer--Smithfield Foods, Inc., Norfolk, VA; *U.S. Public*, pg. 1479
Little, W. Norris, Pres. & Chief Oper. Officer--Shaw Industries, Inc., Dalton, GA; *U.S. Public*, pg. 1464
Litvack, Sanford M., Chief Oper. Officer & Sr. Exec. V.P.--The Walt Disney Company, Burbank, CA; *U.S. Public*, pg. 511
Livonius, Robert, Chief Oper. Officer--Interim Services Inc., Fort Lauderdale, FL; *U.S. Public*, pg. 892
Ljungberg, Robert, Chm. Bd., Pres., Chief Exec. & Chief Oper. Officer--Ultra Tool & Plastics, Inc., Amherst, NY; *U.S. Private*, pg. 1116
Ljungstrom, Bo, Dir.--Helly-Hansen Confeccoes Lda., Moita, Portugal; *Int'l*, pg. 1010
Loebbe, Klaus-Peter, Chief Oper. Officer--BASF Coatings AG, Munster, Germany; *Int'l*, pg. 104
Loftus, Donald, Pres. & Chief Exec. Officer--Sanofi Beaute, Inc., New York, NY; *Int'l*, pg. 445
Logan, Dennis, Chief Oper. Officer-Beaver Foods Limited--Cara Operations Limited, Toronto, Canada; *Int'l*, pg. 266
Logan, Oran, Pres. & Chief Oper. Officer--Alamo Group, Inc., Seguin, TX; *U.S. Public*, pg. 34
Logotheti-Lyra, Elisavet, Chief Oper. Officer--Christie's Hellas Ltd., Athens, Greece; *Int'l*, pg. 290
Loke, Chan Keng, Chief Oper. Officer--Kim Eng Securities USA Inc., New York, NY; *Int'l*, pg. 733
Long, Francis A., Chief Oper. Officer & Exec. V.P.--Pennsylvania Power & Light Company-Lehigh Div., Allentown, PA; *U.S. Public*, pg. 1244
Long, James H., Chief Oper. Officer & V.P.--Long MFG. NC, Inc., Tarboro, NC; *U.S. Private*, pg. 674
Long, James R., Pres. & Chief Oper. Officer-Nortel World Trade--Northern Telecom Limited, Brampton, Canada; *Int'l*, pg. 968
Long, Phil, Pres. & Chief Oper. Officer--Biggs Gilmore Communications, Kalamazoo, MI; *U.S. Private*, pg. 143
Lopez, Francisco Fernandez, Chief Oper. Officer--Banco Santander, Mexico, Mexico; *Int'l*, pg. 144
Lorayes, Roberto, Chief Oper. Officer--Kim Eng Securities Philippines Inc., Manila, Philippines; *Int'l*, pg. 733
Lorber, Howard M., Pres. & Chief Oper. Officer--New Valley Corporation, Miami, FL; *U.S. Public*, pg. 1173
Lorberbaum, Jeffery, Pres. & Chief Oper. Officer--Mohawk Industries, Inc., Calhoun, GA; *U.S. Public*, pg. 1121
Lough, D.K., Pres. & Chief Oper. Officer--The Halifax Insurance Company, Toronto, Canada; *Int'l*, pg. 648
Loughlin, Thomas G., Chief Oper. Officer--Environmental Tectonics Corporation (ETC), Southampton, PA; *U.S. Public*, pg. 587
Louis, Kenneth C., Pres. & Chief Oper. Officer--Ameritas Life Insurance Corp., Lincoln, NE; *U.S. Private*, pg. 65
Lovold, Kjell, Chief Oper. Officer--Norfolier A/S & Co., Fjellhamar, Norway; *Int'l*, pg. 659
Low, Tony, Chief Oper. Officer--Darwin Digital, New York, NY; *U.S. Public*, pg. 1422
Lowater, David B., Pres. & Chief Oper. Officer-Visual Communications Group--Electrohome Ltd., Kitchener, Canada; *Int'l*, pg. 438
Lowe, Alan S., Pres. & Chief oper. Officer--Read-Rite Corporation, Milpitas, CA; *U.S. Public*, pg. 1366
Lowry, Richard M., Chief Oper. Officer & Exec. V.P.--Great Lakes Dredge & Dock Co., Oak Brook, IL; *U.S. Private*, pg. 474
Loy, Robert W., Exec. V.P.-Opers.--Roberts Pharmaceutical Corporation, Eatontown, NJ; *U.S. Public*, pg. 1393
Lubbert, Joachim, Dr., Co-Chief Oper. Officer--Berlin Branch, Berlin, Germany; *Int'l*, pg. 645
Lubetkin, Alvin N., Pres. & Chief Oper. Officer--Oshman's Sporting Goods, Inc., Houston, TX; *U.S. Public*, pg. 1233
Lubman, Irving, Chm. Bd. & Chief Oper. Officer--Nu Horizons Electronics Corp., Melville, NY; *U.S. Public*, pg. 1205
Lubs, John, Pres. & Chief Oper. Officer--Mason Shoe Mfg. Co., Chippewa Falls, WI; *U.S. Private*, pg. 712
Lubs, John A., Pres. & Chief Exec. Officer--Wissota Trader Ltd., Chippewa Falls, WI; *U.S. Private*, pg. 712
Lucci, Mike, Pres. & Chief Oper. Officer--Bally Total Fitness Corporation, Chicago, IL; *U.S. Public*, pg. 171
Luczo, Stephen J., Chm. Bd., Pres. & Chief Oper. Officer--Seagate Technology Inc., Scotts Valley, CA; *U.S. Public*, *pg. 1449*
Luddington, S.J., Chief Oper. Officer--Polycell Products Limited, Welwyn Garden City, United Kingdom; *Int'l*, pg. 1501
Ludes, John T., Pres. & Chief Oper. Officer--Fortune Brands, Inc., Old Greenwich, CT; *U.S. Public*, pg. 674
Ludington, David, Pres. & Chief Oper. Officer--Ludington News Co. Inc., Detroit, MI; *U.S. Private*, pg. 679
Ludlow, Stephen J., Pres. & Chief Oper. Officer--Veritas DGC Inc., Houston, TX; *U.S. Private*, pg. 1136
Ludvigsen, Carl W., Jr., Dr., Chief Oper. Officer & Exec. V.P.--Lab One, Lenexa, KS; *U.S. Public*, pg. 1449
Lugash, Larry, Chief Oper. Officer & Exec. V.P.--Maxon Industries, Inc., Huntington Park, CA; *U.S. Private*, pg. 717
Lukaska, Kenneth F., Pres. & Chief Oper. Officer--Unisource, Minneapolis, MN; *U.S. Public*, pg. 1671
Luke, Donald L., Pres. & Chief Oper. Officer--Group Maintenance America Corp., Houston, TX; *U.S. Public*, pg. 766
Lund, Richard A., Pres. & Chief Oper. Officer--Cade Industries, Inc., Lansing, MI; *U.S. Public*, pg. 289
Lunder, Peter, Pres., Chief Oper. Officer & Sec.--Dexter Shoe Company, Dexter, ME; *U.S. Public*, pg. 217
Lunderstadt, Carl, Pres. & Chief Oper. Officer--Florida Crushed Stone Company, Leesburg, FL; *U.S. Private*, pg. 414
Lundgren, Per S., Chief Oper. Officer--Novo Nordisk A/S, Sao Paulo, Brazil; *Int'l*, pg. 987
Lundstrom, Karen, Chief Oper. Officer--Applied Industrial Materials Corporation, Stamford, CT; *U.S. Public*, pg. 1736
Lung, David D., Pres. & Chief Oper. Officer--Patrick Industries Inc., Elkhart, IN; *U.S. Public*, pg. 1264
Lung, Jim, Chief Oper. Officer--Patrick Metals, Mishawaka, IN; *U.S. Public*, pg. 1265
Lunghi, Fabio, Chief Oper. Officer & Exec. V.P.--INCSTAR Corporation, Stillwater, MN; *Int'l*, pg. 483
Lunoi, Ken, Chief Oper. Officer & Exec. V.P.--Delta Education, Inc., Hudson, NH; *Int'l*, pg. 1402
Luntz, Andrew, Pres. & Chief Oper. Officer--Luntz Corporation, Canton, OH; *U.S. Private*, pg. 681
Luporte, Michael, Chief Oper. Officer--Olsonite Corporation, Newnan, GA; *U.S. Private*, pg. 815
Lussier, Gaetan, Chief Oper. Officer--Drake Bakeries, Inc., Wayne, NJ; *Int'l*, pg. 349
Lust, Kenneth E., Chief Oper. Officer & Sr. V.P.--MainStreet BankGroup Incorporated, Martinsville, VA; *U.S. Public*, pg. 1038
Luthro, John O., Chief Oper. Officer--Rochester Midland Corporation, Rochester, NY; *U.S. Private*, pg. 937
Lutz, John C., Pres., Chief Exec. Officer & Chief Oper. Officer--Elco Textron, Rockford, IL; *U.S. Public*, pg. 1590
Luzi, Armand, Chief Oper. Officer--Seal Products Incorporated, Naugatuck, CT; *U.S. Public*, pg. 849
Lybarger, Stanley A., Chief Exec. Officer--Bank of Oklahoma, N.A., Tulsa, OK; *U.S. Public*, pg. 163
Lydick, J. Lee, Pres., Chief Oper. Officer & Treas.--Grant-Lydick Beverage Co., San Antonio, TX; *U.S. Private*, pg. 470
Lyle, Freeman, Chief Oper. Officer & Chief Fin. Officer--Kennedy-Wilson, Inc., Santa Monica, CA; *U.S. Public*, pg. 951
Lynch, Cliff, Chief Oper. Officer--Burnham, Atlanta, GA; *Int'l*, *pg. 686*
Lynch, Richard, Pres. & Chief Oper. Officer--The Sports Authority Inc., Fort Lauderdale, FL; *U.S. Public*, pg. 1499
Lynett, Patricia, Chief Oper. Officer--Kelly Assisted Living Services, Inc., Troy, MI; *U.S. Public*, pg. 949
Lynne, Michael, Pres. & Chief Oper. Officer--New Line Cinema Corporation, New York, NY; *U.S. Public*, pg. 1614
Lyon, Harald, Chief Oper. Officer--KONE Sowitsch AG, Vienna, Austria; *Int'l*, pg. 748
Lyon, Wayne M., Pres. & Chief Oper. Officer--Masco Corporation, Taylor, MI; *U.S. Public*, pg. 1052
Lyons, Joseph F., Chief Oper. Officer & Gen. Mgr.--Akers Packaging Service Inc., Middletown, OH; *U.S. Private*, pg. 29
Lysenko, Vladimir P., Chief Oper. Officer--Akerlund & Rausing, Kiev, Ukraine; *Int'l*, pg. 33
Mabry, Mike, Chief Oper. Officer--Isolyser Company, Inc., Norcross, GA; *U.S. Public*, pg. 914
Macatee, John C., Pres. & Chief Oper. Officer--Office Depot Inc., Delray Beach, FL; *U.S. Public*, pg. 1212
MacDonald, Erin E., Pres. & Chief Oper. Officer--Sierra Health Services, Inc., Las Vegas, NV; *U.S. Public*, pg. 1469
MacDonald, J. Rory, Chief Oper. Officer & Exec. V.P.--The Bank of Nova Scotia Trust Company, Toronto, Canada; *Int'l*, pg. 155
MacDonald, K. Lin, Pres. & Chief Oper. Officer--Noranda Forest Inc., Toronto, Canada; *Int'l*, pg. 434
MacDonald, Michael, Pres. & Chief Oper. Officer--Carson Pirie Scott & Co., Milwaukee, WI; *U.S. Public*, pg. 309
Macdonald, Roddy, Chief Oper. Officer & Exec. V.P.--Alflex, Long Beach, CA; *U.S. Public*, pg. 415
MacDonald, William F., Jr., Chm. Bd., Pres., Chief Exec. & Chief Oper. Officer--Houghton International Inc., Valley Forge, PA; *U.S. Private*, pg. 541
MacGregor, Bruce, Pres. & Chief Oper. Officer--L.A. Gear, Inc., Santa Monica, CA; *U.S. Public*, pg. 969
Machala, Edward W., V.P.-Opers., Mfg. & Treas.--American Power Conversion Corporation, West Kingston, RI; *U.S. Public*, pg. 89
Machiels, G., Chief Oper. Officer--Gomala Imtech NV, Alken, Belgium; *Int'l*, pg. 681
Machuel, Pascal, Dir. Gen.--Telediffusion de France, Paris, France; *Int'l*, pg. 503
Machulak, Edward L., Chm. Bd., Pres., Chief Exec. Officer & Chief Oper. Officer--Commerce Group Corp., Milwaukee, WI; *U.S. Public*, pg. 410
Mack, Christopher E., Chief Oper. Officer & V.P.--ITC Learning Corp., Herndon, VA; *U.S. Public*, pg. 859
Mack, John J., Pres. & Chief Oper. Officer--Morgan Stanley Dean Witter & Co., New York, NY; *U.S. Public*, pg. 1132
Mackay, E.A.G., Chief Oper. Exec.--South African Breweries, Ltd., Johannesburg, South Africa; *Int'l*, pg. 1286
MacKenzie, G. Allan, Pres. & Chief Oper. Officer--Gendis Inc., Winnipeg, Canada; *Int'l*, pg. 542
Mackii, Callum, Chief Oper. Officer--Protocall Ventures, Marlow, United Kingdom; *U.S. Public*, pg. 740
Mackin, Scott G., Pres. & Chief Oper. Officer--Ogden Energy Group, Inc., Fairfield, NJ; *U.S. Public*, pg. 1213
MacLean, Barry L., Chm. Bd., Pres., Chief Exec. & Chief Oper. Officer--Maclean-Fogg Co., Mundelein, IL; *U.S. Private*, pg. 692
MacLeay, Thomas, Pres. & Chief Oper. Officer--National Life Insurance Company, Montpelier, VT; *U.S. Private*, pg. 785
MacLeod, Richard, Pres. & Chief Oper. Officer--Tapco International Corporation, Plymouth, MI; *U.S. Private*, pg. 1068
MacLeod, Tom, Pres. & Chief Oper. Officer--Iams Company, Dayton, OH; *U.S. Private*, pg. 556
MacMorran, Henry G., Pres. & Chief Oper. Officer--LaSalle Cragin Bank, Chicago, IL; *Int'l*, pg. 10
MacPhail, Keith A.J., Chief Oper. Officer & Exec. V.P.--Canadian Natural Resources Limited, Calgary, Canada; *Int'l*, pg. 258
Macuzak, John A., Pres. & Chief Oper. Officer--National Steel Corporation, Mishawaka, IN; *Int'l*, pg. 902
Madill, Eugene E., Chief Oper. Officer--Dairylea Cooperative Inc., East Syracuse, NY; *U.S. Private*, pg. 307
Madler, Mike, Chief Oper. Officer & Sr. V.P.--Prime Medical Services, Inc., Austin, TX; *U.S. Public*, pg. 1327
Madsen, Dennis, Chief Oper. Officer & Exec. V.P.--Recreational Equipment, Inc., Kent, WA; *U.S. Private*, pg. 914
Maender, Charles R., Pres. & Chief Oper. Officer--Central States Diversified, Inc., Saint Louis, MO; *U.S. Private*, pg. 224
Magid, Richard A., Chief Oper. Officer & Treas.--Ha-Lo Industries, Inc., Niles, IL; *U.S. Public*, pg. 773
Magner, Marjorie, Pres. & Chief Oper. Officer--Commercial Credit Company, Baltimore, MD; *U.S. Public*, pg. 1633
Magruder, Ronald N., Pres. & Chief Oper. Officer--Cracker Barrel Old Country Store, Inc., Lebanon, TN; *U.S. Public*, *pg. 455*
Mahanes, H. Patrick, Chief Oper. Officer & V.P.--Kennametal Inc., Latrobe, PA; *U.S. Public*, pg. 950
Maher, David L., Pres. & Chief Oper. Officer--American Stores Company, Salt Lake City, UT; *U.S. Public*, pg. 92
Mahoney, Michael J., Pres. & Chief Oper. Officer--RCN Corporation, Princeton, NJ; *U.S. Public*, pg. 1354
Mahoney, Richard, Pres. & Chief Oper. Officer--Caesars World, Inc., Las Vegas, NV; *U.S. Public*, pg. 1512
Mailind, Jesper, Pres. & Chief Oper. Officer--GN Danavox A/S, Taastrup, Denmark; *Int'l*, pg. 537
Major, Robert A., Pres. & Chief Oper. Officer--ContiMortgage Corporation, Horsham, PA; *U.S. Public*, pg. 439
Makarewicz, David C., Pres. & Chief Oper. Officer--J2, Inc., Deerfield, IL; *U.S. Private*, pg. 598
Makarewicz, Stephen E., Pres. & Chief Oper. Officer--J.M. Tull Metals Co., Inc., Norcross, GA; *U.S. Public*, pg. 879
Makhani, Madan P., Chm. Bd., Pres., Chief Oper. & Chief Fin. Officer--American Foundry Group, Inc., Bixby, OK; *U.S. Private*, pg. 54
Malenick, Donal H., Pres. & Chief Oper. Officer--Worthington Industries, Inc., Columbus, OH; *U.S. Public*, pg. 1780
Malesevich, Michael, Chief Oper. Officer & V.P.--Miller-St. Nazianz, Inc., Saint Nazianz, WI; *U.S. Private*, pg. 748
Maley, J., Chief Oper. Officer--Amersham Australia Pty. Ltd., Baulkham Hills, Australia; *Int'l*, pg. 992
Malkiewicz, Bob, Co-Pres. & Chief Oper. Officer--Helm, Inc., Detroit, MI; *U.S. Private*, pg. 520
Malmstrom, Kari, Chief Oper. Officer--KONE Elevators Export, Helsinki, Finland; *Int'l*, pg. 746
Malone, Joe N., Chief Oper. Officer & Sr. V.P.--Blockbuster Music, Dallas, TX; *U.S. Private*, pg. 776
Malone, Robert A., Pres., Chief Exec. & Chief Oper. Officer--Alyeska Pipeline Service Company, Anchorage, AK; *U.S.* Private, pg. 47

Malone, Tom, Pres. & Chief Oper. Officer--Milliken & Company, Spartanburg, SC; *U.S. Private*, pg. 748

Maloney, Raymond E., Pres. & Chief Oper. Officer--Farm Press, Clarksdale, MS; *U.S. Public*, pg. 1328

Maloof, Richard C., Pres. & Chief Oper. Officer--Bird Incorporated, Norwood, MA; *Int'l*, pg. 1170

Malschaert, Alain, Chief Oper. Officer--Aalst Local Head Office, Aalst, Belgium; *Int'l*, pg. 147

Malvaso, James J., Pres. & Chief Oper. Officer--The Raymond Corporation, Greene, NY; *Int'l*, pg. 123

Mamo, Dave, Chief Oper. Officer--LINC Financial Services, Inc., Chicago, IL; *U.S. Public*, pg. 996

Manafo, Mark S., Chief Oper. Officer--Partech Communications Group, Inc., Columbus, OH; *U.S. Public*, *pg. 1641*

Mancinelli, Victor A., Chief Oper. Officer & Exec. V.P.--Gehl Company, West Bend, WI; *U.S. Public*, pg. 704

Mandarich, David D., Chief Oper. Officer & Exec. V.P.--M.D.C. Holdings, Inc., Denver, CO; *U.S. Public*, pg. 1025

Mandel, Lon, Pres. & Chief Oper. Officer-List Marketing Services--LCS Industries, Inc., Clifton, NJ; *U.S. Public*, pg. 970

Mandelbaum, Mervyn, Chm. Bd., Pres., Chief Exec. & Chief Oper. Officer--Superba, Inc., Los Angeles, CA; *U.S. Private*, pg. 1054

Manez, Raymond, Chief Oper. Officer--Dynarad Corporation, Deer Park, NY; *U.S. Public*, pg. 494

Mang, Theo, Dr., Chief Tech. Officer--Fuchs Petrolub AG Oel + Chemie, Mannheim, Germany; *Int'l*, pg. 517

Mangini, John K., Chief Oper. Officer--Allied Digital Technologies, Hauppauge, NY; *U.S. Public*, pg. 48

Manhard, Tom, Chief Oper. Officer--Ribbon Narrow Fabric Company, Secaucus, NJ; *U.S. Private*, pg. 927

Manheim, Glen E., Chief Oper. Officer & Sr. V.P.--Empire Life Insurance Company, Seattle, WA; *U.S. Public*, pg. 1742

Maniscalco, Rosemary, Chief Oper. Officer--Comforce/ Uniforce Staffing Services, Woodbury, NY; *U.S. Public*, pg. 409

Manley, Ted R., Exec. V.P.-Opers. & Pres.-Once Upon A Child--Grow Biz International, Inc., Minneapolis, MN; *U.S.* Public, pg. 767

Manning, Kenneth P., Chm. Bd., Pres. & Chief Exec. Officer--Universal Foods Corporation, Milwaukee, WI; *U.S. Public*, pg. 1695

Manning, Wayne, Pres. & Chief Oper. Officer--Bashas, Chandler, AZ; *U.S. Private*, pg. 120

Marasca, Al, Pres. & Chief Oper. Officer--Ralphs Grocery Company, Compton, CA; *U.S. Private*, pg. 1202

Marchand, Gerard, Vice Chm. & Chief Oper. Officer--EMC-Belgique, Brussels, Belgium; *Int'l*, pg. 459

Marchi, David, Pres. & Chief Oper. Officer--TLP East, Wilton, CT; *U.S. Public*, pg. 1224

Marchionne, Sergio, Deputy Chief Exec. Officer & Chief Oper. Officer--Alusuisse-Lonza Holding Ltd., Zurich, Switzerland; *Int'l*, pg. 66

Marciano, Paul, Pres. & Chief Oper. Officer--Guess ?, Inc., Los Angeles, CA; *U.S. Public*, pg. 768

Marcus, Leonard, Pres. & Chief Oper. Officer--Federated Merchandising, New York, NY; *U.S. Public*, pg. 618

Marcus, Richard G., Pres. & Chief Oper. Officer--American Biltrite Inc., Wellesley Hills, MA; *U.S. Public*, pg. 68

Marcus, Stephen C., Chief Oper. Officer--Mars Graphics, Inc., Westville, NJ; *U.S. Public*, pg. 793

Mariani, Harry, Pres. & Chief Oper. Officer--Castello Banfi Srl., Siena, Italy; *U.S. Private*, pg. 113

Mariani, Pierre, Chief Oper. Officer--BANEXI (Banque Pour l'Expansion Industrielle), Paris, France; *Int'l*, pg. 163

Marien, Katherine C., Pres. & Chief Oper. Officer--Allied Capital Lending Corporation, Washington, DC; *U.S. Public*, pg. 48

Marincic, Joseph, Chief Oper. Officer--George & Thomas Cone Co., Hermitage, PA; *U.S. Private*, pg. 448

Marino, David, Chief Oper. Officer--Exotic Rubber & Plastics Corp., Farmington Hills, MI; *U.S. Private*, pg. 388

Mariotta, Claudio, Chief Oper. Officer--SEE Technologies Inc., Fremont, CA; *U.S. Public*, pg. 1421

Maritz, Steve, Pres.--Maritz Inc., Fenton, MO; *U.S. Private*, pg. 703

Mark, Russell, Chief Oper. Officer--Kaufman and Broad New Mexico Division, Albuquerque, NM; *U.S. Public*, pg. 945

Mark, Thomas E., Pres. & Chief Oper. Officer--Detrex Corporation, Southfield, MI; *U.S. Public*, pg. 501

Markel, Anthony F., Pres. & Chief Oper. Officer--Markel Corporation, Glen Allen, VA; *U.S. Public*, pg. 1046

Markey, Jonathan H., Pres. & Chief Oper. Officer--Bergen Record Corp., Hackensack, NJ; *U.S. Private*, pg. 693

Markham, Charles R., Pres. & Chief Oper. Officer--State Gas & Oil Company Division, State College, PA; *U.S. Public*, pg. 1664

Marks, Francis, Chief Oper. Officer--Paris Securities, New York, NY; *U.S. Private*, pg. 839

Marlar, Jerry L., Chief Oper. Officer--Intermedics Orthopedics, Inc., Austin, TX; *Int'l*, pg. 1307

Marlow, Alan, Pres. & Chief Oper. Officer--Harvey Industries, Inc., Waltham, MA; *U.S. Private*, pg. 508

Marnati, Pietro, Chief Oper. Officer--BNP Leasing SPA, Milan, Italy; *Int'l*, pg. 164

Maron, Edward B., Jr., Chief Oper. Officer & Exec. V.P.-Canadian Div.--Costco Wholesale, Issaquah, WA; *U.S. Public*, pg. 451

Marquardt, Arthur C., Pres. & Chief Oper. Officer--CTG Resources, Inc., Hartford, CT; *U.S. Public*, pg. 285

Marquardt, Arthur C., Pres. & Chief Oper. Officer--Connecticut Natural Gas Corporation, Hartford, CT; *U.S. Public*, pg. 285

Marquardt, Arthur C., Pres. & Chief Oper. Officer--Energy Networks, Inc. (ENI), Hartford, CT; *U.S. Public*, pg. 285

Marquart, Clifford L., Chief Oper. Officer & Exec. V.P.--The Morning Star Group, Dallas, TX; *U.S. Public*, pg. 1527

Marron, Ashley, Chief Oper. Officer--Bermo Scotland, Ltd, Glenrothes, United Kingdom; *U.S. Private*, pg. 136

Marsh, R. James, Chief Oper. Officer--Hilb, Rogal and Hamilton Company of Port Huron, Port Huron, MI; *U.S. Public*, pg. 827

Marshall, Dennis, Chief Oper. Officer--Branch Group Inc., Upper Marlboro, MD; *U.S. Private*, pg. 165

Marshall, Griffith M., Pres., Chief Exec. Officer & Chief Oper. Officer--Herbert Malarkey Roofing Company, Portland, OR; *U.S. Private*, pg. 698

Marshall, Harold D., Pres. & Chief Oper. Officer--Associates First Capital Corporation, Dallas, TX; *U.S. Public*, pg. 662

Marsland, D., Chief Oper. Officer--The Sunlight Service Group Ltd., Basingstoke, United Kingdom; *Int'l*, pg. 385

Marten, Randolph L., Chm. Bd., Chief Oper. Officer & Pres.--Marten Transport, Ltd., Mondovi, WI; *U.S. Public*, pg. 1052

Marti, Alfred, Chief Oper. Officer--Mikron Beijing Office, Beijing, China; *Int'l*, pg. 867

Marti, Andreas Molina, Chief Oper. Officer & Tech. Dir.--Union Naval de Levante, S.A., Madrid, Spain; *Int'l*, pg. 1442

Martin, Andrew P., Pres. & Chief Oper. Officer--Premium Budget Plan, Inc., Winston Salem, NC; *U.S. Public*, pg. 1453

Martin, Andrew P., Pres. & Chief Oper. Officer--The Innovative Company, Winston Salem, NC; *U.S. Public*, pg. 1454

Martin, Andrew P., Pres. & Chief Oper. Officer--Universal Insurance Co., Winston Salem, NC; *U.S. Public*, pg. 1454

Martin, Gary, Chief Oper. Officer--Virginia First Mortgage, Woodbridge, VA; *U.S. Public*, pg. 1721

Martin, Gerry L., Pres. & Chief Oper. Officer--Horizon Paper Co., Inc., New York, NY; *U.S. Private*, pg. 539

Martin, James A., Chief Oper. Officer & V.P.--Liberty Media Corporation, Englewood, CO; *U.S. Public*, pg. 1555

Martin, Margaret Ann, Chief Oper. Officer--Tausche Martin Lonsdorf, Atlanta, GA; *U.S. Private*, pg. 1069

Martin, Matthew G., Chief Oper. & Fin. Officer--Cattleman's, Inc., Detroit, MI; *U.S. Public*, pg. 318

Martin, Paul, Chief Oper. Officer--Community Newspaper Holdings Inc., Lexington, KY; *U.S. Private*, pg. 259

Martin, Rex, Chm. Bd., Pres. & Chief Exec. Officer--NIBCO, Inc., Elkhart, IN; *U.S. Private*, pg. 798

Martino, Mark A., Pres. & Chief Oper. Officer--Maaco Enterprises Inc., King of Prussia, PA; *U.S. Private*, pg. 689

Martz, D. Stephen, Pres. & Chief Oper. Officer--Omega Financial Corporation, State College, PA; *U.S. Public*, pg. 1222

Marvin, John W., Pres. & Chief Oper. Officer--Marvin Lumber & Cedar Company, Warroad, MN; *U.S. Private*, pg. 710

Marzloff, Georges, Chief Oper. Officer--Neste Oy, Chemicals, Espoo, Finland; *Int'l*, pg. 913

Marzloff, Georges, Chief Oper. Officer--Neste Chemicals Holding France S.A., Rungis, France; *Int'l*, pg. 914

Mason, Thomas J., Chief Oper. Officer--Tambrands Inc., Cincinnati, OH; *U.S. Public*, pg. 1331

Mason, Thomas R., Pres. & Chief Oper. Officer--CalEnergy Co., Omaha, NE; *U.S. Public*, pg. 292

Massalone, Daniel, V.P.-Sls.--Corporate Express Delivery Systems Southwest, Inc., Houston, TX; *U.S. Public*, pg. 449

Massaro, Mike, Chief Oper. Officer & Exec. V.P.--Goldberg Moser O'Neill, San Francisco, CA; *U.S. Private*, pg. 459

Master, Rex, Chief Oper. Officer--BHF (Los Angeles), Los Angeles, CA; *Int'l*, pg. 119

Masterson, Bill, Chief Oper. Officer--Sparton Engineered Products, Inc.-Flora Group, Flora, IL; *U.S. Public*, pg. 1496

Mastroianni, Martin J., Pres. & Chief Oper. Officer--Mechanical Technology Inc., Latham, NY; *U.S. Public*, pg. 1077

Mastromonaco, Lorenzo, Chief Oper. Officer--Novo Nordisk Farmaceutici Srl, Rome, Italy; *Int'l*, pg. 988

Mathias, James P., Pres. & Chief Oper. Officer--The JPM Company, Lewisburg, PA; *U.S. Public*, pg. 919

Mathot, Jean-Claude, Pres. & Chief Oper. Officer--BFX Hospitality Group, Inc., Fort Worth, TX; *U.S. Public*, pg. 160

Mathouillet, Philippe, Chief Oper. Officer--NATIO-VIE, Paris, France; *Int'l*, pg. 163

Matsik, George, Chief Oper. Officer-Packaging Opers.--Ball Corporation, Muncie, IN; *U.S. Public*, pg. 170

Matsuda, N., V.P.-Affiliated Co., Swift Instruments Intl.--Swift Instruments, Inc., Dorchester, MA; *U.S. Private*, pg. 1058

Matsumoto, Ernesto, Chief Oper. Officer--Tokio Marine Internacional Sociedad Anonima, Mexico, Mexico; *Int'l*, pg. 1393

Matsumoto, Yasushi, Chief Oper. Officer--Fresh Skylark Co., Ltd., Tokyo, Japan; *Int'l*, pg. 1262

Matsuo, Kazuhiko, Chief Oper. Officer--Gunze Sangyo (Osaka), Osaka, Japan; *Int'l*, pg. 578

Matsuyama, K., Chief Oper. Officer--Stettin Bay Lumber Co., Pty., Ltd., Kimbe, Papua New Guinea; *Int'l*, pg. 949

Matsuyama, Norio, Chief Oper. Officer--P.T. Standard Toyo Polymer, Jakarta, Indonesia; *Int'l*, pg. 1408

Matthews, Craig G., Pres. & Chief Oper. Officer--Brooklyn Union, Brooklyn, NY; *U.S. Public*, pg. 259

Matthews, Leo L., Pres. & Chief Oper. Officer--Allied Construction Products, Inc., Cleveland, OH; *U.S. Public*, pg. 1339

Matthiessen, Robert C., Chief Oper. Officer--Warner Publisher Services, Inc., New York, NY; *U.S. Public*, pg. 1614

Mattson, Bradford C., Pres. & Chief Oper. Officer--Vetrotex CertainTeed Corporation, Wichita Falls, TX; *Int'l*, pg. 1171

Mauch, Danna, Ph.D., Pres. & Chief Oper. Officer-Magellan Public Solutions--Magellan Health Services, Inc., Atlanta, GA; *U.S. Public*, pg. 1033

Maughan, H.B., Chief Oper. Officer & Mng. Dir.--Kidde Thorn Fire Protection Limited, Oldham, United Kingdom; *Int'l*, pg. 1500

Maulden, Jerry L., Vice Chm. & Chief Oper. Officer--Entergy Louisiana, Inc., New Orleans, LA; *U.S. Public*, pg. 586

Maulden, Jerry L., Vice Chm. & Chief Oper. Officer--Entergy New Orleans, Inc., New Orleans, LA; *U.S. Public*, pg. 586

Mauney, Charles F., Chief Oper. Officer & Exec. V.P.--Mauney Hosiery Mills, Inc., Kings Mountain, NC; *U.S. Private*, pg. 715

Maurer, Gilbert, Chief Oper. Officer & Exec. V.P.--Cosmopolitan, New York, NY; *U.S. Private*, pg. 517

Maurer, Gilbert C., Chief Oper. Officer & Exec. V.P.--The Hearst Corporation, New York, NY; *U.S. Private*, pg. 515

Maurer, Jeffrey, Pres. & Chief Oper. Officer--U.S. Trust Corporation, New York, NY; *U.S. Public*, pg. 1688

Maurer, Warren, Chief Oper. Officer& Exec. V.P.--Shadow Broadcast Services, Bala Cynwyd, PA; *U.S. Public*, pg. 1763

Mauro, Robert F., Chief Oper. Officer--WTTW (Channel 11), Chicago, IL; *U.S. Private*, pg. 1145

Mavel, James C., Chm. Bd., Pres. & Chief Exec. Officer--Scan-Optics, Inc., Manchester, CT; *U.S. Public*, pg. 1436

Maxwell, R., Chief Oper. Officer--Burgess Saia Co. Inc., Scarborough, Canada; *Int'l*, pg. 1500

May, Alison, Chief Oper. Officer & Chief Fin. Officer--Esprit de Corp., San Francisco, CA; *U.S. Private*, pg. 383

May, Dennis, Chief Oper. Officer & Exec. V.P.--Sun TV & Appliances, Inc., Groveport, OH; *U.S. Public*, pg. 1532

May, Larry, Chief Oper. Officer, Exec. V.P. & Gen. Mgr.--U.S. Filter/Davis Water & Waste Industries, Inc., Thomasville, GA; *U.S. Public*, pg. 1682

May, Peter W., Pres. & Chief Oper. Officer--Triarc Companies, Inc., New York, NY; *U.S. Public*, pg. 1634

May, Robert, Chief Oper Officer--Cablevision Systems Corporation, Woodbury, NY; *U.S. Public*, pg. 288

Mayell, Michael J., Pres. & Chief Oper. Officer--The Meridian Resource Corporation, Houston, TX; *U.S. Public*, pg. 1095

Mayer, Juan, Chief Oper. Officer--Titania Insurance Company of America, South Burlington, VT; *U.S. Public*, pg. 1731

Mayer, Robert A., Chief Oper. Officer--HealthAmerica Pennsylvania, Inc., Pittsburgh, PA; *U.S. Public*, pg. 454

Maynard, Jerome, Chief Oper. Officer--Vitasoy (U.S.A.) Inc., South San Francisco, CA; *Int'l*, pg. 1469

Mazer, Rick, Chief Oper. Officer & Exec. V.P.--Schwegmann Giant Super Markets, New Orleans, LA; *U.S. Private*, pg. 629

Maziarka, Donald, Pres., Chief Exec. & Chief Oper. Officer--George Sollitt Construction, Wood Dale, IL; *U.S. Private*, pg. 1013

Mazion, Francois, Chief Oper. Officer--CAP Sesa Tertiaire, Paris, France; *Int'l*, pg. 263

Mazza, Dick, Chief Oper. Officer--Wright Medical Technology, Arlington, TN; *U.S. Private*, pg. 1192

Mazza, N. Douglas, Chief Oper. Officer & Exec. V.P.--Hyundai Motor America, Fountain Valley, CA; *Int'l*, pg. 641

McAdam, John, Pres. & Chief Oper. Officer--Sequent Computer Systems, Inc., Beaverton, OR; *U.S. Public*, pg. 1459

McAlhaney, W. Hardee, Chief Oper. Officer--Holiday RV Superstores, Inc.-Orlando, Orlando, FL; *U.S. Public*, pg. 830

McAndrew, Kevin J., Chief Oper. & Fin. Officer & Exec. V.P.--Canterbury Corporate Services, Inc., Medford, NJ; *U.S. Public*, pg. 301

McAndrews, J.J., Pres. & Chief Exec. Officer--Mona Industries, Inc., Paterson, NJ; *U.S. Private*, pg. 756

McCaffrey, Gerald, Chief Oper. Officer & V.P.--Jumping Jacks, Monett, MO; *U.S. Private*, pg. 767

McCall, Carol J., Chief Oper. Officer--Humana Inc., Louisville, KY; *U.S. Public*, pg. 847

McCall, Scott, Chief Exec. Officer & V.P.-Acct. Services--McKinney & McKinney Advertising, Redondo Beach, CA; *U.S. Private*, pg. 723

McCann, Richard L., Chief Oper. Officer, Chief Fin. Officer & Exec. V.P.--Union Pump Company, Battle Creek, MI; *U.S. Private*, pg. 1119

McCaren, J. Reilly, Chief Oper. Officer & Exec. V.P.--Wisconsin Central Transportation Corporation, Rosemont, IL; *U.S. Public*, pg. 1772

McCarthy, Charles V., Chief Oper. Officer & Exec. V.P.--Tetley USA Inc., Shelton, CT; *Int'l*, pg. 1377

McCauley, Douglas A., Chief Oper. Officer--Mechanical Technology Inc.-Technology Grp.(Latham), Latham, NY; *U.S. Public*, pg. 1077

McCellan, John, Chief Oper. Officer--Great Scott Food Markets, Inc., Canton, MA; *U.S. Private*, pg. 402

McChord, M. Jackson, Pres. & Chief Oper. Officer--Peco Mfg. Co., Inc., Portland, OR; *U.S. Private*, pg. 846

McClean, Richard, Chief Exec. Officer & Publisher--International Herald Tribune S.A., Neuilly-sur-Seine, France; *U.S. Public*, pg. 1176

McClelland, Kent, Chief Oper. Officer--Colorado Institutional Foods, Commerce City, CO; *U.S. Private*, pg. 989

McCollough, W. Alan, Pres. & Chief Oper. Officer--Circuit City Stores, Inc., Richmond, VA; *U.S. Public*, pg. 374

McCollum, James, Chief Oper. Officer--Warren E. Collins, Inc., Braintree, MA; *U.S. Private*, pg. 253

McConahey, Stephen G., Pres. & Chief Oper. Officer--EVEREN Securities, Inc., Chicago, IL; *U.S. Public*, pg. 597

McCord, P.J., Chief Oper. Officer--Corbin Russwin, Inc., Berlin, CT; *Int'l*, pg. 1499

McCormick, R., III, Pres. & Chief Oper. Officer--American Sweeteners, Inc., Frazer, PA; *U.S. Private*, pg. 63

McCorry, James J., Chief Oper. Officer--Plaid Clothing Company, New York, NY; *U.S. Public*, pg. 796

McCoy, James T., Pres. & Chief Oper. Officer--The John C. Groub Company Inc., Seymour, IN; *U.S. Private*, pg. 484

McCready, James P., Pres. & Chief Oper. Officer--The Cypress Companies, Akron, OH; *U.S. Private*, pg. 299

McCulley, Robert N., Pres. & Chief Oper. Officer--Southern Precision Corporation, Birmingham, AL; *U.S. Public,* pg. 1736

McCullogh, S. Donald, Pres. & Chief Oper. Officer--Signature Brands USA, Inc., Solon, OH; *U.S. Public,* pg. 1472

McDaniel, John, Chief Oper. Officer--Farmers Telephone Co-Op, Kingstree, SC; *U.S. Private,* pg. 395

McDaniel, R. Leon, Pres. & Chief Oper. Officer--Pioneer Oil Company Inc., Fort Worth, TX; *U.S. Private,* pg. 866

McDonagh, William M., Pres. & Chief Oper. Officer--Broderbund Software, Inc., Novato, CA; *U.S. Public,* pg. 258

McDonald, I., Chief Oper. Officer--Yorkshire Bank, Leeds, United Kingdom; *Int'l,* pg. 906

McDonald, Mackey J., Pres., Chief Exec. Officer & Chief Oper. Officer--VF Corporation, Wyomissing, PA; *U.S. Public,* pg. 1702

McDonald, Richard E., Mng. Officer--BVK/McDonald, Milwaukee, WI; *U.S. Private,* pg. 108

McDougall, Kenneth, Chief Oper. Officer--Ellis & McDougall Lifts Ltd., Glasgow, United Kingdom; *Int'l,* pg. 747

McDowell, J. Walter, Pres. & Chief Exec. Officer--Wachovia Bank of North Carolina, N.A., Winston Salem, NC; *U.S. Public,* pg. 1730

McDowell, Jerry T., Chief Oper. Officer & Sr. V.P.--Alltrista Corporation, Muncie, IN; *U.S. Public,* pg. 56

McEwen, Robert R., Chief Oper. Officer--CSA Managed Gold Mutual Funds, Toronto, Canada; *Int'l,* pg. 243

McFadden, David, Chief Oper. Officer--Montgomery KONE Elevator Co. Ltd., Toronto, Canada; *Int'l,* pg. 748

McFarland, James D., Pres. & Chief Oper. Officer--Husky Oil Ltd., Calgary, Canada; *Int'l,* pg. 640

McGagin, Tim A., Pres. & Chief Oper. Officer--Coastal Lumber Company, Weldon, NC; *U.S. Private,* pg. 248

McGarrity, William, Chief Oper. Officer--Telpar, Inc., Addison, TX; *Int'l,* pg. 890

McGauley, Mark, Chief Oper. Officer--Nomura Holding America, Inc., New York, NY; *Int'l,* pg. 956

McGee, Jim, Pres.-Hospital Div., Chief Oper. Officer & Exec. V.P.--Schein Pharmaceutical, Inc., Florham Park, NJ; *U.S. Private,* pg. 969

McGill, J.C., Chm. Bd., Pres., Chief Exec. Officer--McGill Manufacturing Company, Inc., Valparaiso, IN; *U.S. Public,* pg. 573

McGillicuddy, Dennis, Chm. Bd. & Chief Oper. Officer--CCX, Inc., Charlotte, NC; *U.S. Private,* pg. 193

McGinnis, Ana Maria, Chief Oper. Officer--Royal Copenhagen Porcelain Corporation, White Plains, NY; *Int'l,* pg. 1134

McGinnis, William W., Chief Oper. Officer & Exec. V.P.--Jewelers Mutual Insurance Company, Neenah, WI; *U.S. Private,* pg. 587

McGrath, John, Pres., Chief Oper. Officer & Chief Credit Officer--The San Francisco Co., San Francisco, CA; *U.S.* Public, pg. 1430

McGrath, Mike, Chief Oper. Officer--Cadbury Beverages Seven Up, Dallas, TX; *Int'l,* pg. 248

McGraw, Harold W. III, Pres. & Chief Oper. Officer--The McGraw-Hill Companies, New York, NY; *U.S. Public,* pg. 1069

McGregor, John L., Chief Oper. Officer & Exec. V.P.--Willis Corroon Corp. of Wisconsin, Milwaukee, WI; *Int'l,* pg. 1507

McGuigan, Kate, Chief Oper. Officer--CFI Insurers, Ltd., Los Angeles, CA; *U.S. Public,* pg. 1475

McGuinness, Brian, Chief Oper. Officer--Mitchell Shackleton & Co. Ltd., Manchester, United Kingdom; *U.S. Private,* pg. 783

McGuire, James, Chief Oper. Officer--BGS Systems, Inc., Waltham, MA; *U.S. Public,* pg. 161

McGurk, Chris, Chief Oper. Officer--Universal Pictures, Universal City, CA; *Int'l,* pg. 1216

McHale, Judith, Pres. & Chief Oper. Officer--Discovery Communications, Inc., Bethesda, MD; *U.S. Private,* pg. 334

McHugh, M. Joseph, Pres. & Chief Oper. Officer--Triangle Pacific Corporation, Dallas, TX; *U.S. Public,* pg. 1634

McHugh, M. Joseph, Pres. & Chief Oper. Officer--Bruce Hardwood Floors, Dallas, TX; *U.S. Public,* pg. 1634

McHugh, Peter, Pres. & Chief Oper. Officer--Holland America Line Westours, Seattle, WA; *U.S. Public,* pg. 306

McIntyre, Brookes, Chief Oper. Officer--Banco Santander International Miami, Miami, FL; *Int'l,* pg. 143

McIntyre, Melissa E., RN, OCN, Pres. & Chief Oper. Officer--I.V. One, Altamonte Springs, FL; *U.S. Public,* pg. 229

McKee, Dave, Chief Oper. Officer--Dolan Northwest LLC, Seattle, WA; *U.S. Private,* pg. 338

McKee, W.W., Pres., Chief Exec. & Chief Oper. Officer--Pitt-Des Moines, Inc., Pittsburgh, PA; *U.S. Public,* pg. 1304

McKenna, Gerald, Chief Oper. Officer--NAPS United Kingdom, Abingdon, United Kingdom; *Int'l,* pg. 913

McKenna, Gerald, Chief Oper. Officer--Neste Oil Services, Inc., Houston, TX; *Int'l,* pg. 914

McKenna, Gerald, Chief Oper. Officer--Neste Petroleum (Products), Inc., Houston, TX; *Int'l,* pg. 914

McKenna, Michael J., Pres. & Chief Oper. Officer--Crown Cork & Seal Company, Inc., Philadelphia, PA; *U.S. Public,* pg. 462

McKenna, Ronald F., Exec. V.P. & Chief Oper. Officer-Aerospace--Sundstrand Corporation, Rockford, IL; *U.S. Public,* pg. 1533

McKinnon, Richard, Dir.-Opers.--Richey Electronics, Inc., Garden Grove, CA; *U.S. Public,* pg. 1388

McLain, Lucille, Chief Oper. Officer--Group Health Plan, Inc., Saint Louis, MO; *U.S. Public,* pg. 454

McLaine, John J., Pres. & Chief Oper. Officer--Excel Communications, Inc., Dallas, TX; *U.S. Public,* pg. 598

McLane, James W., Pres. & Chief Oper. Officer--NovaCare Inc., King of Prussia, PA; *U.S. Public,* pg. 1203

McLaughlin, David A., Chief Oper. Officer & Sr. V.P.-Opers./Nutritionals--Jones Medical Industries Inc., Saint Louis, MO; *U.S. Public,* pg. 933

McLaughlin, Philip L., Pres. & Chief Oper. Officer--Horizon Bancorp, Inc., Beckley, WV; *U.S. Public,* pg. 836

McLay, William, Chief Oper. Officer--Ryobi Motor Products, Anderson, SC; *Int'l,* pg. 1151

McLean, W., Chief Oper. Officer--Yale-Corbin Canada Limited, Mississauga, Canada; *Int'l,* pg. 1499

McManus, Edward J., Chief Oper. Officer-Procurement & Logistics--American Stores Company, Salt Lake City, UT; *U.S. Public,* pg. 92

McManus, James T., Pres. & Chief Oper. Officer--Taurus Exploration, Inc., Birmingham, AL; *U.S. Public,* pg. 581

McMaster, Malcolm, Chief Oper. Officer--MacGREGOR (USA) Inc., Pine Brook, NJ; *Int'l,* pg. 670

McMillan, Howard L., Jr., Pres. & Chief Oper. Officer--Deposit Guaranty Corp., Jackson, MS; *U.S. Public,* pg. 500

McMillan, Peter B., Pres. & Chief Oper. Officer--The Mills Corporation, Arlington, VA; *U.S. Public,* pg. 1113

McMinn, John A., Chief Oper. Officer & Exec. V.P.--The Cincinnati Cordage & Paper Company, Cincinnati, OH; *U.S. Private,* pg. 239

McMullen, James, Asst. Gen. Mgr. & Asst. Sec.--Tillamook County Creamery Assn., Tillamook, OR; *U.S. Private,* pg. 1086

McNally, Edward R., Jr., Chief Oper. Officer--Rapp Collins Worldwide, New York, NY; *U.S. Public,* pg. 1224

McNamara, John F., Chief Oper. Officer & Exec. V.P.--United Asset Management Corporation, Boston, MA; *U.S. Public,* pg. 1672

McNamee, Charles, Chief Exec. Officer--TIE/Communications, Inc., Overland Park, KS; *U.S. Private,* pg. 1085

McNeel, Clayton W., Pres. & Chief Oper. Officer--McNeel International Corp., Tampa, FL; *U.S. Private,* pg. 724

McNeeley, Donald R., Pres. & Chief Oper. Officer--Chicago Tube & Iron Co., Chicago, IL; *U.S. Private,* pg. 235

McNeil, Gary L., Chief Oper. Officer & Sr. V.P.--ASCG, Inc., Anchorage, AK; *U.S. Private,* pg. 80

McNutt, Robert P., Pres. & Chief Oper. Officer--Collin Street Bakery, Corsicana, TX; *U.S. Private,* pg. 252

McSween, H. Dale, Chief Oper. Officer & Exec. V.P.--Intertape Polymer Group Inc., Saint-Laurent, Canada; *Int'l,* pg. 684

McSweeny, Joseph M., Chief Oper. Officer--Willis Corroon Corp. of New York, New York, NY; *Int'l,* pg. 1506

Mead, Jeff, Chief Oper. Officer--Loomis, Sayles & Co., Boston, MA; *U.S. Private,* pg. 737

Meade, Richard A., Chief Oper. Officer--The Journal, Williamston, SC; *U.S. Private,* pg. 601

Meagher, Ellen, Chief Oper. Officer & V.P.--Paisano Publications, Inc., Agoura, CA; *U.S. Private,* pg. 834

Mealey, George A., Pres. & Chief Oper. Officer--Freeport-McMoRan Copper & Gold, Inc., New Orleans, LA; *U.S. Public,* pg. 680

Meaney, E. Robert, Pres. & Chief Oper. Officer-Intl. Div.--Valmont Industries, Inc., Valley, NE; *U.S. Public,* pg. 1706

Mebane, David C., Chm. Bd., Pres., Chief Exec. & Oper. Officer--Madison Gas and Electric Company, Madison, WI; *U.S. Public,* pg. 1032

Meclot, Ludo, Chief Oper. Officer--Ferrosan Healthcrafts NV/SA, Brussels, Belgium; *Int'l,* pg. 989

Medina, Carlos R., Chief Oper. Officer & Exec. V.P.--BITOR America Corp., Boca Raton, FL; *Int'l,* pg. 1045

Meeks, James E., Chief Oper. Officer & Sr. V.P.--Copart, Inc., Benicia, CA; *U.S. Public,* pg. 446

Meghani, Vijay, Chief Oper. Officer--BHF-Bank Representative Office, Mumbai, India; *Int'l,* pg. 120

Mehiel, Chris, Chief Oper. Officer & Exec. V.P.--Four M Corporation, Inc., Valhalla, NY; *U.S. Private,* pg. 421

Meier, Bernd, Chief Oper. Officer--SCM Microsystems, Inc., Los Gatos, CA; *U.S. Public,* pg. 1417

Meiers, Ronald J., Chief Oper. Officer & Sr. V.P.--Shopping Centre Group, Toronto, Canada; *Int'l,* pg. 253

Meijer, Emmo, Dr., Chief Oper. Officer--Holland Sweetener Company V.O.F., Maastricht, Netherlands; *Int'l,* pg. 1408

Meijer, Emmo, Dr., Chief Oper. Officer--Holland Sweetener Company, Geleen, Netherlands; *Int'l,* pg. 1408

Meirelles, Henrique de Campos, Pres. & Chief Oper. Officer--BankBoston Corporation, Boston, MA; *U.S. Public,* pg. 183

Meldrum, Renee, Chief Oper. Officer & V.P.--Family Healthcare Services, Inc., Las Vegas, NV; *U.S. Public,* pg. 1469

Mellema, Andries, Pres.--A.G. Simpson Co. Limited, Scarborough, Canada; *Int'l,* pg. 1252

Mellon, Christopher I., C.P.A., Chief Oper. Officer & Exec. V.P.--Pioneer American Holding Company, Carbondale, PA; *U.S. Public,* pg. 1298

Melnick, David, Chief Oper. Officer--Pentech International, Inc., Edison, NJ; *U.S. Public,* pg. 1274

Melnuk, Paul D., Chm. Bd., Pres. & Chief Oper. Officer--Clark Refining & Marketing Inc., Saint Louis, MO; *U.S. Private,* pg. 243

Melton, Owen B., Jr., Pres. & Chief Oper. Officer--First Indiana Corporation, Indianapolis, IN; *U.S. Public,* pg. 1484

Meltzer, Howard C., Pres. & Chief Oper. Officer--PC Quote, Inc., Chicago, IL; *U.S. Public,* pg. 1240

Melville, James, Pres.--First Commonwealth Corporation, Springfield, IL; *U.S. Private,* pg. 406

Melville, James, Pres. & Chief Oper. Officer--Abraham Lincoln Insurance Co., Springfield, IL; *U.S. Private,* pg. 406

Melville, James, Pres. & Chief Oper. Officer--Universal Guarantee Life Insurance, Springfield, IL; *U.S. Private,* pg. 406

Mendello, William L., Pres. & Chief Oper. Officer--Fender Musical Instruments, Scottsdale, AZ; *U.S. Private,* pg. 400

Mendelow, Clive, Vice Chm. & Chief Oper. Officer--Binswanger, Philadelphia, PA; *U.S. Private,* pg. 144

Mendez, Ivan A., Pres. & Chief Oper. Officer--Scotiabank de Puerto Rico, Hato Rey, PR; *Int'l,* pg. 156

Meneguetti, Valdecio Guilherize, Chief Oper. Officer--BB Financeira S.A. Credito Financiamento e Investimento, Brasilia, Brazil; *Int'l,* pg. 141

Menitti, Joseph, Chief Oper. Officer--PolyVision Corp., New York, NY; *U.S. Public,* pg. 1315

Mensah, Nana, Chief Oper. Officer & Exec. V.P.--Long John Silver's, Inc., Lexington, KY; *U.S. Private,* pg. 674

Meredith, Edie L., Exec. Asst.--Steel Technologies Inc., Louisville, KY; *U.S. Public,* pg. 1513

Meredith, J., Chief Oper. Officer--Shanks & McEwan (Southern Waste Services) Ltd, Milton Keynes, United Kingdom; *Int'l,* pg. 1228

Meredith, James F., AIA, Chief Oper. Officer--Giffels Strategic Consultants, L.L.C., Southfield, MI; *U.S. Private, pg. 452*

Meringola, Paul D., Chm. Bd., Pres., Chief Exec. Officer & Chief Oper. Officer--Medical Action Industries Inc., Hauppauge, NY; *U.S. Public,* pg. 1079

Merrell, John K., Pres., Chief Exec. Officer & Chief Oper. Officer--Industrial Dielectrics, Inc., Noblesville, IN; *U.S. Private,* pg. 560

Mershad, Fred, Pres. & Chief Oper. Oficer--The Elder-Beerman Stores Corp., Dayton, OH; *U.S. Private,* pg. 367

Merson, Robert, Chief Oper. Officer--Rexel, Inc., Coral Gables, FL; *Int'l,* pg. 1107

Messenger, George L., Pres. & Chief Oper. Officer--Kemper Reinsurance Co., Long Grove, IL; *U.S. Private,* pg. 614

Metta, F., Chief Oper. Officer--Kuehne & Nagel SpA, Milan, Italy; *Int'l,* pg. 763

Metzger, Samuel, Pres. & Chief Oper. Officer--Chipwich Inc., Ridgewood, NJ; *U.S. Private,* pg. 237

Meyer, Bernard, Pres. & Chief Oper. Officer--Allright Corporation, Houston, TX; *U.S. Private,* pg. 42

Meyer, Henry L., III, Vice Chm. & Chief Oper. Officer--Keycorp, Cleveland, OH; *U.S. Public,* pg. 954

Meyer, Lisa, Sr. Partner & Chief Oper. Officer--Carmichael Lynch, Inc., Minneapolis, MN; *U.S. Private,* pg. 213

Meyer, Ron, Pres. & Chief Oper. Officer--Universal Studios, Inc., Universal City, CA; *Int'l,* pg. 1215

Meyers, Gerald A., Pres. & Chief Oper. Officer--Century Aluminum Company, Monterey, CA; *U.S. Public,* pg. 328

Meyers, Gerald A., Pres. & Chief Oper. Officer--Ravenswood Aluminum Corp., Ravenswood, WV; *U.S. Public,* pg. 328

Meyers, Jerome E. Jr., Pres. & Chief Oper Officer--Dugan & Meyers Interests, Inc., Cincinnati, OH; *U.S. Private,* pg. 345

Meyerson, Andrew S., Pres. & Chief Oper. Officer--Metanetics Corp., Bothell, WA; *U.S. Public,* pg. 1573

Meylink, Daniel E., Chief Member Svcs. Officer--CUNA Mutual Insurance Society, Madison, WI; *U.S. Private,* pg. 296

Micek, Ernest S., Pres. & Chief Oper. Officer--Cargill, Wayzata, MN; *U.S. Private,* pg. 210

Michaels, Robert A., Pres. & Chief Oper. Officer--General Growth Properties Inc., Chicago, IL; *U.S. Public,* pg. 715

Michielutti, Peter G., Chief Oper. Officer & Exec. V.P.--Fingerhut Corp., Minnetonka, MN; *U.S. Public,* pg. 623

Michot, Yves, Pres.-Helicopter Div. & Chief Oper. Officer--Aerospatiale, Paris, France; *Int'l,* pg. 28

Mickels, Bror, Chief Oper. Officer--Novo Nordisk Farma OY, Espoo, Finland; *Int'l,* pg. 988

Mickelson, Timothy C., Pres. & Chief Oper. Officer--Marquette Medical Systems, Inc., Milwaukee, WI; *U.S. Public,* pg. 1047

Mignanelli, James, Chief Exec. & Oper. Officer & Treas.--Plastic Engineering Co. Inc., Haverhill, MA; *U.S. Private,* pg. 871

Mignogna, E.M., Chief Oper. Officer--ANSER (Analytic Services Inc.), Arlington, VA; *U.S. Private,* pg. 75

Mihos, James Peter, Chief Oper. Officer--Christy's Markets, Inc., Brockton, MA; *U.S. Private,* pg. 238

Mikel, Steve H., Chief Exec., Oper. & Fin. Officers--Southern Mineral Corporation, Houston, TX; *U.S. Public,* pg. 1490

Miladinovic, Ratko, Chief Oper. Officer--Novo Nordisk A/S, Belgrade, Serbia; *Int'l,* pg. 988

Milano, Mark R., Chief Oper. Officer--Paramount Petroleum Corp., Paramount, CA; *U.S. Private,* pg. 838

Milbrandt, Mike E., Chief Oper. Officer & Exec. V.P.--Lawson Software, Minneapolis, MN; *U.S. Private,* pg. 654

Miles, Kenneth P., Chief Oper. Officer--ARGOSystems, Inc., Sunnyvale, CA; *U.S. Public,* pg. 240

Mileski, Alan S., Pres. & Chief Oper. Officer--Nelson Westerberg, Inc., Elk Grove Village, IL; *U.S. Private,* pg. 1163

Mileski, Alan S., Pres. & Chief Oper. Officer--Nelson Westerberg, Somerville, NJ; *U.S. Private,* pg. 1164

Mileski, Alan S., Pres. & Chief Oper. Officer--Nelson Westerberg Atlas, Mableton, GA; *U.S. Private,* pg. 1164

Militello, Richard, Chief Oper. Officer--Peoples Telephone Company, Inc., Miami, FL; *U.S. Public,* pg. 1275

Millar, John P., Mng. Dir.--Williams de Broe Holdings Ltd., London, United Kingdom; *Int'l,* pg. 148

Millard, Dan, Chm. Bd., Pres., Chief Exec. & Chief Oper. Officer--Central Illinois Steel Company, Carlinville, IL; *U.S. Private,* pg. 223

Miller, Bill, Pres., Chief Exec. & Chief Oper. Officer--Contico International, Inc., Saint Louis, MO; *U.S. Private,* pg. 267

Miller, C. Douglas, Chm. Bd., Pres. & Chief Oper. Officer--Norrell Corporation, Atlanta, GA; *U.S. Public,* pg. 1192

Miller, David, Pres. & Chief Oper. Officer--Holder Corporation, Atlanta, GA; *U.S. Private,* pg. 533

Miller, Donald R., Chief Oper. Officer--Reeves International, Spartanburg, SC; *U.S. Private,* pg. 507

Miller, Eugene A., Chm. Bd. & Chief Exec. Officer--Comerica Incorporated, Detroit, MI; *U.S. Public,* pg. 408

Miller, James R., Chief Oper. Officer & Exec. V.P.--Northern Life Insurance Company, Seattle, WA; *U.S. Public,* pg. 1375

Miller, Jeff, Chief Oper. Officer--American Architectural Products, Inc., Youngstown, OH; *U.S. Public,* pg. 67

Miller, John C., Pres., Chief Exec. Officer & Chief Oper. Officer--Badger Farm Systems, Inc., Saint Nazianz, WI; U.S. Private, pg. 748

Miller, Leonard, Chm. Bd. & Pres.--Lennar Corporation, Miami, FL; U.S. Public, pg. 987

Miller, Mark, Pres. & Chief Oper. Officer--Cogentrix Incorporated, Charlotte, NC; U.S. Private, pg. 249

Miller, Mark, Chief Oper. Officer--The Focus Agency, Inc., Dallas, TX; U.S. Public, pg. 1224

Miller, Marty, Chief Oper. Officer & Exec. V.P.--Melitta U.S.A., Inc., Clearwater, FL; Int'l, pg. 857

Miller, Michael, Chief Oper. Officer--Cragar Industries, Inc., Phoenix, AZ; U.S. Public, pg. 456

Miller, Mitchell O., Chief Oper. Officer--Springfield Manufacturing LLC, Clover, SC; U.S. Private, pg. 546

Miller, Neil, Chief Fin. Officer, Chief Oper. Officer & Exec. V.P.--Partners & Shevack, Inc., New York, NY; U.S. Private, pg. 842

Miller, Philip B., Chm. & Chief Exec. Officer--Saks Fifth Avenue, New York, NY; U.S. Public, pg. 1429

Miller, Richard C., Chief Oper. Officer & Exec. V.P.--E.D. Bullard Company, Cynthiana, KY; U.S. Private, pg. 180

Miller, Richard C., Pres. & Chief Oper. Officer--GoodMark Foods, Inc., Raleigh, NC; U.S. Public, pg. 751

Miller, Thomas B., Chm. Bd., Pres. & Chief Exec. & Oper. Officer--Berry Bearing Company, Lyons, IL; U.S. Public, pg. 732

Millner, Thomas, Chm. Bd., Pres. & Chief Oper. Officer--Remington Arms Company, Inc., Madison, NC; U.S. Private, pg. 921

Millon, Jean-Pierre, Chief Oper. Officer--PCS Health Systems, Inc., Scottsdale, AZ; U.S. Public, pg. 993

Mills, Glenn, Chief Oper. Officer--Union-Transport (Aust) Pty Ltd, Tullamarine, Australia; U.S. Private, pg. 1120

Mills, Richard C., Chief Oper. Officer--Pomeroy Computer Resources, Hebron, KY; U.S. Public, pg. 1315

Mills, Rita Johnson, Chief Oper. Officer & Sr. V.P.--D.C. Chartered Health Plan, Washington, DC; U.S. Public, pg. 1241

Milner, Bruce D., Pres. & Chief Oper. Officer--Carat ICG, Los Angeles, CA; U.S. Private, pg. 207

Milock, R.L., Chief Oper. Officer & Exec. V.P.--Bradford-White Corporation, Ambler, PA; U.S. Private, pg. 164

Milonski, Donna, Chief Oper. Officer--Royal Copenhagen Porcelain Corporation, New York, NY; Int'l, pg. 1134

Milton, Robert A., Chief Oper. Officer--Air Canada, Saint-Laurent, Canada; Int'l, pg. 36

Minakawa, Atsushi, Chief Oper. Officer--Tosoh Hellas A.I.C., Thessaloniki, Greece; Int'l, pg. 1408

Minami, Junichi, Chief Oper. Officer--Nissho Iwai do Brasil S.A., Sao Paulo, Brazil; Int'l, pg. 948

Minami, Junichi, Chief Oper. Officer--Sakata Seed do Brasil Ltda., Sao Paulo, Brazil; Int'l, pg. 1178

Minaud, Pierre, Chief Oper. Officer--Jet Chef, Le Bourget, France; Int'l, pg. 560

Minear, David, Vice Chm. & Chief Oper. Officer-Adelaide/Melbourne--Young & Rubicam Mattingly, Richmond, Australia; U.S. Private, pg. 1198

Minear, David, Vice Chm. & Chief Oper. Officer--Young & Rubicam Adelaide Pty. Ltd., Dulwich, Australia; U.S. Private, pg. 1198

Minerva, Daniel O., Vice Chm. & Co-Chief Oper. Officer--Eastbridge Holdings Inc., New York, NY; Int'l, pg. 933

Minick, L. Scott, Pres. & Chief Oper. Officer--Sequus Pharmaceuticals, Inc., Menlo Park, CA; U.S. Public, pg. 1460

Minier, Michelle, Chief Oper. Officer & Exec. V.P.--Warehouse Lending Corporation of America, Pasadena, CA; U.S. Public, pg. 857

Minnig, Rebecca L., Sr. V.P.-Opers.--The Commercial Bank, Delphos, OH; U.S. Public, pg. 410

Minsky, Robert, Exec. V.P. & Chief Oper. Officer-Translation & Publishng--Berlitz International, Inc., Princeton, NJ; U.S. Public, pg. 221

Minson, Arthur T., Chief Oper. Officer & Gen. Mgr.--Georgette Klinger, Inc., New York, NY; U.S. Private, pg. 626

Mira, Fahad I., Chief Oper. Officer--Arabian Elevator & Escalator Co. Ltd. (AREECO), Jeddah, Saudi Arabia; Int'l, pg. 748

Miranda, Jose J., Chief Oper. Officer & Exec. V.P.--Gator Industries Inc., Hialeah, FL; U.S. Private, pg. 441

Mishima, Shiro, Mng. Dir.--OYO Corporation, Tokyo, Japan; Int'l, pg. 1019

Mitchell, George, Chief Oper. Officer & Exec. V.P.--Corcom, Inc., Libertyville, IL; U.S. Public, pg. 446

Mitchell, J., Chief Oper. Officer & Exec. V.P.--Versa Services Ltd., Etobicoke, Canada; U.S. Private, pg. 79

Mitchell, James E., Chief Fin. Officer & V.P.--Sunset Publishing Corporation, Menlo Park, CA; U.S. Public, pg. 1613

Mitchell, John M., Pres., Chief Exec. & Chief Oper. Officer--Pluess-Staufer Industries, Inc., Proctor, VT; Int'l, pg. 1061

Mitchell, Patrick, Pres. & Chief Oper. Officer--Cold Spring Granite Company, Cold Spring, MN; U.S. Private, pg. 250

Mitchell, Stephen C., Pres. & Chief Oper. Officer--Lester B. Knight & Associates, Inc., Chicago, IL; U.S. Private, pg. 626

Mitchell, W. Thomas, Chief Oper. Officer--Genencor International, Inc., Rochester, NY; Int'l, pg. 349

Mixon, Grover C., Chief Oper. Officer & Exec. V.P.--Phoenix Medical Technology, Inc., Andrews, SC; U.S. Public, pg. 1292

Miyake, T., Chief Oper. Officer--Scholl Japan Limited, Tokyo, Japan; Int'l, pg. 1210

Mizushima, Shigeru, Pres. & Chief Oper. Officer--Daido Hoxan Inc., Tokyo, Japan; Int'l, pg. 363

Mizutani, Satoshi, Chief Oper. Officer--Comdisco Japan Inc., Osaka, Japan; U.S. Public, pg. 408

Moar, James, Chief Oper. Officer & Exec. V.P.--DataCard Corporation, Minnetonka, MN; U.S. Private, pg. 312

Moberly, Thomas, Pres. & Chief Oper. Officer--G&K Services, Inc., Minnetonka, MN; U.S. Public, pg. 690

Mobley, A. Scott, Chief Oper. Officer, Exec. V.P. & Sec.--Noble Roman's Inc., Indianapolis, IN; U.S. Public, pg. 1187

Mockley, Michael E., Exec. V.P. & Chief Oper. Officer--Anchor Gasoline Corporation, Tulsa, OK; U.S. Private, pg. 70

Moe, Henrik, Pres., Chief Oper. & Exec. Officer--DEC International, Inc., Madison, WI; U.S. Private, pg. 301

Moehring, Hartmut, Dr., Pres. & Chief Oper. Officer--BASF Australia Ltd., Melbourne, Australia; Int'l, pg. 105

Mogi, Takemi, Chief Oper. Officer--Nippon Oil (Australia) Pty. Limited, Sydney, Australia; Int'l, pg. 937

Moguol, Christiou, Chief Oper. Officer--Banque Generale du Luxembourg S.A., Milan, Italy; Int'l, pg. 162

Mollins, Greg, Chief Oper. Officer--Metalcenter, Inc., Santa Fe Springs, CA; U.S. Public, pg. 1375

Mollins, Gregg J., Chief Oper. Officer & Exec. V.P.--Reliance Steel & Aluminum Co., Los Angeles, CA; U.S. Public, pg. 1375

Monaghan, Edward J., Chief Oper. Officer & Exec. V.P.--Flexsteel Industries, Inc., Dubuque, IA; U.S. Public, pg. 653

Monahan, Michael T., Pres.-Comerica Inc. & Comerica Bank--Comerica Incorporated, Detroit, MI; U.S. Public, pg. 408

Monahan, Michael T., Pres. & Chief Oper. Officer--Comerica Bank Michigan, Detroit, MI; U.S. Public, pg. 409

Mone, Thomas, Chief Oper. Officer--San Gabriel Valley Medical Center, San Gabriel, CA; U.S. Private, pg. 1118

Monette, Edward A., Chm. Bd., Pres., Chief Exec. Officer & Chief Oper. Officer--St. Croix Press, Inc., New Richmond, WI; U.S. Private, pg. 960

Monnin, Michelle, Chief Oper. Officer--EMS-West, San Jose, CA; U.S. Public, pg. 565

Monroe, Jeff, Chief Oper. Officer & Exec. V.P.--The Johnson Corporation, Three Rivers, MI; U.S. Private, pg. 591

Monson, Mark, Chief Oper. Officer--Monson Trucking, Inc., Duluth, MN; U.S. Private, pg. 758

Mont, Stuart, Chief Oper. Officer, Chief Fin. Officer, Exec. V.P. & Sec.--Recoton Corporation, Lake Mary, FL; U.S. Public, pg. 1369

Montague, William P., Pres. & Chief Oper. Officer--Mark IV Industries Inc., Amherst, NY; U.S. Public, pg. 1044

Montaner, Fernando, Chief Oper. Officer--BHF-Bank Representative Office, Mexico, Mexico; Int'l, pg. 120

Montano, Frank M., Pres. & Chief Oper. Officer--Moto Photo, Inc., Dayton, OH; U.S. Public, pg. 1136

Monteiro, Edson Machado, Chief Oper. Officer--BB Leasing-Arrandemento Mercantil, Brasilia, Brazil; Int'l, pg. 141

Montgomery, D.G., Chief Oper. Officer--Timber Products Company, LP, Springfield, OR; U.S. Private, pg. 1086

Montgoris, William J., Chief Oper. Officer & Sr. Mng. Dir.--The Bear Stearns Companies Inc., New York, NY; U.S. Public, pg. 197

Montgoris, William J., Chief Oper. Officer--Bear, Stearns & Co. Inc., New York, New York, NY; U.S. Public, pg. 198

Monto, Edward A., Pres. & Chief Oper. Officer--Houston Industries Energy, Inc., Houston, TX; U.S. Public, pg. 843

Monty, Jean C., Pres. & Chief Exec. & Oper. Officer--BCE Inc., Montreal, Canada; Int'l, pg. 114

Moody, Ross R., Pres. & Chief Oper. Officer--National Western Life Insurance Company, Austin, TX; U.S. Public, pg. 1161

Moone, Robert H., Pres. & Chief Oper. Officer--State Automobile Mutual Insurance Co., Columbus, OH; U.S. Private, pg. 1036

Mooney, Edward P., Chief Oper. Officer & V.P.--Monsey-Bakor, Kimberton, PA; U.S. Private, pg. 757

Mooney, Eugene C., Pres. & Chief Oper. Officer--Orange-Co., Inc., Bartow, FL; U.S. Public, pg. 1229

Mooney, James P., Chm. Bd. & Chief Oper. Officer--OM Group, Cleveland, OH; U.S. Public, pg. 1208

Mooney, Paul, Chief Oper. Officer--Novo Nordisk Pharmaceuticals Ltd., Dublin, Ireland; Int'l, pg. 988

Moore, Clyde R., Pres. & Chief Oper. Officer--Thomas & Betts Corporation, Memphis, TN; U.S. Public, pg. 1597

Moore, Frank, Chief Oper. Officer & Exec. V.P.--McCall Oil & Chemical Corp., Portland, OR; U.S. Private, pg. 719

Moore, Glenn R., Pres. & Chief Oper. Officer--Maynard Oil Co., Dallas, TX; U.S. Public, pg. 1064

Moore, Jack R., Pres. & Chief Exec. Officer--Stahl Specialty Company, Kingsville, MO; U.S. Private, pg. 1029

Moore, Jackson W., Pres. & Chief Oper. Officer--Union Planters Corporation, Cordova, TN; U.S. Public, pg. 1668

Moore, James L., Pres. & Chief Oper. Officer--Coca-Cola Consolidated, Charlotte, NC; U.S. Public, pg. 392

Moore, James L., Jr., Pres. & Chief Oper. Officer--Coca-Cola Bottling Co. Consolidated, Charlotte, NC; U.S. Public, pg. 391

Moore, John, Pres., Chief Exec. & Oper. Officer--Mindscape, Inc., Novato, CA; Int'l, pg. 1026

Moore, Robert, Chief Oper. Officer--Hawthorne Communications, Inc., Fairfield, IA; U.S. Private, pg. 512

Moore, Roger, Chief Oper. Officer--Novo Nordisk Pharma Ltd., Tokyo, Japan; Int'l, pg. 988

Moore, Thomas E., Chief Oper. Officer & Exec. V.P.--Material Sciences Corporation, Elk Grove Village, IL; U.S. Public, pg. 1056

Mooth, Thomas A., Chief Oper. Officer & Exec. V.P.--Trone Advertising, Inc., Greensboro, NC; U.S. Private, pg. 1104

Morais, Douglas, Exec. V.P.--Ortel Corporation, Alhambra, CA; U.S. Public, pg. 1232

Morales, Otto, Chief Oper. Officer--BIC de Guatemala, Guatemala, Guatemala; Int'l, pg. 1273

Moran, Mike, Pres. & Chief Oper. Officer--The Care Group, Inc., New York, NY; U.S. Public, pg. 305

Moran, Raymond, Chief Oper. Officer & Mng. Dir.--Cowen & Company, New York, NY; U.S. Private, pg. 280

More, Dominick D., Chief Oper. Officer & V.P.-Opers.--Eastern Air Devices, Inc., Dover, NH; U.S. Private, pg. 357

Morehead, C. Richard, Pres. & Chief Oper. Officer--American Heritage Life Investment Corp., Jacksonville, FL; U.S. Public, pg. 78

Morel, Bernard, Chief Oper. Officer--Go Voyages, Paris, France; Int'l, pg. 560

Morelli, B., Chief Oper. Officer--Sibeka, Brussels, Belgium; Int'l, pg. 1442

Morelli, Frank, Chief Oper. Officer & Chief Fin. Officer--MarketSource Corporation, Cranbury, NJ; U.S. Private, pg. 705

Morelli, Michael, Chief Oper. Officer--Littleton Coin Co., Inc., Littleton, NH; U.S. Private, pg. 671

Morgan, Jerry, Pres. & Chief Oper. Officer--Sargent & Greenleaf, Inc., Nicholasville, KY; U.S. Private, pg. 965

Morgano, Tony, Chief Oper. Officer--American Express Publishing Corporation, New York, NY; U.S. Public, pg. 74

Moriel, Donald M., Chief Oper. Officer & Exec. V.P.--Norcal Waste Systems, San Francisco, CA; U.S. Public, pg. 1188

Morikawa, Derek, Pres. & Chief Oper. Officer--Wavetek Corporation, San Diego, CA; U.S. Private, pg. 1154

Morin, Christopher L., Chief Oper. Officer--Noble International Ltd., Bloomfield Hills, MI; U.S. Public, pg. 1187

Morin, Eliane, Chief Oper. Officer--Framatome Connectors France, Versailles, France; Int'l, pg. 503

Morin, K.R., Chief Oper. Officer--Shanks & McEwan (Northern) Ltd, Coatbridge, United Kingdom; Int'l, pg. 1228

Mork, Richard G., Pres., Chief Exec. Officer & Chief Oper. Officer--A.M. Castle & Co., Franklin Park, IL; U.S. Public, pg. 312

Morley, Francis W., Chief Oper. Officer--Midland Paper Co., Elk Grove Village, IL; U.S. Private, pg. 744

Morlock, Greg, Chief Oper. Officer & V.P.-Opers.--Seed Restaurant Group, Inc., Lexington, KY; U.S. Private, pg. 981

Morris, Brian, Pres.--Dailey & Associates, West Hollywood, CA; U.S. Public, pg. 909

Morris, Craig, Chief Fin. Officer--Integral Systems, Inc., Walnut Creek, CA; Int'l, pg. 242

Morris, John R., Pres. & Chief Oper. Officer--Builders Transport, Incorporated, Camden, SC; U.S. Public, pg. 267

Morris, Nigel W., Pres. & Chief Oper. Officer--Capital One Financial Corporation, Falls Church, VA; U.S. Public, pg. 302

Morris, Scott J., Chief Oper. Officer & Exec. V.P.--Commercial Light Company, Hillside, IL; U.S. Private, pg. 258

Morris, T.N., Jr., Chm., Pres. & Chief Exec. Officer--Calcasieu Lumber Company, Austin, TX; U.S. Private, pg. 200

Morrison, Craig, Pres.--Van Leer Containers, Inc., Alsip, IL; Int'l, pg. 1146

Morse, Howard L., Pres. & Chief Oper. Officer--Acurex Environmental Corp., Mountain View, CA; Int'l, pg. 607

Mortell, John F., Chief Oper. Officer & Exec. V.P.--Physician Computer Network, Inc., Morris Plains, NJ; U.S. Public, pg. 1293

Mortimer, Anthony, Chief Oper. Officer--Goethe Management Ltd., Saint Peter Port, United Kingdom; Int'l, pg. 162

Mortimer, Daniel J., Chief Oper. Officer & Exec. V.P.--Halter Marine Group, Inc., Gulfport, MS; U.S. Public, pg. 778

Mosack, Glenn, Chief Oper. Officer--Conbraco Industries Inc., Matthews, NC; U.S. Private, pg. 261

Mosheneck, G. Ken, Chief Oper. Officer--Royster-Clark, Inc., Tarboro, NC; U.S. Private, pg. 949

Mossberg, Alan I., Pres., Chief Exec. & Chief Oper. Officer & Treas.--O.F. Mossberg & Sons, Inc., North Haven, CT; U.S. Private, pg. 764

Mott, David M., Pres. & Chief Oper. Officer--MedImmune, Inc., Gaithersburg, MD; U.S. Public, pg. 1081

Mottola, Thomas D., Pres. & Chief Oper. Officer-SMEI--Sony Music Entertainment, Inc., New York, NY; Int'l, pg. 1281

Mougeot, Robert F., Chief Oper. Officer & Chief Fin. Officer--HEI Diversified, Inc., Honolulu, HI; U.S. Public, pg. 800

Moulton, E., Chief Oper. Officer--Signal Capital Corporation, Danvers, MA; U.S. Public, pg. 115

Mow, Rosa, Chief Oper. Officer--Bugle Boy Industries, Inc., Simi Valley, CA; U.S. Private, pg. 179

Mowatt, Thomas, Pres. & Chief Oper. Officer--Champion Laboratories, Inc., Albion, IL; U.S. Private, pg. 1113

Mower, Don, Pres. & Chief Oper. Officer--Edwards Baking Co., Norcross, GA; U.S. Private, pg. 365

Moyer, Greg, Pres. & Chief Editorial Officer--Discovery Networks, Inc., Bethesda, MD; U.S. Private, pg. 334

Moylan, K.C., Chief Oper. Officer--Champps Entertainment, Inc., Wayzata, MN; Int'l, pg. 325

Moyn, John A., Sr. V.P.-Opers.--Atlantic Aviation Corp., New Castle, DE; U.S. Private, pg. 94

Mruz, Michael J., Pres. & Chief Exec. & Oper. Officer--Nichols Research Corporation, Huntsville, AL; U.S. Public, pg. 1182

Mudge, Fred N., Chief Oper. Officer--Commonwealth Aluminum-Lewisport, Lewisport, KY; U.S. Public, pg. 415

Mueller, David B., Chief Oper. Officer & Exec. V.P.--Spartech Corporation, Clayton, MO; U.S. Public, pg. 1495

Muftuoglu, Zeki, Chief Oper. Officer--Cignasa Sigorta A.S., Istanbul, Turkey; U.S. Public, pg. 363

Muftuoglu, Zeki, Chief Oper. Officer--Cignasa Sigorta A.S., Istanbul, Turkey; Int'l, pg. 1167

Muguerza, Jose, Chief Oper. Officer & Exec. V.P.--Rymer Meat Inc., Chicago, IL; U.S. Public, pg. 1414

Mulchay, Patrick J., Chief Oper. Officer & Exec. V.P.--Northern Indiana Public Service Company, Hammond, IN; U.S. Public, pg. 1185

Muldoon, Greg, Chief Oper. Officer & Exec. V.P.--Browning-Ferris Industries, Inc., Houston, TX; U.S. Public, pg. 262

Muldowney, Michael R., V.P.-Production & Mfg.--King & Prince Seafood Corporation, Brunswick, GA; *U.S. Private*, pg. 620
Mulford, Mark C., Pres. & Chief Oper. Officer--Ameriquest Technologies, Santa Ana, CA; *U.S. Public*, pg. 96
Mulhall, Denis, Chief Oper. Officer--Berisford plc, London, United Kingdom; *Int'l*, pg. 188
Mulhern, Malcolm, Chief Oper. Officer--Frionor (Thailand) Ltd., Bangkok, Thailand; *Int'l*, pg. 516
Mulholland, Paul, Chief Oper. Officer--Chemrock Corporation, Jacksonville, FL; *U.S. Private*, pg. 903
Mullany, Hank, Chief Oper. Officer--Genuardi Family Markets Inc., Norristown, PA; *U.S. Private*, pg. 447
Mullis, Elbert N., Jr., Chief Fin. & Admin. Officer, Exec. V.P. & Treas.--Coca-Cola Bottling Co. United, Inc., Birmingham, AL; *U.S. Private*, pg. 248
Mulloy, Gary M., Pres. & Chief Oper. Officer--ADVO, Inc., Windsor, CT; *U.S. Public*, pg. 23
Mulroney, John P., Pres. & Chief Oper. Officer--Rohm and Haas Company, Philadelphia, PA; *U.S. Public*, pg. 1403
Mulva, J.J., Pres. & Chief Oper. Officer--Phillips Petroleum Company, Bartlesville, OK; *U.S. Public*, pg. 1290
Mulvihill, Merilee J., Chief Oper. Officer--International Capital Equipment Limited, Hamilton, Bermuda; *Int'l*, pg. 683
Muma, Leslie M., Vice Chm., Pres. & Chief Oper. Officer--Fiserv, Inc., Brookfield, WI; *U.S. Public*, pg. 647
Murga, Rogelio M., Pres. & Chief Oper. Officer--EEI Corporation, Manila, Philippines; *Int'l*, pg. 425
Murgolo, Joseph, Pres., Chief Exec. Officer & Chief Oper. Officer--Friendship Dairies, Inc., Friendship, NY; *U.S. Private*, pg. 429
Murnin, Stephen, Pres. & Chief Oper. Officer--Network Real Estate Inc., Capitola, CA; *U.S. Private*, pg. 791
Murphy, Fred, Pres. & Chief Oper. Officer--Fisher Gauge Limited, Peterborough, Canada; *Int'l*, pg. 491
Murphy, Fred, Pres. & Chief Oper. Officer--Fishercast, Peterborough, Canada; *Int'l*, pg. 491
Murphy, Fred, Pres. & Chief Oper. Officer--Fishertech, Peterborough, Canada; *Int'l*, pg. 491
Murphy, G.D., Chm. Bd.--Erly Industries, Inc., Los Angeles, CA; *U.S. Public*, pg. 591
Murphy, Ginny, Chief Oper. Officer-Media--The Arnold Agency, Richmond, VA; *U.S. Private*, pg. 84
Murphy, Gregory E., Pres. & Chief Oper. Officer--Selective Insurance Group, Inc, Branchville, NJ; *U.S. Public*, pg. 1455
Murphy, Peter J., Chief Oper. Officer--Flexible Circuit Products Division, Methuen, MA; *U.S. Public*, pg. 1264
Murray, J. Mikell, Chief Oper. Officer & Sr. V.P.--Utilities Construction Co., Inc. Of South Carolina, Charleston, SC; *U.S. Private*, pg. 1130
Murschel, William H., Pres. & Chief Oper. Officer--Skyline Corporation, Elkhart, IN; *U.S. Public*, pg. 1476
Murset, Hans, Chief Oper. Officer--Mikron France Sarl, La Verriere, France; *Int'l*, pg. 867
Musgrave, William, Chief Oper. Officer & Exec. V.P.--Hendrick Automotive Group, Charlotte, NC; *U.S. Private*, pg. 522
Myers, Gary F., Pres. & Chief Oper. Officer--Kocolene Oil Corp., Seymour, IN; *U.S. Private*, pg. 629
Myers, Robert L., Chief Oper. Officer & Exec. V.P.--Priority Healthcare Corporation, Altamonte Springs, FL; *U.S. Public*, pg. 229
Myracle, Richard N., Chief Oper. Officer & Exec. V.P.--McKinney & Silver, Raleigh, NC; *U.S. Private*, pg. 723
Nadel, Paul, Pres. & Chief Oper. Officer--Ferolie Group, Montvale, NJ; *U.S. Private*, pg. 401
Nader, Anthony, Chief Oper. Officer & V.P.--National Electronics Warranty Corporation, Sterling, VA; *U.S. Private*, pg. 782
Nagataki, S., Chief Oper. Officer--Singapore Electrical Steel Services Private Ltd., Jurong, Singapore; *Int'l*, pg. 949
Nagel, Joe, Chief Oper. Officer & Exec. V.P.--US Ecology, Inc., Houston, TX; *U.S. Public*, pg. 71
Nagel, Joseph J., Pres. & Chief Oper. Officer--American Ecology Corporation, Boise, ID; *U.S. Public*, pg. 71
Nagorske, Lynn A., Pres. & Chief Oper. Officer--TCF Financial Corp., Minneapolis, MN; *U.S. Public*, pg. 1554
Nahas, Mostafa El, Chief Oper. Officer--Marryat & Scott Egypt-S.A., Cairo, Egypt; *Int'l*, pg. 748
Nahkunst, Michael, Chief Oper. Officer & Exec. V.P.--Cheesecake Factory Incorporated, Calabasas Hills, CA; *U.S. Public*, pg. 343
Naimark, Richard, Sr. V.P.--American Arbitration Association, New York, NY; *U.S. Private*, pg. 50
Najarian, Aram H., Chief Oper. Officer--Marketing Displays International, Farmington Hills, MI; *U.S. Private*, pg. 705
Nakamura, Kunio, Chm. Bd., Chief Exec. Officer & Chief Oper. Officer--Matsushita Electric Corporation of America, Secaucus, NJ; *Int'l*, pg. 847
Nakano, Mutsuo, Chief Oper. Officer--The Sumitomo Bank, Ltd.-Cairo Representative Office, Cairo, Egypt; *Int'l*, pg. 1309
Nakashige, Steve L., Pres. & Chief Oper. Officer--Hologic, Inc., Waltham, MA; *U.S. Public*, pg. 831
Nakasone, Robert C., Pres. & Chief Oper. Officer--Toys "R" Us, Inc., Paramus, NJ; *U.S. Public*, pg. 1626
Nalle, Peter, Chief Oper. Officer--Childrens Press Inc., Danbury, CT; *Int'l*, pg. 794
Nally, Michael J., Pres. & Chief Oper. Officer--Sportcraft Ltd., Mount Olive, NJ; *U.S. Private*, pg. 1026
Namekawa, Fumiaki, Chief Oper. Officer--The Tokio Marine International Fund (Luxembourg) S.A., Luxembourg, Luxembourg; *Int'l*, pg. 1393
Namekawa, Fumiaki, Chief Oper. Officer--Tokio Marine International Fund (Bahama) Company Limited, Nassau, Bahamas; *Int'l*, pg. 1393
Naporano, Joseph A., Chief Fin. Officer, Chief Oper. Officer & Exec. V.P.--Long Haymes Carr, Inc., Winston Salem, NC; *U.S. Public*, pg. 909
Nardulli, Ettore, Pres. & Chief Oper. Officer--Black Dot Graphics, Inc., Crystal Lake, IL; *U.S. Public*, pg. 503
Nasser, Albert, Chm. Bd., Chief Exec. Officer & Chief Oper. Officer--Lady Marlene Sales Corp., New York, NY; *U.S. Private*, pg. 642
Nathan, Joseph A., Pres. & Chief Oper. Officer--Compuware Corporation, Farmington Hills, MI; *U.S. Public*, pg. 423
Nattier, Robert, Chief Oper. Officer, Chief Fin. Officer & Gen. Mgr.--Mid-Kansas Co-op Association, Moundridge, KS; *U.S. Private*, pg. 743
Naukkarinen, Tyrki, Chief Oper. Officer--Plastilon, Willich, Germany; *Int'l*, pg. 915
Navarro, Bernabe L. Jr., Chief Oper. & Fin. Officer & Exec. V.P.--La Tondena Distillers, Inc., Manila, Philippines; *Int'l, pg. 785*
Neal, Philip M., Pres. & Chief Oper. Officer--Avery Dennison Corporation, Pasadena, CA; *U.S. Public*, pg. 152
Nedley, Robert E., Pres. & Chief Oper. Officer--St. Joe Corp., Jacksonville, FL; *U.S. Public*, pg. 1426
Nedwin, Glenn E., Chief Oper. Officer--Novo Nordisk Biotech, Inc., Davis, CA; *Int'l*, pg. 987
Needham, Tim, Pres. & Chief Oper. Officer--Williamhouse-Regency, Inc., New York, NY; *U.S. Public*, pg. 89
Neely, Bill, Pres. & Chief Oper. Officer--M.B. Kahn Construction Co., Inc., Columbia, SC; *U.S. Private*, pg. 604
Negishi, Yoshiya, Pres. & Chief Oper. Officer--Tokyo Senko International Inc., Tokyo, Japan; *Int'l*, pg. 1394
Negrini, Roberto, Chief Oper. Officer & Dir.-Production--Caleffi S.p.A., Viadana, Italy; *Int'l*, pg. 252
Neher, Lloyd, Chief Oper. Officer--Valley Food Distributors of Nevada, Las Vegas, NV; *U.S. Public*, pg. 919
Neill, R.A., Pres. & Chief Oper. Officer--Orenda Aerospace Corporation, Mississauga, Canada; *Int'l*, pg. 829
Neill, Richard, Pres. & Chief Oper. Officer--Magellan Aerospace Corporation, Mississauga, Canada; *Int'l*, pg. 829
Nelson, J. Calvin, Chief Oper. Officer & Exec. V.P.--Logan Corporation, Huntington, WV; *U.S. Private*, pg. 672
Nelson, John P., Pres. & Chief Oper. Officer--Acceptance Insurance Co., Inc., Omaha, NE; *U.S. Public*, pg. 14
Nelson, M. Bruce, Pres. & Chief Oper. Officer--Viking Office Products, Torrance, CA; *U.S. Public*, pg. 1720
Nelson, Marilynn C., Vice Chm. & Chief Oper. Officer--Carlson Companies, Inc., Minnetonka, MN; *U.S. Private*, pg. 211
Nelson, P.T., Chief Oper. Officer--Kidde-Graviner Australia Pty. Limited, Mordialloc, Australia; *Int'l*, pg. 1500
Nelson, Robert, Chief Fin. Officer & Chief Oper. Officer--Trace International Holdings, Inc., New York, NY; *U.S. Private*, pg. 1094
Nelson, Ronald, Chief Oper. Officer--Plum Building Systems, Inc., Roseville, MN; *U.S. Private*, pg. 475
Nelson, Roy C., Pres. & Chief Oper. Officer--Bank of Utah, Ogden, UT; *U.S. Private*, pg. 114
Nelson, Tom, Chief Oper. Officer--Fullerton Metals Co., Northbrook, IL; *U.S. Private*, pg. 431
Nelson, William H., Chief Oper. Officer & Exec. V.P.--Intermountain Health Care Inc., Salt Lake City, UT; *U.S. Private*, pg. 568
Nesci, Mark A., Chief Oper. Officer & V.P.-Store Opers.--Burlington Coat Factory Warehouse Corporation, Burlington, NJ; *U.S. Public*, pg. 268
Neugarten, Maks, Chief Oper. Officer--Novo Nordisk A/S, Warsaw, Poland; *Int'l*, pg. 989
Neumann, Dan, Chief Oper. Officer & Sr. V.P.--Onyx Technologies Ltd., Tel Aviv, Israel; *Int'l*, pg. 1007
Newberry, Richard A., Pres. & Chief Oper. Officer--Crown International, Inc., Elkhart, IN; *U.S. Private*, pg. 293
Newberry, Stephen, Chief Oper. Officer & Exec. V.P.--Lam Research Corporation, Fremont, CA; *U.S. Public*, pg. 975
Newbold, Philip, Chief Oper. Officer & Exec. V.P.--Data Dimensions, Inc., Culver City, CA; *U.S. Public*, pg. 485
Newkirk, Gerry, Pres. & Chief Oper. Officer--Tractor Supply Co., Nashville, TN; *U.S. Public*, pg. 1627
Newman, Larry M., Chief Oper. Officer--Call Interactive, Omaha, NE; *U.S. Public*, pg. 631
Newman, Terry G., Chief Oper. Officer & Sr. V.P.--Co-Steel Inc., Toronto, Canada; *Int'l*, pg. 298
Newmann, Heinz, Chief Oper. Officer--Decision Data, Heppenheim, Germany; *Int'l*, pg. 645
Newton, D.V., Pres. & Chief Oper. Officer--Canada Life Casualty Insurance Company, Etobicoke, Canada; *Int'l*, pg. 254
Newton, Thomas Alex, Pres. & Chief Oper. Officer--Daniel Industries, Inc., Houston, TX; *U.S. Public*, pg. 482
Neyer, William L., Sec.--Al Neyer, Inc., Cincinnati, OH; *U.S. Private*, pg. 797
Nezin, Gerard, Chief Oper. Officer--ITMI, Boulogne-Billancourt, France; *Int'l*, pg. 263
Nguyen, Khoa, Chief Oper. Officer & Exec. V.P.--VideoServer, Inc., Burlington, MA; *U.S. Public*, pg. 1720
Nichols, Fred R., Chm. Bd., Pres. & Chief Exec. Officer--TCA Cable TV, Inc., Tyler, TX; *U.S. Public*, pg. 1553
Nichols, Gerald L., Chief Oper. Officer & Exec. V.P.--CSX Transportation, Inc., Jacksonville, FL; *U.S. Public*, pg. 284
Nichols, Mack G., Pres. & Chief Oper. Officer--Mallinckrodt Inc., Saint Louis, MO; *U.S. Public*, pg. 1039
Nicholson, Bruce J., Chief Oper. Officer & Exec. V.P.--Lutheran Brotherhood, Minneapolis, MN; *U.S. Private*, pg. 681
Nickel, Dennis L., Chief Oper. Officer--E.V. Roberts & Associates, Inc., Culver City, CA; *U.S. Private*, pg. 935
Nielsen, Steve, Chief Oper. Officer & Sr. V.P.--Agripac Inc., Salem, OR; *U.S. Private*, pg. 26
Nielsen, Steven E., Pres. & Chief Oper. Officer--Dycom Industries, Inc., Palm Beach Gardens, FL; *U.S. Public*, pg. 538
Nihlmark, Eric, Chief Oper. Officer--Fastighetsaktiebolaget Hufvudstaden, Goteborg, Sweden; *Int'l*, pg. 478
Nii, Takaharu, Chief Oper. Officer--Makita Gulf FZE, Dubai, United Arab Emirates; *Int'l*, pg. 832
Nikkel, John G., Pres. & Chief Oper. Officer--Unit Corporation, Tulsa, OK; *U.S. Public*, pg. 1672
Nink, Trevor, Chief Oper. Officer--KONE Elevators (Australia) Pty. Ltd., Alexandria, Australia; *Int'l*, pg. 748
Nishimura, Koichi, Ph.D., Chm. Bd., Pres. & Chief Exec. Officer--Solectron Corporation, Milpitas, CA; *U.S. Public*, pg. 1483
Nissen, Dietmar, Dr., Pres. & Chief Oper. Officer--BASF Japan Ltd., Tokyo, Japan; *Int'l*, pg. 106
Nizam, Ike, Chief Oper. Officer--Master Distributors, Santa Monica, CA; *U.S. Private*, pg. 714
Noddle, Jeffrey, Exec. V.P., Pres. & Chief Oper. Officer-Wholesale Food Companies--SuperValu, Inc., Eden Prairie, MN; *U.S. Public*, pg. 1540
Nodland, J.M., Pres. & Chief Oper. Officer--McWhorter Technologies, Inc., Carpentersville, IL; *U.S. Public*, pg. 1074
Noelle, Gerald L., Chief Oper. Officer--Philadelphia American Life Insurance Company, Houston, TX; *U.S. Public*, pg. 853
Noels, Jacques, Pres., Chief Exec. Officer & Chief Oper. Officer--Zenith Data Systems, Deerfield, IL; *Int'l*, pg. 317
Nogueira, Artur M., Chief Oper. Officer & V.P.--Sapropur, S.A.R.L., Lisbon, Portugal; *U.S. Public*, pg. 429
Noll, Rich, Chief Exec. Officer--Sara Lee Sock Company, High Point, NC; *U.S. Public*, pg. 1434
Noonan, Terrence A., Pres. & Chief Oper. Officer--Furon Company, Laguna Niguel, CA; *U.S. Public*, pg. 688
Noonan, Timothy J., Pres. & Chief Oper. Officer--Rite Aid Corporation, Camp Hill, PA; *U.S. Public*, pg. 1390
Norberg, Joseph, Chief Oper. Officer--Hill, Holliday, Connors, Cosmopulos, Inc., Boston, MA; *U.S. Private*, pg. 529
Norbitz, Wayne, Pres. & Chief Oper. Officer--Nathan's Famous Inc., Westbury, NY; *U.S. Public*, pg. 1152
Nordin, Stig, Chief Exec. & Oper. Officer--Korsnas AB, Gavle, Sweden; *Int'l*, pg. 759
Nordkild, Peter, Chief Oper. Officer--Novo Nordisk Pharma Gesellschaft mbH, Vienna, Austria; *Int'l*, pg. 988
Nordwall, Anders, Chief Oper. Officer--MacGREGOR Cranes AB, Ornskoldsvik, Sweden; *Int'l*, pg. 670
Norin, Mats, Chief Oper. Officer--KONE Elevator (H.K.) Ltd., Kowloon, Hong Kong; *Int'l*, pg. 747
Norment, Philip, Chief Oper. Officer--Pilot Software, Cambridge, MA; *U.S. Private*, pg. 872
North, Gary, Chief Oper. Officer--Matson Terminals, Inc., San Francisco, CA; *U.S. Public*, pg. 40
Norwood, Mike, Pres. & Chief Oper. Officer--Electron Corp., Littleton, CO; *U.S. Private*, pg. 370
Noto, Lucio A., Chm. Bd., Pres., Chief Exec. & Chief Oper. Officer--Mobil Oil Corporation, Fairfax, VA; *U.S. Public*, pg. 1118
Novak, D., Chief Oper. Officer--Onyx Interactive Multimedia Ltd., Tel Aviv, Israel; *Int'l*, pg. 1007
Novak, Louis R., Chief Oper. Officer & Exec. V.P.--Galoob Toys, Inc., South San Francisco, CA; *U.S. Public*, pg. 698
Noyes, Ken, Pres. & Chief Oper. Officer--Schwan's Sales Enterprises, Marshall, MN; *U.S. Private*, pg. 974
Nozawa, Hiroo, Deputy Chm. & Chief Oper. Officer--Union Bank of California, San Francisco, CA; *Int'l*, pg. 157
Nozawa, Ryoichiro, Pres. & Chief Oper. Officer--Fanuc Ltd., Yamanashi, Japan; *Int'l*, pg. 477
Nozko, Henry W., Jr., Chief Oper. Officer, Exec. V.P. & Treas.--ACMAT Corporation, New Britain, CT; *U.S. Public*, pg. 16
Nuckels, Jim C., Chief Oper Officer-Pacific Recycling--Birmingham Steel Corporation, Birmingham, AL; *U.S. Public*, pg. 232
Nunes, Jawad G., Pres. & Chief Oper. Officer--American Tool Companies, Inc., Hoffman Estates, IL; *U.S. Private*, pg. 63
Nussbaum, Michael, Chief Oper. Officer--Field Container Company, L.P., Elk Grove Village, IL; *U.S. Private*, pg. 403
Nutter, Richard F., Chief Oper. Officer--Washington Service Bureau, Inc., Washington, DC; *Int'l*, pg. 1513
Nutter, W. Lee, Pres. & Chief Oper. Officer--Rayonier Inc., Stamford, CT; *U.S. Public*, pg. 1363
Nygrist, Bo, Chief Oper. Officer--AB Akerlund & Rausing, Norrkoping, Sweden; *Int'l*, pg. 33
O'Brien, Bill, Sr. V.P. & Chief Oper. Officer--Reed Elsevier Business Information, Newton, MA; *Int'l*, pg. 1095
O'Brien, Mark J., Chief Oper. Officer & Exec. V.P.--Pulte Corporation, Bloomfield Hills, MI; *U.S. Public*, pg. 1344
O'Brien, William K., Chief Oper. Officer--Coopers & Lybrand, New York, NY; *U.S. Private*, pg. 274
O'Bryan, P. Jack, Pres. & Chief Oper. Officer--USG Corporation, Chicago, IL; *U.S. Public*, pg. 1660
O'Dea, Patrick, Pres. & Chief Oper. Officer--Mother's Cake & Cookie Co., Oakland, CA; *U.S. Private*, pg. 1022
O'Donnell, James V., Chief Oper. Officer & Exec. V.P.--Gap Stores Division, San Bruno, CA; *U.S. Public*, pg. 702
O'Donnell, Patrick J., Chief Oper. Officer, Treas. & Gen. Mgr.--National Grape Co-Op Association, Inc., Westfield, NY; *U.S. Private*, pg. 784
O'Hanlon, Michael, Chm. Bd., Pres. & Chief Exec. & Oper. Officer--DVI Financial Services Inc., Newport Beach, CA; *U.S. Public*, pg. 476
O'Hanlon, Michael A., Pres. & Chief Oper. Officer--DVI, Inc., Doylestown, PA; *U.S. Public*, pg. 476
O'Hanlon, Michael A., Pres. & Chief Oper. Officer--DVI Business Credit, Inc., Newport Beach, CA; *U.S. Public*, pg. 476
O'Keefe, Tim, Chief Oper. Officer--Rangen Aquaculture Research, Buhl, ID; *U.S. Private*, pg. 909
O'Leary, Daniel J., Chief Oper. Officer--Stupp Corporation, Baton Rouge, LA; *U.S. Private*, pg. 1048
O'Malley, Michael, Chief Oper. & Fin. Officer & V.P.-Fin.--TelCom Semiconductor, Inc., Mountain View, CA; *U.S. Public*, pg. 1569
O'Malley, William, Chm. Bd., Pres. & Chief Oper. Officer--Tidewater Inc., New Orleans, LA; *U.S. Public*, pg. 1608
O'Meara, John M., Chief Oper. Officer & Exec. V.P.--First Midwest Bancorp, Inc., Itasca, IL; *U.S. Public*, pg. 636

O'Neil, Christopher, Chief Oper. Officer--Sound Advice, Inc., Dania, FL; *U.S. Public*, pg. 1488

O'Neil, James P., Pres. & Chief Oper. Officer--Bowne & Co., Inc., New York, NY; *U.S. Public*, pg. 248

O'Reilly, Larry, Chief Oper. Officer--O'Reilly Automotive Inc., Springfield, MO; *U.S. Public*, pg. 1230

O'Rourke, Mike, Chief Oper. Officer--Kaufman and Broad Colorado Division, Denver, CO; *U.S. Public*, pg. 945

O'Shea, Daniel, Chief Oper. Officer--Bill Communications, Inc., New York, NY; *Int'l*, pg. 1446

O'Shei, Donald M., Jr., Pres. & Chief Oper. Officer-CalEnergy Asia--CalEnergy Co., Omaha, NE; *U.S. Public, pg. 292*

Oakerson, William, Pres. & Chief Oper. Officer--Boat America Corp., Alexandria, VA; *U.S. Private*, pg. 153

Oakes, Eric J., Pres. & Chief Oper. Officer--Foster Wheeler Energy International, Inc., Clinton, NJ; *U.S. Public*, pg. 676

Oakes, Gary E., Pres., Chief Exec. & Oper. Officer--American Precast Concrete, Inc., Indianapolis, IN; *U.S. Private*, pg. 60

Obenberger, Robert L., Exec. V.P. & Gen. Mgr.--Four-S Baking Company, Los Angeles, CA; *U.S. Private*, pg. 422

Oberton, Willard D., Chief Oper. Officer & V.P.--Fastenal Company, Winona, MN; *U.S. Public*, pg. 614

Obsbaum, Frederic, Chief Oper. Officer & Chief Fin. Officer--Midland Walwyn Capital Corporation, New York, NY; *Int'l*, pg. 865

Ochiltree, Jock, Pres. & Chief Oper. Officer--Information Storage Devices, San Jose, CA; *U.S. Public*, pg. 876

Ocskay, A., Chief Oper. Officer--SAIA AG, Murten, Switzerland; *Int'l*, pg. 1500

Oden, D. Keith, Pres. & Chief Oper. Officer--Camden Property Trust, Houston, TX; *U.S. Public*, pg. 298

Odlang, Theron, Chief Oper. Officer--Fujisawa U.S.A. Inc., Deerfield, IL; *Int'l*, pg. 525

Odlaug, Theron, Ph.D., Chief Oper. Officer & Exec. V.P.--Fujisawa U.S.A., Deerfield, IL; *Int'l*, pg. 525

Offen, Al, Chief Oper. Officer--Wolf Mansfield Bolling Advertising Inc., Buffalo, NY; *U.S. Private*, pg. 1185

Ofstad, Cort, Chief Oper. Officer & Chief Fin. Officer--GKN Westland Aerospace North America Inc., Compton, CA; *Int'l*, pg. 535

Ogg, Thomas C., Chief Oper. Officer & Exec. V.P.--American Hardware Mutual Insurance Co., Columbus, OH; *U.S. Private*, pg. 764

Ogg, Thomas C., Chief Oper. Officer--American Merchants Casualty Co., Columbus, OH; *U.S. Private*, pg. 764

Ohlhues, Robert D., Pres. & Chief Oper. Officer--Associated Commercial Mortgage, Inc., Green Bay, WI; *U.S. Public*, pg. 140

Okamoto, Hiroshi, Chief Oper. Officer--Makita (Australia) Pty. Ltd., Sydney, Australia; *Int'l*, pg. 831

Okamoto, Shiyo, Chief Oper. Officer--Nippon Oil Exploration U.K. Limited, London, United Kingdom; *Int'l*, pg. 937

Okano, Keith, Chief Oper. Officer--Global Software, Inc., Raleigh, NC; *U.S. Private*, pg. 457

Okazaki, Hyoichi, Chief Oper. Officer--Japan Cargo Co., Ltd., Matsuyama, Japan; *Int'l*, pg. 1262

Oki, G., Chief Oper. Officer--P.T. Pardic Jaya Chemicals, Jakarta, Indonesia; *Int'l*, pg. 949

Okochi, Akira, Chief Oper. Officer & Sr. V.P.--Haseko (New York) Inc., New York, NY; *Int'l*, pg. 600

Okuma, Syuzo, Chief Oper. Officer--Taiwan Nisseki Co., Ltd., Kao-hsiung, Taiwan; *Int'l*, pg. 937

Olen, Gary, Pres., Chief Exec. Officer--The Sportsman's Guide, Inc., Saint Paul, MN; *U.S. Public*, pg. 1499

Oler, R. Wayne, Chief Oper. Officer--Addison-Wesley Higher Education, Reading, MA; *Int'l*, pg. 1026

Oliver, Travis, Chief Oper. Officer--Alcone Marketing Group, Irvine, CA; *U.S. Public*, pg. 1223

Olsman, Robert C., Pres. & Chief Oper. Officer--Reliance Insurance Company, Philadelphia, PA; *U.S. Public*, pg. 1374

Olson, Arthur L., Pres. & Chief Oper. Officer--R.L. Polk & Co., Southfield, MI; *U.S. Private*, pg. 874

Ong, Egil, Chief Oper. Officer--COBE Laboratories, Inc., Singapore, Singapore; *Int'l*, pg. 667

Onoda, Masayoshi, Pres. & Chief Oper. Officer--Yamanouchi Pharmaceutical Co. Ltd., Tokyo, Japan; *Int'l*, pg. 1518

Oran, Frederic M., Chief Oper. Officer & Exec. V.P.--Industrial Acoustics Company, Inc., Bronx, NY; *U.S. Public*, pg. 875

Orchard, William, Chief Oper. Officer--KONE Lifts Ltd., Hounslow, United Kingdom; *Int'l*, pg. 747

Orczyk, Stanley R., Chm. & Chief Oper. Officer--Meenan Oil Co. L.P., Syosset, NY; *U.S. Private*, pg. 729

Orlans, Eric, Gen. Mgr.--Gent Local Head Office, Gent, Belgium; *Int'l*, pg. 147

Orlik, Simon, Chief Oper. Officer--Akerlund & Rausing Ltd., Leicester, United Kingdom; *Int'l*, pg. 33

Orn, Gerald S., Pres., Chief Oper. Officer & Treas.--Central Allied Enterprises, Canton, OH; *U.S. Private*, pg. 222

Orr, Donald, Chief Oper. Officer, Exec. V.P. & Gen. Mgr.--Amperif Corporation, Chatsworth, CA; *U.S. Public*, pg. 1523

Orr, James F., Chief Oper. Officer--Cincinnati Bell Telephone, Cincinnati, OH; *U.S. Public*, pg. 367

Orr, Ron, Chief Oper. Officer--Molded Fiber Glass Companies, Ashtabula, OH; *U.S. Private*, pg. 755

Ortino, Hector R., Pres. & Chief Oper. Officer--Ferro Corporation, Cleveland, OH; *U.S. Public*, pg. 618

Orton, Douglas M., V.P.-Opers.--Cains Foods, L.P., Ayer, MA; *U.S. Private*, pg. 199

Orum, Stephen A., Chief Oper. Officer & Exec. V.P.--Lands' End, Inc., Dodgeville, WI; *U.S. Public*, pg. 977

Osabe, Bunjiro, Chm. Bd., Pres. & Chief Exec. Officer--Ozeki Corporation, Nishinomiya, Japan; *Int'l*, pg. 1019

Osada, Minoru, Chief Oper. Officer--Pentel of America, Ltd., Torrance, CA; *Int'l*, pg. 1035

Osborne, Charles M., Pres. & Chief Oper. Officer--Graco Inc., Golden Valley, MN; *U.S. Public*, pg. 756

Oscherwitz, William, Exec. V.P. & Chief Oper. Officer--Shofar Kosher Foods, Linden, NJ; *U.S. Public*, pg. 1433

Osherwitz, William, Chief Oper. Officer-Corp. Mktg.--Bessin Corporation, Chicago, IL; *U.S. Public*, pg. 1433

Osiek, Ross G., Pres. & Chief Oper. Officer--Nooter Corporation, Saint Louis, MO; *U.S. Private*, pg. 801

Osouf, Serge, Pres. & Chief Oper. Officer--SCOR, Paris, France; *Int'l*, pg. 1152

Osowski, Tom, Pres. & Chief Oper. Officer--Harrison Paint Corp., Canton, OH; *U.S. Private*, pg. 506

Osterman, John C., Pres., Chief Oper. Officer & Treas.--Chicago Rivet & Machine Company, Naperville, IL; *U.S. Public*, pg. 348

Ostrander, Charles, Co-Pres. & Chief Oper. Officer-Slipper Div.--R.G. Barry Corporation, Pickerington, OH; *U.S. Public*, pg. 192

Ostrow, Ronald F., Pres. & Chief Exec. Officer--LeaRonal, Inc., Freeport, NY; *U.S. Public*, pg. 982

Otaki, Katsuhiko, Pres. & Chief Oper. Officer--The Industrial Bank of Japan, Limited (Canada), Toronto, Canada; *Int'l, pg. 675*

Ouimet, Gilles P., Pres. & Chief Oper. Officer--Pratt & Whitney Canada Inc., Longueuil, Canada; *U.S. Public*, pg. 1690

Outlaw, Lanny F., Pres. & Chief Oper. Officer--Western Gas Resources, Inc., Denver, CO; *U.S. Public*, pg. 1758

Ouwehand, Hans, Chief Oper. Officer & Mng. Dir.--Littelfuse B.V., Utrecht, Netherlands; *U.S. Public*, pg. 1001

Overocker, H.L., Chief Oper. Officer--Frazee Industries Inc., San Diego, CA; *Int'l*, pg. 1501

Owen, C. Ray, Chief Oper. Officer & Exec. V.P.--Burlington Resources Inc., Houston, TX; *U.S. Public*, pg. 269

Owens, Phil, Pres. & Chief Oper. Officer--Top-Seal Corp., Phoenix, AZ; *U.S. Private*, pg. 1071

Owens, R. Harold, Pres. & Chief Oper. Officer--World Acceptance Corporation, Greenville, SC; *U.S. Public*, pg. 1778

Owens, Stewart K., Pres. & Chief Oper. Officer--Bob Evans Farms, Inc., Columbus, OH; *U.S. Public*, pg. 596

Owens, William A., Vice Chm., Pres. & Chief Oper. Officer--Science Applications International Corp., San Diego, CA; *U.S. Private*, pg. 975

Oyamada, A., Chief Oper. Officer--Dunlop Tire Corporation, Buffalo, NY; *Int'l*, pg. 1317

Oyster, William, Pres., Chief Oper. Officer & Mgr.-Adv., Sls. & Mktg.--Dallas Gold & Silver Exchange, Inc., Dallas, TX; *U.S. Public*, pg. 478

Pacheco, C., Chief Oper. Officer--Tintas Robbialac S.A., Sacavem, Portugal; *Int'l*, pg. 1501

Pachulski, Sheila, V.P.-Support Services--Prime Technology, Inc., Grand Rapids, MI; *U.S. Private*, pg. 884

Packard, Susan, Chief Oper. Officer--Home & Garden Television, Knoxville, TN; *U.S. Public*, pg. 1447

Paddock, M. David, Chm. Bd., Pres., Chief Exec. & Oper. Officer--Peoples National Bank, Lawrenceville, IL; *U.S. Public*, pg. 1217

Padnos, Jeffrey S., Pres. & Chief Oper. Officer--Louis Padnos Iron & Metal Co., Holland, MI; *U.S. Private*, pg. 834

Page, Timothy B., Chief Oper. Officer & Exec. V.P.--Farah Incorporated, El Paso, TX; *U.S. Public*, pg. 612

Paige, Richard, Pres.--PRO Group, Inc., Englewood, CO; *U.S. Private*, pg. 887

Pailleret, Pierre, Chief Oper. Officer--Orly Air Traiteur, Wissous, France; *Int'l*, pg. 560

Pajak, John J., Pres. & Chief Oper. Officer--Massachusetts Mutual Life Insurance Co., Springfield, MA; *U.S. Private*, pg. 712

Palko, Lorri M., Pres. & Chief Oper. Officer--Dorsey Trailers, Inc., Atlanta, GA; *U.S. Public*, pg. 520

Palle, Robert J., Jr., Chief Oper. Officer & Exec. V.P.--Blonder-Tongue Laboratories, Inc., Old Bridge, NJ; *U.S. Public*, pg. 237

Palleschi, Ralph, Chief Oper. Officer--New York Islanders Hockey Club, Uniondale, NY; *U.S. Private*, pg. 794

Pallien, Joachim, Chief Oper. Officer--Banque Generale du Luxembourg SA, Frankfurt/Main, Germany; *Int'l*, pg. 162

Palmer, Douglas W., Chief Oper. Officer--Norcen Energy Resources Limited, Calgary, Canada; *Int'l*, pg. 434

Palmer, Greg, Chief Oper. Officer & Exec. V.P.--RemedyTemp, Inc., San Juan Capistrano, CA; *U.S. Public*, pg. 1376

Palmer, Stephen, Chief Oper. Officer--Stiles Corporation, Fort Lauderdale, FL; *U.S. Private*, pg. 1043

Palonen, Gary L., Pres. & Chief Oper. Officer--Veridian, Alexandria, VA; *U.S. Private*, pg. 1136

Palonen, Gary L., Pres. & Chief Oper. Officer--Veda International, Inc., Alexandria, VA; *U.S. Private*, pg. 1136

Pamplin, Robert B., Jr., Dr., Pres., Chief Oper. Officer & Sec.--R.B. Pamplin Corp., Portland, OR; *U.S. Private*, pg. 835

Pan, Michael J., Pres. & Chief Oper. Officer--Snyder's Drug Stores, Inc., Minnetonka, MN; *U.S. Private*, pg. 1011

Papanier, George, Chief Oper. Officer--Resorts Casino Hotel, Atlantic City, NJ; *U.S. Public*, pg. 1531

Papciak, Wally, Chief Oper. Officer--Quality Education Data (QED), Denver, CO; *U.S. Private*, pg. 858

Pape, Manfred, Chief Oper. Officer--Thompson-Siegel GmbH, Dusseldorf, Germany; *Int'l*, pg. 610

Papke, Howard, Chief Oper. Officer--American Marine Holdings Inc., Sarasota, FL; *U.S. Private*, pg. 58

Papows, Jeffrey, Pres. & Chief Oper. Officer--Lotus Development Corporation, Cambridge, MA; *U.S. Public*, pg. 896

Papows, Jeffrey, Chief Oper. Officer & Exec. V.P.--Lotus Business Products Div., Cambridge, MA; *U.S. Public*, pg. 896

Paquin, James D., Chief Oper. Officer--American Cometra, Inc., Fort Worth, TX; *Int'l*, pg. 562

Parell, Jeff J., Pres. & Chief Oper. Officer--National Car Rental System, Inc., Minneapolis, MN; *U.S. Public*, pg. 1379

Parent, Mick, V.P.-Opers.--Grist Mill Company, Lakeville, MN; *U.S. Public*, pg. 766

Paris, Dominique, Chief Oper. Officer--Messier-Dowty, Abingdon, United Kingdom; *Int'l*, pg. 1340

Paris, Dominique, Chief Oper. Officer--Messier-Dowty International, Velizy-Villacoublay, France; *Int'l*, pg. 1340

Parise, Andrew J., Pres. & Chief Oper. Officer--Texfi Industries, Inc., Raleigh, NC; *U.S. Public*, pg. 1588

Parise, Thomas, Pres. & Chief Oper. Officer--Inter-Tel, Incorporated, Phoenix, AZ; *U.S. Public*, pg. 888

Pariso, Tim, Chief Oper. Officer & Exec. V.P.--Celotex Corporation, Tampa, FL; *U.S. Private*, pg. 221

Park, Bill, Chief Oper. Officer & Sr. V.P.--Curtis Mathes Holding Corp., Dallas, TX; *U.S. Public*, pg. 1057

Park, Sam Koo, Pres. & Chief Exec. Officer--Asiana Airlines, Los Angeles, CA; *U.S. Private*, pg. 89

Park, Sung-Joon, Chief Oper. Officer & Sr. Exec. V.P.--Daehong Advertising Inc., Seoul, Korea; *Int'l*, pg. 357

Park, Willner, Chief Oper. Officer--Infinicom, Chatham, NJ; *U.S. Private*, pg. 561

Parker, Charles A., Chief Oper. Officer & Exec. V.P.--Diamond Comic Distributors, Inc., Timonium, MD; *U.S. Private*, pg. 330

Parker, Ronald W., Chief Oper. Officer--Pizza Inn, Inc., Dallas, TX; *U.S. Public*, pg. 1307

Parks, Raymond F., Pres. & Chief Oper. Officer--J.H. Fletcher & Co., Huntington, WV; *U.S. Private*, pg. 412

Parmelee, H.J., Pres. & Chief Oper. Officer--The Turner Corporation, New York, NY; *U.S. Public*, pg. 1645

Parra, Luis Guillermo, Pres. & Chief Oper. Officer--BASF Quimica Colombiana S.A., Bogota, Colombia; *Int'l*, pg. 107

Parrette, William, Pres. & Chief Exec. Officer--Solitec Wafer Processing, Inc., San Jose, CA; *U.S. Private*, pg. 1013

Parrinello, John, Jr., Chief Oper. Officer & Exec. V.P.--Frank Briscoe Co. Inc., Kenilworth, NJ; *U.S. Private*, pg. 169

Parrish, James, Chief Oper. Officer--Innovative South, Nashville, TN; *U.S. Private*, pg. 565

Passaglia, Paolo, Chief Oper. Officer--Gambro Sales AB, Trieste, Italy; *Int'l*, pg. 668

Pate, Stephen T., Pres. & Chief Oper. Officer--Western Surety Company, Sioux Falls, SD; *U.S. Public*, pg. 303

Patel, Homi B., Pres. & Chief Oper. Officer--Hartmarx Corporation, Chicago, IL; *U.S. Public*, pg. 795

Patel, Mayur, Chief Oper. Officer--Novo Nordisk A/S, Nairobi, Kenya; *Int'l*, pg. 987

Patent, Patrick H., Chief Oper. Officer & Sr. V.P.--Megapulse, Inc., Bedford, MA; *U.S. Private*, pg. 729

Paterna, Salvatore A., Chm. Bd., Pres., Chief Exec. Officer & Chief Oper. Officer--John Solomon, Inc., Somerville, MA; *U.S. Private*, pg. 1013

Paterson, Ronald, Chief Oper. Officer & Exec. V.P.--Champion HealthCare Corporation, Houston, TX; *U.S. Public*, pg. 333

Patrick, Charles F., Chief Oper.Officer & Exec. V.P.--The Copley Press, Inc., La Jolla, CA; *U.S. Private*, pg. 275

Patrick, D.W., Chief Oper. Officer--Lynden Forwarding, Inc., Seattle, WA; *U.S. Private*, pg. 684

Patterson, A. Glenn, Pres. & Chief Oper. Officer--Patterson Energy, Inc., Snyder, TX; *U.S. Public*, pg. 1265

Patterson, A. Glenn, Pres. & Chief Oper. Officer--Patterson Drilling Co., Snyder, TX; *U.S. Public*, pg. 1265

Patterson, Charles, Pres., Chief Exec. Officer & Chief Oper. Officer--Walman Optical Company, Minneapolis, MN; *U.S. Private*, pg. 1148

Patterson, David S., Chief Oper. Officer & Exec. V.P.--Payco American Corporation, Brookfield, WI; *U.S. Public, pg. 1267*

Patterson, James E., Pres. & Chief Oper. Officer--Fred B. Johnston Company, Inc., Chapin, SC; *U.S. Private*, pg. 595

Patterson, Richard, Pres. & Chief Oper. Officer--Rosenthal Automotive Organization, Arlington, VA; *U.S. Private*, pg. 946

Patterson, William, Chief Oper. Officer & Sr. V.P.--Rundel Products, Inc., Portland, OR; *U.S. Private*, pg. 951

Patton, Charles A., Pres. & Chief Oper. Officer--Virginia First Savings Bank, F.S.B., Petersburg, VA; *U.S. Public*, pg. 1721

Pauek, Tommy, Pres., Chief Exec. & Oper. Officer--Alabama Farmers Co-op, Decatur, AL; *U.S. Private*, pg. 30

Paul, Gerald, Dr., Chief Oper. Officer & Exec. V.P.--Vishay Intertechnology, Inc., Malvern, PA; *U.S. Public*, pg. 1721

Paulson, Henry, Jr., Pres. & Chief Oper. Officer--Goldman, Sachs & Co., New York, NY; *U.S. Private*, pg. 462

Pauly, Jay W., Chief Oper. Officer & Sr. V.P.--BRE Properties, Inc., San Francisco, CA; *U.S. Public*, pg. 163

Pauza, Frank, Pres. & Chief Oper. Officer--Universal Folding Box Company, Inc., Hoboken, NJ; *U.S. Private*, pg. 1127

Pawsey, E.J.B., Chief Oper. Officer--Hart, Fenton & Co. Ltd., Portsmouth, United Kingdom; *Int'l*, pg. 1214

Payne, Paul D., Exec. V.P. & Chief Oper. Officer--Mercedes-Benz Credit Corp., Norwalk, CT; *Int'l*, pg. 368

Paynter, Stacey, Chief Oper. Officer-San Francisco, Exec. V.P. & Dir.--EvansGroup, Salt Lake City, UT; *U.S. Private*, pg. 385

Paynter, Stacey, Chief Oper. Officer & Exec. V.P.--EvansGroup, San Francisco, CA; *U.S. Private*, pg. 385

Payton, Jerry, Chief Oper. Officer & Sr. V.P.--Old America Stores, Howe, TX; *U.S. Public*, pg. 1215

Peabody, C. Matthew, Pres. & Chief Oper. Officer--X-Rite, Incorporated, Grandville, MI; *U.S. Public*, pg. 1783

Peacock, Gary, Gen. Mgr.--Covington Foods, Inc., Covington, IN; *U.S. Private*, pg. 280

Peacock, Lynne, Grp. Dir.-Opers.--Woolwich Plc, Bexley, United Kingdom; *Int'l*, pg. 1514

Pearce, B.D., Chief Oper. Officer--Larch-Lap Limited, Hartlebury, United Kingdom; *Int'l*, pg. 925

Pearce, R.M., Chief Oper. Officer & Exec. V.P.--Coho Energy, Inc., Dallas, TX; *U.S. Public*, pg. 396

Pearson, Neal, Chief Oper. Officer--Enway Inc., Clackamas, OR; *Int'l*, pg. 1262

Peattie, Allan E., Pres. & Chief Oper. Officer--Southeastern Development Company, Port Huron, MI; *U.S. Public*, pg. 1489

Peavey, Melia, Pres. & Chief Oper. Officer--Peavey Electronics Corp., Meridian, MS; *U.S. Private*, pg. 845
Pecchioli, Roberto, Chief Oper. Officer--KONE Ascensori S.p.A., Milan, Italy; *Int'l*, pg. 747
Pecchioli, Roberto, Chief Oper. Officer--KONE Italia S.p.A., Milan, Italy; *Int'l*, pg. 747
Pedersen, Birger, Chief Oper. Officer--Ferrosan AB, Malmo, Sweden; *Int'l*, pg. 989
Pedersen, Bjarne Lynge, Chief Oper. Officer--KONE Elevator A/S, Copenhagen, Denmark; *Int'l*, pg. 747
Pedersen, David, Chief Oper. Officer& Exec. V.P.--Martin K. Eby Construction Company, Inc., Wichita, KS; *U.S. Private*, pg. 359
Pedersen, Knud Odgaard, Chief Oper. Officer--Royal Copenhagen A/S, Frederiksberg, Denmark; *Int'l*, pg. 1134
Pedersen, Mogens C., Chief Oper. Officer--Ferrosan Healthcare Ltd., Byfleet, United Kingdom; *Int'l*, pg. 989
Peery, Tom A., Pres. & Chief Oper. Officer--Heilig Meyers Furniture Co., Richmond, VA; *U.S. Public*, pg. 804
Peery, Troy A., Jr., Pres. & Chief Oper. Officer--Heilig-Meyers Company, Richmond, VA; *U.S. Public*, pg. 804
Pelino, Dennis, Pres. & Chief Oper. Officer--Fritz Companies, Inc., San Francisco, CA; *U.S. Public*, pg. 683
Pendegast, Michael, Chief Oper. Officer-Florida Office & Sr. V.P.--Weatherby Health Care, Norwalk, CT; *U.S. Private*, pg. 1155
Pendleton, Arthur L., Chief Oper. Officer & Exec. V.P.--Roanoke Gas Company, Roanoke, VA; *U.S. Public*, pg. 1392
Pendleton, Arthur L., Chief Oper. Officer--Bluefield Gas Company, Bluefield, WV; *U.S. Public*, pg. 1393
Penner, Phillip B., Chief Oper. Officer--Accurate Perforating Co., Chicago, IL; *U.S. Private*, pg. 12
Penniman, Nicholas G., IV, Sr. V.P.-Newspaper Opers.--Pulitzer Publishing Company, Saint Louis, MO; *U.S. Public*, pg. 1343
Penny, Roger P., Pres. & Chief Oper. Officer--Bethlehem Steel Corporation, Bethlehem, PA; *U.S. Public*, pg. 226
Pentz, Paul E., Pres. & Chief Oper. Officer--TruServ Corporation, Chicago, IL; *U.S. Private*, pg. 1108
Pepperdine, James, Chief Oper. Officer & Exec. V.P.--Yesawich, Pepperdine & Brown, Orlando, FL; *U.S. Private*, pg. 1195
Pereira, Hugo Dantas, Dir.-Tech. & Matl. Resources--Banco do Brasil, Brasilia, Brazil; *Int'l*, pg. 141
Perez Lizaur, Jose Ignacio, Chief Oper. Officer--Wal-Mart Holding Co., Mexico, Mexico; *Int'l*, pg. 241
Perez Lizaur, Jose Ignacio, Chief Oper. Officer--Wal-Mart Holding Co., Mexico, Mexico; *U.S. Public*, pg. 1733
Perez, Enrique, Chief Oper. Officer, Sr. Exec. V.P., Gen. Counsel & Sec.--Philippine Long Distance Telephone Company, Manila, Philippines; *Int'l*, pg. 1051
Perez, Lombardo, Chm. Bd., Pres. & Chief Oper. Officer--Metro Ford Inc., Miami, FL; *U.S. Private*, pg. 736
Perich, Michael, Chief Oper. Officer--Bernina of America Inc., Aurora, IL; *Int'l*, pg. 189
Perkins, Grace, Chief Oper. Officer & Coord.-Benefits--Stern-Leach Company, Attleboro, MA; *Int'l*, pg. 329
Perreault, Fernand, Pres. & Chief Oper. Officer--SITQ Immobilier, Montreal, Canada; *Int'l*, pg. 249
Perrin, Charles, Chief Oper. Officer--Avon Products, Inc., New York, NY; *U.S. Public*, pg. 155
Perris, James W., Chief Oper. Officer & V.P.-Opers.--TRM Copy Centers Corporation, Portland, OR; *U.S. Public*, pg. 1558
Perrone, Michael M., Pres. & Chief Oper. Officer--Fields Financial Services, Inc., Bryan, TX; *U.S. Public*, pg. 942
Perry, Michael W., Pres. & Chief Oper. Officer--INMC Mortgage Holdings, Inc., Pasadena, CA; *U.S. Public*, pg. 857
Pesce, William J., Chief Oper. Officer--John Wiley & Sons, Inc., New York, NY; *U.S. Public*, pg. 1768
Petch, Ronald S., Pres. & Chief Oper. Officer--Calprop Corporation, Marina Del Rey, CA; *U.S. Public*, pg. 296
Peters, James D., Pres. & Chief Oper. Officer--E & B Marine Incorporated, Edison, NJ; *U.S. Public*, pg. 1756
Peters, Joe, ChieF Oper. Officer--Neste Resins B.V., Delfzijl, Netherlands; *Int'l*, pg. 915
Peters, Jon, Co-Chief Exec. Officer--The Guber Peters Entertainment Company, Los Angeles, CA; *Int'l*, pg. 1283
Peters, Lawrence W., Pres. & Chief Oper. Officer--Long Island Bancorp, Inc., Melville, NY; *U.S. Public*, pg. 1013
Petersen, Gary N., Pres. & Chief Oper. Officer--Minnegasco, Minneapolis, MN; *U.S. Public*, pg. 843
Petersen, K.C., Pres. & Chief Oper. Officer--Schenectady International, Inc., Schenectady, NY; *U.S. Private*, pg. 969
Petersen, Mike, Pres. & Chief Oper. Officer--Baker's Supermarkets, Inc., Omaha, NE; *U.S. Public*, pg. 652
Petersen, Steve, Chief Oper. Officer--Southern Paving Co., Moab, UT; *U.S. Private*, pg. 591
Petersmeyer, Gary S., Pres. & Chief Oper. Officer--Collagen Corporation, Palo Alto, CA; *U.S. Public*, pg. 399
Peterson, A., Chief Oper. Officer--Meyer International PLC, London, United Kingdom; *Int'l*, pg. 864
Peterson, Chris, Chief Oper. Officer--Colgate-Palmolive A/S, Glostrup, Denmark; *U.S. Public*, pg. 398
Peterson, John, Pres. & Chief Oper. Officer--Warren Electric Telecommunications-Utilities Company, Houston, TX; *U.S. Private*, pg. 1151
Peterson, Larry, Chief Oper. Officer--Anoka Electric Cooperative, Ramsey, MN; *U.S. Private*, pg. 75
Peterson, Randall J., Pres. & Chief Oper. Officer--Associated Bank Green Bay, Green Bay, WI; *U.S. Public*, *pg. 141*
Peterson, Robert H., Chief Oper. Officer-Metallurgical & Sr. V.P.--Sunshine Mining And Refining Company, Boise, ID; *U.S. Public*, pg. 1536
Petit, Henri, Chief Oper. Officer--Consumer Imaging Division, Rochester, NY; *U.S. Public*, pg. 555
Petit, Henri D., Chief Oper. Officer-Tech., Mfg. & Prod. Devel.--Eastman Kodak Company, Rochester, NY; *U.S. Public*, pg. 550
Petit, Mary E., Sr. V.P.-Opers.--Barr Laboratories Inc., Pomona, NY; *U.S. Public*, pg. 191
Petrello, Anthony G., Pres. & Chief Oper. Officer--Nabors Industries Inc., Houston, TX; *U.S. Public*, pg. 1148
Petrilli, Frank, Pres., Chief Exec. Officer & Chief Oper. Officer--Waterhouse Investor Services, New York, NY; *Int'l*, pg. 1401
Petrou, David, Pres. & Chief Oper. Officer--Eisner, Petrou & Associates, Inc., Baltimore, MD; *U.S. Private*, pg. 366
Petruzzi, Robert J., Chief Oper. Officer--Arnold Transportation Services, Camp Hill, PA; *U.S. Public*, pg. 132
Petry, Paul E., Pres. & Chief Oper. Officer--Boston Mutual Life Insurance Co., Canton, MA; *U.S. Private*, pg. 161
Peyton, Robert G., Pres.--The W.W. Williams Company, Columbus, OH; *U.S. Private*, pg. 1178
Pfeffer, Philip M., Pres. & Chief Oper. Officer--Random House, Inc., New York, NY; *U.S. Private*, pg. 20
Pfluger, Urs N., Chief Oper. Officer--Novo Nordisk Pharma AG, Kusnacht, Switzerland; *Int'l*, pg. 988
Phair, James J., Chief Oper. Officer--Tokio Re Corporation, New York, NY; *Int'l*, pg. 1392
Pherigo, William I., Pres., Chief Oper. Officer & Treas.--NBSC Corporation, Columbia, SC; *U.S. Public*, pg. 1549
Phillips, Don, Chief Oper. Officer--Oldelft Corp. of America, Columbia, MD; *Int'l*, pg. 389
Phillips, Ira H., Pres. & Chief Oper. Officer--Quoizel Inc., Goose Creek, SC; *U.S. Private*, pg. 901
Phillips, Martin, Chief Oper. Officer & Exec. V.P.--Kline Iron & Steel Co., Inc., Columbia, SC; *U.S. Private*, pg. 626
Phippen, Michael, Pres. & Chief Oper. Officer--Western Staff Services, Walnut Creek, CA; *U.S. Public*, pg. 1760
Piccirilli, Joseph, Pres. & Chief Oper. Officer--Pittsburgh Brewing Company, Pittsburgh, PA; *U.S. Private*, pg. 619
Piche, M., Chief Oper. Officer--Detrey Dentsply S.A., Bois-Colombes, France; *U.S. Public*, pg. 500
Picker, Michael, Chief Oper. Officer & Exec. V.P.--Infresco Corporation, Sarasota, FL; *U.S. Public*, pg. 420
Pierce, Harvey, Pres. & Chief Oper. Officer--American Family Mutual Insurance Co., Madison, WI; *U.S. Private*, pg. 53
Pierce, Vince, Pres. & Chief Oper. Officer--McIlhenny Company, Avery Island, LA; *U.S. Private*, pg. 722
Pieters, G. M., Chief Oper. Officer--Eij Imtech NV, Antwerp, Belgium; *Int'l*, pg. 681
Pietramala, Anthony, Pres. & Chief Oper. Officer--Pro-Pastries Inc., Mississauga, Canada; *U.S. Public*, pg. 806
Pietramala, Anthony, Pres. & Chief Oper. Officer--Heinz Bakery Products, Mississauga, Canada; *U.S. Public*, pg. 806
Pietrowski, Philip E., Sr. V.P.-North American Opers.--The Cerplex Group, Inc., Tustin, CA; *U.S. Public*, pg. 332
Pignatelli, James N., Chief Oper. Officer & Sr. V.P.-Bus. Devel.--Tucson Electric Power Company, Tucson, AZ; *U.S. Public*, pg. 1670
Pignatellis, James S., Chief Oper. Officer & Sr. V.P.--UniSource Energy Corporation, Tucson, AZ; *U.S. Public*, pg. 1670
Pihl, Christer, Chief Oper. Officer--Ahlstrom Glassfibre Ltd.-Karhula Plant, Karhula, Finland; *Int'l*, pg. 32
Pilato, Jean Paul, Chief Oper. Officer--MacDermid France S.A., Evry, France; *U.S. Public*, pg. 1030
Pilgrim, Lindy M., Pres. & Chief Oper. Officer--Pilgrim's Pride Corporation, Pittsburg, TX; *U.S. Public*, pg. 1296
Pillard, L.G., Chief Oper. Officer & Mng. Dir.-Sugar & Starch Opers.--Tate & Lyle PLC, London, United Kingdom; *Int'l*, pg. 1356
Pillet-Will, Jacques, Chief Oper. Officer--Chiltem Group SAM, Monaco, Monaco; *Int'l*, pg. 65
Pilon, Marcel, Chief Oper Officer-North America--Lawson Mardon Packaging Inc., Mississauga, Canada; *Int'l*, pg. 68
Pinard, Jean C., Pres. & Chief Oper. Officer--Hypotheques CDPQ, Montreal, Canada; *Int'l*, pg. 249
Pine, Wong Yung, Chief Oper. Officer--GB Holdings, Jurong, Singapore; *Int'l*, pg. 531
Pine, Wong Yung, Chief Oper. Officer--American Marine Pte. Ltd., Jurong, Singapore; *Int'l*, pg. 531
Pink, Ronald A., Pres. & Chief Oper. Officer--Distribution America, Des Plaines, IL; *U.S. Private*, pg. 335
Pinker, Lamont T., Pres. & Chief Oper. Officer--Gateway Communications, Johnson City, NY; *U.S. Private*, pg. 693
Pinkerton, Dennis, Chief Oper. Officer--Senco Products, Inc., Cincinnati, OH; *U.S. Private*, pg. 984
Pinsley, Sol, Chm. Bd., Pres., Chief Exec. & Chief Oper. Officer--Espey Mfg. & Electronics Corp., Saratoga Springs, NY; *U.S. Public*, pg. 592
Pitchford, Terry, Chief Oper. Officer & Exec. V.P.-Distr. Div.--Rolland Inc., Saint-Jerome, Canada; *Int'l*, pg. 273
Pitkowsky, Murray, Chief Oper. Officer--Datascope Investment Corp., Paramus, NJ; *U.S. Public*, pg. 487
Pitschel, Ernest O., Exec. V.P. & Chief Oper. Officer--Atlas Consolidated Mining & Development Corporation, Manila, Philippines; *Int'l*, pg. 95
Pittman, Gary, Chm. Bd., Pres., Chief Exec., Chief Oper. & Chief Fin. Officer--PCI, Austin, TX; *U.S. Private*, pg. 826
Pitts, Jerry M., Pres. & Chief Oper. Officer--Bayou Steel Corporation, La Place, LA; *U.S. Public*, pg. 197
Pitts, Preston, Pres. & Chief Oper. Officer--Legacy Marketing Group, Petaluma, CA; *U.S. Private*, pg. 658
Pizzuti, Everett V., Pres. & Chief Oper. Officer--Astro-Med, Inc., West Warwick, RI; *U.S. Public*, pg. 141
Plack, James, Chief Oper. Officer--Human Affairs International Inc., Sandy, UT; *U.S. Public*, pg. 1036
Plante, Paul J., Chief Oper. Officer--Reptron Electronics, Inc., Tampa, FL; *U.S. Public*, pg. 1377
Plumlee, Daniel L., Chief Oper. Officer & Exec. V.P.--The L & B Group, Dallas, TX; *U.S. Public*, pg. 1673
Podany, William J., Chief Oper. Officer & Exec. V.P.--ShopKo Stores, Inc., Green Bay, WI; *U.S. Public*, pg. 1467
Podsiadlo, Rick, Chief Oper. Officer--Novo Nordisk Canada, Inc., Mississauga, Canada; *Int'l*, pg. 988
Pogorilic, Sani, Chief Oper. Officer--Novo Nordisk A/S, Zagreb, Croatia; *Int'l*, pg. 987
Pohjanheimo, Jikka, Chief Oper. Officer--Neste Chemicals Holding Inc., Houston, TX; *Int'l*, pg. 913
Poignard, John M., Chief Oper. Officer & V.P.-Opers. & Mfg.--E.P. Henry Corporation, Woodbury, NJ; *U.S. Private*, pg. 522
Poirier, Victor L., Pres., Chief Exec. & Oper. Officer--Thermo Cardiosystems Inc., Woburn, MA; *U.S. Public*, pg. 1592
Polivka, Sherri A., Pres. & Chief Oper. Officer--Ivy, Vernon, CA; *U.S. Public*, pg. 948
Polivka, Sherri A., Pres. & Chief Oper. Officer--A.J. Brandon, Vernon, CA; *U.S. Public*, pg. 948
Pollack, Aileen C., Pres. & Chief Oper. Officer--Key Industries, Inc., Fort Scott, KS; *U.S. Private*, pg. 618
Pollack, Dan, Pres. & Chief Oper. Officer--Stock Yards Packing Co., Inc., Chicago, IL; *U.S. Private*, pg. 1043
Pollack, Paul R., Chief Oper. Officer & Exec. V.P.--Hudson General Corporation, Great Neck, NY; *U.S. Public*, pg. 845
Pollack, Stanley C., Chief Oper. Officer & Treas.--Pollack Corporation, Scarborough, ME; *U.S. Private*, pg. 874
Polley, David, Pres. & Chief Oper. Officer--World Carpets, Inc., Dalton, GA; *U.S. Private*, pg. 1190
Polley, R. Stephen, Chm. Bd.. Pres. & Chief Exec. Officer--Interphase Corporation, Dallas, TX; *U.S. Public*, pg. 908
Pollnow, Charles, Chm. Bd., Chief Exec. & Oper. Officer--The Brulin Corporation, Indianapolis, IN; *U.S. Private*, pg. 176
Pollock, Mayer, II, Pres., Chief Exec. Officer & Chief Oper. Officer--The Pollock Corp., Pottstown, PA; *U.S. Private*, pg. 874
Polzing, Helmut, Chief Oper. Officer--Cleveland Precision Systems GmbH, Loffingen, Germany; *U.S. Public*, pg. 482
Pond, Richard G., Chief Fin. Officer, Chief Oper. Officer & Exec. V.P.--Boston Celtics Limited Partnership, Boston, MA; *U.S. Public*, pg. 246
Pong, Cheong Kim, Chm. Bd., Chief Exec. & Oper. Officer--Hong Fok Corporation Ltd., Singapore, Singapore; *Int'l*, pg. 635
Pontikes, Nicholas K., Chief Oper. Officer--Comdisco, Inc., Rosemont, IL; *U.S. Public*, pg. 407
Poole, A. Mitchell, Pres. & Chief Oper. Officer--Allied Holdings, Inc., Decatur, GA; *U.S. Public*, pg. 48
Poon, Liu Kah, Chief Fin. Officer--Malaysian Tobacco Co./B.A.T. Indust., Kuala Lumpur, Malaysia; *Int'l*, pg. 111
Pope, Mark C., IV, Pres. & Chief Oper. Officer--Graphic Industries, Inc., Atlanta, GA; *U.S. Public*, pg. 1735
Pope, Peter T., Chm. Bd. & Chief Exec. Officer--Pope & Talbot, Inc., Portland, OR; *U.S. Public*, pg. 1316
Popescu, Anca, Chief Oper. Officer--Novo Nordisk A/S, Bucharest, Romania; *Int'l*, pg. 988
Popp, Richard L., Chief Oper. Officer--Wandel & Goltermann Technologies, Inc., Research Triangle Park, NC; *Int'l*, pg. 1486
Port, Nancy, Pres. & Chief Oper. Officer--Equity Services, Inc., Montpelier, VT; *U.S. Private*, pg. 785
Porten, Norbert W., Co-Chief Oper Officer--BHF & IKB Immobilien-Leasing GmbH, Dusseldorf, Germany; *Int'l*, pg. 645
Porter, Carl W., Chief Oper. Officer & Sr. V.P.--Southeastern Michigan Gas Enterprises, Inc., Port Huron, MI; *U.S. Public*, pg. 1489
Porter, Norbert W., Chief Oper. Officer--BHF & IKB Immobilien-Leasing GmbH, Dusseldorf, Germany; *Int'l*, pg. 119
Porter, Robert L., Pres. & Chief Oper. Officer--Oliver Products Company, Grand Rapids, MI; *U.S. Private*, pg. 815
Portera, Joseph P., Chief Oper. Officer & Exec. V.P.-Eastern Div.--Costco Wholesale, Issaquah, WA; *U.S. Public*, pg. 451
Posinski, Frank J., Pres. & Chief Oper. Officer--Cincinnati Gear Company, Cincinnati, OH; *U.S. Private*, pg. 240
Post, Peter, Pres. & Chief Oper. Officer--Emmerling Post, Inc., New York, NY; *U.S. Private*, pg. 374
Poston, Henry, Pres. & Chief Oper. Officer--Martin Color-Fi, Edgefield, SC; *U.S. Public*, pg. 1052
Potashner, Kenneth F., Chm. Bd., Pres., Chief Exec. & Chief Oper. Officer--Maxwell Technologies, Inc., San Diego, CA; *U.S. Public*, pg. 1061
Potkin, Harvey, Pres. & Chief Oper. Officer--National Foods Inc., Bronx, NY; *U.S. Public*, pg. 429
Potter, Nelson W., Pres. & Chief Oper. Officer--Fleetwood Enterprises, Inc., Riverside, CA; *U.S. Public*, pg. 650
Pottruck, David S., Pres. & Chief Oper. Officer--The Charles Schwab Corporation, San Francisco, CA; *U.S. Public*, pg. 1442
Poulsen, Preben E., Chief Oper. Officer--FeF Chemicals A/S, Koge, Denmark; *Int'l*, pg. 987
Pountney, Charles W., Chief Oper. Officer & Exec. V.P.--Paul Inman Associates Inc., Farmington, MI; *U.S. Private*, pg. 564
Poure, Timothy, Pres. & Chief Oper. Officer--General Alum & Chemical, Holland, OH; *U.S. Private*, pg. 443
Poutanen, Matti, Chief Oper. Officer--Norlatex Oy, Kulloo, Finland; *Int'l*, pg. 913
Powell, David L., Pres. & Chief Oper. Officer--Coherent Communications Systems Corp., Ashburn, VA; *U.S. Public*, pg. 1424
Powell, H., Chief Oper. Officer - Americas--Labatt Breweries of Canada, Toronto, Canada; *Int'l*, pg. 679
Powell, John, Pres. & Chief Oper. Officer--P. Lawson Travel, Ltd., Islington, Canada; *U.S. Private*, pg. 212
Powell, Michael, Chief Oper. Officer--MacGREGOR (CHN) Ltd., Shanghai, China; *Int'l*, pg. 670

Powell, Michael, Chief Oper. Officer--MacGREGOR (Kor) Ltd., Pusan, Korea; *Int'l,* pg. 671
Powell, Steve C., Chief Oper. Officer--Carolina First Bank, Greenville, SC; *U.S. Public,* pg. 306
Powers, Frank, Chief Oper. Officer & Exec. V.P.--Matria Healthcare, Inc., Marietta, GA; *U.S. Public,* pg. 1057
Powers, William, Chief Oper. Officer--Petroleum Heat & Power Co., Stamford, CT; *U.S. Public,* pg. 1281
Prado, Marta, Chief Oper. Officer & Sr. V.P.-MedPartners Govt. Svcs.--Medpartners Inc., Birmingham, AL; *U.S. Public,* pg. 1082
Prather, Rick, Sr. V.P. & Asst. Gen. Mgr.--Jostens Sportswear, Overland Park, KS; *U.S. Public,* pg. 686
Pratt, Edward T., Jr., Chief Oper. Officer--Greate Bay Casino Corporation, Atlantic City, NJ; *U.S. Public,* pg. 760
Pratt, Robert N., Chm. Bd., Pres. & Chief Oper. & Chief Exec. Officer--Alta Gold Co., Henderson, NV; *U.S. Public,* pg. 58
Preece, Scott, Chief Oper. Officer--Waremart Inc., Boise, ID; *U.S. Private,* pg. 1150
Pressman, James R., Chm. Bd., Pres. & Chief Oper. Officer--Pressman Toy Corp., New York, NY; *U.S. Private,* pg. 882
Previte, Richard, Pres. & Chief Oper. Officer--Advanced Micro Devices, Inc., Sunnyvale, CA; *U.S. Public,* pg. 21
Prevost, Jean-Michel, Chief Oper. Officer--Plastilon France S.A., Sotteville, France; *Int'l,* pg. 915
Prewitt, Verlon, Chief Oper. Officer--Carhartt, Inc., Dearborn, MI; *U.S. Private,* pg. 210
Price, D., Chief Oper. Officer--Northern Bank Limited, Belfast, United Kingdom; *Int'l,* pg. 906
Price, John, Chief Oper. Officer & Exec. V.P.--Flexfab Horizons International, Inc., Hastings, MI; *U.S. Private,* pg. 412
Price, Richard, Chief Oper. Officer--Mesirow Financial, Chicago, IL; *U.S. Private,* pg. 733
Price, Steven, Pres., Chief Oper. & Exec. Officer--Pricellular Corporation, White Plains, NY; *U.S. Public,* pg. 1324
Price, Timothy F., Pres. & Chief Oper. Officer--MCI Communications Corp., Atlanta, GA; *U.S. Public,* pg. 1023
Prichard, John R., Chief Oper. Officer--McGlynn Bakeries Inc., Minneapolis, MN; *U.S. Private,* pg. 721
Primrose, Mike, Pres. & Chief Exec. Officer--Henry Lee Company, Miami, FL; *U.S. Private,* pg. 657
Pritchard, Phillip L., Pres. & Chief Oper. Officer--Cooker Restaurant Corporation, West Palm Beach, FL; *U.S. Public,* pg. 442
Pritchett, Jim, Chief Oper. Officer & Exec. V.P.--Ultrak Inc., Lewisville, TX; *U.S. Public,* pg. 1663
Proano, Stephan, Chief Exec. Officer & Chief Oper. Officer--Punto Aparte Publicidad, S.A., Panama, Panama; *U.S. Private,* pg. 305
Prohaska, John W., Chief Oper. Officer--North Specialty Products, Brea, CA; *Int'l,* pg. 1243
Prosser, P.J., Chief Oper. Officer--Legal & General Assurance Society Limited, London, United Kingdom; *Int'l,* pg. 805
Prosser, P.J., Chief Oper. Officer--Legal & General Finance Plc, London, United Kingdom; *Int'l,* pg. 805
Prot, Baudouin, Pres. & Chief Oper. Officer--Banque Nationale de Paris, Paris, France; *Int'l,* pg. 163
Proto, Rodney R., Pres. & Chief Oper. Officer--USA Waste Services, Inc., Houston, TX; *U.S. Public,* pg. 1686
Proto, Rodney R., Pres. & Chief Oper. Officer--Sanifill, Inc., Houston, TX; *U.S. Public,* pg. 1686
Proulx, Mike, Chief Oper. Officer & Dir.-Franchising--Arthur Treacher's, Inc., Jacksonville, FL; *U.S. Public,* pg. 136
Province, Wendel H., Chief Oper. Officer--The Pep Boys-Manny, Moe & Jack, Philadelphia, PA; *U.S. Public,* pg. 1276
Pruitt, J. Doug, Pres. & Chief Oper. Officer--Sundt Corp., Tucson, AZ; *U.S. Private,* pg. 1051
Pruitt, Larry, Chief Oper. Officer--Atlantic Coast Asphalt, Jacksonville, FL; *U.S. Private,* pg. 544
Pryne, Wilson H., Pres. & Chief Oper. Officer--American Felt & Filter, Newburgh, NY; *U.S. Private,* pg. 54
Puckett, Randall D., Chief Oper. Officer--Alamo Lumber Company, San Antonio, TX; *U.S. Private,* pg. 1135
Pugh, J. Randolph, Chief Oper. Officer--Willis Corroon Corp. of San Diego, San Diego, CA; *Int'l,* pg. 1507
Puglisi, John, Pres. & Chief Oper. Officer--Lowe McAdams Healthcare, New York, NY; *U.S. Private,* pg. 678
Pulido, Mark A., Pres. & Chief Exec. Officer--McKesson Corporation, San Francisco, CA; *U.S. Public,* pg. 1072
Pulli, Juhani, Chief Oper. Officer--Borealis Polymers Oy, Porvoo, Finland; *Int'l,* pg. 913
Pundyk, Jon R., Chief Oper. Officer--Glamorise Foundations, Inc., New York, NY; *U.S. Private,* pg. 455
Puno, Jimmy, Pres., Chief Exec. Officer & Chief Oper. Officer--Dentsu Young & Rubicam-Alcantara Inc. (Manila), Manila, Philippines; *U.S. Private,* pg. 325
Puputti, Mari, Chief Oper. Officer--Ahlstrom Glassfibre Ltd.-Mikkeli Plant, Mikkeli, Finland; *Int'l,* pg. 32
Purinton, James H., Chief Oper. Officer & Deputy Pres.--ORIX Real Estate Equities, Inc., Chicago, IL; *Int'l,* pg. 1009
Purpura, Vicnent M., Pres. & Chief Oper. Officer--D.A. Davidson & Co., Great Falls, MT; *U.S. Private,* pg. 314
Puschel, Gerald W., Pres. & Chief Oper. Officer--F. Schumacher & Co., New York, NY; *U.S. Private,* pg. 973
Putnam, Spencer, Chief Oper. Officer & Sec.--The Vermont Teddy Bear Company, Inc., Shelburne, VT; *U.S. Public,* pg. 1716
Queen, Richard K., Pres. & Chief Oper. Officer--C S Crable Sportswear, Inc., Batavia, OH; *U.S. Public,* pg. 1111
Quesnel, Gregory L., Pres. & Chief Oper. Officer--CNF Transportation Inc., Palo Alto, CA; *U.S. Public,* pg. 281
Queste, Yves, Pres. & Chief Oper. Officer--Ferry-Morse Seed Company, Modesto, CA; *Int'l,* pg. 566
Quick, Thomas C., Pres. & Chief Oper. Officer--The Quick & Reilly Group Inc., Palm Beach, FL; *U.S. Public,* pg. 650
Quicke, John J., Pres. & Chief Oper. Officer--Sequa Corporation, New York, NY; *U.S. Public,* pg. 1458
Quinnell, Bruce A., Pres. & Chief Oper. Officer-Walden--Borders Group, Inc., Ann Arbor, MI; *U.S. Public,* pg. 245
Quirion, Gerard P., Chief Oper. Officer--Novo Nordisk A/S, Budapest, Hungary; *Int'l,* pg. 988
Ra, Jim, Chief Oper. Officer--Scholastic Inc. Information Center, Lyndhurst, NJ; *U.S. Public,* pg. 1440
Raad, Ramzi, Chief Oper. Officer & V.P.-Reg. Opers.--Intermarkets U.A.E., Dubai, United Arab Emirates; *Int'l,* pg. 680
Raaijmakeb, Raoul, Chief Oper. Officer--COBE International Ltd, Zaventem, Belgium; *Int'l,* pg. 667
Raaijmakeb, Raoul, Chief Oper. Officer--COBE Laboratories Europe N.V., Veenendaal, Netherlands; *Int'l,* pg. 667
Raasch, Jona S., Chief Oper. Officer & V.P.--National Research Corporation, Lincoln, NE; *U.S. Public,* pg. 1159
Racz, Janos, Chief Oper. & Quality Officer--Aeroplex of Central Europe Ltd., Budapest, Hungary; *Int'l,* pg. 834
Racz, Janos, Chief Oper. & Quality Officer--Aeroplex of Central Europe Ltd., Budapest, Hungary; *U.S. Public,* pg. 1006
Radano, Robert M., Chief Oper. Officer & Sr. V.P.--J & J Snack Foods Corporation, Pennsauken, NJ; *U.S. Public,* pg. 916
Radford, David, Chirf Oper. Officer--COBE Laboratories Pty Ltd.-Melbourne, Blackburn, Australia; *Int'l,* pg. 667
Radford, David, Chief Oper. Officer--COBE Laboratories Pty Ltd.-Sydney, Frenchs Forest, Australia; *Int'l,* pg. 667
Radler, F. David, Pres. & Chief Oper. Officer--Hollinger Inc., Vancouver, Canada; *Int'l,* pg. 630
Radwill, Scott, Pres., Chief Exec., Oper. & Fin. Officer--Master Appliance Corp., Racine, WI; *U.S. Private,* pg. 713
Radzievsky, Anna, Chief Oper. Officer & Exec. V.P.--YAR Communications, New York, NY; *U.S. Private,* pg. 1195
Rae, John Maitland, Chief Oper. Officer--BHF-Bank Representative Office, Sao Paulo, Brazil; *Int'l,* pg. 120
Raemer, Steven I., Pres. & Chief Oper. Officer--Radix Corporation, Salt Lake City, UT; *U.S. Private,* pg. 906
Ragsdale, M. Terry, Chief Oper. Officer & Exec. V.P.--Southern States Cooperative, Inc., Richmond, VA; *U.S. Private,* pg. 1017
Rahn, David O., Chief Oper. Officer--First American Trust Co., Santa Ana, CA; *U.S. Public,* pg. 626
Rainville, Donald, Pres. & Chief Oper. Officer--Universal Dynamics, Inc., Woodbridge, VA; *Int'l,* pg. 484
Raitis, Teppo, Chief Oper. Officer--KONE Elevators, BU 2, Hyvinkaa, Finland; *Int'l,* pg. 746
Rajala, Ari, Chief Oper. Officer--Neste Oil Poland Ltd., Warsaw, Poland; *Int'l,* pg. 915
Rajic, Val, Acting Chief Oper. Officer--Central Reserve Life Corporation, Strongsville, OH; *U.S. Public,* pg. 326
Raleigh, Richard J., Chief Oper. Officer--U.S. Home & Garden Inc., San Francisco, CA; *U.S. Public,* pg. 1682
Ramaekers, Larry, Pres. & Chief Oper. Officer--Color Tile, Inc., Fort Worth, TX; *Int'l,* pg. 686
Ramella, Daniel J., Pres. & Chief Oper. Officer--Penton Publishing, Inc., Cleveland, OH; *U.S. Public,* pg. 1306
Ramer, Douglas, Pres. & Chief Oper. Officer--Bruning Paint Company, Baltimore, MD; *U.S. Private,* pg. 176
Rampino, Louis J., Pres. & Chief Oper. Officer--Fremont General Corporation, Santa Monica, CA; *U.S. Public,* pg. 681
Ramus, David W., Chief Oper. Officer--M & T Partners, Portland, OR; *U.S. Private,* pg. 684
Rand, David, Pres. & Chief Oper. Officer--Tingley Rubber Corporation, South Plainfield, NJ; *U.S. Private,* pg. 1088
Randell, Joe, Pres. & Chief Oper. Officer--Air Nova, Bedford, Canada; *Int'l,* pg. 36
Ranelli, John, Chief Oper. Officer--Deckers Outdoor Corporation, Goleta, CA; *U.S. Public,* pg. 491
Rangel, Antonio Luis Ferre, V.P.-Opers.--Puerto Rican Cement Co., Inc., Guaynabo, PR; *U.S. Public,* pg. 1341
Rankin, Bonnie L., Pres. & Chief Oper. Officer--New York Casualty Insurance Co., Watertown, NY; *U.S. Public,* pg. 787
Rankin, Les, Chief Oper. Officer--AgPro Grain, Winnipeg, Canada; *Int'l,* pg. 1195
Raos, John G., Pres. & Chief Oper. Officer--U.S. Industries, Inc., Iselin, NJ; *U.S. Public,* pg. 1683
Rascoe, David S., Pres. & Chief Oper. Officer--Thermal Industries, Inc., Pittsburgh, PA; *U.S. Private,* pg. 490
Rasmussen, Karen, Chief Oper. Officer--A/S Akerlund & Rausing, Roedovre, Denmark; *Int'l,* pg. 33
Ratcliffe, Kenneth, Pres. & Chief Oper. Officer--PC Connection, Inc., Milford, MA; *U.S. Private,* pg. 826
Ratcliffe, Peter, Chief Oper. Officer--Princess Cruise Lines, Los Angeles, CA; *Int'l,* pg. 1035
Ratia, Heikki, Chief Oper. Officer--Plastilon Oy, Imatra, Finland; *Int'l,* pg. 913
Rattmann, Thomas, Pres. & Chief Oper. Officer--Columbian Mutual Life Insurance Co., Binghamton, NY; *U.S. Private, pg. 256*
Ravasio, Robert, Chief Oper. Officer & Sr. V.P.--Ketchum Advertising/San Francisco, San Francisco, CA; *U.S. Private,* pg. 616
Ravine, Harris, Chief Admin. Officer & Exec. V.P.--Storage Technology Corporation, Louisville, CO; *U.S. Public,* pg. 1522
Rawl, Robert T., Chief Oper. Officer--Regency Finance Company, Hermitage, PA; *U.S. Public,* pg. 607
Rawle, Robert H., Pres. & Chief Oper. Officer-J. Ray McDermott, S.A.--McDermott International, Inc., New Orleans, LA; *U.S. Public,* pg. 1067
Rawley, Charles E., Chief Oper. Officer--Kentucky Fried Chicken Corporation (KFC), Louisville, KY; *U.S. Public,* pg. 1636
Rawlings, Kyle, Chief Oper. Officer--Monitor Labs, Inc., Englewood, CO; *Int'l,* pg. 208
Ray, Bradford T., Pres. & Chief Oper. Officer--Steel Technologies Inc., Louisville, KY; *U.S. Public,* pg. 1513
Raymond, Charles, Chief Oper. Officer--Sea-Land Service, Inc., Charlotte, NC; *U.S. Public,* pg. 284
Raymond, Jean-Louis, Chief Oper. Officer--GIB Group, Brussels, Belgium; *Int'l,* pg. 532
Raynor, Stephen K., Sr. V.P. & Chief Oper. Officer--Urban Group, Toronto, Canada; *Int'l,* pg. 253
Razmilovic, Tomo, Pres. & Chief Oper. Officer--Symbol Technologies, Inc., Holtsville, NY; *U.S. Public,* pg. 1546
Reardon, Michael, Exec. V.P. & Gen. Mgr.--U.S. Filter, Palm Desert, CA; *U.S. Public,* pg. 61
Reaves, Dennis, Pres. & Chief Oper. Officer--Penn-Daniels, Inc., Quincy, IL; *U.S. Public,* pg. 1467
Reber, Ron, Chief Oper. Officer & Exec. V.P.--SkyWest Inc., Saint George, UT; *U.S. Public,* pg. 1476
Rebmann, Bruce, Chief Oper. Officer--Platinum Technology - Santa Barbara Laboratory, Goleta, CA; *U.S. Public,* pg. 1309
Recchia, Richard D., Chief Oper. Officer & Exec. V.P.--Mitsubishi Motor Sales of America, Inc., Cypress, CA; *Int'l,* pg. 875
Rechler, Scott, Pres. & Chief Oper. Officer--Reckson Associates Realty Corp., Melville, NY; *U.S. Public,* pg. 1368
Recordati, Giovanni, Pres. & Chief Oper. Officer--Recordati Industria Chimica e Farmaceutica S.p.A., Milan, Italy; *Int'l,* pg. 1090
Recoussine, Jean-Louis, Chief Oper. Officer--Bank Brussels Lambert, New York Branch, New York, NY; *Int'l,* pg. 147
Reed, Brad, Chief Oper. Officer, Treas. & Sec.--Kova Fertilizer Inc., Greensburg, IN; *U.S. Private,* pg. 634
Reed, C.W., Pres. & Chief Oper. Officer--Escalade Sports, Evansville, IN; *U.S. Public,* pg. 591
Reed, Clyde A., Jr., Chief Oper. Officer & Exec. V.P.--Kevco, Inc., Fort Worth, TX; *U.S. Public,* pg. 952
Reed, G. Thomas, Pres. & Chief Oper. Officer--Ethika Corporation, Hilton Head Island, SC; *U.S. Public,* pg. 595
Reed, Jim, Chief Oper. Officer--Empire Kosher Poultry, Inc., Mifflintown, PA; *U.S. Private,* pg. 374
Reeves, Donna, Pres. & Chief Oper. Officer--Frontier Cellular, Rochester, NY; *U.S. Public,* pg. 683
Reeves, Graham, Chief Oper. Officer--Frionor (England) Ltd., Grimsby, United Kingdom; *Int'l,* pg. 516
Rehaag, Anton, Co-Chief Oper. Officer--Kohlbecher & Co. GmbH, Voelklingen, Germany; *Int'l,* pg. 1166
Reichert, Lothar, Chief Oper. Officer & Exec. V.P.--Porta Holdings Inc., Clearwater, FL; *Int'l,* pg. 857
Reichmann, Andre, Chief Oper. Officer--Dri Mark Products, Inc., Port Washington, NY; *U.S. Private,* pg. 342
Reid, A. A., Chief Oper. Officer-Foster's China--Carlton & United Breweries Ltd., Southbank, Australia; *Int'l,* pg. 500
Reid, Alan A., Chief Oper. Officer--Foster's China, Central, Hong Kong; *Int'l,* pg. 501
Reid, Jack R., Exec. V.P.-Refining--Holly Corporation, Dallas, TX; *U.S. Public,* pg. 830
Reilly, Paul V., Pres. & Chief Oper. & Fin. Officer--Mail-Well Inc., Englewood, CO; *U.S. Public,* pg. 1037
Reilly, Thomas E., Jr., Chm. Bd., Chief Exec. Officer & Chief Oper. Officer--Reilly Industries, Inc., Indianapolis, IN; *U.S. Private,* pg. 919
Reilly, William F., Chm. Bd., Chief Exec. Officer & Chief Oper. Officer--Primedia Inc., New York, NY; *U.S. Public,* pg. 1327
Reineke, Edward G., V.P.-Opers.--Dynamic Materials Corporation, Lafayette, CO; *U.S. Public,* pg. 539
Reinke, Winfried, Co-Chief Oper. Officer--Luxembourg Branch, Luxembourg, Luxembourg; *Int'l,* pg. 645
Reinke, Winfried, Co-Chief Oper. Officer--IKB International, Luxembourg, Luxembourg; *Int'l,* pg. 646
Reisch, Marc L., Grp. Pres.-Sls., Chief Oper. Officer & Exec. V.P.--World Color Press, Inc., Greenwich, CT; *U.S. Public;* pg. 1778
Rella, William, Chm. Bd., Pres., Chief Exec. & Oper. Officer--LCS Industries, Inc., Clifton, NJ; *U.S. Public,* pg. 970
Remensperger, Thomas, Pres. & Chief Oper. Officer--Ninteman Construction Company, Inc., San Diego, CA; *U.S. Private,* pg. 1052
Remley, William L., Vice Chm., Pres. & Chief Exec. Officer--Weldotron Corporation, Piscataway, NJ; *U.S. Public,* pg. 1752
Renninger, Barry, Exec. V.P. & Chief Oper. Officer--American Foodservice Corp., King of Prussia, PA; *U.S. Private,* pg. 54
Rense, John A., Chief Oper. Officer & V.P.--Nana Regional Corporation, Inc., Anchorage, AK; *U.S. Private,* pg. 774
Rensinghoff, Stefan, Chief Oper. Officer--Hong Kong Representative Office, Hong Kong, Hong Kong; *Int'l,* pg. 645
Rensinghoff, Stefan, Chief Oper. Officer--BHF & IKB Asia Consult Ltd., Hong Kong, Hong Kong,; *Int'l,* pg. 646
Renzi, R., Chief Oper. Officer & Mng. Dir.--Yale Security Products S.p.A. (Italy), Aprilia, Italy; *Int'l,* pg. 1499
Retterath, William, Chief Fin. & Oper. Officer--Dakotah, Inc., Webster, SD; *U.S. Public,* pg. 477
Reuben, George, Pres. & Chief Oper. Officer--Reuben Organization, Philadelphia, PA; *U.S. Private,* pg. 925
Reuven, Y., Chief Oper. Officer--BL Jersey Ltd, Saint Helier, United Kingdom; *Int'l,* pg. 150
Reyman, Meryl Fischman, Pres. & Chief Oper. Officer--Harrison & Star, Inc., New York, NY; *U.S. Private,* pg. 506
Reynolds, Richard I., Chief Oper. Officer & Exec. V.P.--Libbey Owens Ford Co., Toledo, OH; *Int'l,* pg. 1056
Rhein, Arthur, Pres. & Chief Oper. Officer--Pioneer-Standard Electronics, Inc., Cleveland, OH; *U.S. Public,* pg. 1300
Rhodes, Barry, Chief Oper. Officer--Turner Machine Company, Salem, OH; *U.S. Private,* pg. 368
Rhodes, Michael G., Chief Oper. Officer & Chief Fin. Officer--Modtech, Inc., Perris, CA; *U.S. Public,* pg. 1121
Rhulen, Harry W., Chief Oper. Officer & Exec. V.P.--Frontier Insurance Group, Inc., Rock Hill, NY; *U.S. Public,* pg. 684
Ribas, Douglas, Chief Oper. Officer--BIC Industr. Esferografica Brasileira, Sao Paulo, Brazil; *Int'l,* pg. 1273
Ribsam, John, Chief Oper. Officer--Nalle Plastics Inc., Austin, TX; *U.S. Private,* pg. 773

Riccitiello, John S., Pres. & Chief Oper. Officer--Electronic Arts, San Mateo, CA; *U.S. Public*, pg. 569
Rice, David, Chief Oper. Officer--XRE Corporation, Littleton, MA; *U.S. Public*, pg. 1595
Rice, Linda Johnson, Pres. & Chief Oper. Officer--Johnson Publishing Company, Inc., Chicago, IL; *U.S. Private*, pg. 591
Ricedorf, Charles W., Chief Oper. Officer--First Mount Joy Corporation, Mount Joy, PA; *U.S. Private*, pg. 407
Rich, Brad, Chief Oper. Officer--Rena-Ware Distributors Inc., Redmond, WA; *U.S. Private*, pg. 922
Rich, Harold, Exec. V.P. & Chief Oper. Officer--Instinet Corporation, New York, NY; *Int'l*, pg. 1106
Rich, Jeffrey A., Pres. & Chief Oper. Officer--Affiliated Computer Services, Inc., Dallas, TX; *U.S. Public*, pg. 27
Richard, Russell R., Pres. & Chief Oper. Officer--Monticello Management Co., San Diego, CA; *U.S. Private*, pg. 759
Richardi, Ralph, Pres. & Chief Oper. Officer--Simmons American Eagle Airlines, Dallas-Fort Worth Airport, TX; *U.S. Public*, pg. 10
Richards, Jack E., Pres. & Chief Oper. Officer--Adventure Tours USA, Inc., Dallas, TX; *U.S. Private*, pg. 22
Richards, John D., Acting. Chm. Bd., Pres. & Chief Exec. & Oper. Officer--Granite Furniture Co., Salt Lake City, UT; *U.S. Private*, pg. 469
Richards, Penny, Chief Oper. Officer--Joan Fabrics Corp., Tyngsboro, MA; *U.S. Private*, pg. 588
Richards, Thomas S., Chm. Bd., Pres. & Chief Exec. Officer--Rochester Gas And Electric Corporation, Rochester, NY; *U.S. Public*, pg. 1395
Richards, Wells E., Pres. & Chief Oper. Officer--Richards Brothers of Mountain Grove, Mountain Grove, MO; *U.S. Private*, pg. 928
Richardson, Dave, Chief Oper. Officer--Zomba Recording Corp., London, United Kingdom; *Int'l*, pg. 1529
Richardson, F. Darrell, Chief Oper. Officer & V.P.-Opers.--Mesaba Holdings, Inc., Minneapolis, MN; *U.S. Public*, pg. 1099
Richardson, M. Monte, Chief Oper. Officer & Exec. V.P.--Willis Corroon Corp. of Eugene, Eugene, OR; *Int'l*, pg. 1505
Richardson, Marcus F., Chief Oper. Officer--American Crystal Sugar Company, Moorhead, MN; *U.S. Private*, pg. 52
Richardson, Michael A., Chm. Bd., Pres., Chief Exec. Officer & Chief Oper. Officer--American Consumers, Inc., Fort Oglethorpe, GA; *U.S. Public*, pg. 70
Richings, Michael, Pres. & Chief Exec. Officer--Granges, Inc., Denver, CO; *U.S. Public*, pg. 1723
Rickertsen, Bryan C., V.P.-Tech.--Aliant Communications Inc., Lincoln, NE; *U.S. Public*, pg. 40
Rickey, Mark J., Exec. V.P. & Chief Oper. Officer--Markel Service, Inc., Glen Allen, VA; *U.S. Public*, pg. 1046
Rickey, Mark J., Exec. V.P. & Chief Oper. Officer--Markel American Insurance Co., Glen Allen, VA; *U.S. Public*, pg. 1046
Rickson, Kenneth M., Pres. & Chief Oper. Officer--MML Investors Services, Inc., Springfield, MA; *U.S. Private*, pg. 712
Riddle, Ernie, Chief Oper. Officer-Tascor Inc.--Norrell Corporation, Atlanta, GA; *U.S. Public*, pg. 1192
Rideout, Roy P., Pres. & Chief Oper. Officer--Newfoundland Capital Corporation Limited, Dartmouth, Canada; *Int'l*, pg. 924
Riedel, Steven C., Pres. & Chief Oper. Officer--Precision Castparts Corp., Portland, OR; *U.S. Public*, pg. 1320
Riegel, David L., Chief Oper. Officer & Exec. V.P.--Exabyte Corporation, Boulder, CO; *U.S. Public*, pg. 597
Riess, John M., Pres. & Chief Oper. Officer--The Gates Rubber Company, Denver, CO; *Int'l*, pg. 1396
Rietz, Gary, Chief Information Officer & Dir.-MIS--Dean Foods Company, Franklin Park, IL; *U.S. Public*, pg. 489
Rife, John A., Pres. & Chief Oper. Officer--United Life Insurance Company, Cedar Rapids, IA; *U.S. Public*, pg. 1677
Rifkin, Daniel M., Pres. & Chief Oper. Officer--Omnisource Corporation, Fort Wayne, IN; *U.S. Private*, pg. 817
Riker, Robert A., Chief Oper. Officer, V.P. & Gen. Mgr.--Dimensional Merchandising, Inc., Wharton, NJ; *U.S. Private*, pg. 333
Riley, Dale, Chief Oper. Officer & Exec. V.P.--Lund Food Holdings, Inc., Edina, MN; *U.S. Private*, pg. 680
Rimes, Ron, Chief Oper. Officer--Gast Mfg. Corp., Benton Harbor, MI; *U.S. Private*, pg. 440
Rincon, Jose A., Pres. & Chief Oper. Officer--Grupo Industrial Durango S.A. de C.V., Durango, Mexico; *Int'l*, pg. 575
Rini, Charles A., Sr., Pres. & Chief Oper. Officer--Riser Foods, Inc., Bedford, OH; *U.S. Private*, pg. 450
Rink, Robert J., Chief Oper. Officer & Exec. V.P.--Prestige Stamping, Inc., Warren, MI; *U.S. Private*, pg. 882
Rinna, Mark, Chief Oper. Officer--Chesapeake Bagel Bakery, Atlanta, GA; *U.S. Private*, pg. 5
Rinta, Jorma, Chief Oper. Officer--Neste Resins Corporation, Mississauga, Canada; *Int'l*, pg. 915
Riond, N., Chief Oper. Officer--Francaise De Mecanique, Haisnes, France; *Int'l*, pg. 1021
Riordan, Michael T., Pres. & Chief Oper. Officer--Fort James Corporation, Richmond, VA; *U.S. Public*, pg. 670
Riordan, Rip, Chief Oper. Officer & Exec. V.P.--Clear Channel Television, Inc., Minneapolis, MN; *U.S. Public*, pg. 383
Riordan, Rip, Chief Oper. Officer & Exec. V.P.--WFTC-TV, Minneapolis, MN; *U.S. Public*, pg. 385
Risner, Ray D., Pres. & Chief Oper. Officer--Southern Electronics Corporation, Tucker, GA; *U.S. Public*, pg. 1490
Risto, Jikka, Chief Oper. Officer--AS Traffic Service, Tallinn, Estonia; *Int'l*, pg. 915
Ristola, Pentti, Chief Oper. Officer--OY Ferrosan AB, Espoo, Finland; *Int'l*, pg. 989
Ritchie, H.T., Pres. & Chief Oper. Officer--Ritchie Corporation, Wichita, KS; *U.S. Private*, pg. 933
Ritchie, Timothy, Chief Oper. Officer & Exec. V.P.--Kirby Building Systems, Inc., Portland, TN; *Int'l*, pg. 699
Ritter, Henry L., Chief Oper. Officer & Sr. V.P.--Albert Kahn Associates, Inc., Detroit, MI; *U.S. Private*, pg. 604
Rivest, Jeffrey A., Chief Oper. Officer & Exec. V.P.--The Children's Hospital of Philadelphia, Philadelphia, PA; *U.S. Private*, pg. 236
Robb, Paul, Chief Oper. Officer--Duck Head Apparel, Winder, GA; *U.S. Public*, pg. 498
Robbins, Paul, Chief Oper. Officer & Exec. V.P.--Christianity Today, Inc., Carol Stream, IL; *U.S. Private*, pg. 238
Roberts, Budd, Pres. & Chief Oper. Officer--American Automobile Insurance Co., Creve Coeur, MO; *Int'l*, pg. 59
Roberts, Gary, Pres. & Chief Oper. Officer--Greenstone Roberts Advertising, Melville, NY; *U.S. Public*, pg. 763
Roberts, Gary, Pres. & Chief Oper. Officer--Greenstone Roberts Public Relations, Coconut Creek, FL; *U.S. Public*, pg. 763
Roberts, Gary, Pres. & Chief Oper. Officer--Greenstone Roberts/Florida, Orlando, FL; *U.S. Public*, pg. 763
Roberts, John J., Chief Oper. Officer--Coopers & Lybrand, New York, NY; *U.S. Private*, pg. 274
Roberts, Ken, Chief Oper. Officer--Durbin-Durco, Reform, AL; *U.S. Public*, pg. 406
Roberts, Lee, Pres. & Chief Oper. Officer--FileNet Corporation, Costa Mesa, CA; *U.S. Public*, pg. 622
Roberts, Tom, Chief Oper. Officer--Gator Freightways, Inc., Wilmington, OH; *U.S. Private*, pg. 441
Robertson, Charles, Chief Oper. Officer & Exec. V.P.--Conwell Corp., Dallas, TX; *U.S. Public*, pg. 685
Robertson, Charles G., Chief Oper. Officer & Exec. V.P.--Frozen Food Express Industries, Inc., Dallas, TX; *U.S. Public*, pg. 685
Robertson, Charles G., Chief Oper. Officer & Exec. V.P.--FFE Transportation Services, Inc., Dallas, TX; *U.S. Public*, pg. 685
Robertson, Hal, Chief Oper. Officer--Hagglunds Drives Inc., Stoney Creek, Canada; *Int'l*, pg. 670
Robertson, Pledger, V.P.-Opers.--Western Data Systems, Calabasas, CA; *U.S. Private*, pg. 1165
Robertson, William J., Chief Oper. Officer & Sr. V.P.--Cominco, Ltd., Vancouver, Canada; *Int'l*, pg. 307
Robies, J., Chief Oper. Officer--Danone S.A., Barcelona, Spain; *Int'l*, pg. 379
Robinson, Anne E., Chief Oper. Officer--Caswell-Massey Co. Ltd., Edison, NJ; *U.S. Private*, pg. 219
Robinson, Charles, Chief Oper. Officer--T.F. Cushing, Inc., West Springfield, MA; *U.S. Public*, pg. 141
Robinson, Hugh C. III, Pres., Chief Exec. Officer & Chief Oper. Officer--Presto Food Stores, Inc., Plant City, FL; *U.S. Private*, pg. 882
Robinson, Irwin Z., Chm. & Chief Exec. Officer--Famous Music Corporation, New York, NY; *U.S. Private*, pg. 777
Robinson, J. Douglas, Pres. & Chief Oper. Officer--Utica Mutual Insurance Company, New Hartford, NY; *U.S. Private*, pg. 1129
Robinson, Murray, Pres. & Chief Oper. Officer--Delta & Pine Land Company, Scott, MS; *U.S. Public*, pg. 497
Robinson, Thomas E., Pres. & Chief Oper. Officer--The Entwistle Company, Hudson, MA; *U.S. Private*, pg. 378
Robison, Kevin, Pres. & Chief Oper. Officer--Quanta SecurSystems, Inc., Hanover, MD; *U.S. Public*, pg. 420
Roby, Joe L., Pres. & Chief Oper. Officer--Donaldson, Lufkin, & Jenrette, Inc., New York, NY; *U.S. Public*, pg. 589
Roche, P.C. "Hoop", Pres. & Chief Exec. Officer--Erie Plastics, Corry, PA; *U.S. Private*, pg. 381
Rock, Douglas L., Chm. Bd., Pres., Chief Exec. & Oper. Officer--Smith International, Inc., Houston, TX; *U.S. Public*, pg. 1478
Roden, Donald R., Pres., Chief Exec. Officer & Chief Oper. Officer--Bergen Brunswig Corporation, Orange, CA; *U.S. Public*, pg. 213
Roderova, Jana, Chief Officer--Frionor C.R. a.s., Prague, Czech Republic; *Int'l*, pg. 516
Rodewig, John, Chief Oper. Officer--Eaton Leasing Corp., Cleveland, OH; *U.S. Public*, pg. 558
Rodgers, Ronald W., Pres. & Chief Oper. Officer--Tri Tech Laboratories, Inc., Lynchburg, VA; *U.S. Private*, pg. 1101
Roemer, James, Pres. & Chief Exec. Officer--Bell & Howell Holdings, Skokie, IL; *U.S. Public*, pg. 201
Roesler, Gerd, Chief Oper. Officer--MTN Medizintechnik Neubrandenburg GmbH I.G., Neubrandenburg, Germany; *Int'l*, pg. 669
Rogan, T.B., Chief Oper. Officer--Frank R. MacNeill & Son, Inc., Miami, FL; *Int'l*, pg. 705
Rogers, Dale, Pres. & Chief Oper. Officer--Drug Emporium of Arizona, Scottsdale, AZ; *U.S. Private*, pg. 343
Rogers, Don, Chief Oper. Officer--Foster Wheeler Environmental Corporation, Livingston, NJ; *U.S. Public*, pg. 677
Rogers, James E., Vice Chm., Pres. & Chief Exec. Officer--Cinergy Corp., Cincinnati, OH; *U.S. Public*, pg. 368
Rogers, James E., Vice Chm. & Chief Oper. Officer--Cinergy Corp., Cincinnati, OH; *U.S. Public*, pg. 369
Roggeman, M., Chief Oper. Officer--Overpelt-Plascobel, Inc., Brussels, Belgium; *Int'l*, pg. 1442
Rogowski, Alex, Chief Oper. Officer--Eagle Button Co., Inc., Carlstadt, NJ; *U.S. Private*, pg. 354
Rohleder, Claus, Dr., Chief Oper. Officer--Boehringer Ingelheim, Ingelheim, Germany; *Int'l*, pg. 199
Rohm, William, V.P.-Opers.--Chattanooga Group, Inc., Hixson, TN; *U.S. Private*, pg. 231
Roland, Frank, Pres., Chief Exec. Officer & Chief Oper. Officer--Rubatex Corporation, Roanoke, VA; *U.S. Private*, pg. 56
Rolla, M.F., Pres. & Chief Oper. Officer--Gem Industries Finance Corporation, Toccoa, GA; *U.S. Private*, pg. 442
Rolland, Frank, Pres. & Chief Oper. Officer--RBX Corporation, Roanoke, VA; *U.S. Private*, pg. 56
Rolland, Ian M., Chm. Bd., Pres. & Chief Exec. Officer--Lincoln National Corporation, Fort Wayne, IN; *U.S. Public*, pg. 997
Rollins, Gary W., Pres. & Chief Oper. Officer--Rollins, Inc., Atlanta, GA; *U.S. Public*, pg. 1404
Rollins, John W., Jr., Pres. & Chief Oper. Officer--Rollins Truck Leasing Corp., Wilmington, DE; *U.S. Public*, pg. 1405
Romano, Gary M., Chief Oper. Officer & Exec. V.P.--Equis Financial Group, Boston, MA; *U.S. Private*, pg. 379
Romans, William, Chief Oper. Officer--Sierra Technologies Inc., Buffalo, NY; *U.S. Private*, pg. 999
Rominiecki, Ronald R., Pres. & Chief Oper. Officer--National Propane Corp., Cedar Rapids, IA; *U.S. Public*, pg. 1635
Romoren, Bente-Lill B., Chief Oper. Officer--Novo Nordisk Pharma A/S, Rud, Norway; *Int'l*, pg. 988
Rooney, Thomas S., Chief Oper. Officer & Exec. V.P.--Versar Inc., Springfield, VA; *U.S. Public*, pg. 1717
Root, Larry D., Pres. & Chief Oper. Officer--IES Industries Inc., Cedar Rapids, IA; *U.S. Public*, pg. 855
Root, Larry D., Pres. & Chief Oper. Officer--IES Utilities Inc., Cedar Rapids, IA; *U.S. Public*, pg. 855
Roper, John L., IV, Exec. V.P.-Opers. & Sec.--Norfolk Shipbuilding & Drydock Corporation, Norfolk, VA; *U.S. Private*, pg. 802
Rork, Daniel R., Chief Oper. Officer & V.P.--Fabreeka International, Inc., Stoughton, MA; *U.S. Private*, pg. 390
Rose, D.F., Chief Oper. Officer--PPP hc, Tunbridge Wells, United Kingdom; *Int'l*, pg. 1020
Rose, Matthew K., Chief Oper. Officer & Sr. V.P.--Burlington Northern Santa Fe Corporation, Fort Worth, TX; *U.S. Public*, pg. 268
Rosemore, Andrew S., Chief Oper. Officer, Exec. V.P., Treas. & Asst. Sec.--PMC Capital Inc., Dallas, TX; *U.S. Public*, pg. 1242
Rosen, Jeffery, Chief Oper. Officer & Treas.--Rose Art Industries, Livingston, NJ; *U.S. Private*, pg. 945
Rosenbach, W.H., V.P.-Opers.--National Frozen Foods Corp., Seattle, WA; *U.S. Private*, pg. 783
Rosenberg, Gary, Pres. & Chief Oper. Officer--The Homestead L.C., Hot Springs, VA; *U.S. Private*, pg. 247
Rosenberg, Henry A., Jr., Chm. Bd., Pres., Chief Exec. & Oper. Officer--Crown Central Petroleum Corporation, Baltimore, MD; *U.S. Public*, pg. 462
Rosendahl, David E., Pres. & Chief Oper. Officer--The Medical Protective Company, Fort Wayne, IN; *U.S. Private*, pg. 728
Rosenfeld, Leonard, Chief Oper. Officer--International Plastics Company, New York, NY; *U.S. Private*, pg. 571
Rosenkrantz, Howard M., Pres. & Chief Oper. Officer--U.S. Surgical Corp., Norwalk, CT; *U.S. Public*, pg. 1687
Rosenmueller, Frank J., Chief Oper. Officer--Royal Nederland Levensverzekering N.V., Utrecht, Netherlands; *Int'l*, pg. 16
Rosenthal, Mark, Pres. & Chief Oper. Officer--MTV Networks, New York, NY; *U.S. Private*, pg. 779
Rosenthal, Mark, Chief. Oper. Officer, V.P. & Gen. Counsel--Raleigh Enterprises, Inc., Santa Monica, CA; *U.S. Private*, pg. 907
Rosenthal, Robert, Ph.D, Pres., Chief Exec. Officer & Chief Oper. Officer--Thermo Jarrell Ash Corporation, Franklin, MA; *U.S. Public*, pg. 1594
Rosevear, Kenneth A., Pres. & Chief Oper. Officer--MGM Grand Development, Inc., Las Vegas, NV; *U.S. Public*, pg. 1027
Rosica, Gabriel, Chief Oper. Officer--Bailey Controls Company, Wickliffe, OH; *Int'l*, pg. 654
Rosinoer, Serge, Vice Chm. & Chief Oper. Officer--Clarins, Neuilly-sur-Seine, France; *Int'l*, pg. 295
Roskovensky, E. A., Pres. & Chief Oper. Officer--Robertson-Ceco Corporation, San Ramon, CA; *U.S. Public*, pg. 1394
Ross, Donald L., Chief Oper. Officer & Sr. Exec. V.P.--Enterprise Rent-A-Car Company, Saint Louis, MO; *U.S. Private*, pg. 377
Ross, Elliot B., Chief Oper. Officer & Exec. V.P.--Essef Corporation, Chardon, OH; *U.S. Public*, pg. 592
Ross, Frank, Sr., Chm. Bd. & Chief Oper. Officer--HRH Construction Corp., New York, NY; *U.S. Private*, pg. 1035
Ross, Raymond E., Pres. & Chief Oper. Officer--Cincinnati Milacron Inc., Cincinnati, OH; *U.S. Public*, pg. 368
Ross, Ronald R., Pres. & Chief Oper. Officer--CACI International Inc, Arlington, VA; *U.S. Public*, pg. 272
Rosselet, Thomas, Chief Oper. Officer--Milprint Inc., Oshkosh, WI; *U.S. Public*, pg. 210
Rosser, Darryl, Pres. & Chief Oper. Officer--Falcon Products, Inc., Saint Louis, MO; *U.S. Public*, pg. 611
Rossiter, Robert, Pres. & Chief Oper. Officer--Lear Corporation, Southfield, MI; *U.S. Public*, pg. 981
Rosskam, Skip, III, Pres. & Chief Oper. Officer--David Michael & Co. Inc., Philadelphia, PA; *U.S. Private*, pg. 740
Roszkowski, Leszek, Chief Oper. Officer--Gambro Poland sp. z.o.o., Warsaw, Poland; *Int'l*, pg. 668
Roth, Francis H., Pres. & Chief Oper. Officer--HarCor Energy, Inc., Houston, TX; *U.S. Public*, pg. 782
Roth, Fred, Chief Oper. Officer--Production Management Industries, Inc., Harvey, LA; *U.S. Private*, pg. 889
Roth, John, Chief Oper. Officer--Northern Telecom, Nashville, TN; *Int'l*, pg. 969
Roth, John A., Chief Exec. & Oper. Officer & Pres.-Nortel North America--Northern Telecom Limited, Brampton, Canada; *Int'l*, pg. 968
Roth, Myron I., Pres. & Chief Oper. Officer--All American Communications, Inc., Santa Monica, CA; *U.S. Public*, pg. 41
Roth, W.R., Pres.--SJW Corp., San Jose, CA; *U.S. Public*, pg. 1418
Roth, Y., Chief Oper. Officer--Makhteshim-Agan International, Brussels, Belgium; *Int'l*, pg. 831
Rother, Doug C., Chief Oper. Officer & Exec. V.P.--Columbine JDS Systems, Inc., Denver, CO; *U.S. Public*, pg. 228
Rounick, Marvin, Pres., Chief Exec. Officer & Chief Oper. Officer--Deb Shops, Inc., Philadelphia, PA; *U.S. Public*, pg. 491

Rountree, W. Dekle, Jr., Chief Oper. Officer & Exec. V.P.--Ohmeda, Inc., Liberty Corner, NJ; *Int'l*, pg. 121
Roussel, Allen, V.P.-Opers.--Associated Grocers, Inc., Baton Rouge, LA; *U.S. Private*, pg. 90
Roveto, Connie, Chief Oper. Officer--The Trust Company of Bank of Montreal, Toronto, Canada; *Int'l*, pg. 153
Rowberry, Jon H., Pres. & Chief Oper. Officer--Franklin Covey, Salt Lake City, UT; *U.S. Public*, pg. 679
Rowe, William E., Pres. & Chief Oper. Officer--Stewart Enterprises, Inc., Metairie, LA; *U.S. Public*, pg. 1518
Rowland, Lawrence, Chief Oper. Officer--Lincoln National Management Services, Inc., Fort Wayne, IN; *U.S. Public*, *pg. 998*
Rownak, John J., Jr., Chief Oper. Officer--Citizens Bank of Northwest Arkansas, Fayetteville, AR; *U.S. Public*, pg. 163
Roy, Larry, Chief Oper. Officer--Kentucky Manufacturing Co., Louisville, KY; *U.S. Private*, pg. 615
Roy, Pierre-Andre, Pres. & Chief Oper. Officer--Bombardier Capital Group, Colchester, VT; *Int'l*, pg. 200
Royston, Alan, Chief Oper. Officer--LogEtronics Corporation, Springfield, VA; *U.S. Public*, pg. 6
Rozentsvit, Analolij, Chief Oper. Officer--Ahlstrom Representation in Moscow, Moscow, Russia; *Int'l*, pg. 33
Ruboczky, Tamas, Chief Oper. Officer--Akerlund & Rausing, Budapest, Hungary; *Int'l*, pg. 33
Rudolph, Scott, Chm. Bd., Pres., Chief Exec. Officer & Chief Oper. Officer--Nature's Bounty Inc., Bohemia, NY; *U.S. Public*, pg. 1166
Rue, William B., Chief Oper. Officer & Sr. V.P.--Salton/Maxim Housewares, Inc., Mount Prospect, IL; *U.S. Public*, pg. 1430
Ruff, Edward C., Chm. Bd. & Chief Oper. Officer--Interstate/Johnson Lane, Inc., Charlotte, NC; *U.S. Public*, pg. 909
Ruge, K., Chief Oper. Officer--Manitec Consulting AG, Emmen, Switzerland; *Int'l*, pg. 1205
Rugen, Willi, Co-Chief Oper. Officer--Hesse, Rhineland-Palatinate & Saar Branch, Frankfurt/Main, Germany; *Int'l*, pg. 645
Ruggeri, Dennis, Chief Oper. Officer & Exec. V.P.--Hutchins/Young & Rubicam, Rochester, NY; *U.S. Private*, pg. 1197
Ruhlman, Robert G., Pres. & Chief Oper. Officer--Preformed Line Products, Cleveland, OH; *U.S. Public*, pg. 1321
Ruijssenaars, Andries, Pres. & Chief Oper. Officer--Eagle-Picher Industries, Inc., Cincinnati, OH; *U.S. Private*, pg. 355
Ruisi, Christopher S., Pres. & Chief Oper. Officer--USLIFE Corporation, New York, NY; *U.S. Public*, pg. 77
Rummurthy, Gitch, Pres. & Chief Oper. Officer--InfoVest, Inc., Chicago, IL; *U.S. Private*, pg. 562
Rummurthy, Gitch, Pres. & Chief Oper. Officer--CCC Information Services, Chicago, IL; *U.S. Private*, pg. 562
Rumsey, Gary G., Sr. V.P. & Chief Oper. Officer--Security Bank & Trust Co., Mount Carmel, IL; *U.S. Public*, pg. 1217
Runte, Hans-Dieter, Dr., Chief Oper. Officer--BHF Trust Management Gesellschaft fur Vermoegensverwaltung mbH, Frankfurt/Main, Germany; *Int'l*, pg. 119
Rusch, Bruce R., Pres. & Chief Oper. Officer--Analogic Corporation, Peabody, MA; *U.S. Public*, pg. 109
Russano, Richard, Pres. & Chief Oper. Officer--Winstar Global Products, Inc., Fairfield, NJ; *U.S. Public*, pg. 1772
Russek, Michael, Chief Oper. & Fin. Officer--Astronautics Corporation of America, Milwaukee, WI; *U.S. Private*, pg. 93
Russell, Andy, Chief Oper. Officer--AGA Catalog Marketing & Design, New York, NY; *U.S. Private*, pg. 5
Russell, Dennis, Chief Oper. Officer--Baccarat (Cie des Cristalleries), Paris, France; *Int'l*, pg. 132
Russell, R. David, Chief Oper. Officer & V.P.--Getchell Gold Corp., Englewood, CO; *U.S. Public*, pg. 740
Russillo, Thomas R., Pres. & Chief Oper. Officer--Ben Venue Laboratories, Inc., Bedford, OH; *U.S. Private*, pg. 1136
Russo, Carmine, Chief Oper. Officer--Toymax International Inc., Plainview, NY; *U.S. Public*, pg. 1626
Russo, Richard A., Exec. V.P.--Middlesex Water Company, Iselin, NJ; *U.S. Public*, pg. 1110
Rutt, T., Chief Oper. Officer--Molto GmbH, Lohnberg, Germany; *Int'l*, pg. 1501
Rutter, John, Chief Oper. Officer-Keystone--Vail Resorts, Inc., Vail, CO; *U.S. Public*, pg. 1704
Ruutu, Hanno, Chief Oper. Officer--Neste Kide Oy, Espoo, Finland; *Int'l*, pg. 913
Ruwe, Dean M., Chief Oper. Officer--Copeland Corporation, Sidney, OH; *U.S. Public*, pg. 573
Ryan, James P., Chief Oper. Officer--Stevens Point Brewery, Stevens Point, WI; *U.S. Public*, pg. 300
Ryan, John G., Pres. & Chief Oper. Officer--Global Marine Inc., Houston, TX; *U.S. Public*, pg. 748
Ryan, John J., Pres. & Chief Oper. Officer--Charan Realty Group, Garden City, NY; *U.S. Private*, pg. 229
Ryan, Richard O., Pres. & Chief Oper. Officer--Dekalb Genetics Corporation, De Kalb, IL; *U.S. Public*, pg. 493
Ryan, Thomas F., Jr., Pres. & Chief Oper. Officer--The American Stock Exchange, New York, NY; *U.S. Private*, pg. 62
Ryan, Thomas M., Vice Chm., Pres., Chief Exec. Officer & Chief Oper. Officer-CVS--CVS Corp., Woonsocket, RI; *U.S. Public*, pg. 287
Ryan, Tom, Exec. V.P.-Opers.--URS Logistics, Atlanta, GA; *U.S. Private*, pg. 1114
Ryckebosch, Etienne, Chief Oper. Officer--Schleicher & Schuell N.V. S.A., Gent, Belgium; *Int'l*, pg. 1206
Ryder, C.E., V.P.-Opers.--Alco Chemical, Chattanooga, TN; *Int'l*, pg. 1435
Ryder, John, Pres. & Chief Oper. Officer-Retail--Metro/Basics, Baltimore, MD; *U.S. Public*, pg. 1388
Ryerson, Jay, Chief Oper. Officer & Exec. V.P.--Analysis & Technology, Inc., North Stonington, CT; *U.S. Public*, pg. 109
Ryman, Chris, Chief Oper. Officer-Sls./Beaver Creek--Vail Resorts, Inc., Vail, CO; *U.S. Public*, pg. 1704
Sabin, Bruce D., Chief Oper. Officer & Exec. V.P.--Civic Center Corporation, Saint Louis, MO; *U.S. Public*, pg. 114
Sabin, Dan, Chief Oper. Officer--Bangor & Aroostook Railroad Co., Bangor, ME; *U.S. Private*, pg. 575
Sabol, Thomas A., Chief Oper. Officer--Robert Englekirk, Inc., Los Angeles, CA; *U.S. Private*, pg. 377
Sachse, Robert G., Chief Oper. Officer & Exec. V.P.--Mapco Inc., Tulsa, OK; *U.S. Public*, pg. 1042
Sack, Thomas F., Pres., Chief Exec. Officer & Chief Oper. Officer--Haddon Craftsmen, Inc., Scranton, PA; *U.S. Public*, pg. 518
Sackett, David, Chief Oper. Officer & Exec. V.P.--PAID Prescriptions, Inc., Fair Lawn, NJ; *U.S. Public*, pg. 1091
Sadowski, James, Pres. & Chief Oper. Officer--Chart Industries, Inc., Cleveland, OH; *U.S. Public*, pg. 336
Sadowski, James, Pres. & Chief Oper. Officer--PSI-Process Systems International, Inc., Cleveland, OH; *U.S. Public*, pg. 336
Sadowski, Rick, Dir.-Information Services--Acklands Limited, Toronto, Canada; *Int'l*, pg. 23
Saginaw, David, Pres. & Chief Oper. Officer--Roytex, Inc., New York, NY; *U.S. Private*, pg. 949
Sahene, James M., Pres. & Chief Oper. Officer-TCBY Systems, Inc.--TCBY Enterprises Inc., Little Rock, AR; *U.S. Public*, pg. 1553
Sain, Sanjiv, Chief Oper. Officer--Hagglunds Hydraulic Drives (India) Pvt. Ltd., Pune, India; *Int'l*, pg. 670
Sainio, Veikko, Chief Oper. Officer--KONE Lifts a.s., Prague, Czech Republic; *Int'l*, pg. 747
Sais, Joe, Chief Oper. Officer--Paper Enterprises, Inc., Bronx, NY; *U.S. Private*, pg. 837
Saito, Akihiro, Chief Oper. Officer--Sony Corporation of Panama, Panama, Panama; *Int'l*, pg. 1284
Sakaguchi, Ike, Chief Oper. Officer--Land KK, Osaka, Japan; *Int'l*, pg. 798
Saker, Richard, Chief Oper. Officer & V.P.--Foodarama Supermarkets, Inc., Freehold, NJ; *U.S. Public*, pg. 661
Salanski, Charles W., Pres. & Chief Oper. Officer--Wire Rope Corporation of America, Inc., Saint Joseph, MO; *U.S. Private*, pg. 1184
Salerno, Robert, Pres. & Chief Oper. Officer--Avis Car Leasing, Garden City, NY; *U.S. Public*, pg. 321
Salerno, Robert, Pres. & Chief Oper. Officer--Avis Rent A Car System, Inc., Garden City, NY; *U.S. Public*, pg. 321
Salines, Felis, Chief Oper. Officer--Dalworth Concrete Products, Inc., San Antonio, TX; *U.S. Private*, pg. 417
Salmon, Joe, Chief Oper. Officer-OEM--Serigraph, Inc., West Bend, WI; *U.S. Private*, pg. 985
Saloana, Art, Chief Oper. Officer--Omniflight, Inc., Dallas, TX; *U.S. Private*, pg. 816
Salway, Roger A., Chief Oper. Officer & Exec. V.P.--Paper Calmenson & Co., Saint Paul, MN; *U.S. Private*, pg. 837
Samide, Michael, Chief Oper. Officer & V.P.--Titan International, Inc., Quincy, IL; *U.S. Public*, pg. 1618
Samijn, Luc, Chief Oper. Officer--UM Engineering, Ottignies, Belgium; *Int'l*, pg. 1442
Samman, Salim, Mng. Dir., Chief Oper. Officer, Europe & Dir.--BBDO Worldwide Inc., New York, NY; *U.S. Public*, pg. 1223
Samoff, Pete W., Chief Oper. Officer & Exec. V.P.--T.D. Williamson, Inc., Tulsa, OK; *U.S. Private*, pg. 1179
Sample, Wm., Mgr.-Opers.--Fournier Furniture, Saint Paul, VA; *U.S. Private*, pg. 422
Sampson, Gerald A., Pres. & Chief Oper. Officer--Neiman Marcus Co., Dallas, TX; *U.S. Public*, pg. 785
Samson, Claire, Chief Oper. Officer & Exec. V.P.--Reseau de Television Quatre Saisons Inc., Montreal, Canada; *Int'l*, pg. 241
San Fillipo, Steven A., Chief Oper. Officer--Cardinal Inc., Rahway, NJ; *U.S. Private*, pg. 208
Sanada, Takashi, Pres. & Chief Oper. Officer--KYB Corporation of America, Lombard, IL; *Int'l*, pg. 727
Sanchez, Evagio, Chief Oper. Officer--Sol Melia America, Miami, FL; *Int'l*, pg. 1277
Sandelin, Tor-Erik, Chief Oper. Officer--KONE Elevators Finland, Helsinki, Finland; *Int'l*, pg. 746
Sanderbeck, Jim, Chief Oper. Officer--Manatron, Inc., Kalamazoo, MI; *U.S. Public*, pg. 1040
Sanders, O'Neil, Chm. Bd., Pres., Chief Exec. & Chief Oper. Officer--Associated Petroleum Carriers, Spartanburg, SC; *U.S. Private*, pg. 92
Sanders, Wayne R., Chm. Bd. & Chief Exec. Officer--Kimberly-Clark Corporation, Dallas, TX; *U.S. Public*, pg. 958
Sandman, John B., Chief Oper. Officer & Exec. V.P.--A. Teichert & Son, Inc., Sacramento, CA; *U.S. Private*, pg. 1072
Sands, Marvin, Chief Oper. Officer--Manaschewitz Wine Company, Canandaigua, NY; *U.S. Public*, pg. 300
Sanford, J., Pres. & Chief Oper. Officer--Rolls-Royce Inc., Reston, VA; *Int'l*, pg. 1127
Sanford, Phil, Chief Oper. Officer--Hyer Industries Inc./Thayer Scale, Pembroke, MA; *U.S. Private*, pg. 552
Sanguinetti, L. David, Chief Oper. Officer & Exec. V.P.--Florsheim Group Inc., Chicago, IL; *U.S. Public*, pg. 656
Sankarakrishnan, A., Chief Oper. Officer--KONE Elevator India Ltd., Madras, India; *Int'l*, pg. 748
Sant, Stephen R., Chief Oper. Officer & Exec. V.P.--First Western Bancorp, Inc., New Castle, PA; *U.S. Public*, pg. 642
Santacroce, John, Chief Oper. Officer--Delcal Enterprises, Inc., New York, NY; *U.S. Private*, pg. 322
Santelman, Roger D., Chief Oper. Officer--Hammel, Green & Abrahamson, Inc., Minneapolis, MN; *U.S. Private*, pg. 497
Sapan, Joshua, Pres. & Chief Oper. Officer--Rainbow Programming Holdings, Inc., Woodbury, NY; *U.S. Public*, pg. 288
Saponja, Walter, Pres. & Chief Oper. Officer--TransAlta Utilities, Calgary, Canada; *Int'l*, pg. 1416
Sapp, A. Eugene, Jr., Pres. & Chief Oper. Officer--SCI Systems, Inc., Huntsville, AL; *U.S. Public*, pg. 1416
Sarama, John, Chief Oper. Officer & V.P.-Opers.--Evans, Inc., Chicago, IL; *U.S. Public*, pg. 596
Saraneeyatham, Mongkol, V.P. & Chief Oper. Officer--Unicord Public Co. LTD., Bangkok, Thailand; *Int'l*, pg. 1432
Sargent, Charles, Pres. & Chief Oper. Officer--Evans Industries, Inc., Detroit, MI; *U.S. Private*, pg. 385
Sarin, Arun, Pres. & Chief Oper. Officer--AirTouch Communications, Inc., San Francisco, CA; *U.S. Public*, pg. 34
Sarkiewicz-Hirszson, Olga, Chief Oper. Officer--Ferrosan International A/S, Warsaw, Poland; *Int'l*, pg. 989
Sarner, Gary R., Chief Oper. Officer--Christiana Companies, Inc., Milwaukee, WI; *U.S. Public*, pg. 352
Sarney, George, Dr., Chief Oper. Officer--The Foxboro Company, Foxboro, MA; *Int'l*, pg. 1243
Sartain, James T., Pres. & Chief Oper. Officer--FirstCity Financial Corporation, Waco, TX; *U.S. Public*, pg. 644
Sasamoto, Masaki, Chief Oper. Officer--The Wuphoon Insurance Company Limited, Singapore, Singapore; *Int'l*, pg. 1393
Sasser, Stephen A., Pres. & Chief Oper. Officer--Symix Systems, Inc., Columbus, OH; *U.S. Public*, pg. 1546
Sato, Hiroshi, Chief Oper. Officer--Nissho Iwai Corporation (Iran) Ltd., Tehran, Iran; *Int'l*, pg. 948
Satoh, Yoichi, Chief Oper. Officer--Nissho Iwai (Nigeria) Ltd., Victoria Island, Nigeria; *Int'l*, pg. 948
Sauey, Eric W., Pres. & Chief Oper. Officer--Seats Incorporated, Reedsburg, WI; *U.S. Private*, pg. 410
Saul, Leonardo, Oper. Officer--Arcoplus Argentina, Buenos Aires, Argentina; *Int'l*, pg. 576
Saunders, Keith C., Chief Fin. Officer, Exec. V.P. & Sec.--Zions Co-operative Mercantile Institution, Salt Lake City, UT; *U.S. Public*, pg. 1793
Savage, John E., Pres., Chief Oper. Officer, Co-Chief Exec. Officer & Sec.--Amwest Insurance Group, Inc., Calabasas, CA; *U.S. Public*, pg. 106
Savage, Steven A., Sr. V.P.-Mfg.--Terra Nitrogen Company, L.P., Tulsa, OK; *U.S. Public*, pg. 1581
Savely, Michael, V.P.-Opers.--Concorde Career Colleges, Inc., Kansas City, MO; *U.S. Public*, pg. 430
Saviano, Rudy, Chief Oper. Officer & V.P.-Customer Service--Glen Oaks Industries, Inc., New York, NY; *U.S. Private*, pg. 456
Savitsky, David, Chief Oper. Officer, Exec. V.P., Treas. & Sec.--Staff Builders Inc., Lake Success, NY; *U.S. Public*, pg. 1501
Savonet, H., Chief Oper. Officer--Pum Inox, Charleroi, Belgium; *Int'l*, pg. 301
Savoy, Marie Chantal, Chief Info. Officer--Avenor, Inc., Montreal, Canada; *Int'l*, pg. 101
Sawamura, Fumio, Sr. Mng. Dir.--Hosokawa Micron Corporation, Osaka, Japan; *Int'l*, pg. 635
Sawruk, Donald, Chief Oper. Officer & Exec. V.P.--ESELCO, Inc., Sault Sainte Marie, MI; *U.S. Public*, pg. 591
Sawyer, Charles W., Chief Oper. Officer & Exec. V.P.--Colonial Gas Company, Lowell, MA; *U.S. Public*, pg. 400
Sayegh, Paul, Chief Oper. Officer--Bulova Corporation, Woodside, NY; *U.S. Public*, pg. 1010
Scariot, Terry G., Sr., Pres. & Chief Oper. Officer--Desa International, Bowling Green, KY; *U.S. Private*, pg. 326
Sceales, Ralph, Chief Oper. Officer & V.P.-Opers.--Vacu-Dry Company, Sebastopol, CA; *U.S. Public*, pg. 1704
Schade, Albrecht, Co-Chief Oper. Officer--North Rhine Westphalia Branch, Dusseldorf, Germany; *Int'l*, pg. 645
Schaefer, George A., Jr., Pres. & Chief Oper. Officer--The Fifth Third Bank, Cincinnati, OH; *U.S. Public*, pg. 621
Schaefer, Richard, Chief Oper. Officer--Strober Long Island Building Materials Centers, Inc., Valley Stream, NY; *U.S. Private*, pg. 403
Schaffer, Charles L., Chief Oper. Officer--United Parcel Service of America, Inc., Atlanta, GA; *U.S. Private*, pg. 1123
Schardt, Ronald, Chm. Bd., Chief Exec. Officer & Chief Oper. Officer--Reinke Manufacturing Co., Inc., Deshler, NE; *U.S. Private*, pg. 920
Schattin, Neil, V.P.-Opers.--Monarch Tile, Inc., Florence, AL; *U.S. Private*, pg. 287
Schatz, H.J., Chief Oper. Officer--Groupe SEB Hungary, Budapest, Hungary; *Int'l*, pg. 568
Schatz, H.J., Chief Oper. Officer--Groupe SEB Slovensko, Bratislava, Slovakia; *Int'l*, pg. 568
Schautz, Carol A., Chief Oper. Officer & Exec. V.P.--Wunderman Cato Johnson, New York, NY; *U.S. Private*, pg. 1197
Scheff, Debbie, Sr. V.P. & Chief Oper. Officer-Managed Care--PHP Healthcare Corporation, Reston, VA; *U.S. Public*, pg. 1241
Scheiber, Patrice, Pres. & Chief Oper. Officer--I.C. System, Inc., Vadnais Heights, MN; *U.S. Private*, pg. 553
Schepis, Joseph M., Sr., Chief Oper. Officer & Sr. V.P.--Washington Gas Light Co., Springfield, VA; *U.S. Public*, pg. 1740
Scheurer, John M., Pres. & Chief Oper. Officer--Allied Capital Commercial Corporation, Washington, DC; *U.S. Public*, pg. 47
Schichtel, Gerald F., Pres. & Chief Oper. Officer--Hilliard Corporation, Elmira, NY; *U.S. Private*, pg. 530
Schiefler, Roger, Chm. Bd. & Chief Oper. Officer--Synergis Technologies Group, Grand Rapids, MI; *U.S. Private*, pg. 1060
Schiek, Fred A., Chief Oper. Officer & Exec. V.P.--EMC Insurance Companies, Des Moines, IA; *U.S. Public*, pg. 545
Schiek, Frederick A., Chief Oper. Officer & Exec. V.P.--EMC Insurance Group, Inc., Des Moines, IA; *U.S. Public*, pg. 545
Schieman, L. Richard, Chm. Bd., Pres., Chief Exec. Officer & Chief Oper. Officer--Hughes-Peters, Inc., Cincinnati, OH; *U.S. Private*, pg. 546
Schifrin, Arieh, V.P.-Opers.--California Micro Devices, Milpitas, CA; *U.S. Public*, pg. 293

Schilkey, Andrew, Chief Oper. Officer--Bess Eaton Donut Flour Co., Inc., Westerly, RI; U.S. Private, pg. 139

Schimberg, Henry A., Pres. & Chief Oper. Officer--Coca-Cola Enterprises Inc., Atlanta, GA; U.S. Public, pg. 393

Schimkaitis, John R., Pres. & Chief Oper. Officer--Chesapeake Utilities Corporation, Dover, DE; U.S. Public, pg. 347

Schinder, Rainer, Chief Oper. Officer & Exec. V.P.--Ragold, Inc., Chicago, IL; Int'l, pg. 1084

Schipper, Kevin D., Chief Oper. Officer--Ag Services of America, Inc., Cedar Falls, IA; U.S. Public, pg. 6

Schirmacher, Frank, Chief Oper. Officer--Intairdril Ltd., Zug, Switzerland; U.S. Public, pg. 1316

Schischek, W., Chief Oper. Officer--Maschinenfabrik KBA Modling AG, Enzersdorf, Austria; Int'l, pg. 742

Schivley, William W., Exec. V.P. & Chief Oper. Officer-CMS Marketing--Consumers Energy, Jackson, MI; U.S. Public, pg. 280

Schlanger, Marvin O., Chief Oper. Officer & Exec. V.P.--ARCO Chemical Co., Newtown Square, PA; U.S. Public, pg. 144

Schlegel, William A., Chief Oper. Officer--Institute For Scientific Information, Philadelphia, PA; U.S. Public, pg. 1600

Schlicht, Robert A., Pres. & Chief Oper. Officer--M & I Madison Bank, Madison, WI; U.S. Public, pg. 1050

Schliffer, Kent, Chief Oper. Officer--Crankshaft Machine Group, Jackson, MI; U.S. Private, pg. 102

Schlotfeldt, Ken, Chief Oper. Officer, V.P. & Dir.-Mktg.--Badger Air Brush Company, Franklin Park, IL; U.S. Private, pg. 110

Schlotterbeck, David L., Pres. & Chief Oper. Officer--Pacific Scientific Company, Newport Beach, CA; U.S. Public, pg. 1250

Schmelzel, Randy, Chief Oper. Officer--River Ranch - Northeast, Buffalo, NY; Int'l, pg. 491

Schmid, Alfons, Dr., Chief Oper. Officer--NOBIS Societe des Banques Privees, Luxembourg, Luxembourg; Int'l, pg. 119

Schmid, Charles W., Pres. & Chief Oper. Officer--Carlson Travel Group, Inc., Minneapolis, MN; U.S. Private, pg. 212

Schmid, Max, Chief Oper. Officer--Frionor AG, Basel, Switzerland; Int'l, pg. 516

Schmidt, Larry, Pres. & Chief Oper. Officer--Coca-Cola Bottling Co. of Elizabethtown, Elizabethtown, KY; U.S. Private, pg. 248

Schmidt, Peter, Chief Oper. Officer--TOSOH Europe, Wertheim, Germany; Int'l, pg. 1408

Schmidtgall, William H., Chm. Bd., Pres., Chief Exec. Officer & Chief Oper. Officer--DMI, Inc., Goodfield, IL; U.S. Private, pg. 305

Schmitt, Edward A., Pres. & Chief Oper. Officer--Georgia Gulf Corporation, Atlanta, GA; U.S. Public, pg. 734

Schmitz, P., Chief Oper. Officer--Schlatter Benelux B.V., Breda, Netherlands; Int'l, pg. 1206

Schnack, Uwe, Chief Oper. Officer & Exec. V.P.--TSC Shannock Corporation, Burnaby, Canada; Int'l, pg. 1343

Schneck, Peter, Chief Oper. Officer--Mikron Rottweil GmbH, Rottweil, Germany; Int'l, pg. 867

Schneeberger, Donald G., Pres. & Chief Oper. Officer--H.C. Miller Company, Milwaukee, WI; U.S. Private, pg. 747

Schneider, D., Chief Oper. Officer--Busch-Jaeger Ludenscheider Metallwerk GmbH, Ludenscheid, Germany; Int'l, pg. 1427

Schneider, David, Chief Oper. Officer--Fosters Freeze International, Inc., San Luis Obispo, CA; U.S. Public, pg. 677

Schnitz, Bruce A., Chief Oper. Officer--Tarragon Realty Investors, Dallas, TX; U.S. Public, pg. 1561

Schnuck, Craig, Chm. Bd. & Chief Exec. Officer--Schnuck Markets, Inc., Saint Louis, MO; U.S. Private, pg. 971

Schnuck, Scott, Pres. & Chief Oper. Officer--Schnuck Markets, Inc., Saint Louis, MO; U.S. Private, pg. 971

Schoeffler, Michael H., Pres. & Chief Oper. Officer--Starcraft Corporation, Goshen, IN; U.S. Public, pg. 1510

Schoen, Fred, Chief Exec. Officer--Active Tool & Manufacturing Co., Inc., Roseville, MI; U.S. Private, pg. 16

Schoff, James A., Chief Oper. Officer & Exec. V.P.--Developers Diversified Realty Corporation, Moreland Hills, OH; U.S. Public, pg. 502

Scholler, Jack, Chief Oper. Officer & V.P.--Times Printing Company, Inc., Random Lake, WI; U.S. Private, pg. 1087

Scholtens, Martin A., Chief Oper. Officer-Retail--American Stores Company, Salt Lake City, UT; U.S. Public, pg. 92

Schomburger, Rick, Mgr.-Opers.--Keystone Valves and Controls, Inc., Houston, TX; U.S. Public, pg. 1650

Schou, Christian, Chief Oper. Officer--Ferrosan Norge AS, Osteras, Norway; Int'l, pg. 989

Schrader, Thomas F., Pres. & Chief Oper. Officer--WICOR, Inc., Milwaukee, WI; U.S. Public, pg. 1767

Schrager, Harley, Pres. & Chief Oper. Officer--Pacesetter Corporation, Omaha, NE; U.S. Private, pg. 830

Schram, C.R., Chief Oper. Officer & Chief Fin. Officer--RAM Golf Corporation, Melrose Park, IL; U.S. Private, pg. 908

Schreck, Richard H., Pres. & Chief Oper. Officer--Hofmann Industries, Inc., Sinking Spring, PA; U.S. Private, pg. 533

Schreier, Bradley, Pres. & Chief Oper. Officer--Taylor Corporation, Mankato, MN; U.S. Private, pg. 1070

Schrick, Ben, Chief Oper. Officer & Exec. V.P.--Petroleum Helicopters, Inc., Metairie, LA; U.S. Public, pg. 1281

Schrickel, Patrick D., Pres. & Chief Oper. Officer--Wisconsin Public Service Corporation, Green Bay, WI; U.S. Public, pg. 1728

Schrieber, H., Chief Oper. Officer--SAIA-Burgess GmbH, Dresden, Germany; Int'l, pg. 1501

Schroeder, James, Chief Oper. Officer & Exec. V.P.--Sid Tool Co. Inc., Plainview, NY; U.S. Private, pg. 998

Schroeder, Kenneth L., Pres. & Chief Oper. Officer--KLA Tencor Corporation, San Jose, CA; U.S. Public, pg. 939

Schroeder, Richard H., Pres. & Chief Oper. Officer--Harken Energy Corporation, Irving, TX; U.S. Public, pg. 785

Schucht, John F., Chief Oper. Officer--CT Financial Services, Inc., Toronto, Canada; Int'l, pg. 112

Schues, W., Chief Oper. Officer--The Tokio Marine & Fire Insurance Company (U.K.) Limited, Hamburg, Germany; Int'l, pg. 1393

Schuette, Marvin, Chm. Bd., Pres., Chief Exec. Officer & Chief Oper. Officer--Wausau Homes, Inc., Rothschild, WI; U.S. Private, pg. 1154

Schuette, Marvin, Chm. Bd., Pres., Chief Exec. Officer & Chief Oper. Officer--Sterling Building Systems, Inc., Rothschild, WI; U.S. Private, pg. 1154

Schugens, Siegfried, Chief Oper. Officer--Thera Cosmetic GmbH, Dusseldorf, Germany; Int'l, pg. 610

Schult, Robert W., Pres. & Chief Oper. Officer--Nestle USA, Glendale, CA; Int'l, pg. 916

Schulte, Fred, Chief Oper. Officer--Time Warner Cable Liberty Division, Ferndale, NY; U.S. Public, pg. 1611

Schulte, Fred C., Chief Exec. Officer--Elgin National Industries, Inc., Downers Grove, IL; U.S. Private, pg. 370

Schulte, Fritz, Pres. & Chief Oper. Officer--Hampshire Hosiery, Inc., Spruce Pine, NC; U.S. Public, pg. 778

Schultz, Alan F., Chief Oper. Officer & Exec. V.P.--Valassis Communications, Inc., Livonia, MI; U.S. Public, pg. 1704

Schultz, Randy, Chief Oper. Officer & Exec. V.P.--IGI Resources, Inc., Boise, ID; U.S. Private, pg. 568

Schultz, Ronald E., Chief Oper. Officer & Sr. V.P.--MATRIXX Marketing Inc., Cincinnati, OH; U.S. Public, pg. 368

Schulz, Kevin, Chief Oper. Officer & Exec. V.P.--Hoffer's Inc., Schofield, WI; U.S. Private, pg. 239

Schulze, Fred, Pres., Chief Oper. Officer & Gen. Mgr.--Basler Electric Company, Highland, IL; U.S. Private, pg. 121

Schulze, Horst, Pres. & Chief Oper. Officer--The Ritz-Carlton Hotel Company LLC, Atlanta, GA; U.S. Private, pg. 594

Schulze, Kent, Pres. & Chief Oper. Officer--AgriBioTech, Inc., Las Vegas, NV; U.S. Public, pg. 28

Schulze, Rudolf, Chief Oper. Officer--Saarlaendische Kraftwerksgesellschaft mbH, Saarbruecken, Germany; Int'l, pg. 1167

Schumann, Paul D., Chief Oper. Officer & Sr. V.P.--Consumers Water Company, Portland, ME; U.S. Public, pg. 438

Schunder, Gunther, Chief Oper. Officer--Flender Brasil Ltda., Contagem, Brazil; Int'l, pg. 400

Schupp, Rudy E., Chm. Bd., Pres. & Chief Exec. Officer--Republic Security Financial Corporation, West Palm Beach, FL; U.S. Public, pg. 1381

Schwab, James E., Pres. & Chief Oper. Officer--Xtek, Inc., Cincinnati, OH; U.S. Private, pg. 1194

Schwab, Jimmy, Chief Oper. Officer--D&H Distributing Company, Harrisburg, PA; U.S. Private, pg. 300

Schwab, Peter, Pres. & Chief Oper. Officer--The Foothill Group, Inc., Los Angeles, CA; U.S. Public, pg. 1201

Schwamberger, Kurt R., Pres. & Chief Oper. Officer--American Modern Home Insurance Group, Amelia, OH; U.S. Public, pg. 1110

Schwartz, Alan V., Chief Oper. & Fin. Officer & Exec. V.P.--Bernard Hodes Group, New York, NY; U.S. Public, pg. 1224

Schwartz, Leonard, Chm. Bd., Pres. & Chief Exec. Officer--Aceto Corporation, Lake Success, NY; U.S. Public, pg. 15

Schwartz, Mike, Pres. & Chief Oper. Officer--Armstrong Air Conditioning Inc., Bellevue, OH; U.S. Private, pg. 659

Schwartz, Paul N., Pres. & Chief Oper. & Fin. Officer--Maxxam Inc., Houston, TX; U.S. Public, pg. 1062

Schwartzbeck, Tom, Pres., Chief Oper. Officer & Exec. V.P.--Duron, Inc., Beltsville, MD; U.S. Private, pg. 349

Schwarzman, Stephen A., Pres. & Chief Exec. & Oper. Officer--The Blackstone Group, New York, NY; U.S. Private, pg. 147

Schweitzer, Sheila, Chief Oper. Officer--Envoy Corporation, Nashville, TN; U.S. Public, pg. 587

Schwensen, Jurgen, Chief Oper. Officer--Akerlund & Rausing Verpackung GmbH, Hamburg, Germany; Int'l, pg. 33

Scicutella, John V., Exec. Officer-Opers. & Systems--The Prudential Investment Corp., Newark, NJ; U.S. Private, pg. 892

Scodari, Joseph C., Pres. & Chief Oper. Officer--Centocor, Inc., Malvern, PA; U.S. Public, pg. 323

Scott, Alan, Pres.-TELUS Communications--Telus Corporation, Edmonton, Canada; Int'l, pg. 1374

Scott, Billy D., Chief Oper. Officer--Allright Corporation of Delaware, Phoenix, AZ; U.S. Private, pg. 42

Scott, C. Dennis, Vice Chm. & Chief Oper. Officer--Buffets, Inc., Eden Prairie, MN; U.S. Public, pg. 267

Scott, Ed, Pres. & Chief Oper. Officer--Restonic Mattress Corporation, Rosemont, IL; U.S. Private, pg. 925

Scott, John, Chief Oper. Officer--Allright Parking of Georgia, Inc., Savannah, GA; U.S. Private, pg. 43

Scott, John A., Chief Oper. Officer--Cigna Holdings, Inc., Wilmington, DE; U.S. Public, pg. 357

Scott, Samuel C., Pres. & Chief Oper. Officer--Corn Products International, Inc., Bedford Park, IL; U.S. Public, pg. 447

Scricco, Francis M., Chief Oper. Officer & Exec. V.P.--Arrow Electronics, Inc., Melville, NY; U.S. Public, pg. 133

Scroggin, Webster, Sr. V.P.-Opers.--Amperif Corporation, Chatsworth, CA; U.S. Public, pg. 1523

Seagal, Alvin, Chief Oper. Officer & Exec. V.P.--Perry H. Koplik & Sons, New York, NY; U.S. Private, pg. 632

Seaman, P. Jeffrey, V.P.-Opers.--Cyprus Foote Mineral Co., Kings Mountain, NC; U.S. Public, pg. 471

Searles, Mark A., Pres. & Chief Oper. Officer--Eastex Energy Inc., Houston, TX; U.S. Public, pg. 567

Seck, Wee Tai, Chief Oper. Officer--Neste Petroleum (Singapore) PTE. Ltd., Singapore, Singapore; Int'l, pg. 915

Secker, Alan, Chief Oper. Officer--TOSOH Europe B.V., Cheadle, United Kingdom; Int'l, pg. 1408

Seegmiller, Ray R., Pres. & Chief Oper. Officer--Cabot Oil & Gas Corporation, Houston, TX; U.S. Public, pg. 289

Seely, Mike, Chief Oper. Officer--COBE de Mexico, S.A. de C.V., Mexico, Mexico; Int'l, pg. 667

Seely, Timothy A., Pres. & Chief Oper. Officer--Gwaltney of Smithfield, Ltd., Smithfield, VA; U.S. Public, pg. 1479

Seerup, Soeren, V.P.-Opers--Olicom A/S, Lyngby, Denmark; Int'l, pg. 1001

Seidenberg, Ivan G., Pres. & Chief Oper. Officer--Bell Atlantic Corporation, New York, NY; U.S. Public, pg. 201

Seiler, Melvin, Chief Oper. Officer & Exec. V.P.--Micro Warehouse, Inc., Norwalk, CT; U.S. Public, pg. 1104

Sejovia, Jaime Rodriguez, Chief Oper. Officer--Cydsa S.A. Treament Div., Garza Garcia, Mexico; Int'l, pg. 246

Sejpal, David A., Chm. Bd., Pres., Chief Exec. & Oper. Officer & Sec.--Clothestime Stores, Inc., Anaheim, CA; U.S. Public, pg. 387

Sekiguchi, Matt, Chief Oper. Officer & Exec. V.P.--Johnson Yokogawa Corporation, Newnan, GA; Int'l, pg. 1521

Selfridge, Steven G., Chief Oper. Officer & Exec. V.P.--Checkpoint Systems Inc., Thorofare, NJ; U.S. Public, pg. 343

Selhagen, Leif, Chief Oper. Officer--NAPS Sweden AB, Skarholmen, Sweden; Int'l, pg. 913

Selig, Clyde, Pres. & Chief Oper. Officer-CMC Steel Grp.--Structural Metals, Inc., Seguin, TX; U.S. Public, pg. 412

Selig, Tom, Pres. & Chief Oper. Officer--BLH Electronics, Inc., Canton, MA; Int'l, pg. 1289

Sell, Barbara, V.P.-East Opers.--Nobel Education Dynamics, Inc., Media, PA; U.S. Public, pg. 1185

Sellin, Douglas, Chief Oper.Officer--Seattle Pacific Industries, Inc., Seattle, WA; U.S. Private, pg. 980

Sells, James, Pres. & Chief Oper. Officer--Matson Intermodal System, Inc., San Francisco, CA; U.S. Public, pg. 40

Sells, James E., Chief Info. Service & Sr. V.P.-Photo Service--First American Federal Savings Bank, Bristol, VA; U.S. Public, pg. 624

Seltzer, David S., Chief Oper. Officer, Exec. V.P., Treas. & Sec.--Hi-Tech Pharmacal Co., Inc., Amityville, NY; U.S. Public, pg. 825

Semel, Robert K., Pres., Chief Oper. Officer & Sec.--Uniflex, Inc., Hicksville, NY; U.S. Public, pg. 1665

Semel, Terry S., Co-Chm. Bd., Pres. & Chief Oper. Officer--Warner Bros. Studios, Inc., Burbank, CA; U.S. Public, pg. 1611

Senn, Felix, Chief Oper. Officer--Schleicher & Schuell AG, Riehen, Switzerland; Int'l, pg. 1206

Senov, P.A., Chief Oper. Officer--General Paint Ltd., Vancouver, Canada; Int'l, pg. 1501

Serafini, William A., Chief Oper. Officer & Exec. V.P.--Countrywide Partnership Investments, Inc., Pasadena, CA; U.S. Public, pg. 453

Seramur, John C., Pres., Chief Exec. Officer & Chief Oper. Officer--First Financial Corporation, Stevens Point, WI; U.S. Public, pg. 140

Serenbetz, Robert, Chief Oper. Officer--DNA Plant Technology Corp., Oakland, CA; Int'l, pg. 454

Seriati, Ezio, Chief Oper. Officer--Gambro Sales AB, Lund, Sweden; Int'l, pg. 667

Serino, Matthew, Pres. & Chief Oper. Officer--Serino Coyne Inc., New York, NY; U.S. Private, pg. 985

Serls, Phillip, Pres. & Chief Oper. Officer--Colonial Metals Co., Columbia, PA; U.S. Private, pg. 253

Serra, B., Chief Oper. Officer--BFF Italia Srl, Milan, Italy; Int'l, pg. 798

Serrianne, Mark A., Pres. & Chief Oper. Officer--Northlich Stolley LaWarre, Cincinnati, OH; U.S. Private, pg. 806

Servedio, Dominick M., Pres. & Chief Oper. Officer--STV Group, Inc., Douglassville, PA; U.S. Public, pg. 1421

Sevier, Helen, Chm. Bd., Pres., Chief Exec. & Chief Oper. Officer--B.A.S.S., Inc., Montgomery, AL; U.S. Private, pg. 105

Sewaki, Nobuhiro, Chief Oper. Officer--Tokio Marine South-East Servicing Company Limited, Bangkok, Thailand; Int'l, pg. 1393

Seydoux, Jerome, Vice Chm. & Chief Oper. Officer--Chargeurs, Paris, France; Int'l, pg. 280

Shacklett, Dean R., Chief Oper. Officer--National Label Company, Lafayette Hill, PA; U.S. Private, pg. 785

Shaffer, David, Pres. & Chief Oper. Officer--Arrow Tru-Line, Inc., Archbold, OH; U.S. Private, pg. 85

Shaffer, Donald, Chm. & Chief Exec. Officer--Western Auto Supply Company, Kansas City, MO; U.S. Public, pg. 1452

Shanahan, William S., Pres. & Chief Oper. Officer--Colgate-Palmolive Company, New York, NY; U.S. Public, pg. 397

Shanaman, Samuel, Chief Oper. Officer--DM Management Company, Hingham, MA; U.S. Public, pg. 473

Shaner, William, Pres. & Chief Oper. Officer--Laneco, Inc., Easton, PA; U.S. Public, pg. 1541

Shankar, R. Sam, Pres., Chief Oper. Officer & Co-Chief Exec. Officer--Tork, Inc., Mount Vernon, NY; U.S. Private, pg. 1092

Shapiro, Harvey A., Pres. & Chief Oper. Officer--Dynacare, Inc., Toronto, Canada; Int'l, pg. 425

Sharer, Kevin W., Pres. & Chief Oper. Officer--Amgen Inc., Thousand Oaks, CA; U.S. Public, pg. 100

Sharp, David R., Chief Oper. Officer & V.P.--The Flight International Group, Inc., Newport News, VA; U.S. Public, pg. 654

Sharp, David R., Chief Oper. Officer & V.P.--Flight International Aviation, Inc., Newport News, VA; U.S. Public, pg. 654

Sharp, David R., Chief Oper. Officer & V.P.--Flight International, Inc., Newport News, VA; U.S. Public, pg. 654

Sharp, Edward, Chief Oper. Officer--Integrated Systems Analysts, Inc., Arlington, VA; U.S. Private, pg. 566

Sharpe, John L., Pres. & Chief Oper. Officer--Four Seasons Hotels Inc., Don Mills, Canada; Int'l, pg. 502

Sharpe, Ray, Chief Oper. Officer-Electronic Materials Div.--Cookson Group plc, London, United Kingdom; Int'l, pg. 328

Sharrah, Ray, Chief Oper. Officer--Streamlight Inc., Norristown, PA; *U.S. Private*, pg. 1047
Shattuck, Mayo A., III, Pres. & Chief Oper. Officer--BT Alex. Brown Inc., Baltimore, MD; *U.S. Public*, pg. 185
Shaw, Alan E., V.P.-Opers.--Ryan's Family Steak Houses, Inc., Greer, SC; *U.S. Public*, pg. 1413
Shaw, Bill, Chief Oper. Officer--Turner Reciprocal Advertising Corporation, Atlanta, GA; *U.S. Public*, pg. 1615
Shaw, James, Chief Oper. Officer--Handschy Industries, Bellwood, IL; *U.S. Private*, pg. 403
Shaw, Mark, Chief Oper. Officer & Exec. V.P.--Plenum Publishing Corporation, New York, NY; *U.S. Public*, pg. 1311
Shaw, Ray, Chm. Bd., Pres., Chief Exec. Officer & Chief Oper. Officer--American City Business Journals, Inc., Charlotte, NC; *U.S. Private*, pg. 19
Shaw, Robert C., Chief Fin. Officer & Exec. V.P.-Opers.--ELXSI Corporation, Orlando, FL; *U.S. Public*, pg. 545
Shaw, William J., Pres. & Chief Oper. Officer--Marriott International, Inc., Washington, DC; *U.S. Public*, pg. 1047
Shea, Michael D., Pres. & Chief Oper. Officer--Defiance Precision Products, Inc., Defiance, OH; *U.S. Public*, pg. 493
Sheehan, Edward T., Pres. & Chief Oper. Officer--United Waste Systems, Inc., Houston, TX; *U.S. Public*, pg. 1691
Sheldon, J.M., Chm. Bd., Pres., Chief Exec. Officer & Chief Oper. Officer--Sheldons' Inc., Antigo, WI; *U.S. Private*, pg. 992
Sheldon, James V., Chief Oper. Officer--Monaco Coach Corporation, Coburg, OR; *U.S. Public*, pg. 1123
Shelton, E. Kirk, Pres. & Chief Oper. Officer--CUC International, Inc., Stamford, CT; *U.S. Public*, pg. 320
Sheperd, Martin, Chief Oper. Officer--KONE Elevators (Australia) Pty. Ltd., Newton, New Zealand; *Int'l*, pg. 747
Shephard, K. Craig, Pres. & Chief Oper. Officer--QST Energy, Inc., Peoria, IL; *U.S. Public*, pg. 367
Shepherd, Jim, Pres. & Chief Oper. Officer--Crestbrook Forest Industries Ltd., Cranbrook, Canada; *Int'l*, pg. 348
Sherer, Betsy, Chief Oper. Officer--Films for the Humanities & Sciences, Inc., Monmouth Junction, NJ; *U.S. Public*, pg. 1327
Sherman, Malcolm L., Chief Exec. Officer--Ekco Housewares, Inc., Franklin Park, IL; *U.S. Public*, pg. 566
Sherwood, J. B., Chief Oper. Officer--Illustrated London News, London, United Kingdom; *Int'l*, pg. 1214
Shetler, Jim, Chief Oper. Officer--Sacramento Municipal Utility District, Sacramento, CA; *U.S. Private*, pg. 959
Shibuya, Naoaki, Pres. & Chief Oper. Officer--Central Pacific Bank, Honolulu, HI; *U.S. Public*, pg. 283
Shiely, John S., Pres. & Chief Oper. Officer--Briggs & Stratton Corporation, Wauwatosa, WI; *U.S. Public*, pg. 252
Shimada, Shigeyoshi, Chief Oper. Officer--The Sumitomo Bank, Ltd.-Dalian Representative Office, Dalian, China; *Int'l*, pg. 1309
Shimizu, Takuji, Pres., Chief Exec. Officer & Chief Oper. Officer--Meitsu Inc., Tokyo, Japan; *Int'l*, pg. 856
Shimoyama, Sumio, Chief Oper. Officer--Skandia Life Insurance Co. (Japan) Ltd., Tokyo, Japan; *Int'l*, pg. 1258
Shipley, William S., III, Pres.--Shipley Companies, York, PA; *U.S. Private*, pg. 994
Shipman, Jack H., Pres. & Chief Oper. Officer--Great Financial Bank FSB, Louisville, KY; *U.S. Private*, pg. 473
Shirouza, Osamu, Chief Oper. Officer--TM Claims Service, Inc., New York, NY; *Int'l*, pg. 1392
Shockley, Thomas V., III, Pres. & Chief Oper. Officer--Central and South West Corporation, Dallas, TX; *U.S. Public*, pg. 324
Sholakh, Marwan, Chief Oper. Officer & Exec. V.P.--Nexus Plastics, Inc., Hawthorne, NJ; *U.S. Private*, pg. 797
Shoreman, Terence C., Chief Oper. Officer & Exec. V.P.--Unitog Company, Kansas City, MO; *U.S. Public*, pg. 1693
Shuey, John H., Chm. Bd., Pres., Chief Exec. & Oper. Officer--Amcast Industrial Corporation, Dayton, OH; *U.S. Public*, pg. 63
Shull, Thomas C., Pres. & Chief Oper. Officer--Barneys Inc., New York, NY; *U.S. Private*, pg. 116
Shulman, Mark, Chief Oper. & Mdsg. Officer & Exec. V.P.--Talbots, Inc., Hingham, MA; *Int'l*, pg. 28
Shulman, Martin L., Pres. & Chief Oper. Officer--Customedix Corporation, Wallingford, CT; *U.S. Private*, pg. 298
Shultz, K., Pres. & Chief Oper. Officer--Swepco Tube Corporation, Clifton, NJ; *U.S. Private*, pg. 1058
Shuster, Jay, Pres. & Chief Oper. Officer--Rock-Tenn Company, Norcross, GA; *U.S. Public*, pg. 1396
Siddons, Ernest G., Chief Oper. Officer & Exec. V.P.--Ampco-Pittsburgh Corporation, Pittsburgh, PA; *U.S. Public*, pg. 103
Sidgmore, John, Pres. & Chief Oper. Officer--MFS WorldCom, Inc., Omaha, NE; *U.S. Public*, pg. 1779
Sidgmore, John W., Vice Chm. & Chief Oper. Officer--WorldCom, Inc., Jackson, MS; *U.S. Public*, pg. 1779
Siebenburgen, David A., Pres. & Chief Oper. Officer--Comair Holdings, Inc., Erlanger, KY; *U.S. Public*, pg. 406
Siegel, David L., Vice Chm. & Chief Oper. Officer--Blimpie International, Inc., Atlanta, GA; *U.S. Public*, pg. 236
Siegel, L. Pendleton, Pres. & Chief Oper. Officer--Potlatch Corporation, Spokane, WA; *U.S. Public*, pg. 1318
Siegel, William D., Pres. & Chief Oper. Officer--BHC Communications, Inc., New York, NY; *U.S. Public*, pg. 352
Sierman, Stephen, Chief Oper. Officer--QT Optoelectronics, Sunnyvale, CA; *U.S. Private*, pg. 897
Siess, Robert D., P.E., Pres. & Chief Oper. Officer--Tarlton Corporation, Saint Louis, MO; *U.S. Private*, pg. 1069
Siewert, Patrick T., Chief Oper. Officer-Mktg. & Sls.--Eastman Kodak Company, Rochester, NY; *U.S. Public*, pg. 550
Siglar, Harold, Chief Oper. Officer--McAllen Medical Center, McAllen, TX; *U.S. Public*, pg. 1697
Sills, Lawrence I., Pres. & Chief Exec. & Oper. Officer--Standard Motor Products Inc., Long Island City, NY; *U.S.* Public, pg. 1503
Silver, Martin, Chm. Bd., Pres. & Chief Exec. Officer--Star Industries Inc., Syosset, NY; *U.S. Private*, pg. 1034
Silver, Stan, Pres. & Chief Oper. Officer--The Children's Place Retail Stores, Inc., West Caldwell, NJ; *U.S. Private*, pg. 237
Silverman, S.W., Chief Oper. Officer & Exec. V.P.--PQ Corporation, Berwyn, PA; *U.S. Private*, pg. 827
Silverstein, Allan, Pres. & Chief Oper. Officer--The Bethlehem Corporation, Easton, PA; *U.S. Public*, pg. 225
Silverstein, Leon, Chief Oper. Officer--Arch Aluminium & Glass L.C., Tamarac, FL; *U.S. Private*, pg. 79
Simard, Ronald F.E., Pres. & Chief Oper. Officer--Nowsco Well Service Ltd., Calgary, Canada; *Int'l*, pg. 989
Simkins, L.J., Chm. Bd., Pres., Chief Exec. & Chief Oper. Officer--Simkins Industries, Inc., New Haven, CT; *U.S. Private*, pg. 1000
Simm, David, Pres. & Chief Oper. Officer--Doncasters plc, Melbourn, United Kingdom; *Int'l*, pg. 416
Simmonds, P.G.W., Grp. Mng. Dir.--Pauls plc, Ipswich, United Kingdom; *Int'l*, pg. 598
Simmons, Larry, Chief Oper. Officer-Personnel Lines--Royal Insurance, Charlotte, NC; *Int'l*, pg. 1130
Simo, Zoltan, Pres. & Chief Oper. Officer--TecSyn International, Inc., Saint Catharines, Canada; *Int'l*, pg. 1361
Simon, Ira, V.P.--Triangle Brass Manufacturing, Los Angeles, CA; *U.S. Private*, pg. 1101
Simourian, John, II, Pres. & Chief Oper. Officer--Lily Transportation Corp., Needham, MA; *U.S. Private*, pg. 667
Simpson, Bruce W., Pres. & Chief Oper. Officer--Nova Gas Transmission Ltd., Calgary, Canada; *Int'l*, pg. 971
Simpson, Jack, Pres., Chief Exec. Officer & Chief Oper. Officer--Advance Seed Co., Fulton, KY; *Int'l*, pg. 566
Sin, Lau Chan, Deputy Pres. & Deputy Chief Oper. Officer--DBS Bank Ltd., Singapore, Singapore; *Int'l*, pg. 350
Singer, Gary, Mng. Dir. & Chief Oper. Officer--DMB&B St. Louis, Saint Louis, MO; *U.S. Private*, pg. 303
Singer, James O., Pres. & Chief Oper. Officer--International Total Services, Independence, OH; *U.S. Public*, pg. 908
Singer, Joel L., Pres. & Chief Oper. Officer--Bay State Gas Company, Westborough, MA; *U.S. Public*, pg. 196
Singer, Robert W., Pres., Chief Exec. Officer & Chief Oper. Officer--Keystone Consolidated Industries, Inc., Dallas, TX; *U.S. Public*, pg. 955
Sinha, Awadhesh, Chief Oper. Officer & Chief Fin. Officer--Perry Ellis, New York, NY; *U.S. Public*, pg. 1429
Sisson, Thomas W., Pres. & Chief Oper. Officer--Citibank, Federal Savings Bank (Illinois), Chicago, IL; *U.S. Public*, pg. 378
Sitarz, Richard, Pres. & Chief Oper. Officer--Prospect Foundry, Inc., Minneapolis, MN; *U.S. Public*, pg. 142
Skaggs, Gary L., Chief Oper. Officer & V.P.--Cabre Corp., Wilmington, DE; *U.S. Public*, pg. 289
Skelton, Raymond E., Pres. & Chief Oper. Officer--NBD Banking Company, Southwest, Jeffersonville, IN; *U.S. Public*, pg. 628
Skibitsky, William S., Pres. & Chief Oper. Officer--MYR Group Inc., Rolling Meadows, IL; *U.S. Public*, pg. 1029
Skilling, Jeffrey K., Pres. & Chief Oper. Officer--Enron Corp., Houston, TX; *U.S. Public*, pg. 584
Skinner, Brad, Chief Oper. Officer-Multimodal Div.--Transportacion Maritima Mexicana S.A. de C.V., Mexico, Mexico; *Int'l*, pg. 1418
Skinner, Samuel K., Pres.--ComEd, Chicago, IL; *U.S. Public*, *pg. 1664*
Skirka, Kenneth John, Pres., Chief Exec. & Oper. Officer, Mng. Dir.--Australian Oil & Gas Corporation Limited, Sydney, Australia; *Int'l*, pg. 101
Skough, Jan, Pres. & Chief Oper. Officer--Skandia U.S. Holding Corporation, New York, NY; *Int'l*, pg. 1257
Slattery, James F., Pres. & Chief Oper. Officer--Correctional Services Corporation, Sarasota, FL; *U.S. Public*, pg. 450
Slaughter, Randy, V.P.-Franchise--Dr Pepper/Seven Up No. America, Dallas, TX; *Int'l*, pg. 248
Slavitt, Andrew M., Chief Oper. Officer & Sr. V.P.--PAULA Financial, Pasadena, CA; *U.S. Public*, pg. 1266
Sleurs, L., Chief Oper. Officer--Liebig Benelux NV, Schoten, Belgium; *Int'l*, pg. 380
Slingerlend, Mac J., Pres. & Chief Oper. Officer--Ciber, Inc., Englewood, CO; *U.S. Public*, pg. 356
Sloan, David J., Chief Oper. Officer & Exec. V.P.--Bankers Security Life Insurance Society, Woodbury, NY; *U.S. Public*, pg. 1375
Sloma, Greg, Pres. & Chief Oper. Officer--Data Transmission Network Corporation, Omaha, NE; *U.S. Public*, pg. 486
Slusher, Carroll, Dir.-N. American Rehab.--Insituform Technologies, Inc., Chesterfield, MO; *U.S. Public*, pg. 881
Small, David L., Chief Oper. Officer & Treas.--Nelson & Small Inc., Portland, ME; *U.S. Private*, pg. 790
Small, Lawrence M., Pres. & Chief Oper. Officer--Federal National Mortgage Association (Fannie Mae), Washington, DC; *U.S. Public*, pg. 615
Smalley, Robert A., Jr., Chief Oper. Officer & Exec. V.P.--Cruise America, Inc., Mesa, AZ; *U.S. Private*, pg. 178
Smillie, Greg, Pres.--Hennells, Inc., Ferndale, MI; *U.S. Private*, pg. 522
Smith, A. Ledyard, Chief Oper. Officer--Rex Lumber Company, Acton, MA; *U.S. Private*, pg. 926
Smith, Benson F., Pres. & Chief Oper. Officer--C.R. Bard, Inc., Murray Hill, NJ; *U.S. Public*, pg. 189
Smith, Bob, Dir.-Opers.--American Eurocopter Corp., Grand Prairie, TX; *Int'l*, pg. 29
Smith, Bob, Chief Oper. Officer--MacDermid Singapore Pte. Ltd., Singapore, Singapore; *U.S. Public*, pg. 1030
Smith, Brian, Pres. & Chief Oper. Officer--Cole National Corporation, Cleveland, OH; *U.S. Public*, pg. 396
Smith, Bryan Scott, Pres. & Chief Oper. Officer--Sonic Automotive, Inc., Charlotte, NC; *U.S. Public*, pg. 1485
Smith, C. Michael, Pres., Chief Oper. Officer & Sec.--Orders Distributing Co., Greenville, SC; *U.S. Private*, pg. 819
Smith, Carl W., V.P.-Opers.--Cytec Fiberite Inc., Tempe, AZ; *U.S. Public*, pg. 471
Smith, Christopher, Pres.--H.J. Baker & Bro., Inc., Stamford, CT; *U.S. Private*, pg. 112
Smith, Craig R., Chief Oper. Officer & Exec. V.P.--Owens & Minor Inc., Glen Allen, VA; *U.S. Public*, pg. 1236
Smith, D.C., Chief Oper. Officer & Mng. Dir.--Hammerite Products Limited, Prudhoe, United Kingdom; *Int'l*, pg. 1501
Smith, Dennis, Chief Oper. Officer--Medi-Mail, Inc., Las Vegas, NV; *U.S. Private*, pg. 726
Smith, Dennis, Chief Oper. Officer & Exec. V.P.--Mednet, MPC Corporation, Las Vegas, NV; *U.S. Public*, pg. 1082
Smith, Douglass C., Pres. & Chief Oper. Officer--Industrial Distribution Group, Tucker, GA; *U.S. Public*, pg. 875
Smith, Elwood, Pres. & Chief Oper. Officer--Hayes Axle, Inc., Seminole, OK; *U.S. Private*, pg. 299
Smith, Eric, Pres. & Chief Oper. Officer--Howe Furniture Corporation, Trumbull, CT; *U.S. Private*, pg. 543
Smith, George B., Exec. V.P. & Chief Oper. Officer-Textile & Apparel Grp.--The Dixie Group, Inc., Chattanooga, TN; *U.S. Public*, pg. 514
Smith, Gibbert, Chief Oper. Officer & Exec. V.P.--Helene Curtis Industries, Inc., Chicago, IL; *Int'l*, pg. 1434
Smith, Gregory W., Pres. & Chief Oper. Officer--Jay Advertising, Inc., Rochester, NY; *U.S. Private*, pg. 583
Smith, James, Pres. & Chief Oper. Officer--ConAgra Prepared Food Companies, Omaha, NE; *U.S. Public*, pg. 427
Smith, James, Chief Fin. Officer--Amerimark Inc., Raleigh, NC; *U.S. Public*, pg. 1237
Smith, James M., Pres. & Chief Exec. Officer--AIL Systems Inc., Deer Park, NY; *U.S. Public*, pg. 556
Smith, Jerry M., Pres. & Chief Oper. Officer--Tuesday Morning Corporation, Dallas, TX; *U.S. Public*, pg. 1644
Smith, Joseph, Chief Oper. Officer-East--Coram Healthcare Corporation, Denver, CO; *U.S. Public*, pg. 446
Smith, Joseph T., Pres. & Chief Oper. Officer--Right Management Consultants, Inc., Philadelphia, PA; *U.S. Public*, pg. 1390
Smith, Larry, Chief Oper. Officer--Phillips Plastics Corporation, Phillips, WI; *U.S. Private*, pg. 862
Smith, Leighton, Chief Oper. Officer--UVP, Inc., Upland, CA; *U.S. Private*, pg. 1115
Smith, Lou, Chief Oper. Officer--Kaufman and Broad-Monterey Bay, Inc., Salinas, CA; *U.S. Public*, pg. 945
Smith, Michael, Chief Oper. Officer--Astec International Limited, Wan Chai, Hong Kong; *Int'l*, pg. 92
Smith, Orin, Chief Oper. Officer--Starbucks Coffee Company, Seattle, WA; *U.S. Public*, pg. 1510
Smith, Paul A., Chief Oper. Officer & V.P.-Mfg.--Eversharp Pen Co., Franklin Park, IL; *U.S. Private*, pg. 386
Smith, Peter G., Pres. & Chief Oper. Officer--Lawson Products, Inc., Des Plaines, IL; *U.S. Public*, pg. 980
Smith, Richard, Chief Oper. Officer & Exec. V.P.--Providian Auto & Home Insurance Group, Saint Louis, MO; *Int'l*, pg. 27
Smith, Robert A., Pres. & Chief Oper. Officer--GC Companies, Inc., Chestnut Hill, MA; *U.S. Public*, pg. 693
Smith, Ron, Chief Oper. Officer--Morgantown Plastics Company, Morgantown, KY; *U.S. Public*, pg. 1054
Smith, Scott, Chief Oper. Officer--Quality Dining Inc., Mishawaka, IN; *U.S. Public*, pg. 1349
Smith, Theodore B. III, Pres. & Chief Oper. Officer--John Hassall, Inc., Westbury, NY; *U.S. Private*, pg. 509
Smith, Tom, Chief Oper. Officer--URS Logistics, Atlanta, GA; *U.S. Private*, pg. 1114
Smith, Vince, Chief Oper. Officer--Allright Corporation, Omaha, NE; *U.S. Private*, pg. 42
Smithee, Kirk R., Chief Oper. Officer--Rent-Way, Inc., Erie, PA; *U.S. Public*, pg. 1377
Smits, Richard, Chief Oper. Officer & Exec. V.P.--First Northern Capital Corp., Green Bay, WI; *U.S. Public*, pg. 636
Smotrich, Michael H., Dr., Chief Tech. Officer--Palomar Medical Technologies, Lexington, MA; *U.S. Public*, pg. 1255
Snead, Tom, Pres. & Chief Oper. Officer--Trigon Blue Cross & Blue Shield, Richmond, VA; *U.S. Public*, pg. 1637
Snediker, James M., Pres., Chief Exec. Officer & Chief Oper. Officer--Chicago Show Printing Co., Morton Grove, IL; *U.S. Private*, pg. 235
Snell, E.A., Pres. & Chief Oper. Officer--Hunt-Wesson, Inc., Fullerton, CA; *U.S. Public*, pg. 428
Snell, James, Pres. & Chief Oper. Officer--Shield Healthcare Centers, Valencia, CA; *Int'l*, pg. 740
Sniekers, Niek, Chief Oper. Officer--Novo Nordisk Farma B.V., Alphen aan den Rijn, Netherlands; *Int'l*, pg. 988
Snowdon, David, Chief Oper. Officer--Tomkins PLC, London, United Kingdom; *Int'l*, pg. 1395
Snyder, Byron R., Exec. V.P. & Chief. Oper. Officer--Pioneer/Eclipse Corp., Sparta, NC; *Int'l*, pg. 71
Snyder, Doug, Dir.-Mngmnt. Information Systems--Anderson, Greenwood & Co., Stafford, TX; *U.S. Public*, pg. 1650
Snyder, Michele D., Vice Chm. & Chief Oper. Officer--Snyder Communications, Inc., Bethesda, MD; *U.S. Public*, pg. 1481
Snyder, Paul H., Chief Oper. Officer--High Voltage Engineering Corporation, Wakefield, MA; *U.S. Private*, pg. 528
Snyder, Stuart, Pres. Chief Oper. Officer--Feld Productions, Vienna, VA; *U.S. Private*, pg. 399
Snyder, Thomas J., Pres. & Chief Oper. Officer--Delco Remy America, Inc., Anderson, IN; *U.S. Public*, pg. 495
Sobey, John R., Chief Oper. Officer & Exec. V.P.--Sobey Inc., Stellarton, Canada; *Int'l*, pg. 454
Soderholm, Hardy, Chief Oper. Officer--California Hardware Company, Ontario, CA; *U.S. Private*, pg. 335
Soderquist, Donald G., Vice Chm. & Chief Oper. Officer--Wal-Mart Stores, Inc., Bentonville, AR; *U.S. Public*, pg. 1732
Soetanto, Didi, Chief Oper. Officer--PT Kes Sinar Mas Securities, Jakarta, Indonesia; *Int'l*, pg. 733

Soeters, Martin, Chief Oper. Officer--Novo Nordisk Pharmaceutique S.A., Boulogne-Billancourt, France; *Int'l, pg. 988*
Sofia, Zuheir, Pres., Chief Oper. Officer & Treas.--Huntington Bancshares Inc., Columbus, OH; *U.S. Public,* pg. 849
Soila, Anssi, Pres. & Chief Oper. Officer--Kone Corporation, Helsinki, Finland; *Int'l,* pg. 746
Sokol, John, Exec. V.P.--Bancinsurance Corp., Columbus, OH; *U.S. Public,* pg. 175
Sokolov, Richard, Pres. & Chief Oper. Officer--Simon DeBartolo Group, Inc., Indianapolis, IN; *U.S. Public,* pg. 1474
Sola, Enrico, Pres. & Chief Oper. Officer--Del Monte Foods International Limited, Staines, United Kingdom; *Int'l,* pg. 388
Solberg, James L., Pres., Chief Exec. & Oper. Officer--AutoAlliance International Inc., Flat Rock, MI; *Int'l,* pg. 849
Solender, Michael, Chm. Bd. & Chief Oper. Officer--The Solender Group, Inc., Los Angeles, CA; *U.S. Private,* pg. 1012
Solombrino, Scott, Chm. Bd., Pres. & Chief Exec. Officer--Dav-El Worldwide, Chelsea, MA; *U.S. Private,* pg. 314
Solorzano, Eugenio Najera, Chief Oper. Officer--Empressa La Moderna SA de CV, Monterrey, Mexico; *Int'l,* pg. 454
Solso, Theodore M., Pres. & Chief Oper. Officer--Cummins Engine Company, Inc., Columbus, IN; *U.S. Public,* pg. 467
Sommer, Frederick F., Pres. & Chief Oper. Officer--Citation Corporation, Birmingham, AL; *U.S. Public,* pg. 376
Sommer, James, Pres., Chief Oper. & Fin. Officer & Treas.--Service Motor Company, Dale, WI; *U.S. Private,* pg. 986
Sommer, Ron, Pres. & Chief Oper. Officer--Sony Electronics, Park Ridge, NJ; *Int'l,* pg. 1281
Sommerer, Peter, Pres. & Chief Oper. Officer--Newbridge Networks Corporation, Kanata, Canada; *Int'l,* pg. 924
Somnolet, Michel, Chief Oper. Officer--Cosmair, Inc., New York, NY; *Int'l,* pg. 818
Sonderegger, Paul, Chief Oper. Officer--Swissmetal Deutschland Handelsgesellschaft mbH, Schwenningen, Germany; *Int'l,* pg. 1427
Soran, Robert L., Pres. & Chief Oper. Officer--Uniroyal Technology Corporation, Sarasota, FL; *U.S. Public,* pg. 1670
Sorley, Tom, Pres. & Chief Oper. Officer--Rosendin Electric, Inc., San Jose, CA; *U.S. Private,* pg. 945
Sorrentino, Chuck, Pres. & Chief Oper. Officer--Pameco Corp., Norcross, GA; *U.S. Public,* pg. 1255
Sorrentino, Ralph, Pres. & Chief Oper. Officer--Quantum Media International, Inc., New York, NY; *U.S. Private,* pg. 899
Soukris, Dimitri, Chief Oper. Officer--Novo Nordisk A/S, Cairo, Egypt; *Int'l,* pg. 988
Soule, David, Co-Chief Oper. Officer--Forasol S.A., Velizy-Villacoublay, France; *Int'l,* pg. 496
Sovonet, M., Chief Oper. Officer--S.A. Proprete, Assainissement, Gestion de l'Environnement P.A.G.E., Charleroi, Belgium; *Int'l,* pg. 301
Spagnolo, A., Chief Oper. Officer--Danone S.p.A., Milan, Italy; *Int'l,* pg. 379
Spalletti, F., Dr., Chief Oper. Officer--Eurogenetics Italia SRL, Turin, Italy; *Int'l,* pg. 1408
Spangenberg, David R., Chief Oper. Officer & Exec. V.P.--Liberty National Life Insurance Co., Birmingham, AL; *U.S. Public,* pg. 1622
Spanier, Maury L., Chm. Bd. & Chief Oper. Officer--United Aircraft Products, Forest, OH; *U.S. Public,* pg. 1262
Sparks, William B., Pres. & Chief Oper. Officer--Greif Brothers Corporation, Delaware, OH; *U.S. Public,* pg. 763
Speakman, David, Chief Oper. Officer & V.P.--Gertrude Hawk Chocolates, Inc., Dunmore, PA; *U.S. Private,* pg. 449
Specht, Dennis, Chief Oper. Officer & Chief Fin. Officer--Services Group of America, Seattle, WA; *U.S. Private,* pg. 987
Spector, G.A., Chief Oper. Officer & Exec. V.P.--Equity Residential Properties Trust, Chicago, IL; *U.S. Public,* pg. 590
Speers, Douglas E., Pres. & Chief Exec. & Oper. Officer--Emco Limited, London, Canada; *Int'l,* pg. 452
Spendiff, James A., Pres. & Chief Oper. Officer--Freedom Forge Corporation, Burnham, PA; *U.S. Private,* pg. 425
Spiewak, Roy, Pres., Chief Oper. Officer & Chief Fin. Officer--I. Spiewak & Sons, Inc., New York, NY; *U.S. Private,* pg. 1025
Spiller, Ben M., Pres. & Chief Oper. Officer--Southern Pilot Insurance Company, Greensboro, NC; *Int'l,* pg. 346
Spilman, Robert H., Jr., Pres. & Chief Oper. Officer--Bassett Furniture Industries, Incorporated, Bassett, VA; *U.S. Public,* pg. 193
Spina, David A., Pres. & Chief Oper. Officer--State Street Corporation, Boston, MA; *U.S. Public,* pg. 1513
Spina, David A., Pres. & Chief Oper. Officer--State Street Bank & Trust Co., Boston, MA; *U.S. Public,* pg. 1513
Spitznagel, John T., Pres. & Chief Oper. Officer--Roberts Laboratories, Inc., Eatontown, NJ; *U.S. Public,* pg. 1393
Spoon, Alan G., Pres. & Chief Oper. Officer--The Washington Post Company, Washington, DC; *U.S. Public,* pg. 1742
Spriet, F., Chief Oper. Officer--Sidmar N.V., Gent, Belgium; *Int'l,* pg. 79
Springinsfeld, M., Chief Oper. Officer--Mang/DMB&B, Vienna, Vienna, Austria; *U.S. Private,* pg. 305
Spurrier, Hal, Pres. & Chief Oper. Officer--Snyder Industries, Inc., Lincoln, NE; *U.S. Private,* pg. 1011
Squires, Stanley, Chief Oper. Officer & Exec. V.P.--Anorad Corporation, Hauppauge, NY; *U.S. Private,* pg. 75
St. Charles, David P., Pres. & Chief Oper. Officer--Integrated Systems, Inc., Sunnyvale, CA; *U.S. Public,* pg. 885
Staats, Preston, Chief Oper. Officer--CCI/Triad Corporation, Austin, TX; *U.S. Private,* pg. 193
Stacho, Robert, Pres. & Chief Oper. Officer--Midco International Inc., Chicago, IL; *U.S. Private,* pg. 744
Staff, Christopher, Pres. & Chief Oper. Officer--Authentic Fitness Corp., Los Angeles, CA; *U.S. Public,* pg. 147
Stafford, A.J., Chief Oper. Officer--Cuprinol Limited, Frome, United Kingdom; *Int'l,* pg. 1501
Stahl, Dale E., Pres. & Chief Oper. Officer--Gaylord Container Corporation, Deerfield, IL; *U.S. Public,* pg. 704
Stahl, Kirk, Chief Oper. Officer, Exec. V.P. & Acct. Exec.--Caldwell VanRiper, Inc., Indianapolis, IN; *U.S. Private,* pg. 200
Staley, James D., V.P.-Opers.--Roadway Express, Inc., Akron, OH; *U.S. Public,* pg. 1392
Stamp, Robert, Chief Oper. Officer & Exec. V.P.--Hold-E-Zee, Ltd., Meadville, PA; *U.S. Private,* pg. 229
Stanley, Philip, Chief Oper. Officer--Opp Micolas Mills Inc., Opp, AL; *U.S. Public,* pg. 933
Stanners, Bob, Chief Oper. Officer--A.I. Root Company, Medina, OH; *U.S. Private,* pg. 944
Stansfield, Elaine, Pres. & Chief Oper. Officer--The Sunflower Group, Overland Park, KS; *U.S. Private,* pg. 1052
Stanton, Susan M., Pres. & Chief Oper. Officer--Payless Cashways, Inc., Kansas City, MO; *U.S. Public,* pg. 1267
Stanzione, Dan, Chief Oper. Officer & Exec. V.P.--Lucent Technologies Inc., Murray Hill, NJ; *U.S. Public,* pg. 1017
Starke, Jorg, Dr., Chief Oper. Officer--KSB Aktiengesellschaft, Frankenthal, Germany; *Int'l,* pg. 721
Starkey, James D., Chief Oper. Officer--Pace Industries, Inc., Fayetteville, AR; *U.S. Public,* pg. 986
Starr, John, Chief Oper. Officer--Koch Supplies Inc., Kansas City, MO; *U.S. Private,* pg. 628
Staton, Daniel C., Chief Oper. Officer & Exec. V.P.--Duke Realty Investments, Inc., Indianapolis, IN; *U.S. Public,* pg. 535
Stearns, David P., Chief Oper. Officer & Exec. V.P.--J.H. Routh Packing Co., Sandusky, OH; *U.S. Private,* pg. 948
Stearrett, William, Pres. & Chief Oper. Officer--Seradyn, Inc., Indianapolis, IN; *Int'l,* pg. 871
Steckart, James G., Pres. & Chief Oper. Officer--Advantage Companies, Inc., Wichita, KS; *U.S. Private,* pg. 22
Steel, George, Pres. & Chief Oper. Officer--Scientific Software-Intercomp, Inc., Denver, CO; *U.S. Public,* pg. 1443
Steele, Don, Chief Oper. Officer--River Ranch - Southwest, Dallas, TX; *Int'l,* pg. 491
Steen, Erik, Chief Oper. Officer--Novo Nordisk Comercio de Produtos Farmaceuticos, Lda, Rio de Mouro, Portugal; *Int'l,* pg. 988
Stehle, Walter, Chief Oper. Officer--Tricosal GmbH, Illertissen, Germany; *Int'l,* pg. 610
Stein, Bruce L., Pres.-Mattel Worldwide & Chief Oper. Officer--Mattel, Inc., El Segundo, CA; *U.S. Public,* pg. 1057
Stein, Michael Alan, Pres. & Chief Oper. Officer--Electro-Science Laboratories, Inc., King of Prussia, PA; *U.S. Private,* pg. 369
Stein, Steven B., Pres. & Chief Oper. Officer--Allied Security, Inc., Pittsburgh, PA; *U.S. Private,* pg. 40
Steinberg, Robert M., Pres. & Chief Oper. Officer--Reliance Group Holdings, Inc., New York, NY; *U.S. Public,* pg. 1374
Steiner, D., Chief Oper. Officer--Turegum Insurance Company, Zurich, Switzerland; *Int'l,* pg. 1529
Steingrover, Werner, C0-Chief Oper. Officer--North Rhine Westphalia Branch, Dusseldorf, Germany; *Int'l,* pg. 645
Steinke, Klaus, Chief Oper. Officer--Thompson GmbH, Dusseldorf, Germany; *Int'l,* pg. 610
Stemen, Milton, Pres. & Chief Oper. Officer--R & B Machine Tool Co., Saline, MI; *U.S. Private,* pg. 901
Stenberg, Jan, Pres., Chief Exec. Officer & Chief Oper. Officer--Scandinavian Airlines System (SAS), Solna, Sweden; *Int'l,* pg. 1201
Stengel, Karl, Chief Oper. Officer--Borsch, Stengel & Partner GmbH, Frankfurt/Main, Germany; *Int'l,* pg. 203
Stenger, Ethan A., Chief Oper. Officer & V.P.--Bell Atlantic-PA, Philadelphia, PA; *U.S. Public,* pg. 203
Stephen, Elde, Jr., Chief Oper. Officer--Spectra National, Chattanooga, TN; *U.S. Private,* pg. 786
Stephen, Philip, Chm. Bd., Pres., Chief Oper. & Chief Exec. Officer--Aid Auto Stores, Inc., Westbury, NY; *U.S. Public, pg. 29*
Stephens, J.M., Pres. & Chief Oper. Officer--Davis Electrical Constructors, Inc., Greenville, SC; *U.S. Private,* pg. 315
Stephens, Richard T., Pres. & Chief Oper. Officer--Delaware North Companies, Inc., Buffalo, NY; *U.S. Private,* pg. 321
Stephens, Robert, Chief Oper. Officer--Adaptec, Inc., Milpitas, CA; *U.S. Public,* pg. 19
Stephenson, James, Pres. & Chief Oper. Officer--KineticSystems Corporation, Lockport, IL; *U.S. Private,* pg. 620
Sterba, Hans D., Co-Chief Oper. Officer--IKB Consult GmbH, Dusseldorf, Germany; *Int'l,* pg. 645
Stern, Kenneth F., Chief Oper. Officer--Vernitron Sensor Systems, Saint Petersburg, FL; *U.S. Public,* pg. 157
Stern, Mitchell, Pres. & Chief Oper. Officer--Fox Television Stations Inc., Los Angeles, CA; *Int'l,* pg. 926
Sternberg, Seymour, Chm. Bd., Pres., Chief Exec. Officer & Chief Oper. Officer--New York Life Insurance Company, New York, NY; *U.S. Private,* pg. 794
Stevens, Gus, Pres., Chief Oper. Officer & Treas.--Cyberex, Inc., Mentor, OH; *U.S. Public,* pg. 481
Stevens, J. Clark, Pres. & Chief Oper. Officer--Mesa Air Group, Las Vegas, NV; *U.S. Public,* pg. 1098
Stevens, John R., Pres. & Chief Oper. Officer--Eastern Utilities Associates, Boston, MA; *U.S. Public,* pg. 549
Stevens, Richard I., Pres. & Chief Oper. Officer--Stevens International, Inc., Fort Worth, TX; *U.S. Public,* pg. 1517
Stevens, T. Randy, Pres. & Chief Oper. Officer--First Farmers & Merchants National Bank, Columbia, TN; *U.S. Private,* pg. 407
Stevens, William D., Pres. & Chief Oper. Officer--Mitchell Energy & Development Corp., Spring, TX; *U.S. Public,* pg. 1117
Stevenson, Craig H., Jr., Pres., Chief Exec. & Oper. Officer--OMI Corp., New York, NY; *U.S. Public,* pg. 1208
Stevenson, Dan, Chief Oper. Officer--The Vernon Company, Newton, IA; *U.S. Private,* pg. 1137
Stevenson, Gregory D., Chief Oper. Officer--Micron Electronics, Inc., Nampa, ID; *U.S. Public,* pg. 1105
Steves, Sam Bel, II, Pres. & Chief Oper. Officer--Steves & Sons, Inc., San Antonio, TX; *U.S. Private,* pg. 1042
Steves, Tom, Chief Oper. Officer & Exec. V.P.--Cranford Johnson Robinson Woods, Little Rock, AR; *U.S. Private, pg. 286*
Stewart, Barry L., Pres., Chief Exec. Officer, Chief Fin. Officer & Treas.--Eneco Tech Group, Denver, CO; *U.S. Private,* pg. 376
Stewart, William M., Chief Oper. Officer--Conso Products Co., New York, NY; *U.S. Public,* pg. 434
Stewman, Paul H., Chief Oper. Officer--Commercial Lines--Royal Insurance, Charlotte, NC; *Int'l,* pg. 1130
Sticht, Kevin, Chief Oper. Officer--Cannon, Grand Island, NY; *U.S. Private,* pg. 205
Stiglingh, D.J.J., Chief Oper. Officer--Tosas (Pty) Ltd., Wadeville, South Africa; *Int'l,* pg. 1197
Stinson, Terry D., Pres. & Chief Exec. & Oper. Officer--Bell Helicopter Textron, Hurst, TX; *U.S. Public,* pg. 1588
Stirrup, John T., Pres. & Chief Oper. Officer--BWAY Corp., Atlanta, GA; *U.S. Public,* pg. 164
Stockel, Richard F., Dr., Chief Oper. Officer--Tosoh USA, Inc.-New Jersey Office, Bound Brook, NJ; *Int'l,* pg. 1407
Stockhausen, Joseph P., Chief Oper. Officer--Moltrup Steel Products Company, Beaver Falls, PA; *U.S. Private,* pg. 756
Stoecker, Michael, Chief Oper. Officer--Speciality Graphics--Serigraph, Inc., West Bend, WI; *U.S. Private,* pg. 985
Stokoe, Jamie, Chief Oper. Officer--Gambro Pty Ltd., Auckland, New Zealand; *Int'l,* pg. 668
Stokoe, Jamie, Chief Oper. Officer--Gambro Pty. Ltd., Kenmore, Australia; *Int'l,* pg. 668
Stolworthy, R. Randy, Chief Oper. Officer & Exec. V.P.--New Mexico & Arizona Land Co., Phoenix, AZ; *U.S. Public,* pg. 1172
Stolzer, Ernest, Chief Oper. Officer & Exec. V.P.--Quality Bakers of America Cooperative, Inc., Greenwich, CT; *U.S. Private,* pg. 898
Stone, David, Pres. & Chief Oper. Officer--Sterilite Corporation, Townsend, MA; *U.S. Private,* pg. 1040
Stone, Don, Chief Oper. Officer--Cole Hall Lumber Co., Pelham, AL; *U.S. Private,* pg. 680
Stone, John McWilliams, Jr., Chm. Bd., Pres., Chief Exec. Officer & Chief Oper. Officer--Dukane Corporation, Saint Charles, IL; *U.S. Private,* pg. 345
Stone, Patrick F., Chief Oper. Officer--Fidelity National Financial, Inc., Irvine, CA; *U.S. Public,* pg. 620
Storch, David P., Pres., Chief Exec. & Oper. Officer--AAR Corp., Wood Dale, IL; *U.S. Public,* pg. 1
Storrier, John, Chief Oper. Officer & Exec. V.P.--All American Television, Inc., New York, NY; *U.S. Public,* pg. 41
Stott, James, Chief Oper. Officer--Kramer International, Inc., Milwaukee, WI; *U.S. Public,* pg. 142
Stott, James, Chief Oper. Officer--Quaker Alloy, Inc., Myerstown, PA; *U.S. Public,* pg. 142
Stott, Jim, Chief Oper. Officer--Pennsylvania Steel Foundry & Machine Company, Hamburg, PA; *U.S. Public,* pg. 142
Straathof, Jacques, Chief Oper. Officer--Neste Chemicals Benelux Holding B.V., Breda, Netherlands; *Int'l,* pg. 914
Strange, Bruce, Chief Oper. Officer--Frionor Australia Pty. Ltd., Melbourne, Australia; *Int'l,* pg. 516
Strassler, Hans Rudolf, Pres. & Chief Oper. Officer--Forbo Holding SA, Eglisau, Switzerland; *Int'l,* pg. 496
Strassler, Hans-Rudolf, Pres. & Chief Oper. Officer--Forbo International SA, Eglisau, Switzerland; *Int'l,* pg. 497
Street, Chriss W., Chm. Bd., Pres. & Chief Exec. & Oper. Officer--Comprehensive Care Corporation, Corona Del Mar, CA; *U.S. Public,* pg. 419
Street, Gordon P., Jr., Chm. Bd., Pres., Chief Exec. & Chief Oper. Officer--North American Royalties, Inc., Chattanooga, TN; *U.S. Private,* pg. 803
Strickler, Charles O., Pres.--Rocco Inc., Harrisonburg, VA; *U.S. Private,* pg. 937
Strong, Robert F., II, Pres. & Chief Oper. Officer--Longview National Bank, Longview, TX; *U.S. Public,* pg. 630
Stroud, James A., Co-Chm. Bd., Chief Oper. Officer & Sec.--Capital Senior Living, Inc., Dallas, TX; *U.S. Public,* pg. 302
Stroupe, David, Chief Oper. Officer & V.P.--Green Mountain Propane Gas Co., Burlington, VT; *U.S. Public,* pg. 761
Strubi, Vera, Chief Oper. Officer--Thierry Mugler Parfums, Neuilly-sur-Seine, France; *Int'l,* pg. 295
Stuart, Richard W., Chief Oper. Officer--Eastbridge Asset Management Inc., New York, NY; *Int'l,* pg. 933
Stuart, Timothy R., Pres. & Chief Oper. Officer--Stuart Entertainment Inc., Council Bluffs, IA; *U.S. Public,* pg. 1526
Stubbs, Stoney M., Jr., Chm. Bd., Pres. & Chief Exec. Officer--Frozen Food Express Industries, Inc., Dallas, TX; *U.S. Public,* pg. 685
Stubler, Daniel J., Pres. & Chief Oper. Officer--Toastmaster, Inc., Columbia, MO; *U.S. Public,* pg. 1619
Stuckey, James C., Jr., Chief Oper. Officer--Wholesale Wood Products, Dothan, AL; *U.S. Private,* pg. 680
Stuff, Kenneth K., Chief Oper. Officer--Syndicate Systems, Inc., Middlebury, IN; *U.S. Private,* pg. 1060
Stuntz, William, Pres.--Dranetz-BMI, Edison, NJ; *U.S. Private,* pg. 1144
Sturgeon, James D., Jr., Chief Oper. Officer--Datametrics Corporation, Calabasas, CA; *U.S. Public,* pg. 487
Styring, Eddie, Chief Exec.-Comet--Kingfisher plc, London, United Kingdom; *Int'l,* pg. 733
Suchman, Carol, Chief Oper. Officer--Technology Solutions Inc., New York, NY; *U.S. Private,* pg. 1157
Suchordt, Volkert, Chief Oper. Officer--Busch-Jaeger Ludenscheider Metallwerk GmbH, Ludenscheid, Germany; *Int'l,* pg. 1427

Sudo, Masamichi, Chief Oper. Officer--Daikyo Seiko Co., Ltd., Tokyo, Japan; *U.S. Public*, pg. 1756
Suess, Philip J., Chief Oper. Officer & V.P.--D.C. Taylor Co., Cedar Rapids, IA; *U.S. Private*, pg. 1070
Suey, David, Pres.--Dempster Industries Inc., Beatrice, NE; *U.S. Private*, pg. 324
Sugawara, Noriaki, Chief Oper. Officer--Instruments Division, Saitama, Japan; *Int'l*, pg. 1019
Sugimachi, Toshitaka, Pres. & Chief Oper. Officer--Secom Co., Ltd., Tokyo, Japan; *Int'l*, pg. 1217
Sugino, Toshio, Chief Oper. Officer--Nissho Iwai Italia S.P.A., Milan, Italy; *Int'l*, pg. 948
Sullam, Ronaldo, Chief Oper. Officer--S.E. Carburos Metalicos S.A., Barcelona, Spain; *U.S. Public*, pg. 32
Sullivan, David C., Chief Oper. Officer & Exec. V.P.--Promus Hotel Corporation, Memphis, TN; *U.S. Public*, pg. 1335
Sullivan, Douglas B., Pres. & Chief Oper. Officer--Michaels Stores, Inc., Irving, TX; *U.S. Public*, pg. 1104
Sullivan, Shawn, Chief Oper. Officer & Exec V.P.--Van Cleef & Arpels, Inc., New York, NY; *U.S. Private*, pg. 1132
Sullivan, Stephen, Pres. & Chief Oper. Officer--Ling Electronics Inc., Anaheim, CA; *U.S. Public*, pg. 1077
Sulpizio, Richard, Chief Oper. Officer--QUALCOMM, San Diego, CA; *U.S. Public*, pg. 1348
Sumas, James, Chm. Bd., Chief Oper. Officer, Treas., & Dir.-Adv.--Village Super Market Inc., Springfield, NJ; *U.S.* Public, pg. 1721
Summe, Gregory L., Pres. & Chief Oper. Officer--EG & G, Inc., Wellesley, MA; *U.S. Public*, pg. 542
Suntola, Tuomo, Chief Oper. Officer--Mikrokemia Oy, Espoo, Finland; *Int'l*, pg. 913
Surgenor, Keith S., Pres. & Chief Oper. Officer--Tampa Electric Co., Tampa, FL; *U.S. Public*, pg. 1565
Surkis, Wendy, Chief Oper. Officer--BSA Advertising, Inc., New York, NY; *U.S. Private*, pg. 107
Surles, Philip, Chief Oper. Officer--Champion Enterprises, Inc., Auburn Hills, MI; *U.S. Public*, pg. 332
Sussex, David, Gen. Mgr.--Wynn Oil (U.K.) Limited, Reading, United Kingdom; *U.S. Public*, pg. 1783
Sutcliff Almada, E.L., Chief Oper. Officer--Aluplast S.A. de C.V., Morelos, Mexico; *U.S. Public*, pg. 1756
Sutcliff Almada, E.L., Chief Oper. Officer--The West Company Mexico, SA.de C.V., Mexico, Mexico; *U.S. Public*, pg. 1756
Suter, Ulrich H., Exec. V.P.--Alusuisse-Lonza America Inc., New York, NY; *Int'l*, pg. 67
Sutherland, Allan R., Pres. & Chief Oper. Officer-Industrial Technologies--Derlan Industries Limited, Toronto, Canada; *Int'l*, pg. 395
Suthern, Paul C., Pres. & Chief Oper. Officer--MEDCO Containment Services, Inc., Montvale, NJ; *U.S. Public*, pg. 1091
Sutton, D.S., Chief Oper. Officer--Seven Seas Limited, Hull, United Kingdom; *Int'l*, pg. 593
Sutton, Travis D., Chief Oper. Officer--Shealy Electrical Wholesalers, Greenville, SC; *U.S. Private*, pg. 991
Sutton, Yacha, Pres. & Chief Oper. Officer--Laser Industries Ltd., Tel Aviv, Israel; *Int'l*, pg. 429
Suzuki, Kei, Chief Oper. Officer--Nissho Iwai Iberia S.A., Madrid, Spain; *Int'l*, pg. 948
Suzuki, Keita, Pres. & Chief Oper. Officer--Nissho Iwai (Chile) LTDA, Santiago, Chile; *Int'l*, pg. 948
Suzuki, Sadao, Chief Oper. Officer--Berjaya General Insurance Sdn. Bhd., Kuala Lumpur, Malaysia; *Int'l*, pg. 1392
Suzuki, Sadao, Chief Oper. Officer--The Tokio Marine Management (Australia) Pty. Ltd., Sydney, Australia; *Int'l, pg. 1393*
Svuba, Dwight V., Chief Oper. Officer & V.P.-Energy Supply--St. Joseph Light & Power Co., Saint Joseph, MO; *U.S. Public*, pg. 1427
Swain, Jeff, Pres. & Chief Oper. Officer--Townsends, Inc., Wilmington, DE; *U.S. Private*, pg. 1094
Swain, Terrence P., Pres. & Chief Oper. Officer-Aerospace Opers.--Derlan Industries Limited, Toronto, Canada; *Int'l, pg. 395*
Swartz, Dean, Mgr.-Opers.--RNL Facilities Corporation, Denver, CO; *U.S. Private*, pg. 905
Swartz, James K., Pres. & Chief Oper. Officer--NPC International, Inc., Pittsburg, KS; *U.S. Public*, pg. 1146
Swartz, Jeffrey B., Chief Oper. Officer & Exec. V.P.--The Timberland Company, Stratham, NH; *U.S. Public*, pg. 1609
Sweeney, Eugene, Chief Oper. Officer--Hvide Marine Incorporated, Fort Lauderdale, FL; *U.S. Public*, pg. 851
Sweeney, Joan M., Chief Oper. Officer--Allied Capital Corporation, Washington, DC; *U.S. Public*, pg. 47
Sweeney, Joan M., Pres. & Chief Oper. Officer--Allied Capital Advisors, Inc., Washington, DC; *U.S. Public*, pg. 47
Swerlkolte, Steve, Pres. & Chief Oper. Officer--Full Service Beverage Company, Wichita, KS; *U.S. Private*, pg. 34
Swift, Terry E., Chief Oper. Officer & Exec. V.P.--Swift Energy Company, Houston, TX; *U.S. Public*, pg. 1543
Swinehart, Robert E., Exec. V.P. & Chief Oper. Officer--McGill Manufacturing Company, Inc., Valparaiso, IN; *U.S.* Public, pg. 573
Swink, James W., Pres., Chief Exec. Officer & Chief Oper. Officer--Young Pecan Company (A Partnership), Florence, SC; *U.S. Private*, pg. 1201
Switzer, David A., Pres. & Chief Oper. Officer--Battle Creek Gas Company, Battle Creek, MI; *U.S. Public*, pg. 1489
Syar, James M., Pres. & Chief Oper. Officer--Syar Industries, Inc., Napa, CA; *U.S. Private*, pg. 1059
Sylvester, C., Chief Oper. Officer--Barbados Dairy Industries Ltd., Saint Michael, Barbados; *Int'l*, pg. 923
Sylvetsky, Barry, Chief Oper. Officer & Exec. V.P.--Goodman Knitting Company, Brockton, MA; *U.S. Public*, pg. 948
Syms, Marcy, Pres.--Syms Corporation, Secaucus, NJ; *U.S. Public*, pg. 1547
Synowicki, Robert E., Jr., Chief Oper. Officer & Exec. V.P.--Werner Enterprises, Inc., Omaha, NE; *U.S. Public*, pg. 1754
Syversen, Gunnar, Chief Oper. Officer--TA Control System A/S, Oslo, Norway; *Int'l*, pg. 670
Sztykiel, John E., Pres. & Chief Oper. Officer--Spartan Motors, Inc., Charlotte, MI; *U.S. Public*, pg. 1495
Tabaries, Jean, Chief Oper. Officer--UBCI (Tunisia), Tunis, Tunisia; *Int'l*, pg. 163
Takakura, Hisashi, Pres. & Chief Oper. Officer--Clarins KK, Tokyo, Japan; *Int'l*, pg. 295
Takanose, Takaaki, Chief Oper. Officer--Hagglunds Drives Ltd, Yokohama, Japan; *Int'l*, pg. 670
Takanose, Takaaki, Chief Oper. Officer--Hagglunds Ltd. Dept. Drives, Yokohama, Japan; *Int'l*, pg. 670
Takeda, Tsutomu, Pres. & Chief Oper. Officer--Asatsu Inc., Tokyo, Japan; *Int'l*, pg. 85
Takehata, Ryosuke, Chief Oper. Officer--Dhaka Project Office, Dhaka, Bangladesh; *Int'l*, pg. 942
Takumi, Masaaki, Chief Oper. Officer--Industrial Resins (Malaysia) Sdn. Bhd.-Johor Baharu Plant, Johor Baharu, Malaysia; *Int'l*, pg. 1408
Talamantes, Alfred, Chief Oper. Officer & Exec. V.P.--Mid Atlantic Medical Services, Inc., Rockville, MD; *U.S. Public*, pg. 1109
Talbot, Pamela, Pres. & Chief Oper. Officer-Edelman U.S.--Edelman Public Relations Worldwide, Chicago, IL; *U.S. Private*, pg. 362
Talley, Ron, Chief Oper. Officer--Eagle USA Airfreight, Houston, TX; *U.S. Public*, pg. 547
Tan, A.K., Chief Oper. Officer--KONE Elevator (M) Sdn. Bhd., Kuala Lumpur, Malaysia; *Int'l*, pg. 747
Tan, Michael, Chief Oper. Officer--Singapore Airlines, Los Angeles, CA; *Int'l*, pg. 1374
Tanaka, Hitokuni, Chief Oper. Officer--Hong Kong Architectural Project Office, Tsim Tsa Tsui, Hong Kong; *Int'l*, pg. 942
Tangel, Frank, Chief Oper. Officer & Facilities Mgr.--Contadina Dalla Casa Buitoni, Glendale, CA; *Int'l*, pg. 916
Tangel, Richard E., Chief Oper. Officer & V.P.--Edwards & Kelcey Wireless, Morristown, NJ; *U.S. Private*, pg. 364
Tanimoto, Douglas, Dr., Pres. & Chief Oper. Officer--Laser Power Corporation, San Diego, CA; *U.S. Private*, pg. 652
Taniyama, Yasuro, Pres. & Chief Oper. Officer--Suntory International Corp., New York, NY; *Int'l*, pg. 1321
Tanklage, Robert C., Chm. Bd., Chief Exec. & Chief Oper. Officer--La Victoria Foods, Inc., City of Industry, CA; *U.S.* Private, pg. 641
Tannen, L.P., Pres.--Fairmont Snack Group, Inc., Independence, OH; *U.S. Private*, pg. 392
Tansey, Thomas F., Chief Oper., Exec. V.P. & Treas.--Raritan Bancorp Inc., Bridgewater, NJ; *U.S. Public*, pg. 1361
Tapper, Bo, Chief Oper. Officer--Neste Gas AB, Sundsvall, Sweden; *Int'l*, pg. 915
Targoff, Michael B., Pres. & Chief Oper. Officer--Loral Space & Communications, New York, NY; *U.S. Public*, pg. 1014
Tashiro, Robert R., Chief Oper. Officer--Superior Consultant Holdings Corp., Southfield, MI; *U.S. Public*, pg. 1538
Tassara, L., Ing., Chief Oper. Officer--Silectron SPA, Bologna, Italy; *Int'l*, pg. 287
Tassie, John M., Pres. & Chief Oper. Officer-AAA Fin. Service Corp.--American Automobile Association, Heathrow, FL; *U.S. Private*, pg. 50
Taurel, Sidney, Pres. & Chief Oper. Officer--Eli Lilly and Company, Indianapolis, IN; *U.S. Public*, pg. 992
Tavenius, Tapio, Chief Oper. Officer--Raisio Group plc, Raisio, Finland; *Int'l*, pg. 1085
Tay, Denis, Chief Oper. Officer--Singapore Press Holdings Ltd., Singapore, Singapore; *Int'l*, pg. 1253
Taya, Moriyuki, Chief Oper. Officer--Technical Center, Omiya, Japan; *Int'l*, pg. 1019
Taylor, Alec, Pres. & Chief Oper. Officer--Chattem, Inc., Chattanooga, TN; *U.S. Public*, pg. 341
Taylor, Brent, V.P.-Opers.--Rudolph Foods Company, Lima, OH; *U.S. Private*, pg. 950
Taylor, Gerald H., Pres. & Chief Oper. Officer--MCI Telecommunications Corp., Washington, DC; *U.S. Public, pg. 1024*
Taylor, Mike, Chief Oper. Officer--Textiles Morelos S.A. de C.V., Mexico, Mexico; *U.S. Public*, pg. 268
Taylor, Norman J., Pres. & Chief Oper. Officer--Adience Inc., Carnegie, PA; *U.S. Public*, pg. 58
Taylor, Roger K., Chief Oper. Officer--Financial Security Assurance Holdings Ltd., New York, NY; *U.S. Public*, pg. 622
Taylor, Ronald L., Pres. & Chief Oper. Officer--DeVry Institutes, Oak Brook Terrace, IL; *U.S. Public*, pg. 503
Taylor, Stephen, Chief Oper. Officer--Courier International, Ltd., East Kilbride, United Kingdom; *U.S. Public*, pg. 453
Taylor, William, Pres. & Chief Oper. Officer--Taylor-Morley, Inc., Saint Louis, MO; *U.S. Private*, pg. 1071
Teagle, James C., Pres. & Chief Oper. Officer--Koger Equity Inc., Jacksonville, FL; *U.S. Public*, pg. 965
Teague, Robert M., Pres. & Chief Oper. Officer--Thermo Industries Inc., Charlotte, NC; *U.S. Private*, pg. 1080
Tedesco, Colette, Chief Oper. Officer--Georg Jensen S.A.R.L., Paris, France; *Int'l*, pg. 1134
Teel, E. Gerald, Pres., Chief Exec. Officer & Chief Oper. Officer--Vitamilk Dairy, Inc., Seattle, WA; *U.S. Private*, pg. 1142
Teeters, Bruce W., Sr. V.P.-Fin. & Treas.--Consolidated-Tomoka Land Co., Daytona Beach, FL; *U.S. Public*, pg. 437
Teeters, Bruce W., Chief Oper. Officer--Indigo Group Ltd., Daytona Beach, FL; *U.S. Public*, pg. 437
Teets, Peter B., Pres. & Chief Oper. Officer--Lockheed Martin Corporation, Bethesda, MD; *U.S. Public*, pg. 1006
Teich, Dan, Chief Oper. Officer--Ransomes-Cushman-Ryan, Lincoln, NE; *Int'l*, pg. 1088
Telson, Mitch, Sr. Oper. Officer--Color Tile, Inc., Fort Worth, TX; *Int'l*, pg. 686
Temares, Steven H., Chief Oper. Officer & Exec. V.P.--Bed Bath & Beyond Inc., Union, NJ; *U.S. Public*, pg. 200
Tepas, Thomas G., Pres. & Chief Oper. Officer--ChemFirst Inc., Jackson, MS; *U.S. Public*, pg. 344
Terhar, Bill, Pres. & Chief Oper. Officer--Ocean Beauty Seafoods, Inc., Seattle, WA; *U.S. Private*, pg. 810
Terhar, L.F., Chief Oper. Officer--The David J. Joseph Company, Cincinnati, OH; *Int'l*, pg. 1155
Terlato, William A., Pres. & Chief Oper. Officer--Paterno Imports Limited, Lake Bluff, IL; *U.S. Private*, pg. 843
Terrell, James R., Pres. & Chief Oper. Officer-TV Stations--Gaylord Broadcasting Co., Nashville, TN; *U.S. Public*, pg. 704
Terzic, Branko, Pres., Chief Exec./Oper. Officer--Yankee Energy Financial Services Company, Meriden, CT; *U.S. Public*, pg. 1787
Tesi, Aldo, Chief Oper. Officer & Exec. V.P.--First Data Resources, Omaha, NE; *U.S. Public*, pg. 631
Teter, Gordon F., Chm. Bd., Pres. & Chief Oper. Officer--Wendy's International Inc., Dublin, OH; *U.S. Public*, pg. 1754
Teufel, Robert J., Pres. & Chief Oper. Officer--Rodale Press, Inc., Emmaus, PA; *U.S. Private*, pg. 939
Tew, Charles E., Chief Oper. Officer--Southern Pump & Tank Company, Charlotte, NC; *U.S. Private*, pg. 1017
Thampi, P.M., Pres. & Chief Oper. Officer--BASF India Ltd., Mumbai, India; *Int'l*, pg. 106
Then, J.L., Chief Oper. Officer--Kidde Technologies, Inc., Wilson, NC; *Int'l*, pg. 1500
Therkildsen, Erik, Chief Oper. Officer--Novo Nordisk A/S, Vouliagmeni, Greece; *Int'l*, pg. 988
Thewes, Joachim, Chief Oper. Officer--Land Infrarot GmbH, Leverkusen, Germany; *Int'l*, pg. 798
Thexton, Kent P., Chief Oper. Officer & Exec. V.P.--Rogers Cantel Mobile Communications Inc., Saint-Laurent, Canada; *Int'l*, pg. 1122
Thiel, Mark, Chief Oper. Officer, V.P. & Gen. Mgr.--Thiel Cheese Co., Hilbert, WI; *U.S. Private*, pg. 1081
Thielman, David, Chief Exec. Officer--E Z Loader Corporate, Airway Heights, WA; *U.S. Private*, pg. 352
Thing, Jens, Chief Oper. Officer--Mikron Hannover GmbH, Hannover, Germany; *Int'l*, pg. 867
Thodal-Ness, Einar, Chief Oper. Officer--S-E-Banken Custody Service, Stockholm, Sweden; *Int'l*, pg. 1259
Tholan, Kenneth M., Chief Oper. Officer & Exec. V.P.--Team, Inc., Alvin, TX; *U.S. Public*, pg. 1562
Tholey, James M., Sr. V.P.-Audio/Video--Peirce-Phelps, Inc., Philadelphia, PA; *U.S. Private*, pg. 847
Thoman, Richard, Pres. & Chief Oper. Officer--Xerox Corporation, Stamford, CT; *U.S. Public*, pg. 1783
Thomas, Edmond, Pres. & Chief Oper. Officer--The Wet Seal, Inc., Irvine, CA; *U.S. Public*, pg. 1763
Thomas, Matt, Chief Oper. Officer & V.P.--Galles Chevrolet, Albuquerque, NM; *U.S. Private*, pg. 438
Thomas, Merle, Chief Oper. Officer & V.P.--Republic Die & Tool Company, Belleville, MI; *U.S. Private*, pg. 923
Thomas, Patrick L., Exec. V.P. & Chief Oper. Officer-Industry--Sundstrand Corporation, Rockford, IL; *U.S. Public*, pg. 1533
Thomas, Rowland H., Jr., Pres. & Chief Oper. Officer--Encore Computer Corporation, Fort Lauderdale, FL; *U.S.* Public, pg. 580
Thomas, T. Paul, Pres. & Chief Oper. Officer--Artisoft, Inc., Tucson, AZ; *U.S. Public*, pg. 136
Thompson-Draper, Cheryl, Pres. & Chief Oper. Officer--Warren Electric Company, Houston, TX; *U.S. Private*, pg. 1151
Thompson, Bryan, Chief Oper. Officer--Custom Lumber Mfg. Co., Dothan, AL; *U.S. Private*, pg. 680
Thompson, C.M., Chief Exec. Officer--Rentokil Initial plc, East Grinstead, United Kingdom; *Int'l*, pg. 1285
Thompson, J. Kenneth, Chief Oper. Officer--ARCO Transportation Alaska, Inc., Anchorage, AK; *U.S. Public*, pg. 144
Thompson, James W., Pres. & Chief Exec. Officer--Vallen Safety Supply Company, Houston, TX; *U.S. Public*, pg. 1705
Thompson, Jeffrey L., Chief Oper. Officer & Exec. V.P.--Edelbrock Corp., Torrance, CA; *U.S. Public*, pg. 563
Thompson, John F., Pres. & Chief Oper. Officer--Aurora Electronics, Inc., Irvine, CA; *U.S. Public*, pg. 147
Thompson, Michael, Chief Oper. Officer & Exec. V.P.--Merry Land & Investment Company, Inc., Augusta, GA; *U.S. Public*, pg. 1098
Thompson, Tom, Pres. & Chief Oper. Officer--CKE Restaurants Inc., Anaheim, CA; *U.S. Public*, pg. 278
Thompson, William J., Pres. & Chief Oper. Officer--Vital Signs, Englewood, CO; *U.S. Public*, pg. 1723
Thomson, Charles, Dir.-Grp. Opers.--Scottish Widows' Fund & Life Assurance Society, Edinburgh, United Kingdom; *Int'l*, pg. 1212
Thorn, Stuart, Chief Oper. Officer--Beaulieu Group, Dalton, GA; *U.S. Private*, pg. 127
Thorne, Oakleigh B., Pres. & Chief Exec. Officer--CCH Incorporated, Riverwoods, IL; *Int'l*, pg. 1513
Thorner, Peter, Chm. Bd., Chief Exec. Officer & Chief Oper. Officer--Bradlees Inc., Braintree, MA; *U.S. Public*, pg. 249
Thrailkill, Howard A., Pres. & Chief Oper. Officer--ADTRAN, Inc., Huntsville, AL; *U.S. Public*, pg. 20
Thrailkill, Larry, Chief Oper. Officer & Exec. V.P.--The Edward J. DeBartolo Corporation, Youngstown, OH; *U.S.* Private, pg. 319
Thrall, Jerome Jeffrey, Pres. & Chief Oper. Officer--Thrall Enterprises, Inc., Chicago, IL; *U.S. Private*, pg. 1084
Thuesen, Lars, V.P. & Chief Oper. Officer--SAS Financial Services, Stockholm, Sweden; *Int'l*, pg. 1201
Thurston, Ray, Pres. & Chief Oper. Officer--Sonic Couriers of Arizona, Inc., Scottsdale, AZ; *U.S. Private*, pg. 1123
Tice, Gary L., Chief Oper. Officer & Exec. V.P.--F.N.B. Corporation, Hermitage, PA; *U.S. Public*, pg. 607
Tierno, Anthony F., Chief Oper. Officer & Exec. V.P.--MediaNews Group Inc., Denver, CO; *U.S. Private*, pg. 727

Tierno, Anthony F., Chief Oper. Officer & Exec. V.P.--Garden State Newspapers, Inc., Denver, CO; *U.S. Private*, pg. 727
Tillman, Walter L., Jr., Chief Oper. Officer--Prime Bancorp, Inc., Fort Washington, PA; *U.S. Public*, pg. 1326
Tillotson, John, Chief Oper. Officer--Rieter Holdings, Winterthur, Switzerland; *Int'l*, pg. 1116
Tillotson, John R., Chief Oper. Officer--HATCO, Inc., Garland, TX; *U.S. Private*, pg. 510
Timmerman, William B., Chm. Bd., Pres., Chief Exec. & Oper. Officer--SCANA Corporation, Columbia, SC; *U.S. Public*, pg. 1436
Tinley, J. Patrick, Pres. & Chief Oper. Officer--Ross Systems, Inc., Atlanta, GA; *U.S. Public*, pg. 1406
Tipermas, Marc, Pres. & Chief Oper. Officer--ICF Kaiser International Inc., Fairfax, VA; *U.S. Public*, pg. 852
Tirney, Stephen G., Pres. & Chief Oper. Officer--PMA Reinsurance Corporation, Philadelphia, PA; *U.S. Public*, pg. 1272
Tisch, James S., Pres. & Chief Oper. Officer--Loews Corporation, New York, NY; *U.S. Public*, pg. 1010
Tischler, Louis, Chief Exec. Officer, Chief Oper. Officer & Treas--Westwood Computer Corporation, Springfield, NJ; *U.S. Private*, pg. 1170
Tittle, David E., Pres. & Chief Oper. Officer--Cosco Industries, Spring Valley, NY; *U.S. Private*, pg. 277
Toal, Lawrence J., Chm. Bd., Pres. & Chief Exec. Officer--The Dime Savings Bank of New York, New York, NY; *U.S. Public*, pg. 509
Tobias, Stephen C., Exec. V.P.-Opers.--Norfolk Southern Corporation, Norfolk, VA; *U.S. Public*, pg. 1190
Tod, G. Robert, Pres. & Chief Oper. Officer--CML Group, Inc., Acton, MA; *U.S. Public*, pg. 279
Togni, S., Chief Oper. Officer--Makhteshim-Agan Italia S.r.l., Bergamo, Italy; *Int'l*, pg. 831
Toivonen, Hannu, Chief Oper. Officer--Kesoil Oy, Tampere, Finland; *Int'l*, pg. 913
Tolari, Geno P., Chief Oper. Officer & Exec. V.P.--Sterling Software, Inc., Dallas, TX; *U.S. Public*, pg. 1516
Tolone, Thomas A., Pres. & Chief Oper. Officer--Paoli, Inc., Orleans, IN; *U.S. Private*, pg. 837
Tolot, Jerome, Chief Oper. Officer--Groupe GTM, Nanterre, France; *Int'l*, pg. 823
Tomchin, Lawrence, Pres. & Chief Oper. Officer--Rex Stores Corp., Dayton, OH; *U.S. Public*, pg. 1384
Tominaga, Takashi, Chief Oper. Officer--Tokio Marine Realty Co., Ltd., New York, NY; *Int'l*, pg. 1392
Tominaga, Takashi, Chief Oper. Officer--Tokio Marine Property Limited, London, United Kingdom; *Int'l*, pg. 1393
Tomkins, Trevor, Dr., Pres. & Chief Oper. Officer--Milk Specialties Company, Dundee, IL; *U.S. Private*, pg. 746
Tomlinson, Ralph, Jr., V.P.-Opers.--Ferrous Processing & Trading Co., Detroit, MI; *U.S. Private*, pg. 402
Tomlonovic, Vincent J., Chief Oper. Officer & Gen. Mgr.--Hiniker Company, Mankato, MN; *U.S. Private*, pg. 530
Tommasini, Bernard, V.P.--Societe Services Kelly, Troy, MI; *U.S. Public*, pg. 949
Tomomori, Hiroshi, Mng. Dir. & Chief Oper. Officer--Nissho Iwai Deutschland GmbH, Hamburg, Germany; *Int'l*, pg. 948
Tomooka, Yuji, Chief Oper. Officer--Tokio Marine de Venezuela, C.A., Caracas, Venezuela; *Int'l*, pg. 1393
Tompkins, J. Bruce, Exec. V.P.-Cement Grp.--Southdown, Inc., Houston, TX; *U.S. Public*, pg. 1488
Toomey, Kenton C., Chief Oper. Officer & V.P.-Oper.--Osmonics, Inc., Minnetonka, MN; *U.S. Public*, pg. 1233
Tootle, John, Chief Fin. Officer & V.P.-Fin.--Dominguez Water Company, Long Beach, CA; *U.S. Public*, pg. 516
Toran, Daniel J., Pres. & Chief Oper. Officer--The Penn Mutual Life Insurance Company, Philadelphia, PA; *U.S. Private*, pg. 849
Tornabene, Chuck, Chief Oper. Officer--Turtle Wax, Inc., Chicago, IL; *U.S. Private*, pg. 1110
Torranova, Victor, Chief Info. Officer & V.P.--Geneva Pharmaceuticals, Inc., Broomfield, CO; *Int'l*, pg. 973
Tortellot, Peter L., Pres. & Chief Oper. Officer--Carolina Biological Supply Co., Burlington, NC; *U.S. Private*, pg. 213
Tosato, A., Chief Oper. Officer--Swish Italiana Srl, Albignasego, Italy; *Int'l*, pg. 925
Toucet, Eufemio, Chief Oper. Officer--St. Regis Paper & Bag Div., Guaynabo, PR; *U.S. Public*, pg. 1342
Tough, Steven D., Pres. & Chief Oper. Officer--Foundation Health Federal Services, Inc., Rancho Cordova, CA; *U.S. Public*, pg. 678
Toussaint, John-Charles, Chief Oper. Officer & V.P.--Propper Manufacturing Co., Inc., Long Island City, NY; *U.S. Private*, pg. 891
Towers, Robert, Chief Oper. Officer & V.P.--Ark Restaurants Corp., New York, NY; *U.S. Public*, pg. 129
Townsend, Arthur T., Chief Oper. Officer & Chief Fin. Officer--Lat Purser & Associates, Charlotte, NC; *U.S. Private*, pg. 896
Townsend, Roger, Chief Oper. Officer--CTB International Corp., Milford, IN; *U.S. Public*, pg. 284
Trafton, Stephen J., Chm. Bd., Pres., Chief Exec. Officer & Chief Oper. Officer--Glendale Federal Bank, F.S.B., Glendale, CA; *U.S. Public*, pg. 747
Trawick, Jack D., Pres.--STRAFCO, Inc., San Antonio, TX; *U.S. Private*, pg. 1046
Treis, Donald J., Pres. & Chief Oper. Officer--Arandell Corporation, Menomonee Falls, WI; *U.S. Private*, pg. 79
Treis, Donald J., Pres. & Chief Oper. Officer--Arandell-Schmidt, Menomonee Falls, WI; *U.S. Private*, pg. 79
Tremblay, E., Chief Oper. Officer & V.P.-Opers.--P/A Industries, Inc., Bloomfield, CT; *U.S. Private*, pg. 825
Tremblay, Rene, Pres. & Chief Oper. Officer--Ivanhoe, Montreal, Canada; *Int'l*, pg. 249
Trencher, Lewis J., Chief Oper. Officer & Chief Fin. Officer--J. Walter Thompson Company, New York, NY; *Int'l*, pg. 1483
Trepicchio, Michael J., Pres. & Chief Oper. Officer--Klemtner Advertising Inc., New York, NY; *U.S. Public*, pg. 1422
Trewhella, Raymond M., Pres. & Chief Oper. Officer--Glassmaster Company, Lexington, SC; *U.S. Public*, pg. 745
Tribull, Christoph, Chm. Bd., Pres., Chief Exec. Officer & Chief Oper. Officer--Sierracin Corporation, Sylmar, CA; *U.S. Private*, pg. 999
Trickey, Gregory M., Chief Oper. Officer--Wolverine Tube Inc., Huntsville, AL; *U.S. Public*, pg. 1774
Tridle, David, Chief Oper. Officer--Frankel & Company, Chicago, IL; *U.S. Private*, pg. 424
Trigo-Anez, D., Chief Oper. Officer--BHF-Bank Representative Office, Buenos Aires, Argentina; *Int'l*, pg. 120
Tronsrue, George, Chief Oper. Officer--Nextlink Communications Inc., Bellevue, WA; *U.S. Public*, pg. 1181
Trosino, Vincent J., Chief Oper. Officer & Exec. V.P.--State Farm Mutual Automobile Insurance Company, Bloomington, IL; *U.S. Private*, pg. 1036
Trotta, Thomas A., Sr. V.P.--Connecticut Energy Corporation, Bridgeport, CT; *U.S. Public*, pg. 431
Trotter, Mike, Chief Oper. Officer--Ruppman Marketing Technologies, Inc., Peoria, IL; *U.S. Private*, pg. 951
Troup, Brian M., Pres. & Chief Oper. Officer--The Hallwood Group Incorporated, Dallas, TX; *U.S. Public*, pg. 777
Troutmann, Uwe, Co-Chief Oper. Officer--Helaba Invest Kapitalanlagegesellschaft mbH, Frankfurt/Main, Germany; *Int'l*, pg. 799
Troyer, Kermit, Pres. & Chief Oper. Officer--Troyer Foods, Inc., Goshen, IN; *Int'l*, pg. 619
Truby, Charles, Chief Oper. Officer--Isomedix Inc., Whippany, NJ; *U.S. Public*, pg. 1515
Truby, Charles, Chief Oper. Officer--Skyland Scientific Services, Inc., Bozeman, MT; *U.S. Public*, pg. 1515
Truby, Charles, Chief Oper. Officer--Isomedix Operations Inc., Whippany, NJ; *U.S. Public*, pg. 1515
Truby, Charles, Chief Oper. Officer--Isomedix Management Inc., Whippany, NJ; *U.S. Public*, pg. 1515
Truderung, Harry, Pres.-TELUS Mobility--Telus Corporation, Edmonton, Canada; *Int'l*, pg. 1374
Tsai, Y.H., Chief Oper. Officer & V.P.--Target Advertising Agency Limited, Taipei, Taiwan; *Int'l*, pg. 1355
Tsampalieros, Gabriel, Pres. & Chief Oper. Officer--Cara Operations Limited, Toronto, Canada; *Int'l*, pg. 266
Tschorn, Erhardt, Chief Oper. Officer--Perrin GmbH, Nidderau, Germany; *Int'l*, pg. 1528
Tsugami, Koichi, Chief Oper. Officer--Mikron Ltd. Tokyo, Yokohama, Japan; *Int'l*, pg. 867
Tsuge, Hirohumi, Chief Oper. Officer--Makita Werkzeug Gesellschaft m.b.H., Vienna, Austria; *Int'l*, pg. 832
Tsui, John K, Pres. & Chief Oper. Officer--First Hawaiian Bank, Honolulu, HI; *U.S. Public*, pg. 634
Tsujimoto, Hirokazu, Chief Oper. Officer & Exec. V.P.--Kintetsu World Express (U.S.A.), Inc., Roslyn Heights, NY; *Int'l*, pg. 734
Tsuma, Glen, Chief Oper. Officer--Amplicon, Inc., Santa Ana, CA; *U.S. Public*, pg. 104
Tucker, Richard G., V.P.-Mfg.--Lance, Inc., Charlotte, NC; *U.S. Public*, pg. 977
Tuite, James E., Pres. & Chief Oper. Officer--TCF Bank Minnesota FSB, Minneapolis, MN; *U.S. Public*, pg. 1554
Turesky, Jack A., Pres. & Chief Oper. Officer--National Health Care Affiliates, Inc., Buffalo, NY; *U.S. Private*, pg. 784
Turford, Tom, Chief Oper. Officer--APP Chemicals Limited, Market Drayton, United Kingdom; *Int'l*, pg. 234
Turiano, Vincent C., Chief Oper. Officer & Exec. V.P.--Hollidaysburg Trust Company, Hollidaysburg, PA; *U.S. Public*, pg. 1222
Turnbull, Bruce, Chief Oper. Officer--Henkel Australia Pty. Ltd., Kilsyth, Australia; *Int'l*, pg. 611
Turner, James E., Jr., Pres. & Chief Oper. Officer--General Dynamics Corporation, Falls Church, VA; *U.S. Public*, pg. 708
Turner, Jimmie L., Chief Oper. Officer & Exec. V.P.--Gamma Biologicals Inc., Houston, TX; *U.S. Public*, pg. 698
Turner, John L., Exec. V.P. & Chief Oper. Officer--Allied Mineral Products, Inc., Columbus, OH; *U.S. Private*, pg. 39
Turner, W.B., Jr., Pres. & Chief Oper. Officer--W.C. Bradley Co., Columbus, GA; *U.S. Private*, pg. 164
Turrell, Michael F., Grp. Dir.-Global Opers.--Reckitt & Colman plc, London, United Kingdom; *Int'l*, pg. 1089
Tutor, Ronald N., Acting Chief Oper. Officer--Perini Corporation, Framingham, MA; *U.S. Public*, pg. 1278
Tveit, Inge, Chief Oper. Officer--Esmi A/S, Skare, Norway; *Int'l*, pg. 33
Twa, C.O., Pres. & Chief Oper. Officer--ATCO Group Co., Calgary, Canada; *Int'l*, pg. 95
Twa, C.O., Pres. & Chief Oper. Officer--Canadian Utilities Limited, Calgary, Canada; *Int'l*, pg. 95
Tyson, Ted H., Pres., Chief Exec. & Chief Oper. Officer--The Dickerson Group, Inc., Monroe, NC; *U.S. Private*, pg. 331
Uchida, Hisashi, Pres. & Chief Exec. Officer--Mitsubishi Silicon America, Salem, OR; *Int'l*, pg. 875
Uchida, Shun, Pres. & Chief Oper. Officer--Otsuka America, Inc., San Francisco, CA; *Int'l*, pg. 1013
Uding, George E., Jr., Pres. & Chief Oper. Officer--Medusa Corporation, Cleveland, OH; *U.S. Public*, pg. 1084
Uehara, N., Chief Oper. Officer--The Kyoei Life Insurance Co., Ltd.-London Office, London, United Kingdom; *Int'l*, pg. 777
Ukrop, Robert S., Chief Oper. Officer--Ukrop's Super Markets, Richmond, VA; *U.S. Private*, pg. 1115
Ulewicz, Michael, V.P.-Opers.--Kasle Steel Corporation, Dearborn, MI; *U.S. Private*, pg. 608
Ullman, S. Peter, Pres., Chief Exec. & Oper. Officer--Harris Calorific Co., Gainesville, GA; *U.S. Public*, pg. 996
Umans, Craig, Pres.-RHC Spacemaster & Chief Oper. Officer--RHC/Spacemaster Corporation, Melrose Park, IL; *U.S. Private*, pg. 904
Umbach, William, Chief Oper. Officer--Strober New Jersey Building Supply Centers, Inc., Edison, NJ; *U.S. Private*, pg. 403
Umland, Klaus, Co-Chief Oper. Officer--IKB Leasing Berlin GmbH, Berlin, Germany; *Int'l*, pg. 645
Umland, Klaus, Co-Chief Oper. Officer--IKB Leasing GmbH, Hamburg, Germany; *Int'l*, pg. 645
Underhill, Robert L., Chief Oper. Officer & Exec. V.P.--Channing L. Bete Co., Inc., South Deerfield, MA; *U.S. Private*, pg. 140
Unwin, Geoff, Chief Oper. Officer--CAP Gemini S.A., Paris, France; *Int'l*, pg. 263
Urbancic, Joseph J., Chief Oper. Officer--Zaremba Group, Inc., Lakewood, OH; *U.S. Private*, pg. 1204
Urbanek, Michal, Chief Oper. Officer--Ferrosan International A/S, Prague, Czech Republic; *Int'l*, pg. 989
Urbin, Dominique, Chief Oper. Officer--COBE S.A., Rungis, France; *Int'l*, pg. 667
Uretta, Ronald, Chief Oper. Officer & Treas.--Insignia Financial Group, Inc., Greenville, SC; *U.S. Public*, pg. 881
Urso, R., Chief Oper. Officer--Budd Plastics Design Center, Troy, MI; *Int'l*, pg. 1388
Uyeda, Allen B., Pres. & Chief Exec. Officer--First Insurance Co. of Hawaii, Ltd., Honolulu, HI; *U.S. Public*, pg. 1011
Uyeda, Allen B., Pres. & Chief Exec. Officer--First Insurance Co. of Hawaii, Ltd., Honolulu, HI; *Int'l*, pg. 1392
Vaatainn, Maria, Chief Oper. Officer--Valmet Trade Promotion Office, Saint Petersburg, Russia; *Int'l*, pg. 1449
Vacala, John, Chief Oper. Officer--Dann Dee Display Fixtures, Niles, IL; *U.S. Private*, pg. 310
Vadas, James, Chief Oper. Officer--Schleicher & Schuell, Budapest, Hungary; *Int'l*, pg. 1206
Vaharis, Chris, Chief Oper. Officer--Brown & Brown Venture Group, LLC, Mesa, AZ; *U.S. Private*, pg. 172
Valaoras, George, Pres. & Chief Oper. Officer--Tempel Steel Company, Skokie, IL; *U.S. Private*, pg. 1075
Valdes, David, Chief Oper. Officer & Chief Fin. Officer--Zimmerman & Partners Advertising, Inc., Fort Lauderdale, FL; *U.S. Private*, pg. 1206
Valentino, Harry, Pres. & Chief Oper. Officer--Fresh Mark, Inc., Canton, OH; *U.S. Private*, pg. 427
Vallee, Roy, Chm. Bd., Pres. & Chief Exec. & Oper. Officer--Avnet, Inc., Great Neck, NY; *U.S. Public*, pg. 155
Valotaire, J., Pres. & Chief Oper. Officer--Belair Insurance Company, Montreal, Canada; *Int'l*, pg. 648
Valverde, Carlos, Chief Oper. Officer--Banco Quilmes, Buenos Aires, Argentina; *Int'l*, pg. 142
van Cann, J.H., Chief Oper. Officer--VNU Verkoopgroep BV, De Meern, Netherlands; *Int'l*, pg. 1445
Van de Mortel, C., Chief Oper. Officer--Marine Port Terminals Inc., Brunswick, GA; *Int'l*, pg. 758
van den Beemt, C.M., Chief Oper. Officer--SAB Profiel B.V., Ijsselstein, Netherlands; *Int'l*, pg. 754
van der Brugger, R.J.A., Chief Oper. Officer--Installatiegroep Van Buuren-Van Swaay bv, Zoetermeer, Netherlands; *Int'l*, pg. 681
van Iperen, R. L., Chief Oper. Officer & Exec. Dir.-Bus. Unit Supplies--Oce-van der Grinten N.V., Venlo, Netherlands; *Int'l*, pg. 993
Van Kleef, William T., Exec. V.P.-Opers.--Tesoro Petroleum Corporation, San Antonio, TX; *U.S. Public*, pg. 1581
Van Leersum, J., Chief Oper. Officer--Alabastine Holland BV (Manufacturing), Ammerzoden, Netherlands; *Int'l*, pg. 1501
van Lent, Henri J.E.J., Chief Oper. Officer--Royal Nederland Schadeverzekering, Rotterdam, Netherlands; *Int'l*, pg. 16
van Moorleghem, William, Chief Oper. Officer--Advanced Materials and Technologies N.V., Herk-de-Stad, Belgium; *Int'l*, pg. 1427
Van Ort, Dale, Pres. & Chief Oper. Officer--Freeman Decorating Co., Dallas, TX; *U.S. Private*, pg. 426
Van Sickle, Paul B., Exec. V.P.--Tupperware Corporation, Orlando, FL; *U.S. Public*, pg. 1644
Van Wagenen, Paul G., Chm. Bd., Pres. & Chief Exec. Officer--Pogo Producing Company, Houston, TX; *U.S. Public*, pg. 1312
Van Wooten, Richard A., Chief Oper. Officer & Sr. V.P.--Walk, Haydel & Associates, Inc., New Orleans, LA; *Int'l*, pg. 624
Vanden Bulck, Werner, Chief Oper. Officer--Neste Shipping Benelux, N.V., Antwerp, Belgium; *Int'l*, pg. 915
Vanderslice, John, Pres. & Chief Oper. Officer--Aydin Corporation, Horsham, PA; *U.S. Public*, pg. 158
Vandevelde, Luc, Chief Oper. Officer--Promodes SA, Mondeville, France; *Int'l*, pg. 1071
Vandewater, David, Chief Oper. Officer--Columbia/HCA Healthcare Corporation, Nashville, TN; *U.S. Public*, pg. 404
Vargas, Alex, Chief Oper. Officer, V.P. & Pur. Dir.--Cash & Carry Grocer Inc., Chicago, IL; *U.S. Private*, pg. 218
Vargo, Timothy D., Pres. & Chief Oper. Officer--AutoZone, Inc., Memphis, TN; *U.S. Public*, pg. 150
Varner, Ted, Pres. & Chief Oper. Officer--Convenience Stores Distributors, Richmond, IN; *U.S. Public*, pg. 1049
Varnes, Larry, Vice Chm. & Chief Strategic Officer--Grey Advertising Inc., Western Div., Los Angeles, CA; *U.S. Public*, pg. 764
Vastola, Eugene, Chief Oper. Officer & V.P.--Commonwealth Metal, Englewood Cliffs, NJ; *U.S. Public*, *pg. 412*
Vasvari, Hal A., Chief Oper. Officer & Exec. V.P.--Federal Realty Investment Trust, Rockville, MD; *U.S. Public*, pg. 616
Vaughan, George C., Chief Oper. Officer & Exec. V.P.--Vaughan & Sons, Inc., San Antonio, TX; *U.S. Private*, pg. 1134
Vaughn, Donald C., Pres. & Chief Oper. Officer--Dresser Industries, Inc., Dallas, TX; *U.S. Public*, pg. 528

Vayssie, Michel, Chief Oper. Officer--Banco Banque Nationale de Paris Brasil S/A, Sao Paulo, Brazil; *Int'l*, pg. 164
Vega Vazquez, Gustavo, Chief Oper. Officer--Grupo Elektra S.A. de C.V., Mexico, Mexico; *Int'l*, pg. 573
Vegel, Magne G., Chief Oper. Officer--NAPS Norway A/S, Oslo, Norway; *Int'l*, pg. 913
Velasco, Ernesto Vega, Chief Oper. Officer, Chief Fin. Officer & Sec.--Desc, S.A. de C.V., Mexico, Mexico; *Int'l*, *pg. 395*
Vella, William J., Pres. & Chief Oper. Officer--Carsen Group Inc., Markham, Canada; *U.S. Public*, pg. 301
Venison, Peter J., Chief Oper. Officer-Europe & Indian Ocean--Sun International Hotels Limited, Fort Lauderdale, FL; *U.S. Public*, pg. 1531
Venskys, Zigmundas, Chief Oper. Officer--AB Akerlund & Rausing, Litovskaya, Lithuania; *Int'l*, pg. 33
Vent, Richard H., Pres. & Chief Oper. Officer--Caribiner International, Inc., New York, NY; *U.S. Public*, pg. 305
Verdier, Jacques, Chief Oper. Officer--Technip, Paris, France; *Int'l*, pg. 1360
Verdoorn, Sid, Pres., Chief Exec. & Chief Oper. Officer--C.H. Robinson Co., Eden Prairie, MN; *U.S. Public*, pg. 1394
Vergon, James F., Pres. & Chief Oper. Officer--Central Illinois Light Company, Peoria, IL; *U.S. Public*, pg. 367
Verner, James R., Pres. & Chief Oper. Officer--Acousti Engineering Co. of Florida, Orlando, FL; *U.S. Private*, pg. 14
Verrando, R., Pres. & Chief Oper. Officer--Presstek, Inc., Hudson, NH; *U.S. Public*, pg. 1324
Verrecchia, Al, Chief Oper. Officer--Tonka Corporation, Pawtucket, RI; *U.S. Public*, pg. 797
Verrier, John J., Chief Exec. Officer--Primepak Company, Teaneck, NJ; *U.S. Private*, pg. 884
Verrill, Peter J., Chief Oper. Officer, Exec. V.P. & Treas.--Peoples Heritage Financial Group, Inc., Portland, ME; *U.S. Public*, pg. 1275
Verrycken, R., Chief Oper. Officer--N.V. Polyfilla Products SA, Machelen, Belgium; *Int'l*, pg. 1501
Verwaayen, Ben J.M., Chief Oper. Officer--Lucent Technologies Inc., Murray Hill, NJ; *U.S. Public*, pg. 1017
Vestal, David, Pres. & Chief Oper. Officer--Vestal Manufacturing, Sweetwater, TN; *U.S. Public*, pg. 1737
Veyder, Frank, Chief Oper. Officer--Banque Generale du Luxembourg S.A., Central, Hong Kong; *Int'l*, pg. 162
Veyder, Frank, Chief Oper. Officer--BGL Finance (Asia) Ltd., Central, Hong Kong; *Int'l*, pg. 162
Vichich, William M., Chief Oper. Officer--Citizens Federal Bank, F.S.B., Dayton, OH; *U.S. Public*, pg. 376
Vicini, Robert, V.P. & Chief Oper. Officer--Flori Corp., Phoenix, AZ; *U.S. Private*, pg. 414
Vick, R. John, Pres. & Chief Oper. Officer--Perini Land and Development Co., Framingham, MA; *U.S. Public*, pg. 1278
Vierimaa, Johannes, Chief Oper. Officer--Ahlstrom Machinery Karhula Steel Foundry, Karhula, Finland; *Int'l*, pg. 33
Viering, Peter, Co-Chief Oper. Officer--International Finance Division, Dusseldorf, Germany; *Int'l*, pg. 645
Vigh, Donald A., Chief Oper. Officer & Exec. V.P.--Kimble Glass Inc., Vineland, NJ; *Int'l*, pg. 1464
Viinanen, Jukka, Vice Chm., Pres. & Chief Oper. Officer--Neste Oy, Espoo, Finland; *Int'l*, pg. 912
Vikki, Kirsti, Chief Oper. Officer--Novo Nordisk A/S, Espoo, Finland; *Int'l*, pg. 987
Vila, Raul, Chief Oper. Officer--Puerto Rico Tourism Company, New York, NY; *U.S. Private*, pg. 894
Vilgrain, Francis, Chief Oper. Officer--Grands Moulins de Paris S.A., Paris, France; *Int'l*, pg. 556
Vilgrain, Stanislas, Pres. & Chief Oper. Officer--Cuisine Solutions, Inc., Alexandria, VA; *U.S. Public*, pg. 466
Vincent, Daniel L., Chief Oper. Officer & Exec. V.P.--Pacific Coast Producers, Lodi, CA; *U.S. Private*, pg. 830
Vincent, Joseph A., Chief Oper. & Fin. Officer & V.P.-Fin.--Novametrix Medical Systems Inc., Wallingford, CT; *U.S. Public*, pg. 1203
Vincent, Philip S., Pres. & Chief Oper. Officer--Southern Mills, Inc., Union City, GA; *U.S. Private*, pg. 1016
Vinyard, Lee E., Chief Oper. Officer--Intermatic Inc., Spring Grove, IL; *U.S. Private*, pg. 567
Viola, Donn, Chief Oper. Officer-N.A.--Donnelly Corporation, Holland, MI; *U.S. Public*, pg. 519
Visca, Alessandro, Chief Oper. Officer--Ahlstrom Papeis Ltda., Louveira, Brazil; *Int'l*, pg. 35
Vitale, Kevin B., Chief Oper. Officer--Wall Data Incorporated, Kirkland, WA; *U.S. Public*, pg. 1734
Vitale, Neal, Pres. & Chief Oper. Officer--Petersen Publishing Company, L.L.C., Los Angeles, CA; *U.S. Private*, pg. 856
Viviano, Joseph P., Pres. & Chief Oper. Officer--Hershey Foods Corporation, Hershey, PA; *U.S. Public*, pg. 811
Vogl, Charles J., Pres. & Chief Oper. Officer--Wilton Corporation, Palatine, IL; *U.S. Private*, pg. 1181
Vokrouhlikova, Jirina, Chief Oper. Officer--Novo Nordisk A/S, Prague, Czech Republic; *Int'l*, pg. 987
Volk, Christopher H., Chief Oper. Officer & Exec. V.P.--Franchise Finance Corp. of America, Scottsdale, AZ; *U.S. Public*, pg. 679
Vollaro, John D., Pres. & Chief Oper. Officer--W.R. Berkley Corporation, Greenwich, CT; *U.S. Public*, pg. 215
Volpe, C.E., Chief Oper. Officer--Kemet Electronics Corporation, Simpsonville, SC; *U.S. Public*, pg. 949
Volpentesta, Frank, Chief Oper. Officer & V.P.--Bearing Headquarters Co., Broadview, IL; *U.S. Private*, pg. 127
von Gelder, A., Chief Oper. Officer--Van Rietschoten & Houwens Zuid-West bv, Capelle aan den Ijssel, Netherlands; *Int'l*, pg. 681
von Krempelhuber, Michael, Co-Chief Oper. Officer--Bavarian Branch, Munich, Germany; *Int'l*, pg. 645
von Sahr, Leo, Chief Oper. Officer--Leipzig Branch, Leipzig, Germany; *Int'l*, pg. 645
Vonk, Gary, Pres. & Chief Oper. Officer--Snappy Car Rental, Inc., Tulsa, OK; *U.S. Private*, pg. 1010
Vumbacco, Joseph V., Pres. & Chief Oper. Officer--Health Management Associates, Inc., Naples, FL; *U.S. Public*, pg. 802
Wachtel, M.D., Exec. V.P. & Chief Oper. Officer--Domestic Wholesale, Oshkosh, WI; *U.S. Public*, pg. 1233
Wachtel, Michael P., Chief Oper. Officer & Exec. V.P.--OshKosh B'Gosh, Inc., Oshkosh, WI; *U.S. Public*, pg. 1232
Wackenhut, Richard R., Pres. & Chief Oper. Officer--The Wackenhut Corporation, Palm Beach Gardens, FL; *U.S. Public*, pg. 1731
Wade, Daniel M., Pres. & Chief Oper. Officer--MGM Grand Hotel, Inc., Las Vegas, NV; *U.S. Public*, pg. 1027
Wagar, Mark L., Pres. & Chief Oper. Officer--Medpartners Inc., Birmingham, AL; *U.S. Public*, pg. 1082
Wages, Terry W., Chief Oper. Officer--CGF Industries, Topeka, KS; *U.S. Private*, pg. 194
Wagner, Bryan, Gen. Mgr.--Kurt Manufacturing Co. Inc., Fridley, MN; *U.S. Private*, pg. 637
Wagner, Lawrence M., Pres. & Chief Oper. Officer--The Hillman Company, Pittsburgh, PA; *U.S. Private*, pg. 530
Wagniere, Daniel C., Pres.-Exec. Bd. & Chief Oper. Officer--Sandoz (Hellas) S.A.C.I., Athens, Greece; *Int'l*, pg. 984
Wahl, C. Richard, Pres. & Chief Oper. Officer--Wheatland Tube Company, Collingswood, NJ; *U.S. Private*, pg. 1170
Wahl, Lothar, Pres. & Chief Oper. Officer--BOMAG, Boppard, Germany; *U.S. Public*, pg. 1677
Wahle, James L., Pres. & Chief Oper. Officer--Accu-Sort Systems, Inc., Telford, PA; *U.S. Private*, pg. 11
Waichler, Richard, V.P.-Opers. & Sec.--Follett Corporation, River Grove, IL; *U.S. Private*, pg. 416
Waintraub, Lionel, Chief Oper. Officer--Proser, Creteil, France; *Int'l*, pg. 503
Wainwright, R., Chief Oper. Officer--Ancon CLC, Sheffield, United Kingdom; *Int'l*, pg. 925
Wait, Chuck, V.P.-Production--Tetko, Inc., Briarcliff Manor, NY; *U.S. Private*, pg. 1078
Waldron, John, Chief Oper. Officer--Lyman Lumber Company, Excelsior, MN; *U.S. Private*, pg. 683
Waldrop, Richard E., Pres., Chief Oper. Officer & V.P.-Sls.--Edwards Engineering Corporation, Pompton Plains, NJ; *U.S. Private*, pg. 365
Walker, Chris L., Pres. & Chief Oper. Officer--E.W. Blanch Holdings, Inc., Minneapolis, MN; *U.S. Public*, pg. 236
Walker, Harry M., Pres. & Chief Oper. Officer--Trustmark National Bank, Jackson, MS; *U.S. Public*, pg. 1643
Wallace, Ann, Chief Oper. Officer & V.P.--Underwriters & Management Services Inc., Indianapolis, IN; *U.S. Public*, pg. 998
Wallace, Michael R., Pres. & Chief Oper. Officer--Jack Henry & Associates, Inc., Monett, MO; *U.S. Public*, pg. 808
Wallace, Theodore, Chief Oper. Officer & Exec. V.P.--PriceSmart Inc., San Diego, CA; *U.S. Public*, pg. 1324
Wallace, William F., Pres. & Chief Oper. Officer--Plains Petroleum Operating Co., Lakewood, CO; *U.S. Public*, pg. 191
Wallach, James G., Chief Oper.Officer--Lindenmeyr Munroe, Purchase, NY; *U.S. Private*, pg. 224
Wallach, James G., Chief Oper. Officer--Lindenmeyr Munroe, North Reading, MA; *U.S. Private*, pg. 224
Waller, Stephen L., Sr. V.P.-Network Transportation & Plng.--DHL Airways, Inc., Redwood City, CA; *U.S. Private*, pg. 302
Wallgren, Per-Erik, Chief Oper. Officer--Neste Oy, Gas LPG International, Espoo, Finland; *Int'l*, pg. 913
Wallis, Paul, Chief Oper. Officer--Mikron U.K. Ltd., Huddersfield, United Kingdom; *Int'l*, pg. 867
Walls, Rick, V.P.-Admin. & Chief Oper. Officer--Cantex Inc., Mineral Wells, TX; *Int'l*, pg. 1312
Walpole, R.H., Pres. & Chief Oper. Officer--Walbro Engine Management Corporation, Cass City, MI; *U.S. Public*, pg. 1733
Walsh, Kevin M., Pres. & Chief Oper. Officer--Expeditors International of Washington, Inc., Seattle, WA; *U.S. Public*, pg. 600
Walsh, Larry, Chief Oper. Officer--Carr Gottstein Foods, Anchorage, AK; *U.S. Public*, pg. 308
Walsh, Paul S., Chief Exec. Officer-Pillsbury Brands--The Pillsbury Company, Minneapolis, MN; *Int'l*, pg. 411
Walsh, Thomas, Chief Oper. Officer--Stewart Warner Instruments Corporation, Des Plaines, IL; *U.S. Private*, pg. 1042
Walsh, W.J., Chief Oper. Officer--Channellock, Inc., Meadville, PA; *U.S. Private*, pg. 229
Walsh, William J., Jr., Chief Oper. Officer, Exec. V.P. & Sec.--Consumers Financial Corporation, Camp Hill, PA; *U.S. Public*, pg. 437
Waltermire, Thomas, Chief Oper. Officer--The Geon Company, Avon Lake, OH; *U.S. Public*, pg. 733
Wang, Susie, Chief Oper. Officer--Wang's International, Inc., Memphis, TN; *U.S. Private*, pg. 1149
Wannamaker, Gerald, Chief Oper. Officer--Manufactured Housing Div., Caldwell, ID; *U.S. Public*, pg. 962
Wannamaker, Gerald, Chief Oper. Officer--R-4 KIT Mfg. Co., Mc Pherson, KS; *U.S. Public*, pg. 962
Wannamaker, Gerald, Chief Oper. Officer--Recreational Vehicle Div., Caldwell, ID; *U.S. Public*, pg. 962
Ward, Dalet, Chief Oper. Officer--Orchard Supply Hardware, San Jose, CA; *U.S. Public*, pg. 1452
Ward, Henry, Chief Oper. Officer--Massachusetts Envelope Co., Somerville, MA; *U.S. Private*, pg. 712
Ward, Nelson, Pres. & Chief Oper. Officer--Ennis Business Forms, Inc., Ennis, TX; *U.S. Public*, pg. 583
Ward, Thomas J., Pres. & Chief Oper. Officer--WestPoint Stevens Inc., West Point, GA; *U.S. Public*, pg. 1762
Ward, Thomas S., Pres. & Chief Oper. Officer--Whitman's Candies, Inc., Kansas City, MO; *U.S. Private*, pg. 953
Wareham, John P., Pres. & Chief Oper. Officer--Beckman Instruments, Inc., Fullerton, CA; *U.S. Public*, pg. 199
Warlick, Anderson, Pres. & Chief Oper. Officer--Parkdale Mills, Gastonia, NC; *U.S. Private*, pg. 840
Warner, Greg, Chief Oper. Officer & Exec. V.P.--Kia Motors America, Inc., Irvine, CA; *Int'l*, pg. 733
Warren, Will H., Pres. & Chief Fin. Officer--NES Holdings, Inc., Raleigh, NC; *U.S. Private*, pg. 771
Warshaw, Steven G., Pres., Chief Oper. & Fin. Officer--Chiquita Brands International, Inc., Cincinnati, OH; *U.S. Public*, pg. 349
Wasek, Matt K., Pres. & Chief Oper. Officer--Valley Fresh, Inc., Turlock, CA; *U.S. Private*, pg. 1132
Washburn, Frank A., Chief Oper. Officer, Exec. V.P. & Sec.--Pamida Holdings Corporation, Omaha, NE; *U.S. Public*, pg. 1255
Washow, Lawrence E., Chief Oper. Officer & Exec. V.P.--AMCOL International Corp., Arlington Heights, IL; *U.S. Public*, pg. 63
Wasserspring, Fredric R., Pres. & Chief Oper. Officer--Michael Anthony Jewelers, Inc., Mount Vernon, NY; *U.S.* Public, pg. 1103
Watkins, Gary, Pres. & Chief Oper. Officer--Allison-Erwin Co. Inc., Charlotte, NC; *U.S. Private*, pg. 41
Watkins, James H., Chm. Bd. & Chief Oper. Officer--ATCOM, Inc., Research Triangle Park, NC; *U.S. Private*, pg. 94
Watson, Edward A., Chief Oper. Officer & Exec. V.P.--International Dairy Queen, Inc., Minneapolis, MN; *U.S. Public*, pg. 220
Watson, J.H., Chm., Pres. & Chief Exec. Officer--Confed Investment Counselling Limited, Toronto, Canada; *Int'l*, pg. 325
Watson, Karl, Exec. V.P.--Rinker Materials Corp., West Palm Beach, FL; *Int'l*, pg. 246
Watson, Peter D., Pres. & Chief Oper. Officer--Willis Corroon Melling Ltd., Edmonton, Canada; *Int'l*, pg. 1509
Watson, Richard P., Chief Oper. Officer & Exec. V.P.--H & H Tube & Manufacturing Co., Vanderbilt, MI; *U.S. Private*, pg. 489
Watts, J., M.D., Chief Oper. Officer--Armitage Shanks Limited, Rugeley, United Kingdom; *Int'l*, pg. 197
Watts, Nancy, Dir.-Opers.--Hayes Microcomputer Products, Inc., Norcross, GA; *U.S. Public*, pg. 801
Waxman, Laurance S., Chief Oper. Officer--Waxman Industries, Inc., Bedford, OH; *U.S. Public*, pg. 1748
Way, Richard D., Pres. & Chief Oper. Officer--Northwestern Steel & Wire Co., Sterling, IL; *U.S. Public*, pg. 1201
Weathersby, William C., Pres. & Chief Oper. Officer--American Safety Razor Company, Verona, VA; *U.S. Private*, pg. 597
Weaver, Arnold L., Pres. & Chief Oper. Officer--Pinnacle Financial Services Inc., Saint Joseph, MI; *U.S. Public*, pg. 1297
Weaver, B. H., Chief Oper. Officer & Exec. V.P.--Westco Products, Inc., Pico Rivera, CA; *Int'l*, pg. 244
Weaver, Michael E., Pres., Chief Exec. Officer & Chief Oper. Officer--Weaver Popcorn Company, Inc., Van Buren, IN; *U.S. Private*, pg. 1156
Webb, Carl, Pres. & Chief Oper. Officer--California Federal Bank, San Francisco, CA; *U.S. Private*, pg. 690
Webb, Rollie, Pres. & Chief Oper. Officer--Todd Pacific Shipyards Corp., Seattle, WA; *U.S. Public*, pg. 1619
Weber, Jean-Claude, Co-Chief Oper. Officer--Cofhylux SA, Luxembourg, Luxembourg; *Int'l*, pg. 162
Weber, Philip P., Chief Exec. Officer--Farm Family Casualty Insurance Co., Glenmont, NY; *U.S. Private*, pg. 394
Webster, Donald, Chief Oper. Officer--Perstorp Analytical Inc., Silver Spring, MD; *Int'l*, pg. 1039
Wedaman, David H., Chief Oper. Officer, Exec. V.P. & Pres.-Mark VII Transportation--Mark VII, Inc., Memphis, TN; *U.S. Public*, pg. 1046
Weder, Oskar, Chief Oper. Officer--Mikron Corp. Monroe, Monroe, CT; *Int'l*, pg. 866
Weeks, James C., Pres. & Chief Oper. Officer--The New York Times Company Regional Newspaper Group, Atlanta, GA; *U.S. Public*, pg. 1174
Wegner, Arthur E., Chm. Bd., Chief Exec. Officer & Sr. V.P.--Raytheon Aircraft Company, Wichita, KS; *U.S. Public*, pg. 1365
Wehberg, Keith, Chief Oper. Officer & V.P.-Mktg.--Shillcraft, Inc., Baltimore, MD; *U.S. Private*, pg. 994
Weider, Eric, Chief Oper. Officer--Weider Publications, Inc., Woodland Hills, CA; *U.S. Private*, pg. 1159
Weigel, Klaus, Dr., Chief Oper. Officer--Industrie-Beteiligungs Gesellschaftmbh, Frankfurt/Main, Germany; *Int'l*, pg. 119
Weikel, M. Keith, Chief Oper. Officer & Sr. Exec. V.P.--Health Care & Retirement Corporation, Toledo, OH; *U.S.* Public, pg. 801
Weil, David S., Pres., Chief Exec. Officer & Chief Oper. Officer--Ampacet Corporation, Tarrytown, NY; *U.S. Private*, pg. 67
Weil, Robert S., II, Vice Chm. & Chief Oper. Officer--Weil Brothers Cotton Inc., Montgomery, AL; *U.S. Private*, pg. 1159
Weimer, Jerry W., Chief Oper. Officer & Exec. V.P.--Integrity Incorporated, Mobile, AL; *U.S. Public*, pg. 886
Weinberg, Steven J., Pres. & Chief Oper. Officer--Cyborg Systems, Inc., Chicago, IL; *U.S. Private*, pg. 299
Weinman, Michael, Chief Oper. Officer--Teleflora, LLC, Los Angeles, CA; *U.S. Private*, pg. 941
Weinstein, Marc, Chief Oper. Officer--Jan Bell Marketing Inc., Sunrise, FL; *U.S. Public*, pg. 207
Weintraub, Leigh, Chief Oper. Officer--Merit Medical Systems, Inc., South Jordan, UT; *U.S. Public*, pg. 1096
Weir, R. Brian, Pres. & Chief Oper. Officer--Supershuttle Inc., Phoenix, AZ; *U.S. Private*, pg. 1056
Weisner, B.A., Sr. V.P. & Chief Oper. Officer-Service Centres--Fedmet International Inc., Mississauga, Canada; *Int'l*, pg. 1150
Weiss, Gunther, Chief Oper. Officer--Weiss Scientific Glass Blowing Co., Inc., Portland, OR; *Int'l*, pg. 1408
Weiss, Gunther, Chief Oper. Officer--Weiss Glass Technologies, Inc., San Jose, CA; *Int'l*, pg. 1408
Weiss, Ken, Chief Oper. Officer--Environmental Resources Management, Exton, PA; *U.S. Private*, pg. 378
Weiss, Len, Chief Oper. Officer--Investors Services Group, Boston, MA; *U.S. Public*, pg. 631

Weiss, Moti, Chief Oper. Officer--Sapiens USA, Inc., Durham, NC; *Int'l*, pg. 1193
Weiss, Richard, Chief Oper. Officer--United Receptical, Inc., Pottsville, PA; *U.S. Private*, pg. 1123
Weiss, Ronald, Pres. & Chief Oper. Officer--Bell Mobility Paging Inc., Downsview, Canada; *Int'l*, pg. 115
Weitzman, William, Pres. & Chief Oper. Officer--Electro Rent Corporation, Van Nuys, CA; *U.S. Public*, pg. 568
Welch, Norman H., Jr., Pres.--Eva-Tone Inc., Clearwater, FL; *U.S. Private*, pg. 384
Weller, Johnathan B., Pres. & Chief Oper. Officer--Pennsylvania Real Estate Investment Trust, Fort Washington, PA; *U.S. Public*, pg. 1272
Wellington, Donna, Chief Oper. Officer & Exec. V.P.--Ronco, Inventions. LLC, Chatsworth, CA; *U.S. Private*, pg. 943
Wellman, Jon, Pres. & Chief Oper. Officer--American Business Information, Inc., Omaha, NE; *U.S. Public*, pg. 69
Wells, James M., III, Pres. & Chief Oper. Officer--Crestar Financial Corporation, Richmond, VA; *U.S. Public*, pg. 458
Wemyss, Roy D., Chief Oper. Officer--Mackie Designs, Inc., Woodinville, WA; *U.S. Public*, pg. 1030
Wender, Mark D., Chief Oper. Officer & Sec.--Boatmen's National Mortgage Inc., Memphis, TN; *U.S. Public*, pg. 1165
Wenger, Patrick, Chief Oper. Officer--Royal Doulton Plc., Stoke on Trent, United Kingdom; *Int'l*, pg. 1135
Wenk-Wolff, Kai, Pres. & Chief Oper. Officer--NAPP Systems Inc, San Marcos, CA; *U.S. Public*, pg. 984
Wenner, Hal, V.P.-Opers.--Sunroc Corporation, Dover, DE; *U.S. Private*, pg. 1053
Wenz, Richard E., Pres. & Chief Oper. Officer--Safety 1st, Inc., Chestnut Hill, MA; *U.S. Public*, pg. 1425
Wenzel, Robert J., Pres.-LaserMaster Corp. & Chief Oper. Officer--LaserMaster Technologies, Inc., Eden Prairie, MN; *U.S. Public*, pg. 979
Werner Kuehn, Kurt, Chief Oper. Officer--Resart GmbH, Mainz, Germany; *Int'l*, pg. 104
Werner, Seth, Co-Chm. & Chief Oper. Officer-Dallas--Publicis/Bloom Inc., New York, NY; *Int'l*, pg. 470
Wertz, John C., Chief Oper. Officer, Sr. V.P. & Treas.--Banner Aerospace, Inc., Washington, DC; *U.S. Public*, pg. 187
Wessel, Jeffrey W., Chief Oper. Officer--Nippon Silica Glass USA, Inc., Bound Brook, NJ; *Int'l*, pg. 1407
Wesser, Charles, Pres. & Chief Oper. Officer--Arden International Kitchens, Inc., Lakeville, MN; *U.S. Private*, pg. 972
West, Jim, Pres.--Florafax International, Inc., Vero Beach, FL; *U.S. Public*, pg. 654
West, W. Michael, Pres. & Chief Oper. Officer--Octel Messaging Division, Milpitas, CA; *U.S. Public*, pg. 1017
Westerborg, Volker, Co-Chief Oper. Officer--Helaba Invest Kapitalanlagegesellschaft mbH, Frankfurt/Main, Germany; *Int'l*, pg. 799
Westerman, William, Pres. & Chief Oper. Officer--Cogsdill Tool Products, Inc., Lugoff, SC; *U.S. Private*, pg. 250
Westermeyer, A. Neal, Chief Oper. Officer & Exec. V.P.--National Health Enhancement Systems, Inc., Phoenix, AZ; *U.S. Public*, pg. 1157
Westoff, Gregory J., Pres. & Chief Oper. Officer--Alarmguard Holdings, Inc., Orange, CT; *U.S. Public*, pg. 35
Westphal, Gordon E., Pres. & Chief Oper. Officer--Western States Envelope Co., Milwaukee, WI; *U.S. Private*, pg. 1168
Wetzler, Graydon A., Sr. V.P.-Opers.--Rohr, Inc., Chula Vista, CA; *U.S. Public*, pg. 751
Wexler, Lewis P., Chm. Bd., Pres., Chief Exec. Officer & Chief Oper. Officer--Free Service Tire Company, Inc., Johnson City, TN; *U.S. Private*, pg. 425
Weyhausen, E., Chief Oper. Officer--BHF-Bank Liason Office, Melbourne, Australia; *Int'l*, pg. 120
Whalen, Thomas, V.P.-Opers.--The Felters Company, Roebuck, SC; *U.S. Private*, pg. 400
Wharton, Tom, Chief Oper. Officer--Poppe Tyson, New York, NY; *U.S. Public*, pg. 1642
Wheeler, H.A., Pres. & Chief Oper. Officer--Speedway Motorsports, Inc., Concord, NC; *U.S. Public*, pg. 1498
Wheeler, Nigel, Pres. & Chief Oper. Officer--Trikon Technologies Inc., Chatsworth, CA; *U.S. Public*, pg. 1638
Wheeler, Robert R., Pres. & Chief Oper. Officer--AFC Cable Systems, Inc., Providence, RI; *U.S. Public*, pg. 6
Whisler, J. Steven, Pres. & Chief Oper. Officer--Phelps Dodge Corporation, Phoenix, AZ; *U.S. Public*, pg. 1286
Whisler, John L., Chief Oper. Officer--Leo A. Daly Company, Omaha, NE; *U.S. Private*, pg. 309
Whitaker, Tom, V.P.-Opers.--Sanderson Plumbing Products Inc., Columbus, MS; *U.S. Private*, pg. 964
White, Andrew R., Chief Oper. Officer-M Banx--Bank of Montreal, Toronto, Canada; *Int'l*, pg. 153
White, Charles, Pres. & Chief Oper. Officer--Unisource Worldwide, Inc., Berwyn, PA; *U.S. Public*, pg. 1670
White, Connie, Chief Oper. Officer, Sr. V.P. & Media Dir.--EvansGroup, Salt Lake City, UT; *U.S. Private*, pg. 385
White, George, Pres. & Chief Oper. Officer--Cape Breton Development Corporation, Glace Bay, Canada; *Int'l*, pg. 265
White, Michael J., Chief Oper. Officer--National Trustco Inc., Toronto, Canada; *Int'l*, pg. 909
White, Michael J., Pres. & Chief Oper. Officer--National Trust Company, Stratford, Canada; *Int'l*, pg. 910
White, Stan, Chief Oper. Officer--Yogen Fruz Worldwide Inc., Markham, Canada; *Int'l*, pg. 1520
Whitehead, Geoffrey, Chief Oper. Officer--Novo Nordisk Pharmaceuticals Ltd., Auckland, New Zealand; *Int'l*, pg. 988
Whiteman, Jon, Pres. & Chief Oper. Officer--Morris Coupling Co., Erie, PA; *U.S. Private*, pg. 762
Whiting, R. Bruce, Pres. & Chief Oper. Officer--Kaibab Industries, Phoenix, AZ; *U.S. Private*, pg. 605
Whitley, Michael R., Chm. Bd., Pres. & Chief Exec. & Oper. Officer--KU Energy, Lexington, KY; *U.S. Public*, pg. 940
Whitley, Michael R., Chm. Bd., Pres. & Chief Exec. Officer--Kentucky Utilities Company, Lexington, KY; *U.S. Public*, pg. 941
Whitlow, Don, Pres. & Chief Oper. Officer--Barbour Thread, Inc., Blue Mountain, AL; *Int'l*, pg. 618
Whitney, Brad P., Pres. & Chief Oper. Officer--Linfinity Microelectronics Inc., Garden Grove, CA; *U.S. Public*, pg. 1547
Whitney, Nicholas, Chief Oper. Officer & Exec. V.P.--Management Dynamics, New Providence, NJ; *U.S. Public*, pg. 1040
Whitson, James N., Chief Oper. Officer & Exec. V.P.--Sammons Enterprises, Inc., Dallas, TX; *U.S. Private*, pg. 963
Whitt, David, Pres. & Chief Oper. Officer--Elixir Industries, Gardena, CA; *U.S. Private*, pg. 371
Whyte, Ralph, Chief Oper. Officer--Willis Corroon Aerospace, New York, NY; *Int'l*, pg. 1505
Wickli, H.E., Chief Oper. Officer--Buss Holding GmbH, Weingarten, Germany; *Int'l*, pg. 490
Widerschein, Neil, Chief Oper. Officer & Exec. V.P.--SBC Advertising, Columbus, OH; *U.S. Private*, pg. 955
Widerschein, Neil, Chief Oper. Officer--SBC Public Relations, Westerville, OH; *U.S. Private*, pg. 955
Widmer, Hans, Dr., Chm. Bd., Pres., Chief Exec. & Oper. Officer--Oerlikon-Buhrle Holding AG, Zurich, Switzerland; *Int'l*, pg. 996
Wiener, Doc, Chief Oper. Officer--Mission Industries, Las Vegas, NV; *U.S. Private*, pg. 752
Wiersbe, Dale E., Jr., Pres. & Chief Oper. Officer--Inland Steel Products Company, East Chicago, IN; *U.S. Public*, pg. 879
Wiggins, William H., Pres. & Chief Oper. Officer--Thiele Kaolin Co., Sandersville, GA; *U.S. Private*, pg. 1081
Wigley, Wendell, Chief Oper.Officer--Redco Corporation, Red Lion, PA; *U.S. Private*, pg. 915
Wilbur, Mark, Chief Oper. Officer--Kemron Environmental Services, Inc., Vienna, VA; *U.S. Private*, pg. 614
Wilcox, William H., Pres. & Chief Oper. Officer-M.C.I.I.--Columbia/H.C.A., Dallas, TX; *U.S. Public*, pg. 404
Wilhelm, Marcus, Chm. Bd., Chief Exec. Officer & Chief Oper. Officer--Doubleday Direct, Garden City, NY; *Int'l*, pg. 191
Wilkes, John, Pres. & Chief Exec. Officer--John Dusenbery Co., Inc., Randolph, NJ; *U.S. Private*, pg. 349
Wilkie, I. Giaene, Chief Oper. Officer--Pace International L.P., Kirkland, WA; *U.S. Private*, pg. 829
Wilkie, Michael L., Chm. Bd., Pres., Chief Exec. & Chief Oper. Officer--DOALL Company, Des Plaines, IL; *U.S. Private*, pg. 337
Wilkins, Gregory C., Pres. & Chief Oper. Officer--TrizecHahn Corporation, Toronto, Canada; *Int'l*, pg. 1424
Wilkins, Patrick, Exec. V.P. & Chief Oper. Officer--CH & A Corporation, Kingwood, TX; *Int'l*, pg. 1153
Wilkinson, Peter, Grp. Mng. Dir.-Myer Grace Bros.--Coles Myer Ltd., Tooronga, Australia; *Int'l*, pg. 306
Wilks, David M., Pres. & Chief Oper. Officer--Southwestern Public Service Company, Amarillo, TX; *U.S. Public*, pg. 1170
Willans, J.R.D., Chief Oper. Officer--Pillar Engineering Ltd., London, United Kingdom; *Int'l*, pg. 267
Willcox, James, Pres., Chief Exec. & Chief Oper. Officer--American Marketing Industries, Inc., Kansas City, MO; *U.S. Private*, pg. 58
Wille, Wolfgang, Co-Chief Oper. Officer--FernwaermeVerbund Saar GmbH, Voelklingen, Germany; *Int'l*, pg. 1167
Willey, Glenn, V.P.-Sls.--Allfast Fastening Systems, Inc., City of Industry, CA; *U.S. Private*, pg. 37
Willey, John L., V.P.--Electro Metrics, Inc., Johnstown, NY; *U.S. Private*, pg. 369
Williams, C.E., Chief Oper. Officer & Exec. V.P.--Security Pacific Financial Services Inc., San Diego, CA; *U.S. Public*, pg. 181
Williams, David A., Pres., Chief Oper. Officer & Gen. Mgr.--Regency Lincoln Mercury, Inc., Dallas, TX; *U.S. Private*, pg. 918
Williams, David P., Pres. & Chief Oper. Officer--The Budd Company, Troy, MI; *Int'l*, pg. 1388
Williams, Derek T.D., Chief Oper. Officer & Exec. V.P.--Pall Corporation, Greenvale, NY; *U.S. Public*, pg. 1253
Williams, Donald L., Chief Oper. Officer & V.P.--NGO Development Corporation, Newark, OH; *U.S. Public*, pg. 1157
Williams, Edward, Pres. & Chief Oper. Officer--Galaxy Carpet Mills, Inc., Chatsworth, GA; *U.S. Public*, pg. 1121
Williams, Eldridge M., Chief Oper. Officer & Exec. V.P.--Universal Life Insurance Company, Memphis, TN; *U.S. Private*, pg. 1127
Williams, Ellen, Chief Exec. Officer & Chief Fin. Officer--Millennium Technology Services, Inc., White City, OR; *U.S. Private*, pg. 746
Williams, Frank E., III, Chief Oper. Officer--Williams Equipment Corporation, Manassas, VA; *U.S. Public*, pg. 1770
Williams, Gregg G., Pres. & Chief Oper. Officer--Williams International, Walled Lake, MI; *U.S. Private*, pg. 1178
Williams, H. Arthur, Chief Oper. Officer--Williams Steel Erection Co., Inc., Falls Church, VA; *U.S. Public*, pg. 1770
Williams, J.L., Pres.--Minyard Food Stores, Inc., Coppell, TX; *U.S. Private*, pg. 752
Williams, James, Pres. & Chief Oper. Officer-Food Service Group--Cara Operations Limited, Toronto, Canada; *Int'l*, pg. 266
Williams, James B., Pres. & Chief Oper. Officer--Acklands Limited, Toronto, Canada; *Int'l*, pg. 23
Williams, John H., Jr., Pres. & Chief Oper. Officer--Stein Mart, Inc., Jacksonville, FL; *U.S. Public*, pg. 1514
Williams, Jon M., Pres. & Chief Oper. Officer--Integrated Waste Services, Inc., Buffalo, NY; *U.S. Public*, pg. 886
Williams, Kevin, Chief Oper. Officer--Univest Financial Services, LLC, Atlanta, GA; *U.S. Private*, pg. 1128
Williams, R.L., Pres. & Chief Oper. Officer--Dan River Inc., Danville, VA; *U.S. Public*, pg. 478
Williams, Richard B., Pres. & Chief Oper. Officer--Lone Star Gas Co., Dallas, TX; *U.S. Public*, pg. 1587
Williamson, Brad, Chief Oper. Officer--Cascadia Transport, Vancouver, WA; *U.S. Private*, pg. 683
Williamson, Henry, Chief Oper. Officer--BB&T Corporation, Winston Salem, NC; *U.S. Public*, pg. 159
Williamson, John B., III, Chief Oper. Officer--Highland Propane Company, Roanoke, VA; *U.S. Public*, pg. 1393
Willis, John, Chief Oper. Officer--Thermon Manufacturing Company, San Marcos, TX; *U.S. Private*, pg. 1080
Willis, Larry, Pres. & Chief Oper. Officer--IGA, Inc. (Independent Grocers Alliance), Chicago, IL; *U.S. Private*, pg. 555
Willison, Bruce, Pres.-Home Savings & Chief Oper. Officer--H.F. Ahmanson & Co., Irwindale, CA; *U.S. Public*, pg. 29
Willms, Arthur H., Pres. & Chief Oper. Officer--Westcoast Energy Inc., Vancouver, Canada; *Int'l*, pg. 1492
Wills, Travers H., Chief Oper. Officer & Sr. Exec. V.P.--United HealthCare Corporation, Minnetonka, MN; *U.S. Public*, pg. 1677
Wilmore, Melvin A., Pres. & Chief Oper. Officer--Ross Stores, Inc., Newark, CA; *U.S. Public*, pg. 1405
Wilson, Al, Chief Oper. Officer & V.P.--Mylex Corporation, Fremont, CA; *U.S. Public*, pg. 1143
Wilson, C. Richard, Pres. & Chief Oper. Officer--Buckeye Partners, L.P., Allentown, PA; *U.S. Public*, pg. 266
Wilson, Darrell D., Pres. & Chief Oper. Officer--American Waste Services, Inc., Warren, OH; *U.S. Public*, pg. 94
Wilson, Dee, Mng. Dir.-Publications--John Fairfax Holdings Limited, Sydney, Australia; *Int'l*, pg. 477
Wilson, John, Grp. Pres. & Chief Oper. Officer-Transportation Sys. Grp.--Amtech Corporation, Dallas, TX; *U.S. Public*, pg. 105
Wilson, John, Chief Oper. Officer & Dir.--Hilton International Co., Coral Gables, FL; *Int'l*, pg. 787
Wilson, Martin D., Pres., Chief Oper. Officer & Sec.--D & K Healthcare Resources, Inc., Saint Louis, MO; *U.S. Public*, pg. 471
Wilson, Mike, Chief Exec.--J. Rothschild Assurance Holdings, Gloucester, United Kingdom; *Int'l*, pg. 1178
Wilson, Rich A., Chief Oper. Officer & Sr. V.P.--Ensco International Incorporated (ENSCO), Dallas, TX; *U.S. Public*, pg. 585
Wilson, Ron, Pres. & Chief Oper. Officer--Harrison Wilson & Associates, Parsippany, NJ; *U.S. Public*, pg. 1224
Wilson, Steven A., Pres. & Chief Oper. Officer--BASES Worldwide, Covington, KY; *U.S. Private*, pg. 120
Wiltshire, Dennis, Chief Oper. Officer & Exec. V.P.--Klosterman Baking Company, Inc., Cincinnati, OH; *U.S. Private*, pg. 626
Wilzig, Sherry, Chief Oper. Officer--Oil & Gas Operations, Oklahoma City, OK; *U.S. Public*, pg. 1770
Winch, John J., Pres.--The Minster Machine Company, Minster, OH; *U.S. Private*, pg. 751
Winer, Jonathan H., Chief Oper. Officer & V.P.--Mountain Energy, Inc., South Burlington, VT; *U.S. Public*, pg. 761
Winger, William, Chief Oper. Officer--Canada Alloy Castings, Ltd., Kitchener, Canada; *U.S. Public*, pg. 142
Winkler, Thomas R., Chief Oper. Officer & Exec. V.P.--BioWhittaker, Inc., Walkersville, MD; *U.S. Public*, pg. 297
Winkler, William F., Chief Oper. Officer, Treas. & Sec.--Ackerman McQueen, Inc., Oklahoma City, OK; *U.S. Private*, pg. 12
Winslow, Barry, Pres. & Chief Oper. Officer--Great Lakes Bancorp, Ann Arbor, MI; *U.S. Public*, pg. 1554
Winsnes, Arrita, Chief Oper. Officer--Akerlund & Rausing A/S, Drammen, Norway; *Int'l*, pg. 33
Winter, Raymond F., Pres. & Chief Oper. Officer--BIC Corporation, Milford, CT; *Int'l*, pg. 1273
Winter, William R., Jr., Pres. & Chief Oper. Officer--Williams Steel & Hardware Company, Minneapolis, MN; *U.S. Private*, pg. 1178
Wirta, Ray, Pres. & Chief Oper. Officer--Koll Co., Newport Beach, CA; *U.S. Private*, pg. 631
Wise, Ronald, Chief Oper. Officer--Continental Mills, Inc., Tukwila, WA; *U.S. Private*, pg. 269
Wiseman, I., Chief Oper. Officer--Bank Leumi (UK) PLC, Manchester, United Kingdom; *Int'l*, pg. 150
Wisneski, Joseph J., Pres. & Chief Oper. Officer--ERD Waste Corp., Commack, NY; *U.S. Public*, pg. 546
Wissler, Robert C., Pres. & Chief Oper. Officer--Comprehensive Business Services Inc., Mission Viejo, CA; *U.S. Private*, pg. 423
Witteveen, Raoul J., Pres., Chief Oper. Officer & Chief Fin. Officer--Interpool, Inc., Princeton, NJ; *U.S. Public*, pg. 908
Wolcott, Harold R., Exec. V.P. & Gen. Mgr.--Ballard Medical Products, Draper, UT; *U.S. Public*, pg. 171
Wolcott, Peter, Chief Oper. Officer & V.P.--Precision Resource Inc., Shelton, CT; *U.S. Private*, pg. 880
Woldrich, John D., Chief Oper. Officer & Exec. V.P.--Fair, Isaac and Company, Inc., San Rafael, CA; *U.S. Public*, pg. 609
Wolf, Gregory H., Pres. & Chief Oper. Officer--Humana Health Chicago, Inc., Chicago, IL; *U.S. Public*, pg. 847
Wolf, Gregory H., Pres. & Chief Oper. Officer--Employers Health Insurance Company, Green Bay, WI; *U.S. Public*, pg. 847
Wolf, Gregory H., Pres. & Chief Oper. Officer--Humana Health Plan of Alabama, Inc., Montgomery, AL; *U.S. Public*, pg. 848
Wolf, Gregory H., Pres. & Chief Oper. Officer--Humana Wisconsin Health Organization Insurance Corporation, Milwaukee, WI; *U.S. Public*, pg. 848
Wolf, Gregory H., Pres. & Chief Oper. Officer--Network EPO, Inc., Milwaukee, WI; *U.S. Public*, pg. 848
Wolf, Ken, Chief Oper. Officer--Burr-Brown Corporation, Tucson, AZ; *U.S. Public*, pg. 270
Wolfe, David, Chief Oper. Officer--The Vacation Store, Virginia Beach, VA; *U.S. Private*, pg. 649

Wolfe, Jonathan, Pres. & Chief Oper. Officer--Oshawa Foods, Mississauga, Canada; *Int'l*, pg. 1012
Wolfe, Jonathan A., Pres. & Chief Oper. Officer--The Oshawa Group Limited, Etobicoke, Canada; *Int'l*, pg. 1012
Wolfort, David A., Chief Oper. Officer--Olympic Steel Inc., Cleveland, OH; *U.S. Public*, pg. 1221
Wolpert, Michael, Grp. Pres. & Chief Oper. Officer-Cardkey Systems, Inc.--Amtech Corporation, Dallas, TX; *U.S. Public*, pg. 105
Won Bae, Park, Chief Oper. Officer--Union Polymer Co., Ltd., Chung Nam, Korea; *Int'l*, pg. 949
Wood, Donald S., Ph.D., V.P.-Science & Tech. & Chief Oper. Officer-Science Center Div.--IntegraMed America, Purchase, NY; *U.S. Public*, pg. 883
Wood, R. Ray, Chm. Bd., Pres., Chief Exec. & Oper. Officer--Rockford Products Corp., Rockford, IL; *U.S. Private*, pg. 938
Woodard, Jim, Chief Oper. Officer--Vaughan & Sons, Inc. Multi-Family Sales, Austin, TX; *U.S. Private*, pg. 1135
Woods, D., Chief Oper. Officer--Pall Mall Support Services Limited, London, United Kingdom; *Int'l*, pg. 385
Woods, James R., Pres. Chief Oper. Officer--SunBank Capital Management, N.A., Orlando, FL; *U.S. Public*, pg. 1537
Woodson, Glen, II, Pres. & Chief Oper. Officer--Crouch Supply Company, Inc., Fort Worth, TX; *U.S. Private*, pg. 291
Woodward, William, Chief Oper. Officer--Maxcor Manufacturing, Inc., Colorado Springs, CO; *U.S. Private*, pg. 716
Woolf, Robert W., Pres. & Chief Oper. Officer--Chemi-Trol Chemical Co., Gibsonburg, OH; *U.S. Public*, pg. 345
Wooten, Marvin, V.P. & Gen. Mgr.--Southco Distributing Company, Goldsboro, NC; *U.S. Private*, pg. 1014
Workman, David J., Pres. & Chief Oper. Officer--Ultimate Electronics, Thornton, CO; *U.S. Public*, pg. 1662
Worley, Morris T., Chief Oper. Officer & V.P.--Rayrock Yellowknife Resources Inc., Toronto, Canada; *Int'l*, pg. 1089
Worth, Maurice W., Chief Oper. Officer--Delta Air Lines, Inc., Atlanta, GA; *U.S. Public*, pg. 497
Wouters, Guido, Chief Oper. Officer--Brugge-Oostende Local Head Office, Brugge, Belgium; *Int'l*, pg. 147
Wray, Donald E., Pres. & Chief Oper. Officer--Tyson Foods, Inc., Springdale, AR; *U.S. Public*, pg. 1652
Wright, Connie, V.P. & Cashier--Colorado Business Bank, Denver, CO; *U.S. Private*, pg. 255
Wright, Felix E., Pres. & Chief Oper. Officer--Leggett & Platt, Incorporated, Carthage, MO; *U.S. Public*, pg. 985
Wright, Ian, Chief Oper. Officer--Sandusky Limited, Glenrothes, United Kingdom; *U.S. Private*, pg. 965
Wright, Larry M., Pres. & Chief Oper. Officer--Panaco, Inc., Kansas City, MO; *U.S. Public*, pg. 1255
Wright, P.J., Pres. & Chief Oper. Officer--Jefferson Smurfit Group p.l.c., Dublin, Ireland; *Int'l*, pg. 1269
Wright, Robert A., Pres. & Chief Oper. Officer--Amcor Capital Corporation, Coachella, CA; *U.S. Public*, pg. 64
Wright, Ron, Chief Oper. Officer & Exec. V.P.--C & S Wholesale Grocery Inc., Brattleboro, VT; *U.S. Private*, pg. 192
Wright, Russell D., Pres. & Chief Oper. Officer-Electric & Gas Division--Commonwealth Energy System, Cambridge, MA; *U.S. Public*, pg. 414
Wright, Russell D., Pres. & Chief Oper. Officer--Cambridge Electric Light Co., Cambridge, MA; *U.S. Public*, pg. 414
Wright, Russell D., Pres. & Chief Oper. Officer--Commonwealth Energy System, Electric Division, Cambridge, MA; *U.S. Public*, pg. 414
Wright, Russell D., Pres. & Chief Oper. Officer--Canal Electric Co., Cambridge, MA; *U.S. Public*, pg. 415
Wright, Russell D., Pres. & Chief Oper. Officer--Commonwealth Electric Co., Cambridge, MA; *U.S. Public*, pg. 415
Wright, Warren E., Chm Bd. & Chief Oper. Officer--Renosol Corp., Saline, MI; *U.S. Private*, pg. 922
Wrigley, William, Chm. Bd., Pres. & Chief Oper. Officer--Wm. Wrigley Jr. Company, Chicago, IL; *U.S. Public*, pg. 1781
Wruble, Brian F., Pres. & Chief Oper. Officer--Delaware Management Holdings, Inc., Philadelphia, PA; *U.S. Public*, pg. 997
Wu, C.L., Chief Oper. Officer--Thermalloy Ltd., Kowloon, Hong Kong; *Int'l*, pg. 209
Wu, Han Jan, Chief Oper. Officer--Tainan Spinning Co., Ltd., Tai-nan, Taiwan; *Int'l*, pg. 1347
Wyatt, Alan, Chief Oper. Officer--Neste Gas Ltd., London, United Kingdom; *Int'l*, pg. 915
Wyshynski, Mel, Chief Oper. Officer & Sr. V.P.--P.T. International Nickel Indonesia, Jakarta, Indonesia; *Int'l*, pg. 947
Yaeger, Douglas H., Pres. & Chief Oper. Officer--Laclede Gas Company, Saint Louis, MO; *U.S. Public*, pg. 973
Yager, William L., Pres. & Chief Oper. Officer--The Rival Company, Kansas City, MO; *U.S. Public*, pg. 1391
Yamada, Kunio, Chief Oper. Officer & Exec. V.P.--Rohto Pharmaceutical Co., Osaka, Japan; *Int'l*, pg. 1126
Yamaguchi, Kazumitsu, Chief Oper. Officer-Foodstuffs, Lumber & Gen. Merchandise--Nichimen Corporation, Tokyo, Japan; *Int'l*, pg. 927
Yamamoto, Kensei, Chief Oper. Officer--The Tokio Marine & Fire Insurance Company (U.K.) Limited, Paris, France; *Int'l*, pg. 1392
Yamamoto, Toshinori, Chief Oper. Officer--Tosoh Europe B.V., Amsterdam, Netherlands; *Int'l*, pg. 1408
Yancey, George F.T., Jr., Pres.--Perry's Ice Cream Co., Inc., Akron, NY; *U.S. Private*, pg. 855
Yano, Makoto, Chief Oper. Officer--Makita Korea Co., Ltd., Seoul, Korea; *Int'l*, pg. 832
Yanuklis, John, Chief Oper. Officer--Strober King Building Supply Centers, Inc., Congers, NY; *U.S. Private*, pg. 403
Yarborough, W. Glen, V.P.--Allied Research Corporation, Vienna, VA; *U.S. Public*, pg. 48
Yarossi, Paul A., Chief Oper. Officer& Sr. V.P.--HNTB Corporation, Kansas City, MO; *U.S. Private*, pg. 492
Yasuhara, Jiro, Chief Oper. Officer--Lamma Power Station Project Office, Tsim Tsa Tsui, Hong Kong; *Int'l*, pg. 943
Yasui, Shosaku, Pres. & Chief Oper. Officer--Teijin Limited, Osaka, Japan; *Int'l*, pg. 1362
Yazaki, Haruo, Chief Oper. Officer--Aiya Co., Ltd., Tokyo, Japan; *Int'l*, pg. 1262
Yemenidjian, Alex, Pres. & Chief Oper. & Fin. Officer--MGM Grand, Inc., Las Vegas, NV; *U.S. Public*, pg. 1026
Yew, Helen, Chief Oper. Officer--Royal Copenhagen (Hong Kong) Ltd., Hong Kong, Hong Kong; *Int'l*, pg. 1135
Yoder, Trevor, Chief Oper. Officer--Blue Marble Advanced Communications Group, New York, NY; *U.S. Private*, pg. 104
Yokana, Andre, Pres.--Sterling Davis Standard, South Plainfield, NJ; *Int'l*, pg. 1240
Yonemitsu, Keiichi, Chief Oper. Officer--Nippon Oil (Asia) Pte. Ltd., Singapore, Singapore; *Int'l*, pg. 937
Yoneyama, Reiji, Pres.--Chiyoda Mutual Life Insurance Company, Tokyo, Japan; *Int'l*, pg. 286
Yong Chuan, Edwin Lee, Chief Oper. Officer--Lee Kim Tah Holdings Ltd., Singapore, Singapore; *Int'l*, pg. 1346
York, Christopher, Chief Oper. Officer-West--Coram Healthcare Corporation, Denver, CO; *U.S. Public*, pg. 446
Yoshida, Mitsunobu, Chief Oper. Officer--TM Management Services Limited, London, United Kingdom; *Int'l*, pg. 1392
Yoshizawa, Masashi, Chief Oper. Officer--Nippon Oil Exploration U.S.A. Limited, Houston, TX; *Int'l*, pg. 937
Young, Fred C., Pres., Chief Oper. Officer, Treas. & Sec.--Black Box Corporation of PA, Lawrence, PA; *U.S. Public, pg. 235*
Young, James H., Chief Oper. Officer & Exec. V.P.--Reactive Metals & Alloys Corporation (REMACOR), West Pittsburg, PA; *U.S. Private*, pg. 913
Youngblood, Gary C., Pres. & Chief Oper. Officer--Alabama Gas Corporation, Birmingham, AL; *U.S. Public*, pg. 581
Yu, Quincy, Pres. & Chief Oper. Officer--Red Sky Interactive, San Francisco, CA; *U.S. Public*, pg. 1224
Yui, Akira, Pres., Chief Oper. Officer--Dentsu Burson Marsteller, Inc., New York, NY; *Int'l*, pg. 393
Zaagman, Michael E., V.P.-Opers.--Triple S Plastics, Inc., Vicksburg, MI; *U.S. Public*, pg. 1639
Zaccaria, Adrian, Pres. & Chief Oper. Officer--Bechtel Group, Inc., San Francisco, CA; *U.S. Private*, pg. 128
Zaheeruddin, M., Gen. Mgr.-ComTech--National Refinery Limited, Karachi, Pakistan; *Int'l*, pg. 909
Zaidi, S.K.A., Chief Oper. Officer--Novo Nordisk A/S, Karachi, Pakistan; *Int'l*, pg. 988
Zajos, Ferenc, Chief Oper. Officer--Gambro kft, Budapest, Hungary; *Int'l*, pg. 667
Zak, Robert M., Chief Oper. Officer--Merchants Group, Inc., Buffalo, NY; *U.S. Public*, pg. 1090
Zalka, Saul, Chief Oper. Officer--Sun City Industries, Inc., Fort Lauderdale, FL; *U.S. Public*, pg. 1529
Zaloker, Ante, Chief Oper. Officer--Novo Nordisk A/S, Ljubljana, Slovenia; *Int'l*, pg. 988
Zambonini, Ron, Pres. & Chief Oper. Officer--Cognos Corp., Burlington, MA; *Int'l*, pg. 306
Zampetis, Theodore K., Pres. & Chief Oper. Officer--The Standard Products Company, Dearborn, MI; *U.S. Public*, pg. 1504
Zantop, James M., Pres. & Chief Oper. Officer--Zantop International Airlines, Inc., Ypsilanti, MI; *U.S. Private*, pg. 1204
Zatina, Thomas, Chief Oper. Officer, Exec. V.P. & Asst. Sec.--Bozzuto's Inc., Cheshire, CT; *U.S. Public*, pg. 249
Zekger, Ronen, Chief Oper. Officer--Orbotech S.A., Europe, Brussels, Belgium; *Int'l*, pg. 1007
Zelinsky, Doris, Chief Oper. Officer--Country Home Bakery, Inc., Bridgeport, CT; *U.S. Private*, pg. 278
Zellers, C.F., Jr., Pres. & Chief Oper. Officer--Florida East Coast Industries Inc., Saint Augustine, FL; *U.S. Public*, pg. 1427
Zemenick, Carl A., Pres., Chief Exec. Officer & Chief Oper. Officer--GF Office Furniture Ltd., Gallatin, TN; *U.S. Private*, pg. 434
Zenk, Saul, Pres. & Treas.--Monico Alloys, Inc., Los Angeles, CA; *U.S. Private*, pg. 757
Zhou, Leo Yi Feng, Chief Oper. Officer--Hagglunds China Ltd., Shanghai, China; *Int'l*, pg. 670
Zicarelli, Jim, Chm. Bd., Chief Exec. Officer & Chief Oper. Officer--Cramer Inc., Kansas City, KS; *U.S. Private*, pg. 285
Zichlin, Sidney, Chief Oper. Officer & V.P.--Linzer Products Corp., Flushing, NY; *U.S. Private*, pg. 669
Ziegler, William T., Chief Oper. Officer.--Swisher International Group, Inc., Darien, CT; *U.S. Public*, pg. 1543
Zieky, Edward, Chief Oper. Officer--The General Building Supply Company, East Hartford, CT; *U.S. Private*, pg. 403
Zieky, Eliott, Chief Oper. Officer--The General Building Supply Company, East Hartford, CT; *U.S. Private*, pg. 403
Ziering, Michael, Pres. & Chief Oper. Officer--Diagnostic Products Corporation, Los Angeles, CA; *U.S. Public*, pg. 505
Zigrossi, Norman A., Chief Admin. Officer--Tennessee Valley Authority, Knoxville, TN; *U.S. Public*, pg. 1580
Zimm, John, Chief Oper. Officer--G B Stores, Columbus, OH; *U.S. Private*, pg. 972
Zimmerli, Kurt, Chm. Bd., Pres., & Chief Exec. Officer--Zima Corporation, Spartanburg, SC; *U.S. Private*, pg. 637
Zimmic, Tom, Dir.-Bakery Opers.--Grocers Baking Co., Grand Rapids, MI; *U.S. Private*, pg. 482
Zinger, Doron, Chief Oper. Officer & Sr. V.P.--ECI Telecom Ltd., Petah Tiqwa, Israel; *Int'l*, pg. 643
Zolinski, Ned, Chief Oper. Officer--Knurr USA East, Blythewood, SC; *Int'l*, pg. 739
Zook, Dennis R., Chief Oper. Officer & Exec. V.P.-S. Div. & Mexico--Costco Wholesale, Issaquah, WA; *U.S. Public*, pg. 451
Zoss, Howard A., Chief Oper. Officer--Wyse Advertising, Cleveland, OH; *U.S. Private*, pg. 1193
Zoss, Howard A., Chief Oper. Officer--Wyse Advertising/ Cleveland, Cleveland, OH; *U.S. Private*, pg. 1194
Zullig, Weiner, Chief Oper. Officer--CAP Gemini Suisse, Geneva, Switzerland; *Int'l*, pg. 264
Zundel, Randy, Chief Fin. Officer & V.P.--OEC Medical Systems, Inc., Salt Lake City, UT; *U.S. Public*, pg. 1207
Zuppe, William W., Pres. & Chief Oper. Officer--Sterling Financial Corporation, Spokane, WA; *U.S. Public*, pg. 1516
ZurSchmiede, Thomas, Pres. & Chief Oper. Officer--Federal Screw Works, Detroit, MI; *U.S. Public*, pg. 616
ZurSchmiede, W.T., Jr., Chm. Bd., Chief Exec. & Chief Fin. Officer--Federal Screw Works, Detroit, MI; *U.S. Public*, pg. 616
Zuther, Ingo A., Dr., Chief Oper. Officer--AdvoCard Rechtsschutzversicherung AG, Hamburg, Germany; *Int'l*, pg. 15
Zwyssig, Markus, Chief Oper. Officer--BHF-BANK (Switzerland) Ltd., Zurich, Switzerland; *Int'l*, pg. 119

CONTROLLER

Aba, George, V.P. & Controller--Fortune Fashion Inc., City of Commerce, CA; *U.S. Private*, pg. 419
Abad, Jose, Controller & Gen. Mgr.--AEP Industries Packaging Espana, S.A., Alicante, Spain; *U.S. Public*, pg. 5
Abajian, Karen, Controller--Imperial Bancorp, Inglewood, CA; *U.S. Public*, pg. 871
Abajian, Ted, Controller--Summit Family Restaurants, Inc., Salt Lake City, UT; *U.S. Public*, pg. 278
Abatemarco, Michael J., Sr. Mng. Dir., Controller & Asst. Sec.--The Bear Stearns Companies Inc., New York, NY; *U.S. Public*, pg. 197
Abbomonte, Patricia, Controller--TBAC - Prince Gardner, Inc., Arlington, TX; *U.S. Public*, pg. 1560
Abbott, Bradley S., Controller--Omnicare, Inc., Covington, KY; *U.S. Public*, pg. 1223
Abbott, Mike, Controller--Prince Sports Group Inc., Bordentown, NJ; *U.S. Private*, pg. 884
Abbott, Richard, Controller--Allied Plywood Corporation, Concord, MA; *U.S. Public*, pg. 1193
Abbott, William R., Controller--Newport Corporation, Irvine, CA; *U.S. Public*, pg. 1179
Abele, Michael, Controller--Scott Specialty Gases, Plumsteadville, PA; *U.S. Private*, pg. 977
Abels, Wedge, Controller--American City Business Journals, Inc., Charlotte, NC; *U.S. Private*, pg. 19
Aberasturi, Paul, Chief Fin. Officer--Amicale Industries, Inc., New York, NY; *U.S. Private*, pg. 66
Aberdeen, Jeffery, Controller--Commerce Bancshares, Inc., Kansas City, MO; *U.S. Public*, pg. 409
Ables, Thomas, Treas.--The W.W. Williams Company, Columbus, OH; *U.S. Private*, pg. 1178
Aboussafy, Morley, Controller--Weyerhaeuser Canada Ltd., Kamloops, Canada; *U.S. Public*, pg. 1764
Abrahamsen, Patricia, Controller--Aerco International Inc., Northvale, NJ; *U.S. Private*, pg. 23
Abramsky, Rochelle, Controller--Lander Co., Inc., Englewood, NJ; *U.S. Private*, pg. 647
Achs, Donna M., Controller--Charmilles Technologies Corp., Lincolnshire, IL; *Int'l*, pg. 489
Achwarizmi, D., Controller & Dir.-Fin.--Hoogovens Aluminium BV, Amstelveen, Netherlands; *Int'l*, pg. 753
Ackart, Jennifer C., Controller--Raymond James Financial, Inc., Saint Petersburg, FL; *U.S. Public*, pg. 923
Ackerman, Charles, Controller--Grant Geophysical Inc., Houston, TX; *U.S. Private*, pg. 470
Ackerman, Charles, V.P. & Corp. Controller--Veritas DGC Inc, Houston, TX; *U.S. Private*, pg. 1136
Ackerman, Mark B., Comptroller--Massmutual Corporate Investors, Springfield, MA; *U.S. Public*, pg. 1055
Ackerman, Steve, Controller--Save Mart Supermarkets, Modesto, CA; *U.S. Private*, pg. 968
Ackerman, Wayne, Controller--Rapid Industrial Plastics Company, Jersey City, NJ; *U.S. Private*, pg. 910
Acolt, Dennis, V.P. & Controller--Clark Refining & Marketing Inc., Saint Louis, MO; *U.S. Private*, pg. 243
Acosta, Efrain, Controller--W & S Distributors, Inc., Bayamon, PR; *Int'l*, pg. 132
Acri, Robert, Controller & Treas.--Tribune Review Publishing Co., Greensburg, PA; *U.S. Private*, pg. 1102
Adam, Judy, Corp. Controller--WIC Western International Communications Ltd., Vancouver, Canada; *Int'l*, pg. 1481
Adams, Andrew, Controller--Minorco, Luxembourg, Luxembourg; *Int'l*, pg. 77
Adams, Barbara, Controller--Boscarale/Tom Togs, New York, NY; *U.S. Private*, pg. 160
Adams, Bruce, Controller--The Springwall Mattress Co., Akron, OH; *U.S. Private*, pg. 973
Adams, Daryl B., Chief Acctg. Officer, V.P. & Controller--Ladd Furniture, Inc., Greensboro, NC; *U.S. Public*, pg. 974
Adams, Firgal, Controller--McGraw-Hill Book Co. Australia Pty. Ltd., Roseville, Australia; *U.S. Public*, pg. 1072
Adams, Jeff, Controller-RTR Div.--Aaron Rents, Inc., Atlanta, GA; *U.S. Public*, pg. 12
Adams, John, Controller--Diehl Machines, Wabash, IN; *U.S. Public*, pg. 944
Adams, Julie, V.P. & Controller--Bally Total Fitness Corporation, Chicago, IL; *U.S. Public*, pg. 171
Adams, Kevin, V.P., Controller--Restaura, Inc., Phoenix, AZ; *U.S. Public*, pg. 1718
Adams, Paul, Controller--Western Gas Resources, Inc., Denver, CO; *U.S. Public*, pg. 1758
Adams, Steve, Controller--Nana Regional Corporation, Inc., Anchorage, AK; *U.S. Private*, pg. 774
Adams, Tanya, Controller--Costa Cruise Lines, N.V., Miami, FL; *U.S. Private*, pg. 278

Adamson, Duncan, Controller--Braun Canada Ltd., Mississauga, Canada; *U.S. Public*, pg. 744

Adamson, Marilyn, Controller--Lodestar Energy Inc., Lexington, KY; *U.S. Private*, pg. 672

Adamsville, Card, Controller--IA Construction Corp., Concordville, PA; *U.S. Private*, pg. 552

Adase, Steve, Controller--Alpha Metals, Inc., Jersey City, NJ; *Int'l*, pg. 328

Adcock, Dennis, Controller--Standard Candy Co., Inc., Nashville, TN; *U.S. Private*, pg. 1030

Addison, J.E., Controller--MPX Systems, Inc., Cayce, SC; *U.S. Public*, pg. 1436

Addison, Jimmy E., V.P. & Controller--South Carolina Electric & Gas Co. (SCE&G), Columbia, SC; *U.S. Public*, pg. 1436

Addison, Siegrid, Controller--Daniel Caron Sportswear, New York, NY; *U.S. Private*, pg. 309

Adelhardt, Joseph W., V.P. & Controller--Pathmark Stores Incorporated, Woodbridge, NJ; *U.S. Private*, pg. 843

Adelizzi, Rob, Comptroller--Frank W. Winne & Son, Inc., Philadelphia, PA; *U.S. Private*, pg. 1183

Adelt, Bruno, Controller--Volkswagen AG, Wolfsburg, Germany; *Int'l*, pg. 1473

Adfahl, James, Controller--National Computer Systems, Eden Prairie, MN; *U.S. Public*, pg. 1155

Adkins, Craig, Controller--Creative Publications, Mountain View, CA; *U.S. Private*, pg. 288

Adkins, Deborah, V.P. & Controller--Recoton Corporation, Lake Mary, FL; *U.S. Public*, pg. 1369

Adler, Tracy, Controller--New Line Cinema Corporation, New York, NY; *U.S. Public*, pg. 1614

Adloff, Richard C., Corp. V.P. & Controller--Allegiance Healthcare Corp., McGaw Park, IL; *U.S. Public*, pg. 44

Admirand, Peter, Controller & Sec.--Western Beef, Inc., Ridgewood, NY; *U.S. Public*, pg. 1758

Adornetto, David, Controller--Mentor Urology, Inc., Santa Barbara, CA; *U.S. Public*, pg. 1086

Adornetto, John, V.P. & Controller--Dixon Ticonderoga Company, Heathrow, FL; *U.S. Public*, pg. 514

Adrian, Jerry, Controller--Vulcraft Div., Fort Payne, AL; *U.S. Public*, pg. 1206

Adrian, Nancy, Controller--Toastmaster, Inc., Columbia, MO; *U.S. Public*, pg. 1619

Adrian, Patricia M., Controller--Sivyer Steel Corporation, Bettendorf, IA; *U.S. Private*, pg. 1008

Aelvoet, Patrick, V.P.-Acctg. & Controller--USLD Communications Corp., San Antonio, TX; *U.S. Public*, pg. 969

Agarwald, Ramakant, Controller--Windsor Art, Inc., Pico Rivera, CA; *U.S. Public*, pg. 212

Agee, Lloyd, Controller--B&B Molders, Mishawaka, IN; *U.S. Private*, pg. 105

Aghdami, Amanda N., Controller--The Pittston Company, Glen Allen, VA; *U.S. Public*, pg. 1305

Agnell, Bill, Controller--Reynen, Bardis & Winn, Sacramento, CA; *U.S. Private*, pg. 926

Ahearn, Michael J., Controller & Treas.--C.R. Daniels, Inc., Ellicott City, MD; *U.S. Private*, pg. 310

Ahern, John R., Controller-Comml. Analysis & Support--The Lubrizol Corporation, Wickliffe, OH; *U.S. Public*, pg. 1016

Ahlgrimm, Marijo, Sr. V.P. & Controller--ICF Kaiser International Inc., Fairfax, VA; *U.S. Public*, pg. 852

Ahrens, Cheryl, Controller--Grant Thornton LLP, Chicago, IL; *U.S. Private*, pg. 470

Aielli, Joseph, V.P. & Controller--Tombstone Pizza Corporation, Northfield, IL; *U.S. Public*, pg. 1288

Aird, Joseph, V.P. & Controller--General Cigar Holdings Inc, New York, NY; *U.S. Public*, pg. 707

Aisenberg, Bill, Controller--Pinnacle Brands, Inc., Dallas, TX; *U.S. Private*, pg. 866

Aizawa, Hiroshi, Chief Fin. Officer & Div. Mgr.--Sumitomo Bank of California, San Francisco, CA; *Int'l*, pg. 1309

Akkerman, Rich, Controller--Johnson Brothers Wholesale Liquor, Saint Paul, MN; *U.S. Private*, pg. 591

Akman, Tash, Corp. Controller--Champion Parts, Inc., Glen Ellyn, IL; *U.S. Public*, pg. 334

Al-Dukhaikh, M.A., Controller & Dir.-Fin.--Al-Jubail Petrochemical Company, Tareet, Saudi Arabia; *U.S. Public*, pg. 601

Albak, Ozcan, Fin. Controller--Bilar Bilgi Araclari Ticaret A.S., Istanbul, Turkey; *Int'l*, pg. 1115

Albanese, Angel, Controller--Prepress Solutions, Inc., Billerica, MA; *U.S. Private*, pg. 882

Albano, Peter, Controller--Edwin B. Stimpson Company, Inc., Bayport, NY; *U.S. Private*, pg. 1043

Alberici, Joseph, Controller--Softmart, Inc., Downingtown, PA; *U.S. Private*, pg. 1012

Alberston, Evie, Controller--The Arnold Agency, Richmond, VA; *U.S. Private*, pg. 84

Albert, Yvan, V.P.-Fin. & Controller--Security Chimneys International Ltd., Laval, Canada; *Int'l*, pg. 1217

Alberts, David E., V.P. & Controller--G.E. Johnson Construction Co., Inc., Colorado Springs, CO; *U.S. Private*, pg. 591

Alberts, Edward P., Sr. V.P.-Fin. & Controller--Fiserv, Inc., Brookfield, WI; *U.S. Public*, pg. 647

Albrecht, Gene, Controller--Omega World Travel, Inc., Fairfax, VA; *U.S. Private*, pg. 816

Albrecht, Jerry, Controller--Lynch Manufacturing Corporation, Greenwich, CT; *U.S. Public*, pg. 1022

Albrechtsen, Brad, Controller--National R.V., Inc., Perris, CA; *U.S. Public*, pg. 1159

Alcon, Mary Ann, Dir.-Fin.--TCI International Inc., Sunnyvale, CA; *U.S. Public*, pg. 1555

Alcorn, William J., V.P. & Controller--JC Penney Company, Inc., Plano, TX; *U.S. Public*, pg. 916

Aldridge, Joseph, Controller--Gifford-Hill Company, Dallas, TX; *Int'l*, pg. 593

Aleman, Whilma, Controller--The Beverage Source, Inc., Los Angeles, CA; *U.S. Public*, pg. 591

Ales, S.J., Sec. & Controller--Brock-McVey Company, Lexington, KY; *U.S. Private*, pg. 721

Alesia, Steve, Controller--Hurco Companies, Inc., Indianapolis, IN; *U.S. Public*, pg. 850

Alestam, Jan, Controller--Esselte AB, Solna, Sweden; *Int'l*, pg. 459

Alexander, Glenn J., Controller--Blonder-Tongue Laboratories, Inc., Old Bridge, NJ; *U.S. Public*, pg. 237

Alexander, Lynette, Controller--John Burnham & Co., San Diego, CA; *U.S. Private*, pg. 186

Alfano, Sam, Corp. Controller--Wolverine Tube Inc., Huntsville, AL; *U.S. Public*, pg. 1774

Alford, Terri L., Asst. Controller--Tyler Corporation, Dallas, TX; *U.S. Public*, pg. 1651

Alfson, Craig H., Controller--Malcolm Pirnie, Inc., White Plains, NY; *U.S. Private*, pg. 867

Algero, Pete, Jr., Controller--Consolidated Companies Inc. (CONCO), Metairie, LA; *U.S. Private*, pg. 265

Ali, Sadiq, Fin. Controller--Manhattan Pakistan (Private) Limited, Karachi, Pakistan; *U.S. Private*, pg. 186

Alianiello, Rocco, Controller--Sky Bros. Inc., Altoona, PA; *U.S. Public*, pg. 918

Alkins, Christine, Asst. V.P. & Controller--Moyer Packing Company, Souderton, PA; *U.S. Private*, pg. 765

Allchin, Steven J., Corp. Controller & Asst. Treas.--Stanley Consultants, Inc., Muscatine, IA; *U.S. Private*, pg. 1033

Alldian, David, V.P. & Controller--Blue Tee Corporation, New York, NY; *U.S. Private*, pg. 153

Alleman, Raymond H., V.P. & Controller--First State Insurance Company, Boston, MA; *U.S. Public*, pg. 794

Alleman, Raymond H., V.P. & Controller--New England Insurance Company, Boston, MA; *U.S. Public*, pg. 794

Allen, Don, Controller--Patsy's, Inc., Concord, NH; *U.S. Private*, pg. 843

Allen, Gary, Controller & Sec.--Wagnerware Corporation, Sidney, OH; *U.S. Private*, pg. 1146

Allen, John, Controller--Perry Equipment Corporation, Mineral Wells, TX; *U.S. Private*, pg. 855

Allen, Kari A., Dir.-Acctg. & Asst. Controller--USLD Communications Corp., San Antonio, TX; *U.S. Public*, pg. 969

Allen, Mark, Controller--Ziegler Inc., Minneapolis, MN; *U.S. Private*, pg. 1205

Allen, Patricia, Controller--Alkeremes, Cambridge, MA; *U.S. Public*, pg. 41

Allen, Robert A., Controller & Treas.--Skeena Cellulose Inc., Vancouver, Canada; *Int'l*, pg. 1261

Allen, Roger C., Controller--Santa Anita Enterprises, Inc., Arcadia, CA; *U.S. Public*, pg. 1081

Allen, Tom, V.P. & Corp. Controller--Bantam Doubleday Dell Publishing Group, Inc., New York, NY; *Int'l*, pg. 191

Alley, Ralph L., Sr. V.P., Controller & Treas.--CNB Bancshares, Inc., Evansville, IN; *U.S. Public*, pg. 280

Alley, Ralph L., Controller--Citizens National Bank, Evansville, IN; *U.S. Public*, pg. 281

Allison, Bob, V.P.-Fin. & Admin.--Allison-Erwin Co. Inc., Charlotte, NC; *U.S. Private*, pg. 41

Allison, Terry, V.P. & Controller--Quorum Health Group, Inc., Brentwood, TN; *U.S. Public*, pg. 1353

Allmendinger, Bruno, Deputy Treas. & Controller--Sulzer Ltd., Winterthur, Switzerland; *Int'l*, pg. 1305

Allred, John, Controller--Beehive Machinery Co., Sandy, UT; *U.S. Private*, pg. 1160

Allred, John A., Controller--Weiler & Company, Inc., Whitewater, WI; *U.S. Private*, pg. 1160

Allsop, Roger, Controller--Horsehead Resource Development Company, Inc., Palmerton, PA; *U.S. Private*, pg. 540

Almario, Dimingo, Controller--Premier Metal Products, Fontana, CA; *U.S. Private*, pg. 881

Almeida, Isabel, Exec. V.P.--Banco Espirito Santo e Comercial de Lisboa SA, Lisbon, Portugal; *Int'l*, pg. 142

Alstadt, Steven W., Chief Acctg. Officer & Controller--Furniture Brands International Inc., Saint Louis, MO; *U.S. Public*, pg. 688

Altavilla, Peter T., Controller & Sec.--Applied Magnetics Corporation, Goleta, CA; *U.S. Public*, pg. 123

Altenbaumer, Larry F., Chief Fin. Officer, Controller & Treas.--Illinova Inc., Decatur, IL; *U.S. Public*, pg. 869

Altergott, Kurt, Controller--Kaufman and Broad New Mexico Division, Albuquerque, NM; *U.S. Public*, pg. 945

Althoff, Larry, Controller--Van Kampen/American Capital Inc., Oak Brook Terrace, IL; *U.S. Public*, pg. 1132

Altmaier, Chris, Controller & Treas.--Southern Belle Dairy Company, Somerset, KY; *U.S. Private*, pg. 1015

Altman, Annemarie, Controller-N. America--Instron Corporation, Canton, MA; *U.S. Public*, pg. 882

Alvarez, Leslie, V.P. & Controller--Vanstar Corporation, Pleasanton, CA; *U.S. Public*, pg. 1708

Alverez, Jose, Controller--Timesavers Inc., Crystal, MN; *U.S. Private*, pg. 1088

Amaral, Angel M., V.P. & Controller--Puerto Rican Cement Co., Inc., Guaynabo, PR; *U.S. Public*, pg. 1341

Amato, Michael, Controller--Trelleborg-Boliden, Stamford, CT; *Int'l*, pg. 1423

Amato, Robert T., V.P. & Controller--Gap Stores Division, San Bruno, CA; *U.S. Public*, pg. 702

Amaturo, Ciro, V.P. & Controller--Fischbach & Moore, Inc., New York, NY; *U.S. Public*, pg. 84

Ambrose, Peter, Controller--Ford Motor Norge A/S, Kolbotn, Norway; *U.S. Public*, pg. 666

Ameen, Philip D., V.P. & Comptroller--General Electric Company, Fairfield, CT; *U.S. Public*, pg. 709

Ames, Kevin, Sr. V.P. & Controller--Bank of the West, Walnut Creek, CA; *Int'l*, pg. 163

Ametrano, Carmen, Controller & Office Mgr.--Ritter Bros., Inc., Harrisburg, PA; *U.S. Private*, pg. 933

Amory, Robert F., V.P. & Controller--American Financial Group, Cincinnati, OH; *U.S. Public*, pg. 75

Amspacher, Richard, V.P.-Fin. & Controller--Topflight Corp., York, PA; *U.S. Private*, pg. 1091

Amundson, Bille, Controller--Programmed Composites, Inc., Anaheim, CA; *U.S. Private*, pg. 882

An, Sung Yun, Fin. Controller--Grand Hyatt Seoul, Seoul, Korea; *U.S. Private*, pg. 551

Anacker, Tom, Controller--Varity Zecal, Churchville, NY; *Int'l*, pg. 820

Anastasio, Stephen, Corp. Controller--Value Line, Inc., New York, NY; *U.S. Private*, pg. 137

Andersen, Rolf, V.P. & Controller--Northwest Airlines, Inc., Saint Paul, MN; *U.S. Public*, pg. 1200

Anderskow, David, Chief Fin. Officer, Controller & Treas.--Power Contracting & Engineering Corp., Schaumburg, IL; *U.S. Private*, pg. 877

Anderson, Al, V.P.-Fin.--Dreis & Krump Manufacturing Company, Chicago, IL; *U.S. Private*, pg. 342

Anderson, B., Controller--LucasVarity plc, London, United Kingdom; *Int'l*, pg. 819

Anderson, Bill, Controller--Bel Air Markets, West Sacramento, CA; *U.S. Private*, pg. 908

Anderson, Brian P., Controller--Baxter Healthcare Corporation, Deerfield, IL; *U.S. Public*, pg. 196

Anderson, Cathy L., Controller--Key Production Company, Inc., Denver, CO; *U.S. Public*, pg. 953

Anderson, Crystal, Controller--Chicago Machine Tool Company, Elk Grove Village, IL; *U.S. Private*, pg. 235

Anderson, D., Controller--Becker Milk Co. Ltd., Scarborough, Canada; *Int'l*, pg. 182

Anderson, Dave, Controller--Reliable Chevrolet, Richardson, TX; *U.S. Private*, pg. 920

Anderson, David S., Sr. V.P. & Controller--Citizens Savings Bank, Providence, RI; *Int'l*, pg. 1132

Anderson, Debbie, Controller--Gilrichco, Inc., Oxnard, CA; *U.S. Private*, pg. 454

Anderson, Donald W., Sec. & Controller--Interferon Sciences, Inc., New Brunswick, NJ; *U.S. Public*, pg. 694

Anderson, G.D., Controller--J.M. Huber, Calcium Carbonate Division, Quincy, IL; *U.S. Private*, pg. 545

Anderson, Gail, Controller--Catalina Yachts, Inc., Woodland Hills, CA; *U.S. Private*, pg. 219

Anderson, Garn, Controller & Sec.--Superior Industries International, Inc., Van Nuys, CA; *U.S. Public*, pg. 1539

Anderson, Gunnar, Controller--Clements Foods Co., Oklahoma City, OK; *U.S. Private*, pg. 245

Anderson, James, V.P. & Controller--American Furniture Company, Incorporated, Martinsville, VA; *U.S. Public*, pg. 974

Anderson, Jessica, Controller--California Offset Printers, Inc., Glendale, CA; *U.S. Private*, pg. 196

Anderson, Joanne, Controller--Bell Flavors & Fragrances, Northbrook, IL; *U.S. Private*, pg. 131

Anderson, Joseph A., V.P. & Controller--McCormick & Company, Incorporated, Sparks, MD; *U.S. Public*, pg. 1066

Anderson, Judy, Asst. Controller--Body Shop of America, Jacksonville, FL; *U.S. Private*, pg. 154

Anderson, Larry, Asst. Controller--Quantum Media International, Inc., New York, NY; *U.S. Private*, pg. 899

Anderson, Linda, Controller--Erie Plastics, Corry, PA; *U.S. Private*, pg. 381

Anderson, Mark L., Controller--Horizon Bancorp, Inc., Beckley, WV; *U.S. Public*, pg. 836

Anderson, Marvin R., Sr. V.P. & Controller--AMCORE Trust Company, Rockford, IL; *U.S. Public*, pg. 65

Anderson, Paul R., Controller & Principal Acctg. Officer--DPL Inc., Dayton, OH; *U.S. Public*, pg. 473

Anderson, Paul R., Controller--Dayton Power & Light Co., Dayton, OH; *U.S. Public*, pg. 473

Anderson, Richard, Controller--The Chesapeake Life Insurance Co., Oklahoma City, OK; *U.S. Public*, pg. 1679

Anderson, Robert, Controller--Ocean Spray Cranberries-Bordentown Plant, Bordentown, NJ; *U.S. Private*, pg. 811

Anderson, Robert W., Controller, Treas. & Sec.--Superior Oil Co. Inc., Indianapolis, IN; *U.S. Private*, pg. 1055

Anderson, Sandra M., V.P., Controller & Treas.--Quemetco, Inc., Dallas, TX; *U.S. Private*, pg. 900

Anderson, Sandra M., Controller--Quemetco Metals Limited, Inc., Dallas, TX; *U.S. Private*, pg. 900

Anderson, Scott, Controller--Kalmbach Publishing Co., Waukesha, WI; *U.S. Private*, pg. 606

Anderson, Shirley R., C.P.A., Controller--Sholodge, Inc., Hendersonville, TN; *U.S. Public*, pg. 1467

Anderson, Steve, Controller--Gage Marketing Group, Minneapolis, MN; *U.S. Private*, pg. 437

Anderson, William T., V.P. & Controller--Cabot Corporation, Boston, MA; *U.S. Public*, pg. 288

Anderson, William T., Asst. Controller--Cabot Corporation, Boston, MA; *U.S. Public*, pg. 288

Andre, Charles M., Chief Fin. Officer & Controller--Lumber Group Inc., Dothan, AL; *U.S. Private*, pg. 680

Andrea, Gwen, Controller--A.L. Hansen Manufacturing Co., Waukegan, IL; *U.S. Private*, pg. 500

Andreacci, John J., V.P. & Controller--Duro-Lite International, Fairfield, NJ; *U.S. Private*, pg. 349

Andreacci, John J., V.P. & Corp. Controller--Duro-Test Corporation, Fairfield, NJ; *U.S. Private*, pg. 349

Andrews, B.M., V.P. & Controller--Canadian Western Natural Gas Company Limited, Calgary, Canada; *Int'l*, pg. 95

Andrews, Bruce, Controller--First Electric Cooperative, Corp., Jacksonville, AR; *U.S. Private*, pg. 407

Andrews, Mary Lou, Controller--IKG Industries, Clark, NJ; *U.S. Public*, pg. 793

Andrews, R.D., Controller--Redland PLC, Reigate, United Kingdom; *Int'l*, pg. 1090

Andrews, Robert J., Controller--Essex Chemical Corporation, Clifton, NJ; *U.S. Public*, pg. 523

Andrews, William C., V.P. & Controller--Rohm and Haas Company, Philadelphia, PA; *U.S. Public*, pg. 1403

Andritz, Thomas, Controller--Fort Pitt Acquisitions, Inc., Coraopolis, PA; *U.S. Private*, pg. 419

Anesh, Jim, Controller--Eager Beaver, Lake Wales, FL; *U.S. Private*, pg. 354

Angart, Paul, Controller--Blue Coral/Slick 50, Cleveland, OH; *U.S. Public*, pg. 1348

Angelini, Carlo Giuseppe, Dir.-Budget & Controller--Istituto Mobiliare Italiano, Rome, Italy; *Int'l*, pg. 692

Angelo, William M., Controller--Coachmen Industries, Inc., Elkhart, IN; *U.S. Public*, pg. 387

Angelos, Thomas T., V.P. & Controller--Coeur D'Alene Mines Corporation, Coeur D'Alene, ID; *U.S. Public*, pg. 394
Anjolras, Gerard, Comptroller & Inspector Gen.--Electricite de France, Paris, France; *Int'l*, pg. 437
Annett, Michelle, Controller & Treas.--Peters Construction Corp., Waterloo, IA; *U.S. Private*, pg. 856
Anodide, Teri, V.P. & Controller--Kennedy-Wilson, Inc., Santa Monica, CA; *U.S. Public*, pg. 951
Anshus, Gregg, Chief Fin. Officer & Controller--Waters Instruments, Inc., Rochester, MN; *U.S. Public*, pg. 1745
Ansilio, Larry, Controller--SASIB Packaging North America, Skokie, IL; *Int'l*, pg. 1194
Ansley, Lawrence, V.P. & Controller--W.G. Carroll, Inc., Atlanta, GA; *U.S. Public*, pg. 1071
Anstett, William J., Controller--Silver State Disposal Service, Inc., Las Vegas, NV; *U.S. Public*, pg. 1380
Anthony, Bob, V.P. & Controller--Coherent, Inc., Santa Clara, CA; *U.S. Public*, pg. 395
Anthony, James M., Sr. Dir.-Plng. & Analysis--Checkers Drive-In Restaurants, Inc., Clearwater, FL; *U.S. Public*, pg. 342
Anthony, Susan, Asst. Controller--Electric Power Equipment Co., Columbus, OH; *U.S. Private*, pg. 368
Antion, Kathleen, Controller--Chartwell Partners, Los Angeles, CA; *U.S. Private*, pg. 230
Antwerp, Jana Van, V.P.-Acctg. Opers.--Greyhound Lines, Inc., Dallas, TX; *U.S. Public*, pg. 765
Aono, Sumi, Treas. & Sec.--Red Apple, Inc., Ontario, OR; *U.S. Private*, pg. 915
Appel, Bruce, Controller--Stagebill, New York, NY; *U.S. Public*, pg. 1328
Applegate, Henry M., III, Sr. V.P. & Controller--Mirage Resorts Incorporated, Las Vegas, NV; *U.S. Public*, pg. 1116
Appling, Laura, Controller--Sterling Software, Inc., Dallas, TX; *U.S. Public*, pg. 1516
Apuzzo, Joseph F., V.P.-Fin. & Controller--Terex Corporation, Westport, CT; *U.S. Public*, pg. 1581
Aquila, Susan, Chief Fin. Officer & Controller--Edmund Scientific Company, Barrington, NJ; *U.S. Private*, pg. 364
Aratoon, Cheryl, Comtroller--Tetra Tech NUS, Inc., Gaithersburg, MD; *U.S. Public*, pg. 1582
Arborio, Peter, Controller & Asst. Treas.--Dutchess Quarry & Supply Co. Inc., Pleasant Valley, NY; *U.S. Private*, pg. 350
Archard, Phillip, V.P. & Controller--Bridgeport Machines, Inc., Bridgeport, CT; *U.S. Public*, pg. 251
Archbold, Michael G., Asst. Controller--Woolworth Corporation, New York, NY; *U.S. Public*, pg. 1777
Archbold, Thomas G., Controller--United Capital Corp., Great Neck, NY; *U.S. Public*, pg. 1674
Archer, John, V.P. & Controller--Stanley Knight Corporation, New Troy, MI; *U.S. Private*, pg. 1033
Areson, George S., Controller--Rayonier New Zealand Limited, Auckland, New Zealand; *U.S. Public*, pg. 1363
Argentino, Tony, Controller--Squire-Cogswell Company, Gurnee, IL; *U.S. Private*, pg. 1027
Ariano, Martin G., Controller--Phelps Tointon Inc., Greeley, CO; *U.S. Private*, pg. 860
Ariaudo, Corrado, Controller--Olivetti SpA, Turin, Italy; *Int'l*, pg. 1002
Arlea, Michael N., Controller & Mgr.-Personnel--Cardinal Inc., Rahway, NJ; *U.S. Private*, pg. 208
Arling, Steve, Controller--Rich Products Corp., Buffalo, NY; *U.S. Private*, pg. 928
Arliskas, Leslie J., Controller--Helian Health Group, Inc., Monterey, CA; *U.S. Public*, pg. 1715
Armstrong, Bill, Controller--The Fremont Co., Fremont, OH; *U.S. Private*, pg. 426
Armstrong, Don, Controller--Engineer Control Intl., Elon College, NC; *U.S. Private*, pg. 376
Armstrong, H.S., Controller-Mktg.--General Motors of Canada Ltd., Oshawa, Canada; *U.S. Public*, pg. 722
Armstrong, Joan M., Controller--WTVF, Nashville, TN; *U.S. Private*, pg. 647
Arndt, Larry, Chief Fin. Officer, V.P.-Fin. & Controller--WEN Products, Inc., Bensenville, IL; *U.S. Private*, pg. 1144
Arner, Howard, Gen. Mgr. & Controller--SMI Miscellaneous, Cayce, SC; *U.S. Public*, pg. 412
Arnett, Lonnie A., V.P. & Controller--Bethlehem Steel Corporation, Bethlehem, PA; *U.S. Public*, pg. 226
Arnheim, Walter R., V.P. & Treas.--Mobil Oil Corporation, Fairfax, VA; *U.S. Public*, pg. 1118
Arno, Sue, Controller--Munck Automation Technology, Newport News, VA; *U.S. Private*, pg. 767
Arnold, Byron J., Controller--Embraco North America, Inc., Norcross, GA; *U.S. Public*, pg. 1765
Arnold, Byron J., Controller--GPD/Embraco North America, Inc., Norcross, GA; *U.S. Public*, pg. 1765
Arnold, Cherry, Controller--Service Packing Company-United Food Group, Los Angeles, CA; *U.S. Private*, pg. 986
Arnold, Mark S., V.P. & Controller--Sterling Plumbing Group, Inc., Rolling Meadows, IL; *U.S. Private*, pg. 630
Arnold, Michael J., Chief Admin. Officer & Sr. V.P.--Freeport-McMoRan Inc., New Orleans, LA; *U.S. Public*, pg. 680
Arnold, Michael J., V.P. & Controller-Opers.--Freeport-McMoRan Copper & Gold, Inc., New Orleans, LA; *U.S. Public*, pg. 680
Arnold, Richard, Chief Fin. Officer & Controller--Conway Corporation, Conway, AR; *U.S. Private*, pg. 272
Arnold, Thomas W., Corp. Controller--Sabreliner Corporation, Saint Louis, MO; *U.S. Private*, pg. 959
Arsenault, William, V.P. & Controller--Stackhouse Inc., Riverside, CA; *U.S. Public*, pg. 1591
Arsonneaud, F., Controller--Consortium Vinicole de Bordeaux et de la Gironde SA, Parempuyre, France; *Int'l*, pg. 752
Arterburn, Jim, V.P. & Controller--Sooner Pipe & Supply Corp., Tulsa, OK; *U.S. Private*, pg. 1014
Arth, Jerry, V.P.-Fin. & Admin., Controller & Treas.--Malco Products, Inc., Barberton, OH; *U.S. Private*, pg. 698
Arthur, Ray, Controller--General Signal Corporation, Stamford, CT; *U.S. Public*, pg. 726
Artis, Andre, Controller--Worrell Enterprises, Inc., Boca Raton, FL; *U.S. Private*, pg. 1191
Artz, Becky, Controller--Carolina Biological Supply Co., Burlington, NC; *U.S. Private*, pg. 213
Arvia, Mark, Controller--Bennett Brothers, Inc., Chicago, IL; *U.S. Private*, pg. 133
Arwine, Hilary A., Controller--Chemfab Corporation, Merrimack, NH; *U.S. Public*, pg. 344
Arzbaecher, Robert, Chief Fin. Officer--Applied Power Inc., Butler, WI; *U.S. Public*, pg. 124
Asai, Carl C., Controller--Timberline Software Corporation, Beaverton, OR; *U.S. Public*, pg. 1609
Asbury, Lisa, Controller-UKI--Dyersburg Corporation, Dyersburg, TN; *U.S. Public*, pg. 538
Asbury, Lisa, Controller--United Knitting, Inc., Cleveland, TN; *U.S. Public*, pg. 538
Asche, Ronald D., V.P.-Bus. Support, Controller & Treas.--Nebraska Public Power District, Columbus, NE; *U.S. Private*, pg. 789
Ash, Bob, Controller--Orr Safety Company, Louisville, KY; *U.S. Private*, pg. 820
Ashcraft, James, Comptroller--MD Pneumatics, Springfield, MO; *U.S. Private*, pg. 1111
Ashton, Carolyn, Controller--United Distributors, Inc., Smyrna, GA; *U.S. Private*, pg. 1121
Ashworth, Honey, Controller--KTI Fish, Houston, TX; *U.S. Private*, pg. 604
Aspinwall, Linda, Controller--Quaker City Motor Parts Company, Middletown, DE; *U.S. Private*, pg. 898
Aspinwall, Tom, Controller--American Strip Steel Inc., Kearny, NJ; *U.S. Private*, pg. 62
Assmus, Brian, Controller--Buttrey Food & Drug Company, Great Falls, MT; *U.S. Public*, pg. 271
Astrup, Tom, Controller--Midwest Agri-Commodities, Corte Madera, CA; *U.S. Private*, pg. 53
Atencio, Bonnie, Controller--American Furniture Company, Albuquerque, NM; *U.S. Private*, pg. 55
Athing, William, Controller--Quidel Corporation, San Diego, CA; *U.S. Public*, pg. 1352
Atienza, Corazon F., Asst. V.P. & Controller--EEI Corporation, Manila, Philippines; *Int'l*, pg. 425
Atsoff, Michael C., Controller--Genesee Corporation, Rochester, NY; *U.S. Public*, pg. 728
Aubuchon, Donat, Controller--W.E. Aubuchon Co., Inc., Westminster, MA; *U.S. Private*, pg. 98
Auchter, Gisela, Asst. Controller & Asst. Sec.--Semtech Corporation, Newbury Park, CA; *U.S. Public*, pg. 1456
Aucoin, Samuel A., Controller--Gasco, Inc., Honolulu, HI; *Int'l*, pg. 225
Audette, Stephanie D., Controller--Amtrak-National Railroad Passenger Corp., Washington, DC; *U.S. Private*, pg. 68
Aufdembrink, Loeta A., Comptroller--United Missouri Bank of Monett, Monett, MO; *U.S. Public*, pg. 1655
Auger, Mike, Controller--The Jel Sert Co., West Chicago, IL; *U.S. Private*, pg. 585
Augustine, Glenn, Controller--Eaton Corp., Supercharger Div., Athens, GA; *U.S. Public*, pg. 556
Augustine, Joseph L., V.P.-Opers. Controller--Gould Electronics Inc., Foil Division, Eastlake, OH; *U.S. Public*, pg. 1592
Aulen, Kenneth L., Admin. V.P. & Controller--Ashland, Inc., Russell, KY; *U.S. Public*, pg. 138
Ault, Frank H., V.P. & Controller--Enova Corp, San Diego, CA; *U.S. Public*, pg. 583
Ault, Frank H., V.P. & Controller--San Diego Gas & Electric Company, San Diego, CA; *U.S. Public*, pg. 584
Ault, John L., V.P. & Controller--The Sherwin-Williams Company, Cleveland, OH; *U.S. Public*, pg. 1465
Ausanka, John J., III, V.P. & Comptroller--The Record-Journal Publishing Company, Meriden, CT; *U.S. Private*, pg. 914
Austin, Gary S., V.P. & Controller--National City Corporation, Cleveland, OH; *U.S. Public*, pg. 1154
Austin, John D., Controller--Performance Food Group Company, Richmond, VA; *U.S. Public*, pg. 1278
Autry, Sharon, Controller-Sls. & Svcs.--Diagraph Corporation, Earth City, MO; *U.S. Private*, pg. 330
Avellino, Ann Marie, Sr. V.P. & Controller--Stackig Advertising and Public Relations, Mc Lean, VA; *U.S. Private*, pg. 1028
Avisse, Jean-Louis, Controller--Moulinex S.A., Bagnolet, France; *Int'l*, pg. 896
Avonwitz, Lee, Controller--The Monet Group, Inc., New York, NY; *U.S. Private*, pg. 757
Ayers, Michael R., V.P. & Controller--Thiokol Corporation, Ogden, UT; *U.S. Public*, pg. 1596
Azzinnari, Mariella, Controller--Baccardi-Martini Uruguay S.A., Montevideo, Uruguay; *U.S. Private*, pg. 109
Baarda, Cor, Sec. & Controller--Henkel Canada Ltd., Mississauga, Canada; *Int'l*, pg. 612
Babcock, Bill, Controller--Pedus Services, Inc., Los Angeles, CA; *U.S. Private*, pg. 846
Babcock, Gene, Controller--Beckman Instruments, Inc., Fullerton, CA; *U.S. Public*, pg. 199
Bacchioni, Victor, Controller--Medical Action Industries Inc., Hauppauge, NY; *U.S. Public*, pg. 1079
Bachman, G.E., Controller--Diamond Chain Company, Indianapolis, IN; *U.S. Private*, pg. 68
Bachman, George, Dir.-Acctg.--Florida Public Utilities Company, West Palm Beach, FL; *U.S. Public*, pg. 655
Bachmann, Mark R., V.P. & Controller--National Service Industries, Inc., Atlanta, GA; *U.S. Public*, pg. 1160
Bacile, Nick A., V.P. & Controller--Transcontinental Gas Pipe Line Corp., Houston, TX; *U.S. Public*, pg. 1769
Back, Tom, Controller--H S Die & Engineering, Inc., Grand Rapids, MI; *U.S. Private*, pg. 489
Backenson, Peter, Chief Fin. Officer & Controller--Phototype Color Graphics, Inc., Pennsauken, NJ; *U.S. Private*, pg. 864
Bacon, Carol L., Controller & Treas.--Town & Country Homes, Fort Worth, TX; *U.S. Public*, pg. 319
Bacon, Neil F., Chief Fin. Officer, Treas. & Controller--Homasote Company, Trenton, NJ; *U.S. Public*, pg. 831
Badke, John, Controller--Vicon Industries, Inc., Hauppauge, NY; *U.S. Public*, pg. 1719
Baemmert, Joe, Controller & Asst. Treas.--Green Bay Packaging Inc., Green Bay, WI; *U.S. Private*, pg. 476
Baer, Sara, Controller & Mgr.-Human Resources--Hood & Company, Hamburg, PA; *Int'l*, pg. 572
Baetens, Hedwig, Controller--Berlitz Schools of Languages B.V., Amsterdam, Netherlands; *U.S. Public*, pg. 222
Baetens, Hedwig, Controller--Berlitz Schools of Languages of Benelux S.A., Brussels, Belgium; *U.S. Public*, pg. 222
Baga, Louis, Controller--Restaurant Developers Corp., Independence, OH; *U.S. Private*, pg. 925
Baggett, Patrick C., Asst. Sec.--W.S. Badcock Corporation, Mulberry, FL; *U.S. Private*, pg. 109
Bagnal, Jayne, Controller--Sprott Oil Co., Inc., Manning, SC; *U.S. Private*, pg. 1027
Bahmueller, Steve, Controller--Hull Corporation, Hatboro, PA; *U.S. Private*, pg. 547
Baier, Daniel J., Controller--Rochester Gas And Electric Corporation, Rochester, NY; *U.S. Public*, pg. 1395
Bailey-Young, Karen, Controller--Parks LLC, Baltimore, MD; *U.S. Private*, pg. 840
Bailey, Cindy, Controller--KLLM Transport Services, Inc., Jackson, MS; *U.S. Public*, pg. 939
Bailey, John, V.P. & Corp. Controller--Bristol Hotels & Resorts, Dallas, TX; *U.S. Public*, pg. 253
Bailey, Paul J., Controller--CML Group, Inc., Acton, MA; *U.S. Public*, pg. 279
Bailey, Scott, Controller--NationsBank Sunwest, Inc., Albuquerque, NM; *U.S. Public*, pg. 1165
Bain, D.W., Treas. & Controller--Cyanamid Canada Inc., Markham, Canada; *U.S. Public*, pg. 80
Bain, Scott, Controller--Washers, Incorporated, Livonia, MI; *U.S. Private*, pg. 1152
Bain, Scott, Controller--Alpha Coatings, Livonia, MI; *U.S. Private*, pg. 1152
Bair, Clinton, Controller & Sec.--Republic Die & Tool Company, Belleville, MI; *U.S. Private*, pg. 923
Bair, Keith, Corp. Controller--Gencor Industries, Inc., Orlando, FL; *U.S. Public*, pg. 705
Bair, Keith S., Controller--Arrow International, Inc., Reading, PA; *U.S. Public*, pg. 135
Baird, Julie, Controller--Jackson Hole Ski Resort, Teton Village, WY; *U.S. Private*, pg. 579
Bajc, Stephen, Controller--Crown Crafts, Inc., Atlanta, GA; *U.S. Public*, pg. 465
Baker, Ben, Controller--Alamo Industrial Group, San Antonio, TX; *U.S. Private*, pg. 31
Baker, James E., V.P. & Controller--Apria Healthcare Group Inc., Costa Mesa, CA; *U.S. Public*, pg. 125
Baker, Michael, Controller--Tab Products Co., Palo Alto, CA; *U.S. Public*, pg. 1559
Baker, Richard A., Controller--Gorman-Rupp Industries Div., Bellville, OH; *U.S. Public*, pg. 754
Baker, Russell, Controller--Chattanooga Choo-Choo Holiday Inn, Chattanooga, TN; *U.S. Private*, pg. 231
Baker, Steven E., Controller--W.G. Mills, Inc., Sarasota, FL; *U.S. Private*, pg. 749
Baker, Tim, Controller--Mears Transportation Group, Orlando, FL; *U.S. Private*, pg. 726
Baker, Tom, Controller--Nakano Foods Inc., Arlington Heights, IL; *Int'l*, pg. 883
Baker, Tracy, Controller--The Royal China & Porcelain Companies Inc., Moorestown, NJ; *U.S. Private*, pg. 948
Baker, William G., Grp. V.P.-Admin. Services--HarperCollins Publishers, New York, NY; *Int'l*, pg. 926
Bakerman, Eve, Controller--Integra Technologies Corp., Waltham, MA; *U.S. Private*, pg. 565
Balaskovits, Kenneth S., V.P. & Controller--Peoples Energy Corporation, Chicago, IL; *U.S. Public*, pg. 1274
Balaskovits, Kenneth S., V.P. & Controller--Peoples Energy Services Corporation, Chicago, IL; *U.S. Public*, pg. 1275
Balcer, Brian, Treas. & Controller--Lyman Lumber Company, Excelsior, MN; *U.S. Private*, pg. 683
Balconi, Kathy, Controller--Griffin Bacal Inc., New York, NY; *U.S. Private*, pg. 480
Baldi, Alessandro, Controller--Alusuisse-Lonza Holding Ltd., Zurich, Switzerland; *Int'l*, pg. 66
Baldwin, Marie, Controller--AirTronics Co., Elgin, IL; *U.S. Public*, pg. 944
Baldwin, W.R., Controller--Reading & Bates Corporation, Houston, TX; *U.S. Public*, pg. 1354
Bales, Robert, Controller--Price/McNabb, Inc., Charlotte, NC; *U.S. Private*, pg. 883
Balk, Lavern, Controller--Don E. Williams Co., Rock Island, IL; *U.S. Private*, pg. 1177
Balkit, Daniel, Controller--Amkor Electronics, Inc., West Chester, PA; *U.S. Private*, pg. 66
Ball-Miller, Paris M., Sec., Controller & Treas.--Troyer Foods, Inc., Goshen, IN; *Int'l*, pg. 619
Ball, Bruce, Controller--Genesee Metal Stampings, Inc., West Henrietta, NY; *U.S. Private*, pg. 446
Ball, Bruce, Controller--Genesee A & B, Inc., Old Hickory, TN; *U.S. Private*, pg. 446
Ball, G.D., V.P. & Controller--Parsons Corporation, Pasadena, CA; *U.S. Private*, pg. 841
Ballan, Kenneth, Controller--Dexter Chemical Corp., Bronx, NY; *U.S. Private*, pg. 329
Ballew, Charles T., Asst. V.P. & Controller--USAA Buying Service, San Antonio, TX; *U.S. Private*, pg. 1114
Balsys, Raymond, V.P. & Controller--Parlux Fragrances Inc., Fort Lauderdale, FL; *U.S. Public*, pg. 1264
Baltes, John L., Jr., Controller--Central Louisiana Electric Company, Inc., Pineville, LA; *U.S. Public*, pg. 325
Baltz, Jeffrey D., Controller--Apex Oil Company, Inc., Saint Louis, MO; *U.S. Private*, pg. 77
Balzuweit, Herbert, Controller--EIS International Inc., Herndon, VA; *U.S. Public*, pg. 544
Bamberger, George, Controller--Par Enterprises, Inc., Wheeling, WV; *U.S. Private*, pg. 838
Banas, John, Controller--Sun Electric, Lincolnshire, IL; *U.S. Public*, pg. 1480

Banaszek, K.S., Controller--Eriez Magnetics, Erie, PA; *U.S. Private*, pg. 381
Banbury, J. Hunter, Treas.--Cone-Blanchard Machine Company, Windsor, VT; *U.S. Private*, pg. 262
Bancroft, Peter, Controller--The Connecticut Water Company, Clinton, CT; *U.S. Public*, pg. 431
Bancroft, Peter J., Controller & Asst. Treas.--Connecticut Water Service, Inc., Clinton, CT; *U.S. Public*, pg. 431
Bandsma, John E., Controller--Gilman, Janesville, WI; *Int'l*, pg. 1389
Bandusky, Drew M., Intl. Controller--Griffith Laboratories Worldwide, Inc., Alsip, IL; *U.S. Private*, pg. 481
Banfield, William, Controller--Artistic Greetings, Inc., Elmira, NY; *U.S. Public*, pg. 136
Bange, Richard M., Jr., Controller & Asst. Sec.--Baltimore Gas and Electric Company, Baltimore, MD; *U.S. Public*, pg. 172
Bangurah, Sadd, Controller--Ceiling & Partitions, Inc., Landover, MD; *U.S. Private*, pg. 221
Banifazl, Shahrokh, Controller--Hydraulics International, Inc., Chatsworth, CA; *U.S. Private*, pg. 551
Banks, Christine, Controller--Alfin, Inc., New York, NY; *U.S. Public*, pg. 40
Bankus, Daniel M., Controller--Optek Technology, Inc., Carrollton, TX; *U.S. Public*, pg. 1227
Bannell, Stephen G., Reg. Controller--Johnson's Wax (East Africa) Ltd., Nairobi, Kenya; *U.S. Private*, pg. 593
Bannon, Richard, V.P. & Controller--Entex Information Services, Rye Brook, NY; *U.S. Private*, pg. 378
Banquer, C.S., Controller & Treas.--Acme Refrigeration Of Baton Rouge Inc., Baton Rouge, LA; *U.S. Private*, pg. 13
Banu, John E., Comptroller--Westvaco Corporation, New York, NY; *U.S. Public*, pg. 1762
Barbara, Joseph, Controller--Hendrickson International, Woodridge, IL; *U.S. Private*, pg. 155
Barbe, Doug, Controller--Draka U.S.A., Franklin, MA; *Int'l*, pg. 417
Barbee, Tom, Controller & Treas.--Feed Service Corp., Ohiowa, NE; *U.S. Private*, pg. 399
Barber, Alice, Controller & Treas.--Frequency and Time Systems, Inc., Beverly, MA; *U.S. Public*, pg. 488
Barber, David, V.P. & Controller--ICL, Inc., Irvine, CA; *Int'l*, pg. 529
Barber, Donald G., Chief Fin. Officer & Sr. V.P.--Santa Fe International Corporation, Dallas, TX; *Int'l*, pg. 765
Barber, Grant A., Asst. Controller--Northern Telecom Limited, Brampton, Canada; *Int'l*, pg. 968
Barber, John W., Chief Fin. Officer, V.P. & Controller--General American Life Insurance Co., Saint Louis, MO; *U.S. Private*, pg. 443
Barber, Kathy, Controller--Heck Industries, Baton Rouge, LA; *U.S. Private*, pg. 519
Barber, Roger, Controller--The Scoular Company, Omaha, NE; *U.S. Private*, pg. 977
Barcellos, Murilo, Controller--Apolo Produtos de Aco S.A., Rio de Janeiro, Brazil; *Int'l*, pg. 78
Barcher, Paul S., First V.P. & Controller--The Fifth Third Bank of Kentucky, Louisville, Louisville, KY; *U.S. Public*, pg. 621
Barco, Norma, Controller--Pacific Northern Inc., Seattle, WA; *U.S. Private*, pg. 832
Bardaro, Mike, V.P. & Controller--AMF Bowling Worldwide, Richmond, VA; *U.S. Private*, pg. 6
Bardsley, T., Controller--The Budd Company, Troy, MI; *Int'l*, pg. 1388
Bares, Roger, Controller & Dir.-Fin.--Northland Aluminum Products, Inc., Minneapolis, MN; *U.S. Private*, pg. 805
Barfuss, Sheldon K., Controller--Great Salt Lake Minerals Corp., Overland Park, KS; *U.S. Private*, pg. 505
Barina, Ralf, Controller--Knurr AG, Munich, Germany; *Int'l*, pg. 739
Baris, Robert, Controller--D & K Healthcare Resources, Inc., Saint Louis, MO; *U.S. Public*, pg. 471
Barker, Stephen J., Controller--Boeing Realty Corporation, Long Beach, CA; *U.S. Public*, pg. 241
Barker, Steve, Sr. V.P. & Controller--Deposit Guaranty Corp., Jackson, MS; *U.S. Public*, pg. 500
Barkley, Andrew, V.P. & Controller--Six Flags Theme Parks Inc., Parsippany, NJ; *U.S. Public*, pg. 1611
Barkley, Barry R., Sr. V.P. & Controller--Great Western Financial Corporation, Chatsworth, CA; *U.S. Public*, pg. 1741
Barkley, Michael, Controller--ISS International Service System, Inc., Atlanta, GA; *Int'l*, pg. 656
Barkley, Norman, Grp. Fin. Comptroller--International Tool & Supply, PLC, New Malden, United Kingdom; *Int'l*, pg. 684
Barlett, Mark, Controller--Blue Cross & Blue Shield of Michigan, Detroit, MI; *U.S. Private*, pg. 151
Barlow, James, Controller & Treas.--Wynn's International, Inc., Orange, CA; *U.S. Public*, pg. 1782
Barnard, Aubrey D., Sec., Treas. & Controller--SouthTrust Corporation, Birmingham, AL; *U.S. Public*, pg. 1491
Barnard, Gabrielle, Controller--Putt Putt Golf Courses of America, Inc., Fayetteville, NC; *U.S. Private*, pg. 896
Barnard, Randy, Controller--Hall Sign, Inc., Bloomington, IN; *U.S. Private*, pg. 495
Barnes-Wallis, P., Controller & Mgr.-Inv. Rels.--Rolls-Royce plc, London, United Kingdom; *Int'l*, pg. 1126
Barnes, Linda J., V.P. & Controller--INSO Corporation, Boston, MA; *U.S. Public*, pg. 882
Barnes, Peter D., V.P.-Admin. & Controller--TCG International Inc., Burnaby, Canada; *Int'l*, pg. 1336
Barnett, Gregory, Controller--Merit Medical Systems, Inc., South Jordan, UT; *U.S. Public*, pg. 1096
Barnett, James, Controller & Sec.--Delchester Oil Co. Inc., West Chester, PA; *U.S. Private*, pg. 518
Barnham, Robert E., Controller--Container Div. (Dallas), Dallas, TX; *Int'l*, pg. 1269
Barnstable, Steve, Controller--Roper Starch Worldwide, Mamaroneck, NY; *U.S. Private*, pg. 944
Barone, Thomas, V.P. & Controller--NewsEdge Corporation, Burlington, MA; *U.S. Public*, pg. 1180
Baroni, Albert J., Controller--Malden Mills Industries, Inc., Lawrence, MA; *U.S. Private*, pg. 698
Barr, Edward E., Controller--DIC Trading (USA) Inc., Fort Lee, NJ; *Int'l*, pg. 369
Barr, Wendy, Controller-Mfg. Div.--Reptron Electronics, Inc., Tampa, FL; *U.S. Public*, pg. 1377
Barragato, Grace, Controller--Davis Companies, Los Angeles, CA; *U.S. Private*, pg. 315
Barrett, Kent E., Sr. V.P., Controller & Treas.--American General Life & Accident Insurance Co., Nashville, TN; *U.S. Public*, pg. 76
Barrett, Phillip, Controller--Chick-fil-A, Inc., Atlanta, GA; *U.S. Private*, pg. 236
Barrette, Raymond, Controller--Panneaux Malette-OSB Inc., Saint-Georges, Canada; *Int'l*, pg. 833
Barrier, Luther, Comptroller--S&D Coffee Inc., Concord, NC; *U.S. Private*, pg. 954
Barron, John F., Controller--Commonwealth Industries, Inc., Louisville, KY; *U.S. Public*, pg. 415
Barroso, Marjorie, Comptroller & Treas.--Maryland & Virginia Milk Producers Cooperative Association, Inc., Reston, VA; *U.S. Private*, pg. 711
Barrows, Craig, Sr. V.P., Gen. Counsel & Corp. Sec.--M/A-COM Inc., Lowell, MA; *U.S. Public*, pg. 8
Barroy, Dominique, Controller--Groupe Limagrain, Chappes, France; *Int'l*, pg. 566
Barry, Daniel L., V.P. & Controller--Orion Capital Corporation, New York, NY; *U.S. Public*, pg. 1231
Barry, Debby, Controller & Treas.--Vance Industries, Inc., Chicago, IL; *U.S. Private*, pg. 1133
Barry, James, Controller--Varity Dayton Walther, Dayton, OH; *Int'l*, pg. 820
Barry, Jan, Controller--AGI Inc., Melrose Park, IL; *U.S. Private*, pg. 5
Barry, Jeff, Asst. Controller--R.L. Zeigler Co. Inc., Tuscaloosa, AL; *U.S. Private*, pg. 1204
Barry, Raymond, Controller--New Era Cap. Co., Derby, NY; *U.S. Private*, pg. 793
Barry, Robert, Controller--John M. Olson Company, Saint Clair Shores, MI; *U.S. Private*, pg. 815
Barry, Roger, Controller--Capro, Inc., Willis, TX; *U.S. Public*, *pg. 1569*
Barsotti, Deidra D., V.P. & Controller--Raychem Corporation, Menlo Park, CA; *U.S. Public*, pg. 1362
Bartell, Judy, Controller--Federal Process Corp., Cleveland, OH; *U.S. Private*, pg. 399
Bartels, Mary J., Chief Fin. Officer & Controller--American Steamship Company, Williamsville, NY; *U.S. Public*, pg. 690
Bartenstein, Jeff C., Controller, Treas. & Sec.--Alaska Industrial Hardware Inc., Anchorage, AK; *U.S. Private*, pg. 31
Barth, Maggie, Controller--American Enterprise Institute for Public Policy Research, Washington, DC; *U.S. Private*, pg. 53
Barthel, Cindy, Controller--Great Clips, Inc., Minneapolis, MN; *U.S. Private*, pg. 473
Bartholomew, Doug, Controller--Austin Industries, Inc., Dallas, TX; *U.S. Private*, pg. 99
Bartice, Gregory M., First V.P. & Controller--Republic Bank for Savings, New York, NY; *U.S. Public*, pg. 1380
Bartle, Richard, Controller--Economy Folding Box Corp., Chicago, IL; *U.S. Private*, pg. 362
Bartley, Dixie, V.P.-Fin. & Controller--Nashville Steel Corp., Nashville, TN; *U.S. Private*, pg. 775
Bartley, Steven, Controller--Foster & Gallagher, Inc., Peoria, IL; *U.S. Private*, pg. 420
Bartley, Thomas, Controller--Modern Drop Forge Co., Blue Island, IL; *U.S. Private*, pg. 754
Barton, Phil, Controller--SEEQ Technology Inc., Fremont, CA; *U.S. Public*, pg. 1417
Barton, Thom, Controller--PYA/Monarch, Inc., Greenville, SC; *U.S. Public*, pg. 1433
Bartow, Don, Controller--Traylor Brothers, Inc., Evansville, IN; *U.S. Private*, pg. 1098
Basalaj, Paul, Controller--Datapoint Corp. Pty. Ltd., Artarmon, Australia; *Int'l*, pg. 384
Basar, John, Chief Fin. Officer & Controller--National Real Estate Services, Inc., Vancouver, Canada; *Int'l*, pg. 909
Bashaw, Charles E., V.P. & Controller--Kaman Music Corp., Bloomfield, CT; *U.S. Public*, pg. 942
Basile, Vincent F., Controller--WWF Paper Corporation, Bala Cynwyd, PA; *U.S. Private*, pg. 1145
Bass, David, Controller--Galderma Laboratories, Inc., Fort Worth, TX; *Int'l*, pg. 819
Bass, John, Controller--Vulcraft Div., Grapeland, TX; *U.S. Public*, pg. 1206
Bass, Matt, Asst. Fin. Controller--Overhead Door Corporation, Dallas, TX; *U.S. Private*, pg. 822
Basset, John, Controller--Nice-Pak Products, Inc., Orangeburg, NY; *U.S. Private*, pg. 798
Bassett, Martin, Controller--Walman Optical Company, Minneapolis, MN; *U.S. Private*, pg. 1148
Bassette, Bennett, Controller--UNC Johnson Technology, Muskegon, MI; *U.S. Public*, pg. 710
Bassil, Ernest, Controller--Pavey Envelope & Tag Corp., Jersey City, NJ; *U.S. Public*, pg. 1038
Bastian, Jan, Asst. Controller--Superior Die Tool And Machine Company, Columbus, OH; *U.S. Private*, pg. 1054
Batchelder, Herbert W., Controller--Bose Corporation, Framingham, MA; *U.S. Private*, pg. 160
Bates, Noma, Controller--Gish Biomedical, Inc., Irvine, CA; *U.S. Public*, pg. 745
Batesole, Lee, Controller--Vulcraft Div., Saint Joe, IN; *U.S. Public*, pg. 1206
Bath, D., Controller--Corner Brook Pulp & Paper Limited, Corner Brook, Canada; *Int'l*, pg. 761
Bath, David A., V.P. & Controller--Kleinschmidt Inc., Deerfield, IL; *U.S. Private*, pg. 625
Batley, Paul, Controller--Independent Publications, Inc., Bryn Mawr, PA; *U.S. Private*, pg. 559
Batory, Lynn, Controller--Elgin National Industries, Inc., Downers Grove, IL; *U.S. Private*, pg. 370
Batraki, Ronna, Controller--Losurdo Foods, Inc., Hackensack, NJ; *U.S. Private*, pg. 677
Batson, Catherine W., Sr. V.P. & Controller--Carolina First Corporation, Greenville, SC; *U.S. Public*, pg. 306
Batstone, Don, Controller--Castner Knott Co., Nashville, TN; *U.S. Public*, pg. 1090
Batt, Bill, Controller--Kemmons Wilson, Inc., Memphis, TN; *U.S. Private*, pg. 613
Batt, Geoffrey, V.P. & Controller--Alcan Rolled Products Division, Cleveland, OH; *Int'l*, pg. 50
Batt, James M., Pres., Chief Exec. Officer & Controller--Peck Spring Company, Plainville, CT; *U.S. Private*, pg. 846
Batt, Jim, Controller--Coleman Powermate Compressors, Springfield, MN; *U.S. Private*, pg. 691
Battaglini, Rick, Controller--John Paul Mitchell Systems, Santa Clarita, CA; *U.S. Private*, pg. 753
Battan, Thomas A., Comptroller & Treas.--W.L. Hailey & Company, Inc., Nashville, TN; *U.S. Private*, pg. 494
Battey, Brenda, Sr. V.P. & Controller--FirstFed Financial Corp., Santa Monica, CA; *U.S. Public*, pg. 645
Battle, Judith H., V.P.-Fin. & Controller--ServiceCare, Inc., Columbia, SC; *U.S. Public*, pg. 1436
Bauer, Gary, Controller--Champaign Landmark, Inc., Urbana, OH; *U.S. Private*, pg. 227
Bauer, Joel, Controller--On-Cor Frozen Foods Inc., Northbrook, IL; *U.S. Private*, pg. 817
Bauer, Karen, Chief Acctg. Officer, Controller & Sec.--Allied Research Corporation, Vienna, VA; *U.S. Public*, pg. 48
Baughn, Rick, Controller--Bettis Corporation, Waller, TX; *U.S. Public*, pg. 482
Baum, Clemens, Dr., Sr. V.P. & Controller--Deutz AG, Cologne, Germany; *Int'l*, pg. 407
Baum, Lynn, Controller & Mgr.-Acct.--Idea Man, Inc., Los Angeles, CA; *U.S. Private*, pg. 557
Baum, Vicky, Controller--Fiesta Mart Inc., Houston, TX; *U.S. Private*, pg. 403
Baumann, Nancy, Asst. Controller--Crown Holdings, Inc., Roseville, MN; *U.S. Private*, pg. 293
Bauschka, Michael, V.P. & Controller--Montgomery KONE Inc., Moline, IL; *Int'l*, pg. 746
Baxter, Bob, Controller--Volt Directory Services, Blue Bell, PA; *U.S. Public*, pg. 1724
Baxter, Jeffrey, Controller--Evans, Inc., Chicago, IL; *U.S. Public*, pg. 596
Baxter, Warner L., Controller--AmerenUE, Saint Louis, MO; *U.S. Public*, pg. 66
Baydarian, Mark, Controller--Leviton Mfg. Co., Inc., Little Neck, NY; *U.S. Private*, pg. 663
Bayens, Vince, Controller--Metal Sales Manufacturing Corporation, Sellersburg, IN; *U.S. Private*, pg. 567
Bayley, Nicholas, Chief Fin. Officer, V.P.-Fin. & Controller--Knapp Shoes Inc., Penn Yan, NY; *U.S. Private*, pg. 401
Baz, Thomas A., V.P. & Corp. Controller--Cubic Corporation, San Diego, CA; *U.S. Public*, pg. 466
Bazany, LeRoy F., V.P. & Controller--Bemis Company, Inc., Minneapolis, MN; *U.S. Public*, pg. 210
Bazzare, Howard, Controller--Inland Valley Regional Medical Center, Wildomar, CA; *U.S. Public*, pg. 1697
Beach, Jim, V.P.-Fin. & Admin.--Applied Microsystems Corporation, Redmond, WA; *U.S. Public*, pg. 123
Beachy, Alan R., V.P. & Controller--Lear Corporation, Rochester Hills, MI; *U.S. Public*, pg. 982
Beam, Larry, Controller--Houchens Industries Inc., Bowling Green, KY; *U.S. Private*, pg. 541
Beamer, Jerry, Exec. V.P. & Controller--Berry Companies, Inc., Wichita, KS; *U.S. Private*, pg. 137
Beames, Douglas K., Chief Fin. Officer & Controller--Reed Grain & Bean Company, Buhl, ID; *U.S. Private*, pg. 916
Beames, Douglas K., Chief Fin. Officer & Controller--Reed Brothers Inc., Buhl, ID; *U.S. Private*, pg. 916
Bean, Ken, Controller--Uni-Marts, Inc., State College, PA; *U.S. Public*, pg. 1664
Bean, Michael A., Exec. V.P. & Controller--Compass Bank, Birmingham, AL; *U.S. Public*, pg. 418
Bean, Robert, Controller--Lytron Incorporated, Woburn, MA; *U.S. Private*, pg. 684
Beans, Noel, Controller--Nextlink Communications Inc., Bellevue, WA; *U.S. Public*, pg. 1181
Beard, Linda, Controller--Ellwood Group, Inc., Ellwood City, PA; *U.S. Private*, pg. 373
Beardsell, Derek, Controller--Noranda Forest Inc., Toronto, Canada; *Int'l*, pg. 434
Beasley, Gary, Asst. V.P.--E.C. Barton & Company, Jonesboro, AR; *U.S. Private*, pg. 119
Beath, D., Gen. Mgr. & Grp. Audit Controller--HSBC Holdings plc, London, United Kingdom; *Int'l*, pg. 579
Beath, Dave, Controller--Langford Inc., Guelph, Canada; *U.S. Public*, pg. 81
Beaton, Judy, Controller--Yuba Heat Transfer Division, Tulsa, OK; *U.S. Private*, pg. 264
Beauchesne, J.M., Controller--Air Canada Vacations Inc., Montreal, Canada; *Int'l*, pg. 36
Beaudin, Scott, Controller--Better Brands Of Atlanta, Inc., Atlanta, GA; *U.S. Private*, pg. 141
Beaudri, Kenneth, Controller--The Arnold Engineering Company, Marengo, IL; *U.S. Public*, pg. 1420
Beaudry, Chantal, Controller--Kulicke & Soffa, AG, Zug, Switzerland; *U.S. Public*, pg. 969
Beauford, Richard, Controller--Coleman Dairy LLC, Little Rock, AR; *U.S. Private*, pg. 251
Beaulieu, Michael E., V.P. & Controller--Cardinal Distribution, Dublin, OH; *U.S. Public*, pg. 304
Beauregard, David, Controller--Comverse Network Systems, Wakefield, MA; *U.S. Public*, pg. 425
Beavdoin, Dick, Controller--Colgate Oral Pharmaceutical, Canton, MA; *U.S. Public*, pg. 397
Beck, Andrew H., Controller--AGCO Corporation, Duluth, GA; *U.S. Public*, pg. 28
Becker, H.C., Controller--National Rejectors, Inc., G.m.b.H., Hamburg, Germany; *U.S. Public*, pg. 456
Becker, Jerome, Chief Fin. Officer, Controller & Treas.--Masters, Inc., Westbury, NY; *U.S. Private*, pg. 714

Becker, Lawrence K., Mng. Dir. & Controller--OppenheimerFunds Distributor, Inc., New York, NY; *U.S. Private*, pg. 818
Becker, Marc, Mgr.-Coordination & Control--European Investment Bank, Luxembourg, Luxembourg; *Int'l*, pg. 465
Becker, Tom, Asst. Controller--E & B Marine Incorporated, Edison, NJ; *U.S. Public*, pg. 1756
Beczkiewicz, Tom, Controller--Abbyland Foods, Inc., Abbotsford, WI; *U.S. Private*, pg. 10
Bedee, Louise, Controller--The National Super Service Co., Toledo, OH; *U.S. Private*, pg. 787
Bedell, Jenny, Controller--Capital City Press, Inc., Berlin, VT; *U.S. Private*, pg. 205
Bedford, Brian C., Corp. Controller--Marketing Corp. of America, Westport, CT; *U.S. Private*, pg. 704
Bednarz, Richard, Controller, Treas. & Sec.--Loga Athletic/Headwear Inc., Mattapoisett, MA; *U.S. Public*, pg. 1644
Bednorz, Nick, Chief Fin. Officer & Controller--Nichols-Homeshield, Davenport, IA; *U.S. Public*, pg. 1350
Beecher, Chris, Controller--Morris Newspaper Corporation, Savannah, GA; *U.S. Private*, pg. 762
Beekley, Roger J., V.P. & Controller--Harleysville Group, Harleysville, PA; *U.S. Public*, pg. 786
Beere, Don E., V.P., Controller & Mgr.-MIS--Tesoro Petroleum Corporation, San Antonio, TX; *U.S. Public*, pg. 1581
Beeth, Harry R., Asst. Controller--International Business Machines Corporation, Armonk, NY; *U.S. Public*, pg. 895
Begnami, Martiniano, Controller--Nestle Industrial e Commercial Ltda., Sao Paulo, Brazil; *Int'l*, pg. 921
Begue, John S., Comptroller & Treas.--Everlast World Boxing Corp., Bronx, NY; *U.S. Private*, pg. 386
Begue, John S., Comptroller & Treas.--Everlast Sports Manufacturing Corp., Bronx, NY; *U.S. Private*, pg. 386
Behan, Cathy, Controller--TSC Shannock Corporation, Burnaby, Canada; *Int'l*, pg. 1343
Behm, D. Skip, Controller--Spiegel, Inc., Downers Grove, IL; *U.S. Public*, pg. 1498
Behrendt, Don, Controller--A B C Appliance Inc., Pontiac, MI; *U.S. Private*, pg. 2
Behymer, Jean M., Controller--Ghent Manufacturing, Inc., Lebanon, OH; *U.S. Private*, pg. 450
Beica, Gian Franco, Controller--Roltra-Morse S.p.A., Turin, Italy; *U.S. Public*, pg. 857
Beigarde, Norman, V.P. & Controller--Allendale Mutual Insurance Co., Johnston, RI; *U.S. Private*, pg. 37
Beil, Gary W., V.P. & Controller--The Boeing Company, Seattle, WA; *U.S. Public*, pg. 239
Beilke, Terry L., Controller--Lund International Holdings, Inc., Anoka, MN; *U.S. Public*, pg. 1020
Beiriger, Terry, Chief Fin. Officer, Controller & Sec.--International FiberCom, Phoenix, AZ; *U.S. Public*, pg. 898
Beishline, Bob, Controller--Allegiant Physician Services, Atlanta, GA; *U.S. Public*, pg. 45
Beja, Albert, Controller--Bast Chevrolet Inc., Seaford, NY; *U.S. Private*, pg. 122
Belford, Ray, Chief Fin. Officer & Controller--Hayes Axle, Inc., Seminole, OK; *U.S. Private*, pg. 299
Belgya, Mark R., Corp. Controller--J.M. Smucker Company, Orrville, OH; *U.S. Public*, pg. 1480
Beling, Gregory, Controller--Miner Enterprises Inc., Geneva, IL; *U.S. Private*, pg. 749
Belitz, Gary R., Chief Acctg. Officer & Controller--The Williams Companies, Inc., Tulsa, OK; *U.S. Public*, pg. 1769
Belitz, Stanley W., Controller--Unit Corporation, Tulsa, OK; *U.S. Public*, pg. 1672
Belknap, Bob, Controller--Mackie Designs, Inc., Woodinville, WA; *U.S. Public*, pg. 1030
Bell, Bob, Controller & Asst. Treas.--Rose Packing Company, Barrington, IL; *U.S. Private*, pg. 945
Bell, Enrique, Controller--Carfel, Inc., Miami, FL; *U.S. Private*, pg. 210
Bell, Jon, Controller--Washington Real Estate Investment Trust, Kensington, MD; *U.S. Public*, pg. 1743
Bell, Nancy, Controller--Southwest Recreational Industries Inc., Leander, TX; *U.S. Public*, pg. 1018
Bell, Sharon H., Controller--RPR & Associates, Inc., Columbia, SC; *U.S. Private*, pg. 905
Bellavia, Vera, Controller--Doremus & Company, New York, NY; *U.S. Public*, pg. 1223
Belleau, Thomas F., Chief Fin. Officer & V.P.-Fin.--The Langer Biomechanics Group, Inc., Deer Park, NY; *U.S. Public*, pg. 978
Bellis, William J., Chief Fin. Officer, V.P.-Fin., Controller & Treas.--AGR International, Inc., Butler, PA; *U.S. Private*, pg. 5
Bello, George E., Exec. V.P. & Controller--Reliance Group Holdings, Inc., New York, NY; *U.S. Public*, pg. 1374
Bellon, Nolan X., Sr. V.P. & Controller--Zions First National Bank, Salt Lake City, UT; *U.S. Public*, pg. 1793
Belmonte, Cassie, Chief Fin. Officer--Al Neyer, Inc., Cincinnati, OH; *U.S. Private*, pg. 797
Belmonte, Donna, Controller--Performance Automotive Network, Fairfield, OH; *U.S. Private*, pg. 853
Belsky, Joel, Sr. V.P. & Controller--Federated Department Stores, Inc., Cincinnati, OH; *U.S. Public*, pg. 617
Belstock, Richard, Sr. V.P.--Sierra West Bancorp, Truckee, CA; *U.S. Public*, pg. 1470
Belz, Raymond T., V.P. & Controller--USG Corporation, Chicago, IL; *U.S. Public*, pg. 1660
Belzer, Jeff, Controller--Walters & Wolf, Fremont, CA; *U.S. Private*, pg. 1149
Belzinskas, Rem, Controller--Signature Brands USA, Inc., Solon, OH; *U.S. Public*, pg. 1472
Benapfl, William J., Chief Fin. Officer & Controller--California Custom Foods, Lodi, CA; *U.S. Private*, pg. 831
Bench, Sherice, Mgr.--Commemorative Brands, Inc., Austin, TX; *U.S. Private*, pg. 258
Bencivengo, Cathy, Asst. Controller--Middlesex Water Company, Iselin, NJ; *U.S. Public*, pg. 1110
Bencivengo, Kathleen, Controller--Tidewater Utilities, Inc., Odessa, DE; *U.S. Public*, pg. 1110
Bendelius, Ronald A., Sr. V.P. & Comptroller--Arnhold and S. Bleichroeder, Inc., New York, NY; *U.S. Private*, pg. 83
Bender, Brian W., Sr. V.P., Controller & Asst. Treas.--Younkers, Inc., Des Moines, IA; *U.S. Public*, pg. 1334
Bender, Michael, Treas., Controller & Chief Accountant--Lewis Drug, Inc., Sioux Falls, SD; *U.S. Private*, pg. 665
Bender, Mike, V.P. & Controller--Sterner Lighting Systems Incorporated, Eden Prairie, MN; *U.S. Private*, pg. 1042
Bendrihem, Maurice, Controller--The Dreyfus Corporation, New York, NY; *U.S. Public*, pg. 1085
Benedetti, Stephen J., V.P., Controller & Treas.--Resource Mortgage Capital, Inc., Glen Allen, VA; *U.S. Public*, pg. 1382
Benedetto, L., Controller--Manistique Papers, Inc., Manistique, MI; *Int'l*, pg. 762
Benevides, Bill, Controller--Ortronics, Inc., Pawcatuck, CT; *Int'l*, pg. 806
Benjamin, James C., V.P. & Controller--Harnischfeger Industries, Inc., Saint Francis, WI; *U.S. Public*, pg. 788
Benjamin, James L., Controller--United Illuminating Company, New Haven, CT; *U.S. Public*, pg. 1678
Benka, Jim, Controller--Symons Corporation, Des Plaines, IL; *U.S. Private*, pg. 932
Benkert, Jerome A., Jr., V.P. & Controller--Indiana Energy, Inc., Indianapolis, IN; *U.S. Public*, pg. 874
Benne, Vicki L., Controller--Isco, Inc., Lincoln, NE; *U.S. Public*, pg. 913
Bennell, Peter, Fin. Controller--Gestetner Australasia Limited, Brookvale, Australia; *Int'l*, pg. 1115
Benner, Kevin P., Controller, Treas & Sec.--Jasper County Farm Bureau Co-op Association, Inc., Rensselaer, IN; *U.S. Private*, pg. 583
Bennett, Dan, Asst. Controller--Levlad, Inc., Chatsworth, CA; *U.S. Private*, pg. 663
Bennett, Denise, Controller--AppleTree Markets, Houston, TX; *U.S. Private*, pg. 78
Bennett, Ed, Controller--Turning Point Care Center, Moultrie, GA; *U.S. Public*, pg. 1697
Bennett, Gary K., Controller & Treas.--Gerber Scientific, Inc., South Windsor, CT; *U.S. Public*, pg. 740
Bennett, Joseph, Controller--Tidewater Inc., New Orleans, LA; *U.S. Public*, pg. 1608
Bennett, Marvin, V.P. & Controller--GF Industries, Inc., San Mateo, CA; *U.S. Private*, pg. 434
Bennett, Rich, Controller--Hygrade Metal Moulding Mfg. Corp., Bethlehem, PA; *U.S. Private*, pg. 552
Benoit, Marc, Controller--Societe Generale de Financement du Quebec, Montreal, Canada; *Int'l*, pg. 1274
Benrimo, Martin, Controller--Maki Corporation, Lunenburg, MA; *U.S. Private*, pg. 697
Benrubi, Steve, Controller--Domino's Pizza Inc., Ann Arbor, MI; *U.S. Private*, pg. 339
Benson, Art, Division Controller--AST Bearings Division, Montville, NJ; *U.S. Public*, pg. 157
Benson, Bob, Controller (SEG)--Hallmark Cards, Inc., Kansas City, MO; *U.S. Private*, pg. 495
Benson, John, Chief Fin. Officer & Chief Info. Officer--Dallas Gold & Silver Exchange, Inc., Dallas, TX; *U.S. Public*, pg. 478
Benson, Leslie, Controller--The Good Guys, Inc., Brisbane, CA; *U.S. Public*, pg. 750
Benson, Robert, Controller--Komatsu America International Company, Vernon Hills, IL; *Int'l*, pg. 744
Benson, Trace, Controller--Old Dutch Foods, Inc., Roseville, MN; *U.S. Private*, pg. 814
Benson, Vera, Controller & Sec.--Ernst W. Dorn Co., Inc., Gardena, CA; *U.S. Private*, pg. 340
Bentley, Al, Controller--Pearce Industries Inc., Houston, TX; *U.S. Private*, pg. 845
Bentley, Rita P., Controller & Treas.--Daniel F. Young, Inc., New York, NY; *U.S. Private*, pg. 1200
Bentley, Rod, V.P. & Controller--Bentley & Bentley, Fremont, CA; *U.S. Private*, pg. 1186
Benton, Barry L., V.P.-Finance & Controller--Western Atlas Logging Services, Houston, TX; *U.S. Public*, pg. 1757
Benton, Ronald J., Controller--Merry Land & Investment Company, Inc., Augusta, GA; *U.S. Public*, pg. 1098
Benz, Edward, Controller & Asst. Treas.--Wheaton Van Lines, Inc., Indianapolis, IN; *U.S. Private*, pg. 1171
Berecz, Liz, Controller--Quantum Corporation, Milpitas, CA; *U.S. Public*, pg. 1350
Berg, Charlie, Controller--Crabar Business Systems, Dayton, OH; *U.S. Private*, pg. 283
Bergadon, R.N., Controller--Hunter Douglas Architectural Products Inc., Duluth, GA; *Int'l*, pg. 639
Berge, O., Unit Controller--Weatherford Norge, A/S, Stavanger, Norway; *U.S. Public*, pg. 1750
Berger, Connie, Asst. Controller & Mgr.-MIS--Precision Carbide Tool Company, Inc., Niles, IL; *U.S. Private*, pg. 879
Berger, Morris W., Chief Fin. Officer--Careers USA Inc., Philadelphia, PA; *U.S. Private*, pg. 209
Berger, Robert W., Controller & Asst. Treas.--McClatchy Newspapers Inc., Sacramento, CA; *U.S. Public*, pg. 1065
Berger, Ron, Controller--Hughes Christensen, Houston, TX; *U.S. Public*, pg. 166
Bergeron, B. J., Controller--InterBio Inc., Woodlands, TX; *U.S. Private*, pg. 566
Berges, Dianna, Controller--Cummins Southwest Inc., Phoenix, AZ; *U.S. Private*, pg. 296
Berges, Edward S., Asst. Controller--Western Waste Industries, Torrance, CA; *U.S. Public*, pg. 1686
Berges, Orlando, Sr. V.P. & Controller--Banco Popular de Puerto Rico, San Juan, PR; *U.S. Public*, pg. 175
Berghoove, Brad A., Controller--Sackner Products, Grand Rapids, MI; *U.S. Public*, pg. 924
Bergin, Noreen G., V.P. & Corp. Controller--Netscape Communications Corp., Mountain View, CA; *U.S. Public*, pg. 1168
Bergold, James E., V.P.-Fin. & Controller--ITT Fluid Technology Corporation, Midland Park, NJ; *U.S. Public*, pg. 860
Bergonzi, John A., Controller & Asst. Treas.--Equitable Resources, Inc., Pittsburgh, PA; *U.S. Public*, pg. 589
Bergstrom, Stig-Erik, Dep. Pres.-Fin., Treas., Information Mngmt. & Real Estate--OY Stockmann AB, Helsinki, Finland; *Int'l*, pg. 1301
Beringer, Harvey, Controller--Manhattan Store Interiors, Inc., Brooklyn, NY; *U.S. Private*, pg. 699
Berk, Alan, Sr. V.P. & Corp. Controller--A. Epstein and Sons, Intl., Inc., Chicago, IL; *U.S. Private*, pg. 379
Berkland, Marlin, Controller--G.E. Capital Fleet Services, Fort Wayne, IN; *U.S. Public*, pg. 710
Berkowitz, Martin A., Sr. V.P. & Comptroller--The Prudential Insurance Company of America, Newark, NJ; *U.S. Private*, pg. 892
Berkowitz, Steven, Controller--Chase & Sons Division, Randolph, MA; *U.S. Public*, pg. 337
Berkowski, Joe, Controller--Carhartt, Inc., Dearborn, MI; *U.S. Private*, pg. 210
Berman, Alan, Controller--Bee-Gee Shoe Corp., Dayton, OH; *U.S. Private*, pg. 367
Berman, Guy, Mgr.-Coordination & Control--European Investment Bank, Luxembourg, Luxembourg; *Int'l*, pg. 465
Berman, Lawrence, V.P. & Controller--Transammonia Inc., New York, NY; *U.S. Private*, pg. 1096
Berman, Myra, Controller--Goldberger Doll Mfg. Company, Inc., Brooklyn, NY; *U.S. Private*, pg. 459
Bernard, Todd, Asst. Controller--Old Dominion Freight Line, Inc., High Point, NC; *U.S. Public*, pg. 1216
Bernardoni, James A., Controller--Exolon-Esk Company, Tonawanda, NY; *U.S. Public*, pg. 600
Bernardski, Marline, Mgr.-Acctg.--General Tours Inc., Keene, NH; *U.S. Private*, pg. 445
Berner, Alan G., Controller--Ross Bicycles USA Ltd., Farmingdale, NY; *U.S. Private*, pg. 946
Berney, Rand C., V.P. & Controller--Phillips Petroleum Company, Bartlesville, OK; *U.S. Public*, pg. 1290
Berni, Silvio, Controller--The Dyson-Kissner-Moran Corporation, New York, NY; *U.S. Private*, pg. 351
Bernice, Edward, V.P. & Controller--ENSR, Acton, MA; *U.S. Private*, pg. 354
Bernstein, David, Controller--Autodesk, Inc., San Rafael, CA; *U.S. Public*, pg. 148
Bernstein, Herb, Controller--A&E Stores, Inc., Teterboro, NJ; *U.S. Private*, pg. 1
Berntsson, Kristina, Controller--SAS Park Royal Hotel, Lysaker, Norway; *Int'l*, pg. 1202
Berry, Allen W., Controller & Treas.--Wehco Media, Inc., Little Rock, AR; *U.S. Private*, pg. 1159
Berry, James W., Controller & Asst. Treas.--WSMP, Inc., Claremont, NC; *U.S. Public*, pg. 1729
Berry, Nancy, Controller--The Jewell Electrical Instruments Co., Manchester, NH; *U.S. Private*, pg. 36
Berry, William T., Jr., Asst. V.P. & Controller--Eskimo Pie Corporation, Richmond, VA; *U.S. Public*, pg. 592
Berryman, David R., Asst. Controller-Fin. Reporting--International Multifoods Corporation, Minneapolis, MN; *U.S. Public*, pg. 900
Bertolino, Margaret, Chief Fin. Officer--Agri-Mark, Inc., Lawrence, MA; *U.S. Private*, pg. 26
Bertrom, Doris, V.P. & Controller--Miller Meester Advertising Inc., Minneapolis, MN; *U.S. Private*, pg. 747
Berube, Bob, Controller--Three-Five Systems, Tempe, AZ; *U.S. Public*, pg. 1604
Berzenski, Paul, V.P. & Controller--General Instrument Corporation, Horsham, PA; *U.S. Public*, pg. 716
Besel, Daniel G., V.P.-Corp. Controller--BC Gas Inc., Vancouver, Canada; *Int'l*, pg. 114
Besel, Daniel G., V.P. & Corp. Controller--BC Gas Utility, Vancouver, Canada; *Int'l*, pg. 114
Beshada, Don, Controller--The Okonite Company, Ramsey, NJ; *U.S. Private*, pg. 813
Bestow, Mark, Controller--Petersen Publishing Company, L.L.C., Los Angeles, CA; *U.S. Private*, pg. 856
Betencourt, Jorge, Controller--Sensormatic Electronics Corp. de Puerto Rico, Aguadilla, PR; *U.S. Public*, pg. 1457
Betham, Dave, Comptroller--Turtle Bay Hilton Golf & Tennis Resort, Kahuku, HI; *U.S. Public*, pg. 829
Betts, Derek W., V.P. & Controller--Tolko Manitoba, Inc., The Pas, Canada; *Int'l*, pg. 1395
Betz, Gail, Controller--The Advocate, Newark, OH; *U.S. Private*, pg. 23
Betz, Michael, Controller--Allied Chucker & Engineering Company, Jackson, MI; *U.S. Private*, pg. 38
Beuka, Bill, Comptroller--Tetko, Inc., Briarcliff Manor, NY; *U.S. Private*, pg. 1078
Beutler, Tom, Sec., Treas. & Controller--Beutler Heating & Air Conditioning Inc., Sacramento, CA; *U.S. Private*, pg. 141
Beyer, Tom, V.P.-Controller--Sanford Corporation, Bellwood, IL; *U.S. Public*, pg. 1178
Beyerl, Gregory S., V.P. & Controller--Bindley Western Industries, Inc., Indianapolis, IN; *U.S. Public*, pg. 228
Beyerl, Gregory S., V.P. & Controller--Bindley Western Drug Company, Indianapolis, IN; *U.S. Public*, pg. 228
Beynon, Janne M., Controller--CCL Custom Manufacturing, Niles, IL; *Int'l*, pg. 238
Bhatt, Johnny, Asst. Controller--Coggin Automotive Group, Jacksonville, FL; *U.S. Private*, pg. 250
Bianchi, Carl, Controller--Strauss Discount Auto, South River, NJ; *U.S. Private*, pg. 1046
Biancotti, Peter J., V.P. & Controller--Witco Corporation, Greenwich, CT; *U.S. Public*, pg. 1773
Bianquis, R., Fin. Controller & Mgr.--AEP France S.A.S., Fecamp, France; *U.S. Public*, pg. 5
Biar, L. Scott, Controller & Asst. Sec.--Weatherford Enterra Incorporated, Houston, TX; *U.S. Public*, pg. 1749
Bible, Michael, Controller--El Camino Resources, Ltd., Woodland Hills, CA; *U.S. Private*, pg. 366
Bickel, Wes, Controller--Wellington Regional Medical Center, West Palm Beach, FL; *U.S. Public*, pg. 1697
Bickerstaff, David L., V.P. & Controller--Atmos Energy Corporation, Dallas, TX; *U.S. Public*, pg. 145

Biddle, Jim, Jr., Controller & Dir.-Fin.--Mader Construction Corp, Elma, NY; *U.S. Private*, pg. 693
Bidell, Ron, Controller--Office Products Division, Brattleboro, VT; *U.S. Public*, pg. 620
Biederman, Tom, Controller, Treas. & Sec.--Coleman Cadillac Inc., Bethesda, MD; *U.S. Private*, pg. 251
Biedka, Jeff, Controller--Home Juice Co., Melrose Park, IL; *U.S. Private*, pg. 537
Bielhl, Ed, Controller--Condere Corporation, Natchez, MS; *U.S. Private*, pg. 262
Bielski, Ned, Controller--DBA Systems, Inc., Melbourne, FL; *U.S. Public*, pg. 472
Bielun, John A., Chief Fin. Officer, Sr. V.P. & Treas.--Alta Gold Co., Henderson, NV; *U.S. Public*, pg. 58
Bienenfeld, Ellen, Asst. Chief Fin. Officer--The Solender Group, Inc., Los Angeles, CA; *U.S. Private*, pg. 1012
Bierre, Eric, Controller--ISS-International Service System A/S, Holte, Denmark; *Int'l*, pg. 656
Biese, David, Controller--Carson Pirie Scott & Co., Milwaukee, WI; *U.S. Public*, pg. 309
Biette, Steven, Corp. Controller--Reilly Industries, Inc., Indianapolis, IN; *U.S. Private*, pg. 919
Bietz, Steven L., Controller--Williston Basin Interstate Pipeline Company, Bismarck, ND; *U.S. Public*, pg. 1026
Bijl, Rien, Intl. Controller--Inamed B.V., Breda, Netherlands; *U.S. Public*, pg. 874
Bikowsky, Nancy, Controller--Stapo Hollander Industries, Lakewood, NJ; *U.S. Private*, pg. 1033
Bilello, Phil, V.P. & Controller--John Hassall, Inc., Westbury, NY; *U.S. Private*, pg. 509
Billet, Ken, Controller--Maxcor Manufacturing, Inc., Colorado Springs, CO; *U.S. Private*, pg. 716
Billings, Todd, Controller--Ball Horticultural Company, West Chicago, IL; *U.S. Private*, pg. 112
Billis, Stephen, Controller--Educational Insights, Inc., Carson, CA; *U.S. Public*, pg. 565
Binder, David G., V.P. & Controller--A.P. Green Industries, Inc., Mexico, MO; *U.S. Public*, pg. 761
Binder, Joe, Controller & Sec.--Acme Truck Line, Inc., Harvey, LA; *U.S. Private*, pg. 14
Binder, M., Treas. & Reg. Comptroller--Hilton Canada Inc., Montreal, Canada; *Int'l*, pg. 788
Bindon, Diana, Controller--Colfax Envelope Corporation, Buffalo Grove, IL; *U.S. Private*, pg. 252
Binette, Diane, Controller--Barber Industries, Inc., Edmonton, Canada; *Int'l*, pg. 164
Bingenheimer, Charles G., Jr., Controller--Kingsdown, Inc., Mebane, NC; *U.S. Private*, pg. 622
Bingham, B., Controller (Europe)--Kenner Parker Europe, Maidenhead, United Kingdom; *U.S. Public*, pg. 797
Binkley, Ruth, Controller & Treas.--Cummings Inc., Nashville, TN; *U.S. Private*, pg. 295
Biondi, Cathi, Controller--American Appraisal Italia S.r.l., Milan, Italy; *U.S. Private*, pg. 50
Bird, Patti, Controller--IEC Electronics Corp., Newark, NY; *U.S. Public*, pg. 854
Birdsong, Henry, Chief Fin. Officer--Intelligent Systems Corp., Norcross, GA; *U.S. Public*, pg. 888
Birdsong, Randall G., Controller, Treas. & Sec.--Spencer Companies Inc., Huntsville, AL; *U.S. Private*, pg. 1024
Biro, Jon C., Controller & Treas.--Wedco Technology, Bloomsbury, NJ; *U.S. Public*, pg. 854
Bish, Jacqueline, Controller--TIE Systems Northern California, Hayward, CA; *U.S. Private*, pg. 1085
Bishoff, John, Controller--Steiner Corporation, Salt Lake City, UT; *U.S. Private*, pg. 1039
Bishop, David W., II, Controller--Mine Safety Appliances Co., Pittsburgh, PA; *U.S. Public*, pg. 1114
Bishop, M., Treas. & Fin. Controller--Scholl Plc, Newton, United Kingdom; *Int'l*, pg. 1209
Bishop, Wayne, Controller--Laidlaw Inc., Burlington, Canada; *Int'l*, pg. 259
Bistrom, Helena, Sr. V.P. & Controller--Metra Corporation, Helsinki, Finland; *Int'l*, pg. 862
Bitz, Robyn, Controller--Egan Cos., Minneapolis, MN; *U.S. Private*, pg. 365
Bitzer, Joerg, V.P.-Fin.--Software AG, Darmstadt, Germany; *Int'l*, pg. 1276
Bjelajac, Keith, Controller--Viking Office Products, Torrance, CA; *U.S. Public*, pg. 1720
Bjorkqvist, Krister, Grp. V.P.-Bus. Controller--Polarcup Group Headquarters, Espoo, Finland; *Int'l*, pg. 638
Bjorseth, Raymond G., Controller--Joslyn Corporation, Chicago, IL; *U.S. Public*, pg. 481
Black, Clyde, Controller--REDA, Bartlesville, OK; *U.S. Public*, pg. 298
Black, David, V.P. & Gen. Mgr.--Admiral Heintz, Inc., Wadsworth, OH; *U.S. Public*, pg. 1143
Black, David R., Controller--Bangor Hydro-Electric Company, Bangor, ME; *U.S. Public*, pg. 178
Black, Douglas M., Controller--Bradley Printing Company, Des Plaines, IL; *U.S. Public*, pg. 1778
Black, Kenneth A., Chief Fin. Officer, Grp. V.P.-Corp. Fin., Controller & Treas.--First Citizens Banc Shares, Inc., Raleigh, NC; *U.S. Public*, pg. 628
Black, Kenneth W., Jr., Controller--Lowe's Companies, Inc., North Wilkesboro, NC; *U.S. Public*, pg. 1015
Blackham, Steve, Controller--Bonneville Pacific Corporation, Salt Lake City, UT; *U.S. Public*, pg. 244
Blackledge, Bruce, Controller--Johnson Acoustical & Supply Co., Portland, OR; *U.S. Private*, pg. 590
Blackmon, Charles, Controller--Morgan Manufacturing, Oshkosh, WI; *U.S. Public*, pg. 1132
Blackwood, Clay, Mfg. Controller--Furr's/Bishops, Inc., Lubbock, TX; *U.S. Public*, pg. 689
Blade, Kenneth L., Controller--Chicago Lock Company, Pleasant Prairie, WI; *U.S. Private*, pg. 235
Blair, Barry, Controller--Rex Lumber Company, Acton, MA; *U.S. Private*, pg. 926
Blair, Ed, V.P. & Controller--Shakespeare Fishing Tackle, Columbia, SC; *U.S. Public*, pg. 940
Blair, Kevin, Controller--Daw Technologies, Inc., Salt Lake City, UT; *U.S. Public*, pg. 489
Blake, Barry R., V.P. & Controller--Perini Corporation, Framingham, MA; *U.S. Public*, pg. 1278
Blake, Joy, Asst. Controller--Active Tool & Manufacturing Co., Inc., Roseville, MI; *U.S. Private*, pg. 16
Blake, Pat, Controller--Myers Industries, Inc., Akron, OH; *U.S. Public*, pg. 1143
Blake, Roger E., V.P. & Controller--Daubert Coated Products, Inc., Westchester, IL; *U.S. Private*, pg. 313
Blakely, Hugh W., V.P. & Controller--The Ivaco Group, Montreal, Canada; *Int'l*, pg. 695
Blakely, Robert E., Chief Acctg. Officer, V.P. & Controller--Xtra Corporation, Boston, MA; *U.S. Public*, pg. 1786
Blakslee, Ida, Controller--Eckman Construction Company, Bedford, NH; *U.S. Private*, pg. 359
Blanchard, Craig A., V.P.-Fin., Controller & Treas.--Sheldons' Inc., Antigo, WI; *U.S. Private*, pg. 992
Blanchard, Earl, Chief Fin. Officer, V.P. & Controller--Sturm, Ruger & Co., Inc., Southport, CT; *U.S. Public*, pg. 1526
Blanco, Bruce, Controller--ADAC Laboratories Inc., Milpitas, CA; *U.S. Public*, pg. 3
Blanco, Bruce, Controller--CCI/Triad Automotive, Livermore, CA; *U.S. Private*, pg. 193
Blanda, James A., V.P. & Controller--Sears, Roebuck and Co., Hoffman Estates, IL; *U.S. Public*, pg. 1452
Blaney, Joseph A., Controller--Clark Grave Vault Co., Columbus, OH; *U.S. Private*, pg. 243
Blankenship, Rodney W., V.P. & Controller--Blount International, Inc., Montgomery, AL; *U.S. Public*, pg. 237
Blankenship, Rodney W., V.P. & Controller--Blount, Inc., Montgomery, AL; *U.S. Public*, pg. 238
Blanton, Lisa, Controller--Birmingham Steel Corp., Cleveland Div., Cleveland, OH; *U.S. Public*, pg. 232
Blass, Richard C., V.P. & Controller--Informix Software, Menlo Park, CA; *U.S. Public*, pg. 876
Blatt, Mike, Controller & Treas.--Future Foam, Inc., Council Bluffs, IA; *U.S. Private*, pg. 433
Blaxton, Cooper, J., Controller--Lampert Yards, Inc., Saint Paul, MN; *U.S. Private*, pg. 645
Blazie, Al, Controller--Maxxim Medical, Inc., Clearwater, FL; *U.S. Public*, pg. 1063
Bleeker, Mark, Controller--Howard Miller, Zeeland, MI; *U.S. Private*, pg. 747
Bleens, Deidre, Controller--Addington Resources, Inc., Lexington, KY; *U.S. Public*, pg. 1379
Bleier, Frederick L., Treas. & Controller--IP Timberlands, Ltd., Purchase, NY; *U.S. Public*, pg. 904
Bleser, Howard, Controller--American Marine Holdings Inc., Sarasota, FL; *U.S. Private*, pg. 58
Blevins, Terry, Controller--The Virginian-Pilot, Norfolk, VA; *U.S. Private*, pg. 649
Blickens, Robert, V.P.-Fin., Treas. & Controller--Komline-Sanderson Engineering Corp., Peapack, NJ; *U.S. Private*, pg. 631
Block, Karla, Controller--Condon Oil Company, Inc., Ripon, WI; *U.S. Private*, pg. 262
Bloem, Majorie, Controller--Phoenixville Newspapers, Inc., Phoenixville, PA; *U.S. Public*, pg. 935
Blohm, Douglas L., Controller--Riceland Foods, Inc., Stuttgart, AR; *U.S. Private*, pg. 928
Bloom, Richard, Exec. V.P.--TST/Impreso, Inc., Coppell, TX; *U.S. Private*, pg. 1066
Bloom, Ted, Controller--International Data Group, Boston, MA; *U.S. Private*, pg. 569
Bluhm, Robert, Controller--Pope & Talbot, Inc., Portland, OR; *U.S. Public*, pg. 1316
Blum, Michael, Controller--Utility Trailer Manufacturing Co., City of Industry, CA; *U.S. Private*, pg. 1130
Blumberg, Richard, Controller--The Titan Industrial Corp., New York, NY; *U.S. Private*, pg. 1089
Blume, David, Controlller--McInerney-Miller Brothers Inc., Detroit, MI; *U.S. Private*, pg. 722
Blundell, John F., Asst. Comptroller--Westvaco Corporation, New York, NY; *U.S. Public*, pg. 1762
Boada, Andy, Controller--Fedco, Inc., Santa Fe Springs, CA; *U.S. Private*, pg. 398
Boane, Greg, Controller--Noble Offshore Corporation, Houston, TX; *U.S. Public*, pg. 1186
Boardman, Lee, Controller--Ballard Medical Products, Draper, UT; *U.S. Public*, pg. 171
Boase, Steve, Chief Fin. Officer & V.P.--McKinney & Silver, Raleigh, NC; *U.S. Private*, pg. 723
Bobel, Mary, Chief Fin. Officer--Genus Inc., Sunnyvale, CA; *U.S. Public*, pg. 732
Bobo, April, Sec. & Controller--Olen Corporation, Columbus, OH; *U.S. Private*, pg. 631
Bocchini, W. Perry, Asst. Controller--The Penn Traffic Company, Syracuse, NY; *U.S. Public*, pg. 1270
Bock, John, III, Controller--Hamilton Communications Group, Inc., Chicago, IL; *U.S. Private*, pg. 497
Bock, Mike, Controller--Coolidge Glass Co., Inc., Waukesha, WI; *U.S. Private*, pg. 273
Bodinger, Bill, Controller--Kinray Inc., Whitestone, NY; *U.S. Private*, pg. 622
Bodinger, Bill, Controller--Sunbelt Beverages, Lutherville, MD; *U.S. Private*, pg. 1051
Bodinger, Bruce, Controller--Schneider Mills, Inc., New York, NY; *U.S. Private*, pg. 971
Bodnar, Jeff, Controller--Manning Equipment, Inc., Louisville, KY; *U.S. Private*, pg. 700
Bodner, David, Controller--Kraft Hardware, Inc., New York, NY; *U.S. Private*, pg. 634
Bodziony, Dennis, Controller--Atlas Cylinder, Eugene, OR; *U.S. Public*, pg. 1261
Boehmer, Douglas, V.P. & Controller--Associated Wholesale Grocers, Inc., Kansas City, KS; *U.S. Private*, pg. 93
Boen, Kevin, Controller--Maxon Corporation, Muncie, IN; *U.S. Private*, pg. 716
Boergert, Amy, Controller--Contract Interiors Inc., Taylor, MI; *U.S. Private*, pg. 270
Boersma, Mark, Controller--Seton Company, Norristown, PA; *U.S. Private*, pg. 987
Boeshart, Frank, V.P., Controller & Treas.--Terminal Grain Corp., Sioux City, IA; *U.S. Private*, pg. 1077
Bogaert, Jacques, Controller--GEODIS, Paris, France; *Int'l*, pg. 549
Bogdan, JoAnn, Chief Acctg. Officer & Controller--Dayton Hudson Corporation, Minneapolis, MN; *U.S. Public*, pg. 489
Boggio, Gayle, Comptroller--Asoma Corporation, White Plains, NY; *U.S. Private*, pg. 89
Bohner, Dan A., Controller--Adventure Lands of America, Inc., Des Moines, IA; *U.S. Private*, pg. 22
Bohner, Gerhard, Mng. Dir.-Fin. & Controlling--Landis & Staefa AG, Zug, Switzerland; *Int'l*, pg. 800
Bohnsack, M. Gregory, Controller--Dynamics Corporation of America, Greenwich, CT; *U.S. Public*, pg. 286
Boik, Karen, Controller--Great Lakes Wholesale Drugs, Livonia, MI; *U.S. Private*, pg. 475
Boillargeon, Marcel, Comptroller & Treas.--Telebec Ltee, Anjou, Canada; *Int'l*, pg. 116
Boisvert, Catherine M., V.P. & Controller--Farrel Corporation, Ansonia, CT; *U.S. Public*, pg. 614
Boisvert, Kenneth, Controller--Teleflex Fluid Systems Inc., Suffield, CT; *U.S. Public*, pg. 1569
Boka, Nora, Controller--Dacor Corporation, Northfield, IL; *U.S. Private*, pg. 306
Bokfpan, Steve, Controller--Color Spot Nursery, Inc., Pleasant Hill, CA; *U.S. Private*, pg. 254
Boland, James, Controller--Central Illinois Steel Company, Carlinville, IL; *U.S. Private*, pg. 223
Boland, Nick, Exec. Fin. Dir. & Controller--MTI Ireland, Dublin, Ireland; *U.S. Public*, pg. 1028
Boldt, Wendy J., Asst. Controller--Mathews & Boucher, Rochester, NY; *U.S. Private*, pg. 714
Bolha, John, Asst. Controller--Southwest National Corporation, Greensburg, PA; *U.S. Public*, pg. 1493
Boling, Paul F., Controller--Cabot Oil & Gas Corporation, Houston, TX; *U.S. Public*, pg. 289
Bollinger, Michele A., Comptroller--Galamba Metals, Inc., Kansas City, KS; *U.S. Private*, pg. 437
Bolton, Mary Ann, Controller--Wolverine Gasket & Manufacturing Co., Inkster, MI; *U.S. Private*, pg. 355
Bonade, David, Controller--Metpar Corp., Westbury, NY; *U.S. Private*, pg. 735
Bonaker, Dave, Controller--Columbus Mills, Inc., Columbus, GA; *U.S. Private*, pg. 256
Bond, David M., Controller, Sec. & Asst. Treas.--International Dairy Queen, Inc., Minneapolis, MN; *U.S. Public*, pg. 220
Bond, David M., Controller & Asst. Treas.--American Dairy Queen Corporation, Minneapolis, MN; *U.S. Public*, pg. 220
Bond, Lura, Controller--Delta Life Corporation, Memphis, TN; *U.S. Private*, pg. 59
Bondoc, Evelyn, Controller, Computer Opers. & Personnel--GWP, Inc., Los Angeles, CA; *U.S. Private*, pg. 437
Bonds, Gary, Sr. V.P. & Controller--Bancorp South Inc., Tupelo, MS; *U.S. Public*, pg. 176
Bonds, Gary C., Comptroller--Bank of Mississippi, Tupelo, MS; *U.S. Public*, pg. 176
Bonds, Michael, V.P. & Controller--Continental Airlines, Houston, TX; *U.S. Public*, pg. 439
Bonenberger, Lee, Asst. Controller--Versar Inc., Springfield, VA; *U.S. Public*, pg. 1717
Bongiorno, Annette, Controller--DM Management Company, Hingham, MA; *U.S. Public*, pg. 473
Boniello, Michael, V.P.-Fin. & Controller--Penco Products, Oaks, PA; *U.S. Private*, pg. 848
Boniello, Michael P., Controller--Vester Corporation, Newtown Square, PA; *U.S. Private*, pg. 86
Bonk, Michael, V.P. & Controller--Bachman's, Inc., Minneapolis, MN; *U.S. Private*, pg. 109
Bonkoski, Ken J., Controller--Menasha Corporation, Neenah, WI; *U.S. Private*, pg. 731
Bonnar, C.E., Controller--Brenco, Inc., Petersburg, VA; *U.S. Public*, pg. 1710
Bonner, Missy, Controller--Beck Manufacturing, Inc., Waynesboro, PA; *U.S. Private*, pg. 146
Bonner, Nancy D., V.P. & Controller-Opers. Acctg.--Freeport-McMoRan Inc., New Orleans, LA; *U.S. Public*, pg. 680
Bonner, Wendy, Controller--Barton Malow Enterprises, Inc., Southfield, MI; *U.S. Private*, pg. 120
Bonney, Jeffrey A., Chief Acctg. Officer & V.P.--Louis Dreyfus Natural Gas Corp., Oklahoma City, OK; *U.S. Private*, pg. 342
Bonsol, Fernando, Comptroller--Gaffney-Kroese Electrical Supply Corp., Rahway, NJ; *U.S. Private*, pg. 437
Bonyko, Blake, Controller--The Middleby Corporation, Rolling Meadows, IL; *U.S. Public*, pg. 1109
Bonyko, Blake, Controller--Middleby Marshall/CTX, Elgin, IL; *U.S. Public*, pg. 1110
Booher, R.D., Comptroller--Ranger Oil Limited, Calgary, Canada; *Int'l*, pg. 1086
Booker, John P., V.P. & Controller--Old Dominion Freight Line, Inc., High Point, NC; *U.S. Public*, pg. 1216
Boomer, Brian, Controller--Ameripol Synpol Corp., Port Neches, TX; *U.S. Private*, pg. 65
Boomer, Brian, Controller--Engineered Carbons Inc., Borger, TX; *U.S. Private*, pg. 65
Boone, Sharon D., Controller & Asst. Sec.--Public Service Company of North Carolina, Inc., Gastonia, NC; *U.S. Public*, pg. 1340
Booth, Barbara, Controller & Treas.--Space Master International, Atlanta, GA; *U.S. Private*, pg. 1019
Booth, James R., Controller--Beemak Plastics, Gardena, CA; *U.S. Private*, pg. 598
Booth, John, Controller--Bass PLC, London, United Kingdom; *Int'l*, pg. 169
Booth, Marcia, Controller--Main Brothers Oil Company, Inc., Albany, NY; *U.S. Private*, pg. 697
Borak, Robert L., Treas., Controller & Sec.--McGraw-Hill Securities Trading, Inc., New York, NY; *U.S. Public*, pg. 1071
Borg, Frank, Controller--Hyatt Corporation, Chicago, IL; *U.S. Private*, pg. 551

Borgen, P., Comptroller--Opel Norge AS, Skedsmokorset, Norway; *U.S. Public*, pg. 723
Borgersen, Kari, Controller--Sensormatic A/S, Oslo, Norway; *U.S. Public*, pg. 1457
Borgeson, Dan, Controller--Sommer & Maca Industries, Inc., Cicero, IL; *U.S. Private*, pg. 1013
Borgman, Jerry, Controller & Treas.--Lyon's Restaurants, Inc., Foster City, CA; *U.S. Private*, pg. 684
Borinski, Michael, V.P. & Controller--United States Cold Storage, Inc., Cherry Hill, NJ; *U.S. Private*, pg. 1124
Bork, Larry, Controller & Dir.-Admin.--Lundia Div. of MII, Inc., Jacksonville, IL; *U.S. Private*, pg. 680
Borlinghaus, Scott, Controller & Sec.--John Fabick Tractor Company, Fenton, MO; *U.S. Private*, pg. 390
Borman, Gary, V.P. & Corp. Controller--Matthews Studio Equipment, Burbank, CA; *U.S. Public*, pg. 1060
Borocz, Michael S., Sr. V.P. & Controller--PNC Bank, Camp Hill, PA; *U.S. Public*, pg. 1243
Boross, Steve, Asst. Controller--Pioneer Paper Corporation, Carlstadt, NJ; *U.S. Private*, pg. 867
Borowicz, Donna, Controller--American Institute of C.P.A.'s Inc., New York, NY; *U.S. Private*, pg. 57
Borowy, Chester, Controller--Jarvis-Pemco, Kalamazoo, MI; *U.S. Public*, pg. 1506
Borst, Robert, Controller--Universal Composites-U.S.C., Manheim, PA; *U.S. Private*, pg. 1126
Boskelly, Linda, Controller--Wirtz Corporation, Chicago, IL; *U.S. Private*, pg. 1184
Bosscher, Tom, Controller--Bissell Inc., Grand Rapids, MI; *U.S. Private*, pg. 145
Bossert, James P., V.P. & Controller--The New England, Boston, MA; *U.S. Private*, pg. 737
Bost, Walter, Chief Fin. Officer--Ridgeview, Inc., Newton, NC; *U.S. Private*, pg. 930
Boswell, William E., Controller, Accounting Svcs. & Fin. Reporting--BP Oil Co., Cleveland, OH; *Int'l*, pg. 220
Bosworth, Theodore G., Corp. Controller--Schenectady International, Inc., Schenectady, NY; *U.S. Private*, pg. 969
Bothe, Dan, Controller--Trimfoot Company, Farmington, MO; *U.S. Public*, pg. 1684
Bottiglieri, James J., V.P. & Controller--Petroleum Heat & Power Co., Stamford, CT; *U.S. Public*, pg. 1281
Bottini, Giancarlo, Chief Fin. Officer--Benetton Group S.p.A., Ponzano Veneto, Italy; *Int'l*, pg. 186
Bottoms, Beth, Controller--Ilco Unican Corp., Simplex Access Controls Division, Winston Salem, NC; *Int'l*, pg. 1432
Bouchard, Clement, Controller--Imprimerie Quebecor Lebonfon, Val d'Or, Canada; *Int'l*, pg. 1077
Bouchardy, Eric, Controller--Fotolabo S.A., Lausanne, Switzerland; *Int'l*, pg. 501
Boudreau, Gilles, Controller--Drake Bakeries, Inc., Wayne, NJ; *Int'l*, pg. 349
Boulay, David, Controller--Carlson Systems, Omaha, NE; *U.S. Private*, pg. 212
Boulay, Joseph, Comptroller--Catholic Digest, Saint Paul, MN; *U.S. Private*, pg. 220
Bourg, Cindy, Controller--Eatelcorp Inc., Gonzales, LA; *U.S. Private*, pg. 358
Bourque, D., Controller--Presstek, Inc., Hudson, NH; *U.S. Public*, pg. 1324
Boutwell, David, V.P. & Controller--Harbert Corporation, Birmingham, AL; *U.S. Private*, pg. 500
Bowden, Angie, Controller--Spring Engineers of Houston Ltd., Houston, TX; *U.S. Private*, pg. 956
Bowden, David G., V.P., Controller & Sec.--Griffin Group, Inc., New York, NY; *U.S. Private*, pg. 480
Bowden, Mac, Controller--Walker Die Casting, Inc., Lewisburg, TN; *U.S. Private*, pg. 1147
Bowdring, Robert J., Controller--Lifeline Systems, Inc., Cambridge, MA; *U.S. Public*, pg. 992
Bowe, Bob, Controller & Dir.--Network Equipment Technologies, Inc., Redwood City, CA; *U.S. Public*, pg. 1168
Bowen-Ashwin, Graham, V.P. & Controller--Elf Atochem North America, Inc., Philadelphia, PA; *Int'l*, pg. 445
Bowen, James E., Comptroller & Sec.--Better Living Inc., Charlottesville, VA; *U.S. Private*, pg. 141
Bowen, Randy, Controller--Battey Machinery Company, Rome, GA; *U.S. Private*, pg. 123
Bowers, Patrick, Controller--National Machinery, Tiffin, OH; *U.S. Private*, pg. 785
Bowlin, Janet, Controller--Henderson Auctions, Livingston, LA; *U.S. Private*, pg. 577
Bowling, Beverly, V.P. & Controller--Whataburger, Inc., Corpus Christi, TX; *U.S. Private*, pg. 1170
Bowling, John, Controller--FDP Corp., Miami, FL; *U.S. Public*, pg. 603
Bowling, Ron, Controller-Div.--Robertshaw Tennessee, Knoxville, TN; *Int'l*, pg. 1243
Bowman, Kathy, Controller & Treas.--B & K Steel & Supply, Inc., Ogden, UT; *U.S. Private*, pg. 105
Bowman, Richard F., V.P. & Controller--First Virginia Life Insurance Company, Falls Church, VA; *U.S. Public*, pg. 642
Bowman, Timothy P., Asst. Controller--American Electric Power Service Corp., Columbus, OH; *U.S. Public*, pg. 72
Bowshier, Terry, V.P. & Controller--State Automobile Mutual Insurance Co., Columbus, OH; *U.S. Private*, pg. 1036
Boyce, Alan F., Controller--Hosokawa Micron Australia Pty. Ltd., Wetherill Park, Australia; *Int'l*, pg. 636
Boyce, Brian, V.P.-Fin. & Corp. Controller--Arch Communications Group, Inc., Westborough, MA; *U.S. Public*, pg. 127
Boyd, Delen, V.P. & Controller--Avondale Incorporated, Monroe, GA; *U.S. Private*, pg. 102
Boyd, Jean, Controller--Culinary Foods Group, Glendale, CA; *Int'l*, pg. 917
Boyd, Lester D., Controller & Office Mgr.--Harrison Paint Corp., Canton, OH; *U.S. Private*, pg. 506
Boyda, James, Controller--Palmer Moving & Storage Co., Troy, MI; *U.S. Private*, pg. 835
Boyer, George W., Controller--Hamilton Equipment, Inc., Ephrata, PA; *U.S. Private*, pg. 497
Boyer, Jeffrey L., Controller--Duke Energy Corporation, Charlotte, NC; *U.S. Public*, pg. 534
Boyer, Joseph M., Controller--Dunn Reber Glenn Marz, Reno, NV; *U.S. Private*, pg. 347
Boyer, Norman L., Dir.-Fin. & Acct.--United McGill Corp., Groveport, OH; *U.S. Private*, pg. 1122
Boyer, Terry, Controller--Avibank Mfg., Inc., Burbank, CA; *U.S. Private*, pg. 101
Boyet, Charles, Controller & Treas.--Sigmund Cohn Corp., Mount Vernon, NY; *U.S. Private*, pg. 250
Boyette, John G., V.P. & Controller--Cox Enterprises, Inc., Atlanta, GA; *U.S. Private*, pg. 281
Boykin, Frank A., Controller--Mohawk Industries, Inc., Calhoun, GA; *U.S. Public*, pg. 1121
Boylan, Bob, Controller--Sonoma Mission Inn & Spa, Sonoma, CA; *U.S. Private*, pg. 1014
Boyle, Brian, Controller--Dover Flour Mills, Cambridge, Canada; *Int'l*, pg. 417
Boyle, Francis C., Jr., V.P. & Controller--Barnes Group Inc., Bristol, CT; *U.S. Public*, pg. 189
Boyle, James, Sr. V.P., Controller & Treas.--Broad National Bancorporation, Newark, NJ; *U.S. Public*, pg. 257
Boyle, James, Sr. V.P. & Comptroller--Broad National Bank, Newark, NJ; *U.S. Public*, pg. 257
Boyle, Terry, Controller--The Failure Group, Inc., Menlo Park, CA; *U.S. Public*, pg. 609
Boynton, Judith G., V.P. & Controller--Amoco Corporation, Chicago, IL; *U.S. Public*, pg. 101
Bozarth, William T., V.P. & Controller--Travelers Group, New York, NY; *U.S. Public*, pg. 1632
Bozzell, W. Scott, V.P. & Controller--Piccadilly Cafeterias, Inc., Baton Rouge, LA; *U.S. Public*, pg. 1294
Braber, James Den, Controller--Louis Padnos Iron & Metal Co., Holland, MI; *U.S. Private*, pg. 834
Brace, Frederic F., V.P. & Controller--UAL Corporation, Elk Grove Village, IL; *U.S. Public*, pg. 1652
Brace, Frederic F., V.P.-Fin. & Controller--United Air Lines, Inc., Elk Grove Village, IL; *U.S. Public*, pg. 1653
Brace, John, Controller--Astre Corporate Group, Alexandria, VA; *U.S. Private*, pg. 93
Brachna, Michael A., Controller--PMC Industries Inc., Wickliffe, OH; *U.S. Private*, pg. 827
Bracken, Gary, Sr. V.P. & Controller--TCI Communications, Inc., Englewood, CO; *U.S. Public*, pg. 1554
Bracker, Brian, Controller--Packaging Resources, Incorporated, Lake Forest, IL; *U.S. Private*, pg. 833
Brada, Tim, Controller--Emkay, Inc., Itasca, IL; *U.S. Private*, pg. 374
Bradburn, Thomas J., V.P.-Fin. & Controller--Newport News Shipbuilding, Inc., Newport News, VA; *U.S. Public*, pg. 1179
Braddock, David, Controller--Inductotherm Corp., Rancocas, NJ; *U.S. Private*, pg. 560
Bradley, Karyn, Controller--Ruscon Corp., Charleston, SC; *U.S. Private*, pg. 952
Bradley, Kevin B., Chief Oper. Officer & Controller--Taylor & Francis Philadelphia, Bristol, PA; *Int'l*, pg. 1358
Bradley, P.C., Controller--Park Air Electronics Ltd., Peterborough, United Kingdom; *U.S. Public*, pg. 1198
Bradley, Rodney, Controller--Little Switzerland, Inc., Charlotte Amalie, VI; *U.S. Public*, pg. 1001
Bradley, Thomas F., V.P. & Grp. Controller--Newell Co., Freeport, IL; *U.S. Public*, pg. 1176
Bradly, Charles E., Controller & Treas.--Fabreeka International, Inc., Stoughton, MA; *U.S. Private*, pg. 390
Bradshaw, Jim, Chief Fin. Officer & Controller--Bruce Industries, Inc., Dayton, NV; *U.S. Private*, pg. 175
Bradshaw, Karen, Controller--Amspec Chemical Corporation, Gloucester City, NJ; *U.S. Private*, pg. 67
Brady, Darren, Controller--MHM Services Inc., Vienna, VA; *U.S. Public*, pg. 1027
Brady, David, Chief Fin. Officer & Controller--Deluxe Storage Systems, Inc., Warren, PA; *U.S. Private*, pg. 323
Brady, Ed, Controller--Johns Manville Corporation, Denver, CO; *U.S. Public*, pg. 927
Brady, Lona, Treas. & Controller--Army Times Publishing Co., Springfield, VA; *U.S. Public*, pg. 699
Brady, William L., V.P. & Controller--Foodbrands America, Inc., Oklahoma City, OK; *U.S. Public*, pg. 852
Braly, Doug, Controller--Cassens Transport Company, Edwardsville, IL; *U.S. Private*, pg. 219
Branch, Keith, Controller--Bundy Corporation, Cartersville Plant, Cartersville, GA; *Int'l*, pg. 1340
Branche, Francois, Treas. & Controller--Calberson, Paris, France; *Int'l*, pg. 1163
Brancheau, Patrick, V.P. & Controller--Holley Replacement Parts Division, Bowling Green, KY; *U.S. Public*, pg. 402
Brand, Joseph A., Controller--Royal Oak Mines Inc., Kirkland, WA; *U.S. Public*, pg. 1410
Brand, Robert L., V.P. & Controller--McDonnell Aircraft & Missile Systems Div., Berkeley, MO; *U.S. Public*, pg. 241
Brandell, Steven, Controller--Propak Systems Ltd., Airdrie, Canada; *Int'l*, pg. 1071
Brandon, Adrienne H., V.P. & Controller--United Cities Gas Company, Brentwood, TN; *U.S. Public*, pg. 146
Brandsderfer, Richard, Controller--Shipley Companies, York, PA; *U.S. Private*, pg. 994
Brandstein, Zvi, Controller--Elscint Ltd., Haifa, Israel; *Int'l*, pg. 450
Brandt, D.E., V.P. & Controller--Union Electric Development Corporation, Saint Louis, MO; *U.S. Public*, pg. 66
Brandt, D.E., Controller--Union Electric Steel Corp., Carnegie, PA; *U.S. Public*, pg. 103
Brannan, C. Scott, V.P.-Admin. & Controller--Danaher Corporation, Washington, DC; *U.S. Public*, pg. 480
Brannen, Andy, Controller--Amplicon, Inc., Santa Ana, CA; *U.S. Public*, pg. 104
Brannon, M. Lamar, Jr., Controller--Vulcan Materials Company-Mideast Div., Winston Salem, NC; *U.S. Public*, pg. 1725
Brashaw, Gerald L., V.P., Controller & Treas.--Paragon Electric Co., Inc., Two Rivers, WI; *Int'l*, pg. 1243
Brashaw, John, Controller--Danfoss Fluid Power, a division of Danfoss, Inc., Racine, WI; *Int'l*, pg. 377
Brassfield, W. Kirk, Controller--Mapco Petroleum Inc., Tulsa, OK; *U.S. Public*, pg. 1042
Bratton, Mike, Controller--Watt, Roop & Co., Cleveland, OH; *U.S. Private*, pg. 1154
Brattwall, Christer, Controller--BTL AB, Goteborg, Sweden; *Int'l*, pg. 123
Braum, Thomas C., Jr., V.P. & Controller--Handleman Company, Troy, MI; *U.S. Public*, pg. 779
Braun, Charles A., Controller--Communications Systems, Inc., Hector, MN; *U.S. Public*, pg. 415
Braun, James E., V.P. & Controller--Baker Hughes Incorporated, Houston, TX; *U.S. Public*, pg. 165
Brauner, Hans U., Controller--Jagenberg AG, Neuss, Germany; *Int'l*, pg. 1108
Bray, David L., Controller--HPS, Inc., Indianapolis, IN; *U.S. Private*, pg. 492
Bray, Stan, Controller--Bizzack Inc., Lexington, KY; *U.S. Private*, pg. 146
Brayman, Mark, Controller--Electrical Insulation Suppliers, Atlanta, GA; *U.S. Private*, pg. 368
Brazeau, Richard, V.P. & Controller--Standard Manufacturing Co., Inc., Troy, NY; *U.S. Private*, pg. 1031
Brazell, Kim, Controller--Ederer Inc., Seattle, WA; *U.S. Private*, pg. 363
Brazinski, Albert, Controller--E.H. Titchener & Company, Binghamton, NY; *U.S. Private*, pg. 1089
Breece, Lorraine, Chief Acctg. Officer & Controller--Nabi, Boca Raton, FL; *U.S. Public*, pg. 1148
Brega, Rick, Controller--General Automation, Inc., Irvine, CA; *U.S. Public*, pg. 706
Breger, Rex, Chief Fin. Officer & Controller--Milprint Inc., Oshkosh, WI; *U.S. Public*, pg. 210
Breiland, Leslie K., V.P. & Controller--Block Drug Company, Inc., Jersey City, NJ; *U.S. Public*, pg. 236
Breisinger, James R., V.P. & Controller--Kennametal Inc., Latrobe, PA; *U.S. Public*, pg. 950
Breitenstein, Bill, Controller--Nordstrom, Inc., Seattle, WA; *U.S. Public*, pg. 1190
Brekelbaum, J.F., Controller--International Columbia Resources Corporation, Bogota, Colombia; *U.S. Public*, pg. 602
Brendel, Rick, Mgr.-Office--Owen Industries, Inc., Carter Lake, IA; *U.S. Private*, pg. 824
Brenn, James E., V.P. & Controller--Briggs & Stratton Corporation, Wauwatosa, WI; *U.S. Public*, pg. 252
Brennan, Ann, V.P. & Controller--Chicago Creative Partnership, Chicago, IL; *U.S. Private*, pg. 234
Brennan, Diane, Controller & Sec.--Thruway Fasteners Inc., North Tonawanda, NY; *U.S. Private*, pg. 1084
Brennan, Steve, Controller--NWW Properties Limited, Risley, United Kingdom; *Int'l*, pg. 1444
Brenner, Jeffrey, Chief Fin. Officer--Database America Companies, Montvale, NJ; *U.S. Private*, pg. 312
Brenner, Michael D., Corp. Controller--Production Tool Supply Co., Warren, MI; *U.S. Private*, pg. 889
Brenner, Mike, Controller--Power Control Div., Bowling Green, KY; *U.S. Public*, pg. 556
Brenzee, John, Controller--State Industries Inc., Ashland City, TN; *U.S. Private*, pg. 1036
Bresett, Norah K., C.P.A., Asst. V.P. & Controller--Litchfield Financial Corporation, Williamstown, MA; *U.S. Public*, pg. 1001
Breslow, Jay, Controller--Camerican International, Paramus, NJ; *U.S. Public*, pg. 426
Bresnahan, Timothy T., Controller--Hynes Industries Inc., Youngstown, OH; *U.S. Private*, pg. 552
Brever, Ted, Controller--M. Fine & Sons Manufacturing Co., Inc., New York, NY; *U.S. Private*, pg. 405
Brewer, Jackie, V.P. & Controller--Minyard Food Stores, Inc., Coppell, TX; *U.S. Private*, pg. 752
Brewer, Kim, Controller--The Disston Co., Greensboro, NC; *U.S. Public*, pg. 950
Brewton, Gerald, Controller & Mgr.-Cash Mngmt., Employee Ben. & Human Resources--Jerry Hamm Chevrolet Inc., Jacksonville, FL; *U.S. Private*, pg. 497
Breyfogle, Kathy, Controller--Gilmore Bros., Inc., Kalamazoo, MI; *U.S. Private*, pg. 454
Briggs, John, Asst. V.P., Controller & Sec.--Hy-Vee Food Stores Incorporated, West Des Moines, IA; *U.S. Private*, pg. 550
Brigham, Douglas L., Controller--Morrison Knudsen Corporation, Boise, ID; *U.S. Public*, pg. 1133
Brinek, Alfred, Asst. Treas., Controller--Voest-Alpine Industries, Inc., New York, NY; *Int'l*, pg. 1470
Bringham, Nancy F., Asst. Controller--JC Penney Company, Inc., Plano, TX; *U.S. Public*, pg. 916
Brink, Brian, Controller--Bil Mar Foods, Inc., Zeeland, MI; *U.S. Public*, pg. 1433
Brinkley, Michael G., V.P. & Corp. Controller--Whitehall Corporation, Dallas, TX; *U.S. Public*, pg. 1765
Brinkman, Tom, Controller--FMC-Smith Meter Co., Erie, PA; *U.S. Public*, pg. 605
Brisley, Peter, Controller--Klaussner Furniture Industry, Asheboro, NC; *U.S. Private*, pg. 625
Bristol, Gerald A., V.P.-Fin., Controller & Treas.--Red Wing Shoe Co., Inc., Red Wing, MN; *U.S. Private*, pg. 915
Brittelli, Brenda S., Chief Fin. Officer, Controller, Treas. & Sec.--Adams Wine Co., Atlanta, GA; *U.S. Private*, pg. 17
Britton, M.E., Controller--Federal Industries Metals Group, Etobicoke, Canada; *Int'l*, pg. 1150
Britton, Marion E., V.P., Controller & Asst. Sec.--Russel Metals Inc., Mississauga, Canada; *Int'l*, pg. 1149
Broadbent, Curtis, Controller--Vulcraft Div., Brigham City, UT; *U.S. Public*, pg. 1206
Broadhead, George, Acting Controller--Mobil Oil Corporation, Fairfax, VA; *U.S. Public*, pg. 1118
Broady, Maxim, Asst. Comptroller--Avenor, Inc., Montreal, Canada; *Int'l*, pg. 101
Brock, Blake, Controller--Corrections Corporation of America, Nashville, TN; *U.S. Public*, pg. 450
Brock, Laurence M., V.P. & Controller--Unitil Corporation, Hampton, NH; *U.S. Public*, pg. 1692

Brock, Laurence M., Controller--Concord Electric Company, Hampton, NH; *U.S. Public*, pg. 1692
Brock, Laurence M., Controller--UNITIL Resources, Inc., Hampton, NH; *U.S. Public*, pg. 1692
Brock, Laurence M., Controller--UNITIL Service Corporation, Hampton, NH; *U.S. Public*, pg. 1693
Brock, Lynn, Comptroller--Holiday RV Superstores, Inc.-Ft. Myers, Fort Myers, FL; *U.S. Public*, pg. 830
Brockway, M., Fin. Controller & Sec.--Senior Conflow, Nottingham, United Kingdom; *Int'l*, pg. 1220
Broder, Jeff, Controller & Treas.--HLB Communications, Inc., Chicago, IL; *U.S. Private*, pg. 491
Brodigan, Martin, Fin. Controller--Savin Canada Inc., North York, Canada; *Int'l*, pg. 1116
Brodnan, Richard, Controller--Foulds Inc., Libertyville, IL; *U.S. Private*, pg. 421
Broekema, Rita A., Controller--Autocam Corporation, Grand Rapids, MI; *U.S. Public*, pg. 148
Broley, William G., Comptroller--Hawker Siddeley Canada Inc., Mississauga, Canada; *Int'l*, pg. 604
Brolund, Robert T., Controller--Bulldog Co., Memphis, TN; *U.S. Public*, pg. 1176
Bromme, Mike, Controller--North Carolina Mutual Wholesale Drug Co., Durham, NC; *U.S. Private*, pg. 804
Bronson, Deborah, Controller--Pike Industries Inc., Tilton, NH; *Int'l*, pg. 242
Bronstein, Andrew P., V.P. & Controller--SunGard Data Systems Inc., Wayne, PA; *U.S. Public*, pg. 1534
Brook, James S., V.P. & Controller--UtiliCorp United Inc., Kansas City, MO; *U.S. Public*, pg. 1700
Brooks-Brown, Carrie, V.P. & Asst. Controller--The Gap, Inc., San Francisco, CA; *U.S. Public*, pg. 702
Brooks, Donald, Controller--Peabody Office Furniture Corporation, Boston, MA; *U.S. Private*, pg. 844
Brooks, E.B., Chief Acct. Officer & Controller--Trico Products Corporation, Buffalo, NY; *Int'l*, pg. 1397
Brooks, Karyn, Controller--Transcanada Pipelines Limited, Calgary, Canada; *Int'l*, pg. 1416
Brooks, M. S., Grp. Fin. Controller--Bridport-Gundry p.l.c., Dorset, United Kingdom; *Int'l*, pg. 215
Brooks, Ron, V.P.-Fin. & Controller--Gunnebo Fastening Corp., Lonoke, AR; *U.S. Private*, pg. 488
Broome, Burton E., V.P. & Controller--Transamerica Corporation, San Francisco, CA; *U.S. Public*, pg. 1629
Broome, H. Cuy, Jr., Controller & Treas.--Harry Pepper & Associates, Jacksonville, FL; *U.S. Private*, pg. 851
Brophy, Jacqueline R., Asst. Comptroller--Westvaco Corporation, New York, NY; *U.S. Public*, pg. 1762
Brosseau, Bill, Controller--Pollak Division, Boston, MA; *U.S. Private*, pg. 1045
Brost, Betty, Controller--The Minnesota Mutual Life Insurance Company, Saint Paul, MN; *U.S. Private*, pg. 750
Brostek, Greg, Controller--Eaton Corp., Aerospace & Commercial Controls Div., Costa Mesa, CA; *U.S. Public*, pg. 557
Brostowicz, W.W., Controller--Grosvenor Marketing Ltd., Paramus, NJ; *Int'l*, pg. 92
Brostowitz, James, V.P., Treas., Controller & Asst. Sec.--Harley-Davidson, Inc., Milwaukee, WI; *U.S. Public*, pg. 786
Brostowitz, James M., V.P. & Controller--Harley-Davidson Motor Company, Milwaukee, WI; *U.S. Public*, pg. 786
Brotto, Paul E., V.P.-Fin. Plng. & Controller--Air Canada, Saint-Laurent, Canada; *Int'l*, pg. 36
Broussard, Bruce, Controller--Baker Petrolite Corporation, Houston, TX; *U.S. Public*, pg. 166
Brown, Abe, Controller--J & R Music World, New York, NY; *U.S. Private*, pg. 576
Brown, Adam, Chief Fin. Officer--Gelco Information Network, Inc., Eden Prairie, MN; *U.S. Private*, pg. 442
Brown, Andrew, V.P. & Corp. Controller--Adaptec, Inc., Milpitas, CA; *U.S. Public*, pg. 19
Brown, Bill, Controller--Robbins Manufacturing Company, Tampa, FL; *U.S. Private*, pg. 935
Brown, Chris, Controller--Hedstrom Corporation, Mount Prospect, IL; *U.S. Private*, pg. 526
Brown, Chris, Controller--ERO, Inc., Mount Prospect, IL; *U.S. Private*, pg. 526
Brown, Chris, Controller--ERO Industries, Inc., Mount Prospect, IL; *U.S. Private*, pg. 526
Brown, Clifford R., Asst. Controller--The Goodyear Tire & Rubber Company, Akron, OH; *U.S. Public*, pg. 752
Brown, Clydene, Controller--Silver Dollar City, Inc., Branson, MO; *U.S. Private*, pg. 1000
Brown, Dave, Controller--Duro Bag Manufacturing Co., Ludlow, KY; *U.S. Private*, pg. 348
Brown, Deborah, Controller--Environmental Control Inc., Santa Fe, NM; *U.S. Public*, pg. 49
Brown, Deborah, Controller--Sanco Inc., Taos, NM; *U.S. Public*, pg. 49
Brown, Gary, Controller--American Medical Security Holdings, Inc., Green Bay, WI; *U.S. Public*, pg. 1692
Brown, Gehr W., Chief Fin. Officer & V.P.-Fin.--Mona Industries, Inc., Paterson, NJ; *U.S. Private*, pg. 756
Brown, Gregory J., Controller--Dunn Industries Inc., Kansas City, MO; *U.S. Private*, pg. 347
Brown, Gregory J., Asst. V.P. & Controller--J.E. Dunn Construction Co., Kansas City, MO; *U.S. Private*, pg. 347
Brown, Harry, Controller--SPS Industrial Products Div., Cleveland, OH; *U.S. Public*, pg. 1420
Brown, Janie, V.P. & Controller--Merix Corporation, Forest Grove, OR; *U.S. Public*, pg. 1096
Brown, Jeff, Controller--Weichert Company, Morris Plains, NJ; *U.S. Private*, pg. 1159
Brown, Jim, Controller--Thermo Electric Co., Inc., Saddle Brook, NJ; *U.S. Private*, pg. 1080
Brown, John, Controller--CPI Corp., Saint Louis, MO; *U.S. Public*, pg. 283
Brown, Kevin, Controller--Robbins & Myers, Inc., Dayton, OH; *U.S. Public*, pg. 1393
Brown, Laurie, Controller--Sioux Manufacturing Corp., Fort Totten, ND; *U.S. Private*, pg. 1003
Brown, Leonard, Controller--Dettra Flag Company, Oaks, PA; *U.S. Private*, pg. 328
Brown, Lloyd, Controller--Westlake Medical Center, Westlake Village, CA; *U.S. Public*, pg. 1697
Brown, Lyman R., Controller--United Grocers Inc., Portland, OR; *U.S. Private*, pg. 1122
Brown, Mark, Controller--United Farm Tools, Inc., Glasgow, KY; *U.S. Private*, pg. 1122
Brown, Mark A., Controller--Saturn of Greenwood, Greenwood, IN; *U.S. Private*, pg. 672
Brown, Michael, Chief Fin. Officer & Controller--New Plan Realty Trust, New York, NY; *U.S. Public*, pg. 1172
Brown, Mildred, Controller--Manufacturers' News, Inc., Evanston, IL; *U.S. Private*, pg. 700
Brown, Raymond J., Asst. Controller--Gohmann Asphalt & Construction Inc., Clarksville, IN; *U.S. Private*, pg. 459
Brown, Saralyn, V.P. & Controller--Don Miguel Mexican Foods, Inc., Anaheim, CA; *U.S. Private*, pg. 339
Brown, Sheila, V.P. & Controller--Wickland Corporation, Sacramento, CA; *U.S. Private*, pg. 1174
Brown, Susan, Controller--Rex Marine Center, Inc., Norwalk, CT; *U.S. Private*, pg. 926
Brown, Ted T., Controller--Haynes International, Inc., Kokomo, IN; *U.S. Public*, pg. 801
Brown, Tim, Controller--Polar Beverages, Worcester, MA; *U.S. Private*, pg. 873
Brown, Tina, Controller--Bromar Inc., Newport Beach, CA; *U.S. Private*, pg. 171
Brown, Tony, Grp. Fin. Controller--Renold PLC, Manchester, United Kingdom; *Int'l*, pg. 1103
Brown, Vicki, Controller--Polyloom Corp. of America, Dayton, TN; *U.S. Private*, pg. 875
Brown, William C., CPA, V.P.-Fin.--MGI PHARMA INC., Minneapolis, MN; *U.S. Public*, pg. 1026
Brown, William L., V.P.-Fin. & Controller--Jones Medical Industries Inc., Saint Louis, MO; *U.S. Public*, pg. 933
Brown, William M., Chief Fin. Officer, Exec. V.P. & Controller--IMO Industries Inc., Lawrenceville, NJ; *U.S. Public*, pg. 856
Browne, Kathleen A., V.P. & Controller--W.R. Grace & Co., Boca Raton, FL; *U.S. Public*, pg. 754
Brownell, David A., Controller & Treas.--Electro Metrics, Inc., Johnstown, NY; *U.S. Private*, pg. 369
Browning, T.B., Controller--ChemFirst Inc., Jackson, MS; *U.S. Public*, pg. 344
Brozick, J.F., Controller & Asst. Sec.--J & L Specialty Products Corp., Pittsburgh, PA; *Int'l*, pg. 572
Bruce, Linda, Controller--Mark Chevrolet Inc., Wayne, MI; *U.S. Private*, pg. 704
Bruce, Minette, Controller--American Classic Voyagers Company, New Orleans, LA; *U.S. Private*, pg. 380
Bruce, Randy, Controller--Mar-Jac Poultry Inc., Gainesville, GA; *U.S. Private*, pg. 701
Bruce, Sandra, Controller--Hall Contracting Corp., Louisville, KY; *U.S. Private*, pg. 495
Bruce, Tom, Controller--Quality Chekd Dairies, Inc., Naperville, IL; *U.S. Private*, pg. 898
Brucker, David, Controller--Industrial Rubber Products Company, Charleston, WV; *U.S. Private*, pg. 561
Bruening, Ann E., V.P. & Controller--Marshall & Ilsley Trust Company, Milwaukee, WI; *U.S. Public*, pg. 1051
Bruggink, J.C., Corp. Controller--KLM Royal Dutch Airlines, Amstelveen, Netherlands; *Int'l*, pg. 719
Brundell, Martin, Controller-Europe--Datapoint Corporation, Paris, France; *Int'l*, pg. 384
Brunetta, David C., District Controller, Asst. Sec. & Treas.--Ragnar Benson, Inc., Monroeville, PA; *U.S. Private*, pg. 99
Bruno, Edward B., Controller--Carpenter Technology Corporation, Reading, PA; *U.S. Public*, pg. 307
Brunozi, Joao Odair, Controller--Acos Villares S.A., Sao Paulo, Brazil; *Int'l*, pg. 23
Bruns, Michael A., Controller--Roberds, Inc., Carrollton, OH; *U.S. Public*, pg. 1393
Brunton, David W., Controller--Phoenix American Incorporated, San Rafael, CA; *U.S. Private*, pg. 862
Brunton, Tom, V.P. & Controller--Centigram Communications Corporation, San Jose, CA; *U.S. Public*, pg. 323
Brust, Robert, Chief Fin. Officer, Sr. V.P. & Controller--Unisys Corporation, Blue Bell, PA; *U.S. Public*, pg. 1671
Bryan, Sharon M., V.P. & Controller--Reebok International Ltd., Stoughton, MA; *U.S. Public*, pg. 1369
Bryant, Dan C., Controller--Haverty Furniture Companies, Inc., Atlanta, GA; *U.S. Public*, pg. 799
Bryant, David, Controller--Dealers Electrical Supply Co., Waco, TX; *U.S. Private*, pg. 318
Bryant, Lynn, Corp. Controller--Washington Homes, Inc., Landover, MD; *U.S. Public*, pg. 1741
Bryant, Mark C., Controller--Geupel DeMars, Inc., Indianapolis, IN; *U.S. Private*, pg. 449
Bryant, Ron, Controller--Dixon Industries, Inc., Coffeyville, KS; *U.S. Public*, pg. 238
Bryson, John, Controller--Hancock Fabrics, Inc., Tupelo, MS; *U.S. Public*, pg. 779
Brzeczek, Timothy, Controller--Goldenberg Group, Inc., Lynwood, CA; *U.S. Public*, pg. 1193
Bublitz, Brent, Controller--McNally Industries, Inc., Grantsburg, WI; *U.S. Private*, pg. 724
Bubp, Greg, Controller--Eclipse Inc., Rockford, IL; *U.S. Private*, pg. 360
Bucco, Joe, Controller--Integrated Brands Inc., Ronkonkoma, NY; *U.S. Public*, pg. 883
Buchanan, Paul W., Sr. V.P. & Controller--Hovnanian Enterprises, Inc., Red Bank, NJ; *U.S. Public*, pg. 843
Buchanan, Scott, Controller--Dart Transit Company, Eagan, MN; *U.S. Private*, pg. 311
Buchy, Rose, Asst. Controller--Devon Group, Inc., Stamford, CT; *U.S. Public*, pg. 503
Buckel, Mark A., Controller--Valvoline Company, Lexington, KY; *U.S. Public*, pg. 139
Buckheit, John G., V.P. & Controller--Sanchez Computer Associates, Malvern, PA; *U.S. Public*, pg. 1425
Buckner, Clay H., Jr., Controller & Treas.--Krystal Company, Chattanooga, TN; *U.S. Private*, pg. 636
Bucks, Thomas E., V.P. & Controller--Centennial Cellular Corp., New Canaan, CT; *U.S. Public*, pg. 329
Bucys, Frank, Controller--Tridel Enterprises Inc., Downsview, Canada; *Int'l*, pg. 1423
Buczynski, Veronica, Controller--Gamma One, Inc., North Haven, CT; *U.S. Public*, pg. 228
Buddour, Linda, CPA, Dir.-Fin.--Pharmaceutical Product Development, Inc., Wilmington, NC; *U.S. Public*, pg. 1285
Budicin, Jim, Unit Controller--Weatherford Australia Pty. Ltd., Malaga, Australia; *U.S. Public*, pg. 1750
Buehler, Christine, Controller--ASN Incorporated, Winter Park, FL; *U.S. Private*, pg. 8
Bueno, Thomas, Chief Acctg. Officer & Controller--Apco Argentina Inc., Tulsa, OK; *U.S. Public*, pg. 119
Buettner, William P., V.P. & Controller--The Austin Company, Cleveland, OH; *U.S. Private*, pg. 99
Buffington, Sam, Corp. Controller--Giant Industries Inc., Scottsdale, AZ; *U.S. Public*, pg. 741
Buford, T. Mark, V.P. & Controller--Community Health Systems, Inc., Brentwood, TN; *U.S. Private*, pg. 419
Buhl, Michael E., Controller--Suntec Industries Inc., Rockford, IL; *U.S. Private*, pg. 1054
Buhr, Jim, Controller--Bashas, Chandler, AZ; *U.S. Private*, pg. 120
Bukofski, Joseph, V.P. & Controller--Capital Associates, Inc., Lakewood, CO; *U.S. Public*, pg. 302
Bull, George, Controller--Doncasters plc, Melbourn, United Kingdom; *Int'l*, pg. 416
Bull, Stuart, Controller--Rexam PLC, London, United Kingdom; *Int'l*, pg. 1106
Bullis, Sue, Controller--Kragie/Newell, Des Moines, IA; *U.S. Private*, pg. 634
Bullmore, R. Steven, Corp. Controller--Modine Manufacturing Company, Racine, WI; *U.S. Public*, pg. 1121
Bulmer, Gary, Controller--Solon Manufacturing Company, Solon, ME; *U.S. Private*, pg. 1013
Bumbala, Steve, V.P. & Controller--The New York Post, New York, NY; *Int'l*, pg. 927
Bumtus, Susan, Asst. Controller--Shepard Clothing Company, New Bedford, MA; *U.S. Private*, pg. 992
Buncher, Sharon, Controller--Erico International, Solon, OH; *U.S. Private*, pg. 381
Bunker, Steven, Controller--Geneva Steel, Vineyard, UT; *U.S. Public*, pg. 729
Bunker, Theodore, Controller--Flint Manufacturing Co., Burton, MI; *U.S. Private*, pg. 413
Bunton, Diane, Controller--Great Lakes Peterbilt, GMC, Portage, IN; *U.S. Private*, pg. 475
Bunton, Jeffrey L., Controller--Kewaunee Scientific Corporation, Statesville, NC; *U.S. Public*, pg. 953
Buonato, Richard T., V.P. & Controller--Icahn & Co., Inc., New York, NY; *U.S. Private*, pg. 556
Burak, Evan, Controller--Technology Research Corporation, Clearwater, FL; *U.S. Public*, pg. 1564
Burak, Mark A., Controller--Bank of America Illinois, Chicago, IL; *U.S. Public*, pg. 180
Burbon, Louis, Controller--Dena Corporation, Elk Grove Village, IL; *U.S. Private*, pg. 324
Burch, J.E., V.P. & Controller--Guarantee Life Insurance Co., Omaha, NE; *U.S. Public*, pg. 768
Burger, Glenn, Controller--National Steel & Shipbuilding Company, San Diego, CA; *U.S. Private*, pg. 787
Burgess, Chris, Controller--Chesapeake Corporation, Richmond, VA; *U.S. Public*, pg. 346
Burgess, Linda K., Controller & Corp. Sec.--Maynard Oil Co., Dallas, TX; *U.S. Public*, pg. 1064
Burgholzer, Robert A., Jr., V.P. & Controller--Duracell International Inc., Bethel, CT; *U.S. Public*, pg. 743
BurKamper, Rick, Controller--Big A Auto Parts, Davenport, IA; *U.S. Public*, pg. 10
Burke, Brian T., Chief Acctg. Officer, Sr. V.P. & Controller--Symbol Technologies, Inc., Holtsville, NY; *U.S. Public*, pg. 1546
Burke, Donna, Controller--The Long Company, Chicago, IL; *U.S. Private*, pg. 674
Burke, Gerry, Controller--John R. Lyman Company, Chicopee, MA; *U.S. Private*, pg. 683
Burke, Lee, Controller--Simplex Industries, Inc., Scranton, PA; *U.S. Private*, pg. 1001
Burke, Steve, Controller--Edelbrock Corp., Torrance, CA; *U.S. Public*, pg. 563
Burke, Timothy, Mgr.-Financial Control--William Blair & Company L.L.C., Chicago, IL; *U.S. Private*, pg. 148
Burke, Willie, Controller--Graber-Rogg, Inc., Cranford, NJ; *U.S. Private*, pg. 468
Burket, Linda, Controller--American Eurocopter Corp., Grand Prairie, TX; *Int'l*, pg. 29
Burkey, Michelle, Controller & Treas.--The Tobin Corporation, North Ridgeville, OH; *U.S. Private*, pg. 102
Burkhart, Richard, Chief Fin. Officer & Controller--Mid-Continent Screw Products Co., Lincolnwood, IL; *U.S. Private*, pg. 743
Burkholder, Michael, Controller--Gendex-Del Medical Imaging Corp., Franklin Park, IL; *U.S. Public*, pg. 494
Burkman, Rick, Controller--BernzOmatic, Medina, NY; *U.S. Public*, pg. 1177
Burks, John, Controller--Houchens Markets, Bowling Green, KY; *U.S. Private*, pg. 541
Burleson, Thomas W., V.P. & Controller--Citation Corporation, Birmingham, AL; *U.S. Public*, pg. 376
Burley, Mark M., Controller--Joseph Simon & Sons, Inc., Tacoma, WA; *U.S. Private*, pg. 1001
Burlotos, Alex, Controller--Tops Appliance City, Edison, NJ; *U.S. Public*, pg. 1622
Burman, Richard, V.P. & Controller--CRN International, Inc., Hamden, CT; *U.S. Private*, pg. 197
Burness, John G., Asst. Treas.--Scott's Restaurants Inc., Markham, Canada; *Int'l*, pg. 1213

Burnett, Donna M., Chief Acctg. Officer & Controller--Public Service Company of New Mexico, Albuquerque, NM; *U.S. Public*, pg. 1339
Burnett, Peter, Controller--Messier-Dowty Customer Support Center- Americas, Sterling, VA; *Int'l*, pg. 1340
Burns, Craig, Chief Acctg. Officer, V.P. & Controller--Checkpoint Systems Inc., Thorofare, NJ; *U.S. Public*, pg. 343
Burns, Lance, Controller--Hagie Manufacturing Co., Clarion, IA; *U.S. Private*, pg. 493
Burns, Michael, Controller--Davis Tool & Engineering Co., Detroit, MI; *U.S. Private*, pg. 315
Burns, Raymond, V.P. & Controller--Cohen Furniture Company, Peoria Heights, IL; *U.S. Private*, pg. 250
Burns, T.J., Controller--Micropolis Corporation, Chatsworth, CA; *U.S. Private*, pg. 742
Burnworth, David A., Controller--Motor Products Div., Rockford, IL; *U.S. Public*, pg. 1250
Burr, Tracy Lee, Corp. Controller--Albert Fisher North America, Dallas, TX; *Int'l*, pg. 491
Burraell, James F., Sr. V.P. & Controller--Collins Electric Company, Inc., Chicopee, MA; *U.S. Private*, pg. 253
Burrow, Robert D., Controller--Falconbridge Limited, Toronto, Canada; *Int'l*, pg. 433
Burstyn, Richard, Controller--Holiday RV Superstores, Inc.-Tampa, Tampa, FL; *U.S. Public*, pg. 830
Burtness, David, V.P. & Controller--Witcher Construction Co., Minneapolis, MN; *U.S. Private*, pg. 1185
Burton, Brenda, Controller--NicSand, Inc., Cleveland, OH; *U.S. Private*, pg. 799
Burton, Tracey H., Controller--E.V. Roberts & Associates, Inc., Culver City, CA; *U.S. Private*, pg. 935
Busam, Raymond J., V.P.-Admin. & Fin.--L.R. Nelson Corporation, Peoria, IL; *U.S. Private*, pg. 790
Busch, Andrew A., V.P. & Controller--Dominion Textile Inc., Montreal, Canada; *Int'l*, pg. 415
Busch, Thomas, Controller--Salant Corporation, New York, NY; *U.S. Public*, pg. 1429
Bush, Bill, Controller & Mgr.-H.R.--Woodbury Business Forms, Inc., La Grange, GA; *U.S. Private*, pg. 1186
Bushalon, Kevin, Controller--Ideon Group, Inc., Jacksonville, FL; *U.S. Public*, pg. 320
Bushell, tom, Controller--Charter-Provo School, Inc., Provo, UT; *U.S. Public*, pg. 1035
Bushey, Richard K., V.P. & Controller--Edison International, Rosemead, CA; *U.S. Public*, pg. 564
Bushey, Richard K., V.P. & Controller--Southern California Edison Company, Rosemead, CA; *U.S. Public*, pg. 564
Buske, John M., Controller & Dir.-Fin.--St. Jude Medical, Inc., Saint Paul, MN; *U.S. Public*, pg. 1427
Buss, Scott, Controller--United Hardware Distributing Co., Plymouth, MN; *U.S. Private*, pg. 335
Bussard, Alain, Controller--Banco Santander-Suiza, Geneva, Switzerland; *Int'l*, pg. 143
Bussing, Greg, Controller--Sealright Company, Inc., De Soto, KS; *U.S. Public*, pg. 1451
Bustillo, Armando, Fin. Controller--NRG Distribution Corporation, Guaynabo, PR; *Int'l*, pg. 1115
Butash, Carol, V.P. & Controller--Mars Advertising Co., Southfield, MI; *U.S. Private*, pg. 706
Butler, Alice, Controller--Byerly Ford-Nissan Inc., Louisville, KY; *U.S. Private*, pg. 191
Butler, Frank J., Chief Info. Officer & Controller--L & D Group, Aurora, IL; *U.S. Private*, pg. 638
Butler, John, Controller--Producers Livestock, North Salt Lake, UT; *U.S. Private*, pg. 888
Butler, Mark R., Controller--Bridges & Company, Inc., Pittsburgh, PA; *U.S. Private*, pg. 168
Butt, Mazhar, Reg. Controller--Weatherford Oil Tool Middle East Ltd., Dubai, United Arab Emirates; *U.S. Public*, pg. 1750
Butterick, Mike, Controller--AutoZone, Inc., Memphis, TN; *U.S. Public*, pg. 150
Butters, Debbie, Controller--Sebastian Cotton & Grain Corp., Sebastian, TX; *U.S. Private*, pg. 980
Butts, Tom, Controller--Williams Healthcare Systems, Elgin, IL; *U.S. Public*, pg. 1507
Buyers, Greg, Controller--Field Packing Company, Owensboro, KY; *U.S. Private*, pg. 403
Byar, James P., V.P.--American Pacific Corporation, Las Vegas, NV; *U.S. Public*, pg. 88
Bybee, O. Lynn, Controller, Treas. & Sec.--Wick Building Systems, Mazomanie, WI; *U.S. Private*, pg. 1174
Bygge, Johan, Controller--Electrolux, AB, Stockholm, Sweden; *Int'l*, pg. 438
Byrd, Art, Controller--Martin Sprocket & Gear, Inc., Arlington, TX; *U.S. Private*, pg. 709
Byrd, Edward R., V.P. & Controller--Pacific Life Insurance Company, Newport Beach, CA; *U.S. Private*, pg. 831
Byrd, Jeff, V.P.-Admin. & Controller--Halstead Industries, Inc., Greensboro, NC; *U.S. Private*, pg. 496
Byrne, James P., V.P. & Controller--American Country Insurance Co., Chicago, IL; *U.S. Private*, pg. 1030
Byrne, M.A., Controller--Air New Zealand Ltd. (U.S.A.), El Segundo, CA; *Int'l*, pg. 38
Byrne, Michael, V.P. & Controller--Sonat Energy Services Company, Birmingham, AL; *U.S. Public*, pg. 1485
Byrne, T.R., Grp. Fin. Controller--Airtours Plc, Rossendale, United Kingdom; *Int'l*, pg. 39
Byruch, David B., V.P. & Controller--J.E. Berkowitz, LP, Westville, NJ; *U.S. Private*, pg. 135
Cabot, Wayne, Controller--Clark Construction Group, Inc., Bethesda, MD; *U.S. Private*, pg. 242
Cacchioli, Joseph A., V.P. & Controller--E-Z-Em, Inc., Westbury, NY; *U.S. Public*, pg. 540
Cacchiotti, Don, Controller--Spelling Entertainment Group, Inc., Los Angeles, CA; *U.S. Private*, pg. 776
Cacchiotti, John, Controller--Summit Division, Cleveland, OH; *U.S. Public*, pg. 78
Caeballo Madariaga, Jaime, V.P. & Controller--Bufete Industrial S.A. de C.V., Mexico, Mexico; *Int'l*, pg. 232
Cagalj, Mike, Chief Fin. Officer, V.P. & Controller--Atlas Hotels, Inc., San Diego, CA; *U.S. Private*, pg. 96
Cahill, Jerry, V.P.-Fin. & Controller--Grolsch Importers Inc., Atlanta, GA; *Int'l*, pg. 559
Cahill, Kirk, V.P.-Fin., Controller & Treas.--Chicago Extruded Metals Co., Cicero, IL; *U.S. Private*, pg. 234
Cahoon, Philip R., V.P., Controller & Asst. Sec.--QMS, Inc., Mobile, AL; *U.S. Public*, pg. 1346
Cain, Suzy, Controller--Chronicle Publishing Co. Inc., San Francisco, CA; *U.S. Private*, pg. 239
Caiola, Vincent, Controller--The Lane Construction Corp., Meriden, CT; *U.S. Private*, pg. 649
Cairns, Myles S., Jr., V.P.-Opers. & Controller--The Loewen Group, Inc., Burnaby, Canada; *Int'l*, pg. 814
Calabuig, Enrique, Fin. Controller--NRG Comunicaciones S.A., Barcelona, Spain; *Int'l*, pg. 1116
Calderon, Thomas, Controller--PharmChem Laboratories, Inc., Menlo Park, CA; *U.S. Public*, pg. 1285
Caldwell, A., Chief Fin. Officer & Controller--Puritan Maid Ltd., Aylesbury, United Kingdom; *Int'l*, pg. 210
Caliendo, Anthony, Controller--The Strober Organization, Inc., Brooklyn, NY; *U.S. Private*, pg. 403
Caliwara, Climaco E., Asst. V.P.-Comptroller--Atlas Consolidated Mining & Development Corporation, Manila, Philippines; *Int'l*, pg. 95
Call, Anita, Controller--Triangle Brass Manufacturing, Los Angeles, CA; *U.S. Private*, pg. 1101
Call, Harry N., Controller--Chase Corporation, Braintree, MA; *U.S. Public*, pg. 337
Callaghan, J., Controller--Target Rock Corp., Farmingdale, NY; *U.S. Public*, pg. 470
Callahan, James, Controller--Syratech Corporation, East Boston, MA; *U.S. Private*, pg. 1060
Callan, Richard T., Chief Fin. Officer, V.P. & Controller--Alliance Construction Solutions, Inc., Fort Collins, CO; *U.S. Private*, pg. 38
Callaro, Lee, Asst. Controller--Nieco Corporation, Burlingame, CA; *U.S. Private*, pg. 799
Callegan, Lesa, Controller--Coleman Oldsmobile, Inc., Baton Rouge, LA; *U.S. Private*, pg. 252
Callis, Chris, Controller--Central Parking Corp., Nashville, TN; *U.S. Public*, pg. 326
Camacho, Don, Sr. V.P. & Controller--Converse Inc., North Reading, MA; *U.S. Public*, pg. 441
Camalo, Craig, Controller--Code-Alarm, Inc., Madison Heights, MI; *U.S. Public*, pg. 393
Camalo, Craig, Controller & Chief Accounting Officer--Code Alarm Security Systems, Madison Heights, MI; *U.S. Public*, pg. 394
Camarata, Dan, Controller--Pueblo Xtra International, Inc., Pompano Beach, FL; *U.S. Private*, pg. 894
Camarre, Jim, Controller--Mollenberg-Betz Inc., Buffalo, NY; *U.S. Private*, pg. 756
Cameron, Ian, Corp. Controller--Methanex Corporation, Vancouver, Canada; *Int'l*, pg. 862
Camerote, Mark A., Controller--The Pep Boys-Manny, Moe & Jack, Philadelphia, PA; *U.S. Public*, pg. 1276
Camery, Brent, Fin. Controller--Banque Indosuez, New York, NY; *Int'l*, pg. 313
Caminiti, Katherine M., V.P. & Asst. Controller--Century Communications Corp., New Canaan, CT; *U.S. Public*, pg. 329
Camp, Terri, V.P. & Controller--WorldCorp, Inc., Herndon, VA; *U.S. Public*, pg. 1779
Campanella, Richard, Controller--4C Foods Corporation, Brooklyn, NY; *U.S. Private*, pg. 421
Campbell, Alan, V.P. & Controller--Altron Systems Corporation, Fremont, CA; *U.S. Public*, pg. 59
Campbell, Bob, Controller--Automotive Rentals, Inc. (ARI), Mount Laurel, NJ; *U.S. Private*, pg. 535
Campbell, Bobby R., Controller--Murphy Exploration & Production Co., New Orleans, LA; *U.S. Public*, pg. 1142
Campbell, Ed, V.P. & Controller--Keystone Steel & Wire Co., Peoria, IL; *U.S. Public*, pg. 955
Campbell, Edward M., Controller--Edward Hines Lumber Co., Itasca, IL; *U.S. Private*, pg. 530
Campbell, Gregg, V.P.-Fin. & Controller--Thompson-McCully Co., Belleville, MI; *U.S. Private*, pg. 1083
Campbell, Ian, Fin. Controller--AEP Industries (NZ) Ltd., Panmure, New Zealand; *U.S. Public*, pg. 5
Campbell, Jerry, V.P. & Controller--Parade Publications Inc., New York, NY; *U.S. Private*, pg. 20
Campbell, Kathy, Controller--Ziniz Inc., Louisville, KY; *U.S. Private*, pg. 1206
Campbell, Mike, Controller & Sec.--Fareway Stores, Inc., Boone, IA; *U.S. Private*, pg. 393
Campbell, Reid T., Asst. Controller--Fund American Enterprises Holdings, Inc., Hanover, NH; *U.S. Public*, pg. 688
Campbell, William T., Chief Fin. Officer & V.P.-Fin.--Smith Environmental Technologies Corp., Plymouth Meeting, PA; *U.S. Public*, pg. 1477
Campoverte, Jaime, Controller--Nuevo Federal S.A., Buenos Aires, Argentina; *Int'l*, pg. 990
Caneiros, Jose, Controller--Becton Dickinson Infusion Therapy, Inc., Sandy, UT; *U.S. Public*, pg. 199
Cannatelli, Donna, Controller--Autoroll Machine Co., LLC, Middleton, MA; *U.S. Private*, pg. 101
Cannizzaro, Louis A., Controller--Fairfield Maxwell Ltd., New York, NY; *U.S. Private*, pg. 391
Cannon, Rose Marie C., Treas. & Sec.--Cannon Express Inc., Springdale, AR; *U.S. Public*, pg. 301
Canosa, Albert A., Chief Fin. Officer & Corp. V.P.-Admin.--Raytech Corporation, Shelton, CT; *U.S. Public*, pg. 1363
Canty, Sean, Controller--Farnam Sealing Systems Division, Troy, MI; *U.S. Public*, pg. 401
Capani, Pam, V.P. & Controller--Highlights for Children, Inc., Columbus, OH; *U.S. Private*, pg. 528
Cape, Bob, V.P. & Controller--Harris Farms, Inc., Coalinga, CA; *U.S. Private*, pg. 505
Caplow, Peter, Controller--Blumberg Communications Inc., Minneapolis, MN; *U.S. Public*, pg. 305
Cappa, Tony, Controller--Dribeck Importers, Inc., Greenwich, CT; *U.S. Private*, pg. 343
Cappellucci, Robert, Controller--Haydon Switch & Instrument, Inc., Waterbury, CT; *U.S. Private*, pg. 513
Cappucci, Jim, Controller--Black Box Corporation of PA, Lawrence, PA; *U.S. Public*, pg. 235
Carabetta, Jim, Comptroller & Dir.-Personnel & Investor Rels.--Beauty Enterprises Inc., Hartford, CT; *U.S. Private*, pg. 128
Carahan, Steve, Controller--Adams Extract Co., Inc., Austin, TX; *U.S. Private*, pg. 16
Carballo, Larry, Controller--Servico, Inc., West Palm Beach, FL; *U.S. Public*, pg. 1462
Carberry, Patricia, Chief Acctg. Officer, V.P. & Controller--Sotheby's Holdings Inc., New York, NY; *U.S. Public*, pg. 1487
Carbone, David L., V.P-Fin.--Electronic Arts, San Mateo, CA; *U.S. Public*, pg. 569
Carbone, Wendy, Controller--Medusa Aggregate Co., Cleveland, OH; *U.S. Public*, pg. 1084
Cardiello, Sam, Chief Fin. Officer & Controller--Dan's Supreme Super Markets Inc., Hempstead, NY; *U.S. Private*, pg. 310
Cardinal, Lawrence, Jr., Sr. V.P. & Controller--First National Bank of Ohio, Akron, OH; *U.S. Public*, pg. 646
Carek, M., Controller--Stamco Industries Inc., Euclid, OH; *U.S. Private*, pg. 1029
Carey, Christopher J., Sr. V.P. & Controller--CoreStates Financial Corp., Philadelphia, PA; *U.S. Public*, pg. 446
Carey, Gail B., Controller--DeVlieg-Bullard Inc., Westport, CT; *U.S. Public*, pg. 502
Carey, Millie, Controller--Sunrise Nissan of Orange Park, Orange Park, FL; *U.S. Private*, pg. 1053
Carey, William P., Treas.--Scanforms, Inc., Bristol, PA; *U.S. Public*, pg. 228
Cargile, Charles F., Chief Acctg. Officer & Corp. Controller--Flowserve Corporation, Long Beach, CA; *U.S. Public*, pg. 658
Cariara, Augustine, Asst. Comptroller--Eastern Utilities Associates, Boston, MA; *U.S. Public*, pg. 549
Cariolano, Greg, V.P. & Controller--Lyndon Property Insurance Company, Saint Louis, MO; *U.S. Public*, pg. 685
Carland, Diane, Controller-Distr. Div.--Reptron Electronics, Inc., Tampa, FL; *U.S. Public*, pg. 1377
Carleton, Callis, V.P. & Controller--Atlantic Gulf Communities Corporation, Miami, FL; *U.S. Public*, pg. 144
Carlevato, Jeff, Controller & Treas.--QST Industries, Inc., Chicago, IL; *U.S. Private*, pg. 897
Carlile, Tom E., V.P. & Controller--Boise Cascade Corporation, Boise, ID; *U.S. Public*, pg. 242
Carlino, Elio, Controller & Asst. Treas.--Milgray Electronics, Inc., Farmingdale, NY; *U.S. Public*, pg. 205
Carlino, Susanna, Controller--New England Stone Industries, Inc., Esmond, RI; *U.S. Private*, pg. 793
Carloon, L., Mng. Dir. & Controller--Moore Paragon Svenska AB, Vastervik, Sweden; *Int'l*, pg. 890
Carls, Jon, Asst. Controller--AmerenCIPS, Springfield, IL; *U.S. Public*, pg. 65
Carlson, Bruce, Corp. Controller--Delaware North Companies, Inc., Buffalo, NY; *U.S. Private*, pg. 321
Carlson, John, Controller--Reliance Elevator Company, Chicago, IL; *U.S. Private*, pg. 921
Carlson, Kathy, Controller--M.H. Greenebaum, Inc., Parsippany, NJ; *U.S. Private*, pg. 477
Carlson, Ronald P., Controller--Hyde Manufacturing Co., Southbridge, MA; *U.S. Private*, pg. 551
Carlsson, Jan, Controller--Sodra Cell AB, Vaxjo, Sweden; *Int'l*, pg. 1275
Carlstrom, R.A., V.P. & Controller--Albany International Corp., Albany, NY; *U.S. Public*, pg. 36
Carmack, Clint, Controller & Treas.--New Horizons LLC, Cincinnati, OH; *U.S. Private*, pg. 794
Carmany, David J., Chief Fin. Officer, V.P.-Fin., Treas. & Controller--Castleberry/Snow's Brands Inc., Augusta, GA; *U.S. Private*, pg. 219
Carner, John, Controller--McCauley Propeller Systems, Vandalia, OH; *U.S. Public*, pg. 1589
Carnevale, Frank, Controller--Hart Engineering Corporation, Greenville, RI; *U.S. Private*, pg. 507
Carney, Mark, Controller--Great Lakes Confectionery, Cleveland, OH; *Int'l*, pg. 865
Carnthers, Robert, Controller--Ricart Ford Inc., Groveport, OH; *U.S. Private*, pg. 927
Caroll, Chris, Controller--Formation, Inc., Moorestown, NJ; *U.S. Private*, pg. 419
Carpenter, Danny, Controller--Charter Hospital of Mobile, Inc., Mobile, AL; *U.S. Public*, pg. 1034
Carpenter, David G., Controller--CSW Credit, Inc., Dallas, TX; *U.S. Public*, pg. 324
Carpenter, Debbie, Controller--L.M. Sandler & Sons, Virginia Beach, VA; *U.S. Private*, pg. 964
Carpenter, Michael R., V.P. & Asst. Controller--Blockbuster Entertainment Group, Dallas, TX; *U.S. Private*, pg. 775
Carpenter, Michael R., V.P. & Corp. Controller--Republic Industries, Inc., Fort Lauderdale, FL; *U.S. Public*, pg. 1378
Carpenter, Robert L., Jr., Sr. V.P. & Controller--First Maryland Bancorp, Baltimore, MD; *Int'l*, pg. 64
Carpenter, Robert L., Jr., Treas. & Controller--First Maryland Life Insurance Company, Baltimore, MD; *Int'l*, pg. 64
Carpenter, Scott J., Controller--Dairy Queen Corporate Store, Louisville, KY; *U.S. Public*, pg. 220
Carr, Jim, Controller--Koh-I-Noor, Inc., Bloomsbury, NJ; *U.S. Private*, pg. 629
Carr, Michael, Asst. Controller--Penco Products, Oaks, PA; *U.S. Private*, pg. 848
Carradine, John M., V.P.-Fin. & Treas.--Intellicall, Inc., Carrollton, TX; *U.S. Public*, pg. 887
Carreon, Michael R., V.P. & Controller--America West Airlines, Inc., Phoenix, AZ; *U.S. Public*, pg. 67
Carrico, Stephen J., V.P. & Controller--Hensel Phelps Construction Co., Greeley, CO; *U.S. Private*, pg. 523
Carrier, Elaine, Controller--Jouan, Inc., Winchester, VA; *U.S. Private*, pg. 601

Carro, Armando, Comptroller--Braum Ice Cream Stores Inc., Oklahoma City, OK; *U.S. Private*, pg. 166
Carroll-Coelho, Kathaleen M., V.P.-Fin. & Controller--Arrow Automotive Industries, Inc., Framingham, MA; *U.S. Public*, pg. 133
Carroll, Helen M., Asst. Treas.--Troy Savings Bank-East Greenbush, East Greenbush, NY; *U.S. Private*, pg. 1106
Carroll, John, Controller--Sky Bros. Inc., Allentown, PA; *U.S.* Public, pg. 918
Carroll, Patrick, Controller--Buckeye Container, Wooster, OH; *U.S. Private*, pg. 177
Carson, Larry E., Asst. V.P. & Asst. Controller--National Western Life Insurance Company, Austin, TX; *U.S. Public*, pg. 1161
Carstens, I., Controller--Radiometer A/S, Bronshoj, Denmark; *Int'l*, pg. 1083
Carter, Larry R., V.P. & Controller--Advanced Micro Devices, Inc., Sunnyvale, CA; *U.S. Public*, pg. 21
Carter, Lawrence, Controller--Stillman & Hoag, Inc., Englewood, NJ; *U.S. Private*, pg. 1043
Carter, Lisa K., V.P. & Controller--Oakwood Homes Corporation, Greensboro, NC; *U.S. Public*, pg. 1209
Carter, Terry L., Controller--Potlatch Corporation, Spokane, WA; *U.S. Public*, pg. 1318
Cartledge, R.L., Comptroller--Sun Company, Inc. (R&M), Philadelphia, PA; *U.S. Public*, pg. 1530
Carus, Alan, Controller--Overseas Shipholding Group, Inc., New York, NY; *U.S. Public*, pg. 1236
Caruso, Frank A., Controller--Parametric Technology Corporation, Waltham, MA; *U.S. Public*, pg. 1257
Caruso, N.J., Controller & Gen. Auditor--Shell Oil Company, Houston, TX; *Int'l*, pg. 1136
Cary, Richard, Controller--Arthur J. Gallagher & Co., Itasca, IL; *U.S. Public*, pg. 698
Casbon, Thomas, Controller--Current Technology, Inc., Irving, TX; *U.S. Public*, pg. 480
Cascione, Maria, Asst. Corp. Controller--Maidenform Worldwide, New York, NY; *U.S. Private*, pg. 697
Case, David M., V.P. & Controller--MCI Communications Corp., Atlanta, GA; *U.S. Public*, pg. 1023
Case, Lloyd, V.P. & Controller--Forum Communications Company, Fargo, ND; *U.S. Private*, pg. 420
Case, Sharon, Controller--Seattle WA Steel Division, Seattle, WA; *U.S. Public*, pg. 232
Caserza, Daniel M., Controller--Gas Tech, Newark, CA; *U.S.* Public, pg. 1593
Casey, James M., Controller & Sec.--Bituminous Casualty Corp., Rock Island, IL; *U.S. Public*, pg. 1218
Casey, Mike, Controller--Thrall Car Mfg. Co., Chicago Heights, IL; *U.S. Private*, pg. 344
Casey, Ronald, Controller--Alcan Aluminum Corporation, Cleveland, OH; *Int'l*, pg. 50
Cash, Lorene, Controller--Lone Star Corrugated Container Corporation, Irving, TX; *U.S. Private*, pg. 674
Cash, Lorene, Controller--Lone Star Container Sales Corp., Irving, TX; *U.S. Private*, pg. 674
Casillas, Ray, Controller--Phelps Dodge Hidalgo, Playas, NM; *U.S. Public*, pg. 1287
Caso, Rob, Controller--Centocor, Inc., Malvern, PA; *U.S. Public*, pg. 323
Casper, Jack, Comptroller--Clark Pacific, Sacramento, CA; *U.S. Private*, pg. 243
Cassanova, Mike, Controller--Vivitar Corporation, Newbury Park, CA; *Int'l*, pg. 1060
Cassard, Christopher D., Controller--Oregon Steel Mills Inc., Portland, OR; *U.S. Public*, pg. 1230
Cassell, Ronald, Controller--Bassett Furniture Industries, Incorporated, Bassett, VA; *U.S. Public*, pg. 193
Casselman, David, Controller--Westclox, Norcross, GA; *U.S.* Private, pg. 445
Castagno, John D., Tax Controller--Anheuser-Busch Companies, Inc., Saint Louis, MO; *U.S. Public*, pg. 113
Castaldo, John, Controller--Music Sales Corporation, New York, NY; *U.S. Private*, pg. 768
Castaneda, Pacifico M., V.P. & Comptroller--La Tondena Distillers, Inc., Manila, Philippines; *Int'l*, pg. 785
Castellano, J., Controller & Mgr.-Bus.--McGraw Hill Interamericana de Espana S.A., Madrid, Spain; *U.S. Public*, pg. 1072
Castellano, Michael J., Sr. V.P. & Controller--Merrill Lynch & Co., Inc., New York, NY; *U.S. Public*, pg. 1097
Castellano, Michael J., Controller--Merrill Lynch, Pierce, Fenner & Smith, Inc., New York, NY; *U.S. Public*, pg. 1098
Castellano, Michael N., V.P. & Controller--Phibro Division of Salomon Inc., Westport, CT; *U.S. Public*, pg. 1633
Castellow, Ben, Corp. Controller--Tom's Foods, Inc., Columbus, GA; *U.S. Private*, pg. 1090
Castillo, Edwardo, Controller--Gillette Argentina S.A., Buenos Aires, Argentina; *U.S. Public*, pg. 744
Castillo, I., Controller--Grupo Industrial Morgan, S.A. de C.V., Mexico, Mexico; *Int'l*, pg. 895
Castillo, Yolanda, Controller--Lanz, Inc., San Francisco, CA; *U.S. Private*, pg. 650
Castro, Amparo, V.P., Controller & Asst. Treas.--PharmHouse, Inc., New York, NY; *U.S. Public*, pg. 1286
Castronova, Rose, Controller--Hill, Holliday/Altschiller, New York, NY; *U.S. Private*, pg. 529
Caswell, David, Controller--David Boland, Inc., Titusville, FL; *U.S. Private*, pg. 154
Catanzano, Dennis, V.P. & Controller--The Life Insurance Co. of Virginia, Richmond, VA; *U.S. Public*, pg. 712
Catlett, Gary, Controller & V.P.--Winrock Enterprises, Inc., Little Rock, AR; *U.S. Private*, pg. 1183
Catlin, Susan, Controller--Puritan Bakery, Inc., Carson, CA; *U.S. Private*, pg. 895
Catoe, Sam, Controller--Jacobsen Textron, Racine, WI; *U.S.* Public, pg. 1589
Catrinar, Larry, Controller--Amurcon Corporation, Southfield, MI; *U.S. Private*, pg. 69
Catrini, Vincent, Controller--Porta Systems Corp., Syosset, NY; *U.S. Public*, pg. 1317
Caudle, Deena, Controller--Las Vegas Sun, Las Vegas, NV; *U.S. Private*, pg. 652
Caulkins, Sue, Controller--The Shane Group Inc., Hillsdale, MI; *U.S. Private*, pg. 989
Cautillo, John M., Controller & Sec.--Refined Sugars, Inc., Yonkers, NY; *Int'l*, pg. 699
Cavagnero, Al, Controller--Robot Research, Inc., San Diego, CA; *U.S. Public*, pg. 1457
Cavaliere, Vince, Controller--Rosco Laboratories, Inc., Stamford, CT; *U.S. Private*, pg. 944
Cavalli, P.G., Controller--Arnoldo Mondadori Editore S.p.A., Segrate, Italy; *Int'l*, pg. 887
Cavanaugh, Donald, Controller & Dir.-Acctg. Svcs.--American Bible Society, New York, NY; *U.S. Private*, pg. 51
Cavanaugh, M.J., V.P., Gen. Mgr., Controller & Treas.--Day-Glo Color Corp., Cleveland, OH; *U.S. Public*, pg. 1357
Cave, Thomas W., Controller--Elcor Corporation, Dallas, TX; *U.S. Public*, pg. 567
Caveney, Timothy, Controller--Blue Cross and Blue Shield Association, Chicago, IL; *U.S. Private*, pg. 151
Cavin, Mildred C., Controller--The Free Lance-Star Publishing Co., Fredericksburg, VA; *U.S. Private*, pg. 424
Cawthon, Vernon, Chief Fin. Officer, Controller & Treas.--Strachan Shipping Co., Garden City, GA; *U.S. Private*, pg. 1045
Ceccarelli, Joe, Controller--Louis Dreyfus Corporation, Wilton, CT; *U.S. Private*, pg. 342
Cecchini, James, Controller--Tessco Group, Inc., Georgetown, TX; *U.S. Public*, pg. 394
Celentano, Domenick A., Jr., V.P.-Mktg. & Adv.--Celentano Bros. Inc., Verona, NJ; *U.S. Private*, pg. 221
Cella, Barbara T., Controller--Phonetics, Inc., Aston, PA; *U.S. Private*, pg. 863
Celmer, Lee, Controller--R-2 KIT Mfg. Co., Caldwell, ID; *U.S. Public*, pg. 962
Cenci, Dan, Controller--Hughes Family Markets, Inc., Irwindale, CA; *U.S. Public*, pg. 1349
Centera, Mary, V.P. & Controller--Fleetwood Aluminum Products, Corona, CA; *U.S. Private*, pg. 410
Ceplinskas, Darlene J., V.P. & Controller--United Asset Management Corporation, Boston, MA; *U.S. Public*, pg. 1672
Cerami, John, Controller--Chapman Management Group, Berwyn, PA; *U.S. Private*, pg. 229
Ceraolo, Carmine, Asst. Controller--Lynch Corporation, Greenwich, CT; *U.S. Public*, pg. 1021
Cernugel, William J., Sr. V.P.-Fin. & Controller--Alberto-Culver Company, Melrose Park, IL; *U.S. Public*, pg. 37
Cervantes, Jorge, Controller--BYK Gulden, S.A. de C.V., Mexico, Mexico; *Int'l*, pg. 66
Cesario, Sam, Controller--Quebecor Printing MIL Inc., Don Mills, Canada; *Int'l*, pg. 1077
Cestnik, Joe, Controller--C.J. Rush Inc., Scarborough, Canada; *Int'l*, pg. 395
Cetrullo, Rich, Controller--Foster Management Co., King of Prussia, PA; *U.S. Private*, pg. 421
Chabot, Sharyn, Controller--ADAP Inc., Brockton, MA; *U.S. Private*, pg. 4
Chabowski, Jody, Asst. Controller--Applied Industrial Technologies, Cleveland, OH; *U.S. Public*, pg. 122
Chaddick, RoGene, Controller--Allsups Convenience Stores Inc., Clovis, NM; *U.S. Private*, pg. 44
Chadwick, Marshall, Chief Fin. Officer & Controller--Monarch Avalon, Inc., Baltimore, MD; *U.S. Public*, pg. 1123
Chaffin, Chris, Controller--Robert F. Driver Co., Inc., San Diego, CA; *U.S. Private*, pg. 343
Chamberlain, Rich, Controller--Inserra Shoprite, Mahwah, NJ; *U.S. Private*, pg. 565
Chambers, Alfred J., Controller--Emerson Radio Corp., Parsippany, NJ; *U.S. Public*, pg. 578
Chambers, James, Controller--Wyle Laboratories-Eastern Operations, Huntsville, AL; *U.S. Private*, pg. 1193
Chambers, Sam, II, Chief Fin. Officer & Controller--Galaxy Food Company, Orlando, FL; *U.S. Public*, pg. 697
Champion, Bob, Controller--GFG Corporation, Milwaukee, WI; *Int'l*, pg. 395
Champoux, Richard H., Controller--Alox Corporation, Niagara Falls, NY; *U.S. Public*, pg. 1357
Chan, Fay, Controller--Ambrose Carr Linton Carroll Inc., Toronto, Canada; *Int'l*, pg. 71
Chan, Gary, Controller--Sensormatic Asia/Pacific, Singapore, Singapore; *U.S. Public*, pg. 1457
Chan, Kai Leung, Controller--CMC International (S.E. Asia) Pte. Limited, Singapore, Singapore; *U.S. Public*, pg. 413
Chan, VincentY.T., Fin. Controller--Hong Kong Security Ltd., Kowloon, Hong Kong; *Int'l*, pg. 704
Chan, W., Controller--Avex Electronics Pte. Ltd., Singapore, Singapore; *U.S. Private*, pg. 545
Chanani, Madhu S., Exec. V.P., Controller & Asst. Sec.--Western Waste Industries, Torrance, CA; *U.S. Public*, pg. 1686
Chandler, A., Controller--Reckitt & Colman plc, London, United Kingdom; *Int'l*, pg. 1089
Chandler, Sharon, Controller--CPI Prints Plus, Inc., Concord, CA; *U.S. Public*, pg. 283
Chaney, Renee, Controller--Island Lincoln-Mercury, Merritt Island, FL; *U.S. Private*, pg. 576
Chang, Alvin A. C., Controller--Hawaiian Tug & Barge Corp., Honolulu, HI; *U.S. Public*, pg. 800
Chang, Alvin A. C., Controller--Young Brothers, Ltd., Honolulu, HI; *U.S. Public*, pg. 800
Chaopragnoi, Suksri, Accountant--Bangkok Athletic Co., Ltd., Bangkok, Thailand; *Int'l*, pg. 146
Chapell, Jeff, Controller--Prime Tanning Co., Inc., Rochester, NH; *U.S. Private*, pg. 884
Chapin, John E., Controller--Kaiser Aerospace & Electronics Corp., Foster City, CA; *U.S. Private*, pg. 605
Chaplin, Robert L., V.P. & Controller--Maytag Corporation, Newton, IA; *U.S. Public*, pg. 1064
Chapman, Gwen, Controller--Europe Auto Equipment, Pantin, France; *U.S. Public*, pg. 394
Chapman, James A., V.P. & Controller--First American Federal Savings Bank, Bristol, VA; *U.S. Public*, pg. 624
Chapman, Julie, Controller--Outlook Eyewear Company, Denver, CO; *U.S. Public*, pg. 195
Charboneau, Pierre, V.P., Controller & Treas.--Culinar Inc., Montreal, Canada; *Int'l*, pg. 348
Charbonnet, Michael D., Sr. V.P. & Comptroller--Whitney Holding Corporation, New Orleans, LA; *U.S. Public*, pg. 1766
Charles, Catherine, Controller--Selix F. Schoeller Ltd., High Wycombe, United Kingdom; *Int'l*, pg. 1209
Charles, Debbie, Controller--Retail Prods., Ocala, FL; *U.S. Public*, pg. 575
Charow, Ronald, Controller--Westburne Inc., Montreal, Canada; *Int'l*, pg. 1491
Charpentier, Marti R., Controller & Asst. Treas.--Analysts International Corporation, Minneapolis, MN; *U.S. Public*, pg. 110
Charping, Tony, Controller--Designers Knitting Mills, New York, NY; *U.S. Public*, pg. 778
Charping, Tony, Controller--Natalie Knitting Mills, Chilhowie, VA; *U.S. Public*, pg. 779
Charron, Carol, Controller, Treas. & Sec.--Art Moran Pontiac-GMC Inc., Southfield, MI; *U.S. Private*, pg. 760
Charzenko, Anthony, Controller--UNR Home Products Div., Ruston, LA; *U.S. Public*, pg. 1404
Chase, Dee Anne, Controller, Treas., Sec. & Dir.-Employee Benefits--Regency Lincoln Mercury, Inc., Dallas, TX; *U.S.* Private, pg. 918
Chau, Al, Controller--ZMP, Inc., Glendale, CA; *U.S. Private*, pg. 1203
Chausse, Robert J., Controller--Kinross Gold Corporation, Toronto, Canada; *Int'l*, pg. 734
Chavez, Linda, Controller--Marshall Industries, El Monte, CA; *U.S. Public*, pg. 1051
Cheatham, C.L., Treas. & Controller--Brierley & Partners, Dallas, TX; *U.S. Private*, pg. 168
Cheek, Joe, Controller--Fluidtec Engineer Products, Greensboro, NC; *U.S. Public*, pg. 401
Cheeseman, Richard J., Fin. Controller--Photo-Me International plc, Bookham, United Kingdom; *Int'l*, pg. 1055
Cheesman, Bruce, Controller--Quebecor Imaging (Alphatext), Richmond Hill, Canada; *Int'l*, pg. 1077
Chelin, Jeffrey D., V.P.-Fin. & Sec.--ARC International Corporation, Downsview, Canada; *Int'l*, pg. 17
Chen, Heng W., Sr. V.P.-Fin. & Controller--City National Corporation, Beverly Hills, CA; *U.S. Public*, pg. 380
Chen, Jackie, Controller--Pace Advertising, New York, NY; *Int'l*, pg. 1483
Chen, Jane, Controller--John Crane (Taiwan) Co. Ltd., Kaohsiung, Taiwan; *Int'l*, pg. 1339
Chen, Jiunny-Show, Sr. V.P. & Controller--The International Commercial Bank of China, Taipei, Taiwan; *Int'l*, pg. 683
Chen, Stan, Controller--Raleigh Enterprises, Inc., Santa Monica, CA; *U.S. Private*, pg. 907
Chenault, Chuck, V.P. & Controller--Computer City, Fort Worth, TX; *U.S. Public*, pg. 1560
Cheney, Craig, Corp. Controller--Fulton Industries Inc., Wauseon, OH; *U.S. Private*, pg. 431
Cheng, Betty, Controller--Premier Refractories International Inc., King of Prussia, PA; *U.S. Public*, pg. 58
Cheng, Isaac, Fin. Controller--Chubb Hong Kong Ltd., Kowloon, Hong Kong; *Int'l*, pg. 705
Cherry, Terry, Controller--Southern California Air Gas, Lakewood, CA; *U.S. Public*, pg. 33
Chesler, Harvey, Controller--Truevision, Inc., Santa Clara, CA; *U.S. Public*, pg. 1642
Cheung, Newton, Fin. Controller--Johnson Electric Holdings Limited, Tai No, Hong Kong; *Int'l*, pg. 712
Cheung, Wilson, Corp. Controller--Network Peripherals Inc., Milpitas, CA; *U.S. Public*, pg. 1169
Chia Wee Chang, Joseph, Controller--Showpla Asia Limited, Singapore, Singapore; *Int'l*, pg. 1237
Chia, Lim Soo, Controller--UFE Pte Ltd, Singapore, Singapore; *U.S. Private*, pg. 1112
Chico, R., Controller--Worldwide Food Products Inc., Jamaica, NY; *U.S. Private*, pg. 1191
Chidlow, Richard V., Chief Acctg. Officer & Controller--Oceaneering International, Inc., Houston, TX; *U.S. Public*, pg. 1211
Chidlow, Robert V., Chief Acctg. Officer & Controller--Oceaneering International, Inc., Morgan City, LA; *U.S. Public*, pg. 1211
Chiesa, Nancy, Controller--Ziegler Chemical & Mineral Corp., Jericho, NY; *U.S. Private*, pg. 1205
Chik, Mimi, Controller--Straube Regional Center LLC, Pennington, NJ; *U.S. Private*, pg. 1046
Childers, C. Scott, Controller--APAC/Ballenger Paving Company, Inc., Taylors, SC; *U.S. Public*, pg. 139
Childers, Dexter, Jr., Controller--Steel of West Virginia, Inc., Huntington, WV; *U.S. Public*, pg. 1513
Childers, Steve, Controller--Air Industries Corporation, Garden Grove, CA; *U.S. Private*, pg. 28
Childress, Karen, Controller--Homeowners Group, Inc., Sunrise, FL; *U.S. Public*, pg. 832
Childress, Michael, Asst. Controller--AmerenCIPS, Springfield, IL; *U.S. Public*, pg. 65
Childrey, Buster, Controller--Manchester Tank & Equipment Company, Brentwood, TN; *U.S. Private*, pg. 699
Chin, Dan, Controller--Sizzler International, Inc., Los Angeles, CA; *U.S. Public*, pg. 1475
Chircop, Anthony, Controller-Subsidiaries--Air Malta Co. Ltd., Luqa, Malta; *Int'l*, pg. 37
Chirico, Emanuel, V.P. & Controller--Phillips-Van Heusen Corporation, New York, NY; *U.S. Public*, pg. 1291
Chisholm, Wendy, Controller--MM Industra, Ltd., Dartmouth, Canada; *Int'l*, pg. 74
Chism, Earl K., V.P. & Controller--Potomac Electric Power Company, Washington, DC; *U.S. Public*, pg. 1318
Chizak, Tim, Controller--Ripplewood Holdings L.L.C., New York, NY; *U.S. Private*, pg. 931
Chmielewski, Mike, Controller--Bisceglia Brothers Wine Co., Madera, CA; *U.S. Public*, pg. 300
Choi, B.J., Controller--Hyundai Electronics America, San Jose, CA; *Int'l*, pg. 641

Choisser, David, V.P. & Controller--Coda Energy, Inc., Dallas, TX; *U.S. Public*, pg. 584
Chong, David, Controller--Hoover Stainless Pte Ltd., Singapore, Singapore; *Int'l*, pg. 1322
Chores, Mryon, V.P. & Controller--A.O. Smith Electrical Products Company, Tipp City, OH; *U.S. Public*, pg. 1477
Chow, Tony, Controller--Berel Industries Inc., Cerritos, CA; *U.S. Private*, pg. 135
Christen, A., Controller--RetailNet B.V., Amsterdam, Netherlands; *Int'l*, pg. 750
Christensen, D.M., V.P. & Controller--Fairmont Tamper, West Columbia, SC; *U.S. Public*, pg. 793
Christensen, Don, Controller--T.J. Maxx, Framingham, MA; *U.S. Public*, pg. 1557
Christiansen, Christer, Chief Economist & Controller--Sodra Cell AB, Vaxjo, Sweden; *Int'l*, pg. 1275
Christiansen, Lawrence M., Controller--Concrete Technology Corp., Tacoma, WA; *U.S. Private*, pg. 262
Christiansen, Ove, Controller--Vestjyske Slagterier, Struer, Denmark; *Int'l*, pg. 1464
Christianson, Dean, Controller--Owatonna Canning Company, Owatonna, MN; *U.S. Public*, pg. 349
Christianson, Greg, V.P. & Controller--Huntington Bancshares Inc., Columbus, OH; *U.S. Public*, pg. 849
Christofferson, Glen P., V.P. & Controller--Fisher Companies Inc., Seattle, WA; *U.S. Public*, pg. 647
Chu, Chorng-Yi, Controller & Asst. Treas.--Payless Car Rental System, Inc., Saint Petersburg, FL; *U.S. Private*, pg. 844
Chu, Cindy, Controller--Dominguez Services Corporation, Long Beach, CA; *U.S. Public*, pg. 516
Chu, Larry, Fin. Controller--Poppe Tyson, New York, NY; *U.S. Public*, pg. 1642
Chua, Jimmy C., V.P.-Logistics & Pur.--Philippine Airlines, Inc., Manila, Philippines; *Int'l*, pg. 1050
Chua, Ler Ching, Chief Fin. Officer, Treas. & Sec.--GB Holdings, Jurong, Singapore; *Int'l*, pg. 531
Chudler, Clifford, Controller--Sherwood Food Distributors, Detroit, MI; *U.S. Private*, pg. 993
Chui, Ignatius, Grp. Fin. Controller--Cycle & Carriage Industries (1986) Pte. Limited, Singapore, Singapore; *Int'l*, pg. 350
Chukwu, Meeka, Controller--Paradigm Technology, Inc., San Jose, CA; *U.S. Public*, pg. 1256
Chulumovich, Keith, Controller & Treas.--Cambridge Industries Inc., Madison Heights, MI; *U.S. Private*, pg. 202
Chung, A., Controller--Gestetner Office Systems New Zealand Limited, Ponsonby, New Zealand; *Int'l*, pg. 1115
Chung, Nung K., V.P. & Controller--George Uhe Co., Inc., Paramus, NJ; *U.S. Private*, pg. 1115
Church, Julie, Controller--Staodyn Inc., Longmont, CO; *U.S. Public*, pg. 1509
Ciaccio, Peggy, Plant Controller--Kankakee, IL Steel Division, Bourbonnais, IL; *U.S. Public*, pg. 232
Ciano, Mark, Controller--PNY Technologies, Inc., Parsippany, NJ; *U.S. Private*, pg. 827
Cid, Ladislau, Controller--Embraer-Empresa Brasileira de Aeronautica S.A., Sao Jose dos Campos, Brazil; *Int'l*, pg. 452
Ciecko, Richard, Controller--Hanna Corporation, Chicago, IL; *U.S. Private*, pg. 231
Cieply, Lucy, Controller--Rama Group of Companies, Cheektowaga, NY; *U.S. Private*, pg. 908
Cieslak, Rick, Controller--Transpo Electronics, Inc., Orlando, FL; *U.S. Private*, pg. 1097
Cifarelli, John, Controller--The Fusco Corporation, New Haven, CT; *U.S. Private*, pg. 432
Ciklic, Carol, Controller--Shepaug Corporation, New York, NY; *U.S. Private*, pg. 993
Ciklic, Carol, Controller--The Unimax Corporation, New York, NY; *U.S. Private*, pg. 1118
Ciletti, Robert, Controller--SouthCo. Inc., Concordville, PA; *U.S. Private*, pg. 1014
Cimmino, Don, Controller--Stocko Corp., Carlstadt, NJ; *Int'l*, pg. 1301
Cimo, David, Controller--Midwest Litho Arts, Des Plaines, IL; *U.S. Public*, pg. 1779
Cinquin, Carl, Chief Fin. Officer & Controller--Cramer Company, Old Saybrook, CT; *U.S. Public*, pg. 1238
Cioni, Donna, Controller--Sid Harvey Industries, Valley Stream, NY; *U.S. Private*, pg. 998
Cipollone, Floriana G., Corp. Controller--CSA Management Inc., Toronto, Canada; *Int'l*, pg. 243
Cipollone, Floriana G., Controller & Treas.--Goldcorp Inc., Toronto, Canada; *Int'l*, pg. 243
Cipollone, Floriana G., Controller & Treas.--Wharf Resources Ltd., Lead, SD; *Int'l*, pg. 243
Cipollone, Floriana G., Controller & Treas.--Lexam Explorations Inc., Toronto, Canada; *Int'l*, pg. 243
Cirillo, N.J., V.P. & Controller--The F.A. Bartlett Tree Expert Co., Stamford, CT; *U.S. Private*, pg. 119
Cisario, Victor, Controller--Find/SVP, Inc., New York, NY; *U.S. Public*, pg. 623
Cisco, Lyla, Controller--Nalle Plastics Inc., Austin, TX; *U.S. Private*, pg. 773
Claar, T., Controller--Hedstrom Corp., Ashland, OH; *U.S. Private*, pg. 526
Claes, James B., Controller & Asst. Sec.--Laclede Steel Company, Saint Louis, MO; *U.S. Public*, pg. 974
Clafby, Kathleen, Comptroller--NHD Hardware, Stoughton, MA; *U.S. Private*, pg. 3
Clancy, B.K., V.P. & Controller--AEGON USA, Inc., Baltimore, MD; *Int'l*, pg. 26
Clancy, Bob, Controller--Molon Motor & Coil Corp., Rolling Meadows, IL; *U.S. Private*, pg. 756
Claps, Frank, Controller--V-Band Corporation, Elmsford, NY; *U.S. Public*, pg. 1701
Clardy, John, Controller--California Micro Devices, Milpitas, CA; *U.S. Public*, pg. 293
Clare, James, Controller--ITW Woodworth, Ferndale, MI; *U.S. Public*, pg. 867
Clarey, William, Controller--Flex-O-Glass, Inc., Chicago, IL; *U.S. Private*, pg. 412
Clark, Brenda, Corp. Controller--Merchants Rent A Car, Inc., Hooksett, NH; *U.S. Private*, pg. 732
Clark, Harry, V.P. & Controller--Gould Paper Corporation, New York, NY; *U.S. Private*, pg. 466
Clark, Jeanne, Controller--Hinderliter Heat Treating, Inc., Dallas, TX; *U.S. Private*, pg. 530
Clark, Jennifer, Controller--Rough Brothers, Inc., Cincinnati, OH; *U.S. Private*, pg. 947
Clark, Karen K., Controller--Precision Castparts Corp., Portland, OR; *U.S. Public*, pg. 1320
Clark, Katherine P., V.P. & Controller--Philip Morris Companies Inc., New York, NY; *U.S. Public*, pg. 1287
Clark, Larry L., V.P., Controller & Asst. Treas.--Chaparral Steel Co., Midlothian, TX; *U.S. Public*, pg. 1585
Clark, Robert, Controller--Maurice Electric Supply Company, Washington, DC; *U.S. Private*, pg. 715
Clark, Terry L., V.P. & Controller--Ross Aluminum Foundries, Sidney, OH; *U.S. Private*, pg. 355
Clarke, David A., Controller--Lapmaster International Ltd., Morton Grove, IL; *Int'l*, pg. 1338
Clarke, George T., Sr. V.P. & Controller--UST Corporation, Boston, MA; *U.S. Public*, pg. 1660
Clarke, George T., Controller--UST Corporation, Boston, MA; *U.S. Public*, pg. 1660
Clarke, George T., Sr. V.P. & Controller--USTrust, Boston, MA; *U.S. Public*, pg. 1660
Clarke, Graham, Fin. Controller--Whitehall Laboratories Ltd., London, United Kingdom; *U.S. Public*, pg. 82
Clausen, Roger H., Div. V.P.-Corp. Acct. & Corp. Controller--Walgreen Co., Deerfield, IL; *U.S. Public*, pg. 1733
Claverie, Roy E., Sr. V.P.--Ingram Industries Inc., Nashville, TN; *U.S. Private*, pg. 562
Clay, David, Chief Fin. Officer & Controller--Universal Industrial Products Co., Pioneer, OH; *U.S. Public*, pg. 1677
Clay, Debbie, Controller--The Sunflower Group, Overland Park, KS; *U.S. Private*, pg. 1052
Clayton, Tripp, Chief Fin. Officer, V.P. & Controller--Tanner Co., Rutherfordton, NC; *U.S. Private*, pg. 1068
Cleary, John, Controller--DeMaria Building Co. Inc., Novi, MI; *U.S. Private*, pg. 323
Cleasby, Craig L., V.P., Controller & Chief Fin. Officer--ITT Cannon Sealectro, New Britain, CT; *U.S. Public*, pg. 859
Clemens, Blaine, Controller--Lukens Steel Company, Coatesville, PA; *U.S. Public*, pg. 1020
Clemens, P. Blaine, V.P. & Controller--Lukens Inc., Coatesville, PA; *U.S. Public*, pg. 1019
Clement, Jim, Controller--Altama Delta Corporation, Atlanta, GA; *U.S. Private*, pg. 47
Clements, Greg, Controller--Cleveland Group, Inc., Atlanta, GA; *U.S. Private*, pg. 246
Clements, Linda S., Corp. Controller--EXAR Corporation, Fremont, CA; *U.S. Public*, pg. 597
Clendenning, Sara, Controller--Vital Signs, Englewood, CO; *U.S. Public*, pg. 1723
Clifford, Elizabeth A., Controller--Colonial Penn Group, Inc., Wilmington, DE; *U.S. Public*, pg. 990
Clifford, Jane, Controller--Fel-Pro Incorporated, Skokie, IL; *U.S. Private*, pg. 399
Clifford, Peter, Chief Acctg. Officer, Sr. V.P.-Fin. & Controller--John Wiley & Sons, Inc., New York, NY; *U.S. Public*, pg. 1768
Cline, William, V.P. & Controller--Borg Warner Automotive, Inc., Chicago, IL; *U.S. Public*, pg. 245
Cling, Michael, Controller--Multi-Plex, Inc., Howe, IN; *U.S. Private*, pg. 315
Clocheret, Willy, Controller--Datapoint Belgium S.A., Brussels, Belgium; *Int'l*, pg. 384
Closs, Nancy A., V.P. & Controller--Federal Home Loan Bank of New York, New York, NY; *U.S. Private*, pg. 399
Closs, Willie, Sr. V.P. & Controller--North Carolina Mutual Life Insurance Co., Durham, NC; *U.S. Private*, pg. 804
Closterman, Jane, Controller & Asst. Sec.--TIE/Communications, Inc., Overland Park, KS; *U.S. Private*, pg. 1085
Cloue, Alaine, Controller--Mead Europe Engineering, S.A.R.L., Chateauroux, France; *U.S. Public*, pg. 1076
Cloutier, Patrick, Controller--Waterville TG Inc., Waterville, Canada; *Int'l*, pg. 1487
Cloverdale, David G., V.P.-H.R.--Vilter Manufacturing Corporation, Cudahy, WI; *U.S. Private*, pg. 1140
Clubb, Toni, Controller--Vitatech International, Inc., Tustin, CA; *U.S. Private*, pg. 1142
Cluver, Al, Controller--Environmental Development Corp., Hoopeston, IL; *U.S. Public*, pg. 49
Cluver, Al, Controller--Upper Rock Island County Landfill, East Moline, IL; *U.S. Public*, pg. 49
Coates, Paul C., Controller--BWI Plc, Altrincham, United Kingdom; *Int'l*, pg. 130
Coats, W. John, V.P.-Fin.--Nutri/System Inc., Horsham, PA; *U.S. Private*, pg. 859
Cobb, Bruce A., Controller--Tetra Technologies, Woodlands, TX; *U.S. Public*, pg. 1582
Cocca, Tony, Asst. Controller--Metallurg, Inc., New York, NY; *U.S. Private*, pg. 735
Cochenour, Dave, Controller--Fresh Mark, Inc., Canton, OH; *U.S. Private*, pg. 427
Cockrell, F. Edwin, Controller--Tension Envelope Corp., Kansas City, MO; *U.S. Private*, pg. 1077
Cockrell, Mel, Chief Fin. Officer, Controller & Treas.--Ben E. Keith Company, Fort Worth, TX; *U.S. Private*, pg. 611
Cody, Ed, Controller--Grassland Equipment & Irrigation Corp., Latham, NY; *U.S. Private*, pg. 471
Coen, Beverly, Asst. Controller--Nordson Corporation, Westlake, OH; *U.S. Public*, pg. 1188
Coffman, Michael W., V.P. & Controller--Shenandoah Life Insurance Company, Roanoke, VA; *U.S. Private*, pg. 992
Cofsky, Stewart, V.P. & Controller--Finora Company, Inc., Englewood, CO; *U.S. Private*, pg. 802
Coggins, Carol, Controller--Cattleman's, Inc., Detroit, MI; *U.S. Public*, pg. 318
Cohelo, Manny, Controller--Shorewood Packaging Corporation of Canada, Ltd., Scarborough, Canada; *U.S. Public*, pg. 1468
Cohen, Harold, Controller--CES/Card Establishment Services Inc., Melville, NY; *U.S. Public*, pg. 631
Cohen, Jeff, Controller & Treas.--Wavetek Corporation, San Diego, CA; *U.S. Private*, pg. 1154
Cohen, Larry, V.P. & Controller--The Mutual Life Insurance Company of New York, New York, NY; *U.S. Private*, pg. 769
Cohen, Lewis, Controller & Treas.--Kastle Systems LLC, Arlington, VA; *U.S. Private*, pg. 608
Cohen, Silvio, V.P.-Admin. & Controller--Willoughby's, New York, NY; *U.S. Private*, pg. 1180
Cohen, Warren, V.P.-Fin. & Treas.--Unisystems, Inc., New York, NY; *U.S. Private*, pg. 1120
Cohron, Gene M., V.P. & Controller--Fruit of the Loom, Inc., Chicago, IL; *U.S. Public*, pg. 685
Cokely, Liz, Controller--B.T. Mancini Co., Inc., Milpitas, CA; *U.S. Private*, pg. 699
Colditz, Lawrence L., Controller--Avatar Holdings Inc., Coral Gables, FL; *U.S. Public*, pg. 151
Colditz, Lawrence L., Controller--Avatar Properties Inc., Miami, FL; *U.S. Public*, pg. 151
Coldren, Kathy, Controller--Norrell Corporation, Atlanta, GA; *U.S. Public*, pg. 1192
Cole, Amy, Controller--Jay Instrument & Specialty Co., Cincinnati, OH; *U.S. Private*, pg. 583
Cole, David O., Chief Fin. Officer, V.P., Controller, Treas. & Sec.--Lincoln Foodservice Products, Inc., Fort Wayne, IN; *Int'l*, pg. 188
Cole, John, Controller--Avnet, Inc., Great Neck, NY; *U.S. Public*, pg. 155
Cole, John T., Controller--Butler Manufacturing Company, Kansas City, MO; *U.S. Public*, pg. 271
Coleman, Edward F., Asst. Controller--Kimberly-Clark Corporation, Dallas, TX; *U.S. Public*, pg. 958
Coleman, Mike, Controller--The Coe Manufacturing Company, Painesville, OH; *U.S. Private*, pg. 249
Coleman, Rick, Controller--Einstein Moomjy Inc., Pine Brook, NJ; *U.S. Private*, pg. 366
Coleman, William R., Sr. V.P.-Fin. & Controller--Cincinnati Bell Information Systems Inc., Cincinnati, OH; *U.S. Public*, pg. 367
Coley, Dennis, Controller--Bombardier, Learjet Inc., Wichita, KS; *Int'l*, pg. 200
Coley, Larry D., V.P. & Controller--TBC Corporation, Memphis, TN; *U.S. Public*, pg. 1553
Colford, Francis X., V.P. & Controller--New Jersey Natural Gas Co., Wall, NJ; *U.S. Public*, pg. 1172
Colgan, Vincent J., V.P. & Controller--Grolier Inc., Danbury, CT; *Int'l*, pg. 794
Collier, Jackie, V.P. & Controller--Aviall, Inc., Dallas, TX; *U.S. Public*, pg. 154
Collier, Jeff, Controller--Burlington Motor Holdings Inc., Daleville, IN; *U.S. Private*, pg. 183
Collier, Martha, Controller--Culbro Land Resources, Inc., Windsor, CT; *U.S. Public*, pg. 708
Collier, Mary, Controller--Sangamon Industries, Taylorville, IL; *U.S. Private*, pg. 965
Collings, W.R., Controller--National Electrical Carbon Canada, Mississauga, Canada; *Int'l*, pg. 892
Collins, Charles, Controller--Cal-Maine Foods, Inc., Jackson, MS; *U.S. Public*, pg. 292
Collins, Doug, Controller--Refrigeration Supplies Distributors, Monterey Park, CA; *U.S. Private*, pg. 917
Collins, Evan, Controller--Network Associates, Inc., Santa Clara, CA; *U.S. Public*, pg. 1168
Collins, G.M., Controller--J.M. Huber, Wood Products Div., Charlotte, NC; *U.S. Private*, pg. 545
Collins, Grace, V.P. & Controller-Media--Quantum Media International, Inc., New York, NY; *U.S. Private*, pg. 899
Collins, James C., Controller--Ajax Manufacturing Company, Inc., Hillsborough, NJ; *U.S. Private*, pg. 1030
Collins, Kim, Controller--Smith McDonald Corp., Buffalo, NY; *U.S. Private*, pg. 1009
Collins, Sally, Controller--Ventures Group, Minneapolis, MN; *U.S. Private*, pg. 646
Collins, Stephen, Chief Fin. Officer & Controller--Ocean Mist Farms Corp., Castroville, CA; *U.S. Private*, pg. 811
Collins, Susan, Controller--SunPure Ltd., Avon Park, FL; *U.S. Private*, pg. 1053
Collins, William, Controller--Ward Leonard Electric Company, Inc., Mount Vernon, NY; *U.S. Private*, pg. 1118
Collogan, Joan, Controller--Fresh Choice, Inc., Santa Clara, CA; *U.S. Public*, pg. 682
Colon, J., Controller--Moore Business Forms de Puerto Rico, S.A., Hato Rey, PR; *Int'l*, pg. 889
Colon, Ricardo, V.P. & Controller--Banca Serfin, S.A., New York Agency, New York, NY; *Int'l*, pg. 137
Colreavy, Coleen A., Chief Acctg. Officer, V.P. & Controller--Seaman Furniture Company, Inc., Woodbury, NY; *U.S. Public*, pg. 1452
Colter, David, Corp. Controller--General Alum & Chemical, Holland, OH; *U.S. Private*, pg. 443
Colucci, R., Controller--Providence Journal-Bulletin, Providence, RI; *U.S. Public*, pg. 209
Comeford, Kevin, Controller--TMP Worldwide Recruitment Division, New York, NY; *U.S. Private*, pg. 1065
Comer, Mel, Controller--Parfums De Coeur Ltd., Darien, CT; *U.S. Private*, pg. 839
Como, Elizabeth, Controller--Plant Maintenance Service Corporation, Memphis, TN; *U.S. Private*, pg. 869
Como, Patricia, Controller & Asst. Sec.--Offshore Logistics, Inc., Lafayette, LA; *U.S. Public*, pg. 1212
Comport, Bradley, Controller--The Davey Tree Expert Company, Kent, OH; *U.S. Private*, pg. 314
Comstock, Allan L., V.P. & Controller--Atlantic Richfield Company, Los Angeles, CA; *U.S. Public*, pg. 144
Conaghan, Megan, Controller--Naugatuck Glass Company, Naugatuck, CT; *U.S. Private*, pg. 789
Condame, J.R., Controller--Graham Corporation, Batavia, NY; *U.S. Public*, pg. 757
Condie, John, Controller--Mercury Air Group Inc., Los Angeles, CA; *U.S. Public*, pg. 1092

Condne, Mike, Controller--Greenlee Textron, Rockford, IL; *U.S. Public*, pg. 1589
Condrin, J. Paul, III, Chief Fin. Officer & Sr. V.P.--Liberty Mutual Insurance Co., Boston, MA; *U.S. Private*, pg. 666
Conk, Richard, V.P. & Controller--Cometals, New York, NY; *U.S. Public*, pg. 412
Conklin, Shawn, Controller--Menu Foods, Inc., Pennsauken, NJ; *U.S. Private*, pg. 731
Conley, C. Max, Controller--Conley Frog/Switch & Forge Co., Memphis, TN; *U.S. Private*, pg. 263
Conley, Kelly J., Asst. Controller--Berel Industries Inc., Cerritos, CA; *U.S. Private*, pg. 135
Conley, Kenneth L., Controller--Eaton Metal Products Company, Denver, CO; *U.S. Private*, pg. 358
Conley, Perry, Controller--Spartan Mills, Spartanburg, SC; *U.S. Private*, pg. 1020
Conlisk, John, V.P. & Controller--Supercuts, Inc., San Francisco, CA; *U.S. Public*, pg. 1373
Conlon, John S., Controller--C.R. Gibson Co., Norwalk, CT; *U.S. Public*, pg. 1168
Conn, Bill, Controller--Teleflex Automotive, Hillsdale, MI; *U.S. Public*, pg. 1569
Connell, Brian, Controller--Ground Round Inc., Braintree, MA; *U.S. Public*, pg. 766
Connelly, Charles J., Chief Fin. Officer, Exec. V.P. & Controller--Dacon Electronics Plc., Hemel Hempstead, United Kingdom; *U.S. Public*, pg. 395
Connelly, Jim, Controller--Tastee Freez International Inc., Utica, MI; *U.S. Private*, pg. 1069
Connelly, Joe, Controller--Levonian Brothers Inc., Troy, NY; *U.S. Private*, pg. 663
Connelly, Tom, Controller--Planning Systems Inc., Mc Lean, VA; *U.S. Private*, pg. 869
Conner, James, Controller--Gulf Lumber Company, Inc., Mobile, AL; *U.S. Private*, pg. 487
Connolly, Janna L., V.P. & Controller--Riverside Group, Inc., Jacksonville, FL; *U.S. Public*, pg. 1391
Connor, John M., Controller & Treas.--Cives Corporation, Roswell, GA; *U.S. Private*, pg. 241
Connor, Martin J., Jr., Controller--Engelhard Corporation, Iselin, NJ; *U.S. Public*, pg. 582
Conrad, Kim R., Controller, Treas. & Sec.--B & G Wholesalers, Inc., Nashville, TN; *U.S. Private*, pg. 105
Conrado, Mark, Controller--Maxoptix Corp., Fremont, CA; *Int'l*, pg. 762
Conroy, John, Controller--MFRI Inc., Niles, IL; *U.S. Public*, pg. 1026
Conroy, John L., Sr. V.P. & Fin. Controller--Jefferies & Company, Inc., Los Angeles, CA; *U.S. Public*, pg. 925
Conroy, Patrick, V.P. & Controller--Montgomery Ward & Co., Inc., Chicago, IL; *U.S. Private*, pg. 758
Constantine, Ronald, Controller--Rennoc Corporation, Vineland, NJ; *U.S. Private*, pg. 922
Conti, Joseph, Comptroller--Yoo Hoo Chocolate Beverage Corp., Carlstadt, NJ; *Int'l*, pg. 567
Conway, Jack, Sr. V.P. & Controller--Keystone Foods Corporation, Bala Cynwyd, PA; *U.S. Private*, pg. 619
Conway, Kenneth A., V.P. & Controller--PETsMART, Inc., Phoenix, AZ; *U.S. Public*, pg. 1281
Cook, Charles, Controller--Alemite Corporation, Charlotte, NC; *Int'l*, pg. 127
Cook, Dolly, Controller--Surco Products, Inc., Pittsburgh, PA; *U.S. Private*, pg. 1056
Cook, Jean, Controller--Mylon C. Jacobs Supply Co., Broken Arrow, OK; *U.S. Private*, pg. 963
Cook, John F., Jr., V.P. & Controller--ITT Aerospace/Communications Div., Fort Wayne, IN; *U.S. Public*, pg. 859
Cook, Michael, Controller--TruGreen-ChemLawn, Memphis, TN; *U.S. Public*, pg. 1461
Cook, Philip W., V.P. & Controller--Burlington Resources Inc., Houston, TX; *U.S. Public*, pg. 269
Cook, Rob, Fin. Controller--TML Reed Exhibitions (Pty.) Ltd.-Africa, Randburg, South Africa; *Int'l*, pg. 1097
Cook, Sherry, Controller--Draper Texmaco, Inc., Spartanburg, SC; *U.S. Private*, pg. 342
Cook, Stephen B., V.P. & Controller--The Ryland Group, Inc., Columbia, MD; *U.S. Public*, pg. 1414
Cooke, Andrew, Controller--USA Floral Products, Inc., Washington, DC; *U.S. Public*, pg. 1685
Cooke, Belinda, Controller--WKYT-TV, Lexington, KY; *U.S. Public*, pg. 759
Cookingham, Raymond W., V.P. & Controller--Hewlett-Packard Company, Palo Alto, CA; *U.S. Public*, pg. 813
Cookson, Bernard, Controller--Mitre Corporation, Bedford, MA; *U.S. Private*, pg. 753
Cooley, Robert, Controller--The F.X. Matt Brewing Co., Utica, NY; *U.S. Private*, pg. 714
Coomber, Peter D., Fin. Controller--Scientific Software-Intercomp (U.K.) Limited, Egham, United Kingdom; *U.S. Public*, pg. 1444
Coombs, J.C., Controller--Kaman Sciences Corp., Colorado Springs, CO; *U.S. Public*, pg. 942
Coombs, Michael, Controller--Frutarom Meer Corporation, North Bergen, NJ; *U.S. Private*, pg. 554
Coombs, Michael, Controller--Stelar Inc., Chicago, IL; *U.S. Private*, pg. 1040
Coomes, R.E., Sr. V.P. & Controller--Dorr-Oliver Incorporated, Milford, CT; *Int'l*, pg. 839
Coopat, Resa, Controller--Polaris Pool Systems, Inc., San Marcos, CA; *U.S. Private*, pg. 873
Cooper, Alex, V.P. & Controller--Telus Corporation, Edmonton, Canada; *Int'l*, pg. 1374
Cooper, Brent, Controller--Bovaird Supply Co., Tulsa, OK; *U.S. Private*, pg. 162
Cooper, Douglas C., V.P. & Controller--Wampole Laboratories, Cranbury, NJ; *U.S. Public*, pg. 310
Cooper, Lauren, V.P. & Controller--Outback Steakhouse Inc., Tampa, FL; *U.S. Public*, pg. 1235
Cope, Donald G., V.P. & Controller--J.B. Hunt Transport Services, Inc., Lowell, AR; *U.S. Public*, pg. 849
Coppinger, Tommy, Mgr.-Acctg.--Nashville Wire Product Co., Nashville, TN; *U.S. Private*, pg. 775
Coppola, David J., V.P. & Controller--Calton, Inc., Manalapan, NJ; *U.S. Public*, pg. 296
Corcoran, Tom, Controller--Hayward Industries, Inc., Elizabeth, NJ; *U.S. Private*, pg. 513
Corcoran, William B., Controller--Hapco/American Div., Abingdon, VA; *U.S. Private*, pg. 351
Corday, Craig, Controller--Miniature Precision Components, Walworth, WI; *U.S. Private*, pg. 750
Cordek, Lawrence D., Chief Fin. Officer & Corp. Sec.--G B Stores, Columbus, OH; *U.S. Private*, pg. 972
Cordero, Angel, Controller--B & C Bottlers Corp., Cayey, PR; *Int'l*, pg. 131
Cordina, Thomas, V.P. & Controller--American Decal & Mfg. Co., Chicago, IL; *U.S. Private*, pg. 53
Core, Lester A., Controller--Landauer, Inc., Glenwood, IL; *U.S. Public*, pg. 977
Corey, Wayne, V.P. & Controller--Pacesetter Corporation, Omaha, NE; *U.S. Private*, pg. 830
Cormier, John R., V.P. & Controller--Hill, Holliday, Connors, Cosmopulos, Inc., Boston, MA; *U.S. Private*, pg. 529
Cornelius, Tom, Controller--Florida Health Facilities, Inc., Lutz, FL; *U.S. Public*, pg. 1035
Cornell, Lance A., V.P. & Controller--HBOC, Atlanta, GA; *U.S. Public*, pg. 770
Cornette, A.P. Jr., Sr. V.P. & Comptroller--First State Bank, Greenville, KY; *U.S. Public*, pg. 1217
Cornwell, Jeff, V.P. & Controller--Airgas, Inc., Radnor, PA; *U.S. Public*, pg. 33
Cornwell, Virginia, Controller--Cowden Metal Specialties, Inc., Chino, CA; *U.S. Private*, pg. 280
Coronado, William J., Controller--Universal Corporation, Richmond, VA; *U.S. Public*, pg. 1694
Coronado, William J., V.P. & Controller--Universal Leaf Tobacco Company, Inc., Richmond, VA; *U.S. Public*, pg. 1694
Coronis, Dave, Controller--Advanced Circuit Technology, Nashua, NH; *U.S. Private*, pg. 21
Corprew, Lamont, Controller--WJZ-TV, Baltimore, MD; *U.S. Public*, pg. 275
Corr, Robert R., Controller, Treas. & Sec.--BEI Technologies, Inc., San Francisco, CA; *U.S. Public*, pg. 160
Correla, Felisbela, Controller--McGraw-Hill Interamericana de Portugal, Ltda, Lisbon, Portugal; *U.S. Public*, pg. 1072
Corrigan, Billy, Controller--Willis Corroon Asia Pacific Limited, Singapore, Singapore; *Int'l*, pg. 1509
Corry, Peter, V.P. & Controller--The Cornelius Company, Anoka, MN; *Int'l*, pg. 646
Corso, Alfred J., Corp. Controller--Brown & Sharpe Manufacturing Company, North Kingstown, RI; *U.S. Public*, pg. 260
Cortazzo, Susan N., V.P., Controller & Sec.--Lillian Vernon Corporation, New Rochelle, NY; *U.S. Public*, pg. 1716
Cortee, Edwin, Contoller--Stanley Blacker, Inc., New York, NY; *U.S. Private*, pg. 147
Cortiana, Walter, Fin. Controller--NRG Italia S.p.A., Milan, Italy; *Int'l*, pg. 1116
Cory, Charles L., Controller--Abbott Chemical & Agricultural Products Division, Abbott Park, IL; *U.S. Public*, pg. 13
Cosaert, John P., Chief Fin. Officer, Exec. V.P.-Intl. Fin., Treas. & Controller--Heartland Express, Inc., Coralville, IA; *U.S. Public*, pg. 803
Costallano, Joseph, Asst. Controller--Embers Charcoal Company, Inc., Conway, SC; *U.S. Private*, pg. 373
Costello, James, Controller--Dale Industries Inc., Dearborn, MI; *U.S. Private*, pg. 308
Coster, Victor J., Controller & Sec.--Cache, Inc., New York, NY; *U.S. Public*, pg. 289
Costlow Rogers, Annell, Controller--ENSERCH Corporation, Dallas, TX; *U.S. Public*, pg. 1587
Cothern, Carol, Controller--Precision Tune Autocare Inc., Leesburg, VA; *U.S. Public*, pg. 1321
Cotton, Donald, V.P. & Corp. Controller--Rally's Hamburgers, Inc., Louisville, KY; *U.S. Public*, pg. 1359
Cottrell, Adele, Controller--New Hermes Incorporated, Duluth, GA; *U.S. Private*, pg. 793
Cottrell, Paul, Jr., Controller--Pine State Trading Company, Augusta, ME; *U.S. Private*, pg. 865
Couch, Jim A., V.P. & Controller--Rykoff-Sexton, Inc., Wilkes-Barre, PA; *U.S. Public*, pg. 918
Coughlin, Kathy, V.P. & Controller--Spelling Entertainment Group, Inc., Los Angeles, CA; *U.S. Private*, pg. 776
Coughlin, L.L., Controller--Portec, Inc., Shipping Systems Div., Oak Brook, IL; *U.S. Public*, pg. 1318
Coumbe, Frederick R., Controller--Svedala Pumps & Process, Colorado Springs, CO; *Int'l*, pg. 1325
Counts, Duane, Controller--Bush Brothers & Company, Knoxville, TN; *U.S. Private*, pg. 189
Courington, Jerry D., Controller--Western Resources, Inc., Topeka, KS; *U.S. Public*, pg. 1759
Courtney, Doug, Controller--Ray-Carroll County Grain Co-op, Richmond, MO; *U.S. Private*, pg. 911
Courtney, Wayme, Controller--Rangen, Inc., Buhl, ID; *U.S. Private*, pg. 909
Cowan, J. Earl, Controller--Kenan Transport Company, Chapel Hill, NC; *U.S. Public*, pg. 949
Cowan, Steve, Controller--Havens Steel Co., Kansas City, MO; *U.S. Private*, pg. 510
Cowles, Alfred L., III, Chief Fin. Officer, Treas. & Controller--Bluff City Distributing Co., Inc., Memphis, TN; *U.S. Private*, pg. 153
Cowles, Rick, Controller--Sullivan Paper Company, West Springfield, MA; *U.S. Private*, pg. 1050
Cowley, I., Fin. Controller--Meggitt Electronic Components Ltd., Swindon, United Kingdom; *Int'l*, pg. 853
Cowsert, Lilly, Controller--Mashburn Construction Company, Columbia, SC; *U.S. Private*, pg. 711
Cox, Edward, Controller--National Technical Systems, Inc., Calabasas, CA; *U.S. Public*, pg. 1161
Cox, Hiram A., Controller--Delta Air Lines, Inc., Atlanta, GA; *U.S. Public*, pg. 497
Cox, Jack, Controller--Aiwa America, Inc., Mahwah, NJ; *Int'l*, pg. 1280
Cox, Lisa, Controller--McLaughlin Gormley King Company, Minneapolis, MN; *U.S. Private*, pg. 723
Cox, Michael, Controller--Cleveland Brothers Equipment Co., Inc., Harrisburg, PA; *U.S. Private*, pg. 245
Cox, P.G., V.P. & Controller--Siebe plc, Windsor, United Kingdom; *Int'l*, pg. 1240
Cox, Steve, Controller--Shady Brook Farms, Dayton, VA; *U.S. Private*, pg. 937
Coyle, Janet, Asst. Treas.--The Challenge Machinery Co., Grand Haven, MI; *U.S. Private*, pg. 227
Coyne, Bart, Controller--Fred V. Fowler Company, Inc., Newton, MA; *U.S. Private*, pg. 422
Coyne, Timothy E., V.P. & Controller--TransPro, Inc., New Haven, CT; *U.S. Public*, pg. 1631
Crabill, Mike, Controller--Contempo Colors, Kalamazoo, MI; *U.S. Private*, pg. 267
Crabtree, Max, Controller--Contadina/Libby/Trenton Div., Trenton, MO; *Int'l*, pg. 916
Craew, Tom, Controller--Herff Jones Inc., Indianapolis, IN; *U.S. Private*, pg. 523
Crafts, Norbert H., Controller--Doctors Hospital of Shreveport, Shreveport, LA; *U.S. Public*, pg. 1697
Cragen, John R., Controller--Schawk, Inc., Des Plaines, IL; *U.S. Public*, pg. 1437
Craig, Ginger, Controller--Trident Financial Corporation, Raleigh, NC; *U.S. Private*, pg. 1103
Crandall, George T., V.P., Treas., Controller & Sec.--Tridex Corporation, Westport, CT; *U.S. Public*, pg. 1637
Crane, D.M., V.P. & Controller--Computer Sciences Corporation, El Segundo, CA; *U.S. Public*, pg. 422
Crane, Jerry, V.P. & Controller--Harris Contracting Co., Saint Paul, MN; *U.S. Private*, pg. 505
Cravens, L.A., Controller--National Frozen Foods Corp., Seattle, WA; *U.S. Private*, pg. 783
Crawford, Alan G., Controller--York International Corporation, York, PA; *U.S. Public*, pg. 1788
Crawford, Hugh, Controller--Shelby Yarn Company, Shelby, NC; *U.S. Private*, pg. 991
Crawford, James R., Controller--Reeves Brothers Inc., New York, NY; *U.S. Private*, pg. 507
Crawford, Jim, Controller--Capital Tire, Inc., Toledo, OH; *U.S. Private*, pg. 206
Crawley, Dwight W., Controller & Sec.--Harris Teeter, Inc., Charlotte, NC; *U.S. Public*, pg. 1412
Craymer, Peter, Controller--Bernhardt Furniture Co., Lenoir, NC; *U.S. Private*, pg. 137
Creager, Tom, Controller--National Cattlemen's Beef Association, Greenwood Village, CO; *U.S. Private*, pg. 780
Creasey, Frederick A., Controller--Hollinger Inc., Vancouver, Canada; *Int'l*, pg. 630
Creasman, Scott R., V.P. & Controller--Tyler Corporation, Dallas, TX; *U.S. Public*, pg. 1651
Creek, Wallace W., Comptroller--General Motors Corporation, Detroit, MI; *U.S. Public*, pg. 718
Cribley, Fred J., Controller--Cast-Matic Corporation, Stevensville, MI; *U.S. Public*, pg. 894
Crimmins, John, Corp. Controller--Reed Elsevier Business Information, Newton, MA; *Int'l*, pg. 1095
Criste, Casey, Corp. Controller--Pacifica Services, Inc., Pasadena, CA; *U.S. Private*, pg. 832
Cromwell, Tim, Controller--Regency Group Inc., Jacksonville, FL; *U.S. Private*, pg. 918
Cronejo, Aneida, Controller--Apparel Ventures, Inc., Gardena, CA; *U.S. Private*, pg. 78
Cronin, John W., Chief Fin. Officer & V.P.-Fin.--Suitt Construction Company, Inc., Greenville, SC; *U.S. Private*, pg. 106
Crookston, Kelley L., Controller--National Gas & Oil Company, Newark, OH; *U.S. Public*, pg. 1156
Cropper, Karen, Chief Fin. Officer, V.P. & Controller--Theodore Barry & Associates, Los Angeles, CA; *U.S. Private*, pg. 118
Croppo, Tony, Controller--Sigma-Tau Finanziaria S.p.A., Rome, Italy; *Int'l*, pg. 1248
Cross, Daniel, Controller--The Buschman Co., Cincinnati, OH; *U.S. Private*, pg. 188
Cross, J. Robert, Controller--Bell Atlantic-VA, Richmond, VA; *U.S. Public*, pg. 203
Cross, Jim, Asst. Controller--Walker Die Casting, Inc., Lewisburg, TN; *U.S. Private*, pg. 1147
Cross, John C., Asst. Sec.--Mauna Kea Agribusiness Co., Inc., Papaikou, HI; *U.S. Private*, pg. 190
Cross, Mary Lenore, V.P. & Controller--Federal Chicago Corporation, North Chicago, IL; *U.S. Private*, pg. 398
Cross, Scott, Treas., Controller & Chief Accountant--Lewis Drug, Inc., Sioux Falls, SD; *U.S. Private*, pg. 665
Cross, Terry, Controller--Forest View Psychiatric Hospital, Grand Rapids, MI; *U.S. Public*, pg. 1697
Croston, Ann, Comptroller--Preferred Utilities Manufacturing Corp., Danbury, CT; *U.S. Private*, pg. 881
Croteau, Joe, Controller--T. Rowe Price Associates, Inc., Baltimore, MD; *U.S. Public*, pg. 1324
Croteau, Maurice, Controller--New England Newspaper Supply Company, Inc., Millbury, MA; *U.S. Private*, pg. 793
Crothers, Regina, Controller--Puritan/Churchill Chemical Company, Atlanta, GA; *U.S. Private*, pg. 895
Crotty, Eileen C., Controller--Computer Task Group, Inc. (CTG), Buffalo, NY; *U.S. Public*, pg. 423
Crouse, Carol, Controller--Cleveland Capital Holdings, Cliffside, NC; *U.S. Private*, pg. 246
Crouthamel, Michael R., Chief Fin. Officer & Treas.--John Solomon, Inc., Somerville, MA; *U.S. Private*, pg. 1013
Crow, John, Controller--Angelica Image Apparel, Saint Louis, MO; *U.S. Public*, pg. 113
Crowe, Stephen J., Comptroller--Chevron Corporation, San Francisco, CA; *U.S. Public*, pg. 347
Crowell, Larry, Controller--Philadelphia Sign Company, Palmyra, NJ; *U.S. Private*, pg. 861
Crowley, Curtis, Controller--Vencare, Incorporated, Alpharetta, GA; *U.S. Public*, pg. 1715
Crowley, Elaine, Controller--The Bombay Company, Fort Worth, TX; *U.S. Public*, pg. 244

Cruckshank, James W., Controller--Schnitzer Steel Industries, Inc., Portland, OR; *U.S. Public*, pg. 1439

Cruckshank, James W., Controller--Proler International Corp., Portland, OR; *U.S. Public*, pg. 1440

Cruger, Michael H., V.P.-Oper. & Controller--Henningsen Foods, Inc., White Plains, NY; *Int'l*, pg. 1074

Cruickshank, Andrew, Controller--Anchor Lamina Inc., Windsor, Canada; *Int'l*, pg. 75

Crumb, Dan, Controller--Louisiana Gaming Management, Inc., Metairie, LA; *U.S. Private*, pg. 677

Crump, Thomas F., V.P. & Controller--Heilig-Meyers Company, Richmond, VA; *U.S. Public*, pg. 804

Crump, Tom, Chief Fin. Officer & Controller--Heilig Meyers Furniture Co., Richmond, VA; *U.S. Public*, pg. 804

Crunk, Rebecca B., V.P., Controller & Treas.--United Services Life Insurance Co., Arlington, VA; *U.S. Public*, pg. 1376

Cruse, Cookie, Controller--United Parking, Inc., Atlanta, GA; *U.S. Private*, pg. 1123

Cruz, Stan, Controller & Mgr.-Acctg.--Standun, Inc., Inglewood, CA; *U.S. Private*, pg. 1032

Cruz, Stan, Controller & Mgr.-Accts.--Zephyr Mfg. Co., Inglewood, CA; *U.S. Private*, pg. 1032

Csada, Mike, Comptroller--Estevan Brick Division, Estevan, Canada; *Int'l*, pg. 698

Cube, Sig, Controller--Storm Products Company, Inc., Santa Monica, CA; *U.S. Private*, pg. 1045

Culak, Robert G., Asst. Controller--Sysco Corporation, Houston, TX; *U.S. Public*, pg. 1550

Culley, David, Controller--Dee Paper Company, Chester, PA; *U.S. Private*, pg. 320

Culliton, Tim, Controller--Energy West Inc., Great Falls, MT; *U.S. Public*, pg. 581

Culmer, George, Controller--Prudential Corporation PLC, London, United Kingdom; *Int'l*, pg. 1073

Cuma, Kumar, Controller--International Cutlery, LTD, New York, NY; *U.S. Private*, pg. 569

Cummings, Kurt, Controller--AVX Corporation, Myrtle Beach, SC; *Int'l*, pg. 775

Cummings, M. Laurie, Controller & Asst. Treas.--Dartford Partnership, San Francisco, CA; *U.S. Private*, pg. 312

Cummins, Chris, Controller--Mayville Metal Products Division, Mayville, WI; *U.S. Private*, pg. 264

Cumptom, M.E., V.P. & Controller--J.M. Huber, Clay Div., Macon, GA; *U.S. Private*, pg. 545

Cuniff, Jack, Controller--Adidas International, Portland, OR; *Int'l*, pg. 24

Cunningham, Doug, V.P. & Controller--Principal Mutual Life Insurance Co., Des Moines, IA; *U.S. Private*, pg. 886

Cunningham, James, Controller--Hampshire Chemical Corp., Lexington, MA; *U.S. Private*, pg. 498

Cunningham, Pat, Controller & Dir.-Personnel--I. Spiewak & Sons, Inc., New York, NY; *U.S. Private*, pg. 1025

Cunningham, Tim, Comptroller--Moore Document Solutions, Lake Forest, IL; *Int'l*, pg. 890

Cupak, John F., Controller--Drew Industries Incorporated, White Plains, NY; *U.S. Public*, pg. 529

Cupak, John F., Controller--Leslie Building Products, Inc., White Plains, NY; *U.S. Public*, pg. 989

Curbelo, Ray, Controller & Sec.--National Utility Service, Inc., Park Ridge, NJ; *U.S. Private*, pg. 787

Curless, Carroll D., V.P. & Controller--Eagle-Picher Industries, Inc., Cincinnati, OH; *U.S. Private*, pg. 355

Curran, John, Controller--Risser Oil Corp., Clearwater, FL; *U.S. Private*, pg. 932

Curran, Stephen J., Controller--Bay State Gas Company, Westborough, MA; *U.S. Public*, pg. 196

Curran, Thomas A., Controller--Port of Houston Authority, Houston, TX; *U.S. Private*, pg. 876

Curran, William J., Controller--Frigidaire Company Dishwasher Products, Kinston, NC; *Int'l*, pg. 439

Currie, John, V.P. & Controller--The Stroh Brewery Company, Detroit, MI; *U.S. Private*, pg. 1047

Currie, Mary, Corp. Controller--Labatt Brewing Company Limited, Toronto, Canada; *Int'l*, pg. 679

Curry, James T., Controller--Miller Advertising Agency Inc., New York, NY; *U.S. Private*, pg. 746

Curry, Sharon, Comptroller--Blue Boar Cafeteria Co., Louisville, KY; *U.S. Private*, pg. 151

Curtis, John, Comptroller--Taylor Company, Rockton, IL; *U.S. Public*, pg. 1496

Curtis, Stan, Controller, Asst Treas & Asst. Sec.--Continental Forge Company, Compton, CA; *U.S. Private, pg. 268*

Cusumano, Charles A., V.P.-Fin.--Western Atlas Inc., Houston, TX; *U.S. Public*, pg. 1757

Cutilleta, Thomas, Sr. V.P. & Controller--Stone Container Corporation, Chicago, IL; *U.S. Public*, pg. 1520

Cutilletta, Tom, Controller--Stone Forest Industries, Chicago, IL; *U.S. Public*, pg. 1521

Cutler, Donald, Controller--Barr & Barr, Inc., New York, NY; *U.S. Private*, pg. 117

Cvetkovska, Anna, Controller--OzEmail Limited, Sydney, Australia; *Int'l*, pg. 1019

Cyranoski, Dave, Sr. V.P., Controller & Sec.--Northern Illinois Gas Company, Naperville, IL; *U.S. Public*, pg. 1183

Cyranoski, David L., Sr. V.P., Controller & Sec.--NICOR Inc., Naperville, IL; *U.S. Public*, pg. 1182

Czajka, Edward F., V.P. & Controller--Pacific Capital Bancorp, Salinas, CA; *U.S. Public*, pg. 1247

Czajka, Edward J., V.P. & Controller--First National Bank of Central California, Salinas, CA; *U.S. Public*, pg. 1248

Czapala, Robert, Controller--London House, Rosemont, IL; *U.S. Public*, pg. 1070

Czisch, Ernst, Fin. Controller--Eagle-Picher Wolverine GmbH, Ohringen, Germany; *U.S. Private*, pg. 355

Czulada, Charles, Controller--Premier Mill Corp., Reading, PA; *U.S. Private*, pg. 881

Czulno, John J., Comptroller--Naylor Pipe Company, Chicago, IL; *U.S. Private*, pg. 789

Czyz, Douglas, Controller--SK Hand Tool Corp., Chicago, IL; *Int'l*, pg. 570

D'Alessandro, Robert T., Sr. V.P. & Controller--UST Inc., Greenwich, CT; *U.S. Public*, pg. 1660

D'Aloia, G. Peter, V.P. & Controller--AlliedSignal Inc., Morristown, NJ; *U.S. Public*, pg. 49

D'Amico, John, V.P. & Controller--Wechsler Coffee Corp., Moonachie, NJ; *U.S. Private*, pg. 1158

D'Amico, Martin, Controller--Thomas & Betts/Amerace, Brooksville, FL; *U.S. Public*, pg. 1598

D'Angelo, Mario, Controller--FlightSafety International Inc., Flushing, NY; *U.S. Public*, pg. 218

Dachenhaus, Terry, Controller--Seaway Food Town, Inc., Maumee, OH; *U.S. Public*, pg. 1452

Dacquisto, Sherilyn, Controller--Valley Forge Corporation, San Rafael, CA; *U.S. Public*, pg. 1705

Daffin, Alton L., V.P. & Controller--Joy Mining Machinery, Warrendale, PA; *U.S. Public*, pg. 789

Dahm, Anthony, Controller--Giant Food Inc., Landover, MD; *U.S. Public*, pg. 741

Dahm, J.J., Controller--Robert Bryce & Co., Ltd., Wellington, New Zealand; *Int'l*, pg. 682

Dahmus, J.M., Controller--Procter & Gamble Pharmaceuticals, Inc., Cincinnati, OH; *U.S. Public*, pg. 1331

Dai, John, Controller & Sec.--H.S. Crocker Co., Inc., Huntley, IL; *U.S. Private*, pg. 290

Daibo, Naobumi, Controller--OYO Corporation, Tokyo, Japan; *Int'l*, pg. 1019

Daigle, Randy, Controller--Louisiana Utilities Supply Company, Baton Rouge, LA; *U.S. Private*, pg. 245

Daigle, Raymond, Controller--Imprimerie Quebecor Graphique-Couleur, La Salle, Canada; *Int'l*, pg. 1077

Dailey, Jan, Treas.--Seaman Timber Company, Inc., Montevallo, AL; *U.S. Private*, pg. 979

Dailey, John E., Asst. V.P.-Fin. & Controller--NCC Industries, Inc., Cortland, NY; *U.S. Private*, pg. 697

Dailey, Sean, V.P.-Fin.--Horizon/CMS Healthcare Corporation, Albuquerque, NM; *U.S. Public*, pg. 836

Dale, Dennis W., Controller--E'Town Corporation, Westfield, NJ; *U.S. Public*, pg. 540

Dale, Donald, Controller--Berry Petroleum Company, Taft, CA; *U.S. Public*, pg. 223

Daley, C.C., Jr., V.P. & Comptroller-Intl.--The Folger Coffee Company, Cincinnati, OH; *U.S. Public*, pg. 1331

Daley, Marty, Corp. Controller--Monaco Coach Corporation, Coburg, OR; *U.S. Public*, pg. 1123

Dalia, Dan, Controller--Keane, Inc., Boston, MA; *U.S. Public, pg. 946*

Dalla Riva, Robert J., CPA, Controller--Stanbee Company, Inc., Carlstadt, NJ; *U.S. Private*, pg. 1030

Daly, Peter, Comptroller--Pedone & Partners Adv., Inc., New York, NY; *U.S. Private*, pg. 846

Damm, Ulrich, Dir.-Capital Markets Coordination & Control--European Investment Bank, Luxembourg, Luxembourg; *Int'l*, pg. 465

Damon, Robert, V.P. & Controller--Katz Media Group, Inc., New York, NY; *U.S. Public*, pg. 335

Danchuk, Richard, Controller--Kilovac Corporation, Carpinteria, CA; *U.S. Private*, pg. 259

Dandurand, Don, Controller-Jewell Div.--Allard Industries, Manchester, NH; *U.S. Private*, pg. 36

Daniel, Carole J., V.P. & Controllers.--National Print Group, Inc., Chattanooga, TN; *U.S. Private*, pg. 785

Daniel, K.L., V.P. & Controller--Black & Veatch, Kansas City, MO; *U.S. Private*, pg. 146

Daniel, Merl, V.P. & Controller--Farmland Industries, Inc., Kansas City, MO; *U.S. Private*, pg. 395

Daniel, Richard H., Chief Fin. Officer & Exec. V.P.--Bankers Trust New York Corporation, New York, NY; *U.S. Public, pg. 185*

Daniel, William F., Chief Acctg. Officer, Grp. V.P.-Fin. & Grp. Controller--Elan Corporation Plc, Dublin, Ireland; *Int'l*, pg. 435

Daniels, Donna M., V.P. & Controller--Admiral Insurance Company, Cherry Hill, NJ; *U.S. Public*, pg. 216

Daniels, M.C., Controller--LEXIS Document Services, Springfield, IL; *Int'l*, pg. 1096

Daniels, Pamela H., Chief Acctg. Officer, V.P. & Controller--Beverly Enterprises, Inc., Fort Smith, AR; *U.S. Public*, pg. 227

Danielski, Lawrence J., V.P. & Controller--MediVators, Inc., Eagan, MN; *U.S. Public*, pg. 301

Danish, Colleen P., Asst. Treas.--Troy Savings Bank-Hudson Valley Plaza, Troy, NY; *U.S. Private*, pg. 1106

Dankmyer, William, Controller--AFG Industries, Inc., Kingsport, TN; *Int'l*, pg. 84

Danley, William F., Controller--The Homer Laughlin China Company, Newell, WV; *U.S. Private*, pg. 653

Danna, Patrick J., Controller--Journal Register Company, Trenton, NJ; *U.S. Public*, pg. 934

Dannelly, Robert B., Sr., Chief Fin. Officer, V.P.-Fin. & Controller--Piedmont Mechanical, Inc., Spartanburg, SC; *U.S. Private*, pg. 865

Dannhauser, Michael, Asst. Corp. Controller--Playboy Enterprises, Inc., Chicago, IL; *U.S. Public*, pg. 1309

Dansack, Marty, Controller--Hickory Farms, Inc., Maumee, OH; *U.S. Private*, pg. 525

Danski, Jon F., Sr. V.P. & Controller--ITT Corporation, New York, NY; *U.S. Public*, pg. 1512

DaPra, Dennis, Controller--Michigan Gas Storage Co., Jackson, MI; *U.S. Public*, pg. 280

Darby, Guy C., V.P. & Controller--Exide Electronics Group, Inc., Raleigh, NC; *Int'l*, pg. 126

Darby, Mike, Controller--Glentel Inc., Burnaby, Canada; *Int'l, pg. 1336*

Dark, Vicki, Controller--Tennessee Dressed Beef Company, Nashville, TN; *U.S. Private*, pg. 1076

Darnell, Rhonda, Mgr.-Acctg.--W-B Supply Co., Pampa, TX; *U.S. Private*, pg. 1144

Darragh, Rick, Controller--Indianapolis Life Insurance Co., Indianapolis, IN; *U.S. Private*, pg. 560

Darragh, Susan A., Controller & Treas.--C.S. McKee & Company, Inc., Pittsburgh, PA; *U.S. Public*, pg. 1673

Darsow, David, Controller--Palm Beach Beauty Products Co., Minneapolis, MN; *U.S. Private*, pg. 834

Dart, Geoffrey, Dir. & Controller--Marks & Spencer PLC, London, United Kingdom; *Int'l*, pg. 842

Dasher, Rick, Controller--Paterno Imports Limited, Lake Bluff, IL; *U.S. Private*, pg. 843

Dasis, John, Controller--R.T.M. Winners, Atlanta, GA; *U.S. Private*, pg. 906

Daszkiewicz, Tom, Controller--Faygo Beverages, Inc., Detroit, MI; *U.S. Public*, pg. 1153

Datt, Gary, Controller--Pannier Corporation, Pittsburgh, PA; *U.S. Private*, pg. 837

Daura, Juan, Controller--Kalifarma S.A., Barcelona, Spain; *Int'l*, pg. 1279

Dauria, Steven M., V.P. & Controller--Florida Panthers Holdings, Inc., Fort Lauderdale, FL; *U.S. Public*, pg. 654

Dauterive, Henry, Controller--Nestle Beverage Company, New Orleans, LA; *Int'l*, pg. 917

Davenport, Eileen, Controller--Scicom Data Services, Ltd., Minnetonka, MN; *U.S. Private*, pg. 975

Davenport, Warren, Controller--Kellwood Lingerie/Active Group, Summit, MS; *U.S. Public*, pg. 948

Davenport, Wellington, Controller--Polychrome Corp. Div., Fort Lee, NJ; *Int'l*, pg. 370

David, Roland, V.P. & Controller--Fabricon Products, River Rouge, MI; *U.S. Private*, pg. 355

David, Thomas L., Controller--Ira Higdon Grocery, Inc., Cairo, GA; *U.S. Private*, pg. 527

Davidson, Brian, Controller--The Van Metres Companies, Burke, VA; *U.S. Private*, pg. 1132

Davidson, I., Fin. Controller--AAH Pharmaceuticals Limited, Runcorn, United Kingdom; *Int'l*, pg. 591

Davie, Edward, Sr. V.P. & Pres.-Asia Pacific Div.--ITT Sheraton Corporation, Boston, MA; *U.S. Public*, pg. 1512

Davies, David L., Controller--Shopping Centre Group, Toronto, Canada; *Int'l*, pg. 253

Davies, Mike, V.P. & Controller--Imax Corporation, Mississauga, Canada; *Int'l*, pg. 661

Davies, Stephen, Grp. Fin. Controller--Coats Viyella plc, Manchester, United Kingdom; *Int'l*, pg. 299

Davies, Timothy H., Controller & Treas.--Atalanta Corporation, Elizabeth, NJ; *U.S. Private*, pg. 93

Davies, Zachary M., Controller & Sec.--Tweddle Litho Company, Clinton Township, MI; *U.S. Private*, pg. 1111

Davin, Ernest, Controller--MBM, Rocky Mount, NC; *U.S. Private*, pg. 685

Davis-Padron, Ida, Controller--Equitrac Corporation, Coral Gables, FL; *U.S. Public*, pg. 590

Davis, Al, V.P. & Controller--Marley Pump, Overland Park, KS; *U.S. Public*, pg. 1676

Davis, Betty F., V.P. & Controller--Potomac Capital Investment Corporation, Washington, DC; *U.S. Public*, pg. 1319

Davis, Carolyn, Controller--Danish Creamery Association, Fresno, CA; *U.S. Private*, pg. 310

Davis, Daniel R., V.P. & Controller--Firstbank of Illinois Co., Springfield, IL; *U.S. Public*, pg. 643

Davis, Dave J., V.P. & Corp. Controller--PLM Financial Services, Inc., San Francisco, CA; *U.S. Public*, pg. 1241

Davis, David J., V.P. & Corp. Controller--PLM International, Inc., San Francisco, CA; *U.S. Public*, pg. 1241

Davis, David Terrence, V.P. & Controller--Canadian Utilities Limited, Calgary, Canada; *Int'l*, pg. 95

Davis, Deborah L., Controller--Multimedia Newspaper Company, Greenville, SC; *U.S. Public*, pg. 699

Davis, Douglas C., V.P. & Controller--Marsh & McLennan Companies, Inc., New York, NY; *U.S. Public*, pg. 1048

Davis, Eric, Controller--Brothers Gourmet Coffees, Inc., Boca Raton, FL; *U.S. Public*, pg. 259

Davis, Frank, Controller--Insulating Materials, Inc., Schenectady, NY; *U.S. Private*, pg. 565

Davis, G. Michael, Controller--Rauch Industries, Inc., Gastonia, NC; *U.S. Private*, pg. 1061

Davis, Gary, Controller--South Shore Harbour Development, League City, TX; *U.S. Public*, pg. 88

Davis, Gary, Controller--Hunter Contracting Company, Gilbert, AZ; *U.S. Private*, pg. 549

Davis, George W., Controller--Henkels & McCoy, Inc., Blue Bell, PA; *U.S. Private*, pg. 522

Davis, James R., Chief Fin. Officer & Controller--Rinker Materials Corp., West Palm Beach, FL; *Int'l*, pg. 246

Davis, Jeff, Controller--Collman Graphics, Inc., Baltimore, MD; *U.S. Private*, pg. 253

Davis, Jerry, V.P. & Controller--United Dominion Realty Trust, Inc., Richmond, VA; *U.S. Public*, pg. 1677

Davis, Jill, Controller--Pittsburgh Tube Co. Fairbury Div., Fairbury, IL; *U.S. Private*, pg. 868

Davis, John, Controller--E.A. Sween Company, Eden Prairie, MN; *U.S. Private*, pg. 1058

Davis, John L., Chief Fin. Officer--Riggs National Corporation, Washington, DC; *U.S. Public*, pg. 1389

Davis, John N., V.P. & Controller--Armco Inc., Pittsburgh, PA; *U.S. Public*, pg. 131

Davis, K. Michael, Controller--FPL Group, Inc., North Palm Beach, FL; *U.S. Public*, pg. 608

Davis, K.M., Comptroller--Florida Power & Light Company, North Palm Beach, FL; *U.S. Public*, pg. 608

Davis, Kim, Controller--Inman Construction Corporation, Memphis, TN; *U.S. Private*, pg. 564

Davis, Melissa D., Controller--Texas-New Mexico Power Co., Fort Worth, TX; *U.S. Public*, pg. 1557

Davis, Milton, Asst. Controller--Commercial Metals Company, Dallas, TX; *U.S. Public*, pg. 411

Davis, R. Russell, Asst. Controller--Central and South West Corporation, Dallas, TX; *U.S. Public*, pg. 324

Davis, R.C., Controller--Construction & Mining Group, Bethlehem, PA; *U.S. Public*, pg. 876

Davis, Rich, Controller--Amco Folding Cartons, Inc., Towaco, NJ; *U.S. Private*, pg. 48

Davis, Rick, Controller--The Wiser Oil Company, Dallas, TX; *U.S. Public*, pg. 1773

Davis, Robert W., Acting Controller--Woodmen Accident & Life Co., Lincoln, NE; *U.S. Private*, pg. 1187

Davis, Steve, Controller--Stolper-Fabralloy Co. LLC, Brookfield, WI; *U.S. Public*, pg. 1640

Davis, T. Duncan, Controller--Alco Chemical, Chattanooga, TN; Int'l, pg. 1435
Davis, Thomas, Controller--Wahl Clipper Corp., Sterling, IL; U.S. Private, pg. 1146
Davis, Tom, Controller--Tennessee Farmers Co-op, La Vergne, TN; U.S. Private, pg. 1076
Davis, Vandy, Asst. Controller--Flowers Industries, Inc., Thomasville, GA; U.S. Public, pg. 656
Davis, William F., Chief Fin. Officer, V.P. & Treas.--Barnhill Contracting Company, Tarboro, NC; U.S. Private, pg. 117
Dawkins, Anna, Asst. Controller--KTI, Inc., Guttenberg, NJ; U.S. Public, pg. 939
Dawson, John, Controller--Goldsboro Milling Company, Goldsboro, NC; U.S. Private, pg. 462
Dawson, Steven E., V.P.-Fin. & Admin./Network & Controller--Telemundo Group, Inc., Hialeah, FL; U.S. Public, pg. 1570
Day, Brian, Controller--Arrow International, Cleveland, OH; U.S. Private, pg. 85
Day, Donald R., Controller--Gems Sensors, Plainville, CT; U.S. Public, pg. 481
Day, Greg, Controller--R&B, Inc., Colmar, PA; U.S. Public, pg. 1354
Day, James, Chief Fin. Officer, V.P. & Controller--US 1 Industries Inc., Gary, IN; U.S. Public, pg. 1687
Day, James, Controller--Keystone Lines, Gary, IN; U.S. Public, pg. 1687
Day, James, Controller--TC Services, Gary, IN; U.S. Public, pg. 1687
Day, James, Controller--Blue & Gray Brokerage, Gary, IN; U.S. Public, pg. 1687
Day, James, Controller--Blue & Gray Transportation, Gary, IN; U.S. Public, pg. 1687
Day, Kevin, Controller--A.G. Simpson Co. Limited, Scarborough, Canada; Int'l, pg. 1252
Day, Merrie Beth, Controller--Jan Bell Marketing Inc., Sunrise, FL; U.S. Public, pg. 207
De Armas, Eloy R., Sr. V.P.--Business Mens Insurance Corporation, Coral Gables, FL; U.S. Private, pg. 189
De Bono, Nili, V.P.-Fin. & Admin.--Metropolitan Sunday Newspapers, Inc., New York, NY; U.S. Private, pg. 739
De Busscher, C., Controller--N.V. Van Melle S.A., Berchem, Belgium; Int'l, pg. 1451
De Foor, Jerry W., Chief Acctg. Officer, V.P. & Controller--Protective Life Corporation, Birmingham, AL; U.S. Public, pg. 1336
de Gouyon, Herve, Controller--Credit Lyonnais S.A., Paris, France; Int'l, pg. 343
de Jesus Leon, Ruben, Treas. & Comptroller--Componentes Delfa, C.A., Caracas, Venezuela; U.S. Public, pg. 724
de Jong, J., Controller--VNU Verenigde Nederlandse Uitgeversbedrijven B.V., Haarlem, Netherlands; Int'l, pg. 1445
de Nobel, Roel, Controller--Security House, Purmerend, Netherlands; U.S. Public, pg. 1307
De Prefontaine, Kevin, Controller--Ross Technology Corp., Leola, PA; U.S. Private, pg. 946
De Rond, Fons, Fin. Controller--Kulk & Kramer Kantoorsystemen B.V., Zoetermeer, Netherlands; Int'l, pg. 1116
de Roos, Hans, Controller & Mgr.-Opers.--Sensormatic B.V., Bunnik, Netherlands; U.S. Public, pg. 1457
de St. Pastov, B., Unit Controller--Weatherford France, S.A., Billere., France; U.S. Public, pg. 1750
de Wolf, William, Controller--Canadian Tire Acceptance Ltd., Welland, Canada; Int'l, pg. 259
Dean, D.A., Controller--Long Manufacturing, Ltd., Oakville, Canada; Int'l, pg. 815
Dean, Dave, Controller--Packard BioScience Company, Meriden, CT; U.S. Private, pg. 833
Dean, Edward J., Controller--Wolohan Lumber Co., Saginaw, MI; U.S. Public, pg. 1774
Dean, Greg, V.P.-Fin. & Controller--Jim Walter Resources, Inc., Brookwood, AL; U.S. Public, pg. 1737
Dean, Miles, V.P. & Controller--Outboard Marine Corporation, Waukegan, IL; U.S. Private, pg. 478
Dean, Richard, V.P. & Controller--Gulf States Paper Corporation, Tuscaloosa, AL; U.S. Private, pg. 487
Deane, Kathryn A., V.P. & Controller--Prime Group Realty Trust, Chicago, IL; U.S. Public, pg. 1326
DeAngelo, Yvonne, V.P.-Fin. & Controller--Nobel Education Dynamics, Inc., Media, PA; U.S. Public, pg. 1185
Dearden, Brian, Controller--Teleflex Electrical Systems, Sarasota, FL; U.S. Public, pg. 1569
DeBauche, Carol, Controller--La Amistad Residential Treatment Center, Maitland, FL; U.S. Public, pg. 1697
DeBenedetto, Frank, Controller--Acrison, Inc., Moonachie, NJ; U.S. Private, pg. 14
Deblasi, Ugo D., Controller--The Perkin-Elmer Corporation, Norwalk, CT; U.S. Public, pg. 1279
DeBoth, Dale, Controller--AmClyde Engineered Products Co., Inc., Saint Paul, MN; U.S. Public, pg. 778
Debrecht, Donald R., Sr. V.P., Treas. & Controller--Hill-Behan Lumber Company, Saint Louis, MO; U.S. Private, pg. 529
Debusk, Gerald K., Controller--Xaloy, Inc., Pulaski, VA; U.S. Private, pg. 1194
DeChandt, Marcia A., Controller--Herbert Malarkey Roofing Company, Portland, OR; U.S. Private, pg. 698
Decina, Daniel J., Controller & Treas.--Tasty Baking Company, Philadelphia, PA; U.S. Public, pg. 1561
Decker, Barbara, Controller--Anglo Fabrics Company, Inc., New York, NY; U.S. Private, pg. 74
Decker, C. Jeff, Controller--NxTrend Technology, Inc., Colorado Springs, CO; U.S. Private, pg. 809
Decker, Joan L., Controller--Arinc Inc. (Consolidated), Annapolis, MD; U.S. Private, pg. 81
DeCook, Art, Controller & Treas.--Roy O'Brien Inc., Saint Clair Shores, MI; U.S. Private, pg. 810
DeCoster, John, Controller--Wallace Computer Services, Inc., Lisle, IL; U.S. Public, pg. 1735
Dedeker, Cynthia, Controller--CNJ Distributing, Billings, MT; U.S. Private, pg. 196
Dee, Jim, Controller--Keywell Corporation, Chicago, IL; U.S. Private, pg. 619
Dee, John J., Sr. V.P. & Controller--First Union Real Estate Investments, Cleveland, OH; U.S. Public, pg. 640
Dee, Laura, Controller--Pyramid Handbags Inc., New York, NY; U.S. Private, pg. 896
Deel, Jeffrey A., Asst. Controller--Smithfield Foods, Inc., Norfolk, VA; U.S. Public, pg. 1479
Deffet, Suzanne Tabor, V.P., Controller & Treas.--Allied Mineral Products, Inc., Columbus, OH; U.S. Private, pg. 39
DeFino, Frank, Controller--Imperia Bros., Inc., Pelham Manor, NY; U.S. Private, pg. 558
DeFlorio, V., Controller--Bridgestone/Firestone Italia S.p.A., Milan, Italy; Int'l, pg. 214
DeFoor, Jerry W., Chief Acctg. Officer, V.P. & Controller--Protective Life Insurance Co., Birmingham, AL; U.S. Public, pg. 1336
DeFrancesco, James, Controller--Medical Laboratory Automation, Inc., Pleasantville, NY; U.S. Private, pg. 727
DeGady, Sonny, Controller--Trainer Wortham & Company Incorporated, New York, NY; U.S. Private, pg. 1095
DeGain, Marcy A., Controller--Standard Electronics, Inc., Amherst, NY; U.S. Private, pg. 1031
DeGoce, Kathy, Controller--Inverness Corp., Fair Lawn, NJ; U.S. Private, pg. 574
DeGuzman, Renato, Controller--UHP Healthcare, Inglewood, CA; U.S. Private, pg. 1113
Deierlein, Kathie J., V.P. & Controller--NBT Bancorp Inc., Norwich, NY; U.S. Public, pg. 1144
Deierlein, Walter, Controller--Republic Contracting Corp., Columbia, SC; U.S. Private, pg. 923
Deily, Richard H., Controller--Excalibur Technologies Corporation, Vienna, VA; U.S. Public, pg. 598
Deiter, Jon, Controller--Kokomo Sanitary Pottery Corp., Kokomo, IN; U.S. Private, pg. 449
Del Calvo, Teresita, Controller & Dir.-D.P.--E & G Foods, Miami, FL; U.S. Private, pg. 352
Del Grande, David, Controller--Hoogovens Aluminium Corp., Secaucus, NJ; Int'l, pg. 755
Del Rosario, Mimma, Controller--Master Products Mfg. Co., Los Angeles, CA; Int'l, pg. 340
Delassandro, Glenn, Asst. Controller--K & F Industries Inc., New York, NY; U.S. Private, pg. 602
Deldebio, Phillip, Controller--Hipotronics, Inc., Brewster, NY; U.S. Public, pg. 844
Delgado, Elizabeth, Controller & Treas.--Presidential Realty Corporation, White Plains, NY; U.S. Public, pg. 1323
DelGaiso, Dave, Controller--Soap Opera Digest, New York, NY; U.S. Public, pg. 1328
DelGaiso, Dave, Controller--Soap Opera Weekly, New York, NY; U.S. Public, pg. 1328
Dell, John, Controller--Air New Zealand Ltd., Auckland, New Zealand; Int'l, pg. 38
Delly, Gayla, Controller & Treas.--Benchmark Electronics Inc., Angleton, TX; U.S. Public, pg. 210
Delman, Richard, Chief Fin. Officer, Controller, Treas. & Sec.--New Age Intimates Inc., Long Island City, NY; U.S. Private, pg. 792
Delmont, Ray, Controller--Northern Michigan Veneers, Inc., Gladstone, MI; U.S. Private, pg. 805
Deloach, Scott, Controller--The PBS&J Corporation, Miami, FL; U.S. Private, pg. 825
DeLong, Stephen A., Controller & Chief Acct.--The Reynolds and Reynolds Company, Dayton, OH; U.S. Public, pg. 1384
DeLuca, Donald, Controller--General Office Environments Inc., Rochelle Park, NJ; U.S. Private, pg. 445
DeLuca, Susan, Chief Fin. Officer, Exec. V.P. & Controller--Aero Data Metal Crafters, Ronkonkoma, NY; U.S. Private, pg. 23
Demanche, Jacques, Treas.--Gaz Metropolitain & Company, Montreal, Canada; Int'l, pg. 541
DeMaria, Peter J., V.P. & Controller--Kentucky Power Co., Ashland, KY; U.S. Public, pg. 72
DeMaria, Peter J., V.P. & Controller--Indiana Michigan Power Company, Fort Wayne, IN; U.S. Public, pg. 72
DeMaria, Peter J., V.P. & Controller--Ohio Power Company, Canton, OH; U.S. Public, pg. 72
DeMaria, Peter J., V.P. & Controller--Columbus Southern Power Company, Columbus, OH; U.S. Public, pg. 72
DeMaria, Peter J., V.P. & Controller--Appalachian Power Company, Roanoke, VA; U.S. Public, pg. 72
DeMartini, James, Controller--Caere Corporation, Los Gatos, CA; U.S. Public, pg. 291
Demere, Leon, Controller--Meggitt Avionics Inc., Manchester, NH; Int'l, pg. 853
Demeritt, John, Controller--Meditrust Corporation, Needham, MA; U.S. Public, pg. 1081
Demers, Norbert, Chief Fin. Officer & V.P.-Fin.--The Hilsinger Co. L.P., Plainville, MA; U.S. Private, pg. 530
Dempsey, David W., Controller--Gate City Beverage Distributors, San Bernardino, CA; U.S. Private, pg. 441
den Hoed, Jean, Exec. V.P.-Fin. & Control--Akzo Nobel N.V., Arnhem, Netherlands; Int'l, pg. 42
Denault, Daniel, V.P. & Controller--Domtar Inc., Montreal, Canada; Int'l, pg. 416
DeNeve, David J., Controller--Material Sciences Corporation, Elk Grove Village, IL; U.S. Public, pg. 1056
Denman, Jim, Controller--The O'Boise Corporation, Oak Brook, IL; U.S. Private, pg. 810
Denny, Dale, Controller--John Bouchard & Sons Company, Nashville, TN; U.S. Private, pg. 161
Denten, Steve, Controller--A. Finkl & Sons Co., Chicago, IL; U.S. Private, pg. 405
Denton, David, Controller--Farmers Investment Company, Inc., Horse Cave, KY; U.S. Private, pg. 112
DePalo, Lorelei, Controller--Graham-Field Health Products, Inc., Hauppauge, NY; U.S. Public, pg. 757
Depardieux, Mr., Controller--Baccarat (Cie des Cristalleries), Paris, France; Int'l, pg. 132
DePauw, Floyd, Controller--Bollinger Industries Inc., Grand Prairie, TX; U.S. Public, pg. 243
Depenbrock, Thomas J., V.P. & Controller--NS Group, Inc., Newport, KY; U.S. Public, pg. 1147
DePiro, Valerie, Chief Acctg. Officer, V.P. & Controller--Geotek Communications, Montvale, NJ; U.S. Public, pg. 739
Deppert, Mary, Controller--Moran Industries, Inc., Midlothian, IL; U.S. Private, pg. 760
DePrimo, Richard C., Controller--Alpha Associates, Inc., Woodbridge, NJ; U.S. Private, pg. 44
DeRaad, Mark, V.P., Controller & Principal Acctg. Officer--AST Research Inc., Irvine, CA; Int'l, pg. 1181
Derbes, Lew J., Jr., Asst. Controller-Fin.--Avondale Industries, Inc., Avondale, LA; U.S. Public, pg. 156
DeRieux, Jerry, Controller--Vulcan Materials Company-Southern Div., Birmingham, AL; U.S. Public, pg. 1726
Derive, Darryl, V.P. & Controller--Kaufman and Broad of Nevada, Inc., Las Vegas, NV; U.S. Public, pg. 945
Derlath, Bernhard, V.P. & Controller--Bertelsmann Inc., New York, NY; Int'l, pg. 191
Dermer, Charles, Controller--Ogden Newspapers, Inc., Wheeling, WV; U.S. Private, pg. 812
Dermody, Sue, Controller--Paine Furniture Co., Natick, MA; U.S. Private, pg. 834
Dermott, Nancy, Controller--Ocean Spray Cranberries, Inc., Middleboro, MA; U.S. Private, pg. 811
DeRohan, William, Controller--Fansteel VR/Wesson-Plantsville, Plantsville, CT; U.S. Public, pg. 612
Derr, Will T., V.P. & Controller--Staff Builders Inc., Lake Success, NY; U.S. Public, pg. 1501
Derrick, Al, Controller--Cain & Bultman, Jacksonville, FL; U.S. Private, pg. 199
Desai, K.J., Fin. Controller--Tioxide Group Limited, London, United Kingdom; Int'l, pg. 663
Deschenes, Roger, Controller--Hyde Athletic Industries, Inc., Peabody, MA; U.S. Public, pg. 851
Descoteaux, Mary, V.P. & Controller--Sundt Corp., Tucson, AZ; U.S. Private, pg. 1051
Desmond, Richard M., Chief Acctg. Officer, V.P. & Comptroller--Brooklyn Union, Brooklyn, NY; U.S. Public, pg. 259
Desrioux, H., Controller--Hanimex (France) S.A., Gonesse, France; Int'l, pg. 1115
Desrochers, Mitch, Controller--Corel Corporation, Ottawa, Canada; Int'l, pg. 331
Desrosiers, Louis R., Comptroller--Securespace Inc., Beauport, Canada; Int'l, pg. 253
Detamore-Hunsberger, Daniel R., Controller--WLR Foods, Inc., Timberville, VA; U.S. Public, pg. 1727
Deters, Jim, Controller--Grand Prairie Co-op, Inc., Tolono, IL; U.S. Private, pg. 468
Detlefs, Bob, Controller--World Class Film Corporation, Yonkers, NY; U.S. Private, pg. 1190
Detore, James, Controller--Marcam Solutions, Inc., Newton, MA; U.S. Public, pg. 1042
Dettl, J.N., Controller--Maguire Oil Co., Dallas, TX; U.S. Private, pg. 696
Detz, Albert J., V.P. & Controller--Blockbuster Entertainment Group, Dallas, TX; U.S. Private, pg. 775
Deutsch, John, Chief Fin. Officer & Controller--Teleflex (Canada) Ltd., Vancouver, Canada; U.S. Public, pg. 1570
Devault, Sandra J., Controller--Gudebrod, Inc., Pottstown, PA; U.S. Private, pg. 486
Devenburgh, Chuck, Controller--A.H. Hoffman, Inc., Landisville, PA; U.S. Private, pg. 532
DeVenne, H.E., Controller--Searle Canada Inc., Oakville, Canada; U.S. Public, pg. 1126
Deveny, Jack, Controller--Brookhurst, Inc., Compton, CA; U.S. Private, pg. 171
DeVito, Robert D., Asst. Controller--Sequa Corporation, New York, NY; U.S. Public, pg. 1458
Devitt, Paul J., 1st V.P. & Controller--St. Paul Bancorp, Inc., Chicago, IL; U.S. Public, pg. 1428
Devlin, Richard J., V.P. & Controller--American Arbitration Association, New York, NY; U.S. Private, pg. 50
Devoe, Mary Jane, Controller--The Grandoe Corp., Gloversville, NY; U.S. Private, pg. 469
Dewey, Mathew, Controller--Chesapeake Utilities Corporation, Dover, DE; U.S. Public, pg. 347
Dexter, David, Controller--Armstrong International, Inc., Three Rivers, MI; U.S. Private, pg. 83
Dey, Eric, Controller--Excel Communications, Inc., Dallas, TX; U.S. Public, pg. 598
Deys, Shelley N., Controller--Sentinel Self-Storage Corporation, Calgary, Canada; Int'l, pg. 253
Di Iorio, Anthony, Exec. V.P. & Controller--PaineWebber Incorporated, New York, NY; U.S. Public, pg. 1252
Di Roberto, A. Marino, Controller--Acos Villares Steel Unit, Sao Paulo, Brazil; Int'l, pg. 23
Di Roberto, Antonio Marino, Controller-Steel Div.--Acos Villares S.A., Sao Paulo, Brazil; Int'l, pg. 23
Diamond, David, Asst. V.P. & Controller--Nationwide Insurance Enterprise, Columbus, OH; U.S. Private, pg. 788
Diamond, Evan, Controller--Stainless Incorporated, Deerfield Beach, FL; U.S. Private, pg. 1029
Diamond, Howard, Controller--Quantum Sport, New York, NY; U.S. Private, pg. 900
Diasio, James, Controller--Exide Corporation, Reading, PA; U.S. Public, pg. 600
Diaz, Emil, Controller--Magnedyne Div., Vista, CA; U.S. Private, pg. 999
DiCandilo, Michael, V.P. & Controller--AmeriSource Health Corp., Malvern, PA; U.S. Public, pg. 96
Dick, Brian, Controller--Formica Corporation, Wayne, NJ; Int'l, pg. 129
Dickerman, Barry, Controller--Movie Star, Inc., New York, NY; U.S. Public, pg. 1140
Dickerson, Alan, Controller--CompPair LeRoi, Sidney, OH; Int'l, pg. 1242
Dickey, Doug, Controller--F.G. Montabert, Midland Park, NJ; U.S. Private, pg. 758
Dickinson, Joe, V.P. & Controller--AVW Audiovisual, Inc., Dallas, TX; U.S. Private, pg. 426

Dickinson, Stephen Y., Controller--Media General, Inc., Richmond, VA; *U.S. Public*, pg. 1077
Dickler, Mike, Controller--Chicago Union Station Company, Chicago, IL; *U.S. Private*, pg. 69
Dickson, James Douglas, Jr., Controller & Asst. Sec.--Alba-Waldensian, Inc., Valdese, NC; *U.S. Public*, pg. 35
Didia, Thomas, Controller--Mikropul Environmental Systems Div., Summit, NJ; *Int'l*, pg. 636
Dieckmann, Kurt, Controller--Corrigan Bros., Inc., Saint Louis, MO; *U.S. Private*, pg. 277
Diehl, Richard, V.P., Controller & Treas.--North Central Life Insurance Company, Saint Paul, MN; *U.S. Private*, pg. 404
Diehl, Scott, Controller--Guard Publishing Company, Eugene, OR; *U.S. Private*, pg. 485
Diekemper, Joseph, Controller--M. Bruenger & Co., Inc., Wichita, KS; *U.S. Private*, pg. 175
Dieker, John K., Controller--Greif Brothers Corporation, Delaware, OH; *U.S. Public*, pg. 763
Dierker, James W., V.P., Controller & Treas.--United States Filter Corporation, Palm Desert, CA; *U.S. Public*, pg. 1681
Dieschbourg, Edward J., V.P., Treas. & Controller--Replogle Globes, Inc., Broadview, IL; *U.S. Private*, pg. 923
Dietrich, E. Joy, Pres.--Vidar, Inc., New London, MN; *U.S. Private*, pg. 1139
Dietz, Dave, V.P.-Fin.--Hardware Wholesalers, Inc., Fort Wayne, IN; *U.S. Private*, pg. 502
DiFonzo, Kenneth W., V.P. & Controller--ConAgra, Inc., Omaha, NE; *U.S. Public*, pg. 425
Digby, Kimberly, Controller--Elk Supply Company, Clinton, OK; *U.S. Private*, pg. 371
DiGia, Robert M., V.P. & Controller--Ogden Corporation, New York, NY; *U.S. Public*, pg. 1213
DiGiacomo, John, Sr. V.P. & Controller--North Fork Bancorporation, Inc., Melville, NY; *U.S. Public*, pg. 1194
Dilday, Jenell, Controller--Lea Lumber & Plywood LLC, Windsor, NC; *U.S. Private*, pg. 655
Dilfer, Robert W., V.P. & Controller--Premisys Communications, Inc., Fremont, CA; *U.S. Public*, pg. 1323
Dilillo, Ken, Controller--American Restaurant Group, Inc., Newport Beach, CA; *U.S. Private*, pg. 61
Dillard, Allen E., Chief Fin. Officer, V.P. & Treas.--Nichols Research Corporation, Huntsville, AL; *U.S. Public*, pg. 1182
Dillon, Brian, Controller--Creative Playthings Ltd., Framingham, MA; *U.S. Private*, pg. 287
Dillon, James T., V.P.-Fin. & Gen. Mgr.--Up-Right, Inc., Selma, CA; *U.S. Private*, pg. 1128
Dillon, Michael J., V.P. & Corp. Controller--Ikon Office Solutions, Inc., Malvern, PA; *U.S. Public*, pg. 862
Dimaggio, David, Controller--Gelman Sciences, Inc., Ann Arbor, MI; *U.S. Public*, pg. 1253
DiMartino, Mike, Corp. Controller--Bliss-Salem, Inc., Salem, OH; *U.S. Private*, pg. 149
Dimick, David T., V.P.-Fin. Opers. & Admin.--Woodward-Clyde Group, Inc., Denver, CO; *U.S. Public*, pg. 1655
Dindo, Kathryn W., V.P. & Controller--Caliber System, Inc., Akron, OH; *U.S. Public*, pg. 604
Dingley, D., V.P. & Controller--BFC Pipelines, Edmonton, Canada; *Int'l*, pg. 118
Dion, Jim, Controller--Easy Day Manufacturing Company, Holliston, MA; *U.S. Private*, pg. 358
Dippman, Kenneth C., Corp. Controller--Ludlow Composites Corporation, Fremont, OH; *U.S. Private*, pg. 680
DiPreta, Laura L., Asst. V.P. & Asst. Controller--Citizens Utilities Company, Stamford, CT; *U.S. Public*, pg. 379
Diren, Daniel D., Sr. V.P.-Admin. & Controller--R.G. Barry Corporation, Pickerington, OH; *U.S. Public*, pg. 192
Dischler, Richard, Controller--Magnus Metals, Fremont, NE; *U.S. Private*, pg. 394
Dise, Paul R., Controller--Erving Paper Mills, Inc., Erving, MA; *U.S. Private*, pg. 382
Dishian, Sharon, Asst. Controller--Young Dental Manufacturing, Earth City, MO; *U.S. Private*, pg. 1201
Dispenza, Robert, Controller--IPAC, Inc., Niagara Falls, NY; *U.S. Private*, pg. 555
Dispenzirie, Peter J., Controller--Sky Courier, Reston, VA; *U.S. Public*, pg. 33
DiStefano, Glenda, Controller--Manheim's Greater Orlando Auto Auction, Orlando, FL; *U.S. Private*, pg. 282
DiStefano, Tony, Controller--Associated Company, Inc., Wichita, KS; *U.S. Private*, pg. 89
Distel, Daniel J., V.P. & Controller--The Antec Corporation, Rolling Meadows, IL; *U.S. Public*, pg. 116
DiTrolio, Joseph F., Asst. Controller--Comcast Corporation, Philadelphia, PA; *U.S. Public*, pg. 406
Dittmer, Bruce, Controller--Heurikon Corporation, Madison, WI; *U.S. Public*, pg. 422
Dittmer, Jerald K., V.P. & Controller--The Gunlocke Company, Wayland, NY; *U.S. Public*, pg. 772
Dixon, Holley, Controller--Grizzard, Atlanta, GA; *U.S. Private*, pg. 482
Dizon, Romy, Controller--Your Man Tours, Inc., Inglewood, CA; *U.S. Private*, pg. 1202
Do, S.H., Controller--Samsung Electronics North America Inc., Ridgefield Park, NJ; *Int'l*, pg. 1183
Dodd, L. Richard, Controller--Northeast Texas Farmers Co-Op, Sulphur Springs, TX; *U.S. Private*, pg. 805
Dodson, Michael, Controller--Novellus Systems, Inc., San Jose, CA; *U.S. Public*, pg. 1204
Doeleman, A.M.M., Sr. Dir.-Grp. Fin. Control--Koninklijke Hoogovens N.V., Ijmuiden, Netherlands; *Int'l*, pg. 753
Doeleman, A.M.M., Sr. Dir. & Grp. Fin. Controller--Hoogovens Groep B.V., Ijmuiden, Netherlands; *Int'l*, pg. 753
Doherty, Steve, V.P. & Controller--Ingalls, Boston, MA; *U.S. Private*, pg. 562
Dolan, James F., Controller--Lavelle Company, Philadelphia, PA; *U.S. Private*, pg. 653
Dolan, Jim, Controller--Totes/Isotoner, Inc., New York, NY; *U.S. Public*, pg. 1433
Dolan, Robert E., Controller, Asst. Treas. & Asst. Sec.--Lynch Telecommunications Corporation, Greenwich, CT; *U.S. Public*, pg. 1022
Doles, Edward A., Corp. Controller--Medusa Corporation, Cleveland, OH; *U.S. Public*, pg. 1084
Dolf, Darrel, Dir.-MIS & Controller--H & H Distributing Company, Inc., West Union, IA; *U.S. Private*, pg. 489
Dolinick, Craig, Controller--Joseph, Littlejohn & Levy, New York, NY; *U.S. Private*, pg. 601
Domansky, John, Jr., Controller--Columbia Medical Center Dallas Southwest, Dallas, TX; *U.S. Public*, pg. 404
Domena, Carmen, Controller & Dir.-Cash Mngmt. & Leasing--Medtronic Med Rel, Inc., Humacao, PR; *U.S. Public*, pg. 1083
Domeniconi, Reto F., Gen. Mgr.-Fin., Control, Legal, Taxes, Admin.--Nestle S.A., Vevey, Switzerland; *Int'l*, pg. 915
Domey, Alice K., Controller--Sunhill Food Of Vermont, Inc., Swanton, VT; *Int'l*, pg. 1464
Domingo, Clarence, Controller--Shure Brothers Incorporated, Evanston, IL; *U.S. Private*, pg. 997
Dominguez, Armando, Controller--Grupo Sidek, S.A. de C.V., Guadalajara, Mexico; *Int'l*, pg. 576
Dominic, Antoine, Chief Fin. Officer & Controller--Excel Technology, Inc., New York, NY; *U.S. Public*, pg. 599
Dominick, Samuel P. Jr., V.P. & Controller--Occidental Petroleum Corporation, Los Angeles, CA; *U.S. Public*, pg. 1210
Dominitz, Henry, Controller & Sec.--Jean Philippe Fragrances, Inc., New York, NY; *U.S. Public*, pg. 924
Domzalski, Al, Controller--Everfresh Beverages Inc., Chicago, IL; *U.S. Public*, pg. 1153
Donahey, Kenneth C., Sr. V.P. & Controller--Columbia/HCA Healthcare Corporation, Nashville, TN; *U.S. Public*, pg. 403
Donahoe, Michael P., V.P.-Acctg. & Controller--Perkins Family Restaurants, Memphis, TN; *U.S. Private*, pg. 925
Donahue, Timothy J., Sr. V.P. & Controller--Crown Cork & Seal Company, Inc., Philadelphia, PA; *U.S. Public*, pg. 462
Donaldson, Art, Controller--Kaiser Aluminum Corporation, Houston, TX; *U.S. Public*, pg. 1062
Donaldson, Art, Controller--Kaiser Aluminum & Chemical Corporation, Pleasanton, CA; *U.S. Public*, pg. 1062
Donaldson, David, Controller--Americal Corporation, Henderson, NC; *U.S. Private*, pg. 49
Donaldson, Jerry, Controller--Tiffin Enterprises, Inc., Tiffin, OH; *U.S. Public*, pg. 98
Donelle, M.R., Controller--National Sea Products Limited, Lunenburg, Canada; *Int'l*, pg. 909
Dong, Andrew, Controller--Mother Earth News, New York, NY; *U.S. Private*, pg. 1056
Donker, Lennard, Controller--Messier-Dowty Electronics, Peterborough, Canada; *Int'l*, pg. 1340
Donlon, James D., V.P. & Controller--Chrysler Corporation, Auburn Hills, MI; *U.S. Public*, pg. 352
Donnan, Brian D., Controller & Asst. Sec.--Arden Group, Inc., Los Angeles, CA; *U.S. Public*, pg. 128
Donnelly, Dan, Controller--Emson, Inc., Bridgeport, CT; *U.S. Private*, pg. 375
Donnelly, Denise, V.P. & Controller--Yokogawa Corporation of America, Newnan, GA; *Int'l*, pg. 1521
Donnelly, William P , Grp. V.P. & Controller--ELSAG Bailey Process Automation N.V., Schiphol, Netherlands; *Int'l*, pg. 449
Donofrio, F. Allen, Chief Acctg. Officer, V.P. & Controller--GPU, Inc., Morristown, NJ; *U.S. Public*, pg. 695
Donoghue, Adrian J., V.P. & Controller--Northern Telecom Limited, Brampton, Canada; *Int'l*, pg. 968
Donoghue, Michael H., Controller--McCord Winn Textron Company, Manchester, NH; *U.S. Public*, pg. 1590
Donovan, D. Peter, Controller--General Electric Canada Inc., Mississauga, Canada; *U.S. Public*, pg. 713
Donovan, Dan, Controller--The Presmet Corp., Worcester, MA; *U.S. Private*, pg. 882
Donovan, James, V.P. & Controller--J.B. Martin Company, New York, NY; *U.S. Private*, pg. 709
Donovan, Janice, Controller--Ener-Tek International Corporation, Pawcatuck, CT; *U.S. Private*, pg. 376
Donovan, Janice, Controller--Yardney Technical Products, Inc., Pawcatuck, CT; *U.S. Private*, pg. 376
Donovan, S. Peter, Controller--GE Hydro, Lachine, Canada; *U.S. Public*, pg. 713
Donovan, Terrence M., Controller & Dir.-Fin.--Sentry Group, Rochester, NY; *U.S. Private*, pg. 984
Dooher, Terry, Controller--Barry Controls, Brighton, MA; *U.S. Public*, pg. 124
Dooley, Mike, V.P. & Controller--The Brewer Company, Milford, OH; *U.S. Private*, pg. 167
Doolin, Kay, Controller--Lund Acquisition Corp., Oklahoma City, OK; *U.S. Public*, pg. 1020
Doolittle, David M., Controller--ELXSI Corporation, Orlando, FL; *U.S. Public*, pg. 545
Doppelfeld, Volker, Dir.-Fin. & Controlling--Bayerische Motoren Werke Aktiengesellschaft, Munich, Germany; *Int'l*, pg. 177
Doran, Stephen G., Controller--J.J. Kenny Co., Inc., New York, NY; *U.S. Public*, pg. 1070
Dorbert, K., Controller--Kenner Parker Toys International, Rodgau, Germany; *U.S. Public*, pg. 798
Dore, Geoffrey T., Controller & Treas.--Lomak Petroleum Inc., Fort Worth, TX; *U.S. Public*, pg. 1012
Dore, Syd, Controller--Encore Computer (UK) Ltd., Leatherhead, United Kingdom; *U.S. Public*, pg. 580
Dorey, Kevin, Controller--Alvey Systems, Inc, Saint Louis, MO; *U.S. Private*, pg. 47
Dorfman, Sander, Controller--Beber & Silverstein & Partners, Inc., Miami, FL; *U.S. Private*, pg. 128
Dorr, Dennis, Mgr.-Tech. Support--Krause Plow Corp., Hutchinson, KS; *U.S. Private*, pg. 635
Dose, Robert E., Controller, Asst. Sec. & Asst. Treas.--Virco Mfg. Corporation, Torrance, CA; *U.S. Public*, pg. 1721
Dosland, Michael W., V.P.--First Federal Capital Corp., La Crosse, WI; *U.S. Public*, pg. 632
Dotson, Jerry D., V.P. & Controller--California & Hawaiian Sugar Company Inc., Crockett, CA; *U.S. Public*, pg. 39
Doubles, Michael J., Controller & Treas.--Alex J. Etkin, Inc., Farmington, MI; *U.S. Private*, pg. 384
Dougan, R.W., Controller, Sec. & Treas.--Emerson Electric Canada Ltd., Markham, Canada; *U.S. Public*, pg. 576
Douglas, Corey B., Controller--Harza Engineering Co., Chicago, IL; *U.S. Private*, pg. 509
Douglas, Dan, Controller--Kerr-McGee Coal Corp., Oklahoma City, OK; *U.S. Public*, pg. 952
Douglas, Frank, Controller--Gulf States, Inc., Freeport, TX; *U.S. Private*, pg. 487
Douglas, George A., Chief Fin. Officer, Controller & Treas.--Salem Group, Inc., Pittsburgh, PA; *U.S. Private*, pg. 961
Douglas, George A., Chief Fin. Officer, Controller & Treas.--Salem Corporation, Pittsburgh, PA; *U.S. Private*, pg. 961
Douglas, Jo, Controller--Quoizel Inc., Goose Creek, SC; *U.S. Private*, pg. 901
Douglas, Nancy, Controller--EDO Corporation, New York, NY; *U.S. Public*, pg. 541
Douma, Jim, Controller--Spectrum Industries, Grand Rapids, MI; *U.S. Private*, pg. 1024
Douma, Jim, Controller--Crown Coat, Inc., Grand Rapids, MI; *U.S. Private*, pg. 1024
Dove, Barry, Controller--Acorn Products, Inc., Columbus, OH; *U.S. Public*, pg. 17
Dow, Ken, Corp. Controller--SPX Corporation, Muskegon, MI; *U.S. Public*, pg. 1420
Dow, Ronald C., Controller & Treas.--Three D Departments, Inc., Costa Mesa, CA; *U.S. Public*, pg. 1604
Dowd, William, Controller--Asarco Incorporated, New York, NY; *U.S. Public*, pg. 137
Dowling, Thomas J., V.P. & Controller--Concord EFS, Inc., Memphis, TN; *U.S. Public*, pg. 429
Downing, Bert, Jr., Controller--Keystone Consolidated Industries, Inc., Dallas, TX; *U.S. Public*, pg. 955
Doyle, Donna S., Controller--Central Hudson Gas & Electric Corporation, Poughkeepsie, NY; *U.S. Public*, pg. 324
Doyle, J., Controller--Asahi Glass America, Inc., New York, NY; *Int'l*, pg. 84
Doyle, Joseph, Controller--Deluxe Homes Of PA., Inc., Berwick, PA; *U.S. Private*, pg. 323
Doyon, Miguel C., Controller--Pratt & Whitney Canada Inc., Longueuil, Canada; *U.S. Public*, pg. 1690
Drach, Terry, V.P. & Controller--Natkin Group, Inc., Englewood, CO; *U.S. Public*, pg. 84
Drackwics, Bernard, V.P. & Controller--McGraw-Hill Computers & Communications Information Group, New York, NY; *U.S. Public*, pg. 1070
Dragoo, Cheryl A., Controller & Asst. Treas.--Bowl America, Incorporated, Alexandria, VA; *U.S. Public*, pg. 248
Drake, Pat, Comptroller--Washington State Apple Commission, Wenatchee, WA; *U.S. Private*, pg. 1152
Drake, Susan, Controller--Justin Boot Company, Fort Worth, TX; *U.S. Public*, pg. 937
Draney, L.R., Grp. Fin. Controller--Australian Mutual Provident, Sydney, Australia; *Int'l*, pg. 100
Drass, Mark, Controller--Custom Hoists, Inc., Hayesville, OH; *U.S. Public*, pg. 1506
Dratler, Jerry S.B., V.P. & Controller--Williams-Sonoma, Inc., San Francisco, CA; *U.S. Public*, pg. 1770
Drazba, Brian G., V.P.-Fin. & Corp. Controller--Insight Health Services Corp., Newport Beach, CA; *U.S. Public*, pg. 880
Drechney, Daniel P., Controller--Tootsie Roll Industries, Inc., Chicago, IL; *U.S. Public*, pg. 1621
Dreikosen, Dennis, Exec. Dir.-Acctg & Controller--The Swiss Colony, Inc, Monroe, WI; *U.S. Private*, pg. 1059
Drenning, Gary, Controller--Mylan Laboratories, Inc., Pittsburgh, PA; *U.S. Public*, pg. 1143
Drewnowski, Ken, Controller--J.B. Rodgers Mechanical Contractors, Phoenix, AZ; *U.S. Private*, pg. 939
Dridi, Mary D., V.P. & Controller--SRA International Inc., Arlington, VA; *U.S. Private*, pg. 957
Dries, William, V.P. & Controller--United Dominion Industries, Ltd., Charlotte, NC; *U.S. Public*, pg. 1675
Drillock, David M., Controller & Asst. Sec.--Cytec Industries Inc., West Paterson, NJ; *U.S. Public*, pg. 471
Drinen, John W., V.P. & Controller--AFC Enterprises, Atlanta, GA; *U.S. Private*, pg. 5
Drinkwater, Wayne C., Controller--Ethyl Corporation, Richmond, VA; *U.S. Public*, pg. 595
Driscol, Jim, Controller--Lady Baltimore Foods, Inc., Kansas City, KS; *U.S. Public*, pg. 975
Driscoll, Joe, Controller--Safety 1st, Inc., Chestnut Hill, MA; *U.S. Public*, pg. 1425
Driscoll, Michael, Controller--The Arbour Hospital, Boston, MA; *U.S. Public*, pg. 1696
Dritsas, Jim, Controller--Patterson Frozen Foods, Inc., Patterson, CA; *U.S. Private*, pg. 843
Drobeck, Sharon, V.P. & Controller--Mary Kay Corporation, Dallas, TX; *U.S. Private*, pg. 710
Drogy, Rona, Controller--Welsh Carson Anderson & Stowe, New York, NY; *U.S. Private*, pg. 1162
Drossman, Gary, Controller--American Specialties Inc., Yonkers, NY; *U.S. Private*, pg. 62
Drotar, Paul P., V.P. & Controller--Carrols Corporation, Syracuse, NY; *U.S. Private*, pg. 216
Drugacz, Dennis, Controller--EMS-Togo, Taylor, MI; *Int'l*, pg. 981
Drumheller, H.K., Controller--Unimark Plastics Company, Greer, SC; *U.S. Public*, pg. 57
Drummond, Doug, Controller--Associated Grocers, Inc., Baton Rouge, LA; *U.S. Private*, pg. 90
Drummond, Kirk G., V.P. & Controller--Sysco Corporation, Houston, TX; *U.S. Public*, pg. 1550
Druseikis, Raymond, V.P. & Controller--Red Roof Inns, Inc., Hilliard, OH; *U.S. Public*, pg. 1369
Dryer, Ned, Controller & Sec.--Arizona Wholesale Supply Company, Phoenix, AZ; *U.S. Private*, pg. 82
Dryer, Stephen J., V.P. & Controller--Spalding & Evenflo Companies, Inc., Chicopee, MA; *U.S. Private*, pg. 629
Drymala, Wayne J., Controller--Valero Marketing & Supply Company, San Antonio, TX; *U.S. Public*, pg. 1704

Drymala, Wayne J., Controller--Valero Refining Company, San Antonio, TX; *U.S. Public*, pg. 1704

Duane, Dave, Chief Fin. Officer, Controller & Treas.--Heat Controller, Inc., Jackson, MI; *U.S. Private*, pg. 518

Duarte, Danny, Controller--Stewart Warner Instruments Corporation, Des Plaines, IL; *U.S. Private*, pg. 1042

Dube, Larry, Controller--Park Manufacturing, Inc., Oxford, ME; *U.S. Private*, pg. 840

Dubois, Dave, Controller--Daigle Oil Co., Fort Kent, ME; *U.S. Private*, pg. 307

Dubrow, F., Controller--J.M. Huber, Solem Div., Norcross, GA; *U.S. Private*, pg. 545

Duchesneau, M.A., Controller & Treas.--Central Vermont Railway, Inc., Saint Albans, VT; *Int'l*, pg. 258

Duda, David, Controller--A. Duda & Sons Inc., Oviedo, FL; *U.S. Private*, pg. 344

Dugan, David A., Controller & Sec.--Georgia-Bonded Fibers, Inc., Newark, NJ; *U.S. Public*, pg. 734

Dugan, David A., Controller & Sec.--Bontex, Buena Vista, VA; *U.S. Public*, pg. 734

Dugan, David A., Controller--Bontex International (F.S.C.), Buena Vista, VA; *U.S. Public*, pg. 734

Dugan, Joe, Controller--Ringling Bros., Barnum & Bailey Combined Shows, Inc., Vienna, VA; *U.S. Private*, pg. 400

Duggar, Greg, V.P. & Controller--Dowling Textile Manufacturing Co., Mc Donough, GA; *U.S. Private*, pg. 341

Duggar, Greg, Controller--Whiteswan/Meta, Libertyville, IL; *U.S. Private*, pg. 342

Dugger, Joe Lee, Controller--Vinson Supply Company, Dallas, TX; *U.S. Private*, pg. 963

Duhaime, Alice, Controller--R.W. Beck, Inc., Seattle, WA; *U.S. Private*, pg. 128

Duke, Carol, Controller--Flexfab Horizons International, Inc., Hastings, MI; *U.S. Private*, pg. 412

Dumas, Paul, Controller--Collagen Corporation, Palo Alto, CA; *U.S. Public*, pg. 399

Dumovich, Dave, Controller--Westlake Hardware, Inc., Lenexa, KS; *U.S. Private*, pg. 1169

Dunaway, Dick, Controller--Lufkin, Apex, NC; *U.S. Public*, pg. 444

Duncan, Deborah, Controller--Ultrak Inc., Lewisville, TX; *U.S. Public*, pg. 1663

Duncan, Edward, Controller & Treas.--Master Craft Corp., Kalamazoo, MI; *Int'l*, pg. 267

Duncan, Wes, Controller--Ghafari Associates, Inc., Dearborn, MI; *U.S. Private*, pg. 450

Duncan, William, Controller--Poland Spring Corporation, Greenwich, CT; *Int'l*, pg. 919

Duncan, Willis P., Jr., V.P.-Fin. & Treas.--Thomas Built Buses, Inc., High Point, NC; *U.S. Private*, pg. 1082

Duner, Bruce, Controller--Wonderware Corporation, Irvine, CA; *U.S. Public*, pg. 1775

Dunker, K.J., Controller--Zinc Products Company, Greeneville, TN; *U.S. Public*, pg. 57

Dunleavy, James J., Controller--Binswanger, Philadelphia, PA; *U.S. Private*, pg. 144

Dunleavy, Thomas L., V.P. & Controller--Kraus-Anderson Incorporated, Minneapolis, MN; *U.S. Private*, pg. 635

Dunleavy, Tom, Controller--Kraus-Anderson, Incorporated, Minneapolis, MN; *U.S. Private*, pg. 635

Dunn, Dolores, Controller--Eaton Corp. Div., Athens, AL; *U.S. Public*, pg. 556

Dunn, James, Controller--Wheatland Tube Company, Collingswood, NJ; *U.S. Private*, pg. 1170

Dunn, Mary, Controller--E.J. Brooks Company, Newark, NJ; *U.S. Private*, pg. 172

Dunn, Philip J., V.P., Controller & Treas.--Circuit City Stores, Inc., Richmond, VA; *U.S. Public*, pg. 374

Dunn, Raymond, Controller--SIFCO Turbine Component Services, Tampa, FL; *U.S. Public*, pg. 1471

Dunstan, Dolores, Controller--Ellwood City Forge, Ellwood City, PA; *U.S. Private*, pg. 373

Dupree, Doug, Controller--Robbins Auto Parts, Inc., Dover, NH; *U.S. Private*, pg. 934

Duran Trinidad, Ernesto, Controller--Grupo Mexico S.A. de C.V., Mexico, Mexico; *U.S. Public*, pg. 138

Durant, Karen, V.P. & Controller--Pentair, Inc., Saint Paul, MN; *U.S. Public*, pg. 1273

Durbin, Dean, V.P. & Controller--McGraw-Hill Construction Information Group, New York, NY; *U.S. Public*, pg. 1070

Durboraw, Wayne A., Controller--Blessings Corporation, Newport News, VA; *U.S. Private*, pg. 1179

Durfee, J.Lang, V.P. & Sec.--Bethel Mills, Inc., Bethel, VT; *U.S. Private*, pg. 141

Durkin, Joan, Controller--Finlay Enterprises, Inc., New York, NY; *U.S. Public*, pg. 623

Durrett, Kenneth D., Controller--American Home Shield Corporation, Memphis, TN; *U.S. Public*, pg. 1461

Durso, Steve, Controller--Precision Industries, Omaha, NE; *U.S. Private*, pg. 879

Dussault, Dennis, Controller--Parks Corporation, Fall River, MA; *U.S. Private*, pg. 840

Dutton, Larry, Controller--Buffalo Rock Company, Birmingham, AL; *U.S. Private*, pg. 179

Duvall, Ron, Controller--Domore Corporation, Elkhart, IN; *U.S. Private*, pg. 339

Duwaji, Michael, V.P. & Controller--Four Seasons Hotels Inc., Don Mills, Canada; *Int'l*, pg. 502

Dwyer, Fred, Controller--KCS Energy Inc., Edison, NJ; *U.S. Public*, pg. 938

Dyck, Christopher W., Controller--AVA, Atlanta, GA; *U.S. Private*, pg. 8

Dyer, Jacqualine, Controller--Pacific Forge, Inc., Fontana, CA; *U.S. Private*, pg. 102

Dyer, Lee, Controller--Merchants Publishing Co., Kalamazoo, MI; *U.S. Private*, pg. 732

Dykes, A., Controller--Glastic Corporation, Cleveland, OH; *Int'l*, pg. 740

Dykman, Steve, Controller--Gentex Corporation, Zeeland, MI; *U.S. Public*, pg. 731

Dykstra, Karen, Controller--Automatic Data Processing, Inc., Roseland, NJ; *U.S. Public*, pg. 150

Dymowski, Martin, Controller--B. Green & Co., Owings Mills, MD; *U.S. Private*, pg. 476

Dyner, Pamela S., Controller--International Lease Finance Corporation, Los Angeles, CA; *U.S. Public*, pg. 85

Dyson, Doug, Controller--Carolina Builders Corporation, Marietta, GA; *Int'l*, pg. 1512

Dziuma, Alan, Controller--Manning & Lewis Engineering Co., Union, NJ; *U.S. Private*, pg. 700

Eads, Janet, Controller--Resource Marketing, Inc., Columbus, OH; *U.S. Private*, pg. 924

Eads, John T., Controller-Fin.--Freeport-McMoRan Copper & Gold, Inc., New Orleans, LA; *U.S. Public*, pg. 680

Eagan, Peter J., Controller--Nashua Imaging Supplies Div., Nashua, NH; *U.S. Public*, pg. 1152

Eagen, Dave, Controller--Lotto Sport U.S.A., Carrollton, TX; *Int'l*, pg. 819

Eagleson, James, Controller--Jayco Inc., Middlebury, IN; *U.S. Private*, pg. 583

Earehart, Allen M., V.P. & Controller--Reynolds Metals Company, Richmond, VA; *U.S. Public*, pg. 1385

Easterbrook, Trisha, Controller--Alpha Shirt Co., Inc., Philadelphia, PA; *U.S. Private*, pg. 45

Easterman, Dave, Chief Fin. Officer & Controller--B&B Corporate Holdings, Inc., Tampa, FL; *U.S. Private*, pg. 104

Eastland, Katja, Controller--Shamrock Holdings, Inc., Burbank, CA; *U.S. Private*, pg. 989

Easton, Stewart, Controller & Asst. Treas.--Pacific Coast Producers, Lodi, CA; *U.S. Private*, pg. 830

Eaton, E.H., V.P. & Controller--The Folger Coffee Company, Cincinnati, OH; *U.S. Public*, pg. 1331

Eaton, Edwin H., Jr., V.P. & Comptroller--The Procter & Gamble Company, Cincinnati, OH; *U.S. Public*, pg. 1330

Eaton, Mark, V.P. & Controller--Adecco S.A., Lausanne, Switzerland; *Int'l*, pg. 23

Eaton, Scott, Controller & Sec.--Sasco Group, Cerritos, CA; *U.S. Private*, pg. 967

Ebata, Oemis, Controller--JPE Canada Inc., Peterborough, Canada; *U.S. Public*, pg. 919

Eberhardt, Ed, Contoller--Independent Metals, Germantown, WI; *U.S. Private*, pg. 559

Eberhart, H. Paulett, V.P. & Controller--Electronic Data Systems Corporation, Plano, TX; *U.S. Public*, pg. 569

Ebets-huber, Dr., Controller--Burda Holding GmbH & Co., KG, Munich, Germany; *Int'l*, pg. 233

Ebright, John E., Chief Acctg. Officer & Controller--IES Industries Inc., Cedar Rapids, IA; *U.S. Public*, pg. 855

Ebright, John E., Chief Acctg. Officer & Controller--IES Utilities Inc., Cedar Rapids, IA; *U.S. Public*, pg. 855

Echols, Chris, Controller--The Albany Herald Publishing Co., Inc., Albany, GA; *U.S. Public*, pg. 759

Eckhardt, B.N., V.P. & Controller--Emerson Electric Co., Saint Louis, MO; *U.S. Public*, pg. 572

Eckiss, Steve, Controller--Ready Metal Manufacturing Company, Chicago, IL; *U.S. Private*, pg. 913

Eckmann, J.A., V.P. & Controller--Brown & Williamson Tobacco Corp., Louisville, KY; *Int'l*, pg. 111

Eckstein, Michael, Controller--Kulite Semiconductor Products, Inc., Leonia, NJ; *U.S. Private*, pg. 636

Eddy, Debra, Controller--W.R. Case & Sons Cutlery Company, Bradford, PA; *U.S. Private*, pg. 1207

Edelman, Allan, V.P. & Controller--Greater New York Box Co., Clifton, NJ; *U.S. Private*, pg. 476

Edelson, Allan J., V.P., Controller & Asst. Sec.--ABC, Inc, New York, NY; *U.S. Public*, pg. 511

Edenfield, Dave, V.P. & Controller--Reliance Medical Products, Inc., Mason, OH; *U.S. Private*, pg. 921

Edinger, Peg, Controller--OPT Industries, Inc., Phillipsburg, NJ; *U.S. Public*, pg. 1624

Edmond, Robert, Chief Fin. Officer & Controller--Big M, Inc., Totowa, NJ; *U.S. Private*, pg. 143

Edmonds, Fredrick, Controller--Jelmar Company, Lincolnwood, IL; *U.S. Private*, pg. 585

Edmonds, M., Controller--Senior Engineering Group, plc., Rickmansworth, United Kingdom; *Int'l*, pg. 1220

Edmondson, Jack, Controller--Barksdale, Inc., Los Angeles, CA; *U.S. Public*, pg. 457

Edmunds, Thomas, Controller--Waldo Bros. Company, Boston, MA; *U.S. Private*, pg. 1147

Edwards, Coit, Controller--J. Josephson, Inc., South Hackensack, NJ; *U.S. Private*, pg. 601

Edwards, Drew A., Controller & Treas.--Tredegar Industries Inc., Richmond, VA; *U.S. Public*, pg. 1633

Edwards, Earnest J., V.P. & Controller--Aluminum Company of America, Pittsburgh, PA; *U.S. Public*, pg. 60

Edwards, Gary, Controller--Superior Telecommunications, Atlanta, GA; *U.S. Public*, pg. 58

Edwards, Gary L., V.P. & Controller--The Alpine Group, Inc., New York, NY; *U.S. Public*, pg. 58

Edwards, Greg, Sr. V.P. & Controller--The Irvine Company, Newport Beach, CA; *U.S. Private*, pg. 575

Edwards, Jeff, Comptroller--Beaver Street Fisheries, Inc., Jacksonville, FL; *U.S. Private*, pg. 128

Edwards, Michael, Controller--Richmond Technology Inc., Redlands, CA; *U.S. Private*, pg. 929

Edwards, Neil, Controller--Lost Arrow Corporation, Ventura, CA; *U.S. Private*, pg. 676

Edwards, Phil, Asst. Controller--CitFed Bancorp, Inc., Dayton, OH; *U.S. Public*, pg. 376

Edwards, Rodney, Controller--Tyson Foods, Inc., Magee, MS; *U.S. Public*, pg. 1652

Edwards, Steve, Controller--Jerr-Dan Corporation, Greencastle, PA; *U.S. Public*, pg. 537

Edwards, William, V.P., Treas. & Controller--Kyocera International, Inc., San Diego, CA; *Int'l*, pg. 775

Edwards, William E., III, V.P. & Controller--GTE California Incorporated, Irving, TX; *U.S. Public*, pg. 697

Edwards, William M., III, V.P. & Controller--GTE North Incorporated, Irving, TX; *U.S. Public*, pg. 696

Edwards, William M., III, V.P. & Controller--GTE South Incorporated, Irving, TX; *U.S. Public*, pg. 697

Eenhuis, Loretta, Controller & Treas.--Westin, Inc., Omaha, NE; *U.S. Private*, pg. 1169

Effafrits, Richard, Controller--Printco Group, Greenville, MI; *U.S. Public*, pg. 228

Effren, Gary, V.P. & Controller--Knight-Ridder, Inc., Miami, FL; *U.S. Public*, pg. 963

Eftax, William P., Controller--Fullerton Metals Co., Northbrook, IL; *U.S. Private*, pg. 431

Egan, Bernard F., Controller--Lebhar-Friedman, Inc., New York, NY; *U.S. Private*, pg. 656

Egan, Dana, Controller & Asst. Sec.--Republic Industries, Inc., Fort Lauderdale, FL; *U.S. Public*, pg. 1378

Egan, Laurie, Controller--New Haven Mfg. Corp., New Haven, CT; *U.S. Private*, pg. 793

Eggers, Mike, V.P.-Controller & Administration--Vision-Ease Lens Inc., Brooklyn Park, MN; *U.S. Public*, pg. 162

Ehn, Robert, Controller--Diamond Productions, Inc., Wayne, NJ; *U.S. Private*, pg. 330

Ehni, Edwin, Controller--Boury Enterprises, Wheeling, WV; *U.S. Private*, pg. 162

Ehrenzeller, Paul, Controller--Sithe Energies, Inc., New York, NY; *U.S. Private*, pg. 1004

Ehrlich, Richard, V.P. & Comptroller--Frankfurt Balkind Partners, New York, NY; *U.S. Private*, pg. 424

Eich, Roger, Controller--Prostrollo Motor Company, Madison, SD; *U.S. Private*, pg. 891

Eichner, John, Controller--Harold M. Pitman Co., Inc., Totowa, NJ; *U.S. Private*, pg. 867

Eidson, Julian, Sr. V.P. & Controller--Scientific-Atlanta, Inc., Norcross, GA; *U.S. Public*, pg. 1443

Eidson, Julian W., V.P. & Controller--Scientific-Atlanta, Inc., Norcross, GA; *U.S. Public*, pg. 1443

Eikelberner, Ike K., V.P. & Controller--Excel Industries, Inc., Elkhart, IN; *U.S. Public*, pg. 598

Eisch, Cynthia B., Asst. Controller & Tax Dir.--Walter Industries, Inc., Tampa, FL; *U.S. Public*, pg. 1736

Eisele, Mark O., Controller--Applied Industrial Technologies, Cleveland, OH; *U.S. Public*, pg. 122

Elbe, James L., Controller--First Northern Capital Corp., Green Bay, WI; *U.S. Public*, pg. 636

Eldar, Israel, Controller--American Israeli Paper Mills Ltd., Hadera, Israel; *Int'l*, pg. 74

Eldredge, James W., Controller & Sec.--Puget Sound Energy, Inc., Bellevue, WA; *U.S. Public*, pg. 1342

Eldredge, James W., Controller--Puget Western, Inc., Bellevue, WA; *U.S. Public*, pg. 1342

Elenbaas, Marvin, Sr. V.P. & Controller--Comerica Incorporated, Detroit, MI; *U.S. Public*, pg. 408

Elfeldt, Darrell, V.P. & Controller--Boise Cascade Office Products Corporation, Itasca, IL; *U.S. Public*, pg. 243

Eliasson, David, Controller--NavCom Defense Electronics, Inc., El Monte, CA; *U.S. Private*, pg. 789

Elizondo, Jorge Ancira, Chief Fin. Officer--Altos Hornos de Mexico, S.A., Monclova, Mexico; *Int'l*, pg. 66

Elkins, James V., Controller--Signal Apparel Company, Inc., Chattanooga, TN; *U.S. Public*, pg. 1472

Elko, Richard A., Controller--Sovereign Bancorp, Inc., Wyomissing, PA; *U.S. Public*, pg. 1494

Ellen, Barry, Controller--Modern Medical Modalities Corp., Morristown, NJ; *U.S. Public*, pg. 1121

Ellingsworth, Marsha, Controller--Perdue Farms, Inc., Showell, MD; *U.S. Private*, pg. 852

Elliot, Jim, Controller--Artichoke Industries, Inc., Castroville, CA; *U.S. Private*, pg. 86

Elliott, Andrea, Controller--SJW Corp., San Jose, CA; *U.S. Public*, pg. 1418

Elliott, Mike, Chief Fin. Officer & Controller--Anchor Industries Inc., Evansville, IN; *U.S. Private*, pg. 71

Ellis, David, Controller--IMC Magnetics Corp., Tempe, AZ; *Int'l*, pg. 868

Ellis, Gary, V.P. & Corp. Controller--Medtronic, Inc., Minneapolis, MN; *U.S. Public*, pg. 1082

Ellis, Jack W., V.P. & Controller--NorAm Energy Corp., Houston, TX; *U.S. Public*, pg. 843

Ellis, Joe, Controller--Champion Products, Winston Salem, NC; *U.S. Public*, pg. 1433

Ellis, Mark E., Controller--Mapco Natural Gas Liquids Inc., Tulsa, OK; *U.S. Public*, pg. 1042

Ellis, Randy L., Controller--Parker Drilling Company, Tulsa, OK; *U.S. Public*, pg. 1259

Ellmaleh, C., Controller--Danone Group, Paris, France; *Int'l*, pg. 379

Ellsworth, Jeffrey, Controller--Cambridge Street Metal Co., Allston, MA; *U.S. Private*, pg. 203

Elmer, J. Kent, Controller--IQ Software Corporation, Norcross, GA; *U.S. Public*, pg. 858

Elrod, Lake, Controller--Highland Mills Inc., Charlotte, NC; *U.S. Private*, pg. 528

Elsden, Bob, Controller--Hitchcock Chair Company LTD, New Hartford, CT; *U.S. Private*, pg. 531

Elswarth, Jim, Controller--IAC Industries, Brea, CA; *U.S. Private*, pg. 553

Ely, Lynn, Fin. Controller--All American Bottling Corp., Oklahoma City, OK; *U.S. Private*, pg. 34

Emerson, Barry D., V.P. & Controller--Wyle Electronics, Irvine, CA; *Int'l*, pg. 1457

Emerson, Ronnie, Controller & Treas.--Riverchase Homes, Haleyville, AL; *U.S. Public*, pg. 319

Emerson, Victor H., Jr., Asst. V.P., Controller & Chief Acctg. Officer--Moore Medical Corp., New Britain, CT; *U.S. Public*, pg. 1128

Emig, Tom, Controller--Sybex, Inc., Alameda, CA; *U.S. Private*, pg. 1059

Emmanuelli, Milton, Controller & Treas.--Crown Andersen Inc., Peachtree City, GA; *U.S. Public*, pg. 462

Emmet, R., V.P. & Controller--Cliffs Mining Company, Cleveland, OH; *U.S. Public*, pg. 386

Emrick, Mark, Controller--Mid-Western, Berlin, WI; *U.S. Private*, pg. 136

Encarnacion, Irene, Controller--Niches, Inc., San Diego, CA; *U.S. Public*, pg. 1181

Enderli, Ivo, V.P. & Controller--Liechtenstein Global Trust Limited, Vaduz, Liechtenstein; *Int'l*, pg. 809

Eng, James S., Controller--Sanifill, Inc., Houston, TX; *U.S. Public*, pg. 1686

Engel, F.T., V.P. & Controller--ESAB Consumables, Hanover, PA; *Int'l*, pg. 281
Engelbrecht, Steve, Controller--Newport Steel Corporation, Newport, KY; *U.S. Public*, pg. 1147
Engelsem, Vlrik, Controller--Sensormatic A/S (Denmark), Herlev, Denmark; *U.S. Public*, pg. 1457
Engelsgaard, David, Controller--Interplastic Corp., Saint Paul, MN; *U.S. Private*, pg. 572
England, Alice, Asst. Corp. Controller--Alpha Industries, Inc., Woburn, MA; *U.S. Public*, pg. 57
Engler, J.F., V.P. & Controller--Northwestern Utilities Limited, Edmonton, Canada; *Int'l*, pg. 95
English, Ernest C., Jr., Corp. Controller & Asst. Treas.--Gundle/SLT Environmental, Inc., Houston, TX; *U.S. Public*, pg. 769
English, Linda N., Asst. V.P. & Asst. Controller--Circuit City Stores, Inc., Richmond, VA; *U.S. Public*, pg. 374
Ennis, James, Chief Acctg. Officer, V.P. & Controller--Tyson Foods, Inc., Springdale, AR; *U.S. Public*, pg. 1652
Enriquez, Jackie, Controller, Treas., Dir.-Investor Rels. & Internal Auditor--Supertex, Inc., Sunnyvale, CA; *U.S. Public*, pg. 1539
Entsminger, Michelle, Controller--The Orange County Register, Santa Ana, CA; *U.S. Private*, pg. 425
Epler, Jerry L., V.P. & Controller--Unigard Insurance Co., Bellevue, WA; *Int'l*, pg. 345
Epler, Jerry L., V.P. & Controller--Unigard Indemnity Co., Bellevue, WA; *Int'l*, pg. 345
Epley, Janet, V.P. & Controller--Fender Musical Instruments, Scottsdale, AZ; *U.S. Private*, pg. 400
Epperlein, Richard, Controller & Treas.--A. Zeregas Sons, Inc., Fair Lawn, NJ; *U.S. Private*, pg. 1204
Epstein, Richard, V.P. & Controller--Mitsubishi International Corporation, New York, NY; *Int'l*, pg. 871
Erdmann, Lori, Controller--Integrated Material Handling Company, Oshkosh, WI; *Int'l*, pg. 1397
Ericksen, Barry, V.P. & Controller--Associated of Los Angeles, Los Angeles, CA; *U.S. Private*, pg. 92
Erickson, Chris, Controller--Advanced Input Devices, Inc., Coeur D'Alene, ID; *U.S. Private*, pg. 21
Erickson, Donald R., V.P. & Controller--Comcast Cable Communications, Inc., Philadelphia, PA; *U.S. Public*, pg. 407
Erickson, Joyce, Controller--Marine World Africa USA, Vallejo, CA; *U.S. Private*, pg. 703
Erickson, Karen, Controller--Apertus Technologies Incorporated, Eden Prairie, MN; *U.S. Public*, pg. 119
Erickson, Mike, Controller, Treas. & Sec.--Wagstaff Inc., Spokane, WA; *U.S. Private*, pg. 1146
Ericson, Tim, Controller--Arcon Construction Co., Inc., Harris, MN; *U.S. Private*, pg. 80
Ericsson, Thomas, Controller--ABB AB, Stockholm, Sweden; *Int'l*, pg. 7
Erlenbach, Brad, Controller--William Morrow & Co., Inc., New York, NY; *U.S. Private*, pg. 515
Erlenbush, William, Controller--Growmark, Inc., Bloomington, IL; *U.S. Private*, pg. 484
Ernchetti, Thomas, Controller--Aquarion Company, Bridgeport, CT; *U.S. Public*, pg. 126
Ernster, Paul, Controller--Universal Foods Corporation-Bakery Products Div., Milwaukee, WI; *U.S. Public*, pg. 1696
Eromin, Frederick, Controller--Dynamics Research Corporation, Andover, MA; *U.S. Public*, pg. 539
Erskine, Cindy, Controller--Landstar Development Company, Orlando, FL; *U.S. Private*, pg. 649
Ertel, G.E., Controller--Grede Foundries, Inc., Milwaukee, WI; *U.S. Private*, pg. 476
Ertel, G.E., Controller--Grede-Pryor, Inc., Pryor, OK; *U.S. Private*, pg. 476
Ertle, Grant, Controller--Dukane Canada Ltd., Kitchener, Canada; *U.S. Private*, pg. 346
Erwin, Lyle, Controller--Inter-Tel, Incorporated, Phoenix, AZ; *U.S. Public*, pg. 888
Esak, Mary, Chief Fin. Officer & Controller--Nexus Plastics, Inc., Hawthorne, NJ; *U.S. Private*, pg. 797
Esak, Mary Lynn, Controller--Nexus Plastics, Inc., Hawthorne, NJ; *U.S. Private*, pg. 797
Escott, Baerbel, Controller--J.H. Baxter & Company, San Mateo, CA; *U.S. Private*, pg. 124
Escott, Vera K., Controller--Stone & Thomas, Wheeling, WV; *U.S. Private*, pg. 1044
Espinosa, Ignacio Ibarra, Subcomptroller-Normal Activity--Petroleos Mexicanos, Mexico, Mexico; *Int'l*, pg. 1046
Espinosa, Miriam C., Controller--Isabela Shoe Corp., Isabela, PR; *U.S. Public*, pg. 217
Espinoza, Hector, Asst. Mgr.-Control--Chuquicamata Division, Chuquicamata, Chile; *Int'l*, pg. 302
Espiritu, Magdalena P., V.P. & Controller--AGP Industrial Corporation, Manila, Philippines; *Int'l*, pg. 14
Espittia, Sharon, Controller--Aluma Shield Industries, Inc., Daytona Beach, FL; *U.S. Private*, pg. 47
Esposito, Vincent D., Controller--First Central Financial Corporation, Lynbrook, NY; *U.S. Private*, pg. 406
Essex, Elizabeth, Controller--GSD&M, Austin, TX; *U.S. Private*, pg. 436
Estevez, Juan, Controller--Tomco Auto Products, Inc., Los Angeles, CA; *U.S. Private*, pg. 1090
Estill, Roger A., Controller--Vulcan Materials Company-Southeast Div., Atlanta, GA; *U.S. Public*, pg. 1726
Ettl, Ali, Chief Fin. Officer, V.P.-Fin. & Controller--Putzmeister, Inc., Sturtevant, WI; *U.S. Private*, pg. 896
Eugenio, Chuck, Controller--Gans Ink & Supply Company, Inc., Los Angeles, CA; *U.S. Private*, pg. 440
Euteneuer, Joseph J., V.P. & Controller--Comcast Corporation, Philadelphia, PA; *U.S. Public*, pg. 406
Evanchick, Steven, Asst. Controller--Hyperion Software, Stamford, CT; *U.S. Public*, pg. 851
Evangelista, Joao Vicente, Controller & Treas.--Henkel S/A. Industrias Quimicas, Sao Paulo, Brazil; *Int'l*, pg. 613
Evangelista, Louis J., Controller--Nason and Cullen Group Incorporated, King of Prussia, PA; *U.S. Private*, pg. 775
Evans, Bob, Controller--Matrix Essentials, Inc., Solon, OH; *U.S. Public*, pg. 254
Evans, Daren, Controller--Cosco, Inc., Columbus, IN; *U.S. Private*, pg. 277
Evans, Jim, Controller--Rudolph and Sletten, Inc., Foster City, CA; *U.S. Private*, pg. 950
Evans, Jody, Treas. & Sec.--Ray Bell Construction Co. Inc., Brentwood, TN; *U.S. Private*, pg. 131
Evans, R.D., V.P.-Fin. & Controller--Smith Industries, Inc., Montgomery, AL; *U.S. Private*, pg. 1008
Evans, Ray G., Chief Fin. Officer & Controller--American Rug Craftsmen, Sugar Valley, GA; *U.S. Public*, pg. 1121
Evans, Vicki, Controller--Oakland Tool & Manufacturing Company, Fraser, MI; *U.S. Private*, pg. 809
Evason, John, Controller--Ekco Canada, Inc., Niagara Falls, Canada; *U.S. Public*, pg. 566
Evavold, Douglas, Controller--J. Hellman Produce, Inc., Los Angeles, CA; *U.S. Private*, pg. 520
Evavold, Douglas, Controller--J. Hellman Frozen, Inc., Los Angeles, CA; *U.S. Private*, pg. 520
Everett, Joyce A., V.P. & Controller--Comsearch, Inc., Reston, VA; *U.S. Public*, pg. 46
Evers, Emily, Controller--Deltic Timber Corporation, El Dorado, AR; *U.S. Public*, pg. 498
Everson, Elaine E., Controller--Extendicare Inc., Markham, Canada; *Int'l*, pg. 468
Everts, John F., Controller--The Raymond Corporation, Greene, NY; *Int'l*, pg. 123
Ewald, Robbie, Asst. Controller--Salant Corporation, New York, NY; *U.S. Public*, pg. 1429
Ewing, Dean, V.P. & Controller--Camping World, Inc., Bowling Green, KY; *U.S. Private*, pg. 204
Ewing, Jennifer P., Controller--For Better Living, Inc., Auburn, CA; *U.S. Private*, pg. 417
Eynon, Richard R., Asst. Controller--UGI Corporation, King of Prussia, PA; *U.S. Public*, pg. 1653
Eynon, Richard R., Controller--AmeriGas Partners, L.P., Valley Forge, PA; *U.S. Public*, pg. 1653
Fafara, Patricia, Asst. Controller & Client Acctg.--EURO RSCG Tatham, Chicago, IL; *Int'l*, pg. 601
Fagan, Brad, V.P., Controller, Treas. & Asst. Sec.--Pancho's Mexican Buffet, Inc., Fort Worth, TX; *U.S. Public*, pg. 1255
Fagan, G.A., Controller--Jefferson Smurfit Group p.l.c., Dublin, Ireland; *Int'l*, pg. 1269
Fagan, R., Controller--NIDEC, Canton, MA; *Int'l*, pg. 933
Fagan, Richard J., Controller & Treas.--Quaker Chemical Corporation, Conshohocken, PA; *U.S. Public*, pg. 1346
Fagnan, Nathalie, Corp. Controller--BCP Group Ltd., Montreal, Canada; *Int'l*, pg. 116
Fahey, Paul, Asst. Controller--The Oldenburg Group Companies, Milwaukee, WI; *U.S. Private*, pg. 814
Faillo, Robert, Controller--Midland Enterprises Inc., Cincinnati, OH; *U.S. Public*, pg. 549
Fair, B. Ronald, V.P. & Controller--Broad, Vogt & Conant, Inc., Detroit, MI; *U.S. Private*, pg. 170
Fairbrother, M., Controller--MetalTech International PLC, Stourbridge, United Kingdom; *Int'l*, pg. 862
Fairis, John, Controller--American Woodmark Corporation, Winchester, VA; *U.S. Public*, pg. 96
Fake, Michael, Controller--Hanover Wire Cloth, Hanover, PA; *U.S. Private*, pg. 193
Falb, Rosemary, Asst. Controller--Emerson Radio Corp., Parsippany, NJ; *U.S. Public*, pg. 578
Falberg, Kathryn E., Chief Acctg. Officer & Corp. Controller--Amgen Inc., Thousand Oaks, CA; *U.S. Public*, pg. 100
Falgout, Eldon, Controller--Production Management Companies, Inc., Harvey, LA; *U.S. Private*, pg. 888
Falkenberg, Edward, V.P. & Controller--The Seagram Company Ltd., Montreal, Canada; *Int'l*, pg. 1214
Falkenstern, Donald D., Controller--Commercial Travelers Mutual Insurance Company, Utica, NY; *U.S. Private*, pg. 258
Falzon, Andre R., Controller--Barrick Gold Corporation, Toronto, Canada; *Int'l*, pg. 168
Fangman, Roger, Controller--Dean Operations Inc., Kansas City, MO; *U.S. Private*, pg. 318
Fanning, Parker, Controller--SA-SO Company, Dallas, TX; *U.S. Private*, pg. 955
Farabaugh, Gerald E., Controller--Babcock Lumber Company, Pittsburgh, PA; *U.S. Private*, pg. 108
Farah, Georges, V.P. & Controller--Repap New Brunswick Inc., Montreal, Canada; *Int'l*, pg. 1104
Farell, H.D., Sr. V.P. & Controller--TU Electric, Dallas, TX; *U.S. Public*, pg. 1588
Farinick, Charlie, Asst. Controller--All Seasons Services, Inc., Braintree, MA; *U.S. Private*, pg. 35
Farkouh, Brian, Controller--Bestform Foundations, Inc., Long Island City, NY; *U.S. Private*, pg. 140
Farley, Tom, Controller & Mgr.-Daily Opers.--Norman Levy Associates, Inc., Southfield, MI; *U.S. Private*, pg. 664
Farman, Chris G., Controller--Anjou International Company, New York, NY; *Int'l*, pg. 321
Farmer, Robert L., Controller--H.O. Trerice Company, Oak Park, MI; *U.S. Private*, pg. 1099
Farmer, W.A., Comptroller--Oldsmobile Div. General Motors Corp., Lansing, MI; *U.S. Public*, pg. 720
Farnham, Robert E., V.P. & Controller--Health Management Associates, Inc., Naples, FL; *U.S. Public*, pg. 802
Farnsworth, Bradley P., V.P. & Controller--K N Energy, Inc., Lakewood, CO; *U.S. Public*, pg. 937
Farr, Kevin M., Sr. V.P. & Controller--Mattel, Inc., El Segundo, CA; *U.S. Public*, pg. 1057
Farrar, Ann, Controller--Empire Airlines, Coeur D'Alene, ID; *U.S. Private*, pg. 374
Farrell, John, V.P., Gen. Mgr., Controller & Sec.--Reagan Equipment Company, Inc., Gretna, LA; *U.S. Private*, pg. 913
Farrell, Susan, Controller--The Echo Design Group, Inc., New York, NY; *U.S. Private*, pg. 359
Farver, Joanne C., V.P. & Controller--Corporate Express, Inc., Broomfield, CO; *U.S. Public*, pg. 449
Fasani, Dan, Controller--P.L. Porter Co., Woodland Hills, CA; *U.S. Private*, pg. 876
Fasano, George, Jr., V.P. & Controller--South Carolina Pipeline Corporation, Columbia, SC; *U.S. Public*, pg. 1436
Faucher, Denis, V.P. & Controller--Imasco Limited, Montreal, Canada; *Int'l*, pg. 112
Faulkner, Bob, V.P. & Controller--Musicland Group Inc., Minnetonka, MN; *U.S. Public*, pg. 1142
Faurnier, Laura, Controller--Compuware Corporation, Farmington Hills, MI; *U.S. Public*, pg. 423
Favit, Luigi L., Sr. V.P. & Controller--TrizecHahn Corporation, Toronto, Canada; *Int'l*, pg. 1424
Favreau, Joanne, Controller--Jordan's Meats, Portland, ME; *U.S. Private*, pg. 599
Fay, Randy, Controller--Walsworth Publishing Company, Inc., Marceline, MO; *U.S. Private*, pg. 1148
Fay, Robert W., V.P. & Controller--Harris Corporation, Melbourne, FL; *U.S. Public*, pg. 791
Fayard, Gary P., V.P. & Controller--The Coca-Cola Company, Atlanta, GA; *U.S. Public*, pg. 392
Fayteg, Jim, Controller--Starboard Industries, Inc., East Tawas, MI; *U.S. Public*, pg. 919
Fazzolari, Salvatore D., V.P. & Controller--Harsco Corporation, Camp Hill, PA; *U.S. Public*, pg. 792
Fearon, R., V.P.-Plng. & Controller--Kruger Inc., Montreal, Canada; *Int'l*, pg. 761
Febilano, James M., V.P. & Controller--Anixter International, Chicago, IL; *U.S. Public*, pg. 115
Fedock, R.N., Treas. & Controller--Friendswood Development Company, Houston, TX; *U.S. Public*, pg. 988
Feeback, Cynthia, Controller & Principal Acctg. Officer--Plains Resources Inc., Houston, TX; *U.S. Public*, pg. 1307
Feehan, Jim, Controller--NW Transport Service, Inc., Denver, CO; *U.S. Private*, pg. 772
Feeney, Robert, Controller--Monroe Forgings Inc., Rochester, NY; *Int'l*, pg. 488
Fehr, Gregory G., V.P. & Controller--Consolidated Products, Inc., Indianapolis, IN; *U.S. Public*, pg. 436
Fehr, Gregory G., V.P. & Controller--Consolidated Specialty Restaurant, Indianapolis, IN; *U.S. Public*, pg. 436
Fehr, Gregory G., V.P. & Controller--SNS Investment Company, Indianapolis, IN; *U.S. Public*, pg. 436
Feighway, Tina, Controller--U.S. Broach & Machine Company, Sumter, SC; *U.S. Private*, pg. 102
Fejer, Dominic M., V.P. & Controller--Pinnacle Bank, Valparaiso, IN; *U.S. Public*, pg. 1297
Feld, Eric, Controller--Bigg's Hyper Shoppes, Inc., Milford, OH; *U.S. Public*, pg. 1541
Felderman, Douglas, Chief Fin. Officer--Strouds, Inc., City of Industry, CA; *U.S. Public*, pg. 1525
Feldkemp, Lynn E., Controller--The Coleman Company, Inc., Golden, CO; *U.S. Private*, pg. 690
Feldman, Brian J., Controller--USA Networks, Inc., Saint Petersburg, FL; *U.S. Public*, pg. 1685
Feldman, Brian J., Controller--Home Shopping Network, Inc., Saint Petersburg, FL; *U.S. Public*, pg. 1685
Feldman, Steve, Controller--Barneys Inc., New York, NY; *U.S. Private*, pg. 116
Feliu, Rafael, Controller--Stanric, Inc., Puerto Real, PR; *U.S. Public*, pg. 1503
Fellenstein, Mike, Controller, Treas. & Sec.--Biddulph Automotive Group, Glendale, AZ; *U.S. Private*, pg. 142
Feller, Renee, Controller & Corp. Sec.--Fosters Freeze International, Inc., San Luis Obispo, CA; *U.S. Public*, pg. 677
Fellows, DeWayne, Chief Acctg. Officer, V.P. & Controller--Sundstrand Corporation, Rockford, IL; *U.S. Public*, pg. 1533
Felter, Kenneth V., Controller--Jaguar Cars, Mahwah, NJ; *U.S. Public*, pg. 664
Femmer, Paul D., Controller--Zeigler Coal Holding Company, Fairview Heights, IL; *U.S. Public*, pg. 1790
Fendley, F. Tarrant, Controller--Howell Corporation, Houston, TX; *U.S. Public*, pg. 843
Fenichel, Alvin H., Sr. V.P. & Controller--The Equitable Companies Incorporated, New York, NY; *U.S. Public*, pg. 588
Fennell, Anne Marie, Controller--Heller Seasonings & Ingredients, Inc., Bedford Park, IL; *U.S. Private*, pg. 520
Fenner, Robert, Asst. Treas. & Asst. Controller--Mount Snow Resort, Mount Snow, VT; *U.S. Private*, pg. 61
Fenske, Richard, Controller--Stanco Metal Products, Inc., Grand Haven, MI; *U.S. Private*, pg. 1030
Fenster, Andrew L., Asst. Controller--The New York Times Company, New York, NY; *U.S. Public*, pg. 1173
Fenton, A., Grp. Mgr.-Fin.--John Fairfax Holdings Limited, Sydney, Australia; *Int'l*, pg. 477
Ferguson, Gary R., Controller--Mountain States Pipe & Supply Company, Colorado Springs, CO; *U.S. Private*, pg. 764
Ferguson, Larry, Controller--Sierracin/Sylmar Corporation, Sylmar, CA; *U.S. Private*, pg. 999
Ferguson, Paul G., Controller--Fay, Spofford & Thorndike, Inc., Burlington, MA; *U.S. Private*, pg. 397
Ferguson, Susan L., Controller--Bruce Oakley, Inc., North Little Rock, AR; *U.S. Private*, pg. 809
Fernandez, Edwardo, Controller--DMB&B Bilbao, Bilbao, Spain; *U.S. Private*, pg. 303
Fernandez, Edwin, Controller--Colgate-Palmolive (Central America) S.A., Guatemala, Guatemala; *U.S. Public*, pg. 398
Fernandez, Gumersindo M., Controller--Acos Villares Mechanical Engineering Unit, Sao Paulo, Brazil; *Int'l*, pg. 23
Fernelius, Al, Controller--Larry H. Miller Group, Murray, UT; *U.S. Private*, pg. 747
Fernino, Roselaine, Controller--Mark Lighting Fixture Co., Inc., Edison, NJ; *U.S. Private*, pg. 704
Ferrante, Christine, Sr. V.P. & Comptroller--Fiduciary Trust Company International, New York, NY; *U.S. Public*, pg. 621
Ferrari, Mark, V.P. & Corp. Controller--Kronos Incorporated, Waltham, MA; *U.S. Public*, pg. 967

Ferraro, Helen, Controller--Stonco Genlyte, Union, NJ; *U.S. Public*, pg. 730
Ferrello, Lou, Controller--King Fifth Wheel Co., Mountain Top, PA; *Int'l*, pg. 1337
Ferrentino, Dawn, Asst. Controller--Karnak Corporation, Clark, NJ; *U.S. Private*, pg. 607
Ferrera, James J., Controller & Treas.--James Ferrera & Sons, Inc., Canton, MA; *U.S. Private*, pg. 401
Ferri, Mary Ann, Controller--Atlantic Guest, Inc., Meriden, CT; *U.S. Public*, pg. 1705
Ferrier, Robert, Controller--Entron Industries Limited Partnership, Forest Hills, NY; *U.S. Private*, pg. 378
Ferro, Leonard, Controller--Collins & Aikman Corporation, Charlotte, NC; *U.S. Public*, pg. 399
Festenstein, Gerald, Controller--Universal Overall Company, Chicago, IL; *U.S. Private*, pg. 1127
Fetter, James, Controller--AlliedSignal, Automotive Aftermarket, Rumford, RI; *U.S. Public*, pg. 51
Fetzner, Joseph, V.P. & Controller--PAXAR Corporation, White Plains, NY; *U.S. Public*, pg. 1266
Fetzner, Thomas A., V.P. & Controller--Oneida Ltd., Oneida, NY; *U.S. Public*, pg. 1225
Feuchuk, D.G., V.P. & Controller--Gulf Canada Resources Ltd., Calgary, Canada; *Int'l*, pg. 577
Fichtner, Mindy, Controller--Bartlett Cocke, Inc., San Antonio, TX; *U.S. Private*, pg. 249
Fickel, David, Controller--Homestead House Inc., Westminster, CO; *U.S. Private*, pg. 537
Fiebig, Mark, Controller--Brewer Oil Co., Artesia, NM; *U.S. Private*, pg. 167
Fiegel, Richard M., Controller--Johnson Worldwide Associates, Inc., Sturtevant, WI; *U.S. Public*, pg. 932
Field, Edith M., V.P. & Corp. Controller--ATL Ultrasound, Inc., Bothell, WA; *U.S. Public*, pg. 11
Field, Mike, Controller--The Hammerblow Corp., Wausau, WI; *U.S. Private*, pg. 498
Fields, David C., V.P. & Controller--Pittston Minerals Group, Inc., Lebanon, VA; *U.S. Public*, pg. 1305
Fields, L. Macon, Controller--Plasti-Line, Inc., Knoxville, TN; *U.S. Public*, pg. 1308
Fields, Lawrence O., Controller--Maxco, Inc., Lansing, MI; *U.S. Public*, pg. 1061
Fields, William O., Controller & Treas.--Buffalo Color Corporation, Parsippany, NJ; *U.S. Private*, pg. 178
Fife, Tom, Controller--Cassco Ice & Cold Storage, Inc., Harrisonburg, VA; *U.S. Public*, pg. 1727
Figley, Mark, Controller--NAI Systems Division, Columbia, MD; *U.S. Public*, pg. 1144
Filippi, R.A., Controller--Ancon Insurance Company, Inc., Irving, TX; *U.S. Public*, pg. 601
Filippi, R.A., Controller--Exxon Insurance Holdings, Inc., Saint Georges, Bermuda; *U.S. Public*, pg. 602
Filosa, Rolf, Controller--Multiple Allied Services, Inc., Hayward, CA; *U.S. Private*, pg. 767
Filton, Steven G., V.P. & Controller--Universal Health Services, Inc., King of Prussia, PA; *U.S. Public*, pg. 1696
Findlay, I., Controller--LASMO plc, London, United Kingdom; *Int'l*, pg. 803
Findlay, William, Controller--Avex Electronics Ltd., East Kilbride, United Kingdom; *U.S. Private*, pg. 545
Findling, Gary J., Asst. Treas.--Aeroquip-Vickers, Inc., Maumee, OH; *U.S. Public*, pg. 24
Fink, Brenda, Mgr.-Acct.--The Apparel Group, Ltd., Louisville, KY; *U.S. Private*, pg. 78
Finke, Mike, Controller--Hutch Sports USA, Inc., Hebron, KY; *U.S. Public*, pg. 1354
Finke, Rodney, Controller--LTB Ward Constructors, Inc., Houston, TX; *U.S. Private*, pg. 347
Finkenheller, John, Sr. V.P. & Controller--RehabCare Group, Inc., Saint Louis, MO; *U.S. Public*, pg. 1373
Finlay, Jim, Controller--American Natl. Can Co., Monmouth Junction, NJ; *Int'l*, pg. 1029
Finlon, David, Controller--Baker & Taylor, Inc., Charlotte, NC; *U.S. Private*, pg. 111
Finnegan, Kevin, Controller--Aeroflex Incorporated, Plainview, NY; *U.S. Public*, pg. 23
Finnegan, Kevin, V.P.-Fin.--Aeroflex Laboratories Inc., Plainview, NY; *U.S. Public*, pg. 24
Fioravante, Raymond, Chief Fin. Officer & Controller--Fawn Industries, Inc., Hunt Valley, MD; *U.S. Private*, pg. 397
Fiore, Larry, Controller--Objective Systems Integrators, Inc., Folsom, CA; *U.S. Public*, pg. 1209
Fiqurski, John, Controller--PHB Die Casting, Fairview, PA; *U.S. Private*, pg. 826
Fishbach, Philip D., V.P. & Controller--Xerox Corporation, Stamford, CT; *U.S. Public*, pg. 1783
Fishback, Donald R., Controller--Moog Incorporated, East Aurora, NY; *U.S. Public*, pg. 1127
Fisher, Bryan S., V.P. & Controller--National Surgery Centers, Inc., Chicago, IL; *U.S. Public*, pg. 1161
Fisher, John J., Controller, Treas. & Sec.--Tarlton Corporation, Saint Louis, MO; *U.S. Private*, pg. 1069
Fisher, Martha, Controller & Asst. Treas.--Prudential Metal Supply Corp., East Dedham, MA; *U.S. Private*, pg. 893
Fisher, Maureen, Controller--MTI Vacations, Inc., Downers Grove, IL; *U.S. Private*, pg. 688
Fisher, Mike, V.P.-Controller--Thermador, Los Angeles, CA; *U.S. Public*, pg. 1053
Fisher, Roger W., V.P. & Controller--Horace Mann Educators Corporation, Springfield, IL; *U.S. Public*, pg. 835
Fisher, Tom, Controller--Holsum Bakery, Inc., Phoenix, AZ; *U.S. Private*, pg. 536
Fitch, Gerald, V.P. & Controller--Union Bank of California, San Francisco, CA; *Int'l*, pg. 157
Fitzgerald, Dan, Controller--Stu Evans Lincoln-Mercury Inc., Southgate, MI; *U.S. Private*, pg. 385
Fitzgerald, John, Controller & Sec.--The Robert E. Morris Company, Farmington, CT; *U.S. Private*, pg. 762
Fitzgerald, John J., V.P. & Controller--DynCorp, Reston, VA; *U.S. Private*, pg. 351
Fitzgerald, Ken, Chief Fin. Officer, Controller & Sec.--R.L. Zeigler Co. Inc., Tuscaloosa, AL; *U.S. Private*, pg. 1204
Fitzgerald, Matthew D., V.P., Controller & Asst. Sec.--BJ Services Company, Houston, TX; *U.S. Public*, pg. 161
Fitzgerald, R.W., V.P. & Controller--MidCon Corp., Lombard, IL; *U.S. Public*, pg. 1210
Fitzpatrick, David J., V.P. & Controller--Eastman Kodak Company, Rochester, NY; *U.S. Public*, pg. 550
Fitzpatrick, Mike, Controller--Aircap Industries Corp., Verona, MS; *U.S. Private*, pg. 688
Flaherty, William, Asst. V.P. & Controller--Meridian Technology Leasing Services, Deerfield, IL; *U.S. Private*, pg. 732
Flavin, James E., Sr. V.P.-Fin. & Controller--Staples, Inc., Westborough, MA; *U.S. Public*, pg. 1509
Fleck, Donald C., V.P. & Controller--The Hennegan Company, Florence, KY; *U.S. Private*, pg. 522
Fledderman, J.H., Controller--AVEX Electronics, Inc., Huntsville, AL; *U.S. Private*, pg. 545
Fleet, Michelle L., Controller--T.W. Phillips Gas and Oil Co., Butler, PA; *U.S. Private*, pg. 862
Flegger, Allen, Controller--Southern Apparel Corporation, Largo, FL; *U.S. Private*, pg. 1015
Fleishman, Glenn, Controller--Jetro Holdings, Inc., College Point, NY; *U.S. Private*, pg. 587
Fleming, Amy, Controller--Jasper Corp., Birmingham, AL; *U.S. Private*, pg. 583
Fleming, Christine, Controller--The Hartstone Group PLC, London, United Kingdom; *Int'l*, pg. 599
Fleming, Dan, V.P.-Plng. & Controller--Hospital Affiliates Development Corporation, Nashville, TN; *U.S. Private*, pg. 540
Fleming, Dennis, Controller--Screw Conveyor Corp., Hammond, IN; *U.S. Private*, pg. 977
Flener, Michael, V.P. & Controller--J.E. Higgins Lumber Co., Concord, CA; *U.S. Private*, pg. 527
Fletcher, James, Controller--Standex International Limited, Stockport, United Kingdom; *U.S. Public*, pg. 1507
Fletcher, James, Controller--Roehlen England, Stockport, United Kingdom; *U.S. Public*, pg. 1507
Fletcher, Tim, Controller--Buffelen Woodworking Company, Tacoma, WA; *U.S. Private*, pg. 179
Fletcher, Wallace E., Comptroller & Asst. Treas.--Fall River Gas Company, Fall River, MA; *U.S. Public*, pg. 611
Flett, Peggy, Controller--Allen Nelson & Co., Seattle, WA; *U.S. Private*, pg. 790
Fleury, John, V.P. & Controller--SPD Technologies, Philadelphia, PA; *U.S. Private*, pg. 957
Flick, Elaine, Controller--Ingram Materials Co., Nashville, TN; *U.S. Private*, pg. 563
Floden, Louis, Controller--Pella Corporation, Pella, IA; *U.S. Private*, pg. 848
Flood, Brian D., Asst. Controller--Woolworth Corporation, New York, NY; *U.S. Public*, pg. 1777
Flora, Joy L., V.P. & Controller--ServiceMaster International, Downers Grove, IL; *U.S. Public*, pg. 1462
Florence, Russell V., Controller--Equity Oil Company, Salt Lake City, UT; *U.S. Public*, pg. 590
Flores, Rene, Chief Fin. Officer & Controller--Jones & Jones, Inc., McAllen, TX; *U.S. Private*, pg. 596
Florest, Sylvia, Controller--Quality Naturally Foods, City of Industry, CA; *U.S. Private*, pg. 899
Florio, Charles J., V.P. & Controller--JJI Lighting Group Inc., Greenwich, CT; *Int'l*, pg. 821
Florio, Vince, Controller--BMW, Flushing, NY; *U.S. Private*, pg. 107
Floryance, Peter, Controller--Belarus Machinery, Inc., Milwaukee, WI; *Int'l*, pg. 101
Flournoy, Thomas, V.P. & Controller--1st Source Bank Consolidated, South Bend, IN; *U.S. Public*, pg. 638
Flower, Allen E., Chief Fin. Officer, V.P. & Acting Treas.--COMSAT Corporation, Bethesda, MD; *U.S. Public*, pg. 424
Flower, Sally, Controller-Mktg. Services--Scottish & Newcastle plc, Edinburgh, United Kingdom; *Int'l*, pg. 1211
Flowers, Lizanne, Controller--Baines Management Co., Baltimore, MD; *U.S. Private*, pg. 111
Floyd, Chuck, Chief Fin. Officer & Controller--Inland Associates, Olathe, KS; *U.S. Private*, pg. 563
Floyd, Harry, Controller--CEM Corporation, Matthews, NC; *U.S. Public*, pg. 277
Floyd, Stacy, Controller--E-Z Mart Stores, Inc., Texarkana, TX; *U.S. Private*, pg. 353
Fluegeman, Raymond W., Chief Fin. Officer, Treas., Controller & Dir.-D.P.--Robbins, Inc., Cincinnati, OH; *U.S. Private*, pg. 934
Fluke, Terry, Mrs., Controller--Pizza Haven Inc., Bellevue, WA; *U.S. Private*, pg. 868
Flynn, James F., V.P. & Controller--King Kullen Grocery Co., Inc., Westbury, NY; *U.S. Private*, pg. 621
Flynn, Kenneth T., Jr., V.P. & Controller--Echlin Inc., Branford, CT; *U.S. Public*, pg. 560
Flynn, Larry, Mgr.-Credit--M. Rubin & Sons Inc., Long Island City, NY; *U.S. Private*, pg. 949
Flynn, Tim, Controller--American Saw & Mfg. Company, East Longmeadow, MA; *U.S. Private*, pg. 61
Fobert, Diane, Controller--Jason Industrial, Inc., Fairfield, NJ; *U.S. Private*, pg. 583
Focht, Robert, Controller--Reading Tube Corp., Reading, PA; *U.S. Private*, pg. 202
Foege, Rich, Chief Fin. Officer& Controller--Dierbergs Markets Inc., Chesterfield, MO; *U.S. Private*, pg. 332
Fogelman, Mitchell, V.P. & Controller--International Aluminum Corporation, Monterey Park, CA; *U.S. Public*, pg. 894
Foglia, Jennifer, Controller--Equitable Savings & Loan Association, Wauwatosa, WI; *U.S. Private*, pg. 380
Fok, M., Controller--Delft Instruments N.V., Delft, Netherlands; *Int'l*, pg. 388
Foles, Leslie, V.P. & Controller--The Network of City Business Journals, Inc., Kansas City, MO; *U.S. Private*, pg. 19
Foley, Rich, Controller--American Trading & Production Corporation, Oil & Gas Div., Houston, TX; *U.S. Private*, pg. 64
Foley, Ron, Controller--Fruit of the Loom Limited, London, United Kingdom; *U.S. Public*, pg. 686
Folger, Peter M., V.P. & Controller--Courier Corporation, North Chelmsford, MA; *U.S. Public*, pg. 453
Folse, John, Controller--Boh Bros. Construction Co., LLC, New Orleans, LA; *U.S. Private*, pg. 154
Foltz, Mary Chris, Controller--Stephenson Equipment, Inc., Harrisburg, PA; *U.S. Private*, pg. 1040
Folz, Ken, Controller--Delta Consolidated Industries, Inc. (Co. Headquarters), Jonesboro, AR; *U.S. Public*, pg. 481
Fong, Disston, Fin. Controller--CMC (Australia) Pty. Limited, Sydney, Australia; *U.S. Public*, pg. 413
Fontana, Joseph E., V.P. & Controller--Long Island Lighting Company, Hicksville, NY; *U.S. Public*, pg. 1013
Fontana, Joseph E., Controller--Long Island Lighting Company, Hicksville, NY; *U.S. Public*, pg. 1013
Fontenot, Tony, Controller--Pioneer Concrete Of Texas, Inc., Houston, TX; *Int'l*, pg. 1058
Foote, Bill, Controller--Performance Contracting Group, Lenexa, KS; *U.S. Private*, pg. 853
Foote, C.L., Controller--Simplicity Engineering, Inc., Durand, MI; *Int'l*, pg. 1066
Forbes, Jay, Controller--Nova Scotia Power Inc., Halifax, Canada; *Int'l*, pg. 971
Forbes, Laura, Controller--Goodway Technologies Corporation, Stamford, CT; *U.S. Private*, pg. 464
Forbes, Robert, Controller--Hope's Architectural Products Inc., Jamestown, NY; *U.S. Private*, pg. 538
Forbush, David, Controller--Wards Cove Packing Company, Seattle, WA; *U.S. Private*, pg. 1149
Ford, Bruce L., Controller--Pepper-Lawson, Katy, TX; *U.S. Private*, pg. 851
Ford, Danny, Mgr.-Acctg.--Mobile Gas Service Corp., Mobile, AL; *U.S. Public*, pg. 1120
Ford, Diane L., Controller--WPS Resources Corp., Green Bay, WI; *U.S. Public*, pg. 1728
Ford, Diane L., Controller--Wisconsin Public Service Corporation, Green Bay, WI; *U.S. Public*, pg. 1728
Foreman, Norman, Controller--Caroline Hunt Trust Estate, Dallas, TX; *U.S. Private*, pg. 548
Forero, Luis, Controller--Instituto de Idiomas Colombia, S.A., Bogota, Colombia; *U.S. Public*, pg. 222
Forester, R.A., Controller--Jacobs Applied Technology, Inc., Orangeburg, SC; *U.S. Public*, pg. 921
Fornum, Jack, Controller--Corn Products International, Inc., Bedford Park, IL; *U.S. Public*, pg. 447
Forsberg, Barbara J., V.P. & Controller--Robert Half International Inc., Menlo Park, CA; *U.S. Public*, pg. 774
Forsberg, Craig, Controller--Bridgeman's Restaurants Inc., Minnetonka, MN; *U.S. Private*, pg. 167
Forsyth, Linda, Controller--Hulman & Company, Terre Haute, IN; *U.S. Private*, pg. 547
Fortelka, Bruce, V.P.-Admin. & Controller--Rollex Corporation, Elk Grove Village, IL; *U.S. Private*, pg. 941
Forthen, Wendy, Controller--Weibel Winery, Lodi, CA; *U.S. Private*, pg. 1159
Fortier, L., V.P. & Comptroller--Peerless Carpet Corporation, Acton Vale, Canada; *Int'l*, pg. 1032
Fortier, Levis, V.P. & Controller--Peerless Carpet, Acton Vale, Canada; *Int'l*, pg. 1032
Fortin, Paul, Controller--Roehlen Engraving, Rochester, NY; *U.S. Public*, pg. 1506
Fortney, David, Controller & Treas.--United States Lock & Hardware Co., Columbia, PA; *U.S. Private*, pg. 1196
Fortney, David J., Chief Fin. Officer, Controller & Treas.--York Barbell Co., Inc., York, PA; *U.S. Private*, pg. 1196
Fortney, Steven N., Asst. Controller-Acctg. & Reporting--Telephone and Data Systems, Inc., Chicago, IL; *U.S. Public*, pg. 1570
Fortress, Marston J., V.P. & Controller--Harvard Industries, Inc., Tampa, FL; *U.S. Public*, pg. 796
Foshie, Harold, Controller--Family Inns of America, Inc., Pigeon Forge, TN; *U.S. Private*, pg. 392
Fossett, W. Curtis, Controller & Sec.--Educational Development Corporation, Tulsa, OK; *U.S. Public*, pg. 564
Fossum, Jeffrey J., Chief Fin. Officer & V.P.--Effective Management Systems, Milwaukee, WI; *U.S. Public*, pg. 565
Foster, Brenda, V.P. & Controller--Glacier Water Services Inc., Carlsbad, CA; *U.S. Public*, pg. 745
Foster, David, Controller--Snyder Tank Corp., Buffalo, NY; *U.S. Private*, pg. 1011
Foster, Don, Controller--Tidelands Oil Production Co., Long Beach, CA; *U.S. Private*, pg. 1084
Foster, Mark, Controller--U.S.S. Seko Worldwide, Elk Grove Village, IL; *U.S. Private*, pg. 1115
Foulon, Raphael, Controller--Endevco France S.A., Le Pre-Saint-Gervais, France; *Int'l*, pg. 854
Found, P.A., Grp. Fin. Controller--Commercial Union plc, London, United Kingdom; *Int'l*, pg. 308
Fountain, Brad, Controller-Sls. & Mktg.--Jami, Inc., Shawnee Mission, KS; *U.S. Private*, pg. 581
Fourier, Tina, Controller--Furman Lumber Company, Inc., Billerica, MA; *U.S. Private*, pg. 431
Fournier, Paul, Controller--Ivex Packaging Corporation-Industrial Products Division, Newton, MA; *U.S. Public*, pg. 915
Foust, Diana, Controller--GNWC Wire, Cable & Network Products, Downers Grove, IL; *U.S. Private*, pg. 259
Fowler, Bruce, Controller--Hanimex (NZ) Limited, Albany, New Zealand; *Int'l*, pg. 1116
Fowler, Kinton, Controller--Atlas Copco Wagner Inc., Portland, OR; *Int'l*, pg. 96
Fowler, M. Lee, V.P. & Controller--Louisville Gas and Electric Company, Louisville, KY; *U.S. Public*, pg. 970
Fowler, Stan, Controller--Intex Plastics Corporation, Corinth, MS; *U.S. Private*, pg. 574
Fox, David, Controller--Adhesive Films, Santa Ana, CA; *U.S. Public*, pg. 165
Fox, Edward D., Controller--Massachusetts Envelope Co., Somerville, MA; *U.S. Private*, pg. 712
Fox, Fran, Controller--Crowe Rope Industries L.L.C., Waterville, ME; *U.S. Private*, pg. 291

Fox, Larry, Controller--J. Bacon & Sons, Louisville, KY; *U.S. Public*, pg. 1090
Fox, Peter, Controller--AAI/ACL Technologies, Santa Ana, CA; *U.S. Public*, pg. 1679
Fox, Robert C., V.P. & Controller--Best Buy Co., Inc., Eden Prairie, MN; *U.S. Public*, pg. 223
Fozzard, Randy, Controller--Turf Paradise, Inc., Phoenix, AZ; *U.S. Public*, pg. 831
Frady, Charles, Controller--Photomatrix Corporation, San Diego, CA; *U.S. Public*, pg. 1292
Fraiyer, Scott, Controller & Treas.--EVCON Industries, Wichita, KS; *U.S. Public*, pg. 1788
Fraiyer, Scott, Treas. & Controller--Evcon Industries, Inc., Wichita, KS; *U.S. Public*, pg. 1788
Fraizer, Michael, Sr. V.P., Controller & Treas.--American Mutual Life Holding Co., Des Moines, IA; *U.S. Private*, pg. 59
Fraley, Steven, Chief Fin. Officer & V.P.-Fin.--WINCO, Le Center, MN; *U.S. Private*, pg. 350
Frampton, John, Controller--Dynagear Oil Pumps, Inc., Maquoketa, IA; *U.S. Private*, pg. 350
France, Dave, Mgr.-Acctg.--Interstate Van Lines, Inc., Springfield, VA; *U.S. Private*, pg. 573
France, R.A., V.P. & Controller--Cyprus Foote Mineral Co., Kings Mountain, NC; *U.S. Public*, pg. 471
Francione, Lawrence, Controller--Milwaukee Insurance Group, Milwaukee, WI; *U.S. Public*, pg. 1694
Francis, Betty, Comptroller--BankBoston Corporation, Boston, MA; *U.S. Public*, pg. 183
Francis, Greg, Controller--Wajax Limited, Delta, Canada; *Int'l*, pg. 1484
Francis, Nancy, Controller--Kreonite, Inc., Wichita, KS; *U.S. Private*, pg. 635
Francis, Trudy, Asst. Controller--Intelligent Controls Inc., Lynnwood, WA; *U.S. Private*, pg. 566
Francis, William, Chief Fin. Officer, Treas. & Controller--Captive-Aire Systems, Inc., Youngsville, NC; *U.S. Private*, *pg. 207*
Franco, Frank J., Controller & Treas.--Peckham Industries, Inc., White Plains, NY; *U.S. Private*, pg. 846
Francois, Victor, Controller--Designatronics, Inc., New Hyde Park, NY; *U.S. Private*, pg. 327
Franda, Tony, Controller & Mgr.-Property--Robert B. Aikens & Associates LLC., Troy, MI; *U.S. Private*, pg. 28
Frank, Harold D., Controller & Sec.--Research Products Corporation, Madison, WI; *U.S. Private*, pg. 924
Frank, Peter S., V.P. & Controller--The Edward J. DeBartolo Corporation, Youngstown, OH; *U.S. Private*, pg. 319
Franke, Doug, Controller--North American Roofing Systems, Inc., Arden, NC; *U.S. Private*, pg. 803
Frankenfield, Monte S., V.P.-Fin. & Controller--Phycor, Inc., Nashville, TN; *U.S. Public*, pg. 1293
Frankl, Ted, Controller--Capital Mercury Shirt, New York, NY; *U.S. Private*, pg. 206
Franklin, Wayne, Controller & Sec.--The Parman Corporation, Nashville, TN; *U.S. Private*, pg. 840
Frankowski, Frank, V.P., Controller--Atlantic Electric Co., Pleasantville, NJ; *U.S. Public*, pg. 430
Frano, Daniel, Controller--Dormeyer Industries, Chicago, IL; *U.S. Private*, pg. 340
Fransioli, Mark, Controller--RCM Industries, Franklin Park, IL; *U.S. Private*, pg. 902
Franson, Herbert, Controller & Asst. Treas.--Hathaway Corporation, Littleton, CO; *U.S. Public*, pg. 798
Frantz, Richard A., V.P. & Reg. Controller--FirstMerit Corporation, Akron, OH; *U.S. Public*, pg. 646
Frantzen, Ella, Controller--Berlitz International Danmark A/S, Copenhagen, Denmark; *U.S. Public*, pg. 222
Fraser, Annette, Controller--Star Transportation, Inc., Nashville, TN; *U.S. Private*, pg. 1035
Fraser, Christopher S., Controller--Lewis & Saunders Inc., Laconia, NH; *Int'l*, pg. 1337
Fraser, Ian, Controller--Liebert Ltd., Marlow, United Kingdom; *U.S. Public*, pg. 577
Fraser, Lorne D., Controller--Fraser Papers, Inc., Stamford, CT; *Int'l*, pg. 434
Frasure, William R., Controller--Rowan Companies, Inc., Houston, TX; *U.S. Public*, pg. 1409
Frazier, John, Controller--The Airolite Company, Marietta, OH; *U.S. Private*, pg. 29
Frech, Raymond J., Controller--Alusuisse-Lonza America Inc., New York, NY; *Int'l*, pg. 67
Freda, Mike, Controller--Pacor, Inc., Philadelphia, PA; *U.S. Private*, pg. 833
Frede, Ginger, Controller--Trophy Holdings Inc., Elmwood Park, NJ; *U.S. Private*, pg. 1105
Frederick, Gary, Controller--Fibre Glass-Evercoat Company, Cincinnati, OH; *U.S. Public*, pg. 866
Fredette, Sharon, Controller--H. Wilson Company, South Holland, IL; *U.S. Private*, pg. 359
Fredrickson, Bob, Controller--Lund Food Holdings, Inc., Edina, MN; *U.S. Private*, pg. 680
Fredrickson, Glenn, Controller & Sec.--Standard Manifold Company, Inc., Chicago, IL; *U.S. Private*, pg. 1031
Freed, Thomas J., Controller & Sec.--National City Bancorp, Minneapolis, MN; *U.S. Public*, pg. 1153
Freeman, Brian, Controller--Industrial & Automotive Fasteners, Inc., Royal Oak, MI; *U.S. Public*, pg. 919
Freeman, Deborah, Controller--Blue Bird Coach Lines Inc., Olean, NY; *U.S. Private*, pg. 150
Freeman, Jeff, Controller--Terra Tech Labs, Inc., Santa Ana, CA; *U.S. Public*, pg. 1594
Freeman, Peter, Controller--Liberty Fabrics, Inc., New York, NY; *Int'l*, pg. 340
Freeman, Philip L., Jr., V.P. & Controller--Sheetz, Inc., Altoona, PA; *U.S. Private*, pg. 991
Freeman, Phyllis, Exec. V.P., Comptroller, Legal Officer & Dir.-Investor Rels.--Eagle Lincoln Mercury Inc., Dallas, TX; *U.S. Private*, pg. 355
Freeman, Reyanne, Controller--Brady Marketing Company, Pacheco, CA; *U.S. Private*, pg. 165
Freeman, Richard, Controller--Berlitz Schools of Languages Ltd., London, United Kingdom; *U.S. Public*, pg. 222
Freeman, Terry L., V.P. & Controller--Metals USA, Inc., Houston, TX; *U.S. Public*, pg. 1100
Frees, Vincent J., V.P. & Controller--Pulte Corporation, Bloomfield Hills, MI; *U.S. Public*, pg. 1344
Freidel, Chris, Controller--Business Information Technology, Media, PA; *U.S. Public*, pg. 356
Freimuth, David, Controller--Day International Printing Products Co., Dayton, OH; *U.S. Private*, pg. 56
French, Dan, Controller--Senator Ford, Sacramento, CA; *U.S. Private*, pg. 983
French, Jerry, V.P., Controller & Treas.--Shelter Mutual Insurance Company, Columbia, MO; *U.S. Private*, pg. 992
French, John, II, Controller--Nissan Motor Corporation in U.S.A., Gardena, CA; *Int'l*, pg. 945
French, R.G., Controller & Treas.--Sunkist Growers, Inc., Sherman Oaks, CA; *U.S. Private*, pg. 1052
French, Ronda, Controller--Ancira Enterprises Inc., San Antonio, TX; *U.S. Private*, pg. 71
Freney, Kevin, Controller--Circuit-Wise, Inc., North Haven, CT; *U.S. Private*, pg. 240
Frenzen, Darold F., V.P. & Controller--DST Systems, Inc., Kansas City, MO; *U.S. Public*, pg. 943
Frey, Rick J., Controller & Asst. Sec.--Hickman, Williams & Co. Inc., Cincinnati, OH; *U.S. Private*, pg. 525
Frey, Susanne, Controller & Treas.--The Habegger Corporation, Cincinnati, OH; *U.S. Private*, pg. 492
Frick, Elizabeth, Controller--ACS Industries, Inc., Woonsocket, RI; *U.S. Private*, pg. 3
Fricks, Roy, Controller--The Tog Shop, Americus, GA; *U.S. Private*, pg. 1090
Friedburg, Jeff, Controller--Beach City Chevrolet Co., Long Beach, CA; *U.S. Private*, pg. 125
Friedline, William, Controller--Riggs Industries, Inc., Stoystown, PA; *U.S. Private*, pg. 930
Friedman, Matthew, Asst. Controller--Cognizant Corporation, Westport, CT; *U.S. Public*, pg. 395
Friedman, Richard, Controller--RFI Corp., Bay Shore, NY; *U.S. Public*, pg. 494
Friedrichsen, B.T., Treas. & Sec.--Wagner Mills Inc., Schuyler, NE; *U.S. Private*, pg. 1146
Friel, James, Controller--Ajax Paving Industries Inc., Madison Heights, MI; *U.S. Private*, pg. 29
Friesen, Larry, Controller--U.S. Filter/Davis Water & Waste Industries, Inc., Thomasville, GA; *U.S. Public*, pg. 1682
Frietas, Kathy, Controller--Potamkin Toyota, Inc., Miami, FL; *U.S. Private*, pg. 877
Fringnaezrt, David, Controller--Union Pen Company, Greenwich, CT; *U.S. Private*, pg. 1119
Fritsch, Dan, Grp. Controller--Teleflex Automotive, Troy, MI; *U.S. Public*, pg. 1569
Fritts, Bob, V.P. & Controller--Jackson National Life Insurance Company, Lansing, MI; *Int'l*, pg. 1073
Fritz, Chuck, Controller--Anthony and Sylvan Pools Corporation, Doylestown, PA; *U.S. Public*, pg. 593
Fritz, Steve, Controller--Interstate Payco Seed Company, West Fargo, ND; *U.S. Private*, pg. 573
Fritzen, Doris A., Controller & Sec.--C.F. Haglin & Sons, Edina, MN; *U.S. Private*, pg. 493
Fritzen, James, Controller--Advertising Display Co., Englewood Cliffs, NJ; *U.S. Private*, pg. 23
Frix, Dan, Controller--British Aerospace Holdings Inc., Chantilly, VA; *Int'l*, pg. 218
Froehlich, Joe, V.P. & Controller--DeWitt Media, Inc., New York, NY; *U.S. Private*, pg. 329
Froggatt, Chris N., Controller--APS, Phoenix, AZ; *U.S. Public*, pg. 1297
Fromi, Fred, Chief Fin. Officer & Controller--BeefAmerica Operating Co., Inc., Omaha, NE; *U.S. Private*, pg. 130
Frommer, Elmar, Dr., Div. Head.-Plng. & Controlling--BASF AG, Ludwigshafen, Germany; *Int'l*, pg. 103
Frost, Jim, Controller--Frost Company, Chattanooga, TN; *U.S. Private*, pg. 430
Frost, Kurt, Controller--Magnolia Hi-Fi, Inc., Kent, WA; *U.S. Private*, pg. 696
Frothingham, Chuck, Controller--Transmission Div., Kings Mountain, NC; *U.S. Public*, pg. 556
Frotten, Robert, Exec. V.P.-Fin. & Admin. & Controller--New England Frozen Foods, Inc., Southborough, MA; *U.S. Private*, pg. 793
Fry, Darrel K., Controller--Stauffer Communications, Inc., Augusta, GA; *U.S. Private*, pg. 995
Fry, Lowell, Grp. Controller--Heatcraft Inc., Grenada, MS; *U.S. Private*, pg. 659
Fry, M.L., Controller--Pitt-Des Moines, Inc., Pittsburgh, PA; *U.S. Public*, pg. 1304
Fry, Michael W., Asst V.P., Controller & Asst. Treas.--Lincoln National Administrative Services Corp., Fort Wayne, IN; *U.S. Public*, pg. 998
Fryer, Dave, Controller--Can Corporation of America, Blandon, PA; *U.S. Private*, pg. 204
Fryz, Michael W., Asst. V.P., Controller & Asst. Treas.--Lincoln National Risk Management, Inc., Fort Wayne, IN; *U.S. Public*, pg. 998
Fuchs, William, Chief Fin. Officer & Controller--S. Rothchild & Co., Inc., New York, NY; *U.S. Private*, pg. 947
Fucile, Joe, Controller--Goldsmith/Jeffrey Inc., New York, NY; *U.S. Private*, pg. 462
Fuentas, Jackie, Controller--LanChile Airlines, Miami, FL; *U.S. Private*, pg. 645
Fugere, Keith, Controller--Mooney Aircraft Corporation, Kerrville, TX; *U.S. Private*, pg. 759
Fuhring, Joseph, Controller--Quintron Systems, Inc., Santa Maria, CA; *U.S. Private*, pg. 901
Fujihara, Darryl, Controller--Westwood One, Inc., New York, NY; *U.S. Public*, pg. 1763
Fujinago, Keith, Controller--Penford Corp., Bellevue, WA; *U.S. Public*, pg. 1269
Fujitaki, Norm, Corp. Controller--Coastcast Corporation, Gardena, CA; *U.S. Public*, pg. 391
Fulk, Keith W., V.P., Controller & Asst. Treas.--Folger Nolan Fleming Douglas, Washington, DC; *U.S. Private*, pg. 416
Full, Art, Controller--Blockhouse Co., Inc., York, PA; *U.S. Private*, pg. 150
Fuller, Bernard, Controller--Trim Division, Kalkaska, MI; *U.S. Private*, pg. 355
Fuller, Donald A., Controller--W.C. Caye & Company, Inc., Augusta, GA; *U.S. Private*, pg. 220
Fuller, Jepson, Controller--OEA, Inc., Aurora, CO; *U.S. Public*, pg. 1206
Fuller, Neal A., Controller--SAFECO Services Co., Seattle, WA; *U.S. Public*, pg. 1423
Fuller, Randy, Controller--Wellborn - DE Corp., Albuquerque, NM; *U.S. Private*, pg. 347
Fung, A., Controller-Fin. & Admin.--Wyeth (HK) Limited, Wan Chai, Hong Kong; *U.S. Public*, pg. 82
Funk, Joseph, Controller--Davis Mining & Manufacturing, Coeburn, VA; *U.S. Private*, pg. 315
Funke, David L., Controller--CCH Legal Information Services, Inc., New York, NY; *Int'l*, pg. 1513
Funke, F., Controller--Comdial Corporation, Charlottesville, VA; *U.S. Public*, pg. 407
Funkhouser, William E., Controller--Dollar Rent A Car, Tulsa, OK; *U.S. Public*, pg. 354
Furbay, John D., Controller--Aeronca, Inc., Middletown, OH; *Int'l*, pg. 829
Furey, Joseph B., Controller & Sec.--First Brands Corporation, Danbury, CT; *U.S. Public*, pg. 626
Furland, D., Controller--Columbia Gas System Service Corp., Wilmington, DE; *U.S. Public*, pg. 403
Furtbauer, Helmut, Controller--K & P Leykam Austria, Gratkorn, Austria; *Int'l*, pg. 757
Furzer, Lu Ann, Controller--Compas Electronics, Inc., Kanata, Canada; *Int'l*, pg. 36
Fusco, John, Controller--The Phillies-A Limited Partnership, Philadelphia, PA; *U.S. Private*, pg. 861
Fusco, Mario, Controller--National Metal Industries, West Springfield, MA; *U.S. Public*, pg. 1506
Fusmo, G., Jr., Controller--SCANA Energy Marketing Inc., Columbia, SC; *U.S. Public*, pg. 1436
Fuss, Tom, Controller--Triton Industries, Inc., Chicago, IL; *U.S. Private*, pg. 1104
Fusto, John, Sr. V.P. & Controller--Audiovox Corporation, Hauppauge, NY; *U.S. Public*, pg. 147
Fyfe, David, Controller--Waterford Wedgwood Plc, Dublin, Ireland; *Int'l*, pg. 1487
Gabriel, Doug, V.P., Controller & Treas.--Apperson Business Forms, Inc., Los Angeles, CA; *U.S. Private*, pg. 78
Gaches, Thierry, Controller--Accor S.A., Evry, France; *Int'l*, pg. 20
Gacolos, Laura, Controller--Actron Manufacturing Company, Cleveland, OH; *U.S. Private*, pg. 16
Gaddes, Russ, Controller--T O Plastics, Inc., Minneapolis, MN; *U.S. Private*, pg. 1065
Gaetano, Daniel, Controller--JRC Canida, Inc., Fort Worth, TX; *U.S. Private*, pg. 578
Gaffney, Tonyia, Asst. Controller--Lamonts Apparel, Inc., Kirkland, WA; *U.S. Public*, pg. 975
Gafney, Nark, V.P. & Controller--Huron Valley Steel Corp., Belleville, MI; *U.S. Private*, pg. 549
Gage, Gene G., V.P. & Controller--Simon & Schuster, New York, NY; *U.S. Private*, pg. 777
Gage, George E., Controller & Mgr.--Brown Brothers Harriman & Co., New York, NY; *U.S. Private*, pg. 173
Gagne, Russ, Controller--Saunders Brothers, Westbrook, ME; *U.S. Private*, pg. 968
Gagstetter, Gary, Controller--Thomas & Betts Reznor Division, Memphis, TN; *U.S. Public*, pg. 1598
Gaines, Michael J., V.P. & Controller--Hughes Electronics Corporation, Westchester, CA; *U.S. Public*, pg. 720
Gaisser, Thomas, Controller--Lamonts Apparel, Inc., Kirkland, WA; *U.S. Public*, pg. 975
Galan, Valentin F., Controller--Atlantic Sugar Association, Inc., Belle Glade, FL; *U.S. Private*, pg. 95
Galante, Robert, Controller--M. Kamenstein, Inc., Elmsford, NY; *U.S. Private*, pg. 606
Galaznik, Ken, Controller--Powell Electrical Mfg. Co., Houston, TX; *U.S. Public*, pg. 1319
Galenza, Len, V.P. & Controller--Weatherford Canada Ltd., Nisku, Canada; *U.S. Public*, pg. 1750
Galermo, Steve, Controller-Western Div.--Data Business Forms Limited, Brampton, Canada; *Int'l*, pg. 384
Galermo, Steve, Controller--Data Business Forms, Edmonton, Canada; *Int'l*, pg. 384
Galewski, Mark, Controller--Barber-Colman Company, Rockford, IL; *Int'l*, pg. 1242
Gall, Ellen, Controller--Carlisle Companies Incorporated, Syracuse, NY; *U.S. Public*, pg. 305
Gallagher, Carl, V.P.-Controller--Craftlite, Littlestown, PA; *U.S. Public*, pg. 730
Gallagher, Jim, Controller--National Media Corporation, Philadelphia, PA; *U.S. Public*, pg. 1158
Gallagher, Julie, V.P.-Fin. & Controller--Danzas Corporation, Bellevue, WA; *Int'l*, pg. 382
Gallagher, Kevin, Controller--Kathryn Beich, Inc., Bloomington, IL; *Int'l*, pg. 917
Gallagher, Robert, Controller--TSI Incorporated, Shoreview, MN; *U.S. Public*, pg. 1559
Gallagher, Robert R., Controller--Caterpillar Inc., Peoria, IL; *U.S. Public*, pg. 315
Gallagher, William F., Controller--Deb Shops, Inc., Philadelphia, PA; *U.S. Public*, pg. 491
Gallers, Steve, Mgr.-Acctg.--CyberGuard Corporation, Fort Lauderdale, FL; *U.S. Public*, pg. 470
Gallienne, Marina, Fin. Controller--NRG International Ltd. (Bermuda), Saint Peter Port, United Kingdom; *Int'l*, pg. 1116
Gallina, Joseph M., Comptroller--First Financial Bancorp, Hamilton, OH; *U.S. Public*, pg. 632
Gallmore, Larry D., Controller--Condea Vista Company, Houston, TX; *Int'l*, pg. 325
Gallo, Kathy, Controller--809
Gallo, Lawrence R., III, Controller--BPA International, New York, NY; *U.S. Private*, pg. 107
Galvin, Jon, V.P. & Controller--Wainoco Oil Corporation, Houston, TX; *U.S. Public*, pg. 1732
Gamache, David, V.P. & Controller--Stratus Computer, Inc., Marlborough, MA; *U.S. Public*, pg. 1524

Ganahl, John, Controller--Ganahl Lumber Company, Anaheim, CA; *U.S. Private*, pg. 439
Gangnon, Bruce E., Asst. Corp. Controller--Minnesota Power, Duluth, MN; *U.S. Public*, pg. 1116
Gannon, Robert, Controller-News America--The News Corporation Limited, Sydney, Australia; *Int'l*, pg. 925
Gant, Debra, Controller--Mid-South Milling Company, Inc., Memphis, TN; *U.S. Private*, pg. 744
Gantcher, Catherine, Controller--Au Bon Pain Co., Inc., Boston, MA; *U.S. Public*, pg. 146
Gantent, Cecile, Controller--Craftmatic Industries, Inc., Trevose, PA; *U.S. Private*, pg. 284
Gantt, Sharon, Asst. Controller--Erly Industries, Inc., Los Angeles, CA; *U.S. Public*, pg. 591
Garbarini, John, Controller--Chock Full O' Nuts - Food Service Div., Secaucus, NJ; *U.S. Public*, pg. 351
Garbe, Thomas F., Controller--Consolidated Natural Gas Company, Pittsburgh, PA; *U.S. Public*, pg. 435
Garbe, Thomas F., Controller--Consolidated Natural Gas Service Co., Inc., Pittsburgh, PA; *U.S. Public*, pg. 435
Garcia Sandoval, Juan, V.P. & Controller--Grupo Casa Autrey, Mexico, Mexico; *Int'l*, pg. 573
Garcia-Economou, Elizabeth, Dir.-Corp. Acctg. & Fin. Reporting--Envirodyne Industries, Inc., Oak Brook, IL; *U.S. Public*, pg. 586
Garcia, Armando, Controller--Escuelas de Idiomas Berlitz de Espana, S.A., Madrid, Spain; *U.S. Public*, pg. 222
Garcia, George, Controller--COBE Laboratories, Inc., Lakewood, CO; *Int'l*, pg. 667
Garcia, Juan, Controller--Benihana, Inc., Miami, FL; *U.S. Public*, pg. 211
Garcia, Luis, Fin. Controller--Gestetner SA, Caracas, Venezuela; *Int'l*, pg. 1115
Garcia, Peter, Controller--M K Diamond Products, Inc., Torrance, CA; *U.S. Private*, pg. 684
Garcia, Philip A., Sr. V.P. & Controller--Erie Family Life Insurance Company, Erie, PA; *U.S. Public*, pg. 590
Garcia, Ray, Controller--McBride and Associates, Inc., Albuquerque, NM; *U.S. Private*, pg. 719
Gardiner, Robert A., Chief Fin. Officer, V.P. & Controller--Zapata Corporation, Houston, TX; *U.S. Public*, pg. 1789
Gardiner, Tom, Controller--Pioneer Foods, Inc., Los Angeles, CA; *U.S. Private*, pg. 866
Gardiner, William J., Chief Fin. Officer, Sr. V.P. & Treas.--CRSS Inc., Houston, TX; *Int'l*, pg. 1415
Gardner, Andrew J., Sr. V.P. & Controller--CommNet Cellular Inc., Englewood, CO; *U.S. Public*, pg. 414
Gardner, Ella D., Controller--Detection Systems, Inc., Fairport, NY; *U.S. Public*, pg. 501
Gardner, Harold, V.P., Controller & Dir.-Acctg. Services--MCN Energy Group, Inc., Detroit, MI; *U.S. Public*, pg. 1024
Gardner, Harold, V.P. & Controller--MCN Investment, Detroit, MI; *U.S. Public*, pg. 1025
Gardner, James B., Asst. Comptroller--Union Camp Corporation, Wayne, NJ; *U.S. Public*, pg. 1665
Gardner, Jeff, Controller--Daw Technologies, Inc., Salt Lake City, UT; *U.S. Public*, pg. 489
Gardner, Robert G., Controller--Shenango Industries, Terre Haute, IN; *U.S. Private*, pg. 992
Garfinkle, David M., Controller & Treas.--Bradley Real Estate, Inc., Northbrook, IL; *U.S. Public*, pg. 250
Garisci, Frank, Controller--FKI Industries. Inc., Fairfield, CT; *Int'l*, pg. 472
Garlington, John, Chief Fin. Officer--Warmington Homes, Costa Mesa, CA; *U.S. Private*, pg. 1150
Garman, Roy A., Sr. V.P. & Controller--Donaldson, Lufkin, & Jenrette, Inc., New York, NY; *U.S. Public*, pg. 589
Garner, Julia, Controller--Toccoa Metal Technologies, Inc., Elmhurst, IL; *U.S. Private*, pg. 1089
Garnett, Hugh D., V.P.-Controller--Home Beneficial Corporation, Richmond, VA; *U.S. Public*, pg. 76
Garnett, Steve, Controller--Silbrico Corporation, Hodgkins, IL; *U.S. Private*, pg. 1000
Garratt, Paul R., V.P.-H.R.--Air Canada, Saint-Laurent, Canada; *Int'l*, pg. 36
Garrett, Derek, Controller--Protocol Systems, Inc., Beaverton, OR; *U.S. Public*, pg. 1336
Garrett, J. Daniel, V.P. & Controller--Birmingham Steel Corporation, Birmingham, AL; *U.S. Public*, pg. 232
Garrido, Rosanne, V.P. & Controller--Biscayne Apparel Inc., Clifton, NJ; *U.S. Public*, pg. 232
Garrison, Dan, Controller--HCI Chemtech, Chesterfield, MO; *U.S. Private*, pg. 490
Garruto, Anthony, Controller--Environmental Industries, Inc., Calabasas, CA; *U.S. Private*, pg. 378
Gartland, H., Controller--R.T. Vanderbilt Company, Inc., Norwalk, CT; *U.S. Private*, pg. 1133
Garvey, Clem, Controller--Gestetner S.A., Creteil, France; *Int'l*, pg. 1115
Garvin, Connie, Controller--Crest Cadillac, Inc., Nashville, TN; *U.S. Private*, pg. 712
Gast, Alan, Controller--Harden Industries, Inc., Los Angeles, CA; *U.S. Private*, pg. 501
Gast, Edward A., Controller--Abco Markets, Inc., Phoenix, AZ; *U.S. Private*, pg. 10
Gasull, Lluis, Gen. Controller--Caixa d'Estalvis de Catalunya, Barcelona, Spain; *Int'l*, pg. 249
Gatch-Priest, Robyn, V.P.-Controller & Asst. Treas.--CompUSA, Dallas, TX; *U.S. Public*, pg. 420
Gates, Albert L., Controller--Four-S Baking Company, Los Angeles, CA; *U.S. Private*, pg. 422
Gates, Barry, Controller--Geiger Brothers, Lewiston, ME; *U.S. Private*, pg. 442
Gaubert, Daniel R., Chief Fin. Officer, Sr. V.P.-Fin. & Controller--McDermott International, Inc., New Orleans, LA; *U.S. Public*, pg. 1067
Gault, Donna, Controller--The Karges Furniture Company Inc., Evansville, IN; *U.S. Private*, pg. 607
Gauntt, Edward, Controller--Ardell Industries Inc., Union, NJ; *U.S. Private*, pg. 597
Gausvic, Mary, V.P. & Controller--Jacor Communications, Inc., Covington, KY; *U.S. Public*, pg. 922
Gavagan, George R., V.P. & Controller--Gannett Company, Inc., Arlington, VA; *U.S. Public*, pg. 698
Gavin, John J., Jr., V.P. & Controller--Data General Corporation, Westborough, MA; *U.S. Public*, pg. 485
Gavin, Timothy J., Controller--Juno Lighting, Inc., Des Plaines, IL; *U.S. Public*, pg. 935
Gavito, Maximo, Controller--Gestetner Malaysia Sdn Bhd, Petaling Jaya, Malaysia; *Int'l*, pg. 1115
Gawel, Linda, Controller--Acme Mills Co. Inc., Detroit, MI; *U.S. Private*, pg. 13
Gawer, Dan, Controller--Jamison Plastic Corporation, Allentown, PA; *U.S. Private*, pg. 581
Gawrychowski, Peter, V.P. & Intl. Controller--Columbia Tri-Star Home Video, Burbank, CA; *Int'l*, pg. 1282
Gay, Carolyn, Asst. V.P. & Controller--Sterling Financial Corporation, Spokane, WA; *U.S. Public*, pg. 1516
Gazella, Phillip, Controller--Dotco, Hicksville, OH; *U.S. Public*, pg. 444
Gazmarian, Michael C., Chief Fin. Officer & Treas.--Insteel Industries, Inc., Mount Airy, NC; *U.S. Public*, pg. 882
Gearhardt, Mike, V.P. & Controller- North America--Dayco Products Inc., Miamisburg, OH; *U.S. Public*, pg. 1045
Gearns, Janet, Controller--Wavetek Communications Div., Indianapolis, IN; *U.S. Private*, pg. 1155
Gee, D., Dr., Controller--Imperial Chemical Industries PLC, London, United Kingdom; *Int'l*, pg. 662
Geel, Harne, Unit Controller--Weatherford Oil Tool Nederland B.V., Beverwijk, Netherlands; *U.S. Public*, pg. 1750
Gehbauer, Daryl, Controller--May Design & Construction Co., Saint Louis, MO; *U.S. Public*, pg. 1064
Geigle, Aggie, Controller--Griffin Manufacturing Co., Muskogee, OK; *U.S. Private*, pg. 481
Geiser, Edgar, Dir.-Controlling, Fin. & Info. Tech.--SMH Swiss Corporation for Micro Electronics & Watchmaking Indus. Ltd., Bienne, Switzerland; *Int'l*, pg. 1160
Geiser, James, Chief Fin. Officer, Controller & Treas.--Kokosing Construction Company, Inc., Fredericktown, OH; *U.S. Private*, pg. 631
Geiser, Larry, Controller--Amerbelle Corporation, Rockville, CT; *U.S. Private*, pg. 48
Geist, Paul R., V.P. & Controller--Houlihan's Restaurant Group, Kansas City, MO; *U.S. Public*, pg. 841
Gelbart, M., Controller--Geraghty & Miller, Inc., Denver, CO; *Int'l*, pg. 607
Gelbart, Marion, V.P. & Controller--Geraghty & Miller, Inc., Denver, CO; *Int'l*, pg. 607
Geldmacher, Kenneth K., Controller & Treas.--Centrifugal & Mechanical Industries, Saint Louis, MO; *U.S. Private*, pg. 370
Gelinas, Roger, Controller--White Rock Distilleries Inc., Lewiston, ME; *U.S. Private*, pg. 1173
Gelston, Arthur A., Jr., V.P. & Controller--Beiersdorf, Inc., Norwalk, CT; *Int'l*, pg. 182
Gemeinhart, John, Controller--Hamburg Brothers, Pittsburgh, PA; *U.S. Private*, pg. 497
Gencarelli, Paul, Controller--Bess Eaton Donut Flour Co., Inc., Westerly, RI; *U.S. Private*, pg. 139
Gendron, Gerard, V.P. & Controller--ITT Cannon, Santa Ana, CA; *U.S. Public*, pg. 859
Genovese, Mary Ellen, Corp. Controller--Trimble Navigation Limited, Sunnyvale, CA; *U.S. Public*, pg. 1638
Gensler, Jim, Controller--Henry Schein, Inc., Melville, NY; *U.S. Public*, pg. 1437
Gentile, Bob, Controller--Marchon Eyewear, Melville, NY; *U.S. Private*, pg. 702
Gentile, Patrick J., V.P. & Controller--American Banknote Corp., New York, NY; *U.S. Public*, pg. 68
Geoghan, William, Controller--Interpool, Inc., Princeton, NJ; *U.S. Public*, pg. 908
George, B., Grp. Fin. Controller--Ransomes Plc, Ipswich, United Kingdom; *Int'l*, pg. 1087
George, Michael, Controller--George E. Warren Corporation, Vero Beach, FL; *U.S. Private*, pg. 1151
George, Richard, V.P. & Controller--The Andersons Incorporated, Maumee, OH; *U.S. Public*, pg. 111
George, Rick, Controller--Max & Erma's Restaurants, Columbus, OH; *U.S. Public*, pg. 1060
George, Robert D., Controller & Treas.--Esterline Technologies Corporation, Bellevue, WA; *U.S. Public*, pg. 594
Geraghty, Gerard V., V.P. & Controller--Ingersoll-Rand Company, Woodcliff Lake, NJ; *U.S. Public*, pg. 876
Geraghty, Gerard V., Controller-Opers.--Ingersoll-Rand Company, Woodcliff Lake, NJ; *U.S. Public*, pg. 876
Geraghty, Larry, Controller--Trident Seafood Corporation, Seattle, WA; *U.S. Private*, pg. 429
Gerard, Antonia, Chief Oper. & Chief Fin. Officer, Exec. V.P., Sec. & Controller--Bolliger, Inc., Stamford, CT; *U.S. Private*, pg. 155
Gerard, Marc, Controller--The Beverly Hills Hotel, Beverly Hills, CA; *U.S. Private*, pg. 142
Gerber, Robert, Chief Acctg. Officer, Sr. V.P. & Controller--Fabri-Centers of America, Inc., Hudson, OH; *U.S. Public*, pg. 609
Gerbosi, Douglas P., Chief Fin. Officer & Controller--Friendship Dairies, Inc., Friendship, NY; *U.S. Private*, pg. 429
Gerboth, Robert, Controller--F. Schumacher & Co., New York, NY; *U.S. Private*, pg. 973
Gerdes, Sally, V.P. & Controller--Union Insurance Company, Lincoln, NE; *U.S. Public*, pg. 216
Gerics, David, V.P. & Controller--Cadbury Beverages North America, Stamford, CT; *Int'l*, pg. 248
Gerig, D., Controller--Esso Aktiengesellschaft, Hamburg, Germany; *U.S. Public*, pg. 601
Gerlach, Gerald R., V.P. & Controller--PharMerica, Inc., Tampa, FL; *U.S. Public*, pg. 1286
Germeroth, Gary M., Controller & Treas.--QST Enterprises Inc., Peoria, IL; *U.S. Public*, pg. 367
Germeroth, Gary M., Controller & Treas.--QST Communications, Inc., Peoria, IL; *U.S. Public*, pg. 367
Germeroth, Gary M., Controller--QST Energy, Inc., Peoria, IL; *U.S. Public*, pg. 367
Gersen, Rowland C., Sr. V.P. & Controller--QVC, Inc., West Chester, PA; *U.S. Private*, pg. 897
Gerst, Bonnie, Controller--National Travelers Life Co., West Des Moines, IA; *U.S. Private*, pg. 787
Gerstein, Mitchell, V.P., Controller & Treas.--Krantor Corporation, Syosset, NY; *U.S. Public*, pg. 966
Gerstman, Henry, Controller, Treas. & Sec.--Century Business Credit Corporation, New York, NY; *U.S. Private*, pg. 225
Geswein, Barry, Controller--Caldwell Tanks, Inc., Louisville, KY; *U.S. Private*, pg. 200
Geswein, G.T., Controller--The Mead Corporation, Dayton, OH; *U.S. Public*, pg. 1074
Gettings, Thomas L., V.P. & Controller--The Quaker Oats Company, Chicago, IL; *U.S. Public*, pg. 1347
Getty, William, Controller--Michael's Development Company, Marlton, NJ; *U.S. Private*, pg. 740
Geveda, Chester J., Jr., V.P. & Controller--The Dun & Bradstreet Corporation, Murray Hill, NJ; *U.S. Public*, pg. 535
Gewolp, Joe, Controller--Jaco Electronics, Inc., Hauppauge, NY; *U.S. Public*, pg. 920
Geyer, Troy, Controller, Treas. & Sec.--Antenna Products Corp., Mineral Wells, TX; *U.S. Public*, pg. 289
Ghegan, William S., V.P., Controller & Chief Acctg. Officer--Turner Broadcasting System Inc., Atlanta, GA; *U.S. Public*, pg. 1614
Giahpiero, Demaria, Controller--Marcegaglia SpA, Mantova, Italy; *Int'l*, pg. 841
Giannelli, Katy, V.P. & Controller--Williams Scotsman, Inc., Baltimore, MD; *U.S. Private*, pg. 976
Gibbins, Rob, Controller--A.P. Wyott, Dallas, TX; *U.S. Private*, pg. 1193
Gibbs, Jason A., Treas. & Controller--Pulaski Furniture Corporation, Pulaski, VA; *U.S. Public*, pg. 1342
Gibbs, Kim, Asst. Controller--National Western Life Insurance Company, Austin, TX; *U.S. Public*, pg. 1161
Gibbs, Nelson F., V.P. & Controller--Northrop Grumman Corporation, Los Angeles, CA; *U.S. Public*, pg. 1197
Giblin, John, Sr. V.P. & Controller--Crawford & Company, Atlanta, GA; *U.S. Public*, pg. 458
Giblin, M., Controller--Mediterranean Standard Oil Co., Saint Georges, Bermuda; *U.S. Public*, pg. 602
Gibson, Jack, Controller--American Foundry Group, Inc., Bixby, OK; *U.S. Private*, pg. 54
Gibson, Robert V., V.P.-Fin.& Treas.--Datron Incorporated, Windsor, CT; *U.S. Private*, pg. 313
Giddings, Kathleen A., Controller--Flowserve Corporation, Dayton, OH; *U.S. Public*, pg. 658
Giebel, Terry, Controller--Erickson's Diversified Corp., Hudson, WI; *U.S. Private*, pg. 381
Gieger, Josephine, Controller--Petrie Retail, Inc., Secaucus, NJ; *U.S. Private*, pg. 858
Gielish, Gary, Asst. Controller--Western Waste Industries, Torrance, CA; *U.S. Public*, pg. 1686
Gienapp, Dave, Chief Fin. Officer & Controller--Nematron Corp., Ann Arbor, MI; *U.S. Private*, pg. 791
Gieseker, Bill, V.P. & Controller--Greyhound Lines, Inc., Dallas, TX; *U.S. Public*, pg. 765
Giff, Dennis, Controller--Salem National Corporation, Winston Salem, NC; *U.S. Private*, pg. 962
Gigaute, Marie, Controller & Acct. Coord.--National Football League Properties, Inc., New York, NY; *U.S. Private*, pg. 783
Gilbert, Mary V., V.P. & Controller--CRSS Inc., Houston, TX; *Int'l*, pg. 1415
Gilbertson, Phil, Controller--Auto Glass Specialists, Madison, WI; *U.S. Private*, pg. 100
Gilday, Thomas D., Controller--Helix Technology Corp., Mansfield, MA; *U.S. Public*, pg. 808
Gildea, Hugh, Controller--F & W Publications, Inc., Cincinnati, OH; *U.S. Private*, pg. 388
Giles, Cheryl, Controller--Toresco Enterprises, Springfield, NJ; *U.S. Private*, pg. 1092
Giles, Jeanne, Controller--Koo Koo Roo, Inc., Los Angeles, CA; *U.S. Public*, pg. 966
Giles, Mike, Controller--Bush Hog Division, Selma, AL; *U.S. Public*, pg. 48
Gill, Paul, Dir.-Fin. & Controller--Brooke Industrial Holdings Plc, Sheffield, United Kingdom; *Int'l*, pg. 228
Gillaspey, Paul W., Controller--Newell Window Furnishings Co., Freeport, IL; *U.S. Public*, pg. 1177
Gillen, Mike, Controller--IGA, Inc. (Independent Grocers Alliance), Chicago, IL; *U.S. Private*, pg. 555
Gillen, Paul, Controller--L3 Communications Telemetry & Instrumentation Div., San Diego, CA; *U.S. Private*, pg. 639
Gilliam, Rick, Controller--Kusters Corporation, Spartanburg, SC; *U.S. Private*, pg. 637
Gilligan, Jim, Controller--Warren Electric Group, Houston, TX; *U.S. Private*, pg. 1151
Gilliland, Dale, Controller & Treas.--Buccaneer Homes, Inc., Hamilton, AL; *U.S. Public*, pg. 318
Gillingham, Peter, Controller--Total Petroleum Canada Ltd., Calgary, Canada; *Int'l*, pg. 1409
Gillis, Ron B., Controller-ConAgra Specialty Grain Products Company--ConAgra Fruen Milling Co., Omaha, NE; *U.S. Public*, pg. 428
Gilman, Thomas F., V.P. & Controller--Chrysler Financial Corporation, Southfield, MI; *U.S. Public*, pg. 354
Gilmore, Bruce W., V.P., Controller & Sec.--Marquette Bancshares Inc., Minneapolis, MN; *U.S. Private*, pg. 706
Gilmore, Lou Anne, V.P. & Controller--CSC Financial Services Group, Austin, TX; *U.S. Public*, pg. 422
Gilreath, Thomas, Controller--Texfi Blends Division, Rocky Mount, NC; *U.S. Public*, pg. 1588
Gilreath, Thomas M., Corp. Controller & Asst. Sec.--Texfi Industries, Inc., Raleigh, NC; *U.S. Public*, pg. 1588
Gimberline, Jackie, Controller & Treas.--MidAmerican Capital Company, Des Moines, IA; *U.S. Public*, pg. 1109
Gin, Calvin, Controller--Flying Food Fare, Inc., Chicago, IL; *U.S. Private*, pg. 415
Gingras, Alain, Corp. Controller--Aliments Flamingo, Iberville, Canada; *Int'l*, pg. 57

Ginnetti, Dan, Controller--Ryan Herco Products Corp., Burbank, CA; *U.S. Private*, pg. 953
Ginsburg, Ned, Controller--Michael Business Machines Corporation, Charleston, SC; *U.S. Private*, pg. 740
Gioe, Ferrel, Controller--Evans Industries, Inc., Harvey, LA; *U.S. Private*, pg. 385
Giordani, John E., Chief Fin. Officer, Exec. V.P. & Controller--ICN Pharmaceuticals, Inc., Costa Mesa, CA; *U.S. Public*, pg. 853
Giorgio, Michael R., Chief Fin. Officer, Controller & Treas.--Suarez Corporation Industries, Canton, OH; *U.S. Private*, pg. 1048
Giraffa, Pietro, Chief Fin. Officer & Controller--Hanover Foods Corporation, Hanover, PA; *U.S. Private*, pg. 499
Giroux, Dennis, Controller & Treas.--Schwarz Paper Company, Morton Grove, IL; *U.S. Private*, pg. 974
Gispanski, Thomas J., V.P.-Controller--Brinker International, Inc., Dallas, TX; *U.S. Public*, pg. 253
Giustino, Robert, Corp. Controller--Allied Digital Technologies, Hauppauge, NY; *U.S. Public*, pg. 48
Gividen, Tom, Controller--Cardinal Aluminum Co., Louisville, KY; *U.S. Private*, pg. 208
Givler, Robert C., Controller & Asst. Sec.--Ward Trucking Corp., Altoona, PA; *U.S. Private*, pg. 1149
Gladu, Richard E., Controller--The Evening Call Publishing Co.-The Call, Woonsocket, RI; *U.S. Public*, pg. 934
Glascock, Janet L., Controller--George W. Auch Co., Pontiac, MI; *U.S. Private*, pg. 98
Glass, Dennis R., Chief Fin. Officer, Sr. V.P. & Treas.--Jefferson-Pilot Corporation, Greensboro, NC; *U.S. Public*, pg. 925
Glass, William J., Controller--Quebecor Printing (USA) Corp., Greenwich, CT; *Int'l*, pg. 1078
Glasser, J.M., Reg. Fin. Controller & Dir.--New Zealand Milk Products (North Asia) Ltd, Tokyo, Japan; *Int'l*, pg. 923
Glassgow, Perry, Controller--Eaglemark Financial Services, Inc., Chicago, IL; *U.S. Public*, pg. 786
Glazier, John J., Jr., Controller--Pre Finish Metals Incorporated, Elk Grove Village, IL; *U.S. Public*, pg. 1056
Gleason, E.M., Controller, Corp. Treas. & Sec.--Wisconsin Power & Light Company, Madison, WI; *U.S. Public*, pg. 1728
Gledhill, Katherine, Grp. Controller--Commodity Information Services Group, New York, NY; *U.S. Public*, pg. 1071
Glenn, Curt F., V.P., Controller & Principal Acctg. Officer--GATX Capital Corporation, San Francisco, CA; *U.S. Public*, pg. 690
Glogger, Sabine, Controller--Baldwin-Grafotec GmbH, Augsburg, Germany; *U.S. Public*, pg. 170
Glorioso, Joseph A., V.P. & Controller--Walsh Construction Company, Trumbull, CT; *U.S. Public*, pg. 143
Glorit, Bill, Controller--Slim-Fast Foods Company, West Palm Beach, FL; *U.S. Private*, pg. 1006
Glover, James T., V.P. & Controller--Beckman Instruments, Inc., Fullerton, CA; *U.S. Public*, pg. 199
Glover, M., Controller--Interphase Corporation, Dallas, TX; *U.S. Public*, pg. 908
Glover, Thomas W., III, Controller--Golden Flake Snack Foods, Inc., Birmingham, AL; *U.S. Public*, pg. 750
Glover, Timothy, Controller--Olin Microelectronic Materials, Inc., Norwalk, CT; *U.S. Public*, pg. 1219
Glovna, Ginger, Controller--American Frozen Foods, Inc., Stratford, CT; *U.S. Private*, pg. 55
Gluck, Robert J., V.P. & Controller--Sunbeam Corporation, Delray Beach, FL; *U.S. Public*, pg. 1533
Gluck, Robert S., V.P. & Treas.--Bestfoods, Englewood Cliffs, NJ; *U.S. Public*, pg. 223
Glynn, Brian, Controller--Wagner Casters and Wheels, Hustisford, WI; *U.S. Private*, pg. 1146
Gobeil, Claude, Controller--Imprimerie Quebecor L'Eclaireur, Beauceville, Canada; *Int'l*, pg. 1077
Gobeil, Claude, Controller--Imprimerie Quebecor St-Romuald, Saint-Romvald, Canada; *Int'l*, pg. 1077
Gochanour, Rick, Controller--WinCup, Phoenix, AZ; *U.S. Private*, pg. 1182
Goddard, Simon, Grp. Controller--Derby International Corporation S.A., Luxembourg, Luxembourg; *Int'l*, pg. 394
Godfrey, Robert, Treas. & Sec.--Central States Enterprises, Inc., Heathrow, FL; *U.S. Private*, pg. 225
Godier, Ron, Controller--Nixdorff Krein Industries Inc., Saint Louis, MO; *U.S. Private*, pg. 799
Godin, Gary, Chief Acctg. Officer & Controller--Media 100, Inc., Marlborough, MA; *U.S. Public*, pg. 1079
Godin, Robert, Controller--Yorktowne, Inc., Red Lion, PA; *U.S. Private*, pg. 1196
Godlove, John, Controller--Ivex Packaging Corporation-Grove City, Grove City, PA; *U.S. Public*, pg. 915
Godwin, Carter, Controller--Ross Technology, Inc., Austin, TX; *Int'l*, pg. 526
Goens, Donald V., V.P.-Fin. & Controller--Ameritech, Chicago, IL; *U.S. Public*, pg. 97
Goergen, Gregory N., Controller--Farmers Union Co-Operative Insurance Company of Nebraska, Omaha, NE; *U.S. Private*, pg. 395
Goesvch, James A., Controller--Aero Systems Aviation Corp., Miami, FL; *U.S. Private*, pg. 24
Goetz, Pamela, Controller--Robinson Helicopter Company, Torrance, CA; *U.S. Private*, pg. 936
Goggin, Daniel B., V.P. & Controller--Boston Mutual Life Insurance Co., Canton, MA; *U.S. Private*, pg. 161
Gogol, Sharon E., Asst. Controller--Grotech Capital Group, Inc., Timonium, MD; *U.S. Private*, pg. 483
Gohdes, Sherry M., Controller--Rocco Inc., Harrisonburg, VA; *U.S. Private*, pg. 937
Gold, Marc, Controller--Swiss Army Brands, Inc., Shelton, CT; *U.S. Public*, pg. 1544
Goldberg, Frank, Controller & Dir.-Human Resources--Electro-Science Laboratories, Inc., King of Prussia, PA; *U.S. Private*, pg. 369
Goldberg, Jon A., V.P. & Controller--Charming Shoppes, Inc., Bensalem, PA; *U.S. Public*, pg. 335
Goldberg, Neil, Chief Fin. Officer & Controller--Harcrest International, Ltd., Clark, NJ; *U.S. Private*, pg. 500
Goldberg, Sanford D., Controller--Celestial Seasonings, Boulder, CO; *U.S. Public*, pg. 319
Golden, Dawn, Controller--The Kay Company, Inc., Frankfort, IN; *U.S. Private*, pg. 610
Golden, Kerri, V.P. & Comptroller--BCE Mobile Communications Inc., Saint-Laurent, Canada; *Int'l*, pg. 115
Goldenberg, Scott, V.P. & Controller--The TJX Companies, Inc., Framingham, MA; *U.S. Public*, pg. 1556
Goldsmith, I.J., Controller--Senior TIFT Australia Pty Limited, Rockdale, Australia; *Int'l*, pg. 1223
Goldsmith, Kathleen, Controller--Gestetner Corporation, Greenwich, CT; *Int'l*, pg. 1115
Goldsmith, Lee, Asst. Sec. & Controller--Familian Corp., Van Nuys, CA; *Int'l*, pg. 1512
Goldstein, Alan, Controller--Benderson Development Co., Inc., Buffalo, NY; *U.S. Private*, pg. 132
Goldstein, Cliff, Controller--The Sherwood Group, Inc., Jersey City, NJ; *U.S. Public*, pg. 1466
Goldstein, Fred, Controller--Bentex Kiddie Corporation, New York, NY; *U.S. Private*, pg. 134
Goldstein, Stuart J., Asst. Controller--Cognizant Corporation, Westport, CT; *U.S. Public*, pg. 395
Golesh, John, Controller--Monroc, Inc., Salt Lake City, UT; *U.S. Public*, pg. 1124
Gollon, J., Controller--Schlegel Corporation, Rochester, NY; *Int'l*, pg. 128
Golonka, Richard, Controller--Snap-Tite, Inc., Erie, PA; *U.S. Private*, pg. 1010
Gomer, Howard, Controller--Associated Electric Co-op Inc., Springfield, MO; *U.S. Private*, pg. 89
Gomez, C.P. Veronica, Controller--Tablex, S.A. de C.V., Toluca, Mexico; *Int'l*, pg. 1346
Gomez, F. Gregory, Controller--Spontex, Inc., Columbia, TN; *Int'l*, pg. 1409
Gomez, Julie, Controller--Regional Transportation Authority (RTA), Chicago, IL; *U.S. Private*, pg. 918
Gonopolsky, Allan, Chief Fin. Officer, V.P., Controller & Asst. Sec.--Rexel, Inc., Coral Gables, FL; *Int'l*, pg. 1107
Gonzales, Angelo, V.P.-Acctg. & Controller--Cacique, Inc., City of Industry, CA; *U.S. Private*, pg. 198
Gonzalez, April, Controller--RNF Media Corporation Inc., Beverly Hills, CA; *U.S. Private*, pg. 905
Gonzalez, Gabriella, Controller--Alyeska Pipeline Service Company, Anchorage, AK; *U.S. Private*, pg. 47
Gonzalez, J.E., Controller--Esso Trading Company of Abu Dhabi, Saint Georges, Bermuda; *U.S. Public*, pg. 602
Goode, Pam, Controller--Refrigiwear, Inc., Dahlonega, GA; *U.S. Private*, pg. 917
Goodling, Gregory W., Controller--Fenner Drives, Manheim, PA; *U.S. Private*, pg. 400
Goodman, Alan H., Asst. Controller--Future Foam, Inc., Council Bluffs, IA; *U.S. Private*, pg. 433
Goodman, Pat J., V.P. & Controller--CalEnergy Co., Omaha, NE; *U.S. Public*, pg. 292
Goodnight, David L., Controller--Lexmark International Group, Inc., Lexington, KY; *U.S. Public*, pg. 991
Goodnight, David L., Controller--Lexmark International, Inc., Lexington, KY; *U.S. Public*, pg. 991
Goodrich, Marc, Chief Info. Officer & Controller--Banfi Vintners, Old Brookville, NY; *U.S. Private*, pg. 113
Goodspeed, Dan, Controller--M.S. Carriers, Inc., Memphis, TN; *U.S. Public*, pg. 1027
Goodwin, Bradford S., V.P. & Controller--Genentech, Inc., South San Francisco, CA; *Int'l*, pg. 1120
Goodwin, William J., Controller--Trinity Industries Inc., Dallas, TX; *U.S. Public*, pg. 1638
Goold, David, Chief Fin. Officer Controller--AIM Safety Company Inc., Delta, Canada; *Int'l*, pg. 36
Goolsby, Ross, Controller--Cameron Ashley Building Products, Inc, Dallas, TX; *U.S. Public*, pg. 298
Gordon, Ann, Corp. Controller--Gandalf Technologies Inc., Nepean, Canada; *Int'l*, pg. 540
Gordon, Beth G., Controller--Pool Energy Services Co., Houston, TX; *U.S. Public*, pg. 1316
Gordon, John, Controller--Applause Inc., Woodland Hills, CA; *U.S. Private*, pg. 78
Gordon, Kent, Controller--Associated Food Stores Inc., Salt Lake City, UT; *U.S. Private*, pg. 90
Gordon, Richard, Sec., Treas. & Controller--Vital Signs, Inc., Totowa, NJ; *U.S. Public*, pg. 1723
Gordon, Susan C., Chief Acctg. Officer, V.P. & Controller--Viacom Inc., New York, NY; *U.S. Private*, pg. 775
Gordon, Walter, Controller--Mac Papers, Inc., Jacksonville, FL; *U.S. Private*, pg. 689
Gordon, William, Controller--Cottman Transmission Systems, Inc., Fort Washington, PA; *U.S. Private*, pg. 278
Gorman, Barb, Controller--Ford Development Corporation, Cincinnati, OH; *U.S. Private*, pg. 418
Gorman, David J., V.P. & Controller--NFO Research, Inc., Greenwich, CT; *U.S. Public*, pg. 1146
Gorman, Mark, Controller--Ed Mullinax Ford, Inc., Amherst, OH; *U.S. Public*, pg. 1379
Gormley, Charles, Controller & Treas.--Philadelphia Reserve Supply Company, Croydon, PA; *U.S. Private*, pg. 861
Gorzkowski, Thomas W., Asst. Controller--Terex Corporation, Westport, CT; *U.S. Public*, pg. 1581
Goshien, Gerald, Controller & Treas.-Sls. For Meats & Produce--The Mad Butcher, Inc., Pine Bluff, AR; *U.S. Private*, pg. 693
Gotsis, Cheryl, Controller--Amick Construction Ltd., Orlando, FL; *U.S. Private*, pg. 66
Gottfried, P. Gene, V.P. & Reg. Controller--FirstMerit Corporation, Akron, OH; *U.S. Public*, pg. 646
Gougenheim, Jacques-Henri, Controller--Compagnie UAP, Paris, France; *Int'l*, pg. 323
Gough, Russell, Asst. Controller--Savin Corporation, Stamford, CT; *Int'l*, pg. 1114
Gould, Blair, Controller--Royal Caribbean Cruises Ltd., Miami, FL; *U.S. Public*, pg. 1410
Gould, Brian, Controller--Interkal, Inc., Kalamazoo, MI; *Int'l*, pg. 759
Gould, Evan, Controller--Wenner Media, New York, NY; *U.S. Private*, pg. 1162
Gould, Evan, Controller--Rolling Stone Magazine, New York, NY; *U.S. Private*, pg. 1162
Gould, Evan, Controller--Us Magazine, New York, NY; *U.S. Private*, pg. 1162
Gould, Gregory A., Controller--Colorado MEDtech, Inc., Boulder, CO; *U.S. Public*, pg. 401
Gould, Pat, Controller--EPX, Portland, ME; *U.S. Private*, pg. 354
Gourley, William, Controller--Blue Bird Corporation, Macon, GA; *U.S. Private*, pg. 151
Gowdy, Kathy, V.P. & Controller--Valentine Radford, Inc., Kansas City, MO; *U.S. Private*, pg. 1131
Gowey, David, Controller & Treas.--Pacific Trail Inc., Seattle, WA; *U.S. Private*, pg. 673
Goyne, Roger E., Controller--Western Atlas International, Inc., Houston, TX; *U.S. Public*, pg. 1757
Grace, P.W., V.P. & Controller--Mafco Worldwide Corp., Camden, NJ; *U.S. Private*, pg. 690
Graczyk, Darlene, Controller--Osmose Wood Preserving, Inc., Buffalo, NY; *U.S. Private*, pg. 821
Grady, Edward J., V.P., Controller & Asst. Treas.--Shared Medical Systems Corporation, Malvern, PA; *U.S. Public*, pg. 1463
Graf, Michael A., Sr. V.P. & Controller--Norwest Corporation, Minneapolis, MN; *U.S. Public*, pg. 1201
Graf, Michael A., Controller & Cashier--Norwest Bank Minnesota N.A., Minneapolis, MN; *U.S. Public*, pg. 1202
Grafe, Jens, Controller--Sauer Sundstrand Gmbh & Co., Neumunster, Germany; *Int'l*, pg. 1198
Graff, Scott, Controller--S & S Graphics, Inc., Laurel, MD; *U.S. Private*, pg. 955
Grafstrom, Sune, Controller--MoDo Merchants AB, Stockholm, Sweden; *Int'l*, pg. 886
Graham, Brian, Controller--Michael J. Mungo Company, Inc., Irmo, SC; *U.S. Private*, pg. 767
Graham, James, Controller--Brodart Company, Williamsport, PA; *U.S. Private*, pg. 170
Graham, Jerry F., V.P. & Controller--Mercantile Bankshares Corporation, Baltimore, MD; *U.S. Public*, pg. 1088
Graham, Kurt, Controller--Fletcher Cobre Tire Co. Inc., Phoenix, AZ; *U.S. Private*, pg. 411
Graham, Rob-Roy, Chief Fin. Officer , Sec. & Controller--InterVoice, Inc., Dallas, TX; *U.S. Public*, pg. 910
Graham, Robert J., Controller--Hynautic, Sarasota, FL; *U.S. Public*, pg. 857
Gramkee, James, Controller--Mark IV Industries Inc., Amherst, NY; *U.S. Public*, pg. 1044
Grammer, Jennifer, Controller--S.I. Goldman Co., Longwood, FL; *U.S. Private*, pg. 461
Grammer, Rob, Controller--Lakin General Corporation, Chicago, IL; *U.S. Private*, pg. 644
Granberry, Noland, Controller--IKOS Systems, Inc., Cupertino, CA; *U.S. Public*, pg. 864
Granbois, Sharon, Controller--A & S Tribal Industries, Poplar, MT; *U.S. Private*, pg. 1
Grand, Gary, Controller--Telxon Corporation, Akron, OH; *U.S. Public*, pg. 1573
Graner, James A., V.P. & Controller--Graco Inc., Golden Valley, MN; *U.S. Public*, pg. 756
Granger, Robert, V.P.-Controller--Pitco Frialator Inc., Bow, NH; *U.S. Public*, pg. 1065
Granholm, Robert, Controller--KONE Sowitsch AG, Vienna, Austria; *Int'l*, pg. 748
Granneman, Tom, Controller--Ralcorp Holdings Inc., Saint Louis, MO; *U.S. Public*, pg. 1359
Gransie, David, Controller--Eon Labs Manufacturing, Inc., Laurelton, NY; *U.S. Private*, pg. 379
Grant, Edward, Chief Fin. Officer, V.P. & Controller--Zoeller Co., Louisville, KY; *U.S. Private*, pg. 1207
Grant, Nan A., Controller--PHH Corporation, Hunt Valley, MD; *U.S. Public*, pg. 321
Grant, Nathan, Controller--King Cotton Foods, Memphis, TN; *U.S. Public*, pg. 1433
Granzberg, Kathleen L., Controller-Corp.--Capital Senior Living, Inc., Dallas, TX; *U.S. Public*, pg. 302
Grashvis, John, Controller--Eaton Corporation, U.S. Engine Valve Corporation, Westminster, SC; *U.S. Public*, pg. 557
Grassi, Ciro A., V.P. & Controller--ITT Federal Services Corporation, Colorado Springs, CO; *U.S. Public*, pg. 859
Gratton, D., Fin. Controller--Compass Group plc, Chertsey, United Kingdom,; *Int'l*, pg. 324
Grauman, Jerry, Controller--Eaton Corporation, Hydraulics Division, Eden Prairie, MN; *U.S. Public*, pg. 557
Graupensperger, Brian, Controller--Glenn O. Hawbaker, Inc., State College, PA; *U.S. Private*, pg. 511
Graupman, Mark, Controller--Foremost Farms USA Cooperative, Baraboo, WI; *U.S. Private*, pg. 418
Gravel, Jean, Controller Sico Inc., Longueuil, Canada; *Int'l*, pg. 1239
Gravin, Linda B., Controller--Wasco Products, Inc., Sanford, ME; *U.S. Private*, pg. 1152
Gravina, Jean, Controller--Banque Cantonale Vaudoise, Lausanne, Switzerland; *Int'l*, pg. 160
Gray, Donald M., V.P. & Controller--MSI Insurance Companies, Arden Hills, MN; *U.S. Private*, pg. 688
Gray, Jacob T., V.P. & Controller--Clear Channel Communications, Inc., San Antonio, TX; *U.S. Public*, pg. 383
Gray, John, Controller & Asst. Sec.-Treas.--Sugar Cane Growers Cooperative of Florida, Belle Glade, FL; *U.S. Private*, pg. 1049
Gray, Kay, Controller--Citrus World Inc., Lake Wales, FL; *U.S. Private*, pg. 241
Gray, Timothy M., Comptroller--Ryan Construction Company Of Minnesota, Hibbing, MN; *U.S. Private*, pg. 953
Grecco, Mike, Controller--Kingsley Machine Co., Downers Grove, IL; *U.S. Public*, pg. 866
Grecco, Samuel G., V.P., Controller & Treas.--Remington Arms Company, Inc., Madison, NC; *U.S. Private*, pg. 921
Green, Andrew F., V.P.-Corp. Plng. & Controller--Advantica Restaurant Group, Inc., Spartanburg, SC; *U.S. Public*, pg. 22

Green, Charles, Controller--Powers Construction Co., Inc., Florence, SC; *U.S. Private*, pg. 878
Green, Derek, Controller--United Utilities plc, Warrington, United Kingdom; *Int'l*, pg. 1444
Green, Gene, Controller--Rotary Lift, Madison, IN; *U.S. Public*, pg. 521
Green, Sharon, Controller--Memphis Group, Inc., Memphis, TN; *U.S. Private*, pg. 730
Green, Steven R., V.P. & Controller--Franklin Covey, Salt Lake City, UT; *U.S. Public*, pg. 679
Green, Sue, Asst. Controller--DAQ Electronics Inc., Piscataway, NJ; *U.S. Private*, pg. 300
Green, Willis, Controller--All Star Gas Corporation, Lebanon, MO; *U.S. Private*, pg. 35
Greenberg, Dave, Controller--ATC Healthcare Services Inc., Atlanta, GA; *U.S. Private*, pg. 8
Greenberg, Martin, V.P. & Controller--Tuboscope Incorporated, Houston, TX; *U.S. Public*, pg. 1643
Greene, Michael, Controller & Dir.-Fin.--Alex Lee, Inc., Hickory, NC; *U.S. Private*, pg. 657
Greenia, Joel, Controller--Storage Dimensions, Inc., Milpitas, CA; *U.S. Public*, pg. 1522
Greenlee, Daniel D., Sr. V.P. & Controller--D & N Financial Corporation, Hancock, MI; *U.S. Public*, pg. 472
Greenlee, Daniel D., Sr. V.P. & Controller--D & N Bank, Hancock, MI; *U.S. Public*, pg. 472
Greenler, Paul J., Controller--UFP Technology, Georgetown, MA; *U.S. Private*, pg. 1112
Greenman, Bob, Controller--ABC Rail Cogifer Industries, Cincinnati, OH; *U.S. Public*, pg. 2
Greenman, Bob, Controller--Cogifer SA, Croissy-sur-Seine, France; *Int'l*, pg. 386
Greenthal, Richard S., V.P. & Controller--M. Block & Sons, Inc., Chicago, IL; *U.S. Private*, pg. 150
Greenwood, D.A., Controller--Koch Supplies Inc., Kansas City, MO; *U.S. Private*, pg. 628
Greer, Murray H., Controller--Century Telephone Enterprises, Inc., Monroe, LA; *U.S. Public*, pg. 329
Gregg, Michael W., Sr. V.P.-Acctg. & Controller--Illinois Tool Works Inc., Glenview, IL; *U.S. Public*, pg. 865
Gregg, Sherry, Controller--Manna Pro Partner L.P. (Limited Partnership), Denver, CO; *U.S. Private*, pg. 700
Gregorich, Simon, Controller--Discount Auto Parts, Inc., Lakeland, FL; *U.S. Public*, pg. 510
Gregory, Bob, Controller--Powell Industries, Inc., Houston, TX; *U.S. Public*, pg. 1319
Gregory, David J., Controller--The R.J. Marshall Co., Southfield, MI; *U.S. Private*, pg. 708
Greisiger, W., Controller--DeVilbiss Automotive Refinishing Products, Maumee, OH; *U.S. Public*, pg. 865
Grene, Alan, Controller--Coast Packing Company, Vernon, CA; *U.S. Private*, pg. 248
Gress, Ken, Controller--Dempster Industries Inc., Beatrice, NE; *U.S. Private*, pg. 324
Grex, Debbie, Controller--American Antenna Corp, Elgin, IL; *U.S. Private*, pg. 207
Greyling, A.C., Gen. Mgr.-Legal & Admin. Services--Iscor, Pretoria, South Africa; *Int'l*, pg. 688
Grier, Lester, Controller & Asst. Treas.--Welsh Farms, Inc., Long Valley, NJ; *U.S. Private*, pg. 1162
Grietzer, Roland, Controller & Treas.--Alcom Printing Group, Inc., Bethlehem, PA; *U.S. Private*, pg. 33
Griffin, Brian R., Comptroller & Dir.-Fin.--Isuzu-General Motors Australia Ltd., Melbourne, Australia; *Int'l*, pg. 693
Griffin, Brian R., Comptroller & Dir.-Fin.--Isuzu-General Motors Australia Ltd., Melbourne, Australia; *U.S. Public*, pg. 725
Griffin, Clifford E., Jr., Controller--The Copley Press, Inc., La Jolla, CA; *U.S. Private*, pg. 275
Griffin, Jesse O., Sr. V.P. & Controller--United Companies Financial Corporation, Baton Rouge, LA; *U.S. Public*, pg. 1675
Griffin, John, Controller--Autologic Information International, Inc., Thousand Oaks, CA; *U.S. Public*, pg. 1724
Griffin, LaDeane, Chief Fin. Officer, Treas. Controller & Sec.--Jenkins & Associates, Shawnee Mission, KS; *U.S. Private*, pg. 585
Griffin, Michael, Controller--Gayfers, Montgomery, AL; *U.S. Public*, pg. 1090
Griffin, Peter J., V.P. & Controller--Carter-Wallace, Inc., New York, NY; *U.S. Public*, pg. 309
Griffin, Robert J., Controller--Green Mountain Power Corporation, South Burlington, VT; *U.S. Public*, pg. 761
Griffin, Thomas A., Treas. & Controller--Pope Resources, Poulsbo, WA; *U.S. Public*, pg. 1317
Griffin, William L., V.P. & Controller--TECO Energy, Inc., Tampa, FL; *U.S. Public*, pg. 1565
Griffin, William L., V.P. & Controller--Tampa Electric Co., Tampa, FL; *U.S. Public*, pg. 1565
Griffith, Fred, V.P. & Controller--Ceramic Cooling Tower Co., Fort Worth, TX; *U.S. Private*, pg. 68
Griffith, Nelson, Controller--WestPoint Stevens Inc., West Point, GA; *U.S. Public*, pg. 1762
Griggs, John, V.P. & Controller--Thomas & Betts Electronics Division, Memphis, TN; *U.S. Public*, pg. 1597
Griggs, Stacie, Asst. Controller--Econocom-USA Inc., Memphis, TN; *U.S. Private*, pg. 361
Grigsby, Donald, Controller--Crown Vantage Inc., Oakland, CA; *U.S. Public*, pg. 465
Grimes, James A., Controller & Sec.--Sanderson Farms, Inc., Laurel, MS; *U.S. Public*, pg. 1430
Grimwood, Charlotte, Controller--Linn Products, Inc., Charlotte, MI; *U.S. Private*, pg. 669
Grise, Debbie, Controller--Del American Properties, Inc., Maitland, FL; *U.S. Private*, pg. 321
Grisette, Al, Controller--Franklin Baking Co., Inc., Goldsboro, NC; *U.S. Private*, pg. 424
Grisetti, Mike, V.P. & Controller--Nationwide Homes, Inc., Martinsville, VA; *U.S. Private*, pg. 788
Grissom, Lee, V.P. & Controller--Lowe McAdams Healthcare, New York, NY; *U.S. Private*, pg. 678
Grobb, Tony, Controller--Santee Print Works, Inc., New York, NY; *U.S. Private*, pg. 965
Groble, Tom, V.P.-Fin. & Controller--Nordco, Inc., Milwaukee, WI; *U.S. Public*, pg. 1209
Grocholski, Jack, Controller--Norcostco, Inc., Minneapolis, MN; *U.S. Private*, pg. 801
Groeneveld, Jim, Controller--Media Incorporated, New York, NY; *U.S. Private*, pg. 726
Groeneveld, Jim, Comptroller--Media Direct Partners, Incorporated, New York, NY; *U.S. Private*, pg. 726
Groff, Michael, Asst. Controller--Dairy Mart Convenience Stores, Inc., Cuyahoga Falls, OH; *U.S. Public*, pg. 476
Grogan, Dennis, Controller--Eastern Air Devices, Inc., Dover, NH; *U.S. Private*, pg. 357
Grom, Charles P., V.P. & Controller--C.R. Bard, Inc., Murray Hill, NJ; *U.S. Public*, pg. 189
Groneman, Joseph L., V.P. & Controller--Stinnes Corporation, Tarrytown, NY; *Int'l*, pg. 1460
Groos, D. Michael, Comptroller--St. Joe Corp., Jacksonville, FL; *U.S. Public*, pg. 1426
Grose, Brian C., V.P., Controller & Sec.--Hudson's Bay Company, Toronto, Canada; *Int'l*, pg. 637
Groski, Donald, Asst. Controller--Kelly, Scott And Madison, Inc., Chicago, IL; *U.S. Private*, pg. 613
Gross, Gerald E., Comptroller--General Motors Acceptance Corporation (GMAC), Detroit, MI; *U.S. Public*, pg. 719
Gross, Gerald E., Comptroller--GMAC Mortgage Corporation, Horsham, PA; *U.S. Public*, pg. 720
Gross, Loren D., V.P. & Controller--Ceridian Corporation, Bloomington, MN; *U.S. Public*, pg. 330
Gross, Matthew, Comptroller--John Gross & Co., Baltimore, MD; *U.S. Private*, pg. 483
Gross, Paul, Controller--Bike Athletic Co., Knoxville, TN; *U.S. Private*, pg. 143
Gross, Stephen, Controller--Burns Bros. Inc., Portland, OR; *U.S. Private*, pg. 187
Grossman, Bob, Grp. V.P.-Acctg. & Controller--Ralphs Grocery Company, Compton, CA; *U.S. Private*, pg. 1202
Grossman, Jeffrey W., V.P. & Controller--Columbia Energy Group, Reston, VA; *U.S. Public*, pg. 402
Grossman, Lawrence, Controller--Di Giorgio Corporation, Carteret, NJ; *U.S. Private*, pg. 330
Groszek, James D., Controller--Velsicol Chemical Corporation, Rosemont, IL; *U.S. Private*, pg. 1135
Grounds, Dianne, Controller--Spartan Motors, Inc., Charlotte, MI; *U.S. Public*, pg. 1495
Groves, Alan D., V.P. & Controller--3Com Corporation, Santa Clara, CA; *U.S. Public*, pg. 1603
Grubbe, Philip H., Controller--Unigas, Calgary, Canada; *Int'l*, *pg. 1492*
Grubbs, Mary, Comptroller--Environmental Air Systems, Inc., Greensboro, NC; *U.S. Private*, pg. 378
Gruenhagen, Jon D., Controller--EBP Life Insurnace Co., Minneapolis, MN; *U.S. Public*, pg. 635
Grunebach, Brian, Controller--Pittsburgh Brewing Company, Pittsburgh, PA; *U.S. Private*, pg. 619
Grygorcewicz, Chester, Sr. V.P. & Controller--Marcal Paper Mills, Inc., Elmwood Park, NJ; *U.S. Private*, pg. 701
Grzybowski, Peter, Controller--International Seaway Trading Corporation, Boca Raton, FL; *U.S. Private*, pg. 572
Gschiel, Adolf, Controller--Loctite Deutschland G.m.b.H., Munich, Germany; *Int'l*, pg. 611
Gu, Y.B., Controller--Inkel USA Corporation, La Mirada, CA; *U.S. Private*, pg. 563
Guarino, Wes, Controller--Trimark Holdings, Inc., Santa Monica, CA; *U.S. Public*, pg. 1638
Guarnieri, Donald, Controller--Zing Technologies, Inc., Valhalla, NY; *U.S. Public*, pg. 1792
Guarnieri, John J., V.P. & Corp. Controller--Tyco International Ltd., Exeter, NH; *U.S. Public*, pg. 1647
Gubo, Ulrike, Controller--Piher International GmbH, Eckental, Germany; *Int'l*, pg. 854
Gudolawicz, Mary, Controller--Brady Enterprises, Inc., East Weymouth, MA; *U.S. Private*, pg. 165
Guerin, James L., V.P. & Comptroller--New Hampshire Insurance Group, New York, NY; *U.S. Public*, pg. 84
Gueritey, Harold C., Jr., Controller--Parker Hannifin Corporation, Cleveland, OH; *U.S. Public*, pg. 1259
Guerra, Joe, Controller--Oriel Instruments Corporation, Stratford, CT; *U.S. Private*, pg. 819
Guertz, Wendy, Controller--Bristol Industries, Brea, CA; *U.S. Private*, pg. 169
Guest, Christine M., Treas.--Allens Of Hastings, Inc., Hastings, NE; *U.S. Private*, pg. 37
Guest, J. Rodney, Controller & Treas.--Header Products Inc., Romulus, MI; *U.S. Private*, pg. 514
Guetter, Stephen E., Controller--Rosens Diversified, Inc., Fairmont, MN; *U.S. Private*, pg. 945
Guidry, Liss, Controller--Flexitallic LP, Deer Park, TX; *U.S. Private*, pg. 413
Guilbault, Pierre, Sr. V.P.-Fin. & Comptroller--Steinberg Inc., Montreal, Canada; *Int'l*, pg. 1272
Guilford, Tom, Controller--Rentrak Corporation, Portland, OR; *U.S. Public*, pg. 1377
Guirlinger, Rick, Controller--General Parts, Inc., Raleigh, NC; *U.S. Private*, pg. 445
Gulett, Mike, V.P.-Fin. & Controller--The Acacia Group - Acacia Life Insurance Co., Bethesda, MD; *U.S. Private*, pg. 10
Gulis, Stephen L., Chief Fin. Officer & Exec. V.P.--Wolverine World Wide, Inc., Rockford, MI; *U.S. Public*, pg. 1775
Gulling, Douglas R., Sr. V.P. & Corp. Controller--Brenton Banks, Inc., Des Moines, IA; *U.S. Public*, pg. 251
Gullo, Laura, Controller--Sammons Enterprises, Inc., Dallas, TX; *U.S. Private*, pg. 963
Gumpert, Peter, Controller--Beauchamp Distributing Company, Compton, CA; *U.S. Private*, pg. 127
Gumtow, Nancy, Controller--RS Electronics, Livonia, MI; *U.S. Private*, pg. 905
Gundberg, Dale, Controller--Dakota Electric Association, Farmington, MN; *U.S. Private*, pg. 308
Gustavasson, Bosse, Controller--ICA Handlarnas AB, Solna, Sweden; *Int'l*, pg. 642
Gutchewsky, Judith, V.P. & Controller--Merit Behavioral Care Corp., Park Ridge, NJ; *U.S. Public*, pg. 1036
Guthrie, Marie, Controller--Pinnacle Bank, Jasper, AL; *U.S. Public*, pg. 1297
Guthrie, Matt, Controller--Electro Scientific Industries, Inc., Portland, OR; *U.S. Public*, pg. 568
Guthrie, Peter N., Controller--Red Dog, Kotzebue, AK; *Int'l*, pg. 308
Guthrie, Roy A., Sr. V.P. & Comptroller--Associates Financial Services Corporation, Dallas, TX; *U.S. Public*, pg. 663
Gutman, Dale, V.P. & Controller--The Chas. Levy Company, Chicago, IL; *U.S. Private*, pg. 664
Gutmann, Linda L., Controller--Frank Russell Company, Tacoma, WA; *U.S. Private*, pg. 952
Gutolitz, Arthur, Controller--Hask Toiletries, Great Neck, NY; *U.S. Private*, pg. 509
Gutton, Nicolas, Controller--Societe Francaise des Ascenseurs KONE, Asnieres-sur-Seine, France; *Int'l*, pg. 748
Guy, Barry L., V.P. & Controller--Piedmont Natural Gas Co., Inc., Charlotte, NC; *U.S. Public*, pg. 1295
Guy, R., Controller--TK Gray, Minneapolis, MN; *U.S. Public*, pg. 1329
Haag, Leon, Controller--Seabrook Wallcoverings, Inc., Memphis, TN; *U.S. Private*, pg. 978
Haak, Richard S., Jr., Controller--Wheelabrator Technologies Inc., Hampton, NH; *U.S. Public*, pg. 1745
Haas, David, Exec. V.P. & Treas.--Keen Compressed Gas Co., Wilmington, DE; *U.S. Private*, pg. 611
Haas, David R., V.P. & Controller--Warner Communications Inc., New York, NY; *U.S. Public*, pg. 1611
Haas, Del, V.P. & Controller-Kohler Plumbing North America--Kohler Company, Kohler, WI; *U.S. Private*, pg. 630
Haas, Linda, Controller--TRM Copy Centers Corporation, Portland, OR; *U.S. Public*, pg. 1558
Haas, Mary, Controller--Narrow Fabric Industries, Inc., Reading, PA; *U.S. Private*, pg. 774
Haas, Tony, Controller--BFX Hospitality Group, Inc., Fort Worth, TX; *U.S. Public*, pg. 160
Habing, L., Treas. & Controller--Wavin Bv, Zwolle, Netherlands; *Int'l*, pg. 1135
Habisch, Mark, Controller-ARMD--I.C. System, Inc., Vadnais Heights, MN; *U.S. Private*, pg. 553
Hach, Peter, Dr., Controller--Deutsche Lufthansa AG, Cologne, Germany; *Int'l*, pg. 407
Hackamack, Kent W., V.P.-Fin., Controller & Treas.--Titan International, Inc., Quincy, IL; *U.S. Public*, pg. 1618
Hackney, Reid, Asst. V.P. & Controller--The Dress Barn, Inc., Suffern, NY; *U.S. Public*, pg. 528
Haddan, Laverne, Controller, Treas. & Sec.--Dick Bruhn Incorporated, Salinas, CA; *U.S. Private*, pg. 175
Haddock, Marlene, Comptroller--Beacon Sales Corporation, Jacksonville, FL; *U.S. Private*, pg. 126
Hadley, Jeff, Controller--Correct Craft, Inc., Orlando, FL; *U.S. Private*, pg. 276
Hadsworth, Mary, Controller--Winthrop-Atkins Co., Inc., Middleboro, MA; *U.S. Private*, pg. 1183
Haeberlin, Andreas, Controller--NRG Office Systems GmbH, Hannover, Germany; *Int'l*, pg. 1116
Haentjens, Kate, Controller & Treas.--Hazleton Pumps Inc., Hazleton, PA; *Int'l*, pg. 967
Haesser, Inge, Controller--Berlitz Schools of Languages GmbH, Frankfurt/Main, Germany; *U.S. Public*, pg. 222
Haesser, Inge, Controller--Berlitz Sprachschulen GmbH, Vienna, Austria; *U.S. Public*, pg. 222
Haff, Jim, Controller--SSE Telecom, Inc., Vienna, VA; *U.S. Public*, pg. 1421
Hafner, Thomas C., Controller--Continental/Midland, Inc., Park Forest, IL; *U.S. Private*, pg. 268
Hagar, Gary, Controller--Ivex Packaging Corporation-Visalia, Visalia, CA; *U.S. Public*, pg. 915
Hagedorn, Charles K., Treas. & Controller--Distrigas Corp., Boston, MA; *U.S. Public*, pg. 289
Hagel, Shawn, Controller--Precision Castparts Corp., Portland, OR; *U.S. Public*, pg. 1320
Hagele, Dennis, Controller--The Timberland Company, Stratham, NH; *U.S. Public*, pg. 1609
Hagemann, Maryanne, Controller--Super 8 Motels, Inc., Aberdeen, SD; *U.S. Public*, pg. 322
Hagen, Jerry, Controller--Symbol Technologies, Portable Systems Division, Costa Mesa, CA; *U.S. Public*, pg. 1546
Hager, Tina M., Controller--Specialty Industries, Inc., Red Lion, PA; *U.S. Private*, pg. 1022
Hagerty, Denise M., V.P. & Asst. Controller--ConAgra, Inc., Omaha, NE; *U.S. Public*, pg. 425
Hagopian, Betty, Comptroller--Western Reinsurance Brokers, Inc., Los Angeles, CA; *U.S. Private*, pg. 1168
Hagstrom, Edwin A., Controller--Label Products Div., Omaha, NE; *U.S. Public*, pg. 1152
Hague, Diane, V.P. & Controller--Central Lewmar, Newark, NJ; *U.S. Private*, pg. 223
Hahn, Anthony, Controller--Conestoga Wood Specialties Corp., East Earl, PA; *U.S. Private*, pg. 262
Haidemenos, Gregory, Controller--Westerbeke Corporation, Avon, MA; *U.S. Public*, pg. 1757
Hailemichael, Tesfaye, Controller--Artecon, Inc., Carlsbad, CA; *U.S. Private*, pg. 409
Hain, Larry D., Controller--First Data Corporation, Hackensack, NJ; *U.S. Public*, pg. 630
Haines, A.L., V.P., Controller & Treas.--CHEMCENTRAL Corporation, Bedford Park, IL; *U.S. Private*, pg. 231
Haines, Kathleen C., V.P. & Controller--OMI Corp., New York, NY; *U.S. Public*, pg. 1208
Haines, Kenneth C., Controller--Foremost Corporation of America, Caledonia, MI; *U.S. Public*, pg. 667
Haines, Marlin, Controller--Piezo Crystal Co., Carlisle, PA; *U.S. Private*, pg. 865
Haithcoat, Dale, Controller--ARB Inc., Lake Forest, CA; *U.S. Private*, pg. 7
Haje, Peter R., Exec. V.P., Gen. Counsel & Treas.--Time Warner Inc., New York, NY; *U.S. Public*, pg. 1610
Hakim, Farid, V.P. & Controller--CSI International Corporation, New York, NY; *U.S. Private*, pg. 197

Halas, Germaine, Controller--E.T. Browne Drug Co., Inc., Englewood Cliffs, NJ; *U.S. Private*, pg. 175
Hale, Arlyn K., Controller--Jordan Tamraz Caruso Advertising, Inc., Chicago, IL; *U.S. Private*, pg. 599
Hale, Gordon, Controller & Sec.--Yankee Publishing Incorporated, Dublin, NH; *U.S. Private*, pg. 1195
Halker, Gary P., Chief Information Officer, V.P. & Controller--Church & Dwight Co., Inc., Princeton, NJ; *U.S. Public*, pg. 355
Hall, Almon C., III, Chief Acctg. Officer, V.P. & Controller--Nortek, Inc., Providence, RI; *U.S. Public*, pg. 1192
Hall, C.L., Controller--Amoco Credit Corporation, Chicago, IL; *U.S. Public*, pg. 103
Hall, John T., Controller--Dixie Electric Cooperative, Union Springs, AL; *U.S. Private*, pg. 337
Hall, Matthew J., Controller--J.F. Ahern Co., Fond Du Lac, WI; *U.S. Private*, pg. 27
Hall, R. Wayne, Mng. Dir. & Controller--Provident Bank of Maryland, Baltimore, MD; *U.S. Public*, pg. 1337
Hall, Richard, Controller--Alimed, Inc., Dedham, MA; *U.S. Private*, pg. 34
Hall, Steven, Controller--Cecil Saydah Company, Los Angeles, CA; *U.S. Private*, pg. 969
Hall, Timothy, Corp. Controller--Flexsteel Industries, Inc., Dubuque, IA; *U.S. Public*, pg. 653
Hall, Wayne, Asst. Controller--Joslyn Corporation, Chicago, IL; *U.S. Public*, pg. 481
Haller, James, Controller & Dir.-Fin.--Biomet, Inc., Warsaw, IN; *U.S. Public*, pg. 231
Halley, John C., IV, Controller & D.P.--E.W. Knauss & Son, Inc., Quakertown, PA; *U.S. Private*, pg. 626
Hallig, Elizabeth P., Controller--Los Angeles Turf Club, Inc., Arcadia, CA; *U.S. Public*, pg. 1081
Hallman, Sandy, Controller--Cross Creek Apparel, Inc., Mount Airy, NC; *U.S. Public*, pg. 1413
Halmi, Marty, Fin. Controller--Remy Amerique Inc., New York, NY; *Int'l*, pg. 1102
Halpern, Steve, Controller--Commonwealth Metal, Englewood Cliffs, NJ; *U.S. Public*, pg. 412
Halsey, Greg, Controller--Edison Parking Properties, LLC, Newark, NJ; *U.S. Private*, pg. 364
Ham, Dennis, Controller--Hampton Industries, Inc., Kinston, NC; *U.S. Public*, pg. 779
Ham, R.L., Controller--English China Clays Plc, Theale, United Kingdom; *Int'l*, pg. 455
Hamblen, Dan, Controller--Jones Blair Company, Dallas, TX; *U.S. Private*, pg. 596
Hamblen, Dan, Controller--Jones Blair Co., Chattanooga, TN; *U.S. Private*, pg. 596
Hamelin, Ray, Chief Fin. Officer, Comptroller & Treas.--Northwestel Inc., Whitehorse, Canada; *Int'l*, pg. 115
Hameral, Hans, Controller--Hubacher, Cadillac & Landrover Inc., Sacramento, CA; *U.S. Private*, pg. 543
Hamil, Jim, Controller--Homan Lumber Mart, Inc., Elkhart, IN; *U.S. Private*, pg. 536
Hamilton, Cara T., Controller--Builder Marts of America, Inc., Greenville, SC; *U.S. Private*, pg. 179
Hamilton, Charlotte, Controller--Union City Chair Co., Union City, PA; *U.S. Private*, pg. 170
Hamilton, Geo. E., Controller--Anchor Hocking Consumer Glass, Lancaster, OH; *U.S. Public*, pg. 1177
Hamilton, Greg, Corp. Controller--Clayton Homes, Inc., Knoxville, TN; *U.S. Public*, pg. 382
Hamilton, Richard J.M., Sr. V.P. & Controller--ITT Industries, Inc., White Plains, NY; *U.S. Public*, pg. 859
Hamilton, Tracy, Controller--Waxman Industries, Inc., Bedford, OH; *U.S. Public*, pg. 1748
Hamilton, Wanda, Asst. Controller--Harriss & Covington Hosiery Mills, High Point, NC; *U.S. Private*, pg. 506
Hamilton, William B., Controller--The Fairchild Corporation, Chantilly, VA; *U.S. Public*, pg. 610
Hamman, Donald J., Controller--Teradyne, Inc., Boston, MA; *U.S. Public*, pg. 1580
Hammer, Keith, Controller--De-Sta-Co, A Dover Resources Co., Troy, MI; *U.S. Public*, pg. 521
Hammond, D., Grp. Fin. Controller--British Building & Engineering Appliances Plc, Sandy, United Kingdom; *Int'l*, pg. 219
Hammond, Darrell G., Controller & Treas.--The Danis Companies, Dayton, OH; *U.S. Private*, pg. 310
Hamrick, Al, Controller--Variety Wholesalers, Incorporated, Raleigh, NC; *U.S. Private*, pg. 1134
Hanahan, Len, Controller--American Axle & Manufacturing, Detroit, MI; *U.S. Private*, pg. 51
Hanahan, Susan E., Controller--Charles River Data Systems, Inc., Framingham, MA; *U.S. Private*, pg. 230
Hancock, Bonnie V., V.P.-Acctg. & Controller--Carolina Power & Light Company, Raleigh, NC; *U.S. Public*, pg. 306
Hancock, Joyce K., Sr. V.P. & Controller--First Federal of Michigan, Detroit, MI; *U.S. Public*, pg. 330
Hangartner, Brad, Controller--Hanna-Sherman International, Inc., Portland, OR; *U.S. Private*, pg. 499
Hankins, Mattie H., V.P. & Controller--Cracker Barrel Old Country Store, Inc., Lebanon, TN; *U.S. Public*, pg. 455
Hanley, Bob, Controller--Magruder Color Company, Inc., Elizabeth, NJ; *U.S. Private*, pg. 696
Hanley, Kevin, Controller--Checker Motors Corporation, Kalamazoo, MI; *U.S. Private*, pg. 1029
Hanley, Kevin J., Controller--C.R.A. Holdings Inc., Kalamazoo, MI; *U.S. Private*, pg. 1029
Hanley, Kevin J., Controller & Sec.--CMC Kalamazoo Inc., Kalamazoo, MI; *U.S. Private*, pg. 1030
Hanley, Mark A., Controller--J.M. Schneider Inc., Kitchener, Canada; *Int'l*, pg. 1207
Hanlon, Sarah, Production Controller--Activision, Santa Monica, CA; *U.S. Public*, pg. 17
Hannon, John, Controller--Vermont American Corporation-Fountain Inn Div., Fountain Inn, SC; *U.S. Public*, pg. 575
Hans, Edward, V.P., Controller & Sec.--Argo Instruments Inc., Winchester, VA; *Int'l*, pg. 839
Hansel, Kris, V.P. & Controller--OHM Corporation, Findlay, OH; *U.S. Public*, pg. 1207
Hansel, Kris E., V.P. & Controller--OHM Remediation Services Corp., Findlay, OH; *U.S. Public*, pg. 1208
Hansen, Dennis R., Sr. V.P. & Controller--Westamerica Bancorporation, Fairfield, CA; *U.S. Public*, pg. 1756
Hansen, Dennis R., Sr. V.P., Controller & Cashier--Westamerica Bank, San Rafael, CA; *U.S. Public*, pg. 1756
Hansen, Gord, Controller--The Clark Group, Mission, Canada; *Int'l*, pg. 296
Hansen, Roy, Controller--Aurora Pump, North Aurora, IL; *U.S. Public*, pg. 726
Hansen, Stephen, Comptroller--Brookline Savings Bank, Brookline, MA; *U.S. Private*, pg. 171
Hanson, Al, Controller--Prime Source Inc., Carrollton, TX; *U.S. Private*, pg. 884
Hanson, Bill, Controller--Barko Hydraulics, Superior, WI; *U.S. Private*, pg. 859
Hanson, Brian, Controller & Asst. Sec.--Barry's Jewelers, Inc., Monrovia, CA; *U.S. Public*, pg. 192
Hanson, Dwight, Controller--Applied Communications, Inc., Omaha, NE; *U.S. Public*, pg. 1629
Hanson, J. Brent, Chief Fin. Officer, V.P. & Controller--The Barbers, Hairstyling for Men & Women, Inc., Minneapolis, MN; *U.S. Private*, pg. 115
Hanson, Jeff, Controller--ITW Fluid Products Group, Norcross, GA; *U.S. Public*, pg. 866
Hanson, John R., Controller--Pala Group, Inc., Baton Rouge, LA; *U.S. Private*, pg. 834
Hanson, Paul, Controller--Hensley & Co., Phoenix, AZ; *U.S. Private*, pg. 523
Hanson, Robert, Controller--Conklin Co. Inc., Shakopee, MN; *U.S. Private*, pg. 263
Hantangia, Bob, Controller--Frequency Engineering Laboratories, Farmingdale, NJ; *U.S. Private*, pg. 427
Hantke, William, Controller--Tosco Corporation, Stamford, CT; *U.S. Public*, pg. 1624
Hantman, Michael K., V.P. & Controller--Getty Petroleum Marketing Inc., Jericho, NY; *U.S. Public*, pg. 740
Happer, Daniel J., Asst. Controller--PHH Corporation, Hunt Valley, MD; *U.S. Public*, pg. 321
Harada, Curtis Y., Controller--Hawaiian Electric Industries, Inc., Honolulu, HI; *U.S. Public*, pg. 799
Harada, Curtis Y., V.P. & Controller--HEI Investment Corp., Honolulu, HI; *U.S. Public*, pg. 800
Haragos, Mike, Controller--Filtration Systems Division, Angola, NY; *U.S. Public*, pg. 126
Harbaugh, Blake, V.P. & Controller--Grubb & Ellis Company, Northbrook, IL; *U.S. Public*, pg. 767
Harbeson, Kevin, Controller--Neill-LaVielle Supply Co., Louisville, KY; *U.S. Private*, pg. 790
Harden, Ronald, Controller--Unitog Company, Kansas City, MO; *U.S. Public*, pg. 1693
Harding, Ruth, Controller--ATF, Inc., Lincolnwood, IL; *U.S. Private*, pg. 8
Harding, Steve, Chief Fin. Officer & Sr. V.P.--Neiman Marcus Co., Dallas, TX; *U.S. Public*, pg. 785
Hardwe, Angie, Controller--Theochem Labs., Inc., Tampa, FL; *U.S. Private*, pg. 1079
Hardy, Arlene, Controller--Bowles Fluidics Corporation, Columbia, MD; *U.S. Public*, pg. 248
Hardy, Phil, Asst. Controller--Apex Supply Co., Inc., Atlanta, GA; *U.S. Private*, pg. 77
Haren, John F., Controller--Union Camp Corporation, Wayne, NJ; *U.S. Public*, pg. 1665
Hargin, Cheryl, Controller--Foss Maritime Co., Portland, OR; *U.S. Private*, pg. 1092
Hargus, Wendy G., Controller--Central and South West Corporation, Dallas, TX; *U.S. Public*, pg. 324
Harkema, H., Controller--MultiCopy International B.V., Amsterdam, Netherlands; *Int'l*, pg. 890
Harker, Peter, Controller--GTI Corporation, San Diego, CA; *U.S. Public*, pg. 767
Harkins, Heidi, Controller--Michaels Development Group, Inc., Clifton Park, NY; *U.S. Private*, pg. 740
Harner, Carole Jo, Mgr.-Acctg.--ComSonics, Inc., Harrisonburg, VA; *U.S. Private*, pg. 260
Harpel, Jeffrey K., Controller--Wheat First Butcher Singer, Inc., Richmond, VA; *U.S. Public*, pg. 640
Harper, James J., V.P. & Controller--Eastern Enterprises, Weston, MA; *U.S. Public*, pg. 548
Harper, Lee, Controller & Treas.--Affiliated Computer Services, Inc., Dallas, TX; *U.S. Public*, pg. 27
Harper, Sally, Controller--Steel Technologies Inc., Louisville, KY; *U.S. Public*, pg. 1513
Harpothe, Steffen, Sr. V.P. & Grp. Controller--Scandinavian Airlines System (SAS), Solna, Sweden; *Int'l*, pg. 1201
Harrell, Cindy, Controller--Morven Partners LP, Edenton, NC; *U.S. Private*, pg. 763
Harrelson, Ray, V.P. & Controller--Forms & Supply, Inc., Charlotte, NC; *U.S. Private*, pg. 419
Harrigan, Christopher, Controller--Thinking Machines Corporation, Burlington, MA; *U.S. Private*, pg. 1081
Harrington, Brian K., Chief Fin. Officer, Sr. V.P. & Treas.--Kirby Corporation, Houston, TX; *U.S. Public*, pg. 961
Harrington, Everette, Controller--Weilwood Industries, Inc., New York, NY; *U.S. Private*, pg. 965
Harris, Charlotte R., Controller--Massey Cadillac, Inc., Orlando, FL; *U.S. Private*, pg. 713
Harris, David, Controller--Cavenham Forest Industries Inc., Portland, OR; *Int'l*, pg. 593
Harris, Debra, V.P., Controller & Treas.--SBS Enterprises Inc., Waco, TX; *U.S. Private*, pg. 955
Harris, Dennis, V.P. & Controller--Korn/Ferry International, Los Angeles, CA; *U.S. Private*, pg. 632
Harris, Harry, Controller--USA Weekend, New York, NY; *U.S. Public*, pg. 701
Harris, Jim, Controller--Empire National Bank, Traverse City, MI; *U.S. Private*, pg. 374
Harris, Mitch, Controller--Colorado Boxed Beef Co., Auburndale, FL; *U.S. Private*, pg. 254
Harris, R. Kim, Controller--Tom Brown, Inc., Midland, TX; *U.S. Public*, pg. 262
Harris, Rander, Controller--GoodMark Foods, Inc., Raleigh, NC; *U.S. Public*, pg. 751
Harris, Rob, Controller--Topline Imports, Inc., Bellevue, WA; *U.S. Private*, pg. 1091
Harris, Steve, V.P. & Controller--360 Degrees Communications Company, Chicago, IL; *U.S. Public*, pg. 1607
Harris, William, V.P. & Controller--Pacific Combining Corp., Los Angeles, CA; *U.S. Public*, pg. 802
Harrison, Brian, Controller--Felton Brush Inc., Manchester, NH; *U.S. Private*, pg. 400
Harrison, Brian, Controller--TransInstruments, Basingstoke, United Kingdom; *U.S. Public*, pg. 857
Harrison, Jeffrey, Controller--Atkinson, San Bruno, CA; *U.S. Public*, pg. 143
Harrison, Jim, Controller--Knape & Vogt Mfg. Co., Grand Rapids, MI; *U.S. Public*, pg. 963
Harrison, Jimmy L., Controller--Kaneb Pipe Line Partners, L.P., Richardson, TX; *U.S. Public*, pg. 942
Harrison, Roland, Controller--Earle Industries, Inc., Earle, AR; *U.S. Private*, pg. 356
Harrison, Thomas J., Controller--Brunswick Mining & Smelting Corp. Ltd., Bathurst, Canada; *Int'l*, pg. 434
Harrle, Gary, Controller--Hampton Resources Inc., Portland, OR; *U.S. Private*, pg. 498
Harrod, Larry, Chief Fin. Officer & Controller--Charter Clinic Nightingale, London, United Kingdom; *U.S. Public*, pg. 1036
Harrold, Jerry, Controller--Overseas Service Corporation, West Palm Beach, FL; *U.S. Private*, pg. 823
Harsch, Gail, Controller--River Ranch Northeast, Inc., Buffalo, NY; *U.S. Private*, pg. 934
Harstine, Jay A., Controller--L.J. Smith, Inc., Bowerston, OH; *U.S. Private*, pg. 706
Hart, Brent, Controller--Spec's Music, Inc., Miami, FL; *U.S. Public*, pg. 1497
Hart, Brian, V.P. & Corp. Controller--Pioneer Hi-Bred International, Inc., Des Moines, IA; *U.S. Public*, pg. 1298
Hart, Craig J., V.P. & Controller--IBP, Inc., Dakota City, NE; *U.S. Public*, pg. 852
Hart, David W., Controller--Ginsberg's Institutional Foods, Inc., Hudson, NY; *U.S. Private*, pg. 455
Hart, Gary, Controller--Sellen Construction Company, Seattle, WA; *U.S. Private*, pg. 982
Hart, Helen, Controller--The Sharper Image, San Francisco, CA; *U.S. Public*, pg. 1464
Hart, James F., Controller--Ernst & Young, LLP, New York, NY; *U.S. Private*, pg. 381
Hart, Thomas E., V.P. & Controller--Pogo Producing Company, Houston, TX; *U.S. Public*, pg. 1312
Hartley, Roger, Controller--AEP/Borden B.V., Apeldoorn, Netherlands; *U.S. Public*, pg. 5
Hartline, John V., Jr., Controller--Elgin Dairy Foods, Inc., Chicago, IL; *U.S. Private*, pg. 370
Hartman, Bruce L., V.P. & Controller--Woolworth Corporation, New York, NY; *U.S. Public*, pg. 1777
Hartman, Don, Controller--Sports Imprints/Fun Wear, Huber Heights, OH; *U.S. Public*, pg. 1002
Hartman, Jeffrey, Controller--Signature Flight Support, Orlando, FL; *Int'l*, pg. 114
Hartman, Robert, Asst. Controller--Gould Paper Corporation, New York, NY; *U.S. Private*, pg. 466
Hartman, Robert, Controller--Petersen Aluminum Corporation, Elk Grove Village, IL; *U.S. Private*, pg. 856
Hartman, Robert F., V.P., Controller, Sec. & Chief Acctg. Officer--CERBCO, Inc., Landover, MD; *U.S. Public*, pg. 330
Hartman, Sandi, Controller--Robinson Lumber & Export Company, New Orleans, LA; *U.S. Private*, pg. 936
Hartmann, Hans Ulrich, Controller & Dir.-Fin.--AGIE Charmilles Group, Zug, Switzerland; *Int'l*, pg. 488
Hartmann, Hans Ulrich, Mng. Dir.-Fin. & Controller--AGIE AG (Fur Industrielle Elektronik), Lausanne, Switzerland; *Int'l*, pg. 488
Hartwell, Betsy, Controller--Datawatch Corporation, Wilmington, MA; *U.S. Public*, pg. 488
Hartwick, Richard, Controller--AFM, Sterling Heights, MI; *U.S. Public*, pg. 1363
Harvey, Colleen, Controller--Hawthorne Machinery Company, San Diego, CA; *U.S. Private*, pg. 512
Harwell, William J., Controller & Asst. Treas.--Motion Industries, Inc., Irondale, AL; *U.S. Public*, pg. 732
Hasche, Bruce, Controller--Sencore, Inc., Sioux Falls, SD; *U.S. Private*, pg. 983
Hasel, Steve, Controller--Embassy Industries, Inc., Farmingdale, NY; *U.S. Public*, pg. 1240
Hashimoto, Kiyoshi, Chief Fin. Officer & Controller--Tosoh Corporation, Tokyo, Japan; *Int'l*, pg. 1407
Haskell, Coburn, V.P. & Controller--The Todd-AO Corporation, Hollywood, CA; *U.S. Public*, pg. 1619
Haskins, William K., Controller--Tippins Incorporated, Pittsburgh, PA; *U.S. Private*, pg. 1088
Haslam, R.B., Dep. Controller--Canfor Corporation, Vancouver, Canada; *Int'l*, pg. 260
Hastings, G. Melvin, Sr. V.P. & Controller--Capital Development Co., Lacey, WA; *U.S. Private*, pg. 205
Hastings, James S., Controller--Wisconsin Pharmacal Co., Inc., Jackson, WI; *U.S. Private*, pg. 1185
Hastings, Joseph H., V.P. & Corp. Controller--Delaware Management Holdings, Inc., Philadelphia, PA; *U.S. Public*, pg. 997
Hastings, Vaughn, Controller--Daycon Products Company, Inc., Lanham, MD; *U.S. Private*, pg. 317
Hasty, James, Controller--Moore-Handley, Inc., Pelham, AL; *U.S. Public*, pg. 1128
Hatch, James H., Sr. V.P. & Controller--First Union Corporation, Charlotte, NC; *U.S. Public*, pg. 639
Hatchel, G. Don, V.P. & Controller--Paccar Inc., Bellevue, WA; *U.S. Public*, pg. 1246
Hathaway, Don, Controller--Toter Incorporated, Statesville, NC; *U.S. Private*, pg. 1092
Hatterer, Michel, Mgr.-Coordination & Control--European Investment Bank, Luxembourg, Luxembourg; *Int'l*, pg. 465
Hattori, Gerald Y., Controller--Sipex Corporation, Billerica, MA; *Int'l*, pg. 1415

Haug, Elizabeth P., Controller--The Santa Anita Companies, Arcadia, CA; *U.S. Public*, pg. 1081
Haug, Elizabeth P., Controller--Los Angeles Turf Club, Inc., Arcadia, CA; *U.S. Public*, pg. 1081
Haug, Harold C., Mgr.-Acctg.--F.N. Burt Company, Inc., Buffalo, NY; *U.S. Private*, pg. 188
Haug, James E., Chief Acctg. Officer & Controller--Cascade Natural Gas Corporation, Seattle, WA; *U.S. Public*, pg. 311
Haugarth, Janel S., Asst. Controller--SuperValu, Inc., Eden Prairie, MN; *U.S. Public*, pg. 1540
Haugen, Janet Brutschea, V.P. & Controller--Unisys Corporation, Blue Bell, PA; *U.S. Public*, pg. 1671
Hauptman, Myron, Controller--Concord Fabrics Inc., New York, NY; *U.S. Public*, pg. 429
Hauser, Fred P., Sr. V.P. & Controller--Metropolitan Life Insurance Co., New York, NY; *U.S. Private*, pg. 737
Hauser, Pam, V.P. & Controller--Baird & Warner Inc., Chicago, IL; *U.S. Private*, pg. 111
Havens, Brenda J., Comptroller--Chemical Bank Michigan, Clare, MI; *U.S. Public*, pg. 345
Haviland, Richard J., Chief Fin. Officer--Automatic Data Processing, Inc., Roseland, NJ; *U.S. Public*, pg. 150
Havlik, Gregory C., Controller & Sec.--Wm. T. Burnett & Co., Inc., Baltimore, MD; *U.S. Private*, pg. 186
Hawkins, Elvest, Controller--Crown Prince, Inc. (CA), City of Industry, CA; *U.S. Private*, pg. 293
Hawley, Greg, V.P. & Controller--Willamette Industries, Inc., Portland, OR; *U.S. Public*, pg. 1768
Hayden, Carol, Controller--Brance Krachy Company, Inc., Houston, TX; *U.S. Private*, pg. 165
Hayes, Gregory A., Sr. V.P. & Controller--Shoney's, Inc., Nashville, TN; *U.S. Public*, pg. 1467
Hayes, John P., Grp. Fin. Controller--CBT Systems USA Ltd., Menlo Park, CA; *U.S. Public*, pg. 275
Hayes, Robert, Controller, Treas. & Dir.-Fin.--The Gates Corporation, Denver, CO; *Int'l*, pg. 1396
Hayes, Robert D., Controller--The HON Co., Muscatine, IA; *U.S. Public*, pg. 772
Haywood, B.J., Controller & Sec.--Senior Australia Limited, Smithfield, Australia; *Int'l*, pg. 1222
Hazelwood, Elizabeth, Controller--Fone America, Inc., Portland, OR; *U.S. Public*, pg. 661
Heacock, Richard, V.P.-Fin., Treas. & Sec.--Apache Hose & Belting Company, Inc., Cedar Rapids, IA; *U.S. Private*, pg. 76
Healy, William J., Exec. V.P. & Controller--Summit Bancorp, Princeton, NJ; *U.S. Public*, pg. 1527
Hearn, John, V.P.-Fin. & Controller--Federal Signal Corporation, Signal Div., University Park, IL; *U.S. Public*, pg. 616
Hearne, Barbara, Controller--Charlie Thomas Dealerships, Houston, TX; *U.S. Private*, pg. 1082
Hearst, Ilene, Controller--The Topps Company, Inc., New York, NY; *U.S. Public*, pg. 1621
Heatly, Danny J., Controller--Devon Energy Corporation, Oklahoma City, OK; *U.S. Public*, pg. 503
Heaton, Alan, Controller--The Dunlap Company, Fort Worth, TX; *U.S. Private*, pg. 346
Hebert, William L., Chief Fin. Officer, Treas. & Dir.-Investor Rels.--Louisiana Pacific Corporation, Portland, OR; *U.S. Public*, pg. 1015
Hebidter, Howie, Controller--Accurate Box Co., Inc., Paterson, NJ; *U.S. Private*, pg. 11
Hecht, Michael A., V.P. & Controller--Tambrands Inc., Cincinnati, OH; *U.S. Public*, pg. 1331
Heckaman, Alton D., Jr., V.P. & Controller--Swift Energy Company, Houston, TX; *U.S. Public*, pg. 1543
Hecker, Andrew, Controller--Simplicity Holdings Inc., New York, NY; *U.S. Private*, pg. 1002
Hedderman, James, Controller--Bohler-Uddeholm Corp., Rolling Meadows, IL; *Int'l*, pg. 1471
Hedlund, Tordni, Controller--Korsnas AB, Gavle, Sweden; *Int'l*, pg. 759
Hedman, Wayne, Controller--W.J. Flyte Corporation, Apache Junction, AZ; *U.S. Public*, pg. 49
Heenan, Edward S., V.P. & Comptroller--The Western and Southern Life Insurance Company, Cincinnati, OH; *U.S. Private*, pg. 1164
Heftler, Shraga, Controller--Gestetner (Israel) Limited, Tel Aviv, Israel; *Int'l*, pg. 1115
Hegarty, Kevin P., Sr. V.P. & Controller--Associates First Capital Corporation, Dallas, TX; *U.S. Public*, pg. 662
Heid, Michele C., V.P.-Investor Rels. & Corp. Controller--Raytheon Company, Lexington, MA; *U.S. Public*, pg. 1364
Heil, Dennis, Controller--Broadway Chevrolet, Louisville, KY; *U.S. Private*, pg. 170
Heiman, Wayne, Controller--ADC L.P., Wheeling, IL; *U.S. Private*, pg. 4
Heimbuch, Harvey J., V.P. & Controller--Dole Food Company, Inc., Westlake Village, CA; *U.S. Public*, pg. 515
Heimes, Karen, Controller--Jim Koons Management, Vienna, VA; *U.S. Private*, pg. 632
Heinet, Scott Wein, Corp. Controller--FiberMark Inc., Brattleboro, VT; *U.S. Public*, pg. 620
Heintz, Tom, Controller--Aurora Casket Company, Aurora, IN; *U.S. Private*, pg. 99
Heiser, John, Controller--Roussel Corporation, Montvale, NJ; *Int'l*, pg. 625
Heist, Gary A., Controller & Treas.--Continental Machines, Inc., Savage, MN; *U.S. Private*, pg. 268
Helen, Tim, Controller--New Jersey Resources Corporation, Wall, NJ; *U.S. Public*, pg. 1172
Hellbusch, Karl H., Controller--Braun AG, Kronberg, Germany; *U.S. Public*, pg. 744
Heller, Rodney D., Comptroller--Marquette Coppersmithing Co., Inc., Philadelphia, PA; *U.S. Private*, pg. 706
Heller, Theodore, Asst. V.P. & Deputy Comptroller--American International Group, Inc., New York, NY; *U.S. Public*, pg. 83
Hellman, Murray, Chief Fin. Officer, Controller, Sec. & Treas.--Pressman Toy Corp., New York, NY; *U.S. Private*, pg. 882
Helm, Gordon, Controller--Helmerich & Payne, Inc., Tulsa, OK; *U.S. Public*, pg. 808
Helmbrecht, Glen V., Chief Fin. Officer, Controller & Sec.--Mayville Engineering Co., Inc., Mayville, WI; *U.S. Private*, pg. 718
Helmers, Guy, Controller--Building Plastics, Inc., Memphis, TN; *U.S. Private*, pg. 180
Helmig, Robert, Controller--La France Corporation, Philadelphia, PA; *U.S. Private*, pg. 640
Helms, Karen, Controller--Jewell Building Systems, Dallas, NC; *U.S. Private*, pg. 587
Helms, Keith, V.P. & Controller--Jim Wilson & Associates, Inc., Montgomery, AL; *U.S. Private*, pg. 1181
Helstern, Paul K., V.P. & Comptroller--The Bank of New York (Delaware), Newark, DE; *U.S. Public*, pg. 178
Heltemes, Linda, Controller--Bermo, Inc., Circle Pines, MN; *U.S. Private*, pg. 136
Helton, Charles, Controller--American Recreation Centers, Inc., Sacramento, CA; *U.S. Public*, pg. 90
Helton, Elgin, Chief Fin. Officer--Bender Shipbuilding & Repair Company, Inc., Mobile, AL; *U.S. Private*, pg. 132
Helton, P., Controller--KDI Precision Products, Inc., Cincinnati, OH; *U.S. Private*, pg. 603
Hemingway, Peter, Controller--Mentor Opthalmics, Inc., Santa Barbara, CA; *U.S. Public*, pg. 1086
Heminover, Barton, V.P. & Corp. Controller--Bernard Chaus, Inc., New York, NY; *U.S. Public*, pg. 342
Hemmelgarn, Gerald A., Controller & Asst. Treas.--Kennedy Tank & Manufacturing Co., Inc., Indianapolis, IN; *U.S. Private*, pg. 614
Hemmer, David, Controller--Eaton Corporation, Electric Drives Division, Kenosha, WI; *U.S. Public*, pg. 556
Hempel, Susan, Controller--SicolaMartin Inc., Austin, TX; *U.S. Private*, pg. 998
Hemphill, James M., Controller--Inland Steel Industries, Inc., Chicago, IL; *U.S. Public*, pg. 879
Hemple, John, Controller--Mirror Group plc, London, United Kingdom; *Int'l*, pg. 869
Henderson, Greg, Controller--Alabama Electric Cooperative, Inc., Andalusia, AL; *U.S. Private*, pg. 30
Henderson, Gregory J., V.P. & Controller--Rogers Cantel Mobile Communications Inc., Saint-Laurent, Canada; *Int'l*, pg. 1122
Henderson, Karen, V.P. & Controller--Harrowston Corporation, Toronto, Canada; *Int'l*, pg. 599
Henderson, Ronald, Controller & Chief Fin. Officer--Klaus Radio Inc., Peoria, IL; *U.S. Private*, pg. 625
Hendler, John, Controller--Perkasie Industries Corporation, Perkasie, PA; *U.S. Private*, pg. 854
Hendrickson, James N., V.P. & Controller--Metz Baking Company, Deerfield, IL; *U.S. Private*, pg. 1022
Henec, Lisa, Controller--Concorde Career Colleges, Inc., Kansas City, MO; *U.S. Public*, pg. 430
Heneghan, John, V.P. & Controller--Capsure Holdings Corp., Chicago, IL; *U.S. Public*, pg. 303
Henley, Clem, Controller--Riccobon & Company, Inc., Santa Fe Springs, CA; *U.S. Private*, pg. 927
Henley, Malcolm G., Asst. Comptroller--Westvaco Corporation, New York, NY; *U.S. Public*, pg. 1762
Hennecke, Rolf, Controller--Offshore Equities, Inc., New York, NY; *U.S. Public*, pg. 338
Hennen, Michael L., Controller--Universal Foods Corporation, Milwaukee, WI; *U.S. Public*, pg. 1695
Hennessey, F.M., Chief Fin. Officer & Controller--Wilbur Smith Associates, Columbia, SC; *U.S. Private*, pg. 1009
Hennessy, Joseph J., Asst. Treas. & Controller--JSB Financial, Lynbrook, NY; *U.S. Public*, pg. 919
Henning, George T., V.P. & Controller--The LTV Corporation, Cleveland, OH; *U.S. Public*, pg. 971
Henningsen, Art, V.P. & Controller--Ecolab Inc., Saint Paul, MN; *U.S. Public*, pg. 562
Henock, Arlen, V.P., Controller & Chief Tax Counsel--Pitney Bowes Inc., Stamford, CT; *U.S. Public*, pg. 1303
Henry, Bill, Controller--Quarterdeck Corp., Marina Del Rey, CA; *U.S. Public*, pg. 1350
Henry, Daniel T., Sr. V.P. & Comptroller--American Express Company, New York, NY; *U.S. Public*, pg. 73
Henry, Gordon, Controller--Weiser Lock, Tucson, AZ; *U.S. Public*, pg. 1053
Henry, James, Controller--Overland Transportation System, Inc., Indianapolis, IN; *Int'l*, pg. 1469
Henry, Jeaneane, Controller--Church & Church Inc., Auburn Hills, MI; *U.S. Private*, pg. 239
Henry, William G., V.P. & Controller--General Datacomm Industries, Inc., Middlebury, CT; *U.S. Public*, pg. 708
Hensley, Doris, Controller--Cave City Chevrolet, Cave City, KY; *U.S. Private*, pg. 712
Hensley, J.L., Controller--Esso Eastern Inc., Houston, TX; *U.S. Public*, pg. 601
Hensley, J.L., V.P., Treas. & Controller--Exxon Yemen Inc., Houston, TX; *U.S. Public*, pg. 601
Hensley, Samuel M., Controller--Georgia Gulf Corporation, Atlanta, GA; *U.S. Public*, pg. 734
Henss, Laurence R., V.P., Controller & Treas.--Industrial Dielectrics, Inc., Noblesville, IN; *U.S. Private*, pg. 560
Hentges, Mark, Controller--Wagner Spray Tech Corp., Plymouth, MN; *U.S. Private*, pg. 1146
Hepburn, David, Controller--Polytech Netting Industries, Orillia, Canada; *Int'l*, pg. 1362
Herald, Roger L., Sr. Assoc. Controller--Hayes, Seay, Mattern & Mattern, Inc., Roanoke, VA; *U.S. Private*, pg. 513
Herb, C.B., Controller--Tocco, Inc., Boaz, AL; *U.S. Public*, pg. 1259
Herbeger, Bob, Controller--Williams Steel & Hardware Company, Minneapolis, MN; *U.S. Private*, pg. 1178
Herbert, Bruce, Controller--McQuay International, Minneapolis, MN; *U.S. Private*, pg. 3
Herbert, Teresa A., V.P. & Controller--Independence Holding Company, Stamford, CT; *U.S. Private*, pg. 446
Herbst, Dale, Controller--Woodcraft Industries, Inc., Saint Cloud, MN; *U.S. Private*, pg. 1187
Herchenroder, Jayne A., Controller--Ris Paper Company, Long Island City, NY; *U.S. Private*, pg. 932
Herculson, Mary C., Intl. Controller & Mgr.-Tax--EA Engineering, Science & Technology, Inc., Hunt Valley, MD; *U.S. Public*, pg. 540
Herlihy, Tom, Controller--Pepsi-Cola Albany Bottling Co., Inc., Latham, NY; *U.S. Private*, pg. 852
Herman, Debra, Controller--Beckwith Machinery Company, Murrysville, PA; *U.S. Private*, pg. 129
Herman, Robert J., Controller--Sunbelt Nursery Group Inc., Fort Worth, TX; *U.S. Public*, pg. 715
Herman, Ronald W., Controller--Murphy Oil Corporation, El Dorado, AR; *U.S. Public*, pg. 1141
Herman, Ronald W., Controller--Murphy Oil USA, Inc., El Dorado, AR; *U.S. Public*, pg. 1142
Herman, W.A., III, Treas. & Sec.--Shivers Trading & Operating Co., Augusta, GA; *U.S. Private*, pg. 994
Hermes, Jeffrey E., Controller--Patterson Dental Company, Saint Paul, MN; *U.S. Public*, pg. 1265
Hermiston, Jayne, Controller--Lee Enterprises, Incorporated, Davenport, IA; *U.S. Public*, pg. 983
Hernandez Rodriguez, Carlos Joel, Subcomptroller-Auditory--Petroleos Mexicanos, Mexico, Mexico; *Int'l*, pg. 1046
Hernandez, F., Controller--Logo of the Americas, Fort Lauderdale, FL; *Int'l*, pg. 462
Herndon, Carol, Controller & Dir.-Acctg.--Food Lion, Inc., Salisbury, NC; *Int'l*, pg. 463
Heron, Susan, Controller--The Weathervane Retail Corp., New Britain, CT; *U.S. Private*, pg. 1156
Herr, Craig, Controller--First Mount Joy Corporation, Mount Joy, PA; *U.S. Private*, pg. 407
Herr, Craig, Controller--The Sico Company, Mount Joy, PA; *U.S. Private*, pg. 407
Herrin, Lucynda, Asst. Controller--Domain Energy Corporation, Houston, TX; *U.S. Public*, pg. 515
Herring, Gregory J., V.P. & Controller--Healthcare America, Inc., Austin, TX; *U.S. Private*, pg. 515
Herring, Linda, Controller--Two Rivers Psychiatric Hospital, Kansas City, MO; *U.S. Public*, pg. 1697
Herring, Peter E., Controller--AMBI Inc., Tarrytown, NY; *U.S. Public*, pg. 7
Herrmann, Bernie, Controller--Exabyte Corporation, Boulder, CO; *U.S. Public*, pg. 597
Herrmann, Harold, Chief Fin. Officer & Controller--William B. Reily & Co., Inc., New Orleans, LA; *U.S. Private*, pg. 919
Herschuk, Michael J., Controller--Cine Magnetics, Inc., Armonk, NY; *U.S. Private*, pg. 240
Hersh, Steve, Controller--Kelley Company, Inc., Milwaukee, WI; *U.S. Private*, pg. 612
Hershiser, Dave, Controller--Omaha Steaks, Omaha, NE; *U.S. Private*, pg. 815
Herstead, Marty, Controller--Hamlin, Inc., Lake Mills, WI; *U.S. Public*, pg. 251
Hertz, Tom, Controller--Meyer Broadcasting Company, Bismarck, ND; *U.S. Private*, pg. 739
Herwood, Laura, Controller--Simi Winery, Healdsburg, CA; *Int'l*, pg. 781
Herzberg, Lowell, Controller--Hydraulics Div., Shawnee, OK; *U.S. Public*, pg. 557
Herzog, A. Stephen, V.P. & Controller--Golf Host Resorts, Inc., Tarpon Springs, FL; *U.S. Private*, pg. 1036
Herzog, Julie L., Controller--Frank's Nursery & Crafts, Inc., Detroit, MI; *U.S. Public*, pg. 715
Herzog, Timothy, V.P. & Controller--C S Crable Sportswear, Inc., Batavia, OH; *U.S. Public*, pg. 1111
Hess, Craig E., V.P. & Controller--Destec Energy, Inc., Houston, TX; *U.S. Public*, pg. 1146
Hess, James M., V.P & Controller--Borden, Inc., Columbus, OH; *U.S. Private*, pg. 157
Hess, James W., Sr. V.P. & Controller--Farmers and Merchants Bank and Trust, Hagerstown, MD; *U.S. Public*, pg. 1542
Hesse, Coby C., V.P. & Controller--The Coastal Corporation, Houston, TX; *U.S. Public*, pg. 389
Hessel, David, Controller--Aim Family of Funds, Houston, TX; *Int'l*, pg. 685
Hessel, David, Controller--Aim Equity Funds, Inc., Houston, TX; *Int'l*, pg. 685
Hessel, Jean T., Controller--Green Mountain Propane Gas Co., Burlington, VT; *U.S. Public*, pg. 761
Hester, Trey, Controller--Rocky Rococo Corporation, Oconomowoc, WI; *U.S. Private*, pg. 938
Hettinger, Hanno, Controller--Traub AG, Reichenbach, Germany; *Int'l*, pg. 1419
Hetzel, Tom, Comptroller--Dow Jones & Company, Inc., New York, NY; *U.S. Public*, pg. 524
Hetzer, Tom, V.P. & Controller--NCH Corporation, Irving, TX; *U.S. Public*, pg. 1145
Heurung, Bob, Controller--Scherer Bros. Lumber Company, Minneapolis, MN; *U.S. Private*, pg. 970
Hevelhorst, Richard, Controller--Champion Enterprises, Inc., Auburn Hills, MI; *U.S. Public*, pg. 332
Hewett, Fred, Asst. Controller--Homestake Mining Company, San Francisco, CA; *U.S. Public*, pg. 832
Hewitt, C.G.J., V.P. & Controller--Southam Inc., Don Mills, Canada; *Int'l*, pg. 631
Hewitt, Rick, Fin. Controller--NRG Group Limited, Northampton, United Kingdom; *Int'l*, pg. 1114
Heyde, Kendra, Controller--DFI/Inflight, Inc., Ridgefield, CT; *Int'l*, pg. 103
Heye, C., Controller--Moore Belgium NV, Gent, Belgium; *Int'l*, pg. 889
Heyl, Guy L., Controller--Iwerks Entertainment, Sarasota, FL; *U.S. Public*, pg. 915
Hibbard, Timothy A., V.P. & Controller--The Lamson & Sessions Co., Cleveland, OH; *U.S. Public*, pg. 976
Hibo, Henry P., V.P. & Controller--Annin & Company, Roseland, NJ; *U.S. Private*, pg. 75
Hickman, Rickey, Controller--T.L. James & Company, Ruston, LA; *U.S. Private*, pg. 580

Hickok, Chris C., Chief Acctg. Officer, V.P. & Controller--Benton Oil & Gas Company, Carpinteria, CA; *U.S. Public, pg. 212*
Hicks, Bruce, V.P.-Fin. & Controller--Wilen Manufacturing Company, Inc., Atlanta, GA; *U.S. Private*, pg. 1176
Hietikko, Donna, Controller--Mary Maxim, Inc., Port Huron, MI; *U.S. Private*, pg. 716
Higgins, J., Controller--Minwax Company Div., Upper Saddle River, NJ; *U.S. Public*, pg. 1466
Hightower, Linda, Controller--Dean Sellers Ford Inc., Troy, MI; *U.S. Private*, pg. 983
Hilado, Jules, Controller--Tork, Inc., Mount Vernon, NY; *U.S. Private*, pg. 1092
Hilbert, Stan E., Controller--Hecla Mining Company, Coeur D'Alene, ID; *U.S. Public*, pg. 803
Hileman, Steve, V.P. & Controller--Mrs. Baird's Bakeries, Inc., Fort Worth, TX; *U.S. Private*, pg. 765
Hilfiker, Shelley, Controller--PSC Inc., Webster, NY; *U.S. Public*, pg. 1245
Hill, Charles W., Controller & Treas.--Computer Language Research, Inc., Carrollton, TX; *U.S. Public*, pg. 421
Hill, Curtis V., Exec. V.P. & Controller--Body Shop of America, Jacksonville, FL; *U.S. Private*, pg. 154
Hill, David L., Controller-Fin. & Tax--OHM Remediation Services Corp., Findlay, OH; *U.S. Public*, pg. 1208
Hill, Ed, Controller--Orkin Exterminating Co., Inc., Atlanta, GA; *U.S. Public*, pg. 1404
Hill, Faith, Controller--Coast Grain Company, Inc., Ontario, CA; *U.S. Private*, pg. 248
Hill, Joanne, Controller--Transdyn Controls, Inc., Concord, CA; *U.S. Public*, pg. 1319
Hill, John, Controller--O.C. Cluss Lumber Co., Uniontown, PA; *U.S. Private*, pg. 248
Hill, Joyce, Controller--Noble Roman's Inc., Indianapolis, IN; *U.S. Public*, pg. 1187
Hill, Ken, Controller--MacGREGOR (GBR) Ltd., Whitley Bay, United Kingdom; *Int'l*, pg. 670
Hill, Lucie, Controller--Favorite Products Co., Chomedey, Canada; *U.S. Public*, pg. 1215
Hill, Marvin, Controller--AmeriSteel, Tampa, FL; *U.S. Private*, pg. 65
Hill, Thomas E., V.P. & Controller--Heartland Express, Inc., Coralville, IA; *U.S. Public*, pg. 803
Hill, Thomas P., Jr., V.P. & Controller--PECO Energy Company, Philadelphia, PA; *U.S. Public*, pg. 1268
Hillard, Michael W., Chief Acctg. Officer, V.P. & Controller--FDX Corporation, Memphis, TN; *U.S. Public*, pg. 603
Hillier, Elwood, Controller--Lemons Waste Systems Inc., Dexter, MO; *U.S. Public*, pg. 49
Hillyard, Steve, V.P. & Controller--Weyerhaeuser Real Estate Company, Federal Way, WA; *U.S. Public*, pg. 1764
Hilterbrand, Patricia, Controller, Treas. & Sec.--Pinkerton & Laws Inc., Atlanta, GA; *U.S. Private*, pg. 865
Hiltmann, Fredy, Grp. Controller--Saurer AG, Arbon, Switzerland; *Int'l*, pg. 1198
Himmel, Keith, Controller--Paul Harris Stores, Inc., Indianapolis, IN; *U.S. Public*, pg. 792
Hiner, Harold, Controller--Petroleum Inc., Wichita, KS; *U.S. Private*, pg. 858
Hines, Ginny, Controller--Cutter Aviation Albuquerque, Inc, Albuquerque, NM; *U.S. Private*, pg. 298
Hinnendael, Jack, Controller--Coz Plastics Inc., Northbridge, MA; *U.S. Private*, pg. 827
Hintz, Mike, Controller--Outlook Group Corporation, Neenah, WI; *U.S. Public*, pg. 1235
Hirata, Dean K., Sr. V.P. & Controller--First Hawaiian, Inc., Honolulu, HI; *U.S. Public*, pg. 634
Hirata, Dean K., Sr. V.P. & Controller--First Hawaiian Bank, Honolulu, HI; *U.S. Public*, pg. 634
Hiratsuka, Mr., Mgr.-Acctg.--Leader Instruments Corporation, Hauppauge, NY; *U.S. Private*, pg. 655
Hirjibehedin, Farokh, Chief Fin. Officer & Controller--West Mill Clothes, Inc., Woodside, NY; *U.S. Private*, pg. 1163
Hirous, Julie, Comptroller--Galamet, Inc., Kansas City, MO; *U.S. Private*, pg. 437
Hirsch, Sid, Exec. V.P. & Controller--Honey Fashions Ltd., New York, NY; *U.S. Private*, pg. 537
Hirschhorn, Daniel, V.P. & Controller--American Trading and Production Corporation, Baltimore, MD; *U.S. Private*, pg. 63
Hirst, Robert S., V.P. & Controller--ADVO, Inc., Windsor, CT; *U.S. Public*, pg. 23
Hirt, Fred J., Div. V.P. & Controller--Pharmacia & Upjohn, Kalamazoo, MI; *Int'l*, pg. 1048
Hitt, Pat, Controller--Card Pak, Inc., Cleveland, OH; *U.S. Private*, pg. 208
Hjort, Peter W., Jr., Controller--Flowers Industries, Inc., Thomasville, GA; *U.S. Public*, pg. 656
Hlas, Al, Controller--Brown & Haley, Tacoma, WA; *U.S. Private*, pg. 173
Hluchanek, Debra L., Controller--Galveston-Houston Company, Houston, TX; *U.S. Private*, pg. 438
Ho, Angela, Controller--Biospherics Incorporated, Beltsville, MD; *U.S. Public*, pg. 232
Hoagland, R., V.P.-Fin.--Verson Division, Chicago, IL; *U.S. Public*, pg. 48
Hoaglund, Robert W., V.P.-Control--Premark International, Inc., Deerfield, IL; *U.S. Public*, pg. 1321
Hoard, Roger S., V.P. & Controller--Solutia Inc., Saint Louis, MO; *U.S. Public*, pg. 1483
Hobbs, James R., Jr., V.P. & Controller--Echelon International Corporation, Saint Petersburg, FL; *U.S. Public*, pg. 560
Hobbs, Russell, Controller--Power Distribution Div., Cleveland, TN; *U.S. Public*, pg. 557
Hobbs, Terri D., Controller--Rosser International, Inc., Atlanta, GA; *U.S. Private*, pg. 946
Hoboken, Thomas, Controller--Warrantech Corporation, Stamford, CT; *U.S. Public*, pg. 1740
Hodge, Larry, Controller--Thiele Kaolin Co., Sandersville, GA; *U.S. Private*, pg. 1081
Hodges, Cathy, V.P. & Controller--South Trust Bank of Georgia, Atlanta, GA; *U.S. Public*, pg. 1492
Hodges, Charles, Controller & Treas.--Colonial Oil Industries, Savannah, GA; *U.S. Private*, pg. 253
Hodges, Clark, Controller--AMCOL International Corp., Arlington Heights, IL; *U.S. Public*, pg. 63
Hodges, John, Controller--Apple Canada Ltd., Markham, Canada; *U.S. Public*, pg. 121
Hodgkin, Phil, Chief Fin. Officer, Controller & Treas.--Minarik Corp, Glendale, CA; *U.S. Private*, pg. 749
Hodgson, Dave, Controller--Perry's Ice Cream Co., Inc., Akron, NY; *U.S. Private*, pg. 855
Hoe, Johnny Lim Say, Controller--Keppel Corporation Limited, Singapore, Singapore; *Int'l*, pg. 731
Hoe, Tan Kian, Regional Controller--Sandvik South East Asia Ltd., Jurong, Singapore; *Int'l*, pg. 1187
Hoefler, William R., V.P., Controller & Cashier--AMCORE Bank N.A., Rock River Valley, Sterling, IL; *U.S. Public*, pg. 64
Hoener, Jim, Controller--Engineered Products, Inc., Pittsburgh, PA; *U.S. Private*, pg. 376
Hoenscheid, Mary Ann, Controller--Kenwal Products Corp., Dearborn, MI; *U.S. Private*, pg. 615
Hoffman, Kevin, Controller--Carl M. Freeman Associates, Inc., Potomac, MD; *U.S. Private*, pg. 426
Hoffman, Robert C., Controller--Abbott Pharmaceutical Products Division, Abbott Park, IL; *U.S. Public*, pg. 13
Hoffman, Ronald S., Chief Fin. Officer & Sec.--Nantucket Industries, Inc., Melville, NY; *U.S. Public*, pg. 1151
Hoffmann, Donald, Controller--Yantis Corporation, San Antonio, TX; *U.S. Private*, pg. 1195
Hoffmeyer, Mark, Chief Fin. Officer & Controller--United Laboratories, Inc., Saint Charles, IL; *U.S. Private*, pg. 1122
Hofford, Cletus, Gen. Mgr., Controller & Treas.--Paranatal Care of America, Inc., Edina, MN; *U.S. Private*, pg. 839
Hofmann, Thomas W., Comptroller--Sun Company, Inc., Philadelphia, PA; *U.S. Public*, pg. 1530
Hogan, Brian, Controller--Morgan Products Ltd., Williamsburg, VA; *U.S. Public*, pg. 1132
Hogan, Brian, Controller--Morgan Distribution, Mechanicsburg, PA; *U.S. Public*, pg. 1132
Hogan, James D., Sr. V.P. & Controller--Starbanc Corporation, Cincinnati, OH; *U.S. Public*, pg. 1510
Hogan, Michael R., V.P. & Controller--Monsanto Company, Saint Louis, MO; *U.S. Public*, pg. 1124
Hogan, William H., V.P.-Fin. & Controller--Shorewood Packaging Corporation, New York, NY; *U.S. Public*, pg. 1468
Hohl, Steve, Controller--Williams Furnace Co., Colton, CA; *U.S. Public*, pg. 441
Hoiv, James, Plant Controller--Regal Ware, Inc., Jacksonville, AR; *U.S. Private*, pg. 917
Holbrook, Edgar, Controller--Hays Fluid Controls-Division of Romac Industries, Dallas, NC; *U.S. Private*, pg. 942
Holbrook, Jerry, Sr. V.P. & Controller--Wilmington Savings Fund Society (FSB), Wilmington, DE; *U.S. Public*, pg. 1729
Holcomb, Daryl K., Chief Fin. Officer, V.P. & Treas.--Ronson Corporation, Somerset, NJ; *U.S. Public*, pg. 1405
Holcomb, G. Stephen, V.P. & Controller--Kirby Corporation, Houston, TX; *U.S. Public*, pg. 961
Holcomb, John W., Controller--Insteel Wire Products, Mount Airy, NC; *U.S. Public*, pg. 882
Holdcroft, Philip, Controller--Amerifoods Inc., Lancaster, PA; *U.S. Private*, pg. 65
Holden, Scott, Controller--Aetna Plywood, Inc., Barrington, IL; *U.S. Private*, pg. 25
Holden, Shirley, Treas. & Controller--Royal Oldsmobile Mazda, Inc., Metairie, LA; *U.S. Private*, pg. 948
Holian, Robert R., V.P. & Controller--IMCO Recycling Inc., Irving, TX; *U.S. Public*, pg. 870
Holland, Brett, Controller--Inner Ceramic USA, Garland, TX; *U.S. Private*, pg. 564
Holland, Cort, Chief Acctg. Officer & Controller--Broadway & Seymour, Inc., Charlotte, NC; *U.S. Public*, pg. 258
Holland, Paul, Controller--Communication Cable, Inc., Sanford, NC; *U.S. Public*, pg. 968
Holland, Susan, Treas. & Controller--El Chico Restaurants, Inc., Dallas, TX; *U.S. Private*, pg. 283
Holland, W., Controller--Reynolds Extrusion Company, Richmond Hill, Canada; *U.S. Public*, pg. 1387
Hollars, W. Michael, Controller--Hansen Corporation, Princeton, IN; *Int'l*, pg. 868
Holler, Howard, Controller--Curtis Media Group, Raleigh, NC; *U.S. Private*, pg. 297
Holley, John, V.P. & Controller--Alfa Corporation, Montgomery, AL; *U.S. Public*, pg. 40
Holley, John D., Controller--Alfa Life Insurance Corp., Montgomery, AL; *U.S. Public*, pg. 40
Holley, John D., Controller--Alfa Insurance Corp., Montgomery, AL; *U.S. Public*, pg. 40
Holley, John D., Controller--Alfa General Insurance Corp., Montgomery, AL; *U.S. Public*, pg. 40
Hollinger, William R., V.P. & Controller--Kaufman and Broad Home Corporation, Los Angeles, CA; *U.S. Public*, pg. 944
Hollister, Robert F., Controller-Property--Capital Senior Living, Inc., Dallas, TX; *U.S. Public*, pg. 302
Hollomon, Carl, Controller--Neer Manufacturing Company Inc., Lexington, OH; *U.S. Public*, pg. 727
Holloway, Howard H., Grp. Controller--McGraw-Hill Book Co. (U.K.) Ltd., Maidenhead, United Kingdom; *U.S. Public*, pg. 1072
Holloway, Jim, Controller--Liqui-Box Corporation, Worthington, OH; *U.S. Public*, pg. 1000
Hollyman, Roger K., V.P. & Controller--Emco Limited, London, Canada; *Int'l*, pg. 452
Holmes, D.J., V.P. & Corp. Controller--Trans World Airlines, Inc., Saint Louis, MO; *U.S. Public*, pg. 1629
Holmes, Donald R., Asst. Controller--Motion Industries, Inc., Irondale, AL; *U.S. Public*, pg. 732
Holmes, Martha, Controller--Rusch, Duluth, GA; *U.S. Public, pg. 1569*
Holmes, Norman G., V.P. & Controller--Southern Natural Gas Company, Birmingham, AL; *U.S. Public*, pg. 1485
Holmes, Paul, V.P. & Controller--Crystal Oil Company, Shreveport, LA; *U.S. Public*, pg. 466
Holst, Detlef, Dir.-Fin. & Controller--VP-Schickédanz AG, Nuremberg, Germany; *U.S. Public*, pg. 1333
Holt, Ann, V.P. & Controller--OfficeMax, Shaker Heights, OH; *U.S. Public*, pg. 1212
Holt, Donald F., Sr. V.P. & Controller--Keystone Financial Inc., Harrisburg, PA; *U.S. Public*, pg. 956
Holt, Jon H., Controller & Asst. Treas.--Pulitzer Publishing Company, Saint Louis, MO; *U.S. Public*, pg. 1343
Holt, Richard B., Sr. V.P. & Controller--Hasbro, Inc., Pawtucket, RI; *U.S. Public*, pg. 797
Holtkamp, Ronald W., Controller--Property & Casualty Insurance, San Antonio, TX; *U.S. Private*, pg. 1114
Holzheimer, Jorge, Controller--H.F. Coors China Co., Inglewood, CA; *U.S. Public*, pg. 1506
Homann, Richard, Controller--Sound Advice, Inc., Dania, FL; *U.S. Public*, pg. 1488
Hood, Fay, Controller--B.A.S.S., Inc., Montgomery, AL; *U.S. Private*, pg. 105
Hood, Jack, V.P.-Fin. & Controller--Institutional Financing Services, Benicia, CA; *U.S. Public*, pg. 1652
Hood, Joe, Controller--Fibrebond Corporation, Minden, LA; *U.S. Private*, pg. 402
Hood, Philip, Controller--Enco Materials, Inc., Nashville, TN; *U.S. Private*, pg. 375
Hooper, Harry, Controller & Dir.-H.R.--Trailer Wheel & Frame Company, Houston, TX; *U.S. Private*, pg. 1095
Hoover, Ralph E., Controller--Pacific Steel Casting Co., Berkeley, CA; *U.S. Private*, pg. 832
Hope, Brian P., Controller--Hosokawa Micron Ltd., Runcorn, United Kingdom; *Int'l*, pg. 636
Hopkins, David R., V.P., Controller & Chief Acctg. Officer--Browning-Ferris Industries, Inc., Houston, TX; *U.S. Public*, pg. 262
Hopkinson, B. Todd, V.P.-Fin. & Controller--Williams Natural Gas Company, Tulsa, OK; *U.S. Public*, pg. 1769
Hopp, William A., Controller--The Ward Machinery Company, Hunt Valley, MD; *U.S. Private*, pg. 1149
Hopper, Preston D., Sr. V.P.-Plng. & Acctg. & Controller--CMS Energy Corporation, Dearborn, MI; *U.S. Public*, pg. 279
Hopper, Preston D., V.P. & Controller--CMS Generation Co., Dearborn, MI; *U.S. Public*, pg. 280
Hopwood, B., Fin. Controller--Piher International Ltd., Swindon, United Kingdom; *Int'l*, pg. 853
Horak, Al, Controller--The Taney Corporation, Taneytown, MD; *U.S. Private*, pg. 1067
Horan, John, Controller--Miller Curtain Co., Inc., San Antonio, TX; *U.S. Private*, pg. 746
Horan, Michael D., Controller--Cox Communications, Inc., Atlanta, GA; *U.S. Public*, pg. 454
Horan, Tom, Controller--Marilyn Miglin, L.P., Chicago, IL; *U.S. Private*, pg. 745
Horberg, Jane, Controller--Bessin Corporation, Chicago, IL; *U.S. Public*, pg. 1433
Hornaday, Renee, Controller--Warren Distributing Corp., Raleigh, NC; *U.S. Private*, pg. 1151
Horne, P.A., V.P. & Controller--R.J. Reynolds Tobacco Intl., Inc., Geneva, Switzerland; *U.S. Public*, pg. 1355
Horning, John, Controller--SafetyMaster Corporation, Billings, MT; *U.S. Public*, pg. 1523
Horstkotte, Don, Controller--Ceradyne, Inc, Costa Mesa, CA; *U.S. Public*, pg. 330
Horton, Ann N., Controller--Penn Virginia Corporation, Radnor, PA; *U.S. Public*, pg. 1271
Horton, Ann N., Controller--Penn Virginia Equities Corp., Wilmington, DE; *U.S. Public*, pg. 1271
Horton, Betty, Controller--Pic'n Pay Stores, Inc., Matthews, NC; *U.S. Private*, pg. 864
Horton, Chris, Controller--Textile Rubber & Chemical Company, Dalton, GA; *U.S. Private*, pg. 1079
Horton, Paul C., Asst. Controller--Amdahl Corporation, Sunnyvale, CA; *Int'l*, pg. 527
Horton, Ron, Controller--Gas Equipment Company, Inc., Dallas, TX; *U.S. Private*, pg. 440
Horton, Siobhan K., Asst. V.P. & Controller--Amwest Insurance Group, Inc., Calabasas, CA; *U.S. Public*, pg. 106
Horton, Siobhan K., V.P. & Controller--Amwest Surety Insurance Company, Calabasas, CA; *U.S. Public*, pg. 106
Horton, Thomas W., V.P. & Controller--American Airlines, Inc., Fort Worth, TX; *U.S. Public*, pg. 9
Horton, William, Controller--Tru-Fit Products Corp., Medina, OH; *U.S. Private*, pg. 1107
Horvath, Claudette, Controller--Toms Sierra Company, Colfax, CA; *U.S. Private*, pg. 1090
Horvath, Greg, Controller--Rospatch Jessco, Inc., Dowagiac, MI; *U.S. Public*, pg. 98
Horvath, Les, Controller--Rawson-Koenig, Inc., Houston, TX; *U.S. Public*, pg. 1362
Horvath, William, Controller--Benjamin Obdyke, Inc., Warminster, PA; *U.S. Private*, pg. 810
Horwath, J., Division Controller--BEAU Interconnect Systems, Gilford, NH; *U.S. Public*, pg. 157
Hosenitz, Luke, Controller--Arrow Group Industries, Inc., Wayne, NJ; *U.S. Private*, pg. 477
Hoskins, Douglas H., Controller--Shaw Industries, Inc., Dalton, GA; *U.S. Public*, pg. 1464
Hosler, D.H., Controller--Sybron Chemicals Inc., Birmingham, NJ; *U.S. Public*, pg. 1544
Hosokawa, Koichi, Controller--Kingston Technology Corporation, Fountain Valley, CA; *U.S. Private*, pg. 622
Hosokawa, Koichi, Controller--Furon Company, Laguna Niguel, CA; *U.S. Public*, pg. 688
Hough, Gordon, Controller--Collier-Keyworth, Inc., Liberty, NC; *U.S. Public*, pg. 985
House, Paul, Controller--Warren Industries, Inc., Lafayette, IN; *U.S. Private*, pg. 945
Householder, Joseph A., V.P.-Tax & Comptroller--Unocal Corporation, El Segundo, CA; *U.S. Public*, pg. 1698

Houser, Alan, Controller--Power Distribution Div., Lincoln, IL; *U.S. Public*, pg. 557
Houston, Robert P., Exec. V.P. & Comptroller--Regions Financial Corporation, Birmingham, AL; *U.S. Public*, pg. 1371
Houts, Beverly, Controller--Elyria Foundry Company, Elyria, OH; *U.S. Private*, pg. 373
Hovey, Mark, V.P.-Fin. & Controller--Washington Inventory Service, San Diego, CA; *U.S. Public*, pg. 846
Howaldt, Jens P., Dr., Dir.-Fin., Controlling & Law--Continental AG, Hannover, Germany; *Int'l*, pg. 327
Howard, A.C., Controller--Abell-Howe Company, Forest Park, IL; *U.S. Private*, pg. 10
Howard, Connie, Controller--Camalloy, Incorporated, Washington, PA; *U.S. Private*, pg. 202
Howard, Dale, Controller--Aetrium-FSA, Grand Prairie, TX; *U.S. Public*, pg. 27
Howard, Donald, Controller--Phoenix Manufacturing, Inc., Phoenix, AZ; *U.S. Public*, pg. 441
Howard, K.L., V.P. & Controller--Columbus McKinnon Corp., Amherst, NY; *U.S. Public*, pg. 405
Howard, Melvyn, V.P. & Controller--Columbia Tri-Star Home Video, Burbank, CA; *Int'l*, pg. 1282
Howard, Timothy G., V.P. & Controller--Huffy Corporation, Miamisburg, OH; *U.S. Public*, pg. 846
Howard, Wayne, V.P. & Sr. Controller--Rogers Communications, Inc., Toronto, Canada; *Int'l*, pg. 1122
Howard, William K., Controller--Rapid Industries, Inc., Louisville, KY; *U.S. Private*, pg. 910
Howarth, Duncan, Controller & Dir.-Mktg.--Miller Freeman PLC, London, United Kingdom; *Int'l*, pg. 1443
Howden, Denise, Controller--Force 10 Marine Ltd., Richmond, Canada; *U.S. Public*, pg. 1705
Howdle, Tom, Controller--Casco Products Corporation, Bridgeport, CT; *U.S. Public*, pg. 1458
Howells, Kenneth, Controller--Royston Laboratories, Pittsburgh, PA; *U.S. Public*, pg. 337
Hower, Matthew J., Controller--Burgess-Norton Mfg. Co., Geneva, IL; *U.S. Private*, pg. 68
Howerton, M., Controller--Crane National Vendors Co., Ltd., Scarborough, Canada; *U.S. Public*, pg. 456
Hoyer, David, Controller--North Park Lincoln Mercury Inc., San Antonio, TX; *U.S. Private*, pg. 805
Hoylman, M.A., Controller--Esso International Shipping (Bahamas) Co. Limited, Florham Park, NJ; *U.S. Public*, pg. 601
Hritsuk, Dan, Controller--Baldwin Web Controls, Lombard, IL; *U.S. Public*, pg. 170
Hrubes, Brian J., Controller--Winnebago Industries, Inc., Forest City, IA; *U.S. Public*, pg. 1772
Hryciw, R., Controller--ITT Sheraton Hotels, Toronto, Canada; *U.S. Public*, pg. 1512
Huang, George, Sr. V.P. & Gen. Controller--Acer Incorporated, Taipei, Taiwan; *Int'l*, pg. 22
Huard, Benoit, Controller--Quebecor Multimedia Inc., Montreal, Canada; *Int'l*, pg. 1076
Hubbard, Gary M., V.P. & Comptroller--Moore Business Forms & Systems Div., Lake Forest, IL; *Int'l*, pg. 890
Hubbard, Kristi L., Controller--BeautiControl Cosmetics, Inc., Carrollton, TX; *U.S. Public*, pg. 198
Hubbuch, John, Controller--Lennox International Inc., Richardson, TX; *U.S. Private*, pg. 659
Huber, Richard G., V.P. & Controller--Freeman Decorating Co., Dallas, TX; *U.S. Private*, pg. 426
Huber, Rob, Controller--Fenton Press, Inc., Addison, IL; *U.S. Private*, pg. 400
Huber, Thomas, V.P., Comptroller & Corp. Sec.--Long Island Water Corporation, Lynbrook, NY; *U.S. Private*, pg. 674
Hubley, Barry G., Comptroller--Maritime Telegraph & Telephone Company, Ltd., Halifax, Canada; *Int'l*, pg. 116
Huck, Paul E., V.P. & Corp. Controller--Air Products and Chemicals, Inc., Allentown, PA; *U.S. Public*, pg. 30
Hudak, Kevin R., Sr. Grp. Controller--Conair Corporation, Stamford, CT; *U.S. Private*, pg. 261
Hudgin, Patrick, Controller--C.J. Vitner Co., Chicago, IL; *U.S. Private*, pg. 1142
Hudgins, Ron, Comptroller--Kyanite Mining Corporation, Dillwyn, VA; *U.S. Private*, pg. 638
Hudson, H. Bradford, Controller--ADT Security Systems, Inc., Carmel, IN; *U.S. Public*, pg. 1649
Hudson, Phil, Controller--EOC Normalien GmbH & Co. KG, Ludenscheid, Germany; *Int'l*, pg. 75
Hudson, Phil, Controller--EOC Formsystem GmbH, Mahlberg, Germany; *Int'l*, pg. 75
Hudson, Rick E., Controller--Dillard, A ResourceNet International Company, Greensboro, NC; *U.S. Public*, pg. 901
Hudson, W.D., V.P. & Comptroller--Southern Company Services, Inc., Atlanta, GA; *U.S. Public*, pg. 1490
Hudson, William G., Comptroller--NewTel Communications, Saint Johns, Canada; *Int'l*, pg. 115
Huebsch, Thomas M., Controller--American Precision Industries Inc., Buffalo, NY; *U.S. Public*, pg. 90
Huennenkens, Nancy, V.P. & Controller--ServiceMaster Business & Industry Group, Downers Grove, IL; *U.S. Public*, pg. 1462
Huesgen, James H., V.P. & Controller--PacifiCorp, Portland, OR; *U.S. Public*, pg. 1251
Huey, Charles, Controller--S L C Graphics, LP, Pittston, PA; *U.S. Private*, pg. 955
Huff, Craig D., Chief Fin. Officer, V.P.-Fin. & Treas.--Nature's Sunshine Products, Inc., Provo, UT; *U.S. Public*, pg. 1166
Huff, Louise, Controller--Superior Printing Co., Warren, OH; *U.S. Private*, pg. 1055
Huffines, Ray, Controller--Brunner & Lay, Inc., Springdale, AR; *U.S. Private*, pg. 176
Hufft, Robert, Controller--International Chemical Company, Tulsa, OK; *U.S. Private*, pg. 568
Hug, Albert, Head-Corp. Controling--Clariant International Ltd., Muttenz, Switzerland; *Int'l*, pg. 624
Hughes, Brad, Controller--KTI, Inc., Guttenberg, NJ; *U.S. Public*, pg. 939
Hughes, David, Treas.--Central Supply Co., Inc., Indianapolis, IN; *U.S. Private*, pg. 225
Hughes, Rob, Controller--Tenney Environmental, Williamsport, PA; *U.S. Private*, pg. 1076
Hughes, Shawn, Controller--Perryton Equity, Perryton, TX; *U.S. Private*, pg. 855
Hughes, Thomas J., V.P. & Controller--The Hearst Corporation, New York, NY; *U.S. Private*, pg. 515
Hughes, Thomas R., V.P. & Controller--Fred Meyer Stores, Portland, OR; *U.S. Public*, pg. 1103
Hughes, W. Alan, Treas.--Fleischli Oil Company, Inc., Cheyenne, WY; *U.S. Private*, pg. 410
Hughey, Michael K., Controller--Mellon Bank Corporation, Pittsburgh, PA; *U.S. Public*, pg. 1084
Huie, Jeannie, Controller--Greenstone Roberts Advertising, Melville, NY; *U.S. Public*, pg. 763
Hulen, Cathryn C., Controller--Texas Utilities Company, Dallas, TX; *U.S. Public*, pg. 1586
Hull, Jennifer, Controller--Holstein Association USA, Inc., Brattleboro, VT; *U.S. Private*, pg. 536
Hull, John, Controller--Hollywood Casino Corp, Atlantic City, NJ; *U.S. Public*, pg. 830
Hull, Richard C., Controller--Norpac Foods, Inc., Stayton, OR; *U.S. Private*, pg. 802
Hulliger, Sylvie, Chief Fin. Officer & Controller--La Metaire Clinic, Nyon, Switzerland; *U.S. Public*, pg. 1036
Hulse, Tonice, Controller--Sawyer Riley Compton Inc., Atlanta, GA; *U.S. Private*, pg. 969
Hult, Frank A., Chief Acctg. Officer, V.P. & Controller--Walter Industries, Inc., Tampa, FL; *U.S. Public*, pg. 1736
Hultquist, James, Controller--US Airways, Inc., Arlington, VA; *U.S. Public*, pg. 1680
Hultquist, James A., Controller--US Airways Group, Inc., Arlington, VA; *U.S. Public*, pg. 1680
Human, John E., Controller--The McGuire Furniture Company, San Francisco, CA; *U.S. Private*, pg. 630
Humber, Earl D., Controller--Cannon Equipment, Chattanooga, TN; *Int'l*, pg. 646
Hume, James W., Controller--Chi Systems Division, Ann Arbor, MI; *U.S. Public*, pg. 1539
Humes, David G., V.P. & Controller--Lincoln National Income Fund, Inc., Baltimore, MD; *U.S. Public*, pg. 998
Hummel, Lawrence E., V.P. & Controller--Kellwood Company, Chesterfield, MO; *U.S. Public*, pg. 948
Humphrey, J.H., V.P. & Controller--The Pillsbury Company, Minneapolis, MN; *Int'l*, pg. 411
Humphreys, Donald D., V.P. & Controller--Exxon Corporation, Irving, TX; *U.S. Public*, pg. 601
Hums, Scott J., Controller, Treas. & Mgr.-Financial Reporting--DSM Engineering Plastic Products, Reading, PA; *Int'l*, pg. 354
Hund, Larry, Controller--Heller International, Chicago, IL; *U.S. Private*, pg. 520
Hund, Martin H., Controller--Meco Corporation, Greeneville, TN; *U.S. Private*, pg. 726
Hund, Thomas N., V.P. & Controller--Burlington Northern Santa Fe Corporation, Fort Worth, TX; *U.S. Public*, pg. 268
Hunnicutt, Donald P., Controller & Sec.--Graphic Industries, Inc., Atlanta, GA; *U.S. Public*, pg. 1735
Hunot, Jean-Michel, Controller--Electrovert, Grand Prairie, TX; *Int'l*, pg. 328
Hunt, Allen P., Controller--Miller Building Corp., Wilmington, NC; *U.S. Private*, pg. 746
Hunt, Genivieve M., V.P. & Controller--The First National Bank of St. Mary's, Leonardtown, MD; *U.S. Public*, pg. 1089
Hunt, Mike, Intl. Controller--Griffin Corporation, Valdosta, GA; *U.S. Private*, pg. 480
Hunt, Robert, V.P. & Controller--E & A Industries, Inc., Indianapolis, IN; *U.S. Private*, pg. 352
Hunt, Robert C., Controller--Newfoundland Capital Corporation Limited, Dartmouth, Canada; *Int'l*, pg. 924
Hunter, Judy B., Controller--Justin Industries, Inc., Fort Worth, TX; *U.S. Public*, pg. 936
Hunter, Walter R., Controller & Treas.--Virginia Natural Gas, Inc., Norfolk, VA; *U.S. Public*, pg. 436
Huntington, Roger, Controller--Fresh America Corp., Dallas, TX; *U.S. Public*, pg. 681
Huntley, Beverly, Controller--SIGAL CONSTRUCTION CORP., Washington, DC; *U.S. Private*, pg. 999
Huntzinger, Judith, Sr. V.P. & Controller--BDM International, Inc., Mc Lean, VA; *U.S. Public*, pg. 1558
Huovie, Curt, Controller--The Valspar Corp. Protective Coatings Div., Baltimore, MD; *U.S. Public*, pg. 1707
Hupp, Edwin, Controller & Dir.-Fin.--Rain Bird Sprinklers Manufacturing Corp., Glendora, CA; *U.S. Private*, pg. 907
Hurley, Richard, Controller--Alpha Q, Inc., Colchester, CT; *U.S. Private*, pg. 45
Hurlstone, Barbara, Controller--Mitek Systems, Inc., San Diego, CA; *U.S. Public*, pg. 1117
Hurton, Michael, Controller--ECRM, Tewksbury, MA; *U.S. Private*, pg. 353
Husar, R., Controller--Ingersoll-Dresser Pump Company, Liberty Corner, NJ; *U.S. Public*, pg. 529
Husemoen, Cole, Controller--J.R. Abbott Construction, Inc., Seattle, WA; *U.S. Private*, pg. 9
Huser, Larry F., Controller--Republic Group Incorporated, Hutchinson, KS; *U.S. Public*, pg. 1378
Hutcherson, Cecil, Controller & Sec.--Mayfair Mills, Inc., Arcadia, SC; *U.S. Private*, pg. 718
Hutchinson, J.W., Controller--Industrial Resources, Inc., Fairmont, WV; *U.S. Private*, pg. 961
Hutchinson, J.W., Controller--Mountaineer Resources, Inc., Fairmont, WV; *U.S. Private*, pg. 961
Hutchinson, Thomas D., Controller--CILCORP Inc., Peoria, IL; *U.S. Public*, pg. 367
Hutchinson, Thomas D., Controller--Central Illinois Light Company, Peoria, IL; *U.S. Public*, pg. 367
Hutchinson, Thomas D., Controller--CILCORP Investment Management Inc., Peoria, IL; *U.S. Public*, pg. 367
Huth, Nancy, Controller--Fiesta Restaurants, Inc., Oklahoma City, OK; *U.S. Public*, pg. 555
Hutton, David, Controller--Young & Franklin, Inc., Liverpool, NY; *U.S. Private*, pg. 1196
Hutton, Nancy, Controller, Treas. & Sec.--Crustbuster, Inc., Dodge City, KS; *U.S. Private*, pg. 293
Hutzel, Nick, V.P. & Controller--Vertex Computer Cable Products, Farmingdale, NY; *U.S. Public*, pg. 1718
Huxham, Basil C., Controller--Westcoast Energy Inc., Vancouver, Canada; *Int'l*, pg. 1492
Hyde, Thomas F., Controller--Drake Construction Company, Portland, OR; *U.S. Private*, pg. 347
Hyland, Anne, Grp. Fin. Controller--Medeva PLC, London, United Kingdom; *Int'l*, pg. 852
Hymel, Michael G., V.P. & Controller-Corp. Div.--Stewart Enterprises, Inc., Metairie, LA; *U.S. Public*, pg. 1518
Hynes, Edward G., Controller & Sec.--Befab-Safeland, Ltd., Shannon, Ireland; *U.S. Private*, pg. 313
Hynson, Henry R., Controller--Durrett-Sheppard Steel Co., Inc., Baltimore, MD; *U.S. Private*, pg. 349
Iacarella, Tom, Controller--Raven Industries, Inc., Sioux Falls, SD; *U.S. Public*, pg. 1361
Iacovelli, Mike, Grp. Controller--Quebecor Printing Semline Inc., Braintree, MA; *Int'l*, pg. 1078
Ibanez, Ignacio, Controller--Majorica Jewelry Ltd., New York, NY; *U.S. Private*, pg. 697
Ibanez, J.M. Garcia, Controller--Banco Santander, London, United Kingdom; *Int'l*, pg. 144
Ibe, J., Controller--Tonen Corporation, Tokyo, Japan; *Int'l*, pg. 1398
Ignacek, Paul, Asst. Controller--Bally Total Fitness Holdings Corporation, Chicago, IL; *U.S. Public*, pg. 171
Ignatowski, Robert, Controller--DowBrands, L.P., Indianapolis, IN; *U.S. Public*, pg. 523
Iles, Martin A., Controller--Essef Corporation, Chardon, OH; *U.S. Public*, pg. 592
Ilias, Christos, Asst. Controller--Greyvest Capitol Inc., Toronto, Canada; *Int'l*, pg. 559
Imboden, Suzanne, Controller--Flambeau Airmold Corporation, Roanoke Rapids, NC; *U.S. Private*, pg. 409
Ingersoll, Ellen M., V.P. & Controller--Franchise Finance Corp. of America, Scottsdale, AZ; *U.S. Public*, pg. 679
Ingley, Sandy, Controller--RJO Enterprises, Inc., Lanham, MD; *U.S. Private*, pg. 904
Ingold, Richard, Controller--Alpha Industries, Lyndhurst, NJ; *U.S. Private*, pg. 45
Ingold, Richard, Controller--Beta Plastics, Carlstadt, NJ; *U.S. Private*, pg. 45
Ingold, Richard, Controller--Omega Plastics, Lyndhurst, NJ; *U.S. Private*, pg. 45
Ingram, Anna, Asst. Controller--ENSERCH Corporation, Dallas, TX; *U.S. Public*, pg. 1587
Ingram, Kevin S., V.P. & Controller--Protection Mutual Insurance Co., Park Ridge, IL; *U.S. Private*, pg. 891
Ingram, Lina, Controller--International Microwave Corporation, Norwalk, CT; *U.S. Private*, pg. 571
Inman, David L., Controller--Armstrong Air Conditioning Inc., Bellevue, OH; *U.S. Private*, pg. 659
Innes, James A., Controller--Superior Dairy, Inc., Canton, OH; *U.S. Private*, pg. 1054
Inniger, Brian, Controller--Rieth-Riley Construction Co. Inc., Goshen, IN; *U.S. Private*, pg. 930
Inouye, Glenn K., Sr. V.P.-Corp. Control Opers.--Servco Pacific Inc., Honolulu, HI; *U.S. Private*, pg. 986
Inzitari, Frank, Controller--Frank Ix & Sons, Inc., New York, NY; *U.S. Private*, pg. 423
Iopolito, R. I., Controller--Consumer Products Company, Muncie, IN; *U.S. Public*, pg. 56
Ireland, Robert L., Sr. Dir.-Corp. Fin. & Controller--White Hen Pantry, Inc., Elmhurst, IL; *U.S. Private*, pg. 1172
Irlando, Sandra J., V.P.-Acctg. & Sec.--Prima Energy Corporation, Denver, CO; *U.S. Public*, pg. 1325
Irwin, Douglas, Controller & Mgr.-Risk Mngmt.--New Brunswick Scientific Co., Inc., Edison, NJ; *U.S. Public*, pg. 1169
Irwin, Mary Anne, Controller--The Selmer Co., Inc., Elkhart, IN; *U.S. Public*, pg. 1514
Irwin, Mary Anne, Controller--Vincent Bach Co., Elkhart, IN; *U.S. Public*, pg. 1514
Isbister, Robert, Controller--Elwell-Parker, Inc., Farmington, MI; *U.S. Private*, pg. 373
Islam, Mohamed, Controller--Lombardi Holdings Inc., Whittier, CA; *U.S. Private*, pg. 673
Ison, Roger, V.P. & Controller--McSwain Carpets Inc., Cincinnati, OH; *U.S. Private*, pg. 725
Isono, Denis, V.P. & Controller--Bank of Hawaii, Honolulu, HI; *U.S. Public*, pg. 1248
Isono, Denis K., Sr. V.P. & Controller--Pacific Century Financial Corporation, Honolulu, HI; *U.S. Public*, pg. 1248
Issac, Steven, Controller--Cumberland Packing Corp., Brooklyn, NY; *U.S. Private*, pg. 295
Ito, Ken, Dir.-Fin. & Controller--Excerpta Medica Limited-Japan, Tokyo, Japan; *Int'l*, pg. 1099
Ito, Minoro, Controller--Alpine Electronics of America, Inc., Torrance, CA; *Int'l*, pg. 65
Ivankovich, Ivan, Controller--Prime Matrix Wireless Communications, Calabasas, CA; *U.S. Private*, pg. 884
Ives, Bryan, Controller--Finger Furniture Company, Inc., Houston, TX; *U.S. Private*, pg. 405
Izydorek, Ronald, Controller--Synchro-Start Products, Inc., Niles, IL; *U.S. Private*, pg. 627
Jablonsky, Allan J., Controller--OmniQuip International, Inc., Port Washington, WI; *U.S. Private*, pg. 500
Jack, C. E., Controller--Carter Holt Harvey Limited, Auckland, New Zealand; *U.S. Public*, pg. 904
Jackman, B., Grp. Controller--Morgan Crucible Co. Plc, Windsor, United Kingdom; *Int'l*, pg. 890
Jackson, Cliff, Controller--National Airmotive Corporation, Oakland, CA; *U.S. Private*, pg. 775
Jackson, Daniel E., Controller--Ludowici Roof Tile, Inc., New Lexington, OH; *Int'l*, pg. 1171
Jackson, David, Controller--Centennial Homes Inc., Dallas, TX; *U.S. Public*, pg. 1764
Jackson, Edward J., Asst. Controller--Frank's Nursery & Crafts, Inc., Detroit, MI; *U.S. Public*, pg. 715

Jackson, Katie, V.P.--National Income Realty Trust, New York, NY; *U.S. Public*, pg. 1157

Jackson, Linda, Controller--Real World, Andover, MA; *U.S. Private*, pg. 913

Jackson, Ronald C., Asst. Comptroller & Dir.-Investor Rels.--Regions Financial Corporation, Birmingham, AL; *U.S. Public*, pg. 1371

Jackson, Thomas, Controller--National Forge Company, Irvine, PA; *U.S. Private*, pg. 783

Jackson, Tom, V.P. & Controller--Blitz USA, Inc., Miami, OK; *U.S. Private*, pg. 149

Jacobs, Cindy, Controller--The H.T. Hackney Co., Knoxville, TN; *U.S. Private*, pg. 493

Jacobs, Jim, Controller--Polk Audio, Inc., Baltimore, MD; *U.S. Public*, pg. 1315

Jacobs, Joel, Controller--Richter & Ratner Contracting Corporation, Maspeth, NY; *U.S. Private*, pg. 930

Jacobs, Leonard, V.P., Sec., Controller & Treas.--Perry Machinery Corporation, Hainesport, NJ; *U.S. Private*, pg. 855

Jacobs, Todd, Controller--H & H Tube & Manufacturing Co., Vanderbilt, MI; *U.S. Private*, pg. 489

Jacobsen, Scott, Controller--Dorner Manufacturing Corp., Hartland, WI; *U.S. Private*, pg. 340

Jacoby, Hanns-Jorg, Exec. Mgr.-Controlling & Logistics--AE Goetze GmbH, Burscheid, Germany; *Int'l*, pg. 1334

Jacoby, Paul T., V.P.-Fin. & Controller--Heckett MultiServ, Butler, PA; *U.S. Public*, pg. 793

Jaeger, Robert J., Sr. V.P.-Fin., Controller & Treas.--Westmoreland Coal Co., Colorado Springs, CO; *U.S. Public*, pg. 1761

Jaehnert, Frank J., Controller--S-B Power Tool Company, Chicago, IL; *Int'l*, pg. 205

Jafri, Syed S., Treas. & Controller--Sun City Industries, Inc., Fort Lauderdale, FL; *U.S. Public*, pg. 1529

Jagodzinski, Robert E., Controller--Merchants Group, Inc., Buffalo, NY; *U.S. Public*, pg. 1090

Jahina, Birgit, Controller--Madison Graham Colorgraphics, Inc., Los Angeles, CA; *U.S. Private*, pg. 694

Jahn, Syl, Controller--North American Products Corp., Jasper, IN; *U.S. Private*, pg. 803

Jain, Karan, Controller--Interbath, Inc., City of Industry, CA; *U.S. Private*, pg. 566

Jaksich, Daniel K., Controller--Berkshire Hathaway Inc., Omaha, NE; *U.S. Public*, pg. 217

James, David, Controller--Dean Industries, Inc., Gardena, CA; *Int'l*, pg. 188

James, David R., V.P., Corp. Controller & Treas.--Marcam Solutions, Inc., Newton, MA; *U.S. Public*, pg. 1042

James, Jensen, Controller--Crystal Cream & Butter Company, Sacramento, CA; *U.S. Private*, pg. 294

James, Kerry, Controller--Sutter Health, Sacramento, CA; *U.S. Private*, pg. 1057

James, Margaret, Controller--Lazare Kaplan Intl., Inc., New York, NY; *U.S. Public*, pg. 981

James, Michael, V.P.-Fin.--SmithKline Beecham Corporation, Philadelphia, PA; *Int'l*, pg. 1264

James, Randy B., V.P. & Controller--The Toro Company, Bloomington, MN; *U.S. Public*, pg. 1623

James, Ron, Controller & Treas.--ISK BioSciences, Memphis, TN; *Int'l*, pg. 689

James, Stephen, Controller--Promotional Broadcast Services, Los Angeles, CA; *U.S. Private*, pg. 1166

James, Thomas, Controller--Elder Manufacturing Company, Creve Coeur, MO; *U.S. Private*, pg. 367

Jamieson, Christopher W., V.P. & Controller--Unicorp Canada Corporation, Toronto, Canada; *Int'l*, pg. 1433

Jamieson, D., Controller--Moore Business Forms & Systems Ltd., Auckland, New Zealand; *Int'l*, pg. 889

Jamieson, J., Controller--Nuburn Capital, Calgary, Canada; *Int'l*, pg. 990

Jamieson, John, Controller--Quebecor Printing Aurora, Aurora, Canada; *Int'l*, pg. 1076

Jamison, Deborah, Controller--Lester Coggins Trucking, Okahumpka, FL; *U.S. Private*, pg. 250

Janas, Frank, Controller--Aydin Displays (East), Horsham, PA; *U.S. Public*, pg. 158

Janes, Robert, Controller--John D. Lucas Printing Company, Baltimore, MD; *U.S. Private*, pg. 253

Janes, Robert E., V.P. & Controller--Old American Insurance Co., Kansas City, MO; *U.S. Public*, pg. 943

Janette, Ken, Controller--Sunkyong America, Inc., New York, NY; *Int'l*, pg. 1320

Janette, Kenneth P., V.P. & Corp. Controller--Rayonier Inc., Stamford, CT; *U.S. Public*, pg. 1363

Jang, Kee, Controller--Quebecor Merrill Canada Inc., Vancouver, Canada; *Int'l*, pg. 1077

Janikies Simonson, Cynthia, Controller--Jan-Co., Inc., Cranston, RI; *U.S. Private*, pg. 581

Janiszewski, Andrew, Controller--World's Finest Chocolate Australia Pty. Ltd., Stanmore, Australia; *U.S. Private*, pg. 1191

Jankowski, Wendy, Corp. Controller--Horizon Enterprises Group LLC, Taylor, MI; *U.S. Private*, pg. 539

Jankowviak, Diana, Controller--Custom Cheques of Canada, Vancouver, Canada; *Int'l*, pg. 1077

Janofsky, Mark, Controller--Roberts Pharmaceutical Corporation, Eatontown, NJ; *U.S. Public*, pg. 1393

Janofsky, William, Controller--Van Son Holland Ink Corp. of America, Mineola, NY; *U.S. Private*, pg. 1133

Janov, Edward, Chief Acctg. Officer, V.P. & Controller--Southwest Gas Corporation, Las Vegas, NV; *U.S. Public*, pg. 1493

Janov, Mike, Controller--Edgewater Steel Company, Oakmont, PA; *U.S. Private*, pg. 364

Jansen, Dennis, Controller--Central Products Company, Inc., Menasha, WI; *U.S. Public*, pg. 1022

Janssen, Dan, Controller--Sathers Inc., Round Lake, MN; *U.S. Private*, pg. 397

Janssen, Leonard, V.P. & Controller--Mannington Resilient Floors, Salem, NJ; *U.S. Private*, pg. 700

Janulis, John R., V.P. & Controller--Thomas & Betts Corporation, Memphis, TN; *U.S. Public*, pg. 1597

Japcyzk, Jim, Controller--Oil-Dri Corporation of America, Chicago, IL; *U.S. Public*, pg. 1214

Jaradi, Mark, Dir.-IT--Hayes Microcomputer Products, Inc., Norcross, GA; *U.S. Public*, pg. 801

Jarboe, Jeffery, Controller--Bently Nevada Corporation, Minden, NV; *U.S. Private*, pg. 134

Jarka, Don, Controller--Mold-Tech, Villa Park, IL; *U.S. Public*, pg. 1506

Jarrett, Mack, Controller--Harris Enterprises Inc., Hutchinson, KS; *U.S. Private*, pg. 505

Jarvis, Lowell D., Division Controller--Boise Cascade Timber & Wood Products Division, Boise, ID; *U.S. Public*, pg. 243

Jasuirkowski, Albert M., Controller--Vibra-Metrics, Inc., Hamden, CT; *U.S. Private*, pg. 622

Jattu, Ari, V.P. & Controller--Kymi Paper Mills Ltd., Kuusankoski, Finland; *Int'l*, pg. 1428

Jaworski, Edward, Comptroller--Holden's Engine Products Overseas Corporation, Melbourne, Australia; *U.S. Public*, pg. 723

Jeffcoat, David, Fin. Controller--Smiths Industries plc, London, United Kingdom; *Int'l*, pg. 1266

Jellison, Doug, Controller--Nucor Bearing Products, Inc., Wilson, NC; *U.S. Public*, pg. 1206

Jellison, William R., V.P., Controller & Treas.--Donnelly Corporation, Holland, MI; *U.S. Public*, pg. 519

Jenack, Timothy, Controller--Chemonics Fire-Trol, Inc., Phoenix, AZ; *U.S. Public*, pg. 591

Jendra, Glenn, Controller--Advance Mechanical Systems, Inc., Mount Prospect, IL; *U.S. Private*, pg. 18

Jenkins, Albert J., V.P. & Controller--Commonwealth Relocation Services, Inc., Philadelphia, PA; *U.S. Public*, pg. 1374

Jenkins, George W., Controller--STV Group, Inc., Douglassville, PA; *U.S. Public*, pg. 1421

Jenkins, James, Controller--Taco Cabana, San Antonio, TX; *U.S. Public*, pg. 1559

Jenkins, Jim, Controller--Tessco Technologies, Inc., Sparks, MD; *U.S. Public*, pg. 1582

Jenkins, Larry, V.P. & Controller--Kaufman and Broad of Northern California, Inc., San Ramon, CA; *U.S. Public*, pg. 945

Jennings, M., Controller--Dayco Swan Corporation, Worthington, OH; *U.S. Public*, pg. 1045

Jensen, Gary, Controller--Empire Southwest Co., Mesa, AZ; *U.S. Private*, pg. 374

Jensen, Michael J., Controller--QST Environmental Inc., Peoria, IL; *U.S. Public*, pg. 367

Jensen, Owen, Controller & Treas.--M.A. Mortenson Company, Minneapolis, MN; *U.S. Private*, pg. 763

Jensen, Philip, Controller--Graham Manufacturing Co., Marshfield, WI; *Int'l*, pg. 18

Jensen, Solveig, Controller--Robert Englekirk, Inc., Los Angeles, CA; *U.S. Private*, pg. 377

Jenson, Randy, Controller--International Wine Accessories, Inc., Dallas, TX; *U.S. Private*, pg. 572

Jerge, Ed, Controller--Wilhold Inc., Cleveland, OH; *U.S. Public*, pg. 78

Jermanus, Paul, Controller--Michigan Milk Producers Association, Novi, MI; *U.S. Private*, pg. 741

Jewell, Kirk, Controller--Oklahoma Publishing Company, Oklahoma City, OK; *U.S. Private*, pg. 813

Jewison, Patrick D., V.P. & Controller--Nova Corporation, Calgary, Canada; *Int'l*, pg. 971

Jimemez, Maura R., Asst. Controller--AGP Industrial Corporation, Manila, Philippines; *Int'l*, pg. 14

Jin, Alex, Controller--Standard Motor Products Hong Kong Limited, Sha Tin, Hong Kong; *U.S. Public*, pg. 1503

Jinske, Janice L., Asst. Controller--Farmers and Traders Life Insurance Co., Syracuse, NY; *U.S. Private*, pg. 394

Jio, Stacey M., Controller--Maui Pineapple Co., Ltd., Kahului, HI; *U.S. Public*, pg. 1060

Joannidi, Harold A., Controller, Treas. & Sec.--EcoScience Corporation, East Brunswick, NJ; *U.S. Public*, pg. 563

Jog, Vikram, Controller--Hercules Incorporated, Wilmington, DE; *U.S. Public*, pg. 809

Johanson, Lee Anne, Controller--Mediatex Communications Corporation, Austin, TX; *U.S. Private*, pg. 727

Johansson, Bonnie, Controller--PetCare Plus, Inc., Aurora, IL; *U.S. Private*, pg. 856

Johansson, Lennart, Sr. V.P.-Acctg. & Auditing & Controller--Atlas Copco AB, Stockholm, Sweden; *Int'l*, pg. 95

Johansson, Nils-Erik, Controller--Spectra-Physics AB, Stockholm, Sweden; *Int'l*, pg. 1288

John, Hans-Jurgen, Fin. Controller--Westag & Getalit AG, Rheda-Wiedenbruck, Germany; *Int'l*, pg. 1491

Johns, Christopher P., V.P. & Controller--PG&E Corporation, San Francisco, CA; *U.S. Public*, pg. 1240

Johns, Christopher P., V.P. & Controller--Pacific Gas & Electric Company, San Francisco, CA; *U.S. Public*, pg. 1241

Johnson, Betty R., Controller--MYR Group Inc., Rolling Meadows, IL; *U.S. Public*, pg. 1029

Johnson, Bill, Controller--Decorator Industries, Inc., Pembroke Pines, FL; *U.S. Public*, pg. 491

Johnson, Brent E., V.P. & Controller--Mercantile Bank of Iowa, Des Moines, IA; *U.S. Public*, pg. 1087

Johnson, Bruce, Controller--Elan Foods, Buffalo, NY; *U.S. Private*, pg. 484

Johnson, Carl, Controller--Corcom, Inc., Libertyville, IL; *U.S. Public*, pg. 446

Johnson, Charles, Controller--Cab-o-Sil Div. Cabot Corp., Tuscola, IL; *U.S. Public*, pg. 289

Johnson, David, Controller--Smith & Sons Foods, Inc., Macon, GA; *U.S. Private*, pg. 1006

Johnson, David, V.P. & Controller--RadioShack, Fort Worth, TX; *U.S. Public*, pg. 1560

Johnson, David D., V.P. & Corp. Controller--Kent Electronics Corp., Houston, TX; *U.S. Public*, pg. 951

Johnson, David R., Asst. Controller--Colonial Gas Company, Lowell, MA; *U.S. Public*, pg. 400

Johnson, Dennis, Controller--Nicholson File, Cullman, AL; *U.S. Public*, pg. 444

Johnson, Dennis R., V.P. & Controller--International Multifoods Corporation, Minneapolis, MN; *U.S. Public*, pg. 900

Johnson, Doug, Controller--Foss Maritime Co., Seattle, WA; *U.S. Private*, pg. 1092

Johnson, Gloria, Controller--Sabin Robbins Paper Co., Cincinnati, OH; *U.S. Private*, pg. 959

Johnson, Greg A., Controller & Treas.--F.H. Stoltze Land & Lumber Company, Saint Paul, MN; *U.S. Private*, pg. 1044

Johnson, Gregory, Controller--Snap-On Tools Corporation, Kenosha, WI; *U.S. Public*, pg. 1480

Johnson, Hartley, Controller--Reed & Barton Corporation, Taunton, MA; *U.S. Private*, pg. 916

Johnson, Henry, Controller--Connors Brunswick, Inc., South Portland, ME; *U.S. Private*, pg. 264

Johnson, J. Brent, V.P. & Controller--American Family Mutual Insurance Co., Madison, WI; *U.S. Private*, pg. 53

Johnson, J. Peter, V.P.-Fin., Controller, Treas. & Asst. Sec.--Tellabs Operations, Inc., Lisle, IL; *U.S. Public*, pg. 1572

Johnson, James L., Controller & Corp. Sec.--Werner Enterprises, Inc., Omaha, NE; *U.S. Public*, pg. 1754

Johnson, Jeff, Chief Fin. Officer, Treas. & Sec.--Evans Industries, Inc., Detroit, MI; *U.S. Private*, pg. 385

Johnson, Jeffrey, Controller--Scott's Liquid Gold-Inc., Denver, CO; *U.S. Public*, pg. 1447

Johnson, Ken, Controller--Butera Finer Foods Inc., Elgin, IL; *U.S. Private*, pg. 189

Johnson, Kent, Chief Fin. Officer & Asst. Treas.--Paddock Publications, Inc., Arlington Heights, IL; *U.S. Private*, pg. 833

Johnson, Kevin, V.P. & Controller--Cumberland Farms, Inc., Canton, MA; *U.S. Private*, pg. 295

Johnson, Kevin, Controller--Salton/Maxim Housewares, Inc., Mount Prospect, IL; *U.S. Public*, pg. 1430

Johnson, Kim, Controller--PST Vans, Inc., Salt Lake City, UT; *U.S. Public*, pg. 1246

Johnson, Lisa, Controller--Vinings Industries Inc., Atlanta, GA; *U.S. Private*, pg. 1141

Johnson, Lisa L., V.P. & Controller--Regence BlueCross BlueShield of Oregon, Portland, OR; *U.S. Private*, pg. 917

Johnson, Margaret, Controller--H.C. Miller Company, Milwaukee, WI; *U.S. Private*, pg. 747

Johnson, Mark, Controller--Fairmont Snack Group, Inc., Independence, OH; *U.S. Private*, pg. 392

Johnson, Michael, Chief Acctg. Officer & Controller--Ascend Communications, Inc., Alameda, CA; *U.S. Public*, pg. 138

Johnson, Michael, Controller & Cash Mgr.--Intesys Technologies, Gilbert, AZ; *U.S. Private*, pg. 574

Johnson, Nick, Controller--Nucor Steel-Nebraska, Norfolk, NE; *U.S. Public*, pg. 1205

Johnson, Patti, Controller--Modern Controls, Inc., Minneapolis, MN; *U.S. Public*, pg. 1120

Johnson, Richard, Controller--Computer Power Incorporated, High Bridge, NJ; *U.S. Public*, pg. 421

Johnson, Robert, Controller--Chance Industries, Inc., Wichita, KS; *U.S. Private*, pg. 228

Johnson, Robert, Controller--Standard Examiner, Ogden, UT; *U.S. Private*, pg. 1031

Johnson, Ron, Controller--Airmaster Fan Co., Michigan Center, MI; *U.S. Private*, pg. 29

Johnson, Ron, Controller--Bates Container, Inc., North Richland Hills, TX; *U.S. Private*, pg. 122

Johnson, Ron, Controller--Federal Cartridge Co., Anoka, MN; *U.S. Public*, pg. 239

Johnson, Russell E., Controller--Kapalua Land Co., Ltd., Lahaina, HI; *U.S. Public*, pg. 1060

Johnson, Steve, Controller & Treas.--Baxter Research Medical, Inc., Midvale, UT; *U.S. Public*, pg. 196

Johnson, Sue, Controller--Tri-City Oldsmobile Inc., Louisville, KY; *U.S. Private*, pg. 1100

Johnson, Thomas R., V.P. & Controller--Global Marine Inc., Houston, TX; *U.S. Public*, pg. 748

Johnson, W.L., V.P. & Controller--ANR Pipeline Co., Detroit, MI; *U.S. Public*, pg. 389

Johnson, Wayne, Controller--Mark III Industries, Ocala, FL; *U.S. Private*, pg. 704

Johnson, William, Controller--Earle M. Jorgensen Company, Brea, CA; *U.S. Private*, pg. 600

Johnson, William H., V.P., Controller & Sec.--Reuter Manufacturing Inc., Hopkins, MN; *U.S. Public*, pg. 1383

Johnson, William L., V.P. & Controller--Sonat Inc., Birmingham, AL; *U.S. Public*, pg. 1484

Johnson, William L., Jr., V.P. & Controller--Hillerich & Bradsby Co., Louisville, KY; *U.S. Private*, pg. 530

Johnston, Dan, Controller--Bussmann Division, Ellisville, MO; *U.S. Public*, pg. 443

Johnston, Scott, Controller--Omega Environmental Inc., Richmond, VA; *U.S. Public*, pg. 1222

Johnstone, Mark, Controller--Avemco Corporation, Frederick, MD; *U.S. Public*, pg. 151

Johr, Robert H., Controller--Cone Drive Textron, Traverse City, MI; *U.S. Public*, pg. 1589

Jonas, Edward M., Comptroller--Anchor Glass Container Corporation, Tampa, FL; *Int'l*, pg. 327

Jonas, Junona A., V.P. & Controller--Pacific Gas & Electric Company, San Francisco, CA; *U.S. Public*, pg. 1241

Jonas, Steve, Controller--Fidelity Investments (FMR Corp.), Boston, MA; *U.S. Private*, pg. 402

Jones, Barbara, Controller--Plaid Pantries, Inc., Beaverton, OR; *U.S. Private*, pg. 868

Jones, Barry, Controller--MCDR, Inc., Memphis, TN; *U.S. Private*, pg. 686

Jones, Ben B., Controller--Thermal Transfer Corp., Monroeville, PA; *U.S. Public*, pg. 29

Jones, Bennie, Corp. Controller--Rockett, Burkhead, Lewis & Winslow, Raleigh, NC; *U.S. Private*, pg. 938

Jones, Deborah, V.P. & Controller--B.M.J. Financial Corp., Bordentown, NJ; *U.S. Public*, pg. 1528

Jones, Diane O., Controller--The Flexitallic Group, Inc., Houston, TX; *U.S. Private*, pg. 413

Jones, Donald, Controller--Fleet Engineers, Inc., Muskegon, MI; *U.S. Private*, pg. 410

Jones, Doug, Controller--Kimray, Inc., Oklahoma City, OK; *U.S. Private*, pg. 620

Jones, Douglas, Controller--UNC Aerostructures-Washington, Everett, WA; *U.S. Public*, pg. 710

Jones, Eddie, Corp. Controller--Lincoln Property Company, Dallas, TX; *U.S. Private*, pg. 668

Jones, Hal S., Controller--The Washington Post Company, Washington, DC; *U.S. Public*, pg. 1742

Jones, Ian P., Controller--KFW Canada, Inc., Orillia, Canada; *Int'l*, pg. 1338

Jones, Jana, Controller--The Bakersfield Californian, Bakersfield, CA; *U.S. Private*, pg. 112

Jones, Jeff, Controller--The Carbide/Graphite Group, Inc., Pittsburgh, PA; *U.S. Public*, pg. 304

Jones, Jeffrey W., V.P. & Controller--Gai-Tronics Corporation, Mohnton, PA; *U.S. Public*, pg. 1430

Jones, Jim, V.P., Controller & Treas.--LSB Industries, Inc., Oklahoma City, OK; *U.S. Public*, pg. 970

Jones, Keith, Chief Acctg. Officer & Controller--Kollmorgen Corporation, Waltham, MA; *U.S. Public*, pg. 965

Jones, Kenneth M., V.P. & Controller--Allegheny Power System, Inc., Hagerstown, MD; *U.S. Public*, pg. 42

Jones, Larry, Controller--Marmac Corporation, Vienna, WV; *U.S. Private*, pg. 705

Jones, Lewis B., V.P. & Comptroller--USX Corporation, Pittsburgh, PA; *U.S. Public*, pg. 1661

Jones, Michael, Controller--Young Dental Manufacturing, Earth City, MO; *U.S. Private*, pg. 1201

Jones, Michael O., Controller--Buckeye Partners, L.P., Allentown, PA; *U.S. Public*, pg. 266

Jones, Patrick S., V.P.-Fin. & Controller--Intel Corporation, Santa Clara, CA; *U.S. Public*, pg. 886

Jones, Paul, Controller--Pace Oil Co., Inc., Winston Salem, NC; *U.S. Private*, pg. 829

Jones, Paul J., V.P. & Comptroller--American Home Products Corporation, Madison, NJ; *U.S. Public*, pg. 79

Jones, R.D., Controller--The Machine Tool Group, Cleveland, OH; *U.S. Public*, pg. 503

Jones, Rosy, Asst. Controller--Greenwich Air Services, Miami, FL; *U.S. Public*, pg. 710

Jones, Tom, Controller--Citibank N.A., Long Island City, NY; *U.S. Public*, pg. 377

Jonlia, Richard, Controller--Advanced Metallurgy, Inc., Export, PA; *U.S. Public*, pg. 1564

Jordan, Anthony, Treas. & Controller--Kleer-Vu Plastics Corp., Compton, CA; *U.S. Public*, pg. 962

Jordan, Donald J., Controller--D. Canale Food Services, Inc., Memphis, TN; *U.S. Private*, pg. 204

Jordan, J. Randal, Controller--Manke Lumber Company, Inc., Tacoma, WA; *U.S. Private*, pg. 699

Jordan, Jerry C., V.P. & Mdse. Controller-Apparel & Golden Gems--Montgomery Ward & Co., Inc., Chicago, IL; *U.S. Private*, pg. 758

Jordan, R. Steven, Corp. Controller--The Smithfield Companies, Inc., Portsmouth, VA; *U.S. Public*, pg. 1479

Jorgensen, Janet L., V.P. & Controller--S & K Famous Brands, Inc., Glen Allen, VA; *U.S. Public*, pg. 1414

Jormalainen, Paivi, Controller--Ifi OY, Kerava, Finland; *Int'l*, pg. 501

Jorquera, Manuel, Controller--Gestetner Chile S.A., Santiago, Chile; *Int'l*, pg. 1115

Joseph, Don, Controller--Integrated Systems Consulting Group, Wayne, PA; *U.S. Public*, pg. 1425

Joseph, Jeffrey S., Controller--Financial Security Assurance Holdings Ltd., New York, NY; *U.S. Public*, pg. 622

Joshi, Shekhar, Controller--John Crane Middle East- Central Region, Dubai, United Arab Emirates; *Int'l*, pg. 1339

Jossart, C.L., Sr. V.P. & Controller--Marquette Bank Rochester, Rochester, MN; *U.S. Private*, pg. 706

Joves, Elvie, Controller--Pace Die Cast Products, Inc., Gardena, CA; *U.S. Public*, pg. 986

Joy, Ronald, Chief Exec. Officer, V.P.-Fin. & Controller--MacNaughton Einson Graphics, Fair Lawn, NJ; *U.S. Private*, pg. 692

Joyce, Jim, Controller--L. Powell Co., Inc., Culver City, CA; *U.S. Private*, pg. 877

Joyce, John R., V.P. & Controller--International Business Machines Corporation, Armonk, NY; *U.S. Public*, pg. 895

Joyce, Todd, Corp. Controller--Watson Pharmaceuticals, Inc., Corona, CA; *U.S. Public*, pg. 1746

Joyner, Jeffrey T., Corp. Controller--Transportation Technologies, Inc., Washington, NC; *U.S. Private*, pg. 1097

Jrnar, Jeff, Controller-Europe--Datapoint Corporation, Paris, France; *Int'l*, pg. 384

Juay, Edwin Low Eng, Controller--United Overseas Land Limited, Singapore, Singapore; *Int'l*, pg. 1443

Judd, Jane E., V.P. & Controller--The Titan Corporation, San Diego, CA; *U.S. Public*, pg. 1618

Judson, A. E., Grp. Controller--Goodman Fielder Limited, Sydney, Australia; *Int'l*, pg. 555

Judt, Ed, V.P.-Fin. & Controller--Peters-Revington Corp., Delphi, IN; *U.S. Public*, pg. 352

Juengling, Charles R., V.P., Controller & Sec.--Baldwin Piano & Organ Company, Loveland, OH; *U.S. Public*, pg. 169

Jumel, Humfred, Fin. Controller--Lance International S.A., Sarcelles, France; *Int'l*, pg. 1116

Jun, Keith, Controller--Kia Motors America, Inc., Irvine, CA; *Int'l*, pg. 733

Junior, Judy, Controller--Pawtucket Fasteners Inc., Pawtucket, RI; *U.S. Private*, pg. 844

Juraschek, Paul E., Controller--Programart Corporation, Cambridge, MA; *U.S. Private*, pg. 890

Justice, Carol, Controller--Hollingsworth Oil Co. Inc., Springfield, TN; *U.S. Private*, pg. 535

Justiliano, P.R., Sr. V.P. & Controller--Marshall & Ilsley Corporation, Milwaukee, WI; *U.S. Public*, pg. 1049

Justin, Martin, Controller--Print-O-Tape, Inc., Mundelein, IL; *U.S. Private*, pg. 886

Jutte, P., Chief Fin. Officer & Controller--Holmatro Industrial & Rescue Equipment, Raamsdonksveer, Netherlands; *Int'l*, pg. 632

Kaberle, John D., Jr., Exec. V.P. & Comptroller--Republic New York Corporation, New York, NY; *U.S. Public*, pg. 1380

Kacer, Peter, V.P. & Controller--Atlantis Plastic, Inc., Atlanta, GA; *U.S. Public*, pg. 145

Kaczynski, Barbara, Controller--People, New York, NY; *U.S. Public*, pg. 1613

Kadish, Mark, Controller--Axiom Inc., Moorestown, NJ; *U.S. Public*, pg. 157

Kahmeyer, Wayne W., Controller--Tipperary Corporation, Denver, CO; *U.S. Public*, pg. 1618

Kahn, Laurie O., Controller--Bergen Brunswig Medical Corporation, Montgomery, AL; *U.S. Public*, pg. 214

Kahn, Steve, V.P. & Controller--Camerican International, Paramus, NJ; *U.S. Public*, pg. 426

Kahrs, James, Controller--Rose Art Industries, Livingston, NJ; *U.S. Private*, pg. 945

Kaiser, Marvin, V.P. & Controller--McRae Industries, Inc., Mount Gilead, NC; *U.S. Public*, pg. 1073

Kaiser, Norman, Controller--Bassick by Kaspar, Shiner, TX; *U.S. Private*, pg. 122

Kaiser, Norman, Controller--Kaspar Wire Works, Inc., Shiner, TX; *U.S. Private*, pg. 608

Kalin, Richard A., Controller--Telmark, Inc., Syracuse, NY; *U.S. Private*, pg. 27

Kalinowski, Sylvia J., Controller--Tri-Mark Metal Corp., Shelby, MI; *U.S. Private*, pg. 1100

Kalls, K.A., Controller--Nevada Bell, Reno, NV; *U.S. Public*, pg. 1416

Kalmanek, S.P., Controller--George & Thomas Cone Co., Hermitage, PA; *U.S. Private*, pg. 448

Kalmer, Carol, V.P.-Opers. & Controller--Asbury Carbons, Inc., Asbury, NJ; *U.S. Private*, pg. 87

Kalnins, K.A., Controller--Ziegler Leasing Corp., West Bend, WI; *U.S. Public*, pg. 1792

Kalnins, K.A., Controller & Treas.--Ziegler Medical Equipment Group, Inc., Omaha, NE; *U.S. Public*, pg. 1792

Kalumbi, Godfrey H., Controller--Gestetner Limited, Blantyre, Malawi; *Int'l*, pg. 1115

Kam, P.M., Controller--Jardine Matheson Holdings Limited, Hamilton, Bermuda; *Int'l*, pg. 703

Kamm, Rick, V.P., Treas. & Controller--The Blodgett Oven Co., Inc., Burlington, VT; *U.S. Public*, pg. 1064

Kamphaus, T.E., Controller--Rio Algom Mining Corp., Oklahoma City, OK; *Int'l*, pg. 1118

Kandler, Georgianne, Chief Information Officer & Controller--Logicon, Inc., Torrance, CA; *U.S. Public*, pg. 1198

Kandler, John, Controller--Buffalo Truck Center, Buffalo, NY; *U.S. Private*, pg. 179

Kane, B.C., Controller--Southern Pacific Rail Corporation, San Francisco, CA; *U.S. Public*, pg. 1668

Kane, Frank T., Chief Fin. Officer & V.P.-Fin.--Chromcraft Revington, Inc., Delphi, IN; *U.S. Public*, pg. 352

Kane, Kerry M., Controller--C&D Charter Power Systems, Blue Bell, PA; *U.S. Public*, pg. 271

Kane, Linda M., V.P. & Corp. Controller--Forest City Enterprises, Inc., Cleveland, OH; *U.S. Public*, pg. 667

Kane, Ralph, Controller--Jacob Levy & Bros., Inc., Louisville, KY; *U.S. Private*, pg. 664

Kane, Richard, V.P.-Admin. & Controller--Mason Candlelight, Middlesex, NJ; *U.S. Public*, pg. 1506

Kane, Richard, V.P.-Admin. & Controller--Mason Metals Co., Middlesex, NJ; *U.S. Public*, pg. 1506

Kaneig, Dean, Controller--Arandell Corporation, Menomonee Falls, WI; *U.S. Private*, pg. 79

Kanowitz, Gary, Controller--Control Systems Inc., Saint Paul, MN; *U.S. Private*, pg. 271

Kapadia, Padma, Asst. Controller--Century Bancshares, Inc., Washington, DC; *U.S. Public*, pg. 328

Kapeluch, Jill, Controller--Rinke Pontiac-GMC Co., Warren, MI; *U.S. Private*, pg. 931

Kapitzky, George, Controller--John O. Butler Co., Chicago, IL; *Int'l*, pg. 1320

Kaplan, Mark E., Chief Acctg. Officer & Controller--Weirton Steel Corporation, Weirton, WV; *U.S. Public*, pg. 1751

Kaplan, Sam D., Chief Fin. Officer, Controller, Treas. & Sec.--The He-Ro Group, Ltd., New York, NY; *U.S. Public*, pg. 801

Kaplan, William, Controller--Tekni-Plex, Inc., Somerville, NJ; *U.S. Private*, pg. 1073

Kapp, Richard, Controller--Domecq Importers Inc., Old Greenwich, CT; *Int'l*, pg. 63

Kapsimalis, Chris G., V.P. & Controller--Rheem Manufacturing Co., New York, NY; *Int'l*, pg. 1022

Karanko, Seppo, Controller--KONE Lifts Ltd., Hounslow, United Kingdom; *Int'l*, pg. 747

Karchon, Dennis, Chief Oper. Officer & Controller--Engineering Service, Inc., Southfield, MI; *U.S. Private*, pg. 376

Karger, Ron, Controller--Optimaxx International, Rockleigh, NJ; *U.S. Private*, pg. 818

Karl, Bob, Controller--Pipe Fabricating & Supply Company, Santa Fe Springs, CA; *U.S. Private*, pg. 867

Karl, Joseph, Controller--ILC Technology, Inc., Sunnyvale, CA; *U.S. Public*, pg. 856

Karlin, Roger, V.P. & Controller--Svedala Industries Inc., Waukesha, WI; *Int'l*, pg. 1326

Karlovitz, Jim, Controller--McCain Citrus Inc., Oak Brook, IL; *Int'l*, pg. 850

Karlsson, Lars, V.P. & Grp. Controller--Schauman Wood Oy, Lahti, Finland; *Int'l*, pg. 1428

Karmendy, J.C., Controller--The Kingsford Products Company, Oakland, CA; *U.S. Public*, pg. 387

Karow, Alann, Controller--Sargent and Greenleaf, Nicholasville, KY; *U.S. Private*, pg. 981

Karplus, E.J., Treas. & Controller--General Sekiyu K.K., Tokyo, Japan; *U.S. Public*, pg. 602

Karson, Alan, Controller--Boyer Candy Company Inc., Altoona, PA; *U.S. Private*, pg. 162

Karty, Jack, Controller--Koller Enterprises, Inc., Fenton, MO; *U.S. Private*, pg. 631

Kasch, Vincent L., V.P., Controller & Asst. Treas.--National Western Life Insurance Company, Austin, TX; *U.S. Public*, pg. 1161

Kaschinske, Larry, V.P. & Controller--Jones Intercable, Inc., Englewood, CO; *U.S. Private*, pg. 597

Kaskey, Dale, Controller--The Akro Corporation, Canton, OH; *U.S. Public*, pg. 399

Kaskoff, David, Asst. Controller--Farr Company, El Segundo, CA; *U.S. Public*, pg. 613

Kasnicki, Ted, Controller--Publishers Clearing House, Port Washington, NY; *U.S. Private*, pg. 893

Kasper, Albert, V.P.-Fin. & Controller--Savage Arms Inc., Westfield, MA; *U.S. Private*, pg. 968

Kassar, Richard A., V.P.-Opers. & Controller--Chock Full O' Nuts Corporation, New York, NY; *U.S. Public*, pg. 351

Kassens, David, Controller--Transus Intermodal L.L.C., Atlanta, GA; *U.S. Private*, pg. 1097

Kathage, Hans, Chief Fin. Officer & Controller--Kloeckner Industrie-Anlagen Gmbh, Duisburg, Germany; *Int'l*, pg. 1081

Katona, Howard, Controller--New York Envelope Corp, Long Island City, NY; *U.S. Private*, pg. 794

Katz, David, Controller--Reliable Stores, Inc., Columbia, MD; *U.S. Private*, pg. 920

Kaufer, Howard, Controller--I. Appel Corporation, New York, NY; *U.S. Private*, pg. 78

Kauffmann, Herbert, V.P. & Controller--Freightliner Corp., Portland, OR; *Int'l*, pg. 368

Kaufhold, Thomas, Controller--DataCard Corporation, Minnetonka, MN; *U.S. Private*, pg. 312

Kaufhold, Tom, Controller--DataCard Corporation, Minnetonka, MN; *U.S. Private*, pg. 312

Kaufman, Bonnie, Controller--Prime Technology, Inc., Grand Rapids, MI; *U.S. Private*, pg. 884

Kauppinen, Marja-Liisa, V.P. & Group Controller--Metsa-Serla Corporation, Espoo, Finland; *Int'l*, pg. 863

Kauramaki, Kline, Chief Fin. Officer, V.P. & Controller--J.W. Messner, Inc., Grand Rapids, MI; *U.S. Private*, pg. 734

Kavanagh, Paul, Controller--Fishery Products International Ltd., Saint Johns, Canada; *Int'l*, pg. 492

Kawamura, Takuma, Controller--Nippon Keystone Corporation, Kobe, Japan; *U.S. Public*, pg. 1650

Kawanami, Ginger G., Controller--Nationwide Health Properties Inc., Newport Beach, CA; *U.S. Public*, pg. 1166

Kay, Bruce D., V.P. & Controller--Hannaford Bros. Co., Scarborough, ME; *U.S. Public*, pg. 781

Kaye, Jeffrey, Controller--House of Ronnie, Inc., New York, NY; *U.S. Private*, pg. 542

Kaye, Tom, Controller--Imperial, Inc., Green Bay, WI; *U.S. Private*, pg. 558

Kayser, Chris, Controller--Mosinee Converted Products, Columbus, WI; *U.S. Public*, pg. 1747

Kazmierczak, Kenneth J., Controller, Treas. & Sec.--Schreier Malting Co., Sheboygan, WI; *U.S. Private*, pg. 972

Keady, Kurt, Controller--Connell Limited Partnership, Boston, MA; *U.S. Private*, pg. 264

Kealy, Thomas P., Chief Acctg. Officer, V.P. & Controller--BTU International, Inc., North Billerica, MA; *U.S. Public*, pg. 164

Kean, James, Controller & Treas.--Henderson Electric Co., Inc., Louisville, KY; *U.S. Private*, pg. 521

Kean, Lawrence M., Controller & Sec.--A&A Manufacturing Co., New Berlin, WI; *U.S. Private*, pg. 1

Keane, W., V.P. & Controller--GFA Brands, Inc., Cresskill, NJ; *U.S. Private*, pg. 435

Kearney, Joseph W., Controller & Asst. Sec.--First Union Management, Inc., Cleveland, OH; *U.S. Public*, pg. 641

Kearns, Vincent, Controller & Treas.--Electrocatalytic, Inc., Union, NJ; *U.S. Private*, pg. 369

Keating, A.C., Controller--Military Avionics Division, Minneapolis, MN; *U.S. Public*, pg. 834

Keating, William M., V.P. & Controller--Lane Industries, Inc., Northbrook, IL; *U.S. Private*, pg. 649

Keaton, Jim, Controller--Sequentia Inc., Strongsville, OH; *U.S. Private*, pg. 985

Keaver, Dennis, Controller--Seed Corporation of America, Baltimore, MD; *U.S. Private*, pg. 981

Keck, Elizabeth K., Chief Fin. Officer & Controller--Broadcast Electronics, Inc., Quincy, IL; *U.S. Private*, pg. 531

Keck, Elizabeth K., Controller--Broadcast Programming, Seattle, WA; *U.S. Private*, pg. 531

Keck, Steven, Controller--Discovision Associates, Irvine, CA; *Int'l*, pg. 1057

Kedrick, David, Comptroller--Belliss & Morcom (USA) Inc., West Chicago, IL; *Int'l*, pg. 1065

Keeffe, Elmer C., Controller & Sec.--J.H. Harvey Company, Nashville, GA; *U.S. Private*, pg. 508

Keehfus, Thomas, Controller--Muench-Kreuzer Candle Company, Syracuse, NY; *U.S. Private*, pg. 766

Keen, James F., Sr. V.P. & Controller--First Tennessee National Corporation, Memphis, TN; *U.S. Public*, pg. 638

Keen, James F., Sr. V.P. & Controller--First Tennessee Bank National Association, Memphis, TN; *U.S. Public*, pg. 639

Keenan, David J., V.P. & Controller--Comdisco, Inc., Rosemont, IL; *U.S. Public*, pg. 407

Keenan, Ray P., Controller--Phelps Dodge Morenci Inc., Morenci, AZ; *U.S. Public*, pg. 1287

Keene, Laura, V.P. & Controller--Moroch & Assoc., Inc., Dallas, TX; *U.S. Private*, pg. 762

Kegley, John, Controller--U.S. Can Company, Newnan, GA; *U.S. Public*, pg. 1681

Kehl, Kim, V.P.-Fin. & Controller--Electro Brand, Inc., Chicago, IL; *U.S. Private*, pg. 368

Kehnast, Robert, Controller--Diehl Inc., Defiance, OH; *U.S. Private*, pg. 332

Kehnemund, Mark, Controller--Halliburton Energy Services, Houston, TX; *U.S. Public*, pg. 776

Keilman, David W., Exec. V.P. & Treas.--Comark, Bloomingdale, IL; *U.S. Private*, pg. 257

Keilman, Robert E., Comptroller--The Bank of New York Company, Inc., New York, NY; *U.S. Public*, pg. 178
Keily, Donna, Controller--Crested Butte Mountain Resort, Inc., Crested Butte, CO; *U.S. Private*, pg. 289
Keime, Donald J., Controller--Chino Mines Company, Hurley, NM; *U.S. Public*, pg. 1287
Keinert, Francoise, Controller--K-Tron Switzerland-Soder Division, Niederlenz, Switzerland; *U.S. Public*, pg. 938
Keisler, Carl, Controller--Dewberry & Davis, Fairfax, VA; *U.S. Private*, pg. 329
Keitel, Chris, Chief Fin. Officer, V.P.-Fin., Treas. & Controller--Hobart Brothers Co., Troy, OH; *U.S. Public*, pg. 866
Keith, Jeanette, Controller--Malibu Entertainment Worldwide, Dallas, TX; *U.S. Public*, pg. 1039
Kelleher, Diana, Controller--Action Equipment, Candia, NH; *U.S. Private*, pg. 14
Kelleher, Paul F., Controller & Chief Acctg. Officer--Thermo Cardiosystems Inc., Woburn, MA; *U.S. Public*, pg. 1592
Keller, Chris, Controller & Treasurer--Life-Like Products, Inc., Baltimore, MD; *U.S. Private*, pg. 666
Keller, James E., Treas. & Controller--Rapid Mounting & Finishing Co., Chicago, IL; *U.S. Private*, pg. 910
Keller, Jeff, Chief Fin. Officer & Treas.--D.C.I., Inc., Saint Cloud, MN; *U.S. Private*, pg. 301
Keller, Pam, Controller--Ashley F. Ward, Inc., Mason, OH; *U.S. Private*, pg. 1149
Keller, Philip, Controller--United Service Equipment Company, Murfreesboro, TN; *U.S. Public*, pg. 1507
Kellett, Sherry A., Exec. V.P. & Controller--BB&T Corporation, Winston Salem, NC; *U.S. Public*, pg. 159
Kellett, Sherry A., V.P. & Controller--Branch Banking & Trust, Winston Salem, NC; *U.S. Public*, pg. 160
Kelley, Brian P., Controller--Ascom Canada Limited, Markham, Canada; *Int'l*, pg. 86
Kelley, David P., Controller--Hillsdale Tool & Mfg. Co., Hillsdale, MI; *U.S. Private*, pg. 355
Kelley, James C., Controller--Boss Manufacturing Company, Kewanee, IL; *U.S. Private*, pg. 1142
Kelley, John T., V.P. & Corp. Controller--Fort Wayne National Corporation, Fort Wayne, IN; *U.S. Public*, pg. 673
Kelley, Kristina A., Asst. Controller--Bindley Western Drug Company, Indianapolis, IN; *U.S. Public*, pg. 228
Kelliher, John M., V.P.-Fin. & Controller--The Stride Rite Corporation, Lexington, MA; *U.S. Public*, pg. 1524
Kello, Wes, V.P.--Prime Bancshares Inc., Houston, TX; *U.S.* Public, pg. 1326
Kellogg, Gary, Controller--Washington Manufacturing Company, Inc., Washington, IA; *U.S. Public*, pg. 612
Kellough, D. Eugene, V.P. & Controller--Cash America International, Inc., Fort Worth, TX; *U.S. Public*, pg. 312
Kelly, Chris, Controller--Maxitrol Co., Southfield, MI; *U.S. Private*, pg. 716
Kelly, Chris, V.P. & Controller--Remington Products Company, L.L.C., Bridgeport, CT; *U.S. Private*, pg. 921
Kelly, Dennis C., Controller--Handy & Harman, New York, NY; *U.S. Public*, pg. 780
Kelly, Edward J., V.P., Controller & Treas.--Emery Worldwide, Redwood City, CA; *U.S. Public*, pg. 281
Kelly, Gary C., Controller--Southwest Airlines Co., Dallas, TX; *U.S. Public*, pg. 1493
Kelly, James E., Sr. V.P. & Controller--Midlantic Bank, N.A., Philadelphia, PA; *U.S. Public*, pg. 1242
Kelly, James S., V.P. & Controller--Jenny Craig, Inc., La Jolla, CA; *U.S. Public*, pg. 926
Kelly, John F., Asst. Controller--Anheuser-Busch Companies, Inc., Saint Louis, MO; *U.S. Public*, pg. 113
Kelly, Joseph E., Exec. V.P. & Controller--NationsBank South, Atlanta, GA; *U.S. Public*, pg. 1163
Kelly, Kevin R., Controller--Tel-Save Holdings, Inc., New Hope, PA; *U.S. Public*, pg. 1568
Kelly, Mark, Corp. Controller--Meadowcraft, Inc., Birmingham, AL; *U.S. Private*, pg. 725
Kelly, Mike, Controller--Ward Products Corporation, North Brunswick, NJ; *U.S. Private*, pg. 1149
Kelly, Norma, Controller--Fairway Ford, Inc., Greenville, SC; *U.S. Private*, pg. 392
Kelly, Thomas A., Asst. Corp. Controller--Crown Cork & Seal Company, Inc., Philadelphia, PA; *U.S. Public*, pg. 462
Kelly, Thomas H., V.P. & Controller--Schering-Plough Corporation, Madison, NJ; *U.S. Public*, pg. 1438
Kelly, Walter E., Controller--Zions Bancorporation, Salt Lake City, UT; *U.S. Public*, pg. 1792
Kelm, Rick, Controller--J. Lee Hackett Co., Farmington, MI; *U.S. Private*, pg. 492
Kelsheimer, Brad, Controller--General Housewares Corp., Terre Haute, IN; *U.S. Public*, pg. 715
Kemp, Alan L., Controller--Airtex Products, Fairfield, IL; *U.S.* Private, pg. 1113
Kemp, Russell, Asst. Controller--Park Electrochemical Corporation, Lake Success, NY; *U.S. Public*, pg. 1258
Kempa, Steve, V.P. & Controller--M.L. Stern & Company, Inc., Beverly Hills, CA; *U.S. Private*, pg. 1041
Kempen, Bud, Controller--Pabst Brewing Co., San Antonio, TX; *U.S. Private*, pg. 954
Kempski, David, Controller--Mercury Interactive Corp., Sunnyvale, CA; *U.S. Public*, pg. 1093
Kendziera, Craig, V.P. & Corp. Controller--Tollman/Hundley Hotels, Hopewell Junction, NY; *U.S. Private*, pg. 1090
Kenley, Bill, Controller--Seven-Up Bottling Co. of St. Louis, Hazelwood, MO; *U.S. Private*, pg. 142
Kennalley, Thomas R., Treas. & Controller--Advantage Companies, Inc., Wichita, KS; *U.S. Private*, pg. 22
Kennedy, Jean, Controller--Chernin's Shoes, Inc., Chicago, IL; *U.S. Private*, pg. 233
Kennedy, Richard A., Controller--Nashua Photo Products Div., Nashua, NH; *U.S. Public*, pg. 1152
Kennedy, Robert, Controller--PrimeEnergy Corporation, Stamford, CT; *U.S. Public*, pg. 1328
Kennedy, Steve, Controller & Mgr.-MIS--Cincinnati Gear Company, Cincinnati, OH; *U.S. Private*, pg. 240
Kennely, Thomas, Controller--Steiger Tractor, Fargo, ND; *U.S. Public*, pg. 311
Kenney, Clarence J., Controller--Calgon Carbon Corporation, Pittsburgh, PA; *U.S. Public*, pg. 292
Kent, Kevin, Controller--Empress International Ltd., Port Washington, NY; *U.S. Private*, pg. 375
Keolker, Ronald H., V.P.-Fin.--Twin City Foods, Inc., Stanwood, WA; *U.S. Private*, pg. 1111
Kerechek, Bill, Controller--Louis Kemp Seafood Company, Duluth, MN; *U.S. Public*, pg. 1652
Kerfoot, William, 2nd V.P. & Controller--Wetsel-Oviatt Lumber Company, El Dorado Hills, CA; *U.S. Private*, pg. 1170
Kerkman, Leon, V.P. & Controller--Inacom Corp., Omaha, NE; *U.S. Public*, pg. 873
Kerler, Bill, Controller--R.M. Shoemaker Co., West Conshohocken, PA; *U.S. Private*, pg. 996
Kerley, Barbara J., Systems Controller--Willis Corroon Corp. of Northern Ohio, Cleveland, OH; *Int'l*, pg. 1506
Kern, Kevin C., V.P. & Controller--BWAY Corp., Atlanta, GA; *U.S. Public*, pg. 164
Kerney, S. Mark, Controller--SIGCORP, Inc., Evansville, IN; *U.S. Public*, pg. 1471
Kerney, S. Mark, Controller--Southern Indiana Gas & Electric Co., Evansville, IN; *U.S. Public*, pg. 1471
Kerns, Judy, Controller--Riley Creek Lumber Company, Laclede, ID; *U.S. Private*, pg. 931
Kerr, Gordon J., V.P. & Controller--Mark Resources Inc., Calgary, Canada; *Int'l*, pg. 842
Kerr, Robert D., Controller--LVMH Moet Hennessy Louis Vuitton, New York, NY; *Int'l*, pg. 781
Kerr, Rose, Asst. Controller--Washington Homes, Inc., Landover, MD; *U.S. Public*, pg. 1741
Kerrigan, Paul G., V.P. & Controller--Brookfield Homes Ltd., Toronto, Canada; *Int'l*, pg. 228
Kerrigan, Paul G., V.P. & Controller--Brookfield Homes, Del Mar, CA; *Int'l*, pg. 228
Kersten, James, Asst. Controller--Seaway Food Town, Inc., Maumee, OH; *U.S. Public*, pg. 1452
Kessenich, Jim, Controller--Federal Industries, Inc., Belleville, WI; *U.S. Public*, pg. 1506
Kessler, Gary, Controller--American Color, Phoenix, AZ; *U.S. Public*, pg. 1133
Kessler, Lee, Controller & Sec.--Stern & Stern Industries Inc., New York, NY; *U.S. Private*, pg. 1041
Kessler, Paula G., Controller--MasterBrand Industries, Inc., Lincolnshire, IL; *U.S. Public*, pg. 675
Kesteloot, Don, Controller--Joe E. Woods, Inc., Mesa, AZ; *U.S. Private*, pg. 1187
Kestler, Diane M., Controller--Bank of Southern Maryland, La Plata, MD; *U.S. Public*, pg. 1088
Kettinger, Robert R., Controller--Standex International Corporation, Salem, NH; *U.S. Public*, pg. 1505
Keul, Dave, V.P. & Controller--First Charter Corporation, Concord, NC; *U.S. Public*, pg. 627
Keul, Dave, Controller--First Charter National Bank, Concord, NC; *U.S. Public*, pg. 627
Keuper, Robert, Controller--South Bend Plastics, Inc., Mishawaka, IN; *U.S. Private*, pg. 1014
Keyes, Susan, V.P. & Controller--The Dartnell Corporation, Chicago, IL; *U.S. Private*, pg. 312
Keyser, Susan, Controller--Temtrol, Inc., Okarche, OK; *U.S. Public*, pg. 1193
Keyzer, B.J., Controller--Royal Begemann Group, Breda, Netherlands; *Int'l*, pg. 1133
Khachaturian, Armine, Controller--Sinclair Printing & Litho, Inc., Los Angeles, CA; *U.S. Private*, pg. 1003
Khan, Ejaz A., Controller--Vulcan Materials Company, Birmingham, AL; *U.S. Public*, pg. 1725
Khan, Hussain A., Chief Acctg. Officer & Controller--ABM Industries, San Francisco, CA; *U.S. Public*, pg. 2
Khosla, V. Ranjit, V.P., Dir.-Fin. & Controller--ITT Information Services, Inc., New York, NY; *U.S. Public*, pg. 1512
Khoury, E.R., Controller & Treas.--Morrison Textile Machinery Co., Fort Lawn, SC; *U.S. Private*, pg. 762
Khwaja, Shahid, Controller--Bird-Katema, Santee, CA; *U.S. Public*, pg. 166
Kidnie, Beth, V.P. & Controller--Co-Steel Inc., Toronto, Canada; *Int'l*, pg. 298
Kielich, Mary L., Corp. Controller--Hein-Werner Corporation, Waukesha, WI; *U.S. Public*, pg. 805
Kientzler, Nyla, Controller--Giga-Tronics Incorporated, San Ramon, CA; *U.S. Public*, pg. 742
Kieritemeyer, George, Controller--Cresline Plastic Pipe Co. Inc., Evansville, IN; *U.S. Private*, pg. 289
Kiernan, John, Controller--Veeco Instruments, Inc., Plainview, NY; *U.S. Public*, pg. 1711
Kierzek, Marty, V.P. & Controller--Grant/Jacoby, Inc., Chicago, IL; *U.S. Private*, pg. 470
Kies, J.F., Controller--Tultex Corporation, Martinsville, VA; *U.S. Public*, pg. 1644
Kietrys, Gayle, Controller--Mid-West Automation Systems, Inc., Buffalo Grove, IL; *U.S. Public*, pg. 475
Kilgore, John, Controller--Rose Printing Company, Inc., Tallahassee, FL; *U.S. Private*, pg. 945
Kilgour, David, Controller--International Water Limited, Manchester, United Kingdom; *Int'l*, pg. 1444
Kilkenney, Thomas J., V.P. & Controller--The McGraw-Hill Companies, New York, NY; *U.S. Public*, pg. 1069
Killigan, John, Controller--State Farm Mutual Automobile Insurance Company, Bloomington, IL; *U.S. Private*, pg. 1036
Killoran, Michael F., Controller--Paul Arpin Vanlines, Inc., West Warwick, RI; *U.S. Private*, pg. 85
Kim, I.S., Controller--Samsung Electronics America, Inc., Ridgefield Park, NJ; *Int'l*, pg. 1183
Kimball, Donald, V.P.-Fin. & Controller--The Newhall Land And Farming Company, Valencia, CA; *U.S. Public*, pg. 1178
Kimball, Tom, Controller--The Shelburne Corporation, Shelburne, VT; *U.S. Private*, pg. 991
Kimbell, Jerry, Controller--American Sign & Marketing Services, Inc., Florence, KY; *U.S. Public*, pg. 1309
Kimble, Duane D., Controller--Millennium Petrochemicals, Inc., Cincinnati, OH; *Int'l*, pg. 594
Kimble, Jam, Controller--Arthur A. Pozzi Co., Inc., Portland, OR; *U.S. Private*, pg. 878
Kime, Donald, Chief Oper. Officer & Controller--TV Host Inc., Harrisburg, PA; *U.S. Private*, pg. 1066
Kime, Roger, Chief Fin. Officer & Controller--Champion Boxed Beef, Denver, CO; *U.S. Private*, pg. 228
Kimes, J.J., V.P.-Admin. & Controller--NI Industries, Inc., Seal Beach, CA; *U.S. Public*, pg. 1054
Kimmel, Jerold, Controller--Bel Fuse Inc., Jersey City, NJ; *U.S. Public*, pg. 200
Kimura, Yoshimasa, Airfreight Controller--Kwe-Kintetsu World Express(S)Pte Ltd., Singapore, Singapore; *Int'l*, pg. 735
Kincaid, James, Jr., Controller--Reed Minerals, Highland, IN; *U.S. Public*, pg. 793
Kincaid, Mike, Controller & Sec.--Tractor Supply Co., Nashville, TN; *U.S. Public*, pg. 1627
Kinch, Steve, Controller--Rittenhouse Inc., Park Ridge, IL; *U.S. Private*, pg. 933
Kind, John, Controller--Taylor Corporation, Mankato, MN; *U.S. Private*, pg. 1070
Kindl, Nancy A., Chief Fin. Officer, Treas., Controller & Sec.--Portec, Inc., Lake Forest, IL; *U.S. Public*, pg. 1317
Kindler, Stephen, V.P. & Controller--Rite Aid Corporation, Camp Hill, PA; *U.S. Public*, pg. 1390
Kindsfater, Rick, Controller--Time Systems, Inc., Phoenix, AZ; *U.S. Private*, pg. 1086
Kindsvatter, James L., Controller--Cincinnati Sub-Zero Products, Inc., Cincinnati, OH; *U.S. Private*, pg. 240
Kindsvatter, Robert D., V.P. & Reg. Controller--FirstMerit Corporation, Akron, OH; *U.S. Public*, pg. 646
Kindt, Ernest J., Asst. Controller--Montana Power Company, Butte, MT; *U.S. Public*, pg. 1126
King, Dave, Controller--Dann Dee Display Fixtures, Niles, IL; *U.S. Private*, pg. 310
King, Doug, Chief Fin. Officer & Controller--Wilson Products Co., Salt Lake City, UT; *U.S. Private*, pg. 1181
King, Ellen, Controller--Westgate Inc., Port Allen, LA; *U.S. Private*, pg. 1169
King, Emmitt I., Controller--Vulcan Materials Company-Southwest Div., San Antonio, TX; *U.S. Public*, pg. 1726
King, Eugene J., Jr., Sr. V.P. & Asst. Treas.-Corp. Control--A.G. Edwards, Inc., Saint Louis, MO; *U.S. Public*, pg. 565
King, Eugene J., Jr., Sr. V.P., Asst. Treas. & Comptroller--A.G. Edwards & Sons, Inc., Saint Louis, MO; *U.S. Public*, *pg. 565*
King, Jade, Controller--MCM Enterprises, Inc., Crawfordsville, IN; *U.S. Private*, pg. 686
King, John F., Sec. & Controller--Paco Pharmaceutical Services, Inc., Lakewood, NJ; *U.S. Public*, pg. 1755
King, Lawrence R., Controller--Marine Construction & Design Co., Seattle, WA; *U.S. Private*, pg. 703
King, Margaret, Controller--Buffalo Hospital Supply Co., Inc., Buffalo, NY; *U.S. Private*, pg. 179
King, Michael, Controller--Adtec Detention Systems, San Antonio, TX; *U.S. Private*, pg. 18
King, Michael, Asst. Controller--Demoulas Market Basket, Tewksbury, MA; *U.S. Private*, pg. 324
King, Michael H., Controller--Dresher, Inc., Carthage, MO; *U.S. Public*, pg. 986
King, N.J.W., Head-Grp. Compliance--HSBC Holdings plc, London, United Kingdom; *Int'l*, pg. 579
King, Pat, Controller--Rapid Power Technologies, Inc., Brookfield, CT; *U.S. Private*, pg. 910
Kinney, Thomas J., Controller--Mele Manufacturing Co., Inc., Utica, NY; *U.S. Private*, pg. 730
Kinnison, Craig, V.P. & Controller--Federal Farm Credit Banks Funding Corporation, Jersey City, NJ; *U.S. Private*, pg. 398
Kinsey, Patrick R., V.P. & Controller--Eastman Chemical Company, Kingsport, TN; *U.S. Public*, pg. 550
Kinsinger, Freeman J., Controller--AmerenCIPS, Springfield, IL; *U.S. Public*, pg. 65
Kinsinger, Freeman J., Controller, Asst. Treas. & Asst. Sec.--CIPSCO Investment Company, Springfield, IL; *U.S. Public*, pg. 66
Kipfstuhl, Leo A., Asst. Controller-Opers.--Cleveland-Cliffs Inc, Cleveland, OH; *U.S. Public*, pg. 386
Kirby, Maureen, Dir.-Fin. & Acctg.--LoJack Corporation, Dedham, MA; *U.S. Public*, pg. 1012
Kirchoff, Phillip, Chief Fin. Officer & Controller--Farmway Co-Op Inc., Beloit, KS; *U.S. Private*, pg. 396
Kirk, Sherron A., Controller--USAA Investment Management Co., San Antonio, TX; *U.S. Private*, pg. 1114
Kirkish, Mark, Controller--Rite-Hite Corporation, Milwaukee, WI; *U.S. Private*, pg. 933
Kirkland, Roy K., Controller--Encon Safety Products, Inc., Houston, TX; *U.S. Public*, pg. 1705
Kirkman, J., Controller--Hosokawa Micron Ltd., Brampton, Canada; *Int'l*, pg. 636
Kirkscey, Jerry, Controller--Heavy Machines, Inc., Memphis, TN; *U.S. Private*, pg. 518
Kirschner, John, Controller--Connecticut Spring & Stamping Corporation, Farmington, CT; *U.S. Private*, pg. 263
Kiser, Jeff, Controller-Consumer--Playtex Products Inc., Westport, CT; *U.S. Public*, pg. 1310
Kiser, Ron, Controller--FARO Technologies, Inc., Lake Mary, FL; *U.S. Public*, pg. 613
Kissinger, Karen G., V.P. & Controller--Tucson Electric Power Company, Tucson, AZ; *U.S. Public*, pg. 1670
Kissock, James, Controller--Latrobe Brewing Co., Latrobe, PA; *Int'l*, pg. 680
Kist, William A., V.P. & Controller--Stevens International, Inc., Fort Worth, TX; *U.S. Public*, pg. 1517
Kita, John J., Treas. & Controller--A.O. Smith Corporation, Milwaukee, WI; *U.S. Public*, pg. 1476
Kitamura, Kazumi, Controller--The Berlitz Schools of Languages (Japan) Inc., Tokyo, Japan; *U.S. Public*, pg. 222
Kitchens, Deborah, V.P. & Controller--Kerr-McGee Corporation, Oklahoma City, OK; *U.S. Public*, pg. 952

Kitts, Diane L., V.P. & Controller--Jerome-Duncan Ford, Sterling Heights, MI; *U.S. Private*, pg. 586

Kitzelmann, Volker, Controller--J. Dieffenbacher GmbH & Co., Eppingen, Germany; *Int'l*, pg. 413

Klaczkiewicz, David, Controller--Great Lakes-Eglinton, Bridgeport, MI; *U.S. Public*, pg. 1676

Klaers, John, Controller--Minnesota Electric Supply Company, Willmar, MN; *U.S. Private*, pg. 750

Klag, Robert W., Sr. V.P., Controller & Treas.--National Insurance Group, South San Francisco, CA; *U.S. Public*, pg. 1157

Klash, Ron, Controller--RMS Techs, Inc., Lanham, MD; *U.S. Private*, pg. 905

Klatt, David, Controller--Nodak Mutual Insurance Company, Fargo, ND; *U.S. Private*, pg. 800

Klatzkin, Terri, Controller--Clark Enterprises, Inc., Bethesda, MD; *U.S. Private*, pg. 242

Klaus-Owens, Laura, Controller--North Shore Movers, Northbrook, IL; *U.S. Private*, pg. 805

Klauser, Ken, V.P. & Controller--Ciba Specialty Chemicals, Tarrytown, NY; *Int'l*, pg. 291

Klebe, Terry A., V.P. & Controller--Cooper Industries, Inc., Houston, TX; *U.S. Public*, pg. 442

Kleeberger, Kent A., Corp. Controller--The Limited, Inc., Columbus, OH; *U.S. Public*, pg. 995

Klein, Anne, Controller--Dani Michaels, Inc., New York, NY; *U.S. Private*, pg. 309

Klein, Barbara A., V.P. & Comptroller--Ameritech Corporation, Chicago, IL; *U.S. Public*, pg. 97

Klein, Ed, Controller--Benjamin Moore & Co., Montvale, NJ; *U.S. Private*, pg. 133

Klein, Jacqui, Controller--Quebecor Printing Concord, Concord, Canada; *Int'l*, pg. 1077

Klein, R. Chris, Controller--Quest Medical, Inc., Allen, TX; *U.S. Public*, pg. 1352

Klein, Stan, Controller, Treas. & Sec.--Cormier Chevrolet Company, Inc., Carson, CA; *U.S. Private*, pg. 276

Kleinhenz, Dennis, Chief Fin. Officer & Controller--Radix Wire Company, Cleveland, OH; *U.S. Private*, pg. 907

Kleinschmidt, Bob, Asst. Fin. Dir. & V.P. & Controller-Carlson Hospitality Grp.--Carlson Companies, Inc., Minnetonka, MN; *U.S. Private*, pg. 211

Klerk, Bill, Controller & Asst. Treas.--McNeel International Corp., Tampa, FL; *U.S. Private*, pg. 724

Klethschmidt, Ron, Controller--Bay Industries Inc., Green Bay, WI; *U.S. Private*, pg. 124

Klie, Robert, Controller--NBBJ, Columbus, OH; *U.S. Private*, pg. 771

Kline, Michael, Controller--Furnival/State Machinery Co., Hatfield, PA; *Int'l*, pg. 744

Kling, Brad, V.P. & Controller--Alcon Laboratories, Inc., Fort Worth, TX; *Int'l*, pg. 916

Klinge, Robert, Controller--Prab, Inc., Kalamazoo, MI; *U.S. Public*, pg. 1319

Klinger, Robert, Controller--John Copes Food Products, Inc., Rheems, PA; *U.S. Private*, pg. 274

Klingle, Frances R., Chief Admin. Officer & Controller--American Waste Services, Inc., Warren, OH; *U.S. Public*, pg. 94

Klingstedt, John, V.P. & Controller--Marcus Cable Company, L.P., Dallas, TX; *U.S. Private*, pg. 702

Klinker, Kenneth J., Controller--Meridian Insurance Group, Inc., Indianapolis, IN; *U.S. Public*, pg. 1095

Klintworth, Graham, Controller--Command Plastic Corporation, Akron, OH; *U.S. Private*, pg. 257

Klisurich, Anne K., Controller--Wisconsin Energy Corporation, Milwaukee, WI; *U.S. Public*, pg. 1773

Klisurich, Anne K., Controller & Asst. Sec.--Wisconsin Electric Power Company, Milwaukee, WI; *U.S. Public*, pg. 1773

Kloc, Thomas J., Controller--Monongahela Power Co., Fairmont, WV; *U.S. Public*, pg. 42

Kloc, Thomas J., Comptroller--The Potomac Edison Co., Hagerstown, MD; *U.S. Public*, pg. 42

Kloc, Thomas J., Controller--West Penn Power Co., Greensburg, PA; *U.S. Public*, pg. 42

Klocek, Gary, Controller--Jones Apparel Group, Inc., Bristol, PA; *U.S. Public*, pg. 933

Klocke, Tina, Controller & Emp. Benefits--Clayton Corporation, Fenton, MO; *U.S. Private*, pg. 244

Klomes, Joseph, Controller--Azteca Foods, Incorporated, Chicago, IL; *U.S. Private*, pg. 104

Klompas, H., Controller--The Molson Companies Limited, Toronto, Canada; *Int'l*, pg. 887

Klonowski, Len, V.P. & Controller--Candle Corporation of America, Des Plaines, IL; *U.S. Public*, pg. 239

Kloppe, William, Controller--Stuart Circle Hospital Corporation, Atlanta, GA; *U.S. Public*, pg. 1036

Klucharits, James R., Controller--Isomedix Inc., Whippany, NJ; *U.S. Public*, pg. 1515

Kluesner, Rick, Controller--Cablewave Systems, North Haven, CT; *U.S. Private*, pg. 197

Kluttz, Richard S., Controller & Treas.--Brigadier Homes of North Carolina, Nashville, NC; *U.S. Public*, pg. 318

Kmak, Thomas R., V.P. & Controller--MagneTek, Inc., Nashville, TN; *U.S. Public*, pg. 1037

Knapp, Gregory A., Controller & Asst. Treas.--The Empire District Electric Company, Joplin, MO; *U.S. Public*, pg. 579

Kneipp, Jerry D., Mgr.-Acctg.--The Ohio Art Company, Inc., Bryan, OH; *U.S. Public*, pg. 1214

Knepp, Lynn E., Chief Fin. Officer & Controller--Gannett Fleming Affiliates, Inc., Camp Hill, PA; *U.S. Private*, pg. 439

Knese, William F., V.P., Treas. & Controller--CLARCOR, Inc., Rockford, IL; *U.S. Public*, pg. 381

Knesek, Mike, Controller--Enterprise Products Company, Houston, TX; *U.S. Private*, pg. 377

Knetsch, Manfred, Dir.-Lending Opers./Coordination & Control--European Investment Bank, Luxembourg, Luxembourg; *Int'l*, pg. 465

Knight, Howard, Controller--Kemper Insurance Companies, Long Grove, IL; *U.S. Private*, pg. 614

Knight, J.D., Controller--Flowserve Corporation, Valve Div., Cookeville, TN; *U.S. Public*, pg. 658

Knight, Jim, V.P. & Controller--Mount Vernon Mills, Inc., Greenville, SC; *U.S. Private*, pg. 835

Knight, Ken, Chief Fin. Officer & Comptroller--Akers Packaging Service Inc., Middletown, OH; *U.S. Private*, pg. 29

Knight, Will, Controller--Johnson Ross Corporation, Champaign, IL; *U.S. Public*, pg. 279

Knoblauch, Fred, Controller--Willis Corroon Corp. of Kansas, Wichita, KS; *Int'l*, pg. 1506

Knoll, Dave, Controller--Advance Machine Company, Plymouth, MN; *Int'l*, pg. 932

Knoller, Cathy, Controller--S & P Comstock, Harrison, NY; *U.S. Public*, pg. 1071

Knorr, Gerald R., Asst. Controller--American Electric Power Service Corp., Columbus, OH; *U.S. Public*, pg. 72

Knutson, Dan, V.P., Controller & Treas.--Land O'Lakes, Inc., Arden Hills, MN; *U.S. Private*, pg. 645

Kober, Steven E., V.P. & Controller--Sony Electronics, Park Ridge, NJ; *Int'l*, pg. 1281

Kobiernicki, Walter J., Comptroller--Chicago Tube & Iron Co., Chicago, IL; *U.S. Private*, pg. 235

Kobilarcsik, Jim, Controller--Thermal Technology Industries, North Kansas City, MO; *U.S. Private*, pg. 1080

Kobylarz, Michael, V.P. & Controller--The Texwipe Co., Inc., Upper Saddle River, NJ; *U.S. Private*, pg. 1079

Koch, Jerry, V.P.-Corp. Controller--Regal Ware, Inc., Kewaskum, WI; *U.S. Private*, pg. 917

Koch, Mark, Controller--Reunion Industries, Inc., Stamford, CT; *U.S. Public*, pg. 1383

Koch, Richard, Controller--Dale Carnegie & Associates, Garden City, NY; *U.S. Private*, pg. 308

Koch, Richard, Dir.-Acctg.--Seattle City Light, Seattle, WA; *U.S. Private*, pg. 979

Kochanski, Thaddeus M., V.P. & Controller--The Lehigh Press, Inc., Cherry Hill, NJ; *U.S. Private*, pg. 658

Kochevar, Mark, V.P. & Controller--Hoffer's Inc., Schofield, WI; *U.S. Private*, pg. 239

Kochman, Vicki, Controller--Textile Chemical Co., Inc., Reading, PA; *Int'l*, pg. 1458

Kocsi, Carl, Controller--Overton Moore & Associates, Gardena, CA; *U.S. Private*, pg. 823

Koda, Karen, Controller--Ranir Corporation/DCP, Grand Rapids, MI; *U.S. Private*, pg. 909

Kodosky, Thomas M., V.P. & Corp. Controller--Elkay Manufacturing Company, Oak Brook, IL; *U.S. Private*, pg. 372

Koebele, David, Controller--Advance Circuits, Inc., Minnetonka, MN; *Int'l*, pg. 713

Koefer, Erich, Grp. Treas. & Controller--Mikron Holding AG, Biel, Switzerland; *Int'l*, pg. 866

Koegler, Ronald, V.P. & Controller--Lexford Residential Trust, Columbus, OH; *U.S. Public*, pg. 991

Koehler, Bill, Controller--Unity Manufacturing Co., Chicago, IL; *U.S. Private*, pg. 1126

Koehnlein, James E., Controller--Wilkins-Rogers Incorporated, Ellicott City, MD; *U.S. Private*, pg. 1176

Koenig, Jeffrey H., V.P.-Fin., Controller & Treas.--Executive Risk, Inc., Simsbury, CT; *U.S. Public*, pg. 599

Koenig, Manfred, Controller--Cherry Mikroschalter GmbH, Auerbach, Germany; *U.S. Public*, pg. 346

Koenning, George, Controller--Gus Machado Enterprises, Hialeah, FL; *U.S. Private*, pg. 691

Koerner, Jerry, Controller--R-4 KIT Mfg. Co., Mc Pherson, KS; *U.S. Public*, pg. 962

Koernner, Virginia, Controller--Louisville Bedding Company, Louisville, KY; *U.S. Private*, pg. 677

Koetting, John K., V.P. & Controller--Kansas City Life Insurance Co., Kansas City, MO; *U.S. Public*, pg. 942

Koffman, Stephen V., Controller--United States Sugar Corporation, Clewiston, FL; *U.S. Private*, pg. 1126

Koh, Y.H., Controller--Karahm Company Limited, Kyongki, Korea; *Int'l*, pg. 891

Kohany, R.E., Controller--Specialty Products and Insulation Company, Lancaster, PA; *U.S. Public*, pg. 913

Kohler, Roland, Controller--Holderbank Financiere Glaris Ltd., Glaris, Switzerland; *Int'l*, pg. 628

Kohos, Howard, Chief Acctg. Officer & Corp. Controller--Global Direct Mail Corp, Port Washington, NY; *U.S. Public*, pg. 747

Kojima, Teruo, Controller--Haseko Corporation, Tokyo, Japan; *Int'l*, pg. 599

Koletty, Joseph, Controller--American Sweetners, inc., Frazer, PA; *U.S. Private*, pg. 63

Koller, Michael A., Controller--Tube City Inc., Glassport, PA; *U.S. Private*, pg. 1108

Kollias, Ernie, V.P.-Fin. & Controller--North American Publishing Company, Philadelphia, PA; *U.S. Private*, pg. 803

Kolstad, Brenda, Controller--Hubbard Feeds Inc., Mankato, MN; *Int'l*, pg. 1116

Koltz, Ronald A., Controller--Binks Sames Corporation, Franklin Park, IL; *U.S. Public*, pg. 229

Komatz, Lawrence J., V.P. & Controller--Rockwell International Corporation, Costa Mesa, CA; *U.S. Public*, pg. 1397

Komaya, K., Exec. V.P.- Fin. & Controller--Kawasaki Motors Corp., U.S.A., Irvine, CA; *Int'l*, pg. 725

Kometer, Clyde W., Controller--Kohler Company, Kohler, WI; *U.S. Private*, pg. 630

Kondor, Patricia, Controller--IDX Systems Corporation, Burlington, VT; *U.S. Public*, pg. 854

Konicczny, Scott J., Controller--Secom General Corporation, Novi, MI; *U.S. Public*, pg. 1453

Konn, Jeffrey, Controller--Dick Corporation, Large, PA; *U.S. Private*, pg. 331

Kontz, R.J., V.P.-Fin. Reporting--AEGON USA, Inc., Baltimore, MD; *Int'l*, pg. 26

Kooman, Clinton L., Controller--IDEX Corporation, Northbrook, IL; *U.S. Public*, pg. 862

Koons, Kevin, Controller--Allied Building Products Corporation, East Rutherford, NJ; *U.S. Private*, pg. 38

Koos, Gary, Controller--Logistix, Fremont, CA; *U.S. Private*, pg. 673

Kopala, Leonard M., Controller--Cole Hersee Company, Boston, MA; *U.S. Private*, pg. 251

Kopatz, Margaret, Controller & Asst. Treas.--Valu Discount, Incorporated, Louisville, KY; *U.S. Private*, pg. 1132

Kopff, Matthew, Controller--Country Mutual Insurance Company, Bloomington, IL; *U.S. Private*, pg. 279

Kopka, M.W., Controller--Kemlite Company, Joliet, IL; *U.S. Public*, pg. 457

Kopp, Joseph T., Controller, Treas. & Sec.--Massman Construction Company, Kansas City, MO; *U.S. Private*, pg. 713

Kopp, Melvin, Chief Fin. Officer & Controller--Block Drug Company, Inc., Jersey City, NJ; *U.S. Public*, pg. 236

Korade, Donald B., Controller--AK Steel Corporation, Middletown, OH; *U.S. Public*, pg. 7

Korber, Jessica, Controller, Treas. & Sec.--J. Korber & Company, Albuquerque, NM; *U.S. Private*, pg. 632

Kordalewski, Fred, V.P. & Controller--Broan Limited, Mississauga, Canada; *U.S. Public*, pg. 1194

Korducki, Edward J., Chief Fin. Officer & Controller--California Drop Forge, Los Angeles, CA; *U.S. Public*, pg. 612

Kornblatt, Oscar, Controller--SMI Joist Nevada, Fallon, NV; *U.S. Public*, pg. 413

Korobov, Alan G., Controller--COMSAT Corporation, Bethesda, MD; *U.S. Public*, pg. 424

Korpisaari, Hannu, Sr. V.P. & Controller--Valmet Corporation, Helsinki, Finland; *Int'l*, pg. 1447

Korsakov, Allan B., Controller--Southdown, Inc., Houston, TX; *U.S. Public*, pg. 1488

Korsnack, James J., Controller--La-Z-Boy Incorporated, Monroe, MI; *U.S. Public*, pg. 972

Korth, Laurie, Controller--U.M. Holding Limited, Haddonfield, NJ; *U.S. Private*, pg. 1113

Kos, Donald J., Controller & Treas.--Tradehome Shoe Stores, Inc., Saint Paul, MN; *U.S. Private*, pg. 1095

Koser, Sue, V.P. & Controller-ACC--AMCOL International Corp., Arlington Heights, IL; *U.S. Public*, pg. 63

Kosinski, Robert J., Controller--H.D. Hudson Manufacturing Company, Chicago, IL; *U.S. Private*, pg. 545

Koslosky, David A., Controller--Advanced Accessories Systems, LLC., Sterling Heights, MI; *U.S. Private*, pg. 21

Kosmo, Susan J., Asst. Controller--Wisconsin Power & Light Company, Madison, WI; *U.S. Public*, pg. 1728

Kosmo, Susan J., Asst. Controller--South Beloit Water, Gas & Electric Co., South Beloit, IL; *U.S. Public*, pg. 1728

Kost, Ken, Controller--Danisco Ingredients USA, Inc., New Century, KS; *Int'l*, pg. 378

Kostelni, Charles W.J., Asst. Controller--Bontex, Buena Vista, VA; *U.S. Public*, pg. 734

Kostock, Arlene, Controller--Pacifica Real Estate Group, Santa Barbara, CA; *U.S. Private*, pg. 832

Kostopoulos, George, Controller--A.T. Clayton & Company, Inc., Greenwich, CT; *U.S. Private*, pg. 244

Kotara, Ken, Controller--Dresser Industries, Inc., Dallas, TX; *U.S. Public*, pg. 528

Kothe, Linda, V.P. & Controller--Etienne Aigner, New York, NY; *U.S. Private*, pg. 384

Kotlinsky, Gregory, Fin. Controller--ISK Biotech, Mentor, OH; *Int'l*, pg. 689

Koucouthakis, Barbara S., V.P. & Controller--Transocean Offshore, Inc., Houston, TX; *U.S. Public*, pg. 1631

Koury, Don, Controller--Green Spot Packaging Inc., Claremont, CA; *U.S. Private*, pg. 477

Kouts, Robert, Controller--VLSI Technology, Inc., San Jose, CA; *U.S. Public*, pg. 1703

Kovac, Rae, Controller & Dir.-Data Processing--Holiday RV Superstores, Inc., Orlando, FL; *U.S. Public*, pg. 829

Kovack, Roger F., Controller--Unicom Corporation, Chicago, IL; *U.S. Public*, pg. 1664

Kovack, Roger F., Controller--ComEd, Chicago, IL; *U.S. Public*, pg. 1664

Koval, Thomas J., Controller & Asst. Treas.--Pennsylvania Enterprises Inc., Wilkes-Barre, PA; *U.S. Public*, pg. 1271

Koval, Thomas J., Controller & Asst. Treas.--PG Energy, Inc., Wilkes-Barre, PA; *U.S. Public*, pg. 1271

Kovalcheck, Steve, Controller--Mill-Rose Company, Mentor, OH; *U.S. Private*, pg. 746

Kovanda, Gary, Controller--Comark, Bloomingdale, IL; *U.S. Private*, pg. 257

Koved, Lance, Controller--York International Corporation, York, PA; *U.S. Public*, pg. 1789

Kowal, Chris, Controller--YSI Incorporated, Yellow Springs, OH; *U.S. Private*, pg. 1195

Kowal, Peter, Chief Fin. Officer & Controller--Premier Metal Products Company, Bronx, NY; *U.S. Private*, pg. 881

Kowalski, Mary A., Controller--Antares Group Inc., Cleveland, OH; *U.S. Private*, pg. 76

Kowalski, Russell, Controller--Adair Greene Advertising, Atlanta, GA; *U.S. Private*, pg. 16

Kowasodit, M., Controller--Coast Grain Company, Inc., Ontario, CA; *U.S. Private*, pg. 248

Kraeft, Roal H., Controller--Polygram N.V., Baarn, Netherlands; *Int'l*, pg. 1051

Kraemer, Sandra, Controller--Nuevo Energy Company, Houston, TX; *U.S. Public*, pg. 1206

Kraff, Eric, V.P., Controller & Treas.--MediaOne, Boston, MA; *U.S. Public*, pg. 1688

Kraft, Kyle, Controller-CMC Steel Grp.--Structural Metals, Inc., Seguin, TX; *U.S. Public*, pg. 412

Kraft, Peter, Controller--Elektro Metall Export Gmbh, Ingolstadt, Germany; *U.S. Private*, pg. 313

Kraft, Ralph, Controller--Ropak Corporation, Fullerton, CA; *Int'l*, pg. 811

Krakora, Kevin J., V.P. & Controller--Alumax Inc., Atlanta, GA; *U.S. Public*, pg. 59

Krakowiak, Tom, Controller--Union Special Corp., Huntley, IL; *Int'l*, pg. 716

Kramer, William, III, V.P. & Controller--Reuland Electric Company, City of Industry, CA; *U.S. Private*, pg. 925

Krasinski, Joe, Controller--Tri-K Industries, Inc., Northvale, NJ; *U.S. Private*, pg. 1100

Krathe, Kjell, Controller--Helly-Hansen A/S, Moss, Norway; *Int'l*, pg. 1010
Kraupp, Michael J., V.P. & Controller--SkyWest Inc., Saint George, UT; *U.S. Public*, pg. 1476
Kraupp, Michael J., V.P. & Controller--SkyWest Airlines, Inc., Saint George, UT; *U.S. Public*, pg. 1476
Krause, Donald L., Sr. V.P. & Controller--Newell Co., Freeport, IL; *U.S. Public*, pg. 1176
Krause, Eileen, Controller--Vallerie's Transport Service, Inc., Norwalk, CT; *U.S. Private*, pg. 1131
Kready, Dean, Controller--Denlinger, Inc., Paradise, PA; *U.S. Private*, pg. 324
Krebs, David, Controller--Humana Inc., Louisville, KY; *U.S. Public*, pg. 847
Krebs, Douglas, Controller--Alpha Mills Corp., Schuylkill Haven, PA; *U.S. Private*, pg. 45
Kreider, Rich, Asst. Controller--Kohlberg Kravis Roberts & Co., New York, NY; *U.S. Private*, pg. 629
Kreider, Robert A., Treas. & Controller--Banta Corporation, Menasha, WI; *U.S. Public*, pg. 187
Krein, Paul, Controller--Olson Rug Company, Chicago, IL; *U.S. Private*, pg. 815
Kreith, Joe, Controller--Lombard Lincoln-Mercury & Leasing, Inc., Lombard, IL; *U.S. Private*, pg. 673
Kremaric, Mark, Controller--Silgan Containers, La Porte, IN; *U.S. Public*, pg. 1473
Krenek, Wilfred M., Chief Acctg. Officer, V.P. & Controller--Daniel Industries, Inc., Houston, TX; *U.S. Public*, pg. 482
Kresco, Dolores, Controller--Flexcon Co., Inc., Spencer, MA; *U.S. Private*, pg. 412
Kretovic, Michael, Controller & Sec.--Don Alleson, Inc., Rochester, NY; *U.S. Private*, pg. 339
Krikorian, Deborah, Controller--Walker Magnetics Group, Inc., Worcester, MA; *U.S. Private*, pg. 1147
Krikorian, Mark, V.P. & Controller--Armor All Products Group, Oakland, CA; *U.S. Public*, pg. 387
Krill, Steve, Controller--Southtec, Inc., Albany, NY; *U.S. Private*, pg. 1015
Kriste, Keith, Controller--Applied Microsystems Corporation, Redmond, WA; *U.S. Public*, pg. 123
Kritzman, Leslie, Controller--Progressive Driver Services, Inc., Jacksonville, FL; *U.S. Private*, pg. 890
Krizan, Jerry, Controller--Doubleday Bros. & Co., Kalamazoo, MI; *U.S. Public*, pg. 1506
Kroenke, Ralph J., Controller--Lindsay Manufacturing Company, Lindsay, NE; *U.S. Public*, pg. 999
Kroetz, Steven, Controller--NDS, Columbus, OH; *Int'l*, pg. 918
Krol, Casmir, Controller--Milton Bradley Company, East Longmeadow, MA; *U.S. Public*, pg. 797
Kroll, Joe, V.P. & Controller--AAF-International, Louisville, KY; *U.S. Private*, pg. 3
Kroll, Thomas A., Corp. Controller--Fedders Corp., Liberty Corner, NJ; *U.S. Public*, pg. 614
Kron, Jim, Controller--Frigidaire Home Products-Freezer Products, Saint Cloud, MN; *Int'l*, pg. 440
Kropej, K., Controller--Moore Ges.m.b.H., Vienna, Austria; *Int'l*, pg. 889
Krueger, Bruce, Controller--AAF McQuay, Inc., Baltimore, MD; *U.S. Private*, pg. 2
Krueger, John H., Controller--Valero Energy Corporation, San Antonio, TX; *U.S. Public*, pg. 1704
Krueger, Steve, V.P.-Fin.--Marine Travelift, Inc., Sturgeon Bay, WI; *U.S. Private*, pg. 703
Krueger, Terry, Chief Fin. Officer & Controller--Dairy Farmers of America, Inc., Arlington, TX; *U.S. Private*, pg. 307
Kruger, Anders, Controller--Icopal a/s, Herlev, Denmark; *Int'l*, pg. 658
Kruger, Jurgen, Controller--Hoechst Aktiengesellschaft, Frankfurt/Main, Germany; *Int'l*, pg. 624
Kruglik, Bob, Controller--Cooper Instrument Corp., Middlefield, CT; *U.S. Private*, pg. 274
Kruis, Robert, Controller--Ato-Findley, Inc., Wauwatosa, WI; *Int'l*, pg. 445
Kruk, Dan, Controller-Personal--Playtex Products Inc., Westport, CT; *U.S. Public*, pg. 1310
Krumenacker, John J., Controller--Hvide Marine Incorporated, Fort Lauderdale, FL; *U.S. Public*, pg. 851
Kruml, K., Controller--Jetcom, Cincinnati, OH; *U.S. Public*, pg. 1329
Krumsier, Karl, Exec. V.P.-Controlling--Bosch Automotive Group, Farmington, MI; *Int'l*, pg. 204
Krupa, Constance R., Controller--John Dusenbery Co., Inc., Randolph, NJ; *U.S. Private*, pg. 349
Kruzel, Albert, Controller--The Dwyer Group, Inc., Waco, TX; *U.S. Public*, pg. 537
Kruznowski, Pete, Controller--Heat Bath Park Metallurgical Corp., Indian Orchard, MA; *U.S. Private*, pg. 518
Krygiel, Debra, Asst. Controller--Laughlin/Constable, Inc., Milwaukee, WI; *U.S. Private*, pg. 653
Krzeminski, Keith S., V.P. & Controller--Quaker State Corporation, Irving, TX; *U.S. Public*, pg. 1348
Ksiazek, William P., V.P. & Controller--Sequa Corporation, New York, NY; *U.S. Public*, pg. 1458
Kubit, Kenneth, V.P. & Controller--Great Lakes Realty Corp., Livonia, MI; *U.S. Private*, pg. 475
Kubitz, Morris, Controller--Braeburn Alloy Steel, Lower Burrell, PA; *U.S. Private*, pg. 193
Kublic, Mike, V.P. & Controller--BancTec, Inc., Dallas, TX; *U.S. Public*, pg. 176
Kucharski, Frank, Controller--Brawney Plastics, Inc., Chicago, IL; *U.S. Private*, pg. 166
Kuehnau, Robert J., Corp. Controller--Methode Electronics Inc., Chicago, IL; *U.S. Public*, pg. 1101
Kuei, Gina, Controller--Jaran Inc., San Francisco, CA; *U.S. Private*, pg. 582
Kuei, Gina, Controller--Lilli Ann Corporation, San Francisco, CA; *U.S. Private*, pg. 582
Kuensberg, Cornelia V., Controller--Thermoplast und Apparatebau GmbH, Idstein, Germany; *Int'l*, pg. 1381
Kugler, Anthony, Controller & Sec.--Hudson Valley Paper Company, Albany, NY; *U.S. Private*, pg. 546
Kuhn, Arden, Controller--Bou-Matic, Madison, WI; *U.S. Private*, pg. 301
Kujala, Marilyn, Controller--Butler Automatic, Inc., Canton, MA; *U.S. Private*, pg. 189
Kulin, Richard, Controller--The Coon-De Visser Co., Royal Oak, MI; *U.S. Private*, pg. 273
Kulka, Jeffrey, Controller--Aearo Company, Boston, MA; *U.S. Private*, pg. 23
Kulkusky, Robert, Controller--Springfield Precision Instruments, Inc., Wood Ridge, NJ; *U.S. Private*, pg. 1027
Kumar, Neil, Controller--HTL/Kin-Tech Division, Yorba Linda, CA; *U.S. Public*, pg. 1250
Kuneman, Thomas, Controller & Sec.--LK Tool USA, Inc., Brighton, MI; *Int'l*, pg. 1418
Kunkel, David A., Controller--Frigidaire Home Products-Range Products, Springfield, TN; *Int'l*, pg. 440
Kunz, Ray, Controller--Watlow Electric Manufacturing Company, Saint Louis, MO; *U.S. Private*, pg. 1153
Kunzmann, Raymond F., Chief Fin. Officer, V.P.-Fin. & Controller--Axsys Technologies, Inc., New York, NY; *U.S. Public*, pg. 157
Kupfer, James M., V.P. & Controller--Jockey International, Inc., Kenosha, WI; *U.S. Private*, pg. 588
Kureipe, Varkey, Controller--Ranjit Corporation, Cedar Knolls, NJ; *U.S. Private*, pg. 909
Kuriskin, Eileen, Controller--Victory Refrigeration Co. LC, Cherry Hill, NJ; *U.S. Private*, pg. 1139
Kurland, Fred, V.P. & Controller--Syntex, Palo Alto, CA; *Int'l*, pg. 1120
Kuroski, J. Katherine, V.P. & Controller--Payson Casters, Inc., Gurnee, IL; *U.S. Private*, pg. 844
Kurpeck, Kevin, Controller--DKB & Partners, Inc., Morristown, NJ; *U.S. Private*, pg. 302
Kurrie, Harry R., Auditor--General Motors Acceptance Corporation (GMAC), Detroit, MI; *U.S. Public*, pg. 719
Kurtis, Ron, Controller--Journal Broadcast Group, Inc., Milwaukee, WI; *U.S. Private*, pg. 601
Kurtz, Brian M., Chief Admin. Officer & Sr. V.P.--Alexander's, Inc., Saddle Brook, NJ; *U.S. Public*, pg. 1725
Kurtz, Kevin, Controller--Penn Champ, East Butler, PA; *U.S. Private*, pg. 145
Kurtz, Richard E., Controller--Abbott Diagnostic Products, North Chicago, IL; *U.S. Public*, pg. 13
Kurtz, Robert G., Asst. Controller--The New York Times Company, New York, NY; *U.S. Public*, pg. 1173
Kurzenberger, Jed, Controller--The Gerstenslager Company, Wooster, OH; *U.S. Public*, pg. 1780
Kusnic, Richard A., V.P. & Controller--Central Reserve Life Corporation, Strongsville, OH; *U.S. Public*, pg. 326
Kutner, Jeffrey, Corp. Controller--DAQ Electronics Inc., Piscataway, NJ; *U.S. Private*, pg. 300
Kuykendall, James S., Controller & Asst. Sec.--Bar-S Foods Co., Phoenix, AZ; *U.S. Private*, pg. 114
Kuzmar, Richard A., V.P. & Controller--Ameritech, Chicago, IL; *U.S. Public*, pg. 97
Kuzmar, Richard A., V.P. & Comptroller--Ameritech, Detroit, MI; *U.S. Public*, pg. 97
Kuzmar, Richard A., V.P. & Comptroller--Ameritech, Milwaukee, WI; *U.S. Public*, pg. 97
Kuzmar, Richard A., V.P. & Controller--Indiana Bell Telephone Company, Inc., Indianapolis, IN; *U.S. Public*, pg. 98
Kuzmar, Richard A., V.P. & Comptroller--Ameritech Phone Company, Cleveland, OH; *U.S. Public*, pg. 98
Kvapil, David J., V.P. & Controller--Southern Union Company, Austin, TX; *U.S. Public*, pg. 1491
Kvarda, Kathy, Controller--Alliance Semiconductor Corp., San Jose, CA; *U.S. Public*, pg. 47
Kwan, Guy, Controller--Loews Corporation, New York, NY; *U.S. Public*, pg. 1010
Kwong, Stephen T., Controller--Noma Industries Limited, North York, Canada; *Int'l*, pg. 954
Kyle, Marjorie E., V.P. & Controller-Weston Foods--George Weston Limited, Toronto, Canada; *Int'l*, pg. 1494
Kyle, Marjorie E., Controller--Weston Foods, Toronto, Canada; *Int'l*, pg. 1495
Kyllo, Rod, Controller & Mgr.-Fin. & Acctg.--King Company, Owatonna, MN; *U.S. Public*, pg. 1676
La Forgia, Robert, Sr. V.P. & Controller--Hilton Hotels Corporation, Beverly Hills, CA; *U.S. Public*, pg. 828
La Gioia, Giorgio, Controller--SASIB SpA, Bologna, Italy; *Int'l*, pg. 1194
La Rochere, Gael de, V.P. & Controller--Schneider S.A., Boulogne-Billancourt, France; *Int'l*, pg. 1207
Laaksonen, Juha, Controller--Neste Oy, Espoo, Finland; *Int'l*, pg. 912
Labak, Joseph, V.P. & Controller--Rieter Automotive North America Inc, Farmington Hills, MI; *Int'l*, pg. 1117
LaBoskey, John, V.P. & Controller--BEI Sensors and Systems Company, Sylmar, CA; *U.S. Public*, pg. 160
LaBounty, Dale, Controller--National Lamination Co., Des Plaines, IL; *U.S. Private*, pg. 1068
Labrato, Ronnie R., Controller--Gulf Power Company, Pensacola, FL; *U.S. Public*, pg. 1490
LaBrecque, Ray, Controller--NAPCO, Inc., Terryville, CT; *U.S. Public*, pg. 1592
Labrie, R., Controller--Nickerson Lumber Company, Orleans, MA; *U.S. Private*, pg. 798
Labriola, Pat, Controller--Rymer International Seafood Inc., Chicago, IL; *U.S. Public*, pg. 1414
Labrum, Paula, Controller--Robson Communities, Sun Lakes, AZ; *U.S. Private*, pg. 937
Labrusciano, Frank, Controller--Nestle Beverage Company, Freehold, NJ; *Int'l*, pg. 918
Lacey, David E., Chief Fin. Officer & Exec. V.P.--Storage Technology Corporation, Louisville, CO; *U.S. Public*, pg. 1522
Laconi, Paul L., Controller--Allied Security, Inc., Pittsburgh, PA; *U.S. Private*, pg. 40
Lacoste, Cathleen, Controller & Mgr.-Accts.--Newpark Resources, Inc., Metairie, LA; *U.S. Public*, pg. 1179
Lacroix, Robert, Controller--Faucher Industries Inc., Saint Leonard, Canada; *Int'l*, pg. 479
Lacy, Nancy, Asst. Controller--The Van Metres Companies, Burke, VA; *U.S. Private*, pg. 1132
Lada, Dolores, Comptroller--Dennis Chemical Co., Inc., Saint Louis, MO; *U.S. Private*, pg. 324
LaDouceur, James, Controller--James Steel & Tube Company, Madison Heights, MI; *U.S. Private*, pg. 102
Lafferty, Robert, Controller--Hoechst Marion Roussel, Inc., Bridgewater, NJ; *Int'l*, pg. 624
Lafin, Gregory, Controller--Friedman, Eisenstein, Raemer and Schwartz, LLP, Chicago, IL; *U.S. Private*, pg. 428
Laflamme, Mario, Controller--Prodigy Inc., White Plains, NY; *U.S. Private*, pg. 888
Lafollette, Julie, Controller--Cybus Capital Markets, Des Moines, IA; *U.S. Private*, pg. 769
LaForest, Todd, Controller--Genfoot Inc., Montreal, Canada; *Int'l*, pg. 549
Laforge, Rejean, Controller & Treas.--TQM Pipeline Partnership, Montreal, Canada; *Int'l*, pg. 541
LaGrone, Holley S., V.P. & Controller--Taurus Exploration, Inc., Birmingham, AL; *U.S. Public*, pg. 581
Lague, Jack, V.P. & Controler--National Life Insurance Company, Montpelier, VT; *U.S. Private*, pg. 785
Lahar, Dick, Controller--Garelick Farms, Inc., Franklin, MA; *U.S. Public*, pg. 1527
Lahey, Jim, Controller--Highway One Communications, Integrated Marketing Services, San Francisco, CA; *U.S. Private*, pg. 303
Lahiff, William, V.P. & Controller--Things Remembered, Inc., Highland Heights, OH; *U.S. Public*, pg. 397
Lai, Michael, Controller--Tatung Company of America, Long Beach, CA; *Int'l*, pg. 1357
Laine, Gary, Controller--Iroquois Die & Mfg. Co., Warren, MI; *U.S. Private*, pg. 575
Laine, Jorma, Sr. Controller--Partek Corporation, Helsinki, Finland; *Int'l*, pg. 1024
Laing, R.G., Controller--De La Rue plc, London, United Kingdom; *Int'l*, pg. 386
Laird, Dwayne, Controller--Autotote Corporation, Newark, DE; *U.S. Public*, pg. 150
Laird, Neil J., V.P. & Controller--Honeywell-Measurex Corporation, Cupertino, CA; *U.S. Public*, pg. 833
Lakhani, Moe, Controller--FMS Management Systems, Inc., Miami, FL; *U.S. Private*, pg. 389
Lakhani, Moez, Controller--Pollo Tropical, Inc., Miami, FL; *U.S. Public*, pg. 1315
Lalani, Ali, Controller--Cara Operations Limited, Toronto, Canada; *Int'l*, pg. 266
Lalani, Naushad, Controller--A.M. Todd Company, Kalamazoo, MI; *U.S. Private*, pg. 1089
Lalonde, Marcel, V.P. & Controller--Cambior Inc., Montreal, Canada; *Int'l*, pg. 253
LaLumandiere, Dennis, Controller--Laserscope Surgical Systems, San Jose, CA; *U.S. Public*, pg. 979
Lalwani, P.J., Chief Oper. Officer, Chief Info. Officer, Controller & Sec.--Andrew Sports Club Inc., Secaucus, NJ; *U.S. Private*, pg. 73
LaMantia, Anthony, Chief Accountant--Eversharp Pen Co., Franklin Park, IL; *U.S. Private*, pg. 386
LaMarche, Gary D., Controller & Treas.--Welco Lumber Company, Marysville, WA; *U.S. Private*, pg. 1161
Lamars, Brad, Controller--Universal Foods Corp.-Dehydrated Products Div., Turlock, CA; *U.S. Public*, pg. 1696
Lamb, Kent W., Sr. V.P. & Controller--Western National Life Insurance Co., Houston, TX; *U.S. Public*, pg. 76
Lamb, Roy, Controller--UNC Accessory Services-New York, Bay Shore, NY; *U.S. Public*, pg. 710
Lambert, Albert W., Controller--DCG Precision Manufacturing Corporation, Bethel, CT; *U.S. Private*, pg. 301
Lambert, Eddie, Controller--Hardaway Construction Corp. of Tennessee, Inc., Nashville, TN; *U.S. Private*, pg. 501
Lambert, John D., Controller--Stanback Company, Salisbury, NC; *U.S. Private*, pg. 1030
Lambert, Pat, Controller & Treas.--Homestead Homes, Cordele, GA; *U.S. Public*, pg. 318
Lamberti, Nicholas, Controller--J. Crew Group, Inc., New York, NY; *U.S. Private*, pg. 1078
Lambrecht, Jacques, Controller--N.V. Bekaert S.A., Kortrijk, Belgium; *Int'l*, pg. 183
Lamers, Brad, Controller--Rogers Foods, Turlock, CA; *U.S. Public*, pg. 1696
Lamers, Tim, Controller--Fred Usinger, Inc., Milwaukee, WI; *U.S. Private*, pg. 1129
LaMetterey, David, Controller--Aetna Industries, Inc., Center Line, MI; *U.S. Private*, pg. 25
Lamey, Marianne, Asst. Controller--Chemed Corporation, Cincinnati, OH; *U.S. Public*, pg. 343
Lamkay, Harold, Controller--Victoria Packing Corporation, Brooklyn, NY; *U.S. Private*, pg. 1139
Lammers, Jeff, V.P. & Controller--Duralam, Inc., Appleton, WI; *U.S. Private*, pg. 966
Lampa, Primo, Controller--DCA Advertising, Inc., New York, NY; *Int'l*, pg. 393
Lampugnano, Phil, Chief Fin. Officer, V.P.-Fin. & Controller--Danka Business Systems, La Grange, IL; *Int'l*, pg. 379
Lancaster, Ken, Controller--Wilton Corporation, Palatine, IL; *U.S. Private*, pg. 1181
Lancaster, Wallace, Controller, Treas. & Sec.--Crown Buick, Inc., Metairie, LA; *U.S. Private*, pg. 292
Lance, Lisa, Chief Fin. Officer, V.P. & Controller--Gateway Communications, Johnson City, NY; *U.S. Private*, pg. 693
Landquist, Brent, Controller--ATMI, Inc., Danbury, CT; *U.S. Public*, pg. 12
Landrigan, Kathy, Controller--Maidenform Worldwide, New York, NY; *U.S. Private*, pg. 697
Landwehr, Rick, Controller--Ion Beam Systems Division, Austin, TX; *U.S. Public*, pg. 557
Landzaat, J., Dir.-Control--Internatio-Muller N.V., Rotterdam, Netherlands; *Int'l*, pg. 680

Lane, Jerry, Controller--Brandt, Inc., Bensalem, PA; *Int'l*, pg. 387

Lane, Marvin M., Jr., V.P. & Controller--Texas Instruments Incorporated, Dallas, TX; *U.S. Public*, pg. 1585

Lang, John M., Jr., V.P. & Corp. Controller--UNUM Corporation, Portland, ME; *U.S. Public*, pg. 1699

Lang, Karen, Controller--Samuel Bingham Co, Bloomingdale, IL; *U.S. Private*, pg. 144

Lang, Leonard, Dir.-Personnel & Controller--Kaz, Inc., New York, NY; *U.S. Private*, pg. 610

Lang, Mark, Controller--Schottenstein Stores Corporation, Columbus, OH; *U.S. Private*, pg. 972

Langdon, Robert, Controller--Beardsley & Piper, L.L.C., Chicago, IL; *U.S. Private*, pg. 859

Lange, Thomas, Controller--Pentax Precision Instrument Corp., Orangeburg, NY; *Int'l*, pg. 85

Langelier, Marc, Controller--Beaulieu Vineyard, Rutherford, CA; *Int'l*, pg. 410

Langford, J. Curtis, Controller--Wainoco Oil & Gas Company, Houston, TX; *U.S. Public*, pg. 1732

Langford, Vivien, Grp. Fin. Controller--Shandwick International Plc, London, United Kingdom; *Int'l*, pg. 1226

Langin, Robert H., Acting Chief Fin. Officer & Controller--Crestbrook Forest Industries Ltd., Cranbrook, Canada; *Int'l*, pg. 348

Langley, Carol, Asst. Controller--George W. Park Seed Co., Inc., Greenwood, SC; *U.S. Private*, pg. 839

Langley, H.F., Controller--Mississippi Valley Gas Co., Jackson, MS; *U.S. Private*, pg. 753

Langsdorf, Mary, V.P. & Controller--PacifiCare Health Systems, Inc., Cypress, CA; *U.S. Public*, pg. 1250

Lankford, T. Wayne, Controller, Asst. Treas. & Sec.--Old Dominion Box Co., Inc., Madison Heights, VA; *U.S. Private*, pg. 814

Lanthier, Serge, Treas. & Comptroller--Shirmax Leasing Ltd., Montreal, Canada; *Int'l*, pg. 1235

Lanthiew, Elisa M., Controller--Essex Corporation, New York, NY; *U.S. Public*, pg. 320

Lantow, Michelle M., V.P. & Corp. Controller--The Gap, Inc., San Francisco, CA; *U.S. Public*, pg. 702

Lape, Donald E., Sr. V.P. & Controller--United Missouri Bank of St. Louis, Saint Louis, MO; *U.S. Public*, pg. 1655

LaPenta, Robert L., Jr., Chief Acctg. Officer & Controller--Burlington Coat Factory Warehouse Corporation, Burlington, NJ; *U.S. Public*, pg. 268

Lapointe, Edward J., Controller--American Biltrite Inc., Wellesley Hills, MA; *U.S. Public*, pg. 68

Laramee, Gilles, V.P. & Controller--SNC-Lavalin Group Inc., Montreal, Canada; *Int'l*, pg. 1161

Laramy, William, Chief Fin. Officer, Treas. & Controller--The Purdy Corporation, Manchester, CT; *U.S. Private*, pg. 895

Larance, Don, Controller--Uvex Safety, Inc., Smithfield, RI; *Int'l*, pg. 132

Lareau-Kovac, Rae, Comptroller--Holiday RV Superstores, Inc.-Orlando, Orlando, FL; *U.S. Public*, pg. 830

Larken, Gene, Controller--MI-Jack Products, Inc., Hazel Crest, IL; *U.S. Private*, pg. 740

Larkins, Terry, Controller--American Modular Technologies, Liberty, NC; *U.S. Public*, pg. 69

Larocca, John, V.P.-Fin.--Aceto Corporation, Lake Success, NY; *U.S. Public*, pg. 15

Larocco, Joann, Controller--W.J. & Dennis Co., Elgin, IL; *U.S. Private*, pg. 1144

Laroche, David, Asst. Controller--Michaels Stores, Inc., Irving, TX; *U.S. Public*, pg. 1104

LaRochelle, Jean, Controller--HRH/Atlas Construction Inc., Stamford, CT; *U.S. Private*, pg. 1035

Larrimer, Curtis J., V.P. & Corp. Controller--General Nutrition, Inc., Pittsburgh, PA; *U.S. Public*, pg. 725

Larsen, Hans, Chief Acctg. Officer, V.P. & Controller--Digital Equipment Corporation, Maynard, MA; *U.S. Public*, pg. 507

Larsen, Jay R., Controller--ITT Gilfillan, Van Nuys, CA; *U.S. Public*, pg. 859

Larson, Al, Controller--Pacific Coast Building Products Inc., Sacramento, CA; *U.S. Private*, pg. 830

Larson, Barbara, Controller--Rex Moore Electrical Contractors & Engineers, West Sacramento, CA; *U.S. Private*, pg. 760

Larson, Brenda, Controller--Renosol Corp., Saline, MI; *U.S. Private*, pg. 922

Larson, James R., V.P. & Controller--Anadarko Petroleum Corporation, Houston, TX; *U.S. Public*, pg. 107

Larson, Ken, Controller & Treas.--BRW, Inc., Minneapolis, MN; *U.S. Private*, pg. 107

Larson, Larry, Chief Fin. Officer, Controller, Treas. & Sec.--Holmquist Grain & Lumber Co., Oakland, NE; *U.S. Private*, pg. 535

Larson, Linda, Corp. Controller--Quad/Graphics, Inc., Pewaukee, WI; *U.S. Private*, pg. 897

Larson, Linda F., Controller--Magneco/Metrel, Inc., Addison, IL; *U.S. Private*, pg. 695

Larson, Maureen, Controller--Kraus-Anderson Insurance, Burnsville, MN; *U.S. Private*, pg. 635

Larson, Robert J., V.P. & Controller--Century Communications Corp., New Canaan, CT; *U.S. Public*, pg. 329

Larson, William B., Controller--Commercial Metals Company, Dallas, TX; *U.S. Public*, pg. 411

Lasater, D. Eugene, Controller--The Dixie Group, Inc., Chattanooga, TN; *U.S. Public*, pg. 514

Lascoe, John, Controller & Asst. Treas.--Russell Stover Candies, Inc., Kansas City, MO; *U.S. Private*, pg. 953

Lasiter, Paul B., Sr. V.P. & Controller--Imperial Credit Industries, Inc., Torrance, CA; *U.S. Public*, pg. 872

Lasley, T.D., Controller--Pandrol Jackson, Inc., Ludington, MI; *Int'l*, pg. 280

Laspina, Mario, Controller--The Summit Media Group, New York, NY; *U.S. Private*, pg. 1050

Lassila, Kari, Sr. V.P. & Controller--Outokumpu Oyj, Espoo, Finland; *Int'l*, pg. 1015

Latek, Robert, Sr. V.P. & Controller--Energy Absorption Systems, Inc., Chicago, IL; *U.S. Public*, pg. 1353

Lathram, Charles J., Comptroller--BellSouth Products, Inc., Roanoke, VA; *U.S. Public*, pg. 209

LaTorre, Vincent, Controller--The Care Group, Inc., New York, NY; *U.S. Public*, pg. 305

Lau, Diane, Controller & Sec.--Royal Jeep Eagle Chrysler Plymouth, Inc., Casselberry, FL; *U.S. Private*, pg. 948

Lau, Francis, Mgr.-Quality Control--Brown & Haley, Tacoma, WA; *U.S. Private*, pg. 173

Lauck, Kevin D., Controller & Sec.--Chemi-Trol Chemical Co., Gibsonburg, OH; *U.S. Public*, pg. 345

Laudick, Lawrence A., V.P., Controller & Asst. Sec.--Wendy's International Inc., Dublin, OH; *U.S. Public*, pg. 1754

Laudie, Rich, Controller--Barton Nelson Inc., Kansas City, MO; *U.S. Private*, pg. 120

Lauf, John, Controller--Modern Group Ltd., Bristol, PA; *U.S. Private*, pg. 754

Launder, William H., Controller--Cook Moving Systems, Inc., Buffalo, NY; *U.S. Private*, pg. 272

Lavallee, Robert, Controller--Hologic, Inc., Waltham, MA; *U.S. Public*, pg. 831

Lavanway, Keith, Controller--Great Lakes Window, Inc., Toledo, OH; *U.S. Public*, pg. 1193

LaVelle, Bill, Controller--Alenite L.P., Chicago, IL; *U.S. Private*, pg. 33

Lavelle, William J., V.P. & Controller--Columbia Gas Distribution Companies, Columbus, OH; *U.S. Public*, pg. 402

Lavin, David, Controller--FieldBrook Farms, Inc., Dunkirk, NY; *U.S. Private*, pg. 403

Lavin, James P., Controller--Conectiv, Wilmington, DE; *U.S. Public*, pg. 430

Lavin, James P., Chief Acctg. Officer & Comptroller--Delmarva Power & Light Company, Wilmington, DE; *U.S. Public*, pg. 430

Lavin, Jeffrey B., Corp. Controller--Wyman-Gordon, North Grafton, MA; *U.S. Public*, pg. 1782

Laviouette, Craig, Regional Controller--Westinghouse Canada Inc., Hamilton, Canada; *U.S. Public*, pg. 275

Law, William, Comptroller--Integrated Material Handling Company, Mount Sterling, OH; *Int'l*, pg. 1397

Lawhorn, Vicki, Controller--Empire Electric Association, Cortez, CO; *U.S. Private*, pg. 374

Lawless, Floyd J., Controller--Gray Printing Co., Fostoria, OH; *U.S. Private*, pg. 472

Lawrence, Brian, Controller--Lifetime Hoan Corp., Westbury, NY; *U.S. Public*, pg. 992

Lawrence, Chuck, Controller--M1 KIT Mfg. Co., Caldwell, ID; *U.S. Public*, pg. 962

Lawrence, John, Controller--Wickes Inc., Vernon Hills, IL; *U.S. Public*, pg. 1391

Lawrence, John E., Asst. V.P.-Fin.--Asahi/America, Inc., Malden, MA; *U.S. Public*, pg. 137

Lawrence, Roger, Controller--DeBruce Grain Inc., Kansas City, MO; *U.S. Private*, pg. 319

Laws, Anna, Sr. V.P., Sec. & Controller--EJL Advertising/Los Angeles, Los Angeles, CA; *U.S. Private*, pg. 673

Lawson, Bruce, Reg. Controller--Country Mutual Insurance Company, Bloomington, IL; *U.S. Private*, pg. 279

Lawson, Jim, Controller--Rooney Brothers Company, Tulsa, OK; *U.S. Private*, pg. 943

Lawson, Jim, Controller--Manhattan Construction Company, Tulsa, OK; *U.S. Private*, pg. 943

Lawton, Lonnie, Controller--Helzberg's Diamond Shops, Inc., Kansas City, MO; *U.S. Public*, pg. 220

Lay, Ho Ee, Grp. Chief Accountant--Sime Darby Berhad, Kuala Lumpur, Malaysia; *Int'l*, pg. 1249

Layfield, Laura, Controller--AmeriServe of Norcross, Norcross, GA; *U.S. Private*, pg. 533

Layfield, Laurie, Controller--RPC Incorporated, Atlanta, GA; *U.S. Public*, pg. 1356

Layton, Billy, V.P. & Controller--Glenayre Technologies, Inc., Charlotte, NC; *U.S. Public*, pg. 746

Lazar, Allen, Controller--Kreher Steel Co., Inc., Melrose Park, IL; *U.S. Private*, pg. 635

Lazzarato, David A., V.P. & Comptroller--BCE Inc., Montreal, Canada; *Int'l*, pg. 114

Le Bourgeois, Brian, Controller--L & L Oil Company, Inc., Metairie, LA; *U.S. Private*, pg. 638

Lea, James, Sr. V.P. & Controller--The Quadrant Corporation, Bellevue, WA; *U.S. Public*, pg. 1764

Leach, Michael, Controller--Drug Emporium, Inc., Powell, OH; *U.S. Public*, pg. 530

Leach, Ruth, Controller--Syracuse Supply Company, Syracuse, NY; *U.S. Private*, pg. 1060

Leaman, Carol, Controller--Electrohome Ltd., Kitchener, Canada; *Int'l*, pg. 438

Leatherman, Julie, Controller--Ukrop's Super Markets, Richmond, VA; *U.S. Private*, pg. 1115

Leathers, Jane, Controller--C.F. Hathaway, Waterville, ME; *U.S. Private*, pg. 510

Leavitt, Lynn, Controller--The Weathervane Retail Corp., New Britain, CT; *U.S. Private*, pg. 1156

Lebevre, John, Controller--American White Cross, Dayville, CT; *U.S. Public*, pg. 694

LeBlanc, Charles, V.P., Controller, Sec., & Asst. Treas.--National Service Cleaning Corporation, South Windsor, CT; *U.S. Public*, pg. 1208

LeBlanc, Denis, Controller--Lyman Products Corporation, Middletown, CT; *U.S. Private*, pg. 683

LeBlanc, James, Jr., Chief Fin. Officer & Corp. Controller--Gaylord Chemical Corporation, Slidell, LA; *U.S. Public*, pg. 704

Leblanc, Maryanne, Controller & Treas.--Tano Automation, Inc., Harahan, LA; *U.S. Public*, pg. 1763

LeBlanc, Roger D., Chief Fin. Officer & Controller--Pollack Corporation, Scarborough, ME; *U.S. Private*, pg. 874

Lebo, John, Controller--Allied Old English, Inc., Port Reading, NJ; *U.S. Private*, pg. 39

Lebsock, Alan, Controller--Holly Sugar Corporation, Sugar Land, TX; *U.S. Public*, pg. 872

Lechleiter, Richard A., V.P.-Fin. & Corp. Controller--Vencor, Inc., Louisville, KY; *U.S. Public*, pg. 1711

Lechman, Merna L., Corp. Controller--Big O Tires Incorporated, Englewood, CO; *U.S. Public*, pg. 1553

LeClaire, Greg, Controller--Utah Medical Products, Inc., Midvale, UT; *U.S. Public*, pg. 1700

Leduc, Serge, Controller--Imprimerie Quebecor Inc. Division Cheques, Saint Leonard, Canada; *Int'l*, pg. 1077

Lee, Bill, Controller--Tollycraft Yacht Corporation, San Diego, CA; *U.S. Public*, pg. 1620

Lee, Brenda, V.P., Treas. & Controller--Malama Pacific Corp., Honolulu, HI; *U.S. Public*, pg. 800

Lee, Cindy, Controller--Schuff Steel Co., Phoenix, AZ; *U.S. Private*, pg. 973

Lee, Daniel, Controller--Wind River Systems, Inc., Alameda, CA; *U.S. Public*, pg. 1770

Lee, Daniel R., Chief Fin. Officer, Sr. V.P.-Fin. & Devel. & Treas.--Mirage Resorts Incorporated, Las Vegas, NV; *U.S. Public*, pg. 1116

Lee, E.J., Controller--John Crane (Korea) Co., Ltd., Seoul, Korea; *Int'l*, pg. 1339

Lee, Floyd, Controller--Ploof Truck Lines, Inc., Jacksonville, FL; *U.S. Private*, pg. 872

Lee, Howard, Controller--The Canadian Coleman Co., Ltd., Toronto, Canada; *U.S. Private*, pg. 691

Lee, Jerry, Controller--Nobles Mfg. Inc., Saint Croix Falls, WI; *U.S. Private*, pg. 800

Lee, Kyoo, Controller--Rolled Steel Products Corporation, Los Angeles, CA; *U.S. Private*, pg. 941

Lee, Nelson, Controller--Yogen Fruz Worldwide Inc., Markham, Canada; *Int'l*, pg. 1520

Lee, Peter, Controller--St. Clair Paint and Wallpaper Corporation, Toronto, Canada; *Int'l*, pg. 1170

Lee, R.W., Controller--Rhone-Poulenc Basic Chemicals Co., Shelton, CT; *Int'l*, pg. 1110

Lee, Rodney L., Sr. V.P. & Controller--Liberty Bancorp, Inc., Oklahoma City, OK; *U.S. Public*, pg. 174

Lee, Roger, Controller--MeritCare Health System, Fargo, ND; *U.S. Private*, pg. 733

Lee, Thomas H.Y., Controller--Mandarin Oriental, Hong Kong Limited, Central, Hong Kong; *Int'l*, pg. 704

Leech, Bruce A., Jr., Controller--Armstrong World Industries, Inc., Lancaster, PA; *U.S. Public*, pg. 131

Leeper, Barbara, Controller--Ruska Instrument Corporation, Houston, TX; *U.S. Private*, pg. 952

Lees, William, Jr., Controller--Imperial Schrade Corp., Ellenville, NY; *U.S. Private*, pg. 559

Lefebvre, Francis, Controller--Cockerill Sambre, Brussels, Belgium; *Int'l*, pg. 301

Lefeld, Alfred, V.P. & Controller--Moto Photo, Inc., Dayton, OH; *U.S. Public*, pg. 1136

Lefevbre, Thomas, Controller--Chemtex International, Inc., New York, NY; *Int'l*, pg. 872

Leff, David, Controller--A. Pomerantz & Company, Philadelphia, PA; *U.S. Private*, pg. 875

Leffler, Harry, Controller--The Jones Store Co., Kansas City, MO; *U.S. Public*, pg. 1090

Lefko, Marsha, Controller--Sierra Coating Technologies, De Pere, WI; *U.S. Private*, pg. 998

Lefkof, Matt, Controller--Zenith Products Corp., New Castle, DE; *U.S. Public*, pg. 1054

Legge, Jeff, Controller--Otter Tail Power Company, Fergus Falls, MN; *U.S. Public*, pg. 1234

Legostreva, Elizabeth, Fin. Mgr.--Young & Rubicam/Sovero, Moscow, Russia; *U.S. Private*, pg. 1199

Legro, Thomas E., V.P. & Controller--Edison Mission Energy, Irvine, CA; *U.S. Public*, pg. 564

Lehman, Brian H., V.P. & Controller--BT Financial Corporation, Johnstown, PA; *U.S. Public*, pg. 163

Lehman, John, Controller--Thomas Lighting-Sparta Opers., Sparta, TN; *U.S. Public*, pg. 1599

Lehman, Tom, Controller--Cold Spring Granite Company, Cold Spring, MN; *U.S. Private*, pg. 250

Lehmann, Thomas R., Chief. Fin. Officer & Controller--JSB Financial, Lynbrook, NY; *U.S. Public*, pg. 919

Lehmpuhl, William, Controller--Castle Concrete Co., Colorado Springs, CO; *U.S. Public*, pg. 441

Lehmpuhl, William, Controller--Transit Mix Concrete Co., Colorado Springs, CO; *U.S. Public*, pg. 441

Lehmus, Heikki, Controller--Wisapak Oy Ab, Karhula Factory, Karhula, Finland; *Int'l*, pg. 1429

Lehner, Ed, Controller--Nucor Building Systems, Waterloo, IN; *U.S. Public*, pg. 1205

Lehnerer, George, Controller--Magline, Inc., Pinconning, MI; *U.S. Private*, pg. 695

Lehnert, Kevin L., Controller--MacNeal-Schwendler Corp., Costa Mesa, CA; *U.S. Public*, pg. 1031

Lehto, Sarah, Asst. Controller--Cains Foods, L.P., Ayer, MA; *U.S. Private*, pg. 199

Leighton, Robert, Controller--Ludlow Textiles Co., Inc., Ludlow, MA; *U.S. Private*, pg. 680

Leininger, Hart, Controller--Microsemi Corporation, Santa Ana, CA; *U.S. Public*, pg. 1107

Leisey, William, Controller--Ketema, Inc., Denver, CO; *U.S. Private*, pg. 604

Lellio, Rachel, Controller--Icon International, Stamford, CT; *U.S. Private*, pg. 556

Lembeck, Larry, Chief Fin. Officer & Controller--Stadelman Fruit L.L.C., Yakima, WA; *U.S. Private*, pg. 1028

Lemice, Maurine, Chief Fin. Controller--Livingston S.A., Rungis, France; *Int'l*, pg. 212

Lemke, Ted, Controller--Pettibone Michigan Div., Baraga, MI; *U.S. Private*, pg. 860

Lemoine, Gene, Controller--Schwegmann Giant Super Markets, New Orleans, LA; *U.S. Private*, pg. 629

Lemon, Dave, V.P. & Controller-Direct Div.--Inacom Corp., Omaha, NE; *U.S. Public*, pg. 873

Lemonds, Kris K., Asst. Controller--Michael Foods, Inc., Minneapolis, MN; *U.S. Public*, pg. 1103

Lemousa, Dick, Asst. to the Controller--Morven Partners LP, Edenton, NC; *U.S. Private*, pg. 763

Lencke, H., Dr., Dir.-Opers. & Strategic Plng. & Asst. Controller--Deutsche Bahn, Frankfurt/Main, Germany; *Int'l*, pg. 401

Lenhart, Todd M., WHS Divisional Controller--Riser Foods, Inc., Bedford, OH; *U.S. Private*, pg. 450
Lenig, Mike, Controller--Hughes Group, Clarksville, IN; *U.S. Private*, pg. 546
Lenihan, Bernie, V.P. & Controller--NUI Corporation, Bedminster, NJ; *U.S. Public*, pg. 1147
Lenk, Alexander, Controller--Pittler Maschinenfabrik AG, Langen, Germany; *Int'l*, pg. 1128
lennox, Jeff, Controller--Colad Group Inc., Buffalo, NY; *U.S.* Private, pg. 250
Lenz, D., Controller--BGW Systems, Inc., Hawthorne, CA; *U.S. Private*, pg. 107
Lenz, Mark, V.P. & Controller--Zale Corporation, Irving, TX; *U.S. Public*, pg. 1789
Leonard, Coral, Controller--Safe Alarm, Inc., Davie, FL; *U.S.* Private, pg. 960
Leonard, Steve, Controller--Morgan Construction Co., Worcester, MA; *U.S. Private*, pg. 761
Leong, Alan, Controller--Maui Varieties, Ltd., Honolulu, HI; *U.S. Private*, pg. 715
Leong, Calvin, Exec. V.P. & Controller--Maness Industries, Inc., Long Beach, CA; *U.S. Private*, pg. 699
Leong, Raymond, Exec. V.P.-Fin. & Controller--F. J. Benjamin Holdings Ltd., Singapore, Singapore; *Int'l*, pg. 187
LePage, Jenifer, V.P. & Controller--United Advertising Publications, Inc., Dallas, TX; *Int'l*, pg. 1443
Lepik, Richard, Controller--Atotech U.S.A. Inc., Rock Hill, SC; *U.S. Private*, pg. 97
LePorte, James L., III, V.P., Treas. & Controller--Allen Telecom, Inc., Beachwood, OH; *U.S. Public*, pg. 45
Lepow, Norman, Controller--Aluminum Shapes, LLC, Delair, NJ; *U.S. Private*, pg. 47
Leppla, Larry, Controller--Century Fence Company, Pewaukee, WI; *U.S. Private*, pg. 226
Leray, M., Fin. Controller--AEP/Borden Macaple S.A., Pithwiers, France; *U.S. Public*, pg. 5
Lerch, Mike, Controller--Goodman Equipment Corp., Bedford Park, IL; *U.S. Private*, pg. 464
Lerit, Bruce M., Corp. Controller--The Hain Food Group Inc., Uniondale, NY; *U.S. Public*, pg. 774
Lerner, Harry J., V.P. & Controller--Information Builders, New York, NY; *U.S. Private*, pg. 561
Lerum, Stephen, Controller--Deltak Inc., Plymouth, MN; *U.S.* Public, pg. 924
Leslie, Laurence, Controller & Treas.--Fluke Corporation, Everett, WA; *U.S. Public*, pg. 659
Lesner, John, Controller--Interstate Steel Co. Inc., Des Plaines, IL; *Int'l*, pg. 572
Lessin, Andrew R., V.P. & Controller--International Paper Company, Purchase, NY; *U.S. Public*, pg. 901
Lessman, Steve, Controller--Northville Industries Corp., Melville, NY; *U.S. Private*, pg. 806
Lester, Bob, V.P. & Controller--Thoro, Jacksonville, FL; *U.S.* Private, pg. 505
Lester, Mark, Controller--Thurman Industries, Inc., Bothell, WA; *U.S. Private*, pg. 1084
Lester, Rick, Chief Fin. Officer, V.P. & Asst. Sec.--Domain Energy Corporation, Houston, TX; *U.S. Public*, pg. 515
LeTellier, Ronald, Controller-Admin.--Genovese Drug Stores, Inc., Melville, NY; *U.S. Public*, pg. 730
Leuken, Harold, Controller--Los Angeles Die Casting, Los Angeles, CA; *U.S. Public*, pg. 142
Lev, Dalia, Comptroller--PEC Israel Economic Corporation, New York, NY; *Int'l*, pg. 644
Levert, Sylvain, Controller--Quebecor Inc., Montreal, Canada; *Int'l*, pg. 1075
Levert, Sylvain, Controller--Quebecor Printing, Inc., Montreal, Canada; *Int'l*, pg. 1076
Levin, Alan, Controller--VV Publishing Corp., New York, NY; *U.S. Private*, pg. 1131
Levin, Ann, Controller--Emmerling Post, Inc., New York, NY; *U.S. Private*, pg. 374
Levin, Bruce, Chief Fin. Officer & Controller--ADWORKS, Inc., Washington, DC; *U.S. Private*, pg. 23
Levin, Lawrence, V.P. & Controller--Artra Group Incorporated, Northfield, IL; *U.S. Public*, pg. 136
Levine, Eugene, Controller--Entertainment Communications, Bala Cynwyd, PA; *U.S. Private*, pg. 378
Levine, Norman M., Chief Fin. Officer, V.P. & Controller--DeVry Institutes, Oak Brook Terrace, IL; *U.S. Public*, pg. 503
Levine, Steve, Controller--Risdon Corporation, Naugatuck, CT; *U.S. Public*, pg. 463
Levy, Alan, V.P., Controller & Corp. Sec.--Bolt Technology Corporation, Norwalk, CT; *U.S. Public*, pg. 244
Levy, Ed, Controller--Go Jo Industries, Cuyahoga Falls, OH; *U.S. Private*, pg. 458
Levy, Richard, Sr. V.P. & Controller--New York Life Insurance Company, New York, NY; *U.S. Private*, pg. 794
Levys, Allan, V.P., Controller, & Sec.--Level Export Sales Corp., New York, NY; *U.S. Private*, pg. 662
Lewanda, Douglas M., Controller--Bartlett Brainard Eacott, Inc., Bloomfield, CT; *U.S. Private*, pg. 118
Lewandowski, Greg, Controller & Asst. Treas.--Dean Pickle & Specialty Products Co., Green Bay, WI; *U.S. Public*, pg. 490
Lewers, Prescilla, Controller--Capintec Inc., Ramsey, NJ; *U.S. Private*, pg. 205
Lewis, Edward, Controller--Cleaners Hanger Co., Palm Harbor, FL; *U.S. Private*, pg. 245
Lewis, J.A., Controller, Treas. & Sec.--Logo 7, Inc., Indianapolis, IN; *U.S. Public*, pg. 1644
Lewis, Janet, Asst. Controller--Hawkins Chemical, Inc., Minneapolis, MN; *U.S. Public*, pg. 800
Lewis, Kenneth A., Chief Acctg. Officer, V.P. & Controller--Franklin Resources, Inc., San Mateo, CA; *U.S. Public*, pg. 679
Lewis, Kenneth A., V.P. & Controller--Franklin Resources, Inc., San Mateo, CA; *U.S. Public*, pg. 679
Lewis, Robert, Controller--National Electronics Warranty Corporation, Sterling, VA; *U.S. Private*, pg. 782
Lewis, Robert A., V.P. & Controller--Claire's Stores Inc., Pembroke Pines, FL; *U.S. Public*, pg. 381
Lewis, Robert H., Chief Fin. Officer, V.P.-Fin. & Controller--John Boos & Company, Effingham, IL; *U.S. Private*, pg. 156
Lewis, Rosemary, Controller--Holcomb & Hoke Mfg. Company, Inc., Indianapolis, IN; *U.S. Private*, pg. 533
Lewis, Stephen, Controller--Golden Star Inc., Kansas City, MO; *U.S. Private*, pg. 460
Lewis, Terry, Controller--The Ruhlin Company, Sharon Center, OH; *U.S. Private*, pg. 951
Lewitt, Charles, Chief Fin. Officer & Controller--Morrison Berkshire Inc., North Adams, MA; *U.S. Private*, pg. 762
Ley, Steven, V.P.-Fin.--Pfaudler, Inc., Rochester, NY; *U.S. Public*, pg. 1393
Lezan, Jeff, Controller--Brittany Corporation, Cleveland, OH; *U.S. Private*, pg. 169
Lezar, Ann Marie, Controller--Rockbottom Stores, Inc., Lake Success, NY; *U.S. Private*, pg. 938
Li, Alex, Controller--The Excelsior Hotel, Hong Kong, Causeway Bay, Hong Kong; *Int'l*, pg. 704
Liaskos, Stephen M., V.P. & Controller--NUI Corporation, Bedminster, NJ; *U.S. Public*, pg. 1147
Liban, G., Chm. Bd. & Chief Exec. Officer--Heresite Protective Coatings Inc., Manitowoc, WI; *U.S. Private*, pg. 523
Lichtenhagen, Becky, Controller--Zetec, Inc., Issaquah, WA; *U.S. Private*, pg. 1205
Liddell, Donald, Controller--The Calgary Sun, Calgary, Canada; *Int'l*, pg. 1320
Lieb, Gregory P., Controller-Acctg. & Fin. Reporting--The Lubrizol Corporation, Wickliffe, OH; *U.S. Public*, pg. 1016
Liebbe, Ken, Controller--Modern Woodmen of America, Rock Island, IL; *U.S. Private*, pg. 755
Lieberman, Stuart T., V.P., Controller & Chief Acctg. Officer--Bell & Howell Holdings, Skokie, IL; *U.S. Public*, pg. 201
Lieblein, Dan, Controller--October Films, Inc., New York, NY; *Int'l*, pg. 1216
Liebscher, Klaus, Dr., Dir.-Gen. Mngmt.--Raiffeisen Zentralbank Osterreich, Vienna, Austria; *Int'l*, pg. 1084
Lieburn, Thomas A., Controller--SpecialtyChem Products Corporation, Marinette, WI; *Int'l*, pg. 173
Lienard, Claude, Controller--The Eurotunnel Group, London, United Kingdom; *Int'l*, pg. 466
Lienesch, Robert P., Controller--Cincinnati Milacron Inc., Cincinnati, OH; *U.S. Public*, pg. 368
Lieser, Skip, V.P.-Fin. & Controller--Yoplait USA, Minneapolis, MN; *U.S. Public*, pg. 718
Liew, Alvin, Fin. Controller--Sime Darby Commodities Inc., Destin, FL; *Int'l*, pg. 1250
Lifshatz, Stephen J., V.P.-Opers & Controller--Marcam Solutions, Inc., Newton, MA; *U.S. Public*, pg. 1042
Liggett, George, Chief Fin. Officer & Controller--Alliant Foodservice, Bensenville, IL; *U.S. Private*, pg. 244
Light, Irwin, Treas.--Mitchel-Lincoln Packaging, Saint-Laurent, Canada; *Int'l*, pg. 870
Liljedahl, Arne, Sr. V.P. & Controller--Nordbanken AB, Stockholm, Sweden; *Int'l*, pg. 957
Lillis, Bernard F., Chief Fin. Officer--Cucina Classica Italiana, Inc., Lakewood, NJ; *U.S. Public*, pg. 1435
Lima, Marsha, Controller--Lamp Post Franchise Corporation, Tustin, CA; *U.S. Private*, pg. 644
Limauro, Stephen L., V.P. & Comptroller--Everest Reinsurance Holdings, Liberty Corner, NJ; *U.S. Public*, pg. 597
Lin, Frank, V.P.-Corp. Mktg.--Acer Incorporated, Taipei, Taiwan; *Int'l*, pg. 22
Lin, Jennifer, Controller--American Sporting Goods Corporation, Irvine, CA; *U.S. Private*, pg. 62
Lind, Ralph, Controller & Sec.--St. Croix Press, Inc., New Richmond, WI; *U.S. Private*, pg. 960
Lindenhovius, C., Controller-Fin. & Admin.--Oce-van der Grinten N.V., Venlo, Netherlands; *Int'l*, pg. 993
Linderman, Jerry, Controller--Orleans International, Inc., Bloomfield Hills, MI; *U.S. Private*, pg. 820
Lindfors, Tapio, Dir.-Fin. & Control--Nokia Telecommunications, Espoo, Finland; *Int'l*, pg. 952
Lindgren, Alf, Chief Fin. Officer & Controller--Scancem AB, Malmo, Sweden; *Int'l*, pg. 1198
Lindley, Steven E., Controller--Harlan Electric Co., Rochester Hills, MI; *U.S. Public*, pg. 1029
Lindsey, Fred, Controller--Eva-Tone Inc., Clearwater, FL; *U.S. Private*, pg. 384
Lindsey, Steve, Controller--Pinkerton's Inc., Encino, CA; *U.S. Public*, pg. 1296
Lindsey, Thomas E., Controller--M.A. Hanna Company, Cleveland, OH; *U.S. Public*, pg. 780
Lindslet, Deanne, Div. Controller--KTI, Inc., Guttenberg, NJ; *U.S. Public*, pg. 939
Linehan, Gerald F., Exec. V.P.--Pelican Products, Torrance, CA; *U.S. Private*, pg. 848
Linehan, James B., Chief Fin. Officer, V.P.-Fin., Treas. & Controller--Ruslander & Sons, Inc., Buffalo, NY; *U.S. Private*, pg. 952
Linkenauger, Jim, Controller--Richmond Motor Company, Richmond, VA; *U.S. Private*, pg. 929
Linnemeier, Stephen O., Comptroller--General Motors-Holden's Automotive Limited, Melbourne, Australia; *U.S. Public*, pg. 723
Linotto, John, Controller--Illinois Fruit & Produce Corp., Streator, IL; *U.S. Public*, pg. 918
Linschaten, Clint, Controller--Kaufman and Broad Utah Division, Midvale, UT; *U.S. Public*, pg. 945
Linton, Mark, Controller--Midwest Industries, Inc., Ida Grove, IA; *U.S. Private*, pg. 744
Linton, Richard A., Controller & Treas.--Consolidated Midwest, Inc., La Crosse, WI; *U.S. Private*, pg. 265
Lipenski, Jim, Controller--Bigsby & Kruthers Companies, Chicago, IL; *U.S. Private*, pg. 143
Lippard, Thomas R., III, V.P.-Fin. & Controller--Ronco Communications & Electronics Inc., Tonawanda, NY; *U.S. Private*, pg. 943
Lipschitz, Wayne, Controller--Cheesecake Factory Incorporated, Calabasas Hills, CA; *U.S. Public*, pg. 343
Lipton, Steve, Chief Fin. Officer, V.P. & Controller--The Elder-Beerman Stores Corp., Dayton, OH; *U.S. Private*, pg. 367
Lisenby, Terry, V.P. & Controller--Nucor Corporation, Charlotte, NC; *U.S. Public*, pg. 1205
Lista, Leslie G., Controller--Scholastic Corporation, New York, NY; *U.S. Public*, pg. 1440
Liszt, Lewis N., Controller--Morton International Inc., Chicago, IL; *U.S. Public*, pg. 1134
Litchkowski, Ron, V.P. & Controller--Russell-Stanley Corporation, Red Bank, NJ; *U.S. Private*, pg. 953
Little, Edward, Controller--Mountain States Constructors, Inc., Albuquerque, NM; *U.S. Private*, pg. 764
Little, Kathleen, Controller--Centennial Technologies, Inc., Wilmington, MA; *U.S. Public*, pg. 322
Little, Quez, Controller--Hickory Hill Furniture Corporation, Valdese, NC; *U.S. Private*, pg. 808
Liu, Yolanda, Controller--Bugle Boy Industries, Inc., Simi Valley, CA; *U.S. Private*, pg. 179
Livermore, Richard, Controller--Adra Systems, Inc., Chelmsford, MA; *U.S. Private*, pg. 18
Livigni, Roy, Controller--Alterman Transport Lines, Inc., Opa Locka, FL; *U.S. Private*, pg. 47
Livingston, Marge, Treas. & Controller--The Harwood Companies, Inc., Fort Lauderdale, FL; *U.S. Public*, pg. 1433
Livinston, John D., Asst. Controller--Blount International, Inc., Montgomery, AL; *U.S. Public*, pg. 237
Livinston, John D., Asst. Controller--Blount, Inc., Montgomery, AL; *U.S. Public*, pg. 238
Ljungholm, Gunnar, Controller--Datapoint Svenska AB, Stockholm, Sweden; *Int'l*, pg. 384
Lobasso, Steve, Controller--Triangle Services, Inc., Valley Stream, NY; *U.S. Private*, pg. 1102
Loborg, Philip W., Jr., V.P. & Controller--CalComp Technology, Inc., Anaheim, CA; *U.S. Public*, pg. 1007
LoCascio, Steven A., Interim Chief Fin. Officer, V.P. & Controller--King World Productions, Inc., New York, NY; *U.S. Public*, pg. 961
Locastro, Laurel, Controller--Chyron Corp., Melville, NY; *Int'l*, pg. 1372
Lochbaum, S.E., Controller--Morganite Inc., Dunn, NC; *Int'l*, pg. 891
Lock, P.G., Controller--ING Groep N.V., Amsterdam, Netherlands; *Int'l*, pg. 647
Lockett, Clarence, Comptroller--Johnson & Johnson, New Brunswick, NJ; *U.S. Public*, pg. 927
Lockie, Paul, Controller--Catellus Development Corporation, San Francisco, CA; *U.S. Public*, pg. 314
Lockwood, Kimmy, Controller--K-Tel International, Inc., Minneapolis, MN; *U.S. Public*, pg. 937
Loeffler, Bob, Controller--Lee Grocery Company, Everett, WA; *U.S. Private*, pg. 657
Loew, Jack, Controller--Aldan Industries, Philadelphia, PA; *U.S. Private*, pg. 33
Loew, James P., V.P.-Fin., Controller & Treas.--Modern Concrete Septic Tank Company, Ottsville, PA; *U.S. Private*, pg. 754
Lofties, Michael, Controller--Donlee Technologies Inc., York, PA; *U.S. Private*, pg. 339
Loftus, Robert, Controller--General Cigar Company, Inc., Bloomfield, CT; *U.S. Public*, pg. 708
Logan, Barry, Controller--Watsco, Inc., Coconut Grove, FL; *U.S. Public*, pg. 1745
Logan, Donna, Controller--Kleinert's, Inc., of Alabama, Elba, AL; *U.S. Private*, pg. 625
Lohmann, Okonom Rainer, Mgr.-Controlling & Clearing--Gebr. Eickhoff Maschinenfabrik und Eisengiesserei mbH, Bochum, Germany; *Int'l*, pg. 542
Lohsen, Bob, Controller--Four Seasons Solar Products Corp., Holbrook, NY; *U.S. Private*, pg. 422
Lohsen, Robert A., Controller--Fisher Skylights, Inc., Holbrook, NY; *U.S. Private*, pg. 408
Lohwasser, Charles, V.P., Controller & Sls. Mgr.--EG & G Rotron, Woodstock, NY; *U.S. Public*, pg. 543
Lok, Lillan, Controller--Integral Systems, Inc., Walnut Creek, CA; *Int'l*, pg. 242
Lokuciejewski, G.L., Controller--AEGON Financial Services Group (UK) Ltd., London, United Kingdom; *Int'l*, pg. 28
Lombardi, Joseph, V.P. & Controller--Toys "R" Us, Inc., Paramus, NJ; *U.S. Public*, pg. 1626
Lombardo, Rocco, Controller--Frederick Wildman & Sons Ltd., New York, NY; *U.S. Private*, pg. 1176
Lomenzo, Margie, Controller--A&M Records, Hollywood, CA; *Int'l*, pg. 1052
Londry, Larry, Controller--Garland Commercial Ranges, Ltd., Mississauga, Canada; *Int'l*, pg. 189
Long, Dan, Controller--Reeves International, Spartanburg, SC; *U.S. Private*, pg. 507
Long, Gary E., CPA, V.P. & Controller--Northwestern Mutual Life Insurance Co., Milwaukee, WI; *U.S. Private*, pg. 807
Long, Gary H., Controller & Asst. Sec.--Eagle Food Centers, Inc., Milan, IL; *U.S. Public*, pg. 547
Long, Jennifer, Controller--II-VI Incorporated, Saxonburg, PA; *U.S. Public*, pg. 1647
Long, Joan M., Controller--Dunham's Athleisure Corporation, Waterford, MI; *U.S. Private*, pg. 346
Long, Larry, Comptroller--Machining Enterprises Inc., Warren, MI; *U.S. Private*, pg. 691
Long, Martha, V.P.-Fin. & Controller--Insignia Financial Group, Inc., Greenville, SC; *U.S. Public*, pg. 881
Long, Sharee L., Corp. Controller--Plymouth Tube Company, Warrenville, IL; *U.S. Private*, pg. 873
Long, Thomas, Controller--Berean Christian Stores, Cincinnati, OH; *U.S. Public*, pg. 1506
Longaker, Bruce F., V.P.-Fin. & Corp. Controller--Camco International Inc., Houston, TX; *U.S. Public*, pg. 297
Longenbaugh, Vicky, Controller--Columbia Corporation, Brentwood, TN; *U.S. Private*, pg. 255
Longinotti, Michael K., Controller--Cominco, Ltd., Vancouver, Canada; *Int'l*, pg. 307
Longtine, William J., Asst. Controller--JC Penney Company, Inc., Plano, TX; *U.S. Public*, pg. 916

Lookabill, Reid D., Controller--Salem Carpet Mills, Inc., Winston Salem, NC; *U.S. Public*, pg. 1464
Looney, John B., Controller--Supreme Electronics Corp., Greenwood, MS; *U.S. Public*, pg. 825
Looney, T. Joseph, Controller--Industrial Acoustics Company, Inc., Bronx, NY; *U.S. Public*, pg. 875
Lopez, Eduardo, Controller--Perez Trading Co. Inc., Miami, FL; *U.S. Private*, pg. 852
Lopez, Marcelo, Controller--Wheel Tronic Inc., Mississauga, Canada; *U.S. Public*, pg. 1481
Lopez, Terry, Controller--Zoll Medical Corporation, Burlington, MA; *U.S. Private*, pg. 1207
Lopez, Theresa, Controller--KDFW, Dallas, TX; *Int'l*, pg. 926
Lopez, Theresa, Controller--KTBC, Austin, TX; *Int'l*, pg. 926
Lorch, Christopher, Controller--Mercury Computer Systems, Inc., Chelmsford, MA; *U.S. Private*, pg. 732
Lord, Gerald S., V.P.-Fin. & Controller-U.S. Grocery--Campbell USA, Camden, NJ; *U.S. Public*, pg. 299
Lorenz, Gerald, Controller--MNP Corp., Utica, MI; *U.S. Private*, pg. 687
Lorenz, Steve, Controller--Bonney Forge Corporation, Allentown, PA; *U.S. Private*, pg. 156
Lorwy, Ray, Controller--Sierra Pacific Industries, Anderson, CA; *U.S. Private*, pg. 998
Losando, Anthony, Controller--C.H. Heist Corp., Clearwater, FL; *U.S. Public*, pg. 807
Lossin, U.L., Comptroller--ITT Jabsco, Costa Mesa, CA; *U.S. Public*, pg. 860
Loth, C. Lewis, Jr., Controller--Scott & Stringfellow, Inc., Richmond, VA; *U.S. Public*, pg. 1445
Lotti, George, Controller--Heat & Control, Inc., Hayward, CA; *U.S. Private*, pg. 518
Loucks, Scott, Chief Fin. Officer & V.P.-Fin.--Technology Research Corporation, Clearwater, FL; *U.S. Public*, pg. 1564
Lough, I.P., Controller--Pilkington Plc, Saint Helens, United Kingdom; *Int'l*, pg. 1056
Loughery, John J., Controller--Rubber Molding Division, Norwich, CT; *U.S. Private*, pg. 355
Loughlin, Steve, V.P.-Fin. & Controller--Sequent Computer Systems, Inc., Beaverton, OR; *U.S. Public*, pg. 1459
Louie, Jonathan, V.P.-Fin. & Admin.--Marinco/AFI, Napa, CA; *U.S. Public*, pg. 1705
Love, Kathy H., Asst. Controller-Internal Audit--Walter Industries, Inc., Tampa, FL; *U.S. Public*, pg. 1736
Love, Mike, Controller--Danuser Machine Co., Fulton, MO; *U.S. Private*, pg. 310
Lovell, B.J., Comptroller--Bruce Foods Corp., Cade, LA; *U.S. Private*, pg. 175
Lovett, Bill, Controller--Diamond Chemical Co., Inc., East Rutherford, NJ; *U.S. Private*, pg. 330
Lovett, Deborah, Controller--Sun Data Inc., Norcross, GA; *U.S. Private*, pg. 1050
Lovvorn, Joseph, Controller & Treas.--Alabama Farmers Co-op, Decatur, AL; *U.S. Private*, pg. 30
Low, Curtis, Controller--Miller & Smith, Inc., Mc Lean, VA; *U.S. Private*, pg. 746
Lowber, H. Paul, V.P. & Controller--SAFECO Corporation, Seattle, WA; *U.S. Public*, pg. 1423
Lowe, C.N., V.P. & Controller--Hartford Europe, Inc., Hartford, CT; *U.S. Public*, pg. 795
Lowe, William M., Controller--Arvin Industries, Inc., Columbus, IN; *U.S. Public*, pg. 136
Lowenthal, Barbara L., V.P. & Controller--Leucadia National Corporation, New York, NY; *U.S. Public*, pg. 989
Lowery, Everet, Controller--Conbraco Industries Inc., Matthews, NC; *U.S. Private*, pg. 261
Lowery, Janice, Controller--Williams Company Of Orlando, Inc., Orlando, FL; *U.S. Private*, pg. 1177
Lowry, Gary W., V.P. & Controller--Duckwall-Alco Stores, Inc., Abilene, KS; *U.S. Public*, pg. 533
Lowry, Robert L., Controller--Central Newspapers, Inc., Indianapolis, IN; *U.S. Public*, pg. 326
Loyd, Randall M., Controller--Treadco, Inc., Fort Smith, AR; *U.S. Public*, pg. 131
Lozano, Joe, V.P. & Controller--H.B. Zachry, San Antonio, TX; *U.S. Private*, pg. 1203
Lozeno, Ben, Asst. Controller--Dairy Farmers of America, Inc., Arlington, TX; *U.S. Private*, pg. 307
Lozier, Jackie, Controller & Treas.--Washington Homes, Inc., Landover, MD; *U.S. Public*, pg. 1741
Lubin, Julie, Controller--Sue Firestone & Assoc., Santa Barbara, CA; *U.S. Private*, pg. 406
Lubinskas, James, Controller--Subway Franchise Advertising Fund Trust, Milford, CT; *U.S. Private*, pg. 1048
Lubiski, Thomas M., Asst. Controller--Tasty Baking Company, Philadelphia, PA; *U.S. Public*, pg. 1561
Lucarelli, Brian M., Chief Fin. Officer, Controller, Asst Treas. & Asst. Sec.--Alaskan Copper Companies, Seattle, WA; *U.S. Private*, pg. 31
Lucarelli, Cathy, Controller--Anorad Corporation, Hauppauge, NY; *U.S. Private*, pg. 75
Lucas, Christy, Controller--Creative Alliance, Inc., Louisville, KY; *U.S. Private*, pg. 287
Lucas, Kenneth R., Controller--Shaw-Perkins, Inc., West Pittsburg, PA; *U.S. Private*, pg. 913
Lucas, Larry, Controller--Production Operators Inc., Houston, TX; *U.S. Public*, pg. 298
Lucas, Patti, Controller--Rubatex Corporation, Roanoke, VA; *U.S. Private*, pg. 56
Lucas, Scott, Chief Fin. Officer--K & R Express Systems Inc., Hinsdale, IL; *U.S. Private*, pg. 602
Lucas, Tama, Controller--Ameritruck Distribution Corporation, Fort Worth, TX; *U.S. Private*, pg. 65
Luce, Brad, Controller--Bird Products Corporation, Palm Springs, CA; *U.S. Public*, pg. 1591
Lucien, Kent T., Chief Fin. Officer, Exec. V.P. & Treas.--C. Brewer & Company, Limited, Honolulu, HI; *U.S. Private*, pg. 190
Ludlam, Albert W., Jr., Controller--Glaxo Wellcome PLC, Research Triangle Park, NC; *Int'l*, pg. 553
Lue, Connie, Controller--Pride Products, Inc., Elizabeth, NJ; *U.S. Private*, pg. 883
Lueders, Carl L., V.P. & Controller--Polaroid Corporation, Cambridge, MA; *U.S. Public*, pg. 1313
Luedtke, Sally, Controller--Rockbottom Stores, Inc., Lake Success, NY; *U.S. Private*, pg. 938
Luegers, William, Controller--Dean Foods Company, Franklin Park, IL; *U.S. Public*, pg. 489
Luger, Mark, Controller--NIBCO, Inc., Elkhart, IN; *U.S. Private*, pg. 798
Lugi, Tony, Controller--Dataram Corporation, Princeton, NJ; *U.S. Public*, pg. 487
Luhrs, Robert, Controller--Leo A. Daly Company, Omaha, NE; *U.S. Private*, pg. 309
Luker, Betsy, Controller--Opus South Corporation, Tampa, FL; *U.S. Private*, pg. 818
Lund, Mark R., Sr. V.P., Controller & Asst. Treas.--TCF Financial Corp., Minneapolis, MN; *U.S. Public*, pg. 1554
Lund, Mark R., Sr. V.P., Contoller & Asst. Treas.--TCF Bank Minnesota FSB, Minneapolis, MN; *U.S. Public*, pg. 1554
Lundstroo, Fred, Controller--Gestetner Securities B.V., Diemen, Netherlands; *Int'l*, pg. 1115
Lundy, Ronald C., Treas.--Moscom Corporation, Pittsford, NY; *U.S. Public*, pg. 1136
Luneke, Jim, Controller--Free Service Tire Company, Inc., Johnson City, TN; *U.S. Private*, pg. 425
Lupo, Anthony, Controller--Stephen Gould Paper Co., Inc., Whippany, NJ; *U.S. Private*, pg. 467
Luse, Dick, V.P. & Controller--Payless Cashways, Inc., Kansas City, MO; *U.S. Public*, pg. 1267
Lusk, Jim, V.P. & Controller--Lucent Technologies Inc., Murray Hill, NJ; *U.S. Public*, pg. 1017
Lutgen, David, Controller--R.D. Offit Company, Fargo, ND; *U.S. Private*, pg. 812
Luttrell, Bob, Controller--Nellcor Puritan Bennett Incorporated, Pleasanton, CA; *U.S. Public*, pg. 1039
Lutz, Dan, Controller--Sunstone Hotel Investors, Inc., San Clemente, CA; *U.S. Public*, pg. 1536
Lutz, Mark, Controller--Lockhart Cadillac South, Greenwood, IN; *U.S. Private*, pg. 672
Lutz, Max, Comptroller & Sec.--General Motors Suisse S.A., Bienne, Switzerland; *U.S. Public*, pg. 723
Lutzen, William, V.P. & Controller--Journal Communications Inc., Milwaukee, WI; *U.S. Private*, pg. 601
Luzum, James A., Chief Fin. Officer, Controller & Treas.--Villaume Industries, Inc., Saint Paul, MN; *U.S. Private*, pg. 1140
Lyberger, Catherine, Controller--Star Bronze Company, Alliance, OH; *U.S. Private*, pg. 1034
Lych, Greg, Controller--Oneida Rostone Corporation, Oneida, NY; *U.S. Public*, pg. 1383
Lyftogt, Michael, Controller--M.F. Bank & Company, Inc., Minneapolis, MN; *U.S. Private*, pg. 113
Lyke, H. Andersen, V.P. & Controller--Lyke Corporation, Ripon, WI; *U.S. Private*, pg. 682
Lyle, Lorraine, Gen. Mgr. & Corp. Controller--Northwestel Inc., Whitehorse, Canada; *Int'l*, pg. 115
Lynch, Chuck, Corp. Controller--Expeditors International of Washington, Inc., Seattle, WA; *U.S. Public*, pg. 600
Lynch, Diana, Controller--Grand Holdings, Inc., Edina, MN; *U.S. Private*, pg. 468
Lynch, G. Michael, V.P. & Controller--The Dow Chemical Company, Midland, MI; *U.S. Public*, pg. 522
Lynch, James B., Jr., Sr. V.P. & Controller--USLIFE Corporation, New York, NY; *U.S. Public*, pg. 77
Lynch, John, Controller--Ziebart International Corporation, Troy, MI; *U.S. Private*, pg. 1205
Lynch, John, Acting Chief Fin. Officer, Controller & Treas.--Sun TV & Appliances, Inc., Groveport, OH; *U.S. Public*, pg. 1532
Lynch, Joseph E., V.P. & Controller--Warner-Lambert Company, Morris Plains, NJ; *U.S. Public*, pg. 1738
Lynch, Ken, Controller--Abbott Laboratories/Ashland, Ashland, OH; *U.S. Public*, pg. 13
Lynch, Mike, Controller--Insurance Management Associates, Wichita, KS; *U.S. Private*, pg. 565
Lynch, Mike, Controller--Silver Springs Citrus Co-op, Howey in the Hills, FL; *U.S. Private*, pg. 1000
Lyon, Blake D., V.P. & Controller--EdperBrascan Corporation, Toronto, Canada; *Int'l*, pg. 433
Lyon, Howard T., Controller--Roanoke Gas Company, Roanoke, VA; *U.S. Public*, pg. 1392
Lyons, Dolly, Controller--C.W. Zumbiel Company, Norwood, OH; *U.S. Private*, pg. 1207
Lyons, Mary Ellen, Controller--Sterling Vision, Inc., East Meadow, NY; *U.S. Public*, pg. 1516
Lyons, Steve, Controller--The First Years Inc., Avon, MA; *U.S. Public*, pg. 642
Lyons, Terry, Controller--Metro Information Services, Virginia Beach, VA; *U.S. Public*, pg. 1102
Lyvers, Bill, Controller--Brawny Plastics West, Santa Ana, CA; *U.S. Private*, pg. 166
MacAdam, S.F., Controller--The RTZ Corporation PLC, London, United Kingdom; *Int'l*, pg. 1118
Macaluso, Frank, Controller--Merrimac Industries, Inc., West Caldwell, NJ; *U.S. Public*, pg. 1098
MacArther, Allan, Controller--Mazo Lerch Company, Inc., Alexandria, VA; *U.S. Public*, pg. 918
Macaulay, John C., V.P. & Controller--Overhead Door Corporation, Dallas, TX; *U.S. Private*, pg. 822
Macaulay, T., Controller--Synergistics Industries Limited, Mississauga, Canada; *U.S. Public*, pg. 734
MacCready, Robert C., V.P. & Corp. Controller--Town & Country Corporation, Chelsea, MA; *U.S. Public*, pg. 1625
MacDonald, Bruce, Controller--Faribault Foods Inc., Minneapolis, MN; *U.S. Private*, pg. 393
MacDonald, R.J., V.P. & Comptroller--Moore Business Forms & Systems Ltd., Mississauga, Canada; *Int'l*, pg. 889
MacDonald, Robert, Controller--HRI Hospital, Brookline, MA; *U.S. Public*, pg. 1697
MacDonough, Steven, V.P. & Comptroller--ACCEL International Corporation, Dublin, OH; *U.S. Public*, pg. 14
MacDougall, Derrick, Comptroller-McCain Foods (Canada)--McCain Foods Limited, Florenceville, Canada; *Int'l*, pg. 850
Macey, Jonathan, Sr. V.P. & Controller--Beneficial Corporation, Wilmington, DE; *U.S. Public*, pg. 211
Machler, Gary, Controller--Mason Shoe Mfg. Co., Chippewa Falls, WI; *U.S. Private*, pg. 712
Macintosh, John, Controller, Treas. & Sec.--Tamaroff Buick Inc., Southfield, MI; *U.S. Private*, pg. 1067
Mack, Frank J., Controller--Hutchinson Technology Inc., Hutchinson, MN; *U.S. Public*, pg. 850
Mack, Jeff, Asst. Controller--Rochester & Pittsburgh Coal Company, Indiana, PA; *U.S. Public*, pg. 1395
Mack, John, Controller--Miken Companies, Inc., Cheektowaga, NY; *U.S. Private*, pg. 745
Mack, Steve, Controller--Rainfair, Inc., Racine, WI; *U.S. Private*, pg. 907
Mack, Tim, Controller--Plastic Trim, Inc., Dayton, OH; *U.S. Public*, pg. 919
Mackenzie, Steven, Controller--Coast Steel Fabricators Ltd., Port Coquitlam, Canada; *Int'l*, pg. 31
Mackus, Craig R., Controller & Sec.--Bucyrus International, South Milwaukee, WI; *U.S. Private*, pg. 177
MacLachlan, Calum, Controller & Treas.--H.L. Bouton Company Inc., Buzzards Bay, MA; *U.S. Private*, pg. 162
Maclachlan, Calum, Controller & Treas.--Lensclean, Inc., Buzzards Bay, MA; *U.S. Private*, pg. 162
Macleod, Jack, Controller--Inner Secrets, Inc., Harrison, NJ; *U.S. Private*, pg. 564
MacNeill, James, Controller--Polycoat Systems, Inc., Hudson Falls, NY; *U.S. Private*, pg. 875
Macy, Roberta, Controller & Treas.--Edgerton Forge, Inc., Edgerton, OH; *U.S. Private*, pg. 102
Madden, Teresa, Controller & Sec.--New Century Energies, Inc., Denver, CO; *U.S. Public*, pg. 1170
Maddison, A., Fin. Controller--Gestetner Manufacturing Limited, Wellingborough, United Kingdom; *Int'l*, pg. 1114
Madigan, A., Controller & Sec.--Electrical Carbon Limited, Sheffield, United Kingdom; *Int'l*, pg. 891
Madsen, James A., Controller--Bancomm, Anaheim, CA; *U.S. Public*, pg. 488
Madsen, Marilyn, Controller & Site Mgr.--Bayer Corp. Pharmaceuticals, Berkeley, CA; *Int'l*, pg. 173
Maffeo, Steve, V.P.-Fin.--Telco Systems, Inc., Norwood, MA; *U.S. Public*, pg. 1568
Magallanes, Sarah, Controller--River Crest Hospital, San Angelo, TX; *U.S. Public*, pg. 1697
Magasko, John C., Chief Fin. Officer & Controller--Interstate Steel Supply Company, Philadelphia, PA; *U.S. Public*, pg. 1100
Magaw, Linda, Corp. Controller--East Jordan Iron Works, East Jordan, MI; *U.S. Private*, pg. 356
Magee, Mike, Controller--Manufacturers Products Company, Warren, MI; *U.S. Private*, pg. 701
Maggin, Ron, Controller--Georgette Klinger, Inc., New York, NY; *U.S. Private*, pg. 626
Magnemi, Joe, Sr. V.P. & Controller--Cline, Davis & Mann, Inc., New York, NY; *U.S. Private*, pg. 246
Magrisso, Julio, V.P.-Fin. & Controller--Injection Footwear Corp., Miami, FL; *U.S. Private*, pg. 563
Magruder, Neil, Controller--Nucor Steel-South Carolina, Darlington, SC; *U.S. Public*, pg. 1205
Maguier, Mary, Controller--Quarterdeck International Limited, Dun Laoghaire, Ireland; *U.S. Public*, pg. 1351
Maher, Daniel J., Controller--Hollingsworth & Vose Co., East Walpole, MA; *U.S. Private*, pg. 534
Maher, Daniel J., Jr., Controller--Augat, Inc., Mansfield, MA; *U.S. Public*, pg. 1597
Maher, Michael R., Sr. V.P. & Controller--Standard Federal Bank, Troy, MI; *Int'l*, pg. 10
Mahler, Joseph, V.P. & Controller--Deposition Technologies, Inc., San Diego, CA; *U.S. Public*, pg. 1056
Mahler, Mary, Controller--Advanced Marine Enterprises, Inc., Arlington, VA; *U.S. Public*, pg. 1182
Mahoney, Doug, V.P. & Controller--American Mail-Well Envelope, Englewood, CO; *U.S. Public*, pg. 1038
Mahoney, Robert B., V.P. & Controller--National Semiconductor Corporation, Santa Clara, CA; *U.S. Public*, pg. 1159
Maida, Jane M., Controller--Cytogen Corporation, Princeton, NJ; *U.S. Public*, pg. 471
Maier, David J., Controller--Osmonics, Inc., Minnetonka, MN; *U.S. Public*, pg. 1233
Maier, John N., V.P. & Controller--Coltec Industries Inc., Charlotte, NC; *U.S. Public*, pg. 401
Maier, Klaus, Dr., Controller & Dir.-Fin.--Mercedes-Benz AG, Stuttgart, Germany; *Int'l*, pg. 368
Main, D.W., Grp. Fin. Controller--John Menzies plc, Edinburgh, United Kingdom; *Int'l*, pg. 707
Maingot, Linda, Asst. Controller--Bairnco Corporation, Maitland, FL; *U.S. Public*, pg. 165
Maiolo, Joe, Controller--Northeast Div., Beech Creek, PA; *U.S. Public*, pg. 335
Maiter, Kenneth W., Controller--The Seibels Bruce Group, Inc., Columbia, SC; *U.S. Public*, pg. 1453
Majewicz, Ronald J., Sr. V.P. & Controller--Federal Home Loan Mortgage Corporation, Mc Lean, VA; *U.S. Public*, pg. 615
Majors, Alvin L., V.P. & Controller--Rohr, Inc., Chula Vista, CA; *U.S. Public*, pg. 751
Majsiak, George, Controller--Power Conversion, Inc., Elmwood Park, NJ; *Int'l*, pg. 127
Maker, Dana, Controller--Beacon Group, Bloomfield, CT; *U.S. Private*, pg. 126
Maki, David J., V.P. & Controller--H.B. Fuller Company, Saint Paul, MN; *U.S. Public*, pg. 686
Makris, Alexis, V.P. & Controller--Digital Equipment Corporation, Maynard, MA; *U.S. Public*, pg. 507
Malancziek, Kevin, Controller--The Spencer Turbine Co., Windsor, CT; *U.S. Private*, pg. 1025
Malbon, Mark S., V.P. & Controller--Dataproducts Corporation, Simi Valley, CA; *Int'l*, pg. 620
Malensant, Sylvain, Controller--Security Chimneys International Ltd., Laval, Canada; *Int'l*, pg. 1217
Malhorn, Roy, Controller--ICC Industries, Inc., New York, NY; *U.S. Private*, pg. 553

Malik, Krisham, V.P. & Controller--Pick Quick Foods, Jamaica, NY; *U.S. Private*, pg. 864
Malkiewicz, Steven M., Treas. & Controller--SEMCO Energy Services, Inc., Port Huron, MI; *U.S. Public*, pg. 1489
Mallory, R. Mark, V.P. & Controller--Tribune Company, Chicago, IL; *U.S. Public*, pg. 1635
Malloy, Jack, Controller--Radio One Inc., Lanham, MD; *U.S. Private*, pg. 906
Malls, Stephen, Controller--Monumental Millwork, Inc., Westminster, MD; *U.S. Private*, pg. 759
Malone, H.E., Controller--Ensco International Incorporated (ENSCO), Dallas, TX; *U.S. Public*, pg. 585
Malone, James C., Sr. V.P.-Fin. & Controller--Cognizant Corporation, Westport, CT; *U.S. Public*, pg. 395
Maloney, Dave, Intl. Controller--Diagraph Corporation, Earth City, MO; *U.S. Private*, pg. 330
Maloney, Karen, V.P. & Controller--Arrow Shirt Company, New York, NY; *Int'l*, pg. 194
Maloney, Karen, V.P. & Controller--Bernard Chaus, Inc., Secaucus, NJ; *U.S. Public*, pg. 342
Maloney, Phillip, Controller, Treas. & Sec.--Carver, Inc., Savannah, GA; *U.S. Private*, pg. 217
Mamach, Chuck, Controller--Moritz Cadillac-BMW Inc., Arlington, TX; *U.S. Private*, pg. 761
Mambu, Ronald D., V.P. & Controller--FMC Corporation, Chicago, IL; *U.S. Public*, pg. 604
Manacelli, Kevin J., Controller--The Ailing & Cory Company, Rochester, NY; *U.S. Public*, pg. 1666
Manburg, Rick, Controller--Concord Litho Co., Inc., Concord, NH; *U.S. Private*, pg. 261
Manchester, Glen P., Controller & Dir.-Fin.--Algoma Steel Inc., Sault Sainte Marie, Canada; *Int'l*, pg. 56
Mandeza, Rick, Controller--Aviation Sales Company, Miami, FL; *U.S. Public*, pg. 154
Mandile, Diane, Controller--SpecTran Corporation, Sturbridge, MA; *U.S. Public*, pg. 1497
Mandos, Robert R., Jr., Controller--AMETEK, Inc., Paoli, PA; *U.S. Public*, pg. 99
Maness, George, Controller--Ritchie Corporation, Wichita, KS; *U.S. Private*, pg. 933
Mangan, James, Chief Fin. Officer & Controller--Bixby International Corp., Newburyport, MA; *U.S. Private*, pg. 146
Mangan, Peter F., Controller--Kingsbury Corporation, Keene, NH; *U.S. Private*, pg. 621
Mangold, Allan, Controller--Willis Corroon Corp. of Orange County, Santa Ana, CA; *Int'l*, pg. 1506
Mangum, L.W., Controller--Holt Hosiery Mills, Inc., Burlington, NC; *U.S. Private*, pg. 536
Maniscalco, Joe, Controller--Western National Corporation, Houston, TX; *U.S. Public*, pg. 76
Mankovich, Willie, Controller--Colonial Beef Co., Philadelphia, PA; *U.S. Private*, pg. 253
Mann, Janet, Controller--Eaton Corp., Fluid Power Div., Fletcher, NC; *U.S. Public*, pg. 556
Mann, L. Linden, Controller & Asst. Sec.--Angelica Corporation, Chesterfield, MO; *U.S. Public*, pg. 113
Manner, Harold, Controller--United Bankshares, Inc., Parkersburg, WV; *U.S. Public*, pg. 1674
Manning, Diane, Controller--TTA/Newport, Inc., Newport Beach, CA; *U.S. Private*, pg. 1083
Manning, James, Controller & Treas.--Avesta Sheffield East, Inc., Baltimore, MD; *Int'l*, pg. 221
Mannion, Tom, V.P.-Fin. & Controller--Edwards Baking Co., Norcross, GA; *U.S. Private*, pg. 365
Manos, Chris H., Comptroller--Williams Industries, Inc., Falls Church, VA; *U.S. Public*, pg. 1769
Manos, George, Controller--The Holiday Inn Lancaster Host Hotel & Conference Center, Lancaster, PA; *U.S. Private*, pg. 534
Mansie, Angela, Asst. Controller--Johnny Appleseed's, Inc., Beverly, MA; *U.S. Private*, pg. 590
Manske, Donald, Controller--The Fonda Group, Inc., Saint Albans, VT; *U.S. Private*, pg. 421
Manso, Esther, Comptroller, Treas. & Sec.--Metro Ford Inc., Miami, FL; *U.S. Private*, pg. 736
Manto, Mike, V.P. & Controller--Hyperion Software, Stamford, CT; *U.S. Public*, pg. 851
Manu, Hubert, Controller--Connelly Containers, Inc., Bala Cynwyd, PA; *U.S. Private*, pg. 264
Manuel, Dale, Controller--Renfro Corp., Mount Airy, NC; *U.S. Private*, pg. 922
Manwaring, Richard, Controller--TFX Medical Inc., Jaffrey, NH; *U.S. Public*, pg. 1570
Marabito, Richard T., Corp. Controller & Treas.--Olympic Steel Inc., Cleveland, OH; *U.S. Public*, pg. 1221
Marantette, Tom, V.P.-Corp. Controller--Crain Communications, Inc., Chicago, IL; *U.S. Private*, pg. 284
Maratea, Michael J., V.P. & Controller--Pennzoil Company, Houston, TX; *U.S. Public*, pg. 1272
Maraz, Jim, Controller--VARI-FORM, Strathroy, Canada; *Int'l*, pg. 1341
Marcario, Rose, V.P. & Controller--International Rectifier Corporation, El Segundo, CA; *U.S. Public*, pg. 906
Marcelo, Bert, Controller--R.S. Owens, Chicago, IL; *U.S. Private*, pg. 824
March, Jose, Division Controller--Magnet Controls Div., San Diego, CA; *U.S. Public*, pg. 157
Marchant, C., Controller--Sunds Defibrator Woodhandling, Inc., Birmingham, AL; *Int'l*, pg. 1428
Marchese, Mel, Controller--Giesecke & Devrient Engineering, Inc., Bedford, MA; *U.S. Private*, pg. 452
Marchetti, Roger, Chief Acctg. Officer & Corp. Controller--Guidant Corporation, Indianapolis, IN; *U.S. Public*, pg. 768
Marchibroda, Daniel, Controller--Xerox Credit Corporation, Stamford, CT; *U.S. Public*, pg. 1785
Marchibroda, Daniel S., Asst. Controller--Xerox Corporation, Stamford, CT; *U.S. Public*, pg. 1783
Marconi, Jim, Controller--DHL Worldwide Express, Redwood City, CA; *U.S. Private*, pg. 301
Marcopoto, Michael, Controller--Burns & Roe Enterprises, Inc., Oradell, NJ; *U.S. Private*, pg. 187
Marcus, Michael S., Controller--Catherines Stores Corporation, Memphis, TN; *U.S. Public*, pg. 317
Marczewski, Terry M., V.P. & Controller--Homeland Holding Corp., Oklahoma City, OK; *U.S. Public*, pg. 832
Mardirossian, Olga, Sr. V.P. & Controller--Western International Media Corporation, Los Angeles, CA; *U.S. Private*, pg. 1165
Marek, John J., V.P. & Controller--Huffy Sports Company, Sussex, WI; *U.S. Public*, pg. 846
Marfogel, Shimshon, V.P. & Comptroller--The Israel Land Development Co., Ltd., Tel Aviv, Israel; *Int'l*, pg. 691
Marglous, Steve, Controller--Miss Elaine Inc., Saint Louis, MO; *U.S. Private*, pg. 752
Margolies, Mike, Controller--Ocean Chevrolet, Inc., Toms River, NJ; *U.S. Private*, pg. 810
Margolin, Barry, V.P.-Fin. & Plng. & Controller--Ha-Lo Industries, Inc., Niles, IL; *U.S. Public*, pg. 773
Margolis, David, V.P. & Controller--Broder Bros. Co., Plymouth, MI; *U.S. Private*, pg. 170
Margolis, David, Controller--Broder Bros. Co. Of Florida, Inc., Orlando, FL; *U.S. Private*, pg. 171
Mariani, Albert, Jr., Corp. Controller--Precision Valve Corporation, Yonkers, NY; *U.S. Private*, pg. 880
Maricondo, Peter E., V.P.-Admin. & Fin. & Comptroller--GPU Nuclear Corp., Parsippany, NJ; *U.S. Public*, pg. 695
Marini, Mathew J., Controller--Rent-Way, Inc., Erie, PA; *U.S. Public*, pg. 1377
Marino, Joseph, Controller--Winston Tire Company, Burbank, CA; *U.S. Private*, pg. 514
Markalunas, Peter, Controller--US SerVis, West Orange, NJ; *U.S. Public*, pg. 1687
Markerzon, Ram, Controller--ECI Telecom Ltd., Petah Tiqwa, Israel; *Int'l*, pg. 643
Markevich, Fenton, V.P. & Controller--Pip Printing, Agoura Hills, CA; *U.S. Private*, pg. 423
Markiz, Louis, Asst. V.P. & Controller--Aames Financial Corporation, Los Angeles, CA; *U.S. Public*, pg. 12
Markleski, Craig, Controller--Spectra-Tech, Shelton, CT; *U.S. Public*, pg. 1593
Markunas, Rick, Controller--E.J. Footwear Corp., Endicott, NY; *U.S. Public*, pg. 1684
Markus, Robert, Controller--Spire Corporation, Bedford, MA; *U.S. Public*, pg. 1499
Marlega, J., Controller--Chicago Show Printing Co., Morton Grove, IL; *U.S. Private*, pg. 235
Marone, Joseph, Controller--Hooper Holmes Corporation, Basking Ridge, NJ; *U.S. Public*, pg. 835
Maroney, Diane, Controller--DRS Photronics, Inc., Oakland, NJ; *U.S. Public*, pg. 474
Maroney, Sean, Controller--National Auto Credit Inc., Solon, OH; *U.S. Public*, pg. 1152
Marquand, Christopher J., Controller--Monrovia Nursery Co., Azusa, CA; *U.S. Private*, pg. 757
Marquardt, Charles B., Jr., V.P. & Controller--Pearlstine Distributors Inc., Charleston, SC; *U.S. Private*, pg. 845
Marques, Emilio, Jr., Controller--Sao Paulo Alpargatas S.A., Sao Paulo, Brazil; *Int'l*, pg. 1193
Marquis, Richard, Controller--Kendall de Venezuela, C.A., Caracas, Venezuela; *U.S. Public*, pg. 1648
Marquiss, Andrew, Controller--Volt Delta Resources, Inc., New York, NY; *U.S. Public*, pg. 1724
Marr, David, Grp. Controller--Beaulieu Group, Dalton, GA; *U.S. Private*, pg. 127
Marra, Nicholas M., Controller--Malrite Communications Group, Inc., Cleveland, OH; *U.S. Private*, pg. 698
Marrapodi, L.J., Controller--J.M. Huber, Chemicals Division, Havre De Grace, MD; *U.S. Private*, pg. 545
Marrotte, James, Controller--Brush Wellman Inc., Cleveland, OH; *U.S. Public*, pg. 266
Marsh, Cliff, Controller--Lodgistix, Inc., Phoenix, AZ; *U.S. Public*, pg. 1527
Marsh, Greg, V.P. & Controller--AmeriPath, Inc., Riviera Beach, FL; *U.S. Public*, pg. 96
Marsh, Kevin B., Chief Fin. Officer, V.P.-Fin. & Controller--SCANA Corporation, Columbia, SC; *U.S. Public*, pg. 1436
Marsh, Michele, Controller--Harrington's of Vermont, Inc., Richmond, VT; *U.S. Private*, pg. 504
Marshall, Brent, Fin. Controller--AEP/Borden Global Packaging (U.K.) Ltd., Bridgwater, United Kingdom; *U.S. Public*, pg. 5
Marshall, David, Controller--Continental Paper & Supply Co., Detroit, MI; *U.S. Private*, pg. 269
Marshall, Elizabeth L., Controller--E-Z Serve Corp., Houston, TX; *U.S. Public*, pg. 540
Marshall, Lisa, Asst. V.P. & Controller--Virginia First Savings Bank, F.S.B., Petersburg, VA; *U.S. Public*, pg. 1721
Marshall, Mike, Controller-Employee Rels.--Qantas Airways Ltd., London, United Kingdom; *Int'l*, pg. 1075
Marshall, Peter, Controller--Continental Grain Company, New York, NY; *U.S. Private*, pg. 268
Marshall, Robert, Controller & Treas.--Evy Of California, Inc., Los Angeles, CA; *U.S. Private*, pg. 387
Marszowski, Bruno A., Chief Fin. Officer & Controller--The FINOVA Group Inc., Phoenix, AZ; *U.S. Public*, pg. 624
Martel, Mario W., Controller--SNC-Lavalin Inc., Montreal, Canada; *Int'l*, pg. 1162
Martel, Rochelle, Controller--Syncor International Corporation, Woodland Hills, CA; *U.S. Public*, pg. 1548
Martello, June, Controller--The Long & Foster Companies, Inc., Fairfax, VA; *U.S. Private*, pg. 674
Martien, Pam, Controller--Newpark Environmental Services, Inc., Lafayette, LA; *U.S. Public*, pg. 1179
Martin, Antoinette, V.P.-Fin. & Controller--The Bethlehem Corporation, Easton, PA; *U.S. Public*, pg. 225
Martin, April, Controller--Allou Health & Beauty Care, Inc., Brentwood, NY; *U.S. Public*, pg. 55
Martin, Carrie, Controller--Paoli, Inc., Orleans, IN; *U.S. Private*, pg. 837
Martin, Charles, V.P. & Controller--Strategic Distribution Inc., Bensalem, PA; *U.S. Public*, pg. 1523
Martin, David A., Controller-Fin. Reporting & Analysis--Insituform Technologies, Inc., Chesterfield, MO; *U.S. Public*, pg. 881
Martin, Dennis, Controller--AmeriServe Food Distribution, Inc., Dallas, TX; *U.S. Private*, pg. 533
Martin, E. G., Controller--Saunders Oil Company, Inc., Richmond, VA; *U.S. Private*, pg. 968
Martin, Harry A., V.P. & Sec.--Uni-Marts, Inc., State College, PA; *U.S. Public*, pg. 1664
Martin, J.R., Controller--Union Camp Folding Carton Div., Clifton, NJ; *U.S. Public*, pg. 1666
Martin, James, Controller--Glenshaw Glass Co. Inc., Allison Park, PA; *U.S. Private*, pg. 457
Martin, James W., Controller & Treas.--Evening Post Publishing Co., Charleston, SC; *U.S. Private*, pg. 385
Martin, JoAnn M., Chief Fin. Officer, Sr. V.P. & Controller--Ameritas Life Insurance Corp., Lincoln, NE; *U.S. Private*, pg. 65
Martin, Joe, Corp. V.P. & Controller--National Car Rental System, Inc., Minneapolis, MN; *U.S. Public*, pg. 1379
Martin, John, Chief Fin. Officer--Trend Offset Printing Services, Los Alamitos, CA; *U.S. Private*, pg. 1099
Martin, Joseph J., Asst. Controller--International Business Machines Corporation, Armonk, NY; *U.S. Public*, pg. 895
Martin, June, Controller--Cavalier Homes, Inc., Wichita Falls, TX; *U.S. Public*, pg. 318
Martin, Karen, Controller--Thomson MacConnell Cadillac, Inc., Cincinnati, OH; *U.S. Private*, pg. 1084
Martin, Les, Chief Acctg. Officer, V.P. & Controller--Circus Circus - Las Vegas, Las Vegas, NV; *U.S. Public*, pg. 374
Martin, Linda, Controller--Coastal Lumber Company, Weldon, NC; *U.S. Private*, pg. 248
Martin, Lois, V.P. & Controller--Deluxe Corporation, Shoreview, MN; *U.S. Public*, pg. 498
Martin, Paul D., Controller--TVX Gold Inc., Toronto, Canada; *Int'l*, pg. 1345
Martin, Peter J., V.P. & Grp. Controller--Newell Co., Freeport, IL; *U.S. Public*, pg. 1176
Martin, Randall, Controller--World Carpets, Inc., Dalton, GA; *U.S. Private*, pg. 1190
Martin, Richard, Controller--Outdoor Technologies - Canada, Portage la Prairie, Canada; *U.S. Private*, pg. 822
Martin, Susan, Comptroller--Futuro Inc., Milford, OH; *Int'l*, pg. 182
Martin, Tom, Controller--Yokohama Tire Corporation, Fullerton, CA; *Int'l*, pg. 1521
Martin, Tony, Controller--Blue Circle Industries PLC, London, United Kingdom; *Int'l*, pg. 197
Martin, Tony, Controller--National Welders Supply Co. Inc., Charlotte, NC; *U.S. Private*, pg. 788
Martineau, P.R., V.P. & Treas.--GSW Inc., Guelph, Canada,; *Int'l*, pg. 538
Martinek, Linda A., Controller--The C.P. Hall Company, Chicago, IL; *U.S. Private*, pg. 495
Martinez, Ann, Controller--National Restaurant Management, Inc., New York, NY; *U.S. Private*, pg. 786
Martinez, Cliff, Controller--Tampa Bay Ship Building & Repair Co., Tampa, FL; *U.S. Private*, pg. 1067
Martinez, Marcelino, Controller--Berlitz de Mexico, S.A. de C.V., Mexico, Mexico; *U.S. Public*, pg. 221
Martinez, Walfrido A., Chief Fin. Officer, Sr. V.P. & Controller--E & B Marine Incorporated, Edison, NJ; *U.S. Public*, pg. 1756
Martinko, Jane, Controller--Harkins Builders, Inc., Silver Spring, MD; *U.S. Private*, pg. 502
Martinson, Dan, Controller--Fargo Glass & Paint Company, Fargo, ND; *U.S. Private*, pg. 393
Marubashi, Tom, Controller--International Comfort Products, Franklin, TN; *U.S. Public*, pg. 898
Maruszak, Gregory F., V.P. & Controller--Andrew Corporation, Orland Park, IL; *U.S. Public*, pg. 112
Maruta, Takaya, Controller--Nippon Oil Company, Limited (NiSSEKI), Tokyo, Japan; *Int'l*, pg. 936
Marzella, Vincent, Controller--Jos. M. Herman Shoe Co., Armonk, NY; *U.S. Private*, pg. 524
Masaryk, Marilyn R., Controller--Williamhouse-Regency, Inc., New York, NY; *U.S. Public*, pg. 89
Maschmann, Michael, Controller--ATAPCO Office Products Group, Saint Louis, MO; *U.S. Private*, pg. 64
Masci, Thomas A., Jr., Sr. V.P.-Fin. Opers. & Controller--U.S. Healthcare, Inc., Blue Bell, PA; *U.S. Public*, pg. 26
Maskey, Becky, Controller & Treas.--Cowles Media Company, Minneapolis, MN; *U.S. Private*, pg. 280
Maslyn, Jim, Controller--Mindscape, Inc., Novato, CA; *Int'l*, pg. 1026
Mason, Bill, V.P., Controller--The Eureka Company, Bloomington, IL; *Int'l*, pg. 440
Mason, Bruce, Controller--I.C. Thomasson Associates, Inc., Nashville, TN; *U.S. Private*, pg. 1083
Mason, R.C., Controller--Southern Clay Products Inc., Gonzales, TX; *Int'l*, pg. 802
Mason, Robert E., V.P. & Controller--Treasure Chest Advertising Co., Inc., Glendora, CA; *U.S. Public*, pg. 228
Mason, Thomas, V.P. & Controller--National Bank of Alaska, Anchorage, AK; *U.S. Public*, pg. 1153
Mason, Tom, Controller--National Bancorp of Alaska, Inc., Anchorage, AK; *U.S. Public*, pg. 1153
Massad, Leo, Controller--Hertz Corporation, Newark, NJ; *U.S. Public*, pg. 664
Massad, Leo, Controller--Hertz Corporation, Trenton, NJ; *U.S. Public*, pg. 664
Massad, Leo A., Jr., Controller--The Hertz Corporation, Park Ridge, NJ; *U.S. Public*, pg. 664
Masschelin, P.J., Controller--Compania Minera Disputada de Las Condes S.S., Santiago, Chile; *U.S. Public*, pg. 601
Masserant, Tim, Controller--Peterson American Corp., Southfield, MI; *U.S. Private*, pg. 857
Masseth, Leroy, Controller--Quebedeaux Pontiac, Inc., Tucson, AZ; *U.S. Private*, pg. 900
Massey, Curt, V.P. & Corp. Controller--Kulicke & Soffa Industries, Inc., Willow Grove, PA; *U.S. Public*, pg. 968
Massey, Curtis, Controller--Kulicke & Soffa Industries, Inc., Willow Grove, PA; *U.S. Public*, pg. 968
Massey, Ian, Controller-Fin.--Airbus Industrie, Blagnac, France; *Int'l*, pg. 39

Massey, Mark, Controller--Carolina Tractor & Equipment Co., Charlotte, NC; *U.S. Private*, pg. 214
Massimini, Dante J., Sr. V.P. & Treas.--Pennsylvania Real Estate Investment Trust, Fort Washington, PA; *U.S. Public*, pg. 1272
Massimo, Louis S., V.P. & Controller--Olin Corporation, Norwalk, CT; *U.S. Public*, pg. 1218
Massucci, Donald A., V.P., Controller & Treas.--Goodheart-Willcox Publisher, Tinley Park, IL; *U.S. Private*, pg. 464
Mastil, John, Controller--Triboro Electric Co., Doylestown, PA; *U.S. Private*, pg. 1102
Mastrangelo, J.N., Controller--Industrial Plastics Company, Fort Smith, AR; *U.S. Public*, pg. 56
Mastrogiacomo, Steven F., V.P. & Div. Controller-N. American Superstores--Staples, Inc., Westborough, MA; *U.S. Public*, pg. 1509
Matheny, Kenneth L., V.P. & Comptroller--USX Corporation, Pittsburgh, PA; *U.S. Public*, pg. 1661
Matheson, J., Unit Controller--Weatherford Oil Tool Co. (1983) Ltd., Edmonton, Canada; *U.S. Public*, pg. 1750
Matheson, Jim, Controller--Weatherford Enterra Oilfield Rentals, Singapore, Singapore; *U.S. Public*, pg. 1750
Mathews, Dustan, Controller--Burk Royalty Co., Wichita Falls, TX; *U.S. Private*, pg. 182
Mathews, Glenn, Controller--Southeastern Steel Company, Florence, SC; *U.S. Private*, pg. 1015
Mathews, Rajan S., V.P. & Controller--LIN Cellular Group, Kirkland, WA; *U.S. Public*, pg. 11
Mathews, Stephen, Controller--Pharmacia & Upjohn Inter-American Corporation, Auckland, New Zealand; *Int'l*, pg. 1048
Mathieson, Michael R., V.P. & Controller--Avon Products, Inc., New York, NY; *U.S. Public*, pg. 155
Mathieu, Jan T., Controller--Elkay Products, Inc., Shrewsbury, MA; *U.S. Private*, pg. 372
Matlick, Linda J., Controller--Southern California Water Company, San Dimas, CA; *U.S. Public*, pg. 1489
Matlock, Lanell, Controller--American Eco Corporation, Toronto, Canada; *Int'l*, pg. 73
Matoushaya, Lazarus, Controller--Gestetner (Pvt) Limited, Harare, Zimbabwe; *Int'l*, pg. 1115
Matson, Joseph R., Controller--Nashua Corporation, Nashua, NH; *U.S. Public*, pg. 1152
Matsumoto, Ichiro, Gen. Mgr. & Treas.--Asahi International Ltd., New York, NY; *Int'l*, pg. 85
Matsunaga, Kazumi, Comptroller--CAMI Automotive, Inc., Ingersoll, Canada; *U.S. Public*, pg. 722
Matta, Daniel, Comptroller--The Guttman Group, Belle Vernon, PA; *U.S. Private*, pg. 488
Matter, Gary L., Sr. V.P., Controller & Sec.--Commercial Federal Corporation, Omaha, NE; *U.S. Public*, pg. 411
Mattern, Edie, Controller--The Rivet Group L.L.C., Aberdeen, SD; *U.S. Private*, pg. 934
Mattes, Robert A., Asst. Controller--W.R. Berkley Corporation, Greenwich, CT; *U.S. Public*, pg. 215
Matthews, Brad, Controller--Amtrol Inc., West Warwick, RI; *U.S. Private*, pg. 300
Matthews, Ed, Controller--Stoneville Furniture Co. Inc., Stoneville, NC; *U.S. Private*, pg. 1045
Matthews, J. Larry, V.P. & Controller--The Meridian Resource Corporation, Houston, TX; *U.S. Public*, pg. 1095
Matthews, R.V., V.P.-Controller--MacMillan Bloedel Limited, Vancouver, Canada; *Int'l*, pg. 828
Mattingly, Laura, Controller--Cross Motors Corp., Louisville, KY; *U.S. Private*, pg. 291
Mattingly, M., Controller--Mosler Inc., Hamilton, OH; *U.S. Private*, pg. 763
Mattingly, Mike, Chief Fin. Officer, Controller & Treas.--The Court Company, Memphis, TN; *U.S. Private*, pg. 279
Mattis, Connie, Controller--Uniflow Manufacturing Co., Erie, PA; *U.S. Private*, pg. 1117
Mattson, Donald W., V.P. & Controller--Conrail, Inc., Philadelphia, PA; *U.S. Public*, pg. 431
Maturo, Paul J., Controller--Devon Group, Inc., Stamford, CT; *U.S. Public*, pg. 503
Matz, Eldon, Controller & Asst. Treas.--Dynamic Homes, Inc., Detroit Lakes, MN; *U.S. Public*, pg. 538
Maudsley, Robert L., Controller--Markin Tubing, Inc., Wyoming, NY; *U.S. Private*, pg. 705
Maulen, Edward, Controller--Caswell-Massey Co. Ltd., Edison, NJ; *U.S. Private*, pg. 219
Maulit, Nel A., Controller--Peck Jones Construction, Los Angeles, CA; *U.S. Private*, pg. 846
Mauro, Steve, Chief Fin. Officer & Controller--Powell Electronics Inc., Philadelphia, PA; *U.S. Private*, pg. 877
Mause, Joe, V.P. & Controller--Eastern Smelting & Refining Corporation, Lynn, MA; *U.S. Private*, pg. 357
Mautz, Carl, Controller--Watson Wyatt Worldwide, Bethesda, MD; *U.S. Private*, pg. 1154
Mavde, Graeme, Chief Accountant--Fuller, Smith & Turner Plc, London, United Kingdom; *Int'l*, pg. 529
Mavrakis, Kathy, Controller--WWF-Canada, Inc., Montreal, Canada; *U.S. Private*, pg. 1145
Mavrey, James, V.P. & Controller--ShowBiz Pizza Time, Inc., Irving, TX; *U.S. Public*, pg. 1468
Maw, Glen, Controller-Consumer--Robin Hood Multifoods Inc., Markham, Canada; *U.S. Public*, pg. 901
Maxsimic, George, Controller--The Erin Company, Bangor, ME; *U.S. Private*, pg. 381
Maxson, Debbie, Controller--Benchmark Industries, Brookville, OH; *U.S. Private*, pg. 132
Maxwell, Mike, Div.-Controller--Malta Div.-Tomkins Industries, Inc., Malta, OH; *Int'l*, pg. 1398
Maxwell, Ronald, Controller--A.W. Chesterton Company, Stoneham, MA; *U.S. Private*, pg. 234
May, Art, Controller--Ace Novelty Company, Inc., Woodinville, WA; *U.S. Public*, pg. 1309
May, Kenneth, V.P. & Controller--Talley Industries, Inc., Phoenix, AZ; *U.S. Public*, pg. 307
May, Linda, Chief Fin. Officer--Bam Media, Pleasant Hill, CA; *U.S. Private*, pg. 113
May, Mark, Controller--Shopsmith, Inc., Dayton, OH; *U.S. Public*, pg. 1467
May, Morton, Controller--Dana Perfumes Corp., New York, NY; *U.S. Private*, pg. 922
May, Terry, Chief Acctg. Officer--Pride International, Inc., Houston, TX; *U.S. Public*, pg. 1324
May, Timothy William, Grp. Treas.--Eurocamp Plc, Knutsford, United Kingdom; *Int'l*, pg. 464
Maya, J.J., Controller--NRI Iberica, S.A., Barcelona, Spain; *U.S. Public*, pg. 457
Maybury, Christine, Controller--Rhodes International, Inc., Salt Lake City, UT; *U.S. Private*, pg. 927
Mayer, John, Controller--The Blodgett Oven Co., Inc., Burlington, VT; *U.S. Public*, pg. 1064
Mayer, Joseph, Controller--Champ/Pik-A-Nut Service Line, Edwardsville, KS; *U.S. Public*, pg. 1503
Mayer, Les, Controller--Don Massey Cadillac, Inc., Englewood, CO; *U.S. Private*, pg. 713
Mayleben, Tim, Controller--Applied Intelligence Systems, Inc., Ann Arbor, MI; *U.S. Public*, pg. 569
Mayo, Ronald A., V.P.-Fin. & Controller--Garden State Newspapers, Inc., Denver, CO; *U.S. Private*, pg. 727
Mayor, William J., Asst. Controller--Anheuser-Busch Companies, Inc., Saint Louis, MO; *U.S. Public*, pg. 113
Mays, Debra A., Asst. Treas. & Controller--Ash Grove Cement Company, Shawnee Mission, KS; *U.S. Private*, pg. 87
Mazinis, Pat, Controller--Cougle Commission Company, Inc., Chicago, IL; *U.S. Private*, pg. 278
Mazure, Leslie, Controller--Orient-Express Hotels Inc., New York, NY; *Int'l*, pg. 1213
Mazza, Thomas, Asst. Controller--Foster Wheeler Corporation, Clinton, NJ; *U.S. Public*, pg. 676
McAden, Susan J., V.P. & Controller--Coho Energy, Inc., Dallas, TX; *U.S. Public*, pg. 396
McAfee, Nancy G., V.P., Controller & Treas.--Thrall Enterprises, Inc., Chicago, IL; *U.S. Private*, pg. 1084
McAllister, Scott A., V.P. & Controller--J. Gibson McIlvain Co., White Marsh, MD; *U.S. Private*, pg. 722
McArthey, Dennis P., Controller--Phillips Plastics Corporation, Phillips, WI; *U.S. Private*, pg. 862
McAuliffe, Hawley H., Controller--Compendium Systems Corporation, Greenwich, CT; *U.S. Private*, pg. 259
McBride, Mark, Controller--Evans & Sutherland Computer Corporation, Salt Lake City, UT; *U.S. Public*, pg. 595
McBride, Mark, Controller--Simulation Division, Salt Lake City, UT; *U.S. Public*, pg. 596
McBurney, Robert, V.P.-Admin. & Controller--S.E. Huffman Corp., Clover, SC; *U.S. Private*, pg. 546
McCabe, Joseph J., V.P. & Controller--PP&L Resources, Allentown, PA; *U.S. Public*, pg. 1244
McCabe, Joseph J., V.P. & Controller--Pennsylvania Power & Light Company-Lehigh Div., Allentown, PA; *U.S. Public*, pg. 1244
McCabe, Thomas, Controller--Bufkor, Inc., Clearwater, FL; *U.S. Private*, pg. 179
McCain, Thomas K., V.P. & Controller--Edison Brothers Stores, Inc., Saint Louis, MO; *U.S. Public*, pg. 563
McCall, W.A., Controller, Treas., Sec., & Mgr.-D.P.--Dixie Oil Company, Tifton, GA; *U.S. Private*, pg. 337
McCallum, Gerald, Treas. & Comptroller--Acklands Limited, Toronto, Canada; *Int'l*, pg. 23
McCann, Anna, Controller--Zitel Corporation, Fremont, CA; *U.S. Public*, pg. 1793
McCann, Michael, Controller--Genzyme Diagnostics, Medix Biotech, San Carlos, CA; *U.S. Public*, pg. 733
McCann, Patrick J., Chief Acctg. Officer & Controller--Barnett Banks, Inc., Jacksonville, FL; *U.S. Public*, pg. 1162
McCann, Steven F., V.P. & Controller--Service Merchandise Company, Inc., Brentwood, TN; *U.S. Public*, pg. 1461
McCanna, Philip V., Controller--Pittway Corporation, Chicago, IL; *U.S. Public*, pg. 1305
McCarroll, Michael, V.P. & Controller--Standard & Poor's Ratings Services, New York, NY; *U.S. Public*, pg. 1071
McCarthy, John, Controller--Gorges/Quik-To-Fix Foods, Dallas, TX; *U.S. Private*, pg. 465
McCarthy, Joseph, Controller--Linear Dynamics Inc., Parsippany, NJ; *U.S. Private*, pg. 668
McCarthy, Tom, V.P. & Controller--Brown Motors, Toledo, OH; *U.S. Private*, pg. 174
McCartney, William C., V.P.-Fin. & Controller--Watts Industries, Inc., North Andover, MA; *U.S. Public*, pg. 1746
McCarty, Jerry M., V.P. & Controller--Phelps Dodge Mining Company, Phoenix, AZ; *U.S. Public*, pg. 1286
McCaughan, James, V.P. & Controller--Rollins Leasing Corp., Wilmington, DE; *U.S. Public*, pg. 1405
McClain, Andrea D., Controller--ABX Air, Inc., Wilmington, OH; *U.S. Public*, pg. 33
McClanahan, Patricia N., Chief Fin. Officer & Controller--First Farmers & Merchants National Bank, Columbia, TN; *U.S. Private*, pg. 407
McClelland, Bob, Controller & Treas.--Analog Devices, Santa Clara, CA; *U.S. Public*, pg. 108
McClintock, Steve, Controller--Simpson Dura-Vent Co., Inc., Vacaville, CA; *U.S. Public*, pg. 1474
McClister, Debra L., V.P. & Controller--Philips Electronics North America Corporation, New York, NY; *Int'l*, pg. 1053
McCloskey, Brenda, Chief Fin. Officer & Controller--Marketing Displays International, Farmington Hills, MI; *U.S. Private*, pg. 705
McClure, Cynthia, Controller, Treas. & Sec.--The McClure Group, Wayne, PA; *U.S. Private*, pg. 719
McClure, Hal G., Corp. Controller--Pace Resources, Inc., York, PA; *U.S. Private*, pg. 829
McClusky, Laura, Controller--Hayden, Corona, CA; *U.S. Public*, pg. 1503
McCollough, Ben, Controller--Killearn Properties, Inc., Stockbridge, GA; *U.S. Public*, pg. 956
McCollum, Mark A., V.P. & Controller--Tenneco Inc., Greenwich, CT; *U.S. Public*, pg. 1577
McCollum, Martin J., Grp. Controller--Doehler-Jarvis, Inc., Toledo, OH; *U.S. Public*, pg. 796
McComb, Michael, Controller--Lason, Inc., Madison Heights, MI; *U.S. Public*, pg. 979
McConnell, Gordon, V.P. & Controller--Seagull Energy Corporation, Houston, TX; *U.S. Public*, pg. 1450
McConnell, Mike, Controller--Kenwood USA, Long Beach, CA; *Int'l*, pg. 730
McConnell, Thomas M., Controller--Jiffy Lube International, Inc., Houston, TX; *U.S. Public*, pg. 1272
McCorkle, James H., Controller & Asst. Sec.--Speizman Industries, Inc., Charlotte, NC; *U.S. Public*, pg. 1498
McCorkle, Martha A., Controller--Sunrise Carpet Ind. Inc., Dalton, GA; *U.S. Private*, pg. 1190
McCorkle, Martha A., Controller--White-Crest Dorsett Inc., Dalton, GA; *U.S. Private*, pg. 1190
McCormick, Rob, V.P. & Controller--Mirro Company, Manitowoc, WI; *U.S. Public*, pg. 1177
McCormick, Robert, V.P.-Opers. & Controller--Paco Rabanne Compar, New York, NY; *Int'l*, pg. 1073
McCormick, Robert, V.P.-Opers. & Controller--Compar, New York, NY; *Int'l*, pg. 1073
McCourt, Daniel R., Controller--National Meats Inc., Etobicoke, Canada; *Int'l*, pg. 1207
McCoy, Dean A., Controller--Steego Corporation, West Palm Beach, FL; *Int'l*, pg. 216
McCoy, Dean A., V.P. & Controller--National Beverage Corp., Plantation, FL; *U.S. Public*, pg. 1153
McCradey, Ken, Controller--Empire Kosher Poultry, Inc., Mifflintown, PA; *U.S. Private*, pg. 374
McCrary, Louise, Controller--Blue Cross of California, Woodland Hills, CA; *U.S. Private*, pg. 152
McCraw, James R., V.P. & Controller--Texas Industries, Inc., Dallas, TX; *U.S. Public*, pg. 1585
McCubbin, Donald K., Chief Fin. Officer & Controller--Nadel Architects, Inc., Los Angeles, CA; *U.S. Private*, pg. 773
McCullers, Randy, V.P. & Controller--Federal Savings Bank, Fort Smith, AR; *U.S. Private*, pg. 614
McCullouch, Elizabeth V., V.P., Comptroller & Asst. Sec.--Mobile Telecommunications Technologies Corp., Jackson, MS; *U.S. Public*, pg. 1120
McCullough, Donna, Controller--Holiday RV Superstores West, Inc., Sacramento, CA; *U.S. Public*, pg. 830
McCullough, Gayle, Controller--Plains Cotton Co-op Association, Lubbock, TX; *U.S. Private*, pg. 868
McCullough, Tom, Controller--Winchester Electronics, Watertown, CT; *U.S. Public*, pg. 1003
McCurdy, Frankie F., Controller--Veda Incorporated, Alexandria, VA; *U.S. Private*, pg. 1136
McCurrie, Brian, V.P.-Fin. Admin. & Controller--Union Switch & Signal Inc., Pittsburgh, PA; *Int'l*, pg. 77
McCurry, Donna, Controller--Rolane Factory Outlets, Greensboro, NC; *U.S. Private*, pg. 941
McDaniel, W. Valen, Corp. Auditor--Community Bank System, Inc., De Witt, NY; *U.S. Public*, pg. 416
McDevitt, Lawrence R., V.P. & Controller--Levitz Furniture Incorporated, Boca Raton, FL; *U.S. Public*, pg. 990
McDonald, Brian, V.P.-Fin. & Controller--Comair Holdings, Inc., Erlanger, KY; *U.S. Public*, pg. 406
McDonald, Jerry, Controller--E.P. Graphics, Inc., Berne, IN; *U.S. Private*, pg. 354
McDonald, Jerry, Controller--PC Quote, Inc., Chicago, IL; *U.S. Public*, pg. 1240
McDonald, John, Asst. Corp. Controller--Playboy Enterprises, Inc., Chicago, IL; *U.S. Public*, pg. 1309
McDonald, Kevin, Controller & Sec.--Integrated Waste Services, Inc., Buffalo, NY; *U.S. Public*, pg. 886
McDonald, Myles, Controller--Mitre Sports (U.S.), Nashville, TN; *Int'l*, pg. 1036
McDonald, Steven L., V.P. & Controller--Household International, Inc., Prospect Heights, IL; *U.S. Public*, pg. 842
McDonald, William J., Assoc. Controller--Criterion Life Insurance Co., Washington, DC; *U.S. Public*, pg. 219
McDowell, Bill, Controller--Pursell Industries, Sylacauga, AL; *U.S. Private*, pg. 896
McDowell, Howard, Controller--New England Electric System, Westborough, MA; *U.S. Public*, pg. 1171
McDowell, Howard W., Controller--Narragansett Energy Resources Company, Providence, RI; *U.S. Public*, pg. 1171
McDuffie, Anthony D., Asst. Controller--Harrah's Entertainment, Inc., Memphis, TN; *U.S. Public*, pg. 790
McElroy, Tim, Controller--Nature's Recipe Pet Foods, Corona, CA; *U.S. Private*, pg. 789
McEntee, James, Controller--Nob Hill General Store, Inc., Gilroy, CA; *U.S. Private*, pg. 799
McEntrye, Nancy, Controller--Bibler Brothers, Inc., Russellville, AR; *U.S. Private*, pg. 142
McEvoy, Thomas P., Treas. & Controller--New Standard Corporation, Mount Joy, PA; *U.S. Private*, pg. 794
McEwen, Linda, Controller--Shea Homes, Walnut, CA; *U.S. Private*, pg. 990
McEwen, Russell, Controller--RDM Sports Group, Atlanta, GA; *U.S. Public*, pg. 1354
McFarland, Loren L., Controller--Mentor Corporation, Santa Barbara, CA; *U.S. Public*, pg. 1086
McFarland, Paul, Controller--Standex Electronics, Cincinnati, OH; *U.S. Public*, pg. 1507
McFarlane, Barry, Controller--Pitney Bowes Software Systems, Glen Ellyn, IL; *U.S. Public*, pg. 1304
McGarrity, Richard H., Controller--Unilever United States Inc., New York, NY; *Int'l*, pg. 1435
McGaughy, Patrick L., V.P. & Asst. Controller--Prime Group Realty Trust, Chicago, IL; *U.S. Public*, pg. 1326
McGee, G.J., Controller--Salem Furnace Co., Carnegie, PA; *U.S. Private*, pg. 961
McGhee, Dewey, Controller--Allen & Ohara, Inc., Memphis, TN; *U.S. Private*, pg. 36
McGilberry, Leslie, Controller--ICO, Inc., Houston, TX; *U.S. Public*, pg. 853
McGill, Gary, Controller--Communications Instruments Inc., Fairview, NC; *U.S. Private*, pg. 259
McGill, J., Controller--J.L. Hammett Company, Braintree, MA; *U.S. Private*, pg. 498

McGillicuddy, Andy, Controller--Primark Corporation, Waltham, MA; *U.S. Public*, pg. 1325
McGillivrae, Jeff, Controller--Allied Security, International, Spokane, WA; *U.S. Private*, pg. 41
McGinley, Stephen, V.P. & Controller--The Reliable Life Insurance Company, Webster Groves, MO; *U.S. Public*, pg. 1374
McGinnis, Dave, Controller--Kocolene Oil Corp., Seymour, IN; *U.S. Private*, pg. 629
McGirr, Mark K., V.P., Controller & Asst. Sec.--Smith Technologies Corp., Portland, OR; *U.S. Public*, pg. 1478
McGivney, Richard, Controller--Research Triangle Institute, Research Triangle Park, NC; *U.S. Private*, pg. 924
McGoldrick, Kevin F., Controller--Colonial Gas Company, Lowell, MA; *U.S. Public*, pg. 400
McGowan, J.R., V.P. & Controller--U.S. Can Company, Oak Brook, IL; *U.S. Public*, pg. 1681
McGowan, Kelly, Controller & Treas.--NT Dor-omatic, Harwood Heights, IL; *U.S. Private*, pg. 771
McGrady, David, V.P. & Controller--Nocona Boot Co., Nocona, TX; *U.S. Public*, pg. 937
McGrath, Lee, Controller--Digital Link Corporation, Sunnyvale, CA; *U.S. Public*, pg. 508
McGrath, Mike, Controller--Silicon Valley Group, Inc., San Jose, CA; *U.S. Public*, pg. 1474
McGrath, Richard, Chief Fin. Officer & Controller--Budapest Marriott Hotel, Budapest, Hungary; *Int'l*, pg. 232
McGrath, Sara, Controller--Clothestime Stores, Inc., Anaheim, CA; *U.S. Public*, pg. 387
McGraw, Allan, V.P. & Controller--Global Marketing Resources (GMR), New York, NY; *U.S. Private*, pg. 457
McGrow, Bill, Controller--Unibus, Inc., Strongsville, OH; *U.S. Public*, pg. 1319
McGruder, Mel, Controller--Fred's Inc., Memphis, TN; *U.S. Public*, pg. 680
McGuffin, Glenn, Controller--Consolidated Systems, Inc., Columbia, SC; *U.S. Private*, pg. 266
McGuimess, Kimberly, Dir.-Acct.--Lundy Enterprises, Inc., New Orleans, LA; *U.S. Private*, pg. 681
McGuire, Paul F., Asst. Controller--Kimberly-Clark Corporation, Dallas, TX; *U.S. Public*, pg. 958
McGurk, Nancy, Controller--Resource America Field & Accounting Operations Headquarters, Akron, OH; *U.S. Public*, pg. 1382
McIlraith, Marcia, Controller--Boyles Galvanizing Co., Hurst, TX; *U.S. Public*, pg. 960
McInerney, Brian, Controller--Lindberg Corporation, Rosemont, IL; *U.S. Public*, pg. 999
McInerney, Carol, Corp. Controller--Bradley Corporation, Menomonee Falls, WI; *U.S. Private*, pg. 164
McIntosh, Eric, Controller--Varco (U.K.) Ltd. Drilling Systems, Montrose, United Kingdom; *U.S. Public*, pg. 1709
McIntosh, Joe, Controller--Robert James Sales Inc., Buffalo, NY; *U.S. Private*, pg. 935
McIntyre, Jere R., Controller--The David J. Joseph Company, Cincinnati, OH; *Int'l*, pg. 1155
McIntyre, Jerry, Chief Fin. Officer--David Joseph Co., Cincinnati, OH; *U.S. Private*, pg. 601
McKain, Jim, Controller--Allegheny Heat Treating, Chicora, PA; *U.S. Public*, pg. 412
McKamy Hall, F., V.P., Controller & Treas.--Astec Industries, Inc., Chattanooga, TN; *U.S. Public*, pg. 141
McKay, Annette, Plant Controller--Jordan's Foods-Bangor Division, Bangor, ME; *U.S. Private*, pg. 599
McKay, Caroline, Controller--A.P.S., Inc., Houston, TX; *U.S. Public*, pg. 10
McKay, Patricia A., V.P. & Opers. Controller--Republic Industries, Inc., Fort Lauderdale, FL; *U.S. Public*, pg. 1378
McKean, Scott, Controller--Bridgestone/Firestone, Inc., Nashville, TN; *Int'l*, pg. 213
McKee, Chris, Controller--Glazer's Wholesale Drug Co. Inc., Dallas, TX; *U.S. Private*, pg. 455
McKeeby, Charles, Asst. Controller--Hughes Supply, Inc., Orlando, FL; *U.S. Public*, pg. 846
McKeever, Edward C., Controller--Environmental Resources Management, Exton, PA; *U.S. Private*, pg. 378
McKenna, Edward M., Controller--Orange and Rockland Utilities, Inc., Pearl River, NY; *U.S. Public*, pg. 1229
McKenna, Kenneth, V.P. & Controller--Kings Super Markets Inc., West Caldwell, NJ; *Int'l*, pg. 843
McKenny, John, V.P. & Controller--Interstate Bakeries Corporation, Kansas City, MO; *U.S. Public*, pg. 909
McKenny, John F., V.P. & Controller--Interstate Brands Corporation, Kansas City, MO; *U.S. Public*, pg. 909
McKenzie, Julie, Controller--McKenzies of Vermont, Inc., Burlington, VT; *U.S. Private*, pg. 723
McKenzie, Peter, Corp. Controller--PolyMedica Industries, Inc., Woburn, MA; *U.S. Public*, pg. 1315
McKeon, Jim, V.P. & Controller--Genesis Health Ventures, Inc., Kennett Square, PA; *U.S. Public*, pg. 728
McKeon, Jim, V.P. & Controller--Genesis ElderCare, Philadelphia, PA; *U.S. Public*, pg. 728
McKinney, Audra, Controller--New Cooperative Inc., Fort Dodge, IA; *U.S. Private*, pg. 792
McKinney, Donna, Controller--Saturn of Plymouth, Plymouth, MI; *U.S. Private*, pg. 713
McKinney, Jeff, Controller--Heller Bros. Packing Corp., Winter Garden, FL; *U.S. Private*, pg. 520
McKinney, K., Fin. & Controller--Senior Conflow Inc., Washington, PA; *Int'l*, pg. 1222
McKinney, Ronald E., Controller--Black Cadillac Olds, Inc., Greensboro, NC; *U.S. Private*, pg. 146
McKnight, John, Controller--Abdalla's Lafayette, Inc., Lafayette, LA; *U.S. Private*, pg. 10
McLaughlin, Thomas N., Chief Fin. Officer & Controller--Insulate LLC, Auburn, WA; *Int'l*, pg. 1171
McLeod, Robert, Controller--Auto-trol Technology (Canada) Ltd., Calgary, Canada; *U.S. Public*, pg. 148
McLinn, Kirby, Controller--Rocor Transportation Companies Inc., Oklahoma City, OK; *U.S. Private*, pg. 938
Mcllyar, Michael G., Controller--Broughton Foods Company, Marietta, OH; *U.S. Public*, pg. 259
McLoone, Michael E., V.P. & Controller--General Accident Insurance, Philadelphia, PA; *Int'l*, pg. 543
McLoughlin, Chris, V.P. & Controller--The Home Depot, Inc., Atlanta, GA; *U.S. Public*, pg. 831
McLouth, Rick, Controller--Quality Stores Inc., Muskegon, MI; *U.S. Private*, pg. 899
McLure, Howard A., Sr. V.P., Controller & Asst. Sec.--Magellan Health Services, Inc., Atlanta, GA; *U.S. Public*, pg. 1033
McMahon, Chris, Controller--Automatic Signal/Eagle Signal, Austin, TX; *Int'l*, pg. 1245
McMains, Melvin L., Controller--HON Industries Inc., Muscatine, IA; *U.S. Public*, pg. 772
McMakin, Kelly, Chief Fin. Officer & Treas.--Florafax International, Inc., Vero Beach, FL; *U.S. Public*, pg. 654
McManimon, William P., Controller & Dep. Chief Fin. Officer--NJ Transit, Newark, NJ; *U.S. Private*, pg. 794
McMaster, Kevin, V.P. & Controller--Toll Brothers, Inc., Huntingdon Valley, PA; *U.S. Public*, pg. 1620
McMaster, Walter L., V.P. & Controller--Air Express International Corporation, Darien, CT; *U.S. Public*, pg. 30
McMeans, Shaun D., Controller--Burnham, Lancaster, PA; *U.S. Public*, pg. 270
McMenamin, Edward, Controller & V.P.--H.J. Heinz Company, Pittsburgh, PA; *U.S. Public*, pg. 805
McMillen, R.W. III, V.P. & Corp. Controller--Welch Foods Inc., A Cooperative, Concord, MA; *U.S. Private*, pg. 784
McMullan, D.M., V.P. & Controller--Union Texas Petroleum Holdings, Houston, TX; *U.S. Public*, pg. 1669
McNally, Kevin, Controller--SRDS, Des Plaines, IL; *U.S. Private*, pg. 958
McNamara, J., Controller--Crane Manufacturing, Cudahy, WI; *U.S. Private*, pg. 286
McNaughton, G.L., Controller--MTD Products Limited, Kitchener, Canada; *U.S. Private*, pg. 688
McNaul, Mike, Controller--Bayer Clothing Group, New York, NY; *U.S. Private*, pg. 124
McNicholas, John, Controller--Information Resources, Inc., Chicago, IL; *U.S. Public*, pg. 875
McNichols, E., V.P. & Controller--Krause's Furniture Inc., Brea, CA; *U.S. Public*, pg. 967
McNulty, Jamie, Controller--Aladdin Hotel & Casino, Las Vegas, NV; *U.S. Private*, pg. 30
McNulty, Pat, Corp. Controller--Robertson-Ceco Corporation, San Ramon, CA; *U.S. Public*, pg. 1394
McNutt, John, Controller--CAIRE, Inc., Burnsville, MN; *U.S. Private*, pg. 751
McParland, Thomas J., Jr., Controller--U.S. Healthcare, Inc., Blue Bell, PA; *U.S. Public*, pg. 26
McPhee, Don, Controller--Environmental Tectonics Corporation (ETC), Southampton, PA; *U.S. Public*, pg. 587
McPhee, James, Controller--Southwest Marine, Inc., San Diego, CA; *U.S. Private*, pg. 213
McPherson, Michael J., Exec. V.P., Controller & Sec.--Steadly Company, Carthage, MO; *U.S. Public*, pg. 986
McPhie, Christine G., Controller & Sec.--Trimin Enterprises, Inc., Vancouver, Canada; *Int'l*, pg. 1424
McQuade, Robert C., Chief Fin. Officer, Sec. & Controller--Legacy Storage Systems Corp., Markham, Canada; *Int'l*, pg. 805
McQuesten, Brian R., V.P. & Controller--Ekco Group, Inc., Nashua, NH; *U.S. Public*, pg. 566
McShane, Jim, Controller--Comforce Corporation, Lake Success, NY; *U.S. Public*, pg. 409
McSherry, Rollie, V.P. & Controller--True Temper Hardware Company, Camp Hill, PA; *U.S. Public*, pg. 846
McVay, Daniel J., V.P. & Controller--Centimark Corporation, Canonsburg, PA; *U.S. Private*, pg. 222
McVey, Ann Marie, Controller--Temco Service Industries, New York, NY; *U.S. Public*, pg. 1574
McVey, Ross J., Asst. Controller & Dir.-Tax--Telephone and Data Systems, Inc., Chicago, IL; *U.S. Public*, pg. 1570
Meade, Peter, V.P.-Fin. & Controller--Commtek Communications, Corp., Vienna, VA; *U.S. Private*, pg. 258
Meador, David, V.P. & Controller--DTE Energy Company, Detroit, MI; *U.S. Public*, pg. 475
Meadours, Joe, Controller--L3 Communications Narda-Microwave Div., Hauppauge, NY; *U.S. Private*, pg. 638
Meads, Richard H., Controller--Cooper Communities, Inc., Bella Vista, AR; *U.S. Private*, pg. 273
Meads, Richard H., Controller--Cooper Ventures, Inc., Bella Vista, AR; *U.S. Private*, pg. 274
Meads, Richard H., Controller--Apartment Ventures, Inc., Bella Vista, AR; *U.S. Private*, pg. 274
Means, Fred, Controller--Associated Hosts, Inc., Indianapolis, IN; *Int'l*, pg. 215
Mebus, Christopher, Controller--Arrow Metal Products Corporation, Detroit, MI; *U.S. Private*, pg. 85
Mebus, Philip K., Jr., Pres. & Treas.--Arrow Metal Products Corporation, Detroit, MI; *U.S. Private*, pg. 85
Mecaughey, William, Chief Fin. Officer, V.P. & Treas.--Roy F. Weston, Inc., West Chester, PA; *U.S. Public*, pg. 1761
Mechenbier, Dave, Controller--VWS, Inc., Cleveland, OH; *Int'l*, pg. 440
Mechler, H.P., V.P.-Acctg.--Imperial Holly Corporation, Sugar Land, TX; *U.S. Public*, pg. 872
Medding, David, Chief Fin. Officer & Controller--Quadrangle Development Corporation, Washington, DC; *U.S. Private*, pg. 898
Medel, Ariel, Exec. V.P & Controller--Berkliff Corporation, New York, NY; *U.S. Private*, pg. 135
Medel, Teresita, Controller, Treas. & Sec.--AMATI Communications Corp., San Jose, CA; *U.S. Public*, pg. 1585
Medwid, Glen, Asst. Controller--Steck-Vaughn Distribution Company, Austin, TX; *U.S. Public*, pg. 784
Meeker, Thomas C., Controller--Medicalodges, Inc., Coffeyville, KS; *U.S. Private*, pg. 728
Meeker, Tom, Controller--Medicalodges, Inc., Coffeyville, KS; *U.S. Private*, pg. 728
Mehta, Chandresh, Fin. Controller--Gestetner Limited, Nairobi, Kenya; *Int'l*, pg. 1115
Meier, Jeannette P., Exec. V.P.-Fin. & Admin./Sec.--Sterling Software, Inc., Dallas, TX; *U.S. Public*, pg. 1516
Meier, Terry D., V.P. & Controller--Mallinckrodt Inc., Saint Louis, MO; *U.S. Public*, pg. 1039
Meierhans, Gil, Controller--Key Handling Systems, Inc., Moonachie, NJ; *U.S. Private*, pg. 618
Meinkoth, Richard K., Controller & Treas.--Contico International, Inc., Saint Louis, MO; *U.S. Private*, pg. 267
Meinz, Del, Controller--Purina Mills, Inc., Saint Louis, MO; *U.S. Private*, pg. 895
Meisenheimer, Jerry, Controller--Xebec Corporation, Kansas City, MO; *U.S. Private*, pg. 1194
Melenkivitz, J., Controller--Dielectric Polymers, Inc., Holyoke, MA; *U.S. Public*, pg. 1258
Melenyk, Garry P., Controller--Linear Corporation, Carlsbad, CA; *U.S. Public*, pg. 1193
Melenyk, Garry P., Controller--Moore-O-Matic, Inc., Waupaca, WI; *U.S. Public*, pg. 1193
Melkonian, Laura, Controller--Universal Standard Healthcare, Inc., Southfield, MI; *U.S. Public*, pg. 1697
Meller, Barbara, Controller--Sally Lou Fashions Corporation, New York, NY; *U.S. Private*, pg. 962
Melliger, Rene H., Sr. V.P.-Acctg. & Controller--Liechtenstein Global Trust Limited, Vaduz, Liechtenstein; *Int'l*, pg. 809
Mellinger, Kristin, Controller & Dir.-Fin.--ASCG, Inc., Anchorage, AK; *U.S. Private*, pg. 80
Mello, Carlos R., Sr. V.P. & Controller--People's Bank, Bridgeport, CT; *U.S. Public*, pg. 1274
Mellstig, Soren, Exec. V.P. & Corp. Control--Incentive AB, Stockholm, Sweden; *Int'l*, pg. 666
Melo, Frank E., Second V.P. & Asst. Controller--Boston Mutual Life Insurance Co., Canton, MA; *U.S. Private*, pg. 161
Meloni, Glenn W., Controller--LTX Corporation, Westwood, MA; *U.S. Public*, pg. 972
Melore, Daniel G., Controller--Power & Telephone Supply Company, Memphis, TN; *U.S. Private*, pg. 877
Melton, James, Controller--Lance, Inc., Charlotte, NC; *U.S. Public*, pg. 977
Melton, James R., V.P. & Controller--Furnishings International, Inc., Thomasville, NC; *U.S. Private*, pg. 431
Melton, James R., V.P. & Controller--LifeStyle Furnishings International, Ltd., Thomasville, NC; *U.S. Private*, pg. 431
Melton, Michael R., V.P. & Controller--Caldor, Inc., Norwalk, CT; *U.S. Public*, pg. 292
Meltzer, Ronni, Sr. V.P. & Controller--Morse Diesel International, Inc., New York, NY; *U.S. Private*, pg. 762
Melvin, Stuart, Corp. Controller--Porcelain Metals Corp., Louisville, KY; *U.S. Private*, pg. 876
Menchinger, Steven R., Chief. Fin. Officer, Treas. & Sec.--Glassmaster Company, Lexington, SC; *U.S. Public*, pg. 745
Mendela, Paul, Controller--Margeotes/Fertitta & Partners Inc., New York, NY; *U.S. Private*, pg. 702
Mendelavi, Amnon, Controller--Egged Israel Transport Cooperative Society Ltd., Tel Aviv, Israel; *Int'l*, pg. 435
Mendelssohn, Sharon, Controller--Lance Camper Manufacturing Corporation, Lancaster, CA; *U.S. Private*, pg. 645
Mendez, Angel, Comptroller--Rorer (Caribbean) Corp., Hato Rey, PR; *Int'l*, pg. 1111
Mendez, Carlos Mahud, Controller--Empressa La Moderna SA de CV, Monterrey, Mexico; *Int'l*, pg. 454
Mendoza, Denise, Controller--BGM Health Communications, Inc., Los Angeles, CA; *U.S. Public*, pg. 1223
Mengelt, Jurg, Mng. Dir.-Plng. & Control--Landis & Staefa AG, Zug, Switzerland; *Int'l*, pg. 800
Mental, Michael, Corp. Controller--Queens Group, Inc., Long Island City, NY; *U.S. Private*, pg. 900
Menudier, Daniel R., Chief Acctg. Officer & Controller--Intellicorp Inc., Mountain View, CA; *U.S. Public*, pg. 887
Meo, Peter, Controller--Geo. H. Lehleitner & Co., Inc., Kenner, LA; *U.S. Private*, pg. 659
Meo, William A., Controller--Sifco Industries, Inc., Cleveland, OH; *U.S. Public*, pg. 1470
Meola, Thomas P., V.P.-Fin. & Controller--Bowne & Co., Inc., New York, NY; *U.S. Public*, pg. 248
Merano, Paul, Controller--Farmer's Cooperative Association, Lawrence, KS; *U.S. Private*, pg. 395
Meresman, Steve, Controller--Charmer Industries, Astoria, NY; *U.S. Private*, pg. 230
Merkel, Joelen K., V.P. & Controller--BHC Communications, Inc., New York, NY; *U.S. Public*, pg. 352
Merkens, Wim, Controller--Datapoint Nederland B.V., Gouda, Netherlands; *Int'l*, pg. 384
Merker, Lorrie Ford, Controller--Michigan Blueberry Growers Assn., Grand Junction, MI; *U.S. Private*, pg. 740
Merrell, Don C., V.P. & Controller--Continental Homes Holding Corp., Scottsdale, AZ; *U.S. Public*, pg. 440
Merrill, Hardy, Controller--U.S. Repeating Arms Company, New Haven, CT; *U.S. Private*, pg. 1125
Merwin, Jean, Asst. Controller--Frontier Foundry, Inc., Titusville, PA; *U.S. Private*, pg. 430
Merz, Carl, Controller--Cowen & Company, New York, NY; *U.S. Private*, pg. 280
Mesado, Sylvia, Controller--Centro de Idiomas Berlitz de Venezuela, Caracas, Venezuela; *U.S. Public*, pg. 222
Meschel, Edward, Controller--New Zealand Lamb Co., Inc., White Plains, NY; *U.S. Private*, pg. 796
Meschnig, Dennis, Controller--Tecfor Inc., Itasca, IL; *Int'l*, pg. 440
Messing, James, Controller--Hornady Manufacturing Company, Grand Island, NE; *U.S. Private*, pg. 539
Messinger, Harvey, Controller--Andover Togs, Inc., New York, NY; *U.S. Public*, pg. 112
Messman, Mary C., Controller--BASES Worldwide, Covington, KY; *U.S. Private*, pg. 120
Messmer, Steven E., Controller--Weston Paper & Manufacturing Co., Terre Haute, IN; *U.S. Private*, pg. 1169
Metcalf, J.A., Jr., Chief Acctg. Officer, V.P., Controller--Oklahoma Natural Gas Company, Tulsa, OK; *U.S. Public*, *pg. 1226*

Metcalf, Jim, Controller--Tate & Lyle PLC, London, United Kingdom; *Int'l*, pg. 1356
Metz, Tim, Controller--Continental Promotion Group, Tempe, AZ; *U.S. Private*, pg. 269
Metzinger, Marc, Controller--Amerex USA, Inc., New York, NY; *U.S. Private*, pg. 49
Metzler, Charles M., V.P. & Controller--Springs Industries, Inc., Fort Mill, SC; *U.S. Public*, pg. 1499
Metzner, Allen E., V.P.-Admin. & Controller--Reeds Jewelers, Inc., Wilmington, NC; *U.S. Public*, pg. 1370
Meul, M., Controller--Vandemoortele N.V., Izegem, Belgium; *Int'l*, pg. 1451
Meyer, Herb, Controller--Sunnen Products Company, Saint Louis, MO; *U.S. Private*, pg. 1053
Meyer, Jerry, Asst. Controller--Uni-Marts, Inc., State College, PA; *U.S. Public*, pg. 1664
Meyer, John P., Sr. V.P. & Controller--Sprint Corporation, Westwood, KS; *U.S. Public*, pg. 1500
Meyer, Robert, Controller--Minuteman Press International, Farmingdale, NY; *U.S. Private*, pg. 752
Meyer, Russell J., Corp. Controller--White Castle System, Inc., Columbus, OH; *U.S. Private*, pg. 1171
Meyer, Suzanne L., Controller--Kop-Coat, Pittsburgh, PA; *U.S. Public*, pg. 1357
Meyer, William S., Chief Fin. Officer, Sr. V.P. & Controller--American Greetings Corporation, Cleveland, OH; *U.S. Public*, pg. 77
Meyerhans, Urs, Controller--Western Mining Corporation Holdings Limited, Southbank, Australia; *Int'l*, pg. 1494
Meyers, Deborah P., Controller--Christian Children's Fund, Inc., Richmond, VA; *U.S. Private*, pg. 238
Meyers, William E., V.P. & Controller--TriMas Corporation, Ann Arbor, MI; *U.S. Public*, pg. 1054
Micciolo, John, Controller--Pincus Bros., Inc., Philadelphia, PA; *U.S. Private*, pg. 865
Michaels, Lynne, V.P. & Controller--The Norwich Savings Society, Norwich, CT; *U.S. Public*, pg. 1203
Michaelsen, Norman, Controller--Tamura Corporation of America, Temecula, CA; *U.S. Private*, pg. 1067
Michel, George, Controller--Marsh Bellofram Corp., Newell, WV; *U.S. Private*, pg. 707
Michelsen, Timothy W., Controller--Fidelity Oil Co., Bismarck, ND; *U.S. Public*, pg. 1025
Michelsen, Timothy W., Controller--Fidelity Oil Holdings, Inc., Bismarck, ND; *U.S. Public*, pg. 1025
Micin, Bob, Controller--Allied Tire Sales, Orlando, FL; *U.S. Private*, pg. 41
Mickiewicz, Laurie, Controller--Guardian Alarm Co., Southfield, MI; *U.S. Private*, pg. 485
Middleton, Bernie, Chief Fin. Officer & Controller--Cassano's Inc., Dayton, OH; *U.S. Private*, pg. 218
Midgette, Stephen, Controller--NewAge Industries Inc., Willow Grove, PA; *U.S. Private*, pg. 796
Miele, Jim, Controller--A K H Company, Inc., City of Commerce, CA; *U.S. Private*, pg. 2
Migrino, Renato N., Asst. V.P. & Comptroller--Benguet Corporation, Manila, Philippines; *Int'l*, pg. 186
Mihalik, Dennis, Controller--Mayfran International, Inc., Cleveland, OH; *Int'l*, pg. 1397
Mihalik, George, V.P.--Elf Aquitaine, Inc., New York, NY; *Int'l*, pg. 445
Mihalka, Tibor, Controller--Malev Hungarian Airlines, Plc., Budapest, Hungary; *Int'l*, pg. 833
Miher, Bob, V.P. & Controller--Kaufman and Broad of San Diego, Inc., San Diego, CA; *U.S. Public*, pg. 945
Miike, Patrick T., V.P.-Fin. & Treas.--Amelco Corporation, Gardena, CA; *U.S. Public*, pg. 65
Mikelonis, Rudy, Controller--Zima Corporation, Spartanburg, SC; *U.S. Private*, pg. 637
Miklos, Steven, V.P. & Controller--UniCARE Financial Corp., Irvine, CA; *U.S. Private*, pg. 152
Miklos, Steven W., V.P., Asst. Sec. & Controller--UniCARE Insurance Company, Irvine, CA; *U.S. Private*, pg. 152
Mikola, Larry W., Asst. Controller--Westmoreland Coal Co., Colorado Springs, CO; *U.S. Public*, pg. 1761
Mikos, Joe, Controller--Jarke Corporation, Niles, IL; *U.S. Private*, pg. 583
Mikosz, Mark, Controller--Roundy's, Inc., Pewaukee, WI; *U.S. Private*, pg. 948
Milano, George T., V.P. & Controller--EnviroSource, Inc., Horsham, PA; *U.S. Public*, pg. 587
Miley, John, V.P. & Controller--Hachette Filipacchi Magazines Inc., New York, NY; *Int'l*, pg. 794
Miley, John, Controller--Quebecor Printing Federated Inc., Providence, RI; *Int'l*, pg. 1078
Milioti, Dee, Controller & Treas.--Plastic Reel Corp. of America, Lyndhurst, NJ; *U.S. Private*, pg. 871
Milkovich, Jerry, Controller--Alaron Inc., Auburn Hills, MI; *U.S. Private*, pg. 31
Miller, Charles T., Controller & Treas.--Hammond Group Inc., Hammond, IN; *U.S. Private*, pg. 498
Miller, Chris, Controller & Treas.--Bon Jour International Ltd., New York, NY; *U.S. Private*, pg. 156
Miller, Dallas, Controller--Laubeck Corporation/Cross, Carbondale, PA; *U.S. Private*, pg. 652
Miller, Daniel W., V.P.-Controller--SEIKO Corporation of America, Mahwah, NJ; *Int'l*, pg. 1218
Miller, David, Asst. Controller--Amerifoods Inc., Lancaster, PA; *U.S. Private*, pg. 65
Miller, David, Chief Fin. Officer, Controller, Treas. & Sec.--Monterey Mechanical Company, Oakland, CA; *U.S. Private*, pg. 758
Miller, David, Controller--Mike Savoie Chevrolet Inc., Troy, MI; *U.S. Private*, pg. 968
Miller, Dick, Controller--Thorobred Containers Incorporated, Louisville, KY; *U.S. Private*, pg. 567
Miller, Eric, Corp. Controller--Columbia Laboratories, Inc., Miami, FL; *U.S. Public*, pg. 405
Miller, Fred, V.P. & Controller--Byerly's Inc., Edina, MN; *U.S. Private*, pg. 680
Miller, Gerd, Chm. Bd., Pres. & Treas.--Miller Curtain Co., Inc., San Antonio, TX; *U.S. Private*, pg. 746
Miller, Greg, V.P. & Controller--Universal Studios Recreation Services Group, Universal City, CA; *Int'l*, pg. 1216
Miller, Howard, Controller--Keco Industry, Inc., Florence, KY; *U.S. Private*, pg. 611
Miller, Jerry, Controller--Columbia Falls Aluminum Company, Columbia Falls, MT; *U.S. Private*, pg. 255
Miller, Jerry L., Asst. Controller--National Banner Company, Inc., Dallas, TX; *U.S. Private*, pg. 780
Miller, Joan E., Controller--Sentry Technology Corp., Hauppauge, NY; *U.S. Public*, pg. 1458
Miller, John, Controller--FMC FoodTech/Fran Rica, Stockton, CA; *U.S. Public*, pg. 605
Miller, John J., Treas.--The Southern New England Telephone Company, New Haven, CT; *U.S. Public*, pg. 1491
Miller, Larry, Div. Controller-Adv.--Toronto Star Newspapers Ltd., Toronto, Canada; *Int'l*, pg. 1402
Miller, Larry S., Controller--De Vons Jewelers, Sacramento, CA; *U.S. Private*, pg. 318
Miller, Lester, Controller--Times Printing Company, Inc., Random Lake, WI; *U.S. Private*, pg. 1087
Miller, Lori, Controller--Cortland Line Co., Inc., Cortland, NY; *U.S. Private*, pg. 277
Miller, Lynn, Controller--Sierra Pacific Resources, Reno, NV; *U.S. Public*, pg. 1470
Miller, Mark, Controller--Woods Equipment Company, Oregon, IL; *U.S. Private*, pg. 249
Miller, Michael, Controller & Treas.--Astro Homes, Shippenville, PA; *U.S. Public*, pg. 318
Miller, Mike, V.P. & Controller--Peak Technologies Group, Inc., New York, NY; *Int'l*, pg. 890
Miller, Mike, Controller & Mgr.-Acctg.--Shafer Commercial Seating Inc., Denver, CO; *U.S. Private*, pg. 988
Miller, Paul, Controller--Pacer Infotec Inc., Billerica, MA; *U.S. Private*, pg. 830
Miller, Randall, Controller--Georg Fischer Disa Inc., Oswego, IL; *Int'l*, pg. 382
Miller, Richard H., V.P. & Controller--NAC Reinsurance Corporation, Greenwich, CT; *U.S. Public*, pg. 1144
Miller, Richard H., V.P. & Controller--Greenwich Insurance Company, Greenwich, CT; *U.S. Public*, pg. 1144
Miller, Richard H., V.P. & Controller--Indian Harbor Insurance Company, Greenwich, CT; *U.S. Public*, pg. 1144
Miller, Richard J., V.P. & Controller--Cardinal Health Inc., Dublin, OH; *U.S. Public*, pg. 304
Miller, Robert B., Controller--Quantic Industries Inc., Hollister, CA; *U.S. Private*, pg. 899
Miller, Ronald, Controller--The Magee Carpet Company, Bloomsburg, PA; *U.S. Private*, pg. 694
Miller, Steven E., Asst. Controller--Consolidated Stores Corp., Columbus, OH; *U.S. Public*, pg. 437
Miller, Tammy, V.P.-Fin. & Treas.--Border States Industries, Inc., Fargo, ND; *U.S. Private*, pg. 160
Miller, Tammy, Controller--Monticello Management Co., San Diego, CA; *U.S. Private*, pg. 759
Miller, Thomas E., V.P. & Controller--Avery Dennison Corporation, Pasadena, CA; *U.S. Public*, pg. 152
Miller, Vita, Controller--Ebeling & Reuss Company, Allentown, PA; *U.S. Private*, pg. 358
Mills, James F., Jr., V.P. & Controller--Horace Small Apparel Company, Nashville, TN; *Int'l*, pg. 635
Mills, John, Chief Fin. Officer & Controller--Affiliated Foods Southwest, Little Rock, AR; *U.S. Private*, pg. 26
Mills, Kevin, Controller--Sid Tool Co. Inc., Plainview, NY; *U.S. Private*, pg. 998
Mills, R.J., V.P. & Controller--Cummins Engine Company, Inc., Columbus, IN; *U.S. Public*, pg. 467
Mills, Stephen, Controller--Ferrellgas Partners, L.P., Liberty, MO; *U.S. Public*, pg. 618
Mills, Steven R., Controller--Archer Daniels Midland Company (ADM), Decatur, IL; *U.S. Public*, pg. 127
Mills, Val, Controller--McGhan Limited, Arklow, Ireland; *U.S. Public*, pg. 874
Milner, Angela, Controller--Pumpelly Oil, Inc., Westlake, LA; *U.S. Private*, pg. 895
Milner, Leslie, Controller--Ademco Microtech Security Ltd., East Kilbride, United Kingdom; *U.S. Public*, pg. 1307
Milroy, James R., Sr. V.P., Controller & Cashier--Shoreline Bank, Benton Harbor, MI; *U.S. Public*, pg. 1468
Milton, Barry, Controller--Coast Steel Fabricators Ltd., Port Coquitlam, Canada; *Int'l*, pg. 31
Minard, John D., Chief Fin. Officer V.P. & Controller--Manna Pro Corporation, Saint Louis, MO; *U.S. Private*, pg. 700
Mincer, Robert, V.P. & Controller--Kaufman and Broad Coastal, Newport Beach, CA; *U.S. Public*, pg. 945
Minchhoff, Jim, Controller--United Receptical, Inc., Pottsville, PA; *U.S. Private*, pg. 1123
Minella, Roberto, Controller--Berlitz Language Centers, S.R.L., Rome, Italy; *U.S. Public*, pg. 222
Ming, Yang Chiu, Fin. Controller--Singapore Land Limited, Singapore, Singapore; *Int'l*, pg. 1252
Minnich, A.D., Controller--Carvel Hall, Crisfield, MD; *U.S. Private*, pg. 1061
Minnihan, Jack, V.P.-Fin.--Earl Scheib, Inc., Beverly Hills, CA; *U.S. Public*, pg. 1437
Minor, Jackson W., Comptroller--Southern Electric Generating Co., Birmingham, AL; *U.S. Public*, pg. 1490
Minta, Gary, Controller--Revell-Monogram Inc., Morton Grove, IL; *U.S. Private*, pg. 926
Minter, Lynda, Controller--Nucor Steel-Texas, Jewett, TX; *U.S. Public*, pg. 1205
Mintmier, Robert T., Controller & Sec.--Myrick Construction Inc., Biscoe, NC; *U.S. Private*, pg. 771
Miranda, George, First V.P. & Controller--H.F. Ahmanson & Co., Irwindale, CA; *U.S. Public*, pg. 29
Miranda, George, Controller--Home Savings of America, FSB, Irwindale, CA; *U.S. Public*, pg. 29
Miranda, Martin, V.P. & Controller--Quality Dining Inc., Mishawaka, IN; *U.S. Public*, pg. 1349
Mirchin, Howard, Controller--The Curry Corporation, Scarsdale, NY; *U.S. Private*, pg. 297
Mirski, Dan, Division Controller--Ivex Packaging Corporation-Industrial Products Division, Newton, MA; *U.S. Public*, pg. 915
Mishalanie, Phillip G., Controller & Sec.--Barber Dairies, Inc., Birmingham, AL; *U.S. Private*, pg. 115
Miska, Debra, Controller--Labelon Corporation, Canandaigua, NY; *U.S. Private*, pg. 641
Miszak, Michael, Controller & Treas.--Reading Eagle Company, Reading, PA; *U.S. Private*, pg. 913
Mitchell, Arthur N., V.P. & Controller--Moore Corporation Limited, Toronto, Canada; *Int'l*, pg. 888
Mitchell, Bobby, Controller--J.L. Lester & Son, Inc., Rockmart, GA; *U.S. Private*, pg. 660
Mitchell, C. Douglas, Controller--Del Taco, Inc., Laguna Hills, CA; *U.S. Private*, pg. 321
Mitchell, George, Controller--Par Industries, Inc., Medina, OH; *U.S. Private*, pg. 838
Mitchell, Jean, Controller--Lithograph Printing Company, Inc., Memphis, TN; *U.S. Private*, pg. 713
Mitchell, Jeffrey, Comptroller--Sun Bancorp, Inc., Selinsgrove, PA; *U.S. Public*, pg. 1529
Mitchell, John, Controller--Banyan Systems Inc., Westborough, MA; *U.S. Public*, pg. 189
Mitchell, Karen, Controller--King Koil Licensing Company Inc., Saint Paul, MN; *U.S. Private*, pg. 621
Mitchell, Thomas L., Chief Acctg. Officer, V.P. & Controller--Apache Corporation, Houston, TX; *U.S. Public*, pg. 119
Mittakarin, Duangchai, Sr. V.P.-Acctg.--The Industrial Finance Corporation of Thailand, Bangkok, Thailand; *Int'l*, pg. 677
Miyahara, Kenji, Exec. V.P.-Plng., Credit, Investments, Acctng. & Controller--Sumitomo Corporation, Tokyo, Japan; *Int'l*, pg. 1312
Miyajima, N., Controller--Esso Sekiyu Kabushiki Kaisha, Tokyo, Japan; *U.S. Public*, pg. 602
Miyamoto, Gregg, Controller--Virginia Metal Industries, Inc., Orange, VA; *U.S. Private*, pg. 1141
Miyar, Juan, V.P.-Acctg. Svcs. & Corp. Controller--The Wackenhut Corporation, Palm Beach Gardens, FL; *U.S. Public*, pg. 1731
Mocarski, Joan S., Controller--The Hartford Steam Boiler Inspection & Insurance Co., Hartford, CT; *U.S. Public*, pg. 795
Mochizuki, Ellen F., Controller--K2 Inc., Los Angeles, CA; *U.S. Public*, pg. 940
Mocniak, Lawrence G., Controller--Oceaneering Technologies, Upper Marlboro, MD; *U.S. Public*, pg. 1211
Modica, Dave, Controller--Hydraulics Div., Hutchinson, KS; *U.S. Public*, pg. 557
Moehring, Niel, Controller, Treas. & Sec.--Thomas & Skinner, Inc., Indianapolis, IN; *U.S. Private*, pg. 1082
Moeller, Delbert H., Controller--Burlington Basket Co., Burlington, IA; *U.S. Private*, pg. 183
Moeslein, Frank A., Controller--Wells Fargo & Company, San Francisco, CA; *U.S. Public*, pg. 1753
Moffa, Joseph, Controller--American Science & Engineering, Inc., Billerica, MA; *U.S. Public*, pg. 90
Moffat, Robert K., Regional Controller--Mike's Mart, Barrie, Canada; *Int'l*, pg. 1249
Mohan, H.K., V.P. & Controller--Frontec Corporation, Edmonton, Canada; *Int'l*, pg. 95
Moir, C., Controller (U.K.)--Kenner Parker Europe, Maidenhead, United Kingdom; *U.S. Public*, pg. 797
Moisan, Douglas E., CPA, Chief Acctg. Officer, V.P. & Controller--Somerset Savings Bank, Somerville, MA; *U.S. Public*, pg. 1484
Molda, George F., Controller--Chemgraphics Systems, Inc., Secaucus, NJ; *U.S. Public*, pg. 338
Moler, Spencer C., V.P. & Controller--Health Care & Retirement Corporation, Toledo, OH; *U.S. Public*, pg. 801
Moleski, Peter, Controller--Nikon Inc., Melville, NY; *Int'l*, pg. 931
Molineaux, Bob, Controller & Sec.--Willamette Industries Inc., Cleveland, OH; *U.S. Public*, pg. 1768
Moller, Andrew, Controller--Brauns Fashions Corporation, Plymouth, MN; *U.S. Public*, pg. 251
Molta, Donald A., Controller--Bob's Stores, Inc., Meriden, CT; *U.S. Public*, pg. 287
Molton, John, Controller--Ed Miniat, Inc., Chicago, IL; *U.S. Private*, pg. 750
Molvar, Roger H., V.P. & Controller--The Times Mirror Company, Los Angeles, CA; *U.S. Public*, pg. 1615
Monaco, Ralph, Controller--WPT, Inc., Edison, NJ; *U.S. Private*, pg. 1144
Monaco, Ralph, Controller--Dranetz-BMI, Edison, NJ; *U.S. Private*, pg. 1144
Monahan, Dennis, V.P.-Fin. & Corp. Controller--Freedom Chemical Company, Radnor, PA; *U.S. Private*, pg. 425
Monahan, Michael P., Controller--The Monahan Company, Eastpointe, MI; *U.S. Private*, pg. 756
Monk, John H., Jr., Comptroller--Saginaw Overseas Corporation, Detroit, MI; *U.S. Public*, pg. 723
Mono, Tom, Controller--Lettuce Entertain You Enterprises, Inc., Chicago, IL; *U.S. Private*, pg. 661
Monoghan, Dave, Controller & Treas.--Northwestern Public Service, Huron, SD; *U.S. Public*, pg. 1200
Montanari, Dave, Dir.-Fin.--Microtouch Systems, Inc., Methuen, MA; *U.S. Public*, pg. 1108
Montez, Tony, Controller--IDM Equipment Company, Houston, TX; *U.S. Private*, pg. 555
Montgomery, Martha, Controller--MAC Equipment Inc., Houston, TX; *U.S. Private*, pg. 685
Montgomery, Michelle, Controller--The May Apparel Group, Inc., Mebane, NC; *U.S. Private*, pg. 717
Montgomery, Terri, Controller--Grimmer Realty Co. Inc., Birmingham, AL; *U.S. Private*, pg. 482
Montuori, Giorgio, Controller--Recordati Industria Chimica e Farmaceutica S.p.A., Milan, Italy; *Int'l*, pg. 1090
Moody, Sheila, Controller--The Colonial BancGroup, Inc., Montgomery, AL; *U.S. Public*, pg. 400
Mooney, Kevin W., V.P. & Controller--Cincinnati Bell Telephone, Cincinnati, OH; *U.S. Public*, pg. 367
Moore, Bradley, Controller--Postgraduate Medicine, Minneapolis, MN; *U.S. Public*, pg. 1071

Moore, Bradley J., Controller--McGraw-Hill Healthcare Publications Group, Minneapolis, MN; *U.S. Public*, pg. 1071
Moore, Bradley J., Controller--The Physician and Sportsmedicine, Minneapolis, MN; *U.S. Public*, pg. 1071
Moore, Brian, Controller--Temp-Control Mechanical Corp., Portland, OR; *U.S. Private*, pg. 1075
Moore, Chris, Controller--General Bearing Corp., West Nyack, NY; *U.S. Public*, pg. 706
Moore, Cindy A., Chief Fin. Officer, Sr. V.P. & Controller--ACCEL International Corporation, Dublin, OH; *U.S. Public*, pg. 14
Moore, Dick, Controller--JRN, Inc., Columbia, TN; *U.S. Private*, pg. 578
Moore, Jerry, Controller--Altec Industries, Inc., Birmingham, AL; *U.S. Private*, pg. 47
Moore, Roy J., Jr., Corp. Controller--American Cometra, Inc., Fort Worth, TX; *Int'l*, pg. 562
Moore, Terry, Controller--Global Environmental Corp., Hagerstown, MD; *U.S. Public*, pg. 747
Moore, William, Controller--The Renovator's Supply, Inc., Conway, NH; *U.S. Private*, pg. 923
Moorhouse, Mike, Controller--Ceco Concrete Construction LLC, Gladstone, MO; *U.S. Private*, pg. 859
Moorjani, Flor, Dir.-Fin. & Admin.--Mercury Computer Systems, Inc., Chelmsford, MA; *U.S. Private*, pg. 732
Moorman, David, Controller--Carpenter Co., Richmond, VA; *U.S. Private*, pg. 214
Moorman, Timothy D., V.P.-Fin. & Controller--Our Sunday Visitor, Inc., Huntington, IN; *U.S. Private*, pg. 821
Moos, Chris, Controller--Display Technologies Electrohome Inc., Carthage, MO; *Int'l*, pg. 438
Moothart, Gary, Controller--Consolidated-Tomoka Land Co., Daytona Beach, FL; *U.S. Public*, pg. 437
Mora, Roberto, Fin. Controller--F.I.A.P. SpA, Turate, Italy; *U.S. Public*, pg. 5
Morabito, Richard, V.P. & Controller--Dawn Joy Fashions, Inc., New York, NY; *U.S. Private*, pg. 316
Morales, Jose, Controller--Datapoint Iberica S.A., Madrid, Spain; *Int'l*, pg. 384
Morales, Ken, Controller--Universal Fasteners Inc., Lawrenceburg, KY; *Int'l*, pg. 1515
Morales, Rich, Controller--Houston Fearless 76 Inc., Compton, CA; *U.S. Private*, pg. 542
Morales, Virginia E., Comptroller--Detex Corporation, New Braunfels, TX; *U.S. Private*, pg. 327
Moran, D., Controller--Castrol Canada Inc., Toronto, Canada; *Int'l*, pg. 235
Moran, Joe, V.P. & Controller--Peake Printers, Inc., Cheverly, MD; *U.S. Private*, pg. 845
Moran, Paul, Controller--Seaman-Patrick Paper Company, Detroit, MI; *U.S. Private*, pg. 979
Moran, Penny, Controller--Outsource International, Deerfield Beach, FL; *U.S. Public*, pg. 1236
Morcos, Magdi L., Controller--Asian Development Bank, Manila, Philippines; *Int'l*, pg. 88
More, Peter S., Controller--Glit, Wrens, GA; *U.S. Public*, pg. 944
Morehead, Russell R., Controller--Haeger Industries, Inc., Dundee, IL; *U.S. Private*, pg. 493
Morehead, Theresa, Controller--Intermatic Inc., Spring Grove, IL; *U.S. Private*, pg. 567
Moreira, John M., Asst. Comptroller--Eastern Utilities Associates, Boston, MA; *U.S. Public*, pg. 549
Morell, Kris, Controller--Hubbard Construction Co., Winter Park, FL; *U.S. Private*, pg. 544
Morello, Eduardo, Controller--Berlitz Escuelas de Idiomas Ltda., Santiago, Chile; *U.S. Public*, pg. 222
Morello, James J., Chief Fin. Officer & Treas.--Medical Assurance, Inc., Birmingham, AL; *U.S. Public*, pg. 1079
Morgan, Charles C., Controller--SCANA Petroleum Resources, Inc., Houston, TX; *U.S. Public*, pg. 1436
Morgan, David, Grp. Fin. Controller--Meggitt plc, Wimborne Minster, United Kingdom; *Int'l*, pg. 853
Morgan, Donna, Controller--Southgate Ford Inc., Southgate, MI; *U.S. Private*, pg. 1018
Morgan, Felicia, Controller--Rev-A-Shelf, Louisville, KY; *U.S. Private*, pg. 925
Morgan, Gayle, Controller--O'Neal Steel Inc., Birmingham, AL; *U.S. Private*, pg. 817
Morgan, Thomas, Controller--Basic Food International Inc., Fort Lauderdale, FL; *U.S. Private*, pg. 121
Morgione, Vincent, Controller--The Cafaro Co., Youngstown, OH; *U.S. Private*, pg. 198
Morin, Christian, Controller--Credit Mutuel, Paris, France; *Int'l*, pg. 344
Morin, Stephen P., Controller--Ferrofluidics Corporation, Nashua, NH; *U.S. Public*, pg. 620
Morin, Vivianne, Controller--Coscient Group Inc., Montreal, Canada; *Int'l*, pg. 335
Morissette, Art, Controller--Duo-Fast Corporation, Huntley, IL; *U.S. Private*, pg. 347
Morize, Ellen, Controller--Rawlings Sporting Goods Company, Fenton, MO; *U.S. Public*, pg. 1361
Morman, Dave, Controller & Treas.--Farmers Union Marketing & Processing Association, Redwood Falls, MN; *U.S. Private*, pg. 395
Morneau, Michael J., Controller--Kaman Corporation, Bloomfield, CT; *U.S. Public*, pg. 941
Morocco, Robert, Controller--Go-Video, Inc., Scottsdale, AZ; *U.S. Public*, pg. 748
Morozek, Michael, Controller--American Packaging Corporation, Philadelphia, PA; *U.S. Private*, pg. 60
Morrell, Alan, Controller--Simmons-Boardman Publishing Corp., New York, NY; *U.S. Private*, pg. 1000
Morrell, Michael W., Asst. Controller--GTE Corporation, Stamford, CT; *U.S. Public*, pg. 696
Morris, Brenda, Controller--Seattle Pacific Industries, Inc., Seattle, WA; *U.S. Private*, pg. 980
Morris, Cathy, Controller--Anthem Electronics Inc., San Jose, CA; *U.S. Public*, pg. 134
Morris, Dave, Controller--Anderson-Tully Co., Memphis, TN; *U.S. Private*, pg. 73
Morris, David, Controller--Schroders PLC, London, United Kingdom; *Int'l*, pg. 1210
Morris, Douglas, Controller--Avionics Specialities, Inc., Charlottesville, VA; *U.S. Public*, pg. 25
Morris, Edie, Controller--Glen Oaks Hospital, Greenville, TX; *U.S. Public*, pg. 1697
Morris, Gerry, Controller--Selkirk Metalbestos, Dallas, TX; *U.S. Public*, pg. 1794
Morris, James E., V.P., Controller, Treas. & Sec.--SL Industries, Inc., Mount Laurel, NJ; *U.S. Public*, pg. 1418
Morrison, Robert, V.P. & Controller--Navistar International Corporation, Chicago, IL; *U.S. Public*, pg. 1167
Morrison, Robert I., V.P. & Controller--Navistar International Transportation Corp., Chicago, IL; *U.S. Public*, pg. 1167
Morrison, Ross, Controller--Vornado Realty Trust, Saddle Brook, NJ; *U.S. Public*, pg. 1725
Morrow, John C., Sr. V.P. & Controller--BOK Financial Corp., Tulsa, OK; *U.S. Public*, pg. 163
Morrow, John C., Sr. V.P. & Controller--Bank of Oklahoma, N.A., Tulsa, OK; *U.S. Public*, pg. 163
Morrow, Roger, Controller & Treas.--International Pipe Machinery Corp., Sioux City, IA; *U.S. Private*, pg. 571
Morse, L. Thomas, V.P. & Controller--Acuson Corporation, Mountain View, CA; *U.S. Public*, pg. 18
Morstad, Lynn A., Controller--Dorfile Company, Memphis, TN; *U.S. Public*, pg. 1177
Mortensen, Eric, Controller--Peter Kiewit Sons Inc., Omaha, NE; *U.S. Private*, pg. 619
Mortenson, Tim, Controller--Kasco Corporation, Maitland, FL; *U.S. Public*, pg. 165
Morton, Edward F., Controller--Bell Atlantic-WV, Charleston, WV; *U.S. Public*, pg. 203
Morton, Victoria C., Controller--Hollymatic Corporation, Countryside, IL; *U.S. Private*, pg. 535
Mosca, Randell, Controller--Maher Terminals Inc., Jersey City, NJ; *U.S. Private*, pg. 697
Moser, Steve, Controller--Media That Works, Cincinnati, OH; *U.S. Private*, pg. 727
Mosley, Wayne L., V.P. & Controller--Cole National Corporation, Cleveland, OH; *U.S. Public*, pg. 396
Moss, Alan, Controller--Schneider Group, Mississauga, Canada; *Int'l*, pg. 1208
Moss, Bill, Controller--Crown Foods Inc., Saint Louis, MO; *U.S. Private*, pg. 292
Most, Jeff, Controller--Marcus Brothers Textiles, Inc., New York, NY; *U.S. Private*, pg. 702
Mosteller, Mark E., Controller--Boatmen's National Mortgage Inc., Memphis, TN; *U.S. Public*, pg. 1165
Mothet, Hadelin, Controller--Bontex S.A., Stembert, Belgium; *U.S. Public*, pg. 734
Motsenbocker, Terry, Controller--Countrymark Cooperative, Inc., Indianapolis, IN; *U.S. Private*, pg. 279
Mott, Jean, Controller--Meade Group, Inc., Utica, MI; *U.S. Private*, pg. 725
Mould, John T., Sr. V.P.-Controller--HongKong Bank of Canada, Vancouver, Canada; *Int'l*, pg. 583
Mounsey, Ed, Comptroller--Cowtown Boot Company, El Paso, TX; *U.S. Private*, pg. 281
Mountain, J.M., Controller--Morgan Materials Technology Limited, Stourport, United Kingdom; *Int'l*, pg. 894
Mowder, Jim, Controller--Lawrence Paper Company, Lawrence, KS; *U.S. Private*, pg. 654
Mowers, Steven A., Controller--ACC TeleCom, Rochester, NY; *U.S. Public*, pg. 3
Moxley, Doug, Controller--Tekelec, Calabasas, CA; *U.S. Public*, pg. 1566
Moy, Tom, Controller--Pet Life Foods, Inc., Willowbrook, IL; *U.S. Private*, pg. 856
Moyer, Doug, Controller--Clemens Markets Inc., Kulpsville, PA; *U.S. Private*, pg. 245
Moyers, Donald L., Controller, Treas. & Sec.--Riddleberger Bros., Inc., Mount Crawford, VA; *U.S. Private*, pg. 930
Moyle, Michele, Controller--Ensoniq, Malvern, PA; *U.S. Private*, pg. 377
Moynihan, Thomas F., Controller--Brookstone Company, Inc., Nashua, NH; *U.S. Public*, pg. 259
Mozynski, Joanne, Controller--Goodwill Industries International, Bethesda, MD; *U.S. Private*, pg. 464
Mozzillo, Nick, Controller--Norwalk Powdered Metals, Inc., Norwalk, CT; *U.S. Private*, pg. 808
Mraz, Joseph B., Chief Fin. Officer & Controller--Beacon Container Corporation, Birdsboro, PA; *U.S. Private*, pg. 125
Mrowka, James A., Controller--Detroit City Dairy, Inc., Detroit, MI; *U.S. Private*, pg. 328
Muccino, Robert D., Controller & Sec.--Frank Briscoe Co. Inc., Kenilworth, NJ; *U.S. Private*, pg. 169
Mucharino, L., Controller--EIS Brake Parts Div., Berlin, CT; *U.S. Public*, pg. 1503
Muchmore, R. Charles, Jr., V.P. & Controller--Halliburton Company, Dallas, TX; *U.S. Public*, pg. 775
Muck, Janet, Controller--Littleford Day Inc., Florence, KY; *U.S. Private*, pg. 671
Mueller, John M., Controller--ALLTEL Corporation, Little Rock, AR; *U.S. Public*, pg. 55
Mueller, Ken, Sr. V.P. & Controller--Platinum Technology, Inc., Oak Brook Terrace, IL; *U.S. Public*, pg. 1309
Mueller, Lois, Controller--Jergens Inc., Cleveland, OH; *U.S. Private*, pg. 586
Mueller, Robert, Asst. Gen. Mgr.-Fin. & Admin.--Dairyland Power Cooperative, La Crosse, WI; *U.S. Private*, pg. 307
Mueller, Thomas W., Controller & Asst. Treas.--Kentucky Medical Insurance Company (KMIC), Louisville, KY; *U.S. Private*, pg. 741
Muenster, G.E., Controller--ESCO Electronics Corporation, Saint Louis, MO; *U.S. Public*, pg. 546
Muir, Jonathan, Controller--Toymax International Inc., Plainview, NY; *U.S. Public*, pg. 1626
Muis, Jules W., V.P. & Controller--The World Bank, Washington, DC; *U.S. Private*, pg. 1188
Mulady, James, Controller--Edwards Brothers, Inc., Ann Arbor, MI; *U.S. Private*, pg. 365
Mulberry, Zane, Controller & Treas.--Richards Brothers of Mountain Grove, Mountain Grove, MO; *U.S. Private*, pg. 928
Muldowney, Kathryn M., Controller--Mercantile Stores Company, Inc., Fairfield, OH; *U.S. Public*, pg. 1089
Mullaney, Lisa, Controller--The New Piper Aircraft, Inc., Vero Beach, FL; *U.S. Private*, pg. 794
Mullen, Richard J., V.P. & Controller--First Farmers & Merchants National Bank, Columbia, TN; *U.S. Private*, pg. 407
Muller, Alfred, V.P. & Controller--Bitburger Brauerei Th. Simon GmbH, Bitburg, Germany; *Int'l*, pg. 197
Muller, Alfred, Controller--SaniServ Manufacturing Corp., Indianapolis, IN; *U.S. Private*, pg. 965
Muller, Eric, Exec. V.P.-Fin. & Admin.--Sulzer Ltd., Winterthur, Switzerland; *Int'l*, pg. 1305
Mulligan, Dennis, Controller--Branch Group Inc., Upper Marlboro, MD; *U.S. Private*, pg. 165
Mulligan, Donald, V.P. & Controller--Demoulas Market Basket, Tewksbury, MA; *U.S. Private*, pg. 324
Mullins, H.G., Controller & Mgr.-Mfg.--Flowserve Corporation, Foundry Div., Dayton, OH; *U.S. Public*, pg. 658
Mullins, Russ, Controller--The Great Lakes Cheese Co., Newbury, OH; *U.S. Private*, pg. 473
Mullins, Terry, Controller--Central United Life Insurance Co., Houston, TX; *U.S. Private*, pg. 225
Mullins, Terry, Controller--Christian Mutual Life Insurance Co., Houston, TX; *U.S. Private*, pg. 225
Mullis, Robert, Controller--Pulliam Motor Company, Columbia, SC; *U.S. Private*, pg. 894
Mullner, Rebecca, Controller--Byrnes & Kiefer Company, Callery, PA; *U.S. Private*, pg. 191
Multer, Mark, Controller--Union Pump Company, Battle Creek, MI; *U.S. Private*, pg. 1119
Mulvaney, J.V., Controller--Illinois Central Corporation, Chicago, IL; *U.S. Public*, pg. 864
Munch, Robert, Controller--The Laitram Corporation, Harahan, LA; *U.S. Private*, pg. 643
Muncy, Darlene, Chief Fin. Officer, V.P. & Treas.--Caldwell VanRiper, Inc., Indianapolis, IN; *U.S. Private*, pg. 200
Munkacsy, Bill, Controller--UNC Aviation Services, Inc., Annapolis, MD; *U.S. Public*, pg. 710
Murakami, Neil, Controller & Sec.--Jacmar Companies, Inc., Alhambra, CA; *U.S. Private*, pg. 580
Murashige, Mark A., Asst. Controller--Barnwell Industries, Inc., Honolulu, HI; *U.S. Public*, pg. 190
Muretta, Bruce, Chief Fin. Officer & Controller--West Chemical Products, Inc., Princeton, NJ; *U.S. Private*, pg. 1158
Muretta, Bruce, V.P.-Fin. & Admin. & Controller--West Penetone Inc., Ville d'Anjou, Canada; *U.S. Private*, pg. 1158
Murman, Bill, Controller--General Wholesale Company, Inc., Atlanta, GA; *U.S. Private*, pg. 445
Murnin, Joel A., V.P., Treas. & Controller--Manufacturers Railway Company, Saint Louis, MO; *U.S. Public*, pg. 114
Murphy, A.G., Jr., V.P.-Fin. & Controller--BS & B Process Systems, Inc., Houston, TX; *U.S. Private*, pg. 572
Murphy, Daniel L., V.P. & Controller--Designs, Inc., Needham, MA; *U.S. Public*, pg. 501
Murphy, Gerry, Controller--BV Financial (Ireland) Ltd., Dublin, Ireland; *Int'l*, pg. 180
Murphy, Harold, Controller--UniFirst Corporation, Wilmington, MA; *U.S. Public*, pg. 1665
Murphy, James, Controller--Armatron International, Inc., Melrose, MA; *U.S. Public*, pg. 131
Murphy, James, Controller--Lois/EJL New York, New York, NY; *U.S. Public*, pg. 1011
Murphy, Jim, Controller--Lois/USA Inc., New York, NY; *U.S. Public*, pg. 1011
Murphy, John J., Chief Fin. Officer, Exec. V.P. & Treas.--Arrow Financial Corporation, Glens Falls, NY; *U.S. Public*, pg. 135
Murphy, Karty, Controller--Restaurants Unlimited, Seattle, WA; *U.S. Private*, pg. 925
Murphy, M.B., Controller--Thermal Ceramics, Burlington, Canada; *Int'l*, pg. 894
Murphy, Maureen, Controller--Associated Grocers, Inc., Seattle, WA; *U.S. Private*, pg. 90
Murphy, Mike, Controller--Ag-Chem Equipment Co., Inc., Minnetonka, MN; *U.S. Public*, pg. 6
Murphy, Mike, Controller--Federal APD, Inc., Farmington, MI; *U.S. Public*, pg. 616
Murphy, P. Cornell, Controller--Progress Printing Company, Lynchburg, VA; *U.S. Private*, pg. 890
Murphy, Patrick W., Controller--Alico, Inc., La Belle, FL; *U.S. Public*, pg. 41
Murphy, Robert J., Asst. Controller--Oxford Health Plans Inc., Norwalk, CT; *U.S. Public*, pg. 1238
Murphy, Stephanie, V.P. & Controller--Hal Riney & Partners, Inc., San Francisco, CA; *U.S. Private*, pg. 931
Murphy, Steve, Controller--Stamler Corporation, Millersburg, KY; *U.S. Private*, pg. 814
Murphy, Susan, Controller--GenRad, Inc., Westford, MA; *U.S. Public*, pg. 731
Murphy, Thomas G., V.P.-Admin. & Controller--American Kennel Club, Inc., New York, NY; *U.S. Private*, pg. 58
Murphy, William E. IV, V.P.-Admin. & Controller--Enviroq, Birmingham, AL; *U.S. Public*, pg. 881
Murray, Don, Controller--Quebecor Printing Hazleton Inc., Hazleton, PA; *Int'l*, pg. 1076
Murray, Jay, Controller--Bel-Art Products, Pequannock, NJ; *U.S. Private*, pg. 130
Murray, Lowan, Controller--Amana Society, Inc., Amana, IA; *U.S. Private*, pg. 48
Murray, R.W., Chief Fin. Officer, Sr. V.P., Treas., Controller & Sec.--Webb, Murray & Associates, Houston, TX; *U.S. Private*, pg. 1157
Murrell, Robert, Controller--Piedmont Airlines, Inc., Salisbury, MD; *U.S. Public*, pg. 1680
Murrow, Alan J., Controller--National Auto Credit Inc., Solon, OH; *U.S. Public*, pg. 1152

Muschalek, John, Chief Fin. Officer & Controller--First Southwest Company, Dallas, TX; *U.S. Private*, pg. 407

Musil, Daniel, Controller--Heinen's Inc., Cleveland, OH; *U.S. Private*, pg. 519

Muzro, Steve, Controller--Southwest Water Company, West Covina, CA; *U.S. Public*, pg. 1494

Myer, Arthur D., Controller--Western Extrusions, Carrollton, TX; *U.S. Private*, pg. 1165

Myers, Alan, Controller--Kearney Company, Tucker, GA; *U.S. Public*, pg. 444

Myers, Chris, Controller & Mgr.-MIS--Yale/Chase Materials Handling, Inc., City of Industry, CA; *U.S. Private*, pg. 1195

Myers, Deborah, Controller--Weldon Machine Tool, Inc., York, PA; *U.S. Private*, pg. 1161

Myers, Don, Controller--Prestige Ford, Garland, TX; *U.S. Private*, pg. 882

Myers, Lanni, V.P. & Controller--California Microwave, Inc., Sunnyvale, CA; *U.S. Public*, pg. 293

Myers, Leland, Controller--Double-Cola Co.-USA, Chattanooga, TN; *U.S. Private*, pg. 341

Myers, Lisa A., Controller--Muro Pharmaceutical, Inc., Tewksbury, MA; *U.S. Private*, pg. 767

Myers, Rich, Controller--Mark Shale, Burr Ridge, IL; *U.S. Private*, pg. 989

Myers, Rita, V.P. & Comptroller--High Point Financial Corp., Branchville, NJ; *U.S. Public*, pg. 826

Myers, Stephen R., Asst. Controller--Bell & Howell Holdings, Skokie, IL; *U.S. Public*, pg. 201

Mytro, Nicholas A., Sec. & Asst. Controller--Sun TV & Appliances, Inc., Groveport, OH; *U.S. Public*, pg. 1532

Nachtsheim, Bob, Controller--Career Education Corporation, Hoffman Estates, IL; *U.S. Private*, pg. 209

Nackman, Neal S., V.P.-Fin.--Nautica Enterprises, Inc., New York, NY; *U.S. Public*, pg. 1167

Nadeau, Roger, Controller--Success Development International, Jacksonville, FL; *U.S. Private*, pg. 1048

Nadow, Mark, Controller & Dir.-Acctg.--AMI Leasing Corporation, Worcester, MA; *U.S. Private*, pg. 7

Naess, Hans, Controller--John Crane Sverige AB, Goteborg, Sweden; *Int'l*, pg. 1339

Nagengast, Barbara A., Controller--Atlas Refinery, Newark, NJ; *U.S. Private*, pg. 96

Nagle, Rick, Controller--Fire Lite Alarms, Inc./Notifier Co., Northford, CT; *U.S. Public*, pg. 1306

Nagumo, Chuck Y., Controller--Yashica, Inc., Somerset, NJ; *Int'l*, pg. 776

Naidu, R., Controller--Mediquip SDN. BHD., Kangar, Malaysia; *U.S. Public*, pg. 1648

Naim, Bernard, Chief Fin. Officer & Treas.--Forasol S.A., Velizy-Villacoublay, France; *Int'l*, pg. 496

Najera, Carrie, Asst. Controller--Manufacturers Consolidation Service, Inc., Memphis, TN; *U.S. Private*, pg. 700

Najsam, Corrina, Controller--B & R Industrial Automation, Roswell, GA; *U.S. Private*, pg. 105

Nakada, Fumio, Exec. Mng. Dir.--Kubota Corp., Osaka, Japan; *Int'l*, pg. 762

Nakama, Paul Y., Controller--Dillingham Construction Corporation, Pleasanton, CA; *U.S. Private*, pg. 333

Nance, Blair T., Chief Fin. Officer, Controller & Treas.--AFG, Inc., Westmont, IL; *U.S. Public*, pg. 955

Napolez, Mario, Controller--Gator Industries Inc., Hialeah, FL; *U.S. Private*, pg. 441

Naranjo, Carlos, Controller--RIU International Pan American Ocean Resort Hotel, Miami Beach, FL; *U.S. Private*, pg. 904

Narazaki, Keiji, Controller--Berlitz Escola de Idiomas Ltda., Sao Paulo, Brazil; *U.S. Public*, pg. 221

Narbonne, Michel, Controller--Poliet, Courbevoie, France; *Int'l*, pg. 1177

Narciso, Anthony, Sr. V.P. & Controller--Odyssey Reinsurance Corporation, New York, NY; *Int'l*, pg. 1258

Nardi, Barbara, Controller--U.S. Filter/Arrowhead Inc., Rockford, IL; *U.S. Public*, pg. 1682

Nardis, Charles, Controller--Engineered Fasteners Div., Massillon, OH; *U.S. Public*, pg. 557

Naremore, Bruce M., Controller--River Parishes Hospital, La Place, LA; *U.S. Public*, pg. 1697

Nash, James S., Chief Fin. Officer, Treas. & Controller--E.P. Henry Corporation, Woodbury, NJ; *U.S. Private*, pg. 522

Nash, Ralph, Controller--Lechters, Inc., Harrison, NJ; *U.S. Public*, pg. 983

Nash, Roger, Controller--Ervin Industries, Inc., Ann Arbor, MI; *U.S. Private*, pg. 382

Nash, Walter Stephen, Controller--The Bartell Drug Company, Seattle, WA; *U.S. Private*, pg. 118

Nason, Conrad, Controller--Bob Sellers Pontiac GMC Truck Inc., Farmington, MI; *U.S. Private*, pg. 983

Nastasowski, T., Controller--The Grieve Corporation, Round Lake, IL; *U.S. Private*, pg. 480

Naughton, John P., V.P. & Controller--Bergen Brunswig Corporation, Orange, CA; *U.S. Public*, pg. 213

Naughton, John P., V.P. & Controller--Bergen Brunswig Drug Company, Orange, CA; *U.S. Public*, pg. 213

Nault, David, Controller--Rolled Alloys, Inc., Temperance, MI; *U.S. Private*, pg. 941

Navarre, Richard A., V.P.-Finance--Peabody Holding Company, Inc., Saint Louis, MO; *Int'l*, pg. 594

Navarro, Guillermo, V.P. & Controller--Greenwich Air Services, Miami, FL; *U.S. Public*, pg. 710

Navarro, J. Benito Bule, Controller--Compania Espanola de Petroleos, S.A. (CEPSA), Madrid, Spain; *Int'l*, pg. 323

Navarro, Richard J., Grp. V.P. & Controller--Albertson's, Inc., Boise, ID; *U.S. Public*, pg. 38

Navikas, David B., Controller--PPG Industries, Inc., Pittsburgh, PA; *U.S. Public*, pg. 1245

Nayar, Sid, Controller--Congoleum Corporation, Mercerville, NJ; *U.S. Public*, pg. 69

Naylor, Christine, V.P.-Fin. & Controller--Dahlberg, Inc., Golden Valley, MN; *U.S. Public*, pg. 194

Neads, Jeremy, Controller--Logitech International SA, Morges, Switzerland; *Int'l*, pg. 815

Nealy, Lynn, Controller--American Paper Group, Inc., Youngstown, OH; *U.S. Private*, pg. 60

Nearing, John R., Controller--Numac Energy Inc., Calgary, Canada; *Int'l*, pg. 990

Nease, Jim, Dir.-Fin. & Acctg.--Hollingsworth Saco Lowell Corporation, Inc., Easley, SC; *U.S. Private*, pg. 535

Nebiolo, Thomas E., Controller--Pilot Air Freight Corp., Lima, PA; *U.S. Private*, pg. 865

Necikowski, Stan, Controller--ELCO Corporation, Huntingdon, PA; *Int'l*, pg. 775

Neder, Richard, Controller--Poly Pak America, Inc., Los Angeles, CA; *U.S. Private*, pg. 875

Needham, Jack, Controller--The Grand Union Company, Wayne, NJ; *U.S. Public*, pg. 758

Neeley, Wayne P., Controller--The Amalgamated Sugar Company LLC, Ogden, UT; *U.S. Private*, pg. 48

Neese, M.S. Jonnie, Controller--House of Perfection, Inc., New York, NY; *U.S. Private*, pg. 542

Neff, Terry A., Controller--Kissimmee Toyota Inc., Kissimmee, FL; *U.S. Private*, pg. 624

Neil, James, Controller--Treadwell Corporation, Thomaston, CT; *U.S. Private*, pg. 1098

Neira, Mariano, Mgr.-Admin. & Control--CODELCO Chile (Corporacion Nacional Del Cobre De Chile), Santiago, Chile; *Int'l*, pg. 302

Neis, Douglas A., Chief Fin. Officer & Treas.--The Marcus Corporation, Milwaukee, WI; *U.S. Public*, pg. 1044

Nelligan, David T., V.P. & Controller--Miramichi Pulp & Paper Inc., Newcastle, Canada; *Int'l*, pg. 1104

Nelson, Bert, Controller--Sellstrom Manufacturing Co., Palatine, IL; *U.S. Private*, pg. 983

Nelson, Brent, Division Controller--Vernitron Controls Div., San Diego, CA; *U.S. Public*, pg. 158

Nelson, Carol, Controller--Allied Oil & Supply, Inc., Omaha, NE; *U.S. Private*, pg. 39

Nelson, Dale J., Controller--Williams Controls, Inc., Portland, OR; *U.S. Public*, pg. 1769

Nelson, David R., Controller & Asst. Sec.--RJ Associates, Plymouth, MN; *U.S. Private*, pg. 932

Nelson, Don, Controller--Dunn-Edwards Corporation, Los Angeles, CA; *U.S. Private*, pg. 347

Nelson, Elvin, Controller--Gayfers, Mobile, AL; *U.S. Public*, pg. 1090

Nelson, Gary, Controller--Wilson Industries Inc., Houston, TX; *U.S. Private*, pg. 1181

Nelson, Harry, Controller--Punch Press Products, Inc., Los Angeles, CA; *U.S. Private*, pg. 895

Nelson, Keith, Controller--DRI Europe (U.K.) Ltd., London, United Kingdom; *U.S. Public*, pg. 1072

Nelson, Larry, Controller--U.S. Security Associates, Inc., Roswell, GA; *U.S. Private*, pg. 1126

Nelson, Mark D., Controller--Plantronics Inc., Santa Cruz, CA; *U.S. Public*, pg. 1308

Nelson, Paul, Controller--Williams Pipe Line Co., Tulsa, OK; *U.S. Public*, pg. 1769

Nelson, Peter A., Chief Acctg. Officer, V.P. & Controller--American Media, Inc., Lake Worth, FL; *U.S. Public*, pg. 87

Nelson, Steven K., V.P. & Controller--Dillard's, Inc., Little Rock, AR; *U.S. Public*, pg. 509

Nelson, Tom, V.P.-Fin.--Petro-Hunt Corporation, Dallas, TX; *U.S. Private*, pg. 858

Nelson, William F., Controller--Bodine Electric Company, Chicago, IL; *U.S. Private*, pg. 154

Nelson, William H., Controller & Asst. Sec.--Team, Inc., Alvin, TX; *U.S. Public*, pg. 1562

Nemec, Timothy M., Controller & Chief Acctg. Officer--American Income Holding, Inc., Wilmington, DE; *U.S. Public*, pg. 1622

Nemmers, David A., Controller--Advance Packaging Corporation, Grand Rapids, MI; *U.S. Private*, pg. 18

Neo, Catherine, Fin. Controller--Sundstrand Pacific Aerospace (Pte) Ltd., Singapore, Singapore; *U.S. Public*, pg. 1534

Neppl, Christina M., V.P. & Controller--BJ's Wholesale Club, Inc., Natick, MA; *U.S. Public*, pg. 162

Nerland, Nairn L., Controller & Asst. Sec.--Nowsco Well Service Ltd., Calgary, Canada; *Int'l*, pg. 989

Nerone, Maureen, Chief Fin. Officer, V.P. & Controller--Colony Liquor Distributors, Inc., Kingston, NY; *U.S. Private*, pg. 254

Nerud, Mark, Asst. V.P. & Asst. Controller--Jackson National Life Insurance Company, Lansing, MI; *Int'l*, pg. 1073

Nesmith, Ron, Controller--Farmers Telephone Co-Op, Kingstree, SC; *U.S. Private*, pg. 395

Ness, Andrea, Controller--Custom Cheques of Canada, Winnipeg, Canada; *Int'l*, pg. 1077

Ness, Melvin O., Controller--Escast, Inc., Addison, IL; *U.S. Public*, pg. 612

Nesset, Marguerite, V.P. & Controller--Buffets, Inc., Eden Prairie, MN; *U.S. Public*, pg. 267

Nethaway, Cary, Controller & Mgr.-Acctg.--Sacramento Municipal Utility District, Sacramento, CA; *U.S. Private*, pg. 959

Neubauer, Jim, Controller--Barnhardt Manufacturing Co., Charlotte, NC; *U.S. Private*, pg. 116

Neucere, Eileen, Controller--Gamma Biologicals Inc., Houston, TX; *U.S. Public*, pg. 698

Neueschwander, Roy, Controller--Marshall Erdman and Associates, Inc., Madison, WI; *U.S. Private*, pg. 380

Neuman, Ronald W., Chief Fin. Officer, Treas. & Controller--Allen-Edmonds Shoe Corp., Port Washington, WI; *U.S. Private*, pg. 36

Nevendank, Maura, Asst. Controller--Coca-Cola Bottling Co. of Chicago, Niles, IL; *U.S. Private*, pg. 248

Neville, Whit, Controller--Capitol Broadcasting Co., Inc., Raleigh, NC; *U.S. Private*, pg. 206

Newberry, C. Thomas, V.P. & Controller--Hubbard Broadcasting, Inc., Saint Paul, MN; *U.S. Private*, pg. 543

Newburger, John, Controller--American Marking Systems, Clifton, NJ; *U.S. Private*, pg. 58

Newell, Matthew, Sr. V.P. & Controller--Allied Advertising Agency, Public Relations, Boston, MA; *U.S. Private*, pg. 38

Newell, W.F., V.P. & Controller--AP North American Aftermarket Division, Goldsboro, NC; *U.S. Private*, pg. 230

Newhagen, Richard, Controller--Nestle Beverage Company, Suffolk, VA; *Int'l*, pg. 918

Newhart, George T., Controller--CTS Corporation, Elkhart, IN; *U.S. Public*, pg. 285

Newkirk, Dennis G., V.P. & Controller--NL Industries, Inc., Houston, TX; *U.S. Private*, pg. 270

Newkirk, Dennis G., V.P. & Controller--Kronos, Inc., Houston, TX; *U.S. Private*, pg. 270

Newman, Janice, Controller--Quebecor Printing Haughton, Scarborough, Canada; *Int'l*, pg. 1077

Newman, Joe, Controller--Amsted Industries Incorporated, Chicago, IL; *U.S. Private*, pg. 68

Newman, Michael, Corp. Controller--Acrometal Companies, Inc., Plymouth, MN; *U.S. Private*, pg. 14

Newman, Tim, Grp. Treas.--United News & Media plc, London, United Kingdom; *Int'l*, pg. 1443

Newmeyer, Richard, Controller--Alloy Technology International Inc., West Nyack, NY; *U.S. Private*, pg. 42

Newsome, Carla, Controller--Precision Systems, Inc., Saint Petersburg, FL; *U.S. Public*, pg. 1321

Newsome, J. Rick, Controller--Kaiser Permanente, Northeast Division, Farmington, CT; *U.S. Private*, pg. 605

Newson, Joe, Controller & Sec.--Southern Leather Co., Inc., Memphis, TN; *U.S. Private*, pg. 1016

Newson, Martin, Co. Sec. & Controller--Bayer UK Ltd., Newbury, United Kingdom; *Int'l*, pg. 175

Newton, Anne B., Controller--Cyclam SA, Amiens, France; *Int'l*, pg. 1339

Newton, Doug, Acting Controller--Adobe Systems Incorporated, San Jose, CA; *U.S. Public*, pg. 20

Newton, Karen, Controller--Einson Freeman Inc., Paramus, NJ; *Int'l*, pg. 1483

Newton, Stuart, Controller--Best Products Co., Inc., Richmond, VA; *U.S. Private*, pg. 990

Newton, Vicki, Controller--LGC Management, Englewood, CO; *U.S. Private*, pg. 639

Ney, Gene, Controller--Ranchers Cotton Oil, Fresno, CA; *U.S. Private*, pg. 908

Ng, Cindy, Corp. Controller--Right Management Consultants, Inc., Philadelphia, PA; *U.S. Public*, pg. 1390

Ng, Nancy, Controller--Gestetner Private Limited, Singapore, Singapore; *Int'l*, pg. 1115

Ngvyen, Thu, Controller--Casablanca Fan Company, Pomona, CA; *U.S. Private*, pg. 549

Ngvyen, Thu, Controller--Casablanca Fan Co., Inc., Memphis, TN; *U.S. Private*, pg. 549

Nice, Robert, Controller--Rosenbergers Dairies, Inc., Hatfield, PA; *U.S. Private*, pg. 945

Nicholas, Howard D., Controller--Grand Trunk Corporation (GTC), Detroit, MI; *Int'l*, pg. 258

Nicholls, Vicky L., Controller--Spartan Oil Corp., Lansing, MI; *U.S. Private*, pg. 1021

Nichols, Jim, Controller--Farnsworth Companies, Mesa, AZ; *U.S. Private*, pg. 397

Nichols, Ralph, Controller--Frontier Foundry, Inc., Titusville, PA; *U.S. Private*, pg. 430

Nichols, William A., V.P.-Fin. & Controller--Becton Dickinson & Company, Franklin Lakes, NJ; *U.S. Public*, pg. 199

Nichols, William G., Asst. Controller--Aluminum Company of America, Pittsburgh, PA; *U.S. Public*, pg. 60

Nicholson, Peter, Controller--Asher/Gould Advertising, Inc., Los Angeles, CA; *U.S. Private*, pg. 88

Nicholson, Robert C., Chief Fin. Officer & Controller--IMI Cornelius Inc. (MN), Anoka, MN; *Int'l*, pg. 646

Nichter, Mark S., Controller, Sec. & Dir.-Investor Rels.--Continental Materials Corporation, Chicago, IL; *U.S. Public*, pg. 441

Nickelatti, Chris, Controller, Treas. & Sec.--Crown Fence Co., Long Beach, CA; *U.S. Private*, pg. 292

Nickerson, Arthur B., V.P. & Controller--Granite Construction Incorporated, Watsonville, CA; *U.S. Public*, pg. 759

Nicklay, Daniel C., Controller--Colwell Industries, Inc., Minneapolis, MN; *U.S. Private*, pg. 257

Nickolas, John N., Asst. Controller--Safeguard Scientifics, Inc., Wayne, PA; *U.S. Public*, pg. 1424

Nicol, Bruce B., Controller--Placer Dome Inc., Vancouver, Canada; *Int'l*, pg. 1060

Nicola, Steve, Controller--Matthews International Corp., Pittsburgh, PA; *U.S. Public*, pg. 1059

Niehaus, Kevin, Controller--Towne Properties, Cincinnati, OH; *U.S. Private*, pg. 1093

Niehus, Mark A., Corp. Controller--Walbro Corporation, Cass City, MI; *U.S. Public*, pg. 1733

Nielsen, Bryce, Controller--New Bedford Panoramex Corporation, Upland, CA; *U.S. Private*, pg. 792

Niemiec, Joe, Controller--Valley Manufacturing Corporation, Wilkes-Barre, PA; *Int'l*, pg. 1338

Nilles, Gregg, Controller--Columbian Mutual Life Insurance Co., Binghamton, NY; *U.S. Private*, pg. 256

Nilsen, Terje, Chief Fin. Officer, Treas. & Controller--AGA Ges.m.b.H., Vienna, Austria; *Int'l*, pg. 13

Nimons, John M., V.P. & Controller--Champion International Corp., Stamford, CT; *U.S. Public*, pg. 333

Nimtz, D., Controller--Consolidated Papers, Inc., Wisconsin Rapids, WI; *U.S. Public*, pg. 436

Nimura, Yosh, Controller--Kulicke & Soffa (Japan), Ltd., Tokyo, Japan; *U.S. Public*, pg. 969

Nirenberg, Jerry, V.P. & Controller--GAB Robins North America, Inc., Parsippany, NJ; *Int'l*, pg. 1153

Nissen, Elise, Chief Fin. Officer--AFP Imaging Corporation, Elmsford, NY; *U.S. Public*, pg. 6

Nitu, Litsa, Controller--Harrison Div., Burbank, CA; *U.S. Private*, pg. 999

Niwinski, Richard, Controller--Houghton International Inc., Valley Forge, PA; *U.S. Private*, pg. 541

Nix, Jackie, Controller--Valley Hospital Medical Center, Las Vegas, NV; *U.S. Public*, pg. 1697

Noah, Joni, Chief Fin. Officer, Controller & Treas.--Visible Changes, Houston, TX; *U.S. Private*, pg. 1141
Noal, Jack, Controller--Erie Press Systems, Erie, PA; *U.S. Private*, pg. 353
Nobles, M.K., Controller--The Thompson's Company, Memphis, TN; *U.S. Public*, pg. 1466
Nobles, R.L., Controller & Dir.-D.P.--Blevins Inc., Nashville, TN; *U.S. Private*, pg. 149
Nobles, Rob, Controller--Harris Ford, Inc., Lynnwood, WA; *U.S. Private*, pg. 506
Noblitt, Steve, Controller--Universal Flavors-U.S.A., Indianapolis, IN; *U.S. Public*, pg. 1696
Nocito, Michael F., V.P. & Controller--Bowater Incorporated, Greenville, SC; *U.S. Public*, pg. 247
Nocl, Nicholas A., Chief Fin. Officer & Controller--Western Regional Off Track Betting, Batavia, NY; *U.S. Private*, pg. 1168
Noel, David, Controller--Medical Graphics Corp., Saint Paul, MN; *U.S. Public*, pg. 1080
Noga, John, Controller--The Chardon Rubber Co., Chardon, OH; *U.S. Private*, pg. 229
Nogal, Joseph P., Controller, Treas. & Asst. Sec.--Woodhead Industries, Inc., Buffalo Grove, IL; *U.S. Public*, pg. 1776
Nogue, Bob, Controller--Dowell Schlumberger Canada Inc., Calgary, Canada; *U.S. Public*, pg. 1439
Nolan, Charlie, V.P. & Controller--McWane, Inc., Birmingham, AL; *U.S. Private*, pg. 725
Nolan, Larry, Controller--K-D Lamp Company, Cincinnati, OH; *U.S. Private*, pg. 603
Nolan, Liam, Controller--Universal Dynamics, Inc., Woodbridge, VA; *Int'l*, pg. 484
Nolenberg, Walter C., Controller--Intermet Corporation, Troy, MI; *U.S. Public*, pg. 894
Noll, Lawrence R., V.P., Controller & Sec.--AEP Industries, Inc., South Hackensack, NJ; *U.S. Public*, pg. 4
Nolte, William, Controller--Digi International Inc., Minnetonka, MN; *U.S. Public*, pg. 506
Nolterieke, Gary, Controller--Massey Cadillac, Inc., Downey, CA; *U.S. Private*, pg. 713
Nolterieke, Gary, Controller--Massey Chevrolet Geo, Inc., Downey, CA; *U.S. Private*, pg. 713
Nomura, Yoshihide, Controller--Teac America, Inc., Montebello, CA; *Int'l*, pg. 1360
Nonoguchi, Norimichi, Controller & Chief Actuary--Yasuda Mutual Life Insurance Co., Tokyo, Japan; *Int'l*, pg. 1519
Noonan, Chris, Asst. V.P. & Controller--Genovese Drug Stores, Inc., Melville, NY; *U.S. Public*, pg. 730
Noonan, Janice, Controller--Lawn Doctor Inc., Holmdel, NJ; *U.S. Private*, pg. 653
Noonan, W.J., Controller--Wyeth (Ireland) Limited, Limerick, Ireland; *U.S. Public*, pg. 82
Norberg, Mats, V.P. & Grp. Controller--Dahl International AB, Stockholm, Sweden; *Int'l*, pg. 359
Norman, Paul R., Controller--Globe Newspaper Company, Boston, MA; *U.S. Public*, pg. 1175
Normile, Michael T., Sr. V.P.-Fin. & Controller--Mercantile Bancorporation Inc., Saint Louis, MO; *U.S. Public*, pg. 1087
Norris, Dave, Controller--Ross Roy Communications Canada, Limited, Windsor, Canada; *U.S. Private*, pg. 946
Norris, Nick, Controller--Louisville Transportation, Louisville, KY; *U.S. Private*, pg. 567
North, Chris, Controller--Hydril Company, Houston, TX; *U.S. Private*, pg. 551
North, June, Controller--Capitol Cadillac, Corp., Lansing, MI; *U.S. Private*, pg. 712
Novack, Jennifer, Controller--The Equitable Bank, Hales Corners, WI; *U.S. Private*, pg. 380
Novack, Linda, Controller--Minnesota Brewing Company, Saint Paul, MN; *U.S. Public*, pg. 1115
Novak, Tom, Controller--The Richard E. Jacobs Group, Westlake, OH; *U.S. Private*, pg. 580
NovaK, Westley, Gen. Mgr.,Controller & Treas.--H & D Steel Service, Inc., Cleveland, OH; *U.S. Private*, pg. 489
Novakov, Martin J., Asst. Controller--M/G Transportation Services, Inc., Amelia, OH; *U.S. Public*, pg. 1111
Novakowski, Joe, Controller--CMI Holding Corp., Canton, MA; *U.S. Private*, pg. 195
Novakowski, Joe, Controller--Chadwick-Miller Inc., Canton, MA; *U.S. Private*, pg. 195
Novotney, Carri, Controller--Heart Interface Corporation, Kent, WA; *U.S. Public*, pg. 1705
Novotny, Ronald, Controller--Quintana Petroleum Corp., Houston, TX; *U.S. Private*, pg. 901
Nowak, Raymond M., V.P. & Controller--Warner Music Group, Inc., New York, NY; *U.S. Public*, pg. 1612
Nowakowski, David, V.P., Controller & Treas.--MichCon, Detroit, MI; *U.S. Public*, pg. 1025
Nowakowski, Matthew, Controller--FCA International Ltd., Westmount, Canada; *Int'l*, pg. 470
Nowakowski, Matthew, Treas.--Financial Collection Agencies (International) Inc., Mississauga, Canada; *Int'l*, pg. 470
Nowakowski, Matthew, Treas.--FCA Holdings, Inc., Wayne, PA; *Int'l*, pg. 471
Nowaturski, Dave, Controller--Medusa Minerals Co, Thomasville, PA; *U.S. Public*, pg. 1084
Nowling, Eric, Acting Chief Fin. Officer, V.P. & Controller--Standard Microsystems Corp., Hauppauge, NY; *U.S. Public*, pg. 1502
Nsamala, Isaac, Financial Controller & Dir.-Mktg.--National Bank of Malawi, Blantyre, Malawi; *Int'l*, pg. 1296
Nuley, Ray, Controller--The Walworth Company USA, Houston, TX; *U.S. Private*, pg. 1149
Nunnelley, Douglas B., Exec. V.P., Comptroller & Chief Acctg. Officer--AmSouth Bancorporation, Birmingham, AL; *U.S. Public*, pg. 105
Nurpuri, Jatinder, Fin. Controller--Britax International plc, Warwick, United Kingdom; *Int'l*, pg. 216
Nutile, F., Fin. Controller--AEP/Borden S.A., Baudour, Belgium; *U.S. Public*, pg. 5
Nyberg, Sara, Controller--Jillian's Entertainment Corporation, Boston, MA; *U.S. Private*, pg. 587
Nylen, Christina, Controller--Sensormatic AB (Sweden), Stockholm, Sweden; *U.S. Public*, pg. 1457
Nystuen, Mark, First V.P.--ABN/LaSalle North America Inc., Chicago, IL; *Int'l*, pg. 11
O'Brien, Denis G., Controller--Alcan Aluminium Limited, Montreal, Canada; *Int'l*, pg. 50
O'Brien, Dermot, Chief Acct.--Cannon Rubber Ltd., London, United Kingdom; *Int'l*, pg. 261
O'Brien, Jim, Controller--National Waste Services Inc., Chicago, IL; *U.S. Public*, pg. 49
O'Brien, John, Controller--Duferco Steel Inc., Laurence Harbor, NJ; *U.S. Private*, pg. 345
O'Brien, Leo, Controller--Bay State Milling Co., Quincy, MA; *U.S. Private*, pg. 124
O'Brien, Maureen, Controller--Pizzagalli Construction Co., South Burlington, VT; *U.S. Private*, pg. 868
O'Brien, Morgan, Controller--DQE Inc., Coraopolis, PA; *U.S. Public*, pg. 474
O'Brien, Patrick J., Controller--The Belt Railway Co. of Chicago, Bedford Park, IL; *Int'l*, pg. 258
O'Brien, Patrick J., Controller--The Belt Railway Co. of Chicago, Bedford Park, IL; *U.S. Public*, pg. 269
O'Brien, Robert J., Asst. Corp. Controller--Robert Bosch Corporation, Broadview, IL; *Int'l*, pg. 204
O'Brien, Tom, V.P., Controller & Asst. Treas.-Bank Opers.--Ultramar Diamond Shamrock Corporation, San Antonio, TX; *U.S. Public*, pg. 1663
O'Brien, William, Controller--Weis Markets, Inc., Sunbury, PA; *U.S. Public*, pg. 1751
O'Bryant, John, Controller--Zero Enclosures, North Salt Lake, UT; *U.S. Public*, pg. 1791
O'Connell, Francis M., V.P.-Fin. & Controller--VIMRx Pharmaceuticals, Inc., Wilmington, DE; *U.S. Public*, pg. 1702
O'Connell, Michael, Controller--Crane Plastics Company, Columbus, OH; *U.S. Private*, pg. 286
O'Conner, Joe, Pres. & Controller--American Metal & Plastics Inc., Grand Rapids, MI; *U.S. Private*, pg. 59
O'Connor, A. Bruce, V.P. & Controller--Middlesex Water Company, Iselin, NJ; *U.S. Public*, pg. 1110
O'Connor, Chuck, Controller--Daisy Manufacturing Company, Inc., Rogers, AR; *U.S. Private*, pg. 308
O'Connor, Deborah, V.P.--The ServiceMaster Company, Downers Grove, IL; *U.S. Public*, pg. 1461
O'Connor, Joseph E., Jr., V.P. & Controller--Union Pacific Corporation, Dallas, TX; *U.S. Public*, pg. 1667
O'Connor, Kenny, Asst. Controller--Amerbelle Corporation, Rockville, CT; *U.S. Private*, pg. 48
O'Connor, Raymond, Controller--Amprobe Instrument, Lynbrook, NY; *U.S. Public*, pg. 1676
O'Dean, Eric, Controller--Ingram Paper Company, City of Industry, CA; *U.S. Public*, pg. 904
O'Dell, Theodore, Sr. V.P. & Controller--Mutual of America Life Insurance Company, New York, NY; *U.S. Private*, pg. 769
O'Dell, Theodore, Sr. V.P. & Controller--American Life Insurance Company of New York, New York, NY; *U.S. Private*, pg. 769
O'Donnell, Mary, Controller--Concurrent Computer Corporation, Fort Lauderdale, FL; *U.S. Public*, pg. 430
O'Donnell, Patricia, Controller--Murry's, Inc., Upper Marlboro, MD; *U.S. Private*, pg. 768
O'Donnell, Patrick, Controller--Rock of Ages Corporation, Graniteville, VT; *U.S. Public*, pg. 1396
O'Donnell, Raymond, V.P. & Controller--Bank of the Hudson, Poughkeepsie, NY; *U.S. Public*, pg. 1319
O'Donovan, Gerald, Controller--Kepner-Tregoe, Inc., Skillman, NJ; *U.S. Public*, pg. 1659
O'Donovan, Susan E., V.P. & Controller--ContiFinancial Corporation, New York, NY; *U.S. Public*, pg. 439
O'Donovan, Susan E., V.P. & Controller--ContiFinancial Services Corporation, New York, NY; *U.S. Public*, pg. 439
O'Drobinak, James, Chief Fin. Officer, Sr. V.P. & Controller--ABR Information Services, Inc., Palm Harbor, FL; *U.S. Public*, pg. 2
O'Dwyer, Neil, Controller--SPS International Ltd., Shannon, Ireland; *U.S. Public*, pg. 1420
O'Farrell, Michael K., Controller--Applied Materials, Inc., Santa Clara, CA; *U.S. Public*, pg. 123
O'Halloran, William P., Sr. V.P. & Controller--SunTrust Banks, Inc., Atlanta, GA; *U.S. Public*, pg. 1537
O'Hara, Gerald, Controller--Bucilla Corporation, Hazleton, PA; *U.S. Private*, pg. 352
O'Hara, Ralph L., Controller--GATX Corporation, Chicago, IL; *U.S. Public*, pg. 690
O'Herron, Frederick E., Jr., Controller--New England Coffee Company, Malden, MA; *U.S. Private*, pg. 792
O'Hop, Rick, Controller--Panel Prints, Inc., Old Forge, PA; *U.S. Private*, pg. 836
O'Keefe, Jay P., Asst. Controller--Emons Transportation Group, Inc., York, PA; *U.S. Public*, pg. 578
O'Keefe, Timothy J., V.P. & Controller--Salient 3 Communications, Inc., Reading, PA; *U.S. Public*, pg. 1429
O'Leary, Donald F., Controller--Rogers Corporation, Rogers, CT; *U.S. Public*, pg. 1402
O'Leary, James, V.P. & Controller--U.S. Industries, Inc., Iselin, NJ; *U.S. Public*, pg. 1683
O'Loughlin, T.K., V.P.-Fin. & Treas.--Saztec International, Inc., Billerica, MA; *U.S. Public*, pg. 1435
O'Malley, Patrick J., Chief Acctg. Officer--Mercury Finance Co., Lake Forest, IL; *U.S. Public*, pg. 1093
O'Malley, Terry, Controller--AGA Gas, Inc., Independence, OH; *Int'l*, pg. 13
O'Mally, Mary, Controller--Apple Vacations West Inc., Elk Grove Village, IL; *U.S. Private*, pg. 78
O'Neal, Marian, Controller--Sara Lee Direct, Winston Salem, NC; *U.S. Public*, pg. 1434
O'Neil, Steven P., Controller--The Converse Professional Group, Inc., Monrovia, CA; *U.S. Private*, pg. 271
O'Neill, Bob, Controller--Terumo Medical Corporation, Somerset, NJ; *Int'l*, pg. 1376
O'Neill, Peter J., Sr. V.P.-Fin., Controller & Treas.--Agway, Inc., De Witt, NY; *U.S. Private*, pg. 27
O'Neill, Tom, Controller--Putman Publishing Co., Itasca, IL; *U.S. Private*, pg. 896
O'Niel, Amy, Controller--Kaufman and Broad of Texas, Ltd., San Antonio, TX; *U.S. Public*, pg. 945
O'Reilly, John, Controller--Bulova Corporation, Woodside, NY; *U.S. Public*, pg. 1010
O'Rourk, Joanne, Controller--Office Depot, Detroit, MI; *U.S. Public*, pg. 1212
O'Rourke, Eileen M., V.P. & Controller--Legg Mason, Inc., Baltimore, MD; *U.S. Public*, pg. 984
O'Rourke, Liam, Controller--CSP Industries B.V., Kildare, Ireland; *U.S. Public*, pg. 445
O'Rourke, Patrick G., Controller--Stewart & Stevenson Services, Inc., Houston, TX; *U.S. Public*, pg. 1517
O'Shea, Paul, Controller-Eastern Div.--Data Business Forms Limited, Brampton, Canada; *Int'l*, pg. 384
O'Young, Wilfried, Controller--CIBA-GEIGY Australia Ltd., Pendle Hill, Australia; *Int'l*, pg. 976
Oakley, Richard, Controller--Meenan Oil Co. L.P., Syosset, NY; *U.S. Private*, pg. 729
Obendorf, Steven E., Corp. Controller--Varlen Corporation, Naperville, IL; *U.S. Public*, pg. 1710
Ober, J. David, V.P. & Controller-Retail Acctg.--Albertson's, Inc., Boise, ID; *U.S. Public*, pg. 38
Oberg, Catherine, Chief Fin. Officer & Controller--Hudson County News Company, North Bergen, NJ; *U.S. Private*, pg. 545
Oberg, Page, Controller--Consolidated Beverages, Inc., Auburn, MA; *U.S. Private*, pg. 264
Oberhelman, Steve, Controller--Swepco Tube Corporation, Clifton, NJ; *U.S. Private*, pg. 1058
Obradovich, Mark, Controller--Gehl Company, West Bend, WI; *U.S. Public*, pg. 704
Ochoa, Greg, Controller--C.A. Muer Corp., Detroit, MI; *U.S. Private*, pg. 766
Ockey, Jeff, Controller--Recomp, Inc., Sandy, UT; *U.S. Private*, pg. 914
Ocone, Louis M., Sr. V.P. & Controller--Equitable Investment Corporation, New York, NY; *U.S. Public*, pg. 589
Oczkowicz, Thomas J., Controller--Rogers Group Inc., Nashville, TN; *U.S. Private*, pg. 939
Odenahl, Patricia J., Asst. Controller--Federal Paper Board Company, Inc., Montvale, NJ; *U.S. Public*, pg. 903
Odom, Don, Controller--Conwood Company L.P., Memphis, TN; *U.S. Private*, pg. 272
Odom, Elton, Div. V.P. & Controller--Swank, Inc., Attleboro, MA; *U.S. Public*, pg. 1543
Oehlschlaeger, Karl, Controller--Calprop Corporation, Marina Del Rey, CA; *U.S. Public*, pg. 296
Oelkers, Robert C., V.P. & Comptroller--Texaco Inc., White Plains, NY; *U.S. Public*, pg. 1582
Oen, Scott, Opers. Controller--Inmet Mining Corporation, Toronto, Canada; *Int'l*, pg. 678
Offenhauser, Stefan, Controller--Hosokawa MikroPul GmbH, Cologne, Germany; *Int'l*, pg. 636
Ogden, J.E., Controller--UMC Industries, Ltd., Lytham Saint Anne's, United Kingdom; *U.S. Public*, pg. 457
Ogilvy, David, Controller--Branch Electric Supply Co., Inc., Boston, MA; *U.S. Private*, pg. 165
Oglesby, Bill, Controller--Westronics, Inc., Kingwood, TX; *U.S. Public*, pg. 1593
Ohly, Jeffrey W., Sr. V.P., Treas. & Sec.--World Acceptance Corporation, Greenville, SC; *U.S. Public*, pg. 1778
Ohms, Larry T., Controller & Asst. Treas.--United States Lime & Minerals, Dallas, TX; *U.S. Public*, pg. 1684
Oilschlager, Bob, Controller--Andes Candies Inc., Delavan, WI; *U.S. Private*, pg. 163
Okerberg, Tom, Controller--Curtis 1000, Inc., Atlanta, GA; *U.S. Public*, pg. 70
Okonowsky, Gary, Controller--Kaufman and Broad Colorado Division, Denver, CO; *U.S. Public*, pg. 945
Okscin, Allan, Controller--Friendly Ice Cream Corp., Wilbraham, MA; *U.S. Public*, pg. 682
Okumoto, Richard, Controller--Novell Inc., San Jose, CA; *U.S. Public*, pg. 1203
Okuzono, S., Controller--Mikimoto (America) Co. Ltd., New York, NY; *Int'l*, pg. 866
Olander, Stephen, Controller--Dynamic Metal Products Company, Manchester, CT; *U.S. Private*, pg. 350
Oldham, Allen, V.P. & Controller--Ingram Barge Company, Nashville, TN; *U.S. Private*, pg. 563
Oldstein, Bob, Controller--Wire-Pro Inc., Salem, NJ; *U.S. Private*, pg. 1184
Olendzki, Kenneth L., Controller--Park Foods L.P., Barrington, IL; *U.S. Private*, pg. 839
Olidier, Rod, Controller--Retirement Community Specialists, Inc., Phoenix, AZ; *U.S. Private*, pg. 925
Olig, Steve, Controller--Thomas Industries Inc., Sheboygan, WI; *U.S. Public*, pg. 1599
Olinger, Donald, Sr. V.P. & Controller--Host Marriott Corporation, Bethesda, MD; *U.S. Public*, pg. 841
Oliver, David M., V.P. & Controller--The Vons Companies, Inc., Arcadia, CA; *U.S. Public*, pg. 1426
Oliver, Ray, V.P.-Opers. & Pur. & Comptroller--Tatum Farms Int., Inc., Dawsonville, GA; *U.S. Private*, pg. 1069
Oliveri, Carol H., V.P. & Controller--First Federal Savings, East Hartford, CT; *U.S. Public*, pg. 632
Oliveri, Phillip W., V.P. & Controller--Riser Foods, Inc., Bedford, OH; *U.S. Private*, pg. 450
Oliveri, Phillip W., Controller--Rini-Rego Supermarkets, Inc., Cleveland, OH; *U.S. Private*, pg. 451
Olivieri, Carlos, V.P. & Controller--Y.P.F., S.A., Buenos Aires, Argentina; *Int'l*, pg. 1515
Olivos de Castro, Blanca, Controller--Gestetner S.A., San Isidro, Peru; *Int'l*, pg. 1115
Ollinger, Greg, V.P.-Fin. & Controller--Hubert Company, Harrison, OH; *U.S. Private*, pg. 545
Ollis, Allen, Controller--JPS Textile Group, Inc., Greenville, SC; *U.S. Private*, pg. 578
Ollo, Deborah, Controller--Pepsi-Cola Bottling Company of Charlotte Inc., Charlotte, NC; *U.S. Private*, pg. 852

Olsen, Eugene, Controller--Direct Press Modern Litho Corporation, Huntington Station, NY; *U.S. Private*, pg. 334

Olsen, Rodney G., Asst. Controller--Kimberly-Clark Corporation, Dallas, TX; *U.S. Public*, pg. 958

Olson, Al, V.P. & Controller--Hennells, Inc., Ferndale, MI; *U.S. Private*, pg. 522

Olson, Alfred C., Jr., Controller--GAI Consultants, Inc., Monroeville, PA; *U.S. Private*, pg. 433

Olson, Brian, Corp. Controller--AirSensors, Inc., Seattle, WA; *U.S. Public*, pg. 33

Olson, Brian, Controller--IMPCO AirSensors Technologies, Cerritos, CA; *U.S. Public*, pg. 34

Olson, Dale, Controller--Smead Manufacturing Company, Hastings, MN; *U.S. Private*, pg. 1006

Olson, David K., V.P. & Controller--ServiceMaster Healthcare Management Services, Inc., Downers Grove, IL; *U.S. Public*, pg. 1462

Olson, Kim, Controller--Arrow Tank & Engineering Co., Minneapolis, MN; *U.S. Private*, pg. 85

Olson, Lenore, Controller--Meyer Jewelers, Taylor, MI; *U.S. Private*, pg. 739

Olson, Mark, V.P. & Controller--Westcorp, Irvine, CA; *U.S. Public*, pg. 1756

Olson, Rodney E., Chief Fin. Officer & Sr. V.P.-Fin. & Corp. Devel.--Sabreliner Corporation, Saint Louis, MO; *U.S. Private*, pg. 959

Olson, Theodore A., V.P. & Controller--Abbott Laboratories, Abbott Park, IL; *U.S. Public*, pg. 12

Olson, Theodore A., Controller--Abbott Laboratories, Abbott Park, IL; *U.S. Public*, pg. 13

Olson, Timothy J., Asst. Corp. Controller--Phelps Dodge Corporation, Phoenix, AZ; *U.S. Public*, pg. 1286

Onders, Lou, Controller--BMY-Wheeled Vehicles, Marysville, OH; *U.S. Public*, pg. 793

Onufer, Carl W., V.P. & Controller--Southwest National Corporation, Greensburg, PA; *U.S. Public*, pg. 1493

Onufer, Carl W., V.P. & Controller--Southwest National Bank of Pennsylvania, Greensburg, PA; *U.S. Public*, pg. 1493

Oosthuysen, P.C., Asst. Gen. Mgr.-Grp. Fin. & Advisory Svcs.--Standard Bank Investment Corporation Limited, Johannesburg, South Africa; *Int'l*, pg. 1293

Oostveen, Gary, Controller--Hirschfeld, Inc., San Angelo, TX; *U.S. Private*, pg. 530

Oostveen, Gary, Controller--Hirschfeld Steel Company, Inc., San Angelo, TX; *U.S. Private*, pg. 531

Opitz, Rafael, Controller--General Motors do Brasil Ltda., Sao Caetano do Sul, Brazil; *U.S. Public*, pg. 722

Oppenhuizen, A., Controller--Thompack B.V., Apeldoorn, Netherlands; *U.S. Public*, pg. 5

Orem, Barbara, Controller & sec.--Lois/EJL Los Angeles, Los Angeles, CA; *U.S. Private*, pg. 673

Orgill, Kay, V.P. & Controller--Trus Joist MacMillan, Boise, ID; *Int'l*, pg. 829

Orgill, Kay, V.P. & Controller--TJ International, Inc., Boise, ID; *U.S. Public*, pg. 1556

Orgill, Kay, V.P. & Controller--Trus Joist MacMillan, Boise, ID; *U.S. Public*, pg. 1556

Orlando, Jean M., Controller--Spectrum Asset Management, Inc., Stamford, CT; *U.S. Public*, pg. 1674

Orloff, Dale O., Controller--First Federal FSB, Hutchinson, MN; *U.S. Public*, pg. 608

Orman, Roxanne, Controller--Little Lady Foods, Inc., Elk Grove Village, IL; *U.S. Private*, pg. 671

Orr, Sean, Sr. V.P. & Controller--PepsiCo, Inc., Purchase, NY; *U.S. Public*, pg. 1276

Ortiz, J. Ruben, Controller--TII Industries, Inc., Copiague, NY; *U.S. Public*, pg. 1556

Osatczuk, Walter, Controller--Cam Am Casters, Mississauga, Canada; *U.S. Public*, pg. 1507

Osborn, Joyce, Controller--Wechco, Inc., Princeton, NJ; *U.S. Private*, pg. 1158

Osborn, Robert, Controller--Russell Sigler Inc., Phoenix, AZ; *U.S. Private*, pg. 999

Osborn, Skeet, Controller--Ormet Primary Aluminum Corp, Hannibal, OH; *U.S. Private*, pg. 820

Osborn, Steve, Controller--Pepsi-Cola Bottling Co., Denver, CO; *U.S. Public*, pg. 1276

Oskins, James C., Controller & Sec.--George Koch Sons, Inc., Evansville, IN; *U.S. Private*, pg. 628

Osmundson, Michael, Controller--Bearing Distributors, Inc., Columbia, SC; *U.S. Private*, pg. 127

Osoinick, Paul, Asst. Corp. Controller--The Leslie Fay Companies, Inc., New York, NY; *U.S. Public*, pg. 989

Oster, Ralph, Controller--First National Bank in Chicago Heights, Chicago Heights, IL; *U.S. Public*, pg. 760

Ostroff, Arthur J., Controller & Treas.--Standard Medical Imaging, Inc., Columbia, MD; *U.S. Private*, pg. 1032

Ott, Linda, Corp. Controller--RHC/Spacemaster Corporation, Melrose Park, IL; *U.S. Private*, pg. 904

Ottem, Roger, Controller--Hawkins Chemical, Inc., Minneapolis, MN; *U.S. Public*, pg. 800

Otterbeck, Steven, Controller--Brumko Magnetics, Elkhorn, NE; *U.S. Private*, pg. 696

Otterbeck, Steven, Acting Controller--Magnetics Data, Inc., Eden Prairie, MN; *U.S. Private*, pg. 696

Ouderkirk, D.R., Controller--Henry Birks & Sons (1993) Inc., Montreal, Canada; *Int'l*, pg. 196

Ouzts, Daniel R., V.P. & Controller--Medicore Inc., Hialeah, FL; *U.S. Public*, pg. 1080

Ouzts, Daniel R., V.P. & Controller--Techdyne, Inc., Hialeah, FL; *U.S. Public*, pg. 1080

Overby, Gloria, Controller--Slane Hosiery Mills, Inc., High Point, NC; *U.S. Private*, pg. 1005

Overmeyer, George J., Controller--Aqua Care Systems Inc., Coral Springs, FL; *U.S. Public*, pg. 126

Owens, Dick, Controller--Masco Building Products Corp., Seal Beach, CA; *U.S. Public*, pg. 1053

Owens, Gary, Controller--Kohl's Food Stores, Wauwatosa, WI; *Int'l*, pg. 1375

Owens, Mike, Controller & Dir.-Special Projects--Hale-Halsell Company, Tulsa, OK; *U.S. Private*, pg. 494

Owens, Phil, Controller--GN Nettest Fiber Optic Division, Utica, NY; *Int'l*, pg. 536

Owens, Richard M., Controller--Fencourt Reinsurance Co. Ltd., Hamilton, Bermuda; *U.S. Public*, pg. 795

Owens, Tom, Controller--P/A Industries, Inc., Bloomfield, CT; *U.S. Private*, pg. 825

Owens, William T., Grp. V.P.-Fin. & Controller--Healthsouth Corporation, Birmingham, AL; *U.S. Public*, pg. 803

Oyan, Tor, V.P. & Controller--Kvaerner a.s.a., Lysaker, Norway; *Int'l*, pg. 766

Oyster, A.P., Controller--Proudfoot USA Company, West Palm Beach, FL; *Int'l*, pg. 1072

Ozaki, Joe, Controller, Treas. & Sec.--A-Mark Financial, Santa Monica, CA; *U.S. Private*, pg. 2

Ozmun, Robert, Chief Fin. Officer & Controller--Grocers Supply Co. Inc., Houston, TX; *U.S. Private*, pg. 483

Pacchini, Carlo, Chief Fin. Officer, Exec. V.P., Controller & Real Estate--Nyltech North America Inc., Manchester, NH; *Int'l*, pg. 482

Pace, James C., Jr., Controller & Office Mgr.--Inman Mills, Inman, SC; *U.S. Private*, pg. 564

Pachla, Ken, Controller--Ludington News Co. Inc., Detroit, MI; *U.S. Private*, pg. 679

Pacholski, John Joseph, Grp. Controller--Lend Lease Corporation Limited, Sydney, Australia; *Int'l*, pg. 806

Packard, Ralph K., V.P. & Controller--Vanguard Real Estate Fund II, Valley Forge, PA; *U.S. Private*, pg. 1134

Packer, Wayne, Controller--Keysor Century Corporation, Saugus, CA; *U.S. Private*, pg. 618

Padilla, Jorge L., V.P., Treas. & Controller--Universal Insurance Co., San Juan, PR; *U.S. Public*, pg. 962

Padilla, Penny, Controller--Commerical Roofers Inc., Las Vegas, NV; *U.S. Private*, pg. 258

Page, Steve, Controller--Indeck Power Equipment Company, Wheeling, IL; *U.S. Private*, pg. 559

Pagliarini, John, Controller--Columbine JDS Systems, Inc., Denver, CO; *U.S. Public*, pg. 228

Pai, Subhash, Controller & Asst. Sec.--Startec Global Communications Corporation, Bethesda, MD; *U.S. Public*, pg. 1511

Pailing, Jeanne, Comptroller--Philip Laser Magnetic Storage, Colorado Springs, CO; *Int'l*, pg. 1054

Paillaud, Guy, Dir.-Mngmt. Control--Promodes SA, Mondeville, France; *Int'l*, pg. 1071

Pain, John T., Controller--Tennant Company, Minneapolis, MN; *U.S. Public*, pg. 1577

Pairitz, Dave, Controller--Fastec Industrial, Elkhart, IN; *U.S. Private*, pg. 397

Pais, P.E., Comptroller--Kolynos SAIC, Buenos Aires, Argentina; *U.S. Public*, pg. 81

Pakfetrat, Edna, Controller--Haws Drinking Faucet Co., Berkeley, CA; *U.S. Private*, pg. 512

Palazzari, Philip, V.P. & Controller--Honeywell Inc., Minneapolis, MN; *U.S. Public*, pg. 833

Palitza, Carolyn M., V.P. & Controller--Luby's Cafeterias, Inc., San Antonio, TX; *U.S. Public*, pg. 1017

Pallares, Moises, Comptroller--General Motors de Mexico, S.A. de C.V., Ramos Arizpe, Mexico; *U.S. Public*, pg. 722

Pallen, Michael, Controller--Gilman Paper Co., Saint Marys, GA; *U.S. Private*, pg. 454

Palm, Sarah, Controller--Kanthal AB, Hallstahammar, Sweden; *Int'l*, pg. 723

Palmer, Dina, Controller--Summit Food Service Distributors, London, Canada; *Int'l*, pg. 266

Palmer, Donald S., Controller--GuestInformant, Inc., Woodland Hills, CA; *U.S. Public*, pg. 11

Palmer, John, Controller--City Postal, Inc., New York, NY; *U.S. Private*, pg. 241

Palmer, Karen, Controller--Ultimate Technology Corporation, Victor, NY; *U.S. Public*, pg. 1637

Palmer, Paul, Controller--Sierra Health Services, Inc., Las Vegas, NV; *U.S. Public*, pg. 1469

Palmer, Waet, Controller--Chas Roberts Air Conditioning, Inc., Phoenix, AZ; *U.S. Private*, pg. 935

Palu, Michael, Controller--Circle International Group, Inc., San Francisco, CA; *U.S. Public*, pg. 370

Panaro, Robert, V.P. & Controller--CertainTeed Corporation, Valley Forge, PA; *Int'l*, pg. 1170

Pane, Anthony, Controller--The American Stock Exchange, New York, NY; *U.S. Private*, pg. 62

Pankiw, Peter, Controller--The Hartz Mountain Corp., Secaucus, NJ; *U.S. Private*, pg. 508

Pannell, Michael, Sr. V.P. & Controller--Riggs National Corporation, Washington, DC; *U.S. Public*, pg. 1389

Pannu, Mohan, Controller--Executive Car Leasing, Inc., Los Angeles, CA; *U.S. Private*, pg. 388

Pannus, Darrius, Chief Fin. Officer, V.P.-Fin. & Controller--Good Companies, Carson, CA; *U.S. Private*, pg. 463

Panza, Raymond H., Controller--Duquesne Light Company, Pittsburgh, PA; *U.S. Public*, pg. 474

Panzella, Vito, Controller--MobileComm, Ridgefield Park, NJ; *U.S. Public*, pg. 1120

Paolillo, Leonard, Controller--Spincraft Massachusetts, North Billerica, MA; *U.S. Public*, pg. 1506

Paolozzi, Anthony, V.P. & Controller--Utica Mutual Insurance Company, New Hartford, NY; *U.S. Private*, pg. 1129

Pap, Agnes, Controller--American Appraisal Hungary Co. Ltd., Budapest, Hungary; *U.S. Private*, pg. 50

Papa, Bernard, Controller--Troy Corporation, Florham Park, NJ; *U.S. Private*, pg. 1105

Papai, Jacqueline, Exec. V.P. & Controller--Ventre Packing Company, Inc., Syracuse, NY; *U.S. Private*, pg. 1135

Papera, Michael F., Controller--Allstate Can Corporation, Parsippany, NJ; *U.S. Private*, pg. 44

Papletti, Robert A., V.P. & Controller--Service America Corporation, Stamford, CT; *U.S. Private*, pg. 986

Papp, Gregory R., Controller--Aeroquip-Vickers, Inc., Maumee, OH; *U.S. Public*, pg. 24

Pappas, James J., V.P. & Controller-Science & Prod. Devel. Div.--Bristol-Myers Squibb International, Princeton, NJ; *U.S. Public*, pg. 254

Papso, Anna Mae, V.P. & Controller--The West Company, Incorporated, Lionville, PA; *U.S. Public*, pg. 1755

Paquette, Michael S., V.P. & Controller--Fund American Enterprises Holdings, Inc., Hanover, NH; *U.S. Public*, pg. 688

Para, Gregory, Chief Fin. Officer & Controller--Dimensional Merchandising, Inc., Wharton, NJ; *U.S. Private*, pg. 333

Pardi, Richard A., Controller--Western Data Systems, Calabasas, CA; *U.S. Private*, pg. 1165

Parekh, Dilip, V.P. & Controller--Jessica McClintock Inc., San Francisco, CA; *U.S. Private*, pg. 719

Pareyt, Gary, Controller--The Rao Group Inc., Sterling Heights, MI; *U.S. Private*, pg. 910

Parfitt, Elaine, Chief Fin. Officer, V.P. & Controller--Integral Systems, Inc., Lanham, MD; *U.S. Public*, pg. 883

Parikh, Nitin G., V.P.-Fin. & Controller--Frederick's of Hollywood, Inc., Hollywood, CA; *U.S. Private*, pg. 424

Parikh, Viren M., Controller--Quanex Corporation, Houston, TX; *U.S. Public*, pg. 1349

Paris, Chuck, Controller--LubeCon Systems, Inc., White Cloud, MI; *U.S. Private*, pg. 679

Parish, Beth, Controller--ACX Technologies Inc., Golden, CO; *U.S. Public*, pg. 3

Park, Anthony J, Controller--Fidelity National Financial, Inc., Irvine, CA; *U.S. Public*, pg. 620

Park, Brian, Controller--Pipetronix Ltd., Concord, Canada; *Int'l*, pg. 1071

Park, Dwain S., Controller--True Companies, Casper, WY; *U.S. Private*, pg. 1107

Park, Jeffrey B., V.P. & Controller--Gaylord Container Corporation, Deerfield, IL; *U.S. Public*, pg. 704

Parke, James, Controller--Tupman Thurlow Co. Inc., Avon, CT; *U.S. Private*, pg. 1109

Parker, C.W., Controller--StacoEnergy Products Co., Dayton, OH; *U.S. Private*, pg. 260

Parker, E., Controller--Acme Canvas Co., Inc., Malden, MA; *U.S. Private*, pg. 13

Parker, Harold, Controller--CCB Financial Corporation, Durham, NC; *U.S. Public*, pg. 276

Parker, J. Scott, Controller--James N. Gray Construction Co., Inc., Lexington, KY; *U.S. Private*, pg. 472

Parker, Jay E., Controller--Hub Group, Inc., Lombard, IL; *U.S. Public*, pg. 844

Parker, Jerry L., V.P. & Controller--DIMON, Incorporated, Danville, VA; *U.S. Public*, pg. 509

Parker, Phil, Comptroller--Mount Snow Resort, Mount Snow, VT; *U.S. Private*, pg. 61

Parker, Ron, Controller--Venchurs Packaging, Inc., Adrian, MI; *U.S. Private*, pg. 1135

Parkey, Mark A., Controller--J. Alexanders Corporation, Nashville, TN; *U.S. Public*, pg. 40

Parkinson, Brent, Controller & Mgr.-Risk Mngmt.--Dawn Food Products, Inc., Jackson, MI; *U.S. Private*, pg. 316

Parks, Deborah A., CPA, Controller--Parks Products, Inc., Hollywood, CA; *U.S. Private*, pg. 840

Parks, Larry, Controller--Petersen Graphics Group, South Bend, IN; *U.S. Private*, pg. 856

Parks, Larry, Controller--5 Rubber Corporation, Kittanning, PA; *U.S. Public*, pg. 1504

Parks, Steve, Controller--Ernest Paper Products, Inc., Los Angeles, CA; *U.S. Private*, pg. 381

Parmalee, William, Controller--Qualex Inc., Durham, NC; *U.S. Public*, pg. 551

Parnell, Gordon, Controller--Microchip Technology, Inc., Chandler, AZ; *U.S. Public*, pg. 1105

Parra, Mike, Chief Fin. Officer, Controller & Treas.--F.P.A., Inc., Irving, TX; *U.S. Private*, pg. 389

Parra, Mimi, Controller--Prism Integrated Sanitation Management, Inc., Miami, FL; *U.S. Private*, pg. 592

Parrin, David J., Sr. V.P. & Controller--U.S. Bancorp, Minneapolis, MN; *U.S. Public*, pg. 1680

Parrish, Teresa, V.P.-Fin. & Controller--Vincennes Steel Corp., Vincennes, IN; *U.S. Private*, pg. 1141

Parsons, Lena, Controller--World Oil Corp., South Gate, CA; *U.S. Private*, pg. 1190

Parsons, Richard T., Controller--EnerMark Income Fund, Calgary, Canada; *Int'l*, pg. 454

Partaleois, Charles, Controller--Ark-Les Corporation, Stoughton, MA; *U.S. Private*, pg. 82

Pasarro, Dominic, Controller--Technic Incorporated, Cranston, RI; *U.S. Private*, pg. 1071

Pascolini, Mario, Chief Fin. Officer & Treas.--The Will-Burt Company, Orrville, OH; *U.S. Private*, pg. 1177

Pashkowsky, John, Controller--Ketema Division, El Cajon, CA; *Int'l*, pg. 1222

Pasker, Carl, Controller--Spraying Systems Co., Wheaton, IL; *U.S. Private*, pg. 1026

Pasquretta, Mark, Controller--Doral Hotel & Resorts Management Co., New York, NY; *U.S. Private*, pg. 340

Pass, Connie, Controller--American Mathematical Society, Inc., Providence, RI; *U.S. Private*, pg. 59

Passardi, Adriano, Exec. V.P.--Zurich Insurance Company, Zurich, Switzerland; *Int'l*, pg. 1529

Passaro, Larry, Grp. Controller--Industrial Components Group, Shelton, CT; *Int'l*, pg. 127

Passos, Rubens Ferreira, Controller--Aracruz Celulose S.A., Rio de Janeiro, Brazil; *Int'l*, pg. 78

Pata, Kevin R., Corp. Controller--Kit Manufacturing Company, Long Beach, CA; *U.S. Public*, pg. 962

Patafio, Clem, Corp. Controller--Interlaken Capital, Inc., Greenwich, CT; *U.S. Private*, pg. 567

Patafio, Clement P., V.P. & Controller--W.R. Berkley Corporation, Greenwich, CT; *U.S. Public*, pg. 215

Patch, David, Fin. Controller--Hanimex Pty. Limited, Brookvale, Australia; *Int'l*, pg. 1115

Patel, Chandrakant, Controller--Cherokee International LLC, Tustin, CA; *U.S. Private*, pg. 233

Patel, Jay, Controller--Nobart, Inc., Chicago, IL; *U.S. Private*, pg. 800

Patel, Ravi, Controller--Really Useful Holdings Limited, London, United Kingdom; *Int'l*, pg. 1089

Pater, James J., Controller--Aetna Bearing Company, Chicago, IL; *U.S. Private*, pg. 25

Paterson, William A., Sr. V.P. & Controller--Fort James Corporation, Richmond, VA; *U.S. Public*, pg. 670
Patriarcie, Bernie, Controller--Summit Technology, Inc., Waltham, MA; *U.S. Public*, pg. 1528
Patrick, Randy, Controller--Active Tool & Manufacturing Co., Inc., Roseville, MI; *U.S. Private*, pg. 16
Patrick, Stephen C., V.P. & Controller--Colgate-Palmolive Company, New York, NY; *U.S. Public*, pg. 397
Patten, Fred, Controller--American Telecasting, Inc., Colorado Springs, CO; *U.S. Public*, pg. 93
Patten, Robert, Controller--Moran Transporation Company, Greenwich, CT; *U.S. Private*, pg. 760
Patten, Robert J, Controller--Jakobson Shipyard, Inc, Greenwich, CT; *U.S. Private*, pg. 760
Patten, Robert J., Controller--Moran Towing Corporation, Greenwich, CT; *U.S. Private*, pg. 760
Patten, Robert J., Controller & Asst. Sec.--Moran Bulk Corporation, Greenwich, CT; *U.S. Private*, pg. 760
Patten, Robert J., Controller--Moran Insurance Company Limited, Greenwich, CT; *U.S. Private*, pg. 760
Patten, Robert J., Controller--Moran Shipyard Corporation, Greenwich, CT; *U.S. Private*, pg. 761
Patten, Robert J., Controller--Portsmouth Navigation Corporation, Greenwich, CT; *U.S. Private*, pg. 761
Patten, T.J., Controller--Kiwi Brands Pty. Ltd., Clayton, Australia; *U.S. Public*, pg. 1434
Patterson, Mary Lou, Controller--Sherwood, Lockport, NY; *U.S. Public*, pg. 793
Patterson, Michael, Controller--Plunkett-Webster, Inc., New Rochelle, NY; *U.S. Private*, pg. 872
Patterson, Pauline, Controller & Sec.--Maine Potato Growers, Inc., Presque Isle, ME; *U.S. Private*, pg. 697
Patterson, Seth L., V.P. & Controller--Holnam Inc. (West Division), Lakewood, CO; *Int'l*, pg. 628
Patterson, Steve, Controller--Alsons Corporation, Hillsdale, MI; *U.S. Public*, pg. 1053
Patterson, Waldo, V.P.-Fin. & Controller--Super Sagless Corp., Tupelo, MS; *U.S. Public*, pg. 986
Pattison, K., V.P.-Fin. & Controller--Hydro-Aire, Burbank, CA; *U.S. Public*, pg. 457
Patton, Marilyn, Controller--Takatta Inc., Auburn Hills, MI; *U.S. Private*, pg. 528
Patzke, Wallace A., Jr., V.P. & Controller--Florida Rock Industries, Inc., Jacksonville, FL; *U.S. Public*, pg. 655
Paul, Al, Controller--Cosco Fire Protection Inc., Gardena, CA; *U.S. Public*, pg. 1795
Paul, Charles M., Controller--Cedar Fair, L.P., Sandusky, OH; *U.S. Public*, pg. 319
Paul, John H.L., Controller--Sterling Paper Co., Philadelphia, PA; *U.S. Private*, pg. 1041
Paul, Julia, Controller--Nella Oil Company, Auburn, CA; *U.S. Private*, pg. 790
Paul, Steven M., Grp. V.P. & Controller-Pipe Sys. Grp.--Price Brothers Co., Dayton, OH; *U.S. Private*, pg. 883
Paulin, Joel, Controller--Banner Wholesale Grocers, Inc., Chicago, IL; *U.S. Private*, pg. 114
Paulsen, Bruce, V.P. & Controller--Carlson Companies, Inc., Minnetonka, MN; *U.S. Private*, pg. 211
Paulsen, Clifford D., Controller--Fieldcrest Cannon, Inc., Kannapolis, NC; *U.S. Public*, pg. 1296
Paulsen, Clifford D., Controller--Fieldcrest/Cannon Bed Fashions Division, New York, NY; *U.S. Public*, pg. 1296
Paulson, Brian, Controller--Wenger Corporation, Owatonna, MN; *U.S. Private*, pg. 1162
Paulson, David L., Controller--Los Angeles Times, Los Angeles, CA; *U.S. Public*, pg. 1616
Paumen, Douglas, Mgr.-Acctg.--United Power Association, Elk River, MN; *U.S. Private*, pg. 1123
Paur, Shameeron, Controller--Calcitek, Inc., Carlsbad, CA; *Int'l*, pg. 1307
Pavlic, Lynn, Controller--Temple-Inland Forest Products Corporation, Diboll, TX; *U.S. Public*, pg. 1575
Pavlicek, Stephen E., Sr. V.P. & Controller--American National Insurance Company, Galveston, TX; *U.S. Public*, pg. 87
Pavlick, Gary, Controller--Artel Video Systems, Inc., Marlborough, MA; *U.S. Private*, pg. 86
Pavlics, Peter N., Controller--Science Applications International Corp., San Diego, CA; *U.S. Private*, pg. 975
Pavlik, Jeff, Controller & Asst. Treas.--Premier Coatings, Inc., Elk Grove Village, IL; *Int'l*, pg. 1488
Pawelko, E., Fin. Controller--Piher International Corporation, Mount Prospect, IL; *Int'l*, pg. 853
Pawlick, Joseph L., V.P. & Controller--Lawson Products, Inc., Des Plaines, IL; *U.S. Public*, pg. 980
Pawlowski, D.A., Controller--Macwhyte Co., Kenosha, WI; *U.S. Private*, pg. 68
Pawlowski, Walter, Controller--Mestek, Inc., Westfield, MA; *U.S. Public*, pg. 1099
Payette, Paul, Controller--Brittany Dyeing & Printing Corporation, New Bedford, MA; *U.S. Private*, pg. 170
Payne, John, Controller--CorVel Corporation, Irvine, CA; *U.S. Public*, pg. 451
Payne, Robert, Controller--Shape Inc., Kennebunk, ME; *U.S. Private*, pg. 990
Payne, Scott, Controller--Inland Printing Co., Inc., La Crosse, WI; *U.S. Private*, pg. 564
Payton, Fred, Asst. V.P. & Controller--Southwire Company, Carrollton, GA; *U.S. Private*, pg. 1019
Pazurek, John, V.P.-Fin., Treas. & Controller--Northland Cranberries, Inc., Wisconsin Rapids, WI; *U.S. Public*, pg. 1197
Pazurek, John, Chief Fin. Officer & Controller--WildHawk, Inc., Wisconsin Rapids, WI; *U.S. Public*, pg. 1197
Peak, Cam, Fin. Controller--Braum Ice Cream Stores Inc., Oklahoma City, OK; *U.S. Private*, pg. 166
Pearce, Edwin W., III, Asst. Controller--Tencarva Machinery Co., Inc., Greensboro, NC; *U.S. Private*, pg. 1075
Pearl, Ronald, Controller--WNY Group, Englishtown, NJ; *U.S. Private*, pg. 1144
Pearse, Timothy, Controller--Joseph Behr & Sons Inc., Rockford, IL; *U.S. Private*, pg. 130
Pearson, Christopher W., Controller--Tees Storage Company Limited, Middlesbrough, United Kingdom; *U.S. Public*, pg. 693
Peart, Robert, Controller--Chadwick-Helmuth Company, Inc., El Monte, CA; *U.S. Private*, pg. 227
Peat, David W., V.P. & Controller--Homestake Mining Company, San Francisco, CA; *U.S. Public*, pg. 832
Peattie, William W., Treas. & Comptroller--General Motors Acceptance Corporation of Canada Limited, Toronto, Canada; *U.S. Public*, pg. 720
Peck, Larry, Controller--Carr Gottstein Foods, Anchorage, AK; *U.S. Public*, pg. 308
Peck, Robbie, Controller--Marlow Industries, Dallas, TX; *U.S. Private*, pg. 705
Pedersen, Niels, Comptroller--Harmon City, Inc., Salt Lake City, UT; *U.S. Private*, pg. 503
Pegny, Dean, Controller--Dryper's Corp., Vancouver, WA; *U.S. Private*, pg. 344
Peitsch, Dave, Controller--Engine Components Div., Saginaw, MI; *U.S. Public*, pg. 557
Pekins, Julie, Asst. Controller--American Kennel Club, Inc., New York, NY; *U.S. Private*, pg. 58
Pekkala, Keith, Controller--STM Wireless, Inc., Irvine, CA; *U.S. Public*, pg. 1421
Pekrul, Cynthia L., Controller--LaRoche Industries Inc., Atlanta, GA; *U.S. Private*, pg. 651
Pelech, Michael, V.P. & Controller--The Cedarwood Construction Company, Akron, OH; *U.S. Private*, pg. 221
Pelisson, Edward, Asst. V.P. & Controller--Marcel Dekker, Inc., New York, NY; *U.S. Private*, pg. 321
Pell, Debbie, Asst. Cashier & Controller--United Missouri Bank of Springfield, Springfield, MO; *U.S. Public*, pg. 1655
Pellecchia, Nicholas D., V.P.-Fin. & Controller--Nordson Corporation, Westlake, OH; *U.S. Public*, pg. 1188
Pellegrino, Louis, Controller & Sec.--Northway Motorcar Corporation, Latham, NY; *U.S. Private*, pg. 806
Pelletier, Robert, Controller--Intermetrics, Inc., Burlington, MA; *U.S. Private*, pg. 567
Pelton, Teresa, Asst. Controller--PAXAR Corporation, White Plains, NY; *U.S. Public*, pg. 1266
Peltz, Les, Controller--Allied Mutual Insurance Company, Des Moines, IA; *U.S. Private*, pg. 39
Pembroke, James, Controller--CPAC, Inc., Leicester, NY; *U.S. Public*, pg. 282
Penchas, Henri, Exec. V.P. -Acctg. & Control--Banco Itau S.A., Sao Paulo, Brazil; *Int'l*, pg. 142
Pender, William P., Jr., V.P. & Grp. Controller--Realty One, Cleveland, OH; *U.S. Private*, pg. 914
Pendleton, Janet A., V.P. & Controller--John Hancock Mutual Life Insurance Company, Boston, MA; *U.S. Private*, pg. 589
Penfound, C.S., Controller--Mobil Oil Company, Ltd., Milton Keynes, United Kingdom; *U.S. Public*, pg. 1119
Pennell, Richard W., Asst. Gen. Controller--Borden, Inc., Columbus, OH; *U.S. Private*, pg. 157
Penning, Gerald A., Exec. V.P. & Controller--HSBC Americas, Buffalo, NY; *Int'l*, pg. 580
Pennington, Bev, Controller--Wide-Lite, San Marcos, TX; *U.S. Public*, pg. 730
Pennington, James M., Controller--Central Vermont Public Service Corporation, Rutland, VT; *U.S. Public*, pg. 327
Pennington, W.A., Chief Fin. Officer & Controller--Tech-Tran Corporation, Rancocas, NJ; *U.S. Private*, pg. 560
Penno, D. Bruce, Chief Fin. Officer & Treas.--Pridgeon & Clay, Inc., Grand Rapids, MI; *U.S. Private*, pg. 883
Penny, Pamela J., V.P. & Controller--American General Corporation, Houston, TX; *U.S. Public*, pg. 76
Penrod, Dan, Controller--Lancaster Colony Automotive Group, Dublin, OH; *U.S. Public*, pg. 977
Pensky, Wayne C., Controller & Chief Acctg. Officer--Hexcel Corporation, Pleasanton, CA; *U.S. Public*, pg. 824
Pepin, E. Lyle, Controller & Asst. Sec.--The Cleveland Electric Illuminating Company, Independence, OH; *U.S. Public*, pg. 645
Pepin, E. Lyle, Controller & Asst. Sec.--The Toledo Edison Company, Toledo, OH; *U.S. Public*, pg. 645
Pepski, Kathy O., V.P. & Controller--The Valspar Corporation, Minneapolis, MN; *U.S. Public*, pg. 1707
Perdue, Sharon, Sr. V.P.-Fin.--Tropical Sportswear International, Tampa, FL; *U.S. Private*, pg. 1105
Perez, Jenelle, Controller--MG Products, San Antonio, TX; *U.S. Public*, pg. 1026
Perez, Kimberly A., Asst. Controller-Acctg./Strategic Plng.--Walter Industries, Inc., Tampa, FL; *U.S. Public*, pg. 1736
Perez, Manny, Controller--Braman World Car Center, Miami, FL; *U.S. Private*, pg. 165
Perez, Matt, Controller--Peerless Umbrella Co., Inc., Harrison, NJ; *U.S. Private*, pg. 847
Perez, Sergio, Dir.-Control & Mngmnt.--Andina Division, Los Andes, Chile; *Int'l*, pg. 302
Perkins, Elizabeth, Controller--Chicago Magazine, Chicago, IL; *U.S. Public*, pg. 1328
Perkins, Kyle, Controller-Opers.--All American Bottling Corp., Oklahoma City, OK; *U.S. Private*, pg. 34
Perkins, Mark, Chief Fin. Officer & Controller--Handgards Inc., Northbrook, IL; *U.S. Private*, pg. 499
Perkins, Rich, Controller & Treas.--Foxworth-Galbraith Lumber Co., Dallas, TX; *U.S. Private*, pg. 423
Perkins, Richard, Controller--Rotary Multiforms, Inc., Warren, MI; *U.S. Private*, pg. 947
Perricone, Anthony J., Controller--Accu-Sort Systems, Inc., Telford, PA; *U.S. Private*, pg. 11
Perry, Brian M., Chief Fin. Officer & Treas.--Interface Electronics Corporation, Hopkinton, MA; *U.S. Private*, pg. 567
Perry, Carmen, Chief Fin. Officer, Treas., Controller & Sec.--Outdoor Venture Corp., Stearns, KY; *U.S. Private*, pg. 822
Perry, Jay, Controller, Treas. & Sec.--Steiny & Company, Inc., Baldwin Park, CA; *U.S. Private*, pg. 1039
Perry, Julius, Controller--Johanson Manufacturing Corporation, Boonton, NJ; *U.S. Private*, pg. 589
Perry, Rebecca, Controller--Starmet Corporation, Concord, MA; *U.S. Public*, pg. 1511
Perry, Sheri, Controller--Anchor Tool & Die Company, Cleveland, OH; *U.S. Private*, pg. 71
Persson, Sven-Erik, Exec. V.P. & Head-Group Staff--Cardo AB, Malmo, Sweden; *Int'l*, pg. 268
Perugachi, Helen, Controller--White Rock Products Corp., Whitestone, NY; *U.S. Private*, pg. 1173
Pesesky, P. Scott, V.P. & Controller--Gwaltney of Smithfield, Ltd., Smithfield, VA; *U.S. Public*, pg. 1479
Peter, Horst, Controller--Volkswagen Canada, Inc., Ajax, Canada; *Int'l*, pg. 1475
Peters, B.G., Chief Fin. Officer, V.P.-Fin. & Controller--ICI Americas, Inc., Wilmington, DE; *Int'l*, pg. 663
Peters, Barbara, Controller--Brower Company, Kent, WA; *U.S. Private*, pg. 124
Peters, Graham, Controller--The Lincoln Electric Company, Cleveland, OH; *U.S. Public*, pg. 996
Peters, Joey, Chief Fin. Officer & Controller--Specialty Textile Products, Talladega, AL; *U.S. Private*, pg. 1023
Peters, Phillip H., Comptroller & Treas.--Continental Water Company, Saint Louis, MO; *U.S. Private*, pg. 269
Petersen, Dan, Controller--Data Transmission Network Corporation, Omaha, NE; *U.S. Public*, pg. 486
Peterson, Allen, Asst. Controller--The Minnesota Mutual Life Insurance Company, Saint Paul, MN; *U.S. Private*, pg. 750
Peterson, John G., V.P. & Controller--Dep Corporation, Rancho Dominguez, CA; *U.S. Public*, pg. 500
Peterson, Mark, V.P. & Controller--Applebee's International, Inc., Overland Park, KS; *U.S. Public*, pg. 122
Peterson, Norman, V.P. & Comptroller--Jonathan Manufacturing Corp., Fullerton, CA; *U.S. Private*, pg. 595
Peterson, Ronald R., Controller--The Washington Water Power Company, Spokane, WA; *U.S. Public*, pg. 1744
Peterson, Scott R., V.P. & Controller--Phyxis Corporation, San Diego, CA; *U.S. Public*, pg. 305
Peterson, William, Controller--A.O. Smith/Uppco, Inc., Monticello, IL; *U.S. Public*, pg. 1477
Petescia, Joseph L., Controller--Coltec Holdings Inc, Charlotte, NC; *U.S. Public*, pg. 401
Peteshman, Mike, Asst. Controller--Tupperware Corporation, Orlando, FL; *U.S. Public*, pg. 1644
Petito, Phil, Controller--Chugai Boyeki (America) Corp., Commack, NY; *Int'l*, pg. 290
Petka, Bob, Controller--UETA, Inc., Laredo, TX; *Int'l*, pg. 103
Petrangelo, Julie, Controller--John Roberts Company, Minneapolis, MN; *U.S. Private*, pg. 935
Petrie, Patrick D., V.P. & Corp. Controller--H & R Block, Inc., Kansas City, MO; *U.S. Public*, pg. 770
Petrizzo, John, Controller--Tetley USA Inc., Shelton, CT; *Int'l*, pg. 1377
Petroski, Leigh, Mgr.-Acctg.--The Genlyte Group Incorporated, Union, NJ; *U.S. Public*, pg. 729
Petrovich, Dushan, V.P. & Controller--Wm. Wrigley Jr. Company, Chicago, IL; *U.S. Public*, pg. 1781
Petrucelli, M.S., V.P. & Controller--General Electric Investment Corp., Stamford, CT; *U.S. Public*, pg. 712
Petry, Michael, Controller--Peace River Electric Cooperative, Inc., Wauchula, FL; *U.S. Private*, pg. 845
Petsch, Manfred, Controller--The Braas Group, Oberursell, Germany; *Int'l*, pg. 1091
Petterson, David S., Sr. V.P. & Corp. Controller--Costco Wholesale, Issaquah, WA; *U.S. Public*, pg. 451
Petty, Warren, Controller--W.M. Barr & Co., Inc., Memphis, TN; *U.S. Private*, pg. 117
Peyton, Patrick H., V.P., Controller & Asst. Sec.--Pioneer Plastics Corporation, Auburn, ME; *U.S. Private*, pg. 867
Pezzatti, Arnold, Controller--Von Roll AG, Gerlafingen, Switzerland; *Int'l*, pg. 1480
Pfaff, Jeany, Controller--Right Start, Inc., Westlake Village, CA; *U.S. Private*, pg. 930
Pfeiffenberger, Tom, Controller--Reading Body Works, Inc., Reading, PA; *U.S. Private*, pg. 913
Pfeiffer, Doug, Controller--Mercer Transportation Co., Louisville, KY; *U.S. Private*, pg. 732
Pfisterer, Vera B., Controller--CBC-U.S.A Inc., Chicago, IL; *U.S. Public*, pg. 337
Pflaster, Tina, V.P. & Sec.--Arnold Steel Company, Inc., Lakewood, NJ; *U.S. Private*, pg. 84
Pflum, Nancy S., V.P.-Fin. & Controller--Waldom Electronics, Inc., Chicago, IL; *U.S. Public*, pg. 944
Phagans, T.M., Treas. & Sec.--Addison Steel Inc., Albany, GA; *U.S. Private*, pg. 17
Phair, W. Gordon, Controller--Dakota Mining Corporation, Denver, CO; *U.S. Public*, pg. 477
Phalon, Ted, Controller--McCourt Label Co., Lewis Run, PA; *U.S. Private*, pg. 720
Pharand, S., Comptroller--Canadian National Railway Company, Montreal, Canada; *Int'l*, pg. 258
Phelan, James, V.P.-Fin. & Controller--The H.W. Wilson Co., Bronx, NY; *U.S. Private*, pg. 1180
Phelps, Charles B., V.P. & Controller--Phelps Dodge Intl. Corp., Coral Gables, FL; *U.S. Public*, pg. 1286
Phelps, W. Bruce, Sr. V.P. & Controller--NationsBank West, Saint Louis, MO; *U.S. Public*, pg. 1164
Philips, Ronald, Controller--Key Food Stores Co-operative, Inc., Brooklyn, NY; *U.S. Private*, pg. 617
Philley, Pam, Controller--Allied Carbi-Tech, Inc., Topeka, IN; *U.S. Private*, pg. 38
Phillips, Anita, V.P. & Controller--Carlson Wagonlit Travel, Minneapolis, MN; *U.S. Private*, pg. 212
Phillips, David, Controller--South Fresh Farms, Indianola, MS; *U.S. Private*, pg. 1014
Phillips, Greg, Mgr.-Int. Bus. Cont.--MTM Enterprises, Inc., Studio City, CA; *Int'l*, pg. 927
Phillips, Jacqueline R., Corp. Controller--Channellock, Inc., Meadville, PA; *U.S. Private*, pg. 229
Phillips, Jean, Asst. Controller--Musicland Group Inc., Minnetonka, MN; *U.S. Public*, pg. 1142
Phillips, Keith, Controller--Jim Lupient Enterprises, Golden Valley, MN; *U.S. Private*, pg. 681

Phillips, Keith, Controller--Lupient Automotive Group, Minneapolis, MN; *U.S. Private*, pg. 681
Phillips, M. A., Sr. V.P. & Controller--Brown Marketing Communications, Chicago, IL; *U.S. Private*, pg. 174
Phillips, Mike, Controller--Thomas Built Buses, Inc., High Point, NC; *U.S. Private*, pg. 1082
Phillips, Richard T., Controller & Treas.--Canyon Resources Corporation, Golden, CO; *U.S. Public*, pg. 301
Phillips, Ron, Comptroller--Georgia Duck & Cordage Mills, Scottdale, GA; *U.S. Private*, pg. 448
Phillips, Sam, Controller--T.D. Williamson, Inc., Tulsa, OK; *U.S. Private*, pg. 1179
Philpot, David, Controller--Shepherd Construction Co., Inc., Atlanta, GA; *U.S. Private*, pg. 993
Phimister, Mark, Fin. Controller--Instron Schenck Testing Systems Limited, High Wycombe, United Kingdom; *U.S. Public*, pg. 883
Piacenti, Richard W., V.P. & Controller--Cornerstone Natural Gas, Inc., Dallas, TX; *U.S. Public*, pg. 567
Pica, Joseph M., Controller--Rynone Manufacturing Corporation, Sayre, PA; *U.S. Private*, pg. 953
Picard, Raymond H., Asst. Controller-Taxes--Kaman Corporation, Bloomfield, CT; *U.S. Public*, pg. 941
Picco, W. Michael, Controller--Computer Systems Research, Inc., Avon, CT; *U.S. Public*, pg. 1070
Pick, Philip, Controller--Arrow Pneumatics Co. Inc., Lake Zurich, IL; *U.S. Private*, pg. 85
Picket, Tony, Controller--Kettle Restaurants, Houston, TX; *U.S. Private*, pg. 617
Pickle, Scott, Controller & Treas.--Cavalier Insurance Agency, Inc., Hamilton, AL; *U.S. Public*, pg. 318
Pickus, Russ, Controller--Airline Hydraulics Corporation, Bensalem, PA; *U.S. Private*, pg. 29
Pico, Alberto, Controller--InterAmerican Development Bank, Washington, DC; *U.S. Private*, pg. 566
Pidlipchak, John, Controller--Star Gas Corporation, Stamford, CT; *U.S. Public*, pg. 1281
Piebenga, John, Controller--Harris-Kayot, Inc., Fort Wayne, IN; *U.S. Private*, pg. 506
Piecuch, Steve, V.P. & Controller--Newberg Perini, Chicago, IL; *U.S. Public*, pg. 1278
Piecuch, Tom, Controller--List Industries, Inc., Deerfield Beach, FL; *U.S. Private*, pg. 669
Piekarski, David, Controller--Plasticrete Block & Supply Corp., North Haven, CT; *U.S. Private*, pg. 871
Pierrelle, Bernard, Controller--Rhone-Poulenc S.A., Courbevoie, France; *Int'l*, pg. 1108
Pietrzak, Michael, V.P., Controller & Treas.--IDS Trust Co., Minneapolis, MN; *U.S. Public*, pg. 73
Pietrzak, Michael, V.P. & Controller--IDS Deposit Corp., Midvale, UT; *U.S. Public*, pg. 73
Pihl, Larry D., Chief Fin. Officer, V.P.-Fin., Treas. & Controller--UTILX Corporation, Kent, WA; *U.S. Public*, pg. 1701
Pikosky, Kathryn S., Controller--EAO Switch Corporation, Milford, CT; *Int'l*, pg. 444
Pilch, Samuel, V.P. & Controller--The Allstate Corporation, Northbrook, IL; *U.S. Public*, pg. 55
Pilkington, John, Controller--Harding Lawson Associates Group, Inc., Novato, CA; *U.S. Public*, pg. 785
Piller, Wolfgang, Fin. Controller--Daimler-Benz Aerospace AG, Munich, Germany; *Int'l*, pg. 367
Pimsner, Richard, V.P. & Controller--Southwestern Life Insurance Company, Dallas, TX; *U.S. Private*, pg. 1018
Pine, Barry, Controller--Today's Man, Inc., Moorestown, NJ; *U.S. Public*, pg. 1619
Pineda, Tony, Asst. Controller--TMP Worldwide/Recruitment Division, Santa Clara, CA; *U.S. Private*, pg. 1065
Pinedo, Rubin, Controller--Aero Peru Corporation, Coral Gables, FL; *U.S. Private*, pg. 24
Pinkerton, Jerry W., Chief Acctg. Officer, V.P. & Controller--ENSERCH Corporation, Dallas, TX; *U.S. Public*, pg. 1587
Pinkerton, Stan, Asst. V.P. & Controller--Louisiana Downs, Bossier City, LA; *U.S. Private*, pg. 319
Pinos, George, Controller--RI Holdings, Grand Rapids, MI; *U.S. Private*, pg. 904
Pinson, Kathleen S., V.P. & Controller--Pre-Paid Legal Services, Inc., Ada, OK; *U.S. Public*, pg. 1320
Pinto, David, Controller--Irvine Sensors Corporation, Costa Mesa, CA; *U.S. Public*, pg. 913
Pinto, William L., Controller--Cedar Farms Company, Inc., Philadelphia, PA; *U.S. Private*, pg. 221
Piorkowski, Ted, Controller & Asst. Sec.--Crowley, Milner & Company, Detroit, MI; *U.S. Public*, pg. 461
Piorkowski, Ted, Controller--Steinbach Stores, Inc., Detroit, MI; *U.S. Public*, pg. 461
Piper, Jay, Controller--M.D.C. Holdings, Inc., Denver, CO; *U.S. Public*, pg. 1025
Piper, Steve, Controller--Schlumberger Malco Inc., Owings Mills, MD; *Int'l*, pg. 1206
Pipitone, Andrew, Controller--Solar Communications, Inc., Naperville, IL; *U.S. Private*, pg. 1012
Pippen, David, Controller--Air UK Ltd., Stansted, United Kingdom; *Int'l*, pg. 38
Piquard, Vale'rie, Controller-Sofamor, S.N.C.--Sofamor Danek Group, Inc., Memphis, TN; *U.S. Public*, pg. 1482
Pirtle, Ronald M., Comptroller--AC Rochester Overseas Corporation, Southampton, United Kingdom; *U.S. Public*, pg. 722
Pirtle, Ronald M., Comptroller--AC Rochester Overseas Corporation, Detroit, MI; *U.S. Public*, pg. 722
Pitalis, Al, Controller--The W.B. Wood Company, New Providence, NJ; *U.S. Private*, pg. 1186
Pitsellos, Nick, Controller--Autocon Technologies, Inc., Farmington, MI; *U.S. Public*, pg. 850
Pittman, Joe, Controller-Opers.--Jami, Inc., Shawnee Mission, KS; *U.S. Private*, pg. 581
Pitts, Wendy, Controller--Marta Cooperative of America Inc., Scottsdale, AZ; *U.S. Private*, pg. 708
Pizor, Lynne, Controller--Prime Operating Company, Houston, TX; *U.S. Public*, pg. 1329
Pizza, Peter M., Controller--AMREP Corporation, New York, NY; *U.S. Public*, pg. 104
Pizzo, Ronald A., Controller--Cambrex Corporation, East Rutherford, NJ; *U.S. Public*, pg. 297
Place, Brian F., Controller & Asst. Treas.--Todays Temporary, Inc., Dallas, TX; *U.S. Public*, pg. 277
Plahn, Kim, V.P.-Fin.--Damark International, Inc., Minneapolis, MN; *U.S. Public*, pg. 478
Plant, Randy, Controller--Huntsman Corporation, Salt Lake City, UT; *U.S. Private*, pg. 549
Plaskey, Wade, Controller--Federal Screw Works, Detroit, MI; *U.S. Public*, pg. 616
Plate, L.E., Controller--Steiner Co., Inc., Chicago, IL; *U.S. Private*, pg. 1039
Platt, Dan, Controller--California Cedar Products, Inc., Stockton, CA; *U.S. Private*, pg. 200
Platt, Rosemary, Controller--Morris Merchants, Inc., Canton, MA; *U.S. Public*, pg. 1706
Pleasants, Jeff, Controller & Treas.--Pressure Systems, Inc., Hampton, VA; *Int'l*, pg. 1130
Pless, Rodney, Controller--Transmontaigne, Fayetteville, AR; *U.S. Public*, pg. 1631
Pless, Rodney S., Chief Acctg. Officer, V.P. & Controller--TransMontaigne Oil Company, Denver, CO; *U.S. Public*, pg. 1631
Pletcher, Dante, Controller--T & N Industries, Inc., Ann Arbor, MI; *Int'l*, pg. 1334
Pletcher, Jim, Controller--Lee Pharmaceuticals, South El Monte, CA; *U.S. Public*, pg. 984
Plewaki, Jim, Controller--The Bergquist Company, Minneapolis, MN; *U.S. Private*, pg. 135
Plizga, Wayne, V.P.-Fin.--Energy & Environmental Research Corp., Irvine, CA; *U.S. Private*, pg. 376
Plourde, Robert J., V.P. & Controller--GTECH Corporation, West Greenwich, RI; *U.S. Public*, pg. 767
Plumly, Harlen, V.P., Controller & Treas.--Marcam Solutions, Inc., Newton, MA; *U.S. Public*, pg. 1042
Plunkett, Mike, Controller--Hajoca Corp., Ardmore, PA; *U.S. Private*, pg. 494
Plunkett, Stephen J., Controller--Ipalco Enterprises, Inc., Indianapolis, IN; *U.S. Public*, pg. 912
Plunkett, Stephen J., Controller--Indianapolis Power & Light Company, Indianapolis, IN; *U.S. Public*, pg. 913
Plush, Mark J., Controller & Asst. Sec.--Keithley Instruments, Inc., Cleveland, OH; *U.S. Public*, pg. 946
Pluth, Peter J., Controller--Mattel Games/Puzzles, El Segundo, CA; *U.S. Public*, pg. 1058
Ply, Michael, Controller--Booth Newspapers, Inc., Grand Rapids, MI; *U.S. Private*, pg. 157
Poag, Neil W., V.P., Controller & Sec.--Waterloo Furniture Components Limited, Kitchener, Canada; *U.S. Private*, pg. 270
Podber, Gilda, Controller & Treas.--Lone Star Equities Inc., Lynbrook, NY; *U.S. Private*, pg. 674
Podnar, Mike, Controller--Asko, Inc, Homestead, PA; *U.S. Private*, pg. 89
Podojil, James A., Controller & Treas.--A.M. Castle & Co., Franklin Park, IL; *U.S. Public*, pg. 312
Poe, Robert, Controller--Grindmaster Corporation, Louisville, KY; *U.S. Private*, pg. 482
Poelking, John, Controller--WGN-TV, Chicago, IL; *U.S. Public*, pg. 1636
Pofahl, Jim, Controller--Nasco Modesto, Modesto, CA; *U.S. Private*, pg. 446
Poggensee, Thomas, Controller & Treas.--Florsheim Group Inc., Chicago, IL; *U.S. Public*, pg. 656
Pogliaghi, Lino, Controller & Mgr.-Budget Dept.--Cassa di Risparmio delle Provincie Lombarde SpA (CARIPLO), Milan, Italy; *Int'l*, pg. 274
Pohl, Walter F., Jr., Controller--Gold Kist, Inc., Atlanta, GA; *U.S. Private*, pg. 459
Pohlman, Steve, V.P., Controller & Treas.--Huffy Service First, Inc., Miamisburg, OH; *U.S. Public*, pg. 846
Pointon, A.D., Controller--Mead Coated Board U.K. Limited, Rickmansworth, United Kingdom; *U.S. Public*, pg. 1076
Poisson, Daniel, Controller--CFCF Inc., Montreal, Canada; *Int'l*, pg. 240
Pokrajac, William R., Controller--John B. Sanfilippo & Son, Inc., Elk Grove Village, IL; *U.S. Public*, pg. 1431
Polak, Dennis, Controller & Treas.--Gilmore Envelope Corp., Los Angeles, CA; *U.S. Private*, pg. 454
Pole, Bruce, Controller--Nucor Steel-Utah, Plymouth, UT; *U.S. Public*, pg. 1205
Polisar, Janie, Controller--Mesa Air Group, Las Vegas, NV; *U.S. Public*, pg. 1098
Polizzatto, Phil, Controller--A S H, Inc., Phoenix, AZ; *U.S. Private*, pg. 2
Polk, Angie, Controller--Gene Reed Chevrolet, Charleston, SC; *U.S. Private*, pg. 1095
Pollard, Carla, V.P. & Controller--Republic Security Financial Corporation, West Palm Beach, FL; *U.S. Public*, pg. 1381
Pollard, Courtney, Controller--H.J. Russell & Co., Atlanta, GA; *U.S. Private*, pg. 952
Pollock, Maurice, V.P., Controller, Treas. & Sec.--Collin Street Bakery, Corsicana, TX; *U.S. Private*, pg. 252
Polounovsky, G., Controller--Exxon Chemical Polymeres, SNC, Paris, France; *U.S. Public*, pg. 602
Polsky, Martin, Controller--D. Waldner Company, Inc., Farmingdale, NY; *U.S. Private*, pg. 1147
Pomeroy, Amy, Controller--Wyatt Energy Incorporated, New Haven, CT; *U.S. Private*, pg. 1193
Pomilio, Luke, Controller--Conmed Corporation, Utica, NY; *U.S. Public*, pg. 431
Pompa, Mark A., V.P. & Controller--EMCOR Group, Inc., Norwalk, CT; *U.S. Public*, pg. 571
Pompeo, Mario, Controller--Banfi Product Corp, Old Brookville, NY; *U.S. Private*, pg. 113
Pond, Phillip, Controller--Heatcraft, Inc.-Refrigeration Products Division, Stone Mountain, GA; *U.S. Private*, pg. 659
Poniatowski, Bruce H., V.P. & Controller--Raritan Bancorp Inc., Bridgewater, NJ; *U.S. Public*, pg. 1361
Pontier, Roland, Controller & Deputy Mng. Dir.--MacGREGOR (FRA) S.A., Marseilles, France; *Int'l*, pg. 670
Ponzetti, Bill, Chief Fin. Officer, Controller & Treas.--Active Electrical Supply Company, Chicago, IL; *U.S. Private*, pg. 15
Ponzio, Peter J., V.P.-Fin., Controller & Asst. Treas.--Day-Timers, Inc., East Texas, PA; *U.S. Public*, pg. 674
Poole, Hampton R., Jr., V.P. & Controller--Standard Commercial Corporation, Wilson, NC; *U.S. Public*, pg. 1501
Poole, Kevin L., Grp. Taxation Controller--Dalgety Plc, London, United Kingdom; *Int'l*, pg. 376
Pooler, John E., Jr., Controller--Pepper, Hamilton & Scheetz, Philadelphia, PA; *U.S. Private*, pg. 851
Popa, John M., Controller--Republic Powdered Metals, Inc., Medina, OH; *U.S. Public*, pg. 1357
Pope, Andy, Controller--Horizon Distribution Inc., Summerville, SC; *U.S. Private*, pg. 539
Pope, Brian, Controller--Royal Oak Enterprises, Inc., Atlanta, GA; *U.S. Private*, pg. 948
Pope, C. Larry, V.P. & Controller--Smithfield Foods, Inc., Norfolk, VA; *U.S. Public*, pg. 1479
Pope, Paula, Controller--Blue Ridge Electric Membership Corp., Lenoir, NC; *U.S. Private*, pg. 153
Popelars, Frank J., Staff V.P. & Controller--Sonoco Products Company, Hartsville, SC; *U.S. Public*, pg. 1485
Popicg, Pat, Controller--Scott Lumber Company, Bridgeport, OH; *U.S. Private*, pg. 977
Popp, Betty, Controller & Sec.--Red Wing Products, Inc., Plainview, NY; *Int'l*, pg. 480
Porcelli, James A., V.P. & Corp. Controller--Conair Corporation, Stamford, CT; *U.S. Private*, pg. 261
Porcello, Joe, Controller--Anaren Microwave Inc., East Syracuse, NY; *U.S. Public*, pg. 110
Pordon, Robert, Controller--Bobst Group Inc., Roseland, NJ; *Int'l*, pg. 198
Porper, Catherine, Controller--Italia/Gal Advertising, Los Angeles, CA; *U.S. Private*, pg. 576
Porper, Mary, Controller--Suissa Miller Advertising, Inc., Los Angeles, CA; *U.S. Private*, pg. 1049
Porpora, Peter, V.P. & Controller--Briggs Industries, Inc., Tampa, FL; *U.S. Private*, pg. 168
Port, Joseph, V.P.-Fin. & Controller--Kaydon Corporation, Clearwater, FL; *U.S. Public*, pg. 945
Porte, Patrick, Mgr.-Credit--Advance Steel Co., Detroit, MI; *U.S. Private*, pg. 21
Porter, Chuck, Controller--Robert E. Bayley Construction, Seattle, WA; *U.S. Private*, pg. 125
Porter, J.C., V.P. & Comptroller--Lafarge Canada Inc., Montreal, Canada; *Int'l*, pg. 789
Porter, Jeffrey P., Controller--Dreyer's Grand Ice Cream, Inc., Oakland, CA; *U.S. Public*, pg. 529
Porter, John C., V.P. & Controller--Lafarge Corporation, Reston, VA; *Int'l*, pg. 788
Porter, June, Controller--Brown Evans Distributing Co., Mesa, AZ; *U.S. Private*, pg. 174
Porter, Mike, Controller--Eller Media Company, Phoenix, AZ; *U.S. Public*, pg. 383
Porter, Robert C., V.P., Treas., Sec. & Asst. Controller--CIPSCO Investment Company, Springfield, IL; *U.S. Public*, pg. 66
Porter, William, V.P., Corp. Controller & Asst. Sec.--Cadence Design Systems, Inc., San Jose, CA; *U.S. Public*, pg. 290
Portwood, Richard M., V.P.-Controller--Texas, New Mexico & Oklahoma Coaches, Inc., Lubbock, TX; *U.S. Public*, pg. 766
Posluszny, Carl, V.P. & Controller--Chem-Trend Incorporated, Howell, MI; *Int'l*, pg. 235
Posner, Barbara L., V.P.-Fin. & Admin.--EA Engineering, Science & Technology, Inc., Hunt Valley, MD; *U.S. Public*, pg. 540
Posner, Gary, Controller--Darigold, Inc., Seattle, WA; *U.S. Private*, pg. 311
Poston, David J., Controller--Todd Pacific Shipyards Corp., Seattle, WA; *U.S. Public*, pg. 1619
Potapchuk, John, V.P.-Opers. & Controller--Olsten Health Services, Melville, NY; *U.S. Public*, pg. 1221
Potas, Albert T., V.P. & Controller--Old Kent Financial Corporation, Grand Rapids, MI; *U.S. Public*, pg. 1216
Poteraj, Robert S., Controller--Boyle Engineering Corp., Newport Beach, CA; *U.S. Private*, pg. 163
Potka, Vel-Jussi, V.P. & Controller--Enso Oyj, Helsinki, Finland; *Int'l*, pg. 455
Potter, Jim, Controller--Rice Food Markets Inc., Houston, TX; *U.S. Private*, pg. 927
Potter, John, Controller & Sec.--Amlings Flowerland, Hinsdale, IL; *U.S. Private*, pg. 66
Potter, Steve, Controller--Transico Incorporated, Santa Ana, CA; *U.S. Public*, pg. 1630
Potts, Terry, Controller--Binning's Building Products, Inc., Lexington, NC; *U.S. Public*, pg. 67
Poulatian, Alek, Controller--Carpeteria, Inc., Valencia, CA; *U.S. Private*, pg. 215
Poulin, Bern, Div. Controller--Boise Cascade Paper Div., Boise, ID; *U.S. Public*, pg. 243
Poulson, Keith, Controller--EROL'S Internet, Springfield, VA; *U.S. Private*, pg. 382
Pourdieu, J., V.P.-Audits & Control--SNCF, Paris, France; *Int'l*, pg. 1163
Powell, Brad, V.P. & Controller--Omega Environmental Inc., Bothell, WA; *U.S. Public*, pg. 1221
Powell, Frances R., V.P.-Acctg. & Controller--EVI, Inc., Houston, TX; *U.S. Public*, pg. 547
Powell, Larry, Asst. Controller--Revco Scientific, Asheville, NC; *U.S. Public*, pg. 727
Powell, R. Gwynne, Controller--Lustine Oldsmobile & Buick, Inc., Hyattsville, MD; *U.S. Private*, pg. 681
Powell, Rhonda, V.P. & Controller--NTH Consultants, Ltd., Farmington, MI; *U.S. Private*, pg. 772
Powell, Stephen M., Controller--Chattem, Inc., Chattanooga, TN; *U.S. Public*, pg. 341
Powell, Stephen M., Controller--Chattem, Inc., Consumer Products Division, Chattanooga, TN; *U.S. Public*, pg. 341
Powers, Jeffrey L., V.P. & Controller--Battle Mountain Gold Company, Houston, TX; *U.S. Public*, pg. 193

Powers, Kevin, Corp. Controller--Cherry Electrical Products Corporation, Waukegan, IL; *U.S. Public*, pg. 346
Prather, Larry K., Controller--Radiator Specialty Company, Charlotte, NC; *U.S. Private*, pg. 906
Pratt, Hazel, Controller--Bradford Oil Company, Inc., Bradford, VT; *U.S. Private*, pg. 164
Pratten, Robert A., Chief Fin. Officer--Regency Associates Limited Partnership, Champaign, IL; *U.S. Private*, pg. 918
Prechtl, Victor L., V.P. & Controller--Fluor Corporation, Irvine, CA; *U.S. Public*, pg. 659
Preis, P.H., V.P. & Controller--Jersey Central Power & Light Co., Morristown, NJ; *U.S. Public*, pg. 695
Prekop, Lon, Controller--Lake Shore, Inc., Kingsford, MI; *U.S. Private*, pg. 814
Premo, Anita, Controller--Action Manufacturing Co., Philadelphia, PA; *U.S. Private*, pg. 15
Prendergast, Vincent J., Controller--Prime Medical Services, Inc., Austin, TX; *U.S. Public*, pg. 1327
Prescott, Steve, Controller--Idaho Supreme Company, Firth, ID; *U.S. Private*, pg. 557
Presley, Charles R., Controller--Thomaston Mills, Inc., Thomaston, GA; *U.S. Public*, pg. 1599
Presseisen, J.M., Controller--Esso N.V./S.A., Maasmechelen, Belgium; *U.S. Public*, pg. 602
Pressler, Susan, Controller--InteCom, Dallas, TX; *Int'l*, pg. 794
Prestopino, Frank J., Comptroller--Royal Insurance, Charlotte, NC; *Int'l*, pg. 1130
Prestosa, Patrick, Controller--Industrial Wire Products Corporation, Pomona, CA; *U.S. Private*, pg. 561
Previti, F.J., Controller--TTX Co., Chicago, IL; *U.S. Private*, pg. 1066
Pribanic, Gerald, V.P. & Controller--Hoover Company, Canton, OH; *U.S. Public*, pg. 1065
Price, Alf, Controller--Sandwell Inc., Vancouver, Canada; *Int'l*, pg. 1188
Price, Earl W., V.P. & Controller--SNC-Lavalin Inc., Montreal, Canada; *Int'l*, pg. 1162
Price, Gary L., Comptroller & Treas.--Ben Venue Laboratories, Inc., Bedford, OH; *U.S. Private*, pg. 1136
Price, Kerry, V.P. & Controller--Crowder Construction Co., Charlotte, NC; *U.S. Private*, pg. 291
Price, M., Controller--Australian National Industries Limited, Pyrmont, Australia; *Int'l*, pg. 100
Price, Marilyn, V.P. & Controller--Frontier Communications Services, Bingham Farms, MI; *U.S. Public*, pg. 684
Price, Robert J., Controller--Aetna Inc., Hartford, CT; *U.S. Public*, pg. 26
Price, Tim, V.P. & Controller--Kohl's Corporation, Menomonee Falls, WI; *U.S. Public*, pg. 965
Price, Tom, Controller--Villeroy & Boch Tableware, Ltd., Princeton, NJ; *Int'l*, pg. 1468
Prickel, Mary Beth, Controller--Tri-Manufacturing, Terre Haute, IN; *U.S. Public*, pg. 710
Pries, Sue, Controller--Guth Lighting Company, Saint Louis, MO; *Int'l*, pg. 821
Prigg, Blair, Controller--Service Supply Co. Inc. of Indiana, Indianapolis, IN; *U.S. Private*, pg. 987
Primat, Pierre, Controller--Keller-Dorian Graveurs, Div. of Roehlen Industries/Europe, Lyon, France; *U.S. Public*, pg. 1507
Primera, Irene, V.P. & Controller--La Quinta Inns, Inc., San Antonio, TX; *U.S. Public*, pg. 972
Primerano, Richard, V.P. & Controller--Chartwell Re Corporation, Stamford, CT; *U.S. Public*, pg. 336
Prindle, Cheryl, Controller--Restonic Mattress Corporation, Rosemont, IL; *U.S. Private*, pg. 925
Priore, A., Controller--Dassault Falcon Jet Corp., South Hackensack, NJ; *Int'l*, pg. 383
Prisco, Carol, Controller--Safeguard Business Systems, Inc., Fort Washington, PA; *U.S. Private*, pg. 960
Priske, Alan J., Controller--Jewelers Mutual Insurance Company, Neenah, WI; *U.S. Private*, pg. 587
Privette, Herbert, Controller--Lowe's Food Stores, Inc., Winston Salem, NC; *U.S. Private*, pg. 657
Probus, Lawrence K., V.P. & Controller--Brown-Forman Corporation, Louisville, KY; *U.S. Public*, pg. 261
Procik, John, Controller--Sheffield Steel Corporation-Joliet, Joliet, IL; *U.S. Private*, pg. 991
Proctor, Bonnie, Controller--Diamond Forecast, Elgin, IL; *U.S. Public*, pg. 730
Proksch, Fritz, Controller--Osterreichischen Bundesbahnen GmbH, Vienna, Austria; *Int'l*, pg. 1012
Promm, Robert, V.P. & Controller--Apple Computer, Inc., Cupertino, CA; *U.S. Public*, pg. 121
Prosak, Al, Controller--Discount Drug Mart Inc., Medina, OH; *U.S. Private*, pg. 334
Proud, C.F., Controller--ICI Paints, Cleveland, OH; *Int'l*, pg. 663
Proud, C.F., Controller--Sinclair/Ameritone Paint Corp., Los Angeles, CA; *Int'l*, pg. 663
Proulx, R., Controller--Agropur, Granby, Canada; *Int'l*, pg. 31
Provino, Francis, Controller--Paychex, Inc., Rochester, NY; *U.S. Public*, pg. 1267
Provost, David, Controller--Delicato Vineyards, Manteca, CA; *U.S. Private*, pg. 322
Pruim, Elmer G., Controller--Bairnco Corporation, Maitland, FL; *U.S. Public*, pg. 165
Prulidon, Kristein, Controller--Pace International L.P., Kirkland, WA; *U.S. Private*, pg. 829
Prunier, Dominique, Controller--Compagnie Generale Maritime et Financiere, Suresnes, France; *Int'l*, pg. 322
Pruss, Michael A., Controller--Falcon Products, Inc., Saint Louis, MO; *U.S. Public*, pg. 611
Prybylski, Lawrence, Controller--Star Children's Dress Company, Inc., New York, NY; *U.S. Private*, pg. 1034
Przystes, Richard, Controller--Spiegel Meats, Inc., Miami, FL; *U.S. Private*, pg. 1025
Przystes, Richard, Controller--RealCold Storage, Miami, FL; *U.S. Private*, pg. 1025
Puckett, Rick, Corp. Controller--American Business Information, Inc., Omaha, NE; *U.S. Public*, pg. 69
Pucky, Timothy, Controller--Luntz Corporation, Canton, OH; *U.S. Private*, pg. 681
Pugh, Irene G., Controller--Datametrics Corporation, Calabasas, CA; *U.S. Public*, pg. 487
Pugh, James, Controller--McCrometer Inc., Hemet, CA; *U.S. Public*, pg. 482
Pulgar, Teo, Controller--Barouh Eaton Allen Corporation, Brooklyn, NY; *U.S. Private*, pg. 117
Pulgar, Teo, Controller & Mgr.-Credit--Ko-Rec-Type, Brooklyn, NY; *U.S. Private*, pg. 117
Puliam, Joe, Controller--AGCO Inc., Norcross, GA; *U.S. Private*, pg. 26
Pulido, Cecilia, Controller--Precisionaire, Inc., Saint Petersburg, FL; *U.S. Public*, pg. 648
Pullen, Timothy L., V.P. & Controller--Tenet Healthcare Corporation, Santa Barbara, CA; *U.S. Public*, pg. 1576
Puma, Joseph, Controller--Halm Industries Company, Incorporated, Glen Head, NY; *U.S. Private*, pg. 496
Punch, John, Controller--Birmingham AL Steel Division, Birmingham, AL; *U.S. Public*, pg. 232
Punturiero, Cathy, Asst. Controller--JJI Lighting Group Inc., Greenwich, CT; *Int'l*, pg. 821
Purdy, Thomas G., V.P. & Reg. Controller--FirstMerit Corporation, Akron, OH; *U.S. Public*, pg. 646
Purett, Joe, Controller & Treas.--Schlotzsky's, Inc., Austin, TX; *U.S. Public*, pg. 1439
Pye, James P., Controller--Arch Coal, Inc., Saint Louis, MO; *U.S. Public*, pg. 139
Pysnack, John W., Controller--Gleason Corporation, Rochester, NY; *U.S. Public*, pg. 746
Qu, Jun Yi, Controller--John Crane Tianjin Ltd., Tianjin, China; *Int'l*, pg. 1339
Qualls, Laurie, Controller--Family Bargain Corporation, San Diego, CA; *U.S. Public*, pg. 612
Quan, Darryl T., Controller--Watkins-Johnson Company, Palo Alto, CA; *U.S. Public*, pg. 1745
Queen, Andy, Controller--Fitzgerald & Co., Atlanta, GA; *U.S. Private*, pg. 409
Query, Rex, Controller--Vulcraft Div., Florence, SC; *U.S. Public*, pg. 1206
Quievryn, Lou, Controller--Duff-Norton, Charlotte, NC; *U.S. Public*, pg. 406
Quigley, Sharon A., Controller--IRT Property Company, Atlanta, GA; *U.S. Public*, pg. 858
Quigley, Susan, Dir.-Fin.--Toronto Blue Jays Baseball Club, Inc., Toronto, Canada; *Int'l*, pg. 680
Quinlan, James E., Controller--LCS Industries, Inc., Clifton, NJ; *U.S. Public*, pg. 970
Quinlivan, Mick, Controller--Itron Inc., Spokane, WA; *U.S. Public*, pg. 914
Quinn, Cathy, Comptroller--Carefree of Colorado, Broomfield, CO; *U.S. Public*, pg. 217
Quinn, Colleen, Controller--Grybauskas Beatrice, New York, NY; *U.S. Private*, pg. 485
Quinn, John, V.P. & Controller--Waste Management International plc, London, United Kingdom; *U.S. Public*, pg. 1745
Rabe, Debbie, Controller--Wasserstrom Company, Columbus, OH; *U.S. Private*, pg. 1152
Rabinoff, Robert J., Sr. V.P. & Controller--Quick & Reilly, Inc., New York, NY; *U.S. Public*, pg. 650
Racavich, Carl, Controller--California Panel & Veneer Company, Cerritos, CA; *U.S. Private*, pg. 201
Racek, Mary, Controller--Miller Resources International, Inc., North Brunswick, NJ; *U.S. Private*, pg. 748
Rackley, James, Controller--Justrite Manufacturing Company, Des Plaines, IL; *U.S. Public*, pg. 617
Rackowski, Thomas, V.P. & Controller--The IDI Group Companies, Arlington, VA; *U.S. Private*, pg. 554
Rada, John B., Treas. & Controller--Firemen's Insurance Company of Washington, D.C., Bethesda, MD; *U.S. Public*, pg. 215
Radack, John, V.P.-Controller--Bird Products Corporation, Palm Springs, CA; *U.S. Public*, pg. 1591
Radak, John M., V.P. & Controller--Sunrise Medical, Inc., Carlsbad, CA; *U.S. Public*, pg. 1535
Radatovich, Steve, V.P., Controller & Sec.--Vectura Group, Inc., New Orleans, LA; *U.S. Private*, pg. 1135
Rado, Patricia A., V.P. & Controller--Public Service Electric & Gas Co., Newark, NJ; *U.S. Public*, pg. 1340
Radtke, Eldon, Controller--Maze Nails, Peru, IL; *U.S. Private*, pg. 718
Radtke, Phil, Controller--Akzo Nobel Inc., Chicago, IL; *Int'l*, pg. 47
Radusch, L., Controller--Richard Hirschmann GmbH & Co., Neckartenzlingen, Germany; *Int'l*, pg. 1108
Radusch, Stephen K., Controller--Players International, Inc., Atlantic City, NJ; *U.S. Public*, pg. 1310
Raer, Susan, Asst. Controller--The Union Corporation, Greenwich, CT; *U.S. Public*, pg. 1667
Raffia, M.J., V.P.-Fin.--Kane-Miller Corp., Tarrytown, NY; *U.S. Private*, pg. 607
Ragazzo, Richard, V.P. & Controller--Xerox Canada Ltd., North York, Canada; *U.S. Public*, pg. 1785
Rager, Dennis, Controller--Snyder's of Hanover, Inc., Hanover, PA; *U.S. Private*, pg. 1011
Rahe, Ronald F., Controller--Baldwin Technology Company, Inc., Norwalk, CT; *U.S. Public*, pg. 169
Rahn, Jean, Controller--Uncle B's Bakery, Inc., Ellsworth, IA; *U.S. Public*, pg. 1664
Raia, Judy, Controller--Foodarama Supermarkets, Inc., Freehold, NJ; *U.S. Public*, pg. 661
Raible, William, V.P. & Controller--Bacharach Inc., Pittsburgh, PA; *U.S. Private*, pg. 109
Raiche, John T., Controller & Sec.--Divane Bros. Electric Co., Franklin Park, IL; *U.S. Private*, pg. 336
Raile, Vernon A., Chief Acctg. Officer, V.P. & Controller--MDU Resources Group, Inc., Bismarck, ND; *U.S. Public*, pg. 1025
Raimondi, Italo, Controller--McGraw-Hill Libri Italia, S.r.l., Milan, Italy; *U.S. Public*, pg. 1072
Raines, William, Controller--Speedway Motorsports, Inc., Concord, NC; *U.S. Public*, pg. 1498
Rains, Gladys, Controller & Treas.--Davis Paint Company, Kansas City, MO; *U.S. Private*, pg. 315
Raithel, Michael L., Controller--Crane Co., Stamford, CT; *U.S. Public*, pg. 456
Raivio, Richard, V.P.-Fin. & Controller--Pac Paper Inc., Vancouver, WA; *U.S. Private*, pg. 828
Rajappa, Sampath, Sr. V.P. & Controller--Federal National Mortgage Association (Fannie Mae), Washington, DC; *U.S. Public*, pg. 615
Ralph, David, Controller--Thermon Manufacturing Company, San Marcos, TX; *U.S. Private*, pg. 1080
Ralph, Jeff, Controller--Multi-Ad Services, Incorporated, Peoria, IL; *U.S. Private*, pg. 766
Ralston, Helen E.K., Controller--John Crane UK Ltd., Slough, United Kingdom; *Int'l*, pg. 1338
Ramanathan, Sinniah, V.P. & Controller--The Singer Company, Hong Kong, Hong Kong; *Int'l*, pg. 1220
Ramberg, David, Controller--Big Horn Co-Op Marketing Association, Greybull, WY; *U.S. Private*, pg. 143
Ramey, Peter, Comptroller--Lou Fusz Automotive Network, Saint Louis, MO; *U.S. Private*, pg. 432
Rami, Emma, V.P. & Controller--Pathe, Paris, France; *Int'l*, pg. 1024
Ramirez Pineda, Manuel, V.P. & Controller--Grupo Continental S.A., Tampico, Mexico; *Int'l*, pg. 573
Ramirez, Robert, Controller--Vita Food Products, Inc., Chicago, IL; *U.S. Private*, pg. 1142
Ramma, Mike, Asst. Controller--Avatar Holdings Inc., Coral Gables, FL; *U.S. Public*, pg. 151
Ramos, David A., Asst. Controller--Wisconsin Power & Light Company, Madison, WI; *U.S. Public*, pg. 1728
Ramos, David A., Asst. Controller--South Beloit Water, Gas & Electric Co., South Beloit, IL; *U.S. Public*, pg. 1728
Ramsden, Jonathan E., Controller--Omnicom Group Inc., New York, NY; *U.S. Public*, pg. 1223
Ramsey, Bill, Controller--London Litho Aluminum Co., Inc., Lincolnwood, IL; *U.S. Private*, pg. 673
Ramsey, Richard L., V.P. & Controller--Tandy Corporation, Fort Worth, TX; *U.S. Public*, pg. 1560
Rancourt, Cathy, Controller--Diversey Water Technologies, Inc., Chagrin Falls, OH; *U.S. Public*, pg. 1150
Rand, Edward L., Jr., V.P. & Controller--Atlantic American Corporation, Atlanta, GA; *U.S. Public*, pg. 143
Randall, Patrick, Asst. Controller--Valassis Communications, Inc., Livonia, MI; *U.S. Public*, pg. 1704
Randazzo, Martin, Controller--Redco Corporation, Red Lion, PA; *U.S. Private*, pg. 915
Randolph, Gwen, Controller--Span-America Medical Systems Inc., Greenville, SC; *U.S. Public*, pg. 1495
Randolph, Ken, Controller--Chemstone Corp., Strasburg, VA; *U.S. Private*, pg. 233
Rands, Mary, Controller, Treas. & Sec.--Brush Research Manufacturing Company, Los Angeles, CA; *U.S. Private*, pg. 176
Ranshaw, W.A., Controller--Highway Equipment Company, Cedar Rapids, IA; *U.S. Private*, pg. 529
Ransom, Richard, Controller--Chico's Fas Inc, Fort Myers, FL; *U.S. Public*, pg. 349
Ranucci, Vincent, Controller--Alden Auto Parts Warehouse, Inc., Somerset, MA; *U.S. Private*, pg. 33
Rapaport, Jonathan, Chief Fin. Officer, V.P. & Treas.--Pacesetter Steel Service, Inc., Kennesaw, GA; *U.S. Private*, pg. 830
Raper, Jeff, Controller--United States Ceramic Tile Co., East Sparta, OH; *U.S. Private*, pg. 1124
Raposa, Donald, Controller--Whaling Industries, Inc., Fall River, MA; *U.S. Private*, pg. 1170
Rapp, Herbert, Controller--Wandel & Goltermann GmbH & Co., Elektronische Messtechnik, Eningen, Germany; *Int'l*, pg. 1485
Rascon, Roger, Chief Fin. Officer & Controller--Interstate Electronics Corp., Anaheim, CA; *U.S. Public*, pg. 622
Rasfeld, Dave, Controller--Planet Products Corp., Cincinnati, OH; *U.S. Private*, pg. 869
Rashes, Sylvia, Controller & Dir.-Fin--Center Laboratories, Inc., Port Washington, NY; *U.S. Public*, pg. 813
Rashid, Ali, Controller--Weider Publications, Inc., Woodland Hills, CA; *U.S. Private*, pg. 1159
Rasnick, Robert, Controller--The Orvis Company, Inc., Manchester, VT; *U.S. Private*, pg. 820
Raso, James P., Controller--Urstadt Biddle Properties, Inc., Greenwich, CT; *U.S. Public*, pg. 1700
Ratcliffe, Tom, V.P. & Controller--LDB Corporation, Kerrville, TX; *U.S. Private*, pg. 639
Ratcliffe, Tom, Controller--Mr. Gatti's, Inc., Kerrville, TX; *U.S. Private*, pg. 639
Rath, Bob, Controller--Komori Corporation, Tokyo, Japan; *Int'l*, pg. 745
Rath, Bob, Controller--Komori America Corporation, Rolling Meadows, IL; *Int'l*, pg. 745
Rathbone, John P., V.P. & Controller--Norfolk Southern Corporation, Norfolk, VA; *U.S. Public*, pg. 1190
Rather, Jerome, V.P.-Fin. & Controller--Credit Union National Association, Madison, WI; *U.S. Private*, pg. 288
Ratliff, Robert L., Controller--Nalco Chemical Company, Naperville, IL; *U.S. Public*, pg. 1150
Ratson, R. Malcolm, Controller--Dimeling, Schreiber & Park, Philadelphia, PA; *U.S. Private*, pg. 333
Rau, David E., V.P. & Controller--Del Webb Corporation, Phoenix, AZ; *U.S. Public*, pg. 494
Rauch, Art, Controller--The Thermos Company, Schaumburg, IL; *Int'l*, pg. 938
Rauman, Jerry, Controller--Farley, Inc., Chicago, IL; *U.S. Private*, pg. 394
RAuscher, Jurgen, Dir.-Acctg., Controlling & Taxes--IKB Deutsche Industriebank AG, Dusseldorf, Germany; *Int'l*, pg. 645
Raut, S.A., Controller--Weatherford Saudia Arabia Ltd., Al-Krabiyah, Saudi Arabia; *U.S. Public*, pg. 1750
Ravasio, Doris, Controller--Gibbs Wire & Steel Company, Inc., Southington, CT; *U.S. Private*, pg. 451
Raveling, Lyle, Controller--Polka Dot Dairy/Tom Thumb, Inc., Hastings, MN; *U.S. Private*, pg. 874

Rawot, Billie K., V.P. & Controller--Eaton Corporation, Cleveland, OH; *U.S. Public*, pg. 555
Rawson, Glen, Controller--Industrial & Retail Bag Division, Chicago, IL; *U.S. Public*, pg. 1521
Ray, Donna L., Controller--Serologicals Corporation, Clarkston, GA; *U.S. Public*, pg. 1460
Ray, Doug, V.P. & Controller--John Wieland Homes Inc., Atlanta, GA; *U.S. Private*, pg. 1175
Ray, Kurt, Controller--Leslie Metal Arts Co., Inc., Grand Rapids, MI; *U.S. Private*, pg. 660
Ray, Michael, Controller--Marks & Morgan Jewelers Inc, Augusta, GA; *U.S. Private*, pg. 705
Ray, Richard, Controller--Powell ESCO Company, Greenville, TX; *U.S. Public*, pg. 1319
Ray, Thomas E., Controller--Luwa Bahnson, Inc., Winston Salem, NC; *U.S. Private*, pg. 682
Ray, Wendy, Controller--Denny Menholt Frontier Chevrolet, Billings, MT; *U.S. Private*, pg. 324
Rayback, Carolyn, Controller--Pacific Foods, Inc., Kent, WA; *U.S. Private*, pg. 831
Raymonda, David, Controller--Wells Aluminum Corp., Baltimore, MD; *U.S. Private*, pg. 1161
Raynaud, Alain-Pierre, Sr. V.P. & Controller--Renault, Boulogne-Billancourt, France; *Int'l*, pg. 1102
Raynor, Karen, Controller--GSW Jackes-Evans Manufacturing Co., Saint Louis, MO; *Int'l*, pg. 538
Re, Michael, V.P. & Controller--Swinerton Inc., San Francisco, CA; *U.S. Private*, pg. 1059
Rea, Kerry, V.P. & Controller--View-Master, Inc., Mount Laurel, NJ; *U.S. Public*, pg. 1058
Read, J., Controller--Cyanamid of Great Britain Ltd., Gosport, United Kingdom; *U.S. Public*, pg. 81
Readinger, Randall R., Controller--Lowrance Electronics, Inc., Tulsa, OK; *U.S. Public*, pg. 1015
Reagan, Terry, Controller--Metal Seal & Products, Inc., Willoughby, OH; *U.S. Private*, pg. 734
Reardon, Diana, Controller--Amphenol Corporation, Wallingford, CT; *U.S. Private*, pg. 629
Reardon, Gene, Controller--Guy Gannett Communications, Portland, ME; *U.S. Private*, pg. 439
Reardon, J., Controller--The Goldhirsh Group, Boston, MA; *U.S. Private*, pg. 461
Reardon, John, V.P. & Controller--The Goldhirsh Group, New York, NY; *U.S. Private*, pg. 461
Reardon, M. D., Asst. Controller--JC Penney Company, Inc., Plano, TX; *U.S. Public*, pg. 916
Reaves, Dennis, Controller--Singleton Seafood Co., Tampa, FL; *U.S. Public*, pg. 427
Rebholz, Andrrew, Controller--WHX Corporation, New York, NY; *U.S. Public*, pg. 1726
Rebollar, Becky, Controller--JG Industries, Inc., Chicago, IL; *U.S. Public*, pg. 917
Reda, John, Controller--The Frye Company, Great Neck, NY; *U.S. Private*, pg. 430
Redard, Michael, Chief Fin. Officer--Medical Analysis Systems Inc., Camarillo, CA; *U.S. Private*, pg. 727
Redman, Anton, Fin. Controller--BBC Magazines, London, United Kingdom; *Int'l*, pg. 114
Redmon, Gary, Controller--River Oaks Hospital, New Orleans, LA; *U.S. Public*, pg. 1697
Redner, Robert R., Pres. & Controller--General Filters, Inc., Novi, MI; *U.S. Private*, pg. 444
Redwood, Mark, Fin. Controller--CDP, London, United Kingdom; *Int'l*, pg. 239
Reece, Mark, Controller, Treas & Sec.--Young-Phillips Sales Co., Clemmons, NC; *U.S. Private*, pg. 1201
Reed, Brian, Controller--U.S. Trails, Dallas, TX; *U.S. Public*, pg. 1688
Reed, Frank, Controller--High Industries, Inc., Lancaster, PA; *U.S. Private*, pg. 528
Reed, Jim D., V.P. & Controller--Giddings & Lewis, Inc., Fond Du Lac, WI; *Int'l*, pg. 1389
Reed, Laura, Controller--Cherry Central Cooperative, Traverse City, MI; *U.S. Private*, pg. 233
Reed, Robert, Chief Accountant--Laird & Company, Eatontown, NJ; *U.S. Private*, pg. 642
Reed, Thomas E., Controller--Schultz Steel Company, South Gate, CA; *U.S. Private*, pg. 973
Reed, Wayne, Sr. V.P. & Controller--NationsBank of Tennessee, Nashville, TN; *U.S. Public*, pg. 1163
Reeder, Angela, Controller--American Appraisal (U.K.) Ltd., Manchester, United Kingdom; *U.S. Private*, pg. 50
Reel, Brian, Controller--Grafton Fraser Inc., Willowdale, Canada; *Int'l*, pg. 556
Rees, Gary, Controller--Phoenix Fuel Company, Inc., Phoenix, AZ; *U.S. Private*, pg. 863
Reese, Robert A., Controller--Guest Supply, Inc., Monmouth Junction, NJ; *U.S. Public*, pg. 768
Reese, Vicki, Controller--Matrix Service Company, Tulsa, OK; *U.S. Public*, pg. 1057
Reeskamp, R.R., Controller--Williams & Humbert Ltd., Jerez de la Frontera, Spain; *Int'l*, pg. 751
Reeves, Donna A., V.P. & Controller--Global Industrial Technologies, Dallas, TX; *U.S. Public*, pg. 747
Reeves, Stephen F., V.P. & Controller--The Black & Decker Corporation, Towson, MD; *U.S. Public*, pg. 233
Refael, Lebel, Controller--Agis Industries Ltd., Bnei-Brak, Israel; *Int'l*, pg. 30
Regan, Kevin R., V.P. & Controller--Big Y Foods Inc., Springfield, MA; *U.S. Private*, pg. 143
Regan, Michael N., V.P. & Controller--Harrah's Entertainment, Inc., Memphis, TN; *U.S. Public*, pg. 790
Regan, Tony, Dir.-Acctg. & Legal Svcs.--Kaneb Services, Inc., Richardson, TX; *U.S. Public*, pg. 942
Regenstein, Barry I., V.P. & Controller--Hudson General Corporation, Great Neck, NY; *U.S. Public*, pg. 845
Rehm, Sam, Controller--Delagra Corporation, Bridgeville, DE; *U.S. Private*, pg. 321
Reich, E., Controller--El Al Airlines Ltd., Lod, Israel; *Int'l*, pg. 435
Reich, Vicki, V.P. & Controller--Brunswick Corporation, Lake Forest, IL; *U.S. Public*, pg. 265
Reichert, Robert T., Corp. Controller--F.N.B. Corporation, Hermitage, PA; *U.S. Public*, pg. 607
Reid, Brian G., Comptroller--Bruncor, Inc., Saint John, Canada; *Int'l*, pg. 230
Reid, Dale G., Chief Admin. Officer, V.P. & Controller--Allegheny Teledyne Incorporated, Pittsburgh, PA; *U.S. Public*, pg. 43
Reid, Joseph, Controller--Windmere-Durable Holdings, Hialeah, FL; *U.S. Public*, pg. 1771
Reid, Ray, V.P. & Controller--Entex, Houston, TX; *U.S. Public*, pg. 843
Reijtenbagh, L., V.P.-Admin. & Controller--Hunter Douglas N.V., Rotterdam, Netherlands; *Int'l*, pg. 639
Reilly, Donald W., Controller--A.T. Cross Co., Lincoln, RI; *U.S. Public*, pg. 460
Reimer, Elizabeth B., Controller--Pizza Inn, Inc., Dallas, TX; *U.S. Public*, pg. 1307
Reimer, Stan, Controller--Salwasser Manufacturing Company, Inc., Reedley, CA; *U.S. Private*, pg. 963
Reimersma, Della, Controller--Holiday RV Superstores of South Atlanta, Inc., Forest Park, GA; *U.S. Public*, pg. 830
Rein, Harvey, V.P. & Controller--Loral Space & Communications, New York, NY; *U.S. Public*, pg. 1014
Reine, Arthur F., Controller--Astro-Med, Inc., West Warwick, RI; *U.S. Public*, pg. 141
Reiner, Keith, Controller--The Penn Companies, Philadelphia, PA; *U.S. Private*, pg. 849
Reinfort, Ernest B., Comptroller--Gendis Inc., Winnipeg, Canada; *Int'l*, pg. 542
Reinhart, Kevin J., Controller--Canadian Occidental Petroleum Ltd., Calgary, Canada; *U.S. Public*, pg. 1210
Reinke, David, Mgr.-Acctg.--Brazos Electric Power Cooperative, Inc., Waco, TX; *U.S. Private*, pg. 166
Reinke, Len, Controller--Forge Division, Marion, OH; *U.S. Public*, pg. 557
Reinko, Lynn, Controller--Forge Division, South Bend, IN; *U.S. Public*, pg. 557
Reiseck, Rick, Controller--Baldwin InLine Finishing, Willowbrook, IL; *U.S. Public*, pg. 170
Reisinger, Chales M., V.P., Treas. & Controller--The Kitchen Collection Inc., Chillicothe, OH; *U.S. Public*, pg. 1149
Reisinger, Kerry J., Asst. Treas.--Yorktowne Paperboard Corp., York, PA; *U.S. Private*, pg. 796
Reitan, Gunnar, Chief Fin. Officer & Corp. Controller--Scandinavian Airlines System (SAS), Solna, Sweden; *Int'l*, pg. 1201
Reiter, Erich, Controller--Villeroy & Boch AG, Mettlach, Germany; *Int'l*, pg. 1468
Reith, Steve, Controller--Hudepohl-Schoenling Brewing Company, Cincinnati, OH; *U.S. Private*, pg. 545
Reitiman, Judy, Controller--DuCoa L.P., Highland, IL; *U.S. Private*, pg. 301
Reker, David, Controller--Bedford Industries, Inc., Worthington, MN; *U.S. Private*, pg. 129
Reklau, David L., Controller-Fin.--VF Corporation, Wyomissing, PA; *U.S. Public*, pg. 1702
Remmers, Dean, Asst. Controller--TECO Energy, Inc., Tampa, FL; *U.S. Public*, pg. 1565
Remmerswaal, E., Controller--Moore International B.V., Leislen, Netherlands; *Int'l*, pg. 889
Remus, Donna, Controller--Ultimo Ltd., Chicago, IL; *U.S. Private*, pg. 1116
Renehan, John, Controller--COMNET Corporation, Lanham, MD; *U.S. Public*, pg. 416
Rennie, Carole, Controller--The Jean Coutu Group (PJC) Inc., Longueuil, Canada; *Int'l*, pg. 340
Renninger, Linda, Controller--Eat N Park Restaurants, Pittsburgh, PA; *U.S. Private*, pg. 358
Rens, Tim, Controller--Farmland MissChem, Ltd., Port of Spain, Trinidad & Tobago; *U.S. Public*, pg. 1117
Rensi, Chad, Controller--Spartan International Inc., Holt, MI; *U.S. Private*, pg. 1020
Renz, David, Controller--Atlas Copco Comptec Inc., Voorheesville, NY; *Int'l*, pg. 96
Repoliea, Ray, Controller--Drive Train Industries, Denver, CO; *U.S. Private*, pg. 343
Repp, Timothy J., Chief Fin. Officer & V.P.-Fin.--SBE, Inc., San Ramon, CA; *U.S. Public*, pg. 1416
Resnick, Peter, Controller--Bell Industries, Inc., El Segundo, CA; *U.S. Public*, pg. 204
Rettig, Pat, Controller--Turner Industries, Baton Rouge, LA; *U.S. Private*, pg. 1109
Reuben, Rolf, Controller--Daniels Printing Company, Everett, MA; *U.S. Private*, pg. 310
Reuss, Daniel J., Sr. V.P., Controller & Treas.--Dain Rauscher Corporation, Minneapolis, MN; *U.S. Public*, pg. 476
Reves, Ricky, Asst. Controller--Global Van Lines, Inc., Orange, CA; *U.S. Private*, pg. 458
Rex, John, Controller--Reico, Inc., Springfield, VA; *U.S. Private*, pg. 919
Reyburn, Steve, Controller--Star-Kist Foods, Inc., Newport, KY; *U.S. Public*, pg. 806
Reyes, David, Controller--Johnson Storage Moving Co, Denver, CO; *U.S. Private*, pg. 594
Reyes, George, V.P. & Controller--Sun Microsystems, Inc., Palo Alto, CA; *U.S. Public*, pg. 1531
Reyes, Luis, Controller--Beckman Coulter, Miami, FL; *U.S. Public*, pg. 199
Reyes, Rod, Controller--IDM Controls, Houston, TX; *U.S. Private*, pg. 554
Reymann, Mary C., V.P.-Fin., Controller & Sec.--Flanigan's Enterprises, Inc., Fort Lauderdale, FL; *U.S. Public*, pg. 648
Reynolds, Harold E., V.P.--The Dime Savings Bank of New York, New York, NY; *U.S. Public*, pg. 509
Reynolds, Howard, Controller--Kropp Forge Co., Cicero, IL; *U.S. Private*, pg. 1064
Reynolds, Larry J., Controller--Powder River Coal Company, Gillette, WY; *Int'l*, pg. 594
Reynolds, Mike, Controller--The Nielsen Company, Florence, KY; *U.S. Private*, pg. 799
Reynolds, R.C., Controller--Vulcan Materials Company-Midsouth Div., Knoxville, TN; *U.S. Public*, pg. 1726
Rezich, John, V.P. & Controller-True North Communications Inc.--True North Communications Inc., Chicago, IL; *U.S. Public*, pg. 1641
Rhoads, Gary L., Sr. V.P., Controller & Cashier--National Penn Bank, Boyertown, PA; *U.S. Public*, pg. 1159
Rhudy, Huey J., Treas. & Sec.--STRAFCO, Inc., San Antonio, TX; *U.S. Private*, pg. 1046
Ribar, Monika, Controller--Panalpina Welttransport (Holding) AG, Binningen, Switzerland; *Int'l*, pg. 1022
Ribaudo, William J., Corp. Controller--EG & G, Inc., Wellesley, MA; *U.S. Public*, pg. 542
Ricard, Benoit, Controller--Uniboard Canada Inc., Laval, Canada; *Int'l*, pg. 1431
Riccardi, Lisa, Controller--Furniture Consultants, New York, NY; *U.S. Public*, pg. 1686
Ricci, Joe, Controller--Spar Aerospace Limited, Toronto, Canada; *Int'l*, pg. 1287
Ricci, Mike, Controller--American Power Conversion Corporation, West Kingston, RI; *U.S. Public*, pg. 89
Ricciardello, Mary, V.P. & Comptroller--Houston Industries Incorporated, Houston, TX; *U.S. Public*, pg. 842
Rice-Newell, Christine E., Asst. Treas.--International Thoroughbred Breeders, Inc., Cherry Hill, NJ; *U.S. Public*, pg. 908
Rice, David, Chief Fin. Officer--Universal Builders Supply, Inc., Mount Vernon, NY; *U.S. Private*, pg. 1126
Rice, Dianne S., Controller--High Plains Corporation, Wichita, KS; *U.S. Public*, pg. 825
Rice, James, Sr V.P. & Controller--Essex International, Inc., Fort Wayne, IN; *U.S. Public*, pg. 593
Rice, Jim, Controller--Haemonetics Corporation, Braintree, MA; *U.S. Public*, pg. 773
Rice, Kent, Controller--Tokheim Corporation, Fort Wayne, IN; *U.S. Public*, pg. 1620
Rice, Patrick, Controller--Fastenal Company, Winona, MN; *U.S. Public*, pg. 614
Rich, Gerald I., Sr. V.P., Controller & Treas.--Coast Savings Financial, Inc., Los Angeles, CA; *U.S. Public*, pg. 388
Rich, Kenneth S., V.P. & Controller--ServiceMaster Business & Industry Group, Downers Grove, IL; *U.S. Public*, pg. 1462
Rich, Robert, Controller--The Calkins Manufacturing Company, Spokane, WA; *U.S. Private*, pg. 201
Rich, Robert C., Exec. V.P.-Opers. & Fin., Controller & Asst. Sec.--Master Lock Company, Milwaukee, WI; *U.S. Public*, pg. 675
Rich, Thomas, V.P.-Corp. Controller--Gould Electronics Inc., Eastlake, OH; *U.S. Public*, pg. 1591
Richard, Frank, Controller--Engine Components Div., Kearney, NE; *U.S. Public*, pg. 557
Richards, Andy, Controller--Bunnell Plastics Division, Mickleton, NJ; *U.S. Public*, pg. 689
Richards, B., Controller--Jen-Coat Inc., Westfield, MA; *U.S. Public*, pg. 70
Richards, Dave, Controller & Treas.--Pacific Hide & Fur Depot, Great Falls, MT; *U.S. Private*, pg. 831
Richards, Jane, Controller--Barrett Resources Corporation, Denver, CO; *U.S. Public*, pg. 191
Richards, K., Division Controller--Vernitron Sensor Systems, Saint Petersburg, FL; *U.S. Public*, pg. 157
Richards, Neil, Controller--AMF Bakery Systems, Richmond, VA; *U.S. Private*, pg. 6
Richards, Pauline, Grp. Fin. Controller--Rollins Burdick Hunter Co. (Bermuda) Ltd., Hamilton, Bermuda; *U.S. Public*, pg. 119
Richards, Stephen C., V.P. & Controller--Harcourt General, Inc., Chestnut Hill, MA; *U.S. Public*, pg. 782
Richardson, Greg, Controller--Mrs. Winner's Chicken & Biscuit Restaurants, Atlanta, GA; *U.S. Private*, pg. 766
Richardson, K.G., Grp. Fin. Controller--Dobson Park Industries Plc, Wigan, United Kingdom; *U.S. Public*, pg. 789
Richer, Linda, Controller--The Protector Corporation, Elmhurst, IL; *U.S. Private*, pg. 891
Richey, Carol, Controller--Blue Shield of California, San Francisco, CA; *U.S. Private*, pg. 153
Richins, Gerald W., Controller--Phelps Dodge Tyrone, Tyrone, NM; *U.S. Public*, pg. 1287
Richman, Candy, Asst. V.P. & Controller--Centris Group Inc., Costa Mesa, CA; *U.S. Public*, pg. 328
Richter, Darline M., V.P. & Controller--Dycom Industries, Inc., Palm Beach Gardens, FL; *U.S. Public*, pg. 538
Richter, Delroy, V.P. & Controller--Mammoth, Inc., Chaska, MN; *U.S. Public*, pg. 1193
Richter, Delroy J., V.P. & Controller--Commercial Environmental Systems Group, Inc., Chaska, MN; *U.S. Public*, pg. 1193
Richter, Frank, Controller--Nowsco Well Service Inc., Houston, TX; *Int'l*, pg. 990
Richter, Kirk A., Controller--Sigma-Aldrich Corporation, Saint Louis, MO; *U.S. Public*, pg. 1471
Rickard, D.B., Grp. Fin. Controller--Grand Metropolitan Plc, London, United Kingdom; *Int'l*, pg. 408
Rickles, Ed, Controller--Williams Worldwide, Santa Monica, CA; *U.S. Private*, pg. 1179
Rickling, Penny, Chief Fin. Officer & V.P.--Howden Fluid Systems, Santa Barbara, CA; *U.S. Public*, pg. 1045
Ricks, Thomas E., V.P. & Controller--El Paso Natural Gas Co., Houston, TX; *U.S. Public*, pg. 567
Rico, Chuck, V.P. & Controller--La Petite Academy Inc., Overland Park, KS; *U.S. Private*, pg. 640
Riddle, Glynn, Sr. V.P. & Controller--Comdata Corporation, Brentwood, TN; *U.S. Public*, pg. 331
Ridenour, Tom, Controller--Nationwide Credit Inc., Marietta, GA; *U.S. Private*, pg. 788
Ridley, John, Controller--Richardton Mfg. Co., Richardton, ND; *U.S. Public*, pg. 1676
Ridley, Ron, Controller--Brite Voice Systems, Inc., Heathrow, FL; *U.S. Public*, pg. 257
Ridley, Ronald C., Controller--Brite Voice Systems, Canton, MA; *U.S. Public*, pg. 257
Riegert, George, Controller--Robbins, Inc., Cincinnati, OH; *U.S. Private*, pg. 934

Riehl, Christopher, Controller--Fansteel VR/Wesson-Lexington, Lexington, KY; U.S. Public, pg. 612
Riel, Charito, V.P. & Controller--The Chisholm-Mingo Group, New York, NY; U.S. Private, pg. 237
Riggs, Robert, Controller--BTR Precision Die Casting, Inc., Russellville, KY; Int'l, pg. 127
Rigsby, Gary, Controller--Active Voice Corporation, Seattle, WA; U.S. Public, pg. 17
Rigsby, Robert E., Sr. V.P.-Fin. & Controller--Virginia Electric and Power Company, Richmond, VA; U.S. Public, pg. 516
Riley, Jim, Controller--Ross Systems, Inc., Atlanta, GA; U.S. Public, pg. 1406
Riley, Michael, Chief Fin. Officer & Controller--Wellman Dynamics Corp., Creston, IA; U.S. Public, pg. 612
Rilla, J.M., V.P.-Fin.--Koehler Manufacturing Company, Marlborough, MA; U.S. Private, pg. 706
Rimarcik, Joseph C., Sr. V.P.-Accounting & Admin. & Controller--Paul Inman Associates Inc., Farmington, MI; U.S. Private, pg. 564
Rimmington, D.B., Controller--Glynwed International PLC, Birmingham, United Kingdom; Int'l, pg. 554
Rinaldi, Nicholas A., Controller--Yankee Energy System, Inc., Meriden, CT; U.S. Public, pg. 1787
Rinehait, John, Controller--San Francisco Giants Baseball Club, San Francisco, CA; U.S. Private, pg. 964
Ringel, James, Controller--Serfilco, Ltd., Northbrook, IL; U.S. Private, pg. 985
Ringhoffer, Douglas, Controller--E.R. Moore Co., Chicago, IL; U.S. Private, pg. 759
Ringmayr, Georg, Controller--Alpine Aktiengesellschaft, Augsburg, Germany; Int'l, pg. 636
Rinn, Richard D., V.P. & Controller--Kysor Panel Systems, Fort Worth, TX; U.S. Public, pg. 1445
Riodan, Mary Beth, Controller--Cyborg Systems, Inc., Chicago, IL; U.S. Private, pg. 299
Riordan, John, Fin. Controller--Mallinckrodt Medical, Athlone, Ireland; U.S. Public, pg. 1040
Rios da Silva, Antonio Wiz, Controller--Banco do Brasil, Brasilia, Brazil; Int'l, pg. 141
Ripka, David E., Controller--NRG Energy, Inc., Minneapolis, MN; U.S. Public, pg. 1195
Ripley, James W., Comptroller--Bestfoods, Englewood Cliffs, NJ; U.S. Public, pg. 223
Ripple, Patricia L., V.P. & Corp. Controller--American Greetings Corporation, Cleveland, OH; U.S. Public, pg. 77
Ririe, Del, Controller--Waremart Inc., Boise, ID; U.S. Private, pg. 1150
Risher, Ronald D., V.P., Corp. Controller & Sec.--Thorn Apple Valley, Inc., Southfield, MI; U.S. Public, pg. 1602
Rispoli, Carl A., Corp. Controller & Asst. Sec.--Defiance, Inc., Cleveland, OH; U.S. Public, pg. 493
Risser, Rick, Controller--GSE, Inc., Farmington, MI; U.S. Public, pg. 1676
Rissman, Dennis, Chief Fin. Officer & Controller--Bresler's Industries, Inc., Des Plaines, IL; Int'l, pg. 1520
Ristau, O., Controller--Gestetner AB, Spanga, Sweden; Int'l, pg. 1115
Ritchie, John George, Controller--Sime Darby Berhad Insurance Services Division, Kuala Lumpur, Malaysia; Int'l, pg. 1250
Riter, Jerry, Controller--Koppel Steel Corp., Beaver Falls, PA; U.S. Public, pg. 1147
Ritter, George, Controller & Asst. Sec.--VWR Scientific Products, West Chester, PA; U.S. Public, pg. 1703
Ritterband, Larry, V.P. & Controller--American Metal Products, Olive Branch, MS; U.S. Public, pg. 1053
Ritz, Richard L., V.P. & Controller--Federal Signal Corporation, Oak Brook, IL; U.S. Public, pg. 616
Ritzel, Joseph, V.P. & Controller--Day & Zimmermann, Inc., Philadelphia, PA; U.S. Private, pg. 316
Ritzmann, Keith W., V.P. & Controller--The Ackerley Group, Seattle, WA; U.S. Public, pg. 15
Rivard, Peter A., Comptroller--D.D. Bean & Sons Co., Jaffrey, NH; U.S. Private, pg. 126
River, Wesley, Controller--Banco Chase Manhattan, S.A., Santo Amaro, Brazil; U.S. Public, pg. 339
Rivera, Jose, Controller--Henry Lee Company, Miami, FL; U.S. Private, pg. 657
Rivera, Percy, Controller--Wisdom Imports Sales Co. Inc., Irvine, CA; Int'l, pg. 679
Rivera, Tessie, Controller--AMD Industries Inc., Cicero, IL; U.S. Private, pg. 6
Rives, S. Bradford, V.P.-Fin. & Controller--LG & E Energy Corp., Louisville, KY; U.S. Public, pg. 970
Rivet, Roger, V.P. & Controller--Patterson-Kelley Company, Tulsa, OK; U.S. Public, pg. 793
Roach, David, Controller--Speedling Incorporated, Sun City, FL; U.S. Private, pg. 1024
Roach, Donald V., Controller--Footstar Inc., Mahwah, NJ; U.S. Public, pg. 661
Roadman, Neil A., Controller--Kansas City Power & Light Company, Kansas City, MO; U.S. Public, pg. 943
Roback, Lisa, Asst. Controller--Evans, Inc., Chicago, IL; U.S. Public, pg. 596
Roberson, Clayton E., Jr., V.P. & Controller--Stein Mart, Inc., Jacksonville, FL; U.S. Public, pg. 1514
Roberts, Bob, Controller--All-Phase Electric Supply Co., Benton Harbor, MI; U.S. Private, pg. 35
Roberts, Clark, Controller--Trinity Universal Insurance Co., Dallas, TX; U.S. Public, pg. 1694
Roberts, Maureen, Controller--P.C. Richard & Son, Farmingdale, NY; U.S. Private, pg. 928
Roberts, Michael D., First V.P., Controller & Asst. Treas.--W.P. Carey & Co., Inc., New York, NY; U.S. Private, pg. 209
Roberts, Peter W., V.P. & Controller--The Loewen Group, Inc., Burnaby, Canada; Int'l, pg. 814
Roberts, Rodney K., Controller--Idahoan Foods, Lewisville, ID; U.S. Private, pg. 557
Roberts, Stewart, Controller--Nucor Steel-Arkansas, Blytheville, AR; U.S. Public, pg. 1205
Roberts, T.C., Controller--Mead Packaging International, Inc., Atlanta, GA; U.S. Public, pg. 1076
Roberts, William E., Chief Fin. Officer, V.P., Controller & Treas.--Lone Star Industries, Inc., Stamford, CT; U.S. Public, pg. 1012
Robertson, Bud, Controller--M/A-COM Inc., Lowell, MA; U.S. Public, pg. 8
Robertson, Donald B., Asst. Controller--Kimberly-Clark Corporation, Dallas, TX; U.S. Public, pg. 958
Robertson, Gordy, Controller--Malt-O-Meal Company, Minneapolis, MN; U.S. Private, pg. 699
Robertson, Jamie, Controller--Union Carbide (Europe) S.A., Meyrin, Switzerland; U.S. Public, pg. 1667
Robertson, Jennifer, Controller.-Intl;. Sls. & Mktg.--The Gates Rubber Company Ltd., Dumfries, United Kingdom; Int'l, pg. 1397
Robertson, Lowell L., Sr. V.P. & Controller--The Dial Corporation, Phoenix, AZ; U.S. Public, pg. 505
Robertson, Mike, Div. Controller--MMI Products, Inc., Houston, TX; U.S. Private, pg. 687
Robertson, Peter, Controller--Pembina Pipeline Corporation, Calgary, Canada; Int'l, pg. 1032
Robertson, Robert A., Controller--Jannock Limited, Toronto, Canada; Int'l, pg. 698
Robinson, Bob, Controller--Yamaha Motor Corp., U.S.A., Cypress, CA; Int'l, pg. 1516
Robinson, Bruce, Controller--Klipsch, Inc., Hope, AR; U.S. Private, pg. 626
Robinson, Eli E., Controller--Contractors Steel Company, Livonia, MI; U.S. Private, pg. 270
Robinson, Glenn H., V.P. & Controller--Mountain Fuel Supply Company, Salt Lake City, UT; U.S. Public, pg. 1352
Robinson, Glenn H., V.P. & Controller--Questar Pipeline Company, Salt Lake City, UT; U.S. Public, pg. 1352
Robinson, Greg, Controller--Federal Data Corporation, Bethesda, MD; U.S. Private, pg. 398
Robinson, Jack, Controller--Geneva Corporation, Greensboro, NC; U.S. Private, pg. 446
Robinson, James, V.P. & Comptroller--Deere & Company, Moline, IL; U.S. Public, pg. 491
Robinson, John R., Sr. V.P., Controller & Treas.--Purity Dairies Inc., Nashville, TN; U.S. Private, pg. 895
Robinson, Lee J., Controller & Asst. Sec.--Advanced Machine Vision Corp., Medford, OR; U.S. Public, pg. 20
Robinson, Michael D., Controller--KU Energy, Lexington, KY; U.S. Public, pg. 940
Robinson, Michael D., Controller--Kentucky Utilities Company, Lexington, KY; U.S. Public, pg. 941
Robinson, Micheal N., Controller--KU Capital Corporation, Lexington, KY; U.S. Public, pg. 941
Robinson, Phil, Controller--R D I S Corporation, Chicago, IL; U.S. Private, pg. 903
Robinson, Scott L., Sr. V.P. & Controller--SunAmerica Inc., Los Angeles, CA; U.S. Public, pg. 1532
Robisch, Gary, Controller--Richardson Electronics, Ltd., Lafox, IL; U.S. Public, pg. 1387
Robison, Hal, Controller--Taylor Machine Works, Inc., Louisville, MS; U.S. Private, pg. 1070
Robison, James A., Controller & Treas.--Tenera, Inc., San Francisco, CA; U.S. Public, pg. 1576
Roble, Craig, Controller--HEI, Inc., Victoria, MN; U.S. Public, pg. 770
Robles, Josue, Jr., Chief Fin. Officer, Sr. V.P. & Treas.--USAA (United Services Automobile Association), San Antonio, TX; U.S. Private, pg. 1114
Robson, Brian A., V.P. & Controller--Coyote Network Systems, Inc., Westlake Village, CA; U.S. Public, pg. 455
Robson, Robert, Controller--Northern Telecom, Nashville, TN; Int'l, pg. 969
Rocco, Richard, Controller--Pen-Tab Industries, Inc., Front Royal, VA; U.S. Private, pg. 848
Rock, John, Grp. Credit Controller--Schroders PLC, London, United Kingdom; Int'l, pg. 1210
Rockefeller, David, Grp. Controller--New York Magazine, New York, NY; U.S. Public, pg. 1328
Rocktoff, William, Controller & Dir.-Employee Benefits--Kimmins Corp., Tampa, FL; U.S. Public, pg. 960
Rockwood, Craig, Mgr.-Acctg.--Peco Mfg. Co., Inc., Portland, OR; U.S. Private, pg. 846
Rodammer, Gretchen L., Controller--Chemical Bank & Trust Company, Midland, MI; U.S. Public, pg. 345
Rodger, William T., Controller--Computer Products, Inc., Boca Raton, FL; U.S. Public, pg. 422
Rodrigues, Andre, Controller--Cervejarias Kaiser Brasil Ltda., Campinas, Brazil; Int'l, pg. 279
Rodrigues, John C., Controller--The Harodite Finishing Company Inc., North Dighton, MA; U.S. Private, pg. 503
Rodriguez, Gaspar, Controller--Simmons Juvenile Products, Rutherford, NJ; U.S. Private, pg. 1001
Rodriguez, John, Controller--Joseph Kirschner Co., Augusta, ME; U.S. Private, pg. 599
Rodriguez, Juana D., Treas.--Mason Distributors, Inc., Hialeah, FL; U.S. Private, pg. 712
Rodriguez, Mark, Dir.-Human Resources--IMPCO AirSensors Technologies, Cerritos, CA; U.S. Public, pg. 34
Rodriguez, Ray, Treas.--Fiesta Mart Inc., Houston, TX; U.S. Private, pg. 403
Rodriguez, Ruben, Controller--Isolyser Company, Inc., Norcross, GA; U.S. Public, pg. 914
Rodriques, Dennis, Controller--The Liposome Company, Inc., Princeton, NJ; U.S. Public, pg. 1000
Roe, Al, Controller--VPI Mirrex Corp., Delaware City, DE; U.S. Private, pg. 1141
Roe, Debra P., Controller--Monarch Cement Co., Humboldt, KS; U.S. Public, pg. 1123
Roe, Tom, Controller--X-Rite, Incorporated, Grandville, MI; U.S. Public, pg. 1783
Roe, William J., V.P. & Controller--Maytag Galesburg Refrigeration Products, Galesburg, IL; U.S. Public, pg. 1064
Roedl, Suzanne, V.P.-Fin.--Condor D.C. Power Supplies Inc., Oxnard, CA; U.S. Public, pg. 1419
Roehrick, Charles T., V.P. & Controller--ADC Telecommunications, Inc., Minnetonka, MN; U.S. Public, pg. 4
Roenitz, William K., Controller & Treas.--Bio-Logic Systems Corp., Mundelein, IL; U.S. Public, pg. 230
Roenning, Knut, Controller--Bergesen d.y. A.S., Oslo, Norway; Int'l, pg. 188
Roeske, Richard, Controller--Unitrin, Inc., Chicago, IL; U.S. Public, pg. 1693
Roesnheim, John, Controller--FWD/Seagrave Fire Apparatus, Inc., Clintonville, WI; U.S. Private, pg. 390
Rogers, Alvin, Controller--Monumental Millwork, Inc., Westminster, MD; U.S. Private, pg. 759
Rogers, Darrell, Controller--Turner Holding LLC, Covington, TN; U.S. Private, pg. 1109
Rogers, Donald W., Controller--ACCO World Corporation, Lincolnshire, IL; U.S. Public, pg. 674
Rogers, Harrison W., Controller--Birdair, Inc., Amherst, NY; Int'l, pg. 1348
Rogers, John, Treas. & Controller--Mallery Lumber Corp., Emporium, PA; U.S. Private, pg. 698
Rogers, R.C., Controller--Block Industries, Inc., Wilmington, NC; U.S. Private, pg. 150
Rogers, Ralph A., Jr., V.P. & Controller--Provident Companies, Inc., Chattanooga, TN; U.S. Public, pg. 1337
Rogers, Richard, Controller--Vortec, Cincinnati, OH; U.S. Public, pg. 865
Rogers, Steven W., 2nd V.P., Controller & Asst. Sec.--First Penn-Pacific Life Insurance Co., Oak Brook Terrace, IL; U.S. Public, pg. 998
Rohwer, Matthew, Controller--CMI Corporation, Oklahoma City, OK; U.S. Public, pg. 278
Rojas, Lucy, Controller--H.G. Fenton Material Company, San Diego, CA; U.S. Private, pg. 400
Rolan, Oscar, V.P.-Fin. & Controller--Pioneer New Media Technologies, Long Beach, CA; U.S. Private, pg. 866
Roland, David J., Controller--Marinette Marine Corporation, Marinette, WI; U.S. Private, pg. 703
Rold, Stephen K., V.P., Controller, Treas. & Sec.--Roofing Wholesale Co., Inc., Phoenix, AZ; U.S. Private, pg. 943
Roldan, Juan H., Controller--Island Express, Catano, PR; U.S. Private, pg. 211
Roldan, Simeon Y., Chief Fin. Officer & Controller--King Wire Inc., North Chicago, IL; U.S. Private, pg. 621
Rolf, Stephen P., V.P. & Corp. Controller--Hunt Corporation, Philadelphia, PA; U.S. Public, pg. 848
Rolff, Bill D., Controller--Niagara Transformer Corp., Buffalo, NY; U.S. Private, pg. 798
Rollins, John D., Controller--Yale University Press, New Haven, CT; U.S. Private, pg. 1195
Rolls, Steven G., V.P. & Controller--The B.F. Goodrich Company, Richfield, OH; U.S. Public, pg. 751
Roman, John J., V.P. & Controller--Northeast Utilities, Berlin, CT; U.S. Public, pg. 1194
Roman, John J., V.P. & Controller--Public Service Company of New Hampshire, Manchester, NH; U.S. Public, pg. 1195
Roman, Julian, Controller--Grupo Iberia, Madrid, Spain; Int'l, pg. 574
Romer, John, Comptroller--Guest Services, Inc., Fairfax, VA; U.S. Private, pg. 486
Romero, Fernando, Controller--Kaufman y Broad de Mexico SA de CV, Mexico, Mexico; U.S. Public, pg. 945
Romig, Kenneth J., V.P. & Controller--First Western Bancorp, Inc., New Castle, PA; U.S. Public, pg. 642
Romig, Michael V., Chief Fin. Officer & V.P.--Marine Construction & Design Co., Seattle, WA; U.S. Private, pg. 703
Romito, Robert, Controller--Leupold & Stevens, Inc., Beaverton, OR; U.S. Private, pg. 662
Romo, Jesus, Controller--Grupo Industrial Durango S.A. de C.V., Durango, Mexico; Int'l, pg. 575
Rondeau, E.R., Controller--Detrex Corporation, Southfield, MI; U.S. Public, pg. 501
Rondon, Salustiano Jose, Comptroller--Mantex, S.A.C.A., Caracas, Venezuela; Int'l, pg. 840
Rone, B.J., Controller--RenoAir Inc., Reno, NV; U.S. Private, pg. 922
Roose, Donald, V.P. & Controller--Mitchell Energy & Development Corp., Spring, TX; U.S. Public, pg. 1117
Roots, Brian, Grp. Controller--Whatman plc, Maidstone, United Kingdom; Int'l, pg. 1498
Roots, Trevor, Controller--Network Systems Corporation, Minneapolis, MN; U.S. Public, pg. 1522
Roots, Trevor, Controller--Bytex Corporation, Westborough, MA; U.S. Public, pg. 1522
Rosch, Harald, Controller--Boehringer Mannheim GmbH, Mannheim, Germany; Int'l, pg. 331
Rose, Estelle, Chief Fin. Officer--Kobra International Ltd, New York, NY; U.S. Private, pg. 628
Rose, George, Fin. Controller--British Aerospace p.l.c., Farnborough, United Kingdom; Int'l, pg. 217
Rose, Ken, Corp. Controller--TelCom Semiconductor, Inc., Mountain View, CA; U.S. Public, pg. 1569
Rose, Loren, Controller & Dir.D.P.--Pyramid Mountain Lumber, Seeley Lake, MT; U.S. Private, pg. 896
Rose, Meredith, Controller--Bearing Service Company, Pittsburgh, PA; U.S. Private, pg. 127
Rose, P., Grp. Fin. Controller--Babcock International Group PLC, Amersham, United Kingdom; Int'l, pg. 130
Rosebery, Susan, Controller--Environmental Elements Corporation, Baltimore, MD; U.S. Public, pg. 586
Roseborough, Viola G., Controller--Bayex Incorporated, Albion, NY; Int'l, pg. 1170
Rosen, Allen, Grp. Controller--New Balance Athletic Shoe, Inc., Boston, MA; U.S. Private, pg. 792
Rosen, Gary, Controller--Puroflow Incorporated, Van Nuys, CA; U.S. Public, pg. 1345
Rosen, Sylvia F., Controller--Castle-Harlan, Inc., New York, NY; U.S. Private, pg. 219
Rosenberg, Bruce, Controller--Zuckerman-Honickman Inc., King of Prussia, PA; U.S. Private, pg. 1207
Rosenberg, Eric, Controller--Susie's Deals, City of Industry, CA; U.S. Private, pg. 1056

Rosenberg, Harris, Controller--Jaclyn, Inc., West New York, NJ; *U.S. Public*, pg. 920

Rosenberg, Harvey, Controller--A & P Coat, Apron & Linen Supply, Bronx, NY; *U.S. Private*, pg. 1

Rosenberg, Philip G., 1st Sr. V.P., Treas., Controller & Asst. Sec.--Morse Shoe, Inc., Canton, MA; *U.S. Public*, pg. 168

Rosenberger, E. John, Controller--Wampler Foods, Timberville, VA; *U.S. Public*, pg. 1727

Rosenblum, Mark J., V.P. & Controller--Wellman, Inc., Shrewsbury, NJ; *U.S. Public*, pg. 1752

Rosendahl, John, V.P. & Controller--Genmar Holdings, Inc., Minneapolis, MN; *U.S. Private*, pg. 447

Rosengard, Andrew, Sr. V.P. & Controller--Cablevision Systems Corporation, Woodbury, NY; *U.S. Public*, pg. 288

Rosenkranz, Ken, Controller & Dir.-Personnel--Spirite Industries, Inc., Englewood, NJ; *U.S. Private*, pg. 1026

Rosenqvist, Paul, V.P.-Economy & Group Controller--Rautaruukki Oy, Helsinki, Finland; *Int'l*, pg. 1088

Rosenthal, David, V.P. & Controller--Carat MBS, New York, NY; *U.S. Private*, pg. 208

Rosett, Daniel, Sr. V.P. & Controller--Metro-Goldwyn-Mayer Inc., Santa Monica, CA; *U.S. Public*, pg. 1101

Rosner, Ron, Controller--Coast Manufacturing Company, Yonkers, NY; *U.S. Private*, pg. 248

Rosowski, Robert B., V.P. & Controller--Masco Corporation, Taylor, MI; *U.S. Public*, pg. 1052

Ross, D.R., V.P. & Controller--Pyle Inc., Elmhurst, IL; *U.S. Private*, pg. 629

Ross, Gloria, Controller--Bridgeway Hospital, North Little Rock, AR; *U.S. Public*, pg. 1696

Ross, James L., V.P. & Controller--CSX Corporation, Richmond, VA; *U.S. Public*, pg. 284

Ross, Janet, Controller--Ellison Graphics, Jupiter, FL; *U.S. Private*, pg. 524

Ross, John, Corp. Controller--MarketSource Corporation, Cranbury, NJ; *U.S. Private*, pg. 705

Ross, John, Controller--Trafalgar House PLC, London, United Kingdom; *Int'l*, pg. 772

Ross, John, Controller--Imaging Services, Leominster, MA; *Int'l*, pg. 1076

Ross, Livingston E., V.P. & Controller--Citizens Utilities Company, Stamford, CT; *U.S. Public*, pg. 379

Ross, Lyle, Controller--Lan-O-Sheen, Inc., Saint Paul, MN; *U.S. Private*, pg. 645

Ross, Mell, Controller--CVC Products, Inc., Rochester, NY; *U.S. Private*, pg. 197

Ross, Nancy, Controller--BGF Industries Inc., Greensboro, NC; *U.S. Private*, pg. 106

Ross, Rose, Controller--Bodine Assembly and Test Systems, Bridgeport, CT; *U.S. Private*, pg. 154

Ross, S., Comptroller--Monarch Luggage Co. Inc., Brooklyn, NY; *U.S. Private*, pg. 757

Rosset, Bruno, Controller--Datapoint S.A., Rungis, France; *Int'l*, pg. 384

Rossler, Bobbi, Controller--F.H. Bonn Company, Springfield, OH; *U.S. Private*, pg. 156

Rossmeisl, Shirley I., Controller--Hazen Paper Company, Holyoke, MA; *U.S. Private*, pg. 514

Roth, Barbara J., Controller--Nielsen Dillingham Builders, Inc., San Diego, CA; *U.S. Private*, pg. 333

Roth, Doug, Controller--Pony U.S.A., Nashville, TN; *Int'l*, pg. 1036

Roth, Peter, Controller--Brauerei AG, Zurich, Switzerland; *Int'l*, pg. 479

Rothman, Marc, Controller--General Instrument Corporation, Horsham, PA; *U.S. Public*, pg. 716

Rothrock, Gordon, V.P. & Controller--DSC Logistics, Inc., Des Plaines, IL; *U.S. Private*, pg. 306

Rothwell, Ronnie E., Controller--Arrow Industries, Inc., Carrollton, TX; *U.S. Public*, pg. 426

Rotolo, Jan, Controller--Harris, Baio & McCullough Inc., Philadelphia, PA; *U.S. Private*, pg. 504

Rottman, Robert, Mng. Dir. & Controller--Nomura Securities International, Inc., New York, NY; *Int'l*, pg. 956

Rouhselang, Sandra, V.P. & Controller--Edward Don & Company, North Riverside, IL; *U.S. Private*, pg. 339

Rountree, Jane, Controller--MelloButtercup Ice Cream Inc., Wilson, NC; *U.S. Private*, pg. 730

Rouse, John J., Jr., V.P. & Controller--Cox Broadcasting Inc., Atlanta, GA; *U.S. Private*, pg. 281

Rousseau, Scott, V.P.-Admin., Controller, Treas. & Sec.--Palmer Electric Co., Winter Park, FL; *U.S. Private*, pg. 834

Routt, J. Robert, V.P. & Controller--The E.W. Scripps Company, Cincinnati, OH; *U.S. Public*, pg. 1447

Rowan, D., Controller--Union Camp Flexible Packaging, Wayne, NJ; *U.S. Public*, pg. 1666

Rowe, Jean, Controller--Carlton Manufacturing, Inc., Goshen, IN; *U.S. Private*, pg. 212

Rowe, Tim, Controller--Aztex Enterprises, Knoxville, TN; *U.S. Private*, pg. 104

Rowe, W.G., Controller--Ames Taping Tool Systems Co., Duluth, GA; *U.S. Private*, pg. 103

Rowell, Colie, Controller--Central Coca-Cola Bottling Company, Inc., Richmond, VA; *U.S. Private*, pg. 222

Rowland, Don, Controller--Sequa Chemicals, Inc., Chester, SC; *U.S. Public*, pg. 1459

Rowlen, Thomas M., Controller, Treas. & Sec.--Yoder Oil Company Inc., Elkhart, IN; *U.S. Private*, pg. 1196

Rowlett, Donald R., Controller--OGE Energy Corp., Oklahoma City, OK; *U.S. Public*, pg. 1207

Roy, G., Controller--Place Turcot Mill, Montreal, Canada; *Int'l*, pg. 761

Roy, Richard R., V.P. & Controller--Gilbane Building Company, Providence, RI; *U.S. Private*, pg. 452

Rozevink, Ron, Controller--Michigan Cat, Novi, MI; *U.S. Private*, pg. 740

Rubar, W.H., Controller--BE & K, Inc., Birmingham, AL; *U.S. Private*, pg. 106

Rubenovitch, Peter H., Sr. V.P. & Controller--Manulife Financial (The Manufacturers Life Insurance Company), Toronto, Canada; *Int'l*, pg. 840

Rubinson, Irving, V.P. & Asst. Controller--Block Drug Company, Inc., Jersey City, NJ; *U.S. Public*, pg. 236

Ruble, Joyce, Controller--K-VA-T, Abingdon, VA; *U.S. Private*, pg. 603

Rucinski, Bob, Controller--Orthofix Inc., Richardson, TX; *Int'l*, pg. 1011

Rucker, Edward, Controller--Nitram Energy Inc., Orchard Park, NY; *U.S. Private*, pg. 799

Ruddock, Evette, Controller--Del Global Technologies, Valhalla, NY; *U.S. Public*, pg. 493

Rudinsky, Charles, Controller--Global Petroleum Corp., Waltham, MA; *U.S. Private*, pg. 457

Rudolph, Carl J., V.P. & Controller--Aid Association for Lutherans, Appleton, WI; *U.S. Private*, pg. 27

Rudolph, Daniel, Controller--Spartech Corporation, Clayton, MO; *U.S. Public*, pg. 1495

Rudolph, Esmond, Controller--Applied Biosystems, Foster City, CA; *U.S. Public*, pg. 1279

Rudy, Cindy, V.P.-Fin.--Nautilus International, Independence, VA; *U.S. Public*, pg. 498

Rue, Eugene D., Controller & Mgr.-Credit--R.C.A. Rubber Company, Akron, OH; *U.S. Private*, pg. 902

Ruegg, Rudolf, Controller--Landis & Staefa AG, Zug, Switzerland; *Int'l*, pg. 800

Ruf, Walter, Controller--Forbo Holding SA, Eglisau, Switzerland; *Int'l*, pg. 496

Rufai, Charles, Controller--Carver Federal Savings Bank, New York, NY; *U.S. Public*, pg. 310

Rufer, Friedrich, Controller--Georg Fischer Ltd., Schaffhausen, Switzerland; *Int'l*, pg. 488

Ruffing, Robert H., Controller--American Financial Group, Cincinnati, OH; *U.S. Public*, pg. 74

Ruffreux, T., Controller--Moore Paragon (Suisse) S.A., Lausanne, Switzerland; *Int'l*, pg. 890

Ruggieri, Tom, Controller--American Vanguard Corporation, Newport Beach, CA; *U.S. Public*, pg. 94

Rugrugotska, Mary, Controller--Chicago Consolidated, Madison, WI; *U.S. Private*, pg. 533

Ruiz, Paul, Controller--VTEL Corporation, Austin, TX; *U.S. Public*, pg. 1703

Rullie, Richard, Controller--Joan & David Helpern, Inc., New York, NY; *U.S. Private*, pg. 521

Rulon, Robert E., V.P. & Controller--Lockheed Martin Corporation, Bethesda, MD; *U.S. Public*, pg. 1006

Ruminski, Dick, V.P.-Fin. Opers. & Controller--Bergen Brunswig Corporation, Orange, CA; *U.S. Public*, pg. 213

Runge, Scott, Treas.--Calavo Growers of California, Santa Ana, CA; *U.S. Private*, pg. 199

Runtz, James, Controller--Tempel Steel Company, Skokie, IL; *U.S. Private*, pg. 1075

Runz, Robert G., Controller--AEP Industries, Inc., South Hackensack, NJ; *U.S. Public*, pg. 4

Rupke, Jerry I., Controller & Treas.--Public Utility District No. 2 of Grant County, Ephrata, WA; *U.S. Private*, pg. 893

Rupp, Kevin A., Controller--Fina, Inc., Dallas, TX; *Int'l*, pg. 1044

Rushing, Paula H., V.P. & Controller--Alabama Gas Corporation, Birmingham, AL; *U.S. Public*, pg. 581

Russel, Joyce, Chief Fin. Officer, Sr. V.P. & Controller--Jostens Learning Corporation, San Diego, CA; *U.S. Private*, pg. 601

Russell, Barbara, Controller--Hitox Corporation of America, Corpus Christi, TX; *U.S. Public*, pg. 829

Russell, Bonnie, Controller--The Gazette Company, Cedar Rapids, IA; *U.S. Private*, pg. 442

Russell, Dianne, Controller & Mgr.-Admin.--Industra Service Corporation, New Westminster, Canada; *Int'l*, pg. 74

Russell, F. William, Controller--Farmers & Merchants Bank of Central California, Lodi, CA; *U.S. Private*, pg. 394

Russell, Pamela, Controller--Porcelain Products, Carey, OH; *U.S. Public*, pg. 308

Russell, Richard G., Sr. V.P. & Controller--RJR Nabisco Holdings Corp., New York, NY; *U.S. Public*, pg. 1354

Russo, Jeff, Controller--Hadeler Sullivan Ewing, Dallas, TX; *U.S. Private*, pg. 493

Rust, Kevin, Controller--Allied Industrial Group, Inc., Saint Louis, MO; *U.S. Private*, pg. 39

Rust, Kevin, Controller--Chemtech Products Inc., Saint Louis, MO; *U.S. Private*, pg. 39

Ruth, Jim, V.P. & Controller--Modern Welding Co., Inc., Owensboro, KY; *U.S. Private*, pg. 755

Rutkowski, Rick, Controller--La Marche Mfg. Co., Des Plaines, IL; *U.S. Private*, pg. 640

Rutman, Bob, Controller--Frederick Atkins, New York, NY; *U.S. Private*, pg. 94

Rutzer, Franz, Controller--Oerlikon-Buhrle Holding AG, Zurich, Switzerland; *Int'l*, pg. 996

Rutzler, John E., III, V.P. & Controller--Zurn Industries, Inc., Erie, PA; *U.S. Public*, pg. 1794

Ryan, Beverly, Controller--Patch Communications, Titusville, FL; *U.S. Private*, pg. 842

Ryan, Ed, Controller--Magnetic Analysis Corp., Mount Vernon, NY; *U.S. Private*, pg. 695

Ryan, Herbert V., V.P. & Controller--Pfizer Inc., New York, NY; *U.S. Public*, pg. 1281

Ryan, Jack, Controller--Precision Products Corporation, Rockford, IL; *U.S. Private*, pg. 879

Ryan, James, Controller--Power Systems Inc., Bloomfield, CT; *Int'l*, pg. 868

Ryan, Jim, Controller & Treas.--Harker's Distribution, Inc., Le Mars, IA; *U.S. Private*, pg. 502

Ryan, John, Dir.-Corp. Communications--CIBC Oppenheimer Corp., New York, NY; *Int'l*, pg. 257

Ryan, June, Controller--Griffin Bacal Volny, Toronto, Canada; *U.S. Private*, pg. 480

Ryan, William T., Controller--VASA Brougher, Inc., Indianapolis, IN; *Int'l*, pg. 464

Rycroft, Mary, Controller--Richard Lewis Paper Corporation, Northfield, IL; *U.S. Private*, pg. 467

Rydin, Anders, Grp. Controller--Skandinaviska Enskilda Banken, Stockholm, Sweden; *Int'l*, pg. 1258

Rydzewski, Philip, Controller--PHP Healthcare Corporation, Reston, VA; *U.S. Public*, pg. 1241

Rye, Walter L., Chm. Bd. & Chief Exec. Officer--Cincinnati Gear Company, Cincinnati, OH; *U.S. Private*, pg. 240

Rynne, John P., Controller--Eaton Vance Corp., Boston, MA; *U.S. Public*, pg. 559

Ryss, Russ, Controller--Land O'Lakes, Inc., Kiel, WI; *U.S. Private*, pg. 646

Sabater, Carmen M., Controller--MasTec, Inc., Miami, FL; *U.S. Public*, pg. 1055

Sabella, Angela J., V.P. & Controller--Shaklee Corporation, San Francisco, CA; *Int'l*, pg. 1518

Sabella, Bobbe V., Controller--General Electric Capital Aviation Services, San Francisco, CA; *U.S. Public*, pg. 712

Sabina, Frank, Controller & Treas.--Case Paper Co., Inc., Long Island City, NY; *U.S. Private*, pg. 218

Sabocik, William, Plant Controller--Ardmore Farms, De Land, FL; *U.S. Public*, pg. 1348

Sabol, Joseph, Controller--Conap Inc., Olean, NY; *U.S. Private*, pg. 261

Sabourin, Diane, Controller--The Guber Peters Entertainment Company, Los Angeles, CA; *Int'l*, pg. 1283

Sachdeva, Sue, V.P.-Fin. & Controller--Koss Corporation, Milwaukee, WI; *U.S. Public*, pg. 966

Sachno, Andy, Controller--Adler Boschetto Peebles & Partners, Inc., New York, NY; *U.S. Private*, pg. 17

Sack, Dieter, Dir.-Fin. & Controller--Deutsche Bahn, Frankfurt/Main, Germany; *Int'l*, pg. 401

Sacripanti, P., Controller--Lafarge Construction Materials, Canfield, OH; *Int'l*, pg. 788

Sactino, Tony, Controller--O.F. Mossberg & Sons, Inc., North Haven, CT; *U.S. Private*, pg. 764

Sadek, John A., V.P. & Comptroller--Southern New England Telecommunications Corporation, New Haven, CT; *U.S. Public*, pg. 1490

Sadowski, Chester P., Chief Acctg. Officer, V.P. & Controller--U.S. Home Corporation, Houston, TX; *U.S. Public*, pg. 1682

Saenz, R., Controller--Kolana S.A., Callao, Peru; *U.S. Public*, pg. 81

Safir, Judy, Controller--Seventeen Magazine, New York, NY; *U.S. Public*, pg. 1328

Sage, George, Controller--Great Neck Saw Manufacturers, Inc., Mineola, NY; *U.S. Private*, pg. 475

Sagenella, Peggy, Controller--A&Z Hayward, Inc., East Providence, RI; *U.S. Private*, pg. 2

Sahuc, Peter, Controller--Performance Medical Group, Lafayette, LA; *U.S. Private*, pg. 853

Saitta, Richard J., Asst. Comptroller--Broad National Bank, Newark, NJ; *U.S. Public*, pg. 257

Saksa, John, Controller--Sanden International (U.S.A.), Inc., Wylie, TX; *Int'l*, pg. 1184

Saladino, John A., Controller--ROHN Industries, Inc., Peoria, IL; *U.S. Public*, pg. 1404

Salasatinos, Chris, Controller--Reynolds Machine Tool Corp., Melrose Park, IL; *U.S. Private*, pg. 926

Salaz, Brenda, Controller--Rosauers Supermarkets, Inc., Spokane, WA; *U.S. Private*, pg. 944

Salberg, Greg, Controller--Quality Pontiac GMC Buick, Albuquerque, NM; *U.S. Private*, pg. 899

Sale, A.D., Controller--Beaird Industries, Inc., Shreveport, LA; *U.S. Public*, pg. 1639

Salem, Linda, Corp. Controller--Great Plains Manufacturing, Inc., Salina, KS; *U.S. Private*, pg. 475

Salene, Terri, Controller--Pasotex Corporation, El Paso, TX; *U.S. Private*, pg. 842

Sales, Diana, Controller--Williams Patent Crusher and Pulverizer Co., Saint Louis, MO; *U.S. Private*, pg. 1178

Salinas, Jerry, Controller--Frost National Bank, San Antonio, TX; *U.S. Public*, pg. 467

Sall, Ralph, Controller--AFD Contract Furniture, New York, NY; *U.S. Private*, pg. 5

Sallese, Peter, Controller--Newbridge Communications, Inc., New York, NY; *Int'l*, pg. 191

Salmonsen, Valerie, V.P. & Controller--Lawrence Savings Bank, North Andover, MA; *U.S. Public*, pg. 980

Salomon, Lars, Sr. V.P. & Controller--AGA AB, Lidingo, Sweden; *Int'l*, pg. 12

Salonen, Timo, Grp. V.P. & Controller--Leaf Group B.V., Espoo, Finland,; *Int'l*, pg. 638

Saludares, Manny, Controller--The Pervo Paint Company, Los Angeles, CA; *U.S. Private*, pg. 856

Salvator, Charles, Controller--Trifari Jewelers, New York, NY; *U.S. Private*, pg. 757

Salvo, Henry J., Jr., V.P. & Controller--The Clorox Company, Oakland, CA; *U.S. Public*, pg. 386

Salzer, Uwe, Dr., Controller--Degussa AG, Frankfurt/Main, Germany; *Int'l*, pg. 388

Salzwedel, Larry M., Controller--Honeymead Products Co., Mankato, MN; *U.S. Private*, pg. 537

Samford, Ron E., Jr., Exec. V.P. & Controller--Hibernia Corporation, New Orleans, LA; *U.S. Public*, pg. 825

Samide, Thomas D., Asst. Controller--Bachman Company, Reading, PA; *U.S. Private*, pg. 109

Samila, Tatiana, Asst. Controller--Hollinger Inc., Vancouver, Canada; *Int'l*, pg. 630

Sammon, B.P., Controller--Marley PLC, Sevenoaks, United Kingdom; *Int'l*, pg. 843

Sammons, Paul, Controller--Old America Stores, Howe, TX; *U.S. Public*, pg. 1215

Samonek, Kenneth J., Controller--The Producto Machine Co., Bridgeport, CT; *U.S. Private*, pg. 889

Sams, Trent, V.P. & Controller--Bostonian Shoe Co., Newton, MA; *Int'l*, pg. 297

Samuel, Kitty, Controller--Lynden Incorporated, Seattle, WA; *U.S. Private*, pg. 683

Samuels, Gerald M., Controller--Junior Gallery Ltd., New York, NY; *U.S. Private*, pg. 602

Samuelson, Brooke, Controller--Roundtree Automotive Group, Shreveport, LA; *U.S. Private*, pg. 947

Samuelsson, Goran, Controller--Atlet AB, Molnlycke, Sweden; *Int'l*, pg. 97

San Pedro, Jose Luis, Controller, Treas. & Mng. Dir.-Economy & Fin.--Iberdrola, S.A., Bilbao, Spain; *Int'l*, pg. 657
San, L.C., Controller--Esso Production Malaysia Inc., Kuala Lumpur, Malaysia; *U.S. Public*, pg. 602
Sanborn, Steve, Controller--Noble House Hotels and Resorts, Kirkland, WA; *U.S. Private*, pg. 800
Sancher, Raymond, Controller--FATA Production Machinery, Cleveland, OH; *Int'l*, pg. 474
Sand, Eric, Controller--Zero Corporation, Los Angeles, CA; *U.S. Public*, pg. 1791
Sandeen, Roger D., Chief Info. Officer, V.P. & Controller--Northern States Power Company, Minneapolis, MN; *U.S. Public*, pg. 1195
Sandeen, Roger D., Controller--Northern States Power Co. (Wis.), Eau Claire, WI; *U.S. Public*, pg. 1195
Sandefur, Connie, Controller--Hercules Engine Company, Canton, OH; *U.S. Private*, pg. 523
Sandeman, Debbie, Comtroller--Pick's Cove Marina, Tacoma, WA; *U.S. Private*, pg. 865
Sander, Richard W., Jr., V.P. & Controller--Cable Television Division, New Canaan, CT; *U.S. Public*, pg. 329
Sanders, Barry, Controller--Steiner Electric Company, Elk Grove Village, IL; *U.S. Private*, pg. 1039
Sanders, Jeff, V.P. & Controller--Consorcio G. Grupo Dina, S.A. de C.V., Mexico, Mexico; *Int'l*, pg. 326
Sanders, Richard, Controller--Bermil Industries Corp., Inwood, NY; *U.S. Private*, pg. 136
Sanders, Roger L. II, Controller--Imperial Bondware Corp., Montvale, NJ; *U.S. Public*, pg. 903
Sanders, Roger L., II, Controller--Federal Paper Board Company, Inc., Montvale, NJ; *U.S. Public*, pg. 903
Sanders, Thomas J., V.P. & Asst. Controller--Reliance Group Holdings, Inc., New York, NY; *U.S. Public*, pg. 1374
Sanderson, Randy C., V.P. & Controller--Dollar General Corporation, Nashville, TN; *U.S. Public*, pg. 515
Sandler, Robert M., Sr. V.P. & Controller--The Cato Corporation, Charlotte, NC; *U.S. Public*, pg. 318
Sandler, Tom, V.P.-Fin. & Corp. Controller--Lark Luggage Company, Inc., Denver, CO; *U.S. Public*, pg. 1430
Sands, Perry, Controller--Sam Kane Beef Processors, Inc., Corpus Christi, TX; *U.S. Private*, pg. 607
Sands, R.W., Controller--Energizer Eveready Ltd., London, United Kingdom; *U.S. Public*, pg. 1360
Sandy, Phil, Controller--Global Software, Inc., Raleigh, NC; *U.S. Private*, pg. 457
Sanfilppo, James J., Controller--Pentech International, Inc., Edison, NJ; *U.S. Public*, pg. 1274
Sanford, James, Controller--Atlantic Builders Group Inc., Baltimore, MD; *U.S. Private*, pg. 95
Sang, Sit Peng, Fin. Controller--Keppel-Fels Ltd., Singapore, Singapore; *Int'l*, pg. 731
Sangesland, Wendy, Controller--Robotic Vision Systems, Inc., Hauppauge, NY; *U.S. Public*, pg. 1395
Sangster, Gordon, V.P.-Fin. & Controller--Advanced Polymer Systems, Redwood City, CA; *U.S. Public*, pg. 22
Santa Maria, Jerry, Controller--XKD Corporation, Los Gatos, CA; *U.S. Private*, pg. 1194
Santacroce, John, Controller--Argo International Corp., New York, NY; *U.S. Private*, pg. 322
Santamaria, Susana, Controller--Sensormatic del Caribe, Isla Verde, PR; *U.S. Public*, pg. 1457
Santos, Oliver, Controller--AC Martin Partners, Los Angeles, CA; *U.S. Private*, pg. 708
Saperstein, Robert, Controller--Cosco Industries, Spring Valley, NY; *U.S. Private*, pg. 277
Sapieha, Jerry, Corp. Controller--Ocelot Energy Inc., Calgary, Canada; *Int'l*, pg. 996
Saponaro, Steve, Controller--Richey Electronics, Inc., Garden Grove, CA; *U.S. Public*, pg. 1388
Sapp, Roger, Sec. & Controller--Wurzburg, Inc., Memphis, TN; *U.S. Private*, pg. 1192
Sappe, Phyllis, Asst. Controller--Doral Hotel & Resorts Management Co., New York, NY; *U.S. Private*, pg. 340
Sardononi, Ellen, Controller--Boston Digital Corp., Milford, MA; *U.S. Private*, pg. 161
Sarina, Michael L., Controller--Wilbur-Ellis Company & Connell Brothers Company, San Francisco, CA; *U.S. Private*, pg. 1175
Sarmiento, Alice, Controller--Admiral Maintenance Service L.P., Lincolnwood, IL; *U.S. Private*, pg. 17
Sarnese, William E., Controller & Asst. Corp. Sec.--Penn Engineering & Manufacturing Corp., Danboro, PA; *U.S. Public*, pg. 1269
Sartin, David P., Controller & Sec.--Central Power and Light Company, Corpus Christi, TX; *U.S. Public*, pg. 324
Sartor, Robert, V.P. & Controller--Avenor, Inc., Montreal, Canada; *Int'l*, pg. 101
Sarver, David A., V.P. & Reg. Controller--FirstMerit Corporation, Akron, OH; *U.S. Public*, pg. 646
Sassin, Joe, Controller--Tauber Oil Company, Houston, TX; *U.S. Private*, pg. 1069
Sategna, T.G., Controller-Electric--Public Service Company of New Mexico, Albuquerque, NM; *U.S. Public*, pg. 1339
Sato, Kyoko, Controller--Nihon Kenall K.K., Tokyo, Japan; *U.S. Public*, pg. 1648
Sator, Robert, Controller--The Imagination Network, Burlingame, CA; *U.S. Public*, pg. 66
Sattler, James E., Controller--Redland Ohio Inc., Woodville, OH; *Int'l*, pg. 1091
Sauer, Thomas J., V.P., Treas. & Controller--McGrath RentCorp, Livermore, CA; *U.S. Public*, pg. 1069
Sauerwein, Robert A., V.P. & Controller--The Okonite Company, Ramsey, NJ; *U.S. Private*, pg. 813
Saunders, Dan, Controller--Nestle Beverage Company, Sunbury, OH; *Int'l*, pg. 918
Saunders, Douglas C., V.P. & Corp. Controller--InterTAN Inc., Fort Worth, TX; *U.S. Public*, pg. 910
Saunders, F.G., V.P. & Controller--Bradford-White Corporation, Ambler, PA; *U.S. Private*, pg. 164
Saunders, Tim, Corp. Controller--Mitel Corporation, Kanata, Canada; *Int'l*, pg. 870
Savage, Anne, Controller--American Buildings Co., Eufaula, AL; *U.S. Public*, pg. 69
Savage, Jim, Controller--Howell Packaging, Burlington, Canada; *Int'l*, pg. 417
Savery, Susanne, Controller--Glenayre Electronics, Inc., Quincy, IL; *U.S. Public*, pg. 747
Savignano, John, Controller--Carl Zeiss, Inc., Thornwood, NY; *Int'l*, pg. 1523
Savinsky, Sandy, Controller--Den-Mat Corporation, Santa Maria, CA; *U.S. Private*, pg. 324
Savona, Marco, Controller & Treas.--Abbott Ball Company, West Hartford, CT; *U.S. Private*, pg. 9
Savoy, Harold, Jr., Controller--Contadina Dalla Casa Buitoni, Glendale, CA; *Int'l*, pg. 916
Sawhney, Vinay, Asst. Controller--Stowe-Pharr Mills, Inc., Mc Adenville, NC; *U.S. Private*, pg. 1045
Sawicki, Richard J., Comptroller--Warren Equities Inc., Providence, RI; *U.S. Private*, pg. 1151
Sawyer, Jim, Controller--Town & Country Supermarket, Hardy, AR; *U.S. Private*, pg. 1093
Sawyer, Merla, V.P.-Fin., Controller--Elan Pharmaceutical Research Corp., Gainesville, GA; *Int'l*, pg. 436
Sax, Jerry, V.P. & Controller--Berg Electronics, Saint Louis, MO; *U.S. Public*, pg. 212
Saxton, Pam, V.P.-Fin. & Controller--J.D. Edwards & Company, Denver, CO; *U.S. Private*, pg. 365
Sayers, Jo-Anne, Fin. Controller--Inmet Mining Corporation, Toronto, Canada; *Int'l*, pg. 678
Sayers, Jo-Anne, Asst. Controller--Metall Mining Corporation, Toronto, Canada; *Int'l*, pg. 862
Sayre, Larry, Chief Fin. Officer, V.P.-Fin., Controller & Treas.--Collins Industries, Inc., Hutchinson, KS; *U.S. Public*, pg. 399
Sayre, Michael R., Controller--Worthington Industries, Inc., Columbus, OH; *U.S. Public*, pg. 1780
Scallera, Mike, Controller--Head Distributing Co., Smyrna, GA; *U.S. Private*, pg. 514
Scalzi, Barbara, Controller--Chiswick Trading Inc., Sudbury, MA; *U.S. Private*, pg. 237
Scanlon, George B., V.P. & Controller--Ryder System, Inc., Miami, FL; *U.S. Public*, pg. 1413
Scanlon, Patrick, Controller--Penn Security Bank and Trust Co., Scranton, PA; *U.S. Public*, pg. 1270
Scanlon, Rebecca, Controller--Jackson MS Steel Division, Jackson, MS; *U.S. Public*, pg. 232
Scardino, John, Jr., V.P. & Controller--Florida Progress Corporation, Saint Petersburg, FL; *U.S. Public*, pg. 655
Scardino, John, Jr., V.P. & Controller--Florida Power Corporation, Saint Petersburg, FL; *U.S. Public*, pg. 655
Scaringi, Tony, Controller--Imprimerie Quebecor Montreal, Montreal, Canada; *Int'l*, pg. 1077
Scarpati, Steve, Sr. V.P.-Fin. Mngmt. & Controller--The Guardian Life Insurance Company of America, New York, NY; *U.S. Private*, pg. 486
Scavone, Anne M., Controller--IMC Global, Bannockburn, IL; *U.S. Public*, pg. 856
Scerbo, John, Controller--Merco/Savory Inc., Lakewood, NJ; *Int'l*, pg. 189
Schaapveld, Larry, Chief Fin. Officer, V.P., Controller & Treas.--Varied Investments, Inc., Muscatine, IA; *U.S. Private*, pg. 1134
Schachinger, Christoff, Controller--Bennington Iron Works, Inc., Bennington, VT; *U.S. Private*, pg. 133
Schaechterle, Gordon E., Jr., V.P., Controller & Tax Counsel--Mapco Inc., Tulsa, OK; *U.S. Public*, pg. 1042
Schaefer, Robert B., Controller--Matlack Systems, Inc., Wilmington, DE; *U.S. Public*, pg. 1057
Schaefer, Robert B., Controller--Rollins Truck Leasing Corp., Wilmington, DE; *U.S. Public*, pg. 1405
Schafer, Gary, V.P. & Controller--Forstmann & Company, Inc., New York, NY; *U.S. Public*, pg. 670
Schalek, Linda, Controller--Valassis Communications, Inc., Livonia, MI; *U.S. Public*, pg. 1704
Schambach, Stanley L., Controller--Hoffer Plastics Corporation, South Elgin, IL; *U.S. Private*, pg. 532
Schario, Paul V., Controller--Canton Drop Forge, Canton, OH; *U.S. Private*, pg. 205
Schatt-Schneider, S.T., Controller--Somerset Railroad Corp., Ithaca, NY; *U.S. Public*, pg. 1173
Schattschneider, Susan T., Asst. Controller--New York State Electric & Gas Corporation, Binghamton, NY; *U.S. Public*, pg. 1173
Schaus, Sandra L., V.P. & Controller--ServiceMaster Food Management Services, Downers Grove, IL; *U.S. Public*, pg. 1462
Scheerbaum, Heidi, Asst. Controller--American Home Improvement, Monroeville, PA; *U.S. Private*, pg. 56
Scheffy, Hubert, Jr., V.P. & Controller--Lewis Homes Management Corp., Upland, CA; *U.S. Private*, pg. 665
Scheinast, Johann, Controller--Julius Meinl AG, Vienna, Austria; *Int'l*, pg. 856
Scheitlin, Jeff, V.P. & Controller--Bally Total Fitness Holdings Corporation, Chicago, IL; *U.S. Public*, pg. 171
Schelle, Nathan T., V.P., Controller & Asst. Sec.--Bailey, Fischer & Porter Company, Warminster, PA; *Int'l*, pg. 449
Schellenberg, Dawn, Controller--Imprimerie Quebecor Canada, Woodbridge, Canada; *Int'l*, pg. 1077
Schelling, Elmer, Controller--Aurora Metals Division L.P.C., Montgomery, IL; *U.S. Private*, pg. 529
Schempf, David J., V.P. & Controller--COMPAQ Computer Corporation, Houston, TX; *U.S. Public*, pg. 417
Schenker, Robert, V.P. & Controller--The CIT Group/Commercial Services, New York, NY; *Int'l*, pg. 360
Scherer, George F., Chief Fin. Officer, Exec. V.P. & Treas.--McCarthy Building Companies, Saint Louis, MO; *U.S. Private*, pg. 719
Scherer, Michael, Controller--W. Gamby & Co., New York, NY; *U.S. Private*, pg. 439
Scherer, Thomas E., V.P. & Controller--W.H. Brady Co., Milwaukee, WI; *U.S. Public*, pg. 250
Scherff, Kevin, Controller--Case-Swayne Co. Inc., Corona, CA; *U.S. Private*, pg. 218
Scherier, Chris, Asst. V.P. & Asst. Controller--ReliaStar Financial Corp., Minneapolis, MN; *U.S. Public*, pg. 1375
Scherpf, Joseph C., V.P. & Controller--U.S. Surgical Corp., Norwalk, CT; *U.S. Public*, pg. 1687
Schevers, A., Controller--CSM Ingredients Division, Diemen, Netherlands; *Int'l*, pg. 243
Schiappa, Gene, Controller--ZMP, Inc., Glendale, CA; *U.S. Private*, pg. 1203
Schick, Kevin C., Chief Fin. Officer, V.P., Controller & Treas.--Con-Way Transportation Services, Palo Alto, CA; *U.S. Public*, pg. 281
Schiemann, Dirk, Mgr.-Fin.--Apollinaris & Schweppes Gmbh & Co., Hamburg, Germany; *Int'l*, pg. 78
Schierbaum, Wayne D., Sr. V.P.-Fin. & Controller--White Consolidated Industries, Inc., Cleveland, OH; *Int'l*, pg. 439
Schiess, John M., Exec. V.P.-Fin. & Controller--General Brewing Company, Vancouver, WA; *U.S. Private*, pg. 954
Schiff, Frederick S., V.P.-Fin. Opers. & Controller--Bristol-Myers Squibb Company, New York, NY; *U.S. Public*, pg. 253
Schiff, John, Corp. Controller--General Brewing Company, Vancouver, WA; *U.S. Private*, pg. 954
Schiff, John, Corp. Controller--Falstaff Brewing Corporation, San Antonio, TX; *U.S. Private*, pg. 955
Schiffner, Robert A., V.P. & Controller--Nabisco Inc., Parsippany, NJ; *U.S. Public*, pg. 1355
Schilling, Kenneth C., Controller--NACCO Industries, Inc., Cleveland, OH; *U.S. Public*, pg. 1149
Schilperoot, F.A.P., Controller--Industrial Pharmaceutical Products Division, Delft, Netherlands; *Int'l*, pg. 1142
Schimp, Dan, Controller--Mohawk Paper Mills, Inc., Cohoes, NY; *U.S. Private*, pg. 755
Schlange, Richard W., V.P. & Controller--Hormel Foods Corp., Austin, MN; *U.S. Public*, pg. 840
Schlatter, Richard, Corp. V.P. & Controller--Ferro Union, Inc., Torrance, CA; *U.S. Private*, pg. 402
Schlattman, Robert, V.P. & Controller--Whittaker Controls, Inc., North Hollywood, CA; *U.S. Public*, pg. 1767
Schleifer, Steve, V.P. & Controller--SDI Technologies Inc., Rahway, NJ; *U.S. Private*, pg. 956
Schlesinger, Albert R., V.P. & Controller--Ball Corporation, Muncie, IN; *U.S. Public*, pg. 170
Schliess, John, Controller--S & P Company, Mill Valley, CA; *U.S. Private*, pg. 954
Schlosser, P., Treas. & Sec.--Krupp Robins, Inc., Englewood, CO; *Int'l*, pg. 511
Schlotman, Mike, V.P. & Controller--The Kroger Co., Cincinnati, OH; *U.S. Public*, pg. 967
Schlotterbeck, Andrew P., V.P. & Controller--Data Broadcasting Corporation, Jackson, WY; *U.S. Public*, pg. 484
Schlueter, R.J., Asst. Controller--Emerson Electric Co., Saint Louis, MO; *U.S. Public*, pg. 572
Schlukebier, William, Corp. Controller--Jostens, Minneapolis, MN; *U.S. Public*, pg. 934
Schluter, Helmut, Controller--Hermann Pfauter GmbH & Co., Ludwigsburg, Germany; *Int'l*, pg. 617
Schmalz, Douglas J., Chief Fin. Officer & V.P.--Archer Daniels Midland Company (ADM), Decatur, IL; *U.S. Public*, pg. 127
Schmeider, Luke R., Pres., Treas. & Chief Exec. Officer--Mesa Laboratories, Inc., Wheat Ridge, CO; *U.S. Public*, pg. 1099
Schmid, Rolf, Treas.--Wandel & Goltermann GmbH & Co., Elektronische Messtechnik, Eningen, Germany; *Int'l*, pg. 1485
Schmidt, Brenda, Controller--Lawson Software, Minneapolis, MN; *U.S. Private*, pg. 654
Schmidt, Brian L., Controller--Wayne Steel, Inc., Wooster, OH; *U.S. Public*, pg. 1101
Schmidt, Cheryl A., Controller--Fitzpatrick & Weller, Inc., Ellicottville, NY; *U.S. Private*, pg. 409
Schmidt, Dennis, Controller--Milwaukee Electric Tool Corp., Brookfield, WI; *Int'l*, pg. 96
Schmidt, Patrick, Controller & Sec.--Signtech USA, Ltd., San Antonio, TX; *U.S. Private*, pg. 999
Schmidt, R. John, Jr., Sr. V.P. & Controller--Office Depot Inc., Delray Beach, FL; *U.S. Public*, pg. 1212
Schmidt, Richard, Controller--Tecstar Inc., City of Industry, CA; *U.S. Private*, pg. 1072
Schmidt, Steve, Controller--Midwest Auto Parts Distributors, Inc., Saint Paul, MN; *U.S. Private*, pg. 744
Schmidt, Steve, Controller--Sacramento Kings, Sacramento, CA; *U.S. Private*, pg. 959
Schmidt, V., Fin. Controller--F.I.A.P. Deutschland GmbH, Rems, Germany; *U.S. Public*, pg. 5
Schmidt, William C., Asst. Controller--The Dow Chemical Company, Midland, MI; *U.S. Public*, pg. 522
Schmitt, Amy, V.P. & Controller--LINC Capital Group, Chicago, IL; *U.S. Public*, pg. 996
Schmitz, Stephen L., V.P. & Controller--Harmon Industries, Inc., Blue Springs, MO; *U.S. Public*, pg. 788
Schneble, James R., Controller--The Bureau of National Affairs, Inc., Washington, DC; *U.S. Private*, pg. 181
Schneible, William F., Controller, Treas. & Sec.--Brooklyn Bottling Co. of Milton, NY, Milton, NY; *U.S. Private*, pg. 171
Schneider, Charles, Controller--Basel Trading Company Ltd., Basel, Switzerland; *Int'l*, pg. 169
Schneider, David T., Chief Fin. Officer & V.P.--Formica Corporation, Wayne, NJ; *Int'l*, pg. 129
Schneider, E., Controller--Deminex-Deutsche GmbH, Essen, Germany; *Int'l*, pg. 1460
Schneider, James, Controller--Shelter Components Corporation, Elkhart, IN; *U.S. Public*, pg. 952
Schneider, James M., V.P.-Fin. & Corp. Controller--Dell Computer Corporation, Round Rock, TX; *U.S. Public*, pg. 495
Schneider, Todd, Controller--Peterson Builders, Inc., Sturgeon Bay, WI; *U.S. Private*, pg. 857
Schnieber, Steve, Controller--Schnieber Fine Foods, Inc., Lincoln, NE; *U.S. Private*, pg. 971

Schnoor, S.J., Controller--Patent Construction Systems, Paramus, NJ; *U.S. Public*, pg. 793

Schoaly, Lisa, Controller--Quincy Mutual Fire Insurance Company, Quincy, MA; *U.S. Private*, pg. 901

Schober, Mark A., Controller--Minnesota Power, Duluth, MN; *U.S. Public*, pg. 1116

Schocke, Robert P., Chief Fin. Officer, Treas., Controller & Sec.--Greenhorne & O'Mara, Inc., Greenbelt, MD; *U.S. Private*, pg. 477

Schoeffler, Michael H., Pres. & Chief Oper. Officer--Starcraft Corporation, Goshen, IN; *U.S. Public*, pg. 1510

Schoen, Wayne, Controller--Neuman Distributors, Inc., Ridgefield, NJ; *U.S. Public*, pg. 1169

Schoendorfer, Margarita A., V.P. & Controller--Manor Care, Inc., Gaithersburg, MD; *U.S. Public*, pg. 1041

Scholz, Robert, Controller--Edward C. Levy Co., Dearborn, MI; *U.S. Private*, pg. 664

Schoo, Jerry, V.P. & Controller--McCord Payen Inc., Wyandotte, MI; *Int'l*, pg. 1334

Schor, Irwin, Controller--Antwerp Diamond Distributors Inc., New York, NY; *U.S. Private*, pg. 76

Schossler, Frank, Controller--Worthington Foods Inc., Worthington, OH; *U.S. Public*, pg. 1780

Schott, James F., V.P.-Financial Services & Controller--Wisconsin Gas Company, Milwaukee, WI; *U.S. Public*, pg. 1767

Schott, Julie, Controller--Nuttall Gear Corporation, Niagara Falls, NY; *U.S. Private*, pg. 809

Schow, William F., V.P. & Controller--Magic Valley Foods, Inc., Rupert, ID; *U.S. Private*, pg. 695

Schraer, Greg, Controller--Health Management Systems, Inc., New York, NY; *U.S. Public*, pg. 802

Schramm, Dan M., V.P. & Controller--Pettibone Corporation, Lisle, IL; *U.S. Private*, pg. 859

Schramm, Harold, Controller--Schutte & Koerting Division, Bensalem, PA; *U.S. Private*, pg. 604

Schreiber, Eric, Mgr.-Fin.--Ceramtec North America Applications, Inc., Mansfield, MA; *Int'l*, pg. 860

Schreimer, Gregory, Controller--Elgin Watch Company, Long Island City, NY; *U.S. Private*, pg. 371

Schrimpf, Bill, Pres. & Controller--Piasa Motor Fuels Inc., Hartford, IL; *U.S. Private*, pg. 864

Schroder, Jurgen, Controller--Porsche AG, Stuttgart, Germany; *Int'l*, pg. 1063

Schroeder, Vern, Controller--Fresh Food, Inc., Hobart, IN; *U.S. Private*, pg. 427

Schrott, Craig, Controller--Associated Global Systems, New Hyde Park, NY; *U.S. Private*, pg. 90

Schubel, Traci, Corp. Controller--Dairyland Greyhound Park, Inc., Kenosha, WI; *U.S. Private*, pg. 307

Schuering, Jim, Controller & Treas.--J.D. Streett & Co., Inc., Maryland Heights, MO; *U.S. Private*, pg. 1047

Schultz, Gary, Controller--Lund Boats, New York Mills, MN; *U.S. Private*, pg. 447

Schultz, Harry, Controller--Trimfit, Inc., Bristol, PA; *U.S. Private*, pg. 1103

Schultz, Jim, Controller--BHP Copper North America, Tucson, AZ; *Int'l*, pg. 224

Schultz, Ron, Controller--Jack Ross Motors Inc., Tempe, AZ; *U.S. Private*, pg. 946

Schulz, Clifford J., Controller--Safety-Kleen Corp., Elgin, IL; *U.S. Public*, pg. 1425

Schulz, David J., Controller--Patrick Cudahy Inc., Cudahy, WI; *U.S. Public*, pg. 1479

Schulz, Scott L., Controller--Interactive Technologies, Inc., Saint Paul, MN; *U.S. Public*, pg. 888

Schulze, Bill, Controller--LFE Industrial Systems Corporation, Clinton, MA; *U.S. Public*, pg. 1045

Schumacher, Beth, Controller--Granger Construction Co., Lansing, MI; *U.S. Private*, pg. 469

Schumacher, David, Controller--Rogers Tool Works, Inc., Rogers, AR; *U.S. Public*, pg. 950

Schumacher, Norbert, Chief Fin. Officer, Sr. V.P. & Controller--Marathon Cheese Corp., Marathon, WI; *U.S. Private*, pg. 701

Schumacher, Richard C., V.P. & Controller--Brown Group, Inc., Saint Louis, MO; *U.S. Public*, pg. 262

Schuppert, Arno, Controller--Fried. Krupp AG, Essen, Germany; *Int'l*, pg. 507

Schurbon, Steven A., V.P. & Controller--Kaufman and Broad of Arizona, Inc., Phoenix, AZ; *U.S. Public*, pg. 945

Schurer, Bobby, Controller--Edd Helms Electrical Contracting, Miami, FL; *U.S. Private*, pg. 520

Schussel, Robert, Controller--National Distributing Co., Inc., Atlanta, GA; *U.S. Private*, pg. 781

Schuster, Ronald, V.P. & Controller--The Hunt Corporation, Indianapolis, IN; *U.S. Private*, pg. 548

Schwab, Mary Lou, Chief Fin. Officer, Controller & Treas.--Auto-trol Technology Corporation, Denver, CO; *U.S. Public*, pg. 148

Schwall, Jeff, Sr. V.P. & Controller--Warner Cable Communications, Inc., Columbus, OH; *U.S. Public*, pg. 1611

Schwartz-O'Hara, Mary, Controller--Mrs. Smith's Bakeries, Inc., Thomasville, GA; *U.S. Public*, pg. 657

Schwartz, John W., Controller--General Dynamics Corporation, Falls Church, VA; *U.S. Public*, pg. 708

Schwartz, Marvin, Chief Fin. Officer & Controller--Eagle Button Co., Inc., Carlstadt, NJ; *U.S. Private*, pg. 354

Schwartz, Robert, Controller--La Salle County Farm Supply, Ottawa, IL; *U.S. Private*, pg. 640

Schweiger, Barbara, Controller--Sensormatic AG, Cham, Switzerland; *U.S. Public*, pg. 1457

Schweiger, Michael, Controller--Zimmerman & Partners Advertising, Inc., Fort Lauderdale, FL; *U.S. Private*, pg. 1206

Schwenke, Bill, Controller--Donnkenny, Inc., New York, NY; *U.S. Public*, pg. 519

Schwinberg, Rick, Controller--Cloud Corporation, Des Plaines, IL; *U.S. Private*, pg. 247

Sciberras, Mario, Chief Fin. Officer & V.P.--Dearborn Gage Company, Garden City, MI; *U.S. Private*, pg. 319

Sciole, Domenick R., Controller--Pennock, Philadelphia, PA; *U.S. Private*, pg. 850

Sciscoe, Geri, Controller--PTS Electronics Corporation, Bloomington, IN; *U.S. Private*, pg. 828

Sclafani, Joseph L., Exec. V.P. & Controller--The Chase Manhattan Corporation, New York, NY; *U.S. Public*, pg. 337

Scoggins, Rex R., Chief Fin. Officer, Controller & Sec.--C & K Market, Inc., Brookings, OR; *U.S. Private*, pg. 191

Scoggins, Yvonne V., V.P. & Controller--Matria Healthcare, Inc., Marietta, GA; *U.S. Public*, pg. 1057

Scogin, James G., Controller & Treas.--Lot$ Off Corporation, San Antonio, TX; *U.S. Public*, pg. 1014

Scordamaglia, Joe, V.P. & Controller--Raypak, Inc., Westlake Village, CA; *Int'l*, pg. 1022

Scott, Charles, Controller--Mr. Christmas Inc., New York, NY; *U.S. Private*, pg. 765

Scott, Gene, Controller--IHOP Corp., Glendale, CA; *U.S. Public*, pg. 862

Scott, James C., V.P. & Controller--Hickory Specialties, Inc., Brentwood, TN; *U.S. Public*, pg. 596

Scott, Patrick J., V.P., Controller & Asst. Sec.--Bankers Life & Casualty Company, Chicago, IL; *U.S. Public*, pg. 433

Scott, Richard L., Controller--Bock Industries Inc., Elkhart, IN; *Int'l*, pg. 265

Scott, Robert, Controller--Harry Winston, Inc., New York, NY; *U.S. Private*, pg. 1183

Scott, Ron, Controller--Clayton Industries Co., El Monte, CA; *U.S. Private*, pg. 245

Scott, Steven, Controller--Sutherland Lumber Co., Kansas City, MO; *U.S. Private*, pg. 1057

Scoville, Randy, Controller--Certified Grocers of California, Los Angeles, CA; *U.S. Private*, pg. 226

Screnci, Mariano, Controller--Searle S.R.L, Milan, Italy; *Int'l*, pg. 1217

Scrivner, Patricia, Controller--Judson-Atkinson Candies, Inc., San Antonio, TX; *U.S. Private*, pg. 602

Scuron, C., Controller--Cochrane, Inc., King of Prussia, PA; *U.S. Public*, pg. 456

Scurr, R.J., Controller-Fin.--The Hongkong and Shanghai Banking Corporation Limited (HongkongBank), Central, Hong Kong; *Int'l*, pg. 583

Scuuley, Al, Controller--Target Stamped Products Corp., Kinsman, OH; *U.S. Private*, pg. 1069

Seago, Holly, Controller--Homes By Dave Brown, Tempe, AZ; *U.S. Private*, pg. 537

Seagraves, Susan, V.P. & Controller--Regal Cinemas Inc., Knoxville, TN; *U.S. Public*, pg. 1371

Seal, Marianne, Controller--Crest Fruit Co., Alamo, TX; *U.S. Public*, pg. 1506

Seals, Carol E., V.P. & Controller--American Heritage Life Insurance Co., Jacksonville, FL; *U.S. Public*, pg. 79

Sears, Christine, Controller--Penn National Insurance, Harrisburg, PA; *U.S. Private*, pg. 850

Sears, John W., Controller--Republic Engineered Steels, Inc., Massillon, OH; *U.S. Public*, pg. 1378

Sears, Robert, Controller--Clark Foodservice, Inc., Elk Grove Village, IL; *U.S. Private*, pg. 242

Seaton, John R., V.P. & Comptroller--Graybar Electric Company, Inc., Clayton, MO; *U.S. Private*, pg. 472

Sebastian, D.J., Controller--J.M. Huber, Oil & Gas Div., Houston, TX; *U.S. Private*, pg. 545

Seda, Mike, Controller--Orchard Supply Hardware, San Jose, CA; *U.S. Public*, pg. 1452

Sedin, David, Controller--Video Products Distributors, Inc., Sacramento, CA; *U.S. Private*, pg. 1139

See, David, Controller--Spectrum Industries, Inc., Chippewa Falls, WI; *U.S. Private*, pg. 1024

Seebery, Thomas, Dir.--Siemens AG, Munich, Germany; *Int'l*, pg. 1244

Seeley, Paul J., Treas., Controller & Sec.--Lindsay Manufacturing Inc., Ponca City, OK; *U.S. Private*, pg. 668

Seery, Patrick, Chief Fin. Officer, Controller & Treas.--James McHugh Construction Co., Chicago, IL; *U.S. Private*, pg. 721

Segall, Larry M., V.P., Treas. & Controller--Tiffany & Co., New York, NY; *U.S. Public*, pg. 1608

Segui, Gail, Controller--Comtech Telecommunications Corp., Melville, NY; *U.S. Public*, pg. 425

Seibert, Kimberly, Controller--Symix Systems, Inc., Columbus, OH; *U.S. Public*, pg. 1546

Seiden, Neil, Controller--Monitor Aerospace Corporation, Amityville, NY; *U.S. Private*, pg. 757

Seiler, Jerry, Controller--First Health Group Corp., Downers Grove, IL; *U.S. Public*, pg. 635

Seitz, Charles W., V.P. & Controller--Axel Johnson Inc., Stamford, CT; *Int'l*, pg. 709

Sekimura, Owen K., Staff V.P.-Fin., Controller & Chief Acctg. Officer--Aloha Airgroup, Inc., Honolulu, HI; *U.S. Private*, pg. 44

Selby, Patsy J., Controller--Multimedia Cablevision, Co., Wichita, KS; *U.S. Public*, pg. 699

Selk, Thomas L., V.P., Controller & Sec.--Associated Mortgage, Inc., De Pere, WI; *U.S. Public*, pg. 140

Sell, William G., Chief Acctg. Officer, V.P. & Controller--Fairfield Communities, Inc., Little Rock, AR; *U.S. Public*, pg. 610

Seller, J.D., Controller--Technologies Division, Joplin, MO; *U.S. Private*, pg. 355

Sellers, Gregg, Controller--Parkdale Mills, Gastonia, NC; *U.S. Private*, pg. 840

Semel, Semel I., V.P. & Controller--Calvin Klein, Inc., New York, NY; *U.S. Private*, pg. 202

Sempier, Philip J., V.P. & Treas.--The Chubb Corporation, Warren, NJ; *U.S. Public*, pg. 354

Semrad, Myron, Controller--Dr Pepper/Seven Up No. America, Dallas, TX; *Int'l*, pg. 248

Semrud, Ed, Controller--Ramsey Technology, Inc., Minneapolis, MN; *U.S. Public*, pg. 1592

Senecal, Donald, V.P.-Fin. & Distr./Worldwide Controller--Spalding Sports Worldwide, Chicopee, MA; *U.S. Private*, pg. 630

Sentance, Robert F., Controller--Orthofix International N.V., Curacao, Netherlands Antilles; *Int'l*, pg. 1011

Seposs, Ron, Controller--Hendrickson Stamping, Joliet, IL; *U.S. Private*, pg. 155

Serge, Tom, V.P. & Controller--J.R. Simplot Company, Boise, ID; *U.S. Private*, pg. 1002

Serio, Leo, Controller--Premdor Inc., Mississauga, Canada; *Int'l*, pg. 1066

Sermet, Dennis, V.P. & Controller--NVR, Inc., Mc Lean, VA; *U.S. Public*, pg. 1148

Serwick, Dennis, Controller--The Economics Press, Inc., Fairfield, NJ; *U.S. Private*, pg. 362

Sessanta, Sal, Controller--Structural Foam Plastics, Inc., Somerville, NJ; *U.S. Private*, pg. 1047

Severson, W., Controller--Treibacher Schleifmittel Corp., Niagara Falls, NY; *U.S. Private*, pg. 1099

Sevig, David, Chief Fin. Officer & Chief Information Officer--Cooker Restaurant Corporation, West Palm Beach, FL; *U.S. Public*, pg. 442

Sexton, Cliff, V.P.-Fin. & Asst. Sec.--Pioneer/Eclipse Corp., Sparta, NC; *Int'l*, pg. 71

Sexton, Michael J., V.P. & Controller--Prime Bank, Philadelphia, PA; *U.S. Public*, pg. 1326

Sexton, Terry G., Comptroller--Ace Doran Hauling & Rigging Company, Cincinnati, OH; *U.S. Private*, pg. 340

Sexton, Terry G., Comptroller--Ace Doran Brokerage, Cincinnati, OH; *U.S. Private*, pg. 340

Seyffarth, L., V.P. & Controller--Hoffmann-La Roche Inc., Nutley, NJ; *Int'l*, pg. 1120

Sfura, R., Controller--Hunter Douglas Metals, Homewood, IL; *Int'l*, pg. 639

Sgroi, S.B., Controller & Treas.--Elkins Constructors, Inc., Jacksonville, FL; *U.S. Private*, pg. 372

Shaak, W.A., Controller--Northwood Forest Industries, Ltd., Prince George, Canada; *U.S. Public*, pg. 1076

Shackelton, Scott H., V.P. & Controller--International Game Technology, Reno, NV; *U.S. Public*, pg. 900

Shah, Chetan, Division Controller--Gould Electronics Inc., Shawmut Circuit Protection Division, Newburyport, MA; *U.S. Public*, pg. 1592

Shah, Pradip, V.P. & Controller--Smart & Final, Vernon, CA; *Int'l*, pg. 563

Shah, Prashah, Controller--River Ranch Southwest, Inc., Dallas, TX; *U.S. Private*, pg. 934

Shakarisaz, Terry, V.P. & Controller--General Homes Corporation, Houston, TX; *U.S. Private*, pg. 444

Shallberg, Tina, Controller--Stewart-Warner South Wind Corp., Indianapolis, IN; *Int'l*, pg. 127

Shampey, Paul, Controller & Treas.--Kaiser Ventures, Inc., Ontario, CA; *U.S. Public*, pg. 941

Shanahan, Brendan, V.P. & Controller--Oxford Health Plans Inc., Norwalk, CT; *U.S. Public*, pg. 1238

Shandell, Fred, Controller--Injectron Corporation, Plainfield, NJ; *U.S. Private*, pg. 563

Shane, Kenneth A., Controller--White Pigeon Paper Company, White Pigeon, MI; *U.S. Private*, pg. 87

Shannon, W. Patrick, V.P. & Controller--BellSouth Corporation, Atlanta, GA; *U.S. Public*, pg. 207

Shannon, W.P., Comptroller--BellSouth Enterprises, Inc., Atlanta, GA; *U.S. Public*, pg. 208

Shapiro, Mark D., V.P. & Controller--Consolidated Stores Corp., Columbus, OH; *U.S. Public*, pg. 437

Shapiro, Ronald, Sr. V.P., Comptroller--Vitt Media International, Inc., New York, NY; *U.S. Private*, pg. 1142

Shapiro, Steven L., V.P. & Controller--Grossman's, Inc., Stoughton, MA; *U.S. Private*, pg. 585

Shaputis, Brian, Controller--Ektelon, Bordentown, NJ; *U.S. Private*, pg. 884

Shaqfeh, David K., Controller--Hatfield Quality Meats, Hatfield, PA; *U.S. Private*, pg. 510

Share, Jon, Controller--Mautz Paint Co., Madison, WI; *U.S. Private*, pg. 715

Sharkey, John G., V.P.-Fin., Controller & Sec.--TSR Inc., Hauppauge, NY; *U.S. Public*, pg. 1559

Sharp, J., Controller--Production Equipment Group, Woodcliff Lake, NJ; *U.S. Public*, pg. 877

Sharp, Michael, Controller--AAR Corp., Wood Dale, IL; *U.S. Public*, pg. 1

Sharpe, C.L., Grp. Fin. Controller--Q.U.F. Industries Ltd., Brisbane, Australia; *Int'l*, pg. 1074

Sharrock, Paul, Controller--Super Services Waste Management Inc., Flagstaff, AZ; *U.S. Public*, pg. 49

Shary, Teresa, Controller--Hartford Distributors Inc., Manchester, CT; *U.S. Private*, pg. 507

Shaull, Mike, Controller--Block Distributing Company, San Antonio, TX; *U.S. Private*, pg. 149

Shaver, Dean, Controller--Sunstates Corporation, Raleigh, NC; *U.S. Public*, pg. 1536

Shaver, Dean, Controller--Sunstates Realty Group Inc., Raleigh, NC; *U.S. Public*, pg. 1536

Shaw, Angela, Controller & Dir.-Acctg.--Earl May Seed & Nursery L.c., Shenandoah, IA; *U.S. Private*, pg. 356

Shaw, Dan, Controller--Southern Ohio Fabricators, Inc., Batavia, OH; *U.S. Private*, pg. 1017

Shaw, Dennis M., Controller & Sec.--Petroleum Products Corp., Middletown, PA; *U.S. Private*, pg. 859

Shaw, William T., Asst. V.P.-Fin. & Controller--Bird Incorporated, Norwood, MA; *Int'l*, pg. 1170

Shay, S.F., Controller-Mfg.--Citizens Gas & Coke Utility, Indianapolis, IN; *U.S. Private*, pg. 241

Shea, Bill, Controller--800-FLOWERS, Inc., Westbury, NY; *U.S. Private*, pg. 366

Shea, James T., V.P. & Cost Controller--Fruit of the Loom, Inc., Chicago, IL; *U.S. Public*, pg. 685

Shea, Michael J., Controller--Computer Horizons Corp., Mountain Lakes, NJ; *U.S. Public*, pg. 421

Shea, Steven, Controller--Media 100, Inc., Marlborough, MA; *U.S. Public*, pg. 1079

Sheard, Julie, Category Controller--Schweppes Europe Limited, Watford, United Kingdom; *Int'l*, pg. 248

Shearer, Robert K., V.P. & Controller--VF Corporation, Wyomissing, PA; *U.S. Public*, pg. 1702

Sheehan, Brian J., V.P. & Controller--Hills Stores Co., Canton, MA; *U.S. Public*, pg. 828

Sheehan, Heather E., Controller & Treas.--Trans Mountain Pipeline Company Ltd., Vancouver, Canada; *Int'l*, pg. 114

Sheehan, John F., Controller--National Fire Protection Association, Quincy, MA; *U.S. Private*, pg. 782
Sheehan, Pamela S., Controller--Saint-Gobain Advanced Materials Corporation, Louisville, KY; *Int'l*, pg. 1173
Sheehan, T.F., V.P. & Controller--Oak Industries Inc., Waltham, MA; *U.S. Public*, pg. 1209
Sheehy, John F., Asst. Treas.--Troy Savings Bank-Whitehall, Whitehall, NY; *U.S. Private*, pg. 1106
Sheer, Dick, V.P.-Retail & Controller--Safelite AutoGlass, Columbus, OH; *U.S. Private*, pg. 960
Sheinson, Ilene R., Controller--Franklin Electronic Publishers, Inc., Burlington, NJ; *U.S. Public*, pg. 679
Sheldon, Craig A., V.P. & Controller--Cantel Industries, Inc., Clifton, NJ; *U.S. Public*, pg. 301
Shellabarger, Tracy, Controller--Nucor Steel-Indiana, Crawfordsville, IN; *U.S. Public*, pg. 1205
Shelley, D. O., V.P. & Controller--GS Industries, Inc., Charlotte, NC; *U.S. Private*, pg. 435
Shelt, Pat, Asst. Controller--RS Electronics, Livonia, MI; *U.S. Private*, pg. 905
Shelton, Jeff W., Chief Fin. Officer & V.P.-Fin.--Skyline Chili, Inc., Fairfield, OH; *U.S. Public*, pg. 1475
Shelton, Theresa, V.P.-Fin.--Rock Bottom Restaurants, Louisville, CO; *U.S. Public*, pg. 1396
Shenk, Dale M., V.P.-Fin. & Controller--Acushnet Company, Fairhaven, MA; *U.S. Public*, pg. 675
Shenk, David, Controller--Rollins, Inc., Atlanta, GA; *U.S. Public*, pg. 1404
Shepard, Richard, Dir.-Acctg.--The Hall China Company, East Liverpool, OH; *U.S. Private*, pg. 494
Shepherd, Dale L., Controller--Cashco, Inc., Ellsworth, KS; *U.S. Private*, pg. 218
Shepherd, Peter D., Treas.--McKechnie PLC, Walsall, United Kingdom; *Int'l*, pg. 851
Sheridan, Michael, V.P. & Controller--Gale Research Inc., Detroit, MI; *U.S. Public*, pg. 1600
Sheridan, Nikki, V.P. & Controller--CRIIMI MAE, Rockville, MD; *U.S. Public*, pg. 459
Sheridian, James E., Controller--Paper Enterprises, Inc., Bronx, NY; *U.S. Private*, pg. 837
Sherif, Jack, Controller--George Rice & Sons, Los Angeles, CA; *U.S. Public*, pg. 1779
Sherman, Philip S., Sr. V.P. & Grp. Controller--Reliance Group Holdings, Inc., New York, NY; *U.S. Public*, pg. 1374
Sherman, R. Cris, V.P. & Controller--Eastex Energy Inc., Houston, TX; *U.S. Public*, pg. 567
Sherringham, Philip, Sr. V.P. & Controller--Sanwa Bank California, Los Angeles, CA; *Int'l*, pg. 1189
Sherry, Kenneth C., Sec.--Valk Manufacturing Company, New Kingstown, PA; *U.S. Private*, pg. 1131
Sherwin, Marie, Controller--Palmer Jarvis Communications, Vancouver, Canada; *Int'l*, pg. 1022
Sherwood, Robert A., Jr., Controller--FAG Bearings Corporation, Danbury, CT; *Int'l*, pg. 469
Shickluna, R. Michael, Dir.-Control & Corp. Office--Hudson's Bay Company, Toronto, Canada; *Int'l*, pg. 637
Shide, Mark, Controller--Rihm Motor Company, Saint Paul, MN; *U.S. Private*, pg. 931
Shields, Joe, Controller--Progress Paint Mfg. Co., Louisville, KY; *U.S. Private*, pg. 890
Shields, John, Controller--WTTW (Channel 11), Chicago, IL; *U.S. Private*, pg. 1145
Shiffman, Randi, Controller--Complast, Inc., Bloomington, MN; *U.S. Private*, pg. 259
Shigematsu, Masabumi, Gen. Mgr.-Acctg. Controlling Div.--Sumitomo Corporation, Tokyo, Japan; *Int'l*, pg. 1312
Shipengrover, Donald R., Controller--Watkins System Inc., Concordville, PA; *U.S. Private*, pg. 1153
Shipman, Dan, Fin. Controller--Thorntons PLC, Darbyshire, United Kingdom; *Int'l*, pg. 1386
Shiraki, Ernest T., Controller--Hawaiian Electric Company, Inc., Honolulu, HI; *U.S. Public*, pg. 800
Shocklee, Mary E., Controller--Mid Atlantic Medical Services, Inc., Rockville, MD; *U.S. Public*, pg. 1109
Shockley, D., Controller--Menley & James Laboratories, Inc., Horsham, PA; *U.S. Public*, pg. 1086
Shockley, William M., Chief Fin. Officer, V.P. & Controller--SPS Technologies, Inc., Jenkintown, PA; *U.S. Public*, pg. 1419
Shoemaker, Ellen, V.P. & Controller--Clopay Corporation, Cincinnati, OH; *U.S. Public*, pg. 766
Shoemaker, James, Controller--Webb Heavy-Duty Roller Conveyor Systems, Harbor Springs, MI; *U.S. Private*, pg. 1156
Shoemaker, Sally, Controller--Tropical Sportswear International, Tampa, FL; *U.S. Private*, pg. 1105
Shong, Bruce, Chief Fin. Officer & Controller--Burnstad Brothers, Inc., Tomah, WI; *U.S. Private*, pg. 187
Shonka, Mike, Sr. V.P.-Fin. & Controller--The Cessna Aircraft Co., Wichita, KS; *U.S. Public*, pg. 1589
Shorey, Rhonda, Controller--Diversified Communications, Portland, ME; *U.S. Private*, pg. 336
Short, Harry W., Sr. V.P. & Controller--Northern Trust Corporation, Chicago, IL; *U.S. Public*, pg. 1195
Short, William, V.P.-Fin. & Controller--Morrison, Inc., Hammond, IN; *U.S. Private*, pg. 762
Shortley, John, Controller--PS Trading, Inc., Dallas, TX; *U.S. Public*, pg. 1245
Shoup, Patrick, Controller--Spectrum Control, Inc., Erie, PA; *U.S. Public*, pg. 1497
Show, Don, Controller--Plastomer Corp., Livonia, MI; *U.S. Private*, pg. 872
Show, John, Controller--Dover Mills Limited, Halifax, Canada; *Int'l*, pg. 417
Showers, Mark, Chief Fin. Officer, Treas. & Sec.--Spartech Plastics, Portage, WI; *U.S. Public*, pg. 1496
Shrieves, John, Controller & Corp. Sec.--Omniflight, Inc., Dallas, TX; *U.S. Private*, pg. 816
Shrieves, John, Controller & Corp. Sec.--Omniflight Helicopters, Inc., Dallas, TX; *U.S. Private*, pg. 817
Shuda, Michael, Controller--Moxness Products, Inc., Racine, WI; *U.S. Public*, pg. 124
Shuell, Paul R., Asst. Controller--GTE Corporation, Stamford, CT; *U.S. Public*, pg. 696
Shuman, Charles, Controller--Condor Pacific Industries, Inc., Westlake Village, CA; *U.S. Private*, pg. 262
Shure, Daniel B., Pres. & Chief Exec. Officer--Strombecker Corporation, Chicago, IL; *U.S. Private*, pg. 1047
Siano, Michael J., Controller--Stratton Management Company, Plymouth Meeting, PA; *U.S. Private*, pg. 1046
Sidders, Martin, Grp. Fin. Controller--Dixons Group plc, Hemel Hempstead, United Kingdom,; *Int'l*, pg. 413
Siddiqui, M. Irfan, Controller--National Refinery Limited, Karachi, Pakistan; *Int'l*, pg. 909
Siddons, Michael, Controller--Fischbein Co., Statesville, NC; *U.S. Private*, pg. 103
Sider, Jerry, Controller--Royal Farms Inc., Brooklyn, NY; *U.S. Private*, pg. 948
Sidlowe, David A., V.P. & Controller--American Healthcorp Inc., Nashville, TN; *U.S. Public*, pg. 78
Sidman, Alan M., Chief Fin. Officer & Controller--Instrumentarium Imaging, Inc., Milwaukee, WI; *U.S. Private*, pg. 565
Sidwell, David H., Mng. Dir. & Controller--J.P. Morgan Co. Incorporated, New York, NY; *U.S. Public*, pg. 1129
Siebenmorgen, Tom, Controller--Leisure Arts, Inc., Little Rock, AR; *U.S. Public*, pg. 1613
Sieja, Mark, Controller--Central Data Corporation, Champaign, IL; *U.S. Private*, pg. 223
Siek, Greg, Controller--Thermo Black Clawson, Inc., Middletown, OH; *U.S. Public*, pg. 1593
Sieradzki, Richard D., Controller--Ryan's Family Steak Houses, Inc., Greer, SC; *U.S. Public*, pg. 1413
Sievers, Robert D., Comptroller--American Water Works Company, Inc., Voorhees, NJ; *U.S. Public*, pg. 95
Sievers, Sean, Controller--Pacific Crest Capital, Inc., Agoura Hills, CA; *U.S. Public*, pg. 1248
Sifferman, Carolyn, V.P. & Controller--Republic Entertainment, Inc., Los Angeles, CA; *U.S. Private*, pg. 776
Sigler, Jill, Controller--Cohn & Wells, San Francisco, CA; *Int'l*, pg. 601
Sigler, John, Corp. Controller--Kokomo Grain Co., Inc., Kokomo, IN; *U.S. Private*, pg. 631
Sigman, Richard, Chief Fin. Officer--IWI Holding Limited, Westmont, IL; *U.S. Public*, pg. 861
Signorino, Judy, Controller--International Microcircuits, Inc., Milpitas, CA; *U.S. Private*, pg. 571
Sihuvola, Pekka, Controller--Kone Corporation, Helsinki, Finland; *Int'l*, pg. 746
Silberbauer, Gary L., Sr. Partner & Controller--J. Walter Thompson Company, New York, NY; *Int'l*, pg. 1483
Silva, Estanislau, Controller & Gen. Mgr.--Banco Totta & Acores, Lisbon, Portugal; *Int'l*, pg. 144
Silver, Richard D., Sr. V.P. & Controller--Downey Savings & Loan Association, F.A., Newport Beach, CA; *U.S. Public*, pg. 526
Silver, Steve, Controller & Dir.-Fin. Plng. & Reporting--Krasdale Foods Inc., White Plains, NY; *U.S. Private*, pg. 635
Silveria, Robert W., V.P. & Controller--Heery International, Inc., Atlanta, GA; *U.S. Private*, pg. 519
Silverstein, Arthur, Controller--Advance Publications Inc., Staten Island, NY; *U.S. Private*, pg. 18
Silverstein, Kenneth, Corp. Controller--Encore Computer Corporation, Fort Lauderdale, FL; *U.S. Public*, pg. 580
Siman, Gil, Controller--RTG Furniture Corp., Seffner, FL; *U.S. Private*, pg. 905
Simboli, David, Controller--VAW of America, Inc., Ellenville, NY; *Int'l*, pg. 1466
Simella, Dan, Controller--Trigen Energy Corporation, White Plains, NY; *U.S. Public*, pg. 1637
Simmers, Scott, Controller, Treas., & Sec.--Power Process Piping, Inc., Plymouth, MI; *U.S. Private*, pg. 878
Simmons, Dennis, Controller--Rocco Building Supplies Inc., Harrisonburg, VA; *U.S. Private*, pg. 937
Simmons, Grant D., CPA, Controller--Giffels Associates, Inc., Southfield, MI; *U.S. Private*, pg. 452
Simmons, James, Asst. Controller--Cowen & Company, New York, NY; *U.S. Private*, pg. 280
Simmons, John, Controller--Production Operators, Inc., Houston, TX; *U.S. Public*, pg. 298
Simmons, John, Jr., V.P. & Controller--Eckerd Corporation, Largo, FL; *U.S. Public*, pg. 917
Simmons, Rich, Controller--Champion Parts (Canada) Ltd., Concord, Canada; *U.S. Public*, pg. 335
Simmons, Richard, Controller--OEM Div., Hope, AR; *U.S. Public*, pg. 335
Simmons, Tom, Controller--Bongards Creameries Inc., Norwood, MN; *U.S. Private*, pg. 156
Simms, Andrew, Controller--C. Roher Inc., Fleetwood, PA; *U.S. Private*, pg. 940
Simms, Donald G., Controller--United Piece Dye Works, LP, New York, NY; *U.S. Private*, pg. 1123
Simon, Curt, Controller--Hunter Corp., Portage, IN; *U.S. Private*, pg. 549
Simon, G. Ronald, V.P. & Controller--American Standard Inc., Piscataway, NJ; *U.S. Public*, pg. 91
Simon, Guy, Controller--Berlitz France S.A., Paris, France; *U.S. Public*, pg. 222
Simon, Michael A., Controller & Asst. Sec.--Acme Electric Corporation, East Aurora, NY; *U.S. Public*, pg. 16
Simon, Scott, Controller--Penn-Daniels, Inc., Quincy, IL; *U.S. Public*, pg. 1467
Simone, Guy, Controller--Bookazine Company, Inc., Bayonne, NJ; *U.S. Private*, pg. 156
Simoneaux, Darrell, V.P.-Fin. & Controller--Johnson Supply & Equipment Corp., Houston, TX; *U.S. Private*, pg. 594
Simons, R.L., V.P.-Fin.--Hardings, Inc., Elmira, NY; *U.S. Private*, pg. 502
Simpson, David, Controller--W. Braun Company, Chicago, IL; *U.S. Private*, pg. 166
Simpson, Frank, Controller--Plywood Plastics Inc., Buffalo, NY; *U.S. Private*, pg. 873
Simpson, James R., V.P. & Controller--General Host Corporation, Stamford, CT; *U.S. Public*, pg. 715
Sims, Daniel, Controller--Ramsay Health Care, Inc., Coral Gables, FL; *U.S. Public*, pg. 1360
Sims, Jerry L., Jr., Controller--ATC Communications Group, Inc., Dallas, TX; *U.S. Public*, pg. 11
Sims, Mike, Controller--Interform Corporation, Bridgeville, PA; *U.S. Public*, pg. 333
Sinclair, Robert, Corp. Controller--Aaron Rents, Inc., Atlanta, GA; *U.S. Public*, pg. 12
Sinclair, Robert, Controller--Schlumberger Industries, Owenton, KY; *U.S. Public*, pg. 1439
Sindelar, Dave, Controller--Dudek & Bock Spring Manufacturing Company, Chicago, IL; *U.S. Private*, pg. 344
Sindlinger, Dan K., Controller--Reactive Metals & Alloys Corporation (REMACOR), West Pittsburg, PA; *U.S. Private*, pg. 913
Singeisen, E., Controller--Elektro-Apparatebau Olten AG, Olten, Switzerland; *Int'l*, pg. 444
Singer, Gary, Chief Fin. Officer & Controller--Habisat Globe Inc., Buffalo, NY; *Int'l*, pg. 585
Singer, Gary M., Controller--Business Week, New York, NY; *U.S. Public*, pg. 1069
Singleton, Robert G., Controller--Georgia Tent & Awning Inc., Atlanta, GA; *U.S. Private*, pg. 448
Singsank, James, Controller--ABC Rail Products Corp., Chicago, IL; *U.S. Public*, pg. 2
Sinks, Patrick, Chief Acctg. Officer, V.P. & Controller--MGIC Investment Corporation, Milwaukee, WI; *U.S. Public*, pg. 1026
Sinks, Patrick, V.P., Controller & Chief Acctg. Officer--Mortgage Guaranty Insurance Corporation, Milwaukee, WI; *U.S. Public*, pg. 1026
Sinsky, Pete, Interim Controller--Camosy, Inc., Russell, IL; *U.S. Private*, pg. 203
Sipek, Meridith P., Controller--Aztar Corporation, Phoenix, AZ; *U.S. Public*, pg. 158
Siraco, Michael N., V.P. & Controller--Analogic Corporation, Peabody, MA; *U.S. Public*, pg. 109
Sircy, Robert, V.P. & Controller--Southwestern/Great American Inc., Nashville, TN; *U.S. Private*, pg. 1018
Sisel, Larry, V.P. & Controller--Bushnell Corporation, Overland Park, KS; *U.S. Private*, pg. 1191
Siser, Robert, Controller & Treas.--T C Manufacturing Company, Inc., Evanston, IL; *U.S. Private*, pg. 1062
Siska, Charles W., Jr., Controller--North Carolina Natural Gas Corporation, Fayetteville, NC; *U.S. Public*, pg. 1194
Sismondo, Peter R., V.P., Controller, Treas. & Asst. Sec.--Alleghany Corporation, New York, NY; *U.S. Public*, pg. 42
Sison, Rentl, Controller--David L. Peister Co., Inc., New York, NY; *U.S. Private*, pg. 848
Sitman, Anthony, Controller--Bristol-Myers Squibb International, Princeton, NJ; *U.S. Public*, pg. 254
Sitman, Anthony, V.P. & Controller--Bristol-Myers Squibb U.S. Pharmaceutical Group, Plainsboro, NJ; *U.S. Public*, pg. 255
Siu, Kin, Controller--Media Resources International, New York, NY; *U.S. Private*, pg. 727
Sivin, Charles, Controller--Walker-Pioneer Graphics, New York, NY; *U.S. Private*, pg. 1147
Sizemore, Dennis, Sr. V.P. & Controller--Howard Hughes Corporation, Las Vegas, NV; *U.S. Public*, pg. 1407
Sizemore, Louise, Office Mgr. & Controller--WYMT-TV, Hazard, KY; *U.S. Public*, pg. 759
Skalicky, Steven S., Asst. V.P. & Deputy Comptroller--American International Group, Inc., New York, NY; *U.S. Public*, pg. 83
Skalicky, Steven S., Sr. V.P. & Controller--Transatlantic Holdings Inc., New York, NY; *U.S. Public*, pg. 84
Skinner, Marlise C., Controller--Corporate Express Delivery Systems Southwest, Inc., Houston, TX; *U.S. Public*, pg. 449
Skinner, Renee H., Asst. V.P. & Controller--Atlantic Southeast Airlines Inc., Atlanta, GA; *U.S. Public*, pg. 144
Sklar, Fay, Controller--Red Calliope & Associates, Inc., Los Angeles, CA; *U.S. Public*, pg. 465
Sklenicka, George, Sr. V.P.-Admin. & Controller--Vienna Sausage Mfg. Co., Chicago, IL; *U.S. Private*, pg. 1139
Skorupski, John, Controller--Williams International, Walled Lake, MI; *U.S. Private*, pg. 1178
Skott, Allen I., Controller--American Optical Corporation, Greenwich, CT; *U.S. Private*, pg. 60
Skrzysowski, David A., V.P. & Controller--EnergyNorth, Inc., Manchester, NH; *U.S. Public*, pg. 581
Slaby, Kenneth P., V.P. & Controller--Federal-Mogul Corporation, Southfield, MI; *U.S. Public*, pg. 615
Slack, David, V.P., Comptroller, Asst. Sec. & Asst. Treas.--Arkansas Best Corporation, Fort Smith, AR; *U.S. Public*, pg. 130
Slack, Linda, Controller--Morse Controls, Hudson, OH; *U.S. Public*, pg. 857
Slade, Colin L., V.P. & Controller--Tektronix, Inc., Wilsonville, OR; *U.S. Public*, pg. 1567
Slate, Janet, Controller--Affiliated Publishers, Inc., Nashville, TN; *U.S. Private*, pg. 26
Slattery, Kevin, Controller--Bridgestone/Firestone Inc. Retail Operations, Rolling Meadows, IL; *Int'l*, pg. 213
Slattery, Michael, Controller--Couristan Inc., Fort Lee, NJ; *U.S. Private*, pg. 279
Sleath, Alan, Controller--Sun Hill Industries, Inc., Stamford, CT; *U.S. Private*, pg. 1051
Sledge, Brian D., V.P., Controller & Sec.--Utilities Construction Co., Inc. Of South Carolina, Charleston, SC; *U.S. Private*, pg. 1130
Sledge, Chuck, V.P. & Controller--Stage Stores, Inc., Houston, TX; *U.S. Private*, pg. 1028
Sleeman, Donald G., Chief Fin. Officer, Sr. V.P., Controller & Treas.--The Turner Corporation, New York, NY; *U.S. Public*, pg. 1645
Sleeper, Mark, Controller--The Vermont Teddy Bear Company, Inc., Shelburne, VT; *U.S. Public*, pg. 1716
Slezak, Kenneth, Controller--Curtiss-Wright Corp., Lyndhurst, NJ; *U.S. Public*, pg. 469

Sloan, Ben, Controller & Asst. V.P.-Acctg.--Atlas Van Lines, Inc., Evansville, IN; *U.S. Private*, pg. 97
Sloan, John E., Controller--Detroit Coil Company, Ferndale, MI; *U.S. Private*, pg. 328
Slockers, Erik L., V.P. & Controller--Terra Nitrogen Company, L.P., Tulsa, OK; *U.S. Public*, pg. 1581
Slopsema, Martha, Controller--Allomatic Products Company, Sullivan, IN; *U.S. Public*, pg. 1363
Slover, John J., Controller--American Travellers Corporation, Bensalem, PA; *U.S. Public*, pg. 433
Slovin, Alan, Controller--Jarvis (West), South El Monte, CA; *U.S. Public*, pg. 1506
Slukerski, Walter, V.P. & Controller--Fortis, Inc., New York, NY; *Int'l*, pg. 499
Slutz, Larry, Chief Fin. Officer & North American Controller--Zenith Data Systems, Deerfield, IL; *Int'l*, pg. 317
Small, George, V.P. & Controller--Franklin Sports, Inc., Stoughton, MA; *U.S. Private*, pg. 424
Smallman, C., Controller & Treas.--Stanford Telecommunications, Sunnyvale, CA; *U.S. Public*, pg. 1508
Smerz, Susan M., Sr. V.P., Controller & Asst. Sec.--First Midwest Bancorp, Inc., Itasca, IL; *U.S. Public*, pg. 636
Smiley, Beverly L., Controller--Badger Meter, Inc., Milwaukee, WI; *U.S. Public*, pg. 164
Smith, Albert E., V.P. & Controller--Anixter Inc., Skokie, IL; *U.S. Public*, pg. 115
Smith, Alton, Exec. V.P. & Controller--Furr's/Bishops, Inc., Lubbock, TX; *U.S. Public*, pg. 689
Smith, Barry E., Chief Acctg. Officer, V.P. & Controller--NovaCare Inc., King of Prussia, PA; *U.S. Public*, pg. 1203
Smith, Bill, Controller--New Fortis Corp., King, NC; *U.S. Public*, pg. 843
Smith, Brenda H., V.P. & Controller--MainStreet BankGroup Incorporated, Martinsville, VA; *U.S. Public*, pg. 1038
Smith, Brian, Controller--Robson Communities, Sun Lakes, AZ; *U.S. Private*, pg. 937
Smith, C. Matthew, Controller--P.H. Glatfelter Company, Spring Grove, PA; *U.S. Public*, pg. 746
Smith, C. W., Controller--Transport, Inc., Madison, AL; *U.S. Public*, pg. 482
Smith, Carol, Controller--Amloid Corporation, Saddle Brook, NJ; *U.S. Private*, pg. 66
Smith, Cathy, Controller--Gerbig, Snell/Weisheimer & Assoc., Inc., Columbus, OH; *U.S. Private*, pg. 449
Smith, Charisse, Controller--SOR Inc., Lenexa, KS; *U.S. Private*, pg. 957
Smith, Charles T., Controller--Panel Processing, Inc., Alpena, MI; *U.S. Private*, pg. 836
Smith, Craig, Controller--HyClone Laboratories Inc., Logan, UT; *Int'l*, pg. 1037
Smith, Dan, Controller--Grizzard, Atlanta, GA; *U.S. Private*, pg. 482
Smith, Dan, Controller--TABS Direct (Operating Div.), Stafford, TX; *U.S. Private*, pg. 482
Smith, Darrell, Controller--Small Tube Products Co., Inc., Altoona, PA; *U.S. Public*, pg. 1775
Smith, David, Controller--Advanced Energy Industry, Fort Collins, CO; *U.S. Public*, pg. 20
Smith, David, Controller--Democrat Printing & Lithograph Company, Little Rock, AR; *U.S. Private*, pg. 323
Smith, David S., Controller--Montana Power Company, Butte, MT; *U.S. Public*, pg. 1126
Smith, David S., Controller--Entech, Inc., Butte, MT; *U.S. Public*, pg. 1127
Smith, Donald A., Corp. Controller--Sylvan Inc., Saxonburg, PA; *U.S. Public*, pg. 1545
Smith, Eleanor R., Controller & Sec.--Scope Industries, Santa Monica, CA; *U.S. Public*, pg. 1444
Smith, Franca, Controller--George Weston Limited, Toronto, Canada; *Int'l*, pg. 1494
Smith, Frank E., Chief Fin. Officer, Sr. V.P. & Sec.--West Coast Bancorp, Newport Beach, CA; *U.S. Public*, pg. 1755
Smith, Franklin H., Controller--Johnson Controls, Inc., Milwaukee, WI; *U.S. Public*, pg. 932
Smith, Franklin H., Controller--Johnson Controls, Inc., Controls Group, Milwaukee, WI; *U.S. Public*, pg. 932
Smith, Frederick L., Controller--Finch, Pruyn & Co., Inc., Glens Falls, NY; *U.S. Private*, pg. 405
Smith, Gary, Controller--Cone Mills Corporation, Greensboro, NC; *U.S. Public*, pg. 430
Smith, Gary, V.P. & Controller--Odetics Inc., Anaheim, CA; *U.S. Public*, pg. 1212
Smith, Grace, Controller & Treas.--R&R Advertising, Las Vegas, NV; *U.S. Private*, pg. 902
Smith, Greg, V.P. & Controller--Rubin Postaer & Associates, Santa Monica, CA; *U.S. Private*, pg. 949
Smith, Gregory, Controller--The Geon Company, Avon Lake, OH; *U.S. Public*, pg. 733
Smith, Howard I., Chief Fin. Officer, Exec. V.P. & Comptroller--American International Group, Inc., New York, NY; *U.S. Public*, pg. 83
Smith, Jack, Controller--Port of Portland, Portland, OR; *U.S. Private*, pg. 876
Smith, Jack, Controller--Schaedler Brothers, Inc., Harrisburg, PA; *U.S. Private*, pg. 969
Smith, James, V.P. & Controller--AnnTaylor, Inc., New York, NY; *U.S. Public*, pg. 116
Smith, James, Corp. Controller--Durakon Industries, Inc., Lapeer, MI; *U.S. Public*, pg. 537
Smith, Janet, Controller--Capitol Group, Springfield, IL; *U.S. Private*, pg. 206
Smith, Janice, Controller-Intl. Opers.--K-Swiss Inc., Chatsworth, CA; *U.S. Public*, pg. 937
Smith, Joan R., V.P., Controller & Sec.--Marine Drilling Companies, Inc., Sugar Land, TX; *U.S. Public*, pg. 1044
Smith, Julie, Controller--The Bentley Agnew Group Inc., London, Canada; *Int'l*, pg. 187
Smith, Julie, Controller--Agnew Group, London, Canada; *Int'l*, pg. 187
Smith, Julie, Controller--Bentley Leathers Inc., Dollard des Ormeaux, Canada; *Int'l*, pg. 187
Smith, Kathleen, Controller & Asst. Sec.--Algood Food Company, Louisville, KY; *U.S. Private*, pg. 34
Smith, Keith E., V.P. & Controller--Boyd Gaming Corporation, Las Vegas, NV; *U.S. Public*, pg. 249
Smith, Kenneth T., V.P. & Controller--Family Dollar Stores, Inc., Matthews, NC; *U.S. Public*, pg. 612
Smith, Kevin, Controller--Consolidated Biscuit Co., Mc Comb, OH; *U.S. Private*, pg. 265
Smith, Kevin, Controller--Marsh Furniture Company, High Point, NC; *U.S. Private*, pg. 708
Smith, Larry, V.P. & Controller--MidAmerican Energy Holdings, Des Moines, IA; *U.S. Public*, pg. 1109
Smith, Larry D., Staff V.P. & Controller--Allied Products Corporation, Chicago, IL; *U.S. Public*, pg. 48
Smith, Marsha, Controller--Land O'Lakes, Inc., Southampton, PA; *U.S. Private*, pg. 646
Smith, Martyn, Controller & Grp. Dir.-Fin.--Inchcape PLC, London, United Kingdom; *Int'l*, pg. 671
Smith, Michael B., Controller & Asst. Sec.--Burke Mills, Inc., Valdese, NC; *U.S. Public*, pg. 267
Smith, Michael D., Controller--Central and South West Services, Inc., Dallas, TX; *U.S. Public*, pg. 324
Smith, Michael D., Controller--CSW Energy, Inc., Dallas, TX; *U.S. Public*, pg. 324
Smith, Patrick F., V.P & Controller--John Hancock Variable Life Insurance Co., Boston, MA; *U.S. Private*, pg. 590
Smith, Patti, Controller--M & C Specialties Company, Southampton, PA; *U.S. Private*, pg. 684
Smith, Priscilla, Controller--Anthony Forest Products Co., Inc., El Dorado, AR; *U.S. Private*, pg. 76
Smith, Rea, Controller--Q3 Stamped Metal, Columbus, OH; *U.S. Private*, pg. 897
Smith, Rhen D., Treas. & Controller--Hofmann Industries, Inc., Sinking Spring, PA; *U.S. Private*, pg. 533
Smith, Richard A., V.P. & Controller--Frontier Corporation, Rochester, NY; *U.S. Public*, pg. 683
Smith, Robert J., Controller--Great Lakes Chemical Corporation, West Lafayette, IN; *U.S. Public*, pg. 760
Smith, Robert Lewis, Controller, Treas. & Sec.--Hankins Lumber Company, Inc., Elliott, MS; *U.S. Private*, pg. 499
Smith, Roger, Controller--Datapoint (U.K.) Ltd., London, United Kingdom; *Int'l*, pg. 384
Smith, Roger, Controller--Vista Gold Corp., Denver, CO; *U.S. Public*, pg. 1723
Smith, S.A., Sr. V.P. & Controller--Loblaw Companies Limited, North York, Canada; *Int'l*, pg. 1495
Smith, Sally, Controller--Ariel Corporation, Mount Vernon, OH; *U.S. Private*, pg. 81
Smith, Samuel, Controller--Owsley & Sons, Inc., Fort Mill, SC; *U.S. Private*, pg. 824
Smith, Sean T., Controller--Starter Corp., New Haven, CT; *U.S. Public*, pg. 1511
Smith, Sharon A., V.P. & Controller--Golden State Mutual Life Insurance Company, Los Angeles, CA; *U.S. Private*, pg. 461
Smith, Sherry M., Asst. Controller--SuperValu, Inc., Eden Prairie, MN; *U.S. Public*, pg. 1540
Smith, Thomas W., Controller & Treas.--National Retail Hardware Assn., Indianapolis, IN; *U.S. Private*, pg. 786
Smith, Tom, Controller--Godiva Chocolatier, Inc., New York, NY; *U.S. Public*, pg. 299
Smithers, John, Chief Fin. Officer & Controller--B & R Foods, Dover, FL; *U.S. Public*, pg. 1278
Smithers, Rodney, Controller--Elite Lamp, Inc., West Memphis, AR; *U.S. Private*, pg. 371
Smitley, Phil, Controller--Carmike Cinemas, Inc., Columbus, GA; *U.S. Public*, pg. 305
Smyth, Ann F., Controller--Barr Laboratories Inc., Pomona, NY; *U.S. Public*, pg. 191
Snellens, G.M., Controller & Dir.-Acctg.--Ballast Nedam NV, Amstelveen, Netherlands; *Int'l*, pg. 133
Snelling, Randy, Controller--Platinum Solutions, Inglewood, CA; *U.S. Public*, pg. 1309
Sniffen, John, Controller--Nestle Beverage Company, Ripon, CA; *Int'l*, pg. 918
Snoeblen, Roy, Controller--Roger Holler Chevrolet & GEO Co., Winter Park, FL; *U.S. Private*, pg. 534
Snow, Marty, V.P. & Controller--Kash N Karry Food Stores, Inc., Tampa, FL; *Int'l*, pg. 463
Snyder, Barbara S., V.P.-Finance--Rudolph Foods Company, Lima, OH; *U.S. Private*, pg. 950
Snyder, Charles, Controller--Presidential Life Corporation, Nyack, NY; *U.S. Public*, pg. 1323
Snyder, Lance, Controller--McLaughlin Manufacturing Company, Greenville, SC; *U.S. Private*, pg. 724
Snyder, Linda, Controller--Marco Color Labs, Inc., Hawthorne, CA; *U.S. Private*, pg. 702
Snyder, Steven E., Controller--Cray Research, Eagan, MN; *U.S. Public*, pg. 1473
Snyder, Tim, Controller--HPM Corporation, Mount Gilead, OH; *U.S. Private*, pg. 492
Sobota, John J., Controller--CC Industries, Inc., Chicago, IL; *U.S. Private*, pg. 192
Socher, George A., Controller--Sulcus Computer Corp., Greensburg, PA; *U.S. Public*, pg. 1527
Socher, George A., V.P. & Controller--Westinghouse Air Brake Company, Wilmerding, PA; *U.S. Public*, pg. 1760
Sodestrom, Dirk A., V.P. & Controller--Western Staff Services, Walnut Creek, CA; *U.S. Public*, pg. 1760
Soher, Thomas J., Controller--Schlosser Forge Company, Rancho Cucamonga, CA; *U.S. Private*, pg. 970
Sohl, Marvel, Controller & Treas.--Bluewater, Mora, MN; *U.S. Private*, pg. 153
Sokolowski, Anthony, V.P. & Controller--CPM, Inc., Chicago, IL; *U.S. Private*, pg. 196
Solari, Ray, Corp. Controller--MMC Networks, Inc., Sunnyvale, CA; *U.S. Public*, pg. 1027
Solarz, Anthony J., Controller--Market Facts, Inc., Arlington Heights, IL; *U.S. Public*, pg. 1046
Solato, Tom, Chief Fin. Officer & Controller--Roosevelt Paper Co., Philadelphia, PA; *U.S. Private*, pg. 943
Solger, Richard P., Controller--Treasure Island Foodmarts Inc., Chicago, IL; *U.S. Private*, pg. 1098
Solinsky, Mary Ellen, Controller--Vision One, Norwich, CT; *U.S. Private*, pg. 1141
Solomon, Buddy, Controller--Cox Newspapers, Inc., Atlanta, GA; *U.S. Private*, pg. 281
Solomon, Terry, Controller--Best Western International, Inc., Phoenix, AZ; *U.S. Private*, pg. 140
Solomon, William W., V.P. & Controller--American Pad and Paper Company, Dallas, TX; *U.S. Public*, pg. 88
Solvason, Johannes, Controller--IceLandAir, Columbia, MD; *Int'l*, pg. 658
Somerville, Penelope F., Sr. V.P. & Corp. Controller--Bank of Montreal, Toronto, Canada; *Int'l*, pg. 153
Sommer, Charles, Asst. Controller--Sanifill, Inc., Houston, TX; *U.S. Public*, pg. 1686
Sommer, Gary, Controller--Borden Italian Foods, Columbus, OH; *U.S. Private*, pg. 158
Somodi, Thomas, Controller--Albert Trostel & Sons Co., Milwaukee, WI; *U.S. Private*, pg. 1105
Somrak, Wayne P., V.P. & Controller--Varian Associates, Inc., Palo Alto, CA; *U.S. Public*, pg. 1710
Sonnen, Joan, Controller--Forest Oil Corporation, Denver, CO; *U.S. Public*, pg. 670
Sontoro, Tom, V.P. & Controller--Vitalink Pharmacy Services, Inc., Naperville, IL; *U.S. Public*, pg. 1041
Soose, Harry J., Jr., V.P.-Fin. & Controller--International Technology Corporation, Monroeville, PA; *U.S. Public*, pg. 907
Sorensen, Tom, Controller--Poli-Twine Western Inc., Clearfield, UT; *Int'l*, pg. 1362
Sorg, Denise K., Controller--Energy Dynamics Division, Chandler, AZ; *U.S. Public*, pg. 1250
Soro, Linda, Controller--Hanft Byrne Raboy Abrams & Partners, Inc., New York, NY; *U.S. Private*, pg. 499
Sorrentino, Stephen J., Controller--Quebecor Printing Semline Inc., Braintree, MA; *Int'l*, pg. 1078
Sot, Edward J., Controller--Merck & Co., Inc., Whitehouse Station, NJ; *U.S. Public*, pg. 1090
Sou, Betty, Controller & Sec.--Oroamerica, Inc., Burbank, CA; *U.S. Public*, pg. 1232
Soublin, Michel, V.P. & Controller-Oilfield Services--Schlumberger Limited, New York, NY; *U.S. Public*, pg. 1439
Soucie, Edwin, Jr., Asst. Controller & Dir.-Tax--Foster Wheeler Corporation, Clinton, NJ; *U.S. Public*, pg. 676
Soukas, George, Controller--Dodge Regupol, Inc., Lancaster, PA; *U.S. Private*, pg. 337
Soukup, Larry, Controller--J.H. Larson Electrical Company, Golden Valley, MN; *U.S. Private*, pg. 652
Sourdiff, Jerald, Sr. V.P. & Controller--Lutheran Brotherhood, Minneapolis, MN; *U.S. Private*, pg. 681
Southall, Frank, V.P. & Controller--Ruby Tuesday, Inc., Mobile, AL; *U.S. Public*, pg. 1411
Southard, Scott, Controller--Haines & Co., Inc., Canton, OH; *U.S. Private*, pg. 494
Southern, David, Controller--Scios Inc., Mountain View, CA; *U.S. Public*, pg. 1444
Southgate, David, Intl. Controller--Software Publishing Corporation, Fairfield, NJ; *U.S. Public*, pg. 1483
Souza, John P., Controller--Procter & Gamble Venezuela, C.A., Caracas, Venezuela; *U.S. Public*, pg. 1332
Sovine, Judith L., Controller & Mgr.-Tax--The Gorman-Rupp Company, Mansfield, OH; *U.S. Public*, pg. 754
Sovine, Judith L., Controller--Mansfield Div., Mansfield, OH; *U.S. Public*, pg. 754
Sowinski, Dave, V.P. & Controller--American Drew, Greensboro, NC; *U.S. Public*, pg. 974
Sowinski, David, V.P. & Controller--Lea Industries, Greensboro, NC; *U.S. Public*, pg. 974
Spalding, Timothy J., V.P. & Controller--Jacobson Stores Inc., Jackson, MI; *U.S. Public*, pg. 922
Spangenberg, Scott J., Controller--Cascade Corporation, Troutdale, OR; *U.S. Public*, pg. 310
Sparduto, John, Controller--Warren Properties, Escondido, CA; *U.S. Private*, pg. 1151
Sparks, Gary, Chief Fin. Officer & Controller--Trauth Dairy Inc., Newport, KY; *U.S. Private*, pg. 1098
Spary, D.S., Controller--Crane Australia Pty. Ltd., Saint Marys, Australia; *U.S. Public*, pg. 457
Spates, Janet, Mgr.-Opers.--Pax World Fund Family, Portsmouth, NH; *U.S. Public*, pg. 1266
Spear, Robert D., Controller--Helen of Troy Corporation, El Paso, TX; *U.S. Public*, pg. 807
Spears, Mark T., V.P. & Controller--Waste Management, Inc., Oak Brook, IL; *U.S. Public*, pg. 1744
Speed, James, Sr. V.P. & Controller--Hardee's Food Systems, Inc., Rocky Mount, NC; *U.S. Public*, pg. 278
Speer, R.M., Controller--Flexible Technologies Inc., Abbeville, SC; *Int'l*, pg. 1267
Speiller, Michael, V.P. & Controller--Lambda Electronics Inc., Melville, NY; *Int'l*, pg. 1241
Spence, Jeffrey E., Chm. Bd., Pres., Controller & Chief Exec. & Fin. Officer--Controlled Systems of Wisconsin, Inc., Nashotah, WI; *U.S. Private*, pg. 271
Spencer, Daniel, V.P.--ULLICO Inc., Washington, DC; *U.S. Private*, pg. 1115
Spencer, Joe, Controller--Doman Industries Limited, Duncan, Canada; *Int'l*, pg. 414
Spencer, Wes, V.P. & Controller--CBS Radio, New York, NY; *U.S. Public*, pg. 274
Speridakos, John D., Controller--Essex Industries, New Haven, CT; *Int'l*, pg. 18
Spetz, Jan, Controller--AB Industrivarden, Stockholm, Sweden; *Int'l*, pg. 678
Sphar, Kelly, Controller--Automobile Protection Corporation-APCO, Atlanta, GA; *U.S. Public*, pg. 150
Spiczka, Mark, Controller--Dayton Rogers Mfg. Co., Blaine, MN; *U.S. Private*, pg. 318
Spiegel, John, Comptroller--Applied Innovation Inc., Dublin, OH; *U.S. Public*, pg. 123
Spielberger, Thomas, Controller--Jordan Industries, Inc., Deerfield, IL; *U.S. Private*, pg. 598
Spielberger, Thomas C., V.P. & Controller--J2, Inc., Deerfield, IL; *U.S. Private*, pg. 598

Spina, John, Sr. V.P. & Controller--Sudler & Hennessey, New York, NY; *U.S. Private*, pg. 1197
Spindor, Bob, Controller--McGavin Foods Ltd., Langley, Canada; *Int'l*, pg. 841
Spires, Steve, Controller--Nucor Fasteners, Saint Joe, IN; *U.S. Public*, pg. 1205
Spitse, Ruth Ann, Controller--Firstcom Marketing Inc., Toronto, Canada; *U.S. Private*, pg. 1200
Spitz, Brian, Controller--American Tank & Fabricating Co., Cleveland, OH; *U.S. Private*, pg. 63
Spitz, Randy J., Controller, Treas. & Sec.--Hicks Oil-Hicks Gas, Inc., Roberts, IL; *U.S. Private*, pg. 526
Spivack, Michael S., Controller--HLW International LLP, New York, NY; *U.S. Private*, pg. 491
Spivey, Richard, Controller--Sunnyland Refining Co., Inc., Birmingham, AL; *U.S. Private*, pg. 607
Spohn, Richard A., Controller-Acctg.--Ingersoll-Rand Company, Woodcliff Lake, NJ; *U.S. Public*, pg. 876
Sponem, Sandy, Controller--Piper Jaffray Companies, Inc., Minneapolis, MN; *U.S. Public*, pg. 1300
Sponseller, Bob, V.P., Gen. Mgr. & Controller--Golden West Broadcasters, Los Angeles, CA; *U.S. Private*, pg. 461
Spooner, Connie, Controller--Pelican Products, Torrance, CA; *U.S. Private*, pg. 848
Spooner, Steven E., V.P. & Controller--SHL Systemhouse, Ottawa, Canada; *Int'l*, pg. 1154
Spowart, Jay R., V.P.-Fin. & Corp. Sec.--Casio Phone-Mate, Inc., Torrance, CA; *Int'l*, pg. 274
Sprague, Ron, Controller--Wireless One Network LP, Fort Myers, FL; *U.S. Private*, pg. 1184
Spratt, Lee, Controller--Blue Diamond Growers, Sacramento, CA; *U.S. Private*, pg. 152
Sprauer, G., Controller--ITT Flygt, Pointe-Claire, Canada; *U.S. Public*, pg. 860
Sprenger, Charles, Controller--Dakco Distributors, Inc., Minot, ND; *U.S. Private*, pg. 308
Spriester, Fred, Controller--Hydraulics Div., Spencer, IA; *U.S. Public*, pg. 557
Springer, A., Controller--M.H. Rhodes, Inc., Avon, CT; *U.S. Private*, pg. 927
Springer, Branch J., Chief Fin. Officer, V.P. & Treas.--Abbey Etna Machine Company, Perrysburg, OH; *U.S. Private*, pg. 9
Springer, David, Chief Fin. Officer & Controller--Snyder Industries, Inc., Lincoln, NE; *U.S. Private*, pg. 1011
Springer, Jerry M., Controller & Asst. Sec.--NIPSCO Industries, Inc., Hammond, IN; *U.S. Public*, pg. 1185
Springsteen, Greg, Asst. Controller--Christenson Electric, Inc., Portland, OR; *U.S. Private*, pg. 238
Spruill, Rosemary, Controller--Gateway Press, Inc., Louisville, KY; *U.S. Private*, pg. 441
Spuur, Andrew, Controller--Kawai America Corporation, Compton, CA; *Int'l*, pg. 725
Spychala, Michael R., V.P.-Admin. & Controller--First Empire State Corporation, Buffalo, NY; *U.S. Public*, pg. 631
Squierdo, Michael, Controller--Susquehanna Bancshares, Inc., Lititz, PA; *U.S. Public*, pg. 1542
Squinzi, Maurizia, Controller--Compart SpA, Milan, Italy; *Int'l*, *pg. 324*
Sriram, N., Controller--Lovytex SDN. BHD., Kuala Langat, Malaysia; *U.S. Public*, pg. 1648
St. Clair, D.E., Controller--Exxon Asset Management Company, Irving, TX; *U.S. Public*, pg. 601
St. Germain, Dennis, V.P. & Controller--Harper-Wyman Co., Aurora, IL; *U.S. Public*, pg. 1209
St. Jean, Kevin, Controller--Spafas, Inc., Preston, CT; *U.S. Public*, pg. 195
St. Jean, Robert, V.P. & Controller--Provigo Inc., Montreal, Canada; *Int'l*, pg. 1072
St. Jean, Robert, V.P. & Controller--Provigo Distribution, Montreal, Canada; *Int'l*, pg. 1073
St. Michel, Mark, Sec., Treas. & Controller--Aero Systems Engineering Inc., Saint Paul, MN; *Int'l*, pg. 276
St. Pierre, Michel, Controller--Imprimerie Quebecor Joliette, Joliette, Canada; *Int'l*, pg. 1077
St. Pierre, Michel, Controller--Imprimerie Quebecor St-Jean, Saint-Jean, Canada; *Int'l*, pg. 1077
St. Pierre, Serge, Controller--Imprimerie Quebecor Magog, Magog, Canada; *Int'l*, pg. 1077
Staal, W., Controller--Food Products Management BV, Amstelveen, Netherlands; *Int'l*, pg. 751
Stack, Alan R., Controller--Kingsbury, Inc., Philadelphia, PA; *U.S. Private*, pg. 622
Stackelhouse, Dave, Controller--American Marketing Industries, Inc., Kansas City, MO; *U.S. Private*, pg. 58
Stadelman, Tim, Controller--J.H. Findorff & Son, Inc., Madison, WI; *U.S. Private*, pg. 405
Staelgrave, Ralph, Controller--Phillips Service Industries, Inc., Livonia, MI; *U.S. Private*, pg. 862
Staffrude, P.R., Controller & Treas.--Duluth, Winnipeg & Pacific Railway Co., Superior, WI; *Int'l*, pg. 258
Staggs, Brian, Controller--Star Fine Foods, Inc., Fresno, CA; *U.S. Private*, pg. 1034
Stahl, Duane, Controller--LumenX Company, Mogadore, OH; *U.S. Public*, pg. 56
Stahlberger, Geraldine M., Controller--Gold Medal Insurance Co., Minneapolis, MN; *U.S. Public*, pg. 718
Stahlbush, Brent, Controller & Asst. Treas.--APX International, Auburn Hills, MI; *U.S. Private*, pg. 7
Stair, Frederick J., Corp. Controller--Belden & Blake Corporation, Canton, OH; *U.S. Private*, pg. 1078
Stalkfleet, Rick, Chief Fin. Officer, V.P. & Controller--Rauland-Borg Corporation, Skokie, IL; *U.S. Private*, pg. 911
Stamer, Murray, Corp. Controller--Park Electrochemical Corporation, Lake Success, NY; *U.S. Public*, pg. 1258
Stamford, William A., V.P. & Controller--Eli Lilly and Company, Indianapolis, IN; *U.S. Public*, pg. 992
Stammler, Gary, Controller--Brooks Beverage Management, Inc., Columbus, OH; *U.S. Private*, pg. 142
Stancato, Kenneth J., V.P. & Controller--Weyerhaeuser Company, Federal Way, WA; *U.S. Public*, pg. 1764
Stander, Joe W., Sr. V.P. & Controller--Colorado National Bankshares, Inc., Denver, CO; *U.S. Public*, pg. 1680
Standiford, Jeffrey M., Controller & Dir.-Data Processing--Lamb Engineering & Construction Co., Salt Lake City, UT; *U.S. Private*, pg. 644
Stange, Chris, Controller & Dir.-Acctg.--O'Reilly Automotive Inc., Springfield, MO; *U.S. Public*, pg. 1230
Stanko, Laura, Controller--Letica Corporation, Rochester, MI; *U.S. Private*, pg. 661
Stankuis, Bob, Controller--Dav-El Worldwide, Chelsea, MA; *U.S. Private*, pg. 314
Stankus, John C., V.P. & Controller--New Haven Savings Bank, New Haven, CT; *U.S. Private*, pg. 793
Stanley, Brian C., V.P.-Investor Rels. & Controller--Valmont Industries, Inc., Valley, NE; *U.S. Public*, pg. 1706
Stanley, Daniel, Controller--Snappy Air Distribution Products, Detroit Lakes, MN; *U.S. Public*, pg. 1506
Stanley, Jim, Controller--Quincy Compressor Division Coltec Industries, Quincy, IL; *U.S. Public*, pg. 402
Stansberry, Brian, Controller--QT Optoelectronics, Sunnyvale, CA; *U.S. Private*, pg. 897
Stanskey, Dan, V.P. & Controller--Anchor Continental Incorporated, Columbia, SC; *U.S. Private*, pg. 70
Stanton, Laura, Controller--Dunlap & Co. Inc., Columbus, IN; *U.S. Private*, pg. 346
Stanz, Ken, Controller--AVC/Nu-Vision, Inc., Flint, MI; *U.S. Private*, pg. 9
Stanziale, Ronald C., Jr., V.P. & Controller--Hudson Insurance Company, New York, NY; *Int'l*, pg. 1258
Stapleton, Jerry M., Controller--General Shale Products Corp., Johnson City, TN; *Int'l*, pg. 843
Stapleton, Jerry M., Controller--General Shale Products Corp., Elizabethton, TN; *Int'l*, pg. 843
Stark, James R., Controller--Bio-Rad Laboratories, Inc., Hercules, CA; *U.S. Public*, pg. 230
Starr, Marie, Controller--Hamilton Precision Metals, Lancaster, PA; *U.S. Public*, pg. 944
Stasuszen, Rick, Controller--C.R. Anthony Company, Oklahoma City, OK; *U.S. Private*, pg. 1029
Statile, Peter J., V.P. & Controller--Hanson North America, Woodbridge, NJ; *Int'l*, pg. 593
Stawarz, Raymond R., Sr. V.P., Dir.-Corp. Acctg. & Asst. Treas. & Asst. Sec.--Federated Mutual Insurance Company, Owatonna, MN; *U.S. Private*, pg. 399
Steadley, Bob, Controller--Zaremba Group, Inc., Lakewood, OH; *U.S. Private*, pg. 1204
Steeber, Jerry, Controller--Dempster Equipment, Toccoa, GA; *U.S. Private*, pg. 1089
Steele, Harry W., V.P. & Controller--James H. Drew Corp., Indianapolis, IN; *U.S. Public*, pg. 1084
Steele, John, Controller--Carrier Vibrating Equipment, Inc., Louisville, KY; *U.S. Private*, pg. 215
Steele, Kevin S., Controller, Chief Acctg. Officer & Asst. Sec.--UDC Homes, Inc., Scottsdale, AZ; *U.S. Private*, pg. 5
Steenbeke, Joseph J., Chief Fin. Officer, Treas., Sec. & Controller--Spray-Tech, Inc., Longwood, FL; *U.S. Private*, *pg. 1026*
Stefanek, Albert, Controller--Solid State Devices, Inc., La Mirada, CA; *U.S. Private*, pg. 1012
Stefanick, J., Controller & Mgr.-Credit--Tamaqua Cable Products Corp., Schuylkill Haven, PA; *Int'l*, pg. 417
Stefano, Brian R., Chief Fin. Officer & Controller--Peter Pan Bus Lines, Inc., Springfield, MA; *U.S. Private*, pg. 856
Steffan, John P., V.P. & Controller--Cinergy Corp., Cincinnati, OH; *U.S. Public*, pg. 368
Steffen, John P., Asst. Comptroller--Cinergy, Plainfield, IN; *U.S. Public*, pg. 369
Steffen, John P., Asst. Comptroller--CINergy Services, Inc., Cincinnati, OH; *U.S. Public*, pg. 369
Steffen, John P., Asst. Comptroller--KO Transmission Company, Cincinnati, OH; *U.S. Public*, pg. 369
Steffen, John P., Asst. Comptroller--Lawrenceburg Gas Co., Cincinnati, OH; *U.S. Public*, pg. 369
Steffen, John P., Asst. Comptroller--Miami Power Corp., Cincinnati, OH; *U.S. Public*, pg. 369
Steffen, John P., Asst. Comptroller--Tri-State Improvement Co., Cincinnati, OH; *U.S. Public*, pg. 369
Steffen, John P., Asst. Comptroller--Union Light, Heat and Power Co., Cincinnati, OH; *U.S. Public*, pg. 369
Steffen, John P., Asst. Comptroller--Cinergy Corp., Cincinnati, OH; *U.S. Public*, pg. 369
Stegall, Douglas C., Chief Fin. Officer, V.P. & Controller--Global Marine Drilling Co., Houston, TX; *U.S. Public*, pg. 748
Steiner, Dallas, Controller--Dakotah, Inc., Webster, SD; *U.S. Public*, pg. 477
Steiner, Diana, Controller--Westchester Lace, Inc., North Bergen, NJ; *U.S. Private*, pg. 1163
Steinhart, Conrad, Controller, Treas. & Sec.--Happy Holiday Tree Farms, Sheridan, MI; *U.S. Private*, pg. 254
Steins, Bernie, V.P.-Fin. & Controller--Federal Business Products, Inc., Clifton, NJ; *U.S. Private*, pg. 398
Steke, Gary, Controller--Goshen Rubber Co., Inc., Goshen, IN; *U.S. Private*, pg. 465
Stelly, Greg, Controller & Sec.--Carter Chambers Supply, Inc., Baton Rouge, LA; *U.S. Private*, pg. 216
Stemler, Wayne, Controller--Hendrick Motorsports, Harrisburg, NC; *U.S. Private*, pg. 522
Stender, Steve, Controller--Rena-Ware Distributors Inc., Redmond, WA; *U.S. Private*, pg. 922
Stephan, Richard, V.P. & Controller--Viad Corp, Phoenix, AZ; *U.S. Public*, pg. 1718
Stephas, Gus, Sr. V.P. & Controller--CBL & Associates Properties, Inc., Chattanooga, TN; *U.S. Public*, pg. 273
Stephenson, Garry, Controller--Reynolds and Reynolds-Business Forms Division, Oklahoma City, OK; *U.S. Public*, pg. 1385
Stern, Denise, Asst. Controller--Cutler Manufacturing Corporation, Lakeland, FL; *U.S. Private*, pg. 298
Stern, Frederic E., V.P. & Controller--United Retail Group, Inc., Rochelle Park, NJ; *U.S. Public*, pg. 1679
Stern, Jack, V.P. & Controller--Esselte Corporation, Garden City, NY; *Int'l*, pg. 459
Stern, Joyce, Controller--WAXY (FM), Fort Lauderdale, FL; *U.S. Public*, pg. 925
Stetson, Steven, Controller--The J.M. Ney Company, Bloomfield, CT; *U.S. Public*, pg. 111
Steven, Michael T., Asst. Controller--Woolworth Corporation, New York, NY; *U.S. Public*, pg. 1777
Stevens, Art, Controller--Faulkner Cadillac Inc., Trevose, PA; *U.S. Private*, pg. 397
Stevens, Bill, Controller--Eastern American Energy Corporation, Charleston, WV; *U.S. Private*, pg. 357
Stevens, Dennis, Controller--Horizon Paper Co., Inc., New York, NY; *U.S. Private*, pg. 539
Stevens, Doris E., Controller--Trimtex Co. Inc., Williamsport, PA; *U.S. Private*, pg. 1103
Stevens, Doug, Controller & Asst. Sec.--Delta Woodside Industries, Inc., Greenville, SC; *U.S. Public*, pg. 497
Stevens, Fran, V.P.-Operations--Star Video Entertainment, L.P., Jersey City, NJ; *U.S. Private*, pg. 1132
Stevens, Gregory W., V.P. & Controller--Phelps Dodge Corporation, Phoenix, AZ; *U.S. Public*, pg. 1286
Stevens, Michael C., Controller & Asst. Treas.--Connecticut Natural Gas Corporation, Hartford, CT; *U.S. Public*, pg. 285
Stevens, Michael L., Controller--Rayrock Yellowknife Resources Inc., Toronto, Canada; *Int'l*, pg. 1089
Stevens, Robert, Asst. Controller--Domain Energy Corporation, Houston, TX; *U.S. Public*, pg. 515
Stevenson, Allan J., Chief Fin. Officer, Sr. V.P. & Controller--Parsons Brinckerhoff Inc., New York, NY; *U.S. Private*, pg. 841
Stevenson, Brady, Controller--Melling Forging Company, Lansing, MI; *U.S. Private*, pg. 102
Stevenson, Dave, Controller--Rundel Products, Inc., Portland, OR; *U.S. Private*, pg. 951
Stevenson, Jimmie K., Controller--Hygeia Dairy Co., Inc., Harlingen, TX; *U.S. Private*, pg. 552
Stevenson, W.N., V.P. & Controller--Rheem Air Conditioning Div., Fort Smith, AR; *Int'l*, pg. 1022
Steward, Cynthia G., Controller--Illinois Power Company, Decatur, IL; *U.S. Public*, pg. 869
Stewart, James, Controller--Imation Corporation, Oakdale, MN; *U.S. Public*, pg. 870
Stewart, Jeff A., V.P. & Controller--Tricord Systems, Inc., Plymouth, MN; *U.S. Public*, pg. 1637
Stewart, John F., Chief Acctg. Officer & Controller--The Penn Traffic Company, Syracuse, NY; *U.S. Public*, pg. 1270
Stewart, Lynne, Controller--People's Choice TV Corp., Shelton, CT; *U.S. Public*, pg. 1274
Stewart, Michael R., Chief Fin. Officer, V.P., Treas. & Controller--Surgical Laser Technologies, Inc., Montgomeryville, PA; *U.S. Public*, pg. 1542
Stewart, William, Controller--Hunter Marine Corporation, Alachua, FL; *U.S. Private*, pg. 549
Stichalk, George, Controller--M.J. Daly & Sons, Inc., Waterbury, CT; *U.S. Private*, pg. 309
Stichler, Donald L., Controller, Treas. & Sec.--Varco International, Inc., Orange, CA; *U.S. Public*, pg. 1709
Stickles, Pat, Controller--Quality Toyota, Longwood, FL; *U.S. Private*, pg. 899
Stieber, Patrick, Controller--Plastigage Corporation, Jackson, MI; *U.S. Private*, pg. 871
Stiles, Sandra E., V.P. & Controller--Random House, Inc., New York, NY; *U.S. Private*, pg. 20
Stiles, William, Controller--OMNI Products, Inc., Portland, OR; *U.S. Private*, pg. 816
Stillwell, Alex, Controller--Northern Telecom - National Repair & Distribution Center, Nashville, TN; *Int'l*, pg. 970
Stimpfel, John S., V.P. & Controller--The American Stock Exchange, New York, NY; *U.S. Private*, pg. 62
Stipetic, Toni, Controller--Acme Poultry Company, Inc., Renton, WA; *U.S. Private*, pg. 13
Stirl, Mark E., Controller--Sonat Exploration Company, Houston, TX; *U.S. Public*, pg. 1485
Stocelcle, Char, Controller--CRX Inc., Fremont, NE; *U.S. Public*, pg. 49
Stock, Joyce, Controller--Siemer Milling Company, Teutopolis, IL; *U.S. Private*, pg. 998
Stockamp, Robert L., V.P. & Controller--Diebold, Incorporated, Canton, OH; *U.S. Public*, pg. 506
Stockelmann, Cheryl, Controller--Rodney D. Young Insurance, Dallas, TX; *U.S. Private*, pg. 1202
Stocker, Joe, Controller--The Vernon Company, Newton, IA; *U.S. Private*, pg. 1137
Stockman, John, Controller--Ellicott Machine Corporation International, Baltimore, MD; *U.S. Private*, pg. 372
Stockslager, Mark J., Corp. Controller--Krug International Corp., Houston, TX; *U.S. Public*, pg. 967
Stodola, Randy, V.P. & Controller--Met-Coil Systems Corp., Cedar Rapids, IA; *U.S. Public*, pg. 1099
Stodola, Randy, Controller--Iowa Precision Industries, Cedar Rapids, IA; *U.S. Public*, pg. 1100
Stoehr, David, Controller--Associated Banc-Corp, Green Bay, WI; *U.S. Public*, pg. 140
Stoffel, Don, Controller--Keller Construction Company Ltd., El Monte, CA; *U.S. Private*, pg. 612
Stohler, Roger, Controller--Hoboken Wood Flooring Corporation, Wayne, NJ; *U.S. Private*, pg. 532
Stokes, John E., Controller--Riviana Foods Inc., Houston, TX; *U.S. Public*, pg. 1392
Stoller, Stuart, V.P. & Controller--The New York Times Company, New York, NY; *U.S. Public*, pg. 1173
Stollings, Anthony, V.P. & Controller--Provident Financial Group, Inc., Cincinnati, OH; *U.S. Public*, pg. 1338
Stoltz, Robert, V.P. & Controller--Sanford Corporation, Bellwood, IL; *U.S. Public*, pg. 1178
Stoltz, Robert, V.P. & Controller--Sanford Beroc Corp., Brentwood, TN; *U.S. Public*, pg. 1178
Stone, Archie, Chief Fin. Officer & Controller--Fletcher Jones Management Group, Las Vegas, NV; *U.S. Private*, *pg. 597*
Stone, Dan W., Controller-Flowers Bakeries, Inc.--Flowers Industries, Inc., Thomasville, GA; *U.S. Public*, pg. 656
Stone, Lynn, Controller--Bombardier Corporation, Benton, IL; *Int'l*, pg. 200

Stone, Pat, Controller--American Manufacturing Company, Chattanooga, TN; *U.S. Private*, pg. 58
Stone, Patricia, Adv. Controller--Pirelli U.K. Tyres Limited, Burton on Trent, United Kingdom; *Int'l*, pg. 1059
Stone, Spencer, Controller--Torchmark Corporation, Birmingham, AL; *U.S. Public*, pg. 1622
Stone, Stephen, V.P. & Controller--Irwin Toy Ltd., Toronto, Canada; *Int'l*, pg. 688
Stone, Sylvia, Controller--H.O. Penn Machinery Co. Inc., Poughkeepsie, NY; *U.S. Private*, pg. 849
Stonehill, Judy, Controller--Cosmos Communications, Inc., Long Island City, NY; *U.S. Private*, pg. 278
Stooksbury, Hugh T., Controller--Pride Oil Co., Inc., Knoxville, TN; *U.S. Private*, pg. 613
Storck, Bill, Controller--Fike Corporation, Blue Springs, MO; *U.S. Private*, pg. 404
Storck, Raymond L., V.P., Controller & Asst. Treas.--MicroAge, Inc., Tempe, AZ; *U.S. Public*, pg. 1104
Storey, Craig, Controller--Radica USA Limited, Dallas, TX; *U.S. Private*, pg. 906
Storms, Tom, V.P. & Controller--Rodale Press, Inc., Emmaus, PA; *U.S. Private*, pg. 939
Story, Dirk, Controller--EcoScience Produce Systems Corp., Orlando, FL; *U.S. Public*, pg. 563
Stos, Kent S., Controller--National Cooperative Refinery Association, Mc Pherson, KS; *U.S. Private*, pg. 781
Stoudenmire, Stan F., V.P. & Controller--Policy Management Systems Corporation, Blythewood, SC; *U.S. Public*, pg. 1314
Stouffer, Ray, Controller--Greer Steel Co., Dover, OH; *U.S. Private*, pg. 479
Stout, Kenneth L., Controller--Ashland Services Company, Lexington, KY; *U.S. Public*, pg. 139
Stout, Tom, Controller--America Online Incorporated, Dulles, VA; *U.S. Public*, pg. 66
Stoval, Jim, Controller--SRS Technologies, Newport Beach, CA; *U.S. Private*, pg. 958
Strain, Harry, Controller--Ourisman Chevrolet, Marlow Heights, MD; *U.S. Private*, pg. 821
Strain, Ronald R., V.P., Treas. & Controller--Miller Brewing Company, Milwaukee, WI; *U.S. Public*, pg. 1289
Stralkowski, Tom, Controller--Palmer International, Inc., Worcester, PA; *U.S. Private*, pg. 834
Strang, Sara, Controller--General Drug Co., Chicago, IL; *U.S. Private*, pg. 1007
Strasma, Edward J., Chief Fin. Officer, Exec. V.P. & Controller--Interstate Producers Livestock Association, Peoria, IL; *U.S. Private*, pg. 573
Strassburger, Leo, Corp. Controller--Fahlgren, Dublin, OH; *U.S. Private*, pg. 391
Stratman, Joe, Controller--Nucor-Yamato Steel Company, Blytheville, AR; *U.S. Public*, pg. 1206
Straub, Henry, Controller--Old Guard Insurance Group, Lancaster, PA; *U.S. Public*, pg. 1216
Straub, Hubert, Dr., Controller--Heidelberger Druckmaschinen A.G., Heidelberg, Germany; *Int'l*, pg. 604
Strausser, Albert, V.P. & Controller--Capitol Manufacturing Co., Westerville, OH; *U.S. Public*, pg. 793
Strawn, Timothy, V.P. & Controller--Hatteras Yachts, New Bern, NC; *U.S. Private*, pg. 447
Streeby, Harold, Controller--Teleflex Automotive, Lebanon, VA; *U.S. Public*, pg. 1569
Streed, Julie, Controller--Grist Mill Company, Lakeville, MN; *U.S. Public*, pg. 766
Streich, Gordon, Chief Fin. Officer & V.P.--RK Mechanical, Inc., Denver, CO; *U.S. Private*, pg. 904
Streiff, Mark L., Controller--Ducommun Incorporated, Carson, CA; *U.S. Public*, pg. 533
Stribley, D. LeAnne, V.P.-Fin. & Controller--Tennessee Valley Authority, Knoxville, TN; *U.S. Public*, pg. 1580
Strickler, George E., V.P.-Fin.-N. America Tires--The Goodyear Tire & Rubber Company, Akron, OH; *U.S. Public*, pg. 752
Stricko, Nancy, V.P., Controller--Ammirati, Puris & Lintas, Inc., New York, NY; *U.S. Private*, pg. 66
Strif, Rich, Controller--Stuart Entertainment Inc., Council Bluffs, IA; *U.S. Public*, pg. 1526
Stringer, James J., V.P. & Controller--Lyons Lavey Nickel Swift, Inc., New York, NY; *U.S. Public*, pg. 1224
Strittmatter, Melissa, Controller--Blimpie International, Inc., Atlanta, GA; *U.S. Public*, pg. 236
Strobach, Bill, Controller--Wisconsin Automated Machinery Corp., Oshkosh, WI; *U.S. Private*, pg. 1184
Strobel, Steven J., V.P. & Controller--Owens Corning, Toledo, OH; *U.S. Public*, pg. 1236
Strohl, P., Controller--L.B. Smith, Inc., Camp Hill, PA; *U.S. Private*, pg. 1009
Strole, Jon, Controller--Tuffy Associates Corp., Toledo, OH; *U.S. Private*, pg. 1109
Strong, Bob, Controller--National Restaurant Supply Company, El Paso, TX; *U.S. Private*, pg. 786
Strootman, Ann M., V.P. & Controller--The Penn Mutual Life Insurance Company, Philadelphia, PA; *U.S. Private*, pg. 849
Stroud, Mark A., V.P. & Controller--First National Bank of Sweetwater, Sweetwater, TX; *U.S. Public*, pg. 633
Struett, Bill, Controller--Triangle Distributing Company, Santa Fe Springs, CA; *U.S. Private*, pg. 1101
Strulovici, Christian, Gen. Controller--Groupe GAN, Paris, France; *Int'l*, pg. 563
Strunk, Kaye, Controller & Treas.--Carter-Jones Companies, Inc., Kent, OH; *U.S. Private*, pg. 217
Stryker, Gerald, Controller--McGraw-Hill Continuing Education Center, Washington, DC; *U.S. Public*, pg. 1070
Stryker, Gerald, Controller--NRI Schools, Washington, DC; *U.S. Public*, pg. 1071
Strzynski, Greg, Controller--American International Airways, Ypsilanti, MI; *U.S. Private*, pg. 57
Stuart, Ronald W., V.P.-Fin. & Comptroller--S. Schwab Company, Cumberland, MD; *U.S. Private*, pg. 974
Stuckey, Ray, Controller--Harp's Food Stores, Inc., Springdale, AR; *U.S. Private*, pg. 504
Studer, Cathy, Asst. V.P. & Asst. Controller--Raritan Bancorp Inc., Bridgewater, NJ; *U.S. Public*, pg. 1361
Studley, Joseph, V.P. & Controller--The Interpublic Group of Companies, Inc., New York, NY; *U.S. Public*, pg. 908
Stuebgen, William J., V.P. & Controller--APL Limited, Oakland, CA; *Int'l*, pg. 912
Stulik, Bruce, Controller--Nuarc Company, Inc., Niles, IL; *U.S. Private*, pg. 808
Stull, Timothy L., Corp. Controller--DBA Systems, Inc., Melbourne, FL; *U.S. Public*, pg. 472
Stumbaugh, Kenneth E., Controller--Commercial Intertech Corp., Youngstown, OH; *U.S. Public*, pg. 411
Stumme, Brent, Controller--CalMat Co., Los Angeles, CA; *U.S. Public*, pg. 295
Stump, Darwin, Controller--Petroleum Development Corporation, Bridgeport, WV; *U.S. Public*, pg. 1280
Stump, Ken, Controller--Beverage America, Inc., Holland, MI; *U.S. Private*, pg. 141
Stump, Susan, Controller--Futter Lumber Corporation, Rockville Center, NY; *U.S. Private*, pg. 432
Sturtevant, Catherine M., Controller.--Ann Sacks Tile & Stone, Inc., Portland, OR; *U.S. Private*, pg. 630
Stuteville, Rodney, Controller--Graphic Technology, Inc., New Century, KS; *Int'l*, pg. 950
Stutts, Gloria, Controller & Treas.--Mansion Homes, Robbins, NC; *U.S. Public*, pg. 318
Stutvoet, William, Gen. Mgr. & Controller--Thompack B.V., Apeldoorn, Netherlands; *U.S. Public*, pg. 5
Stuver, Craig O., Corp. Controller & Asst. Treas.--Michael Baker Corporation, Pittsburgh, PA; *U.S. Public*, pg. 168
Suarez, Alfonso F., Corp. V.P.-Control--Grupo Iberia, Madrid, Spain; *Int'l*, pg. 574
Suarez, Gerardo, Controller--Bacardi-Martini, USA, Inc., Miami, FL; *U.S. Private*, pg. 109
Subramanian, V., Controller--Semcon Electronics Pvt. Ltd., Mumbai, India; *U.S. Public*, pg. 1107
Suen, Susanna, Controller--Kulicke & Soffa (Asia), Ltd., Kowloon, Hong Kong; *U.S. Public*, pg. 969
Suesser, Alfred, Controller--Dover Corporation, New York, NY; *U.S. Public*, pg. 520
Sugarman, Shawn A., V.P. & Controller--The Minute Maid Company, Houston, TX; *U.S. Public*, pg. 392
Suglia, Victor, Controller--Saks Fifth Avenue, New York, NY; *U.S. Public*, pg. 1429
Suhre, Jim, Controller--Jeff Wyler Dealer Group, Inc., Cincinnati, OH; *U.S. Private*, pg. 1193
Sula, James, Controller--Recoton Auto Corporation, Lincolnshire, IL; *U.S. Public*, pg. 1369
Sullenberger, Dana E., V.P. & Opers. Controller--Republic Industries, Inc., Fort Lauderdale, FL; *U.S. Public*, pg. 1378
Sullivan, Debra, Controller--Johnstown Knitting Mill Co., Johnstown, NY; *U.S. Private*, pg. 595
Sullivan, Dennis, Controller--Metropolitan Transportation Authority, New York, NY; *U.S. Private*, pg. 739
Sullivan, Elizabeth Breen, V.P. & Controller--MBIA Inc., Armonk, NY; *U.S. Public*, pg. 1023
Sullivan, Jerry, Controller--Dynagear Inc., Downers Grove, IL; *U.S. Private*, pg. 350
Sullivan, John, Controller--Texon Materials Inc., Russell, MA; *U.S. Private*, pg. 1079
Sullivan, John L., Controller, Treas. & Sec.--Totsy Manufacturing Company, Inc., Holyoke, MA; *U.S. Private*, *pg. 1093*
Sullivan, John L., III, Controller & Treas.--The Eastern Company, Naugatuck, CT; *U.S. Public*, pg. 548
Sullivan, Mark W., Treas.--Creative Productions, Pittsburgh, PA; *U.S. Private*, pg. 288
Sullivan, Michael, Controller & Bus. Mgr.--KGAN-TV, Cedar Rapids, IA; *U.S. Private*, pg. 439
Sullivan, Sharon, Controller--Twincraft, Inc., Winooski, VT; *U.S. Private*, pg. 1111
Sullivan, Timothy K., Controller--Tri-Remanufacturing, Terre Haute, IN; *U.S. Public*, pg. 710
Sulzbach, D.J., Chief Fin. Officer, V.P. & Controller--Wyman-Gordon Forgings, North Grafton, MA; *U.S. Public*, pg. 1782
Summers, Cheryl, Controller & Asst. Sec.--McCall Oil & Chemical Corp., Portland, OR; *U.S. Private*, pg. 719
Summers, William E., V.P. & Controller--Plant City Steel Co., Plant City, FL; *U.S. Public*, pg. 793
Sumner, Sharon, Chief Fin. Officer & Controller--Craddock-Terry Inc., Lynchburg, VA; *U.S. Private*, pg. 284
Sun, James, Controller--Authentic Fitness Corp., Los Angeles, CA; *U.S. Public*, pg. 147
Sun, Nikki, Controller--Dumore Corporation, Mauston, WI; *U.S. Private*, pg. 346
Sundeen, Dan, Controller--Eaton Office Supply Co., Inc., Amherst, NY; *U.S. Private*, pg. 358
Surerus, William E., Sr. V.P. & Controller--Mesirow Financial, Chicago, IL; *U.S. Private*, pg. 733
Surma, John P., Sr. V.P.-Fin. & Acctg. & Controller--Marathon Oil Company, Houston, TX; *U.S. Public*, pg. 1661
Surma, Ronald F., Chief Fin. Officer & Controller--Processed Plastic Company, Montgomery, IL; *U.S. Private*, pg. 888
Susel, Roman J., Controller--Bauer Sports Inc., Montreal, Canada; *U.S. Public*, pg. 1184
Susen, Vaclav, Controller--John Crane Sigma a.s., Lutin, Czech Republic; *Int'l*, pg. 1339
Sutter, Conrad, Controller--Engine Components Div., Belmond, IA; *U.S. Public*, pg. 556
Suttijiwimoa, Boonsong, Controller--Kendall-Gammatron Ltd., Bangkok, Thailand; *U.S. Public*, pg. 1648
Sutton, Scott, Controller--Fabwel Inc., Elkhart, IN; *U.S. Private*, pg. 390
Sutton, William M., V.P., Comptroller & Treas.--Huntington National Bank, Morgantown, WV; *U.S. Public*, pg. 850
Suzzi, Don, Controller--L. Karp & Sons, Inc., Elk Grove Village, IL; *U.S. Private*, pg. 607
Svendsen, Niels-Ole, Controller--Sophus Berendsen A/S, Soeborg, Denmark; *Int'l*, pg. 1284
Svenson, Ulrik, Sr. V.P.-Fin. Control--Millicom International Cellular SA, Bertrange, Luxembourg; *Int'l*, pg. 867
Swalwell, Greg, Controller--Contran Corporation, Dallas, TX; *U.S. Private*, pg. 270
Swalwell, Gregory M., Controller--Valhi, Inc., Dallas, TX; *U.S. Private*, pg. 270
Swanson, Bill, Controller--Quill Corp., Lincolnshire, IL; *U.S. Private*, pg. 901
Swanson, Randy, Controller--Windsor Fashions, Los Angeles, CA; *U.S. Private*, pg. 1182
Swanson, Ron, Controller--Alkota Cleaning Systems, Inc., Alcester, SD; *U.S. Private*, pg. 34
Swart, J.B., Controller & Dir.-Fin.--Permark International (Pty.) Ltd., Johannesburg, South Africa; *Int'l*, pg. 1036
Swartz, G. I., Chief Fin. Officer, Treas. & Controller--U.S. Borax Inc., Valencia, CA; *Int'l*, pg. 1119
Swatt, Richard, Controller--Cushman & Wakefield, Inc., New York, NY; *Int'l*, pg. 873
Swatzell, Susan, Controller--State Volunteer Mutual Insurance Co., Brentwood, TN; *U.S. Private*, pg. 1037
Swecker, Trudy B., Asst. Comptroller--Huntington National Bank, Morgantown, WV; *U.S. Public*, pg. 850
Sweeney, Frank J., Controller--ITT Avionics Division, Clifton, NJ; *U.S. Public*, pg. 859
Sweeney, Stephen J., Controller--Parsons & Whittemore, Inc., Rye Brook, NY; *U.S. Private*, pg. 840
Sweet, David, V.P. & Controller--David Clark Company Incorporated, Worcester, MA; *U.S. Private*, pg. 242
Sweet, Raymond D., V.P.-Opers., Controller & Treas.--Consolidated Coatings Corp., Brunswick, OH; *U.S. Public*, pg. 1357
Swett, 50805, Controller--Continental Graphics Holdings, Inc., Los Angeles, CA; *U.S. Private*, pg. 268
Swick, Dennis, Controller--North Safety Products, Health Care Division, Rockford, IL; *Int'l*, pg. 1243
Swift, William A., V.P. & Controller FAO--Ford Motor Company, Dearborn, MI; *U.S. Public*, pg. 661
Swink, Laura Marmora, Controller--Willis Corroon Corp. of Penn., Radnor, PA; *Int'l*, pg. 1507
Swinton, Rick, Controller--Crowley Maritime Corporation, Oakland, CA; *U.S. Private*, pg. 292
Swisher, Renee, Controller--Taco John's International, Inc., Cheyenne, WY; *U.S. Private*, pg. 1066
Swisher, Stephen, Corp. Controller--B/E Aerospace, Inc., Wellington, FL; *U.S. Public*, pg. 159
Switalski, Marty, Controller--Schurz Communications, Inc., South Bend, IN; *U.S. Private*, pg. 973
Swizerro, Paul, Controller--C.I. Hayes, Inc., Cranston, RI; *U.S. Private*, pg. 513
Swords, Gary A., V.P. & Chief Acctg. Officer--Cigna Corp., Philadelphia, PA; *U.S. Public*, pg. 356
Syfu, Jaime, Controller--ELE International, Inc./Soiltest, Lake Bluff, IL; *Int'l*, pg. 1287
Sykes, Alan, Controller--Hazen & Sawyer, New York, NY; *U.S. Private*, pg. 514
Sykes, Janelle, Controller--Pioneer Flour Mills, San Antonio, TX; *U.S. Private*, pg. 866
Sylvester, Dale R., Controller--Eaton Corporation, Engineered Fasteners Division, Brunswick, OH; *U.S. Public*, pg. 556
Syrjamaki, Maxine, Controller--Jefferies Group, Inc., Los Angeles, CA; *U.S. Public*, pg. 924
Szabo, Bill, Controller--Niagara Cutter, Inc., Amherst, NY; *U.S. Private*, pg. 798
Szabo, Frank, Controller--ACC Corp., Rochester, NY; *U.S. Public*, pg. 2
Szeglin, Irene, Controller--Enterprise, New York, NY; *U.S. Private*, pg. 377
Szenasi, Frank P., Controller & Treas.--Dover Industries Limited, Burlington, Canada; *Int'l*, pg. 417
Szerwo, Robert, Asst. Controller--Mission Industries, Las Vegas, NV; *U.S. Private*, pg. 752
Szeto, Archie K., V.P.-Fin. & Controller--PerSeptive Biosystems, Inc., Framingham, MA; *U.S. Public*, pg. 1279
Sztraicher, Dan, Controller--La Reina, Inc., Los Angeles, CA; *U.S. Private*, pg. 640
Szubski, Maria, Controller--Pubco Corporation, Cleveland, OH; *U.S. Public*, pg. 1339
Szymanski, Richard, Controller--Prime Hospitality Corp., Fairfield, NJ; *U.S. Public*, pg. 1326
Szypulski, Wayne R., V.P. & Controller--Sara Lee Corporation, Chicago, IL; *U.S. Public*, pg. 1432
Szywala, Dennis, Controller--Graphic Controls Corporation, Buffalo, NY; *U.S. Private*, pg. 470
Tabor, Chuck, Controller--Thonet, Statesville, NC; *U.S. Public*, pg. 1465
Tacinelli, Joseph V., Controller--M & M Precision Systems Corporation, Carrollton, OH; *U.S. Public*, pg. 482
Tacinelli, Joseph V., Controller--Ball Screws & Actuators Co., Inc., San Jose, CA; *U.S. Public*, pg. 482
Tacka, David W., Chief Acctg. Officer & Controller--Hershey Foods Corporation, Hershey, PA; *U.S. Public*, pg. 811
Taets, Jim, Controller--Nord Resources Corporation, Albuquerque, NM; *U.S. Public*, pg. 1188
Tagliaferro, Alphonso, Controller--Westwood One, Inc., New York, NY; *U.S. Public*, pg. 1763
Tajak, Rich, V.P. & Controller--Fujisawa U.S.A., Deerfield, IL; *Int'l*, pg. 525
Talamo, Felix, Controller--Media Partnership Corporation, Norwalk, CT; *U.S. Private*, pg. 1168
Talbot, Ann, Controller--Underground Construction Co., Inc., Benicia, CA; *U.S. Private*, pg. 1116
Taliaferro, Gary D., V.P. & Controller--CNF Transportation Inc., Palo Alto, CA; *U.S. Public*, pg. 281
Talkington, Jack A., Sr. V.P.-Lending, Controller--United Companies Financial Corporation, Baton Rouge, LA; *U.S. Public*, pg. 1675
Tall, Louis, Controller--Fortifiber Corporation, Incline Village, NV; *U.S. Private*, pg. 419
Talley, Kenny, V.P.-Controller--Motel 6 Operating L.P., Dallas, TX; *Int'l*, pg. 21
Talreja, Prakash, Controller--Money Point Diamond Co., Chesapeake, VA; *U.S. Private*, pg. 757

Tamura, Atsuko, Controller--Recreational Equipment, Inc., Kent, WA; U.S. Private, pg. 914
Tamura, Hideo, Controller--Chugai Boyeki Co., Ltd., Tokyo, Japan; Int'l, pg. 290
Tang, Sam, Controller--TMP Worldwide Ltd., Toronto, Canada; U.S. Private, pg. 1065
Tanner, Deloy, Controller--Nebraska Book Co., Inc., Lincoln, NE; U.S. Private, pg. 789
Tanquary, Fred T., Controller--Mail Boxes Etc., San Diego, CA; U.S. Public, pg. 1687
Tansey, James R., Chief Fin. Officer & Sr. V.P.--Jaydon Incorporated, Rock Island, IL; U.S. Private, pg. 584
Tapia, L., Fin. Controller--Dynacast de Mexico, S.A. de C.V., Tultitlan, Mexico; Int'l, pg. 300
Taraba, John, V.P. & Controller--Cyprus Amax Minerals Company, Englewood, CO; U.S. Public, pg. 470
Tarbath, Lynda L., Controller--General Communication, Inc., Anchorage, AK; U.S. Public, pg. 708
Tardiff, Paul, Corp. Controller--Waters Corporation, Milford, MA; U.S. Public, pg. 1745
Tarsia, Pat, Controller--AM Cosmetics Inc., Nyack, NY; U.S. Private, pg. 6
Tart, Maureen B., V.P. & Controller--AT&T Corporation, Basking Ridge, NJ; U.S. Public, pg. 10
Tartaglia, Daniel, V.P. & Controller--Harden Furniture Company, McConnellsville, NY; U.S. Private, pg. 501
Tartre, Don, Controller & Sr. Dir.--Agouron Pharmaceuticals, Inc., La Jolla, CA; U.S. Public, pg. 28
Tarzwell, Jeff, Controller--Sasco/Valley Electric, Mountain View, CA; U.S. Private, pg. 967
Tasker, Steven W., V.P. & Controller--Niagara Mohawk Power Corporation, Syracuse, NY; U.S. Public, pg. 1181
Tassello, Ronald, Comptroller--Baltek Corporation, Northvale, NJ; U.S. Public, pg. 171
Tatasciore, John, Controller--Danaher Tool Group, Lancaster, PA; U.S. Public, pg. 480
Tate, Chris, Asst. Controller--Ingram Merchandising Service Inc., La Vergne, TN; U.S. Private, pg. 563
Tate, Karen, Controller--Automobile Magazine, Ann Arbor, MI; U.S. Public, pg. 1328
Tatters, Douglas R., Asst. Controller--Magna International Inc., Markham, Canada; Int'l, pg. 829
Tattum, George, Controller--AEP Industries Australia Pty. Ltd., Kirrawee, Australia; U.S. Public, pg. 5
Taub, David, Controller & Sec.--Fownes Brothers & Co., Inc., New York, NY; U.S. Private, pg. 422
Taudin, Claude, Treas.--Bull S.A., Louveciennes, France; Int'l, pg. 315
Taunton, Vicki, Controller--Drumheller Bag & Supply, Valdosta, GA; U.S. Private, pg. 802
Tavolette, Fred, Controller--Allen & Hoshall, Inc., Memphis, TN; U.S. Private, pg. 36
Taylor, Alan, V.P.-Corp. Controller--Kellogg Company, Battle Creek, MI; U.S. Public, pg. 947
Taylor, Art, Controller--Coleman Powermate, Inc., Omaha, NE; U.S. Private, pg. 691
Taylor, Cathy, Corp. Controller--Triple S Plastics, Inc., Vicksburg, MI; U.S. Public, pg. 1639
Taylor, Charles, Controller--Anamet Inc., Waterbury, CT; U.S. Private, pg. 70
Taylor, Cindy B., V.P., Controller & Sec.--Cliffs Drilling Company, Houston, TX; U.S. Public, pg. 386
Taylor, Diana, Chief Fin. Officer & Controller--Horizon Bancorp, Michigan City, IN; U.S. Private, pg. 538
Taylor, Everett R., Controller--Martin Electronics, Inc., Perry, FL; U.S. Private, pg. 709
Taylor, Gail, Reg. Controller--Harley Industries, Inc., Tulsa, OK; U.S. Public, pg. 880
Taylor, Harold, Chief Fin. Officer & Controller--RNL Facilities Corporation, Denver, CO; U.S. Private, pg. 905
Taylor, Harold L., Controller--RNL Facilities Corporation, Denver, CO; U.S. Private, pg. 905
Taylor, Louis, Chief Fin. Officer & Controller--Caro Produce & Institutional Foods, Houma, LA; U.S. Public, pg. 1278
Taylor, Robert J., Controller--LaSalle-Talman Bank, Chicago, IL; Int'l, pg. 11
Taylor, Robert W., V.P. & Controller--Southern States Cooperative, Inc., Richmond, VA; U.S. Private, pg. 1017
Taylor, Roy, Controller--Huck International, Inc., Tucson, AZ; U.S. Public, pg. 1597
Taylor, Steve, Controller--Dayton Parts, Inc., Harrisburg, PA; U.S. Public, pg. 919
Taylor, T.S., Fin. Controller--Arjo Wiggins Appleton plc, Basingstoke, United Kingdom; Int'l, pg. 567
Taylor, Terry, Controller--MTL Inc., Plant City, FL; U.S. Public, pg. 1028
Taylor, Terry, Controller--Montgomery Tank Lines, Inc., Plant City, FL; U.S. Public, pg. 1028
Taylor, Thomas, Controller--Volvo and Honda Sales & Service, Lisle, IL; U.S. Private, pg. 1143
Taylor, Tommy Dee, Controller--Media Recovery, Inc., Graham, TX; U.S. Private, pg. 726
Taylor, William, Controller--Governair Corporation, Oklahoma City, OK; U.S. Public, pg. 1193
Tchorzewski, Ronald J., V.P. & Controller--Cadence Design Systems, Inc., San Jose, CA; U.S. Public, pg. 290
Tecmyer, Ken, Controller--Superior Industries of Nebraska, Inc., Omaha, NE; U.S. Private, pg. 1055
Tedesco, Gary, Controller--L. Luria & Son, Inc., Medley, FL; U.S. Public, pg. 1020
Teeman, Steve, Controller--Aaron Brothers, Inc., City of Commerce, CA; U.S. Public, pg. 1104
Teems, Sharon, Controller--KeyStone Center, Chester, PA; U.S. Public, pg. 1697
Teherani, Vicky C., V.P. & Controller--A.H. Belo Corporation, Dallas, TX; U.S. Public, pg. 209
Teichholz, Henry A., V.P., Controller & Treas.--Holly Corporation, Dallas, TX; U.S. Public, pg. 830
Tejon, Jose, Exec. V.P.--Banco Santander, Madrid, Spain; Int'l, pg. 143
Templin, Roy W., V.P. & Corp. Controller--Kimball International, Inc., Jasper, IN; U.S. Public, pg. 956
Ten Berge, J., Controller--Corporate New Business Development Div., Delft, Netherlands; Int'l, pg. 1142
ten Doesschate, M. S., Grp. Controller--CSM N.V., Diemen, Netherlands; Int'l, pg. 243
Ten Eyck, William B., Comptroller--Delco Chassis Overseas Corporation, Detroit, MI; U.S. Public, pg. 723
Ten Eyck, William B., Comptroller--Chassis Overseas Corp., Detroit, MI; U.S. Public, pg. 723
Tencza, Frank, Controller--Royer Industries, Inc., Kingston, PA; Int'l, pg. 1066
Tenore, Nicholas, Controller--Subaru Distributor Corp., Orangeburg, NY; Int'l, pg. 523
Terrell, Dan, Controller--Peebles, Inc., South Hill, VA; U.S. Private, pg. 846
Terrell, James E., V.P. & Controller--Georgia-Pacific Corporation, Atlanta, GA; U.S. Public, pg. 735
Terry, M.E., Grp. Fin. Controller--Cobham plc, Wimborne Minster, United Kingdom; Int'l, pg. 301
Terwilliger, David A., V.P.-Process Mgmnt.--Equitable of Iowa Companies, Des Moines, IA; Int'l, pg. 647
Tesh, Joan J., Controller--United Family Life Insurance Co., Atlanta, GA; Int'l, pg. 499
Tessman, Tom, Controller--TriEnda Corporation, Portage, WI; U.S. Private, pg. 1103
Tester, Ralph, Controller--The St. George Group, Inc., Pittsburgh, PA; U.S. Private, pg. 960
Teter, Dennis, Controller--Mid-Kansas Co-op Association, Moundridge, KS; U.S. Private, pg. 743
Teter, Dennis, Controller--Lubrication Consultants, L.L.C., Moundridge, KS; U.S. Private, pg. 743
Tewksbury, Gregg R., CPA, Chief Fin. Officer & Controller--CFX Bank, Keene, NH; U.S. Public, pg. 277
Thackston, Steve, Controller & Treas.--Dugan & Meyers Interests, Inc., Cincinnati, OH; U.S. Private, pg. 345
Thames, Angela, Controller--PCI, Austin, TX; U.S. Private, pg. 826
Tharp, Glenda, Controller--Channel Technologies, Inc., Santa Barbara, CA; U.S. Private, pg. 228
Tharp, Joseph B., Sr. V.P. & Fin. Controller--BankAmerica Corporation, San Francisco, CA; U.S. Public, pg. 179
Thatcher, Bob, Controller--The Gibson Group Inc., Cincinnati, OH; U.S. Private, pg. 451
Thatcher, Dale A., Asst. Controller--Ohio Casualty Corporation, Hamilton, OH; U.S. Public, pg. 1214
Thauvette, Alain, Controller--Assurance vie Desjardins-Laurentienne, Levis, Canada; Int'l, pg. 396
Thawerbhoy, Nazim G., Sr. V.P. & Controller--Jacobs Engineering Group Inc., Pasadena, CA; U.S. Public, pg. 921
Theing, Gallant, Controller--Microtel International Inc., Ontario, CA; U.S. Public, pg. 1108
Theisen, Bernard J., Controller & Asst. Sec.--The Standard Products Company, Dearborn, MI; U.S. Public, pg. 1504
Theisen, George, Controller--Roman, Inc., Roselle, IL; U.S. Private, pg. 942
Theodorow, James, Controller--Ford Steel Co., Inc., Maryland Heights, MO; U.S. Private, pg. 418
Theriault, Allain, Controller--Purdel, Cooperative Agro-Alimentaire, Bic, Canada; Int'l, pg. 1073
Therrien, Liz, Asst. V.P.-Finance & Controller--Cruise America, Inc., Mesa, AZ; U.S. Private, pg. 178
Thibault, Chuck, V.P., Controller, Treas. & Sec.--Lazy Days R V Center, Inc., Seffner, FL; U.S. Private, pg. 655
Thibault, Steve, Controller--Ansul Incorporated, Marinette, WI; U.S. Public, pg. 1648
Thibault, Steve, Controller--Ansul Fire Protection, Marinette, WI; U.S. Public, pg. 1650
Thies, Mark T., V.P.-Devel. & Controller--Black Hills Corporation, Rapid City, SD; U.S. Public, pg. 235
Thiessen, G.D., Controller & Asst. Sec.--MacDonald Dettwiler & Associates Ltd., Richmond, Canada; U.S. Public, pg. 1229
Thivierge, Claudine, Contoller--MDF La Baie Inc., La Baie, Canada; Int'l, pg. 1432
Thobe, Daniel, Div. V.P. & Controller--The Bon Ton Stores, Inc., York, PA; U.S. Public, pg. 244
Thomas, Bruce, Controller--Chace Precision Metals, Inc., Reidsville, NC; U.S. Public, pg. 1564
Thomas, Dasil, Controller--William H. Sadlier, Inc., New York, NY; U.S. Public, pg. 1422
Thomas, David, Controller--President Baking-Louisville, Louisville, KY; Int'l, pg. 1069
Thomas, Donald E., V.P. & Controller--The Southland Corporation, Dallas, TX; Int'l, pg. 693
Thomas, Jack L., Controller--Sterling Electronics Corporation, Houston, TX; U.S. Public, pg. 1051
Thomas, Jayne, Controller--The Crown Group, Inc., Warren, MI; U.S. Private, pg. 292
Thomas, Jennifer E., Controller--Sport Supply Group, Inc., Dallas, TX; U.S. Public, pg. 1499
Thomas, Kevin, Controller--Econocom-USA Inc., Memphis, TN; U.S. Private, pg. 361
Thomas, Lon, Controller--Carter Holt Harvey Roofing USA, Inc., Houston, TX; U.S. Public, pg. 905
Thomas, Lucia, Controller--Fischbach & Dougherty, Inc., Atlanta, GA; U.S. Private, pg. 408
Thomas, Tim, Controller--Granny Goose Foods, Inc., Oakland, CA; U.S. Private, pg. 469
Thomason, Joel D., Sr. V.P. & Controller--The Pepper Companies, Inc., Chicago, IL; U.S. Private, pg. 851
Thompson, Ann, Comptroller--American Fast Print, Limited, Spartanburg, SC; U.S. Private, pg. 53
Thompson, Brack, Controller--Frehner Construction Company, Inc., North Las Vegas, NV; U.S. Private, pg. 426
Thompson, Chester D., Comptroller--Empire Company Limited, Stellarton, Canada; Int'l, pg. 453
Thompson, Curtis A., V.P. & Controller--Primedia Inc., New York, NY; U.S. Public, pg. 1327
Thompson, D.F., Controller--Flowserve Duriron Canada, Woodbridge, Canada; U.S. Public, pg. 659
Thompson, Ernest B., V.P. & Controller--Amdahl Corporation, Sunnyvale, CA; Int'l, pg. 527
Thompson, George, Controller--Performance Contractors Inc., Baton Rouge, LA; U.S. Private, pg. 853
Thompson, Gregory C., V.P. & Controller--Wang Laboratories, Inc., Billerica, MA; U.S. Public, pg. 1737
Thompson, Jim, Controller--Quality Petroleum Corp., Lakeland, FL; U.S. Private, pg. 899
Thompson, Josh, Controller--Pontiac Bancorp, Inc., Pontiac, IL; U.S. Public, pg. 1316
Thompson, Kevin T., Sr. V.P. & Controller--First of America Bank Corporation, Kalamazoo, MI; U.S. Public, pg. 636
Thompson, Leslie, Controller--Raffi & Swanson, Inc., Wilmington, MA; U.S. Private, pg. 907
Thompson, Michael G., Corp. Controller--RAYOVAC Corporation, Madison, WI; U.S. Private, pg. 912
Thompson, P.C., Controller--S & C Electric Company, Chicago, IL; U.S. Private, pg. 954
Thompson, Paul, Controller--Psomas & Associates, Santa Monica, CA; U.S. Private, pg. 893
Thompson, Ray F., V.P., Treas. & Controller--Tech-Sym Corporation, Houston, TX; U.S. Public, pg. 1563
Thompson, Robert E., V.P. & Controller--Terra Industries, Inc., Sioux City, IA; U.S. Public, pg. 1581
Thompson, Robert G., V.P. & Controller--Whirlpool Corporation, Benton Harbor, MI; U.S. Public, pg. 1764
Thompson, Robert L., Comptroller & Dir.-Corp. Planning--Oryx Energy, Dallas, TX; U.S. Public, pg. 1232
Thompson, Ronnie D., Controller--Bearden Lumber Company, Inc., Bearden, AR; U.S. Private, pg. 127
Thompson, Thomas M., Controller & Asst. Treas.--Up-Right Work Platforms Division, Selma, CA; U.S. Private, pg. 1128
Thompson, Tommie D., Exec. V.P. & Corp. Controller--United of Omaha Life Insurance Company, Omaha, NE; U.S. Private, pg. 770
Thomson, Doug, Dir.-Fin. & Acctg.--Skyway Freight Systems, Inc., Watsonville, CA; U.S. Private, pg. 1005
Thorenz, William R., V.P. & Controller--Bankers Life Insurance Co. of New York, Woodbury, NY; U.S. Private, pg. 560
Thornburg, Katrina, Asst. Controller--Elder Manufacturing Company, Creve Coeur, MO; U.S. Private, pg. 367
Thrapp, Richard, Chief Fin. Officer & Controller--Salant Childrens Apparel Group, New York, NY; U.S. Public, pg. 1429
Thrasher, Cliff S., Chief Acctg. Officer, V.P. & Comptroller--Georgia Power Co., Atlanta, GA; U.S. Public, pg. 1490
Thrasher, Jody, Controller--RNF Media Corporation Inc., Beverly Hills, CA; U.S. Private, pg. 905
Thresher, Lynnette, Corp. Controller--Seattle Packaging Corporation, Seattle, WA; U.S. Private, pg. 980
Thuer, Mark A., Controller--Magnetic Metals Corp., Camden, NJ; U.S. Private, pg. 560
Thune, Maureen C., Controller & Asst. Sec.--CORT Business Services Corporation, Fairfax, VA; U.S. Public, pg. 451
Tibble, D., Controller--BTR plc, London, United Kingdom; Int'l, pg. 124
Tiberia, Thomas V., Corp. Controller--Louis P. Ciminelli Construction Co. Inc., Buffalo, NY; U.S. Private, pg. 239
Ticknor, Mark, Controller--Elco Consumer Products Corp., Rockford, IL; U.S. Public, pg. 1590
Tiemann, L. Scott, V.P. & Controller--Budget Group, Inc., Daytona Beach, FL; U.S. Private, pg. 178
Tierney, William E., Jr., Controller--Facemate Corporation, Chicopee, MA; U.S. Private, pg. 391
Tilder, Brad, Asst. V.P.-Fin. & Controller--Alaska Air Group, Inc., Seattle, WA; U.S. Public, pg. 35
Tilton, Kenneth L., Exec. V.P. & Controller--Texas Commerce Bank, Houston, TX; U.S. Public, pg. 339
Timberlake, Shena, Controller--Victoria Regional Medical Center, Victoria, TX; U.S. Public, pg. 1697
Timm, Bryan, Controller--CF & I Steel, L.P., Pueblo, CO; U.S. Public, pg. 1230
Timm, Fred H., Corp. Controller & Sec.--Twin Disc, Incorporated, Racine, WI; U.S. Public, pg. 1646
Timm, Marcia Marrs, Sr. V.P. & Controller--First Security Bank of Idaho, N.A., Boise, ID; U.S. Public, pg. 637
Timmins, Richard F., V.P. & Corp. Controller--Cisco Systems, Inc., San Jose, CA; U.S. Public, pg. 375
Timmons, Earl L., V.P. & Comptroller--Du Pont (E.I. Du Pont De Nemours & Co.), Wilmington, DE; U.S. Public, pg. 530
Timmons, James T., Controller--Lennar Corporation, Miami, FL; U.S. Public, pg. 987
Timmons, Poe, V.P.-Cooperation & Controller--Safelite AutoGlass, Columbus, OH; U.S. Private, pg. 960
Tims, Ron, Fin. Controller--IGT-Europe b.v., Hoofddorp, Netherlands; U.S. Public, pg. 900
Tinkey, Paula, Controller--Best Access Systems, Indianapolis, IN; U.S. Public, pg. 223
Tirado, Wilfredo, Controller--Banco Popular, Melrose Park, IL; U.S. Public, pg. 176
Tireman, Craig S., Controller--Butler International, Inc., Montvale, NJ; U.S. Public, pg. 270
Tiziani, John, Controller--Naporano Iron & Metal, Newark, NJ; U.S. Private, pg. 774
Tizzard, B., Controller--Heatric Ltd., Poole, United Kingdom; Int'l, pg. 853
Tjards, Jack, Controller--Metz Baking Co., Chicago, IL; U.S. Private, pg. 1022
Tjornemark, Bent, Mng. Dir.--Danisco A/S, Copenhagen, Denmark; Int'l, pg. 378
Tobalski, Michael A., Corp. Controller--Devcon International Corp., Deerfield Beach, FL; U.S. Public, pg. 502
Tobbe, Norge, Asst. Controller--Swagelok Company, Solon, OH; U.S. Private, pg. 1057
Toben, Doreen A., V.P.-Fin. & Controller--Bell Atlantic Corporation, New York, NY; U.S. Public, pg. 201
Tobiasz, Todd, Controller--Mrs. Alison's Cookie Company, Saint Louis, MO; U.S. Private, pg. 765
Tobin, Steve, V.P., Treas. & Controller--Gerber Life Insurance Co., White Plains, NY; Int'l, pg. 973
Tochterman, Florence, Controller--International Components Corporation, Melville, NY; U.S. Private, pg. 569
Toczylowski, Frank A., Controller--Selas Corporation of America, Dresher, PA; U.S. Public, pg. 1454

Todaro, Ralph, V.P. & Controller--Pacific Enterprises, Los Angeles, CA; *U.S. Public*, pg. 1249

Todaro, Ralph, V.P. & Controller--Southern California Gas Co., Los Angeles, CA; *U.S. Public*, pg. 1249

Toister, Adi, Controller--Tiger Direct, Inc., Miami, FL; *U.S. Public*, pg. 747

Tokar, L., Controller--GCI Holdings Corporation, Chicago, IL; *U.S. Private*, pg. 434

Tolentino, Lynn, Controller--Dexol, Torrance, CA; *U.S. Public*, pg. 1390

Tolson, John, V.P. & Controller--Maytag Company, Newton, IA; *U.S. Public*, pg. 1064

Tom, May, Controller--Versar Inc., Springfield, VA; *U.S. Public*, pg. 1717

Tom, Stella, Controller--Kaufman and Broad Central Valley Div., Modesto, CA; *U.S. Public*, pg. 945

Toman, James W., Controller--Spinnaker Industries, Inc., Dallas, TX; *U.S. Public*, pg. 1022

Tomas, Sherry, Controller--MTI/The Image Group, Inc., New York, NY; *U.S. Private*, pg. 688

Tomaska, Kathleen, Asst. Treas.--Anson Industries, Inc., Melrose Park, IL; *U.S. Private*, pg. 76

Tomaszek, Wesley A., Asst. Controller--Mallinckrodt Inc., Saint Louis, MO; *U.S. Public*, pg. 1039

Tomchak, Leonard, Controller--Muskin Leisure Products, Inc., Wilkes-Barre, PA; *U.S. Private*, pg. 768

Tomek, Lawrence C., Controller--Perry Engineering Company, Inc., Winchester, VA; *U.S. Private*, pg. 854

Tomko, Patricia M., RET Divisional Controller--Riser Foods, Inc., Bedford, OH; *U.S. Private*, pg. 450

Tompkins, J.R., Controller--M.D. Moody & Sons Inc., Jacksonville, FL; *U.S. Private*, pg. 759

Toner, Jeffrey, Controller--Keystone Powdered Metal Company, Saint Marys, PA; *U.S. Private*, pg. 619

Tonra, Joan E., Sr. V.P. & Controller--BayBanks, Inc., Boston, MA; *U.S. Public*, pg. 184

Toovey, Doug, Controller--Wilsey Bennett Co., San Francisco, CA; *U.S. Private*, pg. 1180

Topa, Charles, V.P.-Controller--United Refining Company, Warren, PA; *U.S. Private*, pg. 915

Topmiller, Tom, Controller--Vinylweld Division, Chicago, IL; *U.S. Private*, pg. 848

Topor, Cathy, Controller--The Jean Coutu (PJC) USA Inc., Warwick, RI; *Int'l*, pg. 340

Toral, Armando, Controller--Santa Fe Gaming Corporation, Las Vegas, NV; *U.S. Public*, pg. 1432

Torkelson, Eric T., V.P. & Controller--Norwest Financial, Inc., Des Moines, IA; *U.S. Public*, pg. 1202

Torkelson, Larry, Controller--Ameripride Service Company, Minneapolis, MN; *U.S. Private*, pg. 65

Tornquist, K.A., Controller & Asst. Treas.--Maine Public Service Company, Presque Isle, ME; *U.S. Public*, pg. 1038

Torseth, Pete, Controller--Polka Dot Dairy/Tom Thumb Food Markets, Hastings, MN; *U.S. Private*, pg. 874

Tortora, Canio, Controller--PIC Design, Middlebury, CT; *U.S.* Private, pg. 864

Tortora, Dennis J., Controller & Asst. Treas.--Steinway Musical Instruments, Inc., Waltham, MA; *U.S. Public*, pg. 1514

Tortora, Dennis J., Controller & Asst. Treas.--Steinway & Sons, Long Island City, NY; *U.S. Public*, pg. 1514

Tosoni, Melinda, V.P. & Controller--NGC Corporation, Houston, TX; *U.S. Public*, pg. 1146

Toth, Judy, V.P. & Controller--Multifoods Specialty Distribution Inc., Denver, CO; *U.S. Public*, pg. 901

Touri, Jeffrey C., Controller--Gantos, Inc., Grand Rapids, MI; *U.S. Public*, pg. 702

Tousant, Laura, Controller & Treas.--Car-Freshner Corporation, Watertown, NY; *U.S. Private*, pg. 207

Toussaint, Walter, Controller--Freudenberg & Company, Weinheim, Germany; *Int'l*, pg. 505

Towler, John S., Controller--Alpharma Inc., Fort Lee, NJ; *U.S. Public*, pg. 57

Townsend, Arthur T., Chief Oper. Officer & Chief Fin. Officer--Lat Purser & Associates, Charlotte, NC; *U.S. Private*, pg. 896

Townswick, Orrin, Controller--New Apple Lines, Inc., Madison, SD; *U.S. Private*, pg. 792

Tracey, Barbara J., Controller--Scan-Optics, Inc., Manchester, CT; *U.S. Public*, pg. 1436

Trachsel, Roy O., V.P. & Controller--California State Bank-La Habra, La Habra, CA; *U.S. Public*, pg. 294

Tracy, Rusty, Controller--The Vacation Store, Virginia Beach, VA; *U.S. Private*, pg. 649

Tradwick, Jerry, Controller--Mercantile Credit Corp., Baton Rouge, LA; *U.S. Public*, pg. 1090

Traeger, Jeff, V.P. & Controller--Hardin Construction Group, Inc., Atlanta, GA; *U.S. Private*, pg. 501

Traicoff, James T., Controller--Wegener Corporation, Duluth, GA; *U.S. Public*, pg. 1751

Trani, Louis D., Controller--Perry H. Koplik & Sons, New York, NY; *U.S. Private*, pg. 632

Trares, Kevin, Controller--Midway Products Corporation, Monroe, MI; *U.S. Private*, pg. 744

Travis, Len, Controller--Reltec, Inc., Warrenville, IL; *U.S. Private*, pg. 921

Travis, Susan, Controller & Asst. Treas.--C-Line Products, Inc., Des Plaines, IL; *U.S. Private*, pg. 192

Trebing, Rick, Controller--Mentor Graphics Corporation, Wilsonville, OR; *U.S. Public*, pg. 1086

Treinen, James M., Controller--Romac Industries, Inc., Seattle, WA; *U.S. Private*, pg. 942

Treinen, Thomas J., Controller--Special Devices, Incorporated, Newhall, CA; *U.S. Public*, pg. 1496

Tremblay, Richard, Controller--Tembec Inc., Montreal, Canada; *Int'l*, pg. 1374

Tremelling, Terrance, Controller--Bel Air Markets, West Sacramento, CA; *U.S. Private*, pg. 908

Trempe, Jean, Controller--Wausau Metals, Nanik Division, Wausau, WI; *U.S. Public*, pg. 1500

Trent, Joe, Controller--Bob Montgomery Chevrolet/Honda, Louisville, KY; *U.S. Private*, pg. 758

Trepani, Joseph B., V.P. & Controller--Tech Data Corporation, Clearwater, FL; *U.S. Public*, pg. 1562

Tressler, Gary, Fin. Controller--Eagle-Picher Fluid Systems Limited, Market Harborough, United Kingdom; *U.S. Private*, pg. 355

Trevico, Mika, Controller--GS Battery (U.S.A.), Inc., City of Industry, CA; *Int'l*, pg. 702

Trier, James, Controller--Paul Stuart, Inc., New York, NY; *U.S. Private*, pg. 844

Trineman, Paul, Chief Fin. Officer--Life Sciences International Plc, London, United Kingdom; *U.S. Public*, pg. 1594

Triolo, Joseph, Controller--Pioneer Paper Corporation, Carlstadt, NJ; *U.S. Private*, pg. 867

Tripi, Vince, Controller & Bus. Mgr.--WOKR-TV, Rochester, NY; *U.S. Private*, pg. 439

Triplett, Preston, V.P., Controller & Sec.--Brookshire Grocery, Tyler, TX; *U.S. Private*, pg. 172

Tripp, David, Grp. Fin. Controller--APV U.K. Plc, Coaley, United Kingdom; *Int'l*, pg. 1240

Trippetti, Vic, Chief Fin. Officer & Controller--L.A. Gear, Inc., Santa Monica, CA; *U.S. Public*, pg. 969

Troutman, W. Wilson, Controller & Asst. Treas.--Industrial Coatings Group, Inc., Chicago, IL; *U.S. Private*, pg. 434

Troy, William C., Controller--Interstate Power Company, Dubuque, IA; *U.S. Public*, pg. 910

Trubard, Dick, Controller--Promus Hotel Corporation, Memphis, TN; *U.S. Public*, pg. 1335

Truchi, James, Chief Fin. Officer, Controller & Treas.--Trucchis Markets, Raynham, MA; *U.S. Private*, pg. 1107

Trueheart, J.L., Asst. Controller--Dominion Resources, Inc., Richmond, VA; *U.S. Public*, pg. 516

Trueheart, J.L., Controller--Dominion Lands, Inc., Richmond, VA; *U.S. Public*, pg. 516

Truong, Quinn, Controller--Mediaspot, Inc., Corona Del Mar, CA; *U.S. Private*, pg. 727

Truscott, Lorne, Controller--Professional Apartment Management, Inc., Lodi, CA; *U.S. Private*, pg. 889

Truslow, Donald K., Controller--Wachovia Corporation, Winston Salem, NC; *U.S. Public*, pg. 1730

Tryens, Andrew L., Jr., Controller--NAO, Inc., Philadelphia, PA; *U.S. Private*, pg. 771

Tsacalis, William A., V.P. & Controller--Chiquita Brands International, Inc., Cincinnati, OH; *U.S. Public*, pg. 349

Tsang, Cherley, Fin. Controller--Associated Engineers Ltd., Kowloon, Hong Kong; *Int'l*, pg. 705

Tsang, Terence, V.P., Controller & Treas.--Guess ?, Inc., Los Angeles, CA; *U.S. Public*, pg. 768

Tsanos, Scott J., Controller, Treas. & Sec.--Sybra, Inc., Atlanta, GA; *U.S. Private*, pg. 270

Tschumper, D.J., Controller--Badger Equipment Co., Winona, MN; *U.S. Private*, pg. 102

Tseng, Eunice, Controller--MAG Innovision Co., Inc., Santa Ana, CA; *U.S. Private*, pg. 694

Tsuchiya, Michio, Controller--Nemic-Lambda KK, Tokyo, Japan; *Int'l*, pg. 1242

Tubergen, Jim, Controller & Dir.-Acctg.--D & W Food Centers, Inc., Grand Rapids, MI; *U.S. Private*, pg. 300

Tubridy, T., Controller & Dir.--Union Camp Container Div., Wayne, NJ; *U.S. Public*, pg. 1666

Tubridy, Thomas J., Asst. Comptroller--Union Camp Corporation, Wayne, NJ; *U.S. Public*, pg. 1665

Tuccillo, Stephen, Controller--Jordache Enterprises, Inc., New York, NY; *U.S. Private*, pg. 597

Tucker, Arthur V., V.P. & Controller--Chemed Corporation, Cincinnati, OH; *U.S. Public*, pg. 343

Tucker, Bob, Controller--Voltelcon, West Palm Beach, FL; *U.S. Public*, pg. 1724

Tucker, Marshall D., Chief Fin. Officer, V.P., Treas., Controller & Sec.--Dixon Paper Co., Denver, CO; *U.S. Public*, pg. 902

Tucker, Ronald E., Controller--Baldor Electric Company, Fort Smith, AR; *U.S. Public*, pg. 168

Tudor, Brenda S., Controller & Sec.--Ingles Markets, Incorporated, Black Mountain, NC; *U.S. Public*, pg. 878

Tueber, William, Chief Fin. Officer & Controller--EMC Corporation, Hopkinton, MA; *U.S. Public*, pg. 545

Tuffnail, Howard J., Controller--Tech Data Canada, Inc., Mississauga, Canada; *U.S. Public*, pg. 1562

Tummers, Nick, Controller--Tri Valley Growers, San Ramon, CA; *U.S. Private*, pg. 1101

Tunui, Brian J., Dir. & Fin. Controller--Bermuda Trust (Cook Islands) Limited, Rarotonga, Cook Islands; *Int'l*, pg. 151

Tuoriniemi, Robert E., Comptroller--Central Maine Power Company, Augusta, ME; *U.S. Public*, pg. 325

Tuoriniemi, Robert E., Controller--Washington Gas Light Co., Springfield, VA; *U.S. Public*, pg. 1740

Turchetta, Thomas, Controller--Eastern Engraving, Stirling, NJ; *U.S. Public*, pg. 1506

Turchick, Sharon M., Controller & Sec.--Sauer Industries, Inc., Pittsburgh, PA; *U.S. Private*, pg. 967

Turco, Ann, V.P. & Controller--The Weightman Group, Philadelphia, PA; *U.S. Private*, pg. 1159

Turco, Vince, Controller--Lonza Inc., Fair Lawn, NJ; *Int'l*, pg. 67

Turcza, John B., V.P. & Controller--Willis Corroon Corp. of Illinois, Chicago, IL; *Int'l*, pg. 1506

Turgeon, Gilles, Corp. Controller--The Oshawa Group Limited, Etobicoke, Canada; *Int'l*, pg. 1012

Turin, Connie, Controller--Zack Electronics, San Jose, CA; *U.S. Private*, pg. 1203

Turkington, Scott, Controller--Lionel LLC, Chesterfield, MI; *U.S. Private*, pg. 669

Turnbull, Allyson, Controller--Dorsey Trailers, Inc., Atlanta, GA; *U.S. Public*, pg. 520

Turner, Charles, V.P. & Controller--Pier 1 Imports, Inc., Fort Worth, TX; *U.S. Public*, pg. 1295

Turner, Donna, Controller--Turner Electric Corporation, Fairview Heights, IL; *U.S. Public*, pg. 1705

Turner, John J., V.P.-Fin. & Controller--United Water Management & Services, Harrington Park, NJ; *U.S. Public*, pg. 1692

Turner, Mark, Sr. V.P. & Controller--WSFS Financial Corporation, Wilmington, DE; *U.S. Public*, pg. 1728

Turner, T.G., Treas.--Pluess-Staufer Industries, Inc., Proctor, VT; *Int'l*, pg. 1061

Turner, Terry, V.P. & Controller--Huffy Bicycle Company, Celina, OH; *U.S. Public*, pg. 846

Turpin, Roger W., Controller & Principal Fin. Officer--Citicorp, New York, NY; *U.S. Public*, pg. 376

Turton, Gary J., V.P. & Controller--New York State Electric & Gas Corporation, Binghamton, NY; *U.S. Public*, pg. 1173

Tuska, Jim, Controller & Dir.-Fin.--American Fluorescent Corporation, Waukegan, IL; *U.S. Private*, pg. 54

Tussi, Enrico, Controller--Datapoint Italia S.P.A., Milan, Italy; *Int'l*, pg. 384

Tuttle, David J., Controller--Overnite Transportation Co., Richmond, VA; *U.S. Public*, pg. 1668

Twarozynski, James J., V.P. & Controller--Independent Bank Corporation, Ionia, MI; *U.S. Public*, pg. 874

Tweed, Robert E., Controller--Abbott Hospital Products Division, North Chicago, IL; *U.S. Public*, pg. 13

Twilling, Tom, Controller & Treas.--Perry & Derrick Co., Cincinnati, OH; *U.S. Private*, pg. 854

Twining, R., Controller--Kenner Parker (Australia) Ltd., Alexandria, Australia; *U.S. Public*, pg. 797

Twogood, Giles, Controller--Rigel Energy Corporation, Calgary, Canada; *Int'l*, pg. 1117

Twomey, Kevin J., V.P. & Controller--Fleming Companies, Inc., Oklahoma City, OK; *U.S. Public*, pg. 652

Tyburski, Michael, Controller--Valley National Gasses Inc., Wheeling, WV; *U.S. Private*, pg. 1132

Tylenda, Martin, Controller--First Independence National Bank, Detroit, MI; *U.S. Public*, pg. 635

Tyler, Robert L., Chief Fin. Officer & Sr. V.P.--Aliant Communications Inc., Lincoln, NE; *U.S. Public*, pg. 40

Tyner, Carol, Controller--PSDI, Bedford, MA; *U.S. Private*, pg. 828

Tyrell, G.W., Controller--Moore Nederland B.V., Amsterdam, Netherlands; *Int'l*, pg. 890

Tyrpak, Paul M., Treas. & Controller--Comptek Federal Systems, Inc., Buffalo, NY; *U.S. Public*, pg. 419

Tyson, Joseph, Controller--Forman Brothers, Inc., Washington, DC; *U.S. Private*, pg. 418

Tzomg, Mei, Chief Fin. Officer, Treas. & Controller--Pantech Construction Co., Lanham, MD; *U.S. Private*, pg. 837

Uemura, Kenneth, V.P. & Controller--C. Brewer & Company, Limited, Honolulu, HI; *U.S. Private*, pg. 190

Ugolini, Richard P., V.P. & Controller--Central Steel & Wire Company, Chicago, IL; *U.S. Public*, pg. 327

Uhl, Kenneth A., V.P. & Controller--The Great Atlantic & Pacific Tea Company, Inc., Montvale, NJ; *Int'l*, pg. 1375

Uhlich, Reinard W., Controller--Montana-Dakota Utilities Co., Bismarck, ND; *U.S. Public*, pg. 1025

Ullah, Mahmud, Controller--Gestetner Bangladesh Ltd., Dhaka, Bangladesh; *Int'l*, pg. 1115

Umansky, Joseph H., V.P. & Deputy Comptroller--American International Group, Inc., New York, NY; *U.S. Public*, pg. 83

Umland, Kurt, Controller--Wolfer Printing Company, City of Commerce, CA; *U.S. Private*, pg. 1186

Underhill, James F., Sr. V.P. & Controller--McJunkin Corporation, Charleston, WV; *U.S. Private*, pg. 722

Underhill, Stephen M., Chief Fin. Officer, Controller & Dir.-Personnel--R.O. Whitesell & Associates, Inc, Indianapolis, IN; *U.S. Private*, pg. 1173

Underwood, Bob, Controller--Fred B. Johnston Company, Inc., Chapin, SC; *U.S. Private*, pg. 595

Underwood, David, Controller--Teleflex Automotive, Hillsdale, MI; *U.S. Public*, pg. 1569

Unfried, Robert, V.P. & Controller--SMI Steel, Inc., Birmingham, AL; *U.S. Public*, pg. 412

Ungashick, John, Controller--First Financial Building Corporation, Manchester, MO; *U.S. Private*, pg. 407

Unger, Johanna, V.P., Controller & Sec.--PS Group Holdings, San Diego, CA; *U.S. Public*, pg. 1245

Uristiansen, Svein, Asst. V.P. & Controller--A/S Ivaran Rederi, Lysaker, Norway; *Int'l*, pg. 696

Ussery, Michael J., Controller--Triton Energy Limited, Dallas, TX; *U.S. Public*, pg. 1640

Ussery, Suzanne, Controller--Aeroflex Lintek Corp., Powell, OH; *U.S. Public*, pg. 24

Uzzi, Michael, Controller--Lee National Corporation, New York, NY; *U.S. Private*, pg. 658

Uzzi, Michael, Controller--Great Universal Capital Corp., New York, NY; *U.S. Private*, pg. 658

Vacher, P.B.E., Sr. V.P. & Controller--AEGON Nederland N.V., Hague, Netherlands; *Int'l*, pg. 26

Vacosalem, Billy, Controller--Nady Systems, Inc., Emeryville, CA; *U.S. Private*, pg. 773

Vagan, Russ, Asst. Controller--Jays Foods LLC, Chicago, IL; *U.S. Private*, pg. 584

Vahvelainen, Sirpa, Controller--Dun & Bradstreet Finland Oy., Espoo, Finland; *U.S. Public*, pg. 536

Vajda, David J., Controller--Northern Indiana Public Service Company, Hammond, IN; *U.S. Public*, pg. 1185

Valanti, Chuck, Chief Fin. Officer & Controller--Eberline Instrument Corporation, Santa Fe, NM; *U.S. Public*, pg. 1593

Valdes, Max O., Controller--The First American Financial Corporation, Santa Ana, CA; *U.S. Public*, pg. 624

Valdez, Carlos de Luna, Dir.-Fin. & Controller--Altos Hornos de Mexico, S.A., Monclova, Mexico; *Int'l*, pg. 66

Valente, Joe, Controller--Ryan Drossman & Partners, New York, NY; *U.S. Private*, pg. 953

Valenti, Peter, Controller--SRI International, Menlo Park, CA; *U.S. Private*, pg. 958

Valenti, Phyllis, Controller--Star Industries Inc., Syosset, NY; *U.S. Private*, pg. 1034

Valentine, Gary, Controller--U.S. Safety, Lenexa, KS; *U.S. Private*, pg. 1125

Valenzuela, Butch, Controller--Flojet Corporation, Irvine, CA; *U.S. Private*, pg. 414

Valero, Patricia, Controller--Prenatal, S.A., Barcelona, Spain; *Int'l*, pg. 1068

Valladares, Rafael, Sr. V.P. & Controller--PonceBank, F.S.B., Ponce, PR; *U.S. Public*, pg. 1316

Vallaro, Mike, Controller--Jays Foods LLC, Chicago, IL; *U.S. Private*, pg. 584
Valls, Juan, Controller--ITW Espana, S.A., Barcelona, Spain; *U.S. Public*, pg. 868
Van Beolts, Mary, Controller & Acctng.--Almanij N.V., Antwerp, Belgium; *Int'l*, pg. 65
Van Bever, Christiane, Controller--GIB Group, Brussels, Belgium; *Int'l*, pg. 532
Van Brokland, Katie, Controller--Central Lincoln People's Utility District, Newport, OR; *U.S. Private*, pg. 223
Van Bruyssel, Luc, Controller--Kredietbank N.V., Brussels, Belgium; *Int'l*, pg. 760
Van Damme, Paul, V.P. & Controller--Laidlaw Inc., Burlington, Canada; *Int'l*, pg. 259
Van De Velde, James D., V.P. & Controller--Hillenbrand Industries, Inc., Batesville, IN; *U.S. Public*, pg. 828
Van de Visser, Larry W., Controller--Dan River Inc., Danville, VA; *U.S. Public*, pg. 478
van den Berg, O.W.Ph, Controller--CSM Food Division, Diemen, Netherlands; *Int'l*, pg. 243
van der Boon, D., Controller--Bakery Ingredients Division, Delft, Netherlands; *Int'l*, pg. 1142
Van Der Colff, Rasmus, Financial Controller--Activision, Santa Monica, CA; *U.S. Public*, pg. 17
Van Der Heyden, A.J., Controller--Bac Color Franseweg, Steenbergen, Netherlands; *Int'l*, pg. 131
Van Dissel, J.A.H., Controller--Meneba Meel B.V., Rotterdam, Netherlands; *Int'l*, pg. 555
van Eeckhoudt, M., Controller--Esso Inc., Brussels, Belgium; *U.S. Public*, pg. 602
Van Gameren, G., Controller--Mead Packboard B.V., Rotterdam, Netherlands; *U.S. Public*, pg. 1076
Van Handel, Michael J., Chief Acctg. Officer, V.P. & Treas.--Manpower Inc., Milwaukee, WI; *U.S. Public*, pg. 1042
Van Helisden, John, Fin. Controller--Gestetner (Pty) Limited, Johannesburg, South Africa; *Int'l*, pg. 1115
Van Hook, Dennis, Controller--Mikohn Gaming Corporation, Las Vegas, NV; *U.S. Public*, pg. 1111
Van Hook, Donald W., Controller--Strahman Valves, Inc., Florham Park, NJ; *U.S. Private*, pg. 1046
Van Horn, David G., Controller--Gusher Pumps, Inc., Dry Ridge, KY; *U.S. Private*, pg. 488
Van Horn, Louis G., Controller--Kansas City Southern Industries, Inc., Kansas City, MO; *U.S. Public*, pg. 943
Van Houten, Eric, Controller--SBS Products, Inc., Saginaw, MI; *U.S. Private*, pg. 955
Van Kirk, Doug, Controller--Wyle Laboratories, Inc., El Segundo, CA; *U.S. Private*, pg. 1193
Van Mook, Dennis, Comptroller--W. Heath & Co., Los Angeles, CA; *U.S. Public*, pg. 84
van Mourik, R., Controller--Blydenstein-Willink N.V., Hengelo, Netherlands; *Int'l*, pg. 198
Van Ness, Peter, Controller--Jackson Furniture Industries, Cleveland, TN; *U.S. Private*, pg. 579
Van Ness, Peter, Controller--Cleveland Chair Company, Cleveland, TN; *U.S. Private*, pg. 579
van Oostrum, P., Chief Fin. Officer--Schering Nederland B.V., Weesp, Netherlands; *Int'l*, pg. 1204
Van Parys, Henri, Mgr.-Pub. Rels.--Kulicke & Soffa Industries, Inc., Willow Grove, PA; *U.S. Public*, pg. 968
Van Riper, Jeffrey L., Controller & Sec.--Seneca Foods Corporation, Pittsford, NY; *U.S. Public*, pg. 1456
Van Slyke, Paul, Controller--Lasco Bathware, Anaheim, CA; *Int'l*, pg. 1397
Van Stippen, Marty, Chief Fin. Officer & Controller--Creative Group Inc., Appleton, WI; *U.S. Private*, pg. 287
van West, Walter, Controller--British Airways PLC, London, United Kingdom; *Int'l*, pg. 218
Van Wyngarden, Donald L., Controller--Lincoln National Corporation, Fort Wayne, IN; *U.S. Public*, pg. 997
Vance, Gary R., Sr. V.P. & Comptroller--First Security Corporation, Salt Lake City, UT; *U.S. Public*, pg. 637
Vandanmeer, Diane C., Controller--Eastman Worldwide, Buffalo, NY; *U.S. Private*, pg. 358
Vande Hey, Sedona, Controller--Thiel Cheese Co., Hilbert, WI; *U.S. Private*, pg. 1081
VandeLeest, Martha, Controller--Richardson Industries, Inc., Sheboygan Falls, WI; *U.S. Private*, pg. 929
Vander Vorst, Pieter, V.P. & Controller--Sybase, Inc., Emeryville, CA; *U.S. Public*, pg. 1544
Vander, Don, Controller--Benson Automotive World, San Antonio, TX; *U.S. Private*, pg. 133
Vanderburg, Scott, Controller--Timber Products Co., Germantown, TN; *U.S. Private*, pg. 1086
Vanderhoven, Paul, Controller--Sterling Chemicals Holdings, Inc., Houston, TX; *U.S. Public*, pg. 1515
VanderPlueg, David, Controller--Schneider National, Inc., Green Bay, WI; *U.S. Private*, pg. 971
Vandervoort, Kathleen, V.P. & Controller-North America--Harlequin Enterprises Ltd., Don Mills, Canada; *Int'l*, pg. 1402
Vandeveldo, Carl, Controller--Henold, Inc., Westfield, NY; *Int'l*, pg. 1104
Vanhoy, Trish, Controller--Arnold Palmer Cadillac Inc., Charlotte, NC; *U.S. Private*, pg. 713
VanLooy, A., Comptroller--General Motors Luxembourg Operations S.A., Bascharage, Luxembourg; *U.S. Public*, pg. 723
Vannatta, M. Jack, Exec. V.P., Controller & Treas.--First American Corporation, Nashville, TN; *U.S. Public*, pg. 624
Vanneste, Paul, Controller--Daniel Canada, Calgary, Canada; *U.S. Public*, pg. 483
Vanover, R.C., Controller--A.L. Lee Corp., Lester, WV; *U.S. Private*, pg. 961
VanRoekel, Gerald, V.P.-Opers., Gen. Mgr. & Controller--Groschopp, Inc., Sioux Center, IA; *Int'l*, pg. 559
Varnadore, Susan, Controller--One Price Clothing Stores, Inc., Duncan, SC; *U.S. Public*, pg. 1225
Varner, Billy D., Controller--Old Fashion Foods, Inc., Austell, GA; *U.S. Private*, pg. 814
Varner, Mark, Controller--Marsh Supermarkets, Inc., Indianapolis, IN; *U.S. Public*, pg. 1049
Varney, Gary C., Controller--Artesian Resources Corporation, Newark, DE; *U.S. Public*, pg. 135
Varous, Peter, Controller--Rosen Associates Management Corp., Jericho, NY; *U.S. Private*, pg. 945
Vasconcellos, Cesar, Fin. Controller--Gestetner do Brasil, S.A. Sistemas Reprographicos, Rio de Janeiro, Brazil; *Int'l*, pg. 1115
Vasek, Rich, Controller--Royal Appliance Mfg. Co., Cleveland, OH; *U.S. Public*, pg. 1410
Vashon, Julie, V.P. & Plant Controller--Jordan's Foods-Westbrook Division, Westbrook, ME; *U.S. Private*, pg. 599
Vassi, Frank, Controller--Taylor Made-New York, Gloversville, NY; *U.S. Private*, pg. 1070
Vastert, R., Controller--Favory Convenience Food BV, Tilburg, Netherlands; *Int'l*, pg. 751
Vater, Barry, Controller--Specialty Coated Products, Merrimack, NH; *U.S. Public*, pg. 1152
Vaughan, Vaughn V., V.P. & Controller--American Indemnity Financial Corp., Galveston, TX; *U.S. Public*, pg. 83
Vaughn, J., Controller--The Standard Register Company, Dayton, OH; *U.S. Public*, pg. 1505
Vaughn, Polly H., V.P. & Controller--Farah U.S.A., Inc., El Paso, TX; *U.S. Public*, pg. 613
Vaughn, Steve, Controller--Sonic Corporation, Oklahoma City, OK; *U.S. Public*, pg. 1485
Vazoulas, William, Controller--Konica Imaging USA, Inc., Glen Cove, NY; *Int'l*, pg. 749
Vazzano, Joseph F., V.P. & Comptroller--The Prudential Realty Group, Newark, NJ; *U.S. Private*, pg. 892
Veach, Sarah, Controller--Landry's Seafood Restaurants Inc., Houston, TX; *U.S. Public*, pg. 977
Veeck, Ed, Controller--Edward C. Levy Co., Dearborn, MI; *U.S. Private*, pg. 664
Veenboer, G.W.M., Controller--Bols International B.V., Nieuw-Vennep, Netherlands; *Int'l*, pg. 751
Vega, Antonio, Controller--Supreme International Corp., Miami, FL; *U.S. Public*, pg. 1542
Vega, Luz, Controller--Puerto Rico Tourism Company, San Juan, PR; *U.S. Private*, pg. 894
Veilleux, J., Controller--Trois-Rivieres Mill, Trois-Rivieres, Canada; *Int'l*, pg. 761
Velarde, Yolanda, Controller--Crispin Porter & Bogusky, Miami, FL; *U.S. Private*, pg. 290
Velazquez, Domingo, Controller--Sein Mendez Laboratories, Inc., Rio Piedras, PR; *U.S. Public*, pg. 670
Velez, Maria, Controller--Caribe Express, Aguadilla, PR; *U.S. Private*, pg. 211
Velorde, Yolanda, Controller--Crispin Porter & Bogusky Advertising, Miami, FL; *U.S. Private*, pg. 290
Velucci, Frank, Controller--All-Luminum Products, Inc., Philadelphia, PA; *U.S. Private*, pg. 34
Vena, James A., Controller--Delroyd Worm Gear, Trenton, NJ; *U.S. Public*, pg. 857
Vena, James A., Controller--Boston Gear, Quincy, MA; *U.S.* Public, pg. 857
Venditti, Jim, Controller--Heritage Inks International, Edison, NJ; *U.S. Private*, pg. 524
Venesky, Paul, Controller--Mooney Chemicals, Cleveland, OH; *U.S. Public*, pg. 1208
Venneman, Nicholas, Controller--Aurora Packing Co., Inc., North Aurora, IL; *U.S. Private*, pg. 99
Ventigan, Maria, Controller-N. America--Rainbow Technologies, Inc., Irvine, CA; *U.S. Public*, pg. 1359
Ventura, Tom, Controller--Yellow Corporation, Overland Park, KS; *U.S. Public*, pg. 1788
Vercillo, T.M., Corp. Controller--Northwestern Steel & Wire Co., Sterling, IL; *U.S. Public*, pg. 1201
Verdon, John, Controller--Data National, Chantilly, VA; *U.S. Public*, pg. 1724
Vernon-Chancey, Felecia A., V.P. & Controller--Pacific Gateway Properties, San Francisco, CA; *U.S. Public*, pg. 1250
Vernon, Lennox, V.P. & Controller--Fair, Isaac and Company, Inc., San Rafael, CA; *U.S. Public*, pg. 609
Verveld, F., Controller--Campina Melkunie BV, Zaltbommel, Netherlands; *Int'l*, pg. 254
Vesey, Charles W., V.P.-Info Svcs. & Controller--Bandag, Incorporated, Muscatine, IA; *U.S. Public*, pg. 177
Vest, Randy J., V.P. & Controller--Kimberly-Clark Corporation, Dallas, TX; *U.S. Public*, pg. 958
Vetere, Louis J., Controller & Treas.--Marotta Scientific Controls, Inc., Montville, NJ; *U.S. Private*, pg. 706
Vetere, Nicholas, Controller--Fishman & Tobin, Inc., Conshohocken, PA; *U.S. Private*, pg. 408
Viano, Larry, Controller & Treas.--Semitool, Inc., Kalispell, MT; *U.S. Public*, pg. 1456
Viator, Rick, Controller & Mgr.-Office--M.A. Patout & Son, Jeanerette, LA; *U.S. Private*, pg. 843
Viau, Michelle G., Controller--Pegasus Gold Corporation, Spokane, WA; *U.S. Public*, pg. 1269
Vic, Tom, V.P.-Fin. & Controller--World Dryer Corp., Berkeley, IL; *U.S. Public*, pg. 1497
Vicari, Dominick, Controller--Greater New York Mutual Insurance Company, New York, NY; *U.S. Private*, pg. 476
Vicas, Michael, Controller--Teleflex Automotive Manufacturing Corp., Waterbury, CT; *U.S. Public*, pg. 1569
Vierig, Bradley M., Sr. V.P. & Controller--American Stores Company, Salt Lake City, UT; *U.S. Public*, pg. 92
Vietheer, Judy, Controller--Structural Industries, Inc., Hicksville, NY; *U.S. Private*, pg. 1048
Viglino, Claudio, Mgmnt. Acctng.--Barbero 1891 SpA, Canale, Italy; *Int'l*, pg. 164
Vignola, Frank, Controller--VARTA Batteries Inc., Elmsford, NY; *Int'l*, pg. 1452
Villalobos, Norma, Controller--Pace Press, Inc., Moonachie, NJ; *U.S. Private*, pg. 829
Villarino, Laura, Sr. V.P. & Controller--Firstbank Puerto Rico, Santurce, PR; *U.S. Public*, pg. 644
Villarino, Laura, Controller--First Leasing & Rental Corporation, Toa Baja, PR; *U.S. Public*, pg. 644
Villiotti, Anthony J., Treas. & Controller--Duquesne Enterprises, Pittsburgh, PA; *U.S. Public*, pg. 474
Vincent, L.A., Controller--SAE Engineering, Inc., Santa Clara, CA; *U.S. Private*, pg. 955
Vincent, Paul E., Controller--Alpha Industries, Inc., Woburn, MA; *U.S. Public*, pg. 57
Vines, Kenneth R., V.P. & Controller--DSC Communications Corporation, Plano, TX; *U.S. Public*, pg. 475
Vinson, Lynette, Controller--Nevada Power Company, Las Vegas, NV; *U.S. Public*, pg. 1169
Vipond, J.R., V.P. & Controller--Praxair Inc., Danbury, CT; *U.S. Public*, pg. 1319
Virgets, Anne G., Controller--Sullivan Oil Company, Baton Rouge, LA; *U.S. Private*, pg. 1050
Visser, E.M., Group Controller--Van Melle N.V., Breda, Netherlands; *Int'l*, pg. 1450
Vissers, John, Controller--Farr Company, El Segundo, CA; *U.S. Public*, pg. 613
Vitro, Thomas D., Controller--Springborn Testing & Research, Inc., Enfield, CT; *U.S. Private*, pg. 1027
Vitti, James, Controller--Interlaken Capital, Inc., Greenwich, CT; *U.S. Private*, pg. 567
Vloemans, Hans, Controller--NRG Benelux B.V., s Hertogenbosch, Netherlands; *Int'l*, pg. 1116
Vochis, Charles, Controller--Quebecor Printing Modern Inc., Brookfield, CT; *Int'l*, pg. 1078
Voelkerding, Tim, Controller--Cincinnati Industrial Machinery Div., Cincinnati, OH; *U.S. Private*, pg. 355
Vogel, Gerhard, Dr., Chief Fin. Officer, V.P.-Fin. & Controller--Fuchs Petrolub AG Oel + Chemie, Mannheim, Germany; *Int'l*, pg. 517
Vogel, Paul, Controller--Amcel Corp., Watertown, MA; *U.S. Private*, pg. 48
Vogt, A.R., Controller-Gas Opers. & Asst. Sec.--Public Service Company of New Mexico, Albuquerque, NM; *U.S. Public*, pg. 1339
Vogt, Thomas, Corp. Controller--Fingerhut Corp., Minnetonka, MN; *U.S. Public*, pg. 623
Voigt, J., Controller--O&K Orenstein & Koppel Aktiengesellschaft, Dortmund, Germany; *Int'l*, pg. 516
Voigt, Linda, Controller--Hasslocher Enterprises, Inc., San Antonio, TX; *U.S. Private*, pg. 510
Voiss, James, Controller--Acrometal Companies, Inc., Plymouth, MN; *U.S. Private*, pg. 14
Volchko, Michael D., Controller--Park-Ohio Industries, Inc., Cleveland, OH; *U.S. Public*, pg. 1258
Volker, Laura A., Asst. Controller--Chemed Corporation, Cincinnati, OH; *U.S. Public*, pg. 343
Vollmayer, Don, Controller--Charter Communications, Inc., Saint Louis, MO; *U.S. Private*, pg. 230
Volpicelli, Debbie, Controller--CarrAmerica Realty, Washington, DC; *U.S. Public*, pg. 308
Volt, Bryan, Controller--Ryan Construction Company of Minnesota, Inc., Minneapolis, MN; *U.S. Private*, pg. 953
Voltolina, Frank A., Asst. Controller--Mallinckrodt Inc., Saint Louis, MO; *U.S. Public*, pg. 1039
Von Haden, Shelley, Controller--Stark Candy Company, Pewaukee, WI; *U.S. Private*, pg. 1113
von Mayrhauser, Mark, V.P. & Controller--Ames Department Stores, Inc., Rocky Hill, CT; *U.S. Public*, pg. 99
Von Memerty, Sandy, Chief Fin. Officer & Controller--Charter Medical of England Ltd., London, United Kingdom; *U.S. Public*, pg. 1036
Von Rueden, James, Controller & Sec.--Wausau Homes, Inc., Rothschild, WI; *U.S. Private*, pg. 1154
Vorgity, Eric, Chief Fin. Officer & Controller--Dietrich's Milk Products, Inc., Reading, PA; *U.S. Private*, pg. 332
Vos, Harry, Controller--Skandia Insurance Company Limited, Stockholm, Sweden; *Int'l*, pg. 1256
Voss, Brenda B., Controller--Coyne Beahm Inc., Colfax, NC; *U.S. Private*, pg. 283
Voss, Jim, Controller--Dot Printer, Inc., Irvine, CA; *U.S. Private*, pg. 341
Voss, Robert, Controller--Sparks Family Hospital, Sparks, NV; *U.S. Public*, pg. 1697
Voss, Stephen D., Controller--Chicago Rivet & Machine Company, Naperville, IL; *U.S. Public*, pg. 348
Votteler, Erwin, Controller--American Appraisal Espana, S.A., Madrid, Spain; *U.S. Private*, pg. 50
Vouilloz, Daniel, Controller--Fotolabo Club S.A., Lausanne, Switzerland; *Int'l*, pg. 501
Vredenbregt, J.C., V.P., Controller & Asst. Treas.--The Ziegler Companies, Inc., West Bend, WI; *U.S. Public*, pg. 1791
Vredenbregt, J.C., V.P., Controller & Asst. Treas.--B.C. Ziegler & Co., West Bend, WI; *U.S. Public*, pg. 1792
Vrethem, Anders, Controller--Sandvik AB, Sandviken, Sweden; *Int'l*, pg. 1185
Vrtis, Thomas, Controller--RMT Technology, Bellwood, IL; *U.S. Private*, pg. 927
Vukmanic, Donald F., V.P. & Controller--L.B. Foster Company, Pittsburgh, PA; *U.S. Public*, pg. 675
Vyncke, Margaret T., Controller-Broadcast Grp.--The New York Times Company Broadcasting Group, Memphis, TN; *U.S. Public*, pg. 1173
Waak, Terrance, Controller--The Philadelphia Bourse, Inc., Lanham, MD; *U.S. Private*, pg. 861
Wack, Mark, Controller--Struthers Industries Inc., Gulfport, MS; *U.S. Private*, pg. 1048
Waddell, John, Controller--Columbus Steel Drum, Inc., Blacklick, OH; *U.S. Private*, pg. 385
Waddell, Robert N., Corp. Controller--Agra Inc., Calgary, Canada; *Int'l*, pg. 30
Wade, Bob, Controller--Miracle Recreation Equipment Company, Monett, MO; *U.S. Private*, pg. 752
Wade, Cindy, Controller--Black Fin Yacht Corporation, Fort Lauderdale, FL; *U.S. Private*, pg. 147
Wade, Donnie, Controller, Treas. & Sec.--Goodpasture, Inc., Brownfield, TX; *U.S. Private*, pg. 464
Wade, Earl, Controller--Ocean Bio-Chem Inc., Fort Lauderdale, FL; *U.S. Public*, pg. 1211
Wade, Thomas, Exec. V.P. & Controller--Jamison Bedding, Inc., Franklin, TN; *U.S. Private*, pg. 581

Wadhams, Timothy, V.P., Controller & Treas.--MascoTech, Inc., Taylor, MI; *U.S. Public*, pg. 1055
Waggerman, Eugene S., Chief Exec. Officer--Perkins-Goodwin Co. Inc., Stamford, CT; *Int'l*, pg. 586
Waggoner, Henry R., Controller & Sec.--Lakeside Industries, Issaquah, WA; *U.S. Private*, pg. 644
Wagner, Adam, Asst. Controller--Wenner Media, New York, NY; *U.S. Private*, pg. 1162
Wagner, Brooke, Dir.-Fin.--Software Publishing Corporation, Fairfield, NJ; *U.S. Public*, pg. 1483
Wagner, Craig, Controller--Auburn General Hospital, Auburn, WA; *U.S. Public*, pg. 1696
Wagner, Don, Controller--Gifford-Hill Concrete Products Inc., Richmond, VA; *Int'l*, pg. 593
Wagner, Douglas A., Controller--Dothan Apparel, Inc., New York, NY; *U.S. Private*, pg. 540
Wagner, Harvey L., Comptroller--FirstEnergy Corp., Akron, OH; *U.S. Public*, pg. 644
Wagner, James, Controller--Jacuzzi Bros., Jacuzzi, Inc., Little Rock, AR; *U.S. Public*, pg. 1684
Wagner, Mary Jane, Chief Fin. Officer, Treas. & Sec.--American Inks & Coatings Corp., Phoenixville, PA; *U.S. Private*, pg. 56
Wagner, Mike, Controller--Kaufman and Broad Inland Empire, Anaheim, CA; *U.S. Public*, pg. 945
Wagner, Stacy L., V.P.-Fin. & Controller--Plasma-Therm, Inc., Saint Petersburg, FL; *U.S. Public*, pg. 1308
Wagner, Susan, Controller-Spec & Voltec--Sauer Industries, Inc., Pittsburgh, PA; *U.S. Private*, pg. 967
Wagner, Susan, Controller--Voltec, McMurray, PA; *U.S. Private*, pg. 968
Wagner, William, Controller--VR/Wesson Hydro Carbide, Latrobe, PA; *U.S. Public*, pg. 612
Wagstaff, C. Fred, III, Controller--Interstate/Johnson Lane, Inc., Charlotte, NC; *U.S. Public*, pg. 909
Wahl, W. F., Controller--CNG Energy Services Corporation, Pittsburgh, PA; *U.S. Public*, pg. 435
Wahlgren, Leif, Controller--Moore Europe, Lausanne, Switzerland; *Int'l*, pg. 889
Wahlund, Lars, Controller--Saab AB, Linkoping, Sweden; *Int'l*, pg. 686
Wai, Sam, Controller--American Crystal Sugar Company, Moorhead, MN; *U.S. Private*, pg. 52
Wainman, Tracy, Controller--Numetrix Ltd., Toronto, Canada; *Int'l*, pg. 990
Waisanen, Larry, Controller--Lafarge S.A., Paris, France; *Int'l*, pg. 788
Wait, Richard, V.P. & Comptroller--Reitmans (Canada) Limited, Montreal, Canada; *Int'l*, pg. 1102
Wait, Tim, Controller--UDL Laboratories, Inc., Rockford, IL; *U.S. Public*, pg. 1143
Waite, Frank, Controller--Security Mutual Life Insurance Co. of New York, Binghamton, NY; *U.S. Private*, pg. 981
Walbrun, Paul A., V.P. & Controller--Summa Industries, Torrance, CA; *U.S. Public*, pg. 1527
Walchirk, Nina, Controller--OMNI Superstores, Northlake, IL; *U.S. Private*, pg. 1202
Walden, Don, Controller--Cricket Lane, West Bridgewater, MA; *U.S. Public*, pg. 948
Waldhelm, Jack, Controller--First American Title Insurance Co. of Texas, Inc., Houston, TX; *U.S. Public*, pg. 626
Waldrop, Joseph E., V.P.-Fin. Analysis & Planning--Glaxo Wellcome PLC, Research Triangle Park, NC; *Int'l*, pg. 553
Walhatys, Michael, Controller--Albank Financial Corporation, Albany, NY; *U.S. Public*, pg. 36
Waljen, Dale, Controller--Puna Plantation Hawaii Ltd., Hilo, HI; *U.S. Private*, pg. 895
Walker, Alfred J., V.P. & Chief Acctg. Officer--General Communication, Inc., Anchorage, AK; *U.S. Public*, pg. 708
Walker, Baker, Chief Fin. Officer, Controller, Treas. & Sec.--C.B. Ragland Company, Nashville, TN; *U.S. Private*, pg. 907
Walker, Diane, Controller--Andover Bancorp, Inc., Andover, MA; *U.S. Public*, pg. 111
Walker, Donald H., Chief Fin. Officer, V.P.-Fin.--Frisch's Restaurants, Inc., Cincinnati, OH; *U.S. Public*, pg. 682
Walker, Earl, Controller & Treas.--Jitney-Jungle Stores of America, Inc., Jackson, MS; *U.S. Private*, pg. 588
Walker, G.M.A., Dir.-Mktg. & Controller--Cussons (U.K.) LTD., Cheadle, United Kingdom; *Int'l*, pg. 1024
Walker, James, Asst. Controller--Benchmark Electronics Inc., Angleton, TX; *U.S. Public*, pg. 210
Walker, James A., Jr., Sr. V.P. & Controller--Wal-Mart Stores, Inc., Bentonville, AR; *U.S. Public*, pg. 1732
Walker, Jami, Fin. Controller--Lake Region Manufacturing Co., Ltd., New Ross, Ireland; *U.S. Private*, pg. 643
Walker, Jim, V.P.-Controller--Fujitsu Computer Products of America, Inc., San Jose, CA; *Int'l*, pg. 526
Walker, Larry J., V.P. & Controller--Dravo Corporation, Pittsburgh, PA; *U.S. Public*, pg. 527
Walker, Lynette, Controller--Motown Record Company, J.P., New York, NY; *Int'l*, pg. 1052
Walker, Steven, Controller--McKean Oldsmobile Company, Pittsburgh, PA; *U.S. Private*, pg. 722
Wall, Dave, Mgr.-Acctg.--Graymills Corp., Chicago, IL; *U.S. Private*, pg. 473
Wall, Edward F., III, Controller--Geyer-McAllister Publications, Inc., New York, NY; *U.S. Private*, pg. 450
Wall, Nancy, Office Mgr.--Florida Capital Partners, Tampa, FL; *U.S. Private*, pg. 414
Wallace, Albert, V.P. & Controller--GIW Industries, Inc., Grovetown, GA; *Int'l*, pg. 721
Wallace, Bill, Fin. Controller-Rigids Div.--AEP/Borden Global Packaging (U.K.) Ltd., Bridgwater, United Kingdom; *U.S. Public*, pg. 5
Wallace, Mark A., V.P. & Controller--Tremont Corporation, Denver, CO; *U.S. Private*, pg. 270
Wallace, Mary, Controller--Hendrick Automotive Group, Charlotte, NC; *U.S. Private*, pg. 522
Wallach, Fred, V.P. & Controller--Circon Corporation, Santa Barbara, CA; *U.S. Public*, pg. 373
Waller, Alan, Controller- EIS--McGraw-Hill Financial Information Services Group, New York, NY; *U.S. Public*, pg. 1071
Waller, Jeffrey M., V.P. & Corp. Controller--S.C. Johnson & Son, Inc., Racine, WI; *U.S. Private*, pg. 592
Walley, Brad, Controller--The Vagabond Inns, San Diego, CA; *U.S. Private*, pg. 558
Wallin, Eric J., Controller--The Smithfield Packing Co., Inc., Smithfield, VA; *U.S. Public*, pg. 1479
Walling, J., Asst. Controller--Crane Defense Systems, Conroe, TX; *U.S. Public*, pg. 456
Wallingford, Mary Beth, V.P. & Controller--Geneva Pharmaceuticals, Inc., Broomfield, CO; *Int'l*, pg. 973
Wallington, Rich, V.P.-Fin. & Controller--Books-A-Million, Inc., Birmingham, AL; *U.S. Public*, pg. 244
Wallwork, Philip, Controller--Morse Controls Ltd., Basildon, United Kingdom; *U.S. Public*, pg. 857
Walpole, P., Controller--Union Camp Chemical Products Div., Wayne, NJ; *U.S. Public*, pg. 1666
Walsh, Brendan, Controller & Treas.--Monsey-Bakor, Kimberton, PA; *U.S. Private*, pg. 757
Walsh, James, V.P. & Controller--Meijer, Inc., Grand Rapids, MI; *U.S. Private*, pg. 729
Walsh, James F., Controller--Instrument Specialties Company, Delaware Water Gap, PA; *U.S. Private*, pg. 565
Walsh, Janice, Controller--Western Corporate Enterprises Inc., Vancouver, Canada; *Int'l*, pg. 1494
Walsh, John, Controller--O'Donnell-Usen Fisheries Corp., Tampa, FL; *U.S. Public*, pg. 427
Walsh, Paige P., V.P. & Controller--Code, Hennessy & Simmons, Inc., Chicago, IL; *U.S. Private*, pg. 249
Walston, William D., Comptroller--Aristech Chemical Corporation, Pittsburgh, PA; *Int'l*, pg. 872
Walter, Jack A., Chief Acctg. Officer, V.P. & Controller--Calspan SRL Corporation, Washington, DC; *U.S. Private*, pg. 1136
Walters, Gerald, Controller--Flo Control, Inc., Burbank, CA; *U.S. Private*, pg. 414
Walters, Pam, Controller--Angeles Housing Concepts, Canoga Park, CA; *U.S. Private*, pg. 74
Walters, Richard L., Chief Acctg. Officer, V.P. & Controller--Value City Department Stores, Inc., Columbus, OH; *U.S. Private*, pg. 972
Walters, Steven J., Controller--Continental Circuits Corp., Phoenix, AZ; *U.S. Public*, pg. 440
Walters, Thomas M., V.P. & Controller--Drummond Company, Inc., Jasper, AL; *U.S. Private*, pg. 343
Walton, Bill R., Controller--Belk Stores Services Inc., Charlotte, NC; *U.S. Private*, pg. 131
Walton, Mick, Controller--Tyco Toys, Inc., Mount Laurel, NJ; *U.S. Public*, pg. 1058
Walton, Robert, Controller--Lake River Corporation, Berwyn, IL; *U.S. Public*, pg. 961
Walts, Loren W., Comptroller--Johnson Newspaper Corporation, Watertown, NY; *U.S. Private*, pg. 591
Waltzinger, Bill, Controller--Bed Bath & Beyond Inc., Union, NJ; *U.S. Public*, pg. 200
Wampler, Kevin, Controller--Finish Line, Inc., Indianapolis, IN; *U.S. Public*, pg. 623
Wandler, Les R., Controller & Corp. Fin.--Checkers Drive-In Restaurants, Inc., Clearwater, FL; *U.S. Public*, pg. 342
Wandrey, Corina, Controller--Imperial Hotels, El Segundo, CA; *U.S. Private*, pg. 558
Wanjek, Carl, Controller--Giles & Ransome, Inc., Bensalem, PA; *U.S. Private*, pg. 453
Warady, Timothy S., Controller--Dentsply International Inc., York, PA; *U.S. Public*, pg. 498
Warbrick, M. Shane, Grp. Controller--Fletcher Challenge Limited, Auckland, New Zealand; *Int'l*, pg. 494
Ward, Cecily A., V.P. & Controller--Federal Realty Investment Trust, Rockville, MD; *U.S. Public*, pg. 616
Ward, J.M., Controller--John Mowlem & Company plc, Isleworth, United Kingdom; *Int'l*, pg. 896
Ward, Ken, Controller--Grote Industries, Madison, IN; *U.S. Private*, pg. 483
Ward, Robert, Chief Fin. Officer, Chief Acctg. Officer & V.P.--Cavco Industries, Inc., Phoenix, AZ; *U.S. Public*, pg. 323
Ward, Susan, Controller--Four Seasons Air Conditioning Div., Coppell, TX; *U.S. Public*, pg. 1503
Ward, Tim, Controller--Telco Capital Corporation, Chicago, IL; *U.S. Private*, pg. 1073
Warden, Hays R., V.P., Controller & Chief Acctg. Officer--Burlington Resources Inc., Houston, TX; *U.S. Public*, pg. 269
Wardwell, Gary E., Controller--Consumers Water Company, Portland, ME; *U.S. Public*, pg. 438
Ware, D.M., Controller--Radionics, Inc., Salinas, CA; *U.S. Public*, pg. 501
Ware, James, Controller--State Electric Supply Co., Huntington, WV; *U.S. Private*, pg. 1036
Warfield, Bill, Controller--OMRON Systems, Inc., Schaumburg, IL; *Int'l*, pg. 1005
Warfield, Dale, Controller--Kerr-McGee Petroleum Exploration & Production Division, Oklahoma City, OK; *U.S. Public*, pg. 952
Waring, Paul, Corp. Controller & Treas.--Reflectone, Inc., Tampa, FL; *Int'l*, pg. 218
Warkentien, Cathy, Controller--Humphrey Products Company, Kalamazoo, MI; *U.S. Private*, pg. 547
Warr, Sabrina, Controller--TCA Cable TV, Inc., Tyler, TX; *U.S. Public*, pg. 1553
Warr, Sabrina A., Controller--TCA Management Company, Tyler, TX; *U.S. Public*, pg. 1553
Warren, Brandy, Controller--Silver Towne L.P., Winchester, IN; *U.S. Private*, pg. 1000
Warren, James A., Controller--Genzyme Corporation, Cambridge, MA; *U.S. Public*, pg. 733
Warrener, Richard C., Chief Fin. Officer & Sr. V.P.--Rurban Financial Corp., Defiance, OH; *U.S. Public*, pg. 1412
Wasco, Robin, Controller--Nieco Corporation, Burlingame, CA; *U.S. Private*, pg. 799
Washko, John A., V.P. & Sr. Corp. Controller--Crown American Realty Trust, Johnstown, PA; *U.S. Public*, pg. 461
Waskuch, Charles, Controller--Simkins Industries, Inc., New Haven, CT; *U.S. Private*, pg. 1000
Wasserman, Barry, Controller--Hitchcock Automotive Resources, City of Industry, CA; *U.S. Private*, pg. 531
Wassner, Judah, Controller--Arnav Industries, Inc., New York, NY; *U.S. Private*, pg. 83
Wasson, Chester, Controller--Hoffco/Comet Industries, Inc., Richmond, IN; *U.S. Private*, pg. 532
Wasson, Russell D., Controller--Cajun Electric Power Co-op, Baton Rouge, LA; *U.S. Private*, pg. 199
Wat, Tay Lai, Financial Controller--Hai Sun Hup Group Ltd., Singapore, Singapore; *Int'l*, pg. 586
Watanabe, John, Controller-Asia Pacific--Walbro Corporation, Cass City, MI; *U.S. Public*, pg. 1733
Watanabe, T., Controller--Kulicke & Soffa (Japan), Ltd., Tokyo, Japan; *U.S. Public*, pg. 969
Waterbury, Mark, Asst. Controller--Cade Industries, Inc., Lansing, MI; *U.S. Public*, pg. 289
Waterlow, David G., Grp. Fin. Controller--Dalgety Plc, London, United Kingdom; *Int'l*, pg. 376
Waters, John, Controller--Consolidated Metco, Inc., Portland, OR; *U.S. Public*, pg. 1710
Waters, Mike, Controller--Kern Industries, City of Industry, CA; *U.S. Private*, pg. 616
Waters, Tricia, Chief Fin. Officer & Dir.-Fin.--Rice Growers Association of California, West Sacramento, CA; *U.S. Private*, pg. 927
Watkins, Kim A., V.P. & Controller--Ohio Gas Company, Bryan, OH; *U.S. Private*, pg. 812
Watkins, Ron, Controller--Dixieland Food Stores Inc., Geneva, AL; *U.S. Private*, pg. 337
Watkins, Tim, Exec. V.P. & Controller--The Acorn, Kalamazoo, MI; *U.S. Private*, pg. 454
Watroba, Wallace, Controller--Jarvis (East), Palmer, MA; *U.S. Public*, pg. 1506
Watson, Julie, Controller--Phoenix Technologies Ltd., San Jose, CA; *U.S. Public*, pg. 1292
Watson, K.M., V.P. & Controller--ATCO Group Co., Calgary, Canada; *Int'l*, pg. 95
Watson, Michelle, Controller--UNC ARTEX, Addison, TX; *U.S. Public*, pg. 710
Watson, Neil, Gen. Mgr. & Controller--Mike Daugherty's Chevrolet Geo, Inc., Sacramento, CA; *U.S. Private*, pg. 313
Watson, Robert, Controller--Johnston Industries, Inc., Columbus, GA; *U.S. Public*, pg. 933
Watson, Robert, Controller--S.T. Research, Newington, VA; *U.S. Private*, pg. 958
Watson, Robert L., Comptroller--Hilton Equipment Corp., Beverly Hills, CA; *U.S. Public*, pg. 829
Watson, Roberta J., V.P. & Controller--Micros Systems Inc., Beltsville, MD; *U.S. Public*, pg. 1106
Watson, Thomas G., Sr. V.P. & Controller--Shoreline Financial Corp., Benton Harbor, MI; *U.S. Public*, pg. 1467
Watson, Thomas G., Sr. V.P. & Controller--Shoreline Bank, Benton Harbor, MI; *U.S. Public*, pg. 1468
Watterson, Leo, V.P. & Controller--Sun Healthcare Group Inc., Albuquerque, NM; *U.S. Public*, pg. 1530
Wax, Linda, Controller--Ideal Chemical & Supply Company, Memphis, TN; *U.S. Private*, pg. 557
Weafer, Robert, Jr., Chief Acctg. Officer, V.P. & Controller--Boston Edison Company, Boston, MA; *U.S. Public*, pg. 247
Wear, Ray, V.P. & Controller--Peterson Farms, Decatur, AR; *U.S. Private*, pg. 857
Weaver, Joseph, Controller--Florida Residential Treatment Centers, Inc., West Palm Beach, FL; *U.S. Public*, pg. 1035
Weaver, Robert L., V.P. & Controller--Cameron & Barkley Company, Charleston, SC; *U.S. Private*, pg. 203
Weaver, Tom, Controller--BC-USA, New Holland, PA; *Int'l*, pg. 201
Webb, Dan, Controller--Gosnell Builders, Phoenix, AZ; *U.S. Private*, pg. 873
Webb, Katherine, Controller--Hunter Engineering Co., Inc., Riverside, CA; *Int'l*, pg. 474
Webb, Patrick, Controller--Thermwell Products Co., Inc., Paterson, NJ; *U.S. Private*, pg. 1081
Webb, Robert D., Controller & Asst. Sec.--Lester B. Knight & Associates, Inc., Chicago, IL; *U.S. Private*, pg. 626
Webber, Jean G., Asst. Comptroller--American Express Credit Corporation, Wilmington, DE; *U.S. Public*, pg. 74
Webber, Mike, Controller--Web Press Graphics Ltd., Port Coquitlam, Canada; *Int'l*, pg. 1077
Webber, Tom, Asst. Controller--Prairie Farms Dairy, Inc., Carlinville, IL; *U.S. Private*, pg. 878
Webel, Gary, Controller--Bettcher Manufacturing Corp., Cleveland, OH; *U.S. Private*, pg. 169
Weber, Gary, Controller--Oregon Metallurgical Corporation, Albany, OR; *U.S. Public*, pg. 43
Weber, George A., Asst. Controller--Sysco Corporation, Houston, TX; *U.S. Public*, pg. 1550
Weber, Karrie, Controller--Gordon & Ferguson of Delaware, Inc., Plymouth, MN; *U.S. Private*, pg. 465
Weber, Kurt, Corp. Controller--Field Container Company, L.P., Elk Grove Village, IL; *U.S. Private*, pg. 403
Webster, Adam, Controller--ServiceMaster Residential/Commercial Services Co., Memphis, TN; *U.S. Public*, pg. 1461
Webster, Gordon, Controller--Hilliard Corporation, Elmira, NY; *U.S. Private*, pg. 530
Wechsler, Julie, Controller--The Paper House/Southern Paper, Miami, FL; *U.S. Private*, pg. 467
Weeks, Bonnie, Asst. Controller--Clare Rose Inc./Clare Rose of Nassau, Patchogue, NY; *U.S. Private*, pg. 945
Weeks, Darwin, V.P. & Controller--Foodmaker, Inc., San Diego, CA; *U.S. Public*, pg. 661
Weeks, Nancy, Controller--Valley Fresh, Inc., Turlock, CA; *U.S. Private*, pg. 1132

Weeks, Shirley, Controller--Beechmont Investments Inc., Cincinnati, OH; *U.S. Private*, pg. 129
Weerner, Monika G., Controller--Chemoil, San Francisco, CA; *U.S. Private*, pg. 233
Wegener, Kim, Controller--McKellar Companies, San Diego, CA; *U.S. Private*, pg. 723
Wegleitner, Marcia, Controller--Plastech Corporation, Forest Lake, MN; *U.S. Private*, pg. 870
Wehlmann, David W., V.P. & Controller--Grey Wolf, Inc., Houston, TX; *U.S. Public*, pg. 765
Wehmeier, R.T., Controller--The Kirk & Blum Mfg. Co., Cincinnati, OH; *U.S. Private*, pg. 623
Wehner, Todd, Controller--Steck-Vaughn Distribution Company, Austin, TX; *U.S. Public*, pg. 784
Wehner, Todd B., Controller--Steck-Vaughn Company, Austin, TX; *U.S. Public*, pg. 784
Wehner, Todd B., Controller--Steck-Vaughn Publishing Corporation, Austin, TX; *U.S. Public*, pg. 784
Wehr, Patty, Controller--Haskel International, Inc., Burbank, CA; *U.S. Public*, pg. 798
Wehren, Dennis, Controller--The Cerplex Group, Inc., Tustin, CA; *U.S. Public*, pg. 332
Wehrlin, Gerald T., Controller--National Fuel Gas Company, Buffalo, NY; *U.S. Public*, pg. 1156
Wehtje, Ronald M., V.P. & Controller--Pillowtex Corporation, Dallas, TX; *U.S. Public*, pg. 1296
Weiden, Robert, Controller--P & F Industries, Inc., Farmingdale, NY; *U.S. Public*, pg. 1239
Weigand, David, V.P.-Fin.--American Software, Inc., Atlanta, GA; *U.S. Public*, pg. 91
Weigand, James P., Controller--Skyline Corporation, Elkhart, IN; *U.S. Public*, pg. 1476
Weigel, Karen, Controller--Morley Builders, Santa Monica, CA; *U.S. Private*, pg. 761
Weil, Cheryl, Controller--Dominick's Finer Foods, Northlake, IL; *U.S. Private*, pg. 1202
Weil, William S., Controller--Leggett & Platt, Incorporated, Carthage, MO; *U.S. Public*, pg. 985
Weilminster, Robert, V.P.-Fin.--Poly-Seal Corporation, Baltimore, MD; *U.S. Private*, pg. 875
Weimer, Robert C., Dir.-Finance & Admin.--Union City Body Company, L.P., Union City, IN; *U.S. Private*, pg. 1118
Weinberg, Kent E., Controller--Grumman Olson Division, Sturgis, MI; *U.S. Public*, pg. 1198
Weiner, Debbie, Controller--Tillamook County Creamery Assn., Tillamook, OR; *U.S. Private*, pg. 1086
Weinstein, Larry, Controller--Best Provision Co., Inc., Newark, NJ; *U.S. Private*, pg. 140
Weis, Sandy, Comptroller--Holiday RV Superstores West, Inc., Bakersfield, CA; *U.S. Public*, pg. 830
Weisbarth, James A., Sr. V.P. & Controller--Central Reserve Life of North America Insurance Co., Strongsville, OH; *U.S. Public*, pg. 326
Weisman, Susan, Sr. V.P. & Controller--BankAtlantic Bancorp, Inc., Fort Lauderdale, FL; *U.S. Public*, pg. 183
Weisner, Carol A., V.P. & Controller--Litton Industries, Inc., Woodland Hills, CA; *U.S. Public*, pg. 1002
Weiss, Brad, Controller--Tuttle-Click Automobile Group, Irvine, CA; *U.S. Private*, pg. 1111
Weiss, Felix, Div. Mgr. & Controller--Migros, Zurich, Switzerland; *Int'l*, pg. 865
Weiss, George, V.P. & Grp. Controller--Ceco Concrete Construction LLC, Gladstone, MO; *U.S. Private*, pg. 859
Weiss, Neil, Controller--Starrett HRH, New York, NY; *U.S. Private*, pg. 1035
Welber, Herbert, Controller & Asst. Treas.--Aydin Corporation, Horsham, PA; *U.S. Public*, pg. 158
Welbourne, Jack, Controller--Knomark, Inc., Aurora, IL; *U.S.* Private, pg. 627
Welch, Denise, Controller--F.L. Roberts & Co. Inc., Springfield, MA; *U.S. Private*, pg. 935
Welch, Phil, Controller--S.P. Richards Co., Smyrna, GA; *U.S. Public*, pg. 732
Welge, Michael W., Exec. V.P., Treas., Sec. & Comptroller--Gilster Mary Lee Corp., Chester, IL; *U.S. Private*, pg. 455
Welker, Rick, V.P. & Controller--Bradlees Inc., Braintree, MA; *U.S. Public*, pg. 249
Welling, Beverly A., Controller--Jupiter Industries, Inc., Northbrook, IL; *U.S. Private*, pg. 602
Wellings, Gregory, Controller--Bondware, Toronto, Canada; *Int'l*, pg. 417
Wellings, Gregory, Controller--Robinson Cone, Burlington, Canada; *Int'l*, pg. 417
Wellington, Doug, Controller--Sealaska Corporation, Juneau, AK; *U.S. Private*, pg. 978
Welliver, Byron L., Sr. V.P.-Fin., Controller & Treas.--Noble Drilling Corporation, Houston, TX; *U.S. Public*, pg. 1186
Wellman, Thomas A., Controller & Asst. Treas.--Alexander & Baldwin, Inc., Honolulu, HI; *U.S. Public*, pg. 39
Wellman, Thomas A., V.P., Controller & Asst. Treas.--A & B-Hawaii, Inc., Honolulu, HI; *U.S. Public*, pg. 39
Wells, A. Keith, Controller--M. Swift & Sons Inc., Hartford, CT; *U.S. Private*, pg. 1059
Wells, Clyde L., Controller & Treas.--Vestal Manufacturing, Sweetwater, TN; *U.S. Public*, pg. 1737
Wells, Jim, Controller--Cummins Cumberland Inc., Louisville, KY; *U.S. Private*, pg. 295
Wells, Pam, Controller--Madison Newspapers, Inc., Madison, WI; *U.S. Public*, pg. 984
Wells, Penny, Controller--Quality Food Oils, Inc., New Milford, CT; *Int'l*, pg. 92
Wells, Thomas M., Grp. V.P. & Controller--GEICO Corporation, Washington, DC; *U.S. Public*, pg. 219
Wells, Thomas M., Controller--Criterion Life Insurance Co., Washington, DC; *U.S. Public*, pg. 219
Wells, Thomas M., V.P. & Controller--GEICO Indemnity Company, Washington, DC; *U.S. Public*, pg. 220
Welsh, Dale, Controller--Hill & Griffith Company, Cincinnati, OH; *U.S. Private*, pg. 529
Welsh, Philip, V.P.-Fin. & Treas.--Environment/One Corporation, Niskayuna, NY; *U.S. Public*, pg. 586
Welten, B.J.J.V., Controller--Food Specialties Division, Delft, Netherlands; *Int'l*, pg. 1142
Weltz, Kevin, Controller--Danielson Holding Corporation, New York, NY; *U.S. Public*, pg. 483
Wenderlich, Martha, Controller--Helm, Inc., Detroit, MI; *U.S. Private*, pg. 520
Wendt, Lee, Controller--Cerwin Vega, Inc., Simi Valley, CA; *U.S. Private*, pg. 227
Wenger, Scott, Div. Controller--Michigan Tube Co., Eau Claire, MI; *U.S. Private*, pg. 533
Wensel, Deborah, Controller--Great Lakes Dredge & Dock Co., Oak Brook, IL; *U.S. Private*, pg. 474
Wenstrom, Wayne, Controller--Baldwin Graphic Systems, Inc., Shelton, CT; *U.S. Public*, pg. 170
Wentz, William D., V.P. & Controller--Hoover Group, Inc., Alpharetta, GA; *U.S. Private*, pg. 538
Wenzel, Frank, Ph.D., Sr. V.P. & Controller--Bayer Corporation, Pittsburgh, PA; *Int'l*, pg. 172
Werger, Edward M., Asst. Controller--Federal Paper Board Company, Inc., Montvale, NJ; *U.S. Public*, pg. 903
Werner, Lee, Controller--La-Co Industries Markal Company, Elk Grove Village, IL; *U.S. Private*, pg. 640
Werner, Raymond, Controller--Siliconix, Inc., Santa Clara, CA; *Int'l*, pg. 367
Werner, William, Controller--Apache Plastics, L.P., Lodi, CA; *U.S. Private*, pg. 77
Werning, Tom, Controller--Svedala Industries-Universal Engineering, Cedar Rapids, IA; *Int'l*, pg. 1326
Werstak, Joe, Controller--Milk Marketing Inc., Strongsville, OH; *U.S. Private*, pg. 745
Werth, Merv, Controller--Kenetech Corp., San Francisco, CA; *U.S. Public*, pg. 950
Wertz, Carl, Controller--Diodes Incorporated, Westlake Village, CA; *U.S. Public*, pg. 510
Wesolowski, Gerald F., Chief Fin. Officer--H.W. Kaufman Financial Group, Inc., Farmington, MI; *U.S. Private*, pg. 609
Wesorick, L., Chief Fin. Officer & Controller--Rapid Engineering Inc., Comstock Park, MI; *U.S. Private*, pg. 910
Wessman, Troy, Controller--Griffin Envelope, Inc., Seattle, WA; *U.S. Public*, pg. 1038
West, David, Controller--Royal Waterbeds, Maryland Heights, MO; *U.S. Private*, pg. 949
West, Gabriele, Controller--A. Levy & J. Zentner Co., Sacramento, CA; *U.S. Private*, pg. 663
West, Junette C., V.P. & Controller--Apollo Group, Inc., Phoenix, AZ; *U.S. Public*, pg. 120
West, Karen E., V.P. & Controller--The Vanguard Group, Inc., Valley Forge, PA; *U.S. Private*, pg. 1133
West, Kevin D., Controller--SpeedFan International, Inc., Chandler, AZ; *U.S. Public*, pg. 1497
West, L. David, Controller--Accent Furniture, Inc., Maryland Heights, MO; *U.S. Private*, pg. 949
West, L. David, Controller--Boyd Flotation, Inc, Maryland Heights, MO; *U.S. Private*, pg. 949
West, William, Comptroller--Mays Chemical Company, Indianapolis, IN; *U.S. Private*, pg. 718
Westbury, M.J., Controller--M.E. Mack Valves Pty. Limited, Bayswater, Australia; *Int'l*, pg. 1222
Westcott, Ronald H., Comptroller--Alberta Energy Company, Ltd., Calgary, Canada; *Int'l*, pg. 48
Westervelt, James J., Sr. V.P. & Grp. Controller--The Hartford Financial Services Group Inc., Hartford, CT; *U.S. Public*, pg. 794
Westervelt, James J., V.P. & Grp. Controller--Hartford Fire Insurance Co., Hartford, CT; *U.S. Public*, pg. 794
Westh, Mogens, Controller--KONE Elevator A/S, Copenhagen, Denmark; *Int'l*, pg. 747
Westhoff, Joseph A., Controller--Atlantic Concrete Products, Inc., Tullytown, PA; *U.S. Private*, pg. 95
Westhoff, Joseph J., Pres.--Atlantic Concrete Products, Inc., Tullytown, PA; *U.S. Private*, pg. 95
Weston, Thomas, V.P., Controller & Dir.-Mergers/ Acquisitions--BTG, Inc., Fairfax, VA; *U.S. Public*, pg. 164
Westover, Frank T., Sr. V.P. & Controller--Whitman Corporation, Rolling Meadows, IL; *U.S. Public*, pg. 1766
Westphal, Steven D., V.P. & Controller--Coca-Cola Bottling Co. Consolidated, Charlotte, NC; *U.S. Public*, pg. 391
Westphalen, Glen, Corp.Controller--Elixir Industries, Gardena, CA; *U.S. Private*, pg. 371
Wetesnik, Bob, V.P. & Controller--Sea World of Texas, San Antonio, TX; *U.S. Public*, pg. 114
Wethington, Bud, Controller--McAllen Medical Center, McAllen, TX; *U.S. Public*, pg. 1697
Wetmore, Douglas J., Controller--International Flavors & Fragrances, Inc., New York, NY; *U.S. Public*, pg. 898
Wetterlund, Wayne, Controller--Urban Outfitters, Inc., Philadelphia, PA; *U.S. Public*, pg. 1700
Weures, Andrew D., Fin. Controller--Meyer International PLC, London, United Kingdom; *Int'l*, pg. 864
Weverb, Lynn, Controller--Cheyenne Outfitters, Inc., Cheyenne, WY; *U.S. Private*, pg. 234
Weyls, Tim, Controller--Master Builders Inc., Cleveland, OH; *Int'l*, pg. 1465
Whalen, Ann W., Controller--Appleton Papers Inc., Appleton, WI; *Int'l*, pg. 567
Whalen, John A., Comptroller--Commonwealth Energy System, Cambridge, MA; *U.S. Public*, pg. 414
Whalen, Kevin, Controller--Willcox & Gibbs, Inc., Carteret, NJ; *U.S. Private*, pg. 1177
Wharton, Joanne, Controller--The American Bankers Association, Washington, DC; *U.S. Private*, pg. 51
Wheeler, Arnold F., V.P., Controller & Treas.--Bartlett and Company, Kansas City, MO; *U.S. Private*, pg. 118
Wheeler, Ken, Controller--Container Div. (Wilson), Wilson, NC; *Int'l*, pg. 1270
Wheeler, Linda, Controller--Newmont Mining Corporation, Denver, CO; *U.S. Public*, pg. 1178
Wheeler, Linda, Controller--Newmont Gold Company, Denver, CO; *U.S. Public*, pg. 1179
Wheeler, Mike, Chief Fin. Officer, V.P. & Treas.--Hy-Vee Food Stores Incorporated, West Des Moines, IA; *U.S. Private*, pg. 550
Whelply, Gerald, Controller--Pac Rim Holding Corporation, Woodland Hills, CA; *U.S. Public*, pg. 1246
Whepley, Harry, V.P.-Fin.--Tekra Corporation, New Berlin, WI; *U.S. Private*, pg. 1073
Whigham, O. Michael, Chief Acctg. Officer, V.P. & Controller--Coca-Cola Enterprises Inc., Atlanta, GA; *U.S. Public*, pg. 393
Whipple, Brent, Controller--Zions Co-operative Mercantile Institution, Salt Lake City, UT; *U.S. Public*, pg. 1793
Whisnant, John R., Chief Fin. Officer & V.P.-Fin.--Insignia Systems, Inc., Minnetonka, MN; *U.S. Public*, pg. 881
Whitaker, Bill, V.P. & Controller--Great American Industries, Inc., Vestal, NY; *U.S. Private*, pg. 473
White, Betty J., Controller, Treas. & Asst. Sec.--Christiana Companies, Inc., Milwaukee, WI; *U.S. Public*, pg. 352
White, Chris, Controller--Executive Jet Aviation, Inc., Columbus, OH; *U.S. Private*, pg. 388
White, Doug, Controller--Sechrist Industries, Inc., Anaheim, CA; *U.S. Private*, pg. 980
White, Eileen B., Corp. Controller--Cooper Tire & Rubber Company, Findlay, OH; *U.S. Public*, pg. 445
White, George S., V.P. & Controller--Foster Wheeler Corporation, Clinton, NJ; *U.S. Public*, pg. 676
White, Grover L., V.P. & Controller--Longs Drug Stores Corporation, Walnut Creek, CA; *U.S. Public*, pg. 1013
White, James D., V.P. & Controller--AON Corporation, Chicago, IL; *U.S. Public*, pg. 117
White, Matthew, Controller--Virginia First Financial Corp., Petersburg, VA; *U.S. Public*, pg. 1721
White, Richard, Controller--Automatic Machine Products Company, Attleboro, MA; *U.S. Private*, pg. 101
White, Steven E., Controller--Cleveland City Forge, Cleveland, OH; *U.S. Public*, pg. 1258
White, Todd, V.P. & Controller--The Scotts Company, Marysville, OH; *U.S. Public*, pg. 1446
White, W., Controller--Intermodal Transportation Services, Inc., Parsippany, NJ; *Int'l*, pg. 1153
White, Warren L., V.P. & Controller--Plastics, Inc., Saint Paul, MN; *U.S. Public*, pg. 1177
White, Warren L., V.P. & Controller--Anchor Hocking Plastics, Saint Paul, MN; *U.S. Public*, pg. 1177
Whiteford, Stephen, V.P. & Controller--The Cooper Companies, Inc., Irvine, CA; *U.S. Public*, pg. 442
Whitehead, John P., Asst. V.P. & Controller--Selective Insurance Company of South Carolina, Charlotte, NC; *U.S. Public*, pg. 1455
Whitehead, John P., Asst. V.P. & Controller--Selective Insurance Company of America, Branchville, NJ; *U.S. Public*, pg. 1455
Whitehead, John P., Asst. V.P. & Controller--Exchange Insurance Company, Buffalo, NY; *U.S. Public*, pg. 1455
Whitehill, George, Controller--Wolf, Block, Schorr & Solis-Cohen, Philadelphia, PA; *U.S. Private*, pg. 1185
Whitener, Kirk, Controller--United Design Corporation, Noble, OK; *U.S. Private*, pg. 1121
Whitham, Mark D., Comptroller--Firstar Corporation-Iowa, Des Moines, IA; *U.S. Public*, pg. 643
Whiting, Arthur S., V.P. & Controller--Vanguard Cellular Systems, Inc., Greensboro, NC; *U.S. Public*, pg. 1707
Whitlock, Tom, V.P. & Controller--Erly Industries, Inc., Los Angeles, CA; *U.S. Public*, pg. 591
Whitlow, Steve, Controller--Equitable Bag Company, Inc., Florence, KY; *U.S. Private*, pg. 380
Whitman, Lawrence R., V.P. & Controller--GTE Corporation, Stamford, CT; *U.S. Public*, pg. 696
Whitmeyer, Angelyn, Sr. V.P. & Controller--Trone Advertising, Inc., Greensboro, NC; *U.S. Private*, pg. 1104
Whitney, James E., Controller--Hughes Supply, Inc., Orlando, FL; *U.S. Public*, pg. 846
Whitney, Lisa, Controller--Carnation Products Div., Glendale, CA; *Int'l*, pg. 916
Whitney, Philip, Controller--Bollinger Shipyards, Inc., Lockport, LA; *U.S. Private*, pg. 155
Whiton, A.E., V.P. & Controller--Ionics, Incorporated, Watertown, MA; *U.S. Public*, pg. 912
Whitt, William H., Controller--Mueller Steam Specialty, Lumberton, NC; *U.S. Public*, pg. 1676
Whitten, Earl, Chief Fin. Officer, Treas. & Controller--Sherley Grain Company, Bovina, TX; *U.S. Private*, pg. 993
Whitton, Jeffrey, Controller--Freedom Communication Inc., Irvine, CA; *U.S. Private*, pg. 425
Whitty, Ron, Controller--Conso Products Company, Union, SC; *U.S. Public*, pg. 434
Whitworth, Terry, Controller--Samtec Inc., New Albany, IN; *U.S. Private*, pg. 963
Whitworth, Victor, Controller--Giant Cement Holding Inc., Summerville, SC; *U.S. Public*, pg. 741
Wichowski, Andrew, Controller--Quackenbush Co. Inc., Buffalo, NY; *U.S. Private*, pg. 897
Wick, Stephen, Asst. Controller--Sterling Electronics Corporation, Houston, TX; *U.S. Public*, pg. 1051
Widen, Anders, Chief Fin. Officer & Controller--H.A. Schlatter AG, Schlieren, Switzerland; *Int'l*, pg. 1205
Widmark, Walter, V.P.-Control, Acctng. & Taxes & Controller--Mo och Domsjo AB, Stockholm, Sweden; *Int'l*, pg. 885
Widner, Kimberly, Controller--Cavco Industries, Inc., Phoenix, AZ; *U.S. Public*, pg. 323
Wiecek, Dick, Controller--Kay Home Products, Inc., Cleveland, OH; *U.S. Public*, pg. 1258
Wiecek, Richard, Controller--Marshallan Industries, Cleveland, OH; *U.S. Public*, pg. 1259
Wiedenfeld, Linda, Controller--Madison Dairy Produce Company, Madison, WI; *U.S. Private*, pg. 694
Wiehoff, John, Controller--C.H. Robinson Co., Eden Prairie, MN; *U.S. Public*, pg. 1394
Wiepz, Ron, Controller--Pabst Brewing Co./Tumwater, Tumwater, WA; *U.S. Private*, pg. 954
Wiese, Sandy, Controller--Simpson Electric Co., Elgin, IL; *U.S. Private*, pg. 1002
Wiesek, Richard, Controller--Quaker Industries, Antioch, IL; *U.S. Public*, pg. 1259
Wiesner, George R., Asst. Controller--WPS Resources Corp., Green Bay, WI; *U.S. Public*, pg. 1728

Wiest, Dale, Controller--Terre Hill Concrete Products, Inc., Terre Hill, PA; *U.S. Private*, pg. 1077
Wigger, Lisa, V.P. & Controller--BRC Holdings, Dallas, TX; *U.S. Public*, pg. 163
Wigger, Wayne, Controller--Producers Co-op Association, Inc., Girard, KS; *U.S. Private*, pg. 888
Wiklund, Erik, Controller--KONE Hissar AB, Kista, Sweden; *Int'l*, pg. 747
Wilber, S. Michael, Controller--Engineered Specialty Plastics, Hot Springs National Park, AR; *U.S. Public*, pg. 583
Wild, Mark, Fin. Controller--Heywood Williams Group PLC, Huddersfield, United Kingdom; *Int'l*, pg. 618
Wild, Paul, V.P. & Controller--Roman Electric Company, Inc., Milwaukee, WI; *U.S. Private*, pg. 942
Wildman, Murray, Controller--Starcan Corporation, Toronto, Canada; *Int'l*, pg. 1297
Wiles, Stuart, Corp. Controller--Ben & Jerry's Homemade Inc., South Burlington, VT; *U.S. Public*, pg. 210
Wiley, George, Controller--Saratoga Equine Sports Center, Saratoga Springs, NY; *U.S. Private*, pg. 965
Wilhelm, Dale W., V.P. & Controller--Serv-Tech, Inc., Houston, TX; *U.S. Public*, pg. 1460
Wilhoite, John, V.P. & Controller--Intergraph Corporation, Huntsville, AL; *U.S. Public*, pg. 890
Wilke, Nancy J., V.P. & Controller--Encyclopaedia Britannica, Inc., Chicago, IL; *U.S. Private*, pg. 375
Wilkerson, Dale G., Controller--Mapco Coal Inc., Tulsa, OK; *U.S. Public*, pg. 1042
Wilkes, Michael S., Controller--Santa Fe Energy Resources, Inc., Houston, TX; *U.S. Public*, pg. 1431
Wilkinson, Gregory J., V.P. & Controller--Telephone and Data Systems, Inc., Chicago, IL; *U.S. Public*, pg. 1570
Wilkinson, Jim, Asst. Controller--Sasco Group, Cerritos, CA; *U.S. Private*, pg. 967
Wilkosz, David, Controller--P & E, Inc., Orlando, FL; *U.S. Private*, pg. 825
Will, Larry L., Controller--The Law Company, Inc., Wichita, KS; *U.S. Private*, pg. 653
Willard, Ken, V.P., Controller & Treas.--Oxford Realty Financial Group, Bethesda, MD; *U.S. Private*, pg. 825
Willems, Ricardo, Controller--Coats North America, Charlotte, NC; *Int'l*, pg. 300
Willemse, Paul, Controller--Peerless Tube Company, Bloomfield, NJ; *U.S. Public*, pg. 1269
Willett, Susanne, Controller--New Brunswick Power Corporation, Fredericton, Canada; *Int'l*, pg. 923
Willhite, Donald H., V.P. & Controller--Atlantic Aviation Corp., New Castle, DE; *U.S. Private*, pg. 94
Williams-Owen, Cathy, Controller--Dri Mark Products, Inc., Port Washington, NY; *U.S. Private*, pg. 342
Williams, David K., Exec. V.P., Controller & Sec.--Killearn Properties, Inc., Stockbridge, GA; *U.S. Public*, pg. 956
Williams, Delores P., Controller--Phoenix Medical Technology, Inc., Andrews, SC; *U.S. Public*, pg. 1292
Williams, Earl, Controller--Belz Enterprises, Memphis, TN; *U.S. Private*, pg. 132
Williams, Edward W., V.P. & Controller--ITT Defense & Electronics, Inc., Mc Lean, VA; *U.S. Public*, pg. 859
Williams, Gary, Controller--Mitchel & Scott Machine Co., Inc., Indianapolis, IN; *U.S. Private*, pg. 753
Williams, Glen S., Controller--The Goldfield Corporation, Melbourne, FL; *U.S. Public*, pg. 750
Williams, Gloria, V.P., Controller, Treas. & Dir.-Investor Rels.--The Stop & Shop Companies, Inc., Quincy, MA; *Int'l*, pg. 750
Williams, Greg, Controller--Nabholz Construction Corp., Conway, AR; *U.S. Private*, pg. 772
Williams, H.E., Controller--Levlad, Inc., Chatsworth, CA; *U.S. Private*, pg. 663
Williams, Harold, Controller--Vulcraft Div., Norfolk, NE; *U.S. Public*, pg. 1206
Williams, Jeffrey, Controller--Computational Systems Inc., Knoxville, TN; *U.S. Public*, pg. 572
Williams, Jim, Controller--American Home Improvement, Monroeville, PA; *U.S. Private*, pg. 56
Williams, Joan, Controller--Newman's Own, Inc., Westport, CT; *U.S. Private*, pg. 797
Williams, John, V.P. & Controller--Bell Sports Corp., San Jose, CA; *U.S. Public*, pg. 207
Williams, Keith, V.P.-Admin., Controller, Treas. & Sec.--Perry Brothers, Inc., Lufkin, TX; *U.S. Private*, pg. 854
Williams, Kevin, Controller--Senior Flexonics Inc., Bartlett, IL; *Int'l*, pg. 1222
Williams, Lynn, Controller--Intercounty Title Co. of Illinois, Chicago, IL; *U.S. Private*, pg. 567
Williams, Mark A., V.P. & Controller--Canadian Airlines Corporation, Calgary, Canada; *Int'l*, pg. 255
Williams, Mark A., Controller--Electro Kinetics Div., Santa Barbara, CA; *U.S. Public*, pg. 1250
Williams, Patricia, Comptroller--Carlos R. Leffler Inc., Richland, PA; *U.S. Private*, pg. 658
Williams, Paul D., Chief Acctg. Officer & Controller--Genesco Inc., Nashville, TN; *U.S. Public*, pg. 728
Williams, Penny, Controller--Tausche Martin Lonsdorf, Atlanta, GA; *U.S. Private*, pg. 1069
Williams, Peter E., Chief Fin. Officer, V.P.-Fin. & Asst. Sec.--WD-40 Company, San Diego, CA; *U.S. Public*, pg. 1726
Williams, Phil, Controller--Tom James Company, Franklin, TN; *U.S. Private*, pg. 580
Williams, Sam, Controller--Effingham-Clay Service Co., Effingham, IL; *U.S. Private*, pg. 365
Williams, Samuel D., V.P. & Controller--Ducommun Incorporated, Carson, CA; *U.S. Public*, pg. 533
Williams, Sid, Controller--Baker Hughes INTEQ, Houston, TX; *U.S. Public*, pg. 166
Williams, Steve, Controller--Elberta Crate & Box Company, Bainbridge, GA; *U.S. Private*, pg. 367
Williams, Thomas A., V.P. & Controller--Oracle Corporation, Redwood City, CA; *U.S. Public*, pg. 1227
Williams, Thomas C., Treas., Controller & Asst. Sec.--Florida Tile Industries, Inc., Lakeland, FL; *U.S. Public*, pg. 1322
Williams, Tyra S., V.P. & Controller--Willis Faber North America, Inc.-Georgia, Atlanta, GA; *Int'l*, pg. 1503
Williams, W.A., V.P. & Controller--A.O. Smith Water Products Company, Irving, TX; *U.S. Public*, pg. 1477
Williams, Warner, Controller--FFP Marketing Company, Inc., Fort Worth, TX; *U.S. Public*, pg. 604
Williams, Willard, Controller--Howell Metal Company, New Market, VA; *U.S. Public*, pg. 413
Williams, Wygonda, Comptroller--Handling Systems Engineering, Jacksonville, FL; *U.S. Private*, pg. 499
Williamson, Billie I., Sr. V.P.-Fin. & Controller--Marriott International, Inc., Washington, DC; *U.S. Public*, pg. 1047
Williamson, Dick, V.P.-Fin. & Grp. Controller--Tracor Aerospace, Inc., Austin, TX; *U.S. Public*, pg. 1627
Williem, Don, Controller--Kamax-G.B. DuPont L.P., Troy, MI; *U.S. Private*, pg. 606
Willis, Bernard, Controller-Grp. Fin.--J. Sainsbury plc, London, United Kingdom; *Int'l*, pg. 1169
Willis, Bobby J., V.P. & Controller--Entergy Gulf States, Inc., Beaumont, TX; *U.S. Public*, pg. 586
Willis, Chris, Controller--Interpoint, Redmond, WA; *U.S. Public*, pg. 457
Willis, Lawrence I., V.P.-Fin. & Controller--Granite Broadcasting Corporation, New York, NY; *U.S. Public*, pg. 759
Willis, Mitch, Controller--Troyer Potato Products, Inc., Waterford, PA; *U.S. Private*, pg. 1106
Wilsky, Cindy, Controller--Atlanta Hawks, Inc., Atlanta, GA; *U.S. Public*, pg. 1614
Wilson, Allen W., V.P. & Div.-Controller--Mount Snow Resort, Mount Snow, VT; *U.S. Private*, pg. 61
Wilson, Barbara, Controller--Solitec Wafer Processing, Inc., San Jose, CA; *U.S. Private*, pg. 1013
Wilson, Barry, Controller--Amtech Corporation, Dallas, TX; *U.S. Public*, pg. 105
Wilson, Barry G., Controller--Centex Corporation, Dallas, TX; *U.S. Public*, pg. 322
Wilson, Brian R., Comptroller--DoFasco, Inc., Hamilton, Canada; *Int'l*, pg. 414
Wilson, Cynthia, Controller--The Churchill Companies, Minneapolis, MN; *U.S. Private*, pg. 239
Wilson, D. James, Controller & Treas.--Northwest Natural Gas Company, Portland, OR; *U.S. Public*, pg. 1200
Wilson, Gene, Controller--Kool Seal, Inc., Twinsburg, OH; *U.S. Private*, pg. 632
Wilson, Harrison, Controller--TransTechnology Corporation, Liberty Corner, NJ; *U.S. Public*, pg. 1632
Wilson, Jack, Corp. Controller--VicWest Steel Division North American Building Products, Oakville, Canada; *Int'l*, pg. 698
Wilson, Jimmy, Chief Fin. Officer, Treas. & Controller--J.M. Smith Corp., Spartanburg, SC; *U.S. Private*, pg. 1008
Wilson, John, Controller--Circle A.W. Products, Co., Portland, OR; *U.S. Public*, pg. 1471
Wilson, Joy, Controller--North American Company, Fort Lauderdale, FL; *U.S. Private*, pg. 803
Wilson, Linda, Controller--Legacy Audio Inc., Springfield, IL; *U.S. Public*, pg. 45
Wilson, Lynn, Controller--Johnston & Murphy Co., Nashville, TN; *U.S. Public*, pg. 728
Wilson, Martin, Controller--Smith Corona Corp., Cortland, NY; *U.S. Private*, pg. 1007
Wilson, Ray, Controller--Sonoco Engraph, Inc., Atlanta, GA; *U.S. Public*, pg. 1486
Wilson, Raymond, Controller--American Business Products, Inc., Atlanta, GA; *U.S. Public*, pg. 70
Wilson, Robert G., V.P.-Fin. & Controller--Kitchen Kompact, Inc., Jeffersonville, IN; *U.S. Private*, pg. 624
Wilson, Robert W., Chief Fin. Officer, Exec. V.P., Controller, Treas. & Asst. Sec.--Supreme Industries, Inc., Goshen, IN; *U.S. Public*, pg. 1541
Wilson, Sandra, Controller--Sensormatic Canada, Inc., Mississauga, Canada; *U.S. Public*, pg. 1457
Wilson, Teresa, Controller--Cruising Equipment Company, Seattle, WA; *U.S. Public*, pg. 1705
Wilson, Tim, Controller & Asst. Treas.--Beaudry Ford, Inc., Atlanta, GA; *U.S. Private*, pg. 127
Winchell, Chuck, Controller--Schuck & Sons Construction Co., Glendale, AZ; *U.S. Private*, pg. 973
Winchester, Glenda, Controller--Marshall & Williams Co., Greenville, SC; *U.S. Private*, pg. 708
Windfeldt, Thomas A., V.P., Controller & Treas.--Donaldson Company, Inc., Minneapolis, MN; *U.S. Public*, pg. 517
Windhorst, David R., Controller & Dir.-Corp. Acctg.--Vencor, Inc., Louisville, KY; *U.S. Public*, pg. 1711
Windt, Richard L., V.P. & Corp. Controller--Acme United Corporation, Fairfield, CT; *U.S. Public*, pg. 17
Wing, David, V.P.-Fin. & Controller--Amtran, Inc., Indianapolis, IN; *U.S. Public*, pg. 106
Wingaard, Bill, Controller--Tarco, North Little Rock, AR; *U.S. Private*, pg. 1068
Winger, Carl, Controller--Vulcan Materials Company-Midwest Div., Lombard, IL; *U.S. Public*, pg. 1726
Winger, Charles J., Comptroller--Cinergy, Plainfield, IN; *U.S. Public*, pg. 369
Winger, Charles J., Comptroller--Cinergy Investments, Inc., Indianapolis, IN; *U.S. Public*, pg. 369
Winget, Bob, Chief Fin. Officer & Controller--Richards Industries, Inc., Cincinnati, OH; *U.S. Private*, pg. 929
Wingo, Susan, Comptroller--Uniblend Spinners, Inc., Conway, SC; *U.S. Private*, pg. 1117
Winkler, Gary, Controller--Academy Corporation, Katy, TX; *U.S. Private*, pg. 11
Winnacott, Ronald, Fin.. Controller--AEP Canada, Inc., West Hill, Canada; *U.S. Public*, pg. 5
Winoker, Lawrence, Controller--MacAndrews & Forbes Holdings Inc., New York, NY; *U.S. Private*, pg. 689
Winslow, Richard H., Chief Fin. Officer, V.P.-Fin., Controller & Treas.--Norfolk Shipbuilding & Drydock Corporation, Norfolk, VA; *U.S. Private*, pg. 802
Winston, Charles, Controller--Russell Petroleum Corporation, Montgomery, AL; *U.S. Private*, pg. 953
Winter, Bonnie, Controller--Calcor Space Facility, Inc., Whittier, CA; *U.S. Private*, pg. 200
Winter, Edwin T., Jr., Mgr.-Acctg.--Bachmann Industries, Inc., Philadelphia, PA; *U.S. Private*, pg. 109
Winter, Jeffrey R., Controller--Stryker Corporation, Kalamazoo, MI; *U.S. Public*, pg. 1525
Winters, David R., V.P.-Fin. & Controller--M.A. Bruder & Sons, Incorporated, Broomall, PA; *U.S. Private*, pg. 175
Winters, Steve, Controller--International Electronic Research Corp., Burbank, CA; *U.S. Public*, pg. 286
Wirdzek, J.P., Controller--Amecom Div., College Park, MD; *U.S. Public*, pg. 1002
Wisdorf, Douglas G., Sr. V.P. & Controller--Washington Mutual Inc., Seattle, WA; *U.S. Public*, pg. 1741
Wise, Chris, V.P.-Fin., Treas. & Sec.--Southco Distributing Company, Goldsboro, NC; *U.S. Private*, pg. 1014
Wise, Keith, Sr. V.P. & Controller--Allright Corporation, Houston, TX; *U.S. Private*, pg. 42
Wise, Mike, Controller--Hobbs Corporation, Springfield, IL; *Int'l*, pg. 127
Wise, Spence, Controller & Mgr.-Risk--Milliken & Company, Spartanburg, SC; *U.S. Private*, pg. 748
Wiseman, Ronald D., Controller & Asst. Sec.--Thomas Industries Inc., Louisville, KY; *U.S. Public*, pg. 1598
Wishnack, Paula, Controller--Adams Business Forms, Topeka, KS; *U.S. Private*, pg. 16
Wishnowsky, Harvey, Controller--Medalist Industries, Elk Grove Village, IL; *U.S. Public*, pg. 867
Wisiniewsky, Mark, Controller--Check Technology Corporation, Minnetonka, MN; *U.S. Public*, pg. 342
Withycomb, Leslie, Controller--Primesouth, Inc., Columbia, SC; *U.S. Public*, pg. 1436
Witkowski, Chris, Sr. V.P. & Controller--Hubco, Inc., Mahwah, NJ; *U.S. Public*, pg. 845
Witkowski, John, Controller--Ultra Tool & Plastics, Inc., Amherst, NY; *U.S. Private*, pg. 1116
Witt, J., Controller--American Safety Technologies, Inc., Roseland, NJ; *Int'l*, pg. 892
Witt, Scott, Controller--The Stellar Group Inc., Jacksonville, FL; *U.S. Private*, pg. 1040
Wittensolder, L.D., Controller--Gougler Industries, Inc., Kent, OH; *U.S. Private*, pg. 466
Wittingham, Katey, Controller--Medieval Times Dinner & Tournament, Inc., Buena Park, CA; *U.S. Private*, pg. 728
Wittke, Barb, Controller--B & B Homes Corporation, Casper, WY; *U.S. Private*, pg. 105
Wittman, Mike, V.P. & Controller--KPIX-TV, San Francisco, CA; *U.S. Public*, pg. 275
Witty, Tim, V.P. & Controller--Ag Processing Inc., A Cooperative, Omaha, NE; *U.S. Private*, pg. 26
Witzko, Markus, Controller & Office Mgr.--Sensormatic Ges.m.b.H, Salzburg, Austria; *U.S. Public*, pg. 1457
Wnek, Andrew T., V.P. & Controller--Canadian Tire Corporation Limited, Toronto, Canada; *Int'l*, pg. 259
Wnuk, John, Controller--Johanna Foods Inc., Flemington, NJ; *U.S. Private*, pg. 589
Woebenberg, Sue, Controller--Cascade Steel Rolling Mills, Inc., McMinnville, OR; *U.S. Public*, pg. 1440
Wohlman, Richard, V.P. & Controller--Fahnestock & Co., Inc., New York, NY; *Int'l*, pg. 476
Wojtasiak, Lawrence A., Controller--Nash Finch Company, Edina, MN; *U.S. Public*, pg. 1151
Wold, Dennis, Controller--The Cretex Companies, Elk River, MN; *U.S. Private*, pg. 289
Wold, Richard, Controller--Croscill, Inc., New York, NY; *U.S. Private*, pg. 290
Wolf, Brian K., Corp. Controller--Eateries, Inc., Oklahoma City, OK; *U.S. Public*, pg. 555
Wolf, Brian K., Corp. Controller--Pepperoni Grill, Oklahoma City, OK; *U.S. Public*, pg. 555
Wolf, David, Controller--Perstorp Polyols Inc., Toledo, OH; *Int'l*, pg. 1038
Wolf, Kenneth, V.P. & Controller--Callaway Golf Company, Carlsbad, CA; *U.S. Public*, pg. 294
Wolfe, Carroll, Controller & Treas.--The Mad Butcher, Inc., Pine Bluff, AR; *U.S. Private*, pg. 693
Wolfe, Jim, Controller--Carl Zeiss Optical, Inc., Petersburg, VA; *Int'l*, pg. 1523
Wolfe, Nelson, Controller--Beach Mold & Tool Inc., New Albany, IN; *U.S. Private*, pg. 125
Wolfe, Robert F., Comptroller, Treas. & Sec.--Ardco, Inc., Alsip, IL; *U.S. Private*, pg. 80
Wolfe, Victor, Controller--Lithographix, Inc., Los Angeles, CA; *U.S. Private*, pg. 670
Wolfgang, John, Controller--Saarbergwerke Aktiengesellschaft, Saarbruecken, Germany; *Int'l*, pg. 1166
Wolfington, Michael, Controller--Minerals Div., Reno, NV; *U.S. Private*, pg. 355
Wolford, Edward R., Controller--Tuscarora Incorporated, New Brighton, PA; *U.S. Public*, pg. 1646
Wolfrom, Ed, Controller--Burns & McDonnell Engineers-Architects-Consultants, Kansas City, MO; *U.S. Private*, pg. 187
Wolfsheimer, R., Sr. V.P. & Controller--Calvert Group, Ltd., Bethesda, MD; *U.S. Private*, pg. 11
Wollaston, Richard, Asst. Controller--The Stride Rite Corporation, Lexington, MA; *U.S. Public*, pg. 1524
Wollman, F.W., Controller--Carbon Products Operation Inc., East Stroudsburg, PA; *Int'l*, pg. 891
Wolowitz, Charles A., V.P. & Aeropower Grp. Controller--Pall Corporation, Greenvale, NY; *U.S. Public*, pg. 1253
Wolter, Howard J., Controller & Asst. Sec.--Jason Incorporated, Milwaukee, WI; *U.S. Public*, pg. 923
Woltering, D.F., V.P. & Controller--Ferguson Machine Co., Saint Louis, MO; *U.S. Public*, pg. 457
Wolters, John J., Sr. V.P.-Fin. & Controller--ABC Television Network Group, New York, NY; *U.S. Public*, pg. 511
Womac, Ron, Controller--Fritz Air Freight, Irving, TX; *U.S. Public*, pg. 683
Womack, Carol, Controller--Orchids Paper Products Co., Pryor, OK; *U.S. Private*, pg. 819
Womack, Rosalie, Controller--Moeller Products Co., Inc., Greenville, MS; *U.S. Private*, pg. 755
Womer, Wilda G., Controller--NVF Company, Yorklyn, DE; *U.S. Private*, pg. 772

Wong, Cynthia, Controller--First Marathon Inc., Toronto, Canada; *Int'l*, pg. 486
Wong, Garth, Controller--Norcen Energy Resources Limited, Calgary, Canada; *Int'l*, pg. 434
Wong, Gordon, Controller--Mylex Corporation, Fremont, CA; *U.S. Public*, pg. 1143
Wong, S.C., Controller--Exxon Trading Asia Pacific Private Limited, Singapore, Singapore; *U.S. Public*, pg. 602
Wong, Tammy, Controller--Seligman & Associates, Inc., Southfield, MI; *U.S. Private*, pg. 982
Wongphayak, Rangsan, Exec. V.P.--Bangkok Bank Public Company Limited, Bangkok, Thailand; *Int'l*, pg. 146
Wood, Barbara S., V.P., Controller, Treas. & Sec.--Independence Capital Management, Inc., Horsham, PA; *U.S. Private*, pg. 849
Wood, Brad, Controller--St. Louis National Baseball Club L.P., Saint Louis, MO; *U.S. Private*, pg. 961
Wood, Carol S., Chief Fin. Officer, Controller, Treas. & Sec.--Higginbotham-Bartlett Co., Lubbock, TX; *U.S. Private*, pg. 527
Wood, David, Controller--AMC, Inc., Atlanta, GA; *U.S. Private*, pg. 6
Wood, G., Grp. Mgr.-Fin.--South African Breweries, Ltd., Johannesburg, South Africa; *Int'l*, pg. 1286
Wood, Gordon, Controller--Beach Patrol Inc., Carson, CA; *U.S. Private*, pg. 125
Wood, J. David, V.P. & Controller--Derlan Industries Limited, Toronto, Canada; *Int'l*, pg. 395
Wood, John, Comptroller--G.I. Trucking Co., La Mirada, CA; *U.S. Public*, pg. 131
Wood, Kurt, Treas.--RJ Associates, Plymouth, MN; *U.S. Private*, pg. 932
Wood, Mike, Controller--NHT, Benicia, CA; *U.S. Public*, pg. 1369
Wood, Timothy M., Chief Fin. Officer, V.P. & Controller--Borg-Warner Security Corporation, Chicago, IL; *U.S. Public*, pg. 245
Woodard, Michael, Controller--G&K Services, Inc., Minnetonka, MN; *U.S. Public*, pg. 690
Woodard, Tony, Controller--URS Logistics, Atlanta, GA; *U.S. Private*, pg. 1114
Woodbury, Robert W., Jr., V.P. & Controller--Dynatech Corporation, Burlington, MA; *U.S. Public*, pg. 539
Woodlief, Philip, V.P. & Controller--Insilco Corporation, Dublin, OH; *U.S. Public*, pg. 881
Woods, David A., V.P. & Controller--SAFECO Credit Company, Inc., Seattle, WA; *U.S. Public*, pg. 1423
Woods, Thomas, Controller--Tool & Engineering Co., Chicago, IL; *U.S. Private*, pg. 394
Woodward, James H., V.P.-Admin. & Controller--Dana Corporation, Toledo, OH; *U.S. Public*, pg. 479
Woodward, Mae, Controller--Fresh Western International, Salinas, CA; *Int'l*, pg. 491
Workman, Larry E., Controller--Russell Corporation, Alexander City, AL; *U.S. Public*, pg. 1413
Worley, Richard, Controller--Alamo Group, Inc., Seguin, TX; *U.S. Public*, pg. 34
Worner, Ernst, Div. Mgr.--Durkopp Adler AG, Bielefeld, Germany; *Int'l*, pg. 468
Worthington, Carl, Controller--SEI Holding Corp., Dallas, TX; *U.S. Private*, pg. 956
Worthington, O. Douglas, V.P., Controller & Asst. Treas.--The Lincoln National Life Insurance Co., Fort Wayne, IN; *U.S. Public*, pg. 998
Worthington, Richard, Controller--Etec Systems, Inc., Hayward, CA; *U.S. Public*, pg. 594
Wortzman, Howard, V.P.-Fin. Reporting--Counsel Corporation, Toronto, Canada; *Int'l*, pg. 338
Wotta, Paul, Controller--Sunrise Leasing Corporation, Golden Valley, MN; *U.S. Public*, pg. 1535
Wozniak, Bob, Controller--Sterling, Inc., Milwaukee, WI; *U.S. Private*, pg. 1041
Wray, Anita M., V.P. & Controller--Ralston Purina Company, Saint Louis, MO; *U.S. Public*, pg. 1359
Wright, Arlene H., Controller--The Cosmetic Center Inc., Columbia, MD; *U.S. Private*, pg. 689
Wright, George, Controller--Transamerican Natural Gas Corporation, Houston, TX; *U.S. Private*, pg. 1096
Wright, J.L., Asst. Controller--Reading & Bates Corporation, Houston, TX; *U.S. Public*, pg. 1354
Wright, Jeff, Controller--San Francisco Newspaper Agency, San Francisco, CA; *U.S. Private*, pg. 239
Wright, Jeffrey L., Controller--BMC Industries, Inc., Minneapolis, MN; *U.S. Public*, pg. 162
Wright, Julie A., Controller--O.I. Corporation, College Station, TX; *U.S. Public*, pg. 1208
Wright, Patricia, Controller--Star Video Entertainment, L.P., Jersey City, NJ; *U.S. Private*, pg. 1132
Wright, Peter W., V.P. & Opers. Controller--Republic Industries, Inc., Fort Lauderdale, FL; *U.S. Public*, pg. 1378
Wright, W., V.P. & Controller--Atco Gas Services Ltd., Calgary, Canada; *Int'l*, pg. 95
Wright, William, Controller--Lowrance Canada, Mississauga, Canada; *U.S. Public*, pg. 1016
Wrightson, Robert E., Sr. V.P. & Controller--Consolidated Freightways Corp., Menlo Park, CA; *U.S. Public*, pg. 435
Wrinn, Thomas, Controller--Barrister Information Systems Corporation, Buffalo, NY; *U.S. Public*, pg. 192
Wronski, John, Controller--Robinson Bus Service, Evanston, IL; *U.S. Private*, pg. 936
Wuffli, Peter A., Chief Fin. Officer--Swiss Bank Corporation, Basel, Switzerland; *Int'l*, pg. 1329
Wulff, John K., Chief Fin. Officer, V.P. & Controller--Union Carbide Corporation, Danbury, CT; *U.S. Public*, pg. 1666
Wulff, Scott, Controller--Nucor Iron Carbide, Port of Spain, Trinidad & Tobago; *U.S. Public*, pg. 1206
Wuori, Richard W., V.P. & Controller--Watkins Associated Industries Inc., Atlanta, GA; *U.S. Private*, pg. 1153
Wurdemann, Loran, V.P.-Fin. & Controller--Schwartz & Benjamin, Inc., New York, NY; *U.S. Private*, pg. 974
Wurderle, Richard, V.P. & Controller--Revenue Collection Group World Headquarters, San Diego, CA; *U.S. Public*, pg. 466
Wurst, Robert S., Controller--Cyro Industries, Rockaway, NJ; *Int'l*, pg. 1454
Wust, Pierre, Treas., Controller & Chief Fin. Officer--Sandoz Pharma Ltd., Eden Terrace, New Zealand; *Int'l*, pg. 985
Wvest, Glen, Controller--Tulip Corporation, City of Industry, CA; *U.S. Private*, pg. 1109
Wyant, Jim, Controller--Security Bank & Trust Co., Vincennes, IN; *U.S. Public*, pg. 1217
Wyatt, Peter F., Pres. & Controller--N E D Corp., Worcester, MA; *U.S. Private*, pg. 771
Wymer, Cynthia, Controller--B&W Co-op, Inc., Breckenridge, MI; *U.S. Private*, pg. 105
Wynne, Linda, V.P. & Controller--Dunhill Personnel System, Inc., Hauppauge, NY; *U.S. Public*, pg. 1746
Xavier, Kris, V.P. & Controller--Gottschalks Inc., Fresno, CA; *U.S. Public*, pg. 754
Xepoleas, Courtney, Controller--Berryman Products, Inc., Arlington, TX; *U.S. Private*, pg. 138
Yaffee, Jerry, Controller--Otari Corporation, Foster City, CA; *Int'l*, pg. 1013
Yagodines, Nathan, Controller--Laser Industries Ltd., Tel Aviv, Israel; *Int'l*, pg. 429
Yamamoto, Hideo, Dir.-Plng. & Control--UBE Industries Ltd., Tokyo, Japan; *Int'l*, pg. 1426
Yan, Chua Bee, Mgr.-Fin. & Admin.--Orchard Parade Holdings Limited, Singapore, Singapore; *Int'l*, pg. 1007
Yang, Felix, Sr. V.P. & Controller--Partners & Shevack, Inc., New York, NY; *U.S. Private*, pg. 842
Yannazzo, Gary, V.P. & Controller--Metallgesellschaft Corp., New York, NY; *Int'l*, pg. 861
Yansak, Jan, Controller--SofTECH, Inc., Grand Rapids, MI; *U.S. Public*, pg. 1482
Yarborough, David, Controller--Meridell Achievement Center, Liberty Hill, TX; *U.S. Public*, pg. 1697
Yarbrough, Dennis J., Controller-Corp. Acctg.--Wm. Wrigley Jr. Company, Chicago, IL; *U.S. Public*, pg. 1781
Yasbek, Steve, V.P.-Fin. & Plng., Controller--Symbol Technologies, Portable Systems Division, Costa Mesa, CA; *U.S. Public*, pg. 1546
Yasbek, Steven M., Chief Info. Officer, V.P. & Controller--Pacific Scientific Company, Newport Beach, CA; *U.S. Public*, pg. 1250
Yastrzemski, J.R., Comptroller--Florida East Coast Industries Inc., Saint Augustine, FL; *U.S. Public*, pg. 1427
Yates, Brian, Controller--Analytical Surveys, Inc., Colorado Springs, CO; *U.S. Public*, pg. 110
Yates, Richard L., V.P. & Controller--Textron Inc., Providence, RI; *U.S. Public*, pg. 1588
Yaworsky, George, Asst. Controller--Bessemer Group, Inc., New York, NY; *U.S. Private*, pg. 139
Yazdi, Mordechai, Fin. Controller--NRG France S.A., Creteil, France; *Int'l*, pg. 1116
Yeager, Paul, Controller--Ausherman Construction Company, Frederick, MD; *U.S. Private*, pg. 99
Yellen, Maurice, Controller--Dames & Moore Inc., Los Angeles, CA; *Int'l*, pg. 624
Yelpo, Beverly, Controller--Victaulic Company of America, Easton, PA; *U.S. Private*, pg. 1138
Yen, Dominic F., Esq., Controller--Adec International Automation Corp., Cleveland, OH; *U.S. Private*, pg. 17
Yennerell, Rich, Controller--Adience Inc., Carnegie, PA; *U.S.* Public, pg. 58
Yergey, Beth, Controller--Systems & Computer Technology Corporation, Malvern, PA; *U.S. Public*, pg. 1552
Yerkes, Theresa F., V.P. & Controller--The Stanley Works, New Britain, CT; *U.S. Public*, pg. 1508
Yim, Sherri, V.P. & Controller--Central Pacific Bank, Honolulu, HI; *U.S. Public*, pg. 283
Yip, Tom S.A., Controller--Echo Bay Mines Ltd., Englewood, CO; *U.S. Public*, pg. 561
Yoder, Doug, Controller--Ridgeview, Inc., Newton, NC; *U.S. Private*, pg. 930
Yoder, Dwight J., V.P. & Controller--Allergan, Inc., Irvine, CA; *U.S. Public*, pg. 46
Yodowitz, Heidi, Controller--McKesson Corporation, San Francisco, CA; *U.S. Public*, pg. 1072
Yokota, Milton, Controller--Persis Corporation, Honolulu, HI; *U.S. Private*, pg. 855
Yonchek, Jim, Controller--Pilling Weck, Research Triangle Park, NC; *U.S. Public*, pg. 1569
Yonchek, Jim, Controller--Pilling Weck, Fort Washington, PA; *U.S. Public*, pg. 1569
Yonkaitis, Walter, Controller--Folger Adam Security Inc., Lemont, IL; *U.S. Private*, pg. 416
York, Dan, Sec., Treas. & Controller--Peck Road Ford Truck Sales, Whittier, CA; *U.S. Private*, pg. 846
York, Randy, Corp. Controller--First Cash, Inc., Arlington, TX; *U.S. Public*, pg. 627
York, Sally, Controller--Wilton Industries, Inc., Woodridge, IL; *U.S. Private*, pg. 1181
York, Steve, Controller--Darling Envelope Corporation, Shawnee Mission, KS; *U.S. Private*, pg. 311
York, W.R., Controller--Flexible Products Company, Marietta, GA; *U.S. Private*, pg. 412
Yost, William H., Treas. & Controller--Maguire Group Inc., Foxboro, MA; *U.S. Private*, pg. 696
Youga, Tony, V.P. & Controller--E. & J. Gallo Winery, Modesto, CA; *U.S. Private*, pg. 438
Young, Alan, V.P. & Controller--Westwood-Squibb Pharmaceuticals Inc., Buffalo, NY; *U.S. Public*, pg. 255
Young, Barrie, V.P. & Controller--Shaw's Supermarkets, Inc., East Bridgewater, MA; *Int'l*, pg. 1170
Young, Don L., Controller-Audits--OGE Energy Corp., Oklahoma City, OK; *U.S. Public*, pg. 1207
Young, Douglas E., Chief Fin. Officer & Sr. V.P.--Copperweld Fayetteville Division, Fayetteville, TN; *Int'l*, pg. 662
Young, Ian, Fin. Controller--Goodman Fielder Mills Ltd., Eastwood, Australia; *Int'l*, pg. 555
Young, Matthew, Controller--Mechanics Tool Div., Dallas, TX; *U.S. Public*, pg. 1509
Young, Michael, Controller--DeMert & Dougherty, Inc., Coal City, IL; *U.S. Private*, pg. 323
Young, Phillip G., V.P. & Controller--Bergen Brunswig Medical Corporation, Orange, CA; *U.S. Public*, pg. 214
Young, Phillip G., V.P. & Controller--Bergen Brunswig Medical Corporation, Montgomery, AL; *U.S. Public*, pg. 214
Young, Richard, V.P. & Controller--Bill Heard Enterprises, Inc., Columbus, GA; *U.S. Private*, pg. 515
Young, Richard A., V.P. & Asst. Corp. Controller--NS Group, Inc., Newport, KY; *U.S. Public*, pg. 1147
Young, Scott, V.P. & Controller--Green Tree Financial Corporation, Saint Paul, MN; *U.S. Public*, pg. 761
Young, Stephen, Controller--EMI Group plc, London, United Kingdom; *Int'l*, pg. 426
Young, Sylvie, Controller--Image Entertainment, Inc., Chatsworth, CA; *U.S. Public*, pg. 870
Youngman, Matthew J., Controller--The Macneal-Schwendler Corp., Los Angeles, CA; *U.S. Public*, pg. 1030
Younk, James L., V.P.-Fin.--David White, L.L.C., Germantown, WI; *U.S. Public*, pg. 1765
Younk, James L., V.P.-Fin.--David White, L.L.C., Germantown, WI; *U.S. Private*, pg. 1765
Yross, Nancy, Asst. Controller--Efficient Engineering Co., Troy, MI; *U.S. Private*, pg. 365
Yumes, Judith, Controller--The M/A/R/C Group, Irving, TX; *U.S. Public*, pg. 1022
Yungmann, George L., Sr. V.P. & Controller--The Rouse Company, Columbia, MD; *U.S. Public*, pg. 1407
Yurek, Nancy, V.P. & Controller--American Management Systems, Inc., Fairfax, VA; *U.S. Public*, pg. 86
Yust, Dan, Controller--Kansa Corporation, Emporia, KS; *U.S. Public*, pg. 170
Zabinski, A.F., Jr., Chief Fin. Officer, Controller & Treas.--George Sollitt Construction, Wood Dale, IL; *U.S. Private*, pg. 1013
Zabranskey, Audrey, Controller--Smith Metal Arts Company, Inc., Buffalo, NY; *U.S. Private*, pg. 1009
Zachariello, Lori, Controller--Baltic Linen Company, Inc., Valley Stream, NY; *U.S. Private*, pg. 113
Zachary, John L., Controller--Oilfield Marine Services-Americas Region, Morgan City, LA; *U.S. Public*, pg. 1211
Zack, Brian P., Controller--Tech Systems Corp., Thomaston, CT; *U.S. Private*, pg. 313
Zagwoski, Michael, Controller--JCI Data Processing, Inc., Cinnaminson, NJ; *U.S. Private*, pg. 577
Zahnow, Fred, Chief Information Officer, V.P. & Controller--Black Rogers Sullivan Goodnight, Inc., Houston, TX; *U.S. Private*, pg. 147
Zahradka, Lyle, Controller--Robert Gibb & Sons, Inc., Fargo, ND; *U.S. Private*, pg. 451
Zambereny, Robert, Controller--Patriot American Hospitality Operating Company, San Mateo, CA; *U.S. Public*, pg. 1265
Zander, Don, Sr. V.P. & Controller--Benson Motors Corporation, Metairie, LA; *U.S. Private*, pg. 134
Zander, Jeffrey, Pres. & Controller--Zander's Creamery Inc., Cross Plains, WI; *U.S. Private*, pg. 1203
Zang, William L., V.P., Treas., Sec. & Controller--International Power Machines Corporation, Garland, TX; *Int'l*, pg. 126
Zapf, William Q., Asst. Controller--Nordson Corporation, Westlake, OH; *U.S. Public*, pg. 1188
Zappantis, Sylvia, Controller--Spinnerin Inc., South Hackensack, NJ; *U.S. Private*, pg. 1025
Zarembka, Karen, Controller--A.W. Mendenhall Co., Inc., Elk Grove Village, IL; *U.S. Private*, pg. 731
Zatta, Robert J., V.P.-Fin. & Controller-Intl. Grocery--Campbell Soup Company, Camden, NJ; *U.S. Public*, pg. 298
Zavacky, Joseph E., Controller & Asst. Sec.--C-COR Electronics, Inc., State College, PA; *U.S. Public*, pg. 272
Zawicki, Mark, Controller--Sara Lee Bakery, Chicago, IL; *U.S. Public*, pg. 1433
Zearo, Louis F., V.P. & Deputy Comptroller--American International Group, Inc., New York, NY; *U.S. Public*, pg. 83
Zeasman, Joyce M., Asst. Controller-Corp. Reengineering--Telephone and Data Systems, Inc., Chicago, IL; *U.S. Public*, pg. 1570
Zee, Stanley, Controller--Nissin Foods (U.S.A.) Co. Ltd., Gardena, CA; *Int'l*, pg. 949
Zeedik, Bruce, V.P. & Controller--Merisel, Inc., El Segundo, CA; *U.S. Public*, pg. 1095
Zeek, Walt, Controller--Superior Label Systems, Inc., Mason, OH; *U.S. Private*, pg. 1055
Zegers, J.L., Controller--SmithKline Beecham Diergeneeskundige Producten B.V., Zoetermeer, Netherlands; *Int'l*, pg. 1266
Zehr, Kathy, Controller & Asst. Sec.--Meredith Corporation, Des Moines, IA; *U.S. Public*, pg. 1094
Zeilstra, M., Controller--Hosokawa Micron B.V., Doetinchem, Netherlands; *Int'l*, pg. 636
Zele, Jim, Controller--The Euclid Chemical Company, Cleveland, OH; *U.S. Public*, pg. 1358
Zelinski, Rob, Controller--Arthur Treacher's, Inc., Jacksonville, FL; *U.S. Public*, pg. 136
Zelky, Randy, Controller--Hofley Manufacturing Company, Roseville, MI; *U.S. Private*, pg. 532
Zellers, W.L., Controller-Gas Opers.--Citizens Gas & Coke Utility, Indianapolis, IN; *U.S. Private*, pg. 241
Zemba, Steve, Controller--Munroe, Inc., Pittsburgh, PA; *U.S.* Private, pg. 767
Zeock, Ed, Controller--GF Office Furniture Ltd., Gallatin, TN; *U.S. Private*, pg. 434
Zeph, Tamara, Controller--Catalina Marketing Corporation, Saint Petersburg, FL; *U.S. Public*, pg. 314
Zerbini, Elio, Controller--Reece-Campbell, Inc., Cincinnati, OH; *U.S. Private*, pg. 916
Zerrusen, Raymond, V.P. & Controller--World Color Press, Inc., Greenwich, CT; *U.S. Public*, pg. 1778
Zerulas, A.D., Controller--Phelps Dodge Refining Corp., El Paso, TX; *U.S. Public*, pg. 1287
Zich, Larry, Second V.P.& Controller--Pioneer Mutual Life Insurance Company, Fargo, ND; *U.S. Private*, pg. 866

Zichlin, Lenny, Controller--Linzer Products Corp., Flushing, NY; *U.S. Private*, pg. 669
Ziegler, John K., Jr., Chief Fin. Officer & Controller--Willcox & Gibbs, Inc., Carteret, NJ; *U.S. Private*, pg. 1177
Ziegler, Scott F., V.P.-Fin., Controller & Sec.--Emons Transportation Group, Inc., York, PA; *U.S. Public*, pg. 578
Ziegler, Scott F., V.P.-Fin., Controller & Sec.--Maryland & Pennsylvania Railroad, York, PA; *U.S. Public*, pg. 579
Zientck, Brian P., Controller--Rudolph/Libbe, Inc., Walbridge, OH; *U.S. Private*, pg. 950
Zigment, Robert A., Controller, Treas. & Sec.--Kunzler & Company, Inc., Lancaster, PA; *U.S. Private*, pg. 636
Zike, Harry, V.P. & Controller--Siemens Corporation, New York, NY; *Int'l*, pg. 1245
Zilinskas, Matthew J., Controller--Kearney-National, Inc., White Plains, NY; *U.S. Private*, pg. 351
Zimbo, Theodore, Controller--ACO Inc., Farmington Hills, MI; *U.S. Private*, pg. 3
Zimlich, Joe, Controller--Comlinear Corporation, Fort Collins, CO; *U.S. Public*, pg. 1160
Zimmerman, Chuck, Controller--Leson Chevrolet Company, Inc., Harvey, LA; *U.S. Private*, pg. 660
Zimmerman, George J., Controller--Badger Paper Mills, Inc., Peshtigo, WI; *U.S. Public*, pg. 165
Zimmerman, Lee D., Gen. Mgr.-Acctg.--Steelox Systems Inc., Mason, OH; *U.S. Private*, pg. 1038
Zimmerman, Rich, Controller--Sunline Coach Co., Inc., Denver, PA; *U.S. Private*, pg. 1053
Ziolkowski, Gary, Controller-DMSD--I.C. System, Inc., Vadnais Heights, MN; *U.S. Private*, pg. 553
Zipse, David, Controller--Nanocor, Inc., Arlington Heights, IL; *U.S. Public*, pg. 64
Zirolli, Mark, Comptoller--Control Module, Inc., Enfield, CT; *U.S. Private*, pg. 271
Zisko, John, Controller--Wyant Coporation, Somerville, NJ; *U.S. Public*, pg. 1781
Zitnay, Robert, Controller--The William Carter Company, Morrow, GA; *U.S. Private*, pg. 217
Zitzmann, Al, Controller--Evergood Products Corporation, Hicksville, NY; *U.S. Private*, pg. 386
Zmyslinski, Brad, Controller--Sentinel Consumer Products, Inc., Mentor, OH; *U.S. Private*, pg. 984
Znamierowski, Donald J., V.P. & Controller--Hartford Life & Accident Insurance Company, Hartford, CT; *U.S. Public*, pg. 795
Znidarsic, Kenneth, Controller--Convenient Food Mart, Inc., Painesville, OH; *U.S. Private*, pg. 271
Zofkie, Mike, Controller--Hirsh Company, Skokie, IL; *U.S. Public*, pg. 963
Zoller, Tom, V.P.-Plng. & Controlling--BASF Corporation Fiber Products Division, Charlotte, NC; *Int'l*, pg. 105
Zoloty, Gregory M., V.P. & Controller--Hickok Incorporated, Cleveland, OH; *U.S. Public*, pg. 825
Zoppas, Giovanni, Controller--Benetton Group S.p.A., Ponzano Veneto, Italy; *Int'l*, pg. 186
Zorger, John, Controller & V.P.--Mitsubishi Motor Sales of America, Inc., Cypress, CA; *Int'l*, pg. 875
Zuar, Robert D., V.P.--The New England, Boston, MA; *U.S. Private*, pg. 737
Zuber, Harold L., Jr., Chief Fin. Officer & V.P.--Teleflex Incorporated, Plymouth Meeting, PA; *U.S. Public*, pg. 1569
Zuerblis, Ken, V.P.-Fin.--Enzon, Inc., Piscataway, NJ; *U.S. Public*, pg. 587
Zuhlke, Bernd, Controller--Melitta Unternehmensgruppe Bentz KG, Minden, Germany; *Int'l*, pg. 856
Zumbo, Elizabeth, Asst. Controller--The F.X. Matt Brewing Co., Utica, NY; *U.S. Private*, pg. 714
Zupkus, Vince, Controller--The Spring Air Company, Des Plaines, IL; *U.S. Private*, pg. 1027
Zweng, Michael J., Controller--Ferrous Processing & Trading Co., Detroit, MI; *U.S. Private*, pg. 402
Zwiernikowski, Rick, Controller--Hastings Manufacturing Company, Hastings, MI; *U.S. Public*, pg. 798

CORPORATE SECRETARY

Aaron, Art, V.P.-Bus. & Legal Affairs & Sec.--Ascent Entertainment Group, Inc., Denver, CO; *U.S. Public*, pg. 138
Aarvig, Thora A., Sec.--Colorado Business Bankshares, Inc., Denver, CO; *U.S. Private*, pg. 255
Abair, Daniel, Treas. & Sec.--Park Motor Sales Company, Detroit, MI; *U.S. Private*, pg. 840
Abate, Anthony, Sr. V.P. & Sec.--North Fork Bank, Mattituck, NY; *U.S. Public*, pg. 1194
Abate, Anthony J., Sr. V.P. & Corp. Sec.--North Fork Bancorporation, Inc., Melville, NY; *U.S. Public*, pg. 1194
Abatemarco, Michael J., Sr. Mng. Dir., Controller & Asst. Sec.--The Bear Stearns Companies Inc., New York, NY; *U.S. Public*, pg. 197
Abbot, Patricia, Treas. & Sec.--Metro Label Corp., Garland, TX; *U.S. Private*, pg. 736
Abbott, Henry J., Sec. & Gen. Counsel--Central Parking Corp., Nashville, TN; *U.S. Public*, pg. 326
Abbott, R. William, Chief Fin. Officer & Exec. V.P.--WSFS Financial Corporation, Wilmington, DE; *U.S. Public*, pg. 1728
Abbott, Sharon, V.P., Gen. Counsel & Sec.--UniCARE Financial Corp., Irvine, CA; *U.S. Private*, pg. 152
Abbott, Sherry L., Sec.--Southeastern Michigan Gas Enterprises, Inc., Port Huron, MI; *U.S. Public*, pg. 1489
Abdalla, Carolyn, Sec.--Abdalla's Lafayette, Inc., Lafayette, LA; *U.S. Private*, pg. 10
Abdoo, David, Sec.--Carlton Communications Plc, London, United Kingdom; *Int'l*, pg. 272
Abene, William, Chief Exec. Officer & Sec.--Davidson Printing Company, Duluth, MN; *U.S. Private*, pg. 314
Abernethy, Robert C., Pres. & Sec.--Carolina Glove Co., Newton, NC; *U.S. Private*, pg. 214
Abney, Delbert, V.P. & Sec.--Sunniland Corporation, Sanford, FL; *U.S. Private*, pg. 1053
Abraham, Peter, Sec.--CSR Limited, Sydney, Australia; *Int'l*, pg. 245
Abrams, Patricia, Sec.--Abrams & Co. Publishing Inc., Waterbury, CT; *U.S. Private*, pg. 10
Accardo, Jack P., Chief Fin. Officer, V.P., Treas. & Sec.--Kasper Machine Company, Madison Heights, MI; *U.S. Private*, pg. 608
Acey, Thomas M., Treas. & Sec.--Conmed Corporation, Utica, NY; *U.S. Public*, pg. 431
Achard, Aime, Sec.--Banque Nationale de Paris (Suisse) S.A., Basel, Switzerland; *Int'l*, pg. 164
Achatz, Harvey H., V.P.-Admin. & Sec.--Daisytek International Corporation, Plano, TX; *U.S. Public*, pg. 477
Achatz, Harvey H., V.P.-Admin. & Sec.--Daisytek Incorporated, Plano, TX; *U.S. Public*, pg. 477
Achatz, Harvey H., V.P.-Admin. & Sec.--Daisytek (Canada) Inc., Toronto, Canada; *U.S. Public*, pg. 477
Achatz, Harvey H., V.P.-Admin. & Sec.--Daisytek Latin America, Miami, FL; *U.S. Public*, pg. 477
Achatz, Harvey H., V.P.-Admin. & Sec.--Daisytek De Mexico S.A. de C.V., Mexico, Mexico; *U.S. Public*, pg. 477
Achatz, Harvey H., V.P.-Admin. & Sec.--Priority Fulfillment Services, Inc., Plano, TX; *U.S. Public*, pg. 477
Achatz, Harvey H., V.P.-Admin. & Sec.--Daisytek Australia Pty. Ltd., Alexandria, Australia; *U.S. Public*, pg. 477
Ackerman, Sanford S., Chief Fin. Officer & Sr. V.P.--Blair Television, New York, NY; *U.S. Private*, pg. 148
Ackerman, Susan D., V.P. & Sec.--Phoenix American Incorporated, San Rafael, CA; *U.S. Private*, pg. 862
Acklie, Phyllis A., V.P. & Sec.--Crete Carrier Corp., Lincoln, NE; *U.S. Private*, pg. 289
Ackman, Roger S., V.P., Gen. Counsel & Sec.--Imperial Tobacco Limited, Montreal, Canada; *Int'l*, pg. 112
Aclin, Maggie, Asst. Sec.--Burlington Northern Santa Fe Corporation, Fort Worth, TX; *U.S. Public*, pg. 268
Adamo, James, Treas. & Sec.--Burnside Construction Co., Downers Grove, IL; *U.S. Private*, pg. 187
Adamonis, Kyle A., Sec.--Taco Incorporated, Cranston, RI; *U.S. Private*, pg. 1066
Adams, Al, V.P.-Adams Div. & Sec.--M.B. Kahn Construction Co., Inc., Columbia, SC; *U.S. Private*, pg. 604
Adams, Brenda, V.P. & Sec.--Fairfax Financial Holdings Limited, Toronto, Canada; *Int'l*, pg. 476
Adams, Jennifer L., Chief Legal & Admin. Officer, Exec. V.P. & Sec.--World Color Press, Inc., Greenwich, CT; *U.S. Public*, pg. 1778
Adams, John B., Chief Fin. Officer, Exec. V.P.-Fin., Sec. & Treas.--Big O Tires Incorporated, Englewood, CO; *U.S. Public*, pg. 1553
Adams, John M., Jr., Asst. Gen. Counsel & Asst. Sec.--American Electric Power Service Corp., Columbus, OH; *U.S. Public*, pg. 72
Adams, Larry M., V.P.-Info. Systems & Sec.--Carmike Cinemas, Inc., Columbus, GA; *U.S. Public*, pg. 305
Adams, Leigh, Sec.--Reptron Electronics, Inc., Tampa, FL; *U.S. Public*, pg. 1377
Adams, Mark, Sr. V.P., Treas. & Sec.--Hechinger Company Investors II, L.P., Largo, MD; *U.S. Private*, pg. 477
Adams, Richard, Sec.--The Post Office, London, United Kingdom; *Int'l*, pg. 1064
Adams, Tonya, Corp. Sec.--ELSAG Bailey Process Automation N.V., Schiphol, Netherlands; *Int'l*, pg. 449
Adcock, Edward, Chief Fin. Officer, Treas. & Sec.--General Processors, Inc., Oxford, NC; *U.S. Public*, pg. 1502
Adelman, Graham, Sr. V.P., Gen. Counsel & Sec.--Global Industrial Technologies, Dallas, TX; *U.S. Public*, pg. 747
Adikes, Robert K., V.P., Sec. & Gen. Counsel--Spalding & Evenflo Companies, Inc., Chicopee, MA; *U.S. Private*, pg. 629
Adkins, B. Jan, Asst. Sec.--TNP Enterprises, Inc., Fort Worth, TX; *U.S. Public*, pg. 1557
Adkins, B. Jan, Asst. Sec.--Texas-New Mexico Power Co., Fort Worth, TX; *U.S. Public*, pg. 1557
Adler, Cindy F., Sec. & Dir.-Investor Rels.--Homasote Company, Trenton, NJ; *U.S. Public*, pg. 831
Adler, Elaine, Sec.--Myron Manufacturing Corporation, Maywood, NJ; *U.S. Private*, pg. 771
Adler, Jack P., Sec.--EA Global, Inc., Hunt Valley, MD; *U.S. Public*, pg. 541
Adler, Jack P., Esq., V.P., Gen. Counsel & Sec.--EA Engineering, Science & Technology, Inc., Hunt Valley, MD; *U.S. Public*, pg. 540
Adler, Marc S., Asst. Sec.--Rohm and Haas Company, Philadelphia, PA; *U.S. Public*, pg. 1403
Admirand, Peter, Controller & Sec.--Western Beef, Inc., Ridgewood, NY; *U.S. Public*, pg. 1758
Afsher, Carolyn McKinney, Sec.--Columbia Energy Group, Reston, VA; *U.S. Public*, pg. 402
Agache, Gerard, Sec.--Credit Mutuel, Paris, France; *Int'l*, pg. 344
Ager, Rowley, Sec.--Tesco PLC, Cheshunt, United Kingdom; *Int'l*, pg. 1376
Agger, James H., Sr. V.P., Gen. Counsel & Sec.--Air Products and Chemicals, Inc., Allentown, PA; *U.S. Public*, pg. 30
Agler, Nancy L., Corp. Sec.--Guy Gannett Communications, Portland, ME; *U.S. Private*, pg. 439
Agnich, Richard J., Sr. V.P., Gen. Counsel & Sec.--Texas Instruments Incorporated, Dallas, TX; *U.S. Public*, pg. 1585
Agranoff, Gerald N., V.P.-Gen. Counsel & Corp Sec.--Datapoint Corporation, Paris, France; *Int'l*, pg. 384
Agresti, Michael L., V.P.-Fin., Treas. & Sec.--Lee Pharmaceuticals, South El Monte, CA; *U.S. Public*, pg. 984
Aguirre, Monica, Asst. Sec.--TransTechnology Corporation, Liberty Corner, NJ; *U.S. Public*, pg. 1632
Ahart, J.F., Chief Fin. Officer, V.P., Treas. & Sec.--Powell Industries, Inc., Houston, TX; *U.S. Public*, pg. 1319
Ahearn, Ellen, Corp. Sec.--Central Hudson Gas & Electric Corporation, Poughkeepsie, NY; *U.S. Public*, pg. 324
Ahearn, Mark, Sec.--Best Access Systems, Indianapolis, IN; *U.S. Public*, pg. 223
Ahlsen, Brit Magda, Sec.--Helly-Hansen A/S, Moss, Norway; *Int'l*, pg. 1010
Ahmad, Saadat Nasim, Exec. V.P. & Sec.--Habib Bank Ltd., Karachi, Pakistan; *Int'l*, pg. 584
Ahting, Frank, V.P.-Fin.--Athey Products Corporation, Wake Forest, NC; *U.S. Public*, pg. 142
Ailes, Walter, V.P., Treas. & Sec.--McGill Manufacturing Company, Inc., Valparaiso, IN; *U.S. Public*, pg. 573
Ainsworth, Kent P., Chief Fin. Officer, Exec. V.P. & Sec.--URS Corporation, San Francisco, CA; *U.S. Public*, pg. 1655
Ainsworth, Phyllis, Sec.--Charleston Financial Services, Inc., Charleston, SC; *U.S. Public*, pg. 634
Ainsworth, Phyllis B., Corp. Sec.--First Financial Holdings, Inc., Charleston, SC; *U.S. Public*, pg. 634
Aita, John, M.D., Sec.--Physicians Mutual Insurance Co., Omaha, NE; *U.S. Private*, pg. 864
Ajer, Randolph E., Chief Fin. Officer, Exec. V.P., Treas. & Sec.--Mercury Air Group Inc., Los Angeles, CA; *U.S. Public*, pg. 1092
Akin, Paul N., Grp. Pres. & Chief Oper. Officer--Inman Construction Corporation, Memphis, TN; *U.S. Private*, pg. 564
Al-Ghulikah, A.M., Sec.--Al-Jubail Petrochemical Company, Tareet, Saudi Arabia; *U.S. Public*, pg. 601
Alan, Arnold, Sec.--Fisca Oil Co., Inc., Westwood, KS; *U.S. Private*, pg. 408
Alber, K.F., Sec.--Comalco Limited, Brisbane, Australia; *Int'l*, pg. 307
Alberici, John S., Vice Chm., Chief Fin. Officer, Sr. V.P. & Sec.--J.S. Alberici Construction Co., Inc., Saint Louis, MO; *U.S. Private*, pg. 32
Alberico, D., Sec.--Burrows Paper Corporation, Little Falls, NY; *U.S. Private*, pg. 188
Albers, Fern B., Sec.--Canadian Pacific Railway, Minneapolis, MN; *Int'l*, pg. 259
Albert, Stephen A., Sec.--Steel of West Virginia, Inc., Huntington, WV; *U.S. Public*, pg. 1513
Alberts, Robert J., Treas. & Sec.--Templeton, Kenly & Co., Inc., Broadview, IL; *U.S. Private*, pg. 1075
Alberty, Kimberly, Exec. Sec.--Hill & Griffith Company, Cincinnati, OH; *U.S. Private*, pg. 529
Albino, Maria, Sec.--Financial Collection Agencies (International) Inc., Westmount, Canada; *Int'l*, pg. 470
Albino, Maria, Sec.--Financial Collection Agencies (International) Inc., Mississauga, Canada; *Int'l*, pg. 470
Albino, Maria, Sec.--FCA Holdings, Inc., Wayne, PA; *Int'l*, pg. 471
Albino, Maria, Sec.--Financial Collection Agencies of Pennsylvania Inc, Wayne, PA; *Int'l*, pg. 471
Albrecht, Joanna Zisa, Asst. Sec.--Cantel Industries, Inc., Clifton, NJ; *U.S. Public*, pg. 301
Albrecht, Marilyn, Sec.--Red Wing Publishing Company, Red Wing, MN; *U.S. Private*, pg. 915
Alcaraz, D. Heliodoro, Sec.--Seguros De Vida Y Pensiones Antares, S.A., Madrid, Spain; *Int'l*, pg. 1371
Alden, John R., Chief Fin. Officer, Sr. V.P.-Fin. & Sec.--Swift Energy Company, Houston, TX; *U.S. Public*, pg. 1543
Aldred, Heidi, Sec.--Computer Power Group Limited, Melbourne, Australia; *Int'l*, pg. 325
Alem, Nancy, Sec. & Treas.--Compar, New York, NY; *Int'l*, pg. 1073
Alepuz, D. Jose Antonio, Sec.--Sistemas Tecnicos Loterias Del Estado (S.T.L.), Madrid, Spain; *Int'l*, pg. 1372
Ales, S.J., Sec. & Controller--Brock-McVey Company, Lexington, KY; *U.S. Private*, pg. 721
Alesso, Dominick, Gen. Counsel & Sec.--A-P-A Transport Corp., North Bergen, NJ; *U.S. Private*, pg. 2
Alexander, Constantine, Sec.--Nabi, Boca Raton, FL; *U.S. Public*, pg. 1148
Alexander, John R., Sec.--Hilliard Corporation, Elmira, NY; *U.S. Private*, pg. 530
Alexander, John R., Sr. V.P. & Sec.--Orange-Co., Inc., Bartow, FL; *U.S. Public*, pg. 1229
Alexander, Julie, Sec.--TIG Holdings, Inc., New York, NY; *U.S. Public*, pg. 1555
Alexander, Nicholas Z., Sr. V.P.-Gen. Counsel & Sec.--ACCEL International Corporation, Dublin, OH; *U.S. Public*, pg. 14
Alexander, R.M., Treas. & Asst. Sec.--Gulf Canada Resources Ltd., Calgary, Canada; *Int'l*, pg. 577
Alexander, Rosemary, Sec.--Cold Spring Granite Company, Cold Spring, MN; *U.S. Private*, pg. 250
Alflen, J., Treas. & Sec.--Torrance Nissan, Inc., Torrance, CA; *U.S. Public*, pg. 1380
Alguire, William M., Sec.--Electrohome Ltd., Kitchener, Canada; *Int'l*, pg. 438
Aliff, Debbie, Gen. Counsel & Sec.--Washington Homes, Inc., Landover, MD; *U.S. Public*, pg. 1741
Allan, R.J.M., Sec.--Mini Instruments Limited, Burnham-on Crouch, United Kingdom; *Int'l*, pg. 892
Allard, Marcella, Sec.--Starcrest Products of California, Perris, CA; *U.S. Private*, pg. 1035
Allen, Clinton G., Treas. & Sec.--Bill Heard Oldsmobile Company, Columbus, GA; *U.S. Private*, pg. 515
Allen, Craig D., Sec.--Norcen Energy Resources Limited, Calgary, Canada; *Int'l*, pg. 434
Allen, Donna, Exec. Sec.--Cains Foods, L.P., Ayer, MA; *U.S.* Private, pg. 199
Allen, Elizabeth, Sec.--Pemco Die Casting Corporation, Bridgman, MI; *U.S. Private*, pg. 848
Allen, Erik, Sec. & Mgr.-Grocery--Allens Of Hastings, Inc., Hastings, NE; *U.S. Private*, pg. 37
Allen, Gary, Controller & Sec.--Wagnerware Corporation, Sidney, OH; *U.S. Private*, pg. 1146
Allen, Glenda B., V.P.-Contract Admin. & Sec.--Leasing Solutions, Inc., San Jose, CA; *U.S. Public*, pg. 982
Allen, Heath L., Esq., Sec.--Arnold Industries, Inc., Lebanon, PA; *U.S. Public*, pg. 132
Allen, J., Sec.--Babcock International Group PLC, Amersham, United Kingdom; *Int'l*, pg. 130
Allen, John C., V.P.-Human Resources, Corp. Counsel & Sec.--Energy West Inc., Great Falls, MT; *U.S. Public*, pg. 581

Allen, Joseph, Exec. V.P., Treas. & Sec.--Brant Allen Industries, Inc., Greenwich, CT; *U.S. Private*, pg. 165
Allen, Kathleen, Sec.--California Panel & Veneer Company, Cerritos, CA; *U.S. Private*, pg. 201
Allen, Martin J., Jr., Sr. V.P. & Sec.--Old Kent Financial Corporation, Grand Rapids, MI; *U.S. Public*, pg. 1216
Allen, R.J.M., Sec.--Centronic Limited, Croydon, United Kingdom; *Int'l*, pg. 892
Allen, Sharon, Sec.--Republic Alloys, Inc., Charlotte, NC; *U.S. Private*, pg. 923
Allen, Wayne E., Dir.-Sls. & Mktg. & Corp. Sec.--Idaho Supreme Company, Firth, ID; *U.S. Private*, pg. 557
Allender, Patrick W., Chief Fin. Officer, Sr. V.P. & Sec.--Danaher Corporation, Washington, DC; *U.S. Public*, pg. 480
Alles, Charles, Treas. & Sec.--Windemuller Electric Inc., Wayland, MI; *U.S. Private*, pg. 1182
Allgood, Joan U., V.P. & Gen. Counsel--Developers Diversified Realty Corporation, Moreland Hills, OH; *U.S. Public*, pg. 502
Allison, Charles, V.P., Gen. Counsel & Sec.--Gulf States Paper Corporation, Tuscaloosa, AL; *U.S. Private*, pg. 487
Allred, Gary L., Treas. & Sec.--AC Corporation, Greensboro, NC; *U.S. Private*, pg. 3
Allsbury, Fran, Exec. Sec.--Tamaqua Cable Products Corp., Schuylkill Haven, PA; *Int'l*, pg. 417
Allsup, Barbara J., V.P., Sec. & Treas.--Allsups Convenience Stores Inc., Clovis, NM; *U.S. Private*, pg. 44
Allums, Mary B., Sec.--Buffalo Rock Company, Birmingham, AL; *U.S. Private*, pg. 179
Almas, Thomas H., V.P.-Admin. & Sec.--The Newhall Land And Farming Company, Valencia, CA; *U.S. Public*, pg. 1178
Almase, Teodoro, V.P.-Legal & Corp Sec.--Atlas Consolidated Mining & Development Corporation, Manila, Philippines; *Int'l*, pg. 95
Almond, David R., Sr. V.P., Gen. Counsel & Sec.--Fleming Companies, Inc., Oklahoma City, OK; *U.S. Public*, pg. 652
Almond, Roger, Sec.--IMI Plc, Witton, United Kingdom; *Int'l, pg. 646*
Alongi, Linda, Treas. & Sec.--American Furniture Company, Albuquerque, NM; *U.S. Private*, pg. 55
Alonso, Loretta, Sec.--AMREP Corporation, New York, NY; *U.S. Public*, pg. 104
Alperson, Lonnie, Treas. & Sec.--Rolled Steel Products Corporation, Los Angeles, CA; *U.S. Private*, pg. 941
Alphson, Howard C., Gen. Counsel & Sec.--M.C. Gill Corporation, El Monte, CA; *U.S. Private*, pg. 453
Alslen, Joseph C., Treas. & Sec.--Southern California Auto Group, Torrance, CA; *U.S. Private*, pg. 1016
Alsup, James M., Sec.--Tom Brown, Inc., Midland, TX; *U.S. Public*, pg. 262
Altavilla, Peter T., Controller & Sec.--Applied Magnetics Corporation, Goleta, CA; *U.S. Public*, pg. 123
Alter, Robert A., Chm. Bd., Pres. & Sec.--Sunstone Hotel Investors, Inc., San Clemente, CA; *U.S. Public*, pg. 1536
Alteri, Sharon, Sec.--Airguard Industries Inc., Louisville, KY; *U.S. Public*, pg. 382
Altherr, Jack R., Jr., Vice Chm. & Chief Fin. Officer--Avondale Incorporated, Monroe, GA; *U.S. Private*, pg. 102
Althof, Timothy D., Treas. & Sec.--New England Business Service, Inc., Groton, MA; *U.S. Public*, pg. 1170
Althoff, John J., V.P., Gen. Counsel & Sec.--Ekco Group, Inc., Nashua, NH; *U.S. Public*, pg. 566
Altmann, Howard J., First V.P. & Asst. Sec.--W.P. Carey & Co., Inc., New York, NY; *U.S. Private*, pg. 209
Ambrose, Andy, Chief Fin. Officer, Exec. V.P. & Sec.--Miller Freeman Inc., San Francisco, CA; *Int'l*, pg. 1443
Ambutas, Vytas, Asst. Sec.--Tang Industries Inc., Las Vegas, NV; *U.S. Private*, pg. 1068
Amer, John C., Exec. V.P.-Fin. & Sec.--Reactive Metals & Alloys Corporation (REMACOR), West Pittsburg, PA; *U.S. Private*, pg. 913
Amerasinghe, D.C., Sec.--Asian Development Bank, Manila, Philippines; *Int'l*, pg. 88
Ames, J.W., V.P.-Fin., Treas. & Sec.--Milwaukee Electric Tool Corp., Brookfield, WI; *Int'l*, pg. 96
Ames, Roger, Sec.--Waterloo Service Company, Waterloo, IA; *U.S. Private*, pg. 1152
Amini, Michael, Exec. V.P. & Sec.--Sage Energy Company, San Antonio, TX; *U.S. Public*, pg. 1426
Ammons, Dora M., Asst. Sec.--Hickory Construction Company, Hickory, NC; *U.S. Private*, pg. 525
Amrein, Felix, Dr., Sec.--Roche Holding Ltd., Basel, Switzerland; *Int'l*, pg. 1119
Anastasio, Curt, V.P., Gen. Counsel & Corp. Sec.--Ultramar Diamond Shamrock Corporation, San Antonio, TX; *U.S. Public*, pg. 1663
Ancarrow, N. Hopper, V.P., Sec. & Gen. Counsel--Southern States Cooperative, Inc., Richmond, VA; *U.S. Private*, pg. 1017
Anderko, Frank, V.P.-Mfg. & Sec.--Worzalla Publishing Co., Inc., Stevens Point, WI; *U.S. Private*, pg. 1191
Anders, Howard G., Chief Fin. Officer, Exec. V.P. & Sec.--Hospitality Worldwide Services, Inc., New York, NY; *U.S.* Public, pg. 841
Andersen, Darian B., Corp. Sec. & Dir.-Law Dept.--Foodbrands America, Inc., Oklahoma City, OK; *U.S. Public*, pg. 852
Andersen, Joseph G., V.P.-Fin., Treas. & Sec.--Continental Circuits Corp., Phoenix, AZ; *U.S. Public*, pg. 440
Andersen, Mariette, V.P.-Mktg. & Sec.--Coolidge Glass Co., Inc., Waukesha, WI; *U.S. Private*, pg. 273
Andersen, Martin H., Asst. Sec.--Andersen Group, Inc., Bloomfield, CT; *U.S. Public*, pg. 111
Andersen, Michael P., V.P., Gen. Counsel & Sec.--John Alden Financial Corporation, Miami, FL; *U.S. Public*, pg. 39
Anderson, Adair, Sec.--John Menzies plc, Edinburgh, United Kingdom; *Int'l*, pg. 707
Anderson, Al, V.P.-Fin.--Dreis & Krump Manufacturing Company, Chicago, IL; *U.S. Private*, pg. 342
Anderson, Barbara C., V.P., Gen. Counsel & Corp. Sec.--Executone Information Systems, Inc., Milford, CT; *U.S. Public*, pg. 599
Anderson, Carolyn J., Chief Fin. Officer & Corp. Sec.--Scott's Liquid Gold-Inc., Denver, CO; *U.S. Public*, pg. 1447
Anderson, Carolyn J., Sec.--SLG Plastics, Inc., Denver, CO; *U.S. Public*, pg. 1447
Anderson, David B., V.P.-Corp. Devel., Gen. Counsel & Sec.--GATX Corporation, Chicago, IL; *U.S. Public*, pg. 690
Anderson, David C., Gen. Counsel & Corp. Sec.--Airborne Freight Corporation, Seattle, WA; *U.S. Public*, pg. 32
Anderson, Donald W., Sec. & Controller--Interferon Sciences, Inc., New Brunswick, NJ; *U.S. Public*, pg. 694
Anderson, Douglas E., Exec. V.P. & Sec.--Boddie-Noell Enterprises Inc., Rocky Mount, NC; *U.S. Private*, pg. 154
Anderson, Douglas L., Asst. Gen. Counsel & Asst. Sec.--CalEnergy Co., Omaha, NE; *U.S. Public*, pg. 292
Anderson, Garn, Controller & Sec.--Superior Industries International, Inc., Van Nuys, CA; *U.S. Public*, pg. 1539
Anderson, George E., V.P. & Sec.--Crown Holdings, Inc., Roseville, MN; *U.S. Private*, pg. 293
Anderson, Gregory W., Corp. Counsel & Sec.--Martin Color-Fi, Edgefield, SC; *U.S. Public*, pg. 1052
Anderson, J. David, Asst. Treas. & Asst. Sec.--Roanoke Gas Company, Roanoke, VA; *U.S. Public*, pg. 1392
Anderson, Linnea, Sec.--Anderson Brothers Construction Brainerd, Brainerd, MN; *U.S. Private*, pg. 72
Anderson, Lonnie, Sec.--Rugby Farmers Union Elevator Company, Rugby, ND; *U.S. Private*, pg. 950
Anderson, Lyn D., V.P.-Fin., Treas. & Sec.--Tom's Foods, Inc., Columbus, GA; *U.S. Private*, pg. 1090
Anderson, Mark A., Chief Fin. Officer, Sec. & Treas.--Community First Bankshares, Inc., Fargo, ND; *U.S. Public*, pg. 416
Anderson, R.D., Gen. Counsel & Sec.--Procter & Gamble Inc., North York, Canada; *U.S. Public*, pg. 1332
Anderson, Robert W., Controller, Treas. & Sec.--Superior Oil Co. Inc., Indianapolis, IN; *U.S. Private*, pg. 1055
Anderson, Roger, Chief Fin. Officer & Sec.--Pepsi-Cola General Bottlers, Inc., Rolling Meadows, IL; *U.S. Public*, pg. 1277
Anderson, Ronald A., Sec. & Asst. Treas.--St. Joe Corp., Jacksonville, FL; *U.S. Public*, pg. 1426
Anderson, Sandy, Sec.--Orchids Etc., Milwaukie, OR; *Int'l*, pg. 1518
Anderson, Sherry E., Sr. V.P. & Sec.--United Companies Financial Corporation, Baton Rouge, LA; *U.S. Public*, pg. 1675
Anderson, William E., II, Sr. V.P., Sec. & Gen. Counsel--Long John Silver's, Inc., Lexington, KY; *U.S. Private*, pg. 674
Andonian, Hratch K., Co-Chm., Exec. V.P., Treas. & Sec.--A K H Company, Inc., City of Commerce, CA; *U.S. Private*, *pg. 2*
Andre, Janet, Corp. Sec.--Carlyle Holding Corporation, Washington, DC; *U.S. Private*, pg. 213
Andre, Wayne, Treas. & Sec.--Roseville Chrysler Plymouth Jeep Inc., Roseville, MI; *U.S. Private*, pg. 946
Andreola, A.V., Sec.--Holman Enterprises, Pennsauken, NJ; *U.S. Private*, pg. 535
Andres, Keith, Asst. Treas.--Hickory Farms, Inc., Maumee, OH; *U.S. Private*, pg. 525
Andrews, Steven R., V.P., Gen. Counsel & Sec.--Multigraphics Inc., Mount Prospect, IL; *U.S. Public*, pg. 1141
Angermeier, Kurt A., Treas. & Sec.--Battle Creek Gas Company, Battle Creek, MI; *U.S. Public*, pg. 1489
Annis, Michael, V.P., Gen. Counsel & Sec.--Del Taco, Inc., Laguna Hills, CA; *U.S. Private*, pg. 321
Ansara, Suzanne L., Asst. Sec.--Nashua Corporation, Nashua, NH; *U.S. Public*, pg. 1152
Anselmi, A., Dr., Sec.--MCG Morgan Carbon Graphite Srl, Milan, Italy; *Int'l*, pg. 891
Anthony, Aubra, Jr., Gen. Counsel, Treas. & Sec.--Anthony Forest Products Co., Inc., El Dorado, AR; *U.S. Private*, pg. 76
Anthony, Frank S., V.P., Gen. Counsel & Sec.--Bird Incorporated, Norwood, MA; *Int'l*, pg. 1170
Anthony, Steven M., Treas. & Sec.--Bearden Lumber Company, Inc., Bearden, AR; *U.S. Private*, pg. 127
Anton, Charles T., Treas. & Sec.--Lift-All Co., Inc., Manheim, PA; *U.S. Private*, pg. 667
Antwine, Danny, Treas. & Sec.--Choctaw Electric Co-Op, Hugo, OK; *U.S. Private*, pg. 238
Anzaldo, Marianne W., Chief Info. Officer, Sec. & Mgr.-Adv.--E.P. Henry Corporation, Woodbury, NJ; *U.S. Private*, pg. 522
Aono, Sumi, Treas. & Sec.--Red Apple, Inc., Ontario, OR; *U.S. Private*, pg. 915
Aparicio, Anthony, Sr. V.P. & Sec.--Banco Santander, Madrid, Spain; *Int'l*, pg. 143
Appelwick, Karen K., Treas. & Sec.--New Apple Lines, Inc., Madison, SD; *U.S. Private*, pg. 792
Appenzeller, Rebecca H., Gen. Counsel & Corp. Sec.--The Standard Register Company, Dayton, OH; *U.S. Public*, pg. 1505
Applegate, Henry, Chief Fin. Officer, Exec. V.P. & Sec.--Players International, Inc., Atlantic City, NJ; *U.S. Public*, pg. 1310
Appling, Dana, Gen. Counsel & Sec.--Sacramento Municipal Utility District, Sacramento, CA; *U.S. Private*, pg. 959
Aquilino, Vincent, Gen. Counsel & Sec.--Graymills Corp., Chicago, IL; *U.S. Private*, pg. 473
Arakelian, Dorothy J., Treas. & Sec.--Standard Manufacturing Co., Inc., Troy, NY; *U.S. Private*, pg. 1031
Aramian, S. Sue, Vice Chm. & Sec.--Consolidated Specialty Restaurant, Indianapolis, IN; *U.S. Public*, pg. 436
Aramian, S. Sue, Vice Chm. & Sec.--SNS Investment Company, Indianapolis, IN; *U.S. Public*, pg. 436
Aramian, Sue, Vice Chm.--Fairmont Snack Group, Inc., Independence, OH; *U.S. Private*, pg. 392
Arana, Cheryl, Treas. & Sec.--Chase Chevrolet Co., Inc., Stockton, CA; *U.S. Private*, pg. 230
Aranow, Peter J., Exec. V.P., Treas. & Sec.--Players International, Inc., Atlantic City, NJ; *U.S. Public*, pg. 1310
Araujo, Alonso, Corp. Sec.--Mineral San Sebastian S.A., San Salvador, El Salvador; *U.S. Public*, pg. 410
Arbitman, William A., V.P., Sec. & Assoc. Gen. Counsel--The Dial Corporation, Phoenix, AZ; *U.S. Public*, pg. 505
Arcadi, Vincent, Treas. & Sec.--Depew Development Inc., Lancaster, NY; *U.S. Private*, pg. 326
Arcari, John J., Chief Fin. Officer--Robotic Vision Systems, Inc., Hauppauge, NY; *U.S. Public*, pg. 1395
Arcati, Anthony, Corp. Sec.--Champion Aluminum Window Corporation, Syosset, NY; *U.S. Private*, pg. 227
Archibald, Andrew M., Chief Fin. Officer, V.P.-Fin. & Sec.--Intertape Polymer Group Inc., Saint-Laurent, Canada; *Int'l*, pg. 684
Archibald, Andrew M., Treas. & Sec.--International Container Systems, Tampa, FL; *Int'l*, pg. 685
Arduini, Catherine E., Sec.--Intermagnetics General Corporation, Latham, NY; *U.S. Public*, pg. 893
Arena, Daniel E., Treas. & Asst. Sec.--General Microwave Corporation, Amityville, NY; *U.S. Public*, pg. 717
Arenberg, Kathleen, Sec.--Columbia Pipe & Supply Company, Chicago, IL; *U.S. Private*, pg. 256
Arfmann, Bruce L., Chief Fin. Officer, Treas. & Sec.--Colorado MEDtech, Inc., Boulder, CO; *U.S. Public*, pg. 401
Armato, Michael, Sec.--Knutson Construction Co., Minneapolis, MN; *U.S. Private*, pg. 627
Armbrister, Gary, Asst. Treas. & Asst. Sec.--Stanley Furniture Co. Inc., Stanleytown, VA; *U.S. Public*, pg. 1508
Armell, Beverly L., Sec. & Mgr.-Investor Rels.--Helix Technology Corp., Mansfield, MA; *U.S. Public*, pg. 808
Armitage, Rod, Sec. & Dir.-Legal Dept.--Staveley Industries PLC, Croydon, United Kingdom; *Int'l*, pg. 1298
Arms, G. Geoffrey, V.P., Gen. Counsel & Sec.--Pool Energy Services Co., Houston, TX; *U.S. Public*, pg. 1316
Armstrong, B., Sec.--Beazer Group Plc, Bath, United Kingdom; *Int'l*, pg. 181
Armstrong, Connie, Corp. Sec.--Vulcan International Corporation, Wilmington, DE; *U.S. Public*, pg. 1725
Armstrong, Diane, Corp. Sec.--Ryan Herco Products Corp., Burbank, CA; *U.S. Private*, pg. 953
Armstrong, James E., V.P.-Engrng. & Opers. & Sec.--Sundowner Offshore Services, Inc., Houston, TX; *U.S. Public*, pg. 1149
Armstrong, Nelson W., Jr., V.P.-Admin. & Sec.--Aztar Corporation, Phoenix, AZ; *U.S. Public*, pg. 158
Arnaouti, Michael, Sec.--Bowthorpe plc, Crawley, United Kingdom; *Int'l*, pg. 207
Arnerup, Tord, Chief Legal Advisor--Nordbanken AB, Stockholm, Sweden; *Int'l*, pg. 957
Arnesen, Mark R., V.P., Sec. & Corp. Counsel--The First American Financial Corporation, Santa Ana, CA; *U.S. Public*, pg. 624
Arnold, Gail T., Asst. Sec.--Atlantic American Life Insurance Company, Atlanta, GA; *U.S. Public*, pg. 143
Arnold, Linda, V.P.-H.R. & Sec.--Toastmaster, Inc., Columbia, MO; *U.S. Public*, pg. 1619
Arnold, Patricia L., Sec.--Bacco Construction Co., Iron Mountain, MI; *U.S. Private*, pg. 109
Arnold, R., Sec.--Rentokil Initial Pest Control, Duluth, GA; *Int'l*, pg. 1285
Arnopolin, Judith, Sec.--Century Publishing Company, Evanston, IL; *U.S. Private*, pg. 226
Arone, Anne, Sec.--Brookfield Properties Corporation, Toronto, Canada; *Int'l*, pg. 228
Arone, Anne, Corp. Sec.--Unicorp Canada Corporation, Toronto, Canada; *Int'l*, pg. 1433
Arpino, Carlo, Sec.--Banca Nazionale del Lavoro Sj.A., Rome, Italy; *Int'l*, pg. 136
Arrigo, Joseph F., Chief Fin. Officer, Exec. V.P. & Treas.--UIS, Inc., Jersey City, NJ; *U.S. Private*, pg. 1113
Arrigoni, Al A., V.P.-Construction & Asst. Sec.--Longs Drug Stores Corporation, Walnut Creek, CA; *U.S. Public*, pg. 1013
Arrington, Roger W., Sec.--Du Pont (E.I. Du Pont De Nemours & Co.), Wilmington, DE; *U.S. Public*, pg. 530
Arst, Patricia L., Sec.--Goldsmiths, Inc., Wichita, KS; *U.S. Private*, pg. 462
Arterbery, Vivian J., Corp. Sec.--RAND, Santa Monica, CA; *U.S. Private*, pg. 908
Arthur, H. Thomas, II, V.P., Gen. Counsel & Asst. Sec.--SCANA Corporation, Columbia, SC; *U.S. Public*, pg. 1436
Arthur, H. Thomas, II, V.P. & Gen. Counsel--South Carolina Pipeline Corporation, Columbia, SC; *U.S. Public*, pg. 1436
Arthur, H.T., Asst. Sec.--SCANA Energy Marketing Inc., Columbia, SC; *U.S. Public*, pg. 1436
Artindale, G. W., Sec. & Dir.--Fortnum & Mason PLC, London, United Kingdom; *Int'l*, pg. 500
Artistia, Ernest, Sec.--Bush Industries Inc., Jamestown, NY; *U.S. Public*, pg. 270
Asch, David, Exec. V.P.-Treas. & Sec.--Twincraft, Inc., Winooski, VT; *U.S. Private*, pg. 1111
Aselage, Susan Seabury, V.P., Asst. Treas. & Sec.--Sabreliner Corporation, Saint Louis, MO; *U.S. Private*, pg. 959
Ash, Herbert L., Asst. Sec.--Hampton Industries, Inc., Kinston, NC; *U.S. Public*, pg. 779
Ashburn, Joanna, Admin. Asst.--Ellwood City Forge, Ellwood City, PA; *U.S. Private*, pg. 373
Ashcom, N.C., Sec.--Ohio Edison Co.-Akron Div., Akron, OH; *U.S. Public*, pg. 645
Ashcom, Nancy C., Sec.--FirstEnergy Corp., Akron, OH; *U.S. Public*, pg. 644
Ashenbrenner, Tom, Chief Fin. Officer, V.P.-Fin. & Sec.--Outlook Group Corporation, Neenah, WI; *U.S. Public*, pg. 1235

Ashenfelter, Dennis D., Asst. Sec.--Oregon Metallurgical Corporation, Albany, OR; *U.S. Public*, pg. 43

Asher, Norman B., Corp. Sec.--Lifeline Systems, Inc., Cambridge, MA; *U.S. Public*, pg. 992

Ashley, James W., Sec.--Methode Electronics Inc., Chicago, IL; *U.S. Public*, pg. 1101

Ashley, Ken, Treas. & Sec.--CCH Incorporated, Riverwoods, IL; *Int'l*, pg. 1513

Ashley, Kenneth, Chief Fin. Officer & Sec.--National R.V., Inc., Perris, CA; *U.S. Public*, pg. 1159

Ashmore, R.C., V.P. & Asst. Sec.--APAC/Ballenger Paving Company, Inc., Taylors, SC; *U.S. Public*, pg. 139

Ashmun, R.E., Sec.--National Frozen Foods Corp., Seattle, WA; *U.S. Private*, pg. 783

Ashurst, Graham H., Sec. & Chief Solicitor--Derbyshire Building Society, Duffield, United Kingdom; *Int'l*, pg. 394

Ashworth, Brent F., V.P., Gen. Counsel & Sec.--Nature's Sunshine Products, Inc., Provo, UT; *U.S. Public*, pg. 1166

Askey, Darrel F., Chief Fin. Officer, V.P.-Fin., Treas. & Sec.--Celestial Seasonings, Boulder, CO; *U.S. Public*, pg. 319

Aspden, M., Sec.--Clear Communications Limited, Auckland, New Zealand; *Int'l*, pg. 223

Aspegren, Carl, Sr. V.P. & Sec.--Trelleborg AB, Trelleborg, Sweden; *Int'l*, pg. 1419

Assini, Frederick, Gen. Counsel & Corp. Sec.--Plasti-Kote Company Inc., Medina, OH; *U.S. Private*, pg. 870

Astor, Margret, Sec.--Derby International Corporation S.A., Luxembourg, Luxembourg; *Int'l*, pg. 394

Astrue, Michael J., Esq., V.P., Gen. Counsel & Sec.--Biogen, Inc., Cambridge, MA; *U.S. Public*, pg. 230

Astrup, Dan, Treas. & Sec.--Astrup Drugs, Inc., Austin, MN; *U.S. Private*, pg. 93

Ater, William C., Chief Admin. Officer, Sr. V.P. & Sec.--Anacomp, Inc., Indianapolis, IN; *U.S. Public*, pg. 106

Athos, Gus J., Sr. V.P., Gen. Counsel & Sec.--Eagle Industries, Inc., Chicago, IL; *U.S. Private*, pg. 473

Atkin, P.N., Sec.--Ladbroke Group Plc, London, United Kingdom; *Int'l*, pg. 787

Atkin, P.N., Sec.--Ladbroke Group Properties Ltd., London, United Kingdom; *Int'l*, pg. 787

Atkins, Stanley B., V.P. & Sec.--Citation Corporation, Birmingham, AL; *U.S. Public*, pg. 376

Atkinson, Jerome, Sr. V.P., Gen. Counsel & Sec.--Fortis, Inc., New York, NY; *Int'l*, pg. 499

Atkinson, Jerome A., Sr. V.P., Gen. Counsel & Sec.--American Security Group, Atlanta, GA; *Int'l*, pg. 499

Attardi, Charles, Jr., Sec. & Treas.--North Carolina Equipment Co., Raleigh, NC; *U.S. Private*, pg. 804

Atterbury, J.M.D., Sec.--Barclays Bank PLC, London, United Kingdom; *Int'l*, pg. 164

Atterbury, John M.D., Sec.--Barclays Bank Trust Co. Ltd., London, United Kingdom; *Int'l*, pg. 164

Atterbury, Robert Rennie, III, V.P., Gen. Counsel & Sec.--Caterpillar Inc., Peoria, IL; *U.S. Public*, pg. 315

Atwood, Johnnie, Sec.--Atwood Distributing, Inc., Enid, OK; *U.S. Private*, pg. 98

Auchter, Gisela, Asst. Controller & Asst. Sec.--Semtech Corporation, Newbury Park, CA; *U.S. Public*, pg. 1456

Aufox, Jerry M., Legal Counsel & Sec.--A.M. Castle & Co., Franklin Park, IL; *U.S. Public*, pg. 312

Augenbraum, Barry S., Sec.--Raymond James Financial, Inc., Saint Petersburg, FL; *U.S. Public*, pg. 923

Augsburger, Robert L., V.P., Asst. Sec. & Dir.-Contract Admin.--ITT Aerospace/Communications Div., Fort Wayne, IN; *U.S. Public*, pg. 859

August, Robert W., Sr. V.P. & Sec.--Monro Muffler/Brake, Inc., Rochester, NY; *U.S. Public*, pg. 1124

Auriemma, Sam, Chief Fin. Officer & V.P.-Fin.--Wonderware Corporation, Irvine, CA; *U.S. Public*, pg. 1775

Aus, Janice A., Sec.--Bremer Financial Corporation, Saint Paul, MN; *U.S. Private*, pg. 167

Ausburn, Kevin R., Chief Fin. Officer, Treas. & Sec.--Southern Missouri Containers Inc., Springfield, MO; *U.S. Private*, pg. 1017

Austin, D.A., Corp. Sec.--C G Smith Ltd., Sandton, South Africa; *Int'l*, pg. 1263

Austin, Frank E., Sr. V.P., Gen. Counsel & Corp. Sec.--Glenborough Realty Trust Incorporated, San Mateo, CA; *U.S. Public*, pg. 747

Austin, G. Kenneth, III, Sec.--A-Dec, Inc., Newberg, OR; *U.S. Private*, pg. 2

Austin, Lawrence, V.P.-Fin., Sec. & Treas.--Miniature Precision Components, Walworth, WI; *U.S. Private*, pg. 750

Austin, Neil D., V.P.-Gen. Counsel & Sec.--Checkpoint Systems Inc., Thorofare, NJ; *U.S. Public*, pg. 343

Auten, David C., Asst. Sec.--W.P. Carey & Co., Inc., New York, NY; *U.S. Private*, pg. 209

Avallone, Pamela, Sec.--Alpha Associates, Inc., Woodbridge, NJ; *U.S. Private*, pg. 44

Avci, Inal, Sec.--Koc Holding A.S., Istanbul, Turkey; *Int'l*, pg. 741

Avery, James, Treas. & Sec.--Schumacher-Dugan Construction, West Chester, OH; *U.S. Private*, pg. 973

Avery, O. Keith, Treas. & Sec.--Presto Food Stores, Inc., Plant City, FL; *U.S. Private*, pg. 882

Avis, James C., Exec. V.P., Gen. Counsel & Sec.--Newbridge Networks Corporation, Kanata, Canada; *Int'l*, pg. 924

Aydon, Richard, Sec. & Dir.-Legal--Christies International plc, London, United Kingdom; *Int'l*, pg. 289

Ayers, Larry G., Chief Fin. Officer, V.P.-Fin., Treas. & Sec.--Southern Electronics Corporation, Tucker, GA; *U.S. Public*, pg. 1490

Ayers, Larry G., Chief Fin. Officer, V.P.-Fin., Sec. & Treas.--Southern Electronics Distributors International, Tucker, GA; *U.S. Public*, pg. 1490

Azar, Michael C., Gen. Counsel & Sec.--Noble International Ltd., Bloomfield Hills, MI; *U.S. Public*, pg. 1187

Baarda, Cor, Sec. & Controller--Henkel Canada Ltd., Mississauga, Canada; *Int'l*, pg. 612

Baba, Ryutaro, V.P. & Sec.--Ricoh Electronics, Inc., Tustin, CA; *Int'l*, pg. 1114

Babcock, Reginald, V.P.-Corp. Services, Gen. Counsel & Sec.--Connecticut Natural Gas Corporation, Hartford, CT; *U.S. Public*, pg. 285

Babcock, Reginald L., V.P., Gen. Counsel & Sec.--CTG Resources, Inc., Hartford, CT; *U.S. Public*, pg. 285

Babcock, Reginald L., V.P., Gen. Counsel & Sec.--Energy Networks, Inc. (ENI), Hartford, CT; *U.S. Public*, pg. 285

Babcock, Theodore A., V.P., Treas. & Asst. Sec.--Long Island Lighting Company, Hicksville, NY; *U.S. Public*, pg. 1013

Babilla, Terrence, Gen. Counsel & Sec.--Sport Supply Group, Inc., Dallas, TX; *U.S. Public*, pg. 1499

Babin, Mara, Corp. Sec.--HMI Industries, Cleveland, OH; *U.S. Public*, pg. 771

Babin, Mara, Sec. & Gen. Counsel--Sifco Industries, Inc., Cleveland, OH; *U.S. Public*, pg. 1470

Babineau, Anne S., V.P., Gen. Counsel & Sec.--Bell Atlantic-NJ, Newark, NJ; *U.S. Public*, pg. 202

Bacchi, Josephine A., Sec.--John Wiley & Sons, Inc., New York, NY; *U.S. Public*, pg. 1768

Bachand, Jean-Paul, Exec. V.P., Gen. Counsel & Corp. Sec.--Montreal Trustco, Montreal, Canada; *Int'l*, pg. 155

Bachman, Alan, Sec.--Bachman's, Inc., Minneapolis, MN; *U.S. Private*, pg. 109

Bachman, Susan Anderson, Asst. Sec.--Grant, Inc., Huron, SD; *U.S. Public*, pg. 1201

Bachman, Susan Anderson, Asst. Sec.--Northwestern Networks, Inc., Huron, SD; *U.S. Public*, pg. 1201

Bachman, Susan Anderson, Asst. Sec.--Northwestern Systems, Inc., Huron, SD; *U.S. Public*, pg. 1201

Bachman, Susan Anderson, Asst. Sec.--Northwestern Growth Corp., Sioux Falls, SD; *U.S. Public*, pg. 1201

Bachman, Susan Anderson, Asst. Sec.--Northwestern Energy Corp., Huron, SD; *U.S. Public*, pg. 1201

Bachman, Susan Anderson, Asst. Sec.--Nekota Resources Inc., Huron, SD; *U.S. Public*, pg. 1201

Bacigalupo, Charles A., Sr. V.P. & Sec.--Legg Mason, Inc., Baltimore, MD; *U.S. Public*, pg. 984

Bacigalupo, John W., Treas. & Sec.--Kelly-Moore Paint Company, Inc., San Carlos, CA; *U.S. Private*, pg. 613

Backer, Richard I., Exec. V.P.-Devel. & Asst. Sec.--Carlyle & Co. Jewelers, Greensboro, NC; *U.S. Private*, pg. 213

Bacon, Donna L., V.P., Gen. Counsel & Sec.--JPE, Inc., Ann Arbor, MI; *U.S. Public*, pg. 919

Badcock, Wogan S., III, Exec. V.P.-Mngmt. & Admin. Services--W.S. Badcock Corporation, Mulberry, FL; *U.S. Private*, pg. 109

Baddeley, D. Jeffrey, V.P., Gen. Counsel & Sec.--Outboard Marine Corporation, Waukegan, IL; *U.S. Private*, pg. 478

Baddeley, Robert Gregory, Chief Fin. Officer & Sec.--Eurocamp Plc, Knutsford, United Kingdom; *Int'l*, pg. 464

Baden, Marvin, V.P.-Mktg. & Sls., Treas. & Sec.--Producers Rice Mill Inc., Stuttgart, AR; *U.S. Private*, pg. 888

Baer, Luke, V.P., Gen. Counsel & Sec.--Robert Bosch Corporation, Broadview, IL; *Int'l*, pg. 204

Bagan, Kenneth M., Gen. Counsel & Sec.--Nowsco Well Service Ltd., Calgary, Canada; *Int'l*, pg. 989

Bagerdjian, Haig, V.P., Gen. Counsel & Sec.--Syncor International Corporation, Woodland Hills, CA; *U.S. Public*, pg. 1548

Bagg, K.A., Sec.--RMP Properties Ltd., Crown Mines, South Africa; *Int'l*, pg. 1081

Baggett, Patrick C., Asst. Sec.--W.S. Badcock Corporation, Mulberry, FL; *U.S. Private*, pg. 109

Bagley, Suzanne F., Corp. Sec.--The San Francisco Co., San Francisco, CA; *U.S. Public*, pg. 1430

Bahler, Gary M., V.P., Gen. Counsel & Sec.--Woolworth Corporation, New York, NY; *U.S. Public*, pg. 1777

Bahr, Mark A., Exec. V.P. & Sec.--Barton Malow Enterprises, Inc., Southfield, MI; *U.S. Private*, pg. 120

Baiden, Arthur H., III, Exec. V.P. & Sec.--Potter-Shackelford Construction Co., Greenville, SC; *U.S. Private*, pg. 877

Bailey, A.C., Sec.--Stackpole Ltd., Newton, MA; *U.S. Private*, pg. 1028

Bailey, Donna J., Sec.--Sonat Energy Services Company, Birmingham, AL; *U.S. Public*, pg. 1485

Bailey, Mark, V.P., Gen. Counsel & Sec.--SENCORP, Newport, KY; *U.S. Private*, pg. 983

Bailey, Richard A., V.P.-Gen. Counsel & Sec.--Kraft Canada Inc., Don Mills, Canada; *U.S. Public*, pg. 1288

Bailey, Ruth, Sec.--Sunnen Products Company, Saint Louis, MO; *U.S. Private*, pg. 1053

Baillargeon, Marie, Asst. Gen. Counsel & Asst. Sec.--The Ivaco Group, Montreal, Canada; *Int'l*, pg. 695

Baillargeon, Pierre, Sec. Gen.--Hydro-Quebec, Montreal, Canada; *Int'l*, pg. 640

Bain, Irwin A., Gen. Counsel & Sec.--Schottenstein Stores Corporation, Columbus, OH; *U.S. Private*, pg. 972

Bain, R.A., Asst. Sec.--Agra Inc., Calgary, Canada; *Int'l*, pg. 30

Baines, Edith M., Sec.--Baines Management Co., Baltimore, MD; *U.S. Private*, pg. 111

Baines, Harry F., Gen. Counsel & Sec.--T & N Plc, Manchester, United Kingdom; *Int'l*, pg. 1334

Bair, Clinton, Controller & Sec.--Republic Die & Tool Company, Belleville, MI; *U.S. Private*, pg. 923

Bair, Connie S., V.P., Cashier & Sec.--Churubusco State Bank, Churubusco, IN; *U.S. Public*, pg. 674

Bair, Stephen L., V.P., Corp. Counsel & Sec.--Time-Life, Inc., Alexandria, VA; *U.S. Public*, pg. 1613

Baird, D.L., Jr., Sec.--Exxon Corporation, Irving, TX; *U.S. Public*, pg. 601

Baird, John N., Sec. & Gen. Counsel--Air Liquide America Corporation, Houston, TX; *Int'l*, pg. 37

Baisley, James M., Sr. V.P., Gen. Counsel & Sec.--W.W. Grainger, Inc., Lincolnshire, IL; *U.S. Public*, pg. 758

Bakehorn, Peggy, Treas. & Sec.--American Stationery Co., Inc., Peru, IN; *U.S. Private*, pg. 62

Baker, A.B., Corp Sec.--Riggs National Corporation, Washington, DC; *U.S. Public*, pg. 1389

Baker, Bridget, Dir.-Corp. Pub. Rels. & Corp. Sec.--Guard Publishing Company, Eugene, OR; *U.S. Private*, pg. 485

Baker, Debra A., Sec.--UST Inc., Greenwich, CT; *U.S. Public*, pg. 1660

Baker, Marty, Sec.--Madison Grocery Co., Inc., Richmond, KY; *U.S. Private*, pg. 694

Baker, Newell A., Jr., Exec. V.P. & Sec.--J.D. Streett & Co., Inc., Maryland Heights, MO; *U.S. Private*, pg. 1047

Baker, Richard C., V.P., Gen. Counsel & Sec.--H.B. Fuller Company, Saint Paul, MN; *U.S. Public*, pg. 686

Baker, Richard J., V.P. & Sec.--Allmerica Financial Corporation, Worcester, MA; *U.S. Public*, pg. 54

Baker, Robert, V.P., Gen. Counsel & Sec.--IDX Systems Corporation, Burlington, VT; *U.S. Public*, pg. 854

Baker, Simon H., V.P.-Tax & Legal & Sec.--Hosokawa Micron International Inc., New York, NY; *Int'l*, pg. 635

Baker, Susan D., V.P., Sec. & Gen. Counsel-Mngmt. Services--The ServiceMaster Company, Downers Grove, IL; *U.S. Public*, pg. 1461

Baker, Wayne, Sec. & Asst. Treas.--Athey Products Corporation, Wake Forest, NC; *U.S. Public*, pg. 142

Baldauf, David, V.P., Sec. & Gen. Counsel--Benderson Development Co., Inc., Buffalo, NY; *U.S. Private*, pg. 132

Baldwin, Ellen R., Sec.--David A. Bramble, Inc., Chestertown, MD; *U.S. Private*, pg. 165

Balestra, Roger A., V.P.-Fin. & Sec.--Cabre Exploration Ltd., Calgary, Canada; *Int'l*, pg. 247

Balius, Louis M., Assoc. Gen. Counsel & Asst. Sec.--Champion Enterprises, Inc., Auburn Hills, MI; *U.S. Public*, pg. 332

Ball-Miller, Paris M., Sec., Controller & Treas.--Troyer Foods, Inc., Goshen, IN; *Int'l*, pg. 619

Ball, Alice, Treas. & Sec.--Air Power, Inc., High Point, NC; *U.S. Private*, pg. 28

Ball, James H., Sr. V.P., Sec. & Gen. Counsel--Nestle Holdings, Inc., Stamford, CT; *Int'l*, pg. 916

Ballantyne, Richard L., V.P., Gen. Counsel & Sec.--Harris Corporation, Melbourne, FL; *U.S. Public*, pg. 791

Ballard, Augustus S., Sec.--The Kent Manufacturing Co., Pickens, SC; *U.S. Private*, pg. 615

Ballard, John H., Asst. Sec.--Avemco Corporation, Frederick, MD; *U.S. Public*, pg. 151

Ballard, John W., III, Chief Fin. Officer & Sec.--TCI International Inc., Sunnyvale, CA; *U.S. Public*, pg. 1555

Ballenger, Donna, Sec.--Plastic Packaging, Inc., Hickory, NC; *U.S. Private*, pg. 871

Ballentine, Richard O., V.P., Gen. Counsel & Sec.--Butler Manufacturing Company, Kansas City, MO; *U.S. Public*, pg. 271

Ballew, J.A., Sec.--Crystal Eurasia Oil Co., Shreveport, LA; *U.S. Public*, pg. 466

Ballew, Jeffery A., Sr. V.P., Treas. & Sec.--Crystal Oil Company, Shreveport, LA; *U.S. Public*, pg. 466

Ballou, Rebecca W., Sec.--Harrah's Entertainment, Inc., Memphis, TN; *U.S. Public*, pg. 790

Balog, Andrew E., Asst. Sec.--New Valley Corporation, Miami, FL; *U.S. Public*, pg. 1173

Baltasar, Ana Maria, Sec.--Noblex Argentina S.A.C. e I., Buenos Aires, Argentina; *Int'l*, pg. 951

Balter, Moshe, Sec.--Carmel Container Systems Ltd., Petah Tiqwa, Israel; *Int'l*, pg. 75

Bancroft, Brian, Sec.--Lancashire Dairies Ltd., Manchester, United Kingdom; *Int'l*, pg. 798

Bandler, Beth M., V.P., Gen. Counsel & Sec.--Hawker Siddeley Canada Inc., Mississauga, Canada; *Int'l*, pg. 604

Banducci, Dena L., Corp. Sec.--Micron Custom Manufacturing Services, Inc., Nampa, ID; *U.S. Public*, pg. 1105

Bange, Richard M., Jr., Controller & Asst. Sec.--Baltimore Gas and Electric Company, Baltimore, MD; *U.S. Public*, pg. 172

Bangs, Nelson A., V.P., Gen Counsel & Sec.--Dr Pepper/Seven Up No. America, Dallas, TX; *Int'l*, pg. 248

Bank, Malvin, Sec.--Columbia National Group, Inc., Cleveland, OH; *U.S. Private*, pg. 255

Banks, Ada L., Sec.--Ritchie Corporation, Wichita, KS; *U.S. Private*, pg. 933

Bankston, Archie M., Sec. & Assoc. Gen. Counsel--Consolidated Edison Company of New York, Inc., New York, NY; *U.S. Public*, pg. 434

Bann, D., Sec.--Air UK Ltd., Stansted, United Kingdom; *Int'l*, pg. 38

Bannerman, Martha G., Exec. V.P., Gen. Counsel & Sec.--Greenwich Insurance Company, Greenwich, CT; *U.S. Public*, pg. 1144

Bannerman, Martha G., Exec. V.P., Gen. Counsel & Sec.--Indian Harbor Insurance Company, Greenwich, CT; *U.S. Public*, pg. 1144

Banquer, C.S., Controller & Treas.--Acme Refrigeration Of Baton Rouge Inc., Baton Rouge, LA; *U.S. Private*, pg. 13

Banstetter, Robert J., V.P., Gen. Counsel & Sec.--General American Life Insurance Co., Saint Louis, MO; *U.S. Private*, pg. 443

Bar-Chaim, Nadav, Dr., V.P.-Device Structures & Matls. & Corp. Sec.--Ortel Corporation, Alhambra, CA; *U.S. Public*, pg. 1232

Baracos, Victor, Sec.--Weilwood Industries, Inc., New York, NY; *U.S. Private*, pg. 965

Barbarowicz, Robert P., Exec. V.P., Gen. Counsel & Sec.--National Insurance Group, South San Francisco, CA; *U.S. Public*, pg. 1157

Barbas, J.P.E., Dir.-Corp. Communication & Sec.--N.V. Koninklijke KNP BT, Amsterdam, Netherlands; *Int'l*, pg. 756

Barber, A. Lee, V.P. & Sec.--Barber Brothers Contracting Company, Baton Rouge, LA; *U.S. Private*, pg. 115

Barber, Dan, V.P.-Fin., Treas. & Sec.--Barnett Millworks, Inc., Theodore, AL; *U.S. Private*, pg. 116

Barber, Debbie, V.P. & Sec.--Denver Wholesale Florists Company, Denver, CO; *U.S. Private*, pg. 326

Barber, Jean, Sec.--The Bartell Drug Company, Seattle, WA; *U.S. Private*, pg. 118

Barber, Judith A., Sec.--Smithtown Bancorp, Inc., Smithtown, NY; *U.S. Public*, pg. 1479

Barber, R.G., Sec.--HSBC Holdings plc, London, United Kingdom; *Int'l*, pg. 579

Barclay, Bruce, Gen. Counsel & Sec.--Guidant Corporation-Vascular Intervention Group, Santa Clara, CA; *U.S. Public*, pg. 768

Bardin, William E., Jr., V.P. & Sec.--Glen Raven Mills, Inc., Glen Raven, NC; *U.S. Private*, pg. 456

Bardsley, M.J., Grp. Sec.--AMEC Plc, Northwich, United Kingdom; *Int'l*, pg. 16

Bardsley, Michael, Sec.--AMEC Process & Energy, London, United Kingdom; *Int'l*, pg. 16

Bariletti, Robert P., Asst. Treas. & Asst. Sec.--Puget Energy Inc., Bothell, WA; *U.S. Public*, pg. 1342

Barkai, Judith, Gen. Counsel, Sec. & Dir.-Investor Rels.--American Israeli Paper Mills Ltd., Hadera, Israel; *Int'l*, pg. 74

Barkan, Lee, Sr. V.P, Sec. & Gen. Counsel--AVC/Nu-Vision, Inc., Flint, MI; *U.S. Private*, pg. 9

Barker, D.W., Chief Fin. Officer, Treas. & Sec.--Maescher Industries, Inc., Cincinnati, OH; *U.S. Private*, pg. 694

Barker, Everette, Asst. Sec.--Bankhead Enterprises Inc., Atlanta, GA; *U.S. Private*, pg. 114

Barker, Margaret A., Asst. Sec.--Midland Walwyn Inc., Toronto, Canada; *Int'l*, pg. 865

Barker, Mary, Admin. Sec.--Mid-State Wire Company, Crawfordsville, IN; *U.S. Private*, pg. 686

Barkley, Jim, Gen. Counsel & Sec.--Simon DeBartolo Group, Inc., Indianapolis, IN; *U.S. Public*, pg. 1474

Barlett, Lee, V.P., Gen. Counsel & Sec.--Torchmark Corporation, Birmingham, AL; *U.S. Public*, pg. 1622

Barletta, Francis, Sec.--Barletta Materials & Construction, Hazleton, PA; *U.S. Private*, pg. 116

Barlow, B.N., Sec.--The Ritz Hotel (London) Limited, London, United Kingdom; *Int'l*, pg. 773

Barlow, Carol Ann, Treas. & Sec.--Macristy Industries, Inc., New Britain, CT; *U.S. Private*, pg. 693

Barlow, Thomas J., Reg. Counsel & Asst. Sec.--OHM Remediation Services Corp., Findlay, OH; *U.S. Public*, pg. 1208

Barmeier, William G., V.P., Gen. Counsel & Sec.--VeriFone, Inc., Redwood City, CA; *U.S. Public*, pg. 815

Barnard, Aubrey D., Sec., Treas. & Controller--SouthTrust Corporation, Birmingham, AL; *U.S. Public*, pg. 1491

Barnard, Douglas C., V.P., Gen. Counsel & Sec.--Furnishings International, Inc., Thomasville, NC; *U.S. Private*, pg. 431

Barnard, Douglas C., V.P., Gen. Counsel & Sec.--LifeStyle Furnishings International, Ltd., Thomasville, NC; *U.S. Private*, pg. 431

Barnes, Donna E., Sec.--Pacific American Income Shares, Inc., Pasadena, CA; *U.S. Public*, pg. 1247

Barnes, Kaye, Corp. Sec.--Pacific Foods, Inc., Kent, WA; *U.S. Private*, pg. 831

Barnes, Michael H., Chief Fin. Officer, Sr. V.P. & Corp. Sec.--Intellicall, Inc., Carrollton, TX; *U.S. Public*, pg. 887

Barnes, Ned M., Corp. Sec.--Sterling Financial Corporation, Spokane, WA; *U.S. Public*, pg. 1516

Barnes, Phyllis J., Sec.--Spectrulite Consortium, Inc., Madison, IL; *U.S. Private*, pg. 1024

Barnes, Robert M., V.P., Gen. Counsel & Sec.--Unitog Company, Kansas City, MO; *U.S. Public*, pg. 1693

Barnes, Willie R., Sec.--American Shared Hospital Services, San Francisco, CA; *U.S. Public*, pg. 91

Barnett, Gillian H., V.P. & Sec.--Algood Food Company, Louisville, KY; *U.S. Private*, pg. 34

Barnett, James, Controller & Sec.--Delchester Oil Co. Inc., West Chester, PA; *U.S. Private*, pg. 518

Barnett, James, Assoc. Gen. Counsel & Asst. Sec.--MidAmerican Capital Company, Des Moines, IA; *U.S. Public*, pg. 1109

Barnett, Jerome, Corp. Sec.--Marubeni America Corporation, New York, NY; *Int'l*, pg. 844

Barnett, M.J., Sec.--Barlow Ltd., Sandton, South Africa; *Int'l*, *pg. 167*

Barnett, Robert G., Gen. Counsel & Sec.--Deposit Guaranty Corp., Jackson, MS; *U.S. Public*, pg. 500

Barnett, Steve, Sec. & Corp. Counsel--Global Industrial Technologies, Dallas, TX; *U.S. Public*, pg. 747

Barney, Nancy, Treas. & Sec.--Simonds-Shields-Theis Grain Co., Kansas City, MO; *U.S. Private*, pg. 1001

Barnickol, Karl R., Sr. V.P., Gen. Counsel & Sec.--Solutia Inc., Saint Louis, MO; *U.S. Public*, pg. 1483

Barocas, Leon, V.P., Treas. & Sec.--Santee Print Works, Inc., New York, NY; *U.S. Private*, pg. 965

Baron, Charles B., Sec.--Nixdorff Krein Industries Inc., Saint Louis, MO; *U.S. Private*, pg. 799

Barone, Douglas, Asst. Secretary--Fidelity & Guaranty Life Insurance Co., Baltimore, MD; *U.S. Public*, pg. 1659

Baroue, Daren, Treas. & Sec.--Watkins Contracting, Inc., San Diego, CA; *U.S. Public*, pg. 1384

Barr, Charles F., V.P., Gen. Counsel & Sec.--General Re Corporation, Stamford, CT; *U.S. Public*, pg. 725

Barratt, Paul, V.P., Gen. Counsel & Sec.--Triangle Pacific Corporation, Dallas, TX; *U.S. Public*, pg. 1634

Barre, Stephen A., Chm. Bd., Pres., Chief Exec. Officer & Sec.--Servo Corporation of America, Westbury, NY; *U.S. Private*, pg. 987

Barrett, Colleen C., Exec. V.P.-Customers & Corp. Sec.--Southwest Airlines Co., Dallas, TX; *U.S. Public*, pg. 1493

Barrett, JoAnn, V.P.-Opers., Treas. & Sec.--Samuel Bingham Co, Bloomingdale, IL; *U.S. Private*, pg. 144

Barrett, W. Hale, Sec.--Merry Land & Investment Company, Inc., Augusta, GA; *U.S. Public*, pg. 1098

Barrett, William J., Sec. & Asst. Treas.--Supreme Industries, Inc., Goshen, IN; *U.S. Public*, pg. 1541

Barri, Joseph P., Sec.--The Pioneer Group, Inc., Boston, MA; *U.S. Public*, pg. 1298

Barrie, John G., Jr., Mgr.-Pension Fund--Dominion Resources, Inc., Richmond, VA; *U.S. Public*, pg. 516

Barro, Dan, V.P. & Corp. Sec.--Lamp Post Franchise Corporation, Tustin, CA; *U.S. Private*, pg. 644

Barron, Francois, Sec.--Cambior Inc., Montreal, Canada; *Int'l*, pg. 253

Barron, Harold S., Sr. V.P., Gen. Counsel & Sec.--Unisys Corporation, Blue Bell, PA; *U.S. Public*, pg. 1671

Barrow, M.J., Sr. V.P.-Fin. & Admin., Treas., Sec. & Dir.--M.S. Carriers, Inc., Memphis, TN; *U.S. Public*, pg. 1027

Barrow, Steven, V.P.-Corp. Devel. & Sec.--Wall Street Deli, Inc., Birmingham, AL; *U.S. Public*, pg. 1734

Barrows, Craig, Sr. V.P., Gen. Counsel & Corp. Sec.--M/A-COM Inc., Lowell, MA; *U.S. Public*, pg. 8

Barry, Ralph, Chief Fin. Officer, V.P., Treas. & Sec.--Imaging Technologies Corp., San Diego, CA; *U.S. Public*, *pg. 870*

Barss, Natalie, Sec.--Brooks Resources Corporation, Bend, OR; *U.S. Private*, pg. 172

Bart, Todd, Chief Fin. Officer, Treas. & Sec.--Panaco, Inc., Kansas City, MO; *U.S. Public*, pg. 1255

Bartels, Michael G., V.P., Sec. & Treas.--The East Ohio Gas Co., Cleveland, OH; *U.S. Public*, pg. 435

Bartenstein, Jeff C., Controller, Treas. & Sec.--Alaska Industrial Hardware Inc., Anchorage, AK; *U.S. Private*, pg. 31

Barth, Peter H., V.P., Corp. Counsel & Asst. Sec.--Smith's Food & Drug Centers, Inc., Salt Lake City, UT; *U.S. Public*, pg. 1103

Bartholomew, Leonard W., Sec. & Dir.-Personnel--Frozen Food Express Industries, Inc., Dallas, TX; *U.S. Public*, pg. 685

Bartine, Allen, Treas. & Sec.--O'Bryan Brothers Inc., Chicago, IL; *U.S. Private*, pg. 810

Bartl, James F., Sec.--National Presto Industries, Inc., Eau Claire, WI; *U.S. Public*, pg. 1159

Bartlett, Carl, Sr. V.P. & Sec.--Jim Wilson & Associates, Inc., Montgomery, AL; *U.S. Private*, pg. 1181

Bartlett, Jeffrey W., V.P.-Regulatory Affairs--Stepan Company, Northfield, IL; *U.S. Public*, pg. 1514

Bartlett, John B., Sr. V.P., Gen. Counsel & Sec.--Rhone-Poulenc Rorer - U.S., Collegeville, PA; *Int'l*, pg. 1110

Bartoletti, Barbara, Asst. Corp. Sec.--Atlantic Richfield Company, Los Angeles, CA; *U.S. Public*, pg. 144

Barton, John S., Corp. Sec.--Thiele Kaolin Co., Sandersville, GA; *U.S. Private*, pg. 1081

Barton, Nancy E., Sr. V.P., Gen. Counsel & Sec.--General Electric Capital Services, Inc., Stamford, CT; *U.S. Public*, *pg. 711*

Bartram, John C., Sec.--Lord, Sullivan & Yoder Inc. Marketing Communications, Columbus, OH; *U.S. Private*, *pg. 676*

Bartruff, Stuart, Exec. V.P. & Sec.--First Commerce Bancshares, Inc., Lincoln, NE; *U.S. Public*, pg. 629

Bartsch, Noel B., Sec.--Nicholas Paper, Inc., Fitchburg, MA; *U.S. Private*, pg. 798

Barwell, D.M., Sec.--Cyanamid of Great Britain Ltd., Gosport, United Kingdom; *U.S. Public*, pg. 81

Basham, Roxann R., Treas. & Corp. Sec.--Black Hills Corporation, Rapid City, SD; *U.S. Public*, pg. 235

Bashoff, K.H., Sr. V.P.-Gen. Counsel & Sec.--Fidelity Mutual Life Insurance Co., Radnor, PA; *U.S. Private*, pg. 403

Baskins, Ann O., Mng. Counsel & Asst. Sec.--Hewlett-Packard Company, Palo Alto, CA; *U.S. Public*, pg. 813

Bass, Norma, Treas. & Sec.--The Parman Corporation, Nashville, TN; *U.S. Private*, pg. 840

Basset, Geoff, Sec.--Hastings Deering (PNG) Pty Ltd, Boroko, Papua New Guinea; *Int'l*, pg. 1250

Bast, Bonnie R., V.P. & Sec.--Bast Chevrolet Inc., Seaford, NY; *U.S. Private*, pg. 122

Bateman, William E., Corp. Sec. & Gen. Counsel--FTI Foodtech International Inc., Don Mills, Canada; *Int'l*, pg. 476

Bates, Carolyn, Gen. Counsel & Sec.--Imation Corporation, Oakdale, MN; *U.S. Public*, pg. 870

Bates, J.G., Co. Sec.--ICL PLC, Putney, United Kingdom; *Int'l*, pg. 528

Bates, Jackie A., Asst. Sec.--Kimberly-Clark Corporation, Dallas, TX; *U.S. Public*, pg. 958

Bates, Louise, Sec.--Cutco Industries, Inc., Syosset, NY; *U.S. Public*, pg. 470

Bates, Robert E., Sec.--Mobil Oil Corporation, Fairfax, VA; *U.S. Public*, pg. 1118

Batson, Catherine W., Sec.--CF Investment Company, Greenville, SC; *U.S. Public*, pg. 306

Battaglia, Anthony, Sec.--Cunningham-Limp Development Co., Farmington Hills, MI; *U.S. Private*, pg. 297

Battaglini, Tom, V.P.-Small Companion Animals--Schering-Plough Animal Health, Union, NJ; *U.S. Public*, pg. 1438

Battle, Thomas P., Sr. V.P., Gen. Counsel & Sec.--Mitchell Energy & Development Corp., Spring, TX; *U.S. Public*, pg. 1117

Baubonis, Patricia, Corp. Sec. & Dir.-Legal Services--Graphic Controls Corporation, Buffalo, NY; *U.S. Private*, pg. 470

Bauder, Dixie A., Sec.--Coca-Cola Bottling Co. United, Inc., Birmingham, AL; *U.S. Private*, pg. 248

Baudeu, Guy, Sec.--Alcatel Alsthom Compagnie Generale D'Electricite, Paris, France; *Int'l*, pg. 52

Bauer, Douglas F., Gen. Counsel & Sec.--Bowne & Co., Inc., New York, NY; *U.S. Public*, pg. 248

Bauer, Fred D., Asst. Sec.--Applied Industrial Technologies, Cleveland, OH; *U.S. Public*, pg. 122

Bauer, Karen, Chief Acctg. Officer, Controller & Sec.--Allied Research Corporation, Vienna, VA; *U.S. Public*, pg. 48

Bauer, Michael, Exec. V.P., Sec. & Treas.--Al & Ed's Auto Sound Center, Monterey Park, CA; *U.S. Private*, pg. 30

Bauer, Mimi, Treas. & Sec.--Basic Food International Inc., Fort Lauderdale, FL; *U.S. Private*, pg. 121

Bauer, Shirley, Sec.--Empire Electric Association, Cortez, CO; *U.S. Private*, pg. 374

Bauer, Vineeta, Mgr.-Sls. & Retail Mktg.--Firstar Corporation, Milwaukee, WI; *U.S. Public*, pg. 642

Bauer, Walo, Dr., Chief Info. Officer & Sec.--Schweizer Verband der Raiffeisenbanken, Saint Gallen, Switzerland; *Int'l*, pg. 1211

Baugh, Thomas E., Jr., Sec.--Sands Investments, Inc., Myrtle Beach, SC; *U.S. Private*, pg. 964

Baughn, Alan L., V.P.-Corp. Plng. & Devel. & Sec.--The Standard Register Company, Dayton, OH; *U.S. Public*, pg. 1505

Baulig, George L., Treas. & Sec.--South Jersey Industries, Inc., Folsom, NJ; *U.S. Public*, pg. 1488

Baulig, George L., Sec. & Asst. Treas.--South Jersey Gas Co., Folsom, NJ; *U.S. Public*, pg. 1488

Baum, W.A., III, Sec. & Treas.--W.A. Baum Company, Inc., Copiague, NY; *U.S. Private*, pg. 124

Bauman, Colleen T., Asst. Sec.--Champion Enterprises, Inc., Auburn Hills, MI; *U.S. Public*, pg. 332

Baumgardner, Roger L., V.P., Treas. & Sec.--Roanoke Gas Company, Roanoke, VA; *U.S. Public*, pg. 1392

Baumgarte, Virginia, Sec. & Treas.--The Wiegmann Company, Freeburg, IL; *U.S. Public*, pg. 845

Baumgarten, David, V.P. & Sec.--Boulevard Bancorp, Inc., Chicago, IL; *U.S. Public*, pg. 1680

Baumgarten, Herbert J., Sr. V.P., Gen. Counsel & Sec.--Unilever United States Inc., New York, NY; *Int'l*, pg. 1435

Baveis, Edward, Sec. & Treas.--Bell Atlantic Paging, Parsippany, NJ; *U.S. Public*, pg. 203

Bavido, Joe, Sec.--Dairy Farmers of America, Inc., Arlington, TX; *U.S. Private*, pg. 307

Baxter, David K., Sec.--Union Boiler Co., Nitro, WV; *U.S. Private*, pg. 262

Baxter, Mary Beth, Treas. & Asst. Sec.--Lynch Telephone Corporation, Greenwich, CT; *U.S. Public*, pg. 1022

Baxter, Randy P., Sec. & Treas.-Fin. Information Officer--Armada Corporation, Detroit, MI; *U.S. Private*, pg. 82

Baxter, Randy P., Treas. & Sec.--Hoskins Mfg. Co., Detroit, MI; *U.S. Private*, pg. 83

Baxter, Randy P., Sec.--Hoskins Thermal Systems, Inc., Detroit, MI; *U.S. Private*, pg. 83

Bayles, Mary, Sec.--Royal Waterbeds, Maryland Heights, MO; *U.S. Private*, pg. 949

Bayley, Joanne, Treas. & Sec.--Robert E. Bayley Construction, Seattle, WA; *U.S. Private*, pg. 125

Beach, Juanita, Sec. & Treas.--Beach Mold & Tool Inc., New Albany, IN; *U.S. Private*, pg. 125

Beadie, William M., Sec.--API Group Inc., Saint Paul, MN; *U.S. Private*, pg. 7

Beal, Ilene, Exec. V.P. & Sec.--BayBanks, Inc., Boston, MA; *U.S. Public*, pg. 184

Beal, Karen, Sec. & Treas.--E.R. Probyn Ltd., New Westminster, Canada; *Int'l*, pg. 1071

Beal, Karen, Sec. & Treas.--Cedartone Specialties, Kent, WA; *Int'l*, pg. 1071

Beal, Karen, Sec. & Treas.--Crane Creek Cedar, Kent, WA; *Int'l*, pg. 1071

Beale, Susan M., V.P. & Sec.--DTE Energy Company, Detroit, MI; *U.S. Public*, pg. 475

Beall, Pamela K.M., V.P., Treas., & Asst. Sec.--OHM Corporation, Findlay, OH; *U.S. Public*, pg. 1207

Beall, Pamela K.M., V.P., Treas. & Asst. Sec.--OHM Remediation Services Corp., Findlay, OH; *U.S. Public*, pg. 1208

Beall, Pamela K.M., Treas. & Asst. Sec.--OHM International, Inc., Findlay, OH; *U.S. Public*, pg. 1208

Bean, Christopher V., Jr., Sec.--CFX Bank, Keene, NH; *U.S. Public*, pg. 277

Bean, Richard E., Chief Fin. Officer, Exec. V.P. & Sec.--Pearce Industries Inc., Houston, TX; *U.S. Private*, pg. 845

Beans, Patrick E., Chief Fin. Officer, V.P., Treas. & Sec.--National Research Corporation, Lincoln, NE; *U.S. Public*, *pg. 1159*

Bear, Belle, Sec.--The Lewis Bear Company, Pensacola, FL; *U.S. Private*, pg. 127

Beard, C.L., V.P. & Sec.--Annin & Company, Roseland, NJ; *U.S. Private*, pg. 75

Beard, John E., Esq., Sec.--The Timberland Company, Stratham, NH; *U.S. Public*, pg. 1609

Beardsley, Mary Louise, Asst. Gen. Counsel & Asst. Sec.--Barnes Group Inc., Bristol, CT; *U.S. Public*, pg. 189

Bearmon, Lee, V.P., Gen. Counsel & Sec.--Carlson Companies, Inc., Minnetonka, MN; *U.S. Private*, pg. 211

Beary, Michelle, Treas. & Sec.--Marsh Company, Belleville, IL; *U.S. Private*, pg. 707

Beasley, C.J., Sec.--Laporte plc, Luton, United Kingdom; *Int'l*, pg. 801

Beasley, Mark V., V.P., Gen. Counsel & Sec.--Michaels Stores, Inc., Irving, TX; *U.S. Public*, pg. 1104

Beato, Luis, Dr., Sec.--Portuguese Railways (CP), Lisbon, Portugal; *Int'l*, pg. 1063

Beatt, Bruce H., V.P., Gen. Counsel & Sec.--The Dexter Corporation, Windsor Locks, CT; *U.S. Public*, pg. 504

Beatty, J. Guy, Jr., Sec.--Coca-Cola Enterprises Inc., Atlanta, GA; *U.S. Public*, pg. 393

Beauchamp, Jacques, Corp. Sec.--Avenor, Inc., Montreal, Canada; *Int'l*, pg. 101

Beauchemin, Manon, Gen. Counsel & Sec.--Sico Inc., Longueuil, Canada; *Int'l*, pg. 1239

Beaudoin, Marc, Treas. & Sec.--Hancock Lumber, Inc., Casco, ME; *U.S. Private*, pg. 498

Beaudouin, Mark T., Sr. V.P., Gen. Counsel & Asst. Sec.--Morse Shoe, Inc., Canton, MA; *U.S. Public*, pg. 168

Beaudouin, Mark T., 1st Sr. V.P., Gen. Counsel & Asst. Sec.--Casual Male, Inc., Hyde Park, MA; *U.S. Public*, pg. 168

Beaulieu, Dennis P., V.P. & Sec.--Fund American Enterprises Holdings, Inc., Hanover, NH; *U.S. Public*, pg. 688

Beaulieu, Genevieve B., Asst. Sec.--Cadim, Montreal, Canada; *Int'l*, pg. 249

Beaulieu, Genevive B., Asst. Sec.--Cadev, Montreal, Canada; *Int'l*, pg. 249

Beaulieu, Jon C., Treas. & Sec.--Anderson Trucking Service Inc., Saint Cloud, MN; *U.S. Private*, pg. 72

Beck, Connie K., V.P., Sec. & Assoc. Gen. Counsel--The Reader's Digest Association, Inc., Pleasantville, NY; *U.S. Public*, pg. 1367

Beck, Edward W., Sr. V.P., Gen. Counsel & Sec.--Shaklee Corporation, San Francisco, CA; *Int'l*, pg. 1518

Beck, Eileen M., Sec.--Allegheny Power System, Inc., Hagerstown, MD; *U.S. Public*, pg. 42

Beck, Eileen M., Sec.--Monongahela Power Co., Fairmont, WV; *U.S. Public*, pg. 42
Beck, Eileen M., Sec.--The Potomac Edison Co., Hagerstown, MD; *U.S. Public*, pg. 42
Beck, Eileen M., Sec.--West Penn Power Co., Greensburg, PA; *U.S. Public*, pg. 42
Beck, J. Edward, Jr., Sec.--Beck Manufacturing, Inc., Waynesboro, PA; *U.S. Private*, pg. 146
Beck, Nancy M., Sec.--Clark Grave Vault Co., Columbus, OH; *U.S. Private*, pg. 243
Beck, Stephen, V.P. & Sec.--Bitrek Corporation, Waynesboro, PA; *U.S. Private*, pg. 145
Beck, Stuart J., Pres., Sec., Treas. & Dir.--Granite Broadcasting Corporation, New York, NY; *U.S. Public*, pg. 759
Becker, Paul, V.P., Treas., Gen. Counsel & Sec.--Cosco Industries, Spring Valley, NY; *U.S. Private*, pg. 277
Becker, Wolf Dieter, Sec. & Treas.--Traub-Hermle Corporation, Menomonee Falls, WI; *Int'l*, pg. 1419
Beckwith, David E., Sec.--Christiana Companies, Inc., Milwaukee, WI; *U.S. Public*, pg. 352
Becvar, Tom, Sec.--Toccoa Metal Technologies, Inc., Elmhurst, IL; *U.S. Private*, pg. 1089
Bedard, Rene, Corp. Sec.--Gaz Metropolitain & Company, Montreal, Canada; *Int'l*, pg. 541
Bedenbaugh, James R., V.P., Treas. & Asst. Sec.--Magellan Health Services, Inc., Atlanta, GA; *U.S. Public*, pg. 1033
Bedewi, Elizabeth M., Sr. V.P, Sec. & Treas.--New Mexico & Arizona Land Co., Phoenix, AZ; *U.S. Public*, pg. 1172
Bedford, Hilda L., Sec.--Beckwith Elevator Co., Boston, MA; *U.S. Private*, pg. 128
Bednarz, Richard, Controller, Treas. & Sec.--Loga Athletic/ Headwear Inc., Mattapoisett, MA; *U.S. Public*, pg. 1644
Beebe, Lydia I., Sec.--Chevron Corporation, San Francisco, CA; *U.S. Public*, pg. 347
Beebe, Lydia I., Sec.--Chevron Chemical Co., San Ramon, CA; *U.S. Public*, pg. 348
Beebe, Marilyn J., Asst. Sec.--Central Power and Light Company, Corpus Christi, TX; *U.S. Public*, pg. 324
Beebe, Raymond M., V.P., Gen. Counsel & Sec.--Winnebago Industries, Inc., Forest City, IA; *U.S. Public*, pg. 1772
Beeby, Kenneth J., V.P., Gen. Counsel & Sec.--Ocean Spray Cranberries, Inc., Middleboro, MA; *U.S. Private*, pg. 811
Beegan, Geraldine, Sec.--Cla-Val Div., Newport Beach, CA; *U.S. Private*, pg. 482
Beerman, Joel I., V.P., Gen. Counsel & Sec.--Georgia Gulf Corporation, Atlanta, GA; *U.S. Public*, pg. 734
Beers, Nancy D., Sec.--Centrex Corporation, Findlay, OH; *U.S. Private*, pg. 225
Beery, James, Gen. Counsel & Sec.--SmithKline Beecham plc, Brentford, United Kingdom; *Int'l*, pg. 1264
Beg, Loredana, Sec.--Pearson, Inc., New York, NY; *Int'l*, pg. 1026
Begarly, Helen, Sec.--Willis Corroon Americas, Nashville, TN; *Int'l*, pg. 1505
Beggs, Susan L., Asst. V.P.-Shareholder Rels. & Asst. Sec.--Luby's Cafeterias, Inc., San Antonio, TX; *U.S. Public*, pg. 1017
Beha, Ralph W., Gen. Counsel & Sec.--Control Data Systems, Inc., Arden Hills, MN; *U.S. Public*, pg. 441
Behan, William L., III, V.P. & Sec.--Hill-Behan Lumber Company, Saint Louis, MO; *U.S. Private*, pg. 529
Behera, S.C., Sec.--Mahanadi Coalfields Limited, Sambalpur, India; *Int'l*, pg. 298
Behler, Mary G., Treas. & Sec.--Blue Ridge Pressure Castings, Inc., Lehighton, PA; *U.S. Private*, pg. 153
Behrens, James W., Asst. Sec.--American Family Mutual Insurance Co., Madison, WI; *U.S. Private*, pg. 53
Beiriger, Terry, Chief Fin. Officer, Controller & Sec.--International FiberCom, Phoenix, AZ; *U.S. Public*, pg. 898
Beittel, T. Brooks, Sr. V.P., Sec. & Treas.--Duff & Phelps Utilities Income Inc., Chicago, IL; *U.S. Public*, pg. 534
Beland, Michel, Gen. Counsel & Sec.--Societe Generale de Financement du Quebec, Montreal, Canada; *Int'l*, pg. 1274
Belanger, Serge, Asst. Sec.--General Electric Canada Inc., Mississauga, Canada; *U.S. Public*, pg. 713
Belangia, Clyde, V.P. & Sec.--Carftique, Inc., Pulaski, VA; *U.S. Public*, pg. 1342
Belaval, Mario S., Exec. V.P.-Admin. & Asst. Sec.--Bacardi Corporation, San Juan, PR; *Int'l*, pg. 131
Belenguer, Alfonso, Sec.--Union Naval de Levante, S.A., Madrid, Spain; *Int'l*, pg. 1442
Belich, Mel F., Sr. V.P., Gen. Counsel & Sec.--IPL Energy Inc., Calgary, Canada; *Int'l*, pg. 651
Beliveau, Daniele, Gen. Counsel & Sec.--Domco Inc., Farnham, Canada; *Int'l*, pg. 415
Bell, Albert J., Sr. V.P., Gen. Counsel & Sec.--Consolidated Stores Corp., Columbus, OH; *U.S. Public*, pg. 437
Bell, Arthur, V.P. & Sec.--Madison Graham Colorgraphics, Inc., Los Angeles, CA; *U.S. Private*, pg. 694
Bell, Carmela Leone, V.P., Gen. Counsel & Corp. Sec.--Reliable Stores, Inc., Columbia, MD; *U.S. Private*, pg. 920
Bell, Kayden, V.P., Treas. & Sec.--Arnold Machinery Company, Salt Lake City, UT; *U.S. Private*, pg. 84
Bell, Marc N., V.P., Gen. Counsel & Sec.--Brooke Group Ltd., Miami, FL; *U.S. Public*, pg. 259
Bell, Marc N., Sec.--New Valley Corporation, Miami, FL; *U.S. Public*, pg. 1173
Bell, Mary Anne, Acting Corp. Sec.--Westamerica Bancorporation, Fairfield, CA; *U.S. Public*, pg. 1756
Bell, Mary Anne, Acting Corp. Sec.--Westamerica Bank, San Rafael, CA; *U.S. Public*, pg. 1756
Bell, Peter, Sec.--Chicago Reader, Inc., Chicago, IL; *U.S. Private*, pg. 235
Bell, Wayne L., V.P. & Sec.--Virginia Metal Industries, Inc., Orange, VA; *U.S. Private*, pg. 1141
Bellary, Uday, Chief Fin. Officer, V.P. & Asst. Sec.--MMC Networks, Inc., Sunnyvale, CA; *U.S. Public*, pg. 1027
Belt, J. Edward, Chief Tech. Officer, Sr. V.P.-Engrng. & Asst. Sec.--Printronix, Inc., Irvine, CA; *U.S. Public*, pg. 1329
Belt, Marie B., Sr. V.P. & Sec.--Artistic Greetings, Inc., Elmira, NY; *U.S. Public*, pg. 136
Benacin, Philippe, Treas. & Sec.--Jordache Fragrances & Cosmetics, New York, NY; *U.S. Public*, pg. 924
Bencrowsky, Anna M., V.P. & Sec.--1838 Bond-Debenture Trading Fund, Radnor, PA; *U.S. Public*, pg. 566
Bencze, Miklos, Corp. Sec.--Malev Hungarian Airlines, Plc., Budapest, Hungary; *Int'l*, pg. 833
Bender, Brian W., Chief Fin. Officer, V.P. & Sec.--Egghead, Inc., Liberty Lake, WA; *U.S. Public*, pg. 566
Bender, James J., Asst. Gen. Counsel--NRG Energy, Inc., Minneapolis, MN; *U.S. Public*, pg. 1195
Bender, Jeanne, Sec.--Reliance Elevator Company, Chicago, IL; *U.S. Private*, pg. 921
Bendle, Jean D., Asst. Sec.--Joy Mining Machinery, Warrendale, PA; *U.S. Public*, pg. 789
Beng, Lim Hock, Sec.--Lee Kim Tah Holdings Ltd., Singapore, Singapore; *Int'l*, pg. 1346
Benger, Scott C., Sr. V.P.-Fin., Treas. & Sec.--Analytical Surveys, Inc., Colorado Springs, CO; *U.S. Public*, pg. 110
Benik, Tina, V.P., Gen. Counsel & Sec.--A.T. Cross Co., Lincoln, RI; *U.S. Public*, pg. 460
Benjamin, Keith J., Sec.--AC Rochester Overseas Corporation, Southampton, United Kingdom; *U.S. Public*, pg. 722
Benjamin, Michael S., Sr. V.P., Gen. Counsel & Sec.--Meditrust Corporation, Needham, MA; *U.S. Public*, pg. 1081
Benjamin, Robert M., Sec. & Gen. Counsel--E.W. Blanch Holdings, Inc., Minneapolis, MN; *U.S. Public*, pg. 236
Benjamin, Scott, Sec. & Mgr.-Legal Opers.--Bumble Bee Seafoods Inc., San Diego, CA; *U.S. Private*, pg. 526
Benjumea, Ignacio, Exec. V.P.--Banco Santander, Madrid, Spain; *Int'l*, pg. 143
Benner, Kevin P., Controller, Treas & Sec.--Jasper County Farm Bureau Co-op Association, Inc., Rensselaer, IN; *U.S. Private*, pg. 583
Bennett, E. James, Sec. & Asst. Gen. Counsel--Maytag Corporation, Newton, IA; *U.S. Public*, pg. 1064
Bennett, Frank, Chief Oper. Officer, V.P. & Asst. Sec.--Camalloy, Incorporated, Washington, PA; *U.S. Private*, pg. 202
Bennett, George H., Jr., Exec. V.P., Gen. Counsel & Sec.--Cardinal Health Inc., Dublin, OH; *U.S. Public*, pg. 304
Bennett, George O., V.P. & Sec.--Bennett Brothers, Inc., Chicago, IL; *U.S. Private*, pg. 133
Bennett, Kevin D., Sr. Corp. Counsel & Asst. Sec.--Lowe's Companies, Inc., North Wilkesboro, NC; *U.S. Public*, pg. 1015
Bennett, Monty C., V.P.-Employee Rels. & Corp. Sec.--Hastings Manufacturing Company, Hastings, MI; *U.S. Public*, pg. 798
Bennett, P.R., Sec.--McPherson's Limited, Mulgrave, Australia; *Int'l*, pg. 852
Bennett, Shirley O., Asst. V.P. & Asst. Sec.--Bennett Brothers, Inc., Chicago, IL; *U.S. Private*, pg. 133
Bennett, Steven A., Gen. Counsel & Sec.--Banc One Corporation, Columbus, OH; *U.S. Public*, pg. 172
Bennett, Walter L., Chief Admin. Officer, Sr. V.P.-Fin. & Sec.--Thor Industries, Inc., Jackson Center, OH; *U.S. Public*, pg. 1602
Bennett, William, Asst. Sec.--Fairfield Communities, Inc., Little Rock, AR; *U.S. Public*, pg. 610
Bennion, Charlene, Exec. V.P. & Sec.--The Rowe Corporation, Charlotte, NC; *U.S. Private*, pg. 948
Bennitt, Fred Y., Sec. & Treas.--Sylvan Inc., Saxonburg, PA; *U.S. Public*, pg. 1545
Benno, Eli, V.P., Treas. & Sec.--Trading Port, Inc., Albany, NY; *U.S. Private*, pg. 1095
Benoit, Andre, Sec.--Bazar de L'Hotel de Ville, Paris, France; *Int'l*, pg. 181
Benoliel, Joel, Sr. V.P.-Real Estate & Law, Gen. Counsel & Corp. Sec.--Costco Wholesale, Issaquah, WA; *U.S. Public*, pg. 451
Bensen, Eric R., Chief Fin. Officer & V.P.--Cruise America, Inc., Mesa, AZ; *U.S. Private*, pg. 178
Benson, AnnDrea M., Sec.--Piper Trust Company, Minneapolis, MN; *U.S. Public*, pg. 1303
Benson, Betty, Treas. & Sec.--Delaware Electric Co-Op, Greenwood, DE; *U.S. Private*, pg. 321
Benson, James, V.P. & Sec.--Automatic Data Processing, Inc., Roseland, NJ; *U.S. Public*, pg. 150
Benson, Reed L., Gen. Counsel & Corp. Sec.--Data Broadcasting Corporation, Jackson, WY; *U.S. Public*, pg. 484
Benson, Vera, Controller & Sec.--Ernst W. Dorn Co., Inc., Gardena, CA; *U.S. Private*, pg. 340
Bentley, Antoinette C., Sr. V.P., Sec. & Assoc. Gen. Counsel--Talegen Corporation, Seattle, WA; *U.S. Public*, pg. 1784
Bentley, Julia A., Sr. V.P.-Plng. & Inv. Rels. & Sec.--Proffitt's, Inc., Alcoa, TN; *U.S. Public*, pg. 1333
Bentley, Nancy S., Treas. & Sec.--Associated Administrators, Inc., Portland, OR; *U.S. Private*, pg. 918
Bentley, Paul M., Exec. V.P. & Sec.--Cramer-Krasselt, Milwaukee, WI; *U.S. Private*, pg. 285
Benton, Jane, Treas. & Sec.--Monroe Hardware Co., Monroe, NC; *U.S. Private*, pg. 335
Berenzweig, Doris, Sec.--Rag Shops, Inc., Hawthorne, NJ; *U.S. Public*, pg. 1358
Berg, Carole L., V.P. & Sec.--Serfilco, Ltd., Northbrook, IL; *U.S. Private*, pg. 985
Berg, Sture, Corp. Sec.--L.H. Sowles Company, Inc., Minneapolis, MN; *U.S. Private*, pg. 1019
Berg, Thomas C., V.P.-Personnel, Gen. Counsel & Sec.--Amsted Industries Incorporated, Chicago, IL; *U.S. Private*, pg. 68
Bergen, Lee D., Chm. Bd. & Sec.--Peter Lumber Company, Pleasantville, NJ; *U.S. Private*, pg. 856
Berger, Bryan, Sec. & Treas.--Smith Farms, Inc., Flatonia, TX; *U.S. Private*, pg. 1008
Berger, Edward S., V.P., Gen. Counsel & Sec.--Information Resources, Inc., Chicago, IL; *U.S. Public*, pg. 875
Berger, Morris W., Chief Fin. Officer--Careers USA Inc., Philadelphia, PA; *U.S. Private*, pg. 209
Berger, Nol, Sr. V.P.-Legal Affairs & Corp. Sec.--Koninklijke Ahold NV, Zaandam, Netherlands; *Int'l*, pg. 749
Berger, Richard N., Chief Fin. Officer, V.P. & Sec.--Richey Electronics, Inc., Garden Grove, CA; *U.S. Public*, pg. 1388
Bergere, Del, V.P., Gen. Counsel & Sec.--Altera Corporation, San Jose, CA; *U.S. Public*, pg. 59
Bergeson, Margo R., Corp. Sec.--Alta Gold Co., Henderson, NV; *U.S. Public*, pg. 58
Bergholm, Lena, Sec.--AB Industrivarden, Stockholm, Sweden; *Int'l*, pg. 678
Bergholz-Widell, Ragnvi, Sec.--Incentive AB, Stockholm, Sweden; *Int'l*, pg. 666
Bergholz, Eugene W., Sec.--Camtronics Ltd., Hartland, WI; *U.S. Public*, pg. 109
Bergin, J.C., Sec.--Firth-Rixson Plc, Sheffield, United Kingdom; *Int'l*, pg. 487
Berglass, Judith R., Sr. V.P. & Sec.--Dep Corporation, Rancho Dominguez, CA; *U.S. Public*, pg. 500
Bergman, Harry, Treas. & Sec.--The First Republic Corporation of America, New York, NY; *U.S. Public*, pg. 637
Bergman, Robert S., Exec. V.P. & Sec.--Processed Plastic Company, Montgomery, IL; *U.S. Private*, pg. 888
Berick, James H., Sec.--A. Schulman, Inc., Akron, OH; *U.S. Public*, pg. 1441
Berick, James H., Sec.--The Tranzonic Companies, Pepper Pike, OH; *U.S. Public*, pg. 1632
Berkley, Herbert R., Treas. & Sec.--Berkliff Corporation, New York, NY; *U.S. Private*, pg. 135
Berkley, Richard L., Treas. & Sec.--Tension Envelope Corp., Kansas City, MO; *U.S. Private*, pg. 1077
Berlin, Marvin, Treas. & Sec.--New York Carpet World, Dalton, GA; *U.S. Public*, pg. 1464
Berlinsky, Jay S., Sec.--Transco Inc., Chicago, IL; *U.S. Private*, pg. 1096
Berman, Barbara, V.P.-Retail Accts. & Sec.--Ha-Lo Industries, Inc., Niles, IL; *U.S. Public*, pg. 773
Berman, Ira, V.P., Gen. Counsel & Sec.--Gulfstream Aerospace Corporation, Savannah, GA; *U.S. Private*, pg. 419
Berman, Joshua M., Sec.--Tyco International Ltd., Exeter, NH; *U.S. Public*, pg. 1647
Berman, Robert, Treas. & Sec.--Metpar Corp., Westbury, NY; *U.S. Private*, pg. 735
Berman, Stephen G., Chief Oper. Officer, Exec. V.P. & Sec.--JAKKS Pacific, Inc., Malibu, CA; *U.S. Public*, pg. 923
Berman, Steven L., Exec. V.P., Treas. & Sec.--R&B, Inc., Colmar, PA; *U.S. Public*, pg. 1354
Bernadino, Joseph, Sr. Exec. V.P. & Gen. Counsel--Prime Hospitality Corp., Fairfield, NJ; *U.S. Public*, pg. 1326
Bernard, Louis, Sr. V.P.-Admin. & Sec.--Laurentian Trust of Canada, Montreal, Canada; *Int'l*, pg. 396
Bernards, Jeffrey, V.P. & Sec.--Bernards Brothers, Inc., San Fernando, CA; *U.S. Private*, pg. 136
Berndt, Ellen German, Sec.--Borden, Inc., Columbus, OH; *U.S. Private*, pg. 157
Bernfeld, Jeffrey A., V.P. & Gen. Counsel--American Science & Engineering, Inc., Billerica, MA; *U.S. Public*, pg. 90
Bernhardson, Ivy S., V.P., Assoc. Gen. Counsel. & Asst. Sec.--General Mills, Inc., Minneapolis, MN; *U.S. Public*, pg. 717
Bernick, Carol L., Exec. V.P. & Asst. Sec.--Alberto-Culver Company, Melrose Park, IL; *U.S. Public*, pg. 37
Bernstein, Harold L., Gen. Counsel & Sec.--Hi-Shear Industries Inc., New Hyde Park, NY; *U.S. Public*, pg. 824
Bernstein, Marshall E., Sec.--Richton International Corporation, Madison, NJ; *U.S. Public*, pg. 1389
Bernstein, Stephen, Sr. Mng. Dir. & Asst. Sec.--The Bear Stearns Companies Inc., New York, NY; *U.S. Public*, pg. 197
Berrette, Anne Marie, Gen. Sec.--Salomon S.A., Annecy, France; *Int'l*, pg. 1181
Berrie, Suzanne, V.P., Sec. & Exec. Asst. To Chief Exec. Officer--Parfums International Ltd., New York, NY; *Int'l*, pg. 1435
Berritt, Harold E., Gen. Counsel & Sec.--Claire's Stores Inc., Pembroke Pines, FL; *U.S. Public*, pg. 381
Berry, Donald R., V.P.-Tax Mngmt. & Asst. Sec.--Pope & Talbot, Inc., Portland, OR; *U.S. Public*, pg. 1316
Berry, Elizabeth, Asst. Sec.--Metropolitan Mortgage & Securities Co., Inc., Spokane, WA; *U.S. Private*, pg. 738
Berry, Jim, Sec. & Gen. Counsel--SmithKline Beecham Corporation, Philadelphia, PA; *Int'l*, pg. 1264
Berry, John G., Sec.--Iceland Group plc, Deeside, United Kingdom; *Int'l*, pg. 658
Berry, Susan D., Sec.--Arizona Instrument Corporation, Phoenix, AZ; *U.S. Public*, pg. 129
Bersoff, Marilyn, Sr. V.P.-Admin. & Sec.--BTG, Inc., Fairfax, VA; *U.S. Public*, pg. 164
Berson, Joel, Sec. & Gen. Counsel--Tork, Inc., Mount Vernon, NY; *U.S. Private*, pg. 1092
Bertelsen, Mark, Sec. & Attorney--Atmel Corporation, San Jose, CA; *U.S. Public*, pg. 145
Besse, Grey, Sec.--Northern Michigan Veneers, Inc., Gladstone, MI; *U.S. Private*, pg. 805
Betance, P., Asst. Sec.--Arden-Mayfair, Inc., Compton, CA; *U.S. Public*, pg. 129
Betance, Patricia, Asst. Sec.--Arden Group, Inc., Los Angeles, CA; *U.S. Public*, pg. 128
Bethea, Richard W., Jr., V.P., Corp. Counsel & Sec.--Astec Industries, Inc., Chattanooga, TN; *U.S. Public*, pg. 141
Bethurum, Shirley A., Treas. & Sec.--Bethurum Research & Development, Inc., Texas City, TX; *U.S. Private*, pg. 141
Bethurun, Shirley A., V.P., Treas. & Sec.--Bushwhacker Associates, Inc., Texas City, TX; *U.S. Private*, pg. 141
Betro, Karen M., V.P.-Admin. & Sec.--FOTOBALL USA, Inc., San Diego, CA; *U.S. Public*, pg. 678

Betuker, Kenneth S., Chief Fin. Officer, V.P. & Sec.--Noodle Kidoodle Inc., Syosset, NY; *U.S. Public*, pg. 1188
Beusmans, Bart C.M.I., Sec.--Akzo Nobel N.V., Arnhem, Netherlands; *Int'l*, pg. 42
Beutler, Tom, Sec., Treas. & Controller--Beutler Heating & Air Conditioning Inc., Sacramento, CA; *U.S. Private*, pg. 141
Beverage, Bill M., Chief Fin. Officer, Treas. & Sec.--Outdoor Systems, Inc., Phoenix, AZ; *U.S. Public*, pg. 1235
Beveridge, R.E., Gen. Counsel & Sec.--Marley PLC, Sevenoaks, United Kingdom; *Int'l*, pg. 843
Bewley, Linda L., Asst. Sec.--BWI Kartridg Pak, Davenport, IA; *Int'l*, pg. 130
Bewley, Peter D., Sr. V.P., Gen. Counsel & Sec.--NovaCare Inc., King of Prussia, PA; *U.S. Public*, pg. 1203
Bexhed, Jan-Mikael, Gen. Counsel & Sec.--Skandia Insurance Company Limited, Stockholm, Sweden; *Int'l*, pg. 1256
Beyer, Michael K., Sr. V.P., Gen. Counsel & Sec.--Robert Mondavi Winery, Inc., Oakville, CA; *U.S. Public*, pg. 1393
Beyer, Ruth, Corp. Sec.--Precision Castparts Corp., Portland, OR; *U.S. Public*, pg. 1320
Bharti, N., Asst. Sec.--Unitech Plc, Reading, United Kingdom; *Int'l*, pg. 1241
Bialick, David W., Treas. & Asst. Sec.--Computer Horizons Corp., Mountain Lakes, NJ; *U.S. Public*, pg. 421
Bianco, Sally, Sec.--Control Module, Inc., Enfield, CT; *U.S. Private*, pg. 271
Biar, L. Scott, Controller & Asst. Sec.--Weatherford Enterra Incorporated, Houston, TX; *U.S. Public*, pg. 1749
Biasucci, Sam B., Sr. V.P., Sec. & Cashier--First Western Bank, National Association, New Castle, PA; *U.S. Public*, pg. 642
Bibler, Laurie, Chief Fin. Officer, Treas. & Sec.--Bibler Brothers, Inc., Russellville, AR; *U.S. Private*, pg. 142
Bich-Dufour, Marie-Aimee, Exec. V.P., Gen. Counsel & Sec.--Societe BIC S.A., Clichy, France; *Int'l*, pg. 1272
Biederman, Tom, Controller, Treas. & Sec.--Coleman Cadillac Inc., Bethesda, MD; *U.S. Private*, pg. 251
Biehl, George C., Chief Fin. Officer, Sr. V.P. & Sec.--Southwest Gas Corporation, Las Vegas, NV; *U.S. Public*, pg. 1493
Bienvenu, Wayne, Treas. & Sec.--Turnbull Enterprises, Inc., Baltimore, MD; *U.S. Private*, pg. 1109
Biggins, Edward J., Jr., Sec.--Public Service Enterprise Group Incorporated, Newark, NJ; *U.S. Public*, pg. 1340
Biggs, Ricky, Treas. & Sec.--Edmonson Wheat Growers, Inc., Edmonson, TX; *U.S. Private*, pg. 364
Bighan, Rod, Sec.--Farmer's Cooperative Association, Lawrence, KS; *U.S. Private*, pg. 395
Bihler, Theresa, Asst. Sec.--Rent-Way, Inc., Erie, PA; *U.S. Public*, pg. 1377
Bikales, Norman A., Sec. & Clerk--BIW Cable Systems, Inc., Franklin, MA; *Int'l*, pg. 417
Bilawsky, Mark A., V.P., Gen. Counsel & Sec.--Church & Dwight Co., Inc., Princeton, NJ; *U.S. Public*, pg. 355
Billam, Dale J., Sec.--Phillips Petroleum Company, Bartlesville, OK; *U.S. Public*, pg. 1290
Biller, Odd I., Gen. Counsel & Sec.--Norsk Hydro a.s, Oslo, Norway; *Int'l*, pg. 959
Billett, Geoffrey J., Pres. & Sec.--Ecophon CertainTeed, Inc., Valley Forge, PA; *Int'l*, pg. 1171
Billey, Judith A., Sec.--Anarad, Inc., Santa Barbara, CA; *U.S. Public*, pg. 1563
Billingslea, William, Jr., Corp. Counsel & Asst. Sec.--Rohr, Inc., Chula Vista, CA; *U.S. Public*, pg. 751
Billis, Stephen, Controller--Educational Insights, Inc., Carson, CA; *U.S. Public*, pg. 565
Billups, S. Keith, Sec.--Publix Supermarkets Inc., Lakeland, FL; *U.S. Private*, pg. 893
Bilodeau, Gerard L., Sr. V.P. & Sec.--Arrow Financial Corporation, Glens Falls, NY; *U.S. Public*, pg. 135
Bilstrom, Jon W., Gen. Counsel & Sec.--Mercantile Bancorporation Inc., Saint Louis, MO; *U.S. Public*, pg. 1087
Bilstrom, Jon W., Sec.--Mercantile Bank of St. Louis N.A., Saint Louis, MO; *U.S. Public*, pg. 1087
Bilyi, I., Corp. Sec.--Kruger Inc., Montreal, Canada; *Int'l*, pg. 761
Binder, Joe, Controller & Sec.--Acme Truck Line, Inc., Harvey, LA; *U.S. Private*, pg. 14
Binder, Joseph, Sec.--Key Food Stores Co-operative, Inc., Brooklyn, NY; *U.S. Private*, pg. 617
Binder, Lilli A., Asst. Sec.--Rite Aid Corporation, Camp Hill, PA; *U.S. Public*, pg. 1390
Binding, David, Sec.--Legal & General Group PLC, London, United Kingdom; *Int'l*, pg. 805
Bindra, Tejinder S., Asst. Sec.--Columbia Energy Group, Reston, VA; *U.S. Public*, pg. 402
Bingaman, Larry L., V.P.-Corp. Rels. & Sec.--Aquarion Company, Bridgeport, CT; *U.S. Public*, pg. 126
Bingham, H. Raymond, Chief Fin. Officer, Exec. V.P. & Sec.--Cadence Design Systems, Inc., San Jose, CA; *U.S. Public*, pg. 290
Binmore, J.S., Sec.--Thomas Robinson Group Plc, Kilburn, United Kingdom; *Int'l*, pg. 231
Biolchini, Robert R., Gen. Counsel & Sec.--Lowrance Electronics, Inc., Tulsa, OK; *U.S. Public*, pg. 1015
Bird, Thomas J., Jr., Exec. V.P., Gen. Counsel & Sec.--IMO Industries Inc., Lawrenceville, NJ; *U.S. Public*, pg. 856
Birdsong, Randall G., Controller, Treas. & Sec.--Spencer Companies Inc., Huntsville, AL; *U.S. Private*, pg. 1024
Birk, David R., Sr. V.P., Gen. Counsel & Sec.--Avnet, Inc., Great Neck, NY; *U.S. Public*, pg. 155
Birkanshaw, Ralph, Sec.--New England Dairies, Inc., Hartford, CT; *U.S. Private*, pg. 793
Birtwistle, Kathleen A., Asst. Sec.--Waverly, Inc., Baltimore, MD; *U.S. Public*, pg. 1748
Bisaro, Paul, Sr. V.P., Gen. Counsel & Sec.--Barr Laboratories Inc., Pomona, NY; *U.S. Public*, pg. 191
Bishop, Daniel S., V.P., Gen. Counsel & Sec.--PAXAR Corporation, White Plains, NY; *U.S. Public*, pg. 1266
Bishop, E. Liston, III, Deputy Gen. Counsel, Dir.-Acquisitions & Asst. Sec.--Coca-Cola Enterprises Inc., Atlanta, GA; *U.S. Public*, pg. 393
Bishop, Earl, Treas. & Sec.--Free Service Tire Company, Inc., Johnson City, TN; *U.S. Private*, pg. 425
Bishop, J. Randall, Chief Fin. Officer, V.P. & Sec.--Cameron & Barkley Company, Charleston, SC; *U.S. Private*, pg. 203
Bishop, John J., Sr. V.P. & Asst. Sec.--Motorists Mutual Insurance Co., Columbus, OH; *U.S. Private*, pg. 764
Biss, Joyce, Exec. Sec.--PSC Inc., Webster, NY; *U.S. Public*, pg. 1245
Bissara, Philippe, Co. Sec.--Alcatel Alsthom Compagnie Generale D'Electricite, Paris, France; *Int'l*, pg. 52
Bisschops, Theo P.M., Sec. & Dir.-Investor Rels.--Gamma Holding N.V., Helmond, Netherlands; *Int'l*, pg. 539
Bistricer, Nathan, Sec.--Philipp Brothers Chemicals, Inc., Fort Lee, NJ; *U.S. Private*, pg. 861
Bitar, Thomas J., Sec.--Dataram Corporation, Princeton, NJ; *U.S. Public*, pg. 487
Biting, Cynthia, Sec.--Invacare Health Care Furnishings, Chesterfield, MO; *U.S. Public*, pg. 911
Bittenbender, Charles A., V.P., Gen. Counsel & Sec.--NACCO Industries, Inc., Cleveland, OH; *U.S. Public*, pg. 1149
Bitting, Cynthia N., Gen. Counsel & Sec.--Allied Industrial Group, Inc., Saint Louis, MO; *U.S. Private*, pg. 39
Bixler, R. Jeffrey, V.P., Gen. Counsel & Sec.--Health Care & Retirement Corporation, Toledo, OH; *U.S. Public*, pg. 801
Black, Barrie H., Gen. Counsel & Sec.--Bruncor, Inc., Saint John, Canada; *Int'l*, pg. 230
Black, Bryan, Sec.--Vogler Motor Company, Inc., Carbondale, IL; *U.S. Private*, pg. 1143
Black, David, Exec. V.P., Sec. & Gen. Counsel--Affiliated Computer Services, Inc., Dallas, TX; *U.S. Public*, pg. 27
Black, Richard, Asst. Sec.--Brodart Company, Williamsport, PA; *U.S. Private*, pg. 170
Blackburn, G. Templeton, II, V.P.-Real Estate, Gen. Counsel & Sec.--Rose's Stores, Inc., Henderson, NC; *U.S. Public*, pg. 1405
Blackburn, Lisa, Exec. Sec.--Carroll's Foods, Inc., Warsaw, NC; *U.S. Private*, pg. 215
Blackford, Robert N., Asst. Sec.--Hughes Supply, Inc., Orlando, FL; *U.S. Public*, pg. 846
Blackin, Jack, Sr. V.P. & Asst. Sec.--Valley National Bancorp, Wayne, NJ; *U.S. Public*, pg. 1705
Blackstone, Franklin, Jr., Gen. Counsel & Sec.--Bearing Service Company, Pittsburgh, PA; *U.S. Private*, pg. 127
Blackwell, Daisy S., Sec.--Southland Oil Company, Jackson, MS; *U.S. Private*, pg. 1018
Blagbrough, P.H., Sec.--Save & Prosper Group Limited, London, United Kingdom; *Int'l*, pg. 493
Blain, Gerard, Sec.--Meridian Diagnostics, Inc., Cincinnati, OH; *U.S. Public*, pg. 1094
Blair, David A., Sec.--Blair Corporation, Warren, PA; *U.S. Public*, pg. 236
Blair, J.H., Sec.--Air New Zealand Ltd., Auckland, New Zealand; *Int'l*, pg. 38
Blair, Marilyn R., Sec.--Itron Inc., Spokane, WA; *U.S. Public*, pg. 914
Blaisdell-Snowdon, Deborah, Exec. V.P. & Corp. Sec.--The U.S. Baird Corporation, Stratford, CT; *U.S. Private*, pg. 1124
Blake, Allen, Chief Fin. Officer, V.P. & Sec.--First Banks America, Inc., Clayton, MO; *U.S. Public*, pg. 626
Blake, Colin, Dir.-Commercial & Sec.--Neff (UK) Limited, Milton Keynes, United Kingdom; *Int'l*, pg. 912
Blake, Gerald K., Chief Investment Officer, Sr. V.P. & Corp. Sec.--National Travelers Life Co., West Des Moines, IA; *U.S. Private*, pg. 787
Blalock, Alvin C., V.P., Sec. & Dir.-Mfg.--GoodMark Foods, Inc., Raleigh, NC; *U.S. Public*, pg. 751
Blanchard, Eric A., V.P., Sec. & Gen. Counsel--Dean Foods Company, Franklin Park, IL; *U.S. Public*, pg. 489
Blanchard, M.D., Sec.--Texas Generating Company, Fort Worth, TX; *U.S. Public*, pg. 1557
Blanchard, William C., Treas. & Sec.--Wm. Blanchard Co., Springfield, NJ; *U.S. Private*, pg. 148
Bland, Louis T., Jr., V.P.-H.R. & Sec.--Oil-Dri Corporation of America, Chicago, IL; *U.S. Public*, pg. 1214
Blandford, R.G., Sec.--Senior Foster Wheeler Power Division, Wembley, United Kingdom; *Int'l*, pg. 1221
Blank, Julius, Sec.--Xicor, Inc., Milpitas, CA; *U.S. Public*, pg. 1785
Blank, Martin J., Chm. Bd., Chief Oper. Officer & Sec.--Automobile Protection Corporation-APCO, Atlanta, GA; *U.S. Public*, pg. 150
Blank, Randall, Chief Fin. Officer, Exec. V.P. & Sec.--Seacor Smit Inc., Houston, TX; *U.S. Public*, pg. 1449
Blankenheim, Donna C., V.P. & Sec.--CUNA Mutual Insurance Society, Madison, WI; *U.S. Private*, pg. 296
Blankenship, Paula, Corp. Sec. & Mgr.-Employee Compensation & Benefits--Bush Brothers & Company, Knoxville, TN; *U.S. Private*, pg. 189
Blankinship, Scott F., Exec. V.P. & Sec.--Petroleum Marketers, Inc., Roanoke, VA; *U.S. Private*, pg. 859
Blanscet, Glen A., V.P., Gen. Counsel & Sec.--Atmos Energy Corporation, Dallas, TX; *U.S. Public*, pg. 145
Blattner, Stephen C., Chief Fin. Officer, Treas. & Sec.--D.H. Blattner & Sons, Inc., Avon, MN; *U.S. Private*, pg. 148
Blaylock, Marcia, V.P. & Sec.--CLARCOR, Inc., Rockford, IL; *U.S. Public*, pg. 381
Bligh, Diana W., Asst. Sec.--Borg-Warner Security Corporation, Chicago, IL; *U.S. Public*, pg. 245
Blixt, Charles A., Exec. V.P., Sec. & Gen. Counsel--R.J. Reynolds Tobacco Company, Winston Salem, NC; *U.S. Public*, pg. 1355
Bloch, Roland, Sec.--SMH Swiss Corporation for Micro Electronics & Watchmaking Indus. Ltd., Bienne, Switzerland; *Int'l*, pg. 1160
Block, Ira, V.P., Gen. Counsel & Sec.--Wechsler Coffee Corp., Moonachie, NJ; *U.S. Private*, pg. 1158
Block, Stephen A., V.P.-Law & Sec.--International Flavors & Fragrances, Inc., New York, NY; *U.S. Public*, pg. 898
Bloom, Alan, Sr. V.P., Gen. Counsel & Sec.--Maxicare Health Plans, Inc., Los Angeles, CA; *U.S. Public*, pg. 1061
Bloom, Arnold, V.P., Gen. Counsel & Sec.--Russ Berrie and Company, Inc., Oakland, NJ; *U.S. Public*, pg. 222
Bloomberg, Stanley, Exec. V.P. & Sec.--Glen Oaks Industries, Inc., New York, NY; *U.S. Private*, pg. 456
Bloomfield, Kevin L., V.P., Gen. Counsel & Sec.--Belden Inc., Saint Louis, MO; *U.S. Public*, pg. 200
Bloore, J.R., Sec.--Cigna Reinsurance New Zealand Limited, Auckland, New Zealand; *U.S. Public*, pg. 363
Blount, Susan L., V.P. & Sec.--The Prudential Insurance Company of America, Newark, NJ; *U.S. Private*, pg. 892
Blum, Donald R., Treas. & Asst. Sec.--The Weitz Company, Inc., Des Moines, IA; *U.S. Private*, pg. 1160
Blum, Rick, Asst. Sec.--Castle Convertible Fund, Inc., New York, NY; *U.S. Public*, pg. 313
Blumberg, Michael, Sr., Sr. V.P.-Pur. & Sec.--Sound Advice, Inc., Dania, FL; *U.S. Public*, pg. 1488
Blumenthal, Richard A., Sr. V.P., Gen. Counsel & Sec.--Systems & Computer Technology Corporation, Malvern, PA; *U.S. Public*, pg. 1552
Blundell, Charles, Sec.--Rolls-Royce plc, London, United Kingdom; *Int'l*, pg. 1126
Blunier, Doris, Sec.--DMI, Inc., Goodfield, IL; *U.S. Private*, pg. 305
Blunk, Richard, Exec. V.P., Gen. Counsel & Sec.--ShowBiz Pizza Time, Inc., Irving, TX; *U.S. Public*, pg. 1468
Bluth, Lawrence N., V.P., Gen. Counsel & Sec.--Penske Corporation, Detroit, MI; *U.S. Private*, pg. 850
Bluth, Thomas, V.P., Treas. & Sec.--Catalina Lighting, Inc., Miami, FL; *U.S. Public*, pg. 314
Blutstein, Barbara, Sec.--Reliable Knitting Works, Milwaukee, WI; *U.S. Private*, pg. 920
Boardman, Harold F., V.P., Gen. Counsel & Sec.--Hoffmann-La Roche Inc., Nutley, NJ; *Int'l*, pg. 1120
Bobel, Mary, Chief Fin. Officer--Genus Inc., Sunnyvale, CA; *U.S. Public*, pg. 732
Bober, Joanne L., Sr. V.P., Gen. Counsel & Sec.--General Signal Corporation, Stamford, CT; *U.S. Public*, pg. 726
Bobo, April, Sec. & Controller--Olen Corporation, Columbus, OH; *U.S. Private*, pg. 631
Bockart, Richard L., V.P., Treas. & Sec.--Oshman's Sporting Goods, Inc., Houston, TX; *U.S. Public*, pg. 1233
Boda, Tammy, Sec.--Crosman Corp., East Bloomfield, NY; *U.S. Private*, pg. 291
Bodager, Brian R., Sr. V.P., Gen. Counsel & Sec.--Associated Banc-Corp, Green Bay, WI; *U.S. Public*, pg. 140
Bodiford, Lowell, Treas. & Sec.--Fort Worth Lumber Company, Fort Worth, TX; *U.S. Private*, pg. 419
Bodkins, Connie, Sec.--Clark Enterprises, Inc., Bethesda, MD; *U.S. Private*, pg. 242
Boegner, Dieter K., V.P.-Fin., Sec. & Treas.--Installation Products Div., Lancaster, PA; *U.S. Public*, pg. 132
Boehm, Darnell, Chief Fin. Officer--Aetrium Inc., Saint Paul, MN; *U.S. Public*, pg. 27
Boehm, Hannes G., Sec.--Chatsworth Data Corporation, Chatsworth, CA; *U.S. Private*, pg. 231
Boepple, Patricia A., Asst. Sec.--Amdahl Corporation, Sunnyvale, CA; *Int'l*, pg. 527
Bogatz, I. Scott, V.P., Gen. Counsel & Sec.--Rio Hotel & Casino Inc., Las Vegas, NV; *U.S. Public*, pg. 1390
Bogden, John M., V.P., Treas. & Sec.--On Technology Corporation, Cambridge, MA; *U.S. Public*, pg. 1225
Boggs, L. Kennedy, Sec.--BenefitAmerica, Columbia, SC; *U.S. Public*, pg. 1699
Bogomolny, Robert L., V.P., Gen. Counsel & Sec.--Searle Laboratories, Skokie, IL; *U.S. Public*, pg. 1125
Bohling, J. Scott, Chief Fin. Officer, V.P. & Sec.--H.H. Brown Shoe Company, Inc., Greenwich, CT; *U.S. Public*, pg. 217
Bohn, Han C., Asst. Sec.--HTI Export Ltd., Bridgetown, Barbados; *U.S. Public*, pg. 851
Boland, Michael, Treas. & Sec.--David Boland, Inc., Titusville, FL; *U.S. Private*, pg. 154
Bolanowski, Stephen A., Sec.--Hammond Group Inc., Hammond, IN; *U.S. Private*, pg. 498
Bolbach, Cynthia J., Corp. Sec.--The Bureau of National Affairs, Inc., Washington, DC; *U.S. Private*, pg. 181
Boldison, W.F., Asst. Sec.--Rolls-Royce plc, London, United Kingdom; *Int'l*, pg. 1126
Bolduc, Yvon, V.P.-Legal Affairs & Sec.--G.T.C. Transcontinental Group Ltd., Montreal, Canada; *Int'l*, pg. 538
Bolin, Susan C., Chief Fin. Officer, Exec. V.P., Treas. & Sec.--The O'Boise Corporation, Oak Brook, IL; *U.S. Private*, pg. 810
Bollinger, Charlotte, Sec.--Bollinger Shipyards, Inc., Lockport, LA; *U.S. Private*, pg. 155
Bollington, John R., Sr. V.P., Gen. Counsel & Sec.--20th Century Industries, Woodland Hills, CA; *U.S. Public*, pg. 1646
Bolton-Smith, C., V.P. & Corp. Sec.--MCI Communications Corp., Atlanta, GA; *U.S. Public*, pg. 1023
Bolton, William J., Chief Fin. Officer & Corp. Sec.--Carolina Steel Corporation, Greensboro, NC; *U.S. Private*, pg. 214
Bompard, Jean-Jacques, Corp. Sec.--Rossignol S.A., Voiron, France; *Int'l*, pg. 1127
Bonahoom, A. James, Jr., Pres. & Sec.--Wolverine Packing Co., Detroit, MI; *U.S. Private*, pg. 1186
Bond, David M., Controller, Sec. & Asst. Treas.--International Dairy Queen, Inc., Minneapolis, MN; *U.S. Public*, pg. 220
Bond, Richard E., V.P., Gen. Counsel & Sec.--Monaco Coach Corporation, Coburg, OR; *U.S. Public*, pg. 1123
Bond, Rodney S., Chief Fin. Officer, Treas. & Sec.--VTEL Corporation, Austin, TX; *U.S. Public*, pg. 1703
Bond, Thomas A., Chief Fin. Officer, Exec. V.P. & Sec.--Aluma Systems Corp., Toronto, Canada; *Int'l*, pg. 1423
Bondy, Timothy J., Chief Fin. Officer & V.P.--Northwestern Steel & Wire Co., Sterling, IL; *U.S. Public*, pg. 1201

Bonello, Irene, Sec.--P & F Industries, Inc., Farmingdale, NY; *U.S. Public*, pg. 1239
Bonet, Frank J., Asst. Sec.--JC Penney Company, Inc., Plano, TX; *U.S. Public*, pg. 916
Bongrain, Alec, Sec.--BC-USA, New Holland, PA; *Int'l*, pg. 201
Bonk, Robert, Chief Fin. Officer, V.P.-Fin. & Sec.--Northern Labs, Inc., Manitowoc, WI; *U.S. Private*, pg. 805
Bonn, Allan, Treas. & Sec.--F.H. Bonn Company, Springfield, OH; *U.S. Private*, pg. 156
Bonn, Patricia, Mgr.-Admin. & Employee Rels.--Bobst Group Inc., Roseland, NJ; *Int'l*, pg. 198
Bonner, Robert B., Chief Oper. Officer, Exec. V.P. & Sec.--First Federal Savings, East Hartford, CT; *U.S. Public*, pg. 632
Bonner, William R., V.P. & Sec.--Kronos, Inc., Houston, TX; *U.S. Private*, pg. 270
Bonvino, Frank W., V.P., Gen. Counsel & Sec.--International Multifoods Corporation, Minneapolis, MN; *U.S. Public*, pg. 900
Boody, Fran, Sec.--Crescent Genlyte, Barrington, NJ; *U.S. Public*, pg. 730
Boone, D.W., Sec.--Farm Electric Services Ltd., Calgary, Canada; *Int'l*, pg. 1416
Boone, Don W., Corp. Sec.--Transalta Corporation, Calgary, Canada; *Int'l*, pg. 1416
Boone, Donald W., Sec.--TransAlta Energy Corporation, Calgary, Canada; *Int'l*, pg. 1416
Boone, Donald W., Sec.--TransAlta Enterprises Corporation, Calgary, Canada; *Int'l*, pg. 1416
Boone, Donald W., Corp. Sec.--TransAlta Utilities, Calgary, Canada; *Int'l*, pg. 1416
Boone, Jo Ann, Exec. Sec.--MW Manufacturers Inc., Rocky Mount, VA; *Int'l*, pg. 593
Boone, Sharon D., Controller & Asst. Sec.--Public Service Company of North Carolina, Inc., Gastonia, NC; *U.S. Public*, pg. 1340
Boone, William L., V.P.-Fin., Treas. & Sec.--Kenan Transport Company, Chapel Hill, NC; *U.S. Public*, pg. 949
Booth, Brenda, Head-Secretariat--Coats Viyella plc, Manchester, United Kingdom; *Int'l*, pg. 299
Booth, Richard H., Corp. Counsel & Sec.--Standex International Corporation, Salem, NH; *U.S. Public*, pg. 1505
Borak, Robert L., Treas., Controller & Sec.--McGraw-Hill Securities Trading, Inc., New York, NY; *U.S. Public*, pg. 1071
Borawski, Bob, Sec.--Silicon Power Cube Corporation, San Pedro, CA; *U.S. Private*, pg. 1000
Bordwin, Milton, Sec.--NHD Hardware, Stoughton, MA; *U.S. Private*, pg. 3
Borg, Jennifer A., V.P. & Sec.--Macromedia Incorporated, Hackensack, NJ; *U.S. Private*, pg. 693
Borgerding, Bruce J., Deputy Gen. Counsel & Sec.--Tennant Company, Minneapolis, MN; *U.S. Public*, pg. 1577
Borgeson, Steven E., Sr. V.P., Gen. Counsel, Sec., Treas. & Clerk--ChemDesign Corporation, Fitchburg, MA; *Int'l*, pg. 173
Borglijung, Ulrike, Sec.--Stora Papyrus AB, Molndal, Sweden; *Int'l*, pg. 1303
Boris, Fran, Exec. V.P., Sr. Corp. Counsel & Sec.--Blimpie International, Inc., Atlanta, GA; *U.S. Public*, pg. 236
Borish, Arnold P., V.P., Gen. Counsel & Sec.--Roy F. Weston, Inc., West Chester, PA; *U.S. Public*, pg. 1761
Borkowski, Michael W., Asst. Sec.--Alumax Inc., Atlanta, GA; *U.S. Public*, pg. 59
Borlinghaus, Scott, Controller & Sec.--John Fabick Tractor Company, Fenton, MO; *U.S. Private*, pg. 390
Born, J. Ivan, V.P., Treas. & Sec.--Beaudry Ford, Inc., Atlanta, GA; *U.S. Private*, pg. 127
Boron, Walter W., Asst. V.P., Sec. & Trust Officer--First Western Trust Services Co., New Castle, PA; *U.S. Public*, pg. 642
Borton, Ronald, Treas. & Sec.--Sauder Manufacturing Corporation, Archbold, OH; *U.S. Private*, pg. 967
Bosch, Joel, Treas. & Sec.--Minot Builders Supply Association, Minot, ND; *U.S. Private*, pg. 751
Boss, Willard I., Jr., V.P. & Sec.--Nuevo Energy Company, Houston, TX; *U.S. Public*, pg. 1206
Bosser, M. Alain, Gen. Counsel & Sec.--SNECMA - Societe Nationale d'Etude et de Construction de Moteurs d'Aviation, Paris, France; *Int'l*, pg. 1165
Bossio, Salvatore, Corp. Sec.--Swinerton Inc., San Francisco, CA; *U.S. Private*, pg. 1059
Bost, Paula D., Asst. Sec.--American Appraisal Associates, Inc., Milwaukee, WI; *U.S. Private*, pg. 49
Boswell, William P., V.P.-Gen. Counsel & Sec.--The Peoples Natural Gas Co., Pittsburgh, PA; *U.S. Public*, pg. 435
Bothe, Brooke, Sec.--H.W. Kaufman Financial Group, Inc., Farmington, MI; *U.S. Private*, pg. 609
Bottorff, Marilyn C., Sec.--ENSERV, Inc., Madison, WI; *U.S. Public*, pg. 1728
Bottorff, Marilyn C., Asst. Corp. Sec.--Heartland Development Corporation, Madison, WI; *U.S. Public*, pg. 1728
Bottorff, Marilyn C., Sec.--Heartland Energy Services, Inc., Madison, WI; *U.S. Public*, pg. 1728
Bottorff, Marilyn C., Sec.--Heartland Energy Group, Inc., Madison, WI; *U.S. Public*, pg. 1728
Boucher, Joyce J., Sec.--Caldwell Manufacturing Company, Rochester, NY; *U.S. Private*, pg. 200
Boudreau, J.L., Treas. & Asst. Corp. Sec.--The St. Paul Companies, Inc., Saint Paul, MN; *U.S. Public*, pg. 1429
Boughton, Sid, Treas. & Sec.--Jacobsen Manufacturing, Inc., Safety Harbor, FL; *U.S. Private*, pg. 580
Bouland, Steve, V.P. & Asst. Sec.--AMCORE Bank, South Beloit, IL; *U.S. Public*, pg. 64
Boulier, Paul, Asst. Sec.--Nova Chemicals, Inc., Monaca, PA; *Int'l*, pg. 971
Bourgarel, Michel, Exec. V.P. & Sec.--Air Liquide S.A., Paris, France; *Int'l*, pg. 37
Bouthot, Kerry, Sec.--Beacon Group, Bloomfield, CT; *U.S. Private*, pg. 126
Boutonnat, Pierre-Louis, Gen. Sec.--Entreprise Miniere et Chimique, Paris, France; *Int'l*, pg. 458
Bouzitat, Francoise, Sec. Gen.--Arianespace SA, Evry, France; *Int'l*, pg. 81
Bovee, David R., Chief Fin. Officer, V.P. & Asst. Sec.--Dura Automotive Systems, Inc., Minneapolis, MN; *U.S. Public*, pg. 537
Bowden, David G., V.P., Controller & Sec.--Griffin Group, Inc., New York, NY; *U.S. Private*, pg. 480
Bowden, Douglas, Exec. V.P. & Sec.--Sencore, Inc., Sioux Falls, SD; *U.S. Private*, pg. 983
Bowden, Kathleen D., Sec.--Dobson & Johnson, Inc., Nashville, TN; *U.S. Private*, pg. 337
Bowe, William J., Exec. V.P., Gen. Counsel & Sec.--Encyclopaedia Britannica, Inc., Chicago, IL; *U.S. Private*, pg. 375
Bowen, James E., Comptroller & Sec.--Better Living Inc., Charlottesville, VA; *U.S. Private*, pg. 141
Bowen, Pamela A., V.P. & Sec.--The Annapolis Banking & Trust Co., Annapolis, MD; *U.S. Public*, pg. 1088
Bower, Robert R., Sr. V.P.--S.T. Research, Newington, VA; *U.S. Private*, pg. 958
Bowers, Richard, Sr. Exec. V.P., Gen. Counsel & Sec.--Jan Bell Marketing Inc., Sunrise, FL; *U.S. Public*, pg. 207
Bowers, Robert E., V.P.-Fin.--Watt Publishing Co., Mount Morris, IL; *U.S. Private*, pg. 1154
Bowie, M.S., Asst. Sec.--Miller Advertising Agency Inc., New York, NY; *U.S. Private*, pg. 746
Bowling, Lupe, Sec.--Genicom Corporation, Chantilly, VA; *U.S. Public*, pg. 729
Bowman, Claire, Asst. Corp. Sec.--Schuff Steel Co., Phoenix, AZ; *U.S. Private*, pg. 973
Bowman, David W., Sr. V.P., Gen. Counsel & Sec.--Mapco Inc., Tulsa, OK; *U.S. Public*, pg. 1042
Bowman, S.W., Sec.--J. Bibby & Sons Plc, London, United Kingdom; *Int'l*, pg. 167
Bowron-White, Susan, Asst. Sec.--Meridian Insurance Group, Inc., Indianapolis, IN; *U.S. Public*, pg. 1095
Boxer, Robert L., V.P., Gen. Counsel & Sec.--Moscom Corporation, Pittsford, NY; *U.S. Public*, pg. 1136
Boyd, Craig T., Asst. Sec.--Wallace Computer Services, Inc., Lisle, IL; *U.S. Public*, pg. 1735
Boyd, Dale, Chief Fin. Officer, Exec. V.P. & Sec.--MTI Technology Corporation, Anaheim, CA; *U.S. Public*, pg. 1028
Boyd, George M., Sec.--Allmerica Securities Trust, Worcester, MA; *U.S. Public*, pg. 54
Boyd, James, Sec.--Goodkind & O'Dea, Inc., Rutherford, NJ; *U.S. Private*, pg. 329
Boyd, Jeffery, Exec. V.P. & Gen. Counsel--Oxford Health Plans Inc., Norwalk, CT; *U.S. Public*, pg. 1238
Boyd, R.T., Sec. & Corp. Counsel--The Torrington Co., Torrington, CT; *U.S. Public*, pg. 877
Boyd, Wade C., Asst. Sec.--Longview Fibre Company, Longview, WA; *U.S. Public*, pg. 1013
Boyd, William F., V.P., Sec. & Corp. Counsel--Coeur D'Alene Mines Corporation, Coeur D'Alene, ID; *U.S. Public*, pg. 394
Boydell, A. Christopher, Sec.--Bridon PLC, Doncaster, United Kingdom; *Int'l*, pg. 215
Boyer, Tamara, Gen. Counsel & Asst. Sec.--Clayton Homes, Inc., Knoxville, TN; *U.S. Public*, pg. 382
Boylan, John L., Treas. & Asst. Sec.--Lancaster Colony Corporation, Columbus, OH; *U.S. Public*, pg. 976
Boyle, Beatrice W., Sec.--Alico, Inc., La Belle, FL; *U.S. Public*, pg. 41
Boyle, Michael W.P., Gen. Counsel & Asst. Sec.--Trans Mountain Pipeline Company Ltd., Vancouver, Canada; *Int'l*, pg. 114
Boyles, William C., V.P. & Asst. Sec.--Chesapeake Utilities Corporation, Dover, DE; *U.S. Public*, pg. 347
Boynton, Mary, Sec., Librarian & Dir.-Investor Rels.--Newcor, Inc., Bloomfield Hills, MI; *U.S. Public*, pg. 1176
Braam, James R., Chief Fin. Officer, V.P.-Fin., Treas. & Sec.--Virco Mfg. Corporation, Torrance, CA; *U.S. Public*, pg. 1721
Bradford, David, Sr. V.P., Gen. Counsel & Corp. Sec.--Novell, Inc., Orem, UT; *U.S. Public*, pg. 1203
Bradley, Donald D., Gen. Counsel & Sec.--Furon Company, Laguna Niguel, CA; *U.S. Public*, pg. 688
Bradley, Edward, Exec. V.P. & Sec.--Certified Grocers Midwest, Inc., Hodgkins, IL; *U.S. Private*, pg. 226
Bradley, J.S., Gen. Counsel & Sec.--The RTZ Corporation PLC, London, United Kingdom; *Int'l*, pg. 1118
Bradley, P.D., Sec.--Eurotherm plc, Horsham, United Kingdom; *Int'l*, pg. 465
Brady, Julie C., V.P., Gen. Counsel & Sec.--Apertus Technologies Incorporated, Eden Prairie, MN; *U.S. Public*, pg. 119
Brady, William A., V.P.-Law & Asst. Sec.--Ikon Office Solutions, Inc., Malvern, PA; *U.S. Public*, pg. 862
Braeke, Thomas K., Exec. V.P. & Sec.--Hilb, Rogal & Hamilton Company of the Quad Cities, Moline, IL; *U.S. Public*, pg. 827
Braig, Thomas, Sec.--Superior Label Systems, Inc., Mason, OH; *U.S. Private*, pg. 1055
Braine, Anthony, Sec.--The British Land Company PLC, London, United Kingdom; *Int'l*, pg. 219
Braithwaite, Garlan, V.P., Treas. & Sec.--Whitehall Corporation, Dallas, TX; *U.S. Public*, pg. 1765
Brakken, William P., Chief Fin. Officer, Sr. V.P., Treas. & Sec.--Lanoga Corporation, Redmond, WA; *U.S. Private*, pg. 650
Brams, Leonard A., Chief Fin. Officer, Sr. V.P.-Fin. & Sec.--Handleman Company, Troy, MI; *U.S. Public*, pg. 779
Brancaccio, Raymond F., V.P. & Sec.--First Central Financial Corporation, Lynbrook, NY; *U.S. Private*, pg. 406
Branch, Kay, Sec.--Crown International, Inc., Elkhart, IN; *U.S. Private*, pg. 293
Branche, Francois, Treas. & Controller--Calberson, Paris, France; *Int'l*, pg. 1163
Brandin, Patricia A., Sec.--Amoco Corporation, Chicago, IL; *U.S. Public*, pg. 101
Brandon, Lynda, Treas. & Sec.--John J. Campbell Co., Inc., Memphis, TN; *U.S. Private*, pg. 204
Brandon, Terry T., Asst. Treas. & Asst. Sec.--Longview Fibre Company, Longview, WA; *U.S. Public*, pg. 1013
Brannamam, John, Mgr.--Amana Farms, Inc., Amana, IA; *U.S. Private*, pg. 48
Brannen, John T., Treas. & Sec.--Mid America International Trucks, Inc., Memphis, TN; *U.S. Private*, pg. 743
Branson, D.A., Sec.--Totton Pumps Ltd., Southampton, United Kingdom; *Int'l*, pg. 1512
Branson, David A., Sec.--Wolseley Plc., Droitwich, United Kingdom; *Int'l*, pg. 1511
Brasher, James E., Sec. & Gen. Counsel--Western Atlas International, Inc., Houston, TX; *U.S. Public*, pg. 1757
Braswell, Walter M., V.P., Gen. Counsel & Sec.--E'Town Corporation, Westfield, NJ; *U.S. Public*, pg. 540
Braun, Morris, V.P. & Sec.--W. Braun Company, Chicago, IL; *U.S. Private*, pg. 166
Brauner, D.A., Sec.--Bertolli USA, Inc., Secaucus, NJ; *Int'l*, pg. 655
Braybrooks, Colin S., Sr. V.P., Gen. Counsel & Sec.--United Family Life Insurance Co., Atlanta, GA; *Int'l*, pg. 499
Breaux, Ron, Dir.-North American Sls.--Orion Research Inc., Boston, MA; *U.S. Public*, pg. 1592
Brecher, Howard A., V.P. & Sec.--Value Line, Inc., New York, NY; *U.S. Private*, pg. 137
Breeze, Evelyn E., V.P. & Sec.--UMB First National Bank, Collinsville, IL; *U.S. Public*, pg. 1654
Bremer, Craig W., Sec.--The Pfaltzgraff Co., York, PA; *U.S. Private*, pg. 860
Bremer, John M., Sr. V.P., Gen. Counsel & Sec.--Northwestern Mutual Life Insurance Co., Milwaukee, WI; *U.S. Private*, pg. 807
Brendzel, Ronald I., Chief Fin. Officer, Sr. V.P. & Sec.--Safeguard Health Enterprises, Inc., Anaheim, CA; *U.S. Public*, pg. 1424
Brenkus, Teri, Corp. Sec.--The Crawford Group, Cleveland, OH; *U.S. Private*, pg. 287
Brennan, Alice C., V.P. & Sec.--Bristol-Myers Squibb Company, New York, NY; *U.S. Public*, pg. 253
Brennan, Diane, Controller & Sec.--Thruway Fasteners Inc., North Tonawanda, NY; *U.S. Private*, pg. 1084
Brennan, John E., Vice Chm. & Asst. Sec.--Southern Union Company, Austin, TX; *U.S. Public*, pg. 1491
Brennan, Richard S., Gen. Counsel & Sec.--Case Corporation, Racine, WI; *U.S. Public*, pg. 311
Brennan, Walter, Sec. & Treas.--American Fabrics Company, New York, NY; *U.S. Private*, pg. 53
Brenner, David L., Sec.--Aramark Educational Resources Inc. Inc., Golden, CO; *U.S. Private*, pg. 79
Brenner, Jeffrey, Chief Fin. Officer--Database America Companies, Montvale, NJ; *U.S. Private*, pg. 312
Brent, Peter E., V.P.-Legal Affairs & Sec.--MDS Inc., Etobicoke, Canada; *Int'l*, pg. 826
Brenton, Evelyn, Sec.--Autoswage Products, Inc., Shelton, CT; *U.S. Private*, pg. 101
Breslin, Mike, Vice Chm.-Law & H.R. Worldwide--Leo Burnett Company, Inc., Chicago, IL; *U.S. Private*, pg. 183
Bressler, Bernard, Treas. & Sec.--Gradco Systems, Inc., Las Vegas, NV; *U.S. Public*, pg. 757
Bressler, Bernard, Sec.--Plenum Publishing Corporation, New York, NY; *U.S. Public*, pg. 1311
Brett, Stephen M., Exec. V.P. & Sec.--TCI Communications, Inc., Englewood, CO; *U.S. Public*, pg. 1554
Brewer, Sandra S., Sec.--Huttig Sash & Door Co., Chesterfield, MO; *U.S. Public*, pg. 457
Brewer, Scott E., V.P., Gen. Counsel & Sec.--International Total Services, Independence, OH; *U.S. Public*, pg. 908
Brewer, Stanley, Treas. & Sec.--Brewer Oil Co., Artesia, NM; *U.S. Private*, pg. 167
Brewster, Cynthia, Sec. & Mgr.-Adv.--Labelon Corporation, Canandaigua, NY; *U.S. Private*, pg. 641
Brice, Joni, Chief Exec. Officer--Heil-Brice Retail Advertising, Newport Beach, CA; *U.S. Private*, pg. 519
Briceno, Mahim, Sec. of Society--Petroleos de Venezuela S.A., Caracas, Venezuela; *Int'l*, pg. 1045
Bricknell, David J., Sec.--Pilkington Plc, Saint Helens, United Kingdom; *Int'l*, pg. 1056
Brickner, Lynne, V.P., Gen. Counsel & Sec.--Whittaker Corporation, Simi Valley, CA; *U.S. Public*, pg. 1766
Brickson, Richard A., V.P., Sec. & Gen. Counsel--The May Department Stores Company, Saint Louis, MO; *U.S. Public*, pg. 1063
Bridge, John B., V.P., Gen. Counsel & Sec.--Brougher Agency, Inc., Indianapolis, IN; *Int'l*, pg. 464
Bridges, Laura, Treas. & Sec.--Stones, Inc., Bainbridge, GA; *U.S. Private*, pg. 1045
Bridwell, R., Sec.--SGS Industrial Services, Iselin, NJ; *Int'l*, pg. 1153
Bridwell, R.K., Asst. Sec.--SGS Control Services Inc., Edison, NJ; *Int'l*, pg. 1153
Brierley, Tony, Sec.--3i Group plc, London, United Kingdom; *Int'l*, pg. 1386
Briggs, H.J., Deputy Sec.--Halifax plc, Halifax, United Kingdom; *Int'l*, pg. 589
Briggs, John, Asst. V.P., Controller & Sec.--Hy-Vee Food Stores Incorporated, West Des Moines, IA; *U.S. Private*, pg. 550
Brigham, Barbie, Sec. & Mgr.-Risk--Diagraph Corporation, Earth City, MO; *U.S. Private*, pg. 330
Bright, Gerald, V.P. & Sec.--Masco Corporation, Taylor, MI; *U.S. Public*, pg. 1052
Brill, Robert M., V.P., Gen. Counsel & Sec.--Stokely USA, Inc., Oconomowoc, WI; *U.S. Public*, pg. 1518
Brinberg, Simeon, Sr. V.P. & Sec.--Georgetown Partners, Inc., Great Neck, NY; *U.S. Private*, pg. 466
Brindisi, Geraldine M., Sec.--The American Stock Exchange, New York, NY; *U.S. Private*, pg. 62
Brindley, Jennifer, Corp. Sec.--W.A. Roosevelt Co., La Crosse, WI; *U.S. Private*, pg. 943
Brink, Steven L., Chief Fin. Officer, Treas. & Sec.--Quiksilver, Inc., Costa Mesa, CA; *U.S. Public*, pg. 1353

Brinkler, Kenneth C., Sec.--Fairmont Homes, Inc., Nappanee, IN; *U.S. Private*, pg. 391

Brinson, Steve, Sec.--Royal Oldsmobile Mazda, Inc., Metairie, LA; *U.S. Private*, pg. 948

Bristol, Gerald A., V.P.-Fin., Controller & Treas.--Red Wing Shoe Co., Inc., Red Wing, MN; *U.S. Private*, pg. 915

Britt, Kathy, Corp. Sec. & Office Mgr.--Tarrant Service, Inc., Louisville, KY; *U.S. Private*, pg. 1069

Britt, Robert D., Chief Fin. Officer, Treas. & Sec.--Green Mountain Coffee Roasters, Inc., Waterbury, VT; *U.S. Public*, pg. 761

Britt, Sheila, Asst. Sec.--Avenor, Inc., Montreal, Canada; *Int'l*, pg. 101

Brittelli, Brenda S., Chief Fin. Officer, Controller, Treas. & Sec.--Adams Wine Co., Atlanta, GA; *U.S. Private*, pg. 17

Britto, Michael, Sec. & Div. Mgr.-Fin.--Uncas Manufacturing Company, Providence, RI; *U.S. Private*, pg. 1116

Britton, Marion E., V.P., Controller & Asst. Sec.--Russel Metals Inc., Mississauga, Canada; *Int'l*, pg. 1149

Britton, Patricia, Sec. & Gen. Counsel--Porsche Cars North America, Inc., Reno, NV; *Int'l*, pg. 1063

Brizzolara, Paul T., Asst. V.P. & Asst. Sec.--The Midland Company, Cincinnati, OH; *U.S. Public*, pg. 1110

Broadwin, David, Esq., Sec.--S. Bent & Brothers, Inc., Gardner, MA; *U.S. Private*, pg. 134

Brocci, John F., V.P.-Admin. & Sec.--Kaydon Corporation, Clearwater, FL; *U.S. Public*, pg. 945

Brock, Carolyn, Sec.--J.L. Todd Auction Co., Rome, GA; *U.S. Private*, pg. 1090

Brock, Debra, Asst. Sec.--LTB Ward Constructors, Inc., Houston, TX; *U.S. Private*, pg. 347

Brocke, Jim, Sec.--George F. Brocke & Sons, Inc., Kendrick, ID; *U.S. Private*, pg. 170

Brocksher, Jean, Sec. & Asst. Treas.--Allright Corporation, Houston, TX; *U.S. Private*, pg. 42

Brockway, M., Fin. Controller & Sec.--Senior Conflow, Nottingham, United Kingdom; *Int'l*, pg. 1220

Brod, Spencer, Treas. & Sec.--Empire Diamond Corporation, New York, NY; *U.S. Private*, pg. 374

Brodbeck, Tilman, Corp. Sec.--Porsche AG, Stuttgart, Germany; *Int'l*, pg. 1063

Brodell, Albert P., Jr., Sec.--Initio, Inc., Carson City, NV; *U.S. Public*, pg. 879

Brodell, Albert P., Jr., Sec.--Deerskin Trading Post, Inc., North Bergen, NJ; *U.S. Public*, pg. 879

Broderick, Dennis J., Sr. V.P., Gen. Counsel & Sec.--Federated Department Stores, Inc., Cincinnati, OH; *U.S. Public*, pg. 617

Broderick, Lois, Sec.--Echo Bay Mines Ltd., Englewood, CO; *U.S. Public*, pg. 561

Brodie, K.D., Sec.--The News Corporation Limited, Sydney, Australia; *Int'l*, pg. 925

Brodkey, Andrew A., V.P., Gen. Counsel & Sec.--BHP Copper North America, Tucson, AZ; *Int'l*, pg. 224

Brodsky, Bernard, V.P., Treas. & Sec.--Charming Shoppes, Inc., Bensalem, PA; *U.S. Public*, pg. 335

Brodt, John D., Treas. & Sec.--Ohio Valley Electric Corporation, Piketon, OH; *U.S. Private*, pg. 813

Brody, Donald, Sec.--Brodart Company, Williamsport, PA; *U.S. Private*, pg. 170

Broen, John E., V.P.-Corp. Affairs & Sec.--Rothmans Benson & Hedges Inc., North York, Canada; *Int'l*, pg. 1130

Bromfield, Wayne A., Gen. Counsel & Sec.--The JPM Company, Lewisburg, PA; *U.S. Public*, pg. 919

Brommels, Alyce M., Sec.--Bay State Milling Co., Quincy, MA; *U.S. Private*, pg. 124

Bronson, David, Chief Fin. Officer, Sr. V.P.-Fin. & Sec.--VWR Scientific Products, West Chester, PA; *U.S. Public*, pg. 1703

Brooke, Dell S., Corp. Sec.--EBSCO Industries, Inc., Birmingham, AL; *U.S. Private*, pg. 358

Brooker, Peter, V.P.-Plng. & Sec.--The Great Atlantic & Pacific Tea Company, Inc., Montvale, NJ; *Int'l*, pg. 1375

Brookes, H.M., Treas. & Sec--Powerscreen International Plc, Dungannon, United Kingdom; *Int'l*, pg. 1066

Brooks, Barry A., Sec.--Catalina Marketing Corporation, Saint Petersburg, FL; *U.S. Public*, pg. 314

Brooks, Delcy, Corp. Sec.--Slant/Fin Corporation, Greenvale, NY; *U.S. Private*, pg. 1005

Brooks, George S., II, Gen. Counsel & Sec.--KU Energy, Lexington, KY; *U.S. Public*, pg. 940

Brooks, George S., II, Gen. Counsel & Corp. Sec.--KU Capital Corporation, Lexington, KY; *U.S. Public*, pg. 941

Brooks, Priscilla C., Corp. Sec.--The Seibels Bruce Group, Inc., Columbia, SC; *U.S. Public*, pg. 1453

Brooks, Wendell, Pres. & Sec.--Wood Group Pressure Control, Houston, TX; *U.S. Public*, pg. 1775

Brookshire, Alexandra, V.P., Gen. Counsel & Sec.--Wall Data Incorporated, Kirkland, WA; *U.S. Public*, pg. 1734

Brossard, Pierre, Sec.--Confederation Des Caisses Des Jardins, Levis, Canada; *Int'l*, pg. 325

Brostowitz, James, V.P., Treas., Controller & Asst. Sec.--Harley-Davidson, Inc., Milwaukee, WI; *U.S. Public*, pg. 786

Brountas, Paul, Corp. Sec.--Genetics Institute, Inc., Cambridge, MA; *U.S. Public*, pg. 79

Brountas, Paul P., Sec.--CML Group, Inc., Acton, MA; *U.S. Public*, pg. 279

Brown, Alan, Sec.--Petersburg Long Distance Inc., Toronto, Canada; *Int'l*, pg. 1040

Brown, Barbara, Exec. Sec.--Comprehensive Business Services Inc., Mission Viejo, CA; *U.S. Private*, pg. 423

Brown, Cathy E., Sec.--Essex County Gas Company, Amesbury, MA; *U.S. Public*, pg. 593

Brown, Celia R., Sec.--NAC Re Corp., Greenwich, CT; *U.S. Public*, pg. 1144

Brown, Celia R., V.P., Mgr.-H.R. & Asst. Sec.--NAC Reinsurance Corporation, Greenwich, CT; *U.S. Public*, pg. 1144

Brown, Celia R., V.P. & Asst. Sec.--Greenwich Insurance Company, Greenwich, CT; *U.S. Public*, pg. 1144

Brown, Celia R., V.P. & Asst. Sec.--Indian Harbor Insurance Company, Greenwich, CT; *U.S. Public*, pg. 1144

Brown, Chris, Treas. & Sec.--Bruce Foods Corp., Cade, LA; *U.S. Private*, pg. 175

Brown, David H., Sec.--Wyandot Inc., Marion, OH; *U.S. Private*, pg. 1193

Brown, David, Esq., Sec.--Kao Corporation of America (DE), Wilmington, DE; *Int'l*, pg. 717

Brown, Dennis, Sec.--Gateway Press, Inc., Louisville, KY; *U.S. Private*, pg. 441

Brown, Donna, Corp. Sec.--T & N Industries, Inc., Ann Arbor, MI; *Int'l*, pg. 1334

Brown, Eric B., V.P., Gen. Counsel & Sec.--Transocean Offshore, Inc., Houston, TX; *U.S. Public*, pg. 1631

Brown, Eric V., Jr., Sec.--Prab, Inc., Kalamazoo, MI; *U.S. Public*, pg. 1319

Brown, Frank C., V.P., Gen. Counsel & Corp. Sec.--Rexam Inc., Charlotte, NC; *Int'l*, pg. 1106

Brown, Fred, Sec.--Barratt Developments Plc, Newcastle upon Tyne, United Kingdom; *Int'l*, pg. 167

Brown, Harvey J., Sec.--F.M. Brown Sons, Inc., Birdsboro, PA; *U.S. Private*, pg. 174

Brown, Heidi L., V.P. & Gen. Counselor--LSB Industries, Inc., Oklahoma City, OK; *U.S. Public*, pg. 970

Brown, Jack R., Chief Fin. Officer, Treas. & Sec.--Florida Public Utilities Company, West Palm Beach, FL; *U.S. Public*, pg. 655

Brown, James C., Chief Fin. Officer, V.P.-Fin., Treas. & Sec.--Patterson Energy, Inc., Snyder, TX; *U.S. Public*, pg. 1265

Brown, James D., Exec. V.P. & Sec.--Pacor, Inc., Philadelphia, PA; *U.S. Private*, pg. 833

Brown, JoBeth G., V.P. & Sec.--Anheuser-Busch Companies, Inc., Saint Louis, MO; *U.S. Public*, pg. 113

Brown, Kathye W., Pres., Chief Exec. Officer, V.P. & Corp. Sec.--Brown Evans Distributing Co., Mesa, AZ; *U.S. Private*, pg. 174

Brown, Kenneth R., Sr. V.P.-Investments & Sec.--Liberty Bancorp, Inc., Oklahoma City, OK; *U.S. Public*, pg. 174

Brown, Larry G., Sr. V.P., Gen. Counsel & Sec.--AEGON USA, Inc., Baltimore, MD; *Int'l*, pg. 26

Brown, Larry R., V.P. & Gen. Counsel--The Timken Company, Canton, OH; *U.S. Public*, pg. 1617

Brown, Malcolm, Sec.--Hong Kong Telecommunications Limited, Quarry Bay, Hong Kong; *Int'l*, pg. 247

Brown, Malcolm, Company Sec.--Hong Kong Telephone Company Ltd., Wan Chai, Hong Kong; *Int'l*, pg. 247

Brown, Mary E., Asst. Treas. & Asst. Sec.--AmerenCIPS, Springfield, IL; *U.S. Public*, pg. 65

Brown, Michael, V.P.-Corp. Rels. & Sec.--Consolidated Freightways Corp., Menlo Park, CA; *U.S. Public*, pg. 435

Brown, Nancy, Treas. & Sec.--Heintzelman's Truck Center Inc., Orlando, FL; *U.S. Private*, pg. 519

Brown, Philip D, Corp. Sec.--Harrisons & Crosfield plc, London, United Kingdom; *Int'l*, pg. 598

Brown, R. C., Sec. & Gen. Counsel--BTR plc, London, United Kingdom; *Int'l*, pg. 124

Brown, Robert W., Jr., Exec. V.P., Gen. Mgr. & Sec.--Brown Motors, Toledo, OH; *U.S. Private*, pg. 174

Brown, Roger A., Sr. V.P., Sec. & Gen. Counsel--Harleysville Group, Harleysville, PA; *U.S. Public*, pg. 786

Brown, Sandra J., Corp. Sec.--People's Bank, Bridgeport, CT; *U.S. Public*, pg. 1274

Brown, Sandra J., Sec.--Pharmaceutical Formulations, Inc., Edison, NJ; *U.S. Public*, pg. 1284

Brown, Scott M., Sr. V.P., Gen. Counsel & Sec.--Tenet Healthcare Corporation, Santa Barbara, CA; *U.S. Public*, pg. 1576

Brown, Sherrie, Sec.--Baccarat, Inc., Edison, NJ; *Int'l*, pg. 132

Brown, Susan, Sec.--Brown & Brown Venture Group, LLC, Mesa, AZ; *U.S. Private*, pg. 172

Brown, Thomas H., Jr., Sec.--Molin Auto Parts Inc., Buffalo, NY; *U.S. Private*, pg. 756

Brown, Timothy N., Corp. Counsel & Sec.--J.E. Higgins Lumber Co., Concord, CA; *U.S. Private*, pg. 527

Brown, Toni, Asst. Sec.--Dewberry Design Group, Oklahoma City, OK; *U.S. Private*, pg. 329

Brown, William, Sec. & Treas.--CNL Financial Corp., Macon, GA; *U.S. Public*, pg. 281

Brown, William G., Sec.--Medicus Systems Corporation, Evanston, IL; *U.S. Public*, pg. 1080

Brown, William R., Gen. Counsel & Sec.--American United Life Insurance Company, Indianapolis, IN; *U.S. Private*, pg. 64

Brownfield, Debbie, Chief Fin. Officer, Sr. V.P. & Sec.--Lamonts Apparel, Inc., Kirkland, WA; *U.S. Public*, pg. 975

Browning, David S., Gen. Counsel & Sec.--Schlumberger Limited, New York, NY; *U.S. Public*, pg. 1439

Browning, George, Treas. & Sec.--Elk Supply Company, Clinton, OK; *U.S. Private*, pg. 371

Browning, Jean, Treas. & Sec.--Browning Chemical Corporation, White Plains, NY; *U.S. Private*, pg. 175

Browning, Jonathan W., Sec.--Bank of Utah, Ogden, UT; *U.S. Private*, pg. 114

Brownley, William L. Prieur, V.P., Gen. Counsel & Sec.--Telos Corporation, Ashburn, VA; *U.S. Public*, pg. 1573

Broyles, Thomas M., V.P.-Fin. & Sec.--Peerless Pottery, Inc., Rockport, IN; *U.S. Private*, pg. 847

Brozick, J.F., Controller & Asst. Sec.--J & L Specialty Products Corp., Pittsburgh, PA; *Int'l*, pg. 572

Bruckner, Annemarie, Asst. Sec.--Continental Materials Corporation, Chicago, IL; *U.S. Public*, pg. 441

Brucks, Elizabeth, Exec. Sec.--Helwig Carbon Products, Inc., Milwaukee, WI; *U.S. Private*, pg. 521

Bruggeman, G.F., Asst. Sec.--Al Johnson Construction Co., Bloomington, MN; *U.S. Private*, pg. 590

Brull, John J., V.P.-Fin. & Sec.--AGA Gas, Inc., Independence, OH; *Int'l*, pg. 13

Brumber, K. Richard, Sec.--Jones Chemicals, Inc., Le Roy, NY; *U.S. Private*, pg. 596

Brumby, David, Sec.--Pumpelly Oil, Inc., Westlake, LA; *U.S. Private*, pg. 895

Brumleve, David, Sr. V.P., Treas. & Sec.--Siemer Milling Company, Teutopolis, IL; *U.S. Private*, pg. 998

Brumm, James E., Exec. V.P., Sec. & Gen. Counsel--Mitsubishi International Corporation, New York, NY; *Int'l*, pg. 871

Brune, Fred M., Sr. V.P., Treas. & Sec.--Lockwood Greene Engineers, Inc., Spartanburg, SC; *Int'l*, pg. 633

Brunea, Allene, Exec. Asst.--F.N. Burt Company, Inc., Buffalo, NY; *U.S. Private*, pg. 188

Bruneel, Didier, Sec. General--Banque de France, Paris, France; *Int'l*, pg. 160

Brunet, Nicole, Asst. Sec.--Gaz Metropolitain & Company, Montreal, Canada; *Int'l*, pg. 541

Brunetta, David C., District Controller, Asst. Sec. & Treas.--Ragnar Benson, Inc., Monroeville, PA; *U.S. Private*, pg. 99

Brunk, Randy, Sec.--Producers Co-op Association, Inc., Girard, KS; *U.S. Private*, pg. 888

Brunko, C.E., Asst. Treas. & Asst. Sec.--Otter Tail Power Company, Fergus Falls, MN; *U.S. Public*, pg. 1234

Bruno, Richard M., Treas. & Asst. Sec.--Sonoco Engraph, Inc., Atlanta, GA; *U.S. Public*, pg. 1486

Bruno, Robert A., V.P., Gen. Counsel & Sec.--First Medical Group Inc., Stamford, CT; *U.S. Public*, pg. 636

Brunt, George, V.P., Gen. Counsel & Sec.--DSC Communications Corporation, Plano, TX; *U.S. Public*, pg. 475

Brunton, Dale, Reg. Mgr.-Hong Kong--AJC International, Inc., Atlanta, GA; *U.S. Private*, pg. 6

Brusegard, Richard H., Asst. Sec.--Gendis Inc., Winnipeg, Canada; *Int'l*, pg. 542

Brustein, Lawrence, Chief Fin. Officer, Sec. & Treas.--Henry Modell & Company, Inc., New York, NY; *U.S. Private*, pg. 754

Bryan, Charles R., V.P., Treas. & Sec.--AVA, Atlanta, GA; *U.S. Private*, pg. 8

Bryan, Michelle V., Sec.--US Airways Group, Inc., Arlington, VA; *U.S. Public*, pg. 1680

Bryan, Michelle V., V.P. & Dep. Gen Counsel & Sec.--US Airways, Inc., Arlington, VA; *U.S. Public*, pg. 1680

Bryan, William A., V.P.-Fin., Treas. & Sec.--Pardee Construction Company, Los Angeles, CA; *U.S. Public*, pg. 1764

Bryant, Carleton F., III, Chief Oper. Officer, Exec. V.P., Treas. & Sec.--Westerbeke Corporation, Avon, MA; *U.S. Public*, pg. 1757

Bryant, Geraldine D., Treas. & Sec.--Lowell Packing Company, Fitzgerald, GA; *U.S. Private*, pg. 679

Bryant, Randolph W., Sr. V.P., Gen. Counsel & Sec.--Group Maintenance America Corp., Houston, TX; *U.S. Public*, pg. 766

Bryant, Richard J., Treas. & Sec.--Bryant Electric Supply Company, Inc., Lowell, NC; *U.S. Private*, pg. 177

Bryson, Jeanne, Asst. V.P. & Sec.--Universal Life Insurance Company, Memphis, TN; *U.S. Private*, pg. 1127

Bryte, Deccie, Sec.--Ireland Coffee Tea, Inc., Pleasantville, NJ; *U.S. Public*, pg. 351

Bucek, Dennis C., Sr. V.P., Treas. & Asst. Sec.--Coherent, Inc., Santa Clara, CA; *U.S. Public*, pg. 395

Buchanan, James H., Chief Fin. Officer, Treas. & Sec.--Excalibur Technologies Corporation, Vienna, VA; *U.S. Public*, pg. 598

Buchanan, Jeffrey D., Chief Fin. Officer, V.P.-Fin./Admin., Treas. & Sec.--Three-Five Systems, Tempe, AZ; *U.S. Public*, pg. 1604

Bucher, Darlene, Sec.--Woodstream Corporation, Lititz, PA; *U.S. Public*, pg. 566

Bucholtz, Barbara K., Sec.--T.D. Williamson, Inc., Tulsa, OK; *U.S. Private*, pg. 1179

Buckler, Steven N., Pres. & Sec.--ACS Industries, Inc., Woonsocket, RI; *U.S. Private*, pg. 3

Buckly, Ronald W., Gen. Counsel & Sec.--Tekelec, Calabasas, CA; *U.S. Public*, pg. 1566

Buckman Davis, Katherine, Sec. & Asst. Treas--Bulab Holdings, Inc., Memphis, TN; *U.S. Private*, pg. 180

Buckman, James E., Sr. Exec. V.P., Gen. Counsel & Asst. Sec.--HFS, Incorporated, Parsippany, NJ; *U.S. Public*, pg. 321

Buda, T.J., Sr. V.P., Sec. & Gen. Counsel--Auto-Owners Insurance, Lansing, MI; *U.S. Private*, pg. 100

Budd, Geoffrey, Sec.--Dixons Group plc, Hemel Hempstead, United Kingdom,; *Int'l*, pg. 413

Budde, Kenneth C., Chief Acctg. Officer, Sr. V.P.-Fin., Treas. & Sec.--Stewart Enterprises, Inc., Metairie, LA; *U.S. Public*, pg. 1518

Budig, George J., V.P., Treas. & Sec.--Budco Group Inc., Cincinnati, OH; *U.S. Private*, pg. 178

Budnick, David, Treas. & Sec.--Hatfield Quality Meats, Hatfield, PA; *U.S. Private*, pg. 510

Buffum, Paul, V.P., Gen. Counsel & Sec.--Nashua Corporation, Nashua, NH; *U.S. Public*, pg. 1152

Buha, Robert, V.P., Sec. & Treas.--Great Lakes Peterbilt, GMC, Portage, IN; *U.S. Private*, pg. 475

Buhl, Edd R., V.P. & Sec.--Central Mutual Insurance Co., Van Wert, OH; *U.S. Private*, pg. 223

Buhl, Tim, Chief Fin. Officer & Asst. Sec.--Aerco International Inc., Northvale, NJ; *U.S. Private*, pg. 23

Buitenhuis, Theresa, Sec. & Mgr.-H.R.--Dover Industries Limited, Burlington, Canada; *Int'l*, pg. 417

Bull, Harry C., Vice Chm. & Sec.--Bradner Central Company, Chicago, IL; *U.S. Private*, pg. 164

Bullard, Peter H.F., Sec.--RMC Group p.l.c., Egham, United Kingdom; *Int'l*, pg. 1078

Buller, Carloyn J., Esq., Asst. Sec.--Essef Corporation, Chardon, OH; *U.S. Public*, pg. 592

Bulliner, P. Alan, V.P., Gen. Counsel & Sec.--Bell Atlantic Corporation, New York, NY; *U.S. Public*, pg. 201

Bulloch, Steven N., Asst. Sec.--Keycorp, Cleveland, OH; *U.S. Public*, pg. 954

Bullock, Brian, Sec. & Mgr.-Commercial & Legal Affairs--Australian Oil & Gas Corporation Limited, Sydney, Australia; *Int'l*, pg. 101

Bulovas, Marie, Treas. & Asst. Sec.--Donohue Paper Sales Corporation, Jericho, NY; *Int'l*, pg. 1075

Bulpitt, Nigel P., Sec. & Dir.--Gallaher Limited, Weybridge, United Kingdom; *Int'l*, pg. 539

Bumgardner, Eunice L., V.P. & Gen. Counsel--The Bureau of National Affairs, Inc., Washington, DC; *U.S. Private*, pg. 181
Bundage, Warner F., Sec.--Bell Atlantic-VA, Richmond, VA; *U.S. Public*, pg. 203
Bunikis, Caroline G., Asst. Sec.--Continental Homes Holding Corp., Scottsdale, AZ; *U.S. Public*, pg. 440
Bunn, D.V., Dir.-Fin. & Sec.--Morganite Thermal Ceramics Limited, Norton, United Kingdom; *Int'l*, pg. 893
Burak Melchione, Janet, Sr. V.P., Gen. Counsel & Sec.--Everest Reinsurance Holdings, Liberty Corner, NJ; *U.S. Public*, pg. 597
Burbage, Roger, Chief Fin. Officer, V.P.-Fin. & Sec.--Intrenet, Inc., Milford, OH; *U.S. Public*, pg. 910
Burcham, Kay, Treas. & Sec--Manufacturers Consolidation Service, Inc., Memphis, TN; *U.S. Private*, pg. 700
Buren, P.S., Sec.-Concern Secretariate--Koninklijke Hoogovens N.V., Ijmuiden, Netherlands; *Int'l*, pg. 753
Burgart, Richard H., Chief Fin. Officer, Treas. & Sec.--FSF Financial Corp., Hutchinson, MN; *U.S. Public*, pg. 608
Burge, Michael, V.P.-Projects & Sec.--Liechtenstein Global Trust Limited, Vaduz, Liechtenstein; *Int'l*, pg. 809
Burger, Gerald K., V.P. & Sec.--Browning-Ferris Industries, Inc., Houston, TX; *U.S. Public*, pg. 262
Burgess, Linda K., Controller & Corp. Sec.--Maynard Oil Co., Dallas, TX; *U.S. Public*, pg. 1064
Burgess, Virginia Vance, Dir.-Inv. Rels. & Asst. Sec.--Northwest Natural Gas Company, Portland, OR; *U.S. Public;* pg. 1200
Burgon, Barre G., V.P., Corp. Counsel & Sec.--Flying J. Inc., Brigham City, UT; *U.S. Private*, pg. 415
Burgoyne, Mary Louise, Treas. & Sec.--Burgoyne, Inc., Philadelphia, PA; *U.S. Private*, pg. 182
Burke, J. Terence, Gen. Counsel & Sec.--Realty One, Cleveland, OH; *U.S. Private*, pg. 914
Burke, Kelly M., V.P.-Fin., Sec. & Admin.--Burke Engineering Company, South El Monte, CA; *U.S. Private, pg. 183*
Burke, Monica J., Chief. Fin. Officer, Treas. & Sec.--Valley Forge Corporation, San Rafael, CA; *U.S. Public*, pg. 1705
Burke, Raymond T., Sec. & Tres.--Equitable Holding Corporation, Secaucus, NJ; *U.S. Public*, pg. 589
Burke, Steven C., Chief Fin. Officer, V.P.-Fin. & Admin. & Sec.--Quidel Corporation, San Diego, CA; *U.S. Public*, pg. 1352
Burke, William J., Sec. & Treas.--Insulate LLC, Auburn, WA; *Int'l*, pg. 1171
Burkett, Marvin D., Chief Fin. Officer, Sr. V.P. & Treas.--Advanced Micro Devices, Inc., Sunnyvale, CA; *U.S. Public*, pg. 21
Burkey, J. Brent, Sr. V.P., Gen. Counsel & Sec.--Matria Healthcare, Inc., Marietta, GA; *U.S. Public*, pg. 1057
Burkholder, P.W., Sec. & Treas.--AC & S Inc., Lancaster, PA; *U.S. Public*, pg. 913
Burkitt, James, Sec.--Unigate PLC, London, United Kingdom; *Int'l*, pg. 1433
Burks, Ashby Q., V.P., Gen. Counsel & Corp. Sec.--Quorum Health Group, Inc., Brentwood, TN; *U.S. Public*, pg. 1353
Burleson, Barbara E., Sec.--Pepsi-Cola Bottling Company of Charlotte Inc., Charlotte, NC; *U.S. Private*, pg. 852
Burns, Arthur L., Gen. Counsel & Sec.--Interpool, Inc., Princeton, NJ; *U.S. Public*, pg. 908
Burns, B. Bernard, Jr., Sr. V.P., Gen. Counsel & Sec.--United Dominion Industries, Ltd., Charlotte, NC; *U.S. Public*, pg. 1675
Burns, D.C., Sec.--Airtours Plc, Rossendale, United Kingdom; *Int'l*, pg. 39
Burns, Diane W., Sec.--CompuDyne Corporation, Willimantic, CT; *U.S. Public*, pg. 419
Burns, Drew, Sec.--Thomas & Betts, North Attleboro, MA; *U.S. Public*, pg. 1598
Burns, Harmon E., Exec. V.P. & Sec.--Franklin Resources, Inc., San Mateo, CA; *U.S. Public*, pg. 679
Burns, John M., Sec.--United News & Media plc, London, United Kingdom; *Int'l*, pg. 1443
Burns, Lee D., Treas. & Sec.--Servotronics, Inc., Elma, NY; *U.S. Public*, pg. 1462
Burns, Noreen E., Sec.--Brooktree Rockwell Semiconductor Systems Div., San Diego, CA; *U.S. Public*, pg. 1398
Burns, Teresa A., Asst. Sec.--General Housewares Corp., Terre Haute, IN; *U.S. Public*, pg. 715
Burnstad, Rita, Sec.--Burnstad Brothers, Inc., Tomah, WI; *U.S. Private*, pg. 187
Burnstein, Sumner, Sec.--EPX, Portland, ME; *U.S. Private*, pg. 354
Burrell, Richard L., Sr. V.P.-Fin., Treas. & Sec.--R.G. Barry Corporation, Pickerington, OH; *U.S. Public*, pg. 192
Burris, Howard W., V.P. & Asst. Sec.--Burris Foods, Inc., Milford, DE; *U.S. Private*, pg. 188
Burris, Janice B., Asst. Sec.--Family Dollar Stores, Inc., Matthews, NC; *U.S. Public*, pg. 612
Burroughs, Bobbie J., Exec. V.P.-Admin. & Sec.--Aames Financial Corporation, Los Angeles, CA; *U.S. Public*, pg. 12
Burrow, Sharon, Sec.--National Computer Print, Inc., Birmingham, AL; *U.S. Private*, pg. 780
Burrows, Dennis A., Exec V.P., Treas. & Sec.--Roper Bros. Lumber Co., Inc., Petersburg, VA; *U.S. Private*, pg. 944
Bursk, Dana, Sec.--Makino Inc., Mason, OH; *Int'l*, pg. 831
Burslem, William, III, Chief Fin. Officer, V.P. & Sec.--Travel Ports of America Inc., Rochester, NY; *U.S. Public*, pg. 1632
Burstein, Lucien, Sec.--Lazare Kaplan Intl., Inc., New York, NY; *U.S. Public*, pg. 981
Burt, Richard, V.P., Gen. Counsel & Sec.--ABB Inc., Norwalk, CT; *Int'l*, pg. 3
Burt, Victoria L., Asst. Sec.--Lampert Yards, Inc., Saint Paul, MN; *U.S. Private*, pg. 645
Burtness, Dave, V.P., Treas. & Asst. Sec.--Witcher Construction Company, Eden Prairie, MN; *U.S. Private*, pg. 347
Burton, Amanda J., Grp. Sec. & Legal Advisor--Meyer International PLC, London, United Kingdom; *Int'l*, pg. 864
Burton, Jean, Sec.--G.E. Appliances, Louisville, KY; *U.S. Public*, pg. 710
Burton, Sandra, Sec. & Mgr.-Fin.--Moss Telecommunications Services, Grand Rapids, MI; *U.S. Private*, pg. 763
Burton, Steven, Gen. Counsel & Sec.--Sithe Energies, Inc., New York, NY; *U.S. Private*, pg. 1004
Busby, D.J., Sec. & Legal--Tioxide Group Limited, London, United Kingdom; *Int'l*, pg. 663
Busby, Valerie S., Sec.--Pawling Corporation, Pawling, NY; *U.S. Private*, pg. 844
Busch, William R., Jr., Sec. & Gen. Counsel--Cowles Media Company, Minneapolis, MN; *U.S. Private*, pg. 280
Bush, Edwin F., Sec. & Gen. Counsel--Appleton Papers Inc., Appleton, WI; *Int'l*, pg. 567
Bush, John A.H., V.P., Gen. Counsel & Sec.--Rio Algom Limited, Toronto, Canada; *Int'l*, pg. 1118
Buss, Cal, V.P., Treas. & Sec.--Vallet Food Serv Inc., Dubuque, IA; *U.S. Private*, pg. 1131
Butenas, John P., Asst. Gen. Counsel & Asst. Sec.--Manor Care, Inc., Gaithersburg, MD; *U.S. Public*, pg. 1041
Butler, Brenda J., Sec.--Advantage Companies, Inc., Wichita, KS; *U.S. Private*, pg. 22
Butler, Charl L., Chief Fin. Officer, V.P. & Sec.--NBSC Corporation, Columbia, SC; *U.S. Public*, pg. 1549
Butler, William J., Sec.--Uforma Shelby Business Forms, Shelby, OH; *U.S. Private*, pg. 740
Butner, Beverly B., V.P.-Admin. & Sec.--Proto Systems of Atlanta, Alpharetta, GA; *U.S. Private*, pg. 891
Butt, P. Lawrence, V.P., Gen. Counsel & Sec.--Marsh Supermarkets, Inc., Indianapolis, IN; *U.S. Public*, pg. 1049
Buttacavoli, Frank, Chief Fin. Officer & Exec. V.P.--Parlux Fragrances Inc., Fort Lauderdale, FL; *U.S. Public*, pg. 1264
Butterfield, Benjamin P., Sec. & Gen. Counsel--Hughes Supply, Inc., Orlando, FL; *U.S. Public*, pg. 846
Butterfield, P.C., Sec.--British Mohair Spinners Limited, Bradford, United Kingdom; *Int'l*, pg. 219
Button, Russ, Sec. & Treas.--Hastings, Inc., Barrie, Canada; *U.S. Public*, pg. 798
Butts, Edward A., V.P.-Gen. Counsel & Sec.--Ameritech, Chicago, IL; *U.S. Public*, pg. 97
Buxkemper, Melissa, Sec.--Buena Vista Home Video, Burbank, CA; *U.S. Public*, pg. 513
Buzzard, Michael, Sec.--Effingham-Clay Service Co., Effingham, IL; *U.S. Private*, pg. 365
Buzzell, James R., V.P., Treas. & Sec.--ADT Automotive, Inc., Nashville, TN; *U.S. Public*, pg. 1648
Bybee, O. Lynn, Controller, Treas. & Sec.--Wick Building Systems, Mazomanie, WI; *U.S. Private*, pg. 1174
Byer, Marian, Treas. & Sec.--Byer California, San Francisco, CA; *U.S. Private*, pg. 191
Byler, John, Exec. V.P. & Sec.--Carlos R. Leffler Inc., Richland, PA; *U.S. Private*, pg. 658
Bynum, Jeffery A., V.P.-Land & Sec.--Lomak Petroleum Inc., Fort Worth, TX; *U.S. Public*, pg. 1012
Byrne, James T., Jr., Sec.--Bankers Trust New York Corporation, New York, NY; *U.S. Public*, pg. 185
Byrne, Timothy W., Chief Fin. Officer, Sr. V.P. & Sec.--United States Lime & Minerals, Dallas, TX; *U.S. Public*, pg. 1684
Byvanck, Th. Th., Corp. Sec.--Koninklijke Hoogovens N.V., Ijmuiden, Netherlands; *Int'l*, pg. 753
Byvanck, Th. Th., Sec.--Hoogovens Groep B.V., Ijmuiden, Netherlands; *Int'l*, pg. 753
Caban, Desiree Kim, Sec.--Warrantech Corporation, Stamford, CT; *U.S. Public*, pg. 1740
Cabanes, Pierre, Sr. V.P. & Sec.--Thomson S.A., Paris, France; *Int'l*, pg. 1381
Cabanes, Pierre, Sr. V.P. & Corp. Sec.--Thomson-CSF S.A., Paris, France; *Int'l*, pg. 1383
Cabello, David, Sr. V.P., Gen. Counsel & Sec.--COMPAQ Computer Corporation, Houston, TX; *U.S. Public*, pg. 417
Cabot, Christopher, Sec.--Samuel Cabot, Inc., Newburyport, MA; *U.S. Private*, pg. 198
Cabral, Warren, Sec.--Fencourt Reinsurance Co. Ltd., Hamilton, Bermuda; *U.S. Public*, pg. 795
Cader, Arnold, Sec.--A.G. Simpson Co. Limited, Scarborough, Canada; *Int'l*, pg. 1252
Cadman, T.J., Dir.-Fin. & Sec.--Senior Phoenix RFS Limited, Bridgnorth, United Kingdom; *Int'l*, pg. 1221
Cadwallader, Elizabeth E., Sec.--The Fifth Third Bank of Columbus, Columbus, OH; *U.S. Public*, pg. 621
Cagampang-De Castro, Soledad M., V.P.-Legal & Audit & Sec.--Benguet Corporation, Manila, Philippines; *Int'l*, pg. 186
Cahill, James, Chief Fin. Officer, Exec. V.P., Treas. & Sec.--Strattec Securities Corporation, Milwaukee, WI; *U.S. Public*, pg. 1523
Cahill, Kenneth, V.P. & Sec.--Larken Inc., Cedar Rapids, IA; *U.S. Private*, pg. 651
Cahoon, Philip R., V.P., Controller & Asst. Sec.--QMS, Inc., Mobile, AL; *U.S. Public*, pg. 1346
Cain, David P., Sr. V.P., Gen. Counsel & Sec.--International Comfort Products, Franklin, TN; *U.S. Public*, pg. 898
Calabrese, Joseph J., Jr., Chief Fin. Officer, Exec. V.P. & Sec.--Harvey Electronics, Inc., Lyndhurst, NJ; *U.S. Public*, pg. 796
Calder, Kathryn A., V.P. & Sec.--Scott's Restaurants Inc., Markham, Canada; *Int'l*, pg. 1213
Calder, Kathryn A., V.P. & Sec.--Scott's Food Services Inc., Markham, Canada; *Int'l*, pg. 1213
Calder, Kathryn A., V.P. & Sec.--Scott's Management Services Inc., Markham, Canada; *Int'l*, pg. 1213
Caldwell, Allen, Sec.--Koch Industries, Incorporated, Wichita, KS; *U.S. Private*, pg. 628
Caldwell, Harold L., Sec.--Gibson Greetings, Inc., Cincinnati, OH; *U.S. Public*, pg. 742
Calfas, William, Exec. V.P., Gen. Counsel & Sec.--Courtaulds Aerospace, Glendale, CA; *Int'l*, pg. 339
Calhound, Alexander D., Sec.--Union Bank of California, San Francisco, CA; *Int'l*, pg. 157
Caliendo, G.D., Sr. V.P., Gen. Counsel & Sec.--Orange and Rockland Utilities, Inc., Pearl River, NY; *U.S. Public*, pg. 1229
Calier, M., Sec.--ETEX, Vernouillet, France; *Int'l*, pg. 430
Calise, Nicholas J., V.P., Assoc. Gen. Counsel & Sec.--The B.F. Goodrich Company, Richfield, OH; *U.S. Public*, pg. 751
Calise, William J., Jr., Sr. V.P., Gen. Counsel & Sec.--Rockwell International Corporation, Costa Mesa, CA; *U.S. Public*, pg. 1397
Callaghan, Patrick, V.P. & Sec.--Tetko, Inc., Briarcliff Manor, NY; *U.S. Private*, pg. 1078
Callahan, Mary J., Asst. Sec.--Caterpillar Inc., Peoria, IL; *U.S. Public*, pg. 315
Callahan, Sandra W., Treas. & Asst. Sec.--TECO Energy, Inc., Tampa, FL; *U.S. Public*, pg. 1565
Callas, M. Jane, Asst. Sec.--D.C. Taylor Co., Cedar Rapids, IA; *U.S. Private*, pg. 1070
Callaway, Joe, Treas. & Sec.--Coda Energy, Inc., Dallas, TX; *U.S. Public*, pg. 584
Callaway, Karl E., Sec.--Monarch Cement Co., Humboldt, KS; *U.S. Public*, pg. 1123
Calligaro, Darryl, Grp. Sec.--Peters & Brownes Foods Ltd., Balcatta, Australia; *Int'l*, pg. 1040
Cama, Christina B., V.P. & Sec.--American Reliable Insurance Company, Scottsdale, AZ; *U.S. Public*, pg. 67
Cambournac, Francois, Corp. Sec.--Havas Advertising, Levallois-Perret, France; *Int'l*, pg. 600
Camera, Nicholas J., V.P., Gen. Counsel & Sec.--The Interpublic Group of Companies, Inc., New York, NY; *U.S. Public*, pg. 908
Camerlinckx, F.J., Sec.--Esso Inc., Brussels, Belgium; *U.S. Public*, pg. 602
Camerlinckx, F.J., Sec.--Esso N.V./S.A., Maasmechelen, Belgium; *U.S. Public*, pg. 602
Cameron, Beatrice, Sec.--Barger Builders, Saint Petersburg, FL; *U.S. Private*, pg. 116
Cameron, E. Colby, Sec.--Kervick Enterprises, Inc., Worcester, MA; *U.S. Private*, pg. 616
Camosy, John P., Sr. V.P.--Camosy, Inc., Russell, IL; *U.S. Private*, pg. 203
Camp, Tom, V.P., Treas., Gen. Counsel & Sec.--The Apogee Companies, Inc., Lake Oswego, OR; *U.S. Private*, pg. 77
Campbell, Alex, Sec.--Thornton Oil Corp., Louisville, KY; *U.S. Private*, pg. 1084
Campbell, Allan R., Sr. V.P. & Gen. Counsel--Unitrode Corporation, Merrimack, NH; *U.S. Public*, pg. 1694
Campbell, Ann P., Sec.--The Flight International Group, Inc., Newport News, VA; *U.S. Public*, pg. 654
Campbell, E.F., Asst. Sec.--Aero Corporation, Lake City, FL; *U.S. Public*, pg. 1766
Campbell, Eugene B., Jr., V.P.-Fin.--Mrs. Giles Country Kitchens, Inc., Lynchburg, VA; *U.S. Public*, pg. 596
Campbell, G. Anthony, Gen. Counsel & Sec.--Flowers Industries, Inc., Thomasville, GA; *U.S. Public*, pg. 656
Campbell, Mike, Controller & Sec.--Fareway Stores, Inc., Boone, IA; *U.S. Private*, pg. 393
Campbell, Regina, Sec.--Bellsouth Wireless, Inc., Atlanta, GA; *U.S. Public*, pg. 208
Campbell, Robert D., Treas. & Asst. Sec.--Playboy Enterprises, Inc., Chicago, IL; *U.S. Public*, pg. 1309
Campbell, Robert J., V.P. & Sec.--American National Property & Casualty Co., Springfield, MO; *U.S. Public*, pg. 87
Campbell, Ronald, Sec. & Mgr.-Credit--Enco Materials, Inc., Nashville, TN; *U.S. Private*, pg. 375
Campbell, Shirley, Sec.--The Roanoke Times, Roanoke, VA; *U.S. Private*, pg. 649
Candee, William J., III, Sec.--Forest Laboratories, Inc., New York, NY; *U.S. Public*, pg. 670
Candioty, Linda, Exec. V.P.--Cheesecake Factory Incorporated, Calabasas Hills, CA; *U.S. Public*, pg. 343
Cannata, Daphne P., Sr. V.P.-Gen. Admin. & Sec.--The Norwich Savings Society, Norwich, CT; *U.S. Public*, pg. 1203
Canning, John B., Corp. Sec. & Assoc. Gen. Counsel--Rayonier Inc., Stamford, CT; *U.S. Public*, pg. 1363
Canning, Lucretia L., Asst. Sec.--United Fire & Casualty Company, Cedar Rapids, IA; *U.S. Public*, pg. 1677
Cannon, Bruce A., Chief Fin. Officer, Sr. V.P., Treas. & Sec.--SpecTran Corporation, Sturbridge, MA; *U.S. Public, pg. 1497*
Cannon, Harold, Sec.--Advanced Animations, Inc., Stockbridge, VT; *U.S. Public*, pg. 1703
Cannon, Harold, Sec.--Retail Stores, Inc., Smyrna, GA; *U.S.* Public, pg. 1703
Cannon, Harold, Sec.--VISPAC Inc., Livonia, MI; *U.S. Public, pg. 1703*
Cannon, Harold, Sec.--Visual Services Inc., Bloomfield Hills, MI; *U.S. Public*, pg. 1703
Cannon, Harold D., Sec.--VSI Holdings, Inc., Bloomfield Hills, MI; *U.S. Public*, pg. 1703
Cannon, Rose Marie C., Treas. & Sec.--Cannon Express Inc., Springdale, AR; *U.S. Public*, pg. 301
Cano, Norma, Sec.--Penaflor S.A., Buenos Aires, Argentina; *Int'l*, pg. 1032
Cantor, Sheldon, V.P. & Asst. Sec.--American Banknote Corp., New York, NY; *U.S. Public*, pg. 68
Caparros, Ann M., V.P., Gen. Counsel & Sec.--Horace Mann Educators Corporation, Springfield, IL; *U.S. Public, pg. 835*
Caplan, W., Sec.--Harwick Standard Distribution Corporation, Akron, OH; *U.S. Private*, pg. 509
Caporella, Joseph G., Exec. V.P. & Corp Sec.--National Beverage Corp., Plantation, FL; *U.S. Public*, pg. 1153
Cappers, Murray, Sec.--National Fire Protection Association, Quincy, MA; *U.S. Private*, pg. 782
Capps, Rae A., V.P., Gen. Counsel & Sec.--Hawaiian Airlines, Inc., Honolulu, HI; *U.S. Public*, pg. 799
Capps, Sherrill M., V.P., Sec. & Treas.--Washburn Graphics, Inc., Charlotte, NC; *U.S. Public*, pg. 291

Cappuccitti, R., V.P. & Corp. Secretary--Maple Leaf Foods Inc., Toronto, Canada; *Int'l*, pg. 841

Capson, Robert, Asst. Corp. Sec.--Bruncor, Inc., Saint John, Canada; *Int'l*, pg. 230

Caputo, Vincent, V.P., Asst. Treas. & Asst. Sec.--Aris Industries, Inc., New York, NY; *U.S. Public*, pg. 129

Caramazza, Kathi, Sec.--Lasco Bathware, Anaheim, CA; *Int'l*, pg. 1397

Carbone, Gene, Chief Fin. Officer, V.P.-Fin. & Sec.--Calavo Growers of California, Santa Ana, CA; *U.S. Private*, pg. 199

Cardine, Mac, V.P. & Sec.--MCDR, Inc., Memphis, TN; *U.S. Private*, pg. 686

Cardman, Philip N., V.P., Gen. Counsel & Sec.--Objective Systems Integrators, Inc., Folsom, CA; *U.S. Public*, pg. 1209

Cardman, Phillip N., V.P., Gen. Counsel & Sec.--Convex Technology Center - Hewlett-Packard, Richardson, TX; *U.S. Public*, pg. 815

Cardoza, Robert J., Sec.--American Automobile Association, Heathrow, FL; *U.S. Private*, pg. 50

Careless, Robert A., Sec.--Sketchley Plc, Hinckley, United Kingdom; *Int'l*, pg. 1261

Carey-Ranes, Marianne, Asst. Sec.--Medicalodges, Inc., Coffeyville, KS; *U.S. Private*, pg. 728

Carlbom, Chuck, Pres., Chief Exec. Officer & Sec.--United Grocers Inc., Portland, OR; *U.S. Private*, pg. 1122

Carles, Robert S., Sec.--Lance, Inc., Charlotte, NC; *U.S. Public*, pg. 977

Carley, Garry G., Exec. V.P. & Sec.--Standard Federal Bank, Troy, MI; *Int'l*, pg. 10

Carlile, Richard F., Sec.--Van Dyne-Crotty, Inc., Dayton, OH; *U.S. Private*, pg. 1132

Carlin, Donald, V.P. & Sec.--Ridg's Finer Foods, Garland, TX; *U.S. Public*, pg. 1288

Carlin, Edward R., Chief Fin. Officer, Exec. V.P. & Sec.--Goody's Family Clothing, Inc., Knoxville, TN; *U.S. Public*, pg. 753

Carlsen, David R., Chm. Bd., Sec. & Legal Counsel--Upper Midwest Industries, Incorporated, Minneapolis, MN; *U.S. Private*, pg. 1129

Carlson, Bruce R., Treas. & Sec.--Park Construction Company, Minneapolis, MN; *U.S. Private*, pg. 839

Carlson, Jennie P., Sr. V.P., Deputy Gen. Counsel & Asst. Sec.--Starbanc Corporation, Cincinnati, OH; *U.S. Public*, pg. 1510

Carlson, Kathy, Sec.--Papa Gino's Inc., Dedham, MA; *U.S. Private*, pg. 837

Carlson, Kenneth J., Jr., Sec. & Dir.-Bus. Plng.--DSM Engineering Plastic Products, Reading, PA; *Int'l*, pg. 354

Carlson, Larue, Sec.--AXIA Incorporated, Lombard, IL; *U.S. Private*, pg. 103

Carlson, LeRoy, Chief Fin. Officer, Chief Acctg. Officer, Exec. V.P. & Sec.--BRE Properties, Inc., San Francisco, CA; *U.S. Public*, pg. 163

Carlson, Samuel L., Sr. V.P.-Admin. & Sec.--Pancho's Mexican Buffet, Inc., Fort Worth, TX; *U.S. Public*, pg. 1255

Carlson, Stanley A., Sr. V.P., Gen. Counsel & Corp. Sec.--Seafirst Corporation, Seattle, WA; *U.S. Public*, pg. 181

Carlson, Winfield W., V.P. & Asst. Sec.--St. Joe Corp., Jacksonville, FL; *U.S. Public*, pg. 1426

Carlton, Dorothy, Treas. & Sec.--Corrugated Metals, Inc., Bedford Park, IL; *U.S. Private*, pg. 277

Carlton, Jeffrey, Sec.--New Brunswick Power Corporation, Fredericton, Canada; *Int'l*, pg. 923

Carlucci, Christine M., V.P.-Admin. & Opers. & Sec.--Marisa Christina Inc., New Hyde Park, NY; *U.S. Public*, pg. 1044

Carmack, John, Sec.--Amelco Corporation, Gardena, CA; *U.S. Public*, pg. 65

Carman, Dhar, Chief Fin. Officer, Exec. V.P. & Sec.--Statex Petroleum, Inc., Dallas, TX; *U.S. Public*, pg. 1245

Carnahan, John M., Treas. & Sec.--Woodfin Pontiac-Isuzu, Baton Rouge, LA; *U.S. Private*, pg. 1187

Carneal, Drew St. J., Sr. V.P., Corp. Counsel & Sec.--Owens & Minor Inc., Glen Allen, VA; *U.S. Public*, pg. 1236

Carney, Dennis, Chief Fin. Officer, Treas. & Sec.--Midwest Mutual Insurance Co., West Des Moines, IA; *U.S. Private*, pg. 881

Carney, Dennis, Treas. & Sec.--Equity Fire & Casualty Insurance Company, West Des Moines, IA; *U.S. Private*, pg. 881

Carney, Steve, Sec.--Harvest States Cooperatives, Saint Paul, MN; *U.S. Private*, pg. 508

Carney, Thomas D., V.P. & Gen. Counsel--Borders Group, Inc., Ann Arbor, MI; *U.S. Public*, pg. 245

Carolan, Margaret, Exec. Sec.--Macy's East, New York, NY; *U.S. Public*, pg. 618

Carolus, Paul R., Chief Fin. Officer, Treas. & Sec.--Westwood Corporation, Tulsa, OK; *U.S. Public*, pg. 1763

Carolus, Russell S., V.P. & Sec.--Chatwins Group, Inc., Pittsburgh, PA; *U.S. Private*, pg. 231

Carpenter, Barbara J., Asst. Corp. Sec.--MTS Systems Corporation, Eden Prairie, MN; *U.S. Public*, pg. 1028

Carpenter, Ernest A., V.P.-Admin. & Gen. Counsel--Tippins Incorporated, Pittsburgh, PA; *U.S. Private*, pg. 1088

Carpenter, Francis, Sec. Gen.--European Investment Bank, Luxembourg, Luxembourg; *Int'l*, pg. 465

Carpenter, Karen L., Exec. V.P. & Sec.--Curtis-Toledo, Inc., Saint Louis, MO; *U.S. Private*, pg. 298

Carpenter, Phyllis, Sec.--Ahlstrom Machinery, Glens Falls, NY; *Int'l*, pg. 34

Carpenter, W. Geoffrey, Asst. Sec. & Assoc. Gen. Counsel--McCormick & Company, Incorporated, Sparks, MD; *U.S. Public*, pg. 1066

Carr, David, Chief Fin. Officer, Sr. V.P. & Sec.--Latshaw Enterprises, Inc., Wichita, KS; *U.S. Public*, pg. 979

Carr, Gwenn L., V.P., Sec. & Assoc. Gen. Counsel--ITT Industries, Inc., White Plains, NY; *U.S. Public*, pg. 859

Carr, Tina, V.P.-Human Resources & Sec.--First Northern Capital Corp., Green Bay, WI; *U.S. Public*, pg. 636

Carrara, John J., Asst. Gen. Counsel & Asst. Sec.--Westvaco Corporation, New York, NY; *U.S. Public*, pg. 1762

Carrell, Nancy J., V.P., Gen. Counsel & Sec.--Celanese Canada, Inc., Montreal, Canada; *Int'l*, pg. 625

Carrico, F. Donald, Treas. & Sec.--Rapid Industries, Inc., Louisville, KY; *U.S. Private*, pg. 910

Carrico, Patrick, Treas. & Sec.--Holderness Supplies, Tucson, AZ; *U.S. Private*, pg. 534

Carrier, Arthur, Sec.--Associated Electric Co-op Inc., Springfield, MO; *U.S. Private*, pg. 89

Carrigan, Dale, Sec.--Wilsey Bennett Co., San Francisco, CA; *U.S. Private*, pg. 1180

Carroll, Gerald, V.P. & Sec.--Arrowhead Holding Corporation, Brecksville, OH; *U.S. Private*, pg. 86

Carroll, Gerald, V.P. & Sec.--Vesper Corporation, Brecksville, OH; *U.S. Private*, pg. 86

Carroll, Gerald J., Corp. Sec.--Vester Corporation, Newtown Square, PA; *U.S. Private*, pg. 86

Carroll, Gerald J., Sec.--Starboard Data Services, Inc., King of Prussia, PA; *U.S. Private*, pg. 86

Carroll, Kathleen M., V.P., Gen. Counsel & Sec.--Chartwell Re Corporation, Stamford, CT; *U.S. Public*, pg. 336

Carroll, Robert C., Sec.--CBC-U.S.A Inc., Chicago, IL; *U.S. Public*, pg. 337

Carse, Jimmie L., Treas. & Sec.--Carse Oil Co. Inc., Orlando, FL; *U.S. Private*, pg. 216

Carson, Daniel M., V.P., Gen. Counsel & Sec.--Sweetheart Cup Company Inc., Owings Mills, MD; *U.S. Private*, pg. 1058

Carson, Joanne S., Sec.--Irvine Sensors Corporation, Costa Mesa, CA; *U.S. Public*, pg. 913

Carten, John, Asst. Corp. Sec.--Amtrak-National Railroad Passenger Corp., Washington, DC; *U.S. Private*, pg. 68

Carter, Anthony, M.D., Sec.--Health Plan of Nevada, Inc., Las Vegas, NV; *U.S. Public*, pg. 1469

Carter, C. Michael, Exec. V.P., Gen. Counsel & Sec.--Pinkerton's Inc., Encino, CA; *U.S. Public*, pg. 1296

Carter, Cheryl C., Sec. & Dir.-Investor Rels.--Synalloy Corporation, Spartanburg, SC; *U.S. Public*, pg. 1547

Carter, David R., Treas. & Sec.--Trustmark National Bank, Jackson, MS; *U.S. Public*, pg. 1643

Carter, E. Leo, V.P. & Asst. Sec.--Solo Cup Company, Highland Park, IL; *U.S. Private*, pg. 1013

Carter, Helen D., Sec.--Carco Electronics, Menlo Park, CA; *U.S. Private*, pg. 208

Carter, Joan, Pres., Chief Oper. Officer & Corp. Sec.--U.M. Holding Limited, Haddonfield, NJ; *U.S. Private*, pg. 1113

Carter, Larry R., Chief Fin. Officer, V.P.-Fin. & Admin. & Sec.--Cisco Systems, Inc., San Jose, CA; *U.S. Public*, pg. 375

Carter, Nancy Lee, Asst. Sec.--Kimberly-Clark Corporation, Dallas, TX; *U.S. Public*, pg. 958

Carter, Robert D., Sr. V.P. & Asst. Sec.--Regency Finance Company, Hermitage, PA; *U.S. Public*, pg. 607

Caruso, John A., V.P.-Legal Affairs & Sec.--Enzon, Inc., Piscataway, NJ; *U.S. Public*, pg. 587

Caruso, Joseph, V.P. & Corp. Sec.--The Guardian Life Insurance Company of America, New York, NY; *U.S. Private*, pg. 486

Caruso, Vincent, Chief Admin. Officer--Transworld Home Healthcare, Inc., New York, NY; *U.S. Public*, pg. 1632

Carvalho, Jean, Sr. V.P. & Corp. Sec.--BankAtlantic Bancorp, Inc., Fort Lauderdale, FL; *U.S. Public*, pg. 183

Case, C. Wayne, V.P., Corp. Counsel & Sec.--Gundle/SLT Environmental, Inc., Houston, TX; *U.S. Public*, pg. 769

Case, C. Wayne, Asst. Sec.--Gundle/SLT Environmental, Inc., Houston, TX; *U.S. Public*, pg. 769

Case, Robert O., Gen. Counsel & Sec.--Hach Company, Loveland, CO; *U.S. Public*, pg. 773

Casey, James M., Controller & Sec.--Bituminous Casualty Corp., Rock Island, IL; *U.S. Public*, pg. 1218

Casey, Karen L., Sec. & Treas.--Libertyville Lincoln-Mercury Sales, Inc., Libertyville, IL; *U.S. Private*, pg. 666

Casey, William, Exec. V.P. & Sec.--NationsBank Equity Mortgage Corporation, Richmond, VA; *U.S. Public*, pg. 1163

Cashwell, Henry V., Treas. & Sec.--Tencarva Machinery Co., Inc., Greensboro, NC; *U.S. Private*, pg. 1075

Casis, Rachela, Sec.--Sapiens International, Rehovot, Israel; *Int'l*, pg. 1193

Casmere, Vicki L., V.P., Gen. Counsel & Sec.--Varlen Corporation, Naperville, IL; *U.S. Public*, pg. 1710

Cason, Marilynn, V.P., Gen. Counsel & Sec.--DeVry Institutes, Oak Brook Terrace, IL; *U.S. Public*, pg. 503

Cassell, Barbara, Exec. Sec.--R & R Marketing, West Caldwell, NJ; *U.S. Private*, pg. 902

Casselman, David A., V.P.-Fin., Controller, Sec. & Treas.--General Time Corp., Norcross, GA; *U.S. Private*, pg. 445

Cassens, Kay, Treas. & Sec.--Cassens Transport Company, Edwardsville, IL; *U.S. Private*, pg. 219

Cassidy, Emmet P., Treas. & Sec.--Peoples Energy Corporation, Chicago, IL; *U.S. Public*, pg. 1274

Cassidy, R. Brian, Chief Fin. Officer, Treas. & Sec.--Krasdale Foods Inc., White Plains, NY; *U.S. Private*, pg. 635

Cassner, Curtis B., Sec.--Rotary Forms Press, Inc., Hillsboro, OH; *U.S. Private*, pg. 947

Castain, Esther K., Corp. Sec. & Mgr.-Employee Rels.--Vacu-Dry Company, Sebastopol, CA; *U.S. Public*, pg. 1704

Castens, Christopher C., Sec.--International Thoroughbred Breeders, Inc., Cherry Hill, NJ; *U.S. Public*, pg. 908

Castiglione, Philip, Treas. & Sec.--Ray Laethem Pontiac-Buick-GMC-Truck, Inc., Detroit, MI; *U.S. Private*, pg. 642

Castilla, P., Sec.--BT Telecomunicaciones S.A., Madrid, Spain; *Int'l*, pg. 223

Castillo, Karen S., Sec.--Farah Incorporated, El Paso, TX; *U.S. Public*, pg. 612

Castro, Betty S., Sec.--Insurance Brokers & Managers, Inc., New Orleans, LA; *U.S. Public*, pg. 1677

Castro, J., Sec.--Ceramicas Termicas de Guatemala S.A., Guatemala, Guatemala; *Int'l*, pg. 894

Castronuovo, Dr. F., Sec.--Fiat Auto S.p.A., Milan, Italy; *Int'l*, pg. 481

Cato, Glenn P., Pres. & Chief Exec. Officer--Maxum Health Corp., Dallas, TX; *U.S. Public*, pg. 881

Caton, R., Sec.--DSI Transports, Tampa, FL; *Int'l*, pg. 1285

Catron, William G., Chief Admin. Officer, Exec. V.P. & Gen. Counsel--Galoob Toys, Inc., South San Francisco, CA; *U.S. Public*, pg. 698

Catt, R., Sec.--Simon Engineering plc, London, United Kingdom; *Int'l*, pg. 1251

Cattani, Maryellen, Exec. V.P., Gen. Counsel & Sec.--APL Limited, Oakland, CA; *Int'l*, pg. 912

Cattarmole, Carolyn, Sec.--Courtaulds Textiles Plc, London, United Kingdom; *Int'l*, pg. 339

Cattell, Peggy, Asst. Sec.--CompUSA, Dallas, TX; *U.S. Public*, pg. 420

Caudill, Douglas W., Sec.--Nobel Insurance Limited, Hamilton, Bermuda; *Int'l*, pg. 951

Causey, J.P., Jr., Sr. V.P., Gen. Counsel & Sec.--Chesapeake Corporation, Richmond, VA; *U.S. Public*, pg. 346

Cautillo, John M., Controller & Sec.--Refined Sugars, Inc., Yonkers, NY; *Int'l*, pg. 699

Cavanagh, Lucille, Sec.--International Correspondence Schools Canadian Ltd., Montreal, Canada; *U.S. Public*, pg. 784

Cavanaugh, Eugene L., Jr., V.P. & Sec.--1st Source Capital Corporation, South Bend, IN; *U.S. Public*, pg. 638

Cavanaugh, James W., Asst. Sec.--Hormel Foods Corp., Austin, MN; *U.S. Public*, pg. 840

Cavanaugh, Jim, Chm. Bd., Pres., Chief Exec. Officer & Sec.--Jani King International, Inc., Dallas, TX; *U.S. Private*, pg. 581

Cavender, William, Treas. & Sec.--Hallidie Machinery Company, Inc., Seattle, WA; *U.S. Private*, pg. 495

Cawley, C., Sec.--Esso Production Malaysia Inc., Kuala Lumpur, Malaysia; *U.S. Public*, pg. 602

Cawsey, D.R., Mgr.-H.R. & Asst. Corp. Sec.--ATCO Group Co., Calgary, Canada; *Int'l*, pg. 95

Cawsey, Dale, Asst. Sec.--Canadian Utilities Limited, Calgary, Canada; *Int'l*, pg. 95

Celentano, Doris, Treas. & Sec.--Celentano Bros. Inc., Verona, NJ; *U.S. Private*, pg. 221

Cella, Christopher L., V.P., Gen. Counsel & Sec.--Holly Corporation, Dallas, TX; *U.S. Public*, pg. 830

Cellino, Anna Marie, Sec.--National Fuel Gas Company, Buffalo, NY; *U.S. Public*, pg. 1156

Centanza, Jean, Sec.--Paris Foods Corp., Camden, NJ; *U.S. Private*, pg. 839

Cepeda, Sharon K., Asst. Sec.--GPU, Inc., Morristown, NJ; *U.S. Public*, pg. 695

Cernahouz, Ralph, V.P.-Fin. & Corp. Sec.--Schumacher Electric Corporation, Mount Prospect, IL; *U.S. Private*, pg. 973

Cerquinho da Fonesca, Luis, Sec.--UNICER-Uniao Cervejeira, S.A., Mamede de Infesta, Portugal; *Int'l*, pg. 1432

Ceruzzi, Louis, V.P. & Sec.--Massachusetts Container Corporation, Marlborough, MA; *U.S. Private*, pg. 263

Cerviem, Letizia, Corp. Sec.--BDDP S.p.A, Milan, Italy; *Int'l*, pg. 117

Chabod, Rene, Sec.--Aerospatiale, Paris, France; *Int'l*, pg. 28

Chadd, Cindy, Asst. Sec.--Sentinel Consumer Products, Inc., Mentor, OH; *U.S. Private*, pg. 984

Chadwick, William, Chief Admin. Officer, V.P. & Sec.--Ensco International Incorporated (ENSCO), Dallas, TX; *U.S. Public*, pg. 585

Chaifetz, David H., V.P., Gen. Counsel & Sec.--Praxair Inc., Danbury, CT; *U.S. Public*, pg. 1319

Chait, Jon F., Chief Fin. Officer, Exec. V.P. & Sec.--Manpower Inc., Milwaukee, WI; *U.S. Public*, pg. 1042

Chakrabarti, Udayan, Sec.--Eastern Coalfields Limited, Burdwan, India; *Int'l*, pg. 298

Chalela, R.E., Sec.--International Columbia Resources Corporation, Bogota, Colombia; *U.S. Public*, pg. 602

Chalifoux, Michael T., Chief Fin. Officer, Sr. V.P. & Sec.--Circuit City Stores, Inc., Richmond, VA; *U.S. Public*, pg. 374

Challis, J.C., Deputy Sec.--Concert Communications Company, London, United Kingdom; *Int'l*, pg. 223

Chamberlain, Carole R., Asst. Sec.--Allegheny Power System, Inc., Hagerstown, MD; *U.S. Public*, pg. 42

Chamberlain, E. Martin, V.P.-Regulatory Affairs & Sec.--Ballard Medical Products, Draper, UT; *U.S. Public*, pg. 171

Chamberlain, George M., Jr., Sr. V.P. & Sec.--Delaware Management Holdings, Inc., Philadelphia, PA; *U.S. Public*, pg. 997

Chambers, Rufus A., Sec.--W.B. Johnson Properties, LLC, Atlanta, GA; *U.S. Private*, pg. 594

Chambers, T.L., Treas. & Sec.--Rumsey Electric Company, Conshohocken, PA; *U.S. Private*, pg. 951

Chambers, William S., Sr. V.P.-Engrng. & Sec.--Kingsbury, Inc., Philadelphia, PA; *U.S. Private*, pg. 622

Chan, Henderson, Sec.--Sanwa Foods, Inc., City of Industry, CA; *U.S. Public*, pg. 299

Chan, Lincoln, Corp. Sec.--Blue Anchor, Inc., Dinuba, CA; *U.S. Private*, pg. 150

Chan, Toshiko, Sec.--World Oil Corp., South Gate, CA; *U.S. Private*, pg. 1190

Chan, William W., V.P. & Sec.--Authentic Fitness Corp., Los Angeles, CA; *U.S. Public*, pg. 147

Chanani, Madhu S., Exec. V.P., Controller & Asst. Sec.--Western Waste Industries, Torrance, CA; *U.S. Public*, pg. 1686

Chance, Steven K., V.P., Gen. Counsel & Sec.--Teleflex Incorporated, Plymouth Meeting, PA; *U.S. Public*, pg. 1569

Chandler, William E., Chief Fin. Officer, Sr. V.P.-Fin. & Sec.--Hunt Corporation, Philadelphia, PA; *U.S. Public*, pg. 848

Chaney, Mary D., V.P., Sec. & Treas.--Sterling Capital Management Company, Charlotte, NC; *U.S. Public*, pg. 1674

Chantland, Dennis A., Exec. V.P. & Sec.--Williams-Sonoma, Inc., San Francisco, CA; *U.S. Public*, pg. 1770
Chapko, Stephen J., Chief Fin. Officer, Exec. V.P., Treas. & Sec.--Kent Electronics Corp., Houston, TX; *U.S. Public*, pg. 951
Chapline, Edward S., III, Gen. Counsel & Sec.--TIC United Corporation, Dallas, TX; *U.S. Private*, pg. 1063
Chapman, C. Phillip, Chief Fin. Officer, V.P. & Sec.--Microchip Technology, Inc., Chandler, AZ; *U.S. Public*, pg. 1105
Chapman, Carl L., Asst. Sec. & Asst. Treas.--Energy Realty, Inc., Indianapolis, IN; *U.S. Public*, pg. 875
Chapman, Conrad D., Sec.--Davis Industries Inc., Plymouth, MI; *U.S. Private*, pg. 315
Chapman, H., Sec.--Burns, Philp & Company Limited, Sydney, Australia; *Int'l*, pg. 236
Chapman, H.E., Sec.--TNT Limited, Redfern, Australia; *Int'l*, pg. 1342
Chapman, Margaret A., Asst. Sec.--Reliability Incorporated, Houston, TX; *U.S. Public*, pg. 1373
Chapman, Susan E., Asst. Sec.--Datascope Corp., Montvale, NJ; *U.S. Public*, pg. 487
Chappell, Charles G., Asst. Sec.--Helix Technology Corp., Mansfield, MA; *U.S. Public*, pg. 808
Chapple, Thomas L., Sr. V.P., Gen. Counsel & Sec.--Gannett Company, Inc., Arlington, VA; *U.S. Public*, pg. 698
Charlesworth, Tom G., Sr. V.P.--Cousins Properties Incorporated, Atlanta, GA; *U.S. Public*, pg. 453
Charlton, Robin, Company Sec.--EMI Group plc, London, United Kingdom; *Int'l*, pg. 426
Charms, Iris, V.P.-Admin. & Sec.--Octagon Process Inc., Edgewater, NJ; *U.S. Private*, pg. 811
Charping, Julie, Sec.--The Ryland Group, Inc., Columbia, MD; *U.S. Public*, pg. 1414
Charron, Carol, Controller, Treas. & Sec.--Art Moran Pontiac-GMC Inc., Southfield, MI; *U.S. Private*, pg. 760
Chase, Dee Anne, Controller, Treas., Sec. & Dir.-Employee Benefits--Regency Lincoln Mercury, Inc., Dallas, TX; *U.S. Private*, pg. 918
Chase, Kathleen A., Sec.--F.H. Chase, Inc., Mansfield, MA; *U.S. Private*, pg. 230
Chatt, Joseph R., Jr., Gen. Mgr. & Sec.--Caribe Express, Aguadilla, PR; *U.S. Private*, pg. 211
Chattin, Phillip K., Gen. Counsel & Sec.--American Ecology Corporation, Boise, ID; *U.S. Public*, pg. 71
Chauvette, Claude, Sec. & Treas.--St. Lawrence Cement Inc., Montreal, Canada; *Int'l*, pg. 628
Chawla, Vera, Sec.--Information Systems & Network Corporation, Bethesda, MD; *U.S. Private*, pg. 561
Chelin, Jeffrey D., V.P.-Fin. & Sec.--ARC International Corporation, Downsview, Canada; *Int'l*, pg. 17
Chell, Beverly C., Vice Chm., Gen. Counsel & Sec.--Primedia Inc., New York, NY; *U.S. Public*, pg. 1327
Chen, C.C., Gen. Mgr.-Corp. Plng.--China Steel Corporation, Kao-hsiung, Taiwan; *Int'l*, pg. 285
Chen, John, Treas. & Sec.--Tang Industries Inc., Las Vegas, NV; *U.S. Private*, pg. 1068
Cheng, Li Ling, Sec.--Tainan Spinning Co., Ltd., Tai-nan, Taiwan; *Int'l*, pg. 1347
Cheng, Linda Y.H., Asst. Corp. Sec.--PG&E Corporation, San Francisco, CA; *U.S. Public*, pg. 1240
Chernin, Herbert, Sec.--Caravan Brokay, Totowa, NJ; *U.S. Private*, pg. 208
Chero, Thomas H., Sr. V.P.-Legal & Sec.--Avemco Corporation, Frederick, MD; *U.S. Public*, pg. 151
Cherven, Allison, Sec. Reporting Analyst--Jostens, Minneapolis, MN; *U.S. Public*, pg. 934
Chessin, Daniel J., Exec. V.P. & Sec.--Hahn Automotive Warehouse, Inc., Rochester, NY; *U.S. Public*, pg. 774
Chester, Lawrence, V.P.-Sec. & Gen. Counsel--Northern Telecom Inc., Rochester, NY; *Int'l*, pg. 970
Chi-Kin, Stewart Leung, Corp. Sec.--New World Development Co. Ltd., Hong Kong, Hong Kong; *Int'l*, pg. 923
Chiarotti, John M., Chief Oper. Officer, Sec. & Gen. Mgr.--Amos-Hill Associates, Inc., Edinburgh, IN; *U.S. Private*, pg. 67
Child, Patricia, Sec.--R.C. Willey Home Furnishings, Salt Lake City, UT; *U.S. Public*, pg. 221
Childers, James H., V.P., Sec. & Treas.--Medicalodges, Inc., Coffeyville, KS; *U.S. Private*, pg. 728
Childers, Violet, Corp. Sec.--Southern Belle Dairy Company, Somerset, KY; *U.S. Private*, pg. 1015
Chilibeck, Peter J., Asst. Gen. Counsel & Sec.--Northern Telecom Limited, Brampton, Canada; *Int'l*, pg. 968
Chilvers, Anthony, Sec.--The West Company (UK) Ltd., Saint Austell, United Kingdom; *U.S. Public*, pg. 1756
Chin, Henry W., Chief Fin. Officer, V.P.-Fin. & Sec.--Marshall Industries, El Monte, CA; *U.S. Public*, pg. 1051
Ching, Han H., Chm. Bd. & Sec.--Aloha Airgroup, Inc., Honolulu, HI; *U.S. Private*, pg. 44
Chipperfield, Lynn, V.P., Gen. Counsel & Sec.--Furniture Brands International Inc., Saint Louis, MO; *U.S. Public*, pg. 688
Chitolti, Monica, Sec.--Postalmarket, Milan, Italy; *Int'l*, pg. 1064
Chitty, Michael, Corp. Sec.--Willis Corroon Group PLC, London, United Kingdom; *Int'l*, pg. 1501
Chitwood, Frank W., Sr. V.P. & Asst. Sec.--Dewberry Design Group, Oklahoma City, OK; *U.S. Private*, pg. 329
Chiu, Robert J., Sec.--Mizuno Corporation of America, Norcross, GA; *Int'l*, pg. 885
Cho, Y. Eric, V.P. & Sec.--Avanti, Fremont, CA; *U.S. Public*, pg. 151
Choate, A.G., V.P.-Law, Gen. Counsel & Sec.--American Trading and Production Corporation, Baltimore, MD; *U.S. Private*, pg. 63
Choate, Chris A., Sr. V.P., Gen. Counsel & Sec.--AmeriCredit Corp., Fort Worth, TX; *U.S. Public*, pg. 96
Choi, Sang K., Sec.--Crown Confectionery Co., Ltd., Seoul, Korea; *Int'l*, pg. 348
Chow, Shirley, Sr. V.P.-Admin. & Fin. & Corp. Sec.--Bachmann Industries, Inc., Philadelphia, PA; *U.S. Private*, pg. 109
Choy, Benedict, Sr. V.P. & Sec.--Supertex, Inc., Sunnyvale, CA; *U.S. Public*, pg. 1539
Chozianin, H. Judith, Sec.--Ryder System, Inc., Miami, FL; *U.S. Public*, pg. 1413
Chrestman, Flossie, Sec.--ASCG, Inc., Anchorage, AK; *U.S. Private*, pg. 80
Christensen, Edward, V.P., Gen. Counsel & Sec.--Culligan International Company, Northbrook, IL; *U.S. Public*, pg. 467
Christensen, Val John, Exec. V.P.--Franklin Covey, Salt Lake City, UT; *U.S. Public*, pg. 679
Christenson, James E., V.P. & Gen. Counsel & Sec.--Herman Miller, Inc., Zeeland, MI; *U.S. Public*, pg. 1111
Christian, Mark A., V.P. & Sec.--Central Coca-Cola Bottling Company, Inc., Richmond, VA; *U.S. Private*, pg. 222
Christian, Ronald E., Gen. Counsel & Sec.--Indiana Energy, Inc., Indianapolis, IN; *U.S. Public*, pg. 874
Christian, Ronald E., Gen. Counsel & Sec.--Indiana Gas Company, Inc., Indianapolis, IN; *U.S. Public*, pg. 875
Christie, E.H., Sec. & Legal Counsel--Cyanamid Canada Inc., Markham, Canada; *U.S. Public*, pg. 80
Christine, F. Janey, Sec.--Serologicals Corporation, Clarkston, GA; *U.S. Public*, pg. 1460
Christoff, William M., Asst. Treas.-Taxes & Asst. Sec.--Brush Wellman Inc., Cleveland, OH; *U.S. Public*, pg. 266
Christofil, Jim, V.P.-Fin., Treas. & Sec.--Republic Storage Systems Company Inc., Canton, OH; *U.S. Private*, pg. 924
Chu, David, Exec. V.P. & Sec.--Nautica Enterprises, Inc., New York, NY; *U.S. Public*, pg. 1167
Chua, Ler Ching, Chief Fin. Officer, Treas. & Sec.--GB Holdings, Jurong, Singapore; *Int'l*, pg. 531
Chuan Lim, James Koh, Sec.--Jacks International Limited, Singapore, Singapore; *Int'l*, pg. 697
Chuan, Koe Eng, Sec.--Khong Guan Flour Milling Limited, Singapore, Singapore; *Int'l*, pg. 732
Chuang, Lim, Chief Fin. Officer & Sec.--Haw Par Brothers International Limited, Singapore, Singapore; *Int'l*, pg. 603
Chuang, Lim, Sec.--Tiger Medicals Ltd., Singapore, Singapore; *Int'l*, pg. 603
Chuba, Patricia A., Sec. & Asst. Treas.--AGR International, Inc., Butler, PA; *U.S. Private*, pg. 5
Chubb, Thomas C., Assoc. Gen. Counsel & Asst. Sec.--Oxford Industries, Inc., Atlanta, GA; *U.S. Public*, pg. 1239
Chun, I.H., Sec. & Mgr.-Legal & Contracts--Hyundai Electronics America, San Jose, CA; *Int'l*, pg. 641
Church, R.D., Treas. & Sec.--Erico International, Solon, OH; *U.S. Private*, pg. 381
Chused, Andrew, Treas. & Asst. Sec.--Hampton Industries, Inc., Kinston, NC; *U.S. Public*, pg. 779
Chynoweth, Robert, Treas. & Sec.--Wyoming Machinery Company, Casper, WY; *U.S. Private*, pg. 1193
Cianciusi, Diana, Gen. Counsel & Sec.--Gandalf Technologies Inc., Nepean, Canada; *Int'l*, pg. 540
Ciangiulli, Helen Sands, Asst. Sec.--International Thoroughbred Breeders, Inc., Cherry Hill, NJ; *U.S. Public*, pg. 908
Ciccotelli, Teresa T., Esq., V.P., Legal Counsel & Sec.--AmeriSource Health Corp., Malvern, PA; *U.S. Public*, pg. 96
Ciepcielinski, Stanley, Chief Fin. Officer, Exec. V.P. & Sec.--Glenayre Technologies, Inc., Charlotte, NC; *U.S. Public*, pg. 746
Cierenberg, Mr., Sec.--Kloof Gold Mining Company Limited, Johannesburg, South Africa; *Int'l*, pg. 738
Ciola, Marsha, Treas. & Sec.--National Health Products, Orlando, FL; *U.S. Private*, pg. 784
Ciottone, R.T., Sec.--Continental Water Company, Saint Louis, MO; *U.S. Private*, pg. 269
Ciprich, Paula M., Gen. Counsel & Asst. Sec.--National Fuel Gas Distribution Corp., Buffalo, NY; *U.S. Public*, pg. 1156
Ciriello, Joseph, Sec.--Plasticrete Block & Supply Corp., North Haven, CT; *U.S. Private*, pg. 871
Claasens, Jean, Asst. Sec.--BEI Technologies, Inc., San Francisco, CA; *U.S. Public*, pg. 160
Cladianos, Pete, III, Exec. V.P. & Sec.--The Sands Regent, Reno, NV; *U.S. Public*, pg. 1431
Claes, James B., Controller & Asst. Sec.--Laclede Steel Company, Saint Louis, MO; *U.S. Public*, pg. 974
Claiborne, Herbert, III, Legal Counsel & Sec.--Carpenter Co., Richmond, VA; *U.S. Private*, pg. 214
Clancy, Robert A., Sec.--Aydin Corporation, Horsham, PA; *U.S. Public*, pg. 158
Claramunt, Francisco Grau, Corp. Sec.--Compania Espanola de Petroleos, S.A. (CEPSA), Madrid, Spain; *Int'l*, pg. 323
Clariond Reyes, Eugenio, Chief Exec. Officer & Sec.--Grupo IMSA S.A. de C.V., Garza Garcia, Mexico; *Int'l*, pg. 575
Clark, Barry, Mng. Dir. & Sec.--Sime Darby Commodities Limited, London, United Kingdom; *Int'l*, pg. 1250
Clark, Candace, Chief Legal Officer, Sr. V.P. & Sec.--Kaman Corporation, Bloomfield, CT; *U.S. Public*, pg. 941
Clark, Cheryl M., Corp. Clerk--The Berkshire Gas Company, Pittsfield, MA; *U.S. Public*, pg. 216
Clark, David, Asst. Sec.--Meggitt plc, Wimborne Minster, United Kingdom; *Int'l*, pg. 853
Clark, Dennis, Chief Fin. Officer, V.P. & Sec.--Carus Corporation, Peru, IL; *U.S. Private*, pg. 217
Clark, Edith, Sec.--SGS Government Programs Inc., New York, NY; *Int'l*, pg. 1153
Clark, Frederick H., Sec.--ANR Pipeline Co., Detroit, MI; *U.S. Public*, pg. 389
Clark, J. Patrick, V.P., Gen. Counsel & Sec.--Dentsply International Inc., York, PA; *U.S. Public*, pg. 498
Clark, James N., Exec. V.P. & Sec.--The Western and Southern Life Insurance Company, Cincinnati, OH; *U.S. Private*, pg. 1164
Clark, John M., III, Sr. V.P., Gen. Counsel & Sec.--National Semiconductor Corporation, Santa Clara, CA; *U.S. Public*, pg. 1159
Clark, Jonathan M., Gen. Counsel & Sec.--Morgan Stanley Group Inc., New York, NY; *U.S. Public*, pg. 1132
Clark, M.A.C., Sec.--Cadbury Schweppes p.l.c., London, United Kingdom; *Int'l*, pg. 247
Clark, Nancy L., V.P.-Fin. & Sec.--Cowden Metal Specialties, Inc., Chino, CA; *U.S. Private*, pg. 280
Clark, Richard M., Sr. V.P., Gen. Counsel & Sec.--Kellogg Company, Battle Creek, MI; *U.S. Public*, pg. 947
Clark, Robert, Sec.--Eagle Button Co., Inc., Carlstadt, NJ; *U.S. Private*, pg. 354
Clark, Sandy, Sec.--Acme Mills Co. Inc., Detroit, MI; *U.S. Private*, pg. 13
Clark, Scott W., Treas. & Sec.--Construction Management Service, Wilmington, DE; *U.S. Private*, pg. 266
Clark, Susan, V.P., Treas. & Asst. Sec.--Dewberry Design Group, Oklahoma City, OK; *U.S. Private*, pg. 329
Clark, Tom, Treas. & Sec.--Big Horn Co-Op Marketing Association, Greybull, WY; *U.S. Private*, pg. 143
Clarke, Peter C., Sec.--The British Land Corporation Limited, London, United Kingdom; *Int'l*, pg. 219
Clarke, Peter W., Chief Fin. Officer, Exec. V.P. & Sec.--Orthofix International N.V., Curacao, Netherlands Antilles; *Int'l*, pg. 1011
Clarke, Wendolyn C., Asst. Sec.--UNUM Corporation, Portland, ME; *U.S. Public*, pg. 1699
Clarkson, Charles, Sec. & Counsel--TLC Beatrice International Holdings Inc., New York, NY; *U.S. Private*, pg. 1064
Clarkson, Janice, Sec.--Clarkson Construction Companies, Kansas City, MO; *U.S. Private*, pg. 244
Clarkson, S.B., V.P., Gen. Counsel & Sec.--Newport News Shipbuilding, Inc., Newport News, VA; *U.S. Public*, pg. 1179
Claunch, Joe Howard, Treas. & Sec.--Somerset Refinery Inc., Somerset, KY; *U.S. Private*, pg. 1013
Clauser, Fred, Sec.--Koh-I-Noor, Inc., Bloomsbury, NJ; *U.S. Private*, pg. 629
Claussen, Vera, Sec.--Public Utility District No. 2 of Grant County, Ephrata, WA; *U.S. Private*, pg. 893
Clays, P.J., Sec.--Dulmison (U.K.) Limited, Corby, United Kingdom; *Int'l*, pg. 893
Clayton, Charles W., Chief Fin. Officer, V.P. & Treas.--Hampshire Group, Ltd., Anderson, SC; *U.S. Public*, pg. 778
Clayton, John, Sec.--Guardian Royal Exchange Plc, London, United Kingdom; *Int'l*, pg. 577
Clayton, K.B., V.P., Treas. & Asst. Sec.--Taylor Woodrow Homes Florida Inc., Sarasota, FL; *Int'l*, pg. 1359
Clayton, Patricia, Sec.--Putt Putt Golf Courses of America, Inc., Fayetteville, NC; *U.S. Private*, pg. 896
Cleary, Robert T., Chief Exec. Officer, Treas. & Sec.--KineticSystems Corporation, Lockport, IL; *U.S. Private*, pg. 620
Cleary, Robert T., V.P.-Inventory Plng. & Admin.--Columbia House Music Club, New York, NY; *Int'l*, pg. 1281
Cleckner, Richard W., Sec.--Stephenson Equipment, Inc., Harrisburg, PA; *U.S. Private*, pg. 1040
Clegg, Scott, V.P. & Asst. Sec.--Merryhill Country Schools, Inc., Sacramento, CA; *U.S. Public*, pg. 1186
Clemence, Richard R., Vice Chm.--Hyde Manufacturing Co., Southbridge, MA; *U.S. Private*, pg. 551
Clement, Patricia E., Treas. & Asst. Sec.--BNI Coal, Ltd., Bismarck, ND; *U.S. Public*, pg. 1116
Clemente, Sharon, Sec.--Dallas Peterbilt, Inc., Irving, TX; *U.S. Private*, pg. 309
Clementi, Carole Anne, Sec.--General American Investors Company, Inc., New York, NY; *U.S. Public*, pg. 706
Clements, James E., Chief Fin. Officer & Sec.--Dorsey Trailers, Inc., Atlanta, GA; *U.S. Public*, pg. 520
Clements, Norman F., V.P., Sec. & Treas.--EAC Corporation, Saint Louis, MO; *U.S. Private*, pg. 353
Clemmer, Linda, Asst. Sec.--Furnival/State Machinery Co., Hatfield, PA; *Int'l*, pg. 744
Clendenan, R.E., Dir.-Human Resources, Admin. Sec.--Chemetics International Company Ltd Vancouver Operations, Vancouver, Canada; *Int'l*, pg. 774
Cleveland-Booth, Beth, Sec.--Castleberry/Snow's Brands Inc., Augusta, GA; *U.S. Private*, pg. 219
Cleveland, Joe, V.P. & Sec.--NCH Corporation, Irving, TX; *U.S. Public*, pg. 1145
Click, Dennis, V.P. & Sec.--Nationwide Insurance Enterprise, Columbus, OH; *U.S. Private*, pg. 788
Clifton, Harold S., Sec.--The Bakersfield Californian, Bakersfield, CA; *U.S. Private*, pg. 112
Clifton, Jean B., Chief Fin. Officer, Exec. V.P., Treas. & Sec.--Journal Register Company, Trenton, NJ; *U.S. Public*, pg. 934
Climent, Henri, Sec. Gen.--Facom, Morangis, France; *Int'l*, pg. 570
Clinebell, Kenneth M., Chief Fin. Officer, Treas. & Sec.--Precision Systems, Inc., Saint Petersburg, FL; *U.S. Public*, pg. 1321
Clodfetter, Steve, Sec.--Consolidated Foundries, Cudahy, CA; *U.S. Private*, pg. 265
Cloney, Richard M., V.P. & Sec.--Susquehanna Bancshares, Inc., Lititz, PA; *U.S. Public*, pg. 1542
Clonts, Richard, Chief Fin. Officer, V.P.-Fin & Sec.--Sewell Village Cadillac Co., Dallas, TX; *U.S. Private*, pg. 988
Closterman, Jane, Controller & Asst. Sec.--TIE/Communications, Inc., Overland Park, KS; *U.S. Private*, pg. 1085
Cloutier, N. Paul, V.P., Gen. Counsel & Sec.--Gendis Inc., Winnipeg, Canada; *Int'l*, pg. 542
Cloutier, Nicole, Sec.--WF Corroon Canada Inc., Montreal, Canada; *Int'l*, pg. 1502
Clymer, Stuart, Sec.--Universal Voltronics Corporation, Mount Kisco, NY; *U.S. Public*, pg. 1596
Coasson, lawrence P., Treas. & Sec.--FieldBrook Farms, Inc., Dunkirk, NY; *U.S. Private*, pg. 403
Coates, Glenn, Sec.--Racine Federated, Inc., Racine, WI; *U.S. Private*, pg. 906
Coble, Ted C., V.P., Treas. & Asst. Sec.--Piedmont Natural Gas Co., Inc., Charlotte, NC; *U.S. Public*, pg. 1295

Cobley, Martin, Sec.--BHP Steel Europe Middle East Ltd., Bromley, United Kingdom; *Int'l*, pg. 227
Coburn, Anna Mary, Sec.--Host Marriott Corporation, Bethesda, MD; *U.S. Public*, pg. 841
Cocci, Emma Marie, Sec.--Scanforms, Inc., Bristol, PA; *U.S. Public*, pg. 228
Cochius, H., Sec.--Highveld Steel & Vanadium Corporation, Witbank, South Africa; *Int'l*, pg. 76
Cochran, Elizabeth, Sec.--Walker Die Casting, Inc., Lewisburg, TN; *U.S. Private*, pg. 1147
Cochran, Joe, Asst. Sec.--Phillips Petroleum Company, Bartlesville, OK; *U.S. Public*, pg. 1290
Cochrane, E.G., II, V.P.-Sec. & Gen. Counsel--Mount Vernon Mills, Inc., Greenville, SC; *U.S. Private*, pg. 835
Cochrane, Laura J., Gen. Counsel & Sec.--TSI Incorporated, Shoreview, MN; *U.S. Public*, pg. 1559
Cocke, Norman A., Chief Fin. Officer, Sr. V.P. & Sec.--Chronimed Inc., Minnetonka, MN; *U.S. Public*, pg. 352
Codrington, R.G., Sec.--TransTec Plc, Birmingham, United Kingdom; *Int'l*, pg. 1418
Coe, Donna J., Asst. V.P. & Asst. Sec.--Smith Technologies Corp., Portland, OR; *U.S. Public*, pg. 1478
Coefield, Pat, Corp. Secretary--Sunnyland Refining Co., Inc., Birmingham, AL; *U.S. Private*, pg. 607
Cofer, David T., V.P., Gen. Counsel & Sec.--Kennametal Inc., Latrobe, PA; *U.S. Public*, pg. 950
Cogdill, Rick, Chief Fin. Officer & Exec. V.P.--Pilgrim's Pride Corporation, Pittsburg, TX; *U.S. Public*, pg. 1296
Cohane, Timothy, Sec.--Times Fiber Communications, Inc., Wallingford, CT; *U.S. Private*, pg. 629
Cohen de Lara, M.M.I., Sec.--VNU Verenigde Nederlandse Uitgeversbedrijven B.V., Haarlem, Netherlands; *Int'l*, pg. 1445
Cohen, Alan H., Chief Oper. Officer, Exec. V.P. & Sec.--George Uhe Co., Inc., Paramus, NJ; *U.S. Private*, pg. 1115
Cohen, Barbara, Sec.--Familian Corp., Van Nuys, CA; *Int'l*, pg. 1512
Cohen, Clifford A., Asst. Sec.--Lady Baltimore Foods, Inc., Kansas City, KS; *U.S. Public*, pg. 975
Cohen, Howard, V.P.-Admin. & Asst. Sec.--General Microwave Corporation, Amityville, NY; *U.S. Public*, pg. 717
Cohen, Karen G., Sec.--Amwest Surety Insurance Company, Calabasas, CA; *U.S. Public*, pg. 106
Cohen, Lou, Sec.--National Restaurant Management, Inc., New York, NY; *U.S. Private*, pg. 786
Cohen, Marvin, Sr. V.P. & Sec.--LCS Industries, Inc., Clifton, NJ; *U.S. Public*, pg. 970
Cohen, Robert, Gen. Counsel & Sec.--Hall Financial Group, Inc., Dallas, TX; *U.S. Private*, pg. 495
Cohen, Steven, Sec.--Robbins Auto Parts, Inc., Dover, NH; *U.S. Private*, pg. 934
Cohen, Victor, V.P. & Gen. Counsel--Polo/Ralph Lauren Corporation, New York, NY; *U.S. Private*, pg. 874
Cohenca, Emilia, Chm. Bd.--Jason Industrial, Inc., Fairfield, NJ; *U.S. Private*, pg. 583
Cohl, Robert A., V.P.-Admin. & Sec.--Slater Industries Inc., North York, Canada; *Int'l*, pg. 1262
Cohn, Carol, Treas. & Sec.--Decorative Crafts, Inc., Greenwich, CT; *U.S. Private*, pg. 320
Cohn, Kenneth D., V.P.-Benefits & Asst. Sec.--Southdown, Inc., Houston, TX; *U.S. Public*, pg. 1488
Cohn, Martin, Sec.--Emcee Broadcast Products, Inc., White Haven, PA; *U.S. Public*, pg. 570
Coker, D.J., Sec.--Morgan Crucible Co. Plc, Windsor, United Kingdom; *Int'l*, pg. 890
Colaianne, John M., Chief Fin. Officer & Sec.--Cambridge Industries Inc., Madison Heights, MI; *U.S. Private*, pg. 202
Colangelo, Joe, Asst. Sec.--Getty Petroleum Marketing Inc., Jericho, NY; *U.S. Public*, pg. 740
Colantino, M.B., Sec.--Darlene Jewelry Manufacturing Company, Pawtucket, RI; *U.S. Private*, pg. 311
Colbert, M.W., Sec.--Morgan Refractories Inc., Canon City, CO; *Int'l*, pg. 893
Colburn, J. Brian, Exec. V.P.-Special Projects & Sec.--Magna International Inc., Markham, Canada; *Int'l*, pg. 829
Colby, Albert A., Jr., V.P.-Domestic Phosphate, Treas. & Sec.--International Chemical Company, Tulsa, OK; *U.S. Private*, pg. 568
Cole, Betty, Sec.--Trend Line Corporation, Jackson, MS; *U.S. Private*, pg. 1099
Cole, David O., Chief Fin. Officer, V.P., Controller, Treas. & Sec.--Lincoln Foodservice Products, Inc., Fort Wayne, IN; *Int'l*, pg. 188
Cole, Robert B., Sec.--Lennar Corporation, Miami, FL; *U.S. Public*, pg. 987
Cole, Vincent J., V.P., Gen. Counsel & Sec.--Lexmark International Group, Inc., Lexington, KY; *U.S. Public*, pg. 991
Cole, Vincent J., V.P., Gen. Counsel & Sec.--Lexmark International, Inc., Lexington, KY; *U.S. Public*, pg. 991
Coleman, John W., Asst. to the Pres.--American General Life & Accident Insurance Co., Nashville, TN; *U.S. Public*, pg. 76
Coleman, Robert E., Treas. & Sec.--Coleman Oldsmobile, Inc., Baton Rouge, LA; *U.S. Private*, pg. 252
Collette, Bill, V.P.-Engrng. & Devel. & Sec.--Computer Network Technology Corporation, Minneapolis, MN; *U.S. Public*, pg. 421
Collicelli, Gilles, Sec.--Editions d'enseignements-religieux F.P.R. Inc., Montreal, Canada; *Int'l*, pg. 1077
Collin, Mark H., Chief Fin. Officer, Treas. & Sec.--Unitil Corporation, Hampton, NH; *U.S. Public*, pg. 1692
Collins, Donald F., Treas. & Sec.--Collins Electric Company, Inc., Chicopee, MA; *U.S. Private*, pg. 253
Collins, Dorothy, Exec. Sec.--Vester Corporation, Newtown Square, PA; *U.S. Private*, pg. 86
Collins, Frank, Sec.--HMO Texas, L.C., Houston, TX; *U.S. Public*, pg. 1470
Collins, Frank E., Exec. V.P., Gen. Counsel & Sec.--Sierra Health Services, Inc., Las Vegas, NV; *U.S. Public*, pg. 1469
Collins, Gillian, Sec.--Chubb Insurance Company of Europe, Brussels, Belgium; *U.S. Public*, pg. 355
Collins, John J., Jr., V.P., Gen. Counsel & Sec.--Champion Enterprises, Inc., Auburn Hills, MI; *U.S. Public*, pg. 332
Collins, Julie E., Chief Fin. Officer, Treas. & Sec.--Continental Homes Holding Corp., Scottsdale, AZ; *U.S. Public*, pg. 440
Collins, Julie E., Treas. & Sec.--Continental Homes, Inc., Scottsdale, AZ; *U.S. Public*, pg. 440
Collins, Patricia M., V.P., Assoc. Gen. Counsel & Asst. Sec.--Ogden Energy Group, Inc., Fairfield, NJ; *U.S. Public*, pg. 1213
Collins, Thomas P., V.P.-Legal & Sec.--Wilmington Trust Corporation, Wilmington, DE; *U.S. Public*, pg. 1770
Collinsworth, William J., Chief Fin. Officer, V.P.-Fin., Treas. & Asst. Sec.--Optek Technology, Inc., Carrollton, TX; *U.S. Public*, pg. 1227
Collova, J. James, Chief Fin. Officer & Sec.--Paper Calmenson & Co., Saint Paul, MN; *U.S. Private*, pg. 837
Colombo, Aldolfo, Sec.--Metropolitana Milanese S.P.A., Milan, Italy; *Int'l*, pg. 863
Colquhoun, A.T., Sec.--Matthew Clark Taunton, Ltd., Bristol, United Kingdom; *Int'l*, pg. 848
Colton, David J., Sec.--Domestic Uniform Rental Co., Farmington Hills, MI; *U.S. Private*, pg. 338
Colton, Michael L., Sec.--Rodney Hunt Company, Orange, MA; *U.S. Private*, pg. 549
Colville, William W., Sr. V.P., Gen. Counsel & Acting Sec.--Owens Corning, Toledo, OH; *U.S. Public*, pg. 1236
Combs, Katherine K., Sec.--PECO Energy Company, Philadelphia, PA; *U.S. Public*, pg. 1268
Comerford, Thomas M., Asst. Sec.--JC Penney Company, Inc., Plano, TX; *U.S. Public*, pg. 916
Como, Patricia, Controller & Asst. Sec.--Offshore Logistics, Inc., Lafayette, LA; *U.S. Public*, pg. 1212
Compean, J., Pres. & Sec.--Grupo Video Visa S.A. de C.V., Mexico, Mexico; *Int'l*, pg. 577
Compton, Gregory A., Sr. V.P., Sec. & Gen. Counsel--NTS Development Company, Louisville, KY; *U.S. Private*, pg. 772
Compton, Walter K., Sec. & Mgr.-Law Dept.--Murphy Oil Corporation, El Dorado, AR; *U.S. Public*, pg. 1141
Compton, Walter K., Sec.--Murphy Exploration & Production Co., New Orleans, LA; *U.S. Public*, pg. 1142
Comstock, Linda, Exec. Sec.--The Troy Savings Bank, Troy, NY; *U.S. Private*, pg. 1106
Conant, Philip D., V.P. & Sec.--Golden Gem Growers Inc., Umatilla, FL; *U.S. Private*, pg. 460
Condit, Linda F., V.P. & Corp. Sec.--Pennzoil Company, Houston, TX; *U.S. Public*, pg. 1272
Condon, Edward, Asst. Sec.--Playboy Preferred, Inc., Itasca, IL; *U.S. Public*, pg. 1310
Condon, Robert V., Chief Fin. Officer, V.P.-Fin., Treas. & Sec.--Merrimac Industries, Inc., West Caldwell, NJ; *U.S. Public*, pg. 1098
Cone, D.L., Asst. Sec.--Phillips Petroleum Company, Bartlesville, OK; *U.S. Public*, pg. 1290
Cone, H.D., Sec.--Rolls-Royce Power Engineering plc, Newcastle upon Tyne, United Kingdom; *Int'l*, pg. 1127
Congdon, Jeffrey, Chief Fin. Officer & Sec.--Budget Group, Inc., Daytona Beach, FL; *U.S. Private*, pg. 178
Conklin, M.E., Corp. Sec.--Conklin Instrument Corporation, Pleasant Valley, NY; *U.S. Private*, pg. 263
Conklin, Thomas J., Sr. V.P. & Corp. Sec.--The Mutual Life Insurance Company of New York, New York, NY; *U.S. Private*, pg. 769
Conlon, Michael, Sec.--Quanex Corporation, Houston, TX; *U.S. Public*, pg. 1349
Conn, Richard, Treas. & Sec.--Ervin Industries, Inc., Ann Arbor, MI; *U.S. Private*, pg. 382
Connelly, Elizabeth K., Sr. V.P., Corp. Sec., Human Resources & Office Mngmt.--Adler Boschetto Peebles & Partners, Inc., New York, NY; *U.S. Private*, pg. 17
Connors, Joseph J., Asst. Sec.--Kleinert's, Inc., of Alabama, Elba, AL; *U.S. Private*, pg. 625
Connors, Joseph J., Treas. & Asst. Sec.--Kleinert's Inc. of Florida, Largo, FL; *U.S. Private*, pg. 625
Conrad, Kim R., Controller, Treas. & Sec.--B & G Wholesalers, Inc., Nashville, TN; *U.S. Private*, pg. 105
Conrad, Lucius C., V.P.--Chemoil, San Francisco, CA; *U.S. Private*, pg. 233
Conradsen, Jane, Sec.--Agri-Mark, Inc., Lawrence, MA; *U.S. Private*, pg. 26
Conradt, Woody, Chief Fin. Officer, Treas. & Sec.--Telsco Industries, Garland, TX; *U.S. Private*, pg. 1074
Conroy, John P., V.P. & Sec.--Greif Brothers Corporation, Delaware, OH; *U.S. Public*, pg. 763
Consiglio, Lic. R.C., Sec.--Grupo Sitra, S.A. DE C.V., Guadalajara, Mexico; *Int'l*, pg. 775
Convisser, Theodora S., Clerk--Boston Edison Company, Boston, MA; *U.S. Public*, pg. 247
Conway, J.W., Sec. & Treas.--Atlas Tag & Label Inc., Neenah, WI; *U.S. Private*, pg. 145
Conway, Robert D., Treas. & Sec.--Schneider National, Inc., Green Bay, WI; *U.S. Private*, pg. 971
Cook, Debbie, Sec. & Treas.--Cook Manufacturing Corporation, Duncan, OK; *U.S. Private*, pg. 272
Cook, Judy C., Mgr.-Pres. Office Svcs. & Asst. Corp. Sec.--Public Service Company of North Carolina, Inc., Gastonia, NC; *U.S. Public*, pg. 1340
Cook, Linda S., V.P., Treas. & Sec.--Georgia Casualty & Surety Company, Atlanta, GA; *U.S. Public*, pg. 143
Cook, Maureen I., Asst. Sec.--Silcorp Limited, Scarborough, Canada; *Int'l*, pg. 1249
Cook, Mike, Treas. & Sec.--Collins Oldsmobile Inc., Indianapolis, IN; *U.S. Private*, pg. 253
Cook, Richard A., Chief Fin. Officer, Treas. & Sec.--Johanna Foods Inc., Flemington, NJ; *U.S. Private*, pg. 589
Cook, Terry, Sr. V.P., Gen. Counsel & Sec.--Kaiser Ventures, Inc., Ontario, CA; *U.S. Public*, pg. 941
Cooke, Charles M., IV, Sec.--Molokai Ranch Ltd., Honolulu, HI; *Int'l*, pg. 216
Cooke, Roger, Sr. V.P., Gen. Counsel & Sec.--Smith's Food & Drug Centers, Inc., Salt Lake City, UT; *U.S. Public*, pg. 1103
Cooke, Roger A., Sr. V.P., Gen. Counsel & Sec.--Fred Meyer Incorporated, Portland, OR; *U.S. Public*, pg. 1103
Cooke, Roger A., Sr. V.P., Gen. Counsel & Sec.--Fred Meyer Stores, Portland, OR; *U.S. Public*, pg. 1103
Cooke, Stephen D., Sr. V.P., Gen. Counsel & Sec.-AMBAC Assurance Corp.--AMBAC Financial Group, Inc., New York, NY; *U.S. Public*, pg. 62
Cooksey, David C., Chief Fin. Officer, V.P. & Sec.--Contico International, Inc., Saint Louis, MO; *U.S. Private*, pg. 267
Coomer, Ralph, Treas. & Sec.--Ziniz Inc., Louisville, KY; *U.S. Private*, pg. 1206
Cooney, Michael B., Sr. V.P.-Law & Admin. & Sec.--A.P. Green Industries, Inc., Mexico, MO; *U.S. Public*, pg. 761
Coons, Ann M., Assoc. Gen. Counsel & Asst. Sec.--The Times Mirror Company, Los Angeles, CA; *U.S. Public*, pg. 1615
Cooper, Candy, Sec.-Sls.Svcs.--Shell Chemical Co., Houston, TX; *Int'l*, pg. 1136
Cooper, Cary D., Corp. Sec.--Cherokee Inc., Van Nuys, CA; *U.S. Public*, pg. 345
Cooper, D. Page, Dir.-Employee Benefits & Asst. Sec.--Media General, Inc., Richmond, VA; *U.S. Public*, pg. 1077
Cooper, Doris, Asst. Sec. & Mgr.-Communications--General Employment Enterprises, Inc., Oak Brook Terrace, IL; *U.S. Public*, pg. 714
Cooper, Richard F., V.P.-Admin, Gen. Counsel & Sec.--Arkansas Best Corporation, Fort Smith, AR; *U.S. Public*, pg. 130
Cooper, Sheila, Sr. V.P., Gen. Counsel & Sec.--Mary Kay, Inc., Dallas, TX; *U.S. Private*, pg. 711
Cooper, Steven D., Sr. V.P.-Plng., Gen. Counsel & Sec.--Electrolux Corporation, Atlanta, GA; *U.S. Private*, pg. 369
Coopr, Jerome, Treas. & Sec.--Green Bus Lines, Inc., Jamaica, NY; *U.S. Private*, pg. 476
Coots, E. Davis, Sec.--ADT Security Systems, Inc., Carmel, IN; *U.S. Public*, pg. 1649
Cope, Ruth, Sec. & Office Mgr.--John Copes Food Products, Inc., Rheems, PA; *U.S. Private*, pg. 274
Copeland, G.J., Sec.--Whessoe Plc, Newton Aycliffe, United Kingdom; *Int'l*, pg. 1498
Copland, Ronald G., Exec. V.P., Sec. & Asst. Treas.--Copland Fabrics, Inc., Burlington, NC; *U.S. Private*, pg. 274
Coppock, Paul C., Chief Admin. Officer, Sr. V.P., Gen. Counsel & Sec.--Harsco Corporation, Camp Hill, PA; *U.S. Public*, pg. 792
Coppola, Carl, Pres. & Sec.--Mark Lighting Fixture Co., Inc., Edison, NJ; *U.S. Private*, pg. 704
Coquillette, William H., Asst. Sec.--The Lamson & Sessions Co., Cleveland, OH; *U.S. Public*, pg. 976
Corbett, Grafton J., III, Sec.--Textile Rubber & Chemical Company, Dalton, GA; *U.S. Private*, pg. 1079
Corbett, John, Treas. & Sec.--United Feeds, Inc., Sheridan, IN; *U.S. Private*, pg. 1122
Corbin, R. F., Treas. & Sec.--Metal Trades, Inc., Hollywood, SC; *U.S. Private*, pg. 734
Cordek, Lawrence D., Chief Fin. Officer & Corp. Sec.--G B Stores, Columbus, OH; *U.S. Private*, pg. 972
Cormick, Charles B.A., Sec.--The Rank Group PLC, London, United Kingdom; *Int'l*, pg. 1086
Corn, Amy C., Sec. & Assoc. Gen. Counsel--Pitney Bowes Inc., Stamford, CT; *U.S. Public*, pg. 1303
Corn, Pauline G., Chief Info. Officer, Treas. & Sec.--Industrial Maintenance Overflow Corporation, Fletcher, NC; *U.S. Private*, pg. 561
Cornelius, Michael A., V.P.-Law & Admin. & Sec.--Western Digital Corporation, Irvine, CA; *U.S. Public*, pg. 1758
Cornell, Helen, V.P., Treas. & Sec.--Gardner Denver Machinery Inc., Quincy, IL; *U.S. Public*, pg. 703
Cornish, Jeff, Chief Fin. Officer & V.P.--Pilot Corporation, Knoxville, TN; *U.S. Private*, pg. 865
Cornish, Jeffrey L., Treas. & Sec.--Pilot Corporation, Knoxville, TN; *U.S. Private*, pg. 865
Cornish, Jeffrey L., Sec.--Pilot Receivables Corporation, Knoxville, TN; *U.S. Private*, pg. 865
Cornwell, Kevin L., Chm. Bd., Pres. & Chief Exec. Officer--Utah Medical Products, Inc., Midvale, UT; *U.S. Public*, pg. 1700
Corr, Deborah A., Treas. & Asst. Sec.--VWR Scientific Products, West Chester, PA; *U.S. Public*, pg. 1703
Corr, Robert R., Controller, Treas. & Sec.--BEI Technologies, Inc., San Francisco, CA; *U.S. Public*, pg. 160
Corrigan, Joanne, Sec.--JSB Financial, Lynbrook, NY; *U.S. Public*, pg. 919
Corsanico, Toni, Exec. Sec.--Angelo Brothers Co., Philadelphia, PA; *U.S. Private*, pg. 74
Cortazzo, Susan N., V.P., Controller & Sec.--Lillian Vernon Corporation, New Rochelle, NY; *U.S. Public*, pg. 1716
Cortese, Greg, V.P., Gen. Counsel & Sec.--PAR Technology Corporation, New Hartford, NY; *U.S. Public*, pg. 1256
Corteslla, Roser, Sec.--Mattel Espana, S.A., Barcelona, Spain; *U.S. Public*, pg. 1059
Corwin, Laura J., Sec. & Corp. Counsel--The New York Times Company, New York, NY; *U.S. Public*, pg. 1173
Corwine, David B., V.P., Gen. Counsel & Corp. Sec.--Allied Products Corporation, Chicago, IL; *U.S. Public*, pg. 48
Cosbey, J.R., V.P., Treas. & Sec.--Daubert Industries, Inc., Westchester, IL; *U.S. Private*, pg. 313
Cosner, Alan, V.P., Treas. & Sec.--Lady Baltimore Foods, Inc., Kansas City, KS; *U.S. Public*, pg. 975
Cost, John J., Sec.--Bell Industries, Inc., El Segundo, CA; *U.S. Public*, pg. 204
Costantini, Lou, Jr., Chief Fin. Officer, V.P., Sec., & Treas.--Century Door U.S.A. Inc., Tampa, FL; *Int'l*, pg. 1067
Coster, Victor J., Controller & Sec.--Cache, Inc., New York, NY; *U.S. Public*, pg. 289

Costigan, John M., Sr. V.P., Gen. Counsel & Sec.--Premark International, Inc., Deerfield, IL; *U.S. Public*, pg. 1321
Cotanda, Francisco Carballo, Dir.-Legal Affairs & Sec.--Repsol S.A., Madrid, Spain; *Int'l*, pg. 1104
Cothran, Jack T., Corp. Counsel & Asst. Sec.--Abrams Industries, Inc., Atlanta, GA; *U.S. Public*, pg. 14
Coticchia, Michael L., Asst. Sec.--Applied Industrial Technologies, Cleveland, OH; *U.S. Public*, pg. 122
Cottee, K.E., Sec.--Morganite Carbon NZ Ltd, Auckland, New Zealand; *Int'l*, pg. 892
Cotti, Araceli, Sec.--Finlay Enterprises, Inc., New York, NY; *U.S. Public*, pg. 623
Cottick, William R., Sec. & Assoc. Gen. Counsel--Laidlaw Inc., Burlington, Canada; *Int'l*, pg. 259
Cottle, Karen, V.P., Gen. Counsel & Sec.--Raychem Corporation, Menlo Park, CA; *U.S. Public*, pg. 1362
Cottrell, Frank S., V.P., Gen. Counsel & Sec.--Deere & Company, Moline, IL; *U.S. Public*, pg. 491
Cottrell, Frank S., Sec.--John Deere Credit Company, Moline, IL; *U.S. Public*, pg. 492
Coughlin, F.X., Jr., Exec. V.P. & Sec.--F.X. Coughlin Co., Taylor, MI; *U.S. Private*, pg. 278
Coughlin, Joseph P., Sr. V.P. & Sec.--NUI Corporation, Bedminster, NJ; *U.S. Public*, pg. 1147
Coulston, Christy, Asst. Sec.--Sonoma Valley Bank, Sonoma, CA; *U.S. Public*, pg. 1487
Coulter, Chad W., Asst. Sec.--Delphi Financial Group, Inc., Wilmington, DE; *U.S. Public*, pg. 496
Coulter, Chad W., V.P., Gen. Counsel & Sec.--Reliance Standard Life Insurance Company, Philadelphia, PA; *U.S. Public*, pg. 496
Coupe, Bruce A., Treas. & Sec.--Peerless Tyre Co., Denver, CO; *U.S. Private*, pg. 847
Courtade, Arturo Perez, Gen. Counsel & Sec.--Grupo Sidek, S.A. de C.V., Guadalajara, Mexico; *Int'l*, pg. 576
Courteault, Antoine, Gen. Sec.--CERUS - Compagnies Europeennes Reunies, Paris, France; *Int'l*, pg. 240
Courtney, Richard, Sec.--US 1 Industries Inc., Gary, IN; *U.S. Public*, pg. 1687
Covey, Joy D., Chief Fin. Officer, V.P.-Fin., Treas. & Sec.--Amazon.com, Inc., Seattle, WA; *U.S. Public*, pg. 62
Covey, Steven K., Corp. Sec.--Navistar International Corporation, Chicago, IL; *U.S. Public*, pg. 1167
Covez, R.A., Gen. Counsel & Sec.--Foster-Miller, Inc., Waltham, MA; *U.S. Private*, pg. 421
Cowan, Charles G., V.P. & Sec.--Hollinger Inc., Vancouver, Canada; *Int'l*, pg. 630
Cowan, Richard, Chief Fin. Officer, Treas., Controller & Sec.--Wheeler Brothers Grain Co., Watonga, OK; *U.S. Private*, pg. 1171
Coward, John, Sec.--Windsor Shade Tobacco Company, Inc., Hartford, CT; *U.S. Private*, pg. 1182
Cowder, Stephen, Sec.--Glaxo Wellcome plc, London, United Kingdom; *Int'l*, pg. 552
Cowell, Marion A., Jr., Exec. V.P., Gen. Counsel & Sec.--First Union Corporation, Charlotte, NC; *U.S. Public*, pg. 639
Cowen, Robert N., Sr. V.P. & Sec.--Overseas Shipholding Group, Inc., New York, NY; *U.S. Public*, pg. 1236
Cowper-Smith, G. Blair, Corp. Sec. & Special Counsel--Stelco Inc., Hamilton, Canada; *Int'l*, pg. 1299
Cox, William S., V.P., Gen. Counsel & Sec.--Smith Technologies Corp., Portland, OR; *U.S. Public*, pg. 1478
Cox, Arthur, Treas. & Sec.--The Knapheide Mfg. Co., Quincy, IL; *U.S. Private*, pg. 626
Cox, Christeen H., Corp. Sec. & Dir.-Human Resources--American Cometra, Inc., Fort Worth, TX; *Int'l*, pg. 562
Cox, Dennis, Controller, Asst. Sec. & Treas.--McGill Manufacturing Company, Inc., Valparaiso, IN; *U.S. Public*, pg. 573
Cox, Karen E., Sec.--Sunlink Corporation, Atlanta, GA; *U.S. Public*, pg. 208
Cox, Richard, V.P. & Sec.--Cox Furniture, Maxton, NC; *U.S. Private*, pg. 283
Cox, Robert G., Sec.--Kentucky Medical Insurance Company (KMIC), Louisville, KY; *U.S. Private*, pg. 741
Cox, S.A., Sec.--H.J. Tinsley & Co. Limited, Grantham, United Kingdom; *Int'l*, pg. 891
Cox, Stephen, Dir.-Legal Services & Sec.--Laura Ashley Holdings Plc, Maidenhead, United Kingdom; *Int'l*, pg. 804
Cox, Stephen, Sec.--Laura Ashley Holdings Plc, Maidenhead, United Kingdom; *Int'l*, pg. 804
Cox, Thomas P., Sr. V.P.-Fin., Sec. & Treas.--Timberline Software Corporation, Beaverton, OR; *U.S. Public*, pg. 1609
Coyle, Dennis P., Gen. Counsel & Sec.--FPL Group, Inc., North Palm Beach, FL; *U.S. Public*, pg. 608
Cozean, Ronald J., Gen. Counsel & Sec.--Park-Ohio Industries, Inc., Cleveland, OH; *U.S. Public*, pg. 1258
Crabtree, Richard, Treas. & Sec.--SCR, Inc., Tigard, OR; *U.S. Private*, pg. 955
Cradon, R.M., Sec.--The Peninsular and Oriental Steam Navigation Company, London, United Kingdom; *Int'l*, pg. 1032
Craig, David T., Chief Fin. Officer & Sec.--Australia & New Zealand Banking Group Limited, Melbourne, Australia; *Int'l*, pg. 98
Craig, John H., Sec.--Derlan Industries Limited, Toronto, Canada; *Int'l*, pg. 395
Craig, Peter M., Vice Chm. & Exec. V.P.--Rainbow Technologies, Inc., Irvine, CA; *U.S. Public*, pg. 1359
Crain, Merrilee P., Sec.--Crain Communications, Inc., Chicago, IL; *U.S. Private*, pg. 284
Cramer, Dwight, Corp. Sec.--Western National Corporation, Houston, TX; *U.S. Public*, pg. 76
Cramer, Michael J., V.P., Gen. Counsel & Sec.--The Morning Star Group, Dallas, TX; *U.S. Public*, pg. 1527
Cramm, C. Brian, Chief Fin. Officer & V.P.-Fin.--Dakota Mining Corporation, Denver, CO; *U.S. Public*, pg. 477
Crankshaw, H.J., Sec.--De Beers Consolidated Mines Limited, Kimberley, South Africa; *Int'l*, pg. 76
Crans, Rhoda, Exec. Sec.--Tutor-Saliba Corporation, Sylmar, CA; *U.S. Private*, pg. 1111
Craun, Todd R., Gen. Counsel & Sec.--Airgas, Inc., Radnor, PA; *U.S. Public*, pg. 33
Craven, Dorothy W., Corp. Sec.--B.B. Walker Company, Asheboro, NC; *U.S. Public*, pg. 1734
Cravens, Mary Ann, V.P.-Admin. & Sec.--Star Lumber & Supply Company, Inc., Wichita, KS; *U.S. Private*, pg. 1034
Crawford, C. Suzanne, V.P.-Legal Affairs & Sec.--Consoltex Group Inc., Ville Saint Laurent, Canada; *Int'l*, pg. 326
Crawford, Christine, Sec. & Legal Officer--Henkels & McCoy, Inc., Blue Bell, PA; *U.S. Private*, pg. 522
Crawford, D.B., Dir. & Sec.--Pilkington (New Zealand) Limited, Wellington, New Zealand; *Int'l*, pg. 1057
Crawford, Thomas J., Asst. V.P. & Sec.--Roanoke Electric Steel Corporation, Roanoke, VA; *U.S. Public*, pg. 1392
Crawford, Valerie, Sec.--Outboard Marine Corporation, Waukegan, IL; *U.S. Private*, pg. 478
Crawford, Valerie, Sec.--Johnson Outboards Marine Corp., Waukegan, IL; *U.S. Private*, pg. 478
Crawley, Dwight W., Controller & Sec.--Harris Teeter, Inc., Charlotte, NC; *U.S. Public*, pg. 1412
Creasey, Martin, Sec.--The Financial Times Ltd., London, United Kingdom; *Int'l*, pg. 1025
Creasman, William P., Sr. V.P., Gen. Counsel & Sec.--TCBY Enterprises Inc., Little Rock, AR; *U.S. Public*, pg. 1553
Creekmuir, William S., Chief Fin. Officer, Exec. V.P., Treas. & Sec.--Ladd Furniture, Inc., Greensboro, NC; *U.S. Public*, pg. 974
Creel, L. Anderson, Chief Fin. Officer, Sr. V.P., Treas. & Sec.--Prime Bancshares Inc., Houston, TX; *U.S. Public*, pg. 1326
Cremins, William T., Exec. V.P., Gen. Counsel & Sec.--Naugatuck Glass Company, Naugatuck, CT; *U.S. Private*, pg. 789
Crepin, Carmen, V.P. & Sec.--Caisse de depot et placement du Quebec, Montreal, Canada; *Int'l*, pg. 249
Crepin, Carmen, Corp. Sec.--Capital d'Amerique CDPQ, Montreal, Canada; *Int'l*, pg. 249
Crepin, Carmen, Corp. Sec.--Capital Communications CDPQ, Montreal, Canada; *Int'l*, pg. 249
Crepin, Carmen, Corp. Sec.--Capital International CDPQ, Montreal, Canada; *Int'l*, pg. 249
Crepin, Carmen, Corp. Sec.--Sofinov, Montreal, Canada; *Int'l*, pg. 249
Creson, Lenore, Sec.--First Tennessee National Corporation, Memphis, TN; *U.S. Public*, pg. 638
Cress, Sally, Treas. & Sec.--Bancinsurance Corp., Columbus, OH; *U.S. Public*, pg. 175
Crewes, P.W., Sec.--Lend Lease Corporation Limited, Sydney, Australia; *Int'l*, pg. 806
Crews, Donald R., Sr. V.P., Legal & Sec.--Harte-Hanks Communications, Inc., San Antonio, TX; *U.S. Public*, pg. 793
Crider, Karen K., Gen. Counsel & Sec.--The Stride Rite Corporation, Lexington, MA; *U.S. Public*, pg. 1524
Crifasi, Sam J., Corp. Sec.--Associated Grocers, Inc., Baton Rouge, LA; *U.S. Private*, pg. 90
Crill, Scott, Corp. Sec.--Safety-Kleen Corp., Elgin, IL; *U.S. Public*, pg. 1425
Crinks, F. William, Sec.--Hoverspeed Ltd., Dover, United Kingdom; *Int'l*, pg. 1214
Crisafulli, Robert, Jr., Treas. & Sec.--The Orioles, Inc., Baltimore, MD; *U.S. Private*, pg. 819
Criscillis, Paul A., Jr., Chief Fin. Officer & V.P.-Fin.--Crown Crafts, Inc., Atlanta, GA; *U.S. Public*, pg. 465
Crisford, Jane, Sec.--Lyons Seafoods Limited, Warminster, United Kingdom; *Int'l*, pg. 824
Crisp, A., Sec.--Taylor Woodrow Property Holdings Pty. Ltd., Parramatta, Australia; *Int'l*, pg. 1360
Crisp, Linda, Dir.-Admin. & Asst. Sec.--Consolidated-Tomoka Land Co., Daytona Beach, FL; *U.S. Public*, pg. 437
Crisp, Marlene, Sec.--SA-SO Company, Dallas, TX; *U.S. Private*, pg. 955
Crisp, Max, V.P.-Fin., Treas. & Sec.--Stewart Information Services Corporation, Houston, TX; *U.S. Public*, pg. 1518
Critser, Gary P., Sr. Exec. V.P., Treas. & Sec.--Kimball International, Inc., Jasper, IN; *U.S. Public*, pg. 956
Crittenden, J.A., Sec.--CNG Power Services Corporation, Pittsburgh, PA; *U.S. Public*, pg. 435
Croal, Thomas V., Chief Fin. Officer, V.P. & Sec.--Insight Health Services Corp., Newport Beach, CA; *U.S. Public*, pg. 880
Crocker, Frederick G., Jr., Chief Fin. Officer, V.P., Treas. & Sec.--Springborn Testing & Research, Inc., Enfield, CT; *U.S. Private*, pg. 1027
Croke, Jerome P., Exec. V.P., Sec. & Legal Counsel--LaSalle-Talman Bank, Chicago, IL; *Int'l*, pg. 11
Croll, Samuel W., III, Pres.--Croll-Reynolds Company, Inc., Westfield, NJ; *U.S. Private*, pg. 290
Cromwell, Jimmie, Asst. Sec.--City Gas Company of Florida, Hialeah, FL; *U.S. Public*, pg. 1147
Cronen, Vincent, Treas. & Sec.--Whittaker, Clark & Daniels, Inc., South Plainfield, NJ; *U.S. Private*, pg. 1174
Cronin, Michael X., V.P. & Sec.--Central Steel & Wire Company, Chicago, IL; *U.S. Public*, pg. 327
Cronje, C.J., Corp. Sec.--Distillers Corporation S.A., Stellenbosch, South Africa; *Int'l*, pg. 1129
Cronk, Julian, Grp. Sec.--The Hartstone Group PLC, London, United Kingdom; *Int'l*, pg. 599
Crook, Donald M., V.P. & Sec.--Kimberly-Clark Corporation, Dallas, TX; *U.S. Public*, pg. 958
Cross, Eric L., Exec. V.P. & Sec.--Maxco, Inc., Lansing, MI; *U.S. Public*, pg. 1061
Cross, Raymond, V.P. & Sec.--Federal Chicago Corporation, North Chicago, IL; *U.S. Private*, pg. 398
Croteau, Clara, Treas. & Sec.--Spiegel Meats, Inc., Miami, FL; *U.S. Private*, pg. 1025
Crouch, George W., Jr., Treas. & Sec.--Tallapoosa River Electric Co-Op, Lafayette, AL; *U.S. Private*, pg. 1067
Croushore, Bruce J., Sec. & Gen. Counsel--Bender Shipbuilding & Repair Company, Inc., Mobile, AL; *U.S. Private*, pg. 132
Crowe, Marcy, Sec.--Gray Communications Systems, Inc., Albany, GA; *U.S. Public*, pg. 759
Crowell, Leslie, Sec.--East Coast Steel, Inc., Claremont, NH; *U.S. Private*, pg. 356
Crowell, Sheryl, Corp. Sec.--Bent Tube, Inc., Fowlerville, MI; *U.S. Private*, pg. 134
Crowley, Diane N., Corp. Sec.--Superior Auctioneers & Marketing, Inc., San Antonio, TX; *U.S. Private*, pg. 1054
Crowley, James T., Sec.--American Kennel Club, Inc., New York, NY; *U.S. Private*, pg. 58
Crozier, David, Treas. & Sec.--Sharon Tube Company, Sharon, PA; *U.S. Private*, pg. 990
Cruickshank, D.J., Chief Fin. Officer & Sr. V.P.--Flexible Products Company, Marietta, GA; *U.S. Private*, pg. 412
Crum, Mary M., Treas. & Sec.--Crum Electric Supply Co., Inc., Casper, WY; *U.S. Private*, pg. 293
Crumbine, Dennis, Sr. V.P., Sec. & Treas.--Poland Spring Corporation, Greenwich, CT; *Int'l*, pg. 919
Crump, Lynne, V.P. & Sec.--Grizzard, Atlanta, GA; *U.S. Private*, pg. 482
Crump, Vera, Sec.--Babcock Lumber Company, Pittsburgh, PA; *U.S. Private*, pg. 108
Cruncleton, Barbara A., Treas. & Sec.--John S. Frey Enterprises, Los Angeles, CA; *U.S. Private*, pg. 428
Crutcher, Michael B., Sr. V.P., Gen. Counsel & Sec.--Brown-Forman Corporation, Louisville, KY; *U.S. Public*, pg. 261
Crutcher, Shirley, Treas. & Sec.--Atrium Companies, Inc., Dallas, TX; *U.S. Private*, pg. 98
Crutcher, Shirley, Treas. & Sec.--Atrium Companies, Inc., Irving, TX; *U.S. Private*, pg. 98
Cruz, J.A., Sec.--Esso Standard Oil S.A. Limited, Nassau, Bahamas; *U.S. Public*, pg. 602
Crvarich, Gene, Chief Fin. Officer, V.P., Treas. & Sec.--Al Larson Boat Shop, Inc., Terminal Island, CA; *U.S. Private*, pg. 652
Crystal, Joel F., Sr. Counsel & Asst. Sec.--New Plan Realty Trust, New York, NY; *U.S. Public*, pg. 1172
Cuerden, A., Sec.--Carclo Engineering Group plc, Sheffield, United Kingdom; *Int'l*, pg. 268
Cullen, Edward J., Jr., Asst. Sec.--PECO Energy Company, Philadelphia, PA; *U.S. Public*, pg. 1268
Cullen, Gary S., Asst. Sec.--CNF Transportation Inc., Palo Alto, CA; *U.S. Public*, pg. 281
Cullen, Martin J., V.P., Treas & Sec.--Chock Full O' Nuts Corporation, New York, NY; *U.S. Public*, pg. 351
Culleton, James E., Corp. Sec. & Pres.-First Commercial Bank--First Banks, Inc., Sacramento, CA; *U.S. Public*, pg. 626
Culver, Margaret S., Sec.--Henry Vogt Machine Co., Louisville, KY; *U.S. Private*, pg. 1143
Culverwell, Ronald L., Treas. & Asst. Sec.--Zions Co-operative Mercantile Institution, Salt Lake City, UT; *U.S. Public*, pg. 1793
Cummings, Larry E., V.P., Gen. Counsel & Sec.--Harken Energy Corporation, Irving, TX; *U.S. Public*, pg. 785
Cummings, R.C., Gen. Counsel & Sec.--Smith-Lee Co., Inc., Oneida, NY; *U.S. Private*, pg. 1009
Cummins, Joe, Sec.--Conway Corporation, Conway, AR; *U.S. Private*, pg. 272
Cummiskey, Mary, Sec.-Admin. Srvcs.--Bolt Technology Corporation, Norwalk, CT; *U.S. Public*, pg. 244
Cummiskey, Robert D., Jr., V.P.-Risk Mngmt. & Sec.--Petroleum Helicopters, Inc., Metairie, LA; *U.S. Public*, pg. 1281
Cundiff, James N., Gen. Counsel-New Ventures & Corp. Services & Asst. Sec.--Mapco Inc., Tulsa, OK; *U.S. Public*, pg. 1042
Cunningham, Bob, Gen. Counsel & Sec.--Tennessee Farmers Co-op, La Vergne, TN; *U.S. Private*, pg. 1076
Cunningham, John, Press Sec.--Metropolitan Transportation Authority, New York, NY; *U.S. Private*, pg. 739
Cunningham, John, Sir, Sec.--Alloy Technology International Inc., West Nyack, NY; *U.S. Private*, pg. 42
Cunningham, Kathleen J., Chief Oper. Officer, Chief Fin. Officer & Sec.--NxTrend Technology, Inc., Colorado Springs, CO; *U.S. Private*, pg. 809
Cunningham, N.J., Sec.--ATE Investment, Inc., Pleasantville, NJ; *U.S. Public*, pg. 430
Cuozzo, Donald H., V.P. & Sec.--Mine Safety Appliances Co., Pittsburgh, PA; *U.S. Public*, pg. 1114
Curado, Julia Maria, Sec.--Celbi SA, Figueira da Foz, Portugal; *Int'l*, pg. 1303
Curbelo, Ray, Controller & Sec.--National Utility Service, Inc., Park Ridge, NJ; *U.S. Private*, pg. 787
Curley, Denis M., Chief Fin. Officer, Sr. V.P., Treas. & Sec.--The Ackerley Group, Seattle, WA; *U.S. Public*, pg. 15
Curp, John H., Gen. Counsel & Sec.--CitFed Bancorp, Inc., Dayton, OH; *U.S. Public*, pg. 376
Curr, K.D., Grp. Sec.--Standard Bank Investment Corporation Limited, Johannesburg, South Africa; *Int'l*, pg. 1293
Curran-Goodway, Trudy, Asst. Corp. Sec.--Canadian Airlines Corporation, Calgary, Canada; *Int'l*, pg. 255
Curran, B.S., Sec.--ICI American Holdings Inc., Wilmington, DE; *Int'l*, pg. 663
Curran, Barbara S., Sec.--ICI Americas, Inc., Wilmington, DE; *Int'l*, pg. 663
Curran, Catherine, Sec.--Curran Group, Inc., Crystal Lake, IL; *U.S. Private*, pg. 297
Curran, Kevin J., Sr. V.P., Gen. Counsel & Sec.--Parsons Brinckerhoff Inc., New York, NY; *U.S. Private*, pg. 841
Currie, R.M., Gen. Counsel & Sec.--Detrex Corporation, Southfield, MI; *U.S. Public*, pg. 501
Currier, Ronald, Treas. & Sec.--Gilpatrick Construction Company, Inc., Riverton, WY; *U.S. Private*, pg. 454
Curry, Jeffrey, Chief Fin. Officer & Sec.--Kenworth of Indianapolis Inc., Indianapolis, IN; *U.S. Private*, pg. 615
Curry, John, Sec. & Dir.-Fin.--National Consolidated, Melbourne, Australia; *Int'l*, pg. 908
Curry, Paul F., Asst. Sec.--National Grape Co-Op Association, Inc., Westfield, NY; *U.S. Private*, pg. 784
Curson, R. John, Chief Fin. Officer, Sr. V.P.-Fin. & Sec.--Truevision, Inc., Santa Clara, CA; *U.S. Public*, pg. 1642

Curtas, William W., Chief Exec., Chief Oper. & Chief Fin. Officer & Exec. V.P.--Steego Corporation, West Palm Beach, FL; *Int'l*, pg. 216

Curtin, Mary E., V.P., Gen. Counsel & Sec.--Innovex, Inc., Hopkins, MN; *U.S. Public*, pg. 880

Curtis, Harold R., Chief Fin. Officer, Sr. V.P., Treas. & Sec.--The M/A/R/C Group, Irving, TX; *U.S. Public*, pg. 1022

Curtis, Roger William, Chm. Bd., Chief Exec. Officer & Sec.--L.N. Curtis & Sons, Oakland, CA; *U.S. Private*, pg. 297

Curtis, Stan, Controller, Asst Treas & Asst. Sec.--Continental Forge Company, Compton, CA; *U.S. Private, pg. 268*

Curtis, Therese D., Sec.--Topa Equities Ltd, Inc., Los Angeles, CA; *U.S. Private*, pg. 1091

Cusick, Mark A., Sec.--Ferro Corporation, Cleveland, OH; *U.S. Public*, pg. 618

Custedl, Laura, Sec.--C.A. Cigarrera Bigott, Sucs., Caracas, Venezuela; *Int'l*, pg. 111

Cusumano, Vincent, Sec.--TransNet Corporation, Somerville, NJ; *U.S. Public*, pg. 1631

Cutchall, Anita J., V.P.-Legal & Corp. Sec.--Zero Corporation, Los Angeles, CA; *U.S. Public*, pg. 1791

Cutler, Todd D., Asst. Sec.--PECO Energy Company, Philadelphia, PA; *U.S. Public*, pg. 1268

Cutter, Edward A., Sr. V.P., Gen. Counsel & Sec.--The Clorox Company, Oakland, CA; *U.S. Public*, pg. 386

Cutting, Lilian M., Sec.--Greenham Trading Limited, Isleworth, United Kingdom; *Int'l*, pg. 1358

Cyranoski, Dave, Sr. V.P., Controller & Sec.--Northern Illinois Gas Company, Naperville, IL; *U.S. Public*, pg. 1183

Cyranoski, David L., Sr. V.P., Controller & Sec.--NICOR Inc., Naperville, IL; *U.S. Public*, pg. 1182

Cyrus, Kenneth M., Sr. V.P., Gen. Counsel & Sec.--Pharmacia & Upjohn, Inc., Windsor, United Kingdom; *Int'l*, pg. 1047

Cyrus, Kenneth M., Exec. V.P., Gen. Counsel & Sec.--Pharmacia & Upjohn, Kalamazoo, MI; *Int'l*, pg. 1048

Cyrus, Suzanne, Treas. & Sec.--Adams Investment Company, Bartlesville, OK; *U.S. Private*, pg. 16

Czaja, Darlene E., Sec.--PC Quote, Inc., Chicago, IL; *U.S. Public*, pg. 1240

Czaja, Kenneth A., Chief Fin. Officer, V.P.-Fin. & Sec.--Intellicorp Inc., Mountain View, CA; *U.S. Public*, pg. 887

d'Abouville, Christian, Sec.--Compagnie Generale Maritime et Financiere, Suresnes, France; *Int'l*, pg. 322

D'Agostino, Mara, Asst. Corp. Sec.--Rigel Energy Corporation, Calgary, Canada; *Int'l*, pg. 1117

D'Amato, Janice M., Sec.--Paccar Inc., Bellevue, WA; *U.S. Public*, pg. 1246

D'Amour, Charles L., Chief Oper. Officer, Exec. V.P. & Sec.--Big Y Foods Inc., Springfield, MA; *U.S. Private*, pg. 143

D'Anna, Christopher, V.P. & Sec.--Mars Super Markets, Inc., Baltimore, MD; *U.S. Private*, pg. 707

D'Atri, Justin, Gen. Counsel & Sec.--John Boos & Company, Effingham, IL; *U.S. Private*, pg. 156

D'Haeze, T.M., V.P.-Fin. & Acctg., Treas. & Sec.--Dwyer Instruments Inc., Michigan City, IN; *U.S. Private*, pg. 350

d'Hondt, Jean-Claude, Corp. Sec.--Migros, Zurich, Switzerland; *Int'l*, pg. 865

Dadourian, Elise, Gen. Counsel & Sec.--Deluxe Storage Systems, Inc., Warren, PA; *U.S. Private*, pg. 323

Dahl, Carolyn C., Sec.--Colwell Industries, Inc., Minneapolis, MN; *U.S. Private*, pg. 257

Dahl, Valerie J., V.P., Treas. & Asst. Sec.--Stearns Enterprises, Inc., Lexington, KY; *U.S. Private*, pg. 1037

Dahly, John H., Chief Fin. Officer, Exec. V.P. & Sec.--Schultz Sav-O Stores, Inc., Sheboygan, WI; *U.S. Public*, pg. 1442

Dai, John, Controller & Sec.--H.S. Crocker Co., Inc., Huntley, IL; *U.S. Private*, pg. 290

Dainora, Anthony R., Sec.--Republic Automotive Parts, Inc., Brentwood, TN; *U.S. Public*, pg. 1377

Dajer, Antonio, V.P.-Human Resources & Asst. Sec.--Pueblo International, Inc.-P.R. Div., Carolina, PR; *U.S. Private*, pg. 894

Dal Mas, Paolo, Sec.--Cassa di Risparmio delle Provincie Lombarde SpA (CARIPLO), Milan, Italy; *Int'l*, pg. 274

Dalbeck, Richard W., Exec. V.P., Chief Fin. Officer & Sec.--The Guber Peters Entertainment Company, Los Angeles, CA; *Int'l*, pg. 1283

Dale, Thomas E., Sec.--Associates Financial Services Corporation, Dallas, TX; *U.S. Public*, pg. 663

Dalinger, Trudy, Chief Fin. Officer & Sr. V.P.--TSC Shannock Corporation, Burnaby, Canada; *Int'l*, pg. 1343

Dalinger, Trudy, Sec.--Trax Music Vision Ltd., Burnaby, Canada; *Int'l*, pg. 1343

Dallacqua, John, Chief Fin. Officer, V.P.-Fin., Treas. & Sec.--Crowley, Milner & Company, Detroit, MI; *U.S. Public*, pg. 461

Dallob, Naomi C., V.P. & Sec.--Chemed Corporation, Cincinnati, OH; *U.S. Public*, pg. 343

Dalongeville, Jean-Maurice, Sec.--CGG Group, Massy, France; *Int'l*, pg. 241

Dalquist, Dorothy, Sec.--Northland Aluminum Products, Inc., Minneapolis, MN; *U.S. Private*, pg. 805

Dalton, Ronald, Sr. V.P., Treas. & Sec.--Huron Valley Steel Corp., Belleville, MI; *U.S. Private*, pg. 549

Daly, Denis G., Chief Legal Officer, V.P., Gen. Counsel & Sec.--Amcast Industrial Corporation, Dayton, OH; *U.S. Public*, pg. 63

Daly, J.G., Sec.--Leo A. Daly Company, Omaha, NE; *U.S. Private*, pg. 309

Daly, Michael J., III, Sec.--M.J. Daly & Sons, Inc., Waterbury, CT; *U.S. Private*, pg. 309

Damon, E.W., V.P. Fin., Admin. & Asst. Sec.--RPS Inc., Coraopolis, PA; *U.S. Public*, pg. 604

Damon, Nancy J., Sec.--MasTec, Inc., Miami, FL; *U.S. Public*, pg. 1055

Dance, J. Christopher, V.P.-Legal Affairs & Corp. Sec.--Excel Communications, Inc., Dallas, TX; *U.S. Public*, pg. 598

Daneri, Roxanne, Gen. Counsel & Sec.--Chuck Swift Sales & Leasing, Davis, CA; *U.S. Private*, pg. 1058

Dangeau, Jeffrey L., Asst. Sec.--A.W. Realty Co., Fayetteville, AR; *U.S. Public*, pg. 1494

Dangeau, Jeffrey L., Asst. Sec.--Southwestern Energy Pipeline Company, Fayetteville, AR; *U.S. Public*, pg. 1494

Dangeau, Jeffrey L., Asst. Sec.--Arkansas Western Pipeline Company, Fayetteville, AR; *U.S. Public*, pg. 1494

Daniel, Bernard, Sec.--Nestle S.A., Vevey, Switzerland; *Int'l, pg. 915*

Daniel, Lucille H., V.P. & Sec.--Raritan Bancorp Inc., Bridgewater, NJ; *U.S. Public*, pg. 1361

Daniels, Diana M., V.P., Gen. Counsel & Sec.--The Washington Post Company, Washington, DC; *U.S. Public*, pg. 1742

Daniels, R.M., Gen. Counsel & Corp. Sec.--H.P. Bulmer Holdings Plc, Hereford, United Kingdom; *Int'l*, pg. 232

Danielson, Roland, Chief Information Officer & Sec.--ICA Handlarnas AB, Solna, Sweden; *Int'l*, pg. 642

Danielsson, Mona, Sec.--Stora Cell AB, Gavle, Sweden; *Int'l*, pg. 1303

Danko, Douglas B., Chief Fin. Officer & Sec.--Stabler Companies, Inc., Harrisburg, PA; *U.S. Private*, pg. 1028

Danna, Patricia, Sec.--Network Real Estate Inc., Capitola, CA; *U.S. Private*, pg. 791

Danner, Hazel, Sec.--Electronic Tele-Communications, Inc., Waukesha, WI; *U.S. Public*, pg. 570

Darian, Ralph, Sec.--Levonian Brothers Inc., Troy, NY; *U.S. Private*, pg. 663

Darnell, W. Reid, Corp. Sec.--Florida Crushed Stone Company, Leesburg, FL; *U.S. Private*, pg. 414

Darr, James E., Jr., Sr. V.P., Gen. Counsel & Sec.--Dillard's, Inc., Little Rock, AR; *U.S. Public*, pg. 509

Darricau, Aime, Gen. Sec.--COGEMA - Compagnie Generale des Matieres Nucleaires, Velizy-Villacoublay, France; *Int'l*, pg. 304

Darwin, Natalie, Sec.--Cardinal Inc., Rahway, NJ; *U.S. Private*, pg. 208

Dathe, Robert F., Chief Fin. Officer, Sr. V.P.-Fin., & Corp. Sec.--Marotta Scientific Controls, Inc., Montville, NJ; *U.S. Private*, pg. 706

Daugherty, S. Wayne, V.P.-Opers. & Sec.--The Buckle, Inc., Kearney, NE; *U.S. Public*, pg. 267

Davenport, Clarence R., V.P. & Treas.--Newell Co., Freeport, IL; *U.S. Public*, pg. 1176

Davenport, Colleen M., Assoc. Gen. Counsel & Asst. Sec.--Analysts International Corporation, Minneapolis, MN; *U.S. Public*, pg. 110

Davenport, Fred B., Jr., Gen. Counsel & Corp. Sec.--Pharmaceutical Product Development, Inc., Wilmington, NC; *U.S. Public*, pg. 1285

Davenport, Marian, V.P., Gen. Counsel & Sec.--Destec Energy, Inc., Houston, TX; *U.S. Public*, pg. 1146

Davenport, Sally A., Corp. Sec.--Sequus Pharmaceuticals, Inc., Menlo Park, CA; *U.S. Public*, pg. 1460

David, Orna Bar, Gen. Counsel & Sec.--Elscint Ltd., Haifa, Israel; *Int'l*, pg. 450

Davidman, Evan, Reg. Mgr.-Europe--AJC International, Inc., Atlanta, GA; *U.S. Private*, pg. 6

Davidson, Carl B., V.P. & Sec.--Texaco Inc., White Plains, NY; *U.S. Public*, pg. 1582

Davidson, David A., Corp. Sec.--CB Commercial Real Estate, Los Angeles, CA; *U.S. Public*, pg. 272

Davidson, David A., Sr. V.P. & Sec.--Liberty Northwest Insurance Corp., Portland, OR; *U.S. Private*, pg. 666

Davie, Andrew, Chief Oper. Officer, Sec. & Mgr.-Personnel--Campbell Distillers Limited, Brentford, United Kingdom; *Int'l*, pg. 567

Davies, P.P., Sec.--Taylor Woodrow Construction Limited, Southall, United Kingdom; *Int'l*, pg. 1358

Davies, Richard J., Sr. V.P.-Fin., Treas. & Asst. Sec.--Time Warner Cable, Stamford, CT; *U.S. Public*, pg. 1610

Davies, Richard W., Jr., Gen. Counsel & Sec.--Hubbell Incorporated, Orange, CT; *U.S. Public*, pg. 844

Davies, Robin, Sec.--Arjo Wiggins Appleton plc, Basingstoke, United Kingdom; *Int'l*, pg. 567

Davies, Zachary M., Controller & Sec.--Tweddle Litho Company, Clinton Township, MI; *U.S. Private*, pg. 1111

Davis, Ann M., Asst. Sec.--Pinnacle Bank, Jasper, AL; *U.S. Public*, pg. 1297

Davis, Barry E., Sec. & Assoc. Dir.--Eurodis Electron PLC, Reigate, United Kingdom; *Int'l*, pg. 1247

Davis, Bonni G., Gen. Counsel & Sec.--Finlay Enterprises, Inc., New York, NY; *U.S. Public*, pg. 623

Davis, Bonnie, Treas. & Sec.--O.P. Link Handle Company, Salem, IN; *U.S. Private*, pg. 668

Davis, Charles E., Jr., Sec.--Laboratory Supply Company, Inc., Louisville, KY; *U.S. Private*, pg. 641

Davis, Deborah Karen, Sec.--Davis Mining & Manufacturing, Coeburn, VA; *U.S. Private*, pg. 315

Davis, Dennis, V.P.-Adv., Sls. & Mktg.--Davis Wood Products, Inc., Hudson, NC; *U.S. Private*, pg. 315

Davis, Don E., Sec. & Gen. Counsel--Acceptance Insurance Co., Inc., Omaha, NE; *U.S. Public*, pg. 14

Davis, Edna R., Treas. & Sec.--HDW, Incorporated, Shreveport, LA; *U.S. Private*, pg. 335

Davis, G. Gervaise III, V.P., Legal Counsel & Sec.--American Recreation Centers, Inc., Sacramento, CA; *U.S. Public*, pg. 90

Davis, Gary B., Chief Fin. Officer & Treas.--Polk Audio, Inc., Baltimore, MD; *U.S. Public*, pg. 1315

Davis, Gary K., Treas. & Sec.--Bud Davis Cadillac, Inc., Memphis, TN; *U.S. Private*, pg. 314

Davis, J. Kennerly, Jr., V.P. & Sec.--Dominion Resources, Inc., Richmond, VA; *U.S. Public*, pg. 516

Davis, J. Kennerly, Jr., Sr. V.P., Treas. & Corp. Sec.--Virginia Electric and Power Company, Richmond, VA; *U.S. Public*, pg. 516

Davis, Jack, Sec.--Casa Bonita, Inc., Carrollton, TX; *U.S. Public*, pg. 278

Davis, Jane G., V.P., Gen. Counsel & Sec.--Joy Mining Machinery, Warrendale, PA; *U.S. Public*, pg. 789

Davis, Jeannine M., V.P., Gen. Counsel & Sec.--CTS Corporation, Elkhart, IN; *U.S. Public*, pg. 285

Davis, John M., V.P., Gen. Counsel & Sec.--IWC Resources Corporation, Indianapolis, IN; *U.S. Public*, pg. 1185

Davis, John M., V.P., Gen. Counsel & Sec.--Indianapolis Water Company, Indianapolis, IN; *U.S. Public*, pg. 1185

Davis, John S., V.P., Gen. Counsel & Sec.--Cameron Ashley Building Products, Inc, Dallas, TX; *U.S. Public*, pg. 298

Davis, Lewis, Sec.--Crystal Flash Petroleum Corp., Indianapolis, IN; *U.S. Private*, pg. 294

Davis, Lloyd G., Chief Fin. Officer, Exec. V.P.-Fin., Treas. & Sec.--Baldor Electric Company, Fort Smith, AR; *U.S. Public*, pg. 168

Davis, M.A., Gen. Counsel & Sec.--Sterling Pulp Chemicals, Ltd., Etobicoke, Canada; *U.S. Public*, pg. 1580

Davis, Marcie, Exec. V.P., Treas. & Sec.--PharmHouse, Inc., New York, NY; *U.S. Public*, pg. 1286

Davis, Mark A., V.P. & Sec.--Bridges & Company, Inc., Pittsburgh, PA; *U.S. Private*, pg. 168

Davis, Martha O., Treas. & Sec.--Jimmy Davis Enterprises, Inc., Madison, FL; *U.S. Private*, pg. 315

Davis, Michael L., Chief Fin. Officer, Treas. & Sec.--Crouch Supply Company, Inc., Fort Worth, TX; *U.S. Private*, pg. 291

Davis, Norman H., V.P. & Sec.--Signet Star Reinsurance Company, Florham Park, NJ; *U.S. Public*, pg. 216

Davis, Richard, Asst. Sec.--AAH plc, Runcorn, United Kingdom; *Int'l*, pg. 591

Davis, Robert L., Gen. Counsel & Sec.--Provident Bankshares Corporation, Baltimore, MD; *U.S. Public*, pg. 1337

Davis, S.A., Asst. Sec.--South Carolina Pipeline Corporation, Columbia, SC; *U.S. Public*, pg. 1436

Davis, S.J., Sec.--Esso Trading Company of Abu Dhabi, Saint Georges, Bermuda; *U.S. Public*, pg. 602

Davis, Steve J., Chief Admin. Officer, Gen. Counsel & Asst. Sec.--Magellan Health Services, Inc., Atlanta, GA; *U.S. Public*, pg. 1033

Davis, Thomas A., Pres., Chief Exec. Officer & Asst. Sec.--United HealthCare of Utah, Salt Lake City, UT; *U.S. Public*, pg. 1678

Davis, W. William, V.P., Sec. & Gen. Counsel--NationsBank of Tennessee, Nashville, TN; *U.S. Public*, pg. 1163

Davisson, Richard F., Gen. Counsel & Sec.--Pay Less Super Markets, Inc., Anderson, IN; *U.S. Private*, pg. 844

Dawahare, Martin, Treas. & Sec.--Dawahares, Inc., Lexington, KY; *U.S. Private*, pg. 316

Dawbarn, Mark L., Sec. & Legal Dir.--Lincoln Assurance Limited, Uxbridge, United Kingdom; *U.S. Public*, pg. 998

Dawe, Anthony, Sec.--Bain Hogg Group plc, London, United Kingdom; *Int'l*, pg. 671

Dawson, Grant, Gen. Counsel & Company Sec.--Centrica Plc, Slough, United Kingdom; *Int'l*, pg. 279

Dawson, Jay W., Sec. & House Counsel--T.W. Phillips Gas and Oil Co., Butler, PA; *U.S. Private*, pg. 862

Dawson, Richard, Sr. V.P.-Law & Admin., Gen. Counsel & Sec.--Harvard Industries, Inc., Tampa, FL; *U.S. Public*, pg. 796

Day, Kerry, Assoc. Gen. Counsel & Sec.--Telus Corporation, Edmonton, Canada; *Int'l*, pg. 1374

Day, Robert L., Corp. Sec. & Asst. Gen. Counsel--FMC Corporation, Chicago, IL; *U.S. Public*, pg. 604

Day, Sharon, Treas. & Sec.--Catalina Yachts, Inc., Woodland Hills, CA; *U.S. Private*, pg. 219

Daymond, Ian C., Gen. Counsel & Sec.--Delta Gold N.L., Sydney, Australia; *Int'l*, pg. 389

De Araluce y Araluce, D. Manuel M., Sec.--Telecomunicaciones Marinas, S.A. (Temasa), Madrid, Spain; *Int'l*, pg. 1372

de Clippele, Luc J., Gen. Sec.--Vlaamse Investeringsvennootschap (VIV), Zwijnaarde, Belgium; *Int'l*, pg. 547

de Klerk, H.J., Sec.--Iscor, Pretoria, South Africa; *Int'l*, pg. 688

De Lamata Gorostiza, Juan I., Sec.--ENDESA - Empresa Nacional de Electricidad, S.A., Madrid, Spain; *Int'l*, pg. 1224

de Lasa, Jose M., Sr. V.P., Sec. & Gen. Counsel--Abbott Laboratories, Abbott Park, IL; *U.S. Public*, pg. 13

De Leon, Nora, Exec. Sec.--Sudamtex de Uruguay, S.A., Montevideo, Uruguay; *Int'l*, pg. 1304

de Leusse, Guy, Corp. Sec.--Compagnie de Suez, Paris, France; *Int'l*, pg. 313

De Maeyer, Jacquline, Exec. Sec.--Maison Mathieu, S.A., Antwerp, Belgium; *Int'l*, pg. 846

De Majistre, Robert, V.P. & Sec.--Seton Company, Norristown, PA; *U.S. Private*, pg. 987

de Meester, F.D., Sec.--Royal Pakhoed NV, Rotterdam, Netherlands; *Int'l*, pg. 1147

De Mento, Robert, Treas. & Sec.--Brooks Provisions Inc., Philadelphia, PA; *U.S. Private*, pg. 172

de Metz, Robert, Sec.--Compagnie Financiere de Paribas, Paris, France; *Int'l*, pg. 319

de Paredes Castillo, Vicente Santamaria, Gen. Counsel & Dep. Sec.--Tabacalera, S.A., Madrid, Spain; *Int'l*, pg. 1345

De Pass, William K., V.P., Sec. & Treas.--Standard Supply & Hardware Co., New Orleans, LA; *U.S. Private*, pg. 1032

de Pinedo Cabezudo, Ignacio, Sec.--Iberdrola, S.A., Bilbao, Spain; *Int'l*, pg. 657

de Prunele, Stephane, Sec.--Leclerc, Issy-les-Moulineaux, France; *Int'l*, pg. 805

De Rosales Garrido, D. Manuel Martin, General Sec.--T.S. Telefonica Sistemas, S.A., Madrid, Spain; *Int'l*, pg. 1372

De Ruiter, Eleanore, Mgr.-Quality Assuarance & Exec. Asst.--Grocers Baking Co., Grand Rapids, MI; *U.S. Private*, pg. 482

de Verdiere, Jean-Francois Colin, Gen. Counsel, Sec. & Dir.-Medium & Long Term Export Credits Div.--Banque Francaise du Commerce Exterieur, Paris, France; *Int'l*, pg. 160

de Virville, Michel, Sr. V.P. & Corp. Sec.--Renault, Boulogne-Billancourt, France; *Int'l*, pg. 1102
De Wachter, Marcia, Sec.--Banque Nationale de Belgique, Brussels, Belgium; *Int'l*, pg. 162
de With, J.W., Sec.--NORIT N.V., Amersfoort, Netherlands; *Int'l*, pg. 958
Deakin, P., Sec.--Senior Foster Wheeler Construction Division, Snaith, United Kingdom; *Int'l*, pg. 1221
Deamer, Virginia R., V.P. & Sec.--The Russell National Bank, Lewistown, PA; *U.S. Public*, pg. 1222
Dean, Edwin W., Vice Chm., Gen. Counsel & Sec.--Danskin Inc., New York, NY; *U.S. Public*, pg. 483
Dean, Mary T., Asst. Sec.--Washington Real Estate Investment Trust, Kensington, MD; *U.S. Public*, pg. 1743
Deane, Andrea, Corp. Sec.--K-D Lamp Company, Cincinnati, OH; *U.S. Private*, pg. 603
Deane, James R., Sec. & Gen. Counsel--Fiduciary Trust Company International, New York, NY; *U.S. Public*, pg. 621
DeAngelo, Thomas J., Chief Fin. Officer, Treas. & Sec.--Isomedix Inc., Whippany, NJ; *U.S. Public*, pg. 1515
DeAngelo, Yvonne, V.P.-Fin. & Controller--Nobel Education Dynamics, Inc., Media, PA; *U.S. Public*, pg. 1185
DeAngelo, Yvonne, Sec.--Merryhill Country Schools, Inc., Sacramento, CA; *U.S. Public*, pg. 1186
DeAngelo, Yvonne, Sec.--Rocking Horse Development Corporation, Media, PA; *U.S. Public*, pg. 1186
DeAngelo, Yvonne, Sec. & Treas.--Imagine Educational Products, Inc., Media, PA; *U.S. Public*, pg. 1186
Dearborn, Charles H., V.P., Gen. Counsel & Sec.--Acuson Corporation, Mountain View, CA; *U.S. Public*, pg. 18
Deason, J.E., Chief Fin. Officer & Exec. V.P.--Wolverine Tube Inc., Huntsville, AL; *U.S. Public*, pg. 1774
Debaets, Marc, Sec.--Electrabel S.A., Brussels, Belgium; *Int'l*, pg. 436
DeBauche, Julie A., Sec.--Associated Commercial Mortgage, Inc., Green Bay, WI; *U.S. Public*, pg. 140
DeBeliso, Richard J., PE, Exec. V.P. & Sec.--Giffels Hoyem Basso, Inc., Troy, MI; *U.S. Private*, pg. 452
DeBona, Ronald V., Sec.--H & H Tube & Manufacturing Co., Vanderbilt, MI; *U.S. Private*, pg. 489
deBrier, Donald P., Exec. V.P., Sr. Gen. Counsel & Corp. Sec.--Occidental Petroleum Corporation, Los Angeles, CA; *U.S. Public*, pg. 1210
Debulpaep, Jacques, Sec.--SAIT-RadioHolland Group S.A., Brussels, Belgium; *Int'l*, pg. 1151
DeBuono, Laureen, Exec. V.P.-H.R., Gen Counsel & Sec.--Nellcor Puritan Bennett Incorporated, Pleasanton, CA; *U.S. Public*, pg. 1039
DeCarlo, William S., Asst. Sec.--Telephone and Data Systems, Inc., Chicago, IL; *U.S. Public*, pg. 1570
Dechnik, James, Chief Fin. Officer, V.P.-Fin. & Sec.--The Johnson Corporation, Three Rivers, MI; *U.S. Private*, pg. 591
DeCius, Dennis A., Chief Fin. Officer, Exec. V.P. & Asst. Sec.--Pacific Capital Bancorp, Salinas, CA; *U.S. Public*, pg. 1247
Decker, Christopher B., Asst. Corp. Controller & Asst. Sec.--Hein-Werner Corporation, Waukesha, WI; *U.S. Public*, pg. 805
Decker, Richard, Chief Fin. Officer, V.P.-Fin., Treas. & Sec.--CEM Corporation, Matthews, NC; *U.S. Public*, pg. 277
Decker, Thomas A., V.P., Gen. Counsel & Sec.--Vetrotex CertainTeed Corporation, Wichita Falls, TX; *Int'l*, pg. 1171
Dee, James, V.P., Gen. Counsel & Sec.--SPS Technologies, Inc., Jenkintown, PA; *U.S. Public*, pg. 1419
Dee, Jay, Treas., Sec. & Dir.-Sls.--Dee Paper Company, Chester, PA; *U.S. Private*, pg. 320
Deegan, Mary, Sec.--H.J. Baker & Bro., Inc., Stamford, CT; *U.S. Private*, pg. 112
Deeming, Nick, Dir.-Legal & Corp. Sec.--PPP hc, Tunbridge Wells, United Kingdom; *Int'l*, pg. 1020
DeFerrari, Diana, Sr. V.P. & Sec.--Plasma-Therm, Inc., Saint Petersburg, FL; *U.S. Public*, pg. 1308
Deferrari, Ronald H., Chm. Bd., Chief Exec. Officer, Treas. & Sec.--Plasma-Therm, Inc., Saint Petersburg, FL; *U.S. Public*, pg. 1308
Defonte, Robert G., Sr. V.P.-Mdsg. & Sec.--E & B Marine Incorporated, Edison, NJ; *U.S. Public*, pg. 1756
DeForest, Stephen E., Sec.--ABX Air, Inc., Wilmington, OH; *U.S. Public*, pg. 33
Degnan, Martin J., V.P., Assoc. Gen. Counsel & Asst. Sec.--Rubbermaid Incorporated, Wooster, OH; *U.S. Public*, pg. 1411
Deitsch, Sara, Sec.--Deitsch Plastics Company, West Haven, CT; *U.S. Private*, pg. 320
Dekker, H.J., Sec.--Nutricia BV, Zoetermeer, Netherlands; *Int'l*, pg. 991
Dekle, Kazue, Sec.--The Yasuda Trust and Banking Co., Ltd., Tokyo, Japan; *Int'l*, pg. 1520
del Campo Lanz, Javier Martinez, Sec.--Grupo Gigante S.A. de C.V., Mexico, Mexico; *Int'l*, pg. 574
del Campo Rodriguez, Miguel, Dir., Gen. Mgr., Legal Counsel & Sec.--Asland S.A., Madrid, Spain; *Int'l*, pg. 790
Del Corral, D. Julio, General Sec.--Teleinformatica Y Comunicaciones, S.A., Madrid, Spain; *Int'l*, pg. 1372
Del Valle, Etienne Totti, Sec.--Puerto Rican Cement Co., Inc., Guaynabo, PR; *U.S. Public*, pg. 1341
Delahunty, Edward J., Asst. Sec.--Tasty Baking Company, Philadelphia, PA; *U.S. Public*, pg. 1561
Delaney, Dorothy, Sec.--Puget Western, Inc., Bellevue, WA; *U.S. Public*, pg. 1342
Delaney, Dorothy S., Asst. Sec.--Hydro Energy Development Corp., Bothell, WA; *U.S. Public*, pg. 1342
Delaney, Jim, Treas. & Sec.--Curtis Lumber Company, Ballston Spa, NY; *U.S. Private*, pg. 297
Delaney, Patrick, Gen. Counsel & Sec.--MTS Systems Corporation, Eden Prairie, MN; *U.S. Public*, pg. 1028
Delaney, Patrick, Sec.--Vital Signs MN, Inc., Burnsville, MN; *U.S. Public*, pg. 1723
DelCol, John V., V.P., Gen. Counsel & Sec.--Chartwell Re Corporation, Stamford, CT; *U.S. Public*, pg. 336
Delfs, James, Chief Fin. Officer & Sr. V.P.-Fin.--Stein Mart, Inc., Jacksonville, FL; *U.S. Public*, pg. 1514
Delisle, Pat, Sec.--OMC Milwaukee, Milwaukee, WI; *U.S. Private*, pg. 478
Delman, Richard, Chief Fin. Officer, Controller, Treas. & Sec.--New Age Intimates Inc., Long Island City, NY; *U.S. Private*, pg. 792
Delman, Stephen B., Sec.--The Arlen Corporation, New York, NY; *U.S. Public*, pg. 131
Delmore, Timothy C., Chief Fin. Officer & Sec.--Arctic Cat Inc., Thief River Falls, MN; *U.S. Public*, pg. 128
DeLoos, H., Corp. Sec.--DAF Trucks N.V., Eindhoven, Netherlands; *U.S. Public*, pg. 1247
Delvaux, Jean-Louis, Exec. V.P.-Fin. & Corp. Sec.--Financiere Saint Dominique, Paris, France; *Int'l*, pg. 344
DeMatteo, Madelyn M., V.P., Gen. Counsel & Sec.--Southern New England Telecommunications Corporation, New Haven, CT; *U.S. Public*, pg. 1490
Demblowski, Denis A., Asst. Sec.--Aluminum Company of America, Pittsburgh, PA; *U.S. Public*, pg. 60
Dembowski, David M., Sr. V.P. & Sec.--ONBANCorp, Inc., Syracuse, NY; *U.S. Public*, pg. 631
DeMeo, Ronald C., Sr. V.P.-Mktg. & Sls. & Sec.--Marietta Corporation, Cortland, NY; *U.S. Private*, pg. 702
Demers, D., V.P.-H.R. & Admin. & Corp. Sec.--F.W. Myers & Co., Inc., Rouses Point, NY; *U.S. Private*, pg. 770
Demler, Lois, Sec.--Columbus McKinnon Corp., Amherst, NY; *U.S. Public*, pg. 405
Dempsey, Timothy M., V.P., Gen. Counsel & Sec.--Oshkosh Truck Corporation, Oshkosh, WI; *U.S. Public*, pg. 1233
Dempster, Amelia R., Sec.--Wilder Deem, Inc., New York, NY; *U.S. Private*, pg. 1176
Denburg, Richard, Corp. Sec.--Barton Press, Inc., West Orange, NJ; *U.S. Private*, pg. 120
Denegre, George, Sec.--International Shipholding Corporation, New Orleans, LA; *U.S. Public*, pg. 907
Denham, Grey, Sec.--GKN plc, Redditch, United Kingdom; *Int'l*, pg. 534
Denhof, Ronnell P., Sec.--Owen-Ames-Kimball Co., Grand Rapids, MI; *U.S. Private*, pg. 823
Denison, John B., V.P. & Sec.--National Gas & Oil Company, Newark, OH; *U.S. Public*, pg. 1156
Denniston, John, Gen. Counsel & Sec.--Bobit Publishing Company, Torrance, CA; *U.S. Private*, pg. 154
Denny, Douglas, Sec.--World Shipping, Inc., Rocky River, OH; *U.S. Private*, pg. 1190
Denrich, Stuart, V.P.-Information Systems & Sec.--So-Lo-Food, Inc., Baltimore, MD; *U.S. Private*, pg. 1011
Denson, William F., III, V.P.-Law & Sec.--Vulcan Materials Company, Birmingham, AL; *U.S. Public*, pg. 1725
Dent, Thompson S., Exec. V.P.-Corp. Svcs. & Sec.--Phycor, Inc., Nashville, TN; *U.S. Public*, pg. 1293
Denton, Carol D., Asst. Sec.--Duke Energy Corporation, Charlotte, NC; *U.S. Public*, pg. 534
Denton, Patsy, V.P., Treas. & Sec.--Denton Enterprises Inc., Grosse Pointe Woods, MI; *U.S. Private*, pg. 325
Depelteau, Ginette, Asst. Sec.--Capital Communications CDPQ, Montreal, Canada; *Int'l*, pg. 249
DePew, Marian J., Asst. Sec.--GreatBanc, Inc., Aurora, IL; *U.S. Public*, pg. 760
Deptula, George S., Sec.--Syracuse Supply Company, Syracuse, NY; *U.S. Private*, pg. 1060
Derbyshire, J., Sec.--Clarks International, Street, United Kingdom; *Int'l*, pg. 296
Derlath, Karen, Sec.--T.L. Diamond Company, New York, NY; *U.S. Private*, pg. 330
Deron, Johan, Sec.--Kredietbank N.V., Brussels, Belgium; *Int'l*, pg. 760
Dertz, Susan, V.P.-Human Resources & Sec.--Louis Allis Company, Milwaukee, WI; *U.S. Private*, pg. 677
Derungs, Felix, Sec.--Danzas Holding Ltd., Basel, Switzerland; *Int'l*, pg. 382
DeSantis, Lydia M., Sec.--GP Strategies Corporation, New York, NY; *U.S. Public*, pg. 694
Desclee, Francois, Sec.--Tractebel, Brussels, Belgium; *Int'l*, pg. 1414
Desjardins-Siciliano, Yves, V.P.-Law--BCE Mobile Communications Inc., Saint-Laurent, Canada; *Int'l*, pg. 115
Deslauries, Therese, Sec.--Culinar Inc., Montreal, Canada; *Int'l*, pg. 348
Desmarais, Nick, Sec.--Westar Group Ltd., Vancouver, Canada; *Int'l*, pg. 1491
Desmarais, Nicolas, Sec.--Great Pacific Enterprises Inc., Vancouver, Canada; *Int'l*, pg. 557
Despres, Monique, V.P., Gen. Counsel & Sec.--Telemedia Inc., Montreal, Canada; *Int'l*, pg. 1373
Desrosiers, Robert A., V.P.-Fin. & Sec.--Bauer Sports Inc., Montreal, Canada; *U.S. Public*, pg. 1184
Desy, Luc O., Gen. Counsel & Sec.--Rolland Inc., Saint-Jerome, Canada; *Int'l*, pg. 273
Deull, Charles B., Sr. V.P.-Legal & Bus. Affairs & Sec.--Scholastic Corporation, New York, NY; *U.S. Public*, pg. 1440
Deuschle, Mark J., Chief Fin. Officer, V.P.-Fin., Treas. & Sec.--Plasti-Line, Inc., Knoxville, TN; *U.S. Public*, pg. 1308
DeVille, Paul, Pres., Chief Oper. Officer & Sec.--Persis Corporation, Honolulu, HI; *U.S. Private*, pg. 855
Devine, Jack M., Treas. & Sec.--Associated Power, Inc., Wilmington, CA; *U.S. Private*, pg. 92
Devos, Ron, Chief Fin. Officer, V.P.-Fin. & Sec.--Nathan's Famous Inc., Westbury, NY; *U.S. Public*, pg. 1152
Dew, Bruce J., Sec.--Diemolding Corp., Canastota, NY; *U.S. Private*, pg. 332
Dewey, R. Bruce, Sr. V.P. & Gen. Counsel--Mestek, Inc., Westfield, MA; *U.S. Public*, pg. 1099
Dewey, Ronald L., Dir.-Fin. & Sec.--Erdle Perforating Co., Rochester, NY; *U.S. Private*, pg. 380
Dewez, Brigitte M., Deputy Gen. Counsel & Corp. Sec.--Unocal Corporation, El Segundo, CA; *U.S. Public*, pg. 1698
DeWolf, Daniel, Esq., Legal Counsel & Corp. Sec.--Chyron Corp., Melville, NY; *Int'l*, pg. 1372
DeYager, Betty J., Sec.--The Foreign Candy Co., Inc., Hull, IA; *U.S. Private*, pg. 418
DeZure, Thomas J., Asst. Sec.--Ford Motor Company, Dearborn, MI; *U.S. Public*, pg. 661
Di Rienzo, Mary, Sec.--Standard Metals Corporation, New York, NY; *U.S. Public*, pg. 1502
Dial, Lorinda Jewelene, Treas. & Sec.--Plymouth Creameries, Inc., Plymouth, WI; *U.S. Private*, pg. 872
Diamond, Clare W., Treas. & Sec.--T.L. Diamond Company, New York, NY; *U.S. Private*, pg. 330
Diamond, Frederic, Exec. V.P., Treas. & Sec.--Diamond Chemical Co., Inc., East Rutherford, NJ; *U.S. Private*, pg. 330
Diamond, Sari L., V.P. & Sec.--TrizecHahn Corporation, Toronto, Canada; *Int'l*, pg. 1424
Dias Garcia, Joao, Sec.--Caixa Geral de Depositos, Lisbon, Portugal; *Int'l*, pg. 250
Diaz, Saul, V.P. & Sec.--Med-Lab Supply Company, Inc., Miami, FL; *U.S. Private*, pg. 726
Dibble, Leroy E., Treas. & Asst. Sec.--Bulab Holdings, Inc., Memphis, TN; *U.S. Private*, pg. 180
Dicapua, Nicholas, Chief Oper. Officer, Chief Fin. Officer, V.P., Treas. & Sec.--Liberty Fabrics, Inc., New York, NY; *Int'l*, pg. 340
DiCaro, Daniel P., Chief Fin. Officer, V.P. & Asst. Sec.--Medicus Systems Corporation, Evanston, IL; *U.S. Public*, pg. 1080
Dick, Jerome J., Asst. Sec.--Bowl America, Incorporated, Alexandria, VA; *U.S. Public*, pg. 248
Dick, Michael T., Asst. Sec.--Bowl America, Incorporated, Alexandria, VA; *U.S. Public*, pg. 248
Dicke, James F., III, V.P. & Sec.--Crown Equipment Corporation, New Bremen, OH; *U.S. Private*, pg. 292
Dickerson, Mark S., V.P., Gen. Counsel & Sec.--Talley Industries, Inc., Phoenix, AZ; *U.S. Public*, pg. 307
Dickerson, Paige C., Asst. Sec.--Texfi Industries, Inc., Raleigh, NC; *U.S. Public*, pg. 1588
Dickerson, Virginia, Corp. Sec. & Mgr.-Acctg.--Nelson Photo Supplies, San Diego, CA; *U.S. Private*, pg. 791
Dickey, Jane, Sec.--Union City Body Company, L.P., Union City, IN; *U.S. Private*, pg. 1118
Dickey, Sam, Treas. & Sec.--O'Neil Data Systems, Inc., Los Angeles, CA; *U.S. Private*, pg. 817
Dickie, John W., Sec. & Dir.-Human Resources--ComSonics, Inc., Harrisonburg, VA; *U.S. Private*, pg. 260
Dickie, Lawrence F., V.P., Assoc. Gen. Counsel & Asst. Sec.--PepsiCo, Inc., Purchase, NY; *U.S. Public*, pg. 1276
Dickinson, Charles W., IV, V.P. & Sec.--The Eastville Bank, Eastville, VA; *U.S. Public*, pg. 1089
Dickler, Gerard, Sec.--Guideposts Associates, Inc., Carmel, NY; *U.S. Private*, pg. 487
Dickson, James Douglas, Jr., Controller & Asst. Sec.--Alba-Waldensian, Inc., Valdese, NC; *U.S. Public*, pg. 35
Dickson, Thomas E., Treas. & Sec.--Hoover Treated Wood Products, Inc., Thomson, GA; *U.S. Public*, pg. 1193
Diem, Linda L., Treas. & Sec.--Southern Agricultural Insecticides, Inc., Palmetto, FL; *U.S. Private*, pg. 1015
Diemer, Irving, Jr., V.P. & Sec.--Metal Seal & Products, Inc., Willoughby, OH; *U.S. Private*, pg. 734
Dietrich, A.D., Sec.--Grant, Inc., Huron, SD; *U.S. Public*, pg. 1201
Dietrich, A.D., Sec.--Northwestern Networks, Inc., Huron, SD; *U.S. Public*, pg. 1201
Dietrich, A.D., Sec.--Northwestern Systems, Inc., Huron, SD; *U.S. Public*, pg. 1201
Dietrich, A.D., Sec.--Northwestern Growth Corp., Sioux Falls, SD; *U.S. Public*, pg. 1201
Dietrich, A.D., Asst. Sec.--Cornerstone Propane G.P. Inc., Watsonville, CA; *U.S. Public*, pg. 1201
Dietrich, A.D., Sec.--Nekota Resources Inc., Huron, SD; *U.S. Public*, pg. 1201
Dietrich, Alan D., V.P.-Admin. & Sec.--Northwestern Public Service, Huron, SD; *U.S. Public*, pg. 1200
Dietz, D.F., Sec.--National Sea Products Incorporated, Portsmouth, NH; *Int'l*, pg. 909
Dietz, David F., Sec.--Outdoor Communications, Inc., Corinth, MS; *U.S. Private*, pg. 822
Dietz, Gene E., Sec.--Kennedy Tank & Manufacturing Co., Inc., Indianapolis, IN; *U.S. Private*, pg. 614
Dill, Andre, Sec.--Specialty Underwriters Reinsurance Facility, Hamilton, Bermuda; *U.S. Private*, pg. 741
Dill, Andre J., Sec.--Moran Insurance Company Limited, Greenwich, CT; *U.S. Private*, pg. 760
Dillard, Naomi, Treas. & Sec.--Electronic Drives and Controls, Parsippany, NJ; *U.S. Private*, pg. 370
Diller, Keeta, Asst. V.P. & Sec.--Rurban Financial Corp., Defiance, OH; *U.S. Public*, pg. 1412
Dillmann, Todd A., Corp. Counsel & Sec.--Giddings & Lewis, Inc., Fond Du Lac, WI; *Int'l*, pg. 1389
Dillon, Mimi, Dir. & Sec.-Sls.--Catholic Order of Foresters, Naperville, IL; *U.S. Private*, pg. 220
DiLorenzo, John F., Jr., Sec.--Kentucky Power Co., Ashland, KY; *U.S. Public*, pg. 72
DiLorenzo, John F., Jr., Sec.--Indiana Michigan Power Company, Fort Wayne, IN; *U.S. Public*, pg. 72
DiLorenzo, John F., Jr., Sec.--Ohio Power Company, Canton, OH; *U.S. Public*, pg. 72
DiLorenzo, John F., Jr., Sec.--Columbus Southern Power Company, Columbus, OH; *U.S. Public*, pg. 72
DiLorenzo, John F., Jr., Sec.--Appalachian Power Company, Roanoke, VA; *U.S. Public*, pg. 72
DiMatteo, Lynne, Exec. Asst.-Chattanooga Choo-Choo Holiday Inn, Chattanooga, TN; *U.S. Private*, pg. 231
Dimmers, Alan, Sec.--The Shane Group Inc., Hillsdale, MI; *U.S. Private*, pg. 989
Dimun, Anthony, Chief Fin. Officer, Exec. V.P., Treas. & Sec.--Vital Signs, Inc., Totowa, NJ; *U.S. Public*, pg. 1723
Dinger, William S., Pres. & Sec.--William H. Sadlier, Inc., New York, NY; *U.S. Public*, pg. 1422
DiNunzio, Joseph A., V.P. & Sec.--Artesian Water Company, Inc., Newark, DE; *U.S. Public*, pg. 135
Dion, Ronald, Sr. V.P.-Fin.--Altec Lansing Technologies, Inc., Milford, PA; *U.S. Private*, pg. 479

DiOrio, Mary R., Sec.--Spadone Inc., Norwalk, CT; *U.S. Private*, pg. 1019
Dippell, J., V.P.-Fin. & Admin. & Sec.--Dare Foods Limited, Kitchener, Canada; *Int'l*, pg. 383
Diracles, John, Jr., V.P., Treas. & Sec.--Radisson Hotel Corporation, Minneapolis, MN; *U.S. Private*, pg. 212
DiSalvo, Joe, Asst. Sec.--General Electric Canada Inc., Mississauga, Canada; *U.S. Public*, pg. 713
DiSante, Robert, V.P. & Asst. Sec.--FCA Holdings, Inc., Wayne, PA; *Int'l*, pg. 471
DiSante, Robert, V.P. & Asst. Sec.--Financial Collection Agencies of Pennsylvania Inc, Wayne, PA; *Int'l*, pg. 471
Disbrow, Nancy M., V.P.-Human Resources & Corp. Sec.--Liggett-Stashower, Inc., Cleveland, OH; *U.S. Private*, pg. 667
Ditcher, John, V.P. & Sec.--Atlantic Concrete Products, Inc., Tullytown, PA; *U.S. Private*, pg. 95
DiTommaso, Victor, V.P.-Fin., Treas. & Sec.--Ennis Business Forms, Inc., Ennis, TX; *U.S. Public*, pg. 583
Dittmer, R.G., V.P., Sec. & Treas.--AGRA Inc., Calgary, Canada; *Int'l*, pg. 30
Dittmer, R.G., Sec.--Maxum Engineering Enterprises Ltd., Calgary, Canada; *Int'l*, pg. 31
Dittmer, Robert G., Exec. V.P.-Fin./Admin. & Sec.--Agra Inc., Calgary, Canada; *Int'l*, pg. 30
Ditto, Michael E., V.P., Gen. Counsel & Sec.--Republic Financial Services, Inc., Dallas, TX; *Int'l*, pg. 346
Ditto, Michael E., V.P. & Sec.--Republic Diversified Services, Inc., Dallas, TX; *Int'l*, pg. 346
Ditto, Michael E., V.P. & Sec.--Southern Insurance Co., Dallas, TX; *Int'l*, pg. 346
Ditto, Michael E., V.P. & Corp. Sec.--Republic Financial Services, Inc., Dallas, TX; *Int'l*, pg. 346
Ditto, Michael E., V.P. & Corp. Sec.--Southern Underwriters Insurance Company, Dallas, TX; *Int'l*, pg. 346
Ditto, Michael E., V.P. & Corp. Sec.--Republic Fire & Casualty Insurance Company, Dallas, TX; *Int'l*, pg. 346
Ditto, Michael E., V.P. & Sec.--Republic Group No. Two, Dallas, TX; *Int'l*, pg. 346
Ditto, Michael E., V.P. & Sec.--Eagle General Agency, Dallas, TX; *Int'l*, pg. 346
Ditto, Michael E., V.P. & Sec.--Allied Premium Finance, Dallas, TX; *Int'l*, pg. 346
Dixon, Clive Sidney, Sec--How Group Limited, West Bromwich, United Kingdom; *Int'l*, pg. 636
Dixon, Gwen, Asst. Sec.--Iomega Corporation, Roy, UT; *U.S. Public*, pg. 912
Dixon, Paul E., V.P., Gen. Counsel & Sec.--Handy & Harman, New York, NY; *U.S. Public*, pg. 780
Doak, Margaret, Asst. Sec.--Bird Incorporated, Norwood, MA; *Int'l*, pg. 1170
Dobbs, James C., V.P., Gen. Counsel & Sec.--Versar Inc., Springfield, VA; *U.S. Public*, pg. 1717
Dockery, Daniel P., Asst. Gen. Counsel & Asst. Sec.--Miller Brewing Company, Milwaukee, WI; *U.S. Public*, pg. 1289
Dockter, Rebecca L., Treas. & Sec.--PBD, Inc., Alpharetta, GA; *U.S. Private*, pg. 825
Dodd, Martin H., Sr. V.P., Gen. Counsel & Sec.--TRC Companies, Inc., Windsor, CT; *U.S. Public*, pg. 1557
Doder, Milenko, Treas. & Sec.--The Rados Companies, Santa Ana, CA; *U.S. Private*, pg. 907
Dodson, Bob, V.P. & Sec.--Direct Press Modern Litho Corporation, Huntington Station, NY; *U.S. Private*, pg. 334
Doench, Debra, Mgr.-Corp. Communications--Hobart Brothers Co., Troy, OH; *U.S. Public*, pg. 866
Doettling, Robert L., Sr. V.P.-Fin. & Admin. & Sec.--Midland Enterprises Inc., Cincinnati, OH; *U.S. Public*, pg. 549
Dohnal, D.E., Sec. & Counsel--The Kelly-Springfield Tire Company, Cumberland, MD; *U.S. Public*, pg. 753
Dokmo, Harold B., Jr., Chm. Bd., Pres., Owner, Treas. & Sec.--Norcraft Companies, Inc., Saint Paul, MN; *U.S. Private*, pg. 801
Dolan, Maureen, Sec. & Treas.--Cargill Salt, Newark, CA; *U.S. Private*, pg. 210
Dolan, Robert E., Controller, Asst. Treas. & Asst. Sec.--Lynch Telecommunications Corporation, Greenwich, CT; *U.S. Public*, pg. 1022
Dolan, Timothy, V.P., Sec. & Gen. Attorney--Robertshaw Controls Company, Richmond, VA; *Int'l*, pg. 1243
Dolbeare, Gary, V.P.-Fin. & Sec.--Basler Electric Company, Highland, IL; *U.S. Private*, pg. 121
Dolinko, Richard, Sec.--Best Provision Co., Inc., Newark, NJ; *U.S. Private*, pg. 140
Doll, David J., Chief Fin. Officer & Sr. V.P.--Bodine Electric Company, Chicago, IL; *U.S. Private*, pg. 154
Dollarhide, Michael J., Asst. Sec.--John Deere Capital Corporation, Reno, NV; *U.S. Public*, pg. 492
Dolph, Bettie, Treas. & Sec.--Berry Contracting, Corpus Christi, TX; *U.S. Private*, pg. 137
Dominitz, Henry, Controller & Sec.--Jean Philippe Fragrances, Inc., New York, NY; *U.S. Public*, pg. 924
Donadio, Mark C., Gen. Counsel & Sec.--Barrister Information Systems Corporation, Buffalo, NY; *U.S. Public*, pg. 192
Donde, R. Martinez, Sec.--Empaques Ponderosa SA, Mexico, Mexico; *Int'l*, pg. 454
Dongarran, Janet, Asst. Sec.--GATX Corporation, Chicago, IL; *U.S. Public*, pg. 690
Donnan, Brian D., Controller & Asst. Sec.--Arden Group, Inc., Los Angeles, CA; *U.S. Public*, pg. 128
Donnelly, Kevin W., V.P., Gen. Counsel & Sec.--Nortek, Inc., Providence, RI; *U.S. Public*, pg. 1192
Donnels, Chuck, Treas.--Earl Construction Company, West Sacramento, CA; *U.S. Private*, pg. 1051
Donoghue, Denis, Sec.--Irish Biscuits, Dublin, Ireland; *Int'l*, pg. 688
Donohoe, James D., Sec.--Republic Engineered Steels, Inc., Massillon, OH; *U.S. Public*, pg. 1378
Donohue, Robert F., V.P. & Chief Legal Officer--Cirrus Logic, Inc., Fremont, CA; *U.S. Public*, pg. 375
Donovan, David, Treas. & Asst. Sec.--Printpack Inc., Atlanta, GA; *U.S. Private*, pg. 886
Donovan, Jan L., Asst. Sec.--Fluor Corporation, Irvine, CA; *U.S. Public*, pg. 659
Donovan, Sandra J., Sec.--Delco Electronics Overseas Corporation, Detroit, MI; *U.S. Public*, pg. 721
Dooley, Jo Ann C., V.P. & Sec.--Gardner Publications, Inc., Cincinnati, OH; *U.S. Private*, pg. 440
Dopkins, Leonard A., Chm. Bd., Treas. & Sec.--Standard Electronics, Inc., Amherst, NY; *U.S. Private*, pg. 1031
Doran, Michael W., Treas. & Sec.--Midway Ford Truck Center Inc., Kansas City, MO; *U.S. Private*, pg. 744
Doran, Sandra J., V.P., Gen. Counsel & Sec.--Shaw's Supermarkets, Inc., East Bridgewater, MA; *Int'l*, pg. 1170
Doran, William M., Esq., Sec.--SEI Investments, Oaks, PA; *U.S. Public*, pg. 1417
Doremus, Peter, Sec.--Edlund Company, Inc., Burlington, VT; *U.S. Private*, pg. 364
Dorflinger, Peter G., V.P., Gen. Counsel & Corp. Sec.--Sulzermedica USA Inc., Angleton, TX; *Int'l*, pg. 1307
Dornbusch, Arthur A., II, V.P., Gen. Counsel & Sec.--Engelhard Corporation, Iselin, NJ; *U.S. Public*, pg. 582
Dornbush, Darwin C., Sec.--Benihana, Inc., Miami, FL; *U.S. Public*, pg. 211
Dornbush, Darwin C., Sec.--Cantel Industries, Inc., Clifton, NJ; *U.S. Public*, pg. 301
Dorsen, Hariette, Sr. V.P., Sec. & Gen. Counsel--Bantam Doubleday Dell Publishing Group, Inc., New York, NY; *Int'l*, pg. 191
Dorsett, C. Powers, Sr. V.P., Gen. Counsel & Sec.--Springs Industries, Inc., Fort Mill, SC; *U.S. Public*, pg. 1499
Dorsey, Patrick B., Sr. V.P., Gen. Counsel & Sec.--Tiffany & Co., New York, NY; *U.S. Public*, pg. 1608
Dorszynski, Douglas, V.P.-Tax, Treas. & Sec.--Applied Power Inc., Butler, WI; *U.S. Public*, pg. 124
Dorwart, Frederic, Gen. Counsel & Sec.--BOK Financial Corp., Tulsa, OK; *U.S. Public*, pg. 163
Dorwart, Frederic, Sec.--Bank of Oklahoma, N.A., Tulsa, OK; *U.S. Public*, pg. 163
Dory, Leara, V.P.-Fin. & Sec.--Cuisine Solutions, Inc., Alexandria, VA; *U.S. Public*, pg. 466
Dose, Robert E., Controller, Asst. Sec. & Asst. Treas.--Virco Mfg. Corporation, Torrance, CA; *U.S. Public*, pg. 1721
Doss, M. Kenneth, V.P. & Sec.--Fieldcrest Cannon, Inc., Kannapolis, NC; *U.S. Public*, pg. 1296
Doss, M. Kenneth, V.P. & Sec.--Fieldcrest/Cannon Bed Fashions Division, New York, NY; *U.S. Public*, pg. 1296
Dotterer, Herbert T., Chief Fin. Officer, Sr. V.P.-Fin. & Admin. & Sec.--Eagle Food Centers, Inc., Milan, IL; *U.S. Public*, pg. 547
Dougherty, James T., Sr. V.P., Gen. Counsel & Sec.--Lone Star Technologies, Inc., Dallas, TX; *U.S. Public*, pg. 1012
Doughty, H. Court, Jr., Asst. Sec.--Borden, Inc., Columbus, OH; *U.S. Private*, pg. 157
Douglas, Gene, V.P.-Legal & Admin. & Corp. Sec.--Hvide Marine Incorporated, Fort Lauderdale, FL; *U.S. Public*, pg. 851
Douglas, J. Paul, V.P., Corp. Counsel & Sec.--Public Service Company of North Carolina, Inc., Gastonia, NC; *U.S. Public*, pg. 1340
Douglass, Robert, Sec.--Warner Candy Company, Inc., Schiller Park, IL; *U.S. Private*, pg. 1150
Doumenc, Jean-Pierre, Sec.--Schneider S.A., Boulogne-Billancourt, France; *Int'l*, pg. 1207
Douthit, R.E., V.P., Sec. & Treas.--Smith & Sons Foods, Inc., Macon, GA; *U.S. Private*, pg. 1006
Dow, Samuel, Sec.--Coats Viyella plc, Manchester, United Kingdom; *Int'l*, pg. 299
Dowd, Thomas F., V.P., Gen. Counsel & Sec.--Graybar Electric Company, Inc., Clayton, MO; *U.S. Private*, pg. 472
Dowie, Sandra L., Sec.--Freeman Decorating Co., Dallas, TX; *U.S. Private*, pg. 426
Downey, Paul, Pres., Treas. & Sec.--Advanced Circuit Technology, Nashua, NH; *U.S. Private*, pg. 21
Downing, G. Edgar, V.P., Sec. & Gen. Counsel--Mobile Gas Service Corp., Mobile, AL; *U.S. Public*, pg. 1120
Dowsett, S.A., Sec.--Australia Power Pty Ltd, Malaga, Australia; *Int'l*, pg. 894
Doyle, Cecil G., Chief Fin. Officer, Exec. V.P., Treas. & Sec.--Hayes, Seay, Mattern & Mattern, Inc., Roanoke, VA; *U.S. Private*, pg. 513
Doyle, Charles A., V.P., Gen. Counsel & Sec.--Burns & Roe Enterprises, Inc., Oradell, NJ; *U.S. Private*, pg. 187
Doyle, Elizabeth M., V.P.-Admin. & Production & Sec.--My Own Meals, Inc., Deerfield, IL; *U.S. Private*, pg. 770
Doyle, J., Controller--Asahi Glass America, Inc., New York, NY; *Int'l*, pg. 84
Doyle, John A., Jr., Asst. Sec.--Foster Wheeler Corporation, Clinton, NJ; *U.S. Public*, pg. 676
Doyle, N.J., Sec.--Greenham Construction Materials Limited, Isleworth, United Kingdom; *Int'l*, pg. 1358
Drabek, J.A., Sec.--American Flange & Manufacturing Co. Inc., Carol Stream, IL; *Int'l*, pg. 1146
Drader, Kelly I., Chief Fin. Officer, Sr. V.P. & Corp. Sec.--EnerMark Income Fund, Calgary, Canada; *Int'l*, pg. 454
Draffin, Michael C., Sec.--Boeing Realty Corporation, Long Beach, CA; *U.S. Public*, pg. 241
Drake, Lynda, Sec.--Leblanc Communications, Inc., Richardson, TX; *U.S. Private*, pg. 656
Dray, Kari, Exec. Sec.--Falcon Products, Inc., Saint Louis, MO; *U.S. Public*, pg. 611
Drengel, Donna J., Asst. Sec.--Community Bank System, Inc., De Witt, NY; *U.S. Public*, pg. 416
Drenning, John B., Sec.--Astronics Corporation, Buffalo, NY; *U.S. Public*, pg. 142
Drenning, John B., Sec.--Moog Incorporated, East Aurora, NY; *U.S. Public*, pg. 1127
Drenning, John B., Esq., Sec.--Acme Electric Corporation, East Aurora, NY; *U.S. Public*, pg. 16
Dresdow, Mary A., Sec.--A.C. Nielsen Company, Schaumburg, IL; *U.S. Public*, pg. 1183
Dresser, W. Donald, Exec. V.P., Dir.-Devel. & Asst. Sec.--United Foods, Inc., Bells, TN; *U.S. Public*, pg. 1677
Drew, James S., Asst. Sec.--Charleston Insurance Company, Buffalo, NY; *U.S. Public*, pg. 1455
Drew, William J., Sec.--Kohler Company, Kohler, WI; *U.S. Private*, pg. 630
Drillock, David M., Controller & Asst. Sec.--Cytec Industries Inc., West Paterson, NJ; *U.S. Public*, pg. 471
Drinkward, Robert, Pres. & Sec.--Bergelectric Corporation, Los Angeles, CA; *U.S. Private*, pg. 135
Driscoll, Linda, Asst. Sec.--Continental Can Co., Norwalk, CT; *U.S. Public*, pg. 439
Driver, Carole P., Asst. Corp. Sec.--Landmark Graphics Corporation, Houston, TX; *U.S. Public*, pg. 776
Droin, Francois, Sec. Gen.--Groupe Saint Louis, Paris, France; *Int'l*, pg. 567
Dropkin, Philip, Sec. & Gen. Counsel--Time Warner Cable Liberty Division, Ferndale, NY; *U.S. Public*, pg. 1611
Drost, Marianne, Sec.--GTE Corporation, Stamford, CT; *U.S. Public*, pg. 696
Drouin, Sylvie, V.P.-Legal Affairs & Corp. Sec.--Cadim, Montreal, Canada; *Int'l*, pg. 249
Drouin, Sylvie, Corp. Sec.--Cadev, Montreal, Canada; *Int'l*, pg. 249
Drouin, Sylvie, Corp. Sec.--Ivanhoe, Montreal, Canada; *Int'l*, *pg. 249*
Drouin, Sylvie, Corp. Sec.--SITQ Immobilier, Montreal, Canada; *Int'l*, pg. 249
Drouin, Sylvie, Corp. Sec.--Hypotheques CDPQ, Montreal, Canada; *Int'l*, pg. 249
Drucker, Nate, Chief Fin. Officer, Treas. & Sec.--Weber Marking Systems, Inc., Arlington Heights, IL; *U.S. Private*, pg. 1157
Druggish, Thomas R., V.P., Treas. & Sec.--ELXSI Corporation, Orlando, FL; *U.S. Public*, pg. 545
Drury, Richard B., Treas. & Sec.--TJ International, Inc., Boise, ID; *U.S. Public*, pg. 1556
Dryer, Ned, Controller & Sec.--Arizona Wholesale Supply Company, Phoenix, AZ; *U.S. Private*, pg. 82
Dryer, Ned, Treas. & Sec.--National Brands, Inc., Phoenix, AZ; *U.S. Private*, pg. 780
du Bois, Patrick, Exec. V.P. & Sec. Gen.--Sabena, Zaventem, Belgium; *Int'l*, pg. 1168
Du Bose, Sam I., Corp. Sec.--White Electrical Construction Co., Atlanta, GA; *U.S. Private*, pg. 1172
Dubach, Patrick, V.P. & Sec.--Avesta Sheffield East, Inc., Baltimore, MD; *Int'l*, pg. 221
Duback, S.R., Sec.--OshKosh B'Gosh, Inc., Oshkosh, WI; *U.S. Public*, pg. 1232
Dube, Georges, Corp. Sec.--Sand Technology Systems, Westmount, Canada; *Int'l*, pg. 1183
DuBerger, Me Jacques, Sec.--Telebec Ltee, Anjou, Canada; *Int'l*, pg. 116
Dubin, Stephen V., Sr. V.P., Gen. Counsel & Sec.--CSS Industries, Inc., Philadelphia, PA; *U.S. Public*, pg. 283
Dubin, Ursula P., Sec.--Manufacturers' News, Inc., Evanston, IL; *U.S. Private*, pg. 700
Dubner, Miriam, Sec. & Treas.--Gerson & Gerson, Inc., New York, NY; *U.S. Private*, pg. 449
DuBois, Charles H., Sec.--Mobil Oil Corporation, Fairfax, VA; *U.S. Public*, pg. 1118
Dubon, J.L. Gonzalez, Sec.--Refractarios Nacionales S.A., Guatemala, Guatemala; *Int'l*, pg. 894
Dubreuil, Etienne, V.P.-Legal Affairs & Sec.--The Laurentian Group Corporation, Montreal, Canada; *Int'l*, pg. 396
DuChene, Todd, V.P., Gen. Counsel & Sec.--Fisher Scientific International, Hampton, NH; *U.S. Private*, pg. 658
Duckworth, Gary E., Sec.--Frederick Trading Company, Frederick, MD; *U.S. Private*, pg. 335
Duckworth, Norman E., V.P.-Human Resources & Corp. Sec.--ONEOK Inc., Tulsa, OK; *U.S. Public*, pg. 1226
Duda, Luther, V.P. & Sec.--A. Duda & Sons Inc., Oviedo, FL; *U.S. Private*, pg. 344
Duda, Thomas, Chief Fin. Officer & Sec.--Westwood Computer Corporation, Springfield, NJ; *U.S. Private*, pg. 1170
Dudchenko, Peter, V.P.-Corp. Devel. & Asst. Sec.--Citation Corporation, Birmingham, AL; *U.S. Public*, pg. 376
Dudczyk, Lisa, Sec.--Amurol Confections Co., Yorkville, IL; *U.S. Public*, pg. 1781
Dudley, Robert G., Sec.--First United Bancshares, Inc., El Dorado, AR; *U.S. Public*, pg. 641
Duerr, Richard E., Jr., V.P., Gen. Counsel & Sec.--Sofamor Danek Group, Inc., Memphis, TN; *U.S. Public*, pg. 1482
Duersch, Charles A., Treas. & Sec.--Western States Machine Company, Hamilton, OH; *U.S. Private*, pg. 1168
Duffell, David K., Sec.--Wellman, Inc., Shrewsbury, NJ; *U.S. Public*, pg. 1752
Duffield, Anne E., V.P., Div. Counsel & Sec.--ContiMortgage Corporation, Horsham, PA; *U.S. Public*, pg. 439
Duffin, Patricia A., Treas. & Asst. Sec.--CH Mortgage Company, Scottsdale, AZ; *U.S. Public*, pg. 441
Duffy, K.M., Joint Sec.--BT (Worldwide) Ltd., London, United Kingdom; *Int'l*, pg. 222
DuFour, Candace, Sec.--Weingarten Realty Investors, Houston, TX; *U.S. Public*, pg. 1751
Dufour, Didie, Sec. Gen.--BMOI, Antananarivo, Madagascar; *Int'l*, pg. 163
Dugan, David A., Controller & Sec.--Georgia-Bonded Fibers, Inc., Newark, NJ; *U.S. Public*, pg. 734
Dugan, David A., Controller & Sec.--Bontex, Buena Vista, VA; *U.S. Public*, pg. 734
Dugan, Francis R., Chm. Bd. & Chief Exec. Officer--Dugan & Meyers Interests, Inc., Cincinnati, OH; *U.S. Private*, pg. 345
DuGan, Gordon F., Sr. V.P. & Asst. Sec.--W.P. Carey & Co., Inc., New York, NY; *U.S. Private*, pg. 209
Dugan, Joel H., Sr. V.P.-Fin. & Admin., & Sec.--Rhodes, Inc., Atlanta, GA; *U.S. Public*, pg. 805
Dugan, Mary E., Chm. Bd., Treas. & Sec.--Dugan Production Corp., Farmington, NM; *U.S. Private*, pg. 345
Dugan, Ruth, Exec. Admin. Assist.--Carpeteria, Inc., Valencia, CA; *U.S. Private*, pg. 215
Duggan, Ruby, V.P. & Sec.--Duggan Industries, Inc., Dallas, TX; *U.S. Private*, pg. 345

Duggan, Thomas E., Gen. Counsel & Sec.--OppenheimerFunds Distributor, Inc., New York, NY; *U.S. Private*, pg. 818

Duhamel, Beatrice, Sec. Gen.--BNP Luxembourg SA, Luxembourg, Luxembourg; *Int'l*, pg. 164

Duhe, Tommy, Sec.--M.A. Patout & Son, Jeanerette, LA; *U.S. Private*, pg. 843

Duke, Susanna N., Corp. Sec. & Dir.-Law--Plum Creek Timber Co., L.P., Seattle, WA; *U.S. Public*, pg. 1311

Dula, C. Stephen, Chief Fin. Officer, Treas. & Sec.--Salem National Corporation, Winston Salem, NC; *U.S. Private*, pg. 962

Dull, Karen, Chief Fin. Officer & Exec. V.P.--World's Finest Chocolate, Inc., Chicago, IL; *U.S. Private*, pg. 1191

Dumeny, Marcel J., Sr. V.P., Chief Gen. Counsel & Corp. Sec.--Fairfield Communities, Inc., Little Rock, AR; *U.S. Public*, pg. 610

Dumond, Paul G., Sec.--Danka Business Systems PLC, London, United Kingdom; *Int'l*, pg. 379

Dumont, Poerre, Sec.--Etablissements Delhaize Freres Et Cie "Le Lion" S.A., Brussels, Belgium; *Int'l*, pg. 462

Dun, David, Gen. Counsel & Sec.--Sierra Pacific Industries, Anderson, CA; *U.S. Private*, pg. 998

Dunaway, Allen R., Chief Fin. Officer, V.P. & Sec.--Orthologic Corporation, Tempe, AZ; *U.S. Public*, pg. 1232

Dunbar, Peter, V.P. & Sec.--Summit Bank, Bethlehem, PA; *U.S. Public*, pg. 1528

Dunbar, Peter, V.P. & Sec.--First Valley Corporation, Bethlehem, PA; *U.S. Public*, pg. 1528

Duncan, Linda, Sec.--Dewberry Design Group, Oklahoma City, OK; *U.S. Private*, pg. 329

Duncan, Melvin D., Jr., V.P. & Sec.--Red Ball Corporation, Seattle, WA; *U.S. Private*, pg. 97

Duncan, Rosario, Sec.--Business Mens Insurance Corporation, Coral Gables, FL; *U.S. Private*, pg. 189

Dunlap, F. Thomas, Jr., V.P., Gen. Counsel & Sec.--Intel Corporation, Santa Clara, CA; *U.S. Public*, pg. 886

Dunlap, Joanne, V.P.-Admin. Services & Sec.--Logicon Geodynamic, Torrance, CA; *U.S. Public*, pg. 1199

Dunn, E.R., V.P.-Human Resources & Asst. Sec.--Whirlpool Corporation, Benton Harbor, MI; *U.S. Public*, pg. 1764

Dunn, Leslie, Sr. V.P., Gen. Counsel & Sec.--Cole National Corporation, Cleveland, OH; *U.S. Public*, pg. 396

Dunn, Nina Laserson, Exec. V.P., Gen. Counsel & Sec.--DRS Technologies, Inc., Parsippany, NJ; *U.S. Public*, pg. 474

Dunn, P., Sec.--Crane Limited U.K., Ipswich, United Kingdom; *U.S. Public*, pg. 458

Dunn, Robert V., Sr. V.P.-Law & Admin.--General Nutrition, Inc., Pittsburgh, PA; *U.S. Public*, pg. 725

Dunn, Susan S., Asst. Sec.--Glaxo Wellcome PLC, Research Triangle Park, NC; *Int'l*, pg. 553

Dunnavant, Terrell H., Sec.--Kyanite Mining Corporation, Dillwyn, VA; *U.S. Private*, pg. 638

Dunne, Timothy R., V.P., Gen. Counsel & Sec.--CRSS Inc., Houston, TX; *Int'l*, pg. 1415

Dunstan, Ericson M., Sr. V.P.-Corp. Engrng. & Sec.--Micropolis Corporation, Chatsworth, CA; *U.S. Private*, pg. 742

Duplessis, Carol, Sec. & Mgr.-Personnel--Cooper Instrument Corp., Middlefield, CT; *U.S. Private*, pg. 274

DuPlessis, Neil, Sec.--NB Coal Company Limited, Minto, Canada; *Int'l*, pg. 923

duPont, Augustus I., V.P., Gen. Counsel & Sec.--Crane Co., Stamford, CT; *U.S. Public*, pg. 456

Dupont, Julia, V.P. & Sec.--Sani-Tech Inc., Lafayette, NJ; *U.S. Public*, pg. 1545

Dupont, Richard, Chief Fin. Officer & Sec.--Source Services Corporation, Dallas, TX; *U.S. Public*, pg. 1488

Dupps, David M., Treas. & Sec.--Dupps Company, Germantown, OH; *U.S. Private*, pg. 348

Durand, Mary K., Sec.--American Republic Insurance Co., Des Moines, IA; *U.S. Private*, pg. 61

Durant, Charles, V.P.-Legal & Sec.--Interactive Technologies, Inc., Saint Paul, MN; *U.S. Public*, pg. 888

Durbin, A.J., Sec.--Exxon Coal Australia Ltd., Sydney, Australia; *U.S. Public*, pg. 602

Durden, M. Frances, Sr. V.P., Gen. Counsel & Sec.--Michael Anthony Jewelers, Inc., Mount Vernon, NY; *U.S. Public*, pg. 1103

Durfee, J.Lang, V.P. & Sec.--Bethel Mills, Inc., Bethel, VT; *U.S. Private*, pg. 141

Durnin, Jerry L., Treas. & Sec.--A.K. Durnin Chrysler Plymouth, Inc., Baton Rouge, LA; *U.S. Private*, pg. 348

Durning, Peter F., Asst. Gen. Counsel & Asst. Sec.--Stone & Webster, Incorporated, Boston, MA; *U.S. Public*, pg. 1519

Dutton, C.B., Sec.--Sarkes Tarzian, Bloomington, IN; *U.S. Private*, pg. 966

Duwe, John, Treas. & Sec.--United States Bakery, Portland, OR; *U.S. Private*, pg. 1124

Dwyer-Owens, Dina, Exec. V.P.-Opers.--The Dwyer Group, Inc., Waco, TX; *U.S. Public*, pg. 537

Dwyer, Gregg A., Sr. V.P., Gen. Counsel & Sec.--Duracell International Inc., Bethel, CT; *U.S. Public*, pg. 743

Dwyer, Joseph P., Treas. & Sec.--Asplundh Tree Expert Co., Willow Grove, PA; *U.S. Private*, pg. 89

Dye, Edward R., Sec. & Asst. Gen. Counsel--GenCorp Inc., Fairlawn, OH; *U.S. Public*, pg. 705

Dyen, Randall, Sr. V.P., Gen. Counsel & Sec.--General Accident Insurance, Philadelphia, PA; *Int'l*, pg. 543

Dyer, K.E., Dir.-Fin. & Sec.--Senior Hargreaves Limited, Bury, United Kingdom; *Int'l*, pg. 1221

Dyer, Steven, Sec.--Old Guard Insurance Group, Lancaster, PA; *U.S. Public*, pg. 1216

Dykeman, Peter J., Gen. Counsel & Corp. Sec.--New Brunswick Power Corporation, Fredericton, Canada; *Int'l*, *pg. 923*

Dykman, Susan, Exec. Asst.-Investor Rels.--Allegiant Physician Services, Atlanta, GA; *U.S. Public*, pg. 45

Dyson, Harry, Treas. & Sec.--Providence Journal-Bulletin, Providence, RI; *U.S. Public*, pg. 209

Dziadzio, John F., Exec. V.P., Treas. & Sec.--JL Media, Inc., Union, NJ; *U.S. Private*, pg. 507

Dzurick, Robert D., Sec.--Lloyd Controls, Inc., Mountlake Terrace, WA; *U.S. Private*, pg. 672

Eacott, Susan H., Sec.--Bartlett Brainard Eacott, Inc., Bloomfield, CT; *U.S. Private*, pg. 118

Eagle, Marjorie J., Treas. & Sec.--Pipe Fabricating & Supply Company, Santa Fe Springs, CA; *U.S. Private*, pg. 867

Eardley, Barry, Grp. Company Sec.--Alvis plc, London, United Kingdom; *Int'l*, pg. 69

Earl, Jane, Sec.--Sedgwick Group plc, London, United Kingdom; *Int'l*, pg. 1217

Earnhardt, Jim Babe, Treas. & Sec.--Earnhardt's Motor Companies, Gilbert, AZ; *U.S. Private*, pg. 356

Easley, Maria, Sec.--Schrader Bellows Division, Cuyahoga Falls, OH; *U.S. Public*, pg. 1261

Eason, William E., Jr., Sr. V.P., Gen. Counsel & Sec.--Scientific-Atlanta, Inc., Norcross, GA; *U.S. Public*, pg. 1443

East, Ernest E., V.P., Gen. Counsel & Sec.--Artisoft, Inc., Tucson, AZ; *U.S. Public*, pg. 136

Easter, R. Bruce, Jr., V.P., Gen. Counsel & Sec.--Nextlink Communications Inc., Bellevue, WA; *U.S. Public*, pg. 1181

Easter, Steven, V.P.-Govt. Member Rels. & Sec.--Blue Diamond Growers, Sacramento, CA; *U.S. Private*, pg. 152

Eastman, Joel M., V.P., Gen. Counsel & Sec.--Bristol Hotels & Resorts, Dallas, TX; *U.S. Public*, pg. 253

Eaton, Craig L., Asst. Sec.--Narragansett Energy Resources Company, Providence, RI; *U.S. Public*, pg. 1171

Eaton, David, Dir.-Legal & Risk Mngmt. Svcs. & Asst. Sec.--Bandag, Incorporated, Muscatine, IA; *U.S. Public*, pg. 177

Eaton, Scott, Controller & Sec.--Sasco Group, Cerritos, CA; *U.S. Private*, pg. 967

Eberhardt, M.C., V.P., Gen. Counsel & Sec.--Raytheon E-Systems, Greenville, TX; *U.S. Public*, pg. 1365

Ebright, M.A., Sec.--Baker Commodities, Inc., Los Angeles, CA; *U.S. Private*, pg. 111

Eccles, Margot L., V.P. & Asst. Sec.--LDI, Ltd., Indianapolis, IN; *U.S. Private*, pg. 639

Eckberg, David, Gen. Counsel & Sec.--Hart Crowser, Inc., Seattle, WA; *U.S. Private*, pg. 507

Eckenrod, Jeannie, Treas. & Sec.--FKG Oil Company, Belleville, IL; *U.S. Private*, pg. 764

Eckhart, Nathan S., Treas. & Asst. Sec.--Allen Organ Company, Macungie, PA; *U.S. Public*, pg. 45

Eddins, Heidi J., General Counsel & Sec.--Providence and Worcester Railroad Company, Worcester, MA; *U.S. Public*, pg. 1336

Edelman, Joseph M., V.P. & Sec.--Network Long Distance, Inc., Baton Rouge, LA; *U.S. Public*, pg. 1169

Edelman, Ruth, Sec.--Edelman Public Relations Worldwide, Chicago, IL; *U.S. Private*, pg. 362

Edelson, Allan J., V.P., Controller & Asst. Sec.--ABC, Inc, New York, NY; *U.S. Public*, pg. 511

Edelson, James I., Exec. V.P., Gen. Counsel & Sec.--PEC Israel Economic Corporation, New York, NY; *Int'l*, pg. 644

Edelstein, Stanley, Sec.--Pacesetter Corporation, Omaha, NE; *U.S. Private*, pg. 830

Eder, James A., V.P., Gen. Counsel & Sec.--Kollmorgen Corporation, Waltham, MA; *U.S. Public*, pg. 965

Edholm, Monica, Sec.--Gunnebo Industrier AB, Gunnebo, Sweden; *Int'l*, pg. 578

Edidin, Orrin J., V.P., Sec. & Gen. Counsel--WMS Industries Inc., Chicago, IL; *U.S. Public*, pg. 1727

Ediger, Lewis W., V.P.-Risk Mngmt. & Sec.--Collins Industries, Inc., Hutchinson, KS; *U.S. Public*, pg. 399

Edlow, Kenneth L., Sr. Mng. Dir. & Sec.--The Bear Stearns Companies Inc., New York, NY; *U.S. Public*, pg. 197

Edreich, Jack, Treas. & Sec.--Brittany Dyeing & Printing Corporation, New Bedford, MA; *U.S. Private*, pg. 170

Edrington, Jack B., Sec. & Asst. Gen. Counsel--Shell Oil Company, Houston, TX; *Int'l*, pg. 1136

Edson, A.H., Mng. Dir. & Sec.--Senior Engineering (Pty) Limited-South Africa, Vereeniging, South Africa; *Int'l*, pg. 1223

Edstrom, Susan C., V.P.-Admin. & Sec.--Media Arts Group, Inc., San Jose, CA; *U.S. Public*, pg. 1077

Edwards, Carl, Jr., Exec. V.P., Gen. Counsel & Sec.--Lennox International Inc., Richardson, TX; *U.S. Private*, pg. 659

Edwards, Christine, Asst. Sec.--GES Inc., Marianna, AR; *U.S. Private*, pg. 434

Edwards, David, V.P., Legal Counsel & Sec.--Bombardier, Learjet Inc., Wichita, KS; *Int'l*, pg. 200

Edwards, Kenneth N., Corp. Sec.--Dunn-Edwards Corporation, Los Angeles, CA; *U.S. Private*, pg. 347

Edwards, Kent M., V.P.-H.R. & Asst. Sec.--Vallen Corporation, Houston, TX; *U.S. Public*, pg. 1705

Edwards, L. Ward, V.P.-Fin., Treas. & Sec.--Moore-Handley, Inc., Pelham, AL; *U.S. Public*, pg. 1128

Edwards, Mark E., V.P., Gen. Counsel & Sec.--Confederation Life Insurance Company, Toronto, Canada; *Int'l*, pg. 325

Edwards, Sarah M., Sec.--Abrams Industries, Inc., Atlanta, GA; *U.S. Public*, pg. 14

Edwards, Stephanie, Sec.--Power Contracting & Engineering Corp., Schaumburg, IL; *U.S. Private*, pg. 877

Edwards, T.L., Treas. & Sec.--Coastal Wholesale, Inc., Kinston, NC; *U.S. Private*, pg. 248

Edwards, William F., Treas. & Sec.--Pilot Air Freight Corp., Lima, PA; *U.S. Private*, pg. 865

Effinger, Jerry L., Asst. Sec.--Ogden Corporation, New York, NY; *U.S. Public*, pg. 1213

Effstrom, Carroll E., Sec. & Treas.--Farmers Marine Copper Works, Galveston, TX; *U.S. Private*, pg. 422

Egan, Charles J., Jr., V.P., Gen. Counsel & Sec.--Hallmark Cards, Inc., Kansas City, MO; *U.S. Private*, pg. 495

Egan, Dana, Controller & Asst. Sec.--Republic Industries, Inc., Fort Lauderdale, FL; *U.S. Public*, pg. 1378

Egan, Gerald, Treas. & Sec.--The Schebler Co., Bettendorf, IA; *U.S. Private*, pg. 366

Egan, Gerald F., Chief Fin. Officer, V.P.-Fin., Treas. & Sec.--Duty Free International, Inc., Ridgefield, CT; *Int'l*, pg. 103

Egan, Gerald L., Treas. & Sec.--Egan McKay Electrical Contractors, Minneapolis, MN; *U.S. Private*, pg. 366

Egan, Pam, Treas. & Asst. Sec.--JG Industries, Inc., Chicago, IL; *U.S. Public*, pg. 917

Egan, Thomas P., Jr., V.P., Gen. Counsel & Sec.--Valmont Industries, Inc., Valley, NE; *U.S. Public*, pg. 1706

Ege, Russell, Asst. Sec.--United Power Association, Elk River, MN; *U.S. Private*, pg. 1123

Egged, Molly M., Asst. Sec.--Hawaiian Electric Industries, Inc., Honolulu, HI; *U.S. Public*, pg. 799

Egged, Molly M., Sec.--Hawaii Electric Light Co., Inc., Hilo, HI; *U.S. Public*, pg. 800

Egged, Molly M., Asst. Sec.--Hawaiian Tug & Barge Corp., Honolulu, HI; *U.S. Public*, pg. 800

Egged, Molly M., Asst. Sec.--Young Brothers, Ltd., Honolulu, HI; *U.S. Public*, pg. 800

Egged, Molly M., Asst. Sec.--Malama Pacific Corp., Honolulu, HI; *U.S. Public*, pg. 800

Eggeling, Heidi, New Bus. Contact & Corp. Sec.--Young & Rubicam GmbH, Vienna, Austria; *U.S. Private*, pg. 1199

Eggenschwiler, James, Asst. Gen. Counsel & Asst. Sec.--Consolidated Stores Corp., Columbus, OH; *U.S. Public*, pg. 437

Ehresman, William, Sr. V.P. & Sec.--Gannett Fleming Affiliates, Inc., Camp Hill, PA; *U.S. Private*, pg. 439

Ehret, A.D., V.P., Treas. & Sec.--Dexter Company, Fairfield, IA; *U.S. Private*, pg. 329

Eich, R.B., Dr., Sec.--Esso Aktiengesellschaft, Hamburg, Germany; *U.S. Public*, pg. 601

Eichel, Roger, Sec. & Legal--Hampton Industries, Inc., Kinston, NC; *U.S. Public*, pg. 779

Eichel, Roger M., V.P. & Sec.--Hampton Industries, Inc., Kinston, NC; *U.S. Public*, pg. 779

Eichenseer, Mike, V.P. & Gen. Mgr.--Koken Mfg. Co. Inc., Saint Louis, MO; *Int'l*, pg. 1349

Eichlen, Arlene M., Admin. Asst.--MD Pneumatics, Springfield, MO; *U.S. Private*, pg. 1111

Eike, Linda, Sec.--Delphi Financial Group, Inc., Wilmington, DE; *U.S. Public*, pg. 496

Eikenbary, Eldon, Treas. & Asst. Sec.--Clarkson Construction Companies, Kansas City, MO; *U.S. Private*, pg. 244

Eilon, Avia, V.P. & Sec.--Magellan International Trading, Northbrook, IL; *U.S. Private*, pg. 694

Eisenberg, Barbara K., V.P., Assoc. Gen. Counsel & Corp. Sec.--Burlington Industries, Inc., Greensboro, NC; *U.S. Public*, pg. 268

Eisenberg, Craig, Chief Fin. Officer & Treas.--American Strip Steel Inc., Kearny, NJ; *U.S. Private*, pg. 62

Eisenberg, L., Corp. Sec.--Pluess-Staufer Industries, Inc., Proctor, VT; *Int'l*, pg. 1061

Eisenberg, Marshall, Sec.--General Growth Properties Inc., Chicago, IL; *U.S. Public*, pg. 715

Eisenberg, Warren, Chm. Bd., Co-Chief Exec. Officer & Sec.--Bed Bath & Beyond Inc., Union, NJ; *U.S. Public*, pg. 200

Eisenmayer, Mildred F., Sec. & Asst. Treas.--Cullman Ventures, Inc., Norwalk, CT; *U.S. Private*, pg. 294

Eisenmayer, Mildred F., Sec. & Asst. Treas.--Cullman Ventures, Inc., New York, NY; *U.S. Private*, pg. 295

Eisenschenk, Mark, Exec. V.P.--Ringer Corporation, Bloomington, MN; *U.S. Public*, pg. 1390

Eismont, Diane S., Sec.--DQE Inc., Coraopolis, PA; *U.S. Public*, pg. 474

Eisner, Henry, V.P.-Fin & Sec.--MultiQuip, Inc., Carson, CA; *Int'l*, pg. 695

Eisner, William, V.P., Sec. & Gen. Counsel--ITT Federal Services Corporation, Colorado Springs, CO; *U.S. Public*, *pg. 859*

Eitel, Linda M., Sec.--Standard Medical Imaging, Inc., Columbia, MD; *U.S. Private*, pg. 1032

Eitel, Robert C., V.P.-Oper. & Corp. Sec.--The C.P. Hall Company, Chicago, IL; *U.S. Private*, pg. 495

Ekdahl, Mikael, Gen. Counsel & Sec.--Skanska AB, Danderyd, Sweden; *Int'l*, pg. 1260

Ekker, Erik, Company Sec.--Elsevier NV, Amsterdam, Netherlands; *Int'l*, pg. 1093

Eklund, Ann, Sec.--Fleet Engineers, Inc., Muskegon, MI; *U.S. Private*, pg. 410

Eklund, Karen, Sec.--Cardo AB, Malmo, Sweden; *Int'l*, pg. 268

Eksten, Ronald C., V.P., Gen. Counsel & Sec.--Hamilton Beach/Proctor-Silex, Inc., Glen Allen, VA; *U.S. Public*, pg. 1149

Ekstrom, Paul, Sec.--California Water Service Co., San Jose, CA; *U.S. Public*, pg. 294

Elburn, Kathleen M., Sec.--The Arundel Corporation, Sparks, MD; *U.S. Public*, pg. 656

Elden, Carol E., Sec.--Colonial Gas Company, Lowell, MA; *U.S. Public*, pg. 400

Elder, John S., Sec.--Onex Corporation, Toronto, Canada; *Int'l*, pg. 1006

Eldred, N.J., Sec.--Telecom Securicor Cellular Radio Limited, Slough, United Kingdom; *Int'l*, pg. 222

Eldredge, James W., Controller & Sec.--Puget Sound Energy, Inc., Bellevue, WA; *U.S. Public*, pg. 1342

Eldridge, James F., Exec. V.P.-Corp. Legal & Sec.--American Family Mutual Insurance Co., Madison, WI; *U.S. Private*, pg. 53

Elefante, Jeffrey P., Exec. V.P., Gen. Counsel & Sec.--CACI International Inc, Arlington, VA; *U.S. Public*, pg. 272

Eley, P.R., Dir.-Fin. & Sec.--Senior Davis Derby, Derby, United Kingdom; *Int'l*, pg. 1220

Elizondo, Alonso Ancira, Chief Exec. Officer & Exec. V.P.--Altos Hornos de Mexico, S.A., Monclova, Mexico; *Int'l*, pg. 66

Elkins, David G., V.P., Gen. Counsel & Sec.--Sterling Chemicals Holdings, Inc., Houston, TX; *U.S. Public*, pg. 1515

Ellcessor, Steven J., V.P.-Admin., Gen. Counsel & Sec.--J.M. Smucker Company, Orrville, OH; *U.S. Public*, pg. 1480

Elledge, Richard D., Chief Acctg. Officer, Sr. V.P. & Asst. Sec.--Lowe's Companies, Inc., North Wilkesboro, NC; *U.S. Public*, pg. 1015

Ellender, John E., Sec.--Cigna Reinsurance Company (U.K.) Limited, London, United Kingdom; *U.S. Public*, pg. 363

Eller, James, Jr., Sec.--Glendale Federal Bank, F.S.B., Glendale, CA; *U.S. Public*, pg. 747

Elliot, William, Sr. V.P., Gen. Counsel & Asst. Sec.--Gateway 2000, North Sioux City, SD; *U.S. Public*, pg. 703

Elliott, Daniel R., Jr., Sr. V.P., Gen. Counsel & Sec.--White Consolidated Industries, Inc., Cleveland, OH; *Int'l*, pg. 439

Elliott, Deirdre C., V.P., Corp. Counsel & Sec.--Badger Meter, Inc., Milwaukee, WI; *U.S. Public*, pg. 164

Elliott, Irma B., V.P. & Sec.--OGE Energy Corp., Oklahoma City, OK; *U.S. Public*, pg. 1207

Elliott, James V., Sr. V.P., Gen. Counsel & Sec.--AEGON USA, Inc., Louisville, KY; *Int'l*, pg. 26

Elliott, Lilly, Sec.--Mid-Am Building Supply, Inc., Moberly, MO; *U.S. Private*, pg. 743

Elliott, Lynda J., Asst. Sec.--Canadian Occidental Petroleum Ltd., Calgary, Canada; *U.S. Public*, pg. 1210

Elliott, M.B., Asst. Gen. Counsel & Asst. Sec.--Union Camp Corporation, Wayne, NJ; *U.S. Public*, pg. 1665

Elliott, P.M., Sec. & Solicitor--English China Clays Plc, Theale, United Kingdom; *Int'l*, pg. 455

Elliott, Stacy, Exec. Sec.--Lane Limited, Tucker, GA; *Int'l*, pg. 1129

Elliott, Yvonne, Corp. Sec.--Aerosonic Corporation, Clearwater, FL; *U.S. Public*, pg. 25

Ellis, Amy, Admin. to Pres.--Hampshire Hosiery, Inc., Spruce Pine, NC; *U.S. Public*, pg. 778

Ellis, Margaret E., Asst. Sec. & Treas.--SI Handling Systems, Inc., Easton, PA; *U.S. Public*, pg. 1418

Elliston, Michael, V.P.-Fin & Treas.--Holly's Inc., Grand Rapids, MI; *U.S. Private*, pg. 535

Elman, Barry, Sec.--Precision Extrusions, Bensenville, IL; *U.S. Private*, pg. 879

Elmburg, Linda T., Sec.--Blitz USA, Inc., Miami, OK; *U.S. Private*, pg. 149

Elmore, E. Whitehead, Sr. V.P., Gen. Counsel & Sec.--Albemarle Corporation, Richmond, VA; *U.S. Public*, pg. 37

Elwood, Clark D., V.P., Gen. Counsel & Sec.--ITT Educational Services, Inc., Indianapolis, IN; *U.S. Public*, pg. 1512

Emanuel, James M., Sec.--Lincare Holdings Inc., Clearwater, FL; *U.S. Public*, pg. 996

Ember, G. Howard, Jr., V.P.-Fin. & Asst. Sec.--Tootsie Roll Industries, Inc., Chicago, IL; *U.S. Public*, pg. 1621

Ember, G. Howard, Jr., V.P.-Fin. & Asst. Sec.--Charms Company, Chicago, IL; *U.S. Public*, pg. 1621

Emerick, C., Sec.--Munroe, Inc., Pittsburgh, PA; *U.S. Private*, pg. 767

Emery, Lavinia Z., Sec. & Asst. Treas.--Driver-Harris Company, Harrison, NJ; *U.S. Public*, pg. 530

Emmett, Lynne, Sec.--Willis Corroon Melling Inc., Toronto, Canada; *Int'l*, pg. 1509

Emond, Carl E., V.P.-Fin. & Asst. Sec.--Unican Security Systems Ltd., Montreal, Canada; *Int'l*, pg. 1432

Emrick, Charles, V.P. & Sec.--Ken-Mac Metals, Inc., Cleveland, OH; *Int'l*, pg. 1388

End, Ralph P., V.P. & Gen. Counsel--Keystone Consolidated Industries, Inc., Dallas, TX; *U.S. Public*, pg. 955

Endres, Jane F., Asst. Sec.--Capitol Indemnity Corporation, Madison, WI; *U.S. Public*, pg. 302

Endres, Jane F., Asst. Sec.--Capitol Specialty Insurance Corporation, Madison, WI; *U.S. Public*, pg. 302

Engdahl, Walter A., V.P.-Corp. Counsel & Sec.--Sensormatic Electronics Corporation, Boca Raton, FL; *U.S. Public*, pg. 1457

Engelbert, John, V.P.-Fin. & Sec.--Carter Day International, Minneapolis, MN; *U.S. Private*, pg. 216

Engelman, Wayne, Sr. V.P., Treas. & Sec.--Colle & McVoy, Inc., Minneapolis, MN; *U.S. Private*, pg. 252

Engelmann, Glen, Gen. Counsel & Corp. Sec.--Zeneca Inc., Wilmington, DE; *Int'l*, pg. 1525

England, Patricia A., V.P.-Corp. Communications & Sec.--Harding Lawson Associates Group, Inc., Novato, CA; *U.S. Public*, pg. 785

Englefield, F.W., IV, Co-Pres., Chief Exec., Chief Fin. Officer & Sec.--Englefield, Inc., Newark, OH; *U.S. Private*, pg. 377

English, Jim, Sr. V.P.--After Dark Video, Inc., Beverly Hills, CA; *U.S. Public*, pg. 1310

Engwall, K. Wyatt, Sr. V.P.-Fin. & Asst. Sec.--Morrison Health Care Inc., Smyrna, GA; *U.S. Public*, pg. 1133

Eno, Woodrow E., Sr. V.P.-Law & Govt. Rels., Sec. & Gen. Counsel--Aid Association for Lutherans, Appleton, WI; *U.S. Private*, pg. 27

Ensign, Gregory M., V.P., Gen. Counsel & Sec.--Kirkwood Industries, Inc., Cleveland, OH; *U.S. Private*, pg. 623

Ensinger, James, Treas. & Sec.--Rudel Machinery Company, Inc., Shelton, CT; *U.S. Private*, pg. 950

Ensz, Phil, Sec.--Michigan Wheel Corporation, Grand Rapids, MI; *U.S. Private*, pg. 741

Ent, Margaret A., V.P., Sec. & Treas.--CD Products, Inc., New Providence, NJ; *U.S. Public*, pg. 276

Entrekin, Robert L., V.P. & Sec.--Murata Electronics North America, Inc., Smyrna, GA; *Int'l*, pg. 897

Entzinger, J.J.T., Sr. V.P. & Gen. Sec.--KLM Royal Dutch Airlines, Amstelveen, Netherlands; *Int'l*, pg. 719

Entzinger, J.J.T., Sr. V.P. & Gen. Sec.--KLM Royal Dutch Airlines, Elmsford, NY; *Int'l*, pg. 719

Epperson, Margaret A., Sec.--Cooker Restaurant Corporation, West Palm Beach, FL; *U.S. Public*, pg. 442

Epperson, Robert J., Sec. & Treas.--Enterprise Electronics Corp., Enterprise, AL; *U.S. Public*, pg. 1563

Eppinette, Joy B., Subsidiary Sec.--Century Telephone Enterprises, Inc., Monroe, LA; *U.S. Public*, pg. 329

Epprecht, John W., V.P., Treas. & Sec.--The Great Lakes Cheese Co., Newbury, OH; *U.S. Private*, pg. 473

Erani, Albert, Chief Oper. Officer, Treas. & Sec.--A&E Stores, Inc., Teterboro, NJ; *U.S. Private*, pg. 1

Ereckson, Stanley, Jr., Sr. V.P., Gen. Counsel & Sec.--Vicorp Restaurants, Inc., Denver, CO; *U.S. Public*, pg. 1719

Ergoz, Ertugrul, Gen. Sec.--Sabanci Holding A.S., Istanbul, Turkey; *Int'l*, pg. 1167

Erickson, Grant D., Gen. Counsel & Sec.--Nelson Westerberg, Inc., Elk Grove Village, IL; *U.S. Private*, pg. 1163

Erickson, Gregory, V.P. & Sec.--Erickson's Diversified Corp., Hudson, WI; *U.S. Private*, pg. 381

Erickson, Mike, Controller, Treas. & Sec.--Wagstaff Inc., Spokane, WA; *U.S. Private*, pg. 1146

Erickson, Phillip A., Gen. Counsel & Sec.--IMI Cornelius Inc. (MN), Anoka, MN; *Int'l*, pg. 646

Erickson, Rebecca A., Asst. Sec. & Mgr.-Benefits Admin.--Cornerstone Natural Gas, Inc., Dallas, TX; *U.S. Public*, pg. 567

Erickson, Ruth E., Corp. Sec.--Anderson Erickson Dairy Company, Des Moines, IA; *U.S. Private*, pg. 72

Erikson, J. Lance, Exec. V.P., Sec. & Gen Counsel--Great Western Financial Corporation, Chatsworth, CA; *U.S. Public*, pg. 1741

Erl, Gerhard H., V.P.-Corp. Services & Sec.--NewTel Enterprises Limited, Saint Johns, Canada; *Int'l*, pg. 115

Erlandsson, Per, Sec. & Legal--Saab AB, Linkoping, Sweden; *Int'l*, pg. 686

Erola, Tuomo, Sec.--Kone Corporation, Helsinki, Finland; *Int'l*, pg. 746

Erskine, Susan D., Exec. V.P.-Devel. & Sec.--PMR Corporation, San Diego, CA; *U.S. Public*, pg. 1242

Erwin, Robert P., Jr., Gen. Counsel & Sec.--Bartlett and Company, Kansas City, MO; *U.S. Private*, pg. 118

Erwin, Theresa T., Sec.--Mission American Insurance Company, Rancho Dominguez, CA; *U.S. Public*, pg. 483

Esau, Steven, V.P., Gen. Counsel & Sec.--Asymetrix Learning Systems, Inc., Bellevue, WA; *U.S. Private*, pg. 93

Eschbach, Reinhard, Sec.--Iroquois Die & Mfg. Co., Warren, MI; *U.S. Private*, pg. 575

Escriba, Antonio, Sr. V.P. & Sec.--Firstbank Puerto Rico, Santurce, PR; *U.S. Public*, pg. 644

Eskilson, Thomas T., Pres., Treas. & Sec.--Dixie Dairy Company, Gary, IN; *U.S. Private*, pg. 337

Eskow, Alan D., Sr. V.P.-Fin. Admin. & Sec.--Valley National Bancorp, Wayne, NJ; *U.S. Public*, pg. 1705

Eskowitz, Sheldon, Treas. & Sec.--Plascal Corporation, Farmingdale, NY; *U.S. Private*, pg. 870

Essenberg, Ruth, Sec.--Douglas Steel Fabricating Corporation, Lansing, MI; *U.S. Private*, pg. 341

Estrada, Lily, Sec.--H. Salt of Southern California, Inc., Monterey Park, CA; *U.S. Private*, pg. 489

Etheridge, Jean, Sec.--Nobility Homes, Inc., Ocala, FL; *U.S. Public*, pg. 1186

Etherington, Glenn A., Chief Fin. Officer & Sec.--Brite Voice Systems, Inc., Heathrow, FL; *U.S. Public*, pg. 257

Etienne, Michelle, Sec.--Barr Laboratories Inc., Pomona, NY; *U.S. Public*, pg. 191

Ettelson, Stephen, V.P., Sec. & Mgr.-Natl. Sls.--Electro Brand, Inc., Chicago, IL; *U.S. Private*, pg. 368

Etter, Greg V., Gen. Counsel & Sec.--Battle Mountain Gold Company, Houston, TX; *U.S. Public*, pg. 193

Ettor, David, Corp. Sec.--The Hercules Tire & Rubber Company, Findlay, OH; *U.S. Private*, pg. 523

Ettridge, Timothy, Sec. & Treas.--Temps & Company, Washington, DC; *U.S. Private*, pg. 1075

Eustes, Susan, Sec.--Amgen Boulder, Inc., Boulder, CO; *U.S. Public*, pg. 101

Evangelist, Frank E., Sr. V.P.-Fin. & Sec.--Regis Corporation, Minneapolis, MN; *U.S. Public*, pg. 1373

Evanger, Marc, Chief Fin. Officer, V.P., Treas. & Sec.--QFC Holding Company, Stamford, CT; *U.S. Public*, pg. 1349

Evans, Daniel E., Chm. Bd., Chief Exec. Officer & Sec.--Bob Evans Farms, Inc., Columbus, OH; *U.S. Public*, pg. 596

Evans, Daphne, Sec.--Rogers Communications, Inc., Toronto, Canada; *Int'l*, pg. 1122

Evans, Eric W., Asst. V.P.-Investor Rels. & Sec.--Unicorp Canada Corporation, Toronto, Canada; *Int'l*, pg. 1433

Evans, F. Maxwell, V.P., Gen. Counsel & Sec.--Sterling Chemicals, Inc., Houston, TX; *U.S. Public*, pg. 1515

Evans, Jody, Treas. & Sec.--Ray Bell Construction Co. Inc., Brentwood, TN; *U.S. Private*, pg. 131

Evans, John, Sec.--SF Services, North Little Rock, AR; *U.S. Private*, pg. 956

Evans, John T., Vice Chm. & Sec.--GrandeTel Technologies Inc., Richmond, Canada; *Int'l*, pg. 556

Evans, Maureen M., Dir.-Fin., Treas. & Asst. Sec.--Cerner Corporation, Kansas City, MO; *U.S. Public*, pg. 331

Evans, Milo R., Treas. & Sec.--Copes-Vulcan Inc., Lake City, PA; *U.S. Private*, pg. 274

Everett, Leigh Ann, Asst. Sec.--Lincoln Property Company, Dallas, TX; *U.S. Private*, pg. 668

Everett, Leslie H., V.P. & Corp. Sec.--PG&E Corporation, San Francisco, CA; *U.S. Public*, pg. 1240

Everett, Leslie H., V.P. & Corp. Sec.--Pacific Gas & Electric Company, San Francisco, CA; *U.S. Public*, pg. 1241

Evers, Bradley W., V.P., Gen. Counsel & Sec.--Price Brothers Co., Dayton, OH; *U.S. Private*, pg. 883

Ewell, Shirlee, Sec.--Wavetek Communications Div., Indianapolis, IN; *U.S. Private*, pg. 1155

Ewert, Darrell, Sec. & Gen. Counsel--The Oshawa Group Limited, Etobicoke, Canada; *Int'l*, pg. 1012

Ewing, Ron, Chief Fin. Officer, Chief Oper. Officer & Sec.--LVL Advertising, Palo Alto, CA; *U.S. Private*, pg. 640

Eyster, Franklin S., II, Sr. V.P., Gen. Counsel & Sec.--Atlantic Aviation Corp., New Castle, DE; *U.S. Private*, pg. 94

Ezerski, Ronald E., Chief Fin. Officer, Exec. V.P., Treas. & Sec.--Patterson Dental Company, Saint Paul, MN; *U.S. Public*, pg. 1265

Fagan, Brad, V.P., Controller, Treas. & Asst. Sec.--Pancho's Mexican Buffet, Inc., Fort Worth, TX; *U.S. Public*, pg. 1255

Faidley, Julia, Sec.--Banco de la Nacion Argentina, New York, NY; *Int'l*, pg. 140

Faigin, Alan W., Gen. Counsel & Sec.--Fremont General Corporation, Santa Monica, CA; *U.S. Public*, pg. 681

Fairbrook, Susan, Sec.--ALZA International, Palo Alto, CA; *U.S. Public*, pg. 62

Falconer, I.L., Sec.--CRA Limited, Melbourne, Australia; *Int'l*, pg. 1119

Falconer, Linda, Asst. Sec.--Comdial Corporation, Charlottesville, VA; *U.S. Public*, pg. 407

Falconer, Sheila, Corp. Sec.--Curt Bullock Builders, Inc., Danville, IL; *U.S. Private*, pg. 180

Falconi, Robert, Chief Fin. Officer, Treas. & Sec.--Planning Systems Inc., Mc Lean, VA; *U.S. Private*, pg. 869

Faldetta, Marlyce A., Sec.--Kit Manufacturing Company, Long Beach, CA; *U.S. Public*, pg. 962

Falduto, Wilma, Sec.--Valley National Bancorp, Wayne, NJ; *U.S. Public*, pg. 1705

Falk-Drigan, Brydget, Sec.--Dun & Bradstreet Canada Ltd., Mississauga, Canada; *U.S. Public*, pg. 536

Fallon, Ann, Sec.--Ripon Foods, Inc., Ripon, WI; *U.S. Private*, pg. 931

Falvey, Jim, Sec.--Pennock, Philadelphia, PA; *U.S. Private*, pg. 850

Fancher, Jan T., Chief Fin. Officer, Treas. & Sec.--Cadet Manufacturing Company, Vancouver, WA; *U.S. Private*, pg. 198

Fannin, David C., Exec. V.P., Gen. Counsel & Sec.--Sunbeam Corporation, Delray Beach, FL; *U.S. Public*, pg. 1533

Fantin, Louis A., V.P., Gen. Counsel & Sec.--Lenox, Incorporated, Lawrenceville, NJ; *U.S. Public*, pg. 261

Farias, Cecilia, Corp. Sec.--Publicidad Ferrer y Asociados, S.A. de C.V., Mexico, Mexico; *Int'l*, pg. 1073

Faribault, Dominique, Corp. Sec.--CFCF Inc., Montreal, Canada; *Int'l*, pg. 240

Faribault, Dominique, Corp. Sec.--Reseau de Television Quatre Saisons Inc., Montreal, Canada; *Int'l*, pg. 241

Faribault, Dominique, Corp. Sec.--Champlain Productions Inc., Montreal, Canada; *Int'l*, pg. 241

Faris, Wayne G., Sec.--Medical Graphics Corp., Saint Paul, MN; *U.S. Public*, pg. 1080

Farley, Daniel W., V.P. & Sec.--New York State Electric & Gas Corporation, Binghamton, NY; *U.S. Public*, pg. 1173

Farmansson, Bodil, Sec.--Munksjo AB, Jonkoping, Sweden; *Int'l*, pg. 1423

Farmer, John A., Sec.--Newbridge Networks Corporation, Kanata, Canada; *Int'l*, pg. 923

Farnsworth, Philip R., Sec.--ABC, Inc, New York, NY; *U.S. Public*, pg. 511

Faroudja, Yves C., Chief Tech. Officer & Sec.--Faroudja, Inc., Sunnyvale, CA; *U.S. Public*, pg. 613

Farquharson, G.M., Sec.--GSW Inc., Guelph, Canada,; *Int'l*, pg. 538

Farquharson, G.M., Sec.--Shaw Industries Ltd., Etobicoke, Canada; *Int'l*, pg. 1231

Farrar, Fred, Chief Fin. Officer & Sec.--Hospital Affiliates Development Corporation, Nashville, TN; *U.S. Private*, pg. 540

Farrell, Catherine, V.P., Corp. Counsel & Sec.--Fluor Daniel GTI, Inc., Norwood, MA; *U.S. Public*, pg. 660

Farrell, Donna L., Corp. Sec.--Exchange Insurance Company, Buffalo, NY; *U.S. Public*, pg. 1455

Farrell, John, V.P., Gen. Mgr., Controller & Sec.--Reagan Equipment Company, Inc., Gretna, LA; *U.S. Private*, pg. 913

Farrington, Marilyn, Sr. Exec. Sec.--The Bay, Toronto, Canada; *Int'l*, pg. 637

Farris, Donna E., Sec.--American & Efird, Inc., Mount Holly, NC; *U.S. Public*, pg. 1412

Fasel, William, Corp. Sec. & Dir.-Investor Rels.--AON Corporation, Chicago, IL; *U.S. Public*, pg. 117

Fasig, Carl E., Sec.--Arthur J. Gallagher & Co., Itasca, IL; *U.S. Public*, pg. 698

Fasulo, Edward, Sr. V.P. & Asst. Sec.--Elsinore Corporation, Las Vegas, NV; *U.S. Public*, pg. 570

Fato, Martha, Treas. & Sec.--Par Enterprises, Inc., Wheeling, WV; *U.S. Private*, pg. 838

Faulk, Barbara D., Personnel & Exec. Sec.--nexAir, Memphis, TN; *U.S. Private*, pg. 797

Faulkner, Harry F., III, V.P.-Legal & Sec.--North American Royalties, Inc., Chattanooga, TN; *U.S. Private*, pg. 803

Faulkner, Walter T., Sec.--Bacardi Corporation, San Juan, PR; *Int'l*, pg. 131

Fava, Michel, Sec. Gen.--BNP (Mexico) SA, Mexico, Mexico; *Int'l*, pg. 164

Faw, Thomas M., Sec.--Spencer's Inc., Mount Airy, NC; *U.S. Private*, pg. 1025

Fawbert, K.J.A., Deputy Mng. Dir. & Sec.--Birtley Engineering Ltd., Chesterfield, United Kingdom; *Int'l*, pg. 1139

Fawcett, Dwight J., Sec.--White Pigeon Paper Company, White Pigeon, MI; *U.S. Private*, pg. 87

Fawcett, Dwight W., Sec.--Artistic Carton Company, Elgin, IL; *U.S. Private*, pg. 87

Feather, William L., Sr. V.P., Gen. Counsel & Sec.--Allegiance Healthcare Corp., McGaw Park, IL; *U.S. Public*, pg. 44

Featherstone, D.W., Sec.--John Laing PLC, London, United Kingdom; *Int'l*, pg. 796

Feazell, Thomas L., Sr. V.P., Gen. Counsel & Sec.--Ashland, Inc., Russell, KY; *U.S. Public*, pg. 138

Febrer, F., Sec.--Morganite Espanola SA, Vizcaya, Spain; *Int'l*, pg. 892

Fedalen, Richard J., Sec.--The Acacia Group - Acacia Life Insurance Co., Bethesda, MD; *U.S. Private*, pg. 10

Federspiel, Robert W., Corp. Sec.--Boca Research Inc., Boca Raton, FL; *U.S. Public*, pg. 239

Feeney, Francis X., V.P.-Fin. & Sec.--CCX, Inc., Charlotte, NC; *U.S. Private*, pg. 193

Feeney, Helen, V.P. & Sec.--Alumax Inc., Atlanta, GA; *U.S. Public*, pg. 59

Fehr, Lawrence F., Chief Fin. Officer & V.P.-Fin.--Herff Jones Inc., Indianapolis, IN; *U.S. Private*, pg. 523

Fehring, Thomas H., Sec.--Wisconsin Energy Corporation, Milwaukee, WI; *U.S. Public*, pg. 1773

Fehring, Thomas H., Sec.--Badger Service Co., Milwaukee, WI; *U.S. Public*, pg. 1773

Fehring, Thomas H., Sec.--Wisconsin Electric Power Company, Milwaukee, WI; *U.S. Public*, pg. 1773

Fehring, Thomas H., Sec.--Wisconsin Michigan Investment Corp., Milwaukee, WI; *U.S. Public*, pg. 1773

Fehring, Thomas H., Sec.--Wispark Corporation, Milwaukee, WI; *U.S. Public*, pg. 1773

Fehring, Thomas H., Sec.--Wisvest Corporation, Milwaukee, WI; *U.S. Public*, pg. 1773

Fehring, Thomas H., Sec.--Witech Corporation, Milwaukee, WI; *U.S. Public*, pg. 1773

Fehring, Thomas H., Sec.--Syndesis Development Corp., Milwaukee, WI; *U.S. Public*, pg. 1773

Feibel, James B., Sec. & Gen. Counsel--Electric Power Equipment Co., Columbus, OH; *U.S. Private*, pg. 368

Feiner, Stuart F., Exec. V.P., Gen. Counsel & Sec.--Inco Limited, Toronto, Canada; *Int'l*, pg. 672

Fekete, Roger, V.P. & Sec.--Peck Spring Company, Plainville, CT; *U.S. Private*, pg. 846

Feld, Larry, V.P.-Store Devel. & Sec.--Today's Man, Inc., Moorestown, NJ; *U.S. Public*, pg. 1619

Feldkamp, Joseph, Sec.--Jake Sweeney Auto Leasing, Inc., Cincinnati, OH; *U.S. Private*, pg. 1058

Feldman, Leon D., Exec. V.P., Treas. & Sec.--P & F Industries, Inc., Farmingdale, NY; *U.S. Public*, pg. 1239

Feldman, Shirley, Sec. & Treas.--Isfel Company, Inc., Rahway, NJ; *U.S. Private*, pg. 576

Feldner, Ronald A., Chief Fin. Officer & Sec.--Bill Heard Enterprises, Inc., Columbus, GA; *U.S. Private*, pg. 515

Fellenstein, Mike, Controller, Treas. & Sec.--Biddulph Automotive Group, Glendale, AZ; *U.S. Private*, pg. 142

Feller, Alan, Chief Oper. Officer, Chief Fin. Officer, Treas. & Sec.--G-III Apparel Group, Ltd., New York, NY; *U.S. Public*, pg. 690

Feller, Harriet Burns, Exec. V.P., Sec. & Gen Counsel--Westcorp, Irvine, CA; *U.S. Public*, pg. 1756

Feller, Harriet Burns, Sr. V.P., Gen. Counsel & Sec.--Western Financial Bank, Irvine, CA; *U.S. Public*, pg. 1757

Feller, Renee, Controller & Corp. Sec.--Fosters Freeze International, Inc., San Luis Obispo, CA; *U.S. Public*, pg. 677

Fellerman, William, Chief Fin. Officer, Treas. & Sec.--Star Multi Care Services Inc., Hicksville, NY; *U.S. Public*, pg. 1510

Fellowes, Peter, Exec. V.P. & Sec.--Fellowes Manufacturing Co., Itasca, IL; *U.S. Private*, pg. 400

Felsenthal, Daniel L., V.P.-Fin., Treas. & Asst. Sec.--Barry's Jewelers, Inc., Monrovia, CA; *U.S. Public*, pg. 192

Felsher, Steven G., Exec. V.P.-Fin./Worldwide, Treas. & Sec.--Grey Advertising Inc., New York, NY; *U.S. Public*, pg. 764

Fennell, S., Asst. Sec.--The Boots Company PLC, Nottingham, United Kingdom; *Int'l*, pg. 202

Fenster, Fred A., Treas. & Sec.--Capucci Creations International, Inc., Beverly Hills, CA; *U.S. Private*, pg. 207

Fenton, John W., Jr., Treas. & Sec.--National Computer Systems, Eden Prairie, MN; *U.S. Public*, pg. 1155

Fenwick, Graham, Asst. Sec.--Alliance UniChem PLC, Chessington, United Kingdom; *Int'l*, pg. 57

Ferara, Kathryn, Sec.--Transmedia Network Inc., Miami, FL; *U.S. Public*, pg. 1631

Ferenbach, Patricia, Corp. Sec.--Leon-Ferenbach Inc., Hoboken, NJ; *U.S. Private*, pg. 660

Ferguson, Arthur, Corp. Sec.--Minerallac Co., Addison, IL; *U.S. Private*, pg. 750

Ferguson, Brian C., Dir.-Corp. Rels. & Corp. Sec.--Alberta Energy Company, Ltd., Calgary, Canada; *Int'l*, pg. 48

Ferguson, George A., V.P., Cashier & Sec.--The First National Bank of St. Mary's, Leonardtown, MD; *U.S. Public*, pg. 1089

Ferguson, John T., II, Gen. Counsel & Sec.--Crompton & Knowles Corporation, Stamford, CT; *U.S. Public*, pg. 459

Ferguson, Richard R., V.P., Treas. & Asst. Sec.--Great Lakes Chemical Corporation, West Lafayette, IN; *U.S. Public*, pg. 760

Ferguson, Sharon, Asst. Sec.--Fairfield Communities, Inc., Little Rock, AR; *U.S. Public*, pg. 610

Ferguson, Terrence J., Gen. Counsel & Sec.--MFS WorldCom, Inc., Omaha, NE; *U.S. Public*, pg. 1779

Feria, Jose Y., Sec.--San Miguel Corp., Manila, Philippines; *Int'l*, pg. 1183

Ferman, Martha S., Treas. & Sec.--Ferman Oldsmobile, Tampa, FL; *U.S. Private*, pg. 401

Fermor, F.H., Corp. Sec.--Senior Engineering Group, plc., Rickmansworth, United Kingdom; *Int'l*, pg. 1220

Fernandez, D. Jose David Alvarez, Sec.--Compania Gestora de Servicio Mensatel, S.A., Madrid, Spain; *Int'l*, pg. 1372

Fernandez, Frank, Asst Treas. & Sec.--Barr & Barr, Inc., New York, NY; *U.S. Private*, pg. 117

Fernous, Louis F., Jr., V.P. & Sec.--Fortune Brands, Inc., Old Greenwich, CT; *U.S. Public*, pg. 674

Ferrara, David M., Sec.--Anaren Microwave Inc., East Syracuse, NY; *U.S. Public*, pg. 110

Ferraro, Peter, Gen. Counsel & Sec.--Parmalat Canada Ltd., Etobicoke, Canada; *Int'l*, pg. 1023

Ferreira, Maria Jose, Sec.--SmithKline Beecham Laboratorios Ltda., Rio de Janeiro, Brazil; *Int'l*, pg. 1266

Ferrer-Sama y Sama, D. Jose Antonio, Sec.--Hispasat, S.A., Madrid, Spain; *Int'l*, pg. 1372

Ferri, Robert, Sec. & Assoc. Gen. Counsel--Asarco Incorporated, New York, NY; *U.S. Public*, pg. 137

Ferris, Brian W., Asst. Gen. Counsel & Asst. Sec.--CalMat Co., Los Angeles, CA; *U.S. Public*, pg. 295

Ferwerda, H., Corp. Sec.--N.V. Koninklijke Bijenkorf Beheer KBB, Amsterdam, Netherlands; *Int'l*, pg. 750

Festinger, Jonathan, Gen. Counsel & Sec.--WIC Western International Communications Ltd., Vancouver, Canada; *Int'l*, pg. 1481

Festinger, Jonathan B., Sec. & Gen. Counsel--Canadian Satellite Communications Inc., Mississauga, Canada; *Int'l*, pg. 1481

Fetridge, Bonni Jean, Sec.--The Dartnell Corporation, Chicago, IL; *U.S. Private*, pg. 312

Feys, Edwin, V.P. & Sec.--H.O. Trerice Company, Oak Park, MI; *U.S. Private*, pg. 1099

Fialkow, Steven, Sec.--National Home Health Care Corp., Scarsdale, NY; *U.S. Public*, pg. 1157

Ficarra, Debbie, Sec.--The John Johnson Co., Detroit, MI; *U.S. Private*, pg. 591

Ficarro, John R., V.P., Gen. Counsel & Sec.--Phar-Mor, Inc., Youngstown, OH; *U.S. Public*, pg. 1284

Fick, Jerry, Asst. Sec.--Standard Textile Co., Inc., Cincinnati, OH; *U.S. Private*, pg. 1032

Ficke, Michael, Chief Fin. Officer, V.P.-Fin. & Sec.--Alfin, Inc., New York, NY; *U.S. Public*, pg. 40

Fickel, Brigitte, Dr., Sec.--Heidelberger Zement A.G., Heidelberg, Germany; *Int'l*, pg. 605

Fickenscher, Donald A., V.P., Gen. Counsel & Sec.--Virginia Natural Gas, Inc., Norfolk, VA; *U.S. Public*, pg. 436

Fiedler, William L., V.P., Gen. Counsel & Sec.--Philip Industrial Services Group, Houston, TX; *Int'l*, pg. 1050

Field, Bernard, Sec.--Saint-Gobain, Courbevoie, France; *Int'l*, pg. 1170

Field, John Osgood, Sec.--Plan International USA, Inc., Warwick, RI; *U.S. Private*, pg. 869

Field, S.A., Sec.--De La Rue plc, London, United Kingdom; *Int'l*, pg. 386

Fielding, Sharon, Treas. & Sec.--Southwestern Reprographics Inc., Las Vegas, NV; *U.S. Private*, pg. 1176

Fields, Vicky, Asst. Sec.--Gerber International Inc., New York, NY; *U.S. Private*, pg. 448

Fierle, Debra R., Sec.--Cook Moving Systems, Inc., Buffalo, NY; *U.S. Private*, pg. 272

Fierman, Bernice P., Sec.--ANESCO, Kingston, PA; *U.S. Private*, pg. 74

Figg, Rosalind, Sec.--Recordati Industria Chimica e Farmaceutica S.p.A., Milan, Italy; *Int'l*, pg. 1090

Figueredo, Lelin, Sec.--American International Container, Inc., Miami, FL; *U.S. Private*, pg. 57

Fike, Robert M., V.P. & Sec.--Pac Paper Inc., Vancouver, WA; *U.S. Private*, pg. 828

Fikejs, John W., V.P.-Finance.--Plymouth Tube Company, Warrenville, IL; *U.S. Private*, pg. 873

Filippucci, Emanuela, Corp. Sec.--Bulgari SPA, Rome, Italy; *Int'l*, pg. 232

Fillahit, Jill, Sec.--Fostoria Industries, Inc., Fostoria, OH; *U.S. Private*, pg. 421

Fillippo, Thomas A., Pres., Chief Exec. Officer & Corp. Sec.--DeVault Foods, Devault, PA; *U.S. Private*, pg. 329

Filomeno, Elsa, Sec.--Industrias Pacocha S.A. (Unilever), Lima, Peru; *Int'l*, pg. 1437

Filter, Eunice M., V.P., Treas. & Sec.--Xerox Corporation, Stamford, CT; *U.S. Public*, pg. 1783

Finamore, Carole H., Asst. Sec.--Schlumberger Limited, New York, NY; *U.S. Public*, pg. 1439

Finch, Priscilla, Asst. V.P. & Sec.--Coast Savings Financial, Inc., Los Angeles, CA; *U.S. Public*, pg. 388

Findlay, Konstance J.K., Sr. V.P.-Bus. Devel. & Sec.--Conso Products Company, Union, SC; *U.S. Public*, pg. 434

Findley, Hope, Asst. Sec.--Metropolitan Mortgage & Securities Co., Inc., Spokane, WA; *U.S. Private*, pg. 738

Finegood, Daniel, Corp. Sec.--Good Companies, Carson, CA; *U.S. Private*, pg. 463

Finely, Bill R., Chief Fin. Officer, V.P. & Sec.--Micronics Computers, Inc., Fremont, CA; *U.S. Public*, pg. 1106

Fineman, C.P., Sec.--Caldwell Tanks, Inc., Louisville, KY; *U.S. Private*, pg. 200

Fingarson, John L., V.P., Sec. & Gen. Counsel--Trans Mountain Pipeline Company Ltd., Vancouver, Canada; *Int'l*, pg. 114

Fingerle, Larry, Sec. & Treas.--Fingerle Lumber Co., Ann Arbor, MI; *U.S. Private*, pg. 405

Fink, Karen G., V.P., Gen. Counsel & Sec.--Concurrent Computer Corporation, Fort Lauderdale, FL; *U.S. Public*, pg. 430

Fink, Richard, Sec.--Coram Healthcare Corporation, Denver, CO; *U.S. Public*, pg. 446

Finkel, Nathan, V.P. & Sec.--FMS Management Systems, Inc., Miami, FL; *U.S. Private*, pg. 389

Finkelson, Ira, Asst. Sec.--CSW Leasing, Inc., Dallas, TX; *U.S. Public*, pg. 324

Finkelstein, Charles D., Sec.--Faber, Coe & Gregg, Inc., Secaucus, NJ; *U.S. Private*, pg. 390

Finley, Paul C., Gen. Counsel & Sec.--Algoma Steel Inc., Sault Sainte Marie, Canada; *Int'l*, pg. 56

Finn, Steven G., Vice Chm.--Bytex Corporation, Westborough, MA; *U.S. Public*, pg. 1522

Finn, Thomas W., V.P., Gen. Counsel & Sec.--DataCard Corporation, Minnetonka, MN; *U.S. Private*, pg. 312

Finn, William M., Sec. & Clerk--Central Maine Power Company, Augusta, ME; *U.S. Public*, pg. 325

Finn, William M., Sec.--Maine Yankee, Brunswick, ME; *U.S. Public*, pg. 325

Finnegan, Martha Ann, Asst. Sec.--Cabot Corporation, Boston, MA; *U.S. Public*, pg. 288

Finnell, Mary Anne, Sec.--TBG Services, Inc., New York, NY; *Int'l*, pg. 1335

Finneran, John G., Jr., Sr. V.P., Gen. Counsel & Sec.--Capital One Financial Corporation, Falls Church, VA; *U.S. Public*, pg. 302

Fiora, Ann M., Sec.--Dodge Regupol, Inc., Lancaster, PA; *U.S. Private*, pg. 337

Fioravanti, Enrico, Sec.--Istituto Mobiliare Italiano, Rome, Italy; *Int'l*, pg. 692

Fiore, J., Sec.--Ship Analytics, Inc., North Stonington, CT; *U.S. Private*, pg. 994

Fiorini, Pamela A., Sec.--Bergstrom Capital Corporation, Seattle, WA; *U.S. Public*, pg. 215

Firth, John, Gen. Counsel & Sec.--Quality Dining Inc., Mishawaka, IN; *U.S. Public*, pg. 1349

Firth, P. Graham, Sec.--Carbo Plc, Manchester, United Kingdom; *Int'l*, pg. 268

Fischer, Amy, Exec. Sec.--Taiyo Kogyo Corporation, Osaka, Japan; *Int'l*, pg. 1348

Fischer, Eric R., Exec. V.P., Gen. Counsel & Sec.--United States Trust Company, Boston, MA; *U.S. Public*, pg. 1660

Fischer, Eric R., Exec. V.P., Gen. Counsel & Sec.--USTrust, Boston, MA; *U.S. Public*, pg. 1660

Fischer, Jerome, Treas. & Sec.--Buerkle Buick-Honda Co., Saint Paul, MN; *U.S. Private*, pg. 178

Fischer, Klaus P., V.P., Gen. Counsel & Sec.--Elliott Company, Jeannette, PA; *U.S. Private*, pg. 373

Fischer, Michael S., V.P., Gen. Counsel & Sec.--Washington Square Securities, Minneapolis, MN; *U.S. Public*, pg. 1376

Fischer, Philip, Treas. & Sec.--Torcon, Inc., Westfield, NJ; *U.S. Private*, pg. 1092

Fischette, Joseph A., V.P., Gen. Counsel & Sec.--Calgon Carbon Corporation, Pittsburgh, PA; *U.S. Public*, pg. 292

Fischman, Bernard D., Sec.--Shepaug Corporation, New York, NY; *U.S. Private*, pg. 993

Fish, Dale, Treas. & Sec.--Lil'Champ/Food Stores Inc., Jacksonville, FL; *U.S. Private*, pg. 837

Fish, Milton, Jr., V.P. & Sec.--Stelar Inc., Chicago, IL; *U.S. Private*, pg. 1040

Fisher, Arlene Lane, Sec.--ILC Industries, Inc., Bohemia, NY; *U.S. Private*, pg. 555

Fisher, Bruce A., Chief Fin. Officer, Sr. V.P. & Sec.--PCA International, Inc., Matthews, NC; *U.S. Public*, pg. 1240

Fisher, David E., V.P. & Sec.--Minorco, Luxembourg, Luxembourg; *Int'l*, pg. 77

Fisher, David F., V.P., Gen. Counsel & Corp. Sec.--ADC Telecommunications, Inc., Minnetonka, MN; *U.S. Public*, pg. 4

Fisher, Dean, Branch Mgr.--Duellman Electric Supply, Inc., Cleveland, OH; *Int'l*, pg. 1107

Fisher, John J., Controller, Treas. & Sec.--Tarlton Corporation, Saint Louis, MO; *U.S. Private*, pg. 1069

Fisher, Lawrence N., Sr. V.P.-Law & Sec.--Fluor Corporation, Irvine, CA; *U.S. Public*, pg. 659

Fisher, Lisa, Sec.--Gray Printing Co., Fostoria, OH; *U.S. Private*, pg. 472

Fisher, MaryAnn, V.P., Sec. & Gen. Counsel--Condea Vista Company, Houston, TX; *Int'l*, pg. 325

Fisher, Nicole, Sec.--Stella Foods, Inc., Green Bay, WI; *U.S.* Private, pg. 1040

Fisher, Patricia, Sec.--Victaulic Company of America, Easton, PA; *U.S. Private*, pg. 1138

Fisher, R. Douglas, Sr. V.P.- Credit Admin. & Sec.--Mercantile Bank of Iowa, Des Moines, IA; *U.S. Public*, pg. 1087

Fisher, William, V.P.-Admin.--Butterick Company, Inc., New York, NY; *U.S. Private*, pg. 190

Fisk, Hayward D., Gen. Counsel & Sec.--Computer Sciences Corporation, El Segundo, CA; *U.S. Public*, pg. 422

Fissasloo, Bill, Sec. , Treas. & Dir.-Pur.--Gress Foods Inc., Gainesville, GA; *U.S. Private*, pg. 480

Fiszel, Roland, Sec.--Credit Agricole, Bonvin, France; *Int'l*, pg. 341

Fitts, Bill, Sec.--Braid Electric Company, Nashville, TN; *U.S.* Private, pg. 165

Fitzgerald, Amy, V.P. & Sec.--GSC Enterprises, Inc., Chicago, IL; *U.S. Private*, pg. 436

Fitzgerald, Hope, Sec. & Sls. Admin.--Son Chief Electrics, Inc., Winsted, CT; *U.S. Private*, pg. 1014

Fitzgerald, John, Controller & Sec.--The Robert E. Morris Company, Farmington, CT; *U.S. Private*, pg. 762

Fitzgerald, Ken, Chief Fin. Officer, Controller & Sec.--R.L. Zeigler Co. Inc., Tuscaloosa, AL; *U.S. Private*, pg. 1204

Fitzgerald, Matthew D., V.P., Controller & Asst. Sec.--BJ Services Company, Houston, TX; *U.S. Public*, pg. 161

Fitzhugh, A. Chad, Chief Fin. Officer, Treas. & Sec.--O'Charley's Inc., Nashville, TN; *U.S. Public*, pg. 1211

FitzPatrick, James A., Jr., Corp. Sec.--Executive Risk, Inc., Simsbury, CT; *U.S. Public*, pg. 599

Fitzpatrick, Michael, V.P. & Sec.--Fitzpatrick & Weller, Inc., Ellicottville, NY; *U.S. Private*, pg. 409

Fitzpatrick, Nancy S., Partner & Sec.--J. Walter Thompson Company, New York, NY; *Int'l*, pg. 1483

Fitzsimons, John H., Gen. Counsel & Sec.--The Dyson-Kissner-Moran Corporation, New York, NY; *U.S. Private*, pg. 351

Fitzwater, Steven K., Chief Acctg. Officer, V.P. & Sec.--Seafield Capital Corporation, Kansas City, MO; *U.S. Public*, pg. 1449

Flach, Wilma C., Sec.--McClatchy Newspapers Inc., Sacramento, CA; *U.S. Public*, pg. 1065

Flacks, D. M., Gen. Counsel & Sec.--Carter Holt Harvey Limited, Auckland, New Zealand; *U.S. Public*, pg. 904

Flaherty, John, Sec.--Rolex Watch U.S.A., Inc., New York, NY; *Int'l*, pg. 1126

Flanagan, Patrick A., Exec. V.P.-Mergers & Acq. & Sec.--Mac-Gray Corporation, Cambridge, MA; *U.S. Public*, pg. 1029

Flax, Robert J., Exec. V.P., Gen. Counsel & Sec.--Bay View Capital Corporation, San Mateo, CA; *U.S. Public*, pg. 197

Flegenheimer, Roy A., Chief Oper. Officer, Treas. & Sec.--Employee Solutions, Inc., Phoenix, AZ; *U.S. Public*, pg. 579

Fleming, Carol J., Sec.--Merchants Publishing Co., Kalamazoo, MI; *U.S. Private*, pg. 732

Fleming, Gordon, Treas. & Sec.--Brach & Brock Confections Inc., Chattanooga, TN; *U.S. Private*, pg. 163

Fleshman, Betty R., Sec.--Potlatch Corporation, Spokane, WA; *U.S. Public*, pg. 1318

Fletcher, Debbie, Sec.--Cutter Aviation Albuquerque, Inc, Albuquerque, NM; *U.S. Private*, pg. 298

Fletcher, F. Alan, V.P., Gen. Counsel & Sec.--Pegasus Gold Corporation, Spokane, WA; *U.S. Public*, pg. 1269

Fletcher, J.E., V.P.-Legal & Corp. Affairs & Sec.--Ranger Oil Limited, Calgary, Canada; *Int'l*, pg. 1086

Fletcher, Martin W., Sec.--Chefs International, Inc., Point Pleasant Beach, NJ; *U.S. Public*, pg. 343

Flick, Michael A., Chief Admin. Officer, Exec. V.P. & Sec.--First Commerce Corporation, New Orleans, LA; *U.S. Public*, pg. 629

Flicker, D.W., V.P.-Law & Sec.--Canadian Pacific Limited, Calgary, Canada; *Int'l*, pg. 258

Flies, William P., Chief Tech. Officer & Sec.--XATA Corporation, Burnsville, MN; *U.S. Public*, pg. 1783

Fligg, W. Patrick, Asst. Sec.--HEI Power Corp., Honolulu, HI; *U.S. Public*, pg. 800

Flink, Richard A., V.P., Gen. Counsel & Sec.--C.R. Bard, Inc., Murray Hill, NJ; *U.S. Public*, pg. 189

Flinn, Colleen O., Asst. Sec.--Philip Morris Companies Inc., New York, NY; *U.S. Public*, pg. 1287

Flippin, James C., V.P. & Sec.--Reading Eagle Company, Reading, PA; *U.S. Private*, pg. 913

Flodstrom, Johan, Gen. Counsel & Sec.--Mo och Domsjo AB, Stockholm, Sweden; *Int'l*, pg. 885

Flom, Gerald T., Sec.--Smith System Manufacturing Company, Plano, TX; *U.S. Private*, pg. 1009

Floor, Richard, Sec.--Muro Pharmaceutical, Inc., Tewksbury, MA; *U.S. Private*, pg. 767

Floor, Richard, Corp. Sec.--SofTECH, Inc., Grand Rapids, MI; *U.S. Public*, pg. 1482

Florence, Faye A., V.P., Gen. Counsel & Sec.--Syratech Corporation, East Boston, MA; *U.S. Private*, pg. 1060

Flori, James D., V.P. & Sec.--Flori Corp., Phoenix, AZ; *U.S. Private*, pg. 414

Flowers, Genia, Treas. & Sec.--Hickory Construction Company, Hickory, NC; *U.S. Private*, pg. 525

Flowers, Michael L., V.P., Asst. Sec. & Chief In-House Counsel--The Midland Company, Cincinnati, OH; *U.S. Public*, pg. 1110

Floyd, Israel J., Sec. & Asst. Gen. Counsel--Hercules Incorporated, Wilmington, DE; *U.S. Public*, pg. 809

Floyd, Orilla, Sec.--CV Reit, Inc., West Palm Beach, FL; *U.S. Public*, pg. 286

Fluehr, Joseph A., III, Sec.--Prime Bancorp, Inc., Fort Washington, PA; *U.S. Public*, pg. 1326

Flynn, E. Dean, Sec.--The Manitowoc Company, Inc., Manitowoc, WI; *U.S. Public*, pg. 1040

Flynn, John T., Jr., Asst. Sec.--Federal Paper Board Company, Inc., Montvale, NJ; *U.S. Public*, pg. 903

Flynn, Peter E., Exec. V.P. & Sec.--ENStar, Inc., Eden Prairie, MN; *U.S. Public*, pg. 585

Foecking, Leland R., Treas. & Sec.--Joseph Behr & Sons Inc., Rockford, IL; *U.S. Private*, pg. 130

Fogelsong, Linda, Corp. Sec.--Avibank Mfg., Inc., Burbank, CA; *U.S. Private*, pg. 101

Fogg, Glenice D., Treas. & Sec.--Southeastern Medequip, Inc., Jacksonville Beach, FL; *U.S. Private*, pg. 1015

Foglia, Dennis A., Exec. V.P., Treas. & Sec.--Equitable Savings & Loan Association, Wauwatosa, WI; *U.S. Private*, pg. 380

Foglia, Dennis A., Exec. V.P., Sec. & Treas.--The Equitable Bank, Hales Corners, WI; *U.S. Private*, pg. 380

Fohrman, Monica, V.P., Asst. Gen. Counsel & Corp. Sec.--R.R. Donnelley & Sons Company, Chicago, IL; *U.S. Public*, pg. 517

Fokes, W.B., V.P. & Sec.--Equifax Inc., Atlanta, GA; *U.S. Public*, pg. 588

Folan, McDara P., III, V.P., Sec. & Gen. Counsel--Allen Telecom, Inc., Beachwood, OH; *U.S. Public*, pg. 45

Foley, Cheryl M., V.P., Gen. Counsel & Sec.--Cinergy Corp., Cincinnati, OH; *U.S. Public*, pg. 368

Foley, Cheryl M., Sec.--Power Equipment Supply Company, New Washington, IN; *U.S. Public*, pg. 369

Foley, Cheryl M., Sec.--PSI Power Resource Development, Inc., Indianapolis, IN; *U.S. Public*, pg. 369

Foley, Cheryl M., Sec.--PSI Power Resource Operations, Indianapolis, IN; *U.S. Public*, pg. 369

Foley, Cheryl M., Sec.--CGE Eck, Inc., Cincinnati, OH; *U.S. Public*, pg. 369

Foley, Cheryl M., V.P., Gen. Counsel & Corp. Sec.--CINergy Services, Inc., Cincinnati, OH; *U.S. Public*, pg. 369

Foley, Mercedes, Vice Chm. & Sec.--Steve Foley Cadillac, Northbrook, IL; *U.S. Private*, pg. 416

Folle, W., Sec.--Fried. Krupp AG, Essen, Germany; *Int'l*, pg. 507

Folts, John B., Exec. V.P., Treas. & Sec.--Hargro Enterprises, Inc., Stamford, CT; *U.S. Private*, pg. 502

Fondevilla, Esther, Sec.--Salvat Editores S.A., Barcelona, Spain; *Int'l*, pg. 796

Fontenot, Sundra, Sec.--Fugro Group Companies, Houston, TX; *U.S. Private*, pg. 430

Foo, A., Sec.--Esso Singapore Private Limited, Singapore, Singapore; *U.S. Public*, pg. 602

Foo, A., Sec.--Exxon Trading Asia Pacific Private Limited, Singapore, Singapore; *U.S. Public*, pg. 602

Foo, Dennis, Sec.--Scotts Holdings Limited, Singapore, Singapore; *Int'l*, pg. 1212

Fooch, Kelly, Sec.--Temperature Equipment Corporation, Lansing, IL; *U.S. Private*, pg. 1075

Foong Lan, Helen Chong nee Chia, Sec. & Legal Counsel--Singapore Petroleum Company Ltd., Singapore, Singapore; *U.S. Public*, pg. 102

Forbes, Alan, Gen. Mgr.-Corp. Devel. & Sec.--Standard Life Assurance, Edinburgh, United Kingdom; *Int'l*, pg. 1297

Forbes, R.H.A., Sec.--British Alcan Aluminium plc, Gerrards Cross, United Kingdom; *Int'l*, pg. 51

Forbes, Richard E., V.P.-Fin. & Asst. Sec.--Aristokraft, Inc., Jasper, IN; *U.S. Public*, pg. 675

Force, Jill L., Sr. V.P., Gen. Counsel & Sec.--Vencor, Inc., Louisville, KY; *U.S. Public*, pg. 1711

Ford, Beverly, Asst. Sec.--Lario Enterprises, Inc., Wichita, KS; *U.S. Private*, pg. 651

Ford, Elsa, Corp. Sec.--John Burnham & Co., San Diego, CA; *U.S. Private*, pg. 186

Ford, Gary, V.P., Gen. Counsel & Sec.--Axent Technologies, Rockville, MD; *U.S. Public*, pg. 157

Ford, Peggy, V.P., Gen. Counsel & Sec.--La Petite Academy Inc., Overland Park, KS; *U.S. Private*, pg. 640

Ford, Stephen, Treas. & Sec.--Ford Meter Box Company, Wabash, IN; *U.S. Private*, pg. 418

Ford, Steven J., V.P., Gen. Counsel & Sec.--Carlisle Companies Incorporated, Syracuse, NY; *U.S. Public*, pg. 305

Ford, Susan E., Sec.--Knight Architects Engineers Planners, Inc., Chicago, IL; *U.S. Private*, pg. 626

Forehand, Steve R., Sec.--Russell Corporation, Alexander City, AL; *U.S. Public*, pg. 1413

Foreht, Stephen, Sec.--GAF Premium Products, Inc., Wayne, NJ; *U.S. Private*, pg. 433

Foremny, Brian, Gen. Counsel & Sec.--CyberGuard Corporation, Fort Lauderdale, FL; *U.S. Public*, pg. 470

Fornella, Norman G., Chief Fin. Officer, Exec. V.P., Treas. & Sec.--Morse Diesel International, Inc., New York, NY; *U.S. Private*, pg. 762

Forney, James L., Chief Fin. Officer & Treas.--Fone America, Inc., Portland, OR; *U.S. Public*, pg. 661

Fornmark, Inger, Sec.--Atlet AB, Molnlycke, Sweden; *Int'l*, pg. 97

Forsyth, Terrence, Sec.--Bank of Ireland, Dublin, Ireland; *Int'l*, pg. 152

Fortado, Michael G., V.P. & Corp. Sec.--ENSERCH Corporation, Dallas, TX; *U.S. Public*, pg. 1587

Fortin, Raymond D., Sr. V.P. & Sec.--SunTrust Banks, Inc., Atlanta, GA; *U.S. Public*, pg. 1537

Fortmuller, George A., Chief Fin. Officer, V.P., Treas. & Sec.--Edwin B. Stimpson Company, Inc., Bayport, NY; *U.S. Private*, pg. 1043

Fortun, Jay, Gen. Counsel--Wickland Corporation, Sacramento, CA; *U.S. Private*, pg. 1174

Fortunoff, Helene, Treas. & Sec.--Fortunoff, Uniondale, NY; *U.S. Private*, pg. 420

Fossett, W. Curtis, Controller & Sec.--Educational Development Corporation, Tulsa, OK; *U.S. Public*, pg. 564

Fossum, Robert, Sec.--American Mathematical Society, Inc., Providence, RI; *U.S. Private*, pg. 59

Foster, Craig, Sec.--Rex Lumber Company, Acton, MA; *U.S. Private*, pg. 926

Foster, Fran, Sec.--Guaranty Corporation, Baton Rouge, LA; *U.S. Private*, pg. 485

Foster, L. Dale, Treas. & Sec.--Aeronca, Inc., Middletown, OH; *Int'l*, pg. 829

Foster, Marvin L., Sr. V.P. & Sec.--Nationwide Homes, Inc., Martinsville, VA; *U.S. Private*, pg. 788

Foster, Robert, Sr. V.P.-Pub. Affairs--Edison International, Rosemead, CA; *U.S. Public*, pg. 564

Foster, Robert J., V.P.-Fin.--National Machinery, Tiffin, OH; *U.S. Private*, pg. 785

Fothergill, Paul A., Mng. Dir. & Sec.--Analysis & Technology Australia Pty Limited, Kingston, Australia; *U.S. Public*, pg. 110

Foti, Frances, Sec. & Dir.-Personnel--ICC Industries, Inc., New York, NY; *U.S. Private*, pg. 553

Foudree, Charles M., Exec. V.P.-Fin., Treas. & Sec.--Harmon Industries, Inc., Blue Springs, MO; *U.S. Public*, pg. 788

Foulk, David L., Sec.--NationsBank West, Saint Louis, MO; *U.S. Public*, pg. 1164

Fountain, John E., V.P., Gen. Counsel & Sec.--Morrison Health Care Inc., Smyrna, GA; *U.S. Public*, pg. 1133

Fourniadis, Robert A., Sr. V.P., Gen. Counsel & Sec.--Calton, Inc., Manalapan, NJ; *U.S. Public*, pg. 296

Fowler, Ian, Sec.--Trafalgar House PLC, London, United Kingdom; *Int'l*, pg. 772

Fowler, L.C., Sec.--Digital Courier International Inc., Burnaby, Canada; *Int'l*, pg. 413

Fowler, P.D., Sec.--International Systems & Controls Corp., Houston, TX; *U.S. Private*, pg. 572

Fox, Dianne F., Sr. V.P.-Admin. & Sec.--Hilb, Rogal and Hamilton Company, Glen Allen, VA; *U.S. Public*, pg. 826

Fox, Dianne F., V.P. & Sec.--Hilb, Rogal and Hamilton Company of Canada, Limited, Winnipeg, Canada; *U.S. Public*, pg. 828

Fox, Lawrence A., V.P. & Sec.--Champion International Corp., Stamford, CT; *U.S. Public*, pg. 333

Fox, Randolph, V.P.-Fin., Treas. & Sec.--Metal Masters Foodservice Equipment, Clayton, DE; *U.S. Private*, pg. 734

Fox, Raymond A., Chief Oper. Officer, V.P. & Sec.--Active Electrical Supply Company, Chicago, IL; *U.S. Private*, pg. 15

Fox, Robert, Sr. V.P.-Fin. & Admin., Treas. & Sec.--Rocor Transportation Companies Inc., Oklahoma City, OK; *U.S. Private*, pg. 938

Fox, Stephen, V.P., Gen. Counsel & Sec.--Amperif Corporation, Chatsworth, CA; *U.S. Public*, pg. 1523

Foy, John N., Chief Fin. Officer & Exec. V.P.--CBL & Associates Properties, Inc., Chattanooga, TN; *U.S. Public*, pg. 273

Frailing, Judith M., V.P. & Asst. Corp. Sec.--Arandell Corporation, Menomonee Falls, WI; *U.S. Private*, pg. 79

Frame, Peter, V.P. & Sec.--Rotary Multiforms, Inc., Warren, MI; *U.S. Private*, pg. 947

Francis-Vogelsang, Charee, V.P. & Sec.--Diebold, Incorporated, Canton, OH; *U.S. Public*, pg. 506

Francis, Eugene, Jr., Sec.--National Farms Inc., Kansas City, MO; *U.S. Private*, pg. 782

Francis, George E., Chief Fin. Officer, Sr. V.P. & Sec.--First Commonwealth Corporation, Springfield, IL; *U.S. Private, pg. 406*

Francis, Kathleen C., Assoc. Counsel & Asst. Sec.--Interpool, Inc., Princeton, NJ; *U.S. Public*, pg. 908

Francis, M.K.V., Sec.--Pilkington Properties Limited, Saint Helens, United Kingdom; *Int'l*, pg. 1056

Francis, Philip, Sec.--Fuller, Smith & Turner Plc, London, United Kingdom; *Int'l*, pg. 529

Francis, Robert D., Sr. V.P.-Underwriting & Corp. Sec.--Medical Assurance, Inc., Birmingham, AL; *U.S. Public*, pg. 1079

Francois, Guy, Sec. Gen.--Au Bon Marche, Paris, France; *Int'l*, pg. 97

Frank, Bernie, Gen. Counsel & Sec.--Williams Patent Crusher and Pulverizer Co., Saint Louis, MO; *U.S. Private*, pg. 1178

Frank, Harold D., Controller & Sec.--Research Products Corporation, Madison, WI; *U.S. Private*, pg. 924

Frank, Judy, Sec.--CNJ Distributing, Billings, MT; *U.S. Private*, pg. 196

Frank, Lloyd, Gen. Counsel & Sec.--Esquire Radio & Electronics Inc., Brooklyn, NY; *U.S. Private*, pg. 383

Frank, Melvin S., Sec.--Union Industries, Inc., Providence, RI; *U.S. Private*, pg. 1119

Frank, Sanford B., Gen. Counsel & Sec.--Toymax International Inc., Plainview, NY; *U.S. Public*, pg. 1626

Frank, Steven N., V.P., Assoc. Gen. Counsel & Sec.--McDonnell Aircraft & Missile Systems Div., Berkeley, MO; *U.S. Public*, pg. 241

Franke, Thomas, V.P. & Sec.--Riemeier Lumber Company, Inc., Cincinnati, OH; *U.S. Private*, pg. 930

Frankel, Jeffrey A.H., V.P.-Legal & Asst. Sec.--MicroAge, Inc., Tempe, AZ; *U.S. Public*, pg. 1104

Franklin, Carol, Chief Fin. Officer & Sec.--Video Display Corporation, Tucker, GA; *U.S. Public*, pg. 1720

Franklin, Earl R., Sec. & Assoc. Gen. Counsel--Eaton Corporation, Cleveland, OH; *U.S. Public*, pg. 555

Franklin, J.E., II, Sec. & Gen. Counsel--Atlantic Electric Co., Pleasantville, NJ; *U.S. Public*, pg. 430

Franklin, James, Sec. & Dir.-Fin.--Tasco Sales Inc., Miramar, FL; *U.S. Private*, pg. 928

Franklin, Wayne, Controller & Sec.--The Parman Corporation, Nashville, TN; *U.S. Private*, pg. 840

Frankovich, George, Sec. & Gen. Counsel--Sterling Inc., Akron, OH; *Int'l*, pg. 1248

Fransen, Darla A., V.P.-Human Resources & Sec.--Tri-State Insurance Company of Minnesota, Luverne, MN; *U.S. Public*, pg. 215

Frantz, Francis X., Sr. V.P.-External Affairs, Gen Counsel & Sec.--ALLTEL Corporation, Little Rock, AR; *U.S. Public*, pg. 55

Franz, Victor, V.P. & Sec.--Fenton Press, Inc., Addison, IL; *U.S. Private*, pg. 400

Frasco, Robert A., Esq., V.P., Gen. Counsel & Sec.--Devon Group, Inc., Stamford, CT; *U.S. Public*, pg. 503

Fraser, Gregory A., Ph.D., Chief Fin. Officer, Exec. V.P., Treas. & Sec.--FARO Technologies, Inc., Lake Mary, FL; *U.S. Public*, pg. 613

Fraser, Marge, Sec.--Lester B. Knight & Associates, Inc., Chicago, IL; *U.S. Private*, pg. 626

Frasier, Ralph K., Gen. Counsel & Sec.--Huntington Bancshares Inc., Columbus, OH; *U.S. Public*, pg. 849

Frasier, Ralph K., Exec. V.P., Gen. Counsel, Sec. & Cashier--Huntington National Bank, Columbus, OH; *U.S. Public*, pg. 850

Frattin, Piero L., Sec.--Benetton Group S.p.A., Ponzano Veneto, Italy; *Int'l*, pg. 186

Frawley, Frederic, Sec. & Sr. Attorney--Central and South West Corporation, Dallas, TX; *U.S. Public*, pg. 324

Fray, Jennifer H., Gen. Counsel & Sec.--Hart Holding Company, Inc., Norwalk, CT; *U.S. Private*, pg. 507

Frazen, Mary A., Exec. V.P., Sec. & Treas.--Ed Marling Stores, Inc., Topeka, KS; *U.S. Private*, pg. 705

Frazer, Robert H., Esq., V.P., Gen. Counsel & Sec.--ACMAT Corporation, New Britain, CT; *U.S. Public*, pg. 16

Frazer, Robert H., Esq., V.P., Gen. Counsel & Sec.--United Coastal Insurance Company, New Britain, CT; *U.S. Public*, pg. 16

Frazier, C. Clifford, Jr., Sec.--Unifi Inc., Greensboro, NC; *U.S. Public*, pg. 1665

Frazier, Patricia B., Sec.--Dycom Industries, Inc., Palm Beach Gardens, FL; *U.S. Public*, pg. 538

Frease, Belden A., Sr. V.P. & Sec.--Computer Associates International, Inc., Islandia, NY; *U.S. Public*, pg. 420

Fredette, A., Sec.--Lafarge Canada Inc., Montreal, Canada; *Int'l*, pg. 789

Fredianelli, Ronald E., Chief Fin. Officer & Sec.--ILC Technology, Inc., Sunnyvale, CA; *U.S. Public*, pg. 856

Fredrich, Carolyn A., Corp. Sec.--Kinark Corporation, Tulsa, OK; *U.S. Public*, pg. 960

Fredrickson, Glenn, Controller & Sec.--Standard Manifold Company, Inc., Chicago, IL; *U.S. Private*, pg. 1031

Freeborn, Steven J., V.P.-Commercial Lines & Sec.--Union Insurance Company, Lincoln, NE; *U.S. Public*, pg. 216

Freed, Sharon V., V.P., Bank Counsel & Sec.--The Trustcompany Bancorporation, Jersey City, NJ; *U.S. Public*, pg. 1643

Freed, Thomas J., Controller & Sec.--National City Bancorp, Minneapolis, MN; *U.S. Public*, pg. 1153

Freedman, Larry S., Sr. V.P., Gen. Counsel & Sec.--Platinum Technology, Inc., Oak Brook Terrace, IL; *U.S. Public*, pg. 1309

Freedman, Stanley A., Sec.--TBC Corporation, Memphis, TN; *U.S. Public*, pg. 1553

Freehling, Les, Sec.--Oberg Industries Corp., Freeport, PA; *U.S. Private*, pg. 810

Freeman, Jeff E., Sr. V.P.-Fin., Sec. & Treas.--Havatampa, Inc., Tampa, FL; *U.S. Private*, pg. 510

Freeman, Leroy, V.P. & Sec.--The Osterneck Co. Inc., Lumberton, NC; *U.S. Private*, pg. 821

Freeman, Stanley Roger, Chief Acct. & Sec.--Birds Eye Walls Ltd., Walton-on-Thames, United Kingdom; *Int'l*, pg. 1434

Freidheim, John, V.P. & Sec.--Cougle Commission Company, Inc., Chicago, IL; *U.S. Private*, pg. 278

Freilich, Joseph, Treas. & Sec.--Icahn & Co., Inc., New York, NY; *U.S. Private*, pg. 556

Freimark, Jeffrey P., Chief Fin. Officer, Sr. V.P. & Sec.--The Grand Union Company, Wayne, NJ; *U.S. Public*, pg. 758

Freisner, David W., Exec. V.P.--Galamba Metals, Inc., Kansas City, KS; *U.S. Private*, pg. 437

French, J.J., Jr., Sec.--Trinity Industries Inc., Dallas, TX; U.S. Public, pg. 1638

Frenette, Charles J., Treas. & Sec.--Mason Shoe Mfg. Co., Chippewa Falls, WI; U.S. Private, pg. 712

Frenette, Charles J., Treas. & Sec.--Wissota Trader Ltd., Chippewa Falls, WI; U.S. Private, pg. 712

Frese, Shona, Sec.--United Fire & Casualty Company, Cedar Rapids, IA; U.S. Public, pg. 1677

Freundlich, Jana R., Asst. Sec.--Tandy Corporation, Fort Worth, TX; U.S. Public, pg. 1560

Frew, A.D., Sec.--United Biscuits (Holdings) Plc, West Drayton, United Kingdom; Int'l, pg. 1442

Frey, Keith G., Chief Fin. Officer, V.P.-Fin. & Admin. & Sec.--IL International Inc., Stratford, CT; U.S. Public, pg. 855

Frey, Rick J., Controller & Asst. Sec.--Hickman, Williams & Co. Inc., Cincinnati, OH; U.S. Private, pg. 525

Frezel, William J., Exec. V.P. & Sec.--Premier Dental Products Company, King of Prussia, PA; U.S. Private, pg. 881

Friar, Amy, Exec. Admin. Asst.--Bush Hog Division, Selma, AL; U.S. Public, pg. 48

Frick, Dennis D., Sec.--Florida Rock Industries, Inc., Jacksonville, FL; U.S. Public, pg. 655

Fridman, Josef J., Sr. V.P.-Law, Corp. Services & Sec.--BCE Inc., Montreal, Canada; Int'l, pg. 114

Fridman, Josef J., Sec.--Bell Canada, Montreal, Canada; Int'l, pg. 115

Friedman, Charlene Andros, Gen. Counsel & Asst. Sec.--Collagen Corporation, Palo Alto, CA; U.S. Public, pg. 399

Friedman, Dean, Treas. & Sec.--Great Lakes Wholesale Drugs, Livonia, MI; U.S. Private, pg. 475

Friedman, Gary E., Corp. V.P. & Gen. Counsel--Agouron Pharmaceuticals, Inc., La Jolla, CA; U.S. Public, pg. 28

Friedman, Irwin, Asst. Sec.--Banner Wholesale Grocers, Inc., Chicago, IL; U.S. Private, pg. 114

Friedman, Jerry, Exec. V.P., Treas. & Sec.--Marvin Engineering Company, Inc., Inglewood, CA; U.S. Private, pg. 710

Friedman, Marilyn, Sec.--Willis Corroon Melling Inc., Montreal, Canada; Int'l, pg. 1509

Friedman, Mark J., Asst. Corp. Sec.--Atlantic Richfield Company, Los Angeles, CA; U.S. Public, pg. 144

Friedman, Stacey, Sec.--Jaclo Inc., Mountainside, NJ; U.S. Private, pg. 349

Friedrich, Calvin H., Treas. & Asst. Sec.--Seneca Resources Corp., Houston, TX; U.S. Public, pg. 1156

Friedrichsen, B.T., Treas. & Sec.--Wagner Mills Inc., Schuyler, NE; U.S. Private, pg. 1146

Friend, Ross D., Sr. V.P., Gen. Counsel & Sec.--The Franklin Life Insurance Company, Springfield, IL; U.S. Public, pg. 76

Friend, William K., V.P., Sec. & Counsel--Hills Stores Co., Canton, MA; U.S. Public, pg. 828

Frierson, Robert W., V.P. & Asst. Sec.--Republic Financial Services, Inc., Dallas, TX; Int'l, pg. 346

Frierson, Robert W., V.P. & Asst. Sec.--Republic Underwriters Insurance Co., Dallas, TX; Int'l, pg. 346

Frierson, Robert W., V.P. & Asst. Sec.--Republic-Vanguard Life Insurance Co., Dallas, TX; Int'l, pg. 346

Frierson, Robert W., V.P. & Asst. Sec.--Republic Diversified Services, Inc., Dallas, TX; Int'l, pg. 346

Frierson, Robert W., V.P. & Asst. Sec.--Southern Insurance Co., Dallas, TX; Int'l, pg. 346

Frierson, Robert W., V.P. & Asst. Sec.--Republic Financial Services, Inc., Dallas, TX; Int'l, pg. 346

Frierson, Robert W., V.P. & Asst. Sec.--Southern Underwriters Insurance Company, Dallas, TX; Int'l, pg. 346

Frierson, Robert W., V.P. & Asst. Sec.--Republic Fire & Casualty Insurance Company, Dallas, TX; Int'l, pg. 346

Frierson, Robert W., V.P. & Asst. Sec.--Republic Group No. Two, Dallas, TX; Int'l, pg. 346

Frierson, Robert W., V.P. & Asst. Sec.--Eagle General Agency, Dallas, TX; Int'l, pg. 346

Fries-Gardner, Lisa, V.P., Compliance Officer & Sec.--Foster Wheeler Corporation, Clinton, NJ; U.S. Public, pg. 676

Frigard, Wayne R., Asst. Clerk--Boston Edison Company, Boston, MA; U.S. Public, pg. 247

Frisch, Benjamin P., V.P., Treas. & Sec.--Beaver Street Fisheries, Inc., Jacksonville, FL; U.S. Private, pg. 128

Fritzen, Doris A., Controller & Sec.--C.F. Haglin & Sons, Edina, MN; U.S. Private, pg. 493

Froch, Michael I., Sec.--Newcom, Inc., Westlake Village, CA; U.S. Public, pg. 147

Frock, John, Exec. V.P. & Asst. Sec.--Nobel Education Dynamics, Inc., Media, PA; U.S. Public, pg. 1185

Froemming, Herb, Pres. & Chief Oper. Officer--Brauns Fashions Corporation, Plymouth, MN; U.S. Public, pg. 251

Frohnmaier, Nancy C., V.P. & Sec.--General Employment Enterprises, Inc., Oak Brook Terrace, IL; U.S. Public, pg. 714

Frost, William J., V.P., Sec. & Treas.--EDO Western Corporation, Salt Lake City, UT; U.S. Public, pg. 542

Fruchtman, Arthur, V.P.-Legal & Sec.--Ingersoll-Dresser Pump Company, Liberty Corner, NJ; U.S. Public, pg. 529

Fruge, Sherry, Sec. & Treas.--Texas Metal Works, Inc., Beaumont, TX; U.S. Private, pg. 1078

Fruitman, Harvey, Chief Fin. Officer, Exec. V.P. & Sec.--Tridel Enterprises Inc., Downsview, Canada; Int'l, pg. 1423

Fruman, Lee S., M.D., J.D., Sec.--Dale Industries Inc., Dearborn, MI; U.S. Private, pg. 308

Fry, David, Sec.--Anchor Lamina Inc., Windsor, Canada; Int'l, pg. 75

Fry, Thomas W., V.P.-Fin. & Admin., Treas. & Sec.--BEI Medical Systems Company, Hackensack, NJ; U.S. Private, pg. 106

Frye, Darrell, V.P.-Fin. & Sec.--Harriss & Covington Hosiery Mills, High Point, NC; U.S. Private, pg. 506

Fuchs, Werner, Sec. Gen.--The Swissair Group, Zurich, Switzerland; Int'l, pg. 1333

Fugate, Donna M., Mgr.-Office Svc.--United Fire & Casualty Company, Cedar Rapids, IA; U.S. Public, pg. 1677

Fui San, June Low, Sec.--Singapore Reinsurance Corporation Limited, Singapore, Singapore; Int'l, pg. 1253

Fujikawa, Seicho, V.P. & Sec.--Mutual Trading Co., Inc., Los Angeles, CA; U.S. Private, pg. 770

Fukuchi, Sumi, Corp. Sec.--Continental Graphics Corporation, Los Angeles, CA; U.S. Private, pg. 268

Fukuda, M., Corp. Sec.--Miyata Industry Co., Ltd., Chigasaki, Japan; Int'l, pg. 884

Fuller, Glenn, V.P. & Sec.--McKee Foods Corporation, Collegedale, TN; U.S. Private, pg. 723

Fuller, Patricia, Corp. Sec.--Southwestern Petroleum Corporation, Fort Worth, TX; U.S. Private, pg. 1019

Fuller, Richard, V.P.--Woodward-Clyde Group, Inc., Denver, CO; U.S. Public, pg. 1655

Furey, John J., Gen. Counsel & Sec.--Campbell Soup Company, Camden, NJ; U.S. Public, pg. 298

Furey, Joseph B., Controller & Sec.--First Brands Corporation, Danbury, CT; U.S. Public, pg. 626

Furman, Granklin G., Sec.--Furman Foods, Inc., Northumberland, PA; U.S. Private, pg. 431

Furst, Rafael, Sr. V.P., Treas. & Sec.--The Elder-Beerman Stores Corp., Dayton, OH; U.S. Private, pg. 367

Furst, Rafael, Pres., Treas. & Sec.--The El-Bee Chargit Corp., Dayton, OH; U.S. Private, pg. 367

Furstein, Steve, Treas. & Sec.--Duro Dyne Corporation, Farmingdale, NY; U.S. Private, pg. 349

Furter, Ruth, Corp. Sec.--Hilti AG, Schaan, Liechtenstein; Int'l, pg. 619

Furtick, Russell H., V.P. & Asst. Sec.--American Heritage Life Investment Corp., Jacksonville, FL; U.S. Public, pg. 78

Furusho, Takashi, Sec.--Sankyo Company Limited, Tokyo, Japan; Int'l, pg. 1189

Fuser, Jean, Sec.--Kodak Brasileira C.I.L., Sao Paulo, Brazil; U.S. Public, pg. 552

Fushimi, V., Sec.--Dimco-Gray Company, Centerville, OH; U.S. Private, pg. 333

Fuson, Harold W., Jr., Sec. & Chief Legal Officer--The Copley Press, Inc., La Jolla, CA; U.S. Private, pg. 275

Fuster Fernandez, D. Vincente, Sec.--Playa De Madrid, S.A., Madrid, Spain; Int'l, pg. 1371

Futch, M.B., Asst. Sec.--Florida East Coast Industries Inc., Saint Augustine, FL; U.S. Public, pg. 1427

Futch, Michael, V.P., Gen. Counsel & Sec.--Granite Construction Incorporated, Watsonville, CA; U.S. Public, pg. 759

Futter, Kenneth, Treas. & Sec.--Futter Lumber Corporation, Rockville Center, NY; U.S. Private, pg. 432

Gaab, Donna, Asst. Corp. Sec.--Calavo Growers of California, Santa Ana, CA; U.S. Private, pg. 199

Gaccione, Ann, Sec.--Peerless Tube Company, Bloomfield, NJ; U.S. Public, pg. 1269

Gace, James M., V.P., Treas. & Sec.--Financial Industries Corp., Austin, TX; U.S. Public, pg. 622

Gaddis, L.L., V.P. & Sec.--National Posters, Inc., Chattanooga, TN; U.S. Private, pg. 786

Gaertner, Suzie, Chief Fin. Officer--Shealy Electrical Wholesalers, Greenville, SC; U.S. Private, pg. 991

Gaffin, Helen, Sec.--Baris Shoe Company, Inc., New York, NY; U.S. Private, pg. 116

Gagas, Carolyn M., Asst. Sec.--General Ceramics, Inc., Haskell, NJ; Int'l, pg. 1394

Gagne, Irene M., Asst. Sec.--EnergyNorth, Inc., Manchester, NH; U.S. Public, pg. 581

Gagnon, Lawrence J., V.P., Gen. Counsel & Sec.--Southeastern Michigan Gas Enterprises, Inc., Port Huron, MI; U.S. Public, pg. 1489

Gagnon, Louis Gilles, V.P., Gen. Counsel & Sec.--Donohue Inc., Quebec, Canada; Int'l, pg. 1075

Gagnon, Louis Gilles, V.P., Gen. Counsel &Sec.--Westburne Inc., Montreal, Canada; Int'l, pg. 1491

Gaidano, Don J., Sec.--Service Assets Corp., Newport Beach, CA; U.S. Private, pg. 171

Gaier, J. Richard, Sec.--The Orr Felt Company, Piqua, OH; U.S. Private, pg. 820

Gail, Dan, Exec. V.P., Sec. & Gen. Counsel--Southwestern Financial Services Corp., Dallas, TX; U.S. Private, pg. 1018

Gail, Daniel B., Exec. V.P., Gen. Counsel & Sec.--Constitution Life Insurance Co., Dallas, TX; U.S. Private, pg. 1018

Gailey, John, Sec.--Senetics, Boulder, CO; U.S. Public, pg. 1755

Gailey, John R., III, V.P., Gen. Counsel & Sec.--The West Company, Incorporated, Lionville, PA; U.S. Public, pg. 1755

Gajewski, Gary, V.P.-Fin. & Specialties & Asst. Sec.--Moen Incorporated, North Olmsted, OH; U.S. Public, pg. 675

Gajewski, J.L., V.P.-Employee Benefits & Risk Mngmt. & Sec.--Elkins Constructors, Inc., Jacksonville, FL; U.S. Private, pg. 372

Galanes, Philip, V.P., Gen. Counsel & Sec.--Golden Books Family Entertainment Inc., New York, NY; U.S. Public, pg. 749

Galanis, Marian M., Sec.--Sealing Devices Inc., Lancaster, NY; U.S. Private, pg. 978

Galasso, Linda, V.P. & Asst. Sec.--The Equitable Companies Incorporated, New York, NY; U.S. Public, pg. 588

Galbraith, Leslie A., Chief Fin. Officer, Exec. V.P., Treas. & Sec.--First International Bancorp, Inc., Hartford, CT; U.S. Public, pg. 635

Gale, Connie, V.P., Gen. Counsel & Sec.--Frontier Communications Services, Bingham Farms, MI; U.S. Public, pg. 684

Gallagher, Catherine, Sec.--Arrow International, Cleveland, OH; U.S. Private, pg. 85

Gallagher, Cindy, Treas. & Sec.--Jim Fresard Pontiac Buick, Inc., Royal Oak, MI; U.S. Private, pg. 427

Gallagher, Frann M., Asst. Gen. Counsel & Asst. Sec.--International Game Technology, Reno, NV; U.S. Public, pg. 900

Gallagher, James G., V.P., Gen. Counsel & Sec.--USA Networks, Inc., Saint Petersburg, FL; U.S. Public, pg. 1685

Gallagher, Kevin C., Sr. V.P., Gen. Counsel & Sec.--360 Degrees Communications Company, Chicago, IL; U.S. Public, pg. 1607

Gallagher, Nancy L., V.P. & Sec.--AMC Entertainment, Inc., Kansas City, MO; U.S. Private, pg. 6

Gallagher, Thomas W., Sr. V.P., Gen. Counsel & Sec.--Citizens Banking Corporation, Flint, MI; U.S. Public, pg. 379

Gallagher, William T., Asst. Corp. Sec. & Asst. Gen. Counsel--Crown Cork & Seal Company, Inc., Philadelphia, PA; U.S. Public, pg. 462

Gallaher, Jacqueline, Asst. Sec.--Phoenix Medical Technology, Inc., Andrews, SC; U.S. Public, pg. 1292

Gallaher, James A., Sec.--The New England, Boston, MA; U.S. Private, pg. 737

Gallo, Samuel J., Sr. V.P., Gen. Counsel & Sec.--Arthur D. Little, Inc., Cambridge, MA; U.S. Private, pg. 670

Galloway, Peter S., Sec.--Johnson & Johnson, New Brunswick, NJ; U.S. Public, pg. 927

Galowich, Ronald H., Exec. V.P., Sec. & Gen. Counsel--First Health Group Corp., Downers Grove, IL; U.S. Public, pg. 635

Galvin, Kerry, Corp. Sc.--Lyondell Petrochemical Company, Houston, TX; U.S. Public, pg. 1022

Gammon, Krista, Asst. Sec.--Trustmark Corporation, Jackson, MS; U.S. Public, pg. 1643

Gamoran, Saul, Exec. V.P., Gen. Counsel & Sec.--Play by Play Toys & Novelties, Inc., San Antonio, TX; U.S. Public, pg. 1309

Gandal, Robert, V.P.--Management Recruiters International, Inc., Cleveland, OH; U.S. Public, pg. 277

Gandy, Brian E., Sec.--Dalgety Plc, London, United Kingdom; Int'l, pg. 376

Gangopadhyay, M.M., Sec.--Central Coalfields Limited, Ranchi, India; Int'l, pg. 298

Gans, Robert M., Exec. V.P., Gen. Counsel & Sec.--PriceSmart Inc., San Diego, CA; U.S. Public, pg. 1324

Gant, Harry, Chief Fin. Officer, V.P., Treas. & Sec.--Young Radiator Company, Racine, WI; U.S. Private, pg. 1201

Garay, Joseph P., V.P., Sec. & Gen. Counsel--Bailey, Fischer & Porter Company, Warminster, PA; Int'l, pg. 449

Garbade, Nancy C., Sec. & Gen. Counsel--Arrhythmia Research Technology, Inc., Austin, TX; U.S. Public, pg. 133

Garber, M.E., Sec.--Nevada Bell, Reno, NV; U.S. Public, pg. 1416

Garber, Ronald D., Gen. Counsel & Sec.--Koo Koo Roo, Inc., Los Angeles, CA; U.S. Public, pg. 966

Garber, Samuel B., V.P., Gen. Counsel & Sec.--Evans, Inc., Chicago, IL; U.S. Public, pg. 596

Garbus, Samantha K., Second V.P., Asst. Sec. & Assoc. Mgr.-Property Mngmt.--W.P. Carey & Co., Inc., New York, NY; U.S. Private, pg. 209

Garcia-Ovies, Ramiro, Sec.--Tabacalera, S.A., Madrid, Spain; Int'l, pg. 1345

Garcia, Ileana, Treas. & Sec.--International Recovery Corp., Miami Springs, FL; U.S. Public, pg. 906

Garcia, Juan J., Sec.--Aerolineas Argentinas, Buenos Aires, Argentina; Int'l, pg. 575

Gard, Susan, Esq., Corp. Sec.--SaniServ Manufacturing Corp., Indianapolis, IN; U.S. Private, pg. 965

Gardener, Bruce D., Gen. Counsel, Dir.-Legal Opers. & Sec.--Hartford Life & Accident Insurance Company, Hartford, CT; U.S. Public, pg. 795

Gardener, Marvin, Gen. Counsel & Sec.--Loehmann's, Inc., Bronx, NY; U.S. Public, pg. 1010

Gardner, Ashley G., Sec.--Schenectady International, Inc., Schenectady, NY; U.S. Private, pg. 969

Gardner, Betty A., Co-Chm. Bd. & Sec.--Soft Sheen Products, Inc., Chicago, IL; U.S. Private, pg. 1012

Gardner, David A., Exec. V.P., Sls. Mgr. & Sec.--Alfred Nickles Bakery, Inc., Navarre, OH; U.S. Private, pg. 799

Gardner, David A., Exec. V.P. , Sec. & Sls. Mgr.--Nickles Bakery, Inc., Martins Ferry, OH; U.S. Private, pg. 799

Gardner, David A., Exec. V.P., Sls. Mgr. & Sec.--Nickles Bakery of Ohio Inc., Lima, OH; U.S. Private, pg. 799

Gardner, Donald R., Chief Fin. Officer, Sr. V.P. & Sec.--Rigel Energy Corporation, Calgary, Canada; Int'l, pg. 1117

Garety, Andrew, Group Fin. Dir. & Sec.--Liberty PLC, London, United Kingdom; Int'l, pg. 807

Gargiulo, William R. Jr., Asst. Sec.--Wisconsin Pharmacal Co., Inc., Jackson, WI; U.S. Private, pg. 1185

Garner, Robert E. Lee, Sec.--Builders Transport, Incorporated, Camden, SC; U.S. Public, pg. 267

Garonzik, Arnon E., Gen. Counsel & Sec.--Environmental Resources Management, Exton, PA; U.S. Private, pg. 378

Garpow, James E., Asst. Treas. & Asst. Sec.--Simpson Industries, Inc., Plymouth, MI; U.S. Public, pg. 1474

Garrett, Ann, Sec.--The Mad Butcher, Inc., Pine Bluff, AR; U.S. Private, pg. 693

Garrett, Karen L., Corp. Sec.--TCA Cable TV, Inc., Tyler, TX; U.S. Public, pg. 1553

Garrett, Thomas, III, Sec.--Check Technology Corporation, Minnetonka, MN; U.S. Public, pg. 342

Garrison, Tom, V.P., Treas. & Sec.--American Freightways Corporation, Harrison, AR; U.S. Public, pg. 75

Garson, Gary, V.P., Deputy Gen. Counsel & Asst. Sec.--Loews Corporation, New York, NY; U.S. Public, pg. 1010

Garten, David B., V.P., Gen. Counsel & Sec.--NL Industries, Inc., Houston, TX; U.S. Private, pg. 270

Garvey, Jean K., V.P. & Sec.--Garvey Industries, Inc., Wichita, KS; U.S. Private, pg. 440

Garvin, Paul, Sec.--New Balance Athletic Shoe, Inc., Boston, MA; U.S. Private, pg. 792

Gasca, Peter, Treas. & Corp. Sec.--Wards Cove Packing Company, Seattle, WA; U.S. Private, pg. 1149

Gaskin, John R., V.P., Gen. Counsel & Sec.--Duke Realty Investments, Inc., Indianapolis, IN; U.S. Public, pg. 535

Gasper, Leslie, Sec.--Sturm, Ruger & Co., Inc., Southport, CT; *U.S. Public*, pg. 1526
Gates, Albert L., Controller--Four-S Baking Company, Los Angeles, CA; *U.S. Private*, pg. 422
Gates, Deanna M., Sec.--Standard Plywoods, Inc., Clinton, SC; *U.S. Private*, pg. 1032
Gates, Nancy, In-House Council--Exolon-Esk Company, Tonawanda, NY; *U.S. Public*, pg. 600
Gates, Phyllis, Sec.--American Woodmark Corporation, Winchester, VA; *U.S. Public*, pg. 96
Gates, Signe S., V.P., Gen. Counsel & Sec.--Axel Johnson Inc., Stamford, CT; *Int'l*, pg. 709
Gates, William S., Treas. & Sec.--Preferred Risk Life Insurance Co., West Des Moines, IA; *U.S. Private*, pg. 880
Gatewood, Robert C., Sr. Exec. V.P.-Legal Affairs, Sec. & Treas.--Dairy Queen Corporate Store, Louisville, KY; *U.S.* Public, pg. 220
Gatewood, Wanda T., Corp. Sec.--Basic Construction Company, Newport News, VA; *U.S. Private*, pg. 121
Gathany, Eleanor S., Sec.--Hershey Foods Corporation, Hershey, PA; *U.S. Public*, pg. 811
Gattis, James L., Sec.--Pacific Capital Bancorp, Salinas, CA; *U.S. Public*, pg. 1247
Gatzek, Deborah R., Sr. V.P., Gen. Counsel & Asst. Sec.--Franklin Resources, Inc., San Mateo, CA; *U.S. Public*, pg. 679
Gau, Jack, Sec. & Treas.--G.R. Herberger's, Inc., Saint Cloud, MN; *U.S. Public*, pg. 1333
Gauck, Charles H., Sec. & Assoc. Gen. Counsel--Alliant Techsystems, Hopkins, MN; *U.S. Public*, pg. 47
Gaudin, Claude, Gen. Counsel & Board Sec.--Lyonnaise des Eaux S.A., Nanterre, France; *Int'l*, pg. 822
Gaugler, Bonita, Dir.-Corp. Affairs. & Asst. Sec.--Harleysville Group, Harleysville, PA; *U.S. Public*, pg. 786
Gaulter, Andrew M., Sec.--Schroders PLC, London, United Kingdom; *Int'l*, pg. 1210
Gaunt, William L., Sec.--CoreStates Financial Corp., Philadelphia, PA; *U.S. Public*, pg. 446
Gauthier, Adele, V.P. & Gen. Mgr.--Laurentien Cable TV Inc., Montreal, Canada; *Int'l*, pg. 241
Gauthier, Andre H., Sec. & Dir.-Member Rels.--Agropur, Granby, Canada; *Int'l*, pg. 31
Gavin, Carol Coghlan, V.P, Gen. Counsel. & Asst. Sec.--Tellabs Operations, Inc., Lisle, IL; *U.S. Public*, pg. 1572
Gavin, Jon D., Chief Fin. Officer, V.P., Sec. & Treas.--Frontier Oil Corporation, Englewood, CO; *U.S. Public*, pg. 1732
Gavin, Jon D., Chief Fin. Officer, V.P., Sec. & Treas.--Frontier Holdings Inc., Englewood, CO; *U.S. Public*, pg. 1732
Gawelek, Randolph A., Exec. V.P.& Sec.--The Kitchen Collection Inc., Chillicothe, OH; *U.S. Public*, pg. 1149
Gaxiola, F., Sec.--Grupo Industrial Morgan, S.A. de C.V., Mexico, Mexico; *Int'l*, pg. 895
Gay, Mickela D., V.P.-Opers. & Sec.--Kastle Systems LLC, Arlington, VA; *U.S. Private*, pg. 608
Gay, R. Norwood, III, Sr. V.P., Gen. Counsel & Sec.--Attorneys' Title Insurance Fund, Orlando, FL; *U.S. Private*, pg. 98
Gayga, Lorraine, Asst. Sec.--NUI Corporation, Bedminster, NJ; *U.S. Public*, pg. 1147
Gaylord, Thomas M., Treas. & Sec.--Mack Molding Company Inc., Arlington, VT; *U.S. Private*, pg. 691
Gaynor, Mitchell L., V.P., Gen. Counsel & Sec.--Sybase, Inc., Emeryville, CA; *U.S. Public*, pg. 1544
Gebo, L. Evelyn, Treas. & Sec.--Gebo Distributing Co., Inc., Plainview, TX; *U.S. Private*, pg. 442
Geddie, Rowland H., III, V.P., Gen. Counsel & Sec.--O'Sullivan Industries Holdings, Lamar, MO; *U.S. Public*, pg. 1234
Gee, Bruce K., Sec.--Cigna Insurance New Zealand Limited, Auckland, New Zealand; *U.S. Public*, pg. 364
Gee, Edward, Treas. & Sec.--Cloverhill Bakery, Chicago, IL; *U.S. Private*, pg. 247
Gee, Gregory W., Sr. V.P., Gen. Counsel & Sec.--Sun Life Assurance Company of Canada, Toronto, Canada; *Int'l*, pg. 1318
Geiger, Paul E., V.P., Sec. & Treas.--CMS Nomeco, Jackson, MI; *U.S. Public*, pg. 280
Geiman, Pam, Sec.--Craftlite, Littlestown, PA; *U.S. Public*, pg. 730
Geisel, Jean F., Asst. Sec.--Bausch & Lomb Incorporated, Rochester, NY; *U.S. Public*, pg. 194
Geisselbrecht, Elvin, V.P., Treas. & Sec.--YRJ Corporation, Houston, TX; *U.S. Private*, pg. 1176
Geisselbrecht, Elvin R., Treas. & Sec.--Wilco Reprographic, Inc., Las Vegas, NV; *U.S. Private*, pg. 1176
Gelardi, Ronald N., Chief Oper. Officer, Mng. Dir. & Sec.--Barr Brothers & Co., Inc., New York, NY; *U.S. Private*, pg. 117
Gelder, John W., Sec.--Harlan Electric Co., Rochester Hills, MI; *U.S. Public*, pg. 1029
Geller, Eric P., Sr. V.P., Gen. Counsel & Sec.--Harcourt General, Inc., Chestnut Hill, MA; *U.S. Public*, pg. 782
Geller, Richard, Sec.--Novartis Seeds, Inc., Downers Grove, IL; *Int'l*, pg. 974
Gelman, I. Lawrence, V.P., Sec. & Assoc. Counsel--Rite Aid Corporation, Camp Hill, PA; *U.S. Public*, pg. 1390
Gelpi, John J., III, Sec.--Industrial Metals of the South, New Orleans, LA; *U.S. Private*, pg. 561
Gemmill, Esq., Elizabeth H., V.P. & Sec.--Tasty Baking Company, Philadelphia, PA; *U.S. Public*, pg. 1561
Gentile, Robert N., V.P.-Law, Gen. Counsel & Sec.--Transtar Holdings, L.P., Monroeville, PA; *U.S. Private*, pg. 1097
Gentner, Craig, Chief Fin. Officer, Sr. V.P.-Fin. & Admin. & Sec.--Network Equipment Technologies, Inc., Redwood City, CA; *U.S. Public*, pg. 1168
Gentry, Hubert, Jr., Sr. V.P., Gen. Counsel & Sec.--NorAm Energy Corp., Houston, TX; *U.S. Public*, pg. 843
Gentry, Pamela J., Treas. & Asst. Sec.--Signal Apparel Company, Inc., Chattanooga, TN; *U.S. Public*, pg. 1472
Genuardi, Joseph, Jr., Sec.--Genuardi Family Markets Inc., Norristown, PA; *U.S. Private*, pg. 447
Genzer, Marvin D., V.P., Gen. Counsel & Sec.--EDO Corporation, New York, NY; *U.S. Public*, pg. 541
Geoghan, Joseph E., V.P., Gen. Counsel & Sec.--Union Carbide Corporation, Danbury, CT; *U.S. Public*, pg. 1666
Geoghegan, Andrew P., Sr. V.P., Gen. Counsel & Sec.--Hannaford Bros. Co., Scarborough, ME; *U.S. Public*, pg. 781
Geogino, Damian C., V.P., Gen. Counsel & Sec.--United States Filter Corporation, Palm Desert, CA; *U.S. Public*, pg. 1681
George, D.A., Sec.--Monarch Development Corporation, Willowdale, Canada; *Int'l*, pg. 1359
George, Judith E., Sec.--Harrowston Corporation, Toronto, Canada; *Int'l*, pg. 599
George, Leslie, Jr., Treas. & Sec.--King Group, Inc., Ann Arbor, MI; *U.S. Private*, pg. 620
George, P.M., Dir. & Asst. Sec.--London & Leeds (USA) Corporation, New York, NY; *Int'l*, pg. 788
George, Thomas A., Sec. & Treas.--Melody Foods, Inc., Farmington Hills, MI; *U.S. Private*, pg. 730
Georgen, Mary Jo, Asst. Corp. Sec.--UAL Corporation, Elk Grove Village, IL; *U.S. Public*, pg. 1652
Gerard, Antonia, Chief Oper. & Chief Fin. Officer, Exec. V.P., Sec. & Controller--Bolliger, Inc., Stamford, CT; *U.S.* Private, pg. 155
Gerardot, Roger, Corp. Sec.--BCI Mer Rouge, Djibouti, Djibouti; *Int'l*, pg. 163
Gerber, Daryl, Sec.--Gerber Plumbing Fixtures Corporation, Chicago, IL; *U.S. Private*, pg. 449
Gerber, Daryl E., Sec.--Kokomo Sanitary Pottery Corp., Kokomo, IN; *U.S. Private*, pg. 449
Gerdin, Russell A., Chm. Bd., Pres. Chief Exec. Officer, Chief Oper. Officer & Sec.--Heartland Express, Inc., Coralville, IA; *U.S. Public*, pg. 803
Geren, Tracey, Treas. & Sec.--Weldon, Williams & Lick, Inc., Fort Smith, AR; *U.S. Private*, pg. 1161
Gerhart, Betty J., Sec.--High Industries, Inc., Lancaster, PA; *U.S. Private*, pg. 528
Gerlach, John B., Jr., Pres., Chief Exec. Officer, Chief Oper. Officer & Sec.--Lancaster Colony Corporation, Columbus, OH; *U.S. Public*, pg. 976
Gerland, Joseph P., Exec. V.P. & Sec.--Gerland Corp., Houston, TX; *U.S. Private*, pg. 449
Gerlinger, Charles D., Sec.--Cabot Corporation, Boston, MA; *U.S. Public*, pg. 288
Gerstle, Mark R., Chief Admin. Officer & V.P.--Cummins Engine Company, Inc., Columbus, IN; *U.S. Public*, pg. 467
Gerstman, Henry, Controller, Treas. & Sec.--Century Business Credit Corporation, New York, NY; *U.S. Private*, pg. 225
Gertmenian, Russell M., Sec.--Desco Corporation, Columbus, OH; *U.S. Private*, pg. 326
Gerutowski, Ronald, Sec.--Narragansett Electric Co., Providence, RI; *U.S. Public*, pg. 1171
Gervais, P. Andre, Sec.--Hilton Canada Inc., Montreal, Canada; *Int'l*, pg. 788
Gerych, Rita, Exec. Sec.--Foseco Inc., Cleveland, OH; *Int'l*, pg. 234
Gette, Anthony R., Pres., Chief Oper. Officer & Sec.--Mentor Corporation, Santa Barbara, CA; *U.S. Public*, pg. 1086
Gettlefinger, Andrew, Sec. & Treas.--Kelso Oil Company, Knoxville, TN; *U.S. Private*, pg. 613
Gettlegfinger, Herman E., Chief Fin. Officer, Treas. & Sec.--Pride Oil Co., Inc., Knoxville, TN; *U.S. Private*, pg. 613
Getz, Herbert, Sr. V.P., Gen. Counsel & Sec.--Waste Management, Inc., Oak Brook, IL; *U.S. Public*, pg. 1744
Getz, Janie, Sec.--Berryman Products, Inc., Arlington, TX; *U.S. Private*, pg. 138
Getzler, Michael J., V.P. & Attorney--The Dime Savings Bank of New York, New York, NY; *U.S. Public*, pg. 509
Geurin, Lynn K., Chief Fin. Officer, Exec. V.P. & Sec.--Resource Mortgage Capital, Inc., Glen Allen, VA; *U.S. Public*, pg. 1382
Geyer, Troy, Controller, Treas. & Sec.--Antenna Products Corp., Mineral Wells, TX; *U.S. Public*, pg. 289
Ghiz, Sally, Sec.--Paddock Pool Construction Co., Inc., Scottsdale, AZ; *U.S. Private*, pg. 833
Giannavla, John, V.P. & Sec.--T-NETIX, Inc., Englewood, CO; *U.S. Public*, pg. 1553
Giard, A., V.P.-Law & Sec.--Canadian National Railway Company, Montreal, Canada; *Int'l*, pg. 258
Giarrusso, Raymond J., Treas. & Sec.--GAI Consultants, Inc., Monroeville, PA; *U.S. Private*, pg. 433
Gibb, Bradley, Treas. & Sec.--Robert Gibb & Sons, Inc., Fargo, ND; *U.S. Private*, pg. 451
Gibbes, A.H., Asst. Sec.--South Carolina Electric & Gas Co. (SCE&G), Columbia, SC; *U.S. Public*, pg. 1436
Gibbons, Dale M., Exec. V.P.-Fin. & Sec.--Zions Bancorporation, Salt Lake City, UT; *U.S. Public*, pg. 1792
Gibbons, Dale M., Exec. V.P.-Fin. & Sec.--Zions First National Bank, Salt Lake City, UT; *U.S. Public*, pg. 1793
Gibbons, Gregg M., V.P.-Corp. Affairs, Gen. Counsel & Sec.--Wynn's International, Inc., Orange, CA; *U.S. Public, pg. 1782*
Gibbs, A.H., Asst. Sec.--MPX Systems, Inc., Cayce, SC; *U.S. Public*, pg. 1436
Gibbs, Brian, Sec.--Taunton Cider Company P.L.C., Taunton, United Kingdom; *Int'l*, pg. 849
Gibbs, Kathleen, Sec.--Willis Corroon Melling Ltd., Vancouver, Canada; *Int'l*, pg. 1509
Gibert, F.J., Sec.--Consolidated Companies Inc. (CONCO), Metairie, LA; *U.S. Private*, pg. 265
Gibson, B. Baird, Sec. & Treas.--Patterson Pump Company, Toccoa, GA; *U.S. Public*, pg. 754
Gibson, Beverly A., Asst. Sec.--Pier 1 Imports, Inc., Fort Worth, TX; *U.S. Public*, pg. 1295
Gibson, Cynthia, Treas. & Sec.--Wolcott & Lincoln, Inc., Kansas City, MO; *U.S. Private*, pg. 1185
Gibson, David, Sec.--Rexam PLC, London, United Kingdom; *Int'l*, pg. 1106
Gibson, Drue, Corp. Sec.--Lewis Brothers Bakeries, Inc., Evansville, IN; *U.S. Private*, pg. 665
Gibson, Kathleen M., V.P. & Sec.--Honeywell Inc., Minneapolis, MN; *U.S. Public*, pg. 833
Gibson, N.M., Sec. & Treas.--Synergistics Chemicals, Inc., Mississauga, Canada; *U.S. Public*, pg. 734
Gibson, Russell G., Chief Fin. Officer, Exec. V.P., Treas. & Asst. Sec.--Farah Incorporated, El Paso, TX; *U.S. Public, pg. 612*
Gielow, Ronald W., Asst. Sec.--Paul Mueller Company, Springfield, MO; *U.S. Public*, pg. 1141
Giessert, Lisa B., Sec.--The New Piper Aircraft, Inc., Vero Beach, FL; *U.S. Private*, pg. 794
Gifford, S., Sec. & Dir.-Investor Rels.--Tate & Lyle PLC, London, United Kingdom; *Int'l*, pg. 1356
Giglio, Jean, Sec.--The Gazette Company, Cedar Rapids, IA; *U.S. Private*, pg. 442
Gilbane, Robert V., Sec.--Gilbane Building Company, Providence, RI; *U.S. Private*, pg. 452
Gilbert, James B., Sec.--King & Prince Seafood Corporation, Brunswick, GA; *U.S. Private*, pg. 620
Gilbert, James F., Gen. Counsel & Sec.--PrimeEnergy Corporation, Stamford, CT; *U.S. Public*, pg. 1328
Gilbert, Martin G., Asst. Gen. Counsel & Asst Sec.--Wal-Mart Stores, Inc., Bentonville, AR; *U.S. Public*, pg. 1732
Gilbert, Richard D., Chief Fin. Officer, Treas. & Sec.--The Converse Professional Group, Inc., Monrovia, CA; *U.S. Private*, pg. 271
Gilbertson, Jay, Pres., Co-Chief Oper. Officer, Chief Fin. Officer, Treas. & Sec.--HBOC, Atlanta, GA; *U.S. Public*, pg. 770
Gilchrist, David, Sec. & Dir.-Corp. Affairs--Halifax plc, Halifax, United Kingdom; *Int'l*, pg. 589
Gilchrist, Henry, Sec.--Kirby Corporation, Houston, TX; *U.S. Public*, pg. 961
Gill, Elliot, Asst. Sec.--Equitable Resources, Inc., Pittsburgh, PA; *U.S. Public*, pg. 589
Gill, Margaret, Sr. V.P.-Legal & External Affairs & Corp. Sec.--AirTouch Communications, Inc., San Francisco, CA; *U.S. Public*, pg. 34
Gill, Nicholas P., Chief Fin. Officer, V.P., Treas. & Sec.--The Union Corporation, Greenwich, CT; *U.S. Public*, pg. 1667
Gill, Peter, Grp. Dir.-Fin. & Sec.--Dorling Kindersley Holdings plc, London, United Kingdom; *Int'l*, pg. 416
Gille, Lori-Jean, J.D., Sr. V.P., Gen. Counsel & Sec.--MGI PHARMA INC., Minneapolis, MN; *U.S. Public*, pg. 1026
Gillespie, Carol J., V.P., Gen. Counsel & Sec.--The Liposome Company, Inc., Princeton, NJ; *U.S. Public*, pg. 1000
Gillespie, Carol J., V.P. & Sec.--Syntex, Palo Alto, CA; *Int'l*, pg. 1120
Gillespie, Suzanne, Sec.--Poughkeepsie Financial Corp., Poughkeepsie, NY; *U.S. Public*, pg. 1319
Gillespie, Suzanne, Sec.--Bank of the Hudson, Poughkeepsie, NY; *U.S. Public*, pg. 1319
Gillig, Stephen R., Pres., Chief Admin. Officer & Sec.--Fort Wayne National Corporation, Fort Wayne, IN; *U.S. Public*, pg. 673
Gillig, Stephen R., Sec.--Fort Wayne National Bank, Fort Wayne, IN; *U.S. Public*, pg. 674
Gillman, Stephen J., V.P.-Admin. & Asst. Sec.--Rust-Oleum Corporation, Vernon Hills, IL; *U.S. Public*, pg. 1358
Gilmer, Jill A., Sec.--International Murex Technologies Corporation, Guelph, Canada; *Int'l*, pg. 684
Gilmore, Bruce W., V.P., Controller & Sec.--Marquette Bancshares Inc., Minneapolis, MN; *U.S. Private*, pg. 706
Gilmour, Ian M., Grp. Corp. Sec.--Goodman Fielder Limited, Sydney, Australia; *Int'l*, pg. 555
Gilpin, John D., Sr. V.P. & Sec.--Lyman Lumber Company, Excelsior, MN; *U.S. Private*, pg. 683
Gilreath, Thomas M., Corp. Controller & Asst. Sec.--Texfi Industries, Inc., Raleigh, NC; *U.S. Public*, pg. 1588
Gilvar, Barry S., Sec.--Liberty Mutual Insurance Co., Boston, MA; *U.S. Private*, pg. 666
Gimbel, Hermann, Dr., Sec.--Von Roll AG, Gerlafingen, Switzerland; *Int'l*, pg. 1480
Ginebra, Jose Alb., Corp. Sec., Bus.-to-Bus. Consultant & New Bus. Contact--Publicitaria Cumbre, Santo Domingo, Dominican Republic; *U.S. Public*, pg. 1422
Giner, Fernando Liopis, Sec.--AHM ALTOS HORNOS DEL MEDITERRANEO, S.A., Sagunto, Spain; *Int'l*, pg. 1223
Ginn, David K., Gen. Counsel & Sec.--Oxford Industries, Inc., Atlanta, GA; *U.S. Public*, pg. 1239
Ginn, William D., Sec.--Nordson Corporation, Westlake, OH; *U.S. Public*, pg. 1188
Ginns, Daniel, Chm. Bd., Chief Exec. Officer & Corp. Sec.--Datametrics Corporation, Calabasas, CA; *U.S. Public*, pg. 487
Ginsberg, Michael, Sec. & Treas.--F.T. Publications Inc., New York, NY; *Int'l*, pg. 1026
Ginsburg, George B., V.P., Treas. & Sec.--Money Point Diamond Co., Chesapeake, VA; *U.S. Private*, pg. 757
Gioimo, Suzzanne J., Sec.--Nalco Chemical Company, Naperville, IL; *U.S. Public*, pg. 1150
Giordano, Alberto, Sec.--Banca di Roma, Rome, Italy; *Int'l*, pg. 135
Giorgi, Frederick, Sec.--Can Corporation of America, Blandon, PA; *U.S. Private*, pg. 204
Giorgi, G., Sec.--Hotel Cipriani S.p.A., Venice, Italy; *Int'l*, pg. 1214
Giovanetti, Crystal, Exec. Sec.--PYA/Monarch, Inc., Greenville, SC; *U.S. Public*, pg. 1433
Gisler, R.F., Asst. Sec.--Pitt-Des Moines, Inc., Pittsburgh, PA; *U.S. Public*, pg. 1304
Gittelman, Milton, Chief Exec. Officer, V.P, Treas. & Sec.--Triumph Pet Industries, Inc., Warwick, NY; *U.S. Private*, pg. 1104
Giuliani, John, Treas. & Sec.--Lodal, Inc., Kingsford, MI; *U.S. Private*, pg. 672
Givler, Robert C., Controller & Asst. Sec.--Ward Trucking Corp., Altoona, PA; *U.S. Private*, pg. 1149
Givler, Robert R., Asst. Sec.--Ward Trucking Corp., Altoona, PA; *U.S. Private*, pg. 1149

Glade, John F., V.P.-Engrng. & Mfg. & Sec.--Alpha Microsystems, Santa Ana, CA; *U.S. Public*, pg. 57

Glantz, Miles M., Gen. Counsel & Sec.--Wechco, Inc., Princeton, NJ; *U.S. Private*, pg. 1158

Glascoe, Rosalyn B., Sec.--Mississippi Chemical Corporation, Yazoo City, MS; *U.S. Public*, pg. 1117

Glass, Dee Dee, Dir.-Tax & Asst. Sec.--Robertson-Ceco Corporation, San Ramon, CA; *U.S. Public*, pg. 1394

Glass, Susan J., Asst. Sec. & Asst. Gen. Counsel--Allergan, Inc., Irvine, CA; *U.S. Public*, pg. 46

Glassett, Tim, Sr. V.P. & Sec.--H.F. Ahmanson & Co., Irwindale, CA; *U.S. Public*, pg. 29

Gleason, E.M., Controller, Corp. Treas. & Sec.--Wisconsin Power & Light Company, Madison, WI; *U.S. Public*, pg. 1728

Gleason, Edward M., V.P., Treas. & Corp. Sec.--WPL Holdings, Inc., Madison, WI; *U.S. Public*, pg. 1727

Gleason, Edward M., V.P., Controller, Treas. & Corp. Sec.--South Beloit Water, Gas & Electric Co., South Beloit, IL; *U.S. Public*, pg. 1728

Gleason, Edward M., Sec.--REAC, Inc., Madison, WI; *U.S. Public*, pg. 1728

Gleason, Edward M., Asst. Corp. Sec.--Heartland Development Corporation, Madison, WI; *U.S. Public*, pg. 1728

Gleitz, Janet J., Corp. Sec. & Dir.-Investor Rels.--Ryan's Family Steak Houses, Inc., Greer, SC; *U.S. Public*, pg. 1413

Glendening, R. Bradley, Sr. V.P., Sec. & Gen. Counsel--Mary Kay Corporation, Dallas, TX; *U.S. Private*, pg. 710

Glenn, John M., V.P., Gen. Counsel & Sec.--Roadway Express, Inc., Akron, OH; *U.S. Public*, pg. 1392

Glenn, William E., Exec. V.P., Sec. & Acct. Exec.--Willis Corroon Corp. of Knoxville, Knoxville, TN; *Int'l*, pg. 1506

Glessner, Dave, Chief Fin. Officer & Sec.--Agsco, Inc., Grand Forks, ND; *U.S. Private*, pg. 27

Glick, C.S., Chief Fin. Officer, Sr. V.P. & Sec.--Gulf Canada Resources Ltd., Calgary, Canada; *Int'l*, pg. 577

Glorioso, S., Dir. & Asst. Sec.--Lucas Industries Inc., Buffalo, NY; *Int'l*, pg. 820

Gluck, Jerry M., Sec.--Jefferies Group, Inc., Los Angeles, CA; *U.S. Public*, pg. 924

Glynn, John J., Treas. & Sec.--Baird, Patrick & Co., Inc., New York, NY; *U.S. Private*, pg. 111

Glynn, Terry, Treas. & Sec.--Select Canfield, Chicago, IL; *U.S. Private*, pg. 982

Gnat, Albert, Sec.--CCL Industries, Inc., Willowdale, Canada; *Int'l*, pg. 238

Gobris, Joseph J., Asst. Sec. & Asst. Treas.--Voest-Alpine International Corporation, New York, NY; *Int'l*, pg. 1470

Gockley, James M., Sec.--Mellon Bank Corporation, Pittsburgh, PA; *U.S. Public*, pg. 1084

Goddard, Larry, Chief Fin. Officer, Treas. & Sec.--P.A.M. Transport, Inc., Tontitown, AR; *U.S. Private*, pg. 825

Goddard, Linda, Corp. Sec. & Human Resources Dir.--Griffin Bacal Volny, Toronto, Canada; *U.S. Private*, pg. 480

Godefroid, Alain, Sec.--Union Miniere, Brussels, Belgium; *Int'l*, pg. 1441

Godfrey, Cullen M., Sr. V.P., Gen. Counsel & Sec.--Fina, Inc., Dallas, TX; *Int'l*, pg. 1044

Godfrey, Robert, Treas. & Sec.--Central States Enterprises, Inc., Heathrow, FL; *U.S. Private*, pg. 225

Godiner, Donald L., Sr. V.P., Gen. Counsel & Sec.--Laclede Gas Company, Saint Louis, MO; *U.S. Public*, pg. 973

Godts, Benoit, Corp. Sec.--Bernheim-Comofi, Brussels, Belgium; *Int'l*, pg. 562

Goebel, A.E., Treas. & Sec.--Energy Systems Group, Inc., Evansville, IN; *U.S. Public*, pg. 1471

Goebel, A.E., Treas. & Sec.--ComSource, Inc., Evansville, IN; *U.S. Public*, pg. 1471

Goebel, Andrew E., Chief Fin. Officer, Sr. V.P. & Sec.--SIGCORP, Inc., Evansville, IN; *U.S. Public*, pg. 1471

Goebel, Janice R., Corp. Sec.--Kraus-Anderson Incorporated, Minneapolis, MN; *U.S. Private*, pg. 635

Goebel, Janice R., Sec.--Kraus-Anderson, Incorporated, Minneapolis, MN; *U.S. Private*, pg. 635

Goedde, Ronald J., Chief Fin. Officer, Exec. V.P. & Sec.--Cornerstone Propane G.P. Inc., Watsonville, CA; *U.S. Public*, pg. 1201

Goedecke, Barbara, V.P. & Sec.--Otto Goedecke, Inc., Houston, TX; *U.S. Private*, pg. 458

Goedert, Philip H., Sec. & Treas.--Design-Build West, Denver, CO; *U.S. Private*, pg. 905

Goeller, Michael C., Sec. & Gen. Counsel--Hatzel & Buehler, Inc., Wilmington, DE; *U.S. Private*, pg. 266

Goellner, Alfred O., Asst. Sec.--JC Penney Company, Inc., Plano, TX; *U.S. Public*, pg. 916

Goforth, Rene, Pres., Treas. & Sec.--Hilb, Rogal and Hamilton Company of Victoria, Victoria, TX; *U.S. Public*, pg. 827

Goguel, Claude, Sec.--Alcatel Cit (S.A.), Velizy-Villacoublay, France; *Int'l*, pg. 56

Goh, Derek, Gen. Counsel & Sec.--Hai Sun Hup Group Ltd., Singapore, Singapore; *Int'l*, pg. 586

Gohmann, John R., Chief Oper. Officer, V.P., Sec. & Dir.-Pur.--Gohmann Asphalt & Construction Inc., Clarksville, IN; *U.S. Private*, pg. 459

Gohn, Joseph M., Asst. Sec.--Catherines Stores Corporation, Memphis, TN; *U.S. Public*, pg. 317

Goldberg, Cindy, Treas. & Sec.--FDP Corp., Miami, FL; *U.S. Public*, pg. 603

Goldberg, David S., V.P., Gen. Counsel & Sec.--InterTAN Inc., Fort Worth, TX; *U.S. Public*, pg. 910

Goldberg, Eileen, Asst. Sec.--National Income Realty Trust, New York, NY; *U.S. Public*, pg. 1157

Goldberg, Eileen, Asst. Sec.--Tarragon Realty Investors, Dallas, TX; *U.S. Public*, pg. 1561

Goldberg, Larry, Gen. Counsel & Sec.--Gemstar International Group Limited, Pasadena, CA; *U.S. Public*, pg. 705

Goldberg, Marvin A., Sr. Exec. V.P.-Legal & Corp. Affairs & Sec.--Shoppers Drug Mart, Ltd., Toronto, Canada; *Int'l*, pg. 112

Goldberg, Sherman I., Exec. V.P., Gen. Counsel & Sec.--First Chicago NBD Corporation, Chicago, IL; *U.S. Public*, pg. 627

Goldblatt, Jay A., Assoc. Gen. Counsel & Asst. Sec.--Pubco Corporation, Cleveland, OH; *U.S. Public*, pg. 1339

Golden, David, Chief Fin. Officer, Treas. & Sec.--Stephen Gould Paper Co., Inc., Whippany, NJ; *U.S. Private*, pg. 467

Golden, Randal E., Exec. V.P. & Sec.--D.O.C. Optics Corporation, Southfield, MI; *U.S. Private*, pg. 305

Goldenberg, Victoria, Sec. & Treas.--Fashion Shop of Kentucky Inc., Louisville, KY; *U.S. Private*, pg. 397

Goldenetz, James D., Sec.--Modtech, Inc., Perris, CA; *U.S. Public*, pg. 1121

Goldings, Morris, Gen. Counsel & Sec.--Jet Spray Corp., Norwood, MA; *U.S. Private*, pg. 586

Goldman, Bertha, Sec.--Farmland Dairies, Wallington, NJ; *U.S. Private*, pg. 395

Goldman, C. David, Sec. & Clerk--George E. Warren Corporation, Vero Beach, FL; *U.S. Private*, pg. 1151

Goldman, Charles, Sec.--Seaboard Flour Corporation, Newton, MA; *U.S. Public*, pg. 1449

Goldman, Donald L., V.P. & Sec.--Management Recruiters International, Inc., Cleveland, OH; *U.S. Public*, pg. 277

Goldman, Marilyn S., Exec. V.P., Treas. & Sec.--S.I. Goldman Co., Longwood, FL; *U.S. Private*, pg. 461

Goldsmith, Harry L., Gen. Counsel & Sec.--AutoZone, Inc., Memphis, TN; *U.S. Public*, pg. 150

Goldsmith, Lee, Asst. Sec. & Controller--Familian Corp., Van Nuys, CA; *Int'l*, pg. 1512

Goldstein, Barry J., Chief Fin. Officer, Exec. V.P.-Fin. & Sec.--Office Depot Inc., Delray Beach, FL; *U.S. Public*, pg. 1212

Goldstein, Dennis B., Corp. Counsel & Asst. Sec.--Homestake Mining Company, San Francisco, CA; *U.S. Public*, pg. 832

Goldstein, Marlene Kaplan, Sec.--Advanced Magnetics, Inc., Cambridge, MA; *U.S. Public*, pg. 20

Goldstein, Norman R., V.P., Treas. & Asst. Sec.--Barton Incorporated, Chicago, IL; *U.S. Public*, pg. 300

Golias, Ann, Sec.--Helena Laboratories Corporation, Beaumont, TX; *U.S. Private*, pg. 519

Golik, Donald E., Chief Fin. Officer, Sr. V.P. & Sec.--Paul Mueller Company, Springfield, MO; *U.S. Public*, pg. 1141

Golovin, Jonathan J., Chm. Bd. & Sec.--Consilium, Inc., Mountain View, CA; *U.S. Public*, pg. 434

Gonda, Louis L., Exec. V.P. & Sec.--International Lease Finance Corporation, Los Angeles, CA; *U.S. Public*, pg. 85

Gonge, Scott, Sec.--Troy Corporation, Florham Park, NJ; *U.S. Private*, pg. 1105

Gonopolsky, Allan, Chief Fin. Officer, V.P., Controller & Asst. Sec.--Rexel, Inc., Coral Gables, FL; *Int'l*, pg. 1107

Gonzales, Alice Kaeslin, Sec.--Alpine Packing Company, Stockton, CA; *U.S. Private*, pg. 45

Gonzalez, Andrea, Corp. Sec.--Viceversa/Young & Rubicam, Montevideo, Uruguay; *U.S. Private*, pg. 1200

Gonzalez, C., Treas., Sec. & Pur. Agent--Villazon Company Inc., Upper Saddle River, NJ; *U.S. Private*, pg. 1140

Gonzalez, Jose Cue, Sec.--Hulleras Del Norte, S.A. (HUNOSA), Asturias, Spain; *Int'l*, pg. 639

Gonzalez, Rafael Lozano, Sec. General--Amper, S.A., Madrid, Spain; *Int'l*, pg. 1372

Gonzalez, Richard J., Chief Fin. Officer, V.P., Treas. & Sec.--Bayou Steel Corporation, La Place, LA; *U.S. Public*, pg. 197

Good, Charles E., V.P.--Snyder's of Hanover, Inc., Hanover, PA; *U.S. Private*, pg. 1011

Goodell, Brenda, Treas. & Sec.--Willard Grain & Feed, Inc., Celina, TX; *U.S. Private*, pg. 1177

Goodenough, Adrian J., Sec.--Alliance UniChem PLC, Chessington, United Kingdom; *Int'l*, pg. 57

Goodfriend, Herbert J., Vice Chm. & Sec.--Jones Apparel Group, Inc., Bristol, PA; *U.S. Public*, pg. 933

Goodger, John V., V.P., Treas. & Asst. Sec.--Pioneer-Standard Electronics, Inc., Cleveland, OH; *U.S. Public*, pg. 1300

Goodkind, Conrad G., Corp. Sec.--Cade Industries, Inc., Lansing, MI; *U.S. Public*, pg. 289

Goodman, Dorothy, Sec.--Goodmans, Inc., Phoenix, AZ; *U.S. Private*, pg. 464

Goodman, James A., Gen. Counsel & Sec.--Day & Zimmermann, Inc., Philadelphia, PA; *U.S. Private*, pg. 316

Goodman, Michael R., V.P.-Fin. & Sec.--City Machine Tool & Die Company, Inc., Muncie, IN; *U.S. Private*, pg. 241

Goodman, Robert, Corp. Sec.--Telxon Corporation, Akron, OH; *U.S. Public*, pg. 1573

Goodman, Roy B., Sr. V.P.-Fin., Sec. & Treas.--Heilig-Meyers Company, Richmond, VA; *U.S. Public*, pg. 804

Goodman, Stanley, Sec.--Winstar Global Products, Inc., Fairfield, NJ; *U.S. Public*, pg. 1772

Goodrich, H.L., Sec. & Gen. Counsel--Dan River Inc., Danville, VA; *U.S. Public*, pg. 478

Goodwin, Tevor J., Chief Fin. Officer, Company Sec. & Dir.--Norton Healthcare Limited, Harlow, United Kingdom; *U.S. Public*, pg. 915

Goody, Alycia, Gen Counsel & Sec.--Providence Energy Corporation, Providence, RI; *U.S. Public*, pg. 1337

Goodyear, Clarice Cato, Exec. V.P. & Asst. Sec.--The Cato Corporation, Charlotte, NC; *U.S. Public*, pg. 318

Goodyear, E.D., Treas. & Sec.--Dispatch Consumer Services, Westerville, OH; *U.S. Private*, pg. 335

Goossen, Dean H., Sec.--USG Corporation, Chicago, IL; *U.S. Public*, pg. 1660

Gordan, Cynthia, V.P.-Human Resources & Legal Counsel--Quaker Fabric Corporation, Fall River, MA; *U.S. Public*, pg. 1347

Gordon, Amy, Sec.--The Eastern Company, Naugatuck, CT; *U.S. Public*, pg. 548

Gordon, B. Diane, V.P.-Fin., Treas. & Sec.--Buckeye Corrugated Inc., Wooster, OH; *U.S. Private*, pg. 177

Gordon, John, Jr., Sec. & Mgr.-Fin.--Gordon Food Service Inc., Grand Rapids, MI; *U.S. Private*, pg. 465

Gordon, Richard, Sec., Treas. & Controller--Vital Signs, Inc., Totowa, NJ; *U.S. Public*, pg. 1723

Gordon, S. Amber, Sec.--Hadron, Inc., Alexandria, VA; *U.S. Public*, pg. 773

Gordonsmith, John A., Exec. V.P.-Treasury, Legal & Corp. Sec.--FCA International Ltd., Westmount, Canada; *Int'l*, pg. 470

Gore, Genevieve W., Dr., Treas. & Sec.--W.L. Gore & Associates, Inc., Newark, DE; *U.S. Private*, pg. 465

Gore, H. Gearl, Sec.--Republic Security Financial Corporation, West Palm Beach, FL; *U.S. Public*, pg. 1381

Gore, John, Sec.--IPC Magazines Limited, London, United Kingdom; *Int'l*, pg. 651

Gorham, William, Gen. Counsel & Sec.--Zoll Medical Corporation, Burlington, MA; *U.S. Private*, pg. 1207

Gorham, William H., Sec.--UniFirst Corporation, Wilmington, MA; *U.S. Public*, pg. 1665

Gorin, Robert S., Sr. V.P., Gen. Counsel & Sec.--W.R. Berkley Corporation, Greenwich, CT; *U.S. Public*, pg. 215

Goss, Gary S., Sec.--Bay Area Bancshares, Redwood City, CA; *U.S. Private*, pg. 124

Gossett, Darrell, Exec. V.P., Sec. & Treas.--Ermco, Inc., Indianapolis, IN; *U.S. Private*, pg. 381

Gotkin, Michael S., Sr. V.P. & Gen. Counsel--Farley Candy Company, Chicago, IL; *U.S. Private*, pg. 397

Gotschall, George D., Asst. Sec.--Sifco Industries, Inc., Cleveland, OH; *U.S. Public*, pg. 1470

Gottesman, Joel, Sr. V.P. Gen. Counsel & Sec.--Green Tree Financial Corporation, Saint Paul, MN; *U.S. Public*, pg. 761

Gould, Douglas S., V.P. & Sec.--Citation National Insurance Company, San Jose, CA; *U.S. Public*, pg. 376

Gowan, Anne L., Sec.--Community Cash Stores, Spartanburg, SC; *U.S. Private*, pg. 259

Gowan, Bruce W., Chief Fin. Officer & Sec.--Magellan Aerospace Corporation, Mississauga, Canada; *Int'l*, pg. 829

Gower, E.D., Chief Fin. Officer, V.P.-Fin. & Sec.--Farnam Companies, Inc., Phoenix, AZ; *U.S. Private*, pg. 396

Gowland, Karen, V.P., Corp. Sec. & Asst. Gen. Counsel--Boise Cascade Corporation, Boise, ID; *U.S. Public*, pg. 242

Goyal, Prabhat, Chief Fin. Officer & V.P.-Fin.--Network Associates, Inc., Santa Clara, CA; *U.S. Public*, pg. 1168

Gozo, Sara J., V.P. & Corp. Sec.--The Turner Corporation, New York, NY; *U.S. Public*, pg. 1645

Graafland, C.G.C. Hooft, Mr., Sec.--SHV Holdings N.V., Utrecht, Netherlands; *Int'l*, pg. 1154

Grabell, Neil S., Sr. V.P., Gen. Counsel & Sec.--QVC, Inc., West Chester, PA; *U.S. Private*, pg. 897

Grady, Elaine, Treas. & Sec.--Howards TV & Appliances, Inc., La Habra, CA; *U.S. Private*, pg. 543

Grady, Kevin, Mgr.-Credit--OmniQuip International, Inc., Port Washington, WI; *U.S. Private*, pg. 500

Grae, Gary, Treas. & Sec.--Parisi Inc./Royal Store Fixture, Philadelphia, PA; *U.S. Private*, pg. 839

Graff, M., Treas. & Sec.--Douglas Stephen Plastics, Inc., Paterson, NJ; *U.S. Private*, pg. 341

Graham, Brendan, Grp. Sec.--Avonmore Waterford Group plc, Killkenny, Ireland; *Int'l*, pg. 102

Graham, Jack, Mgr.-Corp. Communications--Ethyl Corporation, Richmond, VA; *U.S. Public*, pg. 595

Graham, Linda H., V.P. & Sec.--RPC Incorporated, Atlanta, GA; *U.S. Public*, pg. 1356

Graham, Rob-Roy, Chief Fin. Officer , Sec. & Controller--InterVoice, Inc., Dallas, TX; *U.S. Public*, pg. 910

Graham, William H., V.P., Gen. Counsel & Sec.--Bethlehem Steel Corporation, Bethlehem, PA; *U.S. Public*, pg. 226

Granander, June, Chief Fin. Officer & Sec.--Foster Products Corporation, Minneapolis, MN; *U.S. Public*, pg. 686

Grandle, Pat, Sec. & Mgr.-Mktg. & Adv.--Tricon Industries, Inc., Lisle, IL; *U.S. Private*, pg. 1102

Granicher, John W., Sr. V.P. & Sec. & Treas.--Keller & Gannon, San Francisco, CA; *U.S. Private*, pg. 626

Granoff, Gail P., Sec.--Rohm and Haas Company, Philadelphia, PA; *U.S. Public*, pg. 1403

Gransec, David H., Sec.--Eon Labs, Jamaica, NY; *U.S. Private*, pg. 379

Grant, D.A.G., Sec.--BIL (Far East Holdings) Ltd., Hong Kong, Hong Kong; *Int'l*, pg. 215

Grant, John, Jr., Corp. Sec.--Sealing Equipment Products Co., Inc., Pelham, AL; *U.S. Private*, pg. 978

Grant, K.N., Grp. Co. Sec.--Commercial Union plc, London, United Kingdom; *Int'l*, pg. 308

Grant, Laura, Sec.--ScotiaMocatta, New York, NY; *Int'l*, pg. 156

Grant, Philip J., Co. Sec. & Legal Counsel--Skandia UK Insurance plc, London, United Kingdom; *Int'l*, pg. 1258

Grant, Rhondda E.S., Sec.--Nova Corporation, Calgary, Canada; *Int'l*, pg. 971

Grantner, Francis J., Gen. Counsel & Sec.--Rieth-Riley Construction Co. Inc., Goshen, IN; *U.S. Private*, pg. 930

Granzier, Paul A., V.P., Gen. Counsel & Sec.--RPM, Inc., Medina, OH; *U.S. Public*, pg. 1356

Gratzke, Carol, Chief Fin. Officer--Cherokee Inc., Van Nuys, CA; *U.S. Public*, pg. 345

Graves, James T., Vice Chm., Gen. Counsel & Sec.--Mark VII, Inc., Memphis, TN; *U.S. Public*, pg. 1046

Graves, James T., Gen. Counsel & Sec.--Mark VII Transportation Company, Inc., Greenwood, IN; *U.S. Public*, pg. 1046

Graves, John E., Sec.--Elkay Manufacturing Company, Oak Brook, IL; *U.S. Private*, pg. 372

Graves, Ronald N., V.P., Gen. Counsel & Sec.--J.R. Simplot Company, Boise, ID; *U.S. Private*, pg. 1002

Graves, Walter H., Sec. & Treas.--Tecom Industries, Inc., Chatsworth, CA; *U.S. Public*, pg. 1563

Grawmeyer, Christine S., Asst. Corp. Sec.--UAL Corporation, Elk Grove Village, IL; *U.S. Public*, pg. 1652

Gray, Carol M., Sec.--Ludowici Roof Tile, Inc., New Lexington, OH; *Int'l*, pg. 1171

Gray, Carol M., Sec,--CertainTeed International, Inc., Valley Forge, PA; *Int'l*, pg. 1171

Gray, Carol M., Sec.--CertainTeed Ventures, Inc., Valley Forge, PA; *Int'l*, pg. 1171
Gray, Dawn M., Sec.--American Business Products, Inc., Atlanta, GA; *U.S. Public*, pg. 70
Gray, Franklin N., Exec. V.P., Treas. & Sec.--James N. Gray Construction Co., Inc., Lexington, KY; *U.S. Private*, pg. 472
Gray, Janet, Sec.--Jack Henry & Associates, Inc., Monett, MO; *U.S. Public*, pg. 808
Gray, Jay, Sec.--The Vapormatic Co. Ltd., Exeter, United Kingdom; *Int'l*, pg. 1512
Gray, Jeffrey E., Sr. Corp. Counsel & Asst. Sec.--Lowe's Companies, Inc., North Wilkesboro, NC; *U.S. Public*, pg. 1015
Gray, S. Garrett, Gen. Counsel & Sec.--Minerals Technologies, Inc., New York, NY; *U.S. Public*, pg. 1115
Grazian, David R., Dir.-Corp. Taxation & Asst. Sec.--Granite Construction Incorporated, Watsonville, CA; *U.S. Public*, pg. 759
Graziano, Anthony W., Jr., V.P., Gen. Counsel & Sec.--Stant Corporation, Denver, CO; *Int'l*, pg. 1396
Greb, Christine D., Asst. Sec.--Arthur J. Gallagher & Co., Itasca, IL; *U.S. Public*, pg. 698
Greco, Louis A., Chief Fin. Officer & Sec.--The Macneal-Schwendler Corp., Los Angeles, CA; *U.S. Public*, pg. 1030
Greco, Robert, Chief Tech. Officer, Treas. & Sec.--Active Voice Corporation, Seattle, WA; *U.S. Public*, pg. 17
Green, Albert, Sec.--I.C. Thomasson Associates, Inc., Nashville, TN; *U.S. Private*, pg. 1083
Green, Colin, Sec.--British Telecommunications plc, London, United Kingdom; *Int'l*, pg. 222
Green, David, Corp Sec.--Prudential Corporation PLC, London, United Kingdom; *Int'l*, pg. 1073
Green, John R., Treas. & Sec.--John E. Green Co., Detroit, MI; *U.S. Private*, pg. 477
Green, Joseph T., V.P., Gen. Counsel & Sec.--TCF Bank Minnesota FSB, Minneapolis, MN; *U.S. Public*, pg. 1554
Green, Nancy, Asst. Treas. & Asst. Sec.--Tab Products Co., Palo Alto, CA; *U.S. Public*, pg. 1559
Green, P.E., Grp. Sec.--Meggitt plc, Wimborne Minster, United Kingdom; *Int'l*, pg. 853
Green, Ronald, Sec.--Aven Tools Ltd., Rotherham, United Kingdom; *U.S. Public*, pg. 234
Green, Stewart E., V.P., Gen. Counsel & Sec.--George Weston Limited, Toronto, Canada; *Int'l*, pg. 1494
Green, Thomas B., Gen. Counsel & Sec.--Dell Computer Corporation, Round Rock, TX; *U.S. Public*, pg. 495
Green, Todd, V.P. & Asst. Sec.--The Acacia Group - Acacia Life Insurance Co., Bethesda, MD; *U.S. Private*, pg. 10
Green, William G., Esq., Sr. V.P., Gen. Counsel & Sec.--Chiron Corporation, Emeryville, CA; *U.S. Public*, pg. 349
Green, William T., Exec. V.P., Treas. & Sec.--Art's-Way Manufacturing Co., Inc., Armstrong, IA; *U.S. Public*, pg. 136
Greenberg, J., Sec.--Concert Communications Company, London, United Kingdom; *Int'l*, pg. 223
Greenberger, Joseph, Gen. Counsel & Sec.--Moore Medical Corp., New Britain, CT; *U.S. Public*, pg. 1128
Greenberger, Joseph, Sec.--Rexx Environmental Corp., New York, NY; *U.S. Public*, pg. 1384
Greenberger, Raymond S., Treas. & Asst. Sec.--AFA Protective Systems, Inc., Syosset, NY; *U.S. Public*, pg. 5
Greenblatt, Debra R., V.P. & Sec.--Vaughan & Sons, Inc., San Antonio, TX; *U.S. Private*, pg. 1134
Greene, Cindy, Asst. Sec.--The Dickerson Group, Inc., Monroe, NC; *U.S. Private*, pg. 331
Greene, Jerry W., Sec. & Treas.--Hanes Companies, Inc., Winston Salem, NC; *U.S. Public*, pg. 986
Greene, Julie, Sec.--CSP Inc., Billerica, MA; *U.S. Public*, pg. 283
Greene, Larry H., Sec.--Shoppers Drug Mart, Ltd., London, Canada; *Int'l*, pg. 112
Greenfield, Barry, V.P., Treas. & Sec.--Opus South Corporation, Tampa, FL; *U.S. Private*, pg. 818
Greenfield, Betty, V.P. & Sec.--Commonwealth Toy & Novelty Company, New York, NY; *U.S. Private*, pg. 258
Greenlee, David, Sec.--Ben E. Keith Company, Fort Worth, TX; *U.S. Private*, pg. 611
Greenlee, Elaine B., Treas. & Sec.--Circle Plastics Products, Inc., Circleville, OH; *U.S. Private*, pg. 240
Greenman, Ronald L., Sec.--Portland Food Products Company, Forest Grove, OR; *U.S. Private*, pg. 876
Greenspan, Joseph, Sec.--Masters, Inc., Westbury, NY; *U.S. Private*, pg. 714
Greenstein, Kenneth I., Sec.--Lexington Precision Corporation, New York, NY; *U.S. Public*, pg. 991
Greenwell, Daniel D., Chief Fin. Officer & Sec.--Zoltek Companies, Inc., Saint Louis, MO; *U.S. Public*, pg. 1794
Greer, Jane H., V.P. & Sec.--Delta Woodside Industries, Inc., Greenville, SC; *U.S. Public*, pg. 497
Greer, Jerry M., FLMI, Sr. V.P. & Sec.--Ethika Corporation, Hilton Head Island, SC; *U.S. Public*, pg. 595
Greer, Lawrence, Sec.--Dunn Investment Co., Birmingham, AL; *U.S. Private*, pg. 347
Greer, Robert A., V.P. & Sec.--Autry Greer & Sons, Inc., Prichard, AL; *U.S. Private*, pg. 479
Gregory, Dennis, Chief Fin. Officer & V.P.-Fin.--Woodcraft Industries, Inc., Saint Cloud, MN; *U.S. Private*, pg. 1187
Gregory, Steve, Treas. & Asst. Sec.--Binkley Company, Warrenton, MO; *U.S. Private*, pg. 534
Greiner, Charles L., Asst. Sec.--Modern American Life Insurance Company, Springfield, MO; *U.S. Public*, pg. 853
Greiner, Charles L., Sec. & Treas.--Western Pioneer Life Insurance Co., Louisville, KY; *U.S. Public*, pg. 853
Gress, Ken, Controller--Dempster Industries Inc., Beatrice, NE; *U.S. Private*, pg. 324
Grey, Robert J., Sr. V.P., Gen. Counsel & Sec.--PP&L Resources, Allentown, PA; *U.S. Public*, pg. 1244
Grey, Robert J., Sr. V.P., Gen. Counsel & Sec.--Pennsylvania Power & Light Company-Lehigh Div., Allentown, PA; *U.S. Public*, pg. 1244
Greyling, A.C., Gen. Mgr.-Legal & Admin. Services--Iscor, Pretoria, South Africa; *Int'l*, pg. 688
Griffin, LaDeane, Chief Fin. Officer, Treas. Controller & Sec.--Jenkins & Associates, Shawnee Mission, KS; *U.S. Private*, pg. 585
Griffin, Marna W., Sec.--Griffin Transport Services, Inc., Sparks, NV; *U.S. Private*, pg. 481
Griffin, Thomas A., Treas. & Controller--Pope Resources, Poulsbo, WA; *U.S. Public*, pg. 1317
Griffin, William E., Sec.--Precision Valve Corporation, Yonkers, NY; *U.S. Private*, pg. 880
Griffith, Brian, Sec. & Gen. Counsel--MFA Incorporated, Columbia, MO; *U.S. Private*, pg. 686
Griffith, G. Sanders, III, Sr. Exec. V.P., Gen. Counsel & Sec.--Synovus Financial Corp., Columbus, GA; *U.S. Public*, pg. 1548
Griffith, Robert, V.P., Treas. & Sec.--The Chas. H. Lilly Co., Portland, OR; *U.S. Private*, pg. 667
Griffith, Ronald L., Sr., Chief Fin. Officer, Sr. V.P.-Fin., Treas. & Sec.--Burnham, Lancaster, PA; *U.S. Public*, pg. 270
Griffiths, D.J., Sec.--Unitech Plc, Reading, United Kingdom; *Int'l*, pg. 1241
Griffiths, P.L., Sec.--SEIKO Australia Pty. Ltd., Sydney, Australia; *Int'l*, pg. 1218
Griggs, Forest, Jr., Sec.--Jack Griggs Inc., Exeter, CA; *U.S. Private*, pg. 482
Grillo, Robert T., Exec. V.P., Treas. & Sec.--General Office Environments Inc., Rochelle Park, NJ; *U.S. Private*, pg. 445
Grimes, James A., Controller & Sec.--Sanderson Farms, Inc., Laurel, MS; *U.S. Public*, pg. 1430
Grimes, T.N., Sec.--Bardon Group PLC, Solihull, United Kingdom; *Int'l*, pg. 166
Grimley, Robert, Treas. & Sec.--Duo-Fast Corporation, Huntley, IL; *U.S. Private*, pg. 347
Grimmer, Rose J., Sec.--Grimmer Realty Co. Inc., Birmingham, AL; *U.S. Private*, pg. 482
Grimsley, Janet T., Sec.--Tri-Can International, Ltd., Alsip, IL; *U.S. Public*, pg. 1022
Grimstad, John A., Gen. Counsel & Sec.--Waters Instruments, Inc., Rochester, MN; *U.S. Public*, pg. 1745
Grimwade, Fred S., Sec. & Gen. Mgr.-Share Holder Rels.--Western Mining Corporation Holdings Limited, Southbank, Australia; *Int'l*, pg. 1494
Grinsley, Janet T., Treas. & Sec.--Lynch Machinery, Inc., Bainbridge, GA; *U.S. Public*, pg. 1022
Grinstein, Jeffrey M., Exec. V.P., Gen. Counsel, & Sec.--American Waste Services, Inc., Warren, OH; *U.S. Public*, *pg. 94*
Griswold, James B., Sec.--Keithley Instruments, Inc., Cleveland, OH; *U.S. Public*, pg. 946
Gritchen, Lyle S., Sr. V.P., Gen. Counsel & Sec.--Qual-Med, Inc., Pueblo, CO; *U.S. Public*, pg. 678
Grobbel, Mark A., Asst. Sec.--Frank's Nursery & Crafts, Inc., Detroit, MI; *U.S. Public*, pg. 715
Grobman, Richard, Dir. & Sec.--Key Food Stores Co-operative, Inc., Brooklyn, NY; *U.S. Private*, pg. 617
Groce, R.T., Sec.--IDenticard Systems, Inc., Lancaster, PA; *U.S. Private*, pg. 557
Groen, Keith C., V.P.-Legal & Sec.--Aaron Rents, Inc., Atlanta, GA; *U.S. Public*, pg. 12
Groetzinger, Jon, Jr., Sr. V.P., Gen. Counsel & Sec.--American Greetings Corporation, Cleveland, OH; *U.S. Public*, pg. 77
Grogan, Alice W., Sec.--Wachovia Corporation, Winston Salem, NC; *U.S. Public*, pg. 1730
Grogan, Ed, Corp. Sec.--Environment/One Corporation, Niskayuna, NY; *U.S. Public*, pg. 586
Grondahl, Tom, Sec.--Den norske Bank ASA, Oslo, Norway; *Int'l*, pg. 392
Gronningsaeter, Marius H., Sr. V.P.-Legal, Gen. Counsel & Sec.--Elkem ASA, Oslo, Norway; *Int'l*, pg. 446
Groom, Gary L., Exec. V.P.-Fin. & Sec.--Coachmen Industries, Inc., Elkhart, IN; *U.S. Public*, pg. 387
Groom, Michael, Exec. Sec.--United Dairymen of Arizona, Tempe, AZ; *U.S. Private*, pg. 1121
Grose, Brian C., V.P., Controller & Sec.--Hudson's Bay Company, Toronto, Canada; *Int'l*, pg. 637
Gross, Bennett S., V.P., Gen. Counsel & Sec.--Caldor, Inc., Norwalk, CT; *U.S. Public*, pg. 292
Gross, Donald, Treas. & Sec.--Dan's Supreme Super Markets Inc., Hempstead, NY; *U.S. Private*, pg. 310
Gross, Donald W., Sec.--Genovese Drug Stores, Inc., Melville, NY; *U.S. Public*, pg. 730
Gross, Douglas H., V.P., Gen. Counsel & Sec.--Computer Language Research, Inc., Carrollton, TX; *U.S. Public*, pg. 421
Gross, Lawrence A., V.P., Gen. Counsel & Sec.--SunGard Data Systems Inc., Wayne, PA; *U.S. Public*, pg. 1534
Gross, Murray, Sr. V.P., Gen. Counsel & Clerk--EG & G, Inc., Wellesley, MA; *U.S. Public*, pg. 542
Gross, Richard B., Sr. V.P., Gen. Counsel & Sec.--AMBAC Financial Group, Inc., New York, NY; *U.S. Public*, pg. 62
Gross, Stephen, Sec.--The Wet Seal, Inc., Irvine, CA; *U.S. Public*, pg. 1763
Grossenburg, Blanche, Sec.--Grossenburg Implements, Incorporated, Winner, SD; *U.S. Private*, pg. 483
Grossman, Richard D., Treas. & Sec.--Therm, Inc., Ithaca, NY; *U.S. Private*, pg. 1079
Grossman, Stanley H., Exec. V.P. & Sec.--Catherines Stores Corporation, Memphis, TN; *U.S. Public*, pg. 317
Grossmann, Ralph L., Sec.--The Reliable Life Insurance Company, Webster Groves, MO; *U.S. Public*, pg. 1374
Grove, Ray, Sec.--California Fresh Apricot Council, San Francisco, CA; *U.S. Private*, pg. 200
Grow, David R., Chief Oper. & Fin. Officer & Exec. V.P.--Daw Technologies, Inc., Salt Lake City, UT; *U.S. Public*, pg. 489
Growcott, Carm, Exec. Sec.--Streamlight Inc., Norristown, PA; *U.S. Private*, pg. 1047
Grubbe, K.S., Chief Fin. Officer, Grp. V.P.-Fin. & Asst. Sec.--Ag Processing Inc., A Cooperative, Omaha, NE; *U.S. Private*, pg. 26
Grubek, Vita A., Sec.--Pioneer Life Insurance Co. of Illinois, Rockford, IL; *U.S. Public*, pg. 434
Grubman, Clay H., Sec.--Media Printing Corporation, Pompano Beach, FL; *U.S. Private*, pg. 726
Gruenewald, Dolores, Corp. Secretary--Etec Systems, Inc., Hayward, CA; *U.S. Public*, pg. 594
Grupka, Richard A., Treas. & Sec.--John W. Danforth Co., Buffalo, NY; *U.S. Private*, pg. 309
Guarisco, John, Treas & Sec.--Berwick Bay Oil Co. Inc., Morgan City, LA; *U.S. Private*, pg. 138
Guarriello, Joseph L., Exec. V.P., Gen. Counsel & Sec.--Mid Atlantic Medical Services, Inc., Rockville, MD; *U.S. Public*, pg. 1109
Guber, Alfred M., V.P.-Fin. & Admin.--John Dusenbery Co., Inc., Randolph, NJ; *U.S. Private*, pg. 349
Gubman, Irwin L., Gen. Counsel & Sec.--Imperial Credit Industries, Inc., Torrance, CA; *U.S. Public*, pg. 872
Guccione, Anthony, Treas. & Sec.--General Media International Inc., New York, NY; *U.S. Private*, pg. 444
Gudors, Sandra, Dir.-Mktg.--McAlpin's, Cincinnati, OH; *U.S. Public*, pg. 1090
Guedry, James W., V.P. & Sec.--International Paper Company, Purchase, NY; *U.S. Public*, pg. 901
Guedry, James W., V.P. & Sec.--IP Timberlands, Ltd., Purchase, NY; *U.S. Public*, pg. 904
Guerra, Jorge, Sec.--Real Holding Management Corp., Miami, FL; *U.S. Private*, pg. 913
Guest, Karen, V.P. & Sec.--United Advertising Publications, Inc., Dallas, TX; *Int'l*, pg. 1443
Gugliotta, Missie, Sec.--The H.T. Hackney Co., Knoxville, TN; *U.S. Private*, pg. 493
Gui, John, Sec.--Altair Corporation, Lincolnshire, IL; *U.S. Private*, pg. 46
Guido, Beba, Asst. to Pres.--Gowland Publicidad S.A., Buenos Aires, Argentina; *U.S. Public*, pg. 1642
Guilford, Margaret, Sec.--Kentucky Manufacturing Co., Louisville, KY; *U.S. Private*, pg. 615
Guire, Ronald W., Chief Fin. Officer, Exec. V.P. & Sec.--EXAR Corporation, Fremont, CA; *U.S. Public*, pg. 597
Gulbas, Jacqueline, Treas. & Sec.--National Restaurant Supply Company, El Paso, TX; *U.S. Private*, pg. 786
Guldenstern, David L., V.P. & Sec.--Catskill Savings Bank, Catskill, NY; *U.S. Public*, pg. 318
Gulick, Henry G., V.P. & Sec.--The Chubb Corporation, Warren, NJ; *U.S. Public*, pg. 354
Gulick, Henry G., Sr. V.P. & Sec.--Chubb & Son, Inc., Warren, NJ; *U.S. Public*, pg. 355
Gundersoy, Robert V., Jr., Sec.--Legato Systems, Inc., Palo Alto, CA; *U.S. Public*, pg. 984
Gupta, Narendra K., Chm. Bd., Chief Exec. Officer & Sec.--Integrated Systems, Inc., Sunnyvale, CA; *U.S. Public*, pg. 885
Gupta, R.K., Sec.--Assam Carbon Products Limited, Calcutta, India; *Int'l*, pg. 891
Guriel, Florian, Asst. Sec. & Treas.--Whiting Equipment Canada, Inc., Welland, Canada; *U.S. Private*, pg. 1173
Gurka, Jane, Mgr.-Personnel & Sec.--M. Swift & Sons Inc., Hartford, CT; *U.S. Private*, pg. 1059
Gurney, Sandra, Sec.--Willis Corroon Continental Europe Limited, London, United Kingdom; *Int'l*, pg. 1502
Gurrie, Maureen, Asst. Sec.--Donohue Inc., Quebec, Canada; *Int'l*, pg. 1075
Gurton, Lenora, Corp. Sec.--Benchmark Electronics Inc., Angleton, TX; *U.S. Public*, pg. 210
Gust, Morgan M., V.P.-Admin., Gen. Counsel & Sec.--Giant Industries Inc., Scottsdale, AZ; *U.S. Public*, pg. 741
Gutknecht, James, Treas. & Sec.--Wheaton Inc., Millville, NJ; *Int'l*, pg. 67
Gutmann, Leon J., Asst. Treas. & Asst. Sec.--The Topps Company, Inc., New York, NY; *U.S. Public*, pg. 1621
Guve, Berit, Corp. Sec.--ICA Handlarnas AB, Solna, Sweden; *Int'l*, pg. 642
Guynick, N. Yale, Corp. Sec.--Tribune Review Publishing Co., Greensburg, PA; *U.S. Private*, pg. 1102
Guzik, William, Sec.--Sussex Group, Ltd., Chicago, IL; *U.S. Public*, pg. 918
Guzman, Mary, Mgr.-Corp. Commun. & Asst. Sec.--Credit Lyonnais Americas, New York, NY; *Int'l*, pg. 344
Gwizdala, Lori A., Sec.--CFC Data Corp., Midland, MI; *U.S. Public*, pg. 345
Haack, Arthur L., Chm. Bd. & Sec.--Hickman, Williams Canada, Inc., Cambridge, Canada; *U.S. Private*, pg. 525
Haag, Arliss M., Corp. Sec.--First Federal FSB, Hutchinson, MN; *U.S. Public*, pg. 608
Haag, Joyce P., Corp. Sec.--Eastman Kodak Company, Rochester, NY; *U.S. Public*, pg. 550
Haagensen, Anne, Sec.--ESS-Food, Copenhagen, Denmark; *Int'l*, pg. 429
Haarer, G. Donald, Sec. & Legal Officer--ITT Cannon Sealectro, New Britain, CT; *U.S. Public*, pg. 859
Haas, Christel, Sec.--FPB Holding AG, Dusseldorf, Germany; *Int'l*, pg. 1303
Haas, Janice A., Asst. Sec.--Equitable Resources, Inc., Pittsburgh, PA; *U.S. Public*, pg. 589
Habecker, Eugene B., Pres., Chief Exec. Officer & Sec.--American Bible Society, New York, NY; *U.S. Private*, pg. 51
Habegger, James L., Sec.--The Habegger Corporation, Cincinnati, OH; *U.S. Private*, pg. 492
Habig, John B., Sr. Exec. V.P. & Opers. Officer--Kimball International, Inc., Jasper, IN; *U.S. Public*, pg. 956
Hachey, Barbara G., Sec.--Dunn Industries Inc., Kansas City, MO; *U.S. Private*, pg. 347
Hachey, Barbara G., Sec.--J.E. Dunn Construction Co., Kansas City, MO; *U.S. Private*, pg. 347
Hackemack, Wendy W., Asst. Sec.--Spaghetti Warehouse, Inc., Garland, TX; *U.S. Public*, pg. 1495
Hacking, Earl, Sec.--M.A. Mortenson Company, Minneapolis, MN; *U.S. Private*, pg. 763
Hackman, Tracy L., Sec.--Chrysler Financial Corporation, Southfield, MI; *U.S. Public*, pg. 354
Haddan, Laverne, Controller, Treas. & Sec.--Dick Bruhn Incorporated, Salinas, CA; *U.S. Private*, pg. 175

Haddock, Pamela B., V.P.-Specialty Underwriting & Asst. Sec.--Selective Insurance Company of the Southeast, Charlotte, NC; *U.S. Public*, pg. 1456
Hadfield, Neil, Chm. Bd., Chief Fin. Officer & Sec.--Western Pacific Data Systems, La Jolla, CA; *U.S. Private*, pg. 1168
Hafer, Thomas F., Sr. V.P., Gen. Counsel & Sec.--Salient 3 Communications, Inc., Reading, PA; *U.S. Public*, pg. 1429
Haffner, Louise, Asst. Sec.--Charter One Financial, Inc., Cleveland, OH; *U.S. Public*, pg. 336
Hafstead, Christian R.C., Chief Fin. Officer & Sec.--M.F. Bank & Company, Inc., Minneapolis, MN; *U.S. Private*, pg. 113
Haft, Julie, Sec. & Treas.--Haywin Textile Products, Inc., Brooklyn, NY; *U.S. Private*, pg. 514
Haft, Robert, Asst. Sec.--Health-Chem Corporation, New York, NY; *U.S. Public*, pg. 802
Hagan, Becky, Sec.--Timber Products Co., Germantown, TN; *U.S. Private*, pg. 1086
Hagan, Julia P., Sec. & Corp. Counsel--Vermont American Tool Corp., Louisville, KY; *U.S. Public*, pg. 575
Hage, Richard, Treas. & Sec.--Walser Automotive Group, Bloomington, MN; *U.S. Private*, pg. 1148
Hageman, John A., Sr. V.P.-Legal Affairs, Gen. Counsel & Sec.--Physician Corporation of America, Miami, FL; *U.S. Public*, pg. 1293
Hagemier, Robert, Sec.--Syndicate Systems, Inc., Middlebury, IN; *U.S. Private*, pg. 1060
Hagenau, Steve, Treas. & Sec.--Dayton Andrews Inc., Clearwater, FL; *U.S. Private*, pg. 74
Hager, Jean, Treas. & Sec.--Air Industries Corporation, Garden Grove, CA; *U.S. Private*, pg. 28
Haggard, Tamara C., Corp. Sec.--Cummings Inc., Nashville, TN; *U.S. Private*, pg. 295
Hagge, Stephen, Chief Fin. Officer, Exec. V.P., Treas. & Sec.--AptarGroup, Inc., Crystal Lake, IL; *U.S. Public*, pg. 125
Haggen, Arthur W., Sr. V.P. & Sec.--American Bankers Insurance Co. of Florida, Miami, FL; *U.S. Public*, pg. 67
Hagi, Kurt, Exec. V.P. & Sec.--Sulzer Ltd., Winterthur, Switzerland; *Int'l*, pg. 1305
Hagood, Derrill M., Sec.--William M. Bird & Co., Inc., Charleston, SC; *U.S. Private*, pg. 145
Hagorrt, Thomas H., Gen. Counsel & Sec.--Albany International Corp., Albany, NY; *U.S. Public*, pg. 36
Hahn, Barbara, Exec. Sec.--McNeil & NRM., Inc., Akron, OH; *U.S. Private*, pg. 725
Hahn, Charles J., Asst. Sec.--The Dow Chemical Company, Midland, MI; *U.S. Public*, pg. 522
Hahn, David, Sr. V.P., Gen. Counsel & Sec.--The Titan Corporation, San Diego, CA; *U.S. Public*, pg. 1618
Hahn, Elizabeth, Treas. & Sec.--Conestoga Wood Specialties Corp., East Earl, PA; *U.S. Private*, pg. 262
Hahn, Helen, Sec.--Hahn Equipment Co., Evansville, IN; *U.S. Public*, pg. 1624
Haig, Robert W., V.P. & Sec.--The Imperial Life Assurance Co., Toronto, Canada; *Int'l*, pg. 396
Hain, Mark, V.P., Gen. Counsel & Sec.--Norrell Corporation, Atlanta, GA; *U.S. Public*, pg. 1192
Haines, Dennis, Gen Counsel & Sec.--Zurn Industries, Inc., Erie, PA; *U.S. Public*, pg. 1794
Haines, Gerald A., III, Sec. & Gen. Counsel--Applied Extrusion Technologies, Inc., Peabody, MA; *U.S. Public*, pg. 122
Haist, Dennis P., V.P., Gen. Counsel & Sec.--Dillingham Construction Corporation, Pleasanton, CA; *U.S. Private*, pg. 333
Hakimoglu, Zeynep, Asst. Sec. (West Coast)--Aydin Corporation, Horsham, PA; *U.S. Public*, pg. 158
Halas, Paul J., Sr. V.P., Gen. Counsel & Sec.--Oak Industries Inc., Waltham, MA; *U.S. Public*, pg. 1209
Halbritter, M.A., Gen. Counsel & Sec.--Hope Gas, Inc., Clarksburg, WV; *U.S. Public*, pg. 435
Hald, Alan, Sec.--MicroAge Enterprises, Inc., Tempe, AZ; *U.S. Public*, pg. 1104
Hale, D., Corp. Sec.--Fine Art Developments plc, Bradford, United Kingdom; *Int'l*, pg. 485
Hale, Darrell, Treas. & Asst. Sec.--Dura-Line Corp., Middlesboro, KY; *U.S. Private*, pg. 598
Hale, Denise L., Asst. Sec.--Kleinert's Inc. of Florida, Largo, FL; *U.S. Private*, pg. 625
Hale, Gordon, Controller & Sec.--Yankee Publishing Incorporated, Dublin, NH; *U.S. Private*, pg. 1195
Hale, James R., Gen. Counsel & Sec.--Luby's Cafeterias, Inc., San Antonio, TX; *U.S. Public*, pg. 1017
Hale, James T., Sr. V.P., Gen. Counsel & Sec.--Dayton Hudson Corporation, Minneapolis, MN; *U.S. Public*, pg. 489
Hale, Katherine L., Sec.--First American Federal Savings Bank, Bristol, VA; *U.S. Public*, pg. 624
Hale, Kenneth O., Chief Fin. Officer, V.P. & Sec.--Cable Design Technologies Corporation, Pittsburgh, PA; *U.S. Public*, pg. 287
Hales, Patricia, V.P. & Sec.--SmarTrunk Systems, Inc., Hayward, CA; *U.S. Private*, pg. 1006
Haley, C. James, Jr., Treas. & Sec.--Lufkin Industries, Inc., Lufkin, TX; *U.S. Public*, pg. 1019
Haley, Kathleen M., Sec.--Florida Progress Corporation, Saint Petersburg, FL; *U.S. Public*, pg. 655
Hall, Charles W., Asst. Sec.--Friedman Industries, Inc., Houston, TX; *U.S. Public*, pg. 682
Hall, David K., V.P., Gen. Counsel & Sec.--Bell Atlantic-WV, Charleston, WV; *U.S. Public*, pg. 203
Hall, Deanna L., V.P.-Strategic Plng. & Sec.--Acme Design Technology, Co., Crozet, VA; *U.S. Private*, pg. 13
Hall, John B., Sr. V.P. & Sec.--Norbest, Inc., Midvale, UT; *U.S. Private*, pg. 801
Hall, John F., V.P.-Fin., Sec. & Treas.--Delta Natural Gas Company, Inc., Winchester, KY; *U.S. Public*, pg. 497
Hall, Kaye, Sec.--Linder & Associates, Inc., Wichita, KS; *U.S. Private*, pg. 668
Hall, Kenneth McCrae, Asst. Sec.--San Francisco Insurance Company (U.K.) Ltd., London, United Kingdom; *Int'l*, pg. 59
Hall, Norman E., V.P.-Legal & Corp. Sec.--Ocelot Energy Inc., Calgary, Canada; *Int'l*, pg. 996
Hall, Priscilla, Sec.--All Seasons Services, Inc., Braintree, MA; *U.S. Private*, pg. 35
Hall, Robert, V.P.-Legal Affairs & Sec.--The Cascades Group, Kingsey Falls, Canada; *Int'l*, pg. 273
Hall, Robert F., V.P.-Legal Affairs & Sec.--Cascades, Inc., Kingsey Falls, Canada; *Int'l*, pg. 273
Hall, Rosemary, Asst. Sec.--Dewberry Design Group, Oklahoma City, OK; *U.S. Private*, pg. 329
Hall, Stewart K., Gen. Counsel & Sec.--Howtek, Inc., Hudson, NH; *U.S. Public*, pg. 844
Hall, Virginia M., Sec.--TII Electronics, Inc., Copiague, NY; *U.S. Public*, pg. 1556
Hall, Virginia M., Sec.--TII-Ditel, Hickory, NC; *U.S. Public*, pg. 1556
Hallahan, Virginia, Asst. Sec.--Mid American Elevator Co., Inc., Chicago, IL; *U.S. Private*, pg. 743
Hallam, R.J., Dir.-Fin. & Sec.--Senior Entex, Nottingham, United Kingdom; *Int'l*, pg. 1220
Halleen, Otis H., V.P., Gen. Counsel & Sec.--United Stationers Inc., Des Plaines, IL; *U.S. Public*, pg. 1689
Hallemeesch, Willy, Sec. & Gen. Counsel--N.V. Bekaert S.A., Kortrijk, Belgium; *Int'l*, pg. 183
Hallenbeck, Mark D., Sec.--BellSouth Enterprises, Inc., Atlanta, GA; *U.S. Public*, pg. 208
Halliday, James B., V.P., Treas. & Sec.--Argonaut Group, Inc., Los Angeles, CA; *U.S. Public*, pg. 129
Hallinan, William J., Sr. V.P., Gen. Counsel & Sec.--The FINOVA Group Inc., Phoenix, AZ; *U.S. Public*, pg. 624
Hallman, Michael R., Sec.--Dairyland Greyhound Park, Inc., Kenosha, WI; *U.S. Private*, pg. 307
Halloran, Michael F., Asst. Sec.--Connecticut Water Service, Inc., Clinton, CT; *U.S. Public*, pg. 431
Halloran, Michael J., Chief Fin. Officer, V.P. & Asst. Sec.--Wallace Computer Services, Inc., Lisle, IL; *U.S. Public*, pg. 1735
Hallows, Michael, Sec. & Dir.-Internal Rels.--Joseph E. Seagram & Sons, Inc., New York, NY; *Int'l*, pg. 1215
Hallows, Michael C.L., Sec.--The Seagram Company Ltd., Montreal, Canada; *Int'l*, pg. 1214
Hallquist, Scott G., Sr. V.P., Gen. Counsel & Sec.--Immunex Corporation, Seattle, WA; *U.S. Public*, pg. 871
Halper, Steven H., Chief Oper. Officer, Exec. V.P. & Sec.--Seaman Furniture Company, Inc., Woodbury, NY; *U.S. Public*, pg. 1452
Halsey, Casey S., V.P., Gen. Counsel & Asst. Sec.--Dunn Industries Inc., Kansas City, MO; *U.S. Private*, pg. 347
Halter, Timothy P., V.P. & Sec.--Karts International Inc., Covington, LA; *U.S. Public*, pg. 944
Halterman, Darlene F., Sec. & Asst. Treas.--First Mount Joy Corporation, Mount Joy, PA; *U.S. Private*, pg. 407
Halverson, Philip R., V.P., Gen. Counsel & Sec.--Minnesota Power, Duluth, MN; *U.S. Public*, pg. 1116
Halvorson, Lorraine, Treas. & Sec.--Prospect Motors, Inc., Jackson, CA; *U.S. Private*, pg. 891
Halvorson, Melissa, Jo, Sec.--The Instant Web Companies, Chanhassen, MN; *U.S. Private*, pg. 565
Ham, Benson, Treas. & Sec.--National Rural Utilities Cooperative Finance Corporation, Herndon, VA; *U.S. Private*, pg. 786
Hamblin, Connie, Sec. & Dir.-Corp. Commun.--Gentex Corporation, Zeeland, MI; *U.S. Public*, pg. 731
Hambly, Gail, Gen. Counsel & Company Sec.--John Fairfax Holdings Limited, Sydney, Australia; *Int'l*, pg. 477
Hamilton, D. Steven, Treas. & Sec.--Rish Equipment Company, Bluefield, WV; *U.S. Private*, pg. 932
Hamilton, John, Co. Sec.--Australian Radio Network, Seven Hills, Australia; *U.S. Public*, pg. 386
Hamilton, Nancy E., Sr. Counsel & Sec.--Ralston Purina Company, Saint Louis, MO; *U.S. Public*, pg. 1359
Hamilton, Peter B., Chief Fin. Officer, Sr. V.P. & Sec.--Brunswick Corporation, Lake Forest, IL; *U.S. Public*, pg. 265
Hamilton, Stephen G., Sr. V.P., Gen. Counsel & Sec.--Computer Sales International Inc., Saint Louis, MO; *U.S. Private*, pg. 260
Hammalian, Stephen J., Ph.D., Chief Admin Officer & Exec. V.P.--EA Engineering, Science & Technology, Inc., Hunt Valley, MD; *U.S. Public*, pg. 540
Hammel, Robin, Asst. V.P. & Asst. Sec.--The Shane Group Inc., Hillsdale, MI; *U.S. Private*, pg. 989
Hammer, Jay, Sec. & Dir.-Stores--Urban Outfitters, Inc., Philadelphia, PA; *U.S. Public*, pg. 1700
Hammer, Jay, Sec.--Anthropologie, Philadelphia, PA; *U.S. Public*, pg. 1700
Hammer, Jay, Sec.--Urban Outfitters, Inc., New York, NY; *U.S. Public*, pg. 1700
Hammes, Lynn F., Treas. & Sec.--Amvestors Financial Corporation, Topeka, KS; *U.S. Private*, pg. 59
Hammett, LeMoyne A., Asst. Sec.--Sizzler International, Inc., Los Angeles, CA; *U.S. Public*, pg. 1475
Hammond, Craig, Pres., Chief Oper. Officer & Sec.--L. Perrigo Company, Allegan, MI; *U.S. Public*, pg. 1280
Hammond, Frederic G., Gen. Counsel & Sec.--Avid Technology, Inc., Tewksbury, MA; *U.S. Public*, pg. 154
Hammond, Gilbert P., Jr., V.P.-H.R. & Corp. Sec.--Geupel DeMars, Inc., Indianapolis, IN; *U.S. Private*, pg. 449
Hammonds, P.J.S., Sec.--National Westminster Bank PLC, London, United Kingdom; *Int'l*, pg. 910
Hampel, Robert E., Chief Fin. Officer, Treas. & Sec.--Keller Crescent Co., Evansville, IN; *U.S. Private*, pg. 612
Hampson, Michael D., Sec.--Whitbread PLC, London, United Kingdom; *Int'l*, pg. 1498
Hampson, Roderick W., V.P. & Sec.--The Boiler Inspection & Insurance Co. of Canada, Toronto, Canada; *U.S. Public*, pg. 795
Hampton, John L.M., Sr. V.P., Gen. Counsel & Sec.--Potash Corporation of Saskatchewan Inc., Saskatoon, Canada; *Int'l*, pg. 1064
Hamrick, H.R., Sec., Treas. & Mgr.-Data Processing--Haines City Citrus Growers Association, Haines City, FL; *U.S. Private*, pg. 494
Han, Susan J., Sec.--Midland Walwyn Inc., Toronto, Canada; *Int'l*, pg. 865
Hancey, Don, Sec.--LeGrand Johnson Construction Co., Logan, UT; *U.S. Private*, pg. 591
Hancock, Dale D., V.P. & Sec.--Cowboy Oil Company, Pocatello, ID; *U.S. Private*, pg. 280
Hancox, Anna, Sec.--Smith & Sons Foods, Inc., Macon, GA; *U.S. Private*, pg. 1006
Handelsman, H., Sec.--Northridge Industries, Inc., Chicago, IL; *U.S. Private*, pg. 551
Handley, Richard L., Sr. V.P., Gen. Counsel & Sec.--Republic Industries, Inc., Fort Lauderdale, FL; *U.S. Public*, pg. 1378
Hands, Harold P., Exec. V.P.-Legal & Sec.--Mackenzie Financial Corporation, Toronto, Canada; *Int'l*, pg. 828
Handschuh, Gregory, V.P.-Legal Affairs, Gen. Counsel & Asst. Sec.--Amdahl Corporation, Sunnyvale, CA; *Int'l*, pg. 527
Haney, Sandra, Exec. Sec.--Continental Carbon Company, Houston, TX; *Int'l*, pg. 286
Hankins, David, V.P.-Admin. & Sec.--Hahn Systems, Inc., Indianapolis, IN; *U.S. Private*, pg. 493
Hanks, W. David, Exec. V.P. & Asst. Sec.--Riviana Foods Inc., Houston, TX; *U.S. Public*, pg. 1392
Hanley, Dean, Clerk--CSP Inc., Billerica, MA; *U.S. Public*, pg. 283
Hanley, Kevin J., Controller & Sec.--CMC Kalamazoo Inc., Kalamazoo, MI; *U.S. Private*, pg. 1030
Hann, Daniel P., V.P., Gen. Counsel & Sec.--Biomet, Inc., Warsaw, IN; *U.S. Public*, pg. 231
Hannaford, R.C., Sec.--Imperial Tobacco Group, Ltd., Bristol, United Kingdom; *Int'l*, pg. 666
Hannah, David S., Sec.--Fedco, Inc., Santa Fe Springs, CA; *U.S. Private*, pg. 398
Hannesson, John D., V.P., Gen. Counsel & Sec.--Flowserve Corporation, Long Beach, CA; *U.S. Public*, pg. 658
Hannon, Kevin P., Sr. V.P. & Sec.--Admiral Insurance Company, Cherry Hill, NJ; *U.S. Public*, pg. 216
Hanono, Fanny, Treas. & Sec.--Supreme International Corp., Miami, FL; *U.S. Public*, pg. 1542
Hans, Edward, V.P., Controller & Sec.--Argo Instruments Inc., Winchester, VA; *Int'l*, pg. 839
Hansen, Charles, Legal Counsel--Carson Pirie Scott & Co., Milwaukee, WI; *U.S. Public*, pg. 309
Hansen, Dr. A., Gen. Counsel--Kuehne & Nagel International AG, Schindellegi, Switzerland; *Int'l*, pg. 763
Hansen, Kent E., Sr. V.P. & Sec.--Fedders Corp., Liberty Corner, NJ; *U.S. Public*, pg. 614
Hansen, Linda, V.P., Gen. Counsel & Sec.--BetzDearborn Inc., Trevose, PA; *U.S. Public*, pg. 226
Hansen, Lynne, Sec.--Eagle Iron Works, Des Moines, IA; *U.S. Private*, pg. 354
Hansen, Michael S., V.P.-Fin. & Sec.--Ameritech, Milwaukee, WI; *U.S. Public*, pg. 97
Hansen, Nancy S., V.P.-Admin. & Sec.--Pennsylvania Crusher Corp., Broomall, PA; *U.S. Private*, pg. 850
Hansen, Paul G., Chief Fin. Officer & V.P.-Fin.--Adaptec, Inc., Milpitas, CA; *U.S. Public*, pg. 19
Hansen, Ruth, Exec. V.P. & Sec.--H & H Distributing Company, Inc., West Union, IA; *U.S. Private*, pg. 489
Hanson, Brian, Controller & Asst. Sec.--Barry's Jewelers, Inc., Monrovia, CA; *U.S. Public*, pg. 192
Hanson, D.D., Sec.--Orbex Inc., Circle Pines, MN; *U.S. Public*, pg. 238
Harahan, William J., IV, Sec.--Header Products Inc., Romulus, MI; *U.S. Private*, pg. 514
Harbour, Steven E., V.P.-Legal & Sec.--OHM Corporation, Findlay, OH; *U.S. Public*, pg. 1207
Harbour, Steven E., V.P. & Sec.--OHM Remediation Services Corp., Findlay, OH; *U.S. Public*, pg. 1208
Harbour, Steven E., V.P. & Sec.--OHM Environmental Resources Management Corp., Findlay, OH; *U.S. Public*, pg. 1208
Harbour, Steven E., V.P., Treas. & Sec.--Environmental Treatment & Technologies Corp., Findlay, OH; *U.S. Public*, pg. 1208
Harbour, Steven E., V.P. & Sec.--OHM International, Inc., Findlay, OH; *U.S. Public*, pg. 1208
Harcharek, Janice, Dir.-Human Resources & Corp. Sec.--Universal Dynamics, Inc., Woodbridge, VA; *Int'l*, pg. 484
Harden, Oleta J., Sr. V.P., Gen. Counsel & Corp. Sec.--New Jersey Resources Corporation, Wall, NJ; *U.S. Public*, pg. 1172
Harder, William E., V.P.-Law, Gen. Counsel & Asst. Sec.--Dayton Hudson Corporation, Minneapolis, MN; *U.S. Public*, pg. 489
Hardman, Hugh, V.P.-Fin. & Sec.--Oxford Instruments-Nuclear Measurements Group, Oak Ridge, TN; *Int'l*, pg. 1018
Hardy, Gene, Exec. V.P., Sec. & Gen. Counsel--United Artists Theatre Circuits Incorporated, Englewood, CO; *U.S. Private*, pg. 1120
Hardy, Gene, Sec.--United Artists Theatre Circuits Incorporated, Englewood, CO; *U.S. Private*, pg. 1120
Hardy, Gene M., Treas. & Sec.--La-Z-Boy Incorporated, Monroe, MI; *U.S. Public*, pg. 972
Hardy, Sophia, Sec.--Barnhill Contracting Company, Tarboro, NC; *U.S. Private*, pg. 117
Hare, Jeff, Treas. & Sec.--Road Machinery Company, Phoenix, AZ; *U.S. Private*, pg. 934
Haretakis, John, Treas. & Sec.--Spires Restaurants Inc., Orange, CA; *U.S. Private*, pg. 1026
Harkey, Robert S., Sr. V.P., Gen. Counsel & Sec.--Delta Air Lines, Inc., Atlanta, GA; *U.S. Public*, pg. 497
Harkness, William, Sec.--Weir Group PLC, Glasgow, United Kingdom; *Int'l*, pg. 1488
Harmer, Stanley J., Asst. Sec.--Rohm and Haas Company, Philadelphia, PA; *U.S. Public*, pg. 1403
Harmon, Dan, V.P. & Sec.--Hoffman Corporation, Portland, OR; *U.S. Private*, pg. 532

Harmon, Doreen, Corp. Sec.--Harmon City, Inc., Salt Lake City, UT; *U.S. Private*, pg. 503
Harmon, Ellen T., Asst. Sec.--Sequa Corporation, New York, NY; *U.S. Public*, pg. 1458
Harmon, Tim, Sec.--Hercules Engine Company, Canton, OH; *U.S. Private*, pg. 523
Harmsen, Harlen F., Sec.--WD-40 Company, San Diego, CA; *U.S. Public*, pg. 1726
Harney, Dwayne, Chief Fin. Officer & Sec.--Allied Security, International, Spokane, WA; *U.S. Private*, pg. 41
Harp, Paul L., Sec. & Treas.--Metric Systems Corp., Fort Walton Beach, FL; *U.S. Public*, pg. 1563
Harper, Benny, Sr. V.P.-Fin., Treas. & Sec.--Friedman Industries, Inc., Houston, TX; *U.S. Public*, pg. 682
Harper, Daniel S., Sec.--Harper Bros., Inc., Fort Myers, FL; *U.S. Private*, pg. 504
Harper, Dolores A., Sec.--The Guttman Group, Belle Vernon, PA; *U.S. Private*, pg. 488
Harper, Edith Gaylord, Sec.--Gaylord Broadcasting Co., Nashville, TN; *U.S. Public*, pg. 704
Harper, Mike, Chief Acctg. Officer, V.P. & Asst. Sec.--HMI Industries, Cleveland, OH; *U.S. Public*, pg. 771
Harper, Ralph E., V.P., Gen. Counsel & Sec.--Gleason Corporation, Rochester, NY; *U.S. Public*, pg. 746
Harrell, Kim, Sec.--Golden Cat Corporation, Saint Louis, MO; *U.S. Public*, pg. 1360
Harring, Michael A., Asst. Sec.--John Deere Capital Corporation, Reno, NV; *U.S. Public*, pg. 492
Harring, Michael A., Asst. Sec.--John Deere Credit Company, Moline, IL; *U.S. Public*, pg. 492
Harrington, Brian K., V.P.-Fin. & Sec.--Dixie Carriers, Inc., Houston, TX; *U.S. Public*, pg. 962
Harrington, Jack, Sec.--Ball Horticultural Company, West Chicago, IL; *U.S. Private*, pg. 112
Harrington, Judy D., V.P.-Stockholder Rels. & Asst. Sec.--Bob Evans Farms, Inc., Columbus, OH; *U.S. Public*, pg. 596
Harrington, Roger, V.P., Treas. & Sec.--Midwest Industries, Inc., Ida Grove, IA; *U.S. Private*, pg. 744
Harris, Alice M., Exec. V.P. & Asst. Sec.--City Gas Company of Florida, Hialeah, FL; *U.S. Public*, pg. 1147
Harris, Ann, Sec.--Horner Rausch Optical Company East, Inc., Nashville, TN; *U.S. Private*, pg. 540
Harris, Cecily, Treas. & Sec.--GFA Brands, Inc., Cresskill, NJ; *U.S. Private*, pg. 435
Harris, Charles E., Sec.--American Locker Group, Inc., Jamestown, NY; *U.S. Public*, pg. 85
Harris, Douglas C., V.P. & Sec.--Knight-Ridder, Inc., Miami, FL; *U.S. Public*, pg. 963
Harris, Henry C., Sr. V.P.-Strategic Plng. & Alliance--Zitel Corporation, Fremont, CA; *U.S. Public*, pg. 1793
Harris, James P., V.P. & Sec.--Montgomery Watson, Cleveland, OH; *U.S. Private*, pg. 759
Harris, Jon M., Gen. Counsel & Sec.--Wheat First Butcher Singer, Inc., Richmond, VA; *U.S. Public*, pg. 640
Harris, Karen J., Corp. Sec.--The Flood Company, Hudson, OH; *U.S. Private*, pg. 414
Harris, Lee A., Sr. V.P., Gen. Counsel & Sec.--IRT Property Company, Atlanta, GA; *U.S. Public*, pg. 858
Harris, Lee A., Sec.--VW Mall, Inc., Atlanta, GA; *U.S. Public*, *pg. 858*
Harris, R. Jeffrey, V.P., Gen. Counsel & Sec.--Sybron International Corporation, Milwaukee, WI; *U.S. Public*, pg. 1544
Harris, R. Macy, III, V.P., Sec. & Mgr.-Adv.--The Ailing & Cory Company, Rochester, NY; *U.S. Public*, pg. 1666
Harris, R. Theo, Sec.--Blue Ridge Electric Cooperative Inc., Pickens, SC; *U.S. Private*, pg. 153
Harris, Stuart I., Vice Chm. & Sec.--Pollo Tropical, Inc., Miami, FL; *U.S. Public*, pg. 1315
Harris, Susan L., Sr. V.P., Gen. Counsel & Sec.--SunAmerica Inc., Los Angeles, CA; *U.S. Public*, pg. 1532
Harris, Titus H., III, Chief Fin. Officer & Sec.--The GNI Group, Inc., Deer Park, TX; *U.S. Public*, pg. 693
Harrison, Dean W., Sr. V.P., Gen. Counsel & Sec.--Gibraltar Savings, Simi Valley, CA; *U.S. Public*, pg. 181
Harrison, Ian W., Sec.--Courtaulds plc, London, United Kingdom; *Int'l*, pg. 338
Harrison, James M., Chief Fin. Officer, Exec. V.P., Treas. & Sec.--C.R. Gibson Co., Norwalk, CT; *U.S. Public*, pg. 1168
Harrison, Robert, V.P.--Dominick & Dominick, Incorporated, New York, NY; *U.S. Private*, pg. 338
Harrison, Sandra, Treas. & Sec.--Bill Wink Chevrolet, Dearborn, MI; *U.S. Private*, pg. 144
Harrison, T.F.G., Sec.--Paterson Zochonis Plc, Stockport, United Kingdom; *Int'l*, pg. 1024
Hart, Kenneth A., Pres., Chief Oper. Officer & Sec.--First Trust and Savings Bank of Taylorville, Taylorville, IL; *U.S. Public*, pg. 644
Hart, Pat, Sec.--Thermal Technology Industries, North Kansas City, MO; *U.S. Private*, pg. 1080
Hart, Robert M., Sr. V.P., Gen. Counsel & Sec.--Alleghany Corporation, New York, NY; *U.S. Public*, pg. 42
Hart, Timothy C., Asst. Sec.--The Dial Corporation, Phoenix, AZ; *U.S. Public*, pg. 505
Hart, Wayne L., Sec.--Chesapeake Utilities Corporation, Dover, DE; *U.S. Public*, pg. 347
Hart, William, Sec.--Socanav Inc., Montreal, Canada; *Int'l*, pg. 1272
Harter, Richard M., Clerk--LTX Corporation, Westwood, MA; *U.S. Public*, pg. 972
Harter, Theresa D., Asst. Sec. & Exec. Asst.--Ethika Corporation, Hilton Head Island, SC; *U.S. Public*, pg. 595
Hartill, M., Corp. Sec.--Senior Thermal Engineering Limited, Wembley, United Kingdom; *Int'l*, pg. 1221
Hartman, Charles R., V.P. & Sec.--Stifel Financial Corp., Saint Louis, MO; *U.S. Public*, pg. 1518
Hartman, Lawrence S., Sec.--National Income Realty Trust, New York, NY; *U.S. Public*, pg. 1157
Hartman, Peter A., Treas. & Sec.--Chemung Ford, Inc., Elmira, NY; *U.S. Private*, pg. 233
Hartman, Robert F., V.P., Controller, Sec. & Chief Acctg. Officer--CERBCO, Inc., Landover, MD; *U.S. Public*, pg. 330
Hartman, Sheldon R., Asst. Sec.--Keycorp, Cleveland, OH; *U.S. Public*, pg. 954
Hartmann, Richard J., Sec. & Treas.--Brookville Telephone Company, Brookville, PA; *U.S. Public*, pg. 56
Hartmann, Robert, Sec.--Blumberg Communications Inc., Minneapolis, MN; *U.S. Public*, pg. 305
Harton, Cynthia A., Sec.--Hawthorne Corp., Charleston, SC; *U.S. Private*, pg. 512
Hartwell, Margaret, Treas. & Sec.--Microlog Corporation, Germantown, MD; *U.S. Public*, pg. 1105
Hartwig, Eugene L., Sr. V.P., Gen. Counsel & Sec.--Kelly Services, Inc., Troy, MI; *U.S. Public*, pg. 949
Harvey, Colleen Curran, Sec.--American Express Financial Advisor, Minneapolis, MN; *U.S. Public*, pg. 73
Harvey, Gerald, V.P., Gen. Counsel & Sec.--TransTechnology Corporation, Liberty Corner, NJ; *U.S. Public*, pg. 1632
Harvey, H. Scott, V.P., Assoc. Gen. Counsel & Asst. Sec.--Comdisco, Inc., Rosemont, IL; *U.S. Public*, pg. 407
Harvey, Jr., A. Mosby, V.P., General Counsel & Sec.--HON Industries Inc., Muscatine, IA; *U.S. Public*, pg. 772
Harvey, Michael, V.P., Gen. Counsel & Sec.--Landstar Holding, Shelton, CT; *U.S. Public*, pg. 978
Harwood, George L., Chief Fin. Officer, Sr. V.P.-Information Systems & Sec.--Printronix, Inc., Irvine, CA; *U.S. Public*, pg. 1329
Harwood, Sanford, Asst. Chm. & Sec.--Square Industries, Inc., Jersey City, NJ; *U.S. Public*, pg. 326
Haskell, John, Sec.--Earl Construction Company, West Sacramento, CA; *U.S. Private*, pg. 1051
Haskin, Robert W., Jr., V.P., Gen. Counsel & Sec.--Remington Arms Company, Inc., Madison, NC; *U.S. Private*, pg. 921
Haskins, Betty, Sec.--Arrow Tank & Engineering Co., Minneapolis, MN; *U.S. Private*, pg. 85
Haskins, Jack L., Mgr.-Rates & Regulatory Matters & Asst. Sec.--Gulf Power Company, Pensacola, FL; *U.S. Public*, pg. 1490
Haslem, Cynthia, Sec.--Livernois Engineering Company, Dearborn, MI; *U.S. Private*, pg. 672
Hassinger, Douglas, Treas. & Sec.--Perkasie Industries Corporation, Perkasie, PA; *U.S. Private*, pg. 854
Hastings, John J., Chief Fin. Officer, Exec. V.P., Treas. & Sec.--The Middleby Corporation, Rolling Meadows, IL; *U.S. Public*, pg. 1109
Hasychak, Michael C., Treas. & Sec.--Brush Wellman Inc., Cleveland, OH; *U.S. Public*, pg. 266
Hatfield, M.A., Sr. V.P. & Sec.--Marshall & Ilsley Corporation, Milwaukee, WI; *U.S. Public*, pg. 1049
Hatlen, Joel, Controller & Treas.--Data I/O Corporation, Redmond, WA; *U.S. Public*, pg. 486
Hatton, D.M., Sec.--Kenwood Appliances Plc, Havant, United Kingdom; *Int'l*, pg. 730
Hattox, Patsy L., Chief Admin. Officer, V.P. & Sec.--Nichols Research Corporation, Huntsville, AL; *U.S. Public*, pg. 1182
Haubenreich, George R., Jr., V.P., Gen. Counsel & Sec.--Oceaneering International, Inc., Houston, TX; *U.S. Public*, pg. 1211
Haubenreich, George R., Jr., V.P., Gen. Counsel & Sec.--Oceaneering International, Inc., Morgan City, LA; *U.S. Public*, pg. 1211
Hauk, Donald B., Chief Fin. Officer, Exec. V.P. & Sec.--Republic Automotive Parts, Inc., Brentwood, TN; *U.S. Public*, pg. 1377
Hauser, F.J., Treas. & Sec.--Conley Frog/Switch & Forge Co., Memphis, TN; *U.S. Private*, pg. 263
Hauss, Suesan, Treas. & Sec.--Jeffrey Buick-Nissan Inc., Roseville, MI; *U.S. Private*, pg. 585
Haveisen, Margaret, Sec.--Continental Forge Company, Compton, CA; *U.S. Private*, pg. 268
Haveman, Kenneth, Sec.--Binkley Company, Warrenton, MO; *U.S. Private*, pg. 534
Havlik, Gregory C., Controller & Sec.--Wm. T. Burnett & Co., Inc., Baltimore, MD; *U.S. Private*, pg. 186
Hawbaker, Alan, Treas. & Sec.--Glenn O. Hawbaker, Inc., State College, PA; *U.S. Private*, pg. 511
Hawes, Douglas W., Esq., Sec.--United Water Resources, Harrington Park, NJ; *U.S. Public*, pg. 1691
Hawke, Susan, Asst. Sec.--Montana Power Company, Butte, MT; *U.S. Public*, pg. 1126
Hawken, A.G., Sec.--ECC International Ltd., Theale, United Kingdom; *Int'l*, pg. 455
Hawkes, Cathy, Asst. Sec.--The Raymond Corporation, Greene, NY; *Int'l*, pg. 123
Hawkins, Frank, Treas. & Sec.--World Publishing Company, Tulsa, OK; *U.S. Private*, pg. 1190
Hawkins, John R., Exec. V.P. & Sec.--Hawkins Chemical, Inc., Minneapolis, MN; *U.S. Public*, pg. 800
Hawkins, Ralph L., Jr., Sec.--Northern Life Insurance Company, Seattle, WA; *U.S. Public*, pg. 1375
Hawkins, Steven B., Chief Fin. Officer, V.P.-Fin. & Admin., Treas. & Sec.--FFP Marketing Company, Inc., Fort Worth, TX; *U.S. Public*, pg. 604
Hawkins, Thomas W., Sr. V.P., Gen. Counsel & Sec.--Blockbuster Entertainment Group, Dallas, TX; *U.S. Private*, pg. 775
Hawryluk, Allan A., Gen. Counsel & Sec.--Atomic Energy of Canada Ltd., Mississauga, Canada; *Int'l*, pg. 97
Hawtin, I.A., Sec.--The Boots Company PLC, Nottingham, United Kingdom; *Int'l*, pg. 202
Hay, Mark H., Sec.--Rowan Companies, Inc., Houston, TX; *U.S. Public*, pg. 1409
Hay, William H., V.P., Gen. Counsel & Sec.--Beckman Instruments, Inc., Fullerton, CA; *U.S. Public*, pg. 199
Haydem, Jane, Corp. Sec.--Thermalloy, Inc., Farmers Branch, TX; *Int'l*, pg. 208
Hayes, Alan, Sec.--Tuscarora Yarns Inc., Mount Pleasant, NC; *U.S. Private*, pg. 1110
Hayes, Chester F., Sec. & Gen. Counsel--ARGOSystems, Inc., Sunnyvale, CA; *U.S. Public*, pg. 240
Hayes, D., Grp. Sec.--Scholl Plc, Newton, United Kingdom; *Int'l*, pg. 1209
Hayes, David M., Sr. V.P., Gen. Counsel & Sec.--Agway, Inc., De Witt, NY; *U.S. Private*, pg. 27
Hayes, James W., III, Gen. Counsel & Sec.--Brown & Sharpe Manufacturing Company, North Kingstown, RI; *U.S. Public*, pg. 260
Hayes, Kevin J., Chief Fin. Officer, V.P., Treas. & Asst. Sec.--Methode Electronics Inc., Chicago, IL; *U.S. Public*, pg. 1101
Hayes, Patricia, Gen. Counsel & Sec.--Centimark Corporation, Canonsburg, PA; *U.S. Private*, pg. 222
Hayman, Martin, Grp. Sec.--Standard Chartered Bank PLC, London, United Kingdom; *Int'l*, pg. 1294
Haynes, Regina, Asst. Sec.--Tultex Corporation, Martinsville, VA; *U.S. Public*, pg. 1644
Hays, Barbara Sue, Sec.--Allen & Ohara, Inc., Memphis, TN; *U.S. Private*, pg. 36
Hays, Randy K., Treas. & Sec.--Masek Distributing Inc., Gering, NE; *U.S. Private*, pg. 711
Hays, Richard M., Sec.--RMI Titanium Company, Niles, OH; *U.S. Public*, pg. 1662
Haythe, Thomas M., Sec.--Skyland Scientific Services, Inc., Bozeman, MT; *U.S. Public*, pg. 1515
Haywood, B.J., Controller & Sec.--Senior Australia Limited, Smithfield, Australia; *Int'l*, pg. 1222
Haywood, C.A., Sec. & Treas.--Commercial Interior Builders, Inc., Jessup, MD; *U.S. Public*, pg. 913
Heacock, Richard, V.P.-Fin., Treas. & Sec.--Apache Hose & Belting Company, Inc., Cedar Rapids, IA; *U.S. Private*, pg. 76
Heacox, Helen B., Asst. Sec.--First Union Real Estate Investments, Cleveland, OH; *U.S. Public*, pg. 640
Head, Alva, Exec. Asst.--American Classic Voyagers Company, New Orleans, LA; *U.S. Private*, pg. 380
Head, Christopher A., Exec. V.P., Gen. Counsel & Sec.--Comptek Research, Inc., Buffalo, NY; *U.S. Public*, pg. 419
Head, Christopher A., Sec.--Comptek Federal Systems, Inc., Buffalo, NY; *U.S. Public*, pg. 419
Head, Malcolm, Sr. V.P. & Sec.--TIG Holdings, Inc., New York, NY; *U.S. Public*, pg. 1555
Headley, Tricia, Dir.-Corp. Svcs.--O'Reilly Automotive Inc., Springfield, MO; *U.S. Public*, pg. 1230
Heagney, Larry, Treas. & Sec.--Milliken & Company, Spartanburg, SC; *U.S. Private*, pg. 748
Heal, Kenneth L., Treas. & Sec.--Elco Textron, Rockford, IL; *U.S. Public*, pg. 1590
Healey, Jack P., Chief Fin. Officer, V.P. & Sec.--Industrial Distribution Group, Tucker, GA; *U.S. Public*, pg. 875
Healey, Karen, Chief Fin. Officer & Sec.--Connector Manufacturing Company, Hamilton, OH; *U.S. Private*, pg. 264
Healey, Mary J., V.P., Gen. Counsel & Sec.--Yankee Energy System, Inc., Meriden, CT; *U.S. Public*, pg. 1787
Healy, E. Peter, Chief Fin. Officer, Exec. V.P. & Sec.--Barry's Jewelers, Inc., Monrovia, CA; *U.S. Public*, pg. 192
Healy, Patrick, Sec.--Blue Island Railroad, Chicago, IL; *U.S. Public*, pg. 865
Heard, R.M., Grp. Sec.--BPB Industries PLC, Slough, United Kingdom; *Int'l*, pg. 122
Hearn, Michael D., Gen. Counsel & Sec.--Interstate/Johnson Lane, Inc., Charlotte, NC; *U.S. Public*, pg. 909
Hearn, Michael D., Sr. Mng. Dir., Gen. Counsel & Sec.--Interstate/Johnson Lane Corporation, Charlotte, NC; *U.S. Public*, pg. 910
Heath, Deborah, Sec.--SPS Technologies, Inc., Jenkintown, PA; *U.S. Public*, pg. 1419
Heath, Frederick G., V.P., Treas. & Sec.--Brown Wood Preserving Company, Louisville, KY; *U.S. Private*, pg. 174
Heatherley, P.D., Corp. Sec.--Senior TIFT Limited, Waltham Cross, United Kingdom; *Int'l*, pg. 1221
Heaton, Mary Margaret, Corp. Counsel & Asst. Sec.--Oxford Industries, Inc., Atlanta, GA; *U.S. Public*, pg. 1239
Hebb, Walter M., Sr. V.P.-Mktg. & Prod. Devel.--General Binding Corporation, Northbrook, IL; *U.S. Public*, pg. 707
Hebert, Clifford J., Jr., V.P.-Fin., Treas. & Sec.--Eastern Utilities Associates, Boston, MA; *U.S. Public*, pg. 549
Hecht, Louis A., Sec. & Gen. Counsel--Molex Incorporated, Lisle, IL; *U.S. Public*, pg. 1121
Heck, Shirley A., Sec.--Heck Industries, Baton Rouge, LA; *U.S. Private*, pg. 519
Heckel, Marilyn A., Asst. Corp. Sec.--H.W. Kaufman Financial Group, Inc., Farmington, MI; *U.S. Private*, pg. 609
Hecker, David, Sr. V.P., Sec. & Gen. Counsel--S.C. Johnson & Son, Inc., Racine, WI; *U.S. Private*, pg. 592
Hedrick, Hal C., Jr., Asst. Sec.--The LTV Corporation, Cleveland, OH; *U.S. Public*, pg. 971
Heekin, W. Michael, Sr. V.P., Gen. Counsel & Sec.--American Heritage Life Investment Corp., Jacksonville, FL; *U.S. Public*, pg. 78
Heesh, Steve, Asst. Sec.--Qantas Airways Ltd., Mascot, Australia; *Int'l*, pg. 1074
Heft, Karen, Sec.--Three D Departments, Inc., Costa Mesa, CA; *U.S. Public*, pg. 1604
Hegarty, David J., Pres. & Chief Oper. Officer--Health and Retirement Properties Trust, Newton, MA; *U.S. Public*, pg. 801
Heggen, Arthur, Sec.--Caribbean American Life Assurance Company, Hato Rey, PR; *U.S. Public*, pg. 67
Heggen, Arthur W., Exec. V.P. & Sec.--American Bankers Insurance Group, Inc., Miami, FL; *U.S. Public*, pg. 67
Heggen, Arthur W., Sec.--Bankers American Life Assurance Company, Pearl River, NY; *U.S. Public*, pg. 68
Heggen, Arthur W., Sec.--Voyager Service Warranties, Inc., Fort Worth, TX; *U.S. Public*, pg. 68
Heggland, Roy T., Sr. V.P., Gen. Counsel & Sec.--Cincinnati Bell Information Systems Inc., Cincinnati, OH; *U.S. Public*, pg. 367
Hegi, Joe, Sec.--Premium Tank Line Inc., Jackson, MS; *U.S.* Private, pg. 329

Heidbreder, Warren W., Chief Fin. Officer, V.P. & Sec.--Bandag, Incorporated, Muscatine, IA; *U.S. Public*, pg. 177
Heidorn, Robert E., Deputy Gen. Counsel & Asst. Sec.--Indiana Energy, Inc., Indianapolis, IN; *U.S. Public*, pg. 874
Heil, M., Treas. & Sec.--American Excelsior Company, Arlington, TX; *U.S. Private*, pg. 53
Heiligman, D.C., V.P.-Fin. & Corp. Sec.--Rochester Gas And Electric Corporation, Rochester, NY; *U.S. Public*, pg. 1395
Heim, Stephanie, Asst. Sec.--Federal-Mogul Corporation, Southfield, MI; *U.S. Public*, pg. 615
Heims, Holger, V.P.-Oper. Controlling & Sec.--Ameriquest Technologies, Santa Ana, CA; *U.S. Public*, pg. 96
Heineman, Brett D., V.P., Sec. & Mgr.-East Reg. Sls.--Conway Import Co. Inc., Franklin Park, IL; *U.S. Private*, pg. 272
Heinman, Gregg J., V.P.-Opers., Treas. & Sec.--Conway Import Co. Inc., Franklin Park, IL; *U.S. Private*, pg. 272
Heinrich, Robert, V.P. & Gen. Counsel--Fender Musical Instruments, Scottsdale, AZ; *U.S. Private*, pg. 400
Heinson, Ann, Sec.--Allied Oil & Supply, Inc., Omaha, NE; *U.S. Private*, pg. 39
Heinz, Inge, Sec.--Richard Hirschmann GmbH & Co., Neckartenzlingen, Germany; *Int'l*, pg. 1108
Heinz, Naomi, Sec. & Dir.-Acctg.--JSI, French Lick, IN; *U.S. Private*, pg. 583
Heipt, J. Dennis, Sr. V.P.-Admin. & Sec.--Science Applications International Corp., San Diego, CA; *U.S. Private*, pg. 975
Heiser, James S., Chief Fin. Officer, V.P., Gen. Counsel, Sec. & Treas.--Ducommun Incorporated, Carson, CA; *U.S. Public*, pg. 533
Heisig, Jamie, Sec.--Scientific Protein Laboratories, Inc., Waunakee, WI; *U.S. Public*, pg. 80
Hejna, Silva, Asst. V.P. & Sec.--M & I Thunderbird Bank, Phoenix, AZ; *U.S. Public*, pg. 1050
Helbich, Nancy, Sec. to the Chm.--Monarch Construction Company, Cincinnati, OH; *U.S. Private*, pg. 757
Held, K. Lars, Treas. & Sec.--Overly Manufacturing Co., Greensburg, PA; *U.S. Private*, pg. 823
Helders, G.P., Sec. & Treas.--Hartford Insurance Group of Canada, Willowdale, Canada; *U.S. Public*, pg. 794
Heldman, Julie, Sec.--Signature Eyewear, Inc., Inglewood, CA; *U.S. Public*, pg. 1473
Heldman, Paul W., Sr. V.P., Gen. Counsel & Sec.--The Kroger Co., Cincinnati, OH; *U.S. Public*, pg. 967
Heldt, Patti, Pres. & Sec.--Steven Manufacturing Co., Hermann, MO; *U.S. Private*, pg. 1042
Helfrich, Leonard W., V.P. & Sec.--Allen Organ Company, Macungie, PA; *U.S. Public*, pg. 45
Heller, Edward, Sec.--Blumenthal Print Works, Inc., New Orleans, LA; *U.S. Private*, pg. 153
Heller, Renate, Sec.--Borsch, Stengel & Partner GmbH, Frankfurt/Main, Germany; *Int'l*, pg. 203
Heller, Ronald G., Sec.--Ingersoll-Rand Company, Woodcliff Lake, NJ; *U.S. Public*, pg. 876
Hellman, Murray, Chief Fin. Officer, Controller, Sec. & Treas.--Pressman Toy Corp., New York, NY; *U.S. Private*, pg. 882
Helm, Steve, V.P.-Legal & Corp. Sec.--Allied Waste Industries, Scottsdale, AZ; *U.S. Public*, pg. 49
Helman, Robert A., Sec.--Dresher, Inc., Carthage, MO; *U.S.* Public, pg. 986
Helmbrecht, Glen V., Chief Fin. Officer, Controller & Sec.--Mayville Engineering Co., Inc., Mayville, WI; *U.S. Private, pg. 718*
Helmick, Susan T., Sec.--Helmick Corporation, Fairmont, WV; *U.S. Private*, pg. 520
Hemmer, Donald M., Treas. & Sec.--Paul Hemmer Construction Company, Fort Mitchell, KY; *U.S. Private*, pg. 521
Hemmings, Laura, Sec.--Dixon Ticonderoga Company, Heathrow, FL; *U.S. Public*, pg. 514
Hempstead, George H., III, V.P., Gen. Counsel & Sec.--Hanson North America, Woodbridge, NJ; *Int'l*, pg. 593
Hempt, Gerald L., Sec. & Treas.--Hempt Brothers, Inc., Camp Hill, PA; *U.S. Private*, pg. 521
Hemsted, Stephen, Sec. & Dir.-Fin.--The National Magazine Company Ltd., London, United Kingdom; *U.S. Private*, pg. 518
Henderson, Alan C., Chief Fin. Officer, Exec. V.P. & Sec.--RehabCare Group, Inc., Saint Louis, MO; *U.S. Public*, pg. 1373
Henderson, Clarence, Asst. Sec.--Bank of Montreal, Toronto, Canada; *Int'l*, pg. 153
Henderson, Eugene L., Sec.--Indiana Financial Investors, Inc., Chicago, IL; *U.S. Private*, pg. 903
Henderson, Lisa, Sec.--James Austin Co., Mars, PA; *U.S. Private*, pg. 99
Hendon, Robert C., Jr., V.P., Gen. Counsel & Sec.--Berlitz International, Inc., Princeton, NJ; *U.S. Public*, pg. 221
Hendricks, Diane M., V.P. & Sec.--ABC Supply Company, Inc., Beloit, WI; *U.S. Private*, pg. 3
Hendricks, Ruth Ann, Sec.--Rose Acre Farms, Seymour, IN; *U.S. Private*, pg. 944
Hendrickson, R. David, Sec.--Southern Natural Gas Company, Birmingham, AL; *U.S. Public*, pg. 1485
Hendrix, Sherry, Corp. Sec.--Henco, Inc., Selmer, TN; *U.S. Private*, pg. 521
Hendry, Andrew D., Sr. V.P., Gen. Counsel & Sec.--Colgate-Palmolive Company, New York, NY; *U.S. Public*, pg. 397
Hennequin, Philippe, Sec.--CAP Gemini S.A., Paris, France; *Int'l*, pg. 263
Henning, Edward J., Sr. V.P., Gen. Counsel & Sec.--Health Care Property Investors, Inc., Newport Beach, CA; *U.S. Public*, pg. 801
Henning, Robert V., Jr., Sec.--Belmont Metals, Inc., Brooklyn, NY; *U.S. Private*, pg. 132
Henquinet, Wayne K., Sec. & Treas.--New Mech Companies, Inc., Saint Paul, MN; *U.S. Private*, pg. 794
Henry, Bob J., V.P., Gen. Counsel & Sec.--Allied Van Lines, Inc., Naperville, IL; *Int'l*, pg. 901
Henry, Charles R., Sec.--Cable Constructors, Inc., Iron Mountain, MI; *U.S. Private*, pg. 197
Henry, Corlis L., Sec.--Cajun Electric Power Co-op, Baton Rouge, LA; *U.S. Private*, pg. 199
Henry, Dawn A., Asst. Sec.--Blair Corporation, Warren, PA; *U.S. Public*, pg. 236
Henry, John F., Jr., Sec.--Coca-Cola Bottling Co. Consolidated, Charlotte, NC; *U.S. Public*, pg. 391
Henry, Paula W., Sec.--Dawson Geophysical Company, Midland, TX; *U.S. Public*, pg. 489
Henry, Roni, Mgr.-Admin. & Human Resources & Asst. Sec.--Waters Instruments, Inc., Rochester, MN; *U.S. Public*, pg. 1745
Henry, Sam L., Chief Fin. Officer, Sr. V.P. & Sec.--Helen of Troy Corporation, El Paso, TX; *U.S. Public*, pg. 807
Henry, Stuart W., V.P.-Admin. & Sec.--First Marathon Inc., Toronto, Canada; *Int'l*, pg. 486
Henschel, David F., Sec.--AMP Incorporated, Harrisburg, PA; *U.S. Public*, pg. 7
Hensey, Kim J., V.P. & Sec.--RLI Corp., Peoria, IL; *U.S. Public*, pg. 1356
Hensley, Martha S., V.P.-Admin. & Sec.--TCA Management Company, Tyler, TX; *U.S. Public*, pg. 1553
Hensley, Pat, Sec.--Burk Royalty Co., Wichita Falls, TX; *U.S. Private*, pg. 182
Hensley, William H., V.P.-Gen. Counsel & Sec.--Mueller Industries, Inc., Memphis, TN; *U.S. Public*, pg. 1141
Hepworth, John C., Sec.--Clear Springs Foods, Inc., Buhl, ID; *U.S. Private*, pg. 245
Herald, Gwen, Asst. Sec.--Tractor Supply Co., Nashville, TN; *U.S. Public*, pg. 1627
Herald, James, V.P.-Fin., Sec & Treas.--Morgan Foods, Inc., Austin, IN; *U.S. Private*, pg. 761
Herbert, John, Gen. Counsel & Sec.--Ace Doran Hauling & Rigging Company, Cincinnati, OH; *U.S. Private*, pg. 340
Herbert, John, Gen. Counsel & Sec.--Ace Doran Brokerage, Cincinnati, OH; *U.S. Private*, pg. 340
Herbster, Judith A., Sec.--Conklin Co. Inc., Shakopee, MN; *U.S. Private*, pg. 263
Herlihy, Gerard A., Chief Fin. Officer & Sec.--Williams Controls, Inc., Portland, OR; *U.S. Public*, pg. 1769
Herma, John F., Chief Oper. Officer, Exec. V.P. & Sec.--Kohl's Corporation, Menomonee Falls, WI; *U.S. Public*, pg. 965
Herman, Michael P., Chief Fin. Officer, V.P. & Sec.--Vari-Lite International, Dallas, TX; *U.S. Public*, pg. 1709
Herman, Robin A., Sr. V.P., Gen. Counsel & Sec.--Western Staff Services, Walnut Creek, CA; *U.S. Public*, pg. 1760
Herman, W.A., Treas. & Sec.--Stauffer Communications, Inc., Augusta, GA; *U.S. Private*, pg. 995
Herman, W.A., III, Treas. & Sec.--Shivers Trading & Operating Co., Augusta, GA; *U.S. Private*, pg. 994
Hermanson, Lydia, Sec.--Mr. Christmas Inc., New York, NY; *U.S. Private*, pg. 765
Hermsdorf, Martha A., Corp. Sec.--RMT, Inc., Madison, WI; *U.S. Public*, pg. 1728
Hernandez, Ana Rosa, Corp. Sec.--Crispin Porter & Bogusky Advertising, Miami, FL; *U.S. Private*, pg. 290
Hernandez, Aurora, Corp. Sec.--Publicidad Ferrer y Asociados, S.A. de C.V., Mexico, Mexico; *Int'l*, pg. 1073
Hernandez, Juan Manuel Echevarria, Gen. Mgr., Dir. & Sec.--Banco Central Hispanoamericano S.A., Madrid, Spain; *Int'l*, pg. 139
Hernandez, Louis R., V.P., Treas. & Asst. Sec.--W.P. Carey & Co., Inc., New York, NY; *U.S. Private*, pg. 209
Herner, Donald A., Gen. Counsel & Sec.--JJI Lighting Group Inc., Greenwich, CT; *Int'l*, pg. 821
Herr, J. Michael, Sec.--Shopsmith, Inc., Dayton, OH; *U.S. Public*, pg. 1467
Herring, J. Andrew, Sec.--INCSTAR Corporation, Stillwater, MN; *Int'l*, pg. 483
Herring, Jerome, Sr. V.P. & Sec.--BB&T Corporation, Winston Salem, NC; *U.S. Public*, pg. 159
Herron, Bonnie L., V.P. & Sec.--Intelligent Systems Corp., Norcross, GA; *U.S. Public*, pg. 888
Herschend, Peter, Vice Chm. & Exec. V.P.--Silver Dollar City, Inc., Branson, MO; *U.S. Private*, pg. 1000
Hershkowitz, Thomas, Chief Fin. Officer, V.P., Treas. & Sec.--American Journal of Nursing Company, New York, NY; *Int'l*, pg. 1513
Hertzoff, Charles, Sec.--NationsBank/Miami, Miami, FL; *U.S. Public*, pg. 1162
Herzig, Reginia, Sec.-Mktg.--AGCO Argentina S.A., Haedo, Argentina; *Int'l*, pg. 30
Hess, Carol M., Asst. Sec.--Steck-Vaughn Company, Austin, TX; *U.S. Public*, pg. 784
Hess, Carol M., Asst. Sec.--National Education Credit Corporation, Irvine, CA; *U.S. Public*, pg. 784
Hess, Carol M., Asst. Sec.--National Education Payroll Corp., Irvine, CA; *U.S. Public*, pg. 784
Hess, Carol M., Asst. Sec.--Steck-Vaughn Publishing Corporation, Austin, TX; *U.S. Public*, pg. 784
Hess, Carol M., Asst. Sec.--Steck-Vaughn Distribution Company, Austin, TX; *U.S. Public*, pg. 784
Hess, P.Gregory, Legal Counsel & Sec.--Barr & Barr, Inc., New York, NY; *U.S. Private*, pg. 117
Hess, Peter L., Gen. Counsel & Sec.--Farrel Corporation, Ansonia, CT; *U.S. Public*, pg. 614
Hess, Philip, Sec.--Credit Suisse Group, Zurich, Switzerland; *Int'l*, pg. 345
Hesse, Paul A., V.P.-Communications & Sec.--General Dynamics Corporation, Falls Church, VA; *U.S. Public*, pg. 708
Hesse, Selwyn, Vice Chm., Exec. V.P. & Sec.--Automatic Equipment Mfg. Co., Pender, NE; *U.S. Private*, pg. 101
Hessler, David J., Treas. & Sec.--MTD Products Limited, Kitchener, Canada; *U.S. Private*, pg. 688
Hetherington, Edwin S., Gen. Counsel & Sec.--Sea Containers Ltd., Hamilton, Bermuda; *Int'l*, pg. 1213
Hetherington, Edwin S., Gen. Counsel & Sec.--Orient-Express Hotels Inc., New York, NY; *Int'l*, pg. 1213
Hetherington, John W., V.P. & Sec.--Westvaco Corporation, New York, NY; *U.S. Public*, pg. 1762
Heumann, H. David, Sec.--The Boeing Travel Company, Irvine, CA; *U.S. Public*, pg. 241
Hewes, Philip A., Sr. V.P. & Sec.--Comdisco, Inc., Rosemont, IL; *U.S. Public*, pg. 407
Hewitt, Christopher, Sec.--Optek Technology, Inc., Carrollton, TX; *U.S. Public*, pg. 1227
Hewitt, John, Sec.--Expamet International Plc, London, United Kingdom; *Int'l*, pg. 467
Hewitt, Robert C., Chief Fin. Officer, V.P.-Fin. & Sec.--Newport Corporation, Irvine, CA; *U.S. Public*, pg. 1179
Hewlett-Brown, Wanda, Treas. & Sec.--Heights Heating & Cooling, Auburn Hills, MI; *U.S. Private*, pg. 519
Hiatt, David A., V.P., Treas. & Sec.--The National Super Service Co., Toledo, OH; *U.S. Private*, pg. 787
Hibbs, Glen H., Sec.--Southwestern Electric Service Co., Dallas, TX; *U.S. Public*, pg. 1588
Hickey, Angela, Corp. Sec.--John Ayling and Associates Limited, London, United Kingdom; *Int'l*, pg. 103
Hickey, John E., V.P., Sec. & Asst. Gen. Counsel--International Business Machines Corporation, Armonk, NY; *U.S. Public*, pg. 895
Hickman, Winston E., Chief Fin. Officer, Sr. V.P. & Sec.--Pacific Scientific Company, Newport Beach, CA; *U.S. Public*, pg. 1250
Hicks, A.J., Sec.--Jackpot Enterprises, Inc., Las Vegas, NV; *U.S. Public*, pg. 920
Hicks, J.C., Treas. & Sec.--ECC International Inc., Atlanta, GA; *Int'l*, pg. 455
Hicks, Jeff, Treas. & Sec.--English China Clays, Inc., Atlanta, GA; *Int'l*, pg. 455
Hicks, Maude H., Treas. & Sec.--Horton Homes, Inc., Eatonton, GA; *U.S. Private*, pg. 540
Higbee, David M., Sec.--Apco Argentina Inc., Tulsa, OK; *U.S. Public*, pg. 119
Higbee, David M., Sec.--The Williams Companies, Inc., Tulsa, OK; *U.S. Public*, pg. 1769
Higdon, Lawrence, V.P. & Sec.--Ira Higdon Grocery, Inc., Cairo, GA; *U.S. Private*, pg. 527
Higginbotham, Dorothy, Sec.--Ozark Motor Lines, Memphis, TN; *U.S. Private*, pg. 825
Higgins, Prentiss C., V.P.-Q.A. & ESD Laboratories--ESA, Inc., Chelmsford, MA; *U.S. Private*, pg. 354
Higgins, Robert E., Sec.--Elsinore Corporation, Las Vegas, NV; *U.S. Public*, pg. 570
Higgins, Robert E., Acting Corp. Sec.--Perini Corporation, Framingham, MA; *U.S. Public*, pg. 1278
Highley, Edward, Sec.--Alamo Group, Inc., La Grange, IL; *U.S. Public*, pg. 35
Hignett, Kenneth L., Chief Fin. Officer, Sr. V.P. & Sec.--Morgan's Foods, Inc., Beachwood, OH; *U.S. Public*, pg. 1133
Hignutt, Debbie, Sec.--O.A. Newton & Son Co., Bridgeville, DE; *U.S. Private*, pg. 797
Hildreth, Gary R., V.P., Gen. Counsel & Sec.--Armco Inc., Pittsburgh, PA; *U.S. Public*, pg. 131
Hill, Bruce G., V.P., Gen. Counsel & Sec.--INSO Corporation, Boston, MA; *U.S. Public*, pg. 882
Hill, David L., Sec.--Capital National Insurance Company, Burlington, VT; *U.S. Public*, pg. 1207
Hill, Debra, Sec.--Flanders Corp., Washington, NC; *U.S. Public*, pg. 648
Hill, Joseph G., Chief Fin. Officer, V.P.-Fin., Treas. & Sec.--DMI Furniture Inc., Louisville, KY; *U.S. Public*, pg. 473
Hill, Justin, Jr., Sec. & Treas.--Lawrence Paper Company, Lawrence, KS; *U.S. Private*, pg. 654
Hill, Lewis, III, Sec.--Golf Hosts, Inc., Palm Harbor, FL; *U.S. Private*, pg. 1036
Hill, Maggie, Sec.--McNally Manufacturing, Pittsburg, KS; *Int'l*, pg. 1326
Hill, Max E., Chief Fin. Officer, V.P.-Fin. & Sec.--I.C. System, Inc., Vadnais Heights, MN; *U.S. Private*, pg. 553
Hill, P.C., Sec.--James Walker & Co. Limited, Woking, United Kingdom; *Int'l*, pg. 1485
Hill, Steven H., Sr. V.P. & Sec.--Southern Container Corporation, Hauppauge, NY; *U.S. Private*, pg. 1016
Hill, Susan, Sec.--The Bank Funds Company LLC, Chicago, IL; *U.S. Private*, pg. 113
Hill, Wayne S., Chief Fin. Officer, V.P. & Sec.--Toromont Industries Ltd., Concord, Canada; *Int'l*, pg. 1400
Hilliard, Susan, Exec. Asst.--The Challenge Machinery Co., Grand Haven, MI; *U.S. Private*, pg. 227
Hillin, W.K., Sr. V.P., Gen. Counsel & Sec.--Reading & Bates Corporation, Houston, TX; *U.S. Public*, pg. 1354
Hilterbrand, Patricia, Controller, Treas. & Sec.--Pinkerton & Laws Inc., Atlanta, GA; *U.S. Private*, pg. 865
Himes, Susan, Corp. Sec.--Standard Pacific Corp., Costa Mesa, CA; *U.S. Public*, pg. 1503
Hindman, Donald D., V.P.-Sls. & Mktg.--Clark Foodservice, Inc., Elk Grove Village, IL; *U.S. Private*, pg. 242
Hinds, Susan C., Asst. Sec.--IES Industries Inc., Cedar Rapids, IA; *U.S. Public*, pg. 855
Hinds, Susan C., Asst. Sec.--IES Investments Inc., Cedar Rapids, IA; *U.S. Public*, pg. 855
Hinkley, Richard L., V.P., Chief Counsel & Sec.--Nevada Power Company, Las Vegas, NV; *U.S. Public*, pg. 1169
Hinman, Mark, V.P., Sec. & Mgr.-Sls.--Rome Strip Steel Co., Inc., Rome, NY; *U.S. Private*, pg. 942
Hinton, Helen L., Sec.--Broughton Foods Company, Marietta, OH; *U.S. Public*, pg. 259
Hintz, Murray, Sec.--Cass-Clay Creamery, Fargo, ND; *U.S. Private*, pg. 218
Hirsch, Barry, Sr. V.P., Gen. Counsel & Sec.--Loews Corporation, New York, NY; *U.S. Public*, pg. 1010
Hise, William P., Asst. Sec.--Dayton Hudson Corporation, Minneapolis, MN; *U.S. Public*, pg. 489
Hitchcock, Pat, Treas. & Sec.--WRM, Incoporated, Mabscott, WV; *U.S. Private*, pg. 1144
Hite, David S., Treas & Sec.--McKinnon Bridge Co., Franklin, TN; *U.S. Private*, pg. 723
Hite, E.A., Corp. Sec.--The Hite Company, Altoona, PA; *U.S. Private*, pg. 531
Hittinger, Richelle, Sec.--Belmont Industries, Inc., Bala Cynwyd, PA; *U.S. Private*, pg. 903

Hittler, Daniel L., Chief Admin. Officer & Sec.--Walbro Corporation, Cass City, MI; *U.S. Public*, pg. 1733
Ho, Dorothy, Sec.--Superior Metal Printing Limited, Singapore, Singapore; *Int'l*, pg. 1322
Hoaglund, Donna, Sec.--Knouse Foods Inc., Peach Glen, PA; *U.S. Private*, pg. 627
Hoard, Heidi, V.P., Gen. Counsel & Sec.--Musicland Group Inc., Minnetonka, MN; *U.S. Public*, pg. 1142
Hobbs, George D., V.P., Gen. Counsel & Sec.--Centocor, Inc., Malvern, PA; *U.S. Public*, pg. 323
Hobert, Nancy S., Asst. Sec.--Analysis & Technology, Inc., North Stonington, CT; *U.S. Public*, pg. 109
Hochberg, S., Sec.--L. Karp & Sons, Inc., Elk Grove Village, IL; *U.S. Private*, pg. 607
Hockenberry, John F., Asst. Sec.--The Washington Post Company, Washington, DC; *U.S. Public*, pg. 1742
Hockett, Galen R., Sec. & Treas.--Larrys, Inc., Gillette, WY; *U.S. Private*, pg. 652
Hockett, Lynn M., Asst. Sec.--John Deere Capital Corporation, Reno, NV; *U.S. Public*, pg. 492
Hockman, Ralph C., V.P., Gen. Mgr., Treas. & Sec.-Access Floors--Tate Access Floors, Inc., Jessup, MD; *U.S. Private*, pg. 1069
Hodge, Linda J., Assoc. Gen. Counsel & Asst. Sec.--Amgen Inc., Thousand Oaks, CA; *U.S. Public*, pg. 100
Hodge, Petrina, Sec.--NETG Limited, London, United Kingdom; *U.S. Public*, pg. 784
Hodges, Cheryl D., Sr. V.P., Sec. & Dir. Inv. Rels.--Omnicare, Inc., Covington, KY; *U.S. Public*, pg. 1223
Hodges, John, Asst. Sec.--The Burton Group PLC, London, United Kingdom; *Int'l*, pg. 237
Hodgkinson, M., Asst. Sec.--Britax International plc, Warwick, United Kingdom; *Int'l*, pg. 216
Hoehn, Richard N., Asst. Sec.--Kingsbury Corporation, Keene, NH; *U.S. Private*, pg. 621
Hoehner, J.F., Asst. Gen. Counsel & Asst. Sec.--Sverdrup Corporation, Maryland Heights, MO; *U.S. Private*, pg. 1057
Hofer, Mark, Asst. Sec.--IG Laboratories, Inc., Framingham, MA; *U.S. Public*, pg. 733
Hoff, George H., Treas. & Sec.--Sargento Foods Inc.- Food Service Div., Plymouth, WI; *U.S. Private*, pg. 966
Hoffen, John, Sec.--USF&G Corporation, Baltimore, MD; *U.S. Public*, pg. 1659
Hoffer, Helen, Sec.--Hoffer Plastics Corporation, South Elgin, IL; *U.S. Private*, pg. 532
Hoffman, Barry P., Grp. V.P., Gen. Counsel & Sec.--Valassis Communications, Inc., Livonia, MI; *U.S. Public*, pg. 1704
Hoffman, Becky, Sec.--Automatic Equipment Mfg. Co., Pender, NE; *U.S. Private*, pg. 101
Hoffman, G.L., Chm. Bd., Pres., Chief Exec. Officer & Sec.--Insignia Systems, Inc., Minnetonka, MN; *U.S. Public*, pg. 881
Hoffman, Gary, Sec. & Treas.--Superior Water, Light & Power Company, Superior, WI; *U.S. Public*, pg. 1116
Hoffman, Gary K., V.P., Assoc. Gen. Counsel & Asst. Sec.--Old American Insurance Co., Kansas City, MO; *U.S. Public*, pg. 943
Hoffman, Joyce, V.P. & Corp. Sec.--The Principal Financial Group, Des Moines, IA; *U.S. Private*, pg. 885
Hoffman, Joyce, V.P. & Corp. Sec.--Principal Mutual Life Insurance Co., Des Moines, IA; *U.S. Private*, pg. 886
Hoffman, L.R., Corp. Sec. & Acting Chief Fin. Officer--Sybron Chemicals Inc., Birmingham, NJ; *U.S. Public*, pg. 1544
Hoffman, Richard C., Sec.--Weldotron Corporation, Piscataway, NJ; *U.S. Public*, pg. 1752
Hoffman, Robert L., Sec.--Ag-Chem Equipment Co., Inc., Minnetonka, MN; *U.S. Public*, pg. 6
Hoffman, Ronald S., Chief Fin. Officer & Sec.--Nantucket Industries, Inc., Melville, NY; *U.S. Public*, pg. 1151
Hoffmann, Christoph L., Exec. V.P.-Law & Corp. Admin. & Sec.--Raytheon Company, Lexington, MA; *U.S. Public*, pg. 1364
Hofley, C., V.P. & Sec.--Hofley Manufacturing Company, Roseville, MI; *U.S. Private*, pg. 532
Hogan, Gerald W., Asst. Sec.--Radisson Hotel Corporation, Minneapolis, MN; *U.S. Private*, pg. 212
Hogan, Kenneth W., Chief Fin. Officer, Sr. V.P. & Sec.--Valley Resources, Inc., Cumberland, RI; *U.S. Public*, pg. 1706
Hogan, Kenneth W., Chief Fin. Officer, Sr. V.P. & Sec.--Bristol & Warren Gas Company, Bristol, RI; *U.S. Public*, pg. 1706
Hogan, Vicky, Sec.--Quik Print Inc., Wichita, KS; *U.S. Private*, pg. 421
Hoges, Franziska, Sec.--Durr AG, Stuttgart, Germany; *Int'l*, pg. 421
Hogg, A.S., Sec.--Crane Group Limited, Epping, Australia; *Int'l*, pg. 340
Hogg, G. Scott, Treas. & Sec.--Better Brands Of Atlanta, Inc., Atlanta, GA; *U.S. Private*, pg. 141
Hohener, Dr. M., Sec--Credit Suisse, Zurich, Switzerland; *Int'l*, pg. 345
Hohenstein, Gail A., Asst. Sec.--Humana Health Insurance of Nevada, Inc., Las Vegas, NV; *U.S. Public*, pg. 847
Hohenstein, Gail A., Asst. Sec.--Humana Health Chicago, Inc., Chicago, IL; *U.S. Public*, pg. 847
Hohenstein, Gail A., V.P. & Asst. Sec.--Employers Health Insurance Company, Green Bay, WI; *U.S. Public*, pg. 847
Hohenstein, Gail A., Asst. Sec.--Humana Health Plan of Texas, Inc., San Antonio, TX; *U.S. Public*, pg. 848
Hohenstein, Gail A., Asst. Sec.--Humana Medical Plan Inc.- Miami, Miramar, FL; *U.S. Public*, pg. 848
Hohenstein, Gail A., Asst. Sec.--Humana Health Plan of Georgia, Inc., Louisville, KY; *U.S. Public*, pg. 848
Hohenstein, Gail A., Asst. Sec.--Humana Health Plan of Louisiana, Inc., Louisville, KY; *U.S. Public*, pg. 848
Hohenstein, Gail A., Asst. Sec.--Humana Insurance Company, Kansas City, MO; *U.S. Public*, pg. 848
Hohenstein, Gail A., Asst. Sec.--Humana Health Plan of Ohio, Inc., Cincinnati, OH; *U.S. Public*, pg. 848
Hohenstein, Gail A., Asst. Sec.--Humana Health Plan of Utah, Inc., Salt Lake City, UT; *U.S. Public*, pg. 848
Hohenstein, Gail A., Asst. Sec.--Humana Health Plan, Inc., Louisville, KY; *U.S. Public*, pg. 848
Hohenstein, Gail A., Asst. Sec.--Humana Health Plan of Alabama, Inc., Montgomery, AL; *U.S. Public*, pg. 848
Hohenstein, Gail A., Asst. Sec.--Humana Wisconsin Health Organization Insurance Corporation, Milwaukee, WI; *U.S. Public*, pg. 848
Hohenstein, Gail A., V.P. & Asst. Sec.--Network EPO, Inc., Milwaukee, WI; *U.S. Public*, pg. 848
Hohm, Dale J., V.P.-Fin. & Sec.--Numac Energy Inc., Calgary, Canada; *Int'l*, pg. 990
Hohn, Richard G., Sr. V.P., Sec. & Counsel--USLIFE Corporation, New York, NY; *U.S. Public*, pg. 77
Holbrook, Connie C., V.P. & Sec.--Questar Corporation, Salt Lake City, UT; *U.S. Public*, pg. 1352
Holbrook, Janet, Sec. & Treas.--Morgan Lumber Sales Co., Columbus, OH; *U.S. Private*, pg. 761
Holbrook, Lisa J., Sr. V.P.-Fin., Treas. & Sec.--Longview Fibre Company, Longview, WA; *U.S. Public*, pg. 1013
Holcomb, Robert J., Treas. & Sec.--V.T. Inc., Merriam, KS; *U.S. Private*, pg. 1131
Holcombe, Mary Lou, Asst. V.P. & Sec.--Andal Corp., New York, NY; *U.S. Public*, pg. 111
Holcombe, Paul A., Jr., V.P., Gen. Counsel & Sec.--Glaxo Wellcome PLC, Research Triangle Park, NC; *Int'l*, pg. 553
Holcombe, Robert S., Sr. V.P.,Gen. Counsel & Sec.--Apria Healthcare Group Inc., Costa Mesa, CA; *U.S. Public*, pg. 125
Holden, Pat, Sec.--Trayer Products, Inc., Elmira, NY; *U.S. Private*, pg. 1098
Holder, James T., Exec. V.P., Gen. Counsel & Sec.--Checkers Drive-In Restaurants, Inc., Clearwater, FL; *U.S. Public*, pg. 342
Holder, Walter, V.P. & Sec.--Hershey Creamery Company, Harrisburg, PA; *U.S. Private*, pg. 524
Holderness, Craig, Asst. Treas.--Nalco Chemical Company, Naperville, IL; *U.S. Public*, pg. 1150
Holding, M., Sec.--Dowty Aerospace, Wolverhampton, Wolverhampton, United Kingdom; *Int'l*, pg. 1337
Holihen, Jennifer A., Chief Fin. Officer, Treas. & Sec.--Crossmann Communities, Inc., Indianapolis, IN; *U.S. Public*, pg. 461
Holland, E.J., Jr., Sr. V.P.-H.R. & Sec.--Payless Cashways, Inc., Kansas City, MO; *U.S. Public*, pg. 1267
Holland, James M., Sr. V.P. & Sec.--Atwood Oceanics, Inc., Houston, TX; *U.S. Public*, pg. 146
Holland, Mark, Asst. Sec.--Sierra Health and Life Insurance Company, Inc., Las Vegas, NV; *U.S. Public*, pg. 1469
Holland, Robert B., III, Sr. V.P., Gen. Counsel & Sec.--Triton Energy Limited, Dallas, TX; *U.S. Public*, pg. 1640
Holland, Robert T., Chief Fin. Officer, V.P. & Sec.--Relm Wireless Corp., West Chester, PA; *U.S. Public*, pg. 1376
Holland, Thomas A., Chief Fin. Officer, Exec. V.P. & Sec.--Continental Mortgage and Equity Trust, Dallas, TX; *U.S. Public*, pg. 441
Holler, Judy, Sec.--Roger Holler Chevrolet & GEO Co., Winter Park, FL; *U.S. Private*, pg. 534
Holleran, T. Jerome, Sec.--Arrow International, Inc., Reading, PA; *U.S. Public*, pg. 135
Holley, Cheri, Gen. Counsel & Sec.--Titan International, Inc., Quincy, IL; *U.S. Public*, pg. 1618
Hollifield, Matthew V., Chief Acctg. Officer, V.P.-Acctg. & Asst. Sec.--WSMP, Inc., Claremont, NC; *U.S. Public*, pg. 1729
Hollings, David, Gen. Counsel & Sec.--Tano Automation, Inc., Harahan, LA; *U.S. Public*, pg. 1763
Hollingsworth, John Mark, Sr. Legal Counsel & Asst. Sec.--Valhi, Inc., Dallas, TX; *U.S. Private*, pg. 270
Hollingsworth, Linda, Treas. & Sec.--Sun Bulb Company, Inc., Arcadia, FL; *U.S. Private*, pg. 1050
Holloway, Eugene C., V.P., Gen. Counsel & Sec.--Thomas & Betts/Amerace, Brooksville, FL; *U.S. Public*, pg. 1598
Holloway, Ronald A., Sec., Mgr.-Land & Dir.--States, Inc., Breckenridge, TX; *U.S. Private*, pg. 1037
Holm, Joyce, Sec.--Your Man Tours, Inc., Inglewood, CA; *U.S. Private*, pg. 1202
Holman, Bobby G., Chief Fin. Officer, Treas. & Asst. Sec.--WSMP, Inc., Claremont, NC; *U.S. Public*, pg. 1729
Holman, Don, Sec.--Byers Portland Willamette, Portland, OR; *U.S. Private*, pg. 191
Holman, Robert, Exec. V.P.-Fin.--Reinalt-Thomas Corp., Ann Arbor, MI; *U.S. Private*, pg. 919
Holmen, Robert R., Asst. Sec.--ICS Intangibles Holding Company, Irvine, CA; *U.S. Public*, pg. 783
Holmen, Robert R., Asst. Sec.--Steck-Vaughn Company, Austin, TX; *U.S. Public*, pg. 784
Holmen, Robert R., Asst. Sec.--National Educational International Corp., Irvine, CA; *U.S. Public*, pg. 784
Holmen, Robert R., Asst. Sec.--National Education Credit Corporation, Irvine, CA; *U.S. Public*, pg. 784
Holmen, Robert R., Asst. Sec.--National Education Payroll Corp., Irvine, CA; *U.S. Public*, pg. 784
Holmen, Robert R., Asst. Sec.--Steck-Vaughn Publishing Corporation, Austin, TX; *U.S. Public*, pg. 784
Holmen, Robert R., Asst. Sec.--Steck-Vaughn Distribution Company, Austin, TX; *U.S. Public*, pg. 784
Holmes, Donald D., V.P.-Fin. & Sec.--Scotsman Industries, Inc., Vernon Hills, IL; *U.S. Public*, pg. 1444
Holmes, Frank E., Dr., Exec. V.P., Chief Oper. Officer & Sec.--Semi-Tech Corporation, Markham, Canada; *Int'l*, pg. 1220
Holmes, Hardin, Sec.--COBE Laboratories, Inc., Lakewood, CO; *Int'l*, pg. 667
Holmes, Janet, Asst. Sec.--Coca-Cola Bottling Co. Consolidated, Charlotte, NC; *U.S. Public*, pg. 391
Holmes, William E., Chief Fin. Officer & Sec.--Compas Electronics, Inc., Kanata, Canada; *Int'l*, pg. 36
Holschuh, Laurel A., Sr. V.P., Asst. Gen. Counsel & Sec.--Norwest Corporation, Minneapolis, MN; *U.S. Public*, pg. 1201
Holsenbeck, G. Penn, V.P., Assoc. Gen. Counsel & Sec.--Philip Morris Companies Inc., New York, NY; *U.S. Public*, pg. 1287
Holton, Bill, Sec.--Dakota Electric Association, Farmington, MN; *U.S. Private*, pg. 308
Holtzman, Morton, V.P., Sec. & Treas.--Harve Benard Ltd., Secaucus, NJ; *U.S. Private*, pg. 508
Holtzman, Morton, V.P., Treas. & Sec.--Harve Benard Ltd., New York, NY; *U.S. Private*, pg. 508
Holzman, Donald J., Gen. Counsel & Sec.--Dinaire Corp., Buffalo, NY; *U.S. Private*, pg. 334
Hombre, Juan Bule, Sec.--Banco Central Hispanoamericano S.A., Madrid, Spain; *Int'l*, pg. 139
Homes, Pat, Sec.--Homes & Son Contractors, Inc., Phoenix, AZ; *U.S. Private*, pg. 537
Honaman, David G., Chief Fin. Officer, V.P.-Admin. & Sec.--Wolohan Lumber Co., Saginaw, MI; *U.S. Public*, pg. 1774
Honbarrier, Louise B., Treas. & Sec.--Central Transport, Archdale, NC; *U.S. Private*, pg. 225
Honek, Anna B., Sec.--Connecticut Drive Shaft, Inc., Milford, CT; *U.S. Private*, pg. 263
Hones, Frank W., Asst. Treas. & Asst. Sec.--Jacobson Stores Inc., Jackson, MI; *U.S. Public*, pg. 922
Honeycutt, Travis W., Exec. V.P. & Sec.--Isolyser Company, Inc., Norcross, GA; *U.S. Public*, pg. 914
Hong, Chung Ki, Sec.--Cho Hung Bank, Seoul, Korea; *Int'l*, pg. 287
Honig, David, Treas. & Sec.--Jarchem Industries, Inc., Newark, NJ; *U.S. Private*, pg. 582
Hood, Cecil G., Treas. & Sec.--Batson-Cook Company, West Point, GA; *U.S. Private*, pg. 123
Hoogewind, William H., Sec. & Dir.-Mktg.--Clipper Belt Lacer Company, Grand Rapids, MI; *U.S. Private*, pg. 413
Hook, Gail, Sec.--Tetley USA Inc., Shelton, CT; *Int'l*, pg. 1377
Hooper, D.R., Sec.--Berisford plc, London, United Kingdom; *Int'l*, pg. 188
Hooper, David, Co. Sec.--Magnet Ltd., Keighley, United Kingdom; *Int'l*, pg. 188
Hooper, Lawrence L., Jr., Gen. Counsel & Sec.--Petroleum & Resources Corp., Baltimore, MD; *U.S. Public*, pg. 1280
Hoopman, L. Elizabeth, Sec.--Burris Foods, Inc., Milford, DE; *U.S. Private*, pg. 188
Hootkin, Pamela N., V.P., Treas. & Sec.--Phillips-Van Heusen Corporation, New York, NY; *U.S. Public*, pg. 1291
Hoover, Arthur, Sec. & Prod. Mgr.--T. Bruce Sales, Inc., West Middlesex, PA; *U.S. Private*, pg. 175
Hoover, Rose, Sec. & Legal Asst.--Ampco-Pittsburgh Corporation, Pittsburgh, PA; *U.S. Public*, pg. 103
Hope, R.G., Sec.--Silentnight Holdings Plc, Colne, United Kingdom; *Int'l*, pg. 1249
Hopkins, Jacques V., Sec.--Astro-Med, Inc., West Warwick, RI; *U.S. Public*, pg. 141
Hopkins, Jeff, Sec.--Superior Graphite Co., Chicago, IL; *U.S. Private*, pg. 1054
Hopkins, R. Howard, Sr. V.P., Gen. Counsel & Sec.--SGS North America Inc., New York, NY; *Int'l*, pg. 1153
Hopkinson, Ian, Corp. Sec.--MDIS Group plc, Hemel Hempstead, United Kingdom; *Int'l*, pg. 826
Hopkinson, Mark R., Chief Fin. Officer, Treas. & Asst. Sec.--Artistic Carton Company, Elgin, IL; *U.S. Private*, pg. 87
Hopp, Daniel F., V.P., Gen. Counsel & Sec.--Whirlpool Corporation, Benton Harbor, MI; *U.S. Public*, pg. 1764
Hoppe, Lois, Exec. Sec.--Bradley Corporation, Menomonee Falls, WI; *U.S. Private*, pg. 164
Hopping, K.H., V.P. & Sec.--The Lubrizol Corporation, Wickliffe, OH; *U.S. Public*, pg. 1016
Hopwood, Terry, V.P., Gen. Counsel & Sec.--Suncor Inc., Calgary, Canada; *Int'l*, pg. 1320
Horan, Anthony J., Sr. V.P. & Sec.--The Chase Manhattan Corporation, New York, NY; *U.S. Public*, pg. 337
Horan, Dennis, Chief Fin. Officer, Treas. & Sec.--URM Stores, Inc., Spokane, WA; *U.S. Private*, pg. 1114
Horan, Thomas W., Chief Fin. Officer, Sr. V.P.-Fin. & Sec.--Great Dane Trailers, Inc., Savannah, GA; *U.S. Private*, pg. 1030
Horgan, Denis F., Sec.--Westshore Terminals Ltd., Delta, Canada; *Int'l*, pg. 1491
Horiszny, Laurene H., V.P., Gen. Counsel & Sec.--Borg Warner Automotive, Inc., Chicago, IL; *U.S. Public*, pg. 245
Horn, Randall, Dir.-Investor Rels. & Asst. Sec.--NICOR Inc., Naperville, IL; *U.S. Public*, pg. 1182
Horn, Richard P., V.P., Gen. Counsel & Asst. Sec.--HealthAmerica Pennsylvania, Inc., Pittsburgh, PA; *U.S. Public*, pg. 454
Horner, Robert W., III, Sr. V.P., Gen. Counsel & Sec.--Vitalink Pharmacy Services, Inc., Naperville, IL; *U.S. Public*, pg. 1041
Horner, Russell G., Jr., Sr. V.P., Gen. Counsel & Sec.--Kerr-McGee Corporation, Oklahoma City, OK; *U.S. Public*, pg. 952
Horner, Stephen R., V.P.-Admin. & Asst. Sec.--Renaissance Energy Ltd., Calgary, Canada; *Int'l*, pg. 1102
Horowitz, Donald, Chief Fin. Officer, Treas. & Sec.--Aceto Corporation, Lake Success, NY; *U.S. Public*, pg. 15
Horowitz, Donald, Treas. & Sec.--VGF Corporation, Lake Success, NY; *U.S. Public*, pg. 15
Horowitz, Jeffrey R., Sr. V.P., Gen. Counsel & Sec.--Ogden Energy Group, Inc., Fairfield, NJ; *U.S. Public*, pg. 1213
Horowitz, Roberto, Sec.--Landstar Development Company, Orlando, FL; *U.S. Private*, pg. 649
Horrocks, Alison, Sec.--Shandwick International Plc, London, United Kingdom; *Int'l*, pg. 1226
Horton, Ann N., Treas. & Sec.--Penn Virginia Oil & Gas Company, Kingsport, TN; *U.S. Public*, pg. 1271
Horton, Brenda, Sec.--S&D Coffee Inc., Concord, NC; *U.S. Private*, pg. 954
Horton, Jeffrey, V.P. & Sec.--IDS Deposit Corp., Midvale, UT; *U.S. Public*, pg. 73
Horton, Mark, Sec.--Brierley Investments Limited, Wellington, New Zealand; *Int'l*, pg. 215

Horvat, Peter D., Chief Fin. Officer, V.P., Treas. & Sec.--Lenape Forge, Inc., West Chester, PA; *U.S. Private*, pg. 659
Horwitz, Eugene, V.P.-Admin. & Sec.--Liberty Paper & Bag Co., Auburn Hills, MI; *Int'l*, pg. 233
Horwitz, Stewart, Chief Fin. Officer & Sec.--Elkay Plastics Company, Inc., Los Angeles, CA; *U.S. Private*, pg. 372
Hos, Bruce, V.P., Gen. Mgr. & Sec.--Mizuno Golf Company, Norcross, GA; *Int'l*, pg. 885
Hoshiko, Jim, Mgr.-Product Devel.--McGill Manufacturing Company, Inc., Valparaiso, IN; *U.S. Public*, pg. 573
Hoskin, M.C., Sec.--The Davis Service Group Plc., London, United Kingdom; *Int'l*, pg. 385
Hoskin, Norman J., Asst. Sec.--Aqua Care Systems Inc., Coral Springs, FL; *U.S. Public*, pg. 126
Hoskins, T.J., Sec.--Exxon Coal and Minerals Company, Houston, TX; *U.S. Public*, pg. 601
Hotchkin, R., Sec.--Tech-Tran Corporation, Rancocas, NJ; *U.S. Private*, pg. 560
Hottovy, Ronald J., Chief Fin. Officer, Exec. V.P., Treas. & Sec.--Scientific Software-Intercomp, Inc., Denver, CO; *U.S. Public*, pg. 1443
Hougen, H. Monty, V.P., Sec. & Deputy Gen. Counsel--DynCorp, Reston, VA; *U.S. Private*, pg. 351
Hough, Pam, Asst. Sec.--Family Home Hospice, Inc., Las Vegas, NV; *U.S. Public*, pg. 1469
Houghton, T.P., Sec.--Senior Green Economiser Division, Wakefield, United Kingdom; *Int'l*, pg. 1221
Houle, Patricia S., Sec. & Asst. Treas.--Bozzuto's Inc., Cheshire, CT; *U.S. Public*, pg. 249
House, P.J., V.P. & Sec.--ATCO Group Co., Calgary, Canada; *Int'l*, pg. 95
Houser, Douglas G., Asst. Sec.--Nike, Inc., Beaverton, OR; *U.S. Public*, pg. 1184
Houser, Glena, V.P. & Sec.--Fidelity National Title Insurance Company of Tennessee, Knoxville, TN; *U.S. Public*, pg. 621
Houston, B. Ord, Sec.--The Bethlehem Corporation, Easton, PA; *U.S. Public*, pg. 225
Houston, John, Sec.--PremiumWear, Inc., Minneapolis, MN; *U.S. Public*, pg. 1323
Houston, Tom, Gen. Counsel & Sec.--Scottish Widows' Fund & Life Assurance Society, Edinburgh, United Kingdom; *Int'l*, pg. 1212
Hovanec, Eugene F., Chief Fin. Officer & Sec.--Vitesse Semiconductor Corporation, Camarillo, CA; *U.S. Public*, pg. 1723
Hover-Smoot, Scott R., Gen. Counsel & Sec.--California Micro Devices, Milpitas, CA; *U.S. Public*, pg. 293
Howard, Bill, Treas. & Sec.--Mercer Transportation Co., Louisville, KY; *U.S. Private*, pg. 732
Howard, Connie, Controller--Camalloy, Incorporated, Washington, PA; *U.S. Private*, pg. 202
Howard, Heather, Gen. Counsel & Sec.--The Boeing Company, Seattle, WA; *U.S. Public*, pg. 239
Howard, James H., Chief Fin. Officer & Corp. Sec.--Stowe-Pharr Mills, Inc., Mc Adenville, NC; *U.S. Private*, pg. 1045
Howard, Jan, Sec.--Telsi Ltd., London, United Kingdom; *Int'l*, pg. 1248
Howard, Larry, Asst. Sec.--Health Plan of Nevada, Inc., Las Vegas, NV; *U.S. Public*, pg. 1469
Howard, Patricia J., V.P., Asst. Gen. Counsel & Deputy Sec.--Republic New York Corporation, New York, NY; *U.S. Public*, pg. 1380
Howard, Richard F., Chm. Bd. & Sec.--WSMP, Inc., Claremont, NC; *U.S. Public*, pg. 1729
Howard, Robert I., Sec.--Halma p.l.c., Amersham, United Kingdom; *Int'l*, pg. 589
Howard, Rudy C., CPA, Chief Fin. Officer, V.P.-Fin., Treas. & Sec.--Pharmaceutical Product Development, Inc., Wilmington, NC; *U.S. Public*, pg. 1285
Howard, Thomas, V.P. & Sec.--Carl Weissman & Sons, Inc., Great Falls, MT; *U.S. Private*, pg. 1160
Howard, William J., Exec. V.P. & Sec.--DenAmerica Corp., Scottsdale, AZ; *U.S. Public*, pg. 498
Howat, Bruce B., Corp. Sec.--Ameritech Corporation, Chicago, IL; *U.S. Public*, pg. 97
Howe, Jas Murray, Sec. & Clerk--Courier Kendallville, Inc., Kendallville, IN; *U.S. Public*, pg. 453
Howe, Jos Murray, Clerk--Courier Westford, Inc., Westford, MA; *U.S. Public*, pg. 453
Howell-Saxton, Delight, Chief Fin. Officer, Sr. V.P. & Sec.--McGrath RentCorp, Livermore, CA; *U.S. Public*, pg. 1069
Howell, Dolores, Exec. V.P. & Sec.--Moyer Packing Company, Souderton, PA; *U.S. Private*, pg. 765
Howell, Hilton H., V.P. & Sec.--Bull Run Corporation, Atlanta, GA; *U.S. Public*, pg. 267
Howell, Kenneth, Asst. Sec.--Pioneer Oil Company Inc., Fort Worth, TX; *U.S. Private*, pg. 866
Howell, Margaret, Sec.--Steel Technologies Inc., Louisville, KY; *U.S. Public*, pg. 1513
Howerton, Nancy, Asst. Sec.--Metropolitan Mortgage & Securities Co., Inc., Spokane, WA; *U.S. Private*, pg. 738
Howie, P.R.S., Gen. Counsel & Sec.--Burmah Castrol plc, Swindon, United Kingdom; *Int'l*, pg. 234
Howson, Richard, Treas. & Sec.--Dover Corp. (Canada) Ltd., Mississauga, Canada; *U.S. Public*, pg. 522
Hoyt, Jeffrey E., Chief Oper. Officer, Exec. V.P. & Sec.--Sun Bancorp, Inc., Selinsgrove, PA; *U.S. Public*, pg. 1529
Hrayssi, Walid, Sec.--Gefinor S.A. Luxembourg, Luxembourg, Luxembourg; *Int'l*, pg. 542
Hretzay, Eugene, Gen. Counsel & Sec.--Acklands Limited, Toronto, Canada; *Int'l*, pg. 23
Hron, Michael G., Gen. Counsel & Sec.--Telephone and Data Systems, Inc., Chicago, IL; *U.S. Public*, pg. 1570
Hsiau-Huey Hsieh, Vicki, Sr. V.P. & Sec.--The International Commercial Bank of China, Taipei, Taiwan; *Int'l*, pg. 683
Huben, Christina E., Gen. Counsel & Sec.--EnviroSource, Inc., Horsham, PA; *U.S. Public*, pg. 587
Huber, Judy, Exec. V.P., Treas. & Sec.--Time Systems, Inc., Phoenix, AZ; *U.S. Private*, pg. 1086
Huber, Stephen, Chief Fin. Officer, Treas. & Sec.--Birdsong Corporation, Suffolk, VA; *U.S. Private*, pg. 145
Huber, Thomas, V.P., Comptroller & Corp. Sec.--Long Island Water Corporation, Lynbrook, NY; *U.S. Private*, pg. 674
Huber, Thomas P., Exec. V.P., Gen. Counsel & Asst. Sec.--First Hawaiian Bank, Honolulu, HI; *U.S. Public*, pg. 634
Huber, Thomas P., V.P. & Asst. Sec.--FHB Properties, Inc., Honolulu, HI; *U.S. Public*, pg. 635
Huber, Thomas P., V.P. & Asst. Sec.--FH Center, Inc., Honolulu, HI; *U.S. Public*, pg. 635
Huber, Thomas P., Asst. Sec.--Real Estate Delivery, Inc., Honolulu, HI; *U.S. Public*, pg. 635
Hubler, James T., Sr. V.P.-Industrial Rels., Gen. Counsel & Sec.--Freightliner Corp., Portland, OR; *Int'l*, pg. 368
Hudnut, Stewart S., Sr. V.P., Sec. & Gen. Counsel--Illinois Tool Works Inc., Glenview, IL; *U.S. Public*, pg. 865
Hudson, Beth A., Sec.--Diversco, Inc., Spartanburg, SC; *U.S. Private*, pg. 336
Hudson, Mary, Sec.--Ceco Building Systems, Columbus, MS; *U.S. Private*, pg. 221
Hudson, Richard W., V.P.-Fin. & Sec.--Healthcare Services Group, Inc., Huntingdon Valley, PA; *U.S. Public*, pg. 803
Hudspeth, Forrest, Sec.--Carlton Manufacturing, Inc., Goshen, IN; *U.S. Private*, pg. 212
Huerter, M. Jane, Exec. V.P.-Corp. Resources & Corp. Sec.--Mutual of Omaha Insurance Company, Omaha, NE; *U.S. Private*, pg. 769
Huerter, M. Jane, Sec.--Mutual of Omaha Investor Services, Inc., Omaha, NE; *U.S. Private*, pg. 770
Huerter, M. Jane, Sec.--Tele-Trip Company, Omaha, NE; *U.S. Private*, pg. 770
Huerter, M. Jane, Exec. V.P.-Corp. Resouces & Corp. Sec.--United of Omaha Life Insurance Company, Omaha, NE; *U.S. Private*, pg. 770
Huff, Charles E., V.P., Gen. Counsel & Sec.--Boyd Gaming Corporation, Las Vegas, NV; *U.S. Public*, pg. 249
Hufnagel, Leon C., Jr., Sec.--BPA International, New York, NY; *U.S. Private*, pg. 107
Huftless, Cindy, Sec.--Amwest Insurance Group, Inc., Calabasas, CA; *U.S. Public*, pg. 106
Hughes, B., Sec.--Hilton International Hotels (U.K.) Ltd., Watford, United Kingdom; *Int'l*, pg. 787
Hughes, Catherine L., Gen. Counsel & Sec.--Acxiom Corporation, Conway, AR; *U.S. Public*, pg. 18
Hughes, George M., Corp. Clerk--Chase Corporation, Braintree, MA; *U.S. Public*, pg. 337
Hughes, Karen S., Chief Fin. Officer, V.P. & Sec.--Ridgewood Properties, Inc., Atlanta, GA; *U.S. Public*, pg. 1389
Hughes, Mary L., Sec.--Medtech Inc., Jackson, WY; *U.S. Private*, pg. 728
Hughes, Michael, Sec.--OzEmail Limited, Sydney, Australia; *Int'l*, pg. 1019
Hughes, Paul, Sec.--Hughes Family Markets, Inc., Irwindale, CA; *U.S. Public*, pg. 1349
Hughes, W. Alan, Treas.--Fleischli Oil Company, Inc., Cheyenne, WY; *U.S. Private*, pg. 410
Huitt, E. Larry, Chm. Bd., Exec. V.P., Treas. & Sec.--Huitt-Zollars, Inc., Dallas, TX; *U.S. Private*, pg. 547
Hulin, J. F., Sec.--Clayhithe P.L.C., Aylesbury, United Kingdom; *Int'l*, pg. 297
Hull, Earl J., Sec.--The Monarch Machine Tool Company, Sidney, OH; *U.S. Public*, pg. 1123
Hulme, Michael E., Jr., Asst. Gen. Counsel & Asst. Sec.--United States Filter Corporation, Palm Desert, CA; *U.S. Public*, pg. 1681
Hulseman, John, Exec. V.P. & Sec.--Solo Cup Company, Highland Park, IL; *U.S. Private*, pg. 1013
Hume, D. William, Sr. V.P. & Asst. Sec.--Penn Security Bank and Trust Co., Scranton, PA; *U.S. Public*, pg. 1270
Hummers, William S., III, Chief Fin. Officer & Exec. V.P.--Carolina First Corporation, Greenville, SC; *U.S. Public*, pg. 306
Humpherson, C.M., Sec.--Wagon Industrial Holdings PLC, Birmingham, United Kingdom; *Int'l*, pg. 1484
Humphreys, D.J., Sec.--Morganite Thermal Ceramics Taiwan Limited, Taipei, Taiwan,; *Int'l*, pg. 894
Humphreys, John W., V.P.-Admin. & Asst. Sec.--Norfolk Shipbuilding & Drydock Corporation, Norfolk, VA; *U.S. Private*, pg. 802
Humphreys, Robert K., Chief Fin. Officer, Treas. & Sec.--Valley Detroit Diesel Allison, City of Industry, CA; *U.S. Private*, pg. 1132
Humphreys, Sandy, Sec.--Minor Rubber Co., Inc., Bloomfield, NJ; *U.S. Private*, pg. 751
Humphries, Donnie R., V.P. & Sec.--NCI Building Systems, Inc., Houston, TX; *U.S. Public*, pg. 1145
Hundy, W.M., Co. Sec.--Email Limited, Waterloo, Australia; *Int'l*, pg. 450
Hunnicutt, Donald P., Controller & Sec.--Graphic Industries, Inc., Atlanta, GA; *U.S. Public*, pg. 1735
Hunnicutt, John O., III, V.P.-Admin. & Sec.--DIMON, Incorporated, Danville, VA; *U.S. Public*, pg. 509
Hunt, Darlene, Corp. Sec.--Clairol Canada Inc., Montreal, Canada; *U.S. Public*, pg. 254
Hunt, Johnelle, Sec.--J.B. Hunt Transport Services, Inc., Lowell, AR; *U.S. Public*, pg. 849
Hunt, Julian Richard, Sec.--Tie Rack plc, Brentford, United Kingdom; *Int'l*, pg. 1389
Hunt, Mary E., Asst. Sec.--Central Power and Light Company, Corpus Christi, TX; *U.S. Public*, pg. 324
Hunt, Philip G., Sr. V.P., Gen. Counsel & Sec.--Ruby Tuesday, Inc., Mobile, AL; *U.S. Public*, pg. 1411
Hunt, Tim J., Sec.--Del Monte Foods International Limited, Staines, United Kingdom; *Int'l*, pg. 388
Huntington, David, V.P. & Sec.--IDM Controls, Houston, TX; *U.S. Private*, pg. 554
Huntsman, Barry N., Treas. & Sec.--AMBAR Marine, Inc., Lafayette, LA; *U.S. Private*, pg. 126
Hupfer, C.J., V.P., Treas. & Corp. Sec.--Sonoco Products Company, Hartsville, SC; *U.S. Public*, pg. 1485
Hupp, John W., Sec.--Knowles Electronics, Inc., Itasca, IL; *U.S. Private*, pg. 627
Huppi, Rolf, Chm. Bd. & Chief Exec. Officer--Zurich Insurance Company, Zurich, Switzerland; *Int'l*, pg. 1529
Huras, Lynn, V.P. & Asst. Sec.--Trans-Lux Canada Ltd., Mississauga, Canada; *U.S. Public*, pg. 1629
Hurley, Melissa M., Sr. V.P., Gen. Counsel & Sec.--Northstar Investment Management Corporation, Greenwich, CT; *U.S. Public*, pg. 1375
Hurlstone, Barbara, Controller--Mitek Systems, Inc., San Diego, CA; *U.S. Public*, pg. 1117
Hursh, Alan, Treas. & Sec.--Acousti Engineering Co. of Florida, Orlando, FL; *U.S. Private*, pg. 14
Hurst, David B., Sec.--Adams Resources & Energy, Inc., Houston, TX; *U.S. Public*, pg. 18
Hurt, Robert, V.P.-Maintenance, Asst. Sec. & Dir.--M.S. Carriers, Inc., Memphis, TN; *U.S. Public*, pg. 1027
Hurwich, Robert A., V.P.-Admin., Sec. & Gen. Counsel--Lynch Corporation, Greenwich, CT; *U.S. Public*, pg. 1021
Hurwich, Robert A., Asst. Sec.--M-Tron Industries, Inc., Yankton, SD; *U.S. Public*, pg. 1022
Hurwich, Robert A., Bd. Sec.--The Morgan Group, Inc., Elkhart, IN; *U.S. Public*, pg. 1022
Husain, Altaf, Treas., Sec. & Mgr.-Fin. & Plng.--National Refinery Limited, Karachi, Pakistan; *Int'l*, pg. 909
Husband, W.D., Sec. & Treas.--Canadian Timken Ltd., Saint Thomas, Canada; *U.S. Public*, pg. 1617
Hussain, Masarrat, Dir.-Admin.--Signet Group plc, London, United Kingdom; *Int'l*, pg. 1248
Hussey, Edward Joseph, V.P., Sec. & Asst. Treas.--Liberty Homes, Inc., Goshen, IN; *U.S. Public*, pg. 992
Hussey, Michael F., V.P.-Fin. & Asst. Sec.--Liberty Homes, Inc., Goshen, IN; *U.S. Public*, pg. 992
Hutcherson, Cecil, Controller & Sec.--Mayfair Mills, Inc., Arcadia, SC; *U.S. Private*, pg. 718
Hutcheson, N., Gen. Counsel & Asst. Sec.--The Budd Company, Troy, MI; *Int'l*, pg. 1388
Hutchison, Shawna, Sec.--Johns Manville Corporation, Denver, CO; *U.S. Public*, pg. 927
Hutton, Nancy, Controller, Treas. & Sec.--Crustbuster, Inc., Dodge City, KS; *U.S. Private*, pg. 293
Huxtable, Laurie J., Asst. Sec.--Caterpillar Inc., Peoria, IL; *U.S. Public*, pg. 315
Hyde, Susan C., Mgr.-Investor Rels. & Asst. Sec.--W.P. Carey & Co., Inc., New York, NY; *U.S. Private*, pg. 209
Hyland, John T., Sec. & Treas.--Intercom Systems, Inc., Copiague, NY; *U.S. Public*, pg. 1556
Hyland, Kathi, Corp. Sec.--Pacific Coast Producers, Lodi, CA; *U.S. Private*, pg. 830
Hyndman, Peter S., V.P.-Law, Gen. Counsel & Sec.--The Loewen Group, Inc., Burnaby, Canada; *Int'l*, pg. 814
Hynes, Edward G., Controller & Sec.--Befab-Safeland, Ltd., Shannon, Ireland; *U.S. Private*, pg. 313
Hysler, Lorraine, Sec.--KOA Holdings, New York, NY; *U.S. Private*, pg. 603
Iacovelli, David, Treas. & Sec.--Italian Food Manufacturers, Inc., Vestal, NY; *U.S. Private*, pg. 576
Iacovetti, Benedict J., Asst. Sec.--American Travellers Insurance Services, Bensalem, PA; *U.S. Public*, pg. 433
Iannacone, Michael, Sec.--Consolidated Viscount Resources Ltd., Vancouver, Canada; *Int'l*, pg. 326
Iceland, Philip, Sec. & Gen. Mgr.--Yorkshire Building Society, Bradford, United Kingdom; *Int'l*, pg. 1522
Ichii, Hideo, V.P. & Sec.--Asahi International Ltd., New York, NY; *Int'l*, pg. 85
Ichikawa-Schmid, Susan, V.P. & Sec.--Peck Jones Construction, Los Angeles, CA; *U.S. Private*, pg. 846
Ide, R. William, III, Sr. V.P., Gen. Counsel & Sec.--Monsanto Company, Saint Louis, MO; *U.S. Public*, pg. 1124
Iglesias Elizondo, E., Sec.--Far-Ben S.A. de C.V., Monterrey, Mexico; *Int'l*, pg. 478
Ilitch, Marian, Sec. & Treas.--Little Caesar Enterprises, Inc., Detroit, MI; *U.S. Private*, pg. 671
Imamura, Austin, V.P. & Sec.--CPB Inc., Honolulu, HI; *U.S. Public*, pg. 282
Imbeau, Claude, Gen. Counsel & Sec.--Tembec Inc., Montreal, Canada; *Int'l*, pg. 1374
Imbriaco, James, Assoc. Gen. Counsel & Asst. Sec.--The Times Mirror Company, Los Angeles, CA; *U.S. Public*, pg. 1615
Imperia, Joseph, Treas. & Sec.--Imperia Bros., Inc., Pelham Manor, NY; *U.S. Private*, pg. 558
Indelicato, Frank, Sec.--Delicato Vineyards, Manteca, CA; *U.S. Private*, pg. 322
Ingberman, Israel, Sec. & Treas.--Continental Health Affiliates, Inc., Englewood Cliffs, NJ; *U.S. Public*, pg. 440
Ingemi, Jean-Marie, Asst. Sec.--Stackpole Ltd., Newton, MA; *U.S. Private*, pg. 1028
Ingersoll, Mark K., Sec.--Rochester Midland Corporation, Rochester, NY; *U.S. Private*, pg. 937
Ingleman, John A., Chief Fin. Officer & V.P.--Hutchinson Technology Inc., Hutchinson, MN; *U.S. Public*, pg. 850
Ingraham, James H., V.P.-Legal & Sec.--H & R Block, Inc., Kansas City, MO; *U.S. Public*, pg. 770
Ingram, Betty, Treas. & Sec.--B & B Homes Corporation, Casper, WY; *U.S. Private*, pg. 105
Ingram, E. Michael, Sr. V.P., Gen. Counsel & Sec.--National Data Corporation, Atlanta, GA; *U.S. Public*, pg. 1155
Ingram, Richard S., Jr., Chief Fin. Officer, Treas. & Sec.--T.A. Loving Company, Goldsboro, NC; *U.S. Private*, pg. 677
Ingram, Steve, V.P.-Legal & Sec.--Southern Farm Bureau Casualty Insurance Company, Ridgeland, MS; *U.S. Private*, pg. 1016
Ingram, W. Ronald, Gen. Counsel & Sec.--Chronicle Publishing Co. Inc., San Francisco, CA; *U.S. Private*, pg. 239
Ingulsrud, Brian, Asst. Treas. & Asst. Sec.--American Crystal Sugar Company, Moorhead, MN; *U.S. Private*, pg. 52
Inkpen, A. Robert, V.P.-Fin. & Sec.--Newfoundland Capital Corporation Limited, Dartmouth, Canada; *Int'l*, pg. 924
Innaimo, Linda, Corp. Sec.--Truelove & Maclean Inc., Waterbury, CT; *U.S. Private*, pg. 1107
Inserra, Laurence, Sec.--Wakefern Food Corporation, Elizabeth, NJ; *U.S. Private*, pg. 1146

Iorio, Frank S., Sec.--Dani Michaels, Inc., New York, NY; *U.S. Private*, pg. 309
Ippolito, Robert S., Chief Fin. Officer, Treas. & Sec.--Penn National Gaming, Inc., Wyomissing, PA; *U.S. Public*, pg. 1270
Ippolito, Ugo F., Sec.--IQ Software Corporation, Norcross, GA; *U.S. Public*, pg. 858
Irish, Rebecca R., Sec. & Treas.--A - 1 Medical Equipment, Inc., Orlando, FL; *U.S. Public*, pg. 884
Irish, Rebecca R., Sec. & Treas.--American Medical Rentals, Inc., Orlando, FL; *U.S. Public*, pg. 884
Irish, Roy, Dir.-Fin. & Sec.--Laughton & Sons, Ltd., Birmingham, United Kingdom; *Int'l*, pg. 804
Irlando, Sandra J., V.P.-Acctg. & Sec.--Prima Energy Corporation, Denver, CO; *U.S. Public*, pg. 1325
Irving, J., Dir.-Legal Affairs--Iveco-Ford Truck Ltd., Watford, United Kingdom; *Int'l*, pg. 484
Irwin, Jan, Sec.--Sundt Corp., Tucson, AZ; *U.S. Private*, pg. 1051
Irwin, John D., Sec.--Tolleson Lumber Company, Inc., Perry, GA; *U.S. Private*, pg. 1090
Isaacson, James, V.P.-Fin., Treas. & Sec.--International Airline Support Group, Inc., Atlanta, GA; *U.S. Public*, pg. 894
Isakoff, Lou, Corp. Sec.--MTM Enterprises, Inc., Studio City, CA; *Int'l*, pg. 927
Isakoff, Louis A., Sr. V.P., Gen. Counsel & Sec.--International Family Entertainment, Inc., Virginia Beach, VA; *Int'l*, pg. 927
Iselin, Peter, V.P.-Fin. & Sec.--Rochester & Pittsburgh Coal Company, Indiana, PA; *U.S. Public*, pg. 1395
Isom, Donna, Treas. & Sec.--Quality Foods Inc., Little Rock, AR; *U.S. Private*, pg. 898
Iverach, Sheila J., Asst. Sec.--Westcoast Energy Inc., Vancouver, Canada; *Int'l*, pg. 1492
Iverson, Kenneth A., V.P. & Sec.--Ecolab Inc., Saint Paul, MN; *U.S. Public*, pg. 562
Iwatani, Jon T., Asst. Treas. & Asst. Sec.--Ka'u Agribusiness Co., Inc., Pahala, HI; *U.S. Private*, pg. 190
Iwatani, Jon T., Asst. Treas. & Asst. Sec.--Olokele Sugar Co., Limited, Kaunakakai, HI; *U.S. Private*, pg. 191
Izbicki, Anthony J., V.P. & Sec.--Hood & Company, Hamburg, PA; *Int'l*, pg. 572
Izquierdo, Mireia, Sec.--Caixa d'Estalvis de Catalunya, Barcelona, Spain; *Int'l*, pg. 249
Jabanoski, James R., Asst. Sec.--John Deere Capital Corporation, Reno, NV; *U.S. Public*, pg. 492
Jaccard, Walter B., V.P.- Gen. Counsel & Sec.--U.S. Trails, Dallas, TX; *U.S. Public*, pg. 1688
Jackman, Edward F., V.P., Gen. Counsel & Sec.--Cytec Industries Inc., West Paterson, NJ; *U.S. Public*, pg. 471
Jackman, Ian Peter, Sec.--The Burton Group PLC, London, United Kingdom; *Int'l*, pg. 237
Jackson, John D., Sr. V.P. & Sec.--The Fairchild Corporation, Chantilly, VA; *U.S. Public*, pg. 610
Jackson, Johnnie M., Jr., V.P., Gen. Counsel & Sec.--Olin Corporation, Norwalk, CT; *U.S. Public*, pg. 1218
Jackson, Peter H., Sec. & Mgr.-Special Projects--Humphrey Products Company, Kalamazoo, MI; *U.S. Private*, pg. 547
Jackson, Rex S., V.P., Gen. Counsel & Sec.--Read-Rite Corporation, Milpitas, CA; *U.S. Public*, pg. 1366
Jacob, Linda, Corp. Sec.--Kowalski Sausage Co., Inc., Hamtramck, MI; *U.S. Private*, pg. 634
Jacobs, Andrew F., Sr. V.P.-Control, Treas. & Sec.--Capstead Mortgage Corporation, Dallas, TX; *U.S. Public*, *pg. 303*
Jacobs, Curtis M., Sr. V.P., Chief Counsel & Sec.--National City Bank, Kentucky, Louisville, KY; *U.S. Public*, pg. 1154
Jacobs, Gary, Exec. V.P.& Sec.--Corporate Express, Inc., Broomfield, CO; *U.S. Public*, pg. 449
Jacobs, Herbert V., Asst. Sec.--Rothchild Asset Management Inc., New York, NY; *U.S. Private*, pg. 947
Jacobs, Jack, V.P.-Pur. & Sec.--Allou Health & Beauty Care, Inc., Brentwood, NY; *U.S. Public*, pg. 55
Jacobs, Leonard, V.P., Sec., Controller & Treas.--Perry Machinery Corporation, Hainesport, NJ; *U.S. Private*, pg. 855
Jacobs, Mark N., V.P., Sec. & Deputy Gen. Counsel--The Dreyfus Corporation, New York, NY; *U.S. Public*, pg. 1085
Jacobs, Paul, Sec.--Zygo Corporation, Middlefield, CT; *U.S. Public*, pg. 1795
Jacobsen, Joseph T., Exec. V.P. & Sec.--Environmental Services of America, Inc., Rahway, NJ; *U.S. Public*, pg. 546
Jacobson, Harvey, Pres., Chief Exec. Officer & Sec.--Glencraft Lingerie, Inc., New York, NY; *U.S. Private*, pg. 456
Jacobson, Ken, Chief Fin. Officer, Treas. & Sec.--Idea Engineering & Fabricating, Detroit, MI; *U.S. Private*, pg. 557
Jacobson, Richard N., Gen. Counsel & Sec.--The Standard Products Company, Dearborn, MI; *U.S. Public*, pg. 1504
Jacoy, Catherine E., Gen. Counsel & Sec.--Unigard Insurance Co., Bellevue, WA; *Int'l*, pg. 345
Jacoy, Catherine E., Gen. Counsel & Sec.--Unigard Indemnity Co., Bellevue, WA; *Int'l*, pg. 345
Jaeckel, Manfred, Corp. Sec.--Carl Zeiss, Oberkochen, Germany; *Int'l*, pg. 1522
Jaeger, Mark S., V.P., Gen. Counsel & Asst. Sec.--Jockey International, Inc., Kenosha, WI; *U.S. Private*, pg. 588
Jaffe, Lawrence E., Sec.--Medicore Inc., Hialeah, FL; *U.S. Public*, pg. 1080
Jaffe, Roslyn S., Treas. & Sec.--The Dress Barn, Inc., Suffern, NY; *U.S. Public*, pg. 528
Jaffee, Heidi M., Asst. Sec.--Oil-Dri Corporation of America, Chicago, IL; *U.S. Public*, pg. 1214
Jager, Edward G., Sec.--Horn Packaging Corporation, Ayer, MA; *U.S. Private*, pg. 539
Jagger, Denise, Corp. Sec.--Asda Group Plc, Leeds, United Kingdom; *Int'l*, pg. 17
Jagtap, J.R., Sec.--Air India, Mumbai, India; *Int'l*, pg. 37
Jaisson, J., Sr. V.P. & Sec.--Elf Atochem S.A., Paris, France; *Int'l*, pg. 445
James, David, V.P. & Sec.--California Manufacturing Enterprises, Corona, CA; *U.S. Private*, pg. 201
James, David, Treas. & Sec.--WJW Constructors, LLC, Mesa, AZ; *U.S. Private*, pg. 1187
James, Donald W., V.P. & Sec.--B.M.J. Financial Corp., Bordentown, NJ; *U.S. Public*, pg. 1528
James, Jay, Sec.--W.L. Hailey & Company, Inc., Nashville, TN; *U.S. Private*, pg. 494
James, Stacy J., Sec.--El Paso Natural Gas Co., Houston, TX; *U.S. Public*, pg. 567
Jameson, Kelly J., V.P., Gen. Counsel & Sec.--Cornerstone Natural Gas, Inc., Dallas, TX; *U.S. Public*, pg. 567
Janger, Jerome, Sec. & Legal--Kennington Ltd., Inc., Van Nuys, CA; *U.S. Private*, pg. 615
Jannette, Donald D., Asst. Treas. & Asst. Sec.--Interstate Power Company, Dubuque, IA; *U.S. Public*, pg. 910
Janney, Oliver J., V.P., Gen. Counsel & Sec.--Uniroyal Technology Corporation, Sarasota, FL; *U.S. Public*, pg. 1670
Janochoski, Thomas A., V.P. & Sec.--Great Northern Iron Ore Properties, Saint Paul, MN; *U.S. Public*, pg. 760
Janosko, Nancy M., Sec.--Pulse Bancorp, Inc., South River, NJ; *U.S. Public*, pg. 1344
Janosky, Arnold, V.P., Gen. Counsel & Sec.--Precision Tune Autocare Inc., Leesburg, VA; *U.S. Public*, pg. 1321
Japha, Daniel S., Gen. Counsel-Corp., Sec. & Dir.-Investor Rels.--M.D.C. Holdings, Inc., Denver, CO; *U.S. Public*, pg. 1025
Japha, Daniel S., Sec.--M.D.C. Holdings, Inc., Denver, CO; *U.S. Public*, pg. 1025
Jaqua, John E., Sec.--Nike, Inc., Beaverton, OR; *U.S. Public*, pg. 1184
Jardine, B.R., Grp. Sec.--Q.U.F. Industries Ltd., Brisbane, Australia; *Int'l*, pg. 1074
Jardine, Leo A., Sec.--Alpnet Inc., Salt Lake City, UT; *U.S. Public*, pg. 58
Jarrell, Gary F., V.P. & Sec.--Huntington National Bank, Morgantown, WV; *U.S. Public*, pg. 850
Jarrett, Thomas K., Asst. Sec.--John Deere Capital Corporation, Reno, NV; *U.S. Public*, pg. 492
Jarrett, Thomas K., Asst. Sec.--John Deere Credit Company, Moline, IL; *U.S. Public*, pg. 492
Jartz, John G., Sr. V.P.-Law & Bus. Devel./Corp. Sec.--The Quaker Oats Company, Chicago, IL; *U.S. Public*, pg. 1347
Jarva, T., Dir. & Sec.--Pilkington Lamino Oy, Tampere, Finland; *Int'l*, pg. 1057
Jarzab, Betty Anne, Asst. Sec.--Rayrock Yellowknife Resources Inc., Toronto, Canada; *Int'l*, pg. 1089
Jaster, Kyle M., Chief Fin. Officer, Treas. & Sec.--Mooney Aircraft Corporation, Kerrville, TX; *U.S. Private*, pg. 759
Jaye, Steven A., Sr. V.P., Gen. Counsel & Corp. Sec.--Sunrise Medical, Inc., Carlsbad, CA; *U.S. Public*, pg. 1535
Jeanonougin, David, Sr. V.P. & Sec.--Cintas Corporation, Mason, OH; *U.S. Public*, pg. 370
Jeavons, W.G., Sec.--Caparo Industries Plc, Walsall, United Kingdom; *Int'l*, pg. 264
Jedlinski, Diane M., Sec.--Roman, Inc., Roselle, IL; *U.S. Private*, pg. 942
Jeffcoat, Peggy B., Sec.--Fairfield Electric Cooperative, Winnsboro, SC; *U.S. Private*, pg. 391
Jeffreys, R., Sec.--Bradstock Group plc, London, United Kingdom; *Int'l*, pg. 210
Jeffs, Rohan, Gen. Mgr.-Corp. Services & Corp. Sec.--Woolworths Limited, Yennora, Australia; *Int'l*, pg. 676
Jendruczak, Karen, C.P.S., Sec.--Ridg-U-Rak, Inc., North East, PA; *U.S. Private*, pg. 930
Jenkins, Debra, Sec.--Atlapac Trading Company, Inc., Los Angeles, CA; *U.S. Private*, pg. 96
Jenkins, J., V.P., Gen. Counsel & Sec.--Dow Corning Corporation, Midland, MI; *U.S. Public*, pg. 523
Jenkins, Mary, Sec.--Coral Oil & Gas Inc., Houston, TX; *U.S. Private*, pg. 275
Jenkins, Rebecca J., Exec. V.P. & Sec.--MainStreet BankGroup Incorporated, Martinsville, VA; *U.S. Public*, pg. 1038
Jenkins, W. Lawrence, V.P. & Corp. Sec.--Koger Equity Inc., Jacksonville, FL; *U.S. Public*, pg. 965
Jenks, Rodney P., V.P., Gen. Counsel & Sec.--Hexcel Corporation, Pleasanton, CA; *U.S. Public*, pg. 824
Jenkyn, Richard, Corp. Sec.--International Capital Equipment Limited, Hamilton, Bermuda; *Int'l*, pg. 683
Jenney, Suzanne P., Asst. Sec.--RJR Nabisco Holdings Corp., New York, NY; *U.S. Public*, pg. 1354
Jennings, Michael E., Sr. V.P.--NationsBank West, Saint Louis, MO; *U.S. Public*, pg. 1164
Jennings, Thomas P., Sr. V.P., Gen. Counsel & Sec.--First Virginia Banks, Inc., Falls Church, VA; *U.S. Public*, pg. 641
Jensen, Amie, Sec.--Lambda Advanced Analog, Santa Clara, CA; *Int'l*, pg. 1241
Jensen, Diane, Exec. Sec.--Clarks Cos. N.A., Newton, MA; *Int'l*, pg. 297
Jensen, Don A., V.P. & Sec.--Sprint Corporation, Westwood, KS; *U.S. Public*, pg. 1500
Jensen, Irving F., Jr., Chm. Bd., Treas. & Sec.--Irving F. Jensen Co., Inc., Sioux City, IA; *U.S. Private*, pg. 586
Jensen, Michael J., Treas. & Sec.--Keck Instruments, Inc., Williamston, MI; *U.S. Public*, pg. 367
Jeremiah, Barbara S., Sec. & Asst. Gen. Counsel--Aluminum Company of America, Pittsburgh, PA; *U.S. Public*, pg. 60
Jett, Ernest C., V.P., Mng. Dir.-Legal Dept. & Sec.--Leggett & Platt, Incorporated, Carthage, MO; *U.S. Public*, pg. 985
Jewett, Robert William, Sr. V.P., Gen. Counsel & Sec.--Hooper Holmes Corporation, Basking Ridge, NJ; *U.S. Public*, pg. 835
Jimenez, Carlos, Sec.--Hylsamex, S.A. de C.V., San Nicolas, Mexico; *Int'l*, pg. 56
Jimenez, Ildefonso, Sec.--Jimenez/DMB&B, Manila, Philippines; *U.S. Private*, pg. 304
Joannidi, Harold A., Controller, Treas. & Sec.--EcoScience Corporation, East Brunswick, NJ; *U.S. Public*, pg. 563
Jobe, C., Sec.--Northern Rock PLC, Newcastle upon Tyne, United Kingdom; *Int'l*, pg. 968
Joffe, Carl H., Gen. Counsel & Sec.--Purcell Co., Inc., Diamondhead, MS; *U.S. Private*, pg. 895
Johansson, Asa, Sec.--Jarnia AB, Ulricehammn, Sweden; *Int'l*, pg. 188
Johns, D. Malcolm, Jr., V.P., Gen. Counsel & Sec.--CNG Producing Co., New Orleans, LA; *U.S. Public*, pg. 435
Johnsen, Ken C., V.P., Gen. Counsel & Sec.--Geneva Steel, Vineyard, UT; *U.S. Public*, pg. 729
Johnson, Alan G., Corp. Sec.--KV Pharmaceutical Company, Saint Louis, MO; *U.S. Public*, pg. 941
Johnson, Avis J., Sec.--Suttle Caribe, Inc., Humacao, PR; *U.S. Public*, pg. 415
Johnson, B. S., Gen. Counsel & Corp. Sec.--Qantas Airways Ltd., Mascot, Australia; *Int'l*, pg. 1074
Johnson, Bruce D., Sec.--Meyer Broadcasting Company, Bismarck, ND; *U.S. Private*, pg. 739
Johnson, Catherine C., V.P. & Sec.--Johnson Newspaper Corporation, Watertown, NY; *U.S. Private*, pg. 591
Johnson, Craig, Sec.--Vertel, Woodland Hills, CA; *U.S. Public*, pg. 1717
Johnson, Craig W., Gen. Counsel & Sec.--Laserscope Surgical Systems, San Jose, CA; *U.S. Public*, pg. 979
Johnson, Craig W., Esq., Sec.--Collagen Corporation, Palo Alto, CA; *U.S. Public*, pg. 399
Johnson, Daniel R., Sr. V.P., Gen. Counsel & Sec.--Combe Incorporated, White Plains, NY; *U.S. Private*, pg. 257
Johnson, Douglas A., V.P., Gen. Counsel & Sec.--Pettibone Corporation, Lisle, IL; *U.S. Private*, pg. 859
Johnson, Douglas A., Sec.--Beardsley & Piper, L.L.C., Chicago, IL; *U.S. Private*, pg. 859
Johnson, Elizabeth Pringle, Sr. V.P., Gen. Counsel & Sec.--Camden Property Trust, Houston, TX; *U.S. Public*, pg. 298
Johnson, Eunice W., Treas. & Sec.--Johnson Publishing Company, Inc., Chicago, IL; *U.S. Private*, pg. 591
Johnson, Gary R., V.P., Gen. Counsel & Sec.--Northern States Power Company, Minneapolis, MN; *U.S. Public*, pg. 1195
Johnson, Greg A., Controller & Treas.--F.H. Stoltze Land & Lumber Company, Saint Paul, MN; *U.S. Private*, pg. 1044
Johnson, Guy, Corp. Sec.--Storehouse PLC, London, United Kingdom; *Int'l*, pg. 1304
Johnson, J. Peter, V.P.-Fin., Controller, Treas. & Asst. Sec.--Tellabs Operations, Inc., Lisle, IL; *U.S. Public*, pg. 1572
Johnson, James C., V.P. & Sec.--Northrop Grumman Corporation, Los Angeles, CA; *U.S. Public*, pg. 1197
Johnson, James L., Controller & Corp. Sec.--Werner Enterprises, Inc., Omaha, NE; *U.S. Public*, pg. 1754
Johnson, James R., Exec. V.P. & Sec.--Johnson Storage Moving Co, Denver, CO; *U.S. Private*, pg. 594
Johnson, John, Sec.--Plains Cotton Co-op Association, Lubbock, TX; *U.S. Private*, pg. 868
Johnson, Justin, Esq., V.P., Gen. Counsel & Sec.--Atlanta Life Insurance Company, Atlanta, GA; *U.S. Private*, pg. 94
Johnson, Larry, Sec.--Southern Minnesota Beet Sugar Cooperative, Renville, MN; *U.S. Private*, pg. 1016
Johnson, Margaret R., Asst. Sec.--JC Penney Company, Inc., Plano, TX; *U.S. Public*, pg. 916
Johnson, Marianne Boyd, Asst. Sec.--Boyd Gaming Corporation, Las Vegas, NV; *U.S. Public*, pg. 249
Johnson, Mary Ann, V.P.-Adm. & Corp. Sec.--Knife River Coal Mining Company, Bismarck, ND; *U.S. Public*, pg. 1025
Johnson, Minnie, Asst. Sec. & Asst. Treas.--Saddlebag Lake Resorts, Inc., La Belle, FL; *U.S. Public*, pg. 41
Johnson, Patricia M., Treas., Sec. & Dir.-Fin.--Tony Downs Foods Company, Saint James, MN; *U.S. Private*, pg. 342
Johnson, R.S., Sec.--B. Elliott plc., London, United Kingdom; *Int'l*, pg. 448
Johnson, Robert A., V.P., Gen. Counsel & Sec.--Bonneville International Corp., Salt Lake City, UT; *U.S. Private*, pg. 327
Johnson, Robert T., Sec. & Treas.--Blu-Ray, Middletown, CT; *U.S. Private*, pg. 142
Johnson, S.A., Sec.--Maine and New Brunswick Electrical Power Company, Ltd., Presque Isle, ME; *U.S. Public*, pg. 1038
Johnson, S.A., Sec. & Treas.--WRR Environmental Services Co., Inc., Eau Claire, WI; *U.S. Public*, pg. 1792
Johnson, Scott W., Sr. V.P., Gen. Counsel & Sec.--Bemis Company, Inc., Minneapolis, MN; *U.S. Public*, pg. 210
Johnson, Stanley, Treas. & Sec.--Mueller Sports Medicine, Inc., Prairie Du Sac, WI; *U.S. Private*, pg. 766
Johnson, Steven A., V.P.-Customer Svc., Gen. Counsel & Sec.--Maine Public Service Company, Presque Isle, ME; *U.S. Public*, pg. 1038
Johnson, Stewart H., V.P. & Sec.--APAC/Ballenger Paving Company, Inc., Taylors, SC; *U.S. Public*, pg. 139
Johnson, Teresa H., Sec.--SuperValu, Inc., Eden Prairie, MN; *U.S. Public*, pg. 1540
Johnson, Todd T., Treas. & Sec.--Industrial Construction, Inc., Idaho Falls, ID; *U.S. Private*, pg. 560
Johnson, William D., V.P.-Legal, Sr. Counsel & Asst. Sec.--Carolina Power & Light Company, Raleigh, NC; *U.S. Public*, pg. 306
Johnson, William H., V.P., Controller & Sec.--Reuter Manufacturing Inc., Hopkins, MN; *U.S. Public*, pg. 1383
Johnsrud, Thor, Sec.--Christiania Bank og Kreditkasse ASA, Oslo, Norway; *Int'l*, pg. 289
Johnston, Malcolm, Corp. Sec.--Cannon Rubber Ltd., London, United Kingdom; *Int'l*, pg. 261
Johnston, Murray, V.P., Gen. Counsel & Sec.--H.B. Zachry, San Antonio, TX; *U.S. Private*, pg. 1203
Johnston, Norma, Sec.--National Wine & Spirits Corp., Indianapolis, IN; *U.S. Private*, pg. 788
Johnston, P.J., Dir.-Fin. & Sec.--Senior Heat Treatment Limited, Dunstable, United Kingdom; *Int'l*, pg. 1221

Jones Kane, M'Liss, Sr. V.P., Gen. Counsel & Corp. Sec.--Fidelity National Financial, Inc., Irvine, CA; *U.S. Public*, pg. 620

Jones, A. Morgan, Sec.--Sierra West Bancorp, Truckee, CA; *U.S. Public*, pg. 1470

Jones, Brenda, Asst. Sec.--Delta Woodside Industries, Inc., Greenville, SC; *U.S. Public*, pg. 497

Jones, Brenda, Sec.--Jones Blair Co., Chattanooga, TN; *U.S. Private*, pg. 596

Jones, Carol Ann, Sec.--Dealers Electrical Supply Co., Waco, TX; *U.S. Private*, pg. 318

Jones, Christine M., V.P.-Stockholder Rels. & Sec.--Haverty Furniture Companies, Inc., Atlanta, GA; *U.S. Public*, pg. 799

Jones, Colin D., Gen. Counsel & Sec.--Cambridge Shopping Centres Limited, Toronto, Canada; *Int'l*, pg. 253

Jones, D. Michael, V.P.-Gen. Counsel--Reynolds Metals Company, Richmond, VA; *U.S. Public*, pg. 1385

Jones, D.A., Sec. & Dir.-Fin.--M B M Technology Limited, Brighton, United Kingdom; *Int'l*, pg. 892

Jones, David C., V.P.-Legal Services & Sec.--Lafarge Corporation, Reston, VA; *Int'l*, pg. 788

Jones, Diane R., Sec. & Dir.-Admin. Svcs.--Jack Gray Transport, Inc., Gary, IN; *U.S. Private*, pg. 471

Jones, Diane W., Sec.--Ferguson Publishing Company, Chicago, IL; *U.S. Private*, pg. 401

Jones, Dorothy, Sec.--Magic Valley Foods, Inc., Rupert, ID; *U.S. Private*, pg. 695

Jones, Gary, Treas. & Sec.--Rural Electric Co-op, Lindsay, OK; *U.S. Private*, pg. 952

Jones, Graham, Grp. Sec. & Head of Legal Services--Norwich Union Life Insurance, Norwich, United Kingdom; *Int'l*, pg. 970

Jones, Gregory R., V.P.-Human Resources, Gen. Counsel & Sec.--QMS, Inc., Mobile, AL; *U.S. Public*, pg. 1346

Jones, Helen, Sec.--Kingfisher plc, London, United Kingdom; *Int'l*, pg. 733

Jones, Jacqueline C., Sec.--Jones & Jones, Inc., McAllen, TX; *U.S. Private*, pg. 596

Jones, James E., Chief Fin. Officer, Treas. & Sec.--Modern Welding Co., Inc., Owensboro, KY; *U.S. Private*, pg. 755

Jones, James P., V.P., Gen. Counsel & Sec.--Stone & Webster, Incorporated, Boston, MA; *U.S. Public*, pg. 1519

Jones, James R., Asst. Sec.--Union Camp Corporation, Wayne, NJ; *U.S. Public*, pg. 1665

Jones, K., Gen. Counsel & Sec.--Colonial Pipeline Company, Atlanta, GA; *U.S. Private*, pg. 254

Jones, Kenneth J., Corp. Sec.--Essex Industries, New Haven, CT; *Int'l*, pg. 18

Jones, Kevin C., Asst. Sec.--Hormel Foods Corp., Austin, MN; *U.S. Public*, pg. 840

Jones, L.A., Sec.--Land Securities Plc, London, United Kingdom; *Int'l*, pg. 798

Jones, L.A., Sec.--Land Securities Properties Limited, London, United Kingdom; *Int'l*, pg. 798

Jones, Laird R., Asst. Sec.--Union Camp Corporation, Wayne, NJ; *U.S. Public*, pg. 1665

Jones, M.R., Sec.--Sparex International Ltd., Exeter, United Kingdom; *Int'l*, pg. 1512

Jones, Mark L., V.P.-Finance, Corp. Sec. & Treas.--Sunbelt Nursery Group Inc., Fort Worth, TX; *U.S. Public*, pg. 715

Jones, Marvel C., Sec.--Dawn Food Products, Inc., Jackson, MI; *U.S. Private*, pg. 316

Jones, Miles E., Chief Oper. Officer & Sec.--Dawn Food Products, Inc., Jackson, MI; *U.S. Private*, pg. 316

Jones, Orlo D., Sr. V.P.-Properties & Sec.--Longs Drug Stores Corporation, Walnut Creek, CA; *U.S. Public*, pg. 1013

Jones, Raymond E., Exec. V.P. & Sec.--Shelter Mutual Insurance Company, Columbia, MO; *U.S. Private*, pg. 992

Jones, Velma J., V.P. & Sec.--Bank of Montreal, Toronto, Canada; *Int'l*, pg. 153

Jones, W. Benjamin, III, Sec.--IRT Management Company, Atlanta, GA; *U.S. Public*, pg. 858

Jones, William Allen, Exec. V.P.-Corp. Affairs & Sec.--Metro-Goldwyn-Mayer Inc., Santa Monica, CA; *U.S. Public*, pg. 1101

Jongleux, Lynn B., Gen. Counsel & Sec.--United Farm Family Life Insurance Co., Indianapolis, IN; *U.S. Private*, pg. 1122

Jonker, S.J., Sec.-Supervisory Bd.--Internatio-Muller N.V., Rotterdam, Netherlands; *Int'l*, pg. 680

Jordan, Arthur D., Asst. Sec.--Boeing Realty Corporation, Long Beach, CA; *U.S. Public*, pg. 241

Jordan, Charles A., V.P. & Sec.--Jordan Tamraz Caruso Advertising, Inc., Chicago, IL; *U.S. Private*, pg. 599

Jordan, Nicholas, Asst. Sec.--Minorco, Luxembourg, Luxembourg; *Int'l*, pg. 77

Jordan, Russell W., III, Sr. V.P., Gen. Counsel & Sec.--Lawyers Title Insurance Corporation, Richmond, VA; *U.S. Public*, pg. 981

Jorella, Clairene, Asst. Sec.--Kimberly-Clark Corporation, Dallas, TX; *U.S. Public*, pg. 958

Jorgenson, Mary Ann, Esq., Sec.--Essef Corporation, Chardon, OH; *U.S. Public*, pg. 592

Joroff, Howard, V.P.-Fin. & Sec.--Hudson County News Company, North Bergen, NJ; *U.S. Private*, pg. 545

Josendale, John D., Grp. Pres.-Wire Rope Prods.--Wire Rope Corporation of America, Inc., Saint Joseph, MO; *U.S. Private*, pg. 1184

Josenhans, Paul J., Assoc. Gen. Counsel & Sec.--Borden, Inc., Columbus, OH; *U.S. Private*, pg. 157

Joslin, Mark W., Chief Fin. Officer & Treas.--Lawter International, Inc., Kenosha, WI; *U.S. Public*, pg. 980

Joubert, Nereus, Dr., Gen. Mgr., Gen. Counsel & Sec.--Sasol Limited, Johannesburg, South Africa; *Int'l*, pg. 1196

Journigan, Joanne, Treas. & Asst. Sec.--Heater Utilities, Incorporated, Cary, NC; *U.S. Public*, pg. 1116

Joyner, John F., V.P.-Fin., Treas. & Sec.--The Dickerson Group, Inc., Monroe, NC; *U.S. Private*, pg. 331

Jubelirer, Steven W., Treas. & Sec.--John Reyer Company, Sharon, PA; *U.S. Private*, pg. 926

Juda, Dennis, Sec.--Excelsior Manufacturing & Supply Corp., Itasca, IL; *U.S. Private*, pg. 387

Judy, John G., Sec.--Construcciones Aeronauticas, SA, Madrid, Spain; *U.S. Public*, pg. 242

Juelsgaard, Stephen, V.P., Gen. Counsel & Asst. Sec.--Genentech, Inc., South San Francisco, CA; *Int'l*, pg. 1120

Juengling, Charles R., V.P., Controller & Sec.--Baldwin Piano & Organ Company, Loveland, OH; *U.S. Public*, pg. 169

Juliano, Richard, Chief Fin. Officer, Sec. & Treas.--A.H. Hoffman, Inc., Landisville, PA; *U.S. Private*, pg. 532

Jumonville, Carla, Sec.--Group Insurance Inc. of Louisiana, Baton Rouge, LA; *U.S. Private*, pg. 484

Jumonville, Francis, Treas. & Sec.--Airtrol, Inc., Baton Rouge, LA; *U.S. Private*, pg. 29

Jungmann, Charles J., Sec.--Remmele Engineering, Inc., New Brighton, MN; *U.S. Private*, pg. 921

Juris, Eugene W., V.P.-Fin. & Sec.--Banner Aerospace, Inc., Washington, DC; *U.S. Public*, pg. 187

Jussup, W. John, V.P., Gen. Counsel & Sec.--Cognos Inc., Ottawa, Canada; *Int'l*, pg. 305

Just, Lawrence E., Asst. Sec. & Gen. Counsel--Bradley Printing Company, Des Plaines, IL; *U.S. Public*, pg. 1778

Justesen, Wayne, V.P., Gen. Counsel & Sec.--Greenwood Mills, Inc., Greenwood, SC; *U.S. Private*, pg. 479

Justice, Dale L., Asst. Sec.--Kimberly-Clark Corporation, Dallas, TX; *U.S. Public*, pg. 958

Kaden, Ellen O., Exec. V.P., Gen. Counsel & Sec.--CBS, New York, NY; *U.S. Public*, pg. 273

Kadish, David A., Sec. & Gen. Counsel--Integral Systems, Inc., Walnut Creek, CA; *Int'l*, pg. 242

Kadow, Joe, V.P., Gen. Counsel & Sec.--Outback Steakhouse Inc., Tampa, FL; *U.S. Public*, pg. 1235

Kahanek, Carol F., Sec.--Z-Seven Fund, Inc., Mesa, AZ; *U.S. Public*, pg. 1789

Kahen, Harold I., Gen. Counsel & Sec.--Standard Microsystems Corp., Hauppauge, NY; *U.S. Public*, pg. 1502

Kahle, John H., Exec. V.P., Gen. Counsel & Asst. Sec.--Kimball International, Inc., Jasper, IN; *U.S. Public*, pg. 956

Kahlig, Sandra, Treas. & Sec.--North Park Lincoln Mercury Inc., San Antonio, TX; *U.S. Private*, pg. 805

Kahn, Carol J., Asst. Sec.--Standard Pacific Corp., Costa Mesa, CA; *U.S. Public*, pg. 1503

Kahn, Harry H., V.P., Gen. Counsel & Sec.--ABM Industries, San Francisco, CA; *U.S. Public*, pg. 2

Kahn, Stanley, Vice Chm., Treas. & Sec.--Croscill, Inc., New York, NY; *U.S. Private*, pg. 290

Kahn, Todd, Exec. V.P., Gen. Counsel & Sec.--Salant Corporation, New York, NY; *U.S. Public*, pg. 1429

Kailes, Howard, Sec.--Insituform Technologies, Inc., Chesterfield, MO; *U.S. Public*, pg. 881

Kaiman, Stan C., Sec.--Cooper Tire & Rubber Company, Findlay, OH; *U.S. Public*, pg. 445

Kaitz, Miriam Collins, Treas. & Sec.--Palm Beach Beauty Products Co., Minneapolis, MN; *U.S. Private*, pg. 834

Kalaher, Richard A., V.P., Gen. Counsel & Sec.--American Standard Inc., Piscataway, NJ; *U.S. Public*, pg. 91

Kalaydjian, Catherine A., V.P. & Asst. Sec.--Resolute Management Corp., Stamford, CT; *U.S. Public*, pg. 220

Kalec, John J., Chief Fin. Officer, Sr. V.P. & Sec.--Clayton Homes, Inc., Knoxville, TN; *U.S. Public*, pg. 382

Kalette, Stephen R., V.P.-Admin. & Gen. Counsel--Pubco Corporation, Cleveland, OH; *U.S. Public*, pg. 1339

Kalib, David L., V.P., Gen. Counsel & Sec.--Berkshire Life Insurance Company, Pittsfield, MA; *U.S. Private*, pg. 136

Kalin, Alyce, Sec.--Kalin Enterprises, Inc., Sarasota, FL; *U.S. Private*, pg. 606

Kalin, Alyce, Sec.--Kalin Financial Division, Sarasota, FL; *U.S. Private*, pg. 606

Kalin, Richard S., Gen. Counsel & Sec.--Pentech International, Inc., Edison, NJ; *U.S. Public*, pg. 1274

Kalitte, Stephen R., V.P., Gen. Counsel & Sec.--Kroy Inc., Scottsdale, AZ; *U.S. Public*, pg. 1339

Kallenberger, G., Sec.--Pilkington Floatglas AB, Halmstad, Sweden; *Int'l*, pg. 1057

Kallete, Stephen R., V.P. & Sec.--Aspen Imaging International, Inc., Cleveland, OH; *U.S. Public*, pg. 1339

Kallmeyer, L.B., Treas. & Sec.--The Kirk & Blum Mfg. Co., Cincinnati, OH; *U.S. Private*, pg. 623

Kalsbeck, Kathy, Exec. Sec.--CWC Textron Company, Muskegon, MI; *U.S. Public*, pg. 1590

Kaltman, Martin, Sec.--Queens Group, Inc., Long Island City, NY; *U.S. Private*, pg. 900

Kamins, Howard, V.P., Gen. Counsel & Corp. Sec.--EA Industries, West Long Branch, NJ; *U.S. Public*, pg. 541

Kaminski, Robert J., PE, V.P. & Sec.--Giffels Technologies, Inc., Southfield, MI; *U.S. Private*, pg. 452

Kamitaki, Wayne, Sec.--Maui Varieties, Ltd., Honolulu, HI; *U.S. Private*, pg. 715

Kamsler, J. Scott, Chief Fin. Officer, V.P.-Fin. & Sec.--SymmetriCom, Inc., San Jose, CA; *U.S. Public*, pg. 1547

Kanarek, Arnold W., Sr. V.P. & Sec.--Industrial Acoustics Company, Inc., Bronx, NY; *U.S. Public*, pg. 875

Kandrysawtz, Beth, V.P., Treas. & Sec.--The Motorlease Corp., Farmington, CT; *U.S. Private*, pg. 764

Kane, Frank T., Chief Fin. Officer, V.P. & Sec.--Cochrane Furniture Co., Inc., Lincolnton, NC; *U.S. Public*, pg. 352

Kane, William, Chief Fin. Officer, V.P., Treas. & Sec.--Molded Fiber Glass Companies, Ashtabula, OH; *U.S. Private*, pg. 755

Kaneko, Takasi, Sec.--Nippon Oil Company, Limited (NISSEKI), Tokyo, Japan; *Int'l*, pg. 936

Kangrga, R.L., V.P. & Asst. Sec.--Ziegler Thrift Trading, Inc., Minneapolis, MN; *U.S. Public*, pg. 1792

Kanim, Elvira, Treas. & Sec.--Vivian & Elliette, Inc., Vernon, CA; *U.S. Private*, pg. 1142

Kankel, Keith V., V.P.-Fin., Treas. & Sec.--Patrick Industries Inc., Elkhart, IN; *U.S. Public*, pg. 1264

Kantor, Jonathan, Sr. V.P., Gen. Counsel & Sec.--Continental Assurance Company, Chicago, IL; *U.S. Private*, pg. 267

Kanzig, Robert, Dr., Sec.--Jelmoli AG, Zurich, Switzerland; *Int'l*, pg. 705

Kaplan, Carl E., Sec.--Data General Corporation, Westborough, MA; *U.S. Public*, pg. 485

Kaplan, Elliot S., Gen. Counsel & Sec.--Best Buy Co., Inc., Eden Prairie, MN; *U.S. Public*, pg. 223

Kaplan, Harvey, Treas. & Sec.--Drew Industries Incorporated, White Plains, NY; *U.S. Public*, pg. 529

Kaplan, Haya, Sec.--Orbotech Ltd., Yavne, Israel; *Int'l*, pg. 1007

Kaplan, Sam D., Chief Fin. Officer, Controller, Treas. & Sec.--The He-Ro Group, Ltd., New York, NY; *U.S. Public*, pg. 801

Kaplan, Samuel, Pres., Chief Exec. Officer, Sec. & Dir.-Sls. & Pur.--Admiration Hosiery Mills, Inc., Charlotte, NC; *U.S. Private*, pg. 528

Kaplanek, Rosemary, Treas. & Sec.--Floral Glass & Mirror, Inc., Hauppauge, NY; *U.S. Private*, pg. 414

Karalis, John P., Sr. V.P.-Corp. Devel. & Sec.--Tektronix, Inc., Wilsonville, OR; *U.S. Public*, pg. 1567

Karel, Steven, V.P., Gen. Counsel & Sec.--Robert Half International Inc., Menlo Park, CA; *U.S. Public*, pg. 774

Kargula, Michael R., Exec. V.P., Gen. Counsel & Sec.--Primark Corporation, Waltham, MA; *U.S. Public*, pg. 1325

Kari, Aune, Corp. Sec.--Bronto Skylift Oy AB, Tampere, Finland; *U.S. Public*, pg. 617

Karl, Catherine, V.P.-Admin.--The Times Publishing Co., Saint Petersburg, FL; *U.S. Private*, pg. 1087

Karl, Frederick B., Jr., V.P., Gen. Counsel & Sec.--Medical Manager Corporation, Tampa, FL; *U.S. Public*, pg. 1080

Karlix, Susan E., Asst. Sec.--John Deere Capital Corporation, Reno, NV; *U.S. Public*, pg. 492

Karlshausen, Robert, Gen. Counsel & Sec.--Herstal S.A., Herstal, Belgium; *Int'l*, pg. 617

Karniel, Uzi, Corp. Counsel & Sec.--Teva Pharmaceutical Industries Ltd., Petah Tiqwa, Israel; *Int'l*, pg. 1380

Karsakis, N., Real Estate Mngmt. & Sec.--Taylor Woodrow (Australia) Pty. Limited, Mount Pleasant, Australia; *Int'l*, pg. 1359

Karsian, Andrea, Sec.--Ocean Chevrolet, Inc., Toms River, NJ; *U.S. Private*, pg. 810

Karsk, Bruce C., V.P.-Fin., Treas. & Sec.--Lindsay Manufacturing Company, Lindsay, NE; *U.S. Public*, pg. 999

Karsky, Gloria J., Gen. Counsel & Sec.--TCF Bank Illinois, Oak Brook, IL; *U.S. Public*, pg. 1554

Karvonen, Thomas D., Sec.--Ambrake Corporation, Elizabethtown, KY; *U.S. Public*, pg. 721

Karwacki, Thomas J., Treas. & Sec.--The Park Circle Motor Co., Baltimore, MD; *U.S. Private*, pg. 839

Karwi, T.B., Sec.--Zimbabwe Electricity Supply Authority, Harare, Zimbabwe; *Int'l*, pg. 1528

Kasak, Robert, Gen. Counsel--MTL Inc., Plant City, FL; *U.S. Public*, pg. 1028

Kaskowitz, J., Sec.--B-Line Systems, Inc., Highland, IL; *U.S. Public*, pg. 1471

Kasle, Stephen, Sec.--Kasle Steel Corporation, Dearborn, MI; *U.S. Private*, pg. 608

Kassel, Maureen W., V.P. & Sec.--U.S. Home & Garden Inc., San Francisco, CA; *U.S. Public*, pg. 1682

Kassner, Mark S., Chief Fin. Officer, V.P. & Sec.--Sloan's Supermarkets, Inc., New York, NY; *U.S. Private*, pg. 915

Kastner, Erich, Asst. V.P. & Asst. Sec.-Hydro Div.--Voest-Alpine International Corporation, New York, NY; *Int'l*, pg. 1470

Kastner, Jeffrey, Asst. Sec.--Flanigan's Enterprises, Inc., Fort Lauderdale, FL; *U.S. Public*, pg. 648

Katsumata, Mark, Chief Fin. Officer & Sec.--Durum Energy Corp., Vancouver, Canada; *Int'l*, pg. 422

Katsumata, Mark, Chief Fin. Officer & Sec.--Durum Energy Corp., Sucursal Del Peru, Vancouver, Canada; *Int'l*, pg. 422

Katsumata, Mark, Chief Fin. Officer & Sec.--Durum (Australia) Pty. Ltd., Vancouver, Canada; *Int'l*, pg. 422

Katz, Randall A., V.P.-Taxes & Asst. Sec.--Bumble Bee Seafoods Inc., San Diego, CA; *U.S. Private*, pg. 526

Katz, Solomon, Treas. & Sec.--Manhattan Store Interiors, Inc., Brooklyn, NY; *U.S. Private*, pg. 699

Katz, Stewart, Pres. & Chief Oper. Officer--Noodle Kidoodle Inc., Syosset, NY; *U.S. Public*, pg. 1188

Katzman, Howard, Dr., Sr. V.P. & Sec.--Bowl America, Incorporated, Alexandria, VA; *U.S. Public*, pg. 248

Kauffman, Jeffery R., Asst. Treas. & Asst. Sec.--Lift-All Co., Inc., Manheim, PA; *U.S. Private*, pg. 667

Kaufman, Howard M., Sr. V.P., Treas. & Sec.--Lynch & Mayer, Inc., New York, NY; *U.S. Public*, pg. 998

Kaufman, Jack, Chief Fin. Officer--The Hain Food Group Inc., Uniondale, NY; *U.S. Public*, pg. 774

Kautz, Walter J., Treas. & Sec.--Sugar Cane Growers Cooperative of Florida, Belle Glade, FL; *U.S. Private*, pg. 1049

Kawalick, Steven, Gen. Counsel & Asst. Sec.--Intelligent Electronics, Inc., Exton, PA; *U.S. Public*, pg. 887

Kay, Sanford, V.P.-Human Resources & Sec.--Standard Motor Products Inc., Long Island City, NY; *U.S. Public*, pg. 1503

Kaye, Diane L., V.P., Gen. Counsel & Sec.--Federal-Mogul Corporation, Southfield, MI; *U.S. Public*, pg. 615

Kaye, P., Sec.--Shanks & McEwan Group Plc, Bourne, United Kingdom; *Int'l*, pg. 1228

Kazlo, Ronald, Sr. V.P.-Fin. & Asst. Sec.--ACCO Brands, Inc., Wheeling, IL; *U.S. Public*, pg. 674

Kazmierczak, Kenneth J., Controller, Treas. & Sec.--Schreier Malting Co., Sheboygan, WI; *U.S. Private*, pg. 972

Kazmierczak, Stanley, Chief Fin. Officer, V.P.-Fin. & Admin. & Sec.--Digital Link Corporation, Sunnyvale, CA; *U.S. Public*, pg. 508

Kean, Lawrence M., Controller & Sec.--A&A Manufacturing Co., New Berlin, WI; *U.S. Private*, pg. 1

Keane, Kathleen A., Corp. Sec.--The Stanley Consultants Group, Muscatine, IA; *U.S. Private*, pg. 1032

Keane, Kathleen A., Sec.--Stanley Design-Build, Inc., Muscatine, IA; *U.S. Private*, pg. 1033

Keane, Kathleen A., Sec.--Stanley Enviromental, Inc., Coralville, IA; *U.S. Private*, pg. 1033

Keane, Kathleen A., Corp. Sec.--Stanley Consultants, Inc., Muscatine, IA; *U.S. Private*, pg. 1033

Kearl, Greg, Chief Oper. Officer, Exec. V.P., Treas. & Sec.--Menley & James Laboratories, Inc., Horsham, PA; *U.S. Public*, pg. 1086

Kearney, Barbara W., Sec.--Zippo Manufacturing Company, Bradford, PA; *U.S. Private*, pg. 1207

Kearney, Christopher J., V.P., Gen. Counsel & Sec.--SPX Corporation, Muskegon, MI; *U.S. Public*, pg. 1420

Kearney, Joseph W., Controller & Asst. Sec.--First Union Management, Inc., Cleveland, OH; *U.S. Public*, pg. 641

Kearns, Connie, Exec. Sec.--Airmaster Fan Co., Michigan Center, MI; *U.S. Private*, pg. 29

Keaster, James C., Sec.--The Bradford National Bank of Greenville, Greenville, IL; *U.S. Private*, pg. 164

Keating, Edah, Sec.--Newpark Resources, Inc., Metairie, LA; *U.S. Public*, pg. 1179

Keating, Pamela A., Gen. Counsel & Clerk--LTX Corporation, Westwood, MA; *U.S. Public*, pg. 972

Kec, Janet, Treas. & Sec.--Western States Petroleum Inc., Phoenix, AZ; *U.S. Private*, pg. 1169

Keeffe, Elmer C., Controller & Sec.--J.H. Harvey Company, Nashville, GA; *U.S. Private*, pg. 508

Keeler, Philip, Asst. Treas. & Sec.--Hatfield Quality Meats, Hatfield, PA; *U.S. Private*, pg. 510

Keen, Jon, Sec.--Keen Compressed Gas Co., Wilmington, DE; *U.S. Private*, pg. 611

Keen, Paul R., Gen. Counsel & Sec.--Argo-Tech Corporation, Cleveland, OH; *U.S. Private*, pg. 81

Keene, Robert A., Chm. Bd., Sec. & Treas.--John Roberts Company, Minneapolis, MN; *U.S. Private*, pg. 935

Kees, Ray, Chief Fin. Officer, Corp. Sec. & Treas.--Gem-Dandy, Inc., Madison, NC; *U.S. Private*, pg. 442

Keidar, I., Sec.--Elbit Computers Ltd., Haifa, Israel; *Int'l*, pg. 644

Keim, Patricia M., Dir.-Admin. & Corp. Sec.--Unigas, Calgary, Canada; *Int'l*, pg. 1492

Keith, Jan W., V.P.-Membership & Corp. Sec.--American Arbitration Association, New York, NY; *U.S. Private*, pg. 50

Keith, Paula, Sec.--Sterling Chemicals Holdings, Inc., Houston, TX; *U.S. Public*, pg. 1515

Keith, Paula, Sec.--Sterling Chemicals, Inc., Houston, TX; *U.S. Public*, pg. 1515

Keith, Susan S., V.P., Corp. Counsel & Sec.--Halliburton Company, Dallas, TX; *U.S. Public*, pg. 775

Keith, Susan S., V.P. & Corp. Sec.--Halliburton Energy Services, Inc., Dallas, TX; *U.S. Public*, pg. 776

Kell, Lisa A., Corp Sec.--Eastex Energy Inc., Houston, TX; *U.S. Public*, pg. 567

Kelleher, Harry B., Gen. Counsel & Sec.--Reagan Equipment Company, Inc., Gretna, LA; *U.S. Private*, pg. 913

Kelleher, Thomas M., Sec.--BIC Corporation, Milford, CT; *Int'l*, pg. 1273

Keller, Barbara, Treas. & Sec.--Hotel Corporation of America, Maple Hill, KS; *U.S. Private*, pg. 541

Keller, Bryan, V.P., Gen. Counsel & Sec.--Delaware North Companies, Inc., Buffalo, NY; *U.S. Private*, pg. 321

Keller, J. Frank, Chief Fin. Officer, Exec. V.P. & Sec.--Barrett Resources Corporation, Denver, CO; *U.S. Public*, *pg. 191*

Keller, J.T., Sec.--Exxon Yemen Inc., Houston, TX; *U.S. Public*, pg. 601

Keller, Jim, Chief Fin. Officer & Sec.--Ness Holding Co., Portland, OR; *U.S. Private*, pg. 791

Keller, Roger A., V.P., Gen. Counsel & Sec.--Mallinckrodt Inc., Saint Louis, MO; *U.S. Public*, pg. 1039

Keller, Stephen M., Corp. Sec.--Na-Churs Plant Food Company, Marion, OH; *U.S. Private*, pg. 1096

Keller, Thomas C., Treas. & Sec.--Lou Ana Foods, Inc., Opelousas, LA; *Int'l*, pg. 879

Kellermeyer, Donald V., Pres., Chief Exec. Officer & Treas.--Kellermeyer Co., Toledo, OH; *U.S. Private*, pg. 612

Kellermeyer, Thomas V., Sec.--Kellermeyer Co., Toledo, OH; *U.S. Private*, pg. 612

Kelley, Charles A., Corp. Sec.--SpeedFan International, Inc., Chandler, AZ; *U.S. Public*, pg. 1497

Kelley, Don K., Chief Fin. Officer & Treas.--Kappler Safety Group, Inc., Guntersville, AL; *U.S. Private*, pg. 607

Kelley, Robert L., Exec. V.P. & Sec.--Kelley Bean Co., Inc., Morrill, NE; *U.S. Private*, pg. 612

Kellhofer, Don, Treas. & Sec.--Efco Corporation, Monett, MO; *U.S. Private*, pg. 353

Kellogg, Cynthia P., Chief Fin. Officer, V.P., Treas. & Sec.--Heartland Development Corporation, Madison, WI; *U.S. Public*, pg. 1728

Kelly, Brian, Pres., Chief. Oper. Officer & Sec.--Activision, Santa Monica, CA; *U.S. Public*, pg. 17

Kelly, Brian C., Gen. Counsel & Sec.--Chris-Craft Industries, Inc., New York, NY; *U.S. Public*, pg. 351

Kelly, Brian C., Gen. Counsel & Sec.--BHC Communications, Inc., New York, NY; *U.S. Public*, pg. 352

Kelly, Brian M., Asst. Sec.--General Electric Canada Inc., Mississauga, Canada; *U.S. Public*, pg. 713

Kelly, Claudia, Sec.--Watkins-Johnson Company, Palo Alto, CA; *U.S. Public*, pg. 1745

Kelly, Donald, Chief Fin. Officer, V.P.-Fin. & Sec.--Digital Solutions, Inc., Somerset, NJ; *U.S. Public*, pg. 508

Kelly, Douglas L., Corp. V.P. & Sec.--A.G. Edwards, Inc., Saint Louis, MO; *U.S. Public*, pg. 565

Kelly, Douglas L., Sec.--A.G. Edwards Trust Company, Saint Louis, MO; *U.S. Public*, pg. 565

Kelly, Eileen, V.P.-Personal Lines & Sec.--Acadia Insurance Company, Westbrook, ME; *U.S. Public*, pg. 215

Kelly, James C., Sec.--Shared Medical Systems Corporation, Malvern, PA; *U.S. Public*, pg. 1463

Kelly, Jane, Sec.--Hubbard Farms, Inc., Walpole, NH; *U.S. Public*, pg. 1092

Kelly, Jane, Sec.--Hubbard Farms, Inc., Walpole, NH; *Int'l*, pg. 1114

Kelly, Janet Langford, Sr. V.P., Gen. Counsel & Sec.--Sara Lee Corporation, Chicago, IL; *U.S. Public*, pg. 1432

Kelly, John A., Jr., Sec.--Peerless Confection Company, Chicago, IL; *U.S. Private*, pg. 847

Kelly, John F., V.P., Gen. Counsel & Asst. Sec.--Allmerica Financial Corporation, Worcester, MA; *U.S. Public*, pg. 54

Kelly, John, Jr., V.P. & Sec.--Vanguard Energy Corp., Houston, TX; *U.S. Private*, pg. 1133

Kelly, Joseph T., Chief Fin. Officer, Treas. & Sec.--Ewing Cole Cherry Brott, Philadelphia, PA; *U.S. Private*, pg. 387

Kelly, Kathleen M., V.P.-Admin. & Sec.--American Technical Ceramics Corp., Huntington Station, NY; *U.S. Public*, pg. 93

Kelly, Larry, Mgr.- Mktg.Svcs.--EG & G Rotron, Woodstock, NY; *U.S. Public*, pg. 543

Kelly, Pat, Asst. Corp. Sec.--Synergistics Industries Limited, Mississauga, Canada; *U.S. Public*, pg. 734

Kelly, Paul F., Sec.--Ralston Purina Canada Agri-Division, Woodstock, Canada; *U.S. Public*, pg. 1360

Kelly, Paul J., Chief Fin. Officer, V.P. & Sec.--Il Fornaio America Corporation, Corte Madera, CA; *U.S. Public*, pg. 864

Kelly, Susan, Sr. V.P. & Sec.--Albert M. Greenfield & Company, Philadelphia, PA; *U.S. Private*, pg. 477

Kelso, Kathi, Corp. Sec.--Warn Industries, Inc., Clackamas, OR; *U.S. Private*, pg. 1150

Kelvic, Patrick, Sec.--Grandy's, Inc., Lewisville, TX; *U.S. Private*, pg. 61

Kemezys, K. Peter, V.P., Asst. Gen. Counsel & Asst. Sec.--Manor Care, Inc., Gaithersburg, MD; *U.S. Public*, pg. 1041

Kemmerer, Constance, Corp. Sec.--Jackson Hole Ski Resort, Teton Village, WY; *U.S. Private*, pg. 579

Kemp-Harper, R.L., Sec.--Williams Holdings Plc, Derby, United Kingdom; *Int'l*, pg. 1499

Kempe, Ingegerd, Sec.--Fastighetsaktiebolaget Hufvudstaden, Stockholm, Sweden; *Int'l*, pg. 478

Kempf, LeRoy, Sec.--Condon Oil Company, Inc., Ripon, WI; *U.S. Private*, pg. 262

Kemph, Patricia A., Asst. Sec.--The Goodyear Tire & Rubber Company, Akron, OH; *U.S. Public*, pg. 752

Kendall, Cheryl L., Chief Fin. Officer, V.P., Treas. & Sec.--Acme United Corporation, Fairfield, CT; *U.S. Public*, pg. 17

Kendrick, Marcia, Asst. Sec.--Seitel Geophysical, Inc. dba Eagle Geophysical, Inc., Houston, TX; *U.S. Public*, pg. 1454

Kendrick, Vicki, Sec.--Fresh Mark, Inc., Canton, OH; *U.S. Private*, pg. 427

Kenneally, Mary, Treas. & Sec.--Town Pump, Inc., Butte, MT; *U.S. Private*, pg. 1093

Kenneally, William, Sr. V.P., Gen. Counsel & Sec.--Golub Corporation, Schenectady, NY; *U.S. Private*, pg. 463

Kennedy, Ellen J., Sec.--Hancock Fabrics, Inc., Tupelo, MS; *U.S. Public*, pg. 779

Kennedy, Glenn J., Chief Fin. Officer, Treas. & Sec.--Alba-Waldensian, Inc., Valdese, NC; *U.S. Public*, pg. 35

Kennedy, Jack, Sec.--Abbott Ball Company, West Hartford, CT; *U.S. Private*, pg. 9

Kennedy, James C., Sec.--American Financial Group, Cincinnati, OH; *U.S. Public*, pg. 74

Kennedy, John P., V.P., Gen. Counsel & Sec.--Johnson Controls, Inc., Milwaukee, WI; *U.S. Public*, pg. 932

Kennedy, Quentin J., Exec. V.P. & Sec.--Federal Paper Board Company, Inc., Montvale, NJ; *U.S. Public*, pg. 903

Kennedy, Quentin J., Exec. V.P. & Sec.--Imperial Bondware Corp., Montvale, NJ; *U.S. Public*, pg. 903

Kennedy, Ruth A., Sr. V.P., Gen. Counsel & Sec.--Electronic Arts, San Mateo, CA; *U.S. Public*, pg. 569

Kennedy, Sheralyn, Asst. Corp. Sec.--California State Bank-La Habra, La Habra, CA; *U.S. Public*, pg. 294

Kenney, Crane H., V.P., Gen. Counsel & Sec.--Tribune Company, Chicago, IL; *U.S. Public*, pg. 1635

Kenny, James R., Pres., Chief Exec. Officer & Sec.--SJNB Financial Corp., San Jose, CA; *U.S. Public*, pg. 1418

Kensing, Henry V., V.P., Gen. Counsel & Sec.--Dynamics Corporation of America, Greenwich, CT; *U.S. Public*, pg. 286

Kent, Kristin H., V.P., Sr. Legal Counsel & Asst. Sec.--Gannett Company, Inc., Arlington, VA; *U.S. Public*, pg. 698

Kent, Richard E., V.P., Sec. & Gen. Counsel--Grossman's, Inc., Stoughton, MA; *U.S. Private*, pg. 585

Keoleian, Harry A., Sec.--Marketing Displays International, Farmington Hills, MI; *U.S. Private*, pg. 705

Kephart, R., V.P.-Treas. & Sec.--Furman Lumber Company Inc., Dallas, TX; *U.S. Private*, pg. 431

Ker, Alan S., Chief Fin. Officer, Treas. & Sec.--Universal Standard Healthcare, Inc., Southfield, MI; *U.S. Public*, pg. 1697

Kerbey, David T., Sec.--Bespak plc, Norfolk, United Kingdom; *Int'l*, pg. 193

Kerkstra, Steven, Chief Fin. Officer, V.P. & Asst. Sec.--Three D Departments, Inc., Costa Mesa, CA; *U.S. Public*, *pg. 1604*

Kerley, Gregory D., V.P., Treas. & Sec.--Southwestern Energy Company, Fayetteville, AR; *U.S. Public*, pg. 1494

Kerley, Gregory D., V.P., Sec. & Treas.--Southwestern Energy Pipeline Company, Fayetteville, AR; *U.S. Public*, pg. 1494

Kerley, Gregory D., V.P., Sec. & Treas.--Arkansas Western Pipeline Company, Fayetteville, AR; *U.S. Public*, pg. 1494

Kerley, Marsha L., Treas. & Sec.--Peterson Builders, Inc., Sturgeon Bay, WI; *U.S. Private*, pg. 857

Kern, Weldon, Exec. V.P. & Sec.--Modern American Life Insurance Company, Springfield, MO; *U.S. Public*, pg. 853

Kerr, A., Sec.--Bruntons Areo Product, Musselburgh, United Kingdom; *Int'l*, pg. 268

Kerr, G.F.B., Sec.--Nycomed Amersham plc, Chalfont Saint Giles, United Kingdom; *Int'l*, pg. 992

Kerrigan, Juanita I., V.P. & Sec.--Avatar Holdings Inc., Coral Gables, FL; *U.S. Public*, pg. 151

Kerrigan, Juanita I., V.P. & Sec.--Avatar Properties Inc., Miami, FL; *U.S. Public*, pg. 151

Kersharo, Graham, Grp. Co. Sec.--AAH plc, Runcorn, United Kingdom; *Int'l*, pg. 591

Kershaw, N., Sec.--Magnesium Elektron, Twickenham, United Kingdom; *Int'l*, pg. 51

Kerslake, Ros, Sec.--Booker PLC, London, United Kingdom; *Int'l*, pg. 202

Kerz, Paul J., Sec.--Accelerated Claims Processing, Inc., New York, NY; *U.S. Public*, pg. 802

Kerz, Paul J., Sec.--Quality Medical Adjudication, Inc., Rancho Cordova, CA; *U.S. Public*, pg. 802

Kesler-Corneil, Dian, Sec.--Torstar Corporation, Toronto, Canada; *Int'l*, pg. 1402

Kesner, Harvey J., Esq., Sr. V.P., Gen. Counsel & Sec.--American Banknote Corp., New York, NY; *U.S. Public*, pg. 68

Kessel, Roger H., Sr. V.P., Gen. Counsel & Sec.--TECO Energy, Inc., Tampa, FL; *U.S. Public*, pg. 1565

Kessel, Roger H., Gen. Counsel & Sec.--Tampa Electric Co., Tampa, FL; *U.S. Public*, pg. 1565

Kesseler, Lois, Sec.--S.M. Frank & Co., Inc., Peekskill, NY; *U.S. Private*, pg. 423

Kessler, B.I., Sec.--Formation, Inc., Moorestown, NJ; *U.S. Private*, pg. 419

Kessler, Lee, Controller & Sec.--Stern & Stern Industries Inc., New York, NY; *U.S. Private*, pg. 1041

Kessler, Patricia D., Sec. & Franchise Compliance Officer--The Barbers, Hairstyling for Men & Women, Inc., Minneapolis, MN; *U.S. Private*, pg. 115

Kessler, Paul B., Sec.--Cora Texas Manufacturing Co., Inc., White Castle, LA; *U.S. Private*, pg. 275

Ketner, William O., Jr., Pres. & Sec.--Exclusive Healthcare, Inc., Omaha, NE; *U.S. Private*, pg. 770

Kettig, David T., V.P.-Legal & Sec.--Independence Holding Company, Stamford, CT; *U.S. Private*, pg. 446

Keuler, Lloyd J., Treas. & Sec.--Turner Supply Company, Mobile, AL; *U.S. Private*, pg. 1110

Key, Gary C., Sec.--Fletcher Challenge Limited, Auckland, New Zealand; *Int'l*, pg. 494

Keyes, Bryan F., Treas., Sec. & Dir.-Legal & Fin.--STB Systems, Inc., Richardson, TX; *U.S. Public*, pg. 1421

Khatri, D., Sec.--First State Computing Pty Ltd, Sydney, Australia; *Int'l*, pg. 222

Khazarian, Roxanne, Gen. Counsel & Sec.--Ethan Allen, Inc., Danbury, CT; *U.S. Public*, pg. 595

Khim, Tay Beng, Sec.--CWT Distribution Limited, Singapore, Singapore; *Int'l*, pg. 246

Khoury, Kenneth F., V.P. & Sec.--Georgia-Pacific Corporation, Atlanta, GA; *U.S. Public*, pg. 735

Khoury, Richel G., Vice Chm., Treas. & Sec.--Monticello Management Co., San Diego, CA; *U.S. Private*, pg. 759

Kibblehouse, John R., Treas. & Sec.--Haines Kibblehouse, Skippack, PA; *U.S. Private*, pg. 494

Kibbon, Larry J., Treas. & Sec.--Walsh Group, Chicago, IL; *U.S. Private*, pg. 1148

Kibbon, Larry J., Treas. & Sec.--Walsh Construction Co. of Illinois, Chicago, IL; *U.S. Private*, pg. 1148

Kicsar, Francis J., Sec.--WPS Energy Services, Inc., Green Bay, WI; *U.S. Public*, pg. 1728

Kicsar, Francis J., Sec.--WPS Power Development, Inc., Green Bay, WI; *U.S. Public*, pg. 1728

Kicsar, Francis J., Sec.--WPS Leasing, Inc., Green Bay, WI; *U.S. Public*, pg. 1728

Kiefer, Carl O., V.P.-Fin., Treas. & Sec.--Don E. Williams Co., Rock Island, IL; *U.S. Private*, pg. 1177

Kiefer, Evelyn, Sec.--Bel-Ray Company, Inc., Farmingdale, NJ; *U.S. Private*, pg. 130

Kiefer, William R., V.P.-Law & Sec.--Weirton Steel Corporation, Weirton, WV; *U.S. Public*, pg. 1751

Kieffer, D.A., V.P.-Fin., Treas. & Sec.--McCall Oil & Chemical Corp., Portland, OR; *U.S. Private*, pg. 719

Kiehnle, Robert C., Chief Fin. Officer, Exec. V.P. & Asst. Sec.--Fresh America Corp., Dallas, TX; *U.S. Public*, pg. 681

Kieran, Mary-Anne, Sec.--Willcox & Gibbs, Inc., Carteret, NJ; *U.S. Private*, pg. 1177

Kieseman, John, Asst. Treas. & Asst. Sec.--Allied Mercantile Company, Philadelphia, PA; *U.S. Private*, pg. 39

Kikkawa, Takashi, Sec.--Colonial Beef Co., Philadelphia, PA; *U.S. Private*, pg. 253

Kilanowski, Michael C., Jr., Sec.--Freeport-McMoRan Inc., New Orleans, LA; *U.S. Public*, pg. 680

Kilgannon, Memma S., Treas. & Sec.--Amkor Electronics, Inc., West Chester, PA; *U.S. Private*, pg. 66

Kim, Kenneth H., Chm., Pres., Chief Exec. Officer, Corp. Sec. & Treas.--Medieval Times Dinner & Tournament, Inc., Buena Park, CA; *U.S. Private*, pg. 728

Kim, Y.C., Corp. Sec.--Daewoo International America Corp. - Ridgefield, Ridgefield Park, NJ; *Int'l*, pg. 357

Kimball, Charles, Sec.--South Trust Bank of Georgia, Atlanta, GA; *U.S. Public*, pg. 1492

Kimball, Jenny R., Asst. Sec.--John Deere Capital Corporation, Reno, NV; *U.S. Public*, pg. 492

Kimball, Mark, Sec.--Marten Transport, Ltd., Mondovi, WI; *U.S. Public*, pg. 1052

Kinard, M. Mike, Sec.--American Fuel Cell & Coated Fabrics Co. (Amfuel), Magnolia, AR; *U.S. Private*, pg. 55

Kincaid, Mike, Controller & Sec.--Tractor Supply Co., Nashville, TN; *U.S. Public*, pg. 1627

Kinch, John Patrick, Sec.--Safeway PLC, Hayes, United Kingdom; *Int'l*, pg. 1169

Kindl, Nancy A., Chief Fin. Officer, Treas., Controller & Sec.--Portec, Inc., Lake Forest, IL; *U.S. Public*, pg. 1317

Kindlund, Joanne M., V.P.-Fin., Treas. & Sec.--Holiday RV Superstores, Inc., Orlando, FL; *U.S. Public*, pg. 829

Kindziorski, Arthur C., Gen. Acctg. Mgr.--Besser Company, Alpena, MI; *U.S. Private*, pg. 139
King, Alan, Sec.--Brunel Holdings Plc, Chippenham, United Kingdom; *Int'l*, pg. 230
King, Alan, Sec.--Graham Precision Pumps Ltd., Congleton, United Kingdom; *U.S. Public*, pg. 757
King, Brian E., V.P. & Sec.--Dunlap & Co. Inc., Columbus, IN; *U.S. Private*, pg. 346
King, Dan A., V.P.-Fin., Treas. & Sec.--Cherry Electrical Products Corporation, Waukegan, IL; *U.S. Public*, pg. 346
King, Diana, V.P. & Sec.--King World Productions, Inc., New York, NY; *U.S. Public*, pg. 961
King, F., Sec. & Treas.--Bill Ray Nissan, Inc., Longwood, FL; *U.S. Private*, pg. 911
King, Garnet E., Corp. Sec. & Dir.-Exec. Svcs.--Alltrista Corporation, Muncie, IN; *U.S. Public*, pg. 56
King, Geoffrey W., Grp. Co. Sec.--Guinness Plc, London, United Kingdom; *Int'l*, pg. 412
King, J.B., V.P., Gen. Counsel & Sec.--Guidant Corporation, Indianapolis, IN; *U.S. Public*, pg. 768
King, James C., Sr. V.P. & Sec.--BHA Group Holdings Inc., Kansas City, MO; *U.S. Public*, pg. 161
King, James P., Sec.--Community Finance Corporation, Chicago, IL; *U.S. Public*, pg. 1428
King, Jodie W., Gen. Counsel & Sec.--The Hearst Corporation, New York, NY; *U.S. Private*, pg. 515
King, John F., Sec. & Controller--Paco Pharmaceutical Services, Inc., Lakewood, NJ; *U.S. Public*, pg. 1755
King, Kevan S., Gen. Counsel & Sec.--Poco Petroleums Ltd., Calgary, Canada; *Int'l*, pg. 1061
King, Kimberly N., Corp. Sec. & Assoc. Counsel--Kaufman and Broad Home Corporation, Los Angeles, CA; *U.S. Public*, pg. 944
King, Lawrence E., V.P., Gen. Counsel & Sec.--Flint Ink Corp., Detroit, MI; *U.S. Private*, pg. 413
King, Stephen, Sec.--Datron Incorporated, Windsor, CT; *U.S. Private*, pg. 313
King, Thomas R., Gen. Counsel & Sec.--First Team Sports Inc., Anoka, MN; *U.S. Public*, pg. 638
King, Thomas R., Sec.--Scicom Data Services, Ltd., Minnetonka, MN; *U.S. Private*, pg. 975
King, W. Gary, Gen. Counsel & Sec.--Frisch's Restaurants, Inc., Cincinnati, OH; *U.S. Public*, pg. 682
King, William B., Gen. Counsel & Sec.--Bradley Real Estate, Inc., Northbrook, IL; *U.S. Public*, pg. 250
Kingston, I.G., Sec.--Standard Industries, Inc., Salt Lake City, UT; *U.S. Private*, pg. 1031
Kinman, Luther, Sec.--Burtman Iron Works, Inc., Readville, MA; *U.S. Private*, pg. 188
Kinnard, Michael B., V.P., Gen. Counsel & Sec.--Matlack Systems, Inc., Wilmington, DE; *U.S. Public*, pg. 1057
Kinnard, Michael B., V.P., Gen. Counsel & Sec.--Rollins Truck Leasing Corp., Wilmington, DE; *U.S. Public*, pg. 1405
Kinney, Karin M., Corp. Sec.--Ikon Office Solutions, Inc., Malvern, PA; *U.S. Public*, pg. 862
Kinney, Lori, Exec. Sec.--IMC Agribusiness, Collinsville, IL; *U.S. Public*, pg. 856
Kinney, Patrick J., Gen. Counsel & Sec.--All-Phase Electric Supply Co., Benton Harbor, MI; *U.S. Private*, pg. 35
Kinning, Georgia, Sec.--RK Mechanical, Inc., Denver, CO; *U.S. Private*, pg. 904
Kinsella, Liam, Sec.--Allied Irish Banks, p.l.c., Dublin, Ireland; *Int'l*, pg. 64
Kinsinger, Freeman J., Controller, Asst. Treas. & Asst. Sec.--CIPSCO Investment Company, Springfield, IL; *U.S. Public*, pg. 66
Kinzler, Alexander C., V.P. & Sec.--Barnwell Industries, Inc., Honolulu, HI; *U.S. Public*, pg. 190
Kipp, Terry S., Sr. V.P. & Corp. Sec.--National Bancorp of Alaska, Inc., Anchorage, AK; *U.S. Public*, pg. 1153
Kiraly, Thomas, Chief Fin. Officer, V.P.-Fin. & Sec.--BRC Holdings, Dallas, TX; *U.S. Public*, pg. 163
Kirbie, Ellis, V.P., Treas. & Asst. Sec.--Smith Environmental Technologies Corp., Plymouth Meeting, PA; *U.S. Public*, pg. 1477
Kirby, Dan L., Co.-Chm. Bd., Exec. V.P., Gen. Counsel & Sec.--Western Surety Company, Sioux Falls, SD; *U.S. Public*, pg. 303
Kirchhof, Anton C., Gen. Counsel & Sec.--Louisiana Pacific Corporation, Portland, OR; *U.S. Public*, pg. 1015
Kirhofer, Kimberly A., Sec.--Chicago Rivet & Machine Company, Naperville, IL; *U.S. Public*, pg. 348
Kirk, J., Treas. & Sec.--Exact Equipment Corporation, Langhorne, PA; *U.S. Private*, pg. 387
Kirk, James G., V.P., Gen. Counsel & Sec.--International Technology Corporation, Monroeville, PA; *U.S. Public*, pg. 907
Kirk, Timothy W., V.P., Gen. Counsel & Sec.--ROHN Industries, Inc., Peoria, IL; *U.S. Public*, pg. 1404
Kirk, Wayne, V.P., Gen. Counsel, & Sec.--Homestake Mining Company, San Francisco, CA; *U.S. Public*, pg. 832
Kirkendall, Robert E., Sec. & Asst. Treas.--The Gorman-Rupp Company, Mansfield, OH; *U.S. Public*, pg. 754
Kirkis, Ellen, Sec.--Countrymark Cooperative, Inc., Indianapolis, IN; *U.S. Private*, pg. 279
Kirkland, J. Bryant, III, Asst. Sec.--New Valley Corporation, Miami, FL; *U.S. Public*, pg. 1173
Kirkman, James A., III, Exec. V.P., Gen. Counsel & Sec.--Nabisco Inc., Parsippany, NJ; *U.S. Public*, pg. 1355
Kirkpatrick, Douglas, Gen. Counsel & Sec.--Miken Companies, Inc., Cheektowaga, NY; *U.S. Private*, pg. 745
Kirn, John J., Jr., Asst. Sec.--Oglebay Norton Company, Cleveland, OH; *U.S. Public*, pg. 1213
Kirscher, Ian, Gen. Counsel & Sec.--Danielson Holding Corporation, New York, NY; *U.S. Public*, pg. 483
Kirschner, Kenneth M., Vice Chm. & Sec.--Riverside Group, Inc., Jacksonville, FL; *U.S. Public*, pg. 1391
Kirshner, James E., V.P.-Claims & Sec.--Baldwin & Lyons, Inc., Indianapolis, IN; *U.S. Public*, pg. 169
Kirz, Steve, Mgr.-Sls.--Micro Motion Inc., Boulder, CO; *U.S. Public*, pg. 574
Kiscar, Francis J., Sec.--Wisconsin Public Service Corporation, Green Bay, WI; *U.S. Public*, pg. 1728
Kiser, James W., Corp. Sec.--NationsBank Corporation, Charlotte, NC; *U.S. Public*, pg. 1162
Kiser, Muriel, Sec.--Rehrig Pacific Company, Los Angeles, CA; *U.S. Private*, pg. 919
Kish, David, V.P.-Admin. & Gen. Counsel--American Classic Voyagers Company, New Orleans, LA; *U.S. Private*, pg. 380
Kisleiko, Irene M., Asst. Sec.--Quaker Chemical Corporation, Conshohocken, PA; *U.S. Public*, pg. 1346
Kisler, Dennis B., Sr. V.P., Treas. & Sec.--Agronaut Great Central Insurance Co., Peoria, IL; *U.S. Public*, pg. 129
Kissam, Roger H., Asst. Sec.--Garland Commercial Ranges, Ltd., Mississauga, Canada; *Int'l*, pg. 189
Kissane, Michael, V.P., Gen. Counsel & Sec.--CTB International Corp., Milford, IN; *U.S. Public*, pg. 284
Kissell, Allyson, Corp. Sec.--Auto-trol Technology Corporation, Denver, CO; *U.S. Public*, pg. 148
Kissinger, Thomas, Gen. Counsel & Sec.--The Marcus Corporation, Milwaukee, WI; *U.S. Public*, pg. 1044
Kitchens, Lovett, Sec.--Cox Wood Preserving Co., Orangeburg, SC; *U.S. Private*, pg. 283
Kittilsby, Tim, Treas. & Sec.--Miles Sand & Gravel Company, Auburn, WA; *U.S. Private*, pg. 745
Kittleson, John G., Sec.--Bituminous Roadways, Inc., Inver Grove Heights, MN; *U.S. Private*, pg. 146
Kittner, Marc R., Sec.--Murphey Favre Properties, Inc., Seattle, WA; *U.S. Public*, pg. 1742
Kittridge, Cindy, Exec. Sec.--Federal Cartridge Co., Anoka, MN; *U.S. Public*, pg. 239
Kitz, Edward G., V.P., Treas. & Sec.--Roundy's, Inc., Pewaukee, WI; *U.S. Private*, pg. 948
Kiyono, Naoshi, Mng. Dir., Gen. Mgr.-Intl. Investments & Sec.--Yasuda Mutual Life Insurance Co., Tokyo, Japan; *Int'l*, pg. 1519
Kjos, Anne, Sec.--Luxo A/S, Oslo, Norway; *Int'l*, pg. 821
Klajbor, Jerry, Chief Fin. Officer, V.P. & Sec.--Stanford Telecommunications, Sunnyvale, CA; *U.S. Public*, pg. 1508
Klapinsky, Raymond J., Sr. V.P. & Sec.--The Vanguard Group, Inc., Valley Forge, PA; *U.S. Private*, pg. 1133
Klapinsky, Raymond J., Sec.--Vanguard Real Estate Fund II, Valley Forge, PA; *U.S. Private*, pg. 1134
Klarr, James P., Asst. Sec. & Tax Counsel--La-Z-Boy Incorporated, Monroe, MI; *U.S. Public*, pg. 972
Klaszky, Carl W., Treas. & Sec.--A.N. Deringer, Inc., Saint Albans, VT; *U.S. Private*, pg. 326
Klatt, Roger J., Chief Fin. Officer, Sr. V.P., Treas. & Asst. Sec.--Gundle/SLT Environmental, Inc., Houston, TX; *U.S. Public*, pg. 769
Klawitter, Ronald F., Chief Fin. Officer, V.P.-Fin., Treas. & Sec.--Key Tronic Corporation, Spokane, WA; *U.S. Public*, pg. 953
Kleban, Albert J., Gen. Counsel & Sec.--Chessco Industries, Inc., Westport, CT; *U.S. Private*, pg. 234
Klei, Steven E., Chief Fin. Officer, Sr. V.P.-Fin. & Sec.--ProBusiness Services, Inc., Pleasanton, CA; *U.S. Public*, pg. 1330
Kleidon, Judi, Sec.--Scientific Software-Intercomp, Inc., Denver, CO; *U.S. Public*, pg. 1443
Klein, Douglas P., Chief Fin. Officer, V.P., Sec. & Treas.--Go-Video, Inc., Scottsdale, AZ; *U.S. Public*, pg. 748
Klein, Eric G., Gen. Counsel & Corp. Sec.--Kyocera International, Inc., San Diego, CA; *Int'l*, pg. 775
Klein, Frank J., Exec. V.P. & Sec.--Israel Discount Bank of New York, New York, NY; *Int'l*, pg. 645
Klein, Peter W., V.P., Sec. & Gen. Counsel--Atlantis Plastic, Inc., Atlanta, GA; *U.S. Public*, pg. 145
Klein, Peter W., V.P., Gen. Counsel & Sec.--Biscayne Apparel Inc., Clifton, NJ; *U.S. Public*, pg. 232
Klein, Richard T. Jr., Pres. & Chief Oper. Officer--Klein Tools Inc., Skokie, IL; *U.S. Private*, pg. 625
Klein, Stan, Controller, Treas. & Sec.--Cormier Chevrolet Company, Inc., Carson, CA; *U.S. Private*, pg. 276
Klein, Susan, V.P. & Asst. Sec.--Hibernia Corporation, New Orleans, LA; *U.S. Public*, pg. 825
Kleiner, Madeline, Exec. V.P.-Admin., Gen. Counsel & Sec.--H.F. Ahmanson & Co., Irwindale, CA; *U.S. Public*, pg. 29
Kleinman, Robert D., Exec. V.P., Sec. & Gen. Counsel--AFA Protective Systems, Inc., Syosset, NY; *U.S. Public*, pg. 5
Kleinrock, Stella, Sec.--Technology Transfer Institute, Santa Monica, CA; *U.S. Private*, pg. 1072
Kleman, Charles, Chief Fin. Officer, Sec. & Treas.--Chico's Fas Inc, Fort Myers, FL; *U.S. Public*, pg. 349
Klemer, Thomas, V.P.-Mfg.--Faribault Woolen Mill Co., Faribault, MN; *U.S. Private*, pg. 394
Klemme, Donald, Sec.--EMC Insurance Companies, Des Moines, IA; *U.S. Public*, pg. 545
Klemme, Donald D., V.P.-Admin. & Sec.--EMC Insurance Group, Inc., Des Moines, IA; *U.S. Public*, pg. 545
Klenke, Barbara, V.P.-Admin. & Sec.--The Spencer Turbine Co., Windsor, CT; *U.S. Private*, pg. 1025
Klevecz, Lu Ann, Sec. & Dir.-Corp. Commun. & Investor Rels.--nVIEW Corporation, Newport News, VA; *U.S. Public*, pg. 1206
Klevering, Loren L., AIA, Exec. V.P. & Sec.--Giffels Associates, Inc., Southfield, MI; *U.S. Private*, pg. 452
Klevering, Loren L., AIA, Sec.--Giffels Strategic Consultants, L.L.C., Southfield, MI; *U.S. Private*, pg. 452
Kleveter, Lesley, Asst. Sec.--International Rectifier Corporation, El Segundo, CA; *U.S. Public*, pg. 906
Klimas, Barbara, Exec. Sec.--Mueller's Muehle GmbH, Gelsenkirchen, Germany; *Int'l*, pg. 896
Kline, Sidney D., Jr., Dir.--Bachman Company, Reading, PA; *U.S. Private*, pg. 109
Klinefelter, Gary V., Sec. & Gen. Counsel--Amerco, Reno, NV; *U.S. Private*, pg. 48
Klineman, Kent, Sec.--EIS International Inc., Herndon, VA; *U.S. Public*, pg. 544
Klinger, Jeffery L., V.P., Chief Legal Officer & Sec.--Peabody Holding Company, Inc., Saint Louis, MO; *Int'l*, pg. 594
Klint, Douglas E., V.P., Gen. Counsel & Sec.--Gatefield Corporation, Fremont, CA; *U.S. Public*, pg. 703
Klipsch, Michael, Corp. Sec.--Hospital Affiliates Development Corporation, Nashville, TN; *U.S. Private*, pg. 540
Klisurich, Anne, Asst. Sec.--Wisconsin Michigan Investment Corp., Milwaukee, WI; *U.S. Public*, pg. 1773
Klisurich, Anne K., Asst. Sec.--Badger Service Co., Milwaukee, WI; *U.S. Public*, pg. 1773
Klisurich, Anne K., Controller & Asst. Sec.--Wisconsin Electric Power Company, Milwaukee, WI; *U.S. Public*, pg. 1773
Klisurich, Anne K., Asst. Sec.--Wisvest Corporation, Milwaukee, WI; *U.S. Public*, pg. 1773
Klisurich, Anne K., Asst. Sec.--Witech Corporation, Milwaukee, WI; *U.S. Public*, pg. 1773
Klisurich, Anne K., Asst. Sec.--Syndesis Development Corp., Milwaukee, WI; *U.S. Public*, pg. 1773
Klobasa, E. Alan, Sec.--General Dynamics Corporation, Falls Church, VA; *U.S. Public*, pg. 708
Kloempken, John, Sec.--Office Electronics, Inc., Itasca, IL; *U.S. Private*, pg. 812
Klopper, James J., V.P. & Sec.--Keyport Life Insurance Company, Boston, MA; *U.S. Private*, pg. 666
Klops, Jeff, Sr. V.P. & Sec.--Security Capital Group Incorporated, Santa Fe, NM; *U.S. Private*, pg. 980
Kloska, Ronald F., Vice Chm., Deputy Chief Exec. & Chief Admin. Officer--Skyline Corporation, Elkhart, IN; *U.S. Public*, pg. 1476
Kloster, Burton J. Jr., Sr. V.P., Gen. Counsel & Sec.--General Electric Capital Services, Inc., Stamford, CT; *U.S. Public*, pg. 711
Kloster, Pia, Exec. Sec.--EURO RSCG, Copenhagen, Copenhagen, Denmark; *Int'l*, pg. 602
Klosterman, Ronald, Chief Fin. Officer, V.P.-Fin. & Sec.--Flexsteel Industries, Inc., Dubuque, IA; *U.S. Public*, pg. 653
Klosterman, Scott, Chief Fin. Officer, V.P.-Fin. & Corp. Sec.--Chattanooga Group, Inc., Hixson, TN; *U.S. Private*, pg. 231
Kluting, Duane, Chief Fin. Officer & V.P.--X-Rite, Incorporated, Grandville, MI; *U.S. Public*, pg. 1783
Knapp, Arthur F., Jr., Chief Fin. Officer, Sr. V.P. & Sec.--Boole & Babbage, Inc., San Jose, CA; *U.S. Public*, pg. 244
Knapp, Dee Dee, Sec.--Clark Grave Vault Co., Columbus, OH; *U.S. Private*, pg. 243
Knapp, Michael, Chief Fin. Officer & Sec.--Mission West Properties, Cupertino, CA; *U.S. Public*, pg. 1117
Knauss, Robert H., V.P.-Law, Sec. & Assoc. Gen. Counsel--AmeriGas Partners, L.P., Valley Forge, PA; *U.S. Public*, pg. 1653
Knedlik, Ronald, Chief Fin. Officer, Sr. V.P.-Fin., Treas. & Sec.--Alex Lee, Inc., Hickory, NC; *U.S. Private*, pg. 657
Kneezel, Ronald D., V.P., Gen. Counsel & Sec.--Banta Corporation, Menasha, WI; *U.S. Public*, pg. 187
Kneip, Kurt R., Chief Fin. Officer, V.P. & Sec.--Inter-Tel, Incorporated, Phoenix, AZ; *U.S. Public*, pg. 888
Kneip, Kurt R., Chief Fin. Officer, V.P. & Sec.--Inter-Tel, Incorporated-New Jersey, Phoenix, AZ; *U.S. Public*, pg. 888
Kneip, Kurt R., Chief Fin. Officer, V.P., Sec. & Treas.--Southwest Telephone Systems, Inc., Phoenix, AZ; *U.S. Public*, pg. 888
Kneissl, William L., Sr. V.P., Treas. & Sec.--The Troy Savings Bank, Troy, NY; *U.S. Private*, pg. 1106
Knell, Sandra A., Chief Fin. Officer, Exec. V.P. & Sec.--The Coast Distribution System, San Jose, CA; *U.S. Public*, pg. 388
Kniffen, Janet A., Asst. Sec.--ACF Industries, Inc., Saint Charles, MO; *U.S. Private*, pg. 556
Knight, Alfred C., Asst. Sec.--Westvaco Corporation, New York, NY; *U.S. Public*, pg. 1762
Knight, Betty, Asst. Sec.--Dewberry Design Group, Oklahoma City, OK; *U.S. Private*, pg. 329
Knight, Gail, Treas. & Sec.--Keller Building Products of Charlotte, Inc., Charlotte, NC; *U.S. Private*, pg. 612
Knight, Harold E.H., V.P. & Sec.--Brooklyn Union, Brooklyn, NY; *U.S. Public*, pg. 259
Knight, Jeffrey L., Gen. Counsel & Sec.--Old National Bancorp, Evansville, IN; *U.S. Public*, pg. 1217
Knight, Keith R., Asst. Sec.--John Deere Capital Corporation, Reno, NV; *U.S. Public*, pg. 492
Knight, Mark D., Sr. V.P. & Sec.--The Thomson Corporation, Stamford, CT; *U.S. Public*, pg. 1599
Knipe, P.W., Sec. & Treas.--STV Construction Services, Douglassville, PA; *U.S. Public*, pg. 1421
Knipe, P.W., Sec. & Treas.--STV International, New York, NY; *U.S. Public*, pg. 1421
Knipe, Peter W., Treas. & Sec.--STV Group, Inc., Douglassville, PA; *U.S. Public*, pg. 1421
Knipple, Larry R., Corp. Sec.--Kerr Group, Inc., Lancaster, PA; *U.S. Public*, pg. 952
Kniskern, Gary D., V.P.-Admin. & Sec.--Insteel Industries, Inc., Mount Airy, NC; *U.S. Public*, pg. 882
Knispel, Isabel, Treas. & Sec.--Arrow Fastener Co., Inc., Saddle Brook, NJ; *U.S. Private*, pg. 85
Knoll, J.K., Sec.--Abell-Howe Company, Forest Park, IL; *U.S. Private*, pg. 10
Knolla, Peter A., Asst. Sec.--Acceptance Insurance Co., Inc., Omaha, NE; *U.S. Public*, pg. 14
Knopp, Betty, Exec. Sec.--Holsum Bakery, Inc., Phoenix, AZ; *U.S. Private*, pg. 536
Knott, C.R., Sec.--Taylor Woodrow Property Company Ltd., London, United Kingdom; *Int'l*, pg. 1359
Knottenbelt, P., Sec.--Royal Nedlloyd Group N.V., Rotterdam, Netherlands; *Int'l*, pg. 1143
Knowles, A.S., Sec. & Mgr.-Fin.--Arnotts plc, Dublin, Ireland; *Int'l*, pg. 81

Knowles, Robert E., Chief Fin. Officer & Exec. V.P.--S & K Famous Brands, Inc., Glen Allen, VA; *U.S. Public,* pg. 1414
Knox, James E., Sr. V.P., Gen. Counsel & Sec.--Anixter International, Chicago, IL; *U.S. Public,* pg. 115
Knox, Marion A., Jr., V.P., Treas. & Sec.--Terminix Service, Inc., Columbia, SC; *U.S. Private,* pg. 1077
Knox, Richard, Pres., Treas. & Sec.--Knox Oil of Texas Inc., Dallas, TX; *U.S. Private,* pg. 627
Knudsen, Don, Treas. & Sec.--Denny Menholt Frontier Chevrolet, Billings, MT; *U.S. Private,* pg. 324
Kobayashi, Tomokatsu, V.P. & Sec.--Nippon Steel U.S.A., Inc., New York, NY; *Int'l,* pg. 939
Kobiashvili, Zurab S., V.P., Gen. Counsel & Sec.--Apache Corporation, Houston, TX; *U.S. Public,* pg. 119
Koch, Arthur D., Asst. Sec.--Giant Food Inc., Landover, MD; *U.S. Public,* pg. 741
Koch, Diane M., Asst. Treas. & Asst. Sec.--PP&L Resources, Allentown, PA; *U.S. Public,* pg. 1244
Koch, Elizabeth, Corp. Sec. & Asst. Treas.--Plywood Plastics Inc., Buffalo, NY; *U.S. Private,* pg. 873
Koch, R.E., Asst. Sec.--Texaco Inc., White Plains, NY; *U.S. Public,* pg. 1582
Koch, Richard J., V.P., Sec. & Gen. Counsel--American City Business Journals, Inc., Charlotte, NC; *U.S. Private,* pg. 19
Koch, Valerie, Sec.--New Era Cap. Co., Derby, NY; *U.S. Private,* pg. 793
Koch, W.O., Sec.--The Millgard Corp., Livonia, MI; *U.S. Private,* pg. 748
Kocourek, Edward, V.P. & Asst. Sec.--The Schebler Co., Bettendorf, IA; *U.S. Private,* pg. 366
Kocourek, Edward J., V.P., Treas. & Sec--Egan Cos., Minneapolis, MN; *U.S. Private,* pg. 365
Koebel, Wayne R., Chief Fin. Officer, Exec. V.P., Treas. & Sec.--Shoreline Financial Corp., Benton Harbor, MI; *U.S. Public,* pg. 1467
Koefod, Ghazaleh, Sec.-Investor Rels.--Energy Conversion Devices, Inc., Troy, MI; *U.S. Public,* pg. 581
Koehn, Donald L., Exec. V.P., Treas. & Sec.--Bradbury Company, Inc., Moundridge, KS; *U.S. Private,* pg. 163
Koenig, Joseph T., Treas. & Asst. Sec.--The Hallwood Group Incorporated, Dallas, TX; *U.S. Public,* pg. 777
Koenitzer, Judith, Sec.--Helwig Carbon Products, Inc., Milwaukee, WI; *U.S. Private,* pg. 521
Koepke, Allen C., V.P.-Bus. Devel. & Internal Audit--Regal Ware, Inc., Kewaskum, WI; *U.S. Private,* pg. 917
Koertner, Wm. A., V.P.-Fin. & Sec.--AmerenCIPS, Springfield, IL; *U.S. Public,* pg. 65
Koffman, David L., V.P. & Asst. Sec.--Apparel America, Inc., New Haven, CT; *U.S. Public,* pg. 120
Koffman, Lori G., Asst. Sec.--R.P. Scherer Corporation, Troy, MI; *U.S. Public,* pg. 1437
Koffman, Richard, Sec.--Ben Arnold Co., Inc., Vestal, NY; *U.S. Private,* pg. 83
Koffman, Richard E., Vice Chm., Exec. V.P. & Sec.--Apparel America, Inc., New Haven, CT; *U.S. Public,* pg. 120
Koffman, Robert G., Pres. & Chief Exec. Officer--United Properties, Bay City, MI; *U.S. Private,* pg. 1123
Koger, Donald, Sec.--CENTRIA, Moon Township, PA; *U.S. Private,* pg. 225
Kogod, Marvin, Treas. & Sec.--Maurice Electric Supply Company, Washington, DC; *U.S. Private,* pg. 715
Kogovsek, Conrad J., Treas. & Sec.--Keystone Powdered Metal Company, Saint Marys, PA; *U.S. Private,* pg. 619
Koh, Linda, V.P., Treas. & Sec.--Jupiter Industries, Inc., Northbrook, IL; *U.S. Private,* pg. 602
Kohler, John, V.P.-Franchise Contract Admin. & Sec.--A&W Restaurants, Inc., Livonia, MI; *U.S. Private,* pg. 1
Kohlhof, LaVern L., V.P. & Sec.--ITT Hartford Life & Annuity Insurance Corporation, Minneapolis, MN; *U.S. Public,* pg. 795
Kohls, William R., Chief Fin. Officer & Exec. V.P.--Independent Bank Corporation, Ionia, MI; *U.S. Public,* pg. 874
Kohm, William J., Corp. Sec.--DKB & Partners, Inc., Morristown, NJ; *U.S. Private,* pg. 302
Kohn, Margot W., Sec.--Baltek Corporation, Northvale, NJ; *U.S. Public,* pg. 171
Kohn, Robert H., V.P.-Corp. Affairs & Sec.--Borland International, Inc., Scotts Valley, CA; *U.S. Public,* pg. 246
Kojima, H., Sec.--Esso Sekiyu Kabushiki Kaisha, Tokyo, Japan; *U.S. Public,* pg. 602
Kolb, Bernhard, Sec.--Ascom Holding AG, Bern, Switzerland; *Int'l,* pg. 86
Kolbe, William F., Gen. Counsel & Sec.--Color Arts, Inc., Racine, WI; *U.S. Private,* pg. 254
Koller, Marie, Sec.--Koller Enterprises, Inc., Fenton, MO; *U.S. Private,* pg. 631
Kolodney, Richard S., V.P. & Gen. Counsel--Graham-Field Health Products, Inc., Hauppauge, NY; *U.S. Public,* pg. 757
Komejan, Maryam, Sr. V.P.-Corp. Admin. & Corp. Sec.--Donnelly Corporation, Holland, MI; *U.S. Public,* pg. 519
Komenda, Pamela, Sec.--U.S. Surgical Corp., Norwalk, CT; *U.S. Public,* pg. 1687
Komer, Bernard, Sec.--Artistic Greetings, Inc., Elmira, NY; *U.S. Public,* pg. 136
Komline, Christopher L., V.P. & Dir.-Mktg--Komline-Sanderson Engineering Corp., Peapack, NJ; *U.S. Private, pg. 631*
Kondo, Katsuo, Sec. & Gen. Mgr.--West Japan Railway Company, Osaka, Japan; *Int'l,* pg. 1490
Kong, E.C., Sec.--Moore Products Co. (U.K.) Ltd., Yeovil, United Kingdom; *U.S. Public,* pg. 1129
Konheim, Colleen, Sec.--Kobra International Ltd, New York, NY; *U.S. Private,* pg. 628
Konney, Paul E., Sr. V.P., Gen. Counsel & Sec.--Quaker State Corporation, Irving, TX; *U.S. Public,* pg. 1348
Konop, Thomas F., V.P. & Asst. Sec.--Lord Abbett & Co., New York, NY; *U.S. Private,* pg. 675
Konopko, Elliot, V.P., Gen. Counsel & Sec.--Axsys Technologies, Inc., New York, NY; *U.S. Public,* pg. 157
Konowiecki, Joseph S., Gen. Counsel & Sec.--PacifiCare Health Systems, Inc., Cypress, CA; *U.S. Public,* pg. 1250
Kontje, P.H., Sec.--Esso International Shipping (Bahamas) Co. Limited, Florham Park, NJ; *U.S. Public,* pg. 601
Kopelman, Kenneth P., Sec.--Liz Claiborne, Inc., New York, NY; *U.S. Public,* pg. 1005
Kopf, Kenneth A., Asst. Sec. & Asst. Gen. Counsel--Cubic Applications, Inc., Lacey, WA; *U.S. Public,* pg. 466
Kopf, R.S., Gen. Counsel & Sec.--The Fremont Group, San Francisco, CA; *U.S. Private,* pg. 427
Koplik, Perry, Chm. Bd.--Perry H. Koplik & Sons, New York, NY; *U.S. Private,* pg. 632
Kopp, Joseph T., Controller, Treas. & Sec.--Massman Construction Company, Kansas City, MO; *U.S. Private,* pg. 713
Kopp, Stephanie J., Exec. V.P. & Corp. Sec.--Mutual of America Life Insurance Company, New York, NY; *U.S. Private,* pg. 769
Kopp, Stephanie J., Exec. V.P. & Corp. Sec.--American Life Insurance Company of New York, New York, NY; *U.S. Private,* pg. 769
Koppang, Seming, Sec.--Nycomed Amersham, Oslo, Norway; *Int'l,* pg. 993
Koprowski, D., V.P., Gen. Counsel & Sec.--Kawasaki Motors Corp., U.S.A., Irvine, CA; *Int'l,* pg. 725
Koprowski, Wayne M., V.P., Gen. Counsel & Sec.--Joslyn Corporation, Chicago, IL; *U.S. Public,* pg. 481
Korallus, Guenther, V.P. & Sec.--Volvo and Honda Sales & Service, Lisle, IL; *U.S. Private,* pg. 1143
Korber, Jessica, Controller, Treas. & Sec.--J. Korber & Company, Albuquerque, NM; *U.S. Private,* pg. 632
Kordisch, Larry W., Chief Fin. Officer, Exec. V.P.-Fin. & Sec.--Homeland Holding Corp., Oklahoma City, OK; *U.S.* Public, pg. 832
Koris, Gerald A., Sec.--International Rectifier Corporation, El Segundo, CA; *U.S. Public,* pg. 906
Kornegay-Timmons, Patricia, Asst. Sec.--Carolina Power & Light Company, Raleigh, NC; *U.S. Public,* pg. 306
Korpela, Linda K., V.P. & Sec.--D & N Financial Corporation, Hancock, MI; *U.S. Public,* pg. 472
Korpela, Linda K., V.P. & Sec.--D & N Bank, Hancock, MI; *U.S. Public,* pg. 472
Korpela, Richard A., Exec. V.P., Treas. & Sec.--Lynden Incorporated, Seattle, WA; *U.S. Private,* pg. 683
Korstad, Robert, Sec.--United Hardware Distributing Co., Plymouth, MN; *U.S. Private,* pg. 335
Kosewski, Dan, Sec.--Crystal Cream & Butter Company, Sacramento, CA; *U.S. Private,* pg. 294
Kosowski, Barry, Chief Fin. Officer, Treas. & Sec.--Customedix Corporation, Wallingford, CT; *U.S. Private,* pg. 298
Kost, Kenneth R., Sec.--Danisco Ingredients Canada Inc., Rexdale, Canada; *Int'l,* pg. 378
Kotler, Norman, Sr. Legal Advisor & Sec.--ECI Telecom Ltd., Petah Tiqwa, Israel; *Int'l,* pg. 643
Kotz, Robert, Sec.--ACR Industries Inc., Macomb Township, MI; *U.S. Private,* pg. 3
Koza, Thomas Andrew, V.P. & Sec.-Law Admin.--The North American Coal Corporation, Dallas, TX; *U.S. Public,* pg. 1149
Koziar, Stephen F., Jr., Grp. V.P., Gen. Counsel & Sec.--DPL Inc., Dayton, OH; *U.S. Public,* pg. 473
Koziar, Stephen F., Jr., Grp. V.P. & Sec.--Dayton Power & Light Co., Dayton, OH; *U.S. Public,* pg. 473
Kozik, P. Frank, Sec.--Penn Security Bank and Trust Co., Scranton, PA; *U.S. Public,* pg. 1270
Kozol, Joel A., Sec.--Plymouth Rubber Company, Inc., Canton, MA; *U.S. Public,* pg. 1311
Kraber, Richard, Chief Fin. Officer & Sec.--Wind River Systems, Inc., Alameda, CA; *U.S. Public,* pg. 1770
Kraft, Warren, Sec.--California State Bank-La Habra, La Habra, CA; *U.S. Public,* pg. 294
Kraftsow, Carolyn, Sec.--Craftmatic Industries, Inc., Trevose, PA; *U.S. Private,* pg. 284
Kraftsow, Carolyn, Sec.--Craftmatic Organization, Inc., Trevose, PA; *U.S. Private,* pg. 284
Krahling, Suzanne M., Sec.--Murphey Favre, Inc., Seattle, WA; *U.S. Public,* pg. 1742
Krakauer, Albert A., Sr. Exec. V.P.-Legal & Corp. Affairs & Sec.--Shoppers Drug Mart, Ltd., Toronto, Canada; *Int'l,* pg. 112
Kramer, Stacy, Asst. Corp. Sec.--Western Resources, Inc., Topeka, KS; *U.S. Public,* pg. 1759
Kramer, Worth A., Sec.--Watlow Electric Manufacturing Company, Saint Louis, MO; *U.S. Private,* pg. 1153
Kramme, Gerald A., Sec.--Ace Glass Incorporated, Vineland, NJ; *U.S. Private,* pg. 12
Krannich, Beverley T., V.P.-H.R. & Sec.--Sonat Inc., Birmingham, AL; *U.S. Public,* pg. 1484
Krantz, Mary Jan, V.P. & Sec.--Adventure Lands of America, Inc., Des Moines, IA; *U.S. Private,* pg. 22
Krapohl, James R., Treas. & Asst. Sec.--Wolohan Lumber Co., Saginaw, MI; *U.S. Public,* pg. 1774
Krasinski, Leon G., Sec.--ITT Controls & Instruments Division, Midland Park, NJ; *U.S. Public,* pg. 860
Kraskin, Jo, Exec. Sec.--Downey Savings & Loan Association, F.A., Newport Beach, CA; *U.S. Public,* pg. 526
Krasny, Michael P., Chm. Bd., Chief Exec. Officer, Treas. & Sec.--CDW Computer Centers, Inc., Vernon Hills, IL; *U.S.* Public, pg. 277
Kratter, Leslie M., V.P. & Asst. Sec.--Franklin Resources, Inc., San Mateo, CA; *U.S. Public,* pg. 679
Kraus, Joseph M., V.P., Gen. Counsel & Sec.--Central Vermont Public Service Corporation, Rutland, VT; *U.S. Public,* pg. 327
Krause, Stephen H., Sec.--D.D. Bean & Sons Co., Jaffrey, NH; *U.S. Private,* pg. 126
Krechbiel, Vinson, Sec.--Jamieson Film Company, Inc., Dallas, TX; *U.S. Public,* pg. 551
Krechel, Roger, Treas. & Sec.--Breckenridge Material Company, Saint Louis, MO; *U.S. Private,* pg. 166
Kreger, Brian F., Sec.--WM Life Insurance Company, Seattle, WA; *U.S. Public,* pg. 1742
Kreher, Janit, Sec.--Kreher Steel Co., Inc., Melrose Park, IL; *U.S. Private,* pg. 635
Kreindler, Peter M., Sr. V.P., Gen. Counsel & Sec.--AlliedSignal Inc., Morristown, NJ; *U.S. Public,* pg. 49
Kreiner, Dennis W., Asst. Sec.--MBC Agency, Inc., Baltimore, MD; *U.S. Public,* pg. 1089
Kremsdorf, Arlene, Sec.--Gussco Manufacturing, Inc., Brooklyn, NY; *U.S. Private,* pg. 488
Krenek, Wilfred, Chief Fin. Officer, V.P., Treas. & Sec.--Bettis Corporation, Waller, TX; *U.S. Public,* pg. 482
Krenich, John M., Sec.--Capral Aluminium Limited, Granville, Australia; *Int'l,* pg. 266
Kresl, Miles L., Jr., V.P.-Admin., Treas. & Corp. Sec.--Badger Paper Mills, Inc., Peshtigo, WI; *U.S. Public,* pg. 165
Kress, Edward, Sec.--Rex Stores Corp., Dayton, OH; *U.S. Public,* pg. 1384
Kretovic, Michael, Controller & Sec.--Don Alleson, Inc., Rochester, NY; *U.S. Private,* pg. 339
Kretschman, S.R., Sec.--Bissell Inc., Grand Rapids, MI; *U.S.* Private, pg. 145
Kretschmer, Manfred, Sec.--Haindl Papier GmbH, Augsburg, Germany; *Int'l,* pg. 586
Kreusch, Anita E., Sec.--Leonard Kreusch, Inc., Northvale, NJ; *U.S. Private,* pg. 635
Kreutz, Paul E., Esq., Sec.--KLA Tencor Corporation, San Jose, CA; *U.S. Public,* pg. 939
Krieger, Bruce D., V.P., Gen. Counsel & Sec.--Blyth Industries, Greenwich, CT; *U.S. Public,* pg. 239
Kringel, J.H., Sec.--Wrought Washer Mfg., Inc., Milwaukee, WI; *U.S. Private,* pg. 1192
Krintz, Betty, Sec.--First Financial Building Corporation, Manchester, MO; *U.S. Private,* pg. 407
Kripalani, Eva, V.P., Gen. Counsel & Sec.--KinderCare Learning Centers, Inc., Portland, OR; *U.S. Public,* pg. 961
Kriss, Leonard, Gen. Counsel. & Sec.--Mobile Telecommunications Technologies Corp., Jackson, MS; *U.S. Public,* pg. 1120
Kritzer, Paul, Gen. Counsel & Sec.--Journal Communications Inc., Milwaukee, WI; *U.S. Private,* pg. 601
Krivosha, Norman M., Judge, Exec. V.P., Sec. & Gen. Counsel--Ameritas Life Insurance Corp., Lincoln, NE; *U.S. Private,* pg. 65
Krivoshia, E., Jr., V.P., Gen. Counsel & Sec.--National Steel Corporation, Mishawaka, IN; *Int'l,* pg. 902
Kroese, John S., III, Chief Fin. Officer, Treas. & Sec.--Gaffney-Kroese Electrical Supply Corp., Rahway, NJ; *U.S. Private,* pg. 437
Kroetch, Karen, Treas. & Sec.--Krofam Inc., Philip, SD; *U.S.* Private, pg. 636
Kroger, Joan O., Sec.--Columbia/HCA Healthcare Corporation, Nashville, TN; *U.S. Public,* pg. 403
Kroll, Duncan, Sec.--Saskatchewan Government Insurance, SGI, Regina, Canada; *Int'l,* pg. 1195
Krompholz, Nicole, Sec.--Willis Corroon Melling Ltd., Edmonton, Canada; *Int'l,* pg. 1509
Kroneberg, Ingrid, Sec.--Wilbur-Ellis Company & Connell Brothers Company, San Francisco, CA; *U.S. Private,* pg. 1175
Krucks, Kenneth R., Sec. & Asst. Treas.--Rauland-Borg Corporation, Skokie, IL; *U.S. Private,* pg. 911
Krueger, Blake, Exec. V.P., Gen. Counsel & Sec.--Wolverine World Wide, Inc., Rockford, MI; *U.S. Public,* pg. 1775
Kruger, S.O., Asst. Treas. & Asst. Sec.--Tecumseh Products Company, Tecumseh, MI; *U.S. Public,* pg. 1565
Kruger, Susan, Sec.--Spectrulite Consortium, Inc., Madison, IL; *U.S. Private,* pg. 1024
Krumwiede, Geraldine, Sec.--C-Line Products, Inc., Des Plaines, IL; *U.S. Private,* pg. 192
Krupnick, L.A., Sec. & Legal Officer--Inductotherm Industries, Inc., Rancocas, NJ; *U.S. Private,* pg. 560
Kruth, Harold, Gen. Counsel & Sec.--SRI International, Menlo Park, CA; *U.S. Private,* pg. 958
Krutter, Forrest N., Sec.--Berkshire Hathaway Inc., Omaha, NE; *U.S. Public,* pg. 217
Krutzmann, Ronald L., Treas. & Asst. Sec.--Laclede Gas Company, Saint Louis, MO; *U.S. Public,* pg. 973
Kruys, B.Th., Gen. Counsel & Sec.--Van Leeuwen Pipe and Tube Group B.V., Zwijndrecht, Netherlands; *Int'l,* pg. 1449
Krzyminski, Richard, Chief Fin. Officer, Treas. & Sec.--Baxter Hodell Donnelly Preston Inc., Cincinnati, OH; *U.S.* Private, pg. 124
Krzyzanowski, Richard L., Exec. V.P., Gen. Counsel & Sec.--Crown Cork & Seal Company, Inc., Philadelphia, PA; *U.S. Public,* pg. 462
Kubacki, Robert W., Sr. Counsel & Corp. Sec.--Bourns, Inc., Riverside, CA; *U.S. Private,* pg. 161
Kucera, Philip E., Deputy Gen. Counsel & Asst. Sec.--The Times Mirror Company, Los Angeles, CA; *U.S. Public,* pg. 1615
Kucharczuk, Phyllis L., Asst. Sec.--Penn Virginia Equities Corp., Wilmington, DE; *U.S. Public,* pg. 1271
Kucinski, Bernadine E., Asst. Sec.--Servotronics, Inc., Elma, NY; *U.S. Public,* pg. 1462
Kuck, Timothy W., Gen. Counsel & Sec.--EBP Life Insurnace Co., Minneapolis, MN; *U.S. Public,* pg. 635
Kuck, Timothy W., Chief Fin. Officer, Treas. & Sec.--G&K Services, Inc., Minnetonka, MN; *U.S. Public,* pg. 690
Kuckowski, Joseph, V.P.-Project Mngmnt. & Sec.--Joseph Davis, Inc., Buffalo, NY; *U.S. Private,* pg. 315
Kuckro, Lee G., Sr. V.P., Gen. Counsel & Sec.--The Advest Group, Inc., Hartford, CT; *U.S. Public,* pg. 23
Kuechle, Michael, Sec.--Mid-America Dairymen, Inc., Springfield, MO; *U.S. Private,* pg. 743
Kugler, Anthony, Controller & Sec.--Hudson Valley Paper Company, Albany, NY; *U.S. Private,* pg. 546
Kuhbach, Robert G., V.P., Gen. Counsel & Sec.--Dover Corporation, New York, NY; *U.S. Public,* pg. 520
Kuhlman, Lou B., Sec.--Agriland Company, Byron, MN; *U.S.* Private, pg. 26

Kuhlman, Ryan, Sec.--Kuhlman, Inc., Menomonee Falls, WI; *U.S. Private*, pg. 636
Kuhn, Humberto G., Gen. Counsel & Sec.--Wilson Industries Inc., Houston, TX; *U.S. Private*, pg. 1181
Kuhn, Stephen L., V.P. & Sec.--Massmutual Corporate Investors, Springfield, MA; *U.S. Public*, pg. 1055
Kuhnmuenchijr, John, V.P., Gen. Counsel & Sec.--HK Systems, Inc., New Berlin, WI; *U.S. Private*, pg. 491
Kujawski, Karen, Corp. Sec.--Excel Technology, Inc., New York, NY; *U.S. Public*, pg. 599
Kulla, Raymond, V.P., Gen. Counsel & Sec.--General Housewares Corp., Terre Haute, IN; *U.S. Public*, pg. 715
Kumar, V.S., Sec.--KONE Elevator India Ltd., Madras, India; *Int'l*, pg. 748
Kuneman, Thomas, Chief Fin. Officer & Sec.--Automation Software, Inc., Farmington, MI; *U.S. Public*, pg. 110
Kuneman, Thomas, Controller & Sec.--LK Tool USA, Inc., Brighton, MI; *Int'l*, pg. 1418
Kunzmann, Bruce W., V.P., Sec. & Treas.--Berkley Risk Managers, Somerset, NJ; *U.S. Public*, pg. 215
Kuprionis, M. Denise, Sec.--The E.W. Scripps Company, Cincinnati, OH; *U.S. Public*, pg. 1447
Kupris, Eleanor M., V.P.-Admin. & Sec.--Bowles Fluidics Corporation, Columbia, MD; *U.S. Public*, pg. 248
Kurczewski, Walter W., V.P., Gen. Counsel & Sec.--Square D Company, Palatine, IL; *Int'l*, pg. 1208
Kurland, Richard M., Exec. V.P. & Sec.--Handy Store Fixtures, Inc., Newark, NJ; *U.S. Private*, pg. 499
Kurose, Yuichiro, Mng. Dir.-Sls.--Japan Tobacco Inc., Tokyo, Japan; *Int'l*, pg. 703
Kurten, George W., Sec. & Dir.-H.R.--Walsworth Publishing Company, Inc., Marceline, MO; *U.S. Private*, pg. 1148
Kurtz, Melvin H., V.P., Gen. Counsel & Sec.--Chesebrough-Pond's USA Co., Greenwich, CT; *Int'l*, pg. 1435
Kurtz, Michael, V.P., Legal & Asst. Sec.--Oracle Corporation, Redwood City, CA; *U.S. Public*, pg. 1227
Kurtz, Stephen, Treas. & Sec.--Kulite Semiconductor Products, Inc., Leonia, NJ; *U.S. Private*, pg. 636
Kurtzman, Ellen B., Asst. Sec.--CSS Industries, Inc., Philadelphia, PA; *U.S. Public*, pg. 283
Kushel, Stephen J., Sec.--Cine Magnetics, Inc., Armonk, NY; *U.S. Private*, pg. 240
Kusiak, Phil, Treas. & Sec.--Marsh Furniture Company, High Point, NC; *U.S. Private*, pg. 708
Kutchin, Jill Pollack, V.P.-Corp. Affairs & Clerk--Parlex Corporation, Methuen, MA; *U.S. Public*, pg. 1264
Kutys, James, Dir.-Safety & Asst. Sec.--IA Construction Corp., Concordville, PA; *U.S. Private*, pg. 552
Kuyers, David J., Exec. V.P., Treas. & Sec.--American Seating Company, Grand Rapids, MI; *U.S. Private*, pg. 61
Kuykendall, James S., Controller & Asst. Sec.--Bar-S Foods Co., Phoenix, AZ; *U.S. Private*, pg. 114
Kwak, A.C., V.P.-Gen. Affairs & Sec.--Koninklijke BolsWessanen nv, Amstelveen, Netherlands; *Int'l*, pg. 750
Kwan, Lian, Sec.--Advanced Remediation Inc. (ARM), Kenner, LA; *U.S. Private*, pg. 22
Kwok Fung, June Tay, Sec.--Parkway Holdings Limited, Singapore, Singapore; *Int'l*, pg. 1023
Kyle, Terrence W., Sr. V.P., Treas. & Asst. Sec.--Shared Medical Systems Corporation, Malvern, PA; *U.S. Public*, pg. 1463
La Forte, Brian, Sec.--Polar Beverages, Worcester, MA; *U.S. Private*, pg. 873
La Rue, Mary, Corp. Sec.--Berwind Corporation, Philadelphia, PA; *U.S. Private*, pg. 138
Labadens, Francois, Sec.--Groupe Usinor, Paris, France; *Int'l*, pg. 570
LaBar, John R., V.P. & Sec.--The Midland Company, Cincinnati, OH; *U.S. Public*, pg. 1110
LaBarge, Paul C., Sec. & Treas.--Corel Corporation, Ottawa, Canada; *Int'l*, pg. 331
Laborde, Clifford, Sr. V.P., Gen. Counsel & Sec.--Tidewater Inc., New Orleans, LA; *U.S. Public*, pg. 1608
Lacativa, Roslyn, Corp. Sec.--Presidential Realty Corporation, White Plains, NY; *U.S. Public*, pg. 1323
Lach, Eileen M., Sec.--American Home Products Corporation, Madison, NJ; *U.S. Public*, pg. 79
Lachenmayer, Gregg, V.P. & Sec.--Collegeville/ Imagineering L.P., Collegeville, PA; *U.S. Private*, pg. 252
Lachey, G., V.P.-Admin., Treas. & Sec.--Neenah Foundry Company, Neenah, WI; *U.S. Private*, pg. 790
Lackenby, David, V.P.-Fin. & Asst. Sec.--Eastern Color Printing Company, Avon, CT; *U.S. Private*, pg. 357
Lackey, Robert E.T., V.P., Gen. Counsel & Corp. Sec.--Borg-Warner Security Corporation, Chicago, IL; *U.S. Public*, pg. 245
LaCour, Barry, Gen. Counsel & Sec.--The Laitram Corporation, Harahan, LA; *U.S. Private*, pg. 643
Lacy, S.R., Sec.--Encoat-North Arlington, Inc., Wilmington, DE; *U.S. Public*, pg. 1020
Laderoute, Laurin L., Jr., V.P. & Sec.--Olsten Corporation, Melville, NY; *U.S. Public*, pg. 1220
LaDue, Jack R., Sec.--Rochester Gauges Inc. Of Texas, Dallas, TX; *U.S. Private*, pg. 440
LaDue, M.J., III, V.P. & Sec.--Gas Equipment Company, Inc., Dallas, TX; *U.S. Private*, pg. 440
LaDuke, Nancie, V.P. & Sec.--Kmart Corporation, Troy, MI; *U.S. Public*, pg. 963
Laffan, Donna S., Corp. Sec.--Green Mountain Power Corporation, South Burlington, VT; *U.S. Public*, pg. 761
LaFlame, Gregory F., Mgr.-Investor Rels.--FirstEnergy Corp., Akron, OH; *U.S. Public*, pg. 644
Lafleur, Anthony J., V.P., Assoc. Gen. Counsel & Asst. Sec.--Northern Telecom Limited, Brampton, Canada; *Int'l*, pg. 968
LaFleur, Cheryl A., V.P., Gen. Counsel & Sec.--New England Electric System, Westborough, MA; *U.S. Public*, *pg. 1171*
Lafrance, Patrice D., Asst. Sec.--Falconbridge Limited, Toronto, Canada; *Int'l*, pg. 433
Lagache, Guy, Dir.-Fin. & Admin., Sec.--Generale Sucriere SNC, Paris, France; *Int'l*, pg. 548
Lagoni, Patricia, V.P.-Admin. & Sec.--Consolidated-Tomoka Land Co., Daytona Beach, FL; *U.S. Public*, pg. 437
Lagowski, Lawrence A., Chief Fin. Officer & Sec.--Indeck Power Equipment Company, Wheeling, IL; *U.S. Private*, pg. 559
Lague, Richard, Sec.--Kurdziel Industries, Inc., Muskegon, MI; *U.S. Private*, pg. 637
Lagusch, Jane H., V.P.-Admin. & Sec.--Drug Emporium, Inc., Powell, OH; *U.S. Public*, pg. 530
Lahey, Edward V., Jr., Sr. V.P., Gen. Counsel & Sec.--PepsiCo, Inc., Purchase, NY; *U.S. Public*, pg. 1276
Lahr, Mitch, Chief Fin. Officer, V.P. & Sec.--Morgan Products Ltd., Williamsburg, VA; *U.S. Public*, pg. 1132
Lai, Jeffrey R., Asst. Sec.--Impulse Productions, Inc., Beverly Hills, CA; *U.S. Public*, pg. 1310
Laing, R. Gregory, Sec.--TVX Gold Inc., Toronto, Canada; *Int'l*, pg. 1345
Laird, M.L., Sec.--Laird & Company, Eatontown, NJ; *U.S. Private*, pg. 642
Laird, Rose Marie, Asst. Sec.--Laird & Company, Eatontown, NJ; *U.S. Private*, pg. 642
Lajoie, James R., V.P., Gen. Counsel & Sec.--Xtra Corporation, Boston, MA; *U.S. Public*, pg. 1786
Lake, Frederick A., Gen. Counsel--Glassmaster Company, Lexington, SC; *U.S. Public*, pg. 745
Lake, Ralph B., Sr. V.P., Gen. Counsel & Sec.--Promus Hotel Corporation, Memphis, TN; *U.S. Public*, pg. 1335
Lakin, Thomas J., Exec. V.P., Sec. & Gen. Counsel--Starbanc Corporation, Cincinnati, OH; *U.S. Public*, pg. 1510
Lakner, Brenda S., Sec.--Cedar Fair, L.P., Sandusky, OH; *U.S. Public*, pg. 319
Lalor, Louise, Sec.--Willis Corroon Melling Ltd., Edmonton, Canada; *Int'l*, pg. 1509
Lalwani, P.J., Chief Oper. Officer, Chief Info. Officer, Controller & Sec.--Andrew Sports Club Inc., Secaucus, NJ; *U.S. Private*, pg. 73
Lamadrid, Carlos, Chief Fin. Officer, Sr. V.P. & Sec.--Pope & Talbot, Inc., Portland, OR; *U.S. Public*, pg. 1316
Lamar, Charles W., III, Sec.--Lamar Corporation, Baton Rouge, LA; *U.S. Private*, pg. 644
Lamarre, Denys, Dir.-Legal Dept. & Asst. Sec.--Donohue Inc., Quebec, Canada; *Int'l*, pg. 1075
Lamb, Isabelle S., Treas. & Sec.--Ovalstrapping Inc., Hoquiam, WA; *U.S. Private*, pg. 378
Lamb, Janice B., Treas. & Sec.--Lamb Engineering & Construction Co., Salt Lake City, UT; *U.S. Private*, pg. 644
Lamb, Kevin, V.P.-Fin. & Sec.--Nelsen Steel & Wire Co., Franklin Park, IL; *U.S. Private*, pg. 790
Lambert, Sandra L., Sec.--Thermo Electron Corporation, Waltham, MA; *U.S. Public*, pg. 1591
Lamers, Bradley K., Chief Fin. Officer, V.P., Treas. & Sec.--Alternative Resources Corporation, Lincolnshire, IL; *U.S. Public*, pg. 59
Lamm, Lloyd H., Sr. V.P., Chief Oper. Officer & Sec.--The Metropolitan Savings Bank of Ohio, Youngstown, OH; *U.S. Public*, pg. 608
Lamm, Robert, V.P. & Corp. Sec.--W.R. Grace & Co., Boca Raton, FL; *U.S. Public*, pg. 754
Lammers, Maureen, Exec. Sec.--Grayline Housewares, Carol Stream, IL; *U.S. Private*, pg. 472
Lammert, Richard A., Sr. V.P., Gen. Counsel & Sec.--First Empire State Corporation, Buffalo, NY; *U.S. Public*, pg. 631
Lamont, M.G., Sec.--Lamont Holdings Plc, Belfast, United Kingdom; *Int'l*, pg. 797
Lamoreaux, Dave, Treas. & Sec.--United Producers & Consumers Co-Op, Phoenix, AZ; *U.S. Private*, pg. 1123
Lamy, Pierre, V.P. & Co. Sec.--Brascade Resources Inc., Toronto, Canada; *Int'l*, pg. 433
Lancaster, Tom, Treas. & Sec.--Bell Gas, Inc., Roswell, NM; *U.S. Private*, pg. 131
Lancaster, Wallace, Controller, Treas. & Sec.--Crown Buick, Inc., Metairie, LA; *U.S. Private*, pg. 292
Land, Thomas K., Chief Fin. Officer, Sr. V.P. & Asst. Sec.--Santa Fe Gaming Corporation, Las Vegas, NV; *U.S. Public*, pg. 1432
Land, Thornton R., V.P., Gen. Counsel & Asst. Sec.--Charleston Insurance Company, Buffalo, NY; *U.S. Public*, *pg. 1455*
Landau, Yvette, Sec.--Circus Circus - Las Vegas, Las Vegas, NV; *U.S. Public*, pg. 374
Lander, J. Joyce, Asst. Sec.--Ag-Chem Equipment Co., Inc., Minnetonka, MN; *U.S. Public*, pg. 6
Landergan, Walter L., Jr., Gen. Counsel & Sec.--Components Corporation Of America, Dallas, TX; *U.S. Private*, pg. 259
Landeut, Eliane, Corp. Sec., Admin. & Opers.--Lowe Troost, Brussels, Belgium; *U.S. Private*, pg. 678
Landis, Dean, Treas. & Sec.--United Credit Corp. & Patroit Funding, New York, NY; *U.S. Private*, pg. 1121
Landis, Jay L., Asst. Sec.--Aydin Corporation, Horsham, PA; *U.S. Public*, pg. 158
Landry, Bertha, Asst. Sec.--Riviana Foods Inc., Houston, TX; *U.S. Public*, pg. 1392
Landry, Jaques, Exec. V.P.-Fin. & Sec.--Shirmax Leasing Ltd., Montreal, Canada; *Int'l*, pg. 1235
Landsberger, Anny, Sec.--Bel-Art Products, Pequannock, NJ; *U.S. Private*, pg. 130
Landsman, Emanuel E., V.P. & Clerk--American Power Conversion Corporation, West Kingston, RI; *U.S. Public*, pg. 89
Lane, Jeffrey H., Sr. V.P., Gen. Counsel & Sec.--MGIC Investment Corporation, Milwaukee, WI; *U.S. Public*, pg. 1026
Lane, Jeffrey H., Sr. V.P., Gen. Counsel & Sec.--Mortgage Guaranty Insurance Corporation, Milwaukee, WI; *U.S. Public*, pg. 1026
Lane, Michael H., V.P.-Fin., Treas. & Sec.--Laclede Steel Company, Saint Louis, MO; *U.S. Public*, pg. 974
Lane, Ronald E., Sr. V.P., Legal Counsel & Sec.--Illinois Central Corporation, Chicago, IL; *U.S. Public*, pg. 864
Lane, Warren C., Jr., Sec.--Walker Magnetics Group, Inc., Worcester, MA; *U.S. Private*, pg. 1147
Lang, Gerald, Treas. & Sec.--Delta Power Co., Rockford, IL; *U.S. Private*, pg. 322
Lang, Stephen R., V.P., Gen. Counsel & Sec.--Carter-Wallace, Inc., New York, NY; *U.S. Public*, pg. 309
Langdon, M. Anthony, Sec.--Bristol & West Building Society, Bristol, United Kingdom; *Int'l*, pg. 216
Langdon, P.H., V.P.-Human Resources & Asst. Sec.--Shaw Industries Ltd., Etobicoke, Canada; *Int'l*, pg. 1231
Lange, David A., Sec.--United Fire & Casualty Company, Cedar Rapids, IA; *U.S. Public*, pg. 1677
Lange, Karen E., Sec.--Owatonna Canning Company, Owatonna, MN; *U.S. Public*, pg. 349
Langer, Carol B., Chief Fin. Officer, Treas. & Sec.--Comverse Network Systems, Wakefield, MA; *U.S. Public*, *pg. 425*
Langham, James W., V.P., Gen. Counsel & Sec.--Lone Star Industries, Inc., Stamford, CT; *U.S. Public*, pg. 1012
Langley, Marcia, V.P., Gen. Counsel & Sec.--Atlantic Gulf Communities Corporation, Miami, FL; *U.S. Public*, pg. 144
Langley, Max T., Chief Fin. Officer, Sr. V.P., Treas. & Sec.--Reliability Incorporated, Houston, TX; *U.S. Public*, pg. 1373
Langsner, Scott, Treas. & Sec.--MGM Grand, Inc., Las Vegas, NV; *U.S. Public*, pg. 1026
Langus, Alan L., Chief Counsel, V.P. & Sec.--ContiFinancial Corporation, New York, NY; *U.S. Public*, pg. 439
Langus, Alan L., V.P. & Sec.--ContiFinancial Services Corporation, New York, NY; *U.S. Public*, pg. 439
Lanier, Thomas, Exec. V.P., Chief Fin. Officer & Sec.--Salem Carpet Mills, Inc., Winston Salem, NC; *U.S. Public*, pg. 1464
Lanigan, Lynn L., V.P.--Union Planters Corporation, Cordova, TN; *U.S. Public*, pg. 1668
Lankford, June, Corp. Sec.--Advance Mechanical Systems, Inc., Mount Prospect, IL; *U.S. Private*, pg. 18
Lanni, M., Asst. Sec.--Mayer/Berkshire Corporation, Wayne, NJ; *U.S. Private*, pg. 717
Lannie, P. Anthony, Sr. V.P., Gen. Counsel & Sec.--Tejas Gas Corporation, Houston, TX; *Int'l*, pg. 1136
Lansdell, G. Alan, Sr. V.P. & Sec.--Desjardins Laurentian Life Assurance, Wayne, PA; *Int'l*, pg. 396
Lant, Steven V., Treas. & Asst. Sec.--Central Hudson Gas & Electric Corporation, Poughkeepsie, NY; *U.S. Public*, pg. 324
Lanterman, A., Kirk, Treas. & Sec.--Usibelli Coal Mine, Inc., Healy, AK; *U.S. Private*, pg. 1129
Lanz Duret, P. Suinaga, Sec.--Nadro S.A. de C.V., Mexico, Mexico; *U.S. Public*, pg. 1073
Lapine, Jay M., Sr. V.P., Gen. Counel & Asst. Sec.--HBOC, Atlanta, GA; *U.S. Public*, pg. 770
Lapious, Karen, Sec.--Unitel Video, Inc., New York, NY; *U.S. Public*, pg. 1692
Laporte, Chantal, Asst. Sec.--Ivanhoe, Montreal, Canada; *Int'l*, pg. 249
Lappage, David, Corp. Sec.--Inspectorate Plc, Witham, United Kingdom; *Int'l*, pg. 679
Laprade, Bruno Martin, Sec.--Societe Generale, Paris, France; *Int'l*, pg. 1273
Largay, Timothy L., Sec.--Magellan Petroleum Corporation, Madison, CT; *U.S. Public*, pg. 1036
Largent, Jackie, Sec.--Zack Electronics/Tele-Com Products, Inc., Duarte, CA; *U.S. Private*, pg. 1203
Larkins, Thomas F., Sr. V.P., Gen. Counsel & Sec.--L.A. Gear, Inc., Santa Monica, CA; *U.S. Public*, pg. 969
LaRocca, John Steven, Treas. & Sec.--Roberts Foods, Inc., Springfield, IL; *U.S. Private*, pg. 935
LaRocque, James, Gen. Counsel & Sec.--James McHugh Construction Co., Chicago, IL; *U.S. Private*, pg. 721
Larsen, Pamela J., Asst. V.P. & Asst. Sec.--Mercantile Bank of Iowa, Des Moines, IA; *U.S. Public*, pg. 1087
Larsen, Tom, Treas. & Sec.--Todd & Sargent, Inc., Ames, IA; *U.S. Private*, pg. 1089
Larson, Brian L., Chief Fin. Officer, V.P., Treas. & Sec.--Data Transmission Network Corporation, Omaha, NE; *U.S. Public*, pg. 486
Larson, David J., Sr. V.P., Gen. Counsel & Sec.--Lutheran Brotherhood, Minneapolis, MN; *U.S. Private*, pg. 681
Larson, Jaclyn L., Asst. Sec.--Transamerica Corporation, San Francisco, CA; *U.S. Public*, pg. 1629
Larson, John W., Asst. Sec.--Honeywell-Measurex Corporation, Cupertino, CA; *U.S. Public*, pg. 833
Lasker, Judith O., Gen. Counsel & Sec.--Krause's Furniture Inc., Brea, CA; *U.S. Public*, pg. 967
Latham, David C., Gen. Counsel & Corp. Sec.--Citrus World Inc., Lake Wales, FL; *U.S. Private*, pg. 241
Latham, James D., Sr. V.P., Sec. & Gen. Counsel--ITT Sheraton Corporation, Boston, MA; *U.S. Public*, pg. 1512
Latner, Michael E., Exec. V.P. & Sec.--Dynacare, Inc., Toronto, Canada; *Int'l*, pg. 425
Lattanzio, David, Chief Fin. Officer & V.P.-Fin. & Admin.--PharmChem Laboratories, Inc., Menlo Park, CA; *U.S. Public*, pg. 1285
Latz, Jeanie Sell, Chief Legal Officer & Sr. V.P.-Corp. Services--Kansas City Power & Light Company, Kansas City, MO; *U.S. Public*, pg. 943
Lau, Diane, Controller & Sec.--Royal Jeep Eagle Chrysler Plymouth, Inc., Casselberry, FL; *U.S. Private*, pg. 948
Lauck, Kevin D., Controller & Sec.--Chemi-Trol Chemical Co., Gibsonburg, OH; *U.S. Public*, pg. 345
Laudick, Lawrence A., V.P., Controller & Asst. Sec.--Wendy's International Inc., Dublin, OH; *U.S. Public*, pg. 1754
Laudizio, Michael T., V.P.-Taxes & Sec.--Wallace Computer Services, Inc., Lisle, IL; *U.S. Public*, pg. 1735
Laughead, G. Ross, V.P., Gen. Counsel, & Corp. Sec.--Datapoint Corporation, Paris, France; *Int'l*, pg. 384
Laughter, Bennie M., V.P., Sec. & Gen. Counsel--Shaw Industries, Inc., Dalton, GA; *U.S. Public*, pg. 1464
Laukhuff, R.E., Mgr.-H.R. & Sec.--Universal Composites-U.S.C., Manheim, PA; *U.S. Private*, pg. 1126

Laulhere, Larry, Treas. & Sec.--Lombardi Holdings Inc., Whittier, CA; *U.S. Private*, pg. 673
Launaz, Jean Pierre, Sec. Gen.--Banque Cantonale Vaudoise, Lausanne, Switzerland; *Int'l*, pg. 160
Laurel, Roberto P., Sec.--AGP Industrial Corporation, Manila, Philippines; *Int'l*, pg. 14
Laures, Gerald M., V.P.-Fin., Sec. & Treas.--Cobra Electronics Corporation, Chicago, IL; *U.S. Public*, pg. 391
Laurin, Diane Marcelin, V.P.-Gen. Counsel & Sec.--Steinberg Inc., Montreal, Canada; *Int'l*, pg. 1272
Lausterer, Mary, Corp. Sec.--Hope's Architectural Products Inc., Jamestown, NY; *U.S. Private*, pg. 538
Lautour, Jacques, Sec.--Poliet, Courbevoie, France; *Int'l*, pg. 1177
Lauver, E. Eugene, V.P., Gen. Counsel & Sec.--APS Holding Corporation, Houston, TX; *U.S. Public*, pg. 10
Lauver, E. Eugene, Sr. V.P., Gen. Counsel & Sec.--A.P.S., Inc., Houston, TX; *U.S. Public*, pg. 10
Lauver, E. Eugene, V.P.- Real Estate, Gen. Counsel & Sec.--A.P.S., Memphis, TN; *U.S. Public*, pg. 10
LaValle, John W., Chief Fin. Officer, Sr. V.P. & Sec.--Trikon Technologies Inc., Chatsworth, CA; *U.S. Public*, pg. 1638
Laveissiere, Jean, Sec. & Legal--Forasol S.A., Velizy-Villacoublay, France; *Int'l*, pg. 496
Lavender, Adele, Sec.--New Brunswick Scientific Co., Inc., Edison, NJ; *U.S. Public*, pg. 1169
LaVerdi, Barbara J., Asst. Sec.--Frontier Corporation, Rochester, NY; *U.S. Public*, pg. 683
Laverdiere, Yves, Sec.--SNC-Lavalin Group Inc., Montreal, Canada; *Int'l*, pg. 1161
Laverdiere, Yves, Sec.--SNC-Lavalin Inc., Montreal, Canada; *Int'l*, pg. 1162
Lavigne, Leo R., Chief Fin. Officer & Sec.--Sanitary-Dash Manufacturing Co., Inc., North Grosvenordale, CT; *U.S. Public*, pg. 1795
Lavin, Bernice E., Vice Chm., Treas. & Sec.--Alberto-Culver Company, Melrose Park, IL; *U.S. Public*, pg. 37
Lavine, Gilbert S., Treas. & Sec.--Tax Management, Inc., Washington, DC; *U.S. Private*, pg. 182
Law, Betty J., V.P., Treas. & Sec.--Broadcast Supply Worldwide, Inc., Tacoma, WA; *U.S. Private*, pg. 170
Law, L. William, Jr., Sr. V.P., Gen. Counsel & Sec.--Eastern Enterprises, Weston, MA; *U.S. Public*, pg. 548
Law, Robert, Gen. Counsel & Sec.--Canadian Tire Corporation Limited, Toronto, Canada; *Int'l*, pg. 259
Lawi, David S., Sec. & Treas.--Helm Resources Inc., Greenwich, CT; *U.S. Public*, pg. 808
Lawi, David S., Treas. & Sec.--Unapix Entertainment Inc., New York, NY; *U.S. Public*, pg. 1664
Lawing, Jack L., V.P.-Law & Sec.--Gold Kist, Inc., Atlanta, GA; *U.S. Private*, pg. 459
Lawless, Anette, Sec.--Pearson plc, London, United Kingdom; *Int'l*, pg. 1025
Lawn, Aloysius T., IV, Gen. Counsel & Sec.--Tel-Save Holdings, Inc., New Hope, PA; *U.S. Public*, pg. 1568
Lawnstein, Nancy, Exec. Sec.--Imperial, Inc., Green Bay, WI; *U.S. Private*, pg. 558
Lawrence, David L., Treas. & Asst. Sec.--National-Standard Co., Niles, MI; *U.S. Public*, pg. 1160
Lawrence, J. Rodney, Sr. V.P.-Legal Affairs & Corp. Sec.--Pier 1 Imports, Inc., Fort Worth, TX; *U.S. Public*, pg. 1295
Lawrence, J.P., Sec.--ZF Great Britain Ltd., Nottingham, United Kingdom; *Int'l*, pg. 1522
Lawrence, Joyce A., Asst. Sec.--Chemed Corporation, Cincinnati, OH; *U.S. Public*, pg. 343
Lawrence, Robert A., Treas. & Sec.--Sullivan & Cozart Inc., Louisville, KY; *U.S. Private*, pg. 1049
Lawrence, William B., Exec. V.P.-Corp. Devel. & Intl. & Govt. Rels., Gen. Counsel & Sec--TRW Inc., Cleveland, OH; *U.S. Public*, pg. 1558
Laws, Anna, Sr. V.P., Sec. & Controller--EJL Advertising/Los Angeles, Los Angeles, CA; *U.S. Private*, pg. 673
Lawther, S.D., Sec. & Dir.-Fin.--Wilson Connolly, Northampton, United Kingdom; *Int'l*, pg. 1510
Laxton, Ralph, V.P. & Sec.--Dualite Inc., Williamsburg, OH; *U.S. Private*, pg. 344
Lay, Ken, V.P.-Opers. & Sec.--Lay's Fine Foods, Knoxville, TN; *U.S. Private*, pg. 655
Layman, Debbie, Sec.--Birmingham Steel Corp., Cleveland Div., Cleveland, OH; *U.S. Public*, pg. 232
Laz, Marcia S., Asst. Sec.--The Quaker Oats Company, Chicago, IL; *U.S. Public*, pg. 1347
Lazo, Sennen G., First V.P. & Asst. Sec.--Philippine Long Distance Telephone Company, Manila, Philippines; *Int'l*, pg. 1051
Lea, Leiv, Chief Fin. Officer, V.P. & Sec.--Hill Phoenix, Colonial Heights, VA; *U.S. Public*, pg. 521
League, David W., V.P., Gen. Counsel & Sec.--Ace Hardware Corporation, Oak Brook, IL; *U.S. Private*, pg. 12
Leake, Thomas J., Sec.--Hormel Foods Corp., Austin, MN; *U.S. Public*, pg. 840
Lear, William H., V.P., Gen. Counsel & Sec.--Fleetwood Enterprises, Inc., Riverside, CA; *U.S. Public*, pg. 650
Leberman, Peter, Sec.--Jac Pac Foods, Ltd., Manchester, NH; *U.S. Private*, pg. 579
LeBlanc, Charles, V.P., Controller, Sec., & Asst. Treas.--National Service Cleaning Corporation, South Windsor, CT; *U.S. Public*, pg. 1208
Lebovitz, James A., Sr. V.P., Gen. Counsel & Sec.--FPA Medical Management, Inc., San Diego, CA; *U.S. Public*, pg. 608
Lecaualier, Raynald, Dir.-Legal Affairs & Asst. Sec.--Quebecor Printing, Inc., Montreal, Canada; *Int'l*, pg. 1076
Leckerling, Jon P., Exec. V.P.-Admin., Gen. Counsel & Corp. Sec.--Echlin Inc., Branford, CT; *U.S. Public*, pg. 560
Leclerc, Pierre, Asst. Sec.--Imasco Limited, Montreal, Canada; *Int'l*, pg. 112
Ledbetter, JoAnn, Asst. Sec.--Windmere-Durable Holdings, Hialeah, FL; *U.S. Public*, pg. 1771
Lederer, Ann E., Sr. V.P., Gen. Counsel & Sec.--FirstFed Financial Corp., Santa Monica, CA; *U.S. Public*, pg. 645
Lederer, Leslie T., V.P., Gen. Counsel & Sec.--Stone Container Corporation, Chicago, IL; *U.S. Public*, pg. 1520
Lederman, Ira S., Sr. V.P., Asst. Gen. Counsel & Asst. Sec.--W.R. Berkley Corporation, Greenwich, CT; *U.S. Public*, pg. 215
Lee, Alice H., Sec.--GIW Industries, Inc., Grovetown, GA; *Int'l*, pg. 721
Lee, Dorothy, Asst. Sec.--Dalgety Plc, London, United Kingdom; *Int'l*, pg. 376
Lee, Jeanne Marie, Treas. & Sec.--Lakeside Industries, Issaquah, WA; *U.S. Private*, pg. 644
Lee, Jesse, Chief Fin. Officer, Sr. V.P. & Sec.--The IDI Group Companies, Arlington, VA; *U.S. Private*, pg. 554
Lee, LaNelle F., V.P.-Admin. & Sec.--Oregon Steel Mills Inc., Portland, OR; *U.S. Public*, pg. 1230
Lee, Mary T., V.P. & Sec.--Red Devil Inc., Union, NJ; *U.S. Private*, pg. 915
Lee, Theresa K., Gen. Counsel & Sec.--Eastman Chemical Company, Kingsport, TN; *U.S. Public*, pg. 550
Lee, Thomas H., Sec.--Border States Paving, Inc., Fargo, ND; *U.S. Private*, pg. 160
Lee, Wondy S., Asst. Corp. Sec.--PG&E Corporation, San Francisco, CA; *U.S. Public*, pg. 1240
Lee, Yoon-Jung, Chief Fin. Officer & Mng. Dir.--EMTEC Magnetics GmbH, Ludwigshafen, Germany; *Int'l*, pg. 743
Leeper, Ronald, Sec.--R.M. Palmer Company, Reading, PA; *U.S. Private*, pg. 835
Lefcort, Robert A., Exec. V.P. & Sec.--Outsource International, Deerfield Beach, FL; *U.S. Public*, pg. 1236
LeFevre, John H., Sr. V.P. & Sec.--Deluxe Corporation, Shoreview, MN; *U.S. Public*, pg. 498
Leffler, Darryl, Treas. & Asst. Sec.--National Cooperative Refinery Association, Mc Pherson, KS; *U.S. Private*, pg. 781
Leffler, Donald, Treas. & Sec.--Redburn Tire Company, Phoenix, AZ; *U.S. Private*, pg. 915
Legg, James S., Gen. Counsel & Asst. Sec.--Griffith Laboratories Worldwide, Inc., Alsip, IL; *U.S. Private*, pg. 481
Legg, Robert W., Asst. Sec.--Domgroup Ltd., Toronto, Canada; *Int'l*, pg. 631
LeGrande, W. E., Jr., Exec. V.P.--Gudebrod, Inc., Pottstown, PA; *U.S. Private*, pg. 486
Lehfeldt, Richard, Asst. Gen. Counsel & Asst. Sec.--Edison Mission Energy, Irvine, CA; *U.S. Public*, pg. 564
Lehodey, Robert A., Sec.--Murphy Oil Co., Ltd., Calgary, Canada; *U.S. Public*, pg. 1142
Lehr, Donald A., Chm. Bd., Chief Exec. Officer, Treas. & Sec.--Cubix Corporation, Carson City, NV; *U.S. Private*, pg. 294
Leighton, Paul, V.P. & Corp. Sec.--MidAmerican Energy Holdings, Des Moines, IA; *U.S. Public*, pg. 1109
Leighton, Paul, Sec.--MidAmerican Capital Company, Des Moines, IA; *U.S. Public*, pg. 1109
Leimkuhler, Lyle, V.P.-Fin. & Sec.--News-Press & Gazette Company, Saint Joseph, MO; *U.S. Private*, pg. 797
Leinhardt, Walter F., Sec.--Property Capital Trust, Boston, MA; *U.S. Public*, pg. 1335
Leitner, Virlyn, Sec.--Atlas Wire Corporation, Schiller Park, IL; *U.S. Private*, pg. 97
Leland, Leslie S., Sec.--Burlington Resources Inc., Houston, TX; *U.S. Public*, pg. 269
Lemberg, Thomas M., Sr. V.P., Gen. Counsel & Sec.--Polaroid Corporation, Cambridge, MA; *U.S. Public*, pg. 1313
Lembke, Mark L., Asst. Treas. & Asst. Sec.--American Crystal Sugar Company, Moorhead, MN; *U.S. Private*, pg. 52
Lemen, Juanita, Treas. & Sec.--The Auchter Company, Jacksonville, FL; *U.S. Private*, pg. 98
Lemke, John R., Gen. Counsel & Sec.--The Amalgamated Sugar Company LLC, Ogden, UT; *U.S. Private*, pg. 48
Lemle, Robert S., Sr. V.P., Gen. Counsel & Sec.--Cablevision Systems Corporation, Woodbury, NY; *U.S. Public*, pg. 288
Lemmer, William C., V.P., Gen. Counsel & Sec.--Oryx Energy, Dallas, TX; *U.S. Public*, pg. 1232
Lemmink, Robert D., Asst. Sec.--Cincinnati Bell Telephone, Cincinnati, OH; *U.S. Public*, pg. 367
Lemmon, Richard A., V.P. & Sec.--Tetra Tech, Inc., Pasadena, CA; *U.S. Public*, pg. 1582
Lemon, Robert A., Sec. & Dir.-Fin.--C. B. Fleet Co., Inc., Lynchburg, VA; *U.S. Private*, pg. 410
LeMont, Mary B., Asst. Corp. Sec.--Riggs National Corporation, Washington, DC; *U.S. Public*, pg. 1389
Lemoyne, Stewart, Gen. Counsel & Sec.--Management Dynamics, New Providence, NJ; *U.S. Public*, pg. 1040
Lenahan, Joan O., Sec.--Humana Inc., Louisville, KY; *U.S. Public*, pg. 847
Lenahan, Joan O., Sec.--Humana Health Insurance of Nevada, Inc., Las Vegas, NV; *U.S. Public*, pg. 847
Lenahan, Joan O., Sec.--Humana Health Chicago, Inc., Chicago, IL; *U.S. Public*, pg. 847
Lenahan, Joan O., Sec.--Employers Health Insurance Company, Green Bay, WI; *U.S. Public*, pg. 847
Lenahan, Joan O., Sec.--Humana Health Plan of Texas, Inc., San Antonio, TX; *U.S. Public*, pg. 848
Lenahan, Joan O., Sec.--Humana Medical Plan Inc.-Miami, Miramar, FL; *U.S. Public*, pg. 848
Lenahan, Joan O., Sec.--Humana Health Plan of Georgia, Inc., Louisville, KY; *U.S. Public*, pg. 848
Lenahan, Joan O., Sec.--Humana Health Plan of Louisiana, Inc., Louisville, KY; *U.S. Public*, pg. 848
Lenahan, Joan O., Sec.--Humana Insurance Company, Kansas City, MO; *U.S. Public*, pg. 848
Lenahan, Joan O., Sec.--Humana Health Plan of Ohio, Inc., Cincinnati, OH; *U.S. Public*, pg. 848
Lenahan, Joan O., Sec.--Humana Health Plan of Utah, Inc., Salt Lake City, UT; *U.S. Public*, pg. 848
Lenahan, Joan O., Sec.--Humana Health Plan, Inc., Louisville, KY; *U.S. Public*, pg. 848
Lenahan, Joan O., Sec.--Humana Health Plan of Alabama, Inc., Montgomery, AL; *U.S. Public*, pg. 848
Lenahan, Joan O., Sec.--Humana Wisconsin Health Organization Insurance Corporation, Milwaukee, WI; *U.S. Public*, pg. 848
Lenahan, Joan O., Sec.--Network EPO, Inc., Milwaukee, WI; *U.S. Public*, pg. 848
Lenderman, Gaynell, Treas. & Sec.--Gay Johnson's Inc., Grand Junction, CO; *U.S. Private*, pg. 595
Leness, John S., Gen. Counsel & Sec.--Flow International Corporation, Kent, WA; *U.S. Public*, pg. 656
Lenfestey, Laurel J., V.P., Gen. Counsel & Sec.--Poe & Brown, Inc., Daytona Beach, FL; *U.S. Public*, pg. 1312
Leng, Gee Gek, Sec. & Dir.--Kim Eng Holdings Limited, Singapore, Singapore; *Int'l*, pg. 733
Leng, Teo Jun, Sec.--Transmarco Limited, Singapore, Singapore; *Int'l*, pg. 1417
Lenhard, John E., Assoc. Gen. Counsel & Sec.--Cleveland-Cliffs Inc, Cleveland, OH; *U.S. Public*, pg. 386
Lennes, Gregory, Sec.--Navistar International Corporation, Chicago, IL; *U.S. Public*, pg. 1167
Lennon, Maureen, Sec.--U.S. Borax Inc., Valencia, CA; *Int'l*, pg. 1119
Lennon, S.E., Asst. Sec.--Pilkington Plc, Saint Helens, United Kingdom; *Int'l*, pg. 1056
Lennon, S.E., Sec.--Triplex Safety Glass Limited, Kings Norton, United Kingdom; *Int'l*, pg. 1056
Lennox, D. Craig, V.P., Gen. Counsel & Sec.--The Great-West Life Assurance Company, Winnipeg, Canada; *Int'l*, pg. 557
Lennox, Gregory P., Pres. & Chief Exec. Officer--P.L. Porter Co., Woodland Hills, CA; *U.S. Private*, pg. 876
Lents, Don, Sec.--Miss Elaine Inc., Saint Louis, MO; *U.S. Private*, pg. 752
Lenzi, Louis G., Gen. Counsel & Sec.--MBIA Inc., Armonk, NY; *U.S. Public*, pg. 1023
Lenzmeier, Michael G., V.P.-Opers., Treas. & Asst. Sec.--PrimeVest Financial Services, Inc., Saint Cloud, MN; *U.S. Public*, pg. 1376
Leonard, David A., V.P., Assoc. Gen. Counsel & Asst. Sec.--Southwestern Life Insurance Company, Dallas, TX; *U.S. Private*, pg. 1018
Leonoff, Lawrence, Sr. V.P., Gen. Counsel & Sec.--Ontario Hydro, Toronto, Canada; *Int'l*, pg. 1007
Lergara, Tammy, Exec. Sec.--NW Transport Service, Inc., Denver, CO; *U.S. Private*, pg. 772
LeRoy, Pierre, Gen. Counsel & Sec.--Lagardere Groupe, Paris, France; *Int'l*, pg. 791
LeRoy, Spencer, III, Sr. V.P., Gen. Counsel & Sec.--Old Republic International Corporation, Chicago, IL; *U.S. Public*, pg. 1218
Leslie, C.L., Asst. Treas & Asst. Sec.--Lafarge Canada Inc., Montreal, Canada; *Int'l*, pg. 789
Lespinasse, Jean-Paul, Corp. Sec.--Accor S.A., Evry, France; *Int'l*, pg. 20
Lesser, Robert A., Treas. & Sec.--Alba Forwarding Co., Inc., Jersey City, NJ; *U.S. Private*, pg. 32
Lester, Rick, Chief Fin. Officer, V.P. & Asst. Sec.--Domain Energy Corporation, Houston, TX; *U.S. Public*, pg. 515
Lester, Sandy, Treas. & Sec.--First Financial Bankshares, Inc., Abilene, TX; *U.S. Public*, pg. 633
Lestochi, Robert, Treas. & Sec.--James Industries Inc., Hollidaysburg, PA; *U.S. Private*, pg. 580
Lesueur, Michel, Exec. V.P. & Central Sec.--Credit Nationale, Paris, France; *Int'l*, pg. 344
Letchford, J.W.C., Sec.--NFC plc, London, United Kingdom; *Int'l*, pg. 901
Letendre, Elizabeth R., Sec.--HEICO Corporation, Hollywood, FL; *U.S. Public*, pg. 804
Letica, Gudrun, Sec. & Treas.--Letica Corporation, Rochester, MI; *U.S. Private*, pg. 661
Letizia, Stephen, V.P. & Sec.--The Stephan Company, Fort Lauderdale, FL; *U.S. Public*, pg. 1514
Letourneau, Paul, Sec.--Air Canada, Saint-Laurent, Canada; *Int'l*, pg. 36
Lettenberger, Peter J., Sec.--W.H. Brady Co., Milwaukee, WI; *U.S. Public*, pg. 250
Letwin, Lawrence E., Corp. Sec.--Gamma Biologicals Inc., Houston, TX; *U.S. Public*, pg. 698
Leunig, Mark W., V.P., Gen. Counsel & Sec.--Genesee Corporation, Rochester, NY; *U.S. Public*, pg. 728
Leunis, William G., III, Chief Fin. Officer, Sr. V.P.-Fin., Treas. & Sec.--Ultratech Stepper, Inc., San Jose, CA; *U.S. Public*, pg. 1663
Lev, Bruce L., V.P., Gen. Counsel & Sec.--Micro Warehouse, Inc., Norwalk, CT; *U.S. Public*, pg. 1104
Levesque, Celine, Asst. Sec.--Hypotheques CDPQ, Montreal, Canada; *Int'l*, pg. 249
Levesque, Marc, Sec. & Gen. Counsel--Dominion Textile Inc., Montreal, Canada; *Int'l*, pg. 415
Levin-Hoverter, Mia, Treas. & Sec.--Sturgis Iron & Metal Company, Inc., Sturgis, MI; *U.S. Private*, pg. 1048
Levin, Anne, Sec.--Midwest Petroleum Co., Saint Louis, MO; *U.S. Private*, pg. 745
Levin, Bruce A., V.P., Gen. Counsel & Sec.--Mirage Resorts Incorporated, Las Vegas, NV; *U.S. Public*, pg. 1116
Levin, Karen, V.P.-Commun. & Sec.--Biospherics Incorporated, Beltsville, MD; *U.S. Public*, pg. 232
Levin, Marc B., Exec. V.P.-Investor Rels. & Sec.--Integrated Health Services, Inc., Owings Mills, MD; *U.S. Public*, pg. 884
Levin, Michael D., Sr. V.P., Gen. Counsel & Sec.--Sears, Roebuck and Co., Hoffman Estates, IL; *U.S. Public*, pg. 1452
Levin, Paul F., Sr. V.P., Gen. Counsel & Sec.--First Union Real Estate Investments, Cleveland, OH; *U.S. Public*, pg. 640
Levine, Arnold H., Chief Fin. Officer, V.P.-Fin., Treas. & Asst. Sec.--General Microwave Corporation, Amityville, NY; *U.S. Public*, pg. 717
Levine, Paul, V.P.-Fin., Treas. & Sec.--Magnetic Analysis Corp., Mount Vernon, NY; *U.S. Private*, pg. 695
Levine, Paul, Chief Oper. Officer, Exec. V.P. & Sec.--Hirsch International Corp., Hauppauge, NY; *U.S. Public*, pg. 829

Levine, Theodore, Gen. Counsel & Sec.--PaineWebber Group Incorporated, New York, NY; *U.S. Public*, pg. 1252
Levinson, Lawrence M., Gen. Counsel & Sec.--Arrow Automotive Industries, Inc., Framingham, MA; *U.S. Public*, pg. 133
Levinson, Lawrence M., Sec.--Prime Tanning Co., Inc., Rochester, NH; *U.S. Private*, pg. 884
Levitsky, Asher, Sec.--Norwalk Co., Inc., Norwalk, CT; *U.S. Private*, pg. 807
Levitt, Edward J., Gen. Counsel & Sec.--Gelman Sciences, Inc., Ann Arbor, MI; *U.S. Public*, pg. 1253
Levitt, S., Dir.-Fin. & Corp. Sec.--Standard Products Limited, Huntingdon, United Kingdom; *U.S. Public*, pg. 1505
Levron, Barbara, Sec.--Makhteshim Chemical Works Ltd., Beersheba, Israel; *Int'l*, pg. 830
Levy-Morelle, Jacques, Corp. Sec.--Solvay S.A., Brussels, Belgium; *Int'l*, pg. 1277
Levy, Alan, V.P., Controller & Corp. Sec.--Bolt Technology Corporation, Norwalk, CT; *U.S. Public*, pg. 244
Levy, Arthur J., Asst. Sec.--Avnet, Inc., Great Neck, NY; *U.S. Public*, pg. 155
Levy, Donald R., Sec.--M. Block & Sons, Inc., Chicago, IL; *U.S. Private*, pg. 150
Levy, Harry A., Vice Chm. & Sec.--Oriole Homes Corp., Delray Beach, FL; *U.S. Public*, pg. 1230
Levy, Jo Ann, Asst. Sec.--Oriole Homes Corp., Delray Beach, FL; *U.S. Public*, pg. 1230
Levy, Peter, V.P. & Sec.--Rockville Fabrics Corporation, New York, NY; *U.S. Private*, pg. 938
Levy, Sally, Treas. & Sec.--Jacob Levy & Bros., Inc., Louisville, KY; *U.S. Private*, pg. 664
Levy, Stephen, Corp. Sec.--Dena Corporation, Elk Grove Village, IL; *U.S. Private*, pg. 324
Levy, Stuart, Chief Fin. Officer, V.P., Treas. & Sec.--Donnkenny, Inc., New York, NY; *U.S. Public*, pg. 519
Levys, Allan, V.P., Controller, & Sec.--Level Export Sales Corp., New York, NY; *U.S. Private*, pg. 662
Lew, James W., Exec. V.P., Treas. & Sec.--Lodgistix, Inc., Phoenix, AZ; *U.S. Public*, pg. 1527
Lewis, Delores, Sec.--C.C. Myers, Inc., Rancho Cordova, CA; *U.S. Private*, pg. 770
Lewis, Don L., Sec.--Enfield Holdings Ltd., Bulawayo, Zimbabwe; *Int'l*, pg. 390
Lewis, Harry E., V.P. & Sec.--First Gray Line Corporation, Beverly Hills, CA; *U.S. Private*, pg. 407
Lewis, J.A., Controller, Treas. & Sec.--Logo 7, Inc., Indianapolis, IN; *U.S. Public* pg. 1644
Lewis, Jim, Chief Fin. Officer, V.P., Treas. & Sec.--Hale-Halsell Company, Tulsa, OK; *U.S. Private*, pg. 494
Lewis, Julius, Sec.--Juno Lighting, Inc., Des Plaines, IL; *U.S. Public*, pg. 935
Lewis, Roderic W., V.P.-Legal Affairs, Gen. Counsel & Corp. Sec.--Micron Technology Inc., Boise, ID; *U.S. Public*, pg. 1105
Libbe, Allan J., Treas. & Sec.--Rudolph/Libbe, Inc., Walbridge, OH; *U.S. Private*, pg. 950
Liberman, Betsy, Sec.--Nucor Corporation, Charlotte, NC; *U.S. Public*, pg. 1205
Lichtenstein, Jack, Sec. & Treas.--Auburn Hosiery Mills, Inc., Auburn, KY; *U.S. Private*, pg. 98
Lickert, W.R., Treas. & Sec.--Mason & Hanger Corporation, Inc., Lexington, KY; *U.S. Private*, pg. 711
Lickert, William, Sec.--Mason & Hanger Corporation, Inc., Lexington, KY; *U.S. Private*, pg. 711
Liebentritt, Don, V.P. & Asst. Sec.--Great American Management & Investment, Inc., Chicago, IL; *U.S. Private*, pg. 473
Lieber, Jerome B., Sec.--Decorator Industries, Inc., Pembroke Pines, FL; *U.S. Public*, pg. 491
Lieberg, Eric N., Pres., Chief Fin. Officer & Exec. V.P.--Rundel Products, Inc., Portland, OR; *U.S. Private*, pg. 951
Lieberman, David H., Sec.--Herley Industries, Inc., Lancaster, PA; *U.S. Public*, pg. 811
Lieberman, Kathleen H., Esq., V.P., Assoc. Gen. Counsel & Asst. Sec.--Charming Shoppes, Inc., Bensalem, PA; *U.S. Public*, pg. 335
Liegel, Craig, Chief Fin. Officer & Asst. Sec.--Packerland Packing Co., Green Bay, WI; *U.S. Private*, pg. 833
Life, Philip Bradley, V.P. & Asst. Sec.--Riverside Book & Bible House, Inc., Iowa Falls, IA; *U.S. Private*, pg. 598
Lifland, Bill, V.P.-Circulation & Data Processing--PCI, Austin, TX; *U.S. Private*, pg. 826
Light, Daniel T., Treas. & Sec.--Belle Tire Distributor Inc., Allen Park, MI; *U.S. Private*, pg. 132
Lightfoot, Mark F., V.P. & Gen. Counsel & Sec.--American Home Shield Corporation, Memphis, TN; *U.S. Public*, pg. 1461
Lillard, Joyce B., Sr. V.P.-Admin. & Sec.--American Income Holding, Inc., Wilmington, DE; *U.S. Public*, pg. 1622
Lillycrop, David P., Gen. Counsel & Sec.--TI Group plc, Abingdon, United Kingdom; *Int'l*, pg. 1337
Lim, Ginney, Sec.--Singapore Press Holdings Ltd., Singapore, Singapore; *Int'l*, pg. 1253
Limpus, Jane, Sec.--Hofmann Industries, Inc., Sinking Spring, PA; *U.S. Private*, pg. 533
Lin, Jia-Shyong, V.P.-Mktg./Sls., Sec. & Gen. Mgr.--Amspec Chemical Corporation, Gloucester City, NJ; *U.S. Private*, pg. 67
Linbeck, Constance, Sec.--Linbeck Construction Corp, Houston, TX; *U.S. Private*, pg. 667
Lind, Ralph, Controller & Sec.--St. Croix Press, Inc., New Richmond, WI; *U.S. Private*, pg. 960
Lind, Sheila, Sec.--Peerless Chain Company, Winona, MN; *U.S. Public*, pg. 1268
Lind, Tracy, Corp. Sec. & Mgr.-Tax--North Pacific Lumber Company, Portland, OR; *U.S. Private*, pg. 805
Lindal, Walter, Sir, Chm. Emeritus & Sec.--Lindal Cedar Homes, Inc., Seattle, WA; *U.S. Public*, pg. 998
Lindbloom, Sharon J., Asst. Sec.--Lincoln Foodservice Products, Inc., Fort Wayne, IN; *Int'l*, pg. 188
Linden, David, Chief Fin. Officer & Sec.--Monrovia Nursery Co., Azusa, CA; *U.S. Private*, pg. 757
Linden, Ray, V.P., Gen. Counsel & Sec.--The Canada Life Assurance Company, Toronto, Canada; *Int'l*, pg. 254
Lindenmeyer, Mark R., V.P., Gen. Counsel & Sec.--Hillenbrand Industries, Inc., Batesville, IN; *U.S. Public*, pg. 828
Lindley, William G., Treas. & Sec.--T.H. Rogers Lumber Co., Edmond, OK; *U.S. Private*, pg. 940
Lindsay, Ronald T., V.P., Gen. Counsel & Sec.--Collins & Aikman Corporation, Charlotte, NC; *U.S. Public*, pg. 399
Lines, Jim, Chief Fin. Officer, Gen. Counsel & Sec.--ITI Marketing Services, Inc., Omaha, NE; *U.S. Private*, pg. 555
Ling, Robert M., Sec.--Grocers Equipment Co., Los Angeles, CA; *U.S. Private*, pg. 227
Ling, Robert M., Sec.--Grocers and Merchants Insurance, Inc., Covina, CA; *U.S. Private*, pg. 227
Ling, Robert M., Jr., V.P., Gen. Councel & Sec.--Certified Grocers of California, Los Angeles, CA; *U.S. Private*, pg. 226
Ling, Robert M., Jr., Sec.--Grocers Capital Co., Los Angeles, CA; *U.S. Private*, pg. 227
Ling, Robert M., Jr., Sec.--Grocers Development Co., Los Angeles, CA; *U.S. Private*, pg. 227
Ling, Robert M., Jr., Sec.--Crown Grocers, Inc., Los Angeles, CA; *U.S. Private*, pg. 227
Ling, Robert M., Jr., Sec.--Grocers General Merchandise Co., Los Angeles, CA; *U.S. Private*, pg. 227
Ling, Robert M., Jr., Sec.--Springfield Insurance Company, Covina, CA; *U.S. Private*, pg. 227
Linge, H. Kennedy, V.P., Sec. & Assoc. Gen. Counsel--PPG Industries, Inc., Pittsburgh, PA; *U.S. Public*, pg. 1245
Linge, Julie A., Sec.--Putman Publishing Co., Itasca, IL; *U.S. Private*, pg. 896
Lingen, Charles, Chief Fin. Officer & Sr. V.P.--The Sportsman's Guide, Inc., Saint Paul, MN; *U.S. Public*, pg. 1499
Linkous, Clare, Treas. & Sec.--Linkous Construction Company, Inc., Memphis, TN; *U.S. Private*, pg. 669
Linn, Jeffrey A., V.P. & Sec.--Pennsylvania Real Estate Investment Trust, Fort Washington, PA; *U.S. Public*, pg. 1272
Linn, Peter J., Sec.--Liqui-Box Corporation, Worthington, OH; *U.S. Public*, pg. 1000
Linne, R. Steven, Gen. Counsel & Sec.--Haynes International, Inc., Kokomo, IN; *U.S. Public*, pg. 801
Linnell, Norman C., Gen. Counsel & Sec.--Donaldson Company, Inc., Minneapolis, MN; *U.S. Public*, pg. 517
Linnertz, Ann, Corp. Sec.--Amtrak-National Railroad Passenger Corp., Washington, DC; *U.S. Private*, pg. 68
Linton, Myreel, Treas. & Sec.--Landa, Inc., Portland, OR; *U.S. Private*, pg. 646
Lione, C.A., Sec.--Robert Fleming & Co. Limited, London, United Kingdom; *Int'l*, pg. 493
Lione, Gail, V.P., Gen. Counsel & Sec.--Harley-Davidson, Inc., Milwaukee, WI; *U.S. Public*, pg. 786
Lipchik, Harold, Sec.--National Technical Systems, Inc., Calabasas, CA; *U.S. Public*, pg. 1161
Lipka, Carole, Dir.-Mktg.--Keeney Manufacturing Co., Newington, CT; *U.S. Private*, pg. 611
Lipp, Maria Cecilia, Sec. & Corp. Librarian--Y.P.F., S.A., Buenos Aires, Argentina; *Int'l*, pg. 1515
Lippes, Gerald S., Gen. Counsel & Sec.--Mark IV Industries Inc., Amherst, NY; *U.S. Public*, pg. 1044
Lisker, Meshulam, Sec. & Dir.-Mktg.--Antwerp Diamond Distributors Inc., New York, NY; *U.S. Private*, pg. 76
Lisowski, Brent, Sec.--Garland Commercial Ranges, Ltd., Mississauga, Canada; *Int'l*, pg. 189
Lissy, David H., Sr. V.P., Gen. Counsel & Corp. Sec.--Ames Department Stores, Inc., Rocky Hill, CT; *U.S. Public*, pg. 99
List, Ruth, Treas. & Sec.--Alatec Products, Inc., Chatsworth, CA; *U.S. Private*, pg. 31
Litton, W.H., Asst. Sec.--Electrical Equipment Company, Raleigh, NC; *U.S. Private*, pg. 368
Livingston, Thomas P., Asst. Sec.--The Perkin-Elmer Corporation, Norwalk, CT; *U.S. Public*, pg. 1279
Ljungberg, Maryanne, Dir.-Employee Devel.--Ultra Tool & Plastics, Inc., Amherst, NY; *U.S. Private*, pg. 1116
Llado, Carlos Diaz, Sec.--Vallehermoso, S.A., Madrid, Spain; *Int'l*, pg. 1447
Lloveras, Ramon, V.P., Gen. Counsel & Sec.--Pueblo Xtra International, Inc., Pompano Beach, FL; *U.S. Private*, pg. 894
Lloyd, David G., Chief Fin. Officer & Sr. V.P.--Taco Cabana, San Antonio, TX; *U.S. Public*, pg. 1559
Lloyd, Dwayne, Treas. & Sec.--Texas Electric Cooperatives, Inc., Austin, TX; *U.S. Private*, pg. 1078
Lloyd, T.R., Gen. Counsel & Sec.--Pitt-Des Moines, Inc., Pittsburgh, PA; *U.S. Public*, pg. 1304
Lo, Clement, Exec. Dir. & Sec.--Sun Hung Kai Properties Ltd., Wan Chai, Hong Kong; *Int'l*, pg. 1318
Loble, Lester H., II, Gen. Counsel & Sec.--MDU Resources Group, Inc., Bismarck, ND; *U.S. Public*, pg. 1025
Lochen, K.A., Asst. Sec.--B.C. Ziegler & Co., West Bend, WI; *U.S. Public*, pg. 1792
Locher, M.A., Sec.--Hydro Group, Inc., Bridgewater, NJ; *U.S. Private*, pg. 552
Lock, Larry B., Sec.--Enterprises International Inc., Hoquiam, WA; *U.S. Private*, pg. 377
Lockard, Richard A., Dir.-Risk Mngmt. & Asst. Sec.--Furniture Brands International Inc., Saint Louis, MO; *U.S. Public*, pg. 688
Lockie, V.M., Sec.--Betacom Plc, Brentwood, United Kingdom; *Int'l*, pg. 193
Lockwood, Robert W., V.P., Gen. Counsel & Sec.--Ralcorp Holdings Inc., Saint Louis, MO; *U.S. Public*, pg. 1359
Lodge, Susan M., Sec.--Delaware Ribbon Manufacturers, Inc., Philadelphia, PA; *U.S. Private*, pg. 322
Loeb, Carl, Treas. & Sec.--Piknik Products Company, Inc., Montgomery, AL; *U.S. Private*, pg. 865
Loeber, Michael, Treas. & Sec.--Loeber Motors, Inc., Lincolnwood, IL; *U.S. Private*, pg. 672
Loesch, George, Sec.--Holy Cross Electric Association, Inc., Glenwood Springs, CO; *U.S. Private*, pg. 536
Loesche, Peter, Sec.--Provident Mutual Life Insurance Co., Berwyn, PA; *U.S. Private*, pg. 891
Lofgren, Raye M., Sec.--McAnally Enterprises, Inc., Yucaipa, CA; *U.S. Private*, pg. 718
Lofstrand, Bobby, Treas. & Sec.--Minnkota Power Cooperative, Inc., Grand Forks, ND; *U.S. Private*, pg. 751
Loftin, Nancy C., Chief Legal Counsel, V.P. & Sec.--APS, Phoenix, AZ; *U.S. Public*, pg. 1297
Logan, Beate, Exec. Sec.--Storage Dimensions, Inc., Milpitas, CA; *U.S. Public*, pg. 1522
Logan, Robert, Exec. V.P., Sec. & Treas.--Plastics Manufacturing Company, Dallas, TX; *U.S. Public*, pg. 1530
Logan, Winford, Dir.-Admin. Services & Asst. Sec.--State Automobile Mutual Insurance Co., Columbus, OH; *U.S. Private*, pg. 1036
Logas, George P., V.P., Sec. & Gen. Counsel--New Hampshire Insurance Group, New York, NY; *U.S. Public*, pg. 84
Logghe, Ronald M., V.P. & Sec.--Logghe Stamping Company, Fraser, MI; *U.S. Private*, pg. 672
Logne, Lawrence E., Corp. Sec.--International Lottery & Totalizator Systems, Inc., Carlsbad, CA; *U.S. Public*, pg. 900
Logue, Cheryl A., Sec.--Equitrac Corporation, Coral Gables, FL; *U.S. Public*, pg. 590
Lohec, Helen K., Sec.--American Indemnity Financial Corp., Galveston, TX; *U.S. Public*, pg. 83
Loher, Brian H., Treas., Sec. & Dir.-Investor Rels.--Hall Contracting Corp., Louisville, KY; *U.S. Private*, pg. 495
Lohman, Paul J., Treas. & Asst. Sec.--Sands Investments, Inc., Myrtle Beach, SC; *U.S. Private*, pg. 964
Lomax, Janice M., Corp. Sec.--Calvert Bank & Trust Co., Prince Frederick, MD; *U.S. Public*, pg. 1088
Lombard, John J., Jr., Sec.--Airline Hydraulics Corporation, Bensalem, PA; *U.S. Private*, pg. 29
Lombard, Richard, Sec.--Lombard Architectural Precast Prod. Co, Alsip, IL; *U.S. Private*, pg. 673
Londgren, James, Sec.--United Power Association, Elk River, MN; *U.S. Private*, pg. 1123
London, Edith, Sec.--London Litho Aluminum Co., Inc., Lincolnwood, IL; *U.S. Private*, pg. 673
London, Fredric S., Sr. V.P., Gen. Counsel & Sec.--OMI Corp., New York, NY; *U.S. Public*, pg. 1208
Long-Pearson, Shirley, Sec.--Parrish Tire Company, Inc., Winston Salem, NC; *U.S. Private*, pg. 840
Long, Charles, Sec.--Citibank N.A., Long Island City, NY; *U.S. Public*, pg. 377
Long, Charles E., Exec. V.P.-External Affairs & Sec.--Citicorp, New York, NY; *U.S. Public*, pg. 376
Long, Debbie, Sec.--West Coast Life Insurance Co., San Francisco, CA; *U.S. Public*, pg. 1336
Long, Francis A., V.P. & Sec.--Power Markets Development Company, Allentown, PA; *U.S. Public*, pg. 1244
Long, Gary H., Controller & Asst. Sec.--Eagle Food Centers, Inc., Milan, IL; *U.S. Public*, pg. 547
Long, Gary R., V.P. & Sec.--Sands Motor Company, Inc., Glendale, AZ; *U.S. Private*, pg. 964
Long, W. Audie, Sr., Sr. V.P., Gen. Counsel & Sec.--USLD Communications Corp., San Antonio, TX; *U.S. Public*, pg. 969
Longarzo, Agnes, V.P.-Admin. & Sec.--Morton's Restaurant Group, Inc., New Hyde Park, NY; *U.S. Public*, pg. 1136
Longbons, Jeffrey M., Chief Fin. Officer, V.P., Sec. & Treas.--Monitor Liability Managers, Inc., Rolling Meadows, IL; *U.S. Public*, pg. 215
Longenberger, Robert, Sec.--Sun Bancorp, Inc., Selinsgrove, PA; *U.S. Public*, pg. 1529
Longnecker, Dean, Exec. V.P.-Fin. & Sec.--Central Tractor Farm & Country, Inc., Des Moines, IA; *U.S. Private*, pg. 237
Looby, Lawrence J., V.P. & Sec.--OmniTRAX Inc., Chicago, IL; *U.S. Private*, pg. 171
Loomis, James, Asst. Sec. & Asst. Treas.--Loomis Brothers, Inc., Cedar Rapids, IA; *U.S. Private*, pg. 675
Looper, Tommy E., Chief Fin. Officer, Exec. V.P. & Sec.--Anchor Financial Corporation, Myrtle Beach, SC; *U.S. Public*, pg. 111
Lopez, Alicia, V.P., Sec. & Gen. Counsel--Haemonetics Corporation, Braintree, MA; *U.S. Public*, pg. 773
Lopez, Darla, Office Admin. & Corp. Sec.--The Woodfin Suite Hotels, San Diego, CA; *U.S. Private*, pg. 1187
Lopez, Enrique Pinel, Sec.--Banca March S.A., Palma de Mallorca, Spain; *Int'l*, pg. 136
Lopker, Karl F., Chief Exec. Officer & Sec.--QAD Inc, Carpinteria, CA; *U.S. Public*, pg. 1345
Loree, James H., Gen. Counsel & Sec.--Zantop International Airlines, Inc., Ypsilanti, MI; *U.S. Private*, pg. 1204
Lorig, Alan S., Treas. & Sec.--Dedert Corporation, Olympia Fields, IL; *U.S. Private*, pg. 320
LoStocco, Ralph J., V.P.-Admin.--Bridgeport Machines, Inc., Bridgeport, CT; *U.S. Public*, pg. 251
Losurdo, Mary, Sec.--Losurdo Foods, Inc., Hackensack, NJ; *U.S. Private*, pg. 677
Lotter, Charles R., Exec. V.P., Gen. Counsel & Sec.--JC Penney Company, Inc., Plano, TX; *U.S. Public*, pg. 916
Loudermilk, Joey M., Sr. V.P., Gen. Counsel, & Corp. Sec.--AFLAC Incorporated, Columbus, GA; *U.S. Public*, pg. 28
Loudon, Donald H., Corp. Sec.--Torotel, Inc., Grandview, MO; *U.S. Public*, pg. 1624
Loughlin, Joseph P., Sec.--Frontier Insurance Group, Inc., Rock Hill, NY; *U.S. Public*, pg. 684
Louis, Murray A., V.P.-Communications & Asst. Sec.--SEI Investments, Oaks, PA; *U.S. Public*, pg. 1417
Louttit, Gordon J., Sr. V.P., Gen. Counsel & Sec.--Aerospace Corporation, El Segundo, CA; *U.S. Private*, pg. 24
Love, Alison T., Sec. & Assoc. Gen. Counsel--Transcanada Pipelines Limited, Calgary, Canada; *Int'l*, pg. 1416
Love, D.A., V.P., Gen. Counsel & Sec.--The Molson Companies Limited, Toronto, Canada; *Int'l*, pg. 887

Love, Jimmy, Sr. V.P. & Sec.--T.L. James & Company, Ruston, LA; *U.S. Private*, pg. 580
Lovelace, Belle, Treas. & Sec.--Mar-Mac Manufacturing Company, Inc., McBee, SC; *U.S. Private*, pg. 701
Loveland, Curtis A., Sec.--Applied Innovation Inc., Dublin, OH; *U.S. Public*, pg. 123
Loveless, Keith, Corp. Sec. & Assoc. Gen. Counsel--Alaska Air Group, Inc., Seattle, WA; *U.S. Public*, pg. 35
Lovgren, Rich, Sec.--Lam Research Corporation, Fremont, CA; *U.S. Public*, pg. 975
Lowber, John M., Chief Fin. Officer, Sr. V.P., Treas. & Sec.--General Communication, Inc., Anchorage, AK; *U.S. Public*, pg. 708
Lowden, Francis V., III, Asst. Sec.--Universal Corporation, Richmond, VA; *U.S. Public*, pg. 1694
Lowe, James R., Asst. Sec.--Chesapeake Utilities Corporation, Dover, DE; *U.S. Public*, pg. 347
Lowe, Winston, Sec.--General Electric Capital Railcar Services, Chicago, IL; *U.S. Public*, pg. 712
Lower, Roberta D., Sec.--Ludlow Textiles Co., Inc., Ludlow, MA; *U.S. Private*, pg. 680
Lowes, Robert E., Sec.--Photo-Me International plc, Bookham, United Kingdom; *Int'l*, pg. 1055
Lowney, Gloria, Sec.--Telsmith, Inc., Mequon, WI; *U.S. Public*, pg. 141
Lowrie, James, Sec.--Alcom Printing Group, Inc., Bethlehem, PA; *U.S. Private*, pg. 33
Lowry, Donald M., Sr. V.P., Gen. Counsel & Sec.--Continental Assurance Company, Chicago, IL; *U.S. Private*, pg. 267
Lowry, Mike M., Treas. & Sec.--Moto, Inc., Belleville, IL; *U.S. Private*, pg. 764
Lowther, John, V.P., Sec. & Gen. Counsel--State Automobile Mutual Insurance Co., Columbus, OH; *U.S. Private*, pg. 1036
Lubben, David J., Gen. Counsel & Sec.--United HealthCare Corporation, Minnetonka, MN; *U.S. Public*, pg. 1677
Lucarelli, Brian M., Chief Fin. Officer, Controller, Asst Treas. & Asst. Sec.--Alaskan Copper Companies, Seattle, WA; *U.S. Private*, pg. 31
Lucas, Barbara B., Sr. V.P.-Pub. Affairs & Corp. Sec.--The Black & Decker Corporation, Towson, MD; *U.S. Public*, pg. 233
Lucciola, Ronald, Asst. Sec.--Westburne Inc., Montreal, Canada; *Int'l*, pg. 1491
Luchsinger, John F., Jr., JD,, V.P., Gen. Counsel & Sec.--Farmers and Traders Life Insurance Co., Syracuse, NY; *U.S. Private*, pg. 394
Luckhardt, Robert, Treas. & Sec.--The Fifth Third Bank of Northern Kentucky, Florence, KY; *U.S. Public*, pg. 621
Ludgus, Nancy Lucke, Asst. Sec.--National Semiconductor Corporation, Santa Clara, CA; *U.S. Public*, pg. 1159
Ludlow, Patricia, Sec.--Bedford Industries, Inc., Worthington, MN; *U.S. Private*, pg. 129
Ludlum, Melissa, Corp. Sec.--Macromedia Incorporated, Hackensack, NJ; *U.S. Private*, pg. 693
Lugar, Todd, V.P.-Opers., Treas. & Sec.--Thomas L. Green & Co., Inc., Indianapolis, IN; *U.S. Private*, pg. 477
Lukacs, Bela B., Exec. V.P. & Sec.--National Tool & Manufacturing Company, Kenilworth, NJ; *U.S. Private*, pg. 787
Luke, James P., Chief Fin. Officer & Exec. V.P.--Blessings Corporation, Newport News, VA; *U.S. Private*, pg. 1179
Luke, Paul B., Chief Fin. Officer, Sr. V.P., Treas. & Sec.--T&W Financial Corporation, Tacoma, WA; *U.S. Public*, pg. 1552
Lukman, John C., Sr. V.P. & Sec.--Stanchem Inc., East Berlin, CT; *U.S. Private*, pg. 1030
Lummis, P. Bradley, Sr. V.P., Treas. & Sec.--Mrs. Baird's Bakeries, Inc., Fort Worth, TX; *U.S. Private*, pg. 765
Lund, Clyde R., Jr., Sec.--Dynamic Homes, Inc., Detroit Lakes, MN; *U.S. Public*, pg. 538
Lund, Gordon H., Treas. & Asst. Sec.--Dynamic Homes, Inc., Detroit Lakes, MN; *U.S. Public*, pg. 538
Lund, Ronald E., Sr. V.P., Gen. Counsel & Sec.--Medtronic, Inc., Minneapolis, MN; *U.S. Public*, pg. 1082
Lundberg, Larry T., Gen. Mgr. & Sec.--Trout-Blue Cheliau, Inc., Chelan, WA; *U.S. Private*, pg. 1105
Lunder, Peter, Pres., Chief Oper. Officer & Sec.--Dexter Shoe Company, Dexter, ME; *U.S. Public*, pg. 217
Lundgren, Gary, Chm. Bd. & Sec.--Interpacific Investors Services, Seattle, WA; *U.S. Private*, pg. 572
Lundquist, Gene A., V.P. & Corp. Sec.--Calcot, Ltd., Bakersfield, CA; *U.S. Private*, pg. 200
Lunt, Jack R., Sr. V.P., Asst. Gen. Counsel & Sec.--American Stores Company, Salt Lake City, UT; *U.S. Public*, pg. 92
Lupo, Michael A., Chief Fin. Officer, Exec. V.P. & Sec.--ABT Building Products Corporation, Neenah, WI; *Int'l*, pg. 20
Luraschi, William R., Gen. Counsel & Sec.--AES Corporation, Arlington, VA; *U.S. Public*, pg. 5
Luria, Gloria, Sec.--L. Luria & Son, Inc., Medley, FL; *U.S. Public*, pg. 1020
Lurus, Steven A., Chief Acctg. Officer, Sec. & Dir.-Fin.--Metro Information Services, Virginia Beach, VA; *U.S. Public*, pg. 1102
Luskey, David, Sec. & Mgr.-Mail Order--Luskeys Western Stores, Inc., Fort Worth, TX; *U.S. Private*, pg. 681
Luskin, Jean, Sec.--Luskin's, Inc., Columbia, MD; *U.S. Private*, pg. 681
Lusser, Franz, Sec.--Union Bank of Switzerland, Zurich, Switzerland; *Int'l*, pg. 1439
Lustbader, Brian G., Exec. V.P., Gen. Counsel & Sec.--The P.J. Carlin Construction Company, New Rochelle, NY; *U.S. Private*, pg. 211
Lutringer, Richard, Sec.--FAG Bearings Corporation, Danbury, CT; *Int'l*, pg. 469
Lutynski, Adam M., Gen. Counsel & Sec.--The Reynolds and Reynolds Company, Dayton, OH; *U.S. Public*, pg. 1384
Lutz-van der Kley, M.C.M.N., Sec.--Gist-Brocades, Inc., Wilmington, DE; *Int'l*, pg. 1143
Lutz, Max, Comptroller & Sec.--General Motors Suisse S.A., Bienne, Switzerland; *U.S. Public*, pg. 723
Luykx, Rian, Exec. Sec.--Inamed B.V., Breda, Netherlands; *U.S. Public*, pg. 874
Lyda, Allen E., V.P.-Fin., Treas. & Asst. Sec.--Tejon Ranch Company, Lebec, CA; *U.S. Public*, pg. 1566
Lyden, Olof, Corp. Sec.--Swedbank, Stockholm, Sweden; *Int'l*, pg. 1328
Lyman, Clarence K., V.P.-Fin., Treas. & Asst. Sec.--Hawaiian Airlines, Inc., Honolulu, HI; *U.S. Public*, pg. 799
Lyman, Patricia A., V.P., Asst. Gen. Counsel & Asst. Sec.--Edison Mission Energy, Irvine, CA; *U.S. Public*, pg. 564
Lynch, Hal, Sec.--Sunrise Nissan of Orange Park, Orange Park, FL; *U.S. Private*, pg. 1053
Lyndon, D.A., Sec.--Renold PLC, Manchester, United Kingdom; *Int'l*, pg. 1103
Lynes, Pat, Admin. Asst.--Ionics, Incorporated, Watertown, MA; *U.S. Public*, pg. 912
Lyon, David, Sec.--Hardel Mutual Plywood Corporation, Olympia, WA; *U.S. Private*, pg. 501
Lyon, Mark S., Asst. Sec.--Fortune Brands, Inc., Old Greenwich, CT; *U.S. Public*, pg. 674
Lyons, Jeanne, Corp. Sec.--Gencor Industries, Inc., Orlando, FL; *U.S. Public*, pg. 705
Lyons, Stephen M., III, Asst. Sec.--W.P. Carey & Co., Inc., New York, NY; *U.S. Private*, pg. 209
Lyons, Theresa, V.P. & Sec.--North Carolina Mutual Life Insurance Co., Durham, NC; *U.S. Private*, pg. 804
Mabanta, William, Sec.--Aero Data Metal Crafters, Ronkonkoma, NY; *U.S. Private*, pg. 23
MacConnell, Cynthia S., Treas. & Sec.--Beechmont Investments Inc., Cincinnati, OH; *U.S. Private*, pg. 129
MacCrellish, William, Sec.--Harvey Industries, Inc., Waltham, MA; *U.S. Private*, pg. 508
MacDiarmid, Ann, Corp. Sec.--FOCUS2020, Inc., Tenafly, NJ; *U.S. Private*, pg. 415
MacDonald, George E., Sec.--York Barbell Co., Inc., York, PA; *U.S. Private*, pg. 1196
Macdonald, John, Asst. Sec.--Union Carbide Corporation, Danbury, CT; *U.S. Public*, pg. 1666
MacDonald, Patricia, Asst. Sec.--Kollmorgen Corporation, Waltham, MA; *U.S. Public*, pg. 965
MacDougald, Suzanne M., Sr. V.P. & Sec.--ABR Information Services, Inc., Palm Harbor, FL; *U.S. Public*, pg. 2
MacDougall, Peter, Clerk--The L.S. Starrett Company, Athol, MA; *U.S. Public*, pg. 1511
MacFadyen, Alex, Corp. Sec.--First Citizens Banc Shares, Inc., Raleigh, NC; *U.S. Public*, pg. 628
Macgonigal, Peter, Sec.--Nippon Credit Australia Limited, Sydney, Australia; *Int'l*, pg. 933
Machesney, Lisa A., Gen. Counsel & Sec.--Cabot Oil & Gas Corporation, Houston, TX; *U.S. Public*, pg. 289
Machi, Vito A., Sr. V.P., Sr. Loan Admin., Asst. Sec. & Asst. Treas.--The Metropolitan Savings Bank of Ohio, Youngstown, OH; *U.S. Public*, pg. 608
Machlowitz, David S., Sec.--Siemens Medical Systems, Inc., Iselin, NJ; *Int'l*, pg. 1246
Machov, Steven J., V.P., Gen. Counsel & Sec.--Merrill Corporation, Saint Paul, MN; *U.S. Public*, pg. 1097
Machulak, Edward A., Exec. V.P., Sec. & Mktg., Sls. Promo, Adv. Dir.--Commerce Group Corp., Milwaukee, WI; *U.S. Public*, pg. 410
Machulak, Edward L., Chm. Bd., Pres., Chief Exec. Officer & Chief Oper. Officer--Commerce Group Corp., Milwaukee, WI; *U.S. Public*, pg. 410
Machulak, Walter A., Sec. & Mgr.-Pur.--Homespan Realty Co., Inc., Milwaukee, WI; *U.S. Public*, pg. 410
Maciel, Jose Luis Rico, Sec.--Controladora Comercial Mexicana, S.A. de C.V., Mexico, Mexico; *Int'l*, pg. 328
Macintosh, John, Controller, Treas. & Sec.--Tamaroff Buick Inc., Southfield, MI; *U.S. Private*, pg. 1067
Macintosh, John, Treas. & Sec.--Tamaroff Leasing Co., Southfield, MI; *U.S. Private*, pg. 1067
Macioce, S.F., Asst. Sec.--Commercial Light Company, Hillside, IL; *U.S. Private*, pg. 258
Maciola, Cathy, Corp. Sec.--Nissin Foods (U.S.A.) Co. Ltd., Gardena, CA; *Int'l*, pg. 949
MacIver, Robertson, Gen. Counsel & Sec.--PNC Bank, Philadelphia, PA; *U.S. Public*, pg. 1243
Mack, Catherine R., V.P., Gen. Counsel & Sec.--Federal Realty Investment Trust, Rockville, MD; *U.S. Public*, pg. 616
Mackay, Gordon A., Sec.--Schneider Corp., Kitchener, Canada; *Int'l*, pg. 1207
MacKenzie, Harold, Gen. Counsel & Sec.--Overton Gear & Tool Corp., Addison, IL; *U.S. Private*, pg. 823
MacKenzie, J. Blair, V.P., Gen. Counsel & Sec.--Southam Inc., Don Mills, Canada; *Int'l*, pg. 631
Mackey, Steven, V.P.-Gen. Counsel & Sec.--Helmerich & Payne, Inc., Tulsa, OK; *U.S. Public*, pg. 808
Mackness, Richard, Sec.--Meristem plc, Wetherby, United Kingdom; *Int'l*, pg. 858
Mackus, Craig R., Controller & Sec.--Bucyrus International, South Milwaukee, WI; *U.S. Private*, pg. 177
Maclachlan, A.G., Sec.--Howden Group Plc, Renfrew, United Kingdom; *Int'l*, pg. 636
MacLean, George H., Sr. V.P., Gen. Counsel & Sec.--U.S. Industries, Inc., Iselin, NJ; *U.S. Public*, pg. 1683
Macleod, Jack, Controller--Inner Secrets, Inc., Harrison, NJ; *U.S. Private*, pg. 564
Maclin, Joan, Gen. Counsel--The Scoular Company, Omaha, NE; *U.S. Private*, pg. 977
MacNeil, Robert, V.P.-Fin. & Sec.--Continental Coin Corporation, Van Nuys, CA; *U.S. Private*, pg. 267
MacPartland, D., Sec.--Hubbard Hall Inc., Waterbury, CT; *U.S. Private*, pg. 544
MacSporran, Graham, Sec. & Dir.-Fin.--Bridport-Gundry p.l.c., Dorset, United Kingdom; *Int'l*, pg. 215
Madden, Richard O., Chief Fin. Officer, Exec. V.P., Treas. & Sec.--Vermont Financial Services Corp., Brattleboro, VT; *U.S. Public*, pg. 1716
Madden, Teresa, Controller & Sec.--New Century Energies, Inc., Denver, CO; *U.S. Public*, pg. 1170
Madding, Claudia, Asst. Sec.--Archer Daniels Midland Company (ADM), Decatur, IL; *U.S. Public*, pg. 127
Maddox, Barbara T., Sec.--Lee-Moore Oil Co., Inc., Sanford, NC; *U.S. Private*, pg. 657
Madigan, A., Controller & Sec.--Electrical Carbon Limited, Sheffield, United Kingdom; *Int'l*, pg. 891
Madison, Carolyn B., Sec.--Pace Industries, Inc., Fayetteville, AR; *U.S. Public*, pg. 986
Madison, George W., Exec. V.P., Gen. Counsel & Corp. Sec.--Comerica Incorporated, Detroit, MI; *U.S. Public*, pg. 408
Madlinger, Steven R., Chief Fin. Officer, V.P., Treas. & Sec.--GreatBanc, Inc., Aurora, IL; *U.S. Public*, pg. 760
Madsen, James A., Asst. Sec.--Datum Inc., Irvine, CA; *U.S. Public*, pg. 488
Madsen, Richard W., V.P., Gen. Counsel & Sec.--Rohr, Inc., Chula Vista, CA; *U.S. Public*, pg. 751
Maender, William J., V.P.-Fin. & Sec.--LaBarge, Inc., Saint Louis, MO; *U.S. Public*, pg. 973
Maeo, Naokazu, Corp. Sec.--The Nanto Bank, Ltd., Nara, Japan; *Int'l*, pg. 905
Maffeo, Vincent A., V.P., Gen. Counsel & Sec.--ITT Automotive, Inc., Auburn Hills, MI; *U.S. Public*, pg. 859
Magary, Richard, Sr. V.P.-Admin. & Asst. Sec.--American Shared Hospital Services, San Francisco, CA; *U.S. Public*, pg. 91
Magee, Mark E., Sr. V.P., Gen. Counsel & Sec.--Provident Financial Group, Inc., Cincinnati, OH; *U.S. Public*, pg. 1338
Magid, Ruth Arbel, Corp. Sec.--El Al Airlines Ltd., Lod, Israel; *Int'l*, pg. 435
Magnuson, G.E., Sec.--Research, Incorporated, Eden Prairie, MN; *U.S. Public*, pg. 1382
Magnuson, G.E., Sec. & Legal Counsel--Sheldahl, Inc., Northfield, MN; *U.S. Public*, pg. 1465
Magnuson, Gerald E., Sec.--Washington Scientific Industries, Inc., Long Lake, MN; *U.S. Public*, pg. 1744
Magnusson, Ingmar, Sec. & Gen. Counsel--Gambro AB, Lund, Sweden; *Int'l*, pg. 666
Magnusson, Ulf, Gen. Counsel & Corp. Sec.--Electrolux, AB, Stockholm, Sweden; *Int'l*, pg. 438
Magram, Saul H., Sr. V.P., Gen. Counsel & Sec.--Estee Lauder Companies Inc., New York, NY; *U.S. Public*, pg. 594
Mahan, Patricia T., V.P. & Sec.--American Fund Advisors, Inc., Garden City, NY; *U.S. Private*, pg. 55
Maher, Francesca M., V.P., Gen. Counsel & Sec.--UAL Corporation, Elk Grove Village, IL; *U.S. Public*, pg. 1652
Maher, Francesca M., V.P., Gen. Counsel & Sec.--United Air Lines, Inc., Elk Grove Village, IL; *U.S. Public*, pg. 1653
Maher, John, Sec.--Bill Collins Ford Inc., Louisville, KY; *U.S. Private*, pg. 253
Mahler, Glenn, V.P., Treas. & Sec.--Blue Cross Laboratories, Saugus, CA; *U.S. Private*, pg. 152
Mahler, Thomas R., Sec. & Gen. Counsel--Analysts International Corporation, Minneapolis, MN; *U.S. Public*, pg. 110
Mahler, Tom, Gen. Counsel & Sec.--AIC-FSS Advertising, Minneapolis, MN; *U.S. Private*, pg. 5
Mahone, William L., Asst. Sec.--Strategic Distribution Inc., Bensalem, PA; *U.S. Public*, pg. 1523
Mahoney, George, Sec. & Gen. Counsel--Media General, Inc., Richmond, VA; *U.S. Public*, pg. 1077
Mahoney, George R., Jr., Exec. V.P., Gen. Counsel & Sec.--Family Dollar Stores, Inc., Matthews, NC; *U.S. Public*, pg. 612
Mahowald, Douglass, Asst. Sec. & Mgr.-Cash Mngmt.--MDU Resources Group, Inc., Bismarck, ND; *U.S. Public*, pg. 1025
Mai Hai, Bernard Ngiam, Sec.--IPC Corporation Ltd., Singapore, Singapore; *Int'l*, pg. 651
Mai, Elizabeth, V.P., Gen. Counsel & Sec.--Advanta Corp., Spring House, PA; *U.S. Public*, pg. 22
Maier, Alden M., V.P. & Sec.--Morris Newspaper Corporation, Savannah, GA; *U.S. Private*, pg. 762
Major, Sandra, Mgr.-Risk & Asst. Sec.--AEP Industries, Inc., South Hackensack, NJ; *U.S. Public*, pg. 4
Makarewicz, David C., V.P. & Asst. Sec.--Sate-Lite Manufacturing Company, Niles, IL; *U.S. Private*, pg. 598
Makarewicz, David C., V.P. & Asst. Sec.--Parsons Precision Products, Inc., Parsons, KS; *U.S. Private*, pg. 598
Makarewicz, David C., V.P. & Asst. Sec.--Valmark Industries, Inc., Fremont, CA; *U.S. Private*, pg. 598
Makawicz, David C., V.P. & Asst. Sec.--PAMCO Printed Tape & Label Company, Inc., Des Plaines, IL; *U.S. Private*, pg. 598
Makowski, Joseph G., V.P., Gen. Counsel & Sec.--Computer Task Group, Inc. (CTG), Buffalo, NY; *U.S. Public*, pg. 423
Makowski, Susan, Sec. & Treas.--American Travellers Insurance Services, Bensalem, PA; *U.S. Public*, pg. 433
Malacarne, C. John, V.P., Gen. Counsel & Sec.--Kansas City Life Insurance Co., Kansas City, MO; *U.S. Public*, pg. 942
Malacarne, C. John, Sec.--Sunset Life Insurance Co. of America, Olympia, WA; *U.S. Public*, pg. 943
Male, Henry-Paul, Sec.--Labinal SA, Montigny-le-Bretonneux, France; *Int'l*, pg. 785
Malik, Helen T., Corp. Sec. & Treas.--Mitchell Corporation of Owosso, Owosso, MI; *U.S. Private*, pg. 753
Malin, Herbert, Exec. V.P. & Sec.--Teknor Apex Company, Pawtucket, RI; *U.S. Private*, pg. 1073
Malish, William, Treas. & Sec.--Princeville Corporation, Princeville, HI; *U.S. Private*, pg. 885
Malkasian, Henry A., Sec.--IGI, Inc., Buena, NJ; *U.S. Public*, pg. 855
Mallett, Ross E., Asst. Sec.--Western Mining Corporation Holdings Limited, Southbank, Australia; *Int'l*, pg. 1494
Mallory, Glenn E., Sec.--American Vanguard Corporation, Newport Beach, CA; *U.S. Public*, pg. 94
Mallory, Richard, Treas. & Sec.--C. Weaver Chevrolet, Inc., New York Mills, NY; *U.S. Private*, pg. 1156
Malloy, Edwin, Jr., Sec.--Cheraw Yarn Mills, Inc., Cheraw, SC; *U.S. Private*, pg. 233

Malm, Michael, Sec.--Clean Harbors, Inc., Braintree, MA; *U.S. Public*, pg. 383
Malone, Angela, Sec.--CRH, plc, Dublin, Ireland; *Int'l*, pg. 242
Maloney, Betty Lou, Asst. Sec.--McClatchy Newspapers Inc., Sacramento, CA; *U.S. Public*, pg. 1065
Maloney, James V., Sec. & Dir.-Investor Rels.--Pulitzer Publishing Company, Saint Louis, MO; *U.S. Public*, pg. 1343
Maloney, Joseph J., Treas. & Sec.--Daniel J. Keating Co., Ardmore, PA; *U.S. Private*, pg. 610
Maloney, Michael P., V.P., Gen. Counsel & Sec.--Orion Capital Corporation, New York, NY; *U.S. Public*, pg. 1231
Maloney, Phillip, Controller, Treas. & Sec.--Carver, Inc., Savannah, GA; *U.S. Private*, pg. 217
Maloney, Thomas K., V.P.-Opers. & Fin.--Voyager Emblems, Inc., Sanborn, NY; *U.S. Private*, pg. 1143
Maltzman, Donald, Chm. Bd. & Sec.--Tomco Auto Products, Inc., Los Angeles, CA; *U.S. Private*, pg. 1090
Maltzman, Marvin S., Sr. V.P.-Admin., Sec. & Gen. Counsel--House of Fabrics, Inc., Sherman Oaks, CA; *U.S. Public*, pg. 842
Malysheff, George, Gen. Counsel & Sec.--Telus Corporation, Edmonton, Canada; *Int'l*, pg. 1374
Manchester, Gilbert M., V.P. & Gen. Counsel--Commercial Intertech Corp., Youngstown, OH; *U.S. Public*, pg. 411
Mancinelli, Paolo, Sec.--Olivetti SpA, Turin, Italy; *Int'l*, pg. 1002
Mancino, Peter B., V.P., Gen. Counsel & Sec.--UCAR International Inc., Danbury, CT; *U.S. Public*, pg. 1662
Mandekic, Anthony, Treas. & Sec.--Tracinda Corporation, Las Vegas, NV; *U.S. Private*, pg. 1095
Mandell, Edward L., V.P. & Sec.--ALZA Development Corporation, Palo Alto, CA; *U.S. Public*, pg. 62
Mandeville, Robert, Chief Fin. Officer, Treas. & Sec.--Cranston Print Works Company, Cranston, RI; *U.S. Private*, pg. 286
Manen, Martin Giles, Grp. Sec.--Sime Darby Berhad, Kuala Lumpur, Malaysia; *Int'l*, pg. 1249
Mangan, Margaret A., Asst. V.P. & Asst. Sec.--Barnwell Industries, Inc., Honolulu, HI; *U.S. Public*, pg. 190
Mangan, Pete, Chief Fin. Officer, V.P.-Fin. & Sec.--Trident Microsystems, Inc., Mountain View, CA; *U.S. Public*, pg. 1637
Manger, Sandra, Sec.--Hamilton Stores, Inc., Bozeman, MT; *U.S. Private*, pg. 497
Manikashetti, K.S., Sec.--Bharat Petroleum Corporation Ltd., Mumbai, India; *Int'l*, pg. 194
Maniscalco, Diane, Chief Fin. Officer-Admin./Opers.-Sec. & Treas.--Colonna Bros., Inc., North Bergen, NJ; *U.S. Private*, pg. 254
Maniyar, Prabhav V., Chief Fin. Officer, Sr. V.P. & Sec.--Startec Global Communications Corporation, Bethesda, MD; *U.S. Public*, pg. 1511
Manke, Virgil, Sec.--Manke Lumber Company, Inc., Tacoma, WA; *U.S. Private*, pg. 699
Mankowski, Susan, V.P.-Admin.--American Travellers Corporation, Bensalem, PA; *U.S. Public*, pg. 433
Manluccia, Ann, Sec.--Eller Media Company, Phoenix, AZ; *U.S. Public*, pg. 383
Mann, Emily K., Sec.--Inverness Corp., Fair Lawn, NJ; *U.S. Private*, pg. 574
Mann, Gail S., V.P., Sec., Asst. Gen. Counsel & Clerk--Digital Equipment Corporation, Maynard, MA; *U.S. Public*, pg. 507
Mannetta, Lisa, Sec.--Algonquin Gas Transmission Corporation, Boston, MA; *U.S. Public*, pg. 534
Manning, Carol J., Corp. Sec.--Woodward Governor Company, Rockford, IL; *U.S. Public*, pg. 1776
Manning, Martha E., Sr. V.P., Gen. Counsel & Sec.--U.S. Bioscience, Inc., Conshohocken, PA; *U.S. Public*, pg. 1681
Manny, David P., Exec. V.P. & Sec.--Finch, Pruyn & Co., Inc., Glens Falls, NY; *U.S. Private*, pg. 405
Mansfield, Fred W., Sec.--Great Lakes Financial Resources, Inc., Matteson, IL; *U.S. Private*, pg. 474
Manso, Esther, Comptroller, Treas. & Sec.--Metro Ford Inc., Miami, FL; *U.S. Private*, pg. 736
Manson, James J., V.P. & Sec.--National Concrete Products Company, Plymouth, MI; *U.S. Private*, pg. 781
Mansour, Ned, Pres.-Mattel USA & Sec.--Mattel, Inc., El Segundo, CA; *U.S. Public*, pg. 1057
Mantel, M., Corp. Sec.--CSM N.V., Diemen, Netherlands; *Int'l*, pg. 243
Manuel, G. Leonard, Gen. Counsel & Sec.--Cominco, Ltd., Vancouver, Canada; *Int'l*, pg. 307
Manukas, George, V.P., Treas. & Asst. Sec.--DKM Properties Corporation, Lawrenceville, NJ; *U.S. Private*, pg. 351
Manuola, Colleen E., Asst. Sec.--Tasty Baking Company, Philadelphia, PA; *U.S. Public*, pg. 1561
Manwell, Edmund R., Sec.--Dreyer's Grand Ice Cream, Inc., Oakland, CA; *U.S. Public*, pg. 529
Manz, Terry K., V.P., Treas. & Sec.--Cactus Feeders, Inc., Amarillo, TX; *U.S. Private*, pg. 198
Maradza, C.R., Sec.--T A Holdings Limited, Harare, Zimbabwe; *Int'l*, pg. 1334
Maraone, Michael, Chief Fin. Officer--American International Airways, Ypsilanti, MI; *U.S. Private*, pg. 57
March, L.H.W., Sec.--TSB Hill Samuel Bank Holding Co Plc, London, United Kingdom; *Int'l*, pg. 813
Marchal, Jean-Claude, Sec.--GEODIS, Paris, France; *Int'l*, pg. 549
Marchall, Paul, Sec.--Granite State Electric Co., Lebanon, NH; *U.S. Public*, pg. 1171
Marchant, Richard, Sec. & Dir.-Admin.--Tomkins PLC, London, United Kingdom; *Int'l*, pg. 1395
Marchesi, Donna M., Corp. Sec.--CVB Financial Corp., Ontario, CA; *U.S. Public*, pg. 286
Marchisott, Alan, Sec. & Gen. Counsel--Moran Bulk Corporation, Greenwich, CT; *U.S. Private*, pg. 760
Marchisotto, Alan, Gen. Counsel & Sec.--Moran Towing Of Delaware, Inc, Greenwich, CT; *U.S. Private*, pg. 760
Marchisotto, Alan, Sec. & Gen. Counsel--Jakobson Shipyard, Inc, Greenwich, CT; *U.S. Private*, pg. 760
Marchisotto, Alan, Sec. & Gen. Counsel--Hampton Roads Land Co., Ltd, Greenwich, CT; *U.S. Private*, pg. 760
Marchisotto, Alan, Sec. & Gen. Counsel--Seaboard Barge Corporation, Greenwich, CT; *U.S. Private*, pg. 761
Marchisotto, Alan, Sec. & Gen. Counsel--Petroleum Transportation Corporation, Greenwich, CT; *U.S. Private*, pg. 761
Marchisotto, Alan, Sec. & Gen. Counsel--Moran Shipyard Corporation, Greenwich, CT; *U.S. Private*, pg. 761
Marchisotto, Alan, Sec. & Gen. Counsel--Portsmouth Navigation Corporation, Greenwich, CT; *U.S. Private*, pg. 761
Marchisotto, Alan L., Gen. Counsel & Sec.--Moran Transporation Company, Greenwich, CT; *U.S. Private*, pg. 760
Marchisotto, Alan L., Gen. Counsel & Sec.--Moran Towing Corporation, Greenwich, CT; *U.S. Private*, pg. 760
Marcic, Irene S., Chief Fin. Officer, Exec. V.P., Treas. & Sec.--Astrex, Inc., Plainview, NY; *U.S. Public*, pg. 141
Marcucci, Roy, Sec.--Gonnella Baking Co., Chicago, IL; *U.S.* Private, pg. 463
Marcus, Arthur, V.P. & Sec.--Marcus Brothers Textiles, Inc., New York, NY; *U.S. Private*, pg. 702
Marcus, Beth B., Asst. Corp. Sec.--Napa Valley Bank, Napa, CA; *U.S. Public*, pg. 1756
Marcus, Harriet, Treas. & Sec.--Harold Leonard & Company, Inc., Union, NJ; *U.S. Private*, pg. 660
Marcus, Thomas L., V.P.-Bus Devel., Gen. Counsel & Sec.--Broderbund Software, Inc., Novato, CA; *U.S. Public*, pg. 258
Marczak, David J., Chief Fin. Officer, Treas. & Sec.--Secom General Corporation, Novi, MI; *U.S. Public*, pg. 1453
Mares, Virginia, Sec.--CH2M Hill, Inc., Greenwood Village, CO; *U.S. Private*, pg. 195
Maresca, Anthony R., Chief Fin. Officer, Sr. V.P., Treas. & Sec.--ACR Group, Houston, TX; *U.S. Public*, pg. 3
Margalit, Shlomo, Dr., Chm. Bd., Chief Tech. Officer & Sec.--MRV Communications, Inc., Chatsworth, CA; *U.S. Public*, pg. 1027
Margan, William D., Sec.--John Bouchard & Sons Company, Nashville, TN; *U.S. Private*, pg. 161
Margetts, W. Thomas, Sr. V.P.-Human Resources, Gen. Counsel & Sec.--Stant Corporation, Denver, CO; *Int'l*, pg. 1396
Margolin, Christopher J., V.P., Gen. Counsel & Sec.--XOMA Corporation, Berkeley, CA; *U.S. Public*, pg. 1786
Margolis, Lawrence A., Chief Fin. Officer, Exec. V.P. & Sec.--The Antec Corporation, Rolling Meadows, IL; *U.S. Public*, pg. 116
Marguet, Rene, Corp. Sec.--HPI Holding S.A., Yverdon, Switzerland; *Int'l*, pg. 579
Margulies, Jay, Sec.--Advanced Energy Industry, Fort Collins, CO; *U.S. Public*, pg. 20
Margulis, Irwin, Exec. V.P. & Sec.--Zemco Industries, Inc., Buffalo, NY; *U.S. Private*, pg. 1204
Mariga, Doris, Sec.--Greyvest Capitol Inc., Toronto, Canada; *Int'l*, pg. 559
Marin, Michael J., Asst Sec.--SEIKO Corporation of America, Mahwah, NJ; *Int'l*, pg. 1218
Marinucci, Lisa W., Sec.--Marquette Coppersmithing Co., Inc., Philadelphia, PA; *U.S. Private*, pg. 706
Marion, Kathleen A., V.P.-Corp. Services & Sec.--Long Island Lighting Company, Hicksville, NY; *U.S. Public*, pg. 1013
Markarewicz, David C., V.P. & Asst. Sec.--Beemak Plastics, Gardena, CA; *U.S. Private*, pg. 598
Markesino, Carol, Asst. Sec.--Newfoundland Capital Corporation Limited, Dartmouth, Canada; *Int'l*, pg. 924
Markey, Robert G., Sec.--Blue Coral/Slick 50, Cleveland, OH; *U.S. Public*, pg. 1348
Markey, Thomas, V.P., Treas. & Sec.--National Spinning Co., Inc., New York, NY; *U.S. Private*, pg. 786
Markheim, Steven, V.P. & Sec.--Electro Rent Corporation, Van Nuys, CA; *U.S. Public*, pg. 568
Markl, Thomas L., Sr. V.P.--UTILX Corporation, Kent, WA; *U.S. Public*, pg. 1701
Markowitz, Edwin, Sec.--Monitor Aerospace Corporation, Amityville, NY; *U.S. Private*, pg. 757
Marks, Michael J., V.P., Gen. Counsel & Sec.--Alexander & Baldwin, Inc., Honolulu, HI; *U.S. Public*, pg. 39
Marks, Sam, Exec. V.P., Corp. Sec. & Dir.-Pur.--Triangle Marketing Corp., New York, NY; *U.S. Private*, pg. 1102
Marks, Sam, Exec. V.P., Corp. Sec. & Dir.-Pur.--New Brook Paper, New York, NY; *U.S. Private*, pg. 1102
Markulis, John, V.P. & Sec.--Puritan Bakery, Inc., Carson, CA; *U.S. Private*, pg. 895
MarLett, Charles D., Corp. Sec.--AMR Corporation, Fort Worth, TX; *U.S. Public*, pg. 9
Marlowe, Bob, Chief Acctg. Officer, Treas. & Sec.--Sholodge, Inc., Hendersonville, TN; *U.S. Public*, pg. 1467
Marlowe, Margaret H., Sec. & Asst. Treas.--National Fruit Product Company, Winchester, VA; *U.S. Private*, pg. 783
Marochi, Serge, Gen. Sec.--Damart S.A., Robaix, France; *Int'l*, pg. 376
Marold, Louis, Sec. & Mgr.-H.R.--Maxcor Manufacturing, Inc., Colorado Springs, CO; *U.S. Private*, pg. 716
Maroney, James, V.P., Gen. Counsel & Sec.--Tuboscope Incorporated, Houston, TX; *U.S. Public*, pg. 1643
Marotto, Leslie A., Sec.--American Precision Industries Inc., Buffalo, NY; *U.S. Public*, pg. 90
Marquard, Henry F., Asst. Sec.--Stanley Design-Build, Inc., Muscatine, IA; *U.S. Private*, pg. 1033
Marquard, Henry F., Asst. Sec.--Stanley Enviromental, Inc., Coralville, IA; *U.S. Private*, pg. 1033
Marquard, Henry F., Gen. Counsel & Asst. Sec.--Stanley Consultants, Inc., Muscatine, IA; *U.S. Private*, pg. 1033
Marques, Ana Cristina, Corp. Sec.--Central de Cervejas, S.A., Lisbon, Portugal; *Int'l*, pg. 279
Marras, Alberto, Sec.--Fondiaria S.P.A., Florence, Italy; *Int'l*, pg. 496
Marrero, Manuel, Chief Fin. Officer, Sr. V.P.-Admin., Treas. & Sec.--Autologic Information International, Inc., Thousand Oaks, CA; *U.S. Public*, pg. 1724
Marrero, Victor L., Sr. V.P. & Treas.--MEDCO Containment Services, Inc., Montvale, NJ; *U.S. Public*, pg. 1091
Marrinan, Susan F., V.P., Sec. & Gen. Counsel--Snap-On Tools Corporation, Kenosha, WI; *U.S. Public*, pg. 1480
Marriner, William L., Chief Fin. Officer, Sr. V.P.-Fin. & Admin., & Sec.--Exabyte Corporation, Boulder, CO; *U.S. Public*, pg. 597
Marroquin, Leopoldo, Sec.--Alfa, S.A. de C.V., Garza Garcia, Mexico; *Int'l*, pg. 56
Marsais, Renata, Gen. Mgr. & Sec.--Sodeva, Paris, France; *Int'l*, pg. 557
Marsh, Cheryl, Corp. Sec--Hilton Hotels Corporation, Beverly Hills, CA; *U.S. Public*, pg. 828
Marsh, Donald L., Chief Fin. Officer, Exec. V.P. & Corp. Sec.--Alflex, Long Beach, CA; *U.S. Public*, pg. 415
Marsh, Donald L., Jr., Chief Fin. Officer, Exec. V.P. & Sec.--Commonwealth Industries, Inc., Louisville, KY; *U.S. Public*, pg. 415
Marsh, K.B., Treas. & Sec.--MPX Systems, Inc., Cayce, SC; *U.S. Public*, pg. 1436
Marsh, K.H., Treas. & Sec.--South Carolina Electric & Gas Co. (SCE&G), Columbia, SC; *U.S. Public*, pg. 1436
Marsh, Michael G., Gen. Counsel, Sec. & Mgr.-Human Resources--Todd Pacific Shipyards Corp., Seattle, WA; *U.S. Public*, pg. 1619
Marsh, Normen J., Jr., Asst. Sec.--Sanders, A Lockheed Martin Company, Nashua, NH; *U.S. Public*, pg. 1008
Marsh, W.T., Sec.--Today's Kids, Booneville, AR; *U.S. Private*, pg. 1020
Marsh, William A., V.P., Gen. Counsel & Sec.--Spang & Company, Butler, PA; *U.S. Private*, pg. 1020
Marshal, Douglas, V.P.-Pub. Affairs, Gen. Counsel & Sec.--Darigold, Inc., Seattle, WA; *U.S. Private*, pg. 311
Marshall, Allen, Chief Fin. Officer--Heller Seasonings & Ingredients, Inc., Bedford Park, IL; *U.S. Private*, pg. 520
Marshall, Jim, Sec.--Primus Inc., Dayton, OH; *U.S. Private*, pg. 884
Marshall, Joananne, V.P. & Sec.--ADP Marshall Contractors Inc., Rumford, RI; *U.S. Public*, pg. 660
Marshall, Larry, Sec. & Gen. Counsel--MFA Oil Company, Columbia, MO; *U.S. Private*, pg. 687
Marshall, Richard N., Treas. & Asst. Sec.--Pennsylvania Enterprises Inc., Wilkes-Barre, PA; *U.S. Public*, pg. 1271
Marshall, Richard N., Treas. & Asst. Sec.--PG Energy, Inc., Wilkes-Barre, PA; *U.S. Public*, pg. 1271
Martin, Denise, Asst. Sec.--Telemedia Inc., Montreal, Canada; *Int'l*, pg. 1373
Martin, Dennis, Sec.--Keating Building Corp., Bala Cynwyd, PA; *U.S. Private*, pg. 610
Martin, Derek C., V.P., Gen. Counsel & Sec.--Precision Drilling Corporation, Calgary, Canada; *Int'l*, pg. 1066
Martin, Dezora M., Sec.--Norfolk Southern Corporation, Norfolk, VA; *U.S. Public*, pg. 1190
Martin, Elizabeth, Sec.--Bellsouth Personal Communications, Inc., Atlanta, GA; *U.S. Public*, pg. 208
Martin, Everett A., Sec.--Mid America Steel, Inc., Fargo, ND; *U.S. Private*, pg. 743
Martin, G.G., Gen. Counsel & Sec.--Coats & Clark Inc., Greenville, SC; *Int'l*, pg. 300
Martin, Gladys, Chief Fin. Officer, Treas. & Sec.--Welsco Inc., North Little Rock, AR; *U.S. Private*, pg. 1161
Martin, Harry A., V.P. & Sec.--Uni-Marts, Inc., State College, PA; *U.S. Public*, pg. 1664
Martin, Harry D., Esq., Gen. Counsel & Sec.--Snap-Tite, Inc., Erie, PA; *U.S. Private*, pg. 1010
Martin, John, Chief Fin. Officer--Trend Offset Printing Services, Los Alamitos, CA; *U.S. Private*, pg. 1099
Martin, John C., III, Chief Fin. Officer, V.P., Treas. & Sec.--TransPro, Inc., New Haven, CT; *U.S. Public*, pg. 1631
Martin, Lenore M., Asst. Sec.--PacifiCorp, Portland, OR; *U.S. Public*, pg. 1251
Martin, Matthew G., Chief Oper. & Fin. Officer--Cattleman's, Inc., Detroit, MI; *U.S. Public*, pg. 318
Martin, Robert, V.P.-Fin. & Sec.--UAP, Inc., Montreal, Canada; *Int'l*, pg. 1426
Martin, Roy C., Sr., Chief Exec. Officer & Sec.--Triangle Electric Company, Madison Heights, MI; *U.S. Private*, pg. 1102
Martin, Roy G., Jr., Asst. Sec.--Valero Refining Company, San Antonio, TX; *U.S. Public*, pg. 1704
Martin, Sallie, Corp. Sec. & Admin. Asst.--Hickory Printing Group, Inc., Conover, NC; *U.S. Private*, pg. 525
Martin, Shirley K., Asst. Corp. Sec.--Newell Co., Freeport, IL; *U.S. Public*, pg. 1176
Martin, Steve, Treas. & Sec.--Russell Chevrolet Company, Sherwood, AR; *U.S. Private*, pg. 952
Martin, Thomas O., V.P.-Mktg. & Sec.--Uniflow Manufacturing Co., Erie, PA; *U.S. Private*, pg. 1117
Martin, Virginia H., Treas. & Sec.--Martin Door Mfg., Inc., Salt Lake City, UT; *U.S. Private*, pg. 708
Martin, William A., Chief Fin. Officer, Sr. V.P. & Asst. Sec.--Insituform Technologies, Inc., Chesterfield, MO; *U.S. Public*, pg. 881
Martin, William F. Jr., Sr. V.P.-Legal & Corp. Sec.--Yellow Corporation, Overland Park, KS; *U.S. Public*, pg. 1788
Martinez, Enrique de la Torre, Deputy Mng. Dir. & Sec.--Caja de Madrid Group, Madrid, Spain; *Int'l*, pg. 251
Martinez, Enrique de la Torre, Sec.--A.H.V. Ensidesa Capital, S.A., Madrid, Spain; *Int'l*, pg. 1223
Martinez, Nelson, Asst. Sec.--Tate Access Floors, Inc., Jessup, MD; *U.S. Private*, pg. 1069
Martos, Alberto Manzano, Sec.--Corporacion MAPFRE, Compania Internacional de Reaseguros, S.A., Madrid, Spain; *Int'l*, pg. 332
Marukawa, Kunio, Sec.--Pioneer New Media Technologies, Long Beach, CA; *U.S. Private*, pg. 866
Marx, Loretta, Corp. Sec. & Telecommunications--Community Bank N.A., De Witt, NY; *U.S. Public*, pg. 416
Marx, Loretta L., Sec.--Community Bank System, Inc., De Witt, NY; *U.S. Public*, pg. 416

Maskey, Rebecca S., Treas.--Alta Loma Productions, Inc., Beverly Hills, CA; *U.S. Public*, pg. 1310
Maskey, Rebecca S., Treas.--Playboy Shows, Inc., Beverly Hills, CA; *U.S. Public*, pg. 1310
Maslick, Joseph R., Chief Fin. Officer, Exec. V.P. & Sec.--Griffith Laboratories Worldwide, Inc., Alsip, IL; *U.S. Private*, pg. 481
Mason, B., Dir.- Fin. & Sec.--Dictaphone Co. U.K. Ltd., Royal Leamington Spa, United Kingdom; *U.S. Private*, pg. 1045
Mason, D.W., Sec.--D. Rowe & Co. Ltd., Chichester, United Kingdom; *Int'l*, pg. 1512
Mason, Herman D., Treas. & Sec.--May Supply Company, Inc., Harrisonburg, VA; *U.S. Public*, pg. 1727
Mason, Sharon, Corp. Sec.--Bliss-Salem, Inc., Salem, OH; *U.S. Private*, pg. 149
Mason, Thomas, Gen. Counsel & Sec.--Freeway Corporation, Cleveland, OH; *U.S. Private*, pg. 426
Mason, Wallace, Chief Fin. Officer, V.P., Sec. & Acct. Exec.--Temkin & Temkin, Northbrook, IL; *U.S. Private*, pg. 1074
Massaro, Patti L., Corp. Counsel & Sec.--Landmark Graphics Corporation, Houston, TX; *U.S. Public*, pg. 776
Massengale, Darrell K., Chief Fin. Officer, V.P.-Fin., Treas. & Sec.--Corrections Corporation of America, Nashville, TN; *U.S. Public*, pg. 450
Massicotte, Francis R., Sr. V.P. & Sec.--Potomac Valley Bank, Gaithersburg, MD; *U.S. Public*, pg. 1089
Massicotte, Guy-Paul, V.P., Gen. Counsel & Sec.--The Ivaco Group, Montreal, Canada; *Int'l*, pg. 695
Masterson, Karen, V.P., Gen. Counsel & Sec.--ADAC Laboratories Inc., Milpitas, CA; *U.S. Public*, pg. 3
Masterson, Kenneth R., Exec. V.P., Gen. Counsel & Sec.--FDX Corporation, Memphis, TN; *U.S. Public*, pg. 603
Masuhara, David M., V.P. & Sec.--BC Gas Inc., Vancouver, Canada; *Int'l*, pg. 114
Mataraso, Matthew H., Corp. Sec.--Trans World Entertainment Corporation, Albany, NY; *U.S. Public*, pg. 1629
Mater, Maud, Sr. V.P., Gen. Counsel & Sec.--Federal Home Loan Mortgage Corporation, Mc Lean, VA; *U.S. Public*, pg. 615
Mateu, Jose Francisco, Sec.--Repsol Quimica, Madrid, Spain; *Int'l*, pg. 1104
Mathias, Percival, Sec.--Irwin Toy Ltd., Toronto, Canada; *Int'l*, pg. 688
Mathison, Susan M., V.P -Admin. & Sec.--Payco American Corporation, Brookfield, WI; *U.S. Public*, pg. 1267
Matics, Cheryl W., Asst. Sec.--West Coast Bancorp, Newport Beach, CA; *U.S. Public*, pg. 1755
Matlock, Ron, V.P., Gen. Counsel & Sec.--Sonic Corporation, Oklahoma City, OK; *U.S. Public*, pg. 1485
Matsuyama, Akihiko, V.P. & Treas.--Asahi America Inc., New York, NY; *Int'l*, pg. 85
Matt, F.X., II, Chm. Bd. & Corp. Sec.--The F.X. Matt Brewing Co., Utica, NY; *U.S. Private*, pg. 714
Matter, Gary L., Sr. V.P., Controller & Sec.--Commercial Federal Corporation, Omaha, NE; *U.S. Public*, pg. 411
Matthay, U., Sec.--Apollinaris & Schweppes Gmbh & Co., Hamburg, Germany; *Int'l*, pg. 78
Matthews, B.S., Sec.--SAS Holdings Limited, Reading, United Kingdom; *Int'l*, pg. 1152
Matthews, Clark J. II, Pres., Chief Exec. Officer & Sec.--The Southland Corporation, Dallas, TX; *Int'l*, pg. 693
Matthews, James E., Chief Fin. Officer, V.P.-Fin. & Sec.--Miltope Group, Inc., Hope Hull, AL; *U.S. Public*, pg. 1114
Matthews, Mark, Treas. & Sec.--Porcelanite, Inc., Lexington, NC; *Int'l*, pg. 573
Matthews, Nigel F., Sec. & Dir.-Pub. Affairs--J. Sainsbury plc, London, United Kingdom; *Int'l*, pg. 1169
Matthews, Ron, Corp. Sec.--Australian Guarantee Corporation Limited, Sydney, Australia; *Int'l*, pg. 1496
Matthis, Doris L., Treas. & Sec.--Kentucky Indiana Lumber Co. Inc., Louisville, KY; *U.S. Private*, pg. 615
Mattin, David, Sec.--Severn Trent Plc, Birmingham, United Kingdom; *Int'l*, pg. 1225
Mattin, David William, Sec.--Severn Trent Water Ltd., Birmingham, United Kingdom; *Int'l*, pg. 1225
Mattingly, Barbara A., Treas. & Sec.--Metro Foods, Inc., Olive Branch, MS; *U.S. Private*, pg. 736
Mattison, Ben, V.P., Treas. & Sec.--Malloy Lithographing Inc., Ann Arbor, MI; *U.S. Private*, pg. 698
Mattison, Robert M., V.P., Gen. Counsel & Sec.--Graco Inc., Golden Valley, MN; *U.S. Public*, pg. 756
Mattle, Jean-Pierre, Sec. Gen.--Kaysersberg S.A., Courbevoie, France; *U.S. Public*, pg. 673
Mattox, Richard L., Sec.--Robinson Nugent, Inc., New Albany, IN; *U.S. Public*, pg. 1394
Matula, Amy, Asst. Sec.--Veritas DGC Inc, Houston, TX; *U.S. Private*, pg. 1136
Matute, Conchita, Sec.--Salvat Editores S.A., Barcelona, Spain; *Int'l*, pg. 796
Mauk, Patricia, Treas. & Sec.--Dudek & Bock Spring Manufacturing Company, Chicago, IL; *U.S. Private*, pg. 344
Mauldin, Bill G., Exec. V.P., Sec. & Treas.--First Commercial Mortgage Co., Little Rock, AR; *U.S. Public*, pg. 630
Maulding, B.C., V.P., Gen. Counsel & Sec.--PrimeSource Corporation, Pennsauken, NJ; *U.S. Public*, pg. 1329
Maurer, Lois, V.P. & Asst. Sec.--Penn Security Bank and Trust Co., Scranton, PA; *U.S. Public*, pg. 1270
Maurin, Lois J., Treas. & Sec.--American Fence & Security Company, Phoenix, AZ; *U.S. Private*, pg. 54
Mauro, Albert P., V.P. & Sec.--Kansas City Southern Industries, Inc., Kansas City, MO; *U.S. Public*, pg. 943
Mautz, Louise U., Sec.--Mautz Paint Co., Madison, WI; *U.S. Private*, pg. 715
Maver, Bob, Chief Fin. Officer, V.P. & Sec.--Standard Insurance Co., Portland, OR; *U.S. Private*, pg. 1031
Mawhorter, Robert L., Sr. V.P.-Fin., Admin. & Sec--Millers Mutual Insurance Assn., Alton, IL; *U.S. Private*, pg. 748
Maxam, Joan, Sec.--Stewart's Ice Cream Co., Inc., Saratoga Springs, NY; *U.S. Private*, pg. 1043
May Ling, Carrie Seow, Sec.--Transmarco Limited, Singapore, Singapore; *Int'l*, pg. 1417
May, Allan W., V.P.-Strategic Devel., Gen. Counsel & Sec.--OEC Medical Systems, Inc., Salt Lake City, UT; *U.S. Public*, pg. 1207
May, J. Michael, Gen. Counsel & Sec.--Ameritruck Distribution Corporation, Fort Worth, TX; *U.S. Private*, pg. 65
May, William L., Jr., Asst. Sec.--Cabot Corporation, Boston, MA; *U.S. Public*, pg. 288
Mayer, Harold F., Sec.--Cognitronics Corporation, Danbury, CT; *U.S. Public*, pg. 394
Mayer, Rui, Dr., Corp. Sec.--Petrogal, s.a., Lisbon, Portugal; *Int'l*, pg. 1044
Mayer, Sylvia, Treas. & Sec.--Mayer/Berkshire Corporation, Wayne, NJ; *U.S. Private*, pg. 717
Mayers, J. Thomas, V.P. & Sec.--The Hall China Company, East Liverpool, OH; *U.S. Private*, pg. 494
Mayers, Lois E., Sec. & Treas.--Ace Novelty Company, Inc., Woodinville, WA; *U.S. Public*, pg. 1309
Maylath, Sharon R., Asst. Sec.--Deluxe Corporation, Shoreview, MN; *U.S. Public*, pg. 498
Maynard, Philip C., Pres. & Sec.--ICS Intangibles Holding Company, Irvine, CA; *U.S. Public*, pg. 783
Maynard, Philip C., V.P. & Sec.--National Learning Systems, Inc., Scranton, PA; *U.S. Public*, pg. 783
Maynard, Philip C., V.P. & Sec.--NBD Incorporated, Scranton, PA; *U.S. Public*, pg. 783
Maynard, Philip C., V.P. & Sec.--Steck-Vaughn Company, Austin, TX; *U.S. Public*, pg. 784
Maynard, Philip C., V.P. & Sec.--National Educational International Corp., Irvine, CA; *U.S. Public*, pg. 784
Maynard, Philip C., Sec.--International Correspondence Schools (Australasia) Limited, Lane Cove, Australia; *U.S.* Public, pg. 784
Maynard, Philip C., V.P. & Asst. Sec.--International Correspondence Schools Canadian Ltd., Montreal, Canada; *U.S. Public*, pg. 784
Maynard, Philip C., Sec.--International Correspondence Schools Ltd., Glasgow, United Kingdom; *U.S. Public*, pg. 784
Maynard, Philip C., Sec.--Intertext Group, Ltd., Glasgow, United Kingdom; *U.S. Public*, pg. 784
Maynard, Philip C., V.P. & Sec.--National Education Training Group, Naperville, IL; *U.S. Public*, pg. 784
Maynard, Philip C., Dir. & Asst. Sec.--NETG Limited, London, United Kingdom; *U.S. Public*, pg. 784
Maynard, Philip C., Sec.--James Martin Insight, Inc., Naperville, IL; *U.S. Public*, pg. 784
Maynard, Philip C., V.P. & Sec.--NETG Holding, Inc., Irvine, CA; *U.S. Public*, pg. 784
Maynard, Philip C., Sec.--International Correspondence Schools (New Zealand) Limited, Wellington, New Zealand; *U.S. Public*, pg. 784
Maynard, Philip C., V.P. & Sec.--National Education Credit Corporation, Irvine, CA; *U.S. Public*, pg. 784
Maynard, Philip C., V.P. & Sec.--National Education Payroll Corp., Irvine, CA; *U.S. Public*, pg. 784
Maynard, Philip C., V.P. & Sec.--Steck-Vaughn Publishing Corporation, Austin, TX; *U.S. Public*, pg. 784
Maynard, Philip C., V.P. & Sec.--Steck-Vaughn Distribution Company, Austin, TX; *U.S. Public*, pg. 784
Mayo, James O., Sec.--The Kiplinger Washington Editors, Inc., Washington, DC; *U.S. Private*, pg. 623
Mayo, Jennifer, Treas., Sec. & Mgr.-Personnel--Von Housen Motors, Sacramento, CA; *U.S. Private*, pg. 1143
Mays, Marinan R., Corp. Sec. & Mgr.-Admin.--Caraustar Industries, Inc., Austell, GA; *U.S. Public*, pg. 303
Mays, Mark A., V.P. & Sec.--Box Hill Systems Corporation, New York, NY; *U.S. Public*, pg. 249
Maze, George H., V.P. & Sec.--Maze Nails, Peru, IL; *U.S. Private*, pg. 718
McAdams, Diane M., Asst. Sec.--Philip Morris Companies Inc., New York, NY; *U.S. Public*, pg. 1287
McAllister, Sharon L., Asst. Sec.--John Deere Capital Corporation, Reno, NV; *U.S. Public*, pg. 492
McAlpine, John, Exec. V.P. & Sec.--The Crown Group, Inc., Warren, MI; *U.S. Private*, pg. 292
McAnallen, William J., Asst. Sec.--Martin Marietta International, Inc., Bethesda, MD; *U.S. Public*, pg. 1009
McArdle, John J., III, Sec.--Matec Corporation, Hopkinton, MA; *U.S. Public*, pg. 1056
McArthur, James L., Sec. & Mgr.-Investor Rels.--ChemFirst Inc., Jackson, MS; *U.S. Public*, pg. 344
McArthur, Steven A., Sr. V.P., Gen. Counsel & Sec.--CalEnergy Co., Omaha, NE; *U.S. Public*, pg. 292
Mcaulay, Jeffrey J., V.P. & Asst. Sec.--Jakobson Shipyard, Inc, Greenwich, CT; *U.S. Private*, pg. 760
McBrayer, Suzanne H., Sec.--Ruddick Corporation, Charlotte, NC; *U.S. Public*, pg. 1412
McBride, Beverly, V.P., Gen. Counsel & Sec.--The Andersons Incorporated, Maumee, OH; *U.S. Public*, pg. 111
McBride, David, Chief Information Officer--McBride and Associates, Inc., Albuquerque, NM; *U.S. Private*, pg. 719
McBride, Dorothy Z., Sec./Treas.--Doubleday Canada Ltd., Toronto, Canada; *Int'l*, pg. 192
McBride, H. Colin, V.P., Asst. Gen. Counsel & Asst. Sec.--RJR Nabisco Holdings Corp., New York, NY; *U.S. Public, pg. 1354*
McBride, Rebecca, Sec.--True Temper Sports Division, Memphis, TN; *U.S. Public*, pg. 233
McBride, Terry W., V.P., Gen. Counsel & Sec.--Repap Enterprises Inc., Montreal, Canada; *Int'l*, pg. 1104
McBride, Terry W., V.P., Gen. Counsel & Sec.--Repap New Brunswick Inc., Montreal, Canada; *Int'l*, pg. 1104
McBurnie, A., Asst. Sec.--Northern Rock PLC, Newcastle upon Tyne, United Kingdom; *Int'l*, pg. 968
McCabe, James M., Asst. Sec.--John Deere Capital Corporation, Reno, NV; *U.S. Public*, pg. 492
McCabe, Janet L., V.P. & Sec.--Baltimore Trust Company, Selbyville, DE; *U.S. Public*, pg. 1088
McCabe, John F., Corp. V.P., Gen. Counsel & Sec.--BDM International, Inc., Mc Lean, VA; *U.S. Public*, pg. 1558
McCabe, Thomas E., Sr. V.P., Gen. Counsel & Sec.--GRC International, Inc., Vienna, VA; *U.S. Public*, pg. 695
McCaigue, Dan, Chief Fin. Officer--Perdue Farms, Inc., Showell, MD; *U.S. Private*, pg. 852
McCall, John R., Exec. V.P., Gen. Counsel & Sec.--LG & E Energy Corp., Louisville, KY; *U.S. Public*, pg. 970
McCall, W.A., Contoller, Treas., Sec., & Mgr.-D.P.--Dixie Oil Company, Tifton, GA; *U.S. Private*, pg. 337
McCann, Gregory L., V.P., Gen. Counsel & Sec.--The Danis Companies, Dayton, OH; *U.S. Private*, pg. 310
McCann, Mary, Asst. Sec.--Blue Cross and Blue Shield of Massachusetts, Boston, MA; *U.S. Private*, pg. 151
McCarthy, Jim, Sr. V.P., Gen. Counsel & Sec.--Ponderosa Steakhouse, Dallas, TX; *U.S. Private*, pg. 736
McCarthy, Joseph F., V.P., Gen. Counsel & Sec.--Lear Corporation, Southfield, MI; *U.S. Public*, pg. 981
McCarthy, Michael J., Sr. V.P., Gen. Counsel & Sec.--A.H. Belo Corporation, Dallas, TX; *U.S. Public*, pg. 209
McCarthy, Robert E., Sec.--Entertainment Weekly Inc., New York, NY; *U.S. Public*, pg. 1613
McCarthy, Timothy, Gen. Counsel & Sec.--Western Regional Off Track Betting, Batavia, NY; *U.S. Private*, pg. 1168
McCarty, Joel, Sr. V.P., Gen. Counsel & Sec.--Old Dominion Freight Line, Inc., High Point, NC; *U.S. Public*, pg. 1216
McCaslin, Lorna, Sec.--Carder, Inc., Lamar, CO; *U.S. Private*, pg. 208
McCaslin, S. D., Sec.--Britax International plc, Warwick, United Kingdom; *Int'l*, pg. 216
McCaul, Eugene, Sec.--Saunders Oil Company, Inc., Richmond, VA; *U.S. Private*, pg. 968
McCauley, Daniel, V.P., Gen. Counsel & Sec.--Air Express International Corporation, Darien, CT; *U.S. Public*, pg. 30
McCaw, John E., Exec. V.P. & Sec.--AT&T Wireless Services, Kirkland, WA; *U.S. Public*, pg. 11
McClain, Robert W., Sr. V.P. & Asst. Sec.--McClain Industries, Inc., Sterling Heights, MI; *U.S. Public*, pg. 1065
McClanahan, Mary P., Sec.--Great Lakes Chemical Corporation, West Lafayette, IN; *U.S. Public*, pg. 760
McClary, Mary Anne, Exec. Sec.-Fin.--Sierra Technologies Inc., Buffalo, NY; *U.S. Private*, pg. 999
McClatchy, William Ellery, Asst. Sec.--McClatchy Newspapers Inc., Sacramento, CA; *U.S. Public*, pg. 1065
McClave, Wilkes, III, Sr. V.P., Gen. Counsel & Sec.--Tosco Corporation, Stamford, CT; *U.S. Public*, pg. 1624
McClelland, Frances H., Treas. & Sec.--Shamrock Foods Company, Phoenix, AZ; *U.S. Private*, pg. 989
McClelland, George R., Chief Fin. Officer & V.P.-Admin.--Independent Can Company, Belcamp, MD; *U.S. Private*, pg. 559
McClennan, Howard, Chief Fin. Officer, Treas. & Sec.--Uncle B's Bakery, Inc., Ellsworth, IA; *U.S. Public*, pg. 1664
McClennon, Audrey, Sec. of the Authority--Regional Transportation Authority (RTA), Chicago, IL; *U.S. Private, pg. 918*
McClure, Cynthia, Controller, Treas. & Sec.--The McClure Group, Wayne, PA; *U.S. Private*, pg. 719
McClure, Matt P., Asst. Sec.--The Seibels Bruce Group, Inc., Columbia, SC; *U.S. Public*, pg. 1453
McCluskey, Eugene M., Jr., Dir.-Taxes & Asst. Sec.--IMC Global, Bannockburn, IL; *U.S. Public*, pg. 856
McColl, Walter, Corp. Sec.--The Wella Corporation, Montvale, NJ; *Int'l*, pg. 1489
McCombs, R.N., Chief Fin. Officer, V.P. & Sec.--Erly Industries, Inc., Los Angeles, CA; *U.S. Public*, pg. 591
McConkey, Duane L., V.P.-Admin. & Sec.--C.H. Robinson Co., Eden Prairie, MN; *U.S. Public*, pg. 1394
McConnell, Kirk D., V.P.-Admin. Services & Asst. Sec.--Magellan Health Services, Inc., Atlanta, GA; *U.S. Public*, pg. 1033
McConnell, Mary, V.P., Gen. Counsel & Sec.--Genmar Holdings, Inc., Minneapolis, MN; *U.S. Private*, pg. 447
McConnell, Muriel, Sec.--Willis Corroon Melling Inc., Ottawa, Canada; *Int'l*, pg. 1509
McConnell, Susan E., Sec.--K2 Inc., Los Angeles, CA; *U.S. Public*, pg. 940
McConville, Rita J., Chief Fin. Officer, Treas. & Sec.--Akorn, Inc., Lincolnshire, IL; *U.S. Public*, pg. 34
McCorkell, Peter L., Sr. V.P., Gen. Counsel & Sec.--Fair, Isaac and Company, Inc., San Rafael, CA; *U.S. Public*, pg. 609
McCorkle, James H., Controller & Asst. Sec.--Speizman Industries, Inc., Charlotte, NC; *U.S. Public*, pg. 1498
McCorkle, Martha A., V.P.-Fin., Treas. & Sec.--World Carpets, Inc., Dalton, GA; *U.S. Private*, pg. 1190
McCormick, John M., Sec.--Investors Management Corp., Raleigh, NC; *U.S. Private*, pg. 574
McCormick, Michael D., Exec. V.P., Legal Counsel & Sec.--Bindley Western Industries, Inc., Indianapolis, IN; *U.S. Public*, pg. 228
McCormick, Neil, Gen. Counsel & Sec.--Morrison Petroleums Ltd., Calgary, Canada; *Int'l*, pg. 895
McCormick, Thomas P., Exec. V.P. & Sec.--Horizon Bank, Michigan City, IN; *U.S. Private*, pg. 539
McCormick, Tom, Sec.--Kimray, Inc., Oklahoma City, OK; *U.S. Private*, pg. 620
McCown, D. Layton, V.P.--Forest City Enterprises, Inc., Cleveland, OH; *U.S. Public*, pg. 667
McCoy, Carol A., Sec. & Assoc. Counsel--Torchmark Corporation, Birmingham, AL; *U.S. Public*, pg. 1622
McCoy, Dustan E., Sr. V.P., Gen. Counsel & Corp. Sec.--Witco Corporation, Greenwich, CT; *U.S. Public*, pg. 1773
McCoy, Janice, Sec. & Treas.--Fleetwood Aluminum Products, Corona, CA; *U.S. Private*, pg. 410
McCoy, Phyllis, Sec.--United Dairy Farmers, Inc., Cincinnati, OH; *U.S. Private*, pg. 1121
McCrea, Charles, Jr., Exec. V.P., Gen. Counsel & Sec.--Mikohn Gaming Corporation, Las Vegas, NV; *U.S. Public*, pg. 1111
McCrory, Kelly L., Treas. & Sec.--Steakley Chevrolet GEO Subaru Inc., Dallas, TX; *U.S. Private*, pg. 1037

McCullars, Denise, Chief Fin. Officer, Treas. & Sec.--Dawson Construction Co., Inc., Gadsden, AL; *U.S. Private*, pg. 316
McCullough, Bob, Exec. V.P., Sec. & Treas.--Harris, Baio & McCullough Inc., Philadelphia, PA; *U.S. Private*, pg. 504
McCurdy, Robert D., V.P. & Sec.--SJL of Kansas Corp., Wichita, KS; *U.S. Public*, pg. 984
McCutchan, Gordon E., Exec. V.P., Gen. Counsel & Sec.--Nationwide Mutual Insurance Co., Columbus, OH; *U.S. Private*, pg. 789
McCutcheon, B.R., Sec.--Doman Industries Limited, Duncan, Canada; *Int'l*, pg. 414
McDade, Sandy D., Sec.--Weyerhaeuser Company, Federal Way, WA; *U.S. Public*, pg. 1764
McDaniel, Charles B., Gen. Counsel & Sec.--Hondo Oil & Gas Company, Roswell, NM; *Int'l*, pg. 818
McDaniel, Charles G., Sec.--UniGroup, Inc., Fenton, MO; *U.S. Private*, pg. 1117
McDaniel, F.E., Jr., Sr. V.P., Treas. & Sec.--Shoney's, Inc., Nashville, TN; *U.S. Public*, pg. 1467
McDaniel, Karen L., Asst. Sec.--Stanley Consultants, Inc., Muscatine, IA; *U.S. Private*, pg. 1033
McDermed, Kevin, Sec.--Prospect Foundry, Inc., Minneapolis, MN; *U.S. Public*, pg. 142
McDermed, Kevin T., Chief Fin. Officer, V.P., Treas. & Sec.--Atchison Casting Corporation, Atchison, KS; *U.S. Public*, pg. 142
McDermott, Kathleen E., Chief Legal Officer & Asst. Sec.--American Stores Company, Salt Lake City, UT; *U.S. Public*, pg. 92
McDermott, Marie, Treas. & Sec.--J.M. Process Systems Inc., Orland Park, IL; *U.S. Private*, pg. 577
McDermott, Martin J., Sr. Asst. Sec.--Merck & Co., Inc., Whitehouse Station, NJ; *U.S. Public*, pg. 1090
McDermott, Ronald L., V.P.-Res. & Tech. & Sec.--Worthington Foods Inc., Worthington, OH; *U.S. Public*, pg. 1780
McDermott, William J., Chief Fin. Officer, V.P. & Sec.--Sevenson Environmental Services, Inc., Niagara Falls, NY; *U.S. Public*, pg. 1462
McDonald, Daryl P., Corp. Counsel & Sec.--Tecumseh Products Company, Tecumseh, MI; *U.S. Public*, pg. 1565
McDonald, J.D., Jr., Sec.--PHB Die Casting, Fairview, PA; *U.S. Private*, pg. 826
McDonald, Kevin, Controller & Sec.--Integrated Waste Services, Inc., Buffalo, NY; *U.S. Public*, pg. 886
McDonald, M.B., Sr. V.P. & Corp. Sec.--A.Y. McDonald Industries, Inc., Dubuque, IA; *U.S. Private*, pg. 721
McDonald, M.B., V.P.-Admin. & Corp. Sec.--A.Y. McDonald Mfg. Co., Dubuque, IA; *U.S. Private*, pg. 721
McDonald, M.B., V.P.-Admin. & Corp. Sec.--A.Y.M. Inc., Albia, IA; *U.S. Private*, pg. 721
McDonald, Ross, Sec.--McKechnie PLC, Walsall, United Kingdom; *Int'l*, pg. 851
McDonald, Sandra, Sec.--Keller Kitchen Cabinets, De Land, FL; *U.S. Private*, pg. 612
McDowell, George E., V.P.-Fin., Treas. & Sec.--Clayton Corporation, Fenton, MO; *U.S. Private*, pg. 244
McDowell, Gloria A., Dir.-Human Resources & Sec.--Golden State Mutual Life Insurance Company, Los Angeles, CA; *U.S. Private*, pg. 461
McDowell, Howard, Treas. & Asst. Sec.--Granite State Electric Co., Lebanon, NH; *U.S. Public*, pg. 1171
McDuffie, Ann, Sec.--Dewey Corporation, Jackson, MS; *U.S. Private*, pg. 329
McElligott, Richard Brendan, Sec.--First National Bank Holdings Limited, Johannesburg, South Africa; *Int'l*, pg. 487
McElroy, Bernard K., Asst. V.P.-Fin. & Asst. Sec.--The Pep Boys-Manny, Moe & Jack, Philadelphia, PA; *U.S. Public*, pg. 127€
McElroy, Pender, Gen. Counsel & Sec.--Burke Mills, Inc., Valdese, NC; *U.S. Public*, pg. 267
McEwen, Anne L., Sec.--Modern Group Ltd., Bristol, PA; *U.S. Private*, pg. 754
McFadden, J. Michael, Sec. & Corp. Fin. Mgr.--Monsey-Bakor, Kimberton, PA; *U.S. Private*, pg. 757
McFarland, Julie, Chief Exec. Officer--McNaughton & Gunn, Inc., Saline, MI; *U.S. Private*, pg. 724
McFarland, Patricia J., V.P., Gen. Counsel & Sec.--Norwest Financial, Inc., Des Moines, IA; *U.S. Public*, pg. 1202
McGarvey, Pat, Sec.--Golden Grain Company, Pleasanton, CA; *U.S. Public*, pg. 1348
McGee, F.D., Gen. Counsel & Sec.--National Sea Products Limited, Lunenburg, Canada; *Int'l*, pg. 909
McGeehan, James D., Sec.--Conrail, Inc., Philadelphia, PA; *U.S. Public*, pg. 431
McGehee, Thomas R., Jr., V.P. & Sec.--Mac Papers, Inc., Jacksonville, FL; *U.S. Private*, pg. 689
McGhee, W. Thomas, Gen. Counsel & Sec.--Berg Electronics, Saint Louis, MO; *U.S. Public*, pg. 212
McGill, Jayne F., Sec.--United McGill Corp., Groveport, OH; *U.S. Private*, pg. 1122
McGlasson, P.A., Asst. Sec.--Phillips Petroleum Company, Bartlesville, OK; *U.S. Public*, pg. 1290
McGlockton, Joan R., Sec. & Asst. Gen. Counsel--Marriott International, Inc., Washington, DC; *U.S. Public*, pg. 1047
McGlothlin, Stanley E., Asst. Sec.--Dresser Industries, Inc., Dallas, TX; *U.S. Public*, pg. 528
McGlynn, Thomas, Sec.--McGlynn Bakeries Inc., Minneapolis, MN; *U.S. Private*, pg. 721
McGovern, Ellen S., Asst. To Pres.--Tighe Industries, Inc., York, PA; *U.S. Private*, pg. 1086
McGowan, Gail, Corp. Sec.--The American Bankers Association, Washington, DC; *U.S. Private*, pg. 51
McGowan, Joseph C., Treas. & Sec.--Interstate Power Company, Dubuque, IA; *U.S. Public*, pg. 910
McGrath, Brent P., Chief Fin. Officer, Treas. & Sec.--Mico Inc., North Mankato, MN; *U.S. Private*, pg. 741
McGrath, Bruce, Asst. Sec.--Ranger Oil Limited, Calgary, Canada; *Int'l*, pg. 1086
McGraw, John, V.P., Gen. Counsel & Sec.--Ciba Specialty Chemicals, Tarrytown, NY; *Int'l*, pg. 291
McGraw, Willard G., Sec.--Glines & Rhodes, Inc., Attleboro, MA; *U.S. Private*, pg. 457
McGreal, Eugene P., Asst. Sec.--JC Penney Company, Inc., Plano, TX; *U.S. Public*, pg. 916
McGregor, Michael K., Treas. & Sec.--Pontiac Bancorp, Inc., Pontiac, IL; *U.S. Public*, pg. 1316
McGuinness, Edith C., Asst. Sec.--Cabot Corporation, Boston, MA; *U.S. Public*, pg. 288
McGuinness, Kathleen G., V.P., Gen. Counsel & Sec.--The Times Mirror Company, Los Angeles, CA; *U.S. Public*, pg. 1615
McGuinness, Kevin, Grp. Sec.--Bradford & Bingley Building Society, Bingley, United Kingdom; *Int'l*, pg. 210
McGuire, Agnes A., Sec.--Fabreeka International, Inc., Stoughton, MA; *U.S. Private*, pg. 390
McGuirk, Ronald C., Sec.--First Maryland Life Insurance Company, Baltimore, MD; *Int'l*, pg. 64
McGuone, James R., Sec.--American Software, Inc., Atlanta, GA; *U.S. Public*, pg. 91
McHale, JoAnne, Asst. Sec.--Pennsylvania Enterprises Inc., Wilkes-Barre, PA; *U.S. Public*, pg. 1271
McHale, JoAnne, Asst. Sec.--PG Energy, Inc., Wilkes-Barre, PA; *U.S. Public*, pg. 1271
McIlhenny, Paul C.P., Exec. V.P. & Sec.--McIlhenny Company, Avery Island, LA; *U.S. Private*, pg. 722
McIngvale, Linda, V.P., Treas. & Sec.--Gallery Furniture, Houston, TX; *U.S. Private*, pg. 438
McInnes, D. Joseph, Chief Admin. Officer, Exec. V.P.-Admin. & Corp. Sec.--Blount International, Inc., Montgomery, AL; *U.S. Public*, pg. 237
McInnes, D. Joseph, Chief Admin. Officer, Exec. V.P.-Admin. & Corp. Sec.--Blount, Inc., Montgomery, AL; *U.S. Public*, pg. 238
McInnes, D. Joseph, Sec.--Simmons Outdoor Corporation, Tallahassee, FL; *U.S. Public*, pg. 238
McInnes, Joseph, Dr., Sec.--CTR Manufacturing, Inc., Union Grove, NC; *U.S. Public*, pg. 238
McInnis, Judy, Sec. & Treas.--Southern Electric Supply Co., Inc., Meridian, MS; *Int'l*, pg. 1107
McIntyre, Donald G., V.P.-Human Resources, General Counsel & Sec.--Mitel Corporation, Kanata, Canada; *Int'l*, pg. 870
McIntyre, J. Lawrence, V.P., Gen. Counsel & Sec.--The Toro Company, Bloomington, MN; *U.S. Public*, pg. 1623
McIntyre, John F., V.P., Sec. & Gen. Counsel--Alcon Laboratories, Inc., Fort Worth, TX; *Int'l*, pg. 916
McInvale, Willie K., Jr., Treas. & Sec.--McNamara Pontiac Isuzu Inc., Orlando, FL; *U.S. Private*, pg. 724
McKaig, William D., Treas. & Sec.--Maaco Enterprises Inc., King of Prussia, PA; *U.S. Private*, pg. 689
McKay, Brian, V.P., General Counsel & Sec.--International Game Technology, Reno, NV; *U.S. Public*, pg. 900
McKay, Donald K., Chief Fin. Officer, Exec. V.P., Treas. & Sec.--Specialty Equipment Companies Inc., Aurora, IL; *U.S. Public*, pg. 1496
McKay, Dwight, Sec. & Treas.--Weston Paper & Manufacturing Co., Terre Haute, IN; *U.S. Private*, pg. 1169
McKee, David, V.P., Sec. & Deputy Gen. Counsel--Baxter International Inc., Deerfield, IL; *U.S. Public*, pg. 196
McKee, Kenneth A., Treas. & Sec.--Security Van Lines, Kenner, LA; *U.S. Private*, pg. 594
McKee, Kent A., Treas. & Asst. Sec.--Mueller Industries, Inc., Memphis, TN; *U.S. Public*, pg. 1141
McKee, Thomas, Corp. Sec.--Signature Brands USA, Inc., Solon, OH; *U.S. Public*, pg. 1472
McKee, Thomas F., Sec.--McDonald & Company Investments, Inc., Cleveland, OH; *U.S. Public*, pg. 1068
McKeithen, Smith, V.P., Gen. Counsel & Sec.--Cadence Design Systems, Inc., San Jose, CA; *U.S. Public*, pg. 290
McKenna, Thomas, Exec. V.P.--Westat Inc., Rockville, MD; *U.S. Private*, pg. 1163
McKenney, M.P., Treas. & Sec.--The Figaro Company, Inc., Mesquite, TX; *U.S. Private*, pg. 404
McKenney, Thomas J., Sec. & Treas.--Northern Telephone Limited, New Liskeard, Canada; *Int'l*, pg. 115
McKenzie, James D., Pres.-Petroleum Coke Grp.--Great Lakes Carbon Corp., Houston, TX; *U.S. Private*, pg. 540
McKeown, Laura J., Sec.--Consolidated Natural Gas Company, Pittsburgh, PA; *U.S. Public*, pg. 435
McKeown, Laura J., Sec.--Consolidated Natural Gas Service Co., Inc., Pittsburgh, PA; *U.S. Public*, pg. 435
McKim, John, Sec.--Peoples National Bank, Lawrenceville, IL; *U.S. Public*, pg. 1217
McKinney, Bert, Treas. & Sec.--Contractors Supplies, Inc., Lufkin, TX; *U.S. Private*, pg. 270
McKinney, Mary, Exec. Dir.-Mktg., Communications & Innovation--Merck Human Health Division (U.S. Human Health), West Point, PA; *U.S. Public*, pg. 1091
McKinnon, E., Sec. & Treas.--Datacor/ISM (Information Systems Management Atlantic Corp.), Moncton, Canada; *Int'l*, pg. 230
McKinzie, J. Mark, Sr. V.P., Sec. & Gen. Counsel--Meridian Insurance Group, Inc., Indianapolis, IN; *U.S. Public*, pg. 1095
McKnight, Douglas G., V.P., Gen. Counsel & Sec.--Fluke Corporation, Everett, WA; *U.S. Public*, pg. 659
McKnight, H. James, V.P., Gen. Counsel & Sec.--Michael Baker Corporation, Pittsburgh, PA; *U.S. Public*, pg. 168
McKnight, W.J., Sec.--Grand Trunk Corporation (GTC), Detroit, MI; *Int'l*, pg. 258
McLachlin, Daniel, V.P. & Sec.--Nabors Industries, Inc., Houston, TX; *U.S. Public*, pg. 1148
McLain, Christopher M., Sr. V.P., General Counsel & Sec.--Crown Vantage Inc., Oakland, CA; *U.S. Public*, pg. 465
McLaughlin, James J., Sec.--ITT Flygt Corporation, Trumbull, CT; *U.S. Public*, pg. 860
McLaughlin, John P., Exec. V.P. & Sec.--Genentech, Inc., South San Francisco, CA; *Int'l*, pg. 1120
McLaughlin, Mark, V.P.-Fin. & Asst. Sec.--Socanav Inc., Montreal, Canada; *Int'l*, pg. 1272
McLaughlin, Michael, Sec.--North Central Life Insurance Company, Saint Paul, MN; *U.S. Private*, pg. 404
McLaughlin, Michael W., V.P., Sec. & Dir.-Hazardous Substance Div.--SCS Engineers, Long Beach, CA; *U.S. Private*, pg. 955
McLaughlin, Stephen, Sec. & Gen. Counsel--Martin Exploration Management Company, Alsip, IL; *U.S. Private*, pg. 709
McLean, Douglas C., Sec.--Interstate Distributor Company, Tacoma, WA; *U.S. Private*, pg. 573
McLean, Miller R., Dir.-Grp. Legal & Regulatory Affairs & Grp. Sec.--The Royal Bank of Scotland plc, Edinburgh, United Kingdom; *Int'l*, pg. 1132
McLean, Regal, Sec.--Fraser Papers, Inc., Stamford, CT; *Int'l*, pg. 434
McLemore, Mary Lou, Sec.--Great River Insurance Company, Meridian, MS; *U.S. Public*, pg. 215
McLeod, John G., Jr., Sr. V.P.-Human Resources & Sec.--Apple South, Inc., Madison, GA; *U.S. Public*, pg. 121
McLure, Howard A., Sr. V.P., Controller & Asst. Sec.--Magellan Health Services, Inc., Atlanta, GA; *U.S. Public*, pg. 1033
McMahon, Marshall I., Jr., Sec.--Northwestern Industrial Piping, Niles, IL; *U.S. Private*, pg. 806
McMahon, Peter, Sec.--Chiltem Group SAM, Monaco, Monaco; *Int'l*, pg. 65
McMahon, Terry, Treas. & Sec.--Clark Detroit-Diesel Allison, Cincinnati, OH; *U.S. Private*, pg. 242
McMakin, Kelly, Chief Fin. Officer & Treas.--Florafax International, Inc., Vero Beach, FL; *U.S. Public*, pg. 654
McManigal, Robert M., Gen. Counsel & Sec.--Adams Rite Manufacturing Co., City of Industry, CA; *U.S. Private*, pg. 17
McManus, John V., V.P.-Fin. & Asst. Sec.--Sheldahl, Inc., Northfield, MN; *U.S. Public*, pg. 1465
McManus, Judith T., V.P. & Asst. Sec.--Calvert Bank & Trust Co., Prince Frederick, MD; *U.S. Public*, pg. 1088
McMeekin, Lisa Stein, Asst. Sec.--Loral Space & Communications, New York, NY; *U.S. Public*, pg. 1014
McMillan, Kenneth, Sec.--Country Life Insurance Company, Bloomington, IL; *U.S. Private*, pg. 278
McMillan, Michael K., Gen. Counsel & Sec.--Helian Health Group, Inc., Monterey, CA; *U.S. Public*, pg. 1715
McMillian, Lonnie S., V.P., Treas. & Sec.--ADTRAN, Inc., Huntsville, AL; *U.S. Public*, pg. 20
McNabb, Frederick W., Jr., V.P. & Asst. Sec.--Charles of the Ritz Group Ltd., New York, NY; *U.S. Private*, pg. 689
McNair, James A., V.P. & Asst. Sec.--PAMCO Printed Tape & Label Company, Inc., Des Plaines, IL; *U.S. Private*, pg. 598
McNally, Edward C., V.P.-Corp. Rels. & Sec.--Rand McNally & Company, Skokie, IL; *U.S. Private*, pg. 908
McNally, Mark K., Gen. Counsel & Sec.--Aristech Chemical Corporation, Pittsburgh, PA; *Int'l*, pg. 872
McNamara, Daniel L., Sec.--Forest Oil Corporation, Denver, CO; *U.S. Public*, pg. 670
McNamara, Linda, Dir.-Fin. Plng. & Corp. Asst. Sec.--Strouds, Inc., City of Industry, CA; *U.S. Public*, pg. 1525
McNamee, Bernard J., Exec. V.P., Gen. Counsel & Sec.--Rexene Corporation, Dallas, TX; *U.S. Private*, pg. 549
Mcnamee, Richard B., V.P.-Fin. & Tax, Treas. & Asst. Sec.--Great American Management & Investment, Inc., Chicago, IL; *U.S. Private*, pg. 473
McNeil, Donna, Sec.--Line Equipment Sales Co., Inc., Charleston, SC; *U.S. Private*, pg. 1130
McNeil, Joan, Sec.--Romac Industries, Inc., Seattle, WA; *U.S. Private*, pg. 942
McNeil, John, Sec.--Pridgeon & Clay, Inc., Grand Rapids, MI; *U.S. Private*, pg. 883
McNicholas, Barbara, Corp. Sec.--Rymer Foods Inc., Chicago, IL; *U.S. Public*, pg. 1414
McNish, Thomas A., V.P. & Sec.--CMS Energy Corporation, Dearborn, MI; *U.S. Public*, pg. 279
McNutly, David, Sr. V.P. & Sec.--First Bank National Association, Chicago, IL; *U.S. Public*, pg. 1681
McPherson, Michael J., Exec. V.P., Controller & Sec.--Steadly Company, Carthage, MO; *U.S. Public*, pg. 986
McPhie, Christine G., Controller & Sec.--Trimin Enterprises, Inc., Vancouver, Canada; *Int'l*, pg. 1424
McQuade, Robert C., Chief Fin. Officer, Sec. & Controller--Legacy Storage Systems Corp., Markham, Canada; *Int'l*, pg. 805
McQueston, James K., Counsel & Sec.--National Life Insurance Company, Montpelier, VT; *U.S. Private*, pg. 785
McRae, James W., V.P. & Sec.--McRae Industries, Inc., Mount Gilead, NC; *U.S. Public*, pg. 1073
McSweeney, Maurice J., Gen. Counsel & Sec.--Hein-Werner Corporation, Waukesha, WI; *U.S. Public*, pg. 805
McTyre, Elaine, Asst. Sec.--Electronic Tele-Communications, Inc., Waukesha, WI; *U.S. Public*, pg. 570
McVeigh, Christine, Asst. Sec.--CalMat Co., Los Angeles, CA; *U.S. Public*, pg. 295
McWilliams, John B., Sr. V.P., Gen. Counsel & Sec.--Canadian Occidental Petroleum Ltd., Calgary, Canada; *U.S. Public*, pg. 1210
Meacher, Ross, Corp. Sec.--Whistler Mountain Holdings, Limited, Whistler, Canada; *Int'l*, pg. 685
Meacher, Ross, Corp. Sec.--Copper Mountain Resort, Frisco, CO; *Int'l*, pg. 685
Meacher, Ross J., Corp. Sec.--Intrawest Corporation, Vancouver, Canada; *Int'l*, pg. 685
Meader, Craig, Sec.--Inland Associates, Olathe, KS; *U.S. Private*, pg. 563
Meadors, Terry L., Treas. & Asst. Sec.--Hickman, Williams & Co. Inc., Cincinnati, OH; *U.S. Private*, pg. 525
Meadows, Stanley, Corp. Sec.--Robertson-Ceco Corporation, San Ramon, CA; *U.S. Public*, pg. 1394
Meagher, John B., Sec.--Bestfoods, Englewood Cliffs, NJ; *U.S. Public*, pg. 223
Meaney, Daniel J. Jr., V.P., Sec. & Gen. Counsel--Circon Video Div., Santa Barbara, CA; *U.S. Public*, pg. 373
Mear, Christine, Coord.-Sls. Promo. & Sls. Admin.--Eversharp Pen Co., Franklin Park, IL; *U.S. Private*, pg. 386

Medaglia, Anthony J., Jr., Sec.--Cognex Corporation, Natick, MA; *U.S. Public*, pg. 394
Medel, Teresita, Controller, Treas. & Sec.--AMATI Communications Corp., San Jose, CA; *U.S. Public*, pg. 1585
Medford, Cecil, V.P., Sec. & Gen. Counsel--The Scott Fetzer Company, Westlake, OH; *U.S. Public*, pg. 217
Medico, Cataldo, Sec.--Medico Industries, Inc., Wilkes-Barre, PA; *U.S. Private*, pg. 728
Medina, Enrique, Sec. & Production Dir.--La Banda de Agustin Medina S.A., Madrid, Spain; *Int'l*, pg. 783
Meeuwsen, Christina S., Asst. Corp. Sec.--EnerMark Income Fund, Calgary, Canada; *Int'l*, pg. 454
Mehalko, Jack W., V.P. & Sec.--NS Group, Inc., Newport, KY; *U.S. Public*, pg. 1147
Mehlhorn, Bernhard, Sec.--The Braas Group, Oberursell, Germany; *Int'l*, pg. 1091
Mehra, Ajay, Chief Fin. Officer, V.P. & Sec.--OSI Systems, Inc., Hawthorne, CA; *U.S. Public*, pg. 1208
Mei-Ling, Jennifer Chang, Sec. & Dep. Mgr.-Legal--Orchard Parade Holdings Limited, Singapore, Singapore; *Int'l*, pg. 1007
Meier, Jeannette P., Exec. V.P., Gen. Counsel & Sec.--Sterling Commerce, Inc., Dublin, OH; *U.S. Public*, pg. 1515
Meier, Jeannette P., Exec. V.P.-Fin. & Admin./Sec.--Sterling Software, Inc., Dallas, TX; *U.S. Public*, pg. 1516
Meier, Karen, Sec.--S.B. Foot Tanning Co., Red Wing, MN; *U.S. Private*, pg. 915
Meier, Michael J., Chief Fin. Officer, V.P.-Fin., Treas. & Sec.--Defiance, Inc., Cleveland, OH; *U.S. Public*, pg. 493
Meilahn, J.E., Treas. & Sec.--Federated Mutual Insurance Company, Owatonna, MN; *U.S. Private*, pg. 399
Meisler, Joanne, Sr. V.P., Gen. Counsel & Sec.--Bellemead Development Corp., Roseland, NJ; *U.S. Public*, pg. 355
Mele, Charles A., Exec. V.P. & Gen. Counsel--MEDCO Containment Services, Inc., Montvale, NJ; *U.S. Public*, pg. 1091
Melka, Sandra, Sec.--Bardons & Oliver, Inc., Solon, OH; *U.S. Private*, pg. 116
Mellbye, Danckert, Sec.--Frionor A/S, Lysaker, Norway; *Int'l*, pg. 516
Melle, Melvin J., Chief Fin. Officer, V.P. & Sec.--The Hallwood Group Incorporated, Dallas, TX; *U.S. Public*, pg. 777
Melloy, Patrick C., V.P., Sec. & Treas.--Melloy Bros. Enterprises, Albuquerque, NM; *U.S. Private*, pg. 730
Melton, Jean, Asst. Sec.--Wynn's International, Inc., Orange, CA; *U.S. Public*, pg. 1782
Melton, Jean, Asst. Sec.--Wynn Oil Company, Azusa, CA; *U.S. Public*, pg. 1782
Melton, R. Neal, V.P.-Equipment & Pur. & Sec.--Regal Cinemas Inc., Knoxville, TN; *U.S. Public*, pg. 1371
Meltzer, Jay H., Sr. V.P., Gen. Counsel & Sec.--The TJX Companies, Inc., Framingham, MA; *U.S. Public*, pg. 1556
Menache, Jack, V.P., Gen. Counsel & Sec.--Integrated Device Technology, Inc., Santa Clara, CA; *U.S. Public*, pg. 884
Menchaca, Peggy B., V.P. & Sec.--Enron Corp., Houston, TX; *U.S. Public*, pg. 584
Menchinger, Steven R., Chief. Fin. Officer, Treas. & Sec.--Glassmaster Company, Lexington, SC; *U.S. Public*, pg. 745
Mendell, Peter, Sec.--Peerless Carpet Corporation, Acton Vale, Canada; *Int'l*, pg. 1032
Mendello, William L., Pres. & Chief Oper. Officer--Fender Musical Instruments, Scottsdale, AZ; *U.S. Private*, pg. 400
Mendelson, Alan C., Asst. Sec.--Amgen Inc., Thousand Oaks, CA; *U.S. Public*, pg. 100
Mendelson, Alan C., Gen. Counsel & Sec.--PETsMART, Inc., Phoenix, AZ; *U.S. Public*, pg. 1281
Mendelson, Herbert, V.P. & Asst. Sec.--Georgetown Partners, Inc., Great Neck, NY; *U.S. Private*, pg. 466
Mendoza, Mireya, Sec.--Mantex, S.A.C.A., Caracas, Venezuela; *Int'l*, pg. 840
Menke, Gerald T., Treas. & Sec.--The F.D. Lawrence Electric Co., Cincinnati, OH; *U.S. Private*, pg. 654
Merandi, Jane, Sec.--Alamco, Inc., Charleston, WV; *U.S. Public*, pg. 403
Mercer, J., Sec. & Dir.--Camden Motors Ltd., Leighton Buzzard, United Kingdom; *Int'l*, pg. 165
Mercer, Karla S., Sec.--Institutional Services, Inc., Fort Worth, TX; *U.S. Public*, pg. 1482
Merchant, Bill R., Asst. Treas.--Grey Wolf, Inc., Houston, TX; *U.S. Public*, pg. 765
Merck, Robert M., V.P., Gen. Counsel & Secretary--Mercedes-Benz Credit Corp., Norwalk, CT; *Int'l*, pg. 368
Merdek, Andrew A., V.P.-Legal Affairs & Sec.--Cox Enterprises, Inc., Atlanta, GA; *U.S. Private*, pg. 281
Merdek, Andrew A., Sec.--Manheim Auctions, Inc., Atlanta, GA; *U.S. Private*, pg. 282
Meredith, Frank, Chief Fin. Officer, Gen. Counsel & Sec.--Harman International Industries, Inc., Woodbury, NY; *U.S. Public*, pg. 787
Mergez, Francois, Sec.--SODIAAL, Paris, France; *Int'l*, pg. 1166
Merico, Judith A., Mgr.-Investor Rels. & Asst. Sec.--Huntington National Bank, Morgantown, WV; *U.S. Public*, *pg. 850*
Meringer, Patricia C., Sr. V.P., Corp. Counsel & Sec.--Hibernia Corporation, New Orleans, LA; *U.S. Public*, pg. 825
Merkel, Donald O., V.P., Sec. & Dir.--E.W. Knauss & Son, Inc., Quakertown, PA; *U.S. Private*, pg. 626
Merker, William, V.P. & Sec.--Standard Automotive Corporation, Hillsborough, NJ; *U.S. Private*, pg. 1030
Merksamer, Jon R., V.P. & Sec.--De Vons Jewelers, Sacramento, CA; *U.S. Private*, pg. 318
Merksamer, Steven A., Asst. Sec.--De Vons Jewelers, Sacramento, CA; *U.S. Private*, pg. 318
Merns, Steve, V.P. & Sec.--Syms Corporation, Secaucus, NJ; *U.S. Public*, pg. 1547
Merrell, Pamela K., V.P.-Human Resources & Sec.--Montana Power Company, Butte, MT; *U.S. Public*, pg. 1126
Merricks, Donald W., Exec. V.P. & Sec.--First Virginia Bank-Piedmont, Lynchburg, VA; *U.S. Public*, pg. 642
Merrill, F. Robert, III, Chief Fin. Officer, V.P.-Fin., Treas. & Sec.--Quest Medical, Inc., Allen, TX; *U.S. Public*, pg. 1352
Merritt, Robert S., Chief Fin. Officer, Sr. V.P.-Fin. & Treas.--Outback Steakhouse Inc., Tampa, FL; *U.S. Public*, pg. 1235
Merritt, Terry, Corp. Sec. & Dir.-H.R.--Walbridge Aldinger Company, Detroit, MI; *U.S. Private*, pg. 1146
Merryman, Gregory K., Corp. Sec. & Asst. Gen. Counsel--General Motors Acceptance Corporation (GMAC), Detroit, MI; *U.S. Public*, pg. 719
Mertens, Ceil, Asst. Sec. & Dir.-Admin. Services--Grolier Inc., Danbury, CT; *Int'l*, pg. 794
Mertson, Eleanor, Sec.--Price Waterhouse L.L.P. - U.S., New York, NY; *U.S. Private*, pg. 883
Mertz, Byron M., III, V.P. & Asst. Sec.--Sun Bancorp, Inc., Selinsgrove, PA; *U.S. Public*, pg. 1529
Mesher, John R., V.P. & Sec. & Gen. Counsel--CertainTeed Corporation, Valley Forge, PA; *Int'l*, pg. 1170
Mesher, John R., Sec.--Air Vent Inc., Peoria Heights, IL; *Int'l*, pg. 1170
Mesher, John R., Sec.--CertainTeed Foreign Sales Corp., Valley Forge, PA; *Int'l*, pg. 1171
Meskell, Kevin M., V.P. & Sec.--Quincy Mutual Fire Insurance Company, Quincy, MA; *U.S. Private*, pg. 901
Messemer, Glenn M., V.P., Sec. & Gen. Counsel--Kaman Corporation, Bloomfield, CT; *U.S. Public*, pg. 941
Messick, Rose, Corp. Sec. & Acctg. Svcs. Dir.--Bernstein-Rein Advertising, Inc., Kansas City, MO; *U.S. Private*, pg. 137
Mestayer, Mark L., Exec. V.P., Sec. & Dir.-Fin.--Piccadilly Cafeterias, Inc., Baton Rouge, LA; *U.S. Public*, pg. 1294
Metcalf, Henry, V.P. & Sec.--Flint River Mills, Bainbridge, GA; *U.S. Private*, pg. 413
Metcalf, Linda, V.P.-Admin. Svcs.--Bairnco Corporation, Maitland, FL; *U.S. Public*, pg. 165
Mettler, Jack, Pres. & Sec.--Circuit-Wise, Inc., North Haven, CT; *U.S. Private*, pg. 240
Meyer, A. David, Gen. Counsel & Sec.--R.O. Whitesell & Associates, Inc, Indianapolis, IN; *U.S. Private*, pg. 1173
Meyer, George G., Chief Exec. Officer, Treas. & Sec.--Central Sprinkler Corporation, Lansdale, PA; *U.S. Public*, *pg. 327*
Meyer, Kent, Sr. V.P.-Imaging--Saztec International, Inc., Billerica, MA; *U.S. Public*, pg. 1435
Meyer, Ronald A., V.P.-Fin. & Admin., Treas. & Sec.--Modern Controls, Inc., Minneapolis, MN; *U.S. Public*, pg. 1120
Meyer, Steven A., Sec.--John Solomon, Inc., Somerville, MA; *U.S. Private*, pg. 1013
Meyerding, Charles E., Sec.--Villaume Industries, Inc., Saint Paul, MN; *U.S. Private*, pg. 1140
Meyers, Howard M., Chm. Bd., Pres. & Chief Exec. Officer--Quexco Incorporated, Dallas, TX; *U.S. Private*, pg. 900
Meyers, Jerome E., Sec.--Dugan & Meyers Construction Co., Cincinnati, OH; *U.S. Private*, pg. 345
Micallef, J.S., Sec.--Dietzgen Corporation, Palatine, IL; *U.S. Private*, pg. 332
Micelli, Tony, V.P.-Fin., Treas. & Sec.--Metex Corporation, Edison, NJ; *U.S. Public*, pg. 1674
Michael, Mark D., Sr. V.P., Gen. Counsel & Sec.--3Com Corporation, Santa Clara, CA; *U.S. Public*, pg. 1603
Michaud, Nancy A., V.P., Gen. Counsel & Sec.--Huffy Corporation, Miamisburg, OH; *U.S. Public*, pg. 846
Michener, Sally R., Sec. & Dir.-Personnel & Pub. Rels.--Scott Specialty Gases, Plumsteadville, PA; *U.S. Private*, pg. 977
Michie, A.J., Sec.--Lloyds TSB Group PLC, London, United Kingdom; *Int'l*, pg. 812
Michno, Timothy, Corp. Sec. & Gen. Counsel--Movado Group, Inc., Lyndhurst, NJ; *U.S. Public*, pg. 1140
Mickus, Donald V., V.P., Treas. & Sec.--Del Webb Corporation, Phoenix, AZ; *U.S. Public*, pg. 494
Middleditch, M.R., Mng. Dir. & Sec.--Spar (UK) Ltd., Harrow, United Kingdom; *Int'l*, pg. 1288
Middleton, Linda, Asst. Sec.--Fina, Inc., Dallas, TX; *Int'l*, pg. 1044
Midgley, J., V.P.-Strategic Devel.--HongKong Bank of Canada, Vancouver, Canada; *Int'l*, pg. 583
Miesmaki, Kai, Exec. V.P.-Admn. & Sec.--Tamrock Corp., Tampere, Finland; *Int'l*, pg. 1352
Migallos, Barbara Ann, Corp. Sec.--La Tondena Distillers, Inc., Manila, Philippines; *Int'l*, pg. 785
Mihalko, George R., Jr., Chief Fin. Officer, Sr. V.P., Treas. & Asst. Sec.--Pamida Holdings Corporation, Omaha, NE; *U.S. Public*, pg. 1255
Mijs, C.F., Sec.--Ceteco N.V., Utrecht, Netherlands; *Int'l*, pg. 279
Miklich, Thomas R., Chief Fin. Officer, Treas., Gen. Counsel & Sec.--Invacare Corporation, Elyria, OH; *U.S. Public*, pg. 911
Miklos, Steven W., V.P., Asst. Sec. & Controller--UniCARE Insurance Company, Irvine, CA; *U.S. Private*, pg. 152
Mikos, Susan McDonough, Sec.--RemedyTemp, Inc., San Juan Capistrano, CA; *U.S. Public*, pg. 1376
Mikovich, Fran, Treas. & Sec.--Orleans Materials & Equipment Co., Inc., New Orleans, LA; *U.S. Private*, pg. 820
Miksiewicz, Sally, Vice Chm. & Sec.--East Penn Mfg. Co., Lyon Station, PA; *U.S. Private*, pg. 357
Milack, Joseph, V.P.-Fin., Treas. & Sec.--Brinkmann Instruments, Inc., Westbury, NY; *U.S. Private*, pg. 169
Milano, Sandro, Sec. & Treas.--Butera Finer Foods Inc., Elgin, IL; *U.S. Private*, pg. 189
Milasius, Alan R., Sr. V.P., Sec. & Dir.-Internal Audit--First Midwest Bancorp, Inc., Itasca, IL; *U.S. Public*, pg. 636
Miles, Leroy J., Sec.--Northland Cranberries, Inc., Wisconsin Rapids, WI; *U.S. Public*, pg. 1197
Milet, Pierre, Chief Fin. Officer, V.P. & Sec.--Clarins, Neuilly-sur-Seine, France; *Int'l*, pg. 295
Miley, Samuel A., V.P., Gen. Counsel & Sec.--MagneTek, Inc., Nashville, TN; *U.S. Public*, pg. 1037
Milfs, Audrey L., V.P. & Sec.--Pacific Life Insurance Company, Newport Beach, CA; *U.S. Private*, pg. 831
Millares, Joe M., Chief Fin. Officer, V.P.-Fin. & Sec.--DSP Technology Inc., Fremont, CA; *U.S. Public*, pg. 475
Miller, A.J., Sec.--L-N Safety Glass, SA de CV, Mexicali, Mexico; *Int'l*, pg. 1056
Miller, Alan J., Sec.--Libbey Owens Ford Co., Toledo, OH; *Int'l*, pg. 1056
Miller, Anita, V.P.-Fin, Treas. & Sec.--Wholesale Electronic Supply, Dallas, TX; *U.S. Private*, pg. 1174
Miller, Ann, Sec.--Gensym Corporation, Western Regional Office, Boulder, CO; *U.S. Public*, pg. 731
Miller, Arthur R., Gen. Counsel & Sec.--Katy Industries, Inc., Englewood, CO; *U.S. Public*, pg. 944
Miller, Barbara J., Asst. Corp. Sec.--Ball Corporation, Muncie, IN; *U.S. Public*, pg. 170
Miller, Carmen Strite, Sec.--Shenandoah Mfg. Co. Inc., Harrisonburg, VA; *U.S. Private*, pg. 992
Miller, Catherine, Exec. Sec.--Heck Cellars Winery, Di Giorgio, CA; *U.S. Private*, pg. 632
Miller, Catherine D., Treas. & Sec.--Derst Baking Company, Inc., Savannah, GA; *U.S. Private*, pg. 326
Miller, Charles, Corp. Sec.--PG Vinyl Windows/PG Proglass Construction, Westbrook, ME; *U.S. Private*, pg. 826
Miller, Charlotte L., Sr. V.P., Gen. Counsel & Sec.--Summit Family Restaurants, Inc., Salt Lake City, UT; *U.S. Public*, *pg. 278*
Miller, Chris A., V.P.-Fin., Treas. & Sec.--C-COR Electronics, Inc., State College, PA; *U.S. Public*, pg. 272
Miller, Cory J., Chief Fin. Officer & V.P.-Fin.--Ciprico, Inc., Plymouth, MN; *U.S. Public*, pg. 370
Miller, D. Jamieson, V.P.-Fin. & Sec.--Contrans Corporation, Woodstock, Canada; *Int'l*, pg. 328
Miller, David, Exec. V.P.--Hask Toiletries, Great Neck, NY; *U.S. Private*, pg. 509
Miller, David, Chief Fin. Officer, Controller, Treas. & Sec.--Monterey Mechanical Company, Oakland, CA; *U.S. Private*, pg. 758
Miller, David D., Exec. V.P. & Corp Legal--UMB Financial Corporation, Kansas City, MO; *U.S. Public*, pg. 1653
Miller, David J., Grp. Sec.--Royal & Sun Alliance Insurance Group plc, London, United Kingdom; *Int'l*, pg. 1130
Miller, Debra A., Sec.--Command Security Corporation, Lagrangeville, NY; *U.S. Public*, pg. 409
Miller, Donald, Treas. & Sec.--Lee Grocery Company, Everett, WA; *U.S. Private*, pg. 657
Miller, Donald E., Sr. V.P., Gen. Counsel & Sec.--The Fairchild Corporation, Chantilly, VA; *U.S. Public*, pg. 610
Miller, Elaine, Sec.--Wegener Corporation, Duluth, GA; *U.S. Public*, pg. 1751
Miller, Eugene F., V.P., Sec. & Corp. Gen. Counsel--Loctite Corporation, Rocky Hill, CT; *Int'l*, pg. 611
Miller, Harold, Jr., Sec.--Cashco, Inc., Ellsworth, KS; *U.S. Private*, pg. 218
Miller, Harvey L., Sec.--Quill Corp., Lincolnshire, IL; *U.S. Private*, pg. 901
Miller, Helen P., Sec.--Intermountain Farmers Association, Salt Lake City, UT; *U.S. Private*, pg. 568
Miller, James, Sec.--Ludington News Co. Inc., Detroit, MI; *U.S. Private*, pg. 679
Miller, Jay, Sr. V.P.-Fin., Treas. & Sec.--Perfection Bakeries Inc., Fort Wayne, IN; *U.S. Private*, pg. 852
Miller, Jean F., Asst. Sec.--C.R. Bard, Inc., Murray Hill, NJ; *U.S. Public*, pg. 189
Miller, Jeanne M., Chief Fin. Officer, V.P. & Sec.--Gish Biomedical, Inc., Irvine, CA; *U.S. Public*, pg. 745
Miller, Jeffrey J., Gen. Counsel & Sec.--NeoRx Corporation, Seattle, WA; *U.S. Private*, pg. 791
Miller, Jo H., Asst. Sec.--TBC Corporation, Memphis, TN; *U.S. Public*, pg. 1553
Miller, John T., Chief Fin. Officer & Sr. V.P.-Fin.--E-Z Serve Corp., Houston, TX; *U.S. Public*, pg. 540
Miller, Jonathan, V.P. & Asst. Sec.--Dewberry Design Group, Oklahoma City, OK; *U.S. Private*, pg. 329
Miller, Judy, Asst. Sec.--Central Louisiana Electric Company, Inc., Pineville, LA; *U.S. Public*, pg. 325
Miller, Katherine, Treas. & Sec.--Pyromet, Inc., Aston, PA; *U.S. Private*, pg. 897
Miller, Kathleen C., Sec.--Regency Dodge Inc., Jacksonville, FL; *U.S. Private*, pg. 918
Miller, Kenneth I., Chief Fin. Officer, Treas., Sr. V.P. & Sec.--Johnston, Lemon & Co. Inc., Washington, DC; *U.S. Private*, pg. 595
Miller, Kenneth W., Corp. Sec.--Cerprobe Corporation, Gilbert, AZ; *U.S. Public*, pg. 332
Miller, Kirk, Sr. V.P., Sec. & Gen. Counsel--Kaiser Permanente, Oakland, CA; *U.S. Private*, pg. 605
Miller, Larry H., Treas. & Sec.--Larry H. Miller Group, Murray, UT; *U.S. Private*, pg. 747
Miller, Lloyd A., V.P., Treas. & Sec.--Midway Products Corporation, Monroe, MI; *U.S. Private*, pg. 744
Miller, M., Corp. Sec.--HongKong Bank of Canada, Vancouver, Canada; *Int'l*, pg. 583
Miller, M.L., Sec.--Supreme Electronics Corp., Greenwood, MS; *U.S. Public*, pg. 825
Miller, Margaret, Sec.--Farrar, Straus & Giroux, Inc., New York, NY; *Int'l*, pg. 1479
Miller, Michael, Chief Oper. Officer--Cragar Industries, Inc., Phoenix, AZ; *U.S. Public*, pg. 456
Miller, Michael L., Sec.--Hickok Incorporated, Cleveland, OH; *U.S. Public*, pg. 825
Miller, Nancy A., V.P. & Sec.--Armor All Products Group, Oakland, CA; *U.S. Public*, pg. 387
Miller, Nancy A., V.P. & Sec.--McKesson Corporation, San Francisco, CA; *U.S. Public*, pg. 1072
Miller, Nicole, Sec.--Miller Advertising Agency Inc., New York, NY; *U.S. Private*, pg. 746
Miller, Nina J., Sec.--Prentiss Incorporated, Floral Park, NY; *U.S. Private*, pg. 882

Miller, Paul M., V.P.-Sls. & Sec.--Mill-Rose Company, Mentor, OH; *U.S. Private*, pg. 746
Miller, Peggy, Sec.--Willis Corroon Melling Inc., Montreal, Canada; *Int'l*, pg. 1509
Miller, Peter D., V.P., Gen. Counsel & Sec.--National Auto Credit Inc., Solon, OH; *U.S. Public*, pg. 1152
Miller, Phebe C., Chief Legal Officer & Sec.--The Bank of New York Company, Inc., New York, NY; *U.S. Public*, pg. 178
Miller, Raymond, Chief Fin. Officer, V.P. & Corp. Sec.--Weiners Stores, Inc., Houston, TX; *U.S. Private*, pg. 1160
Miller, Richard L., Gen. Counsel & Sec.--American Institute of C.P.A.'s Inc., New York, NY; *U.S. Private*, pg. 57
Miller, Richard L., Exec. V.P., Treas. & Sec.--Miller Transporters, Inc., Jackson, MS; *U.S. Private*, pg. 329
Miller, Robert M., V.P.-Law & Sec.--FKI Industries, Inc., Fairfield, CT; *Int'l*, pg. 472
Miller, Ross, Sec.--Harris Steel Co., Cicero, IL; *U.S. Private*, *pg. 506*
Miller, Scott, Sr. V.P., Gen. Counsel & Asst. Sec.--Coherent, Inc., Santa Clara, CA; *U.S. Public*, pg. 395
Miller, Sidney, Sec.--Universal Health Realty Income Trust, King of Prussia, PA; *U.S. Public*, pg. 1697
Miller, Susan, Sec.--YSI Incorporated, Yellow Springs, OH; *U.S. Private*, pg. 1195
Miller, Tim M., Sec.--B&W Co-op, Inc., Breckenridge, MI; *U.S. Private*, pg. 105
Miller, Ward M., Jr., Sr. V.P., Gen. Counsel & Sec.--Avon Products, Inc., New York, NY; *U.S. Public*, pg. 155
Miller, Wayne, Chief Fin. Officer, Exec. V.P.-Fin. & Admin. & Sec.--Bernard Chaus, Inc., Secaucus, NJ; *U.S. Public*, pg. 342
Milligan, Robert Colin, Sec.--South West Water PLC, Exeter, United Kingdom; *Int'l*, pg. 1287
Millisor, William P., Reg. Counsel & Asst. Sec.--OHM Remediation Services Corp., Findlay, OH; *U.S. Public*, pg. 1208
Millman, Linda R., Assoc. Gen. Counsel & Asst. Sec.--Ekco Group, Inc., Nashua, NH; *U.S. Public*, pg. 566
Millman, Linda R., Asst. Sec.--Ekco Housewares, Inc., Franklin Park, IL; *U.S. Public*, pg. 566
Millman, Linda R., Sec.--Ekco International, Inc., Nashua, NH; *U.S. Public*, pg. 566
Mills, Elaine K., Mgr.-Corp. Stock Records & Asst. Sec.--Rohr, Inc., Chula Vista, CA; *U.S. Public*, pg. 751
Mills, Olan, II, Chm. Bd. & Sec.--Olan Mills, Inc., Chattanooga, TN; *U.S. Private*, pg. 749
Mills, William R., Chief Fin. Officer & V.P.-Fin.--Weis Markets, Inc., Sunbury, PA; *U.S. Public*, pg. 1751
Milne, Cynthia J., Sec.--Andover Bancorp, Inc., Andover, MA; *U.S. Public*, pg. 111
Milne, John, Vice Chm., Chief Acq. Officer, Sr. V.P., Treas. & Sec.--United Waste Systems, Inc., Houston, TX; *U.S. Public*, pg. 1691
Milner, David, Esq., Sec.--Commercial Travelers Mutual Insurance Company, Utica, NY; *U.S. Private*, pg. 258
Milstein, Andrew R., V.P., Mgr.-Exec. Mdse. & Asst. Sec.--Burlington Coat Factory Warehouse Corporation, Burlington, NJ; *U.S. Public*, pg. 268
Milstein, Henrietta, V.P. & Sec.--Burlington Coat Factory Warehouse Corporation, Burlington, NJ; *U.S. Public*, pg. 268
Milton, Claire, Treas. & Sec.--National Sea Products Limited, Lunenburg, Canada; *Int'l*, pg. 909
Minchin, Donald E., Sec.--Bayex Incorporated, Albion, NY; *Int'l*, pg. 1170
Minchin, Donald E., Sec.--Bay Mills (Delaware), Inc., Wilmington, DE; *Int'l*, pg. 1170
Minchin, Donald E., Sec.--Perma Glas-Mesh, Inc., Dover, OH; *Int'l*, pg. 1171
Miner, Martin P., Sec.--A & P Coat, Apron & Linen Supply, Bronx, NY; *U.S. Private*, pg. 1
Mingasson, Paul, Sec. Gen.--SNCF, Paris, France; *Int'l*, pg. 1163
Miniat, Edmund, Jr., Exec. V.P. & Sec.--Ed Miniat, Inc., Chicago, IL; *U.S. Private*, pg. 750
Minnaugh, Mark, V.P.-Fin. & Acctg.--Giant Eagle, Inc., Pittsburgh, PA; *U.S. Private*, pg. 450
Minnot, Debra F., Sr. V.P. & Gen. Counsel--Essex International, Inc., Fort Wayne, IN; *U.S. Public*, pg. 593
Minor, Charles D., Sec.--Worthington Industries, Inc., Columbus, OH; *U.S. Public*, pg. 1780
Minor, Edward C., Asst. Sec.--Union Camp Corporation, Wayne, NJ; *U.S. Public*, pg. 1665
Minori, Thomas M., Asst. Sec.--Stabler Companies, Inc., Harrisburg, PA; *U.S. Private*, pg. 1028
Mintmier, Robert T., Controller & Sec.--Myrick Construction Inc., Biscoe, NC; *U.S. Private*, pg. 771
Miranda, Jose J., Chief Oper. Officer & Exec. V.P.--Gator Industries Inc., Hialeah, FL; *U.S. Private*, pg. 441
Miro, Jeffrey, Corp. Sec.--Sotheby's Holdings Inc., New York, NY; *U.S. Public*, pg. 1487
Mirza, Yaqub, Dr., Sec.--Mylex Corporation, Fremont, CA; *U.S. Public*, pg. 1143
Mishalanie, Phillip G., Controller & Sec.--Barber Dairies, Inc., Birmingham, AL; *U.S. Private*, pg. 115
Mishoe, Thomas M., Chief Fin. Officer, V.P., Treas. & Sec.--Eskimo Pie Corporation, Richmond, VA; *U.S. Public*, pg. 592
Misialek, Kurt A., Chief Fin. Officer & V.P.--Eggland's Best, Inc., King of Prussia, PA; *U.S. Private*, pg. 366
Mistretta, F. David, V.P., Gen. Counsel & Sec.--Security Mutual Life Insurance Co. of New York, Binghamton, NY; *U.S. Private*, pg. 981
Miswald, R. Scott, Treas. & Sec.--Entree Corporation, Westlake Village, CA; *U.S. Public*, pg. 455
Mitau, Lee R., Exec. V.P., Gen. Counsel & Sec.--U.S. Bancorp, Minneapolis, MN; *U.S. Public*, pg. 1680
Mitchel, Michael M., V.P.--Economy Folding Box Corp., Chicago, IL; *U.S. Private*, pg. 362
Mitchel, Stephen, V.P., Sec. & Treas.--Mitchel & Scott Machine Co., Inc., Indianapolis, IN; *U.S. Private*, pg. 753
Mitchell, Carol L., Esq., Exec. V.P. & Clerk--Peoples Heritage Financial Group, Inc., Portland, ME; *U.S. Public*, *pg. 1275*
Mitchell, Carolyn S., Corp. Sec.--Sysco Corporation, Houston, TX; *U.S. Public*, pg. 1550
Mitchell, D.G., Asst. Sec.--The North American Coal Corporation, Dallas, TX; *U.S. Public*, pg. 1149
Mitchell, D.S., Sec.--Allied Domecq PLC, London, United Kingdom; *Int'l*, pg. 62
Mitchell, E. Benjamin, Jr., V.P., Sec. & Gen. Counsel--Logicon, Inc., Torrance, CA; *U.S. Public*, pg. 1198
Mitchell, Ethel, Exec. Admin. Asst.--C.R.A. Holdings Inc., Kalamazoo, MI; *U.S. Private*, pg. 1029
Mitchell, H. Thomas, V.P., Gen. Counsel & Sec.--Buffets, Inc., Eden Prairie, MN; *U.S. Public*, pg. 267
Mitchell, John M., Sec. & Public Officer--Hyster Australia Pty. Ltd., Milperra, Australia; *U.S. Public*, pg. 1149
Mitchell, Kathy, Sec.--Gould Electronics Inc., Eastlake, OH; *U.S. Public*, pg. 1591
Mitchell, Randy, Treas. & Sec.--The Hotsy Corporation, Englewood, CO; *U.S. Private*, pg. 500
Mitchell, Robert J., Treas. & Asst. Sec.--ACF Industries, Inc., Saint Charles, MO; *U.S. Private*, pg. 556
Mitchell, Sandra L., Treas. & Sec.--Delagra Corporation, Bridgeville, DE; *U.S. Private*, pg. 321
Mitchell, W. Nathan, Asst. Sec. & Sr. Dir.-Trade Payables--Lowe's Companies, Inc., North Wilkesboro, NC; *U.S. Public*, pg. 1015
Mitsdarfer, Richard J., Sr. V.P. & Asst. Sec.--Citizens Banking Corporation, Flint, MI; *U.S. Public*, pg. 379
Mittasch, Randolph J., Sec. & Treas.--The Care Group, Inc., New York, NY; *U.S. Public*, pg. 305
Mitteness, Elaine, Sec.--Tyler Industries, Benson, MN; *U.S. Private*, pg. 1112
Mizanin, Michael, Sec. & Treas.--Graycor International Inc., Homewood, IL; *U.S. Private*, pg. 472
Mlotek, Mark, V.P. & Gen. Counsel--Henry Schein, Inc., Melville, NY; *U.S. Public*, pg. 1437
Mobley, A. Scott, Chief Oper. Officer, Exec. V.P. & Sec.--Noble Roman's Inc., Indianapolis, IN; *U.S. Public*, pg. 1187
Mock, C.A., Chief Fin. Officer, Sr. V.P. & Sec.--Consolidated Pipe & Supply Company, Birmingham, AL; *U.S. Private*, pg. 266
Mock, Steve, Treas. & Sec.--Barenbrug Northeast, Ogdensburg, NJ; *Int'l*, pg. 167
Mocniak, Michael J., V.P., Gen. Counsel & Sec.--Fansteel, Inc., North Chicago, IL; *U.S. Public*, pg. 612
Moderow, Joseph, Sr. V.P. & Sec.--United Parcel Service of America, Inc., Atlanta, GA; *U.S. Private*, pg. 1123
Modlin, Howard S., Sec.--Fedders Corp., Liberty Corner, NJ; *U.S. Public*, pg. 614
Modlin, Howard S., Sec.--General Datacomm Industries, Inc., Middlebury, CT; *U.S. Public*, pg. 708
Moe, Earl, Sec.--Midwest Tire & Muffler, Inc., Rapid City, SD; *U.S. Private*, pg. 745
Moe, James D., V.P., Gen. Counsel & Sec.--Cargill, Wayzata, MN; *U.S. Private*, pg. 210
Moehring, Niel, Controller, Treas. & Sec.--Thomas & Skinner, Inc., Indianapolis, IN; *U.S. Private*, pg. 1082
Moeller, Audrey C., V.P. & Sec.--Equitable Resources, Inc., Pittsburgh, PA; *U.S. Public*, pg. 589
Moen, Richard, Exec. V.P.-Admin., Gen. Counsel & Sec.--Golden Valley Microwave Foods, Inc., Edina, MN; *U.S. Public*, pg. 427
Moerbeek, Peter J., Chief Fin. Officer, V.P.-Fin. & Sec.--Southwest Water Company, West Covina, CA; *U.S. Public*, pg. 1494
Moffett, Robert T., V.P., Gen. Counsel & Sec.--Howell Corporation, Houston, TX; *U.S. Public*, pg. 843
Moffett, Sharon, Sec.--Pillowtex Corporation, Dallas, TX; *U.S. Public*, pg. 1296
Mogle, David B., Treas. & Sec.--F.N.B. Corporation, Hermitage, PA; *U.S. Public*, pg. 607
Mogle, David B., Sr. V.P. & Sec.--First National Bank of Pennsylvania, Hermitage, PA; *U.S. Public*, pg. 607
Mohan, Patrick, Exec. V.P., Gen. Counsel & Sec.--A.E. Staley Manufacturing Co., Decatur, IL; *Int'l*, pg. 1356
Mohl, Anthony S., First V.P., Asst. Sec. & Dir.-Portfolio Mngmt.--W.P. Carey & Co., Inc., New York, NY; *U.S. Private*, pg. 209
Mohl, Marlies, Sec.--Commercial Metals (International) AG, Zug, Switzerland; *U.S. Public*, pg. 414
Mohlman, Kurt, Treas. & Sec.--United Illuminating Company, New Haven, CT; *U.S. Public*, pg. 1678
Moilanen, Todd A., V.P & Sec.--Cloverdale Equipment Co., Oak Park, MI; *U.S. Private*, pg. 247
Moir, R.J., V.P., Sec. & Gen. Counsel--Holnam Inc. (West Division), Lakewood, CO; *Int'l*, pg. 628
Moix, Norbert, Sec. & Treas.--Nabholz Construction Corp., Conway, AR; *U.S. Private*, pg. 772
Molineaux, Bob, Controller & Sec.--Willamette Industries Inc., Cleveland, OH; *U.S. Public*, pg. 1768
Moloshok, Norman, Sec.--Canon U.S.A., Inc., Lake Success, NY; *Int'l*, pg. 262
Momayez, F., Treas. & Sec.--TGM Detectors Inc., Waltham, MA; *Int'l*, pg. 892
Momboisse, R. Michael, Chief Fin. Officer, V.P.-Legal & Sec.--EMCON, San Mateo, CA; *U.S. Public*, pg. 571
Monacelli, Donna, Sec.--Presidential Life Corporation, Nyack, NY; *U.S. Public*, pg. 1323
Moncada, L. Patricia, Gen. Counsel & Asst. Sec.--Oracle Corporation, Redwood City, CA; *U.S. Public*, pg. 1227
Money, Anthony, V.P., Sec. & Treas.--Foseco Holding Inc., Cleveland, OH; *Int'l*, pg. 234
Monfort, Myra H., V.P., Sec. & Gen. Counsel--Monfort, Inc., Greeley, CO; *U.S. Public*, pg. 427
Mongan, Tod V., Sr. V.P., Gen. Counsel, & Sec.--BancTec, Inc., Dallas, TX; *U.S. Public*, pg. 176
Mongelluzzo, John A., Gen. Counsel & Sec.--Structural Dynamics Research Corp., Milford, OH; *U.S. Public*, pg. 1525
Monigle, Gerald E., Asst. Sec.--Kleinert's, Inc., of Alabama, Elba, AL; *U.S. Private*, pg. 625
Monigle, Gerald E., Asst. Sec.--Kleinert's Inc. of Florida, Largo, FL; *U.S. Private*, pg. 625
Monk, Robert D., Treas. & Sec.--Triple S Plastics, Inc., Vicksburg, MI; *U.S. Public*, pg. 1639
Monk, Thomas, Gen. Counsel & Sec.--Lotus Cars USA, Inc., Lawrenceville, GA; *Int'l*, pg. 1071
Monro, R.C., Asst. Sec.--Redland PLC, Reigate, United Kingdom; *Int'l*, pg. 1090
Monsalve, Julio, Sec.--PDV Marina, S.A., Caracas, Venezuela; *Int'l*, pg. 1045
Monsma, Calvin J., Chief Fin. Officer, V.P. & Sec.--Trion, Inc., Sanford, NC; *U.S. Public*, pg. 1639
Monson, John, Sec.--Rock of Ages Corporation, Graniteville, VT; *U.S. Public*, pg. 1396
Monson, Mary, Sec.--Monson Trucking, Inc., Duluth, MN; *U.S. Private*, pg. 758
Monson, Scott G., Gen. Counsel & Asst. Corp. Sec.--JB Oxford Holdings Inc., Beverly Hills, CA; *U.S. Public*, pg. 916
Mont, Stuart, Chief Oper. Officer, Chief Fin. Officer, Exec. V.P. & Sec.--Recoton Corporation, Lake Mary, FL; *U.S. Public*, pg. 1369
Montague, Carlos S., Chief Fin. Officer, V.P., Treas. & Asst. Sec.--Ault Incorporated, Minneapolis, MN; *U.S. Public*, pg. 147
Montgomery, Angie, Sec.--Moeller Products Co., Inc., Greenville, MS; *U.S. Private*, pg. 755
Montgomery, David, Chief Fin. Officer, V.P.-Fin. & Sec.--Advanstar Communications, Cleveland, OH; *U.S. Private*, *pg. 22*
Montgomery, David, Treas. & Sec.--SouthCo. Inc., Concordville, PA; *U.S. Private*, pg. 1014
Montgomery, Pat, Admin. Asst.--Newport Steel Corporation, Newport, KY; *U.S. Public*, pg. 1147
Montizambert, Eric, Asst. Corp. Sec.--PG&E Corporation, San Francisco, CA; *U.S. Public*, pg. 1240
Mood, Alfred, Treas. & Sec.--Pyramid Mountain Lumber, Seeley Lake, MT; *U.S. Private*, pg. 896
Moodispaw, Leonard, Gen. Counsel & Sec.--Essex Corporation, Columbia, MD; *U.S. Public*, pg. 593
Moomjian, Cary A., V.P., Gen. Counsel & Sec.--Santa Fe International Corporation, Dallas, TX; *Int'l*, pg. 765
Moomjy, Walter, Treas. & Sec.--Einstein Moomjy Inc., Pine Brook, NJ; *U.S. Private*, pg. 366
Moon, Marian J., Corp. Sec.--Devon Energy Corporation, Oklahoma City, OK; *U.S. Public*, pg. 503
Moon, R.K., Sec.--The News Corporation Limited, Sydney, Australia; *Int'l*, pg. 925
Moonan, Jeffrey P., Sr. V.P.-Gen. Counsel & Sec.--Photronics, Inc., Brookfield, CT; *U.S. Public*, pg. 1293
Moore, Anne, Sec.--Orbit Valve International, Inc., Little Rock, AR; *U.S. Private*, pg. 819
Moore, Barney M., Jr., Sec.--Unisource, Doraville, GA; *U.S. Public*, pg. 1671
Moore, C. Steven, V.P., Mng. Attorney & Sec.--Service Merchandise Company, Inc., Brentwood, TN; *U.S. Public*, *pg. 1461*
Moore, Charles, Sec.--Affiliated Foods Southwest, Little Rock, AR; *U.S. Private*, pg. 26
Moore, Dennis G., Chief Fin. Officer, Sr. V.P., Treas. & Sec.--J & J Snack Foods Corporation, Pennsauken, NJ; *U.S. Public*, pg. 916
Moore, Donna D., Sec.--Keystone (Canada) Ltd., Burlington, Canada; *U.S. Public*, pg. 1650
Moore, Donna D., Sec.--Keystone International Holdings Corp., Houston, TX; *U.S. Public*, pg. 1650
Moore, Elizabeth, Sec.--Harold Moore & Associates, Inc., Fayetteville, TN; *U.S. Private*, pg. 759
Moore, J.M., Sec.--Baycoat, Hamilton, Canada; *Int'l*, pg. 414
Moore, James O., V.P.-Fin., Treas. & Asst. Sec.--Cullman Ventures, Inc., Norwalk, CT; *U.S. Private*, pg. 294
Moore, James R., Chief Fin. Officer, Exec. V.P. & Sec.--Urstadt Biddle Properties, Inc., Greenwich, CT; *U.S. Public*, pg. 1700
Moore, John P., Sec.--Northern States Power Company, Minneapolis, MN; *U.S. Public*, pg. 1195
Moore, John P., Jr., Sec. & Gen. Counsel--Northern States Power Co. (Wis.), Eau Claire, WI; *U.S. Public*, pg. 1195
Moore, Linda E., Sec.--Stahl Specialty Company, Kingsville, MO; *U.S. Private*, pg. 1029
Moore, P.A., Sec.--Swire Pacific Limited, Central, Hong Kong; *Int'l*, pg. 1328
Moore, Robert A., V.P.-H.R. & Sec.--Dead River Company, Portland, ME; *U.S. Private*, pg. 318
Moore, Robert C., V.P., Gen. Counsel & Sec.--Texas Industries, Inc., Dallas, TX; *U.S. Public*, pg. 1585
Moore, Rosemary A., Sec.--UNUM Sales Corp., Portland, ME; *U.S. Public*, pg. 1700
Moore, Samuel N., Sec.--Fairfax Lumber & Millwork Company Inc., Springfield, VA; *U.S. Private*, pg. 391
Moore, William B., V.P., Gen. Counsel & Sec.--Whitman Corporation, Rolling Meadows, IL; *U.S. Public*, pg. 1766
Moorhead, Bill, Sec. & Treas.--Homewood Corporation, Columbus, OH; *U.S. Private*, pg. 537
Moorhead, Thomas L., V.P.-Law & Asst. Sec.--Nordson Corporation, Westlake, OH; *U.S. Public*, pg. 1188
Moosa, Moosa E., Chief Fin. Officer, V.P.-Fin. & Treas.--Chemfab Corporation, Merrimack, NH; *U.S. Public*, pg. 344
Mora, R.N., Gen. Counsel & Sec.--The HOH Organizations, Chicago, IL; *U.S. Private*, pg. 492
Moran, Glenn, Sr. V.P., Gen. Counsel & Sec.--The LTV Corporation, Cleveland, OH; *U.S. Public*, pg. 971
Moran, Michael R., Exec. V.P., Gen. Counsel & Sec.--Spiegel, Inc., Downers Grove, IL; *U.S. Public*, pg. 1498
Moran, Patricia K., Corp. Sec. & Asst. Treas.--Zemex Corporation, Toronto, Canada; *Int'l*, pg. 1523
Morbey, Richard I., Sec.--Taylor Woodrow plc, London, United Kingdom; *Int'l*, pg. 1358
Moreau, Leslie, Corp. Sec.--Elixir Industries, Gardena, CA; *U.S. Private*, pg. 371
Morehouse, Janet S., Asst. Sec.--Michaels Stores, Inc., Irving, TX; *U.S. Public*, pg. 1104

Morgan-Prager, Karole, Gen. Counsel & Corp. Sec.--McClatchy Newspapers Inc., Sacramento, CA; *U.S. Public*, pg. 1065
Morgan, Dennis K., V.P.-Legal & Sec.--Southern Union Company, Austin, TX; *U.S. Public*, pg. 1491
Morgan, Elizabeth K., Sec.--Hitox Corporation of America, Corpus Christi, TX; *U.S. Public*, pg. 829
Morgan, James A., V.P.-Fin. & Sec.--Tubular Steel Inc., Saint Louis, MO; *U.S. Private*, pg. 1108
Morgan, James A., Sr. V.P., Gen. Counsel & Sec.--Rubbermaid Incorporated, Wooster, OH; *U.S. Public*, pg. 1411
Morgan, John B., Corp. Sec.--Waterford Wedgwood Plc, Dublin, Ireland; *Int'l*, pg. 1487
Morgan, Kirby, Treas. & Sec.--Williamson-Dickie Mfg. Co., Fort Worth, TX; *U.S. Private*, pg. 1179
Morgan, Larkin C., Chief Fin. Officer, Treas. & Sec.--Arrow Gear Company, Downers Grove, IL; *U.S. Private*, pg. 85
Morgan, Marsha K., V.P.-Investor Relations & Sec.--Burlington Northern Santa Fe Corporation, Fort Worth, TX; *U.S. Public*, pg. 268
Morgan, Randall, Sec.--Crown Andersen Inc., Peachtree City, GA; *U.S. Public*, pg. 462
Morgan, Roger J., Sec.--Petroleum Development Corporation, Bridgeport, WV; *U.S. Public*, pg. 1280
Morgan, V. Harley, Pres.--Pac Paper Inc., Vancouver, WA; *U.S. Private*, pg. 828
Morgels, G., Sec.--Flachglas AG, Furth, Germany; *Int'l*, pg. 1056
Morgenstern, Marc, Sec.--Olympic Steel Inc., Cleveland, OH; *U.S. Public*, pg. 1221
Morgis, Linda, Sec.--Mrs. Alison's Cookie Company, Saint Louis, MO; *U.S. Private*, pg. 765
Moriarty, Jeffry, Corp. V.P.-Law & Sec.--B/E Aerospace, Inc., Wellington, FL; *U.S. Public*, pg. 159
Morin, Curtis L., Pres., Treas. & Sec.--Bennington Iron Works, Inc., Bennington, VT; *U.S. Private*, pg. 133
Morisett, Stella, Sec.--Chronos Richardson, Fairfield, NJ; *Int'l*, pg. 1299
Morley, R., Sec.--Compass Group plc, Chertsey, United Kingdom,; *Int'l*, pg. 324
Moroz, Robin, Gen. Counsel & Sec.--Ground Round Inc., Braintree, MA; *U.S. Public*, pg. 766
Morozuk, John J., V.P., Gen. Counsel & Sec.--Enogex Inc., Oklahoma City, OK; *U.S. Public*, pg. 1207
Morphy, John, Chief Fin. Officer, V.P. & Sec.--Paychex, Inc., Rochester, NY; *U.S. Public*, pg. 1267
Morris, Ann P., Sec.--Peirce-Phelps, Inc., Philadelphia, PA; *U.S. Private*, pg. 847
Morris, Cynthia R., Chief Fin. Officer, Exec. V.P, Treas. & Sec.--Sun Coast Industries, Inc, Dallas, TX; *U.S. Public*, pg. 1529
Morris, Donna R., Dir.-Investor Rels., Asst. Sec. & Treas.--Walk, Haydel & Associates, Inc., New Orleans, LA; *Int'l*, pg. 624
Morris, Gregory D., V.P., Gen. Counsel & Sec.--Pioneer Mutual Life Insurance Company, Fargo, ND; *U.S. Private*, *pg. 866*
Morris, James E., V.P., Controller, Treas. & Sec.--SL Industries, Inc., Mount Laurel, NJ; *U.S. Public*, pg. 1418
Morris, Kathryn L., Treas. & Sec.--Acorn Engineering Company, City of Industry, CA; *U.S. Private*, pg. 14
Morris, Margaret M., Dir.-Corp. & Legal Admin. & Asst. Sec.--Transus Intermodal L.L.C., Atlanta, GA; *U.S. Private*, pg. 1097
Morris, Melvin, Treas. & Sec.--Mountain States Constructors, Inc., Albuquerque, NM; *U.S. Private*, pg. 764
Morris, Michael H., V.P., Gen. Counsel & Sec.--Sun Microsystems, Inc., Palo Alto, CA; *U.S. Public*, pg. 1531
Morris, Paul F., V.P., Treas. & Sec.--The Fusco Corporation, New Haven, CT; *U.S. Private*, pg. 432
Morris, Ralph K., Gen. Counsel & Sec.--American Crystal Sugar Company, Moorhead, MN; *U.S. Private*, pg. 52
Morris, Rebecca R., V.P., Corp. Counsel & Sec.--Dresser Industries, Inc., Dallas, TX; *U.S. Public*, pg. 528
Morris, Scott, Exec. V.P.-External Affairs & Sec.--AT&T Wireless Services, Kirkland, WA; *U.S. Public*, pg. 11
Morris, Timothy L., Asst. Sec.--Entergy Gulf States, Inc., Beaumont, TX; *U.S. Public*, pg. 586
Morrison, Corinne, Sec. & Corp. Librarian--CSE Insurance Group, San Francisco, CA; *U.S. Private*, pg. 197
Morrison, J.M., Chm. Bd., Pres. & Sec.--Morrison, Inc., Hammond, IN; *U.S. Private*, pg. 762
Morrison, M.R., Gen. Counsel & Sec.--Woodside Petroleum Ltd., Melbourne, Australia; *Int'l*, pg. 1137
Morrison, Stephen D., V.P., Gen. Counsel & Sec.--Norwest Mortgage, Inc., Des Moines, IA; *U.S. Public*, pg. 1202
Morrison, Stephen G., Chief Admin. Officer, Exec. V.P., Gen. Counsel & Sec.--Policy Management Systems Corporation, Blythewood, SC; *U.S. Public*, pg. 1314
Morrison, Wyatt F., Sec. & Treas.--Safe Harbor Water Power Corp., Conestoga, PA; *U.S. Public*, pg. 172
Morrisson, A.S., Sr. V.P., Gen. Counsel & Sec.--Sverdrup Corporation, Maryland Heights, MO; *U.S. Private*, pg. 1057
Morrow, Richard, Jr., Sec.--Total Research Corporation, Princeton, NJ; *U.S. Public*, pg. 1625
Morse, M. Brinkley, V.P., Gen. Counsel & Sec.--BMC Software, Inc., Houston, TX; *U.S. Public*, pg. 162
Mortellaro, Robert, Sr. V.P. & Sec.--Louis P. Ciminelli Construction Co. Inc., Buffalo, NY; *U.S. Private*, pg. 239
Mortensen, Howard L., Sec.--Edison Mission Energy, Irvine, CA; *U.S. Public*, pg. 564
Mortenson, Jerald H., Chief Fin. Officer, V.P-Fin. & Administration, Treas. & Sec.--HEI, Inc., Victoria, MN; *U.S. Public*, pg. 770
Mortimer, Ann O., Asst. Sec.--The Reader's Digest Association, Inc., Pleasantville, NY; *U.S. Public*, pg. 1367
Morton, Gerald, Sec.--Pogo Producing Company, Houston, TX; *U.S. Public*, pg. 1312
Morton, J.L., Sec.--Southcorp Holdings Ltd., Adelaide, Australia; *Int'l*, pg. 1287
Moseley, Thomas J., V.P.-Acctg. & Sec.--Loxcreen Company, West Columbia, SC; *U.S. Private*, pg. 679
Moser, David L., Gen. Mgr., Treas. & Sec.--Cross Motors Corp., Louisville, KY; *U.S. Private*, pg. 291
Moser, Eugene R., Treas. & Sec.--Sioux Falls Construction Company, Sioux Falls, SD; *U.S. Private*, pg. 1003
Moskowitz, David, Sec.--Berkshire Realty Company, Inc., Boston, MA; *U.S. Public*, pg. 221
Moskowitz, Jules, V.P., Sec. & Gen. Counsel--DST Systems, Inc., Kansas City, MO; *U.S. Public*, pg. 943
Mosli, Stefan, Gen. Counsel & Sec.--Sika Finanz AG, Baar, Switzerland; *Int'l*, pg. 1248
Moss, Phyllis, Sr. Admin. Sec.--Trans World Airlines, Inc., Saint Louis, MO; *U.S. Public*, pg. 1629
Moszer, Irene M., V.P.-Info. Sys., Treas. & Sec.--Virginia Electric and Power Company, Richmond, VA; *U.S. Public*, pg. 516
Motchan, Brent L., V.P., Gen. Counsel & Sec.--Zeigler Coal Holding Company, Fairview Heights, IL; *U.S. Public*, pg. 1790
Mott, Daniel C., Asst. Sec.--American Crystal Sugar Company, Moorhead, MN; *U.S. Private*, pg. 52
Motzer, William R., V.P., Chief Fin. Officer & Sec.--Berwind Pharmaceutical Services, Inc., West Point, PA; *U.S. Private*, pg. 139
Mower, Eugene, Sec.--Spectrum Industries, Inc., Chippewa Falls, WI; *U.S. Private*, pg. 1024
Moyers, Donald L., Controller, Treas. & Sec.--Riddleberger Bros.. Inc., Mount Crawford, VA; *U.S. Private*, pg. 930
Mrozinski, JoAnn, Sec. & Pur. Agent--Facemate Corporation, Chicopee, MA; *U.S. Private*, pg. 391
Muccino, Robert D., Controller & Sec.--Frank Briscoe Co. Inc., Kenilworth, NJ; *U.S. Private*, pg. 169
Muchoney, Mary, Sec.--Littelfuse, Inc., Des Plaines, IL; *U.S.* Public, pg. 1001
Mudrow, Michael, V.P., Gen. Counsel & Sec.--Regence BlueCross BlueShield of Oregon, Portland, OR; *U.S. Private*, pg. 917
Mueller, Kenneth, Treas. & Asst. Sec.--Cincinnati Milacron Inc., Cincinnati, OH; *U.S. Public*, pg. 368
Mueller, Lony, Sec.--Mulberry Metal Products, Inc., Union, NJ; *U.S. Private*, pg. 766
Mueller, Marlin, Asst. Sec.--Sierra Health and Life Insurance Company, Inc., Las Vegas, NV; *U.S. Public*, pg. 1469
Mueller, Mary, Gen. Counsel & Asst. Sec.--Steak 'n Shake, Inc., Indianapolis, IN; *U.S. Public*, pg. 437
Mueller, Mary H., Gen. Counsel & Asst. Sec.--Consolidated Products, Inc., Indianapolis, IN; *U.S. Public*, pg. 436
Mueller, Mary H., Gen. Counsel & Asst. Sec.--Consolidated Specialty Restaurant, Indianapolis, IN; *U.S. Public*, pg. 436
Mueller, Mary H., Gen. Counsel & Asst. Sec.--SNS Investment Company, Indianapolis, IN; *U.S. Public*, pg. 436
Mueller, Paula, V.P. & Sec.--Dualite Sales & Service, Inc., Williamsburg, OH; *U.S. Private*, pg. 344
Muench, Jerry, V.P. & Sec.--Odetics Inc., Anaheim, CA; *U.S. Public*, pg. 1212
Muguette Gagnier, Sr. V.P. & Sec.--Kaufel Group Ltd., Dorval, Canada; *Int'l*, pg. 724
Muhlschlegel, Karen B., V.P. & Sec.--Jevic Transportation, Inc., Delanco, NJ; *U.S. Public*, pg. 927
Muir, Douglas R., Sr. V.P., Treas. & Sec.--Oakwood Homes Corporation, Greensboro, NC; *U.S. Public*, pg. 1209
Mulcahy, M.J., V.P., Gen. Counsel & Sec.--Gehl Company, West Bend, WI; *U.S. Public*, pg. 704
Mule, Ann C., Corp. Sec.--Sun Company, Inc., Philadelphia, PA; *U.S. Public*, pg. 1530
Mulholland, S., Sec.--Gallaher (Dublin) Ltd., Tallaght, Ireland; *Int'l*, pg. 539
Mullany, Brian R., V.P. & Sec.--Consumers Water Company, Portland, ME; *U.S. Public*, pg. 438
Mullarkey, Kathleen, Gen. Counsel & Corp. Sec.--Federal Farm Credit Banks Funding Corporation, Jersey City, NJ; *U.S. Private*, pg. 398
Mullen, K.J., Sec.--Premier Farnell plc, Wetherby, United Kingdom; *Int'l*, pg. 1068
Mullen, Larry J., Mgr.-Mktg., Treas. & Sec.--Terral Seed Co., Inc., Lake Providence, LA; *U.S. Private*, pg. 1077
Mullen, Peter P., Sec.--FlightSafety International Inc., Flushing, NY; *U.S. Public*, pg. 218
Mulligan, James J., Gen. Counsel & Sec.--Krug International Corp., Houston, TX; *U.S. Public*, pg. 967
Mulliken, W.D., V.P., Gen. Counsel & Sec.--CHEMCENTRAL Corporation, Bedford Park, IL; *U.S. Private*, pg. 231
Mullinix, H.M., V.P.-Admin. & Sec.--Ziegler Inc., Minneapolis, MN; *U.S. Private*, pg. 1205
Mullins, Dennis, V.P.-Pub. Affairs, Sec. & Gen. Counsel--Tejon Ranch Company, Lebec, CA; *U.S. Public*, pg. 1566
Mullins, Kay J., Treas. & Sec.--Rockford Acromatic Product Co., Rockford, IL; *U.S. Private*, pg. 938
Mulvaney, Thomas, V.P., Gen. Counsel, & Sec.--VLSI Technology, Inc., San Jose, CA; *U.S. Public*, pg. 1703
Mulvihill, Roger, Corp. Sec.--The Carbide/Graphite Group, Inc., Pittsburgh, PA; *U.S. Public*, pg. 304
Muncy, Julie, Sec. & H.R. Dir.--Caldwell VanRiper, Inc., Indianapolis, IN; *U.S. Private*, pg. 200
Mundy, Peter J., Chief Fin. Officer, V.P.-Fin., Treas. & Sec.--Sentry Technology Corp., Hauppauge, NY; *U.S. Public*, pg. 1458
Munro, D.M., Gen. Counsel & Sec.--M.I.M. Holdings Ltd., Brisbane, Australia; *Int'l*, pg. 827
Munro, K. Doug, Gen. Counsel & Sec.--Manitoba Hydro, Winnipeg, Canada; *Int'l*, pg. 834
Munro, M. Vance, Sec.--Heath Consultants Incorporated, Houston, TX; *U.S. Private*, pg. 518
Munson, Winston E., Corp. Sec.--Norstan, Inc., Plymouth, MN; *U.S. Public*, pg. 1192
Murakami, Neil, Controller & Sec.--Jacmar Companies, Inc., Alhambra, CA; *U.S. Private*, pg. 580
Murgio, Peter, Sec.--BKM Enterprises, Inc., East Hartford, CT; *U.S. Private*, pg. 107
Muro, Nick, Sec.--Daniel F. Young, Inc., New York, NY; *U.S. Private*, pg. 1200
Murphy, Amy M., Sec.--Scherer Healthcare, Inc., Atlanta, GA; *U.S. Public*, pg. 1437
Murphy, B., Sec.--Call Connections Limited, Slough, United Kingdom; *Int'l*, pg. 222
Murphy, B.J., Sec.--Cellnet Solutions Limited, Slough, United Kingdom; *Int'l*, pg. 222
Murphy, Dennis F., Sec. & Dir.-Insurance--Mercantile Stores Company, Inc., Fairfield, OH; *U.S. Public*, pg. 1089
Murphy, Gerald, Sec. & Grp. Fin. Asst.--Campbells/Bewley Group, Dublin, Ireland; *Int'l*, pg. 253
Murphy, Glenn R., Sec.--Maritime Telegraph & Telephone Company, Ltd., Halifax, Canada; *Int'l*, pg. 116
Murphy, Jeffrey J., Sr. V.P.-Law & Human Resources, Sec. & Gen. Counsel--Aviall, Inc., Dallas, TX; *U.S. Public*, pg. 154
Murphy, John, Sec.--Murphy Company, Eugene, OR; *U.S. Private*, pg. 768
Murphy, John, Sec.--Medeva PLC, London, United Kingdom; *Int'l*, pg. 852
Murphy, Joseph M., Pres. & Sec.--838 Investment Group, Inc., Wilmington, DE; *U.S. Public*, pg. 1729
Murphy, Karen A., Asst. Sec.--Jannock Limited, Toronto, Canada; *Int'l*, pg. 698
Murphy, Kenyon W., V.P., Sec. & Assoc. Counsel--National Service Industries, Inc., Atlanta, GA; *U.S. Public*, pg. 1160
Murphy, Kevin P., Asst. Sec.--The Cleveland Electric Illuminating Company, Independence, OH; *U.S. Public*, pg. 645
Murphy, Kevin P., Asst. Sec.--The Toledo Edison Company, Toledo, OH; *U.S. Public*, pg. 645
Murphy, Michael R., Chief Fin. Officer--Cavalier Homes, Inc., Wichita Falls, TX; *U.S. Public*, pg. 318
Murphy, S. Wayne, Sr. V.P., Gen. Counsel & Sec.--McDermott International, Inc., New Orleans, LA; *U.S. Public*, pg. 1067
Murphy, S. Wayne, V.P., Gen. Counsel & Corp. Sec.--McDermott International, Inc., New Orleans, LA; *U.S. Public*, pg. 1067
Murphy, Timothy J., Asst. Sec.--John Deere Capital Corporation, Reno, NV; *U.S. Public*, pg. 492
Murphy, William, Chief Fin. Officer, Exec. V.P. & Sec.--Computer Horizons Corp., Mountain Lakes, NJ; *U.S. Public*, pg. 421
Murray, Alan L., V.P. & Dir.-Legal & Admin. & Sec.--Dave & Buster's, Dallas, TX; *U.S. Public*, pg. 488
Murray, D.M., V.P.-Fin. & Sec.--Alberox Corporation, New Bedford, MA; *Int'l*, pg. 893
Murray, Joe, Sr. V.P.-Sls. & Mktg.--Frank Industries, Inc., Brown City, MI; *U.S. Private*, pg. 423
Murray, John J., V.P.-Fin., Sec. & Treas.--Alcoa Fujikura, Troy, MI; *U.S. Public*, pg. 61
Murray, John T., Treas. & Sec.--Tinius Olsen Testing Machine Co., Inc., Willow Grove, PA; *U.S. Private*, pg. 1088
Murray, Lawrence M., Chief Fin. Officer, V.P. & Sec.--DeVlieg-Bullard Inc., Westport, CT; *U.S. Public*, pg. 502
Murray, Mary Jane, Sec.--Herbert Malarkey Roofing Company, Portland, OR; *U.S. Private*, pg. 698
Murray, R.W., Chief Fin. Officer, Sr. V.P., Treas., Controller & Sec.--Webb, Murray & Associates, Houston, TX; *U.S. Private*, pg. 1157
Murray, Stuart, Sec.--BICC plc, London, United Kingdom; *Int'l*, pg. 120
Murray, Virginia, Sec.--Ashworth Bros., Inc., Fall River, MA; *U.S. Private*, pg. 89
Murrell, Jack O., V.P., Gen. Counsel & Sec.--ITT Defense & Electronics, Inc., Mc Lean, VA; *U.S. Public*, pg. 859
Muse, Charles H., Jr., Chief Fin. Officer & Treas.--Crown Coal & Coke Co. Inc., Pittsburgh, PA; *U.S. Private*, pg. 292
Muselman, Marilyn, Treas. & Sec.--House of White Birches, Inc., Berne, IN; *U.S. Private*, pg. 542
Musgrave, David J.A., Asst. Sec.--Marley PLC, Sevenoaks, United Kingdom; *Int'l*, pg. 843
Musgrave, Stephen T., Sec.--Alamco-Delaware, Inc., Wilmington, DE; *U.S. Public*, pg. 403
Musgraves, Robert E., V.P., Gen. Counsel & Sec.--Tremont Corporation, Denver, CO; *U.S. Private*, pg. 270
Musgraves, Robert E., V.P., Sec. & Gen. Counsel--Titanium Metals Corporation, Denver, CO; *U.S. Private*, pg. 270
Mustard, William, Sec.--Millicom International Cellular SA, Bertrange, Luxembourg; *Int'l*, pg. 867
Muth, Mary M., Sec.--Orco Block Company, Stanton, CA; *U.S. Private*, pg. 819
Muther, Stephen C., Sr. V.P.-Admin., Gen. Counsel & Sec.--Buckeye Partners, L.P., Allentown, PA; *U.S. Public*, pg. 266
Muto, Joseph, Sec. & Treas.--Clarion Corporation of America, Gardena, CA; *Int'l*, pg. 296
Mutterperl, William C., Sr. V.P., Gen. Counsel & Sec.--Fleet Financial Group, Inc., Boston, MA; *U.S. Public*, pg. 648
Mutterties, J.H., V.P. & Sec.--DBT Online, Inc., Las Vegas, NV; *U.S. Public*, pg. 472
Mutty, Paul, Sec.--TIE/Communications, Inc., Overland Park, KS; *U.S. Private*, pg. 1085
Mycek, Patricia M., Sec.--Philadelphia Suburban Corporation, Bryn Mawr, PA; *U.S. Public*, pg. 1287
Myddelton, Roger H., Sec. & Grp. Dir.-Legal--Grand Metropolitan Plc, London, United Kingdom; *Int'l*, pg. 408
Myer, Dale, V.P., Treas. & Sec.--Signet Star Holdings, Inc., Stamford, CT; *U.S. Public*, pg. 216
Myer, Dale A., Sr. V.P., Treas. & Sec.--Signet Star Reinsurance Company, Florham Park, NJ; *U.S. Public*, pg. 216
Myerow, Michael D., Sec.--Cabletron Systems, Inc., Rochester, NH; *U.S. Public*, pg. 288
Myers, Barry D., V.P., Gen. Counsel & Asst. Sec.--R&B, Inc., Colmar, PA; *U.S. Public*, pg. 1354
Myers, Carol, Corp. Sec.--Trek Corporation, Waterloo, WI; *U.S. Private*, pg. 1099

Myers, Gary L., V.P., Gen. Counsel & Sec.--St. Joseph Light & Power Co., Saint Joseph, MO; *U.S. Public*, pg. 1427

Myers, Gary L., Gen. Counsel & Sec.--SJLP Inc., Saint Joseph, MO; *U.S. Public*, pg. 1427

Myers, H.J., Chief Fin. Officer--LubeCon Systems, Inc., White Cloud, MI; *U.S. Private*, pg. 679

Myers, Howard B., Gen. Counsel & Sec.--RSR Corporation, Dallas, TX; *U.S. Private*, pg. 900

Myers, Jacob, Sec.--Moto Photo, Inc., Dayton, OH; *U.S. Public*, pg. 1136

Myers, Larry F., Chief Fin. Officer, Sr. V.P., Treas. & Sec.--Mitre Corporation, Bedford, MA; *U.S. Private*, pg. 753

Myers, Lawrence A., Sec.--Airtite Contractors Inc., Chicago, IL; *U.S. Private*, pg. 29

Myers, R.E., Jr., Asst. Sec.--Lufkin Industries, Inc., Lufkin, TX; *U.S. Public*, pg. 1019

Myers, Robert M., Chief Fin. Officer, Treas. & Sec.--Tri-State Mack Inc, Memphis, TN; *U.S. Private*, pg. 1101

Myers, Sandra K., Sec.--Keystone Consolidated Industries, Inc., Dallas, TX; *U.S. Public*, pg. 955

Myers, Shirley, Sec.--Bellsouth Mobile Data, Inc., Atlanta, GA; *U.S. Public*, pg. 208

Myers, Susan, Asst. Sec.--Steck-Vaughn Company, Austin, TX; *U.S. Public*, pg. 784

Myers, Susan, Asst. Sec.--Steck-Vaughn Publishing Corporation, Austin, TX; *U.S. Public*, pg. 784

Mynett, G.E., Corp. Sec.--MacMillan Bloedel Limited, Vancouver, Canada; *Int'l*, pg. 828

Myslinski, C.E., Dir.-Credit & Collection & Asst. Sec.--SPS Technologies, Inc., Jenkintown, PA; *U.S. Public*, pg. 1419

Myster, Jay D., Sr. V.P.-Govt. & Legal & Sec.--Otter Tail Power Company, Fergus Falls, MN; *U.S. Public*, pg. 1234

Mytro, Nicholas A., Sec. & Asst. Controller--Sun TV & Appliances, Inc., Groveport, OH; *U.S. Public*, pg. 1532

Naderio, Seven, V.P. & Sec.--Bacardi Limited, Pembroke, Bermuda; *Int'l*, pg. 131

Nadler, Mike, Treas. & Asst. Sec.--HMO Texas, L.C., Houston, TX; *U.S. Public*, pg. 1470

Naef, Francois, Sec.--Ares-Serono S.A., Geneva, Switzerland; *Int'l*, pg. 80

Nagy, Al, Chief Admin. Officer--Ferolie Group, Montvale, NJ; *U.S. Private*, pg. 401

Nahmens, Daniel J., Chief Fin. Officer, V.P.-Fin., Treas. & Sec.--Track 'n Trail, El Dorado Hills, CA; *U.S. Public*, pg. 1626

Nail, Lester, V.P.-Legal Affairs & Asst. Sec.--Food Lion, Inc., Salisbury, NC; *Int'l*, pg. 463

Naismith, Linda, Exec. V.P. & Sec.--American Passage Media Corporation, Seattle, WA; *U.S. Private*, pg. 60

Nakagawa, Kenshi, Sr. V.P.-Legal & Sec.--DIC Trading (USA) Inc., Fort Lee, NJ; *Int'l*, pg. 369

Nakamura, Alyson J., Sec.--A & B-Hawaii, Inc., Honolulu, HI; *U.S. Public*, pg. 39

Nakao, Tsuyoshi, Corp. Sec.--CAPCO U.S.A., Inc., Elk Grove Village, IL; *Int'l*, pg. 278

Nakash, Ralph, Treas. & Sec.--Jordache Enterprises, Inc., New York, NY; *U.S. Private*, pg. 597

Nakashima, Katrin, Sec. & Counsel--Imasco Limited, Montreal, Canada; *Int'l*, pg. 112

Nakatani, T., Asst. Sec.--Mitsubishi International Corporation, New York, NY; *Int'l*, pg. 871

Nalewako, Mary A., Sec.--GPU, Inc., Morristown, NJ; *U.S. Public*, pg. 695

Nanson, John, M.D., Sec.--Behavioral Healthcare Options, Inc., Las Vegas, NV; *U.S. Public*, pg. 1469

Napier, D. Martin, Sec.--Allianz of America, Inc., Westport, CT; *Int'l*, pg. 58

Nappo, Margot, Asst. Sec.--F. Schumacher & Co., New York, NY; *U.S. Private*, pg. 973

Naquin, Gasper K., Treas. & Sec.--Intrepid Enterprises, Inc., Harvey, LA; *U.S. Private*, pg. 574

Narayanan, R., Mgr.-Fin. & Co. Sec.--Castrol Singapore Pte. Ltd., Singapore, Singapore; *Int'l*, pg. 236

Narciso, John, Sec.--Delta plc, London, United Kingdom; *Int'l*, pg. 389

Narzisi, Joy J., Sr. V.P., Treas. & Asst. Sec.--Commercial Federal Corporation, Omaha, NE; *U.S. Public*, pg. 411

Nasky, H. Gregory, Exec. V.P. & Sec.--Showboat, Incorporated, Las Vegas, NV; *U.S. Public*, pg. 1469

Nasta, Frank J., Sec.--Tri-Continental Corporation, New York, NY; *U.S. Private*, pg. 982

Natcher, Stephen, Sr. V.P.-Admin., Gen. Counsel, & Sec.--Wyle Electronics, Irvine, CA; *Int'l*, pg. 1457

Nathan, Stuart C., V.P.--JMB Realty Corporation, Chicago, IL; *U.S. Private*, pg. 577

Nativ, Arie, Sec.--Ma'berot Hayarden Limited, Haifa, Israel; *Int'l*, pg. 691

Natsor, Rich, Mgr.-Bldg--Hartz Mountain Industries, Jersey City, NJ; *U.S. Private*, pg. 508

Nault, Robert P., Gen. Counsel & Asst. Sec.--The Pioneer Group, Inc., Boston, MA; *U.S. Public*, pg. 1298

Navarro, Agie, Asst. Corp. Sec.--Optical Coating Laboratory, Inc., Santa Rosa, CA; *U.S. Public*, pg. 1227

Nayler, M.J., Sec. & Mgr.--Amic Industries Limited, Johanesburg, South Africa; *Int'l*, pg. 76

Neago, Rita, Asst. Sec.--The Folger Coffee Company, Cincinnati, OH; *U.S. Public*, pg. 1331

Nebergall, Cynthia A., Gen. Counsel & Corp. Sec.--GTECH Corporation, West Greenwich, RI; *U.S. Public*, pg. 767

Neely, Thomas E., Sec.--Augat, Inc., Mansfield, MA; *U.S. Public*, pg. 1597

Neely, Walter E., V.P., Assoc. Gen. Counsel & Asst. Sec.--Humana Inc., Louisville, KY; *U.S. Public*, pg. 847

Neely, Walter E., V.P., Assoc. Gen. Counsel & Asst. Sec.--Humana Health Insurance of Nevada, Inc., Las Vegas, NV; *U.S. Public*, pg. 847

Neely, Walter E., V.P., Assoc. Gen. Counsel & Asst. Sec.--Humana Health Chicago, Inc., Chicago, IL; *U.S. Public*, pg. 847

Neely, Walter E., V.P., Assoc. Gen. Counsel & Asst. Sec.--Employers Health Insurance Company, Green Bay, WI; *U.S. Public*, pg. 847

Neely, Walter E., V.P., Assoc. Gen. Counsel & Asst. Sec.--Humana Health Plan of Texas, Inc., San Antonio, TX; *U.S. Public*, pg. 848

Neely, Walter E., V.P., Assoc. Gen. Counsel & Asst. Sec.--Humana Medical Plan Inc.-Miami, Miramar, FL; *U.S. Public*, pg. 848

Neely, Walter E., V.P., Assoc. Gen. Counsel & Asst. Sec.--Humana Health Plan of Georgia, Inc., Louisville, KY; *U.S. Public*, pg. 848

Neely, Walter E., V.P., Assoc. Gen. Counsel & Asst. Sec.--Humana Health Plan of Louisiana, Inc., Louisville, KY; *U.S. Public*, pg. 848

Neely, Walter E., V.P., Assoc. Gen. Counsel & Asst. Sec.--Humana Insurance Company, Kansas City, MO; *U.S. Public*, pg. 848

Neely, Walter E., V.P., Assoc. Gen. Counsel & Asst. Sec.--Humana Health Plan of Ohio, Inc., Cincinnati, OH; *U.S. Public*, pg. 848

Neely, Walter E., V.P., Assoc. Gen. Counsel & Asst. Sec.--Humana Health Plan of Utah, Inc., Salt Lake City, UT; *U.S. Public*, pg. 848

Neely, Walter E., V.P., Assoc. Gen. Counsel & Asst. Sec.--Humana Health Plan, Inc., Louisville, KY; *U.S. Public*, pg. 848

Neely, Walter E., V.P., Assoc. Gen. Counsel & Asst. Sec.--Humana Health Plan of Alabama, Inc., Montgomery, AL; *U.S. Public*, pg. 848

Neely, Walter E., V.P., Assoc. Gen. Counsel & Asst. Sec.--Humana Wisconsin Health Organization Insurance Corporation, Milwaukee, WI; *U.S. Public*, pg. 848

Neely, Walter E., V.P., Assoc Gen. Counsel & Asst. Sec.--Network EPO, Inc., Milwaukee, WI; *U.S. Public*, pg. 848

Neeman, E., V.P.-Legal Services & Sec.--Confederation Trust Company, Toronto, Canada; *Int'l*, pg. 326

Nees, David K., Asst. Sec.--Aeroquip-Vickers, Inc., Maumee, OH; *U.S. Public*, pg. 24

Nees, Kenneth, Sr. V.P. & Sec.--Sony Electronics, Park Ridge, NJ; *Int'l*, pg. 1281

Neff, Wheeler K., V.P., Asst. Gen. Counsel & Asst. Sec.--Beneficial Corporation, Wilmington, DE; *U.S. Public*, pg. 211

Nehrkorn, William H., V.P., Gen. Counsel & Sec.--Heil Environmental Industries, Chattanooga, TN; *U.S. Public*, pg. 520

Neill, Regina I., Asst. Sec.--Tom Brown, Inc., Midland, TX; *U.S. Public*, pg. 262

Nelson, Ann, Sec.--Pacific Trail Inc., Seattle, WA; *U.S. Private*, pg. 673

Nelson, Byron, Sec., Treas. & Exec. Dir.-Fin.--Temerlin McClain, Irving, TX; *U.S. Public*, pg. 1642

Nelson, Byron D., Sr. V.P., Sec. & Gen. Counsel--MYR Group Inc., Rolling Meadows, IL; *U.S. Public*, pg. 1029

Nelson, Cloris, Sec.--Michigan Blueberry Growers Assn., Grand Junction, MI; *U.S. Private*, pg. 740

Nelson, David L., Asst. Sec.--Holnam Inc. (West Division), Lakewood, CO; *Int'l*, pg. 628

Nelson, David R., Chief Fin. Officer & Asst. Sec.--RisComp Industries, Inc., Minneapolis, MN; *U.S. Private*, pg. 932

Nelson, David R., Controller & Asst. Sec.--RJ Associates, Plymouth, MN; *U.S. Private*, pg. 932

Nelson, Debra G., Asst. Sec.--BC Gas Inc., Vancouver, Canada; *Int'l*, pg. 114

Nelson, Dennis R., V.P., Gen. Counsel & Sec.--UniSource Energy Corporation, Tucson, AZ; *U.S. Public*, pg. 1670

Nelson, Dennis R., V.P., Gen. Counsel & Corp. Sec.--Tucson Electric Power Company, Tucson, AZ; *U.S. Public*, pg. 1670

Nelson, Douglas T., Asst. Sec.--Unilever United States Inc., New York, NY; *Int'l*, pg. 1435

Nelson, Grant, Chief Fin. Officer, V.P. & Sec.--West Information Publishing Group, Saint Paul, MN; *U.S. Public*, pg. 1602

Nelson, James E., Asst. Treas., Asst. Gen. Counsel & Asst. Sec.--Washington Square Securities, Minneapolis, MN; *U.S. Public*, pg. 1376

Nelson, Jana L., Exec. V.P.& Corp. Sec.--Oxarc Inc., Spokane, WA; *U.S. Private*, pg. 825

Nelson, Jane E., Gen. Counsel & Sec.--CPI Corp., Saint Louis, MO; *U.S. Public*, pg. 283

Nelson, Johanna M., Treas. & Sec.--Allen Nelson & Co., Seattle, WA; *U.S. Private*, pg. 790

Nelson, Julane, Sec. & Treas.--Qualheim, Inc., New Hartford, CT; *U.S. Public*, pg. 286

Nelson, Mike, V.P., Gen. Counsel & Sec.--Beverage America, Inc., Holland, MI; *U.S. Private*, pg. 141

Nelson, Owen, Sec.--The Bergquist Company, Minneapolis, MN; *U.S. Private*, pg. 135

Nelson, Paul A., V.P. & Sec.--Natural Fuels Corporation, Denver, CO; *U.S. Public*, pg. 1170

Nelson, Ralph S., Sr. V.P., Gen. Counsel & Sec.--Burlington Motor Holdings Inc., Daleville, IN; *U.S. Private*, pg. 183

Nelson, Rudolph, Sec. & Treas.--Square Butte Electric Cooperative, Grand Forks, ND; *U.S. Private*, pg. 751

Nelson, Susan L., Asst. Sec.--Investment Technology Group, Inc., New York, NY; *U.S. Public*, pg. 924

Nelson, Wesley, V.P. & Sec.--H.E. Butt Grocery Co., San Antonio, TX; *U.S. Private*, pg. 190

Nelson, Wilfrid D., Gen. Counsel & Sec.--Smith Environmental Technologies Corp., Plymouth Meeting, PA; *U.S. Public*, pg. 1477

Nelson, William H., Controller & Asst. Sec.--Team, Inc., Alvin, TX; *U.S. Public*, pg. 1562

Nemschoff, Leonard, Chm. Bd. & Sec.--Nemschoff Chairs, Inc., Sheboygan, WI; *U.S. Private*, pg. 791

Nemzura, M., Sec.--MidCon Corp., Lombard, IL; *U.S. Public*, pg. 1210

Nerland, Nairn L., Controller & Asst. Sec.--Nowsco Well Service Ltd., Calgary, Canada; *Int'l*, pg. 989

Ness, Paul D., Chief Fin. Officer, Chief Information Officer, Sec. & Treas.--Polymer Composites Inc., Winona, MN; *Int'l*, pg. 624

Neubert, Marie, Sec.--North American Enclosures, Inc., Central Islip, NY; *U.S. Private*, pg. 803

Neukom, William H., Sr. V.P.-Law & Corp. Affairs & Sec.--Microsoft Corporation, Redmond, WA; *U.S. Public*, pg. 1107

Neuman, Clifford L., Gen. Counsel & Sec.--American Educational Products, Boulder, CO; *U.S. Public*, pg. 71

Neumann, Janet, Treas. & Sec.--Valu Discount, Incorporated, Louisville, KY; *U.S. Private*, pg. 1132

Nevers, Gregory B., Sec.--Markel Corporation, Glen Allen, VA; *U.S. Public*, pg. 1046

Neville, James D., Chief Fin. Officer, Exec. V.P., Treas. & Sec.--The North American Manufacturing Co., Cleveland, OH; *U.S. Private*, pg. 803

Neville, James M., V.P., Gen. Counsel & Asst. Sec.--Ralston Purina Company, Saint Louis, MO; *U.S. Public*, pg. 1359

Nevins, John W., Sec.--Simpson Gumpertz & Heger Inc., Arlington, MA; *U.S. Private*, pg. 1002

Newallis, Eleanor, Sec.--Roselle Paper Co., Inc., Roselle, NJ; *U.S. Private*, pg. 945

Newberry, Carol, Exec. Sec.--Den-Mat Corporation, Santa Maria, CA; *U.S. Private*, pg. 324

Newbold, Y.M., Corp. Sec.--Hanson PLC, London, United Kingdom; *Int'l*, pg. 592

Newcomer, F. Peter, V.P. & Sec.--D.W. Newcomer's Sons, Inc., Kansas City, MO; *U.S. Private*, pg. 796

Newlin Schnake, Jean N., Sec.--United Life Insurance Company, Cedar Rapids, IA; *U.S. Public*, pg. 1677

Newlin, Linton C., V.P.-Tax & Sec.--Magellan Health Services, Inc., Atlanta, GA; *U.S. Public*, pg. 1033

Newman, Edward H., V.P. & Asst. Sec.--Citizens Banking Corporation, Flint, MI; *U.S. Public*, pg. 379

Newman, Harry, Sec. & Treas.--Frequency Electronics, Inc., Uniondale, NY; *U.S. Public*, pg. 681

Newman, John H., V.P.-Legal Affairs, Gen. Counsel & Sec.--Scios Inc., Mountain View, CA; *U.S. Public*, pg. 1444

Newman, Pricilla, Sec.--AEA Investors Inc., New York, NY; *U.S. Private*, pg. 4

Newman, Ronald P., Chief Fin. Officer, V.P.-Fin., Treas. & Sec.--Watsco, Inc., Coconut Grove, FL; *U.S. Public*, pg. 1745

Newmaster, Rich, Corp. Sec.--Lebanon Seaboard Corporation, Lebanon, PA; *U.S. Private*, pg. 656

Newsome, Larry J., Chief Fin. Officer, Sr. V.P., Treas. & Sec.--Echelon International Corporation, Saint Petersburg, FL; *U.S. Public*, pg. 560

Newson, Joe, Controller & Sec.--Southern Leather Co., Inc., Memphis, TN; *U.S. Private*, pg. 1016

Newson, Martin, Co. Sec. & Controller--Bayer UK Ltd., Newbury, United Kingdom; *Int'l*, pg. 175

Newson, Michael, Sec.--Pioneer International Ltd., Sydney, Australia; *Int'l*, pg. 1058

Newton, Andrew B., Sec.--Infoseek Corporaton, Sunnyvale, CA; *U.S. Public*, pg. 876

Newton, Clay, Chief Fin. Officer & Treas.--Equity Oil Company, Salt Lake City, UT; *U.S. Public*, pg. 590

Newton, Joseph, Sec. & Treas.--Dairy Queen Canada, Inc., Burlington, Canada; *U.S. Public*, pg. 220

Newton, Millie, Sec.--Waremart Inc., Boise, ID; *U.S. Private*, pg. 1150

Newton, Stanley B., V.P., Treas. & Sec.--Holmes Tuttle Ford, Inc., Tucson, AZ; *U.S. Private*, pg. 535

Neyer, William L., Sec.--Al Neyer, Inc., Cincinnati, OH; *U.S. Private*, pg. 797

Ng, Benjamin M.T., Exec. V.P. & Asst. Sec.--Tommy Hilfiger Corporation, Kowloon, Hong Kong; *Int'l*, pg. 1398

Niarchos, Michael C., Sr. V.P., Gen. Counsel & Sec.--Howard Hughes Corporation, Las Vegas, NV; *U.S. Public*, pg. 1407

Niblock, W.R., V.P. & Sec.--Courtaulds Coatings Inc., Louisville, KY; *Int'l*, pg. 338

Nichols, David R., V.P. & Sec.--Zions Investment Securities, Inc., Salt Lake City, UT; *U.S. Public*, pg. 1793

Nichols, John C., Sr. V.P.-Admin., Gen. Counsel & Sec.--Environmental Elements Corporation, Baltimore, MD; *U.S. Public*, pg. 586

Nichols, R.L., Asst. Treas. & Dir.-Fin.--Lakehead Pipe Line Co., Inc., Superior, WI; *Int'l*, pg. 652

Nichols, Stuart J., V.P., Gen. Counsel & Sec.--Phoenix Technologies Ltd., San Jose, CA; *U.S. Public*, pg. 1292

Nichols, Wade H. III, V.P. & Sec.--Charles of the Ritz Group Ltd., New York, NY; *U.S. Private*, pg. 689

Nicholson, P.R., Sec. & Sls. Mgr.--Senior New Zealand Limited, Auckland, New Zealand; *Int'l*, pg. 1223

Nicholson, P.R., Sec.--Procter & Gamble (Health & Beauty Care) Limited, Egham, United Kingdom; *U.S. Public*, pg. 1332

Nicholson, Ruth, Sec.--Stora Forest Industries, Port Hawkesbury, Canada; *Int'l*, pg. 1304

Nichter, Mark S., Controller, Sec. & Dir.-Investor Rels.--Continental Materials Corporation, Chicago, IL; *U.S. Public*, pg. 441

Nichter, Mark S., Sec.--Continental Catalina, Inc., Chicago, IL; *U.S. Public*, pg. 441

Nichter, Mark S., Sec.--Continental Copper, Inc., Chicago, IL; *U.S. Public*, pg. 441

Nick, Richard, V.P. & Asst. Sec.--North American Salt Company, Overland Park, KS; *U.S. Private*, pg. 505

Nickelatti, Chris, Controller, Treas. & Sec.--Crown Fence Co., Long Beach, CA; *U.S. Private*, pg. 292

Nickels, William F., Pres. & Chief Exec. Officer--Replogle Globes, Inc., Broadview, IL; *U.S. Private*, pg. 923

Nickerson, Louise, Sec.--Nickerson Lumber Company, Orleans, MA; *U.S. Private*, pg. 798

Nickerson, Lucille M., Sec.--Aetna Inc., Hartford, CT; *U.S. Public*, pg. 26

Nicoll, John, Sr. V.P., Corp. Counsel & Sec.--Colorado National Bank, Denver, CO; *U.S. Public*, pg. 1680

Nicoll, Peter, Sec. & Legal Services--Costain Group PLC, London, United Kingdom; *Int'l*, pg. 336

Niebergall, A. Thomas, Asst. Sec.--Nike, Inc., Beaverton, OR; *U.S. Public*, pg. 1184

Niedens, Douglas, Treas. & Sec.--Universal Construction Company, Inc., Kansas City, KS; *U.S. Private*, pg. 1127
Niederhauser, Markus, Asst. V.P. & Sec.--Bobst S.A., Lausanne, Switzerland; *Int'l*, pg. 198
Niegsch, W.C., Jr., Chief Fin. Officer, Exec. V.P., Treas. & Sec.--Max & Erma's Restaurants, Columbus, OH; *U.S. Public*, pg. 1060
Nielsen, Roberta, Sec. & Mgr.-Cash--Eby Corporation, Wichita, KS; *U.S. Private*, pg. 359
Nielsen, Roberta D., Sec.--Martin K. Eby Construction Company, Inc., Wichita, KS; *U.S. Private*, pg. 359
Niemeyer, Vernon, Sec.--New Cooperative Inc., Fort Dodge, IA; *U.S. Private*, pg. 792
Niemiec, Thom, Treas. & Sec.--The Tech Group, Scottsdale, AZ; *U.S. Private*, pg. 1071
Niese, William A., Asst. Sec.--The Times Mirror Company, Los Angeles, CA; *U.S. Public*, pg. 1615
Nietzel, Warren, Gen. Counsel & Corp. Sec.--Bulova Corporation, Woodside, NY; *U.S. Public*, pg. 1010
Nilsen, Barbara Y., Sec.--SJW Corp., San Jose, CA; *U.S. Public*, pg. 1418
Nilsson-Granvik, Katherine, Sec.--Stora Timber AB, Falun, Sweden; *Int'l*, pg. 1303
Nishikawa, Wendy K.K., Asst. Gen. Counsel & Asst. Sec.--Wynn's International, Inc., Orange, CA; *U.S. Public*, pg. 1782
Nishimura, S., Sec./Treas.--Kansai Paint (America), Inc., Fort Lee, NJ; *Int'l*, pg. 723
Nissen, Inge, Sec.--GN Great Nordic Ltd., Copenhagen, Denmark; *Int'l*, pg. 536
Nobile, Beverly, Sec.--Delta Pride Catfish, Inc., Indianola, MS; *U.S. Private*, pg. 322
Noble, Deborah J., Asst. Sec.--Northern Telecom Limited, Brampton, Canada; *Int'l*, pg. 968
Noble, M.J., Sec.--Ladbroke & Co. Ltd., Harrow, United Kingdom; *Int'l*, pg. 787
Noble, Steven P., Chief Fin. Officer & Sec.--Lustine Oldsmobile & Buick, Inc., Hyattsville, MD; *U.S. Private*, pg. 681
Noda, S., Sec.--Mita Copystar America Inc., Fairfield, NJ; *Int'l*, pg. 870
Noelker, Joe, V.P., Gen. Counsel & Sec.--The Earthgrains Company, Clayton, MO; *U.S. Public*, pg. 547
Nofziger, Sally A., V.P. & Sec.--PacifiCorp, Portland, OR; *U.S. Public*, pg. 1251
Nogal, Joseph P., Controller, Treas. & Asst. Sec.--Woodhead Industries, Inc., Buffalo Grove, IL; *U.S. Public*, pg. 1776
Nolan. G., Corp. Sec.--National Australia Bank Limited, Melbourne, Australia; *Int'l*, pg. 906
Nolan, J. Michael, Sr. V.P., Sec. & Gen. Counsel--Argonaut Co., Menlo Park, CA; *U.S. Public*, pg. 129
Nolan, Steve, Chief Fin. Officer & Sec.--Grey Eagle Distributors Inc., Maryland Heights, MO; *U.S. Private*, pg. 480
Nolan, Thomas J., Chief Fin Officer, V.P.-Fin, Treas. & Sec.--Minuteman International, Inc., Addison, IL; *Int'l*, pg. 587
Nolf, David M., Chief Fin. Officer, Exec. V.P.-Admin. & Sec.--Analysis & Technology, Inc., North Stonington, CT; *U.S. Public*, pg. 109
Nolf, David M., Sec.--Applied Science Associates, Inc., Mc Lean, VA; *U.S. Public*, pg. 109
Nolf, David M., Sec.--Integrated Performance Decisions, North Stonington, CT; *U.S. Public*, pg. 110
Nolf, David M., Sec.--Prism-Dae, Inc., Mc Lean, VA; *U.S. Public*, pg. 110
Noll, Dennis E., V.P., Gen. Counsel & Sec.--Kinetic Concepts, Inc., San Antonio, TX; *U.S. Private*, pg. 620
Noll, Lawrence R., V.P., Controller & Sec.--AEP Industries, Inc., South Hackensack, NJ; *U.S. Public*, pg. 4
Nomura, Jean C., Sec.--Union Bank of California, San Diego, CA; *Int'l*, pg. 157
Nonn, James C., Treas. & Sec.--Pemko Manufacturing Company, Ventura, CA; *U.S. Private*, pg. 848
Noonan, Mary, Sec.--Coopers & Lybrand, New York, NY; *U.S. Private*, pg. 274
Nord, Thomas C., V.P., Gen. Counsel & Sec.--GATX Capital Corporation, San Francisco, CA; *U.S. Public*, pg. 690
Nordlund, D. Craig, Assoc. Gen. Counsel & Sec.--Hewlett-Packard Company, Palo Alto, CA; *U.S. Public*, pg. 813
Nordstrom, William, Treas. & Sec.--Amana-Nordstrom Motel Co., Amana, IA; *U.S. Private*, pg. 48
Noren, Florence, Sec.--Marcal Paper Mills, Inc., Elmwood Park, NJ; *U.S. Private*, pg. 701
Norgren, P.W., Gen. Counsel & Asst. Sec.--Lakehead Pipe Line Co., Inc., Superior, WI; *Int'l*, pg. 652
Norlin, Beverly, Asst. Sec.--Otter Tail Power Company, Fergus Falls, MN; *U.S. Public*, pg. 1234
Norman, Barbara, V.P., Corp. Counsel & Sec.--WHG Resorts & Casinos, Carolina, PR; *U.S. Public*, pg. 1265
Norman, David J., Gen. Counsel & Sec.--Davco Restaurants Inc., Crofton, MD; *U.S. Public*, pg. 488
Norman, Donald, Sec.--Firstcorp Merchant Bank Limited, Johannesburg, South Africa; *Int'l*, pg. 487
Norman, E.J., V.P.-Admin., Gen. Counsel & Sec.--Trico Products Corporation, Buffalo, NY; *Int'l*, pg. 1397
Norman, Stephen P., Corp. Sec.--American Express Company, New York, NY; *U.S. Public*, pg. 73
Norris, Alan, Chief Fin. Officer, Sr. V.P. & Sec.--Consolidated Carma Corporation, Calgary, Canada; *Int'l*, pg. 229
Norris, Francis J., V.P., Treas. & Sec.--Mannington Mills, Inc., Salem, NJ; *U.S. Private*, pg. 700
Norris, Michael, Sr. V.P., Gen. Counsel & Sec.--National Financial Insurance Company, Fort Worth, TX; *U.S. Private*, pg. 782
North, Edwin M., Sec.--Thiokol Corporation, Ogden, UT; *U.S. Public*, pg. 1596
North, Richard J., V.P., Sec. & Treas.--Miller & Smith, Inc., Mc Lean, VA; *U.S. Private*, pg. 746
Northcutt, Velma, Exec. Sec.--Overland Transportation System, Inc., Indianapolis, IN; *Int'l*, pg. 1469
Northey, Randy, Sr. V.P., Gen. Counsel & Sec.--O&Y Properties Corporation, Toronto, Canada; *Int'l*, pg. 993
Norton, Gerard, V.P. & Sec.--Advantage Life Products, Inc., Tampa, FL; *U.S. Public*, pg. 22
Noskin, Steven, Exec. V.P.--Polymer Plastics Corporation, Hauppauge, NY; *U.S. Private*, pg. 875
Nota, Kenneth J., Asst. Sec.--Dryvit Systems, Inc., West Warwick, RI; *U.S. Public*, pg. 1357
Notini, Albert A., Sr. V.P., Gen. Counsel & Sec.--Wang Laboratories, Inc., Billerica, MA; *U.S. Public*, pg. 1737
Novack, Kenneth, Asst. Sec.--Ekco Group, Inc., Nashua, NH; *U.S. Public*, pg. 566
Nowe, Kevin G., Asst. Sec. & Asst. Gen. Counsel--Kennametal Inc., Latrobe, PA; *U.S. Public*, pg. 950
Nowell, Christopher C., Treas. & Asst. Sec.--Cameron & Barkley Company, Charleston, SC; *U.S. Private*, pg. 203
Nuernberg, Robert A., Sec.--WICOR, Inc., Milwaukee, WI; *U.S. Public*, pg. 1767
Nuernberg, Robert A., V.P.-Corp. Rels. & Sec.--Wisconsin Gas Company, Milwaukee, WI; *U.S. Public*, pg. 1767
Nugent, Deborah A., Chief Fin. Officer, V.P.-Fin., Treas. & Sec.--Software Spectrum, Inc., Garland, TX; *U.S. Public*, pg. 1483
Null, Lester H., Sr., Treas. & Sec.--ULLICO Inc., Washington, DC; *U.S. Private*, pg. 1115
Nunes, Melbourne, Sr. V.P., Dep. Counsel & Sec.--New York Life Insurance Company, New York, NY; *U.S. Private*, pg. 794
Nunez, Olga M., Sec.--Northwestern Meats Inc., Miami, FL; *U.S. Private*, pg. 807
Nursey, W.C., V.P. & Sec.--London Life Insurance Group, London, Canada; *Int'l*, pg. 435
Nussbaum, Mark A., Sec.--Southern Foods, Inc., Greensboro, NC; *U.S. Private*, pg. 1016
Nussbaumer, Gerhard, V.P.-Fin., Treas.--Voest-Alpine International Corporation, New York, NY; *Int'l*, pg. 1470
Nute, Lee F., Sr. V.P., Gen. Counsel & Sec.--Bayer Corporation, Pittsburgh, PA; *Int'l*, pg. 172
Nute, Leslie, Gen. Counsel & Sec.--Bayer Corporation, Pittsburgh, PA; *Int'l*, pg. 172
Nutt, Frank, Gen. Mgr., Treas. & Sec.--North Electric Supply, Inc., Auburn Hills, MI; *U.S. Private*, pg. 805
Nylander, Riitta, Sec.--Raisio Group, Raisio, Finland; *Int'l*, pg. 1085
O'Brien, Carol, Sec.--Ag Services of America, Inc., Cedar Falls, IA; *U.S. Public*, pg. 6
O'Brien, George A., V.P., Chief Fin. Officer & Sec.--GenRad Electronic Manufacturing Tests Systems, Westford, MA; *U.S. Public*, pg. 731
O'Brien, J. Michael, V.P.-Sls. & Sec.--American Cast Iron Pipe Co., Birmingham, AL; *U.S. Private*, pg. 51
O'Brien, Kathleen D., V.P.-Fin. & Sec.--Amurol Confections Co., Yorkville, IL; *U.S. Public*, pg. 1781
O'Brien, Mary Anne, Sr. Exec. Sec.--Nozaki America, Inc., New York, NY; *Int'l*, pg. 990
O'Brien, Maureen, Sec.--The Boston Globe, Boston, MA; *U.S. Public*, pg. 1175
O'Brien, Paul J., Sec.--TCI Communications, Inc., Englewood, CO; *U.S. Public*, pg. 1554
O'Brien, Paul T., Gen. Counsel & Sec.--Huls America Inc., Somerset, NJ; *Int'l*, pg. 1455
O'Bryan, Kevin M., Sr. V.P. & Asst. Sec.--The Troy Savings Bank, Troy, NY; *U.S. Private*, pg. 1106
O'Callaghan, R.A., Chief Exec. Officer--Universal Builders Supply, Inc., Mount Vernon, NY; *U.S. Private*, pg. 1126
O'Connell, James M., Chief Fin. Officer, V.P., Treas. & Sec.--Landauer, Inc., Glenwood, IL; *U.S. Public*, pg. 977
O'Conner, Dennis, Sec.--Sappi Limited, Braamfontein, South Africa; *Int'l*, pg. 1193
O'Connor, Dennis, Chief Fin. Officer, V.P.-Fin. & Sec.--Pharmaceutical Resources, Spring Valley, NY; *U.S. Public*, pg. 1285
O'Connor, Marie, Sec.--HMI Industries, Cleveland, OH; *U.S. Public*, pg. 771
O'Connor, Paul R., Corp. Sec.--F.A. Wilhelm Construction Co., Inc., Indianapolis, IN; *U.S. Private*, pg. 1176
O'Connor, William G., V.P.-Admin.--The Topps Company, Inc., New York, NY; *U.S. Public*, pg. 1621
O'Dea, Fred, Chief Fin. Officer & V.P.--Hubbard Construction Co., Winter Park, FL; *U.S. Private*, pg. 544
O'Dell, M.P., Sec.--Svedala Pumps & Process, Colorado Springs, CO; *Int'l*, pg. 1325
O'Dell, Michael R., Chief Fin. Officer, Sr. V.P. & Sec.--First Financial Bancorp, Hamilton, OH; *U.S. Public*, pg. 632
O'Donnell, Joyce, Corp. Sec.--Wershow-Ash-Lewis, Tigard, OR; *U.S. Private*, pg. 1162
O'Donnell, Thomas F., Sec.--Southern Pacific Rail Corporation, San Francisco, CA; *U.S. Public*, pg. 1668
O'Donovan, Rossa, Corp. Sec.--Fiat Auto Ireland Ltd., Dublin, Ireland; *Int'l*, pg. 481
O'Dwyer, Paul, Sec.--Hickson International Plc, Castleford, United Kingdom; *Int'l*, pg. 618
O'Gorman, Anne Marie, Sr. V.P.-Corp. Devel. & Sec.--Coho Energy, Inc., Dallas, TX; *U.S. Public*, pg. 396
O'Halloran, Anna, Corp. Sec.--Royer Industries, Inc., Kingston, PA; *Int'l*, pg. 1066
O'Keefe, John M., Gen. Mgr.-Corp. Services & Asst. Sec.--NewTel Enterprises Limited, Saint Johns, Canada; *Int'l*, pg. 115
O'Leary, Judy, Exec. Sec.--Rockbestos-Suprenant Cable Corp., Clinton, MA; *U.S. Private*, pg. 938
O'Mahony, Gerry, Mgr.--Custom Colorants, Inc., Dalton, GA; *U.S. Public*, pg. 1052
O'Malley, Kevin T., V.P. & Gen. Counsel--St. Jude Medical, Inc., Saint Paul, MN; *U.S. Public*, pg. 1427
O'Melia, Patricia E., Asst. Sec.--Republic New York Corporation, New York, NY; *U.S. Public*, pg. 1380
O'Neal, John W., Asst. Sec.--Washington Gas Light Co., Springfield, VA; *U.S. Public*, pg. 1740
O'Neal, W.K., Corp. Sec.--Salt River Project Agricultural Improvement and Power District, Tempe, AZ; *U.S. Private*, pg. 962
O'Neil, Jack, Gen. Counsel & Sec.--The Western Group, Saint Louis, MO; *U.S. Private*, pg. 1165
O'Neil, Michael T., Sec. & Treas.--Ragnar Benson, Inc., Park Ridge, IL; *U.S. Private*, pg. 99
O'Neil, P.A., Treas. & Sec.--O'Neil Industries Inc., Chicago, IL; *U.S. Private*, pg. 817
O'Neil, Ruth, Dir.-Human Resources & Asst. Sec.--The Somerset Group, Inc., Indianapolis, IN; *U.S. Public*, pg. 1484
O'Neill, Robert B., V.P., Gen. Counsel & Sec.--Capitol Industries-EMI Inc., Hollywood, CA; *Int'l*, pg. 427
O'Reilly, Terrence M., V.P., Gen. Counsel & Sec.--Universal Foods Corporation, Milwaukee, WI; *U.S. Public*, pg. 1695
O'Reilly, William, V.P., Gen. Counsel & Corp. Sec.--Sentry Insurance, A Mutual Company, Stevens Point, WI; *U.S. Private*, pg. 984
O'Riordan, Kaye L., Sec.--Albertson's, Inc., Boise, ID; *U.S. Public*, pg. 38
O'Rourke, Judy, Corp. Sec.--Harrington & King, Chicago, IL; *U.S. Private*, pg. 504
O'Shaughnessy, P., V.P. & Sec.--Lario Enterprises, Inc., Wichita, KS; *U.S. Private*, pg. 651
O'Sullivan, D. J., Sec.--Illustrated London News, London, United Kingdom; *Int'l*, pg. 1214
O'Toole, A.M., Sr. V.P. & Sec.--The Coastal Corporation, Houston, TX; *U.S. Public*, pg. 389
O'Toole, Austin M., Sr. V.P. & Sec.--Coastal Refining & Marketing, Wichita, KS; *U.S. Public*, pg. 390
Oakes, Gary D., Corp. Sec.--Estes Express Lines, Inc., Richmond, VA; *U.S. Private*, pg. 384
Oakley, Graham, Sec.--Marks & Spencer PLC, London, United Kingdom; *Int'l*, pg. 842
Oakley, Judy, Treas. & Sec.--Bruce Oakley, Inc., North Little Rock, AR; *U.S. Private*, pg. 809
Oakley, Roy, Sec.--Cornucopia, Inc., Irvine, CA; *U.S. Private*, pg. 276
Oakley, W. Flake, IV, Chief Fin. Officer, Exec. V.P., Treas. & Sec.--The Colonial BancGroup, Inc., Montgomery, AL; *U.S. Public*, pg. 400
Oathout, James M., Assoc. Gen. Counsel & Sec.--Aeroquip-Vickers, Inc., Maumee, OH; *U.S. Public*, pg. 24
Oben, Walter J., Jr., Chm. Bd., Pres., Treas. & Sec.--Southgate Ford Inc., Southgate, MI; *U.S. Private*, pg. 1018
Ober, Richard F., Jr., Exec. V.P., Gen. Counsel & Sec.--Summit Bancorp, Princeton, NJ; *U.S. Public*, pg. 1527
Ober, Thomas M., Sec.--LINSCO Reinsurance Company, Indianapolis, IN; *U.S. Public*, pg. 998
Oberg, R.C., Sec.--Ancon Insurance Company, Inc., Irving, TX; *U.S. Public*, pg. 601
Oberhauser, Louis B., Corp. Sec.--GE Capital/IT Solutions, Minneapolis, MN; *U.S. Public*, pg. 711
Oberholtzer, Craig S., Credit Mgr. & Corp. Sec.--Glen-Gery Corporation, Wyomissing, PA; *Int'l*, pg. 658
Obert, Paul R., V.P., Gen. Counsel & Sec.--CF Industries, Inc., Long Grove, IL; *U.S. Private*, pg. 193
Oberwetter, James C., V.P.-Public & Govt. Affairs--Hunt Oil Company, Dallas, TX; *U.S. Private*, pg. 548
Obuchowski, Susan, Sec.--Capsure Holdings Corp., Chicago, IL; *U.S. Public*, pg. 303
Obuchowski, Susan, Sec.--Great American Management & Investment, Inc., Chicago, IL; *U.S. Private*, pg. 473
Obuchowski, Susan, Sec.--First Capital Financial Corp., Troy, MI; *U.S. Private*, pg. 473
Ocampo, Antonio V., Sr. V.P., Gen. Counsel & Sec.--Philippine Airlines, Inc., Manila, Philippines; *Int'l*, pg. 1050
Ocampo, Raymond L., Jr., Sr. V.P., Gen Counsel & Sec.--Oracle Corporation, Redwood City, CA; *U.S. Public*, pg. 1227
Ochoa, H., Sec.--Fibras Ceramicas, C.A., Valencia, Venezuela; *Int'l*, pg. 894
Odegaard, Janice, Asst. Sec.--Suncor Inc., Calgary, Canada; *Int'l*, pg. 1320
Odelberg, Carl, Sr. V.P.-Legal Affairs & Sec.--Esselte AB, Solna, Sweden; *Int'l*, pg. 459
Odgers, Richard W., Exec. V.P., Gen. Counsel & Sec.--Pacific Telesis Group, San Francisco, CA; *U.S. Public*, pg. 1415
Oettinger, Julian A., V.P., Gen. Counsel & Corp. Sec.--Walgreen Co., Deerfield, IL; *U.S. Public*, pg. 1733
Offer, Mary Ellen, V.P., Senior Counsel & Asst. Corp. Sec.--The Great Atlantic & Pacific Tea Company, Inc., Montvale, NJ; *Int'l*, pg. 1375
Offerdahl, James R., Chief Fin. Officer, V.P.-Fin. & Admin. & Sec.--Pervasive Software Inc., Austin, TX; *U.S. Public*, pg. 1280
Ogborn, Patricia, Treas. & Sec.--Consolidated Lumber Co., Stillwater, MN; *U.S. Private*, pg. 265
Ogden, James A., Treas. & Sec.--Bargain Supply Company, Louisville, KY; *U.S. Private*, pg. 116
Ogden, Jean H., Sec. & Gen. Counsel--Werner & Pfleiderer Corporation, Ramsey, NJ; *Int'l*, pg. 511
Oglesby, Donald D., Treas. & Sec.--Hanson Engineers Inc., Springfield, IL; *U.S. Private*, pg. 500
Ogram, Jay, Chief Fin. Officer & Sec.--Hudson, RCI, Temecula, CA; *U.S. Private*, pg. 546
Oguro, Kiyo, Sec. & Treas.--Nozaki America, Inc., New York, NY; *Int'l*, pg. 990
Ohashi, Masahiko, Sec. & Deputy Gen. Mgr.--Takugin Finance International Ltd., London, United Kingdom; *Int'l*, pg. 627
Ohlmuller, Raymond P., V.P. & Sec.--Becton Dickinson & Company, Franklin Lakes, NJ; *U.S. Public*, pg. 199
Ohlson, Caroline, Sec.--NCC AB, Solna, Sweden; *Int'l*, pg. 898
Ohly, Jeffrey W., Sr. V.P., Treas. & Sec.--World Acceptance Corporation, Greenville, SC; *U.S. Public*, pg. 1778
Ohrenberg, Wesley, Dir.-Fin., Acctg. & Asst. Sec.--Associated Electric Co-op Inc., Springfield, MO; *U.S. Private*, pg. 89
Okamoto, Yasuo, Asst. Sec.--Hosokawa Micron International Inc., New York, NY; *Int'l*, pg. 635
Okarma, Jerome D., Asst. Sec. & Asst. Gen. Counsel--Johnson Controls, Inc., Milwaukee, WI; *U.S. Public*, pg. 932

OKeefe, John M., Sec.--NewTel Communications, Saint Johns, Canada; *Int'l*, pg. 115
Okinow, Harold, Sec.--A&W Restaurants, Inc.-Carousel Div., Minneapolis, MN; *U.S. Private*, pg. 2
Okumura, Yasuhiko, Corp. Sec.--Yamato Transport USA, Inc., Flushing, NY; *Int'l*, pg. 1519
Older, Mark A., Sec.--Santa Fe Energy Resources, Inc., Houston, TX; *U.S. Public*, pg. 1431
Oldfield, Russell M., V.P.-Legal & Corp. Sec.--Rogers Group Inc., Nashville, TN; *U.S. Private*, pg. 939
Oldham, S., Sec. & Gen. Counsel--Boehringer Mannheim Pharmaceuticals Corp., Rockville, MD; *Int'l*, pg. 331
Oleson, George T., Sec. & Legal Officer--Allied Mutual Insurance Company, Des Moines, IA; *U.S. Private*, pg. 39
Olfe, David C., Sec.--The Valspar Corporation, Minneapolis, MN; *U.S. Public*, pg. 1707
Olinde, Humphrey T., Jr., Treas. & Sec.--Olinde Hardware & Supply Co., Baton Rouge, LA; *U.S. Private*, pg. 814
Oliphant, John H., Sec. & Gen. Counsel--Technicolor, Inc., North Hollywood, CA; *Int'l*, pg. 272
Oliver, M.F., Corp. Sec.--Britvic Soft Drinks Ltd., Chelmsford, United Kingdom; *Int'l*, pg. 170
Oliverio, Louis, V.P. & Treas.--Cincinnati Incorporated, Harrison, OH; *U.S. Private*, pg. 240
Oliveros Lara, R., Sec.--Embotelladores del Valle de Anahuac S.A. de C.V., Mexico, Mexico; *Int'l*, pg. 452
Oller, Lynn, V.P.--Quality Chekd Dairies, Inc., Naperville, IL; *U.S. Private*, pg. 898
Olmsted, Daniel, V.P.-Corp. Legal Sec.--Atlantic Mutual Companies, New York, NY; *U.S. Private*, pg. 95
Olsen, Richard J., Sr. V.P. & Asst. Sec.--Candela Corporation, Wayland, MA; *U.S. Public*, pg. 300
Olshan, Marvin L., Sec.--WHX Corporation, New York, NY; *U.S. Public*, pg. 1726
Olson, Carol, Sec.--Interpoint, Redmond, WA; *U.S. Public*, pg. 457
Olson, D. Joseph, V.P., Gen. Counsel & Sec.--Citizens Insurance Company of America, Howell, MI; *U.S. Public*, pg. 54
Olson, Kenneth A., Treas. & Corp. Sec.--Berry Petroleum Company, Taft, CA; *U.S. Public*, pg. 223
Olson, Kenneth A., Corp. Sec. & Treas.--Berry Petroleum Company-Coastal Operations, Oxnard, CA; *U.S. Public*, pg. 223
Olson, Kenneth A., Corp. Sec. & Treas.--Berry Oil Trading and Transportation, Taft, CA; *U.S. Public*, pg. 223
Olson, Phyllis, Sec.--Montgomery KONE Inc., Moline, IL; *Int'l*, pg. 746
Olson, Robert W., Sr. V.P., Gen. Counsel & Sec.--American Financial Group, Cincinnati, OH; *U.S. Public*, pg. 75
Olson, Robert W., V.P., Gen. Counsel & Sec.--Chiquita Brands International, Inc., Cincinnati, OH; *U.S. Public*, pg. 349
Olsrud, Wanda J., Sec.--Sherms Thunderbird Market, Medford, OR; *U.S. Private*, pg. 993
Omata, K., Sec--Hattori Overseas Hong Kong Ltd., Kowloon, Hong Kong; *Int'l*, pg. 1218
Omura, Toshio, Sec.--Steelox Systems Inc., Mason, OH; *U.S. Private*, pg. 1038
Ondrack, Esther S., V.P. & Corp. Sec.--Chieftain International, Inc., Edmonton, Canada; *Int'l*, pg. 284
Onodera, Yasuo, Gen. Mgr.-Corp. Commun.--Toyo Tire & Rubber Co., Ltd., Osaka, Japan; *Int'l*, pg. 1411
Ooyen, A.J., Sec.--Campina Melkunie BV, Zaltbommel, Netherlands; *Int'l*, pg. 254
Opdike, William, Sec.--Dearden's, Los Angeles, CA; *U.S. Private*, pg. 319
Oppenheimer, Robert, Sec.--CPAC, Inc., Leicester, NY; *U.S. Public*, pg. 282
Orem, Barbara, Controller & sec.--Lois/EJL Los Angeles, Los Angeles, CA; *U.S. Private*, pg. 673
Oren, Irit, Sec.--The Israel Land Development Co., Ltd., Tel Aviv, Israel; *Int'l*, pg. 691
Oren, Karen, Sec.--Corporate Express Delivery Systems Southwest, Inc., Houston, TX; *U.S. Public*, pg. 449
Orenstein, John B., V.P., Deputy Gen. Counsel & Asst. Sec.--Dain Rauscher Corporation, Minneapolis, MN; *U.S. Public*, pg. 476
Orenstein, Steve, Sec. & Treas.--Ad Americas, Los Angeles, CA; *U.S. Private*, pg. 316
Orgill, Joseph, III, Chm. Bd. & Sec.--Orgill Inc., Memphis, TN; *U.S. Private*, pg. 819
Oropeza, Anne, V.P. & Sec.--Transpo Electronics, Inc., Orlando, FL; *U.S. Private*, pg. 1097
Oropeza, S., Sec.--Sistema Argos S.A., Ciudad Juarez, Mexico; *Int'l*, pg. 1256
Orrel, Wally, V.P. & Asst. Sec.--Rocking Horse Development Corporation, Media, PA; *U.S. Public*, pg. 1186
Orsi, Bernard, Exec. V.P. & Sec.--S & P Company, Mill Valley, CA; *U.S. Private*, pg. 954
Ortega y Diaz Ambrona, Juan Antonio, Sec. General--Repsol Petroleo, Madrid, Spain; *Int'l*, pg. 1104
Ortiz, Patrick T., Sr. V.P., Gen. Counsel & Sec.--Public Service Company of New Mexico, Albuquerque, NM; *U.S. Public*, pg. 1339
Ortman, Elizabeth J., Treas. & Sec.--Kokomo Grain Co., Inc., Kokomo, IN; *U.S. Private*, pg. 631
Ortolani, Thecly L., Treas. & Sec.--Carton-Craft Corporation, Buffalo, NY; *U.S. Private*, pg. 217
Orza, Patricia L., Sec.--Eateries, Inc., Oklahoma City, OK; *U.S. Public*, pg. 555
Orza, Patricia L., Sec.--Pepperoni Grill, Oklahoma City, OK; *U.S. Public*, pg. 555
Osborn, Cathleen M., V.P. & Sec.--Hallwood Energy Partners, L.P., Denver, CO; *U.S. Public*, pg. 778
Osborne, Jack, Grp. Sec.--Dairy Vale Co-op. Ltd., Adelaide, Australia; *Int'l*, pg. 372
Osborne, Robert S., Sec.--Lands' End, Inc., Dodgeville, WI; *U.S. Public*, pg. 977
Oscherwitz, Jerry, V.P., Asst. Treas. & Sec.--Best Kosher Sausage Co., Chicago, IL; *U.S. Public*, pg. 1433
Oshinski, Jerry P., Exec. V.P., Treas. & Sec.--Hunter Corp., Portage, IN; *U.S. Private*, pg. 549
Oshiro, Kathleen F., Asst. V.P. & Sec.--Buyco, Inc., Honolulu, HI; *U.S. Private*, pg. 190
Oshiro, Kathleen F., V.P.-Admin & Corp. Sec.--C. Brewer & Company, Limited, Honolulu, HI; *U.S. Private*, pg. 190
Oshiro, Kathleen F., Sec.--Mauna Loa Macadamia Nut Corporation, Hilo, HI; *U.S. Private*, pg. 190
Oshiro, Kathleen F., Sec.--Olokele Sugar Co., Limited, Kaunakakai, HI; *U.S. Private*, pg. 191
Oshiro, Kathleen F., Sec.--Superior Coffee & Foods/Hawaii, Aiea, HI; *U.S. Private*, pg. 191
Oshiro, Kathleen F., Sec.--Mauna Loa Macadamia Partners, L.P., Honolulu, HI; *U.S. Public*, pg. 1060
Oshrin, Martin, Treas. & Sec.--Junior Gallery Ltd., New York, NY; *U.S. Private*, pg. 602
Oskandy, James M., Sec.--Protection Mutual Insurance Co., Park Ridge, IL; *U.S. Private*, pg. 891
Oskins, James C., Controller & Sec.--George Koch Sons, Inc., Evansville, IN; *U.S. Private*, pg. 628
Osland, Dean, V.P. & Sec.--Harris Contracting Co., Saint Paul, MN; *U.S. Private*, pg. 505
Osowski, Richard J., Sr. V.P.-Fin. & Asst. Sec.--Criticare Systems, Inc., Waukesha, WI; *U.S. Public*, pg. 459
Osten, Judd, Sr. V.P., Gen. Counsel & Sec.--Crawford & Company, Atlanta, GA; *U.S. Public*, pg. 458
Oster, Helen P., Sec.--Baldwin Technology Company, Inc., Norwalk, CT; *U.S. Public*, pg. 169
Oster, Stephen, Sec.--Gulf Coast Recycling, Tampa, FL; *U.S. Private*, pg. 487
Osterhouse, Donald, Gen. Counsel & Sec.--King Milling Company, Lowell, MI; *U.S. Private*, pg. 621
Ostler, John R., Sec.--Life Sciences International Plc, London, United Kingdom; *U.S. Public*, pg. 1594
Ostrom, Christel, Sec.--Berner Ltd., Helsinki, Finland; *Int'l*, pg. 189
Ostrowski, James, Chief Fin. Officer, Treas. & Sec.--Awrey Bakeries, Inc., Livonia, MI; *U.S. Private*, pg. 103
Otamura-Kester, Judith K., Asst. Sec.--Jefferies Group, Inc., Los Angeles, CA; *U.S. Public*, pg. 924
Otamura-Kester, Judith K., Asst. Sec.--Investment Technology Group, Inc., New York, NY; *U.S. Public*, pg. 924
Otamura-Kester, Judith K., Sr. V.P., Asst. Gen. Counsel & Asst. Sec.--Jefferies & Company, Inc., Los Angeles, CA; *U.S. Public*, pg. 925
Otis, Thomas, V.P., Sec. & Legal--Eaton Vance Corp., Boston, MA; *U.S. Public*, pg. 559
Otte, Ellen C., Asst. Sec.--National Western Life Insurance Company, Austin, TX; *U.S. Public*, pg. 1161
Otto, Jeffrey W., Gen. Counsel & Sec.--Safety National Casualty Corp., Saint Louis, MO; *U.S. Public*, pg. 496
Otto, William, Chief Fin. Officer & Asst. Sec.--Ripon Foods, Inc., Ripon, WI; *U.S. Private*, pg. 931
Ouellet, Germain, V.P.-Human Resources & Sec.--Premier CDN Enterprises Ltd., Dorval, Canada; *Int'l*, pg. 1067
Oughtred, A.W., Sec.--Fahnestock Viner Holdings Inc., Toronto, Canada; *Int'l*, pg. 476
Ounsworth, James A., Sr. V.P., Gen. Counsel & Sec.--Safeguard Scientifics, Inc., Wayne, PA; *U.S. Public*, pg. 1424
Overbey, Terry, Sec. & Corp. Counsel--The Procter & Gamble Company, Cincinnati, OH; *U.S. Public*, pg. 1330
Overmyer, Elizabeth A., Corp. Sec.--Ball Corporation, Muncie, IN; *U.S. Public*, pg. 170
Overstreet, Dorothy M., Sr. V.P. & Sec.--Overstreet Paving Company, Largo, FL; *U.S. Private*, pg. 823
Overtoom, W. J., Sec.--Royal Packaging Industries Van Leer B.V., Amstelveen, Netherlands; *Int'l*, pg. 1145
Ovrut, Barnett D., Assoc. Gen. Counsel & Sec.--The Hanover Insurance Company, Worcester, MA; *U.S. Public*, pg. 54
Owen, Dolores, Sec. & Treas.--Owen Industries, Inc., Carter Lake, IA; *U.S. Private*, pg. 824
Owen, Hayes D., V.P. & Asst. Sec.--Baton Rouge Water Works Company, Baton Rouge, LA; *U.S. Private*, pg. 122
Owen, Hayes D., V.P., Sec. & Asst. Treas.--Ascension Water Co., Baton Rouge, LA; *U.S. Private*, pg. 123
Owen, Judith E., V.P. & Sec.--Avis Industrial Corporation, Upland, IN; *U.S. Private*, pg. 102
Owen, M., Asst. Sec.--The Peninsular and Oriental Steam Navigation Company, London, United Kingdom; *Int'l*, pg. 1032
Owen, Shirley J., Sec.--AJC International, Inc., Atlanta, GA; *U.S. Private*, pg. 6
Owens, Dennis J., Chief Fin. Officer & V.P.-Admin.--The Pollock Corp., Pottstown, PA; *U.S. Private*, pg. 874
Owens, Gary, Sec.--Peerless Lighting Corp., Berkeley, CA; *U.S. Private*, pg. 847
Owens, Jane E., V.P., Gen. Counsel & Asst. Sec.--The Timberland Company, Stratham, NH; *U.S. Public*, pg. 1609
Owens, Stephen K., Asst. Sec.--Owens Country Sausage, Inc., Richardson, TX; *U.S. Public*, pg. 596
Owerstrom, Dan M., Sr. V.P.-Corp. Law & Sec.--Trygg-Hansa, Stockholm, Sweden; *Int'l*, pg. 1425
Oxendine, Helen, Sec.--Lat Purser & Associates, Charlotte, NC; *U.S. Private*, pg. 896
Ozaki, Joe, Controller, Treas. & Sec.--A-Mark Financial, Santa Monica, CA; *U.S. Private*, pg. 2
Ozuna, Rosemary, Treas. & Sec.--New Bedford Panoramex Corporation, Upland, CA; *U.S. Private*, pg. 792
Pace, H. Duane, Exec. V.P. & Sec.--Jefferson Mills, Inc., Pulaski, VA; *U.S. Private*, pg. 584
Pacifico, Michael, Treas. & Sec.--Pacifico Auto Group, Philadelphia, PA; *U.S. Private*, pg. 832
Paddock, David H., Sec. & Sls. Mgr.-NY District--Preferred Utilities Manufacturing Corp., Danbury, CT; *U.S. Private*, pg. 881
Paddon, R. Stephen, Sec.--Extendicare Inc., Markham, Canada; *Int'l*, pg. 468
Padilla, Raymond O., V.P., Sec. & Asst. Treas.--Davis Selected Advisors, L.P., Santa Fe, NM; *U.S. Private*, pg. 315
Page, Scott T., Sr. Exec. V.P. & Sec.--Collective Bank, Cologne, NJ; *U.S. Public*, pg. 1528
Pahl, Joy, Sec.--J.H. Larson Electrical Company, Golden Valley, MN; *U.S. Private*, pg. 652
Pai, Subhash, Controller & Asst. Sec.--Startec Global Communications Corporation, Bethesda, MD; *U.S. Public*, pg. 1511
Pain, George H., V.P., Gen. Counsel & Sec.--Primex Technologies, Inc., Saint Petersburg, FL; *U.S. Public*, pg. 1329
Painter, Sandra E., Sec.--Firemen's Insurance Company of Washington, D.C., Bethesda, MD; *U.S. Public*, pg. 215
Painton, Russell E., V.P., Gen. Counsel & Sec.--Tracor, Inc., Austin, TX; *U.S. Public*, pg. 1627
Pair, Christopher, Exec. V.P.-Intl. & Corp. Admin., Sec.--Herbalife International of America, Inc., Century City, CA; *U.S. Public*, pg. 809
Pal, P.K., V.P. & Sec.--Alcan Aluminium Limited, Montreal, Canada; *Int'l*, pg. 50
Palaska, Y., Sec.--Geo-Young & Rubicam, Athens, Greece; *U.S. Private*, pg. 1199
Palfreeman, Anthony W.H., Sec.--Delta Cables Holdings Ltd., Enfield, United Kingdom; *Int'l*, pg. 390
Pallat, Daniel J., Chief Fin. Officer, V.P., Treas. & Sec.--Home Juice Co., Melrose Park, IL; *U.S. Private*, pg. 537
Palmer, David, Treas. & Sec.--Farnsworth Companies, Mesa, AZ; *U.S. Private*, pg. 397
Palmer, John, Gen. Counsel & Sec.--Dunham's Athleisure Corporation, Waterford, MI; *U.S. Private*, pg. 346
Palmer, Richard L., V.P.-Fin. & Corp. Sec.--Baton Broadcasting Incorporated, Scarborough, Canada; *Int'l*, pg. 170
Palmer, Roberta, Sec.--Palmer International, Inc., Worcester, PA; *U.S. Private*, pg. 834
Palmer, Thomas E., V.P., Gen. Counsel & Sec.--The Mead Corporation, Dayton, OH; *U.S. Public*, pg. 1074
Palomba, Tarz F., Asst. Sec.--Tiffany & Co., New York, NY; *U.S. Public*, pg. 1608
Paltiel, Rae G., Sec.--Warner-Lambert Company, Morris Plains, NJ; *U.S. Public*, pg. 1738
Paluch, Linda, Sec.--G.E. Capital Commercial Real Estate Financing, Stamford, CT; *U.S. Public*, pg. 712
Pamplin, Robert B., Jr., Dr., Pres., Chief Oper. Officer & Sec.--R.B. Pamplin Corp., Portland, OR; *U.S. Private*, pg. 835
Paola, J., Chief Fin. Officer & Sec.--CIBA-GEIGY (Pty.) Ltd., Isando, South Africa; *Int'l*, pg. 978
Paosio, P., Sec.--Pilkington Lahden Lasitehdas Oy, Lahti, Finland; *Int'l*, pg. 1056
Papa, Vincent, Sr. V.P. & Sec.--Metallgesellschaft Corp., New York, NY; *Int'l*, pg. 861
Papenbrock, William P., Sec.--Pioneer-Standard Electronics, Inc., Cleveland, OH; *U.S. Public*, pg. 1300
Papesh, Al, Mgr.-Fin.--Ritchie Industries, Inc., Conrad, IA; *U.S. Private*, pg. 933
Paquet, Marc, Legal Counsel & Asst. Sec.--Societe Generale de Financement du Quebec, Montreal, Canada; *Int'l*, pg. 1274
Paradis, Robert D., Chief Fin. Officer, V.P. & Sec.--Yale/Chase Materials Handling, Inc., City of Industry, CA; *U.S. Private*, pg. 1195
Parasotto, Patricia M., Sec.--Wajax Limited, Delta, Canada; *Int'l*, pg. 1484
Pare, Anne M., Asst. Sec.--Central Maine Power Company, Augusta, ME; *U.S. Public*, pg. 325
Pare, Anne M., Asst. Sec.--Maine Yankee, Brunswick, ME; *U.S. Public*, pg. 325
Parent, Beatrice D., Corp. Sec.--Progressive Bank, Inc., Fishkill, NY; *U.S. Public*, pg. 1334
Pares, Jacques, Secretaire General--Telediffusion de France, Paris, France; *Int'l*, pg. 503
Parfet, Ray T., Jr., Treas. & Sec.--Gilmore Bros., Inc., Kalamazoo, MI; *U.S. Private*, pg. 454
Parish, Rhonda J., Sr. V.P., Gen. Counsel & Sec.--Advantica Restaurant Group, Inc., Spartanburg, SC; *U.S. Public*, pg. 22
Park, Sara M., Sec.--Addington Resources, Inc., Lexington, KY; *U.S. Public*, pg. 1379
Parker, Carter, Treas. & Sec.--Louisiana Utilities Supply Company, Baton Rouge, LA; *U.S. Private*, pg. 245
Parker, Christy, Sec.--Adventure Tours USA, Inc., Dallas, TX; *U.S. Private*, pg. 22
Parker, D. Michael, Chief Fin. Officer, V.P.-Fin., Sec. & Treas.--Kewaunee Scientific Corporation, Statesville, NC; *U.S. Public*, pg. 953
Parker, Gail E., V.P.-Human Resources & Sec.--The Failure Group, Inc., Menlo Park, CA; *U.S. Public*, pg. 609
Parker, J.A., Asst. Sec.--Trimac Corporation, Calgary, Canada; *Int'l*, pg. 1423
Parker, M.J.F., Sec.--Haden Maclellan Holdings plc, Egham, United Kingdom; *Int'l*, pg. 585
Parker, Vivian, Corp. Sec.--Sonoco Ltd., Brantford, Canada; *U.S. Public*, pg. 1487
Parks, Teri, Sec.--Southwestern/Great American Inc., Nashville, TN; *U.S. Private*, pg. 1018
Parr, Phillis, V.P. & Sec.--Budget Marketing, Inc., Des Moines, IA; *U.S. Private*, pg. 178
Parr, Royse M., Gen. Counsel & Sec.--Mapco Natural Gas Liquids Inc., Tulsa, OK; *U.S. Public*, pg. 1042
Parron, Charles K., Sec.--Electrical Equipment Company, Raleigh, NC; *U.S. Private*, pg. 368
Parrott, Charles, Sec.& Gen. Counsel--Fred V. Fowler Company, Inc., Newton, MA; *U.S. Private*, pg. 422
Parry, Josephine, Sec.--Tandem Computers Inc., Cupertino, CA; *U.S. Public*, pg. 417
Parsons, J.A., Chief Fin. Officer, Exec. V.P., Treas. & Sec.--Willamette Industries, Inc., Portland, OR; *U.S. Public*, pg. 1768
Parsons, Michael G., Sec.--Smith & Nephew PLC, London, United Kingdom; *Int'l*, pg. 1263
Parsons, Renee, Asst. Sec.--Pulse Bancorp, Inc., South River, NJ; *U.S. Public*, pg. 1344
Partain, C. Raymond, V.P.-Risk Mngmt. & Sec.--J.A. Jones, Inc., Charlotte, NC; *Int'l*, pg. 633

Pascoe, Christopher J.C., Counsel & Corp. Sec.--Pratt & Whitney Canada Inc., Longueuil, Canada; U.S. Public, pg. 1690
Pascuzzi, Bob, Chief Fin. Officer & Sec.--The Dorris Lumber & Moulding Co., Sacramento, CA; U.S. Private, pg. 341
Paskal, Randy, Sec.--J & R Film / Moviola Digital Co., Hollywood, CA; U.S. Private, pg. 576
Passano, E. Magruder, Jr., Vice Chm. & Sec.--Waverly, Inc., Baltimore, MD; U.S. Public, pg. 1748
Pastor, Marianne V., Sec.--Williams Industries, Inc., Falls Church, VA; U.S. Public, pg. 1769
Pastori, Guido, Deputy Gen. Mgr. & Sec.--Assicurazioni Generali S.p.A., Trieste, Italy; Int'l, pg. 89
Patel, Magan H., Exec. V.P. & Asst. Sec.--Circuit Systems, Inc., Elk Grove Village, IL; U.S. Public, pg. 374
Paterson, William, Sec.--Whiting Equipment Canada, Inc., Welland, Canada; U.S. Private, pg. 1173
Patience, John, Sec.--BG Plc, Reading, United Kingdom; Int'l, pg. 118
Patrasso, Frances, Sec.--Master Molded Products Corporation, Elgin, IL; U.S. Private, pg. 714
Patten, Robert J., Controller & Asst. Sec.--Moran Bulk Corporation, Greenwich, CT; U.S. Private, pg. 760
Patterson, Michael R., V.P., Gen. Counsel & Sec.--Plains Resources Inc., Houston, TX; U.S. Public, pg. 1307
Patterson, Pauline, Controller & Sec.--Maine Potato Growers, Inc., Presque Isle, ME; U.S. Private, pg. 697
Patterson, Peter, Sec.--Austral Bronze Crane Copper Limited, Wetherill Park, Australia; Int'l, pg. 340
Patterson, Shelby, Sec.--American Furniture Company, Incorporated, Martinsville, VA; U.S. Public, pg. 974
Patterson, W. Lin, Gen. Counsel & Sec.--Mapco Petroleum Inc., Tulsa, OK; U.S. Public, pg. 1042
Patton, Kristin, Corp. Sec.--Sahara Enterprises Inc., Chicago, IL; U.S. Private, pg. 960
Patton, Neal, Gen. Counsel & Sec.--AMC, Inc., Atlanta, GA; U.S. Private, pg. 6
Patton, Terry E., Sr. V.P. & Sec.--FirstMerit Corporation, Akron, OH; U.S. Public, pg. 646
Pattullo, Matt S., Corp. Sec.--Stiefel Laboratories, Inc., Coral Gables, FL; U.S. Private, pg. 1043
Patty, David A., Chief Fin. Officer, Treas. & Sec.--Donahue Schriber, Newport Beach, CA; Int'l, pg. 253
Paturzo, Michael R., Treas. & Sec.--Henningsen Foods, Inc., White Plains, NY; Int'l, pg. 1074
Patzke, Pamela, Gen. Counsel & Asst. Sec.--Lands' End, Inc., Dodgeville, WI; U.S. Public, pg. 977
Paul, Barbara H., V.P.& Asst. Sec.--Kimberly-Clark Corporation, Dallas, TX; U.S. Public, pg. 958
Paul, Peter, Dr., Sec.--Coop Switzerland, Basel, Switzerland; Int'l, pg. 329
Paulin, Ira, Treas. & Sec.--Ranchers Supply Company, Inc., Lamar, CO; U.S. Private, pg. 908
Paulson, Donald E., Sec.--Alpha Industries, Inc., Woburn, MA; U.S. Public, pg. 57
Paulson, Stuart M., V.P.-Claims, Gen. Counsel & Sec.--Blue Ridge Insurance Co., Simsbury, CT; Int'l, pg. 345
Paulson, Stuart M., V.P.-Claims, Gen. Counsel & Sec.--Blue Ridge Indemnity Co., Simsbury, CT; Int'l, pg. 345
Paulson, Stuart M., V.P.-Claims, Gen. Counsel & Sec.--MassWest Insurance Company, West Springfield, MA; Int'l, pg. 345
Paulson, Thomas J., V.P.-Fin., Treas. & Sec.--Neurogen Corporation, Branford, CT; U.S. Public, pg. 1169
Pavalos, Christine, Asst. Sec.--The Dreyfus Corporation, New York, NY; U.S. Public, pg. 1085
Pavelik, Richard, Treas. & Sec.--Landau Building Co., Wexford, PA; U.S. Private, pg. 646
Paver, Robert L., Gen. Counsel & Sec.--Jabil Circuit, Inc., Saint Petersburg, FL; U.S. Public, pg. 919
Pavia, G., Corp. Sec.--Italimpianti of America, Incorporated, Coraopolis, PA; Int'l, pg. 655
Pavitt, Richard, Co. Sec.--Lambert Smith Hampton, London, United Kingdom; Int'l, pg. 797
Pavlick, W.E., Sr. V.P., Gen. Counsel & Sec.--Modine Manufacturing Company, Racine, WI; U.S. Public, pg. 1121
Pavlis, Paul, V.P.-Legal Affairs--All American Communications, Inc., Santa Monica, CA; U.S. Public, pg. 41
Pawelek, Randall, Corp. Sec.--Bartlett Cocke, Inc., San Antonio, TX; U.S. Private, pg. 249
Payne, D. W., Controller & Asst. Sec.--Kerr-McGee Chemical Corp., Oklahoma City, OK; U.S. Public, pg. 952
Payne, Douglas, Sr. V.P.-Fin. & Admin.--Stanley Furniture Co. Inc., Stanleytown, VA; U.S. Public, pg. 1508
Payne, E.M., III, Sec.--Horizon Bancorp, Inc., Beckley, WV; U.S. Public, pg. 836
Payne, Eugene, V.P. & Sec.--InternContinental Life Corp., Austin, TX; U.S. Public, pg. 622
Payne, James P., V.P. & Sec.--National Western Life Insurance Company, Austin, TX; U.S. Public, pg. 1161
Payne, James P., V.P. & Sec.--NWL Financial, Inc., Austin, TX; U.S. Public, pg. 1161
Payne, James P., V.P. & Sec.--NWL Services, Inc., Austin, TX; U.S. Public, pg. 1161
Payne, Stanley J., V.P., Gen. Counsel & Sec.--Bassett Furniture Industries, Incorporated, Bassett, VA; U.S. Public, pg. 193
Payne, William B., Sec.--Deltak Inc., Plymouth, MN; U.S. Public, pg. 924
Payne, William J., V.P., Gen. Counsel & Sec.--Rinker Materials Corp., West Palm Beach, FL; Int'l, pg. 246
Peace, John C., V.P., Gen. Counsel & Sec.--Shenandoah Life Insurance Company, Roanoke, VA; U.S. Private, pg. 992
Pean, Alain, Sec. Gen.--BNP UK Holdings Ltd., London, United Kingdom; Int'l, pg. 164
Pearce, Louis, III, V.P. & Asst. Sec.--Pearce Industries Inc., Houston, TX; U.S. Private, pg. 845
Pearce, M.J., Sec.--Lonrho plc, London, United Kingdom; Int'l, pg. 817
Pearce, Richard W., Jr., Sr. V.P. & Sec.--Amica Mutual Insurance Co., Lincoln, RI; U.S. Private, pg. 66
Pearce, S. M., Sec.--Wassall Plc, London, United Kingdom; Int'l, pg. 1486
Pearey, M.J., Sec.--Scottish & Newcastle plc, Edinburgh, United Kingdom; Int'l, pg. 1211
Pearl, Manny, Treas. & Sec.--Pearl-Pressman-Liberty Communications Group, Philadelphia, PA; U.S. Private, pg. 845
Pearlman, Ted, V.P., Sec. & Treas.--Atlite Lighting Equip. Inc., Maspeth, NY; U.S. Public, pg. 443
Pearman, Brooke, Sec.--Bam Media, Pleasant Hill, CA; U.S. Private, pg. 113
Pearson, Audrey, Treas. & Sec.--NEFA Corporation, Southampton, PA; U.S. Public, pg. 1326
Pearson, Don M., Sec.--Nationwide Health Properties Inc., Newport Beach, CA; U.S. Public, pg. 1166
Pearson, J., Sec.--Greenham Trading Limited, Isleworth, United Kingdom; Int'l, pg. 1358
Pearson, Linda J., Sec.--Addison Insurance Company, Lombard, IL; U.S. Public, pg. 1677
Pearson, Linda J., Sec.--Addison Insurance Agency, Lombard, IL; U.S. Public, pg. 1677
Pearson, Mark A., Sec.--Elan Corporation Plc, Dublin, Ireland; Int'l, pg. 435
Pearson, Thomas L., Gen. Counsel & Sec.--Mapco Coal Inc., Tulsa, OK; U.S. Public, pg. 1042
Peary, Stephen, Sr. V.P., Sec. & Gen. Counsel--PLM International, Inc., San Francisco, CA; U.S. Public, pg. 1241
Peary, Stephen, V.P. & Sec.--PLM Trailer Leasing, San Francisco, CA; U.S. Public, pg. 1241
Pease, David H., III, V.P.-Engrng., Mfg. & Sec.--Pease Industries, Inc., Fairfield, OH; U.S. Private, pg. 845
Pecher, Catherine A., V.P. & Sec.--Birmingham Steel Corporation, Birmingham, AL; U.S. Public, pg. 232
Peck, A. John, Jr., Sec.--Corning Incorporated, Corning, NY; U.S. Public, pg. 448
Peck, Gary S., Chief Fin. Officer, V.P.-Fin. & Sec.--HarCor Energy, Inc., Houston, TX; U.S. Public, pg. 782
Pedroso, Vanessa M., Corp. Sec.--Cervejarias Kaiser Brasil Ltda., Campinas, Brazil; Int'l, pg. 279
Peebles, Jill E., Sec. & Clerk--Instron Corporation, Canton, MA; U.S. Public, pg. 882
Peeler, Nancy Carole, Treas. & Sec.--Peelers Rug Company, Inc., Gaffney, SC; U.S. Private, pg. 846
Peet, Jane, Sec.--Willis Corroon Continental Europe Limited, London, United Kingdom; Int'l, pg. 1502
Pellegrino, Kathleen, Asst. Sec.--Humana Inc., Louisville, KY; U.S. Public, pg. 847
Pellegrino, Kathleen, Asst. Sec.--Humana Health Insurance of Nevada, Inc., Las Vegas, NV; U.S. Public, pg. 847
Pellegrino, Kathleen, Asst. Sec.--Humana Health Chicago, Inc., Chicago, IL; U.S. Public, pg. 847
Pellegrino, Kathleen, Asst. Sec.--Employers Health Insurance Company, Green Bay, WI; U.S. Public, pg. 847
Pellegrino, Kathleen, Asst. Sec.--Humana Health Plan of Texas, Inc., San Antonio, TX; U.S. Public, pg. 848
Pellegrino, Kathleen, Asst. Sec.--Humana Medical Plan Inc.-Miami, Miramar, FL; U.S. Public, pg. 848
Pellegrino, Kathleen, Asst. Sec.--Humana Health Plan of Georgia, Inc., Louisville, KY; U.S. Public, pg. 848
Pellegrino, Kathleen, Asst. Sec.--Humana Health Plan of Louisiana, Inc., Louisville, KY; U.S. Public, pg. 848
Pellegrino, Kathleen, Asst. Sec.--Humana Insurance Company, Kansas City, MO; U.S. Public, pg. 848
Pellegrino, Kathleen, Asst. Sec.--Humana Health Plan of Ohio, Inc., Cincinnati, OH; U.S. Public, pg. 848
Pellegrino, Kathleen, Asst. Sec.--Humana Health Plan of Utah, Inc., Salt Lake City, UT; U.S. Public, pg. 848
Pellegrino, Kathleen, Asst. Sec.--Humana Health Plan, Inc., Louisville, KY; U.S. Public, pg. 848
Pellegrino, Kathleen, Asst. Sec.--Humana Health Plan of Alabama, Inc., Montgomery, AL; U.S. Public, pg. 848
Pellegrino, Kathleen, Asst. Sec.--Humana Wisconsin Health Organization Insurance Corporation, Milwaukee, WI; U.S. Public, pg. 848
Pellegrino, Kathleen, Asst. Sec.--Network EPO, Inc., Milwaukee, WI; U.S. Public, pg. 848
Pellegrino, Louis, Controller & Sec.--Northway Motorcar Corporation, Latham, NY; U.S. Private, pg. 806
Pelletier, Peter A., Treas. & Sec.--Velcro USA Inc., Manchester, NH; Int'l, pg. 1462
Pen'du, Jocelyne, Sec.--Sol Melia, Palma de Mallorca, Spain; Int'l, pg. 1277
Pena, Dave, Sec.--Double AA Builders, Ltd., Scottsdale, AZ; U.S. Private, pg. 341
Penberthy, Mary D., Asst. Sec.--Penberthy Lumber Company, Carson, CA; U.S. Private, pg. 848
Pendell, Richard C., Sec.--Quebecor Printing Pendell Inc., Midland, MI; Int'l, pg. 1078
Pendergraft, Jeffrey R., Chief Admin. Officer & Sr. V.P.--Lyondell Petrochemical Company, Houston, TX; U.S. Public, pg. 1022
Pendrey, J.C., Jr., Chief Fin. Officer, Sr. V.P., Treas. & Sec.--Holder Corporation, Atlanta, GA; U.S. Private, pg. 533
Penfield, Doreen R., V.P.-Admin.--Adecco S.A., Lausanne, Switzerland; Int'l, pg. 23
Peng, Philip, V.P.-Fin.--Acer Incorporated, Taipei, Taiwan; Int'l, pg. 22
Penn, Barbara, Sec.--Cummins Mid-South, Inc., Memphis, TN; U.S. Private, pg. 295
Penner, Harold, Treas. & Asst. Sec.--Lechters, Inc., Harrison, NJ; U.S. Public, pg. 983
Penny, MaryJane, Sec.--List Industries, Inc., Deerfield Beach, FL; U.S. Private, pg. 669
Penton, D.M., Sec.--George Wimpey PLC, London, United Kingdom; Int'l, pg. 1510
Pentz, William H., Sr. Assoc. Gen. Counsel & Asst. Sec.--The Penn Mutual Life Insurance Company, Philadelphia, PA; U.S. Private, pg. 849
Penwell, Patricia A., Sec.--America West Airlines, Inc., Phoenix, AZ; U.S. Public, pg. 67
Peoples, Dawn, Asst. Sec.--Fairfield Communities, Inc., Little Rock, AR; U.S. Public, pg. 610
Pepe, Charles, Asst. Treas. & Asst. Sec.--United Illuminating Company, New Haven, CT; U.S. Public, pg. 1678
Peper, Cheri L., Corp. Sec.--Apache Corporation, Houston, TX; U.S. Public, pg. 119
Pepin, E. Lyle, Controller & Asst. Sec.--The Cleveland Electric Illuminating Company, Independence, OH; U.S. Public, pg. 645
Pepin, E. Lyle, Controller & Asst. Sec.--The Toledo Edison Company, Toledo, OH; U.S. Public, pg. 645
Pepper, Martha, Sec.--Harry Pepper & Associates, Jacksonville, FL; U.S. Private, pg. 851
Pepys, Eric, Sec.--Dot Printer, Inc., Irvine, CA; U.S. Private, pg. 341
Peralta, Joaquim Domingos, Sec. Gen.--Banco Totta & Acores, Lisbon, Portugal; Int'l, pg. 144
Percio, Janis T., Sec.--The Cleveland Electric Illuminating Company, Independence, OH; U.S. Public, pg. 645
Percival, Sylvia, Treas. & Sec.--Intelligent Controls Inc., Lynnwood, WA; U.S. Private, pg. 566
Pereira Formosinho, Walter, Corp. Sec.--Petrobras - Petroleo Brasileiro S.A., Rio de Janeiro, Brazil; Int'l, pg. 1041
Pereira, Douglas L., Chief Fin. Officer & Sr. V.P.--Clothestime Stores, Inc., Anaheim, CA; U.S. Public, pg. 387
Perez, Ann, Dir.--InterBio Inc., Woodlands, TX; U.S. Private, pg. 566
Perez, Enrique, Chief Oper. Officer, Sr. Exec. V.P., Gen. Counsel & Sec.--Philippine Long Distance Telephone Company, Manila, Philippines; Int'l, pg. 1051
Perfido, Ruth S., Asst. Sec.--W.P. Carey & Co., Inc., New York, NY; U.S. Private, pg. 209
Perkins, Arthur, Sec.--Patsy's, Inc., Concord, NH; U.S. Private, pg. 843
Perkins, P. Thomas, Treas. & Sec.--Thomas & Howard Co., Columbia, SC; U.S. Private, pg. 1081
Perlman, Charles H., Sec.--GreatBanc, Inc., Aurora, IL; U.S. Public, pg. 760
Perlman, Charles H., Gen. Counsel & Sec.--Grist Mill Company, Lakeville, MN; U.S. Public, pg. 766
Perlmuter, Bruce, Exec. V.P., Treas. & Sec.--Perlmuter Printing Company, Cleveland, OH; Int'l, pg. 1177
Perona, Dale F., Sr. V.P. & Sec.--True North Communications Inc.--True North Communications Inc., Chicago, IL; U.S. Public, pg. 1641
Perrett, George W., V.P. & Sec.--Interface Systems, Inc., Ann Arbor, MI; U.S. Public, pg. 889
Perretta, Susan R., Corp. Sec.--Selective Insurance Group, Inc, Branchville, NJ; U.S. Public, pg. 1455
Perretta, Susan R., Asst. Sec.--Exchange Insurance Company, Buffalo, NY; U.S. Public, pg. 1455
Perretta, Susan R., Sec.--Charleston Insurance Company, Buffalo, NY; U.S. Public, pg. 1455
Perretta, Susan R., Sec.--Niagara Exchange Corporation, Buffalo, NY; U.S. Public, pg. 1455
Perretta, Susan R., Sec.--Wantage Avenue Holding Company, Inc., Branchville, NJ; U.S. Public, pg. 1456
Perretta, Susan R., Sec.--Selective Technical Administrative Services, Inc., Branchville, NJ; U.S. Public, pg. 1456
Perrin, Marie-Helene, Sec.--Banque Indosuez, Paris, France; Int'l, pg. 313
Perron, Allen A., V.P.-Fin., Treas. & Asst. Sec.--Puget Western, Inc., Bellevue, WA; U.S. Public, pg. 1342
Perrone, Dee, Gen. Counsel & Sec.--Newport Electronics, Inc., Santa Ana, CA; U.S. Private, pg. 816
Perry, Carmen, Chief Fin. Officer, Treas., Controller & Sec.--Outdoor Venture Corp., Stearns, KY; U.S. Private, pg. 822
Perry, D., Sec.--Perry Equipment Corporation, Mineral Wells, TX; U.S. Private, pg. 855
Perry, Dana, Chief Fin. Officer & Asst. Sec.--Aztec Manufacturing Co., Crowley, TX; U.S. Public, pg. 159
Perry, Harvey C., II, V.P. & Sec.--Washington Trust Bancorp, Inc., Westerly, RI; U.S. Public, pg. 1744
Perry, Harvey P., Sr. V.P., Gen. Counsel & Sec.--Century Telephone Enterprises, Inc., Monroe, LA; U.S. Public, pg. 329
Perry, Jay, Controller, Treas. & Sec.--Steiny & Company, Inc., Baldwin Park, CA; U.S. Private, pg. 1039
Perry, John W., Corp. Sec.--First Financial Corporation, Terre Haute, IN; U.S. Public, pg. 633
Perry, Marion E., Treas. & Sec.--Cardinal Scale Manufacturing Company, Webb City, MO; U.S. Private, pg. 209
Perry, Marion E., Treas. & Sec.--Detecto Scale Company, Webb City, MO; U.S. Private, pg. 209
Persson, Eva, Chief-Corp. Legal & Sec.--AB Volvo, Goteborg, Sweden; Int'l, pg. 1476
Peske, Milian, Treas. & Sec.--Metric & Multistandard Components, Hawthorne, NY; U.S. Private, pg. 736
Pestinger, Janis C., V.P.-Admin. & Asst. Sec.--Vari-Lite International, Dallas, TX; U.S. Public, pg. 1709
Petelle, James F., Corp. Sec. & Gen. Attorney--Andrew Corporation, Orland Park, IL; U.S. Public, pg. 112
Peters, Cynthia, Sec.--Peters Construction Corp., Waterloo, IA; U.S. Private, pg. 856
Peters, Gary, V.P.-Fin.--Trinidad/Benham Corp., Denver, CO; U.S. Private, pg. 1103
Peters, John E., Sr. V.P., Gen. Counsel & Sec.--Block Drug Company, Inc., Jersey City, NJ; U.S. Public, pg. 236
Peters, Ronald, Sec.--ICM Holdings Inc., New York, NY; U.S. Private, pg. 554
Peters, Susan, Sec.-Mktg. Controller--Lever Brothers West Indies Ltd., Champs Fleurs, Trinidad & Tobago; Int'l, pg. 1437
Petersen, Ann R., Sec.--Petersen Aluminum Corporation, Elk Grove Village, IL; U.S. Private, pg. 856
Petersen, Gordon W., Sec.--Marquette Medical Systems, Inc., Milwaukee, WI; U.S. Public, pg. 1047
Petersen, March, Pres. & Sec.--Petersen Graphics Group, South Bend, IN; U.S. Private, pg. 856
Peterson, Craig D., Gen. Counsel & Sec.--Xerxes Corporation, Minneapolis, MN; U.S. Private, pg. 1194

Peterson, David, Sr. V.P. & Sec.--Rockford Products Corp., Rockford, IL; *U.S. Private*, pg. 938

Peterson, Gary P., Sec. & Treas.--Bay West Paper Corp. Towel & Tissue Div., Middletown, OH; *U.S. Public*, pg. 1747

Peterson, H., Sec.--James Hardie Industries Ltd., Sydney, Australia; *Int'l*, pg. 596

Peterson, Jean, Treas. & Sec.--Peterson Motor Company, Boise, ID; *U.S. Private*, pg. 857

Peterson, L.S., V.P. & Asst. Sec.--MidCon Corp., Lombard, IL; *U.S. Public*, pg. 1210

Peterson, Lorrayne L., Sec.--Peterson Farms, Decatur, AR; *U.S. Private*, pg. 857

Peterson, Paul R., Sr. V.P., Gen. Counsel & Sec.--Technology Solutions Company (TSC), Chicago, IL; *U.S. Public*, pg. 1564

Peterson, Paul R., Sec. & Gen. Counsel--Technology Solutions Company (TSC), Chicago, IL; *U.S. Public*, pg. 1564

Peterson, Scott, Asst. Sec.--Continental Airlines, Houston, TX; *U.S. Public*, pg. 439

Peterson, Stephen L., V.P. & Asst. Sec.--Deluxe Corporation, Shoreview, MN; *U.S. Public*, pg. 498

Peterson, Steven W., Chief Fin. Officer, V.P.-Fin. & Sec.--Mesa Laboratories, Inc., Wheat Ridge, CO; *U.S. Public*, pg. 1099

Peterson, Wayne S., Chief Fin. Officer, Sr. V.P. & Sec.--Buttrey Food & Drug Company, Great Falls, MT; *U.S. Public*, pg. 271

Petmecky, William M., Sr. V.P. & Sec.--Seneca Resources Corp., Houston, TX; *U.S. Public*, pg. 1156

Petovello, Brian G., Asst. Sec.--Computalog Ltd., Calgary, Canada; *Int'l*, pg. 325

Petricca, Virginia R., Sec.--Petricca Industries, Inc., Pittsfield, MA; *U.S. Private*, pg. 858

Pettigrew, M.R.J., Sec.--Jefferson Smurfit Group p.l.c., Dublin, Ireland; *Int'l*, pg. 1269

Pettinella, Nicholas A., Chief Fin. Officer, Sr. V.P., Treas. & Asst. Sec.--Intermetrics, Inc., Burlington, MA; *U.S. Private*, pg. 567

Pettit, Dale A., V.P., Treas. & Sec.--Silcorp Limited, Scarborough, Canada; *Int'l*, pg. 1249

Pettit, Mary Ann C., Asst. Sec.--The Midland Company, Cincinnati, OH; *U.S. Public*, pg. 1110

Petty, George G., V.P.-Fin., Sec. & Treas.--Atrion Corporation, Arab, AL; *U.S. Public*, pg. 146

Peugeot, Robert, Dir.-Organization & Quality & Sec.--Automobiles Citroen, Neuilly, France; *Int'l*, pg. 1020

Pew, Patricia, Sec.--Full Service Beverage Company, Wichita, KS; *U.S. Private*, pg. 34

Peyser, Irwin, Treas. & Sec.--David Peyser Sportswear Inc., Bay Shore, NY; *U.S. Private*, pg. 860

Peyton, Patrick H., V.P., Controller & Asst. Sec.--Pioneer Plastics Corporation, Auburn, ME; *U.S. Private*, pg. 867

Pezze, L.A., Corp. Sec.--Navistar International Corporation Canada, Hamilton, Canada; *U.S. Public*, pg. 1167

Pfaff, Robert, Sec.--Condor Tool & Die, Inc., Cleveland, OH; *U.S. Private*, pg. 71

Pfaff, Robert E., Chief Legal Counsel & Sec.--Anchor Tool & Die Company, Cleveland, OH; *U.S. Private*, pg. 71

Pfeifer, Greg, Chief Fin. Officer & Treas.--Rochester-Midland ICL, Omaha, NE; *U.S. Private*, pg. 937

Pfeil, Thomas B., Chief Fin. Officer, V.P. & Sec.--Vectra Technologies, Inc., San Ramon, CA; *U.S. Public*, pg. 1711

Pfister, Dean W., Sec.--Franklin Electric Co., Inc., Bluffton, IN; *U.S. Public*, pg. 679

Pfister, Terry W., Chief Fin. Officer, V.P.-Fin., Treas. & Sec.--Enerfab Inc., Cincinnati, OH; *U.S. Private*, pg. 376

Pflaster, Tina, V.P. & Sec.--Arnold Steel Company, Inc., Lakewood, NJ; *U.S. Private*, pg. 84

Pfortmiller, Terry, Treas. & Sec.--Aldi Food Inc., Batavia, IL; *U.S. Private*, pg. 33

Phagans, T.M., Treas. & Sec.--Addison Steel Inc., Albany, GA; *U.S. Private*, pg. 17

Phair, Joseph B., V.P., Gen. Counsel & Sec.--Varian Associates, Inc., Palo Alto, CA; *U.S. Public*, pg. 1710

Pharand, Gilles, Sr. V.P.-Corp. Affairs, Gen. Counsel & Sec.--Domtar Inc., Montreal, Canada; *Int'l*, pg. 416

Phelps, P. Michael, V.P. & Sec.--Morton International Inc., Chicago, IL; *U.S. Public*, pg. 1134

Philipp, Elizabeth R., Exec. V.P., Gen. Counsel & Sec.--Collins & Aikman Corporation, Charlotte, NC; *U.S. Public*, pg. 399

Phillips, Brenda, Sec.--Carnrick Laboratories, Inc., Cedar Knolls, NJ; *U.S. Private*, pg. 436

Phillips, Craig, V.P. & Sec.--Lifetime Hoan Corp., Westbury, NY; *U.S. Public*, pg. 992

Phillips, Dayton, Treas. & Sec.--Fischer Companies, Memphis, TN; *U.S. Private*, pg. 408

Phillips, L.E., Sec.--Senior Conflow Inc., Washington, PA; *Int'l*, pg. 1222

Phillips, Leo H., Jr., V.P., Asst. Gen. Counsel & Asst. Sec.--Manor Care, Inc., Gaithersburg, MD; *U.S. Public*, pg. 1041

Phillips, N. LaRon, CPA, Chief Fin. Officer, Treas. & Sec.--The Newtron Group Inc., Baton Rouge, LA; *U.S. Private*, pg. 797

Phillips, R. G., Dir.-Fin. & Sec.--Hepworth Building Products Limited, Stocksbridge, United Kingdom; *Int'l*, pg. 615

Phillips, Rosalind Ann, Sec.--GEICO Corporation, Washington, DC; *U.S. Public*, pg. 219

Phillips, Rosalind Ann, Sec.--Government Employees Financial Corporation, Washington, DC; *U.S. Public*, pg. 220

Phillips, Wendell E., Asst. Sec.--Southdown, Inc., Houston, TX; *U.S. Public*, pg. 1488

Phipps, Virginia F., V.P. & Sec.--Concord General Life Insurance Company, Concord, NH; *U.S. Public*, pg. 79

Piccirillo, Rocco, V.P.-Opers. & Sec.--Beauty Enterprises Inc., Hartford, CT; *U.S. Private*, pg. 128

Pickering, T.H., Exec. V.P. & Sec.--Westfield Companies, Westfield Center, OH; *U.S. Private*, pg. 1169

Pickett, William S., V.P.-Fin. & Sec.--K & G of Wisconsin, Inc., Milwaukee, WI; *U.S. Private*, pg. 602

Pickle, Robert D., V.P., Gen. Counsel & Sec.--Brown Group, Inc., Saint Louis, MO; *U.S. Public*, pg. 262

Picoli Simpson, Rogeria, Corp. Sec.--Aracruz Celulose S.A., Rio de Janeiro, Brazil; *Int'l*, pg. 78

Picut, Genevieve, Sec.--Essilor International Compagnie Generale d'Optique, Charenton-le-Pont, France; *Int'l*, pg. 462

Pidgeon, Ralph A., V.P. & Asst. Sec.--TrustCo Bank Corp., NY, Schenectady, NY; *U.S. Public*, pg. 1643

Pieper, William T., Treas. & Sec.--Stewart & Stevenson Power, Inc., City of Commerce, CA; *U.S. Public*, pg. 1518

Pierce, A. Kenneth, Jr., V.P.--The Dispatch Printing Company, Columbus, OH; *U.S. Private*, pg. 334

Pierce, B.P., Sec.--Friendswood Development Company, Houston, TX; *U.S. Public*, pg. 988

Pierce, Frank R., Chief Fin. Officer, Exec. V.P., Treas. & Sec.--Gulfmark Offshore Inc., Houston, TX; *U.S. Public*, pg. 769

Pierce, Linda, Coord.-Human Resources--The Edward J. DeBartolo Corporation, Youngstown, OH; *U.S. Private*, pg. 319

Pierce, Richard, Sec.--Guardian Alarm Co., Southfield, MI; *U.S. Private*, pg. 485

Pierce, Sandra T., Corp. Sec.--Norfolk Southern Railway Company, Norfolk, VA; *U.S. Public*, pg. 1191

Pieri, Albert, Treas. & Sec.--Artichoke Industries, Inc., Castroville, CA; *U.S. Private*, pg. 86

Pieri, Albert, Sec.--Ocean Mist Farms Corp., Castroville, CA; *U.S. Private*, pg. 811

Pierson, Rodney, Chief Fin. Officer, Sr. V.P. & Sec.--SAFECO Corporation, Seattle, WA; *U.S. Public*, pg. 1423

Piet, William M., V.P.-Corp. Affairs & Sec.--Wm. Wrigley Jr. Company, Chicago, IL; *U.S. Public*, pg. 1781

Pietroski, Joseph J., Sr. V.P., Gen. Counsel & Sec.--Manulife Financial (The Manufacturers Life Insurance Company), Toronto, Canada; *Int'l*, pg. 840

Pifer, Glenn A., Chief Fin. Officer, Treas. & Sec.--Allied Security, Inc., Pittsburgh, PA; *U.S. Private*, pg. 40

Pike, Mary Anne, Treas. & Sec.--Elite Lamp, Inc., West Memphis, AR; *U.S. Private*, pg. 371

Pike, Robert W., Sr. V.P., Sec. & Gen. Counsel--The Allstate Corporation, Northbrook, IL; *U.S. Public*, pg. 55

Pikus, Jean Zwerlin, V.P.-Opers. & Sec.--Canterbury Corporate Services, Inc., Medford, NJ; *U.S. Public*, pg. 301

Pillay, N., Corp. Sec.--International Factors (Singapore) Ltd., Singapore, Singapore; *Int'l*, pg. 684

Pillois, Jean-Marie, Corp. Sec.--Eridania Beghin-Say Group, Neuilly-sur-Seine, France; *Int'l*, pg. 324

Pinches, P.S., Sec.--Boxmag-Rapid Ltd., Birmingham, United Kingdom; *Int'l*, pg. 1511

Pindyck, Mary E., V.P. & Asst. Sec.--Meridian Industries, Inc., Milwaukee, WI; *U.S. Private*, pg. 732

Pinkerton, Jane E., Chief Fin. Officer, V.P.-Admin. & Sec.--Irex Corporation, Lancaster, PA; *U.S. Public*, pg. 913

Pinney, J., Sec. & Gen. Counsel--Courtaulds Aerospace, Littleborough, United Kingdom; *Int'l*, pg. 338

Piorkowski, Ted, Controller & Asst. Sec.--Crowley, Milner & Company, Detroit, MI; *U.S. Public*, pg. 461

Pipitone, Joseph F., Sr. V.P. & Sec.--The Citizens National Bank, Laurel, MD; *U.S. Public*, pg. 1089

Pisa, Veronica, Sec.--Continental Paper & Supply Co., Detroit, MI; *U.S. Private*, pg. 269

Pishko, Dorita A., Sec.--Respironics, Inc., Pittsburgh, PA; *U.S. Public*, pg. 1383

Pitkowsky, Murray, Sr. V.P.--Datascope Corp., Montvale, NJ; *U.S. Public*, pg. 487

Pitler, Barry, Gen. Counsel & Sec.--Rapid Mounting & Finishing Co., Chicago, IL; *U.S. Private*, pg. 910

Pitts, George L., Sec.--Cagle's Inc., Atlanta, GA; *U.S. Public*, pg. 291

Pitts, George L., Sec.--Cagle's Farms Inc., Dalton, GA; *U.S. Public*, pg. 292

Piyayodilokchai, V., Sec.--Esso Standard Thailand Ltd., Bangkok, Thailand; *U.S. Public*, pg. 602

Plaeger, Frederick J., II, V.P., Gen. Counsel & Corp. Sec.--The Louisiana Land and Exploration Company, New Orleans, LA; *U.S. Public*, pg. 269

Planes, John, Pres., Chief Exec. Officer & Sec.--Planes Moving And Storage, Inc., Cincinnati, OH; *U.S. Private*, pg. 869

Planes, Linda, Asst. Sec.--Planes Moving And Storage, Inc., Cincinnati, OH; *U.S. Private*, pg. 869

Platt, Melanie M., Sec.--AGL Resources, Atlanta, GA; *U.S. Public*, pg. 6

Platt, Thomas C., III, V.P., Gen. Counsel & Sec.--Chemfab Corporation, Merrimack, NH; *U.S. Public*, pg. 344

Plecity, Duane A., Sec.--Inter-Community Telephone Company, Nome, ND; *U.S. Public*, pg. 1022

Plotnick, Stanley D., Chm., Chief Exec. Officer & Sec.--Encore Marketing International, Inc., Lanham, MD; *U.S. Public*, pg. 580

Plubell, Ann Marie P., V.P., Sec. & Assoc. Gen. Counsel--SLM Holding Corp., Washington, DC; *U.S. Public*, pg. 1419

Plush, Mark J., Controller & Asst. Sec.--Keithley Instruments, Inc., Cleveland, OH; *U.S. Public*, pg. 946

Poag, Neil W., V.P., Controller & Sec.--Waterloo Furniture Components Limited, Kitchener, Canada; *U.S. Private*, pg. 270

Poch, Gerlad A., Co-Chm. Bd., Pres., Chief Exec. Officer & Sec.--AmeriData Technologies, Inc., Stamford, CT; *U.S. Public*, pg. 711

Pocknee, D.H., Sec.--Robert Fleming Asset Management Limited, London, United Kingdom; *Int'l*, pg. 493

Podkulski, Laura, Sec.--Osmose Wood Preserving, Inc., Buffalo, NY; *U.S. Private*, pg. 821

Poe, Sheena E., V.P., Gen. Counsel & Sec.--Integon Corporation, Winston Salem, NC; *U.S. Public*, pg. 719

Poeschl, Gaylord, V.P. & Sec.--Tank Service, Inc., Knoxville, TN; *U.S. Public*, pg. 521

Pogach, Allan C., V.P., Treas. & Sec.--Veritas DGC Inc, Houston, TX; *U.S. Private*, pg. 1136

Pohl, W. Timothy, Gen. Counsel & Sec.--American Water Works Company, Inc., Voorhees, NJ; *U.S. Public*, pg. 95

Poho, Juhani, Chief Fin. Officer & Sr. V.P.--Tamrock Corp., Tampere, Finland; *Int'l*, pg. 1352

Poirier, Pierre, V.P.-Legal Affairs & Corp. Sec.--Provigo Inc., Montreal, Canada; *Int'l*, pg. 1072

Pokross, David R., Jr., Gen. Counsel & Sec.--Tech/Ops Sevcon, Inc., Boston, MA; *U.S. Public*, pg. 1563

Polack, Robert, V.P., Corp. Counsel & Sec.--Reilly Industries, Inc., Indianapolis, IN; *U.S. Private*, pg. 919

Polansky, Sheldon, V.P., Legal Counsel & Sec.--Spar Aerospace Limited, Toronto, Canada; *Int'l*, pg. 1287

Poling, Kathy, Sec.--Electro-Coatings, Inc., Berkeley, CA; *U.S. Private*, pg. 368

Polishook, David, Chief Fin. Officer, Treas. & Sec.--The Strober Organization, Inc., Brooklyn, NY; *U.S. Private*, pg. 403

Polk, John, Corp. Sec.--Ludlow Composites Corporation, Fremont, OH; *U.S. Private*, pg. 680

Pollack, Carol, Chief Fin. Officer, V.P., Treas. & Sec.--Comprehensive Care Corporation, Corona Del Mar, CA; *U.S. Public*, pg. 419

Pollack, Michael B., First V.P. & Sec.--W.P. Carey & Co., Inc., New York, NY; *U.S. Private*, pg. 209

Pollaers, John, Dir.-Fin.--United Distillers UK Plc, Perth, United Kingdom; *Int'l*, pg. 412

Pollan, Lynn, V.P., Gen. Counsel & Corp. Sec.--Williamhouse-Regency, Inc., New York, NY; *U.S. Public*, pg. 89

Pollard, Bobbie, Exec. Administrator--American Television Time, Inc., Austin, TX; *U.S. Private*, pg. 63

Pollard, Boyd A., Treas. & Sec.--Power & Telephone Supply Company, Memphis, TN; *U.S. Private*, pg. 877

Pollard, Don, Chief Fin. Officer, Treas. & Sec.--Allied Sporting Goods Inc., Louisville, KY; *U.S. Private*, pg. 41

Pollard, Linda, Exec. Sec.--Ardmore Farms, De Land, FL; *U.S. Public*, pg. 1348

Polley, John E., Asst. Corp. Sec.--Cinergy Corp., Cincinnati, OH; *U.S. Public*, pg. 368

Polley, John E., Asst. Sec.--Cinergy, Plainfield, IN; *U.S. Public*, pg. 369

Polley, John E., Asst. Corp. Sec.--CINergy Services, Inc., Cincinnati, OH; *U.S. Public*, pg. 369

Polley, John E., Asst. Corp. Sec.--KO Transmission Company, Cincinnati, OH; *U.S. Public*, pg. 369

Polley, John E., Asst. Corp. Sec.--Lawrenceburg Gas Co., Cincinnati, OH; *U.S. Public*, pg. 369

Polley, John E., Asst. Corp. Sec.--Miami Power Corp., Cincinnati, OH; *U.S. Public*, pg. 369

Polley, John E., Asst. Corp. Sec.--Tri-State Improvement Co., Cincinnati, OH; *U.S. Public*, pg. 369

Polley, John E., Asst. Corp. Sec.--Union Light, Heat and Power Co., Cincinnati, OH; *U.S. Public*, pg. 369

Polley, John E., Asst. Corp. Sec.--Cinergy Corp., Cincinnati, OH; *U.S. Public*, pg. 369

Pollihan, Thomas H., V.P., Gen. Counsel & Sec.--Kellwood Company, Chesterfield, MO; *U.S. Public*, pg. 948

Pollock, B.R., Treas. & Sec.--Morris Coupling Co., Erie, PA; *U.S. Private*, pg. 762

Pollock, Maurice, V.P., Controller, Treas. & Sec.--Collin Street Bakery, Corsicana, TX; *U.S. Private*, pg. 252

Pollock, Robert J., Sec. & Clerk--Fall River Gas Company, Fall River, MA; *U.S. Public*, pg. 611

Pollock, Ross, V.P., Gen. Counsel & Sec.--OfficeMax, Shaker Heights, OH; *U.S. Public*, pg. 1212

Polson, Linda, Asst. Sec.--Dewberry Design Group, Oklahoma City, OK; *U.S. Private*, pg. 329

Pomares, Jim, Treas., Sec. & Mgr.-Personnel--Sacramento Jaguar, Inc., Sacramento, CA; *U.S. Private*, pg. 1143

Pomerantz, Saul, Chief Fin. Officer, Sr. V.P. & Sec.--Movie Star, Inc., New York, NY; *U.S. Public*, pg. 1140

Pomeranz, Harold, Chm. Bd., Treas. & Sec.--Stanley Roberts, Inc., Lodi, NJ; *U.S. Private*, pg. 936

Pomeroy, John J., V.P., Gen. Counsel & Sec.--Allendale Mutual Insurance Co., Johnston, RI; *U.S. Private*, pg. 37

Pommerville, Robert W., Exec. V.P., Gen. Counsel & Sec.--Beverly Enterprises, Inc., Fort Smith, AR; *U.S. Public*, pg. 227

Ponitz, J.A., Gen. Counsel, Asst. Sec.--Grand Trunk Western Railroad, Inc., Detroit, MI; *Int'l*, pg. 258

Pont, M.J., Exec. Dir. & Sec.--Hoechst Australia Ltd., Melbourne, Australia; *Int'l*, pg. 626

Pool, Stanley L., V.P.-Sls. & Mktg. & Sec.--Mity-Lite, Inc., Orem, UT; *U.S. Public*, pg. 1118

Pope, Douglas V., Sec.--Washington Gas Light Co., Springfield, VA; *U.S. Public*, pg. 1740

Pope, J.M., Sec.--Cobham plc, Wimborne Minster, United Kingdom; *Int'l*, pg. 301

Pople, Gloria, Sec.--Delta plc, London, United Kingdom; *Int'l*, pg. 389

Popov, Peter N., V.P., Gen. Counsel & Sec.--Marine Transport Lines, Inc., Weehawken, NJ; *U.S. Private*, pg. 703

Popp, Betty, Controller & Sec.--Red Wing Products, Inc., Plainview, NY; *Int'l*, pg. 480

Porche, Dale P., Treas. & Sec.--SAIA Motor Freight Lines, Houma, LA; *U.S. Public*, pg. 1788

Porro, Jose Manuel Gonzalez, Vice Sec.--Corporacion MAPFRE, Compania Internacional de Reaseguros, S.A., Madrid, Spain; *Int'l*, pg. 332

Porter, Edward A., V.P.-Admin., Gen. Counsel & Sec.--National Gypsum Company, Charlotte, NC; *Int'l*, pg. 790

Porter, Edward A., V.P., Gen. Counsel & Sec.--Walter Industries, Inc., Tampa, FL; *U.S. Public*, pg. 1736

Porter, Marc A., Chief Fin. Officer, V.P., Treas. & Sec.--The Law Company, Inc., Wichita, KS; *U.S. Private*, pg. 653

Porter, Mike, Sec.--FKI Plc, Halifax, United Kingdom; *Int'l*, pg. 471

Porter, N.C., Sec.--The General Electric Company, p.l.c., London, United Kingdom; *Int'l*, pg. 543

Porter, Robert C., Treas. & Asst. Sec.--AmerenCIPS, Springfield, IL; *U.S. Public*, pg. 65

Porter, Robert C., V.P., Treas., Sec. & Asst. Controller--CIPSCO Investment Company, Springfield, IL; *U.S. Public*, pg. 66

Porter, William, V.P., Corp. Controller & Asst. Sec.--Cadence Design Systems, Inc., San Jose, CA; *U.S. Public*, pg. 290

Posen, Fay, Sec.--Beltone Electronics Corporation, Chicago, IL; *U.S. Private*, pg. 132

Posner, E.G., V.P., Gen. Counsel & Sec.--PQ Corporation, Berwyn, PA; *U.S. Private*, pg. 827

Posnick, Adolph, Chm. Bd. & Sec.--First Union Management, Inc., Cleveland, OH; *U.S. Public*, pg. 641

Post, G. Roger, V.P., Gen. Counsel & Sec.--White Castle System, Inc., Columbus, OH; *U.S. Private*, pg. 1171

Potamkin, Robert, Sec.--Potamkin Manhattan, New York, NY; *U.S. Private*, pg. 876

Pote, Hal, Chm. Bd., Pres., Chief Exec. Officer & Sec.--Ambar, Inc., Lafayette, LA; *U.S. Private*, pg. 126

Potter, John, Controller & Sec.--Amlings Flowerland, Hinsdale, IL; *U.S. Private*, pg. 66

Potts, William L., Jr., Chief Fin. Officer, V.P.-Fin. & Sec.--Komag, Incorporated, San Jose, CA; *U.S. Public*, pg. 966

Pouliot, Colleen M., V.P., Gen. Counsel & Sec.--Adobe Systems Incorporated, San Jose, CA; *U.S. Public*, pg. 20

Pourciau, Charles L., Jr., Sec.--TRAK Microwave Corp., Tampa, FL; *U.S. Public*, pg. 1563

Pourciau, Susan, Treas. & Sec.--Fraenkel Company, Baton Rouge, LA; *U.S. Private*, pg. 423

Powell, Caroline E., Sec.--Carolina Biological Supply Co., Burlington, NC; *U.S. Private*, pg. 213

Powell, Doug, V.P.-Mktg.--Descente America Inc., Englewood, CO; *Int'l*, pg. 395

Powell, Jerry, Gen. Counsel & Sec.--Compass Bancshares, Inc., Birmingham, AL; *U.S. Public*, pg. 418

Powell, Joyce, V.P. & Sec.--L. Powell Co., Inc., Culver City, CA; *U.S. Private*, pg. 877

Powell, Robert J., V.P.-Intl. Licensing, Sec. & Gen. Counsel--Signal Apparel Company, Inc., Chattanooga, TN; *U.S. Public*, pg. 1472

Powell, Susan F., V.P. & Sec.--Investors Insurance Group, Inc., Boca Raton, FL; *U.S. Public*, pg. 911

Power, Claire M., Asst. Sec.--Donaldson, Lufkin, & Jenrette, Inc., New York, NY; *U.S. Public*, pg. 589

Powers Barr, Eve, General Counsel & Asst. Sec.--Atotech U.S.A. Inc., Rock Hill, SC; *U.S. Private*, pg. 97

Powers, Ann, Sec.--Powers Construction Co., Inc., Florence, SC; *U.S. Private*, pg. 878

Powers, I.W., Sec.--Powers Fastening, Inc., New Rochelle, NY; *U.S. Private*, pg. 878

Powers, Joe L., Exec. V.P. & Sec.--Thomas Nelson Inc., Nashville, TN; *U.S. Public*, pg. 1167

Powlick, George, Chief Fin. Officer, V.P.-Fin. & Sec.--K-Swiss Inc., Chatsworth, CA; *U.S. Public*, pg. 937

Prager, Joan, Corp. Sec.--AVX Corporation, Myrtle Beach, SC; *Int'l*, pg. 775

Prater, Ronald, Sec.--Owensboro Grain Co., Inc., Owensboro, KY; *U.S. Private*, pg. 824

Prather, Robert L., Chief Fin. Officer, Exec. V.P., Treas. & Sec.--Kocolene Oil Corp., Seymour, IN; *U.S. Private*, pg. 629

Pratt, William D., Exec. V.P., Sec. & Gen. Counsel--Hollywood Casino Corp, Atlantic City, NJ; *U.S. Public*, pg. 830

Pratte, Lise, Corp. Sec.--Bombardier Inc., Montreal, Canada; *Int'l*, pg. 199

Prentice, F. Sheldon, Sr. V.P., Gen. Counsel & Sec.--Chittenden Corporation, Burlington, VT; *U.S. Public*, pg. 350

Presley, Samuel H., Sec.--Clark Specialty Co., Inc., Hammondsport, NY; *U.S. Private*, pg. 243

Presser, Tracy, Treas. & Sec.--J. Hellman Produce, Inc., Los Angeles, CA; *U.S. Private*, pg. 520

Pressman, Kim I., Exec. V.P., Treas. & Sec.--Price Communications Corporation, New York, NY; *U.S. Public*, pg. 1324

Pressman, Kim I., V.P. & Sec.--Pricellular Corporation, White Plains, NY; *U.S. Public*, pg. 1324

Prestage, Ann, Asst. Sec.--Cooper Ventures, Inc., Bella Vista, AR; *U.S. Private*, pg. 274

Prete, Christine, Sec.--Crabtree Premium Finance, Lombard, IL; *U.S. Public*, pg. 1677

Pribisko, Patricia W., V.P., Gen. Counsel & Sec.--Lesco, Inc., Rocky River, OH; *U.S. Public*, pg. 989

Price, Bradford R., Exec. V.P. & Sec.--First Federal Capital Corp., La Crosse, WI; *U.S. Public*, pg. 632

Price, Carol, Sec.--Indo-Pacific Energy Ltd., Vancouver, Canada; *Int'l*, pg. 422

Price, Gerald R., V.P.-Fin. & Sec.--CFCF Inc., Montreal, Canada; *Int'l*, pg. 240

Price, Joseph, V.P.-Mfg. & Sec.--Dettra Flag Company, Oaks, PA; *U.S. Private*, pg. 328

Price, Michael D., Chief Fin. Officer, V.P., Treas. & Sec.--Bentley Pharmaceuticals, Inc., Tampa, FL; *U.S. Public*, pg. 212

Price, Nancy K., Asst. Sec.--CGAS, Inc., Columbus, OH; *U.S. Public*, pg. 585

Price, R. Kevin, Sr. V.P. & Sec.--The Hartford Steam Boiler Inspection & Insurance Co., Hartford, CT; *U.S. Public*, pg. 795

Price, Ronald D., Chief Fin. Officer, Sr. V.P. & Sec.--Slocan Forest Products Ltd., Richmond, Canada; *Int'l*, pg. 1263

Price, Russell L., V.P., Gen. Counsel & Sec.--Tandycrafts, Inc., Fort Worth, TX; *U.S. Public*, pg. 1561

Price, Steven F., Asst. Treas. & Asst. Corp. Sec.--WPL Holdings, Inc., Madison, WI; *U.S. Public*, pg. 1727

Price, Steven F., Asst. Sec.--South Beloit Water, Gas & Electric Co., South Beloit, IL; *U.S. Public*, pg. 1728

Price, Steven F., Asst. Sec.--REAC, Inc., Madison, WI; *U.S. Public*, pg. 1728

Price, Thomas J., V.P.-Fin. & Sec.--The Oilgear Company, Milwaukee, WI; *U.S. Public*, pg. 1215

Price, W. Ralph, Exec. V.P.--Doron Precision Systems, Inc., Binghamton, NY; *U.S. Private*, pg. 341

Priebe, Kathy, Corp. Sec.--Laidlaw Corporation, Scottsdale, AZ; *U.S. Private*, pg. 642

Priest, Gordon W., Asst. Sec. & Asst. Gen. Counsel--PHH Corporation, Hunt Valley, MD; *U.S. Public*, pg. 321

Prifti, William M., Gen. Counsel & Sec.--Pax World Fund Family, Portsmouth, NH; *U.S. Public*, pg. 1266

Primuth, Richard A., Sec.--Ault Incorporated, Minneapolis, MN; *U.S. Public*, pg. 147

Primuth, Richard A., Sec.--Communications Systems, Inc., Hector, MN; *U.S. Public*, pg. 415

Prince, Charles O., III, Exec. V.P., Gen. Counsel & Sec.--Travelers Group, New York, NY; *U.S. Public*, pg. 1632

Prince, William, Sec.--Distribution America, Des Plaines, IL; *U.S. Private*, pg. 335

Prindle, Cheryl, Controller--Restonic Mattress Corporation, Rosemont, IL; *U.S. Private*, pg. 925

Printz, Victoria, Treas. & Sec.--Somerset Pontiac GMC Inc., Troy, MI; *U.S. Private*, pg. 1013

Prior, John C., Chief Fin. Officer, Sr. V.P.-Fin. & Sec.--Curative Health Services, East Setauket, NY; *U.S. Public*, pg. 469

Proctor, Michael, V.P.-Fin. & Corp. Sec.--Battle Mountain Canada Ltd., Toronto, Canada; *U.S. Public*, pg. 193

Proctor, Timothy D., Sr. V.P., Gen. Counsel & Sec.--Glaxo Wellcome Inc., Research Triangle Park, NC; *Int'l*, pg. 552

Profaci, Robert J., V.P.-Pur. & Sec.--Colivita USA, Inc., Linden, NJ; *U.S. Private*, pg. 252

Profeta, Nicholas J., Sec.--Polychrome Corp. Div., Fort Lee, NJ; *Int'l*, pg. 370

Proffit, Nancy, Sec.--Solar Communications, Inc., Naperville, IL; *U.S. Private*, pg. 1012

Prohofsky, Dennis, V.P., Gen. Counsel & Sec.--The Minnesota Mutual Life Insurance Company, Saint Paul, MN; *U.S. Private*, pg. 750

Prokopp, Terry, Sec. & Adv. Mgr.--Pontiac-GMC Division, Detroit, MI; *U.S. Public*, pg. 720

Proll, Douglas A., V.P.-Fin. & Treas.--Renaissance Energy Ltd., Calgary, Canada; *Int'l*, pg. 1102

Proudfit, Debe, Treas. & Sec.--Vanport Manufacturing, Inc., Boring, OR; *U.S. Private*, pg. 1134

Prow, Enoch J., Exec. V.P. & Sec.--NationsBank South, Atlanta, GA; *U.S. Public*, pg. 1163

Pruden, Peter D., III, Exec. V.P. & Sec.--The Smithfield Companies, Inc., Portsmouth, VA; *U.S. Public*, pg. 1479

Prudhomme, Michael P., Sec. & Treas.--Central Louisiana Electric Company, Inc., Pineville, LA; *U.S. Public*, pg. 325

Pruiett, Norma, Office Mgr.--A.C. Humko, Paris, IL; *Int'l*, pg. 92

Pryor, Joe, Treas. & Sec.--Wm. Bolthouse Farms, Inc., Bakersfield, CA; *U.S. Private*, pg. 155

Puerari, Giovanni, Chief Fin. Officer, Sec. & Treas.--Arnoldo Mondadori Editore S.p.A., Segrate, Italy; *Int'l*, pg. 887

Pugh, A.J., Sec.--Liberty of London Prints Limited, London, United Kingdom; *Int'l*, pg. 807

Pugh, Lowell E., II, Gen. Counsel & Asst. Sec.--United Foods, Inc., Bells, TN; *U.S. Public*, pg. 1677

Pugiello, Peter, Chief Fin. Officer, Sr. V.P., Treas. & Asst. Sec.--Blonder-Tongue Laboratories, Inc., Old Bridge, NJ; *U.S. Public*, pg. 237

Pugliese, Fred, Sec.--Mickelberry Communications, Inc., New York, NY; *U.S. Private*, pg. 741

Puhala, James J., V.P., Gen. Counsel & Sec.--Dravo Corporation, Pittsburgh, PA; *U.S. Public*, pg. 527

Pulkrabek, Larry A., Sr. V.P., Sec. & Gen. Counsel--Armstrong World Industries, Inc., Lancaster, PA; *U.S. Public*, pg. 131

Pullin, Judy K., Asst. Sec.--KCL Corporation, Shelbyville, IN; *U.S. Private*, pg. 603

Pullum, Mary, Sec.--Southwestern Public Service Company, Amarillo, TX; *U.S. Public*, pg. 1170

Pulsifer, Howard A., V.P., Gen. Counsel & Sec.--AAR Corp., Wood Dale, IL; *U.S. Public*, pg. 1

Pultz, George S., V.P., Sec. & Gen. Counsel--Robertson-Ceco Corporation, San Ramon, CA; *U.S. Public*, pg. 1394

Purcell, Kevin H., Treas. & Sec.--Empire Fire & Marine Insurance Co., Omaha, NE; *Int'l*, pg. 1530

Purcell, Steven, Chief Fin. Officer & Corp. Sec.--American Business Information, Inc., Omaha, NE; *U.S. Public*, pg. 69

Purcell, Terri L., Deputy Gen. Counsel & Asst. Sec.--Coca-Cola Enterprises Inc., Atlanta, GA; *U.S. Public*, pg. 393

Purpur, Karen, Sec.--Nordstrom, Inc., Seattle, WA; *U.S. Public*, pg. 1190

Pursley, Linda, Sec.--B.F. Goodrich Aerospace, Akron, OH; *U.S. Public*, pg. 751

Purtell, Lawrence R., Sr. V.P., Gen. Counsel & Sec.--McDermott International, Inc., New Orleans, LA; *U.S. Public*, pg. 1067

Purvines, Verne E., V.P., Gen. Counsel & Sec.--National General Insurance Co., Earth City, MO; *U.S. Public*, pg. 721

Purvis, M. T. A., Asst. Sec.--San Francisco Insurance Company (U.K.) Ltd., London, United Kingdom; *Int'l*, pg. 59

Purvis, Martin T.A., Sec.--Brake Bros plc, Ashford, United Kingdom; *Int'l*, pg. 210

Purvis, Sandra K., Exec. V.P. & Sec.--A.C. Legg Packing Company, Inc., Birmingham, AL; *U.S. Private*, pg. 658

Puthoff, Frank M., V.P., Gen. Counsel & Sec.--Miami Subs Corporation, Fort Lauderdale, FL; *U.S. Public*, pg. 1103

Putnam, Spencer, Chief Oper. Officer & Sec.--The Vermont Teddy Bear Company, Inc., Shelburne, VT; *U.S. Public*, pg. 1716

Pyke, John S., Jr., V.P., Sec. & Legal--M.A. Hanna Company, Cleveland, OH; *U.S. Public*, pg. 780

Pyle, Robert M., Jr., Sec.--American Express Credit Corporation, Wilmington, DE; *U.S. Public*, pg. 74

Quails, Robert, Sr. V.P., Corp. Treas. & Asst Sec.--Haggar Corporation, Dallas, TX; *U.S. Public*, pg. 774

Quast, William J., V.P., Treas. & Asst. Sec.--Energy West Inc., Great Falls, MT; *U.S. Public*, pg. 581

Quatela, Laura G., V.P.-Admin., Gen. Counsel & Sec.--General Railway Signal Corp., Rochester, NY; *Int'l*, pg. 1194

Quebedeaux, Carol, Corp. Sec.--Quebedeaux Pontiac, Inc., Tucson, AZ; *U.S. Private*, pg. 900

Querner, Jon W., Corp. Sec.--Kreonite, Inc., Wichita, KS; *U.S. Private*, pg. 635

Quesada, Martha, Treas. & Sec.--Maxine of Hollywood, Inc., Los Angeles, CA; *U.S. Private*, pg. 716

Quevedo Fort, D. Enrique, Sec.--Telefonia y Finanzas, S.A. (Telfisa), Madrid, Spain; *Int'l*, pg. 1372

Quinn, B., Dit., Acct & Sec.--Moore Paragon Central Africa Limited, Harare, Zimbabwe; *Int'l*, pg. 890

Quinn, Jeffry N., Sr. V.P.-Law & Human Resources, Gen. Counsel & Sec.--Arch Coal, Inc., Saint Louis, MO; *U.S. Public*, pg. 139

Quinn, Joellyn, V.P.-Corp. Rels. & Asst. Sec.--Credit Union National Association, Madison, WI; *U.S. Private*, pg. 288

Quintanilla Ochoa, Raul, Sr. Exec. V.P., Gen. Counsel & Sec.--Grupo Casa Autrey, Mexico, Mexico; *Int'l*, pg. 573

Quintanilla, JesusGarcia- Villoslada, Sec.--AESA Astilleros Espanoles, S.A., Madrid, Spain; *Int'l*, pg. 1223

Quintanilla, JesusGarcia- Villoslada, Sec.--ASTANO - Astilleros y Talleres del Noroeste, S.A., Madrid, Spain; *Int'l*, pg. 1223

Quirk, Kathryn L., V.P. & Asst. Sec.--Montgomery St. Income Securities, Inc., San Francisco, CA; *U.S. Public*, pg. 1127

Quist, S.J., Asst. Sec.--Gist-Brocades, Inc., Wilmington, DE; *Int'l*, pg. 1143

Raber, James A., Corp. Sec.--Star Bronze Company, Alliance, OH; *U.S. Private*, pg. 1034

Rabinowitz, Helen, Sec.--Baris Shoe Company, Inc., New York, NY; *U.S. Private*, pg. 116

Rabinowitz, Maynard, Vice Chm.-Fin. Admin. & Legal Affairs & Sec.--American Media, Inc., Lake Worth, FL; *U.S. Public*, pg. 87

Radatovich, Steve, V.P., Controller & Sec.--Vectura Group, Inc., New Orleans, LA; *U.S. Private*, pg. 1135

Radcliffe, Mark, Company Sec. & Dir.-Corp. Services--Reed Elsevier plc, London, United Kingdom; *Int'l*, pg. 1093

Radcliffe, Mark, Company Sec.--Reed International P.L.C., London, United Kingdom; *Int'l*, pg. 1093

Radcliffe, Randy, V.P., Treas. & Sec.--Fisk Electric Company, Houston, TX; *Int'l*, pg. 16

Radde, Donald E., Exec. V.P. & Sec.--Pinnacle Financial Services Inc., Saint Joseph, MI; *U.S. Public*, pg. 1297

Rader, Larry, Gen. Counsel & Sec.--Marine Travelift, Inc., Sturgeon Bay, WI; *U.S. Private*, pg. 703

Rades, Randolph, V.P. & Sec.--Finora Company, Inc., Englewood, CO; *U.S. Private*, pg. 802

Radford, Enoch, V.P. & Sec.--Plant Maintenance Service Corporation, Memphis, TN; *U.S. Private*, pg. 869

Radke, Jolene, Corp. Sec.--Younkers, Inc., Des Moines, IA; *U.S. Public*, pg. 1334

Raduenz, Gary A., Asst. Sec.--Pettibone Corporation, Lisle, IL; *U.S. Private*, pg. 859

Radwill, Linda, V.P. & Sec.--Master Appliance Corp., Racine, WI; *U.S. Private*, pg. 713

Rafanello, Richard A., Treas. & Sec.--E.C.D., Inc., Hillside, NJ; *U.S. Private*, pg. 353

Rafferty, J.T., Sec.--Benjamin Moore & Co., Montvale, NJ; *U.S. Private*, pg. 133

Raggio, William J., V.P., Gen. Counsel & Sec.--Santa Fe Gaming Corporation, Las Vegas, NV; *U.S. Public*, pg. 1432

Ragucci, John A., Sec.--Joshua L. Baily Co., Inc., Hoboken, NJ; *U.S. Private*, pg. 110

Raiche, John T., Controller & Sec.--Divane Bros. Electric Co., Franklin Park, IL; *U.S. Private*, pg. 336

Raimondi, Josephine A., Gen. Counsel & Sec.--Midwest Employer's Casualty Company, Maryland Heights, MO; *U.S. Public*, pg. 215

Raines, Bobby J., V.P. & Treas.--Cal-Maine Foods, Inc., Jackson, MS; *U.S. Public*, pg. 292

Raines, Mary E., Sec.--Delta Air Lines, Inc., Atlanta, GA; *U.S. Public*, pg. 497

Rainwater, Jay Earl, Gen. Counsel & Sec.--Wm. S. Trimble Company, Inc., Knoxville, TN; *U.S. Private*, pg. 1103

Rainwater, Tom, Chief Fin. Officer, Treas. & Sec.--E.C. Barton & Company, Jonesboro, AR; *U.S. Private*, pg. 119

Rajashekar, K.S., Sec.--South Eastern Coalfields Limited, Bilaspur, India; *Int'l*, pg. 299

Rakow, May T., Sr. V.P.-Personnel & Sec.--IHC Group, Inc., South Elgin, IL; *U.S. Private*, pg. 555

Ralph, Rose Marie, Asst. Sec.--Montana Power Company, Butte, MT; *U.S. Public*, pg. 1126

Ralston, James A., V.P., Gen. Counsel & Sec.--Eagle-Picher Industries, Inc., Cincinnati, OH; *U.S. Private*, pg. 355

Ramadan, Tony, Sec.--Campbell's Soups (Aust.) Pty. Ltd., Melbourne, Australia; *U.S. Public*, pg. 299

Ramat, Charles, Chm. Bd., Pres., Chief Exec. Officer & Asst. Sec.--Aris Industries, Inc., New York, NY; *U.S. Public*, pg. 129

Ramirez, Joseph L., Gen. Counsel & Corp. Sec.--Network Computing Devices, Inc., Mountain View, CA; *U.S. Public*, pg. 1168

Ramos, Garcia, Sec.--Tubos de Acero de Mexico, S.A., Mexico, Mexico; *Int'l*, pg. 1426

Ramsay, Scott, Chief Fin. Officer, Sr. V.P., Treas. & Sec.-Admin.--Shaw's Supermarkets, Inc., East Bridgewater, MA; *Int'l*, pg. 1170

Ramsey, James H., Sec.--Darlington Veneer Company, Darlington, SC; *U.S. Private*, pg. 311

Ramsey, Stewart P., Treas. & Sec.--LSJ Sportswear Inc., Deerfield, WI; *U.S. Private*, pg. 732

Ranada, M.G., Dir.-Fin. & Sec.--Cemindia Company Limited, Calcutta, India; *Int'l*, pg. 774

Ranade, M.G., Dir.-Fin. & Sec.--Cemindia Company Limited, Mumbai, India; *Int'l*, pg. 774

Rance, Brent, Chief Fin. Officer, V.P. & Sec.--Universal Folding Box Company, Inc., Hoboken, NJ; *U.S. Private*, pg. 1127

Randall, Robert W., V.P., Gen. Counsel & Sec.--Pride International, Inc., Houston, TX; *U.S. Public*, pg. 1324
Randall, Ron, V.P., Sec. & Gen. Counsel--Camco International Inc., Houston, TX; *U.S. Public*, pg. 298
Randall, Ronald R., V.P., Gen. Counsel & Sec.--Camco International Inc., Houston, TX; *U.S. Public*, pg. 297
Rands, L. William, Chief Fin. Officer, V.P., Treas. & Sec.--Monroc, Inc., Salt Lake City, UT; *U.S. Public*, pg. 1124
Rands, L. William, Sec.--Big Horn Redi-Mix, Powell, WY; *U.S. Public*, pg. 1124
Rands, Mary, Controller, Treas. & Sec.--Brush Research Manufacturing Company, Los Angeles, CA; *U.S. Private*, pg. 176
Raney, Bill, Treas. & Sec.--West Central Cooperative, Ralston, IA; *U.S. Private*, pg. 1163
Rangarajan, K., V.P. & Asst. Sec.--Standard Commercial Corporation, Wilson, NC; *U.S. Public*, pg. 1501
Ranger, Brian, Asst. Sec.--Westburne Inc., Montreal, Canada; *Int'l*, pg. 1491
Ranin, Ursula, Corp. Sec.--Oy Nokia Ab/Nokia Group, Helsinki, Finland; *Int'l*, pg. 951
Rankin, Nancy K., Asst. Sec.--Pulitzer Publishing Company, Saint Louis, MO; *U.S. Public*, pg. 1343
Ransam, Jack, Sec.--Hardware Wholesalers, Inc., Fort Wayne, IN; *U.S. Private*, pg. 502
Rao, Elizabeth, Sec.--The Rao Group Inc., Sterling Heights, MI; *U.S. Private*, pg. 910
Rao, V. Prakasa, Sec.--Central Mine Planning & Design Institute Limited, Ranchi, India; *Int'l*, pg. 298
Raphael, Joanne H., Sec.--PP&L Resources, Allentown, PA; *U.S. Public*, pg. 1244
Rapp, Christian F., V.P.-Fin. & Sec.--Louisville Bedding Company, Louisville, KY; *U.S. Private*, pg. 677
Rapp, Larry T., V.P. & Corp. Sec.--Electro Scientific Industries, Inc., Portland, OR; *U.S. Public*, pg. 568
Rascio, Anthony, V.P., Gen. Counsel & Sec.--Roberts Pharmaceutical Corporation, Eatontown, NJ; *U.S. Public*, *pg. 1393*
Rascio, Anthony A., V.P. & Sec.--VRG International, Inc., Eatontown, NJ; *U.S. Public*, pg. 1393
Rascio, Anthony A., V.P. & Sec.--Roberts Laboratories, Inc., Eatontown, NJ; *U.S. Public*, pg. 1393
Rascio, Anthony A., V.P. & Sec.--Monmouth Pharmaceutical, Ltd., Guildford, United Kingdom; *U.S. Public*, pg. 1394
Rascoe, Eric, Treas. & Sec.--Thermal Industries, Inc., Pittsburgh, PA; *U.S. Private*, pg. 490
Rasmussen, Dale L., Sr. V.P. & Sec.--AirSensors, Inc., Seattle, WA; *U.S. Public*, pg. 33
Rasor, C. Lewis, Jr., Sec.--Wagner Systems Corporation, Greenville, SC; *Int'l*, pg. 1418
Rassman, Joel H., Chief Fin. Officer, Sr. V.P., Treas. & Asst. Sec.--Toll Brothers, Inc., Huntingdon Valley, PA; *U.S. Public*, pg. 1620
Rathke, Francis, Chief Fin. Officer, Treas. & Sec.--Ben & Jerry's Homemade Inc., South Burlington, VT; *U.S. Public*, pg. 210
Ratliff, Donna L., Treas. & Asst. Sec.--The GNI Group, Inc., Deer Park, TX; *U.S. Public*, pg. 693
Ratliff, Donna R., V.P.-Admin. & Corp. Sec.--The Genlyte Group Incorporated, Union, NJ; *U.S. Public*, pg. 729
Rattleff, Sue, Sec.--Bellsouth Mobile Systems Group, Atlanta, GA; *U.S. Public*, pg. 208
Raulin, Philippe, Sec. Gen.--Framatome SA, Paris, France; *Int'l*, pg. 502
Rausch, Nina, Corp. Sec.--NIPSCO Industries, Inc., Hammond, IN; *U.S. Public*, pg. 1185
Rausch, Nina M., Sec.--Northern Indiana Public Service Company, Hammond, IN; *U.S. Public*, pg. 1185
Rauwerdink, William J., Chief Fin. Officer, Exec. V.P., Treas. & Sec.--Lason, Inc., Troy, MI; *U.S. Public*, pg. 979
Rawlings, Dolores B., Sec.--Crown Central Petroleum Corporation, Baltimore, MD; *U.S. Public*, pg. 462
Rawlins, Don, Asst. Sec.--AutoZone, Inc., Memphis, TN; *U.S. Public*, pg. 150
Rawls, Warren L., Chief Fin. Officer & Sec.--Littlefield, Adams & Company, Huber Heights, OH; *U.S. Public*, pg. 1001
Ray, Stuart, Treas. & Sec.--Davis-Moore Oldsmobile, Inc., Wichita, KS; *U.S. Private*, pg. 315
Ray, William C., V.P., Gen. Counsel & Sec.--Guilford Mills, Inc., Greensboro, NC; *U.S. Public*, pg. 768
Raymond, Samuel O., Sec.--Benthos, Inc., North Falmouth, MA; *U.S. Public*, pg. 212
Read, Bob, Treas. & Sec.--Graham, Milwaukee, WI; *Int'l*, pg. 377
Ready, George W., Treas. & Corp. Sec.--Watkins Associated Industries Inc., Atlanta, GA; *U.S. Private*, pg. 1153
Reasoner, Carroll J., Sec.--Met-Coil Systems Corp., Cedar Rapids, IA; *U.S. Public*, pg. 1099
Reaugh, O.H., Sr. V.P. & Asst. Sec.--States, Inc., Breckenridge, TX; *U.S. Private*, pg. 1037
Recht, Sam, Sec.--Milwaukee Bucks, Inc., Milwaukee, WI; *U.S. Private*, pg. 749
Recla, Debbie, Treas. & Corp. Sec.--Champion, Inc., Iron Mountain, MI; *U.S. Private*, pg. 228
Reddy, C.N., Sr. V.P.-Engrng. & Opers. & Sec.--Alliance Semiconductor Corp., San Jose, CA; *U.S. Public*, pg. 47
Reddy, Patrick D., V.P. & Asst. Sec.--American Banknote Corp., New York, NY; *U.S. Public*, pg. 68
Redepenning, Charles W., Jr., Sr. V.P., Gen. Counsel & Sec.--Unique Casual Restaurants, inc., Danvers, MA; *Int'l*, pg. 324
Redman, Clarence O., Corp. Sec.--AMCOL International Corp., Arlington Heights, IL; *U.S. Public*, pg. 63
Redonet De La Vega, D. Eugenio, Sec.--Eritel, S.A., Madrid, Spain; *Int'l*, pg. 1372
Redwine, Jack F., Asst. Sec. & Treas.--Chickasha Cotton Oil Co., Chandler, AZ; *Int'l*, pg. 1395
Reece, Mark, Controller, Treas & Sec.--Young-Phillips Sales Co., Clemmons, NC; *U.S. Private*, pg. 1201
Reed, Austin F., V.P., Gen. Counsel & Sec.--The Pittston Company, Glen Allen, VA; *U.S. Public*, pg. 1305
Reed, Brad, Chief Oper. Officer, Treas. & Sec.--Kova Fertilizer Inc., Greensburg, IN; *U.S. Private*, pg. 634
Reed, Carol O., Sec.--Reed Grain & Bean Company, Buhl, ID; *U.S. Private*, pg. 916
Reed, E.C., Chm. Bd., Pres. & Sec.--Utica Boilers Inc., Utica, NY; *U.S. Private*, pg. 1129
Reed, Harold F., Jr., Sec.--Tuscarora Incorporated, New Brighton, PA; *U.S. Public*, pg. 1646
Reed, James C., Jr., Exec. V.P., Gen. Counsel & Sec.--Tesoro Petroleum Corporation, San Antonio, TX; *U.S. Public*, pg. 1581
Reed, John J., Jr., Gen. Mgr. & Sec.--Reed Motors, Inc., Orlando, FL; *U.S. Private*, pg. 916
Reed, Marsha, Sec.--The Walt Disney Company, Burbank, CA; *U.S. Public*, pg. 511
Reed, Mike, Treas.--Graphic Technology, Inc., New Century, KS; *Int'l*, pg. 950
Reed, Robert A., V.P., Assoc. Gen. Counsel & Sec.--Jefferson-Pilot Corporation, Greensboro, NC; *U.S. Public*, *pg. 925*
Reed, Stephen, Sec.--Green Spot Packaging Inc., Claremont, CA; *U.S. Private*, pg. 477
Rees, John, Treas. & Sec.--Silver Springs Citrus Co-op, Howey in the Hills, FL; *U.S. Private*, pg. 1000
Reese, D. Michael, Sec.--Ace Tank & Equipment Co., Seattle, WA; *U.S. Private*, pg. 12
Reese, Richard, Treas. & Sec.--Century Furniture Industries, Hickory, NC; *U.S. Private*, pg. 226
Reese, Robert M., V.P., Gen. Counsel & Sec.--Hershey Foods Corporation, Hershey, PA; *U.S. Public*, pg. 811
Reeson, Richard L., Asst. Sec.--Canadian Occidental Petroleum Ltd., Calgary, Canada; *U.S. Public*, pg. 1210
Reeves, Laura H., Asst. Sec.--Anheuser-Busch Companies, Inc., Saint Louis, MO; *U.S. Public*, pg. 113
Reeves, R.J., Sec.--British Steel Plc, London, United Kingdom; *Int'l*, pg. 220
Refael, Lebel, Controller--Agis Industries Ltd., Bnei-Brak, Israel; *Int'l*, pg. 30
Reger, David M., Sec.--Bernard Matthews PLC, Norwich, United Kingdom; *Int'l*, pg. 189
Register, Jan, Sec.--Tocco, Inc., Boaz, AL; *U.S. Public*, pg. 1259
Rego, Thomas A., Sr. V.P.-Store Devel. & Sec.--Riser Foods, Inc., Bedford, OH; *U.S. Private*, pg. 450
Reichlin, Lawrence S., Corp. Sec.--Zuckerman-Honickman Inc., King of Prussia, PA; *U.S. Private*, pg. 1207
Reichman, N., Gen. Counsel & Sec.--Airport Group International, Inc., Glendale, CA; *U.S. Public*, pg. 1009
Reichwein, Mary, Sec.--Revcor, Inc., Carpentersville, IL; *U.S. Private*, pg. 925
Reid, Jane, Corp. Sec. & Legal Dir.--The Body Shop International, Littlehampton, United Kingdom; *Int'l*, pg. 199
Reid, John M., Sec.--Spicers Paper Limited, Preston, Australia; *Int'l*, pg. 72
Reid, Malcolm D., V.P., Gen. Counsel & Sec.--Network Systems Corporation, Minneapolis, MN; *U.S. Public*, pg. 1522
Reilly, William P., Asst. Treas. & Asst. Sec.--Central Hudson Gas & Electric Corporation, Poughkeepsie, NY; *U.S. Public*, pg. 324
Reily, Patrick, Sec.--Reily Electrical Supply, Inc., Metairie, LA; *U.S. Private*, pg. 919
Reimer, Jan R., Asst. Sec.--Micron Technology Inc., Boise, ID; *U.S. Public*, pg. 1105
Rein, David, Sec.--M-Tron Industries, Inc., Yankton, SD; *U.S. Public*, pg. 1022
Reinhart, Peter S., Sr. V.P. & Gen. Counsel--Hovnanian Enterprises, Inc., Red Bank, NJ; *U.S. Public*, pg. 843
Reische, Alan, Sec.--Felton Brush Inc., Manchester, NH; *U.S. Private*, pg. 400
Reisman, Kenneth, V.P., Gen. Counsel & Sec.--Technical Aid Corporation, Newton, MA; *U.S. Private*, pg. 1072
Reiss, Clifford E. II, Sec. & Asst. To Pres.--R.C.A. Rubber Company, Akron, OH; *U.S. Private*, pg. 902
Reitz, Carl F., Sec.--Panel Processing, Inc., Alpena, MI; *U.S. Private*, pg. 836
Reizner, Eckarf, Sec.--Gustav Wagner Maschinenfabrik GmbH, Reutlingen, Germany; *Int'l*, pg. 579
Remes, Audrey C., Treas. & Sec.--Deerskin Trading Post, Inc., North Bergen, NJ; *U.S. Public*, pg. 879
Remeta, George R., Vice Chm., Chief Fin. Officer & Sec.--United Retail Group, Inc., Rochelle Park, NJ; *U.S. Public*, *pg. 1679*
Remmell, Robert E., Asst. Sec.--Conmed Corporation, Utica, NY; *U.S. Public*, pg. 431
Rempe, James H., Sr. V.P., Gen. Counsel & Sec.--Manor Care, Inc., Gaithersburg, MD; *U.S. Public*, pg. 1041
Remsbecher, Thomas G., Sec.--Nooter Corporation, Saint Louis, MO; *U.S. Private*, pg. 801
Renaud, Paul G., Chief Fin. Officer, V.P.-Fin. & Sec.--CAE Inc., Toronto, Canada; *Int'l*, pg. 237
Renaud, Robert A., V.P., Treas. & Sec.--Bankers Fidelity Life Insurance Company, Atlanta, GA; *U.S. Public*, pg. 143
Rendle, J.M., Sec.--Pauls plc, Ipswich, United Kingdom; *Int'l*, pg. 598
Renkema, R., Sec.--Rabobank Nederland, Utrecht, Netherlands; *Int'l*, pg. 1082
Renkwitz, Linda, Sr. V.P. & Corp. Sec.--Robert Fleming, Inc., New York, NY; *Int'l*, pg. 493
Rennie, A. Marie, Corp. Sec.--Royal LePage Limited, Don Mills, Canada; *Int'l*, pg. 1143
Rennie, John C., Sec.--Pacific Dunlop Limited, Melbourne, Australia; *Int'l*, pg. 1021
Reno, Carol L., Sec.--Stainless Incorporated, Deerfield Beach, FL; *U.S. Private*, pg. 1029
Renteria, Sergio, Sec.--Grupo Mexicano de Desarrollo, Mexico, Mexico; *Int'l*, pg. 575
Renwick, Scott, Sec.--Unitrin, Inc., Chicago, IL; *U.S. Public*, pg. 1693
Repetti, Peter Q., Chief Fin. Officer & V.P.-Fin. & Admin.--Manugistics Group, Inc., Rockville, MD; *U.S. Public*, pg. 1042
Retterath, James E., V.P.-Res. & Devel & Sec.--LaserMaster Technologies, Inc., Eden Prairie, MN; *U.S. Public*, pg. 979
Rewolinski, Thomas, Chief Fin. Officer, Treas. & Sec.--Western States Envelope Co., Milwaukee, WI; *U.S. Private*, pg. 1168
Rex, Cheryl, Sec.--Rexhall Industries, Inc., Lancaster, CA; *U.S. Public*, pg. 1384
Rey, E. Correa, Sec.--Industrias Traterh, S.A., Madrid, Spain; *Int'l*, pg. 1222
Reyes, Marisol, Sec.--General Motors Chile S.A., Industria Automotriz, Santiago, Chile; *U.S. Public*, pg. 721
Reymann, Mary C., V.P.-Fin., Controller & Sec.--Flanigan's Enterprises, Inc., Fort Lauderdale, FL; *U.S. Public*, pg. 648
Reynaud, Claude P., Mgr. Dir.-Asia/Pacific--Osmonics Asia/Pacific, Ltd., Kowloon, Hong Kong; *U.S. Public*, pg. 1234
Reynen, John D., Treas. & Sec.--Reynen, Bardis & Winn, Sacramento, CA; *U.S. Private*, pg. 926
Reynolds, Craig A., Chief Fin. Officer, Exec. V.P. & Sec.--American Homestar Corporation, League City, TX; *U.S. Public*, pg. 83
Reynolds, Dudley C., Gen. Counsel & Sec.--Energen Corporation, Birmingham, AL; *U.S. Public*, pg. 581
Reynolds, Marion F., V.P., Treas. & Sec.--Middlesex Water Company, Iselin, NJ; *U.S. Public*, pg. 1110
Reynolds, Marion F., Sec.--Tidewater Utilities, Inc., Odessa, DE; *U.S. Public*, pg. 1110
Reynolds, Marion F., Treas. & Sec.--Pinelands Water & Wastewater Co., Broadway, NJ; *U.S. Public*, pg. 1110
Reynolds, Robert H., Sec.--LDI, Ltd., Indianapolis, IN; *U.S. Private*, pg. 639
Rheinhardt, Roger, Gen. Counsel & Sec.--Panneaux Malette-OSB Inc., Saint-Georges, Canada; *Int'l*, pg. 833
Rhinelander, Melvin A., Sec.--Extendicare (Canada) Inc., Markham, Canada; *Int'l*, pg. 468
Rhoads, Robert K., Sr. V.P., Gen. Counsel & Sec.--Wal-Mart Stores, Inc., Bentonville, AR; *U.S. Public*, pg. 1732
Rhoads, Robert K., Gen. Counsel & Sec.--Wal-Mart Stores, Inc., Bentonville, AR; *U.S. Public*, pg. 1732
Rhudy, Huey J., Treas. & Sec.--STRAFCO, Inc., San Antonio, TX; *U.S. Private*, pg. 1046
Ricard, Jean-Pierre, Sec.--Ciments Francais, Paris, France; *Int'l*, pg. 292
Riccardi, Anthony, Pres., Treas. & Sec.--William A. Randolph, Inc., Morton Grove, IL; *U.S. Private*, pg. 909
Rice, Bernard J., Jr., Treas. & Sec.--Blue Grass Quality Meats, Crescent Springs, KY; *U.S. Private*, pg. 152
Rice, Darrel E., Sec.--Tandy Brands Accessories, Inc., Arlington, TX; *U.S. Public*, pg. 1560
Rice, David R., V.P. & Corp. Sec.--New Haven Savings Bank, New Haven, CT; *U.S. Private*, pg. 793
Rice, Donald L., V.P. & Sec.--Warm Brothers Construction Company, Cincinnati, OH; *U.S. Private*, pg. 1150
Rice, Jill H., Sec.--Burr-Brown Corporation, Tucson, AZ; *U.S. Public*, pg. 270
Rice, Kapua, Corp. Sec.--Niagara Mohawk Power Corporation, Syracuse, NY; *U.S. Public*, pg. 1181
Rice, William D., Sr. V.P.-Strategic Devel.--Curtice Burns Foods, Rochester, NY; *U.S. Private*, pg. 887
Ricedorf, Charles, Sec. & Treas.--Rollman Supply Company, Mount Joy, PA; *U.S. Private*, pg. 407
Rich, Bradford W., Gen. Counsel & Sec.--USAA (United Services Automobile Association), San Antonio, TX; *U.S.* Private, pg. 1114
Rich, Bruce, Sec.--American Eco Corporation, Toronto, Canada; *Int'l*, pg. 73
Rich, Carsten, Gen. Counsel & Sec.--ISS-International Service System A/S, Holte, Denmark; *Int'l*, pg. 656
Rich, David R., Sec.--Rich Products Corp., Buffalo, NY; *U.S.* Private, pg. 928
Rich, Rebecca S., Asst. Sec.--B.B. Walker Company, Asheboro, NC; *U.S. Public*, pg. 1734
Rich, Robert C., Exec. V.P.-Opers. & Fin., Controller & Asst. Sec.--Master Lock Company, Milwaukee, WI; *U.S. Public*, *pg. 675*
Richardello, Michael, Co-owner--Butler Wholesale Products, Inc., Adams, MA; *U.S. Private*, pg. 190
Richards, Daniel R., Treas. & Sec.--West Union Corporation, Memphis, TN; *U.S. Private*, pg. 1163
Richards, G.A., Treas. & Sec.--Ohio Gas Company, Bryan, OH; *U.S. Private*, pg. 812
Richards, Lynn S., Sec.--Little America Refining, Inc., Evansville, WY; *U.S. Private*, pg. 1003
Richards, Maureen, Gen. Counsel & Sec.--Footstar Inc., Mahwah, NJ; *U.S. Public*, pg. 661
Richards, Olive, V.P. & Sec.--Richards Brothers of Mountain Grove, Mountain Grove, MO; *U.S. Private*, pg. 928
Richards, R.L., Sec.--CGAS, Inc., Columbus, OH; *U.S. Public*, pg. 585
Richards, Roger T., Chief Fin. Officer & Sec.--Granite Furniture Co., Salt Lake City, UT; *U.S. Private*, pg. 469
Richardson, Alison S., Sr. V.P.-Admin. & Fin.--Integrity Incorporated, Mobile, AL; *U.S. Public*, pg. 886
Richardson, C. Charles, Sec.--Union Electric Steel N.V., Tessenderlo, Belgium; *U.S. Public*, pg. 104
Richardson, Elizabeth, Sec.--Emess PLC, London, United Kingdom; *Int'l*, pg. 453
Richardson, Ian, Sec.--Sun Life and Provincial Holdings plc, London, United Kingdom; *Int'l*, pg. 1318
Richardson, Jill, Sec.--The Gillette Company, Boston, MA; *U.S. Public*, pg. 743
Richardson, Terry L., V.P.-Admin. & Sec.--Riceland Foods, Inc., Stuttgart, AR; *U.S. Private*, pg. 928
Richenthal, Arthur, Gen. Counsel & Corp. Sec.--Carrafiello, Diehl & Associates, Inc., Irvington, NY; *U.S. Private*, pg. 215
Richert, Maxine H., Corp. Sec.--Sealaska Corporation, Juneau, AK; *U.S. Private*, pg. 978
Richey, Ellen, Exec. V.P., Gen. Counsel & Sec.--Providian Financial Corporation, San Francisco, CA; *U.S. Public*, pg. 1338
Richmond, Charles R., Exec. V.P. & Sec.--Washington Federal Savings, Seattle, WA; *U.S. Public*, pg. 1740

Richmond, Valerie, Sec.--Exel Insurance Co. Ltd., Hamilton, Bermuda; *Int'l*, pg. 467
Richter, George, V.P. & Sec.--FDL Foods, Inc., Dubuque, IA; *U.S. Private*, pg. 396
Richter, Lyle H., Chief Fin. Officer, V.P., Treas. & Sec.--Fox Valley Corporation, Appleton, WI; *U.S. Private*, pg. 422
Rico Maciel, Jose Luis, Sec.--Industrias CH, S.A. de C.V., Tlalnepantla, Mexico; *Int'l*, pg. 677
Ridhiroj, Thana, Sr. V.P. & Sec.--Bangkok Bank of Commerce Ltd., Bangkok, Thailand; *Int'l*, pg. 146
Ridings, S., Sec. & Dir.--The Derbyshire (Isle of Man) Ltd., Douglas, United Kingdom; *Int'l*, pg. 395
Rieck, Kim A., Sr. V.P., Gen. Counsel & Sec.--The Edward J. DeBartolo Corporation, Youngstown, OH; *U.S. Private*, *pg. 319*
Rieck, Thomas W., Sec.--Circuit Systems, Inc., Elk Grove Village, IL; *U.S. Public*, pg. 374
Riecke, Robert, Chief Fin. Officer, Treas. & Sec.--Walle Corporation, Harahan, LA; *U.S. Private*, pg. 1148
Riecke, Robert J., V.P.-Admin., Gen. Counsel & Sec.--WTD Industries, Inc., Portland, OR; *U.S. Public*, pg. 1729
Riegel, Marilyn, Exec. Sec.--Pollio Dairy Products, Mineola, NY; *U.S. Public*, pg. 1288
Riely, Sandra, Sec. & Treas.--Hood Communications, Inc., Grand Terrace, CA; *U.S. Private*, pg. 673
Rieman, Stephen R., V.P.-Fin, Treas. & Sec.--Bard Mfg. Co., Bryan, OH; *U.S. Private*, pg. 116
Riesenbach, E. Gerald, Sec.--Kleinert's, Inc., Plymouth Meeting, PA; *U.S. Private*, pg. 625
Riesensbach, E. Gerald, Sec.--Kleinert's Inc. of Florida, Largo, FL; *U.S. Private*, pg. 625
Rife, Janey L., Treas. & Sec.--Republic Group Incorporated, Hutchinson, KS; *U.S. Public*, pg. 1378
Rifkin, Richard S., Exec. V.P. & Sec.--Omnisource Corporation, Fort Wayne, IN; *U.S. Private*, pg. 817
Riganelli, Paul E., V.P.-Admin., Sec. & Gen. Counsel--TecSyn International, Inc., Saint Catharines, Canada; *Int'l*, pg. 1361
Riggins, Larry, Sec.--Dunbarton Corporation, Dothan, AL; *U.S. Private*, pg. 194
Riggins, Larry D., Sec.--CGF Industries, Topeka, KS; *U.S. Private*, pg. 194
Riggs, Sidney W., Chm. Bd., Sec. & Treas.--Somerset Welding & Steel, Inc., Somerset, PA; *U.S. Private*, pg. 930
Rigot, Joseph M., Gen. Counsel & Sec.--Robbins & Myers, Inc., Dayton, OH; *U.S. Public*, pg. 1393
Rigsby, Linda, Corp. Sec.--Crestar Financial Corporation, Richmond, VA; *U.S. Public*, pg. 458
Riha, Frances, Sec. & Treas.--Office Equipment Company Of Chicago, Elmhurst, IL; *U.S. Private*, pg. 812
Riley, David, Esq., Vice Chm. & Sec.--M K Diamond Products, Inc., Torrance, CA; *U.S. Private*, pg. 684
Riley, Joan R., Gen. Counsel, Sec. & Dir.-Investor Rels.--Quixote Corporation, Chicago, IL; *U.S. Public*, pg. 1353
Riley, Karen E., Sec.--Central Securities Corporation, New York, NY; *U.S. Public*, pg. 326
Riley, Kim, Exec. Sec.--Brooks Foods, Mount Summit, IN; *U.S. Private*, pg. 887
Riley, Shelley M., Sec.--Kinross Gold Corporation, Toronto, Canada; *Int'l*, pg. 734
Rinaldi, G.T., Sec.--MCC Group, L.L.C., Metairie, LA; *U.S. Private*, pg. 686
Rinerson, Darrell D., Chm. Bd., Pres. & Sec.--Micron Quantum Devices, Inc., Santa Clara, CA; *U.S. Public*, pg. 1105
Ringer, Walter M., III, Sec.--Foley-PLP Company, Rochester, NY; *U.S. Private*, pg. 416
Ringley, Edward M., Treas. & Sec.--Consolidated Systems, Inc., Columbia, SC; *U.S. Private*, pg. 266
Ringswald, Michael A., First V.P., Gen. Counsel & Sec.--The Fifth Third Bank of Kentucky, Louisville, Louisville, KY; *U.S. Public*, pg. 621
Rinne, Risto, V.P.-Corp. Plng. & Sec.--Neste Oy, Espoo, Finland; *Int'l*, pg. 912
Rintamaki, John M., Sec.--Ford Motor Company, Dearborn, MI; *U.S. Public*, pg. 661
Rintamaki, John M., Sec.--Associates First Capital Corporation, Dallas, TX; *U.S. Public*, pg. 662
Rishel, Joann, Corp. Sec.--Woolrich, Inc., Woolrich, PA; *U.S. Private*, pg. 1188
Risher, Ronald D., V.P., Corp. Controller & Sec.--Thorn Apple Valley, Inc., Southfield, MI; *U.S. Public*, pg. 1602
Risley, Gary E., Chief Legal Officer & Sec.--Mesa Air Group, Las Vegas, NV; *U.S. Public*, pg. 1098
Rispoli, Carl A., Corp. Controller & Asst. Sec.--Defiance, Inc., Cleveland, OH; *U.S. Public*, pg. 493
Ritch, Kathleen, V.P. & Sec.--Ogden Corporation, New York, NY; *U.S. Public*, pg. 1213
Ritchie, H.T., Corp. Sec.--High Plains Corporation, Wichita, KS; *U.S. Public*, pg. 825
Ritchie, Lewis, Chief Fin. Officer & Exec. V.P.-Fin. & Admin.--Cinram Ltd., Scarborough, Canada; *Int'l*, pg. 293
Rittel, Linda, Asst. Sec.--Hershey Creamery Company, Harrisburg, PA; *U.S. Private*, pg. 524
Ritter, George, Controller & Asst. Sec.--VWR Scientific Products, West Chester, PA; *U.S. Public*, pg. 1703
Ritzko, Laura M., Corp. Sec.--The Penn Mutual Life Insurance Company, Philadelphia, PA; *U.S. Private*, pg. 849
Rix, Jane M., Corp. Sec.--Manatron, Inc., Kalamazoo, MI; *U.S. Public*, pg. 1040
Rizzitello, Jack, Co. Sec.--W.W. Norton & Company, Inc., New York, NY; *U.S. Private*, pg. 807
Roach, Dorothy, Sec.--TII Industries, Inc., Copiague, NY; *U.S. Public*, pg. 1556
Robbins, Donald M., Sr. V.P., Gen. Counsel & Sec.--Hasbro, Inc., Pawtucket, RI; *U.S. Public*, pg. 797
Robbins, Donald M., Sec.--Turf Paradise, Inc., Phoenix, AZ; *U.S. Public*, pg. 831
Robbins, Patricia, Sec.--Inman Mills, Inman, SC; *U.S. Private*, pg. 564
Robbinson, R. Courtney, Chief Fin. Officer & Sec.--Robinson Lumber Company, New Orleans, LA; *U.S. Private*, pg. 936
Roberts, Allen, Sec. & Dir.-Fin.--Renishaw plc, Wotton-under-Edge, United Kingdom; *Int'l*, pg. 1103
Roberts, Annette, Sec. to Pres.--H. R. Kaminsky & Sons, Inc., Fitzgerald, GA; *U.S. Private*, pg. 606
Roberts, C.J., Dir.-Fin. & Sec.--Senior Colman Limited, Sale, United Kingdom; *Int'l*, pg. 1220
Roberts, Donald M., Gen. Counsel & Sec.--Maxwell Technologies, Inc., San Diego, CA; *U.S. Public*, pg. 1061
Roberts, F. Kathryn, Sec.--Century Bancshares, Inc., Washington, DC; *U.S. Public*, pg. 328
Roberts, J.M.B., Sec.--Fleming Private Asset Management Limited, London, United Kingdom; *Int'l*, pg. 493
Roberts, Linda, Exec. Sec.--Keystone Consolidated Industries, Inc., Dallas, TX; *U.S. Public*, pg. 955
Roberts, Rex H., V.P., Assoc. Gen. Counsel & Sec.--American General Life & Accident Insurance Co., Nashville, TN; *U.S. Public*, pg. 76
Roberts, Scott A., Asst. Gen. Counsel & Asst. Sec.--Archer Daniels Midland Company (ADM), Decatur, IL; *U.S. Public*, pg. 127
Roberts, Stephen W., Sec.--Triple F, Inc., Des Moines, IA; *U.S. Private*, pg. 1104
Roberts, Steve, Corp. Sec.--Medi-Mail, Inc., Las Vegas, NV; *U.S. Private*, pg. 726
Robertson, Cathy, Corp. Sec.--Bancorp South Inc., Tupelo, MS; *U.S. Public*, pg. 176
Robertson, Cathy M., Corp. Sec.--Bank of Mississippi, Tupelo, MS; *U.S. Public*, pg. 176
Robertson, Charles B., V.P.-Admin. & Corp. Sec.--DBA Systems, Inc., Melbourne, FL; *U.S. Public*, pg. 472
Robertson, Debbie, Sec.--Shelba D. Johnson Trucking, Thomasville, NC; *U.S. Private*, pg. 594
Robertson, Judy, Sec.--Supershuttle Inc., Phoenix, AZ; *U.S. Private*, pg. 1056
Robertson, Julie, V.P.-Admin. & Sec.--Noble Drilling Corporation, Houston, TX; *U.S. Public*, pg. 1186
Robertson, Julie J., V.P.-Admin. & Sec.--Noble Drilling Services Inc., Houston, TX; *U.S. Public*, pg. 1186
Robertson, Julie J., V.P.-Admin. & Sec.--Noble Offshore Corporation, Houston, TX; *U.S. Public*, pg. 1186
Robertson, Monroe W., Sr. V.P. & Sec.--Key Production Company, Inc., Denver, CO; *U.S. Public*, pg. 953
Robertson, William R., V.P. & Sec.--Barrick Gold Corporation, Toronto, Canada; *Int'l*, pg. 168
Robins, Ken, Sec.--Waxman Industries, Inc., Bedford, OH; *U.S. Public*, pg. 1748
Robins, Ken, Sec.--WOC Inc., Bedford, OH; *U.S. Public*, pg. 1748
Robins, Ken, Sec.--Waxman USA Inc., Bedford, OH; *U.S. Public*, pg. 1749
Robins, R. Steven, Chief Fin. Officer, Treas. & Sec--Builder Marts of America, Inc., Greenville, SC; *U.S. Private*, pg. 179
Robinson, Charles T., V.P. & Sec.--Albert Kahn Associates, Inc., Detroit, MI; *U.S. Private*, pg. 604
Robinson, D.G., Sec.--Australian Mutual Provident, Sydney, Australia; *Int'l*, pg. 100
Robinson, Ed, Sr. V.P. & Gen. Counsel--Harrah's Entertainment, Inc., Memphis, TN; *U.S. Public*, pg. 790
Robinson, Harry T., Jr., Chm. Bd. & Sec.--Top Flight, Inc., Chattanooga, TN; *U.S. Private*, pg. 1091
Robinson, J.A., Asst. Corp. Secretary--Maple Leaf Foods Inc., Toronto, Canada; *Int'l*, pg. 841
Robinson, Joseph A., Chief Fin. Officer, Sr. V.P., Treas. & Sec.--Excel Industries, Inc., Elkhart, IN; *U.S. Public*, pg. 598
Robinson, Lee J., Controller & Asst. Sec.--Advanced Machine Vision Corp., Medford, OR; *U.S. Public*, pg. 20
Robinson, Marvin S., V.P., Gen. Counsel & Sec.--Garan, Incorporated, New York, NY; *U.S. Public*, pg. 703
Robinson, Monica, Sec. & Dir.-Personnel--Fritz Industries Inc., Mesquite, TX; *U.S. Private*, pg. 429
Robinson, Steven, Treas. & Sec.--Joy Service, Southfield, MI; *U.S. Private*, pg. 602
Robinson, Thomas G., Sec.--Narragansett Energy Resources Company, Providence, RI; *U.S. Public*, pg. 1171
Robinson, William F., Jr., Asst. Sec.--Cabot Corporation, Boston, MA; *U.S. Public*, pg. 288
Robles, Estela, Treas. & Sec.--La Reina, Inc., Los Angeles, CA; *U.S. Private*, pg. 640
Robson, Donald, Chief Fin. Officer, Treas. & Sec.--Coldwater Creek, Sandpoint, ID; *U.S. Public*, pg. 396
Roche, Arthur D., Chief Fin. Officer & Exec. V.P.--Vicon Industries, Inc., Hauppauge, NY; *U.S. Public*, pg. 1719
Roche, G.P., Sec.--Carbon Brush Mfg. Co., Pty Limited, Rosebery, Australia; *Int'l*, pg. 894
Roche, Sandra L., Esq., Corp. Sec.--Roche Constructors, Inc., Greeley, CO; *U.S. Private*, pg. 937
Roche, Terence P., Exec. V.P., Asst. Treas. & Asst. Sec.--Binks Sames Corporation, Franklin Park, IL; *U.S. Public*, pg. 229
Rochester, Ernest M., Sec.--Chempower, Inc., Akron, OH; *Int'l*, pg. 74
Rochette, Bermanrd, Sec. & Dir.-Legal Affairs--The Jean Coutu Group (PJC) Inc., Longueuil, Canada; *Int'l*, pg. 340
Rockenbach, Michael J., Acting Chief Fin. Officer, V.P.-Fin. & Sec.--Emulex Corporation, Costa Mesa, CA; *U.S. Public*, pg. 579
Rockowitz, Noah E., V.P., Gen. Counsel & Sec.--Hudson General Corporation, Great Neck, NY; *U.S. Public*, pg. 845
Rodbell, Paul N., V.P & Sec.--Apex Supply Co., Inc., Atlanta, GA; *U.S. Private*, pg. 77
Roddick, David, V.P. & Sec.--B.T. Mancini Co., Inc., Milpitas, CA; *U.S. Private*, pg. 699
Rodler, John, Chief Fin. Officer, Sr. V.P., Treas. & Sec.--Folger Nolan Fleming Douglas, Washington, DC; *U.S. Private*, pg. 416
Rodrigues, Neusa, Sec.--DPZ-Duailibi, Petit, Zaragoza, Propaganda S.A., Sao Paulo, Brazil; *Int'l*, pg. 352
Rodriguez Lopez, Dr. Maria Luisa, Sec.--Telefonica Investigacion Y Desarrollo, S.A. (Tidsa), Madrid, Spain; *Int'l*, pg. 1372
Rodriguez, Kathie, Asst. Sec.--Dewberry Design Group, Oklahoma City, OK; *U.S. Private*, pg. 329
Rodriguez, Marianne, V.P., Treas. & Sec.--Deepwater Chemicals, Inc., Woodward, OK; *Int'l*, pg. 1395
Roedl, Suzanne, V.P.-Fin.--Condor D.C. Power Supplies Inc., Oxnard, CA; *U.S. Public*, pg. 1419
Roehl, Katherine S., Sec.--Lake Region Manufacturing, Inc., Chaska, MN; *U.S. Private*, pg. 643
Roehlk, Thomas, Sr. V.P., Gen. Counsel & Sec.--Tupperware Corporation, Orlando, FL; *U.S. Public*, pg. 1644
Roehrig, Allan, Pres.--GFG Corporation, Milwaukee, WI; *Int'l*, pg. 395
Roethler, Charmaine, Sec.--Witcher Construction Company, Eden Prairie, MN; *U.S. Private*, pg. 347
Roethler, Charmaine, Sec.--Witcher Construction Co., Minneapolis, MN; *U.S. Private*, pg. 1185
Rogers, Donna B., Sec.--First Commercial Corporation, Little Rock, AR; *U.S. Public*, pg. 630
Rogers, Ellen Sheriff, Sec. & Asst. Treas.--Potomac Electric Power Company, Washington, DC; *U.S. Public*, pg. 1318
Rogers, Gayle, Asst. Corp. Sec.--Niches, Inc., San Diego, CA; *U.S. Public*, pg. 1181
Rogers, Gloria J., Asst. Sec.--Entech, Inc., Butte, MT; *U.S. Public*, pg. 1127
Rogers, J. Artie, Sr. V.P.-Fin. & Sec.--Empire of Carolina, Inc., Delray Beach, FL; *U.S. Public*, pg. 579
Rogers, Kalen, Sec.--Music Sales Corporation, New York, NY; *U.S. Private*, pg. 768
Rogers, Kathy H., Sec.--Tultex Corporation, Martinsville, VA; *U.S. Public*, pg. 1644
Rogers, M.J., Corp. Sec.--Senior Tube Limited, West Bromwich, United Kingdom; *Int'l*, pg. 1221
Rogers, Margie E., Chief Fin. Officer, V.P., Treas. & Sec.--Team, Inc., Alvin, TX; *U.S. Public*, pg. 1562
Rogers, Margie E., Treas. & Sec.--Team Industrial Services, Inc., Alvin, TX; *U.S. Public*, pg. 1562
Rogers, Margie E., Treas. & Sec.--Pipe Repairs, Inc., Alvin, TX; *U.S. Public*, pg. 1562
Rogers, Margie E., Treas. & Sec.--TECO Manufacturing, Inc., Alvin, TX; *U.S. Public*, pg. 1562
Rogers, Nancy A., Sr. V.P.-Mktg. Svcs. & Sec.--Ameriana Bancorp, New Castle, IN; *U.S. Public*, pg. 66
Rogers, Nigel, Chief Fin. Officer & Sec.--Stadium Limited, Hartlepool, United Kingdom; *Int'l*, pg. 1293
Rogers, Sharon L., V.P.-Legal & Asst. Sec.--Graniteville Company, Graniteville, SC; *U.S. Private*, pg. 103
Rogers, Steven W., 2nd V.P., Controller & Asst. Sec.--First Penn-Pacific Life Insurance Co., Oak Brook Terrace, IL; *U.S. Public*, pg. 998
Rogers, Terry, V.P.-Corp. Admin., Benefits & Human Resources--Herff Jones Inc., Indianapolis, IN; *U.S. Private*, pg. 523
Rogowski, Michael, Sec.--N.G. Bailey & Co. Ltd., Ilkley, United Kingdom; *Int'l*, pg. 132
Rohloff, William M., Chief Fin. Officer, Treas. & Sec.--Stebbins Engineering & Mfg. Co., Watertown, NY; *U.S. Private*, pg. 1037
Rohrer, Joanne M., Treas. & Sec.--Rohrer Corporation, Wadsworth, OH; *U.S. Private*, pg. 940
Rojack, Patricia, Sec.--Bud Industries, Inc., Willoughby, OH; *U.S. Private*, pg. 178
Rokus, Josef W., V.P.-Corp. Devel. & Sec.--Galileo Corp., Sturbridge, MA; *U.S. Public*, pg. 698
Roland, Josette, Gen. Sec.--Dassault Aviation Group, Vaucresson, France; *Int'l*, pg. 383
Rold, Stephen K., V.P., Controller, Treas. & Sec.--Roofing Wholesale Co., Inc., Phoenix, AZ; *U.S. Private*, pg. 943
Rolinson, Becky, Exec. Sec.-Supvr. Financial--Walt Disney Attractions-Walt Disney World, Lake Buena Vista, FL; *U.S. Public*, pg. 513
Rolla, M.F., Pres. & Chief Oper. Officer--Gem Industries Finance Corporation, Toccoa, GA; *U.S. Private*, pg. 442
Rollins, Maureen, Exec. Sec.--Long Island Lighting Company, Hicksville, NY; *U.S. Public*, pg. 1013
Romano, Robert S., Asst. Gen. Counsel & Asst. Sec.--Outboard Marine Corporation, Waukegan, IL; *U.S. Private*, pg. 478
Romano, Vera, Sec.--Universal Photonics, Inc., Hicksville, NY; *U.S. Private*, pg. 1127
Romans, John C., Sr. V.P. & Sec.--H.D. Hudson Manufacturing Company, Chicago, IL; *U.S. Private*, pg. 545
Romig, Michael V., Chief Fin. Officer & V.P.--Marine Construction & Design Co., Seattle, WA; *U.S. Private*, pg. 703
Rominski, Kathryn Hubbard, Sec. & Dir.-Hubbard Foundation--Hubbard Broadcasting, Inc., Saint Paul, MN; *U.S. Private*, pg. 543
Romoser, W. David, V.P., Gen. Counsel & Sec.--A.O. Smith Corporation, Milwaukee, WI; *U.S. Public*, pg. 1476
Ronco, Al, Exec. V.P. & Sec.--Keystone Automotive Industries, Inc., Pomona, CA; *U.S. Public*, pg. 955
Rondeau, Andre, V.P.-Export & Sls.--Uniboard Canada Inc., Laval, Canada; *Int'l*, pg. 1431
Rones, Gail, Treas. & Sec.--Americo Manufacturing Co., Inc., Acworth, GA; *U.S. Private*, pg. 64
Rooke, Ben G., Exec. V.P., Gen. Counsel & Sec.--Keystone Financial Inc., Harrisburg, PA; *U.S. Public*, pg. 956
Root, Carole, Asst. Sec. & Dir.-Shareholder Services--Central Vermont Public Service Corporation, Rutland, VT; *U.S. Public*, pg. 327
Roper, C. Richard, V.P. & Sec.--Ropak Corporation, Fullerton, CA; *Int'l*, pg. 811
Roper, John L., IV, Exec. V.P.-Opers. & Sec.--Norfolk Shipbuilding & Drydock Corporation, Norfolk, VA; *U.S. Private*, pg. 802
Rorebeck, Gretchen, Sec.--Pamida Holdings Corporation, Omaha, NE; *U.S. Public*, pg. 1255
Rorebeck, Gretchen, Sec.--Seaway Importing Company, Omaha, NE; *U.S. Public*, pg. 1255

Rosania, John, Treas. & Sec.--Structural Foam Plastics, Inc., Somerville, NJ; *U.S. Private*, pg. 1047
Rosati, Mario, Sec.--Sierra Semiconductor, San Jose, CA; *U.S. Public*, pg. 1470
Rosati, Mario M., Asst. Sec.--Genus Inc., Sunnyvale, CA; *U.S. Public*, pg. 732
Rosberg, Jacque, Sec.--Citizens Bank of Central Indiana-Central Region, Greenwood, IN; *U.S. Public*, pg. 280
Rose, Cathryne G., Sec.--Roman Electric Company, Inc., Milwaukee, WI; *U.S. Private*, pg. 942
Rose, Donald, V.P., Gen. Counsel & Sec.--Placer Dome Inc., Vancouver, Canada; *Int'l*, pg. 1060
Rose, Howard L., Gen. Counsel--Bowles Fluidics Corporation, Columbia, MD; *U.S. Public*, pg. 248
Rose, Thomas F., V.P. & Sec.--A.M. Todd Company, Kalamazoo, MI; *U.S. Private*, pg. 1089
Rose, Thomas F., Treas. & Sec.--Todd Juice Products, Kalamazoo, MI; *U.S. Private*, pg. 1090
Rosedahl, David Evans, Gen. Counsel & Sec.--Piper Jaffray Companies, Inc., Minneapolis, MN; *U.S. Public*, pg. 1300
Rosemore, Andrew S., Chief Oper. Officer, Exec. V.P., Treas. & Asst. Sec.--PMC Capital Inc., Dallas, TX; *U.S. Public*, pg. 1242
Rosemore, Lance B., Pres., Chief Exec. Officer & Sec.--PMC Capital Inc., Dallas, TX; *U.S. Public*, pg. 1242
Rosen, Deborah A., Asst. Gen. Counsel & Asst. Sec.--Standex International Corporation, Salem, NH; *U.S. Public*, pg. 1505
Rosen, Douglas C., Sec.--Alaskan Copper Companies, Seattle, WA; *U.S. Private*, pg. 31
Rosen, Hermine, Sec.--Star Children's Dress Company, Inc., New York, NY; *U.S. Private*, pg. 1034
Rosen, Jerald I., Sec.--Windmere-Durable Holdings, Hialeah, FL; *U.S. Public*, pg. 1771
Rosen, Michael N., Sec.--Barnes & Noble Inc., New York, NY; *U.S. Public*, pg. 189
Rosen, Sam, Treas. & Sec.--Aztec Manufacturing Co., Crowley, TX; *U.S. Public*, pg. 159
Rosen, Stuart I., V.P., Assoc. Gen. Counsel & Sec.--Triarc Companies, Inc., New York, NY; *U.S. Public*, pg. 1634
Rosen, Thomas, Sec.--Long Prairie Packing Co., Long Prairie, MN; *U.S. Private*, pg. 945
Rosenbaum, III, Ben, Gen. Counsel & Sec.--PHP Healthcare Corporation, Reston, VA; *U.S. Public*, pg. 1241
Rosenberg, Barnett, Sr. V.P., Gen. Counsel & Sec.--Mattel, Inc., El Segundo, CA; *U.S. Public*, pg. 1057
Rosenberg, Bernard, Sec.--Jennie-O Foods, Inc., Willmar, MN; *U.S. Public*, pg. 840
Rosenberg, Ira S., V.P., Gen. Counsel & Sec.--Lechters, Inc., Harrison, NJ; *U.S. Public*, pg. 983
Rosenberg, John K., Exec. V.P. & Gen. Counsel--Western Resources, Inc., Topeka, KS; *U.S. Public*, pg. 1759
Rosenberg, Kenneth B., Pres., Chief Exec. Officer & Sec.--Eastern Smelting & Refining Corporation, Lynn, MA; *U.S. Private*, pg. 357
Rosenberg, Philip G., 1st Sr. V.P., Treas., Controller & Asst. Sec.--Morse Shoe, Inc., Canton, MA; *U.S. Public*, pg. 168
Rosenberg, Philip G., Chief Fin. Officer, Exec. V.P. & Asst. Sec.--Casual Male, Inc., Hyde Park, MA; *U.S. Public*, pg. 168
Rosenberg, Sheli Z., V.P. & Asst. Sec.--Capsure Holdings Corp., Chicago, IL; *U.S. Public*, pg. 303
Rosenberger, Marcus L., Treas. & Sec.--Rosenbergers Dairies, Inc., Hatfield, PA; *U.S. Private*, pg. 945
Rosenblatt, Phillip, Sec.--Joan & David Helpern, Inc., New York, NY; *U.S. Private*, pg. 521
Rosenblum, William F., Sr. V.P., Deputy Gen. Counsel & Corp. Sec.--Republic New York Corporation, New York, NY; *U.S. Public*, pg. 1380
Rosenblum, William F., Jr., Sec.--Republic Bank for Savings, New York, NY; *U.S. Public*, pg. 1380
Rosencutter, Leslie D., V.P.-Admin. & Sec.--Parker Drilling Company, Tulsa, OK; *U.S. Public*, pg. 1259
Rosenfeld, Allen, V.P.-Opers. & Sec.--DAQ Electronics Inc., Piscataway, NJ; *U.S. Private*, pg. 300
Rosenfeld, Richard Z., Sec.--Jacobson Stores Inc., Jackson, MI; *U.S. Public*, pg. 922
Rosensweig, David Z., Sec.--Century Communications Corp., New Canaan, CT; *U.S. Public*, pg. 329
Rosenthal, Benjamin, Treas. & Sec.--Madison Electric Co., Warren, MI; *U.S. Private*, pg. 694
Rosinski, Delores O., Asst. Sec.--Merck & Co., Inc., Whitehouse Station, NJ; *U.S. Public*, pg. 1090
Rosok, Larry, V.P.-H.R. & Corp. Sec.--Cascade Natural Gas Corporation, Seattle, WA; *U.S. Public*, pg. 311
Ross, Bradley, Sec.--Science & Engineering Associates, Albuquerque, NM; *U.S. Private*, pg. 975
Ross, Guy M., V.P. & Sec.--Standard Commercial Corporation, Wilson, NC; *U.S. Public*, pg. 1501
Ross, John E., Sec.--Spelling Entertainment Group, Inc., Los Angeles, CA; *U.S. Private*, pg. 776
Ross, Joseph, Co. Sec.--J. Jarvis & Sons P.L.C., London, United Kingdom; *Int'l*, pg. 705
Ross, Judy, Sec. & Treas.--Layman Candy Company, Inc., Salem, VA; *U.S. Private*, pg. 655
Ross, Jules, V.P.-Fin., Treas. & Sec.--Thackeray Corporation, New York, NY; *U.S. Public*, pg. 1590
Ross, Michael C., Sr. V.P., Gen. Counsel & Sec.--Safeway Inc., Pleasanton, CA; *U.S. Public*, pg. 1426
Ross, Mike, V.P., Gen. Counsel & Asst. Sec.--Atmel Corporation, San Jose, CA; *U.S. Public*, pg. 145
Ross, Robert W., Chief Fin. Officer, V.P., Treas. & Sec.--Selas Corporation of America, Dresher, PA; *U.S. Public*, pg. 1454
Ross, Ronald R., Treas. & Sec.--Ag Processing Inc., A Cooperative, Omaha, NE; *U.S. Private*, pg. 26
Rossi, Roberta M., V.P. & Asst. Sec.--Valero Marketing & Supply Company, San Antonio, TX; *U.S. Public*, pg. 1704
Rossi, Roberta M., V.P. & Asst. Sec.--Valero Refining Company, San Antonio, TX; *U.S. Public*, pg. 1704
Rossini, Edwin R., V.P., Deputy Gen. Counsel & Asst. Sec.-S.C. Johnson & Son, Inc., Racine, WI; *U.S. Private*, pg. 592
Rossiter, Peter L., Exec. V.P., Gen. Counsel & Sec.--Northern Trust Corporation, Chicago, IL; *U.S. Public*, pg. 1195
Rosskamm, Betty, Sr. V.P. & Sec.--Fabri-Centers of America, Inc., Hudson, OH; *U.S. Public*, pg. 609
Rostollan, Jean C., Exec. V.P.-Pur. & Asst. Sec.--Buffets, Inc., Eden Prairie, MN; *U.S. Public*, pg. 267
Rotenberry, William J., Dir.-Corp. Devel. & Asst. Sec.--Joslyn Corporation, Chicago, IL; *U.S. Public*, pg. 481
Roth, J.H., Dir.-Fin. & Sec.--Trafalgar House Property, Inc., Trenton, NJ; *Int'l*, pg. 774
Roth, Laura L., Sec. & Asst. Treas.--BT Financial Corporation, Johnstown, PA; *U.S. Public*, pg. 163
Roth, Laura L., Sec. & Asst. Treas.--Bedford Associates, Inc., Johnstown, PA; *U.S. Public*, pg. 164
Roth, Laura L., Sec. & Asst. Treas.--Laurel Bank, Johnstown, PA; *U.S. Public*, pg. 164
Roth, Laura L., Sec. & Asst. Treas.--Laurel Trust Company, Johnstown, PA; *U.S. Public*, pg. 164
Roth, Laura L., Sec. & Asst. Treas.--Laurel Community Development Corporation, Johnstown, PA; *U.S. Public*, pg. 164
Roth, Walter, Sec.--Corcom, Inc., Libertyville, IL; *U.S. Public*, pg. 446
Roth, Walter, Sec.--Shelby Williams Industries, Inc., Morristown, TN; *U.S. Public*, pg. 1464
Rothe, John E., V.P. & Sec.--Turtle & Hughes, Inc., Linden, NJ; *U.S. Private*, pg. 1110
Rothenberger, Eva, Treas. & Sec.--Vari Tronics Company, Inc., Duarte, CA; *U.S. Private*, pg. 1134
Rother, Doug C., Chief Oper. Officer & Exec. V.P.--Columbine JDS Systems, Inc., Denver, CO; *U.S. Public*, pg. 228
Rother, Mary, Exec. Sec.--Jacobsen Textron, Racine, WI; *U.S. Public*, pg. 1589
Rothman, Henry, Sec.--House of Ronnie, Inc., New York, NY; *U.S. Private*, pg. 542
Rothschild, Bruce I., V.P., Gen. Counsel & Sec.--The Rouse Company, Columbia, MD; *U.S. Public*, pg. 1407
Rothschild, Bruce I., V.P., Gen. Counsel & Sec.--Rouse Legal Div., Columbia, MD; *U.S. Public*, pg. 1407
Rothwell, Peter, Assoc. Counsel & Sec.--Dassault Falcon Jet Corp., South Hackensack, NJ; *Int'l*, pg. 383
Rott, Herbert, Jr., V.P., Treas. & Sec.--Rott-Keller Supply Co., Fargo, ND; *U.S. Private*, pg. 947
Rotter, David H., Pres., Chief Exec. Officer & Sec.--The Rottlund Company, Inc., Roseville, MN; *U.S. Public*, pg. 1406
Rotzien, William A., Asst. Sec.--John Deere Capital Corporation, Reno, NV; *U.S. Public*, pg. 492
Rotzien, William A., Gen. Counsel & Asst. Sec.--John Deere Credit Company, Moline, IL; *U.S. Public*, pg. 492
Rounsaville, Guy, Jr., Gen. Counsel & Sec.--Wells Fargo & Company, San Francisco, CA; *U.S. Public*, pg. 1753
Rouse, John William, Dep. Mng. Dir. & Sec.--Fuji International Finance PLC, London, United Kingdom; *Int'l*, pg. 521
Rouse, Richard F., V.P. & Asst. Sec.--Cubic Applications, Inc., Lacey, WA; *U.S. Public*, pg. 466
Rousseau, Scott, V.P.-Admin., Controller, Treas. & Sec.--Palmer Electric Co., Winter Park, FL; *U.S. Private*, pg. 834
Routs, D.F., Special Duties & Sec.--Hepworth Minerals and Chemicals Limited, Sandbach, United Kingdom; *Int'l*, pg. 615
Rowan, James P., V.P., Assoc. Gen. Counsel & Asst. Sec.--The Wackenhut Corporation, Palm Beach Gardens, FL; *U.S. Public*, pg. 1731
Rowe, Robert C., Sr. V.P. & Sec.--Golden West Financial Corporation, Oakland, CA; *U.S. Public*, pg. 750
Rowe, Rosemary M., Sec.--Community Bancorp, Derby, VT; *U.S. Public*, pg. 416
Rowe, Sharon, Treas. & Sec.--Lou LaRiche Chevrolet Inc., Plymouth, MI; *U.S. Private*, pg. 651
Rowe, W. Bayless, Gen. Counsel & Sec.--Deltic Timber Corporation, El Dorado, AR; *U.S. Public*, pg. 498
Rowland, Susan E., Sec.--Griffon Corp., Jericho, NY; *U.S. Public*, pg. 766
Rowlen, Thomas M., Controller, Treas. & Sec.--Yoder Oil Company Inc., Elkhart, IN; *U.S. Private*, pg. 1196
Rowley, R.O., Dir.-Fin.--Reuters Holdings PLC, London, United Kingdom; *Int'l*, pg. 1105
Rowson, Rachel, Company Sec.--BAA plc, London, United Kingdom; *Int'l*, pg. 103
Roy, Harold, Gen. Counsel & Sec.--Bayer Clothing Group, New York, NY; *U.S. Private*, pg. 124
Royer, Donald E., Exec. V.P. & Gen. Counsel--Downey Financial Corp., Newport Beach, CA; *U.S. Public*, pg. 525
Royer, Donald E., Exec. V.P., Gen. Counsel & Sec.--Downey Savings & Loan Association, F.A., Newport Beach, CA; *U.S. Public*, pg. 526
Rozee, Peter C., Gen. Counsel & Sec.--Inmet Mining Corporation, Toronto, Canada; *Int'l*, pg. 678
Rozel, Samuel J., Chief Legal Officer, Sr. V.P., Gen. Counsel & Sec.--Philips Electronics North America Corporation, New York, NY; *Int'l*, pg. 1053
Roznowski, Jack, Treas. & Sec.--Trerice Tosto Colliers International, Bingham Farms, MI; *U.S. Private*, pg. 1099
Ruault, Jean-Pierre, Sec.--Compagnie UAP, Paris, France; *Int'l*, pg. 323
Rubel, Darrell D., Chief Fin. Officer, Exec. V.P., Treas. & Asst. Sec.--Marten Transport, Ltd., Mondovi, WI; *U.S. Public*, pg. 1052
Rubin, David M., Gen. Counsel & Sec.--CC Industries, Inc., Chicago, IL; *U.S. Private*, pg. 192
Rubin, Milton, Sec. & Gen. Counsel--Argo International Corp., New York, NY; *U.S. Private*, pg. 322
Rubin, Robert, Vice Chm., V.P.-Sls., Treas. & Sec.--M. Rubin & Sons Inc., Long Island City, NY; *U.S. Private*, pg. 949
Rubin, Steven, V.P., Gen. Counsel & Sec.--General Binding Corporation, Northbrook, IL; *U.S. Public*, pg. 707
Rubinfeld, Abraham N., Gen. Counsel & Sec.--CSA Management Inc., Toronto, Canada; *Int'l*, pg. 243
Rubinfeld, Abraham N., Sec.--Goldcorp Inc., Toronto, Canada; *Int'l*, pg. 243
Rubinfeld, Abraham N., Corp. Counsel & Sec.--Wharf Resources Ltd., Lead, SD; *Int'l*, pg. 243
Rubinfeld, Abraham N., Gen. Counsel & Sec.--Lexam Explorations Inc., Toronto, Canada; *Int'l*, pg. 243
Rubow, Arthur H., Sec.--Greif Brothers Corporation, Delaware, OH; *U.S. Public*, pg. 763
Rubright, James A., Exec. V.P., Gen. Counsel & Sec.--Sonat Exploration Company, Houston, TX; *U.S. Public*, pg. 1485
Ruby, G. Mary, V.P.-Legal Affairs, Gen. Counsel & Sec.--Imax Corporation, Mississauga, Canada; *Int'l*, pg. 661
Ruckes, Kerstin, Sec.--Thermoplast und Apparatebau GmbH, Idstein, Germany; *Int'l*, pg. 1381
Ruckriegel, Lovella, V.P., Treas. & Sec.--BR Associates, Inc., Jasper, IN; *U.S. Private*, pg. 107
Rudman, Gerald E., Sec.--Penobscot Shoe Company, Old Town, ME; *U.S. Public*, pg. 1273
Rudnick, Alan A., V.P., Gen. Counsel & Corp. Sec.--CSX Corporation, Richmond, VA; *U.S. Public*, pg. 284
Rudnik, Robert J., Exec. V.P., Gen. Counsel & Sec.--Prime Group Realty Trust, Chicago, IL; *U.S. Public*, pg. 1326
Rudolph, Philip, Treas.--Rudolph Foods Company, Lima, OH; *U.S. Private*, pg. 950
Rue, C.J., Corp. Sec.--Northwest Natural Gas Company, Portland, OR; *U.S. Public*, pg. 1200
Rueb, Roy T., V.P., Treas. & Sec.--Pentair, Inc., Saint Paul, MN; *U.S. Public*, pg. 1273
Ruegsegger, Martin C., V.P., Corp. Counsel & Sec--Piedmont Natural Gas Co., Inc., Charlotte, NC; *U.S. Public*, pg. 1295
Ruen, Daniel P., Sec.--Cleaners Hanger Co., Palm Harbor, FL; *U.S. Private*, pg. 245
Ruff, Ellen T., Sec. & Dep. Gen. Counsel--Duke Energy Corporation, Charlotte, NC; *U.S. Public*, pg. 534
Ruff, John D., Sec.--Criterion Life Insurance Co., Washington, DC; *U.S. Public*, pg. 219
Ruffin, Pat, V.P., Treas. & Sec.--Ruffin Building Systems, Inc., Oak Grove, LA; *U.S. Private*, pg. 950
Ruffin, Robert, V.P.-Human Resources & Sec.--Servico, Inc., West Palm Beach, FL; *U.S. Public*, pg. 1462
Ruffner, Ernest L., Gen. Counsel & Sec.--Halifax Corporation, Alexandria, VA; *U.S. Public*, pg. 775
Rufiange, Manon, Sec.--Willis Corroon Melling Inc., Montreal, Canada; *Int'l*, pg. 1509
Rufo, Beth Ann, Sec. & Meetings Plng.--The PBS&J Corporation, Miami, FL; *U.S. Private*, pg. 825
Rugg, Jonathan, Sec.--Rugg Manufacturing Company, Greenfield, MA; *U.S. Private*, pg. 950
Ruhkala, Peter D., Chief Fin. Officer, Treas. & Sec.--Nor-Cal Beverage Co., Inc., West Sacramento, CA; *U.S. Private*, pg. 801
Ruhle, Robert E., Chief Fin. Officer, Exec. V.P., Treas. & Sec.--Ruhle Companies, Inc., Valhalla, NY; *U.S. Private*, pg. 950
Rule, Christopher, Company Sec.--W.H. Smith Group plc, London, United Kingdom; *Int'l*, pg. 1264
Rumbley, JoAnne C., Asst. Sec.--Fieldcrest Cannon, Inc., Kannapolis, NC; *U.S. Public*, pg. 1296
Rumple, Belinda, Asst. Sec.--WSFS Financial Corporation, Wilmington, DE; *U.S. Public*, pg. 1728
Rundquist, Lorne, V.P.-Finance--Rosendin Electric, Inc., San Jose, CA; *U.S. Private*, pg. 945
Runk, Judith, Sec.--Directory Distributing Associates, Inc., Saint Louis, MO; *U.S. Private*, pg. 334
Ruppert, John L., Gen. Counsel & Corp. Sec.--Brothers Gourmet Coffees, Inc., Boca Raton, FL; *U.S. Public*, pg. 259
Rush, Curt S., Gen. Counsel & Sec.--Global Direct Mail Corp, Port Washington, NY; *U.S. Public*, pg. 747
Rush, Mary, Sec. & Dir.-Investor Rels.--Tyson Foods, Inc., Springdale, AR; *U.S. Public*, pg. 1652
Rushton, K.J., Sec.--Imperial Chemical Industries PLC, London, United Kingdom; *Int'l*, pg. 662
Rusinak, Ronald, V.P., Gen. Counsel & Sec.--Crown American Realty Trust, Johnstown, PA; *U.S. Public*, pg. 461
Rusnell, Joanne D., Sec. & Asst. Gen. Counsel--Labatt Brewing Company Limited, Toronto, Canada; *Int'l*, pg. 679
Russ, Charles P., III, Exec. V.P.-Law & Human Resources, Gen. Counsel & Sec.--U S West Inc., Englewood, CO; *U.S. Public*, pg. 1688
Russell, Barron Jeff, Treas. & Sec.--Food & Gas, Inc., Norcross, GA; *U.S. Private*, pg. 417
Russell, Brian C., Sec.--Elder's Finance Group, Melbourne, Australia; *Int'l*, pg. 500
Russell, David, Assoc. Gen. Counsel & Asst. Sec.--Grow Group, Inc., Cleveland, OH; *Int'l*, pg. 663
Russell, Douglas W., Chief Fin. Officer, Treas. & Asst. Sec.-Rotonics Manufacturing Inc., Gardena, CA; *U.S. Public*, pg. 1406
Russell, George Earl, Treas. & Sec.--Russell Petroleum Corporation, Montgomery, AL; *U.S. Private*, pg. 953
Russell, J. Richard, Sec.--Henderson Administration Group PLC, London, United Kingdom; *Int'l*, pg. 609
Russell, L. Michael, V.P., Gen. Counsel & Sec.--International Rectifier Corporation, El Segundo, CA; *U.S. Public*, pg. 906
Russell, Ronald J., V.P., Gen. Counsel & Sec.--Methanex Corporation, Vancouver, Canada; *Int'l*, pg. 862
Russian, David H., Chief Fin. Officer, V.P.-Fin., Sec. & Treas.--Brooktree Rockwell Semiconductor Systems Div., San Diego, CA; *U.S. Public*, pg. 1398
Russo, Art, Treas. & Sec.--Seco Warwick Corporation, Meadville, PA; *U.S. Private*, pg. 980
Russo, Gregory T., Sec.--Merrill Lynch & Co., Inc., New York, NY; *U.S. Public*, pg. 1097

Ruszin, Thomas E., Jr., Treas. & Asst. Sec.--Baltimore Gas and Electric Company, Baltimore, MD; *U.S. Public*, pg. 172
Rutgers, J.A., Dir.-Legal & Gen Sec.--Philips Electronics N.V., Eindhoven, Netherlands; *Int'l*, pg. 1051
Ruth, James C., V.P., Gen. Counsel & Asst. Sec.--Texas Eastern Products Pipeline Company, L.P., Houston, TX; *U.S. Public*, pg. 535
Rutherford, J. Kenneth, Chief Fin. Officer & Corp. Sec.--NBS Technologies, Inc., Mississauga, Canada; *Int'l*, pg. 898
Rutledge, Michael, Sec.--Farmers Mutual Hail Insurance Co. of Iowa, Des Moines, IA; *U.S. Private*, pg. 395
Rutledge, Susan, Sec.--Product Information Network, Englewood, CO; *U.S. Private*, pg. 597
Rutman, Gregory, V.P., Sec. & Gen. Counsel--The Geon Company, Avon Lake, OH; *U.S. Public*, pg. 733
Ryan, Christopher J., Chief Fin. Officer, Exec. V.P.-Fin. & Sec.--Lakeland Industries, Inc., Ronkonkoma, NY; *U.S. Public*, pg. 975
Ryan, Dwight P., Chief Fin. Officer, V.P., Treas. & Sec.--IntegraMed America, Purchase, NY; *U.S. Public*, pg. 883
Ryan, Edwin, Gen. Counsel & Sec.--Tomkins Industries Inc., Dayton, OH; *Int'l*, pg. 1397
Ryan, Frank J., Chief Fin. Officer & Sec.--Detection Systems, Inc., Fairport, NY; *U.S. Public*, pg. 501
Ryan, Jane G., Asst. Sec.--Indianapolis Water Company, Indianapolis, IN; *U.S. Public*, pg. 1185
Ryan, Janie L., Corp. Sec. & Plan Admin.--Atlantic American Corporation, Atlanta, GA; *U.S. Public*, pg. 143
Ryan, Janie L., Asst. Sec.--Bankers Fidelity Life Insurance Company, Atlanta, GA; *U.S. Public*, pg. 143
Ryan, Janie L., Sec.--Self-Insurance Administrators, Inc., Stone Mountain, GA; *U.S. Public*, pg. 144
Ryan, John F., V.P. & Sec.--Fleming Packaging Corp., Peoria, IL; *U.S. Private*, pg. 411
Ryan, John G., Corp. Sec.--Global Marine Inc., Houston, TX; *U.S. Public*, pg. 748
Ryan, Kevin T., Sr., V.P. & Sec.--Charan Industries, Inc., Garden City, NY; *U.S. Private*, pg. 229
Ryan, Louis F., Exec. V.P., Gen. Counsel & Sec.--Landmark Communications, Inc., Norfolk, VA; *U.S. Private*, pg. 647
Ryan, N. Jeanne, Asst. Sec.--The Toro Company, Bloomington, MN; *U.S. Public*, pg. 1623
Ryan, Patrick, Sr. V.P., Sec. & Gen. Counsel--Hunt-Wesson, Inc., Fullerton, CA; *U.S. Public*, pg. 428
Ryan, Patrick M., Corp. Sec.--Marketing Corp. of America, Westport, CT; *U.S. Private*, pg. 704
Ryan, Robert M., Sec.--Reading Anthracite Co., Pottsville, PA; *U.S. Private*, pg. 913
Ryan, Ron, Chief Fin. Officer, Treas. & Sec.--Punch Press Products, Inc., Los Angeles, CA; *U.S. Private*, pg. 895
Ryan, Russell J., V.P.-Sec. & Treas.--Ryan Construction Company Of Minnesota, Hibbing, MN; *U.S. Private*, pg. 953
Rydel, James W., V.P.-Admin. & Sec.--Intermet Corporation, Troy, MI; *U.S. Public*, pg. 894
Ryder, Beverly, Corp. Sec. & Asst.-Chm.--Edison International, Rosemead, CA; *U.S. Public*, pg. 564
Rydzinski, David, Chief Fin. Officer, V.P. & Asst. Sec.--William A. Randolph, Inc., Morton Grove, IL; *U.S. Private*, pg. 909
Ryland, Joyce, Sr. V.P.& Exec. Sec.--Leiner Health Products, Inc., Carson, CA; *U.S. Private*, pg. 659
Rynn, John A., V.P. & Treas.--Berol Corporation, Brentwood, TN; *U.S. Public*, pg. 1178
Rynone, William J., Treas. & Sec.--Rynone Manufacturing Corporation, Sayre, PA; *U.S. Private*, pg. 953
Ryser, Philip R., V.P.-Franchising, Gen. Counsel & Sec.--Stanley Steemer International, Inc., Dublin, OH; *U.S. Private*, pg. 1033
Saas, Pierre, Sec. Gen.--Bongard, Holtzheim, France; *Int'l*, pg. 570
Sabala, James A., Sec. & Treas.--Pinnacle Exploration, Inc., Coeur D'Alene, ID; *U.S. Public*, pg. 394
Sabin, David C., Chm. Bd. & Sec.--Salton/Maxim Housewares, Inc., Mount Prospect, IL; *U.S. Public*, pg. 1430
Sabl, John J., Exec. V.P., Gen. Counsel & Sec.--Conseco Inc., Carmel, IN; *U.S. Public*, pg. 432
Sachs, Alan, Exec. V.P., Gen. Counsel & Sec.--Edison Brothers Stores, Inc., Saint Louis, MO; *U.S. Public*, pg. 563
Sachs, Arthur S., Sec.--O.F. Mossberg & Sons, Inc., North Haven, CT; *U.S. Private*, pg. 764
Sack, James M., V.P., Gen. Counsel & Sec.--NVR, Inc., Mc Lean, VA; *U.S. Public*, pg. 1148
Sacks, Louis, Treas. & Sec.--S. Freedman & Sons, Inc., Landover, MD; *U.S. Private*, pg. 425
Sacks, Michael B., V.P., Sec. & Gen. Counsel--ADT Security Services, Inc., Aurora, CO; *U.S. Public*, pg. 1649
Sada, Pablo Gonzalez, Pres.-Chemical Fibers & Mining Div. & Sec.-Bd. of Dirs.--Vitro, Sociedad Anonima, Garza Garcia, Mexico; *Int'l*, pg. 1469
Sadler, Robert P., V.P.-Quality Control, Treas. & Sec.--Integral Systems, Inc., Lanham, MD; *U.S. Public*, pg. 883
Sadowski, Raymond, Chief Fin. Officer, Sr. V.P. & Asst. Sec.--Avnet, Inc., Great Neck, NY; *U.S. Public*, pg. 155
Sage, John B., Sec.--Brunswick Mining & Smelting Corp. Ltd., Bathurst, Canada; *Int'l*, pg. 434
Sahm, Judith M., Sec.--SBC Communications Inc., San Antonio, TX; *U.S. Public*, pg. 1415
Sahn, John G., V.P., Gen. Counsel & Sec.--CILCORP Inc., Peoria, IL; *U.S. Public*, pg. 367
Sahn, John G., Sec.--CILCO Energy Corp., Peoria, IL; *U.S. Public*, pg. 367
Sahn, John G., Sec.--CILCO Exploration & Development Co., Peoria, IL; *U.S. Public*, pg. 367
Sahn, John G., Sec.--Central Illinois Light Company, Peoria, IL; *U.S. Public*, pg. 367
Sahn, John G., Sec.--CILCORP Investment Management Inc., Peoria, IL; *U.S. Public*, pg. 367
Sahn, John G., Sec.--CILCORP Ventures Inc., Peoria, IL; *U.S. Public*, pg. 367
Sahn, John G., Sec.--QST Environmental Inc., Peoria, IL; *U.S. Public*, pg. 367
Sahn, John G., Sec.--QST Enterprises Inc., Peoria, IL; *U.S. Public*, pg. 367
Sahn, John G., Sec.--QST Communications, Inc., Peoria, IL; *U.S. Public*, pg. 367
Sahn, John G., Sec.--QST Energy, Inc., Peoria, IL; *U.S. Public*, pg. 367
Saint-Arnaud, Louis, V.P.-Legal Services & Sec.--Quebecor Inc., Montreal, Canada; *Int'l*, pg. 1075
Saint-Arnaud, Louis, V.P.-Legal Affairs & Sec.--Quebecor Communications, Inc., Montreal, Canada; *Int'l*, pg. 1076
Saint-Arnaud, Louis, V.P.-Legal Services & Sec.--Quebecor Multimedia Inc., Montreal, Canada; *Int'l*, pg. 1076
Sakamoto, K., Sec.--SEIKO Hong Kong Ltd., Hong Kong, Hong Kong; *Int'l*, pg. 1218
Saladen, Barbara, Asst. Sec.--Chief Industries, Inc., Grand Island, NE; *U.S. Private*, pg. 236
Salamon, Diane, Treas., Sec. & Legal Counsel--Pic N'Pay Supermarkets, Inc., Dania, FL; *U.S. Private*, pg. 864
Salaysay, Meng, Asst. Sec.--Great Pacific Enterprises Inc., Vancouver, Canada; *Int'l*, pg. 557
Salaysay, Meng, Asst. Sec.--Westar Group Ltd., Vancouver, Canada; *Int'l*, pg. 1491
Sale, Richard H., Sr. V.P. & Sec.--Commercial National Bank, Shreveport, LA; *U.S. Public*, pg. 500
Saleem, M., Dir.-Fin. & Sec.--Parke-Davis & Company, Limited, Karachi, Pakistan; *U.S. Public*, pg. 1739
Salen, Samuel, M.D., Vice Chm. & Sec.--InnoServ Technologies, Inc., Arlington, TX; *U.S. Public*, pg. 879
Salinger, Robert M., Gen. Counsel & Sec.--First Financial Corporation, Stevens Point, WI; *U.S. Public*, pg. 140
Salinger, Robert M., Exec. V.P., Gen. Counsel & Sec.--First Financial Bank, FSB, Stevens Point, WI; *U.S. Public*, pg. 140
Salisbury, George, Chief Fin. Officer, Treas. & Sec.--Symons Corporation, Pasadena, CA; *U.S. Private*, pg. 932
Salit, Gary, Gen. Counsel & Sec.--Bell & Howell Holdings, Skokie, IL; *U.S. Public*, pg. 201
Salomon, Allan, V.P.-Real Estate & Sec.--Reitmans (Canada) Limited, Montreal, Canada; *Int'l*, pg. 1102
Salomons, M.E.J., Sec.-Bd. Mgmnt. & Pub. Rels. Officer--Internatio-Muller N.V., Rotterdam, Netherlands; *Int'l*, pg. 680
Salowitz, Charles B., Sec. & Assoc. Gen. Counsel--Inland Steel Industries, Inc., Chicago, IL; *U.S. Public*, pg. 879
Saltmarsh, P. David, Corp. Sec.--Reckitt & Colman plc, London, United Kingdom; *Int'l*, pg. 1089
Saltzman, Shirley, Sec.--Banner Wholesale Grocers, Inc., Chicago, IL; *U.S. Private*, pg. 114
Salwasser, Margaret, Treas. & Sec.--Salwasser Manufacturing Company, Inc., Reedley, CA; *U.S. Private*, pg. 963
Samet, Andrew B., V.P. & Assoc. Gen. Counsel--AlliedSignal Inc., Morristown, NJ; *U.S. Public*, pg. 49
Samp, Frederick, Gen. Counsel & Corp. Clerk--Bangor Hydro-Electric Company, Bangor, ME; *U.S. Public*, pg. 178
Sampaio, Dr. Orlanda, Sec. Gen.--Transportes Aereos Portugueses, Lisbon, Portugal; *Int'l*, pg. 1418
Samplonius, T., Corp. Sec.--De Bussy Harms N.V., Diemen, Netherlands; *Int'l*, pg. 386
Samuel, Mathew, Sec.--Temasek Holdings Pte. Ltd., Singapore, Singapore; *Int'l*, pg. 1374
Samuel, Matthew, Corp. Sec.--Singapore Airlines Ltd., Singapore, Singapore; *Int'l*, pg. 1374
Samuelian, Karl M., Chm. Exec. Committee & Sec.--Maxwell Technologies, Inc., San Diego, CA; *U.S. Public*, pg. 1061
Samuels, Richard A., Sec.--EnergyNorth, Inc., Manchester, NH; *U.S. Public*, pg. 581
Samuels, Sandor E., Mng. Dir.-Legal, Gen. Counsel & Sec.--Countrywide Home Loans Inc., Pasadena, CA; *U.S. Public*, pg. 452
Sanborn, Barry P., Asst. Sec.--John Hancock Mutual Life Insurance Company, Boston, MA; *U.S. Private*, pg. 589
Sanchez, Eugene, Treas. & Sec.--Distributors Oil Company, Inc., Baton Rouge, LA; *U.S. Private*, pg. 336
Sanchez, Luis Felipe Castresana, Sec. & Legal Counsel--SEPI, Madrid, Spain; *Int'l*, pg. 1223
Sanchez, Raymond, V.P., Treas., Asst. Sec. & Administrator--Hunter Engineering Co., Inc., Riverside, CA; *Int'l*, pg. 474
Sanchez, Sylvia, Sec.--Seagull Energy Corporation, Houston, TX; *U.S. Public*, pg. 1450
Sander, Duane E., Dr., Sec.--Daktronics, Inc., Brookings, SD; *U.S. Public*, pg. 478
Sander, James E., V.P. & Sec.--Hickman, Williams & Co. Inc., Cincinnati, OH; *U.S. Private*, pg. 525
Sander, James M., V.P.-Law & Sec.--General Nutrition, Inc., Pittsburgh, PA; *U.S. Public*, pg. 725
Sander, William C., Exec. V.P., Treas. & Sec.--Hunt Building Corporation, El Paso, TX; *U.S. Private*, pg. 548
Sanders, Al, Dir.-Customer Svc. & Plant Mgr.--Bluewater, Mora, MN; *U.S. Private*, pg. 153
Sanders, Bernard, Sr. V.P. & Corp. Sec.--Farmland Industries, Inc., Kansas City, MO; *U.S. Private*, pg. 395
Sanders, Charles, V.P., Treas. & Sec.--RDM Sports Group, Atlanta, GA; *U.S. Public*, pg. 1354
Sanders, Charles E., Sec.--Hamilton Lamp Corp., North Kansas City, MO; *U.S. Public*, pg. 1354
Sanders, David E., V.P., Gen. Counsel & Sec.--LSI Logic Corp., Milpitas, CA; *U.S. Public*, pg. 971
Sanders, Kenneth W., Chief Fin. Officer, Sr. V.P.-Fin., Treas. & Asst. Sec.--Paging Network, Inc., Plano, TX; *U.S. Public*, pg. 1252
Sanders, Philip P., Treas. & Sec.--The Boeing Company Canada Ltd., Toronto, Canada; *U.S. Public*, pg. 242
Sanders, Stephen, Sec.--St. James's Place Capital plc., London, United Kingdom; *Int'l*, pg. 1177
Sanderson, Tom, Sec.--Monte Vista Co-Op Association, Inc., Monte Vista, CO; *U.S. Private*, pg. 758
Sandgrund, David M., V.P., Gen. Counsel & Sec.--Goody Products, Inc., Peachtree City, GA; *U.S. Public*, pg. 1177
Sandler, Reba, Sec. & Treas.--L.M. Sandler & Sons, Virginia Beach, VA; *U.S. Private*, pg. 964
Sandman, Dan B., Gen. Counsel & Sec.--USX Corporation, Pittsburgh, PA; *U.S. Public*, pg. 1661
Sandman, Paul, Sr. V.P., Gen. Counsel & Sec.--Boston Scientific Corp., Natick, MA; *U.S. Public*, pg. 247
Sands, Paul, Jr., Exec. V.P., Gen. Counsel & Sec.--Chicago Title & Trust Co., Chicago, IL; *U.S. Public*, pg. 42
Sands, Robert, Exec. V.P., Gen. Counsel & Sec.--Canandaigua Wine Company, Inc., Canandaigua, NY; *U.S. Public*, pg. 300
Sandy, Sabra A., Asst. Sec.--Dunn Industries Inc., Kansas City, MO; *U.S. Private*, pg. 347
Sandy, Sabra A., Asst. Sec.--J.E. Dunn Construction Co., Kansas City, MO; *U.S. Private*, pg. 347
Sanford, Sharon J., Sec.--The Somerset Group, Inc., Indianapolis, IN; *U.S. Public*, pg. 1484
Sanger, Thomas C., Sec.--Pacific Enterprises, Los Angeles, CA; *U.S. Public*, pg. 1249
Sanseverino, Diana, Corp. Sec.--Sau-Sea Foods, Inc., Tarrytown, NY; *U.S. Private*, pg. 967
Sansky, Robert, Treas. & Sec.--Emcee Cellular, Inc., Wilmington, DE; *U.S. Public*, pg. 571
Sansom, Walter R., Sec.--Champion Industries, Huntington, WV; *U.S. Public*, pg. 333
Sansone, Joseph, Sec.--Sansone Auto Mall, Avenel, NJ; *U.S. Private*, pg. 965
Santa, Richard A., Chief Fin. Officer--Dynamic Materials Corporation, Lafayette, CO; *U.S. Public*, pg. 539
Santamarina, A., Sec.--Grupo Mexico S.A. de C.V., Mexico, Mexico; *U.S. Public*, pg. 138
Santangelo, Joseph A., Chief Fin. Officer, Treas. & Sec.--FPA Corporation, Bensalem, PA; *U.S. Public*, pg. 608
Santo, James M., Exec. V.P.-Admin.--Eckerd Corporation, Largo, FL; *U.S. Public*, pg. 917
Santone, Margret, Corp. Sec.--Sulcus Computer Corp., Greensburg, PA; *U.S. Public*, pg. 1527
Santos, Dianne, Corp. Sec.--Noteworthy Industries Inc., Amsterdam, NY; *U.S. Private*, pg. 808
Santos, Nury, Sec.--Premier Cruises, Miami, FL; *U.S. Private*, pg. 293
Santry, Nancy, Sec.--The Stop & Shop Companies, Inc., Quincy, MA; *Int'l*, pg. 750
Sanzo, Judi, Sec.--The Todd-AO Corporation, Hollywood, CA; *U.S. Public*, pg. 1619
Sapp, Roger, Sec. & Controller--Wurzburg, Inc., Memphis, TN; *U.S. Private*, pg. 1192
Sarai, Andre, V.P., Treas. & Sec.--Weiss Sheet Metal Company, Gardena, CA; *U.S. Private*, pg. 1160
Sarauer, Lori, Exec. Sec.-Consumer Mktg.--The Pillsbury Company, Minneapolis, MN; *Int'l*, pg. 411
Sarauer, Lori, Exec. Sec.-Consumer Mktg.--Pillsbury Co., Minneapolis, MN; *Int'l*, pg. 411
Saraure, Lori, Exec. Sec.--The Haagen-Dazs Company Inc., Minneapolis, MN; *Int'l*, pg. 411
Sarjoo, Priya, Asst. Treas. & Asst. Sec.--Astrex, Inc., Plainview, NY; *U.S. Public*, pg. 141
Sarkisian, Alex, Exec. V.P. & Sec.--Schawk, Inc., Des Plaines, IL; *U.S. Public*, pg. 1437
Sarkisian, John A., Second Asst. Sec.--Marketing Displays International, Farmington Hills, MI; *U.S. Private*, pg. 705
Sarkisian, Lisa A., Gen. Counsel & Asst. Sec.--Marketing Displays International, Farmington Hills, MI; *U.S. Private*, pg. 705
Sarmiento, Antonio A., Chm. Bd., Pres. & Sec.--Lumas Realty, Inc., Miami, FL; *U.S. Private*, pg. 680
Sarnese, William E., Controller & Asst. Corp. Sec.--Penn Engineering & Manufacturing Corp., Danboro, PA; *U.S. Public*, pg. 1269
Sarosiek, James J., V.P., Gen. Counsel & Sec.--Menasha Corporation, Neenah, WI; *U.S. Private*, pg. 731
Sartin, David P., Controller & Sec.--Central Power and Light Company, Corpus Christi, TX; *U.S. Public*, pg. 324
Sarver, J. William, V.P., Gen. Counsel & Sec.--Bell Atlantic-MD, Baltimore, MD; *U.S. Public*, pg. 202
Sasaki, Sherry, Sec.--Source Capital, Inc., Los Angeles, CA; *U.S. Public*, pg. 1488
Sass, Karen P., Sec.--Gerald H. Phipps, Inc., Denver, CO; *U.S. Private*, pg. 862
Saterbo, John, Sr. V.P. & Sec.--Colorado Boxed Beef Co., Auburndale, FL; *U.S. Private*, pg. 254
Sato, Tetsuhiko, Gen. Mgr. & Corp. Sec.--Tekken Corporation, Tokyo, Japan; *Int'l*, pg. 1362
Satriano, Anita, Asst. Sec.--SGS Control Services Inc., Edison, NJ; *Int'l*, pg. 1153
Satz, Joseph R., Exec. V.P., Gen. Counsel & Sec.--Price Enterprises, Inc., San Diego, CA; *U.S. Public*, pg. 1324
Satzger, Doug, Sr. V.P., Gen. Counsel & Sec.--Air & Water Technologies Corporation, Branchburg, NJ; *U.S. Public*, pg. 29
Sauder, Scot, V.P., Gen. Counsel & Sec.--Continental Medical Systems, Inc., Mechanicsburg, PA; *U.S. Public*, pg. 839
Sauer, Frederick J., V.P. & Sec.--Alliance Construction Solutions, Inc., Fort Collins, CO; *U.S. Private*, pg. 38
Saul, David, Treas. & Sec.--Beach City Chevrolet Co., Long Beach, CA; *U.S. Private*, pg. 125
Saunders, Deirdre D., V.P., Treas. & Asst. Sec.--AMETEK, Inc., Paoli, PA; *U.S. Public*, pg. 99
Saunders, Keith C., Chief Fin. Officer, Exec. V.P. & Sec.--Zions Co-operative Mercantile Institution, Salt Lake City, UT; *U.S. Public*, pg. 1793
Saunders, William B., Sec.--Murphy Family Farms, Rose Hill, NC; *U.S. Private*, pg. 768
Sauve, Nicole, Sec.--Canada Ports Corporation, Ottawa, Canada; *Int'l*, pg. 255
Sauvey, Marian Weilert, V.P.-Law & Corp. Sec.--Atlas World Group, Inc., Evansville, IN; *U.S. Private*, pg. 97
Sauvey, Marian Weilert, V.P.-Law & Corp. Sec.--Atlas Van Lines, Inc., Evansville, IN; *U.S. Private*, pg. 97
Savage, John E., Pres., Chief Oper. Officer, Co-Chief Exec. Officer & Sec.--Amwest Insurance Group, Inc., Calabasas, CA; *U.S. Public*, pg. 106

Savard, J., Sec.--L.B. Smith, Inc., Camp Hill, PA; *U.S. Private*, pg. 1009

Savitsky, David, Chief Oper. Officer, Exec. V.P., Treas. & Sec.--Staff Builders Inc., Lake Success, NY; *U.S. Public*, pg. 1501

Savitz, Richard J., V.P.-Fin., Treas. & Sec.--Justin Industries, Inc., Fort Worth, TX; *U.S. Public*, pg. 936

Sawch, William B., V.P., Gen. Counsel & Sec.--The Perkin-Elmer Corporation, Norwalk, CT; *U.S. Public*, pg. 1279

Sawdei, Milan A., Exec. V.P., Chief Legal Officer & Sec.--Bergen Brunswig Corporation, Orange, CA; *U.S. Public*, pg. 213

Sawyer, Joyce M., Sec.--Congaree Construction Co., Inc., Columbia, SC; *U.S. Private*, pg. 263

Saxon, Franklin N., Chief Fin. Officer, Sr. V.P., Treas. & Sec.--Culp, Inc., High Point, NC; *U.S. Public*, pg. 467

Sayatovic, Wayne P., Chief Fin. Officer & Sr. V.P.-Fin.--IDEX Corporation, Northbrook, IL; *U.S. Public*, pg. 862

Saydah, John, V.P. & Sec.--Cecil Saydah Company, Los Angeles, CA; *U.S. Private*, pg. 969

Sayre, Scott E., Sec. & Assoc. Gen. Counsel--Viad Corp, Phoenix, AZ; *U.S. Public*, pg. 1718

Sbarro, Joseph, Sr. Exec. V.P. & Sec.--Sbarro, Inc., Commack, NY; *U.S. Public*, pg. 1435

Scales, Gene, Treas. & Sec.--Allied Plywood Corp., Alexandria, VA; *U.S. Private*, pg. 40

Scales, M.W., Sec.--The Hongkong and Shanghai Banking Corporation Limited (HongkongBank), Central, Hong Kong; *Int'l*, pg. 583

Scanlan-Smith, Beryl, Sec.--Eatelcorp Inc., Gonzales, LA; *U.S. Private*, pg. 358

Scanlon, Elizabeth A., Gen. Counsel & Sec.--The Wella Corporation, Montvale, NJ; *Int'l*, pg. 1489

Scarfo, Henry J., Mng. Dir.-Corp. Affairs & Asst. Sec.--American Automobile Association, Heathrow, FL; *U.S. Private*, pg. 50

Scarfone, Anthony, Sec. & Gen. Counsel--Dahlberg, Inc., Golden Valley, MN; *U.S. Public*, pg. 194

Scartz, Don T., V.P.-Fin., Treas. & Sec.--Electromagnetic Sciences, Inc., Norcross, GA; *U.S. Public*, pg. 569

Schaedler, Thomas J., Jr., Sec.--Schaedler Brothers, Inc., Harrisburg, PA; *U.S. Private*, pg. 969

Schaefer, John D., Sec.--Plastipak Packaging Inc., Plymouth, MI; *U.S. Private*, pg. 872

Schaefer, John L., Chief Fin. Officer, V.P.-Fin. & Sec.--The Wm. Powell Company, Cincinnati, OH; *U.S. Private*, pg. 877

Schaeff, J., Sec. & Mgr.-Fin.--S.A. Morgan, Brussels, Belgium; *Int'l*, pg. 891

Schaeffer, Becky, Corp. Counsel & Sec.--The PBS&J Corporation, Miami, FL; *U.S. Private*, pg. 825

Schafer, Seymour, Sec.--Asko, Inc, Homestead, PA; *U.S. Private*, pg. 89

Schalk, Michael A., Sec.--Stuart Entertainment Inc., Council Bluffs, IA; *U.S. Public*, pg. 1526

Schall, Valeria, Exec. V.P.--All Star Gas Corporation, Lebanon, MO; *U.S. Private*, pg. 35

Schall, Valerie, Sec.--All Star Gas, Inc., Lebanon, MO; *U.S. Private*, pg. 35

Scharden, Ruth Dale, Sec.--Farmers Investment Company, Inc., Horse Cave, KY; *U.S. Private*, pg. 112

Schauf, Lawrence E., Exec. V.P. & Sec.--Foodmaker, Inc., San Diego, CA; *U.S. Public*, pg. 661

Schaufeld, Karen, Corp. Sec.--National Electronics Warranty Corporation, Sterling, VA; *U.S. Private*, pg. 782

Scheel, Steve, Sec. & Treas.--MeritCare Health System, Fargo, ND; *U.S. Private*, pg. 733

Scheflen, John W., Sr. Exec. V.P., Gen. Counsel & Sec.--MBNA Corporation, Wilmington, DE; *U.S. Public*, pg. 1023

Schein, Steven M., Treas. & Asst. Sec.--IGC Energy, Inc., Indianapolis, IN; *U.S. Public*, pg. 875

Schell, Ivan, Gen. Counsel & Sec.--Roll Forming Corporation, Shelbyville, KY; *U.S. Private*, pg. 941

Schell, Mark E., Gen. Counsel & Sec.--Unit Corporation, Tulsa, OK; *U.S. Public*, pg. 1672

Schelle, Nathan T., V.P., Controller & Asst. Sec.--Bailey, Fischer & Porter Company, Warminster, PA; *Int'l*, pg. 449

Schett, N.B., Gen. Counsel & Sec.--PIMCO Advisors, Stamford, CT; *U.S. Public*, pg. 1296

Scheuer, Thomas, Legal Counsel & Asst. Sec.--Louis Dreyfus Corporation, Wilton, CT; *U.S. Private*, pg. 342

Schey, Walter, Sec.--Putzmeister, Inc., Sturtevant, WI; *U.S. Private*, pg. 896

Schiff, Craig, V.P.-Prods. & Svcs./Corp. Sec.--Hyperion Software, Stamford, CT; *U.S. Public*, pg. 851

Schiffer, Daniel L., Sr. V.P., Gen. Counsel & Sec.--MCN Energy Group, Inc., Detroit, MI; *U.S. Public*, pg. 1024

Schiffer, Daniel L., V.P., Gen. Counsel & Sec.--MCN Investment, Detroit, MI; *U.S. Public*, pg. 1025

Schiffer, Daniel L., V.P. & Sec.--Citizens Gas Fuel Company, Adrian, MI; *U.S. Public*, pg. 1025

Schildge, Ronald, Sec.--Precision Roll Grinders, Inc., Allentown, PA; *U.S. Private*, pg. 880

Schiller, Arthur J., V.P., Gen. Counsel & Sec.--Lane Industries, Inc., Northbrook, IL; *U.S. Private*, pg. 649

Schilling, Richard M., V.P., Gen. Counsel & Sec.--Sundstrand Corporation, Rockford, IL; *U.S. Public*, pg. 1533

Schillinger, Donna, Exec. Sec.--Hirschfeld, Inc., San Angelo, TX; *U.S. Private*, pg. 530

Schiotis, Yvette, Sec.--Metalcenter, Inc., Santa Fe Springs, CA; *U.S. Public*, pg. 1375

Schiotis, Yvette M., Sec.--Reliance Steel & Aluminum Co., Los Angeles, CA; *U.S. Public*, pg. 1375

Schipull, Duane, Treas. & Sec.--Bawden Corporation, Eldridge, IA; *U.S. Private*, pg. 124

Schlagenhauf, John, Treas. & Sec.--Badger Truck Center, Inc., Milwaukee, WI; *U.S. Private*, pg. 110

Schlang, Alan L., Sec.--Guardian Industries Corp., Auburn Hills, MI; *U.S. Private*, pg. 485

Schlanger, Richard, Co-Pres. & Sec.--West Shore Envelope Company, Inc., New York, NY; *U.S. Private*, pg. 1163

Schleif, Lyle, Treas. & Sec.--Anoka Electric Cooperative, Ramsey, MN; *U.S. Private*, pg. 75

Schlingman, William J., Asst. Sec.--The Leslie Fay Companies, Inc., New York, NY; *U.S. Public*, pg. 989

Schlobohm, Jon, Treas. & Sec.--National Corset Supply House, Los Angeles, CA; *U.S. Private*, pg. 781

Schloss, Bruce M., V.P., Gen. Counsel & Sec.--Health-Chem Corporation, New York, NY; *U.S. Public*, pg. 802

Schlosser, Elaine, M., Treas. & Sec.--Schlosser Forge Company, Rancho Cucamonga, CA; *U.S. Private*, pg. 970

Schlosser, P., Treas. & Sec.--Krupp Robins, Inc., Englewood, CO; *Int'l*, pg. 511

Schlothan, Dau, Treas. & Sec.--Oltmans Construction Company, Whittier, CA; *U.S. Private*, pg. 815

Schlott, Thelma, Sec.--Warren Distribution, Inc., Omaha, NE; *U.S. Private*, pg. 1151

Schmeller, Tanya, Sec.--Columbian Mutual Life Insurance Co., Binghamton, NY; *U.S. Private*, pg. 256

Schmider, Susan D., Sec. & Asst. Treas.--Vornado Realty Trust, Saddle Brook, NJ; *U.S. Public*, pg. 1725

Schmidt, Carl G., Chief Fin. Officer, Sr. V.P., Treas. & Sec.--Johnson Worldwide Associates, Inc., Sturtevant, WI; *U.S. Public*, pg. 932

Schmidt, J.R., Sec.--Ziegler Leasing Corp., West Bend, WI; *U.S. Public*, pg. 1792

Schmidt, J.R., Corp. Sec.--Ziegler Collateralized Securities, Inc., West Bend, WI; *U.S. Public*, pg. 1792

Schmidt, J.R., Sec.--Ziegler Medical Equipment Group, Inc., Omaha, NE; *U.S. Public*, pg. 1792

Schmidt, Katitza, V.P. & Sec.--Pacific Handy Cutter, Inc., Costa Mesa, CA; *U.S. Private*, pg. 831

Schmidt, Leslie, Treas. & Sec.--Warrens Waller Press, Inc., South San Francisco, CA; *U.S. Private*, pg. 1151

Schmidt, Patrick, Controller & Sec.--Signtech USA, Ltd., San Antonio, TX; *U.S. Private*, pg. 999

Schmidt, Thomas, V.P., Gen. Counsel & Sec.--Midland Enterprises Inc., Cincinnati, OH; *U.S. Public*, pg. 549

Schmidtman, Scott, Gen. Counsel & Sec.--Olsy North America Inc., Liberty Lake, WA; *Int'l*, pg. 1002

Schmit, James, Gen. Counsel & Sec.--Robert James Sales Inc., Buffalo, NY; *U.S. Private*, pg. 935

Schmitt, David L., Sr. V.P.-Admin., Gen. Counsel & Sec.--Bradlees Inc., Braintree, MA; *U.S. Public*, pg. 249

Schmitt, Timothy J., V.P., Sec., & Asst. Gen. Counsel--Newmont Mining Corporation, Denver, CO; *U.S. Public*, pg. 1178

Schmitz, Don W., Asst. Sec.--Pharmacia & Upjohn, Kalamazoo, MI; *Int'l*, pg. 1048

Schmitz, Michael D., Asst. Sec.--Brunswick Corporation, Lake Forest, IL; *U.S. Public*, pg. 265

Schmoller, Eberhard G.H., Sr. V.P., Gen. Counsel & Sec.--CNF Transportation Inc., Palo Alto, CA; *U.S. Public*, pg. 281

Schmutz, John F., V.P., Gen. Counsel & Sec.--La Quinta Inns, Inc., San Antonio, TX; *U.S. Public*, pg. 972

Schnadig, R., Sec.--Schnadig Corporation, Des Plaines, IL; *U.S. Private*, pg. 971

Schnatter, Charles W., Sr. V.P. & Sec.--Papa John's International Inc., Louisville, KY; *U.S. Public*, pg. 1255

Schneible, William F., Controller, Treas. & Sec.--Brooklyn Bottling Co. of Milton, NY, Milton, NY; *U.S. Private*, pg. 171

Schneider, David M., Chief Legal Officer & Sec.--The Progressive Corporation, Cleveland, OH; *U.S. Public*, pg. 1334

Schneider, Eric N., V.P., Gen. Counsel & Sec.--Schneider Corp., Kitchener, Canada; *Int'l*, pg. 1207

Schneider, Kik, Sec.--Banque Generale du Luxembourg SA, Luxembourg, Luxembourg; *Int'l*, pg. 161

Schneider, Richard A., Chief Fin. Officer--NAI Technologies, Inc., Huntington, NY; *U.S. Public*, pg. 1144

Schneider, Rolf, Sec. Gen.--SIG Schweizersiche Industrie-Gesellschaft Holding AG, Neuhausen, Switzerland; *Int'l*, pg. 1156

Schneider, Scott V., Chief Fin. Officer, V.P., Treas. & Sec.--Saul Centers Inc., Chevy Chase, MD; *U.S. Public*, pg. 1435

Schnell, Lonnie D., Chief Fin. Officer--Haskel International, Inc., Burbank, CA; *U.S. Public*, pg. 798

Schnuck, Terry, Gen. Counsel & Sec.--Schnuck Markets, Inc., Saint Louis, MO; *U.S. Private*, pg. 971

Schnur, Daniel R., Sr. V.P., Gen. Counsel & Sec.--Richfood Holdings, Inc., Glen Allen, VA; *U.S. Public*, pg. 1388

Schochet, William, V.P., Gen. Counsel & Sec.--Overhead Door Corporation, Dallas, TX; *U.S. Private*, pg. 822

Schocke, Robert P., Chief Fin. Officer, Treas., Controller & Sec.--Greenhorne & O'Mara, Inc., Greenbelt, MD; *U.S. Private*, pg. 477

Schoeber, Eldon, V.P., Treas. & Sec.--Site Oil Company of Missouri, Clayton, MO; *U.S. Private*, pg. 1004

Schoenbeck, Lee, Sec.--Dakotah, Inc., Webster, SD; *U.S. Public*, pg. 477

Schoeneman, Cecil, Sec.--Schoeneman Brothers Company, Sioux Falls, SD; *U.S. Private*, pg. 972

Scholler, Bernice, Treas. & Sec.--Times Printing Company, Inc., Random Lake, WI; *U.S. Private*, pg. 1087

Scholtz, Anna Lee, V.P.-Fin. & Sec.--Preussag North America, Greenwich, CT; *Int'l*, pg. 1070

Scholz, David A., Sec.--Unicom Corporation, Chicago, IL; *U.S. Public*, pg. 1664

Scholz, David A., Sec.--ComEd, Chicago, IL; *U.S. Public*, pg. 1664

Schomberg, David, Gen. Sec.--Greater New York Mutual Insurance Company, New York, NY; *U.S. Private*, pg. 476

Schonau, Mark R., Chief Fin. Officer, Sec., Treas., & Investor Rels.--HBO & Company/Cycare Business Group, Scottsdale, AZ; *U.S. Public*, pg. 770

Schonwald, Gary A., Sec. & Legal Officer--General Felt Industries, Inc., Linwood, PA; *U.S. Private*, pg. 1094

Schorr, Stephen I., V.P.-Fin., Treas. & Sec.--Westbrae Natural, Inc., Carson, CA; *U.S. Public*, pg. 774

Schou, Tove, Sec.--Icopal a/s, Herlev, Denmark; *Int'l*, pg. 658

Schoultz, Deborah A., V.P., Treas. & Sec.--The Fibre-Metal Products Company, Concordville, PA; *U.S. Private*, pg. 402

Schrader, Deborah J., Sec.--Zing Technologies, Inc., Valhalla, NY; *U.S. Public*, pg. 1792

Schrader, Richard A., Exec. V.P. & Asst. Sec.--Parsons Brinckerhoff Inc., New York, NY; *U.S. Private*, pg. 841

Schreger, Ira A., Sr. V.P. & Sec.--Sequa Corporation, New York, NY; *U.S. Public*, pg. 1458

Schreiber, David R., Chief Fin. Officer, Treas. & Sec.--Dianon Systems, Inc., Stratford, CT; *U.S. Public*, pg. 506

Schrimpf, Barbara, Sec.--Piasa Motor Fuels Inc., Hartford, IL; *U.S. Private*, pg. 864

Schrimpf, R. William, Asst. Sec.--Hartford-Wood River Terminal, Hartford, IL; *U.S. Private*, pg. 864

Schroeder, Mary Lou, Asst. Sec. & Asst. Treas.--Modern Group Ltd., Bristol, PA; *U.S. Private*, pg. 754

Schropp, Tobin, Asst. Sec.--Peter Kiewit Sons Inc., Omaha, NE; *U.S. Private*, pg. 619

Schuback, Marc G., Asst. Gen. Counsel & Asst. Sec.--Footstar Inc., Mahwah, NJ; *U.S. Public*, pg. 661

Schuchman, Salem D., V.P. & Asst. Sec.--Eagle Food Centers, Inc., Milan, IL; *U.S. Public*, pg. 547

Schueler, Tammy, Chief Fin. Officer--Evans Adhesive Corp., Columbus, OH; *U.S. Private*, pg. 384

Schuering, Michael E., Dir.-Fin. & Corp. Sec--HNTB Corporation, Kansas City, MO; *U.S. Private*, pg. 492

Schuler, Steven T., Chief Fin. Officer, Corp. Sr. V.P., Treas. & Sec.--Brenton Banks, Inc., Des Moines, IA; *U.S. Public*, pg. 251

Schulte, Virgiline M., Sec.--Capitol Indemnity Corporation, Madison, WI; *U.S. Public*, pg. 302

Schulte, Virgiline M., V.P.-Human Resources & Sec.--Capitol Indemnity Corporation, Madison, WI; *U.S. Public*, pg. 302

Schulte, Virgiline M., V.P.-Human Resources & Sec.--Capitol Specialty Insurance Corporation, Madison, WI; *U.S. Public*, pg. 302

Schultz, Fred, V.P.-Admin. & Sec.--Kelley Dock Systems, Milwaukee, WI; *U.S. Private*, pg. 612

Schultz, Gary, Chief Fin. Officer, Treas. & Sec.--Arrowhead Mills, Inc., Hereford, TX; *U.S. Private*, pg. 86

Schultz, James D., Chief Fin. Officer, Sr. V.P., Treas. & Sec.--Old America Stores, Howe, TX; *U.S. Public*, pg. 1215

Schultz, Robert J., Chief Fin. Officer, Treas. & Sec.--Great Lakes Lithograph Co., Cleveland, OH; *U.S. Private*, pg. 474

Schulz, William J., Sr. V.P. & Sec.--Firstar Corporation, Milwaukee, WI; *U.S. Public*, pg. 642

Schulze, Max H., V.P., Treas., Gen. Counsel & Sec.--MCRB Service Bureau, Inc., Chatsworth, CA; *U.S. Private*, pg. 686

Schumacher, D.A., Chief Fin. Officer & Treas.--The Cretex Companies, Elk River, MN; *U.S. Private*, pg. 289

Schumacher, Diane Kosmach, Sr. V.P., Gen. Counsel & Sec.--Cooper Industries, Inc., Houston, TX; *U.S. Public*, pg. 442

Schumacher, Richard M., Asst. Sec.--Northern Indiana Public Service Company, Hammond, IN; *U.S. Public*, pg. 1185

Schuman, Seymour, Chm. Bd. & Sec.--Propper Manufacturing Co., Inc., Long Island City, NY; *U.S. Private*, pg. 891

Schuman, Thomas R., V.P., Gen. Counsel & Sec.--Caremark International Inc, Northbrook, IL; *U.S. Public*, pg. 1082

Schums, William G., V.P., Gen. Counsel & Sec.--Miller Brewing Company, Milwaukee, WI; *U.S. Public*, pg. 1289

Schuster, Richard S., V.P. & Sec.--Nu Horizons Electronics Corp., Melville, NY; *U.S. Public*, pg. 1205

Schuster, Stephen M., V.P., Gen. Counsel & Sec.--Envirodyne Industries, Inc., Oak Brook, IL; *U.S. Public*, pg. 586

Schutzman, Charlotte B., Sec.--Bell Atlantic Financial Services, Wilmington, DE; *U.S. Public*, pg. 202

Schwab, James E., Pres. & Chief Oper. Officer--Xtek, Inc., Cincinnati, OH; *U.S. Private*, pg. 1194

Schwab, Jerry L., Sec.--Farmland Foods, Inc., Kansas City, MO; *U.S. Private*, pg. 396

Schwab, Nelson, Jr., Sec.--Ralph J. Stolle Co., Cincinnati, OH; *U.S. Private*, pg. 1044

Schwartz, Bob, Exec. V.P. & Corp. Sec.--Bozell Retail, Toronto, Canada; *Int'l*, pg. 209

Schwartz, Daniel L., Pres., Treas. & Sec.--Schwartz & Benjamin, Inc., New York, NY; *U.S. Private*, pg. 974

Schwartz, Jack B., Asst. Sec.--Cascade Corporation, Troutdale, OR; *U.S. Public*, pg. 310

Schwartz, Lawrence, Chief Information Officer, V.P. & Sec.--Friendship Dairies, Inc., Friendship, NY; *U.S. Private*, pg. 429

Schwartz, Mel, Gen. Counsel & Sec.--Honeywell Limited, North York, Canada; *U.S. Public*, pg. 835

Schwartz, Sally W., Asst. Sec.--Ford Motor Company, Dearborn, MI; *U.S. Public*, pg. 661

Schwartz, Scott, Sec.--Oxford Health Insurance, Inc., Norwalk, CT; *U.S. Public*, pg. 1239

Schwartz, Scott, Sec.--Oxford Health Plans (FL), Inc., Sarasota, FL; *U.S. Public*, pg. 1239

Schwartz, Scott M., Sec.--Oxford Health Centers, Norwalk, CT; *U.S. Public*, pg. 1239

Schwartz, Scott M., Sec.--Oxford Health Plans (IL), Inc., Rosemont, IL; *U.S. Public*, pg. 1239

Schwartz, Stanley, Exec. V.P. & Sec.--Friendship Dairies, Inc., Jericho, NY; *U.S. Private*, pg. 429

Schwartzman, Peter, Sec.--Pall Corporation, Greenvale, NY; *U.S. Public*, pg. 1253

Schwegler, Tina, Asst. Sec.--Hardel Mutual Plywood Corporation, Olympia, WA; *U.S. Private*, pg. 501

Schweickardt, James L., Sec.--California Custom Foods, Lodi, CA; *U.S. Private*, pg. 831

Schweizer, Robert, Corp. Sec.--Burda Holding GmbH & Co., KG, Munich, Germany; *Int'l*, pg. 233

Schwenke, Bill, Controller--Donnkenny, Inc., New York, NY; *U.S. Public*, pg. 519
Schwer, W.F., Sr. V.P., Gen. Counsel & Sec.--Imperial Holly Corporation, Sugar Land, TX; *U.S. Public*, pg. 872
Schwertz, Joseph D., Jr., Gen. Counsel & Sec.--Whitney Holding Corporation, New Orleans, LA; *U.S. Public*, pg. 1766
Schwind, William F., Jr., Gen. Counsel & Sec.--Marathon Oil Company, Houston, TX; *U.S. Public*, pg. 1661
Scilla, Randy, Asst. Sec. & Asst. Treas.--Pennsylvania Power Co., New Castle, PA; *U.S. Public*, pg. 645
Scobie, M.B., Sec. & Dir.-Corp. Services--Boral Limited, Sydney, Australia; *Int'l*, pg. 203
Scoggins, Rex R., Chief Fin. Officer, Controller & Sec.--C & K Market, Inc., Brookings, OR; *U.S. Private*, pg. 191
Scott, G., Deputy Sec.--Lend Lease Corporation Limited, Sydney, Australia; *Int'l*, pg. 806
Scott, Gary L., V.P.-Natl. Sls. Mgr. & Sec.--Alkota Cleaning Systems, Inc., Alcester, SD; *U.S. Private*, pg. 34
Scott, James H., Sec. & Asst. Treas.--Texas Utilities Company, Dallas, TX; *U.S. Public*, pg. 1586
Scott, John R., V.P., Gen. Counsel & Sec.--Hunt Oil Company, Dallas, TX; *U.S. Private*, pg. 548
Scott, Milton C., Treas. & Sec.--Georgia Duck & Cordage Mills, Scottdale, GA; *U.S. Private*, pg. 448
Scott, Patrick J., Asst. Sec.--Certified Life Insurance, Chicago, IL; *U.S. Public*, pg. 433
Scott, Patty, Exec. Sec.--McLeodUSA Incorporated, Cedar Rapids, IA; *U.S. Public*, pg. 1073
Scott, Stephen, Sec.--Vodafone Group PLC, Newbury, United Kingdom; *Int'l*, pg. 1469
Scott, V. Hollis, Sr. V.P., Treas. & Sec.--The Cato Corporation, Charlotte, NC; *U.S. Public*, pg. 318
Scriven, Jane K., Corp. Sec.--Geest PLC, Spalding, United Kingdom; *Int'l*, pg. 542
Scruff, Monica, Sec.--Pepsi-Co. International, Surrey, United Kingdom; *U.S. Public*, pg. 1277
Scurfield, Ralph K., Sec.--J.E. Baker Co., York, PA; *U.S. Private*, pg. 112
Seabrook, Evelyn T., Sec.--Seabrook Brothers & Sons, Inc., Seabrook, NJ; *U.S. Private*, pg. 978
Seaman, Janet W., Sec.--Seaman Timber Company, Inc., Montevallo, AL; *U.S. Private*, pg. 979
Searcy, Dan, Sec.--Cowin & Company, Inc., Birmingham, AL; *U.S. Private*, pg. 280
Sears, Marvin, Sec.--Jenny Craig, Inc., La Jolla, CA; *U.S. Public*, pg. 926
Sebolt, Walter, Gen. Sec.--Feldschlosschen Hurlimann Holding, Rhaeninfelden, Switzerland; *Int'l*, pg. 479
Seckel, Douglas, Chief Fin. Officer, Treas. & Sec.--Eagle USA Airfreight, Houston, TX; *U.S. Public*, pg. 547
Secker, J., Sec. & Dir.--Miller Freeman PLC, London, United Kingdom; *Int'l*, pg. 1443
Sedder, Shirley, Dir.-Mktg., Sec., Treas.--Andy's Restaurants Inc., Little Rock, AR; *U.S. Private*, pg. 74
Seder, Jeffrey A., Chm. Bd. & Sec.--Craftex Mills Inc. of Pennsylvania, Blue Bell, PA; *U.S. Private*, pg. 284
Sedler, Jordan B., Exec. V.P., Sec. & Treas.--Paper Enterprises, Inc., Bronx, NY; *U.S. Private*, pg. 837
Seeley, James B., Sec.--Bison Canning Co., Inc., Angola, NY; *U.S. Private*, pg. 468
Seeley, Paul J., Treas., Controller & Sec.--Lindsay Manufacturing Inc., Ponca City, OK; *U.S. Private*, pg. 668
Seff, Laura, Sr. V.P.-Corp Quality & Sec.--Sterling Healthcare Group, Inc., Miami, FL; *U.S. Public*, pg. 608
Segale, David S., Treas. & Sec.--Mel Rapton Honda, Sacramento, CA; *U.S. Private*, pg. 911
Seger, Charles F., III, V.P.-Sls. & Mktg. & Sec.--Dennis Chemical Co., Inc., Saint Louis, MO; *U.S. Private*, pg. 324
Seguin, Gilles, Asst. Sec.--Kaufel Group Ltd., Dorval, Canada; *Int'l*, pg. 724
Seidel, Thomas A., Sec.--Growmark, Inc., Bloomington, IL; *U.S. Private*, pg. 484
Seiders, Joseph R., Sr. V.P. & Sec.--CDI Corp., Philadelphia, PA; *U.S. Public*, pg. 276
Seigfreid, Jim, Sec.--Kansas City Chiefs Football Club, Inc., Kansas City, MO; *U.S. Private*, pg. 607
Seigfried, John P., V.P., Gen. Counsel, Sec. & Dir.-Investor Rels.--Medusa Corporation, Cleveland, OH; *U.S. Public*, pg. 1084
Seigner, Maurice, Exec. Dir. & Sec.--France Telecom, Paris, France; *Int'l*, pg. 503
Seils, William G., Sr. V.P., Gen. Counsel & Corp. Sec.--Richardson Electronics, Ltd., Lafox, IL; *U.S. Public*, pg. 1387
Sejpal, David A., Chm. Bd., Pres., Chief Exec. & Oper. Officer & Sec.--Clothestime Stores, Inc., Anaheim, CA; *U.S. Public*, pg. 387
Selawski, Mark, Chief Fin. Officer & Sec.--Medstone International, Inc., Aliso Viejo, CA; *U.S. Public*, pg. 1082
Selcraig, Mark, Asst. Grp. Sec.--First National Bank Holdings Limited, Johannesburg, South Africa; *Int'l*, pg. 487
Self, Susan O., Asst. Corp. Sec.--Fort James Corporation, Richmond, VA; *U.S. Public*, pg. 670
Seli, John D., V.P. & Admin. & Fin.--Chickasha Cotton Oil Co., Chandler, AZ; *Int'l*, pg. 1395
Selk, Thomas L., V.P., Controller & Sec.--Associated Mortgage, Inc., De Pere, WI; *U.S. Public*, pg. 140
Sell, Neil I., Sec.--Rykoff-Sexton, Inc., Wilkes-Barre, PA; *U.S. Public*, pg. 918
Selland, Clay E., Treas. & Asst. Sec.--Longs Drug Stores Corporation, Walnut Creek, CA; *U.S. Public*, pg. 1013
Sellers, Robert P., Treas. & Sec.--Dean Sellers Ford Inc., Troy, MI; *U.S. Private*, pg. 983
Selover, Patricia W., Treas. & Sec.--Selover Buick, Inc., Billings, MT; *U.S. Private*, pg. 983
Seltzer, Agatha, Sec.--Roller Derby Skate Corp., Litchfield, IL; *U.S. Private*, pg. 941
Seltzer, David S., Chief Oper. Officer, Exec. V.P., Treas. & Sec.--Hi-Tech Pharmacal Co., Inc., Amityville, NY; *U.S. Public*, pg. 825
Seltzer, Maryann, Sec.--Farmers Group, Inc., Los Angeles, CA; *Int'l*, pg. 110
Seltzer, Mike, V.P. & Sec.--Red Apple Companies, New York, NY; *U.S. Private*, pg. 914
Selzer, Jim, Chief Fin. Officer, Sr. V.P.-Fin. & Asst. Corp. Sec.--Pico Products, Inc., Lake View Terrace, CA; *U.S. Public*, pg. 1294
Semanick, Ronald J., Sec.--SI Handling Systems, Inc., Easton, PA; *U.S. Public*, pg. 1418
Semel, Robert K., Pres., Chief Oper. Officer & Sec.--Uniflex, Inc., Hicksville, NY; *U.S. Public*, pg. 1665
Semel, Scott N., Exec. V.P., Gen. Counsel & Sec.--Designs, Inc., Needham, MA; *U.S. Public*, pg. 501
Semple, Paul, Sec.--Summa Four, Inc., Manchester, NH; *U.S. Public*, pg. 1527
Senchyshyn, Joan S., Asst. Sec.--DQE Inc., Coraopolis, PA; *U.S. Public*, pg. 474
Seneta, Eugene, Chief Fin. Officer, V.P., Treas. & Sec.--Xyvision, Inc., Wakefield, MA; *U.S. Public*, pg. 1787
Seney, Richard F., Vice Chm. & Sec.--American Telecasting, Inc., Colorado Springs, CO; *U.S. Public*, pg. 93
Sentance, Alan, Sec.--BWI Plc, Altrincham, United Kingdom; *Int'l*, pg. 130
Senty, John L., V.P. & Sec.--Consolidated Midwest, Inc., La Crosse, WI; *U.S. Private*, pg. 265
Serr, Erik, Gen. Counsel & Sec.--R & B Machine Tool Co., Saline, MI; *U.S. Private*, pg. 901
Serrano, George, Pres.-Nuclear Prods., V.P. & Sec.--Packard BioScience Company, Meriden, CT; *U.S. Private*, pg. 833
Serrazin, Belsina, Sec.--Conquest Europe S.A.R.L., Neuilly-sur-Seine, France; *Int'l*, pg. 1484
Serre, Yves De La, Chief Fin. Officer & Sec.--Cegelec, Levallois-Perret, France; *Int'l*, pg. 52
Serwin, Bradley K., Sr. V.P., Gen. Counsel & Sec.--PAULA Financial, Pasadena, CA; *U.S. Public*, pg. 1266
Sessoms, R.D., Chief Fin. Officer & Sec.--Carolina Builders Corporation, Raleigh, NC; *Int'l*, pg. 1512
Seth, E. Anthony, V.P., Gen. Counsel & Sec.--Falconbridge Limited, Toronto, Canada; *Int'l*, pg. 433
Setten, N.V., Sec.--Wavin Bv, Zwolle, Netherlands; *Int'l*, pg. 1135
Severino, Beverly, Sec. & Treas.--Great Scott Advertising Co. Inc., New York, NY; *U.S. Private*, pg. 475
Sevin, Audrey L., Sec.--Petroleum Heat & Power Co., Stamford, CT; *U.S. Public*, pg. 1281
Sexton, Cliff, V.P.-Fin. & Asst. Sec.--Pioneer/Eclipse Corp., Sparta, NC; *Int'l*, pg. 71
Sexton, Robert J., Treas. & Sec.--Tab Products Co., Palo Alto, CA; *U.S. Public*, pg. 1559
Sgambellone, James J., Asst. Sec. & Corp. Dir.-Taxes--The Sherwin-Williams Company, Cleveland, OH; *U.S. Public*, pg. 1465
Sha, J., Treas. & Sec.--Fyrnetics, Inc., Roselle, IL; *Int'l*, pg. 1499
Shackford, Paul, Chief Fin. Officer, V.P., Treas. & Sec.--Park Electrochemical Corporation, Lake Success, NY; *U.S. Public*, pg. 1258
Shaffer, Kathryn, Asst. Sec.--Maynard Oil Co., Dallas, TX; *U.S. Public*, pg. 1064
Shaffer, R.J., V.P., Gen. Counsel & Sec.--NI Industries, Inc., Seal Beach, CA; *U.S. Public*, pg. 1054
Shaffer, Wayne E., Sec.--The Ohio Art Company, Inc., Bryan, OH; *U.S. Public*, pg. 1214
Shaffner, Bob, Chief Fin. Officer & Sec.--Klaussner Corporation, Asheboro, NC; *U.S. Private*, pg. 625
Shah, Dipak, Treas. & Sec.--Village Ford Inc., Dearborn, MI; *U.S. Private*, pg. 1140
Shaker, Helen, Sec.--Shaker Advertising Agency, Oak Park, IL; *U.S. Private*, pg. 988
Shakley, Allan D., Asst. Sec.--United Water Resources, Harrington Park, NJ; *U.S. Public*, pg. 1691
Shakley, Allan D., Sec. & Asst. Treas.--United Water Management & Services, Harrington Park, NJ; *U.S. Public*, pg. 1692
Shandley, E., Sec.--Archer Technicoat Limited, High Wycombe, United Kingdom; *Int'l*, pg. 893
Shanes, Samuel, Exec. V.P. & Sec.--Talk-A-Phone Co., Chicago, IL; *U.S. Private*, pg. 1067
Shanholtzer, Julie V., Asst. Sec.--The Washington Water Power Company, Spokane, WA; *U.S. Public*, pg. 1744
Shank, Roberta, Treas. & Sec.--Chas Roberts Air Conditioning, Inc., Phoenix, AZ; *U.S. Private*, pg. 935
Shannon, Elizabeth O'Neal, Sec.--O'Neal Steel Inc., Birmingham, AL; *U.S. Private*, pg. 817
Shannon, John H., V.P. & Sec.--Golden Enterprises Inc., Birmingham, AL; *U.S. Public*, pg. 749
Shannon, Kathleen E., V.P. & Sec.--American International Group, Inc., New York, NY; *U.S. Public*, pg. 83
Shannon, Margaret B., V.P., Gen. Counsel & Sec.--BJ Services Company, Houston, TX; *U.S. Public*, pg. 161
Shannon, W.K.B., Sec.--Tyco Investments (Australia) Limited, Saint Leonards, Australia; *U.S. Public*, pg. 1651
Shapiro, Amy M., Sr. V.P., Gen. Counsel & Sec.--CommNet Cellular Inc., Englewood, CO; *U.S. Public*, pg. 414
Shapiro, David, Chief Fin. Officer & V.P.-Fin.--Engle Homes, Inc., Boca Raton, FL; *U.S. Public*, pg. 583
Shapiro, Howard, Exec. V.P.-Law & Admin., Gen. Counsel & Sec.--Playboy Enterprises, Inc., Chicago, IL; *U.S. Public*, pg. 1309
Shapiro, Howard, V.P. & Asst. Sec.--Playboy Entertainment Group, Inc., Beverly Hills, CA; *U.S. Public*, pg. 1310
Shapiro, Howard, V.P. & Asst. Sec.--Playboy Models, Inc., Beverly Hills, CA; *U.S. Public*, pg. 1310
Shapiro, Howard, V.P. & Asst. Sec.--Playboy Preferred, Inc., Itasca, IL; *U.S. Public*, pg. 1310
Shapiro, Howard, V.P. & Asst. Sec.--Lifestyle Brands, Ltd., Chicago, IL; *U.S. Public*, pg. 1310
Shapiro, Howard, V.P. & Asst. Sec.--Special Editions, Ltd., Chicago, IL; *U.S. Public*, pg. 1310
Shapiro, Howard, V.P. & Asst. Sec.--Alta Loma Productions, Inc., Beverly Hills, CA; *U.S. Public*, pg. 1310
Shapiro, Howard, V.P. & Asst. Sec.--Critics' Choice Video, Inc., Itasca, IL; *U.S. Public*, pg. 1310
Shapiro, Howard, V.P. & Asst. Sec.--Impulse Productions, Inc., Beverly Hills, CA; *U.S. Public*, pg. 1310
Shapiro, Howard, V.P. & Asst. Sec.--Lake Shore Press, Inc., Chicago, IL; *U.S. Public*, pg. 1310
Shapiro, Howard, V.P. & Asst. Sec.--Playboy Clubs International, Inc., Chicago, IL; *U.S. Public*, pg. 1310
Shapiro, Howard, V.P. & Asst. Sec.--Playboy Shows, Inc., Beverly Hills, CA; *U.S. Public*, pg. 1310
Shapiro, Howard, V.P. & Asst. Sec.--After Dark Video, Inc., Beverly Hills, CA; *U.S. Public*, pg. 1310
Shapiro, Jeffrey M., Exec. V.P. & Sec.--Michael Foods, Inc., Minneapolis, MN; *U.S. Public*, pg. 1103
Sharer, Sharon, V.P.-Admin. & Corp. Sec.--Fisher Broadcasting Inc., Seattle, WA; *U.S. Public*, pg. 648
Sharkey, John G., V.P.-Fin., Controller & Sec.--TSR Inc., Hauppauge, NY; *U.S. Public*, pg. 1559
Sharp, G.M., Sec.--Newhawk Gold Mines LTD., Vancouver, Canada; *U.S. Public*, pg. 833
Sharp, John M., Sec.--Electrical Wholesale Supply Company, Inc., Idaho Falls, ID; *U.S. Private*, pg. 368
Sharpe, J.F., Sec.--Morganite International Limited, Windsor, United Kingdom; *Int'l*, pg. 894
Sharpe, S.J., Sec.--Lend Lease Corporation Limited, Sydney, Australia; *Int'l*, pg. 806
Sharpe, Vivian A., Treas. & Sec.--Texas Refinery Corp., Fort Worth, TX; *U.S. Private*, pg. 1078
Sharwood, Graham, Sec.--Smorgon A.R.C., Sunshine, Australia; *Int'l*, pg. 1269
Shaver, Alan M., Sec.--Kraft Foods, Inc., Northfield, IL; *U.S. Public*, pg. 1287
Shaw, Dennis M., Controller & Sec.--Petroleum Products Corp., Middletown, PA; *U.S. Private*, pg. 859
Shaw, Jerome, Exec. V.P. & Sec.--Volt Information Sciences, Inc., New York, NY; *U.S. Public*, pg. 1724
Shaw, Mary L., Asst. Sec.--The Fairchild Corporation, Chantilly, VA; *U.S. Public*, pg. 610
Shaw, Sarah, Corp. Sec.--Signet Group plc, London, United Kingdom; *Int'l*, pg. 1248
Shaw, Susan E., Sec.--The Coca-Cola Company, Atlanta, GA; *U.S. Public*, pg. 392
Shaw, Trevor H.M., Sec.--Associated British Foods plc, London, United Kingdom; *Int'l*, pg. 92
Shaw, William J., Gen. Counsel & Sec.--Bently Nevada Corporation, Minden, NV; *U.S. Private*, pg. 134
Shay, Paul R., Sec. & Asst. Gen. Counsel--Household International, Inc., Prospect Heights, IL; *U.S. Public*, pg. 842
Shea, Cathy D., Asst. Sec.--Butler International, Inc., Montvale, NJ; *U.S. Public*, pg. 270
Shear, David, V.P. & Sec.--LSB Industries, Inc., Oklahoma City, OK; *U.S. Public*, pg. 970
Shearer, A.K., III, Sec.--Philadelphia Reserve Supply Company, Croydon, PA; *U.S. Private*, pg. 861
Sheehan, Richard H., Jr., Gen. Counsel & Sec.--City National Corporation, Beverly Hills, CA; *U.S. Public*, pg. 380
Sheerin, William K., Sr. V.P.-Admin. & Gen. Services & Corp. Sec.--Astoria Financial Corporation, Lake Success, NY; *U.S. Public*, pg. 141
Sheets, Dennis D., Chief Fin. Officer, Treas. & Sec.--Valley Systems, Inc., Canal Fulton, OH; *U.S. Public*, pg. 1706
Sheetz, Brenda, Sec.--Pinnacle Bank, Valparaiso, IN; *U.S. Public*, pg. 1297
Shefferly, Paul G., Asst. Sec.--Booth American, Detroit, MI; *U.S. Private*, pg. 156
Sheidlower, Arnold M., V.P., Assoc. Gen. Counsel & Asst. Sec.--Harvard Industries, Inc., Tampa, FL; *U.S. Public*, pg. 796
Sheinfeld, David I., Chm. Bd., Chief Exec. Officer & Sec.--Fresh America Corp., Dallas, TX; *U.S. Public*, pg. 681
Sheldon, Craig A., V.P., Treas. & Sec.--MediVators, Inc., Eagan, MN; *U.S. Public*, pg. 301
Sheldon, Cynthia, Sec.--Sheldons' Inc., Antigo, WI; *U.S. Private*, pg. 992
Shelger, James M., Sr. V.P., Gen. Counsel & Sec.--Service Corporation International, Houston, TX; *U.S. Public*, pg. 1460
Shelley, Eulice, Sec.--Global Van Lines, Inc., Orange, CA; *U.S. Private*, pg. 458
Shellman, Jolene L., Asst. Gen. Counsel & Asst. Sec.--A.O. Smith Corporation, Milwaukee, WI; *U.S. Public*, pg. 1476
Shelton, James, Treas. & Sec.--Apex Precision Technology Inc., Indianapolis, IN; *U.S. Private*, pg. 77
Shelton, James D., Chief Fin. Officer, Exec. V.P. & Sec.--PharMerica, Inc., Tampa, FL; *U.S. Public*, pg. 1286
Shemanske, Janet L., Asst. Sec.--W.R. Berkley Corporation, Greenwich, CT; *U.S. Public*, pg. 215
Shepard, Barry, Chief Fin. Officer, Treas. & Asst. Sec.--Scott's Liquid Gold-Inc., Denver, CO; *U.S. Public*, pg. 1447
Shepard, Robert L., Chief Fin. Officer, Dir.-Mngmt. Info. Systems, Treas. & Sec.--Acme Foundry, Inc., Coffeyville, KS; *U.S. Private*, pg. 13
Shepherd, William Clyde, Jr., Treas. & Sec.--Shepherd Construction Co., Inc., Atlanta, GA; *U.S. Private*, pg. 993
Sheppard, M. Jackie, V.P.-Legal, Corp. Projects & Corp. Sec.--Talisman Energy Inc., Calgary, Canada; *Int'l*, pg. 1352
Sheppard, Thomas C., Jr., Asst. Sec.--Allegheny Power System, Inc., Hagerstown, MD; *U.S. Public*, pg. 42
Sherer, Thomas L., Sec.--Pinnacle Bank, Jasper, AL; *U.S. Public*, pg. 1297
Sheridan, William J.V., Sec.--Royal Oak Mines Inc., Kirkland, WA; *U.S. Public*, pg. 1410
Sherlock, Timothy, Chief Fin. Officer & Sec.--Advantage Learning Systems, Inc., Wisconsin Rapids, WI; *U.S. Public*, pg. 22
Sherman, Finda B., Sec. & Dir.-Personnel--MacNeal-Schwendler Corp., Costa Mesa, CA; *U.S. Public*, pg. 1031
Sherman, Gerald M., Asst. Sec.--NWNL Benefits Corp., Minneapolis, MN; *U.S. Public*, pg. 1375

Sherman, Michael, Sr. V.P.-Bus. Devel., Gen. Counsel & Sec.--Fingerhut Corp., Minnetonka, MN; *U.S. Public,* pg. 623
Sherman, Michael, Corp. Sec.--United Grain Growers Ltd., Winnipeg, Canada; *Int'l,* pg. 1442
Sherman, Morris M., Corp. Sec.--Venturian Corp., Hopkins, MN; *U.S. Public,* pg. 1716
Sherman, Pauline, V.P., Sec. & Assoc. Gen. Counsel--The Equitable Companies Incorporated, New York, NY; *U.S. Public,* pg. 588
Sherry, Kenneth C., Sec.--Valk Manufacturing Company, New Kingstown, PA; *U.S. Private,* pg. 1131
Sherry, Peter J., Jr., Asst. Sec.--Ford Motor Company, Dearborn, MI; *U.S. Public,* pg. 661
Sherwood, David, Sec.--Interspiro Inc., Branford, CT; *Int'l,* pg. 1289
Shevchik, Daniel R., Chief Fin. Officer, V.P., Treas. & Sec.--Malcolm Pirnie, Inc., White Plains, NY; *U.S. Private,* pg. 867
Shiba, Wendy C., V.P., Sec. & Asst. Gen. Counsel--Bowater Incorporated, Greenville, SC; *U.S. Public,* pg. 247
Shields, Bobby L., V.P.-Legal & Regulatory Affairs--Hospital Staffing Services, Inc., Fort Lauderdale, FL; *U.S. Public,* pg. 840
Shields, Douglas G., Chief Fin. Officer, V.P. & Sec.--Noma Industries Limited, North York, Canada; *Int'l,* pg. 954
Shields, Shirley M., V.P. & Corp. Sec.--Commercial Intertech Corp., Youngstown, OH; *U.S. Public,* pg. 411
Shimada, Masanori, Treas. & Sec.--Lotte U.S.A., Inc., Battle Creek, MI; *Int'l,* pg. 819
Shimano, Bruce, V.P.-Res. & Devel. & Sec.--Adept Technology, Inc., San Jose, CA; *U.S. Public,* pg. 19
Shimizu, T., Exec. Coord. & Sec.--Mazda Motor of America, Inc., Irvine, CA; *Int'l,* pg. 849
Shimura, Norifumi, Exec. V.P.-Treas. & Sec.--Mitsui Foods, Inc., Norwood, NJ; *Int'l,* pg. 879
Shine, Loretta, Treas. & Sec.--First Financial Group, Inc., Encino, CA; *U.S. Private,* pg. 407
Shine, Philip J., Sec.--Peter Pan Bus Lines, Inc., Springfield, MA; *U.S. Private,* pg. 856
Shinnock, John B., Asst. Gen. Counsel & Asst. Sec.--American Electric Power Service Corp., Columbus, OH; *U.S. Public,* pg. 72
Shipman, Tana, Sec.--Crowley Maritime Corporation, Oakland, CA; *U.S. Private,* pg. 292
Shirk, Betty J., Treas. & Sec.--Beer Nuts, Inc., Bloomington, IL; *U.S. Private,* pg. 130
Shirley, H. Madison, V.P.-Concessions & Asst. Sec.--Carmike Cinemas, Inc., Columbus, GA; *U.S. Public,* pg. 305
Shockey, Paul K., Sec.--JLG Industries, Inc., McConnellsburg, PA; *U.S. Public,* pg. 918
Shockley, Olean, Asst. Sec.--Dewberry Design Group, Oklahoma City, OK; *U.S. Private,* pg. 329
Shone, Rick, Dir.-H.R. & Sec.--Underground Construction Co., Inc., Benicia, CA; *U.S. Private,* pg. 1116
Shonkoff, Fredi, Sec.--Blue Cross and Blue Shield of Massachusetts, Boston, MA; *U.S. Private,* pg. 151
Shook, Gregory R., Sr. V.P.-Admin. & Sec.--Branford Savings Bank, Branford, CT; *U.S. Public,* pg. 250
Shoop, Cynthia A., Asst. Sec.--Allegheny Power System, Inc., Hagerstown, MD; *U.S. Public,* pg. 42
Shor, Alan, Sr. V.P., Gen. Counsel & Sec.--Zale Corporation, Irving, TX; *U.S. Public,* pg. 1789
Short, David G., V.P.-Legal & Sec.--NPC International, Inc., Pittsburg, KS; *U.S. Public,* pg. 1146
Short, Ed, Treas. & Sec.--Alabama Electric Cooperative, Inc., Andalusia, AL; *U.S. Private,* pg. 30
Short, Robert, Mgr.-Personnel & Corp. Sec.--Pacific Hide & Fur Depot, Great Falls, MT; *U.S. Private,* pg. 831
Short, Roland T., Exec. V.P. & Sec.--Alabama Metal Industries Corporation, Birmingham, AL; *U.S. Private,* pg. 30
Shoup, Michael D., Sec.--Amana Society, Inc., Amana, IA; *U.S. Private,* pg. 48
Showers, Mark, Chief Fin. Officer, Treas. & Sec.--Spartech Plastics, Portage, WI; *U.S. Public,* pg. 1496
Shrieves, John, Controller & Corp. Sec.--Omniflight, Inc., Dallas, TX; *U.S. Private,* pg. 816
Shrieves, John, Controller & Corp. Sec.--Omniflight Helicopters, Inc., Dallas, TX; *U.S. Private,* pg. 817
Shrimpton, Patricia, Mgr.-Personnel & Sec.--A.I. Root Company, Medina, OH; *U.S. Private,* pg. 944
Shriver, Jennifer M., Asst. Sec.--The Toledo Edison Company, Toledo, OH; *U.S. Public,* pg. 645
Shropshire, William S., Jr., Chief Fin. Officer, Exec. V.P., Treas. & Sec.--Dyersburg Corporation, Dyersburg, TN; *U.S. Public,* pg. 538
Shuff, Ronald F., V.P., Gen. Counsel & Sec.--Flowserve Corporation, Dayton, OH; *U.S. Public,* pg. 658
Shuford, Arlene, Treas. & Sec.--Bowen Brothers Fruit Co., Inc., Winter Haven, FL; *U.S. Private,* pg. 162
Shulman, David, Sec.--Scitex Corporation Ltd., Holon, Israel; *Int'l,* pg. 644
Shults, Ron, Corp. Sec.--McCormick Distilling Co., Weston, MO; *U.S. Private,* pg. 720
Shuman, Bonnie L., V.P., Gen. Counsel & Asst. Sec.--Shared Medical Systems Corporation, Malvern, PA; *U.S. Public,* pg. 1463
Shuman, Larry E., V.P. & Sec.--Weaber, Inc, Lebanon, PA; *U.S. Private,* pg. 1155
Shuman, N.J., V.P. & Sec.--Salem Asset Management Corp., Wilmington, DE; *U.S. Private,* pg. 961
Shure, R.L., Sec.--Shure Brothers Incorporated, Evanston, IL; *U.S. Private,* pg. 997
Shuttleworth, P.J.W., Sec.--Powell Duffryn PLC, Bracknell, United Kingdom; *Int'l,* pg. 1065
Shutts, Kenneth R., Sr. V.P., Gen. Counsel & Sec.--Penn National Insurance, Harrisburg, PA; *U.S. Private,* pg. 850
Sial, Vic, V.P., Treas. & Asst. Sec.--Advanced Logic Research, Inc., Irvine, CA; *U.S. Public,* pg. 703
Sicks, J.N., Gen. Counsel & Asst. Sec.--Berwind Corporation, Philadelphia, PA; *U.S. Private,* pg. 138
Siebels, Scott A., V.P., Sec. & Assoc. Counsel--Beneficial Corporation, Wilmington, DE; *U.S. Public,* pg. 211
Siegel Steven F., Gen. Counsel & Sec.--New Plan Realty Trust, New York, NY; *U.S. Public,* pg. 1172
Siegel, Cynthia, Sec.--Butler Ventamatic Corp., Mineral Wells, TX; *U.S. Private,* pg. 190
Siegel, June, Sec.--Blue Ridge Farms, Inc., Brooklyn, NY; *U.S. Private,* pg. 153
Siegel, Kenneth S., Sr. V.P., Gen. Counsel & Corp. Sec.--Cognizant Corporation, Westport, CT; *U.S. Public,* pg. 395
Siegel, Richard D., Sec.--Comair Holdings, Inc., Erlanger, KY; *U.S. Public,* pg. 406
Siegel, S.L., Treas. & Sec.--R.S. Owens, Chicago, IL; *U.S. Private,* pg. 824
Siegel, Samuel, Co-Vice Chm., Chief Fin. Officer, Treas. & Sec.--Nucor Corporation, Charlotte, NC; *U.S. Public,* pg. 1205
Siegert, Gerda, Sec.--AGA Ges.m.b.H., Vienna, Austria; *Int'l,* pg. 13
Siegfried, Peter, V.P., Gen. Counsel & Sec.--Central National-Gottesman Inc., Purchase, NY; *U.S. Private,* pg. 224
Siegler, Thomas E., Sr. V.P. & Sec.--Donaldson, Lufkin, & Jenrette, Inc., New York, NY; *U.S. Public,* pg. 589
Sieple, Jeanne, Treas. & Sec.--Mike Daugherty's Chevrolet Geo, Inc., Sacramento, CA; *U.S. Private,* pg. 313
Sigman, Benjamin L., V.P. & Sec.--B. Green & Co., Owings Mills, MD; *U.S. Private,* pg. 476
Sikkema, Gary D., Sec.--Seaway Food Town, Inc., Maumee, OH; *U.S. Public,* pg. 1452
Silberbogen, Paul M., Treas. & Sec.--Oakite Products, Inc., Berkeley Heights, NJ; *Int'l,* pg. 861
Silberman, Michael D., Chief Fin. Officer & Sec.--Retrospettiva, Inc., Beverly Hills, CA; *U.S. Public,* pg. 1383
Silberstein, Dr. Jack, Sec.--Columbus Pipe & Equipment Company, Columbus, OH; *U.S. Private,* pg. 257
Silbey, William J., Staff V.P., Sec. & Assoc. Gen. Counsel--Schering-Plough Corporation, Madison, NJ; *U.S. Public,* pg. 1438
Silipelli, Claire, Sec.--Dana Perfumes Corp., New York, NY; *U.S. Private,* pg. 922
Siljestrom, Sten, Sec.--ABB AB, Stockholm, Sweden; *Int'l,* pg. 7
Silva, Charles J., Jr., Asst. Gen. Counsel & Asst. Sec.--Albany International Corp., Albany, NY; *U.S. Public,* pg. 36
Silva, Guillermo, Jr., Sec.--El Paso Electric Company, El Paso, TX; *U.S. Public,* pg. 567
Silver, David, V.P. & Sec.--Winston Resources, Inc., New York, NY; *U.S. Public,* pg. 1772
Silver, Joyce, Sec.--Sterling Paper Co., Philadelphia, PA; *U.S. Private,* pg. 1041
Silverman, Scott D., Sr. V.P., Gen. Counsel & Sec.--PennCorp Financial Group, Inc., New York, NY; *U.S. Public,* pg. 1271
Silvers, Robert, Sr. V.P., Exec. Publr. & Sec.--Benjamin Franklin Literary & Medical Society, Inc., Indianapolis, IN; *U.S. Private,* pg. 133
Silverstein, Stanley P., V.P., Gen. Counsel & Sec.--Warnaco Inc., New York, NY; *U.S. Public,* pg. 1738
Silverthorn, Richard W., Gen. Counsel & Sec.--Koss Corporation, Milwaukee, WI; *U.S. Public,* pg. 966
Silvestri, Vincent E., V.P.-Corp. Communications--Rockefeller Group, Inc., New York, NY; *Int'l,* pg. 873
Simandl, Robert, Gen. Counsel & Sec.--Bel Fuse Inc., Jersey City, NJ; *U.S. Public,* pg. 200
Simkins, Richard C., Chief Fin. Officer, Exec. V.P., Treas. & Sec.--Knape & Vogt Mfg. Co., Grand Rapids, MI; *U.S. Public,* pg. 963
Simmers, Scott, Controller, Treas., & Sec.--Power Process Piping, Inc., Plymouth, MI; *U.S. Private,* pg. 878
Simmie, Monica F., Corp. Sec.--Maclean Hunter Publishing Ltd., Toronto, Canada; *Int'l,* pg. 1123
Simmonds, John, Sec.--Whatman plc, Maidstone, United Kingdom; *Int'l,* pg. 1498
Simmonds, John A., Corp. Sec.--David Jones Limited, Sydney, Australia; *Int'l,* pg. 714
Simmons, Brian, Exec. V.P. & Sec.--M. Kamenstein, Inc., Elmsford, NY; *U.S. Private,* pg. 606
Simmons, D. Ramsay, III, V.P., Treas., & Sec.--Elberta Crate & Box Company, Bainbridge, GA; *U.S. Private,* pg. 367
Simmons, Harvey O., III, Gen. Counsel & Sec.--Crucible Materials Corp., Solvay, NY; *U.S. Private,* pg. 293
Simmons, Jay B., Sr. V.P., Gen. Counsel & Sec.--Trans Financial, Inc., Bowling Green, KY; *U.S. Public,* pg. 1628
Simmons, Martin E., Exec. V.P.-Admin., Gen. Counsel & Sec.--First American Corporation, Nashville, TN; *U.S. Public,* pg. 624
Simms, Carl, Supvr.--Kelso Oil Company, Knoxville, TN; *U.S. Private,* pg. 613
Simon, Esther, Sec.--Contractors Steel Company, Livonia, MI; *U.S. Private,* pg. 270
Simon, Gloria, V.P.--Triangle Brass Manufacturing, Los Angeles, CA; *U.S. Private,* pg. 1101
Simon, Laurence B., Sr. V.P. & Corp. Sec.--Health Management Systems, Inc., New York, NY; *U.S. Public,* pg. 802
Simon, Mark W., V.P.-Fin. & Corp. Sec.--Penn Engineering & Manufacturing Corp., Danboro, PA; *U.S. Public,* pg. 1269
Simon, Mary T., Treas., Sec. & Dir.-Personnel--J.L. Lester & Son, Inc., Rockmart, GA; *U.S. Private,* pg. 660
Simon, Michael A., Controller & Asst. Sec.--Acme Electric Corporation, East Aurora, NY; *U.S. Public,* pg. 16
Simon, Norman, V.P., Treas. & Sec.--Joseph Simon & Sons, Inc., Tacoma, WA; *U.S. Private,* pg. 1001
Simonart, Hubert, Sec.--Generale de Banque S.A., Brussels, Belgium; *Int'l,* pg. 546
Simonett, Mark J., Sec.--Photo Control Corporation, Minneapolis, MN; *U.S. Public,* pg. 1292
Simons, Drew, V.P., Sec. & Gen. Counsel--Circon Corporation, Santa Barbara, CA; *U.S. Public,* pg. 373
Simonsen, Charlotte, Sec.--MD Foods, Viby, Denmark; *Int'l,* pg. 826
Simpson, D.L., III, Gen. Counsel & Sec.--Conwood Company L.P., Memphis, TN; *U.S. Private,* pg. 272
Simpson, David J., Chief Fin. Officer, V.P. & Sec.--Stryker Corporation, Kalamazoo, MI; *U.S. Public,* pg. 1525
Simpson, Elizabeth, Sec.--Hampshire Group, Ltd., Anderson, SC; *U.S. Public,* pg. 778
Simpson, Hugh A., Sr. V.P., Gen. Counsel & Sec.--Cash America International, Inc., Fort Worth, TX; *U.S. Public,* pg. 312
Simpson, John S., Mgr.-New Bus. & Asst. Sec.--California Water Service Co., San Jose, CA; *U.S. Public,* pg. 294
Simpson, Lynda, Corp. Sec.--Liuski International, Inc., Norcross, GA; *U.S. Public,* pg. 1005
Simpson, Margaret M., Asst. Sec.--National Western Life Insurance Company, Austin, TX; *U.S. Public,* pg. 1161
Simpson, Phyllis T., Asst. Sec.--Duke Energy Corporation, Charlotte, NC; *U.S. Public,* pg. 534
Simpson, Timothy J., V.P., Assoc. Gen. Counsel & Asst. Sec.--Ogden Energy Group, Inc., Fairfield, NJ; *U.S. Public,* pg. 1213
Sims, P. Gerald, V.P.-Admin. & Sec.--Wajax Limited, Delta, Canada; *Int'l,* pg. 1484
Sin, Jenifer, Sec.--Playmates Holdings Ltd., Kowloon, Hong Kong; *Int'l,* pg. 1060
Sinasohn, Sam, V.P.-Taxes & Special Projects--Sunrise Medical, Inc., Carlsbad, CA; *U.S. Public,* pg. 1535
Sinclair, Coral, V.P.--DEECO Industries, Hillside, NJ; *U.S. Private,* pg. 320
Sinclair, Maxine, Sec.--Gensym Corporation, South Central Regional Office, Spring, TX; *U.S. Public,* pg. 731
Sinclair, Wayne, Sr. V.P., Gen. Counsel & Sec.--MMI Companies, Inc., Deerfield, IL; *U.S. Public,* pg. 1027
Singleton, Arthur W., V.P., Treas. & Sec.--Tech Data Corporation, Clearwater, FL; *U.S. Public,* pg. 1562
Singleton, Jane, Asst. Sec.--Ladbroke Group Plc, London, United Kingdom; *Int'l,* pg. 787
Sipkovich, Ronald J., Chief Fin. Officer, V.P.-Fin. & Admin. & Sec.--Advanced Logic Research, Inc., Irvine, CA; *U.S. Public,* pg. 703
Sirett, Wm., Sec.--Vista Gold Corp., Denver, CO; *U.S. Public,* pg. 1723
Sirkin, Samuel, Sec. & Dir.-Mktg.--Clay-Park Labs, Inc., Bronx, NY; *Int'l,* pg. 30
Sirota, Bohdan I., Gen. Counsel & Asst. Sec.--CCL Industries, Inc., Willowdale, Canada; *Int'l,* pg. 238
Sirotkin, Martin, Sec.--Rapid Industrial Plastics Company, Jersey City, NJ; *U.S. Private,* pg. 910
Siskind, David A., Sec. & Asst. Gen. Counsel--The Kendall Company, Mansfield, MA; *U.S. Public,* pg. 1647
Sisler, David G., V.P., Gen. Counsel & Sec.--Elcor Corporation, Dallas, TX; *U.S. Public,* pg. 567
Sisley, G. William, Gen. Counsel & Sec.--Smith Corona Corp., Cortland, NY; *U.S. Private,* pg. 1007
Sisley, G. William, Sec.--Silgan Corporation, Stamford, CT; *U.S. Public,* pg. 1473
Sismondo, Peter R., V.P., Controller, Treas. & Asst. Sec.--Alleghany Corporation, New York, NY; *U.S. Public,* pg. 42
Sisson, Jill B.W., Gen. Counsel & Sec.--ACX Technologies Inc., Golden, CO; *U.S. Public,* pg. 3
Sisson, Roger G., Gen. Counsel & Sec.--Genesco Inc., Nashville, TN; *U.S. Public,* pg. 728
Siverd, Robert J., Sec. & Gen. Counsel--General Cable Corporation, Highland Heights, KY; *Int'l,* pg. 1486
Sjoreen, James P., V.P., Treas. & Sec.--First Penn-Pacific Life Insurance Co., Oak Brook Terrace, IL; *U.S. Public,* pg. 998
Skaff, Ramez G., Treas. & Sec.--Interstate Resources, Inc., Rosslyn, VA; *U.S. Private,* pg. 573
Skaggs, Stephen, Chief Fin. Officer & Sr. V.P.--Lattice Semiconductor Corporation, Hillsboro, OR; *U.S. Public,* pg. 979
Skamoto, Lester, V.P.-Fin. & Sec.--Isemoto Contracting Co. Ltd., Hilo, HI; *U.S. Private,* pg. 575
Skelton, Robert W., V.P., Gen. Counsel & Sec.--McCormick & Company, Incorporated, Sparks, MD; *U.S. Public,* pg. 1066
Skiera, Dorothy A., Corp. Sec.--S & C Electric Company, Chicago, IL; *U.S. Private,* pg. 954
Skinner, James E., Chief Fin. Officer, Exec. V.P., Treas. & Asst. Sec.--CompUSA, Dallas, TX; *U.S. Public,* pg. 420
Skinner, Peter G., Sr. V.P., Gen. Counsel, Sec. & Pres.-Television--Dow Jones & Company, Inc., New York, NY; *U.S. Public,* pg. 524
Sklarz, Mark G., Sec.--Starter Corp., New Haven, CT; *U.S. Public,* pg. 1511
Sklut, Josef, V.P.-Fin., Treas., Sec.--Speizman Industries, Inc., Charlotte, NC; *U.S. Public,* pg. 1498
Skolyan, Mary Rose, Corp. Sec.--Knight Equipment International Inc., Costa Mesa, CA; *U.S. Public,* pg. 862
Skophammer, Robin W., Chief Fin. Officer, Treas. & Sec.--Craig Corporation, Los Angeles, CA; *U.S. Public,* pg. 456
Skornicka, Carol N., V.P., Gen. Counsel & Sec.--Midwest Express Holdings, Inc., Oak Creek, WI; *U.S. Public,* pg. 1111
Skornicka, Carol N., V.P., Sec. & Gen. Counsel--Midwest Express Airlines, Inc., Oak Creek, WI; *U.S. Public,* pg. 1111
Skrine, Bruce E., V.P., Gen. Counsel & Sec.--John Hancock Mutual Life Insurance Company, Boston, MA; *U.S. Private,* pg. 589
Skrobola, A.W., Sr. V.P.-Fin., Treas. & Sec.--Thomas Steel Strip Corp., Warren, OH; *Int'l,* pg. 756
Skuba, William C., Chm. Bd., Pres., Chief Exec. Officer & Sec.--Eastern Environmental Services, Inc., Drums, PA; *U.S. Public,* pg. 549
Skubas, Charles E., Chief Fin. Officer & Sec.--Herlin Press Inc., West Haven, CT; *U.S. Private,* pg. 524
Sladen, J.B., Sec.--Buckman Laboratories Inc., Memphis, TN; *U.S. Private,* pg. 180

Sladnick, Clifford, Sr. V.P., Gen. Counsel & Sec.--St. Paul Bancorp, Inc., Chicago, IL; *U.S. Public*, pg. 1428
Sladnick, Clifford M., Sec.--SPF Insurance Agency, Franklin Park, IL; *U.S. Public*, pg. 1428
Sladnick, Clifford M., Sec.--Custom Source Realty Corporation, Saint Charles, IL; *U.S. Public*, pg. 1429
Slagel, Gerald L., V.P., Engrng. & Sec.--Stanco Metal Products, Inc., Grand Haven, MI; *U.S. Private*, pg. 1030
Slaggie, Stephen M., Sec.--Fastenal Company, Winona, MN; *U.S. Public*, pg. 614
Slater, Craig, Sec.--Anschutz Corporation, Denver, CO; *U.S. Private*, pg. 75
Slattery, James, Gen. Counsel & Sec.--Paradyne, Largo, FL; *U.S. Private*, pg. 838
Slattery, William H., Asst. Sec.--Republic New York Corporation, New York, NY; *U.S. Public*, pg. 1380
Slaughter, Deborah H., Asst. Sec.--DIMON, Incorporated, Danville, VA; *U.S. Public*, pg. 509
Slaughter, Richard G., V.P.-Plng. & Sec.--U.S. Home Corporation, Houston, TX; *U.S. Public*, pg. 1682
Slaughter, Thomas L., V.P., Gen. Counsel & Sec.--Meredith Corporation, Des Moines, IA; *U.S. Public*, pg. 1094
Slaven, R. Michael, Sec.--AEGON USA, Inc., Louisville, KY; *Int'l*, pg. 26
Sledge, Brian D., V.P., Controller & Sec.--Utilities Construction Co., Inc. Of South Carolina, Charleston, SC; *U.S. Private*, pg. 1130
Slezak, David G., Sec. & Dir.-Legal Affairs--Oglebay Norton Company, Cleveland, OH; *U.S. Public*, pg. 1213
Slichter, Donald A., Gen. Counsel & Sec.--Applied Materials, Inc., Santa Clara, CA; *U.S. Public*, pg. 123
Sliker, Carol A., Asst. Sec.--Elizabethtown Gas Co., Union, NJ; *U.S. Public*, pg. 1147
Sliva, Catherine L., Exec. V.P.--Domain Energy Corporation, Houston, TX; *U.S. Public*, pg. 515
Sloan, Mary V., Asst. V.P. & Asst. Sec.--American Stores Company, Salt Lake City, UT; *U.S. Public*, pg. 92
Sloan, Mike, V.P., Gen. Counsel & Sec.--Circus Circus - Las Vegas, Las Vegas, NV; *U.S. Public*, pg. 374
Sloan, Patricia L., Sec. & Treas.--Stratton Growth Fund, Inc., Plymouth Meeting, PA; *U.S. Private*, pg. 1046
Sloan, William E. II, Exec. V.P., Treas. & Sec.--Sloan Valve Company, Franklin Park, IL; *U.S. Private*, pg. 1006
Slockers, Erik L., V.P. & Controller--Terra Nitrogen Company, L.P., Tulsa, OK; *U.S. Public*, pg. 1581
Sloneker, Howard L., III, V.P. & Sec.--Ohio Casualty Corporation, Hamilton, OH; *U.S. Public*, pg. 1214
Slote, Richard B., V.P. & Sec.--King Fuels Inc., Troy, NY; *U.S. Private*, pg. 620
Smallenberger, James Andrew, Sr. V.P. & Sec.--American Mutual Life Holding Co., Des Moines, IA; *U.S. Private*, pg. 59
Smalley, Kathleen, Sr. V.P., Gen. Counsel & Sec.--Catellus Development Corporation, San Francisco, CA; *U.S. Public*, pg. 314
Smalley, R.L., V.P.-Fin. & Sec.--Thermal Ceramics Inc., Augusta, GA; *Int'l*, pg. 894
Smead, H.J., Chm. Bd., Chief Exec. & Chief Fin. Officer & Sec.--Kaiser Aerospace & Electronics Corp., Foster City, CA; *U.S. Private*, pg. 605
Smelthurst, William, Jr., Asst. Treas. & Asst. Sec.--South Jersey Industries, Inc., Folsom, NJ; *U.S. Public*, pg. 1488
Smerge, Raymond G., Exec. V.P., Gen. Counsel & Sec.--Centex Corporation, Dallas, TX; *U.S. Public*, pg. 322
Smerz, Susan M., Sr. V.P., Controller & Asst. Sec.--First Midwest Bancorp, Inc., Itasca, IL; *U.S. Public*, pg. 636
Smiley, Robert W., Sec.--Mylan Laboratories, Inc., Pittsburgh, PA; *U.S. Public*, pg. 1143
Smilowitz, Bernard, Treas. & Sec.--Allied Building Products Corporation, East Rutherford, NJ; *U.S. Private*, pg. 38
Smisek, Jeffrey A., Exec. V.P., Gen. Counsel & Sec.--Continental Airlines, Houston, TX; *U.S. Public*, pg. 439
Smisor, Bradley K., Sec.--Builders Inc., Wichita, KS; *U.S. Private*, pg. 440
Smith, Alan, Sec.--Smiths Industries plc, London, United Kingdom; *Int'l*, pg. 1266
Smith, Alexander J., Sec.--John Hassall, Inc., Westbury, NY; *U.S. Private*, pg. 509
Smith, Alton, Exec. V.P. & Controller--Furr's/Bishops, Inc., Lubbock, TX; *U.S. Public*, pg. 689
Smith, Andrew, Sec.--Tarmac plc, Wolverhampton, United Kingdom; *Int'l*, pg. 1355
Smith, Anne, Gen. Counsel & Sec.--General Casualty Company of Wisconsin, Sun Prairie, WI; *Int'l*, pg. 345
Smith, Anne, Gen. Counsel & Sec.--General Casualty Company of Illinois, Freeport, IL; *Int'l*, pg. 346
Smith, Anne, Gen. Counsel & Sec.--Hoosier Insurance Company, Indianapolis, IN; *Int'l*, pg. 346
Smith, Beryl S., Sec.--East Ascension Telephone Company, Inc., Gonzales, LA; *U.S. Private*, pg. 358
Smith, C. Michael, Pres., Chief Oper. Officer & Sec.--Orders Distributing Co., Greenville, SC; *U.S. Private*, pg. 819
Smith, Carla J., Sr. V.P., Gen. Counsel & Sec.--Dain Rauscher Corporation, Minneapolis, MN; *U.S. Public*, pg. 476
Smith, Christine J., V.P. & Sec.--Berol Corporation, Brentwood, TN; *U.S. Public*, pg. 1178
Smith, Cindy W., Treas. & Sec.--Camping World, Inc., Bowling Green, KY; *U.S. Private*, pg. 204
Smith, David J., V.P., Gen. Counsel & Sec.--Archer Daniels Midland Company (ADM), Decatur, IL; *U.S. Public*, pg. 127
Smith, Dominic, Co.-Sec.--Industrial Equity Limited, Sydney, Australia; *Int'l*, pg. 676
Smith, Don C., V.P. & Sec.--Griffin Manufacturing Co., Muskogee, OK; *U.S. Private*, pg. 481
Smith, Donna Beck, V.P., Sec. & Treas.--Allied Healthcare Products, Inc., Saint Louis, MO; *U.S. Public*, pg. 48
Smith, Doris A., Sec.--Childcraft Education Corporation, Lancaster, PA; *U.S. Public*, pg. 513
Smith, Ed, Treas. & Sec.--Martin & Bayley Inc., Carmi, IL; *U.S. Private*, pg. 708
Smith, Eleanor R., Controller & Sec.--Scope Industries, Santa Monica, CA; *U.S. Public*, pg. 1444
Smith, Emery W., Asst. Gen. Counsel & Asst. Sec.--Cleveland-Cliffs Inc, Cleveland, OH; *U.S. Public*, pg. 386
Smith, Frank E., Chief Fin. Officer, Sr. V.P. & Sec.--West Coast Bancorp, Newport Beach, CA; *U.S. Public*, pg. 1755
Smith, Gary V., Exec. V.P., Treas. & Sec.--Hughes Construction, Inc., North Salt Lake, UT; *U.S. Private*, pg. 546
Smith, Gene, Chief Fin. Officer, Treas. & Sec.--Rollins, Inc., Atlanta, GA; *U.S. Public*, pg. 1404
Smith, Gregory G., Asst. Sec.--General Electric Canada Inc., Mississauga, Canada; *U.S. Public*, pg. 713
Smith, H.M., Asst. Sec.--Emerson Electric Co., Saint Louis, MO; *U.S. Public*, pg. 572
Smith, Harry C., Treas. & Sec.--Daily Express, Inc., Carlisle, PA; *U.S. Private*, pg. 307
Smith, Jane A., V.P. & Sec.--O.I. Corporation, College Station, TX; *U.S. Public*, pg. 1208
Smith, Joan R., V.P., Controller & Sec.--Marine Drilling Companies, Inc., Sugar Land, TX; *U.S. Public*, pg. 1044
Smith, John B., Sr. V.P., Gen. Counsel & Sec.--Interim Services Inc., Fort Lauderdale, FL; *U.S. Public*, pg. 892
Smith, John C., Sec. & Gen. Counsel--Arinc Inc. (Consolidated), Annapolis, MD; *U.S. Private*, pg. 81
Smith, Julie B., Asst. Sec.--Harris Teeter, Inc., Charlotte, NC; *U.S. Public*, pg. 1412
Smith, Kathi, Treas. & Sec.--Damsmith Corp., Sanford, NC; *U.S. Private*, pg. 309
Smith, Kathleen, Controller & Asst. Sec.--Algood Food Company, Louisville, KY; *U.S. Private*, pg. 34
Smith, Kathy, Corp. Sec.--Lund International Holdings, Inc., Anoka, MN; *U.S. Public*, pg. 1020
Smith, Kevin D., Asst. Sec.--McKechnie PLC, Walsall, United Kingdom; *Int'l*, pg. 851
Smith, Klara, Sec.--Terre Hill Concrete Products, Inc., Terre Hill, PA; *U.S. Private*, pg. 1077
Smith, L.S., Dr., Chm. Bd., Chief Exec. Officer, Treas. & Sec.--Dallas Gold & Silver Exchange, Inc., Dallas, TX; *U.S. Public*, pg. 478
Smith, Lawrence A., V.P.-Legal--The Home Depot, Inc., Atlanta, GA; *U.S. Public*, pg. 831
Smith, Lawson K., Sec.--Sparton Corporation, Jackson, MI; *U.S. Public*, pg. 1496
Smith, Les, Treas. & Sec.--Buhrman-Pharr Hardware Company, Texarkana, AR; *U.S. Private*, pg. 179
Smith, Linda, Sec.--Brittany Dyeing & Printing Corporation, New Bedford, MA; *U.S. Private*, pg. 170
Smith, Linda J., Sec.--Baker Hughes Incorporated, Houston, TX; *U.S. Public*, pg. 165
Smith, M. Lynne, Asst. Sec.--Extendicare Inc., Markham, Canada; *Int'l*, pg. 468
Smith, Margaret, Corp. Sec.--Candle Corporation, Santa Monica, CA; *U.S. Private*, pg. 204
Smith, Margaret, Corp. Sec.--Webb Builders Hardware, Arlington, TX; *U.S. Private*, pg. 1156
Smith, Marla, Sec.--Spray-Tech, Inc., Longwood, FL; *U.S. Private*, pg. 1026
Smith, Marschall I., Sr. V.P., Gen. Counsel & Asst. Sec.--IMC Global, Bannockburn, IL; *U.S. Public*, pg. 856
Smith, Marsden, Corp. Sec.--Thorn plc, Chertsey, United Kingdom; *Int'l*, pg. 1385
Smith, Mary, Sec.--The Fifth Third Bank of Kentucky, Paris, KY; *U.S. Public*, pg. 621
Smith, Mary Elizabeth, Sec.--Spenco Medical Corporation, Waco, TX; *U.S. Private*, pg. 955
Smith, Michael B., Controller & Asst. Sec.--Burke Mills, Inc., Valdese, NC; *U.S. Public*, pg. 267
Smith, Michael J., Gen. Counsel & Sec.--Royal Caribbean Cruises Ltd., Miami, FL; *U.S. Public*, pg. 1410
Smith, Michelle, Treas. & Sec.--Aycock, Inc., Hummelstown, PA; *U.S. Private*, pg. 103
Smith, Mike, Treas. & Sec.--Kelsey Construction, Inc., Orlando, FL; *U.S. Private*, pg. 613
Smith, Patricia J., Sec.--Adolph Coors Company, Golden, CO; *U.S. Public*, pg. 445
Smith, Patricia J., Sec.--Coors Brewing Company, Golden, CO; *U.S. Public*, pg. 445
Smith, Philip, Sec.--BBA Group plc, London, United Kingdom; *Int'l*, pg. 112
Smith, R., Dir.-Fin. & Co. Sec.--Cincinnati Milacron U.K. Limited, Birmingham, United Kingdom; *U.S. Public*, pg. 368
Smith, Richard H., Sr. V.P., Gen. Counsel & Sec.--Cooper Communities, Inc., Bella Vista, AR; *U.S. Private*, pg. 273
Smith, Richard H., V.P., Gen. Counsel & Sec.--Cooper Ventures, Inc., Bella Vista, AR; *U.S. Private*, pg. 274
Smith, Richard H., V.P. & Sec.--Apartment Ventures, Inc., Bella Vista, AR; *U.S. Private*, pg. 274
Smith, Rick, Gen. Counsel & Sec.--Nova Scotia Power Inc., Halifax, Canada; *Int'l*, pg. 971
Smith, Robert C., Sr. V.P., Gen. Counsel & Sec.--White Hen Pantry, Inc., Elmhurst, IL; *U.S. Private*, pg. 1172
Smith, Robert H., Chief Fin. Officer & Exec. V.P.-Fin. & Admin.--Novellus Systems, Inc., San Jose, CA; *U.S. Public*, pg. 1204
Smith, Robert Lewis, Controller, Treas. & Sec.--Hankins Lumber Company, Inc., Elliott, MS; *U.S. Private*, pg. 499
Smith, Roger P., Sec.--3M, Saint Paul, MN; *U.S. Public*, pg. 1604
Smith, Ruth, Dr., Sec.--Cavco Industries, Inc., Phoenix, AZ; *U.S. Public*, pg. 323
Smith, S. A., Corp. Sec.--Mail Well Services Inc., Memphis, TN; *U.S. Public*, pg. 1328
Smith, Shelby, Sr., Treas. & Sec.--Smith Management Co., Inc., Shreveport, LA; *U.S. Private*, pg. 1009
Smith, Shirley R., V.P., Gen. Counsel & Sec.--Coventry Corporation, Nashville, TN; *U.S. Public*, pg. 454
Smith, Stephen R., V.P., Gen. Counsel & Sec.--The Interlake Corporation, Lisle, IL; *U.S. Public*, pg. 892
Smith, Sue, Corp. Sec.--Wilcox Electric, Inc., Kansas City, MO; *Int'l*, pg. 1384
Smith, Susan, H.R. Sec.--Sierra West Bancorp, Truckee, CA; *U.S. Public*, pg. 1470
Smith, T.N., V.P. & Sec.--Florida East Coast Industries Inc., Saint Augustine, FL; *U.S. Public*, pg. 1427
Smith, Terry D., Chief Fin. Officer, Exec. V.P. & Sec.--Easco Inc., Girard, OH; *U.S. Public*, pg. 548
Smith, Thomas G., Chief Fin. Officer, Sr. V.P. & Sec.--Forest City Enterprises, Inc., Cleveland, OH; *U.S. Public*, pg. 667
Smith, Tom E., Chm. Bd., Pres. & Chief Exec. Officer--Food Lion, Inc., Salisbury, NC; *Int'l*, pg. 463
Smith, Toni, Admin. Asst.--Indian Head Industries Inc., Charlotte, NC; *U.S. Private*, pg. 559
Smith, Virginia, Admin. Sec.--Fleetwood Enterprises, Inc., Riverside, CA; *U.S. Public*, pg. 650
Smith, Walter L., V.P., Gen. Counsel & Asst. Sec.--Hilb, Rogal and Hamilton Company, Glen Allen, VA; *U.S. Public*, pg. 826
Smith, Walter L., V.P. & Asst. Sec.--Hilb, Rogal and Hamilton Company of Canada, Limited, Winnipeg, Canada; *U.S. Public*, pg. 828
Smoak, Robert R., V.P., Treas. & Sec.--Bernhardt Furniture Co., Lenoir, NC; *U.S. Private*, pg. 137
Smolinski, Edward A., Asst. Sec.--United Industrial Corporation, New York, NY; *U.S. Public*, pg. 1679
Smyre, Dane, Sec. & Treas.--Diamond Hill Plywood Company, Darlington, SC; *U.S. Private*, pg. 311
Smyth, Jeff, Sec.--Tubular & Equipment Services, LLC (TES), Independence, KS; *U.S. Private*, pg. 162
Snavely, Theresa V., Sec.--Snavely Forest Products, Inc., Pittsburgh, PA; *U.S. Private*, pg. 1010
Snaw, Karee, Exec. Sec.--Cincinnati Gear Company, Cincinnati, OH; *U.S. Private*, pg. 240
Snead, Elizabeth P., Sec.--The Paty Company, Piney Flats, TN; *U.S. Private*, pg. 844
Snelling, Andrew P., Treas. & Sec.--The Shelburne Corporation, Shelburne, VT; *U.S. Private*, pg. 991
Snitzer, Isadore, Gen. Counsel & Sec.--C.H. Heist Corp., Clearwater, FL; *U.S. Public*, pg. 807
Snow, Iris E., V.P. & Asst. Sec.--World Acceptance Corporation, Greenville, SC; *U.S. Public*, pg. 1778
Snyder, Catherine, Sec.--Gensym Corporation, Mid-Atlantic Area Office, Chantilly, VA; *U.S. Public*, pg. 731
Snyder, Clark L., Sec.--Cleveland District Cooling Corp., Cleveland, OH; *U.S. Public*, pg. 913
Snyder, Colby H., V.P.-Fin. & Sec.--Namico, Inc., Philadelphia, PA; *U.S. Private*, pg. 773
Snyder, Judith, Sec.--McLean-Thomas Inc., Buffalo, NY; *U.S. Private*, pg. 724
Snyder, Nancy, Sec.--Penn Virginia Corporation, Radnor, PA; *U.S. Public*, pg. 1271
Snyder, Ronald R., V.P. & Gen Counsel, Sec.--Arvin Industries, Inc., Columbus, IN; *U.S. Public*, pg. 136
Snyder, S.I., Chief Fin. Officer, Sr. V.P.-Fin., Treas. & Sec.--Kaufman Footwear, Kitchener, Canada; *Int'l*, pg. 725
Snyder, Wayne, Sr. V.P. & Chief Fin. Officer--Anthem Electronics Inc., San Jose, CA; *U.S. Public*, pg. 134
Soares, H.J., Sec. & Mgr.-Admin.--Morganite Isolantes Termicos Limitada, Rio de Janeiro, Brazil; *Int'l*, pg. 895
Sober, David W., V.P.-Human Resources & Sec.--Performance Food Group Company, Richmond, VA; *U.S. Public*, pg. 1278
Sobey, Paul D., V.P. & Sec.--Empire Company Limited, Stellarton, Canada; *Int'l*, pg. 453
Soefje, Shannon A., Sr. V.P.-Corp. Commun. & Sec.--HD Vest Financial Services, Irving, TX; *U.S. Public*, pg. 770
Soer, Gladys, V.P. & Sec.--Carsen Group Inc., Markham, Canada; *U.S. Public*, pg. 301
Soffer, Robert M., Treas. & Asst. Sec.--Rogers Corporation, Rogers, CT; *U.S. Public*, pg. 1402
Solan, Bob, Sec.--S & S Graphics, Inc., Laurel, MD; *U.S. Private*, pg. 955
Soland, Norman R., V.P., Gen. Counsel & Sec.--Nash Finch Company, Edina, MN; *U.S. Public*, pg. 1151
Soled, Kathleen A., Assoc. Gen. Counsel & Sec.--Trans World Airlines, Inc., Saint Louis, MO; *U.S. Public*, pg. 1629
Soler, Vincent E., Jr., V.P., Treas. & Sec.--American National Insurance Company, Galveston, TX; *U.S. Public*, pg. 87
Solis, Javier, Sr. V.P.-Admin., Gen. Counsel & Sec.--Ameron International Corporation, Pasadena, CA; *U.S. Public*, pg. 98
Sollenberger, Mark L., Exec. V.P., Treas. & Asst. Sec.--BT Financial Corporation, Johnstown, PA; *U.S. Public*, pg. 163
Sollenberger, Mark L., Treas. & Asst. Sec.--Bedford Associates, Inc., Johnstown, PA; *U.S. Public*, pg. 164
Sollenberger, Mark L., Treas. & Asst. Sec.--Laurel Community Development Corporation, Johnstown, PA; *U.S. Public*, pg. 164
Solock, Douglas J., V.P., Sec. & Treas.--Regency Finance Company, Hermitage, PA; *U.S. Public*, pg. 607
Solombrino, Scott, Chm. Bd., Pres. & Chief Exec. Officer--Dav-El Worldwide, Chelsea, MA; *U.S. Private*, pg. 314
Solomon, Deryck J., Sec.--Glynwed International PLC, Birmingham, United Kingdom; *Int'l*, pg. 554
Solomon, Hadar, Esq., V.P., Gen. Counsel & Sec.--Laser Industries Ltd., Tel Aviv, Israel; *Int'l*, pg. 429
Solomon, J. Stuart, Asst. Sec.--Central and South West Corporation, Dallas, TX; *U.S. Public*, pg. 324
Solomon, Martin, Sec.--Checker Motors Corporation, Kalamazoo, MI; *U.S. Private*, pg. 1029
Solomon, William W., V.P. & Controller--American Pad and Paper Company, Dallas, TX; *U.S. Public*, pg. 88
Soloway, Richard, Chm. Bd. & Sec.--Napco Security Systems, Inc., Amityville, NY; *U.S. Public*, pg. 1151
Solt, Russell, Exec. V.P.-Fin. & Admin. & Sec.--Venture Stores, Inc., O Fallon, MO; *U.S. Public*, pg. 1716
Solt, Russell E., Chief Fin. Officer, Sr. V.P.-Fin. & Sec.--Williams-Sonoma, Inc., San Francisco, CA; *U.S. Public*, pg. 1770
Somerville, H., Corp. Sec.--Dawson International PLC, Edinburgh, United Kingdom; *Int'l*, pg. 385
Somes, Charles J., Sec.--GTE North Incorporated, Irving, TX; *U.S. Public*, pg. 696

Somes, Charles J., Sec.--GTE South Incorporated, Irving, TX; *U.S. Public*, pg. 697

Sommer, Nila, Sec.--Service Motor Company, Dale, WI; *U.S. Private*, pg. 986

Sommer, Regina, Chief Fin. Officer & Sr. V.P.--Open Market, Inc., Burlington, MA; *U.S. Public*, pg. 1226

Sommerville, Christine, Sec.--The Marine Container Insurance Co. Ltd., Hamilton, Bermuda; *Int'l*, pg. 1213

Sondag, Robert H., Chief Admin. Officer--Gage Marketing Group, Minneapolis, MN; *U.S. Private*, pg. 437

Sonderman, Andy, Gen. Counsel & Sec.--Columbia Gas Distribution Companies, Columbus, OH; *U.S. Public*, pg. 402

Sonksen, David R., Chief Fin Officer, V.P.-Fin., Treas. & Sec.--Microsemi Corporation, Santa Ana, CA; *U.S. Public*, pg. 1107

Sonnabend, Peter J., Gen. Counsel & Sec.--Sonesta International Hotels Corporation, Boston, MA; *U.S. Public*, pg. 1485

Sons, Kevin, Treas. & Sec.--Bongards Creameries Inc., Norwood, MN; *U.S. Private*, pg. 156

Sonsini, Larry W., Sec.--Silicon Valley Group, Inc., San Jose, CA; *U.S. Public*, pg. 1474

Sonsini, Lawrence W., Sec.--Coherent, Inc., Santa Clara, CA; *U.S. Public*, pg. 395

Soomet, Urmas, Sec.--DoFasco, Inc., Hamilton, Canada; *Int'l*, pg. 414

Sorden, Michael R., Sec. & Treas.--Commercial Light Company, Hillside, IL; *U.S. Private*, pg. 258

Sorensen, Stuart L., Exec. V.P., Chief Actuary & Sec.--Security American Financial Enterprises, Inc., Minnetonka, MN; *U.S. Private*, pg. 980

Sorheim, Dennis R., Treas. & Sec.--Peoples Electric Contractor, Inc., Saint Paul, MN; *U.S. Private*, pg. 851

Sorokin, Cheryl A., Sec.--Airlease Ltd., San Francisco, CA; *U.S. Public*, pg. 33

Sorokin, Cheryl A., Exec. V.P. & Corp. Sec.--BankAmerica Corporation, San Francisco, CA; *U.S. Public*, pg. 179

Soshnick, Julian, V.P. & Gen. Counsel--Analogic Corporation, Peabody, MA; *U.S. Public*, pg. 109

Sottile, Emily J., Asst. Sec. & Asst. Treas.--Consolidated-Tomoka Land Co., Daytona Beach, FL; *U.S. Public*, pg. 437

Sou, Betty, Controller & Sec.--Oroamerica, Inc., Burbank, CA; *U.S. Public*, pg. 1232

Soucy, Barbara, Sec.--British Aerospace Holdings Inc., Chantilly, VA; *Int'l*, pg. 218

Soutendijk, D.R., V.P., Gen. Counsel & Sec.--Union Camp Corporation, Wayne, NJ; *U.S. Public*, pg. 1665

Southern, Reba S., Sec.--American Consumers, Inc., Fort Oglethorpe, GA; *U.S. Public*, pg. 70

Southerst, Mark, V.P., Gen. Counsel & Sec.--Greyhound Lines, Inc., Dallas, TX; *U.S. Public*, pg. 765

Southerst, Mark, Sr. V.P., Gen. Counsel & Sec.--Greyhound Lines, Inc., Dallas, TX; *U.S. Public*, pg. 765

Southwick, Stephen W., V.P., Gen. Counsel & Sec.--IES Industries Inc., Cedar Rapids, IA; *U.S. Public*, pg. 855

Southwick, Stephen W., Sec.--IES Transportation, Inc., Cedar Rapids, IA; *U.S. Public*, pg. 855

Southwick, Stephen W., Sec.--IES Investments Inc., Cedar Rapids, IA; *U.S. Public*, pg. 855

Southwick, Stephen W., V.P., Gen. Counsel & Sec.--IES Utilities Inc., Cedar Rapids, IA; *U.S. Public*, pg. 855

Sowell, L. Dale, Chief Fin. Officer & Asst. Sec.--Winchester Homes, Inc., Calverton, MD; *U.S. Public*, pg. 1764

Sowerby, Ronald E., Chief Fin. Officer, Exec. V.P.-Fin., & Sec.--TCG International Inc., Burnaby, Canada; *Int'l*, pg. 1336

Sowerby, Ronald E., Sec.--Glentel Inc., Burnaby, Canada; *Int'l*, pg. 1336

Sowers, Sally T., Sec.--North Carolina Natural Gas Corporation, Fayetteville, NC; *U.S. Public*, pg. 1194

Spadone, John C., Pres. & Treas.--Spadone Inc., Norwalk, CT; *U.S. Private*, pg. 1019

Spaeth, Karl H., Sec.--Quaker Chemical Corporation, Conshohocken, PA; *U.S. Public*, pg. 1346

Sparks, William, Chief Fin. Officer, V.P. & Sec.--Tutor-Saliba Corporation, Sylmar, CA; *U.S. Private*, pg. 1111

Sparrow, Charlotte A., Sec.--LincAm Properties, Inc., Chicago, IL; *U.S. Public*, pg. 997

Spatz, Ruth Carol, Corp. Sec.--Osmonics, Inc., Minnetonka, MN; *U.S. Public*, pg. 1233

Spayd, Sandra L., Sec.--National Penn Bancshares, Inc., Boyertown, PA; *U.S. Public*, pg. 1158

Spayd, Sandra L., Sr. V.P. & Corp. Sec.--National Penn Bank, Boyertown, PA; *U.S. Public*, pg. 1159

Spears, G.H., Sec.--Kemet Corporation, Simpsonville, SC; *U.S. Public*, pg. 949

Spears, Robert, V.P. & Gen. Counsel--Lone Star Technologies, Inc., Dallas, TX; *U.S. Public*, pg. 1012

Spears, Robert F., Sec.--Lone Star Steel Company, Dallas, TX; *U.S. Public*, pg. 1012

Spector, Dorothy J., Sec.--Spec's Music, Inc., Miami, FL; *U.S. Public*, pg. 1497

Spector, Martin W., Exec. V.P. & Gen. Counsel--Aramark Corp., Philadelphia, PA; *U.S. Private*, pg. 78

Spector, Paul, Chief Fin. Officer, Sr. V.P., Treas. & Sec.--Aris Industries, Inc., New York, NY; *U.S. Public*, pg. 129

Speer, G. William, Esq., Sec.--QMS, Inc., Mobile, AL; *U.S. Public*, pg. 1346

Speiser, Laurence A., Sec.--Paul-Son Gaming Corporation, Las Vegas, NV; *U.S. Public*, pg. 1265

Speisman, Aaron, Sec.--Correctional Services Corporation, Sarasota, FL; *U.S. Public*, pg. 450

Spellberg, Vic, Sec.--Office Connection, Inc., Fort Lauderdale, FL; *U.S. Public*, pg. 1687

Spellman, Richard A., Sr. V.P., Gen. Counsel & Sec.--Guarantee Life Insurance Co., Omaha, NE; *U.S. Public*, pg. 768

Spence, G. Robert, Treas. & Asst. Sec.--Dacco, Inc., Cookeville, TN; *U.S. Private*, pg. 598

Spence, Greg, Sec. & Treas.--Ancira Enterprises Inc., San Antonio, TX; *U.S. Private*, pg. 71

Spencer, David, Sec.--Tokyo-Mitsubishi International plc, London, United Kingdom; *Int'l*, pg. 158

Spencer, J. Greg, Sr. V.P., Treas. & Asst. Sec.--American Stores Company, Salt Lake City, UT; *U.S. Public*, pg. 92

Spencer, Marilyn, Sec. & Treas.--Faber Enterprises, Inc., Canoga Park, CA; *U.S. Private*, pg. 390

Spenny, Richard, Treas. & Sec.--S&S Domestic International Sales Corp., Houston, TX; *U.S. Public*, pg. 1517

Spenny, Richard, Sec. & Treas.--Stewart & Stevenson Holdings, Inc., Houston, TX; *U.S. Public*, pg. 1517

Speranza, Paul S., Gen. Counsel & Sec.--Wegmans Food Markets, Inc., Rochester, NY; *U.S. Private*, pg. 1158

Speranzella, Charles J., Jr., Exec. V.P., Gen. Counsel & Sec.--Breed Technologies, Inc., Lakeland, FL; *U.S. Public*, pg. 251

Sperger, John M., Sec.--Midlantic Bank, N.A., Philadelphia, PA; *U.S. Public*, pg. 1242

Sperling, Peter V., V.P.-Admin., Treas. & Sec.--Apollo Group, Inc., Phoenix, AZ; *U.S. Public*, pg. 120

Sperrazza, Barbara, V.P. & Corp. Sec.--Federal Home Loan Bank of New York, New York, NY; *U.S. Private*, pg. 399

Sperry, A.R., Sr. V.P. & Sec.--Royal Oak Enterprises, Inc., Atlanta, GA; *U.S. Private*, pg. 948

Spetze, Eric, M.L., Sec. & Legal--Pharmacia & Upjohn Biosystems AB, Uppsala, Sweden; *Int'l*, pg. 1047

Sphar, Joe D., V.P.-Minerals & Asst. Sec.--New Mexico & Arizona Land Co., Phoenix, AZ; *U.S. Public*, pg. 1172

Spicola, Brigid M., Asst. Sec.--United HealthCare Corporation, Minnetonka, MN; *U.S. Public*, pg. 1677

Spicola, Brigid M., Sec.--HealthWise of America, Nashville, TN; *U.S. Public*, pg. 1678

Spidel, John W., V.P.-Admin. & Sec.--American Aggregates Corp., Dayton, OH; *Int'l*, pg. 245

Spiegel, Gary J., Sec.--Southwark Metal Manufacturing Company, Philadelphia, PA; *U.S. Private*, pg. 1018

Spiegel, John, Sec. & Treas.--Bucyrus Blades Inc., Bucyrus, OH; *U.S. Private*, pg. 383

Spiess, Gary A., Gen. Counsel & Clerk--BankBoston Corporation, Boston, MA; *U.S. Public*, pg. 183

Spillane, George L., Chief Fin. Officer, V.P. & Sec.--California Microwave, Inc., Sunnyvale, CA; *U.S. Public*, pg. 293

Spiller, Jurg, Dr., Corp. Sec.--Winterthur Schweizerische Versicherungs Gesellschaft, Winterthur, Switzerland; *Int'l*, pg. 345

Spiller, Scott, Gen. Counsel & Sec.--Raytheon Appliances, Ripon, WI; *U.S. Public*, pg. 1366

Spina, Paul, Sec.--Town & Country Ford Inc., Louisville, KY; *U.S. Private*, pg. 1093

Spires, Roy, Treas. & Sec.--B C Sugar Refinery, Ltd., Vancouver, Canada; *Int'l*, pg. 103

Spires, William J., V.P.-Indus. Rels. & Sec.--Vishay Intertechnology, Inc., Malvern, PA; *U.S. Public*, pg. 1721

Spiro, Mark F., Chief Fin. Officer, V.P.-Fin., Treas. & Sec.--Calprop Corporation, Marina Del Rey, CA; *U.S. Public*, pg. 296

Spitz, Arnold J., Exec. V.P., Treas. & Sec.--International Seaway Trading Corporation, Boca Raton, FL; *U.S. Private*, pg. 572

Spitz, Randy J., Controller, Treas. & Sec.--Hicks Oil-Hicks Gas, Inc., Roberts, IL; *U.S. Private*, pg. 526

Spitzer, Eric, Sec.--The Spring Air Company, Des Plaines, IL; *U.S. Private*, pg. 1027

Splinter, Betty Ann M., Sec.--Hawaiian Electric Industries, Inc., Honolulu, HI; *U.S. Public*, pg. 799

Splinter, Betty Ann M., Sec.--HEI Power Corp., Honolulu, HI; *U.S. Public*, pg. 800

Splinter, Betty Ann U., Sec.--Pacific Energy Conservation Services, Inc., Honolulu, HI; *U.S. Public*, pg. 800

Sporn, Benjamin T., V.P.-Legal & Sec.--AMBI Inc., Tarrytown, NY; *U.S. Public*, pg. 7

Spors, Karen, V.P., Gen. Counsel & Sec.--Sta-Rite Industries, Inc., Delavan, WI; *U.S. Public*, pg. 1767

Spowart, Jay R., V.P.-Fin. & Corp. Sec.--Casio Phone-Mate, Inc., Torrance, CA; *Int'l*, pg. 274

Spradley, James W., Jr., Pres. & Chief Exec. Officer--Standard Candy Co., Inc., Nashville, TN; *U.S. Private*, pg. 1030

Sprague, Charles W., Exec. V.P., Gen. Counsel & Sec.--Fiserv, Inc., Brookfield, WI; *U.S. Public*, pg. 647

Sprague, William D., V.P. & Gen. Counsel--Lukens Inc., Coatesville, PA; *U.S. Public*, pg. 1019

Spransy, Joseph W., Corp. Counsel & Asst. Sec.--United States Pipe & Foundry Company, Inc., Birmingham, AL; *U.S. Public*, pg. 1736

Spratling, B.B., Jr., Treas. & Sec.--Dixie Electric Cooperative, Union Springs, AL; *U.S. Private*, pg. 337

Spratt, Crawford W., Sec.--Chubb Insurance Co. of Canada, Toronto, Canada; *U.S. Public*, pg. 355

Sprauve, Gershwain, Asst. Treas.--Little Switzerland, Inc., Charlotte Amalie, VI; *U.S. Public*, pg. 1001

Sprengher, Giorgio, Sec.--Banco Ambrosiano Veneto S.p.A., Milan, Italy; *Int'l*, pg. 138

Sprieser, John R., Chief Fin. Officer, Sr. V.P. & Sec.--IDC Services, Inc., Chicago, IL; *U.S. Private*, pg. 554

Spriexr, John R., V.P.-Fin. & Sec.--Production Payments, Inc., Chicago, IL; *U.S. Private*, pg. 554

Springer, Jerry M., Controller & Asst. Sec.--NIPSCO Industries, Inc., Hammond, IN; *U.S. Public*, pg. 1185

Springer, June, Treas. & Sec.--Smith Motors, Inc., Hammond, IN; *U.S. Private*, pg. 1009

Springer, Patricia, Sec.--C.H. Robinson Co., Eden Prairie, MN; *U.S. Public*, pg. 1394

Sprott, H.B., III, V.P. & Sec.--Sprott Oil Co., Inc., Manning, SC; *U.S. Private*, pg. 1027

Squires, Vernon T., V.P. & Asst. Sec.--American Home Shield Corporation, Memphis, TN; *U.S. Public*, pg. 1461

Srivastava, S.K., Sec.--Northern Coalfields Limited, Sidhi, India; *Int'l*, pg. 299

Srivido, Lena, Sec.--Metro Label Corp., Belleville, NJ; *U.S. Private*, pg. 736

St. Claire, Joy, Sec.--Senator Ford, Sacramento, CA; *U.S. Private*, pg. 983

St. Clare, Mark S., Chief Fin. Officer, Sr. V.P.-Fin. & Sec.--FileNet Corporation, Costa Mesa, CA; *U.S. Public*, pg. 622

St. Louis, Robert, Sec.--The Odom Corporation, Seattle, WA; *U.S. Private*, pg. 811

St. Michel, Mark, Sec., Treas. & Controller--Aero Systems Engineering Inc., Saint Paul, MN; *Int'l*, pg. 276

Stachowicz, Mary, Asst. Sec.--Carus Corporation, Peru, IL; *U.S. Private*, pg. 217

Stacy, Alice, Asst. Sec.--Tech-Sym Corporation, Houston, TX; *U.S. Public*, pg. 1563

Stadtmiller, Martin B., Chief Mfg. Officer, V.P.-Opers. & Sec.--Edwards Brothers, Inc., Ann Arbor, MI; *U.S. Private*, pg. 365

Staelens, Peter, Chief Fin. Officer, Treas. & Asst. Sec.--Dawn Food Products, Inc., Jackson, MI; *U.S. Private*, pg. 316

Stafford, A., V.P. & Sec.--Cassidy's Ltd., Brossard, Canada; *Int'l*, pg. 275

Stafford, Rose Ann, Treas. & Sec.--Equity Supply Company, Kalispell, MT; *U.S. Private*, pg. 380

Stagg, Dard F., V.P., Gen. Counsel & Sec.--Greenwich Air Services, Miami, FL; *U.S. Public*, pg. 710

Stahman, Robert W., V.P., Gen. Counsel & Sec.--Idaho Power Company, Boise, ID; *U.S. Public*, pg. 861

Staines, Michael L., Sr. V.P. & Sec.--Resource America, Inc., Philadelphia, PA; *U.S. Public*, pg. 1382

Stalzer, Robert J., Sr. V.P.-Admin., Fin., Treas. & Asst. Sec.--Servo Corporation of America, Westbury, NY; *U.S. Private*, pg. 987

Stammer, Doris W., Sr. V.P. & Sec.--Peoples Federal Savings Bank, Wooster, OH; *U.S. Public*, pg. 647

Stamper, Sue, Sec.--United Steel & Wire Co., Battle Creek, MI; *U.S. Private*, pg. 1126

Stampone, Frederick A., Chief Admin. Officer, Sr. V.P. & Sec.--The Pep Boys-Manny, Moe & Jack, Philadelphia, PA; *U.S. Public*, pg. 1276

Stanczak, Stephen P., V.P.-Legal & Sec.--Waste Management International plc, London, United Kingdom; *U.S. Public*, pg. 1745

Standaert, James V., Sec.--Modern Woodmen of America, Rock Island, IL; *U.S. Private*, pg. 755

Standish, Linda S., Gen. Counsel & Corp. Sec.--Central Reserve Life Corporation, Strongsville, OH; *U.S. Public*, pg. 326

Stanford, Paul, Exec. V.P.-Admin., Gen. Counsel & Sec.--CalMat Co., Los Angeles, CA; *U.S. Public*, pg. 295

Stanford, Paul, Sec.--CalMat Co. of Arizona, Los Angeles, CA; *U.S. Public*, pg. 295

Stanford, Paul, Sec.--CalMat of Central California, Los Angeles, CA; *U.S. Public*, pg. 295

Stanford, Paul, Sec.--CC Plaza Co., Los Angeles, CA; *U.S. Public*, pg. 295

Stanford, Paul, Sec.--Mission Valley Development Co., Los Angeles, CA; *U.S. Public*, pg. 295

Stanford, Paul, Sec.--CalMat Properties Co., Los Angeles, CA; *U.S. Public*, pg. 295

Stanford, Paul, Sec.--Coast Asphalt, Inc., Los Angeles, CA; *U.S. Public*, pg. 295

Stanford, Paul, Sec.--CalMat Co. of New Mexico, Los Angeles, CA; *U.S. Public*, pg. 295

Stanford, Paul, Sec.--Allied Concrete, Inc., Los Angeles, CA; *U.S. Public*, pg. 295

Stanford, Paul, Sec.--CalMat Land Co., Los Angeles, CA; *U.S. Public*, pg. 295

Stanford, Paul, Sec.--CalMat Leasing Co., Los Angeles, CA; *U.S. Public*, pg. 295

Stanford, Paul, Sec.--Azusa Rock, Inc., Los Angeles, CA; *U.S. Public*, pg. 295

Stanford, Paul, Sec.--Huntmix, Inc., Los Angeles, CA; *U.S. Public*, pg. 296

Stanford, Paul, Sec.--Palomar Transit Mix Co., Los Angeles, CA; *U.S. Public*, pg. 296

Stanford, Paul, Sec.--Hidden Valley Coal Company, Los Angeles, CA; *U.S. Public*, pg. 296

Stanford, Paul, Sec.--Kirst Construction Co., Inc., Los Angeles, CA; *U.S. Public*, pg. 296

Stanford, Paul, Sec.--Reliance Land Co., Los Angeles, CA; *U.S. Public*, pg. 296

Stanford, Paul, Sec.--Rio Norte Este Co., Los Angeles, CA; *U.S. Public*, pg. 296

Stang, Jim, Mgr.--Arden International Kitchens, Inc., Lakeville, MN; *U.S. Private*, pg. 972

Stanger, Kent W., Chief Fin. Officer, Treas. & Sec.--Merit Medical Systems, Inc., South Jordan, UT; *U.S. Public*, pg. 1096

Stanley, David H., V.P.-Legal, Gen. Counsel & Sec.--Informix Software, Menlo Park, CA; *U.S. Public*, pg. 876

Stanley, Tresea, Sec.--Prep - STAT/Spectrum, Franklin, KY; *U.S. Private*, pg. 882

Stansel, Eugene A., Jr., V.P.-H.R. & Sec.--Staple Cotton Cooperative Association, Greenwood, MS; *U.S. Private*, pg. 1033

Stanton, Margaret P., Exec. V.P. & Corp. Sec.--Jazzercise, Inc., Carlsbad, CA; *U.S. Private*, pg. 584

Stanton, Victoria, Exec. V.P., Gen. Counsel & Sec.--Farm Family Casualty Insurance Co., Glenmont, NY; *U.S. Private*, pg. 394

Staples, F. Dudley, Jr., Sec. & Gen. Counsel--BioWhittaker, Inc., Walkersville, MD; *U.S. Public*, pg. 297

Stapleton, Kathleen M., Sec.--GMAC Mortgage Corporation, Horsham, PA; *U.S. Public*, pg. 720

Stapleton, Richard, Exec. V.P.-Fin. & Admin., Gen. Counsel & Sec.--The Lane Construction Corp., Meriden, CT; *U.S. Private*, pg. 649

Stark, W., Sr. V.P., Gen. Counsel & Sec.--ESCO Electronics Corporation, Saint Louis, MO; *U.S. Public*, pg. 546

Starke, Phyllis, Corp. Sec.--Aurora Pump, North Aurora, IL; *U.S. Public*, pg. 726

Starkey, Richard L., Sec.--The Wiser Oil Company, Dallas, TX; *U.S. Public*, pg. 1773

Starkey, Teresa B., Sec.--Anderson Electric, Inc., Springfield, IL; *U.S. Private*, pg. 72

Starling, John M., Sec.--The Goldfield Corporation, Melbourne, FL; *U.S. Public*, pg. 750

Staskiel, James, V.P., Legal Counsel & Sec.--McCarthy Building Companies, Saint Louis, MO; *U.S. Private*, pg. 719

Staudohar, J.E., Sec. & Dir.-Corp. Services--Lakehead Pipe Line Co., Inc., Superior, WI; *Int'l*, pg. 652

Stavely, Richard W., V.P., Sec. & Gen. Counsel--Misco Industries, Wichita, KS; *U.S. Private*, pg. 752

Stavely, Richard W., Sec.--Mountain Iron & Supply Company, Wichita, KS; *U.S. Private*, pg. 764

Steadman, Cathryn, Sec.--Brown Automotive Group, Fairfax, VA; *U.S. Private*, pg. 173

Steele, Alan, Chief Fin. Officer, V.P.-Fin. & Sec.--Advanced Machine Vision Corp., Medford, OR; *U.S. Public*, pg. 20

Steele, Colin, Sec.--Caparo Group Ltd., London, United Kingdom; *Int'l*, pg. 264

Steele, Donald K., V.P.-Sls. & Sec.--Industrial Dielectrics, Inc., Noblesville, IN; *U.S. Private*, pg. 560

Steele, Elizabeth M., Sec.--Jones International, Ltd., Englewood, CO; *U.S. Private*, pg. 597

Steele, Elizabeth M., V.P., Gen. Counsel & Sec.--Jones Intercable, Inc., Englewood, CO; *U.S. Private*, pg. 597

Steele, Kevin S., Controller, Chief Acctg. Officer & Asst. Sec.--UDC Homes, Inc., Scottsdale, AZ; *U.S. Private*, pg. 5

Steele, Lori, Asst. Sec.--Sundt Corp., Tucson, AZ; *U.S. Private*, pg. 1051

Steele, Marcia, V.P. & Sec.--H S Die & Engineering, Inc., Grand Rapids, MI; *U.S. Private*, pg. 489

Steen, Barbara, Sec.--EA Financial, Inc., Wilmington, DE; *U.S. Public*, pg. 541

Steenbeke, Joseph J., Chief Fin. Officer, Treas., Sec. & Controller--Spray-Tech, Inc., Longwood, FL; *U.S. Private*, pg. 1026

Stefaniw, Maria, Sec.--Butcher & Co., Inc., Philadelphia, PA; *U.S. Private*, pg. 189

Stefaniw, Maria, Sec.--Butcher Energy, Philadelphia, PA; *U.S. Private*, pg. 189

Stefanowicz, Sandra, Asst. Sec.--THETA Land Corporation, Wilkes-Barre, PA; *U.S. Public*, pg. 1272

Stefanowicz, Sandra M., Asst. Sec.--Pennsylvania Enterprises Inc., Wilkes-Barre, PA; *U.S. Public*, pg. 1271

Stefanowicz, Sandra M., Asst. Sec.--PG Energy, Inc., Wilkes-Barre, PA; *U.S. Public*, pg. 1271

Stefanowicz, Sandra M., Asst. Sec.--PG Energy Services, Wilkes-Barre, PA; *U.S. Public*, pg. 1272

Steffan, Mike, Pres.-Distr. & Opers. & Corp. Sec.--Inacom Corp., Omaha, NE; *U.S. Public*, pg. 873

Stegner, Geraldine H., Asst. Sec.--Petroleum & Resources Corp., Baltimore, MD; *U.S. Public*, pg. 1280

Stein, Lewis, Treas. & Sec.--RTG Furniture Corp., Seffner, FL; *U.S. Private*, pg. 905

Steinberg, Howard E., Sr. V.P., Sec. & Gen. Counsel--Reliance Group Holdings, Inc., New York, NY; *U.S. Public*, pg. 1374

Steinhart, Conrad, Controller, Treas. & Sec.--Happy Holiday Tree Farms, Sheridan, MI; *U.S. Private*, pg. 254

Steinhauer, Gary, Treas. & Sec.--Madison Dairy Produce Company, Madison, WI; *U.S. Private*, pg. 694

Steinkamp, Robert, V.P., Sec. & Gen. Counsel--Applebee's International, Inc., Overland Park, KS; *U.S. Public*, pg. 122

Steinman, Seymour, Asst. Sec.--Laura Ashley Shops Ltd., Calgary, Canada; *Int'l*, pg. 804

Stellato, Louis E, V.P., Gen. Counsel & Sec.--The Sherwin-Williams Company, Cleveland, OH; *U.S. Public*, pg. 1465

Stelly, Greg, Controller & Sec.--Carter Chambers Supply, Inc., Baton Rouge, LA; *U.S. Private*, pg. 216

Steltmann, Harry F., Chief Fin. Officer, V.P., Treas & Sec.--Eclipse Inc., Rockford, IL; *U.S. Private*, pg. 360

Stempler, Deana, Sec.--Textilease Corporation, Beltsville, MD; *U.S. Private*, pg. 1079

Stendel, David, Sec.--Unican Security Systems Ltd., Montreal, Canada; *Int'l*, pg. 1432

Stensman, Lars, Head-Grp. Staff Law & Corp. Sec.--BTL AB, Goteborg, Sweden; *Int'l*, pg. 123

Stephen, Linda, Sec.--Sunkist Growers, Inc., Sherman Oaks, CA; *U.S. Private*, pg. 1052

Stephens, Barry L., Chief Fin. Officer, V.P. & Sec.--Extendicare Inc., Markham, Canada; *Int'l*, pg. 468

Stephens, Gloria J., Sec.--W.S. Badcock Corporation, Mulberry, FL; *U.S. Private*, pg. 109

Stephens, Philip A., Treas. & Asst. Sec.--Parsons Precision Products, Inc., Parsons, KS; *U.S. Private*, pg. 598

Stephenson, Leighton J., V.P.-Fin., Treas. & Sec.--Vallen Corporation, Houston, TX; *U.S. Public*, pg. 1705

Stephenson, Louise S., Sec.--Capitol Broadcasting Co., Inc., Raleigh, NC; *U.S. Private*, pg. 206

Sterling, Donald R., V.P.-Legal Affairs & Sec.--Iomega Corporation, Roy, UT; *U.S. Public*, pg. 912

Sterling, Marcia, V.P.-Bus. Devel. & Gen. Counsel--Autodesk, Inc., San Rafael, CA; *U.S. Public*, pg. 148

Stern, Bruce E., Gen. Counsel & Sec.--Financial Security Assurance Holdings Ltd., New York, NY; *U.S. Public*, pg. 622

Stern, Gary, Sec.--Stocko Corp., Carlstadt, NJ; *Int'l*, pg. 1301

Stern, Herbert L., Jr., Chm.-Exec. Committee & Sec.--T C Manufacturing Company, Inc., Evanston, IL; *U.S. Private*, pg. 1062

Stern, Julian N., Corp. Sec.--Alza Corporation, Palo Alto, CA; *U.S. Public*, pg. 62

Stern, Julian N., Esq., Sec.--Advanced Polymer Systems, Redwood City, CA; *U.S. Public*, pg. 22

Stern, Laurence R., Asst. Sec.--Republic New York Corporation, New York, NY; *U.S. Public*, pg. 1380

Stern, Maxine E., Sec.--M.L. Stern & Company, Inc., Beverly Hills, CA; *U.S. Private*, pg. 1041

Stern, Robert E., V.P., Gen. Counsel & Sec.--The Bon Ton Stores, Inc., York, PA; *U.S. Public*, pg. 244

Stern, Sandra, Asst. Sec.--Republic New York Corporation, New York, NY; *U.S. Public*, pg. 1380

Sternberg, Paul J., V.P., Gen. Counsel & Sec.--The Raymond Corporation, Greene, NY; *Int'l*, pg. 123

Sterner, Gene E., Treas. & Sec.--Jordon Commercial Refrigerator Co., Philadelphia, PA; *U.S. Private*, pg. 599

Sterrett, W.E., Pres., Chief Fin. Officer & Sec.--Wheaton Van Lines, Inc., Indianapolis, IN; *U.S. Private*, pg. 1171

Stetzner, Leah Manning, Gen. Counsel & Corp. Sec.--Illinova Inc., Decatur, IL; *U.S. Public*, pg. 869

Stetzner, Leah Manning, V.P., Gen. Counsel & Sec.--Illinois Power Company, Decatur, IL; *U.S. Public*, pg. 869

Stetzner, Leah Manning, Sec.--Illinova Generating Co., Decatur, IL; *U.S. Public*, pg. 870

Stetzner, Leah Manning, Corp. Sec.--Illinova Energy Partners, Inc., Oak Brook, IL; *U.S. Public*, pg. 870

Steuber, Frederick G., Sr. V.P., Gen. Counsel & Sec.--The Lincoln Electric Company, Cleveland, OH; *U.S. Public*, pg. 996

Stevens, Constance I., V.P.-Admin. & Asst. Sec.--Stevens International, Inc., Fort Worth, TX; *U.S. Public*, pg. 1517

Stevens, Dave, Chief Fin. Officer, Treas. & Sec.--Scott Sports Group, Ketchum, ID; *U.S. Private*, pg. 977

Stevens, Doug, Controller & Asst. Sec.--Delta Woodside Industries, Inc., Greenville, SC; *U.S. Public*, pg. 497

Stevens, Glenn H., V.P., Gen. Counsel & Sec.--Maxtor Corporation, Milpitas, CA; *Int'l*, pg. 641

Stevens, Jim, J., Jr., Treas. & Sec.--Lincoln Provision, Inc., Chicago, IL; *U.S. Private*, pg. 668

Stevens, Richard A., Exec. Dir. & Sec.--Pentland Group PLC, London, United Kingdom; *Int'l*, pg. 1035

Stevens, Thomas C., Exec. V.P., Gen. Counsel & Sec.--Keycorp, Cleveland, OH; *U.S. Public*, pg. 954

Stevens, Ward C., Ph.D., V.P.-Admin. & Sec.--ATMI, Inc., Danbury, CT; *U.S. Public*, pg. 12

Stevenson, Bobby G., Chm. Bd., Chief Exec. Officer & Sec.--Ciber, Inc., Englewood, CO; *U.S. Public*, pg. 356

Stevenson, Robert W., Chief Fin. Officer, Exec. V.P. & Sec.--Esterline Technologies Corporation, Bellevue, WA; *U.S. Public*, pg. 594

Stevenson, Scott, Corp. Sec.--National Parks Transportation, Inc., Saint George, UT; *U.S. Public*, pg. 1476

Stewart, Barbara E., Sec.--Seligman & Associates, Inc., Southfield, MI; *U.S. Private*, pg. 982

Stewart, Bernard F., Exec. V.P., Gen. Counsel & Sec.--Exide Corporation, Reading, PA; *U.S. Public*, pg. 600

Stewart, Guthrie, Exec. V.P.-Corp. Devel. & Sec.--Teleglobe, Inc., Montreal, Canada; *Int'l*, pg. 1373

Stewart, JoAn B., Sec.--Fair Grounds Corporation, New Orleans, LA; *U.S. Public*, pg. 609

Stewart, John F., Chief Acctg. Officer & Controller--The Penn Traffic Company, Syracuse, NY; *U.S. Public*, pg. 1270

Stewart, Karl A., V.P. & Sec.--Tenneco Inc., Greenwich, CT; *U.S. Public*, pg. 1577

Stewart, Lever, Gen. Counsel & Asst. Sec.--Rock-Tenn Company, Norcross, GA; *U.S. Public*, pg. 1396

Stewart, Lindsay D., V.P. & Asst. Sec.--Nike, Inc., Beaverton, OR; *U.S. Public*, pg. 1184

Stewart, Ronald G., Chief Fin. Officer & V.P.--North Coast Electric Company, Bellevue, WA; *U.S. Private*, pg. 804

Stewart, William C., Jr., V.P., Gen. Counsel & Sec.--Cubic Corporation, San Diego, CA; *U.S. Public*, pg. 466

Stewart, William C., Jr., V.P. & Sec.--Cubic Applications, Inc., Lacey, WA; *U.S. Public*, pg. 466

Stichler, Donald L., Controller, Treas. & Sec.--Varco International, Inc., Orange, CA; *U.S. Public*, pg. 1709

Stichter, Richard D., Sec.--Capital Tire, Inc., Toledo, OH; *U.S. Private*, pg. 206

Sticker, Nina, Sec.--Pioneer American Holding Company, Carbondale, PA; *U.S. Public*, pg. 1298

Stigall, Geraldine M., Asst. Sec.--The Midland Company, Cincinnati, OH; *U.S. Public*, pg. 1110

Stigler, David M., Sr. V.P.-Legal & Pub. Affairs, Gen. Counsel & Sec.--ADVO, Inc., Windsor, CT; *U.S. Public*, pg. 23

Stillman, John C., Exec. V.P. & Sec.--Stillman & Hoag, Inc., Englewood, NJ; *U.S. Private*, pg. 1043

Stimpson, Gordon S., Treas. & Sec.--Gulf Lumber Company, Inc., Mobile, AL; *U.S. Private*, pg. 487

Stimpson, James R., Treas. & Sec.--Channellock, Inc., Meadville, PA; *U.S. Private*, pg. 229

Stimson, Jack, Sec.--Brammer plc, Altrincham, United Kingdom; *Int'l*, pg. 212

Stinchfield, John E., Gen. Counsel & Sec.--The Donohoe Companies, Inc., Washington, DC; *U.S. Private*, pg. 340

Stinnett, J. Daniel, V.P., Sec. & Gen. Counsel--Commerce Bancshares, Inc., Kansas City, MO; *U.S. Public*, pg. 409

Stinson, Peggy J., Asst. Sec.--IWC Resources Corporation, Indianapolis, IN; *U.S. Public*, pg. 1185

Stinson, Robert C., V.P.-Admin. & H.R., Gen. Counsel & Sec.--Applied Industrial Technologies, Cleveland, OH; *U.S. Public*, pg. 122

Stipe, Moyalana T., Asst. Sec.--Institutional Services, Inc., Fort Worth, TX; *U.S. Public*, pg. 1482

Stitzer, H. Todd, V.P., Gen. Counsel & Sec.--Cadbury Beverages North America, Stamford, CT; *Int'l*, pg. 248

Stivers, R.N., Chief Fin. Officer, V.P.-Fin., Treas. & Sec.--Temtex Industries Inc., Dallas, TX; *U.S. Public*, pg. 1575

Stivers, R.N., V.P.-Fin., Sec. & Treas.--Temco Fireplace Products, Inc., Nashville, TN; *U.S. Public*, pg. 1576

Stockwell, Barbara, Sec.--Trico Electric Co-Op, Tucson, AZ; *U.S. Private*, pg. 1102

Stockwell, T., Sec.--Electro Metrics, Inc., Johnstown, NY; *U.S. Private*, pg. 369

Stolk, T., Sec--Delft Instruments N.V., Delft, Netherlands; *Int'l*, pg. 388

Stoll, Larry J., V.P.-Fin., Treas. & Asst. Sec.--St. Joseph Light & Power Co., Saint Joseph, MO; *U.S. Public*, pg. 1427

Stoller, Herbert, Sec.--Materials Research Corporation, Gilbert, AZ; *Int'l*, pg. 1283

Stoller, John R., V.P., Gen. Counsel & Sec.--Pulte Corporation, Bloomfield Hills, MI; *U.S. Public*, pg. 1344

Stolmeier, Judith D., Sec.--KCL Corporation, Shelbyville, IN; *U.S. Private*, pg. 603

Stolte, Sandra L., Pres., Chief Exec. Officer & Sec.--Central Bank, Fairview Heights, IL; *U.S. Public*, pg. 643

Stolzar, Michael, Sec. & Asst. Treas.--General Microwave Corporation, Amityville, NY; *U.S. Public*, pg. 717

Stone, Bruce W., Asst. Sec.--Ogden Corporation, New York, NY; *U.S. Public*, pg. 1213

Stone, Edward B., V.P. & Sec.--W.O. Bankston Enterprises Inc., Dallas, TX; *U.S. Public*, pg. 1379

Stone, Gary L., Sr. V.P., Gen. Counsel & Sec.--Parsons Corporation, Pasadena, CA; *U.S. Private*, pg. 841

Stone, Howard S., Pres. & Sec.--Bake-Line Products, Inc., Des Plaines, IL; *U.S. Public*, pg. 657

Stone, Kathy, V.P., Treas. & Sec.--Ergon, Inc., Jackson, MS; *U.S. Private*, pg. 380

Stone, Marc J., V.P.-Corp. Plng. & Devel., Gen. Counsel & Sec.--Omega Research Inc., Miami, FL; *U.S. Public*, pg. 1222

Stone, Robert H., V.P., Gen. Counsel & Sec.--Avatex Corporation, Dallas, TX; *U.S. Public*, pg. 151

Stoops, Richard, Sec.--George & Lynch, Inc., New Castle, DE; *U.S. Private*, pg. 448

Storakers, Birgitta, Sec.--Stora Power AB, Falun, Sweden; *Int'l*, pg. 1303

Storey, Christopher, Dir. & Sec.--Vaux Group Plc, Sunderland, United Kingdom; *Int'l*, pg. 1453

Storey, David, Chief Fin. Officer & Sec.--Poulter Communications PLC, Leeds, United Kingdom; *Int'l*, pg. 1065

Stork, Alfred E., Treas. & Asst. Sec.--The Imperial Electric Company, Akron, OH; *U.S. Private*, pg. 598

Stortz, Thomas C., V.P. & Sec.--Peter Kiewit Sons Inc., Omaha, NE; *U.S. Private*, pg. 619

Story, Arlene, Asst. Corp. Sec.--Data I/O Corporation, Redmond, WA; *U.S. Public*, pg. 486

Stoudenmire, Stan, Chief Fin. Officer, V.P.-Fin. & Admin. & Sec.--Ross Systems, Inc., Atlanta, GA; *U.S. Public*, pg. 1406

Strahman, Cora, Sec. & Mgr.-Mktg.--Strahman Valves, Inc., Florham Park, NJ; *U.S. Private*, pg. 1046

Straka, Angeline C., V.P., Sec. & Assoc. Gen. Counsel--CBS Corporation, Pittsburgh, PA; *U.S. Public*, pg. 273

Strasburg, Sari Ann, Gen. Counsel & Sec--Velcro Industries N.V., Willemstad, Netherlands Antilles; *Int'l*, pg. 1462

Strassberg, Roslyn, Sec.--Anglers Roslyn Group Ltd., Flushing, NY; *U.S. Private*, pg. 74

Strassler, Marc, Gen. Counsel & Sec.--Pathmark Stores Incorporated, Woodbridge, NJ; *U.S. Private*, pg. 843

Straub, Donald A., Gen. Counsel & Sec.--NT Dor-omatic, Harwood Heights, IL; *U.S. Private*, pg. 771

Straube, Hildegard, Treas. & Sec.--Straube Regional Center LLC, Pennington, NJ; *U.S. Private*, pg. 1046

Straw, Ralph L., Jr., V.P., Gen. Cousel & Sec.--United National Bancorp, Bridgewater, NJ; *U.S. Public*, pg. 1679

Streeper, Norene, Sec.--Wilson Products Co., Salt Lake City, UT; *U.S. Private*, pg. 1181

Street, Paul, Sec.--FiberMark Inc., Brattleboro, VT; *U.S. Public*, pg. 620

Strelioff, Susan J., Sr. V.P. Corp. Governance & Sec.--National Trustco Inc., Toronto, Canada; *Int'l*, pg. 909

Strickstein, Irvin, V.P. & Sec.--National Lumber Co., Warren, MI; *U.S. Private*, pg. 785

Strobel, Martin J., V.P., Gen. Counsel & Sec.--Dana Corporation, Toledo, OH; *U.S. Public*, pg. 479

Strobel, Victoria L., Asst. V.P. & Asst. Sec.--Marshall & Ilsley Corporation, Milwaukee, WI; *U.S. Public*, pg. 1049

Strohm, B.C., Exec. V.P., Gen. Counsel & Sec.--Equity Residential Properties Trust, Chicago, IL; *U.S. Public*, pg. 590

Stroman, Randy, Dir.-Mktg. Communications--Stainless Incorporated, Deerfield Beach, FL; *U.S. Private*, pg. 1029

Strong, Barry P., Gen. Counsel & Sec.--The National Mutual Life Association of Australia Limited, Melbourne, Australia; *Int'l*, pg. 909

Strong, Curt, Treas. & Sec.--Zieman Manufacturing Company, Whittier, CA; *U.S. Private*, pg. 1205

Stropple, Peter W., V.P.-Fin. & Sec.--Ris Paper Company, Long Island City, NY; *U.S. Private*, pg. 932

Stroud, D. Michael, V.P., Gen. Counsel & Sec.--Bell Atlantic-PA, Philadelphia, PA; *U.S. Public*, pg. 203

Stroud, James A., Co-Chm. Bd., Chief Oper. Officer & Sec.--Capital Senior Living, Inc., Dallas, TX; *U.S. Public*, pg. 302

Struck, Theodore F., II, Asst. Treas. & Asst. Sec.--FirstEnergy Corp., Akron, OH; *U.S. Public*, pg. 644

Struckhoff, Charles O., Chief Fin. Officer, V.P.-Fin. & Admin., Treas. & Sec.--Maverick Tube Corporation, Chesterfield, MO; *U.S. Public*, pg. 1060

Strupp, Robert, Treas. & Sec.--Mozel Development Corp., Baileys Crossroads, VA; *U.S. Private*, pg. 765

Struth, D.D., Sec.--Salem Erectors, Carnegie, PA; *U.S. Private*, pg. 961

Struth, David D., Sec.--Salem Corporation, Pittsburgh, PA; *U.S. Private*, pg. 961

Strutt, David, Chief Fin. Officer, Gen. Counsel & Sec.--The Weitz Company, Inc., Des Moines, IA; *U.S. Private*, pg. 1160

Stuart, Gloria, Grp. Dir.-Legal Affairs & Sec.--The BOC Group plc, Windlesham, United Kingdom; *Int'l*, pg. 121

Stuber, Fred, Sr. V.P. & Sec.--Foster & Gallagher, Inc., Peoria, IL; *U.S. Private*, pg. 420

Studebaker, David C., Sec.--Spectra-Physics Laserplane Inc., Dayton, OH; *U.S. Public*, pg. 1594

Stuecker, Phillip J., Chief Fin. Officer, V.P.-Fin. & Sec.--Thomas Industries Inc., Louisville, KY; *U.S. Public*, pg. 1598

Stumler, David J., Asst. Sec.--Thomas Industries Inc., Louisville, KY; *U.S. Public*, pg. 1598

Stumpo, Frank D., Chief Fin. Officer & V.P.-Finance--Resco Products, Inc., Conshohocken, PA; *U.S. Private*, pg. 924

Stutzman, Byron W., Sec.--Programart Corporation, Cambridge, MA; *U.S. Private*, pg. 890

Styer, Paul A., Sr. V.P., Gen. Counsel & Sec.--Copart, Inc., Benicia, CA; *U.S. Public*, pg. 446

Suan, Susan Tay, Sec.--Singapore Land Limited, Singapore, Singapore; *Int'l*, pg. 1252

Suchil, Sally, V.P. & Sec.--MGM Entertainment Company, Culver City, CA; *U.S. Public*, pg. 1614

Sudbury, David M., V.P., Gen. Counsel & Sec.--Commercial Metals Company, Dallas, TX; *U.S. Public*, pg. 411

Sudhoff, Robert, Chief Fin. Officer, V.P.-Fin. & Sec.--The Minster Machine Company, Minster, OH; *U.S. Private*, pg. 751

Sue, Christopher E., Chief Fin. Officer & Sec.--Osicom Technologies Inc., Santa Monica, CA; *U.S. Public*, pg. 1233

Suffredini, J. Michael, Asst. Sec.--Sony Trans Com Systems Inc., Costa Mesa, CA; *Int'l*, pg. 1281

Sugar, David C., V.P., Sec. & Dir.-Mktg.--National Guardian Life Insurance Company, Madison, WI; *U.S. Private*, pg. 784

Sugar, David C., V.P. & Sec.--NGL Holdings Inc., Madison, WI; *U.S. Private*, pg. 784

Sugar, David C., V.P. & Sec.--NGL Financial Services Inc., Madison, WI; *U.S. Private*, pg. 784

Sugar, David C., V.P. & Sec.--NGL Investment Services Inc., Madison, WI; *U.S. Private*, pg. 784

Suleman, Farid, Chief Fin. Officer & Sec.--Westwood One, Inc., New York, NY; *U.S. Public*, pg. 1763

Sullivan, Dennis G., V.P., Gen. Counsel, Asst. Treas. & Asst. Sec.--Middlesex Water Company, Iselin, NJ; *U.S. Public*, pg. 1110

Sullivan, Dennis G., Asst. Treas. & Asst. sec.--Tidewater Utilities, Inc., Odessa, DE; *U.S. Public*, pg. 1110

Sullivan, Dennis G., Sec.--Utility Service Affiliates, Inc., Iselin, NJ; *U.S. Public*, pg. 1110

Sullivan, Glenda D., Sec.--Sullivan Oil Company, Baton Rouge, LA; *U.S. Private*, pg. 1050

Sullivan, John B., Sec.--The Portfolio Group, Inc., New York, NY; *U.S. Public*, pg. 338

Sullivan, John L., Controller, Treas. & Sec.--Totsy Manufacturing Company, Inc., Holyoke, MA; *U.S. Private*, *pg. 1093*

Sullivan, John L., Gen. Counsel & Corp. Sec.--Cray Research, Eagan, MN; *U.S. Public*, pg. 1473

Sullivan, Judith A., Gen. Counsel & Sec.--Citizens Financial Group, Inc., Providence, RI; *Int'l*, pg. 1132

Sullivan, Judith A., Sec.--Citizens Mortgage Corporation, Atlanta, GA; *Int'l*, pg. 1132

Sullivan, Laura P., V.P. & Sec.--State Farm Mutual Automobile Insurance Company, Bloomington, IL; *U.S. Private*, pg. 1036

Sullivan, Mark, Treas. & Sec.--ColeJon Corporation, Cleveland, OH; *U.S. Private*, pg. 251

Sullivan, Michael M., Corp. Counsel & Sec.--SCI Systems, Inc., Huntsville, AL; *U.S. Public*, pg. 1416

Sullivan, Michael P., V.P., Gen. Counsel & Sec.--Commonwealth Energy System, Cambridge, MA; *U.S. Public*, pg. 414

Sullivan, Peter T., Treas. & Sec.--SierraCom, Hopkinton, MA; *U.S. Private*, pg. 999

Sullivan, Robert W., Asst. Sec.--Springs Industries, Inc., Fort Mill, SC; *U.S. Public*, pg. 1499

Sullivan, Scott D., Chief Fin. Officer & Sec.--WorldCom, Inc., Jackson, MS; *U.S. Public*, pg. 1779

Sullivan, Shauna J., Asst. Sec.--Cox Communications, Inc., Atlanta, GA; *U.S. Public*, pg. 454

Sullivan, Sylvia, Chief Fin. Officer & Sec.--McDonald Equipment Co., Willoughby, OH; *U.S. Private*, pg. 721

Sullivan, Timothy J., Chief Fin. Officer, Chief Admin. Officer, Sr. V.P., Treas. & Sec.--Market Facts, Inc., Arlington Heights, IL; *U.S. Public*, pg. 1046

Sulser, Claude, Corp. Sec.--Brauerei AG, Zurich, Switzerland; *Int'l*, pg. 479

Sumas, Robert, Exec. V.P. & Sec.--Village Super Market Inc., Springfield, NJ; *U.S. Public*, pg. 1721

Sumida, Adele, Corp. Sec.--Maui Land & Pineapple Co., Inc., Kahului, HI; *U.S. Public*, pg. 1060

Summers, Cheryl, Controller & Asst. Sec.--McCall Oil & Chemical Corp., Portland, OR; *U.S. Private*, pg. 719

Summers, Kathy, Controller & Sec.--Harold Ziegler Ford-Elkhart, Elkhart, IN; *U.S. Private*, pg. 1205

Sumrall, K.R., Acting Chief Fin. Officer & Sec.--Texas Micro, Inc., Houston, TX; *U.S. Public*, pg. 1586

Sumrall, O. Malcolm, Chief Fin. Officer, Treas. & Sec.--Associated Equipment Company of Delaware, Mobile, AL; *U.S. Private*, pg. 90

Sun, D., Sec.--Esso Singapore Private Limited, Singapore, Singapore; *U.S. Public*, pg. 602

Sun, D., Sec.--Exxon Trading Asia Pacific Private Limited, Singapore, Singapore; *U.S. Public*, pg. 602

Sund, Mike, V.P.-Commun./Investor Rels. & Sec.--Mycogen Corporation, San Diego, CA; *U.S. Public*, pg. 1142

Sunderhaft, Eugene R., Chief Fin. Officer, Sr. V.P.-Fin. & Sec.--The Penn Traffic Company, Syracuse, NY; *U.S. Public*, pg. 1270

Sunderland, Kent W., V.P. & Sec.--Ash Grove Cement Company, Shawnee Mission, KS; *U.S. Private*, pg. 87

Sunkin, David, V.P.-Legal, Gen. Counsel & Sec.--Earl Scheib, Inc., Beverly Hills, CA; *U.S. Public*, pg. 1437

Surface, Katheryn E., Sec. & Gen. Counsel--United Dominion Realty Trust, Inc., Richmond, VA; *U.S. Public*, pg. 1677

Surhan, Pat, Sec.--National Welders Supply Co. Inc., Charlotte, NC; *U.S. Private*, pg. 788

Suryanarayana, U., Sec.--Coal India Limited, Calcutta, India; *Int'l*, pg. 298

Susco, Vincent F., Jr., V.P.-Admin. & Sec.--Connecticut Water Service, Inc., Clinton, CT; *U.S. Public*, pg. 431

Sussis, Mitchell, Corp. Sec.--The Dun & Bradstreet Corporation, Murray Hill, NJ; *U.S. Public*, pg. 535

Sussman, Greta, Sec. & Treas.--Pretty Neat Products, Kearny, NJ; *U.S. Public*, pg. 1177

Suter, Suzanne, Sec.--Anadarko Petroleum Corporation, Houston, TX; *U.S. Public*, pg. 107

Sutherland, Betty C., Sec.--Carolina Casualty Insurance Company, Jacksonville, FL; *U.S. Public*, pg. 216

Sutherland, John, Sec.--Vision One, Norwich, CT; *U.S. Private*, pg. 1141

Sutter, Blanche M., Chief Fin. Officer, Exec. V.P. & Sec.--Caere Corporation, Los Gatos, CA; *U.S. Public*, pg. 291

Suttmeier, Catherine H., V.P., Gen. Counsel & Sec.--Oneida Ltd., Oneida, NY; *U.S. Public*, pg. 1225

Sutton, V.P.-Admin. & Sec.--K & R Express Systems Inc., Hinsdale, IL; *U.S. Private*, pg. 602

Sutton, Neal, Sr. V.P., Gen. Counsel & Sec.--Smith International, Inc., Houston, TX; *U.S. Public*, pg. 1478

Sutton, Ray Sandy, V.P.-Corp. Sec. & Gen. Counsel--Interstate Bakeries Corporation, Kansas City, MO; *U.S. Public*, pg. 909

Suzaki, M., Asst. Sec.--Mitsubishi International Corporation, New York, NY; *Int'l*, pg. 871

Suzuki, Junichi, Pres.--Komatsu America Industries Corp., Wood Dale, IL; *Int'l*, pg. 744

Suzuki, Teiji, Chief Fin. Officer, Sec. & Mng. Dir.--Achilles Corporation, Tokyo, Japan; *Int'l*, pg. 22

Swallow, Jeff, V.P.-Admin., Sec. & Dir.-H.R.--Magnetrol International, Downers Grove, IL; *U.S. Private*, pg. 696

Swallow, Jeff, Dir.-Corp. Sec.--Introtek International, Edgewood, NY; *U.S. Private*, pg. 696

Swan, A.W., Sec. & Dir.-Human Resources--Energizer Eveready Ltd., London, United Kingdom; *U.S. Public*, pg. 1360

Swan, Neil, Sec. & Gen. Counsel--London International Group plc, London, United Kingdom; *Int'l*, pg. 815

Swan, Robert C., V.P. & Sec.--Phelps Dodge Corporation, Phoenix, AZ; *U.S. Public*, pg. 1286

Swander, Michelle, Sec.--National Machinery, Tiffin, OH; *U.S. Private*, pg. 785

Swaner, Beverly, Sec.--Swaner Hardwood Company, Inc., Burbank, CA; *U.S. Private*, pg. 1057

Swanson, Craig M., Chief Fin. Officer, V.P.-Fin. & Sec.--Protocol Systems, Inc., Beaverton, OR; *U.S. Public*, pg. 1336

Swanson, Julie, Sec.--International Research & Evaluation, Eagan, MN; *U.S. Private*, pg. 571

Swanson, Reuel, Corp. Sec.--Metropolitan Mortgage & Securities Co., Inc., Spokane, WA; *U.S. Private*, pg. 738

Swanson, Robert E., Sec.--CertainTeed Manatee Insulation Ltd., Montreal, Canada; *Int'l*, pg. 1176

Swanson, Robin E., Sec.--Amcor Capital Corporation, Coachella, CA; *U.S. Public*, pg. 64

Swanson, Stanley, Sec. & Treas.--Minuteman Press International, Farmingdale, NY; *U.S. Private*, pg. 752

Swantak, Judy L., V.P. & Sec.--Union Pacific Corporation, Dallas, TX; *U.S. Public*, pg. 1667

Sweeney, Frank B., Sec.--Oryx Energy, Dallas, TX; *U.S. Public*, pg. 1232

Sweeney, Mary, Sec.--The Albert Fisher Group PLC, Stoke Poges, United Kingdom; *Int'l*, pg. 491

Sweeney, Patrick E., Asst. Sec.--W.P. Carey & Co., Inc., New York, NY; *U.S. Private*, pg. 209

Sweeney, Thomas, Gen. Counsel & Sec.--HDS Services, Farmington Hills, MI; *U.S. Private*, pg. 490

Sweerts, F.W., Sec.--Philips Electronics N.V., Eindhoven, Netherlands; *Int'l*, pg. 1051

Sweetland, Cynthia, Sec.--Dugan Production Corp., Farmington, NM; *U.S. Private*, pg. 345

Swick, Michael F., V.P., Gen. Counsel & Corp. Sec.--AGCO Corporation, Duluth, GA; *U.S. Public*, pg. 28

Swift, Dean A., V.P., Gen. Counsel & Asst. Sec.--Belden & Blake Corporation, Canton, OH; *U.S. Private*, pg. 1078

Swinnerton, B.R.G., Sec.--Morganite Hong Kong Company Limited, Kowloon, Hong Kong; *Int'l*, pg. 892

Swisher, Thane, V.P. & Sec.--CMI Corporation, Oklahoma City, OK; *U.S. Public*, pg. 278

Switalski, Gillian, Gen. Counsel & Sec.--Proudfoot USA Company, West Palm Beach, FL; *Int'l*, pg. 1072

Switalski, Gillian E., Gen. Counsel & Sec.--Proudfoot plc, Richmond, United Kingdom; *Int'l*, pg. 1071

Swoish, Craig, Exec. V.P., Sec. & Treas.--Lamina Inc., Oak Park, MI; *Int'l*, pg. 75

Sydney-Smith, P.E., Dir.-Fin. & Sec.--British Gypsum Ltd., Loughborough, United Kingdom; *Int'l*, pg. 122

Sykes, James E., Jr., Treas. & Sec.--Noland Company, Newport News, VA; *U.S. Public*, pg. 1187

Sylva, JoAnne, Treas. & Sec.--Dimensional Merchandising, Inc., Wharton, NJ; *U.S. Private*, pg. 333

Syms, Terry L., Sec.--The Washington Water Power Company, Spokane, WA; *U.S. Public*, pg. 1744

Syring, Robert G., V.P. & Sec.--Maxon Corporation, Muncie, IN; *U.S. Private*, pg. 716

Szekely, Steven, Treas. & Sec.--Monarch Avalon, Inc., Baltimore, MD; *U.S. Public*, pg. 1123

Szidon, Bonnie Bixler, Sec.--Ranch-Way Feed Inc., Fort Collins, CO; *U.S. Private*, pg. 908

Szulman-Jones, Marilyn, Treas. & Sec.--Airco Mechanical Inc., Sacramento, CA; *U.S. Private*, pg. 29

Taber, Michael H., Chief Acctg. Officer, V.P.-Fin. & Sec.--Del Global Technologies, Valhalla, NY; *U.S. Public*, pg. 493

Tabernilla, Armando A., V.P.-Legal Affairs, Gen. Counsel & Sec.--IVAX Corporation, Miami, FL; *U.S. Public*, pg. 914

Tabler, Bryan G., V.P., Gen. Counsel & Sec.--Ipalco Enterprises, Inc., Indianapolis, IN; *U.S. Public*, pg. 912

Tabone, Catherine, Dr., Sec.--Air Malta Co. Ltd., Luqa, Malta; *Int'l*, pg. 37

Tack, Kim P., Sec. & Treas.--BWI Kartridg Pak, Davenport, IA; *Int'l*, pg. 130

Tacke, Kelly, Chief Fin. Officer, V.P.-Fin. & Sec.--Palm Harbor Homes, Inc., Dallas, TX; *U.S. Public*, pg. 1254

Taddei, Mirian H., Sec.--Hunter Contracting Company, Gilbert, AZ; *U.S. Private*, pg. 549

Tagesson, Ann-Katrin, Sec.--Stora Building Products AB, Jonkoping, Sweden; *Int'l*, pg. 1302

Taggart, David, Sr. V.P. & Sec.--Montgomery Watson, Pasadena, CA; *U.S. Private*, pg. 759

Tai, Henry T., Dr., Sec.--I-Flow Corporation, Lake Forest, CA; *U.S. Public*, pg. 851

Tait, George, Corp. Sec.--William Grant & Sons Distillers Ltd., Bellshill, United Kingdom; *Int'l*, pg. 557

Takada, J., Sec. & Treas.--Yamaha Motor Canada Ltd., North York, Canada; *Int'l*, pg. 1516

Takahashi, Jin, Sec. & Dir.-Pub. Rels.--Mercian Corporation, Tokyo, Japan; *Int'l*, pg. 858

Takeda, Akio, Sec.--Nisshin Steel USA, Inc., New York, NY; *Int'l*, pg. 946

Talbot, Brian R., Asst. V.P. & Branch Mgr.--Independent Bank, Ionia, MI; *U.S. Public*, pg. 874

Talbot, Paul W., Corp. Sec.--TNP Enterprises, Inc., Fort Worth, TX; *U.S. Public*, pg. 1557

Talcott, Joel, V.P. & Sec.--Ampex Corporation, Redwood City, CA; *U.S. Public*, pg. 104

Talley, Joseph J., Treas. & Asst. Sec.--American Crystal Sugar Company, Moorhead, MN; *U.S. Private*, pg. 52

Talley, Kathleen A., Sec. & Asst. Treas.--Advance Ross Corporation, Chicago, IL; *U.S. Public*, pg. 320

Tallichet, Cecilia, V.P. & Sec.--Specialty Restaurants Corporation, Anaheim, CA; *U.S. Private*, pg. 1022

Tam, Peter, Sec.--Jacks International Limited, Singapore, Singapore; *Int'l*, pg. 697

Tamburo, Vincent A., Gen. Counsel & Sec.--1st Source Corporation, South Bend, IN; *U.S. Public*, pg. 638

Tamburo, Vincent A., Sr. V.P., Gen. Counsel & Sec.--1st Source Bank Consolidated, South Bend, IN; *U.S. Public*, pg. 638

Tanaka, David F., V.P., Gen. Counsel & Sec.--Gaylord Container Corporation, Deerfield, IL; *U.S. Public*, pg. 704

Tanaka, Hidetoshi, V.P., Sec. & Treas.--Mazda (North America), Inc., Irvine, CA; *Int'l*, pg. 849

Tanenberg, Marc T., Chief Fin. Officer, V.P.-Fin. & Sec.--Recoton Auto Corporation, Lincolnshire, IL; *U.S. Public*, pg. 1369

Tang, Paul, V.P., Gen. Counsel & Asst. Sec.--Burlington Coat Factory Warehouse Corporation, Burlington, NJ; *U.S. Public*, pg. 268

Taniguchi, Lon, V.P. & Sec.--Puna Plantation Hawaii Ltd., Hilo, HI; *U.S. Private*, pg. 895

Tankard, Chris, Sec.--Thorn Security Group, Ltd., Sunbury, United Kingdom; *Int'l*, pg. 1386

Tankersley, Daniel B., Vice Chm. & Sec.--United Foods, Inc., Bells, TN; *U.S. Public*, pg. 1677

Tanner, Anthony J., Exec. V.P.-Admin. & Sec.--Healthsouth Corporation, Birmingham, AL; *U.S. Public*, pg. 803

Tanner, B.E., Sec.--Cementation Mining Limited, Doncaster, United Kingdom; *Int'l*, pg. 772

Tanner, B.E., Sec.--Cementation Piling & Foundations Limited, Rickmansworth, United Kingdom; *Int'l*, pg. 772

Tanooka, Yoshio, Sec.--Showpla Asia Limited, Singapore, Singapore; *Int'l*, pg. 1237

Tanski, Ronald J., Sec. & Treas.--National Fuel Resources, Buffalo, NY; *U.S. Public*, pg. 1156

Tanto, Tsuyoshi, Sec.--Kobe Steel U.S.A. Inc. (New York), New York, NY; *Int'l*, pg. 740

Tapp, Richard, Sec. & Chief Legal Advisor--Blue Circle Industries PLC, London, United Kingdom; *Int'l*, pg. 197

Tapscott, James T., Chief Fin. Officer, Treas. & Sec.--Columbus Mills, Inc., Columbus, GA; *U.S. Private*, pg. 256

Tarakajian, Gloria, Asst. Corp. Sec.--Fruit Growers Supply Co., Sherman Oaks, CA; *U.S. Private*, pg. 430

Tassin, William, V.P. & Sec.--IBL Limited, Inc., Scarsdale, NY; *Int'l*, pg. 21

Tat, Ho Yeng, Sec.--Cycle & Carriage Industries (1986) Pte. Limited, Singapore, Singapore; *Int'l*, pg. 350

Tate, Janet, Exec. Sec.--The Kingsford Products Company, Oakland, CA; *U.S. Public*, pg. 387

Tate, Warren E., Gen. Mgr., Treas. & Sec.-Information Services--Gulf Power Company, Pensacola, FL; *U.S. Public*, pg. 1490

Taten, Bruce M., V.P. & Asst. Sec.--Keystone International Holdings Corp., Houston, TX; *U.S. Public*, pg. 1650

Taub, David, Controller & Sec.--Fownes Brothers & Co., Inc., New York, NY; *U.S. Private*, pg. 422

Taub, Jon, Sec.--PVS Chemicals, Inc., Detroit, MI; *U.S. Private*, pg. 828

Taubman, Gerard, Sec. & Dir.-Admin.--Remy Cointreau, Paris, France; *Int'l*, pg. 1102

Tauras, Fran, Sec.--Acheson Industries, Inc., Port Huron, MI; *U.S. Private*, pg. 12

Tauras, Fran, Sec.--Acheson Colloids Company, Port Huron, MI; *U.S. Private*, pg. 12

Tavlin, Michael J., V.P., Treas. & Sec.--Aliant Communications Inc., Lincoln, NE; *U.S. Public*, pg. 40

Tawil, Fred, Sec.--Tawil Associates Inc., Carteret, NJ; *U.S. Private*, pg. 1070

Taylor, A. Alexander, II, Asst. Sec.--Krystal Company, Chattanooga, TN; *U.S. Private*, pg. 636

Taylor, Charles, Sec.--Graham Group, Inc., Des Moines, IA; *U.S. Private*, pg. 468

Taylor, Cindy B., V.P., Controller & Sec.--Cliffs Drilling Company, Houston, TX; *U.S. Public*, pg. 386

Taylor, Dana, Gen. Counsel & Sec.--Curtiss-Wright Corp., Lyndhurst, NJ; *U.S. Public*, pg. 469

Taylor, David H., Chief Fin. Officer, Exec. V.P.-Fin. & Sec.--JPS Textile Group, Inc., Greenville, SC; *U.S. Private*, pg. 578

Taylor, James, V.P., Gen. Counsel & Sec.--Southwestern Bell Telephone Co., Saint Louis, MO; *U.S. Public*, pg. 1416

Taylor, Martha, Sec.--J.H. Routh Packing Co., Sandusky, OH; *U.S. Private*, pg. 948

Taylor, Michael, Sec.--Thunderbird Steel Corporation, Albuquerque, NM; *U.S. Public*, pg. 298

Taylor, Nancy M., Corp. Counsel & Sec.--Tredegar Industries Inc., Richmond, VA; *U.S. Public*, pg. 1633

Taylor, R.T., V.P., Sec. & Asst. Treas.--Al Johnson Construction Co., Bloomington, MN; *U.S. Private*, pg. 590

Taylor, Richard, V.P. & Sec.--Testcom, Inc., Albany, NY; *Int'l*, pg. 1154

Taylor, Ruth A., Treas. & Sec.--The Belt Railway Co. of Chicago, Bedford Park, IL; *Int'l*, pg. 258

Taylor, Ruth A., Treas. & Sec.--The Belt Railway Co. of Chicago, Bedford Park, IL; *U.S. Public*, pg. 269
Taylor, Suzanne Schulze, Sr. Attorney & Asst. Sec.--NACCO Industries, Inc., Cleveland, OH; *U.S. Public*, pg. 1149
Taylor, Terry, Sr. V.P., Gen. Counsel & Sec.--Club Corporation International, Dallas, TX; *U.S. Private*, pg. 247
Taylor, Wayne F., V.P., Gen. Counsel & Sec.--Cincinnati Milacron Inc., Cincinnati, OH; *U.S. Public*, pg. 368
Teasley, Karla Olson, V.P. & Sec.--Lehigh Utilities Inc., Apopka, FL; *U.S. Public*, pg. 1116
Teele, Ross C., Company Sec.--Harris Scarfe Holdings Limited, Toorak, Australia; *Int'l*, pg. 597
Teglo, D.P., Sec.--DFC Ceramics Inc., Canon City, CO; *Int'l*, *pg. 893*
Teigen, Philip J., V.P., Gen. Counsel & Sec.--Capital Associates, Inc., Lakewood, CO; *U.S. Public*, pg. 302
Teixeira, Marcelo Gomes, Exec. Sec.--Banco do Brasil, Brasilia, Brazil; *Int'l*, pg. 141
Tellier, James P., Treas. & Sec.--Jefferson Chevrolet Co., Detroit, MI; *U.S. Private*, pg. 584
Temel, Selim, V.P. & Corp. Sec.--Microphase Corporation, Norwalk, CT; *U.S. Private*, pg. 742
Tenney, Charles H., III, Sec.--Bay State Gas Company, Westborough, MA; *U.S. Public*, pg. 196
Teoh, Elizabeth, Sec.--The Great Eastern Life Assurance Company Limited, Singapore, Singapore; *Int'l*, pg. 557
ter Hark, Eric, Sec.-Corp. Law--GIB Group, Brussels, Belgium; *Int'l*, pg. 532
Terrill, Richard D., Sec. & Assoc. Gen. Counsel--Western Resources, Inc., Topeka, KS; *U.S. Public*, pg. 1759
Terry, David, Sec. & Treas.--Fonar Corporation, Melville, NY; *U.S. Public*, pg. 661
Terry, William F., Sec.--TrustCo Bank Corp., NY, Schenectady, NY; *U.S. Public*, pg. 1643
Teruya, Ethel, Sec.--Armstrong Produce Ltd., Honolulu, HI; *U.S. Private*, pg. 83
Tessier, Charles A., V.P.-Legal Affairs & Sec.--BioChem Pharma Inc., Laval, Canada; *Int'l*, pg. 196
Testa, John W., V.P., Treas. & Sec.--WHX Corporation, New York, NY; *U.S. Public*, pg. 1726
Testa, Richard, Sec.--Teradyne, Inc., Boston, MA; *U.S. Public*, pg. 1580
Tetlow, John, Sec.--United Utilities plc, Warrington, United Kingdom; *Int'l*, pg. 1444
Thanepohn, D.A., Sec.--L & D Group, Aurora, IL; *U.S. Private*, pg. 638
Thaney, Becky, Sec.--American Inks & Coatings Corp., Phoenixville, PA; *U.S. Private*, pg. 56
Thauer, Peter E., V.P.-Law & Environment, Gen. Counsel, & Sec.--Cambrex Corporation, East Rutherford, NJ; *U.S. Public*, pg. 297
Theisen, Bernard J., Controller & Asst. Sec.--The Standard Products Company, Dearborn, MI; *U.S. Public*, pg. 1504
Theodores, Thomas, Legal/Asst. Sec.--Oracle Corporation, Redwood City, CA; *U.S. Public*, pg. 1227
Theurer, Jeffrey L., Sec.--PST Vans, Inc., Salt Lake City, UT; *U.S. Public*, pg. 1246
Thibault, Chuck, V.P., Controller, Treas. & Sec.--Lazy Days R V Center, Inc., Seffner, FL; *U.S. Private*, pg. 655
Thiel, David N., Sr. V.P. & Sec.--Omega Financial Corporation, State College, PA; *U.S. Public*, pg. 1222
Thiel, David N., Sr. V.P. & Sec.--Omega Bank, N.A., State College, PA; *U.S. Public*, pg. 1222
Thielman, David, Chief Exec. Officer--E Z Loader Corporate, Airway Heights, WA; *U.S. Private*, pg. 352
Thies, Doug, Chief Fin. Officer, Treas. & Sec.--Field Packing Company, Owensboro, KY; *U.S. Private*, pg. 403
Thiessen, G.D., Controller & Asst. Sec.--MacDonald Dettwiler & Associates Ltd., Richmond, Canada; *U.S. Public*, pg. 1229
Thindwa, G.H., Sec.--National Bank of Malawi, Blantyre, Malawi; *Int'l*, pg. 1296
Thole, James A., Sec.--Ultra Pac, Inc., Rogers, MN; *U.S. Public*, pg. 1662
Thomas, Benjamin E., Jr., Corp. Sec. & Assoc. Gen. Counsel--H.J. Heinz Company, Pittsburgh, PA; *U.S. Public*, pg. 805
Thomas, Carolyn, Sec.--Superior Federal Bank, Fort Smith, AR; *U.S. Private*, pg. 1054
Thomas, Charles C., Sec.--Mr. Gatti's, Inc., Kerrville, TX; *U.S. Private*, pg. 639
Thomas, Diana Lyn, Sec.--Cornerstone Natural Gas, Inc., Dallas, TX; *U.S. Public*, pg. 567
Thomas, Doris, J., Sec.--National Print Group, Inc., Chattanooga, TN; *U.S. Private*, pg. 785
Thomas, Elisabeth, Asst. Sec.--The Molson Companies Limited, Toronto, Canada; *Int'l*, pg. 887
Thomas, Eugene C., Gen. Counsel & Sec.--Intermountain Industries, Inc., Boise, ID; *U.S. Private*, pg. 568
Thomas, H. Suzanne, Sr. V.P., Gen. Counsel & Sec.--Weatherford Enterra Incorporated, Houston, TX; *U.S. Public*, pg. 1749
Thomas, H. Suzanne, Sr. V.P. & Sec.--Weatherford U.S., Inc., Houston, TX; *U.S. Public*, pg. 1749
Thomas, Helen, Treas. & Sec.--Camino Real Chevrolet & Geo, Monterey Park, CA; *U.S. Private*, pg. 203
Thomas, Jeanette M., V.P., Sec. & Asst. Gen. Counsel--Litton Industries, Inc., Woodland Hills, CA; *U.S. Public*, pg. 1002
Thomas, L.B., Sr. V.P. & Sec.--ConAgra, Inc., Omaha, NE; *U.S. Public*, pg. 425
Thomas, Lee, Sec. & Mgr.-H.R.--California Cedar Products, Inc., Stockton, CA; *U.S. Private*, pg. 200
Thomas, Lee, Sec.--Inter-Tel Equipment UK, Ltd., Wellingborough, United Kingdom; *U.S. Public*, pg. 888
Thomas, Mark, Corp. Sec.--Great Lakes Dredge & Dock Co., Oak Brook, IL; *U.S. Private*, pg. 474
Thomas, Shonnie, Treas. & Sec.--V.B. Hook & Co., Inc., Columbia, SC; *U.S. Private*, pg. 538
Thompson, A.B., Jr., Treas. & Sec.--Woodruff Electric Co-Op, Forrest City, AR; *U.S. Private*, pg. 1187
Thompson, David, Treas. & Sec.--Vulcan Inc., Foley, AL; *U.S. Private*, pg. 1144
Thompson, Gary L., Chief Fin. Officer, V.P.-Fin. & Asst. Sec.--Legato Systems, Inc., Palo Alto, CA; *U.S. Public*, pg. 984
Thompson, Helga Finlay, Sec.--GZA GeoEnvironmental Technologies, Inc., Newton, MA; *U.S. Public*, pg. 697
Thompson, James C., Sec.--AmerenUE, Saint Louis, MO; *U.S. Public*, pg. 66
Thompson, Kevin N., V.P., Sec. & Gen. Counsel--Noranda Inc., Toronto, Canada; *Int'l*, pg. 433
Thompson, Lawrence M., Jr., Corp. Sec.--Sovereign Bancorp, Inc., Wyomissing, PA; *U.S. Public*, pg. 1494
Thompson, Linda, Asst. Sec. & Dir.-Investor Rels.--Interstate Bakeries Corporation, Kansas City, MO; *U.S. Public*, pg. 909
Thompson, Linda L., Dir.-Shareholder Rels. & Asst. Corp. Sec.--Interstate Brands Corporation, Kansas City, MO; *U.S. Public*, pg. 909
Thompson, Martin W., V.P., Treas. & Sec.--Hydro Energy Development Corp., Bothell, WA; *U.S. Public*, pg. 1342
Thompson, Michael G., Sr. V.P., Gen. Counsel & Sec.--Entergy Corporation, New Orleans, LA; *U.S. Public*, pg. 585
Thompson, Pam, Treas. & Sec.--Key Cadillac, Inc., Edina, MN; *U.S. Private*, pg. 617
Thompson, R. Keith, Sr. V.P.-Real Estate & Devel. & Asst. Sec.--Regal Cinemas Inc., Knoxville, TN; *U.S. Public*, pg. 1371
Thompson, Richard J., Chief Fin. Officer, V.P.-Fin., Treas. & Sec.--Computer Products, Inc., Boca Raton, FL; *U.S. Public*, pg. 422
Thompson, Samuel S., Corp. Sec.--Skyline Corporation, Elkhart, IN; *U.S. Public*, pg. 1476
Thomsen, Carl, Chief Fin. Officer, V.P. & Sec.--Digital Microwave Corporation, San Jose, CA; *U.S. Public*, pg. 508
Thomsen, Stan K., Sr. V.P.-Admin. & Sec.--Golden Sun Feeds, Inc., Estherville, IA; *U.S. Private*, pg. 895
Thomsen, Walter L., Treas. & Sec.--Schoep's Ice Cream, Inc., Madison, WI; *U.S. Private*, pg. 972
Thomson, Christine, Corp. Sec.--Mott's Holdings, Inc., Glastonbury, CT; *U.S. Private*, pg. 764
Thomson, John A., Chief Fin. Officer, Sr. V.P. & Sec.--Renaissance Energy Ltd., Calgary, Canada; *Int'l*, pg. 1102
Thomson, Roger F., Exec. V.P., Gen. Counsel & Sec.--Brinker International, Inc., Dallas, TX; *U.S. Public*, pg. 253
Thomson, Steve, Treas. & Sec.--Cambro Manufacturing Company, Huntington Beach, CA; *U.S. Private*, pg. 203
Thorburn, I.G., Exec. Dir.-Admin. & Sec.--Johnson Matthey Public Limited Company, London, United Kingdom; *Int'l*, pg. 713
Thorell, C. Scott, Exec. V.P. & Sec.--Integrated Systems Analysts, Inc., Arlington, VA; *U.S. Private*, pg. 566
Thorelli, Thomas, Sec.--Aetna Bearing Company, Chicago, IL; *U.S. Private*, pg. 25
Thoresen, Trygve M., V.P., Gen. Counsel & Sec.--Summa Industries, Torrance, CA; *U.S. Public*, pg. 1527
Thornhill, Christine, V.P. & Asst. Sec.--Thornhill Oil Company, Inc., Fort Wayne, IN; *U.S. Private*, pg. 1084
Thornhill, Norma, Sec.--Thornhill Oil Company, Inc., Fort Wayne, IN; *U.S. Private*, pg. 1084
Thornton, A.J., Treas. & Sec.--Consolidated Publishing Company, Anniston, AL; *U.S. Private*, pg. 266
Thornton, Donald W., Sr. V.P. & Sec.--Vesta Insurance Group, Inc., Birmingham, AL; *U.S. Public*, pg. 1718
Thornton, Michael, Deputy Chm. & Sec.--Thorntons PLC, Darbyshire, United Kingdom; *Int'l*, pg. 1386
Thornton, Toni, Sec.--Unitog Company, Kansas City, MO; *U.S. Public*, pg. 1693
Thorrez, Morris C., Sec.--Allied Chucker & Engineering Company, Jackson, MI; *U.S. Private*, pg. 38
Thrall, James Randall, V.P. & Sec.--Thrall Enterprises, Inc., Chicago, IL; *U.S. Private*, pg. 1084
Thrasher, Tracy P., Exec. V.P.-Admin. & Corp. Sec.--Medpartners Inc., Birmingham, AL; *U.S. Public*, pg. 1082
Thune, Maureen C., Controller & Asst. Sec.--CORT Business Services Corporation, Fairfax, VA; *U.S. Public*, pg. 451
Thwaite, P.M., Sec.--Charter plc, London, United Kingdom; *Int'l*, pg. 280
Tiang, Koh Chay, Chief Fin. Officer, V.P.-Acctg. & Sec.--Hong Fok Corporation Ltd., Singapore, Singapore; *Int'l*, pg. 635
Tiano, J. Richard, V.P., Gen. Counsel & Sec.--Connecticut Energy Corporation, Bridgeport, CT; *U.S. Public*, pg. 431
Tibbitts, J. Brett, V.P. & Gen. Counsel--Dole Food Company, Inc., Westlake Village, CA; *U.S. Public*, pg. 515
Tibus, Karen, Sec.--Don Massey Cadillac Inc., Plymouth, MI; *U.S. Private*, pg. 712
Tickle, M.G., Corp. Sec.--Senior Bigwood Limited, West Bromwich, United Kingdom; *Int'l*, pg. 1220
Tickner, John J., Sr. V.P. & Sec.--Zenith National Insurance Corp., Woodland Hills, CA; *U.S. Public*, pg. 1790
Tiedemann, Alvin, Sr. V.P. & Sec.--The Intertech Group Inc., Charleston, SC; *Int'l*, pg. 113
Tieger, Jeffrey, V.P. & Sec.--Ocean Bio-Chem Inc., Fort Lauderdale, FL; *U.S. Public*, pg. 1211
Tiemann, Linda K., Asst. Sec.--SIGCORP, Inc., Evansville, IN; *U.S. Public*, pg. 1471
Tiemann, Linda K., Asst. Sec.--Southern Indiana Gas & Electric Co., Evansville, IN; *U.S. Public*, pg. 1471
Tierney, Kevin J., Sr. V.P., Gen. Counsel & Sec.--UNUM Corporation, Portland, ME; *U.S. Public*, pg. 1699
Tiffin, R. Alex, Sr., Treas. & Sec.--Tiffin Motor Homes, Inc., Red Bay, AL; *U.S. Private*, pg. 1086
Tilley, Michael, Sec.--Doncasters plc, Melbourn, United Kingdom; *Int'l*, pg. 416
Tilson, Sheila M., V.P. & Asst. Sec.--Mercury Finance Co., Lake Forest, IL; *U.S. Public*, pg. 1093
Timbie, Thomas E., Chief Fin. Officer, V.P. & Sec.--Xomed Surgical Products, Jacksonville, FL; *U.S. Public*, pg. 253
Timm, Fred H., Corp. Controller & Sec.--Twin Disc, Incorporated, Racine, WI; *U.S. Public*, pg. 1646
Timm, Theodore, Gen. Counsel & Sec.--DOALL Company, Des Plaines, IL; *U.S. Private*, pg. 337
Timma, Michael C., V.P.-Fin., Treas. & Sec.--M M Systems Corporation, Tucker, GA; *U.S. Private*, pg. 685
Timmerman, Bruce, V.P.-Fin. & Sec.--Harris Steel Group Inc., Willowdale, Canada; *Int'l*, pg. 597
Timmins, Val, Sec.--Ranjit Corporation, Cedar Knolls, NJ; *U.S. Private*, pg. 909
Ting, Amy, Exec. Sec.--Dentsu Young & Rubicam Limited (Hong Kong), Hong Kong, Hong Kong; *U.S. Private*, pg. 325
Tingay, Sarah, Sec.--Thames Television Ltd., Teddington, United Kingdom; *Int'l*, pg. 1026
Tinius, Barry, Treas. & Sec.--Love Packaging Group, Wichita, KS; *U.S. Private*, pg. 677
Tinkham, P.B., Sec.--Basic Resources, Inc., Dallas, TX; *U.S.* Public, pg. 1587
Tinkham, Peter B., Treas. & Asst. Sec.--Texas Utilities Company, Dallas, TX; *U.S. Public*, pg. 1586
Tippins, J. Rankin, Gen. Counsel & Sec.--Tech-Sym Corporation, Houston, TX; *U.S. Public*, pg. 1563
Tippitt, Coma L., Sec. & Treas.--Snyder-Crown, Inc., Marked Tree, AR; *U.S. Private*, pg. 1011
Titus, John, Chm. Bd.--Aero Systems Aviation Corp., Miami, FL; *U.S. Private*, pg. 24
Tiwari, K.K., Sec.--Bharat Coking Coal Limited, Dhanbad, India; *Int'l*, pg. 298
Toberman, David, Treas. & Sec.--Toberman, Clayton, MO; *U.S. Private*, pg. 1089
Tobin, David S., Corp. Sec.--Peoples Telephone Company, Inc., Miami, FL; *U.S. Public*, pg. 1275
Tobin, Thomas M., V.P., Gen. Counsel & Sec.--Hudson Insurance Company, New York, NY; *Int'l*, pg. 1258
Tobin, Thomas M., Sr. V.P., Gen. Counsel & Corp. Sec.--Odyssey Reinsurance Corporation, New York, NY; *Int'l*, pg. 1258
Toburen, J.R., V.P. & Sec.--Flexfab Horizons International, Inc., Hastings, MI; *U.S. Private*, pg. 412
Todd, James A., V.P.--Todd Juice Products, Kalamazoo, MI; *U.S. Private*, pg. 1090
Todd, W.F., Sec.--TTX Co., Chicago, IL; *U.S. Private*, pg. 1066
Todd, William H., Jr., Asst. Sec.--Brown & Sharpe Manufacturing Company, North Kingstown, RI; *U.S. Public*, pg. 260
Toll, Bruce E., Pres., Chief Oper. Officer & Sec.--Toll Brothers, Inc., Huntingdon Valley, PA; *U.S. Public*, pg. 1620
Tollinger, Preston, Sec.--Daimler-Benz Capital Inc., Wilmington, DE; *Int'l*, pg. 368
Tolliver, Delno, Treas. & Sec.--East Kentucky Power Co-op, Winchester, KY; *U.S. Private*, pg. 356
Toma, George, Chief Fin. Officer, Treas. & Sec.--Wells-Gardner Electronics Corp., Chicago, IL; *U.S. Public*, pg. 1753
Tombers, Pat, Sec.--North Star Steel Co., Wayzata, MN; *U.S. Private*, pg. 210
Tome, Sandra, Corp. Sec.--Beverly Bancorporation Inc., Chicago, IL; *U.S. Public*, pg. 227
Tominaga, Naoya, Sec. & Dir.--Asahi Investment Australia Ltd., Sydney, Australia; *Int'l*, pg. 85
Tominaga, Naoya, Sec. & Dir.--Asahi Property Australia Pty. Ltd., Sydney, Australia; *Int'l*, pg. 85
Tomiyama, N., Sr. Mng. Dir. & Sec.--General Sekiyu K.K., Tokyo, Japan; *U.S. Public*, pg. 602
Tomlinson, Percy C., Jr., Treas & Sec.--Apogee Enterprises, Inc., Minneapolis, MN; *U.S. Public*, pg. 120
Tompkins, C. Craig, Treas. & Sec.--Citadel Holdings Corp., Los Angeles, CA; *U.S. Public*, pg. 456
Tonegawa, Masaki, V.P., Sec. & Treas.--Pentax Precision Instrument Corp., Orangeburg, NY; *Int'l*, pg. 85
Toner, Gerard, V.P., Gen. Counsel & Sec.--Doubleday Publishing Company, New York, NY; *Int'l*, pg. 191
Toney, Virginia, Sec.--Gensym Corporation, South Central Regional Office, Spring, TX; *U.S. Public*, pg. 731
Tonkin, William H., Treas. & Sec.--Pennsylvania Power & Light Company-Northeast Div., Wilkes-Barre, PA; *U.S. Public*, pg. 1244
Tonkinson, A.O.C., Sec.--South African Breweries, Ltd., Johannesburg, South Africa; *Int'l*, pg. 1286
Tonkovich, E. Paul, Sec. & Dir.--Rotonics Manufacturing Inc., Gardena, CA; *U.S. Public*, pg. 1406
Toohey, James F., Sec.--Spectrum Control, Inc., Erie, PA; *U.S. Public*, pg. 1497
Toohey, Philip S., Exec. V.P., Gen. Counsel & Sec.--HSBC Americas, Buffalo, NY; *Int'l*, pg. 580
Tooker, Trevor N., Asst. V.P. & Comml. Loan Officer--Independent Bank, Ionia, MI; *U.S. Public*, pg. 874
Toole, Edward D., V.P., Assoc. Gen. Counsel & Asst. Sec.--Echlin Inc., Branford, CT; *U.S. Public*, pg. 560
Tootle, John S., Chief Fin. Officer, V.P. & Sec.--Dominguez Services Corporation, Long Beach, CA; *U.S. Public*, pg. 516
Toporkoff, Michel, Corp. Sec.--Nestle France, Courbevoie, France; *Int'l*, pg. 921
Toppi, Angela, Chief Fin. Officer, Sr. V.P., Treas. & Sec.--Trans-Lux Corporation, Norwalk, CT; *U.S. Public*, pg. 1628
Torgerson, Robert, Gen. Counsel & Sec.--Jewelers Mutual Insurance Company, Neenah, WI; *U.S. Private*, pg. 587
Tornberg, Edward, Sec.--Cyberex, Inc., Mentor, OH; *U.S. Public*, pg. 481
Torre, Jean-Marc, Sec. Gen.--Banco Banque Nationale de Paris Brasil S/A, Sao Paulo, Brazil; *Int'l*, pg. 164
Torres, Alfonso Escamez, Corp. Vice Sec.--Compania Espanola de Petroleos, S.A. (CEPSA), Madrid, Spain; *Int'l*, pg. 323
Torres, Jose O., V.P.-Fin., Treas. & Sec.--Puerto Rican Cement Co., Inc., Guaynabo, PR; *U.S. Public*, pg. 1341

Torres, Osvaldo F., Asst. Gen. Counsel & Sec.--Telemundo Group, Inc., Hialeah, FL; *U.S. Public*, pg. 1570
Torres, Vera Trinchero, Sec. & Treas.--Sutter Home Winery, Inc., Saint Helena, CA; *U.S. Private*, pg. 1057
Tortorello, Robert J., V.P., Gen. Counsel & Sec.--Woodhead Industries, Inc., Buffalo Grove, IL; *U.S. Public*, pg. 1776
Toter, Benjamin, V.P.-Fin., Sec. & Treas.--Quality Markets, Inc., Jamestown, NY; *U.S. Public*, pg. 1270
Touhey, C.L., V.P. & Sec.--Orange Motor Company Inc., Albany, NY; *U.S. Private*, pg. 818
Touretz, William, Sec.--Tootsie Roll Industries, Inc., Chicago, IL; *U.S. Public*, pg. 1621
Touse, James L., V.P., Gen. Counsel & Sec.--Group Health Plan, Inc., Saint Louis, MO; *U.S. Public*, pg. 454
Towell, Anthony P., Co-Chm.--Eastco Industrial Safety Corp., Huntington Station, NY; *U.S. Public*, pg. 548
Towers, John R., Sec.--State Street Corporation, Boston, MA; *U.S. Public*, pg. 1513
Towers, John R., Sr. V.P., Gen. Counsel & Sec.--State Street Bank & Trust Co., Boston, MA; *U.S. Public*, pg. 1513
Towey, Ed, Sec.--Hammel, Green & Abrahamson, Inc., Minneapolis, MN; *U.S. Private*, pg. 497
Townsend, Arthur Vincent, Sec.--Guardian Media Group plc, Manchester, United Kingdom; *Int'l*, pg. 577
Townsend, James W., Jr., Sr. V.P. & Sec.--First Charter Corporation, Concord, NC; *U.S. Public*, pg. 627
Toyoda, Shinobu, Chief Fin. Officer, Exec. V.P. & Sec.--Sega of America Inc., Redwood City, CA; *Int'l*, pg. 1218
Trabbuco, John E., Gen. Counsel & Sec.--Beckwith Machinery Company, Murrysville, PA; *U.S. Private*, pg. 129
Trace, Frances O., Asst. Sec.--Bailey, Fischer & Porter Company, Warminster, PA; *Int'l*, pg. 449
Trachimovsky, S., Gen. Counsel & Corp. Sec.--Du Pont Canada Inc., Mississauga, Canada; *U.S. Public*, pg. 532
Trachsel, William H., V.P., Gen. Counsel & Sec.--United Technologies Corporation, Hartford, CT; *U.S. Public*, pg. 1689
Trachtenberg, Michael, Chief Fin. Officer, Chief Acctg. Officer, Exec. V.P. & Sec.--York Research Corporation, New York, NY; *U.S. Public*, pg. 1789
Tracy, James D., Sec.--Roy O'Brien Inc., Saint Clair Shores, MI; *U.S. Private*, pg. 810
Trador, Jack L., V.P. & Asst. Sec.--White Castle System, Inc., Columbus, OH; *U.S. Private*, pg. 1171
Train, Mark, Pres. & Sec.--Jason Incorporated, Milwaukee, WI; *U.S. Public*, pg. 923
Trametzki, Thomas, Chief Fin. Officer, V.P., Treas. & Sec.--Orval Kent Food Co., Wheeling, IL; *U.S. Private*, pg. 820
Trauth, Steven A., V.P.-Prod. & Sec.--Trauth Dairy Inc., Newport, KY; *U.S. Private*, pg. 1098
Travers, Bernard F., III, Dir.-Law & Tax & Asst. Sec.--Andersen Group, Inc., Bloomfield, CT; *U.S. Public*, pg. 111
Travers, Bernard F., III, Esq., Asst. Sec.--The J.M. Ney Company, Bloomfield, CT; *U.S. Public*, pg. 111
Travers, Ronda, Asst. Sec.--Nebraska Public Power District, Columbus, NE; *U.S. Private*, pg. 789
Travis, Margaret, Asst. Sec.--Union Special Corp., Huntley, IL; *Int'l*, pg. 716
Treacy, Richard F., Jr., Sec. & Gen. Counsel--Gerber Scientific, Inc., South Windsor, CT; *U.S. Public*, pg. 740
Treece, Elaine R., Sec. & Fin. Acct.--Tipperary Corporation, Denver, CO; *U.S. Public*, pg. 1618
Treinen, David C., Sr. V.P.-Fin. & Sec.--International Aluminum Corporation, Monterey Park, CA; *U.S. Public*, pg. 894
Treinin, Thomas F., Chm. Bd. & Pres.--Special Devices, Incorporated, Newhall, CA; *U.S. Public*, pg. 1496
Tremayne, F.A.M., V.P., Gen. Counsel & Sec.--BFC Construction Corporation, Scarborough, Canada; *Int'l*, pg. 118
Trembath, Peter H., Esq., V.P., Gen. Counsel & Sec.--BEC Group, Inc., Rye, NY; *U.S. Public*, pg. 160
Tremblax, Mary, Gen. Counsel & Sec.--Lydall, Inc., Manchester, CT; *U.S. Public*, pg. 1020
Tremblay, Claudine, Asst. Sec.--Quebecor Inc., Montreal, Canada; *Int'l*, pg. 1075
Tremblay, Claudine, Asst. Sec.--Quebecor Printing, Inc., Montreal, Canada; *Int'l*, pg. 1076
Tremblay, Claudine, Asst. Sec.--Quebecor Multimedia Inc., Montreal, Canada; *Int'l*, pg. 1076
Tremont, James, Sec. & Treas.--See's Candy Shops, Inc., South San Francisco, CA; *U.S. Public*, pg. 221
Trepanier, Dens, Sec. & Dir.-Communications--Purdel, Cooperative Agro-Alimentaire, Bic, Canada; *Int'l*, pg. 1073
Trewin, P.C., Sec.--British Railways Board, London, United Kingdom; *Int'l*, pg. 220
Tribble, Jay, Sec.--Tribble & Stephens Co., Houston, TX; *U.S. Private*, pg. 1102
Trickett, Deborah, Asst. Sec.--Danka Business Systems PLC, London, United Kingdom; *Int'l*, pg. 379
Tricot, H., Chief Fin. Officer & Corp. Sec.--Dumez-GTM, Nanterre, France; *Int'l*, pg. 823
Trigg, Donald C., Sr. V.P.-Sec. & Gen. Counsel--Anthem, Inc., Indianapolis, IN; *U.S. Private*, pg. 76
Trimble, Robert A., Sec.--Trimble Navigation Limited, Sunnyvale, CA; *U.S. Public*, pg. 1638
Trimble, Robert A., Sec.--TR Navigation Corporation, Austin, TX; *U.S. Public*, pg. 1638
Trimble, Robert A., Sec.--Trimble Navigation International Limited, Sunnyvale, CA; *U.S. Public*, pg. 1638
Trimble, Robert A., Sec.--Trimble Navigation International Foreign Sales Corporation, Sunnyvale, CA; *U.S. Public*, pg. 1638
Trinidad, Myrna T., Asst. Corp. Sec.--Atlas Consolidated Mining & Development Corporation, Manila, Philippines; *Int'l*, pg. 95
Triplett, Preston, V.P., Controller & Sec.--Brookshire Grocery, Tyler, TX; *U.S. Private*, pg. 172
Trippel, Joe, Chief Fin. Officer, Treas. & Sec.--Creation Windows of Indiana, Inc., Elkhart, IN; *U.S. Private*, pg. 287
Trippett, Lillian M., Sec. & Assoc. Gen. Counsel--Lockheed Martin Corporation, Bethesda, MD; *U.S. Public*, pg. 1006
Trobaugh, John, Chief Fin. Officer, Treas. & Sec.--Delta Foremost Chemical Corp., Memphis, TN; *U.S. Private*, pg. 322
Trost, T.W., Sec.--Morganite Canada Corporation, Mississauga, Canada; *Int'l*, pg. 895
Troutman, Nancy G., Asst. Sec.--Esset Corporation, Chardon, OH; *U.S. Public*, pg. 592
Trub, Aaron D., V.P., Treas. & Sec.--Smithfield Foods, Inc., Norfolk, VA; *U.S. Public*, pg. 1479
Trub, Aaron D., Treas. & Sec.--The Smithfield Packing Co., Inc., Smithfield, VA; *U.S. Public*, pg. 1479
Trub, Aaron D., Sec. & Treas.--Esskay, Riderwood, MD; *U.S. Public*, pg. 1479
Trub, Aaron D., Sec.--John Morrell & Co., Cincinnati, OH; *U.S. Public*, pg. 1479
Trubek, Josephine S., Sec.--Frontier Corporation, Rochester, NY; *U.S. Public*, pg. 683
Truesdale, John, V.P.-Admin. & Sec.--Carolina Mills, Inc., Maiden, NC; *U.S. Private*, pg. 214
Truesdell, J.E., Jr., Pres. & Sec.--Austin Group, Flint, MI; *U.S. Private*, pg. 99
Trump, Arthur, Sec. & Gen. Counsel--Atlantic Builders Group Inc., Baltimore, MD; *U.S. Private*, pg. 95
Tsang, P.Y., Sec.--Intex Corp., Long Beach, CA; *U.S. Private*, pg. 574
Tsanos, Scott J., Controller, Treas. & Sec.--Sybra, Inc., Atlanta, GA; *U.S. Private*, pg. 270
Tschirhart, Paul M., Sr. V.P., Gen. Counsel & Sec.--The Hertz Corporation, Park Ridge, NJ; *U.S. Public*, pg. 664
Tsubouchi, Daniel T., Sr. V.P.-Corp. Affairs & Fin. & Sec.--Mark Resources Inc., Calgary, Canada; *Int'l*, pg. 842
Tsujino, Kanzo, V.P. & Corp. Sec.--ASICS Tiger Corporation, Fountain Valley, CA; *U.S. Private*, pg. 89
Tsujioka, Dan, Exec. V.P.-Mdsg. & Sec.--White Cap Industries, Inc., Costa Mesa, CA; *U.S. Public*, pg. 1765
Tubbs, Robert J., Exec. V.P., Gen. Counsel & Sec.--Coltec Holdings Inc, Charlotte, NC; *U.S. Public*, pg. 401
Tucci, Gerard M., V.P.-Opers. & Sec.--Integrated Brands Inc., Ronkonkoma, NY; *U.S. Public*, pg. 883
Tuck, Elizabeth M., Sec.--Transatlantic Holdings Inc., New York, NY; *U.S. Public*, pg. 84
Tucker, Carolyn C., Sec.--The Shoe Show of Rocky Mt., Inc., Concord, NC; *U.S. Private*, pg. 996
Tucker, M. Douglas, Chief Fin. & Acctg. Officer, Sr. V.P.-Fin. & Sec.--BeautiControl Cosmetics, Inc., Carrollton, TX; *U.S. Public*, pg. 198
Tucker, Marshall D., Chief Fin. Officer, V.P., Treas., Controller & Sec.--Dixon Paper Co., Denver, CO; *U.S. Public*, pg. 902
Tucker, Rebbeca C., Sec.--Bovaird Supply Co., Tulsa, OK; *U.S. Private*, pg. 162
Tucker, Richard S., Sec.--Kevco, Inc., Fort Worth, TX; *U.S. Public*, pg. 952
Tucker, Robert T., Sec.--CUC International, Inc., Stamford, CT; *U.S. Public*, pg. 320
Tudor, Brenda S., Controller & Sec.--Ingles Markets, Incorporated, Black Mountain, NC; *U.S. Public*, pg. 878
Tufenkian, Savey, Exec. V.P., Treas. & Sec.--Western Waste Industries, Torrance, CA; *U.S. Public*, pg. 1686
Tufnell, John F.D., Gen. Counsel & Sec.--Air Products Europe, Inc., Allentown, PA; *U.S. Public*, pg. 30
Tuit, Peter, V.P. & Sec.--AEGON N.V., Hague, Netherlands; *Int'l*, pg. 25
Tull, Richard M., V.P. & Sec.--Prime Abstract, Inc., Philadelphia, PA; *U.S. Public*, pg. 1326
Tully, David M., Treas. & Sec.--Mackie Designs, Inc., Woodinville, WA; *U.S. Public*, pg. 1030
Tumminello, Theodore, Sr. V.P., Gen. Counsel & Sec.--Pan-American Life Insurance Company, New Orleans, LA; *U.S. Private*, pg. 836
Tunmore, E. Roger, Pres. & Sec.--Tunmore Oldsmobile Inc., Buffalo, NY; *U.S. Private*, pg. 1109
Tunney, Francis R., Jr., Corp. V.P., Gen. Counsel & Sec.--Allergan, Inc., Irvine, CA; *U.S. Public*, pg. 46
Tupa, John J., Exec. V.P. & Sec.--American West Insurance Company, Grand Forks, ND; *U.S. Public*, pg. 216
Tupper, Kimberly A., Asst. Sec.--DeVry Institutes, Oak Brook Terrace, IL; *U.S. Public*, pg. 503
Turchick, Sharon M., Controller & Sec.--Sauer Industries, Inc., Pittsburgh, PA; *U.S. Private*, pg. 967
Turem, Lois, Asst. Sec.--Gabbert's, Inc., Minneapolis, MN; *U.S. Private*, pg. 437
Turgeon, Nancy, Sec.--Robertson's Auto Salvage, Wareham, MA; *U.S. Private*, pg. 936
Turkin, Todd, Exec. V.P., Sec. & Dir.-Telecomm.--Broder Bros. Co., Plymouth, MI; *U.S. Private*, pg. 170
Turnbeau, Patricia A., Asst. Sec.--Standard Pacific Corp., Costa Mesa, CA; *U.S. Public*, pg. 1503
Turnbull, James H., Sec. & Treas.--Southeastern Development Company, Port Huron, MI; *U.S. Public*, pg. 1489
Turner, Judy, Corp. Sec.--Bureau of Engraving, Minneapolis, MN; *U.S. Private*, pg. 181
Turner, Keith M., Sec. & Dir.-Legal & Bus. Affairs--Really Useful Holdings Limited, London, United Kingdom; *Int'l*, pg. 1089
Turner, M. Caroline, Sr. V.P., Gen. Counsel & Asst. Sec.--Adolph Coors Company, Golden, CO; *U.S. Public*, pg. 445
Turner, M. Caroline, Sr. V.P., Gen. Counsel & Asst. Sec.--Coors Brewing Company, Golden, CO; *U.S. Public*, pg. 445
Tursi, Carl T., V.P. & Sec.--Amerada Hess Corporation, New York, NY; *U.S. Public*, pg. 65
Tushman, J. Lawrence, Chief Exec. Officer & Sec.--Orleans International, Inc., Bloomfield Hills, MI; *U.S. Private*, pg. 820
Tuthill, John, Exec. V.P. & Sec.--Hallwood Commercial Real Estate, Inc., Dallas, TX; *U.S. Public*, pg. 778
Tutt, Carolyn, Asst. Sec.--Danisco Ingredients Canada Inc., Rexdale, Canada; *Int'l*, pg. 378
Tuttle, Howard G., Treas. & Sec.--Lee Company, Westbrook, CT; *U.S. Private*, pg. 657
Tutton, Lawrence, Co. Sec.--GUD Holdings Limited, Sunshine, Australia; *Int'l*, pg. 539
Tuura, Doris K., Gen. Counsel & Asst. Sec.--International Multifoods Corporation, Minneapolis, MN; *U.S. Public*, pg. 900
Tuvikene, Matti, Asst. Sec.--Stelco Inc., Hamilton, Canada; *Int'l*, pg. 1299
Twine, Elizabeth, Corp. Sec.--Western Corporate Enterprises Inc., Vancouver, Canada; *Int'l*, pg. 1494
Tyll, Betty, Treas. & Sec.--Sterling Heights Dodge, Inc., Sterling Heights, MI; *U.S. Private*, pg. 1041
Tymchuk, Tom, Sec.--Central Lincoln People's Utility District, Newport, OR; *U.S. Private*, pg. 223
Tyson, G., Dir.-Fin. & Sec.--Senior Moducel Limited, Stoke on Trent, United Kingdom; *Int'l*, pg. 1221
Tyson, Joe, Jr., Sec.--Meridian Industries, Inc., Milwaukee, WI; *U.S. Private*, pg. 732
Tyson, Ron, Exec. V.P., Treas. & Sec.--Miracle Recreation Equipment Company, Monett, MO; *U.S. Private*, pg. 752
Tzi, Helena Tsalki, Sec.-Mktg.--Henkel Hellas, Moschato, Greece; *Int'l*, pg. 612
Ugarte, J.A., Sec.--Compania Minera Disputada de Las Condes S.S., Santiago, Chile; *U.S. Public*, pg. 601
Uhl, Hannelore, Sec.--Villeroy & Boch Tableware, Ltd., Princeton, NJ; *Int'l*, pg. 1468
Uhley, David W., Sec.--Farmer Brothers Company, Torrance, CA; *U.S. Public*, pg. 613
Ulbrandt, Laura, Sec.--Leucadia National Corporation, New York, NY; *U.S. Public*, pg. 989
Ullo, Kristine, Sec.--Ullo International, Inc., Altamonte Springs, FL; *U.S. Private*, pg. 1116
Ulster, Harley, Sec.--Premdor Inc., Mississauga, Canada; *Int'l*, pg. 1066
Underwood, Alysia, Corp. Secretary--N.B.F. Bollinger Industries, Americus, GA; *U.S. Public*, pg. 243
Underwood, William E., Jr., Sec. & Gen. Counsel--Republic Automotive-AEA Division, Charlotte, NC; *U.S. Public*, pg. 1377
Unger, Johanna, V.P., Controller & Sec.--PS Group Holdings, San Diego, CA; *U.S. Public*, pg. 1245
Unruh, David G., Sr. V.P.-Law & Sec.--Westcoast Energy Inc., Vancouver, Canada; *Int'l*, pg. 1492
Unterrainer, Bernard C., Sec.--Voyager Life Insurance Company, Fort Worth, TX; *U.S. Public*, pg. 68
Unterreiner, Bernard C., Sec.--Voyager Group, Inc., Jacksonville, FL; *U.S. Public*, pg. 68
Unterreiner, Bernard C., Sec.--Voyager Indemnity Insurance Company, Fort Worth, TX; *U.S. Public*, pg. 68
Unterreiner, Bernard C., Sr. V.P. & Sec.--Voyager Service Warranties, Inc., Fort Worth, TX; *U.S. Public*, pg. 68
Upchurch, Samuel E., Jr., Gen. Counsel & Corp. Sec.--Regions Financial Corporation, Birmingham, AL; *U.S. Public*, pg. 1371
Urban, Tony J., Treas. & Sec.--Calumet Construction Corporation, Hammond, IN; *U.S. Private*, pg. 201
Urschel, Elena V., V.P. & Sec.--Urschel Labs Incorporated, Valparaiso, IN; *U.S. Private*, pg. 1129
Urso, Frank P., Sec.--Sugarloaf/USA, Kingfield, ME; *U.S. Private*, pg. 62
Urso, Frank P., Sec.--Waterville Valley Ski Area Ltd., Waterville Valley, NH; *U.S. Private*, pg. 62
Ury, Robert, Mgr.--Heyman Corporation, Niles, IL; *U.S. Private*, pg. 524
Utecht, Andrea, Sr. V.P., Gen. Counsel & Sec.--Elf Atochem North America, Inc., Philadelphia, PA; *Int'l*, pg. 445
Utsunomiya, Takaharu, Grp. V.P.-Fin., Treas. & Asst. Sec.--Sega of America Inc., Redwood City, CA; *Int'l*, pg. 1218
Uy, Conrad, Sec., Dir.-Personnel, & Pur. Agent--Atalanta Corporation, Elizabeth, NJ; *U.S. Private*, pg. 93
Vaccaro, Thomas S., Chief Fin. Officer & Sec.--The Orvis Company, Inc., Manchester, VT; *U.S. Private*, pg. 820
Vacek, Richard, Chief Fin. Officer & Sr. V.P.--Horace Small Apparel Company, Nashville, TN; *Int'l*, pg. 635
Vacek, Richard B., Jr., V.P. & Sec.--R & R Uniforms, Nashville, TN; *Int'l*, pg. 635
Vagnini, K.L., V.P., Sec. & Treas.--The Gerstenslager Company, Wooster, OH; *U.S. Public*, pg. 1780
Vahlsing, Donald W., V.P. & Sec.--Effective Management Systems, Milwaukee, WI; *U.S. Public*, pg. 565
Vail, Charles, Corp. Sec.--Fred's Inc., Memphis, TN; *U.S. Public*, pg. 680
Vakil, Farooq U., Exec. V.P. & Sec.--Lights Of America, Inc., Walnut, CA; *U.S. Private*, pg. 667
Valdivieso, Lucas P., Sec. & Dir.--PonceBank, F.S.B., Ponce, PR; *U.S. Public*, pg. 1316
Valenti, Edward, V.P., Treas. & Sec.--Temco Service Industries, New York, NY; *U.S. Public*, pg. 1574
Valentine, Catherine L., V.P., Gen. Counsel & Sec.--Intuit, Inc., Mountain View, CA; *U.S. Public*, pg. 911
Valentine, George H., V.P. & Sec.--Terra Industries, Inc., Sioux City, IA; *U.S. Public*, pg. 1581
Valentine, James, V.P. & Sec.--Ilsco, Cincinnati, OH; *U.S. Private*, pg. 558
Valerio, Mylin, Asst. to Exec. V.P.-Admin.--Polygram Records, Inc., New York, NY; *Int'l*, pg. 1052
Valice, Debra D., Chief Fin. Officer, Treas. & Corp. Sec.--Seitel, Inc., Houston, TX; *U.S. Public*, pg. 1454
Vallerie, Raymond, Treas. & Sec.--Vallerie's Transport Service, Inc., Norwalk, CT; *U.S. Private*, pg. 1131
Van Amburg, Sheldon, Treas. & Sec.--Farmway Co-Op Inc., Beloit, KS; *U.S. Private*, pg. 396
Van Auken, Bradley A., Sr. V.P., Gen. Counsel & Sec.--Lexford Residential Trust, Columbus, OH; *U.S. Public*, pg. 991
Van Bebber, David L., Asst. Sec.--Tyson Foods, Inc., Springdale, AR; *U.S. Public*, pg. 1652
Van Beckum, Jim, Sec. & Treas.--KRC (Hewitt) Inc., Neenah, WI; *Int'l*, pg. 1202
van Bergen, Anja M., Sec.--Heidemij N.V., Arnhem, Netherlands; *Int'l*, pg. 606

Van Bibber, Roxanne, Asst. Sec.--CNB Bancshares, Inc., Evansville, IN; *U.S. Public*, pg. 280

Van Borkulo-Nuzzo, D. Lynn, Exec. V.P. & Corp. Sec.--Hubco, Inc., Mahwah, NJ; *U.S. Public*, pg. 845

Van Dam, Tina S., Asst. Sec.--The Dow Chemical Company, Midland, MI; *U.S. Public*, pg. 522

Van Den Top, Jay, Treas. & Sec.--L.G. Everist Inc., Sioux Falls, SD; *U.S. Private*, pg. 386

Van Der Hart, Sheri A., Asst. Sec.--John Deere Capital Corporation, Reno, NV; *U.S. Public*, pg. 492

van der Klaauw, J.W.E., Gen. Counsel & Sec.--CSM N.V., Diemen, Netherlands; *Int'l*, pg. 243

van der Velden, Jan M.M., Gen. Counsel & Sec.--Oce-van der Grinten N.V., Venlo, Netherlands; *Int'l*, pg. 993

van der Wal, W.H., Sec. & Gen. Counsel--Ballast Nedam NV, Amstelveen, Netherlands; *Int'l*, pg. 133

van der Walt, L.H., Sec.--Reunert Ltd., Sandton, South Africa; *Int'l*, pg. 1105

Van Deventer, Allen H., Sr. V.P. & Sec.--Van Deventer & Hoch, Glendale, CA; *U.S. Public*, pg. 339

Van Dijk, Mirium, Sec.--Eureko B.V., Amsterdam, Netherlands; *Int'l*, pg. 464

Van Duzer, Charles B., Sec.--Reunion Industries, Inc., Stamford, CT; *U.S. Public*, pg. 1383

Van Duzer, Charles B., V.P. & Sec.--Reunion Energy Company, Houston, TX; *U.S. Public*, pg. 1383

Van Dyke, Thomas W., Sec.--Sealright Company, Inc., De Soto, KS; *U.S. Public*, pg. 1451

van Es-de Moree, M., Corp. Sec.--Hunter Douglas N.V., Rotterdam, Netherlands; *Int'l*, pg. 639

Van Gorder, Jan R., Sr. Exec. V.P., Gen. Counsel & Sec.--Erie Family Life Insurance Company, Erie, PA; *U.S. Public*, pg. 590

Van Gundy, Kari L., V.P., Treas. & Asst. Sec.--CalFarm Insurance Agency, Sacramento, CA; *U.S. Public*, pg. 1791

Van Horn, James R., V.P., Gen. Counsel & Sec.--NUI Corporation, Bedminster, NJ; *U.S. Public*, pg. 1147

Van Horn, L.R., Sec. & Treas.--First Church Financing Corporation, West Bend, WI; *U.S. Public*, pg. 1792

Van Houten, Kent J., Chief Fin. Officer, Treas. & Sec.--Peerless Mfg. Co., Dallas, TX; *U.S. Public*, pg. 1268

Van Kirk, W. Philip, Sec.--E-Z-Em, Inc., Westbury, NY; *U.S. Public*, pg. 540

Van Langen, James, V.P. & Sec.--SGS International Certification Services, Inc., Rutherford, NJ; *Int'l*, pg. 1153

Van Luven, G.A., Chief Fin. Officer, V.P., Treas. & Sec.--The Gage Company, Pittsburgh, PA; *U.S. Private*, pg. 437

van Meerten, Hendrik Jan, Sec.--N.V. Deli-Universal, Rotterdam, Netherlands; *U.S. Public*, pg. 1695

Van Orden, Charles, V.P., Gen. Counsel & Sec.--Honeywell-Measurex Corporation, Cupertino, CA; *U.S. Public*, pg. 833

Van Rees, Cornelius S., Sec.--Graham Corporation, Batavia, NY; *U.S. Public*, pg. 757

Van Riper, Jeffrey L., Controller & Sec.--Seneca Foods Corporation, Pittsford, NY; *U.S. Public*, pg. 1456

van Sambeet-Ronde, Pauwla, Joint Sec.--Velcro Industries N.V., Willemstad, Netherlands Antilles; *Int'l*, pg. 1462

van Schoonenberg, Robert G., Sr. V.P., Gen. Counsel & Sec.--Avery Dennison Corporation, Pasadena, CA; *U.S. Public*, pg. 152

Van Vlierbergen, Brian R., V.P., Gen. Counsel & Sec.--Blue Cross & Blue Shield of Illinois, Chicago, IL; *U.S. Private*, pg. 151

Van Vooren, V.C., Sr. V.P., Treas. & Asst. Sec.--The Ziegler Companies, Inc., West Bend, WI; *U.S. Public*, pg. 1791

Van Vooren, V.C., Asst. Sec.--Ziegler Leasing Corp., West Bend, WI; *U.S. Public*, pg. 1792

Van Wely, Robert P., Dir.-Fin. & Sec.--Andres Wines Ltd., Winona, Canada; *Int'l*, pg. 75

van Wensen, H.P.A., Exec. V.P. & Sec.--ABN-AMRO Holding N.V., Amsterdam, Netherlands; *Int'l*, pg. 8

van Wyhe, J.L., Corp. Sec.--Schering Nederland B.V., Weesp, Netherlands; *Int'l*, pg. 1204

Vana, Robert J., Chief Corp. Counsel & Sec.--Charter One Financial, Inc., Cleveland, OH; *U.S. Public*, pg. 336

Vandeman, George A., Sr. V.P., Gen. Counsel & Sec.--Amgen Inc., Thousand Oaks, CA; *U.S. Public*, pg. 100

Vandenbergh, Robert A., Sec.--High Point Financial Corp., Branchville, NJ; *U.S. Public*, pg. 826

VandenBrand, Rene M.J., V.P.-Corp. Devel. & Sec.--Veritas DGC Inc., Houston, TX; *U.S. Private*, pg. 1136

Vander Pol, Daryl L., Chief Fin. Officer, Exec. V.P., Treas. & Sec.--Vitamilk Dairy, Inc., Seattle, WA; *U.S. Private*, pg. 1142

Vanderah, Phil, Treas. & Sec.--Central Property & Casualty Insurance Company, West Des Moines, IA; *U.S. Private*, pg. 880

Vanderah, Phil, Sec.--Preferred Abstainers Insurance Compan, West Des Moines, IA; *U.S. Private*, pg. 880

Vanderberry, James G., Gen. Counsel & Sec.--Wachovia Bank of North Carolina, N.A., Winston Salem, NC; *U.S. Public*, pg. 1730

Vanderbilt, P., V.P.-Environmental & Sec.--R.T. Vanderbilt Company, Inc., Norwalk, CT; *U.S. Private*, pg. 1133

Vanderminden, Henry J.W., III, Exec. V.P. & Sec.--Mettowee Lumber & Plastic Co., Inc., Granville, NY; *U.S. Private*, pg. 1074

Vandervoort, Peter, Sec.--Essex Chemical Corporation, Clifton, NJ; *U.S. Public*, pg. 523

VanderVorst, Gary D., V.P. Fin. Treas. & Sec.--Erickson Oil Products, Inc., Hudson, WI; *U.S. Private*, pg. 381

Vanderwal, Richard B., Chief Fin. Officer & Sr. V.P.-Fin.--Gingiss International, Addison, IL; *U.S. Private*, pg. 455

Vane, Robert J., Gen. Counsel & Sec.--Charter One Bank, Cleveland, OH; *U.S. Public*, pg. 336

VanHouten, Ronald W., Sec.--Thomaston Mills, Inc., Thomaston, GA; *U.S. Public*, pg. 1599

Varela, Patricia, Sec.-Mktg.--Sancor Cooperativas Unidas Limitadas, Buenos Aires, Argentina; *Int'l*, pg. 1183

Varghese, Roy A., Sec.--Inchcape Bdh, Singapore, Singapore; *Int'l*, pg. 672

Vargo, James D., Treas. & Sec.--Daniels Manufacturing Corporation, Orlando, FL; *U.S. Private*, pg. 310

Vaterlaus, Walter, Sec.--Clariant International Ltd., Muttenz, Switzerland; *Int'l*, pg. 624

Vaughan, Gaye, Sec.--The Van Metres Companies, Burke, VA; *U.S. Private*, pg. 1132

Vaughn, Patrick, V.P.-Fin., Sec. & Treas.--Akzo Nobel Coatings Inc. (KY), Louisville, KY; *Int'l*, pg. 47

Vaupen, Hy, Chief Fin. Officer, Exec. V.P. & Sec.--BCI Holding Corporation, Miami, FL; *U.S. Private*, pg. 106

Vaupen, Hy, Chief Fin. Officer, Exec. V.P. & Sec.--Beverage Canners International Corp., Miami, FL; *U.S. Private*, pg. 106

Vautier, N.J., Sec. & Legal Counsel--Feltrax International, Inc., Auckland, New Zealand; *Int'l*, pg. 130

Vawrinek, Jeffrey J., Asst. Sec.--JC Penney Company, Inc., Plano, TX; *U.S. Public*, pg. 916

Vecsler, Robert, Esq., Gen. Counsel & Sec.--Geotek Communications, Montvale, NJ; *U.S. Public*, pg. 739

Veilleux, Martin J., Chief Fin. Officer, Exec. V.P.-Fin., Treas. & Sec.--Boron LePore Group, Fair Lawn, NJ; *U.S. Public*, *pg. 246*

Veitenheimer, Michael, V.P., Gen. Counsel & Sec.--The Bombay Company, Inc., Fort Worth, TX; *U.S. Public*, pg. 244

Veitenheimer, Mike, V.P., Gen. Counsel & Sec.--The Bombay Company, Fort Worth, TX; *U.S. Public*, pg. 244

Velasco, Ernesto Vega, Chief Oper. Officer, Chief Fin. Officer & Sec.--Desc, S.A. de C.V., Mexico, Mexico; *Int'l*, *pg. 395*

Velasco, Jose A., Sr. V.P., Gen. Counsel & Sec.--Centris Group Inc., Costa Mesa, CA; *U.S. Public*, pg. 328

Vellanueva, Scott, Sec.--Tropic Communications Inc., Columbus, OH; *U.S. Public*, pg. 1641

Veltman, Warren A., Chief Fin. Officer--Autocam Corporation, Grand Rapids, MI; *U.S. Public*, pg. 148

Venechanos, Steven, Chief Fin. Officer & Sec.--Suprema Specialties, Inc., Paterson, NJ; *U.S. Public*, pg. 1541

Venechanos, Steven, Chief Fin. Officer & Sec.--Suprema Specialties Northeast, Inc., Ogdensburg, NY; *U.S. Public*, *pg. 1541*

Vennemann, Jerome A., Asst. Corp. Sec.--Cinergy Corp., Cincinnati, OH; *U.S. Public*, pg. 368

Vennemann, Jerome A., Asst. Sec.--Cinergy, Plainfield, IN; *U.S. Public*, pg. 369

Vennemann, Jerome A., Asst. Corp. Sec.--CINergy Services, Inc., Cincinnati, OH; *U.S. Public*, pg. 369

Vennemann, Jerome A., Asst. Corp. Sec.--KO Transmission Company, Cincinnati, OH; *U.S. Public*, pg. 369

Vennemann, Jerome A., Asst. Corp. Sec.--Lawrenceburg Gas Co., Cincinnati, OH; *U.S. Public*, pg. 369

Vennemann, Jerome A., Asst. Corp. Sec.--Miami Power Corp., Cincinnati, OH; *U.S. Public*, pg. 369

Vennemann, Jerome A., Asst. Corp. Sec.--Tri-State Improvement Co., Cincinnati, OH; *U.S. Public*, pg. 369

Vennemann, Jerome A., Asst. Corp. Sec.--Union Light, Heat and Power Co., Cincinnati, OH; *U.S. Public*, pg. 369

Vennemann, Jerome A., Asst. Corp. Sec.--Cinergy Corp., Cincinnati, OH; *U.S. Public*, pg. 369

Vento, Darlene, Sec.--King Industries, Inc., Norwalk, CT; *U.S. Private*, pg. 620

Verga, Joseph, Sr. V.P., Treas. & Sec.--Techdyne, Inc., Hialeah, FL; *U.S. Public*, pg. 1080

Verglas, Alain, V.P., Treas. & Asst. Sec.--IBL Limited, Inc., Scarsdale, NY; *Int'l*, pg. 21

Verhagen, C.H., V.P., Treas. & Sec.--AEGON Reinsurance Company of America, Short Hills, NJ; *Int'l*, pg. 26

Verhagen, C.H., V.P.-Tres. & Sec.--AEGON U.S. Holding Corp., Short Hills, NJ; *Int'l*, pg. 26

Verkruyse, Anthony J., V.P., Treas. & Sec.--Huntco Inc., Town and Country, MO; *U.S. Public*, pg. 849

Verkruyse, Anthony J., V.P. & Sec.--HSI Aviation, Inc., Springfield, MO; *U.S. Public*, pg. 849

Verlander, Chris A., Sr. V.P. & Sec.--First Colonial Insurance Company, Jacksonville, FL; *U.S. Public*, pg. 79

Verly, Philippe, Sec. & Asst. Gen. Mgr.--Almanij N.V., Antwerp, Belgium; *Int'l*, pg. 65

Vermylen, Mark E., V.P. & Sec.--A. Zeregas Sons, Inc., Fair Lawn, NJ; *U.S. Private*, pg. 1204

Vermylen, Paul A., Jr., Pres., Treas. & Sec.--Meenan Oil Co. L.P., Syosset, NY; *U.S. Private*, *pg. 729*

Vernon, Shirley A., Sec. & Treas.--Gilvin-Terrill Inc., Amarillo, TX; *U.S. Private*, pg. 455

Verny, Jean-Francois, Chief Admin. Officer & Sec.--Credit Lyonnais S.A., Paris, France; *Int'l*, pg. 343

Versaggi, Diane, Asst. Sec.--SGS North America Inc., New York, NY; *Int'l*, pg. 1153

Versraeten, P., Sec.--Sidmar N.V., Gent, Belgium; *Int'l*, pg. 79

Vetsch, K., Sec.--Morganite AG, Kloten, Switzerland; *Int'l*, pg. 891

Vetter, Sandra, Sec.--Better Baked Foods, Inc., North East, PA; *U.S. Private*, pg. 141

Vezza, Carlo, V.P.-Fin. & Sec.--Aluma Shield Industries, Inc., Daytona Beach, FL; *U.S. Private*, pg. 47

Vicente, Julio Pedrosa, Sec.--Barreras Hijos De J. Barreras, S.A., Vigo, Spain; *Int'l*, pg. 1223

Vickers, John, III, Sr. V.P.-Opers.--American Dental Technologies, Southfield, MI; *U.S. Public*, pg. 70

Vickers, Julie, Asst. Sec.--Eurocamp Plc, Knutsford, United Kingdom; *Int'l*, pg. 464

Vickers, Paul, Sec.--Mirror Group plc, London, United Kingdom; *Int'l*, pg. 869

Vickers, 40919 L., Sec.--Universal Fidelity Life Insurance Company, Duncan, OK; *U.S. Private*, pg. 1127

Vickery, Sharlene A., Sec.--General Motors Corporation, Detroit, MI; *U.S. Public*, pg. 718

Vignerot, Ann T., V.P. & Sec.--Boat America Corp., Alexandria, VA; *U.S. Private*, pg. 153

Villafuerte, Ferdinand G., V.P.-Admin. & Corp. Sec.--EEI Corporation, Manila, Philippines; *Int'l*, pg. 425

Villano, Michael J., Chief Fin. Officer, V.P., Treas. & Asst. Sec.--Scan-Optics, Inc., Manchester, CT; *U.S. Public*, pg. 1436

Villarreal, Irma, Sec.--Playboy Enterprises, Inc., Chicago, IL; *U.S. Public*, pg. 1309

Villarreal, Irma, Sec.--Playboy Entertainment Group, Inc., Beverly Hills, CA; *U.S. Public*, pg. 1310

Villarreal, Irma, Sec.--Playboy Models, Inc., Beverly Hills, CA; *U.S. Public*, pg. 1310

Villarreal, Irma, Sec.--Playboy Preferred, Inc., Itasca, IL; *U.S. Public*, pg. 1310

Villarreal, Irma, Sec.--Lifestyle Brands, Ltd., Chicago, IL; *U.S. Public*, pg. 1310

Villarreal, Irma, Sec.--Alta Loma Productions, Inc., Beverly Hills, CA; *U.S. Public*, pg. 1310

Villarreal, Irma, Sec.--Critics' Choice Video, Inc., Itasca, IL; *U.S. Public*, pg. 1310

Villarreal, Irma, Sec.--Impulse Productions, Inc., Beverly Hills, CA; *U.S. Public*, pg. 1310

Villarreal, Irma, Sec.--Lake Shore Press, Inc., Chicago, IL; *U.S. Public*, pg. 1310

Villarreal, Irma, Sec.--Playboy Clubs International, Inc., Chicago, IL; *U.S. Public*, pg. 1310

Villarreal, Irma, Sec.--Playboy Shows, Inc., Beverly Hills, CA; *U.S. Public*, pg. 1310

Villarreal, Irma, Sec.--After Dark Video, Inc., Beverly Hills, CA; *U.S. Public*, pg. 1310

Villegas, Gabriel, Sec.--Grupo Industrial Durango S.A. de C.V., Durango, Mexico; *Int'l*, pg. 575

Vincent, Jacques, Chief Admin. Officer & Corp. Sec.--Rexel, S.A., Paris, France; *Int'l*, pg. 1107

Vincent, James W., Sr. V.P.-Loans & Sec.--The Commercial Bank, Delphos, OH; *U.S. Public*, pg. 410

Vincent, Susan, V.P.-Corp. Sec.--Amerisure Companies, Farmington Hills, MI; *U.S. Private*, pg. 65

Vincke, Francois, Sec. Gen.--Petrofina S.A., Brussels, Belgium; *Int'l*, pg. 1043

Vineberg, Robert S., Asst. Sec.--Reitmans (Canada) Limited, Montreal, Canada; *Int'l*, pg. 1102

Viner, Lucinda, Sec.-Adv. Dept.--Elsevier Science Limited, Kidlington, United Kingdom; *Int'l*, pg. 1100

Vinokour, J.L., Dir. & Sec.--BT North America, Inc., New York, NY; *Int'l*, pg. 223

Virojanadul, Suvit, Corp. Sec.--The Siam Cement Public Company Limited, Bangkok, Thailand; *Int'l*, pg. 1237

Visosky, Leonard M., Chief Fin. Officer & Exec. V.P. & Sec.--Tapco International Corporation, Plymouth, MI; *U.S. Private*, pg. 1068

Vitale, Joseph M., Sr. V.P., Gen. Counsel & Sec.--Belden & Blake Corporation, Canton, OH; *U.S. Private*, pg. 1078

Vitkus, Richard F., Sr. V.P., Gen. Counsel & Sec.--Zenith Electronics Corp., Glenview, IL; *U.S. Public*, pg. 1790

Vitt, A. Francis, Jr., Sec.--Wilkins-Rogers Incorporated, Ellicott City, MD; *U.S. Private*, pg. 1176

Vix, Carol A., Sr. Attorney & Asst. Sec.--Premark International, Inc., Deerfield, IL; *U.S. Public*, pg. 1321

Vlach, Robert, V.P., Gen. Sec. & Gen. Counsel--The Chesapeake Life Insurance Co., Oklahoma City, OK; *U.S. Public*, pg. 1679

Vlach, Robert B., V.P., Gen. Counsel & Sec.--United Insurance Companies, Inc., Dallas, TX; *U.S. Public*, pg. 1679

Vlahakis, Glenda, Treas. & Sec.--Trailer Wheel & Frame Company, Houston, TX; *U.S. Private*, pg. 1095

Vlk, Leroy F., Exec. Sec.--The Florists Assn. of Greater Cleveland, Inc., Cleveland, OH; *U.S. Private*, pg. 415

Vocca, Joe, Treas. & Sec.--Atotech U.S.A. Inc., Rock Hill, SC; *U.S. Private*, pg. 97

Voet, Martin A., Asst. Sec. & Assoc. Gen. Counsel--Allergan, Inc., Irvine, CA; *U.S. Public*, pg. 46

Vogue, Sherry, Sec.--Aquion, Elk Grove Village, IL; *U.S. Private*, pg. 78

Voigt, Howard K., Asst. Sec.--Joy Mining Machinery, Warrendale, PA; *U.S. Public*, pg. 789

Volk, Christopher H., Chief Oper. Officer & Exec. V.P.--Franchise Finance Corp. of America, Scottsdale, AZ; *U.S. Public*, pg. 679

Vollmer, Steve, Treas. & Sec.--Anritsu Wiltron, Morgan Hill, CA; *Int'l*, pg. 77

Volpi, Walter M., V.P., Sec. & Gen. Counsel--Lever Brothers Co., New York, NY; *Int'l*, pg. 1435

Voltz, David L., V.P., Gen. Counsel & Sec.--L.B. Foster Company, Pittsburgh, PA; *U.S. Public*, pg. 675

von Gesau, A., Sec.--The Southern Life Association Limited, Cape Town, South Africa; *Int'l*, pg. 77

Von Hoene, Robert, Sec.--Princeton Bank & Trust Company National Association, East Brunswick, NJ; *U.S. Public*, pg. 338

von Luhrte, Richard L., Exec. V.P., Sec. & Dir.--RNL Facilities Corporation, Denver, CO; *U.S. Private*, pg. 905

von Luhrte, Richard L., Sec.--RNL Design, Denver, CO; *U.S. Private*, pg. 905

von Luhrte, Richard L., Sec.--RNL/Interplan, Los Angeles, CA; *U.S. Private*, pg. 905

Von Rueden, James, Controller & Sec.--Wausau Homes, Inc., Rothschild, WI; *U.S. Private*, pg. 1154

Von Wald, Richard B., Sr. V.P., Gen. Counsel & Sec.--Johns Manville Corporation, Denver, CO; *U.S. Public*, pg. 927

Vondrak, James F., Sec.--Pittway Corporation, Chicago, IL; *U.S. Public*, pg. 1305

Vora, S.B., Sec.--SmithGroup, Inc., Detroit, MI; *U.S. Private*, *pg. 1010*

Vorbach, Joseph, V.P., Gen. Counsel & Sec.--American Bureau of Shipping, New York, NY; *U.S. Private*, pg. 51

Voss, Chris, Office Mgr.--Mattel Games/Puzzles, El Segundo, CA; *U.S. Public*, pg. 1058

Voss, Theodore R., Gen. Counsel & Asst. Sec.--Starter Corp., New Haven, CT; *U.S. Public*, pg. 1511

Voysey, Peter, Gen. Counsel & Sec.--Comdata Corporation, Brentwood, TN; *U.S. Public*, pg. 331

Vozick, David, Chm. Bd., Treas. & Sec.--AFP Imaging Corporation, Elmsford, NY; *U.S. Public*, pg. 6

Vuori, Ulla, Sec.--SO Oviteollisuus OY, Kuopio, Finland; *Int'l*, pg. 1302

Wachi, Eileen S., Asst Sec.--Maui Electric Co., Ltd., Kahului, HI; *U.S. Public*, pg. 800

Wachner, Barbara Jo, Exec. V.P.-Mktg., Personnel & Sec.--BGW Systems, Inc., Hawthorne, CA; *U.S. Private*, pg. 107

Wachterman, Richard M., Sr. V.P., Gen. Counsel & Sec.--Gradison Division, Cincinnati, OH; *U.S. Public*, pg. 1068

Wackenhut, Ruth J., Sec.--The Wackenhut Corporation, Palm Beach Gardens, FL; *U.S. Public*, pg. 1731

Wackerman, Dorothy C., Sec.--CertainTeed Corporation Foundation, Valley Forge, PA; *Int'l*, pg. 1171

Waclawik, James J., Chief Fin. Officer, Sr. V.P. & Sec.--Material Sciences Corporation, Elk Grove Village, IL; *U.S. Public*, pg. 1056

Waddell, James S., Chief Admin. Officer, Exec. V.P. & Sec.--Amcore Financial, Inc., Rockford, IL; *U.S. Public*, pg. 64

Waddington, Bruce A., Sr. V.P.-Engrng. & Sec.--FileNet Corporation, Costa Mesa, CA; *U.S. Public*, pg. 622

Wade, Donnie, Controller, Treas. & Sec.--Goodpasture, Inc., Brownfield, TX; *U.S. Private*, pg. 464

Wade, Kathleen, Sec.--Laura Ashley Shops Ltd., Calgary, Canada; *Int'l*, pg. 804

Wadler, Arnold, Sr. V.P., Gen. Counsel & Sec.--Metromedia Company, East Rutherford, NJ; *U.S. Private*, pg. 736

Wadler, Arnold L., Sr. V.P., Gen. Counsel & Sec.--Metromedia International Group, Inc., East Rutherford, NJ; *U.S. Public*, pg. 1102

Wadler, Sanford S., Gen. Counsel & Sec.--Bio-Rad Laboratories, Inc., Hercules, CA; *U.S. Public*, pg. 230

Wadsworth, Howard, V.P.-Fin. & Admin., Treas. & Sec.--Kaneb Services, Inc., Richardson, TX; *U.S. Public*, pg. 942

Wadsworth, Howard C., V.P., Treas. & Sec.--Kaneb Pipe Line Partners, L.P., Richardson, TX; *U.S. Public*, pg. 942

Wagar, Harvey, Gen. Counsel & Sec.--Lundy Enterprises, Inc., New Orleans, LA; *U.S. Private*, pg. 681

Wagenhals, Tod J., Exec. V.P. & Sec.--Action Performance Companies, Inc., Phoenix, AZ; *U.S. Public*, pg. 17

Waggoner, Henry R., Controller & Sec.--Lakeside Industries, Issaquah, WA; *U.S. Private*, pg. 644

Wagner, Barry J., Gen. Counsel & Sec.--Omnicom Group Inc., New York, NY; *U.S. Public*, pg. 1223

Wagner, Jay H., Reg. Counsel & Asst. Sec.--OHM Remediation Services Corp., Findlay, OH; *U.S. Public*, pg. 1208

Wagner, Martin S., Asst. Sec.--Xerox Corporation, Stamford, CT; *U.S. Public*, pg. 1783

Wagner, Mary Jane, Chief Fin. Officer, Treas. & Sec.--American Inks & Coatings Corp., Phoenixville, PA; *U.S. Private*, pg. 56

Wagner, Pamela L., Corp. Sec.--Allegiant Physician Services, Atlanta, GA; *U.S. Public*, pg. 45

Wagner, Robert V., Chief Fin. Officer, V.P.-Fin., Sec. & Treas.--Code-Alarm, Inc., Madison Heights, MI; *U.S. Public*, pg. 393

Wagstaff, T.W., Sec.--Cook Composites & Polymers Inc., Kansas City, MO; *Int'l*, pg. 1409

Wahl, Edie, Sec.--Service Supply Co. Inc. of Indiana, Indianapolis, IN; *U.S. Private*, pg. 987

Wahl, Rich, V.P.-Adv. & Sec.--Vibra Screw Inc., Totowa, NJ; *U.S. Private*, pg. 1138

Wahrsager, Stewart H., Sr. V.P., Gen. Counsel & Sec.--The Alpine Group, Inc., New York, NY; *U.S. Public*, pg. 58

Wahsrager, Stewart H., Corp. Sec.--Superior Telecommunications, Atlanta, GA; *U.S. Public*, pg. 58

Wai, Charles Chan Man, Sec.--The Sincere Co. Ltd., Hong Kong, Hong Kong; *Int'l*, pg. 1252

Waichler, Richard, V.P.-Opers. & Sec.--Follett Corporation, River Grove, IL; *U.S. Private*, pg. 416

Wainscott, James, Asst. Treas & Asst. Sec.--National Steel Corporation, Mishawaka, IN; *Int'l*, pg. 902

Waite, Donald L., Chief Fin. Officer, Exec. V.P.-Fin. & Sec.--Seagate Technology Inc., Scotts Valley, CA; *U.S. Public*, *pg. 1449*

Waiwood, Michael F., Exec. V.P., Gen. Cousel & Sec.--Midland Title Security, Inc., Cleveland, OH; *U.S. Public*, pg. 626

Wakai, Mayumi, Sec.--Shizuki Electric Corporation, Nishinomiya, Japan; *Int'l*, pg. 1236

Walder, Justin P., Sec.--Ronson Corporation, Somerset, NJ; *U.S. Public*, pg. 1405

Walder, Ken, Sec. & Dir.-Legal--British Airways PLC, London, United Kingdom; *Int'l*, pg. 218

Waldman, David S., Sec.--MONY Life Insurance Co. of America, New York, NY; *U.S. Private*, pg. 769

Waldman, Gary, Sec.--Service Packing Company-United Food Group, Los Angeles, CA; *U.S. Private*, pg. 986

Waldman, Robert A., Sr. V.P. & Gen. Counsel--Transcontinental Realty Investors, Inc., Dallas, TX; *U.S. Public*, pg. 1630

Waldorf, Toby, Treas. & Sec.--Idea Man, Inc., Los Angeles, CA; *U.S. Private*, pg. 557

Waldrop, Alexander M., V.P.-Admin., Gen. Counsel & Sec.--Churchill Downs, Inc., Louisville, KY; *U.S. Public*, pg. 356

Waldrop, Helen, Sec.--Edwards Engineering Corporation, Pompton Plains, NJ; *U.S. Private*, pg. 365

Wales, Gwynne H., Asst. Sec.--Super Discount Markets, Inc., Lithia Springs, GA; *Int'l*, pg. 463

Wales, Gwynne H., Asst. Sec.--Super Discount Markets, Inc., Lithia Springs, GA; *U.S. Public*, pg. 1540

Walford, Brian G., Exec. V.P., Chief Fin. Officer & Sec.--Exel Insurance Co. Ltd., Hamilton, Bermuda; *Int'l*, pg. 467

Walgrove, George R., Jr., Gen. Mgr. & Sec.--Maryland & Virginia Milk Producers Cooperative Association, Inc., Reston, VA; *U.S. Private*, pg. 711

Walk, Consuelo F., Sec.--Walk, Haydel & Associates, Inc., New Orleans, LA; *Int'l*, pg. 624

Walker, Audrey, Corp. Exec. Sec.--Wavetek Corporation, San Diego, CA; *U.S. Private*, pg. 1154

Walker, Baker, Chief Fin. Officer, Controller, Treas. & Sec.--C.B. Ragland Company, Nashville, TN; *U.S. Private*, pg. 907

Walker, Charlotte D., Sec.--Charleston Financial Services, Inc., Charleston, SC; *U.S. Public*, pg. 634

Walker, Clarence A., Sec.-Kennedy Covington--Phoenix Medical Technology, Inc., Andrews, SC; *U.S. Public*, pg. 1292

Walker, Diane E., Sr. V.P., Gen. Counsel & Sec.--CT Financial Services, Inc., Toronto, Canada; *Int'l*, pg. 112

Walker, Hans-Peter, Sec.--Oerlikon-Buhrle Holding AG, Zurich, Switzerland; *Int'l*, pg. 996

Walker, Harry M., Sec.--Trustmark Corporation, Jackson, MS; *U.S. Public*, pg. 1643

Walker, John D., Sec. & Treas.--Anco Insulations, Inc., Baton Rouge, LA; *U.S. Private*, pg. 71

Walker, K.A., Joint Sec.--BT (Worldwide) Ltd., London, United Kingdom; *Int'l*, pg. 222

Walker, Kandee Jo, Treas. & Sec.--Eldorado Chemical Company, San Antonio, TX; *U.S. Private*, pg. 367

Walker, Ken, V.P., Gen. Counsel & Copr. Sec.--Sealy Corporation, Cleveland, OH; *U.S. Private*, pg. 978

Walker, Kevin P., Chief Fin. Officer, Treas. & Sec.--Duncanson & Holt, New York, NY; *U.S. Public*, pg. 1699

Walker, Mark R., V.P.-Gen. Counsel & Sec.--CompUSA, Dallas, TX; *U.S. Public*, pg. 420

Walker, Max N., Treas. & Sec.--Gaston County Dyeing Machine Co., Mount Holly, NC; *U.S. Private*, pg. 441

Walker, Neal, Treas. & Asst. Sec.--Welcome Home, Inc., Wilmington, NC; *U.S. Private*, pg. 598

Walker, Richard A., Chief Admin. Officer, Exec. V.P., Gen. Counsel & Sec.--Kuhlman Corporation, Savannah, GA; *U.S. Public*, pg. 968

Walker, S.A., Grp. Sec.--The Eurotunnel Group, London, United Kingdom; *Int'l*, pg. 466

Walker, Sharon, Exec. Sec.-Corp. Commun.--Canadian Pacific Limited, Calgary, Canada; *Int'l*, pg. 258

Walker, Stacy L., Exec. Asst.--U.S. Safety, Lenexa, KS; *U.S. Private*, pg. 1125

Walker, T.P., Vice Chm. & Sec.--Stonecutter Mills Corp., Spindale, NC; *U.S. Private*, pg. 1044

Walker, Weldon W., Dir.-Tax, Asst. Treas. & Asst. Sec.--Weatherford Enterra Incorporated, Houston, TX; *U.S. Public*, pg. 1749

Walker, Weldon W., V.P., Asst. Treas. & Asst. Sec.--Weatherford U.S., Inc., Houston, TX; *U.S. Public*, pg. 1749

Wall, Anthony J., Exec. V.P.-Bus. Affairs, Gen. Counsel & Sec.--Big Dog Holdings Inc., Santa Barbara, CA; *U.S. Public*, pg. 227

Wall, Kay D., Chief Exec. Officer, Treas. & Sec.--Bryant Electric Company, Inc., High Point, NC; *U.S. Private*, pg. 176

Wall, Richard J. Jr., V.P., Gen. Counsel & Sec.--Cerner Corporation, Kansas City, MO; *U.S. Public*, pg. 331

Wallace, Bass C., Jr., Corp. Counsel & Sec.--Tetra Technologies, Woodlands, TX; *U.S. Public*, pg. 1582

Wallace, Harry, Sec.--Everett Smith Group, Ltd., Milwaukee, WI; *U.S. Private*, pg. 1007

Wallace, Mark D., Sec.--Renex Corp., Coral Gables, FL; *U.S. Public*, pg. 1377

Wallace, Wayne, V.P.-Gen. Counsel & Corp. Sec.--Raytheon Aircraft Company, Wichita, KS; *U.S. Public*, pg. 1365

Wallant, Jean-Claude Coppieters 't, Chief Fin. Officer & Sec.--Etablissements Delhaize Freres Et Cie "Le Lion" S.A., Brussels, Belgium; *Int'l*, pg. 462

Wallen, Birgitta, Sec.--Duni AB, Stockholm, Sweden; *Int'l*, pg. 421

Wallens, E., Sec.--John Gross & Co., Baltimore, MD; *U.S. Private*, pg. 483

Waller, William A., Sr. V.P., Gen. Counsel & Sec.--Petty Company, Inc., Effingham, IL; *U.S. Private*, pg. 860

Wallinder, Ingrid Westin, Corp. Sec.--Avesta Sheffield AB, Stockholm, Sweden; *Int'l*, pg. 221

Wallock, Terrence, Sr. V.P., Sec. & Gen. Counsel--Ralphs Grocery Company, Compton, CA; *U.S. Private*, pg. 1202

Wallock, Terrence J., Exec. V.P., General Counsel & Sec.--The Vons Companies, Inc., Arcadia, CA; *U.S. Public*, pg. 1426

Walls, Clyde, Treas. & Sec.--Commemorative Brands, Inc., Austin, TX; *U.S. Private*, pg. 258

Walls, Maurice D., Gen. Agent & Sec.--Texas Pacific Land Trust, New York, NY; *U.S. Public*, pg. 1586

Walner, Robert, Sr. V.P. & Sec.--Grubb & Ellis Management Services, Inc., Northbrook, IL; *U.S. Public*, pg. 767

Walner, Robert J., Sr. V.P., Gen. Counsel & Corp. Sec.--Grubb & Ellis Company, Northbrook, IL; *U.S. Public*, pg. 767

Walraven, M. Orville, V.P.-Land & Sec.--Noble Affiliates, Inc., Ardmore, OK; *U.S. Public*, pg. 1186

Walraven, Orville, V.P.-Land--Samedan Oil Corporation, Ardmore, OK; *U.S. Public*, pg. 1186

Walseth, Daniel G., V.P., Dir.-Legal Opers. & Sec.--ITT Hartford Life & Annuity Insurance Corporation, Minneapolis, MN; *U.S. Public*, pg. 795

Walsh, William J., Jr., Chief Oper. Officer, Exec. V.P. & Sec.--Consumers Financial Corporation, Camp Hill, PA; *U.S. Public*, pg. 437

Walter, Anna C., V.P. & Sec.--Thermo Electric Co., Inc., Saddle Brook, NJ; *U.S. Private*, pg. 1080

Walter, Fred, V.P. & Sec.--Noville, South Hackensack, NJ; *U.S. Private*, pg. 808

Walters, H., Sec.--ACI International Ltd., Melbourne, Australia; *Int'l*, pg. 128

Walters, Judy A., Sec.--Mercury General Corporation, Los Angeles, CA; *U.S. Public*, pg. 1093

Waltersdorf, Margaret S., Sec.--Tristate Electrical Supply Co., Inc., Hagerstown, MD; *U.S. Private*, pg. 1104

Walton, F. Ferrell, Treas. & Sec.--Johnston Industries, Inc., Columbus, GA; *U.S. Public*, pg. 933

Walton, H. Steven, V.P.-Govt. Affairs, Gen. Counsel & Sec.--Sanifill, Inc., Houston, TX; *U.S. Public*, pg. 1686

Walton, John, Sec.--S L C Graphics, LP, Pittston, PA; *U.S. Private*, pg. 955

Walton, Jon D., Sr. V.P., Gen. Counsel & Sec.--Allegheny Teledyne Incorporated, Pittsburgh, PA; *U.S. Public*, pg. 43

Walton, Louise, Mgr.-Office Services--The Reynolds and Reynolds Company, Dayton, OH; *U.S. Public*, pg. 1384

Walton, Wesley S., Sec.--Market Facts, Inc., Arlington Heights, IL; *U.S. Public*, pg. 1046

Waltzer, Julius, V.P., Treas. & Sec.--Jack Young Associates, Hazleton, PA; *U.S. Private*, pg. 1201

Wamhoff, Fredrick, V.P., Gn. Counsel & Sec.--Rawson-Koenig, Inc., Houston, TX; *U.S. Public*, pg. 1362

Wan, Tracy, Chief Fin. Officer, Sr. V.P. & Sec.--The Sharper Image, San Francisco, CA; *U.S. Public*, pg. 1464

Wanders, A.C.M., Sec.--DSM N.V., Heerlen, Netherlands; *Int'l*, pg. 352

Wang, Stanley L., Sr. V.P., Gen. Counsel & Sec.--Comcast Corporation, Philadelphia, PA; *U.S. Public*, pg. 406

Wang, Susan S., Chief Fin. Officer, Sr. V.P. & Sec.--Solectron Corporation, Milpitas, CA; *U.S. Public*, pg. 1483

Wanner, James E., Exec. V.P. & Sec.--Chase Financial Management Corp., Cleveland, OH; *U.S. Public*, pg. 338

Ward-Jones, R., Sec.--Rentokil Initial plc, East Grinstead, United Kingdom; *Int'l*, pg. 1285

Ward, Bill, Sr. V.P., Gen. Counsel & Sec.--NW Transport Service, Inc., Denver, CO; *U.S. Private*, pg. 772

Ward, C., Sec. & Dir.-Fin.--Aylesbury Automation Ltd., Aylesbury, United Kingdom; *Int'l*, pg. 297

Ward, C., Sec.--Master International Corp., Santa Monica, CA; *U.S. Private*, pg. 713

Ward, Carol J., Corp. Sec.--Cigna Corp., Philadelphia, PA; *U.S. Public*, pg. 356

Ward, Craig, Pres. & Sec.--LTB Ward Constructors, Inc., Houston, TX; *U.S. Private*, pg. 347

Ward, John P., V.P.-Fin. & Sec.--American Uniform Co., Cleveland, TN; *U.S. Private*, pg. 1039

Ward, Richard S., Exec. V.P., Gen. Counsel & Sec.--ITT Corporation, New York, NY; *U.S. Public*, pg. 1512

Ward, Robert, Sec. & Treas.--SunBuilt Homes, Inc., Phoenix, AZ; *U.S. Public*, pg. 323

Ward, Thomas J., V.P.-Admin. & Sec.--Pennsylvania Enterprises Inc., Wilkes-Barre, PA; *U.S. Public*, pg. 1271

Warden, William C., Jr., Chief Admin. Officer, Exec. V.P., Gen. Counsel & Sec.--Lowe's Companies, Inc., North Wilkesboro, NC; *U.S. Public*, pg. 1015

Wardlaw, Sharon, Chief Fin. Officer, Treas. & Sec.--Polydex Pharmaceuticals Limited, Scarborough, Canada; *Int'l*, pg. 1062

Wardley, George, Sec.--Utica Mutual Insurance Company, New Hartford, NY; *U.S. Private*, pg. 1129

Wardlow, Anne V., V.P., Gen. Counsel & Sec.--John Alden Life Insurance Company, Miami, FL; *U.S. Public*, pg. 39

Wark, Dale A., Chief Fin. Officer, Exec. V.P., Treas. & Sec.--R.M. Shoemaker Co., West Conshohocken, PA; *U.S. Private*, pg. 996

Warner, L., Sec.--Laubeck Corporation/Cross, Carbondale, PA; *U.S. Private*, pg. 652

Warner, M. Richard, V.P., Gen. Counsel & Sec.--Temple-Inland Inc., Diboll, TX; *U.S. Public*, pg. 1574

Warnock, Inez, Sec.--Smith Frozen Foods, Inc., Weston, OR; *U.S. Private*, pg. 1008

Warren, George P., Jr., Asst. Sec.--Alamco-Delaware, Inc., Wilmington, DE; *U.S. Public*, pg. 403

Warren, Jeffrey H., V.P.-Land & Minerals & Asst. Sec.--Tejon Ranch Company, Lebec, CA; *U.S. Public*, pg. 1566

Warren, Joseph G., Chief Fin. Officer, V.P.-Fin., Treas. & Sec.--Bowmar Instrument Corporation, Phoenix, AZ; *U.S. Public*, pg. 248

Warren, William M., Sr. V.P., Gen. Counsel & Asst. Sec.--Forest City Enterprises, Inc., Cleveland, OH; *U.S. Public*, *pg. 667*

Warsinske, Steven W., Treas. & Sec.--Southeastern Michigan Gas Company, Port Huron, MI; *U.S. Public*, pg. 1489

Wartman, C.H., Gen. Counsel & Sec.--Consolidated Papers, Inc., Wisconsin Rapids, WI; *U.S. Public*, pg. 436

Washburn, Frank A., Chief Oper. Officer, Exec. V.P. & Sec.--Pamida Holdings Corporation, Omaha, NE; *U.S. Public*, pg. 1255

Washburn, Richard V., Exec. V.P.-H.R. & Sec.--First of America Bank Corporation, Kalamazoo, MI; *U.S. Public*, pg. 636

Washlow, Robert J., Sec.--Lawson Products, Inc., Des Plaines, IL; *U.S. Public*, pg. 980

Wassenaar, Craig G., Chief Fin. Officer, V.P. & Sec.--Ameriwood Industries International Inc., Grand Rapids, MI; *U.S. Public*, pg. 98

Wasser, Marilyn J., V.P.-Law & Sec.--AT&T Corporation, Basking Ridge, NJ; *U.S. Public*, pg. 10

Watddingham, Tony, Corp. Sec.--Foodcorp Limited, Bedfordview, South Africa; *Int'l*, pg. 496

Waterman, C. D. III, Sec.--Lee Enterprises, Incorporated, Davenport, IA; *U.S. Public*, pg. 983

Waterman, Rose, Exec. Sec.--The Kruse Company, Fairfield, OH; *U.S. Private*, pg. 636

Waters, Raymond S., Sec.--One Price Clothing Stores, Inc., Duncan, SC; *U.S. Public*, pg. 1225

Waters, Susan, Asst. Sec.--Kulicke & Soffa Industries, Inc., Willow Grove, PA; *U.S. Public*, pg. 968

Watkin, Nancy, Gen. Counsel & Sec.--Tiger Direct, Inc., Miami, FL; *U.S. Public*, pg. 747

Watkins, A.J., Sec.--Union Texas Petroleum Holdings, Houston, TX; *U.S. Public*, pg. 1669

Watkins, Helen K., Asst. Sec.--Edison International, Rosemead, CA; *U.S. Public*, pg. 564

Watkins, L. Earl, Jr., Gen. Counsel & Sec.--Sunflower Electric Power Corporation, Hays, KS; *U.S. Private*, pg. 1052

Watkins, Matthew M., V.P.-Opers. & Sec.--The Alpha Corporation Of Tennessee, Collierville, TN; *U.S. Private*, pg. 44

Watkins, Norma L., Sec.--Akrochem Corporation, Akron, OH; *U.S. Private*, pg. 30

Watkins, Ophelia, Treas. & Sec.--Stahmann Farms, Inc., La Mesa, NM; *U.S. Private*, pg. 1029

Watkiss, A.H., Asst. Sec.--Unigate PLC, London, United Kingdom; *Int'l*, pg. 1433
Watson, Alonzo W., Jr., Sec.--First Security Corporation, Salt Lake City, UT; *U.S. Public*, pg. 637
Watson, Gwen, Bd. Sec.--NJ Transit, Newark, NJ; *U.S. Private*, pg. 794
Watson, Janet S., Treas. & Sec.--The Empire District Electric Company, Joplin, MO; *U.S. Public*, pg. 579
Watson, L.G., Sec. & Grp. Legal Counsel--London & Edinburgh Insurance Group Limited, Worthing, United Kingdom; *U.S. Public*, pg. 795
Watson, Ronald L., Sec.--Keystone Bank, Horsham, PA; *U.S. Public*, pg. 956
Watson, S.A., Asst. Sec.--The Rank Group PLC, London, United Kingdom; *Int'l*, pg. 1086
Watson, Sarah A., Asst. Corp. Sec.--Delchamps, Inc., Mobile, AL; *U.S. Private*, pg. 588
Watson, Steven L., V.P. & Sec.--Contran Corporation, Dallas, TX; *U.S. Private*, pg. 270
Watson, Steven L., V.P. & Sec.--Valhi, Inc., Dallas, TX; *U.S. Private*, pg. 270
Watson, Susan, Sec.--Scottish Enterprise, Glasgow, United Kingdom; *Int'l*, pg. 1212
Watt, David C., Exec. V.P., Gen. Counsel & Sec.--ICN Pharmaceuticals, Inc., Costa Mesa, CA; *U.S. Public*, pg. 853
Watters, Charles P., Grp. Sec. & Gen. Counsel--Allied Colloids Group Plc., Bradford, United Kingdom; *Int'l*, pg. 62
Watts, T.L., Sec.--Plains Electric Generation Transmission Co-Op, Inc., Albuquerque, NM; *U.S. Private*, pg. 868
Watts, W.J.C., Sec.--Watts Blake Bearne & Co. Plc, Newton Abbot, United Kingdom; *Int'l*, pg. 1487
Watzke, Garry B., Sec.--Arch Communications Group, Inc., Westborough, MA; *U.S. Public*, pg. 127
Wavra, Pat, Sec.-Mktg. Services--Jaguar Cars, Mahwah, NJ; *U.S. Public*, pg. 664
Wax, Robert P., V.P., Gen. Counsel & Sec.--Northeast Utilities, Berlin, CT; *U.S. Public*, pg. 1194
Waxman, Susan, V.P.-Fin. & Admin. & Sec.--Sand Technology Systems, Westmount, Canada; *Int'l*, pg. 1183
Way, Janice H., Sec.--Thomas & Betts Corporation, Memphis, TN; *U.S. Public*, pg. 1597
Way, Michael G., Chief Fin. Officer, Legal, Treas. & Sec.--Bristile Clay Tiles, Ltd., Caversham, Australia; *Int'l*, pg. 216
Way, Radd C., V.P. & Asst. Sec.--The Weitz Company, Inc., Des Moines, IA; *U.S. Private*, pg. 1160
Wayman, W. Russell, Corp. V.P., Gen. Counsel & Sec.--Storage Technology Corporation, Louisville, CO; *U.S. Public*, pg. 1522
Wear, Frank J., Sec.--Omaha Public Power District, Omaha, NE; *U.S. Private*, pg. 815
Weatherford, Terry L., V.P. & Sec.--Cone Mills Corporation, Greensboro, NC; *U.S. Public*, pg. 430
Weaver, Amy S., Pres., Treas. & Sec.--Emons Finance Corporation, Wilmington, DE; *U.S. Public*, pg. 578
Weaver, Anna, Sec.--Adelphia Lamp & Shade Inc., Philadelphia, PA; *U.S. Private*, pg. 17
Weaver, Joseph R., Jr., Gen. Counsel & Sec.--Darling International, Inc, Irving, TX; *U.S. Public*, pg. 484
Weaver, Kennard, Gen. Counsel--Jayco Inc., Middlebury, IN; *U.S. Private*, pg. 583
Weaver, Paul D., Sr. V.P., Clerk, Sec. & Gen. Counsel--Houghton Mifflin Company, Boston, MA; *U.S. Public*, pg. 841
Weaver, Richard T., Chief Exec. & Fin. Officer, Treas. & Sec.--Hamburg Brothers, Pittsburgh, PA; *U.S. Private*, pg. 497
Webb, Maudine, Sec. & Corp. Travel Planner--Alco Chemical, Chattanooga, TN; *Int'l*, pg. 1435
Webb, Robert D., Controller & Asst. Sec.--Lester B. Knight & Associates, Inc., Chicago, IL; *U.S. Private*, pg. 626
Webb, Susan M., V.P.-Human Resoures--Jervis B. Webb Company, Farmington Hills, MI; *U.S. Private*, pg. 1156
Webber, Robert N., V.P., Gen. Counsel & Asst. Sec.--Seaman Furniture Company, Inc., Woodbury, NY; *U.S. Public*, pg. 1452
Weber, Edward D. Jr., V.P., Gen. Counsel & Sec.--Acme Metals Incorporated, Riverdale, IL; *U.S. Public*, pg. 16
Weber, Floyd R,, Sec.--Speakman Company, Wilmington, DE; *U.S. Private*, pg. 1021
Weber, Phillip, Dr., Corp. Sec.--Landis & Staefa AG, Zug, Switzerland; *Int'l*, pg. 800
Weber, Stanley G., Chief Fin. Officer, Sr. V.P.-Fin. & Sec.--Sceptre Resources Limited, Calgary, Canada; *Int'l*, pg. 1203
Webster, Martin, Sec.--Dexion Group plc, Hemel Hempstead, United Kingdom; *U.S. Public*, pg. 893
Wechsler, Barbara, Sec. & Dir.-Personnel & Employee Benefits--Continental Plastic Card Co., Coral Springs, FL; *U.S. Private*, pg. 269
Wechsler, Robert R., Corp. Sec.--Einson Freeman Inc., Paramus, NJ; *Int'l*, pg. 1483
Weddle, Stephen S., V.P., Sec. & Gen. Counsel--The Stanley Works, New Britain, CT; *U.S. Public*, pg. 1508
Wedgwood, J.A.T., Sec.--LASMO plc, London, United Kingdom; *Int'l*, pg. 803
Weed, Monica M., Asst. Sec.--Information Resources, Inc., Chicago, IL; *U.S. Public*, pg. 875
Weeks, Paul, II, Sr. V.P., Gen. Counsel & Sec.--ICF Kaiser International Inc., Fairfax, VA; *U.S. Public*, pg. 852
Weeks, William D., Sec.--Reed & Barton Corporation, Taunton, MA; *U.S. Private*, pg. 916
Wegmann, Leo F., Jr., Sec.--Lafayette Insurance Company, New Orleans, LA; *U.S. Public*, pg. 1677
Wehrenberg, Kim A., V.P.-Gen. Counsel & Sec.--Federal Signal Corporation, Oak Brook, IL; *U.S. Public*, pg. 616
Wehrmeyer, Robert A., Jr., Sr. V.P.-Admin. & Sec.--Kinetic Concepts, Inc., San Antonio, TX; *U.S. Private*, pg. 620
Weibel, Marlene, Treas. & Sec.--Weibel Winery, Lodi, CA; *U.S. Private*, pg. 1159
Weidler, Allen, V.P.-Fin. & Sec.--Fred Usinger, Inc., Milwaukee, WI; *U.S. Private*, pg. 1129
Weiland, Lee, Sec.--Dairyland Power Cooperative, La Crosse, WI; *U.S. Private*, pg. 307
Weiler, Judith, Exec. Asst.--EMS-Togo, Taylor, MI; *Int'l*, pg. 981
Weiler, Timothy, Sec.--Steiner Corporation, Salt Lake City, UT; *U.S. Private*, pg. 1039
Weinberg, David L., Chief Fin. Officer, V.P.-Fin. & Admin., Treas. & Sec.--Columbia Laboratories, Inc., Miami, FL; *U.S. Public*, pg. 405
Weinberg, Herschel M., Gen. Counsel & Sec.--Milgray Electronics, Inc., Farmingdale, NY; *U.S. Public*, pg. 205
Weinberg, Richard A., Exec. V.P., Gen. Counsel & Sec.--GAF Materials Corporation, Wayne, NJ; *U.S. Private*, pg. 433
Weinberg, Richard G., Sr. V.P., Gen. Counsel & Sec.--GAF Corporation, Wayne, NJ; *U.S. Private*, pg. 433
Weiner, Eugene L., Exec. V.P., Sec. & Treas.--Paradise, Inc., Plant City, FL; *U.S. Public*, pg. 1256
Weiner, Ronald, V.P., Gen. Counsel & Sec.--Radiator Specialty Company, Charlotte, NC; *U.S. Private*, pg. 906
Weiner, Warren, Exec. V.P., Treas. & Sec.--Deb Shops, Inc., Philadelphia, PA; *U.S. Public*, pg. 491
Weinfeld, Lewis A., Chief Fin. Officer & Exec. V.P.--Starrett HRH, New York, NY; *U.S. Private*, pg. 1035
Weinman, Richard F., V.P. & Sec.--Canfor Corporation, Vancouver, Canada; *Int'l*, pg. 260
Weinstein, Alan I., Chief Fin. & Admin. Officer, Sr. Exec. V.P. & Sec.--Morse Shoe, Inc., Canton, MA; *U.S. Public*, pg. 168
Weinstein, Edwin S., V.P.-Fin., Treas. & Sec.--Pomeroy Computer Resources, Hebron, KY; *U.S. Public*, pg. 1315
Weinstein, Joan, Sec.--Concord Fabrics Inc., New York, NY; *U.S. Public*, pg. 429
Weinstein, Mark, Sec.--The Cosmetic Center Inc., Columbia, MD; *U.S. Private*, pg. 689
Weintraub, Stephen, Sr. V.P. & Sec.--Counsel Corporation, Toronto, Canada; *Int'l*, pg. 338
Weir, M.A., Gen. Counsel & Sec.--Australian National Industries Limited, Pyrmont, Australia; *Int'l*, pg. 100
Weir, R. Harold, V.P., Gen. Counsel & Sec.--Jannock Limited, Toronto, Canada; *Int'l*, pg. 698
Weisbarth, James, Sr. V.P., Treas. & Asst. Sec.--Central Reserve Life Corporation, Strongsville, OH; *U.S. Public*, pg. 326
Weisberg, David D., V.P. & Sec.--Technic Incorporated, Cranston, RI; *U.S. Private*, pg. 1071
Weisberg, Jerome, V.P. & Sec.--Jacob Stern & Sons, Inc., Santa Barbara, CA; *U.S. Private*, pg. 1041
Weisberg, Martin E. Esq., Sec.--Dick Clark Productions, Inc., Burbank, CA; *U.S. Public*, pg. 382
Weisberger, Mark, V.P., Sec. & Gen. Counsel--IHOP Corp., Glendale, CA; *U.S. Public*, pg. 862
Weise, Rita, Corp. Sec.--Weber-Stephen Products Co., Palatine, IL; *U.S. Private*, pg. 1157
Weiser, Paul D., Sr. V.P., Sec. & Corp. Counsel--Dataproducts Corporation, Simi Valley, CA; *Int'l*, pg. 620
Weiser, Susann, Sec.--Wurzner Dauerbackwaren GmbH, Wurzen, Germany; *Int'l*, pg. 1514
Weiss, Andre, Sec. & Gen. Counsel--Toys "R" Us, Inc., Paramus, NJ; *U.S. Public*, pg. 1626
Weiss, Charles J., Asst. V.P. & Sec.--Citizens Utilities Company, Stamford, CT; *U.S. Public*, pg. 379
Weiss, Ed, Gen. Counsel & Sec.--Group 1 Software, Inc., Lanham, MD; *U.S. Public*, pg. 417
Weiss, Edward, Gen. Counsel & Sec.--COMNET Corporation, Lanham, MD; *U.S. Public*, pg. 416
Weiss, James A., Sec. & Treas.--James Chevrolet Inc., Clinton Township, MI; *U.S. Private*, pg. 580
Weiss, Larry, Chm. Bd., Pres., Chief Exec. Officer & Sec.--Fresh Food, Inc., Hobart, IN; *U.S. Private*, pg. 427
Weiss, Michael B., Asst. Sec.--Harley-Davidson, Inc., Milwaukee, WI; *U.S. Public*, pg. 786
Weiss, Paul, Legal Counsel & Corp. Sec.--Gandalf Systems Corporation, Delran, NJ; *Int'l*, pg. 540
Weiss, R.W., Sec.--Idaho Forest Industry, Inc., Coeur D'Alene, ID; *U.S. Private*, pg. 556
Weiss, Robert L., Sec.--The Wooster Brush Company, Wooster, OH; *U.S. Private*, pg. 1188
Weiss, William L., Sec. & Gen. Counsel--Jetronic Industries, Inc., Philadelphia, PA; *U.S. Public*, pg. 926
Weissbrum, Yoram, Corp. Sec.--Bank Hapoalim, Tel Aviv, Israel; *Int'l*, pg. 149
Weisse, Claude, Sec.--N. Schlumberger & Cie, Guebwiller, France; *Int'l*, pg. 1206
Weitzenfeld, Marvin, Chief Fin. Officer, Sec. & Treas.--Globe-Amerada Glass Company, Elk Grove Village, IL; *U.S. Private*, pg. 458
Weitzenfeld, Marvin, Chief Fin. Officer, Treas. & Sec.--Assurance Glass Co. of Alabama, Selma, AL; *U.S. Private*, pg. 458
Wekstein, Walter, Sec.--Au Bon Pain Co., Inc., Boston, MA; *U.S. Public*, pg. 146
Welch, Cathy, Sec.--Ben Schwartz Market, Inc., Peoria, IL; *U.S. Private*, pg. 974
Weldon, Norman G., V.P. & Sec.--Zions Credit Corporation, Salt Lake City, UT; *U.S. Public*, pg. 1793
Welge, Michael W., Exec. V.P., Treas., Sec. & Comptroller--Gilster Mary Lee Corp., Chester, IL; *U.S. Private*, pg. 455
Weling, S.M., Sec.--Indian Oil Corporation Limited, New Delhi, India; *Int'l*, pg. 673
Weller, Andrew M., Chief Fin. Officer, Exec. V.P., Dir. & Sec--Johnstown America Industries, Chicago, IL; *U.S. Public*, pg. 933
Weller, Joseph C., Chief Fin. Officer, Treas. & Sec.--Morgan Keegan, Inc., Memphis, TN; *U.S. Public*, pg. 1131
Wellington, Foo Thiam Fong, Sec.--United Overseas Land Limited, Singapore, Singapore; *Int'l*, pg. 1443
Wellington, Roger U., Chief Fin. Officer & Treas.--The L.S. Starrett Company, Athol, MA; *U.S. Public*, pg. 1511
Wells, Gary H., Chief Fin. Officer,Treas & Sec.--Chittenden & Eastman Co., Burlington, IA; *U.S. Private*, pg. 237
Wells, Gary H., Chief Fin. Officer, Treas. & Sec--Eastman House Of California, Inc., Burlington, IA; *U.S. Private*, pg. 238
Wells, Gary H., Chief Fin. Officer, Treas. & Sec.--Eastman House Of Alabama, Inc., Burlington, IA; *U.S. Private*, pg. 238
Wells, J.M., III, Exec. V.P. & Sec.--The Homer Laughlin China Company, Newell, WV; *U.S. Private*, pg. 653
Wells, J.M., III, Exec. V.P. & Sec.--The Newell Company, Newell, WV; *U.S. Private*, pg. 653
Wells, J.M., III, Exec. V.P. & Sec.--Newell Bridge & Railway Company, Newell, WV; *U.S. Private*, pg. 653
Wells, Linda K., Corp. Sec.--MPSI Systems Inc., Tulsa, OK; *U.S. Public*, pg. 1027
Welshhans, Richard W., Chief Fin. Officer, V.P. & Treas.--Reflectone, Inc., Tampa, FL; *Int'l*, pg. 218
Welty, John R., V.P., Gen. Counsel & Sec.--Carpenter Technology Corporation, Reading, PA; *U.S. Public*, pg. 307
Wender, Mark D., Chief Oper. Officer & Sec.--Boatmen's National Mortgage Inc., Memphis, TN; *U.S. Public*, pg. 1165
Wendt, T.M., V.P., Div. Counsel & Asst. Sec.--Zimmer, Inc., Warsaw, IN; *U.S. Public*, pg. 254
Wengler, Diann P., Asst. Sec.--Duff & Phelps Utilities Income Inc., Chicago, IL; *U.S. Public*, pg. 534
Wennett, Richard W., Sec.--Blauer Manufacturing Co., Inc., Boston, MA; *U.S. Private*, pg. 149
Wentworth, Francis M., Jr., Sr. V.P., Sec. & General Counsel--Gaylord Entertainment Co., Nashville, TN; *U.S. Public*, pg. 704
Wenzler, Joseph P., Treas. & Sec.--Shurflo Pump Manufacturing Co., Santa Ana, CA; *U.S. Public*, pg. 1767
Wenzler, Joseph P., Treas. & Sec.--Hypro Corporation, New Brighton, MN; *U.S. Public*, pg. 1767
Werber, Richard, V.P.-Legal Affairs, Gen. Counsel & Sec.--Rexall Sundown Inc., Boca Raton, FL; *U.S. Public*, pg. 1384
Werner, Rupert W., Pres. & Sec.--Perry Engineering Company, Inc., Winchester, VA; *U.S. Private*, pg. 854
Wernick, Justin, Dr., Exec. V.P. & Sec.--The Langer Biomechanics Group, Inc., Deer Park, NY; *U.S. Public*, pg. 978
Wertheimer, Robert, V.P., Gen. Counsel & Sec.--American Mail-Well Envelope, Englewood, CO; *U.S. Public*, pg. 1038
Wesemann, Jeannie, Sec.--Affiliated Foods Cooperative Inc., Norfolk, NE; *U.S. Private*, pg. 25
Wessel, Rick L., Chief Fin. Officer, Treas. & Sec.--First Cash, Inc., Arlington, TX; *U.S. Public*, pg. 627
West, David, Controller--Royal Waterbeds, Maryland Heights, MO; *U.S. Private*, pg. 949
West, David M., Sr. V.P. & Sec.-Fin. & Gen. Group--Toyota Motor Sales, U.S.A., Inc., Torrance, CA; *Int'l*, pg. 1412
West, G.P., Treas. & Asst. Sec.--Florida East Coast Industries Inc., Saint Augustine, FL; *U.S. Public*, pg. 1427
West, G.R., Chief Fin. Officer, Corp. Sec. & Treas.--Alley-Cassetty Coal Co., Nashville, TN; *U.S. Private*, pg. 37
West, Kevin, Exec. V.P.--Southwest Recreational Industries Inc., Leander, TX; *U.S. Private*, pg. 1018
West, M. Rudolph, Sec.--Ethyl Corporation, Richmond, VA; *U.S. Public*, pg. 595
West, Steve, Sec.--Arkansas Electric Cooperatives Inc., Little Rock, AR; *U.S. Private*, pg. 82
West, Todd K., Chief Fin. Officer, V.P.-Fin. & Sec.--Noel Group, Inc., New York, NY; *U.S. Public*, pg. 1187
Westen, B. Curtis, Sr. V.P., Gen. Counsel & Sec.--Foundation Health Systems, Inc., Pueblo, CO; *U.S. Public*, pg. 678
Westerbeck, David F., Sr. V.P., Gen. Counsel & Sec.--The Union Central Life Insurance Co., Cincinnati, OH; *U.S. Private*, pg. 1118
Westerbergen, J.W.B., Joint Sec.--Unilever Plc, London, United Kingdom; *Int'l*, pg. 1433
Westermann, John L., III, Chief Fin. Officer, V.P., Treas. & Sec.--CSC Financial Services Group, Austin, TX; *U.S. Public*, pg. 422
Westermeyer, Michael T., V.P. & Sec.--Allianz Life Insurance Company of North America, Minneapolis, MN; *Int'l*, pg. 58
Westlie, James H., Treas. & Sec.--Westlie Motor Company, Minot, ND; *U.S. Private*, pg. 1169
Westlund, Birgitta, Sec.--Stora Forest AB, Falun, Sweden; *Int'l*, pg. 1303
Westmeyer, E.A., Chief Fin. Officer, V.P., Treas. & Sec.--Zeller Corp., Defiance, OH; *U.S. Private*, pg. 1204
Weston, Cori C., V.P. & Sec.--Pacific Century Financial Corporation, Honolulu, HI; *U.S. Public*, pg. 1248
Wetherald, David, Gen. Counsel & Sec.--Torstar Corporation, Toronto, Canada; *Int'l*, pg. 1402
Wetherell, K.J., Asst. Sec.--Farm Electric Services Ltd., Calgary, Canada; *Int'l*, pg. 1416
Wetherell, Ken J., Asst. Corp. Sec.--Transalta Corporation, Calgary, Canada; *Int'l*, pg. 1416
Wetherell, Ken J., Asst. Corp. Sec.--TransAlta Utilities, Calgary, Canada; *Int'l*, pg. 1416
Wetherell, Kenneth J., Asst. Corp. Sec.--TransAlta Enterprises Corporation, Calgary, Canada; *Int'l*, pg. 1416
Wetmore, Edward C., Sec. & Gen. Counsel--Amphenol Corporation, Wallingford, CT; *U.S. Private*, pg. 629
Wetzel, Edward M., V.P.-Fin. & Sec.--Standard Locknut, Inc., Westfield, IN; *U.S. Private*, pg. 1031
Wetzel, Robert, Gen. Counsel & Sec.--KTI, Inc., Guttenberg, NJ; *U.S. Public*, pg. 939
Weyand, Victoria P., V.P. & Sec.--John H. Harland Company, Decatur, GA; *U.S. Public*, pg. 785
Whaley, John A., V.P., Gen. Counsel & Sec.--CT Financial Services, Inc., Toronto, Canada; *Int'l*, pg. 112
Wharton, Garry, Corp. Counsel & Sec.--Motorists Mutual Insurance Co., Columbus, OH; *U.S. Private*, pg. 764
Wharton, Garry L., Gen. Counsel & Sec.--American Hardware Mutual Insurance Co., Columbus, OH; *U.S. Private*, pg. 764

Whatcott, Lee A., Chief Fin. Officer & Sr. V.P.--Westcorp, Irvine, CA; *U.S. Public*, pg. 1756
Wheeler, C., Asst. Treas., Asst. Sec. & Controller--American Welding & Manufacturing Co., Warren, OH; *U.S. Private*, pg. 425
Wheeler, Joyce, Gen. Counsel & Sec.--Royal Insurance, Charlotte, NC; *Int'l*, pg. 1130
Wheeler, Michael B., V.P., Treas. & Asst. Sec.--Stone Container Corporation, Chicago, IL; *U.S. Public*, pg. 1520
Wheeler, Michael B., V.P., Treas. & Asst. Sec.--Stone Forest Industries, Chicago, IL; *U.S. Public*, pg. 1521
Whitaker, R.A., Sec.--General Accident Fire and Life Assurance Corporation p.l.c., Perth, United Kingdom; *Int'l*, pg. 542
Whitbread, Kevin R., Company Sec.--SEIKO UK Limited, Maidenhead, United Kingdom; *Int'l*, pg. 1218
White, Barbara, Corp. Sec.--Seed Restaurant Group, Inc., Lexington, KY; *U.S. Private*, pg. 981
White, Betty J., Controller, Treas. & Asst. Sec.--Christiana Companies, Inc., Milwaukee, WI; *U.S. Public*, pg. 352
White, Billy, V.P. & Sec.--Foxworth-Galbraith Lumber Co., Dallas, TX; *U.S. Private*, pg. 423
White, Colin M., Dir.-Fin. & Sec.--Dowty Aerospace Hydraulics, Cheltenham, Cheltenham, United Kingdom; *Int'l*, pg. 1337
White, Gary W., V.P. & Sec.--Nautilus Insurance Company, Scottsdale, AZ; *U.S. Public*, pg. 216
White, H. Katherine, Sec. & Asst. Gen. Counsel--Sealed Air Corporation, Saddle Brook, NJ; *U.S. Public*, pg. 1450
White, James M., III, Gen. Counsel & Sec.--Universal Corporation, Richmond, VA; *U.S. Public*, pg. 1694
White, James M., III, Asst. Sec.--N.V. Deli-Universal, Rotterdam, Netherlands; *U.S. Public*, pg. 1695
White, Janet, Sec.--Ariel Corporation, Mount Vernon, OH; *U.S. Private*, pg. 81
White, Judy, Sec. & Exec. Asst.--Spirol International Corp., Danielson, CT; *U.S. Private*, pg. 1026
White, Michael B., V.P., Gen. Counsel & Corp. Sec.--Hecla Mining Company, Coeur D'Alene, ID; *U.S. Public*, pg. 803
White, Paul H., Gen. Counsel & Asst. Sec.--AirTouch Communications, Inc., San Francisco, CA; *U.S. Public*, pg. 34
White, Robert W., V.P. & Sec.--Industrial Rubber Products Company, Charleston, WV; *U.S. Private*, pg. 561
White, Stan, Chief Fin. Officer, V.P.-Fin., Sec. & Treas.--U.S. Filter/Davis Water & Waste Industries, Inc., Thomasville, GA; *U.S. Public*, pg. 1682
White, Turner, Sec.--Positronic Industries, Inc., Springfield, MO; *U.S. Private*, pg. 876
White, Virginia, V.P.-Commun. & Asst. Sec.--Staple Cotton Cooperative Association, Greenwood, MS; *U.S. Private*, pg. 1033
White, Virginia L., Treas. & Sec.--Perpetual Corporation, Washington, DC; *U.S. Private*, pg. 854
White, Virginia L., Sec. & Treas.--WJLA-TV, Washington, DC; *U.S. Private*, pg. 854
White, Virginia L., Treas. & Sec.--Allnewsco, Inc., Springfield, VA; *U.S. Private*, pg. 854
White, Virginia L., Treas. & Sec.--WSET Incorporatd, Lynchburg, VA; *U.S. Private*, pg. 854
White, Virginia L., Treas. & Sec.--WCIV, LLC, Mount Pleasant, SC; *U.S. Private*, pg. 854
White, Virginia L., Treas. & Sec.--Allbritton Group, Inc., Washington, DC; *U.S. Private*, pg. 854
White, Virginia L., Treas. & Sec.--Allfinco, Inc., Wilmington, DE; *U.S. Private*, pg. 854
White, Virginia L., Treas. & Sec.--Allbritton Jacksonville, Inc, Jacksonville, FL; *U.S. Private*, pg. 854
White, Virginia L., Treas. & Sec.--Harrisburg Television, Inc, Harrisburg, PA; *U.S. Private*, pg. 854
White, Virginia L., Treas. & Sec.--TV Alabama, Inc., Birmingham, AL; *U.S. Private*, pg. 854
Whitecotton, Liz, Sec. to Pres.--Eaton Metal Products Company, Denver, CO; *U.S. Private*, pg. 358
Whitehead, Adrian, Sec.--Siemens Corporation, New York, NY; *Int'l*, pg. 1245
Whiteman, Joseph D., V.P., Gen. Counsel & Sec.--Parker Hannifin Corporation, Cleveland, OH; *U.S. Public*, pg. 1259
Whiteside, Jeffrey W., Asst. Sec.--Indiana Gas Company, Inc., Indianapolis, IN; *U.S. Public*, pg. 875
Whitman, Barton D., Sec.--UGI Corporation, King of Prussia, PA; *U.S. Public*, pg. 1653
Whitmore, Bruce G., Sr. V.P., Gen. Counsel & Sec.--Atlantic Richfield Company, Los Angeles, CA; *U.S. Public*, pg. 144
Whitmore, Donald E., Jr., Chief Fin. Officer & Exec. V.P.--The Eastern Company, Naugatuck, CT; *U.S. Public*, pg. 548
Whitney, Wallace F., V.P.-Legal, Gen. Counsel & Clerk--Wyman-Gordon, North Grafton, MA; *U.S. Public*, pg. 1782
Whitsell, Helen J., Chm. Bd., Chief Exec. Officer & Treas.--Copeland Lumber Yard, Inc., Portland, OR; *U.S. Private*, pg. 274
Whitson, Brenda, Treas. & Sec.--Ricart Ford Inc., Groveport, OH; *U.S. Private*, pg. 927
Whitt, John R., Sr. V.P.-Mktg., Sls. & Sec.--Sherman & Reilly, Inc., Chattanooga, TN; *U.S. Private*, pg. 993
Whittaker, D., Gen. Counsel & Sec.--Racal Electronics Plc, Bracknell, United Kingdom; *Int'l*, pg. 1082
Whittaker, Martin, Sec.--Sunbeam Victa Holdings Ltd., Campsie, Australia; *Int'l*, pg. 539
Whitters, James P., III, Sec.--Robertson Factories, Inc., Taunton, MA; *U.S. Private*, pg. 936
Whittle, Susan Thomas, V.P., Gen. Counsel & Sec.--Paragon Health Network, Inc., Atlanta, GA; *U.S. Public*, pg. 1256
Wickham, Richard J., Sec.--Boeing Services, Inc., Khamis Mushayt, Saudi Arabia; *U.S. Public*, pg. 242
Wickman, Robert, Treas. & Sec.--Wigwam Mills, Inc., Sheboygan, WI; *U.S. Private*, pg. 1175
Widener, J.C., Sec.--Marley Floors (USA) Inc., Tuscumbia, AL; *Int'l*, pg. 843
Widener, James C., Sec.--General Shale Products Corp., Johnson City, TN; *Int'l*, pg. 843
Widener, James C., Sec.--General Shale Products Corp., Elizabethton, TN; *Int'l*, pg. 843
Widenmann, Faye, V.P.-Corp. Rels., Admin. & Sec.--Pinnacle West Capital Corporation, Phoenix, AZ; *U.S. Public*, pg. 1297
Widmark, K., Sec.--Perstorp Pharma AB, Lund, Sweden; *Int'l*, pg. 1036
Wieczorek, Robert R., V.P., Treas. & Sec.--Brooklyn Union, Brooklyn, NY; *U.S. Public*, pg. 259
Wiener, Michael A., Sec.--CBS Radio, New York, NY; *U.S. Public*, pg. 274
Wiener, Norma, Sec.--Lone Star Equities Inc., Lynbrook, NY; *U.S. Private*, pg. 674
Wiethoff, Charlotte, V.P.-Admin. & Sec.--Viking Office Products, Torrance, CA; *U.S. Public*, pg. 1720
Wiggins, Robert S., Chm. Bd., Chief Exec. Officer & Sec.--Technology Research Corporation, Clearwater, FL; *U.S. Public*, pg. 1564
Wigley, Spencer, Sec. & Dir.-, Legal, Internal Audit & Risk Mngmt.--Bass PLC, London, United Kingdom; *Int'l*, pg. 169
Wilbert, Judith F., Sec.--Micros Systems Inc., Beltsville, MD; *U.S. Public*, pg. 1106
Wilbur, Peter, Sec.--BP America Inc., Cleveland, OH; *Int'l*, pg. 220
Wilcox, Arthur M., Sec.--Evening Post Publishing Co., Charleston, SC; *U.S. Private*, pg. 385
Wilcox, Terry, Treas. & Sec.--Charles Machine Works, Inc., Perry, OK; *U.S. Private*, pg. 230
Wild, Julian, Sec.--Northern Foods plc, Hull, United Kingdom; *Int'l*, pg. 967
Wilder, Margaret T., Asst. Sec.--Trustmark National Bank, Jackson, MS; *U.S. Public*, pg. 1643
Wilder, Michael S., Sec. & Gen. Counsel--Hartford International Insurance Company, Hartford, CT; *U.S. Public*, pg. 795
Wiley, Alan E., Chief Fin. & Admin. Officer, Sr. Exec. V.P. & Sec.--The Cato Corporation, Charlotte, NC; *U.S. Public*, pg. 318
Wiley, Edwin P., Sec.--The Shaler Company, Waupun, WI; *U.S. Private*, pg. 786
Wilhelmi, Darlene, Exec. Sec.--Aurora Pump, North Aurora, IL; *U.S. Public*, pg. 726
Wilhoit, T.A., Sec.--Phoenix Fuel Company, Inc., Phoenix, AZ; *U.S. Private*, pg. 863
Wiliiams, Roy C., Gen. Counsel & Sec.--Inchcape PLC, London, United Kingdom; *Int'l*, pg. 671
Wilke, J.A., Asst. Sec. & Corp. Attorney--Hein-Werner Corporation, Waukesha, WI; *U.S. Public*, pg. 805
Wilken, C.H., Sec.--Jardine Matheson Holdings Limited, Hamilton, Bermuda; *Int'l*, pg. 703
Wilkerson, O.A., III, Sr. V.P., Treas. & Sec.--Smith Industries, Inc., Montgomery, AL; *U.S. Private*, pg. 1008
Wilkerson, Patricia A., Corp. Sec.--Dominion Lands, Inc., Richmond, VA; *U.S. Public*, pg. 516
Wilkerson, Wayne, Sec.--Brookshire Bros., Ltd., Lufkin, TX; *U.S. Private*, pg. 172
Wilkie, Ian C., Sr. V.P.-Strategic Devel., Gen. Counsel & Sec.--Cara Operations Limited, Toronto, Canada; *Int'l*, pg. 266
Wilkinson, Anthony, Sec.--Allied Domecq Retailing Limited, Burton on Trent, United Kingdom; *Int'l*, pg. 63
Wilks, Marylaurel E., V.P.-Commun., Gen. Counsel & Sec.--Speedway Motorsports, Inc., Concord, NC; *U.S. Public*, pg. 1498
Willems, Ilse P., Assoc. Gen. Counsel & Asst. Sec.--Alleghany Corporation, New York, NY; *U.S. Public*, pg. 42
Willert, Willimae C., V.P. & Sec.--Willert Home Products, Inc., Saint Louis, MO; *U.S. Private*, pg. 1177
Willi, Ernst, Dr., Sr. V.P.-Admin. & Opers. & Sec.--Georg Fischer Ltd., Schaffhausen, Switzerland; *Int'l*, pg. 488
Williams, Alan R., V.P. & Sec.--Williams Company Of Orlando, Inc., Orlando, FL; *U.S. Private*, pg. 1177
Williams, Belton R., Corp. & Sec.--George W. Auch Co., Pontiac, MI; *U.S. Private*, pg. 98
Williams, Beverly J., V.P.-Personnel/Admin. & Sec.--Boss Manufacturing Company, Kewanee, IL; *U.S. Private*, pg. 1142
Williams, Blanche, Treas. & Sec.--Fountain Powerboat Industries, Inc., Washington, NC; *U.S. Public*, pg. 678
Williams, Byron, Co-Chm. Bd. & Sec.--Clayton, Williams & Sherwood, Inc., Newport Beach, CA; *U.S. Private*, pg. 245
Williams, Cheryl, Chief Fin. Officer & Sec.--Prime Medical Services, Inc., Austin, TX; *U.S. Public*, pg. 1327
Williams, David E., Chief Fin. Officer, Sr. V.P., Sec. & Treas.--Ethika Corporation, Hilton Head Island, SC; *U.S. Public*, pg. 595
Williams, David H., V.P.-Fin. & Sec.--TVESCO, Inc., Memphis, TN; *U.S. Private*, pg. 1066
Williams, David K., Exec. V.P., Controller & Sec.--Killearn Properties, Inc., Stockbridge, GA; *U.S. Public*, pg. 956
Williams, Doris, Exec. V.P. & Sec.--Jay Jacobs, Inc., Seattle, WA; *U.S. Public*, pg. 922
Williams, Faye M., Treas. & Sec.--Northwest Tobacco & Candy Co., Fayetteville, AR; *U.S. Private*, pg. 806
Williams, G.G., Treas. & Sec.--Williams-Rolls, Inc., Walled Lake, MI; *U.S. Private*, pg. 1178
Williams, Gregory O., Sr. V.P., Sec. & Treas.--Rothchild Asset Management Inc., New York, NY; *U.S. Private*, pg. 947
Williams, J. Vernon, Asst. Sec.--Airborne Freight Corporation, Seattle, WA; *U.S. Public*, pg. 32
Williams, Jill L., Sec.--Genova Products, Inc., Davison, MI; *U.S. Private*, pg. 447
Williams, Jimmie D., Chief Fin. Officer, Exec. V.P., Treas. & Sec.--Belz Enterprises, Memphis, TN; *U.S. Private*, pg. 132
Williams, JoAnn, Exec. Sec.--Laboratory Supply Company, Inc., Louisville, KY; *U.S. Private*, pg. 641
Williams, Joseph M., Treas. & Sec.--Kimmins Corp., Tampa, FL; *U.S. Public*, pg. 960
Williams, Keith, V.P.-Admin., Controller, Treas. & Sec.--Perry Brothers, Inc., Lufkin, TX; *U.S. Private*, pg. 854
Williams, Lynn M., Sec.--SCANA Corporation, Columbia, SC; *U.S. Public*, pg. 1436
Williams, Marianne S., Asst. Sec.--Martin Marietta International, Inc., Bethesda, MD; *U.S. Public*, pg. 1009
Williams, Martha G., V.P., Sec. & Legal--Liberty Corporation, Greenville, SC; *U.S. Public*, pg. 991
Williams, Mary, Sr. V.P. & Asst. Sec.--American Reliable Insurance Company, Scottsdale, AZ; *U.S. Public*, pg. 67
Williams, Maude C., Asst. Sec.--FHB Properties, Inc., Honolulu, HI; *U.S. Public*, pg. 635
Williams, Maude C., Asst. Sec.--Pacific One Dealer Center, Inc., Costa Mesa, CA; *U.S. Public*, pg. 635
Williams, Maude C., Asst. Sec.--Real Estate Delivery, Inc., Honolulu, HI; *U.S. Public*, pg. 635
Williams, Melvin, Sec. & Treas.--Besche Oil Company, Inc., Waldorf, MD; *U.S. Private*, pg. 139
Williams, Nancy, Sec.--Lowe's Food Stores, Inc., Winston Salem, NC; *U.S. Private*, pg. 657
Williams, Nicole S., Chief Fin. Officer, Exec. V.P.-Fin. & Sec.--R.P. Scherer Corporation, Troy, MI; *U.S. Public*, pg. 1437
Williams, Peter E., Chief Fin. Officer, V.P.-Fin. & Asst. Sec.--WD-40 Company, San Diego, CA; *U.S. Public*, pg. 1726
Williams, Philip A., Pres., Trust Officer & Sec. of the Bd.--Farmers and Merchants Bank of Carlinville, Carlinville, IL; *U.S. Public*, pg. 644
Williams, R.A., Vice Chm., Chief Exec. Officer & Sec.--Presstek, Inc., Hudson, NH; *U.S. Public*, pg. 1324
Williams, Robert I., Reg. Counsel & Asst. Sec.--OHM Remediation Services Corp., Findlay, OH; *U.S. Public*, pg. 1208
Williams, Robert M., Asst. Sec.--Carolina Power & Light Company, Raleigh, NC; *U.S. Public*, pg. 306
Williams, Ronald E., V.P.-Fin. & Sec.--Anaheim Manufacturing Company, Anaheim, CA; *U.S. Private*, pg. 70
Williams, Rose Marie, Corp. Sec.--IMC Global, Bannockburn, IL; *U.S. Public*, pg. 856
Williams, Rose Marie, Corp. Sec.--The Vigoro Corporation, Chicago, IL; *U.S. Public*, pg. 856
Williams, S.G., Joint Sec.--Unilever Plc, London, United Kingdom; *Int'l*, pg. 1433
Williams, Thomas A., Chief Fin. Officer, V.P., Treas. & Sec.--Houghton International Inc., Valley Forge, PA; *U.S. Private*, pg. 541
Williams, Thomas C., Treas., Controller & Asst. Sec.--Florida Tile Industries, Inc., Lakeland, FL; *U.S. Public*, pg. 1322
Williams, Thomas J., Assoc. Gen. Counsel & Asst. Sec.--The Stanley Works, New Britain, CT; *U.S. Public*, pg. 1508
Williams, Victor J., Treas. & Sec.--Select Sires, Inc., Plain City, OH; *U.S. Private*, pg. 982
Williamson, Daphne, Treas. & Sec.--Airline Manufacturing Company, Inc., Columbus, MS; *U.S. Private*, pg. 29
Williamson, Dennis, Treas. & Asst. Sec.--Barnes & Reinecke, Inc., Arlington Heights, IL; *U.S. Public*, pg. 49
Williamson, Warren, Sec.--Hollywood Park, Inc., Inglewood, CA; *U.S. Public*, pg. 830
Willis, A.J., Sec.--LucasVarity plc, London, United Kingdom; *Int'l*, pg. 819
Willis, Mary S., Asst. Sec.--Holnam Inc. (West Division), Lakewood, CO; *Int'l*, pg. 628
Willmschen, Robert W., Chief Fin. Officer, Sr. V.P. & Sec.--ABC Rail Products Corp., Chicago, IL; *U.S. Public*, pg. 2
Willoch, Raymond S., V.P., Gen. Counsel & Sec.--Interface Inc., Atlanta, GA; *U.S. Public*, pg. 889
Willoughby, H. William, Pres. & Sec.--CRIIMI MAE, Rockville, MD; *U.S. Public*, pg. 459
Wills, R.J., Treas. & Sec.--A. Tenenbaum Co. Inc., North Little Rock, AR; *U.S. Private*, pg. 1076
Willson, Roxanne, Sec. & Mgr.-Human Resources--Griffin Envelope, Inc., Seattle, WA; *U.S. Public*, pg. 1038
Wilson, Alan A., Grp. Mng. Dir.--Skandia Life Assurance Co. Ltd., Southampton, United Kingdom; *Int'l*, pg. 1258
Wilson, Charles, Sec.--Nationwide Building Society, Swindon, United Kingdom; *Int'l*, pg. 912
Wilson, David, Sec.--B.A.T Industries P.L.C., London, United Kingdom; *Int'l*, pg. 110
Wilson, Donald, Corp. Sec.--ESELCO, Inc., Sault Sainte Marie, MI; *U.S. Public*, pg. 591
Wilson, J. Lynn, Chief Fin. Officer, Treas. & Sec.--Nashville Machine Co. Inc., Nashville, TN; *U.S. Private*, pg. 774
Wilson, Jesse M., Sr., Treas. & Sec.--Apollo Colors Inc., Northbrook, IL; *U.S. Private*, pg. 77
Wilson, Joan M., V.P. & Sec.--Moore Corporation Limited, Toronto, Canada; *Int'l*, pg. 888
Wilson, Kim, Sec.--Miller & Smith, Inc., Mc Lean, VA; *U.S. Private*, pg. 746
Wilson, Laurence E., V.P. & Sec.--Cypress Acquisition, Inc., Houston, TX; *U.S. Public*, pg. 1517
Wilson, Laurence E., V.P. & Sec.--S & S (Dihall) Cogeneration, Inc., Houston, TX; *U.S. Public*, pg. 1517
Wilson, Laurence E., V.P. & Sec.--Stewart & Stevenson de las Americas, Inc., Houston, TX; *U.S. Public*, pg. 1517
Wilson, Laurence E., V.P. & Sec.--Stewart & Stevenson Vehicle Services, Inc., Houston, TX; *U.S. Public*, pg. 1518
Wilson, Laurence E., V.P. & Sec.--Takumei Kumiai Holdings, Inc., Houston, TX; *U.S. Public*, pg. 1518
Wilson, Lawrence E., V.P. & Sec.--Stewart & Stevenson Services, Inc., Houston, TX; *U.S. Public*, pg. 1517
Wilson, Lawrence E., V.P. & Sec.--Stewart & Stevenson International, Inc., Houston, TX; *U.S. Public*, pg. 1517
Wilson, Lawrence E., Sec.--Machinery Acceptance Corporation, Houston, TX; *U.S. Public*, pg. 1517
Wilson, Logan J., V.P.-Legal Affairs & Sec.--Fike Corporation, Blue Springs, MO; *U.S. Private*, pg. 404

Wilson, Lorie Ann, Sec.--BellSouth Information Systems, Inc. (BIS), Atlanta, GA; *U.S. Public*, pg. 208
Wilson, Martin D., Pres., Chief Oper. Officer & Sec.--D & K Healthcare Resources, Inc., Saint Louis, MO; *U.S. Public*, pg. 471
Wilson, N.W., III, V.P.-Americas--Union Texas Petroleum Holdings, Houston, TX; *U.S. Public*, pg. 1669
Wilson, Paige H., V.P., Treas. & Sec.--Heilig-Meyers Company, Richmond, VA; *U.S. Public*, pg. 804
Wilson, Paul, Asst. Sec.--Allied Colloids Group Plc., Bradford, United Kingdom; *Int'l*, pg. 62
Wilson, Rob, Treas. & Sec.--Hubler Chevrolet Inc., Indianapolis, IN; *U.S. Private*, pg. 545
Wilson, Robert M., Chief Fin. Officer, Exec. V.P., Gen. Counsel & Sec.--Roberds, Inc., Carrollton, OH; *U.S. Public*, pg. 1393
Wilson, Robert W., Chief Fin. Officer, Exec. V.P., Controller, Treas. & Asst. Sec.--Supreme Industries, Inc., Goshen, IN; *U.S. Public*, pg. 1541
Wilson, Sarah L., Exec. Sec.--Cives Corporation, Roswell, GA; *U.S. Private*, pg. 241
Wilson, Steven E., Chief Fin. Officer, Exec. V.P., Treas. & Sec.--United Bankshares, Inc., Parkersburg, WV; *U.S. Public*, pg. 1674
Wilson, William T., Sec.--Siemens Automotive Corporation, Auburn Hills, MI; *Int'l*, pg. 1245
Wiltshire, J.A., Corp. Sec.--Eagle Star, Cheltenham, United Kingdom; *Int'l*, pg. 110
Wiltshire, J.M., Jr., V.P., Gen. Counsel & Sec.--Home Beneficial Corporation, Richmond, VA; *U.S. Public*, pg. 76
Wilzig, Alan J., Sec.--The Trust Company of New Jersey, Jersey City, NJ; *U.S. Public*, pg. 1643
Windridge, Susan, Sec.--British Aerospace p.l.c., Farnborough, United Kingdom; *Int'l*, pg. 217
Wine, Mitchell S.T., Sec.--JB Oxford Holdings Inc., Beverly Hills, CA; *U.S. Public*, pg. 916
Winfree, Sara Lynn, Asst. Sec.--Wynn's-Precision, Inc., Lebanon, TN; *U.S. Public*, pg. 1783
Wing, A. Shoon Poo, Sec.--Teamwork Corporation Sdn Bhd, Kuala Lumpur, Malaysia; *Int'l*, pg. 1360
Wingfield, E.N., Corp. Sec.--Rothmans (UK) Ltd., Aylesbury, United Kingdom; *Int'l*, pg. 1130
Winiarski, Victor A., Treas. & Sec.--Progressive Tool & Industries Co., Southfield, MI; *U.S. Private*, pg. 890
Winkels, Thomas, Sec. & Treas.--McNeilus Companies, Dodge Center, MN; *U.S. Private*, pg. 725
Winkleman, Henry W., Sec.--American Biltrite Inc., Wellesley Hills, MA; *U.S. Public*, pg. 68
Winkler, William F., Chief Oper. Officer, Treas. & Sec.--Ackerman McQueen, Inc., Oklahoma City, OK; *U.S. Private*, pg. 12
Winnick, Burton, Gen. Counsel--Asahi/America, Inc., Malden, MA; *U.S. Public*, pg. 137
Winquist, Donna F., V.P., Gen. Counsel & Sec.--AMETEK, Inc., Paoli, PA; *U.S. Public*, pg. 99
Winslow, James E., Chief Fin. Officer, Exec. V.P. & Sec.--Home Products International, Inc., Chicago, IL; *U.S. Public*, pg. 832
Winston, Carolyn, Asst. Sec.--Dewberry Design Group, Oklahoma City, OK; *U.S. Private*, pg. 329
Winter, Dee, Corp. Sec. & Admin./Opers.--J.W. Messner, Inc., Grand Rapids, MI; *U.S. Private*, pg. 734
Wirackara, Anil, Chief Fin. Officer & Sec.--MacDonald Dettwiler & Associates Ltd., Richmond, Canada; *U.S. Public*, pg. 1229
Wirth, Peter, Sec.--IG Laboratories, Inc., Framingham, MA; *U.S. Public*, pg. 733
Wise, Barbara, Sec.--Alfin, Inc., New York, NY; *U.S. Public*, pg. 40
Wise, Chris, Sec.--Grand Prairie Co-op, Inc., Tolono, IL; *U.S. Private*, pg. 468
Wise, Chris, V.P.-Fin., Treas. & Sec.--Southco Distributing Company, Goldsboro, NC; *U.S. Private*, pg. 1014
Wise, Gerald, Asst. Treas. & Asst. Sec.--Fina, Inc., Dallas, TX; *Int'l*, pg. 1044
Wise, John A., Jr., Sec.--HomeTown Communications Network, Inc., Livonia, MI; *U.S. Private*, pg. 537
Wise, Richard, Sec. & Gen. Counsel--Mississippi Valley Gas Co., Jackson, MS; *U.S. Private*, pg. 753
Wise, Ronald L., Treas. & Sec.--E & A Industries, Inc., Indianapolis, IN; *U.S. Private*, pg. 352
Wiseman, Donald F., V.P., Gen. Counsel & Sec.--Perkins Family Restaurants, Memphis, TN; *U.S. Private*, pg. 925
Wiseman, Ronald D., Controller & Asst. Sec.--Thomas Industries Inc., Louisville, KY; *U.S. Public*, pg. 1598
Wiskind, Milton I., Sr. V.P. & Sec.--Myers Industries, Inc., Akron, OH; *U.S. Public*, pg. 1143
Wiskowski, Carol A., Asst. V.P.-Admin. & Asst. Sec.--Madison Gas and Electric Company, Madison, WI; *U.S. Public*, pg. 1032
Wisniewski, Robert E., Treas. & Sec.--Moore Products Co., Spring House, PA; *U.S. Public*, pg. 1128
Wisotsky, Helen E., Chm. Bd., Sec. & Treas.--Imperial Litho & Dryography, Inc., Phoenix, AZ; *U.S. Private*, pg. 558
Withers, W.W., Sr. V.P., Gen. Counsel & Sec.--Emerson Electric Co., Saint Louis, MO; *U.S. Public*, pg. 572
Witmer, John H., Jr., Sr. V.P., Gen. Counsel & Sec.--Dekalb Genetics Corporation, De Kalb, IL; *U.S. Public*, pg. 493
Witmer, John H., Jr., V.P. & Sec.--DeKalb Swine Breeders, Inc., De Kalb, IL; *U.S. Public*, pg. 493
Witter, Jill, V.P., Sec. & Gen. Counsel--Angelica Corporation, Chesterfield, MO; *U.S. Public*, pg. 113
Wittkowske, John, Sec. & Treas.--Weyco Group, Inc., Milwaukee, WI; *U.S. Public*, pg. 1763
Wittman, T. Scott, Pres., Sec. & Treas.--Vantage Global Advisors, Inc., New York, NY; *U.S. Public*, pg. 998
Wittmeyer, K.E., V.P. & Sec.--Blue Chip Stamps, Los Angeles, CA; *U.S. Public*, pg. 217
Wiznitzer, Jane T., V.P.-Legal Affairs & Sec.--Trenwick Group Inc., Stamford, CT; *U.S. Public*, pg. 1634
Woessner, Ron, Gen. Counsel & Sec.--Amtech Corporation, Dallas, TX; *U.S. Public*, pg. 105
Wohl, Richard H., Sr. Exec. V.P., Gen. Counsel & Sec.--INMC Mortgage Holdings, Inc., Pasadena, CA; *U.S. Public*, pg. 857
Wohlman, Herbert, Dr., Gen. Counsel, Sec. & Head-Legal Dept.--Clariant International Ltd., Muttenz, Switzerland; *Int'l*, pg. 624
Wohnsen, Joraen, Exec. V.P. & Sec.--Nykredit, Copenhagen, Denmark; *Int'l*, pg. 993
Woizeski, Debbie, Asst. Sec.--Northwestern Engineering Co., Rapid City, SD; *U.S. Private*, pg. 806
Wojnowski, Leon A., Chief Oper. Officer, Chief Fin. Officer, Treas. & Sec.--Connelly Containers, Inc., Bala Cynwyd, PA; *U.S. Private*, pg. 264
Wojtowecz, Reita, Dir.-Personnel & Sec.--Espey Mfg. & Electronics Corp., Saratoga Springs, NY; *U.S. Public*, pg. 592
Wolf, Christopher F., Chief Fin. Officer, Sr. V.P., Treas. & Sec.--Swank, Inc., Attleboro, MA; *U.S. Public*, pg. 1543
Wolf, Dale J., V.P.-Fin. & Sec.--UtiliCorp United Inc., Kansas City, MO; *U.S. Public*, pg. 1700
Wolf, Howard B., Chm. Bd. & Sec.--Howard B. Wolf, Inc., Dallas, TX; *U.S. Public*, pg. 1774
Wolf, Karen, Sec.--Kitchell Corporation, Phoenix, AZ; *U.S. Private*, pg. 624
Wolf, Lawrence, Pres., Chief Exec. Officer, Treas. & Sec.--Leonard Wholesale, Inc., Springfield, NJ; *U.S. Private*, pg. 660
Wolf, Norman, Chief Exec. Officer, Treas. & Sec.--Carole Wren, Inc., New York, NY; *U.S. Private*, pg. 1192
Wolf, Philip C., Sr. V.P., Gen. Counsel & Sec.--Cyprus Amax Minerals Company, Englewood, CO; *U.S. Public*, pg. 470
Wolf, R. B., Sec.--Brunner & Lay, Inc., Springdale, AR; *U.S. Private*, pg. 176
Wolf, Roger J., Chief Fin. Officer, Sr. V.P., Sec. & Treas.--Hurco Companies, Inc., Indianapolis, IN; *U.S. Public*, pg. 850
Wolf, Steven A., Chief Fin. Officer & Sec.--Ryka Incorporated, King of Prussia, PA; *U.S. Public*, pg. 1414
Wolfcale, A.D., V.P., Deputy Gen. Counsel & Sec.--The Edward J. DeBartolo Corporation, Youngstown, OH; *U.S. Private*, pg. 319
Wolfe, Carroll, Controller & Treas.--The Mad Butcher, Inc., Pine Bluff, AR; *U.S. Private*, pg. 693
Wolfe, J.H., V.P., Gen. Counsel & Sec.--Raytheon Engineers & Constructors International, Inc., Lexington, MA; *U.S. Public*, pg. 1366
Wolfe, Lawrence A., Exec. V.P. & Sec.--Production Tool Supply Co., Warren, MI; *U.S. Private*, pg. 889
Wolfe, Robert F., Comptroller, Treas. & Sec.--Ardco, Inc., Alsip, IL; *U.S. Private*, pg. 80
Wolfeiler, Bernard, Mgr.-Risk Mngmt.--General Cigar Holdings Inc, New York, NY; *U.S. Public*, pg. 707
Wolff, Herbert E., Sr. V.P. & Sec.--First Hawaiian, Inc., Honolulu, HI; *U.S. Public*, pg. 634
Wolff, Herbert E., Sr. V.P. & Sec.--First Hawaiian Bank, Honolulu, HI; *U.S. Public*, pg. 634
Wolff, Herbert E., V.P. & Sec.--FHB Properties, Inc., Honolulu, HI; *U.S. Public*, pg. 635
Wolff, Herbert E., Sec.--FH Center, Inc., Honolulu, HI; *U.S. Public*, pg. 635
Wolff, Herbert E., Sec.--Pacific One Dealer Center, Inc., Costa Mesa, CA; *U.S. Public*, pg. 635
Wolff, Herbert E., V.P. & Sec.--Real Estate Delivery, Inc., Honolulu, HI; *U.S. Public*, pg. 635
Wolff, Herbert E., V.P. & Sec.--First Hawaiian Leasing, Inc., Honolulu, HI; *U.S. Public*, pg. 635
Wolff, Herbert E., V.P. & Sec.--American Security Properties, Inc., Honolulu, HI; *U.S. Public*, pg. 635
Wolff, Kathy, Exec. Sec. & Mgr.-Shareholder Rels.--Simpson Industries, Inc., Plymouth, MI; *U.S. Public*, pg. 1474
Wolff, Richard H., Sec. & Assoc. Gen. Counsel--Newell Co., Freeport, IL; *U.S. Public*, pg. 1176
Wolfgang, Dennis E., Mgr.-Employee Benefits & Asst. Sec.--North American Royalties, Inc., Chattanooga, TN; *U.S. Private*, pg. 803
Wolfington, James E., Exec. V.P. & Sec.--Wolfington Body Company, Exton, PA; *U.S. Private*, pg. 1186
Woll, Kathy, Sec.-Prod. Mgr.--General Microwave Corporation, Amityville, NY; *U.S. Public*, pg. 717
Wollen, A. Ross, Sr. V.P., Gen. Counsel & Sec.--General Cigar Holdings Inc, New York, NY; *U.S. Public*, pg. 707
Wolosky, Steven, Asst. Sec.--WHX Corporation, New York, NY; *U.S. Public*, pg. 1726
Wolski, Christine M., Asst. Corp. Sec.--Commerce Group Corp., Milwaukee, WI; *U.S. Public*, pg. 410
Wolter, Gary J., Sr. V.P.-Admin. & Sec.--Madison Gas and Electric Company, Madison, WI; *U.S. Public*, pg. 1032
Wolter, Howard J., Controller & Asst. Sec.--Jason Incorporated, Milwaukee, WI; *U.S. Public*, pg. 923
Woltz, William, Sr., Treas. & Sec.--Page Holdings, Inc., Mount Airy, NC; *U.S. Private*, pg. 834
Wolynec, Gail, Asst. V.P. & Asst. Sec.--Pulse Bancorp, Inc., South River, NJ; *U.S. Public*, pg. 1344
Womack, C. Suzanne, Sec.--Lincoln National Corporation, Fort Wayne, IN; *U.S. Public*, pg. 997
Womack, C. Suzanne, Sec.--Lincoln Financial Group, Inc., Fort Wayne, IN; *U.S. Public*, pg. 997
Womack, C. Suzanne, Sec.--The Richard Leahy Corporation, Fort Wayne, IN; *U.S. Public*, pg. 997
Womack, C. Suzanne, Sec.--Lincoln Investment Management Inc., Fort Wayne, IN; *U.S. Public*, pg. 998
Womack, C. Suzanne, Asst. V.P. & Sec.--The Lincoln National Life Insurance Co., Fort Wayne, IN; *U.S. Public*, pg. 998
Womack, C. Suzanne, Sec.--Lincoln Financial Advisors, Fort Wayne, IN; *U.S. Public*, pg. 998
Womack, C. Suzanne, Sec.--Lincoln National Administrative Services Corp., Fort Wayne, IN; *U.S. Public*, pg. 998
Womack, C. Suzanne, Sec.--Lincoln National Intermediaries, Inc., Fort Wayne, IN; *U.S. Public*, pg. 998
Womack, C. Suzanne, Sec.--Lincoln National Health & Casualty Insurance Co., Fort Wayne, IN; *U.S. Public*, pg. 998
Womack, C. Suzanne, Sec.--Lincoln National Realty Corporation, Fort Wayne, IN; *U.S. Public*, pg. 998
Womack, C. Suzanne, Sec.--Lincoln National (China) Inc., Fort Wayne, IN; *U.S. Public*, pg. 998
Womack, C. Suzanne, Sec.--Lincoln National Reinsurance Company (Barbados) Limited, Fort Wayne, IN; *U.S. Public*, pg. 998
Womack, C. Suzanne, Sec.--Lincoln National Reinsurance Company (Bermuda) Limited, Fort Wayne, IN; *U.S. Public*, pg. 998
Womack, C. Suzanne, Sec.--Lincoln National Risk Management, Inc., Fort Wayne, IN; *U.S. Public*, pg. 998
Womack, C. Suzanne, Sec.--Lincoln National Structured Settlement, Inc., Fort Wayne, IN; *U.S. Public*, pg. 998
Womack, C. Suzanne, Sec.--Old Fort Insurance Co., Ltd. (Bermuda), Hamilton, Bermuda; *U.S. Public*, pg. 998
Womack, C. Suzanne, Sec.--Underwriters & Management Services Inc., Indianapolis, IN; *U.S. Public*, pg. 998
Womble, W.R., Sec.--Vertex Communications Corporation, Kilgore, TX; *U.S. Public*, pg. 1717
Wong, Francis T., Treas. & Asst. Sec.--Homeland Holding Corp., Oklahoma City, OK; *U.S. Public*, pg. 832
Wong, Sandra C.H., Sec.--Servco Pacific Inc., Honolulu, HI; *U.S. Private*, pg. 986
Wong, Thomas H., Asst. Treas. & Asst. Sec.--Homestake Mining Company, San Francisco, CA; *U.S. Public*, pg. 832
Wonnell, Donn T., V.P.-Regulatory Affairs & Corp. Sec.--Pacific Telecom Cellular, Inc., Vancouver, WA; *U.S. Public*, pg. 1252
Wood, Barbara S., V.P., Controller, Treas. & Sec.--Independence Capital Management, Inc., Horsham, PA; *U.S. Private*, pg. 849
Wood, Betty T., Sec.--J.M. Smith Corp., Spartanburg, SC; *U.S. Private*, pg. 1008
Wood, Carol L., Asst. Sec.--Albertson's, Inc., Boise, ID; *U.S.* Public, pg. 38
Wood, Carol S., Chief Fin. Officer, Controller, Treas. & Sec.--Higginbotham-Bartlett Co., Lubbock, TX; *U.S. Private*, pg. 527
Wood, David, V.P. & Gen. Counsel--Safelite AutoGlass, Columbus, OH; *U.S. Private*, pg. 960
Wood, George N., V.P., Gen. Counsel & Sec.--Celotex Corporation, Tampa, FL; *U.S. Private*, pg. 221
Wood, Kathryn C., V.P.-Human Resources--Plasti-Line, Inc., Knoxville, TN; *U.S. Public*, pg. 1308
Wood, Ken, V.P. & Sec.--Barringer Technologies Inc., New Providence, NJ; *U.S. Public*, pg. 191
Wood, Kenneth R., Sec.--J.R. Wood Inc., Atwater, CA; *U.S. Private*, pg. 1186
Wood, Larry, Treas. & Sec.--First Electric Cooperative, Corp., Jacksonville, AR; *U.S. Private*, pg. 407
Wood, Linda J., Asst. Sec.--IMC Global, Bannockburn, IL; *U.S. Public*, pg. 856
Wood, Nell, Sec.--Chuck Hutton Chevrolet Company, Memphis, TN; *U.S. Private*, pg. 550
Wood, R.S., Sec. & Asst. Treas.--P.H. Glatfelter Company, Spring Grove, PA; *U.S. Public*, pg. 746
Wood, Rene M., V.P.-Fin. & Sec.--McNeel International Corp., Tampa, FL; *U.S. Private*, pg. 724
Wood, Richard A., Jr., Gen. Counsel & Asst. Sec--Wellco Enterprises, Inc., Waynesville, NC; *U.S. Public*, pg. 1752
Woodard, Elizabeth B., V.P., Gen. Counsel & Sec.--Riviana Foods Inc., Houston, TX; *U.S. Public*, pg. 1392
Woodbury, A.T., V.P., Sec. & Assoc. Counsel--Fidelity Mutual Life Insurance Co., Radnor, PA; *U.S. Private*, pg. 403
Woodham, Peggy S., Sec.--American Buildings Co., Eufaula, AL; *U.S. Public*, pg. 69
Woodland, Paul R., Chief Fin. Officer, V.P.-Fin. & Admin. & Asst. Sec.--Dreyer's Grand Ice Cream, Inc., Oakland, CA; *U.S. Public*, pg. 529
Woodruff, J. David, Jr., V.P.-Legal & Corp. Devel. & Asst. Sec.--Energen Corporation, Birmingham, AL; *U.S. Public*, pg. 581
Woods, Andrew, Sec.--Gestetner Holdings PLC, London, United Kingdom; *Int'l*, pg. 1114
Woods, Chris, Mgr.-Sls.--Howell Packaging, Burlington, Canada; *Int'l*, pg. 417
Woods, Marilyn, Sec.--ISI Norgen, Inc., Fraser, MI; *Int'l*, pg. 646
Woods, Nina Jo, Sec.--Joe E. Woods, Inc., Mesa, AZ; *U.S. Private*, pg. 1187
Woodward, A. Davis, V.P.-Legal, Sec., Asst. Gen. Counsel & Dir.-Tax Plng.--Surgical Laser Technologies, Inc., Montgomeryville, PA; *U.S. Public*, pg. 1542
Woodward, Chontelle, Sec.--Meridian Medical Technology, Inc., Columbia, MD; *U.S. Public*, pg. 1095
Woodward, David A., Treas.--Grocers Capital Co., Los Angeles, CA; *U.S. Private*, pg. 227
Woodward, David A., Treas.--Grocers Development Co., Los Angeles, CA; *U.S. Private*, pg. 227
Woodward, David A., Treas.--Crown Grocers, Inc., Los Angeles, CA; *U.S. Private*, pg. 227
Woodward, Fielden, Sec.--Kitchen Kompact, Inc., Jeffersonville, IN; *U.S. Private*, pg. 624
Woodward, K., Chief Legal Officer & Sec.--John Mowlem & Company plc, Isleworth, United Kingdom; *Int'l*, pg. 896
Wooters, Thoams A., Sec. & Gen. Counsel--LoJack Corporation, Dedham, MA; *U.S. Public*, pg. 1012
Wooters, Thomas A., Sec. & Clerk--Starmet Corporation, Concord, MA; *U.S. Public*, pg. 1511
Worcester, Theodore E., Sr. V.P.-Law & Admin. & Gen. Counsel--Westmoreland Coal Co., Colorado Springs, CO; *U.S. Public*, pg. 1761
Word, Tammy, Dir.-H.R. & Sec.--URS Logistics, Atlanta, GA; *U.S. Private*, pg. 1114
Worner, Meredith, Sec.--Menard Electric Cooperative, Petersburg, IL; *U.S. Private*, pg. 731
Worrell, Judy, Treas. & Sec.--Berry Companies, Inc., Wichita, KS; *U.S. Private*, pg. 137
Worthing, Robert W., V.P., Gen. Counsel & Sec.--AAI Corporation, Hunt Valley, MD; *U.S. Public*, pg. 1679

Woudstra, F. Robert, Exec. V.P. & Treas.--American Federation Insurance Co., Grand Rapids, MI; *U.S. Public, pg. 667*
Wraight, Clark, V.P., Treas. & Sec.--Cabre Corp., Wilmington, DE; *U.S. Public*, pg. 289
Wright Jr., Jackson, Attorney--Semco Industries Inc., Stoughton, MA; *U.S. Private*, pg. 983
Wright, D. J., Exec. Dir. & Sec.--Chloride Group PLC, London, United Kingdom; *Int'l*, pg. 287
Wright, Donald J., V.P.-Admin. & Sec.--United States Cold Storage, Inc., Cherry Hill, NJ; *U.S. Private*, pg. 1124
Wright, G.J., V.P., Gen. Counsel & Sec.--ABB Lummus Global Inc., Bloomfield, NJ; *Int'l*, pg. 4
Wright, James W., V.P. & Sec.--Bankmanagers Corp., Milwaukee, WI; *U.S. Private*, pg. 114
Wright, James W., V.P.-Legal Affairs & Sec.--Lord Corporation, Cary, NC; *U.S. Private*, pg. 675
Wright, John, Sec. & Treas.--American National Insurance Service Co., Springfield, MO; *U.S. Public*, pg. 88
Wright, John K., V.P., Sr. Assoc. Counsel & Sec.--Protective Life Insurance Co., Birmingham, AL; *U.S. Public*, pg. 1336
Wright, Lori, V.P.-Fin., Treas. & Sec.--Helm, Inc., Detroit, MI; *U.S. Private*, pg. 520
Wright, Mary Ann, V.P. & Asst. Sec.--American Heritage Life Investment Corp., Jacksonville, FL; *U.S. Public*, pg. 78
Wright, Mary Ann, V.P. & Asst. Sec.--American Heritage Life Insurance Co., Jacksonville, FL; *U.S. Public*, pg. 79
Wright, Norman B., Exec. V.P. & Corp. Sec.--Alias Wavefront, Toronto, Canada; *U.S. Public*, pg. 1474
Wright, P. Jane, Sec.--Ralph C. Wilson Enterprises, Detroit, MI; *U.S. Private*, pg. 1181
Wright, Robert, V.P.-Fin., Treas. & Sec.--W.C. Bradley Co., Columbus, GA; *U.S. Private*, pg. 164
Wright, Rosemary, Treas. & Sec.--Mayfield Building Supply Co., Arlington, TX; *U.S. Private*, pg. 686
Wright, Steven J., Asst. Sec.--Republic New York Corporation, New York, NY; *U.S. Public*, pg. 1380
Wright, Theodore M., Chief Fin. Officer, V.P.-Fin., Treas. & Sec.--Sonic Automotive, Inc., Charlotte, NC; *U.S. Public*, pg. 1485
Wright, Timothy C., Gen. Counsel & Sec.--National-Standard Co., Niles, MI; *U.S. Public*, pg. 1160
Wright, Wayne C., Treas. & Sec.--Copper & Brass Sales, Inc., Eastpointe, MI; *Int'l*, pg. 1389
Wrobel, Robert, Chief Legal Officer & V.P.--Alpharma Inc., Fort Lee, NJ; *U.S. Public*, pg. 57
Wu, Chia-Ling, Chief Sec.-Bd.--Chinese Petroleum Corporation, Taipei, Taiwan; *Int'l*, pg. 286
Wu, Silas, Sec.--Kintetsu World Express (H.K.) Ltd., Kowloon, Hong Kong; *Int'l*, pg. 735
Wuestner, Joseph A., Assoc. Gen. Counsel & Asst. Sec.--Mallinckrodt Inc., Saint Louis, MO; *U.S. Public*, pg. 1039
Wujcik, Grace, Treas. & Sec.--Peace River Electric Cooperative, Inc., Wauchula, FL; *U.S. Private*, pg. 845
Wulf, Lloyd G., Sec.--Rissler & McMurry Company, Casper, WY; *U.S. Private*, pg. 933
Wulff, Robert, Sec. & Clerk--New England Power Service Co., Westborough, MA; *U.S. Public*, pg. 1171
Wurbs, Wolfgang, Sec.--Stadtsparkasse Munchen, Munich, Germany; *Int'l*, pg. 1293
Wurz, Jane, Treas. & Sec.--Accu-Sort Systems, Inc., Telford, PA; *U.S. Private*, pg. 11
Wushinske, Robert P., V.P., Treas., Gen. Counsel & Sec.--Pennsylvania Power Co., New Castle, PA; *U.S. Public*, pg. 645
Wust, Pierre, Treas., Controller & Chief Fin. Officer--Sandoz Pharma Ltd., Eden Terrace, New Zealand; *Int'l*, pg. 985
Wyatt, Bruce H., V.P., Gen. Counsel, Sec. & Clerk--Stanhome Inc., Westfield, MA; *U.S. Public*, pg. 1508
Wyatt, Jack D., Asst. Sec.--Nestle Holdings, Inc., Stamford, CT; *Int'l*, pg. 916
Wyche, C.T., Sec.--RSI Holdings Inc., Greenville, SC; *U.S. Public*, pg. 1358
Wynn, Jane M., Exec. V.P., Sec. & Treas.--Miller Electric Company, Jacksonville, FL; *U.S. Private*, pg. 747
Wynn, John R., Sec.--Intergraph Corporation, Huntsville, AL; *U.S. Public*, pg. 890
Wynn, Robert P., Chief Fin. Officer, Exec. V.P. & Sec.--AmeriPath, Inc., Riviera Beach, FL; *U.S. Public*, pg. 96
Wynne, Scott C., Exec. V.P.-Opers. & Sec.--Just For Feet, Inc., Pelham, AL; *U.S. Public*, pg. 935
Wynns, Carolyn, V.P.-H.R. & Sec.--Tri-State Armature & Electric Works, Memphis, TN; *U.S. Private*, pg. 1100
Wyrsch, Martha B., V.P., Deputy Gen. Counsel & Sec.--K N Energy, Inc., Lakewood, CO; *U.S. Public*, pg. 937
Wysinski, Robert, Chief Fin. Officer, V.P., Treas. & Sec.--Value City Department Stores, Inc., Columbus, OH; *U.S. Private*, pg. 972
Wysong, Phil, Chief Fin. Officer, Treas & Sec.--Jones Company, Inc., Waycross, GA; *U.S. Private*, pg. 596
Wysong, Phil, V.P. & Treas.--Fuel South, Inc., Hazlehurst, GA; *U.S. Private*, pg. 596
Xenis, Paul T., V.P.-Fin. & Sec.--Guest Supply, Inc., Monmouth Junction, NJ; *U.S. Public*, pg. 768
Yada, David, Treas. & Sec.--TACT Holding, South Pasadena, CA; *U.S. Private*, pg. 1067
Yager, Earl L., Chief Fin. Officer, Sr. V.P. & Sec.--Chad Therapeutics, Chatsworth, CA; *U.S. Public*, pg. 332
Yagi, Clyde H., Treas., Sec. & Dir.-Data Processing--Mutual Welding Co., Ltd, Honolulu, HI; *U.S. Private*, pg. 770
Yahav, David, Gen. Counsel & Sec.--The Israel Electric Corporation Ltd., Haifa, Israel; *Int'l*, pg. 690
Yamada, Yasu, Exec. Asst. to Chm. Bd.--Crestbrook Forest Industries Ltd., Cranbrook, Canada; *Int'l*, pg. 348
Yamaguchi, Kenji, Deputy Pres., Dir.-Plng., Pub. Rels., Gen. Affairs & Sec.--Yasuda Mutual Life Insurance Co., Tokyo, Japan; *Int'l*, pg. 1519
Yamamoto, Masashi, Asst. Sec.--Murata Electronics North America, Inc., Smyrna, GA; *Int'l*, pg. 897
Yamashita, Shuichi, V.P., Gen. Mgr. & Sec.--Nippo Marketing & Advertising, Inc., Torrance, CA; *Int'l*, pg. 932
Yancey, Carol B., Corp. Sec.--Genuine Parts Company, Atlanta, GA; *U.S. Public*, pg. 732
Yanes, Clementina, Gen. Counsel & Sec.--Corporacion Grupo Quimico, S.A.C.A., Caracas, Venezuela; *Int'l*, pg. 331
Yankovitch, Esraim, Sec.--Dubek Ltd., Tel Aviv, Israel; *Int'l*, pg. 421
Yannotti, Marie J., Asst. Sec.--Oriole Homes Corp., Delray Beach, FL; *U.S. Public*, pg. 1230
Yantis, Thomas G., Pres. & Chief Exec. Officer--Yantis Corporation, San Antonio, TX; *U.S. Private*, pg. 1195
Yara, Ronald T., Sr. V.P.-Strategic Mktg. & Sec.--S3 Incorporated, Santa Clara, CA; *U.S. Public*, pg. 1415
Yarbro, Alan D., Sr. V.P. & Sec.--Mercantile Bankshares Corporation, Baltimore, MD; *U.S. Public*, pg. 1088
Yarbro, Alan D., Sec.--MBC Agency, Inc., Baltimore, MD; *U.S. Public*, pg. 1089
Yared, Paul D., Sr. V.P., Gen. Counsel & Sec.--Foremost Corporation of America, Caledonia, MI; *U.S. Public*, pg. 667
Yastow, Shelby, Exec. V.P., Gen. Counsel & Sec.--McDonald's Corporation, Oak Brook, IL; *U.S. Public*, pg. 1068
Yates, J.M., Sec.--Graystone PLC, Wilmslow, United Kingdom; *Int'l*, pg. 557
Yates, Thomas H., Treas. & Sec.--Hopkinsville Milling Co., Hopkinsville, KY; *U.S. Private*, pg. 538
Yazgi, Abdo, Exec. V.P. & Sec.--Continental Can Co., Norwalk, CT; *U.S. Public*, pg. 439
Yeargan, Victor B., Jr., Treas. & Sec.--Battey Machinery Company, Rome, GA; *U.S. Private*, pg. 123
Yeary, Wilma, FLMI, Corp. Sec.--Kentucky Investors, Inc., Frankfort, KY; *U.S. Public*, pg. 951
Yeip, Robert L., Treas. & Corp. Sec.--Overhead Conveyor Co., Ferndale, MI; *U.S. Private*, pg. 822
Yellin, Michael R., V.P., Treas. & Sec.--Daniel Industries, Inc., Houston, TX; *U.S. Public*, pg. 482
Yerkes, Wendy V., Asst. Sec.--Indianapolis Power & Light Company, Indianapolis, IN; *U.S. Public*, pg. 913
Yestrumskas, Paul E., V.P., Gen. Counsel & Sec.--Playtex Products Inc., Westport, CT; *U.S. Public*, pg. 1310
Yetter, Thomas G., Treas. & Asst. Sec.--Frozen Food Express Industries, Inc., Dallas, TX; *U.S. Public*, pg. 685
Yip, Susan, Corp. Sec.--Johnson Electric Holdings Limited, Tai No, Hong Kong; *Int'l*, pg. 712
Ylitalo, Joe A., Gen. Counsel & Asst. Sec.--Vertex Communications Corporation, Kilgore, TX; *U.S. Public*, pg. 1717
Yoda, David, Sec. & Treas.--Trader Joe's Co., South Pasadena, CA; *U.S. Private*, pg. 1067
Yokley, Arlen G., Sr. V.P.-Corp. Compliance & Sec.--BellSouth Corporation, Atlanta, GA; *U.S. Public*, pg. 207
Yonker, Michael D., Chief Fin. Officer, V.P.-Fin. & Admin. & Treas.--In Focus Systems, Inc., Wilsonville, OR; *U.S. Public*, pg. 873
Yoo, Paul J., Chief Fin. Officer, Exec. V.P. & Sec.--Jockey International, Inc., Kenosha, WI; *U.S. Private*, pg. 588
York, Dan, Sec., Treas. & Controller--Peck Road Ford Truck Sales, Whittier, CA; *U.S. Private*, pg. 846
Yorks, W. Brinton, V.P. & Sec.--ATL Ultrasound, Inc., Bothell, WA; *U.S. Public*, pg. 11
Yosowitz, Sanford, V.P., Gen. Counsel & Sec.--Alcan Aluminum Corporation, Cleveland, OH; *Int'l*, pg. 50
Yost, Jan, Pres., Treas. & Sec.--D.S.U.-Peterbilt & GMC, Inc., Portland, OR; *U.S. Private*, pg. 306
Younanpour, Ailen, Asst. Corp. Sec.--Pacific Scientific Company, Newport Beach, CA; *U.S. Public*, pg. 1250
Young, Anita J.T., V.P. & Treas.--Lutheran Brotherhood, Minneapolis, MN; *U.S. Private*, pg. 681
Young, David L., First V.P. & Sec.--Atlantic Sugar Association, Inc., Belle Glade, FL; *U.S. Private*, pg. 95
Young, Dona D., Exec. V.P.-Individual Insurance Counsel--Phoenix Home Life Mutual Insurance Company, Hartford, CT; *U.S. Private*, pg. 863
Young, Fred C., Pres., Chief Oper. Officer, Treas. & Sec.--Black Box Corporation of PA, Lawrence, PA; *U.S. Public*, pg. 235
Young, George C., V.P.-Law & Sec.--Canyon Resources Corporation, Golden, CO; *U.S. Public*, pg. 301
Young, James B., V.P. & Sec.--Zilber, Ltd., Milwaukee, WI; *U.S. Private*, pg. 1206
Young, Jeffrey S., Sec.--Young Electric Sign Company, Salt Lake City, UT; *U.S. Private*, pg. 1201
Young, Judy, Sec.--Front Royal, Inc., Morrisville, NC; *U.S. Private*, pg. 430
Young, LeGrande L., V.P., Gen. Counsel & Sec.--Raytech Corporation, Shelton, CT; *U.S. Public*, pg. 1363
Young, Mark, Sec.--Lex Service PLC, Bourne, United Kingdom; *Int'l*, pg. 806
Young, Michael J., Sec.--NRG Energy, Inc., Minneapolis, MN; *U.S. Public*, pg. 1195
Young, Peter A., Exec. V.P. & Sec.--Burd & Fletcher Company, Kansas City, MO; *U.S. Private*, pg. 181
Young, Robert H., Chief Fin. Officer, Exec. V.P., Treas. & Corp. Sec.--First Western Bancorp, Inc., New Castle, PA; *U.S. Public*, pg. 642
Young, Sharon L., Asst. Sec.--Oriole Homes Corp., Delray Beach, FL; *U.S. Public*, pg. 1230
Young, Thomas L., Exec. V.P.-Admin., Gen. Counsel & Sec.--Owens-Illinois, Inc., Toledo, OH; *U.S. Public*, pg. 1238
Young, Virginia S., V.P. & Sec.--Western Atlas Inc., Houston, TX; *U.S. Public*, pg. 1757
Young, William D., Jr., V.P. & Sec.--General Wholesale Company, Inc., Atlanta, GA; *U.S. Private*, pg. 445
Youngblood, John F., Sec.--Meade Group, Inc., Utica, MI; *U.S. Private*, pg. 725
Youngblood, Wilfred E., Pres., Treas. & Sec.--Louisiana Gaming Management, Inc., Metairie, LA; *U.S. Private*, pg. 677
Youngchild, Linda L., Asst. Treas. & Sec.--The Metal Ware Corp., Two Rivers, WI; *U.S. Private*, pg. 734
Younger, Alvin M., Jr., Chief Fin. Officer, Mng. Dir., Treas. & Sec.--T. Rowe Price Associates, Inc., Baltimore, MD; *U.S. Public*, pg. 1324
Younggren, Pamela L., Sec.--Firstbank of Illinois Co., Springfield, IL; *U.S. Public*, pg. 643
Younk, James L., V.P.-Fin.--David White, L.L.C., Germantown, WI; *U.S. Public*, pg. 1765
Younk, James L., V.P.-Fin.--David White, L.L.C., Germantown, WI; *U.S. Private*, pg. 1765
Youssefzadeh, Emil, Pres., Chief Exec. Officer & Sec.--STM Wireless, Inc., Irvine, CA; *U.S. Public*, pg. 1421
Yovanovich, J.R., Sec.--The Ziegler Companies, Inc., West Bend, WI; *U.S. Public*, pg. 1791
Yovanovich, J.R., Sec.--B.C. Ziegler & Co., West Bend, WI; *U.S. Public*, pg. 1792
Yovanovich, J.R., Sec.--Ziegler Asset Management, Inc., West Bend, WI; *U.S. Public*, pg. 1792
Yu, Margaret, Deputy Sec.--Swire Pacific Limited, Central, Hong Kong; *Int'l*, pg. 1328
Yu, Victoria, Corp. Sec.--Keng Hua Paper Products Co., Inc., Manila, Philippines; *Int'l*, pg. 729
Yulman, E. Richard, Treas. & Sec.--National Bedding Co., Beloit, WI; *U.S. Private*, pg. 780
Yuracko, Ellen, Sr. V.P.-Mktg. & Sec.--Gerber Life Insurance Co., White Plains, NY; *Int'l*, pg. 973
Yusoff, R.M., Sec.--Esso Malaysia Berhad, Kuala Lumpur, Malaysia; *U.S. Public*, pg. 602
Zabek, Donald F., Sec. & Treas.--Phoenix Newspapers, Inc., Phoenix, AZ; *U.S. Public*, pg. 326
Zabitchuck, Suzanne M., Corp. Counsel & Asst. Sec.--Watts Industries, Inc., North Andover, MA; *U.S. Public*, pg. 1746
Zachrich, C.S., Sec.--Haeger Industries, Inc., Dundee, IL; *U.S. Private*, pg. 493
Zackim, Carre, Sec.--Alfin, Inc., New York, NY; *U.S. Public*, pg. 40
Zacky, Robert, Sec.--Zacky Farms, Inc., South El Monte, CA; *U.S. Private*, pg. 1203
Zahler, Eric J., V.P., Gen. Counsel & Sec.--Loral Space & Communications, New York, NY; *U.S. Public*, pg. 1014
Zahra, E. Ellis, V.P., Gen. Counsel & Sec.--Winn-Dixie Stores, Inc., Jacksonville, FL; *U.S. Public*, pg. 1771
Zak, S. Arieh, Esq., V.P.-Regulatory Affairs, Corp. Counsel & Asst. Sec.--Datascope Corp., Montvale, NJ; *U.S. Public*, pg. 487
Zakas, Marietta Edmunds, V.P.-Investor Rels. & Corp. Sec.--Equifax Inc., Atlanta, GA; *U.S. Public*, pg. 588
Zakos, Dean R., Assoc. Gen. Counsel & Asst. Sec.--Modine Manufacturing Company, Racine, WI; *U.S. Public*, pg. 1121
Zakutney, Ray, Treas. & Sec.--McConnell Automotive, Mobile, AL; *U.S. Private*, pg. 720
Zalak, Timothy F., Chief Fin. Officer, Treas. & Sec.--Multi-Local Media Corporation, Rockville Centre, NY; *U.S. Private*, pg. 767
Zalka, Ivy, V.P.-Human Resources & Asst. Sec.--Sun City Industries, Inc., Fort Lauderdale, FL; *U.S. Public*, pg. 1529
Zall, Betty, Treas. & Sec.--Paris Presents, Gurnee, IL; *U.S. Private*, pg. 839
Zambelli, Thomas, Chief Fin. Officer & Sr. V.P.--Tops Appliance City, Edison, NJ; *U.S. Public*, pg. 1622
Zambri, Robert R., Sr. V.P., Gen. Counsel & Sec.--Fortis Benefits Insurance Company, Kansas City, MO; *Int'l*, pg. 499
Zanders, Lorette, Sec.--Boury Enterprises, Wheeling, WV; *U.S. Private*, pg. 162
Zang, William L., V.P., Treas., Sec. & Controller--International Power Machines Corporation, Garland, TX; *Int'l*, pg. 126
Zanotelli, Michele, Sec. & Creative Dir.--Kaufmann's, Pittsburgh, PA; *U.S. Public*, pg. 1063
Zanotti, Emanuele, Sec.--Coeclerici Group, Genoa, Italy; *Int'l*, pg. 303
Zarada, Nancy, Sec.--Kemper Insurance Companies, Long Grove, IL; *U.S. Private*, pg. 614
Zatina, Thomas, Chief Oper. Officer, Exec. V.P. & Asst. Sec.--Bozzuto's Inc., Cheshire, CT; *U.S. Public*, pg. 249
Zavacky, Joseph E., Controller & Asst. Sec.--C-COR Electronics, Inc., State College, PA; *U.S. Public*, pg. 272
Zawel, Susan Fein, V.P.-Corp. Commun., Sec. & Assoc. Gen. Counsel--United Industrial Corporation, New York, NY; *U.S. Public*, pg. 1679
Zeger, Warren Y., V.P., Gen. Counsel & Sec.--COMSAT Corporation, Bethesda, MD; *U.S. Public*, pg. 424
Zehner, Andrew, Asst. Sec.--People's Choice TV Corp., Shelton, CT; *U.S. Public*, pg. 1274
Zeller, Paul W., V.P., Deputy Gen. Counsel & Asst. Sec.--Reliance Group Holdings, Inc., New York, NY; *U.S. Public*, pg. 1374
Zellers, C.F., Jr., Pres. & Chief Oper. Officer--Florida East Coast Industries Inc., Saint Augustine, FL; *U.S. Public*, pg. 1427
Zemanek, Louis M., Treas. & Sec.--Gate Petroleum Company, Jacksonville, FL; *U.S. Private*, pg. 441
Zemlin, Raymond, Sec.--Swift Instruments, Inc., Dorchester, MA; *U.S. Private*, pg. 1058
Zenk, Barbara, Chm. Bd.--Monico Alloys, Inc., Los Angeles, CA; *U.S. Private*, pg. 757
Zennedjian, Violet, Treas. & Sec.--Adray Appliance & Photo Center, Inc., Dearborn, MI; *U.S. Private*, pg. 18
Zergman, Carmen, Corp. Sec.--U.S. Divers Co., Inc., Santa Ana, CA; *U.S. Private*, pg. 1125
Zessner, Michael, Sec.--Brookfield Homes Ltd., Toronto, Canada; *Int'l*, pg. 228
Zessner, Michael, Sec.--Brookfield Homes, Del Mar, CA; *Int'l*, pg. 228
Zhang, Shengman, V.P. & Sec.--The World Bank, Washington, DC; *U.S. Private*, pg. 1188
Zieger, Juscy, V.P. & Sec.--Interbath, Inc., City of Industry, CA; *U.S. Private*, pg. 566
Ziegler, Dennis, Asst. Sec.--RHC/Spacemaster Corporation, Melrose Park, IL; *U.S. Private*, pg. 904

Ziegler, Karl H., Sec.--Swisher International Group, Inc., Darien, CT; *U.S. Public*, pg. 1543
Ziegler, Marie Z., Mgr.-Investor & Banking Rels. & Asst. Sec.--Deere & Company, Moline, IL; *U.S. Public*, pg. 491
Ziegler, Marie Z., Asst. Sec.--John Deere Capital Corporation, Reno, NV; *U.S. Public*, pg. 492
Ziegler, Scott F., V.P.-Fin., Controller & Sec.--Emons Transportation Group, Inc., York, PA; *U.S. Public*, pg. 578
Ziegler, Scott F., V.P.-Fin., Controller & Sec.--Maryland & Pennsylvania Railroad, York, PA; *U.S. Public*, pg. 579
Ziegler, William C., Treas. & Sec.--Ziegler Tire & Supply Company, Inc., Canton, OH; *U.S. Private*, pg. 1205
Ziemniak, Frances Ann, Chief Fin. Officer, V.P.-Fin. & Asst. Sec.--CORT Business Services Corporation, Fairfax, VA; *U.S. Public*, pg. 451
Ziering, Marilyn, V.P.-Mktg. Communications & Sec.--Diagnostic Products Corporation, Los Angeles, CA; *U.S. Public*, pg. 505
Zigel, James M., Gen. Counsel & Sec.--LucasVarity Inc., Buffalo, NY; *Int'l*, pg. 820
Zigment, Robert A., Controller, Treas. & Sec.--Kunzler & Company, Inc., Lancaster, PA; *U.S. Private*, pg. 636
Ziino, Joseph J., Jr., V.P. & Asst. Sec.--MGIC Investment Corporation, Milwaukee, WI; *U.S. Public*, pg. 1026
Ziino, Joseph J., Jr., V.P., Assoc. Gen. Counsel & Asst. Sec.--Mortgage Guaranty Insurance Corporation, Milwaukee, WI; *U.S. Public*, pg. 1026
Zils, Joseph C., V.P. & Corp. Sec.--Optical Coating Laboratory, Inc., Santa Rosa, CA; *U.S. Public*, pg. 1227
Zimk, Robbie, Chief Fin. Officer, Treas. & Sec.--Schmieding Enterprises Inc., Springdale, AR; *U.S. Private*, pg. 971
Zimmer, Edward, Sr. V.P., Sec. & Gen. Counsel--Levitz Furniture Incorporated, Boca Raton, FL; *U.S. Public*, pg. 990
Zimmer, Edward P., Sec.--John M. Smyth Co., Downers Grove, IL; *U.S. Public*, pg. 990
Zimmer, Joan C., Mgr.-Ivestor Rels. & Asst. Sec.--Badger Meter, Inc., Milwaukee, WI; *U.S. Public*, pg. 164
Zimmer, Richard, Chief Fin. Officer, Treas., Sec. & Dir.-Acctg.--Active Tool & Manufacturing Co., Inc., Roseville, MI; *U.S. Private*, pg. 16
Zimmer, Robert J., Chief Fin. Officer, V.P.-Fin. & Sec.--Acheson Industries, Inc., Port Huron, MI; *U.S. Private*, pg. 12
Zimmer, Roberta G., Sec.--Reeds Jewelers, Inc., Wilmington, NC; *U.S. Public*, pg. 1370
Zimmer, William H., III, Treas. & Sec.--Cincinnati Bell Telephone, Cincinnati, OH; *U.S. Public*, pg. 367
Zimmerman, Joyce I., Treas. & Sec.--Marval Industries, Inc., Mamaroneck, NY; *U.S. Private*, pg. 710
Zimmerman, Justin, Sr. V.P. & Asst. Sec.--Fabri-Centers of America, Inc., Hudson, OH; *U.S. Public*, pg. 609
Zimmerman, Rod, V.P. & Gen. Mgr.-KMOX-AM--CBS Radio Div., New York, NY; *U.S. Public*, pg. 274
Zimmermann, W.K., Treas. & Sec.--March Manufacturing Inc., Glenview, IL; *U.S. Private*, pg. 702
Zink, Darell E., Jr., Chief Fin. Officer, Exec. V.P. & Asst. Sec.--Duke Realty Investments, Inc., Indianapolis, IN; *U.S. Public*, pg. 535
Zinn, Frank K., Gen. Counsel & Sec.--Simpson Industries, Inc., Plymouth, MI; *U.S. Public*, pg. 1474
Zinn, Thomas R., Pres. & Sec.--Stearns Enterprises, Inc., Lexington, KY; *U.S. Private*, pg. 1037
Zirkman, Joseph A., V.P., Gen. Counsel & Sec.--Carrols Corporation, Syracuse, NY; *U.S. Private*, pg. 216
Zirolla, Beverly, Sec.--Devcon International Corp., Deerfield Beach, FL; *U.S. Public*, pg. 502
Zistler, Betty, V.P. & Sec.--Singleton Seafood Co., Tampa, FL; *U.S. Public*, pg. 427
Zodrow, Christopher N., Sec.--WestPoint Stevens Inc., West Point, GA; *U.S. Public*, pg. 1762
Zoeller, David L., Sr. V.P., Gen. Counsel & Sec.--National City Corporation, Cleveland, OH; *U.S. Public*, pg. 1154
Zoeller, John, V.P. & Sec.--Zoeller Co., Louisville, KY; *U.S. Private*, pg. 1207
Zoellick, Robert B., Exec. V.P., Gen. Counsel & Sec.--Federal National Mortgage Association (Fannie Mae), Washington, DC; *U.S. Public*, pg. 615
Zoobkoff, Anthony A., Sr. Counsel & Asst. Sec.--Cominco, Ltd., Vancouver, Canada; *Int'l*, pg. 307
Zook, Sam, Sec.--Excel Co-Op Inc., Monticello, IN; *U.S. Private*, pg. 387
Zopp, E. Frederick, Sr. V.P., Sec. & Gen. Counsel--PNC Bank, Louisville, KY; *U.S. Public*, pg. 1242
Zuckerman, Dan, V.P.-Real Estate & Sec.--Mac Frugal's Bargains Close-Outs Inc., Rancho Dominguez, CA; *U.S. Public*, pg. 437
Zumbiel, Thomas J., Exec. V.P. & Sec.--C.W. Zumbiel Company, Norwood, OH; *U.S. Private*, pg. 1207
Zummo, Mark, Corp. Sec.--Skyline Chili, Inc., Fairfield, OH; *U.S. Public*, pg. 1475
Zumpkehr, Charles E., Sec.--Donley's, Inc., Cleveland, OH; *U.S. Private*, pg. 340
Zumwalt, LeAnne M., Chief Fin. Officer, Treas. & Sec.--Vivra Incorporated, San Mateo, CA; *U.S. Public*, pg. 1723
Zurcher, Walter, Sec. & Treas.--Panalpina, Inc., Jersey City, NJ; *Int'l*, pg. 1022
Zvesper, Joseph P., Chief Fin. Officer, Exec. V.P., Treas. & Sec.--American Appraisal Associates, Inc., Milwaukee, WI; *U.S. Private*, pg. 49
Zwiauer, Roswitha, Sec.--Mikron Holding AG, Biel, Switzerland; *Int'l*, pg. 866
Zych, J., Corp. Sec.--Imperial Oil Limited, Toronto, Canada; *U.S. Public*, pg. 602
Zylstra, Michael, Corp. Sec. & Gen. Counsel--Cracker Barrel Old Country Store, Inc., Lebanon, TN; *U.S. Public*, pg. 455

EXECUTIVE VICE PRESIDENT

Aaby, James, Exec. V.P.-Creative Services--Jordan, McGrath, Case & Taylor Inc., New York, NY; *U.S. Private*, pg. 598
Aaron, Peter, Exec. V.P.--Lamonts Apparel, Inc., Kirkland, WA; *U.S. Public*, pg. 975
Aarons, Larry, Exec. V.P. & Exec. Creative Dir.--The Chisholm-Mingo Group, New York, NY; *U.S. Private*, pg. 237
Aaronson, Robert J., Exec. V.P.--Airport Group International, Inc., Glendale, CA; *U.S. Public*, pg. 1009
Aas, Stein Wessel, Grp. Exec. V.P.--Christiania Bank og Kreditkasse ASA, Oslo, Norway; *Int'l*, pg. 289
Abbey, Robert A., Exec. V.P.- Sls.--Abbey Etna Machine Company, Perrysburg, OH; *U.S. Private*, pg. 9
Abbott, R. William, Chief Fin. Officer & Exec. V.P.--WSFS Financial Corporation, Wilmington, DE; *U.S. Public*, pg. 1728
Abbott, Wayne, Exec. V.P.--Multiple Allied Services, Inc., Hayward, CA; *U.S. Private*, pg. 767
Abdalla, Edward IV, Exec. V.P.--Abdalla's Lafayette, Inc., Lafayette, LA; *U.S. Private*, pg. 10
Abdalla, Harold C., Exec. V.P.--Abdalla's Lafayette, Inc., Lafayette, LA; *U.S. Private*, pg. 10
Abe, Masahiro, Exec. V.P.--Chemtex International, Inc., New York, NY; *Int'l*, pg. 872
Abe, Masaru, Exec. V.P.--Nippon Shokubai Co., Ltd., Osaka, Japan; *Int'l*, pg. 939
Abe, Sadao, Exec. V.P.--Shiseido Company Ltd., Tokyo, Japan; *Int'l*, pg. 1235
Abe, Susumu, Exec. V.P.--Toshiba Corporation, Tokyo, Japan; *Int'l*, pg. 1402
Abney, David, Mgr.-Opers.--Sonic Couriers of Arizona, Inc., Scottsdale, AZ; *U.S. Private*, pg. 1123
Abrahamson, David A., Exec. V.P.--Cardinal Health Inc., Dublin, OH; *U.S. Public*, pg. 304
Abram, Nancy, Sr. V.P.-Mktg.--Hardee's Food Systems, Inc., Rocky Mount, NC; *U.S. Public*, pg. 278
Abramowitz, Joel, Exec. V.P.--U.S. Trust Corporation, New York, NY; *U.S. Public*, pg. 1688
Abrams, Alan R., Exec. V.P.--Abrams Industries, Inc., Atlanta, GA; *U.S. Public*, pg. 14
Abrams, J. Andrew, Exec. V.P.--Abrams Industries, Inc., Atlanta, GA; *U.S. Public*, pg. 14
Abrams, Jack, Chief Oper. Officer & Exec. V.P.--Nikon Inc., Melville, NY; *Int'l*, pg. 931
Abrams, Jan E., Exec. V.P.-Bus. Affairs--Columbia TriStar Television, Culver City, CA; *Int'l*, pg. 1282
Abrams, Joseph, Exec. V.P.--Mindscape, Inc., Novato, CA; *Int'l*, pg. 1026
Abramson, David, Chief Oper. Officer & Exec. V.P.--Rapid Mounting & Finishing Co., Chicago, IL; *U.S. Private*, pg. 910
Abramson, Stephanie W., Exec. V.P. & Gen. Counsel--Young & Rubicam Inc., New York, NY; *U.S. Private*, pg. 1196
Abreo, Norman F., Exec. V.P.-Opers.--American Italian Pasta Company, Excelsior Springs, MO; *U.S. Public*, pg. 85
Abruzzo, Joe, Exec. V.P. & Media & Mktg. Res. Dir.--The Media Edge, New York, NY; *U.S. Private*, pg. 1079
Accinno, Paul, Exec. V.P.--J.W. Messner, Inc., Grand Rapids, MI; *U.S. Private*, pg. 734
Acevedo, Luis, Principal--Richards, Brock, Miller, Mitchell & Assoc. Inc., Dallas, TX; *U.S. Private*, pg. 929
Acheson, Marcus W., Exec. V.P.--Bank of America Illinois, Chicago, IL; *U.S. Public*, pg. 180
Ackerman, Carl, Exec. V.P.-Fin.--SSD&W Integrated Marketing Communications, Montville, NJ; *U.S. Private*, pg. 958
Ackerman, Francis, Exec. V.P.--Bull S.A., Louveciennes, France; *Int'l*, pg. 315
Ackerman, Philip C., Exec. V.P.--National Fuel Gas Supply Corp., Erie, PA; *U.S. Public*, pg. 1156
Ackstein, Harry, Exec. V.P.-Banking Opers.--Harris Bankcorp, Inc., Chicago, IL; *Int'l*, pg. 154
Acuff, Keith, Exec. V.P. & Chief Mktg. Officer--Noble & Associates, Springfield, MO; *U.S. Private*, pg. 800
Adair, A. Jayson, Exec. V.P.--Copart, Inc., Benicia, CA; *U.S. Public*, pg. 446
Adami, Gary, Chief Fin. Officer & Exec. V.P.--Ruppman Marketing Technologies, Inc., Peoria, IL; *U.S. Private*, pg. 951
Adamo, Charles D., Exec. V.P.-Corp. Devel. & Gen. Counsel--Sun International Hotels Limited, Fort Lauderdale, FL; *U.S. Public*, pg. 1531
Adams, Douglass H., Exec. V.P.--United Bankshares, Inc., Parkersburg, WV; *U.S. Public*, pg. 1674
Adams, Frederick M., Jr., Exec. V.P.-Retail Banking Services--First Chicago NBD Corporation, Chicago, IL; *U.S. Public*, pg. 627
Adams, J. Phillip, Pres.--Flying J. Inc., Brigham City, UT; *U.S. Private*, pg. 415
Adams, Jack, Exec. V.P.--Zima Corporation, Spartanburg, SC; *U.S. Private*, pg. 637
Adams, James E., Chief Fin. Officer, Exec. V.P. & Treas.--MainStreet BankGroup Incorporated, Martinsville, VA; *U.S. Public*, pg. 1038
Adams, Jennifer L., Chief Legal & Admin. Officer, Exec. V.P. & Sec.--World Color Press, Inc., Greenwich, CT; *U.S. Public*, pg. 1778
Adams, Jim, Exec. V.P.-Stores--Parisian, Inc., Birmingham, AL; *U.S. Public*, pg. 1333
Adams, Joe, Exec. V.P. & Treas.--Creative Alliance, Inc., Louisville, KY; *U.S. Private*, pg. 287
Adams, John B., Chief Fin. Officer, Exec. V.P.-Fin., Sec. & Treas.--Big O Tires Incorporated, Englewood, CO; *U.S. Public*, pg. 1553
Adams, John C., Jr., Exec. V.P.--Hilb, Rogal and Hamilton Company, Glen Allen, VA; *U.S. Public*, pg. 826
Adams, Robert, Exec. Dir.--Rio Tinto PLC, London, United Kingdom; *Int'l*, pg. 1118
Adams, Robert A., Chief Oper. Officer & Exec. V.P.--American Annuity Group, Cincinnati, OH; *U.S. Public*, pg. 74
Adams, Robert E., Exec. V.P.-Mortgage Banking Div.--Westcorp, Irvine, CA; *U.S. Public*, pg. 1756
Adams, Robert E., Exec. V.P.-Mortgage Banking--Western Financial Bank, Irvine, CA; *U.S. Public*, pg. 1757
Adams, Thomas H., Exec. V.P.-Human Resources--American National Bank & Trust Co. of Chicago, Chicago, IL; *U.S. Public*, pg. 628
Adams, William J., Exec. V.P. & Gen. Mgr.-Siding--ABT Building Products Corporation, Neenah, WI; *Int'l*, pg. 20
Adamson, Thomas, IV, Exec. V.P.--Scott & Stringfellow, Inc., Richmond, VA; *U.S. Public*, pg. 1445
Addesso, Dominic J., Exec. V.P.-Strategy & Systems Integration--Selective Insurance Group, Inc, Branchville, NJ; *U.S. Public*, pg. 1455
Addis, Paul D., Exec. V.P.--American Electric Power Service Corp., Columbus, OH; *U.S. Public*, pg. 72
Addison, Edwin R., Exec. V.P.--Excalibur Technologies Corporation, Vienna, VA; *U.S. Public*, pg. 598
Addy, George, Exec. V.P. & Chief Gen. Counsel--Telus Corporation, Edmonton, Canada; *Int'l*, pg. 1374
Ader, Jack R., Exec. V.P.--United Jersey Bank Services Co, Paramus, NJ; *U.S. Public*, pg. 1528
Ader, Jack R., Exec. V.P.--UJB Investor Services Company, Paramus, NJ; *U.S. Public*, pg. 1528
Adik, Stephen P., Chief Fin. Officer & Exec. V.P.--Northern Indiana Public Service Company, Hammond, IN; *U.S. Public*, pg. 1185
Adkerson, Richard, Exec. V.P.--P.T. Freeport Indonesia Co., New Orleans, LA; *U.S. Public*, pg. 681
Adler, Robert, Exec. V.P. & Media Dir.--Gotham Incorporated, New York, NY; *U.S. Private*, pg. 677
Adler, Robert J., Exec. V.P. & Dir.-Sls.--Northstar Investment Management Corporation, Greenwich, CT; *U.S. Public*, pg. 1375
Adrean, Lee, Chief Fin. Officer & Exec. V.P.--First Data Corporation, Hackensack, NJ; *U.S. Public*, pg. 630
Adriaasens, T.M.T., Exec. V.P.--ABN-AMRO Holding N.V., Amsterdam, Netherlands; *Int'l*, pg. 8
Adrien, Dan, Exec. V.P.-Mktg.--Burgess Pigment Co., Sandersville, GA; *U.S. Private*, pg. 182
Aebel, Charles F., Chief Fin. Officer & Exec. V.P.--Central States Diversified, Inc., Saint Louis, MO; *U.S. Private*, pg. 224
Aersten, Guillaem, Exec. V.P.--BankBoston Corporation, Boston, MA; *U.S. Public*, pg. 183
Aggers, Jane, Exec. V.P.-Mdsg. & Mktg.--Fabri-Centers of America, Inc., Hudson, OH; *U.S. Public*, pg. 609
Agnello, Alexis, Sr. Exec. V.P.-Opers.--Club Mediterranee SA, Paris, France; *Int'l*, pg. 298
Agneta, Rol, Exec. V.P.--Chyron Corp., Melville, NY; *Int'l*, pg. 1372
Agoglia, John, Exec. V.P.-NBC TV Bus. Affairs--National Broadcasting Co., Inc., New York, NY; *U.S. Public*, pg. 712
Agostinelli, Richard, Chief Fin. Officer & Exec. V.P.--Continental Graphics Corporation, Los Angeles, CA; *U.S.* Private, pg. 268
Agresti, Jack J., Pres. & Chief Exec. Officer--Atkinson, San Bruno, CA; *U.S. Public*, pg. 143
Aguiar, Carlos Agusto, Chief Oper. Officer & Exec. V.P.--Aracruz Celulose S.A., Rio de Janeiro, Brazil; *Int'l*, pg. 78
Aguirre, Jesse, Exec. V.P.-Mexico--Anheuser-Busch International, Inc., Saint Louis, MO; *U.S. Public*, pg. 114
Ahlqvist, Fritz, Exec. V.P.--Koninklijke Ahold NV, Zaandam, Netherlands; *Int'l*, pg. 749
Ahmad, Saadat Nasim, Exec. V.P. & Sec.--Habib Bank Ltd., Karachi, Pakistan; *Int'l*, pg. 584
Aho, Eero, Exec. V.P.--Huhtamaki Oy, Espoo, Finland; *Int'l*, pg. 638
Aidem, Lawrence, Exec. V.P.-Bus. Devel.--Showtime Networks Inc., New York, NY; *U.S. Private*, pg. 779
Aiken, Max C., Exec. V.P.--A.P. Green Industries, Inc., Mexico, MO; *U.S. Public*, pg. 761
Ainsworth, Kent P., Chief Fin. Officer, Exec. V.P. & Sec.--URS Corporation, San Francisco, CA; *U.S. Public*, pg. 1655
Ajer, Randolph E., Chief Fin. Officer, Exec. V.P., Treas. & Sec.--Mercury Air Group Inc., Los Angeles, CA; *U.S. Public*, pg. 1092
Ak Ro, Yong, Exec. V.P.-Overseas Business Opers.--LG Group, Seoul, Korea; *Int'l*, pg. 778
Akashi, Hideyoki, Exec. V.P.--Uniden Corporation, Tokyo, Japan; *Int'l*, pg. 1433
Akdemir, Sabri Yalcin, Exec. V.P.-Fin.--Arcelik A.S., Istanbul, Turkey; *Int'l*, pg. 741
Akermann, Markus, Exec. V.P.--Holderbank Financiere Glaris Ltd., Glaris, Switzerland; *Int'l*, pg. 628
Akerson, Alan W., Sr. Partner & Exec. V.P.--Fleishman-Hillard Inc., Saint Louis, MO; *U.S. Private*, pg. 411
Akesson, Kjell, Exec. V.P.--Svedala Industri AB, Malmo, Sweden; *Int'l*, pg. 1323
Akhtar, M. Saleem, Chief Exec. Officer & Sr. Exec. V.P.--Habib Credit & Exchange Bank Ltd., Karachi, Pakistan; *Int'l*, pg. 584
Akin, Bruce, Exec. V.P. & Chief Exec. Officer-Oxmoor House Books--Southern Progress Corporation, Birmingham, AL; *U.S. Public*, pg. 1612
Akitt, J.E., Exec. V.P.--Exxon Chemical Company, Houston, TX; *U.S. Public*, pg. 601
Akiyama, Hirokazu, Exec. V.P.--NEC Corporation, Tokyo, Japan; *Int'l*, pg. 899
Akkermans, L., Sr. Exec. V.P.--SGS Societe Generale de Surveillance Holding S.A., Geneva, Switzerland; *Int'l*, pg. 1153
Alanis de Penaloza, Adriana, Vice Chm. & Exec. V.P.--Grupo Tribasa S.A. de C.V., Mexico, Mexico; *Int'l*, pg. 577
Alayeto, George I., Exec. V.P.--Connell Co., Westfield, NJ; *U.S. Private*, pg. 264

Albanese, Joseph, Exec. V.P.--Huffman Koos, River Edge, NJ; *U.S. Private*, pg. 546
Alberg, Tom A., Exec. V.P.-Legal & Corp. Affairs--AT&T Wireless Services, Kirkland, WA; *U.S. Public*, pg. 11
Albert, Robert, Exec. V.P.--Trinkle Sales, Inc., Cherry Hill, NJ; *U.S. Private*, pg. 1103
Alberti, Kerry B., Exec. V.P.-Investment Services--Marine Midland Bank, Buffalo, NY; *Int'l*, pg. 581
Albonetti, Joseph G., Exec. V.P. & Hispanic/Intl. Mktg. Dir.--Tinsley Advertising, Miami, FL; *U.S. Private*, pg. 1088
Albrecht, Fred, Exec. V.P.-Fin.--First Worthing Company, Dallas, TX; *U.S. Private*, pg. 408
Albrecht, Richard R., Exec. V.P.-Customer Service--Boeing Commercial Airplane Group, Renton, WA; *U.S. Public*, pg. 240
Albrecht, Steve, Exec. V.P.--Albrecht Inc., Akron, OH; *U.S. Private*, pg. 32
Albright, Sam Z., Exec. V.P.--Jefferies & Company, Inc., Los Angeles, CA; *U.S. Public*, pg. 925
Albritton, Karen, Exec. V.P. & Media Dir.--FGI Inc., Chapel Hill, NC; *U.S. Private*, pg. 389
Alcorn, S. Russell, Exec. V.P.--United Missouri Bank of Joplin, Joplin, MO; *U.S. Public*, pg. 1655
Aldeborgh, John E., Exec. V.P.-Ion Tech. Prods.--Genus Inc., Sunnyvale, CA; *U.S. Public*, pg. 732
Alden, Harold, Exec. V.P.--Bomaine Corporation, Santa Monica, CA; *U.S. Private*, pg. 155
Aldridge, Roger, Exec. Dir.-Store Devel., Equipment & Grp. Estates--Marks & Spencer PLC, London, United Kingdom; *Int'l*, pg. 842
Alepian, Taro, Exec. V.P.-Indus.--SNC-Lavalin Group Inc., Montreal, Canada; *Int'l*, pg. 1161
Alesi, Charles, Exec. V.P.--Walker Magnetics Group, Inc., Worcester, MA; *U.S. Private*, pg. 1147
Alesio, Steven W., Exec. V.P. & Gen. Mgr.-Corp. Card--American Express Travel Related Services Co., Inc., New York, NY; *U.S. Public*, pg. 73
Alexander, Anthony J., Exec. V.P. & Gen. Counsel--FirstEnergy Corp., Akron, OH; *U.S. Public*, pg. 644
Alexander, Gerard C., Exec. V.P. & Pres.-Central Div.--Stewart Enterprises, Inc., Metairie, LA; *U.S. Public*, pg. 1518
Alexander, Glynn M., Exec. V.P.--Building Plastics, Inc., Memphis, TN; *U.S. Private*, pg. 180
Alexander, I.R., Chief Fin. Officer & Exec. V.P.--Purina Mills, Inc., Saint Louis, MO; *U.S. Private*, pg. 895
Alexander, John, Chief Oper. Officer & Exec. V.P.-Admin./Opers.--Dugan Production Corp., Farmington, NM; *U.S. Private*, pg. 345
Alexander, Ron L., Chief Oper. Officer & Exec. V.P.--Willis Corroon Corp. of Knoxville, Knoxville, TN; *Int'l*, pg. 1506
Alexander, Thomas J., Exec. V.P. & Cashier--Chemical Bank & Trust Company, Midland, MI; *U.S. Public*, pg. 345
Alfheim, Roar L., Grp. Exec. V.P.--Jotun Polymer A/S, Sandefjord, Norway; *Int'l*, pg. 714
Alfonso, Charles, Exec. V.P.--Southern California Auto Group, Torrance, CA; *U.S. Private*, pg. 1016
Alford, Walter H., Exec. V.P. & Sr. Gen. Counsel--BellSouth Corporation, Atlanta, GA; *U.S. Public*, pg. 207
Alfroid, Philippe, Chief Fin. Officer & Exec. V.P.-Admin. & Fin.--Essilor International Compagnie Generale d'Optique, Charenton-le-Pont, France; *Int'l*, pg. 462
Allard, Claude, Exec. V.P.-Pharmaprix--Shoppers Drug Mart, Ltd., Toronto, Canada; *Int'l*, pg. 112
Allbritton, Robert L., Exec. V.P.--Allbritton Communications Company, Washington, DC; *U.S. Private*, pg. 854
Allen, Andrew, Exec. V.P.-Intl. Opers.--Bozell Worldwide, Inc., New York, NY; *U.S. Public*, pg. 1642
Allen, Barbara R., Exec. V.P.-Intl. Food Prods.--The Quaker Oats Company, Chicago, IL; *U.S. Public*, pg. 1347
Allen, Barbara R., Exec. V.P.-Intl.--International Quaker Food Products, Chicago, IL; *U.S. Public*, pg. 1347
Allen, Barry K., Exec. V.P.-Consumer & Bus. Services--Ameritech Corporation, Chicago, IL; *U.S. Public*, pg. 97
Allen, Gary R., Chief Banking Officer & Sr. Exec. V.P.--Keycorp, Cleveland, OH; *U.S. Public*, pg. 954
Allen, James D., Chief Fin. Officer & Exec. V.P.--Tandycrafts, Inc., Fort Worth, TX; *U.S. Public*, pg. 1561
Allen, James P., Chief Fin. Officer & Exec. V.P.--CACI International Inc, Arlington, VA; *U.S. Public*, pg. 272
Allen, Jim, Exec. V.P.--Royal Oak Enterprises, Inc., Atlanta, GA; *U.S. Private*, pg. 948
Allen, Joseph, Exec. V.P., Treas. & Sec.--Brant Allen Industries, Inc., Greenwich, CT; *U.S. Private*, pg. 165
Allen, Mitchel, Exec. V.P.-Opers.--Spartan Mills, Spartanburg, SC; *U.S. Private*, pg. 1020
Allen, R. Thomas M., Exec. V.P.-Investments--London Life Insurance Group, London, Canada; *Int'l*, pg. 435
Allen, Russ, Exec. V.P.-Corp. Sls.--Glenayre Technologies, Inc., Charlotte, NC, *U.S. Public*, pg. 746
Allen, Stephen L., Exec. V.P.--MCRB Service Bureau, Inc., Chatsworth, CA; *U.S. Private*, pg. 686
Allen, William G., Exec. V.P.-E. Region--Bergen Brunswig Corporation, Orange, CA; *U.S. Public*, pg. 213
Allen, Woods W., Exec. V.P.-Exploration--Murphy Exploration & Production Co., New Orleans, LA; *U.S. Public*, pg. 1142
Alley, B. James, Exec. V.P.-Mktg.--Tyco Toys, Inc., Mount Laurel, NJ; *U.S. Public*, pg. 1058
Allick, Christopher W., Exec. V.P. & Dir.-Fin.--Jefferies & Company, Inc., Los Angeles, CA; *U.S. Public*, pg. 925
Allinson, A. Edward, Exec. V.P.--State Street Corporation, Boston, MA; *U.S. Public*, pg. 1513
Allison, G., Exec. V.P.--McCormick Paint Works Company, Rockville, MD; *U.S. Private*, pg. 720
Allison, H.B., Exec. V.P.--Lockheed Aeronautical Systems Company, Marietta, GA; *U.S. Public*, pg. 1007
Allison, John R., Chief Fin. Officer & Exec. V.P.--Sun International Hotels Limited, Fort Lauderdale, FL; *U.S. Public*, pg. 1531
Allison, Linda M., Exec. V.P.-Opers. & Admin. Div.--AmSouth Bancorporation, Birmingham, AL; *U.S. Public*, pg. 105
Allison, Robert, Exec. V.P.--Aurora Electronics, Marina Del Rey, CA; *U.S. Public*, pg. 147
Allison, Robert, Exec. V.P.--Southwest Recreational Industries Inc., Leander, TX; *U.S. Private*, pg. 1018
Allyn, William N., Exec. V.P.--Jefferies & Company, Inc., Los Angeles, CA; *U.S. Public*, pg. 925
Almeida, Isabel, Exec. V.P.--Banco Espirito Santo e Comercial de Lisboa SA, Lisbon, Portugal; *Int'l*, pg. 142
Almond, Paul, Exec. V.P.-Programming--LIVE Film & Mediaworks, Van Nuys, CA; *U.S. Private*, pg. 671
Almy, Richard E., Chief Oper. Officer & Exec. V.P.--Walter Industries, Inc., Tampa, FL; *U.S. Public*, pg. 1736
Alonso, Rafael, Exec. V.P.--Banco Santander, Madrid, Spain; *Int'l*, pg. 143
Alper, Merlin L., Exec. V.P. & Chief Fin. Officer--Madison Square Garden Corporation, New York, NY; *U.S. Public*, pg. 288
Alperson, Steven, Exec. V.P.--Rolled Steel Products Corporation, Los Angeles, CA; *U.S. Private*, pg. 941
Alstodt, Harvey, Exec. V.P.-Sls.--Del Laboratories, Inc., Farmingdale, NY; *U.S. Public*, pg. 494
Altick, James A., Exec. V.P.--First Commerce Corporation, New Orleans, LA; *U.S. Public*, pg. 629
Altman, Steven R., Exec. V.P. & Gen. Counsel--QUALCOMM, San Diego, CA; *U.S. Public*, pg. 1348
Altruda, Vin, Exec. V.P.-Store Opers.--Borders Group, Inc., Ann Arbor, MI; *U.S. Public*, pg. 245
Altstadt, Manfred, Chief Fin. Officer & Sr. Exec. V.P.--Mutual of America Life Insurance Company, New York, NY; *U.S. Private*, pg. 769
Altstadt, Manfred, Chief Fin. Officer & Sr. Exec. V.P.--American Life Insurance Company of New York, New York, NY; *U.S. Private*, pg. 769
Alvarado, Joseph, Exec. V.P.-Commercial--Birmingham Steel Corporation, Birmingham, AL; *U.S. Public*, pg. 232
Alvarez, David, Exec. V.P.--Providian Financial Corporation, San Francisco, CA; *U.S. Public*, pg. 1338
Alvarez, Jose, Exec. V.P.--Sugar Cane Growers Cooperative of Florida, Belle Glade, FL; *U.S. Private*, pg. 1049
Alves-Bronson, Nadia, Exec. V.P.-Intl.--Universal Pictures, Universal City, CA; *Int'l*, pg. 1216
Amafia, Julio Gavito, Exec. V.P.--ASTANO - Astilleros y Talleres del Noroeste, S.A., Madrid, Spain; *Int'l*, pg. 1223
Amakasu, Tadao, Exec. V.P. & Gen. Mgr.--Mitsubishi Electric Corporation, Tokyo, Japan; *Int'l*, pg. 872
Amano, Hidetake, Sr. Exec. Dir.--The Japan Development Bank, Tokyo, Japan; *Int'l*, pg. 701
Amano, Junichi, Exec. V.P.--Mitsui & Co., Ltd., Tokyo, Japan; *Int'l*, pg. 877
Amas, Gus J., Exec. V.P. & Gen. Counsel--Eagle Industries, Inc., Chicago, IL; *U.S. Private*, pg. 473
Amason, Tony, Exec. V.P. & Gen. Mgr.-WSM--Lanier Worldwide Inc., Atlanta, GA; *U.S. Public*, pg. 791
Amato, Michael L., Exec. V.P.-Consumer Banking--Washington Mutual Inc., Seattle, WA; *U.S. Public*, pg. 1741
Ambrose, Andy, Chief Fin. Officer, Exec. V.P. & Sec.--Miller Freeman Inc., San Francisco, CA; *Int'l*, pg. 1443
Ambrose, Don, Exec. V.P.--Ambrose Carr Linton Carroll Inc., Toronto, Canada; *Int'l*, pg. 71
Ambrose, William, Exec. V.P.--Entrepreneur, Inc., Wilmington, NC; *U.S. Private*, pg. 1191
Ambrose, William A., Exec. V.P. & Treas.--Worsley Companies Inc., Wilmington, NC; *U.S. Private*, pg. 1191
Ambroseo, John, Dr., Exec. V.P. & Pres.-GM Coherent Laser Grp.--Coherent, Inc., Santa Clara, CA; *U.S. Public*, pg. 395
Ambroseo, John, Dr., Exec. V.P.--Coherent, Inc.-Laser Group, Santa Clara, CA; *U.S. Public*, pg. 395
Ambrosino, Allan, Exec. V.P.--American Business Information, Inc., Omaha, NE; *U.S. Public*, pg. 69
Ambrove, Dennis, Exec. V.P.--Deutsch Engineered Connecting Devices Co., Hemet, CA; *U.S. Private*, pg. 328
Amend, H., Exec. V.P.-Opers.--Shure Brothers Incorporated, Evanston, IL; *U.S. Private*, pg. 997
Amer, John C., Exec. V.P.-Fin. & Sec.--Reactive Metals & Alloys Corporation (REMACOR), West Pittsburg, PA; *U.S. Private*, pg. 913
Ames, Stephen C., Exec. V.P.-Acquisitions--Marine Midland Bank, Buffalo, NY; *Int'l*, pg. 581
Amick, W. Michael, Exec. V.P.-Forest Prods. & Industrial Pkg.--International Paper Company, Purchase, NY; *U.S. Public*, pg. 901
Amini, Michael, Exec. V.P. & Sec.--Sage Energy Company, San Antonio, TX; *U.S. Public*, pg. 1426
Amini, Rex, Exec. V.P. & Treas.--Sage Energy Company, San Antonio, TX; *U.S. Public*, pg. 1426
Amini, Ronald, Exec. V.P.--Sage Energy Company, San Antonio, TX; *U.S. Public*, pg. 1426
Anaya, Raul, Exec. V.P.--Banco Nacional de Mexico, S.A., New York, NY; *Int'l*, pg. 574
Anchor, J.A., Exec. V.P.--KLM Royal Dutch Airlines, Amstelveen, Netherlands; *Int'l*, pg. 719
Ancona, Henry, Exec. V.P.-Comml. Grp.--Polaroid Corporation, Cambridge, MA; *U.S. Public*, pg. 1313
Andalou, Richard, Chief Oper. Officer & Exec. V.P.--McKinney & McKinney Advertising, Redondo Beach, CA; *U.S. Private*, pg. 723
Anders, Howard G., Chief Fin. Officer, Exec. V.P. & Sec.--Hospitality Worldwide Services, Inc., New York, NY; *U.S. Public*, pg. 841
Andersen, Jorgen Vendel, Chief Fin. Officer & Exec. V.P.--ISS-International Service System A/S, Holte, Denmark; *Int'l*, pg. 656
Andersen, Kurt, Exec. V.P.--Republic National Bank of New York, New York, NY; *U.S. Public*, pg. 1380
Anderson, Alexander M., Grp. Exec. V.P.-Investment Mngmt.--Bank of America NT&SA, San Francisco, CA; *U.S. Public*, pg. 180
Anderson, Anne-Drue, Exec. V.P. & Treas.--H.F. Ahmanson & Co., Irwindale, CA; *U.S. Public*, pg. 29
Anderson, Anne-Drue, Exec. V.P.-Corp.--Home Savings of America, FSB, Irwindale, CA; *U.S. Public*, pg. 29
Anderson, Basil L., Chief Fin. Officer, Exec. V.P. & Treas.--Campbell Soup Company, Camden, NJ; *U.S. Public*, pg. 298
Anderson, Bill, Sr. Partner & Exec. V.P.--Fleishman-Hillard Inc., Saint Louis, MO; *U.S. Private*, pg. 411
Anderson, Bill, Exec. V.P. & Gen. Mgr.--IEC Electronics Corp., Newark, NY; *U.S. Public*, pg. 854
Anderson, Bruce, Exec. V.P., Gen. Mgr. & Acct. Services Dir.--Larkin Meeder & Schweidel, Dallas, TX; *U.S. Private*, pg. 651
Anderson, Carolyn J., Exec. V.P.--SLG Chemicals, Inc., Denver, CO; *U.S. Public*, pg. 1447
Anderson, Dave, Exec. V.P.-Opers.--Regal Ware, Inc., Kewaskum, WI; *U.S. Private*, pg. 917
Anderson, Dick, Exec. V.P. & Co-Mng. Dir.--The Healthcare Connection, New York, NY; *U.S. Public*, pg. 1422
Anderson, Douglas E., Exec. V.P. & Sec.--Boddie-Noell Enterprises Inc., Rocky Mount, NC; *U.S. Private*, pg. 154
Anderson, Douglas W., Exec. V.P.--Replacements, Ltd., Mc Leansville, NC; *U.S. Private*, pg. 923
Anderson, Ed, Exec. V.P.--National Auto Credit Inc., Solon, OH; *U.S. Public*, pg. 1152
Anderson, Eric, Exec. V.P. & Treas.--The Conde Nast Publications Inc., New York, NY; *U.S. Private*, pg. 20
Anderson, Fred D., Chief Fin. Officer & Exec. V.P.--Apple Computer, Inc., Cupertino, CA; *U.S. Public*, pg. 121
Anderson, Gary, Chief Fin. Officer & Exec. V.P.--Detroit Newspapers, Detroit, MI; *U.S. Public*, pg. 965
Anderson, Gary J., Exec. V.P.-Fund Mngmt.--TL Ventures, Wayne, PA; *U.S. Public*, pg. 1424
Anderson, Gerard M., Exec. V.P.--DTE Energy Company, Detroit, MI; *U.S. Public*, pg. 475
Anderson, Glenn, Exec. V.P.-Commercial Lines--United States Fidelity & Guaranty Company, Baltimore, MD; *U.S. Public*, pg. 1659
Anderson, Gregory, Chief Fin. Officer--Electrovert, Grand Prairie, TX; *Int'l*, pg. 328
Anderson, James C., Exec. V.P.--Bank of Utah, Ogden, UT; *U.S. Private*, pg. 114
Anderson, James T., Acting Exec. V.P. & Chief Fin. Officer--U S West Inc., Englewood, CO; *U.S. Public*, pg. 1688
Anderson, Joe D., Exec. V.P.-Consumer Mkts. Div.--Countrywide Home Loans Inc., Pasadena, CA; *U.S. Public*, pg. 452
Anderson, John K., Chief Fin. Officer, Exec. V.P. & Treas.--American Heritage Life Insurance Co., Jacksonville, FL; *U.S. Public*, pg. 79
Anderson, John K., Jr., Chief Fin. Officer, Exec. V.P. & Treas.--American Heritage Life Investment Corp., Jacksonville, FL; *U.S. Public*, pg. 78
Anderson, Jon, Exec. V.P. & Chief Creative Officer--Colle & McVoy, Inc., Minneapolis, MN; *U.S. Private*, pg. 252
Anderson, Ole Steen, Exec. V.P.--Danfoss A/S, Nordborg, Denmark; *Int'l*, pg. 376
Anderson, Phelps, Chief Oper. Officer & Exec. V.P.--Hondo Oil & Gas Company, Roswell, NM; *Int'l*, pg. 818
Anderson, Richard, Exec. V.P.-Mfg.--Valassis Communications, Inc., Livonia, MI; *U.S. Public*, pg. 1704
Anderson, Robert, Exec. V.P.--C.J. Vitner Co., Chicago, IL; *U.S. Private*, pg. 1142
Anderson, Robert E., III, Exec. V.P.-Plng. & Devel.--Owens & Minor Inc., Glen Allen, VA; *U.S. Public*, pg. 1236
Anderson, Scott, Exec. V.P.--Thrifty Rent-a-Car System, Inc., Tulsa, OK; *U.S. Public*, pg. 354
Anderson, Walter, Exec. V.P. & Editor--Parade Publications Inc., New York, NY; *U.S. Private*, pg. 20
Anderson, Will, Exec. V.P. & Gen. Mgr.--Karakas, VanSickle, Ouellette Advertising & Public Relations, Portland, OR; *U.S. Private*, pg. 607
Andersson, Bjorn C., Exec. V.P.-Handelsbanken Markets--Svenska Handelsbanken, Stockholm, Sweden; *Int'l*, pg. 1327
Andersson, Hans-Erik, Exec. V.P.--Skandia Insurance Company Limited, Stockholm, Sweden; *Int'l*, pg. 1256
Andersson, Nil-Ove, Exec. V.P.-Fin. & Treas.--Celsius AB, Stockholm, Sweden; *Int'l*, pg. 276
Ando, Goran A., M.D., Exec. V.P.-Worldwide Science & Tech.--Pharmacia & Upjohn, Inc., Windsor, United Kingdom; *Int'l*, pg. 1047
Ando, Terumasa, Exec. V.P.--Kobe Steel, Ltd., Kobe, Japan; *Int'l*, pg. 740
Ando, Tetsuo, Chief Fin. Officer, Exec. V.P. & Treas.--Bridgestone/Firestone, Inc., Nashville, TN; *Int'l*, pg. 213
Andre, Michael G., Exec. V.P.--Interconnect Products Division, Rolling Meadows, IL; *U.S. Public*, pg. 1101
Andreas, Ursula E., Exec. V.P.--Lantzsch-Andreas Enterprises, Inc., Vienna, VA; *U.S. Private*, pg. 650
Andreu, Jean-Louis, Exec. V.P.-Intl. Div./Schneider Electric--Schneider S.A., Boulogne-Billancourt, France; *Int'l*, pg. 1207
Andrews, Amy, Exec. V.P. & Print Dir.--Zenith Media Services, Inc., New York, NY; *U.S. Private*, pg. 1204
Andrews, Charles, Chief Oper. Officer & Exec. V.P.--Ripon Foods, Inc., Ripon, WI; *U.S. Private*, pg. 931
Andrews, Dale, Exec. V.P.--WIC Entertainment Ltd., Vancouver, Canada; *Int'l*, pg. 1482
Andrews, Duane P., Exec. V.P.-Corp. Devel.--Science Applications International Corp., San Diego, CA; *U.S. Private*, pg. 975
Andrews, Nigel D.T., Exec. V.P.-G.E. Capital Components--General Electric Capital Services, Inc., Stamford, CT; *U.S. Public*, pg. 711
Andrews, Nigel D.T., Exec. V.P.--G.E. Capital Commercial Real Estate Financing, Stamford, CT; *U.S. Public*, pg. 712
Andrews, Steven C., Chief Oper. Officer & Exec. V.P.--Integon Corporation, Winston Salem, NC; *U.S. Public*, pg. 719
Andrews, Steven C., Chief Oper. Officer & Exec. V.P.--Integon Indemnity Corporation, Winston Salem, NC; *U.S. Public*, pg. 720
Andrews, Steven C., Chief Oper. Officer & Exec. V.P.--Integon General Insurance Corporation, Winston Salem, NC; *U.S. Public*, pg. 720

Andrews, Steven C., Chief Oper. Officer & Exec. V.P.--New South Insurance Company, Winston Salem, NC; *U.S. Public*, pg. 720
Andrews, Steven C., Chief Oper. Officer & Exec. V.P.--Integon Specialty Insurance Company, Winston Salem, NC; *U.S. Public*, pg. 720
Andrews, Steven C., Chief Oper. Officer & Exec. V.P.--Integon Preferred Insurance Company, Winston Salem, NC; *U.S. Public*, pg. 720
Andrews, Steven C., Chief Oper. Officer & Exec. V.P.--Integon Casualty Insurance Company, Winston Salem, NC; *U.S. Public*, pg. 720
Anello, Ric, Exec. V.P. & Exec. Creative Dir.--DMB&B St. Louis, Saint Louis, MO; *U.S. Private*, pg. 303
Ang, Eric, Exec. V.P.--DBS Bank Ltd., Singapore, Singapore; *Int'l*, pg. 350
Ange, Zhao, Exec. V.P.--Bank of China, Beijing, China; *Int'l*, *pg. 152*
Angeles, Almario L., Exec. V.P.-Fin.--Dentsu Young & Rubicam-Alcantara Inc. (Manila), Manila, Philippines; *U.S. Private*, pg. 325
Angelich, Mark, Exec. V.P.--Amelco Corporation, Gardena, CA; *U.S. Public*, pg. 65
Angeline, Steve, Exec. V.P.-Sls. & Mktg.--Voyager Emblems, Inc., Sanborn, NY; *U.S. Private*, pg. 1143
Angelo, David, Exec. V.P. & Exec. Creative Dir.--Cliff Freeman & Partners, New York, NY; *U.S. Public*, pg. 1422
Angelo, John, Exec. V.P.-Opers.--Angelo Brothers Co., Philadelphia, PA; *U.S. Private*, pg. 74
Angelo, Thomas, Exec. V.P.--Dribeck Importers, Inc., Greenwich, CT; *U.S. Private*, pg. 343
Angelos, Peter, Exec. V.P. & Creative Dir.--Young & Rubicam San Francisco, San Francisco, CA; *U.S. Private*, pg. 1198
Angliss, Kevin, Exec. V.P.--Auburn Hosiery Mills, Inc., Auburn, KY; *U.S. Private*, pg. 98
Angst, Larry, Chief Mdsg. Officer & Exec. V.P.--Hills Stores Co., Canton, MA; *U.S. Public*, pg. 828
Annala, Mauri, Exec. V.P.-Internal Audit--FinnAir Oy, Helsinki, Finland; *Int'l*, pg. 485
Annexstad, A.T., Exec. V.P. & Dir.-Opers.--Federated Mutual Insurance Company, Owatonna, MN; *U.S. Private*, pg. 399
Annibaldi,Cesare, Exec. V.P.-Public Affairs--Fiat Auto SpA, Turin, Italy; *Int'l*, pg. 480
Anthony, G.F. Kym, Exec. V.P.-Corp. & Investment Banking-CIBG--The Toronto Dominion Bank, Toronto, Canada; *Int'l*, pg. 1401
Anthony, Michele, Exec. V.P.-SMEI--Sony Music Entertainment, Inc., New York, NY; *Int'l*, pg. 1281
Antonazzo, Nicholas O., Esq., Exec. V.P.-Real Estate Devel.--Crown American Realty Trust, Johnstown, PA; *U.S. Public*, pg. 461
Antonini, Jack M., Exec. V.P.-Consumer Group--First Union Corporation, Charlotte, NC; *U.S. Public*, pg. 639
Antonio, Franklin P., Chief Tech. Officer & Exec. V.P.--QUALCOMM, San Diego, CA; *U.S. Public*, pg. 1348
Aoki, Hideo, Sr. Exec. V.P.--All Nippon Airways Co. Ltd., Tokyo, Japan; *Int'l*, pg. 57
Aoki, Toshiharu, Sr. Exec. V.P.--Nippon Telegraph and Telephone Corporation, Tokyo, Japan; *Int'l*, pg. 940
Apgar, William, Jr., Exec. V.P.--Dairyland Marketing Services, Inc., Kenosha, WI; *U.S. Private*, pg. 307
Aphaiwongse, Teera, Chief Information Officer & Sr. Exec. V.P.--Bangkok Bank Public Company Limited, Bangkok, Thailand; *Int'l*, pg. 146
Appel, Arthur S., Exec. V.P.--Fire Control Instruments, Inc., Waltham, MA; *U.S. Private*, pg. 406
Appel, Arthur S., Chief Fin. Officer & Exec. V.P.--Fire Controls Instruments, Waltham, MA; *U.S. Public*, pg. 1306
Appel, Gloria, Exec. V.P.-Acct. Mngmt.--Grey Advertising Inc., New York, NY; *U.S. Public*, pg. 764
Appel, John C., Vice Chm. & Chief Fin. Officer--Dain Rauscher Corporation, Minneapolis, MN; *U.S. Public*, pg. 476
Appel, John C., Exec. V.P.-Telephone Opers.--GTE Corporation, Stamford, CT; *U.S. Public*, pg. 696
Appel, John C., Pres. & Exec. V.P.-Network Opers.--GTE North Incorporated, Irving, TX; *U.S. Public*, pg. 696
Appelbaum, Joel, Exec. V.P.-Storage Systems Div.--Micropolis Corporation, Chatsworth, CA; *U.S. Private*, pg. 742
Applegate, Henry, Chief Fin. Officer, Exec. V.P. & Sec.--Players International, Inc., Atlantic City, NJ; *U.S. Public*, pg. 1310
Aquino, Manolo E., Exec. V.P.-Admin. & Procurement--Philippine Airlines, Inc., Manila, Philippines; *Int'l*, pg. 1050
Arai, Kazuhiko, Exec. V.P.--Chubu Electric Power Company, Inc., Nagoya, Japan; *Int'l*, pg. 290
Arai, Tasashi, Exec. Dir.--Minolta Co., Ltd., Osaka, Japan; *Int'l*, pg. 869
Arakawa, Toshiteru, Exec. V.P.--Obayashi Corporation, Tokyo, Japan; *Int'l*, pg. 995
Aramoto, Magohiro, Sr. Exec. Dir.-Corp. Res. & Devel.--Sharp Corporation, Osaka, Japan; *Int'l*, pg. 1228
Aranow, Peter J., Exec. V.P., Treas. & Sec.--Players International, Inc., Atlantic City, NJ; *U.S. Public*, pg. 1310
Arata, Muneo, Exec. V.P.--Sanyo Electric Co., Ltd., Osaka, Japan; *Int'l*, pg. 1190
Arbuckle, James E., Chief Fin. Officer, Exec. V.P. & Treas.--Besser Company, Alpena, MI; *U.S. Private*, pg. 139
Arce, David, Exec. V.P. & Chief Internal Auditor--Banco Santander, Madrid, Spain; *Int'l*, pg. 143
Archambault, Philippe, Exec. V.P.--C.E.P. Communication Group, Paris, France; *Int'l*, pg. 239
Archer, William C., III, Exec. V.P.-External Affairs--Georgia Power Co., Atlanta, GA; *U.S. Public*, pg. 1490
Archinaco, Frank A., Exec. V.P.-Glass--PPG Industries, Inc., Pittsburgh, PA; *U.S. Public*, pg. 1245
Arena, Nick F., Exec. V.P. & Treas.--The Flood Company, Hudson, OH; *U.S. Private*, pg. 414
Arendt, Dan, Exec. V.P.-Fin.--CLT-UFA, Luxembourg, Luxembourg; *Int'l*, pg. 561
Arle, Henrik, Chief Fin. Officer & Exec. V.P.--FinnAir Oy, Helsinki, Finland; *Int'l*, pg. 485
Arledge, David A., Exec. V.P.--Coastal Refining & Marketing, Wichita, KS; *U.S. Public*, pg. 390
Arledge, David A., Exec. V.P.--Coastal States Energy Co., Salt Lake City, UT; *U.S. Public*, pg. 390
Armand, Richard, Exec. V.P.-Environment, Energy & Safety--Pechiney S.A., Courbevoie, France; *Int'l*, pg. 1027
Armbruster, William C., Chief Fin. Officer & Exec. V.P.--Peregrine Incorporated, Southfield, MI; *U.S. Private*, pg. 852
Armistead, James C., Jr., Exec. V.P.-Middle Market/Corp. Banking--First American Corporation, Nashville, TN; *U.S.* Public, pg. 624
Armstrong, Bill, Exec. V.P.--Greer Steel Co., Dover, OH; *U.S. Private*, pg. 479
Armstrong, Brad, Exec. V.P.--The Martin Agency, Richmond, VA; *U.S. Private*, pg. 678
Armstrong, Brad, Exec. V.P.--The Martin Agency, Richmond, VA; *U.S. Public*, pg. 909
Armstrong, J.K., Exec. V.P.--Cigna Investment Group, Inc., Bloomfield, CT; *U.S. Public*, pg. 357
Armstrong, Katharine C., Exec. V.P.-Commercial Lending--UST Corporation, Boston, MA; *U.S. Public*, pg. 1660
Armstrong, Paul O., Exec. V.P.--Aurora Casket Company, Aurora, IN; *U.S. Private*, pg. 99
Armstrong, R. Brock, Exec. V.P.-Corp. Devel.--London Life Insurance Group, London, Canada; *Int'l*, pg. 435
Armstrong, Robert D., Exec. V.P.--First Commercial Bank, N.A., Little Rock, AR; *U.S. Public*, pg. 630
Armstrong, Stuart, Exec. V.P.-Audit--Marine Midland Bank, Buffalo, NY; *Int'l*, pg. 581
Armstrong, Thomas R., Chief Oper. Officer & Exec. V.P.--Advent International, Boston, MA; *U.S. Private*, pg. 22
Arnold, John Q., Chief Fin. Officer & Sr. Exec. V.P.--Mercantile Bancorporation Inc., Saint Louis, MO; *U.S. Public*, pg. 1087
Arnold, John Q., Sr. Exec. V.P. & Chief Fin. Officer--Mercantile Bank of St. Louis N.A., Saint Louis, MO; *U.S. Public*, pg. 1087
Arnold, Richard E., Exec. V.P. & Dir.-Sls. & Banking Admin.--Bay View Capital Corporation, San Mateo, CA; *U.S. Public*, pg. 197
Arnold, Simon, Exec. Dir.-Insurance Services--Inchcape PLC, London, United Kingdom; *Int'l*, pg. 671
Arnold, Tim, Exec. V.P.-New Bus. Devel.-North America--DMB&B Communications, New York, NY; *U.S. Private*, pg. 302
Aron, Mark G., Exec. V.P.-Law & Pub. Affairs--CSX Corporation, Richmond, VA; *U.S. Public*, pg. 284
Aronson, Arthur H., Exec. V.P.-Segment Exec. Specialty Metals--Allegheny Teledyne Incorporated, Pittsburgh, PA; *U.S. Public*, pg. 43
Aronson, Herb, Exec. V.P.--Salant Corporation, New York, NY; *U.S. Public*, pg. 1429
Arp, Fredrik, Exec. V.P.--Trelleborg AB, Trelleborg, Sweden; *Int'l*, pg. 1419
Arrell, Ralph, Exec. V.P.--Eddins-Walcher Company, Midland, TX; *U.S. Private*, pg. 362
Arseneau, George, Exec. V.P.-Human Resources--Alliant Foodservice, Inc., Deerfield, IL; *U.S. Private*, pg. 244
Arter, Marty, Exec. V.P.--Affiliated Foods Cooperative Inc., Norfolk, NE; *U.S. Private*, pg. 25
Arthur, Bach, Exec. V.P.--Star Video Entertainment, L.P., Jersey City, NJ; *U.S. Private*, pg. 1132
Arthur, Barry, Chief Fin. Officer & Exec. V.P.-Fin.--CPI Corp., Saint Louis, MO; *U.S. Public*, pg. 283
Asaba, Michiro, Exec. V.P. & Gen. Mgr.--Bank of Yokohama New York, New York, NY; *Int'l*, pg. 159
Asada, Atsushi, Sr. Exec. V.P.--Sharp Corporation, Osaka, Japan; *Int'l*, pg. 1228
Asada, Kazuo, Sr. Exec. V.P.--Nippon Telegraph and Telephone Corporation, Tokyo, Japan; *Int'l*, pg. 940
Asada, Kentaro, Sr. Exec. V.P.--Meiji Seika Kaisha, Ltd., Tokyo, Japan; *Int'l*, pg. 855
Asada, Masazo, Exec. V.P.--The Green Cross Corporation, Osaka, Japan; *Int'l*, pg. 558
Asada, Shunji, Exec. V.P.--Kintetsu World Express, Inc., Tokyo, Japan; *Int'l*, pg. 734
Asakawa, Minato, Exec. V.P.--Kodansha America, Inc., New York, NY; *Int'l*, pg. 742
Asche, Phil, Exec. V.P. & Area Dir.-Australia & New Zealand--Young & Rubicam New York, New York, NY; *U.S. Private*, pg. 1198
Aschkenasy, Penny, Exec. V.P.--E.N.C., City of Commerce, CA; *U.S. Public*, pg. 948
Ascolese, Richard A., Exec. V.P.--American Home Shield Corporation, Memphis, TN; *U.S. Public*, pg. 1461
Ash, Dennis, Exec. V.P.--Wershow-Ash-Lewis, Tigard, OR; *U.S. Private*, pg. 1162
Ash, William J., III, Exec. V.P.--Avatar Properties Inc., Miami, FL; *U.S. Public*, pg. 151
Ash, William James, III, Exec. V.P.-Avatar Properties Inc.--Avatar Holdings Inc., Coral Gables, FL; *U.S. Public*, pg. 151
Ashar, Mike, Exec. V.P.-Oil Sands Group--Suncor Oil Sands Group, Fort McMurray, Canada; *Int'l*, pg. 1320
Ashby, Michael, Chief Fin. Officer & Exec. V.P.--Ascend Communications, Inc., Alameda, CA; *U.S. Public*, pg. 138
Ashenhurst, Harry, Exec. V.P.-Human Resources--Lennox International Inc., Richardson, TX; *U.S. Private*, pg. 659
Asher, B.H., Exec. Dir.-Investment Banking--HSBC Holdings plc, London, United Kingdom; *Int'l*, pg. 579
Asher, Thomas J., Exec. V.P. & Dir.--The Robinson-Humphrey Company, Inc., Atlanta, GA; *U.S. Public*, pg. 1633
Ashken, Ian, Chief Fin. Officer & Exec. V.P.--BEC Group, Inc., Rye, NY; *U.S. Public*, pg. 160
Ashley, Gary, Exec. V.P.-Artist & Repertoire--MCA Records, Inc., Universal City, CA; *Int'l*, pg. 1215
Askew, William E., Exec. V.P.- Retail Banking--Regions Financial Corporation, Birmingham, AL; *U.S. Public*, pg. 1371
Askren, Stanley A., Exec. V.P.--Heatilator Inc., Mount Pleasant, IA; *U.S. Public*, pg. 772
Assmann, Herbert, Exec. V.P.--Nema Warmetauscher GmbH, Netzschkau, Germany; *Int'l*, pg. 399
Asta, Richard A., Chief Fin. Officer & Exec. V.P.-Fin.--Dixon Ticonderoga Company, Heathrow, FL; *U.S. Public*, pg. 514
Astiar, Mike, Exec. V.P.-Oil Sands Group--Suncor Inc., Calgary, Canada; *Int'l*, pg. 1320
Aston, David L., Exec. V.P.--Pueblo Xtra International, Inc., Pompano Beach, FL; *U.S. Private*, pg. 894
Atkin, Douglas, Exec. V.P. & Plng. Dir.--Wells BDDP, Inc., New York, NY; *Int'l*, pg. 117
Atkin, William W., Chief Fin. Officer & Exec. V.P.--Security Mutual Life Insurance Co. of New York, Binghamton, NY; *U.S. Private*, pg. 981
Atkins, Howard I., Chief Fin. Officer & Exec. V.P.--New York Life Insurance Company, New York, NY; *U.S. Private*, pg. 794
Atols, James L., Exec. V.P.--Atols Tool and Mold Corp., Schiller Park, IL; *U.S. Private*, pg. 97
Attenborough, T. Neale, Exec. V.P.-Opers. & Pres.-Wholesale Opers.--Genesco Inc., Nashville, TN; *U.S. Public*, pg. 728
Atwater, N. William, Exec. V.P.-Engrng. & Construction Grp.--Foster Wheeler Corporation, Clinton, NJ; *U.S. Public*, pg. 676
Atwater, Peter W., Exec. V.P. & Treas.--First USA, Inc., Dallas, TX; *U.S. Public*, pg. 174
Atwell, Michael J., Exec. V.P. & Creative Dir.--Arocom Marketing Group, Inc., Cleveland, OH; *U.S. Private*, pg. 730
Atwood, John, Executive Editor--Men's Journal, New York, NY; *U.S. Private*, pg. 1162
Aubin, Christian, Sr. Exec. V.P.-Strategy, Acctg., Control & Strategy--Banque Nationale de Paris, Paris, France; *Int'l*, *pg. 163*
Aubrey, Stever, Exec. V.P. & Grp. Acct. Dir.--Hill, Holliday, Connors, Cosmopulos, Inc., Boston, MA; *U.S. Private*, pg. 529
Augenbraun, Barry S., Exec. V.P. & Gen. Counsel--Home Shopping Network, Inc., Saint Petersburg, FL; *U.S. Public*, pg. 1685
August, S.M., Exec. V.P.--Cadillac Plastic & Chemical Co., Troy, MI; *U.S. Public*, pg. 781
Auld, Michael S., Exec. V.P.--Merco/Savory Inc., Lakewood, NJ; *Int'l*, pg. 189
Ault, R. Robert, Exec. V.P. & Art Dir.--McKinney & McKinney Advertising, Redondo Beach, CA; *U.S. Private*, *pg. 723*
Aumiller, Gerald E., Sr. V.P. & Dir.-Human Resources--Keystone Financial Inc., Harrisburg, PA; *U.S. Public*, pg. 956
Aurelio, Richard A., Exec. V.P.-Semiconductor Equipment--Varian Associates, Inc., Palo Alto, CA; *U.S. Public*, pg. 1710
Auriemma, Louis, Exec. V.P.--Haddon Craftsmen, Inc., Scranton, PA; *U.S. Public*, pg. 518
Austin, H. Brent, Chief Fin. Officer & Exec. V.P.--El Paso Natural Gas Co., Houston, TX; *U.S. Public*, pg. 567
Austin, Ian G., Exec. V.P.--Placer Dome Inc., Vancouver, Canada; *Int'l*, pg. 1060
Autry, Jacqueline, Exec. V.P.--Golden West Broadcasters, Los Angeles, CA; *U.S. Private*, pg. 461
Aveleyra, Pablo, Exec. V.P.--Grupo Financiero Banamex/Accival, S.A. de C.V., Mexico, Mexico; *Int'l*, pg. 574
Avent, Sharon, Sr. Exec. V.P.--Smead Manufacturing Company, Hastings, MN; *U.S. Private*, pg. 1006
Avery, James F., Exec. V.P.--Clyde Savings Bank Company, Clyde, OH; *U.S. Public*, pg. 632
Avery, James R., Exec. V.P.-Opers. Plng. & Control--The Stroh Brewery Company, Detroit, MI; *U.S. Private*, pg. 1047
Avery, Robert J., Exec. V.P.--Cape Coral National Bank, Cape Coral, FL; *U.S. Public*, pg. 607
Avis, James C., Exec. V.P., Gen. Counsel & Sec.--Newbridge Networks Corporation, Kanata, Canada; *Int'l*, pg. 924
Avis, Robert G., Vice Chm., Exec. V.P. & Dir.-Investment Banking--A.G. Edwards, Inc., Saint Louis, MO; *U.S. Public*, pg. 565
Axthelm, Nancy, Exec. V.P. & Brdcst. Production Dir.--Grey Advertising Inc., New York, NY; *U.S. Public*, pg. 764
Ayers, Lawrence F., Jr., Exec. V.P.--Intergraph Corporation, Huntsville, AL; *U.S. Public*, pg. 890
Ayers, Les, Exec. V.P.-Sls. & Mktg.--Simmons Company, Atlanta, GA; *Int'l*, pg. 686
Ayres, John E., Exec. V.P.-Bus. Devel.--GZA GeoEnvironmental Technologies, Inc., Newton, MA; *U.S.* Public, pg. 697
Ayres, John E., Exec. V.P.-Business Development--GZA GeoEnvironmental, Inc., Newton, MA; *U.S. Public*, pg. 697
Ayres, Robert L., Chief Oper. Officer, Chief Fin. Officer & Exec. V.P.--Bush Industries Inc., Jamestown, NY; *U.S. Public*, pg. 270
Ayres, Robin, Principal--Richards, Brock, Miller, Mitchell & Assoc. Inc., Dallas, TX; *U.S. Private*, pg. 929
Azcarraga, Alejandro Burillo, Grp. Exec. V.P.--Grupo Televisa, S.A. de C.V., Mexico, Mexico; *Int'l*, pg. 576
Azorin, Harry, Exec. V.P. & Exec. Creative Dir.-Consumer Healthcare Grp.--Klemtner Advertising Inc., New York, NY; *U.S. Public*, pg. 1422
Baach, Michael K., Exec. V.P.-Sls. & Mktg.--Corrpro Companies, Inc., Medina, OH; *U.S. Public*, pg. 451
Baars, W.F.C., Exec. V.P.--ABN-AMRO Holding N.V., Amsterdam, Netherlands; *Int'l*, pg. 8
Babb, Ralph, Chief Fin. Officer & Exec. V.P.-Comerica Inc. & Comerica Bank--Comerica Incorporated, Detroit, MI; *U.S. Public*, pg. 408

Babic, Milan, Exec. V.P.--Jugobanka Banking Group, Belgrade, Serbia; *Int'l*, pg. 716
Babin, W.E., Exec. V.P.-Pulp & Paper--Georgia-Pacific Corporation, Atlanta, GA; *U.S. Public*, pg. 735
Babrowski, Claire, Exec. V.P.--McDonald's Corporation, Oak Brook, IL; *U.S. Public*, pg. 1068
Baca, Mal, Exec. V.P.--TACTech, Inc., Yorba Linda, CA; *U.S. Public*, pg. 1792
Bace, Lynn, Exec. V.P. & Gen. Mgr.-Enhancers Div.--Kraft Foods Inc., Glenview, IL; *U.S. Public*, pg. 1288
Bach, Peter, Chief Fin. Officer & Exec. V.P.--Campbell Mithun Esty, Minneapolis, MN; *U.S. Private*, pg. 204
Bacher, Philip J., Exec. V.P. & DMB&B Worldwide Human Resources Dir.--DMB&B Communications, New York, NY; *U.S. Private*, pg. 302
Bachinger, Konrad, Dr., Exec. V.P.-Commercial Banking & Legal Affairs--Liechtenstein Global Trust Limited, Vaduz, Liechtenstein; *Int'l*, pg. 809
Bachman, Ed, Exec. V.P.--Remco Toys, New York, NY; *U.S. Public*, pg. 923
Bachmann, Peter, Sr. V.P.-Bus. Affairs--Spelling Entertainment Group, Inc., Los Angeles, CA; *U.S. Private*, pg. 776
Bachrach, Chuck, Exec. V.P., Media Resources & Programming Dir.--Rubin Postaer & Associates, Santa Monica, CA; *U.S. Private*, pg. 949
Bachrach, Hillel, Exec. V.P.--ESC Medical Systems Ltd., Yokneam, Israel; *Int'l*, pg. 429
Bachrach, Nancy, Exec. V.P.--Grey Advertising Inc., New York, NY; *U.S. Public*, pg. 764
Back, Gregory, Exec. V.P.-Corp. Plng. & Devel.--American Business Information, Inc., Omaha, NE; *U.S. Public*, pg. 69
Backes, Wilfried, Chief Fin. Officer, Exec. V.P. & Treas.--Osram Sylvania Inc., Malvern, PA; *Int'l*, pg. 1245
Backman, William D., III, Exec. V.P.--Aurora Casket Company, Aurora, IN; *U.S. Private*, pg. 99
Backus, James, Exec. V.P.-Engrng. & Construction--Wilmorite, Inc., Rochester, NY; *U.S. Private*, pg. 1180
Bacon, Ernest, Chief Oper. Officer & Exec. V.P.--Community Health Systems, Inc., Brentwood, TN; *U.S. Private*, pg. 419
Badcock, Henry C., Exec. V.P.-Dealers Opers.--W.S. Badcock Corporation, Mulberry, FL; *U.S. Private*, pg. 109
Badcock, Mary R., Exec. V.P.--W.S. Badcock Corporation, Mulberry, FL; *U.S. Private*, pg. 109
Badcock, Wogan S., III, Exec. V.P.-Mngmt. & Admin. Services--W.S. Badcock Corporation, Mulberry, FL; *U.S. Private*, pg. 109
Badenhop, Stephen, Exec. V.P.-Client Services--Jordan, McGrath, Case & Taylor Inc., New York, NY; *U.S. Private*, pg. 598
Baer, Larry, Chief Oper. Officer & Exec. V.P.--San Francisco Giants Baseball Club, San Francisco, CA; *U.S. Private*, pg. 964
Baer, Stephen, Exec. V.P. & Mng. Partner-Creative--Wells BDDP, Inc., New York, NY; *Int'l*, pg. 117
Baesler, David M., Exec. V.P.--Brother International Corporation, Somerset, NJ; *Int'l*, pg. 229
Baez, Carmen, Exec. V.P.-Latin America--Diversified Agency Services, New York, NY; *U.S. Public*, pg. 1223
Bagby, Robert L., Vice Chm., Exec. V.P. & Dir.-Branches--A.G. Edwards, Inc., Saint Louis, MO; *U.S. Public*, pg. 565
Bahash, Robert J., Chief Fin. Officer & Exec. V.P.--The McGraw-Hill Companies, New York, NY; *U.S. Public*, pg. 1069
Bahr, H.T., Sr. V.P.--Miller Freeman Inc., San Francisco, CA; *Int'l*, pg. 1443
Bahr, Mark A., Exec V.P. & Sec.--Barton Malow Co., Southfield, MI; *U.S. Private*, pg. 120
Baiden, Arthur H., III, Exec. V.P. & Sec.--Potter-Shackelford Construction Co., Greenville, SC; *U.S. Private*, pg. 877
Bailey, Charles E., Exec. V.P.--Trustmark National Bank, Jackson, MS; *U.S. Public*, pg. 1643
Bailey, Dan, Dr., Exec. V.P.--UHP Healthcare, Inglewood, CA; *U.S. Private*, pg. 1113
Bailey, David T., Exec. V.P.--Policy Management Systems Corporation, Blythewood, SC; *U.S. Public*, pg. 1314
Bailey, Richard D., Exec. V.P.-Corp. Banking--Shoreline Bank, Benton Harbor, MI; *U.S. Public*, pg. 1468
Bailey, Richard D., II, Exec. V.P.-Corp. Banking--Shoreline Financial Corp., Benton Harbor, MI; *U.S. Public*, pg. 1467
Bailey, Wayne R., Chief Fin. Officer & Exec. V.P.--Fremont General Corporation, Santa Monica, CA; *U.S. Public*, pg. 681
Bailly, Richard L., Exec. V.P.--UFP Technology, Georgetown, MA; *U.S. Private*, pg. 1112
Bain, Howard, III, Chief Fin. Officer & Exec. V.P.-Worldwide Opers.--Symantec Corporation, Cupertino, CA; *U.S. Public*, pg. 1545
Bains, Leslie E., Exec. V.P.--Republic National Bank of New York, New York, NY; *U.S. Public*, pg. 1380
Baird, Arthur, Exec. V.P.--Mrs. Baird's Bakeries, Inc., Fort Worth, TX; *U.S. Private*, pg. 765
Bakane, John L., Exec. V.P.--Cone Mills Corporation, Greensboro, NC; *U.S. Public*, pg. 430
Baker, Alfred, Chief Fin. Officer & Exec. V.P.--Pro-Line Corporation, Dallas, TX; *U.S. Private*, pg. 887
Baker, Allen, Exec. V.P.-Surgical--Alcon Laboratories, Inc., Fort Worth, TX; *Int'l*, pg. 916
Baker, Dan, Exec. V.P.--F. Korbel Bros. Inc., Guerneville, CA; *U.S. Private*, pg. 632
Baker, J. Curtis, Exec. V.P.--Cameron Ashley Building Products, Inc, Dallas, TX; *U.S. Public*, pg. 298
Baker, Larry, Exec. V.P.-Opers.--Invacare Health Care Furnishings, Chesterfield, MO; *U.S. Public*, pg. 911
Baker, Michael C., Sr. Exec. V.P. & Head-Capital Mngmt. Grp.--AmSouth Bancorporation, Birmingham, AL; *U.S. Public*, pg. 105
Baker, Michael D., Exec. V.P.--Fifth Third Bancorp, Cincinnati, OH; *U.S. Public*, pg. 621
Baker, Newell A., Jr., Exec. V.P. & Sec.--J.D. Streett & Co., Inc., Maryland Heights, MO; *U.S. Private*, pg. 1047
Baker, Newton D., Exec. V.P. & Treas.--Access Corporation, Cincinnati, OH; *Int'l*, pg. 994
Baker, Phillips S., Jr., Chief Fin. Officer & Exec. V.P.--Pegasus Gold Corporation, Spokane, WA; *U.S. Public*, pg. 1269
Baker, R. Daniel, Exec. V.P.-Field Opers.--TIE/Communications, Inc., Overland Park, KS; *U.S. Private*, pg. 1085
Baker, Robert W., Chief Oper. Officer--AMR Corporation, Fort Worth, TX; *U.S. Public*, pg. 9
Baker, S. Emery, Exec. V.P.-Opers.--United Family Life Insurance Co., Atlanta, GA; *Int'l*, pg. 499
Baker, T.L., Exec. V.P.--TU Electric, Dallas, TX; *U.S. Public*, pg. 1588
Baker, Tom, Exec. V.P.--TU Services, Dallas, TX; *U.S. Public*, pg. 1588
Baker, W. Randolph, Chief Fin. Officer & Exec. V.P.--Anheuser-Busch Companies, Inc., Saint Louis, MO; *U.S. Public*, pg. 113
Bakker, S.M.M.A.J., Exec. V.P.--ABN-AMRO Holding N.V., Amsterdam, Netherlands; *Int'l*, pg. 8
Balakrishnan, V., Exec. V.P.--Republic Container Corp., Jersey City, NJ; *U.S. Private*, pg. 923
Balanson, Richard, Dr., Exec. V.P. & Gen. Mgr.--Maxtor Corporation, Milpitas, CA; *Int'l*, pg. 641
Balber, Michael B., Exec. V.P.--Sports Imprints/Fun Wear, Huber Heights, OH; *U.S. Public*, pg. 1002
Baldauf, Sari, Exec. V.P.-Nokia APAC--Oy Nokia Ab/Nokia Group, Helsinki, Finland; *Int'l*, pg. 951
Baldi, Joseph, Jr., Exec. V.P.--Baldi, Bloom & Whelan Advertising, New York, NY; *U.S. Private*, pg. 112
Baldwin, Richard O., Jr., Exec. V.P. & Pres.-Corp. Devel. Div.--Stewart Enterprises, Inc., Metairie, LA; *U.S. Public*, pg. 1518
Baldwin, Thomas J., Chief Fin. Officer & Exec. V.P.--Morton's Restaurant Group, Inc., New Hyde Park, NY; *U.S. Public*, pg. 1136
Balfe, Edward T., Exec. V.P.-Construction Mtls.--Lafarge Corporation, Reston, VA; *Int'l*, pg. 788
Balkema, Gary S., Exec. V.P. & Pres.-Consumer Care Division--Bayer Corporation, Pittsburgh, PA; *Int'l*, pg. 172
Balkema, Gary S., Pres.-Consumer Care Div. & Exec. V.P.--Bayer Corporation, Pittsburgh, PA; *Int'l*, pg. 172
Balkema, Gary S., Exec. V.P. & Pres.-Consumer Care Div.--Bayer Corporation, Parsippany, NJ; *Int'l*, pg. 172
Ball, Don H., Sr. Exec. V.P.-Mktg.--Willis Corroon Corp. of Illinois, Chicago, IL; *Int'l*, pg. 1506
Ball, Robert L., Exec. V.P.-Rolled Prods., North America--Alcan Aluminium Limited, Montreal, Canada; *Int'l*, pg. 50
Ballantine, John W., Exec. V.P.-Corp. & Institutional Banking--First Chicago NBD Corporation, Chicago, IL; *U.S. Public*, pg. 627
Ballantine, Wm. Thomas, Exec. V.P.--Newpark Resources, Inc., Metairie, LA; *U.S. Public*, pg. 1179
Ballard, Bob, Exec. V.P.-Opers.--Steelcase Inc., Grand Rapids, MI; *U.S. Private*, pg. 1038
Balle, Ole, Chief Fin. Officer & Exec. V.P.--Sophus Berendsen A/S, Soeborg, Denmark; *Int'l*, pg. 1284
Ballmer, Steven A., Exec. V.P.-Sls. & Support--Microsoft Corporation, Redmond, WA; *U.S. Public*, pg. 1107
Balogh, Mike, Exec. V.P.--Sunflower Group In-Store Services, Des Plaines, IL; *U.S. Private*, pg. 1052
Balter, Wendy, Exec. V.P. & Mng. Dir.-Phase V--Grey Healthcare Group, New York, NY; *U.S. Public*, pg. 765
Balthasar, Norman J., Corp. Exec. V.P.-Saving & Commercial Bank Grp.--Fiserv, Inc., Brookfield, WI; *U.S. Public*, pg. 647
Bamberger, tomas J., Exec. V.P.--Summit Bank, Bethlehem, PA; *U.S. Public*, pg. 1528
Bamberger, Tomas J., Exec. V.P.--First Valley Corporation, Bethlehem, PA; *U.S. Public*, pg. 1528
Bambrick, James E., Exec. V.P.--Farrell Lines Incorporated, New York, NY; *U.S. Private*, pg. 397
Banch, Tom, Exec. V.P.--QST Industries, Inc., Chicago, IL; *U.S. Private*, pg. 897
Bandeira Vieira, Henrique, Exec. Dir.-Mktg.--Petrofina S.A., Brussels, Belgium; *Int'l*, pg. 1043
Bane, Dennis D., Exec. V.P.--Gibson County Bank, Princeton, IN; *U.S. Public*, pg. 1217
Banerjee, Nic, Sr. V.P.-Mktg.--Union Bank of California, San Francisco, CA; *Int'l*, pg. 157
Bankier, Alain, Exec. V.P. & Mng. Dir.--Banexi International Financial Services (North America) Corp., New York, NY; *Int'l*, pg. 163
Banks, James, Exec. V.P.-Third Party Lending--INMC Mortgage Holdings, Inc., Pasadena, CA; *U.S. Public*, pg. 857
Bannerman, Martha G., Exec. V.P., Gen. Counsel & Sec.--Greenwich Insurance Company, Greenwich, CT; *U.S. Public*, pg. 1144
Bannerman, Martha G., Exec. V.P., Gen. Counsel & Sec.--Indian Harbor Insurance Company, Greenwich, CT; *U.S. Public*, pg. 1144
Bannerman, W. Douglas, Exec. V.P.-Corp. Banking--National City Corporation, Cleveland, OH; *U.S. Public*, pg. 1154
Bannon, Kevin J., Exec. V.P. & Chief Investment Officer-Institutional Investment--The Bank of New York Company, Inc., New York, NY; *U.S. Public*, pg. 178
Banta, Robert R., Chief Fin. Officer & Exec. V.P.--Moog Incorporated, East Aurora, NY; *U.S. Public*, pg. 1127
Bar-Giora, Elan, Exec. V.P.-Opers.--Hi-Tech Pharmacal Co., Inc., Amityville, NY; *U.S. Public*, pg. 825
Bar-Ziv, Haim, Exec. V.P.--Israel Discount Bank of New York, New York, NY; *Int'l*, pg. 645
Barad, Seth A., Exec. V.P.-Unbanked Bus.--AEGON USA, Inc., Louisville, KY; *Int'l*, pg. 26
Barad, Seth A., Exec. V.P.--Providian Financial Corporation, San Francisco, CA; *U.S. Public*, pg. 1338
Barathon, Claude, Exec. V.P.-Worldwide Sls.--Quantum Corporation, Milpitas, CA; *U.S. Public*, pg. 1350
Barbarowicz, Robert P., Exec. V.P., Gen. Counsel & Sec.--National Insurance Group, South San Francisco, CA; *U.S. Public*, pg. 1157
Barbera, Tom, Vice Chm. & Exec. V.P.-Govt. Prods.--Mid Atlantic Medical Services, Inc., Rockville, MD; *U.S. Public*, pg. 1109
Barberia, Anthony, Exec. V.P. & Treas.--Amloid Corporation, Saddle Brook, NJ; *U.S. Private*, pg. 66
Barclay, R. Lee, Chief Fin. Officer & Exec. V.P.--Midas-International Corp., Chicago, IL; *U.S. Public*, pg. 1766
Barden, Thomas, Chief Exec. Officer & Exec. V.P.--Barden & Robeson Corporation, Middleport, NY; *U.S. Private*, pg. 116
Bared, Carlos, Exec. V.P.--Farm Stores, Miami, FL; *U.S. Private*, pg. 394
Bareuther, James, Exec. V.P. & Dir.-Sls.--Brown-Forman Corporation, Louisville, KY; *U.S. Public*, pg. 261
Bareuther, James L., Exec. V.P.-Spirits Brands Co.--Brown-Forman Beverages Worldwide, Louisville, KY; *U.S. Public*, pg. 261
Barfus, Richard, Exec. V.P.-Field Opers.--Brightware, Inc., Novato, CA; *U.S. Private*, pg. 168
Barger, Jack, Exec. V.P.--Hop-In Michigan, Inc., Ann Arbor, MI; *Int'l*, pg. 1249
Barger, Maurice W., Jr., Exec. V.P. & Chief Mktg. Officer--NACOLAH Holding Corp. Inc., Chicago, IL; *U.S. Private*, pg. 963
Barger, Steven B., Sr. Exec. V.P.--Primerica Financial Services, Duluth, GA; *U.S. Public*, pg. 1633
Barilli, Luigi, Exec. V.P.-Opers.--I.B.I.S.-S.p.A., Busseto, Italy; *Int'l*, pg. 642
Barker, Brian, Exec. V.P.--Hogan Systems, Inc., Dallas, TX; *U.S. Public*, pg. 422
Barker, Floyd, Exec. V.P.--Coast Manufacturing Company, Yonkers, NY; *U.S. Private*, pg. 248
Barker, Robert L., Exec. V.P.-Worldwide Telecommunications--SHL Systemhouse, Ottawa, Canada; *Int'l*, pg. 1154
Barkhorn, Henry C., III, Exec. V.P.--Fiduciary Trust Company International, New York, NY; *U.S. Public*, pg. 621
Barnard, Andrew A., Exec. V.P.-Bus. Plng. & Devel.--Transatlantic Holdings Inc., New York, NY; *U.S. Public*, pg. 84
Barnard, L. Scott, Exec. V.P.-Sls.--Champion International Corp., Stamford, CT; *U.S. Public*, pg. 333
Barnard, Michael C., Exec. V.P.-Corp.--Royal Insurance Company of Canada, Toronto, Canada; *Int'l*, pg. 1131
Barnes, Andrew, Exec. V.P.-Strategic Bus. Devel.--Mycogen Corporation, San Diego, CA; *U.S. Public*, pg. 1142
Barnes, Charles D., Exec. V.P.--National City Bank, Kentucky, Louisville, KY; *U.S. Public*, pg. 1154
Barnes, Pierre, Chief Oper. Officer & Exec. V.P.--Federation des caisses populaires Desjardins, Montreal, Canada; *Int'l*, pg. 479
Barnes, Robert E., Exec. V.P.-Residential Mortgage Lending--Compass Bank Houston, Houston, TX; *U.S. Public*, pg. 419
Barnet, Bruce, Exec. V.P. & Dir.-Real Estate & Devel.--Long Island Bancorp, Inc., Melville, NY; *U.S. Public*, pg. 1013
Barnett, Barry, Exec. V.P.--Publix Supermarkets Inc., Lakeland, FL; *U.S. Private*, pg. 893
Barnett, Dana G., Vice Chm. & Exec. V.P.--Mylan Laboratories, Inc., Pittsburgh, PA; *U.S. Public*, pg. 1143
Barnett, Ken, Exec. V.P. & Gen. Mgr.--Mars Advertising Co., Southfield, MI; *U.S. Private*, pg. 706
Barnett, Ken, Exec. V.P. & Gen. Mgr.--Mars Public Relations Group, Southfield, MI; *U.S. Private*, pg. 707
Barnett, Lester A., Exec. V.P. & Exec. Creative Dir.--FCB HealthCare, San Francisco, CA; *U.S. Public*, pg. 1641
Barnett, Marjorie, Exec. V.P.--Farmers Copper & Industrial Supply, Galveston, TX; *U.S. Private*, pg. 422
Barnhill, John W., Jr., Exec. V.P. & Gen. Mgr.-Sls.--Blue Bell Creameries, L.P., Brenham, TX; *U.S. Private*, pg. 150
Barnholt, Brandon, Exec. V.P.-Mktg. (St. Louis)--Clark Refining & Marketing Inc., Saint Louis, MO; *U.S. Private*, pg. 243
Barnholt, Edward W., Exec. V.P. & Gen. Mgr.-Test & Meas. Org.--Hewlett-Packard Company, Palo Alto, CA; *U.S. Public*, pg. 813
Baron, Rene, Exec. V.P.-Plng. & Devel.--N. Schlumberger & Cie, Guebwiller, France; *Int'l*, pg. 1206
Barr, Daniel C., Exec. V.P.-Human Resources--First USA, Inc., Dallas, TX; *U.S. Public*, pg. 174
Barr, David C., Chief Oper. Officer & Exec. V.P.--Genesis ElderCare, Philadelphia, PA; *U.S. Public*, pg. 728
Barr, David T., Exec. V.P.--Barr & Barr, Inc., New York, NY; *U.S. Private*, pg. 117
Barr, Greg, Chief Oper. Officer & Exec. V.P.--Nob Hill General Store, Inc., Gilroy, CA; *U.S. Private*, pg. 799
Barr, Michael R., Chief Oper. Officer & Exec. V.P.--Vencor, Inc., Louisville, KY; *U.S. Public*, pg. 1711
Barr, Nancy P., Exec. V.P. & Client Services Dir.--Lord, Sullivan & Yoder Inc. Marketing Communications, Columbus, OH; *U.S. Private*, pg. 676
Barranco, Robert G., Exec. V.P.-Opers.--Kelly Services, Inc., Troy, MI; *U.S. Public*, pg. 949
Barrath, Paul, Exec. V.P.-Fin. Facilities--HBE Corporation/Design Build Divisions, Saint Louis, MO; *U.S. Private*, pg. 489
Barravecchia, John R., Chief Fin. Officer & Exec. V.P.--Franchise Finance Corp. of America, Scottsdale, AZ; *U.S. Public*, pg. 679
Barreira Sotelino, Fernando, Exec. V.P.--Uniao de Bancos Brasileiros S.A. (Unibanco), Sao Paulo, Brazil; *Int'l*, pg. 1431
Barrentine, C. David, Jr., Exec. V.P.--Commercial National Bank, Shreveport, LA; *U.S. Public*, pg. 500
Barrett, Colleen C., Exec. V.P.-Customers & Corp. Sec.--Southwest Airlines Co., Dallas, TX; *U.S. Public*, pg. 1493
Barrett, David J., Chief Oper. Officer & Exec. V.P.--Hearst-Argyle Television Incorporated, New York, NY; *U.S. Private*, pg. 516
Barrett, Robert, Exec. V.P.--Frontier Corporation, Rochester, NY; *U.S. Public*, pg. 683
Barrett, Robert E., Exec. V.P.--UST Inc., Greenwich, CT; *U.S. Public*, pg. 1660

Barrette, Kathy, Exec. V.P.--First American CREDCO, San Diego, CA; *U.S. Public*, pg. 625
Barretto, Alberto Dias de Mattos, Exec. V.P.-Intl. Area--Banco Itau S.A., Sao Paulo, Brazil; *Int'l*, pg. 142
Barringer, Fred A., Exec. V.P. & Gen. Mgr.--Taracorp Evans, Inc., Atlanta, GA; *U.S. Private*, pg. 1068
Barringer, Fred A., Exec. V.P. & Gen. Mgr.--Taracorp Imaco, Inc., Winston Salem, NC; *U.S. Private*, pg. 1068
Barrocas, Eddie, Exec. V.P.--Injection Footwear Corp., Miami, FL; *U.S. Private*, pg. 563
Barron, Gary A., Chief Oper. Officer & Exec. V.P.--Southwest Airlines Co., Dallas, TX; *U.S. Public*, pg. 1493
Barron, Millard, Exec. V.P.--Hudson's Bay Company, Toronto, Canada; *Int'l*, pg. 637
Barrow, M. Brantley, Exec. V.P.-Admin.--Hardin Construction Group, Inc., Atlanta, GA; *U.S. Private*, pg. 501
Barrow, Tommy J., Exec. V.P.--First Financial Bankshares, Inc., Abilene, TX; *U.S. Public*, pg. 633
Bart, Dave, Exec. V.P.-Wine Division--NWS Inc., Chicago, IL; *U.S. Private*, pg. 772
Bartels, Juergen, Exec. V.P.--Carlson Companies, Inc., Minnetonka, MN; *U.S. Private*, pg. 211
Bartelt, Bruce, Chief Oper. Officer & Exec. V.P.--Rainfair, Inc., Racine, WI; *U.S. Private*, pg. 907
Bartelt, Wilbert B., Exec. V.P.--Rust-Oleum Corporation, Vernon Hills, IL; *U.S. Public*, pg. 1358
Barter, John W., Exec. V.P. & Pres.-AlliedSignal Automotive--AlliedSignal Inc., Morristown, NJ; *U.S. Public*, pg. 49
Barth, John, Exec. V.P.--Dairy Queen Canada, Inc., Burlington, Canada; *U.S. Public*, pg. 220
Barth, John M., Exec. V.P.--Johnson Controls, Inc., Controls Group, Milwaukee, WI; *U.S. Public*, pg. 932
Barth, John M., Exec. V.P. & Gen. Mgr.--Johnson Controls, Inc., Plymouth, MI; *U.S. Public*, pg. 932
Bartholomew, Chuck, Exec. V.P. & Client Services Dir.--EvansGroup, Salt Lake City, UT; *U.S. Private*, pg. 385
Bartlett, John C., M.D., Exec. V.P.-Clinical Staff--Magellan Health Services, Inc., Atlanta, GA; *U.S. Public*, pg. 1033
Barton, Peter A., Exec. V.P.--OMI Corp., New York, NY; *U.S. Public*, pg. 1208
Barton, Randy, Exec. V.P.--Quail Piping Products, Inc., Magnolia, AR; *U.S. Public*, pg. 137
Barton, Steven A., Chief Oper. Officer & Exec. V.P.--Benchmark Electronics Inc., Angleton, TX; *U.S. Public*, pg. 210
Bartruff, Stuart, Exec. V.P. & Sec.--First Commerce Bancshares, Inc., Lincoln, NE; *U.S. Public*, pg. 629
Barttett, Richard, Exec. V.P.-McCain International Inc.--McCain Foods Limited, Florenceville, Canada; *Int'l*, pg. 850
Baruc, Robert, Exec. V.P.--Unapix Entertainment Inc., New York, NY; *U.S. Public*, pg. 1664
Baruch, Steven, Exec. V.P.--Presidential Realty Corporation, White Plains, NY; *U.S. Public*, pg. 1323
Baruch, Steven, Exec. V.P.--Presidential Realty of Iowa, Inc., White Plains, NY; *U.S. Public*, pg. 1324
Barzilay, Zvi, Exec. V.P.--Toll Brothers, Inc., Huntingdon Valley, PA; *U.S. Public*, pg. 1620
Basan, Kazim, Exec. V.P.-Engrg.--Arcelik A.S., Istanbul, Turkey; *Int'l*, pg. 741
Basarico, Frank, Jr., Exec. V.P.-Credit Mngmt. Div.--CVB Financial Corp., Ontario, CA; *U.S. Public*, pg. 286
Bascomb, Stuart, Exec. V.P.-Sls. & Mktg.--Express Scripts, Inc., Maryland Heights, MO; *U.S. Public*, pg. 600
Baseler, Theodore, Exec. V.P.-Sls., Mktg. & Corp. Affairs--Stimson Lane Ltd., Woodinville, WA; *U.S. Public*, pg. 1661
Basil, Neal, Exec. V.P. & Acting Gen. Mgr.--SMC Environmental Services Group Inc., King of Prussia, PA; *U.S. Public*, pg. 1717
Baskin, Steve, Exec. V.P.--Mark Shale, Burr Ridge, IL; *U.S. Private*, pg. 989
Bass, Charles W., Chief Oper. Officer & Exec. V.P.--AGL Resources, Atlanta, GA; *U.S. Public*, pg. 6
Bassick, Jack, Exec. V.P.--David Clark Company Incorporated, Worcester, MA; *U.S. Private*, pg. 242
Batayas, Dimitri, Exec. V.P.-Media--Leo Burnett Athens, Athens, Greece; *U.S. Private*, pg. 184
Bateman, R.J., Exec. V.P.--Emerson Electric Co., Saint Louis, MO; *U.S. Public*, pg. 572
Batiwala, Jim, Exec. V.P.--Tata Inc., New York, NY; *Int'l*, pg. 1356
Batten, Frank, Jr., Exec. V.P.--Landmark Communications, Inc., Norfolk, VA; *U.S. Private*, pg. 647
Battenburg, J.T., III, Exec. V.P.--General Motors Corporation, Detroit, MI; *U.S. Public*, pg. 718
Batteux, Armand, Exec. V.P.--Bertrand Faure, Boulogne, France; *Int'l*, pg. 192
Battison, William J., Exec. V.P.-Mktg. & Sls.--Iwerks Entertainment, Burbank, CA; *U.S. Public*, pg. 915
Battle, Fernando, Chief Oper./Retail Banking Officer& Exec. V.P.--Firstbank Puerto Rico, Santurce, PR; *U.S. Public*, pg. 644
Battles, Dennis O., Exec. V.P.--Mercantile Bancorporation Inc., Saint Louis, MO; *U.S. Public*, pg. 1087
Bauchwitz, Barry, Chief Oper. Officer & Exec. V.P.--Account Specific Marketing, Inc. (ASM), Morristown, NJ; *U.S. Private*, pg. 345
Baudo, Jeff, Exec. V.P.--United Advertising Publications, Inc., Dallas, TX; *Int'l*, pg. 1443
Baudouin, Jean-Paul, Exec. V.P.--Fernand Nathan, Paris, France; *Int'l*, pg. 240
Bauer, Carl, Exec. V.P.--C.C. Myers, Inc., Rancho Cordova, CA; *U.S. Private*, pg. 770
Bauer, Chris M., Sr. Exec. V.P.--Firstar Corporation, Milwaukee, WI; *U.S. Public*, pg. 642
Bauer, Craig E., Exec. V.P.--Videojet Systems International, Inc., Wood Dale, IL; *Int'l*, pg. 545
Bauer, Michael, Exec. V.P., Sec. & Treas.--Al & Ed's Auto Sound Center, Monterey Park, CA; *U.S. Private*, pg. 30
Bauer, Mike, Exec. V.P.-Sls. & Mktg.--Empire of Carolina, Inc., Delray Beach, FL; *U.S. Public*, pg. 579
Baugh, Jammie, Exec. V.P. & Gen. Mgr.-Southern California--Nordstrom, Inc., Seattle, WA; *U.S. Public*, pg. 1190
Baughman, David, Exec. V.P.--Plastomer Corp., Livonia, MI; *U.S. Private*, pg. 872
Baukol, R.O., Exec. V.P.-Intl. Opers.--3M, Saint Paul, MN; *U.S. Public*, pg. 1604
Bauler, Beth, Chief Oper. Officer & Exec. V.P.--Alpha Omega Publications, Chandler, AZ; *U.S. Private*, pg. 168
Baum, Nick, Exec. V.P.-Euro RSCG Worldwide--Havas Advertising, Levallois-Perret, France; *Int'l*, pg. 600
Baum, Robert H., Vice Chm. & Gen. Counsel--The Inland Group, Inc., Oak Brook, IL; *U.S. Private*, pg. 564
Baum, William A., Chief Fin. Officer & Exec. V.P.--Peoples Telephone Company, Inc., Miami, FL; *U.S. Public*, pg. 1275
Baumgarten, Jean Claude, Exec. V.P.-Intl. Agreements & Industry Affairs--Groupe Air France, Roissy, France; *Int'l*, *pg. 559*
Baumgartner, Steven M., Exec. V.P. & Sector Pres.-Global Printing--R.R. Donnelley & Sons Company, Chicago, IL; *U.S. Public*, pg. 517
Bavely, Donald, Chief Fin. Officer & Exec. V.P.--Rosenthal Automotive Organization, Arlington, VA; *U.S. Private*, pg. 946
Baxter, Philip, Chief Fin. Officer & Exec. V.P.--Mapco Inc., Tulsa, OK; *U.S. Public*, pg. 1042
Bayle, Michel, Exec. V.P.-Res.--Gaz de France, Paris, France; *Int'l*, pg. 541
Bayless, Charles T., Exec. V.P.-Worldwide Processing Opers.--Archer Daniels Midland Company (ADM), Decatur, IL; *U.S. Public*, pg. 127
Bazoche, Noel, Exec. V.P.-Intl. Devel.--Credit Commercial de France, Paris, France; *Int'l*, pg. 341
Bazy, Dominique, Sr. Exec. V.P.--AXA-UAP, Paris, France; *Int'l*, pg. 18
Beahm, Clyde W., Exec. V.P.-Mktg.--Pennzoil Products Co., Houston, TX; *U.S. Public*, pg. 1272
Beal, Franklyn H., Exec. V.P.-Inland International, Inc.--Inland Steel Industries, Inc., Chicago, IL; *U.S. Public*, pg. 879
Beal, Franklyn H., Exec. V.P.--Inland International, Inc., Chicago, IL; *U.S. Public*, pg. 879
Beal, Ilene, Exec. V.P. & Sec.--BayBanks, Inc., Boston, MA; *U.S. Public*, pg. 184
Beale, John, Exec. V.P.--City National Corporation, Beverly Hills, CA; *U.S. Public*, pg. 380
Bealle, James, Exec. V.P.--Carter & Associates, Atlanta, GA; *U.S. Private*, pg. 216
Bealle, Kim, Exec. V.P. & Acct. Mngmt. Dir.--Young & Rubicam New York, New York, NY; *U.S. Private*, pg. 1198
Beaman, Catherine, Exec. V.P.--Countrywide Title Corporation, Pasadena, CA; *U.S. Public*, pg. 453
Beamer, Jerry, Exec. V.P. & Controller--Berry Companies, Inc., Wichita, KS; *U.S. Private*, pg. 137
Bean, John M., Exec. V.P. & Gen. Mgr.--SHL Systemhouse - Asia/Pacific, Vancouver, Canada; *Int'l*, pg. 1154
Bean, Michael A., Exec. V.P. & Controller--Compass Bank, Birmingham, AL; *U.S. Public*, pg. 418
Bean, Walter C., Exec. V.P.--C.S. McKee & Company, Inc., Pittsburgh, PA; *U.S. Public*, pg. 1673
Beard, Frederick K., Exec. V.P. & Chm. Bd., Pres. & Chief Exec. Officer-Mellon Bank--Mellon Bank Corporation, Pittsburgh, PA; *U.S. Public*, pg. 1084
Beardall, Dennis, Exec. V.P.--Crawford Industries, Crawfordsville, IN; *U.S. Private*, pg. 64
Bearden, James, Exec. V.P., Gen. Mgr. & Chief Oper. Officer--Bush Hog Division, Selma, AL; *U.S. Public*, pg. 48
Bearden, Walter, Exec. V.P.-Foxcroft--The Apparel Group, Ltd., Louisville, KY; *U.S. Private*, pg. 78
Bearman, David, Chief Fin. Officer & Exec. V.P.--Cardinal Health Inc., Dublin, OH; *U.S. Public*, pg. 304
Beartl, Luis J., Sr. V.P.-South American Corp. Devel.--Barrick Gold Corporation, Toronto, Canada; *Int'l*, pg. 168
Beasley, G.E., Sr. Exec. V.P.-Risk Mngmt.--The CIBC Wood Gundy Corporation, Toronto, Canada; *Int'l*, pg. 256
Beasley, Gerald E., Exec. V.P.-Eastern Canada/Europe, Corporate Bank, CIBC--Canadian Imperial Bank of Commerce, Toronto, Canada; *Int'l*, pg. 256
Beaston, Geoff, Exec. V.P.--Lexington Furniture Industries, Lexington, NC; *U.S. Private*, pg. 432
Beatty, Vincent L., Exec. V.P. & Dir.-Loan Sls. & Opers.--Glendale Federal Bank, F.S.B., Glendale, CA; *U.S. Public*, pg. 747
Beauchamp, Luis M., Chief Lending Officer & Sr. Exec. V.P.--Firstbank Puerto Rico, Santurce, PR; *U.S. Public*, pg. 644
Beaudoin, Bernard, Chief Fin. Officer & Exec. V.P.--Kansas City Power & Light Company, Kansas City, MO; *U.S. Public*, pg. 943
Beaudoin, Jean-Pierre, Exec. V.P.-Paper & Board Machines--Valmet Inc., Charlotte Division, Charlotte, NC; *Int'l*, pg. 1448
Beaulieu, Kenneth, Exec. V.P.-Opers.--The Berlin Steel Construction Company, Berlin, CT; *U.S. Private*, pg. 136
Beaver, Andrew, Exec. V.P. & Grp. Dir.--Deutsch, Inc., New York, NY; *U.S. Private*, pg. 328
Beavers, Shirley C., Jr., Exec. V.P.--First Virginia Banks, Inc., Falls Church, VA; *U.S. Public*, pg. 641
Beber, Robert H., Exec. V.P. & Gen. Counsel--W.R. Grace & Co., Boca Raton, FL; *U.S. Public*, pg. 754
Becchetti, Serge, Exec. V.P.--Labinal SA, Montigny-le-Bretonneux, France; *Int'l*, pg. 785
Bechard, Yvon, First Exec. V.P. & Asst. Sec.--The Jean Coutu Group (PJC) Inc., Longueuil, Canada; *Int'l*, pg. 340
Becher, Henry, Exec. V.P.--Dow Jones Markets, Jersey City, NJ; *U.S. Public*, pg. 525
Bechtol, Michael, Exec. V.P.-Retail--Catalina Marketing Corporation, Saint Petersburg, FL; *U.S. Public*, pg. 314
Beck, William F., Exec. V.P.-Europe & Gen. Mgr.-Chemical Prods. Grp.--FMC Corporation, Chicago, IL; *U.S. Public*, pg. 604
Becker, Folke, Exec. V.P. & Pres.-BT Products AB--BT Industries AB, Mjolby, Sweden; *Int'l*, pg. 123
Becker, Larry K., Chief Fin. Officer & Exec. V.P.--Horace Mann Educators Corporation, Springfield, IL; *U.S. Public*, *pg. 835*
Becker, Marc I., Chief Oper. Officer & Exec. V.P.--Network Long Distance, Inc., Baton Rouge, LA; *U.S. Public*, pg. 1169
Beckergel, Steven M., Exec. V.P.--Schoep's Ice Cream, Inc., Madison, WI; *U.S. Private*, pg. 972
Beckerman, Gary, Exec. V.P.--Teac America, Inc., Montebello, CA; *Int'l*, pg. 1360
Beckert, John A., Chief Oper. Officer & Exec. V.P.--Bristol Hotels & Resorts, Dallas, TX; *U.S. Public*, pg. 253
Beckley, David, Chief Fin. Officer & Exec. V.P.--Century Aluminum Company, Monterey, CA; *U.S. Public*, pg. 328
Beckley, Ken, Exec. V.P.--Gregg Appliances Inc., Indianapolis, IN; *U.S. Private*, pg. 479
Beckman, Bryce, Exec. V.P.--Community First Bank & Trust, Celina, OH; *U.S. Public*, pg. 633
Beckman, Karen, Exec. V.P. & Grp. Dir.--Deutsch, Inc., New York, NY; *U.S. Private*, pg. 328
Bedbrook, John R., Dr., Exec. V.P. & Dir.-Science--DNAP Holding Corp., Oakland, CA; *Int'l*, pg. 454
Beebe, Kevin L., Exec. V.P.-Opers.--360 Degrees Communications Company, Chicago, IL; *U.S. Public*, pg. 1607
Beebower, Gilbert L., Exec. V.P.--SEI Investments, Oaks, PA; *U.S. Public*, pg. 1417
Beeken, Dave, Exec. V.P.--Eagle Window & Door, Inc., Dubuque, IA; *U.S. Public*, pg. 67
Beeks, Steven P., Exec. V.P.--Republic Entertainment, Inc., Los Angeles, CA; *U.S. Private*, pg. 776
Begasse, Ken, Exec. V.P.-Client Services & Grp. Mngmt. Supvr.--Lowe McAdams Healthcare, New York, NY; *U.S. Private*, pg. 678
Beglinger, Viktor, Exec. V.P.-Sulzer Infra Group--Sulzer Ltd., Winterthur, Switzerland; *Int'l*, pg. 1305
Beideman, Paul S., Exec. V.P.-Retail Fin. Svcs.--Mellon Bank Corporation, Pittsburgh, PA; *U.S. Public*, pg. 1084
Beilstein, Frederick B., Chief Fin. Officer & Exec. V.P.--URS Logistics, Atlanta, GA; *U.S. Private*, pg. 1114
Beimier, Irving R., Chief Credit Officer & Exec. V.P.--Riggs National Corporation, Washington, DC; *U.S. Public*, pg. 1389
Beindorff, Michael, Exec. V.P.-Mktg. & Product Mngmt.--Visa U.S.A. Inc., San Francisco, CA; *U.S. Private*, pg. 1141
Beitzel, Thomas, Exec. V.P.-Sls.--Dodge Regupol, Inc., Lancaster, PA; *U.S. Private*, pg. 337
Belanger, Jean-Pierre, Exec. V.P.--National Bank of Canada, Montreal, Canada; *Int'l*, pg. 907
Belardi, James R., Exec. V.P.--SunAmerica Inc., Los Angeles, CA; *U.S. Public*, pg. 1532
Belasco, Kent S., Chief Information Officer & Exec. V.P.-MIS--First Midwest Bancorp, Inc., Itasca, IL; *U.S. Public*, pg. 636
Belasco, Kent S., Exec. V.P.--First Midwest Bank, N.A., Itasca, IL; *U.S. Public*, pg. 636
Belcher, B.M., Jr., Exec. V.P.--Benjamin Moore & Co., Montvale, NJ; *U.S. Private*, pg. 133
Belcher, S. Dennis N., Exec. V.P.-Investment Banking & Credit Policy--The Bank of Nova Scotia, Toronto, Canada; *Int'l*, pg. 155
Belford, Jeffrey B., Exec. V.P.-Opers.--Lawson Products, Inc., Des Plaines, IL; *U.S. Public*, pg. 980
Belfrage, B. Bengt, Exec. V.P.--Pharmacia & Upjohn Biotech AB, Uppsala, Sweden; *Int'l*, pg. 1047
Belitsos, Michael G., Exec. V.P. & Exec. Creative Dir.--Young & Rubicam Detroit, Detroit, MI; *U.S. Private*, pg. 1198
Belknap, John C., Chief Fin. Officer & Exec. V.P.--OfficeMax, Shaker Heights, OH; *U.S. Public*, pg. 1212
Bell, Charles L., Grp. Exec. V.P.-Commercial Bus. Grp.--Bank of America NT&SA, San Francisco, CA; *U.S. Public*, pg. 180
Bell, Peter, Exec. V.P.--TCF Financial Corp., Minneapolis, MN; *U.S. Public*, pg. 1554
Bell, Peter, Exec. V.P.--TCF Bank Minnesota FSB, Minneapolis, MN; *U.S. Public*, pg. 1554
Bell, Ronald J., Exec. V.P.-Northern Europe--Kraft Foods International, Rye Brook, NY; *U.S. Public*, pg. 1288
Belle, Thomas, Exec. V.P.--Gage Marketing Group, Minneapolis, MN; *U.S. Private*, pg. 437
Beller, Gary A., Exec. V.P. & Gen. Counsel--Metropolitan Life Insurance Co., New York, NY; *U.S. Private*, pg. 737
Bellew, Steve, Exec. V.P.--The Great Frame Up Systems, Inc., Franklin Park, IL; *U.S. Private*, pg. 473
Bello, George E., Exec. V.P. & Controller--Reliance Group Holdings, Inc., New York, NY; *U.S. Public*, pg. 1374
Bellows, Timothy W., Exec. V.P.--Associates Relocation Management Company, Inc., Dallas, TX; *U.S. Public*, pg. 663
Bellucci, Eunice, Exec. V.P.-Arts & Entertainment Div.--Great Scott Advertising Co. Inc., New York, NY; *U.S. Private*, pg. 475
Bellucci, Joseph, Exec. V.P.--Coken Company, Inc., Providence, RI; *U.S. Private*, pg. 250
Bellucci, Louis V., Sr., Exec. V.P. & Mgr.-Natl. Equities Sls.--Jefferies & Company, Inc., Los Angeles, CA; *U.S. Public*, *pg. 925*
Belluzzo, Richard E., Exec. V.P. & Gen. Mgr.-Computer Org.--Hewlett-Packard Company, Palo Alto, CA; *U.S. Public*, pg. 813
Belskus, Jeff, Exec. V.P. & Treas.--Hulman & Company, Terre Haute, IN; *U.S. Private*, pg. 547
Beltrand, Thomas L., Exec. V.P.-Opers.--Reuter Manufacturing Inc., Hopkins, MN; *U.S. Public*, pg. 1383
Bement, Christian, Chief Oper. Officer & Exec. V.P.--Earl Scheib, Inc., Beverly Hills, CA; *U.S. Public*, pg. 1437
Bemis, Michael B., Exec. V.P.-Intl. Retail Opers.--Entergy Corporation, New Orleans, LA; *U.S. Public*, pg. 585
Bemis, Michael B., Exec. V.P.-Retail Sls.--Entergy Louisiana, Inc., New Orleans, LA; *U.S. Public*, pg. 586

Benadiba, Mark, Exec. V.P.--Cott Corporation - Central Division, Toronto, Canada; *Int'l*, pg. 337
Bencivengo, Richard, Exec. V.P.-Programming--Playboy Entertainment Group, Inc., Beverly Hills, CA; *U.S. Public*, *pg. 1310*
Bender, Jay B., Exec. V.P.--Norwest Mortgage, Inc., Des Moines, IA; *U.S. Public*, pg. 1202
Benedek, Melinda, Exec. V.P.-Bus. Affairs--Showtime Networks Inc., New York, NY; *U.S. Private*, pg. 779
Benedict, Francis E., Exec. V.P.-Banking & Investments--Tompkins County Trust Company, Ithaca, NY; *U.S. Public*, pg. 1621
Benfield, James, Exec. Dir.-Childrenswear & Home Furnishings--Marks & Spencer PLC, London, United Kingdom; *Int'l*, pg. 842
Bengoa, Francisco J., Exec. V.P.-Flight Opers.--Grupo Iberia, Madrid, Spain; *Int'l*, pg. 574
Bengston, John N., Chief Oper. Officer & Exec. V.P.--The Sands Regent, Reno, NV; *U.S. Public*, pg. 1431
Benhase, Daniel B., Exec. V.P.-Trust Fin. Services & Private Banking--Starbanc Corporation, Cincinnati, OH; *U.S. Public*, pg. 1510
Benjamin, Douglas, Exec. V.P. & Chief Exec. Officer-FJB Fashions--F. J. Benjamin Holdings Ltd., Singapore, Singapore; *Int'l*, pg. 187
Benjamin, Floyd, Exec. V.P. & Pres.-Injectable Div.--Akorn, Inc., Lincolnshire, IL; *U.S. Public*, pg. 34
Benjamin, G.R., Exec. V.P.--Champion, Inc., Iron Mountain, MI; *U.S. Private*, pg. 228
Benjamin, Mavis, Exec. V.P.-Store Plng. & Design--F. J. Benjamin Holdings Ltd., Singapore, Singapore; *Int'l*, pg. 187
Benjumea, Ignacio, Exec. V.P.--Banco Santander, Madrid, Spain; *Int'l*, pg. 143
Bennett, Arthur C., Chief Human Res. Officer & Exec. V.P.--The Dime Savings Bank of New York, New York, NY; *U.S. Public*, pg. 509
Bennett, Brad, Chief Acctg. Officer & Exec. V.P.--Integrated Health Services, Inc., Owings Mills, MD; *U.S. Public*, pg. 884
Bennett, Carman, Exec. V.P.-Automotive Grp.--UAP, Inc., Montreal, Canada; *Int'l*, pg. 1426
Bennett, Gary, Exec. V.P.-Sls.--Hitachi Home Electronics, Norcross, GA; *Int'l*, pg. 621
Bennett, George H., Jr., Exec. V.P., Gen. Counsel & Sec.--Cardinal Health Inc., Dublin, OH; *U.S. Public*, pg. 304
Bennett, Marcus C., Chief Fin. Officer & Exec. V.P.--Lockheed Martin Corporation, Bethesda, MD; *U.S. Public*, pg. 1006
Bennett, Michael, Chief Oper. Officer & Exec. V.P.--Terra Industries, Inc., Sioux City, IA; *U.S. Public*, pg. 1581
Bennett, Nicholas J M, Exec. Dir.--WF Corroon-London, London, United Kingdom; *Int'l*, pg. 1502
Bennett, Robert L., Exec. V.P.-Construction--Ruscon Corp., Charleston, SC; *U.S. Private*, pg. 952
Bennington, Richard M., Exec. V.P. & Admin./Fin. Dir.--Don Coleman Advertising, Inc., Southfield, MI; *U.S. Private*, pg. 251
Bennion, Charlene, Exec. V.P. & Sec.--The Rowe Corporation, Charlotte, NC; *U.S. Private*, pg. 948
Benrubi, Sam, Exec. V.P. & Dir.-Sls.--Westwood One, Inc., New York, NY; *U.S. Public*, pg. 1763
Benson, Bill, Chief Fin. Officer & Exec. V.P.--Physicians Mutual Insurance Co., Omaha, NE; *U.S. Private*, pg. 864
Benson, Donald E., Exec. V.P.--Marquette Bancshares Inc., Minneapolis, MN; *U.S. Private*, pg. 706
Benson, Donald E., Chief Fin. Officer & Exec. V.P.--Rieter Automotive North America Inc, Farmington Hills, MI; *Int'l*, *pg. 1117*
Benson, Richard E., Exec. V.P.-Loan Review--Citizens Trust Company, Providence, RI; *Int'l*, pg. 1132
Benson, Thomas H., Exec. V.P. & Chief Oper. Officer-Atlanta Gas Light Company--AGL Resources, Atlanta, GA; *U.S. Public*, pg. 6
Bentley, Barry, Exec. V.P.--Bentley Systems, Inc., Exton, PA; *U.S. Private*, pg. 134
Bentley, Jack L., Exec. V.P.--Western New Mexico Telephone Co., Silver City, NM; *U.S. Public*, pg. 1022
Bentley, Paul M., Exec. V.P. & Sec.--Cramer-Krasselt, Milwaukee, WI; *U.S. Private*, pg. 285
Bentley, Richard, Exec. V.P.--Marshall Industries, El Monte, CA; *U.S. Public*, pg. 1051
Bentley, Scott, Exec. V.P.-Opers. & Services--Bentley Systems, Inc., Exton, PA; *U.S. Private*, pg. 134
Bento, James, Exec. V.P.--Trumpf Inc., Farmington, CT; *U.S. Private*, pg. 1108
Benton, Bill, Exec. V.P.-Stores--Roberds, Inc., Carrollton, OH; *U.S. Public*, pg. 1393
Benvenuto, Robert, Exec. V.P.--Harry Winston, Inc., New York, NY; *U.S. Private*, pg. 1183
Benya, Ben, Exec. V.P. & Client Services Dir.--DavisElen Advertising, Inc., Los Angeles, CA; *U.S. Private*, pg. 316
Benzie, J. Peter, Jr., Exec. V.P.-Retail--Fidelity Investments (FMR Corp.), Boston, MA; *U.S. Private*, pg. 402
Beradinelli, C., Exec. V.P.--Hypertronics Corporation, Hudson, MA; *Int'l*, pg. 1268
Beran, John, Chief Info. Officer & Exec. V.P.--Comerica Incorporated, Detroit, MI; *U.S. Public*, pg. 408
Berardi, John F., Chief Oper. Officer & Exec V.P.-Grain Bus.--Farmland Industries, Inc., Kansas City, MO; *U.S. Private*, pg. 395
Berardi, Martin, Exec. V.P. & Mng. Dir.--Tubos de Acero de Mexico, S.A., Mexico, Mexico; *Int'l*, pg. 1426
Berardinucci, Don A., Exec. V.P.-Opers. & Service Delivery--Royal Bank of Canada, Toronto, Canada; *Int'l*, pg. 1131
Beren, Peter, Exec. V.P.--Misco Industries, Wichita, KS; *U.S. Private*, pg. 752
Berens, Ronald J., Exec. V.P.-Worldwide Specialty Opers.--Woolworth Corporation, New York, NY; *U.S. Public*, pg. 1777
Berg, David, Chief Oper. Officer & Exec. V.P.-Sls.--PremiumWear, Inc., Minneapolis, MN; *U.S. Public*, pg. 1323
Bergant, Paul R., Exec. V.P.-Mktg.--J.B. Hunt Transport Services, Inc., Lowell, AR; *U.S. Public*, pg. 849
Berge, Didier, Exec. V.P.-Houston--Elf Trading, Inc., Houston, TX; *Int'l*, pg. 445
Bergem, Torstein, Exec. V.P.--Norsk Hydro a.s, Oslo, Norway; *Int'l*, pg. 959
Berger, H. Gene, Exec. V.P.--Transworld Home Healthcare, Inc., New York, NY; *U.S. Public*, pg. 1632
Berger, Knut, Exec. V.P.--BTE Brauerel-Technik Essen GmbH, Essen, Germany; *Int'l*, pg. 400
Berger, Stephen, Exec. V.P.--General Electric Capital Services, Inc., Stamford, CT; *U.S. Public*, pg. 711
Berger, Stuart, Exec. V.P.--Integrated Marketing Group, Harrison, NY; *U.S. Private*, pg. 566
Bergeron, N.W., Exec. V.P. & Gen. Mgr.--Plymkraft Inc., Newport News, VA; *U.S. Private*, pg. 256
Berges, J.G., Vice Chm. & Exec. V.P.--Emerson Electric Co., Saint Louis, MO; *U.S. Public*, pg. 572
Bergevin, Paul, Exec. V.P., Gen. Mgr. & Global Tech. Dir.--Edelman Worldwide, Inc., Palo Alto, CA; *U.S. Private*, pg. 362
Bergfalk, Addison, Exec. V.P.--Shade Foods, Inc., Union City, CA; *U.S. Private*, pg. 802
Berghash, Mark, Exec. V.P.--Brimms Inc., Tonawanda, NY; *U.S. Private*, pg. 169
Bergler, Gerald, Chief Oper. Officer & Exec. V.P.--American Speedy Printing Centers, Inc., Troy, MI; *U.S. Private*, pg. 62
Berglund, Ulf, Chief Fin. Officer & Exec. V.P.--Granges AB, Stockholm, Sweden; *Int'l*, pg. 439
Bergman, Robert S., Exec. V.P. & Sec.--Processed Plastic Company, Montgomery, IL; *U.S. Private*, pg. 888
Bergonzi, Frank, Chief Fin. Officer & Exec. V.P.--Rite Aid Corporation, Camp Hill, PA; *U.S. Public*, pg. 1390
Bergren, Paul L., Exec. V.P.-Construction Sector--Ingersoll-Rand Company, Woodcliff Lake, NJ; *U.S. Public*, pg. 876
Bergstrom, Carl-Gustaf, Exec. V.P.--Partek Corporation, Helsinki, Finland; *Int'l*, pg. 1024
Berkbigler, Dale T., Vice Chm., Exec. V.P. & Chief Medical Officer--Foundation Health Systems, Inc., Pueblo, CO; *U.S. Public*, pg. 678
Berkett, Barry, Exec. V.P.--Thrifty Oil Co., Santa Fe Springs, CA; *U.S. Private*, pg. 1084
Berkin, Michael, Exec. V.P.--Dun & Bradstreet, Murray Hill, NJ; *U.S. Public*, pg. 535
Berlan, Denis, Chief Oper. Officer & Exec. V.P.--Altera Corporation, San Jose, CA; *U.S. Public*, pg. 59
Berling, Henry, Exec. V.P.-Partnership Devel.--Owens & Minor Inc., Glen Allen, VA; *U.S. Public*, pg. 1236
Berman, Cliff, Exec. V.P. & Gen. Mgr.-Consumer--Edelman Worldwide, Inc., New York, NY; *U.S. Private*, pg. 362
Berman, Knight, Exec. V.P.--Willis Corroon Corp. of Birmingham, Montgomery, AL; *Int'l*, pg. 1505
Berman, Stephen G., Chief Oper. Officer, Exec. V.P. & Sec.--JAKKS Pacific, Inc., Malibu, CA; *U.S. Public*, pg. 923
Berman, Steven L., Exec. V.P., Treas. & Sec.--R&B, Inc., Colmar, PA; *U.S. Public*, pg. 1354
Bernard, Mary Ellen, Exec. V.P.--Frederick Atkins, New York, NY; *U.S. Private*, pg. 94
Bernd, James D., Exec. V.P.--Kimberly-Clark Corporation, Dallas, TX; *U.S. Public*, pg. 958
Berndt, Wolfgang C., Exec. V.P. & Pres.-N. America--The Procter & Gamble Company, Cincinnati, OH; *U.S. Public*, *pg. 1330*
Berner, Hannes, Exec. V.P.--Berner Ltd., Helsinki, Finland; *Int'l*, pg. 189
Bernick, Carol L., Exec. V.P. & Asst. Sec.--Alberto-Culver Company, Melrose Park, IL; *U.S. Public*, pg. 37
Bernon, Peter M., Chm. Bd. & Chief Exec. Officer--Garelick Farms, Inc., Franklin, MA; *U.S. Public*, pg. 1527
Bernstein, Alan B., Exec. V.P. & Pres.-N. American Opers. Grp.--The Wackenhut Corporation, Palm Beach Gardens, FL; *U.S. Public*, pg. 1731
Bernstein, Emil S., Chief Fin. Officer, Exec. V.P. & Treas.--Chelsea Industries, Inc., Peabody, MA; *U.S. Private*, pg. 231
Bernstein, Hank, Exec. V.P. & Dir.-DMB&B Worldwide Strategic Resources--DMB&B Communications, New York, NY; *U.S. Private*, pg. 302
Bernstein, Martin M., Exec. V.P.-Real Estate--Carlyle & Co. Jewelers, Greensboro, NC; *U.S. Private*, pg. 213
Bernstein, Michael, Exec. V.P.--Safety 1st, Inc., Chestnut Hill, MA; *U.S. Public*, pg. 1425
Bernstein, William, Exec. V.P.-Paramount Pictures--Paramount Pictures Corporation, Los Angeles, CA; *U.S. Private*, pg. 776
Bernstock, Robert F., Pres.-U.S. Grocery & Exec. V.P.--Campbell Soup Company, Camden, NJ; *U.S. Public*, pg. 298
Bero, Ronald A., Sr. Exec. V.P.--Firstar Corporation, Milwaukee, WI; *U.S. Public*, pg. 642
Berry, Claude A., III, Exec. V.P.--Wehr Constructors Inc., Louisville, KY; *U.S. Private*, pg. 1159
Berry, Elsa, Exec. V.P.--Banexi International Financial Services (North America) Corp., New York, NY; *Int'l*, pg. 163
Berry, Glenn A., Chief Fin. Officer & Exec. V.P.--The Dixie Group, Inc., Chattanooga, TN; *U.S. Public*, pg. 514
Berry, Harry E., Exec. V.P. & Chief Credit Officer--First Maryland Bancorp, Baltimore, MD; *Int'l*, pg. 64
Berry, Ira R., Exec. V.P.--Banner Pharmacaps Inc., High Point, NC; *Int'l*, pg. 1272
Berry, Lester, Exec. V.P.--Microtek Medical, Inc., Columbus, MS; *U.S. Public*, pg. 914
Berry, William S., Exec. V.P.--Forest Resources & Corp. Devel.--Rayonier Inc., Stamford, CT; *U.S. Public*, pg. 1363
Berson, Judith S., Exec. V.P.-Specialty Leasing--The Mills Corporation, Arlington, VA; *U.S. Public*, pg. 1113
Bert, Raymond, Exec. V.P.--Credit Commercial de France, Paris, France; *Int'l*, pg. 341
Bertasso, Michael, Exec. V.P.--Star-Kist Foods Inc., Newport, KY; *U.S. Public*, pg. 805
Bertier, Etienne, Exec. V.P. & Head-Corp. Services--Electricite de France, Paris, France; *Int'l*, pg. 437
Bertoncini, Jean-Serge, Exec. V.P.-Info., Tech., Production & Systems--PSA Peugeot Citroen, Paris, France; *Int'l*, pg. 1020
Bertrand, Francois, Exec. V.P.--Commercial Risk Partners Ltd., Hamilton, Bermuda; *Int'l*, pg. 1152
Besemer, Deborah, Exec. V.P.-World-Wide Field Opers.--Lotus Development Corporation, Cambridge, MA; *U.S. Public*, pg. 896
Besig, Hans-Michael, Exec. V.P.--Bayerische Hypotheken- und Wechsel-Bank Aktiengesellschaft, Munich, Germany; *Int'l*, pg. 175
Best, David J., Exec. V.P.-Transportation Svcs.--American Waste Services, Inc., Warren, OH; *U.S. Public*, pg. 94
Bethea, David, Chief Exec. Officer & Exec. V.P.--E.K. Williams, Waco, TX; *U.S. Public*, pg. 538
Bethscheider, Alan, Exec. V.P.-Admin.--Color Tile, Inc., Fort Worth, TX; *Int'l*, pg. 686
Betsinger, Larry L., Exec. V.P.--UJB Discount Brokerage, Ridgefield Park, NJ; *U.S. Public*, pg. 1528
Bettini, James, Exec. V.P.-Opers.--Farm Family Casualty Insurance Co., Glenmont, NY; *U.S. Private*, pg. 394
Bettner, Jurgen, Exec. V.P.--Chema Balcke-Durr Verfahrenstechnik GmbH Rudisleben, Rudisleben, Germany; *Int'l*, pg. 399
Betz, J., Exec. V.P.-Fleet--Thrifty Rent-a-Car System, Inc., Tulsa, OK; *U.S. Public*, pg. 354
Betz, Rolf-Michael, Exec. V.P.--DG Bank, Frankfurt/Main, Germany; *Int'l*, pg. 351
Beu, Robert, Chief Strategic Officer & Exec. V.P.--Hutchins/Young & Rubicam, Rochester, NY; *U.S. Private*, pg. 1197
Beuroth, Arne, Exec. V.P.-Southern Regional Bank--Nordbanken AB, Stockholm, Sweden; *Int'l*, pg. 957
Beusse, Carlton G., Sr. V.P., Mng. Dir.-RMS, Exec. V.P. & Chief Oper. Officer-CRRUX--Willis Corroon Corp. of Wisconsin, Milwaukee, WI; *Int'l*, pg. 1507
Beutgen, J.J., Exec. V.P.-Mktg.--Olive Garden Italian Restaurants, Orlando, FL; *U.S. Public*, pg. 484
Beyer, Anthony F., Exec. V.P.-Commercial Lending--First Farmers & Merchants National Bank, Columbia, TN; *U.S. Private*, pg. 407
Beyer, Gerald D., Exec. V.P. & Chief Admin. Officer--Chicago Mercantile Exchange, Chicago, IL; *U.S. Private*, pg. 235
Bezalel, Yohaman, Exec. V.P.-Human Resources--The Israel Electric Corporation Ltd., Haifa, Israel; *Int'l*, pg. 690
Bhutani, Neelam, Exec. V.P.--Alra Laboratories, Inc., Gurnee, IL; *U.S. Private*, pg. 45
Biamo, Adrian, Dr., Exec. V.P.-Planning, Devel. & Tech.--The Israel Electric Corporation Ltd., Haifa, Israel; *Int'l*, pg. 690
Bianchi, Dorival Antonio, Exec. V.P.--Banco Bradesco S.A., Sao Paulo, Brazil; *Int'l*, pg. 139
Bich-Dufour, Marie-Aimee, Exec. V.P., Gen. Counsel & Sec.--Societe BIC S.A., Clichy, France; *Int'l*, pg. 1272
Bich, Francois, Exec. V.P.--Societe BIC S.A., Clichy, France; *Int'l*, pg. 1272
Bickerstaff, Bernie, Sr. Exec. V.P.--Denver Nuggets Limited Partnership, Denver, CO; *U.S. Public*, pg. 138
Bieber, Carole, Exec. V.P. & Design Dir.-Flapdoodles--Marisa Christina Inc., New Hyde Park, NY; *U.S. Public*, pg. 1044
Bieber, Paul D., Exec. V.P.--Floral Glass & Mirror, Inc., Hauppauge, NY; *U.S. Private*, pg. 414
Biederman, Charles L., Exec. V.P.--Sunstone Hotel Investors, Inc., San Clemente, CA; *U.S. Public*, pg. 1536
Biele, Anthony R., Chief Fin. Officer & Exec. V.P.--Talegen Corporation, Seattle, WA; *U.S. Public*, pg. 1784
Bieler, Mark, Exec. V.P.-Human Resources--Bankers Trust New York Corporation, New York, NY; *U.S. Public*, pg. 185
Bieri, Urs, Exec. V.P.--Holderbank Financiere Glaris Ltd., Glaris, Switzerland; *Int'l*, pg. 628
Bierman, Norman F., Exec. V.P.-Corp. Mktg. & Sls.--Intellisource, Fairfield, CT; *U.S. Public*, pg. 1425
Bies, Susan Schmidt, Exec. V.P.-Risk Mngmt. & ALCO--First Tennessee National Corporation, Memphis, TN; *U.S. Public*, pg. 638
Biffis, Alex, Exec. V.P.--Anchor Lamina Inc., Windsor, Canada; *Int'l*, pg. 75
Bigelow, Jonathan L., Chief Oper. Officer & Exec. V.P.--Cliggott Publishing, Greenwich, CT; *U.S. Private*, pg. 246
Biggemann, Rainer, Exec. V.P.--Associated Fuel Pump Systems Corp., Anderson, SC; *Int'l*, pg. 205
Billis, Leon B., Chief Information Officer & Sr. V.P.--The Equitable Companies Incorporated, New York, NY; *U.S. Public*, pg. 588
Bills, Michael J., Sr. Exec. V.P.--Firstar Corporation, Milwaukee, WI; *U.S. Public*, pg. 642
Bilton, Stuart, Exec. V.P.-Fin. Services Grp.--Chicago Title & Trust Co., Chicago, IL; *U.S. Public*, pg. 42
Biltz, Timothy G., Pres.-U.S. Wireless Opers.--Vanguard Cellular Systems, Inc., Greensboro, NC; *U.S. Public*, pg. 1707
Binder, Kenneth, Chief Fin. Officer & Exec. V.P.-Fin.--Chromalloy Gas Turbine Corp., San Antonio, TX; *U.S. Public*, pg. 1458
Bindley, Thomas L., Exec. V.P.--Whitman Corporation, Rolling Meadows, IL; *U.S. Public*, pg. 1766
Binet, Stephen H., Exec. V.P.--Trenwick America Reinsurance Corporation, Stamford, CT; *U.S. Public*, pg. 1634
Bingham, H. Raymond, Chief Fin. Officer, Exec. V.P. & Sec.--Cadence Design Systems, Inc., San Jose, CA; *U.S. Public*, pg. 290
Binkley, Gregory R., Chief Oper. Officer & Exec. V.P.--The Sportsman's Guide, Inc., Saint Paul, MN; *U.S. Public*, pg. 1499
Bintrock, William T., Exec. V.P.--Commercial Union Corporation, Boston, MA; *Int'l*, pg. 308

Biorck, Hans, Chief Fin. Officer & Exec. V.P.--Esselte AB, Solna, Sweden; *Int'l*, pg. 459
Birch, Paul, Chief Fin. Officer, Treas. & Exec. V.P.-Fin. & Admin.--PSDI, Bedford, MA; *U.S. Private*, pg. 828
Birch, William J., Exec. V.P.-Retail Banking--Glendale Federal Bank, F.S.B., Glendale, CA; *U.S. Public*, pg. 747
Bird, David A., Chief Mktg. Officer & Exec. V.P.--American Heritage Life Investment Corp., Jacksonville, FL; *U.S. Public*, pg. 78
Bird, David A., Chief Mktg. Officer & Exec. V.P.--American Heritage Life Insurance Co., Jacksonville, FL; *U.S. Public*, pg. 79
Bird, George K., IV, Exec. V.P.--State Street Corporation, Boston, MA; *U.S. Public*, pg. 1513
Bird, R. Craig, Chief Fin. Officer, Exec. V.P.-Fin. & Devel. & Admin.--Showboat, Incorporated, Las Vegas, NV; *U.S. Public*, pg. 1469
Bird, Robert D., Exec. V.P.--Allen & Ohara, Inc., Memphis, TN; *U.S. Private*, pg. 36
Bird, Thomas J., Jr., Exec. V.P., Gen. Counsel & Sec.--IMO Industries Inc., Lawrenceville, NJ; *U.S. Public*, pg. 856
Birdsall, Nancy, Exec. V.P.--InterAmerican Development Bank, Washington, DC; *U.S. Private*, pg. 566
Birdsong, Vicki, Exec. V.P.--Concord Computing Corp., Elk Grove Village, IL; *U.S. Public*, pg. 429
Birnbaum, Richard, Exec. V.P.-Mktg. & Opers.--Circuit City Stores, Inc., Richmond, VA; *U.S. Public*, pg. 374
Bischoff-Bogon, Werner, Exec. V.P.--euroflamm GmbH, Bremen, Germany; *Int'l*, pg. 400
Bischoff, Peter G., Exec. V.P.--Read-Rite Corporation, Milpitas, CA; *U.S. Public*, pg. 1366
Bischoff, William C., Exec. V.P.--Pierce National Life Insurance Co., Greenville, SC; *U.S. Public*, pg. 992
Biscieglia, Charles, Chief Oper. Officer & Exec. V.P.--South Jersey Gas Co., Folsom, NJ; *U.S. Public*, pg. 1488
Bishop, James C., Jr., Exec. V.P.-Law--Norfolk Southern Corporation, Norfolk, VA; *U.S. Public*, pg. 1190
Bisset, Ronald J., Exec. V.P.--Canadian Imperial Bank of Commerce, Toronto, Canada; *Int'l*, pg. 256
Bitner, Curtis, Exec. V.P.--A-B Emblem Div. of Conrad Industries, Inc., Weaverville, NC; *U.S. Private*, pg. 2
Bitter, Mark J., Exec. V.P.--Scalamandre, Inc., Long Island City, NY; *U.S. Private*, pg. 969
Bitter, Robert Franco, Exec. V.P.-New Prods. & Promo.--Scalamandre, Inc., Long Island City, NY; *U.S. Private*, pg. 969
Bitting, Bill, Exec. V.P. & Gen. Counsel--Pabst Brewing Co., San Antonio, TX; *U.S. Private*, pg. 954
Bitting, Bill, Exec. V.P. & Gen. Counsel--Pabst Brewing Co./Tumwater, Tumwater, WA; *U.S. Private*, pg. 954
Bittman, Robert A., Exec. V.P.-Prod. Devel.--International Game Technology, Reno, NV; *U.S. Public*, pg. 900
Bixby, R. Philip, Exec. V.P.--Kansas City Life Insurance Co., Kansas City, MO; *U.S. Public*, pg. 942
Bixby, Robert, Exec. V.P.-Engrng. & Opers.--Tippins Incorporated, Pittsburgh, PA; *U.S. Private*, pg. 1088
Bjelland, Rolf F., Exec. V.P.-Investment Mngmt.--Lutheran Brotherhood, Minneapolis, MN; *U.S. Private*, pg. 681
Bjorklund, Gunnar, Exec. V.P.--Sandvik AB, Sandviken, Sweden; *Int'l*, pg. 1185
Bjorling, Goran, Exec. V.P.-Central Credit--Svenska Handelsbanken, Stockholm, Sweden; *Int'l*, pg. 1327
Blachowicz, Leon F., Exec. V.P.-Opers.--California Microwave, Inc., Sunnyvale, CA; *U.S. Public*, pg. 293
Black, David, Exec. V.P., Sec. & Gen. Counsel--Affiliated Computer Services, Inc., Dallas, TX; *U.S. Public*, pg. 27
Black, Gary E., Exec. V.P.--Fireman's Fund Insurance Company, Novato, CA; *Int'l*, pg. 58
Blackham, J. William, Exec. V.P.--Corporex Companies, Inc., Cincinnati, OH; *U.S. Private*, pg. 276
Blackmon, Charles, Chief Fin. Officer & Exec. V.P.--American Buildings Co., Eufaula, AL; *U.S. Public*, pg. 69
Blackwell, Michael D., Exec. V.P. & Gen. Mgr.--MPX Systems, Inc., Cayce, SC; *U.S. Public*, pg. 1436
Blair, Mike, Exec. V.P. & Creative Dir.--GSD&M, Austin, TX; *U.S. Private*, pg. 436
Blair, Patrice, Exec. V.P.--Harris Drury Cohen, Fort Lauderdale, FL; *U.S. Private*, pg. 505
Blair, Rick, Exec. V.P.-Sls. & Mktg.--Weider Nutrition Intl., Salt Lake City, UT; *U.S. Private*, pg. 1159
Blair, William T., Exec. V.P. & Gen. Mgr.- N. American Sls. & Service--Diebold, Incorporated, Canton, OH; *U.S. Public*, pg. 506
Blaisdell-Snowdon, Deborah, Exec. V.P. & Corp. Sec.--The U.S. Baird Corporation, Stratford, CT; *U.S. Private*, pg. 1124
Blajsezak, Claire, Exec. V.P.--RCB Baking Company, Fargo, ND; *U.S. Public*, pg. 1354
Blake, Patrick H., Exec. V.P.-Opers.--Consolidated Freightways Corp., Menlo Park, CA; *U.S. Public*, pg. 435
Blakely, David W.D., Exec. V.P.--Charterways Transportation Limited, London, Canada; *Int'l*, pg. 1213
Blakely, Kevin M., Exec. V.P.--Keycorp, Cleveland, OH; *U.S. Public*, pg. 954
Blakely, Robert T., Chief Fin. Officer & Exec. V.P.--Tenneco Inc., Greenwich, CT; *U.S. Public*, pg. 1577
Blakeslee, Eugene E., Exec. V.P. & Chief Fin. Officer--SJNB Financial Corp., San Jose, CA; *U.S. Public*, pg. 1418
Blanc, Caryn, Exec. V.P.-Distr. & Stores Admin.--Kohl's Corporation, Menomonee Falls, WI; *U.S. Public*, pg. 965
Blanc, Francois, Exec. Dir.--Union Miniere, Brussels, Belgium; *Int'l*, pg. 1441
Blanchard, Ron, Exec. V.P.--Standard Communications Corp., Torrance, CA; *Int'l*, pg. 841
Blank, George, Chief Fin. Officer & Exec. V.P.--Univision Ltd. Partnership, New York, NY; *U.S. Private*, pg. 230
Blank, Randall, Chief Fin. Officer, Exec. V.P. & Sec.--Seacor Smit Inc., Houston, TX; *U.S. Public*, pg. 1449
Blankenhorn, David T., Exec. V.P.--California State Bank, West Covina, CA; *U.S. Public*, pg. 294
Blankenship, Maurice, Exec. V.P.--Berryman Products, Inc., Arlington, TX; *U.S. Private*, pg. 138
Blankenstein, Bernd, Exec. V.P. & Gen. Mgr.-TRW Steering, Suspension & Engine Grp.--TRW Inc., Cleveland, OH; *U.S. Public*, pg. 1558
Blankenstein, Bernd, Exec. V.P. & Gen. Mgr.--TRW Steering, Suspension & Engine Group, Cleveland, OH; *U.S. Public*, pg. 1558
Blankinship, Scott F., Exec. V.P. & Sec.--Petroleum Marketers, Inc., Roanoke, VA; *U.S. Private*, pg. 859
Blanksteen, Merill, Exec. V.P.--New Haven Savings Bank, New Haven, CT; *U.S. Private*, pg. 793
Blanton, Cooper, Exec. V.P.-Underwriting--Mercury General Corporation, Los Angeles, CA; *U.S. Public*, pg. 1093
Blasso, Barbara, Exec. V.P. & Mng. Dir.-Phase V--Grey Healthcare Group, New York, NY; *U.S. Public*, pg. 765
Blattner, Christopher J., Exec. V.P.--D.H. Blattner & Sons, Inc., Avon, MN; *U.S. Private*, pg. 148
Blattner, Edward W., Exec. V.P.--Panalpina, Inc., Jersey City, NJ; *Int'l*, pg. 1022
Blatz, Jean-Charles, Sr. Exec. V.P.--Cementia Holding AG, Zurich, Switzerland; *Int'l*, pg. 790
Blau, Peter, Exec. V.P. & Chief Creative Officer--Blau Marketing Technologies, Inc., Wilton, CT; *U.S. Private*, pg. 148
Blease, Doug, Chief Oper. Officer & Exec. V.P.--D & W Food Centers, Inc., Grand Rapids, MI; *U.S. Private*, pg. 300
Blechschmidt, Edward, Exec. V.P.--Siemens Nixdorf Informationssysteme AG, Kloten, Switzerland; *Int'l*, pg. 1245
Bleiler, James V., Exec. V.P.--Michael's Development Company, Marlton, NJ; *U.S. Private*, pg. 740
Blish, Jeffrey, Exec. V.P. & Acct. Plng. Dir.-L.A.--Deutsch LA, Santa Monica, CA; *U.S. Private*, pg. 328
Blitz, Harvey, Sr. V.P. & Deputy Chief Fin. Officer--The Equitable Companies Incorporated, New York, NY; *U.S. Public*, pg. 588
Blixt, Charles A., Exec. V.P., Sec. & Gen. Counsel--R.J. Reynolds Tobacco Company, Winston Salem, NC; *U.S. Public*, pg. 1355
Blobel, Peter, Chief Oper. Officer & Exec. V.P.--Bertelsmann Inc., New York, NY; *Int'l*, pg. 191
Bloch, Julia Chang, Grp. Exec. V.P.-Corp. Rels.--Bank of America NT&SA, San Francisco, CA; *U.S. Public*, pg. 180
Block, Roger, Exec. V.P.--Carlson Wagonlit Travel, Minneapolis, MN; *U.S. Private*, pg. 212
Block, Terry, Exec. V.P.-Pet Prods.--Ralston Purina Company, Saint Louis, MO; *U.S. Public*, pg. 1359
Block, Thomas, Exec. V.P. & Chief Oper. Officer--Ingalls, Boston, MA; *U.S. Private*, pg. 562
Blocklin, June, Exec. V.P. & Bus. Devel. Dir.--Young & Rubicam New York, New York, NY; *U.S. Private*, pg. 1198
Blondeau, Jean, Sr. Exec. V.P.--PSA Peugeot Citroen, Paris, France; *Int'l*, pg. 1020
Bloom, Martin, Exec. V.P.--National Electronics Warranty Corporation, Sterling, VA; *U.S. Private*, pg. 782
Bloom, Richard, Exec. V.P.--TST/Impreso, Inc., Coppell, TX; *U.S. Private*, pg. 1066
Bloss, David A., Sr., Exec. V.P.--Watts Industries, Inc., North Andover, MA; *U.S. Public*, pg. 1746
Bloss, David A., Sr., Exec. V.P.--Jameco Industries, Inc., Spindale, NC; *U.S. Public*, pg. 1746
Blossfield, W. G., Exec. V.P.--Sears Portrait Studios, Saint Louis, MO; *U.S. Public*, pg. 283
Blount, Ben B., Jr., Chief Fin. Officer & Exec. V.P.-Plng., Admin. & Fin.--Oxford Industries, Inc., Atlanta, GA; *U.S. Public*, pg. 1239
Blount, Robert G., Sr. Exec. V.P.--American Home Products Corporation, Madison, NJ; *U.S. Public*, pg. 79
Bluhm, Leonard A., Chief Fin. Officer & Exec. V.P.--NRG Energy, Inc., Minneapolis, MN; *U.S. Public*, pg. 1195
Blum, Larry R., Exec. V.P.-Admin.--Lillian Vernon Corporation, New Rochelle, NY; *U.S. Public*, pg. 1716
Blume, Gary A., Exec. V.P.--Capital Development Co., Lacey, WA; *U.S. Private*, pg. 205
Blunk, Richard, Exec. V.P., Gen. Counsel & Sec.--ShowBiz Pizza Time, Inc., Irving, TX; *U.S. Public*, pg. 1468
Blystone, John B., Exec. V.P.--Nuovo Pignone S.p.a., Florence, Italy; *Int'l*, pg. 990
Boal, Frank D.A., Exec. V.P.-Opers., Individual Bank CIBC--Canadian Imperial Bank of Commerce, Toronto, Canada; *Int'l*, pg. 256
Boan, Edward E., Exec. V.P.-Fresh Pork & Human Resources--Thorn Apple Valley, Inc., Southfield, MI; *U.S. Public*, pg. 1602
Boardman, William P., Sr. Exec. V.P.--Banc One Corporation, Columbus, OH; *U.S. Public*, pg. 172
Bobowski, Steve, Exec. V.P. & Gen. Mgr.--Fleer-Skybox International Inc., Mount Laurel, NJ; *U.S. Public*, pg. 1052
Bocco, Claudio, Exec. V.P.-Personnel--Istituto Bancario San Paolo Di Torino S.p.A., Turin, Italy; *Int'l*, pg. 691
Bochner, Brian, Exec. V.P.--Barton-Aschman Associates, Inc., Evanston, IL; *U.S. Private*, pg. 841
Bochsler, Karl, Exec. V.P.--Sulzer Ltd., Winterthur, Switzerland; *Int'l*, pg. 1305
Bock, Daniel M., Exec. V.P.--Carquest Corporation, Lakewood, CO; *U.S. Private*, pg. 215
Boddie, Michael W., Exec. V.P.--Hardee's Opers. Grp.--Boddie-Noell Enterprises Inc., Rocky Mount, NC; *U.S. Private*, pg. 154
Boden, A., Exec. V.P., Natl. Media Dir. & Pres.-McKim Media Grp.--BBDO Canada, Toronto, Canada; *U.S. Private*, pg. 104
Bodenheimer, George W., Exec. V.P.-Mktg. & Sls.--ESPN, Inc., Bristol, CT; *U.S. Public*, pg. 512
Bodger, Stephen, Exec. V.P.--Transport Development Group Plc, London, United Kingdom; *Int'l*, pg. 1418
Bodine, Jeffrey P., Exec. V.P.--Bodine Electric Company, Chicago, IL; *U.S. Private*, pg. 154
Bodiou, Joel, Exec. V.P.-Building Matls.--Imetal, Paris, France; *Int'l*, pg. 661
Bodnar, Emery J., Exec. V.P. & Gen. Mgr.--Grant-Lydick Beverage Co., San Antonio, TX; *U.S. Private*, pg. 470
Bodt, H., Exec. V.P.--Philips Electronics N.V., Eindhoven, Netherlands; *Int'l*, pg. 1051
Bodt, Henk, Exec. V.P.--Philips International B.V., Eindhoven, Netherlands; *Int'l*, pg. 1051
Boegler, Pierre, Exec. V.P.-Communications--N. Schlumberger & Cie, Guebwiller, France; *Int'l*, pg. 1206
Boehmler, Robert H., Jr., Exec. V.P.--Commercial National Bank, Shreveport, LA; *U.S. Public*, pg. 500
Boesenberg, Charles M., Exec. V.P. & Gen. Mgr.-Satellite Access Prods. Grp.--Orbital Sciences Corporation, Dulles, VA; *U.S. Public*, pg. 1229
Boettcher, Gerald, Exec. V.P. & Treas.--Kalmbach Publishing Co., Waukesha, WI; *U.S. Private*, pg. 606
Boeve, Roger L., Chief Fin. Officer & Exec. V.P.--Performance Food Group Company, Richmond, VA; *U.S. Public*, pg. 1278
Bogart, Frederic S., Exec. V.P.--Republic National Bank of New York, New York, NY; *U.S. Public*, pg. 1380
Bogart, Robert B., Exec. V.P.-Human Resources--Mutual of Omaha Insurance Company, Omaha, NE; *U.S. Private*, pg. 769
Bogyay, Stephen, Exec. V.P.--Yogen Fruz Worldwide Inc., Markham, Canada; *Int'l*, pg. 1520
Bohl, Rune, Exec. V.P.--Bergman & Beving AB, Stockholm, Sweden; *Int'l*, pg. 188
Bohlin, Garen G., Chief Fin. Officer & Exec. V.P.--Genetics Institute, Inc., Cambridge, MA; *U.S. Public*, pg. 79
Bohn, Susan B., Exec. V.P.-Corp. Dev., Communications & Pub. Rels.--PNC Bank Corp., Pittsburgh, PA; *U.S. Public*, pg. 1242
Bohn, W. Peter, Exec. V.P.--Mellon First Business Bank, Los Angeles, CA; *U.S. Public*, pg. 1085
Bohs, G. Lee, Chief Fin. Officer & Exec. V.P.--Right Management Consultants, Inc., Philadelphia, PA; *U.S. Public*, pg. 1390
Boinet, Sven, Exec. V.P.-Hotels--Accor S.A., Evry, France; *Int'l*, pg. 20
Boireau, Christian, Exec. V.P.-Sls--Groupe Air France, Roissy, France; *Int'l*, pg. 559
Boisvert, M., Exec. V.P.-Western Europe--Labatt Breweries of Canada, Toronto, Canada; *Int'l*, pg. 679
Bolda, Richard R., Exec. V.P.--M & I Northern Bank, Brookfield, WI; *U.S. Public*, pg. 1050
Bolduc, James P., Chief Fin. Officer & Exec. V.P.--CTG Resources, Inc., Hartford, CT; *U.S. Public*, pg. 285
Bolduc, James P., Chief Fin. Officer & Exec. V.P.--Connecticut Natural Gas Corporation, Hartford, CT; *U.S. Public*, pg. 285
Bolduc, James P., Chief Fin. Officer & Exec. V.P.--Energy Networks, Inc. (ENI), Hartford, CT; *U.S. Public*, pg. 285
Bolduc, Pierre, Exec. V.P.-New Business Devel. & Intl. Affairs--Hydro-Quebec, Montreal, Canada; *Int'l*, pg. 640
Boles, Christina L., Exec. V.P.-Loan Admin.--Compass Bank, Birmingham, AL; *U.S. Public*, pg. 418
Bolger, David P., Exec. V.P.-Illinois Reg. Banking--First Chicago NBD Corporation, Chicago, IL; *U.S. Public*, pg. 627
Bolger, Tom, Chief Oper. Officer & Exec. V.P.--EvansGroup, Dallas, TX; *U.S. Private*, pg. 385
Bolin, Susan C., Chief Fin. Officer, Exec. V.P., Treas. & Sec.--The O'Boise Corporation, Oak Brook, IL; *U.S. Private*, pg. 810
Bolinder, William H., Exec. V.P.-Intl./North & South America--Zurich Insurance Company, Zurich, Switzerland; *Int'l*, pg. 1529
Bollen, Boudewijn, Exec. V.P.-Worldwide Sls., Svcs. & Distr.--Nellcor Puritan Bennett Incorporated, Pleasanton, CA; *U.S. Public*, pg. 1039
Bollinger, Donald T., Chm. Bd. & Chief Exec. Officer--Bollinger Shipyards, Inc., Lockport, LA; *U.S. Private*, pg. 155
Bolte, Gunter, Exec. V.P.-Van Houten--Kraft Jacobs Suchard AG, Zurich, Switzerland; *U.S. Public*, pg. 1288
Boltwood, George M., Exec. V.P.-Corp. Banking--Compass Bank, Birmingham, AL; *U.S. Public*, pg. 418
Bolza-Schunemann, Claus, Exec. V.P.-Engrng.--Koenig & Bauer-Albert AG, Wurzburg, Germany; *Int'l*, pg. 742
Bomberger, Glen R., Chief Fin. Officer & Exec. V.P.--A.O. Smith Corporation, Milwaukee, WI; *U.S. Public*, pg. 1476
Bonadurer, Werner, Exec. V.P.--Union Bank of Switzerland, Zurich, Switzerland; *Int'l*, pg. 1439
Bonaiuto, Paul, Chief Fin. Officer & Exec. V.P.-Fin.--Journal Communications Inc., Milwaukee, WI; *U.S. Private*, pg. 601
Bonanni, Luciano, Exec. V.P.--Fonar Corporation, Melville, NY; *U.S. Public*, pg. 661
Bonanno, Salvatore J., Exec. V.P.-Mfr.--Foamex International Inc., Linwood, PA; *U.S. Private*, pg. 1094
Bonaventure, Bob, Exec. V.P.--Beretta U.S.A. Corp., Accokeek, MD; *Int'l*, pg. 188
Bond, Alex M., Exec. V.P.-Strategic Devel.--Just For Feet, Inc., Pelham, AL; *U.S. Public*, pg. 935
Bond, Alice, Exec. V.P.-Client Services--Jordan, McGrath, Case & Taylor Inc., New York, NY; *U.S. Private*, pg. 598
Bond, Dwight, Exec. V.P.--ConAgra Poultry Co., Duluth, GA; *U.S. Public*, pg. 427
Bond, P.C., Mng. Dir.-Nonferrous Sector & Exec. V.P.-S.F. Opers.--Davy International, San Francisco, San Ramon, CA; *Int'l*, pg. 774
Bonetto, Frank J., Exec. V.P.-Community Banking--Bank of the West, Walnut Creek, CA; *Int'l*, pg. 163
Bonham, Carol, Chief Oper. Officer & Exec. V.P.--Interpacific Investors Services, Seattle, WA; *U.S. Private*, pg. 572
Boniface, Andrew, Exec. V.P.--Bonland Industries, Inc., Wayne, NJ; *U.S. Private*, pg. 156
Bonitatibus, Paul J., Exec. V.P.-Retail Banking--Hibernia Corporation, New Orleans, LA; *U.S. Public*, pg. 825
Bonneau, Jacques Q., Sr. Exec. V.P. & Chief Underwriting Officer--Chartwell Re Corporation, Stamford, CT; *U.S. Public*, pg. 336

Bonneau, Jacques Q., Exec. V.P. & Chief Underwriter--The Insurance Corp. of New York, New York, NY; *U.S. Public*, pg. 336
Bonner, Robert B., Chief Oper. Officer, Exec. V.P. & Sec.--First Federal Savings, East Hartford, CT; *U.S. Public*, pg. 632
Bonnet, Yves, Chief Oper. Officer & Exec. V.P.--SNECMA - Societe Nationale d'Etude et de Construction de Moteurs d'Aviation, Paris, France; *Int'l*, pg. 1165
Bonnette, Dennis, Chief Oper. Officer & Exec. V.P.--Advanced Circuit Technology, Nashua, NH; *U.S. Private*, pg. 21
Bonta, Patricio, Exec. V.P., Pres. & CEO JWT/Argentina--J. Walter Thompson Company, New York, NY; *Int'l*, pg. 1483
Bontoux, Bernard, Sr. Exec. V.P.-Legal--Promodes SA, Mondeville, France; *Int'l*, pg. 1071
Bontrager, Derald, Exec. V.P.--Jayco Inc., Middlebury, IN; *U.S. Private*, pg. 583
Bontrager, Ervin L., Exec. V.P.--Schult Homes Corporation, Middlebury, IN; *U.S. Public*, pg. 1442
Boocher, James, Exec. V.P.-Devel.--Sun International Hotels Limited, Fort Lauderdale, FL; *U.S. Public*, pg. 1531
Bookbinder, David, Exec. V.P.--Harrowston Capital Corporation, Toronto, Canada; *Int'l*, pg. 599
Bookman, Michael, Exec. V.P.--Advertising Checking Bureau Incorporated, New York, NY; *U.S. Private*, pg. 23
Booma, Stephen R., Exec. V.P.-Health Care Mngmt. Opers.--Mutual of Omaha Insurance Company, Omaha, NE; *U.S. Private*, pg. 769
Boone Isaacs, Cheryl, Sr. V.P.-Worldwide Publicity--Paramount Pictures Corporation, Los Angeles, CA; *U.S. Private*, pg. 776
Boone, William R., Exec. V.P.--Deposit Guaranty Corp., Jackson, MS; *U.S. Public*, pg. 500
Booth, David, Exec. V.P.-Retail Grp.--Clayton Homes, Inc., Knoxville, TN; *U.S. Public*, pg. 382
Booth, Richard H., Exec. V.P.--Phoenix Home Life Mutual Insurance Company, Hartford, CT; *U.S. Private*, pg. 863
Booth, Robert L., Exec. V.P.--Union Planters Corporation, Cordova, TN; *U.S. Public*, pg. 1668
Booth, Robert L., Exec. V.P.--Union Planters Bank, Memphis, TN; *U.S. Public*, pg. 1669
Boozer, Young J., III, Exec. V.P.-Investments--The Colonial BancGroup, Inc., Montgomery, AL; *U.S. Public*, pg. 400
Bopp, William C., Chief Fin. Officer & Exec. V.P.--C.R. Bard, Inc., Murray Hill, NJ; *U.S. Public*, pg. 189
Borchers, Leon J., Exec. V.P. & Dir.--The Robinson-Humphrey Company, Inc., Atlanta, GA; *U.S. Public*, pg. 1633
Borchers, Richard H., Exec. V.P.-H.R.--Davco Restaurants Inc., Crofton, MD; *U.S. Public*, pg. 488
Borck, George, Exec. V.P.-Store Opers.--Leather Center, Inc., Carrollton, TX; *U.S. Private*, pg. 656
Borges, Bill, Exec. V.P.--Ventura Coastal Corporation, Ventura, CA; *U.S. Private*, pg. 1136
Borghi, Richard, Chief Oper. Officer & Exec. V.P.--Advanced Accessories Systems, LLC., Sterling Heights, MI; *U.S. Private*, pg. 21
Boris, Fran, Exec. V.P., Sr. Corp. Counsel & Sec.--Blimpie International, Inc., Atlanta, GA; *U.S. Public*, pg. 236
Borja Navarrete, Jorge, Exec. V.P.--Empresas ICA Sociedad Controladora S.A.C.V., Mexico, Mexico; *Int'l*, pg. 454
Borjesson, Bjorn, Exec. V.P.-Reg. Bank, Southern Sweden--Svenska Handelsbanken, Stockholm, Sweden; *Int'l*, pg. 1327
Borkan, Al, Exec. V.P.-Media--McKinney & McKinney Advertising, Redondo Beach, CA; *U.S. Private*, pg. 723
Borland, Mark, Exec. V.P.--Au Bon Pain Co., Inc., Boston, MA; *U.S. Public*, pg. 146
Bornia, Antonio, Exec. V.P.--Banco Bradesco S.A., Sao Paulo, Brazil; *Int'l*, pg. 139
Boron, Gregory F., Chief Oper. Officer & Exec. V.P.--Boron LePore Group, Fair Lawn, NJ; *U.S. Public*, pg. 246
Borow, Leonard, Chief Oper. Officer & Exec. V.P.--Aeroflex Incorporated, Plainview, NY; *U.S. Public*, pg. 23
Borrelli, Lou, Chief Oper. Officer & Exec. V.P.--Marcus Cable Company, L.P., Dallas, TX; *U.S. Private*, pg. 702
Boryenace, Charles, Exec. V.P.-Strategic Plng.--American Waste Services, Inc., Warren, OH; *U.S. Public*, pg. 94
Boschetto, Laurence J., Exec. V.P. & Acct. Services Dir.--Adler Boschetto Peebles & Partners, Inc., New York, NY; *U.S. Private*, pg. 17
Bosma, Hille, Exec. V.P.--Albert Heijn B.V., Zaandam, Netherlands; *Int'l*, pg. 749
Bosma, Tiemen, V.P.-Y&R Europe--PMSVW/Young & Rubicam B.V., Amsterdam, Netherlands; *U.S. Private*, pg. 1199
Bosman, Ruud H., Exec. V.P.--Allendale Mutual Insurance Co., Johnston, RI; *U.S. Private*, pg. 37
Bospflug, Lance F., Chief Fin. Officer, Exec. V.P. & Treas.--T.L. James & Company, Ruston, LA; *U.S. Private*, pg. 580
Bosserman, David N., Chief Fin. Officer, Exec. V.P. & Treas.--Best Software, Inc., Reston, VA; *U.S. Public*, pg. 223
Botica, Luke F., Chief Fin. Officer & Exec. V.P.--Dames & Moore Inc., Los Angeles, CA; *Int'l*, pg. 624
Botin, Ana Patricia, Exec. V.P.-Investment Banking--Banco Santander, Madrid, Spain; *Int'l*, pg. 143
Botwinick, Allen G., Exec. V.P.-Admin. & Opers.--The Advest Group, Inc., Hartford, CT; *U.S. Public*, pg. 23
Boughner, Robert L., Chief Oper. Officer & Exec. V.P.--Boyd Gaming Corporation, Las Vegas, NV; *U.S. Public*, pg. 249
Boujoukos, George, Exec. V.P.-Capital Mkts.--The Advest Group, Inc., Hartford, CT; *U.S. Public*, pg. 23
Boujoukos, George A., Exec. V.P.--Advest, Inc., Hartford, CT; *U.S. Public*, pg. 23
Bouma, H., Exec. V.P.--ABN-AMRO Holding N.V., Amsterdam, Netherlands; *Int'l*, pg. 8
Bourdeau, Yvan J.P., Exec. V.P. & Head of Global Treasury Group--Bank of Montreal, Toronto, Canada; *Int'l*, pg. 153
Bourdier, Jean-Pierre, Exec. V.P.-Environ.--Electricite de France, Paris, France; *Int'l*, pg. 437
Bourgarel, Michel, Exec. V.P. & Sec.--Air Liquide S.A., Paris, France; *Int'l*, pg. 37
Bourgeault, Jean-Jacques, Sr. Exec. V.P.-Fin., Gen. Counsel, & Information Tech.--Air Canada, Saint-Laurent, Canada; *Int'l*, pg. 36
Bourgeois, Ronald, Exec. V.P.--Anco Insulations, Inc., Baton Rouge, LA; *U.S. Private*, pg. 71
Bourmand, Claude, Exec. Dir.--La Poste Group, Boulogne-Billancourt, France; *Int'l*, pg. 785
Bourne, Kenneth A., Jr., Exec. V.P.--Mercantile-Safe Deposit & Trust Co., Baltimore, MD; *U.S. Public*, pg. 1089
Bourne, R. W., Jr., Vice Chm. & Exec. V.P.--Eastman Chemical Company, Kingsport, TN; *U.S. Public*, pg. 550
Bourne, Richard, Acting Chief Fin. Officer, Exec. V.P. & Gen. Mgr.--ASICS Tiger Corporation, Fountain Valley, CA; *U.S. Private*, pg. 89
Bourque, Normand R., Exec. V.P. & Pres.-NORDX/CDT--Cable Design Technologies Corporation, Pittsburgh, PA; *U.S. Public*, pg. 287
Bourrut-Lacouture, Patrice, Grp. Dir.-Property--Bouygues, Saint Quentin-en-Yvelines, France; *Int'l*, pg. 206
Boushelle, J. Paul, Exec. V.P.-Community Banking Group--First Security Bank of New Mexico, Albuquerque, NM; *U.S. Public*, pg. 637
Bousquette, Kevin A., Chief Oper. Officer & Exec. V.P.--Sotheby's Holdings Inc., New York, NY; *U.S. Public*, pg. 1487
Bousquette, Matt, Exec. V.P.-Mktg.-Boys Line--Mattel, Inc., El Segundo, CA; *U.S. Public*, pg. 1057
Bouwens, J., Exec. V.P.-Chemical Logistics Europe--Royal Pakhoed NV, Rotterdam, Netherlands; *Int'l*, pg. 1147
Bovaird, J.R., Chief Oper. Officer & Exec. V.P.--Bovaird Supply Co., Tulsa, OK; *U.S. Private*, pg. 162
Boverizer, J.G.F., Exec. V.P. & Treas.--Lloyds Bank Plc., New York, NY; *Int'l*, pg. 813
Bowden, Douglas, Exec. V.P. & Sec.--Sencore, Inc., Sioux Falls, SD; *U.S. Private*, pg. 983
Bowden, John W., Exec. V.P.-Ontario & USA, Corporate Bank CIBC--Canadian Imperial Bank of Commerce, Toronto, Canada; *Int'l*, pg. 256
Bowe, William J., Exec. V.P., Gen. Counsel & Sec.--Encyclopaedia Britannica, Inc., Chicago, IL; *U.S. Private*, pg. 375
Bowerman, C.L., Exec. V.P.-Plng., Corp. Rels. & Svcs.--Phillips Petroleum Company, Bartlesville, OK; *U.S. Public*, pg. 1290
Bowers, Nelson E., II, Exec. V.P.--Sonic Automotive, Inc., Charlotte, NC; *U.S. Public*, pg. 1485
Bowers, Richard, Sr. Exec. V.P., Gen. Counsel & Sec.--Jan Bell Marketing Inc., Sunrise, FL; *U.S. Public*, pg. 207
Bowles, Crandall C., Exec. V.P.-Bath Fashions--Home Furnishings Segment, Fort Mill, SC; *U.S. Public*, pg. 1500
Bowling, Bill J., Exec. V.P. & Pres.-Steel--The Timken Company, Canton, OH; *U.S. Public*, pg. 1617
Bowman, Elizabeth, Exec. V.P.-Fin. & Treas.--Universal Forest Products, Inc., Grand Rapids, MI; *U.S. Public*, pg. 1696
Bowman, John, Exec. V.P. & Strategic Plng. & Res. Dir.--N.W. Ayer & Partners New York, New York, NY; *U.S. Private*, pg. 104
Bowns, Edward E., Exec. V.P. & Gen. Mgr.-Industrial Prods. Grp.--Rock-Tenn Company, Norcross, GA; *U.S. Public*, pg. 1396
Box, Jerry W., Chief Oper. Officer & Exec. V.P.--Oryx Energy, Dallas, TX; *U.S. Public*, pg. 1232
Boyce, Thomas M., Exec. V.P.--Centex Real Estate Corp./Centex Homes, Dallas, TX; *U.S. Public*, pg. 323
Boyd, Brian, Principal--Richards, Brock, Miller, Mitchell & Assoc. Inc., Dallas, TX; *U.S. Private*, pg. 929
Boyd, Dale, Chief Fin. Officer, Exec. V.P. & Sec.--MTI Technology Corporation, Anaheim, CA; *U.S. Public*, pg. 1028
Boyd, Jeffery, Exec. V.P. & Gen. Counsel--Oxford Health Plans Inc., Norwalk, CT; *U.S. Public*, pg. 1238
Boyd, R.B., Exec. V.P.--Puget Western, Inc., Bellevue, WA; *U.S. Public*, pg. 1342
Boyer, Yves, Exec. V.P.--Nissan Canada Inc., Mississauga, Canada; *Int'l*, pg. 945
Boyers, Charles F., Exec. V.P.-Admin. & Fin.--Wills Group, Inc., La Plata, MD; *U.S. Private*, pg. 1180
Boyko, Rick, Exec. V.P. & Creative Head-NY--Ogilvy & Mather Worldwide, Inc., New York, NY; *Int'l*, pg. 1483
Boylan, Michael A., Exec. V.P.--Maxum Health Corp., Dallas, TX; *U.S. Public*, pg. 881
Boyle, David L., Sr. Exec. V.P.--AMBAC Financial Group, Inc., New York, NY; *U.S. Public*, pg. 62
Boyle, Edward F., Exec. V.P.--Intergraph Corporation, Huntsville, AL; *U.S. Public*, pg. 890
Boyle, James R., Exec. V.P. & Chief Asset Mngmt. Officer--Coast Savings Financial, Inc., Los Angeles, CA; *U.S. Public*, pg. 388
Boyle, Lester J., Exec. V.P.--JL Media, Inc., Tulsa, OK; *U.S. Private*, pg. 577
Boyle, Sandra, Exec. V.P.-Asset--Glenborough Realty Trust Incorporated, San Mateo, CA; *U.S. Public*, pg. 747
Bracher, Paul H., Exec. V.P.--Cullen/Frost Bankers, Inc., San Antonio, TX; *U.S. Public*, pg. 467
Bracken, Charles O., Exec. V.P.--Superior Consultant Holdings Corp., Southfield, MI; *U.S. Public*, pg. 1538
Bradberry, John H., Exec. V.P.--Cameron Ashley Building Products, Inc, Dallas, TX; *U.S. Public*, pg. 298
Braddock, William H., Exec. V.P.-Property & Casualty Opers.--Farmers Group, Inc., Los Angeles, CA; *Int'l*, pg. 110
Bradley, Andrew, Exec. V.P.-Mktg., Nestle Ice Cream Co.--Nestle Frozen, Refrigerated, and Ice Cream Companies, Solon, OH; *Int'l*, pg. 918
Bradley, Andrew, Exec. V.P. & Gen. Mgr.--Nestle Ice Cream Co., Columbus, OH; *Int'l*, pg. 918
Bradley, Edward, Exec. V.P. & Sec.--Certified Grocers Midwest, Inc., Hodgkins, IL; *U.S. Private*, pg. 226
Bradley, Joseph A., Exec. V.P.--Foulds Inc., Libertyville, IL; *U.S. Private*, pg. 421
Bradley, Peter, Exec. V.P.--American Bible Society, New York, NY; *U.S. Private*, pg. 51
Bradshaw, John P., Chm. Bd. & Exec. V.P.--Hayes, Seay, Mattern & Mattern, Inc., Roanoke, VA; *U.S. Private*, pg. 513
Bradshaw, Thomas, Chief Fin. Officer & Sr. Exec. V.P.--All American Communications, Inc., Santa Monica, CA; *U.S. Public*, pg. 41
Brady, Don, Exec. V.P.--United Mailing, Inc., Chanhassen, MN; *U.S. Private*, pg. 565
Braeke, Thomas K., Exec. V.P. & Sec.--Hilb, Rogal & Hamilton Company of the Quad Cities, Moline, IL; *U.S. Public*, pg. 827
Bragado, Teodoro, Exec. V.P.-Corp. Banking & Trade Fin.--Banco Santander, Madrid, Spain; *Int'l*, pg. 143
Bragg, D.K., Exec. V.P.--Loblaw Companies Limited, North York, Canada; *Int'l*, pg. 1495
Bramblett, Michael T., Exec. V.P.--Jones Medical Industries Inc., Saint Louis, MO; *U.S. Public*, pg. 933
Brancato, Anthony S., Exec. V.P.-Training Services--Reflectone, Inc., Tampa, FL; *Int'l*, pg. 218
Branciforte, Joseph L., Exec. V.P.--UJB Discount Brokerage, Ridgefield Park, NJ; *U.S. Public*, pg. 1528
Brandenberg, Peter, Head-Textile--Clariant International Ltd., Muttenz, Switzerland; *Int'l*, pg. 624
Brandt, Barry, Exec. V.P.--Weiler & Company, Inc., Whitewater, WI; *U.S. Private*, pg. 1160
Brandt, Paul E., Chief Fin. Officer & Exec. V.P.--California State Bank, West Covina, CA; *U.S. Public*, pg. 294
Brann, Raymond E., Jr., Exec. V.P.--First Virginia Banks, Inc., Falls Church, VA; *U.S. Public*, pg. 641
Brann, Robert, Exec. V.P.--Trak Auto Corporation, Landover, MD; *U.S. Public*, pg. 484
Branning, Harry H., Exec. V.P.-Natl. Sls. Mgr.--The Advest Group, Inc., Hartford, CT; *U.S. Public*, pg. 23
Brashears, Don, Exec. V.P.--Cramer-Krasselt, Chicago, IL; *U.S. Private*, pg. 285
Brasher, William N., III, Exec. V.P.--Commercial Bank at Alma, Alma, AR; *U.S. Public*, pg. 641
Brasseaux, Murray E., Exec. V.P.-Energy Lending--Compass Bank Houston, Houston, TX; *U.S. Public*, pg. 419
Brauer, Norbert, Exec. V.P.--DG Bank, Frankfurt/Main, Germany; *Int'l*, pg. 351
Braun, Donald L., Chief Oper. Officer, Exec. V.P. & Treas.--Hall Financial Group, Inc., Dallas, TX; *U.S. Private*, pg. 495
Braun, Kathryn A., Exec. V.P.-Personal Storage Grp.--Western Digital Corporation, Irvine, CA; *U.S. Public*, pg. 1758
Bravo de Souza, Paul Sergio, Exec. V.P.--Uniao de Bancos Brasileiros S.A. (Unibanco), Sao Paulo, Brazil; *Int'l*, pg. 1431
Bravo, Massimo, Exec. V.P.-Mktg.--Istituto Bancario San Paolo Di Torino S.p.A., Turin, Italy; *Int'l*, pg. 691
Bray, Barry D., Chief Credit Officer & Exec. V.P.--Trans Financial, Inc., Bowling Green, KY; *U.S. Public*, pg. 1628
Brayman, John A., Exec. V.P.-Bus. Devel.--Entergy Corporation, New Orleans, LA; *U.S. Public*, pg. 585
Brazeal, Michael, Exec. V.P. & Creative Dir.--Lois/EJL Chicago, Chicago, IL; *U.S. Public*, pg. 1011
Brazzale, Alfeo, Exec. V.P.-Machining Systems--Mikron Holding AG, Biel, Switzerland; *Int'l*, pg. 866
Brechbill, Terry, Exec. V.P.--D.L. Blair Inc., Garden City, NY; *U.S. Private*, pg. 148
Brecht, Edwin, Exec. V.P.--IKB Deutsche Industriebank AG, Dusseldorf, Germany; *Int'l*, pg. 645
Brecht, Robert P., Exec. V.P.--FirstMerit Corporation, Akron, OH; *U.S. Public*, pg. 646
Breckles, William T., Exec. V.P.--Commercial Union Assurance Company of Canada, Toronto, Canada; *Int'l*, pg. 308
Bredemeier, Sonning, Dr., Exec. V.P. & Dir.-Pub. Rels.--Norddeutsche Landesbank (NORD/LB), Hannover, Germany; *Int'l*, pg. 957
Breedlove, J. Lloyed, Exec. V.P.--Steris Corporation, Mentor, OH; *U.S. Public*, pg. 1515
Bregar, Raymond E., Exec. V.P.-Corp. Opers.--Semtech Corporation, Newbury Park, CA; *U.S. Public*, pg. 1456
Bregman, Barry I., Exec. V.P.--ORIX COMMODITIES Corporation, Tokyo, Japan; *Int'l*, pg. 1008
Brehm, Robert T., Exec. V.P.--ABN AMRO Chicago Corp., Chicago, IL; *Int'l*, pg. 10
Brehmer, Stig, Exec. V.P.-Strip, Foil & Autoplastics--Granges AB, Stockholm, Sweden; *Int'l*, pg. 439
Bremser, Jeff, Exec. V.P. & Exec. Creative Dir.--Bernstein-Rein Advertising, Inc., Kansas City, MO; *U.S. Private*, pg. 137
Breneisen, William, Exec. V.P.-Tech.--Mutual of America Life Insurance Company, New York, NY; *U.S. Private*, pg. 769
Breneisen, William, Exec. V.P.-Tech.--American Life Insurance Company of New York, New York, NY; *U.S. Private*, pg. 769
Brennan, James G., Chief Fin. Officer & Exec. V.P.--Taylor-Morley, Inc., Saint Louis, MO; *U.S. Private*, pg. 1071
Brennan, John V., Chief Fin. Officer, Exec. V.P. & Treas.--Webster Financial Corporation, Waterbury, CT; *U.S. Public*, pg. 1751
Brennan, Robert J., Exec. V.P.--College Division, Greenwich, CT; *U.S. Private*, pg. 57
Brenneman, David L., Exec. V.P.--Drake Construction Company, Portland, OR; *U.S. Private*, pg. 347
Brenner, Arnold S., Exec. V.P. & Gen. Mgr.-Japan Grp.--Motorola, Inc., Schaumburg, IL; *U.S. Public*, pg. 1136
Brenner, Stephen, Chief Oper. Officer, Exec. V.P.-Bus. Affairs. & Gen. Counsel--USA Networks, New York, NY; *U.S. Public*, pg. 1686
Brenner, Walter, Exec. V.P.--Credit Lyonnais Americas, New York, NY; *Int'l*, pg. 344

Breslawski, James, Exec. V.P.--Henry Schein, Inc., Melville, NY; *U.S. Public*, pg. 1437
Brett, Paul, Exec. V.P.--The Thomson Corporation, Stamford, CT; *U.S. Public*, pg. 1599
Brett, Stephen M., Exec. V.P. & Sec.--TCI Communications, Inc., Englewood, CO; *U.S. Public*, pg. 1554
Brevik, John, Exec. V.P.-Sls., Adv. & Mktg.--Exotic Rubber & Plastics Corp., Farmington Hills, MI; *U.S. Private*, pg. 388
Brewer, Michael, Exec. V.P.--Linkous Construction Company, Inc., Memphis, TN; *U.S. Private*, pg. 669
Bricout, Michel, Exec. V.P.-Fin. Cos.--PSA Peugeot Citroen, Paris, France; *Int'l*, pg. 1020
Bridenbaugh, Peter R., Exec. V.P.-Automotive--Aluminum Company of America, Pittsburgh, PA; *U.S. Public*, pg. 60
Bridge, John B., Exec. V.P.--VASA Brougher, Inc., Indianapolis, IN; *Int'l*, pg. 464
Bridges, James, Exec. V.P.-IS--URS Logistics, Atlanta, GA; *U.S. Private*, pg. 1114
Briggs, R. Stephen, Exec. V.P.--Protective Life Corporation, Birmingham, AL; *U.S. Public*, pg. 1336
Briggs, R. Stephen, Exec. V.P.--Protective Life Insurance Co., Birmingham, AL; *U.S. Public*, pg. 1336
Brightman, Jon S., Trust Dept. Exec.--Harris & Bank, Chicago, IL; *Int'l*, pg. 154
Briley, John W., Exec. V.P.-Mark VII Risk Management Div.--Mark VII, Inc., Memphis, TN; *U.S. Public*, pg. 1046
Briller-Burke, Beverly, Exec. V.P.-Fin.--Outdoor Services, San Francisco, CA; *U.S. Private*, pg. 1166
Brilliant, Robert, Exec. V.P.- Fin. & Admin.--Klemtner Advertising Inc., New York, NY; *U.S. Public*, pg. 1422
Brindley, Thomas M., Chief Oper. Officer & Exec. V.P.--W.A. Roosevelt Co., La Crosse, WI; *U.S. Private*, pg. 943
Bring, Murray H., Exec. V.P.-External Affairs & Gen. Counsel--Philip Morris Companies Inc., New York, NY; *U.S. Public*, pg. 1287
Brink, K. Robert, Exec. V.P.--Hearst Magazines Division, New York, NY; *U.S. Private*, pg. 516
Brink, K. Robert, Exec. V.P.--Cosmopolitan, New York, NY; *U.S. Private*, pg. 517
Brinkley, James W., Sr. Exec. V.P.--Legg Mason, Inc., Baltimore, MD; *U.S. Public*, pg. 984
Brinzo, J.S., Exec. V.P.-Fin.--The Cleveland-Cliffs Iron Company, Cleveland, OH; *U.S. Public*, pg. 386
Brisbin, Thomas D., Chief Oper. Officer & Exec. V.P.--Tetra Tech, Inc., Pasadena, CA; *U.S. Public*, pg. 1582
Briscoe, Don L., Exec. V.P.--Bergelectric Corporation, Los Angeles, CA; *U.S. Private*, pg. 135
Bristow, Donald A., Chief Fin. Officer & Exec. V.P.--Voith Hydro, Inc., York, PA; *Int'l*, pg. 1473
Britelle, Douglas, Exec. V.P.--Essef Corporation, Chardon, OH; *U.S. Public*, pg. 592
Britson, Wesley G., Sr. V.P.--Dewberry Design Group, Oklahoma City, OK; *U.S. Private*, pg. 329
Britt, Glenn A., Exec. V.P.--State Farm Life Insurance Co., Bloomington, IL; *U.S. Private*, pg. 1036
Britt, Wayne, Chief Fin. Officer & Exec. V.P.-Fin.--Tyson Foods, Inc., Springdale, AR; *U.S. Public*, pg. 1652
Britton, Jerry W., Exec. V.P.-Commercial Fin. Div.--Green Tree Financial Corporation, Saint Paul, MN; *U.S. Public*, pg. 761
Britton, Robert A., Chief Fin. Officer & Exec. V.P.--Swisher International Group, Inc., Darien, CT; *U.S. Public*, pg. 1543
Broaddus, Jack, Exec. V.P.--Wampler Foods, Timberville, VA; *U.S. Public*, pg. 1727
Broadley, David C., Chief Fin. Officer & Exec. V.P.--Sierra West Bancorp, Truckee, CA; *U.S. Public*, pg. 1470
Brock, Ed, Principal--Richards, Brock, Miller, Mitchell & Assoc. Inc., Dallas, TX; *U.S. Private*, pg. 929
Brock, Kathleen K., Exec. V.P.-Acct. Service--EvansGroup, Denver, CO; *U.S. Private*, pg. 385
Brock, Tony, Exec. V.P. & Treas.--Beadles Lumber Company, Inc., Moultrie, GA; *U.S. Private*, pg. 126
Brockett, Patrick J., Exec. V.P.-World Wide Mktg. & Sls.--National Semiconductor Corporation, Santa Clara, CA; *U.S. Public*, pg. 1159
Brockman, Rob, Exec. V.P.-Admin.--Cash America International, Inc., Fort Worth, TX; *U.S. Public*, pg. 312
Brockshire, Brent, Exec. V.P.--Brookshire Bros., Ltd., Lufkin, TX; *U.S. Private*, pg. 172
Broda, Lothar, Exec. V.P.--Bayerische Hypotheken-und Wechsel-Bank Aktiengesellschaft, Munich, Germany; *Int'l*, pg. 175
Broderick, Joseph E., Exec. V.P.-Client Sls. & Services--Manugistics Group, Inc., Rockville, MD; *U.S. Public*, pg. 1042
Broderick, Robert, Exec. V.P.--Dakota Electric Association, Farmington, MN; *U.S. Private*, pg. 308
Brodie, Nancy S., Chief Fin. Officer & Exec. V.P.--The Penn Mutual Life Insurance Company, Philadelphia, PA; *U.S. Private*, pg. 849
Brodie, Richard, Exec. V.P.--Norman Levy Associates, Inc., Southfield, MI; *U.S. Private*, pg. 664
Brodsky, Howard, Chief Fin. Officer & Exec. V.P.--Grey Direct, New York, NY; *U.S. Public*, pg. 764
Brody, David B., Exec. V.P.-Info. Systems & Opers.--FASTRAC Systems, Inc.-Insurance Agent & Broker, South San Francisco, CA; *U.S. Public*, pg. 1158
Brogan, R. Alan, Exec. V.P.-Transportation Logistics--Norfolk Southern Corporation, Norfolk, VA; *U.S. Public*, pg. 1190
Brognola, Michael J., Chief Oper. Officer & Exec. V.P.--Laidlaw Environmental Services, Inc., Columbia, SC; *U.S. Public*, pg. 975
Bromage, William T., Exec. V.P.-Bus. Banking & Trusts--Webster Financial Corporation, Waterbury, CT; *U.S. Public*, pg. 1751
Bromlow, Terry, Exec. V.P.--Hereford State Bank, Hereford, TX; *U.S. Public*, pg. 633
Brongniart, Philippe, Exec. V.P.--Lyonnaise des Eaux S.A., Nanterre, France; *Int'l*, pg. 822
Bronsard, Joseph A., Exec. V.P. & Plant Mgr.--Homasote Company, Trenton, NJ; *U.S. Public*, pg. 831
Brooks, Mitch, Exec. V.P. & Gen. Mgr.--Trader Publishing Company, Norfolk, VA; *U.S. Private*, pg. 649
Brooks, R. Jeffrey R., Exec. V.P.-Card Services--First Commerce Corporation, New Orleans, LA; *U.S. Public*, pg. 629
Brooks, Robert L., Exec. V.P.-Investment Banking--The Bank of Nova Scotia, Toronto, Canada; *Int'l*, pg. 155
Brookshire, Tim, Exec. V.P.-H.R.--Brookshire Grocery, Tyler, TX; *U.S. Private*, pg. 172
Broomfield, A. D., Exec. V.P., Administrative Bank CIBC--Canadian Imperial Bank of Commerce, Toronto, Canada; *Int'l*, pg. 256
Bross, Richard E., Exec. V.P.-Land & Opers.--Louis Dreyfus Natural Gas Corp., Oklahoma City, OK; *U.S. Private*, pg. 342
Brost, Jim, Exec. V.P.--Miniature Precision Components, Walworth, WI; *U.S. Private*, pg. 750
Brothers, John A., Exec. V.P.--Ashland, Inc., Russell, KY; *U.S. Public*, pg. 138
Broughton, George W., Exec. V.P.-Sls. & Mktg.--Broughton Foods Company, Marietta, OH; *U.S. Public*, pg. 259
Brouilette, Alan, Exec. V.P.--Strombecker Corporation, Chicago, IL; *U.S. Private*, pg. 1047
Broussard, Charles-Henry, Deputy Mgr.--GEODIS, Paris, France; *Int'l*, pg. 549
Brouwer, J., Exec. V.P.-Oil Logistics Europe/Pakhoed Asia--Royal Pakhoed NV, Rotterdam, Netherlands; *Int'l*, pg. 1147
Brouwer, W.J.C., Exec. V.P.--Labouchere N.V., Amsterdam, Netherlands; *Int'l*, pg. 26
Brown, Alan, Exec. V.P.- & WW Media Dir.--Active International, Pearl River, NY; *U.S. Private*, pg. 15
Brown, Anthony S., Exec. V.P., Treas. & Portfolio Mgr.--Pax World Fund Family, Portsmouth, NH; *U.S. Public*, pg. 1266
Brown, Bob, Exec. V.P.-Consumer Mkts. Prod./Midwest & Northeast Div.--Countrywide Home Loans Inc., Pasadena, CA; *U.S. Public*, pg. 452
Brown, Cary, Exec. V.P.-Sls. & Customer Services--American Eurocopter Corp., Grand Prairie, TX; *Int'l*, pg. 29
Brown, Christopher A., Exec. V.P.-Procurement--Richfood Holdings, Inc., Glen Allen, VA; *U.S. Public*, pg. 1388
Brown, Craig, Chief Fin. Officer & Exec. V.P.-DMB&B Fin. & Opers.--DMB&B Communications, New York, NY; *U.S. Private*, pg. 302
Brown, Eddie R., Exec. V.P.--Landstar Holding, Shelton, CT; *U.S. Public*, pg. 978
Brown, Franklin C., Vice Chm., Exec. V.P. & Gen. Counsel--Rite Aid Corporation, Camp Hill, PA; *U.S. Public*, pg. 1390
Brown, Gene, Exec. V.P.-Sls. & Mktg.--Groendyke Transports, Inc., Enid, OK; *U.S. Private*, pg. 483
Brown, Glenn W., Jr., Chief Oper. Officer & Exec. V.P.--Sherman & Reilly, Inc., Chattanooga, TN; *U.S. Private*, pg. 993
Brown, Harry, Exec. V.P. & Chief Mdsg. Officer--Stage Stores, Inc., Houston, TX; *U.S. Private*, pg. 1028
Brown, J. Michael, Exec. V.P.--First National Bank of Commerce, New Orleans, LA; *U.S. Public*, pg. 629
Brown, James D., Exec. V.P. & Sec.--Pacor, Inc., Philadelphia, PA; *U.S. Private*, pg. 833
Brown, Jeffrey N., Exec. V.P.-Mktg.--Webster Financial Corporation, Waterbury, CT; *U.S. Public*, pg. 1751
Brown, Jeremy J., Exec. V.P. & Chief Actuary--Mutual of America Life Insurance Company, New York, NY; *U.S. Private*, pg. 769
Brown, Jeremy J., Exec. V.P. & Chief Actuary--American Life Insurance Company of New York, New York, NY; *U.S. Private*, pg. 769
Brown, Kenneth R., Exec. V.P.--Liberty Bank & Trust Company of Oklahoma City, Oklahoma City, OK; *U.S. Public*, pg. 174
Brown, Larry, V.P.-Prod. Assurance--Analog Devices, Santa Clara, CA; *U.S. Public*, pg. 108
Brown, Mark H., Exec. V.P.-Association & Club Svcs.--American Automobile Association, Heathrow, FL; *U.S. Private*, pg. 50
Brown, Mark H., Exec. V.P.--Edison Brothers Stores, Inc., Saint Louis, MO; *U.S. Public*, pg. 563
Brown, Martin S., Exec. V.P.-Sls. & Mktg.--Foster Wheeler Environmental Corporation, Livingston, NJ; *U.S. Public*, pg. 677
Brown, Michael, Exec. V.P.--House of Fabrics, Inc., Sherman Oaks, CA; *U.S. Public*, pg. 842
Brown, Michael I., Exec. V.P.-Corporate Mngmt. Serv. Admin.--The New England, Boston, MA; *U.S. Private*, pg. 737
Brown, Richard G., Exec. V.P.--Trinity Railcar Leasing, Dallas, TX; *U.S. Public*, pg. 1639
Brown, Richard J., Community Bank Exec.--Harris & Bank, Chicago, IL; *Int'l*, pg. 154
Brown, Thomas G., Exec. V.P. & Chm. & Chief Exec. Off.-Duncanson & Holt, Inc.--UNUM Corporation, Portland, ME; *U.S. Public*, pg. 1699
Brown, Thomas G., Exec. V.P.--UNUM Life Insurance Company of America, Portland, ME; *U.S. Public*, pg. 1699
Brown, Timothy, Exec. V.P.--Agsco, Inc., Grand Forks, ND; *U.S. Private*, pg. 27
Brown, Todd, Exec. V.P. & Gen. Mgr.-Desserts & Snacks Div.--Kraft Foods, Inc., Northfield, IL; *U.S. Public*, pg. 1287
Brown, V.G., Exec. V.P.--ING North America Insurance Company, Atlanta, GA; *Int'l*, pg. 648
Brown, W. Lee, Exec. V.P.--N.B.M. Corp., McAlester, OK; *U.S. Private*, pg. 771
Brown, William M., Chief Fin. Officer, Exec. V.P. & Controller--IMO Industries Inc., Lawrenceville, NJ; *U.S. Public*, pg. 856
Browne, Jon, Chief Admin. Officer & Exec. V.P.--Chernin's Shoes, Inc., Chicago, IL; *U.S. Private*, pg. 233
Browning, Alan D., Exec. V.P.--Jefferies Group, Inc., Los Angeles, CA; *U.S. Public*, pg. 924
Browning, Alan D., Exec. V.P.--Jefferies & Company, Inc., Los Angeles, CA; *U.S. Public*, pg. 925
Browning, David J., Exec. V.P.--Citicorp, New York, NY; *U.S. Public*, pg. 376
Browning, Doyle F., Exec. V.P. & Gen. Mgr.--Chrysler Insurance Co., Southfield, MI; *U.S. Public*, pg. 354
Brownson, John B., Chief Oper. Officer & Exec. V.P.--G.R. Herberger's, Inc., Saint Cloud, MN; *U.S. Public*, pg. 1333
Broxterman, Bruce, Exec. V.P.--Richards Industries, Inc., Cincinnati, OH; *U.S. Private*, pg. 929
Brua, Denny, Exec. V.P.-Opers.--84 Lumber Company, Eighty Four, PA; *U.S. Private*, pg. 366
Brubaker, J. Robert, Exec. V.P. & Sr. Opers. Officer--NationsBank West, Saint Louis, MO; *U.S. Public*, pg. 1164
Bruce, Joseph, Exec. V.P.-Strategic Plng.--Eisner & Associates, Inc., Baltimore, MD; *U.S. Private*, pg. 366
Bruce, Peter W., Exec. V.P.--Northwestern Mutual Life Insurance Co., Milwaukee, WI; *U.S. Private*, pg. 807
Bruchner, Helmut, Dr., Exec. V.P.--Bayerische Hypotheken-und Wechsel-Bank Aktiengesellschaft, Munich, Germany; *Int'l*, pg. 175
Bruder, James J., Exec. V.P.--M.A. Bruder & Sons, Incorporated, Broomall, PA; *U.S. Private*, pg. 175
Bruening, R.P., Sr. V.P. & Gen. Counsel--The Kansas City Southern Railway Co., Kansas City, MO; *U.S. Public*, pg. 944
Bruggemann, C.W.H., Exec. V.P.--ABN-AMRO Holding N.V., Amsterdam, Netherlands; *Int'l*, pg. 8
Brumm, James E., Exec. V.P., Sec. & Gen. Counsel--Mitsubishi International Corporation, New York, NY; *Int'l*, pg. 871
Brumm, P. Michael, Exec. V.P.--Fifth Third Bancorp, Cincinnati, OH; *U.S. Public*, pg. 621
Brunell, Donald A. Jr., Exec. V.P.-Fin.--Union Bank of California, San Francisco, CA; *Int'l*, pg. 157
Brunelle, John, Exec. V.P.--The Conde Nast Publications Inc., New York, NY; *U.S. Private*, pg. 20
Bruner, James D., Exec. V.P.--National Bank of Arizona, Tucson, AZ; *U.S. Public*, pg. 1793
Brunett, Michael, Exec. V.P.--John E. Green Co., Detroit, MI; *U.S. Private*, pg. 477
Brunett, Ray, Exec. V.P.--John E. Green Co., Detroit, MI; *U.S. Private*, pg. 477
Brunk, Marten F., Dr., Exec. V.P.--H. Krantz-TKT GmbH, Bergisch Gladbach, Germany; *Int'l*, pg. 399
Brunner, Daniel S., Exec. V.P.-Govt. Affairs--First Health Group Corp., Downers Grove, IL; *U.S. Public*, pg. 635
Brunner, Vernon A., Exec. V.P.-Mktg.--Walgreen Co., Deerfield, IL; *U.S. Public*, pg. 1733
Brush, James, Exec. V.P.-Sls. & Mktg.--Sentry Group, Rochester, NY; *U.S. Private*, pg. 984
Brust, Susan, Exec. V.P.--Nordic Ware, Minneapolis, MN; *U.S. Private*, pg. 806
Brutsche, Peter, Chief Exec. Officer & Exec. V.P.-Japan--Union Bank of Switzerland, Zurich, Switzerland; *Int'l*, pg. 1439
Bryan, Larry J., Exec. V.P.--Norrell Corporation, Atlanta, GA; *U.S. Public*, pg. 1192
Bryan, Richard, Exec. V.P.--H.B. Zachry, San Antonio, TX; *U.S. Private*, pg. 1203
Bryant, Barbara, Exec. V.P.--The Phoenix Learning Group, Inc., Saint Louis, MO; *U.S. Private*, pg. 863
Bryant, Carleton F., III, Chief Oper. Officer, Exec. V.P., Treas. & Sec.--Westerbeke Corporation, Avon, MA; *U.S. Public*, pg. 1757
Bryant, Carole Y., Exec. V.P.-Corp. & Business Svcs.--SaskPower, Regina, Canada; *Int'l*, pg. 1195
Bryant, George, Reg. V.P.--Dillard Paper Co. of Tampa, Tampa, FL; *U.S. Public*, pg. 902
Bryant, Harry M., Jr., Exec. V.P.--Bryant Electric Supply Company, Inc., Lowell, NC; *U.S. Private*, pg. 177
Bryant, Roy, Exec. V.P.-Sls. & Mktg.--Castleberry/Snow's Brands Inc., Augusta, GA; *U.S. Private*, pg. 219
Bryant, Thaire B., Exec. V.P.--Hallsmith-Sysco Food Services, Norton, MA; *U.S. Public*, pg. 1550
Bryce, Rodolfo C., Exec. V.P.--Schering-Plough Corporation, Madison, NJ; *U.S. Public*, pg. 1438
Brynildsen, Jon Chr., Exec. V.P.-Shipping--Kvaerner a.s.a., Lysaker, Norway; *Int'l*, pg. 766
Bryson, Lee R., Exec. V.P.-Sls.--Piggly Wiggly Co., Memphis, TN; *U.S. Public*, pg. 653
Bubnick, James J., Exec. V.P.-Potash--Potash Corporation of Saskatchewan Inc., Saskatoon, Canada; *Int'l*, pg. 1064
Bucaille, Alain, Sr. Exec. V.P.--Lafarge Aluminates, Paris, France; *Int'l*, pg. 789
Buchanan, Danne L., Exec. V.P.-Opers. & Info. Sys.--Zions Bancorporation, Salt Lake City, UT; *U.S. Public*, pg. 1792
Buchanan, James R., Exec. V.P.-Sls.--Central Sprinkler Company, Lansdale, PA; *U.S. Public*, pg. 327
Buchanan, Richard W., Chief Oper. Officer & Exec. V.P.-Corp. Asset & Fin.--First American Federal Savings Bank, Bristol, VA; *U.S. Public*, pg. 624
Buchanan, Susan S., Exec. V.P.--Nielsen Media Research, New York, NY; *U.S. Public*, pg. 395
Buchel, Andre P., Exec. V.P.-Sulzermedica Group--Sulzer Ltd., Winterthur, Switzerland; *Int'l*, pg. 1305
Bucht, Henri, Exec. V.P.-Finnish Department Stores--Stockmann Department Store Div., Helsinki, Finland; *Int'l*, pg. 1301
Buck, C.J., Chief Oper. Officer & Exec. V.P.--Buck Knives, Inc., El Cajon, CA; *U.S. Private*, pg. 177
Buckalew, Steve, Exec. V.P.--Countrymark Cooperative, Inc., Indianapolis, IN; *U.S. Private*, pg. 279
Buckingham, Robert W., Exec. V.P.--Jack Nadel, Inc., Culver City, CA; *U.S. Private*, pg. 773
Bucklew, Phyllis, Exec. V.P.-Consumer Mkts. Prod./Southeast Div.--Countrywide Home Loans Inc., Pasadena, CA; *U.S. Public*, pg. 452
Buckley, John E., Chief Oper. Officer & Exec. V.P.--A.T. Cross Co., Lincoln, RI; *U.S. Public*, pg. 460

Buckley, John N., Exec. V.P. & Dir.-Credit Admin.--Bay View Capital Corporation, San Mateo, CA; *U.S. Public*, pg. 197

Buckley, Joseph R., Exec. V.P.--Manor Care, Inc., Gaithersburg, MD; *U.S. Public*, pg. 1041

Buckman, James E., Sr. Exec. V.P., Gen. Counsel & Asst. Sec.--HFS, Incorporated, Parsippany, NJ; *U.S. Public*, pg. 321

Bucksbaum, John, Exec. V.P.--General Growth Properties Inc., Chicago, IL; *U.S. Public*, pg. 715

Bucnis, Edward H., Exec. V.P.-Opers. Div.--People's Bank, Bridgeport, CT; *U.S. Public*, pg. 1274

Budnick, Neil G., Exec. V.P.-Pub. Fin. Grp.--Municipal Bond Investors Assurance Corporation, Armonk, NY; *U.S. Public*, pg. 1023

Budolfsen, Elsebeth, Exec. V.P.--Chr. Hansen Holding A/S, Horsholm, Denmark; *Int'l*, pg. 288

Budwick, Robert T., Exec. V.P. & Chief Investment Officer--MBL Life Assurance Corporation, Newark, NJ; *U.S. Private*, pg. 685

Buehler, William F., Exec. V.P. & Chief Staff Officer--Xerox Corporation, Stamford, CT; *U.S. Public*, pg. 1783

Buell, Dick, Chief Oper. Officer & Exec. V.P.--Griffith Laboratories Worldwide, Inc., Alsip, IL; *U.S. Private*, pg. 481

Buerges, Ronald A., Chief Oper. Officer & Sr. Exec. V.P.--Magna Group, Inc., Saint Louis, MO; *U.S. Public*, pg. 1037

Buerkle, John R., Exec. V.P. & Reg. Dir.-Consumer Products-Asia-Pacific--S.C. Johnson & Son, Inc., Racine, WI; *U.S. Private*, pg. 592

Buff, George, III, Exec. V.P.--Penny Plate, Inc., Cherry Hill, NJ; *U.S. Private*, pg. 850

Buffington, M. Dean, Exec. V.P. & Mgr.-Trust--First Security Bank of Idaho, N.A., Boise, ID; *U.S. Public*, pg. 637

Buicko, David M., Chief Oper. Officer & Exec. V.P.--Rotterdam Ventures Inc., Guilderland Center, NY; *U.S. Private*, pg. 437

Bulkeley, John Z., Exec. V.P.-Credit Management Group--Union Bank of California, San Francisco, CA; *Int'l*, pg. 157

Bull, Alfred W., Exec. V.P.-Gases & Equipment--Air Products Europe, Inc., Allentown, PA; *U.S. Public*, pg. 30

Bull, Christopher R.H., Exec. Dir.--Rio Tinto PLC, London, United Kingdom; *Int'l*, pg. 1118

Bullina, Tony, Exec. V.P.-Mdsg.--Carson Pirie Scott & Co., Milwaukee, WI; *U.S. Public*, pg. 309

Bullock, William N., Exec. V.P.--Environmental Air Systems, Inc., Greensboro, NC; *U.S. Private*, pg. 378

Bulow, Anders, Exec. V.P.--Trelleborg AB, Trelleborg, Sweden; *Int'l*, pg. 1419

Bumstead, David L., Exec. V.P.--Noranda Inc., Toronto, Canada; *Int'l*, pg. 433

Bunkers, E.W., Chief Exec. Officer & Exec. V.P.-Fin.--Mueller Industries, Inc., Memphis, TN; *U.S. Public*, pg. 1141

Bunnell, Keith, Exec. V.P. & Mng. Partner-Acct.--Wells BDDP, Inc., New York, NY; *Int'l*, pg. 117

Bunting, William V., Grp. Exec. V.P.-Consumer Fin.--Crestar Financial Corporation, Richmond, VA; *U.S. Public*, pg. 458

Burch, Gail, Exec. V.P., Client Svcs. Dir. & Acct. Supvr.--Cash Plus, Inc., Minneapolis, MN; *U.S. Private*, pg. 218

Burch, Larry, Exec. V.P.-Central Region--Bergen Brunswig Corporation, Orange, CA; *U.S. Public*, pg. 213

Burch, Robert K., Exec. V.P.-Retail Banking--Shoreline Financial Corp., Benton Harbor, MI; *U.S. Public*, pg. 1467

Burch, Robert L., Exec. V.P.-Retail Banking--Shoreline Bank, Benton Harbor, MI; *U.S. Public*, pg. 1468

Burchfield, William H., Exec. V.P.--Champion International Corp., Stamford, CT; *U.S. Public*, pg. 333

Burchill, Frederick J., Exec. V.P.--CRIIMI MAE, Rockville, MD; *U.S. Public*, pg. 459

Burden, Thomas, Exec. V.P. & Creative Dir.-TBC Direct--Trahan, Burden & Charles, Inc., Baltimore, MD; *U.S. Private*, pg. 1095

Burg, Mitchell, Exec. V.P. & Retail Plng. Dir.--The Media Edge, New York, NY; *U.S. Private*, pg. 1079

Burg, Robert J., Exec. V.P.-East Coast--FPA Medical Management, Inc., San Diego, CA; *U.S. Public*, pg. 608

Burger, Hartmut W., Exec. V.P.--Electronic Data Systems Corporation, Plano, TX; *U.S. Public*, pg. 569

Burger, Paul, Exec. V.P. & Client Service Dir.--The Weightman Group, Philadelphia, PA; *U.S. Private*, pg. 1159

Burger, Richard, Exec. V.P.--Sulzer Ltd., Winterthur, Switzerland; *Int'l*, pg. 1305

Burgert, Werner, Exec. V.P.-Fiber Products--BASF Corporation, Mount Olive, NJ; *Int'l*, pg. 105

Burgess, John, Exec. V.P.-American President Lines--APL Limited, Oakland, CA; *Int'l*, pg. 912

Burgi, Daniel, Exec. V.P.--Impuls Advertising AG, Kusnacht, Switzerland; *Int'l*, pg. 666

Burgos, J. Louis, Exec. V.P.-Commercial--Royal LePage Limited, Don Mills, Canada; *Int'l*, pg. 1143

Burie, Hilde, Exec. V.P.-Human Resources--Sabena, Zaventem, Belgium; *Int'l*, pg. 1168

Burk, Herbert, Exec. V.P.--Life-Like Products, Inc., Baltimore, MD; *U.S. Private*, pg. 666

Burka, Mark B., Exec. Dir.--AON Advisors, Inc., Chicago, IL; *U.S. Public*, pg. 117

Burke, David, Exec. V.P.-Sls. & Mktg.--B&G Foods, Inc., Roseland, NJ; *U.S. Private*, pg. 105

Burke, Donald B., Exec. V.P.-Mktg. & Sls.--Worthington Foods Inc., Worthington, OH; *U.S. Public*, pg. 1780

Burke, John D., Chief Mktg. Officer & Exec. V.P.-Plasti-Line, Inc., Knoxville, TN; *U.S. Public*, pg. 1308

Burke, Patrick, Exec. V.P.-Brokerage Svcs.--Automobile Protection Corporation-APCO, Atlanta, GA; *U.S. Public*, pg. 150

Burkett, Lawrence V., Exec. V.P. & Gen. Counsel--Massachusetts Mutual Life Insurance Co., Springfield, MA; *U.S. Private*, pg. 712

Burkett, Linda, Chief Information Officer & Exec. V.P.--Bergen Brunswig Corporation, Orange, CA; *U.S. Public*, pg. 213

Burks, Keith W., Chief Oper. Officer & Exec. V.P.--Bindley Western Industries, Inc., Indianapolis, IN; *U.S. Public*, pg. 228

Burlin, Daniel, Sr. Exec. V.P.-Fin. & Control--Technip, Paris, France; *Int'l*, pg. 1360

Burlingame, Harold W., Exec. V.P.-Human Resources--AT&T Corporation, Basking Ridge, NJ; *U.S. Public*, pg. 10

Burney, Derek H., Exec. V.P.-Intl.--BCE Inc., Montreal, Canada; *Int'l*, pg. 114

Burnham, Daniel P., Exec. V.P. & Pres.-AlliedSignal Aerospace Co.--AlliedSignal Inc., Morristown, NJ; *U.S. Public*, pg. 49

Burniston, Kevin, Exec. Dir.--Willis Corroon Risk Consulting Limited, London, United Kingdom; *Int'l*, pg. 1503

Burns, David J., Exec. V.P.--Gleason Corporation, Rochester, NY; *U.S. Public*, pg. 746

Burns, David T., Exec. V.P.-Beacon Div.--Pillowtex Corporation, Dallas, TX; *U.S. Public*, pg. 1296

Burns, Glenn S., Exec. V.P.-Buildings--Michael Baker Corporation, Pittsburgh, PA; *U.S. Public*, pg. 168

Burns, Harmon E., Exec. V.P. & Sec.--Franklin Resources, Inc., San Mateo, CA; *U.S. Public*, pg. 679

Burns, Jan, Exec. V.P. & Gen. Mgr.--Promotion Information Management (PIM), Chicago, IL; *U.S. Private*, pg. 649

Burns, Patrick, Sr. Exec. V.P. & Gen. Counsel--Mutual of America Life Insurance Company, New York, NY; *U.S. Private*, pg. 769

Burns, Patrick, Sr. Exec. V.P. & Gen. Counsel--American Life Insurance Company of New York, New York, NY; *U.S. Private*, pg. 769

Burns, Ronald S., Exec V.P., Pres. Global Bus. & Global Bus Dir.-Kraft--J. Walter Thompson Company, New York, NY; *Int'l*, pg. 1483

Burnside, Mary M., Exec. V.P.--Novell, Inc., Orem, UT; *U.S. Public*, pg. 1203

Burr, Peter K., Exec. V.P.-Corp. Banking--HSBC Americas, Buffalo, NY; *Int'l*, pg. 580

Burrice, Robert N., Chief Oper. Officer & Exec. V.P.--Gateway Press, Inc., Louisville, KY; *U.S. Private*, pg. 441

Burroughs, Bobbie J., Exec. V.P.-Admin. & Sec.--Aames Financial Corporation, Los Angeles, CA; *U.S. Public*, pg. 12

Burroughs, Michael, Exec. V.P.-Mktg.--Cragar Industries, Inc., Phoenix, AZ; *U.S. Public*, pg. 456

Burrows, Dennis A., Exec V.P., Treas. & Sec.--Roper Bros. Lumber Co., Inc., Petersburg, VA; *U.S. Private*, pg. 944

Burruss, Robert C., Exec. V.P.--Grey Advertising Inc., New York, NY; *U.S. Public*, pg. 764

Bursiek, Dave, Exec. V.P.-North and Latin America--Sapiens International Corporation N.V., Curacao, Netherlands Antilles; *Int'l*, pg. 1193

Bursma, Albert, Jr., Exec. V.P. & Pres.-Great Source Education Group--Houghton Mifflin Company, Boston, MA; *U.S. Public*, pg. 841

Burtelow, John F., Chief Fin. Officer & Exec. V.P.--Ames Department Stores, Inc., Rocky Hill, CT; *U.S. Public*, pg. 99

Burton, Dennis C., Exec. V.P.--Chronimed Inc., Minnetonka, MN; *U.S. Public*, pg. 352

Burton, Patrick H., Exec. V.P.--Sysco Food Services of Montana, Inc., Billings, MT; *U.S. Public*, pg. 1551

Burton, Steven, Worldwide Fin. Dir.--DDB Needham Worldwide Inc., New York, NY; *Int'l*, pg. 357

Burton, Steven, Worldwide Fin. Dir.--DDB Needham Worldwide Inc., New York, NY; *U.S. Public*, pg. 1223

Busby, Robert B., Exec. V.P. & Dir.-Sls.--Pawling Corporation, Pawling, NY; *U.S. Private*, pg. 844

Busch, Joseph F., Exec. V.P.--Ederer Inc., Seattle, WA; *U.S. Private*, pg. 363

Buschey, Larry, Exec. V.P.--Astro Dairy Products Ltd., Etobicoke, Canada; *Int'l*, pg. 95

Buselmeier, Bernard J., Chief Fin. Officer & Exec. V.P.-Fin. & Admin.--Integon Corporation, Winston Salem, NC; *U.S.* Public, pg. 719

Buselmeier, Bernard J., Chief Fin. Officer & Exec. V.P.--Integon National Insurance Co., Winston Salem, NC; *U.S. Public*, pg. 720

Buselmeier, Bernard J., Chief Fin. Officer & Exec. V.P.--Integon Indemnity Corporation, Winston Salem, NC; *U.S.* Public, pg. 720

Buselmeier, Bernard J., Chief Fin. Officer & Exec. V.P.--Integon General Insurance Corporation, Winston Salem, NC; *U.S. Public*, pg. 720

Buselmeier, Bernard J., Chief Fin. Officer & Exec. V.P.--New South Insurance Company, Winston Salem, NC; *U.S. Public*, pg. 720

Buselmeier, Bernard J., Chief Fin. Officer & Exec. V.P.--Integon Specialty Insurance Company, Winston Salem, NC; *U.S. Public*, pg. 720

Buselmeier, Bernard J., Chief Fin. Officer & Exec. V.P.--Integon Preferred Insurance Company, Winston Salem, NC; *U.S. Public*, pg. 720

Buselmeier, Bernard J., Chief Fin. Officer & Exec. V.P.--Integon Casualty Insurance Company, Winston Salem, NC; *U.S. Public*, pg. 720

Bush, Michael J., Chief Oper. Officer & Exec. V.P.--Movado Group, Inc., Lyndhurst, NJ; *U.S. Public*, pg. 1140

Bush, Robert, Exec. V.P.-Individual Markets--Ameritas Life Insurance Corp., Lincoln, NE; *U.S. Private*, pg. 65

Busquet, Anne M., Exec. V.P.-Charge Card Mktg.; Consumer Grp.--American Express Travel Related Services Co., Inc., New York, NY; *U.S. Public*, pg. 73

Bust, Jeffrey, Exec. V.P. & Gen. Mgr.--Manitowoc Engineering Co., Manitowoc, WI; *U.S. Public*, pg. 1041

Busto, Rafael Tresgallo, Exec. V.P.--Banco Santander Puerto Rico, Hato Rey, PR; *Int'l*, pg. 143

Butare, Paul R., Exec. V.P.--Policy Management Systems Corporation, Blythewood, SC; *U.S. Public*, pg. 1314

Butcher, Clive, Exec. V.P. & Gen. Mgr.--Bayerische Landesbank - Singapore Branch, Singapore, Singapore; *Int'l*, pg. 176

Butcher, Peter R., Exec. V.P.-Credit Management Group--Union Bank of California, San Francisco, CA; *Int'l*, pg. 157

Butcher, Robert M., Chief Fin. Officer & Sr. Exec. V.P.--HSBC Americas, Buffalo, NY; *Int'l*, pg. 580

Butcher, Robert M., Chief Fin. Officer & Exec. V.P.--Marine Midland Bank, Buffalo, NY; *Int'l*, pg. 581

Butler, Allen, Exec. V.P. & Gen. Mgr.--Sony Music Entertainment, Inc., New York, NY; *Int'l*, pg. 1281

Butler, Jerry, Exec. V.P.-WW Opers. & Mfg.--Brite Voice Systems, Inc., Heathrow, FL; *U.S. Public*, pg. 257

Butler, John D., Exec. V.P.-Admin. & H.R.--Textron Inc., Providence, RI; *U.S. Public*, pg. 1588

Butler, Michael A., Exec. V.P.--Keycorp, Cleveland, OH; *U.S. Public*, pg. 954

Butler, Robert D., Exec. V.P.-Opers.--Baldor Electric Company, Fort Smith, AR; *U.S. Public*, pg. 168

Butler, Robert L., Exec. V.P.--The Pioneer Group, Inc., Boston, MA; *U.S. Public*, pg. 1298

Butler, Ronald H., Exec. V.P.-Mktg.--PETsMART, Inc., Phoenix, AZ; *U.S. Public*, pg. 1281

Butler, William, Exec. V.P.--Girgenti, Hughes, Butler & McDowell, New York, NY; *U.S. Private*, pg. 455

Butrus, Paul R., Chief Oper. Officer & Exec V.P.--Medical Assurance, Inc., Birmingham, AL; *U.S. Public*, pg. 1079

Butsuntorn, Tawee, Exec. V.P.--The Siam Cement Public Company Limited, Bangkok, Thailand; *Int'l*, pg. 1237

Buttacavoli, Frank, Chief Fin. Officer & Exec. V.P.--Parlux Fragrances Inc., Fort Lauderdale, FL; *U.S. Public*, pg. 1264

Butter, Dave, Exec. V.P.-Europe--Wunderman Worldwide Limited, London, United Kingdom; *U.S. Private*, pg. 1199

Butterfield, Jeffrey, Exec. V.P.-Corp. & Institutional Banking--Harris Bankcorp, Inc., Chicago, IL; *Int'l*, pg. 154

Butterick, Jack L., Exec. V.P.--Gerber Products Company of Puerto Rico, Inc., Carolina, PR; *Int'l*, pg. 973

Buttigieg, Joseph V., Exec. V.P.-Global Banking--Comerica Incorporated, Detroit, MI; *U.S. Public*, pg. 408

Butts, Mervin, Exec. V.P.-Engrng.--ZEXEL Inc., Decatur, IL; *Int'l*, pg. 1528

Butz, Terrell J., Exec. V.P.-Admin.--Cambiar Investors, Inc., Englewood, CO; *U.S. Public*, pg. 1672

Buzogany, R.J. "Buzz", Exec. V.P.--Wyse-Landau Public Relations, Cleveland, OH; *U.S. Private*, pg. 1194

Bwers, John, Exec. V.P.-Sls.--AEP Industries, Inc., South Hackensack, NJ; *U.S. Public*, pg. 4

Byer, Howard O., Exec. V.P.--Martin Marietta Canada Ltd., Ottawa, Canada; *U.S. Public*, pg. 1009

Bykerk, Cecil D., Exec. V.P. & Chief Actuary--Mutual of Omaha Insurance Company, Omaha, NE; *U.S. Private*, pg. 769

Byland, Peter, Exec. V.P.--Holderbank Financiere Glaris Ltd., Glaris, Switzerland; *Int'l*, pg. 628

Byqvist, Goran, Exec. V.P.--Axel Johnson AB, Stockholm, Sweden; *Int'l*, pg. 707

Byran, James, Exec. V.P.--Old World Industries, Inc., Northbrook, IL; *U.S. Private*, pg. 814

Byrd, Arthur A., Exec. V.P.-Opers.--Kellogg USA Inc., Battle Creek, MI; *U.S. Public*, pg. 947

Byrd, David, Exec. V.P.--San Angelo National Bank, San Angelo, TX; *U.S. Public*, pg. 633

Byrd, Jim, Exec. V.P.-Equities--Fortis Advisers, Inc., New York, NY; *Int'l*, pg. 499

Byrne, Blake, Exec. V.P.--Hearst-Argyle Television Incorporated, New York, NY; *U.S. Private*, pg. 516

Byrne, Chris, V.P. & Gen. Mgr.--NHT, Benicia, CA; *U.S. Public*, pg. 1369

Byrne, Paul, Exec. V.P.--Transport Development Group Plc, London, United Kingdom; *Int'l*, pg. 1418

Byrnes, John, V.P.-Opers.--NDS, Columbus, OH; *Int'l*, pg. 918

Bystrxycki, Tom, Exec. V.P.-Opers. & Tech.--U S West Inc., Englewood, CO; *U.S. Public*, pg. 1688

Byun, Byung Joo, Exec. V.P. & Dir.--Cho Hung Bank, Seoul, Korea; *Int'l*, pg. 287

Caballero, Theresa, Exec. V.P.-Mktg. & Promo.--Puerto Rico Tourism Company, San Juan, PR; *U.S. Private*, pg. 894

Cabiallavetta, Mathis, Exec. V.P.-Trading & Sls. & Risk Mngmt.--Union Bank of Switzerland, Zurich, Switzerland; *Int'l*, pg. 1439

Caccamo, Joe, Exec. V.P. & Gen. Mgr.--Central Grocers Co-op, Franklin Park, IL; *U.S. Private*, pg. 223

Cachin, Antoine, Sr. Exec. V.P.-Strategy--Club Mediterranee SA, Paris, France; *Int'l*, pg. 298

Caeymaex, Thierry, Exec. Dir.--Union Miniere, Brussels, Belgium; *Int'l*, pg. 1441

Cafasjian, G.L., Exec. V.P.--West Information Publishing Group, Saint Paul, MN; *U.S. Public*, pg. 1602

Caffarelli, Joseph J., Chief Fin. Officer & Exec. V.P.-Fin.--Physio-Control Corporation, Redmond, WA; *U.S. Public*, pg. 1294

Caffi, Alain, Exec. V.P.--Saint Dominique Participations, Paris, France; *Int'l*, pg. 344

Caffrey, Laura, Chief Fin. Officer & Exec. V.P.--FCB, New York, NY; *U.S. Private*, pg. 389

Cahill, James, Chief Fin. Officer, Exec. V.P., Treas. & Sec.--Strattec Securities Corporation, Milwaukee, WI; *U.S. Public*, pg. 1523

Cahuzac, Antoine, Exec. V.P.-Foreign Markets--Credit Commercial de France, Paris, France; *Int'l*, pg. 341

Cain, Phillip W., Chief Exec. Officer & Exec. V.P.--First National Bank in Marlinton, Marlinton, WV; *U.S. Public*, pg. 836

Caine, Bill, Jr., Exec. V.P.--The Accor Group, Inc., Corona Del Mar, CA; *Int'l*, pg. 21

Caine, Franklyn A., Chief Fin. Officer & Exec. V.P.--Wang Laboratories, Inc., Billerica, MA; *U.S. Public*, pg. 1737

Caine, William, T., Exec. V.P.--Metal Seal & Products, Inc., Willoughby, OH; *U.S. Private*, pg. 734

Caire Obregon, Andres, Exec. V.P.--Grupo Tribasa S.A. de C.V., Mexico, Mexico; *Int'l*, pg. 577

Cajno, John, Exec. V.P.--Brookstone Company, Inc., Nashua, NH; *U.S. Public*, pg. 259
Calabrese, Joseph J., Jr., Chief Fin. Officer, Exec. V.P. & Sec.--Harvey Electronics, Inc., Lyndhurst, NJ; *U.S. Public*, pg. 796
Calabro, Nicholas A., Exec. V.P.--Republic Bank for Savings, New York, NY; *U.S. Public*, pg. 1380
Calder, Iain, Exec. V.P.--American Media, Inc., Lake Worth, FL; *U.S. Public*, pg. 87
Caldu, R., Exec. V.P.-Sls.--Waterville TG Inc., Waterville, Canada; *Int'l*, pg. 1487
Caldwell, Kim A., Exec. V.P.-Global Tech. & New Bus. Devel.--Avery Dennison Corporation, Pasadena, CA; *U.S.* Public, pg. 152
Caldwell, Leonard A., Exec. V.P.--CoreStates Bank, N.A., Philadelphia, PA; *U.S. Public*, pg. 446
Caldwell, Richard C., Exec. V.P.-Investment Mngmt. & Trust--PNC Bank Corp., Pittsburgh, PA; *U.S. Public*, pg. 1242
Caldwell, Robert F., Chief Fin. Officer & Exec. V.P.--Southeastern Michigan Gas Enterprises, Inc., Port Huron, MI; *U.S. Public*, pg. 1489
Calfee, William R., Exec. V.P.-Commercial--Cleveland-Cliffs Inc, Cleveland, OH; *U.S. Public*, pg. 386
Calhoun, Don, Exec. V.P.--Aloe-Vera of America, Dallas, TX; *U.S. Private*, pg. 418
Calkins, Harlan D., Chm. Bd. & Chief Exec. Officer--Rochester Midland Corporation, Rochester, NY; *U.S. Private*, pg. 937
Callahan, James C., Exec. V.P.-IS--SSD&W Integrated Marketing Communications, Montville, NJ; *U.S. Private*, pg. 958
Callahan, Michael J., Chief Fin. Officer & Exec. V.P.--FMC Corporation, Chicago, IL; *U.S. Public*, pg. 604
Callahan, William Michael, Exec. V.P.-Trng., Tech. & Field Support--Group Maintenance America Corp., Houston, TX; *U.S. Public*, pg. 766
Callan, Cheryl, Exec. V.P. & Sr. Partner--N.W. Ayer & Partners New York, New York, NY; *U.S. Private*, pg. 104
Callan, Sherri, Exec. V.P., Dir.-West Coast Div.--Great Scott Advertising Co. Inc., New York, NY; *U.S. Private*, pg. 475
Callero, Christopher, Grp. Exec. V.P.-Natl. Consumer Assets--Bank of America NT&SA, San Francisco, CA; *U.S. Public*, pg. 180
Callicutt, Thomas L., Jr., Exec. V.P., Controller & Principal Acctg. Officer--First Commerce Corporation, New Orleans, LA; *U.S. Public*, pg. 629
Callieri, C., Exec. V.P.--Fiat Auto SpA, Turin, Italy; *Int'l*, pg. 480
Calvert, Horace A., Chief Oper. Officer & Exec. V.P.--Seitel, Inc., Houston, TX; *U.S. Public*, pg. 1454
Camacho, P. Bruce, Exec. V.P.-Investor Rels. & Dir.-Internal Devel.--American Bankers Life Assurance Co. of Florida, Miami, FL; *U.S. Public*, pg. 67
Camaelo, Bruce, Exec. V.P.--American Bankers Insurance Group, Inc., Miami, FL; *U.S. Public*, pg. 67
Camara, Paul, Exec. V.P.-Creative, Sls. & Mktg.--TMP Worldwide, Inc., New York, NY; *U.S. Private*, pg. 1064
Camarata, C.J., Exec. V.P.--Caltex Petroleum Corporation, Irving, TX; *U.S. Public*, pg. 348
Cambournac, Bruno, Exec. V.P.--Monnoyeur SCA, Saint Denis, France; *Int'l*, pg. 888
Cambra, Alan K., Exec. V.P.-Opers.--Omni Hotels, Irving, TX; *U.S. Private*, pg. 1065
Cambra, Kevin, Exec. V.P.-Store Opers.--Sterling Vision, Inc., East Meadow, NY; *U.S. Public*, pg. 1516
Camden, Carl, Exec. V.P.-Mktg., Sls. & Pub. Rels.--Kelly Services, Inc., Troy, MI; *U.S. Public*, pg. 949
Cameron, Doug, Exec. V.P.--Urban Retail Properties, Inc., Chicago, IL; *U.S. Public*, pg. 1700
Cameron, Patricia, Exec. V.P. & Strategic Plng. Dir.--Campbell Mithun Esty, Minneapolis, MN; *U.S. Private*, pg. 204
Cammaker, Sheldon I., Exec. V.P. & Gen. Counsel--EMCOR Group, Inc., Norwalk, CT; *U.S. Public*, pg. 571
Camp, Tom, V.P., Treas., Gen. Counsel & Sec.--The Apogee Companies, Inc., Lake Oswego, OR; *U.S. Private*, pg. 77
Campagnola, Gino, Exec. V.P. & Gen. Sls. Mgr.--Paramount Pictures Corporation, Los Angeles, CA; *U.S. Private*, pg. 776
Campanella, Joseph A., Exec. V.P.-Community Banking--Starbanc Corporation, Cincinnati, OH; *U.S. Public*, pg. 1510
Campbell, Billy, Exec. V.P.--CBS Entertainment, Los Angeles, CA; *U.S. Public*, pg. 274
Campbell, Bruce, Exec. V.P. & Chief Creative Officer--Ketchum Advertising/San Francisco, San Francisco, CA; *U.S. Private*, pg. 616
Campbell, C. Robert, Chief Fin. Officer & Exec. V.P.--Advantica Restaurant Group, Inc., Spartanburg, SC; *U.S.* Public, pg. 22
Campbell, Chuck, Exec. V.P.--Cosmetique, Inc., Vernon Hills, IL; *U.S. Private*, pg. 277
Campbell, Donald, Chief Fin. Officer & Exec. V.P.--The TJX Companies, Inc., Framingham, MA; *U.S. Public*, pg. 1556
Campbell, James I., Exec. V.P.-Opers.--Pittston Minerals Group, Inc., Lebanon, VA; *U.S. Public*, pg. 1305
Campbell, James R., Exec. V.P.--Norwest Corporation, Minneapolis, MN; *U.S. Public*, pg. 1201
Campbell, John, Exec. V.P. & Gen. Mgr.-MXP Bus. Grp.--Marcam Solutions, Inc., Newton, MA; *U.S. Public*, pg. 1042
Campbell, Larry, Exec. V.P.-Health Care Opers.--Staff Builders Inc., Lake Success, NY; *U.S. Public*, pg. 1501
Campbell, Michael E., Exec. V.P.--Olin Corporation, Norwalk, CT; *U.S. Public*, pg. 1218
Campbell, Patricia, Exec. V.P.--Today's Homeowner, New York, NY; *U.S. Public*, pg. 1617
Campbell, R. Bruce, Exec. V.P.--Scott & Stringfellow, Inc., Richmond, VA; *U.S. Public*, pg. 1445
Campbell, Richard, Exec. V.P. & Mktg.--Lally, McFarland & Pantello Inc., New York, NY; *Int'l*, pg. 601
Campbell, Robert E., Exec. V.P.--T. Bruce Sales, Inc., West Middlesex, PA; *U.S. Private*, pg. 175
Campbell, Terry, Chief Fin. Officer & Exec. V.P.--Farmland Industries, Inc., Kansas City, MO; *U.S. Private*, pg. 395
Campion, Jim, Exec. V.P.--Tyton Corporation, Milwaukee, WI; *Int'l*, pg. 208
Campos Parra, Javier, Sr. Exec. Dir.--Grupo Comercial Chedraui S.A. de C.V., Veracruz, Mexico; *Int'l*, pg. 573
Campos Parra, Javier, Sr. Exec. Dir.--Tiendas Chedraui S.A. de C.V., Veracruz, Mexico; *Int'l*, pg. 573
Camus, Daniel, Chief Fin. Officer & Exec. V.P.--Roussel UCLAF S.A., Romainville, France; *Int'l*, pg. 626
Cancela, Jose, Exec. V.P.--Telemundo Group, Inc., Hialeah, FL; *U.S. Public*, pg. 1570
Candioty, Linda, Exec. V.P.--Cheesecake Factory Incorporated, Calabasas Hills, CA; *U.S. Public*, pg. 343
Cangemi, Michael, Chief Fin. Officer & Exec. V.P.--Etienne Aigner, New York, NY; *U.S. Private*, pg. 384
Canizares, Lydia, Exec. V.P. & Dir. Client Services--Lally, McFarland & Pantello Inc., New York, NY; *Int'l*, pg. 601
Cannataro, James R., Exec. V.P.-Fin. & Admin.--Eddie Bauer, Inc., Redmond, WA; *U.S. Public*, pg. 1499
Cannon, Roger F., Exec. V.P.-Sls. & Mktg.--Lawson Products, Inc., Des Plaines, IL; *U.S. Public*, pg. 980
Canova, Antonio, Exec. V.P.--MagneTek, Inc., Nashville, TN; *U.S. Public*, pg. 1037
Cante, Christian, Exec. V.P.-Nuclear Engrng. & Fuel Activities--Framatome SA, Paris, France; *Int'l*, pg. 502
Canter, Peg, Exec. V.P. & Gen. Mgr.-Apparel Mart--AMC, Inc., Atlanta, GA; *U.S. Private*, pg. 6
Cantrell, Duane L., Exec. V.P.-Retail Opers.--Payless ShoeSource, Inc., Topeka, KS; *U.S. Public*, pg. 1268
Capano, Judy, Exec. V.P. & Client Services Dir.--Harrison & Star, New York, NY; *U.S. Private*, pg. 506
Caparros, Pedro, Exec. V.P.-Fin. Opers.--Credit Nationale, Paris, France; *Int'l*, pg. 344
Caporella, Joseph G., Exec. V.P. & Corp Sec.--National Beverage Corp., Plantation, FL; *U.S. Public*, pg. 1153
Capstaff, Diane M., Exec. V.P.-Corp. Sector--John Hancock Mutual Life Insurance Company, Boston, MA; *U.S. Private*, pg. 589
Carballo, Bernard A., Exec. V.P.-Sls., Mktg. & Product Line Mngmt.--Seagate Technology Inc., Scotts Valley, CA; *U.S. Public*, pg. 1449
Carbone, Anthony J., Exec. V.P.-Plastics, Hydrocarbons & Energy--The Dow Chemical Company, Midland, MI; *U.S. Public*, pg. 522
Carbone, Roberto, Exec. V.P.--Taca International Airlines, S. A., San Salvador, El Salvador; *Int'l*, pg. 1346
Card, Larry J., Exec. V.P.-Securities--Pacific Life Insurance Company, Newport Beach, CA; *U.S. Private*, pg. 831
Carden, Charles B., Chief Fin. Officer & Exec. V.P.--Paragon Health Network, Inc., Atlanta, GA; *U.S. Public*, pg. 1256
Carden, Joe, Exec. V.P.-Northern Region--AmSouth Bancorporation, Birmingham, AL; *U.S. Public*, pg. 105
Carendi, Jan R., First Exec. V.P.--Skandia Insurance Company Limited, Stockholm, Sweden; *Int'l*, pg. 1256
Carendi, Jan R., First Exec. V.P.--Assurance & Financial Services, Stockholm, Sweden; *Int'l*, pg. 1256
Carenza, John L., Exec. V.P.--Bell Sports Corp., San Jose, CA; *U.S. Public*, pg. 207
Carey, J. Paul, Exec. V.P.-Mktg & Servicing--SLM Holding Corp., Washington, DC; *U.S. Public*, pg. 1419
Cargotch, Paul, Chief Fin. Officer & Exec. V.P.--Russ Berrie and Company, Inc., Oakland, NJ; *U.S. Public*, pg. 222
Carl, John L., Chief Fin. Officer & Exec. V.P.--Amoco Corporation, Chicago, IL; *U.S. Public*, pg. 101
Carlen, John T., Exec. V.P.--Paychex, Inc., Rochester, NY; *U.S. Public*, pg. 1267
Carleton, James T., Exec. V.P. & Grp. Acct. Dir.--Hill, Holliday, Connors, Cosmopulos, Inc., Boston, MA; *U.S. Private*, pg. 529
Carley, Garry G., Exec. V.P. & Sec.--Standard Federal Bank, Troy, MI; *Int'l*, pg. 10
Carlier, Pierre, Exec. V.P. & Head-Generation & Transmission Div.--Electricite de France, Paris, France; *Int'l*, pg. 437
Carlin, Carlo, Exec. V.P.--Adriatica de Seguros C.A., Caracas, Venezuela; *Int'l*, pg. 61
Carlin, Ira, Exec. V.P. & Media Dir.-Worldwide--McCann-Erickson Worldwide, New York, NY; *U.S. Public*, pg. 909
Carlisle, John C., Chief Oper. Officer & Exec. V.P.--Nabi, Boca Raton, FL; *U.S. Public*, pg. 1148
Carlsen, Steven, Exec. V.P.--Kurt Manufacturing Co. Inc., Fridley, MN; *U.S. Private*, pg. 637
Carlson, James G., Exec. V.P.-Field Opers.--United HealthCare Corporation, Minnetonka, MN; *U.S. Public*, pg. 1677
Carlson, Jane, Exec. V.P. & Mng. Partner-Acct.--Wells BDDP, Inc., New York, NY; *Int'l*, pg. 117
Carlson, Kenneth J., Exec. V.P. & Gen. Mgr.--Jarvis (East), Palmer, MA; *U.S. Public*, pg. 1506
Carlson, Larry P., Exec. V.P.-Satellite Svcs.--Home Box Office, Inc., New York, NY; *U.S. Public*, pg. 1612
Carlson, LeRoy, Chief Fin. Officer, Chief Acctg. Officer, Exec. V.P. & Sec.--BRE Properties, Inc., San Francisco, CA; *U.S. Public*, pg. 163
Carlson, Robert E., Exec. V.P.--Northwestern Mutual Life Insurance Co., Milwaukee, WI; *U.S. Private*, pg. 807
Carluccio, James S., Exec. V.P.--Technology Solutions Company (TSC), Chicago, IL; *U.S. Public*, pg. 1564
Carman, Dhar, Chief Fin. Officer, Exec. V.P. & Sec.--Statex Petroleum, Inc., Dallas, TX; *U.S. Public*, pg. 1245
Carmichael, Ian B., Exec. V.P.-Corp Tech.--Crown Cork & Seal Company, Inc., Philadelphia, PA; *U.S. Public*, pg. 462
Carmichael, Ian B., Exec. V.P.--Crown Cork & Seal Company, Inc.-Corporate Technologies, Wantage, United Kingdom; *U.S. Public*, pg. 464
Carne, Ron, Exec. V.P.--American Systems Technologies, Verona, WI; *U.S. Public*, pg. 2
Carney, John D., Exec. V.P.--Eastern Utilities Associates, Boston, MA; *U.S. Public*, pg. 549
Carney, Lloyd A., Exec. V.P. & Gen. Mgr.-Enterprise Bus. Grp.--Bay Networks, Inc., Santa Clara, CA; *U.S. Public*, pg. 196
Carolan, Douglas, Chief Oper. Officer & Exec. V.P.--Associated Wholesale Grocers, Inc., Kansas City, KS; *U.S. Private*, pg. 93
Caropino, Stephen, Exec. V.P.--Pacifica Services, Inc., Pasadena, CA; *U.S. Private*, pg. 832
Carothers, Rick J., Exec. V.P.--CTX Mortgage Co., Inc., Dallas, TX; *U.S. Public*, pg. 323
Carothers, Robert, Exec. V.P.--Union Electric Steel Corp., Carnegie, PA; *U.S. Public*, pg. 103
Carpenter, Charles J., Chief Procurement Officer & Exec. V.P.--Bergen Brunswig Corporation, Orange, CA; *U.S. Public*, pg. 213
Carpenter, Karen L., Exec. V.P. & Sec.--Curtis-Toledo, Inc., Saint Louis, MO; *U.S. Private*, pg. 298
Carpenter, Mary Anne, Exec. V.P.-Clinical Opers. & Claims Pricing--First Health Group Corp., Downers Grove, IL; *U.S. Public*, pg. 635
Carpenter, Michael A., Vice Chm. & Exec. V.P.-Strategic Plng.--Travelers Group, New York, NY; *U.S. Public*, pg. 1632
Carpenter, Robert W., Jr., Exec. V.P. & Sr. Credit Officer--First National Bank of Ohio, Akron, OH; *U.S. Public*, pg. 646
Carpou, Nick, Exec. V.P. & Natl. Sls. Mgr.-Distribution--Universal Pictures, Universal City, CA; *Int'l*, pg. 1216
Carr, Jeremiah T., Exec. V.P.--Frontier Corporation, Rochester, NY; *U.S. Public*, pg. 683
Carr, John J., Exec. V.P.-Pumps Power Transmission & Instrumentation--IMO Industries Inc., Lawrenceville, NJ; *U.S. Public*, pg. 856
Carr, Robert O., Chm. Bd. & Pres.--Carr Real Estate Services, Washington, DC; *U.S. Public*, pg. 309
Carrington, H.G., Jr., Chief Fin. Officer & Exec. V.P.--Spaghetti Warehouse, Inc., Garland, TX; *U.S. Public*, pg. 1495
Carrithers, Pat, Exec. V.P.-Mktg.--Bollinger Industries Inc., Grand Prairie, TX; *U.S. Public*, pg. 243
Carroll, Ed, Exec. V.P.-Adv.--Carson Pirie Scott & Company, Chicago, IL; *U.S. Public*, pg. 309
Carroll, L. Vane, Exec. V.P.--Blazer Financial Services, Cordova, TN; *U.S. Public*, pg. 1741
Carroll, Loren, Exec. V.P.--Smith International, Inc., Houston, TX; *U.S. Public*, pg. 1478
Carroll, Michael J., Exec. V.P.--Steel Technologies Inc., Louisville, KY; *U.S. Public*, pg. 1513
Carroll, Thomas S., Exec. V.P.-Mktg.--Viking Yacht Co., New Gretna, NJ; *U.S. Private*, pg. 1140
Carroll, Vane, L., Exec. V.P.--Consumer Finance Group, Tampa, FL; *U.S. Public*, pg. 1741
Carrubba, F.P., Exec. V.P.--Philips Electronics N.V., Eindhoven, Netherlands; *Int'l*, pg. 1051
Carrubba, Frank P., Exec. V.P.--Philips International B.V., Eindhoven, Netherlands; *Int'l*, pg. 1051
Carson, Randy, Exec. V.P.--Reliance Electric Company, Cleveland, OH; *U.S. Public*, pg. 1398
Carson, Randy W., Exec. V.P.-Electrical Groups--Reliance Electric, Cleveland, OH; *U.S. Public*, pg. 1397
Carson, Robin, Exec. V.P. & Gen. Mgr.--Sea World of Texas, San Antonio, TX; *U.S. Public*, pg. 114
Carter, Paul R., Exec. V.P. & Pres.-Wal-Mart Realty--Wal-Mart Stores, Inc., Bentonville, AR; *U.S. Public*, pg. 1732
Carter, Reginald, Exec. V.P.--Americold Compressor Co., Cullman, AL; *Int'l*, pg. 439
Carter, Wanda, Exec. V.P.--CACI International Inc, Arlington, VA; *U.S. Public*, pg. 272
Carter, Wayne C., III, Exec. V.P.--National Programs Division, Tampa, FL; *U.S. Public*, pg. 1312
Carter, William H., Chief Fin. Officer & Exec. V.P.--Borden, Inc., Columbus, OH; *U.S. Private*, pg. 157
Carty, Brian, Mng. Dir.-Fin. Svcs. & Exec. V.P.-New Bus./ Human Resources--Hill, Holliday, Connors, Cosmopulos, Inc., Boston, MA; *U.S. Private*, pg. 529
Carus, Paul, Exec. V.P.--Carus Corporation, Peru, IL; *U.S. Private*, pg. 217
Caruso, Bob, Exec. V.P. & Gen. Mgr.--Sesame Place, Langhorne, PA; *U.S. Public*, pg. 114
Caruso, Edward V., Exec. V.P.--Midlantic Bank, N.A., Philadelphia, PA; *U.S. Public*, pg. 1242
Caruso, Frank, Chief Oper. Officer & Exec. V.P.--Willis Corroon Corp. of Nashville, Nashville, TN; *Int'l*, pg. 1506
Casa, Joann, Exec. V.P. & Gen. Mgr.--Melrose, Chatsworth, CA; *U.S. Public*, pg. 948
Casabona, George, Chief Fin. Officer & Exec. V.P.--Dugan Valva Contess Inc., Morristown, NJ; *U.S. Private*, pg. 345
Casabona, Joseph E., Exec. V.P.--Eastern American Energy Corporation, Charleston, WV; *U.S. Private*, pg. 357
Casciano, Frank, Exec. V.P. & Gen. Counsel--MBL Life Assurance Corporation, Newark, NJ; *U.S. Private*, pg. 685
Cascio, Bill, Exec. V.P.-Natl. Sls. & Mktg.--Fetzer Vineyards California Wines, Hopland, CA; *U.S. Public*, pg. 261
Cascisa, Ron P., Exec. V.P.--Sysco Food Services of Portland, Inc., Wilsonville, OR; *U.S. Public*, pg. 1552
Case, Gary L., Exec. V.P.--Associated Administrators, Inc., Portland, OR; *U.S. Private*, pg. 918
Case, Roger, Exec. V.P.--Krause Publications, Inc., Iola, WI; *U.S. Private*, pg. 635
Casey, Daniel P., Chief Fin. Officer & Exec. V.P.--Gaylord Container Corporation, Deerfield, IL; *U.S. Public*, pg. 704
Casey, John, Chief Fin. Officer & Exec. V.P.--BWAY Corp., Atlanta, GA; *U.S. Public*, pg. 164
Casey, John, Exec. V.P. & Chief Fin. Officer--Brierley & Partners, Dallas, TX; *U.S. Private*, pg. 168
Casey, Robert E. Jr., Exec. V.P.--Robinhood Homes, Inc., Solana Beach, CA; *U.S. Private*, pg. 936
Cash, Thomas A., Exec. V.P. & Gen. Mgr.-Intl. Oper. & Re-engineering--American Express Travel Related Services Co., Inc., New York, NY; *U.S. Public*, pg. 73
Cashin, John R., Exec. V.P. & Dir.-Mktg.--Willis Faber North America, Inc.-New York, New York, NY; *Int'l*, pg. 1503

Cashman, Edmund J., Jr., Sr. Exec. V.P.--Legg Mason, Inc., Baltimore, MD; *U.S. Public*, pg. 984

Casio, Rick, Exec. V.P. & Creative Dir.--McKinney & McKinney Advertising, Redondo Beach, CA; *U.S. Private, pg. 723*

Casper, Wayne, Exec. V.P.-Consumer Prods. Div.--Sargento Foods Inc., Plymouth, WI; *U.S. Private*, pg. 966

Cassar, Claude, Chief Fin. Officer & Sr. Exec. V.P.--Dentsu Young & Rubicam brand communications (Network Center), Singapore, Singapore; *U.S. Private*, pg. 325

Cassell, Ralph H., Exec. V.P.-Northern Reg.--Compass Bank, Birmingham, AL; *U.S. Public*, pg. 418

Cassels, William A., Exec. V.P.--Washington Federal Savings, Seattle, WA; *U.S. Public*, pg. 1740

Cassiani, S.M., Exec. V.P.--Exxon Exploration Company, Houston, TX; *U.S. Public*, pg. 601

Cassidy, David B., Exec. V.P.--American Vanguard Corporation, Newport Beach, CA; *U.S. Public*, pg. 94

Castaing, Francois J., Exec. V.P.-Intl. Opers. & Gen. Mgr.-Power Train Opers.--Chrysler Corporation, Auburn Hills, MI; *U.S. Public*, pg. 352

Castaneda, Jose Maria, Exec. V.P.--Banco Santander, Madrid, Spain; *Int'l*, pg. 143

Castellana, Joseph, Vice Chm. & Exec. V.P.-Retail Opers.--Western Beef, Inc., Ridgewood, NY; *U.S. Public*, pg. 1758

Castellani, John J., Exec. V.P.--Tenneco Inc., Greenwich, CT; *U.S. Public*, pg. 1577

Castle, John, Jr., Exec. V.P.--Electronic Data Systems Corporation, Plano, TX; *U.S. Public*, pg. 569

Castleman, Christopher, Exec. Dir.-Strategic Projects--Standard Chartered Bank PLC, London, United Kingdom; *Int'l*, pg. 1294

Castorina, Orlando, V.P.-Opers.--Monroe Forgings Inc., Rochester, NY; *Int'l*, pg. 488

Cataldo, Donna, Exec. V.P. & Media Dir.--Gotham Incorporated, New York, NY; *U.S. Private*, pg. 677

Catenacci, Joseph E., Exec. V.P.--John Carlo Inc., Clinton Township, MI; *U.S. Private*, pg. 211

Cathcart, Richard J., Exec. V.P.--Pentair, Inc., Saint Paul, MN; *U.S. Public*, pg. 1273

Cathy, Dan T., Pres.-Intl. & Exec. V.P.--Chick-fil-A, Inc., Atlanta, GA; *U.S. Private*, pg. 236

Catlow, Walter S., Pres.-Intl. & Exec. V.P.--Ameritech Corporation, Chicago, IL; *U.S. Public*, pg. 97

Catmull, Edwin, Chief Tech. Officer & Exec. V.P.--Pixar Animation Studios, Richmond, CA; *U.S. Public*, pg. 1307

Catron, William G., Chief Admin. Officer, Exec. V.P. & Gen. Counsel--Galoob Toys, Inc., South San Francisco, CA; *U.S. Public*, pg. 698

Catt, Randall L., Exec. V.P.-Human Resources--Kimball International, Inc., Jasper, IN; *U.S. Public*, pg. 956

Cattani, Maryellen, Exec. V.P., Gen. Counsel & Sec.--APL Limited, Oakland, CA; *Int'l*, pg. 912

Cau, Antoine, Exec V.P.-Intl. Opers.--The Hertz Corporation, Park Ridge, NJ; *U.S. Public*, pg. 664

Caughran, Carl, Pres.-Nalleys Fine Foods Div. & Exec. V.P.--Curtice Burns Foods, Rochester, NY; *U.S. Private*, pg. 887

Caulfield, Gary L., Exec. V.P.-Information Mngmt. Grp.--First Hawaiian Bank, Honolulu, HI; *U.S. Public*, pg. 634

Caulo, Ralph D., Exec. V.P. & Pres.-Educational Publishing--Simon & Schuster, New York, NY; *U.S. Private*, pg. 777

Cavalieros, Pierre, Exec. V.P.--Gaz de France, Paris, France; *Int'l*, pg. 541

Cavitt, Glen, Exec. V.P.--Eddins-Walcher Company, Midland, TX; *U.S. Private*, pg. 362

Cavoores, John P., Exec. V.P.--Chubb & Son, Inc., Warren, NJ; *U.S. Public*, pg. 355

Cawthon, A. Alexander, Exec. V.P. & Dir.-H.R.--Thiele Kaolin Co., Sandersville, GA; *U.S. Private*, pg. 1081

Cayre, Jack J., Exec. V.P.--GT Interactive Software Corp., New York, NY; *U.S. Public*, pg. 696

Cayre, Ken, Exec. V.P.--GoodTimes Entertainment Co., New York, NY; *U.S. Private*, pg. 464

Celi, M. Joseph, Exec. V.P.-Remediation Services--GZA GeoEnvironmental Technologies, Inc., Newton, MA; *U.S.* Public, pg. 697

Celia, Joe, Exec. V.P.--Grey Advertising Inc., New York, NY; *U.S. Public*, pg. 764

Cella, John J., Exec. V.P.-Intl. Div.--Airborne Freight Corporation, Seattle, WA; *U.S. Public*, pg. 32

Celusniak, Mark J., Dr., Exec. V.P.-Engine Rings--King Fifth Wheel Co., Mountain Top, PA; *Int'l*, pg. 1337

Cerza, James F., Jr., Exec. V.P. & Opers.--Heilig-Meyers Company, Richmond, VA; *U.S. Public*, pg. 804

Cesan, Raul E., Exec. V.P.--Schering-Plough Corporation, Madison, NJ; *U.S. Public*, pg. 1438

Cevera, Nicholas J., Jr., Exec. V.P.--Swisher International Group, Inc., Darien, CT; *U.S. Public*, pg. 1543

Chadburn, Carl T., Exec. V.P.-H.R.--Phoenix Home Life Mutual Insurance Company, Hartford, CT; *U.S. Private*, pg. 863

Chafey, David H. Jr., Sr. Exec. V.P.-Investments & Trust--Banco Popular de Puerto Rico, San Juan, PR; *U.S. Public*, pg. 175

Chafey, David H., Jr., Sr. Exec. V.P.--BanPonce Corporation, Hato Rey, PR; *U.S. Public*, pg. 176

Chai, Jay W., Exec. V.P.--Itochu Corporation, Tokyo, Japan; *Int'l*, pg. 694

Chaiken, Roslyn, Exec. V.P.--Almo Corp., Philadelphia, PA; *U.S. Private*, pg. 44

Chait, Jon F., Chief Fin. Officer, Exec. V.P. & Sec.--Manpower Inc., Milwaukee, WI; *U.S. Public*, pg. 1042

Chaiyabhat, Sanchai, Exec. V.P.--Siam City Bank Public Company Limited, Bangkok, Thailand; *Int'l*, pg. 1239

Chalden, Jack, Exec. V.P.-Atlanta Giftmart--AMC, Inc., Atlanta, GA; *U.S. Private*, pg. 6

Chalk, W. Kendall, Sr. Exec. V.P.--BB&T Corporation, Winston Salem, NC; *U.S. Public*, pg. 159

Chalkin, Alan, Exec. V.P.--Kay-Bee Toy & Hobby Shops, Inc., Pittsfield, MA; *U.S. Public*, pg. 437

Chall, Ken, Exec. V.P.-Retail Lending--Branch Banking & Trust, Winston Salem, NC; *U.S. Public*, pg. 160

Chamberlain, Garry G., Exec. V.P.-Opers.--MEG, Cambridge City, IN; *U.S. Private*, pg. 686

Chamberlain, J.J., Exec. V.P.--Stowe-Pharr Mills, Inc., Mc Adenville, NC; *U.S. Private*, pg. 1045

Chamberlain, Lisa, Exec. V.P.-Fin. & Admin.--Motown Record Company, J.P., New York, NY; *Int'l*, pg. 1052

Chamberland, Claude, Exec. V.P.-Smelting and Power--Alcan Aluminium Limited, Montreal, Canada; *Int'l*, pg. 50

Chamberland, Claude, Exec. V.P.--Alcan Aluminum Corporation, Cleveland, OH; *Int'l*, pg. 50

Chambrello, Michael R., Exec. V.P. & Pres.-GTECH Lottery--GTECH Corporation, West Greenwich, RI; *U.S. Public*, pg. 767

Chamoto, Michiaki, Exec. Dir.--Advantest Corporation, Tokyo, Japan; *Int'l*, pg. 25

Champeaux, Jacques, Exec. Dir.-Bus. Services--France Telecom, Paris, France; *Int'l*, pg. 503

Champion, Michael J., Dr., Exec. V.P.-Opers.--Riverdale Chemical Co., Glenwood, IL; *U.S. Private*, pg. 934

Chan, Ricky, Exec. V.P.-Far East Opers. & Sr. V.P.-Prod. Devel.--Russ Berrie and Company, Inc., Oakland, NJ; *U.S. Public*, pg. 222

Chan, Thomas, Exec. Dir.-Project Plng.--Sun Hung Kai Properties Ltd., Wan Chai, Hong Kong; *Int'l*, pg. 1318

Chanani, Madhu S., Exec. V.P., Controller & Asst. Sec.--Western Waste Industries, Torrance, CA; *U.S. Public*, pg. 1686

Chandler, Steven L., Sr. V.P.--L.N. Curtis & Sons, Oakland, CA; *U.S. Private*, pg. 297

Chaney, Scott, Exec. V.P.--Palm Harbor Homes, Inc., Dallas, TX; *U.S. Public*, pg. 1254

Chang Bloch, Julia, Grp. Exec. V.P.-Corp. Communications & Govt. Affairs--BankAmerica Corporation, San Francisco, CA; *U.S. Public*, pg. 179

Chang Park, Kyu, Exec. V.P.-Advanced Tech.--LG Group, Seoul, Korea; *Int'l*, pg. 778

Chang, Joshua, Exec. V.P.--American Machine & Tool Company, Inc., Royersford, PA; *U.S. Private*, pg. 58

Chang, Karen W., Exec. V.P.-Retail Branch Network--The Charles Schwab Corporation, San Francisco, CA; *U.S. Public*, pg. 1442

Chantiam, Clement F., Exec. V.P.-Mfg.--Stuart Entertainment Inc., Council Bluffs, IA; *U.S. Public*, pg. 1526

Chantland, Dennis A., Exec. V.P. & Sec.--Williams-Sonoma, Inc., San Francisco, CA; *U.S. Public*, pg. 1770

Chapko, Stephen J., Chief Fin. Officer, Exec. V.P., Treas. & Sec.--Kent Electronics Corp., Houston, TX; *U.S. Public*, pg. 951

Chapman, Chuck, Chief Info. Officer & Exec. V.P.--AON Corporation, Chicago, IL; *U.S. Public*, pg. 117

Chapman, David, Exec. V.P. & Mng. Dir.--Thomas G. Ferguson Associates, Inc., Parsippany, NJ; *Int'l*, pg. 1483

Chapman, Donald R., Chief Fin. Officer & Exec. V.P.--Crawford & Company, Atlanta, GA; *U.S. Public*, pg. 458

Chapman, R. Booth, Exec. V.P.-Independent Loan Review--First American Corporation, Nashville, TN; *U.S. Public*, pg. 624

Chappell, Anthony G., Exec. V.P.--Republic National Bank of New York, New York, NY; *U.S. Public*, pg. 1380

Chappell, Anthony G., Exec. V.P.--Republic National Bank of New York (U.K.), London, United Kingdom; *U.S. Public*, pg. 1381

Chard, R. D., Exec. V.P., Administrative Bank CIBC--Canadian Imperial Bank of Commerce, Toronto, Canada; *Int'l*, pg. 256

Charlebois, Brian J., Chief Oper. Officer & Exec. V.P.--First International Bancorp, Inc., Hartford, CT; *U.S. Public*, pg. 635

Charles, Allan, Exec. V.P. & Corp. Creative Dir.--Trahan, Burden & Charles, Inc., Baltimore, MD; *U.S. Private*, pg. 1095

Charlton, John S.N., Exec. Dir.-Consumer Prods.--Pentland Group PLC, London, United Kingdom; *Int'l*, pg. 1035

Charpak, Zvi, Exec. V.P.-Information Systems & Communications--The Israel Electric Corporation Ltd., Haifa, Israel; *Int'l*, pg. 690

Chartrand, J.C., Exec. V.P.--Equifax Inc., Atlanta, GA; *U.S. Public*, pg. 588

Chase, Edmund, Exec. V.P.-Strategic Devel.--CPI Corp., Saint Louis, MO; *U.S. Public*, pg. 283

Chase, William, Exec. V.P.-Sls. & Mktg.--American Business Information, Inc., Omaha, NE; *U.S. Public*, pg. 69

Chasse, Bill, Exec. V.P.--American Business Advertising, Omaha, NE; *U.S. Private*, pg. 51

Chatham, Don, Assoc. Exec. Dir.-Publishing--American Library Association, Chicago, IL; *U.S. Private*, pg. 58

Chauvin, Jacques, Exec. V.P. & Head-Fin.--Electricite de France, Paris, France; *Int'l*, pg. 437

Chayavadhanangkun, Chotivid, Exec. V.P. & Gen. Mgr.--Bangkok Bank Public Company Limited, Bangkok, Thailand; *Int'l*, pg. 146

Chazen, Stephen I., Exec. V.P.-Corp. Devel.--Occidental Petroleum Corporation, Los Angeles, CA; *U.S. Public*, pg. 1210

Chbosky, Frederick G., Chief Fin. Officer & Exec. V.P.--WHX Corporation, New York, NY; *U.S. Public*, pg. 1726

Che, Byung Yun, Exec. V.P. & Dir.--Cho Hung Bank, Seoul, Korea; *Int'l*, pg. 287

Chemerow, David I., Chief Fin. Officer, Exec. V.P.-Fin. & Opers.--Lifestyle Brands, Ltd., Chicago, IL; *U.S. Public*, pg. 1310

Chen, Chi-Chu, Exec. V.P.--The International Commercial Bank of China, Taipei, Taiwan; *Int'l*, pg. 683

Chen, Lily C., Dr., Chief Fin. Officer, Exec. V.P. & Treas.--General Sciences Corp., Laurel, MD; *U.S. Private*, pg. 976

Chen, Steve, Exec. V.P. & Chief Tech. Officer--Sequent Computer Systems, Inc., Beaverton, OR; *U.S. Public*, pg. 1459

Chen, Ted, Exec. V.P.-Mktg. & Corp. Devel.--Storage Dimensions, Inc., Milpitas, CA; *U.S. Public*, pg. 1522

Chen, Y.C., Exec. V.P.--China Steel Corporation, Kao-hsiung, Taiwan; *Int'l*, pg. 285

Chenevich, William L., Exec. V.P.--Visa U.S.A. Inc., San Francisco, CA; *U.S. Private*, pg. 1141

Chenevier, Francois, Exec. V.P.--Groupe GTM, Nanterre, France; *Int'l*, pg. 823

Cheng, Laurence W., Exec. V.P.--Zurich Insurance Company, Zurich, Switzerland; *Int'l*, pg. 1529

Cheong, Chong Kie, Exec. V.P.-Correspondent Banking & Intl.--DBS Bank Ltd., Singapore, Singapore; *Int'l*, pg. 350

Cherry, Dean E., Exec. V.P.-Investor Rels. & Corp. Communications--World Color Press, Inc., Greenwich, CT; *U.S. Public*, pg. 1778

Chesley, Faris F., Exec. V.P.--ABN AMRO Chicago Corp., Chicago, IL; *Int'l*, pg. 10

Chesser, Leicle E., Chief Fin. Officer & Exec. V.P.--EMCOR Group, Inc., Norwalk, CT; *U.S. Public*, pg. 571

Chessin, Daniel J., Exec. V.P. & Sec.--Hahn Automotive Warehouse, Inc., Rochester, NY; *U.S. Public*, pg. 774

Chessin, Daniel J., Exec. V.P.--Professional Auto Warehouse, Rochester, NY; *U.S. Public*, pg. 774

Chessman, Frank, Exec. V.P.-Retail--Simon Marketing, Inc., Los Angeles, CA; *U.S. Private*, pg. 1001

Cheung, Caroline, Exec. V.P.--F. J. Benjamin Holdings Ltd., Singapore, Singapore; *Int'l*, pg. 187

Chevallier, Alain, Chm. Bd., Stepan Europe--Stepan Europe, Voreppe, France; *U.S. Public*, pg. 1514

Chiapparone, Paul J., Exec. V.P.--Electronic Data Systems Corporation, Plano, TX; *U.S. Public*, pg. 569

Chicharro, Pedro, Exec. V.P.-Plng. & Res.--Banco Santander, Madrid, Spain; *Int'l*, pg. 143

Chihara, Kaoru, Sr. Mng. Dir.--Asahi Breweries Ltd., Tokyo, Japan; *Int'l*, pg. 83

Childers, Bruce S., Exec. V.P.-Mktg. Info. Services--Meldrum & Fewsmith Communications Inc., Cleveland, OH; *U.S. Private*, pg. 730

Childers, Harvey, Exec. V.P.--Garvey Industries, Inc., Wichita, KS; *U.S. Private*, pg. 440

Childs, Julian, Chief Oper. Officer & Exec. V.P.--Dow Jones Markets, Jersey City, NJ; *U.S. Public*, pg. 525

Chinalai, Charden, Exec. V.P.--Bangkok Bank Public Company Limited, Bangkok, Thailand; *Int'l*, pg. 146

Chiocca, Enrico, Sr. Exec. V.P.-Personnel & Org. Div.--Istituto Bancario San Paolo Di Torino S.p.A., Turin, Italy; *Int'l*, pg. 691

Chiocchi, Roger, Exec. V.P. & Gen. Mgr.--The Lord Group, New York, NY; *U.S. Private*, pg. 325

Chipman, Stephen D., Exec. V.P.-Private Client Grp.--Compass Bank Houston, Houston, TX; *U.S. Public*, pg. 419

Chittenden, Jeffrey G.J., Chief Information Officer & Exec. V.P.--First USA, Inc., Dallas, TX; *U.S. Public*, pg. 174

Chiumenti, Paolo, Exec. V.P.-Acctg.--Istituto Bancario San Paolo Di Torino S.p.A., Turin, Italy; *Int'l*, pg. 691

Chiyar, Ramon, Exec. V.P.--Banacol Marketing Corp., Coral Gables, FL; *U.S. Private*, pg. 113

Cho, Kwan-Haeng, Exec. V.P.--Pohang Iron & Steel Co., Ltd., Kyongbuk, Korea; *Int'l*, pg. 1061

Cho, Nam Yong, Exec. V.P. & Dir.--Cho Hung Bank, Seoul, Korea; *Int'l*, pg. 287

Cho, Soo Ho, Exec. V.P.-Sls., Mktg. & Traffic--Korean Airlines Co., Ltd., Seoul, Korea; *Int'l*, pg. 758

Choi, Chong Kun, Exec. V.P. & Dir.--Cho Hung Bank, Seoul, Korea; *Int'l*, pg. 287

Chokey, James A., Exec. V.P.-Law & Govt. Affairs--Harnischfeger Industries, Inc., Saint Francis, WI; *U.S. Public*, pg. 788

Chong, Grace D., Exec. V.P.-Creative Dir. & New Bus. Dir.--Dentsu Young & Rubicam-Alcantara Inc. (Manila), Manila, Philippines; *U.S. Private*, pg. 325

Chotipruk, Santa, Exec. V.P.--The Industrial Finance Corporation of Thailand, Bangkok, Thailand; *Int'l*, pg. 677

Chouraqui, Gerard, Exec. V.P.-Consumer Products--L'Oreal S.A., Clichy, France; *Int'l*, pg. 818

Chow, Joseph W., Exec. V.P.--State Street Corporation, Boston, MA; *U.S. Public*, pg. 1513

Chow, R.H., Exec. V.P.--Permacel, New Brunswick, NJ; *Int'l, pg. 950*

Chow, Winston K.H., Exec. V.P.--First Hawaiian Creditcorp, Inc., Honolulu, HI; *U.S. Public*, pg. 635

Chrenc, Robert J., Chief Fin. Officer & Exec. V.P.--A.C. Nielsen, Stamford, CT; *U.S. Public*, pg. 1183

Christenberry, Boyd E., Exec. V.P.-Mktg.--Alfa Life Insurance Corp., Montgomery, AL; *U.S. Public*, pg. 40

Christensen, Val John, Exec. V.P.--Franklin Covey, Salt Lake City, UT; *U.S. Public*, pg. 679

Christiansen, Winston B., Exec. V.P.--McDonald's Corporation, Oak Brook, IL; *U.S. Public*, pg. 1068

Christie, Doris, Exec. V.P.--J.I. Kislak Inc., Hialeah, FL; *U.S. Private*, pg. 624

Christofferson, Hans, Exec. V.P.-Reg. Bank, Stockholm--Svenska Handelsbanken, Stockholm, Sweden; *Int'l*, pg. 1327

Christopher, Dave, Exec. V.P.--RadioShack, Fort Worth, TX; *U.S. Public*, pg. 1560

Christopher, Lynne, Exec. V.P. & Corp. Media Dir.--HMS Partners, Columbus, OH; *U.S. Private*, pg. 491

Christopher, M., Exec. V.P.--Lantzsch-Andreas Enterprises, Inc., Vienna, VA; *U.S. Private*, pg. 650

Christopher, Philip, Exec. V.P.--Audiovox Corporation, Hauppauge, NY; *U.S. Public*, pg. 147

Christopherson, Robert L., Exec. V.P.--American Bank Note Co., Horsham, PA; *U.S. Public*, pg. 68

Chrominska, Sylvia D., Exec. V.P.-H.R.--The Bank of Nova Scotia, Toronto, Canada; *Int'l*, pg. 155

Chu, Charles C.J., Exec. V.P.--OPICOIL Houston, Inc., Houston, TX; *Int'l*, pg. 286

Chu, David, Exec. V.P. & Sec.--Nautica Enterprises, Inc., New York, NY; *U.S. Public*, pg. 1167

Chun, Kwong, Exec. Dir.-Building Mngmt.--Sun Hung Kai Properties Ltd., Wan Chai, Hong Kong; *Int'l*, pg. 1318

Chun, Thomas K., Exec. V.P.--Mutual Welding Co., Ltd, Honolulu, HI; *U.S. Private*, pg. 770

Chung, Ray, Chief Fin. Officer, Exec. V.P. & Treas.--Dartford Partnership, San Francisco, CA; *U.S. Private*, pg. 312
Church, Jeffrey W., Chief Fin. Officer & Exec. V.P.--Biospherics Incorporated, Beltsville, MD; *U.S. Public*, pg. 232
Church, Kenneth E., Exec. V.P. & Pres.-Upholstery Group--Ladd Furniture, Inc., Greensboro, NC; *U.S. Public*, pg. 974
Churinske, Paul J., Exec. V.P.--Integra Technologies Corp., Waltham, MA; *U.S. Private*, pg. 565
Cialone, Mike, Exec. V.P.--Merchants National Bank, Fort Smith, AR; *U.S. Public*, pg. 501
Ciccone, Marshall, Exec. V.P.-Fin.--Will & Baumer Incorporated, Liverpool, NY; *U.S. Private*, pg. 1176
Ciepcielinski, Stanley, Chief Fin. Officer, Exec. V.P. & Sec.--Glenayre Technologies, Inc., Charlotte, NC; *U.S. Public*, pg. 746
Cierpiszewski, Lawrence, Exec. V.P.--Washington Federal Savings, Seattle, WA; *U.S. Public*, pg. 1740
Cieslak, Terrance, Chief Tech. Officer & Exec. V.P.--May & Speh, Inc., Downers Grove, IL; *U.S. Public*, pg. 1063
Cihiy, Kenneth, Exec. V.P.-Claim--USF&G Corporation, Baltimore, MD; *U.S. Public*, pg. 1659
Cilfone, Nicholas J., Exec. V.P.--Second National Bank of Saginaw, Saginaw, MI; *U.S. Public*, pg. 379
Cimini, Ricardo, Exec. V.P.--Uniao de Bancos Brasileiros S.A. (Unibanco), Sao Paulo, Brazil; *Int'l*, pg. 1431
Ciotti, John, Chief Fin. Officer & Exec. V.P.--Eisner & Associates, Inc., Baltimore, MD; *U.S. Private*, pg. 366
Ciraulo, Jerry, Chief Oper. Officer & Exec. V.P.--Carillon Importers, Ltd., Fort Lee, NJ; *Int'l*, pg. 409
Cirello, John, Exec. V.P. & Pres. & Chief Exec. Officer-Florida Water Services--Minnesota Power, Duluth, MN; *U.S. Public*, pg. 1116
Civalleri, Roberto, Sr. Exec. V.P.-Corp. Div.--Istituto Bancario San Paolo Di Torino S.p.A., Turin, Italy; *Int'l*, pg. 691
Civello, Nelson D., Sr. Exec. V.P.-Fixed Income Capital Markets--Dain Rauscher Corporation, Minneapolis, MN; *U.S. Public*, pg. 476
Civello, Nelson D., Exec. V.P.--Dain Rauscher Incorporated, Minneapolis, MN; *U.S. Public*, pg. 476
Cizain, Jack, Exec. V.P. & Head-Intl. Div.--Electricite de France, Paris, France; *Int'l*, pg. 437
Cladianos, Pete, III, Exec. V.P. & Sec.--The Sands Regent, Reno, NV; *U.S. Public*, pg. 1431
Clancy, John P., Exec. V.P.--Douglas Elliman, New York, NY; *U.S. Private*, pg. 341
Clapps, John, Exec. V.P. & Co-Creative Dir.--Biederman, Kelly & Shaffer, Inc., New York, NY; *U.S. Private*, pg. 142
Claramunt, Dennis D., V.P. & Grp. Exec.--Danaher Corporation, Washington, DC; *U.S. Public*, pg. 480
Clark, A. Bayard, Chief Fin. Officer, Exec. V.P. & Treas.--Commerce Bancshares, Inc., Kansas City, MO; *U.S. Public*, pg. 409
Clark, Edwin R., Exec. V.P.--Speedway Motorsports, Inc., Concord, NC; *U.S. Public*, pg. 1498
Clark, Gerald, Chief Investment Officer & Sr. Exec. V.P.--Metropolitan Life Insurance Co., New York, NY; *U.S. Private*, pg. 737
Clark, James N., Exec. V.P. & Sec.--The Western and Southern Life Insurance Company, Cincinnati, OH; *U.S. Private*, pg. 1164
Clark, Jeffrey C., Exec. V.P. & Asst. Treas.--Branford Savings Bank, Branford, CT; *U.S. Public*, pg. 250
Clark, Kristin, Exec. V.P.-Bus. Devel. & Customer Rels.--Seattle Pacific Industries, Inc., Seattle, WA; *U.S. Private*, *pg. 980*
Clark, Leslie F., II, Exec. V.P.--Timberline Software Corporation, Beaverton, OR; *U.S. Public*, pg. 1609
Clark, Richard B., Exec. V.P.-Leasing--World Financial Properties, Inc., New York, NY; *Int'l*, pg. 1004
Clark, Susan, Exec. V.P. & Mngmt. Supvr.--EvansGroup, Los Angeles, CA; *U.S. Private*, pg. 385
Clark, Terry L., Exec. V.P.-Opers.--Collins Industries, Inc., Hutchinson, KS; *U.S. Public*, pg. 399
Clark, Timothy, Exec. V.P.-Opers.--Ameriana Bancorp, New Castle, IN; *U.S. Public*, pg. 66
Clark, W. Roger, Exec. V.P.-Mortgage--United Companies Financial Corporation, Baton Rouge, LA; *U.S. Public*, pg. 1675
Clark, William P., Jr., Exec. V.P.--Wall Colmonoy Corp., Madison Heights, MI; *U.S. Private*, pg. 1148
Clarke, Frank, Exec. V.P.-Americas--Grey Advertising Inc., New York, NY; *U.S. Public*, pg. 764
Clarke, Frank W., Exec. V.P. & Area Dir.--Grey Advertising, New York, NY; *U.S. Public*, pg. 764
Clarke, Fred, Exec. V.P.--Generale Investment Banking Corporation, New York, NY; *Int'l*, pg. 547
Clarke, George, Exec. V.P.--Stewart Smith Specialty Risks, Inc., Southfield, MI; *Int'l*, pg. 1508
Clarke, Gerald, Exec. V.P.--Coldwater Seafood Corporation, Rowayton, CT; *U.S. Private*, pg. 251
Clarke, Martin, Exec. V.P.--Republic National Bank of New York (U.K.), London, United Kingdom; *U.S. Public*, pg. 1381
Clarke, Peter W., Chief Fin. Officer, Exec. V.P. & Sec.--Orthofix International N.V., Curacao, Netherlands Antilles; *Int'l*, pg. 1011
Classon, Rolf A., Exec. V.P. & Pres.-Diagnostics Div.--Bayer Corporation, Pittsburgh, PA; *Int'l*, pg. 172
Classon, Rolf A., Pres.-Diagnostics Div. & Exec. V.P.--Bayer Corporation, Pittsburgh, PA; *Int'l*, pg. 172
Classon, Rolf A., Exec. V.P. & Pres.-Diagnostics Div.--Bayer Corporation, Parsippany, NJ; *Int'l*, pg. 172
Classon, Rolx, Exec. V.P.-Worldwide Mktg. & Sls. Services--Bayer Corporation/Diagnostics Division, Tarrytown, NY; *Int'l*, pg. 173
Clay, Richter, Exec. V.P.-Motel Opers.--The Rivet Group L.L.C., Aberdeen, SD; *U.S. Private*, pg. 934
Clayton, J. Kerry, Exec. V.P. & Treas.--Fortis, Inc., New York, NY; *Int'l*, pg. 499
Cleary, Gerald V., Exec. V.P.-Sls.--Tyco Preschool, New York, NY; *U.S. Public*, pg. 1058
Cleary, Michael, Exec. V.P.--Pinnacle Brands, Inc., Dallas, TX; *U.S. Private*, pg. 866
Cleberg, Anthony S., Chief Fin. Officer & Exec. V.P.--Morrison Knudsen Corporation, Boise, ID; *U.S. Public*, pg. 1133
Clein, Mark P., Chief Fin. Officer & Exec. V.P.--PMR Corporation, San Diego, CA; *U.S. Public*, pg. 1242
Clemens, Peter J., III, Exec. V.P. & Chief Admin. Officer--Vulcan Materials Company, Birmingham, AL; *U.S. Public*, *pg. 1725*
Clemente, Chuck, Chief Oper. Officer & Exec. V.P.--Redgate Communications Corp., Vero Beach, FL; *U.S. Public*, pg. 66
Clements, Janice, Exec. V.P. & Strategy & Bus. Devel. Dir.--Zenith Media Services, Inc., New York, NY; *U.S. Private*, *pg. 1204*
Clements, Robert H., Exec. V.P.--Clements Foods Co., Oklahoma City, OK; *U.S. Private*, pg. 245
Clemmer, Richard L., Chief Fin. Officer & Exec. V.P.-Fin.--Quantum Corporation, Milpitas, CA; *U.S. Public*, pg. 1350
Clemons, Robert, Exec. V.P.--Herrmidifier Co., Inc., Lancaster, PA; *U.S. Public*, pg. 1639
Clifford, Leigh, Exec. Dir.--Rio Tinto PLC, London, United Kingdom; *Int'l*, pg. 1118
Clifford, Patrick J., Exec. V.P.-Bus. Units--Sonat Exploration Company, Houston, TX; *U.S. Public*, pg. 1485
Clifton, Jean B., Chief Fin. Officer, Exec. V.P., Treas. & Sec.--Journal Register Company, Trenton, NJ; *U.S. Public*, pg. 934
Cline, Peter J., Exec. V.P. & Pres.-Handleman Entertainment Resources--Handleman Company, Troy, MI; *U.S. Public*, pg. 779
Clinton, John, Exec. V.P. & Gen. Mgr.-JWT/Chicago--J. Walter Thompson Company, New York, NY; *Int'l*, pg. 1483
Clist, Todd, Exec. V.P.-Marriott Lodging--Marriott International, Inc., Washington, DC; *U.S. Public*, pg. 1047
Clist, Todd, Exec. V.P. & Gen. Mgr.--Courtyard by Marriott, Washington, DC; *U.S. Public*, pg. 1048
Clock, Douglas G., Chief Fin. Officer & Exec. V.P.--Byerly's Inc., Edina, MN; *U.S. Private*, pg. 680
Cloherty, Michael J., Exec. V.P.--Arthur J. Gallagher & Co., Itasca, IL; *U.S. Public*, pg. 698
Cloniger, Kriss, III, Chief Fin. Officer & Exec. V.P.--AFLAC Incorporated, Columbus, GA; *U.S. Public*, pg. 28
Closterman, Royce D., Exec. V.P.--DST Systems, Inc., Kansas City, MO; *U.S. Public*, pg. 943
Cloud, James, Exec. V.P.--National Bank of Alaska, Anchorage, AK; *U.S. Public*, pg. 1153
Clout, Richard J.S., Exec. V.P.-Intl. Opers.--General Motors Acceptance Corporation (GMAC), Detroit, MI; *U.S. Public*, pg. 719
Clubb, Gary D., Exec. V.P.--Texas Instruments Incorporated, Dallas, TX; *U.S. Public*, pg. 1585
Cluer, Allen, Exec. V.P. & Gen. Mgr.--Clayton Industries Co., El Monte, CA; *U.S. Private*, pg. 245
Clyde, Larry F., Exec. V.P.-Gobal Securities Lending--Mellon Bank Corporation, Pittsburgh, PA; *U.S. Public*, pg. 1084
Clyde, Robert W., Exec. V.P.-Mktg. & Sls.--The Acacia Group - Acacia Life Insurance Co., Bethesda, MD; *U.S. Private*, pg. 10
Clyde, Robert W., Exec. V.P.--Acacia Financial Corporation, Bethesda, MD; *U.S. Private*, pg. 11
Coates, Al, Exec. V.P. & Gen. Mgr.--Calgary Flames Hockey Club, Calgary, Canada; *Int'l*, pg. 252
Coats, Douglas J., Pres.-Acceleration Nat. Insurance Co. & Exec. V.P.--ACCEL International Corporation, Dublin, OH; *U.S. Public*, pg. 14
Cobb, William S., Exec. V.P.--Countrywide Funding Corporation, Pasadena, CA; *U.S. Public*, pg. 453
Cobb, William S., Jr., Div. Exec. V.P.-Wholesale Opers.--Countrywide Home Loans Inc., Pasadena, CA; *U.S. Public*, pg. 452
Coben, John B., Exec. V.P.--Nashville Machine Co. Inc., Nashville, TN; *U.S. Private*, pg. 774
Cobet, Dr. Hermann, Exec. V.P.--Hochtief AG, Essen, Germany; *Int'l*, pg. 623
Cobos, Horacio, Principal--Richards, Brock, Miller, Mitchell & Assoc. Inc., Dallas, TX; *U.S. Private*, pg. 929
Coburn, Al, Exec. V.P. & Chief Oper. Officer--Salem Sportswear, Hudson, NH; *U.S. Public*, pg. 686
Cocheteux, Jean-Bernard, Exec. V.P.--Labinal SA, Montigny-le-Bretonneux, France; *Int'l*, pg. 785
Cochran, James G., Chief Oper. Officer & Exec. V.P.--United Services Life Insurance Co., Arlington, VA; *U.S. Public*, pg. 1376
Cody, Thomas G., Exec. V.P.-Legal & Human Resources--Federated Department Stores, Inc., Cincinnati, OH; *U.S. Public*, pg. 617
Coe, Alan C., Exec. V.P. & Dir.--GATX Capital Corporation, San Francisco, CA; *U.S. Public*, pg. 690
Coffee, M. Terry, Exec. V.P.--Murphy Family Farms, Rose Hill, NC; *U.S. Private*, pg. 768
Coffey, Charles S., Exec. V.P.-Bus. Banking--Royal Bank of Canada, Toronto, Canada; *Int'l*, pg. 1131
Coffey, Shelby III, Exec. V.P. & Editor--Los Angeles Times, Los Angeles, CA; *U.S. Public*, pg. 1616
Coffman, Gregory M., Exec. V.P.--K & G of Wisconsin, Inc., Milwaukee, WI; *U.S. Private*, pg. 602
Cogdill, Rick, Chief Fin. Officer & Exec. V.P.--Pilgrim's Pride Corporation, Pittsburg, TX; *U.S. Public*, pg. 1296
Coggin, Robert W., Exec. V.P.-Mktg.--Delta Air Lines, Inc., Atlanta, GA; *U.S. Public*, pg. 497
Coggiola, Donald A., Exec. V.P.--Policy Management Systems Corporation, Blythewood, SC; *U.S. Public*, pg. 1314
Coghill, C. C., Exec. V.P.--First National Bank of Naples, Naples, FL; *U.S. Public*, pg. 607
Coghlan, John Philip, Exec. V.P.-Schwab Institutional--The Charles Schwab Corporation, San Francisco, CA; *U.S. Public*, pg. 1442
Cohan, James S., Exec. V.P. & Mngmt. Supvr.--Stern Advertising, Inc., Cleveland, OH; *U.S. Private*, pg. 1041
Cohen, Aaron, Exec. V.P. & Brdcst. & Programming Dir.--The Media Edge, New York, NY; *U.S. Private*, pg. 1079
Cohen, Alan, Exec. V.P.-Mktg.-ABC Television Network--ABC, Inc, New York, NY; *U.S. Public*, pg. 511
Cohen, Alan H., Chief Oper. Officer, Exec. V.P. & Sec.--George Uhe Co., Inc., Paramus, NJ; *U.S. Private*, pg. 1115
Cohen, Benjamin, Exec. V.P.-Fin. & Investments--Accor S.A., Evry, France; *Int'l*, pg. 20
Cohen, Bert, Chief Oper. Officer & Exec. V.P.--Worldvision Enterprises, New York, NY; *U.S. Private*, pg. 776
Cohen, Brian, Exec. V.P.--Weber Public Relations Worldwide, Cambridge, MA; *U.S. Private*, pg. 1157
Cohen, Jay R., Exec. V.P. & Treas.--CRI Liquidating REIT, Inc., Rockville, MD; *U.S. Public*, pg. 459
Cohen, Joseph M., Exec. V.P.--Madison Square Garden Network, New York, NY; *U.S. Public*, pg. 288
Cohen, Mark, Exec. V.P.--Atlas Copco North America Inc., Wayne, NJ; *Int'l*, pg. 96
Cohen, Mark J., Exec. V.P.-Sls. & Mktg.--All-Luminum Products, Inc., Philadelphia, PA; *U.S. Private*, pg. 34
Cohen, Peter, Exec. V.P.-TV Production--Jordan, McGrath, Case & Taylor Inc., New York, NY; *U.S. Private*, pg. 598
Cohen, Steven, Exec. V.P.--Host Apparel, Inc., New York, NY; *U.S. Private*, pg. 540
Cohen, Stuart, Exec. V.P.--Amerex USA, Inc., New York, NY; *U.S. Private*, pg. 49
Cohen, Ted, Exec. V.P.--AFD Contract Furniture, New York, NY; *U.S. Private*, pg. 5
Cohn, Julie Ann, Exec. V.P. & Database Mktg. Dir.--Western International Media Corporation, Los Angeles, CA; *U.S. Private*, pg. 1165
Coignard, Gilbert, Exec. V.P.-Mngmt. Control--Credit Commercial de France, Paris, France; *Int'l*, pg. 341
Coimbra, Roberto, Exec. V.P., Pres. & CEO-JWT/Venezuela--J. Walter Thompson Company, New York, NY; *Int'l*, pg. 1483
Colaiacovo, Mario, Chief Fin. Officer & Exec. V.P.--Societe d'Applications Generales d'Electricite et de Mechanique, Paris, France; *Int'l*, pg. 1273
Colasacco, Domenic, Exec. V.P.--UST Corporation, Boston, MA; *U.S. Public*, pg. 1660
Colavito, Michael, Chief Fin. Officer & Exec. V.P.--SCP Direct Inc., New York, NY; *U.S. Public*, pg. 1224
Colburn, J. Brian, Exec. V.P.-Special Projects & Sec.--Magna International Inc., Markham, Canada; *Int'l*, pg. 829
Cole, James J., Jr., Exec. V.P.--Alex J. Etkin, Inc., Farmington, MI; *U.S. Private*, pg. 384
Cole, Michael, Exec. V.P.-Electronic Media & Info. Tech.--Reed Elsevier Business Information, Newton, MA; *Int'l*, pg. 1095
Cole, Steve, Exec. V.P.--S&D Coffee Inc., Concord, NC; *U.S. Private*, pg. 954
Cole, Tom, Chief Fin. Officer & Exec. V.P.--Maxum Health Corp., Dallas, TX; *U.S. Public*, pg. 881
Cole, Tommy W., Exec. V.P.-Corp. Fin. Services--Trans Financial, Inc., Bowling Green, KY; *U.S. Public*, pg. 1628
Cole, William R., Exec. V.P.--Comml. Div.--First of America Bank Corporation, Kalamazoo, MI; *U.S. Public*, pg. 636
Colebrook, Miles, Exec. V.P., Grp. Pres.-JWT/Intl., & Global Bus. Dir.-Nestle--J. Walter Thompson Company, New York, NY; *Int'l*, pg. 1483
Coleman, Jay W., Exec. V.P.-Sls. & Service--CVB Financial Corp., Ontario, CA; *U.S. Public*, pg. 286
Coleman, Lester L., Exec. V.P. & Gen. Counsel--Halliburton Company, Dallas, TX; *U.S. Public*, pg. 775
Coleman, Lester L., Exec. V.P. & Gen. Counsel--Halliburton Energy Services, Inc., Dallas, TX; *U.S. Public*, pg. 776
Coleman, Richard J., Exec. V.P.--Florasynth Inc., Teterboro, NJ; *Int'l*, pg. 173
Coleman, Steven J., Exec. V.P.--Thermo Fibertek, Inc., Waltham, MA; *U.S. Public*, pg. 1593
Colen, Fred A., Exec. V.P.-Quality Speed to Market--Pacesetter Inc., Sylmar, CA; *U.S. Public*, pg. 1428
Colgan, Robert T., Exec. V.P. & Asst. Mgr.-Natl. Sls.--Jefferies & Company, Inc., Los Angeles, CA; *U.S. Public*, *pg. 925*
Collier, Jeffry H., Exec. V.P.-Graphics Corp.--Outlook Group Corporation, Neenah, WI; *U.S. Public*, pg. 1235
Collins, Atwood, III, Exec. V.P.--First Empire State Corporation, Buffalo, NY; *U.S. Public*, pg. 631
Collins, Atwood, III, Exec. V.P.--Manufacturers & Traders Trust Company, Buffalo, NY; *U.S. Public*, pg. 631
Collins, Cindy S., Exec. V.P.-Risk Mngmt.--Hibernia Corporation, New Orleans, LA; *U.S. Public*, pg. 825
Collins, Cornell E., Sr. V.P.-Special Projects--Sundt Corp., Tucson, AZ; *U.S. Private*, pg. 1051
Collins, Frank E., Exec. V.P., Gen. Counsel & Sec.--Sierra Health Services, Inc., Las Vegas, NV; *U.S. Public*, pg. 1469
Collins, Joseph R., Exec. V.P.--Pentair, Inc., Saint Paul, MN; *U.S. Public*, pg. 1273
Collins, Roger, Chief Fin. Officer & Exec. V.P.--Harp's Food Stores, Inc., Springdale, AR; *U.S. Private*, pg. 504
Collins, T. Jay, Exec. V.P.-Marine Oilfield Services--Oceaneering International, Inc., Houston, TX; *U.S. Public*, pg. 1211
Collins, T. Jay, Exec. V.P.--Oilfield Marine Services-Americas Region, Morgan City, LA; *U.S. Public*, pg. 1211
Collins, T. Jay, Exec. V.P.--Oceaneering International, Inc., Morgan City, LA; *U.S. Public*, pg. 1211
Collister, Richard A., Exec. V.P. & Chief H.R. Officer--Comerica Incorporated, Detroit, MI; *U.S. Public*, pg. 408
Colloc'h, Francoise, Sr. Exec. V.P.-Grp. Human Resources & Communications--AXA-UAP, Paris, France; *Int'l*, pg. 18
Coltharp, Douglas E., Chief Fin. Officer & Exec. V.P.--Proffitt's, Inc., Alcoa, TN; *U.S. Public*, pg. 1333
Coltman, David A., Sr. V.P.-Mktg.--UAL Corporation, Elk Grove Village, IL; *U.S. Public*, pg. 1652
Colucci, Joe, Exec. V.P.--Optimaxx International, Rockleigh, NJ; *U.S. Private*, pg. 818

Colvill, Robert, Exec. Dir.-Fin. Activities--Marks & Spencer PLC, London, United Kingdom; *Int'l*, pg. 842
Combe, Roger G., Exec. V.P.--Robert F. Driver Co., Inc., San Diego, CA; *U.S. Private*, pg. 343
Combs, Anastasia, Exec. V.P.--Ace Doran Hauling & Rigging Company, Cincinnati, OH; *U.S. Private*, pg. 340
Combs, George M., Exec. V.P.--Tamaqua Cable Products Corp., Schuylkill Haven, PA; *Int'l*, pg. 417
Comeau, Susan, Exec. V.P.-Human Resources--State Street Corporation, Boston, MA; *U.S. Public*, pg. 1513
Comeau, Susan, Exec. V.P.--State Street Bank & Trust Co., Boston, MA; *U.S. Public*, pg. 1513
Comer, William E., Exec. V.P.-Fin.--Traylor Chemical & Supply Co., Orlando, FL; *U.S. Private*, pg. 1098
Comes, Anastasia M., V.P. & Treas.--Ace Doran Hauling & Rigging Company, Cincinnati, OH; *U.S. Private*, pg. 340
Comins, Ric, Exec. V.P.-Human Resources--OfficeMax, Shaker Heights, OH; *U.S. Public*, pg. 1212
Comley, John, Exec. V.P.--Clearing-Niagara, Buffalo, NY; *U.S. Private*, pg. 196
Compofelice, Joseph S., Exec. V.P.--Valhi, Inc., Dallas, TX; *U.S. Private*, pg. 270
Compton, Harold, Chief Oper. Officer & Exec. V.P.--CompUSA, Dallas, TX; *U.S. Public*, pg. 420
Conacher, John C., Exec. Dir.-America--Halma p.l.c., Amersham, United Kingdom; *Int'l*, pg. 589
Conant, Douglas R., Exec. V.P. & Gen. Mgr.--Specialty Products Co., Parsippany, NJ; *U.S. Public*, pg. 1355
Concannon, Bill, Chief Exec. Officer-Corp. Services & Exec. V.P.--Trammell Crow Company, Dallas, TX; *U.S. Public*, pg. 1628
Condon, Michelle, Exec. V.P.-Retail Banking--The Colonial BancGroup, Inc., Montgomery, AL; *U.S. Public*, pg. 400
Condos, George, Exec. V.P.-Devel.--Wendy's International Inc., Dublin, OH; *U.S. Public*, pg. 1754
Condray, A.L., Exec. V.P.--Exxon Company, U.S.A., Houston, TX; *U.S. Public*, pg. 601
Cone, Stephen A., Exec. V.P. & Chief Mktg. Officer--Keycorp, Cleveland, OH; *U.S. Public*, pg. 954
Cone, W. Mike, Exec. V.P.--The Bank of North Arkansas, Melbourne, AR; *U.S. Public*, pg. 641
Conforti, Joanne, Exec. V.P.-H.R.--Bozell Worldwide, Inc., New York, NY; *U.S. Public*, pg. 1642
Cong-Duk, Park, Exec. V.P.-Construction Mngmt.--Daewoo Corporation, Seoul, Korea; *Int'l*, pg. 357
Conklin, Carroll, Exec. V.P. & Strategic Services Dir.--Lord, Sullivan & Yoder Inc. Marketing Communications, Columbus, OH; *U.S. Private*, pg. 676
Conklin, David J., Exec. V.P.--Conklin Instrument Corporation, Pleasant Valley, NY; *U.S. Private*, pg. 263
Conklin, Deane L., III, Exec. V.P.--First Commercial Bank, N.A., Little Rock, AR; *U.S. Public*, pg. 630
Conklin, Donald R., Exec. V.P.--Schering-Plough Corporation, Madison, NJ; *U.S. Public*, pg. 1438
Conley, Hampton, Exec. V.P.--Greater Construction Corp., Altamonte Springs, FL; *U.S. Private*, pg. 476
Conley, Terrence, Sr. V.P.--Kraco Enterprises, Inc., Compton, CA; *U.S. Private*, pg. 634
Conlon, Brian T., Exec. V.P.--D.L. Blair Inc., Garden City, NY; *U.S. Private*, pg. 148
Connell, Ted, Exec. V.P.--Connell Co., Westfield, NJ; *U.S. Private*, pg. 264
Connelly, T.T., Exec. V.P.--Hardings, Inc., Elmira, NY; *U.S. Private*, pg. 502
Conner, Frank, Chief Fin. Officer & Exec. V.P.-Acctg.--American Freightways Corporation, Harrison, AR; *U.S. Public*, pg. 75
Conners, John B., Exec. V.P.--Liberty Mutual Insurance Co., Boston, MA; *U.S. Private*, pg. 666
Conners, William, Exec. V.P.--Pearl-Pressman-Liberty Communications Group, Philadelphia, PA; *U.S. Private*, pg. 845
Connolly, James, Exec. V.P.--Congressional Information Service (CIS), Bethesda, MD; *Int'l*, pg. 1096
Connolly, Patrick, Exec. V.P.-Specialized Fin.--Dresdner Bank AG, New York, NY; *Int'l*, pg. 418
Connolly, Patrick J., Exec. V.P. & Gen. Mgr.-Catalog--Williams-Sonoma, Inc., San Francisco, CA; *U.S. Public*, pg. 1770
Connor, Thomas G., Jr., Exec. V.P.--Affiliated Computer Services, Inc., Dallas, TX; *U.S. Public*, pg. 27
Connors, Frank, Vice Chm. & Exec. V.P.--STM Wireless, Inc., Irvine, CA; *U.S. Public*, pg. 1421
Connors, Joseph C., Exec. V.P. & Gen. Counsel--Schering-Plough Corporation, Madison, NJ; *U.S. Public*, pg. 1438
Connors, Joseph J., Exec. V.P.--Kleinert's, Inc., Plymouth Meeting, PA; *U.S. Private*, pg. 625
Connors, Kevin P., Exec. V.P. & Pres.-GM Coherent Medical--Coherent, Inc., Santa Clara, CA; *U.S. Public*, pg. 395
Conover, Steve, Sr. V.P. & Exec. Creative Dir.--Ambrose Carr Linton Carroll Inc., Toronto, Canada; *Int'l*, pg. 71
Conrad, E.T., Exec. V.P.--SCS Engineers, Long Beach, CA; *U.S. Private*, pg. 955
Conrad, Gary L., Exec. V.P.-Distr. & Logistics--Richfood Holdings, Inc., Glen Allen, VA; *U.S. Public*, pg. 1388
Constantini, Ben, Exec. V.P.-Sls.--Wavetek Corporation, San Diego, CA; *U.S. Private*, pg. 1154
Constantinides, Patrick, Exec. V.P.--Republic National Bank of New York, New York, NY; *U.S. Public*, pg. 1380
Constantino, Charles A., Exec. V.P.--PAR Technology Corporation, New Hartford, NY; *U.S. Public*, pg. 1256
Constien, Robert W., Exec. V.P.-Investment & Trust Services--The State Bank and Trust Company, Defiance, OH; *U.S. Public*, pg. 1413
Contadino, Joseph, Exec. V.P. & Pres.-Coventry Homes--Del Webb Corporation, Phoenix, AZ; *U.S. Public*, pg. 494
Conte, Courtney B., Exec. V.P.-Production--Carsey-Werner Company, LLC, Studio City, CA; *U.S. Private*, pg. 216
Converso, Frank, Exec. V.P.-Production--Canac Kitchens Ltd, Thornhill, Canada; *U.S. Private*, pg. 630
Conway, Barry, Exec. V.P.-Sls. & Mktg.--Adams Business Forms, Topeka, KS; *U.S. Private*, pg. 16
Conway, Charles C., Chief Fin. Officer & Exec. V.P.--CVS Corp., Woonsocket, RI; *U.S. Public*, pg. 287
Conway, Joe, Exec. V.P. & Gen. Mgr.--Manitex, Inc., Georgetown, TX; *U.S. Public*, pg. 1041
Conway, John W., Exec. V.P.--Crown Cork & Seal Company, Inc., Philadelphia, PA; *U.S. Public*, pg. 462
Conway, Kelly D., Exec. V.P.--Technology Solutions Company (TSC), Chicago, IL; *U.S. Public*, pg. 1564
Conway, William S., Exec. V.P.-Mktg.--American Life Insurance Company of New York, New York, NY; *U.S. Private*, pg. 769
Conwill, Daniel O., Exec. V.P. & Dir.-Fin.--Jefferies & Company, Inc., Los Angeles, CA; *U.S. Public*, pg. 925
Conybeare, H.J., Exec. Dir.--Swire Pacific Limited, Central, Hong Kong; *Int'l*, pg. 1328
Conyers, Rita, Exec. V.P.-Corp. Commun. & Trng. & Leadership--Mutual of America Life Insurance Company, New York, NY; *U.S. Private*, pg. 769
Conyers, Rita, Exec. V.P.-Corp. Commun. & Trng. Leadership--American Life Insurance Company of New York, New York, NY; *U.S. Private*, pg. 769
Coogan, Keith R., Chief Oper. Officer & Exec. V.P.--Software Spectrum, Inc., Garland, TX; *U.S. Public*, pg. 1483
Cook, Bob, Exec. V.P.-CBS Enterprises & Eyemark Entertainment--CBS Enterprises Division, New York, NY; *U.S. Public*, pg. 274
Cook, Jan, Chief Fin. Officer & Exec. V.P.--Polygram N.V., Baarn, Netherlands; *Int'l*, pg. 1051
Cook, John, Chief Oper. Officer & Exec. V.P.--Magruder Color Company, Inc., Elizabeth, NJ; *U.S. Private*, pg. 696
Cook, Norman, Exec. V.P.-Import--Genfoot Inc., Montreal, Canada; *Int'l*, pg. 549
Cook, Paul R., Chief Fin. Officer, Exec. V.P. & Treas.--American Consumers, Inc., Fort Oglethorpe, GA; *U.S. Public*, pg. 70
Cook, Rosanne, Chief Fin. Officer & Exec. V.P.--Dominick & Dominick, Incorporated, New York, NY; *U.S. Private*, pg. 338
Cook, Stephani, Exec. V.P. & Strategic Plng. Dir.--Lowe & Partners/SMS, New York, NY; *U.S. Private*, pg. 678
Cook, Stephen, Exec. V.P.-Export--Genfoot Inc., Montreal, Canada; *Int'l*, pg. 549
Cook, Walter R., Exec. V.P.--Republic National Bank of New York, New York, NY; *U.S. Public*, pg. 1380
Cooke, John F., Exec. V.P.-Corp. Affairs--The Walt Disney Company, Burbank, CA; *U.S. Public*, pg. 511
Cooke, William J., Pres.-Advanstar Mktg. Svcs. & Exec. V.P.--Advanstar Communications, Cleveland, OH; *U.S. Private*, pg. 22
Cooler, Charles, Exec. V.P. & Gen. Mgr.-BASES Intl. Research Div.--BASES Worldwide, Covington, KY; *U.S. Private*, pg. 120
Cooley, Ted C., Exec. V.P.-Individual Div.--Guarantee Life Insurance Co., Omaha, NE; *U.S. Public*, pg. 768
Coombs, Paul D., Exec. V.P.-Oil & Gas Services--Tetra Technologies, Woodlands, TX; *U.S. Public*, pg. 1582
Cooney, John T., Exec. V.P.--Nilfisk A/S, Brondby, Denmark; *Int'l*, pg. 932
Cooper, Arthur G., Exec. V.P.-Fin. & Oper.--Showtime Networks Inc., New York, NY; *U.S. Private*, pg. 779
Cooper, David, Exec. V.P.--C. Weaver Chevrolet, Inc., New York Mills, NY; *U.S. Private*, pg. 1156
Cooper, David B., Chief Fin. Officer & Exec. V.P.--Edison Brothers Stores, Inc., Saint Louis, MO; *U.S. Public*, pg. 563
Cooper, Debbie, Exec. V.P.--Turner Private Networks, Atlanta, GA; *U.S. Public*, pg. 1614
Cooper, Douglas K., Exec. V.P. & Gen. Counsel--Peregrine Incorporated, Southfield, MI; *U.S. Private*, pg. 852
Cooper, Flint, Exec. V.P. & Gen. Mgr.-Security Systems Div.--Richardson Electronics, Ltd., Lafox, IL; *U.S. Public*, pg. 1387
Cooper, Gary, Exec. V.P.-Mfg.--Trelleborg YSH, Inc., South Haven, MI; *Int'l*, pg. 1422
Cooper, Joseph, Chief Information Officer & Exec. V.P.--First Citizens Banc Shares, Inc., Raleigh, NC; *U.S. Public*, pg. 628
Cooper, M. Lynn, Exec. V.P.--CNB Bancshares, Inc., Evansville, IN; *U.S. Public*, pg. 280
Cooper, Scott, Exec. V.P.-Opers.--Players International, Inc., Atlantic City, NJ; *U.S. Public*, pg. 1310
Cooper, Terri, Exec. V.P.--American International Industries, City of Commerce, CA; *U.S. Private*, pg. 57
Cooper, Warren, Exec. V.P.-Human Resources & Admin.--Kmart Corporation, Troy, MI; *U.S. Public*, pg. 963
Cooper, William L., Exec. V.P.--Barnhill Contracting Company, Tarboro, NC; *U.S. Private*, pg. 117
Coopersmith, Harold, Exec. V.P.--Smith-Edwards-Dunlap Company, Philadelphia, PA; *U.S. Private*, pg. 1007
Copland, Ronald G., Exec. V.P., Sec. & Asst. Treas.--Copland Fabrics, Inc., Burlington, NC; *U.S. Private*, pg. 274
Coppedge, Ferrell L., Exec. V.P.--Southern Group, Atlanta, GA; *U.S. Public*, pg. 649
Coppola, Edward, Exec. V.P.-Acquisitions--The Macerich Company, Santa Monica, CA; *U.S. Public*, pg. 1030
Copps, Donald C., Exec. V.P.-Mdsg.--The Copps Corp., Stevens Point, WI; *U.S. Private*, pg. 275
Copps, Frederick C., Exec. V.P.-Wholesale--The Copps Corp., Stevens Point, WI; *U.S. Private*, pg. 275
Copps, Thomas R., Exec. V.P.-Pub. Rels.--The Copps Corp., Stevens Point, WI; *U.S. Private*, pg. 275
Corben, David, Exec. V.P.--JIB Group plc, London, United Kingdom; *Int'l*, pg. 705
Corbett, Larry R., Exec. V.P.--DIMON, International, Inc., Farmville, NC; *U.S. Public*, pg. 510
Corbett, Mike, Exec. V.P.-Opers.--Crane Manufacturing, Cudahy, WI; *U.S. Private*, pg. 286
Corbin, Larry C., Exec. V.P.-Restaurant Div.--Bob Evans Farms, Inc., Columbus, OH; *U.S. Public*, pg. 596
Corbin, Larry C., Exec. V.P.-Bus. Devel.--Bob Evans Farms, Inc. Restaurant Division, Columbus, OH; *U.S. Public*, pg. 596
Corbin, William R., Exec. V.P.-Timberlands & Dis.--Weyerhaeuser Company, Federal Way, WA; *U.S. Public*, pg. 1764
Corby, Francis M. Jr., Exec. V.P.-Fin. & Admin.--Harnischfeger Industries, Inc., Saint Francis, WI; *U.S. Public*, pg. 788
Corcoran, John, Chief Oper. Officer & Exec. V.P.--FCB HealthCare, San Francisco, CA; *U.S. Public*, pg. 1641
Cordaro, C. Roberto, Grp. Pres.-Automotive & Exec. V.P.--Cummins Engine Company, Inc., Columbus, IN; *U.S. Public*, pg. 467
Cordes, Don L., Exec. V.P. & Chief Legal Officer--Koch Industries, Incorporated, Wichita, KS; *U.S. Private*, pg. 628
Cordes, Michael S., Chief Oper. Officer & Exec. V.P.--Mercantile Mortgage Corp., Baltimore, MD; *U.S. Public*, pg. 1089
Cordial, C. Alan, Exec. V.P.--Creative Productions, Pittsburgh, PA; *U.S. Private*, pg. 288
Corey, Bob L., Chief Fin. Officer & Exec. V.P.-Fin.--SyQuest Technology, Inc., Fremont, CA; *U.S. Public*, pg. 1550
Corkran, James, Exec. V.P.--Cottman Transmission Systems, Inc., Fort Washington, PA; *U.S. Private*, pg. 278
Cornelissen, G.P.J., Exec. V.P.--ABN-AMRO Holding N.V., Amsterdam, Netherlands; *Int'l*, pg. 8
Cornell, C. Smith, Exec. V.P.--Fuji Securities Inc.-New York, New York, NY; *Int'l*, pg. 519
Cornell, Ed, Exec. V.P.-New Bus. Devel.--OfficeMax, Shaker Heights, OH; *U.S. Public*, pg. 1212
Cornick, Jack A., Exec. V.P.-Consumer Banking Opers.--Washington Mutual Inc., Seattle, WA; *U.S. Public*, pg. 1741
Cornick, Jack A., Exec. V.P.--Washington Mutual Federal Savings Bank, Seattle, WA; *U.S. Public*, pg. 1742
Cornu, Joseph, Exec. V.P.-Technical & Opers.--Alcatel N.V., Amsterdam, Netherlands; *Int'l*, pg. 55
Corporron, Randy J., Exec. V.P.--Kent Electronics Corp., Houston, TX; *U.S. Public*, pg. 951
Corporron, Rodney J., Exec. V.P.--K-Tec Electronics, Sugar Land, TX; *U.S. Public*, pg. 951
Corrigan, C. Rory, Exec. V.P. & Mgr.-N.Y. Sls. Mgr.--Jefferies & Company, Inc., Los Angeles, CA; *U.S. Public*, *pg. 925*
Corry, Lawrence L., Chief Oper. Officer & Exec. V.P.--The Amalgamated Sugar Company LLC, Ogden, UT; *U.S. Private*, pg. 48
Cort, Fredric B., Exec. V.P.--First Valley Corporation, Bethlehem, PA; *U.S. Public*, pg. 1528
Cortes Moreno, Luis G., Exec. V.P.-Mktg.--Grupo Casa Autrey, Mexico, Mexico; *Int'l*, pg. 573
Cortes, Francisco, Exec. V.P.-Mortgage & Admin. Svcs.--Firstbank Puerto Rico, Santurce, PR; *U.S. Public*, pg. 644
Cortlett, Murray A., Exec. V.P.-Risk Mngmt.--Royal Bank of Canada, Toronto, Canada; *Int'l*, pg. 1131
Corujo, Jose A., Chief Fin. Officer & Exec. V.P.--Puerto Rico Tourism Company, San Juan, PR; *U.S. Private*, pg. 894
Corwin, Ronald D., Exec. V.P.-Mktg.--The American Stock Exchange, New York, NY; *U.S. Private*, pg. 62
Cosenza, Albert, Exec. V.P.--MTA Long Island Rail Road, Jamaica, NY; *U.S. Private*, pg. 739
Cosgrove, Jeff, Exec. V.P.-Mktg.--The Rockport Company, Marlborough, MA; *U.S. Public*, pg. 1370
Cossano, Rick, Exec. V.P.-Wholesale Div.--Countrywide Home Loans Inc., Pasadena, CA; *U.S. Public*, pg. 452
Cosson, Robert, Exec. V.P.-Fin. & Legal--Gaz de France, Paris, France; *Int'l*, pg. 541
Costello, Craig T., Chief Oper. Officer & Exec. V.P.-Opers.--Weirton Steel Corporation, Weirton, WV; *U.S. Public*, pg. 1751
Costello, Daniel W., Exec. V.P.--BankAmerica Corporation, San Francisco, CA; *U.S. Public*, pg. 179
Costello, John H., Sr. Exec. V.P. & Gen. Mgr.-Mktg.--Sears, Roebuck and Co., Hoffman Estates, IL; *U.S. Public*, pg. 1452
Costello, William F., Chief Fin. Officer & Exec. V.P.--QVC, Inc., West Chester, PA; *U.S. Public*, pg. 407
Costello, William F., Chief Fin. Officer & Exec. V.P.--QVC, Inc., West Chester, PA; *U.S. Private*, pg. 897
Costello, William F., Chief Fin. Officer & Exec. V.P.--QVC, Inc., West Chester, PA; *U.S. Public*, pg. 1555
Cote, Louis, Exec. V.P.-Quebec--Cossette Communication Marketing, Quebec, Canada; *Int'l*, pg. 335
Cote, Louis, Exec. V.P.--Cossette Communication-Marketing (Quebec) Inc., Quebec, Canada; *Int'l*, pg. 336
Cote, Richard L., Chief Fin. Officer & Exec. V.P.--Transact Technologies Incorporated, Wallingford, CT; *U.S. Public*, pg. 1629
Cote, Rick B., Exec. V.P.--Acadia Insurance Company, Westbrook, ME; *U.S. Public*, pg. 215
Cotler, Ira, Exec. V.P.-Fin.--Correctional Services Corporation, Sarasota, FL; *U.S. Public*, pg. 450
Cotliar, George, Exec. V.P.--Los Angeles Times, Los Angeles, CA; *U.S. Public*, pg. 1616
Cotros, Charles H., Chief Oper. Officer & Exec. V.P.--Sysco Corporation, Houston, TX; *U.S. Public*, pg. 1550
Cottingham, James P., Exec. V.P.--Time Warner Cable, Stamford, CT; *U.S. Public*, pg. 1610
Cottle, Gail, Exec. V.P.-Prod. Devel.--Nordstrom, Inc., Seattle, WA; *U.S. Public*, pg. 1190
Cotunaccio, Luciano, Exec. Dir.--Marco del Pont S.A., Buenos Aires, Argentina; *Int'l*, pg. 842
Coudray, Georges, Vice Chm.--Credit Mutuel, Paris, France; *Int'l*, pg. 344
Coughlin, E., Exec. V.P.--Lake Shore, Inc., Kingsford, MI; *U.S. Private*, pg. 814
Coughlin, F.X., Jr., Exec. V.P. & Sec.--F.X. Coughlin Co., Taylor, MI; *U.S. Private*, pg. 278
Coughlin, Thomas M., Exec. V.P.-Opers.--Wal-Mart Stores, Inc., Bentonville, AR; *U.S. Public*, pg. 1732
Courides, George, Exec. V.P. & Creative Dir.--Collegeville Advertising, Norristown, PA; *U.S. Public*, pg. 1422

Courtney, David W., Chief Oper. Officer & Exec. V.P.--CHEMCENTRAL Corporation, Bedford Park, IL; *U.S. Private*, pg. 231
Courtney, Michael A., Exec. V.P.--Imperial Tobacco Limited, Montreal, Canada; *Int'l*, pg. 112
Cousin, Yves, Exec. V.P. & Head-Engrng. & Construction--Electricite de France, Paris, France; *Int'l*, pg. 437
Cousins, Steve, Exec. V.P.-Sls. & Mktg.--Delicato Vineyards, Manteca, CA; *U.S. Private*, pg. 322
Coussement, Marc, Exec. Dir.--Union Miniere, Brussels, Belgium; *Int'l*, pg. 1441
Coutard, Jean Pierre, Exec. V.P.--JS Telecommunications S.A., Louveciennes, France; *Int'l*, pg. 706
Coutry, Ezzat, Chief Oper. Officer & Exec. V.P.--La Quinta Inns, Inc., San Antonio, TX; *U.S. Public*, pg. 972
Couzin, Mark S., Exec. V.P.--Mid-Continent Screw Products Co., Lincolnwood, IL; *U.S. Private*, pg. 743
Coverdale, Jac, Exec. V.P. & Creative Dir.--Clarity Coverdale Fury Advertising, Minneapolis, MN; *U.S. Private*, pg. 242
Covey, Stephen M.R., Exec. V.P.-Mktg. & Innovation--Franklin Covey, Salt Lake City, UT; *U.S. Public*, pg. 679
Coviello, Arthur W., Jr., Exec. V.P.-Fin. & Opers.--Security Dynamics Technologies, Bedford, MA; *U.S. Public*, pg. 1453
Covington, Alec C., Exec. V.P. & Chief Oper. Officer-Wholesale Opers.--Richfood Holdings, Inc., Glen Allen, VA; *U.S. Public*, pg. 1388
Cowan, Rory J., Exec. V.P.--R.R. Donnelley & Sons Company, Chicago, IL; *U.S. Public*, pg. 517
Cowan, Roy, Exec. V.P. & Grp. Dir.--DavisElen Advertising, Inc., Los Angeles, CA; *U.S. Private*, pg. 316
Cowie, Bruce, Chief Oper. Officer & Exec. V.P.--Baton Broadcasting Incorporated, Scarborough, Canada; *Int'l*, pg. 170
Cox, Daniel T., Exec. V.P.--AON Corporation, Chicago, IL; *U.S. Public*, pg. 117
Cox, F. Kim, Chief Fin. Officer & Exec. V.P.--Rentrak Corporation, Portland, OR; *U.S. Public*, pg. 1377
Cox, John E., Chief Oper. Officer & Exec. V.P.--Safeguard Health Enterprises, Inc., Anaheim, CA; *U.S. Public*, pg. 1424
Cox, Lamar, Chief Fin. Officer & Exec. V.P.--NationsBank of Tennessee, Nashville, TN; *U.S. Public*, pg. 1163
Cox, Michael, Exec. V.P.--Transport Development Group Plc, London, United Kingdom; *Int'l*, pg. 1418
Cox, Mike, Exec. V.P.-Opers.--Monro Muffler/Brake, Inc., Rochester, NY; *U.S. Public*, pg. 1124
Cox, Robert L., Chief Oper. Officer & Exec. V.P.--Tower Realty Trust, Inc., New York, NY; *U.S. Public*, pg. 1625
Cox, Sam, Chief Oper. Officer & Exec. V.P.--Goodwill Industries International, Bethesda, MD; *U.S. Private*, pg. 464
Coyne, Bill, Exec. V.P.-Sls.--Cable & Wireless Communications Inc., Vienna, VA; *Int'l*, pg. 247
Coyne, James A., Exec. V.P.-Capital Mkts.--Equis Financial Group, Boston, MA; *U.S. Private*, pg. 379
Crabtree, Ray, Exec. V.P.--The Principal Financial Group, Des Moines, IA; *U.S. Private*, pg. 885
Crabtree, Ray, Exec. V.P.--Principal Mutual Life Insurance Co., Des Moines, IA; *U.S. Private*, pg. 886
Craig, Paul, Chief Fin. Officer, Exec. V.P. & Treas.--Pac Rim Holding Corporation, Woodland Hills, CA; *U.S. Public*, pg. 1246
Craig, Peter M., Vice Chm. & Exec. V.P.--Rainbow Technologies, Inc., Irvine, CA; *U.S. Public*, pg. 1359
Craig, Walter M., Jr., Chief Oper. Officer & Exec. V.P.--Helm Resources Inc., Greenwich, CT; *U.S. Public*, pg. 808
Craigie, James, Exec. V.P. & Gen. Mgr.-Beverage Div.--Kraft Foods Inc., Glenview, IL; *U.S. Public*, pg. 1288
Crane, Steve, Exec. V.P. & Creative Dir.--Emmerling Post, Inc., New York, NY; *U.S. Private*, pg. 374
Cranford, William, Exec. V.P.--SouthTrust Corporation, Birmingham, AL; *U.S. Public*, pg. 1491
Crawford, John D., Chm. Bd., Chief Oper. Officer & Exec. V.P.--Network Long Distance, Inc., Baton Rouge, LA; *U.S. Public*, pg. 1169
Crean, John F.M., Sr. Exec. V.P.-Credit & Risk Mgmnt.--The Bank of Nova Scotia, Toronto, Canada; *Int'l*, pg. 155
Cree, Brian J., Chief Oper. Officer & Exec. V.P.--Patina Oil & Gas Corp., Denver, CO; *U.S. Public*, pg. 1264
Creekmuir, William S., Chief Fin. Officer, Exec. V.P., Treas. & Sec.--Ladd Furniture, Inc., Greensboro, NC; *U.S. Public*, pg. 974
Creet, S., Exec. V.P. & Grp. Creative Dir.--BBDO Canada, Toronto, Canada; *U.S. Private*, pg. 104
Cregg, Roger, III, Chief Fin. Officer & Exec. V.P.--Zenith Electronics Corp., Glenview, IL; *U.S. Public*, pg. 1790
Creighton, Dale E., Exec. V.P.-Opers.--London Life Insurance Group, London, Canada; *Int'l*, pg. 435
Crenshaw, Clarke, Exec. V.P.--National Fruit Product Company, Winchester, VA; *U.S. Private*, pg. 783
Crenshaw, Randall, Exec. V.P.-Procurement & Logistics--CommScope, Inc., Hickory, NC; *U.S. Public*, pg. 415
Crepon, Michel, Exec. V.P.--Pathe, Paris, France; *Int'l*, pg. 1024
Crew, William L., Exec. V.P.--Calsonic Climate Control, Inc., Irvine, CA; *Int'l*, pg. 944
Crews, Jesse V., Chief Investment Officer & Exec. V.P.--GATX Capital Corporation, San Francisco, CA; *U.S. Public*, pg. 690
Crichton, David R., Exec. V.P.-Opers.--Standex International Corporation, Salem, NH; *U.S. Public*, pg. 1505
Crigger, Gary B., Exec. V.P.--Bridgestone/Firestone, Inc., Nashville, TN; *Int'l*, pg. 213
Crippin, Ronald L., Exec. V.P.--American Modern Home Insurance Group, Amelia, OH; *U.S. Public*, pg. 1110
Cristo, Gus, Exec. V.P. & Dir.-Sls. & Mktg.--Ferguson International, Inc., Dallas, TX; *U.S. Private*, pg. 401
Critchlow, Norman, Exec. V.P.-Project Fin. Officer--Morse Diesel International, Inc., New York, NY; *U.S. Private*, pg. 762
Critser, Gary P., Sr. Exec. V.P., Treas. & Sec.--Kimball International, Inc., Jasper, IN; *U.S. Public*, pg. 956
Crittenden, Bruce, Exec. V.P.-Mortgage Services/Retail Services--Green Tree Financial Corporation, Saint Paul, MN; *U.S. Public*, pg. 761
Crneckiy, Martin, Jr., Chief Fin. Officer & Exec. V.P.--The Vollrath Company, L.L.C., Sheboygan, WI; *U.S. Private*, pg. 1143
Croatti, Robert L., Exec. V.P.--UniFirst Corporation, Wilmington, MA; *U.S. Public*, pg. 1665
Crocitto, Peter, Exec. V.P.--Valley National Bancorp, Wayne, NJ; *U.S. Public*, pg. 1705
Crombie, Christina, Chief Oper. Officer & Exec. V.P.--Talent Partners, Chicago, IL; *U.S. Private*, pg. 554
Cromeek, Henry, Chief Fin. Officer & Exec. V.P.-Fin.--Artco-Bell Corporation, Temple, TX; *U.S. Private*, pg. 86
Cron, David, Exec. V.P.-Mfg.--AEP Industries, Inc., South Hackensack, NJ; *U.S. Public*, pg. 4
Cronin, David M., Exec. V.P. & Treas.--First Maryland Bancorp, Baltimore, MD; *Int'l*, pg. 64
Cronin, James P., Chief Fin. Officer & Exec. V.P.--Cytec Industries Inc., West Paterson, NJ; *U.S. Public*, pg. 471
Cronin, Jim, Chief Oper. Officer & Exec. V.P.-Fin.--Ascent Entertainment Group, Inc., Denver, CO; *U.S. Public*, pg. 138
Cronin, William F., Exec. V.P.-Mktg.--CPI Corp., Saint Louis, MO; *U.S. Public*, pg. 283
Cronkhite, John, Exec. V.P. & Gen. Counsel--Sea Ray, Knoxville, TN; *U.S. Public*, pg. 266
Cross, Andy, Exec. V.P.-Sls. & Mktg.--MobileComm, Ridgefield Park, NJ; *U.S. Public*, pg. 1120
Cross, Eugene P., Chief Fin. Officer & Exec. V.P.-Fin.--Flowserve Corporation, Long Beach, CA; *U.S. Public*, pg. 658
Crosson, John, Exec. V.P.--Dailey & Associates, West Hollywood, CA; *U.S. Public*, pg. 909
Crosta, Edward A., Chief Exec. Officer & Exec. V.P. & Sec.--West Building Materials, Atlanta, GA; *U.S. Private*, pg. 1163
Crotty, Brian, Exec. V.P.-Bus. Plng.--Elan Corporation Plc, Dublin, Ireland; *Int'l*, pg. 435
Crotty, Kevin M., Exec. V.P.--Van Dyne-Crotty, Inc., Dayton, OH; *U.S. Private*, pg. 1132
Crowder, W.T., Jr., Exec. V.P.--Crowder Construction Co., Charlotte, NC; *U.S. Private*, pg. 291
Crowe, James Q., Exec. V.P.--Peter Kiewit Sons Inc., Omaha, NE; *U.S. Private*, pg. 619
Crowley, J. Samuel, Exec. V.P.-Opers.--CompUSA, Dallas, TX; *U.S. Public*, pg. 420
Crowley, Neil, Exec. V.P.-Retail Services--Pathmark Stores Incorporated, Woodbridge, NJ; *U.S. Private*, pg. 843
Crowley, Patrick, Chief Fin. Officer & Exec. V.P.--Abitibi-Consolidated Inc., Montreal, Canada; *Int'l*, pg. 19
Crowley, Robert A., Exec. V.P.-Commercial Real Estate--Citizens Bank of Massachusetts, Fairhaven, MA; *Int'l*, pg. 1132
Croyle, R.G., Exec. V.P.--Rowan Companies, Inc., Houston, TX; *U.S. Public*, pg. 1409
Crumley, William F., Exec. V.P.-Mfg.--WestPoint Stevens Inc., West Point, GA; *U.S. Public*, pg. 1762
Cudd, Bobby Joe, Exec. V.P.--RPC Incorporated, Atlanta, GA; *U.S. Public*, pg. 1356
Cuddihy, Tim, Exec. V.P. & Gen. Mgr.--Water Country USA, Williamsburg, VA; *U.S. Public*, pg. 114
Cuello, Alfredo, Exec. V.P. & Pres.-Opers./Europe--Avon Products, Inc., New York, NY; *U.S. Public*, pg. 155
Cuenin, James E., Jr., Exec. V.P.--Edwin B. Stimpson Company, Inc., Bayport, NY; *U.S. Private*, pg. 1043
Cuffaro, Joseph A., Jr., Chief Oper. Officer & Exec. V.P.--First American Appraisal Services, San Diego, CA; *U.S. Public*, pg. 625
Culhane, Patrick G., Exec. V.P.-Credit--Fair, Isaac and Company, Inc., San Rafael, CA; *U.S. Public*, pg. 609
Cullen, Brian C., Exec. V.P.-Opers.--King Kullen Grocery Co., Inc., Westbury, NY; *U.S. Private*, pg. 621
Cullen, Brian D., Exec. V.P.--Raytheon Systems Company, Arlington, VA; *U.S. Public*, pg. 1364
Cullen, Karen M., Exec. V.P. & Gen. Counsel--Long Island Bancorp, Inc., Melville, NY; *U.S. Public*, pg. 1013
Cullen, Nicholas T., Exec. V.P. & Pres.-Performance Prods. Div.--Bayer Corporation, Pittsburgh, PA; *Int'l*, pg. 172
Cullen, Nick T., Exec. V.P.-Coatings Indus. Chemicals Div.--Bayer Corporation, Pittsburgh, PA; *Int'l*, pg. 172
Culler, Eugene R., Jr., Exec. V.P.-N. American Tires--The Goodyear Tire & Rubber Company, Akron, OH; *U.S. Public*, pg. 752
Cullimore, Neil R., Exec. V.P.--CSC Financial Services Group, Austin, TX; *U.S. Public*, pg. 422
Cullinane, Michael P., Chief Fin. Officer, Exec. V.P. & Treas.--Platinum Technology, Inc., Oak Brook Terrace, IL; *U.S. Public*, pg. 1309
Culver, Curt S., Exec. V.P.--MGIC Investment Corporation, Milwaukee, WI; *U.S. Public*, pg. 1026
Culver, Larry G., Chief Oper. & Fin. Officer & Exec. V.P.--CellPro, Incorporated, Bothell, WA; *U.S. Public*, pg. 320
Cumming, Donald A., Exec. V.P.-Opers.--Rio Algom Limited, Toronto, Canada; *Int'l*, pg. 1118
Cummings, Craig M., Exec. V.P. & Gen. Mgr.--Vermilion County Division, Danville, IL; *U.S. Public*, pg. 438
Cummins, Bernard J., Chief Admin. Officer, Exec. V.P. & Dir.--EvansGroup, Salt Lake City, UT; *U.S. Private*, pg. 385
Cuneo, Ngaire E., Exec. V.P.-Corp. Devel.--Conseco Inc., Carmel, IN; *U.S. Public*, pg. 432
Cunnane, Joseph F., III, Exec. V.P.-Opers.--Davco Restaurants Inc., Crofton, MD; *U.S. Public*, pg. 488
Cunningham, David, Exec. V.P. & Gen. Mgr.--Utica National Life Insurance Company, Utica, NY; *U.S. Private*, pg. 1130
Cunningham, John P., Chief Fin. Officer & Exec. V.P.--Whirlpool Corporation, Benton Harbor, MI; *U.S. Public*, pg. 1764
Cunningham, Jonathan R., Exec. V.P. & Mgr.-N.Y. Reg. Sls.--Jefferies & Company, Inc., Los Angeles, CA; *U.S. Public*, pg. 925
Cunningham, Philip F., Exec. V.P.-Mktg. & Pres.-Mackenzie Financial Services Inc.--Mackenzie Financial Corporation, Toronto, Canada; *Int'l*, pg. 828
Cunningham, Robert, Exec. V.P.--Swift Transportation Co., Sparks, NV; *U.S. Public*, pg. 1543
Cunningham, Theodore R., Exec. V.P.--Chrysler Corporation, Auburn Hills, MI; *U.S. Public*, pg. 352
Cuoco, Renato Roberto, Exec. V.P.-EDP & Back Office--Banco Itau S.A., Sao Paulo, Brazil; *Int'l*, pg. 142
Curiale, Salvatore R., Sr. Exec. V.P.--American Life Insurance Company of New York, New York, NY; *U.S. Private*, pg. 769
Curiale, Salvatore R., Sr., Sr. Exec. V.P.-Technical Opers.--Mutual of America Life Insurance Company, New York, NY; *U.S. Private*, pg. 769
Curran, Stephen H., Chief Fin. Officer & Exec. V.P.--Primark Corporation, Waltham, MA; *U.S. Public*, pg. 1325
Curran, Timothy J., Exec. V.P. & Gen. Counsel--Curran Group, Inc., Crystal Lake, IL; *U.S. Private*, pg. 297
Curran, William, Chief Fin. Officer & Exec. V.P.--Philips Electronics North America Corporation, New York, NY; *Int'l*, pg. 1053
Currence, Richard M., Exec. V.P.--Tidewater Inc., New Orleans, LA; *U.S. Public*, pg. 1608
Currence, Richard M., Exec. V.P.--Pan-Marine International, Inc., New Orleans, LA; *U.S. Public*, pg. 1608
Currid, Grace, Exec. V.P.--Globe Mortgage America, LLC., River Edge, NJ; *U.S. Private*, pg. 458
Currier, Jeffrey, Chief Fin. Officer & Exec. V.P.-Fin.--Empire of Carolina, Inc., Delray Beach, FL; *U.S. Public*, pg. 579
Curry, Edward J., Chief Oper. Officer & Exec. V.P.--Moore Products Co., Spring House, PA; *U.S. Public*, pg. 1128
Curry, R.T., Exec. V.P.--Brock-McVey Company, Lexington, KY; *U.S. Private*, pg. 721
Curtan, Deborah, Exec. V.P.-Comedy--Columbia TriStar Television, Culver City, CA; *Int'l*, pg. 1282
Curti, Joseph T., M.D., Exec. V.P.--Searle & Co., Skokie, IL; *U.S. Public*, pg. 1125
Curtin, Thomas A., Exec. V.P.--Simplex Time Recorder Co., Gardner, MA; *U.S. Private*, pg. 1002
Curtin, Thomas J., Pres. & Chief Exec. Officer--Princeton Bank & Trust Company National Association, East Brunswick, NJ; *U.S. Public*, pg. 338
Curwen, Richard, Chief Fin. Officer & Exec. V.P.--Appleton Papers Inc., Appleton, WI; *Int'l*, pg. 567
Cusack, Thomas J., Exec. V.P.--Transamerica Corporation, San Francisco, CA; *U.S. Public*, pg. 1629
Cusano, Sam, Chief Fin. Officer & Exec.V.P.--Service Merchandise Company, Inc., Brentwood, TN; *U.S. Public*, pg. 1461
Cuylenberg, Peter van, Exec. V.P.-Opers.--Xerox Corporation, Stamford, CT; *U.S. Public*, pg. 1783
Cypriano, Marcio Artur Laurelli, Exec. V.P.--Banco Bradesco S.A., Sao Paulo, Brazil; *Int'l*, pg. 139
Cyr, Michele, Exec. V.P.-French Language Publishing--Telemedia Inc., Montreal, Canada; *Int'l*, pg. 1373
Czarnecki, Mark J., Exec. V.P.--Manufacturers & Traders Trust Company, Buffalo, NY; *U.S. Public*, pg. 631
Czura, Antony, Sr. Exec. V.P.--SGS Societe Generale de Surveillance Holding S.A., Geneva, Switzerland; *Int'l*, pg. 1153
D'Alessandro, David F., Sr. Exec. V.P.-Retail Sector--John Hancock Mutual Life Insurance Company, Boston, MA; *U.S. Private*, pg. 589
D'Amour, Charles L., Chief Oper. Officer, Exec. V.P. & Sec.--Big Y Foods Inc., Springfield, MA; *U.S. Private*, pg. 143
D'Angelo, Peter R., Chief Fin. Officer & Exec. V.P.--Raytheon Company, Lexington, MA; *U.S. Public*, pg. 1364
D'Antuono, F.M., Chief Oper. Officer & Exec. V.P.--MidCon Corp., Lombard, IL; *U.S. Public*, pg. 1210
D'arcy, John B., Exec. V.P.-Lending--Zions First National Bank, Salt Lake City, UT; *U.S. Public*, pg. 1793
D'Arcy, Katherine McKenzie, Exec. V.P. & Dir.-Human Resources--Citizens Financial Group, Inc., Providence, RI; *Int'l*, pg. 1132
Dabrowski, Mary, Exec. V.P.-Mktg., Fashion--Hampshire Hosiery, Inc., Spruce Pine, NC; *U.S. Public*, pg. 778
Dach, Leslie, Vice Chm. & Sr. Exec. V.P.--Edelman Worldwide, Inc., Washington, DC; *U.S. Private*, pg. 362
Dachowski, Peter R., Exec. V.P.-Insulation--CertainTeed Corporation, Valley Forge, PA; *Int'l*, pg. 1170
Dadario, Michael J., Div. Exec. V.P.-Stores & Opers.--Banana Republic, San Francisco, CA; *U.S. Public*, pg. 702
Daddario, Richard, Chief Fin. Officer & Exec. V.P.--The Mutual Life Insurance Company of New York, New York, NY; *U.S. Private*, pg. 769
Daddino, Anthony F., Chief Fin. Officer & Exec. V.P.--Donaldson, Lufkin, & Jenrette, Inc., New York, NY; *U.S. Public*, pg. 589
Daggett, Darlene M., Exec. V.P.-QVC Mdsg.--QVC, Inc., West Chester, PA; *U.S. Private*, pg. 897
Dagley, Larry J., Chief Fin. Officer & Exec. V.P.--Atmos Energy Corporation, Dallas, TX; *U.S. Public*, pg. 145
Daher, Thomas, Chief Fin. Officer & Exec. V.P.--Motch Corporation, Cleveland, OH; *Int'l*, pg. 1128
Dahl, Tor-Olof, Exec. V.P.--W. Rosenlew Ltd., Helsinki, Finland; *Int'l*, pg. 1428
Dahlberg, Leonard D., Jr., Exec. V.P.--Dixon Ticonderoga Company, Heathrow, FL; *U.S. Public*, pg. 514
Dahlen, R. Daniel, Chief Oper. Officer & Exec. V.P.--Meldrum & Fewsmith Communications Inc., Cleveland, OH; *U.S. Private*, pg. 730
Dahlman, Charles R., Exec. V.P.--Homestead House Inc., Westminster, CO; *U.S. Private*, pg. 537
Dahlstrand, Harold S., Exec. V.P.-H.R.--Spiegel, Inc., Downers Grove, IL; *U.S. Public*, pg. 1498
Dahly, John H., Chief Fin. Officer, Exec. V.P. & Sec.--Schultz Sav-O Stores, Inc., Sheboygan, WI; *U.S. Public*, pg. 1442
Dal Porto, James, Chief Oper. Officer & Exec. V.P.--I-Flow Corporation, Lake Forest, CA; *U.S. Public*, pg. 851

Dal Porto, Todd, Div. Exec. V.P.-Wholesale Prod.--Countrywide Home Loans Inc., Pasadena, CA; *U.S. Public*, pg. 452
Dale, T.J., Exec. V.P.--Manitowoc Western Company, Inc., La Mirada, CA; *U.S. Public*, pg. 1041
Daley, Charles D., Chief Oper. Officer & Exec. V.P.--QMS, Inc., Mobile, AL; *U.S. Public*, pg. 1346
Daley, Michael R., Chief Fin. Officer & Exec. V.P.--ACC Corp., Rochester, NY; *U.S. Public*, pg. 2
Dalgetty, Douglas R., Exec. V.P.--Canadian Western Bank, Edmonton, Canada; *Int'l*, pg. 259
Dallman, Dennis M., Exec. V.P.--Dryvit Systems, Inc., West Warwick, RI; *U.S. Public*, pg. 1357
Dalloy, Pierre, Exec. V.P.-H.R.--Credit Nationale, Paris, France; *Int'l*, pg. 344
Dally, Martha M., Exec. V.P.-Personal Prods.--Sara Lee Corporation, Chicago, IL; *U.S. Public*, pg. 1432
Dalton, Gary, Exec. V.P.--National Bancorp of Alaska, Inc., Anchorage, AK; *U.S. Public*, pg. 1153
Dalton, Gary, Exec. V.P.--National Bank of Alaska, Anchorage, AK; *U.S. Public*, pg. 1153
Dalton, Michael J., Sr. Exec. V.P.--UNITIL Service Corporation, Hampton, NH; *U.S. Public*, pg. 1693
Damlamian, Jean-Jacques, Exec. Dir.-Corp. Devel. & Tech.--France Telecom, Paris, France; *Int'l*, pg. 503
Dammenman, Charles J., Exec. V.P.--LNR Communications, Hauppauge, NY; *U.S. Private*, pg. 639
Dammers, Steven W., Exec. V.P.-Acct. Mngmt.--Grey Advertising Inc., New York, NY; *U.S. Public*, pg. 764
Damveld, Gary, Exec. V.P. & Dir.-Mktg.--S & P Company, Mill Valley, CA; *U.S. Private*, pg. 954
Dana, Charles H., Exec. V.P.-Devel., Plng. & Sourcing--Owens Corning, Toledo, OH; *U.S. Public*, pg. 1236
Dane, Joseph, Exec. V.P.--Deering Ice Cream, Inc., Portland, ME; *U.S. Private*, pg. 403
Daniel, E. Leaon, Exec. V.P.-Intl. EOR & Bus. Devel.--Occidental Oil & Gas Corporation, Bakersfield, CA; *U.S. Public*, pg. 1210
Daniel, Jeanne B., Exec. V.P.-Mdsg. & Mktg.--Tiffany & Co., New York, NY; *U.S. Public*, pg. 1608
Daniel, Richard, Chief Fin. Officer & Mng. Dir.--Bankers Trust Company, New York, NY; *U.S. Public*, pg. 185
Daniel, Richard H., Chief Fin. Officer & Exec. V.P.--Bankers Trust New York Corporation, New York, NY; *U.S. Public*, pg. 185
Daniels, Dennis, Exec. V.P.-Domestic Devel.--United Artists Theatre Circuits Incorporated, Englewood, CO; *U.S. Private*, pg. 1120
Daniels, Leroy, Exec. V.P.--Doosan Crown Can Mfg. Co. Ltd., Seoul, Korea; *U.S. Public*, pg. 465
Daniels, Sam, Exec. V.P.--Amtrol Inc., West Warwick, RI; *U.S. Private*, pg. 300
Dannenberg, John C., Exec. V.P.--International Pipe Machinery Corp., Sioux City, IA; *U.S. Private*, pg. 571
Danner, Bryant C., Exec. V.P. & Gen. Counsel--Edison International, Rosemead, CA; *U.S. Public*, pg. 564
Dansby, Ronald, Exec. V.P.--Western Towing Company, Channelview, TX; *U.S. Public*, pg. 961
Danz, E.B., Exec. V.P.--Donohue Paper Sales Corporation, Jericho, NY; *Int'l*, pg. 1075
Daoust, Paul R., Chief Oper. Officer & Exec. V.P.--Watson Wyatt Worldwide, Bethesda, MD; *U.S. Private*, pg. 1154
Darby, Stephen J., Jr., Exec. V.P.--U.S. Trust Corporation, New York, NY; *U.S. Public*, pg. 1688
Dardel, Pierre Emmanuel, Sr. Exec. V.P.--Financiere Saint Dominique, Paris, France; *Int'l*, pg. 344
Dardis, Stan K., Exec. V.P. & Retail Banking Services Dir.--Bremer Financial Corporation, Saint Paul, MN; *U.S. Private*, pg. 167
Dardis, Stan K., Exec. V.P. & Dir.-Retail Banking--Bremer Financial Services, Inc., Saint Paul, MN; *U.S. Private*, pg. 167
Dare, G.N., Exec. V.P.--Dare Foods Limited, Kitchener, Canada; *Int'l*, pg. 383
Darkazanli, S.K., Exec. V.P.--Loblaw Companies Limited, North York, Canada; *Int'l*, pg. 1495
Darland, Stephen A., Exec. V.P.--J. Walter Thompson Company, New York, NY; *Int'l*, pg. 1483
Darnell, Jerry R., Exec. V.P.-Franchise--Sterling Vision, Inc., East Meadow, NY; *U.S. Public*, pg. 1516
Darr, James J., Exec. V.P.--State Street Corporation, Boston, MA; *U.S. Public*, pg. 1513
Darwin, Gary R., Exec. V.P.--Cardinal Inc., Rahway, NJ; *U.S. Private*, pg. 208
Dauer, John L., Exec. Dir.-Plng. & Devel.--Campbell-Ewald Advertising, Warren, MI; *U.S. Public*, pg. 908
Dauger, Jean-Marie, Exec. V.P.-Corp. Plng. & Control--Gaz de France, Paris, France; *Int'l*, pg. 541
Daugherty, Wayne F., Exec. V.P & Gen. Mgr.-Railroad Div.--XTRA, Inc., Portland, ME; *U.S. Public*, pg. 1787
Daugherty, William T., Exec. V.P.-Corp. Retail Store Opers.--W.S. Badcock Corporation, Mulberry, FL; *U.S. Private*, pg. 109
Dauman, Philippe, Dep. Chm., Chief Admin. Officer, Exec. V.P. & Gen. Counsel--Viacom Inc., New York, NY; *U.S. Private*, pg. 775
Daunhauer, John Paul, Exec. V.P.--Byerly Ford-Nissan Inc., Louisville, KY; *U.S. Private*, pg. 191
Dausch, James F., Exec. V.P.-Devel.--The Mills Corporation, Arlington, VA; *U.S. Public*, pg. 1113
Dautray, Robert, Dir.-Scientific--CEA-Industrie (Commissariat a l'Energie Atomique), Paris, France; *Int'l*, pg. 239
Dauvillaire, Pierre, Exec. Dir.-Corp. Resources--France Telecom, Paris, France; *Int'l*, pg. 503
Davenport, J. Sidney, IV, Exec. V.P.--Ryland Mortgage Co., Columbia, MD; *U.S. Public*, pg. 1414
Davenport, Mark, Exec. V.P. & Gen. Mgr.--J.T. Davenport & Sons, Inc., Sanford, NC; *U.S. Private*, pg. 314
Davey, Robert G., Chief Fin. Officer & Exec. V.P.--McCormick & Company, Incorporated, Sparks, MD; *U.S. Public*, pg. 1066
David, Romeo S., Exec. V.P.--Philippine Airlines, Inc., Manila, Philippines; *Int'l*, pg. 1050
David, William W., Chief Fin. Officer & Exec. V.P.--Sunshine Mining And Refining Company, Boise, ID; *U.S. Public*, pg. 1536
Davidson, Alexander J., Sr. V.P.-Exploration--Barrick Gold Corporation, Toronto, Canada; *Int'l*, pg. 168
Davidson, Brian, Exec. V.P.-Devel.--Integrated Health Services, Inc., Owings Mills, MD; *U.S. Public*, pg. 884
Davidson, D. Dewayne, Exec. V.P.--Liberty Bank & Trust Company of Oklahoma City, Oklahoma City, OK; *U.S. Public*, pg. 174
Davidson, Howard, Exec. V.P. & Creative Dir.--J. Brown/LMC Group, Stamford, CT; *U.S. Public*, pg. 764
Davies, Gareth, Exec. V.P.-U.K., Sweden, Norway & Denmark--Fiskars Oy AB, Helsinki, Finland; *Int'l*, pg. 492
Davies, John B., Exec. V.P.--Massachusetts Mutual Life Insurance Co., Springfield, MA; *U.S. Private*, pg. 712
Davies, John H., Exec. V.P.--Barringer Technologies Inc., New Providence, NJ; *U.S. Public*, pg. 191
Davies, Patrick, Exec. Officer--Sasol Limited, Johannesburg, South Africa; *Int'l*, pg. 1196
Davis, Alan, Chief Fin. Officer & Exec. V.P.--Shape Inc., Kennebunk, ME; *U.S. Private*, pg. 990
Davis, Anne, Exec. V.P.-Admin--New Balance Athletic Shoe, Inc., Boston, MA; *U.S. Private*, pg. 792
Davis, Arnold, Exec. V.P.--DG Bank (Switzerland) Ltd., Zurich, Switzerland; *Int'l*, pg. 352
Davis, Baird, Sr. V.P.-Circulation--Ziff-Davis Publishing Company, New York, NY; *Int'l*, pg. 1276
Davis, Bill, Exec. V.P. & Gen. Mgr.--Sea World of Florida, Orlando, FL; *U.S. Public*, pg. 114
Davis, Charles H., Chief Credit Officer--Harris Bankcorp, Inc., Chicago, IL; *Int'l*, pg. 154
Davis, Chris A., Chief Fin. Officer & Exec. V.P.--Gulfstream Aerospace Corporation, Savannah, GA; *U.S. Private*, pg. 419
Davis, Craig S., Exec. V.P.-Lending & Fin. Services--Washington Mutual Inc., Seattle, WA; *U.S. Public*, pg. 1741
Davis, David J., Chief Oper. Officer & Exec. V.P.--Kleer-Vu Plastics Corp., Compton, CA; *U.S. Public*, pg. 962
Davis, Debbie, Exec. V.P.--Generations Gold, West Palm Beach, FL; *U.S. Private*, pg. 463
Davis, Donald, Exec. V.P. & Media Plng. Dir.--Young & Rubicam New York, New York, NY; *U.S. Private*, pg. 1198
Davis, E. Stephen, Exec. V.P.-Scrivner Grp.--Fleming Companies, Inc., Oklahoma City, OK; *U.S. Public*, pg. 652
Davis, Earl E., Exec. V.P.-Commercial--Weirton Steel Corporation, Weirton, WV; *U.S. Public*, pg. 1751
Davis, H. Stewart, Exec. V.P.-Finishing--Thomaston Mills, Inc., Thomaston, GA; *U.S. Public*, pg. 1599
Davis, Hillel, Exec. V.P.--Republic National Bank of New York, New York, NY; *U.S. Public*, pg. 1380
Davis, Hillel, Exec. V.P.--Republic Bank for Savings, New York, NY; *U.S. Public*, pg. 1380
Davis, Jack E., Exec. V.P.-Commercial Opers.--APS, Phoenix, AZ; *U.S. Public*, pg. 1297
Davis, James H., Chief Oper. Officer & Exec. V.P.--Quanex Corporation, Houston, TX; *U.S. Public*, pg. 1349
Davis, Jeffery H., Exec. V.P.--Davis Industries Inc., Plymouth, MI; *U.S. Private*, pg. 315
Davis, John W., Exec. V.P.-Non-Textile Opers.--Greenwood Mills, Inc., Greenwood, SC; *U.S. Private*, pg. 479
Davis, John J., Exec. V.P.--CACI International Inc, Arlington, VA; *U.S. Public*, pg. 272
Davis, Kenneth C., Exec. V.P.-Far East--ConAgra International, Omaha, NE; *U.S. Public*, pg. 426
Davis, Leon, Exec. Dir.--Rio Tinto PLC, London, United Kingdom; *Int'l*, pg. 1118
Davis, Lloyd G., Chief Fin. Officer, Exec. V.P.-Fin., Treas. & Sec.--Baldor Electric Company, Fort Smith, AR; *U.S. Public*, pg. 168
Davis, M., Exec. V.P.--Waterville TG Inc., Waterville, Canada; *Int'l*, pg. 1487
Davis, Marcie, Exec. V.P., Treas. & Sec.--PharmHouse, Inc., New York, NY; *U.S. Public*, pg. 1286
Davis, Mike, Exec. V.P.-Mktg./Locum Tenens, Inc.--Allegiant Physician Services, Atlanta, GA; *U.S. Public*, pg. 45
Davis, Nancy, Natl. Chief Fin. Officer & Exec. V.P.--Lincoln Property Company, Dallas, TX; *U.S. Private*, pg. 668
Davis, Paul, Exec. V.P.--Uniden America Corporation, Fort Worth, TX; *Int'l*, pg. 1433
Davis, Richard K., Exec. V.P.-Consumer Banking--Starbanc Corporation, Cincinnati, OH; *U.S. Public*, pg. 1510
Davis, Richard L., Exec. V.P. & Gen. Mgr.--American Drug Stores Inc., Oak Brook, IL; *U.S. Public*, pg. 93
Davis, Robert, Exec. V.P.--Reyco Industries, Inc., Springfield, MO; *U.S. Private*, pg. 926
Davis, Russell S., Exec. V.P.--Sears, Roebuck and Co., Hoffman Estates, IL; *U.S. Public*, pg. 1452
Davis, Sam R., Jr., Exec. V.P.-Fin.--Igloo Products Corporation, Houston, TX; *U.S. Public*, pg. 265
Davis, Thomas W., Exec. V.P.--Merrill Lynch & Co., Inc., New York, NY; *U.S. Public*, pg. 1097
Davis, Tim, Exec. V.P. & Global Bus. Dir.-Shell, Unilever--J. Walter Thompson Company, New York, NY; *Int'l*, pg. 1483
Davis, Tracy, Exec. V.P.-Mktg. & Operations--AppleTree Markets, Houston, TX; *U.S. Private*, pg. 78
Davison, John M., Chief Fin. Officer & Exec. V.P.-Opers.--Imax Corporation, Mississauga, Canada; *Int'l*, pg. 661
Day, George R., Exec. V.P. & Chief Credit Officer--Trustmark Corporation, Jackson, MS; *U.S. Public*, pg. 1643
Day, George R., Exec. V.P.--Trustmark National Bank, Jackson, MS; *U.S. Public*, pg. 1643
Day, Julian, Chief Fin. Officer & Exec. V.P.--Safeway Inc., Pleasanton, CA; *U.S. Public*, pg. 1426
Day, Martha Bonsal, Exec. V.P.--Joshua L. Baily Co., Inc., Hoboken, NJ; *U.S. Private*, pg. 110
Day, Roy, Exec. V.P.--Essex Grain Products, Inc., Frazer, PA; *U.S. Private*, pg. 383
De Angelis, J.D., Exec. V.P.--California Products Corp., Cambridge, MA; *U.S. Private*, pg. 201
de Belloy, Geoffrey, Exec. V.P.-Midrange Markets/Europe--Storage Technology Corporation, Louisville, CO; *U.S. Public*, pg. 1522
de Blieck, J.L., Exec. V.P.--KTI Group B.V., Zoetermeer, Netherlands; *Int'l*, pg. 837
de Bodinat, Henri, Sr. Exec. V.P.-Mktg., Sls. & Prods.--Club Mediterranee SA, Paris, France; *Int'l*, pg. 298
de Boer, A.J.M., Exec. V.P.--ABN-AMRO Holding N.V., Amsterdam, Netherlands; *Int'l*, pg. 8
de Boer, R.J., Exec. V.P.--ABN-AMRO Holding N.V., Amsterdam, Netherlands; *Int'l*, pg. 8
de Broqueville, Axel, Exec. Dir.-Chemicals, Paints & Res.--Petrofina S.A., Brussels, Belgium; *Int'l*, pg. 1043
de Burckhart, Maria Isabel P., Exec. V.P.--BanPonce Corporation, Hato Rey, PR; *U.S. Public*, pg. 176
de Carbonell, Annie Astor, Chief Fin. Officer & Sr. Exec. V.P.--Firstbank Puerto Rico, Santurce, PR; *U.S. Public*, pg. 644
de Castejon, Jose M. Gonzalez, Exec. V.P.--Banco Santander Puerto Rico, Hato Rey, PR; *Int'l*, pg. 143
de Cler, W.J.J., Exec. V.P.--ABN-AMRO Holding N.V., Amsterdam, Netherlands; *Int'l*, pg. 8
de Courcel, Georges Chodron, Grp. Exec. V.P.-Intl. Banking & Fin.--Banque Nationale de Paris, Paris, France; *Int'l*, pg. 163
de David-Beauregard, Arnaud, Exec. V.P.-Mechanical Engrng. & Svcs.--PSA Peugeot Citroen, Paris, France; *Int'l*, pg. 1020
de Guillebon, Marc, Exec. V.P.-Intl. Opers.--Credit Commercial de France, Paris, France; *Int'l*, pg. 341
de Jonge, R., Exec. V.P.--Campina Melkunie BV, Zaltbommel, Netherlands; *Int'l*, pg. 254
de Kalbermatten, Thierry, Exec. V.P.-Mngmt.--Bobst S.A., Lausanne, Switzerland; *Int'l*, pg. 198
De Keersmaecker, Guido, Exec. V.P.-Industrial Adhesives & Technical Consumer Prods.--Henkel KGaA, Dusseldorf, Germany; *Int'l*, pg. 609
de Kleuver, Wim, Exec. V.P.--Philips International B.V., Eindhoven, Netherlands; *Int'l*, pg. 1051
de la Calle, Antonio, Exec. V.P.-Maintenance & Construction--Sol Melia, Palma de Mallorca, Spain; *Int'l*, pg. 1277
de la Martiniere, Garard, Chief Fin. Officer & Sr. Exec. V.P.-Holding Companies--AXA-UAP, Paris, France; *Int'l*, pg. 18
de la Mora, Casto, Exec. V.P.--Banco Santander, Madrid, Spain; *Int'l*, pg. 143
de Lagausie, Patrice, Exec. V.P.-Legal Affairs--PSA Peugeot Citroen, Paris, France; *Int'l*, pg. 1020
de Lange, B.J., Exec. V.P.--Campina Melkunie BV, Zaltbommel, Netherlands; *Int'l*, pg. 254
de las Heras, Gonzalo, Exec. V.P.--Banco Santander, Madrid, Spain; *Int'l*, pg. 143
de Lencquesaing, Edouard, Exec. V.P.-Logistics & Opers.--Credit Commercial de France, Paris, France; *Int'l*, pg. 341
de Moraes Schettert, Adalberto, Exec. V.P.--Uniao de Bancos Brasileiros S.A. (Unibanco), Sao Paulo, Brazil; *Int'l*, pg. 1431
De Ney, Richard L., Exec. V.P.-Corp. Strategy & Devel.--Borden, Inc., Columbus, OH; *U.S. Private*, pg. 157
de Noce, Vicente, Chief Fin. Officer & Exec. V.P.--LPC Industrias Alimenticias S.A., Vila Jaguara, Brazil; *Int'l*, pg. 380
de Oliveiro, Evandro Lopes, Exec. V.P.--Banco do Brasil, Brasilia, Brazil; *Int'l*, pg. 141
de Pear, Ron, Exec. V.P., Exec. Media Dir.-JWT/Europe, Chm.-Global Media Group--J. Walter Thompson Company, New York, NY; *Int'l*, pg. 1483
de Puppi, L., Exec. Dir.--Zanussi Componenti Plastica S.p.A., Oderzo, Italy; *Int'l*, pg. 442
de Reus, J., Exec. V.P.--ABN-AMRO Holding N.V., Amsterdam, Netherlands; *Int'l*, pg. 8
de Segonzac, Patrick, Exec. V.P.--Credit Commercial de France, Paris, France; *Int'l*, pg. 341
de Seze, Amaury-Daniel, Sr. Exec. V.P.--Banque Paribas, Paris, France; *Int'l*, pg. 319
de Souza, Alvaro A.C., Exec. V.P.--Citicorp, New York, NY; *U.S. Public*, pg. 376
de Souza, Jose Carlos, Exec. V.P.--Uniao de Bancos Brasileiros S.A. (Unibanco), Sao Paulo, Brazil; *Int'l*, pg. 1431
de St. Paer, Jerry M., Exec. V.P.--The Equitable Companies Incorporated, New York, NY; *U.S. Public*, pg. 588
de Waij, J., Exec. V.P.--Labouchere N.V., Amsterdam, Netherlands; *Int'l*, pg. 26
de Weck, Pierre, Exec. V.P.--Union Bank of Switzerland, Zurich, Switzerland; *Int'l*, pg. 1439
Deal, James A., Exec. V.P. & Pres.-DTCA--American Healthcorp Inc., Nashville, TN; *U.S. Public*, pg. 78
Dean, Alexander L., Exec. V.P.--Builders Inc., Wichita, KS; *U.S. Private*, pg. 440
Dean, Lloyd H., Exec. V.P.-Central Regional Opers.--Advocate Health Care, Oak Brook, IL; *U.S. Private*, pg. 23
Dean, Simon P., Exec. V.P.-Residential--Royal LePage Limited, Don Mills, Canada; *Int'l*, pg. 1143
Deason, J.E., Chief Fin. Officer & Exec. V.P.--Wolverine Tube Inc., Huntsville, AL; *U.S. Public*, pg. 1774
Deaver, Michael, Exec. V.P.--Edelman Worldwide, Inc., Washington, DC; *U.S. Private*, pg. 362
DeBard, Daniel L., Exec. V.P.--Merchants National Bank, Terre Haute, IN; *U.S. Public*, pg. 1217
DeBarr, Alex, Exec. V.P.--Advanstar Communications, Cleveland, OH; *U.S. Private*, pg. 22
DeBeliso, Richard J., PE, Exec. V.P. & Sec.--Giffels Hoyem Basso, Inc., Troy, MI; *U.S. Private*, pg. 452
deBoer, Louis II, Exec. V.P.-HBO Enterprises--Home Box Office, Inc., New York, NY; *U.S. Public*, pg. 1612
DeBoer, Richard B., Exec. V.P.--Morgan Drive Away, Inc., Elkhart, IN; *U.S. Public*, pg. 1022

DeBone, Louis J., Exec. V.P.--Mylan Pharmaceuticals Inc., Morgantown, WV; *U.S. Public*, pg. 1143

DeBoni, Graziano, Exec. V.P. & Chief Fin. Officer--Hugo Boss USA, Inc., New York, NY; *Int'l*, pg. 637

deBrier, Donald P., Exec. V.P., Sr. Gen. Counsel & Corp. Sec.--Occidental Petroleum Corporation, Los Angeles, CA; *U.S. Public*, pg. 1210

DeBuono, Laureen, Exec. V.P.-H.R., Gen Counsel & Sec.--Nellcor Puritan Bennett Incorporated, Pleasanton, CA; *U.S. Public*, pg. 1039

DeCardenas, Jennie, Exec. V.P.--Cacique, Inc., City of Industry, CA; *U.S. Private*, pg. 198

Dechin, Patrick, Chief of Staff--Lagardere Groupe, Paris, France; *Int'l*, pg. 791

Decina, John A., Exec. V.P.--Barr & Barr, Inc., New York, NY; *U.S. Private*, pg. 117

Decio, Terrence M., Sr. Exec. V.P.-Sls. & Mktg.--Skyline Corporation, Elkhart, IN; *U.S. Public*, pg. 1476

DeCius, Dennis A., Chief Fin. Officer, Exec. V.P. & Asst. Sec.--Pacific Capital Bancorp, Salinas, CA; *U.S. Public*, pg. 1247

Deck, Walter S., Exec. V.P.--Hardin's-Sysco Food Services, Inc., Memphis, TN; *U.S. Public*, pg. 1551

Decker, Gayle, Exec. V.P.--Blumenthal/Lansing Company, Lansing, IA; *U.S. Public*, pg. 1187

Deckop, Joe, Exec. V.P. & Chief Fin. Officer--Victoria's Secret Stores, Reynoldsburg, OH; *U.S. Public*, pg. 995

DeCordova, Bryan, Chief Fin. Officer & Exec. V.P.--Michaels Stores, Inc., Irving, TX; *U.S. Public*, pg. 1104

Decoster, Richard B., Chief Oper. Officer & Exec. V.P.--Willis Corroon Corp. of Missouri, Saint Louis, MO; *Int'l*, pg. 1506

Decressac, Anne, Exec. V.P.-Personnel & Communication--Technip, Paris, France; *Int'l*, pg. 1360

Decurtins, Arthur, Exec. V.P.-Private Banking & Securities Admin.--Union Bank of Switzerland, Zurich, Switzerland; *Int'l*, pg. 1439

Dederer, James W., Exec. V.P.& Gen. Counsel--Transamerica Life Companies, Los Angeles, CA; *U.S. Public*, pg. 1630

Deegan, Gail, Chief Fin. Officer, Exec. V.P. & Treas.--Houghton Mifflin Company, Boston, MA; *U.S. Public*, pg. 841

Dees, Alvin H., Jr., Exec. V.P.-Mktg.--Alfa Corporation, Montgomery, AL; *U.S. Public*, pg. 40

Dees, G. Michael, Exec. V.P.-Marisa Christina Design & Mdsg.--Marisa Christina Inc., New Hyde Park, NY; *U.S. Public*, pg. 1044

Dees, Steve, Exec. V.P.-Corp. Rels., Commun. & Intl. Svcs.--Farmland Industries, Inc., Kansas City, MO; *U.S. Private, pg. 395*

DeForest, James V., Exec. V.P.--Peckham Industries, Inc., White Plains, NY; *U.S. Private*, pg. 846

DeFries, Douglas L., Exec. V.P.-Fin.--Bank of Utah, Ogden, UT; *U.S. Private*, pg. 114

Degee, F., Exec. V.P.-Personnel--Cockerill Sambre, Brussels, Belgium; *Int'l*, pg. 301

DeGraan, Edward F., Exec. V.P.-Duracell N. Atlantic Grp.--The Gillette Company, Boston, MA; *U.S. Public*, pg. 743

DeGraan, Edward F., Exec. V.P.-N. Atlantic Grp.--Duracell International Inc., Bethel, CT; *U.S. Public*, pg. 743

Dehecq, Jean Francois, Exec. V.P.-Health Div.--Elf Aquitane, Paris, France; *Int'l*, pg. 444

Dehelly, Charles, Exec. V.P.--Bull S.A., Louveciennes, France; *Int'l*, pg. 315

Dehner, J. B., Exec. V.P. & Chief Oper. Officer--The Kansas City Southern Railway Co., Kansas City, MO; *U.S. Public, pg. 944*

Deignan, John M., Exec. V.P.--U.S. Trust Corporation, New York, NY; *U.S. Public*, pg. 1688

Deily, Linnet F., Exec. V.P.-Services for Investment Mgrs.--The Charles Schwab Corporation, San Francisco, CA; *U.S. Public*, pg. 1442

Deitchle, Gerald W., Chief Fin. Officer & Exec. V.P.--Cheesecake Factory Incorporated, Calabasas Hills, CA; *U.S. Public*, pg. 343

Deiters, F.B., Exec. V.P.--ABN-AMRO Holding N.V., Amsterdam, Netherlands; *Int'l*, pg. 8

Dekel, Elie, Exec. V.P.-Mktg. & Adv.--Saban Entertainment, Los Angeles, CA; *U.S. Private*, pg. 959

del Fonso, Edgardo, Exec. V.P.-Fin.--Philippine Long Distance Telephone Company, Manila, Philippines; *Int'l*, pg. 1051

Del Neri, Edoardo, Exec. V.P.-Sls. & Mktg.--Merloni Elettrodomestici S.P.A., Fabriano, Italy; *Int'l*, pg. 860

Delabriere, Yann, Exec. V.P.-Fin.--PSA Peugeot Citroen, Paris, France; *Int'l*, pg. 1020

Delamasantiere, Claude, Exec. V.P.--Microturbo Division, Toulouse, France; *Int'l*, pg. 786

Delaney, Steven C., Exec. V.P. & Dir.-Capital Mkts.--Scott & Stringfellow Financial, Inc., Richmond, VA; *U.S. Public*, pg. 1445

DeLaney, Steven C., Exec. V.P.--Scott & Stringfellow, Inc., Richmond, VA; *U.S. Public*, pg. 1445

Delaye, Michel, Corp. Exec. V.P.-Space & Defense--Aerospatiale, Paris, France; *Int'l*, pg. 28

Delcommune, Michel-Marc, Exec. Dir.-Corp. Fin. & Insurance--Petrofina S.A., Brussels, Belgium; *Int'l*, pg. 1043

DeLeo, Daniel, Exec. V.P.--American Country Insurance Co., Chicago, IL; *U.S. Private*, pg. 1030

Deletang, Bruno, Exec. V.P.-Fin.--CGG American Services Inc., Houston, TX; *Int'l*, pg. 241

Deleuze, R., Exec. V.P.--Elf Atochem S.A., Paris, France; *Int'l*, pg. 445

Delfino, Enrique Conde, Exec. V.P.--Mantex, S.A.C.A., Caracas, Venezuela; *Int'l*, pg. 840

Delgado, Robert M., Exec. V.P.--Hensley & Co., Phoenix, AZ; *U.S. Private*, pg. 523

Delin, Jan-Arthur, Exec. V.P.--Aritmos AB, Helsingborg, Sweden; *Int'l*, pg. 1072

Delisle, Andre, Chief Fin. Officer & Exec. V.P.-Corp. Plng.--Hydro-Quebec, Montreal, Canada; *Int'l*, pg. 640

DeLitizia, Alfred T., Exec. V.P. & Gen. Mgr.--Gem Industries Finance Corporation, Toccoa, GA; *U.S. Private*, pg. 442

Della Noce, Joseph, Jr., Exec. V.P.--Rotelle, Inc., West Point, PA; *U.S. Public*, pg. 1389

Delldvigne, John P., Exec. V.P.-Plastics--Huls America Inc., Somerset, NJ; *Int'l*, pg. 1455

DeLoach, Harris E., Jr., Exec. V.P.--Sonoco Products Company, Hartsville, SC; *U.S. Public*, pg. 1485

Delp, Mark, Sr. V.P.-Sls. & Mktg.--Gemtron Corporation, Sweetwater, TN; *Int'l*, pg. 1523

DeLuca, Susan, Chief Fin. Officer, Exec. V.P. & Controller--Aero Data Metal Crafters, Ronkonkoma, NY; *U.S. Private*, pg. 23

Delvaux, Jean-Louis, Exec. V.P.-Fin. & Corp. Sec.--Financiere Saint Dominique, Paris, France; *Int'l*, pg. 344

DelZotto, Leo, Exec. V.P.--Tridel Enterprises Inc., Downsview, Canada; *Int'l*, pg. 1423

DeMagistris, Manny, Exec. Grp. Creative Dir.--Avrett, Free & Ginsberg, Inc., New York, NY; *U.S. Private*, pg. 103

deMaio, Mike, Chief Oper. Officer & Exec. V.P.--Lois/USA Inc., New York, NY; *U.S. Public*, pg. 1011

DeMaire, J. Douglas, Exec. V.P.--Primex Technologies, Inc., Saint Petersburg, FL; *U.S. Public*, pg. 1329

DeMaria, Joseph A., Jr., Exec. V.P.--DeMaria Building Co. Inc., Novi, MI; *U.S. Private*, pg. 323

Demeritt, Stephen R., Exec. V.P. & Chief Exec. Officer-Cereal Partners Worldwide--General Mills, Inc., Minneapolis, MN; *U.S. Public*, pg. 717

Demeritt, William, Exec. V.P.--Keller Ladders Inc., Fort Lauderdale, FL; *U.S. Public*, pg. 1684

Demers, Clement, Exec. V.P.--Cadev, Montreal, Canada; *Int'l*, pg. 249

DeMichele, Lawrence, Exec. V.P.--Excell Manufacturing Company, Providence, RI; *U.S. Private*, pg. 387

DeMille, Wallace J., Exec. V.P. & Chief Oper. Officer--Monumental Life Insurance Company, Baltimore, MD; *Int'l*, pg. 27

DeMilt, William A., Exec. V.P.-Real Estate Mngmt.--Mutual of America Life Insurance Company, New York, NY; *U.S.* Private, pg. 769

Dempsey, Donald H., Chief Fin. Officer & Exec. V.P.--Choice Hotels International, Inc., Silver Spring, MD; *U.S. Public*, pg. 351

den Hoed, Jean, Exec. V.P.-Fin. & Control--Akzo Nobel N.V., Arnhem, Netherlands; *Int'l*, pg. 42

Denda, Nobuyuki, Exec. V.P.--Intel Japan, Tokyo, Japan; *U.S. Public*, pg. 887

Denhardt, Gerry, Chief Oper. Officer & Exec. V.P.--Projects Unlimited, Inc., Dayton, OH; *U.S. Private*, pg. 890

Denis, Etienne, Exec. Dir.--Union Miniere, Brussels, Belgium; *Int'l*, pg. 1441

Denison, Floyd G., Exec. V.P.-Fin.--American Bankers Insurance Group, Inc., Miami, FL; *U.S. Public*, pg. 67

Denison, Floyd G., Exec. V.P.-Fin.--American Bankers Life Assurance Co. of Florida, Miami, FL; *U.S. Public*, pg. 67

Denison, John G., Exec. V.P.-Corp. Srvcs.--Southwest Airlines Co., Dallas, TX; *U.S. Public*, pg. 1493

Denk, Gregory P., Exec. V.P.--Kitchell Corporation, Phoenix, AZ; *U.S. Private*, pg. 624

Dennis, Robert, Sr. Exec. V.P.--Asbury Automotive Group, Conshohocken, PA; *U.S. Private*, pg. 87

Denny, Dwight D., Exec. V.P.-Devel.--Ryder System, Inc., Miami, FL; *U.S. Public*, pg. 1413

DeNovellis, Donato A., Chief Fin. Officer & Exec. V.P.--Ekco Group, Inc., Nashua, NH; *U.S. Public*, pg. 566

Denoyel, Gilles, Chief Fin. Officer & Exec. V.P.--Credit Commercial de France, Paris, France; *Int'l*, pg. 341

Dent, Gerald J., Exec. V.P.-Credit Admin.--Zions Bancorporation, Salt Lake City, UT; *U.S. Public*, pg. 1792

Dent, Gerald J., Exec. V.P.-Credit Admin.--Zions First National Bank, Salt Lake City, UT; *U.S. Public*, pg. 1793

Dent, Thompson S., Exec. V.P.-Corp. Svcs. & Sec.--Phycor, Inc., Nashville, TN; *U.S. Public*, pg. 1293

Dentice, Thomas S., Exec. V.P.--McDonald's Corporation, Oak Brook, IL; *U.S. Public*, pg. 1068

Depp, Herbert P., Exec. V.P.--General Electric Capital Aviation Services, San Francisco, CA; *U.S. Public*, pg. 712

Deputy, Howard, Exec. V.P.-Central Region--Bergen Brunswig Corporation, Orange, CA; *U.S. Public*, pg. 213

Der Boghosian, Andrea, Exec. V.P.--Miller Shandwick Technologies, Boston, MA; *Int'l*, pg. 1227

Deramo, Frank, Exec. V.P.-Eastern Opers.--Syroco Inc., Peabody, MA; *Int'l*, pg. 844

Derby, Beth, Exec. V.P.--Health Resources International, West Hartford, CT; *U.S. Private*, pg. 514

Deremo, John B., Exec. V.P.--IPD Marketing Services, Inc., Cincinnati, OH; *U.S. Public*, pg. 1336

DeRoeck, Walter A., Chm. Bd. & Chief Exec. Officer--TCC Industries, Austin, TX; *U.S. Public*, pg. 1554

Deromedi, Roger, Pres.-W. Europe & Exec. V.P.--Kraft Jacobs Suchard AG, Zurich, Switzerland; *U.S. Public*, pg. 1288

DeRosa, Paul R., Mng. Dir.--Eastbridge Capital Inc., New York, NY; *Int'l*, pg. 933

DeRosa, Terence, Exec. V.P.--Electronic Systems Group, Gaithersburg, MD; *U.S. Public*, pg. 474

DeRosa, Terrence, Exec. V.P.--DRS Electronic Systems, Inc., Gaithersburg, MD; *U.S. Public*, pg. 474

DeRossett, Tommy, Exec. V.P.--Associated Aircraft Supply Company, Dallas, TX; *U.S. Private*, pg. 89

DeRoy, Craig I., Exec. V.P. & Gen. Counsel--The First American Financial Corporation, Santa Ana, CA; *U.S. Public*, pg. 624

DeRuiter, Henry, Exec. V.P.--The Pervo Paint Company, Los Angeles, CA; *U.S. Private*, pg. 856

DeRuvo, Alf, Exec. V.P. & Dir.-Res. & Devel.--Svenska Cellulosa Aktiebolaget (SCA), Stockholm, Sweden; *Int'l*, pg. 1326

DeSalvo, Dan, Exec. V.P.-Sls.--American Family Mutual Insurance Co., Madison, WI; *U.S. Private*, pg. 53

DeSantis, Damon, Exec. V.P.--Rexall Sundown Inc., Boca Raton, FL; *U.S. Public*, pg. 1384

Deschamps, Jean-Dominique, Exec. V.P.--Compagnie Generale Des Eaux, Paris, France; *Int'l*, pg. 321

DeShong, Harry B., Exec. V.P.-Mktg.--U-Haul International, Inc., Phoenix, AZ; *U.S. Private*, pg. 49

Despres, Germain L., Exec. V.P.--Danisco Ingredients USA, Inc., New Century, KS; *Int'l*, pg. 378

Desrosier, Jim, Exec. V.P.-Corp. Mktg.--Excite, Inc., Redwood City, CA; *U.S. Public*, pg. 599

Destin, Raymond, Exec. V.P.-Europe--ConAgra International, Omaha, NE; *U.S. Public*, pg. 426

Deutsch, Howard R., Exec. V.P.--Lincare Holdings Inc., Clearwater, FL; *U.S. Public*, pg. 996

Deutsch, Lester, Exec. V.P.--The Deutsch Company, Santa Monica, CA; *U.S. Private*, pg. 328

Deutsch, Robert V., Chief Fin. Officer & Exec. V.P.--Executive Risk, Inc., Simsbury, CT; *U.S. Public*, pg. 599

Devane, John, Ph.D., Exec. V.P.-Res. & Devel. & Acting Chief Scientific Officer--Elan Corporation Plc, Dublin, Ireland; *Int'l*, pg. 435

DeVaux, Lloyd, Exec. V.P.-Corp. Support Services--Union Planters Bank, Memphis, TN; *U.S. Public*, pg. 1669

Devine, John M., Chief Fin. Officer & Exec. V.P.--Ford Motor Company, Dearborn, MI; *U.S. Public*, pg. 661

Devine, Matthew E., Chief Fin. Officer, Exec. V.P. & Treas.--Chancellor Media Corporation, Irving, TX; *U.S. Public*, pg. 335

Devito, Jerry, Exec. V.P.--WFS Financial, Inc., Irvine, CA; *U.S. Public*, pg. 1757

Devlin, J. Richard, Exec. V.P.-Law & External Affairs--Sprint Corporation, Westwood, KS; *U.S. Public*, pg. 1500

DeVries, Klay, Exec. V.P.-Opers.--Periscope Marketing Communications, Minneapolis, MN; *U.S. Private*, pg. 853

DeWitt, Thomas H., Exec. V.P.-Admin. & Gen. Counsel--Standex International Corporation, Salem, NH; *U.S. Public*, pg. 1505

Dexmier, Jean-Yves, Chief Fin. Officer. & Exec. V.P.--Informix Software, Menlo Park, CA; *U.S. Public*, pg. 876

Deyirmendjian, Jacques, Exec. V.P.-Intl.--Gaz de France, Paris, France; *Int'l*, pg. 541

Di Iorio, Anthony, Exec. V.P. & Controller--PaineWebber Incorporated, New York, NY; *U.S. Public*, pg. 1252

Dial, Thomas Ole, Exec. V.P. & Chief Investment Officer--Northstar Investment Management Corporation, Greenwich, CT; *U.S. Public*, pg. 1375

Diamond, David, Exec. V.P.-Mktg. & New Applications--Catalina Marketing Corporation, Saint Petersburg, FL; *U.S. Public*, pg. 314

Diamond, Harry A., AIA, Exec. V.P. & Treas.--Giffels Hoyem Basso, Inc., Troy, MI; *U.S. Private*, pg. 452

Diamond, Jay, Exec. V.P.--DeCorp, Carrollton, TX; *U.S. Public*, pg. 948

Diamond, Jay, Exec. V.P.--Halmode Apparel, Inc., New York, NY; *U.S. Public*, pg. 948

Diamond, Mark, Exec. V.P.--Southern Electronics Corporation, Tucker, GA; *U.S. Public*, pg. 1490

Diamond, Mark, Exec. V.P.--Southern Electronics Distributors International, Tucker, GA; *U.S. Public*, pg. 1490

Diamond, Shelley, Exec. V.P. & Acct. Mng. Dir.--Young & Rubicam New York, New York, NY; *U.S. Private*, pg. 1198

Diaz, Jose Luis, Exec. V.P.--Banco Santander, Madrid, Spain; *Int'l*, pg. 143

Diaz, Manuel L., Exec. V.P.--Republic National Bank of New York, New York, NY; *U.S. Public*, pg. 1380

Dible, David, Exec. V.P.-Specialty Div.--Wal-Mart Stores, Inc., Bentonville, AR; *U.S. Public*, pg. 1732

DiCerchio, Richard D., Chief Oper. Officer & Sr. Exec. V.P.--Costco Wholesale, Issaquah, WA; *U.S. Public*, pg. 451

Dick, Stacy S., Exec. V.P.--Tenneco Inc., Greenwich, CT; *U.S. Public*, pg. 1577

Dicke, Arnold A., Exec. V.P.-Chief Prods.--USLIFE Corporation, New York, NY; *U.S. Public*, pg. 77

Dickerson, Robert C., Exec. V.P.--Southwestern Petroleum Corporation, Fort Worth, TX; *U.S. Private*, pg. 1019

Dickes, Lyle, Exec. V.P.--Foster & Gallagher, Inc., Peoria, IL; *U.S. Private*, pg. 420

Dickinson, Gary W., Exec. V.P.--Hughes Electronics Corporation, Westchester, CA; *U.S. Public*, pg. 720

DiCosimo, Vincent J., Exec. V.P.--Cornerstone Propane G.P. Inc., Watsonville, CA; *U.S. Public*, pg. 1201

DiCristofaro, Leonard, Exec. V.P.--Majorica Jewelry Ltd., New York, NY; *U.S. Private*, pg. 697

Diederick, Dale R., Exec. V.P.--Pacific Capital Bancorp, Salinas, CA; *U.S. Public*, pg. 1247

Dieffenbach, N., Exec. V.P.--Hauck Manufacturing Company Inc., Lebanon, PA; *Int'l*, pg. 1149

Diehl, Michelle, Chief Fin. Officer & Exec. V.P.--Kragie/Newell, Des Moines, IA; *U.S. Private*, pg. 634

Diels, Jean-Pierre, Exec. V.P.--Republic National Bank of New York, New York, NY; *U.S. Public*, pg. 1380

Dierbeck, John J., Exec. V.P.--The Rottlund Company, Inc., Roseville, MN; *U.S. Public*, pg. 1406

Dieter, Mary Q., Chief Oper. Officer, Chief Fin. Officer & Exec. V.P.--Sonoma Valley Bank, Sonoma, CA; *U.S. Public*, pg. 1487

Dietrich, Mark M., Exec. V.P.--First Midwest Bank, N.A., Itasca, IL; *U.S. Public*, pg. 636

Dietrich, William V., Exec. V.P.--Kastle Systems LLC, Arlington, VA; *U.S. Private*, pg. 608

Dietz, James F., Exec. V.P.--PCS Nitrogen, Memphis, TN; *Int'l*, pg. 1064

Dietz, Robert J., Vice Chm. & Exec. V.P.--Gannett Fleming Affiliates, Inc., Camp Hill, PA; *U.S. Private*, pg. 439

Digby, Kent S., Exec. V.P.-Mngmt. & Mktg.--The Mills Corporation, Arlington, VA; *U.S. Public*, pg. 1113

Diggs, Lawrence N., Chief Oper. Officer & Exec. V.P.--Willis Corroon Corp. of Michigan, Livonia, MI; *Int'l*, pg. 1506

Dignam, Arthur F., Chief Fin. Officer, Chief Acctg. Officer & Exec. V.P.--Caribiner International, Inc., New York, NY; *U.S. Public*, pg. 305

Dilissen, Theo, Exec. V.P.-European Div.--ISS-International Service System A/S, Holte, Denmark; *Int'l*, pg. 656

Dill, Peter, Exec. V.P.-Sulzer Escher Wyss Group--Sulzer Ltd., Winterthur, Switzerland; *Int'l*, pg. 1305

Dillard, Alex, Exec. V.P.--Dillard's, Inc., Little Rock, AR; *U.S.* Public, pg. 509

Dillard, Mike, Exec. V.P.--Dillard's, Inc., Little Rock, AR; *U.S. Public*, pg. 509

Diller, Charles H., Jr., Chief Fin. Officer & Exec. V.P.--JLG Industries, Inc., McConnellsburg, PA; *U.S. Public*, pg. 918

Dillon, Adrian T., Chief Fin. Officer, Plng. Officer & Exec. V.P.--Eaton Corporation, Cleveland, OH; *U.S. Public*, pg. 555

Dillon, John H., Exec. V.P.--NationsBank of Tennessee, Nashville, TN; *U.S. Public*, pg. 1163

Dillon, R.I., Exec. V.P. & Treas.--Lafarge Construction Materials, Canfield, OH; *Int'l*, pg. 788

Dillon, Robert, Exec. V.P.--Sony Electronics, Park Ridge, NJ; *Int'l*, pg. 1281

Dills, Patrick G., Exec. V.P.-Sls.--First Health Group Corp., Downers Grove, IL; *U.S. Public*, pg. 635

DiLouis, Anthony J., Exec. V.P.--Nason and Cullen Inc., King of Prussia, PA; *U.S. Private*, pg. 775

DiMeola, Richard, Chief Oper. Officer & Exec. V.P.--Consolidated Cigar Corporation, Fort Lauderdale, FL; *U.S. Private*, pg. 690

Dimick, Neil F., Chief Fin. Officer & Exec. V.P.--Bergen Brunswig Corporation, Orange, CA; *U.S. Public*, pg. 213

Dimmick, Paul H., Exec. V.P.-Capital Markets--Mellon Bank Corporation, Pittsburgh, PA; *U.S. Public*, pg. 1084

Dimmock, Graham, Exec. V.P.--PartnerRe Ltd., Pembroke, Bermuda; *Int'l*, pg. 1024

Dimock, R. R., Exec. V.P.--Kennecott Holdings Corporation, Magna, UT; *Int'l*, pg. 1119

Dimos, Steven G., Exec. V.P.--First National Bank in Massillon, Massillon, OH; *U.S. Public*, pg. 646

Dimun, Anthony, Chief Fin. Officer, Exec. V.P., Treas. & Sec.--Vital Signs, Inc., Totowa, NJ; *U.S. Public*, pg. 1723

Dingman, Joseph W., Exec. V.P.-Fin. & Admin.--The L & B Group, Dallas, TX; *U.S. Public*, pg. 1673

DiNicola, Joseph A., Exec. V.P.--Payless Car Rental System, Inc., Saint Petersburg, FL; *U.S. Private*, pg. 844

Dinius, Raymond L., Exec. V.P.--Countrywide Servicing Exchange, Pasadena, CA; *U.S. Public*, pg. 453

Dinkel, Gene, Chief Oper. Officer & Exec. V.P.--Connector Manufacturing Company, Hamilton, OH; *U.S. Private*, pg. 264

Dinkelacker, Kurt E., Chief Fin. Officer & Exec. V.P.--Ikon Office Solutions, Inc., Malvern, PA; *U.S. Public*, pg. 862

Dionne, Alfred, Exec. V.P.--Barr & Barr, Inc., New York, NY; *U.S. Private*, pg. 117

Dionne, Gervais, Ph.D., Exec. V.P.-Res. & Devel.--BioChem Pharma Inc., Laval, Canada; *Int'l*, pg. 196

DiPofi, Daniel J., Exec. V.P.--Niagara Frontier Hockey, L.P., Buffalo, NY; *U.S. Private*, pg. 798

DiSante, Robert, Exec. V.P.-Fin.--FCA International Ltd., Westmount, Canada; *Int'l*, pg. 470

DiSomma, Joseph, Exec. V.P.-Res. & Devel.--Merle Norman Cosmetics, Inc., Los Angeles, CA; *U.S. Private*, pg. 733

Dissett, Robert C., Exec. V.P., Asst. Treas. & Dir.-Opers.--A.G. Edwards, Inc., Saint Louis, MO; *U.S. Public*, pg. 565

Ditmer, Erik, Exec. V.P.-New York--Right Management Consultants, Inc., Philadelphia, PA; *U.S. Public*, pg. 1390

Ditomassi, George R., Jr., Exec. V.P. & Pres.-Global Innovation--Hasbro, Inc., Pawtucket, RI; *U.S. Public*, pg. 797

Dittmer, Robert G., Exec. V.P.-Fin./Admin. & Sec.--Agra Inc., Calgary, Canada; *Int'l*, pg. 30

Dittrich, Roger, Exec. V.P.--T & D Metal Products, Wasco, IL; *U.S. Private*, pg. 638

Divet, P.Y., Exec. V.P.-Chemical Distr. Europe--Royal Pakhoed NV, Rotterdam, Netherlands; *Int'l*, pg. 1147

Dixler, Joseph M., Exec. V.P.--Nuarc Company, Inc., Niles, IL; *U.S. Private*, pg. 808

Dixon, James M., Exec. V.P.--Nextel Communications, Mc Lean, VA; *U.S. Public*, pg. 1180

Doan, Dan, Exec. V.P.--Merchants National Bank, Terre Haute, IN; *U.S. Public*, pg. 1217

Doane, Paul J., Exec. V.P.-Opers.--Indianapolis Water Company, Indianapolis, IN; *U.S. Public*, pg. 1185

Dobbs, David L., Exec. V.P.-Pur.--Shoney's, Inc., Nashville, TN; *U.S. Public*, pg. 1467

Dobranowski, Anthony E., Chief Fin. Officer & Exec. V.P.--Tesma International Inc., Concord, Canada; *Int'l*, pg. 830

Dobrez, Dan, Exec. V.P.--Dober Chemical Corp., Midlothian, IL; *U.S. Private*, pg. 337

Docherty, Bill, Exec. V.P.-Consumer Prods.--MTD Products, Inc., Valley City, OH; *U.S. Private*, pg. 688

Dodd, J. David, Exec. V.P.--American Publishing Management Services Inc., West Frankfort, IL; *Int'l*, pg. 632

Dodd, Pete, Exec. V.P.--InterAmerican-Star Group, Los Angeles, CA; *Int'l*, pg. 1529

Dodelin, F.J., Chief Fin. Officer & Exec. V.P.--The Hardaway Company, Columbus, GA; *U.S. Private*, pg. 501

Dodge, E.V., Exec. V.P.--Canadian Pacific Railway, Calgary, Canada; *Int'l*, pg. 258

Dodwell, Keith, Exec. V.P.--Autotote Corporation, Newark, DE; *U.S. Public*, pg. 150

Doeren, William B., Exec. V.P.--GC International, Inc., Chestnut Hill, MA; *U.S. Public*, pg. 693

Doerges, Norman, Exec. V.P.--Disneyland, Anaheim, CA; *U.S. Public*, pg. 511

Doherty, Gerald, Grp. Exec. V.P.-Global Capital Markets Grp.--Bank of America NT&SA, San Francisco, CA; *U.S. Public*, pg. 180

Dohmen, Robert, Exec. V.P.--The F. Dohmen Company, Germantown, WI; *U.S. Private*, pg. 338

Dolan, Michael, Exec. V.P.-Hospital Sls. & Devel.--HBE Corporation/Design Build Divisions, Saint Louis, MO; *U.S. Private*, pg. 489

Dolan, Michael, Chief Oper. Officer & Exec. V.P.--Smead Manufacturing Company, Hastings, MN; *U.S. Private*, pg. 1006

Dolan, Paul E., III, Exec. V.P. & Mng. Dir.-Fetzer Winery--Brown-Forman Beverages Worldwide, Louisville, KY; *U.S. Public*, pg. 261

Dolanski, P., Exec. V.P.-Sys. & Fin.--SLM Holding Corp., Washington, DC; *U.S. Public*, pg. 1419

Dolgin, Tracy, Exec. V.P.-Mktg./Fox Sports--Fox Broadcasting Company (FBC), Beverly Hills, CA; *Int'l*, pg. 926

Dolle, Guy, Exec. V.P.--Groupe Usinor, Paris, France; *Int'l*, pg. 570

Dollinger, Joel M., Exec. V.P.--First Central Financial Corporation, Lynbrook, NY; *U.S. Private*, pg. 406

Domingos, K. Kirk, III, Sr. Exec. V.P.-Admin.--Hibernia Corporation, New Orleans, LA; *U.S. Public*, pg. 825

Dominguez, Ronald, Exec. V.P.-Walt Disney Attractions/West Coast--Disneyland, Anaheim, CA; *U.S. Public*, pg. 511

Domis, Raymond C., Chief Fin. Officer & Exec. V.P.--GraphLine Inc., Tamarac, FL; *U.S. Private*, pg. 471

Don, Michael H., Exec. V.P.-Apparel, PEM & Home Grp.--Fred Meyer Stores, Portland, OR; *U.S. Public*, pg. 1103

Donahue, Robert, Chief Fin. Officer & Exec. V.P.--Manufacturers' Services Ltd., Concord, MA; *U.S. Private*, *pg. 701*

Donald, Joe K., Exec. V.P.--Champion International Corp., Stamford, CT; *U.S. Public*, pg. 333

Donaldson, Jerry, Exec. V.P. & Chief Exec. Officer--First National Bank of Saxton, Allentown, PA; *U.S. Public*, pg. 1222

Donch, John, Exec. V.P. & Exec. Creative Dir.--EvansGroup, San Francisco, CA; *U.S. Private*, pg. 385

Donegan, Mark, Exec. V.P.--Precision Castparts Corp., Portland, OR; *U.S. Public*, pg. 1320

Donmoyer, Tim, Chief Fin. Officer & Exec. V.P.--Eller Media Company, Phoenix, AZ; *U.S. Public*, pg. 383

Donnelly, Richard, Exec. V.P.--George Kovacs Lighting, Inc., Glendale, NY; *U.S. Private*, pg. 634

Donnelly, Robert, Exec. V.P.-Sls. & Mktg.--Glastic Corporation, Cleveland, OH; *Int'l*, pg. 740

Donner, Robert D., Exec. V.P.--Champion Business Forms, Glendale Heights, IL; *U.S. Private*, pg. 228

Donovan, John S., Exec. V.P. & Gen. Counsel--Cives Corporation, Roswell, GA; *U.S. Private*, pg. 241

Donovan, Patrick J., Exec. V.P.--Norwest Bank Minnesota N.A., Minneapolis, MN; *U.S. Public*, pg. 1202

Donovan, Paul, Chief Fin. Officer & Exec. V.P.--Sundstrand Corporation, Rockford, IL; *U.S. Public*, pg. 1533

Donovan, Richard G., Exec. V.P.-Construction--Willis Corroon Corp. of Minnesota, Minneapolis, MN; *Int'l*, pg. 1506

Doo, Burton, Exec. V.P.--Altron Incorporated, Wilmington, MA; *U.S. Public*, pg. 59

Dooley, Thomas E., Dep. Chm. & Exec. V.P.-Fin., Corp. Devel. & Communications--Viacom Inc., New York, NY; *U.S. Private*, pg. 775

Doolin, Wallace, Exec. V.P.-Franchise & Corp. Devel.--TGI Friday's, Inc., Addison, TX; *U.S. Private*, pg. 212

Doppelt, Earl H., Exec. V.P. & Gen. Counsel.--A.C. Nielsen, Stamford, CT; *U.S. Public*, pg. 1183

Doppelt, Lawrence, Exec. V.P.--Goldberger Doll Mfg. Company, Inc., Brooklyn, NY; *U.S. Private*, pg. 459

Doramus, W. Michael, Exec. V.P.--Echelon International Corporation, Saint Petersburg, FL; *U.S. Public*, pg. 560

Doran, Don, Exec. V.P.--W.J. & Dennis Co., Elgin, IL; *U.S. Private*, pg. 1144

Doran, Robert J., Exec. V.P.--McDonald's Corporation, Oak Brook, IL; *U.S. Public*, pg. 1068

Dorio, Patrick J., Exec. V.P.-Commerciel Banking Group--First Security Bank of New Mexico, Albuquerque, NM; *U.S. Public*, pg. 637

Dorman, Timothy, Exec. V.P.-W. U.S. Region--Right Management Consultants, Inc., Philadelphia, PA; *U.S. Public*, pg. 1390

Dornemann, Michael, Dr., Mng. Dir.--Bertelsmann AG, Gutersloh, Germany; *Int'l*, pg. 189

Dorner, Horst, Exec. V.P.--Dorner Manufacturing Corp., Hartland, WI; *U.S. Private*, pg. 340

Doroff, Frank, Exec. V.P.-GMM RTW--Bloomingdale's, New York, NY; *U.S. Public*, pg. 617

Dorsen, Hariette, Sr. V.P., Sec. & Gen. Counsel--Bantam Doubleday Dell Publishing Group, Inc., New York, NY; *Int'l*, pg. 191

Dorsey, C. Donald, Exec. V.P.--PETsMART, Inc., Phoenix, AZ; *U.S. Public*, pg. 1281

Dorsey, Jerry E., Chief Oper. Officer & Exec. V.P.--The West Company, Incorporated, Lionville, PA; *U.S. Public*, pg. 1755

Dorso, Michelle, Exec. V.P. & Out of Home Dir.--Zenith Media Services, Inc., New York, NY; *U.S. Private*, pg. 1204

Dorward, Don, Exec. V.P. & Mng. Dir.-San Francisco--Grey Advertising Inc., Western Div., Los Angeles, CA; *U.S. Public*, pg. 764

Dorward, Don, Exec. V.P. & Mng. Dir.--Grey Advertising Inc., San Francisco, CA; *U.S. Public*, pg. 764

Doshan, Jeffrey R., Exec. V.P.--Things Remembered, Inc., Highland Heights, OH; *U.S. Public*, pg. 397

Douay, Philippe, Chief Fin. Officer & Exec. V.P.--Bertrand Faure, Boulogne, France; *Int'l*, pg. 192

Doug-Min, Moon, Exec. V.P.-Project & Energy--Daewoo Corporation, Seoul, Korea; *Int'l*, pg. 357

Douglas, Frank L., M.D., Exec. V.P.-Global Res.--Hoechst Marion Roussel, Inc., Bridgewater, NJ; *Int'l*, pg. 624

Douglas, Jim, Chief Fin. Officer & Exec. V.P.--World Airways, Inc., Herndon, VA; *U.S. Public*, pg. 1780

Douglas, Luis A., Sr. Exec. V.P.-Corp. Clients--The Bank of Bermuda Limited, Hamilton, Bermuda; *Int'l*, pg. 150

Douglas, Robert L., Exec. V.P.--Laurel Trust Company, Johnstown, PA; *U.S. Public*, pg. 164

Douin, Georges, Exec. V.P.-Strategic Plng. & Intl. Opers.--Renault, Boulogne-Billancourt, France; *Int'l*, pg. 1102

Dout, A. Jacqueline, Chief Fin. Officer & Exec. V.P.--Champion Enterprises, Inc., Auburn Hills, MI; *U.S. Public*, *pg. 332*

Douthit, Randy, Exec. V.P.-Television Production--Quincy Jones Entertainment, Los Angeles, CA; *U.S. Public*, pg. 1611

Dowdle, James C., Exec. V.P.--Tribune Company, Chicago, IL; *U.S. Public*, pg. 1635

Dowlan, James R., Sr. Exec. V.P.-Dealer Ctr. Div.--Westcorp, Irvine, CA; *U.S. Public*, pg. 1756

Dowling, John, Exec. V.P.--Cushman & Wakefield, Inc., New York, NY; *Int'l*, pg. 873

Dowling, Robert, Pres. & Exec. V.P.-The Hollywood Reporter--BPI Communications Inc., New York, NY; *Int'l*, pg. 1446

Downe, Bill, Exec. V.P.-Noth American Corp. Banking--Bank of Montreal - Chicago, Chicago, IL; *Int'l*, pg. 154

Downe, William A., Exec. V.P.-N. American Corp. Banking--Bank of Montreal, Toronto, Canada; *Int'l*, pg. 153

Downie, John F., Sr. V.P.--Things Remembered, Inc., Highland Heights, OH; *U.S. Public*, pg. 397

Downing, Andrew J., Chief Oper. Officer & Exec. V.P.--Metro Information Services, Virginia Beach, VA; *U.S. Public*, pg. 1102

Downing, Scott L., Exec. V.P.--Lowell Packing Company, Fitzgerald, GA; *U.S. Private*, pg. 679

Downing, William E., Chief Fin. Officer, Exec. V.P. & Treas.--Pacific Telesis Group, San Francisco, CA; *U.S. Public*, pg. 1415

Downs, Michael, Exec. V.P.--Tokyo-Mitsubishi Futures (USA) Inc., Chicago, IL; *Int'l*, pg. 157

Downs, Thomas, Exec. V.P.-Opers. & Service--QVC, Inc., West Chester, PA; *U.S. Private*, pg. 897

Doyle, Anthony E., Exec. V.P.-Licensee--Le Peep's Grill Inc., Littleton, CO; *U.S. Private*, pg. 655

Doyle, Cecil G., Chief Fin. Officer, Exec. V.P., Treas. & Sec.--Hayes, Seay, Mattern & Mattern, Inc., Roanoke, VA; *U.S. Private*, pg. 513

Doyle, Dennis M., Exec. V.P. & Pres.-Far & Middle East, Austral/Asia--Chiquita Banana North America, Cincinnati, OH; *U.S. Public*, pg. 349

Doyle, Edward G., Exec. V.P.--Chivas Products Ltd., Sterling Heights, MI; *U.S. Private*, pg. 238

Doyle, Jack T., Exec. V.P.--The Fifth Third Bank of Kentucky, Louisville, Louisville, KY; *U.S. Public*, pg. 621

Doyle, James F., Exec. V.P.-Worldwide--Worldwide Quaker Beverages, Chicago, IL; *U.S. Public*, pg. 1347

Drainville, Gary P., Exec. V.P.-H.R. & Trust Asset Mngmt.--Citizens Banking Corporation, Flint, MI; *U.S. Public*, pg. 379

Drake, J.S., Exec. V.P.--Camelot Communications, Inc., Dallas, TX; *U.S. Private*, pg. 203

Drapeau, Norman, Exec. V.P.-Worldwide Sls. & Mktg.--PSDI, Bedford, MA; *U.S. Private*, pg. 828

Drappier, Jacques, Exec. V.P.-Flight Opers.--Sabena, Zaventem, Belgium; *Int'l*, pg. 1168

Drasher, Glenn D., Exec. V.P.-Mktg.--Buffets, Inc., Eden Prairie, MN; *U.S. Public*, pg. 267

Dreeben, Alan, Exec. V.P.--Block Distributing Company, San Antonio, TX; *U.S. Private*, pg. 149

Dreibelbis, David E., Exec. V.P. & Gen. Mgr.-Mill Grp.--Rock-Tenn Company, Norcross, GA; *U.S. Public*, pg. 1396

Dreisbach, Albert, Exec. V.P.--E.J. Brooks Company, Newark, NJ; *U.S. Private*, pg. 172

Drennan, Joseph T., Exec. V.P.--CoreStates Bank, N.A., Philadelphia, PA; *U.S. Public*, pg. 446

Dresel, John, Pres.--Full House Sports & Entertainment, Seattle, WA; *U.S. Public*, pg. 16

Dresmann, Robert, Exec. V.P.-Admin.--The Hennegan Company, Florence, KY; *U.S. Private*, pg. 522

Dresser, W. Donald, Exec. V.P., Dir.-Devel. & Asst. Sec.--United Foods, Inc., Bells, TN; *U.S. Public*, pg. 1677

Dreyer, William E., Sr. Exec. V.P.-External Affairs--SBC Communications Inc., San Antonio, TX; *U.S. Public*, pg. 1415

Driessen, Christine F., Chief Fin. Officer & Sr. V.P.--ESPN, Inc., Bristol, CT; *U.S. Public*, pg. 512

Driessen, P.E., Exec. V.P.--ABN-AMRO Holding N.V., Amsterdam, Netherlands; *Int'l*, pg. 8

Drinan, Helen G., Exec. V.P. & Dir.-H.R.--BankBoston Corporation, Boston, MA; *U.S. Public*, pg. 183

Driscoll, Daniel J., Exec. V.P.-Bus. Devel.--Arnold Advertising, Mc Lean, VA; *U.S. Private*, pg. 84

Driscoll, Karen, Exec. V.P.--Arnold Communications, Inc., Boston, MA; *U.S. Private*, pg. 83

Drnec, Richard, Exec. V.P.--Jelmar Company, Lincolnwood, IL; *U.S. Private*, pg. 585

Dromer, Alain, Exec. V.P.-Asset Mngmt. Grp.--Credit Commercial de France, Paris, France; *Int'l*, pg. 341

Droppert, Marc, Exec. V.P.-Legal, H.R. & Corp. Affairs--Physio-Control Corporation, Redmond, WA; *U.S. Public*, pg. 1294

Drumm, Curtis W., Exec. V.P.-Opers.--The Metal Ware Corp., Two Rivers, WI; *U.S. Private*, pg. 734

Drumm, Robert, Exec. V.P.--Lanoga Corporation, Redmond, WA; *U.S. Private*, pg. 650

Drury, Dan, Exec. V.P.--Mautz Paint Co., Madison, WI; *U.S. Private*, pg. 715

Drury, Robert E., Chief Admin. Officer & Exec. V.P.--United Dominion Industries, Ltd., Charlotte, NC; *U.S. Public*, pg. 1675

Druten, Robert J., Chief Fin. Officer & Hallmark-V.P.-Admin.--Hallmark Cards, Inc., Kansas City, MO; *U.S. Private*, pg. 495

Dry, Mickey W., Exec. V.P. & Chief Credit Officer--Wachovia Corporation, Winston Salem, NC; *U.S. Public*, pg. 1730

Dryden, Robert L., Exec. V.P.-Airplane Prod.--Boeing Commercial Airplane Group, Renton, WA; *U.S. Public*, pg. 240

du Bois, Patrick, Exec. V.P. & Sec. Gen.--Sabena, Zaventem, Belgium; *Int'l*, pg. 1168

Du Monceau, John, Exec. V.P.-Service Vouchers & Car Rental--Accor S.A., Evry, France; *Int'l*, pg. 20

du Toit, Andre G., Exec. Officer--Sasol Limited, Johannesburg, South Africa; *Int'l*, pg. 1196

Du, Yu Hong, Vice Chm. & Exec. V.P.--Keng Hua Paper Products Co., Inc., Manila, Philippines; *Int'l*, pg. 729
Dubelko, Robert, Exec. V.P.--Carsey-Werner Company, LLC, Studio City, CA; *U.S. Private*, pg. 216
Dubiel, Robert S., Exec. V.P.--Acushnet Company, Fairhaven, MA; *U.S. Public*, pg. 675
Dubin, Fred, Exec. V.P. & Natl. Brdcst. Dir.--The Media Edge, New York, NY; *U.S. Private*, pg. 1079
Dublon, Dina, Exec. V.P.-Corp. Plng.--The Chase Manhattan Corporation, New York, NY; *U.S. Public*, pg. 337
DuBois, Richard, Exec. V.P.-Sls.--Astec America Inc., Carlsbad, CA; *Int'l*, pg. 93
DuBroe, Carmen, Exec. V.P.-Mktg.--Weight Watchers International, Inc., Woodbury, NY; *U.S. Public*, pg. 806
Dubrow, Louis A., Exec. V.P.--Trans-Apparel Group, Michigan City, IN; *U.S. Public*, pg. 796
Dubuque, Kenneth R., Exec. V.P.-Intl. Trust & Investments--Mellon Bank Corporation, Pittsburgh, PA; *U.S. Public*, pg. 1084
Duchesne, Yvan, Chief Oper. Officer & Exec. V.P.-Fine Papers Div.--Rolland Inc., Saint-Jerome, Canada; *Int'l*, pg. 273
Duck Yu, Hwan, Exec. V.P.--LG Group, Seoul, Korea; *Int'l*, pg. 778
Duda, Andrew L., Exec. V.P.--A. Duda & Sons Inc., Oviedo, FL; *U.S. Private*, pg. 344
Dudek, John, Chief Oper. Officer & Exec. V.P.--Dudek & Bock Spring Manufacturing Company, Chicago, IL; *U.S. Private*, pg. 344
Dudley, Michael A., Exec. V.P. & Pres.-CDT Intl.--Cable Design Technologies Corporation, Pittsburgh, PA; *U.S. Public*, pg. 287
Dudley, Steve, Exec. V.P.-Sls.--Rossignol Ski Co., Williston, VT; *Int'l*, pg. 1127
Dudley, William H., Exec. V.P.-Investment Opers.--American Express Financial Advisor, Minneapolis, MN; *U.S. Public*, *pg. 73*
Dueker, William A. Jr., Exec. V.P.--Republic National Bank of New York, New York, NY; *U.S. Public*, pg. 1380
Duer, Ted D., Exec. V.P.--Farmers & Merchants Bank-Eastern Shore, Onley, VA; *U.S. Public*, pg. 1089
Duesberg, Michael, Exec. V.P.--Bayerische Hypotheken-und Wechsel-Bank Aktiengesellschaft, Munich, Germany; *Int'l*, pg. 175
Duff, Peter J., Exec. V.P.--E.J. Footwear Corp., Endicott, NY; *U.S. Public*, pg. 1684
Duffar, Francois, Exec. V.P.-National--Cossette Communication Marketing, Quebec, Canada; *Int'l*, pg. 335
Duffy, Bill, Chief Oper. Officer & Exec. V.P.--Barnes & Noble Direct, Rockleigh, NJ; *U.S. Public*, pg. 189
Duffy, Bill, Chief Oper. Officer & Exec. V.P.--B. Dalton Bookseller, Inc., New York, NY; *U.S. Public*, pg. 189
Duffy, James F., Exec. V.P. & Gen. Counsel--The American Stock Exchange, New York, NY; *U.S. Private*, pg. 62
Duffy, John, Sr. Exec. V.P. & Chief of Mfg.--Callaway Golf Company, Carlsbad, CA; *U.S. Public*, pg. 294
Duffy, Karen, Exec. V.P. & Media Dir.--Laughlin/Constable, Inc., Milwaukee, WI; *U.S. Private*, pg. 653
Duffy, Steven M., Exec. V.P.--Wolverine World Wide, Inc., Rockford, MI; *U.S. Public*, pg. 1775
Dufour, Paul V., Chief Fin. Officer & Exec. V.P.-Fin. & Admin.--IMCO Recycling Inc., Irving, TX; *U.S. Public*, pg. 870
Dufresne, J. Stevens, Exec. V.P.-Provider Networks--Mid Atlantic Medical Services, Inc., Rockville, MD; *U.S. Public*, pg. 1109
Dugan, Brendan J., Exec. V.P.-Corp. Banking--European American Bank & Trust Co., Uniondale, NY; *Int'l*, pg. 9
Duhen, Michel, Exec. V.P.-Comml.--Gaz de France, Paris, France; *Int'l*, pg. 541
Duignan, Walter A., Exec. V.P.-Strategy & Plng.--Mohawk Paper Mills, Inc., Cohoes, NY; *U.S. Private*, pg. 755
Duijne, U.K.G., Exec. V.P.--ABN-AMRO Holding N.V., Amsterdam, Netherlands; *Int'l*, pg. 8
Dull, Karen, Chief Fin. Officer & Exec. V.P.--World's Finest Chocolate, Inc., Chicago, IL; *U.S. Private*, pg. 1191
Dumas, Jean-Louis, Exec. V.P.-Mfg.--N. Schlumberger & Cie, Guebwiller, France; *Int'l*, pg. 1206
Duncan, Deborah L., Exec. V.P. & Treas.--The Chase Manhattan Corporation, New York, NY; *U.S. Public*, pg. 337
Duncan, Paul R., Exec. V.P.--Reebok International Ltd., Stoughton, MA; *U.S. Public*, pg. 1369
Duncan, Wayne D., Exec. V.P.--First Citizens Banc Shares, Inc., Raleigh, NC; *U.S. Public*, pg. 628
Dundon, Brian R., Exec. V.P.--MagneTek, Inc., Nashville, TN; *U.S. Public*, pg. 1037
Dundore, Bruce, Exec. V.P. & Creative Dir.--Asher/Gould Advertising, Inc., Los Angeles, CA; *U.S. Private*, pg. 88
Dunham, Jamie, Chief Oper. Officer-Buntin Advertising, Inc. & Exec. V.P.--The Buntin Group, Nashville, TN; *U.S. Private*, pg. 181
Dunham, John L., Chief Fin. Officer & Exec. V.P.--The May Department Stores Company, Saint Louis, MO; *U.S. Public*, pg. 1063
Dunkel, Gunter, Exec. V.P. & Gen. Mgr.--Bayerische Hypotheken-und Wechsel-Bank Aktiengesellschaft New York Branch, New York, NY; *Int'l*, pg. 176
Dunkel, Gunter, Dr., Exec. V.P.--Bayerische Hypotheken-und Wechsel-Bank Aktiengesellschaft, Munich, Germany; *Int'l*, pg. 175
Dunlap, Angela O., Exec. V.P.-Corp. Communications--MCI Communications Corp., Atlanta, GA; *U.S. Public*, pg. 1023
Dunlap, Robert, Exec. V.P.-Bus. Devel.--BFA Educational Media, Saint Louis, MO; *U.S. Private*, pg. 863
Dunlap, Robert, Exec. V.P.-Bus. Devel.--Phoenix Films & Video, Saint Louis, MO; *U.S. Private*, pg. 863
Dunlop, Edward, Exec. V.P.--Chubb & Son, Inc., Warren, NJ; *U.S. Public*, pg. 355
Dunn, E. Paul, Exec. V.P.--Bradley Real Estate, Inc., Northbrook, IL; *U.S. Public*, pg. 250
Dunn, Gregory W., Chief Oper. Officer & Exec. V.P.--Regal Cinemas Inc., Knoxville, TN; *U.S. Public*, pg. 1371
Dunn, Jeffrey, Exec. V.P.--Nickelodeon/Nick At Nite, New York, NY; *U.S. Private*, pg. 779
Dunn, Melvin B., Exec. V.P. & Indiv. Ins. Oper--Security Mutual Life Insurance Co. of New York, Binghamton, NY; *U.S. Private*, pg. 981
Dunn, Nina Laserson, Exec. V.P., Gen. Counsel & Sec.--DRS Technologies, Inc., Parsippany, NJ; *U.S. Public*, pg. 474
Dunn, Stephen D., Exec. V.P. & Treas.--Dunn Industries Inc., Kansas City, MO; *U.S. Private*, pg. 347
Dunn, Stephen D., Exec. V.P. & Treas.--J.E. Dunn Construction Co., Kansas City, MO; *U.S. Private*, pg. 347
Dunton, Gary C., Exec. V.P.-Field Opers.--United States Fidelity & Guaranty Company, Baltimore, MD; *U.S. Public*, pg. 1659
Dupont-Lauren, Randi, Dir.-Sls.--EMPI, Inc., Saint Paul, MN; *U.S. Public*, pg. 545
Dupps, Frank N., Exec. V.P.--Dupps Company, Germantown, OH; *U.S. Private*, pg. 348
Dupuy, Enrique, Sr. Exec. V.P.-Corp. Fin.--Grupo Iberia, Madrid, Spain; *Int'l*, pg. 574
Durden, Hugh M., Exec. V.P.-Corp. Services--Wachovia Corporation, Winston Salem, NC; *U.S. Public*, pg. 1730
Durden, Liston, Exec. V.P.-Mktg. & Prod. Devel.--Viking Range Corp., Greenwood, MS; *U.S. Private*, pg. 1140
Durette, Andrew, Exec. V.P.--Cherry Semiconductor Corp., East Greenwich, RI; *U.S. Public*, pg. 346
Durette, Paul, Exec. V.P.-Opers.--Dansk International Designs Ltd., White Plains, NY; *U.S. Public*, pg. 261
Durfee, J.Lang, V.P. & Sec.--Bethel Mills, Inc., Bethel, VT; *U.S. Private*, pg. 141
Durfee, Robert L., Exec. V.P.--Versar Inc., Springfield, VA; *U.S. Public*, pg. 1717
Durham, B.W., Jr., Exec. V.P.-Mktg.--Simmons, Durham & Associates, Saint Louis, MO; *U.S. Private*, pg. 1000
Durig, Gregory, Chief Fin. Officer & Exec. V.P.--Discovery Communications, Inc., Bethesda, MD; *U.S. Private*, pg. 334
Durkes, Richard W., Exec. V.P.--ABN AMRO Chicago Corp., Chicago, IL; *Int'l*, pg. 10
Durrett, Stephen E., Exec. V.P.--The First National Bank of Lafayette, Lafayette, LA; *U.S. Public*, pg. 630
Durso, Edwin M., Exec. V.P.-Admin.--ESPN, Inc., Bristol, CT; *U.S. Public*, pg. 512
Durston, Marshall, Exec. V.P.--Spaulding & Slye, Boston, MA; *U.S. Private*, pg. 1021
Dutkowsky, Robert M., Exec. V.P.-Markets & Channels--EMC Corporation, Hopkinton, MA; *U.S. Public*, pg. 545
Dutreix, Guy, Sr. Exec. V.P.--SEITA, Societe Nationale D'Exploitation Industrielle des Tabacs et des Allumettes, Paris, France; *Int'l*, pg. 1219
Dvorak, Vera, M.D., Exec. V.P.-Medical Affairs--Mid Atlantic Medical Services, Inc., Rockville, MD; *U.S. Public*, pg. 1109
Dworak, Alfred, Dr., Exec. V.P.--Veba AG, Dusseldorf, Germany; *Int'l*, pg. 1454
Dwyer-Owens, Dina, Exec. V.P.-Opers.--The Dwyer Group, Inc., Waco, TX; *U.S. Public*, pg. 537
Dwyer, Carrie E., Exec. V.P.-Corp. Oversight--The Charles Schwab Corporation, San Francisco, CA; *U.S. Public*, pg. 1442
Dwyer, Daniel P., Chief Fin. Officer, Exec. V.P.-Fin. & Treas.--CommNet Cellular Inc., Englewood, CO; *U.S. Public*, pg. 414
Dwyer, Robert, Chief Oper. Officer & Exec. V.P.--Industrial Coatings Group, Inc., Chicago, IL; *U.S. Private*, pg. 434
Dykema, Bill, V.P.-Mktg.--MEG, Cambridge City, IN; *U.S. Private*, pg. 686
Dykes, Ronald M., Chief Fin. Officer & Exec. V.P.--BellSouth Corporation, Atlanta, GA; *U.S. Public*, pg. 207
Dykstra, Nicholas, Exec. V.P.--Panlabs International Operations, Bothell, WA; *Int'l*, pg. 827
Eaccarino, Lou, Exec. V.P.-Sls. & Mktg.--A.J. Brandon, Vernon, CA; *U.S. Public*, pg. 948
Eaccarino, Lou, Exec. V.P.-Sls.--Goodman Knitting Company, Brockton, MA; *U.S. Public*, pg. 948
Eadie, Graeme, Chief Fin. Officer & Exec. V.P.--Dylex Limited, Toronto, Canada; *Int'l*, pg. 425
Eager, Robert M., Jr., Exec. V.P.--General Reinsurance Corp., Stamford, CT; *U.S. Public*, pg. 725
Eanes, Jasper R., Chief Fin. Officer, Exec. V.P. & Treas.--BankAtlantic Bancorp, Inc., Fort Lauderdale, FL; *U.S. Public*, pg. 183
Earley, Robert H., Exec. V.P.--Adams Business Media, Arlington Heights, IL; *U.S. Private*, pg. 16
Early, Creighton, Chief Fin. Officer & Exec. V.P.--Earth Technology Corp. USA, Long Beach, CA; *U.S. Public*, pg. 1648
Early, Robert C., Exec. V.P.-Corp. Devel.--May & Speh, Inc., Downers Grove, IL; *U.S. Public*, pg. 1063
Early, Terry, Exec. V.P.--Sysco Food Services of Houston, Inc., Houston, TX; *U.S. Public*, pg. 1551
Eastin, Raymond, Exec. V.P. & Chief Exec. Officer--Blue Circle America Inc., Marietta, GA; *Int'l*, pg. 197
Eaton, Randall D., Exec. V.P. & Compliance Officer--United Missouri Bank of Warsaw, Warsaw, MO; *U.S. Public*, pg. 1655
Eberhardt, George J., Chief Fin. Officer & Exec. V.P.--Pinnacle Bank, Valparaiso, IN; *U.S. Public*, pg. 1297
Ebihara, Kiyoshi, Exec. V.P. & Rep. Dir.--Juki Corporation, Tokyo, Japan; *Int'l*, pg. 716
Ebling, Timothy A., Chief Fin. Officer & Exec. V.P.--Greate Bay Casino Corporation, Atlantic City, NJ; *U.S. Public*, pg. 760
Ebrom, Charles, Exec. V.P.--H.B. Zachry, San Antonio, TX; *U.S. Private*, pg. 1203
Ebron, James A., Exec. V.P.-Media Sls.--Black Entertainment Television Holdings Inc., Washington, DC; *U.S. Public*, pg. 235
Ebsworth, David R., Exec. V.P. & Pres.-Pharmaceutical Division--Bayer Corporation, Pittsburgh, PA; *Int'l*, pg. 172
Ebsworth, David, Ph.D., Pres.-Pharmaceutical Div. & Exec. V.P.--Bayer Corporation, Pittsburgh, PA; *Int'l*, pg. 172
Ebsworth, David, Ph.D., Exec. V.P. & Pres.-Pharmaceutical Div.--Bayer Corporation, Parsippany, NJ; *Int'l*, pg. 172
Eby, Carl J., Exec. V.P.--Capital Tire, Inc., Toledo, OH; *U.S. Private*, pg. 206
Eby, Charles K., Exec. V.P.-Quality Assurance & Corporate Estimating--Eby Corporation, Wichita, KS; *U.S. Private*, pg. 359
Eby, Charles K., Exec. V.P.--Martin K. Eby Construction Company, Inc., Wichita, KS; *U.S. Private*, pg. 359
Eck, Robert L., Exec. V.P.--Albert Kahn Associates, Inc., Detroit, MI; *U.S. Private*, pg. 604
Eckardt, Carl R., Exec. V.P.-Corp. Devel.--G-I Holdings Inc., Wilmington, DE; *U.S. Private*, pg. 433
Eckardt, Carl R., Exec. V.P.-Corp. Devel.--International Specialty Products, Inc., Wayne, NJ; *U.S. Public*, pg. 858
Eckert, Peter, Exec. V.P.--Zurich Insurance Company, Zurich, Switzerland; *Int'l*, pg. 1529
Eckis, Thomas M., Corp. Exec. V.P.-Corp. Banking--Crestar Financial Corporation, Richmond, VA; *U.S. Public*, pg. 458
Eckis, Thomas M., Grp. Exec. V.P.-Corp. Banking--Crestar Bank, Richmond, VA; *U.S. Public*, pg. 458
Eckman, Harold R., Exec. V.P.--Eckman Construction Company, Bedford, NH; *U.S. Private*, pg. 359
Edelen, Chris, Exec. V.P.-Opers.--Fox Photo, Inc., Saint Louis, MO; *U.S. Public*, pg. 283
Edell, Dunnan, Sr. Exec. V.P.-Sls.--CCA Industries, Inc., East Rutherford, NJ; *U.S. Public*, pg. 276
Edelman, Jules, Exec. V.P.--Greater New York Box Co., Clifton, NJ; *U.S. Private*, pg. 476
Edelman, Steven M., Chief Fin. & Investment Officer & Exec. V.P.--First Union Real Estate Investments, Cleveland, OH; *U.S. Public*, pg. 640
Edelmann, Klaus, Chief Fin. Officer & Exec. V.P.--Deutz AG, Cologne, Germany; *Int'l*, pg. 407
Edelstein, Arthur, Exec. V.P.--National Technical Systems, Inc., Calabasas, CA; *U.S. Public*, pg. 1161
Edelstenne, Charles, Exec. V.P.-Economic & Fin. Affairs.--Dassault Aviation Group, Vaucresson, France; *Int'l*, pg. 383
Edelstone, Gordon, Exec. V.P.-Menswear--Dylex Limited, Toronto, Canada; *Int'l*, pg. 425
Eden, Avi D., Vice Chm. & Exec. V.P.--Vishay Intertechnology, Inc., Malvern, PA; *U.S. Public*, pg. 1721
Edenfield, J Michael, Exec. V.P. & Chief Oper. Officer--ASI Properties, Inc., Atlanta, GA; *U.S. Public*, pg. 91
Edenfield, J. Michael, Chief Oper. Officer & Exec. V.P.--American Software, Inc., Atlanta, GA; *U.S. Public*, pg. 91
Edge, Kenneth E., Exec. V.P.-Retail--AMCORE Bank N.A., Rockford, Rockford, IL; *U.S. Public*, pg. 64
Edgell, Robert M., Exec. V.P.--Edison Mission Energy, Irvine, CA; *U.S. Public*, pg. 564
Edgington, Kenen, Exec. V.P.--Baldwin Piano & Organ Company, Loveland, OH; *U.S. Public*, pg. 169
Edington, Jeff, Exec. V.P.-Tech.--British Steel Plc, London, United Kingdom; *Int'l*, pg. 220
Edmiston, William R., Exec. V.P.-Old Chicago Opers.--Rock Bottom Restaurants, Louisville, CO; *U.S. Public*, pg. 1396
Edmonds, David B., Exec. V.P.-Human Resources--AmSouth Bancorporation, Birmingham, AL; *U.S. Public*, pg. 105
Edmondson, John, Chief Oper. Officer & Exec. V.P.--Duty Free International, Inc., Ridgefield, CT; *Int'l*, pg. 103
Edwards, Benjamin F., IV, Exec. V.P. & Dir.-Sls. & Mktg.--A.G. Edwards, Inc., Saint Louis, MO; *U.S. Public*, pg. 565
Edwards, C. Webb, Chief Tech. Officer & Exec. V.P.--Norwest Corporation, Minneapolis, MN; *U.S. Public*, pg. 1201
Edwards, Carl, Jr., Exec. V.P., Gen. Counsel & Sec.--Lennox International Inc., Richardson, TX; *U.S. Private*, pg. 659
Edwards, Christine, Exec. V.P. & Chief Legal Officer--Morgan Stanley Dean Witter & Co., New York, NY; *U.S. Public*, pg. 1132
Edwards, Christine A., Exec. V.P. & Chief Legal Officer--Dean Witter, Discover & Co., New York, NY; *U.S. Public*, *pg. 1132*
Edwards, D. Kirk, Exec. V.P.--Key Energy Group Inc., East Brunswick, NJ; *U.S. Public*, pg. 953
Edwards, Gary W., Exec. V.P.-Refining, Mktg. & Supply--Conoco Inc., Houston, TX; *U.S. Public*, pg. 531
Edwards, Henry, Exec. V.P.-Human Resources--FINAST, Maple Heights, OH; *Int'l*, pg. 750
Edwards, John K., Grp. Pres.-Power Generation & Exec. V.P.--Cummins Engine Company, Inc., Columbus, IN; *U.S. Public*, pg. 467
Edwards, Kenneth G., Grp. Exec. V.P.-Commercial Real Estate--Bank of America NT&SA, San Francisco, CA; *U.S. Public*, pg. 180
Edwards, Michael, Exec. V.P. & Treas.--Citizens Savings Bank, Providence, RI; *Int'l*, pg. 1132
Edwards, Michael, Exec. V.P. & Treas.--Citizens Trust Company, Providence, RI; *Int'l*, pg. 1132
Edwards, Robert, Exec. V.P.--Rural Metro Corporation, Scottsdale, AZ; *U.S. Public*, pg. 1412
Edwards, Robert D., Pres.-M.P. Electric & Exec. V.P.--Minnesota Power, Duluth, MN; *U.S. Public*, pg. 1116
Edwards, William G., Exec. V.P.-Housing Opers.--Oakwood Homes Corporation, Greensboro, NC; *U.S. Public*, pg. 1209
Egan, Raymond C., Exec. V.P.--Bristol-Myers Squibb Pharmaceutical & Nutritional Group, New York, NY; *U.S. Public*, pg. 254
Egawa, Hideharu, Sr. Exec. V.P.--Toshiba Corporation, Tokyo, Japan; *Int'l*, pg. 1402
Egawa, Masazumi, Exec. V.P.--Kumagai Gumi Co., Ltd., Tokyo, Japan; *Int'l*, pg. 763
Egeland, John, Chief Fin. Officer & Exec. V.P.--Centex Corporation, Dallas, TX; *U.S. Public*, pg. 322
Egle, Carol, Exec. V.P.--Muench-Kreuzer Candle Company, Syracuse, NY; *U.S. Private*, pg. 766

Eglinton, William M., Chief Oper. Officer & Exec. V.P.--Public Service Company of New Mexico, Albuquerque, NM; *U.S. Public*, pg. 1339

Ehlers, David W., Exec. V.P. & Dir.-Fin.--Union Bank of California, San Francisco, CA; *Int'l*, pg. 157

Ehrenthal, Herb, Exec. V.P.--Girgenti, Hughes, Butler & McDowell, New York, NY; *U.S. Private*, pg. 455

Eichel, Beverly, Chief Fin. Officer & Exec. V.P.--Danskin Inc., New York, NY; *U.S. Public*, pg. 483

Eichorn, Peter K., Exec. V.P.-Europe, Middle East & Africa--Mattel, Inc., El Segundo, CA; *U.S. Public*, pg. 1057

Eickhoff, John R., Chief Fin. Officer & Exec. V.P.--Ceridian Corporation, Bloomington, MN; *U.S. Public*, pg. 330

Eide, R., Exec. V.P. & Mng. Dir.-Benelux--Dun & Bradstreet Eurinform SA-NV, Brussels, Belgium; *U.S. Public*, pg. 536

Eidel, Paula, Exec. V.P.--Tri-City Electrical Contractors Inc., Altamonte Springs, FL; *U.S. Private*, pg. 1100

Eie, Olaf, Exec. V.P.--Orkla A.S.A., Oslo, Norway; *Int'l*, pg. 1010

Eikenberry, Michael, Exec. V.P.-Loan Admin.--Fort Wayne National Corporation, Fort Wayne, IN; *U.S. Public*, pg. 673

Eilender, A., Exec. V.P.-Corp. Devel.--Sybron Chemicals Inc., Birmingham, NJ; *U.S. Public*, pg. 1544

Einhauser, James G., Exec. V.P.-Sls. & Mktg.--Wigwam Mills, Inc., Sheboygan, WI; *U.S. Private*, pg. 1175

Einsmann, Harald, Exec. V.P. & Pres.-Europe, Middle East & Africa--The Procter & Gamble Company, Cincinnati, OH; *U.S. Public*, pg. 1330

Eipp, Donald, Exec. V.P.-Dairy Plant Opers.--Richfood Dairy, Richmond, VA; *U.S. Public*, pg. 1389

Eisenbach, Randall D., Chief Oper. Officer & Exec. V.P.--STB Systems, Inc., Richardson, TX; *U.S. Public*, pg. 1421

Eisenberg, Joseph B., Exec. V.P.--Uniroyal Chemical Corporation, Middlebury, CT; *U.S. Public*, pg. 459

Eisenberg, Joseph B., Exec. V.P.--Uniroyal Chemical Company, Inc., Middlebury, CT; *U.S. Public*, pg. 460

Eisenschenk, Mark, Exec. V.P.--Ringer Corporation, Bloomington, MN; *U.S. Public*, pg. 1390

Eisler, Susan, Exec. V.P. & Res. Dir.--Gotham Incorporated, New York, NY; *U.S. Private*, pg. 677

Eisner, David F., Exec. V.P.--Jefferies Group, Inc., Los Angeles, CA; *U.S. Public*, pg. 924

Eisner, David F., Exec. V.P.--Jefferies & Company, Inc., Los Angeles, CA; *U.S. Public*, pg. 925

Ejima, Kenji, Exec. V.P.--Toppan Printing Company, Ltd., Tokyo, Japan; *Int'l*, pg. 1399

Ek, F. Donald, Exec. V.P.--Tenax Corporation, Danbury, CT; *Int'l*, pg. 193

Ek, Sven, Exec. V.P.--Svedala Industri AB, Malmo, Sweden; *Int'l*, pg. 1323

Eklundh, Fredrik, Exec. V.P.--Stockmann Automotive Sales Div., Helsinki, Finland; *Int'l*, pg. 1301

Ekrek, Sekita, Exec. Dir.-Publicity & Promo.--Allied Advertising Agency, Public Relations, Washington, DC; *U.S. Private*, pg. 38

El Sabeh, Hani, Exec. V.P.--Republic National Bank of New York, New York, NY; *U.S. Public*, pg. 1380

Elbert, Paul A., Exec. V.P. & Chief Oper. Officer-Natural Gas--Consumers Energy, Jackson, MI; *U.S. Public*, pg. 280

Eldridge, James F., Exec. V.P.-Corp. Legal & Sec.--American Family Mutual Insurance Co., Madison, WI; *U.S. Private*, pg. 53

Eldridge, Robert H., Chief Fin. Officer & Exec. V.P.--Briggs & Stratton Corporation, Wauwatosa, WI; *U.S. Public*, pg. 252

Elefante, Jeffrey P., Exec. V.P., Gen. Counsel & Sec.--CACI International Inc, Arlington, VA; *U.S. Public*, pg. 272

Eleniewski, Mark A., Exec. V.P.-Sls. & Engrng.--Detroit Stoker Co., Monroe, MI; *U.S. Public*, pg. 1679

Elia, Richard A., Exec. V.P.--Sevenson Environmental Services, Inc., Niagara Falls, NY; *U.S. Public*, pg. 1462

Elias, John W., Exec. V.P.--Seagull Energy Corporation, Houston, TX; *U.S. Public*, pg. 1450

Eliasberg, James A., Exec V.P. & Gen. Counsel--Taco Cabana, San Antonio, TX; *U.S. Public*, pg. 1559

Eliot, Daniel R., Exec. V.P.-Comml. Banking--FirstFed Financial Corp., Santa Monica, CA; *U.S. Public*, pg. 645

Elizondo, Alonso Ancira, Chief Exec. Officer & Exec. V.P.--Altos Hornos de Mexico, S.A., Monclova, Mexico; *Int'l*, pg. 66

Elkins, Marshall A., Exec. V.P. & Gen. Counsel--Integrated Health Services, Inc., Owings Mills, MD; *U.S. Public*, pg. 884

Ellenbogen, Eric, Exec. V.P.--Golden Books Family Entertainment Inc., New York, NY; *U.S. Public*, pg. 749

Ellington, Richard V., Exec. V.P.-Acct. Mngmt.--Lotas Minard Patton McGiver, New York, NY; *U.S. Private*, pg. 677

Elliot, Tom, Exec. V.P.-Intl. Devel.--United Artists Theatre Circuits Incorporated, Englewood, CO; *U.S. Private*, pg. 1120

Elliott, A. Wright, Exec. V.P.-Corp. Mktg. & Communications--The Chase Manhattan Corporation, New York, NY; *U.S. Public*, pg. 337

Elliott, Jeanette, Exec. V.P. & Creative Dir.--Ackerman McQueen, Inc., Oklahoma City, OK; *U.S. Private*, pg. 12

Elliott, John, Exec. V.P.--BetzDearborn Hydrocarbon Process Group, Woodlands, TX; *U.S. Public*, pg. 226

Elliott, John E., Exec. V.P.--Gencor Industries, Inc., Orlando, FL; *U.S. Public*, pg. 705

Elliott, Robert C., Sr. Exec. V.P.--Bessemer Group, Inc., New York, NY; *U.S. Private*, pg. 139

Elliott, Ross J., Exec. V.P.-Devel.--NxTrend Technology, Inc., Colorado Springs, CO; *U.S. Private*, pg. 809

Ellis, Charles W., Exec. V.P.-Opers.--Warner Cable Communications, Inc., Columbus, OH; *U.S. Public*, pg. 1611

Ellis, Edwin E., Exec. V.P.--OmniTRAX Inc., Chicago, IL; *U.S. Private*, pg. 171

Ellis, Gary L., Chief Oper. Officer & Exec. V.P.--United Bankshares, Inc., Parkersburg, WV; *U.S. Public*, pg. 1674

Ellis, George, Exec. V.P.-Technical Svcs.--American Waste Services, Inc., Warren, OH; *U.S. Public*, pg. 94

Ellis, Robert, Exec. V.P.--Warwick International Ltd., Flintshire, United Kingdom; *U.S. Public*, pg. 1459

Ellison, Gary L., Exec. V.P.--Emkay, Inc., Itasca, IL; *U.S. Private*, pg. 374

Ellison, Peter K., Exec. V.P.-Trust--Zions First National Bank, Salt Lake City, UT; *U.S. Public*, pg. 1793

Eloranta, Jorma, Exec. V.P.-Flight Opers. Div.--FinnAir Oy, Helsinki, Finland; *Int'l*, pg. 485

Elson, Barry R., Exec. V.P.-Opers.--Cox Communications, Inc., Atlanta, GA; *U.S. Public*, pg. 454

Elstner, Judy, Exec. V.P.--J. Korber & Company, Albuquerque, NM; *U.S. Private*, pg. 632

Elvang, Goran, Exec. V.P.-Information Systems--Svenska Handelsbanken, Stockholm, Sweden; *Int'l*, pg. 1327

Elwer, Ronald R., Exec. V.P.--The Commercial Bank, Delphos, OH; *U.S. Public*, pg. 410

Elwood, John, Chief Fin. Officer & Exec. V.P.--Prime Hospitality Corp., Fairfield, NJ; *U.S. Public*, pg. 1326

Emanuel, A., Exec. V.P.--Coil-Tec Corporation, Bessemer, AL; *Int'l*, pg. 79

Emerson, Thomas E., Exec. V.P. & Chief Auditor--Norwest Corporation, Minneapolis, MN; *U.S. Public*, pg. 1201

Emory, L.B., Exec. V.P.--ING North America Insurance Company, Atlanta, GA; *Int'l*, pg. 648

End, Jackie, Exec. V.P. & Mng. Partner-Creative--Wells BDDP, Inc., New York, NY; *Int'l*, pg. 117

Endendyk, Bruce A., Exec. V.P.--Transcontinental Realty Investors, Inc., Dallas, TX; *U.S. Public*, pg. 1630

Ender, Jon T., Exec. V.P.--ABN AMRO Chicago Corp., Chicago, IL; *Int'l*, pg. 10

Endo-Dizon, Ellen, Exec. V.P.-Republic Pictures Productions, Inc.--Republic Entertainment, Inc., Los Angeles, CA; *U.S. Private*, pg. 776

Endres, Ronald J., Chief Fin. Officer & Exec. V.P.--Southern Union Company, Austin, TX; *U.S. Public*, pg. 1491

Enendyk, Bruce A., Exec. V.P.--Continental Mortgage and Equity Trust, Dallas, TX; *U.S. Public*, pg. 441

Engebretson, Duane, Exec. V.P. & Chief Mktg. Officer--Pioneer Mutual Life Insurance Company, Fargo, ND; *U.S. Private*, pg. 866

Engel, David, Chief Fin. Officer & Exec. V.P.--Del Global Technologies, Valhalla, NY; *U.S. Public*, pg. 493

Engel, David, Exec. V.P.--Dynarad Corporation, Deer Park, NY; *U.S. Public*, pg. 494

Engel, Gerard, Grp. Exec. V.P.-Domestic Retail Banking--Credit Commercial de France, Paris, France; *Int'l*, pg. 341

Engelbert, Joseph, Exec. V.P. & Acctg. Svcs. Dir.--TN Services Inc., Omaha, NE; *U.S. Public*, pg. 1642

Engelhart, Debbie, Exec. V.P. & Media Plng. Dir.--Western International Media Corporation, New York, NY; *U.S. Private*, pg. 1166

Engelhaupt, Dave, Exec. V.P.--Affiliated Foods Cooperative Inc., Norfolk, NE; *U.S. Private*, pg. 25

Engelman, Stephen E., Exec. V.P.--SPS Industrial Products Div., Cleveland, OH; *U.S. Public*, pg. 1420

Engelsma, Daniel W., Vice Chm. & Exec. V.P.--Kraus-Anderson Incorporated, Minneapolis, MN; *U.S. Private*, pg. 635

Engelstein, Harry, Exec. V.P. & Chief Construction Officer--Engle Homes, Inc., Boca Raton, FL; *U.S. Public*, pg. 583

England, Gordon R., Exec. V.P.--General Dynamics Corporation, Falls Church, VA; *U.S. Public*, pg. 708

England, Paul J., Exec. V.P. & Gen. Mgr.-Recycled Fiber Div.--Rock-Tenn Company, Norcross, GA; *U.S. Public*, pg. 1396

English, James, Exec. V.P.--The Bethlehem Corporation, Easton, PA; *U.S. Public*, pg. 225

English, L. Arthur, Exec. V.P.-Fin. Services--The Toronto Dominion Bank, Toronto, Canada; *Int'l*, pg. 1401

Engman, Gert, Dir.-Savings Bank Zone West--Swedbank, Stockholm, Sweden; *Int'l*, pg. 1328

Engman, Gosta, Exec. V.P.-Personnel & Admin.--Rautaruukki Oy, Helsinki, Finland; *Int'l*, pg. 1088

Engstrom, Anders, Exec. V.P.--Bergman & Beving AB, Stockholm, Sweden; *Int'l*, pg. 188

Ennis, Joseph L., Exec. V.P.--Globe Mortgage America, LLC., River Edge, NJ; *U.S. Private*, pg. 458

Ennis, Richard A., Exec. V.P. & Treas.--Associated Grocers of New England, Inc., Manchester, NH; *U.S. Private*, pg. 91

Enns, Jo Ellen, Exec. V.P.--revolution, inc., Kansas City, MO; *U.S. Private*, pg. 1131

Ensor, Phillip E., Exec. V.P.-Fin. & Admin.--Marine World Africa USA, Vallejo, CA; *U.S. Private*, pg. 703

Enticknap, Joan, Chief Fin. Officer & Exec. V.P.--Seafirst Corporation, Seattle, WA; *U.S. Public*, pg. 181

Eppler, David M., Exec. V.P.--Central Louisiana Electric Company, Inc., Pineville, LA; *U.S. Public*, pg. 325

Epstein, Jerry, Sr. Partner & Exec. V.P.--Fleishman-Hillard Inc., Saint Louis, MO; *U.S. Private*, pg. 411

Epstein, Phil, Div. Exec. V.P.--KTI, Inc., Guttenberg, NJ; *U.S. Public*, pg. 939

Epstein, Robert S., Chief Info. Officer & Exec. V.P.--Sybase, Inc., Emeryville, CA; *U.S. Public*, pg. 1544

Epton, Delmar F., Exec. V.P.-Opers. Grp.--Regions Financial Corporation, Birmingham, AL; *U.S. Public*, pg. 1371

Erani, Dennis, Exec. V.P. & Gen. Mgr.--A&E Stores, Inc., Teterboro, NJ; *U.S. Private*, pg. 1

Erazmus, Walter T., Chief Fin. Officer & Exec. V.P.--Gibraltar Steel Corp., Buffalo, NY; *U.S. Public*, pg. 742

Erhardt, Ingo, Exec. V.P.--Embraco North America, Inc., Norcross, GA; *U.S. Public*, pg. 1765

Erhardt, Ingo, Exec. V.P.--GPD/Embraco North America, Inc., Norcross, GA; *U.S. Public*, pg. 1765

Erickson, Andrew, Exec. V.P.--Amica Mutual Insurance Co., Lincoln, RI; *U.S. Private*, pg. 66

Erickson, Charles E., Exec. V.P.-Specialty Opers.--Signet Star Reinsurance Company, Florham Park, NJ; *U.S. Public*, pg. 216

Erickson, David B., Pres.--Erickson Oil Products, Inc., Hudson, WI; *U.S. Private*, pg. 381

Erickson, Dennis D., Chief Fin. Officer, Treas. & Exec. V.P.--Norwest Bank Colorado N.A., Denver, CO; *U.S. Public*, pg. 1202

Erickson, S.K., Exec. V.P. & Treas.--Ziegler Inc., Minneapolis, MN; *U.S. Private*, pg. 1205

Erickson, W.E., Exec. V.P.--National Forge Company, Irvine, PA; *U.S. Private*, pg. 783

Erickson, Walter W., Exec. V.P.--Carlson Marketing Group, Inc., Minneapolis, MN; *U.S. Private*, pg. 212

Erikson, Penny, Exec. V.P.-Acct. Mngmt.--Young & Rubicam New York, New York, NY; *U.S. Private*, pg. 1198

Erlen, Hubertus, Dr., Exec. Dir.-Personnel, Production & Environmental Protection--Schering AG, Berlin, Germany; *Int'l*, pg. 1203

Ernst, Markus M., Chief Oper. Officer & Exec. V.P.--Arbor Drugs, Inc., Troy, MI; *U.S. Public*, pg. 126

Erskine, Fred H., Exec. V.P.--Namanco LLC, Tulsa, OK; *U.S. Private*, pg. 773

Erskine, Susan D., Exec. V.P.-Devel. & Sec.--PMR Corporation, San Diego, CA; *U.S. Public*, pg. 1242

Erwin, Larry E., Exec. V.P.--New England Newspaper Supply Company, Inc., Millbury, MA; *U.S. Private*, pg. 793

Erwin, Terry, Exec. V.P.--San Angelo National Bank, San Angelo, TX; *U.S. Public*, pg. 633

Escarrer, Maria Antonia, Exec. V.P.-Human Resources--Sol Melia, Palma de Mallorca, Spain; *Int'l*, pg. 1277

Eschbach, Alan R., Exec. V.P. & Chief Oper. Officer--Rheometric Scientific, Piscataway, NJ; *U.S. Public*, pg. 1387

Eshelman, George, Exec. V.P.-Investment Bank--Comerica Incorporated, Detroit, MI; *U.S. Public*, pg. 408

Espalioux, Jean-Marc, Exec. V.P.-Investor Rels.--Compagnie Generale Des Eaux, Paris, France; *Int'l*, pg. 321

Espegard, Duaine C., Exec. V.P. & Grp. Pres.--Bremer Financial Corporation, Saint Paul, MN; *U.S. Private*, pg. 167

Espi, Jose Maria, Exec. V.P.-Human Resources, Systems & Opers.--Banco Santander, Madrid, Spain; *Int'l*, pg. 143

Esposito, Joseph, Exec. V.P.--Fisher Skylights, Inc., Holbrook, NY; *U.S. Private*, pg. 408

Esposito, Joseph, Chief Oper. Officer & Exec. V.P.--Four Seasons Solar Products Corp., Holbrook, NY; *U.S. Private*, pg. 422

Essary, David K., Exec. V.P.-Opers.--Jitney-Jungle Stores of America, Inc., Jackson, MS; *U.S. Private*, pg. 588

Esselmann, Wilhelm, Dr., Exec. V.P.--DG Bank, Frankfurt/Main, Germany; *Int'l*, pg. 351

Essner, Robert A., Exec. V.P.-Global Medical Device & Specialty Pharmaceuticals--American Home Products Corporation, Madison, NJ; *U.S. Public*, pg. 79

Esstman, Edward H., Exec. V.P.-Auto Fin. Div.--AmeriCredit Corp., Fort Worth, TX; *U.S. Public*, pg. 96

Esstman, Michael B., Exec. V.P.-Telephone Opers.--GTE Corporation, Stamford, CT; *U.S. Public*, pg. 696

Estell, Richard J., Exec. V.P.--United Insurance Companies, Inc., Dallas, TX; *U.S. Public*, pg. 1679

Etherington, Glenn A., Chief Fin. Officer & Exec. V.P.--Brite Voice Systems, Canton, MA; *U.S. Public*, pg. 257

Etter, Christoph, Exec. V.P.--Sulzer Ltd., Winterthur, Switzerland; *Int'l*, pg. 1305

Etter, David J., Chief Credit Officer & Exec. V.P.--First International Bancorp, Inc., Hartford, CT; *U.S. Public*, pg. 635

Ettinger, Irwin R., Chief Acctg. Officer & Exec. V.P.--Travelers Group, New York, NY; *U.S. Public*, pg. 1632

Eubank, Sandy, Exec. V.P. & Gen. Mgr.-Intl.--BASES Worldwide, Covington, KY; *U.S. Private*, pg. 120

Euringer, George P., Exec. V.P. & Chief Creative Officer--Trone Advertising, Inc., Greensboro, NC; *U.S. Private*, pg. 1104

Eustace, D.G., Chief Fin. Officer & Exec. V.P.--Philips Electronics N.V., Eindhoven, Netherlands; *Int'l*, pg. 1051

Eustace, Dudley G., Chief Fin. Officer & Exec. V.P.--Philips International B.V., Eindhoven, Netherlands; *Int'l*, pg. 1051

Evander, Lars, Exec. V.P.--Svenska Handelsbanken, Stockholm, Sweden; *Int'l*, pg. 1327

Evans, Andrew C., Chief Fin. Officer & Exec. V.P.--Simon & Schuster, New York, NY; *U.S. Private*, pg. 777

Evans, Clarence, Chief Oper. Officer & Exec. V.P.-Personal Training & Devel.--The Mad Butcher, Inc., Pine Bluff, AR; *U.S. Private*, pg. 693

Evans, Dan V., Exec. V.P.--Treadco, Inc., Fort Smith, AR; *U.S. Public*, pg. 131

Evans, Drew, Exec. V.P.-Property & Casualty--Willis Corroon Corp. of South Carolina, Columbia, SC; *Int'l*, pg. 1507

Evans, Dwight R., Exec. V.P.--F&G Re, Inc., Morristown, NJ; *U.S. Public*, pg. 1659

Evans, Gary, Exec. V.P. & Chief Oper Officer-Meats Grp.--Farmland Industries, Inc., Kansas City, MO; *U.S. Private*, pg. 395

Evans, James, Exec. V.P.-Opers.--Doubletree Corporation, Memphis, TN; *U.S. Public*, pg. 1335

Evans, Jerome W., Chief Fin. Officer & Exec. V.P.--First Maryland Bancorp, Baltimore, MD; *Int'l*, pg. 64

Evans, John, Exec. V.P.--Alcan Aluminum Corporation, Cleveland, OH; *Int'l*, pg. 50

Evans, John, Exec. V.P. & Creative Dir.--DavisElen Advertising, Inc., Los Angeles, CA; *U.S. Private*, pg. 316

Evans, Karen, Exec. V.P. & Acct. Plng. Dir.--Cliff Freeman & Partners, New York, NY; *U.S. Public*, pg. 1422

Evans, Lawrence E., Exec. V.P.-Store Devel.--AutoZone, Inc., Memphis, TN; *U.S. Public*, pg. 150

Evans, Richard, Chief Oper. Officer & Exec. V.P.--Gaylord Entertainment/Opryland USA, Nashville, TN; *U.S. Public*, pg. 704

Evans, Richard G., Exec. V.P.-Admin.--Green Tree Financial Corporation, Saint Paul, MN; *U.S. Public*, pg. 761

Evans, Richard L., Chief Oper. Officer, Chief Fin. Officer, Exec. V.P. & Treas.--Reunion Industries, Inc., Stamford, CT; *U.S. Public*, pg. 1383

Evans, Robert E., Exec. V.P.--TCF Bank Minnesota FSB, Minneapolis, MN; *U.S. Public*, pg. 1554
Evanson, Robert E., Exec. V.P.-Corp. Devel.--The McGraw-Hill Companies, New York, NY; *U.S. Public*, pg. 1069
Everaert, P.J., Exec. V.P.--Philips Electronics N.V., Eindhoven, Netherlands; *Int'l*, pg. 1051
Everakes, Howard C., Exec. V.P. & Gen. Counsel--Glendale Federal Bank, F.S.B., Glendale, CA; *U.S. Public*, pg. 747
Everard, John D., Exec. V.P. & Gen. Mgr.-European Region--Newbridge Networks Corporation, Kanata, Canada; *Int'l*, pg. 923
Everett, Lewis C., Exec. V.P.-Private Client Grp.--Wheat First Butcher Singer, Inc., Richmond, VA; *U.S. Public*, pg. 640
Everett, Rich, Chief Oper. Officer & Exec. V.P.--West Marine, Inc., Watsonville, CA; *U.S. Public*, pg. 1756
Evertt, Larry, Exec. V.P.--Reily Foods Company, New Orleans, LA; *U.S. Private*, pg. 919
Ewald, Robert H., Chief Oper. Officer & Exec. V.P.-Computer Sys.--Silicon Graphics, Inc., Mountain View, CA; *U.S. Public*, pg. 1473
Eyles, David L., Chief Credit Policy Officer & Exec. V.P.--Fleet Financial Group, Inc., Boston, MA; *U.S. Public*, pg. 648
Ezerski, Ronald E., Chief Fin. Officer, Exec. V.P., Treas. & Sec.--Patterson Dental Company, Saint Paul, MN; *U.S. Public*, pg. 1265
Fabel, Linda K., Exec. V.P.-Retail Banking--Magna Group, Inc., Saint Louis, MO; *U.S. Public*, pg. 1037
Fadden, Jerome T., Chief Fin. Officer, Exec. V.P. & Treas.--NAC Reinsurance Corporation, Greenwich, CT; *U.S. Public*, pg. 1144
Fadden, Jerome T., Chief Fin. Officer, Exec. V.P. & Treas.--Greenwich Insurance Company, Greenwich, CT; *U.S. Public*, pg. 1144
Fadden, Jerome T., Chief Fin. Officer, Exec. V.P. & Treas.--Indian Harbor Insurance Company, Greenwich, CT; *U.S. Public*, pg. 1144
Faems, Michael J., Exec. V.P. & Exec. Creative Dir.--Young & Rubicam Chicago, Chicago, IL; *U.S. Private*, pg. 1198
Fagan, James F., Chief Fin. Officer, Exec. V.P. & Treas.--Arrow Automotive Industries, Inc., Framingham, MA; *U.S. Public*, pg. 133
Fagan, Ray, Exec. V.P.-Fin. & Opers.--Reed Travel Group, Secaucus, NJ; *Int'l*, pg. 1097
Fagerberg, Howard, Chief Fin. Officer & Exec. V.P.--Childrens Press Inc., Danbury, CT; *Int'l*, pg. 794
Fagerstone, Dennis E., Exec. V.P.-Opers.--Pioneer Natural Resources Co., Irving, TX; *U.S. Public*, pg. 1299
Fagin, David, Exec. V.P.--Finish Line, Inc., Indianapolis, IN; *U.S. Public*, pg. 623
Fagnernas, Peter, Exec. V.P.--Merita Ltd., Helsinki, Finland; *Int'l*, pg. 858
Faibish, Mair, Chief Fin. Officer & Exec. V.P.--Krantor Corporation, Syosset, NY; *U.S. Public*, pg. 966
Fair, Jeremy G., Grp. Exec. V.P.-U.S. Corp. Grp.--Bank of America NT&SA, San Francisco, CA; *U.S. Public*, pg. 180
Fairbairn, Ursula, Exec. V.P.-Quality & Human Resources--American Express Company, New York, NY; *U.S. Public*, pg. 73
Fairchild, John B., Exec. V.P.--ABC, Inc, New York, NY; *U.S. Public*, pg. 511
Fairnington, Alan, Exec. V.P., Pres.-JWT/Asia Pacific--J. Walter Thompson Company, New York, NY; *Int'l*, pg. 1483
Fairweather, Howard H., Exec. V.P.--State Street Corporation, Boston, MA; *U.S. Public*, pg. 1513
Falce, Louis R., Exec. V.P.-Cathodes--Ceradyne, Inc, Costa Mesa, CA; *U.S. Public*, pg. 330
Falciani, Robert A., Exec. V.P.--Keller & Gannon, San Francisco, CA; *U.S. Private*, pg. 626
Falduto, James M., Exec. V.P.-Sls. & Mktg.--Wilton Corporation, Palatine, IL; *U.S. Private*, pg. 1181
Falk, Dan, Exec. V.P.-Fin. & Admin.--Orbotech Ltd., Yavne, Israel; *Int'l*, pg. 1007
Falk, Harry, Exec. V.P.--Heller Bros. Packing Corp., Winter Garden, FL; *U.S. Private*, pg. 520
Falkowski, Michael, Exec. V.P.--The Brulin Corporation, Indianapolis, IN; *U.S. Private*, pg. 176
Fallenstein, Albert, Exec. V.P.--Taylor Corporation, Mankato, MN; *U.S. Private*, pg. 1070
Fallis, Stanley, Sr. Exec. V.P. & Dir.-Admin.--EVEREN Securities, Inc., Chicago, IL; *U.S. Public*, pg. 597
Faloon, Donald H., Exec. V.P.-Devel.--Prime Group Realty Trust, Chicago, IL; *U.S. Public*, pg. 1326
Fannin, David C., Exec. V.P., Gen. Counsel & Sec.--Sunbeam Corporation, Delray Beach, FL; *U.S. Public*, pg. 1533
Fanning, Michael R., Exec. V.P. & Chief Mktg. Officer--Washington Square Securities, Minneapolis, MN; *U.S. Public*, pg. 1376
Farb, Marty, Exec. V.P.-Industry Affairs--Sherwood-Davis & Geck, Saint Louis, MO; *U.S. Public*, pg. 80
Farcouli, Pascal, Exec. V.P.-TV--CLT-UFA, Luxembourg, Luxembourg; *Int'l*, pg. 561
Faris, Richard K., Exec. V.P.--Primavera Systems, Inc., Bala Cynwyd, PA; *U.S. Private*, pg. 884
Farley, Michael A., Exec. V.P. & Resource Dir.-Corp. Resources--Fleet Capital Corporation, Glastonbury, CT; *U.S. Public*, pg. 649
Farnham, Raymond J., Exec. V.P.--Integrated Device Technology, Inc., Santa Clara, CA; *U.S. Public*, pg. 884
Farnsworth, Ken, Jr., Chm. Bd., Pres. & Exec. V.P.--Rhodes International, Inc., Salt Lake City, UT; *U.S. Private*, pg. 927
Farnsworth, Robert, Exec. V.P.-Mktg. & Mdsg.--The Pfaltzgraff Co., York, PA; *U.S. Private*, pg. 860
Farnsworth, Robert, Exec. V.P.-Mktg.--The Pfaltzgraff Co., York, PA; *U.S. Private*, pg. 860
Farr, D.N., Exec. V.P.--Emerson Electric Co., Saint Louis, MO; *U.S. Public*, pg. 572
Farr, David, Sr. V.P. & Gen. Mgr.-Corp. Communications Div.--Canon U.S.A., Inc., Lake Success, NY; *Int'l*, pg. 262
Farr, Joe H., Exec. V.P. & Chief Fin. Officer--Temple-Inland Mortgage Corporation, Austin, TX; *U.S. Public*, pg. 1575
Farraker, Stephen, Exec. Dir.--WF Corroon-Manchester, Manchester, United Kingdom; *Int'l*, pg. 1502
Farrar, Greg, Exec. V.P.--Billcom Exposition & Conference, Sterling, VA; *Int'l*, pg. 1446
Farrell, John J., Exec. V.P.-Human Resources--The Chase Manhattan Corporation, New York, NY; *U.S. Public*, pg. 337
Farrell, Mary, Chief Oper. Officer & Exec. V.P.--Mintz & Hoke Inc., Avon, CT; *U.S. Private*, pg. 751
Farrell, Tana J., Chief Oper. Officer & Exec. V.P.--The Woodfin Suite Hotels, San Diego, CA; *U.S. Private*, pg. 1187
Farrelly, Joseph W., Chief Info. Officer & Exec. V.P.--Nabisco Inc., Parsippany, NJ; *U.S. Public*, pg. 1355
Fash, Victoria R., Chief Fin. Officer & Exec. V.P.--Cognizant Corporation, Westport, CT; *U.S. Public*, pg. 395
Fasorile, Tom, Exec. V.P.-Sls.--Bulova Corporation, Woodside, NY; *U.S. Public*, pg. 1010
Fass, Stan, Exec. V.P.-Sls.--Elgin Watch Company, Long Island City, NY; *U.S. Private*, pg. 371
Fassbind, Renato, Exec. V.P.-Fin.--ABB Asea Brown Boveri (Holding) Ltd., Zurich, Switzerland; *Int'l*, pg. 1
Fassinotti, Antonio Ello, Chief Exec. Officer & Exec. V.P.--Ferrero U.S.A., Inc., Somerset, NJ; *Int'l*, pg. 480
Fattor, D., Exec. Dir. & Gen. Mgr.--Zanussi Componenti Plastica S.p.A., Oderzo, Italy; *Int'l*, pg. 442
Fatzinger, Walter R., Jr., Exec. V.P.--First Maryland Bancorp, Baltimore, MD; *Int'l*, pg. 64
Faucher, Robert J., Exec. V.P.-Devel.--Essex International, Inc., Fort Wayne, IN; *U.S. Public*, pg. 593
Faulders, C. Thomas, III, Chief Fin. Officer & Exec. V.P.--BDM International, Inc., Mc Lean, VA; *U.S. Public*, pg. 1558
Faulhaber, Alan M., Exec. V.P.--The F.D. Lawrence Electric Co., Cincinnati, OH; *U.S. Private*, pg. 654
Faulkner, Jack C., Exec. V.P.--Wackenhut Services, Inc., Coral Gables, FL; *U.S. Public*, pg. 1731
Faulkner, Laurence, Exec. V.P.-Equity Trading & Sls.--Fidelity Investments (FMR Corp.), Boston, MA; *U.S. Private*, pg. 402
Fausel, Charles E., Exec. V.P.--Lester B. Knight & Associates, Inc., Chicago, IL; *U.S. Private*, pg. 626
Faust, James L., Exec. V.P. & Pres.-Antec International--The Antec Corporation, Rolling Meadows, IL; *U.S. Public*, pg. 116
Fauve, Jean-Michel, Sr. Exec. V.P.-Devel.--Electricite de France, Paris, France; *Int'l*, pg. 437
Fayne, Henry, Exec. V.P.-Fin. Svcs.--American Electric Power Company, Inc., Columbus, OH; *U.S. Public*, pg. 71
Fayne, Henry W., Exec. V.P.-Fin. Svcs.--American Electric Power Service Corp., Columbus, OH; *U.S. Public*, pg. 72
Feather, Harold E., Exec. V.P.-Strategic Plng.--Rykoff-Sexton, Inc., Wilkes-Barre, PA; *U.S. Public*, pg. 918
Federlin, Gerd, Dr., Exec. V.P.--MAN Aktiengesellschaft, Munich, Germany; *Int'l*, pg. 824
Fee, Kevin T., Exec. V.P.--Reliable Automatic Sprinkler Co., Inc., Mount Vernon, NY; *U.S. Private*, pg. 920
Feekin, Duane D., Exec. V.P.-H.R. Division--Pacific Century Financial Corporation, Honolulu, HI; *U.S. Public*, pg. 1248
Feekin, Duane D., Exec. V.P.-H.R.--Bank of Hawaii, Honolulu, HI; *U.S. Public*, pg. 1248
Feeley, Stanton J., Chief Investment Officer & Exec. V.P.--SunAmerica Inc., Los Angeles, CA; *U.S. Public*, pg. 1532
Feeley, Stanton J., Exec. V.P. & Chief Investment Officer--SunAmerica Asset Management Corporation, New York, NY; *U.S. Public*, pg. 1533
Feeney, John R., Exec. V.P.--Summit Bancorp, Princeton, NJ; *U.S. Public*, pg. 1527
Feeney, Paul M., Chief Fin. Officer & Exec. V.P.--AEP Industries, Inc., South Hackensack, NJ; *U.S. Public*, pg. 4
Feeney, William, Exec. V.P.--International Home Foods Inc., Parsippany, NJ; *U.S. Private*, pg. 526
Feigin, Barbara S., Exec. V.P. & Strategic Svcs. Dir.--Grey Advertising Inc., New York, NY; *U.S. Public*, pg. 764
Feinberg, Steven, Exec. V.P. & Exec. Creative Dir.--N.W. Ayer & Partners New York, New York, NY; *U.S. Private*, pg. 104
Feiner, Stuart F., Exec. V.P., Gen. Counsel & Sec.--Inco Limited, Toronto, Canada; *Int'l*, pg. 672
Feinour, Eugene P., Exec. V.P.--CoreStates Bank, N.A., Philadelphia, PA; *U.S. Public*, pg. 446
Feldman, Clark, Exec. V.P. & Dir.-Mktg.--Vita Food Products, Inc., Chicago, IL; *U.S. Private*, pg. 1142
Feldman, Joel D., Exec. V.P.--Byer California, San Francisco, CA; *U.S. Private*, pg. 191
Feldman, Leon D., Exec. V.P., Treas. & Sec.--P & F Industries, Inc., Farmingdale, NY; *U.S. Public*, pg. 1239
Feldman, Trudy, Exec. V.P.-Sls.--Careers USA Inc., Philadelphia, PA; *U.S. Private*, pg. 209
Feldsher, Paul, Exec. V.P.--Trenwick America Reinsurance Corporation, Stamford, CT; *U.S. Public*, pg. 1634
Feldstein, Eric A., Chief Fin. Officer & Exec. V.P.--General Motors Acceptance Corporation (GMAC), Detroit, MI; *U.S. Public*, pg. 719
Feles, Gust, Exec. V.P.--Carhartt, Inc., Dearborn, MI; *U.S. Private*, pg. 210
Felix, Robert F., Chief Fin. Officer, Exec. V.P. & Treas.--First Federal Savings, East Hartford, CT; *U.S. Public*, pg. 632
Feller, Harriet Burns, Exec. V.P., Sec. & Gen Counsel--Westcorp, Irvine, CA; *U.S. Public*, pg. 1756
Fellman, Lisa, Exec. V.P.--RBT/Strum, Cherry Hill, NJ; *U.S. Private*, pg. 902
Fellowes, Peter, Exec. V.P. & Sec.--Fellowes Manufacturing Co., Itasca, IL; *U.S. Private*, pg. 400
Felmet, Mark H., Exec. V.P.--Pacific One Dealer Center, Inc., Costa Mesa, CA; *U.S. Public*, pg. 635
Fels, Xavier, Exec. V.P.-Pub. Affairs--PSA Peugeot Citroen, Paris, France; *Int'l*, pg. 1020
Felsher, Steven G., Exec. V.P.-Fin./Worldwide, Treas. & Sec.--Grey Advertising Inc., New York, NY; *U.S. Public*, pg. 764
Fenn, Wade R., Exec. V.P.-Mktg.--Best Buy Co., Inc., Eden Prairie, MN; *U.S. Public*, pg. 223
Fenning, Andrew, Exec. V.P., Strategic Devel. Dir.--J. Walter Thompson Company, New York, NY; *Int'l*, pg. 1483
Fenster, Larry C., Exec. V.P. & P.O.M. Devel.--ServiceMaster Energy Management, Englewood, CO; *U.S. Public*, pg. 1462
Ferdinandtsen, G.R., Sr. Exec. V.P.--American National Insurance Company, Galveston, TX; *U.S. Public*, pg. 87
Ferguson, C. Randolph, Exec. V.P.-Grp.--Jefferson-Pilot Life Insurance Co., Greensboro, NC; *U.S. Public*, pg. 926
Ferguson, Clint S., Exec. V.P.--Eastland National Bank, Eastland, TX; *U.S. Public*, pg. 633
Ferguson, D. Stevenson, Jr., Exec. V.P.-Asset Mngmt.--Compass Bank, Birmingham, AL; *U.S. Public*, pg. 418
Ferguson, Donald J., Exec. V.P.-Sls. & Mktg.--Intermatic Inc., Spring Grove, IL; *U.S. Private*, pg. 567
Ferguson, G. Blair, Exec. V.P. & Dir.-Trust Div.--Whitney Holding Corporation, New Orleans, LA; *U.S. Public*, pg. 1766
Ferguson, Roy C., III, Exec. V.P.--Liberty Bank & Trust Company of Tulsa, Tulsa, OK; *U.S. Public*, pg. 174
Fernandes, Anthony G., Exec. V.P.-Products, Global Energy Ventures, Aluminum & Coal--Atlantic Richfield Company, Los Angeles, CA; *U.S. Public*, pg. 144
Fernandez, Claude, Chief Fin. Officer, Exec. V.P., Sr. V.P. & Mng. Dir.--W.P. Carey & Co., Inc., New York, NY; *U.S. Private*, pg. 209
Fernandez, Gonzalo, Exec. V.P.-Commercial Opers.--Pacific Crest Capital, Inc., Agoura Hills, CA; *U.S. Public*, pg. 1248
Fernandez, Manuel, Exec. V.P. & Chief Oper. Officer-Worldwide Instruction--Berlitz International, Inc., Princeton, NJ; *U.S. Public*, pg. 221
Fernstrom, H. Allen, Chief Oper. Officer & Exec. V.P.--Marine Construction & Design Co., Seattle, WA; *U.S. Private*, pg. 703
Ferran, Rene J., Chief Fin. Officer & Exec. V.P.--The Martin Agency, Richmond, VA; *U.S. Private*, pg. 678
Ferran, Rene J., Chief Fin. Officer & Exec. V.P.--The Martin Agency, Richmond, VA; *U.S. Public*, pg. 909
Ferrante, Frank, Exec. V.P.-Sls.--Farmland Dairies, Wallington, NJ; *U.S. Private*, pg. 395
Ferreira Pinto Lima, Luiz Eduardo, Exec. V.P.--Uniao de Bancos Brasileiros S.A. (Unibanco), Sao Paulo, Brazil; *Int'l*, pg. 1431
Ferreira, Jose, Jr., Exec. V.P. & Pres.-Asia Pacific--Avon Products, Inc., New York, NY; *U.S. Public*, pg. 155
Ferreira, Richard S., Chief Fin. Officer & Exec. V.P.--Golf Hosts, Inc., Palm Harbor, FL; *U.S. Private*, pg. 1036
Ferro, Thom, Exec. V.P. & Gen. Mgr.--Westwood One, Inc., New York, NY; *U.S. Public*, pg. 1763
Ferstl, James H., Chief Mdsg. Officer & Exec. V.P.--Venture Stores, Inc., O Fallon, MO; *U.S. Public*, pg. 1716
Fessler, Donald F., Exec. V.P.--Zurn Industries, Inc., Erie, PA; *U.S. Public*, pg. 1794
Fethke, Wayne G., Exec. V.P.-Consumer Prods. Grp.--Fiskars Oy AB, Helsinki, Finland; *Int'l*, pg. 492
Fetter, Trevor, Chief Fin. Officer & Exec. V.P.--Tenet Healthcare Corporation, Santa Barbara, CA; *U.S. Public*, pg. 1576
Fettig, Jeff M., Pres.-Whirlpool Europe B.V. & Exec. V.P.--Whirlpool Corporation, Benton Harbor, MI; *U.S. Public*, pg. 1764
Feuerman, Kerry, Exec. V.P. & Grp. Creative Dir.--The Martin Agency, Richmond, VA; *U.S. Private*, pg. 678
Feuerman, Kerry, Exec. V.P. & Grp. Creative Dir.--The Martin Agency, Richmond, VA; *U.S. Public*, pg. 909
Feulner, Andreas, Exec. V.P.--Astra AB, Sodertalje, Sweden; *Int'l*, pg. 93
Fiamingo, Joseph, Exec. V.P.-Opers.--General Cable Corporation, Highland Heights, KY; *Int'l*, pg. 1486
Fichtner, Lawrence C., Exec. V.P.-Corp. Commun.--Veritas DGC Inc., Houston, TX; *U.S. Private*, pg. 1136
Fidoten, Douglas, Exec. V.P. & Strategic Plng. Dir.--DCA Advertising, Inc., New York, NY; *Int'l*, pg. 393
Field, David O., Exec. V.P.--Petty Company, Inc., Effingham, IL; *U.S. Private*, pg. 860
Fields, Oscar, Exec. V.P.--Motown Record Company, J.P., New York, NY; *Int'l*, pg. 1052
Fieramosca, Charles, Exec. V.P.-Mdsg.--Arrow Shirt Company, New York, NY; *Int'l*, pg. 194
Fierman, Daniel J., Chief Oper. Officer & Exec. V.P.--ANESCO, Kingston, PA; *U.S. Private*, pg. 74
Fierman, Ronald S., Exec. V.P. & Gen. Mgr.--Warwick Baker O'Neill, New York, NY; *U.S. Private*, pg. 1152
Fife, Michael, Exec. V.P.--Fairfax Lumber & Millwork Company Inc., Springfield, VA; *U.S. Private*, pg. 391
Figer, Jean Paul, Grp. V.P.--CAP Gemini S.A., Paris, France; *Int'l*, pg. 263
Figliulo, David A., Exec. V.P.--SPR, Inc., Oak Brook, IL; *U.S. Public*, pg. 1419
Fike, William H., Vice Chm. & Exec. V.P.--Magna International Inc., Markham, Canada; *Int'l*, pg. 829
Filion, Yves, Exec. V.P.-Generation, Transmission & Telecommunications--Hydro-Quebec, Montreal, Canada; *Int'l*, pg. 640
Filippi, Charles-Henri, Grp. Exec. V.P.-Investment Banking--Credit Commercial de France, Paris, France; *Int'l*, pg. 341
Filippo, Sam, Exec. V.P.--Schumacher Electric Corporation, Mount Prospect, IL; *U.S. Private*, pg. 973
Fincher, Joseph, Exec. V.P. & Gen. Mgr.--Adventure Island, Tampa, FL; *U.S. Public*, pg. 114
Fincher, Joseph, Exec. V.P. & Gen. Mgr.--Busch Gardens Tampa, Tampa, FL; *U.S. Public*, pg. 114
Fincher, Larry, Chief Fin. Officer & Exec. V.P.--Truman Arnold Companies, Texarkana, TX; *U.S. Private*, pg. 84
Fine, Jay, Chief Oper. Officer & Exec. V.P.--Fort Lock Corporation, River Grove, IL; *U.S. Private*, pg. 419

Fine, Larry, Exec. V.P. & Mgr.-Gen. Mdse.--Michaels Stores, Inc., Irving, TX; *U.S. Public*, pg. 1104

Finegan, Paul G., Exec. V.P.--CoreStates Bank, N.A., Philadelphia, PA; *U.S. Public*, pg. 446

Finelli, Mary Lynn, Chief Fin. Officer & Exec. V.P.--Provident Mutual Life Insurance Co., Berwyn, PA; *U.S. Private*, pg. 891

Finestone, Ron, Exec. V.P.--Members Only By Europe Craft, New York, NY; *U.S. Public*, pg. 129

Fink, Dennis L., Chief Fin. Officer & Exec. V.P.--Haverty Furniture Companies, Inc., Atlanta, GA; *U.S. Public*, pg. 799

Fink, Jim H., Exec. V.P.--TCBY Enterprises Inc., Little Rock, AR; *U.S. Public*, pg. 1553

Finkel-Green, Janice, Exec. V.P. & Reg. Brdcst. Dir.--Western International Media Corporation, Los Angeles, CA; *U.S. Private*, pg. 1165

Finkel, Janice, Exec. V.P. & Reg. Brdcst. Dir.--Western International Media Corporation, New York, NY; *U.S. Private*, pg. 1166

Finkelstein, David, Sr. Exec. V.P.--Century Business Credit Corporation, New York, NY; *U.S. Private*, pg. 225

Finkelstein, Howard, Exec. V.P.--Metromedia International Telecommunications, Inc., Stamford, CT; *U.S. Public*, pg. 1103

Finley, David, Chief Fin. Officer & Exec. V.P.--Broadway & Seymour, Inc., Charlotte, NC; *U.S. Public*, pg. 258

Finn, Edward L., Chief Fin. Officer & Exec. V.P.--Green Tree Financial Corporation, Saint Paul, MN; *U.S. Public*, pg. 761

Finn, Richard H., Exec. V.P.-Fin. Opers.--Transamerica Corporation, San Francisco, CA; *U.S. Public*, pg. 1629

Finneran, Tom, Chief Fin. Officer & Exec. V.P.--Jordan, McGrath, Case & Taylor Inc., New York, NY; *U.S. Private*, pg. 598

Finnigan, G. Michael, Chief Fin. Officer, Exec. V.P., Treas. & Pres.-Gaming Div.--Hollywood Park, Inc., Inglewood, CA; *U.S. Public*, pg. 830

Finnigan, Joseph T., Sr. Partner & Exec. V.P.--Fleishman-Hillard Inc., Saint Louis, MO; *U.S. Private*, pg. 411

Fiore, Anthony, Exec. V.P.-Intl. Sls.--Active International, Pearl River, NY; *U.S. Private*, pg. 15

Fiorillo, Peter J., Chief Fin. Officer & Exec. V.P.-Fin. & Admin.--Find/SVP, Inc., New York, NY; *U.S. Public*, pg. 623

Firpo, Roberto, Exec. V.P.-Merchant Banking--Istituto Bancario San Paolo Di Torino S.p.A., Turin, Italy; *Int'l*, pg. 691

Fischer, Carolyn, Exec. V.P.-Genecom--Robert A. Becker, New York, NY; *Int'l*, pg. 601

Fischer, Charles W., Chief Oper. Officer & Exec. V.P.--Canadian Occidental Petroleum Ltd., Calgary, Canada; *U.S. Public*, pg. 1210

Fischer, Eric R., Exec. V.P.& Gen. Counsel--UST Corporation, Boston, MA; *U.S. Public*, pg. 1660

Fischer, Eric R., Exec. V.P., Gen. Counsel & Sec.--United States Trust Company, Boston, MA; *U.S. Public*, pg. 1660

Fischer, Eric R., Exec. V.P., Gen. Counsel & Sec.--USTrust, Boston, MA; *U.S. Public*, pg. 1660

Fischer, Hans, Sr. Exec. V.P.--SGS Societe Generale de Surveillance Holding S.A., Geneva, Switzerland; *Int'l*, pg. 1153

Fischer, Richard L., Exec. V.P.--Aluminum Company of America, Pittsburgh, PA; *U.S. Public*, pg. 60

Fischer, Warren L., Exec. V.P.-Acct. Mngmt.--Grey Advertising Inc., New York, NY; *U.S. Public*, pg. 764

Fisher, Andrew S., Exec. V.P.-Affiliates--Cox Broadcasting Inc., Atlanta, GA; *U.S. Private*, pg. 281

Fisher, C. Douglas, Exec. V.P. & Creative Services Dir.--Lord, Sullivan & Yoder Inc. Marketing Communications, Columbus, OH; *U.S. Private*, pg. 676

Fisher, David M., Exec. V.P.--Matthew Clark Taunton, Ltd., Bristol, United Kingdom; *Int'l*, pg. 848

Fisher, Edward, Exec. V.P.-The Private Bank--Bank of Boston Connecticut, Hartford, CT; *U.S. Public*, pg. 184

Fisher, Edwin, Exec. V.P. & Chief Mktg. Officer--The Medical Protective Company, Fort Wayne, IN; *U.S. Private*, pg. 728

Fisher, Judith Dunn, Exec. V.P.--Huntington Bancshares Inc., Columbus, OH; *U.S. Public*, pg. 849

Fisher, Judith Dunn, Exec. V.P.--Huntington National Bank, Columbus, OH; *U.S. Public*, pg. 850

Fisher, Lucy, Exec. V.P.--Warner Bros. Studios, Inc., Burbank, CA; *U.S. Public*, pg. 1611

Fisher, Michael, Exec. V.P.-Stores--Stein Mart, Inc., Jacksonville, FL; *U.S. Public*, pg. 1514

Fisher, Phelps, Exec. V.P.-Mktg. Dir.--Fisher Broadcasting Inc., Seattle, WA; *U.S. Public*, pg. 648

Fisher, Randy, Exec. V.P.-Sls.--John J. Campbell Co., Inc., Memphis, TN; *U.S. Private*, pg. 204

Fisher, Robert J., Chief Oper. Officer & Exec. V.P.--The Gap, Inc., San Francisco, CA; *U.S. Public*, pg. 702

Fisher, William R., Exec. V.P.--Willis Corroon Corp. of Minnesota, Minneapolis, MN; *Int'l*, pg. 1506

Fisi, Louis S., Exec. V.P.--Advanced Lighting Technologies, Inc., Twinsburg, OH; *U.S. Public*, pg. 20

Fisk, Douglas R., Chief Oper. Officer & Exec. V.P.--Mustang Tractor & Equip. Co., Houston, TX; *U.S. Private*, pg. 768

Fisk, John, Exec. V.P.-Single Family Securitization Grp.--Federal Home Loan Mortgage Corporation, Mc Lean, VA; *U.S. Public*, pg. 615

Fitts, Jay T., Exec. V.P. & Chief Credit Officer--LaSalle-Talman Bank, Chicago, IL; *Int'l*, pg. 11

Fitzek, Candace, Exex. V.P.-Retail Banking--Bank of Boston Connecticut, Hartford, CT; *U.S. Public*, pg. 184

Fitzgerald, Connie, Exec. V.P.--BTI Americas, Inc., Northbrook, IL; *U.S. Private*, pg. 108

Fitzgerald, Daniel J., Chief Fin. Officer & Exec. V.P.--Massachusetts Mutual Life Insurance Co., Springfield, MA; *U.S. Private*, pg. 712

Fitzgerald, John, Exec. V.P.--J. Josephson, Inc., South Hackensack, NJ; *U.S. Private*, pg. 601

Fitzgerald, Rusell E., Exec. V.P.--Midlantic Bank, N.A., Philadelphia, PA; *U.S. Public*, pg. 1242

Fitzgibbon, Chuck, Exec. V.P.--Shandwick Baltimore, Baltimore, MD; *Int'l*, pg. 1227

Fitzpatrick, Dana G., Exec. V.P.--Fitzpatrick & Weller, Inc., Ellicottville, NY; *U.S. Private*, pg. 409

Fitzpatrick, Eugene E., Exec. V.P.-Nuclear Generation--American Electric Power Service Corp., Columbus, OH; *U.S. Public*, pg. 72

Fitzpatrick, G.I., Exec. V.P.--Al-Jubail Petrochemical Company, Tareet, Saudi Arabia; *U.S. Public*, pg. 601

Fitzpatrick, Richard J., Exec. V.P.--Banknorth Group Inc., Burlington, VT; *U.S. Public*, pg. 186

Fitzpatrick, Sean, Exec. V.P.--McCann-Erickson Worldwide, New York, NY; *U.S. Public*, pg. 909

Fitzsimons, Michael J., Exec. V.P.--Copper & Brass Sales, Inc., Eastpointe, MI; *Int'l*, pg. 1389

Flach, Oster, Exec. V.P.--Knorr-Bremse Systeme Fur Nutzfahrzeuge GmbH, Munich, Germany; *Int'l*, pg. 738

Flaherty, Patrick, Exec. V.P. & Mng. Partner-Creative--Wells BDDP, Inc., New York, NY; *Int'l*, pg. 117

Flaherty, William, Chief Fin. Officer & Exec. V.P.--Kemper Reinsurance Co., Long Grove, IL; *U.S. Private*, pg. 614

Flanagan, Patrick A., Exec. V.P.-Mergers & Acq. & Sec.--Mac-Gray Corporation, Cambridge, MA; *U.S. Public*, pg. 1029

Flanagan, Patrick B., Chief Oper. Officer & Exec. V.P.--The Austin Company, Cleveland, OH; *U.S. Private*, pg. 99

Flanders, Dudley K., Pres. & Chief Exec. Officer--Flanders Industries, Inc., Fort Smith, AR; *U.S. Private*, pg. 410

Flanders, Howard L., Chief Fin. Officer & Exec. V.P.--All American Semiconductor, Inc., Miami, FL; *U.S. Public*, pg. 41

Flaum, Russell M., Exec. V.P.--Illinois Tool Works Inc., Glenview, IL; *U.S. Public*, pg. 865

Flax, Robert J., Exec. V.P., Gen. Counsel & Sec.--Bay View Capital Corporation, San Mateo, CA; *U.S. Public*, pg. 197

Flechsig, Rolf, Dr., Exec. V.P.--Norddeutsche Landesbank (NORD/LB), Hannover, Germany; *Int'l*, pg. 957

Fleczok, Richard, Exec. V.P.--New Hampshire Ball Bearings, Inc., Peterborough, NH; *Int'l*, pg. 868

Fleischhacker, Joe F., Jr., Chief Exec. Officer & Exec. V.P.--Lake Region Manufacturing, Inc., Chaska, MN; *U.S. Private*, pg. 643

Fleming, Brian, Chief Fin. Officer & Exec. V.P.--The Santa Anita Companies, Arcadia, CA; *U.S. Public*, pg. 1081

Fleming, Charles, Exec. V.P.--IMI Cornelius Inc. (MN), Anoka, MN; *Int'l*, pg. 646

Fleming, Charles E., Jr., Exec. V.P.--IMI Cornelius, Inc. (IA), Mason City, IA; *Int'l*, pg. 646

Fleming, Eugene C., Chief Oper. Officer & Exec. V.P.--Quorum Health Group, Inc., Brentwood, TN; *U.S. Public*, pg. 1353

Fleming, John, Exec. V.P.-Emerging Markets--IXC Communications, Inc., Austin, TX; *U.S. Private*, pg. 556

Fleming, Robert T., Chief Fin. Officer & Exec. V.P.--Universal Studios TV, Universal City, CA; *Int'l*, pg. 1215

Fletcher, Adrian H., Exec. V.P., Gen. Mgr. & Chief Oper. Officer-RNB London--Republic National Bank of New York, New York, NY; *U.S. Public*, pg. 1380

Fletcher, Daniel, Exec. V.P.-Los Angeles--J.W. Messner, Inc., Grand Rapids, MI; *U.S. Private*, pg. 734

Fletcher, Daniel G., Exec. V.P. & Mng. Dir.--J.W. Messner, Inc., Los Angeles, CA; *U.S. Private*, pg. 734

Fletcher, Harold J., Chief Oper. Officer & Exec. V.P.--Federal Home Loan Bank of New York, New York, NY; *U.S. Private*, pg. 399

Fletcher, Michael J., Exec. V.P. & Gen. Mgr.-Tulsa--SPR, Inc., Oak Brook, IL; *U.S. Public*, pg. 1419

Flick, Michael A., Chief Admin. Officer, Exec. V.P. & Sec.--First Commerce Corporation, New Orleans, LA; *U.S. Public*, pg. 629

Fligg, James E., Sr. Exec. V.P.-Strategic Plng. & Intl. Bus. Devel.--Amoco Corporation, Chicago, IL; *U.S. Public*, pg. 101

Flint, David B., Exec. V.P.--Flint Ink Corp., Detroit, MI; *U.S. Private*, pg. 413

Flock, Joseph E., Exec. V.P.-Select Brands Co.--Brown-Forman Beverages Worldwide, Louisville, KY; *U.S. Public*, pg. 261

Flora, Jim, Exec. V.P.--Blue Seal Feeds, Inc., Londonderry, NH; *U.S. Private*, pg. 1134

Flores, Raul Quintero, Exec. V.P.--Hylsa S.A.-Technology Division, San Nicolas, Mexico; *Int'l*, pg. 56

FlorJancic, Ronald J., Exec. V.P.-Mktg.--Consol, Pittsburgh, PA; *U.S. Public*, pg. 531

FlorJancic, Ronald J., Exec. V.P.-Mktg.--Consol, Pittsburgh, PA; *Int'l*, pg. 1081

Flowers, David M., Exec. V.P.-Mktg.--AmeriSource Health Corp., Malvern, PA; *U.S. Public*, pg. 96

Flowers, Lee, Exec. V.P.--Dade Behring Inc., Deerfield, IL; *U.S. Private*, pg. 110

Flowers, Lee, Exec. V.P.--Dade Behring Inc., Deerfield, IL; *Int'l*, pg. 626

Floyd, Phillip M., Exec. V.P.--First Charter Corporation, Concord, NC; *U.S. Public*, pg. 627

Flury, L. Richard, Exec. V.P.-Exploration & Production--Amoco Corporation, Chicago, IL; *U.S. Public*, pg. 101

Flynn, Gary, Exec. V.P. & Treas.--Rotary Multiforms, Inc., Warren, MI; *U.S. Private*, pg. 947

Flynn, Ken, Exec. V.P.-Store Opers.--Eckerd Corporation, Largo, FL; *U.S. Public*, pg. 917

Flynn, Patrick J., Exec. V.P.--McDonald's Corporation, Oak Brook, IL; *U.S. Public*, pg. 1068

Flynn, Peter E., Exec. V.P. & Sec.--ENStar, Inc., Eden Prairie, MN; *U.S. Public*, pg. 585

Flynn, Steven, Exec. V.P.-Mktg.--Gramercy Pictures, Beverly Hills, CA; *U.S. Private*, pg. 468

Fogarty, Steve, Exec. V.P.--Colgate U.S.A., New York, NY; *U.S. Public*, pg. 397

Fogarty, Timothy J., Exec. V.P.-Mortgage Banking--Starbanc Corporation, Cincinnati, OH; *U.S. Public*, pg. 1510

Fogge, Len, Exec. V.P.-Creative/Mktg. Services--Showtime Networks Inc., New York, NY; *U.S. Private*, pg. 779

Fogle, Ron, Exec. V.P.-Commercial Loans--First National Bank of Abilene, Abilene, TX; *U.S. Public*, pg. 633

Foglia, Dennis A., Exec. V.P., Treas. & Sec.--Equitable Savings & Loan Association, Wauwatosa, WI; *U.S. Private*, pg. 380

Foglia, Dennis A., Exec. V.P., Sec. & Treas.--The Equitable Bank, Hales Corners, WI; *U.S. Private*, pg. 380

Foh, Elsie, Exec. V.P.--DBS Bank Ltd., Singapore, Singapore; *Int'l*, pg. 350

Fohrer, Alan J., Chief Fin. Officer & Exec. V.P.--Edison International, Rosemead, CA; *U.S. Public*, pg. 564

Fokker, J.P., Exec. V.P.--SHV Holdings N.V., Utrecht, Netherlands; *Int'l*, pg. 1154

Foley Murphy, Kathy, Exec. V.P. & Gen. Mgr.--Young & Rubicam San Francisco, San Francisco, CA; *U.S. Private*, pg. 1198

Foley, Ann, Exec. V.P.-East Coast Programming--Showtime Networks Inc., New York, NY; *U.S. Private*, pg. 779

Foley, James, Exec. V.P.--Dentsu Young & Rubicam/Seoul, Seoul, Korea; *U.S. Private*, pg. 325

Foley, Peter H., Exec. V.P.-M & A--Frontier Insurance Group, Inc., Rock Hill, NY; *U.S. Public*, pg. 684

Folick, Jeffrey, Chief Oper. Officer & Exec. V.P.--PacifiCare Health Systems, Inc., Cypress, CA; *U.S. Public*, pg. 1250

Folts, John B., Exec. V.P., Treas. & Sec.--Hargro Enterprises, Inc., Stamford, CT; *U.S. Private*, pg. 502

Fontana, Joe, Exec. V.P. & Creative Services Dir.--Ziccardi & Partners, Inc., New York, NY; *U.S. Private*, pg. 1205

Fooks, V. Thomas, Exec. V.P.--RMS Techs, Inc., Lanham, MD; *U.S. Private*, pg. 905

Foote, E.L., Exec. V.P. & Pres.-Indus. Chemicals Division--Bayer Corporation, Pittsburgh, PA; *Int'l*, pg. 172

Forassiepi, Lee, Exec. V.P.--CFB Industries, Inc., Chicago, IL; *U.S. Private*, pg. 194

Forassippi, Lee, Exec. V.P.--Chicago Fire Brick Co., Chicago, IL; *U.S. Private*, pg. 194

Ford, Dave, Exec. V.P.--Heating Oil Partners L.P., Darien, CT; *U.S. Private*, pg. 518

Ford, Scott T., Exec. V.P.--ALLTEL Corporation, Little Rock, AR; *U.S. Public*, pg. 55

Ford, Stephen A., Exec. V.P.-Sls. & Distr.--D & K Healthcare Resources-Lexington Division, Lexington, KY; *U.S. Public*, pg. 472

Ford, Thomas, Exec. V.P.-Opers.-Eastern Div.--Grossman's, Inc., Stoughton, MA; *U.S. Private*, pg. 585

Ford, W. Douglas, Exec. V.P.-Petroleum Prods.--Amoco Corporation, Chicago, IL; *U.S. Public*, pg. 101

Forell, David C., Chief Fin. Officer & Exec. V.P.--Catherines Stores Corporation, Memphis, TN; *U.S. Public*, pg. 317

Forman, Fred L., Chief Info. Officer & Exec. V.P.--American Management Systems, Inc., Fairfax, VA; *U.S. Public*, pg. 86

Forman, Maxine, Exec. V.P.--Cricket Lane, West Bridgewater, MA; *U.S. Public*, pg. 948

Fornaro, Robert L., Sr. V.P.-Plng.--US Airways Group, Inc., Arlington, VA; *U.S. Public*, pg. 1680

Fornella, Norman G., Chief Fin. Officer, Exec. V.P., Treas. & Sec.--Morse Diesel International, Inc., New York, NY; *U.S. Private*, pg. 762

Forney, Guy S., Pres. & Exec. V.P.-Bourns Trimpot--Bourns, Inc., Riverside, CA; *U.S. Private*, pg. 161

Forrer, Christophe Veyrin, Exec. V. P.--Editions du Juris-Classeur, Paris, France; *Int'l*, pg. 1095

Forsberg, Bo, Exec. V.P.-Fin. Institutions & Trade--Svenska Handelsbanken, Stockholm, Sweden; *Int'l*, pg. 1327

Forses, James J., Pres.-Intl. Opers. & Exec. V.P.--Ikon Office Solutions, Inc., Malvern, PA; *U.S. Public*, pg. 862

Forsgren, John H., Chief Fin. Officer & Exec. V.P.--Northeast Utilities, Berlin, CT; *U.S. Public*, pg. 1194

Forsguen, John H., Chief Fin. Officer & Exec. V.P.--Public Service Company of New Hampshire, Manchester, NH; *U.S. Public*, pg. 1195

Forsythe, Carl, Exec. V.P.-Retail Savings--H.F. Ahmanson & Co., Irwindale, CA; *U.S. Public*, pg. 29

Fort, Vance, Exec. V.P.-Govt. & Intl. Rels.--World Airways, Inc., Herndon, VA; *U.S. Public*, pg. 1780

Forte, Deborah A., Exec. V.P. & Div. Head-Scholastic Productions--Scholastic Corporation, New York, NY; *U.S. Public*, pg. 1440

Fortson, Carl, Exec. V.P.--Journal of Commerce, Inc., New York, NY; *Int'l*, pg. 1026

Forward, Frank D., Chief Fin. Officer & Exec. V.P.--BJ's Wholesale Club, Inc., Natick, MA; *U.S. Public*, pg. 162

Foss, Robert E., Chief Fin. Officer & Exec. V.P.--Mid Atlantic Medical Services, Inc., Rockville, MD; *U.S. Public*, pg. 1109

Fossati-Bellani, Vittorio, Dr., Exec. V.P. & Pres.-GM Semiconductor Grp.--Coherent, Inc., Santa Clara, CA; *U.S. Public*, pg. 395

Foster, Arthur L., Exec. V.P.--Collective Bank, Cologne, NJ; *U.S. Public*, pg. 1528

Foster, James H., Exec. V.P., Chm.-Brouillard Communications--J. Walter Thompson Company, New York, NY; *Int'l*, pg. 1483

Foster, Jim, Chief Fin. Officer & Exec. V.P.--JM Family Enterprises Inc., Deerfield Beach, FL; *U.S. Private*, pg. 577

Foster, Norman P., Exec. V.P.-Corp. Fin.--AFLAC Incorporated, Columbus, GA; *U.S. Public*, pg. 28

Fourie, Jan H., Exec. Officer--Sasol Limited, Johannesburg, South Africa; *Int'l*, pg. 1196

Foust, Larry, Exec. V.P. & Gen. Mgr.-Consolidated Wholesale Lumber Co.--Calcasieu Lumber Company, Austin, TX; *U.S. Private*, pg. 200

Fowler, Peggy Y., Chief Oper. Officer & Exec. V.P.--Portland General Electric Co., Portland, OR; *U.S. Public*, pg. 584

Fowler, Susan, Exec. V.P. & Dir.-Human Resources--Sanwa Bank California, Los Angeles, CA; *Int'l*, pg. 1189

Fowlie, Robert G., Exec. V.P.-Opers--Brush Research Manufacturing Company, Los Angeles, CA; *U.S. Private*, pg. 176

Fox, Byron, Exec. V.P.--BRE Properties, Inc., San Francisco, CA; *U.S. Public*, pg. 163

Fox, Christopher A., Exec. V.P.--Regis Corporation, Minneapolis, MN; *U.S. Public*, pg. 1373
Fox, Duane, Exec. V.P.--Spangler Candy Company, Bryan, OH; *U.S. Private*, pg. 1020
Fox, Jonathan E., Chief Exec. Officer, Exec. V.P.-Intl. & Reg. Dir.-Asia Pacific--Grey Asia Pacific, Quarry Bay, Hong Kong; *U.S. Public*, pg. 765
Fox, Leslie B., Chief Oper. Officer & Exec. V.P.--Lexford Residential Trust, Columbus, OH; *U.S. Public*, pg. 991
Fox, Richard, Exec. V.P.--Camp Dresser & McKee Inc., Cambridge, MA; *U.S. Private*, pg. 203
Fox, Robert G., Exec. V.P.--First Charter Corporation, Concord, NC; *U.S. Public*, pg. 627
Fox, Robert J., Exec. V.P.-Raw Matls. & Chemicals--Alcan Aluminium Limited, Montreal, Canada; *Int'l*, pg. 50
Fox, William J., Chief Fin. Officer & Sr. Exec. V.P.--Revlon, Inc., New York, NY; *U.S. Private*, pg. 689
Foxcroft, Ken B., Exec. V.P. & Treas.--The Toronto Dominion Bank, Toronto, Canada; *Int'l*, pg. 1401
Foxworthy, Randolph, Exec. V.P.-Corp. Devel.--Simon DeBartolo Group, Inc., Indianapolis, IN; *U.S. Public*, pg. 1474
Foxx, M.J., Chief Oper. Officer & Exec. V.P.--Handgards Inc., Northbrook, IL; *U.S. Private*, pg. 499
Foy, John N., Chief Fin. Officer & Exec. V.P.--CBL & Associates Properties, Inc., Chattanooga, TN; *U.S. Public*, pg. 273
Fraedrich, David S., Chief Fin. Officer, Exec. V.P. & Treas.--Rocky Shoes & Boots, Inc., Nelsonville, OH; *U.S. Public, pg. 1402*
Fraley, John, Exec. V.P.-Opers.--Louisville Bedding Company, Louisville, KY; *U.S. Private*, pg. 677
Frame, Jim, Exec. V.P. & Production Dir.--Deutsch, Inc., New York, NY; *U.S. Private*, pg. 328
Francis, C.F., Exec. V.P.--Azcon Corp., Chicago, IL; *U.S. Private*, pg. 153
Francis, Dennis B., Exec. V.P. & Chief Tech. Officer--Vanguard Cellular Systems, Inc., Greensboro, NC; *U.S. Public*, pg. 1707
Francis, John H., Exec. V.P.--First Citizens Banc Shares, Inc., Raleigh, NC; *U.S. Public*, pg. 628
Francisco de Castro, Joachim, Exec. V.P.--Uniao de Bancos Brasileiros S.A. (Unibanco), Sao Paulo, Brazil; *Int'l*, pg. 1431
Franco, Elmer, Exec. V.P. & Partner--OfficeMax De Mexico, Mexico, Mexico; *U.S. Public*, pg. 1212
Francois, Georges, Exec. V.P.--Labinal SA, Montigny-le-Bretonneux, France; *Int'l*, pg. 785
Francony, Michel, Exec. V.P. & Head-Distrib.--Electricite de France, Paris, France; *Int'l*, pg. 437
Francony, Michel, Exec. V.P.-Distr.--Gaz de France, Paris, France; *Int'l*, pg. 541
Frangipane, Joe, Exec. V.P.-Sls. & Mktg. (U.S. & Canada)--Alcan Cable Division, Atlanta, GA; *Int'l*, pg. 50
Frank, Betsy, Exec. V.P.-Res. & Bus. Devel.--Viacom Inc., New York, NY; *U.S. Private*, pg. 775
Frank, Betsy, Exec. V.P.-Res. & Bus. Devel.--MTV Networks, New York, NY; *U.S. Private*, pg. 779
Frank, J. Louis, Exec. V.P.-Refining, Mktg. & Transportation--Marathon Oil Company, Houston, TX; *U.S. Public*, pg. 1661
Frank, Robert A., Exec. V.P.--Legg Mason, Inc., Baltimore, MD; *U.S. Public*, pg. 984
Frank, Ronald L., Exec. V.P.-Fin. & Admin.--Ecology and Environment, Inc., Lancaster, NY; *U.S. Public*, pg. 562
Frank, Susan, Chief Oper. Officer & Exec. V.P.--Hanna-Barbera Productions, Inc., Hollywood, CA; *U.S. Public*, pg. 1614
Frank, Werner L., Exec. V.P.--Sterling Software, Inc., Dallas, TX; *U.S. Public*, pg. 1516
Frankel, Arnold, Exec. V.P.--National Utility Service, Inc., Park Ridge, NJ; *U.S. Private*, pg. 787
Franklin, Doug, Exec. V.P. & Gen. Mgr.--Dayton Newspapers, Inc., Dayton, OH; *U.S. Private*, pg. 281
Franklin, E. Thomas, Jr., Exec. V.P.--Franklin Baking Co., Inc., Goldsboro, NC; *U.S. Private*, pg. 424
Franklin, Lawrence, Exec. V.P. & Gen. Mgr.-North America--Elizabeth Arden Company, New York, NY; *Int'l*, pg. 1435
Franklin, Ronald, Exec. V.P. & Mktg. Services Dir.--Don Coleman Advertising, Inc., Southfield, MI; *U.S. Private*, pg. 251
Franklin, Thomas F., Exec. V.P.--First Midwest Bank, N.A., Itasca, IL; *U.S. Public*, pg. 636
Franks, J. Scott, Chief Oper. Officer & Exec. V.P.--Tierney & Partners, Philadelphia, PA; *U.S. Public*, pg. 1641
Franks, Ronald G., Div. Exec. V.P.-Stores & Opers.--GapKids Division, San Bruno, CA; *U.S. Public*, pg. 702
Franzel, Philip A., Chief Fin. Officer & Exec. V.P.--Salant Corporation, New York, NY; *U.S. Public*, pg. 1429
Franzem, Joseph T., Exec. V.P.--The Stroh Brewery Company, Detroit, MI; *U.S. Private*, pg. 1047
Frascarolo, Alessandro, Exec. V.P.-Fin.--Istituto Bancario San Paolo Di Torino S.p.A., Turin, Italy; *Int'l*, pg. 691
Fraser, Donald H., Chief Oper. Officer & Exec. V.P.--Farmers & Merchants Bank of Central California, Lodi, CA; *U.S. Private*, pg. 394
Fraser, Gregory A., Ph.D., Chief Fin. Officer, Exec. V.P., Treas. & Sec.--FARO Technologies, Inc., Lake Mary, FL; *U.S. Public*, pg. 613
Fraser, Richard L., Exec. V.P. & Acct. Exec.--Willis Corroon Corp. of Knoxville, Knoxville, TN; *Int'l*, pg. 1506
Fraser, Steven, Exec. V.P.-Global Retail--Regal Ware, Inc., Kewaskum, WI; *U.S. Private*, pg. 917
Fraser, Stuart W., Exec. V.P.-Logistics, Distr. & Info. Svcs.--Hudson's Bay Company, Toronto, Canada; *Int'l*, pg. 637
Frashure, Ronald D., Exec. V.P.--Acadian Asset Management, Boston, MA; *U.S. Public*, pg. 1672
Frasier, Ralph K., Exec. V.P., Gen. Counsel, Sec. & Cashier--Huntington National Bank, Columbus, OH; *U.S. Public*, pg. 850
Frauenfelder, Martin, Exec. V.P.-Assembly Systems--Mikron Holding AG, Biel, Switzerland; *Int'l*, pg. 866
Frazer, Lewis, III, Chief Fin. Officer, Exec. V.P. & Treas.--Regal Cinemas Inc., Knoxville, TN; *U.S. Public*, pg. 1371
Frazier, Ben, Exec. V.P.--Klaussner Corporation, Asheboro, NC; *U.S. Private*, pg. 625
Frazier, Reid J., Exec. V.P.--Hercules Incorporated, Wilmington, DE; *U.S. Public*, pg. 809
Frazier, Vern, Exec. V.P.--Aldi Food Inc., Batavia, IL; *U.S. Private*, pg. 33
Freadman, Tommy, Exec. V.P.-Engrng.--Altec Lansing Technologies, Inc., Milford, PA; *U.S. Private*, pg. 479
Frederick, Hank, Exec. V.P.--Zacky Farms, Inc., South El Monte, CA; *U.S. Private*, pg. 1203
Frederick, Hank, Exec. V.P.--Zacky Foods, South El Monte, CA; *U.S. Private*, pg. 1203
Fredericks, Eric, Exec. V.P.--Young & Rubicam Europe, Zurich, Switzerland; *U.S. Private*, pg. 1199
Freed, Robert, Exec. V.P.--Kaufman and Broad-South Bay Inc., Fremont, CA; *U.S. Public*, pg. 945
Freedman, Eugene, Vice Chm. & Exec. V.P.--Stanhome Inc., Westfield, MA; *U.S. Public*, pg. 1508
Freedman, Michael, Exec. V.P.--Kepner-Tregoe, Inc., Skillman, NJ; *U.S. Public*, pg. 1659
Freedman, Tom, Chief Fin. Officer & Sr. Exec. V.P.--Les Schwab Tire Centers, Prineville, OR; *U.S. Private*, pg. 974
Freeland, A. Jerome, Exec. V.P. -Journal & Continuity Publishing--Mosby-Year Book, Inc., Saint Louis, MO; *U.S.* Public, pg. 1616
Freeman, Clara, Exec. Dir.-Personnel--Marks & Spencer PLC, London, United Kingdom; *Int'l*, pg. 842
Freeman, Phyllis, Exec. V.P., Comptroller, Legal Officer & Dir.-Investor Rels.--Eagle Lincoln Mercury Inc., Dallas, TX; *U.S. Private*, pg. 355
Freesmeier, Eric, Exec. V.P.--Edison Brothers Stores, Inc., Saint Louis, MO; *U.S. Public*, pg. 563
Freilicher, David, Exec. V.P.--Grey Advertising Inc., New York, NY; *U.S. Public*, pg. 764
Freimuth, Steven P., Exec. V.P.-Corp. Lending Admin.--Washington Mutual Inc., Seattle, WA; *U.S. Public*, pg. 1741
Freisner, David W., Exec. V.P.--Galamba Metals, Inc., Kansas City, KS; *U.S. Private*, pg. 437
Freitas, Noreen, Exec. V.P.--Den-Mat Corporation, Santa Maria, CA; *U.S. Private*, pg. 324
French, C. William, Exec. V.P.-Bus. Devel.--Cinram Ltd., Scarborough, Canada; *Int'l*, pg. 293
French, James T., Exec. V.P.--ITT Hartford Life & Annuity Insurance Corporation, Minneapolis, MN; *U.S. Public*, pg. 795
French, Peter, Chief Oper. Officer & Exec. V.P.--Global Marketing Resources (GMR), New York, NY; *U.S. Private*, pg. 457
Fresu, Aldo Angelo, Exec. V.P.-Admmin.--Istituto Bancario San Paolo Di Torino S.p.A., Turin, Italy; *Int'l*, pg. 691
Fretthold, Timothy J., Chief Admin. Officer & Exec. V.P.--Ultramar Diamond Shamrock Corporation, San Antonio, TX; *U.S. Public*, pg. 1663
Freudenberger, Kent W., Exec. V.P.-Mktg. Div.--Airborne Freight Corporation, Seattle, WA; *U.S. Public*, pg. 32
Freudenthal, John, Exec. V.P.-Mdsg.--Carson Pirie Scott & Co., Milwaukee, WI; *U.S. Public*, pg. 309
Frew, Ridge, Exec. V.P.-Property Opers.--Berkshire Realty Company, Inc., Boston, MA; *U.S. Public*, pg. 221
Frey, Hans-Georg, Exec. V.P.--Spindelfabrik Suessen, Suessen, Germany; *Int'l*, pg. 1290
Frey, Michael, Exec. V.P.--Turkey Hill Dairy, Inc., Conestoga, PA; *U.S. Private*, pg. 1109
Frey, Robert, Exec. V.P.-Intl.--Herman Miller, Inc., Zeeland, MI; *U.S. Public*, pg. 1111
Frezel, William J., Exec. V.P. & Sec.--Premier Dental Products Company, King of Prussia, PA; *U.S. Private*, pg. 881
Fricchione, Patrick, Sr., Exec. V.P.--Simplex Industries, Inc., Scranton, PA; *U.S. Private*, pg. 1001
Fridlington, John W., Exec. V.P.-Comml. Lending--Peoples Heritage Financial Group, Inc., Portland, ME; *U.S. Public, pg. 1275*
Frie, Leonard W., Chief Oper. Officer & Exec. V.P.--Total Renal Care Holdings, Inc., Torrance, CA; *U.S. Public*, pg. 1625
Friedberg, Barry S., Exec. V.P.--Merrill Lynch & Co., Inc., New York, NY; *U.S. Public*, pg. 1097
Friederichs, Peter, Exec. V.P.--Bayerische Hypotheken-und Wechsel-Bank Aktiengesellschaft, Munich, Germany; *Int'l*, pg. 175
Friedlander, Rick D., Exec. V.P.--Republic National Bank of New York, New York, NY; *U.S. Public*, pg. 1380
Friedman, James A., Exec. V.P. & Mngmt. Supvr.--Carrafiello, Diehl & Associates, Inc., Irvington, NY; *U.S. Private*, pg. 215
Friedman, Jane Becker, Exec. V.P.--Alfred A. Knopf, Inc., New York, NY; *U.S. Private*, pg. 21
Friedman, Jerold B., Exec. V.P.--Executive Jet Aviation, Inc., Columbus, OH; *U.S. Private*, pg. 388
Friedman, Norman E., Chief Oper. Officer & Exec. V.P.--Herbalife International of America, Inc., Century City, CA; *U.S. Public*, pg. 809
Friedman, Paul, Exec. V.P.--ABC News, Inc., New York, NY; *U.S. Public*, pg. 511
Friedmann, Daniel E., Exec. V.P. & Gen. Mgr.-Systems Integration & Software Grp.--Orbital Sciences Corporation, Dulles, VA; *U.S. Public*, pg. 1229
Friehe, Bob, Exec. V.P.--Reinke Manufacturing Co., Inc., Deshler, NE; *U.S. Private*, pg. 920
Friendly, Andy, Exec. V.P.-Programming & Prod.--King World Productions, Inc., New York, NY; *U.S. Public*, pg. 961
Fries, Alexis, Exec. V.P.-Asia Pacific--ABB Asea Brown Boveri (Holding) Ltd., Zurich, Switzerland; *Int'l*, pg. 1
Friese, E., Exec. V.P.--AEGON Levensverzekering NV, Hague, Netherlands; *Int'l*, pg. 25
Frinier, Richard, Exec. V.P.-Design & Mktg.--Brown Jordan Company, El Monte, CA; *U.S. Private*, pg. 174
Frisch, Hans, Exec. V.P.--Beaver Street Fisheries, Inc., Jacksonville, FL; *U.S. Private*, pg. 128
Fritz, Donald G., Exec. V.P. & Pres.-Kellogg Europe--Kellogg Company, Battle Creek, MI; *U.S. Public*, pg. 947
Frock, John, Exec. V.P. & Asst. Sec.--Nobel Education Dynamics, Inc., Media, PA; *U.S. Public*, pg. 1185
Froelich, Eugene, Chief Fin. Officer & Exec. V.P.-Fin. & Admin.--Maxicare Health Plans, Inc., Los Angeles, CA; *U.S. Public*, pg. 1061
Froeschle, Duane R., Exec. V.P.--National Bank of Arizona, Tucson, AZ; *U.S. Public*, pg. 1793
Frons, Brian, Exec. V.P.-New World Televison--New World Entertainment, Inc., Los Angeles, CA; *Int'l*, pg. 926
Frotten, Robert, Exec. V.P.-Fin. & Admin. & Controller--New England Frozen Foods, Inc., Southborough, MA; *U.S. Private*, pg. 793
Fruitman, Harvey, Chief Fin. Officer, Exec. V.P. & Sec.--Tridel Enterprises Inc., Downsview, Canada; *Int'l*, pg. 1423
Frutko, David, Chief Fin. Officer & Exec. V.P.--Mezzina/Brown Inc., New York, NY; *U.S. Private*, pg. 739
Fry, Randy, Exec. V.P.--Fry's Electronics, Inc., San Jose, CA; *U.S. Private*, pg. 430
Fry, William N., IV, Exec. V.P. & Chief Oper. Officer-Floorcovering Grp.--The Dixie Group, Inc., Chattanooga, TN; *U.S. Public*, pg. 514
Fryer, Robert L., Exec. V.P.--First Maryland Bancorp, Baltimore, MD; *Int'l*, pg. 64
Fryman, Norman, Exec.V.P.-Mdsg. Sls.--Bayer Clothing Group, New York, NY; *U.S. Private*, pg. 124
Fryman, Norman, Exec. V.P.--Arrow Shirt Company, New York, NY; *Int'l*, pg. 194
Fu, Cary, Chief Fin. Officer & Exec. V.P.--Benchmark Electronics Inc., Angleton, TX; *U.S. Public*, pg. 210
Fuchs, Frederick E., Jr., Exec. V.P. & Dir.-Real Estate--Piccadilly Cafeterias, Inc., Baton Rouge, LA; *U.S. Public*, pg. 1294
Fuchs, Joseph L., Exec. V.P.--The Conde Nast Publications Inc., New York, NY; *U.S. Private*, pg. 20
Fuchs, Ronald, Chief Tech. Officer & Exec. V.P.--Bayer Corporation, Pittsburgh, PA; *Int'l*, pg. 172
Fuchs, Wilhelm, Exec. V.P.--Stora Feldmuhle AG, Dusseldorf, Germany; *Int'l*, pg. 1303
Fudge, Ann, Exec. V.P. & Gen. Mgr.-Maxwell House Div.--Kraft Foods Inc., Glenview, IL; *U.S. Public*, pg. 1288
Fudge, Ann M., Exec. V.P. & Gen. Mgr.-Maxwell House Dix.--Kraft Foods, Inc., Northfield, IL; *U.S. Public*, pg. 1287
Fuest, Frederick, Exec. V.P.-Intl.--Active International, Pearl River, NY; *U.S. Private*, pg. 15
Fugmann, Hans W., Exec. V.P.--Nilfisk A/S, Brondby, Denmark; *Int'l*, pg. 932
Fuhrman, Zvi, Exec. V.P.-Intl. Activity--Bank Hapoalim, Tel Aviv, Israel; *Int'l*, pg. 149
Fujiharo, Toshiro, Exec. V.P.--Nippon Steel Corporation, Tokyo, Japan; *Int'l*, pg. 939
Fujii, Masahiro, Exec. V.P.--Toppan Printing Company, Ltd., Tokyo, Japan; *Int'l*, pg. 1399
Fujii, Mutsuo, Exec. V.P.-Domestic & Overseas Acct. Services--Dentsu Inc., Tokyo, Japan; *Int'l*, pg. 392
Fujii, Toshio, Exec. V.P.--NHK Spring Co., Ltd., Yokohama, Japan; *Int'l*, pg. 901
Fujimori, Toshiyuki, Sr. Exec. V.P.--The Book Club Finance and Securities Public Company Ltd., Bangkok, Thailand; *Int'l*, pg. 816
Fujino, Shigeru, Gen. Mgr.-Logistics--Asahi Breweries Ltd., Tokyo, Japan; *Int'l*, pg. 83
Fujisawa, Hiroyasu, Exec. V.P.--Asahi Breweries Ltd., Tokyo, Japan; *Int'l*, pg. 83
Fujisawa, Susumu, Exec. V.P.--Taisei Corporation, Tokyo, Japan; *Int'l*, pg. 1347
Fukaya, Takashi, Exec. V.P.--Nippon Life Insurance Co., Osaka, Japan; *Int'l*, pg. 934
Fukayama, Gary P., Exec. V.P.--Borg Warner Automotive, Inc., Chicago, IL; *U.S. Public*, pg. 245
Fukazawa, Shigeyoshi, Exec. V.P.-Internal--NKK Corporation, Tokyo, Japan; *Int'l*, pg. 902
Fukuchi, Junji, Exec. V.P.--Mitsubishi Materials Corp., Tokyo, Japan; *Int'l*, pg. 874
Fukuchi, Shigeo, Sr. Mng. Dir.--Asahi Breweries Ltd., Tokyo, Japan; *Int'l*, pg. 83
Fukuda, Hiroyuki, Exec. V.P.--Mycal, Corp., Osaka, Japan; *Int'l*, pg. 897
Fukuda, Morihiro, Exec. V.P.--Shimizu Corporation, Tokyo, Japan; *Int'l*, pg. 1233
Fuller, Donn, Exec. V.P.--MEPC American Properties, Dallas, TX; *U.S. Private*, pg. 686
Fuller, Mark A., Jr., Exec. V.P.--Champion International Corp., Stamford, CT; *U.S. Public*, pg. 333
Fulton, William R., Exec. V.P. & Chief Fin. Officer--Midland Walwyn Inc., Toronto, Canada; *Int'l*, pg. 865
Fumero, Silvano, Sr. Exec. V.P.-Res. & Devel.--Ares-Serono S.A., Geneva, Switzerland; *Int'l*, pg. 80
Funicelli, Joseph, Exec. V.P. & Gen. Mgr.--Unifoil Corporation, Passaic, NJ; *U.S. Private*, pg. 1117
Funke, Mark W., Exec. V.P. & Chief Oper. Officer-Oklahoma City--Bank of Oklahoma, N.A., Tulsa, OK; *U.S.* Public, pg. 163
Fuoco, Dino, Chief Fin. Officer & Exec. V.P.--Alliance Forest Products Inc., Montreal, Canada; *Int'l*, pg. 57
Furlong, Daniel R., Exec. V.P. & Treas.--Paradigm Communications, Tampa, FL; *U.S. Private*, pg. 838
Furlong, Sue, Mng. Partner & Exec. V.P.--Dugan Valva Contess Inc., Morristown, NJ; *U.S. Private*, pg. 345
Furnaro, Frank, Partner & Exec. V.P.--Stawasz & Partners/Health Care Communications, New York, NY; *U.S. Private*, pg. 599
Furst, Dietrich, Exec. V.P.--Norddeutsche Landesbank (NORD/LB), Hannover, Germany; *Int'l*, pg. 957
Furukawa, Takashi, Exec. V.P.--The Chugoku Electric Power Co., Inc., Hiroshima, Japan; *Int'l*, pg. 291
Furukawa, Yasuhiko, Sr. Exec. V.P.--Asahi Glass Co., Ltd., Tokyo, Japan; *Int'l*, pg. 84
Furuya, Seinosuke, Exec. V.P.--Kirin Brewery Co., Ltd., Tokyo, Japan; *Int'l*, pg. 735

Fusarelli, Tony, Exec. V.P.-Worldwide Sls. & Service--General Signal Networks, Shelton, CT; *U.S. Public*, pg. 727
Fusco, Robert A., Exec. V.P.--Olsten Corporation, Melville, NY; *U.S. Public*, pg. 1220
Fuselier, Rudy, Exec. V.P.--Alamo Industrial Group, San Antonio, TX; *U.S. Private*, pg. 31
Fusilli, Donald P., Jr., Exec. V.P. & Gen. Mgr.-Energy--Michael Baker Corporation, Pittsburgh, PA; *U.S. Public*, pg. 168
Fuss, Michael D., Chief Fin. Officer & Exec. V.P.--Wm. E. Wright Limited Partnership, West Warren, MA; *U.S. Private*, pg. 1192
Gabbe, Fred, Exec V.P.-Worldwide Opers.--Mr. Christmas Inc., New York, NY; *U.S. Private*, pg. 765
Gabbert, Wayne B., Exec. V.P.--The First National Bank of Lake Charles, Lake Charles, LA; *U.S. Public*, pg. 630
Gable, W. Bradley, Exec. V.P.--The Van Metres Companies, Burke, VA; *U.S. Private*, pg. 1132
Gabrielsen, Robert, Chief Fin. Officer, Exec. V.P. & Treas.--Pawling Savings Bank, Pawling, NY; *U.S. Public*, pg. 1334
Gadomski, Robert E., Exec. V.P.-Chemicals--Air Products and Chemicals, Inc., Allentown, PA; *U.S. Public*, pg. 30
Gaertner, Mike, Exec. V.P.--Grey Advertising Inc., New York, NY; *U.S. Public*, pg. 764
Gaffney, George F., Exec. V.P.-Personal Fin. & Gen. Mgr.-Metro Toronto--Royal Bank of Canada, Toronto, Canada; *Int'l*, pg. 1131
Gaffney, John, Exec. V.P. & Media Dir.--Arnold Communications, Inc., Boston, MA; *U.S. Private*, pg. 83
Gaffrey, Mike, Exec. V.P. & Dir.-Corp. Devel.--ICF Kaiser International Inc., Fairfax, VA; *U.S. Public*, pg. 852
Gage, Duncan, Exec. V.P.-Opers.--Lafarge Corporation, Reston, VA; *Int'l*, pg. 788
Gagen, George J., Exec. V.P.--Union Pacific Technologies, Saint Louis, MO; *U.S. Public*, pg. 1668
Gagliano, Charles, Exec. V.P.-Mktg.--Pepsi-Cola General Bottlers, Inc., Rolling Meadows, IL; *U.S. Public*, pg. 1277
Gagliardi, Gerald, Exec. V.P. & Pres.-Global Customer Services--Unisys Corporation, Blue Bell, PA; *U.S. Public*, pg. 1671
Gagnier, Charles E., Exec. V.P.-Bank Mergers & Acquisitions--Amcore Financial, Inc., Rockford, IL; *U.S. Public*, pg. 64
Gagnon, Stephen L., Exec. V.P.--Republic Group Incorporated, Hutchinson, KS; *U.S. Public*, pg. 1378
Gail, Dan, Exec. V.P., Sec. & Gen. Counsel--Southwestern Financial Services Corp., Dallas, TX; *U.S. Private*, pg. 1018
Gail, Daniel B., Exec. V.P., Gen. Counsel & Sec.--Constitution Life Insurance Co., Dallas, TX; *U.S. Private*, pg. 1018
Gaines, Brenda, Exec. V.P.--Diners Club Inc., Chicago, IL; *U.S. Public*, pg. 377
Gaines, Howard C., Exec. V.P.--First Commerce Corporation, New Orleans, LA; *U.S. Public*, pg. 629
Gaines, Mark, Exec. V.P. & Natl. Sls. Mgr.-Distribution--Universal Pictures, Universal City, CA; *Int'l*, pg. 1216
Galanos, Nicholas, Exec. V.P.-Opers.--TGI Friday's, Inc., Addison, TX; *U.S. Private*, pg. 212
Galanti, Richard A., Chief Fin. Officer & Exec. V.P.--Costco Wholesale, Issaquah, WA; *U.S. Public*, pg. 451
Galbraith, Leslie A., Chief Fin. Officer, Exec. V.P., Treas. & Sec.--First International Bancorp, Inc., Hartford, CT; *U.S. Public*, pg. 635
Gale, Thomas C., Exec. V.P. & Gen. Mgr.-Jeep Opers.--Chrysler Corporation, Auburn Hills, MI; *U.S. Public*, pg. 352
Galifi, Vincent J., Exec. V.P.-Fin.--Magna International Inc., Markham, Canada; *Int'l*, pg. 829
Gallagher, Daniel, Chief Oper. Officer & Exec. V.P.--Southern Health Services, Inc., Richmond, VA; *U.S. Public*, pg. 454
Gallagher, H. James, Chief Fin. Officer, Exec. V.P.-Fin. & Acting Treas.--CalMat Co., Los Angeles, CA; *U.S. Public*, pg. 295
Gallagher, Pat, Exec. V.P.--ServiceMaster Food Management Services, Downers Grove, IL; *U.S. Public*, pg. 1462
Gallagher, Robert C., Vice Chm. & Exec. V.P.--Associated Banc-Corp, Green Bay, WI; *U.S. Public*, pg. 140
Gallagher, Thomas E., Exec. V.P. & Gen. Counsel--Hilton Hotels Corporation, Beverly Hills, CA; *U.S. Public*, pg. 828
Gallaher, Frank F., Exec. V.P.-Opers.--Entergy Corporation, New Orleans, LA; *U.S. Public*, pg. 585
Gallaher, J. Kirk, Chief Fin. Officer & Exec. V.P.--Uni-Marts, Inc., State College, PA; *U.S. Public*, pg. 1664
Galli, Joseph, Exec. V.P. & Pres.-Power Tools--The Black & Decker Corporation, Towson, MD; *U.S. Public*, pg. 233
Gallian, Robert, Exec. V.P. & V.P.-Sls. & Mktg.--Pet Life Foods, Inc., Willowbrook, IL; *U.S. Private*, pg. 856
Gallo, Aldo, Exec. V.P.-Budget & Performance Control--Istituto Bancario San Paolo Di Torino S.p.A., Turin, Italy; *Int'l*, pg. 691
Gallo, Fred T., Exec. V.P.-Feature Prod. Mngmnt.--Paramount Pictures Corporation, Los Angeles, CA; *U.S. Private*, pg. 776
Gallogly, Jerry T., Exec. V.P.--American States Insurance Companies, Indianapolis, IN; *U.S. Public*, pg. 997
Galloway, H.E., Exec. V.P.-Retail & Community Banking Div.--Sanwa Bank California, Los Angeles, CA; *Int'l*, pg. 1189
Galt, Jeff, Exec. V.P.--The Dialog Corporation plc, London, United Kingdom; *Int'l*, pg. 412
Galt, Jeffrey S., Exec. V.P.--The DIALOG Corporation, Mountain View, CA; *Int'l*, pg. 412
Galuten, Keith, Exec. V.P.--SGD International Corp., Riverdale, NY; *U.S. Private*, pg. 957
Galvin, Frank J., Exec. V.P.--U.S. Can Company, Oak Brook, IL; *U.S. Public*, pg. 1681
Galvin, Robert, Chief Fin. Officer & Exec. V.P.--Nine West Group, Inc., Stamford, CT; *U.S. Public*, pg. 1185
Gambill, Thomas K., Exec. V.P.--Braid Electric Company, Nashville, TN; *U.S. Private*, pg. 165
Gamble, G.C., Exec. V.P.--Westfield Companies, Westfield Center, OH; *U.S. Private*, pg. 1169
Gamey, R.K., Exec. V.P.--Canadian Pacific Limited, Calgary, Canada; *Int'l*, pg. 258
Gamoran, Saul, Exec. V.P., Gen. Counsel & Sec.--Play by Play Toys & Novelties, Inc., San Antonio, TX; *U.S. Public*, pg. 1309
Gandolfi, Gary, Exec. V.P.--Carter Chambers Supply, Inc., Baton Rouge, LA; *U.S. Private*, pg. 216
Ganesan, N., Exec. V.P. & Dir.-Insurance Corp. of Singapore--DBS Bank Ltd., Singapore, Singapore; *Int'l*, pg. 350
Ganis, Andrea, Exec. Sr. V.P.-Promo.--Atlantic Recording Corporation, New York, NY; *U.S. Public*, pg. 1611
Gann, L. Keith, Exec. V.P. & Gen. Mgr.--SOR Inc., Lenexa, KS; *U.S. Private*, pg. 957
Ganoe, John E., Exec. V.P.-Corp. Devel.--Norwest Corporation, Minneapolis, MN; *U.S. Public*, pg. 1201
Gans, Robert M., Exec. V.P., Gen. Counsel & Sec.--PriceSmart Inc., San Diego, CA; *U.S. Public*, pg. 1324
Gantaume, Arturo, Exec. V.P.--Banco Provincial S.A. Banco Universal, Caracas, Venezuela; *Int'l*, pg. 142
Gantz, Charles V., Exec. V.P.--Midlantic Bank, N.A., Edison, NJ; *U.S. Public*, pg. 1242
Ganz, Isaac, V.P.--Villaume Industries, Inc., Saint Paul, MN; *U.S. Private*, pg. 1140
Ganzi, Victor F., Chief Fin. Officer, Exec. V.P. & Legal Officer--The Hearst Corporation, New York, NY; *U.S. Private*, pg. 515
Garbarding, Larry G., Chief Fin. Officer & Exec. V.P.--DTE Energy Company, Detroit, MI; *U.S. Public*, pg. 475
Garber, David, Exec. V.P.-T.V. & New Media--LIVE Film & Mediaworks, Van Nuys, CA; *U.S. Private*, pg. 671
Garber, Robert E., Exec. V.P. & Gen. Counsel--The Equitable Companies Incorporated, New York, NY; *U.S. Public*, pg. 588
Garbutt, George A., Exec. V.P.-Gen. Mgr. & Dir.-Adv.--Maserati Automobiles, Incorporated, Baltimore, MD; *Int'l*, pg. 482
Garcia Barrios, Jorge Luis, Sr. Exec. V.P.-Electronic D.P.--Grupo Casa Autrey, Mexico, Mexico; *Int'l*, pg. 573
Garcia Segovia, Armando J., Exec. V.P.-Devel.--Cemex, S.A. de C.V., Monterrey, Mexico; *Int'l*, pg. 278
Gardner, David A., Exec. V.P., Sls. Mgr. & Sec.--Alfred Nickles Bakery, Inc., Navarre, OH; *U.S. Private*, pg. 799
Gardner, David A., Exec. V.P. , Sec. & Sls. Mgr.--Nickles Bakery, Inc., Martins Ferry, OH; *U.S. Private*, pg. 799
Gardner, David A., Exec. V.P.-Sls.--Nickles Bakery of Indiana Inc., Elkhart, IN; *U.S. Private*, pg. 799
Gardner, David A., Exec. V.P., Sls. Mgr. & Sec.--Nickles Bakery of Ohio Inc., Lima, OH; *U.S. Private*, pg. 799
Gardner, John, Chief Fin. Officer & Exec. V.P.--New Balance Athletic Shoe, Inc., Boston, MA; *U.S. Private*, pg. 792
Gardner, Stephen, Exec. V.P.--Ammirati, Puris & Lintas, Inc., New York, NY; *U.S. Private*, pg. 66
Gareau, Joseph H., Exec. V.P. & Chief Investment Officer--Hartford Fire Insurance Co., Hartford, CT; *U.S. Public*, pg. 794
Gareau, Josheph H., Chief Investment Officer & Exec. V.P.--The Hartford Financial Services Group Inc., Hartford, CT; *U.S. Public*, pg. 794
Garg, Gulshan, Exec. V.P. & Dir.-Info. Tech.--INMC Mortgage Holdings, Inc., Pasadena, CA; *U.S. Public*, pg. 857
Garlick, Ralph W., Exec. V.P. & Sr. Credit Officer--Old Kent Financial Corporation, Grand Rapids, MI; *U.S. Public*, pg. 1216
Garneau, Robert M., Chief Fin. Officer & Exec. V.P.--Kaman Corporation, Bloomfield, CT; *U.S. Public*, pg. 941
Garnett, Gerald, Chief Exec. Officer & Exec. V.P.--Southern Farm Bureau Casualty Insurance Company, Ridgeland, MS; *U.S. Private*, pg. 1016
Garnett, Gerald, Chief Fin. Officer & Exec. V.P.--Mississippi Farm Bureau Casualty Insurance Company, Jackson, MS; *U.S. Private*, pg. 1016
Garnett, Gerald, Chief Fin. Officer & Exec. V.P.--Louisiana Farm Bureau Casualty Insurance Company, Baton Rouge, LA; *U.S. Private*, pg. 1016
Garnett, Stanley I., II, Exec. V.P.--Florida Progress Corporation, Saint Petersburg, FL; *U.S. Public*, pg. 655
Garr, Louis J., Jr., Exec. V.P. & Gen. Counsel--The May Department Stores Company, Saint Louis, MO; *U.S. Public*, pg. 1063
Garratt, Graham, Exec. V.P. & Publr.--Marcel Dekker, Inc., New York, NY; *U.S. Private*, pg. 321
Garris, Ron, Exec. V.P.--Dale Industries Inc., Dearborn, MI; *U.S. Private*, pg. 308
Garrison, Foster C. III, Exec. V.P.--BT Financial Corporation, Johnstown, PA; *U.S. Public*, pg. 163
Garrison, Kenny, Principal--Richards, Brock, Miller, Mitchell & Assoc. Inc., Dallas, TX; *U.S. Private*, pg. 929
Garrity, Jim, Sr. V.P. & Dir.-Adv. & Mktg.--First Union Corporation, Charlotte, NC; *U.S. Public*, pg. 639
Garschagen, D.H., Exec. V.P. & Reg. Mgr.--Bank of America NT&SA, Hong Kong, Hong Kong; *U.S. Public*, pg. 182
Gartfinkel, Steven R., Chief Fin. Officer & Exec. V.P.--DVI, Inc., Doylestown, PA; *U.S. Public*, pg. 476
Gartner, Elliott M., Exec. V.P.--New England Investment Associates, Boston, MA; *U.S. Private*, pg. 737
Garver, Patrick J., Exec. V.P. & Gen. Counsel--Barrick Gold Corporation, Toronto, Canada; *Int'l*, pg. 168
Garvey, Christine N., Grp. Exec. V.P.-Corp. Real Estate/OREO--Bank of America NT&SA, San Francisco, CA; *U.S. Public*, pg. 180
Garvey, Jerry, Exec. V.P.-Property Devel.--Simon DeBartolo Group, Inc., Indianapolis, IN; *U.S. Public*, pg. 1474
Garvey, Thomas E., Exec. V.P.-Benefits--Willis Corroon Corp. of Northern Ohio, Cleveland, OH; *Int'l*, pg. 1506
Garvey, William P., Exec. V.P. & Chief Fin. Officer-U.S.--Grey Advertising Inc., New York, NY; *U.S. Public*, pg. 764
Garvin, Ed, Exec. V.P. & Gen. Mgr.--South Carolina Steel, Taylors, SC; *U.S. Public*, pg. 412
Garza, Regulo Salinas, Exec. V.P.--Hylsa S.A.-Bar and Rod Division, Puebla, Mexico; *Int'l*, pg. 56
Gasmovic, David J., Exec. V.P.--McLaughlin Manufacturing Company, Greenville, SC; *U.S. Private*, pg. 724
Gasner, Thomas M., Exec. V.P.-Opers.--ERO, Inc., Mount Prospect, IL; *U.S. Private*, pg. 526
Gasner, Thomas M., Exec. V.P.-Opers.--ERO Industries, Inc., Mount Prospect, IL; *U.S. Private*, pg. 526
Gassan, Marsha M., Chief Fin. Officer & Sr. Exec. V.P.--Hibernia Corporation, New Orleans, LA; *U.S. Public*, pg. 825
Gaston, Roger, Exec. V.P.-Human Resources--Carson Pirie Scott & Co., Milwaukee, WI; *U.S. Public*, pg. 309
Gaston, Ron, Chief Fin. Officer & Exec. V.P.--Fabri-Centers of America, Inc., Hudson, OH; *U.S. Public*, pg. 609
Gatepithaya, Anant, Sr. Exec. V.P.--SCF Finance & Securities Co., Ltd., Bangkok, Thailand; *Int'l*, pg. 1239
Gates, Carole O'Connor, Exec. V.P.-Mktg.--Star Markets Company, Inc., Cambridge, MA; *U.S. Private*, pg. 1035
Gatto, Andrew K., Exec. V.P.-Mktg.--Toy Biz, Inc., New York, NY; *U.S. Public*, pg. 1625
Gatto, Dominick J., Exec. V.P.--Knight Architects Engineers Planners, Inc., Chicago, IL; *U.S. Private*, pg. 626
Gault, Bob, Chief Oper. Officer & Exec. V.P.--Universal Studios Japan, Ltd., Tokyo, Japan; *Int'l*, pg. 1216
Gault, John, Exec. V.P.--Time Warner Cable, Stamford, CT; *U.S. Public*, pg. 1610
Gauthier, Alan E., Chief Fin. Officer & Exec. V.P.-Fin.--Exide Corporation, Reading, PA; *U.S. Public*, pg. 600
Gautier, John W., Exec. V.P.--Deposit Guaranty National Bank of Louisiana, Hammond, LA; *U.S. Public*, pg. 500
Gavin, John, Exec. V.P.--Right Management Consultants, Inc., Philadelphia, PA; *U.S. Public*, pg. 1390
Gavin, Mark A., CPA, Chief Oper. Officer & Exec. V.P.--CFX Bank, Keene, NH; *U.S. Public*, pg. 277
Gavin, Pat, Chief Fin. Officer, Exec. V.P. & Treas.--General Media International Inc., New York, NY; *U.S. Private*, pg. 444
Gavotto, Andrea, Exec. V.P. & Mng. Dir.--Testa International, Milan, Italy; *Int'l*, pg. 1376
Gavotto, Andrea, Exec. V.P. & Creative Dir.--L'Altra, Turin, Italy; *Int'l*, pg. 1377
Gavzer, Charles A., Exec. V.P.-Devel. & Acquisitions--Hostmark Management Group, Rolling Meadows, IL; *U.S. Private*, pg. 541
Gazerwitz, George, Exec. V.P. & Pres.-Computer Systems Prods. Grp.--Unisys Corporation, Blue Bell, PA; *U.S. Public*, pg. 1671
Gazzola, Kenneth, Exec. V.P. & Publisher--McGraw-Hill Aviation Week Group, New York, NY; *U.S. Public*, pg. 1070
Geary, Robert, Exec. V.P.-Bus. Affairs--TriStar Pictures, Culver City, CA; *Int'l*, pg. 1283
Gebhardt, Barbara, Exec. V.P.--Career Blazers Inc., New York, NY; *U.S. Private*, pg. 209
Gecowets, Jerry, Exec. V.P.--Gosiger Inc., Dayton, OH; *U.S. Private*, pg. 466
Gedacht, Leon, Exec. V.P.--Power Systems Inc., Bloomfield, CT; *Int'l*, pg. 868
Gedeon, Charles C., Exec. V.P.-Raw Matls. & Diversified Bus.--U.S. Steel International, Inc., Pittsburgh, PA; *U.S. Public*, pg. 1661
Gedra, Ted, Exec. V.P.-Wolverine Footwear Grp.--Wolverine Brand Div., Rockford, MI; *U.S. Public*, pg. 1775
Gehring, George A., Jr., Exec. V.P.-Eastern Regional Opers.--Corrpro Companies, Inc., Medina, OH; *U.S. Public*, pg. 451
Geiger, Larry, Exec. V.P.-Acct. Mngmt.--Grey Advertising Inc., New York, NY; *U.S. Public*, pg. 764
Geiger, S. Kay, Exec. V.P.-Intl.--Starbanc Corporation, Cincinnati, OH; *U.S. Public*, pg. 1510
Geisler, Bernd, Exec. V.P.--EMTEC Magnetics GmbH, Ludwigshafen, Germany; *Int'l*, pg. 743
Gelber, Robert M., Exec. V.P. & Pres.-GM Coherent Auburn Grp.--Coherent, Inc., Santa Clara, CA; *U.S. Public*, pg. 395
Gellert, Robert S., Exec. V.P.--Atalanta Corporation, Elizabeth, NJ; *U.S. Private*, pg. 93
Gelman, Howard, Chief Fin. Officer & Exec. V.P.--Adler Boschetto Peebles & Partners, Inc., New York, NY; *U.S. Private*, pg. 17
Genader, Robert J., Sr. Exec. V.P.--AMBAC Financial Group, Inc., New York, NY; *U.S. Public*, pg. 62
Gencarelli, Frank, Exec. V.P.-Mktg.--First Colony Life Insurance Co., Lynchburg, VA; *U.S. Public*, pg. 711
Gendry, Antoine, Exec. V.P.-France, Belgium, Spain--Ciments Francais, Paris, France; *Int'l*, pg. 292
Genecco, Vincent P., Exec. V.P.--P & C Food Markets, Inc., Syracuse, NY; *U.S. Public*, pg. 1270
Genel, Alain, Exec. V.P. & Head-Bus. Devel.--Electricite de France, Paris, France; *Int'l*, pg. 437
Genma, Akira, Sr. Exec. Dir.--Shiseido Company Ltd., Tokyo, Japan; *Int'l*, pg. 1235
Genovese, Anthony, Exec. V.P.--HRH Construction Interiors, Inc., New York, NY; *U.S. Private*, pg. 1035
Gensler, Hugo, Exec. V.P.--Bayerische Hypotheken-und Wechsel-Bank Aktiengesellschaft, Munich, Germany; *Int'l*, pg. 175
Gentry, Richard, Exec. V.P.-Mdsg.--Staples, Inc., Westborough, MA; *U.S. Public*, pg. 1509
Gentry, Robert T., Exec. V.P.-Credit--Omega Financial Corporation, State College, PA; *U.S. Public*, pg. 1222
George, David A., Exec. V.P.-Strategic Svcs. Grp.--United HealthCare Corporation, Minnetonka, MN; *U.S. Public*, pg. 1677
George, Jean-Paul, Exec. V.P.--Gaz de France, Paris, France; *Int'l*, pg. 541
George, John, Exec. V.P.-GHG--Grey Healthcare Group, New York, NY; *U.S. Public*, pg. 765

George, Leonard F., Exec. V.P.--NCI Building Systems, Inc., Houston, TX; *U.S. Public*, pg. 1145

George, Nicholas G., Exec. V.P. & Gen. Mgr.-Folding Carton Div.--Rock-Tenn Company, Norcross, GA; *U.S. Public*, pg. 1396

George, Thomas D., Exec. V.P. & Pres. & Gen. Mgr.-Semiconductor Prods.--Motorola, Inc., Schaumburg, IL; *U.S. Public*, pg. 1136

Georgeou, Tina, Exec. V.P. & Client Svcs. Dir.--DeWitt Media, Inc., New York, NY; *U.S. Private*, pg. 329

Georges-Francois, Jean-Claude, Exec. V.P.--Groupe Usinor, Paris, France; *Int'l*, pg. 570

Georgiadis, Gus P., Exec. V.P.-Sls. & Mktg.--Highmark Inc., Pittsburgh, PA; *U.S. Private*, pg. 528

Gerard, Antonia, Chief Oper. & Chief Fin. Officer, Exec. V.P., Sec. & Controller--Bolliger, Inc., Stamford, CT; *U.S. Private*, pg. 155

Gerber, Stan, Exec. V.P.--JL Media, Inc., Union, NJ; *U.S. Private*, pg. 577

Gergens, L. A., Exec. V.P.--Marigold Foods, Inc., Minneapolis, MN; *Int'l*, pg. 752

Gerhardt, Gary C., Chief Fin. Officer & Exec. V.P.--Engineered Support Systems Inc., Saint Louis, MO; *U.S. Public*, pg. 583

Gerhardt, Gary C., Chief Fin. Officer & Exec. V.P.--Engineered Specialty Plastics, Hot Springs National Park, AR; *U.S. Public*, pg. 583

Gerkens, Henry H., Chief Fin. Officer & Exec. V.P.--Landstar Holding, Shelton, CT; *U.S. Public*, pg. 978

German, Michael I., Exec. V.P.--New York State Electric & Gas Corporation, Binghamton, NY; *U.S. Public*, pg. 1173

Gernert, Douglas P., Chief Oper. Officer & Exec. V.P.--Totes Incorporated, Loveland, OH; *U.S. Private*, pg. 111

Geron, Stephen, Exec. V.P.--Morton Automotive Coatings, Lansing, IL; *U.S. Public*, pg. 1135

Gerson, David, Exec. V.P.--American Enterprise Institute for Public Policy Research, Washington, DC; *U.S. Private*, pg. 53

Gerson, Ralph J., Exec. V.P.--Guardian Industries Corp., Auburn Hills, MI; *U.S. Private*, pg. 485

Gerster, J. Alec, Exec. V.P. & Media/Programming Svcs. Dir.--Grey Advertising Inc., New York, NY; *U.S. Public*, pg. 764

Gersuk, D. Joseph, Chief Fin. Officer & Exec. V.P.--MapInfo Corp., Troy, NY; *U.S. Public*, pg. 1042

Gertenbach, L.V., Exec. V.P.--ABN-AMRO Holding N.V., Amsterdam, Netherlands; *Int'l*, pg. 8

Gertler, Eric J., Exec. V.P.--U.S. News & World Report, New York, NY; *U.S. Private*, pg. 1125

Gervason, Robert J., Exec. V.P. & Exec. Media Dir.--Campbell-Ewald Advertising, Warren, MI; *U.S. Public*, pg. 908

Getman, Dennis J., Exec. V.P. & Gen. Counsel--Avatar Holdings Inc., Coral Gables, FL; *U.S. Public*, pg. 151

Getman, Dennis J., Exec. V.P.--Avatar Properties Inc., Miami, FL; *U.S. Public*, pg. 151

Geurin, Lynn K., Chief Fin. Officer, Exec. V.P. & Sec.--Resource Mortgage Capital, Inc., Glen Allen, VA; *U.S. Public*, pg. 1382

Gewelb, Robert, Chief Oper. Officer & Exec. V.P.--Krasdale Foods Inc., White Plains, NY; *U.S. Private*, pg. 635

Ghaswala, Navaz, Exec. V.P.--Forever Living Products International, Inc., Scottsdale, AZ; *U.S. Private*, pg. 418

Ghazey, Kenneth A., Chief Fin. Officer & Exec. V.P.-Fin. & Admin.--Entex Information Services, Rye Brook, NY; *U.S. Private*, pg. 378

Gherlein, Gerald L., Exec. V.P. & Gen. Counsel--Eaton Corporation, Cleveland, OH; *U.S. Public*, pg. 555

Ghosn, Carlos, Exec. V.P.--Renault, Boulogne-Billancourt, France; *Int'l*, pg. 1102

Giaimo, Robert, Exec. V.P. & Creative Dir.--Grey Advertising Inc., Western Div., Los Angeles, CA; *U.S. Public*, pg. 764

Giambo, Robert A., Exec. V.P. & Chief Actuary--Trenwick America Reinsurance Corporation, Stamford, CT; *U.S. Public*, pg. 1634

Giardini, C.P., Exec. V.P.-Exploration & Production--Marathon Oil Company, Houston, TX; *U.S. Public*, pg. 1661

Giardini, Carl P., Exec. V.P.-Marathon Oil Co.--USX Corporation, Pittsburgh, PA; *U.S. Public*, pg. 1661

Giarratano, Frank P., Exec. V.P.-Client Services--SSD&W Integrated Marketing Communications, Montville, NJ; *U.S. Private*, pg. 958

Gibb, Michael, Exec. V.P.--Manila Mandarin Hotel Incorporated, Manila, Philippines; *Int'l*, pg. 704

Gibbions, Ed, Exec. V.P. & Sec.--Almo Corp., Philadelphia, PA; *U.S. Private*, pg. 44

Gibbons, Dale M., Exec. V.P.-Fin. & Sec.--Zions Bancorporation, Salt Lake City, UT; *U.S. Public*, pg. 1792

Gibbons, Dale M., Exec. V.P.-Fin. & Sec.--Zions First National Bank, Salt Lake City, UT; *U.S. Public*, pg. 1793

Gibbons, Jim, Exec. V.P.-Creative Services--Paramount Pictures Corporation, Los Angeles, CA; *U.S. Private*, pg. 776

Gibbs, Richard L., Exec.V.P.-Fin. & Plng.--Teachers Insurance and Annuity Association, New York, NY; *U.S. Private*, pg. 1071

Gibbs, Robert, Exec. V.P.--Uniden America Corporation, Fort Worth, TX; *Int'l*, pg. 1433

Gibney, Charles W., Chief Fin. Officer, Exec. V.P. & Treas.--Bergen Record Corp., Hackensack, NJ; *U.S. Private*, pg. 693

Gibson Sawi, Elizabeth, Exec. V.P.-Electronic Brokerage--The Charles Schwab Corporation, San Francisco, CA; *U.S. Public*, pg. 1442

Gibson, J. Duncan, Exec. V.P.-Wealth Mgmnt.--The Toronto Dominion Bank, Toronto, Canada; *Int'l*, pg. 1401

Gibson, John E., Exec. V.P.-North American Opers.--General Motors Acceptance Corporation (GMAC), Detroit, MI; *U.S. Public*, pg. 719

Gibson, John W., Jr., Exec. V.P.-Integrated Prods.--Landmark Graphics Corporation, Houston, TX; *U.S. Public*, pg. 776

Gibson, Russell G., Chief Fin. Officer, Exec. V.P., Treas. & Asst. Sec.--Farah Incorporated, El Paso, TX; *U.S. Public*, pg. 612

Gibson, Sloan D., IV, Sr. Exec. V.P. & Head-Commerical Banking--AmSouth Bancorporation, Birmingham, AL; *U.S. Public*, pg. 105

Giegerich, Matthew, Exec. V.P. & Mng. Dir.--Thomas G. Ferguson Associates, Inc., Parsippany, NJ; *Int'l*, pg. 1483

Gielty, Anthony J., Exec. V.P.-RMS--Willis Corroon Corp. of Northern Ohio, Cleveland, OH; *Int'l*, pg. 1506

Giencke, James R., Exec. V.P. & Gen. Mgr.--Arandell Corporation, Menomonee Falls, WI; *U.S. Private*, pg. 79

Giesberts, J.H., Exec. V.P.--ABN-AMRO Holding N.V., Amsterdam, Netherlands; *Int'l*, pg. 8

Gieszl, Yale L., Exec. V.P.--Toyota Motor Sales, U.S.A., Inc., Torrance, CA; *Int'l*, pg. 1412

Gignac, Edward, Exec. V.P.--Elgin Dairy Foods, Inc., Chicago, IL; *U.S. Private*, pg. 370

Gil Antillon, Oscar Robles, Exec. V.P.--Hylsa Bekaert, Tultitlan, Mexico; *Int'l*, pg. 56

Gilbane, Robert F., Exec. V.P.-Gemchem, Inc.--American Vanguard Corporation, Newport Beach, CA; *U.S. Public*, pg. 94

Gilbert, R.W., Exec. V.P.-Sls. & Mktg. & Treas.--Shure Brothers Incorporated, Evanston, IL; *U.S. Private*, pg. 997

Gilbert, Suzanne H., Chief Fin. Officer, Chief Admin. Officer & Exec. V.P.--Campbell-Ewald Advertising, Warren, MI; *U.S. Public*, pg. 908

Gilbertson, John, Chief Oper. Officer & Exec. V.P.--AVX Corporation, Myrtle Beach, SC; *Int'l*, pg. 775

Gilbride, Joe, Chief Fin. Officer & Exec. V.P.--Lowe & Partners/SMS, New York, NY; *U.S. Private*, pg. 678

Gilbride, Joseph, Chief Fin. Officer & Exec. V.P.--The Lowe Group, New York, NY; *U.S. Private*, pg. 677

Gilburne, Adam J., Exec. V.P.-Mdsg.--Just For Feet, Inc., Pelham, AL; *U.S. Public*, pg. 935

Gilchrist, William D., Jr., Exec. V.P.--Compass Bancshares, Inc., Houston, TX; *U.S. Public*, pg. 419

Gilchrist, William D., Jr., Exec. V.P.--Compass Bank Dallas, Richardson, TX; *U.S. Public*, pg. 419

Giles, Jack, Exec. V.P.--Remec, Inc., San Diego, CA; *U.S. Public*, pg. 1376

Giles, R.D., Exec. V.P.-Intl. Retailing--QVC, Inc., West Chester, PA; *U.S. Private*, pg. 897

Gill, Eric W., Exec. V.P. & Central Reg. Pres.--Marine Midland Bank, Buffalo, NY; *Int'l*, pg. 581

Gill, James P., Chief Oper. Officer, Exec. V.P., Gen. Mgr. & Dir.-Mktg.--Jackson Hole Ski Resort, Teton Village, WY; *U.S. Private*, pg. 579

Gilleland, Robert L., Exec. V.P.--LaBarge Pipe & Steel Company, Saint Louis, MO; *U.S. Private*, pg. 641

Gillespie, Robert J., Exec. V.P.-Strategy Plng. & Bus. Devel.--Bestfoods, Englewood Cliffs, NJ; *U.S. Public*, pg. 223

Gillette, Vance, Exec. V.P. & Gen. Mgr.--Teledyne Laars/Jandy Products, Novato, CA; *U.S. Public*, pg. 43

Gilliam, James H., Jr., Exec. V.P. & Gen. Counsel--Beneficial Corporation, Wilmington, DE; *U.S. Public*, pg. 211

Gilliam, James H., Jr., Exec. V.P.--Beneficial Management Corporation of America & Affiliated Corps., Wilmington, DE; *U.S. Public*, pg. 211

Gilliam, Penman R., Exec. V.P.--Intergraph Corporation, Huntsville, AL; *U.S. Public*, pg. 890

Gilliam, Thomas E., Exec. V.P. & Asst. to Vice Chm.--Mutual of America Life Insurance Company, New York, NY; *U.S. Private*, pg. 769

Gillies, Duncan A., Exec. V.P.--Trinity Leasing, Dallas, TX; *U.S. Public*, pg. 1639

Gillis, Edwin J., Chief Fin. Officer, Exec. V.P. & Treas.--Parametric Technology Corporation, Waltham, MA; *U.S. Public*, pg. 1257

Gillis, John, Exec. V.P. & Res./Devel. Dir.--Ross Roy Communications, Inc., Bloomfield Hills, MI; *U.S. Private*, pg. 946

Gillis, Robert, Chief Oper. Officer & Exec. V.P.--Elopak, Inc., New Hudson, MI; *Int'l*, pg. 1390

Gillis, Robert M., Exec. V.P.--Banknorth Group Inc., Burlington, VT; *U.S. Public*, pg. 186

Gillula, E. William, Chief Fin. Officer & Exec. V.P.--Computer Sales International Inc., Saint Louis, MO; *U.S. Private*, pg. 260

Gilman, Kenneth B., Chief Admin. Officer & Exec. V.P.--The Limited, Inc., Columbus, OH; *U.S. Public*, pg. 995

Gilmore, Merle L., Exec. V.P. & Pres.-Europe, Middle East & Africa--Motorola, Inc., Schaumburg, IL; *U.S. Public*, pg. 1136

Gilmore, Ronald J., Exec. V.P.-Adv. & Mktg.--CompUSA, Dallas, TX; *U.S. Public*, pg. 420

Gilmour, Barry K., Exec. V.P.-Systems--Bank of Montreal, Toronto, Canada; *Int'l*, pg. 153

Gilpin, Larry, Exec. V.P.-Team, Guest & Community Rels.--Target Stores, Minneapolis, MN; *U.S. Public*, pg. 489

Ginden, Charles B., Exec. V.P.--SunTrust Banks of Georgia, Inc., Atlanta, GA; *U.S. Public*, pg. 1538

Gingrich, William D., II, Chief Fin. Officer & Exec. V.P.--Hostmark Management Group, Rolling Meadows, IL; *U.S. Private*, pg. 541

Ginibre, Jean-Louis, Exec. V.P. & Editorial Dir.--Hachette Filipacchi Magazines Inc., New York, NY; *Int'l*, pg. 794

Ginn, David R., Exec. V.P.--Thiele Kaolin Co., Sandersville, GA; *U.S. Private*, pg. 1081

Ginsberg, Ira M., Exec. V.P.--Ginsberg's Institutional Foods, Inc., Hudson, NY; *U.S. Private*, pg. 455

Ginsberg, Sheldon, Chief Fin. Officer & Exec. V.P.--Lazare Kaplan Intl., Inc., New York, NY; *U.S. Public*, pg. 981

Ginther, William M., Grp. Exec. V.P.-Tech. & Opers.--Crestar Bank, Richmond, VA; *U.S. Public*, pg. 458

Giordani, John E., Chief Fin. Officer, Exec. V.P. & Controller--ICN Pharmaceuticals, Inc., Costa Mesa, CA; *U.S. Public*, pg. 853

Giordano, Alexander, Exec. V.P. & Chief Mktg. Officer--Standard Security Life Insurance Company of New York, New York, NY; *U.S. Private*, pg. 446

Giordano, Dick, Exec. V.P.--Potomac Graphic Industries, Inc., New York, NY; *Int'l*, pg. 699

Giordano, James A., Exec. V.P.--Chartwell Re Corporation, Stamford, CT; *U.S. Public*, pg. 336

Giorgio, Pier, Exec. V.P. & Reg. Mgr.--Bank of America NT&SA, Milan, Italy; *U.S. Public*, pg. 182

Giraldin, James, Chief Oper. Officer & Sr. Exec. V.P.--FirstFed Financial Corp., Santa Monica, CA; *U.S. Public*, pg. 645

Giraldin, James, Chief Oper. Officer & Sr. Exec. V.P.--First Federal Bank of California, FSB, Santa Monica, CA; *U.S. Public*, pg. 646

Girod, Rene, Exec. V.P.--Rolex Watch U.S.A., Inc., New York, NY; *Int'l*, pg. 1126

Girsky, Charles, Exec. V.P.--Jaco Electronics, Inc., Westlake Village, CA; *U.S. Public*, pg. 921

Gisel, William G., Jr., Exec. V.P.--Rich Products Corp., Buffalo, NY; *U.S. Private*, pg. 928

Gisiger, Michel, Sr. Exec. V.P.--SGS Societe Generale de Surveillance Holding S.A., Geneva, Switzerland; *Int'l*, pg. 1153

Gisriel, William F., Jr., Exec. V.P.--Fairfax Savings Bank, Baltimore, MD; *U.S. Public*, pg. 1543

Givens, Donald, Exec. V.P.--Standco Industries, Inc., Houston, TX; *U.S. Private*, pg. 1032

Gjovik, Mark, Exec. V.P. & Grp. Acct. Dir.--DMB&B Detroit, Troy, MI; *U.S. Private*, pg. 302

Gladding, Gary, Exec. V.P. & Gen. Mgr.-Mdsg.--Gottschalks Inc., Fresno, CA; *U.S. Public*, pg. 754

Gladstone, Peter, Exec. V.P. & Acct. Services Dir.--Eisner & Associates, Inc., Baltimore, MD; *U.S. Private*, pg. 366

Glah, Roy A., Exec. V.P.-Admin.--J. Walter Thompson Company, New York, NY; *Int'l*, pg. 1483

Glancy, John E., Exec. V.P.--Science Applications International Corp., San Diego, CA; *U.S. Private*, pg. 975

Glaser, Gary A., Exec. V.P.--National City Corporation, Cleveland, OH; *U.S. Public*, pg. 1154

Glass, Dennis R., Chief Fin. Officer, Exec. V.P. & Treas.--Jefferson-Pilot Life Insurance Co., Greensboro, NC; *U.S. Public*, pg. 926

Glass, Donald L., Exec. V.P.-Bldg. Prods., Mfg. & Sls.--Georgia-Pacific Corporation, Atlanta, GA; *U.S. Public*, pg. 735

Glass, J. Kenneth, Exec. V.P. & Pres.-Tennessee Banking Grp.--First Tennessee Bank National Association, Memphis, TN; *U.S. Public*, pg. 639

Glasser, David, Exec. V.P.-Fin. & Admin.--The Apparel Group, Ltd., Louisville, KY; *U.S. Private*, pg. 78

Glasser, Stuart, Exec. V.P.-GMM-Mens/Boys/Next Generation/Cosmetics--Bloomingdale's, New York, NY; *U.S. Public*, pg. 617

Glatthaar, Wolfgang, Dr., Exec. V.P.--DG Bank, Frankfurt/Main, Germany; *Int'l*, pg. 351

Glazier, Louis, Exec. V.P.-Fin. & Admin.--Thorn Apple Valley, Inc., Southfield, MI; *U.S. Public*, pg. 1602

Gleason, John F., Exec. V.P.--Grow Group, Inc., Cleveland, OH; *Int'l*, pg. 663

Gleeson, David W., Exec. V.P.-Multifamily Div.--The L & B Group, Dallas, TX; *U.S. Public*, pg. 1673

Glenn, Robert J., Exec. V.P.--Cook Moving Systems, Inc., Buffalo, NY; *U.S. Private*, pg. 272

Glenn, Robert J., Exec. V.P. & Dir.--The Robinson-Humphrey Company, Inc., Atlanta, GA; *U.S. Public*, pg. 1633

Glenn, Stephen C., Exec. V.P.-Admin.--Bank of the West, Walnut Creek, CA; *Int'l*, pg. 163

Glenn, William E., Exec. V.P., Sec. & Acct. Exec.--Willis Corroon Corp. of Knoxville, Knoxville, TN; *Int'l*, pg. 1506

Glickman, Edward, Chief Fin. Officer & Exec. V.P.--Reuben Organization, Philadelphia, PA; *U.S. Private*, pg. 925

Glinert, Floyd S., Exec. V.P.-Mktg.--Shorewood Packaging Corporation, New York, NY; *U.S. Public*, pg. 1468

Glinsky, Michael P., Chief Fin. Officer & Exec. V.P.--U S West Inc., Englewood, CO; *U.S. Public*, pg. 1688

Glosz, George C., Exec. V.P.-Commercial Landing--Riggs Bank N.A., Washington, DC; *U.S. Public*, pg. 1390

Glover, Barbara, Exec. V.P.--Barouh Eaton Allen Corporation, Brooklyn, NY; *U.S. Private*, pg. 117

Glover, Reynaldo, Exec. V.P. & Gen. Counsel--TLC Beatrice International Holdings Inc., New York, NY; *U.S. Private*, pg. 1064

Gluck, Michael, Exec. V.P.--Fujitsu Computer Products of America, Inc., San Jose, CA; *Int'l*, pg. 526

Gluckstern, Steven M., Exec. V.P.--Zurich Insurance Company, Zurich, Switzerland; *Int'l*, pg. 1529

Gluth, Robert C., Exec. V.P. & Treas.--The Marmon Group, Inc., Chicago, IL; *U.S. Private*, pg. 706

Glynn, Martin, Exec. V.P.--HongKong Bank of Canada, Vancouver, Canada; *Int'l*, pg. 583

Gnesda, Thomas A., V.P.-Sls. & Mktg.--EcoScience Produce Systems Corp., Orlando, FL; *U.S. Public*, pg. 563

Gobert, Christian, Exec. V.P.--COGEMA - Compagnie Generale des Matieres Nucleaires, Velizy-Villacoublay, France; *Int'l*, pg. 304

Goddard, Douglas, Chief Fin. Officer & Exec. V.P.--FirstFed Financial Corp., Santa Monica, CA; *U.S. Public*, pg. 645

Goddard, J.H., Jr., Exec. V.P.--PrimeSource Corporation, Pennsauken, NJ; *U.S. Public*, pg. 1329

Goddu, Roger V., Exec. V.P. & Gen. Mdse. Mgr.--Toys "R" Us United States, Paramus, NJ; *U.S. Public*, pg. 1626

Godefroid, Alain, Exec. Dir.--Union Miniere, Brussels, Belgium; *Int'l*, pg. 1441

Godfrey, Debbie, Exec. V.P. & Creative Res. Dir.-Y&RNY--Young & Rubicam New York, New York, NY; *U.S. Private*, pg. 1198

Godfrey, William R., Exec. V.P.-Admin. Svcs.--Sierra Health Services, Inc., Las Vegas, NV; *U.S. Public*, pg. 1469

Godin, Paul, Exec. V.P. & Head-Econ. Forecasting--Electricite de France, Paris, France; *Int'l*, pg. 437

Goding, Keith L, Chief Devel. Officer & Exec. V.P.--RehabCare Group, Inc., Saint Louis, MO; *U.S. Public*, pg. 1373

Godino, Gilberto, Exec. V.P.--Istituto Bancario San Paolo Di Torino S.p.A., Turin, Italy; *Int'l*, pg. 691

Godlasky, Thomas, Exec. V.P.-Investments--American Mutual Life Holding Co., Des Moines, IA; *U.S. Private*, pg. 59

Godoff, Ann, Exec. V.P. & Editor-in-Chief--Random House, New York, NY; *U.S. Private*, pg. 21

Godshalk, Ernie, Chief Oper. Officer & Exec. V.P.--Prodigy Inc., White Plains, NY; *U.S. Private*, pg. 888

Goebel, Sandy, Exec. V.P. & Grp. Mngmt. Supvr.--FerrellCalvillo Communications, Inc., New York, NY; *U.S. Private*, pg. 401

Goedde, Ronald J., Chief Fin. Officer, Exec. V.P. & Sec.--Cornerstone Propane G.P. Inc., Watsonville, CA; *U.S. Public*, pg. 1201

Goelman, Louis M., Exec. V.P.-Logistics--Shoppers Drug Mart, Ltd., Toronto, Canada; *Int'l*, pg. 112

Goertz, Gary, Chief Fin. Officer & Exec. V.P.-Fin.--Telus Corporation, Edmonton, Canada; *Int'l*, pg. 1374

Goes, Joaquim, Exec. V.P.--Banco Espirito Santo e Comercial de Lisboa SA, Lisbon, Portugal; *Int'l*, pg. 142

Goetsch, Tim, Exec. V.P.--Affiliated Foods Cooperative Inc., Norfolk, NE; *U.S. Private*, pg. 25

Goh, Michael P.Y., Exec. V.P.--APL Limited, Oakland, CA; *Int'l*, pg. 912

Gohl, Axel J., Chief Technology Officer & Exec. V.P.--Bayer Corporation, Pittsburgh, PA; *Int'l*, pg. 172

Gold, Charles L., Exec. V.P.--Scott & Stringfellow, Inc., Richmond, VA; *U.S. Public*, pg. 1445

Gold, Christina A., Exec. V.P.-Global Direct-Selling Devel. & Pres.-North America--Avon Products, Inc., New York, NY; *U.S. Public*, pg. 155

Goldberg, Arthur M., Exec. V.P. & Pres.-Gambling Opers.--Hilton Hotels Corporation, Beverly Hills, CA; *U.S. Public*, pg. 828

Goldberg, Gene L., Exec. V.P.--Bradley Pharmaceuticals, Fairfield, NJ; *U.S. Public*, pg. 249

Goldberg, Gene L., Exec. V.P.--Doak Dermatologics, Westbury, NY; *U.S. Public*, pg. 250

Goldberg, Harvey, Exec. V.P.--Toymax International Inc., Plainview, NY; *U.S. Public*, pg. 1626

Goldberg, Michael, Exec. V.P.--Harris Drury Cohen, Fort Lauderdale, FL; *U.S. Private*, pg. 505

Goldberg, Mike, Chief Fin. Officer & Exec. V.P.--Oil-Dri Corporation of America, Chicago, IL; *U.S. Public*, pg. 1214

Goldberg, Moshe, Exec. V.P.--Gitam/BBDO, Ramat Gan, Israel; *Int'l*, pg. 552

Goldberg, Norman, Chief Oper. Officer & Exec. V.P.--Fortunoff, Uniondale, NY; *U.S. Private*, pg. 420

Goldberg, Sherman I., Exec. V.P., Gen. Counsel & Sec.--First Chicago NBD Corporation, Chicago, IL; *U.S. Public*, pg. 627

Golden, Charles E., Chief Fin. Officer & Exec. V.P.--Eli Lilly and Company, Indianapolis, IN; *U.S. Public*, pg. 992

Golden, John, Exec. V.P.--Stephen Gould Paper Co., Inc., Whippany, NJ; *U.S. Private*, pg. 467

Golden, Michael, Exec. V.P. & Gen. Mgr.--Women's Magazines Group, New York, NY; *Int'l*, pg. 190

Golden, Randal E., Exec. V.P. & Sec.--D.O.C. Optics Corporation, Southfield, MI; *U.S. Private*, pg. 305

Goldman, Dan, Exec. V.P.--Amerimark Inc., Raleigh, NC; *U.S. Public*, pg. 1237

Goldman, David, Exec. V.P.--Executive Car Leasing Company, Los Angeles, CA; *U.S. Private*, pg. 388

Goldman, James, Exec. V.P. & Gen. Mgr.-Pub. Affairs--Edelman Worldwide, Inc., New York, NY; *U.S. Private*, pg. 362

Goldman, Michael K., Chief Admin. Officer & Exec. V.P.--ICF Kaiser International Inc., Fairfax, VA; *U.S. Public*, pg. 852

Goldman, Murray A., Exec. V.P. & Asst. Gen. Mgr.-Semiconductor Prods. Sector--Motorola, Inc., Schaumburg, IL; *U.S. Public*, pg. 1136

Goldsmith, J. Wickliffe, Jr., Exec. V.P. & Dir.-Training--Piccadilly Cafeterias, Inc., Baton Rouge, LA; *U.S. Public*, pg. 1294

Goldstein, Barry J., Chief Fin. Officer, Exec. V.P.-Fin. & Sec.--Office Depot Inc., Delray Beach, FL; *U.S. Public*, pg. 1212

Goldstein, Steve, Chief Fin. Officer & Exec. V.P.--Ogilvy & Mather Worldwide, Inc., New York, NY; *Int'l*, pg. 1483

Gomberg, Neal, Exec. V.P. & Grp. Creative Dir.--N.W. Ayer & Partners, New York, NY; *U.S. Private*, pg. 103

Gomez, Enidio, Exec. V.P.-Opers.--Security Plastics, Inc., Hialeah, FL; *U.S. Private*, pg. 981

Goniffes, Jean-Yves, Exec. Dir.-Network Opers.--France Telecom, Paris, France; *Int'l*, pg. 503

Gonthier, Jean-Marie, Exec. V.P.-Quality & Human Resources--Hydro-Quebec, Montreal, Canada; *Int'l*, pg. 640

Gonzales, Bernard, Exec. V.P.--Cullen/Frost Bankers, Inc., San Antonio, TX; *U.S. Public*, pg. 467

Gonzales, Kenda, Chief Fin. Officer & Sr. Exec. V.P.--UDC Homes, Inc., Scottsdale, AZ; *U.S. Private*, pg. 5

Gonzalez, Alejandro, Exec. V.P. & Partner--OfficeMax De Mexico, Mexico, Mexico; *U.S. Public*, pg. 1212

Gonzalez, Jaime, Exec. V.P.-Plng. & Devel.--Puerto Rico Tourism Company, San Juan, PR; *U.S. Private*, pg. 894

Gooch, Lowell Thomas, Exec. V.P. & Gen. Mgr.-Network Systems--Storage Technology Corporation, Louisville, CO; *U.S. Public*, pg. 1522

Goocher, Robert L., Exec. V.P. & Chief Oper. Officer-AGL Resources Svcs. Company--AGL Resources, Atlanta, GA; *U.S. Public*, pg. 6

Good, Gerald, Exec. V.P.-Mktg. & Mdsg.--The Great Atlantic & Pacific Tea Company, Inc., Montvale, NJ; *Int'l*, pg. 1375

Gooding, David E., Exec. V.P.--Transamerica Life Companies, Los Angeles, CA; *U.S. Public*, pg. 1630

Goodman, Ellis, Exec. V.P. & Chief Exec. Officer-Spirits & Beers--Canandaigua Wine Company, Inc., Canandaigua, NY; *U.S. Public*, pg. 300

Goodman, J. Charles, Exec. V.P.-Opers.--Atmos Energy Corporation, Dallas, TX; *U.S. Public*, pg. 145

Goodman, Larry, Exec. V.P.-CNN Sls.--CNN Headline News, Atlanta, GA; *U.S. Public*, pg. 1614

Goodrich, Clifford C., Exec. V.P.-Racing--The Santa Anita Companies, Arcadia, CA; *U.S. Public*, pg. 1081

Goodwin, H. Clark, Exec. V.P.--First Charter Corporation, Concord, NC; *U.S. Public*, pg. 627

Goodwin, Paul R., Chief Fin. Officer & Exec. V.P.-Fin.--CSX Corporation, Richmond, VA; *U.S. Public*, pg. 284

Goodwyn, William H., Jr., Exec. V.P.-Sls. & Mktg.--Lawyers Title Insurance Corporation, Richmond, VA; *U.S. Public*, pg. 981

Goodyear, Clarice Cato, Exec. V.P. & Asst. Sec.--The Cato Corporation, Charlotte, NC; *U.S. Public*, pg. 318

Goralnick, L. Arnold, Exec. V.P.--Geo. E. Keith Company, Brockton, MA; *U.S. Private*, pg. 611

Goralnick, L. Arnold, Exec. V.P.--Keith Highlanders Shoes, Bridgewater, MA; *U.S. Private*, pg. 612

Gordon, Geoff, Exec. V.P.--Shape Inc., Kennebunk, ME; *U.S. Private*, pg. 990

Gordon, Lindsay, Exec. V.P.--HongKong Bank of Canada, Vancouver, Canada; *Int'l*, pg. 583

Gordon, Lynn, Exec. V.P.-Mktg.--Reading Body Works, Inc., Reading, PA; *U.S. Private*, pg. 913

Gordon, Robert R., Jr., Exec. V.P.-Human Resources--R.J. Reynolds Tobacco Company, Winston Salem, NC; *U.S. Public*, pg. 1355

Gordon, Scott, Exec. V.P.--Tokyo-Mitsubishi Futures (USA) Inc., Chicago, IL; *Int'l*, pg. 157

Gordon, Steve, Exec. V.P. & Dir.-Sls. & Mktg.--Columbia Paint & Coatings, Spokane, WA; *U.S. Private*, pg. 256

Gordon, William, Exec. V.P.-Mktg.--Electronic Arts, San Mateo, CA; *U.S. Public*, pg. 569

Gordon, William T., Chief Fin. Officer, Exec. V.P.-Fin. & Treas.--Black Entertainment Television Holdings Inc., Washington, DC; *U.S. Public*, pg. 235

Gordonsmith, John A., Exec. V.P.-Treasury, Legal & Corp. Sec.--FCA International Ltd., Westmount, Canada; *Int'l*, pg. 470

Gordy, Mike, Exec. V.P.-Opers.--Sargento Foods Inc., Plymouth, WI; *U.S. Private*, pg. 966

Gore, S. Tony, III, Exec. V.P.-Acq. & Corp. Devel.--Vanguard Cellular Systems, Inc., Greensboro, NC; *U.S. Public*, pg. 1707

Gorga, Steve, Exec. V.P.-Americas--Utell International-Omaha, Omaha, NE; *Int'l*, pg. 1098

Gorman, D., Exec. V.P.-Sls.--R.T. Vanderbilt Company, Inc., Norwalk, CT; *U.S. Private*, pg. 1133

Gorman, Gerard P., Exec. V.P.--MagneTek, Inc., Nashville, TN; *U.S. Public*, pg. 1037

Gorman, Jerry, Exec. V.P.--Avesta Sheffield AB, Stockholm, Sweden; *Int'l*, pg. 221

Gorman, John R., Exec. V.P.--Republic National Bank of New York, New York, NY; *U.S. Public*, pg. 1380

Gorman, John T., Chief Fin. Officer & Exec. V.P.--American Banknote Corp., New York, NY; *U.S. Public*, pg. 68

Gorman, Lon, Exec. V.P.-Capital Markets & Trading--The Charles Schwab Corporation, San Francisco, CA; *U.S. Public*, pg. 1442

Gorman, Peter E., Exec. V.P.--Harte-Hanks Communications, Inc., San Antonio, TX; *U.S. Public*, pg. 793

Gormley, Robert T., Exec. V.P.-Corp. Banking Grp.--Citizens Trust Company, Providence, RI; *Int'l*, pg. 1132

Gorney, Jon L., Exec. V.P.-MIS--National City Corporation, Cleveland, OH; *U.S. Public*, pg. 1154

Goronkin, David, Exec. V.P.-Opers.--Buffets, Inc., Eden Prairie, MN; *U.S. Public*, pg. 267

Goss, Michael, Chief Fin. Officer & Exec. V.P.--Playtex Products Inc., Westport, CT; *U.S. Public*, pg. 1310

Gossen, Emmett, Exec. V.P.--Motel 6 Operating L.P., Dallas, TX; *Int'l*, pg. 21

Goto, Kazuhiro, Exec. V.P.-Bus. & Prods. Grp.--Minolta Corporation, Ramsey, NJ; *Int'l*, pg. 869

Gottdenker, Michael, Exec V.P.--Commonwealth Telephone Co., Dallas, PA; *U.S. Public*, pg. 415

Gottesman, Charles, Chief Oper. Officer & Exec. V.P.--Hyde Athletic Industries, Inc., Peabody, MA; *U.S. Public*, pg. 851

Goudie, Peter G., Exec. V.P.-Primary Metals Mktg.--Inco Limited, Toronto, Canada; *Int'l*, pg. 672

Gouezel, Herve, Exec. V.P.-Information Systems & Organization--Banque Nationale de Paris, Paris, France; *Int'l*, pg. 163

Gould, Donald L., Exec. V.P. & Creative Dir.--Campbell-Ewald Advertising, Warren, MI; *U.S. Public*, pg. 908

Gourbin, Jean-Louis, Exec. V.P.--Kellogg Company, Battle Creek, MI; *U.S. Public*, pg. 947

Gowland, Pablo Eduardo, Jr., Pres., Gen. Mgr., Exec. V.P., Opers. Dir.--Gowland Publicidad S.A., Buenos Aires, Argentina; *U.S. Public*, pg. 1642

Goyal, Sandeep, Exec. V.P.-Delhi--Rediffusion-DY&R Pvt. Ltd., Mumbai, India; *U.S. Private*, pg. 326

Goyal, Sandeep, Exec. V.P.--Rediffusion-Dentsu, Young & Rubicam (New Delhi), New Delhi, India; *U.S. Private*, pg. 326

Goydan, Paul A., Exec. V.P.--Osmose Wood Preserving, Inc., Buffalo, NY; *U.S. Private*, pg. 821

Gozon, Richard, Exec. V.P.-Pulp, Paper & Pkgng.--Weyerhaeuser Company, Federal Way, WA; *U.S. Public*, pg. 1764

Grabowski, Michael, Exec. V.P.--Bayerische Vereinsbank AG, Hong Kong, Hong Kong; *Int'l*, pg. 180

Graden, Brian, Exec. V.P.-Programming--MTV Networks, New York, NY; *U.S. Private*, pg. 779

Grader, R.H., Exec. V.P.-Sls.--National Frozen Foods Corp., Seattle, WA; *U.S. Private*, pg. 783

Graeber, George C., Exec. V.P. & Pres.-Montrose/CDT--Cable Design Technologies Corporation, Pittsburgh, PA; *U.S. Public*, pg. 287

Graf, Alan B., Jr., Chief Fin. Officer & Exec. V.P.--FDX Corporation, Memphis, TN; *U.S. Public*, pg. 603

Graf, Robert, Exec. V.P.--Pacific Coast Producers, Lodi, CA; *U.S. Private*, pg. 830

Graff, Glenn D., Exec. V.P.--Linbeck Construction Corp, Houston, TX; *U.S. Private*, pg. 667

Grafstrom, Nils, Exec. V.P. & Gen. Counsel--Stora Kopparbergs Bergslags AB, Falun, Sweden; *Int'l*, pg. 1302

Graham, E.G.B., Exec. V.P.-Opers.--Canfor Corporation, Vancouver, Canada; *Int'l*, pg. 260

Graham, George, Exec. V.P.-U.S. Opers.--The Great Atlantic & Pacific Tea Company, Inc., Montvale, NJ; *Int'l*, pg. 1375

Graham, Marc, Exec. V.P. & Gen. Mgr.--PACCAR Automotive Inc., Renton, WA; *U.S. Public*, pg. 1247

Graham, Martin, Exec. V.P.-Opers.--Thrall Car Mfg. Co., Chicago Heights, IL; *U.S. Private*, pg. 344

Graham, Peter, Chief Oper. Officer & Exec. V.P.--Maxxim Medical, Inc., Clearwater, FL; *U.S. Public*, pg. 1063

Grall, Wayne R., Chief Fin. Officer & Exec. V.P.--Serigraph, Inc., West Bend, WI; *U.S. Private*, pg. 985

Granborg, Mogens, Exec. V.P.--Danisco A/S, Copenhagen, Denmark; *Int'l*, pg. 378

Grande, Emilio Lopez, Exec. V.P.-Fin.--Corporacion Internacional de Aviacion (CINTRA), Mexico, Mexico; *Int'l*, pg. 332

Grandin, Michael, Chief Fin. Officer & Exec. V.P.--Canadian Pacific Limited, Calgary, Canada; *Int'l*, pg. 258

Granetz, Nancy, Chief Fin. Officer & Exec. V.P.--Jerry & Ketchum, New York, NY; *U.S. Private*, pg. 616

Grange, Richard A., Exec. V.P.--Intercon Security Limited, Toronto, Canada; *Int'l*, pg. 699

Granger, Daniel D., Exec. V.P. & Pres.-Catalina Mktg. Services--Catalina Marketing Corporation, Saint Petersburg, FL; *U.S. Public*, pg. 314

Grangier, Jean-Claude, Deputy Pres.-Exec. Bd. & Exec. V.P.--Banque Cantonale Vaudoise, Lausanne, Switzerland; *Int'l*, pg. 160

Granholm, Martin, Exec. V.P.--UPM-Kymmene Corporation, Helsinki, Finland; *Int'l*, pg. 1427

Granskog, Christer, Exec. V.P.--Partek Corporation, Helsinki, Finland; *Int'l*, pg. 1024

Grant, A. James, Exec. V.P.-Comml. Banking--Compass Bank Dallas, Richardson, TX; *U.S. Public*, pg. 419

Grant, Clark C., Exec. V.P.-Fin. & Treas.--Buffets, Inc., Eden Prairie, MN; *U.S. Public*, pg. 267

Grant, Joseph M., Chief Fin. Officer & Exec. V.P.--Electronic Data Systems Corporation, Plano, TX; *U.S. Public*, pg. 569

Gras, Phillippe, Exec. V.P.--Renault, Boulogne-Billancourt, France; *Int'l*, pg. 1102

Grassley, Raymond W., Exec. V.P.-Container & Marine Services Div.--XTRA, Inc., Portland, ME; *U.S. Public*, pg. 1787

Grasso, William D., Exec. V.P.--Trans-Apparel Group, Michigan City, IN; *U.S. Public*, pg. 796

Grau, Charles M., Exec. V.P.--ConAgra Feed Ingredient, Knoxville, TN; *U.S. Public*, pg. 426

Graves, Earl G., Jr., Chief Exec. Officer & Exec. V.P.--Earl G. Graves, Ltd., New York, NY; *U.S. Private*, pg. 471

Graves, W. Michael, Exec. V.P.-Central Region--AmSouth Bancorporation, Birmingham, AL; *U.S. Public*, pg. 105

Graves, William T., Exec. V.P.--Torchmark Corporation, Birmingham, AL; *U.S. Public*, pg. 1622

Gravo, Jack R., Exec. V.P.-Fin. & Admin.--FirstMerit Corporation, Akron, OH; *U.S. Public*, pg. 646

Gray, Claudia, Exec. V.P.-Publicity--Gramercy Pictures, Beverly Hills, CA; *U.S. Private*, pg. 468

Gray, Franklin N., Exec. V.P., Treas. & Sec.--James N. Gray Construction Co., Inc., Lexington, KY; *U.S. Private*, pg. 472

Gray, James P., II, Exec. V.P.--James N. Gray Construction Co., Inc., Lexington, KY; *U.S. Private*, pg. 472

Gray, Jerry E., Exec. V.P.--Norwest Bank Minnesota N.A., Minneapolis, MN; *U.S. Public*, pg. 1202

Gray, John H., Exec. V.P. & Chief Admin. Officer--Club Corporation International, Dallas, TX; *U.S. Private*, pg. 247

Gray, Scott, Chief Lending Officer & Exec. V.P.--FirstFed Financial Corp., Santa Monica, CA; *U.S. Public*, pg. 645

Gray, W. Keith, Exec. V.P.--Green Line Investor Service, Toronto, Canada; *Int'l*, pg. 1401

Gray, William C., Exec. V.P.--Atlantic Plumbing Supply Company, Washington, DC; *U.S. Private*, pg. 95

Grayson, Merwin, Jr., Exec. V.P.-Southern Ohio Region--Huntington National Bank, Columbus, OH; *U.S. Public*, pg. 850

Greatwood, Fred E., Exec. V.P.--Willis Corroon Corp. of Eugene, Eugene, OR; *Int'l*, pg. 1505

Greed, John R., Exec. V.P. & Treas.--Mutual of America Life Insurance Company, New York, NY; *U.S. Private*, pg. 769

Green, Benjamin L., Exec. V.P.--B. Green & Co., Owings Mills, MD; *U.S. Private*, pg. 476

Green, George, Pres. & Exec V.P.-Hearst Magazines Intl.--Hearst Magazines Division, New York, NY; *U.S. Private*, pg. 516

Green, James P., Exec. V.P.--AMCORE Bank, Rock River Valley, Dixon, IL; *U.S. Public*, pg. 64

Green, James R., Chief Fin. & Oper. Officer & Exec. V.P.--Bearden Lumber Company, Inc., Bearden, AR; *U.S. Private*, pg. 127

Green, Jay M., Chief Fin. Officer, Exec. V.P. & Treas.--General Cigar Holdings Inc, New York, NY; *U.S. Public*, pg. 707

Green, Joe C., Chief Admin. Officer & Exec. V.P.--Moog Incorporated, East Aurora, NY; *U.S. Public*, pg. 1127

Green, Peggy, Exec. V.P. & Natl. Brdcst. Dir.--Zenith Media Services, Inc., New York, NY; *U.S. Private*, pg. 1204

Green, Phillip D., Chief Fin. Officer & Exec. V.P.--Cullen/Frost Bankers, Inc., San Antonio, TX; *U.S. Public*, pg. 467

Green, Stanley D., Exec. V.P.-Fin. & Corp. Devel.--Southwestern Energy Pipeline Company, Fayetteville, AR; *U.S. Public*, pg. 1494

Green, Stanley D., Exec. V.P.-Fin. & Corp. Devel.--Arkansas Western Pipeline Company, Fayetteville, AR; *U.S. Public*, *pg. 1494*

Green, Susan P., Exec. V.P.-Hotels & Property--Colonial Williamsburg Foundation, Williamsburg, VA; *U.S. Private*, pg. 254

Green, William, Exec. V.P. & Acct. Mng. Dir.--Young & Rubicam New York, New York, NY; *U.S. Private*, pg. 1198

Green, William T., Exec. V.P., Treas. & Sec.--Art's-Way Manufacturing Co., Inc., Armstrong, IA; *U.S. Public*, pg. 136

Greenberg, George, Exec. V.P.-Mktg.--Fox Broadcasting Company (FBC), Beverly Hills, CA; *Int'l*, pg. 926

Greenberg, Russell, Chief Fin. Officer & Exec. V.P.--Jean Philippe Fragrances, Inc., New York, NY; *U.S. Public*, pg. 924

Greenberg, Stuart, Sr. Exec. V.P.-Sls--Bestform Foundations, Inc., Long Island City, NY; *U.S. Private*, pg. 140

Greenberg, Stuart, Sr. Exec. V.P.-Sls.--Lily of France, Inc., New York, NY; *U.S. Private*, pg. 140

Greendale, Christopher H., Exec. V.P.-Mktg.--Cambridge Technology Partners, Cambridge, MA; *U.S. Public*, pg. 1424

Greene, Dale E., Exec. V.P.-Credit Admin.--Comerica Incorporated, Detroit, MI; *U.S. Public*, pg. 408

Greene, Harold H., Exec. V.P.-Real Estate Grp.--Seafirst Corporation, Seattle, WA; *U.S. Public*, pg. 181

Greene, Laurence T., Exec. V.P.-Procurement & Govt. Affairs--Diamond Star Motors, Normal, IL; *Int'l*, pg. 875

Greene, M. Anthony, Exec. V.P.--Raymond James Financial, Inc., Saint Petersburg, FL; *U.S. Public*, pg. 923

Greene, M.J., Exec. V.P.--Federal Industries Metals Group, Etobicoke, Canada; *Int'l*, pg. 1150

Greene, M.S., Exec. V.P.--Texas Utilities Fuel Co., Dallas, TX; *U.S. Public*, pg. 1588

Greene, M.S., Exec. V.P.--Texas Utilities Mining Co., Dallas, TX; *U.S. Public*, pg. 1588

Greene, Rob, Exec. V.P.--Branch Banking & Trust, Winston Salem, NC; *U.S. Public*, pg. 160

Greene, Robert E., Sr. Exec. V.P.--BB&T Corporation, Winston Salem, NC; *U.S. Public*, pg. 159

Greenhalgh, Thomas J., Exec. V.P.-Admin.--Auto Glass Specialists, Madison, WI; *U.S. Private*, pg. 100

Greenquist, Roy, Exec. V.P.--Sofco-Mead, Inc., Scotia, NY; *U.S. Private*, pg. 1012

Greenstein, Michael K., Exec. V.P. & Gen. Mgr.-Avon Books--Avon Books, New York, NY; *U.S. Private*, pg. 515

Greenwald, Deborah Polkes, Exec. V.P. & Exec. Creative Dir.--Harrison & Star, Inc., New York, NY; *U.S. Private*, pg. 506

Greer, John, Chief Oper. Officer, Exec. V.P. & New Bus. Contact--Cohn & Wells, San Francisco, CA; *Int'l*, pg. 601

Greer, Leonard W., Exec. V.P.--Israel Discount Bank of New York, New York, NY; *Int'l*, pg. 645

Gregg, Gary R., Exec. V.P.--Liberty Mutual Insurance Co., Boston, MA; *U.S. Private*, pg. 666

Gregoire, John, Exec. V.P.-Assoc. Svcs.--Credit Union National Association, Madison, WI; *U.S. Private*, pg. 288

Grehan, Harold S., Jr., Exec. V.P.--Central Gulf Lines, Inc., New Orleans, LA; *U.S. Public*, pg. 907

Gremmen, T., Exec. V.P.--DSM Resins B.V., Zwolle, Netherlands; *Int'l*, pg. 353

Grenier, Charles P., Exec. V.P.--Plum Creek Timber Co., L.P., Seattle, WA; *U.S. Public*, pg. 1311

Gress, Steven R., Exec. V.P.--Sysco Food Services of Iowa, Inc., West Des Moines, IA; *U.S. Public*, pg. 1551

Gretchen, Michael G., Exec. V.P.-Comml. Banking--Hibernia Corporation, New Orleans, LA; *U.S. Public*, pg. 825

Grete, Ulrich, Dr., Exec. V.P.-Resources & Mngmt. Support--Union Bank of Switzerland, Zurich, Switzerland; *Int'l*, pg. 1439

Greth, Phillip A., Chief Information Officer & Exec. V.P.--Cardinal Health Inc., Dublin, OH; *U.S. Public*, pg. 304

Grevelius, Sven, Exec. V.P.-Central Control & Acctg.--Svenska Handelsbanken, Stockholm, Sweden; *Int'l*, pg. 1327

Grevey, Robert A., Exec. V.P.-RMS--Willis Corroon Corp. of Northern Ohio, Cleveland, OH; *Int'l*, pg. 1506

Grew, Dennis, Exec. V.P.--SGS Control Services Inc., Edison, NJ; *Int'l*, pg. 1153

Gribbin, Michael, Exec. V.P.--JIB Group plc, London, United Kingdom; *Int'l*, pg. 705

Gribble, Dave, Exec. V.P.--Green Seed Co., Baltimore, MD; *U.S. Private*, pg. 477

Grier, Mark B., Exec. V.P.-Fin. Mngmt.--The Prudential Insurance Company of America, Newark, NJ; *U.S. Private*, pg. 892

Grieveson, Jeremy J., Exec. V.P.--Arbor Acres Farm, Inc., Glastonbury, CT; *Int'l*, pg. 202

Griffin, Bobby, Exec. V.P.-Pacing Bus.--Pacing Business Unit, Minneapolis, MN; *U.S. Public*, pg. 1083

Griffin, Bobby I., Exec. V.P. & Pres.-Pacing Business--Medtronic, Inc., Minneapolis, MN; *U.S. Public*, pg. 1082

Griffin, John M., Exec. V.P.--Griffin Industries, Inc., Cold Spring, KY; *U.S. Private*, pg. 480

Griffin, Michael D., Chief Tech. Officer & Exec. V.P.--Orbital Sciences Corporation, Dulles, VA; *U.S. Public*, pg. 1229

Griffith, G. Sanders, III, Sr. Exec. V.P., Gen. Counsel & Sec.--Synovus Financial Corp., Columbus, GA; *U.S. Public*, pg. 1548

Griffith, Jerry L., Exec. V.P.--J.A. Riggs Tractor Co., Little Rock, AR; *U.S. Private*, pg. 930

Griggs, John W., Chief Fin. Officer & Exec. V.P.--The Alpha Corporation Of Tennessee, Collierville, TN; *U.S. Private*, pg. 44

Grignon, Michel, Exec. V.P.-Mktg.--Hydro-Quebec, Montreal, Canada; *Int'l*, pg. 640

Grigsby, Douglas C., Chief Fin. Officer & Exec. V.P.--Bank of the West, Walnut Creek, CA; *Int'l*, pg. 163

Grigsby, Lonnie O., Exec. V.P. & Gen. Counsel--IBP, Inc., Dakota City, NE; *U.S. Public*, pg. 852

Grijalva, Victor E., Exec. V.P.-Oilfield Services--Schlumberger Limited, New York, NY; *U.S. Public*, pg. 1439

Grijpma, A., Exec. V.P.--ABN-AMRO Holding N.V., Amsterdam, Netherlands; *Int'l*, pg. 8

Grillo, Robert T., Exec. V.P., Treas. & Sec.--General Office Environments Inc., Rochelle Park, NJ; *U.S. Private*, pg. 445

Grimaldi, Joseph A., Sr. Exec. V.P.-Factoring & Comml. Fin.--The Bank of New York Company, Inc., New York, NY; *U.S. Public*, pg. 178

Grimball, Edward B., Chief Fin. Officer & Exec. V.P.--Whitney Holding Corporation, New Orleans, LA; *U.S. Public*, pg. 1766

Grimes, Sean, Exec. V.P.--Pace Advertising, New York, NY; *Int'l*, pg. 1483

Grimland, Gene, Exec. V.P.-Sls.--United American Insurance Co., Dallas, TX; *U.S. Public*, pg. 1623

Grimm, Michael, Exec. V.P.-Sls. & Mktg.--MTL Inc., Plant City, FL; *U.S. Public*, pg. 1028

Grimm, Michael, Exec. V.P.-Sls. & Mktg.--Montgomery Tank Lines, Inc., Plant City, FL; *U.S. Public*, pg. 1028

Grimm, Richard E., Exec. V.P. & Cashier--Penn Security Bank and Trust Co., Scranton, PA; *U.S. Public*, pg. 1270

Grimone, Frank W., Chief Fin. Officer & Sr. Exec. V.P.--Central Reserve Life Corporation, Strongsville, OH; *U.S. Public*, pg. 326

Grimshaw, John M., Exec. V.P.--CACI International Inc, Arlington, VA; *U.S. Public*, pg. 272

Grindon, Michael, Exec. V.P.--Columbia Tri-Star International Television, Culver City, CA; *Int'l*, pg. 1281

Gringarten, Alain C., Dr., Exec. V.P.--Scientific Software-Intercomp, Inc., Denver, CO; *U.S. Public*, pg. 1443

Grinstein, Jeffrey M., Exec. V.P., Gen. Counsel, & Sec.--American Waste Services, Inc., Warren, OH; *U.S. Public*, *pg. 94*

Grissom, Kenneth R., II, Exec. V.P.-Mountasia Development Co.--Malibu Entertainment Worldwide, Dallas, TX; *U.S. Public*, pg. 1039

Griswell, Barry, Exec. V.P.--The Principal Financial Group, Des Moines, IA; *U.S. Private*, pg. 885

Griswell, Barry, Exec. V.P.--Principal Mutual Life Insurance Co., Des Moines, IA; *U.S. Private*, pg. 886

Gritton, Hollis, Exec. V.P.--Florence Deposit Bank, Florence, KY; *U.S. Public*, pg. 173

Gritton, Mark T., Exec. V.P.-U.S.--Brink's, Inc., Darien, CT; *U.S. Public*, pg. 1305

Grivna, Howard, Exec. V.P.-North America--Timesavers Inc., Crystal, MN; *U.S. Private*, pg. 1088

Groce, A. Ben, Sr. V.P.-Mfg.--Boise Cascade Paper Div., Boise, ID; *U.S. Public*, pg. 243

Grode, George F., Exec. V.P.-Govt. Bus. & Corp. Affairs--Highmark Inc., Pittsburgh, PA; *U.S. Private*, pg. 528

Groenewegen, W.Ph., Exec. V.P.--Van Leeuwen Pipe & Tube Corp., Houston, TX; *Int'l*, pg. 1449

Groenning, Per, Exec. V.P.--Copenhagen--Scan-Ad Gruppen A/S, Arhus, Denmark; *Int'l*, pg. 1198

Grogan, James, Sr. Exec. V.P.--UDC Homes, Inc., Scottsdale, AZ; *U.S. Private*, pg. 5

Gronbacher, Frederick J., Exec. V.P. & Deputy Mgr.-Retail Banking--PNC Bank Corp., Pittsburgh, PA; *U.S. Public*, pg. 1242

Grondelli, Ugo, Sr. Exec. V.P. & Deputy Mng. Dir.--Gambro AB, Lund, Sweden; *Int'l*, pg. 666

Gronefeld, Ralph, Exec. V.P.-Youth Svcs. Div.--Res-Care Incorporated, Louisville, KY; *U.S. Public*, pg. 1382

Groninger, Donald L., Exec. V.P., Gen. Counsel & Sr. Compliance Officer--Bridgestone/Firestone, Inc., Nashville, TN; *Int'l*, pg. 213

Gronstedt, Lars O., Exec. V.P.-Bus. Devel.--Svenska Handelsbanken, Stockholm, Sweden; *Int'l*, pg. 1327

Groom, Gary L., Exec. V.P.-Fin. & Sec.--Coachmen Industries, Inc., Elkhart, IN; *U.S. Public*, pg. 387

Groover, L. Clyde, Jr., Exec. V.P.--Associates Relocation Management Company, Inc., Dallas, TX; *U.S. Public*, pg. 663

Groscurth, Hans Christoph, Sr. Exec. V.P.-New Issues Div.--Bayerische Landesbank, Munich, Germany; *Int'l*, pg. 176

Groshong, David E., Exec. V.P.-Fin. Service--Community First Bankshares, Inc., Fargo, ND; *U.S. Public*, pg. 416

Grosklaus, James G., Exec. V.P.--Kimberly-Clark Corporation, Dallas, TX; *U.S. Public*, pg. 958

Gross, Edward H., Exec. V.P.-Fin. & Admin.--Baker & Taylor, Inc., Charlotte, NC; *U.S. Private*, pg. 111

Gross, Lewis, Exec. V.P.--Pioneer Paper Corporation, Carlstadt, NJ; *U.S. Private*, pg. 867

Gross, Mark D., Exec. V.P.-Retail Banking--Charter One Bank, Cleveland, OH; *U.S. Public*, pg. 336

Gross, Ulrich, Exec. V.P.--Hochtief AG, Essen, Germany; *Int'l*, pg. 623

Grossi, Len, Sr. Exec. V.P.--UPN-United Paramount Network, Los Angeles, CA; *U.S. Public*, pg. 352

Grossi, Len, Sr. Exec. V.P.--UPN-United Paramount Network, Los Angeles, CA; *U.S. Private*, pg. 777

Grossman, Janice, Exec. V.P.-Mktg. & Adv.--New York Magazine, New York, NY; *U.S. Public*, pg. 1328

Grossman, Skip, Exec. V.P.--Grossman Iron & Steel Company, Saint Louis, MO; *U.S. Private*, pg. 483

Grossmann, Hartmut G., Exec. V.P.-Opers.--Dresdner Bank AG, New York, NY; *Int'l*, pg. 418

Grosso, Gail Anne, Exec. V.P. & Creative Dir.--EvansGroup, Seattle, WA; *U.S. Private*, pg. 385

Grote, Roger, Exec. V.P.-Acct. Services--Kragie/Newell, Des Moines, IA; *U.S. Private*, pg. 634

Grout, James M., Exec. V.P.--Sholodge, Inc., Hendersonville, TN; *U.S. Public*, pg. 1467

Grove, Janet, Exec. V.P.-Women's Accessories--Federated Merchandising, New York, NY; *U.S. Public*, pg. 618

Grover, Charles W., Exec. V.P.--The Union Central Life Insurance Co., Cincinnati, OH; *U.S. Private*, pg. 1118

Grow, David R., Chief Oper. & Fin. Officer & Exec. V.P.--Daw Technologies, Inc., Salt Lake City, UT; *U.S. Public*, pg. 489

Grubb, Edgar H., Chief Fin. Officer & Exec. V.P.--Transamerica Corporation, San Francisco, CA; *U.S. Public*, pg. 1629

Gruber, Guenther, Exec. V.P. & Chief Fin. Officer--Siemens Nixdorf Information Systems Inc., Burlington, MA; *Int'l*, pg. 1245

Gruber, Jerome, V.P.-Natl. Accts.--Spartech Plastics, Portage, WI; *U.S. Public*, pg. 1496

Gruenberg, Andy, Exec. V.P.-MGM/UA Dist. Co.--MGM/UA Distribution Co., Santa Monica, CA; *U.S. Public*, pg. 1102

Gruenhut, E., Exec. V.P.--Zim-American Israeli Shipping Co., New York, NY; *U.S. Private*, pg. 1206

Grumbly, Thomas P., Grp. Pres.-Environ. & Facilities Mngmt. Grp. & V.P.--ICF Kaiser International Inc., Fairfax, VA; *U.S. Public*, pg. 852

Grundon, Steve, Exec. V.P.--Comdisco Electronics Group, San Diego, CA; *U.S. Public*, pg. 408

Grunther, Hans-Herbert, Exec. V.P.--Landesbank Hessen-Thuringen Girozentrale, Frankfurt/Main, Germany; *Int'l*, pg. 798

Grusin, Dave, Co-Founder & Exec. V.P.--GRP Records, New York, NY; *Int'l*, pg. 1215

Grzenia, Richard, Exec. V.P.-Mfg.--Tekra Corporation, New Berlin, WI; *U.S. Private*, pg. 1073

Gsand, William L., Exec. V.P.--Hitachi America, Ltd., Tarrytown, NY; *Int'l*, pg. 622

Guarend, Michel, Exec. V.P.-Opers.--FCA!BMZ, Suresnes, France; *Int'l*, pg. 469

Guarriello, Joseph L., Exec. V.P., Gen. Counsel & Sec.--Mid Atlantic Medical Services, Inc., Rockville, MD; *U.S. Public*, pg. 1109

Guccione, Nina, Exec. V.P. & Pres.-New Media--General Media International Inc., New York, NY; *U.S. Private*, pg. 444

Guenthner, David, Chief Fin. Officer & Exec. V.P.--Inacom Corp., Omaha, NE; *U.S. Public*, pg. 873

Guerci, Giovanni, Exec. V.P.-Information Systems--Istituto Bancario San Paolo Di Torino S.p.A., Turin, Italy; *Int'l*, pg. 691

Guercio, Thomas R., Chief Fin. Officer, Exec. V.P. & Treas.--Reliable Stores, Inc., Columbia, MD; *U.S. Private*, pg. 920

Guerra, Enrico, Sr. Exec. V.P.-Intl. Collaboration--Agusta S.P.A., Varese, Italy; *Int'l*, pg. 32

Guerra, Joseph L., Exec. V.P.-Acquisitions--American Golf Corporation, Santa Monica, CA; *U.S. Private*, pg. 55

Guerrero Alvarez, Jose Luis, Exec. V.P.--Empresas ICA Sociedad Controladora S.A.C.V., Mexico, Mexico; *Int'l*, pg. 454

Guerrero, Anthony R., Jr., Exec. V.P.-Branch Banking Grp.--First Hawaiian Bank, Honolulu, HI; *U.S. Public*, pg. 634

Guerrieri, Gary L., Exec. V.P.--Laurel Bank, Johnstown, PA; *U.S. Public*, pg. 164

Guezuraga, Robert M., Chief Oper. Officer & Exec. V.P.--Physio-Control Corporation, Redmond, WA; *U.S. Public*, pg. 1294

Guiardo, Paul, Exec. V.P.-Mktg.--America's Store, Saint Petersburg, FL; *U.S. Public*, pg. 1685

Guidotti, Bruce, Exec. V.P.-Client Services--Jordan, McGrath, Case & Taylor Inc., New York, NY; *U.S. Private*, pg. 598

Guiles, Edwin A., Exec. V.P.--Enova Corp, San Diego, CA; *U.S. Public*, pg. 583

Guilford, David J., Exec. V.P. & Dir.-Loan Prod. & Admin.--Barclays American/Mortgage Corp., Charlotte, NC; *Int'l*, pg. 165

Guimond, Clarence, Exec. V.P.-Internal Affairs--Brown & Haley, Tacoma, WA; *U.S. Private*, pg. 173

Guinan, Joseph M., Exec. V.P.--Fuji Securities Inc.-Chicago, Chicago, IL; *Int'l*, pg. 519

Guinan, Joseph M., Exec. V.P.--Fuji Securities Inc.-New York, New York, NY; *Int'l*, pg. 519

Guindon, Robert, Exec. V.P.-Intl.--Franklin Covey, Salt Lake City, UT; *U.S. Public*, pg. 679

Guire, Ronald W., Chief Fin. Officer, Exec. V.P. & Sec.--EXAR Corporation, Fremont, CA; *U.S. Public*, pg. 597

Guiton, John H., Exec. V.P.--Republic National Bank of New York, New York, NY; *U.S. Public*, pg. 1380

Gula, Allen J., Jr., Exec. V.P.--Keycorp, Cleveland, OH; *U.S. Public*, pg. 954

Gulis, Stephen L., Chief Fin. Officer & Exec. V.P.--Wolverine World Wide, Inc., Rockford, MI; *U.S. Public*, pg. 1775

Gumpert, Jon, Exec. V.P.--Universal Pictures, Universal City, CA; *Int'l*, pg. 1216

Gunkel, Thomas F., Exec. V.P.--M.A. Mortenson Company, Minneapolis, MN; *U.S. Private*, pg. 763

Gunn, Marie, Exec. V.P.-Quality of Service--Seafirst Corporation, Seattle, WA; *U.S. Public*, pg. 181

Gunnink, K., Exec. V.P.--ABN-AMRO Holding N.V., Amsterdam, Netherlands; *Int'l*, pg. 8

Gunnlaugsson, G.H., Exec. V.P.--Marshall & Ilsley Corporation, Milwaukee, WI; *U.S. Public*, pg. 1049

Gunther, Robert A., Sr. V.P. & Assoc. Counsel--Summit Bancorp, Princeton, NJ; *U.S. Public*, pg. 1527

Guntner, Christian R., Chief Oper. Officer & Exec. V.P.-Corp. Dev.--Publicker Industries Inc., Fairfield, CT; *U.S. Public*, pg. 1341

Guowen, Zhang, Exec. V.P.--Bank of China, Beijing, China; *Int'l*, pg. 152

Gurgovits, Stephen J., Exec. V.P.--F.N.B. Corporation, Hermitage, PA; *U.S. Public*, pg. 607

Gurley, James A., Exec. V.P.--Union Planters Corporation, Cordova, TN; *U.S. Public*, pg. 1668

Gustaferro, William R., Chief Fin. Officer & Exec. V.P.--Ameritech Phone Company, Cleveland, OH; *U.S. Public*, pg. 98

Gustafson, Paul A., Exec. V.P. & Pres.-Fastening Sys.--The Black & Decker Corporation, Towson, MD; *U.S. Public*, pg. 233

Gustafsson, Lars, Exec. V.P.--Skandinaviska Enskilda Banken, Stockholm, Sweden; *Int'l*, pg. 1258

Gustavsson, Lennart, Exec. V.P.-Grp. Admin. & Control--Componenta Dynapac AB, Vastra Frolunda, Sweden; *Int'l*, pg. 1419
Guterl, Thomas F., Exec. V.P.--U.S. Aviation Underwriters, Inc., New York, NY; *U.S. Public*, pg. 726
Guth, Bernard, Exec. V.P.--Albert M. Greenfield & Company, Philadelphia, PA; *U.S. Private*, pg. 477
Guthire, Jim, Chief Fin. Officer & Exec. V.P.--IXC Communications, Inc., Austin, TX; *U.S. Private*, pg. 556
Guthrie, Frances, Exec. V.P.-Mktg. & Sls.--Fortis Benefits Insurance Company, Kansas City, MO; *Int'l*, pg. 499
Guthrie, Roy A., Chief Fin. Officer & Exec. V.P.--Associates First Capital Corporation, Dallas, TX; *U.S. Public*, pg. 662
Gutierrez, Carlos M., Exec. V.P. & Pres.-Kellogg Asia-Pacific--Kellogg Company, Battle Creek, MI; *U.S. Public*, pg. 947
Gutierrez, Jose Maciel, Exec. V.P.--Hylsa S.A.-Mining and Pelletiing Division, Cuauhtemoc, Mexico; *Int'l*, pg. 56
Gutterman, Gerald S., Chief Fin. Officer & Exec. V.P.-Fin. & Admin.--Sequa Corporation, New York, NY; *U.S. Public*, pg. 1458
Guttman, Richard M., Exec. V.P.--The Guttman Group, Belle Vernon, PA; *U.S. Private*, pg. 488
Guy, Dennis, Exec. V.P.--JIB Group plc, London, United Kingdom; *Int'l*, pg. 705
Guyatt, Raymond E., Chief Fin. Officer & Exec. V.P.--Imasco Limited, Montreal, Canada; *Int'l*, pg. 112
Guzzetti, William L., Exec. V.P.--The Hallwood Group Incorporated, Dallas, TX; *U.S. Public*, pg. 777
Gwaltney, Alton H., Exec. V.P.-The Smithfield Ham & Prods. Co.--The Smithfield Companies, Inc., Portsmouth, VA; *U.S. Public*, pg. 1479
Gyani, Mohan S., Chief Fin. Officer & Exec. V.P.--AirTouch Communications, Inc., San Francisco, CA; *U.S. Public*, pg. 34
Ha-Ngoc, Tuan, Exec. V.P.--Genetics Institute, Inc., Cambridge, MA; *U.S. Public*, pg. 79
Haack, Arthur L., Exec. V.P.-Fin & Admin.--Hickman, Williams & Co. Inc., Cincinnati, OH; *U.S. Private*, pg. 525
Haaland, Ole Jacob, Exec. V.P.-Oil & Gas--Kvaerner a.s.a., Lysaker, Norway; *Int'l*, pg. 766
Haapanen, Pekka, Exec. V.P.--Valmet Inc.- Appleton Division, Appleton, WI; *Int'l*, pg. 1448
Haas, David, Exec. V.P. & Treas.--Keen Compressed Gas Co., Wilmington, DE; *U.S. Private*, pg. 611
Haber, Mitchell L., Exec. V.P. & Gen. Mgr.--Simon & Schuster International & Business & Professional Group, Paramus, NJ; *U.S. Private*, pg. 778
Haberlein, Heinzpeter, Exec. V.P.--Bayerische Hypotheken-und Wechsel-Bank Aktiengesellschaft, Munich, Germany; *Int'l*, pg. 175
Haberli, Ernst, Chief Fin. Officer & Exec. V.P.--Fort James Corporation, Richmond, VA; *U.S. Public*, pg. 670
Habig, Brian, Exec. V.P.-Sls. & Mktg., Kimball--Kimball International, Inc., Jasper, IN; *U.S. Public*, pg. 956
Habig, John B., Sr. Exec. V.P. & Opers. Officer--Kimball International, Inc., Jasper, IN; *U.S. Public*, pg. 956
Hacaj, Rosemary, Exec. V.P.--Metric & Multistandard Components, Hawthorne, NY; *U.S. Private*, pg. 736
Hack, Bruce L., Chief Fin. Officer & Exec. V.P.--Universal Studios, Inc., Universal City, CA; *Int'l*, pg. 1215
Hacker, Benjamin T., Chief Admin. Officer & Exec. V.P.--USAA (United Services Automobile Association), San Antonio, TX; *U.S. Private*, pg. 1114
Hackett, Lee P., Exec. V.P.--American Appraisal Associates, Inc., Milwaukee, WI; *U.S. Private*, pg. 49
Hackney, Hodges, Exec. V.P.-Intl. Sls.--Transportation Technologies, Inc., Washington, NC; *U.S. Private*, pg. 1097
Hackney, F. Hodges, Exec. V.P.-Intl. Sls.--Hackney and Sons, Inc., Washington, NC; *U.S. Private*, pg. 1097
Haddad, Richard, Exec. V.P. & Exec. Creative Dir.--Mintz & Hoke Inc., Avon, CT; *U.S. Private*, pg. 751
Haddock, Robert M., Chief Fin. Officer & Exec. V.P.--Aztar Corporation, Phoenix, AZ; *U.S. Public*, pg. 158
Haden, Richard M., Exec. V.P.-Field Services--Western Resources, Inc., Topeka, KS; *U.S. Public*, pg. 1759
Haeringer, Stephan, Exec. V.P.-Private Banking & Institutional Asset Mngmt.--Union Bank of Switzerland, Zurich, Switzerland; *Int'l*, pg. 1439
Haffey, John, Chief Oper. Officer & Exec. V.P./Energy & Telecommunications--Montana Power Company, Butte, MT; *U.S. Public*, pg. 1126
Haffmans, C.A.M., Exec. V.P.--ABN-AMRO Holding N.V., Amsterdam, Netherlands; *Int'l*, pg. 8
Haffner, David S., Exec. V.P.--Leggett & Platt, Incorporated, Carthage, MO; *U.S. Public*, pg. 985
Hagale, John E., Chief Fin. Officer & Exec. V.P.--Burlington Resources Inc., Houston, TX; *U.S. Public*, pg. 269
Hagan, Bernard F., Chief Oper. Officer & Exec. V.P.--Henkels & McCoy, Inc., Blue Bell, PA; *U.S. Private*, pg. 522
Hagan, James J., Chief Fin. Officer & Exec. V.P.-Fin.--Bruno's Inc., Birmingham, AL; *U.S. Public*, pg. 265
Hagedorn, James, Exec. V.P.-U.S. Bus. Grp.--The Scotts Company, Marysville, OH; *U.S. Public*, pg. 1446
Hagelstein, Bill, Exec. V.P.--Rubin Postaer & Associates, Santa Monica, CA; *U.S. Private*, pg. 950
Hagelstein, William C., Exec. V.P.--Rubin Postaer & Associates, Santa Monica, CA; *U.S. Private*, pg. 949
Hagen, C. Garland, Corp. Exec. V.P.-Corp. Devel. & Funds Mngmt.--Crestar Financial Corporation, Richmond, VA; *U.S. Public*, pg. 458
Hager, Hampton C., Exec. V.P.--Cleveland Capital Holdings, Cliffside, NC; *U.S. Private*, pg. 246
Hager, Hampton C., Exec. V.P.--Petroleum World, Cliffside, NC; *U.S. Private*, pg. 246
Haggar, Paul, Exec. V.P.-Post Production--Paramount Pictures Corporation, Los Angeles, CA; *U.S. Private*, pg. 776
Haggar, Thomas, Chief Oper. Officer & Exec. V.P.--Premarc Corporation, Durand, MI; *U.S. Private*, pg. 881
Hagge, Stephen, Chief Fin. Officer, Exec. V.P., Treas. & Sec.--AptarGroup, Inc., Crystal Lake, IL; *U.S. Public*, pg. 125
Haggerty, John R., Exec. V.P.--Consumer Fin.--Comerica Incorporated, Detroit, MI; *U.S. Public*, pg. 408
Haggerty, John R., Chief Fin. Officer & Sr. Exec. V.P.--Summit Bancorp, Princeton, NJ; *U.S. Public*, pg. 1527
Haggerty, Michael, Exec. V.P. & Media Dir.--Wells BDDP, Inc., New York, NY; *Int'l*, pg. 117
Haggerty, Richard, Exec. V.P.-Sls.--Gilman Paper Co., Saint Marys, GA; *U.S. Private*, pg. 454
Haggle, John E., Chief Fin. Officer & Exec. V.P.--Meridian Oil Holding Inc., Houston, TX; *U.S. Public*, pg. 269
Hagi, Kurt, Exec. V.P. & Sec.--Sulzer Ltd., Winterthur, Switzerland; *Int'l*, pg. 1305
Hagin, Barbara, Exec. V.P. & Gen. Mgr.--Technology Solutions Inc., San Jose, CA; *U.S. Private*, pg. 1157
Hagiwara, Tad, Exec. V.P.-Sls.--Hitachi Home Electronics, Norcross, GA; *Int'l*, pg. 621
Hagsten, Goran, Exec. V.P.--Bergman & Beving AB, Stockholm, Sweden; *Int'l*, pg. 188
Hagstroem, Lennart, Sr. Exec. V.P.--Bergman & Beving AB, Stockholm, Sweden; *Int'l*, pg. 188
Hahn, Arnold C., Chief Fin. Officer & Exec. V.P.--Western Bancorp, Newport Beach, CA; *U.S. Public*, pg. 1757
Hahn, David L., Chief Oper. Officer & Exec. V.P.--Ogden Aviation Services, New York, NY; *U.S. Public*, pg. 1213
Hahn, John W., Exec. V.P.-Information Tech.--Atlantic Mutual Companies, New York, NY; *U.S. Private*, pg. 95
Hahn, Kenneth, Exec. V.P.--Hahn Equipment Co., Evansville, IN; *U.S. Public*, pg. 1624
Hahn, Kent, Exec. V.P.--Hahn Equipment Co., Evansville, IN; *U.S. Public*, pg. 1624
Haifleigh, David, Exec. V.P.-Mktg.--EvansGroup, Denver, CO; *U.S. Private*, pg. 385
Hailey, V. Ann, Chief Fin. Officer & Exec. V.P.--The Limited, Inc., Columbus, OH; *U.S. Public*, pg. 995
Hainich, Matthias, Exec. V.P.--Hochtief AG, Essen, Germany; *Int'l*, pg. 623
Hairston, William G., III, Exec. V.P.-Nuclear--Georgia Power Co., Atlanta, GA; *U.S. Public*, pg. 1490
Hajek, Anna Marie, Exec. V.P. & Pres.-MMI Healthcare Svcs. Grp.--MMI Companies, Inc., Deerfield, IL; *U.S. Public*, pg. 1027
Hake, Ralph F., Sr. Exec. V.P.-Opers.--Whirlpool Corporation, Benton Harbor, MI; *U.S. Public*, pg. 1764
Hakler, Robert, Chief Fin. Officer & Exec. V.P.--Magna Group, Inc., Saint Louis, MO; *U.S. Public*, pg. 1037
Hakstad, Thor, Exec. V.P.--Norsk Hydro a.s, Oslo, Norway; *Int'l*, pg. 959
Halbron, Jean-Pierre, Sr. Exec. V.P.--Alcatel Alsthom Compagnie Generale D'Electricite, Paris, France; *Int'l*, pg. 52
Hale, Dan, Chief Fin. Officer & Exec. V.P.--USF&G Corporation, Baltimore, MD; *U.S. Public*, pg. 1659
Hale, James, Exec. V.P.--Gores Technology Group, Sherman Oaks, CA; *U.S. Private*, pg. 465
Hale, Martin M., Exec. V.P.--Hellman, Jordan Management Company, Inc., Boston, MA; *U.S. Public*, pg. 1673
Haley, Michael P., Exec. V.P. & Pres.-Contract Sls. Grp.--Ladd Furniture, Inc., Greensboro, NC; *U.S. Public*, pg. 974
Hall, Greg, V.P.-Fin. & Admin.--Pentax Canada Inc., Mississauga, Canada; *Int'l*, pg. 85
Hall, Jerry, Chief Oper. Officer & Exec. V.P.--Robert F. Driver Co., Inc., San Diego, CA; *U.S. Private*, pg. 343
Hall, Jerry D., Exec. V.P.--Jack Henry & Associates, Inc., Monett, MO; *U.S. Public*, pg. 808
Hall, John A., Exec. V.P.--Lankford-Sysco Food Services, Inc., Pocomoke City, MD; *U.S. Public*, pg. 1551
Hall, John C., Exec. V.P.--Lusk, Irvine, CA; *U.S. Private*, pg. 681
Hall, Kurt C., Chief Fin. Officer & Exec. V.P.--United Artists Theatre Circuits Incorporated, Englewood, CO; *U.S. Private*, pg. 1120
Hall, Mark, Exec. V.P. & Dir.-Adv. & Sls.--Monarch Avalon, Inc., Baltimore, MD; *U.S. Public*, pg. 1123
Hall, Rick, Chief Fin. Officer & Exec. V.P.--Hardee's Food Systems, Inc., Rocky Mount, NC; *U.S. Public*, pg. 278
Hall, Robert C., Exec. V.P.--Thomson U.S. Inc., Stamford, CT; *U.S. Public*, pg. 1601
Hall, Robert D., Pres.-Whirlpool Asia, Inc. & Exec. V.P.--Whirlpool Corporation, Benton Harbor, MI; *U.S. Public*, pg. 1764
Hall, Scott, Chief Oper. Officer & Exec. V.P.--Kragie/Newell, Des Moines, IA; *U.S. Private*, pg. 634
Halley, Tom, Exec. V.P.-Consumer Mkts. Div./Central Div.--Countrywide Home Loans Inc., Pasadena, CA; *U.S. Public*, pg. 452
Halliwell, Frank, Deputy Chief Exec. & Comml. Dir.--Canada Maritime Limited, London, United Kingdom; *Int'l*, pg. 259
Hallock, Richard W., Exec. V.P.-H.R.--Occidental Petroleum Corporation, Los Angeles, CA; *U.S. Public*, pg. 1210
Halloran, Michael J., Grp. Exec. V.P. & Gen. Counsel--Bank of America NT&SA, San Francisco, CA; *U.S. Public*, pg. 180
Hallstrom, Sture, Exec. V.P.--Svenska Handelsbanken, Stockholm, Sweden; *Int'l*, pg. 1327
Halonen, Eino, Exec. V.P.--Merita Ltd., Helsinki, Finland; *Int'l*, pg. 858
Halper, Steven H., Chief Oper. Officer, Exec. V.P. & Sec.--Seaman Furniture Company, Inc., Woodbury, NY; *U.S. Public*, pg. 1452
Halpert, Lew, Exec. V.P.--Kennedy-Wilson, Inc., Santa Monica, CA; *U.S. Public*, pg. 951
Halpin, Gerard B., Exec. V.P.--Richard De Boo Publishers, Scarborough, Canada; *U.S. Public*, pg. 1601
Halsky, Sheff, Exec. V.P.--Arnold Communications, Inc., Boston, MA; *U.S. Private*, pg. 83
Haltiner, Eugen, Exec. V.P.-Retail Banking--Union Bank of Switzerland, Zurich, Switzerland; *Int'l*, pg. 1439
Halverson, Duane, Chief Oper. Officer & Exec. V.P.--Land O'Lakes, Inc., Arden Hills, MN; *U.S. Private*, pg. 645
Halverson, Gordon E., Exec. V.P.-Sls.--The Antec Corporation, Rolling Meadows, IL; *U.S. Public*, pg. 116
Halvorsen, Andrew C., Exec. V.P.--Beneficial Management Corporation, Peapack, NJ; *U.S. Public*, pg. 211
Hamacher, Samuel, Exec. V.P.--Harbour Group Ltd., Saint Louis, MO; *U.S. Private*, pg. 500
Hamada, Hironobu, Exec. V.P. & Dir.--Kodansha Ltd., Tokyo, Japan; *Int'l*, pg. 742
Hamada, Masayoshi, Exec. V.P. & Rep. Dir.--Juki Corporation, Tokyo, Japan; *Int'l*, pg. 716
Hamann, Rodney, Exec. V.P.-Prods.--Murphy Family Farms, Rose Hill, NC; *U.S. Private*, pg. 768
Hamblode-Gesinn, Sylvie, Exec. V.P.--DG Bank, Frankfurt/Main, Germany; *Int'l*, pg. 351
Hambrick, David W., Exec. V.P.--Horizon Bancorp, Inc., Beckley, WV; *U.S. Public*, pg. 836
Hambrick, David W., Exec. V.P.--Greenbrier Valley National Bank, Lewisburg, WV; *U.S. Public*, pg. 836
Hamerling, Wayne, Exec. V.P.--Jean Philippe Fragrances, Inc., New York, NY; *U.S. Public*, pg. 924
Hamilton, Bernard J., Exec. V.P.--American Express Travel Related Services Co., Inc., New York, NY; *U.S. Public*, pg. 73
Hamilton, Bill, Exec. V.P. & Creative Head- O&M/NY--Ogilvy & Mather Worldwide, Inc., New York, NY; *Int'l*, pg. 1483
Hamilton, Gary, Exec. V.P.--Evans Industries, Inc., Harvey, LA; *U.S. Private*, pg. 385
Hamilton, Henry, Exec. V.P.-Commodity Svcs.--New Century Energies, Inc., Denver, CO; *U.S. Public*, pg. 1170
Hamilton, Henry H., Exec. V.P.--Southwestern Public Service Company, Amarillo, TX; *U.S. Public*, pg. 1170
Hamilton, John A., Exec. V.P.-Information Technology--Marine Midland Bank, Buffalo, NY; *Int'l*, pg. 581
Hamilton, John C., Exec. V.P.--City National Bank of Baton Rouge, Baton Rouge, LA; *U.S. Public*, pg. 629
Hamilton, Michael, Exec. V.P.-Stores & Distr.--Hills Stores Co., Canton, MA; *U.S. Public*, pg. 828
Hamilton, Peter, Exec. V.P.--McCann-Erickson Worldwide, New York, NY; *U.S. Public*, pg. 909
Hamilton, Victoria, Chief Oper. Officer & Exec. V.P.--General American Investors Company, Inc., New York, NY; *U.S. Public*, pg. 706
Hamlin, Bill, Exec. V.P.-Mdsg.--The Home Depot, Inc., Atlanta, GA; *U.S. Public*, pg. 831
Hamm, John G., Exec. V.P.--Artra Group Incorporated, Northfield, IL; *U.S. Public*, pg. 136
Hamm, Raymond A., Jr., Exec. V.P.--County Banking & Trust Company, Elkton, MD; *U.S. Public*, pg. 1089
Hamm, Willi, Chief Oper. Officer & Exec. V.P.--Industra Service Corporation, New Westminster, Canada; *Int'l*, pg. 74
Hammalian, Stephen J., Ph.D., Chief Admin Officer & Exec. V.P.--EA Engineering, Science & Technology, Inc., Hunt Valley, MD; *U.S. Public*, pg. 540
Hammar, Ralph, Exec. V.P.--Axel Johnson AB, Stockholm, Sweden; *Int'l*, pg. 707
Hammer, Kouhaila G., Chief Oper. Officer & Exec. V.P.--Ghafari Associates, Inc., Dearborn, MI; *U.S. Private*, pg. 450
Hammer, Randolf, Grp. Exec. V.P.-Security--Christiania Bank og Kreditkasse ASA, Oslo, Norway; *Int'l*, pg. 289
Hammerling, Harry K., Exec. V.P.--First Financial Bank, FSB, Stevens Point, WI; *U.S. Public*, pg. 140
Hammes, Lynn F., Chief Fin. Officer & Exec. V.P.--American Investors Life Insurance Company, Topeka, KS; *U.S. Private*, pg. 59
Hammock, M. Hill, Exec. V.P.-Comml. Lending--ABN/LaSalle North America Inc., Chicago, IL; *Int'l*, pg. 11
Hammock, Steve, Exec. V.P.--Watkins Manufacturing Corp./Hot Spring Portable Spas, Vista, CA; *U.S. Public*, pg. 1054
Hammond, C.F., III, Exec. V.P.--Great Dane Trailers, Inc., Savannah, GA; *U.S. Private*, pg. 1030
Hampton, Michael, Exec. V.P. & Co-Creative Dir.--The Lord Group, New York, NY; *U.S. Private*, pg. 325
Hampton, Philip, Exec. V.P.-Fin.--British Steel Plc, London, United Kingdom; *Int'l*, pg. 220
Han'ya, Tetsuo, Exec. V.P.--Kajima Corporation, Tokyo, Japan; *Int'l*, pg. 721
Hanawa, Shoji, Exec. V.P.--The Tokyo Electric Power Co., Inc., Tokyo, Japan; *Int'l*, pg. 1394
Hancock, Kevin, Chief Oper. Officer & Exec. V.P.--Hancock Lumber, Inc., Casco, ME; *U.S. Private*, pg. 498
Hancock, Michael, Exec. V.P.-Restaurant Devel.--Boddie-Noell Enterprises Inc., Rocky Mount, NC; *U.S. Private*, pg. 154
Handler, Richard B., Exec. V.P.--Jefferies & Company, Inc., Los Angeles, CA; *U.S. Public*, pg. 925
Handler, Richard B., Exec. V.P.--Jefferies & Company, Inc., Stamford, CT; *U.S. Public*, pg. 925
Hands, Harold P., Exec. V.P.-Legal & Sec.--Mackenzie Financial Corporation, Toronto, Canada; *Int'l*, pg. 828
Hanert, Eckehard, Exec. V.P.--Von Roll AG, Gerlafingen, Switzerland; *Int'l*, pg. 1480
Haney, William V., Exec. V.P.-Corp. & Public Affairs--The MacManus Group, Inc., New York, NY; *U.S. Private*, pg. 692
Hankerson, Neil, Exec. V.P.--Dark Horse Comics, Inc., Milwaukie, OR; *U.S. Private*, pg. 311
Hanks, Alan, Exec. V.P.-Opers.--Telonic Berkeley, Inc., Laguna Beach, CA; *U.S. Private*, pg. 1074
Hanks, Stephen G., Chief Legal Officer & Exec. V.P.--Morrison Knudsen Corporation, Boise, ID; *U.S. Public*, pg. 1133
Hanks, W. David, Exec. V.P. & Asst. Sec.--Riviana Foods Inc., Houston, TX; *U.S. Public*, pg. 1392
Hanley, Peter, Exec. V.P.-Global Opers.--Novellus Systems, Inc., San Jose, CA; *U.S. Public*, pg. 1204
Hanlon, David P., Chief Oper. Officer & Exec. V.P.--Rio Hotel & Casino Inc., Las Vegas, NV; *U.S. Public*, pg. 1390
Hanna, David H., Exec. V.P.--Southwest National Corporation, Greensburg, PA; *U.S. Public*, pg. 1493

Hanna, David M., Exec. V.P.--Southwest National Bank of Pennsylvania, Greensburg, PA; *U.S. Public*, pg. 1493
Hanna, Michael D., Exec. V.P.--Louisiana Pacific Corporation, Portland, OR; *U.S. Public*, pg. 1015
Hanna, Steven R., Exec. V.P. & Chief Info. Officer--Ross Roy Communications, Inc., Bloomfield Hills, MI; *U.S. Private*, pg. 946
Hanna, William B., Exec. V.P.-Fin.--Motor Coach Industries International, Inc., Phoenix, AZ; *Int'l*, pg. 326
Hanneman, LeRoy C., Jr., Exec. V.P.--Del Webb Corporation, Phoenix, AZ; *U.S. Public*, pg. 494
Hannemann, Timothy W., Exec. V.P. & Gen. Mgr.-TRW Space & Electronics Grp.--TRW Inc., Cleveland, OH; *U.S. Public*, pg. 1558
Hannemann, Timothy W., Exec. V.P. & Gen. Mgr.--TRW Space & Electronics Group, Redondo Beach, CA; *U.S. Public*, pg. 1558
Hannigan, Andrew J., Chief Oper. Officer & Exec. V.P.--Centex Real Estate Corp./Centex Homes, Dallas, TX; *U.S. Public*, pg. 323
Hannon, Cyril F., Exec. V.P.-Worldwide Opers.--LSI Logic Corp., Milpitas, CA; *U.S. Public*, pg. 971
Hansen, Andrew, Exec. V.P.--Old American Insurance Co., Kansas City, MO; *U.S. Public*, pg. 943
Hansen, James K., Exec. V.P. & Gen. Mgr.-Mill Div.--Rock-Tenn Company, Norcross, GA; *U.S. Public*, pg. 1396
Hansen, Janet M., Chief Fin. Officer, Exec. V.P. & Treas.--Aquarion Company, Bridgeport, CT; *U.S. Public*, pg. 126
Hansen, Poul, Exec. V.P.--Chr. Hansen Holding A/S, Horsholm, Denmark; *Int'l*, pg. 288
Hansen, Stephen W., Exec. V.P. & Dir.-Human Resources--Norwest Corporation, Minneapolis, MN; *U.S. Public*, pg. 1201
Hansen, Tim, Exec. V.P.-CT/X-ray--Picker International, Inc., Cleveland, OH; *Int'l*, pg. 545
Hanson, Dennis R., Exec. V.P.-Transportation Svcs.--Comdata Corporation, Brentwood, TN; *U.S. Public*, pg. 331
Hanson, James L., Exec. V.P. & Dir.-IS--Mutual of Omaha Insurance Company, Omaha, NE; *U.S. Private*, pg. 769
Hanssen, Stein Rohde, Exec. Dir.--Union Bank of Norway, Oslo, Norway; *Int'l*, pg. 1439
Hansson, Birger, Exec. V.P.--Jimek, Arlov, Sweden; *U.S. Public*, pg. 170
Hantak, Susan, Exec. V.P.--Willert Home Products, Inc., Saint Louis, MO; *U.S. Private*, pg. 1177
Hapka, Catherine, Exec. V.P.-Markets--U S West Inc., Englewood, CO; *U.S. Public*, pg. 1688
Hara, Kimimochi, Exec. Mng. Dir.--Sumitomo Heavy Industries, Ltd., Tokyo, Japan; *Int'l*, pg. 1314
Harada, Yoshihiro, Exec. V.P.--Toray Industries, Inc., Tokyo, Japan; *Int'l*, pg. 1399
Harald, Bo, Exec. V.P.--Merita Ltd., Helsinki, Finland; *Int'l*, pg. 858
Haraldson, William, Chief Oper. Officer & Exec. V.P.-Mktg.--Rosauers Supermarkets, Inc., Spokane, WA; *U.S. Private*, pg. 944
Harari, O., Exec. V.P.--Israel Aircraft Industries Ltd., Israel; *Int'l*, pg. 689
Harayama, Kiyomi, Exec. V.P.-Railway Opers.--East Japan Railway Company, Tokyo, Japan; *Int'l*, pg. 431
Harbeck, Peter A., Chief Admin. Officer & Exec. V.P.--SunAmerica Inc., Los Angeles, CA; *U.S. Public*, pg. 1532
Harbecke, William F., Sr. V.P.-Fin. & Admin.--American Stores Properties, Inc., Salt Lake City, UT; *U.S. Public*, pg. 93
Harbert, David, Chief Fin. Officer & Exec. V.P.--Delco Remy International, Inc., Anderson, IN; *U.S. Public*, pg. 495
Harbert, David L., Chief Fin. Officer & Exec. V.P.--Delco Remy America, Inc., Anderson, IN; *U.S. Public*, pg. 495
Harbert, Timothy B., Exec. V.P.--State Street Corporation, Boston, MA; *U.S. Public*, pg. 1513
Harbin, Henry, M.D., Exec. V.P.-Green Spring Health Services--Magellan Health Services, Inc., Atlanta, GA; *U.S. Public*, pg. 1033
Harden, Tom, Exec. V.P.-IS--L.L. Bean, Inc., Freeport, ME; *U.S. Private*, pg. 639
Harder, Glenn E., Chief Fin. Officer & Exec. V.P.-Fin. Svcs.--Carolina Power & Light Company, Raleigh, NC; *U.S. Public*, pg. 306
Hardin, Joseph S., Jr., Exec. V.P. & Pres.-Sam's--Wal-Mart Stores, Inc., Bentonville, AR; *U.S. Public*, pg. 1732
Harding, Eleanor, Exec. V.P.--Integrated Health Services, Inc., Owings Mills, MD; *U.S. Public*, pg. 884
Harding, Enoch, Jr., Exec. V.P.-Opers.--Kellwood Company, Chesterfield, MO; *U.S. Public*, pg. 948
Hardy, Brad D., Exec. V.P.-Corp. Svcs. & Gen. Counsel--First Security Corporation, Salt Lake City, UT; *U.S. Public*, pg. 637
Hardy, Dennis, Exec. V.P. & Mngmt. Supvr.--Evans, Hardy & Young, Inc., Santa Barbara, CA; *U.S. Private*, pg. 384
Hardy, Gene, Exec. V.P., Sec. & Gen. Counsel--United Artists Theatre Circuits Incorporated, Englewood, CO; *U.S. Private*, pg. 1120
Hardy, Ivad, Exec. V.P.-Strategic Opers.--National Car Rental System, Inc., Minneapolis, MN; *U.S. Public*, pg. 1379
Hare, Steve, Chief Fin. Officer & Exec. V.P.--AMF Bowling Worldwide, Richmond, VA; *U.S. Private*, pg. 6
Harel, Roland, Chief Fin. Officer & Exec. V.P.--Provigo Inc., Montreal, Canada; *Int'l*, pg. 1072
Hargis, Norton B., Jr., Exec. V.P.--Cullen/Frost Bankers, Inc., San Antonio, TX; *U.S. Public*, pg. 467
Hargis, Wen, Exec. V.P.--Cavco Industries, Inc., Phoenix, AZ; *U.S. Public*, pg. 323
Hargrove, G. Thomas, Exec. V.P.--Cullman Ventures, Inc., Norwalk, CT; *U.S. Private*, pg. 294
Harigaya, Hiroshi, Exec. V.P.--Seiko Corporation, Tokyo, Japan; *Int'l*, pg. 1218
Harjuvaaara, Heikki, Exec. V.P.--Akerlund & Rausing, Leerdam, Netherlands; *Int'l*, pg. 33
Harker, Brian J., Chief Fin. Officer & Exec. V.P.--DIMON, Incorporated, Danville, VA; *U.S. Public*, pg. 509
Harker, Brian J., Chief Fin. Officer & Exec. V.P.--DIMON, International, Inc., Farmville, NC; *U.S. Public*, pg. 510
Harker, Gary, Exec. V.P.-Sls.--California Panel & Veneer Company, Cerritos, CA; *U.S. Private*, pg. 201
Harkless, Brad, Exec. V.P.-Sls. & Mktg.--L & S Bearing Co., Oklahoma City, OK; *U.S. Public*, pg. 970
Harman, Gina, Exec. V.P., Sls. & Brand Mgr.--Harman Consumer Group, Woodbury, NY; *U.S. Public*, pg. 787
Harman, Tommy W., Exec. V.P.--National Systems & Research Co., Colorado Springs, CO; *U.S. Private*, pg. 787
Harmon, C.R., Exec. V.P.-Intl. Bus.--Oasis Corp., Columbus, OH; *U.S. Private*, pg. 810
Harmon, Gary, Exec. V.P.-Sls.--Kraft Foods Inc., Glenview, IL; *U.S. Public*, pg. 1288
Harmon, J.A., Exec. V.P.--Emerson Electric Co., Saint Louis, MO; *U.S. Public*, pg. 572
Harms, Steve, Exec. V.P.-Sls.--Sika Corporation, Lyndhurst, NJ; *Int'l*, pg. 1249
Harold, Ann, Exec. V.P.-Mktg. & Sls.--Weber-Stephen Products Co., Palatine, IL; *U.S. Private*, pg. 1157
Harp, Milford B., Exec. V.P.-Opers.--Nalco Chemical Company, Naperville, IL; *U.S. Public*, pg. 1150
Harp, Sidney, II, Exec. V.P. & Agency Dir.--Security Industrial Insurance Co., Inc., Donaldsonville, LA; *Int'l*, pg. 814
Harper, Craig, Exec. V.P.-Opers.--J.B. Hunt Transport Services, Inc., Lowell, AR; *U.S. Public*, pg. 849
Harper, Daniel K., Exec. V.P.-Opers.--Family Smacks, Inc., Liberty, MO; *U.S. Private*, pg. 393
Harps, Cheryl, Exec. V.P. & Media Communications Dir.--Don Coleman Advertising, Inc., Southfield, MI; *U.S. Private*, pg. 251
Harr, Lawrence F., Exec. V.P. & Exec. Counsel--Mutual of Omaha Insurance Company, Omaha, NE; *U.S. Private*, pg. 769
Harra, Tapio, Exec. V.P.-Energy--Neste Oy, Espoo, Finland; *Int'l*, pg. 912
Harrell, Don, Exec. V.P.-External Affairs--Teachers Insurance and Annuity Association, New York, NY; *U.S. Private*, pg. 1071
Harri, Diane, Exec. V.P.--Lally, McFarland & Pantello Inc., New York, NY; *Int'l*, pg. 601
Harrington, Matthew, Exec. V.P. & Gen. Mgr.--Edelman Worldwide, Inc., San Francisco, CA; *U.S. Private*, pg. 362
Harris, Alan F., Exec. V.P. & Pres.-Kellogg Latin America--Kellogg Company, Battle Creek, MI; *U.S. Public*, pg. 947
Harris, Alan F., Exec. V.P.-Cereal Div.-Mktg. & Sls.--Kellogg USA Inc., Battle Creek, MI; *U.S. Public*, pg. 947
Harris, Alice M., Exec. V.P. & Asst. Sec.--City Gas Company of Florida, Hialeah, FL; *U.S. Public*, pg. 1147
Harris, David S., Chief Fin. Officer & Exec. V.P.--Korey, Kay & Partners, New York, NY; *U.S. Private*, pg. 632
Harris, E. Lee, Jr., Exec. V.P.-Human Resources--Compass Bank, Birmingham, AL; *U.S. Public*, pg. 418
Harris, Eugene A., Exec. V.P.-Comml. Banking--BOK Financial Corp., Tulsa, OK; *U.S. Public*, pg. 163
Harris, Eugene A., Exec. V.P.-Commercial Banking--Bank of Oklahoma, N.A., Tulsa, OK; *U.S. Public*, pg. 163
Harris, Gerald, Chief Oper. Officer & Exec. V.P.--Charles Komar & Sons, Inc., New York, NY; *U.S. Private*, pg. 631
Harris, John C., Exec. V.P.--ABN AMRO Chicago Corp., Chicago, IL; *Int'l*, pg. 10
Harris, Karen, Exec. V.P. & Media Dir.--Grey Direct, New York, NY; *U.S. Public*, pg. 764
Harris, Lloyd F., Exec. V.P.--First National Bank of Sweetwater, Sweetwater, TX; *U.S. Public*, pg. 633
Harris, William, Exec. V.P.--Wal-Mart Shoe Div., Bentonville, AR; *U.S. Public*, pg. 1733
Harris, William H., Jr., Exec. V.P.--Intuit, Inc., Mountain View, CA; *U.S. Public*, pg. 911
Harrison, David H., Chief Fin. Officer & Exec. V.P.--Coltec Industries Inc., Charlotte, NC; *U.S. Public*, pg. 401
Harrison, Hans-Olof, Exec. V.P.-Reg. Bank, Eastern Sweden--Svenska Handelsbanken, Stockholm, Sweden; *Int'l*, pg. 1327
Harrison, James M., Chief Fin. Officer, Exec. V.P., Treas. & Sec.--C.R. Gibson Co., Norwalk, CT; *U.S. Public*, pg. 1168
Harrison, James W., Pres. & Exec. V.P.-Metal Chemicals North America--Henkel Surface Technologies, Madison Heights, MI; *Int'l*, pg. 610
Harrison, Nigel R., Chief Fin. Officer & Exec. V.P.--The Thomson Corporation, Stamford, CT; *U.S. Public*, pg. 1599
Harrison, Patrick W., Exec. V.P. & Gen. Mgr.--NationsBank of Tennessee, Nashville, TN; *U.S. Public*, pg. 1163
Harrison, R.W., Exec. V.P.--International Center for Entrepreneurial Development, Inc., Cypress, TX; *U.S. Private*, pg. 568
Harrison, William J., Exec. V.P.--Cascade Corporation, Troutdale, OR; *U.S. Public*, pg. 310
Harsh, John, Exec. V.P.--Pratt-Read Corporation, Bridgeport, CT; *U.S. Private*, pg. 879
Harsh, John, Exec. V.P.--Safari Tool, Bridgeport, CT; *U.S. Private*, pg. 879
Harsmann, Bent, Exec. V.P.--Royal Copenhagen A/S, Frederiksberg, Denmark; *Int'l*, pg. 1134
Hart, Matthew J., Chief Fin. Officer & Exec. V.P.--Hilton Hotels Corporation, Beverly Hills, CA; *U.S. Public*, pg. 828
Hart, Norman, Exec. V.P.--Idahoan Foods, Lewisville, ID; *U.S. Private*, pg. 557
Hartl, Michael J., Exec. V.P., Chief Fin. Officer & Treas.--Norwich Financial Corp., Norwich, CT; *U.S. Public*, pg. 1203
Hartley, S.L., Chief Fin. Officer & Exec. V.P.--The Molson Companies Limited, Toronto, Canada; *Int'l*, pg. 887
Hartman, Lawrence M., Chief Fin. Officer & Exec. V.P.--Velsicol Chemical Corporation, Rosemont, IL; *U.S. Private*, pg. 1135
Hartman, Mark W., Exec. V.P.-Office of Chm.--Crown Cork & Seal Company, Inc., Philadelphia, PA; *U.S. Public*, pg. 462
Hartman, P.F., Exec. V.P.-Personnel & Organization--KLM Royal Dutch Airlines, Amstelveen, Netherlands; *Int'l*, pg. 719
Hartmann, Hans, Exec. V.P.--Norddeutsche Landesbank (NORD/LB), Hannover, Germany; *Int'l*, pg. 957
Hartmann, M., Exec. V.P. & Gen. Mgr.--Deutsche Babcock Technologies, Inc., Duluth, GA; *Int'l*, pg. 401
Hartner, Craig, Chief Fin. Officer & Exec. V.P.--AEC, Inc., Wood Dale, IL; *U.S. Private*, pg. 500
Hartoch, Kenneth, Exec. V.P.--Gerber International Inc., New York, NY; *U.S. Private*, pg. 448
Hartoch, Kenneth, Exec. V.P.--J. Gerber & Co. Inc., New York, NY; *U.S. Private*, pg. 449
Haruna, Akira, Exec. V.P. & Gen. Mgr.--The Industrial Bank of Japan (Canada), Vancouver, Canada; *Int'l*, pg. 676
Harvatine, John, Exec. V.P.--GE Capital/IT Solutions, Minneapolis, MN; *U.S. Public*, pg. 711
Harvey, Cannon Y., Exec. V.P.-Fin. & Law & Gen. Counsel--Southern Pacific Rail Corporation, San Francisco, CA; *U.S. Public*, pg. 1668
Harvey, Curtis R., Chief Fin. Officer & Exec. V.P.--First Financial Bankshares, Inc., Abilene, TX; *U.S. Public*, pg. 633
Harwood, Charlie, Chief Fin. Officer & Exec. V.P.--Covance, Inc., Princeton, NJ; *U.S. Public*, pg. 453
Harwood, Herbert A., Exec. V.P.--Detecto Scale Company, Webb City, MO; *U.S. Private*, pg. 209
Hasegawa, Akira, Sr. Exec. V.P.--All Nippon Airways Co. Ltd., Tokyo, Japan; *Int'l*, pg. 57
Hasegawa, Yoshihiko, Exec. V.P.--Daido Steel Co., Ltd., Nagoya, Japan; *Int'l*, pg. 364
Hashimoto, Mutsumi, Exec. V.P.-Western Japan--Sumitomo Corporation, Tokyo, Japan; *Int'l*, pg. 1312
Hashimoto, Shigehiko, Exec. V.P.--Sumitomo Sitix Corporation, Amagasaki, Japan; *Int'l*, pg. 1317
Haskins, Richard J., Exec. V.P.--Republic Security Financial Corporation, West Palm Beach, FL; *U.S. Public*, pg. 1381
Haslam, Douglas, Chief Fin. Officer & Exec. V.P.--Menu Foods, Inc., Pennsauken, NJ; *U.S. Private*, pg. 731
Hassell, Gerald L., Sr. Exec. V.P.-Corp. Banking--The Bank of New York Company, Inc., New York, NY; *U.S. Public*, pg. 178
Hassell, June, Exec. V.P. & Mng. Dir.--Outdoor Services, New York, NY; *U.S. Private*, pg. 1166
Hassman, Howard, Dr., Exec. V.P.-Corp. Devel.--FPA Medical Management, Inc., San Diego, CA; *U.S. Public*, pg. 608
Hasson, Raymond I., Exec. V.P.--Alba Forwarding Co., Inc., Jersey City, NJ; *U.S. Private*, pg. 32
Hastings-Bass, John, Exec. V.P.--JIB Group plc, London, United Kingdom; *Int'l*, pg. 705
Hastings, Donald M., Sr. V.P. & Exec. V.P.-West Penn/CDT--Cable Design Technologies Corporation, Pittsburgh, PA; *U.S. Public*, pg. 287
Hastings, John J., Chief Fin. Officer, Exec. V.P., Treas. & Sec.--The Middleby Corporation, Rolling Meadows, IL; *U.S. Public*, pg. 1109
Hasumi, Kouichi, Exec. V.P.--Chubu Electric Power Company, Inc., Nagoya, Japan; *Int'l*, pg. 290
Hatakeyama, Takuzo, Sr. Mng. Dir.--Daido Steel Co., Ltd., Nagoya, Japan; *Int'l*, pg. 364
Hatch, Rebecca A., Pres.-Bed & Bath Div. & Exec. V.P.--CHF Industries, Inc., New York, NY; *U.S. Private*, pg. 1094
Hatcher, Betty F., Exec. V.P.-Product Devel.--Gamma Biologicals Inc., Houston, TX; *U.S. Public*, pg. 698
Hatcher, Stephen R., Chief Fin. Officer & Exec. V.P.--The Union Central Life Insurance Co., Cincinnati, OH; *U.S. Private*, pg. 1118
Hatton, Carl, Exec. V.P.--Windsor Industries, Inc., Englewood, CO; *U.S. Private*, pg. 1182
Hatton, Frederick L., Exec. V.P.--GATX Capital Corporation, San Francisco, CA; *U.S. Public*, pg. 690
Hattox, Brock A., Chief Fin. Officer & Exec. V.P.--National Service Industries, Inc., Atlanta, GA; *U.S. Public*, pg. 1160
Hauer, Frank, Exec. V.P.--Olympia & York Developments Ltd., Toronto, Canada; *Int'l*, pg. 1004
Haugsland, Jack W., Chief Oper. Officer & Exec. V.P.--Greyhound Lines, Inc., Dallas, TX; *U.S. Public*, pg. 765
Haunschild, Harold E., Exec. V.P.-Human Resources & Admin.--Meridian Oil Holding Inc., Houston, TX; *U.S. Public*, pg. 269
Hausen, Larry A., Chief Fin. Officer & Exec. V.P.--Signet Star Reinsurance Company, Florham Park, NJ; *U.S. Public*, pg. 216
Hauser, Gerard, Exec. V.P.-Beverage Packaging Activities--Pechiney S.A., Courbevoie, France; *Int'l*, pg. 1027
Hauss, Dieter, Exec. V.P.--Stocko Corp., Carlstadt, NJ; *Int'l*, pg. 1301
Haverty, Michael R., Exec. V.P.--Kansas City Southern Industries, Inc., Kansas City, MO; *U.S. Public*, pg. 943
Hawes, Ken, Exec. V.P.-Bus. Opers.--Merit Behavioral Care Corp., Park Ridge, NJ; *U.S. Public*, pg. 1036
Hawk, Robert, Exec. V.P.--Northland Cranberries, Inc., Wisconsin Rapids, WI; *U.S. Public*, pg. 1197
Hawkins, John A., Sr. Exec. V.P.-Private Clients--The Bank of Bermuda Limited, Hamilton, Bermuda; *Int'l*, pg. 150
Hawkins, John R., Exec. V.P. & Sec.--Hawkins Chemical, Inc., Minneapolis, MN; *U.S. Public*, pg. 800
Hawkins, Ralph W., Exec. V.P. & Mgr.-Community Banking--First Security Bank of Idaho, N.A., Boise, ID; *U.S. Public*, pg. 637
Hawthorne, Nancy, Exec. V.P.--MediaOne, Boston, MA; *U.S. Public*, pg. 1688
Hawver, Daniel, Sr. Exec. V.P.-Property & Casualty & Prod. & Service--Willis Corroon Corp. of Illinois, Chicago, IL; *Int'l*, pg. 1506
Hayashi, Junichi, Exec.Dir.--Thai Orix Leasing Co., Ltd., Bangkok, Thailand; *Int'l*, pg. 677

Hayashi, Junji, Exec. V.P.--Kawasaki Heavy Industries, Ltd., Kobe, Japan; *Int'l*, pg. 725
Hayashi, Keiichi, Exec. V.P.--Alyeska Seafoods, Inc., Unalaska, AK; *Int'l*, pg. 845
Hayashi, Sin-Ichi, Exec. V.P.--Rohto Pharmaceutical Co., Osaka, Japan; *Int'l*, pg. 1126
Hayata, Toshio, Exec. V.P.--Nippon Telegraph and Telephone Corporation, Tokyo, Japan; *Int'l*, pg. 940
Hayden, Jack N., Exec. V.P.--Technology Solutions Company (TSC), Chicago, IL; *U.S. Public*, pg. 1564
Hayden, John W., Sr. Exec. V.P.--The Midland Company, Cincinnati, OH; *U.S. Public*, pg. 1110
Hayes, Arthur, Grp. Exec. Dir.--Royal & Sun Alliance Insurance Group plc, London, United Kingdom; *Int'l*, pg. 1130
Hayes, Derek, Exec. Dir.-Retail Opers. Europe & Intl. Franchise--Marks & Spencer PLC, London, United Kingdom; *Int'l*, pg. 842
Hayes, Glenn W., Exec. V.P.--First National Bank of Commerce, New Orleans, LA; *U.S. Public*, pg. 629
Hayes, John D., Exec. V.P.-Global Adv.--American Express Company, New York, NY; *U.S. Public*, pg. 73
Hayes, John J., Exec. V.P.-Mktg.--DM Management Company, Hingham, MA; *U.S. Public*, pg. 473
Hayes, Michael H., Exec. V.P.--Chartwell Re Corporation, Stamford, CT; *U.S. Public*, pg. 336
Hayes, Michael H., Exec. V.P.--The Insurance Corp. of New York, New York, NY; *U.S. Public*, pg. 336
Hayhurst, James B., Jr., Exec. V.P.--United Bankshares, Inc., Parkersburg, WV; *U.S. Public*, pg. 1674
Haynes, John E., Chief Fin. Officer & Exec. V.P.--Glendale Federal Bank, F.S.B., Glendale, CA; *U.S. Public*, pg. 747
Hays, Russell, Exec. V.P. & Pres.-Hospital Bus.--Nellcor Puritan Bennett Incorporated, Pleasanton, CA; *U.S. Public*, pg. 1039
Hayward, John C., Exec. V.P.-Transportation--Michael Baker Corporation, Pittsburgh, PA; *U.S. Public*, pg. 168
Hazarian, Jeffrey R., Chief Fin. Officer & Exec. V.P.--Tenera, Inc., San Francisco, CA; *U.S. Public*, pg. 1576
Heaberlin, David A., Chief Fin. Officer & Exec. V.P.--Bay View Capital Corporation, San Mateo, CA; *U.S. Public*, pg. 197
Head, Christopher A., Exec. V.P., Gen. Counsel & Sec.--Comptek Research, Inc., Buffalo, NY; *U.S. Public*, pg. 419
Head, J. Michael, Exec. V.P.--Mark VII, Inc., Memphis, TN; *U.S. Public*, pg. 1046
Headrick, Jon C., Exec. V.P.-Investments--Ameritas Life Insurance Corp., Lincoln, NE; *U.S. Private*, pg. 65
Headrick, Michael S., Exec. V.P.--Sysco Food Services of South Florida, Inc., Miami, FL; *U.S. Public*, pg. 1552
Heagy, Linda, Exec. V.P.-Service Prods.--ABN/LaSalle North America Inc., Chicago, IL; *Int'l*, pg. 11
Healey, Dennis W., Exec. V.P.--Techdyne, Inc., Hialeah, FL; *U.S. Public*, pg. 1080
Healey, James E., Chief Fin. Officer & Exec. V.P.--Nabisco Inc., Parsippany, NJ; *U.S. Public*, pg. 1355
Healy, Daniel M., Chief Fin. Officer & Exec. V.P.--North Fork Bancorporation, Inc., Melville, NY; *U.S. Public*, pg. 1194
Healy, Daniel M., Chief Fin. Officer & Exec. V.P.--North Fork Bank, Mattituck, NY; *U.S. Public*, pg. 1194
Healy, E. Peter, Chief Fin. Officer, Exec. V.P. & Sec.--Barry's Jewelers, Inc., Monrovia, CA; *U.S. Public*, pg. 192
Healy, Pat G., Exec. V.P.-Fin. & Admin.--NFO Research, Inc., Greenwich, CT; *U.S. Public*, pg. 1146
Healy, William J., Exec. V.P. & Controller--Summit Bancorp, Princeton, NJ; *U.S. Public*, pg. 1527
Healy, William J., Exec. V.P.--First Valley Corporation, Bethlehem, PA; *U.S. Public*, pg. 1528
Hearnburg, William V., Exec. V.P.-Legal--Southwire Company, Carrollton, GA; *U.S. Private*, pg. 1019
Hearne, Craig, Exec. V.P.--CDB Infotec Inc., Santa Ana, CA; *U.S. Private*, pg. 193
Heath, Rob, Sr. V.P.--CareerTrack Inc., Boulder, CO; *U.S. Public*, pg. 1555
Heatherly, David A., Exec. V.P.-Prod. Devel./Claims--Foremost Corporation of America, Caledonia, MI; *U.S. Public*, pg. 667
Heatwole, Milton W., Exec. V.P. & Treas.--Shenandoah Mfg. Co. Inc., Harrisonburg, VA; *U.S. Private*, pg. 992
Heavener, Michael P., Exec. V.P.--CoreStates Bank, N.A., Philadelphia, PA; *U.S. Public*, pg. 446
Hechler, H.W., Exec. V.P.--Braas GmbH, Oberursell, Germany; *Int'l*, pg. 1091
Hedberg, Douglas P., Exec. V.P. & Managing Dir.--Washington Square Advisors, Inc., Minneapolis, MN; *U.S. Public*, pg. 1376
Hedenstedt, Anders, Exec. V.P.--Vattenfall AB, Stockholm, Sweden; *Int'l*, pg. 1452
Hedrick, K.L., Exec. V.P.-Upstream--Phillips Petroleum Company, Bartlesville, OK; *U.S. Public*, pg. 1290
Heeder, Frank, Exec. V.P.--Ward Products Corporation, North Brunswick, NJ; *U.S. Private*, pg. 1149
Heekin, James R., Exec. V.P. & Reg. Dir.-North America--McCann-Erickson Worldwide, New York, NY; *U.S. Public*, *pg. 909*
Heeps, John, Exec. V.P.-Small Business Banking--Bank of Boston Connecticut, Hartford, CT; *U.S. Public*, pg. 184
Heffer, John M., Exec. V.P.--Republic National Bank of New York, New York, NY; *U.S. Public*, pg. 1380
Hefferman, Brian, Exec. V.P. & Global New Bus. Dir.--J. Walter Thompson Company, New York, NY; *Int'l*, pg. 1483
Hefter, Leonard R., Exec. V.P.--Jefferies & Company, Inc., Los Angeles, CA; *U.S. Public*, pg. 925
Hefton, Carl W., Exec. V.P.--Ketchum, Inc., Pittsburgh, PA; *U.S. Private*, pg. 617
Hegemann, Werner, Exec. V.P.--H. Krantz-TKT GmbH, Bergisch Gladbach, Germany; *Int'l*, pg. 399
Hegener, Karen C., Exec. V.P.--Peterson's Guides, Inc., Princeton, NJ; *U.S. Private*, pg. 858
Heggen, Arthur W., Exec. V.P. & Sec.--American Bankers Insurance Group, Inc., Miami, FL; *U.S. Public*, pg. 67
Hegquist, John, Exec. V.P. & Chief Creative Officer-GHG--Grey Healthcare Group, New York, NY; *U.S. Public*, pg. 765
Heicklen, Steve, Exec. V.P. & Mngmt. Supvr.--Carrafiello, Diehl & Associates, Inc., Irvington, NY; *U.S. Private*, pg. 215
Heidecorn, David, Chief Fin. Officer & Exec. V.P.--Alarmguard Holdings, Inc., Orange, CT; *U.S. Public*, pg. 35
Heilala, John A., Exec. V.P.-Chloralkali--Vulcan Chemicals, Birmingham, AL; *U.S. Public*, pg. 1725
Heim, Greg, Chief Exec. Officer--Modern Drop Forge Co., Blue Island, IL; *U.S. Private*, pg. 754
Heiman, Dr. Frederic P., Chief Tech. Officer & Exec. V.P.--Symbol Technologies, Inc., Holtsville, NY; *U.S. Public*, pg. 1546
Heiman, Mark, Exec. V.P.--Standard Textile Co., Inc., Cincinnati, OH; *U.S. Private*, pg. 1032
Heine, Spencer H., Exec. V.P. & Gen. Counsel--Montgomery Ward & Co., Inc., Chicago, IL; *U.S. Private*, pg. 758
Heine, Wolfgang, Chief Oper. Officer & Exec. V.P.--Voith Hydro, Inc., York, PA; *Int'l*, pg. 1473
Heiner, Dennis G., Exec. V.P. & Pres.-Security Hardware Grp.--The Black & Decker Corporation, Towson, MD; *U.S. Public*, pg. 233
Heinrich, H.E., Exec. V.P.--Apex Broach & Machine Co., Detroit, MI; *U.S. Private*, pg. 77
Heinrich, William R., Exec. V.P.--Ausco Products, Inc., Benton Harbor, MI; *U.S. Private*, pg. 299
Heintel, Carl C., Jr., Exec. V.P.--Keycorp, Cleveland, OH; *U.S. Public*, pg. 954
Heinz, Edward, Exec. V.P.--Bell Flavors & Fragrances, Northbrook, IL; *U.S. Private*, pg. 131
Heinz, Jim, Exec. V.P.--Colle & McVoy Marketing Communications, Minneapolis, MN; *U.S. Private*, pg. 252
Heister, S. Bruce, Exec. V.P.-Asia/Pacific--Alcan Aluminium Limited, Montreal, Canada; *Int'l*, pg. 50
Heitner, Philip, Exec. V.P.-Research--The Nesbitt Thomson Corporation Limited, Toronto, Canada; *Int'l*, pg. 153
Helf, Peter J., Chief Oper. Officer & Exec. V.P.--Marcus Restaurants Inc., Milwaukee, WI; *U.S. Public*, pg. 1044
Helfand, Michael D., Chief Fin. Officer & Exec. V.P.--World Color Press, Inc., Greenwich, CT; *U.S. Public*, pg. 1778
Helfrich, Thomas E., Exec. V.P.-Human Resources--Keycorp, Cleveland, OH; *U.S. Public*, pg. 954
Heller, Andrew T., Exec. V.P.--Marquette Coppersmithing Co., Inc., Philadelphia, PA; *U.S. Private*, pg. 706
Heller, Francie, Exec. V.P.--MBIA Municipal Investors Service Corporation, Armonk, NY; *U.S. Public*, pg. 1023
Heller, H. Robert, Exec. V.P.--Fair, Isaac and Company, Inc., San Rafael, CA; *U.S. Public*, pg. 609
Hellstrom, Kurt, Exec. V.P.-Radio Communications--Telefonaktiebolaget LM Ericsson, Stockholm, Sweden; *Int'l*, pg. 1363
Helmstetter, Richard C., Sr. Exec. V.P. & Chief of New Prods.--Callaway Golf Company, Carlsbad, CA; *U.S. Public*, pg. 294
Helvey, J.L., Chief Fin. Officer, Exec. V.P. & Investor Rels. Officer--Golden West Financial Corporation, Oakland, CA; *U.S. Public*, pg. 750
Hemingway, W. David, Exec. V.P.-Capital Markets & Investments--Zions Bancorporation, Salt Lake City, UT; *U.S. Public*, pg. 1792
Hemingway, W. David, Exec. V.P.-Investments--Zions First National Bank, Salt Lake City, UT; *U.S. Public*, pg. 1793
Hemmer, Gary D., Exec. V.P.-Fin. Markets--Magna Group, Inc., Saint Louis, MO; *U.S. Public*, pg. 1037
Hempson, David P., Exec. V.P.-Opers.--Marietta Corporation, Cortland, NY; *U.S. Private*, pg. 702
Hemrich, Kurt J., Sr. Exec. V.P.--Fender Musical Instruments, Scottsdale, AZ; *U.S. Private*, pg. 400
Hemsley, Stephen J., Sr. Exec. V.P.--United HealthCare Corporation, Minnetonka, MN; *U.S. Public*, pg. 1677
Henderson, Alan C., Chief Fin. Officer, Exec. V.P. & Sec.--RehabCare Group, Inc., Saint Louis, MO; *U.S. Public*, pg. 1373
Henderson, David R., Chief Oper. Officer & Exec. V.P.--EEX Corporation, Houston, TX; *U.S. Public*, pg. 542
Henderson, Donald E., Chief Exec. Officer & Exec. V.P.--United Farm Family Life Insurance Co., Indianapolis, IN; *U.S. Private*, pg. 1122
Henderson, Geneva, Exec. V.P.-Florida-Jacksonville--Lat Purser & Associates, Charlotte, NC; *U.S. Private*, pg. 896
Henderson, J.C., Exec. V.P.--Davis Electrical Constructors, Inc., Greenville, SC; *U.S. Private*, pg. 315
Henderson, Jim, Exec. V.P.-Sls. & Mktg.--BGF Industries Inc., Greensboro, NC; *U.S. Private*, pg. 106
Henderson, Jim, Exec. V.P.--Poe & Brown, Inc., Daytona Beach, FL; *U.S. Public*, pg. 1312
Henderson, Martha, Exec. V.P.-Entertainment Banking--City National Corporation, Beverly Hills, CA; *U.S. Public*, pg. 380
Henderson, Paul, Chief Fin. Officer & Exec. V.P.-Fin. & Admin.--Cott Corporation, Pointe-Claire, Canada; *Int'l*, pg. 337
Henderson, Roger, Exec. V.P.--Chyron Corp., Melville, NY; *Int'l*, pg. 1372
Henderson, Terry, Exec. V.P.--Mahlo America Inc., Spartanburg, SC; *Int'l*, pg. 830
Hendler, D., Exec. V.P.--Leviton Mfg. Co., Inc., Little Neck, NY; *U.S. Private*, pg. 663
Hendrix, John A., Exec. V.P. & Gen. Mgr.--Carolina Tractor & Equipment Co., Charlotte, NC; *U.S. Private*, pg. 214
Hendrix, Robert L., Exec. V.P.-Opers.--Pilgrim's Pride Corporation, Pittsburg, TX; *U.S. Public*, pg. 1296
Heng, Raymond, Exec. V.P.--Turbomeca Microturbo Division, Bordes, France; *Int'l*, pg. 786
Henigson, David, Exec. V.P.--Value Line Publishing, New York, NY; *U.S. Private*, pg. 137
Henkel, Claes, Exec. V.P.--Dun & Bradstreet Ltd., High Wycombe, United Kingdom; *U.S. Public*, pg. 536
Henley, Jeffrey O., Chief Fin. Officer & Exec. V.P.--Oracle Corporation, Redwood City, CA; *U.S. Public*, pg. 1227
Hennessey, Frank M., Exec. V.P.--Masco Corporation, Taylor, MI; *U.S. Public*, pg. 1052
Hennie, Robert A., Exec. V.P.--R&R Advertising, Las Vegas, NV; *U.S. Private*, pg. 902
Henrikson, C. Robert, Sr. Exec. V.P.-Pensions--Metropolitan Life Insurance Co., New York, NY; *U.S. Private*, pg. 737
Henry, Brian C., Chief Fin. Officer & Exec. V.P.--Cincinnati Bell Telephone, Cincinnati, OH; *U.S. Public*, pg. 367
Henry, Edwin P., Exec. V.P.--First Commercial Bank, N.A., Little Rock, AR; *U.S. Public*, pg. 630
Henry, Linda, Exec. V.P.-Alcone Interactive--Alcone Marketing Group, Irvine, CA; *U.S. Public*, pg. 1223
Henry, Paul J., Exec. V.P.-Tech. Services--IMI Cornelius Inc. (MN), Anoka, MN; *Int'l*, pg. 646
Henry, Susie, Exec. V.P.--Bass Pro Shops, Inc., Springfield, MO; *U.S. Private*, pg. 122
Henseler, Gerald A., Chief Fin. Officer & Exec. V.P.--Banta Corporation, Menasha, WI; *U.S. Public*, pg. 187
Hepburn, Victor C., Exec. V.P.--Jannock Limited, Toronto, Canada; *Int'l*, pg. 698
Herb, Ike, Chief Oper. Officer & Sr. V.P.--Hickory Farms, Inc., Maumee, OH; *U.S. Private*, pg. 525
Herbold, Robert J., Chief Oper. Officer & Exec. V.P.--Microsoft Corporation, Redmond, WA; *U.S. Public*, pg. 1107
Herbst, James, Exec. V.P.--Kendale Industries, Inc., Valley View, OH; *U.S. Private*, pg. 614
Herbst, Thomas A., Exec. V.P.--Marquette Bancshares Inc., Minneapolis, MN; *U.S. Private*, pg. 706
Herchin, Michel, Exec. V.P.-Indus. & Social Affairs--Dassault Aviation Group, Vaucresson, France; *Int'l*, pg. 383
Heren, Dieter E., Exec. V.P.-Credit Admin.--Huntington Bancshares Inc., Columbus, OH; *U.S. Public*, pg. 849
Herencia, Roberto R., Exec. V.P.--Banco Popular de Puerto Rico, San Juan, PR; *U.S. Public*, pg. 175
Herencia, Roberto R., Exec. V.P.--BanPonce Corporation, Hato Rey, PR; *U.S. Public*, pg. 176
Hering, Kurt, Exec. V.P.--Bayerische Landesbank Girozentrale - Nuremberg Branch, Nuremberg, Germany; *Int'l*, pg. 176
Herlinger, Charles, Chief Fin. Officer & Exec. V.P.--Siemens Energy & Automation Inc., Alpharetta, GA; *Int'l*, pg. 1245
Herman, Howard L., Exec. V.P.--FASTRAC Systems, Inc., San Bruno, CA; *U.S. Public*, pg. 1158
Herman, Howard L., Exec. V.P.--FASTRAC Systems, Inc.-Insurance Agent & Broker, South San Francisco, CA; *U.S. Public*, pg. 1158
Hermsen, John, Exec. V.P.--Fabri-Centers of America, Inc., Hudson, OH; *U.S. Public*, pg. 609
Hernandez, Robert M., Chm. Bd., Chief Fin. Officer & Exec. V.P.-Fin./USX Corp.--RMI Titanium Company, Niles, OH; *U.S. Public*, pg. 1662
Herndon, Peter, Exec. V.P.--Haseko (Hawaii) Inc., Honolulu, HI; *Int'l*, pg. 600
Herr, Henry D., Chief Fin. Officer & Exec. V.P.--American Healthcorp Inc., Nashville, TN; *U.S. Public*, pg. 78
Herrema, Donald J., Sr. Exec. V.P.--Bessemer Group, Inc., New York, NY; *U.S. Private*, pg. 139
Herrmann, Mary, Exec. V.P.--Ammirati, Puris & Lintas, Inc., New York, NY; *U.S. Private*, pg. 66
Hershaft, Victor, Exec. V.P.--PAXAR Corporation, White Plains, NY; *U.S. Public*, pg. 1266
Hershberger, Mary, Exec. V.P.--EFG Technologies Inc., Saint Paul, MN; *U.S. Public*, pg. 1679
Hershfield, Lawrence S., Exec. V.P.--Leucadia National Corporation, New York, NY; *U.S. Public*, pg. 989
Herskowitz, Ron, Exec. V.P.--Refractive Centers International, Waltham, MA; *U.S. Public*, pg. 1529
Hertel, Geoffrey M., Chief Fin. Officer & Exec. V.P.-Fin. & Admin.--Tetra Technologies, Woodlands, TX; *U.S. Public*, *pg. 1582*
Hertwig, James R., Exec. V.P.--Landstar Holding, Shelton, CT; *U.S. Public*, pg. 978
Herzog, Earl, Exec. V.P. & Media Dir.--Campbell Mithun Esty, Minneapolis, MN; *U.S. Private*, pg. 204
Heschel, Michael S., Chief Info. Officer & Exec. V.P.--The Kroger Co., Cincinnati, OH; *U.S. Public*, pg. 967
Heslet, Fred, Dr., Exec. V.P.-Quality & H.R.--Genus Inc., Sunnyvale, CA; *U.S. Public*, pg. 732
Heslop, James G., Exec. V.P.-Metro Rail Banking--Compass Bank, Birmingham, AL; *U.S. Public*, pg. 418
Hespe, Thomas J., Exec. V.P.-Clinical Sls.--Lab One, Lenexa, KS; *U.S. Public*, pg. 1449
Hess, Terry D., Exec. V.P. & Chief Credit Officer--Glendale Federal Bank, F.S.B., Glendale, CA; *U.S. Public*, pg. 747
Hess, William R., Exec. V.P.-Mktg. & Sls.--Farmers and Traders Life Insurance Co., Syracuse, NY; *U.S. Private*, pg. 394
Hesse, Daniel, Pres.-AT&T Wireless Services & Exec. V.P.--AT&T Corporation, Basking Ridge, NJ; *U.S. Public*, pg. 10
Hesse, James D., Chief Oper. Officer & Exec. V.P.-Commercial--WHX Corporation, New York, NY; *U.S. Public*, pg. 1726
Hesse, Selwyn, Vice Chm., Exec. V.P. & Sec.--Automatic Equipment Mfg. Co., Pender, NE; *U.S. Private*, pg. 101
Heuer, Richard, Exec. V.P.--Bradley Real Estate, Inc., Northbrook, IL; *U.S. Public*, pg. 250
Hewat, W. Brian, Exec. V.P.--Northern Telecom Limited, Brampton, Canada; *Int'l*, pg. 968
Hewgley, William M., Jr., Exec. V.P.-Sls. & Mktg.--American Manufacturing Company, Chattanooga, TN; *U.S. Private*, pg. 58
Heywood, J. C., Exec. V.P.--Beneficial Management Corporation of America & Affiliated Corps., Wilmington, DE; *U.S. Public*, pg. 211
Heywood, J.C., Exec. V.P.--Beneficial Management Corporation, Peapack, NJ; *U.S. Public*, pg. 211
Hi Yu, Kun, Exec. V.P.--LG Group, Seoul, Korea; *Int'l*, pg. 778

Hickey, Brian E., Exec. V.P.--First Empire State Corporation, Buffalo, NY; *U.S. Public*, pg. 631
Hickey, Brian E., Exec. V.P.--Manufacturers & Traders Trust Company, Buffalo, NY; *U.S. Public*, pg. 631
Hickey, David M., Exec. V.P.-Mfg. & Intl. Opers.--Corrpro Companies, Inc., Medina, OH; *U.S. Public*, pg. 451
Hickey, Kevin, Exec. V.P.-Opers.--Oxford Health Plans Inc., Norwalk, CT; *U.S. Public*, pg. 1238
Hicks, Lawrence R., Exec. V.P.-Sls. & Mdsg.--Handleman Company, Troy, MI; *U.S. Public*, pg. 779
Hidaka, M., Exec. V.P.--Nippon Kaiji Kyokai, Tokyo, Japan; *Int'l*, pg. 934
Hidayatallah, Munawar H., Chief Fin. Officer & Exec. V.P.--IRI International Corporation, Houston, TX; *U.S. Public*, pg. 858
Hiemenz, Duane, Chief Oper. Officer & Exec. V.P.-Store Opers.--Michaels Stores, Inc., Irving, TX; *U.S. Public*, pg. 1104
Hienonen, Jukka, Exec. V.P.-Intl. Opers.--Stockmann Department Store Div., Helsinki, Finland; *Int'l*, pg. 1301
Higashisono, Motomasa, Exec. Dir.--Isuzu Motors Limited, Tokyo, Japan; *Int'l*, pg. 692
Higashiyama, Yoshihiko, Exec. Dir.--Minolta Co., Ltd., Osaka, Japan; *Int'l*, pg. 869
Higgins, John J., Exec. V.P. & Chief Admin. Officer--Bank of America Illinois, Chicago, IL; *U.S. Public*, pg. 180
Higgins, Michael J., Chief Fin. Officer & Exec. V.P.--Service America Corporation, Stamford, CT; *U.S. Private*, pg. 986
Higgins, Nancy, Exec. V.P. & Gen. Mgr.--Chapman Warwick Inc., San Diego, CA; *U.S. Private*, pg. 1152
Highet, Mac, Exec. V.P.-Corp. Devel.--Reed Elsevier Inc., New York, NY; *Int'l*, pg. 1095
Hightower, George H., Jr., Exec. V.P.-Sls. & Adv.--Thomaston Mills, Inc., Thomaston, GA; *U.S. Public*, pg. 1599
Hikida, Akira, Exec. V.P.--Kyushu Electric Power Co., Inc., Fukuoka, Japan; *Int'l*, pg. 778
Hikida, Akira, Exec. V.P.--Meiji Milk Products Co., Ltd., Tokyo, Japan; *Int'l*, pg. 855
Hildebrand, Loren, Exec. V.P.-Sls.--Galoob Toys, Inc., South San Francisco, CA; *U.S. Public*, pg. 698
Hildebrand, Phillip, Exec. V.P.-Sls. & Mktg.--New York Life Insurance Company, New York, NY; *U.S. Private*, pg. 794
Hildon, Michael, Exec. V.P.--Commercial Testing & Engineering Co., Lombard, IL; *Int'l*, pg. 1153
Hiles, Thomas M., Exec. V.P.--Cott Corporation, Pointe-Claire, Canada; *Int'l*, pg. 337
Hill, Alan R., Exec. V.P.-Corp. Devel.--Barrick Gold Corporation, Toronto, Canada; *Int'l*, pg. 168
Hill, Alden E., Exec. V.P.--Rogers N.K. Seed Co., Boise, ID; *Int'l*, pg. 974
Hill, C.T., Jr., Corp. Exec. V.P. & Sr. Credit Officer--Crestar Financial Corporation, Richmond, VA; *U.S. Public*, pg. 458
Hill, Gary M., Chief Fin. Officer & Exec. V.P.--Information Resources, Inc., Chicago, IL; *U.S. Public*, pg. 875
Hill, Kenneth E., Exec. V.P.--Poe & Brown, Inc., Daytona Beach, FL; *U.S. Public*, pg. 1312
Hill, Larry D., Sr. Exec. V.P.--Icicle Seafoods, Inc., Seattle, WA; *U.S. Private*, pg. 556
Hill, Melanie, Exec. V.P. & Mng. Dir.--Ackerman McQueen, Inc., Tulsa, OK; *U.S. Private*, pg. 13
Hill, P.J., Dr., Exec. V.P.-E & P--Deminex-Deutsche GmbH, Essen, Germany; *Int'l*, pg. 1460
Hill, Richard T., Exec. V.P.--City National Bank of Baton Rouge, Baton Rouge, LA; *U.S. Public*, pg. 629
Hill, Thomas A., Exec. V.P.--Kimray, Inc., Oklahoma City, OK; *U.S. Private*, pg. 620
Hillenmeyer, Jean-Claude, Exec. V.P.--Cementia Holding AG, Zurich, Switzerland; *Int'l*, pg. 790
Hilliard, M., Exec. V.P. & Mng. Dir.--BBDO Canada, Toronto, Canada; *U.S. Private*, pg. 104
Hillman, Sandra, Exec. V.P. & Pub. Rels. Dir.--Trahan, Burden & Charles, Inc., Baltimore, MD; *U.S. Private*, pg. 1095
Hillmann, Robert, Exec. V.P.--Centex Real Estate Corp./Centex Homes, Dallas, TX; *U.S. Public*, pg. 323
Hilton, David C., Exec. V.P.--The Foothill Group, Inc., Los Angeles, CA; *U.S. Public*, pg. 1201
Himelfarb, Richard J., Sr. Exec. V.P.--Legg Mason, Inc., Baltimore, MD; *U.S. Public*, pg. 984
Hinckley, Bruce, Chief Fin. Officer & Exec. V.P.--Iwerks Entertainment, Burbank, CA; *U.S. Public*, pg. 915
Hinderer, H. William III, Chief Fin. Officer & Exec. V.P.-Fin. & Admin.--Tacony Corporation, Fenton, MO; *U.S. Private*, pg. 1066
Hinds, John A., Exec. V.P.--VeriFone, Inc., Redwood City, CA; *U.S. Public*, pg. 815
Hines, Barbara, Exec. V.P.--Porter Novelli International, New York, NY; *U.S. Public*, pg. 1224
Hiniker, Paul, Exec. V.P.--Argosy Electronics, Inc., Eden Prairie, MN; *U.S. Private*, pg. 81
Hinkamp, James B., II, Exec. V.P.--Chemical Bank West, Cadillac, MI; *U.S. Public*, pg. 345
Hinkle, Allan, Exec. V.P. & Chief Actuary--Provident Mutual Life Insurance Co., Berwyn, PA; *U.S. Private*, pg. 891
Hintz, Donald C., Chief Nuclear Officer & Exec. V.P.--Entergy Corporation, New Orleans, LA; *U.S. Public*, pg. 585
Hipp, Fred, Exec. V.P.--Curtin & Pease/Peneco, Inc, Dunedin, FL; *U.S. Public*, pg. 1306
Hiraga, Sumio, Sr. Exec. V.P.--Kodansha International Ltd, Tokyo, Japan; *Int'l*, pg. 742
Hirao, Shunichi, Exec. V.P.--Takenaka Corporation, Osaka, Japan; *Int'l*, pg. 1351
Hirashima, Osamu, Exec. V.P.--Taisei Corporation, Tokyo, Japan; *Int'l*, pg. 1347
Hirata, Hideo, Exec. V.P.--Tomen Corporation, Osaka, Japan; *Int'l*, pg. 1395
Hirata, Tatsuo, Exec. V.P.--Nissho Iwai Corporation, Tokyo, Japan; *Int'l*, pg. 946
Hiratam, Tsuyoshi, Exec. V.P. & Gen. Mgr.--Mitsubishi Electric Corporation, Tokyo, Japan; *Int'l*, pg. 872
Hirl, J. Roger, Exec. V.P.--Occidental Petroleum Corporation, Los Angeles, CA; *U.S. Public*, pg. 1210
Hirsch, David J., Exec. V.P.--Charles Leonard, Inc., Glendale, NY; *U.S. Private*, pg. 660
Hirsch, Sid, Exec. V.P. & Controller--Honey Fashions Ltd., New York, NY; *U.S. Private*, pg. 537
Hirschfeld, Dennis C., Chief Fin. Officer & Exec. V.P.--Hirschfeld, Inc., San Angelo, TX; *U.S. Private*, pg. 530
Hirshberg, Eric, Exec. V.P. & Creative Dir.-L.A.--Deutsch LA, Santa Monica, CA; *U.S. Private*, pg. 328
Hirst, William F., Exec. V.P.--Laramie Tire Distributors Inc., Norristown, PA; *Int'l*, pg. 1312
Hisai, Isao, Exec. V.P.-Berlitz Japan--Berlitz International, Inc., Princeton, NJ; *U.S. Public*, pg. 221
Hislop, Steven J., Chief Oper. Officer & Exec. V.P.--O'Charley's Inc., Nashville, TN; *U.S. Public*, pg. 1211
Hitchcock, T.P., Exec. V.P. & Treas.--Northwestern Energy Corp., Huron, SD; *U.S. Public*, pg. 1201
Hivon, Larry D., Exec. V.P.-Credit, Corporate Bank CIBC--Canadian Imperial Bank of Commerce, Toronto, Canada; *Int'l*, pg. 256
Hlavacek, James H., Chief Oper. Officer & Exec. V.P.--Amtran, Inc., Indianapolis, IN; *U.S. Public*, pg. 106
Ho, D., Exec. Dir.--Swire Pacific Limited, Central, Hong Kong; *Int'l*, pg. 1328
Ho, Eunice, Exec. Dir.--DBS Securities Singapore Pte. Ltd., Singapore, Singapore; *Int'l*, pg. 351
Hoadley, Russell S., Exec. V.P.-Employee & Pub. Rels.--Hibernia Corporation, New Orleans, LA; *U.S. Public*, pg. 825
Hoadley, Thomas C., Chief Oper. Officer & Exec. V.P.--Lanai Co., Ltd., Lanai City, HI; *U.S. Public*, pg. 313
Hoashi, Kenzo, Exec. V.P.--Komatsu Ltd., Tokyo, Japan; *Int'l*, pg. 743
Hobbs, Nancy J., Exec. V.P. & Gen. Mgr.-Southern Calif.--AirTouch Cellular, Walnut Creek, CA; *U.S. Public*, pg. 34
Hobday, Charles W., Exec. V.P. & Gen. Mgr.--Lancaster Malleable Castings Company, Lancaster, PA; *U.S. Private*, pg. 645
Hobratschk, M. Glenn, Chief Fin. Officer & Exec. V.P.--The Austin Company, Cleveland, OH; *U.S. Private*, pg. 99
Hobson, Andrew, Exec. V.P.--Univision Ltd. Partnership, New York, NY; *U.S. Private*, pg. 230
Hochhauser, Richard M., Exec. V.P.--Harte-Hanks Communications, Inc., San Antonio, TX; *U.S. Public*, pg. 793
Hodapp, Don J., Chief Fin. Officer & Exec. V.P.--Hormel Foods Corp., Austin, MN; *U.S. Public*, pg. 840
Hodge, Allan, Exec. V.P. & Treas.--Foster's Brewing Group, Toronto, Canada; *Int'l*, pg. 501
Hodges, Bill, Exec. V.P. & Gen. Mgr.-Discover Card--NOVUS Services, Inc., Riverwoods, IL; *U.S. Public*, pg. 1132
Hodges, Gene R., Exec. V.P.-Customer Opers.--Georgia Power Co., Atlanta, GA; *U.S. Public*, pg. 1490
Hodges, Tom, Exec. V.P.--Chicago Title & Trust Co., Chicago, IL; *U.S. Public*, pg. 42
Hodges, Tom, Exec. V.P.--Chicago Title Insurance Co., Chicago, IL; *U.S. Public*, pg. 42
Hodgkins, Chuck, Exec. V.P.--Stewart Smith Specialty Risks, Inc., Southfield, MI; *Int'l*, pg. 1508
Hodgman, Jeffrey J., Exec. V.P.--Metropolitan Life Insurance Co., New York, NY; *U.S. Private*, pg. 737
Hodgson, R. Brian, Exec. V.P.--Consolidated Carma Corporation, Calgary, Canada; *Int'l*, pg. 229
Hodgson, R.L., Sr. V.P.--Kelley Advertising Inc., Toronto, Canada; *U.S. Public*, pg. 765
Hoefle, John G., Exec. V.P.--Overland Transportation System, Inc., Indianapolis, IN; *Int'l*, pg. 1469
Hoel, Pat, Chief Oper. Officer & Exec. V.P.--Baltimore Stationery Co./Total Office, Baltimore, MD; *U.S. Private*, pg. 113
Hoenig, Bruce, Exec. V.P. & Plng. Dir.--Western International Media Corporation, Los Angeles, CA; *U.S. Private*, pg. 1165
Hoenmans, Paul J., Exec. V.P.--Mobil Oil Corporation, Fairfax, VA; *U.S. Public*, pg. 1118
Hoenn, Dominique, Sr. Exec. V.P.--Banque Paribas, Paris, France; *Int'l*, pg. 319
Hofer, Harald, Exec. V.P.--Bayerische Hypotheken-und Wechsel-Bank Aktiengesellschaft, Munich, Germany; *Int'l*, pg. 175
Hoff, George H., Chief Fin. Officer & Exec. V.P.--Sargento Foods Inc., Plymouth, WI; *U.S. Private*, pg. 966
Hoff, Walter M., Exec. V.P.--First Data Corporation, Hackensack, NJ; *U.S. Public*, pg. 630
Hoffeller, Charles L., Exec. V.P.-Real Estate--Grossman's, Inc., Stoughton, MA; *U.S. Private*, pg. 585
Hoffine, Bruce, Exec. V.P.--The Zippertubing Co., Los Angeles, CA; *U.S. Private*, pg. 1207
Hoffman, Alan B., Exec. V.P.-Corp. Logistics--Kimball International, Inc., Jasper, IN; *U.S. Public*, pg. 956
Hoffman, James, Exec. V.P.--IES Industries Inc., Cedar Rapids, IA; *U.S. Public*, pg. 855
Hoffman, James E., Exec. V.P.-Customer Svcs. & Energy Delivery--IES Utilities Inc., Cedar Rapids, IA; *U.S. Public*, pg. 855
Hoffman, James L., Exec. V.P.--First Empire State Corporation, Buffalo, NY; *U.S. Public*, pg. 631
Hoffman, James L., Exec. V.P.--Manufacturers & Traders Trust Company, Buffalo, NY; *U.S. Public*, pg. 631
Hoffman, Linda A., Exec. V.P.-Lending Law--Hibernia Corporation, New Orleans, LA; *U.S. Public*, pg. 825
Hoffman, Mark, Exec. V.P.--Claire's Boutiques, Inc., Pembroke Pines, FL; *U.S. Public*, pg. 381
Hoffman, Richard R., Chief Oper. Officer & Exec. V.P.--Alamco, Inc., Charleston, WV; *U.S. Public*, pg. 403
Hoffmann, Christoph L., Exec. V.P.-Law & Corp. Admin. & Sec.--Raytheon Company, Lexington, MA; *U.S. Public*, pg. 1364
Hofmeister, Ernst K., Exec. V.P.--Norddeutsche Landesbank (NORD/LB), Hannover, Germany; *Int'l*, pg. 957
Hofmeister, Ronald T., Exec. V.P.--Medicine Shoppe International, Inc., Saint Louis, MO; *U.S. Public*, pg. 304
Hogan, Lee W., Exec. V.P.--Houston Industries Incorporated, Houston, TX; *U.S. Public*, pg. 842
Hogan, Paul, Chief Oper. Officer--Overseas Service Corporation, West Palm Beach, FL; *U.S. Private*, pg. 823
Hogan, Robert N.D., Exec. V.P.-Credit, Fin. & Mktg. Svcs.--Hudson's Bay Company, Toronto, Canada; *Int'l*, pg. 637
Hogan, Thomas D., Grp. Exec. V.P.-Crestar Investment Grp.--Crestar Financial Corporation, Richmond, VA; *U.S. Public*, pg. 458
Hogan, Thomas D., Grp. Exec. V.P.-Trust & Investment Mgmt.--Crestar Bank, Richmond, VA; *U.S. Public*, pg. 458
Hogan, Timothy K., Exec. V.P.--Sysco Food Services of Minnesota, Inc., Saint Paul, MN; *U.S. Public*, pg. 1551
Hogan, William, Exec. V.P.-Sls. & Mktg.--Clestra Hauserman, Inc., Solon, OH; *Int'l*, pg. 569
Hoglund, William E., Exec. V.P.-Corp. Affairs & Staff Support Grp.--General Motors Corporation, Detroit, MI; *U.S. Public*, pg. 718
Hohage, Frederick, Exec. V.P. & Pres.-Sls. Grp.--Robert Bosch Corporation, Broadview, IL; *Int'l*, pg. 204
Hohlefelder, Walter, Dr., Exec. V.P.--Veba AG, Dusseldorf, Germany; *Int'l*, pg. 1454
Hokin, Richard, Exec.V.P.--Century America Corporation, Chicago, IL; *U.S. Private*, pg. 225
Hokura, Yutaka, Exec. V.P. & Gen. Mgr.--Nippon Steel U.S.A., Inc., Chicago, IL; *Int'l*, pg. 940
Holbert, Daniel, Exec. V.P.--Moss Telecommunications Services, Grand Rapids, MI; *U.S. Private*, pg. 763
Holcombe, Hubert, Jr., Chief Oper. Officer & Exec. V.P.--Arrowhead Mills, Inc., Hereford, TX; *U.S. Private*, pg. 86
Holcombe, Mary Lou, Asst. V.P. & Sec.--Andal Corp., New York, NY; *U.S. Public*, pg. 111
Holcombe, Stephen L., Chief Fin. Officer & Exec. V.P.--Vanguard Cellular Systems, Inc., Greensboro, NC; *U.S. Public*, pg. 1707
Holdaway, Eugene, Exec. V.P.--Lodestar Energy Inc., Lexington, KY; *U.S. Private*, pg. 672
Holdcroft, John P. Jr., Exec. V.P.--Republic New York Corporation, New York, NY; *U.S. Public*, pg. 1380
Holden, Betsy D., Exec. V.P. & Gen. Mgr.-Kraft Cheese Div.--Kraft Foods Inc., Glenview, IL; *U.S. Public*, pg. 1288
Holden, James P., Exec. V.P.-Sls. & Mktg.--Chrysler Corporation, Auburn Hills, MI; *U.S. Public*, pg. 352
Holden, John S., III, Exec. V.P.--Automatic Machine Products Company, Attleboro, MA; *U.S. Private*, pg. 101
Holder, James T., Exec. V.P., Gen. Counsel & Sec.--Checkers Drive-In Restaurants, Inc., Clearwater, FL; U.S. Public, pg. 342
Holder, Randy, Exec. V.P. & Gen. Counsel--Thrifty Rent-a-Car System, Inc., Tulsa, OK; *U.S. Public*, pg. 354
Holekamp, William F., Exec. V.P.--Enterprise Rent-A-Car Company, Saint Louis, MO; *U.S. Private*, pg. 377
Holland, Darrell M., Exec. V.P.--Pepsi-Cola Bottling Company of Charlotte Inc., Charlotte, NC; *U.S. Private*, pg. 852
Holland, Henry P., Exec. V.P.-Integrated Solutions Grp.--Landmark Graphics Corporation, Houston, TX; *U.S. Public*, pg. 776
Holland, Lewis E., Vice Chm., Chief Fin. Officer & Exec. V.P.--National Commerce Bancorporation, Memphis, TN; *U.S. Public*, pg. 1154
Holland, R. Van Ness, Jr., Chief Fin. Officer, Exec. V.P.-Fin. & Treas.--Wyle Electronics, Irvine, CA; *Int'l*, pg. 1457
Holland, Thomas, Chief Fin. Officer & Exec. V.P.--Transcontinental Realty Investors, Inc., Dallas, TX; *U.S. Public*, pg. 1630
Holland, Thomas A., Chief Fin. Officer, Exec. V.P. & Sec.--Continental Mortgage and Equity Trust, Dallas, TX; *U.S. Public*, pg. 441
Holland, Willis J., Exec. V.P.--United Agri Products Co., Greeley, CO; *U.S. Public*, pg. 426
Hollands, P.F.B., Chief Oper. Officer & Exec. V.P.--A&W Food Services of Canada Inc., North Vancouver, Canada; *Int'l*, pg. 1
Hollerbach, Michael D., Chief Fin. Officer & Exec. V.P.--Pulte Corporation, Bloomfield Hills, MI; *U.S. Public*, pg. 1344
Hollerbach, Michael D., Exec. V.P. & Chief Fin. Officer--Pulte Home Corporation, Bloomfield Hills, MI; *U.S. Public*, pg. 1344
Hollinger, Frederic L., Chief Oper. Officer & Exec. V.P.--Giant Industries Arizona, Inc., Scottsdale, AZ; *U.S. Public*, pg. 742
Hollis, Deborah D., Exec. V.P.-Human Resources & Govt. Rels.--Shoney's, Inc., Nashville, TN; *U.S. Public*, pg. 1467
Hollister, Thomas J., Exec. V.P.--BankBoston Corporation, Boston, MA; *U.S. Public*, pg. 183
Hollmen, Harri, Exec. V.P.--Merita Ltd., Helsinki, Finland; *Int'l*, pg. 858
Holloman, H. James, Exec. V.P.-Trust Div.--BOK Financial Corp., Tulsa, OK; *U.S. Public*, pg. 163
Hollowell, Paul C., Exec. V.P. & Gen. Mgr.-Defense Bus.--Oshkosh Truck Corporation, Oshkosh, WI; *U.S. Public*, pg. 1233
Holman, Robert, Exec. V.P.-Fin.--Reinalt-Thomas Corp., Ann Arbor, MI; *U.S. Private*, pg. 919
Holme of Cheltenham, Lord, Exec. Dir.--Rio Tinto PLC, London, United Kingdom; *Int'l*, pg. 1118
Holmes, Douglas, Chief Fin. Officer & Exec. V.P.--MediaOne, Boston, MA; *U.S. Public*, pg. 1688
Holmes, Frank E., Dr., Exec. V.P., Chief Oper. Officer & Sec.--Semi-Tech Corporation, Markham, Canada; *Int'l*, pg. 1220
Holmes, Jay T., Chief Admin. Officer & Exec. V.P.--Bausch & Lomb Incorporated, Rochester, NY; *U.S. Public*, pg. 194
Holmes, John, Exec. V.P., Mktg. Dir. & Sec.--Paradigm Communications, Tampa, FL; *U.S. Private*, pg. 838
Holmes, John E., Exec. V.P. & Pres.-JWT/Latin America & Caribbean--J. Walter Thompson Company, New York, NY; *Int'l*, pg. 1483

Holmes, Paul, Exec. V.P.-Mortgage Banking--Mellon Bank Corporation, Pittsburgh, PA; *U.S. Public*, pg. 1084
Holmes, Robert, Exec. V.P.-SPE Music Group--TriStar Pictures, Culver City, CA; *Int'l*, pg. 1283
Holmson, Cato A., Exec. V.P.--Scancem AB, Malmo, Sweden; *Int'l*, pg. 1198
Holoubek, Terri, Exec. V.P.--Holoubek Inc., Waukesha, WI; *U.S. Private*, pg. 536
Holroyd, Charles, Exec. V.P.-Mktg.--Countrywide Home Loans Inc., Pasadena, CA; *U.S. Public*, pg. 452
Holstein, Hans-Joachim, Exec. V.P. & Sls. Dir.--Traub AG, Reichenbach, Germany; *Int'l*, pg. 1419
Holsten, Joseph M., Chief Oper. Officer & Exec. V.P.--Waste Management, Inc., Oak Brook, IL; *U.S. Public*, pg. 1744
Holterhoff, Volker, Exec. V.P.--Bayerische Hypotheken-und Wechsel-Bank Aktiengesellschaft, Munich, Germany; *Int'l*, pg. 175
Holterhus, Gerhard, Dr., Exec. V.P.--Norddeutsche Landesbank (NORD/LB), Hannover, Germany; *Int'l*, pg. 957
Holzwarth, Gregory, Exec. V.P.-Fin. Services--Epsilon, Burlington, MA; *U.S. Public*, pg. 74
Homann, Claus-Dieter, Exec. V.P.-Intl. Div.--Deutsche Girozentrale-Deutsche Kommunalbank, Frankfurt/Main, Germany; *Int'l*, pg. 406
Homcha, S.F., Exec. V.P.-Engrng. & Prod. Plng.--Mack Trucks, Inc., Allentown, PA; *Int'l*, pg. 1102
Homishak, Conrad, Exec. V.P.--Bridgestone Multi-Media Group, Chandler, AZ; *U.S. Private*, pg. 168
Honda, Katsuhiko, Exec. V.P.-Tobacco--Japan Tobacco Inc., Tokyo, Japan; *Int'l*, pg. 703
Hone, Frank, Exec. V.P. & Mngmt. Dir.--Rubin Ehrenthal & Associates, New York, NY; *U.S. Private*, pg. 949
Honeycutt, Travis W., Exec. V.P. & Sec.--Isolyser Company, Inc., Norcross, GA; *U.S. Public*, pg. 914
Honeysett, William L., Exec. V.P.--McClatchy Newspapers Inc., Sacramento, CA; *U.S. Public*, pg. 1065
Hong, Sang-Bok, Exec. V.P.--Pohang Iron & Steel Co., Ltd., Kyongbuk, Korea; *Int'l*, pg. 1061
Hong, Yee-Tang Jee, Exec. V.P.--DBS Bank Ltd., Singapore, Singapore; *Int'l*, pg. 350
Hongo, Terutsugu, Exec. V.P.--Takeda Chemical Industries, Ltd., Osaka, Japan; *Int'l*, pg. 1350
Honkala, Matti, Exec. V.P.-Fin. & Admin.--Kesko Ltd., Helsinki, Finland; *Int'l*, pg. 732
Honse, Robert, Exec. V.P. & Chief Oper. Officer-Agriculture Input Bus.--Farmland Industries, Inc., Kansas City, MO; *U.S. Private*, pg. 395
Hontzas, Thomas M., Exec. V.P.--Deposit Guaranty National Bank, Jackson, MS; *U.S. Public*, pg. 500
Hoo, Mae Soo, Exec. V.P. & Gen. Mdse. Mgr.--Cache, Inc., New York, NY; *U.S. Public*, pg. 289
Hood, James, Exec. V.P. & Bus. Devel. Dir.--Young & Rubicam New York, New York, NY; *U.S. Private*, pg. 1198
Hooi, Teoh Tee, Sr. V.P.-Americas--Singapore Airlines, Los Angeles, CA; *Int'l*, pg. 1374
Hoopis, Michael P., Exec. V.P. & Pres.-Household Prods.--The Black & Decker Corporation, Towson, MD; *U.S. Public*, pg. 233
Hoover, William D., Exec. V.P.--Centura Banks, Inc., Rocky Mount, NC; *U.S. Public*, pg. 328
Hope, John C., III, Exec. V.P.- Southern Region & Corp. Banking Div.--AmSouth Bancorporation, Birmingham, AL; *U.S. Public*, pg. 105
Hopkins, George W., Exec. V.P.-Corp. Staff--Bank of Montreal, Toronto, Canada; *Int'l*, pg. 153
Hopkins, John D., Exec. V.P. & Gen. Counsel--Jefferson-Pilot Life Insurance Co., Greensboro, NC; *U.S. Public*, pg. 926
Hoppe, William S., Chief Fin. Officer & Exec. V.P.--Rock Bottom Restaurants, Louisville, CO; *U.S. Public*, pg. 1396
Horey, Thomas, Chief Fin. Officer & Exec. V.P.--Plaid Pantries, Inc., Beaverton, OR; *U.S. Private*, pg. 868
Hori, Kazuo, Exec. V.P.--Kumagai Gumi Co., Ltd., Tokyo, Japan; *Int'l*, pg. 763
Horichi, Shiro, Exec. V.P.--The Tokio Marine & Fire Insurance Company, Ltd., Tokyo, Japan; *Int'l*, pg. 1391
Horie, Tetsuya, Chm. Bd.--Long-Term Credit Bank of Japan (Schweiz) AG, Zurich, Switzerland; *Int'l*, pg. 816
Horie, Wilfred Y., Exec. V.P.-Intl.--Associates First Capital Corporation, Dallas, TX; *U.S. Public*, pg. 662
Horio, Tomishi, Exec. Mng. Dir.--Sankyo Company Limited, Tokyo, Japan; *Int'l*, pg. 1189
Horn, James C., Exec. V.P. & Gen. Mgr.--Acme Markets, Malvern, PA; *U.S. Public*, pg. 93
Horn, Randall C., Exec. V.P.-Grp. Opers.--Mutual of Omaha Insurance Company, Omaha, NE; *U.S. Private*, pg. 769
Horn, Robert E., V.P. & Chief Fin. Officer--Pace Resources, Inc., York, PA; *U.S. Private*, pg. 829
Hornady-David, Margaret, Exec. V.P.--Hornady Manufacturing Company, Grand Island, NE; *U.S. Private*, *pg. 539*
Horne, Richard E., Exec. V.P. & Chief Lending Officer--Trustmark Corporation, Jackson, MS; *U.S. Public*, pg. 1643
Horne, Richard E., Exec. V.P.--Trustmark National Bank, Jackson, MS; *U.S. Public*, pg. 1643
Horner, Donald G., Exec. V.P.--First Hawaiian, Inc., Honolulu, HI; *U.S. Public*, pg. 634
Horner, H.B., Exec. V.P.--Florida Rock Industries, Inc., Jacksonville, FL; *U.S. Public*, pg. 655
Horner, Matina S., Exec. V.P.-Human Resources--Teachers Insurance and Annuity Association, New York, NY; *U.S. Private*, pg. 1071
Hornsby, Richard L., Exec. V.P.--Devcon International Corp., Deerfield Beach, FL; *U.S. Public*, pg. 502
Horovitz, Jean-Marie, Exec. V.P.-Credit/Policy & Admin.--European American Bank & Trust Co., Uniondale, NY; *Int'l*, pg. 9
Horowitz, Kenneth J., Exec. V.P.--Scott Printing Corporation, New Providence, NJ; *U.S. Private*, pg. 977
Horowitz, Robert S., Exec. V.P.--Lamb-Weston, Inc., Kennewick, WA; *U.S. Public*, pg. 427
Horsman, Raymond, Chief Oper. Officer & Exec. V.P.--MPS Corporation, Pittsburgh, PA; *U.S. Private*, pg. 687
Horsman, Raymond D., Exec. V.P.--Mulach Steel Corporation, Leetsdale, PA; *U.S. Private*, pg. 766
Hortenstine, Henry, Exec. V.P.--Affiliated Computer Services, Inc., Dallas, TX; *U.S. Public*, pg. 27
Horton, Gerald W., Exec. V.P.--H.W. Kaufman Financial Group, Inc., Farmington, MI; *U.S. Private*, pg. 609
Horvath, Robert G., Chief Fin. Officer & Exec. V.P.--Rapp Collins Worldwide, New York, NY; *U.S. Public*, pg. 1224
Hoshiba, Hideo, Exec. V.P.--Dentsu USA-Los Angeles, Santa Monica, CA; *Int'l*, pg. 393
Hosler, Darrell, Exec. V.P.--Burns & McDonnell Engineers-Architects-Consultants, Kansas City, MO; *U.S. Private*, pg. 187
Host, Gerard R., Chief Fin. Officer & Exec. V.P.--Trustmark National Bank, Jackson, MS; *U.S. Public*, pg. 1643
Hotarek, Brian W., Chief Fin. Officer & Exec. V.P.--The Stop & Shop Companies, Inc., Quincy, MA; *Int'l*, pg. 750
Hoth, Kenneth J., Exec. V.P.--Semiconductor Packaging Materials Co., Inc., Armonk, NY; *U.S. Public*, pg. 1456
Hottlet, Andre, Exec. V.P.--T-Fal Corporation, Pine Brook, NJ; *Int'l*, pg. 568
Hottovy, Ronald J., Chief Fin. Officer, Exec. V.P., Treas. & Sec.--Scientific Software-Intercomp, Inc., Denver, CO; *U.S. Public*, pg. 1443
Houck, Charles S., Exec. V.P.--Bank of Raleigh, Beckley, WV; *U.S. Public*, pg. 836
Houel, Patrick, Chief Fin. Officer & Exec. V.P.--LVMH Moet Hennessy Louis Vuitton, Paris, France; *Int'l*, pg. 779
Hough, P., Exec. V.P.-Chemical Distr. America--Royal Pakhoed NV, Rotterdam, Netherlands; *Int'l*, pg. 1147
Houle, David A., Chief Fin. Officer, Exec. V.P. & Treas.--Pacific Century Financial Corporation, Honolulu, HI; *U.S. Public*, pg. 1248
Houle, David A., Chief Fin. Officer & Exec. V.P.-Treas. Admin.--Bank of Hawaii, Honolulu, HI; *U.S. Public*, pg. 1248
House, James E., Exec. V.P.--Union Planters Bank, Memphis, TN; *U.S. Public*, pg. 1669
House, Paul R., Exec. V.P.--Indiana Lawrence Bank, North Manchester, IN; *U.S. Public*, pg. 633
Houseman, Dave E., Chief Fin. Officer & Exec. V.P.--Signal Apparel Company, Inc., Chattanooga, TN; *U.S. Public*, pg. 1472
Houser, Michael R., Exec. V.P. & Dir.-Mktg. & Mdsg.--Schultz Sav-O Stores, Inc., Sheboygan, WI; *U.S. Public*, pg. 1442
Houston, Alfred D., Chief Fin. Officer & Exec. V.P.--New England Electric System, Westborough, MA; *U.S. Public*, *pg. 1171*
Houston, Robert P., Exec. V.P. & Comptroller--Regions Financial Corporation, Birmingham, AL; *U.S. Public*, pg. 1371
Hover, John C., II, Exec. V.P.--U.S. Trust Corporation, New York, NY; *U.S. Public*, pg. 1688
Hoverson, Robert L., Exec. V.P.--Provident Financial Group, Inc., Cincinnati, OH; *U.S. Public*, pg. 1338
Hoverson, Robert L., Exec. V.P.--The Provident Bank, Cincinnati, OH; *U.S. Public*, pg. 1338
Howard, Bill, Exec. V.P.--Blackeyed Pea Restaurants Inc., Scottsdale, AZ; *U.S. Public*, pg. 498
Howard, Robert C., Exec. V.P.--Thermo Electron Corporation, Waltham, MA; *U.S. Public*, pg. 1591
Howard, Scott P., Sr. Exec. V.P.-Comml. Banking--Hibernia Corporation, New Orleans, LA; *U.S. Public*, pg. 825
Howard, William J., Exec. V.P. & Sec.--DenAmerica Corp., Scottsdale, AZ; *U.S. Public*, pg. 498
Howarth, Peter, Exec. V.P.--Zantop International Airlines, Inc., Ypsilanti, MI; *U.S. Private*, pg. 1204
Howe, Thomas N., Exec. V.P.-Trust & Investment Services--Citizens Savings Bank, Providence, RI; *Int'l*, pg. 1132
Howell, Mary L., Exec. V.P.-Govt. & Intl. Affairs--Textron Inc., Providence, RI; *U.S. Public*, pg. 1588
Howells, Ted, Jr., Chief Fin. Officer & Exec. V.P.--Sony Pictures Entertainment, Culver City, CA; *Int'l*, pg. 1281
Hower, Paul, Exec. V.P.-Opers.--Prime Hospitality Corp., Fairfield, NJ; *U.S. Public*, pg. 1326
Howerton, Al, Exec. V.P.-Store Devel.--QuikTrip Corporation, Tulsa, OK; *U.S. Private*, pg. 901
Howes, William B., Exec. V.P.--Temple-Inland Inc., Diboll, TX; *U.S. Public*, pg. 1574
Howting, Richard M., Exec. V.P. & Global Creative Dir.-Ford--J. Walter Thompson Company, New York, NY; *Int'l*, pg. 1483
Howton, Debbie F., Exec. V.P.--The First National Bank of Lafayette, Lafayette, LA; *U.S. Public*, pg. 630
Hoye, Don, Exec. V.P.-Bus. Devel.--TruServ Corporation, Chicago, IL; *U.S. Private*, pg. 1108
Hoyle, Richard, Exec. V.P.--A.W. Chesterton Company, Stoneham, MA; *U.S. Private*, pg. 234
Hoyt, Jeffrey E., Chief Oper. Officer, Exec. V.P. & Sec.--Sun Bancorp, Inc., Selinsgrove, PA; *U.S. Public*, pg. 1529
Hoyt, Susan, Exec. V.P.-H.R.--Staples, Inc., Westborough, MA; *U.S. Public*, pg. 1509
Hubbard, Thomas F., Exec. V.P.-Real Estate & Devel.--Buffets, Inc., Eden Prairie, MN; *U.S. Public*, pg. 267
Hubbell, Alan C., Exec. V.P.--TCF Bank Minnesota FSB, Minneapolis, MN; *U.S. Public*, pg. 1554
Hubbell, Peter, Exec. V.P.--The Folger Coffee Company, Cincinnati, OH; *U.S. Public*, pg. 1331
Huber, John V., Exec. V.P.--The Vigoro Corporation, Chicago, IL; *U.S. Public*, pg. 856
Huber, Thomas P., Exec. V.P., Gen. Counsel & Asst. Sec.--First Hawaiian Bank, Honolulu, HI; *U.S. Public*, pg. 634
Huckesrein, Dieter H., Exec. V.P.-Opers. & Pres.-Hotel Opers.--Hilton Hotels Corporation, Beverly Hills, CA; *U.S. Public*, pg. 828
Hudak, Kristen M., Chief Fin. Officer & Sr. Exec. V.P.--AmSouth Bancorporation, Birmingham, AL; *U.S. Public*, pg. 105
Hudepohe, James J., Exec. V.P.--Fifth Third Bancorp, Cincinnati, OH; *U.S. Public*, pg. 621
Hudson, Charles, Exec. V.P.-Men's Apparel--Hanover Direct, Inc., Weehawken, NJ; *U.S. Public*, pg. 782
Hudson, Dawn, Exec. V.P.-Global Brands--Frito-Lay Company, Plano, TX; *U.S. Public*, pg. 1277
Hudson, Howard G., Exec. V.P.-Fixed Income--Fortis Advisers, Inc., New York, NY; *Int'l*, pg. 499
Hudson, Larry, Exec. V.P.--Beehive Machinery Co., Sandy, UT; *U.S. Private*, pg. 1160
Huebner, Richard, Exec. V.P.-Fin.--Calmar Inc., City of Industry, CA; *U.S. Private*, pg. 201
Hueneke, Terry A., Exec. V.P.--Manpower Inc., Milwaukee, WI; *U.S. Public*, pg. 1042
Huerter, M. Jane, Exec. V.P.-Corp. Resources & Corp. Sec.--Mutual of Omaha Insurance Company, Omaha, NE; *U.S. Private*, pg. 769
Huerter, M. Jane, Exec. V.P.-Corp. Resouces & Corp. Sec.--United of Omaha Life Insurance Company, Omaha, NE; *U.S. Private*, pg. 770
Huesgen, James H., Chief Fin. Officer & Exec. V.P.--Pacific Telecom Cellular, Inc., Vancouver, WA; *U.S. Public*, pg. 1252
Huff, Marvin Jr., Exec. V.P.--CNB Bancshares, Inc., Evansville, IN; *U.S. Public*, pg. 280
Huff, William B., Exec. V.P.--Globe Newspaper Company, Boston, MA; *U.S. Public*, pg. 1175
Huffhires, Thomas D., Exec. V.P.--Sysco Food Services of Dallas, Dallas, TX; *U.S. Public*, pg. 1551
Hufnagel, Leon, Exec. V.P.--Reed Elsevier Business Information, Newton, MA; *Int'l*, pg. 1095
Hughes-Hallett, J.W.J., Exec. Dir.--Swire Pacific Limited, Central, Hong Kong; *Int'l*, pg. 1328
Hughes, Frank, Exec. V.P. & Chief Creative Officer--Girgenti, Hughes, Butler & McDowell, New York, NY; *U.S. Private*, pg. 455
Hughes, G. Wilson, Exec. V.P. & Gen. Mgr.--General Communication, Inc., Anchorage, AK; *U.S. Public*, pg. 708
Hughes, Garry M., Exec. V.P.--Kinross Gold Corporation, Toronto, Canada; *Int'l*, pg. 734
Hughes, J. Lowell, Chief Fin. Officer & Exec. V.P.-Fin.--Davis Electrical Constructors, Inc., Greenville, SC; *U.S. Private*, pg. 315
Hughes, John F., Exec. V.P. & Treas.--Associates First Capital Corporation, Dallas, TX; *U.S. Public*, pg. 662
Hughes, Louis R., Exec. V.P., Pres. & Gen. Mgr.-Intl. Opers.--General Motors Corporation, Detroit, MI; *U.S. Public*, pg. 718
Hughes, Patrick H., Exec. V.P.--Ryan Insurance Group, Inc., Chicago, IL; *U.S. Public*, pg. 118
Hughes, Peter G., Exec. V.P.--Universal Studios TV, Universal City, CA; *Int'l*, pg. 1215
Hughes, Robert J., Chief Fin. Officer & Exec. V.P.--Poughkeepsie Financial Corp., Poughkeepsie, NY; *U.S. Public*, pg. 1319
Hughes, Robert J., Chief Fin. Officer & Exec. V.P.--Bank of the Hudson, Poughkeepsie, NY; *U.S. Public*, pg. 1319
Hughes, William J., Exec. V.P.-Admin. & Fin.--E.C.D., Inc., Hillside, NJ; *U.S. Private*, pg. 353
Huhtamaki, Martti, Exec. V.P.-Fin.--Merita Ltd., Helsinki, Finland; *Int'l*, pg. 858
Huiquiu, Yang, Vice Chm. & Exec. V.P.--Bank of China, Beijing, China; *Int'l*, pg. 152
Huisjes, J., Exec. V.P.--ABN-AMRO Holding N.V., Amsterdam, Netherlands; *Int'l*, pg. 8
Huitt, E. Larry, Chm. Bd., Exec. V.P., Treas. & Sec.--Huitt-Zollars, Inc., Dallas, TX; *U.S. Private*, pg. 547
Huizer, M.C., Exec. V.P.--ABN-AMRO Holding N.V., Amsterdam, Netherlands; *Int'l*, pg. 8
Hulett, Michael, Exec. Partner--MeritCare Health System, Fargo, ND; *U.S. Private*, pg. 733
Hulihan, James E., Jr., Grp. Exec. V.P.-Asia Retail Banking--Bank of America NT&SA, San Francisco, CA; *U.S. Public*, pg. 180
Hulseman, John F., Exec. V.P.--Solo Cup Company, Highland Park, IL; *U.S. Private*, pg. 1013
Hulvat, Scott, Sr. V.P.-Sls. & Mktg.--F&F Foods, Chicago, IL; *U.S. Private*, pg. 388
Human, Dries, Exec. Dir.-Synserv--Sasol Synthetic Fuels (Pty.) Ltd., Secunda, South Africa; *Int'l*, pg. 1197
Humenansky, Paul L., Chief Oper. Officer & Exec. V.P.--Platinum Technology, Inc., Oak Brook Terrace, IL; *U.S. Public*, pg. 1309
Hummers, William S., III, Chief Fin. Officer & Exec. V.P.--Carolina First Corporation, Greenville, SC; *U.S. Public*, pg. 306
Humphries, French P., Exec. V.P.--B.B. Walker Company, Asheboro, NC; *U.S. Public*, pg. 1734
Hunkapiller, Michael, Ph.D., Exec. V.P.--Applied Biosystems, Foster City, CA; *U.S. Public*, pg. 1279
Hunke, David, Exec. V.P.-Mktg.--The Cincinnati Enquirer, Inc., Cincinnati, OH; *U.S. Public*, pg. 700
Hunstad, Robert E., Exec. V.P.--The Minnesota Mutual Life Insurance Company, Saint Paul, MN; *U.S. Private*, pg. 750
Hunt, Amy, Exec V.P. & Creative Dir.--Wickersham Hunt Schwantner, Boston, MA; *U.S. Private*, pg. 84
Hunt, David A., Exec. V.P.--Biggs Gilmore Communications, Kalamazoo, MI; *U.S. Private*, pg. 143
Hunt, James K., Chief Fin. Officer, Exec. V.P. & Treas.--UST Corporation, Boston, MA; *U.S. Public*, pg. 1660
Hunt, James K., Chief Fin. Officer & Exec. V.P.--USTrust, Boston, MA; *U.S. Public*, pg. 1660
Hunt, Robert J., Chief Fin. Officer & Exec. V.P.--AutoZone, Inc., Memphis, TN; *U.S. Public*, pg. 150
Hunt, Robin R., Exec. V.P.--Allied Security, International, Spokane, WA; *U.S. Private*, pg. 41
Hunte, Alan L., Chief Fin. Officer, Exec. V.P. & Treas.--Trenwick America Reinsurance Corporation, Stamford, CT; *U.S. Public*, pg. 1634
Hunter, George J., Exec. V.P.--Bonanza Bus Lines, Inc., Providence, RI; *U.S. Private*, pg. 156

Hunter, Jack D., Exec. V.P. & Gen. Counsel--Lincoln National Corporation, Fort Wayne, IN; *U.S. Public*, pg. 997
Hunter, Jack D., Exec. V.P. & Gen. Counsel--The Lincoln National Life Insurance Co., Fort Wayne, IN; *U.S. Public*, *pg. 998*
Hunter, Peter A., Exec. V.P.-Fin.--Data Instruments, Inc., Acton, MA; *U.S. Private*, pg. 312
Hunter, Shawn, Exec. V.P.--Denver Nuggets Limited Partnership, Denver, CO; *U.S. Public*, pg. 138
Hunter, Warren, Exec. V.P. & Chief Mktg. Officer--The McClure Group, Wayne, PA; *U.S. Private*, pg. 719
Huntley, Peter W., Exec. V.P.-Business Devel.--Matthew Clark Taunton, Ltd., Bristol, United Kingdom; *Int'l*, pg. 848
Huopalahti, Kari, Exec. V.P.-Intl. Opers.--Imatran Voima Oy, Helsinki, Finland; *Int'l*, pg. 660
Huppe, Ulrich, Exec. V.P.--Veba AG, Dusseldorf, Germany; *Int'l*, pg. 1454
Huppert, Arnold E., Exec. V.P.--Teledyne Water Pik, Fort Collins, CO; *U.S. Public*, pg. 44
Hurley, Brian J., Exec. V.P.--Allendale Mutual Insurance Co., Johnston, RI; *U.S. Private*, pg. 37
Hurley, Charles T., Chief Fin. Officer & Exec. V.P.--Meldrum & Fewsmith Communications Inc., Cleveland, OH; *U.S. Private*, pg. 730
Hurley, Edward, Exec. V.P.-HDI--Hampshire Group, Ltd., Anderson, SC; *U.S. Public*, pg. 778
Hurley, Edward, Exec. V.P.--Hampshire Designers Inc., Anderson, SC; *U.S. Public*, pg. 778
Hurshman, J., Exec. V.P.--Hedstrom Corporation, Mount Prospect, IL; *U.S. Private*, pg. 526
Hurst, D.K., Exec. V.P.--Federal Industries Metals Group, Etobicoke, Canada; *Int'l*, pg. 1150
Hurst, John L., III, Exec. V.P.-Mfg. & Engrng.--Occidental Chemical Corporation, Dallas, TX; *U.S. Public*, pg. 1210
Huschke, Hubert, Exec. V.P.-Basic Services & Logistics--Union Bank of Switzerland, Zurich, Switzerland; *Int'l*, pg. 1439
Huseman, Kenneth V., Chief Oper. Officer & Exec. V.P.--Key Energy Group Inc., East Brunswick, NJ; *U.S. Public*, pg. 953
Huskins, Walter E., Jr., Exec. V.P.-Admin.--UST Corporation, Boston, MA; *U.S. Public*, pg. 1660
Huss, Ron, Exec. V.P.--Mid Atlantic Construction, Inc., Charlotte, NC; *U.S. Private*, pg. 939
Hussain, Aitaf, Exec. V.P.-Fin.--Habib Bank Ltd., Karachi, Pakistan; *Int'l*, pg. 584
Hussey, Peter A., Exec. V.P.--Hussey Corporation, North Berwick, ME; *U.S. Private*, pg. 550
Huston, John, Exec. V.P.-Mktg.--National Cattlemen's Beef Association, Chicago, IL; *U.S. Private*, pg. 780
Huston, Richard T., Exec. V.P.-Mktg.--ShowBiz Pizza Time, Inc., Irving, TX; *U.S. Public*, pg. 1468
Hutchings, Peter L., Chief Fin. Officer & Exec. V.P.--The Guardian Life Insurance Company of America, New York, NY; *U.S. Private*, pg. 486
Hutchins, Bruce, Chief Fin. Officer & Exec. V.P.--Alabama Power Co., Birmingham, AL; *U.S. Public*, pg. 1489
Hutchins, Robert W., Exec. V.P.--Century Bancshares, Inc., Washington, DC; *U.S. Public*, pg. 328
Hutchinson, Mark, Exec. V.P.--R & R Marketing, West Caldwell, NJ; *U.S. Private*, pg. 902
Hutchison, M.N., Sr. V.P.-S.F. Opers. & Dir.-Sls. & Mktg.-Nonferrous Sector--Davy International, San Francisco, San Ramon, CA; *Int'l*, pg. 774
Hutton, David A., Exec. V.P.-Exploration & Devel.--Rayrock Yellowknife Resources Inc., Toronto, Canada; *Int'l*, pg. 1089
Huzl, James F., Chief Fin. Officer & Exec. V.P.--Hendrick Automotive Group, Charlotte, NC; *U.S. Private*, pg. 522
Hyams, Joe, Exec. V.P.-Special Projects--Warner Bros. Studios, Inc., Burbank, CA; *U.S. Public*, pg. 1611
Hyatt, Donald, Exec. V.P.--Lifetime Doors Inc., Farmington, MI; *U.S. Private*, pg. 666
Hyer, Frederick L., Jr., Exec. V.P.--Chubb & Son, Inc., Warren, NJ; *U.S. Public*, pg. 355
Hyland, Gregory E., Exec. V.P.--Keystone Valvtron, Inc., Houston, TX; *U.S. Public*, pg. 1650
Hylland, R.R., Exec. V.P.--Grant, Inc., Huron, SD; *U.S. Public*, pg. 1201
Hylland, R.R., Exec. V.P.--Northwestern Networks, Inc., Huron, SD; *U.S. Public*, pg. 1201
Hylland, R.R., Exec. V.P.--Northwestern Systems, Inc., Huron, SD; *U.S. Public*, pg. 1201
Hylland, Richard R., Exec. V.P.--Northwestern Public Service, Huron, SD; *U.S. Public*, pg. 1200
Hyman, Richard, Exec. V.P.-Electronics Distribution Group--Bell Industries, Inc., El Segundo, CA; *U.S. Public*, pg. 204
Hyman, Richard, Chief Oper. Officer & Exec. V.P.--Milgray/New England, Inc., Wilmington, MA; *U.S. Public*, pg. 206
Hyman, Richard, Chief Oper. Officer & Exec. V.P.--Birnbach Company, Inc., Farmingdale, NY; *U.S. Public*, pg. 207
Hymphreys, David, Exec. V.P.--Minor Rubber Co., Inc., Bloomfield, NJ; *U.S. Private*, pg. 751
Hyon-Ku, Lee, Exec. V.P.-Enrng.--Daewoo Corporation, Seoul, Korea; *Int'l*, pg. 357
Hypponen, Heiki, Exec. V.P.--Merita Ltd., Helsinki, Finland; *Int'l*, pg. 858
Hytheir, M., Exec. V.P.-Systems Sales--Compagnie Generale de Geophysique, Massy, France; *Int'l*, pg. 241
Ianna, Frank, Exec. V.P.--AT&T Corporation, Basking Ridge, NJ; *U.S. Public*, pg. 10
Iannaccone, Emil, Exec. V.P. & Mktg. Dir.--Western International Media Corporation, Los Angeles, CA; *U.S. Private*, pg. 1165
Iapalucci, Sam, Chief Fin. Officer & Exec. V.P.--CH2M Hill Companies, Ltd., Greenwood Village, CO; *U.S. Private*, pg. 195
Iba, Tamotsu, Exec. Deputy Pres.--Sony Corporation, Tokyo, Japan; *Int'l*, pg. 1280
Ichikawa, Hideo, Exec. V.P.--Cosmo Oil Co., Ltd., Tokyo, Japan; *Int'l*, pg. 335
Ichikawa, Masanori, Exec. V.P.-Home Electronics, & Dir.--Pioneer Electronics (USA) Inc., Long Beach, CA; *Int'l*, pg. 1058
Ichikawa, Namio, Exec. V.P.--Namco Ltd., Tokyo, Japan; *Int'l*, pg. 905
Ida, Yoshinori, Exec. Dir.--Isuzu Motors Limited, Tokyo, Japan; *Int'l*, pg. 692
Idemitsu, Akira, Exec. V.P.--Idemitsu Kosan Co., Ltd., Tokyo, Japan; *Int'l*, pg. 659
Ido, Hiroshi, Exec. V.P.--Achilles Corporation, Tokyo, Japan; *Int'l*, pg. 22
Ielmini, Angelo, Exec. V.P.--Patterson Frozen Foods, Inc., Patterson, CA; *U.S. Private*, pg. 843
Igel, Anders, Exec. V.P.-Pub. Telecommunications--Telefonaktiebolaget LM Ericsson, Stockholm, Sweden; *Int'l*, pg. 1363
Igiel, Bob, Exec. V.P.-Brdcst. Programming & Pur.--Young & Rubicam New York, New York, NY; *U.S. Private*, pg. 1198
Ihara, Kuniyoshi, Exec. V.P.--Tokyu Corporation, Tokyo, Japan; *Int'l*, pg. 1394
Ihara, Sozaburo, Exec. V.P.--Mitsubishi Electric Corporation, Tokyo, Japan; *Int'l*, pg. 872
Ikeda, Morio, Exec. Dir.--Shiseido Company Ltd., Tokyo, Japan; *Int'l*, pg. 1235
Ikeda, Shigeru, Exec. V.P.--Nippon Telegraph and Telephone Corporation, Tokyo, Japan; *Int'l*, pg. 940
Ikeda, Tsutomu, Exec. V.P.--The Furukawa Electric Co., Ltd., Tokyo, Japan; *Int'l*, pg. 530
Ikegame, Ryo, Exec. V.P.--The Tokyo Electric Power Co., Inc., Tokyo, Japan; *Int'l*, pg. 1394
Illingworth, David, Exec. V.P. & Pres.-Alternatecare Bus.--Nellcor Puritan Bennett Incorporated, Pleasanton, CA; *U.S. Public*, pg. 1039
Imai, Hiroshi, Exec. V.P.--Ryobi Ltd., Tokyo, Japan; *Int'l*, pg. 1151
Imai, Minoru, Exec. V.P.--Oki Electric Industry Company, Ltd., Tokyo, Japan; *Int'l*, pg. 999
Inaba, Kunihiko, Exec. V.P.--Aoki Corporation, Tokyo, Japan; *Int'l*, pg. 78
Inaba, Yoshiharu, Exec. V.P.--Fanuc Ltd., Yamanashi, Japan; *Int'l*, pg. 477
Inaki, Atsushi, Exec. V.P.--Kajima Corporation, Tokyo, Japan; *Int'l*, pg. 721
Inamura, Akira, Exec. Dir.--Dentsu Inc., Tokyo, Japan; *Int'l*, pg. 392
Inbe, Kazuya, Exec. V.P.--Kao Corporation, Tokyo, Japan; *Int'l*, pg. 717
Inborr, Jan, Grp. Exec. V.P.-Ahlstrom Gen. Prods.--A. Ahlstrom Corporation, Helsinki, Finland; *Int'l*, pg. 32
Inborr, Jan, Grp. Exec. V.P.--A. Ahlstrom Corporation, Helsinki, Finland; *Int'l*, pg. 32
Inciarte, Matias R., Vice Chm., Chief Fin. Officer & Exec. V.P.--Banco Santander, Madrid, Spain; *Int'l*, pg. 143
Infalvi, Daman, Exec. V.P.--Fibre Glass-Evercoat Company, Cincinnati, OH; *U.S. Public*, pg. 866
Infantino, Teresa C., Exec. V.P.--Combe Incorporated, White Plains, NY; *U.S. Private*, pg. 257
Ingemarson, Bo, Exec. V.P.-Fin. & Economy--Skanska AB, Danderyd, Sweden; *Int'l*, pg. 1260
Ingermarson, Bo, Exec. V.P. & Chief Investment Officer--Skandia Insurance Company Limited, Stockholm, Sweden; *Int'l*, pg. 1256
Ingman, Richard W., Chief Fin. Officer & Exec. V.P.--Pentair, Inc., Saint Paul, MN; *U.S. Public*, pg. 1273
Ingram, John M., Exec. V.P.--Ingram Paper Company, City of Industry, CA; *U.S. Public*, pg. 904
Ingrando, Leonard V., Chief Oper. Officer & Exec. V.P.--Crowley Foods, Inc., Binghamton, NY; *Int'l*, pg. 752
Ingulli, Alfred F., Exec. V.P.--Uniroyal Chemical Corporation, Middlebury, CT; *U.S. Public*, pg. 459
Ingulli, Alfred F., Exec. V.P.--Uniroyal Chemical Company, Inc., Middlebury, CT; *U.S. Public*, pg. 460
Innanen, L., Exec. V.P.-Legal & Gen. Counsel--Labatt Breweries of Canada, Toronto, Canada; *Int'l*, pg. 679
Innes, Roger, Exec. V.P.-Sls.--Comdisco Electronics Group, San Diego, CA; *U.S. Public*, pg. 408
Inoue, Hidekazu, Sr. Exec. V.P.--Nippon Telegraph and Telephone Corporation, Tokyo, Japan; *Int'l*, pg. 940
Inoue, Hiroshi, Sr. Exec. Dir. & Grp. Gen. Mgr.-Audio/Visual Systems--Sharp Corporation, Osaka, Japan; *Int'l*, pg. 1228
Inoue, Ichizo, Exec. Dir.--Tanabe Seiyaku Co., Ltd., Osaka, Japan; *Int'l*, pg. 1354
Inoue, Masatoshi, Exec. V.P.--Obayashi Corporation, Tokyo, Japan; *Int'l*, pg. 995
Inoue, Yukio, Exec. V.P.--The Chugoku Electric Power Co., Inc., Hiroshima, Japan; *Int'l*, pg. 291
Inove, Masa, Exec. V.P.--Shaklee Corporation, San Francisco, CA; *Int'l*, pg. 1518
Intaseni, Thiva, Exec. V.P.--The Industrial Finance Corporation of Thailand, Bangkok, Thailand; *Int'l*, pg. 677
Inukai, Nobuo, Exec. V.P.--The Kyoei Mutual Fire & Marine Insurance Company, Tokyo, Japan; *Int'l*, pg. 777
Ionna, Greg, Exec. V.P.--Gibson Greetings, Inc., Cincinnati, OH; *U.S. Public*, pg. 742
Irani, Barry K., Chief Tech. Officer & Exec. V.P.--EEX Corporation, Houston, TX; *U.S. Public*, pg. 542
Irelan, E. Glenn, Exec. V.P.-Mktg., Stores & Real Estate--Catherines Stores Corporation, Memphis, TN; *U.S. Public*, pg. 317
Iribe, P. Chrisman, Chief Oper. Officer & Exec. V.P.--U.S. Generating Company, Bethesda, MD; *U.S. Public*, pg. 1241
Irick, John E., Exec. V.P.--McBride and Associates, Inc., Albuquerque, NM; *U.S. Private*, pg. 719
Irimajiri, Shoichiro, Exec. V.P.-Res., Devel. & Mfg.--Sega Enterprises Ltd., Tokyo, Japan; *Int'l*, pg. 1218
Irish, Charles A., Sr. Exec. V.P.--The Whiting-Turner Contracting Co., Baltimore, MD; *U.S. Private*, pg. 1174
Irish, Jon, Exec. V.P.--MRA, An Integrated Marketing Communications Agency, Overland Park, KS; *U.S. Private*, pg. 687
Irons, Ronald R., Exec. V.P. & Creative Dir.--Trone Advertising, Inc., Greensboro, NC; *U.S. Private*, pg. 1104
Irving, Jack, Exec. V.P.-Menswear--Nordstrom, Inc., Seattle, WA; *U.S. Public*, pg. 1190
Irwin, Joe R., Chief Investment Officer & Exec. V.P.--PNC Bank Corp., Pittsburgh, PA; *U.S. Public*, pg. 1242
Irwin, Phillip D., Chief Oper. Officer & Exec. V.P.--Ranger Oil Limited, Calgary, Canada; *Int'l*, pg. 1086
Irwin, Thomas S., Chief Fin. Officer & Exec. V.P.--HEICO Corporation, Hollywood, FL; *U.S. Public*, pg. 804
Isaacs, Herb, Exec. V.P.--Kelly, Scott And Madison, Inc., Chicago, IL; *U.S. Private*, pg. 613
Isaacson, Helen, Exec. V.P.-Worldwide Licensing--Marvel Entertainment Group, New York, NY; *U.S. Public*, pg. 1052
Isaacson, Kay, Exec. V.P.-Mdsg.--Victoria's Secret Stores, Reynoldsburg, OH; *U.S. Public*, pg. 995
Isacson, Claus-Inge, Exec. V.P.-Pulp & Magazine Paper--Norske Skogindustrier A.S, Skogn, Norway; *Int'l*, pg. 965
Isacsson, Lars, Chief Fin. Officer & Exec. V.P.--Skandinaviska Enskilda Banken, Stockholm, Sweden; *Int'l*, pg. 1258
Isahaya, Shoji, Exec. V.P.--Takeda America Inc., New York, NY; *Int'l*, pg. 1350
Isaly, Thomas G., Exec. V.P.-Admin.--MariTrend, Inc., New Orleans, LA; *U.S. Private*, pg. 1135
Isenberg, Susan, Exec. V.P. & Gen. Mgr.-Healthcare--Edelman Worldwide, Inc., New York, NY; *U.S. Private*, pg. 362
Isenberg, William L., Exec. V.P.--Albert M. Greenfield & Company, Philadelphia, PA; *U.S. Private*, pg. 477
Ishibashi, Nobuyasu, Exec. V.P.--Daiwa House Industry Co., Ltd., Osaka, Japan; *Int'l*, pg. 374
Ishiguro, Masahiro, Sr. Exec. Dir.--The Japan Development Bank, Tokyo, Japan; *Int'l*, pg. 701
Ishihara, Hiroshi, Exec. V.P.--Nippon Telegraph and Telephone Corporation, Tokyo, Japan; *Int'l*, pg. 940
Ishii, J., Exec. V.P.--Otto Sumisho Inc., Tokyo, Japan; *Int'l*, pg. 1015
Ishikawa, Hiroshi, Exec. V.P.--Nippon Telegraph and Telephone Corporation, Tokyo, Japan; *Int'l*, pg. 940
Ishikawa, Shiro, Exec. V.P.--Takenaka Corporation, Osaka, Japan; *Int'l*, pg. 1351
Ishiko, Ryoichi, Exec. V.P.--Aoki Corporation, Tokyo, Japan; *Int'l*, pg. 78
Ishimaru, Yuichi, Chief Oper. Officer & Exec. V.P.--Marubeni America Corporation, New York, NY; *Int'l*, pg. 844
Ishiwata, Masatoshi, Exec. V.P.--Meiji Seika Kaisha, Ltd., Tokyo, Japan; *Int'l*, pg. 855
Ishizu, Shiro, Exec. V.P.--Mitsui Fudosan Co., Ltd., Tokyo, Japan; *Int'l*, pg. 882
Isoard, Frederic, Exec. V.P.-Oil & Gas Div.--Elf Aquitane, Paris, France; *Int'l*, pg. 444
Israel, Jason, Exec. V.P.--American Bankers Insurance Group, Inc., Miami, FL; *U.S. Public*, pg. 67
Israel, Jason J., Exec. V.P.-Opers.--American Bankers Life Assurance Co. of Florida, Miami, FL; *U.S. Public*, pg. 67
Itkowitz, Mark, Exec. V.P.-Creative Services--Jordan, McGrath, Case & Taylor Inc., New York, NY; *U.S. Private*, pg. 598
Ito, Fujio, Exec. V.P.--Ishikawajima-Harima Heavy Industries Co., Ltd., Tokyo, Japan; *Int'l*, pg. 689
Ito, Kanichi, Exec. V.P.--Toshiba Corporation, Tokyo, Japan; *Int'l*, pg. 1402
Ito, Kigen, Exec. Dir.--Isuzu Motors Limited, Tokyo, Japan; *Int'l*, pg. 692
Ito, Kohei, Exec. V.P.--Fanuc Ltd., Yamanashi, Japan; *Int'l*, pg. 477
Ito, Osamu, Exec. V.P.-Human Resources & Gen. Affairs--Diamond Star Motors, Normal, IL; *Int'l*, pg. 875
Ito, Shigeru, Exec. V.P.--Sapporo Breweries Ltd., Tokyo, Japan; *Int'l*, pg. 1193
Itoh, Shunro, Exec. V.P.--Nichimen Corporation, Tokyo, Japan; *Int'l*, pg. 927
Ivans, Paul, Mng. Partner & Exec. V.P.--Dugan Valva Contess Inc., Morristown, NJ; *U.S. Private*, pg. 345
Ivany, John W., Exec. V.P.--Kinross Gold Corporation, Toronto, Canada; *Int'l*, pg. 734
Iwahashi, Keiichi, Exec. V.P.--Kajima Corporation, Tokyo, Japan; *Int'l*, pg. 721
Iwaki, Koichiro, Sr. Mng. Dir.--Asahi Breweries Ltd., Tokyo, Japan; *Int'l*, pg. 83
Iwanicka, Lorraine, Exec. V.P.-Opers.--WWF Paper Corporation, Bala Cynwyd, PA; *U.S. Private*, pg. 1145
Iwanisziw, Nick, Exec. V.P.-Opers.--Menu Foods, Inc., Pennsauken, NJ; *U.S. Private*, pg. 731
Iwasaki, Takashi, Exec. V.P.--The Kansai Electric Power Co., Inc., Osaka, Japan; *Int'l*, pg. 722
Iwata, Sadao, Sr. Exec. Dir.--The Japan Development Bank, Tokyo, Japan; *Int'l*, pg. 701
Iwaya, Sadao, Exec. V.P.--TDK Corporation, Tokyo, Japan; *Int'l*, pg. 1336
Izawa, Ryouzou, Exec. V.P.--Fuji Bank (Schweiz) AG, Zurich, Switzerland; *Int'l*, pg. 521
Izumitani, Hiroshi, Exec. V.P.--Murata Manufacturing Co., Ltd., Kyoto, Japan; *Int'l*, pg. 897
Jaakonaho, Mauri, Exec. V.P.-Fin.--Valmet Corporation, Helsinki, Finland; *Int'l*, pg. 1447
Jaala, Jyrki, Exec. V.P.--Stockmann Automotive Sales Div., Helsinki, Finland; *Int'l*, pg. 1301
Jablonski, Brian J., Exec. V.P.-Sls. & Mktg.--Lason, Inc., Troy, MI; *U.S. Public*, pg. 979
Jachimiec, Chester J., Exec. V.P.-Acq.--Group Maintenance America Corp., Houston, TX; *U.S. Public*, pg. 766
Jachino, R.J., Exec. V.P.--Thomson U.S. Inc., Stamford, CT; *U.S. Public*, pg. 1601
Jack, James E., Chief Fin. Officer & Sr. Exec. V.P.--Associates Financial Services Corporation, Dallas, TX; *U.S. Public*, pg. 663
Jackson, Allan, Dr., Exec. V.P.-Prod.--Vincor International, Niagara Falls, Canada; *Int'l*, pg. 1468
Jackson, Brett, Exec. V.P.-Sls. & Mktg.--Axent Technologies, Rockville, MD; *U.S. Public*, pg. 157

Jackson, Jerry D., Exec. V.P.-External Affairs--Entergy Corporation, New Orleans, LA; *U.S. Public*, pg. 585
Jackson, John, Exec. V.P. & Gen. Mgr.--Kahului Trucking & Storage, Inc., Kahului, HI; *U.S. Public*, pg. 39
Jackson, Kathryn J., Exec. V.P.-Resource Grp.--Tennessee Valley Authority, Knoxville, TN; *U.S. Public*, pg. 1580
Jackson, Liz, Exec. V.P.--Shandwick Baltimore, Baltimore, MD; *Int'l*, pg. 1227
Jackson, Marcus, Chief Oper. Officer & Exec. V.P.--Kansas City Power & Light Company, Kansas City, MO; *U.S. Public*, pg. 943
Jackson, Norman E., Exec. V.P.-Electric Opers.--Western Resources, Inc., Topeka, KS; *U.S. Public*, pg. 1759
Jackson, Ralph E., Jr., Exec. V.P.-Opers.--Cooper Industries, Inc., Houston, TX; *U.S. Public*, pg. 442
Jackson, Robert, Exec. V.P.--Bostrom Seating, Inc., Piedmont, AL; *U.S. Public*, pg. 933
Jackson, Terry A., Exec. V.P.-Asset Mngmt. Services--Bank of Montreal, Toronto, Canada; *Int'l*, pg. 153
Jackson, Terry A., Exec. V.P.-Asset Mgmnt. Svcs.--The Nesbitt Thomson Corporation Limited, Toronto, Canada; *Int'l*, pg. 153
Jacob, Ellis, Chief Fin. Officer & Exec. V.P.--Cineplex Odeon Corporation, Toronto, Canada; *Int'l*, pg. 292
Jacob, John E., Chief Communications Officer & Exec. V.P.--Anheuser-Busch Companies, Inc., Saint Louis, MO; *U.S. Public*, pg. 113
Jacob, Xavier, Sr. Exec. V.P.-Engrng., Procurement & Construction--Technip, Paris, France; *Int'l*, pg. 1360
Jacobi, Ronald N., Exec. V.P & Gen. Counsel--Sony Pictures Entertainment, Culver City, CA; *Int'l*, pg. 1281
Jacobs, Allan, Exec. V.P.--Burlington House Area Rugs, New York, NY; *U.S. Public*, pg. 268
Jacobs, Gary, Exec. V.P.& Sec.--Corporate Express, Inc., Broomfield, CO; *U.S. Public*, pg. 449
Jacobs, Jeremy M., Jr., Exec. V.P.--Delaware North Companies, Inc., Buffalo, NY; *U.S. Private*, pg. 321
Jacobs, John H., Exec. V.P.--The Union Central Life Insurance Co., Cincinnati, OH; *U.S. Private*, pg. 1118
Jacobs, Louis M., Exec. V.P.--Delaware North Companies, Inc., Buffalo, NY; *U.S. Private*, pg. 321
Jacobs, Ray, Exec. V.P. & Creative Dir.--Friedland Jacobs Communications, Burbank, CA; *U.S. Private*, pg. 428
Jacobs, Rodney L., Vice Chm. & Chief Fin. Officer--Wells Fargo & Company, San Francisco, CA; *U.S. Public*, pg. 1753
Jacobs, William I., Exec. V.P.-Global Resources--Mastercard International, Inc., Purchase, NY; *U.S. Private*, pg. 714
Jacobsen, Gregory M., Exec. V.P.-Network Services--Strategic Technology Services, Cerritos, CA; *Int'l*, pg. 1154
Jacobsen, Joseph T., Exec. V.P.--ERD Waste Corp., Commack, NY; *U.S. Public*, pg. 546
Jacobson, L.H., Exec. V.P. & Gen. Counsel--Nuburn Capital, Calgary, Canada; *Int'l*, pg. 990
Jacobsson, Bo, Chief Fin. Officer & Exec. V.P.--Trelleborg AB, Trelleborg, Sweden; *Int'l*, pg. 1419
Jacot, H. Dean, Exec. V.P. & Chief Oper. Officer--Bellaire Corporation, Dallas, TX; *U.S. Public*, pg. 1149
Jacquinot, Bernard, Exec. V.P.-Field Oper.--J.E. Dunn Construction Co., Kansas City, MO; *U.S. Private*, pg. 347
Jacuzzi, Paul V., Exec. V.P. & Gen. Mgr.--Watts Industries (Canada) Inc., Burlington, Canada; *U.S. Public*, pg. 1747
Jae-Hak, Kim, Exec. Mng. Dir.-Engrng. & Tech.--Korea Heavy Industries & Construction Co., Ltd., Seoul, Korea; *Int'l*, pg. 758
Jaeckin, Philippe, Exec. V.P.--Danone Group, Paris, France; *Int'l*, pg. 379
Jaeger, Eric, Exec. V.P.-Investments--Bartlett and Company, Kansas City, MO; *U.S. Private*, pg. 118
Jaeger, Klaus, Exec. V.P.-Info. Tech. & Org.--Landesbank Rheinland-Pfalz, Mainz, Germany; *Int'l*, pg. 799
Jaffee, Steven B., Exec. V.P.--Enron Acess, Dublin, OH; *U.S. Public*, pg. 584
Jagerfelt, Lars, Exec. V.P.-Corp. Communications & Pub. Affairs--Saab AB, Linkoping, Sweden; *Int'l*, pg. 686
Jago, Richard, Exec. V.P.-Mktg.--Old World Industries, Inc., Northbrook, IL; *U.S. Private*, pg. 814
Jahn, Hans V., Exec. V.P.--Klockner Pentaplast of America, Inc., Gordonsville, VA; *Int'l*, pg. 737
Jahnke, Keith, Exec. V.P.-Processed Meats--Thorn Apple Valley, Inc., Southfield, MI; *U.S. Public*, pg. 1602
Jaksa, E.A. Al, Jr., Chief Oper. Officer & Exec. V.P.--Landry's Seafood Restaurants Inc., Houston, TX; *U.S. Public*, pg. 977
James, E., Exec. V.P.--ABN-AMRO Holding N.V., Amsterdam, Netherlands; *Int'l*, pg. 8
James, Edward B., Exec. V.P.--SunTrust Banks of Georgia, Inc., Atlanta, GA; *U.S. Public*, pg. 1538
James, J. Bradford, Exec. V.P.-Corp. Devel. & Distr.--USG Corporation, Chicago, IL; *U.S. Public*, pg. 1660
James, Kenneth T., Chief Oper. Officer & Exec. V.P.--Rauland-Borg Corporation, Skokie, IL; *U.S. Private*, pg. 911
James, Philip J., Exec. V.P.--ConAgra Agri-Products Co., Greeley, CO; *U.S. Public*, pg. 426
Janeczek, Edward J., Exec. V.P. & Treas.--R.O. Whitesell & Associates, Inc, Indianapolis, IN; *U.S. Private*, pg. 1173
Janicek, Anthony, Exec. V.P.--Forest City Land Group, Cleveland, OH; *U.S. Public*, pg. 668
Janjori, Karl, Exec. V.P.-Country Exposures & Gen. Banking--Union Bank of Switzerland, Zurich, Switzerland; *Int'l*, pg. 1439
Jankowski, Henry, Exec. V.P.--DeVault Foods, Devault, PA; *U.S. Private*, pg. 329
Jansen, P.G., Exec. V.P.--ABN-AMRO Holding N.V., Amsterdam, Netherlands; *Int'l*, pg. 8
Jansen, Rolf R., Exec. V.P.--Stora Feldmuhle AG, Dusseldorf, Germany; *Int'l*, pg. 1303
Jansky, Sandra W., Exec. V.P.--SunTrust, Orlando, FL; *U.S. Public*, pg. 1537
Janson, Kenneth R., Chief Fin. Officer, Exec. V.P.-Fin. & Treas.--D & N Financial Corporation, Hancock, MI; *U.S. Public*, pg. 472
Janssens, J.A.H., Exec. V.P.--ABN-AMRO Holding N.V., Amsterdam, Netherlands; *Int'l*, pg. 8
Jansson, Harri, Exec. V.P.-Central Ontario Div./Personal & Comml. Banking--Bank of Montreal - Ottawa, Ottawa, Canada; *Int'l*, pg. 153
Jansson, Harri, Exec. V.P.-Central Ontario Div./Personal & Comml. Banking--Bank of Montreal - Vancouver, Vancouver, Canada; *Int'l*, pg. 153
Jansson, Harri E., Exec. V.P.-Central Ontario Div.--Bank of Montreal, Toronto, Canada; *Int'l*, pg. 153
Janz, Gary, Exec. V.P. & Gen. Mgr.--Greenstone Roberts/Florida, Orlando, FL; *U.S. Public*, pg. 763
Jarc, Frank, Chief Fin. Officer & Exec. V.P.--Viking Office Products, Torrance, CA; *U.S. Public*, pg. 1720
Jarc, Frank R., Chief Fin. Officer & Exec. V.P.--R.R. Donnelley & Sons Company, Chicago, IL; *U.S. Public*, pg. 517
Jarvinen, Juha, Exec. V.P.-Baking Div.--Cultor Ltd., Helsinki, Finland; *Int'l*, pg. 349
Jarvis, Daniel O., Chief Fin. Officer & Exec. V.P.--Intrawest Corporation, Vancouver, Canada; *Int'l*, pg. 685
Jaunch, Robert A., Exec. V.P.--Baraboo-Sysco Food Services, Inc., Baraboo, WI; *U.S. Public*, pg. 1550
Jaunich, Robert, Exec. V.P.-Asia/America--Kraft Jacobs Suchard AG, Zurich, Switzerland; *U.S. Public*, pg. 1288
Jean, Denis, Exec. V.P.-Pulp & Paper--Donohue Inc., Quebec, Canada; *Int'l*, pg. 1075
Jeansson, Lennart, Exec. V.P.--AB Volvo, Goteborg, Sweden; *Int'l*, pg. 1476
Jeanteur, Robert, Exec. V.P.--Schneider S.A., Boulogne-Billancourt, France; *Int'l*, pg. 1207
Jebsen, Finn, Exec. V.P. & Mng. Dir. Denofa-Lilleborg--Orkla A.S.A., Oslo, Norway; *Int'l*, pg. 1010
Jeffares, Robert T., Chief Fin. Officer & Exec. V.P.--Great Lakes Chemical Corporation, West Lafayette, IN; *U.S. Public*, pg. 760
Jefferson, Antwine, III, Exec. V.P.--New England Investment Associates, Boston, MA; *U.S. Private*, pg. 737
Jeffrey, Robert, Exec. V.P. & Mng. Dir.-San Francisco--Lowe & Partners/SMS, New York, NY; *U.S. Private*, pg. 678
Jeffrey, Thomas W., Chief Fin. Officer & Exec. V.P.--Atlantic Gulf Communities Corporation, Miami, FL; *U.S. Public*, pg. 144
Jeffries, Patrick W., Chief Devel. Officer & Exec. V.P.--Salick Health Care, Inc., Los Angeles, CA; *Int'l*, pg. 1524
Jeleersnyder, Jean-Luc, Exec. Dir.--Union Miniere, Brussels, Belgium; *Int'l*, pg. 1441
Jelinek, W. Craig, Chief Oper. Officer & Exec. V.P.-N. Div.--Costco Wholesale, Issaquah, WA; *U.S. Public*, pg. 451
Jellison, Brian D., Exec. V.P.-Indus. Div.--Ingersoll-Rand Company, Woodcliff Lake, NJ; *U.S. Public*, pg. 876
Jeltrup, Eric H., Chief Tech. Officer & Exec. V.P.--PCA International, Inc., Matthews, NC; *U.S. Public*, pg. 1240
Jemal, Marvin, Exec. V.P.--Nobody Beats the Wiz, Carteret, NJ; *U.S. Private*, pg. 800
Jemal, Stephen, Exec. V.P.--Nobody Beats the Wiz, Carteret, NJ; *U.S. Private*, pg. 800
Jeniec, John D., Exec. V.P.--Centex Construction Company, Dallas, TX; *U.S. Public*, pg. 322
Jenkins, Janice, Exec. V.P.-Mktg.--Fox Photo, Inc., Saint Louis, MO; *U.S. Public*, pg. 283
Jenkins, Joseph R., Chief Fin. Officer & Exec. V.P.--Heilig-Meyers Company, Richmond, VA; *U.S. Public*, pg. 804
Jenkins, Joseph R., Chief Exec. Officer & Exec. V.P.--Heilig Meyers Furniture Co., Richmond, VA; *U.S. Public*, pg. 804
Jenkins, Rebecca J., Exec. V.P. & Sec.--MainStreet BankGroup Incorporated, Martinsville, VA; *U.S. Public*, pg. 1038
Jennings, Carl, Exec. V.P.-North American Chemicals--BASF Corporation, Mount Olive, NJ; *Int'l*, pg. 105
Jennings, James B., Exec. V.P.--Hunt Oil Company, Dallas, TX; *U.S. Private*, pg. 548
Jensen, Bernard J., Exec. V.P.--Fuji Securities Inc.-New York, New York, NY; *Int'l*, pg. 519
Jensen, Charles, Exec. V.P.--Generation Metals Corp., Hauppauge, NY; *U.S. Private*, pg. 446
Jensen, Dieter, Exec. V.P.-Prod.--Koenig & Bauer-Albert AG, Wurzburg, Germany; *Int'l*, pg. 742
Jensen, Erik M., Exec. V.P.--Irving F. Jensen Co., Inc., Sioux City, IA; *U.S. Private*, pg. 586
Jensen, Finn O., Grp. Exec. V.P.--Jotun Powder Coatings Pty. Ltd., Brooklyn, Australia; *Int'l*, pg. 715
Jepsen, Edward, Chief Fin. Officer & Exec. V.P.--Times Fiber Communications, Inc., Wallingford, CT; *U.S. Private*, pg. 629
Jessop, Ralph R., Exec. Dir.-Gas Detection--Halma p.l.c., Amersham, United Kingdom; *Int'l*, pg. 589
Jessup, Winthrop S., Exec. V.P.--Delaware Management Holdings, Inc., Philadelphia, PA; *U.S. Public*, pg. 997
Jeter, Mark L., Exec. V.P.--TCF Bank Minnesota FSB, Minneapolis, MN; *U.S. Public*, pg. 1554
Jett, Richard J., Exec. V.P. & SBA Admin.--California State Bank, West Covina, CA; *U.S. Public*, pg. 294
Jim, Jin-Joo, Exec. V.P.--Pohang Iron & Steel Co., Ltd., Kyongbuk, Korea; *Int'l*, pg. 1061
Jimenez, Joseph, Exec. V.P.-Mktg.--Atlantic City Hilton, Atlantic City, NJ; *U.S. Public*, pg. 829
Jinks, Roger, Exec. V.P.-Opers./North Central & International--AGRA Earth & Environmental Limited, Calgary, Canada; *Int'l*, pg. 30
Jiropinyo, Pilik, Chief Fin. Officer & Exec. V.P.--JMP Newcor Holdings Inc., Northbrook, IL; *Int'l*, pg. 1025
Jirsa, James, Chief Fin. Officer & Exec. V.P.--A. Epstein and Sons, Intl., Inc., Chicago, IL; *U.S. Private*, pg. 379
Jobe, Warren Y., Chief Fin. Officer, Exec. V.P. & Treas.--Georgia Power Co., Atlanta, GA; *U.S. Public*, pg. 1490
Joerges, Dan, Exec. V.P.-Sls.--Green Forest Lumber Corporation, Toronto, Canada; *Int'l*, pg. 828
Joffee, Philip M., Exec. V.P.--CalFarm Insurance Company, Sacramento, CA; *U.S. Public*, pg. 1791
Johansson, Barbro, Exec. V.P.-Personnel--Svenska Handelsbanken, Stockholm, Sweden; *Int'l*, pg. 1327
Johansson, Kent, Exec. V.P.-Information, Admin. & Personnel--Celsius AB, Stockholm, Sweden; *Int'l*, pg. 276
Johansson, Kjell, Exec. V.P.--Astra AB, Sodertalje, Sweden; *Int'l*, pg. 93
Johansson, Ole, Exec. V.P.--Metra Corporation, Helsinki, Finland; *Int'l*, pg. 862
Johansson, Stig, Exec. V.P.-Intl. Mkt. Issues--Telia AB, Farsta, Sweden; *Int'l*, pg. 1373
Johansson, Sven Ake, Exec. V.P.-Fin. & Prod.--Nordbanken AB, Stockholm, Sweden; *Int'l*, pg. 957
John, Andrew, Exec. Dir.--Vickers PLC, London, United Kingdom; *Int'l*, pg. 1466
John, James W., Exec. V.P.--Mastercard International, Inc., Purchase, NY; *U.S. Private*, pg. 714
Johns, John D., Chief Fin. Officer & Exec. V.P.--Protective Life Insurance Co., Birmingham, AL; *U.S. Public*, pg. 1336
Johnson, Alan C., Exec V.P.-Powertrain Sys.--Federal-Mogul Corporation, Southfield, MI; *U.S. Public*, pg. 615
Johnson, Ann, Exec. V.P.--Adrien Arpel, New York, NY; *U.S. Public*, pg. 40
Johnson, Bob, Chm. Bd. & Exec. V.P.--Southeastern Realty Group Inc., Orlando, FL; *U.S. Private*, pg. 1015
Johnson, Carl, Exec. V.P. & Gen. Mgr.-Meals Div.--Kraft Foods Inc., Glenview, IL; *U.S. Public*, pg. 1288
Johnson, Carl I., Jr., Exec. V.P.--Johnson Supply & Equipment Corp., Houston, TX; *U.S. Private*, pg. 594
Johnson, Charles B., Exec. V.P.--Metric Systems Corp., Fort Walton Beach, FL; *U.S. Public*, pg. 1563
Johnson, Charles W., Exec. V.P.--Mission Land Company, Irvine, CA; *U.S. Public*, pg. 564
Johnson, Charlie, Exec. V.P.-Opers.--The Cessna Aircraft Co., Wichita, KS; *U.S. Public*, pg. 1589
Johnson, Christina, Exec. V.P. & Dir.-Stores--Saks Fifth Avenue, New York, NY; *U.S. Public*, pg. 1429
Johnson, Dan, Exec. V.P. & Gen. Mgr.-Tommy Nelson--Thomas Nelson Inc., Nashville, TN; *U.S. Public*, pg. 1167
Johnson, Daryl P., Chief Fin. Officer & Exec. V.P.--Response Oncology, Inc., Memphis, TN; *U.S. Public*, pg. 1449
Johnson, Daryle G., Exec. V.P.-Pension Investments--Pacific Life Insurance Company, Newport Beach, CA; *U.S. Private*, pg. 831
Johnson, David G., Sr. Exec. V.P. & Gen. Counsel--Metro-Goldwyn-Mayer Inc., Santa Monica, CA; *U.S. Public*, pg. 1101
Johnson, Debby, Exec. V.P. & Mktg Dir.--Ackerman McQueen, Inc., Oklahoma City, OK; *U.S. Private*, pg. 12
Johnson, Denise, Exec. V.P.--Arnold Communications, Inc., Boston, MA; *U.S. Private*, pg. 83
Johnson, Duane, Exec. V.P.--Berger Transfer & Storage, Inc., Saint Paul, MN; *U.S. Private*, pg. 135
Johnson, Dwight T., Exec. V.P.--Scitex Corporation Ltd., Holon, Israel; *Int'l*, pg. 644
Johnson, Ed, Exec. V.P.-Sls. & Mktg.--Star-Kist Foods Inc., Newport, KY; *U.S. Public*, pg. 805
Johnson, Frank, Chief Fin. Officer, Exec. V.P. & Treas.--Today's Man, Inc., Moorestown, NJ; *U.S. Public*, pg. 1619
Johnson, Harold H., III, Exec V.P.--Provident Bankshares Corporation, Baltimore, MD; *U.S. Public*, pg. 1337
Johnson, Harry A., III, Exec. V.P. & Gen. Counsel--First Tennessee Bank National Association, Memphis, TN; *U.S. Public*, pg. 639
Johnson, Horace M., Jr., Exec. V.P. & Reg. Mgr.--Willis Faber North America, Inc.-North Carolina, Greensboro, NC; *Int'l*, pg. 1503
Johnson, J. Fred, Chief Fin. Officer, Exec. V.P. & Treas.--Piccadilly Cafeterias, Inc., Baton Rouge, LA; *U.S. Public*, pg. 1294
Johnson, James P., Exec. V.P.--Sommer & Maca Industries, Inc., Cicero, IL; *U.S. Private*, pg. 1013
Johnson, James R., Exec. V.P. & Sec.--Johnson Storage Moving Co, Denver, CO; *U.S. Private*, pg. 594
Johnson, James R., Exec. V.P.--Security Van Lines, Kenner, LA; *U.S. Private*, pg. 594
Johnson, James R., Exec. V.P.--Denver Moving & Storage Co., Denver, CO; *U.S. Private*, pg. 594
Johnson, Joanna, Exec. V.P.-Intl./Motion Pictures--Paramount Pictures Corporation, Los Angeles, CA; *U.S. Private*, pg. 776
Johnson, Mercedes, Chief Fin. Officer & V.P.-Fin.--Lam Research Corporation, Fremont, CA; *U.S. Public*, pg. 975
Johnson, Michael A., Exec. V.P.-Admin. & Mktg.--Western Financial Bank, Irvine, CA; *U.S. Public*, pg. 1757
Johnson, Paul E., Jr., Exec. V.P. & Gen. Mgr.--Marriott Senior Living Services, Washington, DC; *U.S. Public*, pg. 1048
Johnson, Peter, Exec. V.P.--MEPC American Properties, Dallas, TX; *U.S. Private*, pg. 686
Johnson, Peter, Exec. V.P.--Little America Refining, Inc., Evansville, WY; *U.S. Private*, pg. 1003
Johnson, R.M., Exec. V.P.--Photo Control Corporation, Minneapolis, MN; *U.S. Public*, pg. 1292
Johnson, Reid, Chief Fin. Officer & Exec. V.P.--Musicland Group Inc., Minnetonka, MN; *U.S. Public*, pg. 1142
Johnson, Richard F., Exec. V.P.--Zurich Insurance Company, Zurich, Switzerland; *Int'l*, pg. 1529
Johnson, Richard L., Exec. V.P.--Sholodge, Inc., Hendersonville, TN; *U.S. Public*, pg. 1467
Johnson, Robert B., Chief Oper. Officer & Exec. V.P.--The Detroit Medical Center, Detroit, MI; *U.S. Private*, pg. 328
Johnson, Rupert H., Jr., Exec. V.P.--Franklin Resources, Inc., San Mateo, CA; *U.S. Public*, pg. 679
Johnson, Sheila Crump, Exec. V.P.-Corp. Affairs--Black Entertainment Television Holdings Inc., Washington, DC; *U.S. Public*, pg. 235

Johnson, Stephen, Chief Oper. Officer & Exec. V.P.--CFA Holding Company, Charlotte, MI; *U.S. Private*, pg. 194
Johnson, Stephen M., Chief Oper. Officer & Exec. V.P.--The Alpine Group, Inc., New York, NY; *U.S. Public*, pg. 58
Johnson, Steve, Sr. V.P.-Pub. Rels.--Union Bank of California, San Francisco, CA; *Int'l*, pg. 157
Johnson, Thomas P., Jr., Exec. V.P.-Retail Banking--NationsBank West, Saint Louis, MO; *U.S. Public*, pg. 1164
Johnson, Thomas R., Exec. V.P.-Credit Policy--Comerica Incorporated, Detroit, MI; *U.S. Public*, pg. 408
Johnson, Thomas R., Jr., Exec. V.P.-Mfg.--Russell Corporation, Alexander City, AL; *U.S. Public*, pg. 1413
Johnson, W. Parks, Exec. V.P.--Deposit Guaranty Corp., Jackson, MS; *U.S. Public*, pg. 500
Johnson, W. Parks, Exec. V.P.--Deposit Guaranty National Bank, Jackson, MS; *U.S. Public*, pg. 500
Johnson, William, Chief Fin. Officer & Exec. V.P.--Camping World, Inc., Bowling Green, KY; *U.S. Private*, pg. 204
Johnston, Doug, Exec. V.P.-Fin.--Platinum Equity Holdings, LLC, Los Angeles, CA; *U.S. Private*, pg. 872
Johnston, Richard W., Exec. V.P.--Pierce & Stevens Corp., Buffalo, NY; *U.S. Private*, pg. 1019
Johnstone, Rudolph G., Jr., Exec. V.P.--Westvaco Corporation, New York, NY; *U.S. Public*, pg. 1762
Johnstone, William B., III, Exec. V.P.-Portfolio Mngmt. Div.--First Hawaiian Bank, Honolulu, HI; *U.S. Public*, pg. 634
Jolain, Pierre, Exec. V.P.-Ethics--Credit Commercial de France, Paris, France; *Int'l*, pg. 341
Jolley, James D., Exec. V.P.-Correspondent Banking Dept.--Magna Group, Inc., Saint Louis, MO; *U.S. Public*, pg. 1037
Jonegard, Rolf, Chief Fin. Officer & Exec. V.P.--Svedala Industri AB, Malmo, Sweden; *Int'l*, pg. 1323
Joneja, Raj, Exec. V.P.-Mdsg.--Mervyn's California, Hayward, CA; *U.S. Public*, pg. 489
Jones, Barclay G., III, Exec. V.P. & Mng. Dir.--W.P. Carey & Co., Inc., New York, NY; *U.S. Private*, pg. 209
Jones, Barry, Gen. Mgr. & Exec. V.P.--Paramount Canada's Wonderland, Vaughan, Canada; *U.S. Private*, pg. 776
Jones, Benjamin, III, W., Exec. V.P.-Legal & Acq.--IRT Property Company, Atlanta, GA; *U.S. Public*, pg. 858
Jones, Bruce, Exec. V.P.--Whittenberg Construction Co., Louisville, KY; *U.S. Private*, pg. 1174
Jones, Clarke C., Exec. V.P.-Adv.--Saunders Oil Company, Inc., Richmond, VA; *U.S. Private*, pg. 968
Jones, Dennis P., Exec. V.P.-Opers.--TLC Beatrice International Holdings Inc., New York, NY; *U.S. Private*, pg. 1064
Jones, E. Richard, Exec. V.P.-Supply Opers.--Safeway Inc., Pleasanton, CA; *U.S. Public*, pg. 1426
Jones, E.R., Exec. V.P.--Safeway Supply, Inc., Walnut Creek, CA; *U.S. Public*, pg. 1426
Jones, Elliott M., Exec. V.P.-Mktg. & Tech. Services--Willis Corroon Corp. of Illinois, Chicago, IL; *Int'l*, pg. 1506
Jones, Harrison P., Exec. V.P.--Vincent Metal Goods-Northern Division, Coon Rapids, MN; *Int'l*, pg. 1118
Jones, James D., Exec. V.P.--American Security Group, Atlanta, GA; *Int'l*, pg. 499
Jones, James G., Grp. Exec. V.P.-Consumer Credit--Bank of America NT&SA, San Francisco, CA; *U.S. Public*, pg. 180
Jones, John P., III, Exec. V.P.-Gases & Equipment--Air Products and Chemicals, Inc., Allentown, PA; *U.S. Public*, pg. 30
Jones, Kathy, Exec. V.P.-Mktg.--Universal Pictures, Universal City, CA; *Int'l*, pg. 1216
Jones, Larry, Exec. V.P. & Treas.--Patriot American Hospitality, Inc., Dallas, TX; *U.S. Public*, pg. 1265
Jones, Lloyd, Exec. V.P.--A.G. Simpson Co. Limited, Scarborough, Canada; *Int'l*, pg. 1252
Jones, Peter, Exec. V.P.--First Marathon Securities Limited, Toronto, Canada; *Int'l*, pg. 486
Jones, Peter C., Exec. V.P.-Tech. & Project Devel.--Inco Limited, Toronto, Canada; *Int'l*, pg. 672
Jones, Philip S., Exec. V.P.-Corp. & Institutional Banking--First Chicago NBD Corporation, Chicago, IL; *U.S. Public*, *pg. 627*
Jones, Richard, Exec. V.P.-Fin.--Vincor International, Niagara Falls, Canada; *Int'l*, pg. 1468
Jones, Stephen M., Exec. V.P.--P.T. Freeport Indonesia Co., New Orleans, LA; *U.S. Public*, pg. 681
Jones, Thomas E., Principal Fin. Officer & Exec. V.P.--Citicorp, New York, NY; *U.S. Public*, pg. 376
Jones, Timothy, Exec. V.P.--ScotiaMocatta, New York, NY; *Int'l*, pg. 156
Jones, Wellington D. III, Exec. V.P.-Personal Banking & Small Bus. Banking Grp.--1st Source Corporation, South Bend, IN; *U.S. Public*, pg. 638
Jones, Wellington D., III, Exec. V.P.-Personal & Small Bus. Banking Grp.--1st Source Bank Consolidated, South Bend, IN; *U.S. Public*, pg. 638
Jones, William Allen, Exec. V.P.-Corp. Affairs & Sec.--Metro-Goldwyn-Mayer Inc., Santa Monica, CA; *U.S. Public*, pg. 1101
Jons, Otto P., Exec. V.P.--Advanced Marine Enterprises, Inc., Arlington, VA; *U.S. Public*, pg. 1182
Joos, David W., Exec. V.P. & Chief Oper. Officer-Electric--Consumers Energy, Jackson, MI; *U.S. Public*, pg. 280
Jordan, Joyce, Exec. V.P.-Sls.--Dart Transit Company, Eagan, MN; *U.S. Private*, pg. 311
Jordan, Kari, Exec. V.P.--Merita Ltd., Helsinki, Finland; *Int'l*, pg. 858
Jordan, Nicholas, Exec. V.P.-Sls. & Mktg.--CPS Corporation, Franklin, TN; *U.S. Private*, pg. 422
Jordan, Shirley, Exec. V.P. & Chief Investment Officer--Presidential Life Corporation, Nyack, NY; *U.S. Public*, pg. 1323
Jordon, Charles "Kip", Exec. V.P. & Publr.-Word Publishing--Thomas Nelson Inc., Nashville, TN; *U.S. Public*, pg. 1167
Jordon, Larry C., Exec. V.P.--New Mech Companies, Inc., Saint Paul, MN; *U.S. Private*, pg. 794
Jorgensen, Hans A., Exec. V.P. & Gen. Mgr.--U.S. Divers Co., Inc., Santa Ana, CA; *U.S. Private*, pg. 1125
Jorgensen, Marty, Sr. V.P.-Pur. & Adv.--Video Products Distributors, Inc., Sacramento, CA; *U.S. Private*, pg. 1139
Josefsen, Turi, Exec. V.P. & Pres.-Intl. Opers.--U.S. Surgical Corp., Norwalk, CT; *U.S. Public*, pg. 1687
Joseph, Isaac, Exec. V.P.-ICO Oilfield Services--ICO, Inc., Houston, TX; *U.S. Public*, pg. 853
Josten, Bruce, Exec. V.P.--Nation's Business, Washington, DC; *U.S. Private*, pg. 788
Jourdan, Bernard, Exec. V.P.--Anjou International Company, New York, NY; *Int'l*, pg. 321
Joyce, Rene R., Sr. Exec. V.P.--Tejas Gas Corporation, Houston, TX; *Int'l*, pg. 1136
Jubiler, Lois, Exec. V.P.-N. America & Europe--Colgate-Palmolive Company, New York, NY; *U.S. Public*, pg. 397
Judd, James T., Sr. Exec. V.P.--Golden West Financial Corporation, Oakland, CA; *U.S. Public*, pg. 750
Julian, Malcolm, Exec. V.P.-Sls. & Mktg.--Winstar Global Products, Inc., Fairfield, NJ; *U.S. Public*, pg. 1772
Juneau, J. Bradley, Exec. V.P.-Exploration--Sonat Exploration GOM Inc., Houston, TX; *U.S. Public*, pg. 1485
Jung, Andrea, Exec. V.P. & Pres.-Global Mktg. & New Bus.--Avon Products, Inc., New York, NY; *U.S. Public*, pg. 155
Jung, Jae-Uk, Exec. V.P.--Daehong Advertising Inc., Seoul, Korea; *Int'l*, pg. 357
Jungmann, Norman, Exec. V.P.-Opers.--Just Born, Inc., Bethlehem, PA; *U.S. Private*, pg. 602
Junquera Diez, Jorge A., Sr. Exec. V.P.--Banco Popular de Puerto Rico, San Juan, PR; *U.S. Public*, pg. 175
Junquera, Jorge A., Sr. Exec. V.P.--BanPonce Corporation, Hato Rey, PR; *U.S. Public*, pg. 176
Jurgeleit, Deborah, Exec. V.P.-Acct. Mngmt.--RBT/Strum, Cherry Hill, NJ; *U.S. Private*, pg. 902
Jurgensen, W.G., Exec. V.P.-Credit Cards--First Chicago NBD Corporation, Chicago, IL; *U.S. Public*, pg. 627
Justice, Hal, Exec. V.P.-Sls. & Mktg.--URS Logistics, Atlanta, GA; *U.S. Private*, pg. 1114
Juvakka, Pentti, Exec. V.P.--Enso Oyj, Helsinki, Finland; *Int'l*, pg. 455
Kabat, Kevin, Sr. Exec. V.P.--Old Kent Bank, Grand Rapids, MI; *U.S. Public*, pg. 1216
Kabat, Kevin T., Exec. V.P.-Retail Admin. & Tech.--Old Kent Financial Corporation, Grand Rapids, MI; *U.S. Public*, pg. 1216
Kabcenell, Derry, Chief Tech. Officer--Oracle Corporation, Redwood City, CA; *U.S. Public*, pg. 1227
Kaczynski, Steve, Exec. V.P.-Sls. & Mktg.--Giant Food Stores Inc., Carlisle, PA; *Int'l*, pg. 750
Kadanoff, Marcia, Partner & Exec. V.P.--Miller/Kadanoff/Huber Direct & Interactive, San Francisco, CA; *U.S. Private*, pg. 747
Kaden, Ellen O., Exec. V.P., Gen. Counsel & Sec.--CBS, New York, NY; *U.S. Public*, pg. 273
Kagan, Michael, Chief Fin. Officer & Exec. V.P.--Tropical Sportswear International, Tampa, FL; *U.S. Private*, pg. 1105
Kageyama, Kenichi, Exec. V.P.--NHK Spring Co., Ltd., Yokohama, Japan; *Int'l*, pg. 901
Kahan, Jay, Exec. V.P.--Tyco Toys, Inc., Mount Laurel, NJ; *U.S. Public*, pg. 1058
Kahle, Gary L., Exec. V.P.--DeKalb Swine Breeders, Inc., De Kalb, IL; *U.S. Public*, pg. 493
Kahle, John H., Exec. V.P., Gen. Counsel & Asst. Sec.--Kimball International, Inc., Jasper, IN; *U.S. Public*, pg. 956
Kahlmann, R.J., Exec. V.P.--FGH Bank N.V., Utrecht, Netherlands; *Int'l*, pg. 26
Kahn, Charles, Exec. V.P.--Things Remembered, Inc., Highland Heights, OH; *U.S. Public*, pg. 397
Kahn, Richie, Partner, Exec. V.P. & Co-Creative Dir.--Harris Drury Cohen, Fort Lauderdale, FL; *U.S. Private*, pg. 505
Kahn, Todd, Exec. V.P., Gen. Counsel & Sec.--Salant Corporation, New York, NY; *U.S. Public*, pg. 1429
Kai-ming, Chan, Exec. Dir.-Architectural & Engrng.--Sun Hung Kai Properties Ltd., Wan Chai, Hong Kong; *Int'l*, pg. 1318
Kairey, Andrew, Exec. V.P.-Universal Studios Home Video--Universal Pictures, Universal City, CA; *Int'l*, pg. 1216
Kaisand, Duane E., Exec. V.P.--Webcraft Technologies, Inc., North Brunswick, NJ; *U.S. Public*, pg. 228
Kaiser, Lloyd T., Exec. V.P.-Systems--Harmon Industries, Inc., Blue Springs, MO; *U.S. Public*, pg. 788
Kaiser, William, Exec. V.P. & Treas.--KTI, Inc., Guttenberg, NJ; *U.S. Public*, pg. 939
Kaitz, Richard A., Exec. V.P.--Palm Beach Beauty Products Co., Minneapolis, MN; *U.S. Private*, pg. 834
Kajinishi, Shogo, Deputy Pres.--Orix Corporation, Tokyo, Japan; *Int'l*, pg. 1008
Kajita, Kunitaka, Sr. Exec. Dir.--The Japan Development Bank, Tokyo, Japan; *Int'l*, pg. 701
Kajiyama, Tohru, Exec. Dir.--Isuzu Motors Limited, Tokyo, Japan; *Int'l*, pg. 692
Kakurai, Takaomi, Exec. V.P.--Yokogawa Electric Corporation, Tokyo, Japan; *Int'l*, pg. 1520
Kalagher, Steven, Exec. V.P. & Pres.-Spirits & Wine Grp.--The Seagram Company Ltd., Montreal, Canada; *Int'l*, pg. 1214
Kalajian, H., Chief Fin. Officer & Exec. V.P.--Ameritech, Detroit, MI; *U.S. Public*, pg. 97
Kalajian, Nectar, Exec. V.P.-Correspondent Div.--Countrywide Funding Corporation, Pasadena, CA; *U.S. Public*, pg. 453
Kalebic, Thomas V., Chief Oper. Officer & Exec. V.P.--Lane Industries, Inc., Northbrook, IL; *U.S. Private*, pg. 649
Kalela, Kimmo, Exec. V.P.--Enso Oyj, Helsinki, Finland; *Int'l*, *pg. 455*
Kalff, G.J., Sr. Exec. V.P.--ABN-AMRO Holding N.V., Amsterdam, Netherlands; *Int'l*, pg. 8
Kalkitis, Herbert, Sr. V.P.--Inman Construction Corporation, Memphis, TN; *U.S. Private*, pg. 564
Kallasvuo, Olli-Pekka, Exec. V.P.-Nokia Americas--Oy Nokia Ab/Nokia Group, Helsinki, Finland; *Int'l*, pg. 951
Kallfass, Heinz, Exec. V.P.--H. Krantz-TKT GmbH, Bergisch Gladbach, Germany; *Int'l*, pg. 399
Kallstromer, Curt, Exec. V.P.-Reg. Bank, Central Sweden--Svenska Handelsbanken, Stockholm, Sweden; *Int'l*, pg. 1327
Kalt, S. Richard, Exec. V.P.--CRN International, Inc., Hamden, CT; *U.S. Private*, pg. 197
Kalter, Marjorie, Exec. V.P. & Mktg. Dir.--Wunderman Cato Johnson, New York, NY; *U.S. Private*, pg. 1197
Kaman, C. William, II, Exec. V.P. & Pres.-Kaman Music--Kaman Corporation, Bloomfield, CT; *U.S. Public*, pg. 941
Kamata, Michisada, Exec. V.P.--Meiji Milk Products Co., Ltd., Tokyo, Japan; *Int'l*, pg. 855
Kamdar, Taroon, Pres.-Asia Pacific Div. & Exec. V.P.--Micropolis Corporation, Chatsworth, CA; *U.S. Private*, pg. 742
Kamil, Harvey, Chief Fin. Officer & Exec. V.P.--Nature's Bounty Inc., Bohemia, NY; *U.S. Public*, pg. 1166
Kamimura, Tetsuo, Exec. V.P. & Dir.-Admin.--Mitsubishi Corporation, Tokyo, Japan; *Int'l*, pg. 871
Kamimura, Tokichi, Exec. Dir.--Dentsu Inc., Tokyo, Japan; *Int'l*, pg. 392
Kamimura, Tomoya, Exec. V.P.--Kajima Corporation, Tokyo, Japan; *Int'l*, pg. 721
Kaminski, Joseph J., Exec. V.P.--Air Products and Chemicals, Inc., Allentown, PA; *U.S. Public*, pg. 30
Kaminsky, Kenneth, Chief Oper. Officer & Exec. V.P.--New Haven Savings Bank, New Haven, CT; *U.S. Private*, pg. 793
Kaminsky, Sergi, Exec. V.P.-Eastern Europe & Chem. Demil.--Environmental/Government Group, Boise, ID; *U.S. Public*, pg. 1134
Kaminsky, Thomas, Exec. V.P.-Sls.--Domecq Importers Inc., Old Greenwich, CT; *Int'l*, pg. 63
Kamioka, Kojiro, Exec. V.P.--Meiji Seika Kaisha, Ltd., Tokyo, Japan; *Int'l*, pg. 855
Kanade, Ichiro, Exec. V.P.--Itochu Corporation, Tokyo, Japan; *Int'l*, pg. 694
Kanai, Akinori, Exec. V.P.--Snow Brand Milk Products Co. Ltd., Tokyo, Japan; *Int'l*, pg. 1271
Kanakubo, Hideyuki, Exec. V.P.--Uniden America Corporation, Fort Worth, TX; *Int'l*, pg. 1433
Kanari, Yoshiaki, Exec. V.P.--Cosmo Securities Co., Ltd., Osaka, Japan; *Int'l*, pg. 335
Kanarick, Arnold F., Exec. V.P. & Dir.-Human Resources--The Limited, Inc., Columbus, OH; *U.S. Public*, pg. 995
Kanazawa, Seiji, Exec. V.P.--Sumitomo Sitix Corporation, Amagasaki, Japan; *Int'l*, pg. 1317
Kane, Alice T., Exec. V.P.-Asset Mngmnt. & Investment Prods. & Gen. Counsel--New York Life Insurance Company, New York, NY; *U.S. Private*, pg. 794
Kane, Douglas C., Chief Oper. Officer & Exec. V.P.--MDU Resources Group, Inc., Bismarck, ND; *U.S. Public*, pg. 1025
Kane, Edward K., Exec. V.P.--The Guardian Life Insurance Company of America, New York, NY; *U.S. Private*, pg. 486
Kaneda, Yoshiyuki, Exec. Deputy Pres.--Sony Corporation, Tokyo, Japan; *Int'l*, pg. 1280
Kang, Jung-Moon, Sr. Exec. V.P. & Creative Dir.--Daehong Advertising Inc., Seoul, Korea; *Int'l*, pg. 357
Kanoff, Chris M., Exec. V.P. & Dir.-Fin.--Jefferies & Company, Inc., Los Angeles, CA; *U.S. Public*, pg. 925
Kanter, Alan, Exec. V.P.-Syratech--Carvel Hall, Crisfield, MD; *U.S. Private*, pg. 1061
Kapalko, Gerald J., Exec. V.P.--Olsten Corporation, Melville, NY; *U.S. Public*, pg. 1220
Kapalla, Elizabeth, Exec. V.P.--Health Education Technologies (HET) Div., New York, NY; *U.S. Public*, pg. 1224
Kapalla, Elizabeth A., Exec. V.P.--PRISM International, New York, NY; *U.S. Public*, pg. 1224
Kaphingst, Richard J., Exec. V.P.--TCF Bank Wisconsin, Milwaukee, WI; *U.S. Public*, pg. 1554
Kaplan Thaler, Linda, Exec. V.P. & Exec. Creative Dir.--Wells BDDP, Inc., New York, NY; *Int'l*, pg. 117
Kaplan, Beth, Exec. V.P.-Mktg.--Rite Aid Corporation, Camp Hill, PA; *U.S. Public*, pg. 1390
Kaplan, Daniel I., Exec. V.P.-HERC--The Hertz Corporation, Park Ridge, NJ; *U.S. Public*, pg. 664
Kaplan, Ronald W., Exec. V.P.--Plant City Steel Co., Plant City, FL; *U.S. Public*, pg. 793
Kaplan, Stan, Exec. V.P. & Creative Dir.--DavisElen Advertising, Inc., Los Angeles, CA; *U.S. Private*, pg. 316
Kappauf, Donald W., Chief Oper. Officer & Exec. V.P.--Digital Solutions, Inc., Somerset, NJ; *U.S. Public*, pg. 508
Kappauf, Donald W., Exec. V.P.--Digital Solutions, Inc., Somerset, NJ; *U.S. Public*, pg. 508
Kappler, Gale, V.P.--Kappler Safety Group, Inc., Guntersville, AL; *U.S. Private*, pg. 607
Karake, Timo, Deputy Chief Exec. Officer & Exec. V.P.-Foodstuffs--Kesko Ltd., Helsinki, Finland; *Int'l*, pg. 732
Karayiannis, Akis, Exec. Dir.--Lehman Brothers International Limited, New York, NY; *U.S. Public*, pg. 987
Kardys, Richard, Exec. V.P. & Exec. Trust Officer--Cullen/Frost Bankers, Inc., San Antonio, TX; *U.S. Public*, pg. 467
Kargula, Michael R., Exec. V.P., Gen. Counsel & Sec.--Primark Corporation, Waltham, MA; *U.S. Public*, pg. 1325
Kari, Juhani, Exec. V.P.--Kemira Oy, Helsinki, Finland; *Int'l*, pg. 727
Karlberg, Ulf, Exec. V.P.--Astra AB, Sodertalje, Sweden; *Int'l*, pg. 93
Karlsson, Goran, Exec. V.P.--Northern Regional Bank--Nordbanken AB, Stockholm, Sweden; *Int'l*, pg. 957
Karlsson, Sanne, Exec. V.P.-Power Trans. & Distrib.--ABB Asea Brown Boveri (Holding) Ltd., Zurich, Switzerland; *Int'l*, pg. 1
Karlsson, Tommy, Exec. V.P.--Crown Cork & Seal Company, Inc., Philadelphia, PA; *U.S. Public*, pg. 462
Karnei, Clifton, Exec. V.P. & Gen. Mgr.--Brazos Electric Power Cooperative, Inc., Waco, TX; *U.S. Private*, pg. 166
Karnei, Clifton, Exec. V.P.--Brazos Fuel Company Inc., Waco, TX; *U.S. Private*, pg. 166

Karnes, W. Michael, Chief Fin. Officer & Exec. V.P.--Prime Group Realty Trust, Chicago, IL; *U.S. Public*, pg. 1326
Karp, Jeff, Exec. V.P.--Power Contracting & Engineering Corp., Schaumburg, IL; *U.S. Private*, pg. 877
Karpa, Carol A., Exec. V.P. & Strategic Media Services Dir.--Doremus & Company, New York, NY; *U.S. Public*, pg. 1223
Karper, Donald J., Exec. V.P.--Alva/Amco Pharmacal Companies, Inc., Chicago, IL; *U.S. Private*, pg. 47
Karr, B.L., Exec. V.P.-Acct. Mngmt.--Brierley & Partners, Dallas, TX; *U.S. Private*, pg. 168
Karr, Howard H., Exec. V.P. & Treas.--First Hawaiian, Inc., Honolulu, HI; *U.S. Public*, pg. 634
Karrass, Stath, Exec. V.P.-Real Estate--John Burnham & Co., San Diego, CA; *U.S. Private*, pg. 186
Karsukura, Shuichi, Exec. V.P.--Uniden America Corporation, Fort Worth, TX; *Int'l*, pg. 1433
Karter, Elias M., Exec. V.P.--The Mead Corporation, Dayton, OH; *U.S. Public*, pg. 1074
Kasai, Hiroshi, Exec. V.P.--Oji Paper Co., Ltd., Tokyo, Japan; *Int'l*, pg. 998
Kasai, Masao, Exec. V.P.--Nichimen Corporation, Tokyo, Japan; *Int'l*, pg. 927
Kasen, Keith, Exec. V.P. & Gen. Mgr.--Busch Gardens Williamsburg, Williamsburg, VA; *U.S. Public*, pg. 114
Kasenter, Robert A., Exec. V.P.-H.R.--Montgomery Ward & Co., Inc., Chicago, IL; *U.S. Private*, pg. 758
Kash, John, Exec. V.P.--Ingersoll-Dresser Pump Company, Liberty Corner, NJ; *U.S. Public*, pg. 529
Kashio, Yukio, Exec. V.P.--Casio Computer Co., Ltd., Tokyo, Japan; *Int'l*, pg. 274
Kashiwagi, Takashi, Exec. V.P.--Hitachi, Ltd., Tokyo, Japan; *Int'l*, pg. 621
Kashmer, Bernard A., Chief Oper Officer & Exec. V.P.--Hull Corporation, Hatboro, PA; *U.S. Private*, pg. 547
Kasle, Donald H., Chief Admin. Officer & Sr. Exec. V.P.--Westcorp, Irvine, CA; *U.S. Public*, pg. 1756
Kasmann, Ludwig, Exec. V.P.--Landesbank Hessen-Thuringen Girozentrale, Frankfurt/Main, Germany; *Int'l*, pg. 798
Kaspi, Paul, Exec. V.P.-Credit Control--Credit Commercial de France, Paris, France; *Int'l*, pg. 341
Kassab, Thomas M., Exec. V.P.--Stainless Incorporated, Deerfield Beach, FL; *U.S. Private*, pg. 1029
Katanyutanon, Prasarn, Exec. V.P.- Banking Grp.--Nakornthon Bank Public Company Limited, Bangkok, Thailand; *Int'l*, pg. 904
Katayama, Kaoru, Exec. Mng. Dir.--Tokuyama Corporation, Tokyo, Japan; *Int'l*, pg. 1393
Katchuk, Richard F., Chief Fin. Officer & Corp. Exec. V.P.--Crestar Financial Corporation, Richmond, VA; *U.S. Public*, pg. 458
Katchuk, Richard F., Chief Fin. Officer & Exec. V.P.--Crestar Bank, Richmond, VA; *U.S. Public*, pg. 458
Kately, Richard, Exec. V.P.-Mktg.--Heitman Financial Ltd., Chicago, IL; *U.S. Public*, pg. 1673
Katen, Karen L., V.P., Exec. V.P.-Pfizer Pharmaceuticals Grp. & Pres.-U.S. Pharm.--Pfizer Inc., New York, NY; *U.S. Public*, pg. 1281
Kathcart, Chris, Exec. V.P.--CMI-Toronto, Toronto, Canada; *U.S. Private*, pg. 287
Kato, Isao, Exec. V.P.--Brother Industries, Ltd., Nagoya, Japan; *Int'l*, pg. 229
Kato, Junsuke, Exec. V.P.--Koito Manufacturing Co., Tokyo, Japan; *Int'l*, pg. 743
Kato, Katsutake, Exec. V.P.--Meitsu Inc., Tokyo, Japan; *Int'l*, *pg. 856*
Kato, Osamu, Exec. V.P.--Sato Kogyo Co., Ltd., Tokyo, Japan; *Int'l*, pg. 1197
Kato, Shimpei, Sr. Exec. V.P.--Fanuc Ltd., Yamanashi, Japan; *Int'l*, pg. 477
Kato, Tomoyuki, Sr. Exec. V.P.--Sumitomo Bank of California, San Francisco, CA; *Int'l*, pg. 1309
Katoyama, Kyozo, Exec. V.P.--Rohto Pharmaceutical Co., Osaka, Japan; *Int'l*, pg. 1126
Katsarakes, George S., Chief Oper. Officer & Exec. V.P.--TII Industries, Inc., Copiague, NY; *U.S. Public*, pg. 1556
Katsura, Akihiko, Deputy Pres.--Chiba Kogyo Bank, Chiba, Japan; *Int'l*, pg. 283
Katsura, Taizo, Sr. Exec. V.P.--Sharp Corporation, Osaka, Japan; *Int'l*, pg. 1228
Katsurada, Teruyoshi, Exec. V.P.--Dentsu Inc., Tokyo, Japan; *Int'l*, pg. 392
Katz, Howard, Exec. V.P.--Reynolds Machine Tool Corp., Melrose Park, IL; *U.S. Private*, pg. 926
Katz, Howard, Exec. V.P.--RMT Technology, Bellwood, IL; *U.S. Private*, pg. 927
Katz, Howard C., Exec. V.P.-Prod.--ESPN, Inc., Bristol, CT; *U.S. Public*, pg. 512
Katz, William E., Exec. V.P.--Ionics, Incorporated, Watertown, MA; *U.S. Public*, pg. 912
Katzin, David B., Chm.-Scientific Advisory Bd. & Exec. V.P.--Herbalife International of America, Inc., Century City, CA; *U.S. Public*, pg. 809
Katzoff, James H., Exec. V.P.-TI Group--TI Group plc, Abingdon, United Kingdom; *Int'l*, pg. 1337
Kauffman, James H., Exec. V.P.-U.S. Pawn Ops--Cash America International, Inc., Fort Worth, TX; *U.S. Public*, pg. 312
Kauffman, Roger A., Chief Oper. Officer & Exec. V.P.--Hecla Mining Company, Coeur D'Alene, ID; *U.S. Public*, pg. 803
Kaufman, Jeffrey V., Chief Oper. Officer & Exec. V.P.--Wall Street Deli, Inc., Birmingham, AL; *U.S. Public*, pg. 1734
Kaufman, Leon, Exec. V.P.--President Baking-Plantation, Lake Bluff, IL; *Int'l*, pg. 1069
Kaufman, Steve, Exec. V.P.--Edelman Worldwide, Inc., New York, NY; *U.S. Private*, pg. 362
Kaufman, Suzanne, Exec. V.P. & Systems & New Technologies Dir.--The Media Edge, New York, NY; *U.S.* Private, pg. 1079
Kaul, Rajendera, Exec. V.P.--F. J. Benjamin Holdings Ltd., Singapore, Singapore; *Int'l*, pg. 187
Kavanaugh, Terrence P., Exec. V.P.--Tembec Inc., Montreal, Canada; *Int'l*, pg. 1374
Kavetas, Harry L., Chief Fin. Officer & Exec. V.P.--Eastman Kodak Company, Rochester, NY; *U.S. Public*, pg. 550
Kavetas, Harry L., Exec. V.P. & Chief Fin. Officer--Scientific Imaging Systems, New Haven, CT; *U.S. Public*, pg. 550
Kawabe, Susumu, Exec. V.P.--Sankyo Company Limited, Tokyo, Japan; *Int'l*, pg. 1189
Kawahara, Hiroshi, Exec. V.P.--NHK Spring Co., Ltd., Yokohama, Japan; *Int'l*, pg. 901
Kawai, Zenjiro, Exec. V.P.--Kajima Corporation, Tokyo, Japan; *Int'l*, pg. 721
Kawana, Yoshikazu, Exec. V.P.--Nissan Motor Co., Ltd., Tokyo, Japan; *Int'l*, pg. 943
Kawano, Yoshiro, Exec. V.P.--Matsushita Electric Works, Ltd., Osaka, Japan; *Int'l*, pg. 847
Kawasaki, Hiroshi, Exec. V.P.--The Tokyo Electric Power Co., Inc., Tokyo, Japan; *Int'l*, pg. 1394
Kawashima, Takeshi, Exec. V.P.--JGC Corporation, Tokyo, Japan; *Int'l*, pg. 697
Kawauchi, Shunsuke, Exec. V.P.--Glory Ltd., Himeji, Japan; *Int'l*, pg. 554
KcKibben, Craig, Exec. V.P.--WRQ, Inc., Seattle, WA; *U.S. Private*, pg. 1145
Keane, Anthony J., Exec. V.P.--Partners & Shevack, Inc., New York, NY; *U.S. Private*, pg. 842
Kearl, Greg, Chief Oper. Officer, Exec. V.P., Treas. & Sec.--Menley & James Laboratories, Inc., Horsham, PA; *U.S. Public*, pg. 1086
Kearney, Daniel P., Exec. V.P.-Investments & Fin. Services--Aetna Inc., Hartford, CT; *U.S. Public*, pg. 26
Kearney, George B., Exec. V.P.--Northwestern Industrial Piping, Niles, IL; *U.S. Private*, pg. 806
Kearns, Robert J., III, Chief Oper. Officer & Exec. V.P.-Fin.--Leasing Solutions, Inc., San Jose, CA; *U.S. Public*, pg. 982
Keating, Brian A., Exec. V.P. & Western Reg. Pres.--Marine Midland Bank, Buffalo, NY; *Int'l*, pg. 581
Keating, Michael K., Exec. V.P. & Gen. Counsel--Fifth Third Bancorp, Cincinnati, OH; *U.S. Public*, pg. 621
Keating, Philip R., Exec. V.P.--Chemical Bank Central, Big Rapids, MI; *U.S. Public*, pg. 345
Keating, Susan, Exec. V.P. & Pres.-Dauphin Deposit Bank--First Maryland Bancorp, Baltimore, MD; *Int'l*, pg. 64
Keay, Steven L., Chief Fin. Officer & Exec. V.P.--Textron Inc., Providence, RI; *U.S. Public*, pg. 1588
Kee, Lim Ho, Chief Exec. Officer & Exec. V.P.-Far East--Union Bank of Switzerland, Zurich, Switzerland; *Int'l*, pg. 1439
Keeble, Donald W., Exec. V.P.-Store Opers.--Kmart Corporation, Troy, MI; *U.S. Public*, pg. 963
Keefe, Patrick E., Exec. V.P.-Opers.--Omnicare, Inc., Covington, KY; *U.S. Public*, pg. 1223
Keehbler, Nicholas, Chief Oper. Officer & Exec. V.P.--PennCorp Financial Group, Inc., New York, NY; *U.S. Public*, pg. 1271
Keeler, Robert, Exec. V.P.-Mktg--WWF Paper Corporation, Bala Cynwyd, PA; *U.S. Private*, pg. 1145
Keenan, John, Exec. V.P. & Chief Creative Officer--Ross Roy Communications, Inc., Bloomfield Hills, MI; *U.S. Private*, pg. 946
Keener, Bruce D., Exec. V.P.--Kepner-Tregoe, Inc., Skillman, NJ; *U.S. Public*, pg. 1659
Keilman, David W., Exec. V.P. & Treas.--Comark, Bloomingdale, IL; *U.S. Private*, pg. 257
Keirstead, Allan G., Vice Chm., Chief Fin. & Admin. Officer & Exec. V.P.--Stanhome Inc., Westfield, MA; *U.S. Public*, *pg. 1508*
Keith, Neil E., Exec. V.P.--Intergraph Corporation, Huntsville, AL; *U.S. Public*, pg. 890
Kelbley, Stephen P., Exec. V.P.--Springs Industries, Inc., Fort Mill, SC; *U.S. Public*, pg. 1499
Kelleher, K.B., Exec. V.P.-Mktg. & Sls.--CNB International, Inc., Charleston, SC; *U.S. Private*, pg. 196
Kelleher, K.B., Exec. V.P.-Mktg. & Sls.--Clearing-Niagara, Buffalo, NY; *U.S. Private*, pg. 196
Keller, J. Frank, Chief Fin. Officer, Exec. V.P. & Sec.--Barrett Resources Corporation, Denver, CO; *U.S. Public*, *pg. 191*
Keller, James J., Chief Oper. Officer & Exec. V.P.--J.J. Keller & Associates, Inc., Neenah, WI; *U.S. Private*, pg. 612
Keller, Michael, Exec. V.P.--Chicago Title & Trust Co., Chicago, IL; *U.S. Public*, pg. 42
Keller, Michael, Exec. V.P.--Chicago Title Insurance Co., Chicago, IL; *U.S. Public*, pg. 42
Keller, Michael, Exec. V.P.-Mktg.--Koo Koo Roo, Inc., Los Angeles, CA; *U.S. Public*, pg. 966
Keller, Michael J., Exec. V.P.--Norwest Mortgage, Inc., Des Moines, IA; *U.S. Public*, pg. 1202
Keller, R. E., Exec. V.P.--Invista Capital Management Inc., Des Moines, IA; *U.S. Private*, pg. 885
Keller, Robert, Chief Fin. Officer & Exec. V.P.--Gateway Apparel, Inc., Saint Louis, MO; *U.S. Private*, pg. 441
Keller, Robert, Exec. V.P.--Dun & Bradstreet, Murray Hill, NJ; *U.S. Public*, pg. 535
Keller, Ron, Exec. V.P.--The Principal Financial Group, Des Moines, IA; *U.S. Private*, pg. 885
Keller, Ron, Exec. V.P.--Sturgeon Electric Company, Henderson, CO; *U.S. Public*, pg. 1029
Keller, Ronald, Exec. V.P.--Principal Mutual Life Insurance Co., Des Moines, IA; *U.S. Private*, pg. 886
Kellett, Sherry A., Exec. V.P. & Controller--BB&T Corporation, Winston Salem, NC; *U.S. Public*, pg. 159
Kelley, Bob, Exec. V.P.-Universal Television Entertainment--Universal Studios TV, Universal City, CA; *Int'l*, pg. 1215
Kelley, James J., Grp. Exec. V.P.-Mngmt. Resources Grp. & Dir.-Human Resources--Crestar Financial Corporation, Richmond, VA; *U.S. Public*, pg. 458
Kelley, James J., Grp. Exec. V.P. & Dir.-Human Resources--Crestar Bank, Richmond, VA; *U.S. Public*, pg. 458
Kelley, Jeffrey D., Exec. V.P.-Investments--National City Corporation, Cleveland, OH; *U.S. Public*, pg. 1154
Kelley, John C., Jr., Exec. V.P. & Pres.-Memphis Banking Grp.--First Tennessee Bank National Association, Memphis, TN; *U.S. Public*, pg. 639
Kellogg, Tom N., Exec. V.P.--General Re Corporation, Stamford, CT; *U.S. Public*, pg. 725
Kelly, Albert J., Exec. V.P.--Hyatt Hotels Corporation, Chicago, IL; *U.S. Private*, pg. 551
Kelly, Bert, Exec. V.P.-Brdcst. Production--DavisElen Advertising, Inc., Los Angeles, CA; *U.S. Private*, pg. 316
Kelly, Craig J., Exec. V.P.-Strategic mktg.--Crestar Financial Corporation, Richmond, VA; *U.S. Public*, pg. 458
Kelly, Craig T., Grp. Exec. V.P.-Strategic Mktg.--Crestar Bank, Richmond, VA; *U.S. Public*, pg. 458
Kelly, Doyle, Exec. V.P.--CNL Financial Corp., Macon, GA; *U.S. Public*, pg. 281
Kelly, Ed, Exec. V.P.-Mdsg. & Mktg.--Eckerd Corporation, Largo, FL; *U.S. Public*, pg. 917
Kelly, Edward W., Jr., Chief Fin. Officer & Exec. V.P.--Cottman Transmission Systems, Inc., Fort Washington, PA; *U.S. Private*, pg. 278
Kelly, Francis T., Exec. V.P.--Productos Gerber de Centroamerica, S.A., San Jose, Costa Rica; *Int'l*, pg. 973
Kelly, Harold V., Exec. V.P. & Gen. Counsel--Republic Engineered Steels, Inc., Massillon, OH; *U.S. Public*, pg. 1378
Kelly, Hugh Rice, Exec. V.P. & Gen. Counsel--Houston Industries Incorporated, Houston, TX; *U.S. Public*, pg. 842
Kelly, James, Chief Fin. Officer & Exec. V.P.--Midlantic Bank, N.A., Edison, NJ; *U.S. Public*, pg. 1242
Kelly, John M., Exec. V.P.-Mktg. & Sls.--Desa International, Bowling Green, KY; *U.S. Private*, pg. 326
Kelly, Michael D., Exec. V.P.-Mktg.--Perkins Family Restaurants, Memphis, TN; *U.S. Private*, pg. 925
Kelly, Richard C., Chief Fin. Officer & Exec. V.P.--New Century Energies, Inc., Denver, CO; *U.S. Public*, pg. 1170
Kelly, Richard C., Chief Fin. Officer, Exec. V.P.-Fin. & Treas.--Public Service Company of Colorado, Denver, CO; *U.S. Public*, pg. 1170
Kelly, Robert C., Chief Strategy Officer & Exec. V.P.--Enron Corp., Houston, TX; *U.S. Public*, pg. 584
Kelly, Suzanne, Exec. V.P.--California Reconveyance Co., Chatsworth, CA; *U.S. Public*, pg. 1741
Kelly, Thomas R., Jr., Exec. V.P. & Mgr.-Gen. Mdse.--Goody's Family Clothing, Inc., Knoxville, TN; *U.S. Public*, *pg. 753*
Kelly, William, Exec. V.P. & Acct. Mng. Dir.--Young & Rubicam New York, New York, NY; *U.S. Private*, pg. 1198
Kelman, J. Brent, Exec. V.P.-Corp. Services--Canada Trustco Mortgage Company, London, Canada; *Int'l*, pg. 112
Kelsey, Glenn B., Chief Fin. Officer & Exec. V.P.--Oneida Ltd., Oneida, NY; *U.S. Public*, pg. 1225
Kelso, David B., Chief Fin. Officer & Exec. V.P.--The Chubb Corporation, Warren, NJ; *U.S. Public*, pg. 354
Kelson, Richard B., Chief Fin. Officer & Exec. V.P.--Aluminum Company of America, Pittsburgh, PA; *U.S. Public*, pg. 60
Keltner, Thomas, Chief Devel. Officer & Exec. V.P.--Promus Hotel Corporation, Memphis, TN; *U.S. Public*, pg. 1335
Kelvie, William E., Chief Information Officer & Exec. V.P.--Federal National Mortgage Association (Fannie Mae), Washington, DC; *U.S. Public*, pg. 615
Kemp, Herb, Exec. V.P. & Client Services Dir.--The Chisholm-Mingo Group, New York, NY; *U.S. Private*, pg. 237
Kemp, K. Thomas, Exec. V.P. & Treas.--Fund American Enterprises Holdings, Inc., Hanover, NH; *U.S. Public*, pg. 688
Kemper, James S., III, Exec. V.P.-Comml. Lines--Kemper Insurance Companies, Long Grove, IL; *U.S. Private*, pg. 614
Kempert, David, Chief Store Opers. Officer & Exec. V.P.--The Cato Corporation, Charlotte, NC; *U.S. Public*, pg. 318
Kemph, Chris, V.P.-Mktg.--Site Oil Company of Missouri, Clayton, MO; *U.S. Private*, pg. 1004
Kempinski, Chet, Chief Oper. Officer & Exec. V.P.--PHB Die Casting, Fairview, PA; *U.S. Private*, pg. 826
Kempinski, Chet, Chief Oper. Officer & Exec. V.P.--PHB Machining Division, Fairview, PA; *U.S. Private*, pg. 826
Kempinski, Chet, Chief Oper. Officer & Exec. V.P--PHB Tool & Die, Girard, PA; *U.S. Private*, pg. 826
Kempinski, Chet, Chief Oper. Officer & Exec. V.P.--PHB Plastic & Rubber Molding Division, Fairview, PA; *U.S. Private*, pg. 826
Kennedy, Arthur S., Exec. V.P.--Carat MBS, New York, NY; *U.S. Private*, pg. 208
Kennedy, Brian J., Exec. V.P.-Sls. & Mktg.--The Hertz Corporation, Park Ridge, NJ; *U.S. Public*, pg. 664
Kennedy, Charles G., Chief Fin. Officer & Exec. V.P.-Finance--Henley Paper Company, Greensboro, NC; *U.S. Private*, pg. 522
Kennedy, Douglas, Exec. V.P.--FDP Corp., Miami, FL; *U.S. Public*, pg. 603
Kennedy, J. Donald, Chief Fin. Officer & Exec. V.P.-Fin. & Admin.--King Kullen Grocery Co., Inc., Westbury, NY; *U.S. Private*, pg. 621
Kennedy, John, Exec. V.P.--Yorktowne Paperboard Corp., York, PA; *U.S. Private*, pg. 796
Kennedy, Martin E., Jr., Exec. V.P.--Simon & Schuster Education Group, Upper Saddle River, NJ; *U.S. Private*, pg. 778
Kennedy, Quentin J., Exec. V.P. & Sec.--Federal Paper Board Company, Inc., Montvale, NJ; *U.S. Public*, pg. 903
Kennedy, Raymond F., Exec. V.P.--Masco Corporation, Taylor, MI; *U.S. Public*, pg. 1052
Kennedy, Walter, Exec. V.P.-Hole 'N One--The Apparel Group, Ltd., Louisville, KY; *U.S. Private*, pg. 78
Kenney, Donald J., Exec. V.P.-Automation/Opers. & Retail Credit--First of America Bank Corporation, Kalamazoo, MI; *U.S. Public*, pg. 636

Kenney, Jerome P., Exec. V.P.-Corp. Strategy & Research--Merrill Lynch & Co., Inc., New York, NY; *U.S. Public*, pg. 1097
Kenney, Tricia, Pres. & Exec. V.P.--Ayer Public Relations, New York, NY; *U.S. Private*, pg. 104
Kenning, John C., Exec. V.P.--Comdisco, Inc., Rosemont, IL; *U.S. Public*, pg. 407
Kenny, Gregory, Exec. V.P.--General Cable Corporation, Highland Heights, KY; *Int'l*, pg. 1486
Kenswil, Larry, Exec. V.P.--MCA Records, Inc., Universal City, CA; *Int'l*, pg. 1215
Kent, James L., Sr. V.P.-Logistics & Special Div.--McLane Company, Inc., Temple, TX; *U.S. Public*, pg. 1733
Kenyon, Robert, Exec. V.P.--Sleepeck Printing Company, Bellwood, IL; *U.S. Private*, pg. 1005
Kephart, Bruce M., Exec. V.P.--FirstMerit Corporation, Akron, OH; *U.S. Public*, pg. 646
Kerber, Ronald L., Chief Technology Officer & Exec. V.P.--Whirlpool Corporation, Benton Harbor, MI; *U.S. Public*, pg. 1764
Kerdraon, Jean Michel, Exec. V.P.-Radio--CLT-UFA, Luxembourg, Luxembourg; *Int'l*, pg. 561
Kerin, Joe, Exec. V.P.-Stores--American Eagles Outfitters Inc., Warrendale, PA; *U.S. Private*, pg. 53
Kerler, William R., Exec. V.P.-Opers.--Jacobs Engineering Group Inc., Pasadena, CA; *U.S. Public*, pg. 921
Kerman, Richard, Exec. V.P.-Mktg.--Steiner Electric Company, Chicago, IL; *U.S. Private*, pg. 1039
Kermott, Gary, Exec. V.P.--First American Title Insurance Co., Santa Ana, CA; *U.S. Public*, pg. 625
Kern, R.E., Exec. V.P.--Morgan Grenfell Capital Management Incorporated, New York, NY; *Int'l*, pg. 405
Kernan, Richard M., Jr., Exec. V.P.-Investments--New York Life Insurance Company, New York, NY; *U.S. Private*, pg. 794
Kerr, Christopher, Exec. V.P.--Blackwell Publishers, Inc., Cambridge, MA; *Int'l*, pg. 197
Kerr, K.G., Exec. Dir.--Swire Pacific Limited, Central, Hong Kong; *Int'l*, pg. 1328
Kerr, Robert, Exec. V.P.--Consolidated Pipe & Supply Company, Birmingham, AL; *U.S. Private*, pg. 266
Kerr, Stephen R., Chief Exec. Officer--Holstein Association USA, Inc., Brattleboro, VT; *U.S. Private*, pg. 536
Kerr, Stephen R., Exec. V.P.--Holstein-Friesian Services, Inc., Brattleboro, VT; *U.S. Private*, pg. 536
Kerschner, Alan, Exec. V.P.-Fin.--Fox Photo, Inc., Saint Louis, MO; *U.S. Public*, pg. 283
Kersh, Russ, Exec. V.P.-Admin. & Fin.--Sunbeam Corporation, Delray Beach, FL; *U.S. Public*, pg. 1533
Kerstein, David, Exec. V.P.-Retail & Mktg.--Old Kent Bank, Grand Rapids, MI; *U.S. Public*, pg. 1216
Kerstein, David L., Exec. V.P.-Retail Banking--Old Kent Financial Corporation, Grand Rapids, MI; *U.S. Public*, pg. 1216
Kerstetter, Bill, Chief Oper. Officer & Exec. V.P.--New World Entertainment, Inc., Los Angeles, CA; *Int'l*, pg. 926
Kervick, Kevin M., Exec. V.P.--Kervick Enterprises, Inc., Worcester, MA; *U.S. Private*, pg. 616
Kerwin, James J., Exec. V.P.-Opers.--Bankers Life Insurance Co. of New York, Woodbury, NY; *U.S. Private*, *pg. 560*
Kerzner, Jay J., Chief Oper. Officer & Exec. V.P.--Rainoldi, Kerzner & Radcliffe, San Francisco, CA; *U.S. Public*, pg. 1224
Kesler, Larry, Exec. V.P.--BanPonce Corporation, Hato Rey, PR; *U.S. Public*, pg. 176
Keslo, Michael, Mng. Dir.-Corp. Enterntainment--Viacom Entertainment, New York, NY; *U.S. Private*, pg. 779
Kessavan, Sudakar, Grp. Pres. & Exec. V.P.--ICF Kaiser International Inc., Fairfax, VA; *U.S. Public*, pg. 852
Kessel, Fred, Exec. V.P.--Chema Balcke-Durr Verfahrenstechnik GmbH Rudisleben, Rudisleben, Germany; *Int'l*, pg. 399
Kesselman, Ronald C., Exec. V.P.--Borden, Inc., Columbus, OH; *U.S. Private*, pg. 157
Kessenich, Mark F., Jr., Mng. Dir.--Eastbridge Capital Inc., New York, NY; *Int'l*, pg. 933
Kessler, Richard, Exec. V.P.--LeaRonal, Inc., Freeport, NY; *U.S. Public*, pg. 982
Ketcham, Geoffrey C., Chief Fin. Officer, Exec. V.P. & Treas.--Energen Corporation, Birmingham, AL; *U.S. Public*, pg. 581
Kettle, Franklin H., Exec V.P.-Aquisitions & Dir.-Corp. Devel.--United Asset Management Corporation, Boston, MA; *U.S. Public*, pg. 1672
Kettler, James M., Pres., Exec. V.P. & Gen Mgr.--Kettler Brothers, Inc., Montgomery Village, MD; *U.S. Private*, pg. 617
Key, Magnus, Exec. V.P.--JM Byggnads och Fastighets AB, Stockholm, Sweden; *Int'l*, pg. 1260
Keyes, James W., Chief Fin. Officer & Exec. V.P.--The Southland Corporation, Dallas, TX; *Int'l*, pg. 693
Keys, James F., Exec. V.P.-Intl. Opers.--The Standard Products Company, Dearborn, MI; *U.S. Public*, pg. 1504
Keyte, David H., Chief Fin. Officer & Exec. V.P.--Forest Oil Corporation, Denver, CO; *U.S. Public*, pg. 670
Khan, S.U., Exec. V.P.--R.J. Brown and Associates Corporation AG, Zug, Switzerland; *Int'l*, pg. 766
Khanna, M.K. "Mike", Exec. V.P., Area Dir.-Central Asia & CEO Hindustan Thompson--J. Walter Thompson Company, New York, NY; *Int'l*, pg. 1483
Khant, Asif M., Exec. V.P.--Newcom, Inc., Westlake Village, CA; *U.S. Public*, pg. 147
Khatib, Ahmad M., Exec. V.P.--WorldCorp, Inc., Herndon, VA; *U.S. Public*, pg. 1779
Kiedrowski, Peter J., Exec. V.P.--Norwest Bank Minnesota N.A., Minneapolis, MN; *U.S. Public*, pg. 1202
Kiefer, Glenn, Exec. V.P.--Barr & Barr, Inc., New York, NY; *U.S. Private*, pg. 117
Kiefer, Joseph T., Exec. V.P. & Gen. Counsel--Pacific Century Financial Corporation, Honolulu, HI; *U.S. Public*, pg. 1248
Kiefer, Joseph T., Exec. V.P.-Legal Division--Bank of Hawaii, Honolulu, HI; *U.S. Public*, pg. 1248
Kiefner, James D., Exec. V.P.--Utility Data Corporation, Indianapolis, IN; *U.S. Public*, pg. 1185
Kiefus, Barry, Exec. V.P.--Big Joe Manufacturing Co., Lincolnwood, IL; *U.S. Private*, pg. 143
Kiehnle, Robert C., Chief Fin. Officer, Exec. V.P. & Asst. Sec.--Fresh America Corp., Dallas, TX; *U.S. Public*, pg. 681
Kiely, Kathy, Exec. V.P. & Creative Dir.--Arnold Communications, Inc., Boston, MA; *U.S. Private*, pg. 83
Kienker, James W., Chief Fin. Officer & Exec. V.P.--NationsBank West, Saint Louis, MO; *U.S. Public*, pg. 1164
Kilbourne, C. Michael, Chief Fin. Officer & Exec. V.P.--Oakwood Homes Corporation, Greensboro, NC; *U.S. Public*, pg. 1209
Kilchenman, Mark, Sr. Exec. V.P.--Lifetouch, Portrait Studios, Eden Prairie, MN; *U.S. Private*, pg. 667
Kilcullen, Daniel M., Exec. V.P.-Global Securities Svcs.--Mellon Bank Corporation, Pittsburgh, PA; *U.S. Public*, pg. 1084
Kildal, Jan, Chief Fin. Officer & Exec. V.P.-Fin.--Norske Skogindustrier A.S, Skogn, Norway; *Int'l*, pg. 965
Kiley, Michael T., Partner, Chief Fin. Officer, & Exec. V.P.--Media That Works, Cincinnati, OH; *U.S. Private*, pg. 727
Kilgore, Jon W., Exec. V.P. & Dir.--The Robinson-Humphrey Company, Inc., Atlanta, GA; *U.S. Public*, pg. 1633
Kilguss, Jr., George E., Exec. V.P.-Trust & Private Banking--Citizens Trust Company, Providence, RI; *Int'l*, pg. 1132
Kilijanski, Joe, Exec. V.P.--Mollenberg-Betz Inc., Buffalo, NY; *U.S. Private*, pg. 756
Killingsworth, Marti, Exec. V.P. & Treas.--Griffin Manufacturing Co., Muskogee, OK; *U.S. Private*, pg. 481
Kilper, Stephen, Exec. V.P.-Disposal Svcs.--American Waste Services, Inc., Warren, OH; *U.S. Public*, pg. 94
Kilroy, Bruce G., Exec. V.P. & Pres.-Lehigh Valley Div.--National Penn Bank, Boyertown, PA; *U.S. Public*, pg. 1159
Kim, Charles G., Exec. V.P.--Commerce Bancshares, Inc., Kansas City, MO; *U.S. Public*, pg. 409
Kim, Hak Soo, Exec. V.P. & Dir.--Cho Hung Bank, Seoul, Korea; *Int'l*, pg. 287
Kim, K.H., Chief Oper. Officer & Exec. V.P.--Kodak Korea Ltd., Seoul, Korea; *U.S. Public*, pg. 555
Kim, Kwang-Ho, Exec. V.P.--Daehong Advertising Inc., Seoul, Korea; *Int'l*, pg. 357
Kim, Leo, Chief Technical Officer & Exec. V.P.--Mycogen Corporation, San Diego, CA; *U.S. Public*, pg. 1142
Kim, Moo N., Chief Exec. Officer, Exec. V.P. & Mgr.-Mfg.--Crown Confectionery Co., Ltd., Seoul, Korea; *Int'l*, pg. 348
Kim, Young C., Exec. V.P. & Mng. Dir.--Sunkyong America, Inc., New York, NY; *Int'l*, pg. 1320
Kimball, Kevin M., Exec. V.P.-Fin./Marriott Lodging--Marriott International, Inc., Washington, DC; *U.S. Public*, pg. 1047
Kimbara, Yoshiro, Exec. V.P.--Toyota Motor Corporation, Tokyo, Japan; *Int'l*, pg. 1411
Kimishima, Hidehiko, Exec. V.P.-Engrng. & Construction--Kawasaki Steel Corporation, Tokyo, Japan; *Int'l*, pg. 726
Kimoto, Yutaka, Exec. V.P.--Sanyo Electric Co., Ltd., Osaka, Japan; *Int'l*, pg. 1190
Kimura, Hideo, Exec. V.P.-Machinery--Kawasaki Heavy Industries, Ltd., Kobe, Japan; *Int'l*, pg. 725
Kimura, Mitsuaki, Exec. V.P.--Asahi Breweries Ltd., Tokyo, Japan; *Int'l*, pg. 83
Kimura, Shigeru, Exec. V.P.--Matsushita Electric Works, Ltd., Osaka, Japan; *Int'l*, pg. 847
Kimura, Yasuo, Exec. V.P.-Tech. Res. & Devel., Media Business, C&C Systems--Sumitomo Corporation, Tokyo, Japan; *Int'l*, pg. 1312
Kimzey, James R., Exec. V.P.-Res. & Engrng.--Baldor Electric Company, Fort Smith, AR; *U.S. Public*, pg. 168
Kindler, Jeffrey B., Exec. V.P. & Gen. Counsel--McDonald's Corporation, Oak Brook, IL; *U.S. Public*, pg. 1068
King-wan, Law, Exec. Dir.-Sls.--Sun Hung Kai Properties Ltd., Wan Chai, Hong Kong; *Int'l*, pg. 1318
King, Brian L., Exec. V.P.--First Maryland Bancorp, Baltimore, MD; *Int'l*, pg. 64
King, E. Cameron, Exec. V.P.-Electronic Commerce Div.--Countrywide Home Loans Inc., Pasadena, CA; *U.S. Public*, pg. 452
King, J. Joseph, Exec. V.P.--Molex Incorporated, Lisle, IL; *U.S. Public*, pg. 1121
King, Kelly, Exec. V.P.-Branch Network--Branch Banking & Trust, Winston Salem, NC; *U.S. Public*, pg. 160
King, Kernan F., Exec. V.P.-Admin.--The New England, Boston, MA; *U.S. Private*, pg. 737
King, Mark A., Chief Fin. Officer & Exec. V.P.--Affiliated Computer Services, Inc., Dallas, TX; *U.S. Public*, pg. 27
King, Michael, Exec. V.P. & Gen. Mgr.--Bayerische Landesbank - Singapore Branch, Singapore, Singapore; *Int'l*, pg. 176
King, Paul L., Exec. V.P. & Treas.--American Family Mutual Insurance Co., Madison, WI; *U.S. Private*, pg. 53
King, Richard, Exec. V.P. & New Bus. Contact--Zimmerman & Partners Advertising, Inc., Elmwood Park, NJ; *U.S. Private*, pg. 1206
King, Richard W., Exec. V.P.-Netware Systems Group--Novell, Inc., Orem, UT; *U.S. Public*, pg. 1203
King, Robert C., Exec. V.P. & Dir.--The Robinson-Humphrey Company, Inc., Atlanta, GA; *U.S. Public*, pg. 1633
King, Robert G., Exec. V.P.-Gillette N. Atlantic Grp.--The Gillette Company, Boston, MA; *U.S. Public*, pg. 743
King, Rufus B., Chief Credit Officer & Exec. V.P.--First American Corporation, Nashville, TN; *U.S. Public*, pg. 624
King, Sheldon S., Exec. V.P. & Dir.-Academic Affairs--Salick Health Care, Inc., Los Angeles, CA; *Int'l*, pg. 1524
Kinney, Richard, Exec. V.P.--All-Phase Electric Supply Co., Benton Harbor, MI; *U.S. Private*, pg. 35
Kinney, Steven, Exec. V.P.--All-Phase Electric Supply Co., Benton Harbor, MI; *U.S. Private*, pg. 35
Kinnune, William P., Exec. V.P.-Corrugated Containers & Bags--Willamette Industries, Inc., Portland, OR; *U.S. Public*, pg. 1768
Kinoshita, Hiroo, Exec. V.P.-Transportation & Insurance Div.--Sumitomo Corporation, Tokyo, Japan; *Int'l*, pg. 1312
Kinzer, Charles, Exec. V.P.-Opers.--Barton Brands, Ltd., Chicago, IL; *U.S. Public*, pg. 300
Kiousis, Martin J., Exec. V.P.--Lynch Manufacturing Corporation, Greenwich, CT; *U.S. Public*, pg. 1022
Kipnis, Gregory P., Exec. V.P.--Jefferies & Company, Inc., Los Angeles, CA; *U.S. Public*, pg. 925
Kippur, Stephen, Exec. V.P. & Grp. Pres.--Professional Reference & Trade Group, New York, NY; *U.S. Public*, pg. 1768
Kippur, Stephen A., Exec. V.P. & Grp. Pres., PRT--John Wiley & Sons, Inc., New York, NY; *U.S. Public*, pg. 1768
Kirby, Dan L., Co.-Chm. Bd., Exec. V.P., Gen. Counsel & Sec.--Western Surety Company, Sioux Falls, SD; *U.S. Public*, pg. 303
Kirby, John, Chief Fin. Officer & Exec. V.P.--U.S. Trust Corporation, New York, NY; *U.S. Public*, pg. 1688
Kirby, Kerry J., Chief Fin. Officer & Exec. V.P.-Fin.--TruServ Corporation, Chicago, IL; *U.S. Private*, pg. 1108
Kirchhoff, William T., Sr., Exec. V.P.--Cleveland Brothers Equipment Co., Inc., Harrisburg, PA; *U.S. Private*, pg. 245
Kirk, Hans, Exec. V.P.--Danfoss A/S, Nordborg, Denmark; *Int'l*, pg. 376
Kirk, Joseph R., Exec. V.P.--OHM Corporation, Findlay, OH; *U.S. Public*, pg. 1207
Kirkman, Allan C., Exec. V.P.-Real Estate Fin.--Mellon Bank Corporation, Pittsburgh, PA; *U.S. Public*, pg. 1084
Kirkman, James A., III, Exec. V.P., Gen. Counsel & Sec.--Nabisco Inc., Parsippany, NJ; *U.S. Public*, pg. 1355
Kirkman, Paul, Exec. V.P.-Mktg. & Sls.--Beverage Canners International Corp., Miami, FL; *U.S. Private*, pg. 106
Kirkowski, Michael, Exec. V.P.--Condor D.C. Power Supplies Inc., Oxnard, CA; *U.S. Public*, pg. 1419
Kirkwood, R., V.P. & Gen. Mgr.--Pyroil Canada Limited, Mississauga, Canada; *Int'l*, pg. 955
Kirkwood, William T., Chief Fin. Officer & Exec. V.P.--Worthington Foods Inc., Worthington, OH; *U.S. Public*, pg. 1780
Kirlin, Peter S., Ph.D., Exec. V.P.--ATMI, Inc., Danbury, CT; *U.S. Public*, pg. 12
Kirwin, Keith, Exec. V.P.--J.B. Coxwell Contract, Inc., Jacksonville, FL; *U.S. Private*, pg. 283
Kiser, Arthur G., Exec. V.P.--Wachovia Bank, Charlottesville, VA; *U.S. Public*, pg. 1730
Kiser, Gerald L., Chief Oper. Officer & Exec. V.P.--La-Z-Boy Incorporated, Monroe, MI; *U.S. Public*, pg. 972
Kish, Timothy E., Esq., Exec. V.P. & Gen. Counsel--Capital Factors, Inc., Fort Lauderdale, FL; *U.S. Public*, pg. 1669
Kishner, Gerald S., Chief Fin. Officer & Exec. V.P.-Fin. & Admin.--Canadian Tire Corporation Limited, Toronto, Canada; *Int'l*, pg. 259
Kissin, Roger, Exec. V.P. & Integrated Programming Dir.--Carrafiello, Diehl & Associates, Inc., Irvington, NY; *U.S. Private*, pg. 215
Kitagawa, Taizoo, Sr. Mng. Dir.--NSK Ltd., Tokyo, Japan; *Int'l*, pg. 903
Kitani, Takaharu, Exec. Dir.--Dentsu Inc., Tokyo, Japan; *Int'l*, pg. 392
Kitao, Yoshitaka, Chief Fin. Officer & Exec. V.P.--Softbank Corporation, Tokyo, Japan; *Int'l*, pg. 1276
Kitch, Gerald C., Exec. V.P. & Pres.-Intl. Bus. Devel.--Pentair, Inc., Saint Paul, MN; *U.S. Public*, pg. 1273
Kitchen, G.J., Chief Admin. Officer & Exec. V.P.--Century Aluminum Company, Monterey, CA; *U.S. Public*, pg. 328
Kitchen, Steven L., Chief Fin. Officer & Exec. V.P.--Western Resources, Inc., Topeka, KS; *U.S. Public*, pg. 1759
Kitei, Michael, Exec. V.P. & Creative Dir.--Sive/Young & Rubicam L.P., Cincinnati, OH; *U.S. Private*, pg. 1197
Kittrell, Charles J., Chief Oper. Officer & Exec. V.P.--Cornerstone Propane G.P. Inc., Watsonville, CA; *U.S. Public*, pg. 1201
Kiyoshi, Katsumi, Exec. V.P.--Dai-Ichi Kangyo Bank of California-Los Angeles, Los Angeles, CA; *Int'l*, pg. 360
Kizuka, Shuichi, Exec. V.P.--Nippon Telegraph and Telephone Corporation, Tokyo, Japan; *Int'l*, pg. 940
Klapper, Dave, Exec. V.P.--Finish Line, Inc., Indianapolis, IN; *U.S. Public*, pg. 623
Klatell, Robert, Exec. V.P.--Arrow Electronics, Inc., Melville, NY; *U.S. Public*, pg. 133
Klauber, James, Exec. V.P.-North American Sls.--Adecco S.A., Lausanne, Switzerland; *Int'l*, pg. 23
Klein, Adam, Exec. V.P.-Global Strategy--Hasbro, Inc., Pawtucket, RI; *U.S. Public*, pg. 797
Klein, Christian A.J., Exec. V.P.--Landesbank Hessen-Thuringen Girozentrale, Frankfurt/Main, Germany; *Int'l*, pg. 798
Klein, Gary, Exec. V.P. & Natl. Sls. Mgr.--Lane Bryant, Reynoldsburg, OH; *U.S. Public*, pg. 995
Klein, Joel, Exec. V.P.--Stamford Capital, Stamford, CT; *U.S. Private*, pg. 1029
Klein, John A., Exec. V.P.-Consumer Banking Div.--People's Bank, Bridgeport, CT; *U.S. Public*, pg. 1274
Klein, Jonathan C., Exec. V.P.--CBS News, New York, NY; *U.S. Public*, pg. 274
Klein, Mathias A., III, Exec. V.P.--Klein Tools Inc., Skokie, IL; *U.S. Private*, pg. 625
Klein, Tom, Exec. V.P.-Mfg.--MNP Corp., Utica, MI; *U.S. Private*, pg. 687
Klein, Walter C., Jr., Exec. V.P.-PNC Mortgage Bank, N.A.--PNC Bank Corp., Pittsburgh, PA; *U.S. Public*, pg. 1242
Kleiner, Madeline, Exec. V.P.-Admin., Gen. Counsel & Sec.--H.F. Ahmanson & Co., Irwindale, CA; *U.S. Public*, pg. 29
Kleinert, Robert, Exec. V.P.--Dade Behring Inc., Deerfield, IL; *U.S. Private*, pg. 110
Kleinert, Robert, Exec. V.P.--Dade Behring Inc., Deerfield, IL; *Int'l*, pg. 626
Kleinman, Mel, Exec. V.P.-Sls.--El Camino Resources, Ltd., Woodland Hills, CA; *U.S. Private*, pg. 366
Kleinman, Robert D., Exec. V.P., Sec. & Gen. Counsel--AFA Protective Systems, Inc., Syosset, NY; *U.S. Public*, pg. 5

Klemann, Gilbert L., II, Exec. V.P.-Strategic & Legal Affairs--Fortune Brands, Inc., Old Greenwich, CT; *U.S. Public*, pg. 674

Klemens, Thomas A., Chief Fin. Officer & Exec. V.P.--The First American Financial Corporation, Santa Ana, CA; *U.S. Public*, pg. 624

Klene, Brian C., Exec. V.P.-Sls. & Mktg.--Micron Electronics, Inc., Nampa, ID; *U.S. Public*, pg. 1105

Kleopa, Lena, Exec. V.P. & Gen. Mgr.--Leo Burnett Athens, Athens, Greece; *U.S. Private*, pg. 184

Klesse, William R., Exec. V.P.--Ultramar Diamond Shamrock Corporation, San Antonio, TX; *U.S. Public*, pg. 1663

Kleva, Gregory, Exec. V.P. & Deputy Gen. Counsel--American Life Insurance Company of New York, New York, NY; *U.S. Private*, pg. 769

Kleva, Gregory A., Jr., Exec. V.P. & Deputy Gen. Counsel--Mutual of America Life Insurance Company, New York, NY; *U.S. Private*, pg. 769

Klevering, Loren L., AIA, Exec. V.P. & Sec.--Giffels Associates, Inc., Southfield, MI; *U.S. Private*, pg. 452

Kliger, Jack, Exec. V.P.--Parade Publications Inc., New York, NY; *U.S. Private*, pg. 20

Klimm, Gerhard, Sr. Exec. V.P.-Sls. & Institutional Investments--Landesbank Rheinland-Pfalz, Mainz, Germany; *Int'l*, pg. 799

Kline, Gary, Exec. V.P.--Uniden America Corporation, Fort Worth, TX; *Int'l*, pg. 1433

Kline, Steven R., Chief Fin. Officer & Exec. V.P.--Gardner Publications, Inc., Cincinnati, OH; *U.S. Private*, pg. 440

Klingensmith, James E., Grp. Exec. V.P.-Health Insurance Opers.--Highmark Inc., Pittsburgh, PA; *U.S. Private*, pg. 528

Klingham, Walter, Exec. V.P.--The Princess Marcella Borghese, Inc., New York, NY; *U.S. Private*, pg. 690

Klipp, William J., Exec. V.P.-SchwabFunds--The Charles Schwab Corporation, San Francisco, CA; *U.S. Public*, pg. 1442

Klipper, Mitchell, Chief Fin. Officer & Exec. V.P.--B. Dalton Bookseller, Inc., New York, NY; *U.S. Public*, pg. 189

Klokner, James R., Exec. V.P.-Admin.--American Family Mutual Insurance Co., Madison, WI; *U.S. Private*, pg. 53

Klosk, Steven M., Exec. V.P.-Admin.--Cambrex Corporation, East Rutherford, NJ; *U.S. Public*, pg. 297

Klues, Jack, Exec. V.P. & Worldwide Media Dir.--Leo Burnett Company, Inc., Chicago, IL; *U.S. Private*, pg. 183

Kluge, Bernhard, Exec. V.P.-Securities Trading--Landesbank Rheinland-Pfalz, Mainz, Germany; *Int'l*, pg. 799

Klyszeiko, Michael A., Exec. V.P.-Opers.--Read-Rite Corporation, Milpitas, CA; *U.S. Public*, pg. 1366

Knapp, David L., Exec. V.P.--CNB Bancshares, Inc., Evansville, IN; *U.S. Public*, pg. 280

Knappik, Klaus, Exec. V.P.-Logistics--The Swissair Group, Zurich, Switzerland; *Int'l*, pg. 1333

Knarr, Robert A., Exec. V.P.-Sls. & Mktg., N. America--U.S. Surgical Corp., Norwalk, CT; *U.S. Public*, pg. 1687

Knell, Sandra A., Chief Fin. Officer, Exec. V.P. & Sec.--The Coast Distribution System, San Jose, CA; *U.S. Public*, pg. 388

Knezevie, Miro, Exec. V.P.--TRC Environmental Solutions, Inc., Irvine, CA; *U.S. Public*, pg. 1558

Knicely, Howard V., Exec. V.P.-Human Resources & Communications--TRW Inc., Cleveland, OH; *U.S. Public*, pg. 1558

Knieling, Hermann, Chief Oper. Officer & Exec. V.P.--Airgas, Inc., Radnor, PA; *U.S. Public*, pg. 33

Knight, Ernest, Exec. V.P.-Sls.& Mktg.- Intl.--Miracle Recreation Equipment Company, Monett, MO; *U.S. Private*, pg. 752

Knight, Harold O., Jr., Chief Fin. Officer & Exec. V.P.--Medpartners Inc., Birmingham, AL; *U.S. Public*, pg. 1082

Knipmeyer, Ken, Exec. V.P. & Gen. Mgr.-BASES C1 Svc.--BASES Worldwide, Covington, KY; *U.S. Private*, pg. 120

Knipp, Kurt S., Exec. V.P.-Bankcard Services--National City Processing, Inc., Louisville, KY; *U.S. Public*, pg. 1154

Knisely, Gary T., Exec. V.P.--Hanover Foods Corporation, Hanover, PA; *U.S. Private*, pg. 499

Kniskern, Pauline A., Chief Fin. Officer & Exec. V.P.--CD Products, Inc., New Providence, NJ; *U.S. Public*, pg. 276

Knispel, Barry, Exec. V.P.--Arrow Fastener Co., Inc., Saddle Brook, NJ; *U.S. Private*, pg. 85

Knopik, Stephen M., Exec. V.P.--Beall's, Inc., Bradenton, FL; *U.S. Private*, pg. 126

Knorr, Carol, Exec. V.P.-Mktg. & Devel.--GMAC Insurance Holdings, Detroit, MI; *U.S. Public*, pg. 719

Knott, Jack E., Exec. V.P. & Pres.-Rexene Prods.--Rexene Corporation, Dallas, TX; *U.S. Private*, pg. 549

Knous, Pamela K., Chief Fin. Officer & Exec. V.P.--SuperValu, Inc., Eden Prairie, MN; *U.S. Public*, pg. 1540

Knowles, Marie L., Chief Fin. Officer & Exec. V.P.--Atlantic Richfield Company, Los Angeles, CA; *U.S. Public*, pg. 144

Knowles, Rick L., Exec. V.P.-Fixed Income & Institutional Equity--The Nesbitt Thomson Corporation Limited, Toronto, Canada; *Int'l*, pg. 153

Knowles, Robert E., Chief Fin. Officer & Exec. V.P.--S & K Famous Brands, Inc., Glen Allen, VA; *U.S. Public*, pg. 1414

Knowlton, Thomas A., Exec. V.P. & Pres.-Kellogg Europe--Kellogg Company, Battle Creek, MI; *U.S. Public*, pg. 947

Knox, John, Exec. V.P.--Great American Management & Investment, Inc., Chicago, IL; *U.S. Private*, pg. 473

Knox, Robert, Exec. V.P.--Knox Oil of Texas Inc., Dallas, TX; *U.S. Private*, pg. 627

Knueppel, Henry W., Exec. V.P.-Opers.--Regal-Beloit Corporation, Beloit, WI; *U.S. Public*, pg. 1370

Knueuen, Gerald R., Chief Fin. Officer, Exec. V.P. & Treas.--Harold M. Pitman Co., Inc., Totowa, NJ; *U.S. Private*, pg. 867

Knupfer, Hans-Georg, Exec. V.P.--Bayerische Hypotheken- und Wechsel-Bank Aktiengesellschaft, Munich, Germany; *Int'l*, pg. 175

Knuts, Per, Exec. V.P.--Stora Kopparbergs Bergslags AB, Falun, Sweden; *Int'l*, pg. 1302

Knutson, G.H., Exec. V.P. & Exec. Creative Dir.--Howard, Merrell & Partners, Inc., Raleigh, NC; *U.S. Private*, pg. 542

Knutson, Jon, Exec. V.P.--Executive Software, Glendale, CA; *U.S. Private*, pg. 388

Knutsson, Jan, Exec. V.P.--Svedala Industri AB, Malmo, Sweden; *Int'l*, pg. 1323

Ko, Chung Sam, Exec. V.P.-Intl.--Korean Airlines Co., Ltd., Seoul, Korea; *Int'l*, pg. 758

Kobacker, Edward J., Chief Oper. Officer & Exec. V.P.--U.S. Timberlands Company, L.P., Klamath Falls, OR; *U.S. Public*, pg. 1688

Kobayakawa, Yohtaro, Exec. V.P.--Takenaka Corporation, Osaka, Japan; *Int'l*, pg. 1351

Kobayashi, Hirokuni, Exec. V.P.--Mycal, Corp., Osaka, Japan; *Int'l*, pg. 897

Kobayashi, Tadashi, Exec. V.P.--Mitsubishi Motors Corporation, Tokyo, Japan; *Int'l*, pg. 875

Kobiela, Peter, Exec. V.P.--Landesbank Hessen-Thuringen Girozentrale, Frankfurt/Main, Germany; *Int'l*, pg. 798

Kobs, Duane, Chief Oper. Officer & Exec. V.P.--Quest Technologies, Inc., Oconomowoc, WI; *U.S. Private*, pg. 900

Kobuna, Kunio, Exec. Dir.--Yamaichi Securities (Singapore) Pte. Ltd., Singapore, Singapore; *Int'l*, pg. 1518

Kocela, Erin, Exec. V.P.-Creative Services--Frankel & Company, Orange, CA; *U.S. Private*, pg. 424

Koch, Benoit H., Exec. V.P.--Holderbank Financiere Glaris Ltd., Glaris, Switzerland; *Int'l*, pg. 628

Koch, Bruce K., Chief Fin. Officer & Exec. V.P.-Opers. & Fin.--Devon Group, Inc., Stamford, CT; *U.S. Public*, pg. 503

Koch, David H., Exec. V.P.-Chemical Tech. Grp.--Koch Industries, Incorporated, Wichita, KS; *U.S. Private*, pg. 628

Koch, Glenn, Exec. V.P.--New Era Cap. Co., Derby, NY; *U.S. Private*, pg. 793

Koch, Jeffrey, Exec. V.P.--National Spinning Co., Inc., New York, NY; *U.S. Private*, pg. 786

Koch, John D., Exec. V.P.-Lending & Subsidiaries--Charter One Bank, Cleveland, OH; *U.S. Public*, pg. 336

Koch, Tim, Chief Fin. Officer, Exec. V.P. & Treas.--EBP Life Insurnace Co., Minneapolis, MN; *U.S. Public*, pg. 635

Kochanski, John A., V.P.-Mktg. & Sls.--Pegasus International Corporation, Pennington, NJ; *U.S. Private*, pg. 1046

Kodayashi, Tsuneki, Sr. Exec. Mng. Dir.--Hitachi Koki Co., Ltd., Tokyo, Japan; *Int'l*, pg. 620

Koebel, Wayne R., Chief Fin. Officer & Exec. V.P.--Shoreline Bank, Benton Harbor, MI; *U.S. Public*, pg. 1468

Koehn, Donald L., Exec. V.P., Treas. & Sec.--Bradbury Company, Inc., Moundridge, KS; *U.S. Private*, pg. 163

Koeneman, Bradford W., Exec. V.P.-Investor Rels. & Mktg.--Magna Group, Inc., Saint Louis, MO; *U.S. Public*, pg. 1037

Koenemann, Carl F., Chief Fin. Officer & Exec. V.P.--Motorola, Inc., Schaumburg, IL; *U.S. Public*, pg. 1136

Koerber, Kathleen, Exec.V.P. & Chief Admin. Officer--MBL Life Assurance Corporation, Newark, NJ; *U.S. Private*, pg. 685

Koerber, Kathleen M., Chief Oper. Officer & Exec. V.P.--MBL Life Assurance Corporation, Newark, NJ; *U.S. Private*, pg. 685

Koff, S., Sr. V.P.-Opers.--Davy International, San Francisco, San Ramon, CA; *Int'l*, pg. 774

Koffman, Richard E., Vice Chm., Exec. V.P. & Sec.--Apparel America, Inc., New Haven, CT; *U.S. Public*, pg. 120

Koga, Masaichi, Sr. Exec. V.P.--Toshiba Corporation, Tokyo, Japan; *Int'l*, pg. 1402

Koh, P.C., Chief Fin. Officer & Exec. V.P.--Husky Oil Ltd., Calgary, Canada; *Int'l*, pg. 640

Kohler, Manfred W., Exec. V.P.--Dun & Bradstreet Schimmelpfeng GmbH, Vienna, Austria; *U.S. Public*, pg. 537

Kohler, W. Manfred, Exec. V.P.--Dun & Bradstreet Deutschland GmbH, Frankfurt/Main, Germany; *U.S. Public*, pg. 536

Kohlhase, Mary, Exec. V.P. & Media Dir.--Media Resources International, New York, NY; *U.S. Private*, pg. 727

Kohlhepp, Jerome C., Exec. V.P.-Specialized Lending--Starbanc Corporation, Cincinnati, OH; *U.S. Public*, pg. 1510

Kohls, Kris, Exec. V.P.-Strategic Devel.--Dart Transit Company, Eagan, MN; *U.S. Private*, pg. 311

Kohls, William R., Chief Fin. Officer & Exec. V.P.--Independent Bank Corporation, Ionia, MI; *U.S. Public*, pg. 874

Kohn, Henri-Armand, Exec. V.P.--Baltek Corporation, Northvale, NJ; *U.S. Public*, pg. 171

Kohn, Jean, Exec. V.P.--Baltek Corporation, Northvale, NJ; *U.S. Public*, pg. 171

Kohnhorst, E.E., Chief Oper. Officer & Exec. V.P.--Brown & Williamson Tobacco Corp., Louisville, KY; *Int'l*, pg. 111

Kohrt, Carl F., Exec. V.P. & Asst. Chief Oper. Officer--Eastman Kodak Company, Rochester, NY; *U.S. Public*, pg. 550

Koike, Takayuki, Exec. V.P.--Kumagai Gumi Co., Ltd., Tokyo, Japan; *Int'l*, pg. 763

Kojima, Akira, Exec. V.P.--Brother Industries, Ltd., Nagoya, Japan; *Int'l*, pg. 229

Kojima, Susumu, Exec. V.P.-Asia Div.--Berlitz International, Inc., Princeton, NJ; *U.S. Public*, pg. 221

Kok, B.R., Exec. V.P.--ABN-AMRO Holding N.V., Amsterdam, Netherlands; *Int'l*, pg. 8

Kokkou, Mary, Exec. V.P.-Client Services--Leo Burnett Athens, Athens, Greece; *U.S. Private*, pg. 184

Kolacki, Paul W., Chief Oper. Officer & Exec. V.P.--Hooper Holmes Corporation, Basking Ridge, NJ; *U.S. Public*, pg. 835

Kolman, Robert, Exec. V.P.-Fin. & Admin.--Discount Tire, Scottsdale, AZ; *U.S. Private*, pg. 334

Kolowratnik, P., Exec. V.P.--Braas GmbH, Oberursell, Germany; *Int'l*, pg. 1091

Kolson, Ronald J., Chief Oper. Officer & Exec. V.P.--Micros Systems Inc., Beltsville, MD; *U.S. Public*, pg. 1106

Kolsted, Darrell, Chief Oper. Officer & Exec. V.P.--Wick Building Systems, Mazomanie, WI; *U.S. Private*, pg. 1174

Komaya, K., Exec. V.P.- Fin. & Controller--Kawasaki Motors Corp., U.S.A., Irvine, CA; *Int'l*, pg. 725

Komoda, Makoto, Exec. V.P.--TDK Corporation, Tokyo, Japan; *Int'l*, pg. 1336

Kondo, Koichi, Exec. V.P.-Mngmt. Planning--Japan Aviation Electronics Industry, Ltd., Tokyo, Japan; *Int'l*, pg. 701

Kondo, Yuzo, Exec. V.P.--Daido Life Insurance Company, Osaka, Japan; *Int'l*, pg. 363

Kondor, George J., Jr., Exec. V.P.--BT Financial Corporation, Johnstown, PA; *U.S. Public*, pg. 163

Konings, Bert J., Exec. V.P.--Sysco/Konings Wholesale, Port Coquitlam, Canada; *U.S. Public*, pg. 1552

Konishi, Masaki, Exec. V.P.--Nippon Express Co., Ltd., Tokyo, Japan; *Int'l*, pg. 933

Konopacki, Thomas, Chief Fin. Officer & Exec. V.P.--Pulse Bancorp, Inc., South River, NJ; *U.S. Public*, pg. 1344

Konopacki, Thomas, Chief Fin. Officer & Exec. V.P.--Pulse Savings Bank, South River, NJ; *U.S. Public*, pg. 1344

Konopik, M. Gene, Exec. V.P. & Grp. Pres.--Sterling Software, Inc., Dallas, TX; *U.S. Public*, pg. 1516

Konowich, Abbey, Exec. V.P.-Mktg.--MCA Records, Inc., Universal City, CA; *Int'l*, pg. 1215

Konowitch, Paul, Exec. V.P.--Medical Economics Company Inc., Montvale, NJ; *U.S. Public*, pg. 1601

Kontinen, Kalevi, Exec. V.P.--Merita Ltd., Helsinki, Finland; *Int'l*, pg. 858

Koo, John, Exec. V.P.-Strategy & Resource Mngmt.--LG Group, Seoul, Korea; *Int'l*, pg. 778

Koo, Young Chi, Exec. V.P. & Dir.--Cho Hung Bank, Seoul, Korea; *Int'l*, pg. 287

Koopman, J., Exec. V.P.--ABN-AMRO Holding N.V., Amsterdam, Netherlands; *Int'l*, pg. 8

Kopp, Stephanie J., Exec. V.P. & Corp. Sec.--Mutual of America Life Insurance Company, New York, NY; *U.S. Private*, pg. 769

Kopp, Stephanie J., Exec. V.P. & Corp. Sec.--American Life Insurance Company of New York, New York, NY; *U.S. Private*, pg. 769

Koppe, David P., Exec. V.P. & Asst. Treas.--United HealthCare of North Carolina, Inc., Greensboro, NC; *U.S. Public*, pg. 1678

Koppe, David P., Exec. V.P. & Asst. Treas.--United HealthCare of Nevada, Inc., Las Vegas, NV; *U.S. Public*, pg. 1678

Kopstick, Marvin, Exec. V.P.-Ontario East--Shoppers Drug Mart, Ltd., Toronto, Canada; *Int'l*, pg. 112

Koraleski, John J., Exec. V.P.-Fin. & Admin.--Union Pacific Railroad Company, Omaha, NE; *U.S. Public*, pg. 1668

Korby, Steve, Chief Fin. Officer & Exec. V.P.--Greyhound Lines, Inc., Dallas, TX; *U.S. Public*, pg. 765

Korby, Steven L., Chief Fin. Officer & Exec. V.P.--Greyhound Lines, Inc., Dallas, TX; *U.S. Public*, pg. 765

Korchek, Jeffrey A., Exec. V.P.-Legal & Business Affairs--Universal Pictures, Universal City, CA; *Int'l*, pg. 1216

Korde, Satish, Exec. V.P. & WW Res. Dir.--Young & Rubicam New York, New York, NY; *U.S. Private*, pg. 1198

Kordisch, Larry W., Chief Fin. Officer, Exec. V.P.-Fin. & Sec.--Homeland Holding Corp., Oklahoma City, OK; *U.S. Public*, pg. 832

Kordyback, Michael R., Exec. V.P.-Stategy, Fin. & Devel.--Jannock Limited, Toronto, Canada; *Int'l*, pg. 698

Korell, Brad, Exec. V.P.--First Commerce Bancshares, Inc., Lincoln, NE; *U.S. Public*, pg. 629

Korell, Harold M., Exec. V.P.-Opers.--Southwestern Energy Company, Fayetteville, AR; *U.S. Public*, pg. 1494

Korell, Harold M., Exec. V.P.-Opers.--Arkansas Western Gas Co., Fayetteville, AR; *U.S. Public*, pg. 1494

Korell, Harold M., Exec. V.P.-Opers.--SEECO, Inc., Fayetteville, AR; *U.S. Public*, pg. 1494

Korell, Harold M., Exec. V.P.-Opers.--Southwestern Energy Pipeline Company, Fayetteville, AR; *U.S. Public*, pg. 1494

Korell, Harold M., Exec. V.P.-Opers.--Southwestern Energy Production Co., Houston, TX; *U.S. Public*, pg. 1494

Korell, Harold M., Exec. V.P.-Opers.--Arkansas Western Pipeline Company, Fayetteville, AR; *U.S. Public*, pg. 1494

Korman, Timothy J., Exec. V.P.-Fin. & Admin.--Hilb, Rogal and Hamilton Company, Glen Allen, VA; *U.S. Public*, pg. 826

Korn, Bill, Exec. V.P.-Strategic Plng., Bus. Devel. & Brdcst. Opers.--CBS, New York, NY; *U.S. Public*, pg. 273

Korn, Michael, Mng. Partner & Exec. V.P.--Ryan Drossman & Partners, New York, NY; *U.S. Private*, pg. 953

Kornecki, Robert, Exec. V.P. & Gen. Mgr.-Bus.--Edelman Public Relations Worldwide, Chicago, IL; *U.S. Private*, pg. 362

Kornegay, H. Tom, Exec. Dir.--Port of Houston Authority, Houston, TX; *U.S. Private*, pg. 876

Kornswiet, Neil B., Exec. V.P., Chm. Bd. & Chief Exec. Officer-One Stop Mortgage, Inc--Aames Financial Corporation, Los Angeles, CA; *U.S. Public*, pg. 12

Koslow, Robert, Exec. V.P. & Production Dir.--Leo Burnett Company, Inc., Chicago, IL; *U.S. Private*, pg. 183

Kostlin, Ulrich, Dr., Exec. Dir.-Mktg. & Sls.--Schering AG, Berlin, Germany; *Int'l*, pg. 1203

Kostock, Arlene M., Exec. V.P.--Invest West Financial Corporation, Santa Barbara, CA; *U.S. Private*, pg. 832

Kosturko, William T., Exec. V.P.-Legal Dept. & Gen. Counsel--People's Bank, Bridgeport, CT; *U.S. Public*, pg. 1274

Kotek, Freddie, Exec. V.P.-Resource Properties, Inc.--Resource America, Inc., Philadelphia, PA; *U.S. Public*, pg. 1382

Kott, Stanley J., Exec. V.P. & Mgr.-Property--NAC Reinsurance Corporation, Greenwich, CT; *U.S. Public*, pg. 1144

Kott, Stanley J., Exec. V.P.--Greenwich Insurance Company, Greenwich, CT; *U.S. Public*, pg. 1144

Kott, Stanley J., Exec. V.P.--Indian Harbor Insurance Company, Greenwich, CT; *U.S. Public*, pg. 1144
Kouno, Akio, Exec. V.P.-Pub. Rels.--Japan Airlines Company, Ltd., Tokyo, Japan; *Int'l*, pg. 699
Koupal, Carl M., Jr., Exec. V.P. & Chief Admin. Officer--Western Resources, Inc., Topeka, KS; *U.S. Public*, pg. 1759
Kouzuma, Makoto, Chief Oper. Officer, Exec. V.P. & Gen. Mgr.--SpeedFam Co Ltd., Ayase, Japan; *U.S. Public*, pg. 1498
Kovaleski, Joe, Exec. V.P.--The Lathrop Company, Toledo, OH; *U.S. Public*, pg. 1645
Kovalic, Fred M., Exec. V.P.--Borg Warner Automotive, Inc., Chicago, IL; *U.S. Public*, pg. 245
Kovel, Ira, Exec. V.P.--W. Gamby & Co., New York, NY; *U.S. Private*, pg. 439
Kowaleski, Dianne, Chief Oper. Officer & Exec. V.P.--Jack Levy Associates, Chicago, IL; *U.S. Private*, pg. 664
Kowalsky, Roger J., Chief Fin. Officer & Exec. V.P.-Fin.--Galoob Toys, Inc., South San Francisco, CA; *U.S. Public*, *pg. 698*
Koyonagi, Shunichi, Exec. V.P.--Shin-Etsu Chemical Co. ltd., Tokyo, Japan; *Int'l*, pg. 1234
Kozai, Yoshinori, Exec. V.P.--Fanuc Ltd., Yamanashi, Japan; *Int'l*, pg. 477
Kozawa, Takeshi, Exec. V.P.--Meiji Seika Kaisha, Ltd., Tokyo, Japan; *Int'l*, pg. 855
Koziol, Donald, Chief Oper. Officer & Exec. V.P.--AON Risk Services, Inc., Chicago, IL; *U.S. Public*, pg. 117
Kozlen, Vern, Exec. V.P.-Investment Mngmt. & Trust Svcs.--City National Corporation, Beverly Hills, CA; *U.S. Public*, pg. 380
Kozlowski, Edwin J., Chief Fin. Officer & Exec. V.P.--General Nutrition, Inc., Pittsburgh, PA; *U.S. Public*, pg. 725
Kraemer, Robert B., Exec. V.P.--Precision Dynamics Corporation, San Fernando, CA; *U.S. Private*, pg. 879
Krafthefer, Kerry M., Exec. V.P.--Berg Electronics, Saint Louis, MO; *U.S. Public*, pg. 212
Krail, Jesse, Deputy Superintendent, Electrical Services Branch--Seattle City Light, Seattle, WA; *U.S. Private*, pg. 979
Krairiksh, Kraithip, Exec. V.P.--The Industrial Finance Corporation of Thailand, Bangkok, Thailand; *Int'l*, pg. 677
Kraiss, Glenn S., Exec. V.P.-Store Opers.--Walgreen Co., Deerfield, IL; *U.S. Public*, pg. 1733
Krakauer, Albert A., Sr. Exec. V.P.-Legal & Corp. Affairs & Sec.--Shoppers Drug Mart, Ltd., Toronto, Canada; *Int'l*, pg. 112
Kramer, Alfred, Member-Bd. of Mngmt.--Wella Group, Darmstadt, Germany; *Int'l*, pg. 1489
Kramer, J. Matthew, Exec. V.P. & Gen. Mgr.-Dallas Trading Div.--Commercial Metals Company, Dallas, TX; *U.S. Public*, pg. 411
Kramer, J. Matthew, Exec. V.P. & Gen. Mgr.--Commercial Metals Co.-Dallas Trading Div., Dallas, TX; *U.S. Public*, pg. 413
Kramer, John P., Exec. V.P. & New Bus. Contact--Icon International, Stamford, CT; *U.S. Private*, pg. 556
Kramer, Peter R., Exec. V.P.--Zoom Telephonics, Inc., Boston, MA; *U.S. Public*, pg. 1794
Kramer, Shlomo, Exec. V.P. & Co-Founder--Check Point Software Technologies Ltd., Redwood City, CA; *U.S. Public*, pg. 342
Krammer, George, Sr. Exec. V.P.-Bus. & Opers.--Technip, Paris, France; *Int'l*, pg. 1360
Kramp, Harry, Exec. V.P., Chm. & Chief Creative Officer-PPGH/JWT-Netherlands--J. Walter Thompson Company, New York, NY; *Int'l*, pg. 1483
Kranenburg, Hendrik J., Exec. V.P.-Global Ratings Dev.--Standard & Poor's Ratings Services, New York, NY; *U.S. Public*, pg. 1071
Krasnow, Todd J., Exec. V.P.-Mktg.--Staples, Inc., Westborough, MA; *U.S. Public*, pg. 1509
Krattenmaker, Kelly, Chief Oper. Officer & Exec. V.P.--E Prime, Inc., Denver, CO; *U.S. Public*, pg. 1170
Kratzer, Kurt A., Exec. V.P.-RDSI--Rurban Financial Corp., Defiance, OH; *U.S. Public*, pg. 1412
Kratzer, Kurt A., Exec. V.P.--Rurbanc Data Services, Inc., Defiance, OH; *U.S. Public*, pg. 1413
Kraus, Dieter, Chief Exec. Officer & Exec. V.P.--Union Air Transport GmbH, Dusseldorf, Germany; *U.S. Private*, pg. 1120
Kraus, Frederick H., Exec. V.P. & Gen. Counsel--Greate Bay Casino Corporation, Atlantic City, NJ; *U.S. Public*, pg. 760
Krause, Arthur B., Chief Fin. Officer & Exec. V.P.--Sprint Corporation, Westwood, KS; *U.S. Public*, pg. 1500
Krause, Roy, Chief Fin. Officer & Exec. V.P.--Interim Services Inc., Fort Lauderdale, FL; *U.S. Public*, pg. 892
Krauss, Charles W., Exec. V.P.--Sysco Food Services of San Francisco, Inc., Fremont, CA; *U.S. Public*, pg. 1552
Krauss, Christine L., Exec. V.P.--Lakewood Engineering & Manufacturing Co., Chicago, IL; *U.S. Private*, pg. 644
Krautter, Jochen, Dr., Exec. V.P.-Metal Chemical/Information Systems--Henkel KGaA, Dusseldorf, Germany; *Int'l*, pg. 609
Krawczyk, David T., Exec. V.P. & Pres.-Contractor's Warehouse Div.--Grossman's, Inc., Stoughton, MA; *U.S. Private*, pg. 585
Krayem, Elie, Exec. V.P.--Republic National Bank of New York, New York, NY; *U.S. Public*, pg. 1380
Krayem, Elie, Exec. V.P.--Republic National Bank of New York (U.K.), London, United Kingdom; *U.S. Public*, pg. 1381
Kreisberg, Neil I., Exec. V.P. & Grp. Dir.--Grey Advertising Inc., New York, NY; *U.S. Public*, pg. 764
Kreiter, Abe E., Exec. V.P.--Castcraft Industries, Inc., Skokie, IL; *U.S. Private*, pg. 219
Kremer, Richard E., Exec. V.P.-Mktg.--Coast Savings Financial, Inc., Los Angeles, CA; *U.S. Public*, pg. 388
Krenek, Gene, Sr. Exec. V.P.--Hollingsworth Saco Lowell Corporation, Inc., Easley, SC; *U.S. Private*, pg. 535
Krentzel, Theodore, Exec. V.P.--Jac Pac Foods, Ltd., Manchester, NH; *U.S. Private*, pg. 579
Kress, E.C., Exec. V.P.--EdperBrascan Corporation, Toronto, Canada; *Int'l*, pg. 433
Kress, Norma L., Exec. V.P.-Tech. Advisor--Kimball International, Inc., Jasper, IN; *U.S. Public*, pg. 956
Kreussling, Charles, Exec. V.P.-Mfg.--Shorewood Packaging Corporation, New York, NY; *U.S. Public*, pg. 1468
Kriak, John M., Chief Fin. Officer & Exec. V.P.--Crown American Realty Trust, Johnstown, PA; *U.S. Public*, pg. 461
Krick, Rainer, Exec. V.P.--Landesbank Hessen-Thuringen Girozentrale, Frankfurt/Main, Germany; *Int'l*, pg. 798
Kriebel, Robert I., Chief Fin. Officer & Exec. V.P.--U.S. Bioscience, Inc., Conshohocken, PA; *U.S. Public*, pg. 1681
Krimstein, Kenneth, Exec. V.P. & Co-Creative Dir.--Biederman, Kelly & Shaffer, Inc., New York, NY; *U.S. Private*, pg. 142
Krinsky, Sharon, Exec. V.P. & Creative Dir.--Hoffman/Lewis, San Francisco, CA; *U.S. Private*, pg. 532
Krinsley, R., Exec. V.P.--Book Div., New York, NY; *U.S. Public*, pg. 1440
Krinsly, S.Z., Sr. Exec. V.P. & Gen. Counsel--Sequa Corporation, New York, NY; *U.S. Public*, pg. 1458
Kristobak, Vincent M., Exec. V.P.--Laurel Bank, Johnstown, PA; *U.S. Public*, pg. 164
Krivel, Richard W., Exec. V.P.--National Bank of Arizona, Tucson, AZ; *U.S. Public*, pg. 1793
Krivosha, Norman M., Judge, Exec. V.P., Sec. & Gen. Counsel--Ameritas Life Insurance Corp., Lincoln, NE; *U.S. Private*, pg. 65
Krizelman, Sheldon, Exec. V.P.-Mktg.--Quorum Health Resources, Inc., Brentwood, TN; *U.S. Public*, pg. 1354
Kroeger, Thomas, Exec. V.P.-H.R.--Office Depot Inc., Delray Beach, FL; *U.S. Public*, pg. 1212
Kroll, Wolfgang, Exec. V.P.-Bus. Admin. & Fin. & Treas.--Siemens Medical Systems, Inc., Iselin, NJ; *Int'l*, pg. 1246
Kron, Patrick, Exec. V.P.-Food, Healthcare & Beauty Packaging--Pechiney S.A., Courbevoie, France; *Int'l*, pg. 1027
Kron, R.B., Exec. V.P.-Dyes & Organic Specialties--Morton International Inc., Chicago, IL; *U.S. Public*, pg. 1135
Kronung, Hans-Dieter, Exec. V.P.--DG Bank, Frankfurt/Main, Germany; *Int'l*, pg. 351
Kroon, David H., Exec. V.P.-Central Regional Opers.--Corrpro Companies, Inc., Medina, OH; *U.S. Public*, pg. 451
Kropf, Omer G., Exec. V.P.--Supreme Industries, Inc., Goshen, IN; *U.S. Public*, pg. 1541
Kropf, Susan J., Exec. V.P. & Pres.-U.S. Opers.--Avon Products, Inc., New York, NY; *U.S. Public*, pg. 155
Krueger, Blake, Exec. V.P., Gen. Counsel & Sec.--Wolverine World Wide, Inc., Rockford, MI; *U.S. Public*, pg. 1775
Krueger, Martin, Exec. V.P.--Blommer Chocolate Co., Chicago, IL; *U.S. Private*, pg. 150
Kruger, Mark, Exec. V.P. & Gen. Mgr.--Pragmaton, Chicago, IL; *U.S. Public*, pg. 1224
Kruggel, H., Exec. V.P.--KTI Group B.V., Zoetermeer, Netherlands; *Int'l*, pg. 837
Krumholz, Stephen B., Chief Oper. Officer & Exec. V.P.--The Southland Corporation, Dallas, TX; *Int'l*, pg. 693
Kryder, R. Stanley, Exec. V.P.--First Union National Bank of Georgia, Atlanta, GA; *U.S. Public*, pg. 640
Krzyzanowski, Richard L., Exec. V.P., Gen. Counsel & Sec.--Crown Cork & Seal Company, Inc., Philadelphia, PA; *U.S. Public*, pg. 462
Krzyzanski, Victor, Exec. V.P.-Mktg.--McCain Bindery Systems, Inc., Chicago, IL; *U.S. Private*, pg. 719
Ku Kang, In, Exec. V.P.-Res. & Devel.--LG Group, Seoul, Korea; *Int'l*, pg. 778
Kubie, David, Exec. V.P.-Corp. Banking--Dresdner Bank AG, New York, NY; *Int'l*, pg. 418
Kublin, Barry S., Exec. V.P.--Benefit Plans Administrative Services, Inc., Utica, NY; *U.S. Public*, pg. 416
Kubo, Kazuo, Sr. Exec. V.P.--Sharp Corporation, Osaka, Japan; *Int'l*, pg. 1228
Kubota, Isamu, Exec. Dir.--Minolta Co., Ltd., Osaka, Japan; *Int'l*, pg. 869
Kucenski, Mary Ann, Exec. V.P.--BT Financial Corporation, Johnstown, PA; *U.S. Public*, pg. 163
Kudoh, Ryuji, Exec. V.P.--Obayashi Corporation, Tokyo, Japan; *Int'l*, pg. 995
Kuechner, Albert A., Exec. V.P.--Collective Bank, Cologne, NJ; *U.S. Public*, pg. 1528
Kuehn, George E., Exec. V.P. & Gen. Counsel--The Stroh Brewery Company, Detroit, MI; *U.S. Private*, pg. 1047
Kuhn, John, Chief Oper. Officer & Exec. V.P.--Heyman Corporation, Niles, IL; *U.S. Private*, pg. 524
Kuhn, Joseph W., Chief Fin. Officer & Exec. V.P.--ALARIS Medical, Inc., San Diego, CA; *U.S. Public*, pg. 35
Kuhn, Joseph W., Chief Fin. Officer & Exec. V.P.--ALARIS Medical Systems, Inc., San Diego, CA; *U.S. Public*, pg. 35
Kuhne, Victor, Exec. V.P.--Knorr-Bremse Systeme Fur Nutzfahrzeuge GmbH, Munich, Germany; *Int'l*, pg. 738
Kuhnemund, Robert F., Chief Fin. Officer & Exec. V.P.--First Data Corporation, Englewood, CO; *U.S. Public*, pg. 631
Kuisma, Maaret, Exec. V.P.-Mktg.--Stockmann Department Store Div., Helsinki, Finland; *Int'l*, pg. 1301
Kukielka, Harald, Exec. V.P.--DG Bank, Frankfurt/Main, Germany; *Int'l*, pg. 351
Kun, Hong Tuck, Exec. V.P.--DBS Bank Ltd., Singapore, Singapore; *Int'l*, pg. 350
Kunert, Manfred, Exec. V.P.--DG Bank, Frankfurt/Main, Germany; *Int'l*, pg. 351
Kunieda, Mikishi, Exec. V.P.--Takenaka Corporation, Osaka, Japan; *Int'l*, pg. 1351
Kunikata, Tsuneo, Exec. V.P.--Seiko Corporation, Tokyo, Japan; *Int'l*, pg. 1218
Kunk, James E., Exec. V.P.-Central Ohio Region--Huntington National Bank, Columbus, OH; *U.S. Public*, pg. 850
Kuntz, Lawrence J., Exec. V.P.-Electronics--Kimball International, Inc., Jasper, IN; *U.S. Public*, pg. 956
Kuntz, Lawrence J., Exec. V.P.--Kimball Electronics Group, Jasper, IN; *U.S. Public*, pg. 957
Kunzler, Christian C., III, Exec. V.P.--Kunzler & Company, Inc., Lancaster, PA; *U.S. Private*, pg. 636
Kunzler, Jurgen, Dr., Exec. V.P.--Balcke-Durr Kuhlturmbau Leipzig GmbH, Leipzig, Germany; *Int'l*, pg. 400
Kuper, Gregory W., Exec. V.P.-Mfg./Office Furniture--Kimball International, Inc., Jasper, IN; *U.S. Public*, pg. 956
Kuras, Paul, Exec. V.P.-London Office--Shoppers Drug Mart, Ltd., London, Canada; *Int'l*, pg. 112
Kurashige, Tomoaki, Exec. V.P.--Taisei Corporation, Tokyo, Japan; *Int'l*, pg. 1347
Kuribayashi, Teiichi, Exec. V.P.--Japan Airlines Company, Ltd., Tokyo, Japan; *Int'l*, pg. 699
Kurihara, Tsutomu, Exec. Mng. Dir.--Sumitomo Heavy Industries, Ltd., Tokyo, Japan; *Int'l*, pg. 1314
Kurimoto, Koji, Exec. V.P.--Mazda Research & Development of North America, Inc., Irvine, CA; *Int'l*, pg. 849
Kurland, Richard M., Exec. V.P. & Sec.--Handy Store Fixtures, Inc., Newark, NJ; *U.S. Private*, pg. 499
Kuroda, Norimasa, Exec. V.P.--Fuji Bank, New York Branch, New York, NY; *Int'l*, pg. 519
Kuruchittham, Thavisakdi, Exec. V.P.-Mngmt.--Nakornthon Bank Public Company Limited, Bangkok, Thailand; *Int'l*, pg. 904
Kurylowicz, Stanley R., Exec. V.P. & Gen. Mgr.--SHL Systemhouse - Ottawa Region, Ottawa, Canada; *Int'l*, pg. 1154
Kusamichi, Masatake, Exec. V.P.--Nissho Iwai Corporation, Tokyo, Japan; *Int'l*, pg. 946
Kushkin, Larry A., Exec. V.P.-Intl. Automotive Opers.--A. Schulman, Inc., Akron, OH; *U.S. Public*, pg. 1441
Kuula, Tapio, Exec. V.P.--Imatran Voima Oy, Helsinki, Finland; *Int'l*, pg. 660
Kuwahara, Hiroshi, Exec. V.P.--Hitachi, Ltd., Tokyo, Japan; *Int'l*, pg. 621
Kuyers, David J., Exec. V.P., Treas. & Sec.--American Seating Company, Grand Rapids, MI; *U.S. Private*, pg. 61
Kuyper, G., Exec. V.P.--ABN-AMRO Holding N.V., Amsterdam, Netherlands; *Int'l*, pg. 8
Kuypers, John, Exec. V.P.--Pentech International, Inc., Edison, NJ; *U.S. Public*, pg. 1274
Kuzia, Paul H., Exec. V.P.-Tech. & Regulatory Affairs--Arch Communications Group, Inc., Westborough, MA; *U.S. Public*, pg. 127
Kye-Yong, Choi, Exec. V.P.-Trading & Corp. Plng.--Daewoo Corporation, Seoul, Korea; *Int'l*, pg. 357
Kyees, John, Chief Fin. Officer & Exec. V.P.--HC Holdings, Columbus, OH; *U.S. Private*, pg. 489
Kyees, John, Chief Fin. Officer & Exec. V.P.--Huntington Clothiers, Inc., Columbus, OH; *U.S. Private*, pg. 490
Kyle, Wayne, Exec. V.P.-Human Resources--Waterhouse Investor Services, New York, NY; *Int'l*, pg. 1401
Kyono, Yorio, Exec. V.P.--Mitsubishi Motors Corporation, Tokyo, Japan; *Int'l*, pg. 875
La Forge, Francis K., Exec. V.P.--Warren Equities Inc., Providence, RI; *U.S. Private*, pg. 1151
La Grand, Kenneth, Exec. V.P.--Gentex Corporation, Zeeland, MI; *U.S. Public*, pg. 731
La Greca, Salvatore, Exec. V.P. & Chief Fin. Officer-Intl.--McCann-Erickson Worldwide, New York, NY; *U.S. Public*, *pg. 909*
La Rosa, Mark, Exec. V.P. & Dir.-Opers--La Rosa's, Inc., Cincinnati, OH; *U.S. Private*, pg. 640
Laabs, David Q., Exec. V.P.-Risk Mngmt. Services--Willis Corroon Corp. of Michigan, Livonia, MI; *Int'l*, pg. 1506
Laakkonen, Jorma, Exec. V.P.--Merita Ltd., Helsinki, Finland; *Int'l*, pg. 858
Laakso, Ari, Exec. V.P.-Admin.--Merita Ltd., Helsinki, Finland; *Int'l*, pg. 858
Laakso, Ari, Exec. V.P.--Merita Bank Ltd., Helsinki, Finland; *Int'l*, pg. 858
Laaksonen, Pekka, Exec. V.P.--Enso Oyj, Helsinki, Finland; *Int'l*, pg. 455
Labanics, Charles, Exec. V.P.--The Frymaster Corp., Shreveport, LA; *Int'l*, pg. 188
Labarge, Suzanne B., Exec. V.P.-Corp. Treasury--Royal Bank of Canada, Toronto, Canada; *Int'l*, pg. 1131
Labbe, Louis-Thomas, Exec. V.P. & Reg. Mgr.--Willis Corroon Melling Inc., Montreal, Canada; *Int'l*, pg. 1509
Labergere, Alain, Exec. V.P. & Pres.-CPC Europe--Bestfoods, Englewood Cliffs, NJ; *U.S. Public*, pg. 223
LaBonge, Chris, Exec. V.P. & Gen. Mgr.-60 West--Grey Direct, New York, NY; *U.S. Public*, pg. 764
Labonte, Michel, Exec. V.P.-Fin. & Admin.--Hydro-Quebec, Montreal, Canada; *Int'l*, pg. 640
Laborde, Cliffe F., Exec. V.P.--Pental Insurance Co., Ltd., New Orleans, LA; *U.S. Public*, pg. 1608
Labs, Rotraut, M.D., Exec. V.P.-Global Drug Devel.--Hoechst Marion Roussel, Inc., Bridgewater, NJ; *Int'l*, pg. 624
Lacey, Brian, Exec. V.P.-Intl. Syndication--The Summit Media Group, New York, NY; *U.S. Private*, pg. 1050
Lacey, David E., Chief Fin. Officer & Exec. V.P.--Storage Technology Corporation, Louisville, CO; *U.S. Public*, pg. 1522
Lacny, Tom, Exec. V.P.--BTI Americas, Inc., Northbrook, IL; *U.S. Private*, pg. 108
Lacourciere, Paul A., Exec. V.P.-Watts Regulatory Co.--Watts Industries, Inc., North Andover, MA; *U.S. Public*, pg. 1746
Lacourse, Julian, Exec. V.P.--Demoulas Market Basket, Tewksbury, MA; *U.S. Private*, pg. 324
Lacourt, Liliane, Exec. V.P.-Commun.--PSA Peugeot Citroen, Paris, France; *Int'l*, pg. 1020
Lacroix, Richard J., Exec. V.P.-Sls.--Potash Corporation of Saskatchewan Inc., Saskatoon, Canada; *Int'l*, pg. 1064
Lacy, Alan J., Chief Fin. Officer & Exec. V.P.--Sears, Roebuck and Co., Hoffman Estates, IL; *U.S. Public*, pg. 1452

Ladd, David J., Chief Tech. Officer & Exec. V.P.--Octel Messaging Division, Milpitas, CA; *U.S. Public*, pg. 1017
LaDouceur, Robert N., Exec. V.P.--Maxum Health Corp., Dallas, TX; *U.S. Public*, pg. 881
Ladt, Thomas T., Exec. V.P.-Opers.--Vencor, Inc., Louisville, KY; *U.S. Public*, pg. 1711
Lae, Byung-Tae, Chief Oper. Officer & Exec. V.P.--Jaeneung Education Co., Ltd., Seoul, Korea; *Int'l*, pg. 697
LaFayette, David R., Exec. V.P. & Chief Agent-Canada--Mutual of Omaha Insurance Company, Omaha, NE; *U.S. Private*, pg. 769
Laffon, Glen A., Exec. V.P.-Prod. Devel.--Central Reserve Life Corporation, Strongsville, OH; *U.S. Public*, pg. 326
LaFleur, Gerlad W., Exec. V.P.--Dole Food Company, Inc., Westlake Village, CA; *U.S. Public*, pg. 515
Lafley, Alan G., Exec. V.P. & Pres.-Asia--The Procter & Gamble Company, Cincinnati, OH; *U.S. Public*, pg. 1330
Lafont, Bruno, Exec. V.P.-Fin.--Lafarge S.A., Paris, France; *Int'l*, pg. 788
LaForte, M.J., Exec. V.P.--Distributed Systems Division, Lisle, IL; *U.S. Public*, pg. 1522
Lagarde, Jacques, Exec. V.P.-Diversified Grp.--The Gillette Company, Boston, MA; *U.S. Public*, pg. 743
Lagarde, Jacques, Exec. V.P.--Diversified Group, Boston, MA; *U.S. Public*, pg. 743
Lagardere, Arnaud, Exec. V.P.-Corp. Mngmt.--Lagardere Groupe, Paris, France; *Int'l*, pg. 791
Lagasse, Charles, Exec. V.P.--G.I. Plastek, Elyria, OH; *U.S. Private*, pg. 435
LaGraize, Edward J., Exec. V.P.--Gerber Systems Corporation, South Windsor, CT; *U.S. Public*, pg. 740
Lahde, Jorma, Exec. V.P.--Korpivaara Oy - Toyota Group, Korso, Finland; *Int'l*, pg. 72
Lai, Keisuke, Exec. V.P. & Dir.--Settsu Corporation, Amagasaki, Japan; *Int'l*, pg. 1225
Laidlaw, Brian K., Exec. V.P.--Genstar Development Company, San Diego, CA; *Int'l*, pg. 112
Laird, A.M. Sandy, Exec. V.P.--Placer Dome Inc., Vancouver, Canada; *Int'l*, pg. 1060
Lakin, Thomas J., Exec. V.P., Sec. & Gen. Counsel--Starbanc Corporation, Cincinnati, OH; *U.S. Public*, pg. 1510
Lakios, Emmanuel, Exec. V.P.-Worldwide Field Opers.--Veeco Instruments, Inc., Plainview, NY; *U.S. Public*, pg. 1711
Lal, Victor, Exec. V.P. & Chief Oper. Officer-New World Television--New World Entertainment, Inc., Los Angeles, CA; *Int'l*, pg. 926
Lala, D.J., Exec. V.P.--Gould Paper Corporation, New York, NY; *U.S. Private*, pg. 466
Lalich, Sandra J., Chief Oper. Officer & Sr. Exec. V.P.--Willis Corroon Corp. of Illinois, Chicago, IL; *Int'l*, pg. 1506
Lalonde, Timothy, Exec. V.P.-Fin. & Treas.--Carrols Corporation, Syracuse, NY; *U.S. Private*, pg. 216
Lam, John, Sr. V.P.-Ontario--HongKong Bank of Canada, Vancouver, Canada; *Int'l*, pg. 583
Lamarque, David T., Exec. V.P. & Mgr.-Service Center--Environmental/Government Group, Boise, ID; *U.S. Public*, pg. 1134
Lamb, David, Exec. V.P. & Global Bus. Dir.-DeBeers--J. Walter Thompson Company, New York, NY; *Int'l*, pg. 1483
Lamb, Frank, Exec. V.P.-Fin.--J B Labs, Inc., Holland, MI; *U.S. Private*, pg. 576
Lamb, James R., Exec. V.P.--Lamb Engineering & Construction Co., Salt Lake City, UT; *U.S. Private*, pg. 644
Lamb, Phillip, Exec. Dir.-Construction--Willis Corroon South Limited, Maidstone, United Kingdom; *Int'l*, pg. 1503
Lamb, Robert C., Jr., Chief Acctg. Officer & Controller--Fleet Financial Group, Inc., Boston, MA; *U.S. Public*, pg. 648
Lamb, Steven G., Chief Oper. Officer & Exec. V.P.--Case Corporation, Racine, WI; *U.S. Public*, pg. 311
Lambeck, Rolf, Exec. V.P.--BTE Brauerel-Technik Essen GmbH, Essen, Germany; *Int'l*, pg. 400
Lambert, John S., Exec. V.P. & Gen. Mgr.--Foster Wheeler USA Corporation, Clinton, NJ; *U.S. Public*, pg. 677
Lambert, Paul T., Exec. V.P.--Harza Engineering Company of California, Oakland, CA; *U.S. Private*, pg. 509
Lambert, Thomas W., Chief Fin. Officer & Exec. V.P.--First of America Bank Corporation, Kalamazoo, MI; *U.S. Public*, pg. 636
Lampen, Richard J., Exec. V.P.--BGLS Inc., Miami, FL; *U.S. Public*, pg. 259
Lampen, Richard J., Exec. V.P. & Gen. Counsel--New Valley Corporation, Miami, FL; *U.S. Public*, pg. 1173
Lamy, Jean-Lucien, Exec. V.P.--Labinal SA, Montigny-le-Bretonneux, France; *Int'l*, pg. 785
Lamz, Richard, Exec. V.P.--Magnetrol International, Downers Grove, IL; *U.S. Private*, pg. 696
Lamz, Richard, Exec. V.P.--Introtek International, Edgewood, NY; *U.S. Private*, pg. 696
Lance, Larry K., Exec. V.P.--Hartford Life & Accident Insurance Company, Hartford, CT; *U.S. Public*, pg. 795
Lanctot, Edmund W., Jr., Exec. V.P. & Mgr.-Opers.--J.W. Window Components, Inc., Elizabethton, TN; *U.S. Public*, pg. 1736
Land, Thornton R., Exec. V.P.-Admin. & Gen. Counsel--Selective Insurance Group, Inc, Branchville, NJ; *U.S. Public*, pg. 1455
Landau, Ellis, Chief Fin. Officer, Exec. V.P. & Treas.--Boyd Gaming Corporation, Las Vegas, NV; *U.S. Public*, pg. 249
Landau, Richard, Exec. V.P.-Hosiery Sls.--Union Underwear Co., Inc., Bowling Green, KY; *U.S. Public*, pg. 686
Lander, Howard, Pres.-Music Group & Exec. V.P.--BPI Communications Inc., New York, NY; *Int'l*, pg. 1446
Landgren, Berne, Exec. V.P.-Grp. Devel.--Telia AB, Farsta, Sweden; *Int'l*, pg. 1373
Landis, Edgar D., Exec. V.P.-Fin.--CDI Corp., Philadelphia, PA; *U.S. Public*, pg. 276
Landress, Ben S., Chief Info. Officer & Exec. V.P.--CBL & Associates Properties, Inc., Chattanooga, TN; *U.S. Public*, pg. 273
Landry, D. Thomas, Exec. V.P. & Dir.-Maintenance & Construction--Piccadilly Cafeterias, Inc., Baton Rouge, LA; *U.S. Public*, pg. 1294
Landry, George W., Exec. V.P. & Dir.-Data Processing & Pur.--Fifth Third Bancorp, Cincinnati, OH; *U.S. Public*, pg. 621
Landry, Gregory G., Chief Fin. Officer & Exec. V.P.-Fin.--Dairy Mart Convenience Stores, Inc., Cuyahoga Falls, OH; *U.S. Public*, pg. 476
Landry, James E., Chief Fin. Officer & Exec. V.P.--United Piece Dye Works, LP, New York, NY; *U.S. Private*, pg. 1123
Landry, Jaques, Exec. V.P.-Fin. & Sec.--Shirmax Leasing Ltd., Montreal, Canada; *Int'l*, pg. 1235
Landry, Michael G., Exec. V.P. & Pres.-Mackenzie Investment Management Inc.--Mackenzie Financial Corporation, Toronto, Canada; *Int'l*, pg. 828
Lane, James A., Jr., Exec. V.P.--RPC Incorporated, Atlanta, GA; *U.S. Public*, pg. 1356
Lane, Lynda, Exec. V.P.-Admin. Corp. Communications--Koll Co., Newport Beach, CA; *U.S. Private*, pg. 631
Lane, Michael J., Exec. V.P.--Schal Bovis Inc., Chicago, IL; *Int'l*, pg. 1033
Lane, Raymond W., Exec. V.P.--The Mead Corporation, Dayton, OH; *U.S. Public*, pg. 1074
Lane, Richard T., Exec. V.P.-Strategic Devel.--World Color Press, Inc., Greenwich, CT; *U.S. Public*, pg. 1778
Laney, Herb, Pres.-Catalogs & Exec. V.P.--Playboy Enterprises, Inc., Chicago, IL; *U.S. Public*, pg. 1309
Langdon, Richard S., Chief Fin. Officer & Exec. V.P.-Fin. & Admin.--EEX Corporation, Houston, TX; *U.S. Public*, pg. 542
Langer, Robert, Exec. V.P.-Fin.--Van Son Holland Ink Corp. of America, Mineola, NY; *U.S. Private*, pg. 1133
Langevin, Charles B., Exec. V.P.--Napco International, Inc., Hopkins, MN; *U.S. Public*, pg. 1716
Langevin, David J., Exec. V.P.--Terex Corporation, Westport, CT; *U.S. Public*, pg. 1581
Langford, Robert M., Chief Oper. Officer & Sr. Exec. V.P.--Shoney's, Inc., Nashville, TN; *U.S. Public*, pg. 1467
Langford, Thomas L., Chief Fin. Officer & Exec. V.P.--Stone & Webster, Incorporated, Boston, MA; *U.S. Public*, pg. 1519
Langille, Brian, Exec. V.P.--Advanstar Communications, Cleveland, OH; *U.S. Private*, pg. 22
Langlois, Norman, Chief Fin. Officer & Exec. V.P.--Butterworth-Heinemann USA, Newton, MA; *Int'l*, pg. 1094
Langsdorf, William B., Chief Fin. Officer & Exec. V.P.--HomeBase, Inc., Irvine, CA; *U.S. Public*, pg. 832
Lanigan, Michael, Pres.-Mi-Jack & Exec. V.P.--MI-Jack Products, Inc., Hazel Crest, IL; *U.S. Private*, pg. 740
Lanigan, William J., Exec. V.P.-Opers.--MI-Jack Products, Inc., Hazel Crest, IL; *U.S. Private*, pg. 740
Lankford, George, Exec. V.P.--Affiliated Foods, Inc., Amarillo, TX; *U.S. Private*, pg. 25
Lannert, Robert C., Chief Fin. Officer & Exec. V.P.--Navistar International Corporation, Chicago, IL; *U.S. Public*, pg. 1167
Lannoye, Lee D., Exec. V.P.-Corp. Admin. & Credit--Washington Mutual Inc., Seattle, WA; *U.S. Public*, pg. 1741
Lansciardi, James, Exec. V.P.--Robert E. Bayley Construction, Seattle, WA; *U.S. Private*, pg. 125
Lansky, Mitchell, Exec. V.P.--Econocom-USA Inc., Memphis, TN; *U.S. Private*, pg. 361
Lansu, Emil, Exec. V.P. & Pres.-Agriculture Division--Bayer Corporation, Pittsburgh, PA; *Int'l*, pg. 172
Lansue, Emil, Pres.-Agricultural Div. & Exec. V.P.--Bayer Corporation, Pittsburgh, PA; *Int'l*, pg. 172
Lantonen, Pauli, Exec. V.P.-Inha Works--Fiskars Oy AB, Helsinki, Finland; *Int'l*, pg. 492
Lantzsch, Margarete G., Exec. V.P.--Lantzsch-Andreas Enterprises, Inc., Vienna, VA; *U.S. Private*, pg. 650
Lanwermeyer, L.F., Exec. V.P.-Mktg.--Harris Bankcorp, Inc., Chicago, IL; *Int'l*, pg. 154
Lanza, Marco C., Exec. V.P.--B/E Aerospace, Inc., Wellington, FL; *U.S. Public*, pg. 159
Lanzani, Emanuele, Exec. V.P.--Scotsman Industries, Inc., Vernon Hills, IL; *U.S. Public*, pg. 1444
Lapekas, Edward, Chief Oper. Officer-Beverage & Sr. Exec. V.P.--American National Can Company, Chicago, IL; *Int'l*, pg. 1029
Lapides, James A., Exec. V.P.-Mktg. & Opers.--United Aluminum Corporation, North Haven, CT; *U.S. Private*, pg. 1120
Lapointe, George, Exec. V.P. & Gen. Mgr.--Solon Manufacturing Company, Solon, ME; *U.S. Private*, pg. 1013
Lara, Juan Jose, Vice Chm., Exec. V.P. & Chief Exec. Officer--Durakon Mexicana, S.A. de C.V., Lerma, Mexico; *U.S. Public*, pg. 537
Larini, Ernest, Chief Fin. Officer & Exec. V.P.--Warner-Lambert Consumer Healthcare, Morris Plains, NJ; *U.S. Public*, pg. 1739
Larkin, William B., Exec. V.P.--F.X. Coughlin Co., Taylor, MI; *U.S. Private*, pg. 278
LaRocco, James, Exec. V.P.-Corp.Devel.--Apcoa, Inc., Cleveland, OH; *U.S. Private*, pg. 533
Larsen, Joe, Chief Oper. Officer & Exec. V.P.--TrizecHahn Centers Inc., San Diego, CA; *Int'l*, pg. 1425
Larsen, Marshall O., Exec. V.P.--The B.F. Goodrich Company, Richfield, OH; *U.S. Public*, pg. 751
Larson, Clayton C., Chief Admin. Officer & Exec. V.P.--First National Bank of Central California, Salinas, CA; *U.S. Public*, pg. 1248
Larson, Kenneth, Exec. V.P.--Monico Alloys, Inc., Los Angeles, CA; *U.S. Private*, pg. 757
Larson, Mark, V.P.-Intl. Devel. & Exec. V.P.-Carlson Market--Carlson Companies, Inc., Minnetonka, MN; *U.S. Private*, pg. 211
Larson, Roland, Exec. V.P.-Stockholm Regional Bank--Nordbanken AB, Stockholm, Sweden; *Int'l*, pg. 957
Larssen, Sverre A., Exec. V.P.-Building Matls.--Norske Skogindustrier A.S, Skogn, Norway; *Int'l*, pg. 965
Larsson, Carl Goran, Exec. V.P.-Network Services Div.--Telia Nattganster Division, Farsta, Sweden; *Int'l*, pg. 1373
Larsson, Peter, Exec. V.P. & Mgr.-Fin. & Admin.--Kanthal AB, Hallstahammar, Sweden; *Int'l*, pg. 723
Larsson, Stig-Arne, Chief Fin. Officer & Exec. V.P.--Telia AB, Farsta, Sweden; *Int'l*, pg. 1373
LaRue, David J., Chief Oper. Officer & Exec. V.P.--Forest City Commercial Construction Company, Inc., Cleveland, OH; *U.S. Public*, pg. 668
Larvor, Jean-Francois, Exec. V.P.-Production & Transmission--Gaz de France, Paris, France; *Int'l*, pg. 541
Lash, Steven M., Chief Fin. Officer, Exec. V.P. & Treas.--FPA Medical Management, Inc., San Diego, CA; *U.S. Public*, pg. 608
Laskey, Walter, Exec. V.P.-Asset Mngmt. & Private Client Market--Bank of Hawaii, Honolulu, HI; *U.S. Public*, pg. 1248
Lassila, Leena, Exec. V.P.-Buying & Fashion--Stockmann Department Store Div., Helsinki, Finland; *Int'l*, pg. 1301
Laster, Larry J., Exec. V.P.--Intergraph Corporation, Huntsville, AL; *U.S. Public*, pg. 890
Latella, Robert N., Chief Oper. Officer & Exec. V.P.--Genesee Corporation, Rochester, NY; *U.S. Public*, pg. 728
Latella, Robert N., Exec. V.P.--The Genesee Brewing Company, Inc., Rochester, NY; *U.S. Public*, pg. 728
Lathrop, J., Exec. V.P.-Admin.--R.T. Vanderbilt Company, Inc., Norwalk, CT; *U.S. Private*, pg. 1133
Latner, Michael E., Exec. V.P. & Sec.--Dynacare, Inc., Toronto, Canada; *Int'l*, pg. 425
Laubie, Christian, Sr. Exec. V.P.-Fin.--Danone Group, Paris, France; *Int'l*, pg. 379
Lauer, Allen J., Exec. V.P.-Instruments--Varian Associates, Inc., Palo Alto, CA; *U.S. Public*, pg. 1710
Lauer, J. Michael, Chief Fin. Officer & Exec. V.P.--MGIC Investment Corporation, Milwaukee, WI; *U.S. Public*, pg. 1026
Lauer, J. Michael, Chief Fin. Officer & Exec. V.P.--Mortgage Guaranty Insurance Corporation, Milwaukee, WI; *U.S. Public*, pg. 1026
Lauer, Steven, Chief Fin. Officer & Exec. V.P.--Topco Associates, Inc., Skokie, IL; *U.S. Private*, pg. 1091
Laughlin, Barbara L., Exec. V.P.--First Empire State Corporation, Buffalo, NY; *U.S. Public*, pg. 631
Laughlin, Barbara L., Exec. V.P.--Manufacturers & Traders Trust Company, Buffalo, NY; *U.S. Public*, pg. 631
Laughlin, J. Rodney, Exec. V.P.-Devel.--Magellan Health Services, Inc., Atlanta, GA; *U.S. Public*, pg. 1033
Laughlin, Leo, Exec. V.P.-Sls.--Dribeck Importers, Inc., Greenwich, CT; *U.S. Private*, pg. 343
Laughlin, Michael E., Exec. V.P.-User Support Svcs.--Norstan, Inc., Plymouth, MN; *U.S. Public*, pg. 1192
Laughren, Judy, Exec. V.P. & Sr. Partner--Blue Marble Advanced Communications Group, New York, NY; *U.S. Private*, pg. 104
Laughridge, Terry, Exec. V.P. & New Bus. Contact--Zimmerman & Partners Advertising, Inc., Fort Lauderdale, FL; *U.S. Private*, pg. 1206
Laughridge, Terry, Exec. V.P. & New Bus. Contact--Zimmerman & Partners Advertising, Inc., Atlanta, GA; *U.S. Private*, pg. 1206
Laukaikul, Thamnoon, Sr. Exec. V.P.--Bangkok Bank Public Company Limited, Bangkok, Thailand; *Int'l*, pg. 146
Lauren, Hakan, Exec. V.P.-Sweetening Div.--Cultor Ltd., Helsinki, Finland; *Int'l*, pg. 349
Laurence, Joseph A., Chief Fin. Officer & Exec. V.P.--LCI International, Inc., Dublin, OH; *U.S. Public*, pg. 969
Laurent-Bellue, Jean, Exec. V.P.-Advisory Activities--Credit Commercial de France, Paris, France; *Int'l*, pg. 341
Laurent, Robert Jr., Chief Fin. Officer & Exec. V.P.-Fin. & Admin.--Fedders Corp., Liberty Corner, NJ; *U.S. Public*, pg. 614
Laurenzi, Mark V., Exec. V.P.-Sls. & Mktg.--Marotta Scientific Controls, Inc., Montville, NJ; *U.S. Private*, pg. 706
Lauriero, Paul, Exec. V.P.--Suprema Specialties, Inc., Paterson, NJ; *U.S. Public*, pg. 1541
Lauriero, Paul, Exec. V.P.--Suprema Specialties Northeast, Inc., Ogdensburg, NY; *U.S. Public*, pg. 1541
Lausin, Gerald M., Exec. V.P.--Prestige Fragrances, Ltd., New York, NY; *U.S. Private*, pg. 690
Lauzier, Marijean, Exec. V.P.--Weber Public Relations Worldwide, Cambridge, MA; *U.S. Private*, pg. 1157
Lavan, Thomas J., Exec. V.P. & Gen. Mgr.--O'Donnell-Usen Fisheries Corp., Tampa, FL; *U.S. Public*, pg. 427
LaVergne, Marc, Exec. V.P.-Mngmt. Audit & Inspection--Banque Nationale de Paris, Paris, France; *Int'l*, pg. 163
Lavinia, Robert J., Exec. V.P. & Pres.-The Circle K Company & Tosco Mktg. Company--Tosco Corporation, Stamford, CT; *U.S. Public*, pg. 1624
Law, Gale, Exec. V.P.--TCBY Enterprises Inc., Little Rock, AR; *U.S. Public*, pg. 1553
Lawder, Kenneth A., Jr., Exec. V.P. & Dir.-Comml. Lending--Whitney Holding Corporation, New Orleans, LA; *U.S. Public*, pg. 1766
Lawrence, Guy, Exec. V.P.-Intl. Distr. & Mktg.--MGM/UA Distribution Co., Santa Monica, CA; *U.S. Public*, pg. 1102
Lawrence, James A., Chief Fin. Officer & Exec. V.P.--Northwest Airlines Corp., Saint Paul, MN; *U.S. Public*, pg. 1199
Lawrence, Lindsey C., Exec. V.P.--BankBoston Corporation, Boston, MA; *U.S. Public*, pg. 183
Lawrence, State, Exec. V.P. & Mng. Partner-Acct.--Wells BDDP, Inc., New York, NY; *Int'l*, pg. 117
Lawrence, Ted, Exec. V.P. & Mngmt. Supvr.--Sudler & Hennessey, New York, NY; *U.S. Private*, pg. 1197

Lawrence, William B., Exec. V.P.-Corp. Devel. & Intl. & Govt. Rels., Gen. Counsel & Sec--TRW Inc., Cleveland, OH; *U.S. Public*, pg. 1558
Lawry, Donald A., Exec. V.P.-Corp. Fin.--Southwest National Corporation, Greensburg, PA; *U.S. Public*, pg. 1493
Lawry, Donald A., Exec. V.P.--Southwest National Bank of Pennsylvania, Greensburg, PA; *U.S. Public*, pg. 1493
Lawson, A. Lowell, Exec. V.P., Chm. Bd. & Chief Exec. Officer-Raytheon E-Systems--Raytheon Company, Lexington, MA; *U.S. Public*, pg. 1364
Lawson, Rodger A., Exec. V.P.-Mktg. & Plng.--The Prudential Insurance Company of America, Newark, NJ; *U.S. Private*, pg. 892
Lawton, Bradley L., Pres.--Star Cutter Co., Farmington, MI; *U.S. Private*, pg. 1034
Layman, Harold E., Chief Fin. Officer & Exec. V.P.--Blount, Inc., Montgomery, AL; *U.S. Public*, pg. 238
Layman, Ralph R., Exec. V.P.-Intl. Equity--General Electric Investment Corp., Stamford, CT; *U.S. Public*, pg. 712
Lazarus, Franz E., Chief Oper. Officer & Exec. V.P.-Intl. Opers.--Costco Wholesale, Issaquah, WA; *U.S. Public*, pg. 451
Lazenby, Thomas E., Exec. V.P.-Consumer Fin.--Compass Bank, Birmingham, AL; *U.S. Public*, pg. 418
Lazo, Samson C., Exec. V.P.--EEI Corporation, Manila, Philippines; *Int'l*, pg. 425
Lazo, Samson C., Exec. V.P.--EEI-Construction Div., Manila, Philippines; *Int'l*, pg. 426
Le Blanc, Theodore, Exec. V.P.-Dealer Sls./Dist. Western Hemisphere--Konica Business Machines USA, Inc., Windsor, CT; *Int'l*, pg. 748
Le Fevre, Paul, Chief Fin. Officer & Exec. V.P.-Strategic Plng. & Mktg.--Keyport Life Insurance Company, Boston, MA; *U.S. Private*, pg. 666
Le Noury, Peter W., Exec. V.P.-Sys. & Opers.--The Bank of Bermuda Limited, Hamilton, Bermuda; *Int'l*, pg. 150
Leach, Anthony, Chief Fin. Officer & Exec. V.P.--Occidental Petroleum Corporation, Los Angeles, CA; *U.S. Public*, pg. 1210
Leader, Morton, Exec. V.P.--Republic National Bank of New York, New York, NY; *U.S. Public*, pg. 1380
Leal, Roberto, Exec. V.P., Pres. & CEO-JWT/Brazil--J. Walter Thompson Company, New York, NY; *Int'l*, pg. 1483
Leamer, Jim, Exec. V.P.-Sls. & Mktg.--McSwain Carpets Inc., Cincinnati, OH; *U.S. Private*, pg. 725
Leary, Gary, Exec. V.P.--UniHealth, Burbank, CA; *U.S. Private*, pg. 1117
Leath, Jerry L., Chief Oper. Officer & Exec. V.P.--Sabreliner Corporation, Saint Louis, MO; *U.S. Private*, pg. 959
Leatherman, Sheila T., Exec. V.P.-Pub. Policy & Govt. Affairs--United HealthCare Corporation, Minnetonka, MN; *U.S. Public*, pg. 1677
Leatherwood, Lucy L., Exec. V.P.-Residential Construction Lending--Compass Bank Houston, Houston, TX; *U.S. Public*, pg. 419
Lebedev, Greg, Chief Oper. Officer & Exec. V.P.--Nation's Business, Washington, DC; *U.S. Private*, pg. 788
Leblanc, Bernard, Exec. V.P.--Gaz de France, Paris, France; *Int'l*, pg. 541
Leblois, Axel, Exec. V.P.--Bull S.A., Louveciennes, France; *Int'l*, pg. 315
Lebovitz, Stephen D., Exec. V.P. & Treas.--CBL & Associates Properties, Inc., Chattanooga, TN; *U.S. Public*, pg. 273
Leckerling, Jon P., Exec. V.P.-Admin., Gen. Counsel & Corp. Sec.--Echlin Inc., Branford, CT; *U.S. Public*, pg. 560
Leckle, Mark M., Exec. V.P. & Gen. Mgr.-Post Div.--Kraft Foods, Inc., Northfield, IL; *U.S. Public*, pg. 1287
Leclaire, Serge, Exec. V.P.-Personal Services Div.--Montreal Trustco, Montreal, Canada; *Int'l*, pg. 155
Lecy, Gerald, Exec. V.P.--Creative Group Inc., Appleton, WI; *U.S. Private*, pg. 287
Ledeboer, K.H., Exec. V.P.-Opers.--KLM Royal Dutch Airlines, Amstelveen, Netherlands; *Int'l*, pg. 719
Lederer, David, Chief Oper. Officer & Exec. V.P.--Detection Systems, Inc., Fairport, NY; *U.S. Public*, pg. 501
Lederer, Paul R., Exec. V.P.-Worldwide Aftermarket--Federal-Mogul Corporation, Southfield, MI; *U.S. Public*, pg. 615
Ledrew, Fred, Exec. V.P.-Spirits & Wines--Heublein, Inc., Hartford, CT; *Int'l*, pg. 410
Lee, Candy, Exec. V.P.-Retail Publr.--Harlequin Enterprises Ltd., Don Mills, Canada; *Int'l*, pg. 1402
Lee, Christopher, Exec. V.P.-Production--TriStar Pictures, Culver City, CA; *Int'l*, pg. 1283
Lee, Chun-Ho, Exec. V.P.--Pohang Iron & Steel Co., Ltd., Kyongbuk, Korea; *Int'l*, pg. 1061
Lee, Dennis M., Exec. V.P.-Human Resources--Caldor, Inc., Norwalk, CT; *U.S. Public*, pg. 292
Lee, George L., Jr., Exec. V.P.--Red Devil Inc., Union, NJ; *U.S. Private*, pg. 915
Lee, Greg, Exec. V.P.-Sls., Mktg. & Tech. Svcs.--Tyson Foods, Inc., Springdale, AR; *U.S. Public*, pg. 1652
Lee, Hyung-Pal, Exec. V.P.--Pohang Iron & Steel Co., Ltd., Kyongbuk, Korea; *Int'l*, pg. 1061
Lee, J.R., Exec. V.P.--Columbia Gas Distribution Companies, Columbus, OH; *U.S. Public*, pg. 402
Lee, James, Exec. V.P. & Pres.-Licensed Discount Div.--J. Baker, Inc., Canton, MA; *U.S. Public*, pg. 167
Lee, Jeff, Exec. V.P.--Davis Paint Company, Kansas City, MO; *U.S. Private*, pg. 315
Lee, Jefferi K., Exec. V.P.-Network Opers. & Programming--Black Entertainment Television Holdings Inc., Washington, DC; *U.S. Public*, pg. 235
Lee, Jong Keun, Exec. V.P. & Dir.--Cho Hung Bank, Seoul, Korea; *Int'l*, pg. 287
Lee, Jong-Deok, Exec. V.P.--Daehong Advertising Inc., Seoul, Korea; *Int'l*, pg. 357
Lee, Kent, Exec. V.P.--USCO, Incorporated, Monroe, NC; *U.S. Public*, pg. 847
Lee, Kimberly Y., Exec. V.P. & Chief Internal Auditor--First Commerce Corporation, New Orleans, LA; *U.S. Public*, pg. 629
Lee, Kisik, Exec. V.P.--Daewoo Securities Co., Ltd., Seoul, Korea; *Int'l*, pg. 358
Lee, Kiwhan, Sr. V.P.-Sls. & Mktg.--American Tape Co., Secaucus, NJ; *Int'l*, pg. 685
Lee, Kyung-Kyoon, Exec. V.P.-Human Resources--Korean Airlines Co., Ltd., Seoul, Korea; *Int'l*, pg. 758
Lee, Michael T., Exec. V.P.--CACI International Inc, Arlington, VA; *U.S. Public*, pg. 272
Lee, Paul L., Exec. V.P. & Gen. Counsel--Republic New York Corporation, New York, NY; *U.S. Public*, pg. 1380
Lee, Paul L., Exec. V.P.--Republic National Bank of New York, New York, NY; *U.S. Public*, pg. 1380
Lee, Robert R., Exec. V.P.--Progressive Driver Services, Inc., Jacksonville, FL; *U.S. Private*, pg. 890
Lee, Wee Guan, Exec. Dir.--DBS Securities UK Ltd., London, United Kingdom; *Int'l*, pg. 351
Lee, Won Soon, Exec. V.P. & Dir.-Personnel--Cho Hung Bank, Seoul, Korea; *Int'l*, pg. 287
Lee, Yong Won, Exec. V.P. & Dir.--Cho Hung Bank, Seoul, Korea; *Int'l*, pg. 287
Leedom, John N., Jr., Exec.-V.P.--Wholesale Electronic Supply, Dallas, TX; *U.S. Private*, pg. 1174
Leeds, Jeffrey W., Exec. V.P. & Chief Lending Officer--Lawrence Savings Bank, North Andover, MA; *U.S. Public*, pg. 980
Leeks, Michael, V.P.-Corp. Devel.--Slater Industries Inc., North York, Canada; *Int'l*, pg. 1262
Leemon, Daniel O., Exec. V.P.-Bus. Strategy--The Charles Schwab Corporation, San Francisco, CA; *U.S. Public*, pg. 1442
Leemputte, Peter G., Exec. V.P.--Chicago Title & Trust Co., Chicago, IL; *U.S. Public*, pg. 42
Leemputte, Peter G., Exec. V.P.--Chicago Title Insurance Co., Chicago, IL; *U.S. Public*, pg. 42
Lefcort, Robert A., Exec. V.P. & Sec.--Outsource International, Deerfield Beach, FL; *U.S. Public*, pg. 1236
Lefever, Allon H., Exec. V.P.-Affiliated Cos.--High Industries, Inc., Lancaster, PA; *U.S. Private*, pg. 528
Lefever, Terry, Exec. V.P.-Welding Prods.--Hobart Brothers Co., Troy, OH; *U.S. Public*, pg. 866
Leff, Sherwin, Exec. V.P.--Impact Communications Group, Chicago, IL; *U.S. Public*, pg. 1641
Lefkowitz, Ira, Exec. V.P.--Hoboken Wood Flooring Corporation, Wayne, NJ; *U.S. Private*, pg. 532
LeFlore, Bonita, Exec. V.P. & Local Brdcst. Dir.--Zenith Media Services, Inc., New York, NY; *U.S. Private*, pg. 1204
Legall, Gerard, Exec. V.P.--Sofamor, S.N.C., Rang-du-Fliers, France; *U.S. Public*, pg. 1482
Legasey, Edward E., Chief Oper. Officer & Exec. V.P.--SRA International Inc., Arlington, VA; *U.S. Private*, pg. 957
Leger, Dominique, Grp. Exec. V.P.-Central Resources--Credit Commercial de France, Paris, France; *Int'l*, pg. 341
Leggetter, Barry, Pres., Sr. Partner, Mng. Dir. & Exec. V.P.--Fleishman-Hillard U.K. Limited, London, United Kingdom; *U.S. Private*, pg. 411
Legrain, Olivier, Exec. V.P.-Specialty Prods.--Lafarge S.A., Paris, France; *Int'l*, pg. 788
Legrand, Bernard, Exec. V.P.-Aluminum Sector--Pechiney S.A., Courbevoie, France; *Int'l*, pg. 1027
LeGrande, W. E., Jr., Exec. V.P.--Gudebrod, Inc., Pottstown, PA; *U.S. Private*, pg. 486
Lehman, Mark E., Exec. V.P. & Sr. Mng. Dir.--The Bear Stearns Companies Inc., New York, NY; *U.S. Public*, pg. 197
Lehmuskoski, Pekka, Exec. V.P.-Fiskars Power Systems--Fiskars Oy AB, Helsinki, Finland; *Int'l*, pg. 492
Lehnertz, George M., Exec. V.P.--Sanwa Business Credit Corporation, Chicago, IL; *Int'l*, pg. 1189
Lehrberg, Dick, Exec. V.P.--Interplay Productions, Inc., Irvine, CA; *U.S. Private*, pg. 572
Leibensperger, Robert L., Exec. V.P. & Pres.-Bearings--The Timken Company, Canton, OH; *U.S. Public*, pg. 1617
Leichnitz, Wolfhard, Dr., Exec. V.P.--Hochtief AG, Essen, Germany; *Int'l*, pg. 623
Leifheit, Dennis, Chief Oper. Officer & Exec. V.P.--IHOP Corp., Glendale, CA; *U.S. Public*, pg. 862
Leininger, C.R., Exec. V.P.-Community Reg.--Magna Group, Inc., Saint Louis, MO; *U.S. Public*, pg. 1037
Leinwohl, Neil R., Exec. V.P. & Exec. Creative Dir.--Korey, Kay & Partners, New York, NY; *U.S. Private*, pg. 632
Leisenring, Carol A., Exec. V.P.-Fin.--CoreStates Financial Corp., Philadelphia, PA; *U.S. Public*, pg. 446
Lemaire, Alain, Exec. V.P.--The Cascades Group, Kingsey Falls, Canada; *Int'l*, pg. 273
Lemay, Raymond, Exec. V.P.--Quebecor Inc., Montreal, Canada; *Int'l*, pg. 1075
Lemberg, Eero, Exec. V.P.--Stockmann Automotive Sales Div., Helsinki, Finland; *Int'l*, pg. 1301
Lemberger, Kenneth, Exec. V.P.--Sony Pictures Entertainment, Culver City, CA; *Int'l*, pg. 1281
Lemec, Bernard, Exec. V.P.-H.R.--Banque Nationale de Paris, Paris, France; *Int'l*, pg. 163
Lemerise, Paul, Chief Info. Officer & Exec. V.P.-Sys. & Distr.--TruServ Corporation, Chicago, IL; *U.S. Private*, pg. 1108
Lemire, Denis T., Exec. V.P.-Mdsg.--Ames Department Stores, Inc., Rocky Hill, CT; *U.S. Public*, pg. 99
Lemke, Robert O., Exec. V.P.--Firstar Community Investment Corp., Milwaukee, WI; *U.S. Public*, pg. 643
Lemman, Dean M., Exec. V.P.--North Coast Electric Company, Bellevue, WA; *U.S. Private*, pg. 804
Lemon, David W., Exec. V.P.-Field Opers.--American Hardware Mutual Insurance Co., Columbus, OH; *U.S. Private*, pg. 764
Lenain, Philippe, Vice Chm. & Chief Oper. Officer--Danone Group, Paris, France; *Int'l*, pg. 379
Lenke, Joanne M., Exec. V.P.--The Psychological Corp., San Antonio, TX; *U.S. Public*, pg. 784
Lennegren, Bjorn, Exec. V.P.-Grp. Corp. Fin.--Componenta Dynapac AB, Vastra Frolunda, Sweden; *Int'l*, pg. 1419
Lennick, Douglas, Exec. V.P.-Private Client Grp.--American Express Financial Advisor, Minneapolis, MN; *U.S. Public*, pg. 73
Lennick, Douglas, Exec. V.P.-Private Client Services--IDS Financial Services, Inc., Minneapolis, MN; *U.S. Public*, pg. 73
Lennon, Terence I., Exec. V.P.-Mergers & Aquisitions--Metropolitan Life Insurance Co., New York, NY; *U.S. Private*, pg. 737
Leno, Sam R., Chief Fin. Officer & Exec. V.P.--Corporate Express, Inc., Broomfield, CO; *U.S. Public*, pg. 449
Lenoir, James S., Exec. V.P.--Deposit Guaranty Corp., Jackson, MS; *U.S. Public*, pg. 500
Lents, Shelaghmichael, Exec. V.P.-Retail Banking--Texas Commerce Bank, Houston, TX; *U.S. Public*, pg. 339
Lenzmeier, Allen U., Chief Fin. Officer & Exec. V.P.--Best Buy Co., Inc., Eden Prairie, MN; *U.S. Public*, pg. 223
Leon-DuFour, Pierre, Exec. V.P.--Groupe GTM, Nanterre, France; *Int'l*, pg. 823
Leonard, Ralph R., Exec. V.P.--First Midwest Bank, N.A., Itasca, IL; *U.S. Public*, pg. 636
Leonard, Russ, Exec. V.P.-Opers. & Programs--Howtek, Inc., Hudson, NH; *U.S. Public*, pg. 844
Leonard, Walter E., Jr., Exec. V.P.-Opers./Tech.--Wachovia Corporation, Winston Salem, NC; *U.S. Public*, pg. 1730
Leonardo, John C., Jr., Chief Oper. Officer & Exec. V.P.--Texas Micro, Inc., Houston, TX; *U.S. Public*, pg. 1586
Leonberger, Jimmy R., Exec. V.P.--Cochran/Sysco Food Services, Jackson, MS; *U.S. Public*, pg. 1550
Leong, Calvin, Exec. V.P. & Controller--Maness Industries, Inc., Long Beach, CA; *U.S. Private*, pg. 699
Leong, Raymond, Exec. V.P.-Fin. & Controller--F. J. Benjamin Holdings Ltd., Singapore, Singapore; *Int'l*, pg. 187
Leonhardt, Jeald D., Exec. V.P.-Fin. & Admin. & Treas.--CommScope, Inc., Hickory, NC; *U.S. Public*, pg. 415
Leophard, Jim, Exec. V.P.--Duff-Norton, Charlotte, NC; *U.S. Public*, pg. 406
Lepley, Fred, Exec. V.P.--Hoffman Seeds, Inc., Landisville, PA; *U.S. Private*, pg. 532
Lepore, Dawn Gould, Chief Info. Officer & Exec. V.P.--The Charles Schwab Corporation, San Francisco, CA; *U.S. Public*, pg. 1442
Lerch, Stephen E., Chief Fin. Officer & Exec. V.P.--Transmedia Network Inc., Miami, FL; *U.S. Public*, pg. 1631
Lerner, Alan B., Sr. Exec. V.P.-Corp. Staff--Associates Financial Services Corporation, Dallas, TX; *U.S. Public*, pg. 663
Lervick, John S., Exec. V.P.--Twin City Foods, Inc., Stanwood, WA; *U.S. Private*, pg. 1111
Lesley, Richard, Chief Oper. Officer & Exec. V.P.--Booth American, Detroit, MI; *U.S. Private*, pg. 156
Leslie, Jonathan C.A., Exec. Dir.--Rio Tinto PLC, London, United Kingdom; *Int'l*, pg. 1118
Lesser, Seymour H., Chief Fin. & Chief Admin. Officer & Exec. V.P.--Arts & Entertainment Network/ABC/NBC, New York, NY; *U.S. Public*, pg. 512
Lesser, Seymour H., Chief Fin. & Chief Admin. Officer & Exec. V.P.--Arts & Entertainment Network/ABC/NBC, New York, NY; *U.S. Private*, pg. 516
Lessor, David, Exec. V.P.--Kinro, Inc., Arlington, TX; *U.S. Public*, pg. 529
Lester, Nelle, Exec. V.P.--J.L. Lester & Son, Inc., Rockmart, GA; *U.S. Private*, pg. 660
Lester, Simon, Exec. V.P.--Cott Corporation, Pointe-Claire, Canada; *Int'l*, pg. 337
Lester, Simon, Exec. V.P.--Cott Europe (Pontefract), Pontefract, United Kingdom; *Int'l*, pg. 338
Lester, Susan E., Chief Fin. Officer & Exec. V.P.--U.S. Bancorp, Minneapolis, MN; *U.S. Public*, pg. 1680
Lesueur, Michel, Exec. V.P. & Central Sec.--Credit Nationale, Paris, France; *Int'l*, pg. 344
Leto, Rick, Exec. V.P. & Gen. Mgr.-Apparel & Access--Kohl's Corporation, Menomonee Falls, WI; *U.S. Public*, pg. 965
Leugers, William J., Jr., Exec. V.P.--Gradison Division, Cincinnati, OH; *U.S. Public*, pg. 1068
LeVeen, Thomas, Chief Oper. Officer & Exec. V.P.--Facemate Corporation, Chicopee, MA; *U.S. Private*, pg. 391
Levene, David A., Exec. V.P.-Mfg. & Admin.--Metropolitan Life Insurance Co., New York, NY; *U.S. Private*, pg. 737
Levenson, Robert J., Sr. Exec. V.P.--MEDCO Containment Services, Inc., Montvale, NJ; *U.S. Public*, pg. 1091
Levin, Harriett, Exec. V.P.-Bus. Devel.--Frankfurt Balkind Partners, New York, NY; *U.S. Private*, pg. 424
Levin, Marc B., Exec. V.P.-Investor Rels. & Sec.--Integrated Health Services, Inc., Owings Mills, MD; *U.S. Public*, pg. 884
Levin, Stephen J., Exec. V.P.-Sls.--Telemundo Group, Inc., Hialeah, FL; *U.S. Public*, pg. 1570
Levine, Fred, Exec. V.P.--United Advertising Publications, Inc., Dallas, TX; *Int'l*, pg. 1443
Levine, Kenneth M., Exec. V.P. & Chief Investment Officer--The Mutual Life Insurance Company of New York, New York, NY; *U.S. Private*, pg. 769
Levine, Mark, Exec. V.P. & Strategic Devel. Dir.--Wunderman Cato Johnson, New York, NY; *U.S. Private*, pg. 1197
Levine, Michael E., Exec. V.P.-Mktg. & Intl.--Northwest Airlines Corp., Saint Paul, MN; *U.S. Public*, pg. 1199
Levine, Michael E., Exec. V.P.-Mktg. & Intl.--Northwest Airlines, Inc., Saint Paul, MN; *U.S. Public*, pg. 1200
Levine, Paul, Chief Oper. Officer, Exec. V.P. & Sec.--Hirsch International Corp., Hauppauge, NY; *U.S. Public*, pg. 829
Levine, Steve, Exec. V.P.-Mktg.--Bel-Art Products, Pequannock, NJ; *U.S. Private*, pg. 130
Levinson, Donald M., Exec. V.P.-H.R.--Cigna Corp., Philadelphia, PA; *U.S. Public*, pg. 356
Levit, Gerald, Exec. V.P.--Grocers Supply Co. Inc., Houston, TX; *U.S. Private*, pg. 483

Levitt, Barton G., Exec. V.P.--Columbian Advertising Inc., Chicago, IL; *U.S. Private*, pg. 256
Levitt, Keith, Sr. V.P.-Fin. & Admin.--Sports/Leisure Magazines Group, Trumbull, CT; *U.S. Public*, pg. 1174
Levitz, Paul, Exec. V.P. & Publisher--DC Comics, Inc., New York, NY; *U.S. Public*, pg. 1614
Levy-Garboua, Vivien, Grp. Exec. V.P.-Intl. Banking & Fin.--Banque Nationale de Paris, Paris, France; *Int'l*, pg. 163
Levy, David, Chief Fin. Officer & Exec. V.P.--Norman Levy Associates, Inc., Southfield, MI; *U.S. Private*, pg. 664
Levy, David, Exec. V.P.-Admin. & Counsel--National Service Industries, Inc., Atlanta, GA; *U.S. Public*, pg. 1160
Levy, Gilles-Pierre, Exec. V.P.-Human Resources--Pechiney S.A., Courbevoie, France; *Int'l*, pg. 1027
Levy, Kenneth, Exec. V.P.-Acct. Mngmt.--Grey Advertising Inc., New York, NY; *U.S. Public*, pg. 764
Levy, Lawrence B., Chief Fin. Officer & Exec. V.P.--Pixar Animation Studios, Richmond, CA; *U.S. Public*, pg. 1307
Levy, Martin, Exec. V.P.--Landau & Heyman Inc., Chicago, IL; *U.S. Private*, pg. 646
Levy, Philip R., Chief Fin. Officer & Exec. V.P.--American Reliable Insurance Company, Scottsdale, AZ; *U.S. Public*, pg. 67
Levy, Richard M., Exec. V.P.-Healthcare--Varian Associates, Inc., Palo Alto, CA; *U.S. Public*, pg. 1710
Levy, Steven A., Exec. V.P. & Treas.--The Titan Industrial Corp., New York, NY; *U.S. Private*, pg. 1089
Lewczyk, Henry, Exec. V.P.--Levenson & Hill, Inc., Dallas, TX; *U.S. Private*, pg. 662
Lewerer, Gary, Exec. V.P.--L.H. Sowles Company, Inc., Minneapolis, MN; *U.S. Private*, pg. 1019
Lewis, Carol D., Exec. V.P.--Squire-Cogswell Company, Gurnee, IL; *U.S. Private*, pg. 1027
Lewis, Charles E., Exec. V.P.--Amspec Chemical Corporation, Gloucester City, NJ; *U.S. Private*, pg. 67
Lewis, Claude W., Exec. V.P.--Canadian Satellite Communications Inc., Mississauga, Canada; *Int'l*, pg. 1481
Lewis, Conrad W., Exec. V.P.-Bus. Units--Newbridge Networks Corporation, Kanata, Canada; *Int'l*, pg. 923
Lewis, Conrad W., Exec. V.P.-Business Units--Newbridge Networks Corporation, Kanata, Canada; *Int'l*, pg. 924
Lewis, Goldy S., Exec. V.P.--Lewis Homes Management Corp., Upland, CA; *U.S. Private*, pg. 665
Lewis, James E., Exec. V.P.-Opers. & Engrng.--Cogentrix Incorporated, Charlotte, NC; *U.S. Private*, pg. 249
Lewis, John, Exec. V.P.--MAC America Communications, Inc., Phoenix, AZ; *U.S. Private*, pg. 685
Lewis, Joseph W., Exec. V.P.--Johnson Controls, Inc., Milwaukee, WI; *U.S. Public*, pg. 932
Lewis, Madeline, Exec. V.P. & Acct. Mng. Dir.--Young & Rubicam New York, New York, NY; *U.S. Private*, pg. 1198
Lewis, Mark, Exec. V.P.-Intl.--Electronic Arts, San Mateo, CA; *U.S. Public*, pg. 569
Lewis, Peggy S., Exec. V.P.--Lewis Brothers Bakeries, Inc., Evansville, IN; *U.S. Private*, pg. 665
Lewis, Randal W., Exec. V.P.--Lewis Homes Management Corp., Upland, CA; *U.S. Private*, pg. 665
Lewis, Robert E., Pres.-NV Opers. & Exec. V.P.--Lewis Homes Management Corp., Upland, CA; *U.S. Private*, pg. 665
Lewis, Roger G., Exec. V.P.--Lewis Homes Management Corp., Upland, CA; *U.S. Private*, pg. 665
Lewis, Thomas, Chief Info. Officer & Exec. V.P.--USF&G Corporation, Baltimore, MD; *U.S. Public*, pg. 1659
Leyden, Paul, Sr. V.P.-Pub. Rels.--The Bank of New York, New York, NY; *U.S. Public*, pg. 178
Leysen, Thomas, Exec. Dir.--Union Miniere, Brussels, Belgium; *Int'l*, pg. 1441
Lezama, Fernando, Exec. V.P. & Pres.-Mexico, Central & South America--Avon Products, Inc., New York, NY; *U.S. Public*, pg. 155
Lhota, William J., Exec. V.P.--American Electric Power Service Corp., Columbus, OH; *U.S. Public*, pg. 72
Lia, Gary, Exec. V.P.--Liberty Mutual Insurance Co., Boston, MA; *U.S. Private*, pg. 666
Libbe, Scott Wm., Exec. V.P.-Sls.--Rudolph/Libbe, Inc., Walbridge, OH; *U.S. Private*, pg. 950
Lichliter, Larry, Exec. V.P.-Mountain Opers.--Vail Associates, Inc., Vail, CO; *U.S. Public*, pg. 1704
Lichtenstein, Michael, Exec. V.P.--Joan & David Helpern, Inc., New York, NY; *U.S. Private*, pg. 521
Lichter, Jonathan, Exec. V.P. & Acct. & Media Svcs. Dir.--Kelly, Scott And Madison, Inc., Chicago, IL; *U.S. Private*, *pg. 613*
Lichter, Lester M., Chief Info. Officer & Exec. V.P.--Excel Communications, Inc., Dallas, TX; *U.S. Public*, pg. 598
Lidvall, Ned, Exec. V.P.-Brewery Opers.--Rock Bottom Restaurants, Louisville, CO; *U.S. Public*, pg. 1396
Lieb, James, Sr. V.P.--The Trump Group, Miami, FL; *U.S. Private*, pg. 1107
Lieb, Richard B., Exec. V.P.--SEI Investments, Oaks, PA; *U.S. Public*, pg. 1417
Lieberg, Eric N., Pres., Chief Fin. Officer & Exec. V.P.--Rundel Products, Inc., Portland, OR; *U.S. Private*, pg. 951
Lieberman, Mark, Exec. V.P.-Entertainment, Commun. & Media--Reed Elsevier Business Information, Newton, MA; *Int'l*, pg. 1095
Liebman, Howard M., Chief Fin. Officer & Exec. V.P.--Shorewood Packaging Corporation, New York, NY; *U.S. Public*, pg. 1468
Liebman, Martin, Exec. V.P. & New York/Long Island Reg. Pres.--Marine Midland Bank, Buffalo, NY; *Int'l*, pg. 581
Lien, Richard C., Exec. V.P.-Opers.--M.F. Bank & Company, Inc., Minneapolis, MN; *U.S. Private*, pg. 113
Lietz, Richard A., Chief Oper. Officer & Exec. V.P.--ANR Pipeline Co., Detroit, MI; *U.S. Public*, pg. 389
Liewald, Robert, Exec. V.P.--Fila USA, Sparks, MD; *Int'l*, pg. 484
Light, Kenneth B., Chief Fin. Officer, Chief Admin. Officer & Exec. V.P.--Allied Products Corporation, Chicago, IL; *U.S. Public*, pg. 48
Ligherink, Martin, Exec. V.P.--Kaufman and Broad of San Diego, Inc., San Diego, CA; *U.S. Public*, pg. 945
Lightstone, Ronald, Chief Oper. Officer & Exec. V.P.--Spelling Television, Los Angeles, CA; *U.S. Private*, pg. 776
Liguori, Ralph, Exec. V.P.-Opers.--Graham-Field Health Products, Inc., Hauppauge, NY; *U.S. Public*, pg. 757
Lilenthal, Stephen W., Exec. V.P.-Field Devel. & Opers.--USF&G Corporation, Baltimore, MD; *U.S. Public*, pg. 1659
Liljebeck, Roy C., Chief Fin. Officer & Exec. V.P.--Airborne Freight Corporation, Seattle, WA; *U.S. Public*, pg. 32
Lilley, Bob, Exec. V.P.--Western International Media Corporation, New York, NY; *U.S. Private*, pg. 1166
lillie, James, Exec. V.P.-Opers.--World Color Press, Inc., Greenwich, CT; *U.S. Public*, pg. 1778
Limburg, E.F., Exec. V.P.--ABN-AMRO Holding N.V., Amsterdam, Netherlands; *Int'l*, pg. 8
Limpe, Emily T., Exec. V.P.--Petro Chem Development Company, New York, NY; *U.S. Private*, pg. 858
Lin, P.C., Exec. V.P.--Taiwan Glass Industry Corp., Taipei, Taiwan; *Int'l*, pg. 1348
Lincoln, Stephen B., Jr., Exec. V.P.--Garelick Farms, Inc., Franklin, MA; *U.S. Public*, pg. 1527
Lind, William, Exec. V.P. & Gen. Mgr.--Barenbrug Northeast, Ogdensburg, NJ; *Int'l*, pg. 167
Lindberg, Ingmar, Exec. V.P.-Admin. & Real Estate--Fiskars Oy AB, Helsinki, Finland; *Int'l*, pg. 492
Lindbleau, Sten, Exec. V.P.-Western Regional Bank--Nordbanken AB, Stockholm, Sweden; *Int'l*, pg. 957
Lindel, Randy, Exec. V.P.--Arnold Communications, Inc., Boston, MA; *U.S. Private*, pg. 83
Linden, Lars, Exec. V.P.--Atlas Copco ACT, Wilrijk, Belgium; *Int'l*, pg. 96
Lindenauer, Arthur, Chief Fin. Officer & Exec. V.P.-Fin.--Schlumberger Limited, New York, NY; *U.S. Public*, pg. 1439
Linder, Steven W., Exec. V.P.--Minnesota Electric Supply Company, Willmar, MN; *U.S. Private*, pg. 750
Lindheim, Richard, Exec. V.P.-TV Grp.--Paramount Pictures Corporation, Los Angeles, CA; *U.S. Private*, pg. 776
Lindholm, Rita, Chief Fin. Officer & Exec. V.P.--Ross Roy Communications, Inc., Bloomfield Hills, MI; *U.S. Private*, pg. 946
Lindner, Alan B., Exec. V.P.--United Dairy Farmers, Inc., Cincinnati, OH; *U.S. Private*, pg. 1121
Lindsay, Tony, Exec. V.P. & Gen. Mgr.--Taracorp Industries, Inc., Granite City, IL; *U.S. Private*, pg. 1068
Lindsey, Kris, Exec. V.P.--All Star Gas Corporation, Lebanon, MO; *U.S. Private*, pg. 35
Linehan, John C., Chief Fin. Officer & Exec. V.P.--Kerr-McGee Corporation, Oklahoma City, OK; *U.S. Public*, pg. 952
Ling, Clara, Exec. Dir.--Playmates Holdings Ltd., Kowloon, Hong Kong; *Int'l*, pg. 1060
Link, John F., Chief Info. Officer & Exec. V.P.-Information Tech.--QVC, Inc., West Chester, PA; *U.S. Private*, pg. 897
Linn, James W., Chief Oper. Officer & Exec. V.P.--Parker Drilling Company, Tulsa, OK; *U.S. Public*, pg. 1259
Linsley, Patrick M., Exec. V.P.-Corp. Mktg.--The National Enquirer, New York, NY; *U.S. Public*, pg. 87
Linton, Bill, Chief Fin. Officer & Exec. V.P.--SHL Systemhouse, Ottawa, Canada; *Int'l*, pg. 1154
Linton, Jeff, Exec. V.P.-Corp. Communications--Dix & Eaton Incorporated, Cleveland, OH; *U.S. Private*, pg. 336
Lipke, Neil E., Exec. V.P.--Gibraltar Steel Corp., Buffalo, NY; *U.S. Public*, pg. 742
Lipp, Cheryl, Exec. V.P.--Community First Bank & Trust, Celina, OH; *U.S. Public*, pg. 633
Lippert, Robert L., Exec. V.P.--Premium Budget Plan, Inc., Winston Salem, NC; *U.S. Public*, pg. 1453
Lippert, Robert L., Exec. V.P.--The Innovative Company, Winston Salem, NC; *U.S. Public*, pg. 1454
Lippert, Robert L., Exec. V.P.--Universal Insurance Co., Winston Salem, NC; *U.S. Public*, pg. 1454
Lippincott, Barbara, Exec. V.P.--United Missouri Bank of Springfield, Springfield, MO; *U.S. Public*, pg. 1655
Lipschitz, Louis, Chief Fin. Officer & Exec. V.P.--Toys "R" Us, Inc., Paramus, NJ; *U.S. Public*, pg. 1626
Lipsky, Barry J., Exec. V.P.--Franklin Electronic Publishers, Inc., Burlington, NJ; *U.S. Public*, pg. 679
Lipsky, John, Exec. V.P. & Chief Economist--The Chase Manhattan Corporation, New York, NY; *U.S. Public*, pg. 337
Lipson, Brian, Exec. V.P.--TrizecHahn Properties Inc., Chicago, IL; *Int'l*, pg. 1425
Liska, P.J., Chief Fin. Officer & Exec. V.P.--The St. Paul Companies, Inc., Saint Paul, MN; *U.S. Public*, pg. 1429
Listen, Robert P., Exec. V.P. & Dir.-Tech. Svcs.--Piccadilly Cafeterias, Inc., Baton Rouge, LA; *U.S. Public*, pg. 1294
Lister, Roy L., Exec. V.P.--Stuart Entertainment Inc., Council Bluffs, IA; *U.S. Public*, pg. 1526
Lister, Roy L., Exec. V.P.--Bazaar & Novelty, Saint Catharines, Canada; *U.S. Public*, pg. 1526
Lister, Stephen L., Exec. V.P.-Member-Firm Regulation--The American Stock Exchange, New York, NY; *U.S. Private*, pg. 62
Litman, Peter, Exec. V.P. & Gen. Counsel--Summit Technology, Inc., Waltham, MA; *U.S. Public*, pg. 1528
Litschi, R.L., Exec. V.P. & Gen. Mgr.--Trico Industries, Inc., San Marcos, TX; *U.S. Public*, pg. 1247
Litten, C. Scott, Chief Fin. Officer & Exec. V.P.--Hills Stores Co., Canton, MA; *U.S. Public*, pg. 828
Little, Christopher, Exec. V.P.--Meredith Corporation, Des Moines, IA; *U.S. Public*, pg. 1094
Littlefield, Benjamin, Exec. V.P.-Real Estate & Devel.--Mann Theatres, Encino, CA; *U.S. Private*, pg. 239
Littmoden, Chris, Exec. Dir.-Retail, The Americas--Marks & Spencer PLC, London, United Kingdom; *Int'l*, pg. 842
Litvack, Sanford M., Chief Oper. Officer & Sr. Exec. V.P.--The Walt Disney Company, Burbank, CA; *U.S. Public*, pg. 511
Litwak, Jim, Exec. V.P.-Mdsg. & Mktg.--Trans World Entertainment Corporation, Albany, NY; *U.S. Public*, pg. 1629
Litwin, Michael J., Chief Credit Officer & Exec. V.P.--Heller Financial, Inc., Chicago, IL; *Int'l*, pg. 519
Litzsinger, P.S., Sr. V.P.-Sls. & Mktg.--Carboline Co., Saint Louis, MO; *U.S. Public*, pg. 1357
Livesay, Rod, Exec. V.P.--Thomason Auto Group, Gladstone, OR; *U.S. Private*, pg. 1083
Livingston, John T., Exec. V.P.--Tishman Realty & Construction Co., Inc., New York, NY; *U.S. Private*, pg. 1089
Ljungberg, Susan L., Exec. V.P. & Gen. Mgr.--Ultra Tool & Plastics, Inc., Amherst, NY; *U.S. Private*, pg. 1116
Llewellyn, Trefor, Exec. Dir.--Caradon Plc, Weybridge, United Kingdom; *Int'l*, pg. 266
Lloyd, Eldon K., Exec. V.P.-Commercial Banking--Imperial Bank, Inglewood, CA; *U.S. Public*, pg. 871
Lloyd, Gary, Exec. V.P.--Plymouth Tube Company, Warrenville, IL; *U.S. Private*, pg. 873
Lloyd, Patrick D., Exec. V.P.-Customer Opers.--BC Gas Utility, Vancouver, Canada; *Int'l*, pg. 114
Lloyd, Rjay, Vice Chm. & Chief Fin. Officer--Forever Living Products International, Inc., Scottsdale, AZ; *U.S. Private*, *pg. 418*
Lloyd, Ronald S., Exec. V.P.--TrizecHahn Corporation, Toronto, Canada; *Int'l*, pg. 1424
Lloyd, Terrance G., Exec. V.P.--Republic National Bank of New York, New York, NY; *U.S. Public*, pg. 1380
Lo, Clement, Exec. Dir. & Sec.--Sun Hung Kai Properties Ltd., Wan Chai, Hong Kong; *Int'l*, pg. 1318
Lochner, James V., Exec. V.P.-Tech. Services--IBP, Inc., Dakota City, NE; *U.S. Public*, pg. 852
Locicero, Joseph A., Exec. V.P. & Pres./Chief Exec. Officer-Bulk Consultants, Inc.--Mellon Bank Corporation, Pittsburgh, PA; *U.S. Public*, pg. 1084
Locke, Chris, Exec. Dir.-TV--The Media Centre, London, United Kingdom; *Int'l*, pg. 852
Lodge, H. Cabot, III, Exec. V.P. & Mng. Dir.--W.P. Carey & Co., Inc., New York, NY; *U.S. Private*, pg. 209
Lodovic, Joseph, Chief Fin. Officer & Exec. V.P.--MediaNews Group Inc., Denver, CO; *U.S. Private*, pg. 727
Lodovic, Joseph J., IV, Chief Fin. Officer & Exec. V.P.--Garden State Newspapers, Inc., Denver, CO; *U.S. Private*, pg. 727
Lodwick, Lyle, Exec. V.P.-Branch Opers.--Pacific Crest Capital, Inc., Agoura Hills, CA; *U.S. Public*, pg. 1248
Loeffler, Michael, Exec. V.P.-Direct Mktg. Svcs.--May & Speh, Inc., Downers Grove, IL; *U.S. Public*, pg. 1063
Lof, Roland Martin, Exec. V.P.-Pulping Tech.--Kvaerner a.s.a., Lysaker, Norway; *Int'l*, pg. 766
Loffa, Michael, Chief Fin. Officer & Exec. V. P.--Midland Life Insurance Co., Columbus, OH; *U.S. Private*, pg. 744
Lofgren, Frederick, Chief Fin. Officer & Exec. V.P.--Hitchiner Manufacturing Company, Inc., Milford, NH; *U.S. Private*, pg. 531
Lofkvist, Bengt, Exec. V.P.--Trelleborg AB, Trelleborg, Sweden; *Int'l*, pg. 1419
Loftis, Jack, Exec. V.P. & Editor--Houston Chronicle, Houston, TX; *U.S. Private*, pg. 517
Lofton, A.L., Jr., Exec. V.P. & Treas.--Utilities Construction Co., Inc. Of South Carolina, Charleston, SC; *U.S. Private*, *pg. 1130*
Loftus, William A., Exec. V.P.-Retail--Ace Hardware Corporation, Oak Brook, IL; *U.S. Private*, pg. 12
Logan, Ann D., Chief Credit Officer & Exec. V.P.--Federal National Mortgage Association (Fannie Mae), Washington, DC; *U.S. Public*, pg. 615
Logan, Harold R., Jr., Exec. V.P.-Fin. & Treas.--TransMontaigne Oil Company, Denver, CO; *U.S. Public*, pg. 1631
Logan, Robert, Exec. V.P., Sec. & Treas.--Plastics Manufacturing Company, Dallas, TX; *U.S. Public*, pg. 1530
Logan, Vicki, Exec. V.P.-Creative Services--Jordan, McGrath, Case & Taylor Inc., New York, NY; *U.S. Private*, pg. 598
LoGatto, James R., Exec. V.P.--Republic Bank for Savings, New York, NY; *U.S. Public*, pg. 1380
Loge, David B., Exec. V.P.-Mfg. & Ancillary Bus.--Costco Wholesale, Issaquah, WA; *U.S. Public*, pg. 451
Logue, Ronald E., Exec. V.P.--State Street Corporation, Boston, MA; *U.S. Public*, pg. 1513
Lohrs, Eugene, Exec. V.P.--Lee Company, Westbrook, CT; *U.S. Private*, pg. 657
Lolas, C. William, Exec. V.P.--Pony U.S.A., Nashville, TN; *Int'l*, pg. 1036
Lom, Tom, Exec. V.P. & Co-Mng. Dir.--The Healthcare Connection, New York, NY; *U.S. Public*, pg. 1422
Londen, Lars E., Exec. V.P.--Central National-Gottesman Inc., Purchase, NY; *U.S. Private*, pg. 224
Long, Donald, Chief Fin. Officer & Exec. V.P.--Amerifoods Inc., Lancaster, PA; *U.S. Private*, pg. 65
Long, Francis A., Exec. V.P.--PP&L Resources, Allentown, PA; *U.S. Public*, pg. 1244
Long, Francis A., Chief Oper. Officer & Exec. V.P.--Pennsylvania Power & Light Company-Lehigh Div., Allentown, PA; *U.S. Public*, pg. 1244
Long, James R., Pres. & Chief Oper. Officer-Nortel World Trade--Northern Telecom Limited, Brampton, Canada; *Int'l*, pg. 968
Long, John R., III, Exec. V.P.-Human Resources--US Airways Group, Inc., Arlington, VA; *U.S. Public*, pg. 1680
Long, Lisa Valk, Exec. V.P.--Time Inc., New York, NY; *U.S. Public*, pg. 1612
Long, Tan Choo, Exec. V.P.--Bangkok Bank Berhad, Kuala Lumpur, Malaysia; *Int'l*, pg. 146
Long, William E., Exec. V.P.--LaSalle-Talman Bank, Chicago, IL; *Int'l*, pg. 11
Longbrake, William A., Chief Fin. Officer, Exec. V.P.-Corp. Finance--Washington Mutual Inc., Seattle, WA; *U.S. Public*, pg. 1741

Longenecker, Chester D., Exec. V.P. & Gen. Counsel--Associates First Capital Corporation, Dallas, TX; *U.S. Public*, pg. 662
Longerbone, Douglas, Exec. V.P.-Opers.--Red Roof Inns, Inc., Hilliard, OH; *U.S. Public*, pg. 1369
Longnecker, Dean, Exec. V.P.-Fin. & Sec.--Central Tractor Farm & Country, Inc., Des Moines, IA; *U.S. Private*, pg. 237
Longo, Peter, Exec. V.P.--Ohio Sealants Inc., Mentor, OH; *Int'l*, pg. 802
Lonnqvist, Markku, Exec. V.P.--Stockmann Automotive Sales Div., Helsinki, Finland; *Int'l*, pg. 1301
Lonson, Tom, Exec. V.P.--Capitol Group, Springfield, IL; *U.S. Private*, pg. 206
Loon, Oon Kum, Exec. V.P.--DBS Bank Ltd., Singapore, Singapore; *Int'l*, pg. 350
Lopez Roldan, Raul, Exec. V.P.--Empresas ICA Sociedad Controladora S.A.C.V., Mexico, Mexico; *Int'l*, pg. 454
Lopez, Johnny O., Exec. V.P.--Platinum Equity Holdings, LLC, Los Angeles, CA; *U.S. Private*, pg. 872
Lopez, Manuel, Exec. V.P.-Network Management--Grupo Iberia, Madrid, Spain; *Int'l*, pg. 574
Loran, Allan Z., Exec. V.P.-Technologies & New Prod. Devel.--American Express Travel Related Services Co., Inc., New York, NY; *U.S. Public*, pg. 73
Loren, Allan Z., Chief Information Officer & Exec. V.P.--American Express Company, New York, NY; *U.S. Public*, pg. 73
Loring, R., Exec. V.P.--Presstek, Inc., Hudson, NH; *U.S. Public*, pg. 1324
Lorraine, Richard A., Chief Fin. Officer & Exec. V.P.--Occidental Chemical Corporation, Dallas, TX; *U.S. Public*, pg. 1210
Losgren, Paul, Exec. V.P.--Alliance Gaming Corporation, Las Vegas, NV; *U.S. Public*, pg. 46
Losh, J. Michael, Chief Fin. Officer & Exec. V.P.--General Motors Corporation, Detroit, MI; *U.S. Public*, pg. 718
Losurdo, Mark, Exec. V.P.--Losurdo Foods, Inc., Hackensack, NJ; *U.S. Private*, pg. 677
Losurdo, Michael, Jr., Exec. V.P.--Losurdo Foods, Inc., Hackensack, NJ; *U.S. Private*, pg. 677
Loudiades, Constantin, Exec. V.P. & Gen. Mgr.-Asia Pacific & Russian Region--Newbridge Networks Corporation, Kanata, Canada; *Int'l*, pg. 923
Loughlin, Edward D., Exec. V.P.--SEI Investments, Oaks, PA; *U.S. Public*, pg. 1417
Loughlin, Richard, Exec. V.P.--Willis Corroon Corp. of New York, New York, NY; *Int'l*, pg. 1506
Loughmiller, Eric M., Chief Fin. Officer & Exec. V.P.--May & Speh, Inc., Downers Grove, IL; *U.S. Public*, pg. 1063
Loughrey, F. Joseph, Grp. Pres.-Indus. & Exec. V.P.--Cummins Engine Company, Inc., Columbus, IN; *U.S. Public*, pg. 467
Loukidis, D.K. Jim, Exec. V.P.--Wisconsin Automated Machinery Corp., Oshkosh, WI; *U.S. Private*, pg. 1184
Lounsberry, Fred, Exec. V.P.-Sls. & Mktg.--Universal Studios Music Australia, Sydney, Australia; *Int'l*, pg. 1216
Louvet, Bertrand, Exec. V.P.-Chemical--Rhone-Poulenc S.A., Courbevoie, France; *Int'l*, pg. 1108
Love, Wm. Timothy, Exec. V.P. & Worldwide Account Dir.-P&G--DMB&B Communications, New York, NY; *U.S. Private*, pg. 302
Lovell, Robert R., Exec. V.P. & Gen. Mgr.-Space Systems Grp.--Orbital Sciences Corporation, Dulles, VA; *U.S. Public*, pg. 1229
Lovell, Stephen, Exec. V.P. & Dir.-Stores--Stage Stores, Inc., Houston, TX; *U.S. Private*, pg. 1028
Low, Dennis, Exec. V.P.-Fin. Services--The Great-West Life Assurance Company, Winnipeg, Canada; *Int'l*, pg. 557
Lowden, Christopher, Exec. V.P.-Opers.--Santa Fe Gaming Corporation, Las Vegas, NV; *U.S. Public*, pg. 1432
Lowden, Suzanne, Exec. V.P.--Santa Fe Gaming Corporation, Las Vegas, NV; *U.S. Public*, pg. 1432
Lowe, Terry, Exec. V.P. & Gen. Mgr.--J.D. Diffenbaugh, Inc., Riverside, CA; *U.S. Private*, pg. 332
Lowe, Thomas M., III, Exec. V.P.--Rosser International, Inc., Atlanta, GA; *U.S. Private*, pg. 946
Lowe, William, Exec. V.P.--Moore Corporation Limited, Toronto, Canada; *Int'l*, pg. 888
Lowenstein, David C., Exec. V.P.--R & R Marketing, West Caldwell, NJ; *U.S. Private*, pg. 902
Lowenstein, Irwin L., Exec. V.P.-Rhodes--Heilig-Meyers Company, Richmond, VA; *U.S. Public*, pg. 804
Lowery, R.C., Exec. V.P.-Western Div.--Interstate Brands Corporation, Kansas City, MO; *U.S. Public*, pg. 909
Lowry, Richard M., Chief Oper. Officer & Exec. V.P.--Great Lakes Dredge & Dock Co., Oak Brook, IL; *U.S. Private*, pg. 474
Loy, Robert W., Exec. V.P.-Opers.--Roberts Pharmaceutical Corporation, Eatontown, NJ; *U.S. Public*, pg. 1393
Lozelle, James R., Exec. V.P.--Tower Automotive, Inc., Grand Rapids, MI; *U.S. Public*, pg. 1625
Lozier, Robert D., Exec. V.P.--Freeman Decorating Co., Dallas, TX; *U.S. Private*, pg. 426
Lozyniak, Andrew, Chief Fin. Officer & Exec. V.P.--Semiconductor Packaging Materials Co., Inc., Armonk, NY; *U.S. Public*, pg. 1456
Lubeck, David A., Exec V.P. & Client Svcs. Dir.--Bernstein-Rein Advertising, Inc., Kansas City, MO; *U.S. Private*, pg. 137
Lubin, William J., Chief Exec. Officer & Exec. V.P.-Commercial Managed Care--PHP Healthcare Corporation, Reston, VA; *U.S. Public*, pg. 1241
Lubrano, Vincent, Chief Fin. Officer & Exec. V.P.--Ammirati Puris Lintas Worldwide, New York, NY; *U.S. Public*, pg. 908
Luby, Dallas W., Exec. V.P.--General Reinsurance Corp., Stamford, CT; *U.S. Public*, pg. 725
Lucas, Blair, Exec. V.P.-Mktg.--Jonathan Manufacturing Corp., Fullerton, CA; *U.S. Private*, pg. 595
Lucas, Maurice, Exec. V.P.--Conair Corporation, Stamford, CT; *U.S. Private*, pg. 261
Lucas, Robert W., Exec. V.P.--Huntington National Bank, Columbus, OH; *U.S. Public*, pg. 850
Lucas, William R., Jr., Exec. V.P.-Admin. & Gen. Counsel--Birmingham Steel Corporation, Birmingham, AL; *U.S. Public*, pg. 232
Luce, James W., Exec. V.P.--ULLICO Inc., Washington, DC; *U.S. Private*, pg. 1115
Luce, James W., Exec. V.P.--Unioncare, Inc., Washington, DC; *U.S. Private*, pg. 1116
Luchs, Charles M., Exec. V.P.--Chubb & Son, Inc., Warren, NJ; *U.S. Public*, pg. 355
Lucien, Kent T., Chief Fin. Officer, Exec. V.P. & Treas.--Buyco, Inc., Honolulu, HI; *U.S. Private*, pg. 190
Lucien, Kent T., Chief Fin. Officer, Exec. V.P. & Treas.--C. Brewer & Company, Limited, Honolulu, HI; *U.S. Private*, pg. 190
Luckenotto, Peter, Exec. V.P.--Norddeutsche Landesbank (NORD/LB), Hannover, Germany; *Int'l*, pg. 957
Luckey, George, Exec. V.P. & Gen. Mgr.-Mdse.--OfficeMax, Shaker Heights, OH; *U.S. Public*, pg. 1212
Ludeman, Steve, Exec. V.P.--Jantzen, Portland, OR; *U.S. Public*, pg. 1702
Ludvigsen, Carl W., Jr., Dr., Chief Oper. Officer & Exec. V.P.--Lab One, Lenexa, KS; *U.S. Public*, pg. 1449
Luffman, Peter J., Pres.-Newsweek Intl. & Exec. V.P.--Newsweek, Inc., New York, NY; *U.S. Public*, pg. 1743
Lugash, Larry, Chief Oper. Officer & Exec. V.P.--Maxon Industries, Inc., Huntington Park, CA; *U.S. Private*, pg. 717
Lugbauer, Catherine, Exec. V.P.--Weber Public Relations Worldwide, Cambridge, MA; *U.S. Private*, pg. 1157
Lukassen, Gary J., Chief Fin. Officer & Exec. V.P.--Hudson's Bay Company, Toronto, Canada; *Int'l*, pg. 637
Lundberg, Lennart, Sr. Exec. V.P.--Vattenfall AB, Stockholm, Sweden; *Int'l*, pg. 1452
Lundstrom, Leif, Exec. V.P.-Mktg. Div.--FinnAir Oy, Helsinki, Finland; *Int'l*, pg. 485
Lundy, Gerald, Exec. V.P.--Shandwick Detroit, Southfield, MI; *Int'l*, pg. 1227
Lundy, James H., Exec. V.P.--National Bank of Arizona, Tucson, AZ; *U.S. Public*, pg. 1793
Lundy, Marilyn, Exec. V.P.--Lundy Enterprises, Inc., New Orleans, LA; *U.S. Private*, pg. 681
Lungberg, Goran, Exec. V.P.-Power Plants--ABB Asea Brown Boveri (Holding) Ltd., Zurich, Switzerland; *Int'l*, pg. 1
Lunghi, Fabio, Chief Oper. Officer & Exec. V.P.--INCSTAR Corporation, Stillwater, MN; *Int'l*, pg. 483
Lunn, Evanline K., Exec. V.P.--First Farmers & Merchants National Bank, Columbia, TN; *U.S. Private*, pg. 407
Lunoi, Ken, Chief Oper. Officer & Exec. V.P.--Delta Education, Inc., Hudson, NH; *Int'l*, pg. 1402
Lunt, Jack, Exec. V.P.-Law & Admin.--American Stores Properties, Inc., Salt Lake City, UT; *U.S. Public*, pg. 93
Lupo, Michael A., Chief Fin. Officer, Exec. V.P. & Sec.--ABT Building Products Corporation, Neenah, WI; *Int'l*, pg. 20
Luppino, Mario, Exec. V.P.--First National Bank of Abilene, Abilene, TX; *U.S. Public*, pg. 633
Lurio, David, Exec. V.P.--Elbeco Incorporated, Reading, PA; *U.S. Private*, pg. 367
Luscinski, Steven, Exec. V.P. & Gen. Mgr.--Accu-Sort Systems, Inc., Telford, PA; *U.S. Private*, pg. 11
Lussier, Arthur E., Exec. V.P. & Mgr.-Real Estate Div.--Imperial Bank, Inglewood, CA; *U.S. Public*, pg. 871
Lussier, Richard H., Exec. V.P.--Intergraph Corporation, Huntsville, AL; *U.S. Public*, pg. 890
Lussky, William, Jr., Exec. V.P.--Progress Paint Mfg. Co., Louisville, KY; *U.S. Private*, pg. 890
Lustbader, Brian G., Exec. V.P., Gen. Counsel & Sec.--The P.J. Carlin Construction Company, New Rochelle, NY; *U.S. Private*, pg. 211
Luter, Barry R.F., Exec. V.P.-Eastern U.S.A.--The Bank of Nova Scotia, Toronto, Canada; *Int'l*, pg. 155
Lutin, Barry S., Exec. V.P.--FieldBrook Farms, Inc., Dunkirk, NY; *U.S. Private*, pg. 403
Lutke-Bornefeld, Peter, Dr., Exec. V.P.--General Re Corporation, Stamford, CT; *U.S. Public*, pg. 725
Lutz, Emil, Exec. V.P.--Sulzer Ltd., Winterthur, Switzerland; *Int'l*, pg. 1305
Lutz, Michael, Exec. V.P.-Opers.--Hanover Direct, Inc., Weehawken, NJ; *U.S. Public*, pg. 782
Lux, Harald, Exec. V.P.--Lux GmbH & Co. KG, Wermelskirchen, Germany; *Int'l*, pg. 993
Luyten, Ben, Exec. V.P.-Human Resources--Interbrew S.A., Leuven, Belgium; *Int'l*, pg. 679
Luzuriaga, Francesca, Exec. V.P.-Worldwide Bus. Plng. & Resources--Mattel, Inc., El Segundo, CA; *U.S. Public*, pg. 1057
Lydon, Coleman, Exec. V.P. & Treas.--Bank of Ireland (U.S.A.), New York, NY; *Int'l*, pg. 152
Lye, Ong Yim, Exec. Dir.--DBS Trustee Ltd., Singapore, Singapore; *Int'l*, pg. 351
Lykins, B.C., Exec. V.P.--Valley Asphalt Corporation, Cincinnati, OH; *U.S. Private*, pg. 1131
Lynch, John, Exec. V.P.-Comml. Lending--ABN/LaSalle North America Inc., Chicago, IL; *Int'l*, pg. 11
Lynch, John, Exec. V.P.-Consumer Prods. Grp.--Olympus America Inc., Melville, NY; *Int'l*, pg. 1005
Lynch, Martin A., Chief Fin. Officer & Exec. V.P.--Smart & Final, Vernon, CA; *Int'l*, pg. 563
Lynch, Robert B., Exec. V.P.-Customer Service--Siemens Nixdorf Information Systems Inc., Burlington, MA; *Int'l*, pg. 1245
Lynch, Ron, Exec. V.P.-Physical Production--TriStar Pictures, Culver City, CA; *Int'l*, pg. 1283
Lynch, Thomas G., Chief Fin. Officer & Exec. V.P.--Elan Corporation Plc, Dublin, Ireland; *Int'l*, pg. 435
Lynch, Tim, Chief Fin. Officer & Exec. V.P.--The Crown Group, Inc., Warren, MI; *U.S. Private*, pg. 292
Lynch, Will, Exec. V.P.--Bright Star Industries, Inc., Wilkes-Barre, PA; *U.S. Public*, pg. 1341
Lynn, Anthony J., Exec. V.P. & Pres. Entertainment Grp.--Playboy Enterprises, Inc., Chicago, IL; *U.S. Public*, pg. 1309
Lyons, Richard M., Exec. V.P.--The Gap, Inc., San Francisco, CA; *U.S. Public*, pg. 702
Lyons, Susanne, Exec. V.P.-Retail Mktg.--Charles Schwab & Co. Inc., San Francisco, CA; *U.S. Public*, pg. 1443
Lyons, Susanne D., Exec. V.P.-Retail Mktg.--The Charles Schwab Corporation, San Francisco, CA; *U.S. Public*, pg. 1442
Ma, John K.K., Exec. Dir.--The Sincere Co. Ltd., Hong Kong, Hong Kong; *Int'l*, pg. 1252
Mabee, Keith, Sr. Exec. V.P.--Dix & Eaton Incorporated, Cleveland, OH; *U.S. Private*, pg. 336
Mac Lachlan, Neil T., Exec. V.P.-Investment--Barrick Gold Corporation, Toronto, Canada; *Int'l*, pg. 168
Macalister, Kim, Exec. V.P., Pres. & Gen. Mgr.-JWT/Singapore--J. Walter Thompson Company, New York, NY; *Int'l*, pg. 1483
Macaluso, Carlos, Exec. V.P.-Sls. & Mktg.--Golden Eagle Group, Inc., Humble, TX; *U.S. Public*, pg. 749
MacAniff, John K., Exec. V.P.--Ogden Entertainment, Inc., New York, NY; *U.S. Public*, pg. 1213
MacArthur, Burton G., Exec. V.P.--Champion International Corp., Stamford, CT; *U.S. Public*, pg. 333
MacArthur, Maxwell B., Exec. V.P.-Store Opers.--The Elder-Beerman Stores Corp., Dayton, OH; *U.S. Private*, pg. 367
Macauley, L., Exec. V.P. & Chief Tax Officer--Labatt Breweries of Canada, Toronto, Canada; *Int'l*, pg. 679
MacCarthur, Twig, Exec. V.P.-Mktg.--Champion International Corp., Stamford, CT; *U.S. Public*, pg. 333
MacColl, John A., Exec. V.P.-Human Resources & Gen. Counsel--USF&G Corporation, Baltimore, MD; *U.S. Public*, pg. 1659
MacDonald, Bill, Exec. V.P.-Strategic Plng.--ICN Pharmaceuticals, Inc., Costa Mesa, CA; *U.S. Public*, pg. 853
MacDonald, Colin, Exec. V.P.--Clearwater Fine Foods Inc., Bedford, Canada; *Int'l*, pg. 297
MacDonald, Grant, Partner & Exec. V.P.--North Castle Partners Advertising, Inc., Stamford, CT; *U.S. Private*, pg. 804
MacDonald, J. Rory, Chief Oper. Officer & Exec. V.P.--The Bank of Nova Scotia Trust Company, Toronto, Canada; *Int'l*, pg. 155
MacDonald, Louis N., Exec. V.P. & Gen. Mgr.--Commercial Record Center, Elk Grove Village, IL; *U.S. Private*, pg. 1164
MacDonald, Malcolm, Exec. Dir.-Fin.--Iscor, Pretoria, South Africa; *Int'l*, pg. 688
Macdonald, Roddy, Chief Oper. Officer & Exec. V.P.--Alflex, Long Beach, CA; *U.S. Public*, pg. 415
MacDonald, William E., III, Exec. V.P.--National City Corporation, Cleveland, OH; *U.S. Public*, pg. 1154
Mace, Edward E., Exec. V.P.--The Fairmont Hotels, San Francisco, CA; *U.S. Private*, pg. 391
Mace, Yvon, Exec. V.P.--Bertrand Faure, Boulogne, France; *Int'l*, pg. 192
Machida, Katsuhiko, Sr. Exec. Dir.-Intl. Bus.--Sharp Corporation, Osaka, Japan; *Int'l*, pg. 1228
Machida, Yoichi, Exec. V.P.--Kawasho Corporation, Tokyo, Japan; *Int'l*, pg. 726
Machles, Cindy, Exec. V.P. & Co-Dir.-Adv.--Grey Healthcare Group, New York, NY; *U.S. Public*, pg. 765
Machribie, Adrianto, Exec. V.P.--P.T. Freeport Indonesia Co., New Orleans, LA; *U.S. Public*, pg. 681
Mack, Ruth, Exec. V.P.-Sls.--WLR Foods, Inc., Timberville, VA; *U.S. Public*, pg. 1727
MacKay, John G., Sr. V.P. & Exec. V.P.-Europe--United Dominion Industries, Ltd., Charlotte, NC; *U.S. Public*, pg. 1675
Macken, John A., Exec. V.P.--P.T. Freeport Indonesia Co., New Orleans, LA; *U.S. Public*, pg. 681
Mackey, Thomas B., Exec. V.P.-Western Opers.--Tenet Healthcare Corporation, Santa Barbara, CA; *U.S. Public*, pg. 1576
Mackie, G.R., Exec. V.P.--Canadian Pacific Railway, Calgary, Canada; *Int'l*, pg. 258
Mackin, Mike, Exec. V.P.--Ohio Valley Aluminum Company, Shelbyville, KY; *U.S. Private*, pg. 567
Mackin, Scott G., Exec. V.P.--Ogden Corporation, New York, NY; *U.S. Public*, pg. 1213
Mackler, Harvey S., Chief Oper. Officer & Exec. V.P.--Gibraltar Corp. of America, New York, NY; *U.S. Public*, pg. 1528
Mackoul, Sabry J., Sr. Exec. V.P.--Summit Bancorp, Princeton, NJ; *U.S. Public*, pg. 1527
MacLean, Clive, Exec. V.P. & Mktg. Dir.--CM Partners, Inc., Rolling Meadows, IL; *U.S. Private*, pg. 195
MacLeish, Donald E., Exec. V.P.--Northern Capital Management, Inc., Madison, WI; *U.S. Public*, pg. 1673
MacLellan, Neil F., III, Exec. V.P.-Sls. & Mktg.--Mac-Gray Corporation, Cambridge, MA; *U.S. Public*, pg. 1029
MacLennan, Alan D., Exec. V.P.-Employee Benefits--The Great-West Life Assurance Company, Winnipeg, Canada; *Int'l*, pg. 557
MacLennan, Mark A., Exec. V.P.--BankBoston Corporation, Boston, MA; *U.S. Public*, pg. 183
MacLeod, Daniel E., Exec. V.P. & Gen. Mgr.--Cajun Electric Power Co-op, Baton Rouge, LA; *U.S. Private*, pg. 199
MacMaster, Norman A., Exec. V.P. & Global Bus. Dir.-Kellogg--J. Walter Thompson Company, New York, NY; *Int'l*, pg. 1483
MacMorran, Henry G., Exec. V.P.-Individual Banking--ABN/LaSalle North America Inc., Chicago, IL; *Int'l*, pg. 11
MacPhail, Keith A.J., Chief Oper. Officer & Exec. V.P.--Canadian Natural Resources Limited, Calgary, Canada; *Int'l*, pg. 258
MacPhee, Gary, Exec. V.P.-Atlantic--Shoppers Drug Mart, Ltd., Toronto, Canada; *Int'l*, pg. 112
Macur, Walter, Exec. V.P.-Asset Based Lending--LaSalle National Bank, Chicago, IL; *Int'l*, pg. 10
Macur, Walter, Exec. V.P.-Asset-Based Lending--ABN/LaSalle North America Inc., Chicago, IL; *Int'l*, pg. 11
Madden, Bruce, Exec. V.P.-Sls. & Mktg.--Maharam, Hauppauge, NY; *U.S. Private*, pg. 696

Madden, Richard O., Chief Fin. Officer, Exec. V.P., Treas. & Sec.--Vermont Financial Services Corp., Brattleboro, VT; U.S. Public, pg. 1716
Maddox, Jay R., Exec. V.P.-Personal Trust--AMCORE Trust Company, Rockford, IL; U.S. Public, pg. 65
Maddox, Jeffrey D., Exec. V.P.--First Maryland Bancorp, Baltimore, MD; Int'l, pg. 64
Madel, Michael, Exec. V.P., Chm., Pres. & Chief Exec. Officer-JWT/Europe--J. Walter Thompson Company, New York, NY; Int'l, pg. 1483
Madison, David W., Exec. V.P.-Branch Loan Div.--First Hawaiian Bank, Honolulu, HI; U.S. Public, pg. 634
Madison, George W., Exec. V.P., Gen. Counsel & Corp. Sec.--Comerica Incorporated, Detroit, MI; U.S. Public, pg. 408
Madley, Richard, Exec. V.P.-NYC--Phillips Fine Art Auctioneers, New York, NY; U.S. Private, pg. 861
Madormo, Patrick, Exec. V.P.--Flo Control, Inc., Burbank, CA; U.S. Private, pg. 414
Madre, Menoit, Sr. Exec. V.P.--Asland S.A., Madrid, Spain; Int'l, pg. 788
Madsen, C. Fred, Exec. V.P. & Mgr.-Casualty--NAC Reinsurance Corporation, Greenwich, CT; U.S. Public, pg. 1144
Madsen, Dennis, Chief Oper. Officer & Exec. V.P.--Recreational Equipment, Inc., Kent, WA; U.S. Private, pg. 914
Maeda, Koichi, Exec. Dir.--Dentsu Inc., Tokyo, Japan; Int'l, pg. 392
Maeda, Koichi, Exec. V.P.--Maruha Corporation, Tokyo, Japan; Int'l, pg. 845
Maese Cordero, Humberto, Exec. V.P.--Internacional de Ceramica S.A. de C.V., Chihuahua, Mexico; Int'l, pg. 680
Magd, Patrick, Exec. V.P.-Corp. Commun.--Gaz de France, Paris, France; Int'l, pg. 541
Magee, Frank, Exec. V.P.--Orthologic Corporation, Tempe, AZ; U.S. Public, pg. 1232
Maggio, Thomas E., Exec. V.P.-Colorants & Additives--Huls America Inc., Somerset, NJ; Int'l, pg. 1455
Maginn, John L., Exec. V.P., Chief Investment Officer & Treas.--Mutual of Omaha Insurance Company, Omaha, NE; U.S. Private, pg. 769
Maginn, John L., Exec. V.P., Chief Investment Officer & Treas.--United of Omaha Life Insurance Company, Omaha, NE; U.S. Private, pg. 770
Maginniss, Christopher M., Chief Fin. Officer & Exec. V.P.--Microdyne Corporation, Alexandria, VA; U.S. Public, pg. 1105
Magnant, Lawrence C., Jr., Exec. V.P.--Herbert Clough, Inc., New York, NY; U.S. Public, pg. 726
Magnin, Laurent, Exec. V.P. & Gen. Mgr.--Great Lakes Confectionery, Cleveland, OH; Int'l, pg. 865
Magnuson, Chris, Exec. V.P.-Admin.--Wasco Products, Inc., Sanford, ME; U.S. Private, pg. 1152
Magrann, Robert P., Exec. V.P.--Brach & Brock Confections, Inc., Chicago, IL; U.S. Private, pg. 163
Magrino, Robert, Exec. V.P.-Sls.--Mita Copystar America Inc., Fairfield, NJ; Int'l, pg. 870
Mahan, Richard, Exec. V.P. & Mng. Partner -Creative--Wells BDDP, Inc., New York, NY; Int'l, pg. 117
Maharam, Michael, Exec. V.P.-Design & Mktg.--Maharam, Hauppauge, NY; U.S. Private, pg. 696
Maharam, Stephen, Exec. V.P.-Fin. & Personnel--Maharam, Hauppauge, NY; U.S. Private, pg. 696
Mahlman, Edward, Exec. V.P. & Client Services Dir.--Tierney & Partners, Philadelphia, PA; U.S. Public, pg. 1641
Mahoney, Andrew, Exec. V.P.-Construction--Willis Corroon Corp. of Minnesota, Minneapolis, MN; Int'l, pg. 1506
Mahoney, George R., Jr., Exec. V.P., Gen. Counsel & Sec.--Family Dollar Stores, Inc., Matthews, NC; U.S. Public, pg. 612
Mahoney, James, Exec. V.P.-Sls.--Plasti-Kote Company Inc., Medina, OH; U.S. Private, pg. 870
Mahoney, John, Chief Fin. Officer & Exec. V.P.--Staples, Inc., Westborough, MA; U.S. Public, pg. 1509
Mahurin, Daniel W., Exec. V.P.--SunTrust, Orlando, FL; U.S. Public, pg. 1537
Maich, Peter A., Exec. V.P.-Mdsg.--T.J. Maxx, Framingham, MA; U.S. Public, pg. 1557
Maier, Ed, Exec. V.P.--ENI, Rochester, NY; U.S. Private, pg. 354
Maila, Michel G., Exec. V.P.-Mexico & Latin America--Bank of Montreal, Toronto, Canada; Int'l, pg. 153
Mailleret, Michel, Exec. V.P.--Labinal SA, Montigny-le-Bretonneux, France; Int'l, pg. 785
Maiman, Dana, Exec. V.P. & Co-Dir.-Client Services-GHG--Grey Healthcare Group, New York, NY; U.S. Public, pg. 765
Maiman, Thomas J., Exec. V.P.--ComEd, Chicago, IL; U.S. Public, pg. 1664
Main, Guy A., Exec. V.P.-Property & Casualty--Amwest Surety Insurance Company, Calabasas, CA; U.S. Public, pg. 106
Maine, Douglas, Chief Fin. Officer & Exec. V.P.--MCI Communications Corp., Atlanta, GA; U.S. Public, pg. 1023
Maio, Keith D., Exec. V.P.--National Bank of Arizona, Tucson, AZ; U.S. Public, pg. 1793
Maitner, Robert E., Exec. V.P.-Opers.--Standard & Poor's Ratings Services, New York, NY; U.S. Public, pg. 1071
Major, John E., Exec. V.P. & Pres.-Infrastructure Prods. Division--QUALCOMM, San Diego, CA; U.S. Public, pg. 1348
Major, Laurence H., Jr., Exec. V.P.--General Accident Insurance, Philadelphia, PA; Int'l, pg. 543
Major, Robert A., Exec. V.P.--ContiFinancial Corporation, New York, NY; U.S. Public, pg. 439
Makelainen, Esko, Exec. V.P.--Enso Oyj, Helsinki, Finland; Int'l, pg. 455
Maki, Yoshio, Exec. V.P.--Mitsubishi Materials Corp., Tokyo, Japan; Int'l, pg. 874
Makinen, Juho, Exec. V.P.-Tech.--Outokumpu Oyj, Espoo, Finland; Int'l, pg. 1015
Makino, Toshimasa, Exec. V.P.--Sumitomo Heavy Industries, Ltd., Tokyo, Japan; Int'l, pg. 1314
Makise, Yoshitake, Exec. V.P.--Mitsubishi Heavy Industries Ltd., Tokyo, Japan; Int'l, pg. 873
Makuta, Keiichi, Exec. V.P.--Tohoku Electric Power Co., Ltd., Sendai, Japan; Int'l, pg. 1390
Malan, Sergio, Exec. V.P.-Electronic Banking--Istituto Bancario San Paolo Di Torino S.p.A., Turin, Italy; Int'l, pg. 691
Malden, Terry L., Exec. V.P.--Maclean Hunter Publishing Ltd., Toronto, Canada; Int'l, pg. 1123
Malden, Terry L., Exec. V.P.--Canadian Publishing, Toronto, Canada; Int'l, pg. 1123
Malen, Juoko, Exec. V.P.-Tech Div.--FinnAir Oy, Helsinki, Finland; Int'l, pg. 485
Maliani, Michael, Exec. V.P.-Devel.--DIC Entertainment, Burbank, CA; U.S. Public, pg. 513
Malinsky, Aaron, Exec. V.P.-Devel. & Strategic Plng.--The Great Atlantic & Pacific Tea Company, Inc., Montvale, NJ; Int'l, pg. 1375
Malling, James E., Exec. V.P.--MBIA Inc., Armonk, NY; U.S. Public, pg. 1023
Malling, James E., Sr. Exec. V.P.-Corp. Mktg. & Devel.--Municipal Bond Investors Assurance Corporation, Armonk, NY; U.S. Public, pg. 1023
Mallon, William G., Chief Credit Officer & Exec. V.P.--Fleet Bank NH, Manchester, NH; U.S. Public, pg. 649
Malloy, Terry, Sr. V.P.-Mktg. & Planning--Osco Drug, Salt Lake City, UT; U.S. Public, pg. 93
Malone, Michael, Chief Fin. Officer & Exec. V.P.--Polaris Industries, Inc., Minneapolis, MN; U.S. Public, pg. 1313
Maloney, John, Exec. V.P.-Sls. & Mktg.--Tacony Corporation, Fenton, MO; U.S. Private, pg. 1066
Malpass, Tad, Exec. V.P.--East Jordan Iron Works, East Jordan, MI; U.S. Private, pg. 356
Malpass, Tracy, Exec. V.P.--East Jordan Iron Works, East Jordan, MI; U.S. Private, pg. 356
Maltempo, Robert S., Exec. V.P.--CSC Financial Services Group, Austin, TX; U.S. Public, pg. 422
Maltese, John, Exec. V.P.-Fin. (New York)--Burson-Marsteller, New York, NY; U.S. Private, pg. 1197
Maltz, Alan, Exec. V.P.-TSL Div.--Brite Voice Systems, Inc., Heathrow, FL; U.S. Public, pg. 257
Maltz, Alan, Exec. V.P.--TSL, New York, NY; U.S. Public, pg. 257
Maltz, Scott, Exec. V.P.-TSL--Brite Voice Systems, Inc., Heathrow, FL; U.S. Public, pg. 257
Malwitz, Donald W., Chief Fin. Officer & Exec. V.P.--United National Bancorp, Bridgewater, NJ; U.S. Public, pg. 1679
Mambro, Jamie, Exec. V.P. & Grp. Creative Dir.--Hill, Holliday, Connors, Cosmopulos, Inc., Boston, MA; U.S. Private, pg. 529
Manabe, Yoshiro, Exec. V.P.-Ship Group & Rolling Stock Grp.--Kawasaki Heavy Industries, Ltd., Kobe, Japan; Int'l, pg. 725
Mancinelli, Victor A., Chief Oper. Officer & Exec. V.P.--Gehl Company, West Bend, WI; U.S. Public, pg. 704
Mancini, Antonio, Chief Oper. Officer--Hospal S.p.A., Bologna, Italy; Int'l, pg. 668
Mancuso, Ross, Exec. V.P. & Gen. Mgr.--Grocers Equipment Co., Los Angeles, CA; U.S. Private, pg. 227
Mandarano, C. Patrick, Exec. V.P.-Medical--Carrafiello, Diehl & Associates, Inc., Irvington, NY; U.S. Private, pg. 215
Mandarich, David D., Chief Oper. Officer & Exec. V.P.--M.D.C. Holdings, Inc., Denver, CO; U.S. Public, pg. 1025
Mandel, Benny, Vice Chm. & Exec. V.P.--Agis Industries Ltd., Bnei-Brak, Israel; Int'l, pg. 30
Mandelbaum, Jay, Exec. V.P.-Mktg.--Salomon Smith Barney Holdings, Inc., New York, NY; U.S. Public, pg. 1633
Mandia, Albert W., Chief Fin. Officer & Exec. V.P.--CoreStates Financial Corp., Philadelphia, PA; U.S. Public, pg. 446
Mandick, Dennis J., Exec. V.P.--Associates Commercial Corporation, Dallas, TX; U.S. Public, pg. 663
Mandini, Roberto, Exec. V.P.--Citgo Petroleum Corporation, Tulsa, OK; Int'l, pg. 1045
Mandles, Martinn H., Chm. Bd., Chief Admin. Officer & Exec. V.P.--ABM Industries, San Francisco, CA; U.S. Public, pg. 2
Manfredi, John F., Exec. V.P.-Corp. Affairs--Nabisco Inc., Parsippany, NJ; U.S. Public, pg. 1355
Mangan, Michael D., Chief Fin. Officer & Exec. V.P.--The Ryland Group, Inc., Columbia, MD; U.S. Public, pg. 1414
Manganello, Joseph A., Jr., Chief Credit Officer & Exec. V.P.-Credit Policy--Bankers Trust New York Corporation, New York, NY; U.S. Public, pg. 185
Mangel, Steven E., Exec. V.P.-Legal & Bus. Affairs & Gen. Counsel--LIVE Film & Mediaworks, Van Nuys, CA; U.S. Private, pg. 671
Maniscalco, Rosemary, Chief Oper. Officer--Comforce/Uniforce Staffing Services, Woodbury, NY; U.S. Public, pg. 409
Manley, Ted R., Exec. V.P.-Opers. & Pres.-Once Upon A Child--Grow Biz International, Inc., Minneapolis, MN; U.S. Public, pg. 767
Manly, Robert W., IV, Exec. V.P.--Smithfield Foods, Inc., Norfolk, VA; U.S. Public, pg. 1479
Mann, Johnny, Exec. V.P.--Associated Aircraft Supply Company, Dallas, TX; U.S. Private, pg. 89
Mann, Kevin J., Exec. V.P.-Category Mngmt.--Rite Aid Corporation, Camp Hill, PA; U.S. Public, pg. 1390
Mann, Michael R., Exec. V.P.--Colonial Metals Co., Columbia, PA; U.S. Private, pg. 253
Mann, Robert A., Chief Fin. Officer & Exec. V.P.-Fin. & Admin.--Park Foods L.P., Barrington, IL; U.S. Private, pg. 839
Manne, S. Anthony, Exec. V.P.-Intl.--Columbia Tri-Star Film Distributors International, Culver City, CA; Int'l, pg. 1281
Mannerkoski, Lauri, Vice Chm. & Exec. V.P.-Mktg.--Rautaruukki Oy, Helsinki, Finland; Int'l, pg. 1088
Mannesson, Magnus, Exec. Dir.--Machinery West, Hisings Karra, Sweden; Int'l, pg. 899
Manning, E. Baines, Exec. V.P.--Valero Marketing & Supply Company, San Antonio, TX; U.S. Public, pg. 1704
Manning, E. Baines, Exec. V.P.--Valero Refining Company, San Antonio, TX; U.S. Public, pg. 1704
Manning, James V., Chief Fin. Officer & Sr. Exec. V.P.--MEDCO Containment Services, Inc., Montvale, NJ; U.S. Public, pg. 1091
Manning, Ray, Jr., Exec. V.P.-E. Region--Bergen Brunswig Corporation, Orange, CA; U.S. Public, pg. 213
Manning, Robert J., Exec. V.P.--ComEd, Chicago, IL; U.S. Public, pg. 1664
Manny, David P., Exec. V.P. & Sec.--Finch, Pruyn & Co., Inc., Glens Falls, NY; U.S. Private, pg. 405
Manoforte, Filippo, Exec. V.P.-Auditing--Istituto Bancario San Paolo Di Torino S.p.A., Turin, Italy; Int'l, pg. 691
Mansell, Kevin, Exec. V.P.-Hardlines Mdse.--Kohl's Corporation, Menomonee Falls, WI; U.S. Public, pg. 965
Manso, Antonio Luiz, Chief Fin. Officer & Exec. V.P.-Fin.--Embraer-Empresa Brasileira de Aeronautica S.A., Sao Jose dos Campos, Brazil; Int'l, pg. 452
Mansur, Danilo M.C., Exec. V.P.-Middle Mkt.--Uniao de Bancos Brasileiros S.A. (Unibanco), Sao Paulo, Brazil; Int'l, pg. 1431
Manz, Chuck, Exec. V.P.--Graham, Milwaukee, WI; Int'l, pg. 377
Mara, Thomas E., Exec. V.P. & Treas.--Leucadia National Corporation, New York, NY; U.S. Public, pg. 989
Marcheteau, A., Sr. Exec. V.P.--Compagnie de Suez, Paris, France; Int'l, pg. 313
Marchilena, Francis S., Exec. V.P.--Raytheon Systems Company, Arlington, VA; U.S. Public, pg. 1364
Marciano, Armand, Exec. V.P.--Guess ?, Inc., Los Angeles, CA; U.S. Public, pg. 768
Marcic, Irene S., Chief Fin. Officer, Exec. V.P., Treas. & Sec.--Astrex, Inc., Plainview, NY; U.S. Public, pg. 141
Marcinuli, Ronald P., Exec. V.P.-Asset Based Bus.--Comerica Incorporated, Detroit, MI; U.S. Public, pg. 408
Marcucci, Frank J., Exec. V.P.-Fin. & Admin.--Amkor Electronics, Inc., West Chester, PA; U.S. Private, pg. 66
Marcus, Alan, Exec. V.P.--Arnold Communications, Inc., Boston, MA; U.S. Private, pg. 83
Marcus, Barbara A., Exec. V.P.-Children's Book Publishing--Scholastic Corporation, New York, NY; U.S. Public, pg. 1440
Marcus, Gwen, Exec. V.P., Gen. Counsel & Admin.--Showtime Networks Inc., New York, NY; U.S. Private, pg. 779
Marcus, Joan, Exec. V.P.-Syndication Svcs.--The Summit Media Group, New York, NY; U.S. Private, pg. 1050
Marcus, Paul, Exec. V.P.-Entertainment Mktg.--Simon Marketing, Inc., Los Angeles, CA; U.S. Private, pg. 1001
Mardiks, Ellen Ryan, Exec. V.P. & Gen. Mgr.- Consumer--Edelman Public Relations Worldwide, Chicago, IL; U.S. Private, pg. 362
Mared, Mats, Exec. V.P.-Real Estate--Skanska AB, Danderyd, Sweden; Int'l, pg. 1260
Marek, Alan J., Chief Fin. Officer & Exec. V.P.--DG Foods, LLC, Chicago, IL; U.S. Private, pg. 301
Margolis, Lawrence A., Chief Fin. Officer, Exec. V.P. & Sec.--The Antec Corporation, Rolling Meadows, IL; U.S. Public, pg. 116
Margulies, Warren, Exec. V.P. & Creative Dir.--Trone Advertising, Inc., Greensboro, NC; U.S. Private, pg. 1104
Marinez Salas, Federico, Exec. V.P.--Empresas ICA Sociedad Controladora S.A.C.V., Mexico, Mexico; Int'l, pg. 454
Marino, Thomas, Exec. V.P.-Network Opers.--Excel Communications, Inc., Dallas, TX; U.S. Public, pg. 598
Marion, Jesse R., Exec. V.P. & Dir.--Datatel, Inc., Houston, TX; U.S. Public, pg. 1454
Mark, Michael, Exec. V.P. & Mng. Partner-Creative--Wells BDDP, Inc., New York, NY; Int'l, pg. 117
Markel, Lynn, Exec. V.P.-Fin. & Admin.--Koch Industries, Incorporated, Wichita, KS; U.S. Private, pg. 628
Markman, Steven, Exec. V.P.-Novell Products--Novell, Inc., Orem, UT; U.S. Public, pg. 1203
Markowsky, Dr. James J., Exec. V.P.-Power Generation--American Electric Power Service Corp., Columbus, OH; U.S. Public, pg. 72
Marks, Gordon W., Exec. V.P.--Swinerton Inc., San Francisco, CA; U.S. Private, pg. 1059
Marks, Harry, Exec. V.P.--Allied Sporting Goods Inc., Louisville, KY; U.S. Private, pg. 41
Marks, Michael, Exec. V.P.--Allied Sporting Goods Inc., Louisville, KY; U.S. Private, pg. 41
Marks, Richard, Exec. V.P.-Sls.--Shadow Broadcast Services, Bala Cynwyd, PA; U.S. Public, pg. 1763
Marks, Sam, Exec. V.P., Corp. Sec. & Dir.-Pur.--Triangle Marketing Corp., New York, NY; U.S. Private, pg. 1102
Marks, Sam, Exec. V.P., Corp. Sec. & Dir.-Pur.--New Brook Paper, New York, NY; U.S. Private, pg. 1102
Markson, Mitchell, Exec. V.P. & Gen. Mgr.-Consumer--Edelman Worldwide, Inc., New York, NY; U.S. Private, pg. 362
Markum, James A., Chief Fin. Officer & Exec. V.P.--Stage Stores, Inc., Houston, TX; U.S. Private, pg. 1028
Marley, Morris, Sr. Exec. V.P.--BB&T Corporation, Winston Salem, NC; U.S. Public, pg. 159
Marlowe, Brian, Exec. V.P. & Pres.-Eastern Div.--Stewart Enterprises, Inc., Metairie, LA; U.S. Public, pg. 1518
Marmon, Larry, Exec. V.P.-Mktg. Opers.--Time-Life, Inc., Alexandria, VA; U.S. Public, pg. 1613
Marois, Paul, Exec. V.P.--Anglo Fabrics Company, Inc., New York, NY; U.S. Private, pg. 74
Maron, Edward B., Jr., Chief Oper. Officer & Exec. V.P.-Canadian Div.--Costco Wholesale, Issaquah, WA; U.S. Public, pg. 451
Marquardt, Klaus-Detlef, Dr., Exec. V.P.--DG Bank, Frankfurt/Main, Germany; Int'l, pg. 351
Marquart, Clifford L., Chief Oper. Officer & Exec. V.P.--The Morning Star Group, Dallas, TX; U.S. Public, pg. 1527
Marra, Edward A., Exec. V.P. & Gen. Mgr.-Nestle Frozen Food Co.--Nestle Frozen, Refrigerated, and Ice Cream Companies, Solon, OH; Int'l, pg. 918
Marram, Ellen, Exec. V.P.--The Seagram Company Ltd., Montreal, Canada; Int'l, pg. 1214

Marro, Anthony, Exec. V.P.--Newsday, Melville, NY; *U.S. Public*, pg. 1616
Marsh, Charles L., Sr. Exec. V.P.-Pur. & Mktg.--Southern Electronics Distributors International, Tucker, GA; *U.S. Public*, pg. 1490
Marsh, Donald L., Chief Fin. Officer, Exec. V.P. & Corp. Sec.--Alflex, Long Beach, CA; *U.S. Public*, pg. 415
Marsh, Donald L., Jr., Chief Fin. Officer, Exec. V.P. & Sec.--Commonwealth Industries, Inc., Louisville, KY; *U.S. Public*, pg. 415
Marshall, David D., Exec. V.P.--Duquesne Light Company, Pittsburgh, PA; *U.S. Public*, pg. 474
Marshall, E., Exec. V.P.-Opers.--Trans World Entertainment Corporation, Albany, NY; *U.S. Public*, pg. 1629
Marshall, I. David, Chief Information Officer & Exec. V.P.--Bankers Trust New York Corporation, New York, NY; *U.S. Public*, pg. 185
Marshall, Joan, Exec. V.P.--The R.J. Marshall Co., Southfield, MI; *U.S. Private*, pg. 708
Marshall, Robert J., Exec. V.P.-Retail Banking--The Bank of Nova Scotia, Toronto, Canada; *Int'l*, pg. 155
Marshall, Ron, Chief Fin. Officer & Exec. V.P.--Pathmark Stores Incorporated, Woodbridge, NJ; *U.S. Private*, pg. 843
Marshall, Scott W., Exec. V.P.-Res. & Devel.--Newbridge Networks Corporation, Kanata, Canada; *Int'l*, pg. 923
Marsilius, Richard A., Exec. V.P. & Sec.--Moore Tool Company, Inc., Bridgeport, CT; *U.S. Private*, pg. 889
Marson, Jacques- Philippe, Exec. V.P.--State Street Corporation, Boston, MA; *U.S. Public*, pg. 1513
Martell, Kenneth, Exec. V.P. & Gen. Mgr.--Plews/Edelmann, Buffalo Grove, IL; *Int'l*, pg. 1396
Marten, Ralph, Exec. V.P.--First Northern Capital Corp., Green Bay, WI; *U.S. Public*, pg. 636
Martens, Harry, Exec. V.P.--Commercial Union Corporation, Boston, MA; *Int'l*, pg. 308
Martens, Herbert R., Exec. V.P.-Wealth Mngmt.--National City Corporation, Cleveland, OH; *U.S. Public*, pg. 1154
Marti, John, Exec. V.P.--Drug Emporium of Arizona, Scottsdale, AZ; *U.S. Private*, pg. 343
Martial, Robin L., Exec. V.P.-Western Grp.--Cardinal Distribution, Dublin, OH; *U.S. Public*, pg. 304
Martin, Barry, Exec. V.P. & Acct. Plng. Dir.--Partners & Shevack, Inc., New York, NY; *U.S. Private*, pg. 842
Martin, Bob L., Exec. V.P. & Pres.-Intl.--Wal-Mart Stores, Inc., Bentonville, AR; *U.S. Public*, pg. 1732
Martin, Clarence, Chief Exec. Officer & Chief Fin. Officer--State Electric Supply Co., Huntington, WV; *U.S. Private*, pg. 1036
Martin, Darrel D., Chief Fin. Officer & Exec. V.P.--Markel Corporation, Glen Allen, VA; *U.S. Public*, pg. 1046
Martin, Daryl, Chief Fin. Officer & Exec. V.P.--Elwell-Parker Limited, Cleveland, OH; *U.S. Private*, pg. 373
Martin, David D., Exec. V.P.--Texas Instruments Incorporated, Dallas, TX; *U.S. Public*, pg. 1585
Martin, Deborah, Exec. V.P. & Gen. Mgr.--Hill, Holliday, Connors, Cosmopulos, Inc., Boston, MA; *U.S. Private*, pg. 529
Martin, Dennis J., Exec. V.P.--Illinois Tool Works Inc., Glenview, IL; *U.S. Public*, pg. 865
Martin, Ed, Exec. V.P.-Human Resources--Showboat, Incorporated, Las Vegas, NV; *U.S. Public*, pg. 1469
Martin, Ernest, Exec. V.P.--United Advertising Publications, Inc., Dallas, TX; *Int'l*, pg. 1443
Martin, Francisco, Exec. V.P.-Intl. Div.--Banco Santander, Madrid, Spain; *Int'l*, pg. 143
Martin, George W., Exec. V.P.--Dun & Bradstreet, Murray Hill, NJ; *U.S. Public*, pg. 535
Martin, Humberto, Exec. V.P.--Banco Popular de Puerto Rico, San Juan, PR; *U.S. Public*, pg. 175
Martin, Humberto, Exec. V.P.--BanPonce Corporation, Hato Rey, PR; *U.S. Public*, pg. 176
Martin, J.E., Exec. V.P.--TU Electric, Dallas, TX; *U.S. Public, pg. 1588*
Martin, Joe, Exec. V.P. & Principal Corp. Affairs Officer--NationsBank Corporation, Charlotte, NC; *U.S. Public*, pg. 1162
Martin, John C., Chief Info. Officer & Exec. V.P.--Citizens Financial Group, Inc., Providence, RI; *Int'l*, pg. 1132
Martin, Ken, Chm. & Chief Exec. Officer--Sedgwick Noble Lowndes, Memphis, TN; *Int'l*, pg. 1218
Martin, Lauralee E., Chief Fin. Officer & Exec. V.P.--Heller International Corporation, Chicago, IL; *Int'l*, pg. 519
Martin, Lauralee E., Chief Fin. Officer & Exec. V.P.--Heller Financial, Inc., Chicago, IL; *Int'l*, pg. 519
Martin, Louis, Exec. V.P.--Sunline Coach Co., Inc., Denver, PA; *U.S. Private*, pg. 1053
Martin, Michael D., Chief Fin. Officer, Exec. V.P. & Treas.--Healthsouth Corporation, Birmingham, AL; *U.S. Public*, pg. 803
Martin, Norbert, Member Bd.--Clouth Gummiwerke AG, Cologne, Germany; *Int'l*, pg. 297
Martin, Richard J., Chief Fin. Officer & Exec. V.P.--Rykoff-Sexton, Inc., Wilkes-Barre, PA; *U.S. Public*, pg. 918
Martin, Robert A., Exec. V.P.-Mktg.--Applebee's International, Inc., Overland Park, KS; *U.S. Public*, pg. 122
Martin, Sally, Exec. V.P. & Gen. Mgr.-Mdsg.-Hosiery--Victoria's Secret Stores, Reynoldsburg, OH; *U.S. Public*, pg. 995
Martin, Samuel, Exec. V.P.--The Holland Hitch Company, Holland, MI; *U.S. Private*, pg. 534
Martin, Samuel A., Exec. V.P.--Binkley Company, Warrenton, MO; *U.S. Private*, pg. 534
Martin, Steven T., Exec. V.P.-Components Segment--Ingersoll-Rand Company, Woodcliff Lake, NJ; *U.S. Public*, pg. 876
Martin, Terence D., Chief Fin. Officer & Exec. V.P.--General Signal Corporation, Stamford, CT; *U.S. Public*, pg. 726
Martin, Thomas E., III, Chief Fin. Officer & Exec. V.P.--Taracorp, Inc., Atlanta, GA; *U.S. Private*, pg. 1068
Martin, Walter, Exec. V.P.--MTS, Inc., West Sacramento, CA; *U.S. Private*, pg. 688
Martin, Walter, Exec. V.P.--Tower Records, West Sacramento, CA; *U.S. Private*, pg. 688
Martineau, Eugene P., Exec. V.P.--Concrete Products Grp.--Southdown, Inc., Houston, TX; *U.S. Public*, pg. 1488
Martineau, James L., Exec. V.P.--Apogee Enterprises, Inc., Minneapolis, MN; *U.S. Public*, pg. 120
Martinez Lozano, Gustavo, Exec. V.P.--Internacional de Ceramica S.A. de C.V., Chihuahua, Mexico; *Int'l*, pg. 680
Martinez, Eliezer Galvan, Exec. V.P.--Acerex S.A., San Nicolas, Mexico; *Int'l*, pg. 56
Martinez, L.E., Exec. V.P.--The Pipelines of Puerto Rico, Inc., San Juan, PR; *U.S. Public*, pg. 1584
Martino, Michael, Exec. V.P. & Chief Investment Officer--Back Bay Advisors, Inc., Boston, MA; *U.S. Private*, pg. 737
Martire, Frank R., Corp. Exec. V.P.-Bank & Credit Union Grp.--Fiserv, Inc., Brookfield, WI; *U.S. Public*, pg. 647
Martyn, Simon A., Exec. V.P.-Grp. Human Resources-USA--Marine Midland Bank, Buffalo, NY; *Int'l*, pg. 581
Martyna, Bobby, Exec. V.P.--Vertel, Woodland Hills, CA; *U.S. Public*, pg. 1717
Maruyama, Hiromi, Exec. Dir.--Advantest Corporation, Tokyo, Japan; *Int'l*, pg. 25
Marx, Jurg, Exec. V.P.-Human Resources--The Swissair Group, Zurich, Switzerland; *Int'l*, pg. 1333
Marzloff, Georges, Exec. V.P.-Chemicals--Neste Oy, Espoo, Finland; *Int'l*, pg. 912
Masada, Fumio, Exec. V.P.--Nippon Life Insurance Co., Osaka, Japan; *Int'l*, pg. 934
Masberg, Ulrich, Dr., Member Bd.--Clouth Gummiwerke AG, Cologne, Germany; *Int'l*, pg. 297
Masco, John R., Exec. V.P.--FirstMerit Corporation, Akron, OH; *U.S. Public*, pg. 646
Maslick, Joseph R., Chief Fin. Officer, Exec. V.P. & Sec.--Griffith Laboratories Worldwide, Inc., Alsip, IL; *U.S. Private*, pg. 481
Mason, David A., Chief Fin. Officer, Exec. V.P. & Treas.--Moto Photo, Inc., Dayton, OH; *U.S. Public*, pg. 1136
Mason, Phil, Exec. V.P.--Taylor Impression, Inc., Nashville, TN; *U.S. Private*, pg. 1070
Mason, Ron, Exec. V.P.--Kentucky Indiana Lumber Co. Inc., Louisville, KY; *U.S. Private*, pg. 615
Massaro, Louis L., Chief Fin. Officer, Chief Admin. Officer & Exec. V.P.--Frontier Corporation, Rochester, NY; *U.S. Public*, pg. 683
Massaro, Mike, Chief Oper. Officer & Exec. V.P.--Goldberg Moser O'Neill, San Francisco, CA; *U.S. Private*, pg. 459
Massengale, Jim E., Exec. V.P.--Protective Life Corporation, Birmingham, AL; *U.S. Public*, pg. 1336
Massengill, Bill, Exec. V.P.--Lexington Furniture Industries, Lexington, NC; *U.S. Private*, pg. 432
Massey, Mitchell, Exec. V.P.--G.H. Bass & Co., South Portland, ME; *U.S. Public*, pg. 1291
Massie, William C., Exec. V.P.--B.B. Walker Company, Asheboro, NC; *U.S. Public*, pg. 1734
Massillon, Gilbert, Exec. Dir.--Union Miniere, Brussels, Belgium; *Int'l*, pg. 1441
Massingill, Doug, Exec. V.P.-Worldwide Opers.--J.D. Edwards & Company, Denver, CO; *U.S. Private*, pg. 365
Mastaler, Richard M., Exec. V.P.-Bus. Devel.--Magellan Health Services, Inc., Atlanta, GA; *U.S. Public*, pg. 1033
Mastandrea, James C., Chm. Bd., Pres. & Chief Exec. Officer--First Union Real Estate Investments, Cleveland, OH; *U.S. Public*, pg. 640
Mastellon, Bill, Chief Fin. Officer & Exec. V.P.--DeWitt Media, Inc., New York, NY; *U.S. Private*, pg. 329
Masterson, Kenneth R., Exec. V.P., Gen. Counsel & Sec.--FDX Corporation, Memphis, TN; *U.S. Public*, pg. 603
Mastrodicasa, B., Exec. V.P.-Mfg. & Distribution--Great Lakes Confectionery, Cleveland, OH; *Int'l*, pg. 865
Mastromarino, John J., Exec. V.P.--BankBoston Corporation, Boston, MA; *U.S. Public*, pg. 183
Masturzo, Paul, Exec. V.P. & Gen. Mgr.-U.S., Elizabeth Arden--Elizabeth Arden Company, New York, NY; *Int'l*, pg. 1435
Masuda, Kohei, Exec. V.P. & Gen. Mgr.-Western Div.--The Sakura Bank (Canada), Vancouver Office, Vancouver, Canada; *Int'l*, pg. 1180
Masukawa, Hitoei, Exec. V.P.-Personnel--Ito-Yokado Co., Ltd., Tokyo, Japan; *Int'l*, pg. 693
Masuko, Mike K., Exec. V.P.--Bundy Japan Ltd., Nagoya, Japan; *Int'l*, pg. 1341
Matar, Stig, Exec. V.P.-Finland, Germany, France, Italy & Eastern Europe--Fiskars Oy AB, Helsinki, Finland; *Int'l*, pg. 492
Mather, Deborah C., Exec. V.P.--Kepner-Tregoe, Inc., Skillman, NJ; *U.S. Public*, pg. 1659
Matheus, Euler, Exec. V.P.-Rio de Janeiro & Brasilia--Salles/DMB&B Publicidade S.A., Sao Paulo, Brazil; *U.S. Private*, pg. 305
Mathias, Jean-Louis, Exec. V.P. & Head-Human Resources--Electricite de France, Paris, France; *Int'l*, pg. 437
Mathias, Jean-Louis, Exec. V.P.-H.R.--Gaz de France, Paris, France; *Int'l*, pg. 541
Mathias, Robert, Exec. V.P.-Credit Admin.--Magna Group, Inc., Saint Louis, MO; *U.S. Public*, pg. 1037
Mathies, William A., Exec. V.P. & Pres.-Beverly Health & Rehab.--Beverly Enterprises, Inc., Fort Smith, AR; *U.S. Public*, pg. 227
Mathis, Daniel W., Exec. V.P. & Dir.-Corp. Banking--First Union Corporation, Charlotte, NC; *U.S. Public*, pg. 639
Mathrani, Arjun K., Exec. V.P.-Global Asset Mngmnt. & Private Banking--The Chase Manhattan Corporation, New York, NY; *U.S. Public*, pg. 337
Matsui, Takeshi, Exec. V.P.--Daikin Industries, Ltd., Osaka, Japan,; *Int'l*, pg. 365
Matsumoto, Arata, Exec. V.P.-Plng. & Control--Kawasaki Heavy Industries, Ltd., Kobe, Japan; *Int'l*, pg. 725
Matsumoto, Raymond, Exec. V.P.-Credit Risk Mngmt.--INMC Mortgage Holdings, Inc., Pasadena, CA; *U.S. Public*, pg. 857
Matsumoto, Shoji, Exec. V.P.--Ryobi Ltd., Tokyo, Japan; *Int'l*, pg. 1151
Matsuno, Syuji, Sr. Exec. Dir.--The Japan Development Bank, Tokyo, Japan; *Int'l*, pg. 701
Matsuo, Yuji, Exec. V.P.--Nippon Telegraph and Telephone Corporation, Tokyo, Japan; *Int'l*, pg. 940
Matsuoka, Iwao, Exec. V.P.--Hitachi, Ltd., Tokyo, Japan; *Int'l*, pg. 621
Matsushita, Masayuki, Exec. V.P.--Matsushita Electric Industrial Co., Ltd., Kadoma, Japan; *Int'l*, pg. 846
Matsuura, Takao, Exec. Dir. & Advisor--Koito Manufacturing Co., Tokyo, Japan; *Int'l*, pg. 743
Matteo, Maxine, Exec. V.P.-Adv., Mktg. & Bus. Devel.--INMC Mortgage Holdings, Inc., Pasadena, CA; *U.S. Public*, pg. 857
Matteson, John, Exec. V.P.-Sls. & Mktg.--Fleischer Manufacturing, Inc., Columbus, NE; *U.S. Private*, pg. 410
Matthews, Bruce H., Exec. V.P.--Sysco Food Services of Charlotte, Inc., Concord, NC; *U.S. Public*, pg. 1551
Matthews, John L., Exec. V.P.--CTX Mortgage Co., Inc., Dallas, TX; *U.S. Public*, pg. 323
Matthews, L. White, III, Exec. V.P.-Fin.--Union Pacific Corporation, Dallas, TX; *U.S. Public*, pg. 1667
Matthews, Michael, Exec. V.P.-Worldwide Mktg.--Platinum Technology, Inc., Oak Brook Terrace, IL; *U.S. Public*, pg. 1309
Matthews, Robert C., Jr., Exec. V.P.--Commerce Bancshares, Inc., Kansas City, MO; *U.S. Public*, pg. 409
Mattingly, David F., Chief Fin. Officer & Exec. V.P.--Metro Foods, Inc., Olive Branch, MS; *U.S. Private*, pg. 736
Mattingly, Thomas M., Exec. V.P.--Metro Foods, Inc., Olive Branch, MS; *U.S. Private*, pg. 736
Mattioli, F.P., Exec. V.P.--Fiat Auto SpA, Turin, Italy; *Int'l*, pg. 480
Matton, Clermont, Exec. V.P.-Measurement & Systems--Schlumberger Limited, New York, NY; *U.S. Public*, pg. 1439
Mattoon, David S., Exec. V.P. & Asst. Mgr.-Natl. Sls.--Jefferies & Company, Inc., Los Angeles, CA; *U.S. Public, pg. 925*
Mattox, William C., Exec. V.P.-Federal Govt. Affairs--Mutual of Omaha Insurance Company, Omaha, NE; *U.S. Private*, pg. 769
Mattrick, Don, Exec. V.P.-Studio--Electronic Arts, San Mateo, CA; *U.S. Public*, pg. 569
Mattson, Bradford C., Exec. V.P.-Interior Building Prods.--CertainTeed Corporation, Valley Forge, PA; *Int'l*, pg. 1170
Mattson, Gary, Exec. V.P.--General Business Services, Inc., Waco, TX; *U.S. Public*, pg. 538
Matysik, James T., Exec. V.P.--Laurel Bank, Johnstown, PA; *U.S. Public*, pg. 164
Mauldin, Michael, Exec. V.P.-Black Music--Sony Music Entertainment, Inc., New York, NY; *Int'l*, pg. 1281
Mauney, Charles F., Chief Oper. Officer & Exec. V.P.--Mauney Hosiery Mills, Inc., Kings Mountain, NC; *U.S. Private*, pg. 715
Maurer, Gilbert, Chief Oper. Officer & Exec. V.P.--Cosmopolitan, New York, NY; *U.S. Private*, pg. 517
Maurer, Gilbert C., Chief Oper. Officer & Exec. V.P.--The Hearst Corporation, New York, NY; *U.S. Private*, pg. 515
Maurer, Warren, Chief Oper. Officer& Exec. V.P.--Shadow Broadcast Services, Bala Cynwyd, PA; *U.S. Public*, pg. 1763
Maurin, Robert A., III, Exec. V.P.--Deposit Guaranty National Bank of Louisiana, Hammond, LA; *U.S. Public*, pg. 500
Maus, Manfred, Exec. V.P.--Lux GmbH & Co. KG, Wermelskirchen, Germany; *Int'l*, pg. 993
Mavis, Todd, Exec. V.P.-Mktg. & Sls.--Mitchell International, San Diego, CA; *U.S. Public*, pg. 1601
May, Dennis, Chief Oper. Officer & Exec. V.P.--Sun TV & Appliances, Inc., Groveport, OH; *U.S. Public*, pg. 1532
May, Joseph W., Exec. V.P. & Dir.-Credit Admin.--Whitney Holding Corporation, New Orleans, LA; *U.S. Public*, pg. 1766
May, Larry, Chief Oper. Officer, Exec. V.P. & Gen. Mgr.--U.S. Filter/Davis Water & Waste Industries, Inc., Thomasville, GA; *U.S. Public*, pg. 1682
May, Thomas L., Chief Mktg. Officer & Exec. V.P.--Equitable Life Insurance Company of Iowa, Des Moines, IA; *Int'l*, pg. 647
May, Tom L., Exec. V.P.-Sls. & Chief Mktg. Officer--Equitable of Iowa Companies, Des Moines, IA; *Int'l*, pg. 647
Mayer, Chester, Exec. V.P.--Mayer/Berkshire Corporation, Wayne, NJ; *U.S. Private*, pg. 717
Mayer, Daniel W., Exec. V.P.--Modern Controls, Inc., Minneapolis, MN; *U.S. Public*, pg. 1120
Mayer, Margery W., Exec. V.P.-Instructional Publishing--Scholastic Corporation, New York, NY; *U.S. Public*, pg. 1440
Mayer, Michael, Exec. V.P.--Mayer/Berkshire Corporation, Wayne, NJ; *U.S. Private*, pg. 717
Mayer, Michael J., Exec. V.P.--Beneficial Management Corporation, Peapack, NJ; *U.S. Public*, pg. 211
Mayer, Michael J., Exec. V.P.--Beneficial Management Corporation of America & Affiliated Corps., Wilmington, DE; *U.S. Public*, pg. 211
Mayer, W. Charles, III, Sr. Exec. V.P. & Head-Alabama Banking Grp. & Birmingham Grp.--AmSouth Bancorporation, Birmingham, AL; *U.S. Public*, pg. 105
Mayeux, David R., Exec. V.P.-Venture Devel.--Tenet Healthcare Corporation, Santa Barbara, CA; *U.S. Public*, pg. 1576
Mayhew, Mary Ann, Exec. V.P.-Contracts & Legal Services--Computer Data Systems, Inc., Rockville, MD; *U.S. Public*, pg. 28
Mayotte, Clifford, Chief Fin. Officer--Bromar Inc., Newport Beach, CA; *U.S. Private*, pg. 171
Mays, Greg, Exec. V.P.-Fin. & Admin.--Ralphs Grocery Company, Compton, CA; *U.S. Private*, pg. 1202
Mazer, Rick, Chief Oper. Officer & Exec. V.P.--Schwegmann Giant Super Markets, New Orleans, LA; *U.S. Private*, pg. 629

Mazza, N. Douglas, Chief Oper. Officer & Exec. V.P.--Hyundai Motor America, Fountain Valley, CA; *Int'l*, pg. 641

Mazzetta, Bruno, Sr. Exec. V.P.-Retail Network Div.--Istituto Bancario San Paolo Di Torino S.p.A., Turin, Italy; *Int'l*, pg. 691

McAdams, Richard E., Exec. V.P.-Contract Admin.--Environmental Tectonics Corporation (ETC), Southampton, PA; *U.S. Public*, pg. 587

McAfee, Lawrence W., Chief Fin. Officer & Exec. V.P.--ITEQ, Inc., Houston, TX; *U.S. Public*, pg. 914

McAlear, Robert T., Exec. V.P.-Controlled Loans--UST Corporation, Boston, MA; *U.S. Public*, pg. 1660

McAllister, Francis R., Exec. V.P.-Copper Oper.--Asarco Incorporated, New York, NY; *U.S. Public*, pg. 137

McAllister, Kenneth W., Exec. V.P. & Gen. Counsel--Wachovia Corporation, Winston Salem, NC; *U.S. Public*, pg. 1730

McAlpine, John, Exec. V.P. & Sec.--The Crown Group, Inc., Warren, MI; *U.S. Private*, pg. 292

McAmis, K. Wayne, Chief Oper. Officer & Exec. V.P.--Southwire Company, Carrollton, GA; *U.S. Private*, pg. 1019

McAndrew, Kevin J., Chief Oper. & Fin. Officer & Exec. V.P.--Canterbury Corporate Services, Inc., Medford, NJ; *U.S. Public*, pg. 301

McAssey, Edward, Exec. V.P.--Lasko Metal Products, Inc., West Chester, PA; *U.S. Private*, pg. 652

McAuvic, Karen, Exec. V.P.-Retail Div.--Gianettino & Meredith Advertising, Short Hills, NJ; *U.S. Private*, pg. 450

McAvoy, Kenneth J., Chief Fin. Officer--Watts Industries, Inc., North Andover, MA; *U.S. Public*, pg. 1746

McBane, Alan, Exec. V.P.--Superior Printing Co., Warren, OH; *U.S. Private*, pg. 1055

McBeth, Steve, Exec. V.P.--Walt Disney Consumer Products, Burbank, CA; *U.S. Public*, pg. 511

McBride, Robert G., Exec. V.P.--Central National-Gottesman Inc., Purchase, NY; *U.S. Private*, pg. 224

McBride, Vince, Exec. V.P.-Sls. & Mktg.--The Selmer Co., Inc., Elkhart, IN; *U.S. Public*, pg. 1514

McBride, Vince, Exec. V.P.-Sales & Mktg.--Ludwig Industries, Monroe, NC; *U.S. Public*, pg. 1514

McCabe, W.G., Exec. V.P.--Mead Johnson Nutritional Group, Evansville, IN; *U.S. Public*, pg. 254

McCafferty, Michael G., Exec. V.P.--Mattel, Inc., El Segundo, CA; *U.S. Public*, pg. 1057

McCall, Donald M., Exec. V.P.--Shea Communications Co., Smyrna, GA; *U.S. Private*, pg. 990

McCall, John R., Exec. V.P., Gen. Counsel & Sec.--LG & E Energy Corp., Louisville, KY; *U.S. Public*, pg. 970

McCallion, Anne D., Exec. V.P. & Dir.-H.R.--Countrywide Home Loans Inc., Pasadena, CA; *U.S. Public*, pg. 452

McCallion, Joseph, Exec. V.P.--Competitive Media Reporting, New York, NY; *Int'l*, pg. 1447

McCallum, Jim, Exec. V.P.--Lees Carpets, Greensboro, NC; *U.S. Public*, pg. 268

McCampbell, Chris C., Exec. V.P.-Hydrocarbon Grp.--Koch Industries, Incorporated, Wichita, KS; *U.S. Private*, pg. 628

McCann, Bob, Exec. V.P. & Mng. Dir., KGF--A.C. Nielsen Company, Schaumburg, IL; *U.S. Public*, pg. 1183

McCann, James B., Exec. V.P.--Maui Land & Pineapple Co., Inc., Kahului, HI; *U.S. Public*, pg. 1060

McCann, James B., Exec. V.P.-Sls. & Mktg.--Maui Pineapple Co., Ltd., Kahului, HI; *U.S. Public*, pg. 1060

McCann, Richard L., Chief Oper. Officer, Chief Fin. Officer & Exec. V.P.--Union Pump Company, Battle Creek, MI; *U.S. Private*, pg. 1119

McCaren, J. Reilly, Chief Oper. Officer & Exec. V.P.--Wisconsin Central Transportation Corporation, Rosemont, IL; *U.S. Public*, pg. 1772

McCarrey, Mike, Exec. V.P.--Webb Builders Hardware, Arlington, TX; *U.S. Private*, pg. 1156

McCarter, Thomas, Exec. V.P.--Republic Bank for Savings, New York, NY; *U.S. Public*, pg. 1380

McCarthy, Bill, Exec. V.P.-Sls.--Risdon Corporation, Naugatuck, CT; *U.S. Public*, pg. 463

McCarthy, Charles V., Chief Oper. Officer & Exec. V.P.--Tetley USA Inc., Shelton, CT; *Int'l*, pg. 1377

McCarthy, Colm, Exec. V.P. & Reg. Mgr.--Bank of America NT&SA, Singapore, Singapore; *U.S. Public*, pg. 182

McCarthy, Frank, Exec. V.P. & Gen. Counsel--North Central Life Insurance Company, Saint Paul, MN; *U.S. Private*, pg. 404

McCarthy, Patrick J., Exec. V.P.-Editorial--Fairchild Publications, New York, NY; *U.S. Public*, pg. 513

McCarthy, Thomas J., Jr., Exec. V.P.--General Re Europe Limited, London, United Kingdom; *U.S. Public*, pg. 726

McCarthy, Timothy, Exec. V.P.-Fin. Prods. & Intl. Grp.--The Charles Schwab Corporation, San Francisco, CA; *U.S. Public*, pg. 1442

McCauley, James T., Exec. V.P.--Kimberly-Clark Corporation, Dallas, TX; *U.S. Public*, pg. 958

McCauley, Sean N., Exec. V.P.--Albert M. Greenfield & Company, Philadelphia, PA; *U.S. Private*, pg. 477

McClellan, Steven R., Chief Fin. Officer & Exec. V.P.--Perkins Family Restaurants, Memphis, TN; *U.S. Private*, pg. 925

McCloskey, James, Chief Fin. Officer & Exec. V.P.--Pinkerton's Inc., Encino, CA; *U.S. Public*, pg. 1296

McCloskey, W.D., Exec. V.P.--Baltimore Aircoil Company, Jessup, MD; *U.S. Private*, pg. 68

McClung, Jay C., Exec. V.P.-Credit Admin.--Synovus Financial Corp., Columbus, GA; *U.S. Public*, pg. 1548

McClung, Perry, Pres.-Managed Care Corp.--Universal Standard Healthcare, Inc., Southfield, MI; *U.S. Public*, pg. 1697

McClure, Tim, Exec. V.P.-Creative--GSD&M, Austin, TX; *U.S. Private*, pg. 436

McColl, I.G., Exec. V.P.--Davy International, Canada, Toronto, Canada; *Int'l*, pg. 775

McCollum, Bruce, Exec. V.P.-Adv., Mktg. & Sls.--Tingley Rubber Corporation, South Plainfield, NJ; *U.S. Private*, pg. 1088

McCombs, Richard N., Exec. V.P.- Fin. & Admin.--American Rice Inc., Houston, TX; *U.S. Public*, pg. 591

McCool, Robert J., Exec. V.P.-Americas--Mobil Oil Corporation, Fairfax, VA; *U.S. Public*, pg. 1118

McCord, W. Shiles, Exec. V.P.-Trust Division--First Commerce Corporation, New Orleans, LA; *U.S. Public*, pg. 629

McCormack, John J., Exec. V.P.-Opers. Support--Teachers Insurance and Annuity Association, New York, NY; *U.S. Private*, pg. 1071

McCormick, John, Exec. V.P.-Tire Equipment Sls.--McNeil & NRM., Inc., Akron, OH; *U.S. Private*, pg. 725

McCoy, Dennis, Exec. V.P.--Mars Super Markets, Inc., Baltimore, MD; *U.S. Private*, pg. 707

McCoy, James W., Exec. V.P.--Union Planters Bank, Memphis, TN; *U.S. Public*, pg. 1669

McCoy, Robert S., Jr., Chief Fin. Officer & Exec. V.P.--Wachovia Corporation, Winston Salem, NC; *U.S. Public*, pg. 1730

McCracken, Alan L., Chief Fin. Officer & Exec. V.P.-Fin.--Baltimore Stationery Co./Total Office, Baltimore, MD; *U.S. Private*, pg. 113

McCranie, G. Edwin, Exec. V.P.-Pur.--Ryan's Family Steak Houses, Inc., Greer, SC; *U.S. Public*, pg. 1413

McCrary, Charles, Exec. V.P.--Alabama Power Co., Birmingham, AL; *U.S. Public*, pg. 1489

McCraw, Tom, Exec. V.P.-Admin.--Voyager Group, Inc., Jacksonville, FL; *U.S. Public*, pg. 68

McCray, Simona, Exec. V.P.--WQXR/FM, WQEW/AM, New York, NY; *U.S. Public*, pg. 1174

McCrea, Charles, Jr., Exec. V.P., Gen. Counsel & Sec.--Mikohn Gaming Corporation, Las Vegas, NV; *U.S. Public*, pg. 1111

McCreary, Kirk, Gen. Mgr.--Michigan Blueberry Growers Assn., Grand Junction, MI; *U.S. Private*, pg. 740

McCroskey, M.W., Exec. V.P.-Investments--American National Insurance Company, Galveston, TX; *U.S. Public*, pg. 87

McCullough, Bob, Exec. V.P., Sec. & Treas.--Harris, Baio & McCullough Inc., Philadelphia, PA; *U.S. Private*, pg. 504

McCullough, Thomas A., Exec. V.P.--DST Systems, Inc., Kansas City, MO; *U.S. Public*, pg. 943

McCusker, Thomas J., Exec. V.P. & Gen. Counsel--Mutual of Omaha Insurance Company, Omaha, NE; *U.S. Private*, pg. 769

McCutchan, Gordon E., Exec. V.P., Law & Corp. Services--Nationwide Insurance Enterprise, Columbus, OH; *U.S. Private*, pg. 788

McCutchan, Gordon E., Exec. V.P., Gen. Counsel & Sec.--Nationwide Mutual Insurance Co., Columbus, OH; *U.S. Private*, pg. 789

McDaniel, Thomas R., Pres. & Chief Exec. Officer--Mission Land Company, Irvine, CA; *U.S. Public*, pg. 564

McDavid, William H., Exec. V.P. & Gen. Counsel--The Chase Manhattan Corporation, New York, NY; *U.S. Public*, pg. 337

McDonald, Erroll, Exec. V.P.--Pantheon Books, Inc., New York, NY; *U.S. Private*, pg. 21

McDonald, James S., Exec. V.P. & Mng. Dir.--Pell, Rudman & Company, Boston, MA; *U.S. Public*, pg. 1673

McDonald, James S., Exec. V.P.--Rothschild/Pell, Rudman & Co., Inc., Baltimore, MD; *U.S. Public*, pg. 1674

McDonald, Paul, Chief Acctg. Officer & Sr. Exec. V.P.--Friendly Ice Cream Corp., Wilbraham, MA; *U.S. Public*, pg. 682

McDonald, Steve D., Exec. V.P.-CIBG--The Toronto Dominion Bank, Toronto, Canada; *Int'l*, pg. 1401

McDonald, William F., Exec. V.P.--Sunnyland Refining Co., Inc., Birmingham, AL; *U.S. Private*, pg. 607

McDonnell, Bernard J., Exec. V.P.-Real Estate & Corp. Devel.--Provigo Inc., Montreal, Canada; *Int'l*, pg. 1072

McDonnell, Francis W., Chief Fin. Officer & Exec. V.P.--Pennsylvania Manufacturers Corp., Blue Bell, PA; *U.S. Public*, pg. 1272

McDonnell, Gordon R., Exec. V.P.--Jefferies & Company, Inc., Los Angeles, CA; *U.S. Public*, pg. 925

McDonough, Thomas P., Exec. V.P.-Customer Svcs. Grp.--United HealthCare Corporation, Minnetonka, MN; *U.S. Public*, pg. 1677

McDowell, Thomas J., Exec. V.P.-Corp. & Institutional Banking--First Chicago NBD Corporation, Chicago, IL; *U.S. Public*, pg. 627

McEnany, Robert, Exec. V.P. & Acct. Plng. Dir.--Levenson & Hill, Inc., Dallas, TX; *U.S. Private*, pg. 662

McEneely, Kevin, Exec. V.P.--Nightingale-Conant Corp., Niles, IL; *U.S. Private*, pg. 799

McEnery, Kevin J., Chief Fin. Officer & Exec. V.P.--Scholastic Corporation, New York, NY; *U.S. Public*, pg. 1440

McEvoy, Charles, Exec. V.P.--Western Extrusions, Carrollton, TX; *U.S. Private*, pg. 1165

McEvoy, Patrick J., Exec. V.P.--Industrial Electronic Engineers, Inc., Van Nuys, CA; *U.S. Private*, pg. 561

McFadden, Edward H., Chief Fin. Officer & Exec. V.P.--Breed Technologies, Inc., Lakeland, FL; *U.S. Public*, pg. 251

McFadden, Rick, Exec. V.P.-U.S.A.--Ketchum Directory Advertising/Los Angeles, Los Angeles, CA; *U.S. Private*, pg. 616

McGann, Edward L., Exec. V.P.--Megapulse, Inc., Bedford, MA; *U.S. Private*, pg. 729

McGee, Gerald, Exec. V.P. & Mng. Dir.-O & M L.A.--Ogilvy & Mather Worldwide, Inc., New York, NY; *Int'l*, pg. 1483

McGee, Jim, Pres.-Hospital Div., Chief Oper. Officer & Exec. V.P.--Schein Pharmaceutical, Inc., Florham Park, NJ; *U.S. Private*, pg. 969

McGee, Liam E., Grp. Exec. V.P.-California Retail--Bank of America NT&SA, San Francisco, CA; *U.S. Public*, pg. 180

McGehee, David S., Exec. V.P.--Mac Papers, Inc., Jacksonville, FL; *U.S. Private*, pg. 689

McGeough, Peter, Chief Fin. & Admin. Officer & Exec. V.P.--Seaman Furniture Company, Inc., Woodbury, NY; *U.S. Public*, pg. 1452

McGhee, Shawn P., Exec. V.P.-Mdsg.--AutoZone, Inc., Memphis, TN; *U.S. Public*, pg. 150

McGhinnis, Willis T., Exec. V.P.--Central Bank of Monroe, Monroe, LA; *U.S. Public*, pg. 629

McGill, J.C., Chm. Bd., Pres., Chief Exec. Officer--McGill Manufacturing Company, Inc., Valparaiso, IN; *U.S. Public*, pg. 573

McGill, S.R., Exec. V.P.--Exxon Company International, Florham Park, NJ; *U.S. Public*, pg. 601

McGinnis, Bernard C., III, Exec. V.P.--Horizon Bancorp, Inc., Beckley, WV; *U.S. Public*, pg. 836

McGinnis, Gerald L., Exec. V.P.-Devel.--Hardee's Food Systems, Inc., Rocky Mount, NC; *U.S. Public*, pg. 278

McGinnis, William W., Chief Oper. Officer & Exec. V.P.--Jewelers Mutual Insurance Company, Neenah, WI; *U.S. Private*, pg. 587

McGinty, Pete, Exec. V.P. & Corp. Devel. Dir.--Lord, Sullivan & Yoder Inc. Marketing Communications, Columbus, OH; *U.S. Private*, pg. 676

McGlynn, Dan J., Exec. V.P.--McGlynn Bakeries Inc., Minneapolis, MN; *U.S. Private*, pg. 721

McGoldrick, Richard T., Exec. V.P.--Bank of the West, Walnut Creek, CA; *Int'l*, pg. 163

McGovern, Eastmen, Exec. V.P.-Worldwide Sls.--Storage Dimensions, Inc., Milpitas, CA; *U.S. Public*, pg. 1522

McGovern, Gail J., Exec. V.P.-Consumer & Small Bus. Div.--AT&T Corporation, Basking Ridge, NJ; *U.S. Public*, pg. 10

McGovern, John F., Chief Fin. Officer & Exec. V.P.-Fin.--Georgia-Pacific Corporation, Atlanta, GA; *U.S. Public*, pg. 735

McGovern, Renee, Exec. V.P.-Sls.--David Dart, Chatsworth, CA; *U.S. Public*, pg. 948

McGraime, Douglas, Chief Fin. Officer, Exec. V.P. & Treas.--Combe Incorporated, White Plains, NY; *U.S. Private*, pg. 257

McGrath, Mike, Sr. V.P.-Sls.-Independent Bottling Systems--Cadbury Beverages, Stamford, CT; *Int'l*, pg. 248

McGrath, Stephen, Exec. V.P.-Corp. Fin.--CIBC Oppenheimer Corp., New York, NY; *Int'l*, pg. 257

McGregor, Charles W., Exec. V.P.-Magnet Wire & Insulation Sector--Essex International, Inc., Fort Wayne, IN; *U.S. Public*, pg. 593

McGregor, Douglas A., Exec. V.P.-Oper. Devel.--The Rouse Company, Columbia, MD; *U.S. Public*, pg. 1407

McGregor, Douglas A., Exec. V.P.-Devel. & Opers.--Rouse Office & Community Development Div., Columbia, MD; *U.S. Public*, pg. 1407

McGregor, John L., Chief Oper. Officer & Exec. V.P.--Willis Corroon Corp. of Wisconsin, Milwaukee, WI; *Int'l*, pg. 1507

McGrody, James J., Exec. V.P.--The Psychological Corp., San Antonio, TX; *U.S. Public*, pg. 784

McGrogan, Michael, Exec. V.P. & Lending Mgr.--LaSalle Cragin Bank, Chicago, IL; *Int'l*, pg. 10

McGuinness, Michael E., Exec. V.P.-Res. & Devel.--Parametric Technology Corporation, Waltham, MA; *U.S. Public*, pg. 1257

McHugh, James R., Exec. V.P.--James McHugh Construction Co., Chicago, IL; *U.S. Private*, pg. 721

McIlhenny, Paul C.P., Exec. V.P. & Sec.--McIlhenny Company, Avery Island, LA; *U.S. Private*, pg. 722

McInis, Ronald, Exec. V.P.-Employee Benefits Opers.--Pan-American Life Insurance Company, New Orleans, LA; *U.S. Private*, pg. 836

McInnes, D. Joseph, Chief Admin. Officer, Exec. V.P.-Admin. & Corp. Sec.--Blount International, Inc., Montgomery, AL; *U.S. Public*, pg. 237

McInnes, D. Joseph, Chief Admin. Officer, Exec. V.P.-Admin. & Corp. Sec.--Blount, Inc., Montgomery, AL; *U.S.* Public, pg. 238

McIntosh, Daniel W., Exec. V.P.--Appleton Papers Inc., Appleton, WI; *Int'l*, pg. 567

McIntyre, Norman F., Exec. V.P.--Petro-Canada, Calgary, Canada; *Int'l*, pg. 1041

McIntyre, Timothy J., Exec. V.P. & Pres.-Promo. Conferencing Svcs. Div.--Boron LePore Group, Fair Lawn, NJ; *U.S. Public*, pg. 246

McInvale, Gerald D., Chief Fin. Officer & Exec. V.P.--Entergy Corporation, New Orleans, LA; *U.S. Public*, pg. 585

McJeed, Sam, Exec. V.P & Gen. Mgr.--American Gasket & Rubber, Schaumburg, IL; *U.S. Private*, pg. 15

McKay, Bob, Mgr.-Contracts & Matls.--Southwest Marine, Inc., San Diego, CA; *U.S. Private*, pg. 213

McKay, Donald A., Chief Fin. Officer & Exec. V.P.--JC Penney Company, Inc., Plano, TX; *U.S. Public*, pg. 916

McKay, Donald K., Chief Fin. Officer, Exec. V.P., Treas. & Sec.--Specialty Equipment Companies Inc., Aurora, IL; *U.S. Public*, pg. 1496

McKee, E. Stanton, Jr., Chief Fin. & Chief Admin. Officer & Exec. V.P.--Electronic Arts, San Mateo, CA; *U.S. Public*, pg. 569

McKee, Paul, Chief Exec. Officer & Exec. V.P.--The Martin Agency, Richmond, VA; *U.S. Private*, pg. 678

McKee, Paul, Chief Exec. Officer & Exec. V.P.--The Martin Agency, Richmond, VA; *U.S. Public*, pg. 909

McKee, William P., Exec. V.P.--Automotive Rentals, Inc. (ARI), Mount Laurel, NJ; *U.S. Private*, pg. 535

McKeever, Steve, Exec. V.P.-Creative Affairs--Motown Record Company, J.P., New York, NY; *Int'l*, pg. 1052

McKellar, C.H., Exec. V.P.--Winn-Dixie Stores, Inc., Jacksonville, FL; *U.S. Public*, pg. 1771

McKenna, Christine, Exec. V.P.-Mktg. & Adv.--Plasti-Kote Company Inc., Medina, OH; *U.S. Private*, pg. 870

McKenna, Ronald F., Exec. V.P. & Chief Oper. Officer-Aerospace--Sundstrand Corporation, Rockford, IL; *U.S. Public*, pg. 1533

McKenna, Steve, Chief Fin. Officer & Sr. Exec. V.P.-Singapore--Dentsu Young & Rubicam Partnerships, New York, NY; *U.S. Private*, pg. 325

McKenna, Thomas, Exec. V.P.--Westat Inc., Rockville, MD; *U.S. Private*, pg. 1163

McKenzie, Dave, Exec. V.P.-Car Electronics & Dir.--Pioneer Electronics (USA) Inc., Long Beach, CA; *Int'l*, pg. 1058

McKeon, Kevin J., Chief Fin. Officer & Exec. V.P.--Home Shopping Network, Inc., Saint Petersburg, FL; *U.S. Public*, pg. 1685

McKeon, Ross W., Chief Fin. Officer & Exec. V.P.-Field Opers.--News America Marketing, Norwalk, CT; *Int'l*, pg. 925

McKernan, Peter, Exec. V.P.--Herculite Products, Inc., York, PA; *U.S. Public*, pg. 802

McKinnell, Henry A., Ph.D., Exec. V.P. & Pres.-Pfizer Pharmaceuticals Grp.--Pfizer Inc., New York, NY; *U.S. Public*, pg. 1281

McKinney, William P., Exec. V.P.--Laurel Bank, Johnstown, PA; *U.S. Public*, pg. 164

McKinnon, John Q., Exec. V.P.-Comml. Banking--American National Bank & Trust Co. of Chicago, Chicago, IL; *U.S. Public*, pg. 628

McKinnon, Thomas E., Exec. V.P.-Human Resources--Ryder System, Inc., Miami, FL; *U.S. Public*, pg. 1413

McKnight, Craig, Chief Fin. Officer & Exec. V.P.--Magellan Health Services, Inc., Atlanta, GA; *U.S. Public*, pg. 1033

McL. Doelp, John, Exec. V.P.--Sony Music Entertainment, Inc., New York, NY; *Int'l*, pg. 1281

McLamb, George T., Chief Fin. Officer, Exec. V.P. & Treas.--Kingsdown, Inc., Mebane, NC; *U.S. Private*, pg. 622

McLane, James W., Exec. V.P.-Health & Grp. Life--Aetna Inc., Hartford, CT; *U.S. Public*, pg. 26

McLaughlin, F. Christopher, Exec. V.P.-Human Resources--Marine Midland Bank, Buffalo, NY; *Int'l*, pg. 581

McLaughlin, John P., Exec. V.P. & Sec.--Genentech, Inc., South San Francisco, CA; *Int'l*, pg. 1120

McLaughlin, Kathy J., Exec. V.P.--Mediaspot, Inc., Corona Del Mar, CA; *U.S. Private*, pg. 727

McLaughlin, M., Exec. V.P. & Grp. Creative Dir.--BBDO Canada, Toronto, Canada; *U.S. Private*, pg. 104

McLaughlin, Marcia, Exec. V.P. & Client Service Dir.--KPR, New York, NY; *U.S. Public*, pg. 1224

McLaughlin, Michael, Exec. V.P.--Technology Solutions Company (TSC), Chicago, IL; *U.S. Public*, pg. 1564

McLean, C.D., Exec. V.P.-Opers.--Continental Airlines, Houston, TX; *U.S. Public*, pg. 439

McLeod, Christopher K., Exec. V.P.--CUC International, Inc., Stamford, CT; *U.S. Public*, pg. 320

McLeod, John, Sr., Exec. V.P.--Lone Star Container Sales Corp., Irving, TX; *U.S. Private*, pg. 674

McLeod, Rod, Exec. V.P.--Royal Caribbean Cruises Ltd., Miami, FL; *U.S. Public*, pg. 1410

McLoughlin, Philip R., Exec. V.P. & Investments--Phoenix Home Life Mutual Insurance Company, Hartford, CT; *U.S. Private*, pg. 863

McLoughlin, Philip R., Exec. V.P.-Investments--Phoenix Home Life Mutual Insurance Co., Hartford, CT; *U.S. Private*, pg. 863

McLuckey, John A., Exec. V.P.-Space & Missles--Boeing Defense & Space Group, Kent, WA; *U.S. Public*, pg. 240

McMahon, Dan, Exec. V.P.--Amloid Corporation, Saddle Brook, NJ; *U.S. Private*, pg. 66

McMahon, John, Exec. V.P.-Worldwide Sls.--Parametric Technology Corporation, Waltham, MA; *U.S. Public*, pg. 1257

McManus, R.W., Exec. V.P.--Westfield Companies, Westfield Center, OH; *U.S. Private*, pg. 1169

McMasters, R.G., Exec. V.P.--AFG Industries, Inc., Kingsport, TN; *Int'l*, pg. 84

McMeekin, H. Thomas, Chief Investment Officer & Exec. V.P.--Lincoln National Corporation, Fort Wayne, IN; *U.S. Public*, pg. 997

McMenemy, William, Exec. V.P.-Mktg.--Sally Hansen, Farmingdale, NY; *U.S. Public*, pg. 494

McMennamin, Michael J., Chief Fin. Officer & Exec. V.P.--Banc One Corporation, Columbus, OH; *U.S. Public*, pg. 172

McMillan, Bayne, Exec. V.P.--Cummins Intermountain Diesel, Salt Lake City, UT; *U.S. Private*, pg. 295

McMillan, Harry, Exec. V.P.--Komori America Corporation, Rolling Meadows, IL; *Int'l*, pg. 745

McMillan, J.T., Exec. V.P.--Exxon Company, U.S.A., Houston, TX; *U.S. Public*, pg. 601

McMinn, John A., Chief Oper. Officer & Exec. V.P.--The Cincinnati Cordage & Paper Company, Cincinnati, OH; *U.S. Private*, pg. 239

McMullen, Mark J., Sr. Exec. V.P.--Associated Bank Green Bay, Green Bay, WI; *U.S. Public*, pg. 141

McMurray, J. Patrick, Exec. V.P.--First Security Corporation, Salt Lake City, UT; *U.S. Public*, pg. 637

McNabb, Larry D., Grp. Exec. V.P.-Global Payment Services--Bank of America NT&SA, San Francisco, CA; *U.S. Public*, pg. 180

McNairy, Charles, Chief Fin. Officer, Exec. V.P. & Treas.--Avatar Holdings Inc., Coral Gables, FL; *U.S. Public*, pg. 151

McNally, Michael J., Exec. V.P.--TU Electric, Dallas, TX; *U.S. Public*, pg. 1588

McNamara, John, Exec. V.P.-Corp. Banking--Bank of Boston Connecticut, Hartford, CT; *U.S. Public*, pg. 184

McNamara, John F., Chief Oper. Officer & Exec. V.P.--United Asset Management Corporation, Boston, MA; *U.S. Public*, pg. 1672

McNamara, Joseph, Exec. V.P. & Gen. Mgr.--Edelman Worldwide, Inc., Dallas, TX; *U.S. Private*, pg. 362

McNamee, Bernard J., Exec. V.P., Gen. Counsel & Sec.--Rexene Corporation, Dallas, TX; *U.S. Private*, pg. 549

McNeir-Tillman, G., Exec. V.P.--Wachovia Bank, Charlottesville, VA; *U.S. Public*, pg. 1730

McNulty, James E., Exec. V.P.-Human Resources & Admin.--Thiokol Corporation, Ogden, UT; *U.S. Public*, pg. 1596

McPartland, Deborah, Exec. V.P. & Buying Opers. Dir.--Cash Plus, Inc., Minneapolis, MN; *U.S. Private*, pg. 218

McPhedrain, Larry L., Exec. V.P.-Opers.--Mary Maxim, Inc., Port Huron, MI; *U.S. Private*, pg. 716

McPherson, David L., Exec. V.P.--Raytheon Systems Company, Arlington, VA; *U.S. Public*, pg. 1364

McPherson, J. Robb, Exec. V.P. & Acct. Exec.--N.W. Ayer & Partners Chicago, Chicago, IL; *U.S. Private*, pg. 104

McPherson, Michael J., Exec. V.P., Controller & Sec.--Steadly Company, Carthage, MO; *U.S. Public*, pg. 986

McPherson, Thomas A., Exec. V.P.--United Bankshares, Inc., Parkersburg, WV; *U.S. Public*, pg. 1674

McQuade, Eugene M., Vice Chm., Chief Fin. Officer & Exec. V.P.--Fleet Financial Group, Inc., Boston, MA; *U.S. Public*, pg. 648

McQuade, Ted M., Exec. V.P.--North American Automobile Opers.--The Standard Products Company, Dearborn, MI; *U.S. Public*, pg. 1504

McQueen, Josh, Exec. V.P. & Worldwide Plng. Dir.--Leo Burnett Company, Inc., Chicago, IL; *U.S. Private*, pg. 183

McQueeney, Thomas, Exec. V.P. & Bus. Affairs & Admin. Dir.--Young & Rubicam New York, New York, NY; *U.S. Private*, pg. 1198

McReynolds, John L., Exec. V.P.-Underwriting--Universal Surety of America, Houston, TX; *U.S. Public*, pg. 303

McShane, John, Exec. V.P.-Devel.--Koo Koo Roo, Inc., Los Angeles, CA; *U.S. Public*, pg. 966

McSween, H. Dale, Chief Oper. Officer & Exec. V.P.--Intertape Polymer Group Inc., Saint-Laurent, Canada; *Int'l*, pg. 684

McTavish, G.L. Larry, Exec. V.P.-Tech. Assessment & Bus. Devel.--Ceridian Corporation, Bloomington, MN; *U.S. Public*, pg. 330

McWilliams, Timothy C., Exec. V.P.--McWilliams Forge Co., Rockaway, NJ; *U.S. Private*, pg. 725

Mead, George C., Exec. V.P.--Cullen/Frost Bankers, Inc., San Antonio, TX; *U.S. Public*, pg. 467

Meade, Peter, Exec. V.P.--Blue Cross and Blue Shield of Massachusetts, Boston, MA; *U.S. Private*, pg. 151

Meadlock, James W., Chm. Bd., Pres. & Chief Exec. Officer--Intergraph Corporation, Huntsville, AL; *U.S. Public*, pg. 890

Meadows, Allen D., Chief Fin. Officer, Exec. V.P. & Treas.--Fidelity National Financial, Inc., Irvine, CA; *U.S. Public*, pg. 620

Meadows, Allen D., Chief Fin. Officer, Exec. V.P. & Treas.--Fidelity National Title Insurance Company, Irvine, CA; *U.S. Public*, pg. 620

Mealman, Glenn E., Exec. V.P.-Natl. Accounts--Fleming Companies, Inc., Oklahoma City, OK; *U.S. Public*, pg. 652

Mears, Charles L., Exec. V.P.-Chlorovinyls--Occidental Chemical Corporation, Dallas, TX; *U.S. Public*, pg. 1210

Medel, Ariel, Exec. V.P & Controller--Berkliff Corporation, New York, NY; *U.S. Private*, pg. 135

Meder, William J., Exec. V.P.--Henry Birks & Sons (1993) Inc., Montreal, Canada; *Int'l*, pg. 196

Medford, Mark O., Exec. V.P.-Customer Service Mktg.--Tennessee Valley Authority, Knoxville, TN; *U.S. Public*, pg. 1580

Medina, Carlos R., Chief Oper. Officer & Exec. V.P.--BITOR America Corp., Boca Raton, FL; *Int'l*, pg. 1045

Medina, Felipe Garza, Exec. V.P.--Hylsa S.A.-Flat Rolled Division, San Nicolas, Mexico; *Int'l*, pg. 56

Medina, Hector, Exec. V.P.-Plng. & Fin.--Cemex, S.A. de C.V., Monterrey, Mexico; *Int'l*, pg. 278

Medina, John, Exec. V.P.-Pigment Grp.--Degussa Corporation, Ridgefield Park, NJ; *Int'l*, pg. 388

Medina, Rubin, Exec. V.P.--Young & Rubicam, S.A. de C.V., Mexico, Mexico; *U.S. Private*, pg. 1200

Medina, Victor, Exec. V.P.--Condal Distributors Inc., Bronx, NY; *U.S. Private*, pg. 262

Meduna, Russell P., Exec. V.P.--Hallwood Energy Partners, L.P., Denver, CO; *U.S. Public*, pg. 778

Medvin, Harvey N., Chief Fin. Officer, Exec. V.P. & Treas.--AON Corporation, Chicago, IL; *U.S. Public*, pg. 117

Medvin, Harvey N., Chief Fin. Officer & Exec. V.P.--Combined Insurance Company of America, Chicago, IL; *U.S. Public*, pg. 118

Meeder, Bill, Exec. V.P.-Bus. Devel.--Larkin Meeder & Schweidel, Dallas, TX; *U.S. Private*, pg. 651

Meehan, Andrew, Exec. Dir.--Brierley Investments Limited, Wellington, New Zealand; *Int'l*, pg. 215

Meehan, Andrew, Exec. Dir.--BIL Asia Holdings Ltd., Central, Hong Kong; *Int'l*, pg. 215

Meehan, Gregory W.A., Chief Fin. Officer, V.P. & Treas.--High Point Financial Corp., Branchville, NJ; *U.S. Public*, pg. 826

Meehan, James, Exec. V.P. & Dir. -Opers.--Brown and Caldwell, Pleasant Hill, CA; *U.S. Private*, pg. 173

Meetze, G. Allen, Sr. Exec. V.P.--NBSC Corporation, Columbia, SC; *U.S. Public*, pg. 1549

Meggy, Robert, Exec. Dir.--Bank of Bermuda (Guernsey) Limited, Saint Peter Port, United Kingdom; *Int'l*, pg. 151

Mehallow, Michael, Exec. V.P.-Mktg.--Borg-Warner Protective Services Corporation, Parsippany, NJ; *U.S. Public*, pg. 245

Mehiel, Chris, Chief Oper. Officer & Exec. V.P.--Four M Corporation, Inc., Valhalla, NY; *U.S. Private*, pg. 421

Mehra, Ajit, Exec. V.P.--Hunter Douglas, Inc., Upper Saddle River, NJ; *Int'l*, pg. 639

Mehra, Ravinder, Exec. V.P.--Banco Santander, Madrid, Spain; *Int'l*, pg. 143

Mehrlich, Richard W., Exec. V.P.-Sls & Mktg.--Medical Manager Corporation, Tampa, FL; *U.S. Public*, pg. 1080

Meier, Arlene, Chief Fin. Officer & Exec. V.P.--Kohl's Corporation, Menomonee Falls, WI; *U.S. Public*, pg. 965

Meier, Jeannette P., Exec. V.P., Gen. Counsel & Sec.--Sterling Commerce, Inc., Dublin, OH; *U.S. Public*, pg. 1515

Meier, Jeannette P., Exec. V.P.-Fin. & Admin./Sec.--Sterling Software, Inc., Dallas, TX; *U.S. Public*, pg. 1516

Meiser, Frederick E., Exec. V.P.-Mdsg.--Heilig-Meyers Company, Richmond, VA; *U.S. Public*, pg. 804

Meister, John M., Exec. V.P.-Transit Prods.--Westinghouse Air Brake Company, Wilmerding, PA; *U.S. Public*, pg. 1760

Melani, Kenneth R., M.D., Exec. V.P.-Health Svcs.--Highmark Inc., Pittsburgh, PA; *U.S. Private*, pg. 528

Melcalfe, Randolph C., Exec. V.P.--ABR Information Services, Inc., Palm Harbor, FL; *U.S. Public*, pg. 2

Mele, Raymond, Exec. V.P.--Mele Manufacturing Co., Inc., Utica, NY; *U.S. Private*, pg. 730

Melek, Al, Exec. V.P.--McNeil & NRM., Inc., Akron, OH; *U.S. Private*, pg. 725

Melican, James P., Exec. V.P.-Legal & External Affairs--International Paper Company, Purchase, NY; *U.S. Public*, pg. 901

Melldye, Peter, Exec. V.P.--Statoil, Stavanger, Norway; *Int'l*, pg. 1297

Mellett, Paul, Exec. V.P.-Fin.--ADP Marshall Contractors Inc., Rumford, RI; *U.S. Public*, pg. 660

Mellon, Christopher I., C.P.A., Chief Oper. Officer & Exec. V.P.--Pioneer American Holding Company, Carbondale, PA; *U.S. Public*, pg. 1298

Mellott, Robert H., Exec. V.P.--Knight Architects Engineers Planners, Inc., Chicago, IL; *U.S. Private*, pg. 626

Mellstig, Soren, Exec. V.P. & Corp. Control--Incentive AB, Stockholm, Sweden; *Int'l*, pg. 666

Mellstrom, Thord, Exec. V.P.--Svenska Handelsbanken, Stockholm, Sweden; *Int'l*, pg. 1327

Melton, H. Burt, Sr. V.P.-Consumer Credit & Bank Related Services--First Union Corporation, Charlotte, NC; *U.S. Public*, pg. 639

Melville, James, Pres.--First Commonwealth Corporation, Springfield, IL; *U.S. Private*, pg. 406

Melzer, William, Exec. V.P. & Acct. Mng. Dir.--Young & Rubicam New York, New York, NY; *U.S. Private*, pg. 1198

Memmo, Nicholas C., Exec. V.P.-Water Process Grp.--United States Filter Corporation, Palm Desert, CA; *U.S. Public*, pg. 1681

Mendelson, Morrie, Exec. V.P.-Intl. Sls.--Shorewood Packaging Corporation of Canada, Ltd., Scarborough, Canada; *U.S. Public*, pg. 1468

Mendez, Manuel A., Exec. V.P.-Risk--Banco Santander, Madrid, Spain; *Int'l*, pg. 143

Mendoza Escalante, Luis Felipe, Exec. V.P.--Bufete Industrial S.A. de C.V., Mexico, Mexico; *Int'l*, pg. 232

Mendoza Fernandez, Jose, Chm. Bd. & Exec. V.P.--Bufete Industrial S.A. de C.V., Mexico, Mexico; *Int'l*, pg. 232

Menjon, Gerard, Exec. V.P. & Head-Res. & Devel.--Electricite de France, Paris, France; *Int'l*, pg. 437

Mensah, Nana, Chief Oper. Officer & Exec. V.P.--Long John Silver's, Inc., Lexington, KY; *U.S. Private*, pg. 674

Menzer, John, Chief Fin. Officer & Exec. V.P.--Wal-Mart Stores, Inc., Bentonville, AR; *U.S. Public*, pg. 1732

Merahn, Steve, M.D., Exec. V.P. & Medical Dir.-Constituency Rels.--Carrafiello, Diehl & Associates, Inc., Irvington, NY; *U.S. Private*, pg. 215

Meranus, Arthur, Exec. V.P. & Exec. Creative Dir.--N.W. Ayer & Partners New York, New York, NY; *U.S. Private*, pg. 104

Mercadante, Blaise, Exec. V.P.-Mktg.--Universal Studios Music Australia, Sydney, Australia; *Int'l*, pg. 1216

Mercer, Harold B., Chief Fin. Officer,Exec. V.P. & Treas.--Swift Instruments, Inc., Dorchester, MA; *U.S. Private*, pg. 1058

Meredith, W.G., Exec. V.P.-Life Sciences Sector & Corp. Svcs.--3M, Saint Paul, MN; *U.S. Public*, pg. 1604

Meric, Jean-Paul, Exec. V.P.-U.S., Canada, Morocco, Greece, Turkey & Czech Republic--Ciments Francais, Paris, France; *Int'l*, pg. 292

Merideth, Ed, Exec. V.P.-Sls.--Barton Beers, Ltd., Chicago, IL; *U.S. Public*, pg. 300

Merk, Richard, Exec. V.P.--Hancock Lumber, Inc., Casco, ME; *U.S. Private*, pg. 498

Merola, Ralph, Exec. V.P.--House of Ronnie, Inc., New York, NY; *U.S. Private*, pg. 542

Merrick, Nicholas A., Chief Fin. Officer & Exec. V.P.--Excel Communications, Inc., Dallas, TX; *U.S. Public*, pg. 598

Merrill, Newton P.S., Sr. Exec. V.P.--The Bank of New York Company, Inc., New York, NY; *U.S. Public*, pg. 178

Merry, Edward C., Exec. V.P.--Sysco Food Services of Philadelphia, Inc., Philadelphia, PA; *U.S. Public*, pg. 1552

Mervine, Tim, Exec. V.P.-Stationery--Baltimore Stationery Co./Total Office, Baltimore, MD; *U.S. Private*, pg. 113

Mesnel, Gerard H., Exec. V.P.-Advanced Tech., Worldwide--The Standard Products Company, Dearborn, MI; *U.S. Public*, pg. 1504

Messer, Monica, Chief Info. Officer & Exec. V.P.--American Business Information, Inc., Omaha, NE; *U.S. Public*, pg. 69

Messinger, Craig, Exec. V.P.-Fixed Income Trading & Sls.--Fidelity Investments (FMR Corp.), Boston, MA; *U.S. Private*, pg. 402

Messinger, Scott, Exec. V.P. & Acct. Dir.--Trahan, Burden & Charles, Inc., Baltimore, MD; *U.S. Private*, pg. 1095

Mestayer, Mark L., Exec. V.P., Sec. & Dir.-Fin.--Piccadilly Cafeterias, Inc., Baton Rouge, LA; *U.S. Public*, pg. 1294

Mestayer, Suzanne T., Exec. V.P.--First National Bank of Commerce, New Orleans, LA; *U.S. Public*, pg. 629

Metelenis, Michael, Exec. V.P. & Exec. Creative Dir.--KPR, New York, NY; *U.S. Public*, pg. 1224

Metsavirta, Aarre, Sr. Exec. V.P.-Paper Grp.--Metsa-Serla Corporation, Espoo, Finland; *Int'l*, pg. 863

Metzer, Andreas, Exec. Dir.-Mktg., Buying & Store Opers.--Julius Meinl AG, Vienna, Austria; *Int'l*, pg. 856

Metzger, Daniel, Exec. V.P.-Mktg.--Lawson Software, Minneapolis, MN; *U.S. Private*, pg. 654

Metzler, David, Exec. V.P.-High-Growth Markets--Colgate-Palmolive Company, New York, NY; *U.S. Public*, pg. 397

Meunier, Jean-Louis, Sr. Exec. V.P. & Chief Actuary--AXA-UAP, Paris, France; *Int'l*, pg. 18

Mew, Calvin, Exec. V.P.-Latin America--Bozell Worldwide, Inc., New York, NY; *U.S. Public*, pg. 1642

Meyer, Armin, Exec. V.P.-Power Generation--ABB Asea Brown Boveri (Holding) Ltd., Zurich, Switzerland; *Int'l*, pg. 1

Meyer, Barry M., Exec. V.P.--Warner Bros. Studios, Inc., Burbank, CA; *U.S. Public*, pg. 1611

Meyer, Bernard F., Exec. V.P.--Amplex/SGNIC, Bloomfield, CT; *Int'l*, pg. 1173
Meyer, Dwight, Exec. V.P.-Sourcing--AnnTaylor, Inc., New York, NY; *U.S. Public*, pg. 116
Meyer, John F., Chief Fin. Officer & Exec. V.P.--Fireman's Fund Insurance Company, Novato, CA; *Int'l*, pg. 58
Meyer, Paul, Exec. V.P. & Legal Counsel--Eller Media Company, Phoenix, AZ; *U.S. Public*, pg. 383
Meyer, Paul J., Exec. V.P.-Fin.--Maui Land & Pineapple Co., Inc., Kahului, HI; *U.S. Public*, pg. 1060
Meyer, Raymond, Exec. V.P.-Deltec--Fiskars Oy AB, Helsinki, Finland; *Int'l*, pg. 492
Meyer, Rick, Exec. V.P.--Gramex Corporation, Bridgeton, MO; *U.S. Private*, pg. 468
Meyer, Robert, Exec. V.P.--Valley National Bancorp, Wayne, NJ; *U.S. Public*, pg. 1705
Meyer, Stephen J., Exec. V.P.--Central Sprinkler Company, Lansdale, PA; *U.S. Public*, pg. 327
Meyer, Thomas, Exec. V.P.--Bayerische Hypotheken-und Wechsel-Bank Aktiengesellschaft, Munich, Germany; *Int'l*, pg. 175
Meyer, Val, Exec. V.P.--Dempster Industries Inc., Beatrice, NE; *U.S. Private*, pg. 324
Meyercord, Edward B., III, Exec. V.P.-Mktg. & Corp. Devel.--Tel-Save Holdings, Inc., New Hope, PA; *U.S. Public*, pg. 1568
Meyers, Charles E., Chief Fin. Officer & Sr. V.P.--The Insurance Corp. of New York, New York, NY; *U.S. Public*, pg. 336
Meyers, David L., Chief Fin. Officer & Exec. V.P.--Del Monte Foods, San Francisco, CA; *U.S. Private*, pg. 321
Meyers, Geoffrey G., Chief Fin. Officer, Exec. V.P. & Treas.--Health Care & Retirement Corporation, Toledo, OH; *U.S. Public*, pg. 801
Meynial, Yves, Exec. V.P.--Credit Commercial de France, Paris, France; *Int'l*, pg. 341
Meyrowitz, Carol, Exec. V.P.-Mdsg.--Chadwick's of Boston, West Bridgewater, MA; *U.S. Public*, pg. 996
Meysman, Frank L., Exec. V.P.--Sara Lee Corporation, Chicago, IL; *U.S. Public*, pg. 1432
Miamis, James D., Exec. V.P.-Meat Opers.--Demoulas Market Basket, Tewksbury, MA; *U.S. Private*, pg. 324
Micali, Jim, Chief Fin. Officer & Exec. V.P.--Michelin Americas Small Tires (MAST), Greenville, SC; *Int'l*, pg. 322
Micati, Victor P., V.P., Exec. V.P.-Pfizer Pharmaceuticals & Area Pres.-Europe--Pfizer Inc., New York, NY; *U.S. Public*, pg. 1281
Michael, H. Martin, Exec. V.P.--Chromcraft Revington, Inc., Delphi, IN; *U.S. Public*, pg. 352
Michael, Ralph S., III, Exec. V.P.-Corp. Banking--PNC Bank Corp., Pittsburgh, PA; *U.S. Public*, pg. 1242
Michalec, Alice, Exec. V.P. & Gen. Mgr.--Rives Carlberg, Houston, TX; *U.S. Private*, pg. 934
Michalossky, Michael, Chief Fin. Officer & Exec. V.P.--Kinney System, Inc., New York, NY; *U.S. Private*, pg. 622
Michel, M., Exec. V.P.--El Puerto de Liverpool S.A., Mexico, Mexico; *Int'l*, pg. 435
Michiels, Baudoin, Exec. V.P.-Belgium, Holland, Great Britain, Denmark & Greece--Kraft Jacobs Suchard AG, Zurich, Switzerland; *U.S. Public*, pg. 1288
Michielutti, Peter G., Chief Oper. Officer & Exec. V.P.--Fingerhut Corp., Minnetonka, MN; *U.S. Public*, pg. 623
Michner, Karl W., Sr. Exec. V.P.--Edison Brothers Stores, Inc., Saint Louis, MO; *U.S. Public*, pg. 563
Micone, Ed, Exec. V.P. & Exec. Producer-Entertainment--Radio City Productions, New York, NY; *Int'l*, pg. 873
Middelhoff, Thomas, Dr., Mng. Dir.--Bertelsmann AG, Gutersloh, Germany; *Int'l*, pg. 189
Middleton, Tom, Exec. V.P.--Goodpasture, Inc., Brownfield, TX; *U.S. Private*, pg. 464
Middleton, Vernon C., Exec. V.P.--United Missouri Bank of Warrensburg, Warrensburg, MO; *U.S. Public*, pg. 1655
Miears, Don, Exec. V.P. & Gen. Mgr.--Cedar Point, Sandusky, OH; *U.S. Public*, pg. 319
Migliorini, James F., Exec. V.P.-Standard Opers.--Signet Star Reinsurance Company, Florham Park, NJ; *U.S. Public*, pg. 216
Mihalko, George R., Jr., Chief Fin. Officer, Sr. V.P., Treas. & Asst. Sec.--Pamida Holdings Corporation, Omaha, NE; *U.S. Public*, pg. 1255
Mike LeNoue, Exec. V.P.--UMB Bank of the West, N.A., Colorado Springs, CO; *U.S. Public*, pg. 1654
Miki, Masaki, Exec. V.P. & Gen. Mgr.--Kikkoman International, Inc., San Francisco, CA; *Int'l*, pg. 733
Miki, Tomonori, Exec. V.P.--Sankyo Company Limited, Tokyo, Japan; *Int'l*, pg. 1189
Miki, Toshio, Exec. V.P.--Nippon Steel Corporation, Tokyo, Japan; *Int'l*, pg. 939
Mikoshiba, Takao, Exec. V.P.--Ishikawajima-Harima Heavy Industries Co., Ltd., Tokyo, Japan; *Int'l*, pg. 689
Milbrandt, Mike E., Chief Oper. Officer & Exec. V.P.--Lawson Software, Minneapolis, MN; *U.S. Private*, pg. 654
Milby, William E., Exec. V.P.--The National Bank of Fredericksburg, Fredericksburg, VA; *U.S. Public*, pg. 1089
Milcent, Jean-Claude, Exec. V.P.-H.R.--PSA Peugeot Citroen, Paris, France; *Int'l*, pg. 1020
Miles, Richard, Sr. Exec. V.P.--CSE Insurance Group, San Francisco, CA; *U.S. Private*, pg. 197
Miles, Richard J., Exec. V.P.--Palmer-American National Bank, Danville, IL; *U.S. Public*, pg. 1217
Miley, John, Exec. V.P. & Corp. Plng. Dir.--G2 Advertising, Huntington Beach, CA; *U.S. Public*, pg. 764
Millar, John F., Exec. V.P.--Dixon Ticonderoga Company, Heathrow, FL; *U.S. Public*, pg. 514
Millard, Frank W., Exec. V.P.--Turtle & Hughes, Inc., Linden, NJ; *U.S. Private*, pg. 1110
Millard, Shannon, Chief Credit Officer & Exec. V.P.--FirstFed Financial Corp., Santa Monica, CA; *U.S. Public*, pg. 645
Millas, Tim, Exec. V.P. & Exec. Creative Dir.--Lowe McAdams Healthcare, New York, NY; *U.S. Private*, pg. 678
Milleman, Laura K., Chief Acctg. Officer & Exec. V.P.--Countrywide Home Loans Inc., Pasadena, CA; *U.S. Public*, pg. 452
Miller, Bill, Exec. V.P.--MAC America Communications, Inc., Phoenix, AZ; *U.S. Private*, pg. 685
Miller, Charles Q., Exec. V.P., Chm. Bd. & Chief Exec. Officer-Raytheon Engrs.--Raytheon Company, Lexington, MA; *U.S. Public*, pg. 1364
Miller, Cliff, Exec. V.P. & Exec. Creative Dir.--Ketchum Advertising/Pittsburgh, Pittsburgh, PA; *U.S. Private*, pg. 616
Miller, Dan, Exec. V.P.-Latin America--Whirlpool Corporation, Benton Harbor, MI; *U.S. Public*, pg. 1764
Miller, David, Exec. V.P.--Hask Toiletries, Great Neck, NY; *U.S. Private*, pg. 509
Miller, David D., Exec. V.P. & Corp Legal--UMB Financial Corporation, Kansas City, MO; *U.S. Public*, pg. 1653
Miller, Duane L., Chief Exec. Officer & Exec. V.P.--Country Life Insurance Company, Bloomington, IL; *U.S. Private*, pg. 278
Miller, George F., Sr. Exec. V.P.-Business Insurance Sector--John Hancock Mutual Life Insurance Company, Boston, MA; *U.S. Private*, pg. 589
Miller, Herry G., Exec. V.P.--Collective Bank, Cologne, NJ; *U.S. Public*, pg. 1528
Miller, James, Exec. V.P.--Bank of America Illinois, Chicago, IL; *U.S. Public*, pg. 180
Miller, James P., Exec. V.P.-Fin.--Cascade Corporation, Troutdale, OR; *U.S. Public*, pg. 310
Miller, James R., Chief Oper. Officer & Exec. V.P.--Northern Life Insurance Company, Seattle, WA; *U.S. Public*, pg. 1375
Miller, James R., Exec. V.P.-Worldwide Bus. Affairs--Warner Bros. Studios, Inc., Burbank, CA; *U.S. Public*, pg. 1611
Miller, Janis, Exec. V.P.--IDS Life Insurance Co. of New York, Albany, NY; *U.S. Public*, pg. 73
Miller, Jim, Exec. V.P.-Sls. & Mktg.--Sutter Home Winery, Inc., Saint Helena, CA; *U.S. Private*, pg. 1057
Miller, John, Exec. V.P.--Young Stuff Apparel Group, Inc., New York, NY; *U.S. Private*, pg. 1202
Miller, Joni, Exec. V.P. & Media Services Dir.--EvansGroup, San Francisco, CA; *U.S. Private*, pg. 385
Miller, Kelly S., Exec. V.P.--CalFarm Insurance Agency, Sacramento, CA; *U.S. Public*, pg. 1791
Miller, Kenneth, Exec. V.P.--Perry Machinery Corporation, Hainesport, NJ; *U.S. Private*, pg. 855
Miller, Larry F., Chief Fin. Officer & Exec. V.P.--Gannett Company, Inc., Arlington, VA; *U.S. Public*, pg. 698
Miller, Lawrence, Exec. V.P.-Opers.--The Loewen Group, Inc., Burnaby, Canada; *Int'l*, pg. 814
Miller, Lynn C., Exec. V.P.-Individual Insurance--Pacific Life Insurance Company, Newport Beach, CA; *U.S. Private*, pg. 831
Miller, Mark, Exec. V.P.-Opers.--Showboat, Incorporated, Las Vegas, NV; *U.S. Public*, pg. 1469
Miller, Mark F., Exec. V.P. & Gen. Mgr.--Hearst Magazines Division, New York, NY; *U.S. Private*, pg. 516
Miller, Mark F., Exec. V.P.--Cosmopolitan, New York, NY; *U.S. Private*, pg. 517
Miller, Mark J., Exec. V.P.-Mdsg. & Stores--Mac Frugal's Bargains Close-Outs Inc., Rancho Dominguez, CA; *U.S. Public*, pg. 437
Miller, Marty, Chief Oper. Officer & Exec. V.P.--Melitta U.S.A., Inc., Clearwater, FL; *Int'l*, pg. 857
Miller, Neil, Chief Fin. Officer, Chief Oper. Officer & Exec. V.P.--Partners & Shevack, Inc., New York, NY; *U.S. Private*, pg. 842
Miller, Philip D., Exec. V.P.--Howard Miller, Zeeland, MI; *U.S. Private*, pg. 747
Miller, Randy, Exec. V.P.-Mktg.--Waterhouse Investor Services, New York, NY; *Int'l*, pg. 1401
Miller, Richard, Exec. V.P.--DVI, Inc., Doylestown, PA; *U.S. Public*, pg. 476
Miller, Richard C., Chief Oper. Officer & Exec. V.P.--E.D. Bullard Company, Cynthiana, KY; *U.S. Private*, pg. 180
Miller, Robert A., Exec. V.P. & Gen. Mgr.--Marriott Ownership Resorts, Washington, DC; *U.S. Public*, pg. 1048
Miller, Steve, Principal--Richards, Brock, Miller, Mitchell & Assoc. Inc., Dallas, TX; *U.S. Private*, pg. 929
Miller, Susan, Exec. V.P. & Client Services Dir.--Cline, Davis & Mann, Inc., New York, NY; *U.S. Private*, pg. 246
Miller, Wayne, Chief Fin. Officer, Exec. V.P.-Fin. & Admin. & Sec.--Bernard Chaus, Inc., Secaucus, NJ; *U.S. Public*, pg. 342
Millgard, C. Richard, Exec. V.P.--The Millgard Corp., Livonia, MI; *U.S. Private*, pg. 748
Millman, Jeffrey I., Exec. V.P. & Creative Dir.--Gray Kirk/VanSant Advertising, Inc., Baltimore, MD; *U.S. Private*, pg. 472
Mills, Bradford A., Exec. V.P.-Bus. Plng. & Devel.--BHP Copper North America, Tucson, AZ; *Int'l*, pg. 224
Mills, Douglas W., Exec. V.P.-U.S. & Canada Foods Prods.--The Quaker Oats Company, Chicago, IL; *U.S. Public*, pg. 1347
Mills, Douglas W., Exec. V.P.--U.S. & Canadian Food Products, Chicago, IL; *U.S. Public*, pg. 1347
Millweard, Tom, Exec. V.P. & Mng. Dir.--Ackerman McQueen, Inc., Irving, TX; *U.S. Private*, pg. 13
Milo, Bob, Exec. V.P.-Mfg.--Coastcast Corporation, Gardena, CA; *U.S. Public*, pg. 391
Milock, R.L., Chief Oper. Officer & Exec. V.P.--Bradford-White Corporation, Ambler, PA; *U.S. Private*, pg. 164
Milostan, Thomas, Exec. V.P.--Excelsior Manufacturing & Supply Corp., Itasca, IL; *U.S. Private*, pg. 387
Milot, Charles, Exec. V.P.--Winthrop-Atkins Co., Inc., Middleboro, MA; *U.S. Private*, pg. 1183
Milroy, James R., Exec. V.P. & Cashier--Shoreline Financial Corp., Benton Harbor, MI; *U.S. Public*, pg. 1467
Minagawa, Fumio, Exec. Dir.--United ORIX Leasing Berhad, Kuala Lumpur, Malaysia; *Int'l*, pg. 1010
Minami, Kenji, Exec. V.P.--The Kansai Electric Power Co., Inc., Osaka, Japan; *Int'l*, pg. 722
Minami, Nobuya, Exec. V.P.--The Tokyo Electric Power Co., Inc., Tokyo, Japan; *Int'l*, pg. 1394
Mineshima, Toshiyuki, Exec. V.P.--Nippon Telegraph and Telephone Corporation, Tokyo, Japan; *Int'l*, pg. 940
Miniat, Edmund, Jr., Exec. V.P. & Sec.--Ed Miniat, Inc., Chicago, IL; *U.S. Private*, pg. 750
Minier, Michelle, Chief Oper. Officer & Exec. V.P.--Warehouse Lending Corporation of America, Pasadena, CA; *U.S. Public*, pg. 857
Minihan, William H., Chief Information Officer & Exec. V.P.--Bank of America Illinois, Chicago, IL; *U.S. Public*, pg. 180
Minkoff, Bruce, Exec. V.P.--Fraenkel Company, Baton Rouge, LA; *U.S. Private*, pg. 423
Minkus, Sabra, Exec. V.P.--Transilwrap Company, Inc., Chicago, IL; *U.S. Private*, pg. 1097
Minor-Hoffman, Julie, Exec. V.P.-Client Services--Grey Entertainment Inc., New York, NY; *U.S. Public*, pg. 764
Minor, Leslie W., Exec. V.P.--Wachovia Bank, Charlottesville, VA; *U.S. Public*, pg. 1730
Minsky, Robert, Exec. V.P. & Chief Oper. Officer-Translation & Publishng--Berlitz International, Inc., Princeton, NJ; *U.S. Public*, pg. 221
Mintern, Fred, Chief Fin. Officer & Exec. V.P.--APX International, Auburn Hills, MI; *U.S. Private*, pg. 7
Minto, Clive, Exec. V.P.-Diversified Bus. Grp.--Canadian Tire Corporation Limited, Toronto, Canada; *Int'l*, pg. 259
Minton, Don, Exec. V.P.--Keller Crescent Co., Evansville, IN; *U.S. Private*, pg. 612
Mintum, Brian, Exec. V.P.-Mktg.--Invesco Funds Group, Denver, CO; *Int'l*, pg. 685
Mirisch, Don, Exec. V.P.-MGM Animation--MGM Worldwide Television, Group., Santa Monica, CA; *U.S. Public*, pg. 1102
Misaka, Shigeo, Sr. Exec. Dir.-Electronic Components & Devices--Sharp Corporation, Osaka, Japan; *Int'l*, pg. 1228
Mischler, Harland L., Chief Fin. Officer & Exec. V.P.--Gradco Systems, Inc., Las Vegas, NV; *U.S. Public*, pg. 757
Mischler, Paul, Exec. V.P. & Treas.--Norfoods, Inc., Overland Park, KS; *U.S. Private*, pg. 802
Misevicius, Milda, Exec. V.P. & New Bus. Devel. Dir.--Korey, Kay & Partners, New York, NY; *U.S. Private*, pg. 632
Misfeldt, Colleen, Exec. V.P.--First Security Bank of Nevada, Las Vegas, NV; *U.S. Public*, pg. 637
Misray, Mary-Lou, Exec. V.P.--USA Casualty Company, Chino, CA; *U.S. Private*, pg. 1116
Missad, Matthew, Exec. V.P.-Corp. Compliance--Universal Forest Products, Inc., Grand Rapids, MI; *U.S. Public*, pg. 1696
Missel, Diane, Exec. V.P. & Gen. Mgr.-Mdse.--The Cato Corporation, Charlotte, NC; *U.S. Public*, pg. 318
Missorten, L., Exec. V.P. & Chief Fin. Officer--Labatt Breweries of Canada, Toronto, Canada; *Int'l*, pg. 679
Misunas, William, Exec. V.P.-Americas--Utell International-Secaucus, Secaucus, NJ; *Int'l*, pg. 1098
Mitch, John Tim, Exec. V.P.--Roy Anderson Corp., Gulfport, MS; *U.S. Private*, pg. 72
Mitchell, Bill, Exec. V.P. & Creative Dir.--Eisner & Associates, Inc., Baltimore, MD; *U.S. Private*, pg. 366
Mitchell, Bruce W., Exec. V.P. & Gen. Auditor--BankAmerica Corporation, San Francisco, CA; *U.S. Public*, pg. 179
Mitchell, Bruce W., Grp. Exec. V.P. & Gen. Auditor--Bank of America NT&SA, San Francisco, CA; *U.S. Public*, pg. 180
Mitchell, Carol L., Esq., Exec. V.P. & Clerk--Peoples Heritage Financial Group, Inc., Portland, ME; *U.S. Public*, *pg. 1275*
Mitchell, Charlie, Chief Exec. Officer--Heckethorn Mfg. Company, Inc., Dyersburg, TN; *U.S. Private*, pg. 519
Mitchell, Christine L., Exec. V.P.--Mitchell Corporation of Owosso, Owosso, MI; *U.S. Private*, pg. 753
Mitchell, Dick, Principal--Richards, Brock, Miller, Mitchell & Assoc. Inc., Dallas, TX; *U.S. Private*, pg. 929
Mitchell, Don, Exec. V.P.--Cogsdill Tool Products, Inc., Lugoff, SC; *U.S. Private*, pg. 250
Mitchell, Donald L., Exec. V.P. & Pres.-Ladd Casegoods Grp.--Ladd Furniture, Inc., Greensboro, NC; *U.S. Public*, pg. 974
Mitchell, E. G., Exec V.P.-Human Resources--Royal Bank of Canada, Toronto, Canada; *Int'l*, pg. 1131
Mitchell, George, Chief Oper. Officer & Exec. V.P.--Corcom, Inc., Libertyville, IL; *U.S. Public*, pg. 446
Mitchell, J., Chief Oper. Officer & Exec. V.P.--Versa Services Ltd., Etobicoke, Canada; *U.S. Private*, pg. 79
Mitchell, James, Exec. V.P.-Mktg. & Prods.--IDS Financial Services, Inc., Minneapolis, MN; *U.S. Public*, pg. 73
Mitchell, James A., Exec. V.P.-Mktg. & Prods.--American Express Financial Advisor, Minneapolis, MN; *U.S. Public*, *pg. 73*
Mitchell, James J., Exec. V.P.-Worldwide Opers. & Tech.--Northern Trust Corporation, Chicago, IL; *U.S. Public*, pg. 1195
Mitchell, Leah, Exec. V.P. & Media Dir.--Asher/Gould Advertising, Inc., Los Angeles, CA; *U.S. Private*, pg. 88
Mitchell, Paul, Chief Fin. Officer & Exec. V.P.--Edelman Public Relations Worldwide, Chicago, IL; *U.S. Private*, pg. 362
Mitchell, Robert I., Exec. V.P. & Exec. Media Dir.--Campbell-Ewald Advertising, Warren, MI; *U.S. Public*, pg. 908
Mitsch, Ronald A., Vice Chm. & Exec. V.P.-Indus. & Consumer Sector/Corp. Svcs.--3M, Saint Paul, MN; *U.S. Public*, pg. 1604
Mitsui, Shigeo, Exec. V.P.--Toray Industries, Inc., Tokyo, Japan; *Int'l*, pg. 1399
Mitsumoto, Kazuhiko, Exec. V.P.--Cosmo Oil Co., Ltd., Tokyo, Japan; *Int'l*, pg. 335
Mitton, Rod, Exec. V.P.--CompAir LeRoi, Sidney, OH; *Int'l*, pg. 1242

Mitzel, Robert E., Exec. V.P.-Asset Mngmt.--IRT Property Company, Atlanta, GA; *U.S. Public*, pg. 858
Mixon, Grover C., Chief Oper. Officer & Exec. V.P.--Phoenix Medical Technology, Inc., Andrews, SC; *U.S. Public*, pg. 1292
Miyagawa, Yasushige, Exec. V.P.--Nisshin Steel Co., Ltd., Tokyo, Japan; *Int'l*, pg. 946
Miyahara, Kenji, Exec. V.P.-Plng., Credit, Investments, Acctng. & Controller--Sumitomo Corporation, Tokyo, Japan; *Int'l*, pg. 1312
Miyahara, M., Exec. V.P. & Gen. Mgr.--Asahi Glass America, Inc., New York, NY; *Int'l*, pg. 84
Miyairi, Tetsuo, Exec. V.P.--Fanuc Ltd., Yamanashi, Japan; *Int'l*, pg. 477
Miyaji, Makoto, Exec. V.P.-Corp. Planning & Fin. Mngmt.--Mazda Motor Corporation, Hiroshima, Japan; *Int'l*, pg. 849
Miyajima, Toyoaki, Exec. V.P.--Sato Kogyo Co., Ltd., Tokyo, Japan; *Int'l*, pg. 1197
Miyake, Kazuhiro, Exec. V.P.--Subaru of America, Inc., Cherry Hill, NJ; *Int'l*, pg. 523
Miyamoto, Hajime, Exec. V.P.--The Kansai Electric Power Co., Inc., Osaka, Japan; *Int'l*, pg. 722
Miyamoto, Hidetoshi, Exec. V.P.--Daido Life Insurance Company, Osaka, Japan; *Int'l*, pg. 363
Miyamoto, Jiro, Exec. V.P.--Daido Steel Co., Ltd., Nagoya, Japan; *Int'l*, pg. 364
Miyata, Akinori, Exec. V.P.--The Tokyo Electric Power Co., Inc., Tokyo, Japan; *Int'l*, pg. 1394
Miyata, Akira, Exec. V.P. & Dir.--China Kang Fu International Leasing Co., Ltd., Beijing, China; *Int'l*, pg. 521
Miyata, Mitsuto, Exec. V.P.--Fanuc Ltd., Yamanashi, Japan; *Int'l*, pg. 477
Miyatake, Yasuyoshi, Exec. V.P.--Shimizu Corporation, Tokyo, Japan; *Int'l*, pg. 1233
Miyawaki, Tomoo, Exec. V.P.--NEC Corporation, Tokyo, Japan; *Int'l*, pg. 899
Miyazaki, Fumiohi, Exec. V.P.--Sumitomo Heavy Industries, Ltd., Tokyo, Japan; *Int'l*, pg. 1314
Miyoshi, Daiya, Exec. V.P.--Showa Denko K.K., Tokyo, Japan; *Int'l*, pg. 1236
Miyoshi, Daiya, Exec. V.P.--Showa Denko Kawasaki Works, Kawasaki, Japan; *Int'l*, pg. 1236
Mizialko, John, Exec. V.P.-Opers.--Allou Personal Care Corp., Saugus, CA; *U.S. Public*, pg. 55
Mizukoshi, Koshi, Exec. V.P.--Kobe Steel, Ltd., Kobe, Japan; *Int'l*, pg. 740
Mizusaki, Iwao, Exec. V.P.--Marubeni Corporation, Osaka, Japan; *Int'l*, pg. 844
Mizutari, Shunicki, Sr. V.P.--Mitsui Foods Export, Burlingame, CA; *Int'l*, pg. 879
Mlekush, Kenneth C., Exec. V.P.-Individual--Jefferson-Pilot Life Insurance Co., Greensboro, NC; *U.S. Public*, pg. 926
Mlynaryk, W., Exec. V.P.-Opers.--Kruger Inc., Montreal, Canada; *Int'l*, pg. 761
Mlynaryk, Walter, Exec. V.P.-Opers.--Corner Brook Pulp & Paper Limited, Corner Brook, Canada; *Int'l*, pg. 761
Moar, James, Chief Oper. Officer & Exec. V.P.--DataCard Corporation, Minnetonka, MN; *U.S. Private*, pg. 312
Moberg, Jim R., Exec. V.P.-Human Resources--Pacific Telesis Group, San Francisco, CA; *U.S. Public*, pg. 1415
Moberly, Thomas, Pres. & Chief Oper. Officer--G&K Services, Inc., Minnetonka, MN; *U.S. Public*, pg. 690
Mobley, A. Scott, Chief Oper. Officer, Exec. V.P. & Sec.--Noble Roman's Inc., Indianapolis, IN; *U.S. Public*, pg. 1187
Mockley, Michael E., Exec. V.P. & Chief Oper. Officer--Anchor Gasoline Corporation, Tulsa, OK; *U.S. Private*, pg. 70
Modzelewski, John F., Sr. Partner, Exec. V.P. & Gen. Mgr.--Fleishman-Hillard, Inc., Chicago, IL; *U.S. Private*, pg. 411
Moeller, Joe W., Exec. V.P.-Supply, Trading & Transportation Grp.--Koch Industries, Incorporated, Wichita, KS; *U.S. Private*, pg. 628
Moellering, John, Exec. V.P.--UNC Aviation Services, Inc., Annapolis, MD; *U.S. Public*, pg. 710
Moen, Donald J., Exec. V.P. & Creative Dir.--Integrity Incorporated, Mobile, AL; *U.S. Public*, pg. 886
Moen, Timothy P., Exec. V.P.-Human Resources--First Chicago NBD Corporation, Chicago, IL; *U.S. Public*, pg. 627
Moerk, Edward, Exec. V.P.--Koninklijke Ahold NV, Zaandam, Netherlands; *Int'l*, pg. 749
Moes, Francois, Exec. V.P.-Institutional Mkts.--Banque Internationale a Luxembourg S.A., Luxembourg, Luxembourg; *Int'l*, pg. 162
Mogavero, Pete, Chief Exec. Officer--Anchor Industries Inc., Evansville, IN; *U.S. Private*, pg. 71
Mohler, Hugh W., Exec. V.P.--Mercantile Bankshares Corporation, Baltimore, MD; *U.S. Public*, pg. 1088
Mohler, Hugh W., Exec. V.P.--Mercantile-Safe Deposit & Trust Co., Baltimore, MD; *U.S. Public*, pg. 1089
Mohlin, Katarina, Exec. V.P. & Corp. Commun. Officer--Skandia Insurance Company Limited, Stockholm, Sweden; *Int'l*, pg. 1256
Moine, Gerard, Exec. Dir.-Pub. Affairs--France Telecom, Paris, France; *Int'l*, pg. 503
Moisen, Chandler J., Exec. V.P.--TransTechnology Corporation, Liberty Corner, NJ; *U.S. Public*, pg. 1632
Molder, Barry, Exec. V.P.--First Commercial Mortgage Co., Little Rock, AR; *U.S. Public*, pg. 630
Molesworth, Richard C., Exec. V.P.--Frederick Trading Company, Frederick, MD; *U.S. Private*, pg. 335
Moley, Miriam, Exec. V.P.-Mktg.--Carson Products Company, Savannah, GA; *U.S. Public*, pg. 309
Moll, Karl Rudolf, Dr., Exec. V.P.--Bayerische Hypotheken- und Wechsel-Bank Aktiengesellschaft, Munich, Germany; *Int'l*, pg. 175
Mollins, Gregg J., Chief Oper. Officer & Exec. V.P.--Reliance Steel & Aluminum Co., Los Angeles, CA; *U.S. Public*, pg. 1375
Molloy, Brian, Mng. Dir.-Paper, Packaging & Print--James Crean PLC, Dublin, Ireland; *Int'l*, pg. 340
Molloy, Charles D., Exec. V.P.--Angelica Image Apparel, Saint Louis, MO; *U.S. Public*, pg. 113
Molyneux, Richard A., Exec. V.P.--Keycorp, Cleveland, OH; *U.S. Public*, pg. 954
Mommers, R.J.W., Exec. V.P.--ABN-AMRO Holding N.V., Amsterdam, Netherlands; *Int'l*, pg. 8
Momose, Nobuo, Exec. V.P.--Dentsu Inc., Tokyo, Japan; *Int'l*, pg. 392
Monaghan, Bruce, Exec. V.P.--Catalina Lighting Canada, Dorval, Canada; *U.S. Public*, pg. 314
Monaghan, Edward J., Chief Oper. Officer & Exec. V.P.--Flexsteel Industries, Inc., Dubuque, IA; *U.S. Public*, pg. 653
Monahan, Grace, Exec. V.P.--CMP Media, Inc., Manhasset, NY; *U.S. Public*, pg. 279
Monden, Minoru, Exec. V.P.--Japan Securities Finance Co. Ltd., Tokyo, Japan; *Int'l*, pg. 702
Mondry, Lawrence N., Exec. V.P.-Mdsg.--CompUSA, Dallas, TX; *U.S. Public*, pg. 420
Monks, Donald R., Sr. Exec. V.P.-Opers. & Tech.--The Bank of New York Company, Inc., New York, NY; *U.S. Public*, pg. 178
Monroe, Janis R., Exec. V.P.-Bus. Devel. Grp.--ICS Learning Systems, Inc., Scranton, PA; *U.S. Public*, pg. 783
Monroe, Jeff, Chief Oper. Officer & Exec. V.P.--The Johnson Corporation, Three Rivers, MI; *U.S. Private*, pg. 591
Mont, Stuart, Chief Oper. Officer, Chief Fin. Officer, Exec. V.P. & Sec.--Recoton Corporation, Lake Mary, FL; *U.S. Public*, pg. 1369
Monteiro, Milton Luis Ubach, Exec. V.P.-Retail Banking--Banco Itau S.A., Sao Paulo, Brazil; *Int'l*, pg. 142
Montes, Ramon, Exec. V.P.--Allou Health & Beauty Care, Inc., Brentwood, NY; *U.S. Public*, pg. 55
Montezemolo, Gianni, Sr. Exec. V.P.-Europe--Johnson Wax S.p.A., Milan, Italy; *U.S. Private*, pg. 593
Montgomery, Clark T., Exec. V.P. & Grp. Dir.--Grey Advertising Inc., New York, NY; *U.S. Public*, pg. 764
Montgomery, Jeffrey A., Chief Oper. Officer & Exec. V.P.--Washington Square Securities, Minneapolis, MN; *U.S. Public*, pg. 1376
Montgomery, R.L., Chief Fin. Officer, Exec. V.P. & Treas.--Columbus McKinnon Corp., Amherst, NY; *U.S. Public*, pg. 405
Montgomery, Robert R., Vice Chm. & Exec. V.P.--Alcon Systems, Inc., Fort Worth, TX; *Int'l*, pg. 916
Monti, Roberto, Chief Exec. Officer--Y.P.F., S.A., Buenos Aires, Argentina; *Int'l*, pg. 1515
Montoni, Richard A., Chief Fin. Officer & Exec. V.P.--Ciber, Inc., Englewood, CO; *U.S. Public*, pg. 356
Montoya, Jorge P., Exec. V.P. & Pres.-Latin America--The Procter & Gamble Company, Cincinnati, OH; *U.S. Public*, pg. 1330
Montupet, J-P L., Exec. V.P.--Emerson Electric Co., Saint Louis, MO; *U.S. Public*, pg. 572
Moody, Susan S., Exec. V.P.-Corp. & Institutional Banking--First Chicago NBD Corporation, Chicago, IL; *U.S. Public*, pg. 627
Moon, Thomas Y., Exec. V.P.--Bankers Security Life Insurance Society, Woodbury, NY; *U.S. Public*, pg. 1375
Mooney, Michael A., Exec. V.P.-Underwriting & Pricing--United HealthCare Corporation, Minnetonka, MN; *U.S. Public*, pg. 1677
Moont, Derry L., Exec. V.P.--Mid Atlantic Medical Services, Inc., Rockville, MD; *U.S. Public*, pg. 1109
Moonves, Leslie, Exec. V.P.--CBS, New York, NY; *U.S. Public*, pg. 273
Moonves, Leslie, Pres. & Exec. V.P.-CBS--CBS Entertainment, Los Angeles, CA; *U.S. Public*, pg. 274
Moorby, Tony, Exec. V.P.--ADT Automotive, Inc., Nashville, TN; *U.S. Public*, pg. 1648
Moore, Brian L., Exec. V.P.-Canadian Insurance Opers.--Manulife Financial (The Manufacturers Life Insurance Company), Toronto, Canada; *Int'l*, pg. 840
Moore, David, Exec. V.P.-Grp. Ins.--Ameritas Life Insurance Corp., Lincoln, NE; *U.S. Private*, pg. 65
Moore, Emmett E., Exec. V.P.-M.C.I.I.--Columbia/H.C.A., Dallas, TX; *U.S. Public*, pg. 404
Moore, Frank, Chief Oper. Officer & Exec. V.P.--McCall Oil & Chemical Corp., Portland, OR; *U.S. Private*, pg. 719
Moore, James R., Chief Fin. Officer, Exec. V.P. & Sec.--Urstadt Biddle Properties, Inc., Greenwich, CT; *U.S. Public*, pg. 1700
Moore, John A., Exec. V.P.-Fin--World Financial Properties, Inc., New York, NY; *Int'l*, pg. 1004
Moore, Kurt, Exec. V.P.-Ablest Svcs. Corp.--C.H. Heist Corp., Clearwater, FL; *U.S. Public*, pg. 807
Moore, Larry, Exec. V.P.--ScanTron Corporation, Tustin, CA; *U.S. Public*, pg. 786
Moore, Maureen, Exec. V.P. & Sr. Partner--N.W. Ayer & Partners New York, New York, NY; *U.S. Private*, pg. 104
Moore, Max, Exec. V.P.--Global Steel Products Corporation, Deer Park, NY; *U.S. Private*, pg. 457
Moore, Michael D., Exec. V.P. & DMB&B Worldwide Media DiR.--DMB&B Communications, New York, NY; *U.S. Private*, pg. 302
Moore, Phillip A., Exec. V.P.--Sterling Commerce, Inc., Dublin, OH; *U.S. Public*, pg. 1515
Moore, Sam Joseph, Exec. V.P. & Pres.-Thomas Nelson Gifts--Thomas Nelson Inc., Nashville, TN; *U.S. Public*, pg. 1167
Moore, Scott, Chief Fin. Officer & Exec. V.P.--PartnerRe Ltd., Pembroke, Bermuda; *Int'l*, pg. 1024
Moore, T. Jerald, Exec. V.P.-Bus. Devel. & Plng.--Beverly Enterprises, Inc., Fort Smith, AR; *U.S. Public*, pg. 227
Moore, Thomas A., Exec. V.P. & Acct. Grp. Dir.--Liggett-Stashower, Inc., Cleveland, OH; *U.S. Private*, pg. 667
Moore, Thomas E., Chief Oper. Officer & Exec. V.P.--Material Sciences Corporation, Elk Grove Village, IL; *U.S. Public*, pg. 1056
Moore, Tim, Exec. V.P.--Philips Electronics Ltd., Scarborough, Canada; *Int'l*, pg. 1055
Moore, William J., Exec. V.P.-Multi-Family Housing Lending--Resource Mortgage Capital, Inc., Glen Allen, VA; *U.S. Public*, pg. 1382
Moorehead, David J., Exec. V.P.--BT Financial Corporation, Johnstown, PA; *U.S. Public*, pg. 163
Moorman, Robert, Exec. V.P.-Client Services--Jordan, McGrath, Case & Taylor Inc., New York, NY; *U.S. Private*, pg. 598
Moosmuller, Martin, Sr. Exec. V.P.-Securities Div.--Bayerische Landesbank, Munich, Germany; *Int'l*, pg. 176
Moot, Suzanne, Exec. V.P.-Mktg. & Retail Banking--UST Corporation, Boston, MA; *U.S. Public*, pg. 1660
Moot, Suzanne, Exec. V.P.-Retail Banking & Mktg.--USTrust, Boston, MA; *U.S. Public*, pg. 1660
Mooter, Ken E., Exec. V.P.-Fin.--Lincoln Property Company, Dallas, TX; *U.S. Private*, pg. 668
Mooth, Thomas A., Chief Oper. Officer & Exec. V.P.--Trone Advertising, Inc., Greensboro, NC; *U.S. Private*, pg. 1104
Moquist, Paul A., Exec. V.P.-Sls. & Mktg.--Insignia Systems, Inc., Minnetonka, MN; *U.S. Public*, pg. 881
Moquist, Ronald M., Exec. V.P.--Raven Industries, Inc., Sioux Falls, SD; *U.S. Public*, pg. 1361
Morais, Douglas, Exec. V.P.--Ortel Corporation, Alhambra, CA; *U.S. Public*, pg. 1232
Morais, Robert J., Exec. V.P.-Consumer--Carrafiello, Diehl & Associates, Inc., Irvington, NY; *U.S. Private*, pg. 215
Moran, Harry J., Exec. V.P.--Sonoco Products Company, Hartsville, SC; *U.S. Public*, pg. 1485
Moran, Michael R., Exec. V.P., Gen. Counsel & Sec.--Spiegel, Inc., Downers Grove, IL; *U.S. Public*, pg. 1498
Moran, Richard E., Jr., Chief Fin. Officer & Exec. V.P.--Irvine Apartment Communities Incorporated, Newport Beach, CA; *U.S. Private*, pg. 575
Morano, Jerry, Exec. V.P.-Mktg. & Commun.--Quality Bakers of America Cooperative, Inc., Greenwich, CT; *U.S. Private*, pg. 898
Morash, David L., Chief Fin. Officer & Exec. V.P.--Safeskin Corporation, San Diego, CA; *U.S. Public*, pg. 1425
Morberg, Per Ove, Exec. V.P.-Strategic Bus. Devel.--Celsius AB, Stockholm, Sweden; *Int'l*, pg. 276
Mordo, Jean H., Chief Fin. Officer & Exec. V.P.--The Scotts Company, Marysville, OH; *U.S. Public*, pg. 1446
Moreira, Marcio, Exec. V.P., Chief Creative Officer & Reg. Dir.-Asia Pacific--McCann-Erickson Worldwide, New York, NY; *U.S. Public*, pg. 909
Morgan, Charles R., Exec. V.P. & Gen. Counsel--BellSouth Corporation, Atlanta, GA; *U.S. Public*, pg. 207
Morgan, D.D., Exec. V.P.--M.A. Hanna Color, Cleveland, OH; *U.S. Public*, pg. 781
Morgan, Glenn R., Chief Fin. Officer & Exec. V.P.--Hartmarx Corporation, Chicago, IL; *U.S. Public*, pg. 795
Morgan, James, Exec. V.P.--Daktronics, Inc., Brookings, SD; *U.S. Public*, pg. 478
Morgan, Mitch, Exec. V.P.-Opers.--Kauffman Products, Inc., Carmel, IN; *U.S. Private*, pg. 609
Morgan, W. Tommy, III, Exec. V.P.--Havatampa, Inc., Tampa, FL; *U.S. Private*, pg. 510
Morgan, William H., Sr. Exec. V.P.--Elias Brothers Restaurants, Inc., Warren, MI; *U.S. Private*, pg. 371
Morgenstern, Barbara, Exec. V.P.--Nuarc Company, Inc., Niles, IL; *U.S. Private*, pg. 808
Morice, James L., Sr. Partner & Exec. V.P.--Fleishman-Hillard Inc., Saint Louis, MO; *U.S. Private*, pg. 411
Moriel, Donald M., Chief Oper. Officer & Exec. V.P.--Norcal Waste Systems, San Francisco, CA; *U.S. Public*, pg. 1188
Morimoto, Katsumi, Exec. V.P.--Daiwa House Industry Co., Ltd., Osaka, Japan; *Int'l*, pg. 374
Morin, Emmanuel, Exec. V.P.--NGTC, Boucherville, Canada; *Int'l*, pg. 541
Morin, Michael, Exec. V.P.--Yaffe & Company, Southfield, MI; *U.S. Private*, pg. 1195
Morin, Rudolph G., Chief Fin. Officer & Exec. V.P.-Opers. & Fin.--Network Computing Devices, Inc., Mountain View, CA; *U.S. Public*, pg. 1168
Morio, Minoru, Exec. Deputy Pres.--Sony Corporation, Tokyo, Japan; *Int'l*, pg. 1280
Morisawa, Kanji, Exec. V.P.--Itochu Corporation, Tokyo, Japan; *Int'l*, pg. 694
Morita, Atsuo, Exec. V.P.--Shikishima Baking Co., Ltd., Nagoya, Japan; *Int'l*, pg. 1231
Morita, Hyozo, Exec. V.P.-Opers.--Ito-Yokado Co., Ltd., Tokyo, Japan; *Int'l*, pg. 693
Morita, Junji, Exec. V.P.--Meiji Seika Kaisha, Ltd., Tokyo, Japan; *Int'l*, pg. 855
Morita, Kazuo, Exec. V.P.--Hitachi, Ltd., Tokyo, Japan; *Int'l*, pg. 621
Mork, Stuart R., Chief Fin. Officer & Sr. V.P.--The Newhall Land And Farming Company, Valencia, CA; *U.S. Public*, pg. 1178
Morris, Barry, Exec. Dir.-Food--Marks & Spencer PLC, London, United Kingdom; *Int'l*, pg. 842
Morris, C. Carson, Exec. V.P.--CACI International Inc, Arlington, VA; *U.S. Public*, pg. 272
Morris, Cynthia R., Chief Fin. Officer, Exec. V.P, Treas. & Sec.--Sun Coast Industries, Inc, Dallas, TX; *U.S. Public*, pg. 1529
Morris, David W., Exec. V.P.--Keystone Morin, Inc., Pelham, AL; *U.S. Public*, pg. 1650
Morris, Edna K., Exec. V.P.--Advantica Restaurant Group, Inc., Spartanburg, SC; *U.S. Public*, pg. 22
Morris, Gary, Chief Fin. Officer & Exec. V.P.--Halliburton Company, Dallas, TX; *U.S. Public*, pg. 775
Morris, Gerald F., Chief Fin. Officer & Exec. V.P.--Diebold, Incorporated, Canton, OH; *U.S. Public*, pg. 506
Morris, Graham, Exec. V.P.-English Language Publishing--Telemedia Inc., Montreal, Canada; *Int'l*, pg. 1373
Morris, Graham J., Exec. V.P.--Comdisco Canada Ltd., Toronto, Canada; *U.S. Public*, pg. 408
Morris, Graham J., Exec. V.P.--Comdisco Canada Ltd., Montreal, Canada; *U.S. Public*, pg. 408
Morris, John, Exec. V.P. & Acct. Dir.--Wunderman Cato Johnson, New York, NY; *U.S. Private*, pg. 1197

Morris, John H., Exec. V.P.--RPM, Inc., Medina, OH; *U.S. Public*, pg. 1356

Morris, Larry G., Sr. Exec. V.P.--ADVO, Inc., Windsor, CT; *U.S. Public*, pg. 23

Morris, Malcolm, Sr. Exec. V.P.--Stewart Information Services Corporation, Houston, TX; *U.S. Public*, pg. 1518

Morris, Patrick J., Sr. Exec. V.P.--CPI Corp., Saint Louis, MO; *U.S. Public*, pg. 283

Morris, R. Don, Chief Fin. Officer& Exec. V.P.--Michaels Stores, Inc., Irving, TX; *U.S. Public*, pg. 1104

Morris, Richard A., Exec. V.P.-RMS--Willis Corroon Corp. of Western Michigan, Grand Rapids, MI; *Int'l*, pg. 1507

Morris, Scott J., Chief Oper. Officer & Exec. V.P.--Commercial Light Company, Hillside, IL; *U.S. Private*, pg. 258

Morris, Stewart, Jr., Sr. Exec. V.P.--Stewart Information Services Corporation, Houston, TX; *U.S. Public*, pg. 1518

Morris, Timothy J., Sr. Exec. V.P.--Bessemer Group, Inc., New York, NY; *U.S. Private*, pg. 139

Morrison, Carolyn, Exec. V.P.-Stores--F.A.O. Schwarz, New York, NY; *Int'l*, pg. 750

Morrison, Charles E., Partner, Exec. V.P., Strategic Plng. Dir. & New Bus. Contact--Don Coleman Advertising, Inc., Southfield, MI; *U.S. Private*, pg. 251

Morrison, David F., Chief Fin. Officer, Exec. V.P. & Treas.--Consolidated Freightways Corp., Menlo Park, CA; *U.S. Public*, pg. 435

Morrison, John H., Exec. V.P. & Gen. Mgr.-Corrugated Div.--Rock-Tenn Company, Norcross, GA; *U.S. Public*, pg. 1396

Morrison, Scott, Pres. & Chief Exec. Officer--Commercial Testing & Engineering Co., Lombard, IL; *Int'l*, pg. 1153

Morrison, Stephen G., Chief Admin. Officer, Exec. V.P., Gen. Counsel & Sec.--Policy Management Systems Corporation, Blythewood, SC; *U.S. Public*, pg. 1314

Morrison, Terry, Exec. V.P.-B.C.--Shoppers Drug Mart, Ltd., Toronto, Canada; *Int'l*, pg. 112

Morriss, George W., Chief Fin. Officer & Exec. V.P.--People's Bank, Bridgeport, CT; *U.S. Public*, pg. 1274

Morrissey, James R., Exec. V.P. & Exec. Creative Dir.--Grey Advertising Inc., New York, NY; *U.S. Public*, pg. 764

Morrissey, Mark, Exec. V.P. & Mng. Dir.--Mezzina/Brown Inc., New York, NY; *U.S. Private*, pg. 739

Morrone, Mario O., Exec. V.P.--BTM Leasing & Finance, Inc., New York, NY; *Int'l*, pg. 157

Morrow, David L., Exec. V.P.-Carolina First Bank--Carolina First Corporation, Greenville, SC; *U.S. Public*, pg. 306

Morrow, Robert P., III, Grp. Exec. V.P.-Asia Wholesale Grp.--Bank of America NT&SA, San Francisco, CA; *U.S. Public*, pg. 180

Morschel, John, Exec. Dir.-Australian Banking--Westpac Banking Corporation, Sydney, Australia; *Int'l*, pg. 1495

Mortell, John F., Chief Oper. Officer & Exec. V.P.--Physician Computer Network, Inc., Morris Plains, NJ; *U.S. Public*, pg. 1293

Mortensen, Davis K., Exec. V.P.-Bldg. Prods.--Georgia-Pacific Corporation, Atlanta, GA; *U.S. Public*, pg. 735

Mortenson, Jim, Exec. V.P.-Sls. & Mktg.--Arrowhead Mills, Inc., Hereford, TX; *U.S. Private*, pg. 86

Mortier, Denis, Exec. V.P.-Equity Fin.--Credit Nationale, Paris, France; *Int'l*, pg. 344

Mortimer, Daniel J., Chief Oper. Officer & Exec. V.P.--Halter Marine Group, Inc., Gulfport, MS; *U.S. Public*, pg. 778

Mortine, Neil, Exec. V.P., Pub. Rels. Dir. & Investor Rels. Dir.--Lord, Sullivan & Yoder Inc. Marketing Communications, Columbus, OH; *U.S. Private*, pg. 676

Mortine, Neil R., Exec. V.P., Pub. Rels. Dir. & Investor Rels. Dir.--Lord, Sullivan & Yoder Public Relations, Columbus, OH; *U.S. Private*, pg. 676

Morton, Alex, Exec. V.P., Grp. Acct. Dir.-Worldwide & Gen. Motors Corp.--DMB&B Detroit, Troy, MI; *U.S. Private*, pg. 302

Morton, Richard, Exec. V.P.--Moran Industries, Inc., Midlothian, IL; *U.S. Private*, pg. 760

Morton, William, Exec. V.P., Mngmt. Rep.--Vitt Media International, Inc., New York, NY; *U.S. Private*, pg. 1142

Morwin, Klaus, Dr., Exec. V.P.-Detergent & Household Cleansers--Henkel KGaA, Dusseldorf, Germany; *Int'l*, pg. 609

Moschini, Andrea, Exec. Dir.-Prod.--Bulgari SPA, Rome, Italy; *Int'l*, pg. 232

Moseley, Ellis E., Exec. V.P.--Freeman Decorating Co., Dallas, TX; *U.S. Private*, pg. 426

Moser, Michael J., Exec. V.P.--Trans Financial, Inc., Bowling Green, KY; *U.S. Public*, pg. 1628

Moser, Mike, Exec. V.P.--Goldberg Moser O'Neill, San Francisco, CA; *U.S. Private*, pg. 459

Moser, Robert W., Exec. V.P.--Springs Industries, Inc., Fort Mill, SC; *U.S. Public*, pg. 1499

Moser, Robert W., Exec. V.P.-Bath Fashions--Home Furnishings Segment, Fort Mill, SC; *U.S. Public*, pg. 1500

Moses, Senn, Exec. V.P.-Mktg.--Universal Studios Recreation Services Group, Universal City, CA; *Int'l*, pg. 1216

Mosier, Jerry, Exec. V.P. & Copy Chief--Keyes Martin, East Hanover, NJ; *U.S. Private*, pg. 618

Mosig Zambrano, Guillermo, Exec. V.P.-Sls., Office Prods.--Grupo Casa Autrey, Mexico, Mexico; *Int'l*, pg. 573

Moskal, Alfred J., Exec. V.P.-Gemchem, Inc.--American Vanguard Corporation, Newport Beach, CA; *U.S. Public*, pg. 94

Moske, Klaus, Exec. V.P.--Wella Group, Darmstadt, Germany; *Int'l*, pg. 1489

Mosley, John, Chief Fin. Officer & Exec. V.P.--Sheplers, Inc., Wichita, KS; *U.S. Private*, pg. 993

Mosner, Lawrence J., Exec. V.P.--Deluxe Corporation, Shoreview, MN; *U.S. Public*, pg. 498

Moss, Dale, Exec. V.P.-Sls. & Mktg.--British Airways, Flushing, NY; *Int'l*, pg. 219

Moss, Wendy, Sr. V.P.-Mktg./Sony Wonder--Sony Music Entertainment, Inc., New York, NY; *Int'l*, pg. 1281

Mossberg, Per, Exec. V.P.-Corp. & Mktg. Communications--Telia AB, Farsta, Sweden; *Int'l*, pg. 1373

Mostek, Charles F., Exec. V.P.-Fresh Meats Sls. & Mktg.--IBP, Inc., Dakota City, NE; *U.S. Public*, pg. 852

Mottern, Chris, Exec. V.P.-Spirits & Wines--Heublein, Inc., Hartford, CT; *Int'l*, pg. 410

Moulie, Pierre, Sr. Exec. V.P.-Human Resources--Electricite de France, Paris, France; *Int'l*, pg. 437

Moulton, Hugh G., Exec. V.P.--Ikon Office Solutions, Inc., Malvern, PA; *U.S. Public*, pg. 862

Moulton, Hugh G., Chief Admin. Officer & Exec. V.P.--Unisource Worldwide, Inc., Berwyn, PA; *U.S. Public*, pg. 1670

Moulton, John, Exec. V.P.-Mfg.--Robert Bosch Corporation, Broadview, IL; *Int'l*, pg. 204

Moynahan, John D., Jr., Exec. V.P.-Group Insurance--Metropolitan Life Insurance Co., New York, NY; *U.S. Private*, pg. 737

Moynihan, Stephen H., V.P. & Treas.--Clean Harbors, Inc., Braintree, MA; *U.S. Public*, pg. 383

Moynot, Alain, Exec. V.P.-Domestic Network--Banque Nationale de Paris, Paris, France; *Int'l*, pg. 163

Mozilo, Ralph S., Chief Underwriting & Compliance Officer & Exec. V.P.--Countrywide Home Loans Inc., Pasadena, CA; *U.S. Public*, pg. 452

Muchnick, Alberto, Exec. V.P.--Republic National Bank of New York, New York, NY; *U.S. Public*, pg. 1380

Muchow, James L., Exec. V.P.--Commercial National Bank of Berwyn, Berwyn, IL; *U.S. Public*, pg. 379

Mucke, B., Exec. V.P.--Braas GmbH, Oberursell, Germany; *Int'l*, pg. 1091

Muehlbauer, James H., Exec. V.P.--George Koch Sons, Inc., Evansville, IN; *U.S. Private*, pg. 628

Mueller, David B., Chief Oper. Officer & Exec. V.P.--Spartech Corporation, Clayton, MO; *U.S. Public*, pg. 1495

Mueller, Gerd D., Chief Fin. Officer, Chief Admin. Officer & Exec. V.P.--Bayer Corporation, Pittsburgh, PA; *Int'l*, pg. 172

Mueller, Gerd D., Chief Admin. & Fin. Officer & Exec. V.P.--Bayer Corporation, Pittsburgh, PA; *Int'l*, pg. 172

Mueller, Gerd D., Chief Fin. Officer, Chief Admin. Officer & Exec. V.P.--Bayer Corporation, Parsippany, NJ; *Int'l*, pg. 172

Mueller, Peter, Exec. V.P.-Mfg.--Stihl Inc., Virginia Beach, VA; *Int'l*, pg. 1301

Mueller, Richard E., Exec. V.P.-Sls.--Mulberry Metal Products, Inc., Union, NJ; *U.S. Private*, pg. 766

Mueller, Robert J., Sr. Exec. V.P.--The Bank of New York Company, Inc., New York, NY; *U.S. Public*, pg. 178

Mueller, Robert J., Exec. V.P.-External Affairs & Bus. Devel.--International Rectifier Corporation, El Segundo, CA; *U.S. Public*, pg. 906

Muguerza, Jose, Chief Oper. Officer & Exec. V.P.--Rymer Meat Inc., Chicago, IL; *U.S. Public*, pg. 1414

Muhlhauser, Eckhard E., Exec. V.P.--ChemDesign Corporation, Fitchburg, MA; *Int'l*, pg. 173

Muir Gonzalez, Ian C., Exec. V.P.--Bufete Industrial S.A. de C.V., Mexico, Mexico; *Int'l*, pg. 232

Muir, Tom, Chief Fin. Officer & Exec. V.P.--Maple Leaf Foods Inc., Toronto, Canada; *Int'l*, pg. 841

Mukasa, Shinji, Exec. V.P.--Obayashi Corporation, Tokyo, Japan; *Int'l*, pg. 995

Mulcahy, Michael R., Exec. V.P.--Trans-Lux Corporation, Norwalk, CT; *U.S. Public*, pg. 1628

Mulchay, Patrick J., Exec. V.P.--NIPSCO Industries, Inc., Hammond, IN; *U.S. Public*, pg. 1185

Mulchay, Patrick J., Chief Oper. Officer & Exec. V.P.--Northern Indiana Public Service Company, Hammond, IN; *U.S. Public*, pg. 1185

Mulder, Kees, Exec. V.P.--Colorbus Inc., Irvine, CA; *U.S. Private*, pg. 255

Muldoon, Greg, Chief Oper. Officer & Exec. V.P.--Browning-Ferris Industries, Inc., Houston, TX; *U.S. Public*, pg. 262

Mullane, Tom, Exec. V.P.--Springfield Precision Instruments, Inc., Wood Ridge, NJ; *U.S. Private*, pg. 1027

Mullenbach, Gerald, Exec. V.P.--Harris Contracting Co., Saint Paul, MN; *U.S. Private*, pg. 505

Muller, Eric, Exec. V.P.-Fin. & Admin.--Sulzer Ltd., Winterthur, Switzerland; *Int'l*, pg. 1305

Muller, Heinz, Exec. V.P.-Commercial Banking--Union Bank of Switzerland, Zurich, Switzerland; *Int'l*, pg. 1439

Muller, Rudolf G., Exec. V.P.-Europe--Union Bank of Switzerland, Zurich, Switzerland; *Int'l*, pg. 1439

Muller, Steven R., Exec. V.P.--Centex Real Estate Corp./Centex Homes, Dallas, TX; *U.S. Public*, pg. 323

Mulligan, Peter K., Exec. V.P.-Consumer Banking--Webster Financial Corporation, Waterbury, CT; *U.S. Public*, pg. 1751

Mullis, Elbert N., Jr., Chief Fin. & Admin. Officer, Exec. V.P. & Treas.--Coca-Cola Bottling Co. United, Inc., Birmingham, AL; *U.S. Private*, pg. 248

Mulroy, Richard, Sr. V.P. & Gen. Counsel--The Mutual Life Insurance Company of New York, New York, NY; *U.S. Private*, pg. 769

Munday, Anthony E., Chief Fin. Officer & Exec. V.P.--Inco Limited, Toronto, Canada; *Int'l*, pg. 672

Munday, Warren, Chief Fin. Officer & Exec. V.P.--CHF Industries, Inc., New York, NY; *U.S. Private*, pg. 1094

Mundt, G. Henry, III, Exec. V.P.-Global Debit Services--Mastercard International, Inc., Purchase, NY; *U.S. Private*, pg. 714

Munekuni, Yoshihide, Exec. V.P. & Rep. Dir.--Honda Motor Co., Ltd., Tokyo, Japan; *Int'l*, pg. 634

Mungo, Billy, Exec. V.P.--Michael J. Mungo Company, Inc., Irmo, SC; *U.S. Private*, pg. 767

Mungon, Terrance P., Exec. V.P.-Equity Lending Grp.--Western Financial Bank, Irvine, CA; *U.S. Public*, pg. 1757

Mungon, Terry, Exec. V.P.-Consumer Lending--Westcorp, Irvine, CA; *U.S. Public*, pg. 1756

Munoz, Carlos R., Chief Credit Officer & Exec. V.P.--The Dime Savings Bank of New York, New York, NY; *U.S. Public*, pg. 509

Munsell, William A., Exec. V.P.--Genmar Holdings, Inc., Minneapolis, MN; *U.S. Private*, pg. 447

Murai, Masayoshi, Exec. V.P.--YKK Corporation, Tokyo, Japan; *Int'l*, pg. 1514

Murakami, Masatoshi, Exec. Dir.--Dentsu Inc., Tokyo, Japan; *Int'l*, pg. 392

Murakami, Takuo, Sr. Mng. Dir.--NSK Ltd., Tokyo, Japan; *Int'l*, pg. 903

Muramatsu, Makoto, Exec. V.P.--Nippon Express Co., Ltd., Tokyo, Japan; *Int'l*, pg. 933

Murano, Koichi, Exec. V.P.--Seiko Corporation, Tokyo, Japan; *Int'l*, pg. 1218

Murdy, James L., Chief Fin. Officer & Exec. V.P.-Fin. & Admin.--Allegheny Teledyne Incorporated, Pittsburgh, PA; *U.S. Public*, pg. 43

Murdy, Wayne W., Chief Fin. Officer & Exec. V.P.--Newmont Mining Corporation, Denver, CO; *U.S. Public*, pg. 1178

Murdy, Wayne W., Chief Fin. Officer & Exec. V.P.--Newmont Gold Company, Denver, CO; *U.S. Public*, pg. 1179

Murn, Edward J., Exec. V.P.--Mercantile Mortgage Corp., Baltimore, MD; *U.S. Public*, pg. 1089

Murnane, George, III, Chief Fin. Officer & Exec. V.P.--International Airline Support Group, Inc., Atlanta, GA; *U.S. Public*, pg. 894

Murphy, David E., Exec. V.P.--Owned Television Stations, New York, NY; *U.S. Private*, pg. 148

Murphy, Evelyn, Exec. V.P.-Corp. Affairs--Blue Cross and Blue Shield of Massachusetts, Boston, MA; *U.S. Private*, pg. 151

Murphy, Evelyn F., Exec. V.P.-Corp. Affairs--Physician Partners of New England, Inc., Boston, MA; *U.S. Private*, pg. 151

Murphy, Jack, Exec. V.P.-Govern. Managed Care--PHP Healthcare Corporation, Reston, VA; *U.S. Public*, pg. 1241

Murphy, John J., Chief Fin. Officer, Exec. V.P. & Treas.--Arrow Financial Corporation, Glens Falls, NY; *U.S. Public*, pg. 135

Murphy, John, Jr., Chm.--First Trust National Association, Saint Paul, MN; *U.S. Public*, pg. 1681

Murphy, Lawrence P., Chief Strategic Officer & Exec. V.P.--The Walt Disney Company, Burbank, CA; *U.S. Public*, pg. 511

Murphy, Melissa, Exec. V.P. & Global Bus. Dir.-Citibank--J. Walter Thompson Company, New York, NY; *Int'l*, pg. 1483

Murphy, Patrick T., Exec. V.P.--Western Regional Off Track Betting, Batavia, NY; *U.S. Private*, pg. 1168

Murphy, Paul S., Exec. V.P.--P.T. Freeport Indonesia Co., New Orleans, LA; *U.S. Public*, pg. 681

Murphy, William, Chief Fin. Officer, Exec. V.P. & Sec.--Computer Horizons Corp., Mountain Lakes, NJ; *U.S. Public*, pg. 421

Murray, David, Exec. V.P.-U.S. Sls. & Prod. Mktg.--The Dun & Bradstreet Corporation, Murray Hill, NJ; *U.S. Public*, pg. 535

Murray, David, Exec. V.P.--Dun & Bradstreet, Murray Hill, NJ; *U.S. Public*, pg. 535

Murray, F.W. Jr., Exec. V.P.--SouthTrust Corporation, Birmingham, AL; *U.S. Public*, pg. 1491

Murray, Kenneth R., Exec. V.P.-Community Banking--Norwest Corporation, Minneapolis, MN; *U.S. Public*, pg. 1201

Murray, Malcolm T., Chief Credit Officer & Exec. V.P.--First Union Corporation, Charlotte, NC; *U.S. Public*, pg. 639

Murray, Mark, Exec. V.P.-Mktg. & Sls.--FAG Bearings Corporation, Danbury, CT; *Int'l*, pg. 469

Murray, Martin, Exec. V.P.--Community Bio-Resources, Hoover, AL; *U.S. Public*, pg. 196

Murray, Michael, Exec. V.P.--Tandy Leather Co., Fort Worth, TX; *U.S. Public*, pg. 1561

Murray, Robert C., Chief Fin. Officer & Exec. V.P.--Public Service Enterprise Group Incorporated, Newark, NJ; *U.S. Public*, pg. 1340

Murrell, Mike, Partner, Exec. V.P. & Dir.-Integrated Svcs.--Miller Meester Advertising Inc., Minneapolis, MN; *U.S. Private*, pg. 747

Murren, James J., Chief Fin. Officer & Exec. V.P.--MGM Grand, Inc., Las Vegas, NV; *U.S. Public*, pg. 1026

Murrin, Stephanie, Exec. V.P. & Creative Dir.--Dugan Valva Contess Inc., Morristown, NJ; *U.S. Private*, pg. 345

Musa, Edson Vaz, Exec. V.P.--Rhone-Poulenc S.A., Courbevoie, France; *Int'l*, pg. 1108

Museler, William J., Exec. V.P.-Transmission & Power Supply Grp.--Tennessee Valley Authority, Knoxville, TN; *U.S. Public*, pg. 1580

Muselman, Roger, Exec. V.P.-Sls.--E.P. Graphics, Inc., Berne, IN; *U.S. Private*, pg. 354

Muselman, Thomas, Exec. V.P.-Mfg.--E.P. Graphics, Inc., Berne, IN; *U.S. Private*, pg. 354

Musgrave, William, Chief Oper. Officer & Exec. V.P.--Hendrick Automotive Group, Charlotte, NC; *U.S. Private*, pg. 522

Musick, Ronald E., Exec. V.P.--Wendy's International Inc., Dublin, OH; *U.S. Public*, pg. 1754

Muskovich, John A., Exec. V.P.--The Elder-Beerman Stores Corp., Dayton, OH; *U.S. Private*, pg. 367

Musselman, John, Exec. V.P.--G. Leblanc Corporation, Kenosha, WI; *U.S. Private*, pg. 656

Mussenden, Felix, Exec. V.P. & Gen. Mgr.--Universal Studios Music Australia, Sydney, Australia; *Int'l*, pg. 1216

Mutch, Robert E., Exec. V.P.--Curtiss-Wright Corp., Lyndhurst, NJ; *U.S. Public*, pg. 469

Muth, Robert, Exec. V.P.-Opers.--Marine Midland Bank, Buffalo, NY; *Int'l*, pg. 581

Muzarco, Frank, Exec. V.P.--Steinway Musical Instruments, Inc., Waltham, MA; *U.S. Public*, pg. 1514

Muzyczko, T., Exec. V.P.--Samuel Bingham Co, Bloomingdale, IL; *U.S. Private*, pg. 144

Mycoff, Chuck, Exec. V.P.-Client Service--Focus Media, Santa Monica, CA; *U.S. Private*, pg. 415

Myers, Dennis A., Exec. V.P.--Nalleys Fine Foods, Tacoma, WA; *U.S. Private*, pg. 887

Myers, John A., Exec. V.P.-Canada, Individual Bank CIBC--Canadian Imperial Bank of Commerce, Toronto, Canada; *Int'l*, pg. 256

Myers, Philip R., Sr. Exec. V.P.--Provident Financial Group, Inc., Cincinnati, OH; *U.S. Public*, pg. 1338

Myers, Philip R., Sr. Exec. V.P.--The Provident Bank, Cincinnati, OH; *U.S. Public*, pg. 1338

Myers, Robert L., Chief Oper. Officer & Exec. V.P.--Priority Healthcare Corporation, Altamonte Springs, FL; *U.S. Public*, pg. 229

Myracle, Richard N., Chief Oper. Officer & Exec. V.P.--McKinney & Silver, Raleigh, NC; *U.S. Private*, pg. 723

Myrby, Seth, Exec. V.P.-Telecom Services--Telia AB, Farsta, Sweden; *Int'l*, pg. 1373

Nabors, James D., Chief Fin. Officer & Exec. V.P.--Russell Corporation, Alexander City, AL; *U.S. Public*, pg. 1413

Nachman, G., Exec. V.P.--Curtiss-Wright Corp., Lyndhurst, NJ; *U.S. Public*, pg. 469

Nadal, Christian, Exec. V.P.-Corp. Communication & Pub. Affairs--Electricite de France, Paris, France; *Int'l*, pg. 437

Nadeau, Marie-Jose, Exec. V.P.-Human Resources--Hydro-Quebec, Montreal, Canada; *Int'l*, pg. 640

Nadel, George, Chief Fin. Officer, Exec. V.P. & Treas.--Jennifer Convertibles Inc., Woodbury, NY; *U.S. Public*, pg. 926

Naeve, Stephen W., Chief Fin. Officer & Exec. V.P.--Houston Industries Incorporated, Houston, TX; *U.S. Public*, pg. 842

Naftaly, Robert H., Chief Fin. Officer & Exec. V.P.--Blue Cross & Blue Shield of Michigan, Detroit, MI; *U.S. Private*, pg. 151

Nagamoto, Takao, Exec. V.P.--The Chugoku Electric Power Co., Inc., Hiroshima, Japan; *Int'l*, pg. 291

Nagano, Hironori, Exec. V.P.--Dentsu USA Inc.-New York, New York, NY; *Int'l*, pg. 393

Nagano, Sunao, Exec. V.P.--Marubeni Corporation, Osaka, Japan; *Int'l*, pg. 844

Nagatoshi, Hisashi, Exec. V.P.--Tokyu Corporation, Tokyo, Japan; *Int'l*, pg. 1394

Nagayasu, Hideo, Exec. V.P.--Fuji Bank (Mexico) S.A., Mexico, Mexico; *Int'l*, pg. 521

Nagel, Chris, Exec. V.P.-Science & Tech.--Molten Metal Technology, Inc., Fall River, MA; *U.S. Public*, pg. 1123

Nagel, Joe, Chief Oper. Officer & Exec. V.P.--US Ecology, Inc., Houston, TX; *U.S. Public*, pg. 71

Nagel, Vernon J., Chief Fin. Officer, Exec. V.P.-Fin. & Treas.--Kuhlman Corporation, Savannah, GA; *U.S. Public*, pg. 968

Nagin, Lawrence M., Exec. V.P.-Corp. Affairs & Gen. Counsel--US Airways Group, Inc., Arlington, VA; *U.S. Public*, pg. 1680

Nagle, T.W., Exec. V.P.-Fin. & Admin.--Reading & Bates Corporation, Houston, TX; *U.S. Public*, pg. 1354

Nagler, Herbert, Exec. V.P.--Bayerische Hypotheken-und Wechsel-Bank Aktiengesellschaft, Munich, Germany; *Int'l*, pg. 175

Nagler, Stewart G., Chief Fin. Officer & Sr. Exec. V.P.--Metropolitan Life Insurance Co., New York, NY; *U.S. Private*, pg. 737

Nagorske, Lynn A., Exec. V.P.--TCF Bank Minnesota FSB, Minneapolis, MN; *U.S. Public*, pg. 1554

Nagumo, Masayuki, Exec. V.P.--Kyowa Hakko U.S.A., Inc., New York, NY; *Int'l*, pg. 778

Nahara, Tsuyoshi, Exec. V.P.--Nippon Life Insurance Co., Osaka, Japan; *Int'l*, pg. 934

Nahirny, Michael, Chief Fin. Officer & Exec. V.P.-Fin. & Admin.--Cara Operations Limited, Toronto, Canada; *Int'l*, pg. 266

Nahkunst, Michael, Chief Oper. Officer & Exec. V.P.--Cheesecake Factory Incorporated, Calabasas Hills, CA; *U.S. Public*, pg. 343

Nahmias, R., Exec. V.P.--Gentex Optics, Inc., Simpson, PA; *Int'l*, pg. 462

Nairn, Brian, Exec. V.P.-Business Publications--Reed Elsevier Business Information, Newton, MA; *Int'l*, pg. 1095

Naismith, Linda, Exec. V.P. & Sec.--American Passage Media Corporation, Seattle, WA; *U.S. Private*, pg. 60

Najim, Edward L., Exec. V.P.-Sls. & Mktg.--Horace Mann Educators Corporation, Springfield, IL; *U.S. Public*, pg. 835

Nakagaki, Eisei, Exec. V.P.-Mktg.--Casio, Inc., Dover, NJ; *Int'l*, pg. 274

Nakagawa, Jean H., Exec. V.P.-Corp.--Servco Pacific Inc., Honolulu, HI; *U.S. Private*, pg. 986

Nakagawa, Takao, Exec. V.P.--Aoki Corporation, Tokyo, Japan; *Int'l*, pg. 78

Nakagome, Ryuzo, Exec. V.P.--Takenaka Corporation, Osaka, Japan; *Int'l*, pg. 1351

Nakahara, Asuka, Chief Fin. Officer & Exec. V.P.--Trammell Crow Company, Dallas, TX; *U.S. Public*, pg. 1628

Nakajima, Shigeo, Exec. V.P.--Nippon Paper Industries Company Limited, Tokyo, Japan; *Int'l*, pg. 937

Nakajima, Takashi, Exec. V.P.--Kajima Corporation, Tokyo, Japan; *Int'l*, pg. 721

Nakamoto, Arlene M., Exec. V.P.-Sls. & Mktg.--American Savings Bank, F.S.B., Honolulu, HI; *U.S. Public*, pg. 800

Nakamura, Akikazu, Exec. V.P.-Tech.--Kawasaki Heavy Industries, Ltd., Kobe, Japan; *Int'l*, pg. 725

Nakamura, Hideaki, Exec. V.P.--The Fuji Bank & Trust Co., New York, NY; *Int'l*, pg. 519

Nakamura, Mark, Exec. V.P.--Sure Save Super Market Ltd., Keaau, HI; *U.S. Private*, pg. 1056

Nakamura, Naoki, Exec. V.P.--Fuji Electric Co., Ltd., Tokyo, Japan; *Int'l*, pg. 522

Nakamura, Ryuhei, Exec. V.P-Textile Grp.--Marubeni Corporation, Osaka, Japan; *Int'l*, pg. 844

Nakamura, Shinichiro, Exec. V.P.--Kyushu Electric Power Co., Inc., Fukuoka, Japan; *Int'l*, pg. 778

Nakaprom, Kulthon, Exec. V.P.--Siam City Bank Public Company Limited, Bangkok, Thailand; *Int'l*, pg. 1239

Nakash, Avi, Exec. V.P.--Jordache Enterprises, Inc., New York, NY; *U.S. Private*, pg. 597

Nakashoji, Masataka, Sr. Exec. Dir.--Sumitomo Bank (Schweiz) AG, Zurich, Switzerland; *Int'l*, pg. 1310

Nakata, Shinji, Exec. V.P.--Haseko Corporation, Tokyo, Japan; *Int'l*, pg. 599

Nakata, Takeshi, Exec. V.P.--Toyobo Co., Ltd., Osaka, Japan; *Int'l*, pg. 1411

Nakatsuka, Ralph Y., Exec. V.P.-Lending & Fin.--American Savings Bank, F.S.B., Honolulu, HI; *U.S. Public*, pg. 800

Nalle, Ned, Exec. V.P.-Univeral TV--Universal Studios TV, Universal City, CA; *Int'l*, pg. 1215

Nally, Mike, Exec. V.P.--Carl M. Freeman Associates, Inc., Potomac, MD; *U.S. Private*, pg. 426

Namchaisiri, Julaporn, Sr. Exec. V.P.--SCF Finance & Securities Co., Ltd., Bangkok, Thailand; *Int'l*, pg. 1239

Namiki, Tadao, Sr. Exec. V.P.--Asahi Glass Co., Ltd., Tokyo, Japan; *Int'l*, pg. 84

Nan, Tan Soo, Sr. Exec. V.P.-Corp. Fin., Ivestments & Trust Services--DBS Bank Ltd., Singapore, Singapore; *Int'l*, pg. 350

Nanula, Richard D., Chief Fin. Officer & Sr. Exec. V.P.--The Walt Disney Company, Burbank, CA; *U.S. Public*, pg. 511

Napoli, Jim, Exec. V.P.-Leasing--Simon DeBartolo Group, Inc., Indianapolis, IN; *U.S. Public*, pg. 1474

Napoli, Paul K., Exec. V.P.--U.S. Trust Corporation, New York, NY; *U.S. Public*, pg. 1688

Naporano, Joseph A., Chief Fin. Officer, Chief Oper. Officer & Exec. V.P.--Long Haymes Carr, Inc., Winston Salem, NC; *U.S. Public*, pg. 909

Naquin, Michael A., Exec. V.P.--Central Bank of Monroe, Monroe, LA; *U.S. Public*, pg. 629

Naquin, Michael A., Exec. V.P.--Rapides Bank & Trust Company of Alexandria, Alexandria, LA; *U.S. Public*, pg. 630

Narasaki, Masahiro, Exec. V.P.--The Kansai Electric Power Co., Inc., Osaka, Japan; *Int'l*, pg. 722

Nasky, H. Gregory, Exec. V.P. & Sec.--Showboat, Incorporated, Las Vegas, NV; *U.S. Public*, pg. 1469

Nasky, Thomas G., Exec. V.P.-Mktg. & Sls.--Dualite Inc., Williamsburg, OH; *U.S. Private*, pg. 344

Nasky, Thomas G., Exec. V.P.-Sls. & Mktg.--Dualite Sales & Service, Inc., Williamsburg, OH; *U.S. Private*, pg. 344

Nasser, Jacques A., Exec. V.P.--Ford Motor Company, Dearborn, MI; *U.S. Public*, pg. 661

Nassetta, Christopher J., Exec. V.P.--Host Marriott Corporation, Bethesda, MD; *U.S. Public*, pg. 841

Nast, Bill, Exec. V.P.-Sls. & Mktg.--Tech Industries, Inc., Woonsocket, RI; *U.S. Private*, pg. 1071

Nathanson, David, Exec. V.P. & Creative Dir.-DDB Needham--The Bank of New York Company, Inc., New York, NY; *U.S. Public*, pg. 178

Natsumeda, Tsuneyoshi, Exec. V.P.-Affiliate Rels., Property & Legal Affairs--Nihon Keizai Shimbun, Inc., Tokyo, Japan; *Int'l*, pg. 929

Nau, Donald H., Jr., Exec. V.P.--Waffle House, Incorporated, Norcross, GA; *U.S. Private*, pg. 1146

Nauber, Noel, Exec. V.P. & Exec. Creative Dir.--DMB&B Detroit, Troy, MI; *U.S. Private*, pg. 302

Navarro, Bernabe L. Jr., Chief Oper. & Fin. Officer & Exec. V.P.--La Tondena Distillers, Inc., Manila, Philippines; *Int'l, pg. 785*

Nayden, Denis J., Exec. V.P.--General Electric Capital Services, Inc., Stamford, CT; *U.S. Public*, pg. 711

Nayden, Denis J., Exec. V.P.--G.E. Capital Commercial Real Estate Financing, Stamford, CT; *U.S. Public*, pg. 712

Neag, Raymond, Exec. V.P.--Arrow International, Inc., Reading, PA; *U.S. Public*, pg. 135

Neal, George E., Exec. V.P.-Investment Opers.--Manulife Financial, Toronto, Canada; *Int'l*, pg. 840

Nearpass, Paul, Exec. V.P.--Grayline Housewares, Carol Stream, IL; *U.S. Private*, pg. 472

Neeb, L.A., Exec. V.P.--Chrysler Credit Corp., Southfield, MI; *U.S. Public*, pg. 354

Needham, Timothy, Exec. V.P.--American Pad and Paper Company, Dallas, TX; *U.S. Public*, pg. 88

Neels, Jan K., Exec. V.P.-AirTouch Intl.--AirTouch Communications, Inc., San Francisco, CA; *U.S. Public*, pg. 34

Neels, Jan K., Exec. V.P.--AirTouch International, Walnut Creek, CA; *U.S. Public*, pg. 34

Nees, Bernard J., Exec. V.P.--Johnston, Lemon & Co. Inc., Washington, DC; *U.S. Private*, pg. 595

Negri, Gian Piero, Exec. V.P.-Asset Mngmt.--Istituto Bancario San Paolo Di Torino S.p.A., Turin, Italy; *Int'l*, pg. 691

Nehring, Maynard, Exec. V.P.--Pepsi-Cola General Bottlers, Inc., Rolling Meadows, IL; *U.S. Public*, pg. 1277

Neidus, Stuart D., Chief Fin. Officer & Exec. V.P.--Essef Corporation, Chardon, OH; *U.S. Public*, pg. 592

Neil, Robert F., Exec. V.P.-Radio--Cox Broadcasting Inc., Atlanta, GA; *U.S. Private*, pg. 281

Neil, Robert W., Exec. V.P.--CACI International Inc, Arlington, VA; *U.S. Public*, pg. 272

Neill, Arthur K., Exec. V.P.-Generation & Transmission--Montana Power Company, Butte, MT; *U.S. Public*, pg. 1126

Neill, Thomas A., Corp. Exec. V.P.-Indus. Prods. & Services Grp.--Fiserv, Inc., Brookfield, WI; *U.S. Public*, pg. 647

Neilson, Martin F., Exec. V.P. & Mgr.-Consumer Assets Div.--Seafirst Corporation, Seattle, WA; *U.S. Public*, pg. 181

Neiman, John C., Exec. V.P.-National Industries--Compass Bank, Birmingham, AL; *U.S. Public*, pg. 418

Neithercut, D.J., Chief Fin. Officer & Exec. V.P.--Equity Residential Properties Trust, Chicago, IL; *U.S. Public*, pg. 590

Nelman, Richard, Exec. V.P. & Gen. Counsel--Waterhouse Investor Services, New York, NY; *Int'l*, pg. 1401

Nelson, Bob, Exec. V.P.-Brdcst. Production--Lowe & Partners/SMS, New York, NY; *U.S. Private*, pg. 678

Nelson, Bruce, Exec. V.P.--McCann-Erickson Worldwide, New York, NY; *U.S. Public*, pg. 909

Nelson, Frank J., Exec. V.P.--SunTrust, Orlando, FL; *U.S. Public*, pg. 1537

Nelson, J. Calvin, Chief Oper. Officer & Exec. V.P.--Logan Corporation, Huntington, WV; *U.S. Private*, pg. 672

Nelson, Jana L., Exec. V.P.& Corp. Sec.--Oxarc Inc., Spokane, WA; *U.S. Private*, pg. 825

Nelson, Kenneth P., Exec. V.P. & Grp. Pres.--Bremer Financial Corporation, Saint Paul, MN; *U.S. Private*, pg. 167

Nelson, L. Scott, Exec. V.P.-Investor Rels.--First Security Corporation, Salt Lake City, UT; *U.S. Public*, pg. 637

Nelson, Larry W., Exec. V.P.-Devel.--CommScope, Inc., Hickory, NC; *U.S. Public*, pg. 415

Nelson, William H., Chief Oper. Officer & Exec. V.P.--Intermountain Health Care Inc., Salt Lake City, UT; *U.S. Private*, pg. 568

Nen, Richard W., Chief Fin. Officer & Exec. V.P.--Charter One Bank, Cleveland, OH; *U.S. Public*, pg. 336

Nergaard, Leiv L., Chief Fin. Officer & Exec. V.P.--Norsk Hydro a.s, Oslo, Norway; *Int'l*, pg. 959

Neskey, David A., Chief Fin. Officer & Exec. V.P.--Spaulding & Slye, Boston, MA; *U.S. Private*, pg. 1021

Neuhoff, Robert, Exec. V.P.--Fahnestock & Co., Inc., New York, NY; *Int'l*, pg. 476

Neumann, Jurgen, Exec. V.P.--Balcke-Durr Kuhlturmbau Leipzig GmbH, Leipzig, Germany; *Int'l*, pg. 400

Neumann, Thomas, Exec. V.P.--The Sherwood Group, Inc., Jersey City, NJ; *U.S. Public*, pg. 1466

Neuner, Mark C., Exec. V.P. & Dir.-Res.--Jefferies & Company, Inc., Los Angeles, CA; *U.S. Public*, pg. 925

Neuschaefer, Thomas H., Chief Fin. Officer & Exec. V.P.--First Financial Bank, FSB, Stevens Point, WI; *U.S. Public*, pg. 140

Neutzling, John, Exec. V.P.-Property Mngmt.--Simon DeBartolo Group, Inc., Indianapolis, IN; *U.S. Public*, pg. 1474

Nevin, John, Exec. V.P.-Opers.--Fieldcrest Cannon, Inc., Kannapolis, NC; *U.S. Public*, pg. 1296

Nevsimal, Charles J., Exec. V.P.-Sls. & Mktg--Wisconsin Pharmacal Co., Inc., Jackson, WI; *U.S. Private*, pg. 1185

Newberry, Stephen, Chief Oper. Officer & Exec. V.P.--Lam Research Corporation, Fremont, CA; *U.S. Public*, pg. 975

Newbold, Philip, Chief Oper. Officer & Exec. V.P.--Data Dimensions, Inc., Culver City, CA; *U.S. Public*, pg. 485

Newell, D.K., Exec. V.P.--Northwestern Growth Corp., Sioux Falls, SD; *U.S. Public*, pg. 1201

Newey, Francois, Exec. V.P.-Fin.--Pechiney S.A., Courbevoie, France; *Int'l*, pg. 1027

Newhouse, Herbert A., Exec. V.P.--Domain Energy Corporation, Houston, TX; *U.S. Public*, pg. 515

Newi, George H., Exec. V.P.-Affiliate Rels.--ABC Television Network, New York, NY; *U.S. Public*, pg. 511

Newman, Arthur E., Exec. V.P.--Waverly, Inc., Baltimore, MD; *U.S. Public*, pg. 1748

Newman, Eric H., Exec. V.P. & Legal Counsel--Bojangles' Restaraunts, Inc., Charlotte, NC; *U.S. Private*, pg. 154

Newman, Gary, Exec. V.P.-Human Resources--Information Resources, Inc., Chicago, IL; *U.S. Public*, pg. 875

Newman, Gary L., Exec. V.P.-Sls., Sls. Promo. & Direct Mktg.--Cooper Communities, Inc., Bella Vista, AR; *U.S. Private*, pg. 273

Newman, Jack A., Jr., Exec. V.P.-Client Organization--Cerner Corporation, Kansas City, MO; *U.S. Public*, pg. 331

Newman, John, Exec. V.P.-Specialty Banking--ABN/LaSalle North America Inc., Chicago, IL; *Int'l*, pg. 11

Newman, Larry, Exec. V.P.-Mktg. & Sls.-Angelica Image Apparel--Angelica Corporation, Chesterfield, MO; *U.S. Public*, pg. 113

Newman, Larry, Exec. V.P.-Mktg. & Sls.--Angelica Image Apparel, Saint Louis, MO; *U.S. Public*, pg. 113

Newman, Larry M., Chief Oper. Officer--Call Interactive, Omaha, NE; *U.S. Public*, pg. 631

Newmann, Dennis, Exec. V.P.--The Bank of New York Company, Inc., New York, NY; *U.S. Public*, pg. 178

Newmark, Amy, Exec. V.P.-Strategic Plng.--Winstar Communications, New York, NY; *U.S. Public*, pg. 1772

Newrkla, Johannes, Exec. V.P. & Creative Dir.--Demner, Merlicek & Bergmann Werbegesellschaft mbH, Vienna, Austria; *Int'l*, pg. 392

Newsome, J.I., Exec. V.P.-North America--Nedlloyd Lines B.V., Rotterdam, Netherlands; *Int'l*, pg. 1145

Newton, Christopher C., Exec. V.P.--Transico Incorporated, Santa Ana, CA; *U.S. Public*, pg. 1630

Neyzi, Mehmet Ali, Exec. V.P.-Mktg.--Arcelik A.S., Istanbul, Turkey; *Int'l*, pg. 741

Nezu, Yukio, Sr. Mng. Dir.--Daido Steel Co., Ltd., Nagoya, Japan; *Int'l*, pg. 364

Ng, Benjamin M.T., Exec. V.P. & Asst. Sec.--Tommy Hilfiger Corporation, Kowloon, Hong Kong; *Int'l*, pg. 1398

Ngandee, Suthira, Exec. V.P.--The Industrial Finance Corporation of Thailand, Bangkok, Thailand; *Int'l*, pg. 677

Nguyen, Khoa, Chief Oper. Officer & Exec. V.P.--VideoServer, Inc., Burlington, MA; *U.S. Public*, pg. 1720

Niblack, John F., Ph.D., Exec. V.P.--Pfizer Inc., New York, NY; *U.S. Public*, pg. 1281

Nic Vold, Johan, Grp. Exec. V.P.--Statoil, Stavanger, Norway; *Int'l*, pg. 1297

Nichol, Josh, Exec. V.P. & Gen. Mgr.--Hoffman/Lewis, San Francisco, CA; *U.S. Private*, pg. 532

Nicholas, Charles R., Chief Fin. Officer & Exec. V.P.-Fin./Admin.--Andrew Corporation, Orland Park, IL; *U.S. Public*, pg. 112

Nicholl, Donald G.E., Exec. V.P.--Pall Corporation, Greenvale, NY; *U.S. Public*, pg. 1253

Nichols, Gerald L., Chief Oper. Officer & Exec. V.P.--CSX Transportation, Inc., Jacksonville, FL; *U.S. Public*, pg. 284

Nichols, Jim, Exec. V.P.--The Coon-De Visser Co., Royal Oak, MI; *U.S. Private*, pg. 273

Nicholson, Bob, Exec. V.P.--Toronto Blue Jays Baseball Club, Inc., Toronto, Canada; *Int'l*, pg. 680

Nicholson, Bruce J., Chief Oper. Officer & Exec. V.P.--Lutheran Brotherhood, Minneapolis, MN; *U.S. Private*, pg. 681

Nicolai, Frank A., Chief Fin. Officer & Exec. V.P.--American Management Systems, Inc., Fairfax, VA; *U.S. Public*, pg. 86

Nicolas, Jean-Louis, Sr. Exec. V.P.--Lafarge PlatresInternational, Sorges, France; *Int'l*, pg. 789

Nicolosi, John, Exec. V.P.-Construction--The Kaempfer Company, Investment Builders, Washington, DC; *U.S. Private*, pg. 604

Nicolson, Ian M., Exec. V.P. & Gen. Mgr.-High Value Products Division--North American Van Lines, Inc., Fort Wayne, IN; *U.S. Public*, pg. 1191

Niehaus, Robert P., Exec. V.P.--Fifth Third Bancorp, Cincinnati, OH; *U.S. Public*, pg. 621

Nields, Charles, Exec. V.P.-Direct Bus. Grp.--Physicians Mutual Insurance Co., Omaha, NE; *U.S. Private*, pg. 864

Nielsen, Judith Doering, Sr. V.P. & Senior Credit Officer--SJNB Financial Corp., San Jose, CA; *U.S. Public*, pg. 1418

Nielsen, Soren Bjerre, Chief Fin. Officer & Exec. V.P.--Danisco A/S, Copenhagen, Denmark; *Int'l*, pg. 378

Nielson, Gary W., Chief Fin. Officer & Exec. V.P.--Price Enterprises, Inc., San Diego, CA; *U.S. Public*, pg. 1324

Niemayer, W. Phil, Chief Fin. Officer & Exec. V.P.-Sls.--Nasco International, Inc., Fort Atkinson, WI; *U.S. Private*, pg. 446

Niemela, Juha, Exec. V.P.--United Paper Mills Ltd., Valkeakoski, Finland; *Int'l*, pg. 1429

Niemeyer, Phil, Exec. V.P.--Nasco Modesto, Modesto, CA; *U.S. Private*, pg. 446

Niemeyer, W. Pil, Chief Fin. Officer & Exec. V.P.--Nasco, Fort Atkinson, WI; *U.S. Private*, pg. 446

Niemiec, Jeff, Exec. V.P.--Ingrid Division of Lawnware, Morton Grove, IL; *U.S. Private*, pg. 654

Nierenberg, Bruce W., Exec. V.P.--Norwegian Cruise Line, Miami, FL; *U.S. Private*, pg. 808

Nightingale, Glen, Exec. Dir.--Pilkington Plc, Saint Helens, United Kingdom; *Int'l*, pg. 1056

Niijima, Kohichi, Sr. Mng. Dir.--NSK Ltd., Tokyo, Japan; *Int'l*, pg. 903

Nilsen, Douglas N., Exec. V.P.-Mdsg.--Big Dog Holdings Inc., Santa Barbara, CA; *U.S. Public*, pg. 227

Nilsson, Stefan, Exec. V.P.-Reg. Bank, Northern Norrland--Svenska Handelsbanken, Stockholm, Sweden; *Int'l*, pg. 1327

Nipp, Heinz, Chief Exec. Officer & Exec. V.P.-Fin.--Liechtenstein Global Trust Limited, Vaduz, Liechtenstein; *Int'l*, pg. 809

Nippes, K.N., Exec. V.P. & Gen. Mgr.--Vapor, Niles, IL; *U.S. Public*, pg. 1761

Nishida, Masao, Exec. V.P.--Teijin Limited, Osaka, Japan; *Int'l*, pg. 1362

Nishida, Masayuki, Exec. V.P.--The Green Cross Corporation, Osaka, Japan; *Int'l*, pg. 558

Nishigaki, Kouji, Exec. V.P.--NEC Corporation, Tokyo, Japan; *Int'l*, pg. 899

Nishiyama, Reitaro, Exec. V.P.--Takenaka Corporation, Osaka, Japan; *Int'l*, pg. 1351

Nishizaki, Seijiro, Exec. V.P.--YKK Corporation, Tokyo, Japan; *Int'l*, pg. 1514

Nishizawa, Yasunori, Exec. V.P.--Oki Electric Industry Company, Ltd., Tokyo, Japan; *Int'l*, pg. 999

Nistendirk, Jack, Chief Fin. Officer & Exec. V.P.--J.H. Fletcher & Co., Huntington, WV; *U.S. Private*, pg. 412

Nitschke, Albrecht, Exec. V.P.-European Opers.--Nielsen Design GmbH, Rheda-Wiedenbruck, Germany; *Int'l*, pg. 462

Nitta, Kenjiro, Exec. V.P.--NEC Corporation, Tokyo, Japan; *Int'l*, pg. 899

Nitti, Raymond M., Exec. V.P.--Joe E. Woods, Inc., Mesa, AZ; *U.S. Private*, pg. 1187

Nivert, Marianne, Exec. V.P.-Corp. Network Services--Telia AB, Farsta, Sweden; *Int'l*, pg. 1373

Nixon, James, Exec. V.P.--Cosmair, Inc., New York, NY; *Int'l*, pg. 818

Nizich, Amy, Exec. V.P. & Reg. Brcst. Dir.--Western International Media Corporation, Los Angeles, CA; *U.S. Private*, pg. 1165

Noble, H. Lee, Exec. V.P. & Pres.-Polymers Division--Bayer Corporation, Pittsburgh, PA; *Int'l*, pg. 172

Noble, H. Lee, Pres.-Polymers Div. & Exec. V.P.--Bayer Corporation, Pittsburgh, PA; *Int'l*, pg. 172

Noble, H. Lee, Exec. V.P. & Pres.-Polymers Div.--Bayer Corporation, Parsippany, NJ; *Int'l*, pg. 172

Noble, Mark, Exec. V.P.-Construction Prods.--Sika Corporation, Lyndhurst, NJ; *Int'l*, pg. 1249

Noda, Tadayoshi, Exec. V.P.--Sumitomo Metal Industries, Ltd., Tokyo, Japan; *Int'l*, pg. 1315

Noddle, Jeffrey, Exec. V.P., Pres. & Chief Oper. Officer-Wholesale Food Companies--SuperValu, Inc., Eden Prairie, MN; *U.S. Public*, pg. 1540

Node-Langlois, Patrick, Exec. V.P.-Environment & Public Affairs--Lafarge S.A., Paris, France; *Int'l*, pg. 788

Noden, Philip Thomas, Exec. Dir.--Sanderson Technology Ltd., Sheffield, United Kingdom; *Int'l*, pg. 1184

Noe, Brad, Exec. V.P.-Sls. & Mktg.--Henredon Furniture Industries, Inc., Morganton, NC; *U.S. Private*, pg. 493

Noe, Daniel R., Exec. V.P. & Chief Credit Officer--Starbanc Corporation, Cincinnati, OH; *U.S. Public*, pg. 1510

Noel, Michael L., Exec. V.P.--Mission Land Company, Irvine, CA; *U.S. Public*, pg. 564

Noels, Jacques, Exec. V.P.--Bull S.A., Louveciennes, France; *Int'l*, pg. 315

Noels, Jaques, Exec. V.P.--Compagnie des Machines Bull, Louveciennes, France; *Int'l*, pg. 315

Noguchi, Teruhisa, Exec. V.P.--Yamanouchi Pharmaceutical Co. Ltd., Tokyo, Japan; *Int'l*, pg. 1518

Nolind, Richard, Exec. V.P.--Merle Norman Cosmetics, Inc., Los Angeles, CA; *U.S. Private*, pg. 733

Noll, William B., Chief Fin. Officer & Exec. V.P.--GMAC Insurance Holdings, Detroit, MI; *U.S. Public*, pg. 719

Nomura, Akio, Exec. V.P.--Osaka Gas Co., Ltd., Osaka, Japan; *Int'l*, pg. 1011

Nomura, Shigeru, Exec. V.P.--Minebea Co., Ltd., Tokyo, Japan; *Int'l*, pg. 867

Nontapunthawat, Nimit, Exec. V.P. & Gen. Mgr.--Bangkok Bank Public Company Limited, Bangkok, Thailand; *Int'l*, pg. 146

Nooney, Charles, Sr. V.P.-Sls. & Mktg.--The Disney Channel, Burbank, CA; *U.S. Public*, pg. 513

Norberg, Paul A., Chief Fin. Officer & Exec. V.P.--Western Staff Services, Walnut Creek, CA; *U.S. Public*, pg. 1760

Nordhoff, Carroll, Exec. V.P.--McCormick & Company, Incorporated, Sparks, MD; *U.S. Public*, pg. 1066

Nordin, Bengt, Exec. V.P.--Korsnas AB, Gavle, Sweden; *Int'l*, pg. 759

Nordloh, Gary L., Exec. V.P.--Questar Corporation, Salt Lake City, UT; *U.S. Public*, pg. 1352

Nordstrand, Anders, Exec. V.P.-Tech.--Mo och Domsjo AB, Stockholm, Sweden; *Int'l*, pg. 885

Nordstrom, Lars G., Deputy Chief Exec. Officer & Exec. V.P.--Nordbanken AB, Stockholm, Sweden; *Int'l*, pg. 957

Nordyke, David H., Exec. V.P.--Commercial National Bank, Shreveport, LA; *U.S. Public*, pg. 500

Noris, Peter D., Exec. V.P. & Chief Investment Officer--The Equitable Companies Incorporated, New York, NY; *U.S. Public*, pg. 588

Norishita, Hikodama, Exec. V.P.--Fuji Heavy Industries, Ltd., Tokyo, Japan; *Int'l*, pg. 522

Norling, James A., Exec. V.P. & Pres.-Messaging, Info. & Media--Motorola, Inc., Schaumburg, IL; *U.S. Public*, pg. 1136

Norman, G.R., Exec. V.P. (GEIM)--General Electric Investment Corp., Stamford, CT; *U.S. Public*, pg. 712

Normile, Michael T., Exec. V.P.-Fin.--Mercantile Bank of St. Louis N.A., Saint Louis, MO; *U.S. Public*, pg. 1087

Norris, David G., Exec. V.P.-Fin. & Bus. Devel.--Fishery Products International Ltd., Saint Johns, Canada; *Int'l*, pg. 492

Norris, David W., Exec. V.P.--Precision Castparts Corp., Portland, OR; *U.S. Public*, pg. 1320

Norris, Michael, Exec. V.P. & Gen. Mgr.--Loews Theatre Management Corp., New York, NY; *Int'l*, pg. 1282

Norris, Robin G., Exec. V.P.-Strategic Plng.--Zellers Inc., Toronto, Canada; *Int'l*, pg. 637

North, William A., Exec. V.P.--C.R. Anthony Company, Oklahoma City, OK; *U.S. Private*, pg. 1029

Norton, Donn H., Exec. V.P.-Real Estate--The Chubb Corporation, Warren, NJ; *U.S. Public*, pg. 354

Norton, Richard G., Exec. V.P. & Mng. Officer--First National Bank of Ohio, Akron, OH; *U.S. Public*, pg. 646

Noskin, Steven, Exec. V.P.--Polymer Plastics Corporation, Hauppauge, NY; *U.S. Private*, pg. 875

Notarides, Susan, Exec. V.P.-Licensing & Mdsg.--Metro-Goldwyn-Mayer Inc., Santa Monica, CA; *U.S. Public*, pg. 1101

Notarides, Susan, Exec. V.P.--MGM/UA Licensing & Merchandising, Santa Monica, CA; *U.S. Public*, pg. 1102

Notarnicola, Jim, Exec. V.P.-Mktg.--Blockbuster Entertainment Group, Dallas, TX; *U.S. Private*, pg. 775

Novack, Kenneth M., Pres.-Schnitzer Investment Corp. & Exec. V.P.-Schnitzer Steel--Schnitzer Steel Industries, Inc., Portland, OR; *U.S. Public*, pg. 1439

Novak, George P., Exec. V.P. & Dir.--The Robinson-Humphrey Company, Inc., Atlanta, GA; *U.S. Public*, pg. 1633

Novak, L.A., Exec. V.P.-Opers.--Clearing-Niagara, Buffalo, NY; *U.S. Private*, pg. 196

Novak, Paul, Exec. V.P.-Aquisitions--Patriot American Hospitality, Inc., Dallas, TX; *U.S. Public*, pg. 1265

Novak, William T., Exec. V.P.-Admin.--Riverdale Chemical Co., Glenwood, IL; *U.S. Private*, pg. 934

Novello, R.J., Exec. V.P.--Emerson Electric Co., Saint Louis, MO; *U.S. Public*, pg. 572

Novick, Stephen A., Exec. V.P.-Creative Svcs.--Grey Advertising Inc., New York, NY; *U.S. Public*, pg. 764

Novinski, Edward J., Exec. V.P.-Managed Care--Medpartners Inc., Birmingham, AL; *U.S. Public*, pg. 1082

Novotny, Eva, Exec. V.P.-Sls. & Mktg.--Medstone International, Inc., Aliso Viejo, CA; *U.S. Public*, pg. 1082

Nowak, Paul J., Exec. V.P.--VWR Scientific Products, West Chester, PA; *U.S. Public*, pg. 1703

Nozko, Henry W., Jr., Chief Oper. Officer, Exec. V.P. & Treas.--ACMAT Corporation, New Britain, CT; *U.S. Public*, pg. 16

Nozoe, Yuki, Exec. V.P.--Sony Pictures Entertainment, Culver City, CA; *Int'l*, pg. 1281

Nucian, Richard, Exec. V.P.--Norman Levy Associates, Inc., Southfield, MI; *U.S. Private*, pg. 664

Nudam, Freck, Sr. Exec. V.P.--Atlas Copco AB, Stockholm, Sweden; *Int'l*, pg. 95

Nugent, Charles J., Chief Fin. Officer & Exec. V.P.--Fulton Financial Corp., Lancaster, PA; *U.S. Public*, pg. 687

Numata, Kenji, Exec. V.P.--Hanwa Co., Ltd., Tokyo, Japan; *Int'l*, pg. 595

Nunziata, Charles, Exec. V.P.--Vernitron Sensor Systems, Saint Petersburg, FL; *U.S. Public*, pg. 157

Nurmimaki, Kalervo, Exec. V.P.--Imatran Voima Oy, Helsinki, Finland; *Int'l*, pg. 660

Nussdorf, Lawrence C., Exec. V.P. & Treas.--Clark Enterprises, Inc., Bethesda, MD; *U.S. Private*, pg. 242

Nussrallah, John R., Exec. V.P.--Trinity Railcar Leasing, Dallas, TX; *U.S. Public*, pg. 1639

Nutting, Ron, Exec. V.P.--OMNI Products, Inc., Portland, OR; *U.S. Private*, pg. 816

Nuzum, Jerry, Exec. V.P.--CAP Gemini America, New York, NY; *Int'l*, pg. 263

Nylander, Mark, Exec. V.P. & Gen. Mgr.--Liggett-Stashower Public Relations, Cleveland, OH; *U.S. Private*, pg. 667

Nylander, Mark C., Exec. V.P. & Gen. Mgr. Pub. Rels.--Liggett-Stashower, Inc., Cleveland, OH; *U.S. Private*, pg. 667

Nyren, Anders, Exec. V.P.-Fin. & Economy--Skanska AB, Danderyd, Sweden; *Int'l*, pg. 1260

O'Brien, John M., Exec. V.P. & Deputy Gen. Mgr.--The New York Times, New York, NY; *U.S. Public*, pg. 1174

O'Brien, John P., Exec. V.P.--CalFarm Insurance Company, Sacramento, CA; *U.S. Public*, pg. 1791

O'Brien, Judy, Sr. V.P.-Managed Health Solutions--Robert A. Becker, New York, NY; *Int'l*, pg. 601

O'Brien, Kevin P., Exec. V.P.-Independents--Cox Broadcasting Inc., Atlanta, GA; *U.S. Private*, pg. 281

O'Brien, Mark J., Chief Oper. Officer & Exec. V.P.--Pulte Corporation, Bloomfield Hills, MI; *U.S. Public*, pg. 1344

O'Brien, Michael W., Exec. V.P.-Sunoco Grp.--Suncor Inc., Calgary, Canada; *Int'l*, pg. 1320

O'Bryan, Henry E., Exec. V.P.--Owensboro Grain Co., Inc., Owensboro, KY; *U.S. Private*, pg. 824

O'Bryan, Stephen F., Exec. V.P.--O'Bryan Brothers Inc., Chicago, IL; *U.S. Private*, pg. 810

O'Byrne, L.F., Exec. V.P.--MidCon Gas Services Corp., Houston, TX; *U.S. Public*, pg. 1210

O'Connell, Kevin P., Exec. V.P. & Chief Mktg. Officer--UNUM Corporation, Portland, ME; *U.S. Public*, pg. 1699

O'Connell, Kevin P., Exec. V.P.--UNUM Life Insurance Company of America, Portland, ME; *U.S. Public*, pg. 1699

O'Connell, Michael, Chief Fin. Officer, Chief Admin. Officer & Exec. V.P.--Advanced Polymer Systems, Redwood City, CA; *U.S. Public*, pg. 22

O'Connor, John, Chief Exec. Officer & Exec. Gen. Mgr.--BHP Petroleum, Melbourne, Australia; *Int'l*, pg. 224

O'Connor, John P., Chief Credit Officer & Exec. V.P.--First Tennessee National Corporation, Memphis, TN; *U.S. Public*, pg. 638

O'Connor, John P., Exec. V.P. & Chief Credit Officer--First Tennessee Bank National Association, Memphis, TN; *U.S. Public*, pg. 639

O'Connor, Thomas P., Exec. V.P.--Springs Industries, Inc., Fort Mill, SC; *U.S. Public*, pg. 1499

O'Connor, Thomas P., Exec. V.P.-Bed Fashions--Home Furnishings Segment, Fort Mill, SC; *U.S. Public*, pg. 1500

O'Dell, Don, Exec. V.P. & Mngmt. Supvr.--Stern Advertising, Inc., Cleveland, OH; *U.S. Private*, pg. 1041

O'Dell, Ervin E., Exec. V.P.--Westfall GMC Truck Inc., Kansas City, MO; *U.S. Private*, pg. 1169

O'Dell, Mark, Exec. V.P.--Westfall GMC Truck Inc., Kansas City, MO; *U.S. Private*, pg. 1169

O'Donnell, Gene, Exec. V.P.-Mdsg.--TruServ Corporation, Chicago, IL; *U.S. Private*, pg. 1108

O'Donnell, James V., Chief Oper. Officer & Exec. V.P.--Gap Stores Division, San Bruno, CA; *U.S. Public*, pg. 702

O'Donovan, V.A., Exec. Dir.--Rockware Group Plc, London, United Kingdom; *Int'l*, pg. 124

O'Gorman, Peter J., Exec. V.P.-Intl. Store & Prod. Devel.--The Great Atlantic & Pacific Tea Company, Inc., Montvale, NJ; *Int'l*, pg. 1375

O'Gorman, Timothy, Exec. V.P.--ABN AMRO Chicago Corp., Chicago, IL; *Int'l*, pg. 10

O'Gorman, Timothy, Exec. V.P.--ABN AMRO Chicago Corp Financial Services, Chicago, IL; *Int'l*, pg. 10

O'Grady, Jeremiah P., Exec. V.P.--Jefferies & Company, Inc., Los Angeles, CA; *U.S. Public*, pg. 925

O'Hare, Edward J., Exec. V.P.--Fortis, Inc., New York, NY; *Int'l*, pg. 499

O'Keefe, T. Scott, Chief Fin. & Info. Officer & Exec. V.P.--Marine Drilling Companies, Inc., Sugar Land, TX; *U.S. Public*, pg. 1044

O'Leary, Carolyn D., Exec. V.P.--The Annapolis Banking & Trust Co., Annapolis, MD; *U.S. Public*, pg. 1088

O'leary, Dan, Chief Fin. Officer & Exec. V.P.--Pueblo Xtra International, Inc., Pompano Beach, FL; *U.S. Private*, pg. 894

O'Leary, Michael a., Exec. Dir.--Rio Tinto PLC, London, United Kingdom; *Int'l*, pg. 1118

O'Malia, David T., Exec. V.P. & Gen. Counsel--O'Malia Food Markets Inc., Carmel, IN; *U.S. Private*, pg. 816

O'Malia, Dennis S., Exec. V.P.--O'Malia Food Markets Inc., Carmel, IN; *U.S. Private*, pg. 816

O'Malley, John C., Exec. V.P.--Dain Rauscher Incorporated, Minneapolis, MN; *U.S. Public*, pg. 476

O'Meara, John M., Chief Oper. Officer & Exec. V.P.--First Midwest Bancorp, Inc., Itasca, IL; *U.S. Public*, pg. 636

O'Meara, Spencer, Exec. V.P.--Hunt Corporation, Philadelphia, PA; *U.S. Public*, pg. 848

O'Meara, Vicki A., Exec. V.P. & Gen. Counsel--Ryder System, Inc., Miami, FL; *U.S. Public*, pg. 1413

O'Neal, E. Stanley, Exec. V.P.--Merrill Lynch & Co., Inc., New York, NY; *U.S. Public*, pg. 1097

O'Neal, Larry, Exec. V.P. & Exec. Creative Dir.--Stern Advertising, Inc., Cleveland, OH; *U.S. Private*, pg. 1041

O'Neil, Christopher, Exec. V.P.-Opers.--Sound Advice, Inc., Dania, FL; *U.S. Public*, pg. 1488

O'Neil, Roger, Grp. Exec. V.P.--Statoil, Stavanger, Norway; *Int'l*, pg. 1297

O'Neil, Thomas J., Exec. V.P.-Opers.--Cleveland-Cliffs Inc, Cleveland, OH; *U.S. Public*, pg. 386

O'Neill, Brian, Exec. V.P. & Creative Dir.--Goldberg Moser O'Neill, San Francisco, CA; *U.S. Private*, pg. 459

O'Neill, James A., Exec. V.P. & Dir.--The Robinson-Humphrey Company, Inc., Atlanta, GA; *U.S. Public*, pg. 1633

O'Neill, Tim, Exec. V.P. & Chief Economist--Bank of Montreal, Toronto, Canada; *Int'l*, pg. 153

O'Neill, William J., Jr., Pres.-Bus. Devel. & Exec. V.P.--Polaroid Corporation, Cambridge, MA; *U.S. Public*, pg. 1313

O'Rourke, William J., Exec. V.P.--North Central Crane & Excavator Sales Corp., Mokena, IL; *U.S. Public*, pg. 1041

O'Shaughnessy, Joseph A., Sr. Exec. V.P.--Friendly Ice Cream Corp., Wilbraham, MA; *U.S. Public*, pg. 682

O'Toole, Timothy S., Exec. V.P. & Treas.--Chemed Corporation, Cincinnati, OH; *U.S. Public*, pg. 343

O"Donnell, John P., Dr., Exec. V.P.--Mylan Pharmaceuticals Inc., Morgantown, WV; *U.S. Public*, pg. 1143

Oakley, Bruce, Exec. V.P.--Bruce Oakley, Inc., North Little Rock, AR; *U.S. Private*, pg. 809

Oakley, W. Flake, IV, Chief Fin. Officer, Exec. V.P., Treas. & Sec.--The Colonial BancGroup, Inc., Montgomery, AL; *U.S. Public*, pg. 400

Obata, Shigeki, Exec. V.P. & Representative Dir.--Mycal, Corp., Osaka, Japan; *Int'l*, pg. 897
Obenberger, Robert L., Exec. V.P. & Gen. Mgr.--Four-S Baking Company, Los Angeles, CA; *U.S. Private*, pg. 422
Obermiller, Gary J., Exec. V.P.--Deltak Inc., Plymouth, MN; *U.S. Public*, pg. 924
Oberting, Gary, Exec. V.P.--Interstate Commodities Inc., Troy, NY; *U.S. Private*, pg. 573
Oberting, V.A., Jr., Pres.--Interstate Commodities Inc., Troy, NY; *U.S. Private*, pg. 573
Oder, Kenneth W., Exec. V.P.-Labor Rels., Human Resources, Law & Pub. Affairs--Safeway Inc., Pleasanton, CA; *U.S. Public*, pg. 1426
Odgers, Richard W., Exec. V.P., Gen. Counsel & Sec.--Pacific Telesis Group, San Francisco, CA; *U.S. Public*, pg. 1415
Odlaug, Theron, Ph.D., Chief Oper. Officer & Exec. V.P.--Fujisawa U.S.A., Deerfield, IL; *Int'l*, pg. 525
Odle, John H., Exec. V.P.-Commercial, Mfg. & Pur.--RMI Titanium Company, Niles, OH; *U.S. Public*, pg. 1662
Odom, William, Co-Chm. Bd. & Exec. V.P.--The Odom Corporation, Seattle, WA; *U.S. Private*, pg. 811
Odom, William, Exec. V.P.--Anchorage Cold Storage Co., Anchorage, AK; *U.S. Private*, pg. 812
Oertli, Roger S., Exec. V.P.-Construction Div.--Guarantee Electrical Company, Saint Louis, MO; *U.S. Private*, pg. 485
Oestreicher, Paul, Exec. V.P.--Edelman Public Relations Worldwide, Chicago, IL; *U.S. Private*, pg. 362
Ofeloch, Charles, Exec. V.P.--Beverly Bancorporation Inc., Chicago, IL; *U.S. Public*, pg. 227
Offermann, Peter, Chief Fin. Officer & Exec. V.P.--TLC Beatrice International Holdings Inc., New York, NY; *U.S. Private*, pg. 1064
Officer, J. David, Exec. V.P.-Mellon Private Asset Mngmt.--Mellon Bank Corporation, Pittsburgh, PA; *U.S. Public*, pg. 1084
Ogan, Roby, Chief Fin. Officer & Sr. Exec. V.P.--TeleCheck Services, Inc., Houston, TX; *U.S. Public*, pg. 631
Ogard, Bjorn, Exec. V.P.--Trelleborg AB, Trelleborg, Sweden; *Int'l*, pg. 1419
Ogasawara, Yasuyuki, Exec. V.P. & Treas.--Mitsubishi International Corporation, New York, NY; *Int'l*, pg. 871
Ogata, Yuji, Exec. V.P.--Kansai Paint Co., Ltd., Osaka, Japan; *Int'l*, pg. 723
Ogawa, Kinya, Exec. V.P.--Shimizu Corporation, Tokyo, Japan; *Int'l*, pg. 1233
Ogawa, Kunio, Exec. V.P.-Energy Grp.--Marubeni Corporation, Osaka, Japan; *Int'l*, pg. 844
Ogawa, Yutaka, Sr. Exec. V.P.--Meiji Seika Kaisha, Ltd., Tokyo, Japan; *Int'l*, pg. 855
Ogg, Larry B., Exec. V.P. & Mgr.-Human Resources Grp.--Seafirst Corporation, Seattle, WA; *U.S. Public*, pg. 181
Ogg, Thomas, Exec. V.P.--Motorists Mutual Insurance Co., Columbus, OH; *U.S. Private*, pg. 764
Ogg, Thomas C., Chief Oper. Officer & Exec. V.P.--American Hardware Mutual Insurance Co., Columbus, OH; *U.S. Private*, pg. 764
Ogi, Takeshichi, Exec. V.P.--Minebea Co., Ltd., Tokyo, Japan; *Int'l*, pg. 867
Ogilvie, Donald, Exec. V.P.--The American Bankers Association, Washington, DC; *U.S. Private*, pg. 51
Oglethorpe, Ray, Exec. V.P.--Redgate Communications Corp., Vero Beach, FL; *U.S. Public*, pg. 66
Ogletree, Terry L., Exec. V.P.-Intl.--Entergy Corporation, New Orleans, LA; *U.S. Public*, pg. 585
Oh, Hosoo, Exec. V.P.--Daewoo Securities Co., Ltd., Seoul, Korea; *Int'l*, pg. 358
Ohba, Nobuo, Exec. V.P.--Daido Steel Co., Ltd., Nagoya, Japan; *Int'l*, pg. 364
Ohbayashi, Takeo, Exec. V.P.--Obayashi Corporation, Tokyo, Japan; *Int'l*, pg. 995
Ohira, Akira, Exec. V.P.--Taisho Pharmaceutical Co., Ltd., Tokyo, Japan; *Int'l*, pg. 1348
Ohishi, Yasuhiro, Exec. V.P.--Toyobo Co., Ltd., Osaka, Japan; *Int'l*, pg. 1411
Ohjimi, Shozo, Exec. V.P.--Ishikawajima-Harima Heavy Industries Co., Ltd., Tokyo, Japan; *Int'l*, pg. 689
Ohki, Makio, Exec. V.P--Sapporo Breweries Ltd., Tokyo, Japan; *Int'l*, pg. 1193
Ohno, Shinji, Sr. Exec. Dir.--The Japan Development Bank, Tokyo, Japan; *Int'l*, pg. 701
Ohori, Ken, Exec. V.P.-U.S.--Tsumura & Co., Tokyo, Japan; *Int'l*, pg. 1425
Ohshima, Hiroshi, Exec. Dir.--Isuzu Motors Limited, Tokyo, Japan; *Int'l*, pg. 692
Ohsone, Kozo, Exec. Deputy Pres.--Sony Corporation, Tokyo, Japan; *Int'l*, pg. 1280
Ohtake, Takashi, Exec. V.P.--Koito Manufacturing Co., Tokyo, Japan; *Int'l*, pg. 743
Ohtsuki, Mikio, Exec. V.P. & Rep. Dir.--Fujitsu Limited, Tokyo, Japan; *Int'l*, pg. 525
Okada, Beverly, Exec. V.P. & Mng. Partner-Creative--Wells BDDP, Inc., New York, NY; *Int'l*, pg. 117
Okada, Hajime, Exec. V.P.--Chubu Electric Power Company, Inc., Nagoya, Japan; *Int'l*, pg. 290
Okada, Kenji, Exec. V.P.--Tohoku Electric Power Co., Ltd., Sendai, Japan; *Int'l*, pg. 1390
Okada, Natsuo, Exec. V.P.--Sumitomo Bank Financial Services, Inc., New York, NY; *Int'l*, pg. 1308
Okada, Natsuo, Exec. V.P.--Sumitomo Bank Securities, Inc., New York, NY; *Int'l*, pg. 1309
Okajima, N., Sr. Exec. V.P.-Opers.--Dunlop Tire Corporation, Buffalo, NY; *Int'l*, pg. 1317
Okamamoto, Kiichi, Exec. V.P.--Murata Machinery, Ltd., Kyoto, Japan; *Int'l*, pg. 897
Okamoto, Koya, Exec. V.P.--Mitsubishi Motors Corporation, Tokyo, Japan; *Int'l*, pg. 875
Okano, Masayoshi, Deputy Pres.--Chiba Kogyo Bank, Chiba, Japan; *Int'l*, pg. 283
Okano, Mitsutake, Exec. V.P. & Dir.-Admin. & Internal Audit--Mitsubishi Corporation, Tokyo, Japan; *Int'l*, pg. 871
Okatomi, Takeshi, Exec. V.P.--Toshiba Corporation, Tokyo, Japan; *Int'l*, pg. 1402
Oketani, Taiichi, Exec. V.P.--Banco Sumitomo Brasileiro S.A., Sao Paulo, Brazil; *Int'l*, pg. 1310
Okijima, Iwao, Exec. V.P.--Toyota Motor Corporation, Tokyo, Japan; *Int'l*, pg. 1411
Okorn, Dennis W., Exec. V.P.--GAI Consultants, Inc., Monroeville, PA; *U.S. Private*, pg. 433
Okoso, Teruchika, Exec. V.P.--Nippon Meat Packers, Inc., Osaka, Japan; *Int'l*, pg. 936
Okubo, Kazuo, Exec. V.P.--Toyo Seikan Kaisha, Ltd., Tokyo, Japan; *Int'l*, pg. 1411
Okubo, Mitsuya, Exec. V.P.--Minebea Co., Ltd., Tokyo, Japan; *Int'l*, pg. 867
Okun, Fred, Exec. V.P.-Sls.--Mattel, Inc., El Segundo, CA; *U.S. Public*, pg. 1057
Okuyama, Toshihiro, Exec. V.P.--Nisshin Steel Co., Ltd., Tokyo, Japan; *Int'l*, pg. 946
Olander, Gary M., Exec. V.P.-Comml. Real Estate--Compass Bank Houston, Houston, TX; *U.S. Public*, pg. 419
Oldano, Ugo, Exec. V.P.-Receipts--Istituto Bancario San Paolo Di Torino S.p.A., Turin, Italy; *Int'l*, pg. 691
Oldfather, David R., Exec. V.P.-Opers.--Tristate Electrical Supply Co., Inc., Hagerstown, MD; *U.S. Private*, pg. 1104
Oldham, Dennis M., Chief Fin. Officer & Exec. V.P.--Willis Corroon Melling Inc., Montreal, Canada; *Int'l*, pg. 1509
Olegen, Robert W., Chief Fin. Officer & Exec.V.P.--Renaissance Hotel Group N.V., Central, Hong Kong; *U.S. Public*, pg. 1048
Olesen, Jens, Exec. V.P. & Reg. Dir.-Latin America--McCann-Erickson Worldwide, New York, NY; *U.S. Public*, pg. 909
Olesnavage, Mark P., Exec. V.P.--L. Perrigo Company, Allegan, MI; *U.S. Public*, pg. 1280
Olinger, Jack, Exec. V.P.-Adv.--The Hammerblow Corp., Wausau, WI; *U.S. Private*, pg. 498
Oliphant, Randall, Chief Fin. Officer & Exec. V.P.--Barrick Gold Corporation, Toronto, Canada; *Int'l*, pg. 168
Oliver, E.Vic, Exec. V.P.-Opers--ComputerLand Canada, Brampton, Canada; *Int'l*, pg. 1154
Oliver, Paul W., Jr., Exec. V.P.--ABN AMRO Chicago Corp., Chicago, IL; *Int'l*, pg. 10
Oliver, R. John, Exec. V.P & Acct. Svcs. Dir.--Ross Roy Communications, Inc., Bloomfield Hills, MI; *U.S. Private*, pg. 946
Oliver, Robert, Exec. V.P.-Stores--McRae's, Inc., Jackson, MS; *U.S. Public*, pg. 1333
Olivier, Louison, Exec. V.P. & Pres.-Groundwood Opers. & Sls.--Abitibi-Consolidated Inc., Montreal, Canada; *Int'l*, pg. 19
Olmo, Luis Del, Exec. V.P.-Mktg.--Sol Melia, Palma de Mallorca, Spain; *Int'l*, pg. 1277
Olpak, Ahmet, Exec. V.P.-Pur.--Arcelik A.S., Istanbul, Turkey; *Int'l*, pg. 741
Olsen, Ernest, Exec. V.P.--Arnold Steel Company, Inc., Lakewood, NJ; *U.S. Private*, pg. 84
Olsen, Rhoda, Exec. V.P.-Franchise Svc.--Great Clips, Inc., Minneapolis, MN; *U.S. Private*, pg. 473
Olsen, Robert M., Jr., Exec. V.P.-Opers. & Technology--Magna Group, Inc., Saint Louis, MO; *U.S. Public*, pg. 1037
Olsen, Ronald Y., Exec. V.P.--First American Title Co. of Los Angeles, Glendale, CA; *U.S. Public*, pg. 625
Olson, Don, Exec. V.P.-Prods. Div.--Peacock Inc., La Salle, Canada; *Int'l*, pg. 1489
Olson, Gene L., Chief Fin. Officer & Exec. V.P.--Golden State Foods, Irvine, CA; *U.S. Private*, pg. 460
Olson, John R., Chief Fin. Officer & Exec. V.P.--Farmers & Merchants Bank of Central California, Lodi, CA; *U.S. Private*, pg. 394
Olson, Larry D., Exec. V.P. & Pres.-Kent Components--Kent Electronics Corp., Houston, TX; *U.S. Public*, pg. 951
Olson, Norman, Exec. V.P. & Media Dir.--Harris Drury Cohen, Fort Lauderdale, FL; *U.S. Private*, pg. 505
Olson, Terry, Exec. V.P.-Sls. & Mktg.--Brothers Gourmet Coffees, Inc., Boca Raton, FL; *U.S. Public*, pg. 259
Olson, Timothy J., Exec. V.P.--F&G Re, Inc., Morristown, NJ; *U.S. Public*, pg. 1659
Olsson, Dave, Exec. V.P. & Creative Dir.--Marketing Support, Incorporated, Chicago, IL; *U.S. Private*, pg. 705
Olsson, Roland, Exec. V.P.-Product Area Payments--Nordbanken AB, Stockholm, Sweden; *Int'l*, pg. 957
Oman, Mark C., Exec. V.P.--Norwest Corporation, Minneapolis, MN; *U.S. Public*, pg. 1201
Omori, Yasuharu, Exec. V.P. & Gen. Mgr.--Dentsu, Sudler & Hennessey Inc., Tokyo, Japan; *U.S. Private*, pg. 325
Omura, Tsutomu, Exec. V.P.--Fuji Photo Film Co., Ltd., Tokyo, Japan; *Int'l*, pg. 523
Ono, Allen K., Exec. V.P.-Admin.--American Savings Bank, F.S.B., Honolulu, HI; *U.S. Public*, pg. 800
Ono, Mikiya, Exec. V.P.--Mitsubishi Materials Corp., Tokyo, Japan; *Int'l*, pg. 874
Onodera, Shinichi, Exec. V.P.--Fuji Bank Canada, Toronto, Canada; *Int'l*, pg. 521
Ophey, Lothar, Dr. Ing., Exec. V.P.-Prod.--Traub AG, Reichenbach, Germany; *Int'l*, pg. 1419
Oppenheimer, Deanna W., Exec. V.P.-Corp. Mktg. & Consumer Bank Div.--Washington Mutual Inc., Seattle, WA; *U.S. Public*, pg. 1741
Oran, Frederic M., Chief Oper. Officer & Exec. V.P.--Industrial Acoustics Company, Inc., Bronx, NY; *U.S. Public*, pg. 875
Oran, Stuart I., Exec. V.P.-Corp. Affairs--UAL Corporation, Elk Grove Village, IL; *U.S. Public*, pg. 1652
Orange, Larry J., Exec. V.P.--Foremost Corporation of America, Caledonia, MI; *U.S. Public*, pg. 667
Orange, Larry J., Exec. V.P.--Foremost Financial Services Corp., Grand Rapids, MI; *U.S. Public*, pg. 667
Orchard, James A., Exec. V.P.-Prof. Programs Div.--Poe & Brown, Inc., Daytona Beach, FL; *U.S. Public*, pg. 1312
Orell, Lawrence, Exec. V.P. & Media Dir.--The Lord Group, New York, NY; *U.S. Private*, pg. 325
Oren, Beverly J., Exec. V.P.--Dart Transit Company, Eagan, MN; *U.S. Private*, pg. 311
Orenstein, Steven, Chief Fin. Officer & Exec. V.P.--DavisElen Advertising, Inc., Los Angeles, CA; *U.S. Private*, pg. 316
Oria y Barros, Jorge, Exec. V.P.-Corp. Devel. & Fin. Plng.--Grupo Casa Autrey, Mexico, Mexico; *Int'l*, pg. 573
Oringer, Kenneth W., Chief Fin. Officer, Exec. V.P. & Treas.--U.S. Security Associates, Inc., Roswell, GA; *U.S. Private*, pg. 1126
Orito, Haruo, Exec. V.P.--Meiji Seika Kaisha, Ltd., Tokyo, Japan; *Int'l*, pg. 855
Ormerod, C. Warren, Exec. V.P.--Midlantic Bank, N.A., Edison, NJ; *U.S. Public*, pg. 1242
Ormsby, Clarence, Exec. V.P. & Treas.--Servaas, Inc., Indianapolis, IN; *U.S. Private*, pg. 986
Orphanides, James A., Exec. V.P.--First American Title Insurance Co. of N.Y., New York, NY; *U.S. Public*, pg. 626
Orr, Graham, Exec. V.P.-Corp. Develop.--Magna International Inc., Markham, Canada; *Int'l*, pg. 829
Orr, William C., Exec. V.P.--First Citizens Banc Shares, Inc., Raleigh, NC; *U.S. Public*, pg. 628
Orser, William S., Chief Nuclear Officer & Exec. V.P.-Energy Supply--Carolina Power & Light Company, Raleigh, NC; *U.S. Public*, pg. 306
Orsi, Bernard, Exec. V.P.--Pabst Brewing Co., San Antonio, TX; *U.S. Private*, pg. 954
Orsi, Bernard, Exec. V.P.--Pabst Brewing Co./Tumwater, Tumwater, WA; *U.S. Private*, pg. 954
Orsini, Tom T., Exec. V.P.--ALLTEL Corporation, Little Rock, AR; *U.S. Public*, pg. 55
Ortiz, Antonio J., Exec. V.P.--Universal Insurance Co., San Juan, PR; *U.S. Public*, pg. 962
Ortiz, Hector, Exec. V.P. Sls. & Mktg.--Miller Products Company, Inc., North Bergen, NJ; *U.S. Private*, pg. 747
Ortiz, Myrna, Exec. V.P.-Branch Banking & Opers.--Firstbank Puerto Rico, Santurce, PR; *U.S. Public*, pg. 644
Orum, Stephen A., Chief Oper. Officer & Exec. V.P.--Lands' End, Inc., Dodgeville, WI; *U.S. Public*, pg. 977
Orzech, Paul M., Chief Fin. Officer & Exec. V.P.--MMI Companies, Inc., Deerfield, IL; *U.S. Public*, pg. 1027
Osabe, Jiro, Exec. V.P.--Ozeki Corporation, Nishinomiya, Japan; *Int'l*, pg. 1019
Osaka, Hiroshi, Exec. V.P.--Snow Brand Milk Products Co. Ltd., Tokyo, Japan; *Int'l*, pg. 1271
Osawa, Yutaka, Exec. Sr. V.P.--Chuo Senko Advertising Co., Ltd., Tokyo, Japan; *Int'l*, pg. 291
Osborne, John M., Exec. V.P.-Franchise Sls. & Devel.--HFS, Incorporated, Parsippany, NJ; *U.S. Public*, pg. 321
Osborne, Roger, Pres.-Work 'n Gear Stores & Exec. V.P.--J. Baker, Inc., Canton, MA; *U.S. Public*, pg. 167
Oscherwitz, William, Exec. V.P. & Chief Oper. Officer--Shofar Kosher Foods, Linden, NJ; *U.S. Public*, pg. 1433
Osgood, Dennis, Exec. V.P.--Cole Vision Corporation, Cleveland, OH; *U.S. Public*, pg. 396
Oshinski, Jerry P., Exec. V.P., Treas. & Sec.--Hunter Corp., Portage, IN; *U.S. Private*, pg. 549
Oskin, David W., Exec. V.P.-Consumer Pkgng.--International Paper Company, Purchase, NY; *U.S. Public*, pg. 901
Ostberg, Claes, Exec. V.P.-Credit--Nordbanken AB, Stockholm, Sweden; *Int'l*, pg. 957
Ostholm, Lars, Exec. V.P.--Sandvik AB, Sandviken, Sweden; *Int'l*, pg. 1185
Ostroff, Alan M., Exec. V.P.-Opers. & Tech.--Compass Bank, Birmingham, AL; *U.S. Public*, pg. 418
Ostroff, Jeffrey, Exec. V.P.--Central Lewmar, Newark, NJ; *U.S. Private*, pg. 223
Osweiler, Stanley, Exec. V.P. & Sr. V.P.-Sls.--Service Supply Co. Inc. of Indiana, Indianapolis, IN; *U.S. Private*, pg. 987
Ota, Yoshikatsu, Exec. Dir.--Minolta Co., Ltd., Osaka, Japan; *Int'l*, pg. 869
Otani, Tetsuro, Exec. V.P.-Components--Japan Aviation Electronics Industry, Ltd., Tokyo, Japan; *Int'l*, pg. 701
Otelsberg, Barry L., Exec. V.P.-Commercial Mktg.--Pacific Crest Capital, Inc., Agoura Hills, CA; *U.S. Public*, pg. 1248
Oteri, James, Sr. V.P.--Nob Hill General Store, Inc., Gilroy, CA; *U.S. Private*, pg. 799
Otero-Smart, Ingrid, Exec. V.P. & Client Services Dir.--Mendoza, Dillon & Asociados, Inc., Newport Beach, CA; *Int'l*, pg. 1483
Otsuka, Mutsutake, Exec. V.P.-Corp. Plng. & Personnel--East Japan Railway Company, Tokyo, Japan; *Int'l*, pg. 431
Otsuka, Yuya, Exec. V.P.--Otsuka Pharmaceutical Co., Ltd., Tokyo, Japan; *Int'l*, pg. 1013
Ott, Kevin D., Exec. V.P.--The Hennegan Company, Florence, KY; *U.S. Private*, pg. 522
Otte, Ruth, Exec. V.P.-New Media--Scholastic Corporation, New York, NY; *U.S. Public*, pg. 1440
Otten, Robert J., Exec. V.P.--Lat Purser & Associates, Charlotte, NC; *U.S. Private*, pg. 896
Otterbein, Gregory, Exec. V.P.-Mdse. & Mktg.--Sysco Food Services-Albany, Albany, NY; *U.S. Public*, pg. 1551
Otto, Barbara Z., Grp. Exec. V.P.-Latin America & Canada Grp.--Bank of America NT&SA, San Francisco, CA; *U.S. Public*, pg. 180
Ouellette, Ray, Exec. V.P.-Sls. & Mktg.--IMI Cornelius Inc. (MN), Anoka, MN; *Int'l*, pg. 646
Ouellette, Ray, Exec. V.P.-Sls. & Mktg.--IMI Cornelius, Inc. (IA), Mason City, IA; *Int'l*, pg. 646
Overland, Thorstein, Grp. Exec. V.P.--Christiania Bank og Kreditkasse ASA, Oslo, Norway; *Int'l*, pg. 289
Overmeer, J.M., Chief Investment Officer & Exec. V.P.--AEGON Nederland N.V., Hague, Netherlands; *Int'l*, pg. 26
Owada, Peter, Exec. V.P. & Treas.--Casio, Inc., Dover, NJ; *Int'l*, pg. 274
Owada, Yasuo, Exec. V.P.--Tohoku Electric Power Co., Ltd., Sendai, Japan; *Int'l*, pg. 1390
Owen, C. Ray, Chief Oper. Officer & Exec. V.P.--Burlington Resources Inc., Houston, TX; *U.S. Public*, pg. 269
Owen, David, Exec. V.P.--Cactus Feeders, Inc., Amarillo, TX; *U.S. Private*, pg. 198

Owen, David, Chief Fin. Officer & Exec. V.P.--Essex International, Inc., Fort Wayne, IN; *U.S. Public*, pg. 593
Owen, Richard F., Pres.-Southern Divisions & Exec. V.P.--Owen Industries, Inc., Carter Lake, IA; *U.S. Private*, pg. 824
Owen, Russel, Exec. V.P.-Strategic Devel.--Brinker International, Inc., Dallas, TX; *U.S. Public*, pg. 253
Owsley, R.M., Exec. V.P.--Owsley & Sons, Inc., Fort Mill, SC; *U.S. Private*, pg. 824
Oxendine, Tom, Exec. V.P.-Systems--Olsy North America Inc., Liberty Lake, WA; *Int'l*, pg. 1002
Oyama, Masanobu, Sr. Exec. V.P.--Toshiba Corporation, Tokyo, Japan; *Int'l*, pg. 1402
Oyama, Shigeaki, Sr. Exec. V.P.--Fanuc Ltd., Yamanashi, Japan; *Int'l*, pg. 477
Oyama, Tsunaaki, Exec. V.P.--Suntory Ltd., Osaka, Japan; *Int'l*, pg. 1321
Ozawa, Hajime, Exec. V.P.--Fuji Bank International, Inc., San Francisco, CA; *Int'l*, pg. 519
Ozawa, Tatsuya, Sr. Exec. Dir.--Shiseido Company Ltd., Tokyo, Japan; *Int'l*, pg. 1235
Paavela, Jaakko, Exec. V.P.--MTV Finland, Helsinki, Finland; *Int'l*, pg. 827
Pacchini, Carlo, Chief Fin. Officer, Exec. V.P., Controller & Real Estate--Nyltech North America Inc., Manchester, NH; *Int'l*, pg. 482
Pace, H. Duane, Exec. V.P. & Sec.--Jefferson Mills, Inc., Pulaski, VA; *U.S. Private*, pg. 584
Pace, Richard A., Exec. V.P.--The Bank of New York Company, Inc., New York, NY; *U.S. Public*, pg. 178
Pace, Wayne H., Chief Fin. Officer & Exec. V.P.--Turner Broadcasting System Inc., Atlanta, GA; *U.S. Public*, pg. 1614
Pacheco Villagran, Eduardo, Sr. Exec. V.P.-Strategic Plng.--Grupo Casa Autrey, Mexico, Mexico; *Int'l*, pg. 573
Pacheco, M., Exec. V.P.-Chile & Latin America--Carter Holt Harvey Limited, Auckland, New Zealand; *U.S. Public*, pg. 904
Pacifico, Joe, Exec. V.P.-Mktg.--The William Carter Company, Morrow, GA; *U.S. Private*, pg. 217
Packett, Jack, Exec. V.P.--Ezon Products, Inc., Germantown, TN; *U.S. Private*, pg. 388
Packman, Michael, Chief Fin. Officer & Exec. V.P.--Active International, Pearl River, NY; *U.S. Private*, pg. 15
Packwood, Jan B., Exec. V.P.--Idaho Power Company, Boise, ID; *U.S. Public*, pg. 861
Pados, Frank J., Jr., Exec. V.P.--Desai Capital Management Incorporated, New York, NY; *U.S. Private*, pg. 326
Pafenzinger, Friedrich, Exec. V.P.--Bayerische Hypotheken-und Wechsel-Bank Aktiengesellschaft, Munich, Germany; *Int'l*, pg. 175
Page, Douglas F., Exec. V.P.--UMB Financial Corporation, Kansas City, MO; *U.S. Public*, pg. 1653
Page, Larry, Chief Fin. Officer, Exec. V.P. & Treas.--ShowBiz Pizza Time, Inc., Irving, TX; *U.S. Public*, pg. 1468
Page, Scott T., Sr. Exec. V.P. & Sec.--Collective Bank, Cologne, NJ; *U.S. Public*, pg. 1528
Page, Stephan F., Chief Fin. Officer & Exec. V.P.--United Technologies Corporation, Hartford, CT; *U.S. Public*, pg. 1689
Page, Timothy B., Chief Oper. Officer & Exec. V.P.--Farah Incorporated, El Paso, TX; *U.S. Public*, pg. 612
Paglieri, Wayne C., Exec. V.P.--F&G Re, Inc., Morristown, NJ; *U.S. Public*, pg. 1659
Pagonis, William G., Exec. V.P.-Logistics--Sears, Roebuck and Co., Hoffman Estates, IL; *U.S. Public*, pg. 1452
Paidas, George P., Exec. V.P.--FirstMerit Corporation, Akron, OH; *U.S. Public*, pg. 646
Paillart, Philippe, Exec. Dir.-Personal Banking--Standard Chartered Bank PLC, London, United Kingdom; *Int'l*, pg. 1294
Paine, Andrew J., Jr., Exec. V.P. & Pres.-NBD Indiana--First Chicago NBD Corporation, Chicago, IL; *U.S. Public*, pg. 627
Paite, Louis, Exec. V.P.--Restonic Mattress Corporation, Rosemont, IL; *U.S. Private*, pg. 925
Paladino, Daniel R., Exec. V.P.-Legal & Environmental Affairs--The Seagram Company Ltd., Montreal, Canada; *Int'l*, pg. 1214
Paladino, Robert C., Exec. V.P.--York Research Corporation, New York, NY; *U.S. Public*, pg. 1789
Palagonia, Chris, Exec. V.P.--J.M.P. Bakery Co., Inc., Brooklyn, NY; *U.S. Private*, pg. 578
Palesny, John P., V.P.--Petersen Aluminum Corporation, Elk Grove Village, IL; *U.S. Private*, pg. 856
Paley, Steve, Exec. V.P.--The Texwipe Co., Inc., Upper Saddle River, NJ; *U.S. Private*, pg. 1079
Paley, William, Exec. V.P.--The Texwipe Co., Inc., Upper Saddle River, NJ; *U.S. Private*, pg. 1079
Palle, Robert J., Jr., Chief Oper. Officer & Exec. V.P.--Blonder-Tongue Laboratories, Inc., Old Bridge, NJ; *U.S. Public*, pg. 237
Palles, Allen P., Chief Fin. Officer & Exec. V.P.--LINC Capital Group, Chicago, IL; *U.S. Public*, pg. 996
Palmer, Greg, Chief Oper. Officer & Exec. V.P.--RemedyTemp, Inc., San Juan Capistrano, CA; *U.S. Public*, pg. 1376
Palmer, Lothar, Exec. V.P.--Stora Feldmuhle AG, Dusseldorf, Germany; *Int'l*, pg. 1303
Palmer, Ronald A., Chief Fin. Officer, Exec. V.P. & Treas.--TCF Financial Corp., Minneapolis, MN; *U.S. Public*, pg. 1554
Palmer, Ronald J., Chief Fin. Officer, Exec. V.P. & Treas.--TCF Bank Minnesota FSB, Minneapolis, MN; *U.S. Public*, *pg. 1554*
Palmero, Claude, Exec. V.P.--Sabena, Zaventem, Belgium; *Int'l*, pg. 1168
Palmgren, Anders, Exec. V.P.--Power & Heat Generation--Imatran Voima Oy, Helsinki, Finland; *Int'l*, pg. 660
Palo, Neil, Exec. V.P.--McNeil Specialty Products Company, New Brunswick, NJ; *U.S. Public*, pg. 928
Palomino, Angel, Exec. V.P.-Europe City Hotels--Sol Melia, Palma de Mallorca, Spain; *Int'l*, pg. 1277
Pan, Karl K.Y., Exec. V.P.-Intl. & Pacific Markets--Bank of Hawaii, Honolulu, HI; *U.S. Public*, pg. 1248
Paneyko, Stephen H., Sr. Exec. V.P.-Wholesale Banking--Summit Bancorp, Princeton, NJ; *U.S. Public*, pg. 1527
Pang, Gerald M., Exec. V.P. & Chief Credit Officer--First Hawaiian Bank, Honolulu, HI; *U.S. Public*, pg. 634
Pangan, E.S., Exec. V.P. & Gen. Mgr.--Philippines Dairy Products Corp., Manila, Philippines; *Int'l*, pg. 923
Pannenberg, Dieter, Exec. V.P.--Norddeutsche Landesbank (NORD/LB), Hannover, Germany; *Int'l*, pg. 957
Pantelidis, James, Exec. V.P.--Petro-Canada, Calgary, Canada; *Int'l*, pg. 1041
Paolercio, Anthony, Jr., Co. Chm. Bd. & Exec. V.P.--Michael Anthony Jewelers, Inc., Mount Vernon, NY; *U.S. Public*, pg. 1103
Papageorge, Deno D., Sr. Exec. V.P.--The Bank of New York Company, Inc., New York, NY; *U.S. Public*, pg. 178
Papageorge, Deno D., Sr. Exec. V.P.--The Bank of New York, New York, NY; *U.S. Public*, pg. 178
Papai, Jacqueline, Exec. V.P. & Controller--Ventre Packing Company, Inc., Syracuse, NY; *U.S. Private*, pg. 1135
Pape, Eldon C., Chief Fin. & Plng. Officer & Exec. V.P.--Omaha Public Power District, Omaha, NE; *U.S. Private*, pg. 815
Papetti, Steven, Exec. V.P.--Papetti Hygrade Egg Products, Elizabeth, NJ; *U.S. Public*, pg. 1104
Papows, Jeffrey, Chief Oper. Officer & Exec. V.P.--Lotus Business Products Div., Cambridge, MA; *U.S. Public*, pg. 896
Paprocki, Thomas R., Exec. V.P.--Huntington Bancshares Inc., Columbus, OH; *U.S. Public*, pg. 849
Papushka, Harry R., Exec. V.P.-Pulp--Repap New Brunswick Inc., Montreal, Canada; *Int'l*, pg. 1104
Paquelet, Clare, Chief Fin. Officer & Exec. V.P.- Fin. & Admin.--FINAST, Maple Heights, OH; *Int'l*, pg. 750
Paquette, Pierre, Sr. Exec. V.P.-Opers.--National Bank of Canada, Montreal, Canada; *Int'l*, pg. 907
Pardi, Louis E., Exec. V.P.-Power--Morrison Knudsen Corp.-Engineering & Construction, Cleveland, OH; *U.S. Public*, pg. 1134
Pardi, Louis E., Exec. V.P.--Power Division, Cleveland, OH; *U.S. Public*, pg. 1134
Pardue, William J., Exec. V.P.--Central Sprinkler Company, Lansdale, PA; *U.S. Public*, pg. 327
Parent, Jean-Pierre, Exec. V.P. & Gen. Mgr.--Muskin Leisure Products, Inc., Wilkes-Barre, PA; *U.S. Private*, pg. 768
Parent, Louise M., Exec. V.P. & Gen. Counsel--American Express Company, New York, NY; *U.S. Public*, pg. 73
Parfet, Donald R., Exec. V.P.-Worldwide Animal Health & Pharmaceutical Comml. Servs.--Pharmacia & Upjohn, Kalamazoo, MI; *Int'l*, pg. 1048
Parham, Buff, Exec. V.P. & Corp. Dir.-Entertainment--Fahlgren, Atlanta, GA; *U.S. Private*, pg. 391
Parios, Chris P., Exec. V.P.--CommonHealth USA, Parsippany, NJ; *Int'l*, pg. 1483
Paris, Robert W., Exec. V.P.-Credit Division--Pacific Century Financial Corporation, Honolulu, HI; *U.S. Public*, pg. 1248
Paris, Robert W., Exec. V.P.-Credit Division--Bank of Hawaii, Honolulu, HI; *U.S. Public*, pg. 1248
Parish, Robert C., Dr., Exec. V.P. & Mng. Dir.-London--Scientific Software-Intercomp, Inc., Denver, CO; *U.S. Public*, pg. 1443
Pariso, Tim, Chief Oper. Officer & Exec. V.P.--Celotex Corporation, Tampa, FL; *U.S. Private*, pg. 221
Park, Charles, Chief Fin. Officer, Exec. V.P.-Fin. & Sec.--Briggs Industries, Inc., Tampa, FL; *U.S. Private*, pg. 168
Park, Mahlon S., Exec. V.P. & Mgr.-Commercial Banking--First Security Bank of Idaho, N.A., Boise, ID; *U.S. Public*, *pg. 637*
Park, Sung-Joon, Chief Oper. Officer & Sr. Exec. V.P.--Daehong Advertising Inc., Seoul, Korea; *Int'l*, pg. 357
Park, William H., Chief Fin. Officer & Exec. V.P.--United Asset Management Corporation, Boston, MA; *U.S. Public*, pg. 1672
Parker, Bruce, Sr. Exec. V.P. & Chief Merchant--Callaway Golf Company, Carlsbad, CA; *U.S. Public*, pg. 294
Parker, Charles A., Chief Oper. Officer & Exec. V.P.--Diamond Comic Distributors, Inc., Timonium, MD; *U.S. Private*, pg. 330
Parker, Don, Exec. V.P. & Chief H.R. Officer--Ammirati Puris Lintas Worldwide, New York, NY; *U.S. Public*, pg. 908
Parker, Jack, Exec. V.P.-Commercial Admin.--Lincoln Property Company, Dallas, TX; *U.S. Private*, pg. 668
Parker, Jack, Chief Fin. Officer & Exec. V.P.--Union Planters Corporation, Cordova, TN; *U.S. Public*, pg. 1668
Parker, James M., Exec. V.P.--First Citizens Banc Shares, Inc., Raleigh, NC; *U.S. Public*, pg. 628
Parker, Jane, Exec. V.P. & Client Services Dir.-Consumer Heath Grp.--Klemtner Advertising Inc., New York, NY; *U.S. Public*, pg. 1422
Parker, John A. H., Exec. V.P. & Dir.-Sls.--Universal Leaf Tobacco Company, Inc., Richmond, VA; *U.S. Public*, pg. 1694
Parker, John W., Chief Fin. Officer & Exec. V.P.--Union Planters Bank, Memphis, TN; *U.S. Public*, pg. 1669
Parker, L. Edward, Exec. V.P.-Mktg.--Burlington Resources Inc., Houston, TX; *U.S. Public*, pg. 269
Parker, L. Edward, Exec. V.P.-Mktg.--Meridian Oil Holding Inc., Houston, TX; *U.S. Public*, pg. 269
Parker, Michael D., Exec. V.P.--The Dow Chemical Company, Midland, MI; *U.S. Public*, pg. 522
Parker, Pat F., Chief Oper. Officer & Exec. V.P.--Southwestern Bell Mobile Systems, Inc., Dallas, TX; *U.S. Public*, pg. 1415
Parker, Richard E., Exec. V.P.-Hardboard/Plastics--ABT Building Products Corporation, Neenah, WI; *Int'l*, pg. 20
Parker, Richard M., Exec. V.P.--Midlantic Bank, N.A., Edison, NJ; *U.S. Public*, pg. 1242
Parker, William M., Exec. V.P.-Bus. Devel.--CACI International Inc, Arlington, VA; *U.S. Public*, pg. 272
Parkerson, Eugene C., Exec. V.P.--Chemical Leaman Corporation, Exton, PA; *U.S. Private*, pg. 233
Parkinson, Robert M., Exec. V.P. & Corp. Chief Auditor--Mellon Bank Corporation, Pittsburgh, PA; *U.S. Public*, pg. 1084
Parlato, Charles, Exec. V.P. & Media Services Dir.--Partners & Shevack, Inc., New York, NY; *U.S. Private*, pg. 842
Parodi, Dennis R., Div. Exec. V.P.-Stores & Opers.--Gap Stores Division, San Bruno, CA; *U.S. Public*, pg. 702
Parr, Jack, Exec. V.P.-Res. & Devel.--Wright Medical Technology, Arlington, TN; *U.S. Private*, pg. 1192
Parrinello, John, Jr., Chief Oper. Officer & Exec. V.P.--Frank Briscoe Co. Inc., Kenilworth, NJ; *U.S. Private*, pg. 169
Parrish, Edward L., Exec. V.P.-Corp. Services Div.--AmSouth Bancorporation, Birmingham, AL; *U.S. Public*, pg. 105
Parrish, James N., Exec. V.P.--North Carolina Mutual Life Insurance Co., Durham, NC; *U.S. Private*, pg. 804
Parrish, Mark, Exec. V.P.-Sls. & Mktg.--Cardinal Health Inc., Dublin, OH; *U.S. Public*, pg. 304
Parrish, Mark W., Exec. V.P.-Sls. & Mktg.--Cardinal Distribution, Dublin, OH; *U.S. Public*, pg. 304
Parrish, O.H., Pres.-Virginia Banking--Crestar Bank, Richmond, VA; *U.S. Public*, pg. 458
Parrish, Richard B., Sr. V.P.-Bldg. Prods.--Boise Cascade Corporation, Boise, ID; *U.S. Public*, pg. 242
Parry, Carol J., Exec. V.P.-Community Devel.--The Chase Manhattan Corporation, New York, NY; *U.S. Public*, pg. 337
Parsons, Robert E., Jr., Chief Fin. Officer & Exec. V.P.--Host Marriott Corporation, Bethesda, MD; *U.S. Public*, pg. 841
Partain, Joe, Exec. V.P.--General Homes Corporation, Houston, TX; *U.S. Private*, pg. 444
Parton, Wayne, Exec. V.P.-Opers.--Allegiant Physician Services, Atlanta, GA; *U.S. Public*, pg. 45
Parton, Wayne, Exec. V.P.-Opers.--Quest Staffing, Atlanta, GA; *U.S. Public*, pg. 45
Pascoe, F. Michael, Exec. V.P. & Gen. Mgr.-Americas Region--Newbridge Networks Corporation, Kanata, Canada; *Int'l*, pg. 923
Paseornek, Helene, Exec. V.P. & Gen. Mgr.-STRATIS KPR--KPR, New York, NY; *U.S. Public*, pg. 1224
Passant, Michel, Exec. V.P.-Operational & Technical Support--Banque Nationale de Paris, Paris, France; *Int'l*, pg. 163
Passardi, Adriano, Exec. V.P.--Zurich Insurance Company, Zurich, Switzerland; *Int'l*, pg. 1529
Passatore, Giuseppe, Sr. Exec. V.P.--Istituto Bancario San Paolo Di Torino S.p.A., Turin, Italy; *Int'l*, pg. 691
Pastore, Robert, Exec. V.P.--Cine Magnetics, Inc., Armonk, NY; *U.S. Private*, pg. 240
Paszamant, David, Vice Chm., Exec. V.P. & Dir.-Mktg.--Adams Wine Co., Atlanta, GA; *U.S. Private*, pg. 17
Pate, George W., Exec. V.P.--TRAK Microwave Corp., Tampa, FL; *U.S. Public*, pg. 1563
Pate, Robert, Exec. V.P.--San Angelo National Bank, San Angelo, TX; *U.S. Public*, pg. 633
Patel, Magan C., Exec. V.P.-Intl. Banking Grp.--Union Bank of California, San Francisco, CA; *Int'l*, pg. 157
Patel, Magan H., Exec. V.P. & Asst. Sec.--Circuit Systems, Inc., Elk Grove Village, IL; *U.S. Public*, pg. 374
Patel, Shashi, Exec. V.P.--Muralo Co., Inc., Bayonne, NJ; *U.S. Private*, pg. 767
Paterson, Ronald, Chief Oper. Officer & Exec. V.P.--Champion HealthCare Corporation, Houston, TX; *U.S. Public*, pg. 333
Patrick, Allan, Exec. V.P.- Mdsg., Adv. & Distr.--Genovese Drug Stores, Inc., Melville, NY; *U.S. Public*, pg. 730
Patrick, Charles F., Chief Oper.Officer & Exec. V.P.--The Copley Press, Inc., La Jolla, CA; *U.S. Private*, pg. 275
Patrick, David, Exec. V.P.-World-Wide Sls.--The Learning Co., Inc., Cambridge, MA; *U.S. Public*, pg. 982
Patrick, Jean A., Exec. V.P. & Dir.-Mktg.--The W.W. Williams Company, Columbus, OH; *U.S. Private*, pg. 1178
Patrick, Thomas H., Exec. V.P.--Merrill Lynch & Co., Inc., New York, NY; *U.S. Public*, pg. 1097
Patrick, Thomas M., Exec. V.P.--Peoples Energy Corporation, Chicago, IL; *U.S. Public*, pg. 1274
Patrick, Thomas M., Exec. V.P.--North Shore Gas Co., Waukegan, IL; *U.S. Public*, pg. 1275
Patrick, Thomas M., Exec. V.P.--The Peoples Gas Light & Coke Co., Chicago, IL; *U.S. Public*, pg. 1275
Patriee, Brisson, Exec. V.P.-Tech.--N. Schlumberger & Cie, Guebwiller, France; *Int'l*, pg. 1206
Patron, Ronald H., Chief Fin. Officer, Pres.-Corp. Div. & Exec. V.P.--Stewart Enterprises, Inc., Metairie, LA; *U.S. Public*, pg. 1518
Patterson, David S., Chief Oper. Officer & Exec. V.P.--Payco American Corporation, Brookfield, WI; *U.S. Public*, *pg. 1267*
Patterson, Donald H. Jr., Pres.-Landmark Broadcasting & Exec. V.P.--Landmark Communications, Inc., Norfolk, VA; *U.S. Private*, pg. 647
Patterson, Jeffrey A., Chief Investment Officer & Exec. V.P.--Prime Group Realty Trust, Chicago, IL; *U.S. Public*, pg. 1326
Patterson, Peyton R., Exec. V.P. & Gen. Mgr.-Consumer Lending--The Dime Savings Bank of New York, New York, NY; *U.S. Public*, pg. 509
Patterson, Robert S., Exec. V.P. & Sr. Trust Officer--First National Bank of Abilene, Abilene, TX; *U.S. Public*, pg. 633
Patterson, Wade C., Exec. V.P.--Intergraph Corporation, Huntsville, AL; *U.S. Public*, pg. 890
Patton, Richard, Exec. V.P.-Res. & Devel.--Lawson Software, Minneapolis, MN; *U.S. Private*, pg. 654
Pattusch, Gunter, Exec. Dir.-Counsel--Schering AG, Berlin, Germany; *Int'l*, pg. 1203
Paul, Charles S., Pres.-MCA Enterprises, Inc. & Exec. V.P.--Universal Studios, Inc., Universal City, CA; *Int'l*, pg. 1215
Paul, Gerald, Dr., Chief Oper. Officer & Exec. V.P.--Vishay Intertechnology, Inc., Malvern, PA; *U.S. Public*, pg. 1721
Paul, S., Exec. V.P.-Pub. Affairs--Labatt Breweries of Canada, Toronto, Canada; *Int'l*, pg. 679

Paul, William F., Exec. V.P.--United Technologies Corporation, Hartford, CT; *U.S. Public*, pg. 1689
Paulikas, George A., Dr., Exec. V.P.--Aerospace Corporation, El Segundo, CA; *U.S. Private*, pg. 24
Paulson, Jerome S., Exec. V.P.--Flexible Steel Lacing Company, Downers Grove, IL; *U.S. Private*, pg. 413
Paulson, Stephanie, Exec. V.P., Treas & Creative Dir.--The Stephenz Group, Inc., San Jose, CA; *U.S. Private*, pg. 1040
Paulus, Michael S., Exec. V.P.-Mktg. Communications--Dix & Eaton Incorporated, Cleveland, OH; *U.S. Private*, pg. 336
Pavlas, Gerald F., Exec. V.P. & Chief Credit Officer--Hibernia Corporation, New Orleans, LA; *U.S. Public*, pg. 825
Pavlovic, Dragan, Exec. V.P.--Jugobanka Banking Group, Belgrade, Serbia; *Int'l*, pg. 716
Pawley, Dennis K., Exec. V.P.-Mfg.--Chrysler Corporation, Auburn Hills, MI; *U.S. Public*, pg. 352
Pawlowski, Norbert, Exec. V.P.--Bayerische Hypotheken-und Wechsel-Bank Aktiengesellschaft, Munich, Germany; *Int'l*, pg. 175
Paxton, John, Pres.-Printing Solutions & Exec. V.P.--PAXAR Corporation, White Plains, NY; *U.S. Public*, pg. 1266
Paxton, John W., Exec. V.P.--Monarch Marking Systems, Miamisburg, OH; *U.S. Public*, pg. 1266
Paydos, Charles J., Exec. V.P.--Phoenix Home Life Mutual Insurance Company, Hartford, CT; *U.S. Private*, pg. 863
Payeras, Miguel, Exec. V.P.-Asia & Pacific--Sol Melia, Palma de Mallorca, Spain; *Int'l*, pg. 1277
Paylor, C. Alan, Exec. V.P.-Sls.--National Insurance Group, South San Francisco, CA; *U.S. Public*, pg. 1157
Payne, I.K., Exec. Dir.--Commonwealth Bank Group, Sydney, Australia; *Int'l*, pg. 312
Payne, Lisa, Chief Fin. Officer & Exec. V.P.--Taubman Centers, Inc., Bloomfield Hills, MI; *U.S. Public*, pg. 1561
Payne, Paul D., Exec. V.P. & Chief Oper. Officer--Mercedes-Benz Credit Corp., Norwalk, CT; *Int'l*, pg. 368
Payne, Sharon, Exec. V.P. & Cashier--Old-First National Bank in Bluffton, Bluffton, IN; *U.S. Public*, pg. 674
Payne, Thomas H., Exec. V.P.--Market Facts-New York, Inc., New York, NY; *U.S. Public*, pg. 1047
Paynter, Stacey, Chief Oper. Officer-San Francisco, Exec. V.P. & Dir.--EvansGroup, Salt Lake City, UT; *U.S. Private*, pg. 385
Paynter, Stacey, Chief Oper. Officer & Exec. V.P.--EvansGroup, San Francisco, CA; *U.S. Private*, pg. 385
Payton, Harry F., Exec. V.P.--BWAY Corp., Atlanta, GA; *U.S. Public*, pg. 164
Paz, Alberto, Exec. V.P. & Client Services Dir.--Robert A. Becker, New York, NY; *Int'l*, pg. 601
Pazos, Guillermo B., Exec. V.P.-South American Opers. & Pres.-Bridgestone Brazil--Bridgestone/Firestone, Inc., Nashville, TN; *Int'l*, pg. 213
Pazour, Don, Exec. V.P.--Miller Freeman Inc., San Francisco, CA; *Int'l*, pg. 1443
Peabody, Carl Mathew, Exec. V.P.--L. Perrigo Company, Allegan, MI; *U.S. Public*, pg. 1280
Peal, Leonard B., Exec. V.P.-Cost & Leased Depts.--The Elder-Beerman Stores Corp., Dayton, OH; *U.S. Private*, pg. 367
Pearce, R.M., Chief Oper. Officer & Exec. V.P.--Coho Energy, Inc., Dallas, TX; *U.S. Public*, pg. 396
Pearce, Richard A., Exec. V.P.-Mktg.--Purina Grocery Products Group, Saint Louis, MO; *U.S. Public*, pg. 1360
Pearl, Martin, Exec. V.P.--Faber, Coe & Gregg, Inc., Secaucus, NJ; *U.S. Private*, pg. 390
Pearse, Stephen G., Exec. V.P. & Gen. Mgr.-Internet/Telecom Bus. Grp.--Bay Networks, Inc., Santa Clara, CA; *U.S. Public*, pg. 196
Pearson, Bruce A., Exec. V.P.-Property & Casualty div.--Willis Corroon Corp. of Kansas, Wichita, KS; *Int'l*, pg. 1506
Pearson, Douglas N., Pres.-North America Opers. & Exec. V.P.--Exide Corporation, Reading, PA; *U.S. Public*, pg. 600
Pearson, Ford G., Exec. V.P.--Frank Consolidated Enterprises Inc., Des Plaines, IL; *U.S. Private*, pg. 423
Peck, Charles H., Exec. V.P.--Brookline Savings Bank, Brookline, MA; *U.S. Private*, pg. 171
Peckham, Rod J., Exec. V.P.-Fin. & Admin. & Strategic Plng.--Forstmann & Company, Inc., New York, NY; *U.S. Public*, pg. 670
Pedersen, Charles, Exec. V.P.-Systems Tech. & Item Processing Group--Union Bank of California, San Francisco, CA; *Int'l*, pg. 157
Pedersen, David, Chief Oper. Officer& Exec. V.P.--Martin K. Eby Construction Company, Inc., Wichita, KS; *U.S. Private*, pg. 359
Pedersen, Gary, Chief Admin. Officer & Exec. V.P.--Gabbert's, Inc., Minneapolis, MN; *U.S. Private*, pg. 437
Peebles, John, Exec. V.P. & Creative Dir.--Adler Boschetto Peebles & Partners, Inc., New York, NY; *U.S. Private*, pg. 17
Peets, Terry R., Exec. V.P.--The Vons Companies, Inc., Arcadia, CA; *U.S. Public*, pg. 1426
Peetz, Jack, Exec. V.P.--Crete Carrier Corp., Lincoln, NE; *U.S. Private*, pg. 289
Pegan, Robert, Exec. V.P.--Central States Enterprises, Inc., Heathrow, FL; *U.S. Private*, pg. 225
Pegg, William S., Exec. V.P.--RPC Incorporated, Atlanta, GA; *U.S. Public*, pg. 1356
Peipers, Harald, Dr., Exec. V.P.--Hochtief AG, Essen, Germany; *Int'l*, pg. 623
Peister, Milton, Exec. V.P.--David L. Peister Co., Inc., New York, NY; *U.S. Private*, pg. 848
Pekeler, Markus, Exec. V.P. & New Bus. Contact--Impuls Advertising AG, Kusnacht, Switzerland; *Int'l*, pg. 666
Pelka, Lawrence J., Exec. V.P.-Commercial--Associates First Capital Corporation, Dallas, TX; *U.S. Public*, pg. 662
Pellegrene, John, Exec. V.P.-Mktg.--Target Stores, Minneapolis, MN; *U.S. Public*, pg. 489
Pellenberg, Charles I., Exec. V.P.-Home Fashion--Hanover Direct, Inc., Weehawken, NJ; *U.S. Public*, pg. 782
Pena, Miguel Tomas, Exec. V.P.--Avantel, S.A., Mexico, Mexico; *Int'l*, pg. 574
Penaloza Sandoval, David, Chm. Bd. & Pres.--Grupo Tribasa S.A. de C.V., Mexico, Mexico; *Int'l*, pg. 577
Penchas, Henri, Exec. V.P. -Acctg. & Control--Banco Itau S.A., Sao Paulo, Brazil; *Int'l*, pg. 142
Penchina, Steven, Exec. V.P. & Exec. Creative Dir.--DCA Advertising, Inc., New York, NY; *Int'l*, pg. 393
Pendleton, Arthur L., Chief Oper. Officer & Exec. V.P.--Roanoke Gas Company, Roanoke, VA; *U.S. Public*, pg. 1392
Peninon, Dominique, Exec. V.P.-Dev.--Financiere Saint Dominique, Paris, France; *Int'l*, pg. 344
Pennella, Mike, Exec. V.P.--Lamb-Weston, Inc., Kennewick, WA; *U.S. Public*, pg. 427
Pennella, William, Exec. V.P.--Crowley Maritime Corporation, Oakland, CA; *U.S. Private*, pg. 292
Penning, Gerald A., Exec. V.P. & Controller--HSBC Americas, Buffalo, NY; *Int'l*, pg. 580
Penrose, Sheila A., Exec. V.P.-Corp. & Institutional Services--Northern Trust Corporation, Chicago, IL; *U.S. Public*, pg. 1195
Pensabene, Susan, Exec. V.P.--SCP Direct Inc., New York, NY; *U.S. Public*, pg. 1224
Pentland, Lawrence, Exec. V.P.--Cott Corporation, Pointe-Claire, Canada; *Int'l*, pg. 337
Pentland, Lawrence, Exec. V.P.--Cott Corporation - North East Division, Toronto, Canada; *Int'l*, pg. 337
Penttila, Risto, Exec. V.P.-Admin.--Stockmann Department Store Div., Helsinki, Finland; *Int'l*, pg. 1301
Penz, William F., Exec. V.P. & Treas.--Ludington News Co. Inc., Detroit, MI; *U.S. Private*, pg. 679
Pepper, Frederick W., Exec. V.P.--Pepper Construction Company, Irvine, CA; *U.S. Private*, pg. 851
Pepper, J. David, Exec. V.P.--The Pepper Companies, Inc., Chicago, IL; *U.S. Private*, pg. 851
Peppercorn, Wayne M., Exec. V.P.--Abolite Lighting Inc., Cincinnati, OH; *U.S. Public*, pg. 971
Pepys Lowe, Renee, Exec. V.P.-Sls. & Mktg.--Noel Joanna, Inc., Rancho Santa Margarita, CA; *U.S. Public*, pg. 465
Peralta, Javier, Exec. V.P.-Credit Dept.--Banco Santander, Madrid, Spain; *Int'l*, pg. 143
Perchick, Morton K., Exec. V.P.--Kulicke & Soffa Industries, Inc., Willow Grove, PA; *U.S. Public*, pg. 968
Perera, Geff, Chief Fin. Officer & Exec. V.P.--Rexene Corporation, Dallas, TX; *U.S. Private*, pg. 549
Perez, Enrique, Chief Oper. Officer, Sr. Exec. V.P., Gen. Counsel & Sec.--Philippine Long Distance Telephone Company, Manila, Philippines; *Int'l*, pg. 1051
Perez, Georgina, Exec. V.P.--Associated Grocers of Florida, Inc., Miami, FL; *U.S. Private*, pg. 91
Perez, Joseph, Exec. V.P.--Credit Commercial de France, Paris, France; *Int'l*, pg. 341
Perez, Milagros, Exec. V.P. & Chief Lending Officer--PonceBank, F.S.B., Ponce, PR; *U.S. Public*, pg. 1316
Perez, Ramon M., Exec. V.P.-Pur.--Cardinal Health Inc., Dublin, OH; *U.S. Public*, pg. 304
Perez, Ramon M., Exec. V.P.-Pur.--Cardinal Distribution, Dublin, OH; *U.S. Public*, pg. 304
Perezgrovas, Armando, Exec. V.P.--Publicidad Ferrer y Asociados, S.A. de C.V., Mexico, Mexico; *Int'l*, pg. 1073
Pericola, Julius L., Exec. V.P.--Bristol-Myers International Group, New York, NY; *U.S. Public*, pg. 254
Perier, F., Exec. V.P.--Elf Atochem S.A., Paris, France; *Int'l*, pg. 445
Perillo, Mike, Exec. V.P.--Dana Lighting, Inc., Easton, MA; *U.S. Public*, pg. 314
Perin, R.L., Jr., Exec. V.P.-Commercial--U.S. Steel International, Inc., Pittsburgh, PA; *U.S. Public*, pg. 1661
Perlegos, Gust, Exec. V.P. & Gen. Mgr.--Atmel Corporation, San Jose, CA; *U.S. Public*, pg. 145
Perlis, Barry, Exec. V.P.--S. Freedman & Sons, Inc., Landover, MD; *U.S. Private*, pg. 425
Perlitz, Frank A., Jr., Exec. V.P.-Opers.--First Federal Savings, East Hartford, CT; *U.S. Public*, pg. 632
Perlman, Alan, Exec. V.P.--E.W. Howell Company, Inc., Port Washington, NY; *Int'l*, pg. 995
Perlmuter, Bruce, Exec. V.P., Treas. & Sec.--Perlmuter Printing Company, Cleveland, OH; *Int'l*, pg. 1177
Perlmutter, Stephen M., Exec. V.P.-Corp. Devel.--Heitman Financial Ltd., Chicago, IL; *U.S. Public*, pg. 1673
Perlyn, Donald L., Exec. V.P.--Miami Subs Corporation, Fort Lauderdale, FL; *U.S. Public*, pg. 1103
Perna, Thomas J., Exec. V.P.-Investment Company Services--The Bank of New York Company, Inc., New York, NY; *U.S. Public*, pg. 178
Perocchi, William, Chief Fin. Officer, Exec. V.P. & Treas.--Doubletree Corporation, Memphis, TN; *U.S. Public*, pg. 1335
Perotti, William L., Jr., Exec. V.P.--Cullen/Frost Bankers, Inc., San Antonio, TX; *U.S. Public*, pg. 467
Peroutka, Michael S., Exec. V.P.-Sls. & Mktg.--Faribault Foods Inc., Minneapolis, MN; *U.S. Private*, pg. 393
Perper, Alan, Exec. V.P.-New Bus. Devel.--Simon Marketing, Inc., Los Angeles, CA; *U.S. Private*, pg. 1001
Perreault, Robert P., Exec. V.P. & Treas.--Lawrence Savings Bank, North Andover, MA; *U.S. Public*, pg. 980
Perron, Eric, Exec. V.P.--Bio-Tek Instruments, Inc., Winooski, VT; *U.S. Private*, pg. 144
Perrotty, P. Sue, Exec. V.P.--CoreStates Financial Corp., Philadelphia, PA; *U.S. Public*, pg. 446
Perry, Brendan J., Sr. Exec. V.P.--Interface Electronics Corporation, Hopkinton, MA; *U.S. Private*, pg. 567
Perry, Ed, Exec. V.P.--Trident Seafood Corporation, Seattle, WA; *U.S. Public*, pg. 429
Perry, Michael W., Chief Oper. Officer & Exec. V.P.--Countrywide Asset Management Corporation, Pasadena, CA; *U.S. Public*, pg. 452
Perry, Rebecca L., Exec. V.P.--La Petite Academy Inc., Overland Park, KS; *U.S. Private*, pg. 640
Perry, Robert M., Exec. V.P.-Corp. Affairs--Dames & Moore Inc., Los Angeles, CA; *Int'l*, pg. 624
Perry, Robert S., Exec. V.P.--Pacific Metal Company, Portland, OR; *U.S. Private*, pg. 832
Perskie, Steven P., Exec. V.P. & Gen. Counsel--Players International, Inc., Atlantic City, NJ; *U.S. Public*, pg. 1310
Persky, James L., Exec. V.P.-Admin. & Fin.--Southdown, Inc., Houston, TX; *U.S. Public*, pg. 1488
Persofsky, Barry, Exec. V.P.--Commerce & Industry Insurance Co., New York, NY; *U.S. Public*, pg. 84
Pestalozzi, Andreas, Exec. V.P.--Holderbank Financiere Glaris Ltd., Glaris, Switzerland; *Int'l*, pg. 628
Pestillo, Peter J., Exec. V.P.-Corp. Rels.--Ford Motor Company, Dearborn, MI; *U.S. Public*, pg. 661
Peter, Hugh M., Sr., Exec. V.P.--Peter Lumber Company, Pleasantville, NJ; *U.S. Private*, pg. 856
Peter, N.R., Exec. V.P.--Hudson's Bay Company, Toronto, Canada; *Int'l*, pg. 637
Peters, Donald E., Exec. V.P.--First Financial Bank, FSB, Stevens Point, WI; *U.S. Public*, pg. 140
Peters, Frederick C., III, Exec. V.P. & Pres.-First Main Line Bank Div.--National Penn Bank, Boyertown, PA; *U.S. Public*, pg. 1159
Peters, Henry, Exec. V.P.-Sales--Miami Systems Corporation, Cincinnati, OH; *U.S. Private*, pg. 740
Peters, John D., Exec. V.P.-Information Tech.--Phillips-Van Heusen Corporation, New York, NY; *U.S. Public*, pg. 1291
Peters, Phillip E., Chief Investment Officer & Exec. V.P.--NationsBank West, Saint Louis, MO; *U.S. Public*, pg. 1164
Peters, Raymond R., Exec. V.P. & Treas.--BankAmerica Corporation, San Francisco, CA; *U.S. Public*, pg. 179
Peters, Raymond R., Grp. Exec. V.P. & Treas.--Bank of America NT&SA, San Francisco, CA; *U.S. Public*, pg. 180
Petersen, Albert E., Exec. V.P.--State Street Corporation, Boston, MA; *U.S. Public*, pg. 1513
Petersen, Susan J., Exec. V.P.--The Putnam Berkley Group, Inc., New York, NY; *Int'l*, pg. 1027
Petersen, Thomas H., Exec. V.P. & Gen. Mgr.--CFC Data Corp., Midland, MI; *U.S. Public*, pg. 345
Peterson, Don, Chief Fin. Officer & Exec. V.P.--Lucent Technologies Inc., Murray Hill, NJ; *U.S. Public*, pg. 1017
Peterson, J. Craig, Chief Fin. & Admin. Officer & Exec. V.P.--Unitog Company, Kansas City, MO; *U.S. Public*, pg. 1693
Peterson, Jack, Exec. V.P. & Chief Fin. Officer--Alliant Foodservice, Inc., Deerfield, IL; *U.S. Private*, pg. 244
Peterson, Keith, Exec. V.P.-Global Direct--Regal Ware, Inc., Kewaskum, WI; *U.S. Private*, pg. 917
Peterson, Keith, Exec. V.P.--Kitchen Fair, Jacksonville, AR; *U.S. Private*, pg. 917
Peterson, Keith, Exec. V.P.--Saladmaster, Inc., Arlington, TX; *U.S. Private*, pg. 917
Peterson, Michael A., Exec. V.P.-Fin. & Legal--Geupel DeMars, Inc., Indianapolis, IN; *U.S. Private*, pg. 449
Peterson, Randy O., Exec. V.P.--Flexible Products Company, Marietta, GA; *U.S. Private*, pg. 412
Peterson, Raymond J., Exec. V.P.-Adv.--Hearst Magazines Division, New York, NY; *U.S. Private*, pg. 516
Petersson, Ingvar, Chief Fin. Officer & Exec. V.P.--Stora Kopparbergs Bergslags AB, Falun, Sweden; *Int'l*, pg. 1302
Petinaux, Marcel A., Ph.D., Chief Tech. Officer & Exec. V.P.--Bayer Corporation, Parsippany, NJ; *Int'l*, pg. 172
Petit, Helmut, Dr., Exec. V.P.--Bayerische Hypotheken-und Wechsel-Bank Aktiengesellschaft, Munich, Germany; *Int'l*, pg. 175
Petit, Marc, Exec. V.P.-Fin.--Sabena, Zaventem, Belgium; *Int'l*, pg. 1168
Petnick, Patrick, Exec. V.P.--Texas Homestead Mortgage Co., San Antonio, TX; *U.S. Public*, pg. 945
Petrak, Michael R., Exec. V.P. & Gen. Mgr.--The Kansas City Star Company, Kansas City, MO; *U.S. Public*, pg. 964
Petras, Michael B., Exec. V.P.-Retail Opers.--Riser Foods, Inc., Bedford, OH; *U.S. Private*, pg. 450
Petrecca, Vincent R., Exec. V.P.--Hubbell Incorporated, Orange, CT; *U.S. Public*, pg. 844
Petri, Eberhard, Exec. V.P.-Res. & Devel.--Siemens Nixdorf Information Systems Inc., Burlington, MA; *Int'l*, pg. 1245
Petricca, Perri C., Exec. V.P.--Petricca Industries, Inc., Pittsfield, MA; *U.S. Private*, pg. 858
Petrich, James R., Exec. V.P.-Grp. Opers.--Willis Corroon Corp. of Kansas, Wichita, KS; *Int'l*, pg. 1506
Petrillo, John C., Exec. V.P.-Strategy & New Service Innovation--AT&T Corporation, Basking Ridge, NJ; *U.S. Public*, pg. 10
Petro, Kenneth, Exec. V.P.--Cal-Air Inc., Whittier, CA; *U.S. Private*, pg. 199
Petrovich, Jon, Exec. V.P. & Brand Mgr.--CNN Headline News, Atlanta, GA; *U.S. Public*, pg. 1614
Petrovich, Jon, Exec. V.P., News Dir.-Headline News & Brand Mgr.--CNN (Cable News Network), Atlanta, GA; *U.S. Public*, pg. 1614
Petry, Paul E., Pres. & Chief Oper. Officer--Boston Mutual Life Insurance Co., Canton, MA; *U.S. Private*, pg. 161
Pett, John L., Chief Credit Officer & Exec. V.P.--First Empire State Corporation, Buffalo, NY; *U.S. Public*, pg. 631
Pett, John L., Exec. V.P.--Manufacturers & Traders Trust Company, Buffalo, NY; *U.S. Public*, pg. 631
Pettiette, Patrick L., Exec. V.P.-Intl.--Heavy Civil Construction, Boise, ID; *U.S. Public*, pg. 1134
Pettiette, Patrick L., Exec. V.P.-Intl. Infrastructure--International Infrastructure Division, Boise, ID; *U.S. Public*, pg. 1134
Pettus, Robert D., Jr., Exec. V.P.--Coca-Cola Bottling Co. Consolidated, Charlotte, NC; *U.S. Public*, pg. 391
Peugeot, Pierre, Sr. Exec. V.P.--PSA Peugeot Citroen, Paris, France; *Int'l*, pg. 1020
Peus, Busso, Dr., Exec. V.P.--Hochtief AG, Essen, Germany; *Int'l*, pg. 623
Peyrache, Marie-Claude, Exec. Dir.-Communications--France Telecom, Paris, France; *Int'l*, pg. 503
Pezier, Jacques, Exec. Dir.--Tokyo-Mitsubishi International plc, London, United Kingdom; *Int'l*, pg. 158

Pfau, Nancy, Exec. V.P.--International Wine Accessories, Inc., Dallas, TX; *U.S. Private*, pg. 572

Pflaster, Leon, Exec. V.P.--Arnold Steel Company, Inc., Lakewood, NJ; *U.S. Private*, pg. 84

Pfluger, Bob, Exec. V.P.--San Angelo National Bank, San Angelo, TX; *U.S. Public*, pg. 633

Pforzheimer, Harry, Exec. V.P.-W. Coast Opers.--The Weber Group, Palo Alto, CA; *U.S. Private*, pg. 1157

Phansuwan, Kunjanaphan, Exec. V.P.--Siam City Credit Finance & Securities Co., Ltd., Bangkok, Thailand; *Int'l*, pg. 1239

Philipp, Elizabeth R., Exec. V.P., Gen. Counsel & Sec.--Collins & Aikman Corporation, Charlotte, NC; *U.S. Public*, pg. 399

Phillips, Carole, Exec. V.P. & Media Dir.--Focus Media, Santa Monica, CA; *U.S. Private*, pg. 415

Phillips, Donald J.M., Exec. V.P.--Ted Thomas Associates Inc. Advertising, Philadelphia, PA; *U.S. Private*, pg. 1083

Phillips, Gary, Chief Fin. Officer & Exec V.P.--Associated Wholesale Grocers, Inc., Kansas City, KS; *U.S. Private*, pg. 93

Phillips, Kurt A., Chief Fin. Officer & Exec. V.P.--Lebanon Valley Farmers Bank, Lebanon, PA; *U.S. Public*, pg. 688

Phillips, Martin, Chief Oper. Officer & Exec. V.P.--Kline Iron & Steel Co., Inc., Columbia, SC; *U.S. Private*, pg. 626

Phillips, Peter, Exec. V.P. -Admin. & Gen. Counsel--The Stop & Shop Companies, Inc., Quincy, MA; *Int'l*, pg. 750

Phillips, Steve, Exec. V.P. & Gen. Counsel--Intergraph Corporation, Huntsville, AL; *U.S. Public*, pg. 890

Phillips, Steven D., Exec. V.P.-Consumer Div.--Countrywide Funding Corporation, Pasadena, CA; *U.S. Public*, pg. 453

Phillips, Todd, Exec. V.P.--Quoizel Inc., Goose Creek, SC; *U.S. Private*, pg. 901

Phillips, Tom, Exec. V.P.--Edelman Worldwide, Inc., New York, NY; *U.S. Private*, pg. 362

Phillips, Toni, Exec. V.P.--Quoizel Inc., Goose Creek, SC; *U.S. Private*, pg. 901

Philosophe, Jacques, Exec. V.P.-Opers.--Cinram Ltd., Scarborough, Canada; *Int'l*, pg. 293

Philport, Joseph, Exec. V.P.-National Media--Competitive Media Reporting, New York, NY; *Int'l*, pg. 1447

Philpott, Joseph, Exec. V.P.-Mfg.--Bassett Furniture Industries, Incorporated, Bassett, VA; *U.S. Public*, pg. 193

Phinyawatana, Thermchai, Exec. V.P.--Finance One Public Company Limited, Bangkok, Thailand; *Int'l*, pg. 484

Phornprapha, Phornpun, Exec. V.P.--Bumble Bee Seafoods Inc., San Diego, CA; *U.S. Private*, pg. 526

Picca, Bruno, Sr. Exec. V.P.-Acctg. & Admin.--Istituto Bancario San Paolo Di Torino S.p.A., Turin, Italy; *Int'l*, pg. 691

Piccioni, Samuel A., Exec. V.P.--Laurel Bank, Johnstown, PA; *U.S. Public*, pg. 164

Piccola, Jay, Exec. V.P.--Puma North America, Brockton, MA; *Int'l*, pg. 1072

Picini, Anthony M., Chief Fin. Officer & Exec. V.P.--PHP Healthcare Corporation, Reston, VA; *U.S. Public*, pg. 1241

Picker, Michael, Chief Oper. Officer & Exec. V.P.--Infresco Corporation, Sarasota, FL; *U.S. Public*, pg. 420

Pickering, T.H., Exec. V.P. & Sec.--Westfield Companies, Westfield Center, OH; *U.S. Private*, pg. 1169

Pickett, Edwin G., Chief Fin. Officer & Exec. V.P.--TIG Holdings, Inc., New York, NY; *U.S. Public*, pg. 1555

Pickryl, W. Jeffrey, Exec. V.P.--Liberty Bank & Trust Company of Oklahoma City, Oklahoma City, OK; *U.S. Public*, pg. 174

Piecuch, John, Exec. V.P.-Cement Strategy, Concrete & Aggregates--Lafarge S.A., Paris, France; *Int'l*, pg. 788

Pielsticker, James E., Exec. V.P.--Arrow Gear Company, Downers Grove, IL; *U.S. Private*, pg. 85

Pierce, Frank R., Chief Fin. Officer, Exec. V.P., Treas. & Sec.--Gulfmark Offshore Inc., Houston, TX; *U.S. Public*, pg. 769

Pierce, Howard, Exec. V.P.-Americas--ABB Asea Brown Boveri (Holding) Ltd., Zurich, Switzerland; *Int'l*, pg. 1

Pierce, Jon P., Exec. V.P.-Human Resources--Mercantile Bancorporation Inc., Saint Louis, MO; *U.S. Public*, pg. 1087

Pierne, James G., Exec. V.P.--Farmers and Merchants Bank and Trust, Hagerstown, MD; *U.S. Public*, pg. 1542

Pierson, J. David, Exec. V.P.--Cole Vision Corporation, Cleveland, OH; *U.S. Public*, pg. 396

Pierucci, P.J., Exec. V.P.-Retail B.U.--The Chinet Co., Norwalk, CT; *Int'l*, pg. 1146

Pierzchalski, Lawrence J., Exec. V.P.-Risk Mngmt.--Mortgage Guaranty Insurance Corporation, Milwaukee, WI; *U.S. Public*, pg. 1026

Pieterse, H.M.L., Exec. V.P.--ABN-AMRO Holding N.V., Amsterdam, Netherlands; *Int'l*, pg. 8

Pietrafesa, Michael, Exec. V.P.--Goldberger Doll Mfg. Company, Inc., Brooklyn, NY; *U.S. Private*, pg. 459

Pigott, Daniel S., Exec. V.P.-Cashiers Div.--First Security Bank of New Mexico, Albuquerque, NM; *U.S. Public*, pg. 637

Pike, Raymond D., Exec. V.P.-Intl. Corp. Devel.--International Game Technology, Reno, NV; *U.S. Public*, pg. 900

Pilch, Patrick, Exec. V.P.--Andrea Electronics Corporation, Long Island City, NY; *U.S. Public*, pg. 112

Pillow, Glen E., Exec. V.P.--Centex-Rodgers Construction Company, Nashville, TN; *U.S. Public*, pg. 322

Pinault, Michel, Sr. Exec. V.P.-Grp. Admin.--AXA-UAP, Paris, France; *Int'l*, pg. 18

Pinero Ferrer, Emilio E., Esq., Exec. V.P.--BanPonce Corporation, Hato Rey, PR; *U.S. Public*, pg. 176

Pines, Robert, Exec. V.P.-Opers.--Vanity Fair, New York, NY; *U.S. Public*, pg. 1702

Pinnick, Larry V., Exec. V.P.--Spangler Inc., Kansas City, KS; *U.S. Private*, pg. 1020

Pinoncely, Geoffroy, Exec. V.P.-Grocery Prods. Div.--Danone Group, Paris, France; *Int'l*, pg. 379

Pinotti, Humberto Fabio Fischer, Exec. V.P.-Retail Banking--Banco Itau S.A., Sao Paulo, Brazil; *Int'l*, pg. 142

Pinto, Michael, Chief Fin. Officer & Exec. V.P.--First Empire State Corporation, Buffalo, NY; *U.S. Public*, pg. 631

Pinto, Michael P., Exec. V.P.--Manufacturers & Traders Trust Company, Buffalo, NY; *U.S. Public*, pg. 631

Piontkowski, John, Chief Fin. Officer & Exec. V.P.--Smith Corona Corp., Cortland, NY; *U.S. Private*, pg. 1007

Piper, A. Coleman, Exec. V.P.-Stores--Proffitt's, Inc., Alcoa, TN; *U.S. Public*, pg. 1333

Piper, A. Coleman, Exec. V.P.-Stores--Proffitt's of Tri-Cities, Inc., Alcoa, TN; *U.S. Public*, pg. 1334

Piper, Steve, Exec. V.P.-Sls.--Grassland Equipment & Irrigation Corp., Latham, NY; *U.S. Private*, pg. 471

Pirchl, Helmut, Exec. V.P.-Sulzer Ruti Group--Sulzer Ltd., Winterthur, Switzerland; *Int'l*, pg. 1305

Pirchl, Helmut, Exec. V.P.--Sulzer Ruti Group, Bern, Switzerland; *Int'l*, pg. 1307

Pirkau, Arno F., Exec. V.P.--Sun Coast Industries, Inc., Dallas, TX; *U.S. Public*, pg. 1529

Pirone, Jeffrey V., Chief Fin. Officer & Exec. V.P.--Orbital Sciences Corporation, Dulles, VA; *U.S. Public*, pg. 1229

Pisano, Robert A., Exec. V.P.--Metro-Goldwyn-Mayer Inc., Santa Monica, CA; *U.S. Public*, pg. 1101

Piscopo, Phillip, Chief Fin. Officer & Exec. V.P.--Neuman Distributors, Inc., Ridgefield, NJ; *U.S. Public*, pg. 1169

Piske, Richard A., III, Exec. V.P.--Olsten Corporation, Melville, NY; *U.S. Public*, pg. 1220

Pitcher, Max G., Exec. V.P.-Exploration & Production--Conoco Inc., Houston, TX; *U.S. Public*, pg. 531

Pitchford, Terry, Chief Oper. Officer & Exec. V.P.-Distr. Div.--Rolland Inc., Saint-Jerome, Canada; *Int'l*, pg. 273

Pitschel, Ernest O., Exec. V.P. & Chief Oper. Officer--Atlas Consolidated Mining & Development Corporation, Manila, Philippines; *Int'l*, pg. 95

Pittman, Homer S., Exec. V.P. & Cashier--First National Bank of Abilene, Abilene, TX; *U.S. Public*, pg. 633

Pittman, Robert, Exec. V.P.--Trend Offset Printing Services, Los Alamitos, CA; *U.S. Private*, pg. 1099

Pizzo, Thomas V., Exec. V.P.--Century Business Credit Corporation, New York, NY; *U.S. Private*, pg. 225

Plageman, David, Exec. V.P.--Scott & Stringfellow, Inc., Richmond, VA; *U.S. Public*, pg. 1445

Plais, Marie-Helene, M.D., Exec. V.P.--Sofamor Danek Group, Inc., Memphis, TN; *U.S. Public*, pg. 1482

Plakias, Greg, Sr. Exec. V.P.--A.W. Chesterton Company, Stoneham, MA; *U.S. Private*, pg. 234

Plansker, Dennis H., Exec. V.P. & Broadcast Services Dir.--Campbell-Ewald Advertising, Warren, MI; *U.S. Public*, pg. 908

Platt, Roger, Chief Fin. Officer & Exec. V.P.--Brooks Brothers, New York, NY; *Int'l*, pg. 843

Pleasant, Richard, Chief Fin. Officer & Exec. V.P.--Industrial Electronic Engineers, Inc., Van Nuys, CA; *U.S. Private*, pg. 561

Plumlee, Daniel L., Chief Oper. Officer & Exec. V.P.--The L & B Group, Dallas, TX; *U.S. Public*, pg. 1673

Pockmire, James, Exec. V.P.-Fin.--Wyse Advertising, Cleveland, OH; *U.S. Private*, pg. 1193

Podany, William J., Chief Oper. Officer & Exec. V.P.--ShopKo Stores, Inc., Green Bay, WI; *U.S. Public*, pg. 1467

Podovsky, Walter, Exec. V.P.--Leblanc Communications, Inc., Richardson, TX; *U.S. Private*, pg. 656

Poer, Bryard, Chief Oper. Officer & Exec. V.P.--First American Field Services, Lakewood, NJ; *U.S. Public*, pg. 625

Poero, Edgardo, Exec. V.P.-Legal--Istituto Bancario San Paolo Di Torino S.p.A., Turin, Italy; *Int'l*, pg. 691

Pogge, Hans J., Exec. V.P.--Grassland Equipment & Irrigation Corp., Blasdell, NY; *U.S. Private*, pg. 471

Pohjola, Markku, Exec. V.P.--Merita Bank Ltd., Helsinki, Finland; *Int'l*, pg. 858

Pohjolainen, Juhani, Vice Chm. & Sr. Exec. V.P.--Enso Oyj, Helsinki, Finland; *Int'l*, pg. 455

Pohle, Klaus, Dr., Exec. Dir.-Fin. & Admin.--Schering AG, Berlin, Germany; *Int'l*, pg. 1203

Pohlhaus, Mark G., Exec. V.P.--Westminster Bank & Trust Co. of Carroll County, Westminster, MD; *U.S. Public*, pg. 1089

Pohlig, Rolf, Dr., Exec. V.P.--Veba AG, Dusseldorf, Germany; *Int'l*, pg. 1454

Pohlmann, Edwin G, Exec. V.P.-Stores & Opers.--Montgomery Ward & Co., Inc., Chicago, IL; *U.S. Private*, pg. 758

Polack, James, Exec. V.P.--Acme Poultry Company, Inc., Renton, WA; *U.S. Private*, pg. 13

Polin, Allan B., Exec. V.P.-Loan Admin.--Aames Financial Corporation, Los Angeles, CA; *U.S. Public*, pg. 12

Polito, Joseph S., Exec. V.P. & Gen. Mgr.--Piccadilly Cafeterias, Inc., Baton Rouge, LA; *U.S. Public*, pg. 1294

Pollack, Matt, Exec. V.P.--Stock Yards Packing Co., Inc., Chicago, IL; *U.S. Private*, pg. 1043

Pollack, Paul R., Chief Oper. Officer & Exec. V.P.--Hudson General Corporation, Great Neck, NY; *U.S. Public*, pg. 845

Pollack, Thomas, Exec. V.P. & Chm.-Universal Studios Motion Picture Grp.--Universal Studios, Inc., Universal City, CA; *Int'l*, pg. 1215

Pollak, William L., Exec. V.P.-Circulation--The New York Times, New York, NY; *U.S. Public*, pg. 1174

Pollard, Kevin H., Exec. V.P.--P.T. Freeport Indonesia Co., New Orleans, LA; *U.S. Public*, pg. 681

Pollock, Duncan, Exec. V.P.--Ammirati, Puris & Lintas, Inc., New York, NY; *U.S. Private*, pg. 66

Pollock, E. Kears, Exec. V.P.-Coatings & Resins--PPG Industries, Inc., Pittsburgh, PA; *U.S. Public*, pg. 1245

Pollock, Jerry, Exec. V.P.--Zenith Administrators, Inc., Washington, DC; *U.S. Private*, pg. 1116

Polosky, Michael J., Exec. V.P.-Network & Systems Opers.--AirTouch Cellular, Walnut Creek, CA; *U.S. Public*, pg. 34

Polsky, Larry M., Exec. V.P.-Admin.--Coltec Holdings Inc, Charlotte, NC; *U.S. Public*, pg. 401

Poltrack, David, Exec. V.P.-Plng. & Res.--CBS Television Network, New York, NY; *U.S. Public*, pg. 274

Pommerville, Robert W., Exec. V.P., Gen. Counsel & Sec.--Beverly Enterprises, Inc., Fort Smith, AR; *U.S. Public*, pg. 227

Pompeo, Patrick, Exec. V.P. & Gen. Mgr.--Blimpie International, Inc., Atlanta, GA; *U.S. Public*, pg. 236

Pomplun, Edwin, Exec. V.P.-Asset Mngmt. Division--CVB Financial Corp., Ontario, CA; *U.S. Public*, pg. 286

Pond, Richard G., Chief Fin. Officer, Chief Oper. Officer & Exec. V.P.--Boston Celtics Limited Partnership, Boston, MA; *U.S. Public*, pg. 246

Pont, Neil F., Exec. V.P.-Branch Delivery Sys.--Amwest Surety Insurance Company, Calabasas, CA; *U.S. Public*, pg. 106

Pontal, Jean-Francois, Exec. V.P.-Consumer Services--France Telecom, Paris, France; *Int'l*, pg. 503

Pontikes, William N., Exec. V.P.--Comdisco, Inc., Rosemont, IL; *U.S. Public*, pg. 407

Pool, Jean D., Exec. V.P. & Dir. of North America Media Services--J. Walter Thompson Company, New York, NY; *Int'l*, pg. 1483

Pope, Bill, Exec. V.P.-Ins.--John Burnham & Co., San Diego, CA; *U.S. Private*, pg. 186

Pope, James Arthur, Chief Fin. Officer, Exec. V.P. & Gen. Counsel--Variety Wholesalers, Incorporated, Raleigh, NC; *U.S. Private*, pg. 1134

Pope, N.W., Exec. V.P.-Mktg. Grp.--First Hawaiian Bank, Honolulu, HI; *U.S. Public*, pg. 634

Popielarski, Pamela, Exec. V.P. & Asst. Gen. Mgr.-Opers.--Tropicana Casino & Resort, Atlantic City, NJ; *U.S. Public*, pg. 159

Popkowski, John, Exec. V.P.-Adv. Sls.-MTV Networks--MTV Networks, New York, NY; *U.S. Private*, pg. 779

Porcherot, Claude, Exec. V.P.-Domestic Subsidiaries & Real Estate--Banque Nationale de Paris, Paris, France; *Int'l*, pg. 163

Port, Frederick, Exec. V.P.-Intl. Sls.--Callaway Golf Company, Carlsbad, CA; *U.S. Public*, pg. 294

Porter, W. Thomas, Jr., Exec. V.P. & Mgr.-Capital Mngmnt. Grp.--Seafirst Corporation, Seattle, WA; *U.S. Public*, pg. 181

Porter, William E., Exec. V.P.--Comdial Corporation, Charlottesville, VA; *U.S. Public*, pg. 407

Portera, Joseph P., Chief Oper. Officer & Exec. V.P.-Eastern Div.--Costco Wholesale, Issaquah, WA; *U.S. Public*, pg. 451

Porterfield, Richard, Exec. V.P.-Forest Products--Champion International Corp., Stamford, CT; *U.S. Public*, pg. 333

Portman, Jeff, Exec. V.P.-Sls. & Mktg.--AMC, Inc., Atlanta, GA; *U.S. Private*, pg. 6

Posa, Sandy, Exec. V.P. & Pres.-Consumer Imaging Grp.--Polaroid Corporation, Cambridge, MA; *U.S. Public*, pg. 1313

Poser, Gerald J., Exec. V.P.--New Mech Companies, Inc., Saint Paul, MN; *U.S. Private*, pg. 794

Poses, Frederic M., Exec. V.P. & Pres.-Engineered Materials--AlliedSignal Inc., Morristown, NJ; *U.S. Public*, pg. 49

Post, D., Exec. V.P.--ABN-AMRO Holding N.V., Amsterdam, Netherlands; *Int'l*, pg. 8

Postaer, Larry, Exec. V.P.-Creative Services--Rubin Postaer & Associates, Santa Monica, CA; *U.S. Private*, pg. 949

Potier, Benoit, Exec. V.P.--Air Liquide S.A., Paris, France; *Int'l*, pg. 37

Potter-Brotman, Jennifer, Exec. V.P.-Corp.--The Forum Corporation, Boston, MA; *U.S. Private*, pg. 420

Potter, Billy, Exec. V.P.--Enco Materials, Inc., Nashville, TN; *U.S. Private*, pg. 375

Potter, Kevin, Exec. V.P.--Optima Direct, Inc., Vienna, VA; *U.S. Public*, pg. 1224

Potter, Linda, Chief Fin. Officer & Exec. V.P.--SunTrust Banks of Tennessee, Inc., Nashville, TN; *U.S. Public*, pg. 1538

Potts, M. William, Chief Fin. Officer & Exec. V.P.--Johnny Appleseed's, Inc., Beverly, MA; *U.S. Private*, pg. 590

Pountney, Charles W., Chief Oper. Officer & Exec. V.P.--Paul Inman Associates Inc., Farmington, MI; *U.S. Private*, pg. 564

Powderly, Robert G., Exec. V.P.--Eastern Utilities Associates, Boston, MA; *U.S. Public*, pg. 549

Powell, H. Verne, Exec. V.P.-Corp. Devel. & External Affairs--Shaw's Supermarkets, Inc., East Bridgewater, MA; *Int'l*, pg. 1170

Powell, H.E., Exec. V.P.--Auto-Owners Insurance, Lansing, MI; *U.S. Private*, pg. 100

Powell, Harry H., Exec. V.P.--Mills & Lupton Supply Co., Chattanooga, TN; *U.S. Public*, pg. 847

Powell, Larry, Exec. V.P.--Frank B. Ross Co. Inc., Jersey City, NJ; *U.S. Private*, pg. 946

Powell, P. Paul, Exec. V.P.--Louisville Transportation, Louisville, KY; *U.S. Private*, pg. 567

Powell, Robert L., Exec. V.P.--Custom Control Sensors, Inc., Chatsworth, CA; *U.S. Private*, pg. 298

Power, John, Exec. V.P.-Comml. Affairs--Groupe Air France, Roissy, France; *Int'l*, pg. 559

Power, Perry J., Exec. Dir.--Tokyo-Mitsubishi International plc, London, United Kingdom; *Int'l*, pg. 158

Power, Thomas F., Jr., Chief Fin. Officer & Exec. V.P.--Wisconsin Central Transportation Corporation, Rosemont, IL; *U.S. Public*, pg. 1772

Powers, Frank, Chief Oper. Officer & Exec. V.P.--Matria Healthcare, Inc., Marietta, GA; *U.S. Public*, pg. 1057

Powers, Joe L., Exec. V.P. & Sec.--Thomas Nelson Inc., Nashville, TN; *U.S. Public*, pg. 1167

Powers, John J., Exec. V.P.-Sls. & Mktg.--AEP Industries, Inc., South Hackensack, NJ; *U.S. Public*, pg. 4

Powers, Raymond, Chief Fin. Officer & Exec. V.P.-Fin.--Barton Incorporated, Chicago, IL; *U.S. Public*, pg. 300

Powis, Rick, Exec. V.P.-Pharmacy--Eckerd Corporation, Largo, FL; *U.S. Public*, pg. 917

Poyfair, Paul B., Exec. V.P.-Svcs.--CompUSA, Dallas, TX; *U.S. Public*, pg. 420

Prabhat, Shivakumar, Chief Fin. Officer & Exec. V.P.-Admin--DCA Advertising, Inc., New York, NY; *Int'l*, pg. 393

Prapinmongkolkarn, Yada, Exec. V.P.--The Industrial Finance Corporation of Thailand, Bangkok, Thailand; *Int'l*, pg. 677

Pras, Robert T., Exec. V.P. & Gen. Mgr.--Marriott Distribution Services (MDS), Washington, DC; *U.S. Public*, pg. 1048

Prather, Robert L., Chief Fin. Officer, Exec. V.P., Treas. & Sec.--Kocolene Oil Corp., Seymour, IN; *U.S. Private*, pg. 629

Pratt, Edward T., III, Exec. V.P.--Greate Bay Casino Corporation, Atlantic City, NJ; *U.S. Public*, pg. 760

Pratt, Edward, III, Exec. V.P.--Pratt Casino Corporation, Dallas, TX; *U.S. Public*, pg. 761

Pratt, Stan, Exec. V.P.-Corp.--Deposit Guaranty Corp., Jackson, MS; *U.S. Public*, pg. 500

Pratt, W. Stanley, Exec. V.P.--Deposit Guaranty National Bank, Jackson, MS; *U.S. Public*, pg. 500

Prechter, Suzette J., Exec. V.P.-Credit Approval--Hibernia Corporation, New Orleans, LA; *U.S. Public*, pg. 825

Precious, W. Ernest, Exec. V.P.--Hunt Corporation, Philadelphia, PA; *U.S. Public*, pg. 848

Prendergast, G. Joseph, Exec. V.P.-General Banking--Wachovia Corporation, Winston Salem, NC; *U.S. Public*, pg. 1730

Prendergast, Thomas J., Chief Exec. Officer & Exec. V.P.--R.P. Scherer Korea Limited, Seoul, Korea; *U.S. Public*, pg. 1438

Prescott, Thomas J., Chief Fin. Officer & Exec. V.P.--Synovus Financial Corp., Columbus, GA; *U.S. Public*, pg. 1548

Pressman, Kim I., Exec. V.P., Treas. & Sec.--Price Communications Corporation, New York, NY; *U.S. Public*, pg. 1324

Prestage, Roy, Exec. V.P.-Americas--Fiskars Oy AB, Helsinki, Finland; *Int'l*, pg. 492

Prestridge, James A., Vice Chm. & Exec. V.P.--Teradyne, Inc., Boston, MA; *U.S. Public*, pg. 1580

Preyer, L. Richardson, Jr., Exec. V.P. & Treas.--Vanguard Cellular Systems, Inc., Greensboro, NC; *U.S. Public*, pg. 1707

Prezzano, Wilbur J., Exec. V.P.--Scientific Imaging Systems, New Haven, CT; *U.S. Public*, pg. 550

Pribanic, Gerald J., Chief Fin. Officer & Exec. V.P.--Maytag Corporation, Newton, IA; *U.S. Public*, pg. 1064

Price, Bradford R., Exec. V.P. & Sec.--First Federal Capital Corp., La Crosse, WI; *U.S. Public*, pg. 632

Price, Donald H., Exec. V.P.--Wawa, Inc., Media, PA; *U.S. Private*, pg. 1155

Price, Gerald F., Exec. V.P.-Mfg. & Engrng.--Barr Laboratories Inc., Pomona, NY; *U.S. Public*, pg. 191

Price, John, Chief Oper. Officer & Exec. V.P.--Flexfab Horizons International, Inc., Hastings, MI; *U.S. Private*, pg. 412

Price, R.K., Sr. Exec. V.P.-Mining & Mfg.--R.T. Vanderbilt Company, Inc., Norwalk, CT; *U.S. Private*, pg. 1133

Price, Rodney, Exec. Dir.--Brierley Investments Limited, Wellington, New Zealand; *Int'l*, pg. 215

Price, Rodney, Exec. Dir.--Brierley Investments Ltd., London, United Kingdom; *Int'l*, pg. 215

Price, W. Ralph, Exec. V.P.--Doron Precision Systems, Inc., Binghamton, NY; *U.S. Private*, pg. 341

Priddle, Donald F., Chief Fin. Officer & Exec. V.P.--Cambridge Shopping Centres Limited, Toronto, Canada; *Int'l*, pg. 253

Prieto, Robert, Exec. V.P. & Dir.-Corp. Devel.--Parsons Brinckerhoff Inc., New York, NY; *U.S. Private*, pg. 841

Priez, David B., Exec. V.P.--The B.F. Goodrich Company, Richfield, OH; *U.S. Public*, pg. 751

Prillaman, L.I., Exec. V.P.-Mktg.--Norfolk Southern Corporation, Norfolk, VA; *U.S. Public*, pg. 1190

Primasing, John R., Exec. V.P. & Chief Lending Officer--Farmers & Merchants Bank of Central California, Lodi, CA; *U.S. Private*, pg. 394

Prince, Alan N., Sr. Exec. V.P.-Tile Opers.--Chicago Title Insurance Co., Chicago, IL; *U.S. Public*, pg. 42

Prince, Charles O., III, Exec. V.P., Gen. Counsel & Sec.--Travelers Group, New York, NY; *U.S. Public*, pg. 1632

Prince, Joshua, Exec. V.P. & Assoc. Creative Dir.--Cline, Davis & Mann, Inc., New York, NY; *U.S. Private*, pg. 246

Prince, Robert J., Exec. V.P.-Institutional & Govt. Sls./N. America--FCA International Ltd., Westmount, Canada; *Int'l*, pg. 470

Prince, Thomas E., Chief Fin. Officer & Exec. V.P.--Downey Financial Corp., Newport Beach, CA; *U.S. Public*, pg. 525

Prince, Thomas E., Chief Fin. Officer & Exec. V.P.--Downey Savings & Loan Association, F.A., Newport Beach, CA; *U.S. Public*, pg. 526

Prindiville, R.A., Exec. V.P.--PIMCO Advisors, Stamford, CT; *U.S. Public*, pg. 1296

Prins, E.J., Exec. V.P.--ABN-AMRO Holding N.V., Amsterdam, Netherlands; *Int'l*, pg. 8

Pritchard, Andrew, Exec. Dir.--Iceland Group plc, Deeside, United Kingdom; *Int'l*, pg. 658

Pritchett, Donald W., Exec. V.P.--Union Bank & Trust Co., North Vernon, IN; *U.S. Public*, pg. 633

Pritchett, Jim, Chief Oper. Officer & Exec. V.P.--Ultrak Inc., Lewisville, TX; *U.S. Public*, pg. 1663

Probolus, Jack X., Exec. V.P. & Dir.-Servicing--Willis Corroon Corp. of Massachusetts, Boston, MA; *Int'l*, pg. 1506

Proceviat, Cliff, Exec. V.P.-Prairies--Shoppers Drug Mart, Ltd., Toronto, Canada; *Int'l*, pg. 112

Proctor, Dominic, Exec. V.P., CEO-JWT/London & Area Dir.-UK & Ireland--J. Walter Thompson Company, New York, NY; *Int'l*, pg. 1483

Prohaska, James A., Exec. V.P.-Opers.--Forest City Residential Development Inc., Cleveland, OH; *U.S. Public*, pg. 669

Prokes, James A., Chief Fin. Officer & Exec. V.P.--Ferrous Processing & Trading Co., Detroit, MI; *U.S. Private*, pg. 402

Proulx, Jerard, Exec. V.P.--Purdel, Cooperative Agro-Alimentaire, Bic, Canada; *Int'l*, pg. 1073

Prouty, Dale A., Exec. V.P.--Investment Technology Group, inc., New York, NY; *U.S. Public*, pg. 924

Provato, M.D., Frank L., Exec. V.P. & Corp. Medical Dir.--PHP Healthcare Corporation, Reston, VA; *U.S. Public*, pg. 1241

Pruden, Peter D., III, Exec. V.P. & Sec.--The Smithfield Companies, Inc., Portsmouth, VA; *U.S. Public*, pg. 1479

Prudhomme, Patrick R., Exec. V.P. & Gen. Mgr.-Ralph & Kacoo's--Piccadilly Cafeterias, Inc., Baton Rouge, LA; *U.S. Public*, pg. 1294

Prudhomme, Patrick R., Exec. V.P. & Gen. Mgr.--Piccadilly Restaurants, Inc., Baton Rouge, LA; *U.S. Public*, pg. 1294

Pruett, William, Exec. V.P.--Total System Services, Inc., Columbus, GA; *U.S. Public*, pg. 1550

Pruitt, Thomas J., Chief Fin. Officer & Exec. V.P.--Banknorth Group Inc., Burlington, VT; *U.S. Public*, pg. 186

Pucher, Andrew, Exec. V.P.--Republic National Bank of New York (U.K.), London, United Kingdom; *U.S. Public*, pg. 1381

Puechal, Jacques, Exec. V.P.-Chemicals--Elf Aquitane, Paris, France; *Int'l*, pg. 444

Puglia, Gingen, Exec. V.P.--House of Perfection, Inc., New York, NY; *U.S. Private*, pg. 542

Pulaski, Mark L., Chief Fin. Officer, Exec. V.P. & Treas.--Keystone Financial Inc., Harrisburg, PA; *U.S. Public*, pg. 956

Pulles, Gregory J., Exec. V.P.--TCF Bank Minnesota FSB, Minneapolis, MN; *U.S. Public*, pg. 1554

Pulley, Frank, Chief Fin. Officer--Interstate Van Lines, Inc., Springfield, VA; *U.S. Private*, pg. 573

Pulliam, Eugene S., Exec. V.P. & Publisher--Central Newspapers, Inc., Indianapolis, IN; *U.S. Public*, pg. 326

Pullins, Jerald A., Exec. V.P.-European Opers.--Service Corporation International, Houston, TX; *U.S. Public*, pg. 1460

Pulton, Ted, Exec. V.P. & New Bus. Devel. Dir.--Gotham Incorporated, New York, NY; *U.S. Private*, pg. 677

Purcell, Patrick B., Exec. V.P. & Chief Fin. & Admin. Officer--Paramount Pictures Corporation, Los Angeles, CA; *U.S. Private*, pg. 776

Purdie, Alexander M., Jr., Exec. V.P. & Dir.--The Robinson-Humphrey Company, Inc., Atlanta, GA; *U.S. Public*, pg. 1633

Purdom, Stephen, E., Exec. V.P.-U.S. Opers.--AFLAC Incorporated, Columbus, GA; *U.S. Public*, pg. 28

Purpura, Salvatore, Chief Fin. Officer & Exec. V.P.--Asoma Corporation, White Plains, NY; *U.S. Private*, pg. 89

Purtle, David S., Exec. V.P.-Opers., Transportation & Warehousing--Tyson Foods, Inc., Springdale, AR; *U.S. Public*, pg. 1652

Purvis, Ed, Exec. V.P.--Benjamin Metals Company, Gardena, CA; *U.S. Private*, pg. 133

Purvis, Sandra K., Exec. V.P. & Sec.--A.C. Legg Packing Company, Inc., Birmingham, AL; *U.S. Private*, pg. 658

Pusateri, Paul, Exec. V.P.--Bally's Grand Inc. (Las Vegas), Las Vegas, NV; *U.S. Public*, pg. 829

Putnam, J. Stephen, Exec. V.P.--Raymond James Financial, Inc., Saint Petersburg, FL; *U.S. Public*, pg. 923

Putnam, Kenneth, Exec. V.P.--MultiQuip, Inc., Carson, CA; *Int'l*, pg. 695

Putnam, Ned, Exec. V.P. & Dir.-Team Roche--Sudler & Hennessey, New York, NY; *U.S. Private*, pg. 1197

Putney, John A., Jr., Exec. V.P.-Pension & Annuity Services--Teachers Insurance and Annuity Association, New York, NY; *U.S. Private*, pg. 1071

Puzder, Andrew F., Exec. V.P.--Fidelity National Financial, Inc., Irvine, CA; *U.S. Public*, pg. 620

Pyle, Cynthia, Exec. V.P.--NationsBank of Tennessee, Nashville, TN; *U.S. Public*, pg. 1163

Quartner, Andrew A., Exec. V.P.--AT&T Wireless Services, Kirkland, WA; *U.S. Public*, pg. 11

Quast, Harry S., Exec. V.P.--CACI International Inc, Arlington, VA; *U.S. Public*, pg. 272

Quattro, L., Chief Fin. Officer & Exec. V.P.--BBDO Canada, Toronto, Canada; *U.S. Private*, pg. 104

Quay, Sharon R., Exec. V.P. & Dir.-Human Resources--Dain Rauscher Corporation, Minneapolis, MN; *U.S. Public*, pg. 476

Quee, Lim Kim, Exec. V.P.--DBS Bank Ltd., Singapore, Singapore; *Int'l*, pg. 350

Queenan, William H., Chief Credit Officer & Exec. V.P.--Norwest Corporation, Minneapolis, MN; *U.S. Public*, pg. 1201

Quick, Peter D., Exec. V.P.--Midlantic Bank, N.A., Edison, NJ; *U.S. Public*, pg. 1242

Quillinan, Robert J., Chief Fin. Officer & Exec. V.P.--Coherent, Inc., Santa Clara, CA; *U.S. Public*, pg. 395

Quilty, Jay, Exec. V.P. & Mng. Dir.--The Sawtooth Group, Woodbridge, NJ; *U.S. Private*, pg. 969

Quinio, Jean-Pierre, Sr. V.P.--Compagnie Generale Des Eaux, Paris, France; *Int'l*, pg. 321

Quinn, J.M., Exec. V.P.--The Spencer Group Inc., Princeton, NJ; *U.S. Private*, pg. 1025

Quinn, James E., Exec. V.P.--Tiffany & Co., New York, NY; *U.S. Public*, pg. 1608

Quinn, Jody, Exec. V.P. & Gen. Mgr.--Edelman Worldwide, Inc., New York, NY; *U.S. Private*, pg. 362

Quinn, Neil, Exec. Dir.-Fire Detection--Halma p.l.c., Amersham, United Kingdom; *Int'l*, pg. 589

Quinn, Robert, Exec. V.P. & Gen. Mgr.--San Francisco Giants Baseball Club, San Francisco, CA; *U.S. Private*, pg. 964

Quinn, Vincent K., Exec. V.P.-Admin. & Claims--GMAC Insurance Holdings, Detroit, MI; *U.S. Public*, pg. 719

Quintanilla Ochoa, Raul, Sr. Exec. V.P., Gen. Counsel & Sec.--Grupo Casa Autrey, Mexico, Mexico; *Int'l*, pg. 573

Quirk, Brian, Exec. V.P.-Sls. & Affiliate Rels.--Playboy Entertainment Group, Inc., Beverly Hills, CA; *U.S. Public*, pg. 1310

Raad, Ramzi, Exec. V.P.--Intermarkets Advertising, Beirut, Lebanon; *Int'l*, pg. 680

Raasch, Jeff, Exec. V.P.-Sls. & Mktg.--Enerfab Inc., Cincinnati, OH; *U.S. Private*, pg. 376

Rabil, Richard J., Pres. & Exec. V.P.--The Van Metres Companies, Burke, VA; *U.S. Private*, pg. 1132

Rabin, Ed, Exec. V.P.--Hyatt Corporation, Chicago, IL; *U.S. Private*, pg. 551

Rabin, Ed, Exec. V.P.--Hyatt Hotels Corporation, Chicago, IL; *U.S. Private*, pg. 551

Rabinowicz, Daniel, Exec. V.P.-Montreal--Cossette Communication Marketing, Quebec, Canada; *Int'l*, pg. 335

Rabinowicz, Daniel, Exec. V.P.--Cossette Communication-Marketing (Montreal) Inc., Montreal, Canada; *Int'l*, pg. 336

Rabinowitz, Marvin, Exec. V.P.--Republic National Bank of New York, New York, NY; *U.S. Public*, pg. 1380

Rabito, Joe, Exec. V.P.-Opers.--Trans Leasing International Inc., Northbrook, IL; *U.S. Public*, pg. 1628

Race, Kevin D., Chief Fin. Officer, Exec. V.P. & Treas.--Fleet Mortgage Group, Inc., Columbia, SC; *U.S. Public*, pg. 650

Radabaugh, James, Exec. V.P.--Norstan, Inc., Plymouth, MN; *U.S. Public*, pg. 1192

Radcliffe, R. Stephen, Exec. V.P.--American United Life Insurance Company, Indianapolis, IN; *U.S. Private*, pg. 64

Radde, Donald E., Exec. V.P. & Sec.--Pinnacle Financial Services Inc., Saint Joseph, MI; *U.S. Public*, pg. 1297

Radecki, Joseph J., Jr., Exec. V.P. & Dir.-Fin. Restructuring--Jefferies & Company, Inc., Los Angeles, CA; *U.S. Public*, pg. 925

Radigan, Robert, Sr. Exec. V.P.--Plasti-Kote Company Inc., Medina, OH; *U.S. Private*, pg. 870

Radzievsky, Anna, Chief Oper. Officer & Exec. V.P.--YAR Communications, New York, NY; *U.S. Private*, pg. 1195

Raevis, John J., Exec. V.P., Gen. Mgr. & New Bus. Contact--de la Cruz & Associates, San Juan, PR; *U.S. Private*, pg. 318

Raff, Beryl, Chief Oper. Officer & Exec. V.P.--Zale Corporation, Irving, TX; *U.S. Public*, pg. 1789

Raft, Steve, Exec. V.P.-Mktg.--Oshman's Sporting Goods, Inc., Houston, TX; *U.S. Public*, pg. 1233

Rager, Jim T., Exec. V.P.-Personal Fin. Services--Royal Bank of Canada, Toronto, Canada; *Int'l*, pg. 1131

Ragsdale, Charles S., Exec. V.P.--Embers Charcoal Company, Inc., Conway, SC; *U.S. Private*, pg. 373

Ragsdale, M. Terry, Chief Oper. Officer & Exec. V.P.--Southern States Cooperative, Inc., Richmond, VA; *U.S. Private*, pg. 1017

Raiden, Norman H., Exec. V.P.-Legal & Subsidiaries--Coast Savings Financial, Inc., Los Angeles, CA; *U.S. Public*, pg. 388

Rainer, J.W. Jr., Exec. V.P.--SouthTrust Corporation, Birmingham, AL; *U.S. Public*, pg. 1491

Rainey, William O., Exec. V.P. & Chief Banking Officer--Trustmark Corporation, Jackson, MS; *U.S. Public*, pg. 1643

Rainey, William O., Exec. V.P.--Trustmark National Bank, Jackson, MS; *U.S. Public*, pg. 1643

Rains, Kenneth A., Exec. V.P. & Trust Grp. Exec.--Hibernia Corporation, New Orleans, LA; *U.S. Public*, pg. 825

Rajan, Ramesh, Exec. V.P. & Chief Fin. Officer--Bozell Worldwide, Inc., New York, NY; *U.S. Public*, pg. 1642

Rajewski, Ray, Exec. V.P.-Stations Grp.--Paramount Pictures Corporation, Los Angeles, CA; *U.S. Private*, pg. 776

Ralser, W. Paul, Exec. V.P.-House America--Countrywide Funding Corporation, Pasadena, CA; *U.S. Public*, pg. 453

Ralston, Bob D., Exec. V.P.-Maintenance--J.B. Hunt Transport Services, Inc., Lowell, AR; *U.S. Public*, pg. 849

Ralston, Ronald, Exec. V.P.-Mktg. & Sls.--Parfums International Ltd., New York, NY; *Int'l*, pg. 1435

Ramaker, David B., Exec. V.P.--Chemical Financial Corporation, Midland, MI; *U.S. Public*, pg. 345

Rambo, Barbara L., Grp. Exec. V.P.-Commercial Banking--Bank of America NT&SA, San Francisco, CA; *U.S. Public*, pg. 180

Ramseth, Paul R., Exec. V.P.-Strategic Devel.--Lutheran Brotherhood, Minneapolis, MN; *U.S. Private*, pg. 681

Ramsey, James H., Exec. V.P.--Diamond Hill Plywood Company, Darlington, SC; *U.S. Private*, pg. 311

Ramseyer, Bryon J., Exec. V.P.--Gamma One, Inc., North Haven, CT; *U.S. Public*, pg. 228

Ramstedt, Ola, Exec. V.P.--Skandia Insurance Company Limited, Stockholm, Sweden; *Int'l*, pg. 1256

Rand, A. Barry, Exec. V.P.-Opers.--Xerox Corporation, Stamford, CT; *U.S. Public*, pg. 1783

Randall, Andrew E., Exec. V.P.-Reg. Chm.-Cash Mngmt.--Starbanc Corporation, Cincinnati, OH; *U.S. Public*, pg. 1510

Randazzo, Chuck, Exec. V.P.--Creative Marketing International Corp., West Chicago, IL; *U.S. Private*, pg. 287

Ranelli, John R., Exec. V.P.--The Stride Rite Corporation, Lexington, MA; *U.S. Public*, pg. 1524

Rankin, Harley, Jr., Chief Fin. Officer & Exec. V.P.--Silgan Corporation, Stamford, CT; *U.S. Public*, pg. 1473

Rankin, William, Exec. V.P.-Group Opers.--Exide Corporation, Reading, PA; *U.S. Public*, pg. 600

Ranson, James, Exec. V.P.--Everbrite, Inc., Greenfield, WI; *U.S. Private*, pg. 386

Rao, Robert, Exec. V.P.--Tyco Preschool, New York, NY; *U.S. Public*, pg. 1058

Rapaport, Steve, Exec. V.P.-Sls. Opers.--Paramount Pictures Corporation, Los Angeles, CA; *U.S. Private*, pg. 776

Rapenne, Daniel, Sr. Exec. V.P.--Thomson-CSF S.A., Paris, France; *Int'l*, pg. 1383

Rapp, Charles, Chief Fin. Officer & Exec. V.P.-Opers.--Stimson Lane Ltd., Woodinville, WA; *U.S. Public*, pg. 1661

Rapp, James F., Exec. V.P.-Intl. Sls.--Plasti-Kote Company Inc., Medina, OH; *U.S. Private*, pg. 870

Rapp, John B., Exec. V.P.-Trust & Fin. Svcs.--First of America Bank Corporation, Kalamazoo, MI; *U.S. Public*, pg. 636

Rapp, Ronald J., Exec. V.P.-Opers.--Jabil Circuit, Inc., Saint Petersburg, FL; *U.S. Public*, pg. 919

Rapp, William E., Exec. V.P.-Mdsg. & Buying--House of Fabrics, Inc., Sherman Oaks, CA; *U.S. Public*, pg. 842

Rappanello, Daniel, Exec. V.P.--Labinal SA, Montigny-le-Bretonneux, France; *Int'l*, pg. 785

Rappaport, Dean S., Chief Oper. Officer & Exec. V.P.--Catalina Lighting, Inc., Miami, FL; *U.S. Public*, pg. 314

Rappaport, Stanley, Exec. V.P.--House of Ronnie, Inc., New York, NY; *U.S. Private*, pg. 542

Rappold, Charles E., Exec. V.P.--The Bank of New York Company, Inc., New York, NY; *U.S. Public*, pg. 178

Rappolt, William C., Exec. V.P. & Treas.--First Empire State Corporation, Buffalo, NY; *U.S. Public*, pg. 631

Rappolt, William C., Exec. V.P.--Manufacturers & Traders Trust Company, Buffalo, NY; *U.S. Public*, pg. 631

Rascoe, Todd, Exec. V.P.--Thermal Industries, Inc., Pittsburgh, PA; *U.S. Private*, pg. 490

Rasmussen, Robert, Exec. V.P.-Odense--Scan-Ad Gruppen A/S, Arhus, Denmark; *Int'l*, pg. 1198

Rassmann, Michael, Exec. V.P. & Gen. Mgr.--Deutsche Bank AG (New York Branch), New York, NY; *Int'l*, pg. 403

Ratcliff, Karen J., Chief Fin. Officer & Exec. V.P.--PriceSmart Inc., San Diego, CA; *U.S. Public*, pg. 1324

Rath, Charles W., Exec. V.P.-Mktg.--Wendy's International Inc., Dublin, OH; *U.S. Public*, pg. 1754

Rath, John, Exec. V.P.--National Programs Division, Tampa, FL; *U.S. Public*, pg. 1312

Rathlisberger, Arnold, Exec. V.P. & Gen. Counsel--Western Waste Industries, Torrance, CA; *U.S. Public*, pg. 1686

Ratner, James A., Exec. V.P.-Real Estate--Forest City Enterprises, Inc., Cleveland, OH; *U.S. Public*, pg. 667

Ratner, Ronald A., Exec. V.P.--Forest City Enterprises, Inc., Cleveland, OH; *U.S. Public*, pg. 667

Ratner, Warren, Exec. V.P.--Creative Hairdressers, Falls Church, VA; *U.S. Private*, pg. 287

Ratoff, Steven B., Chief Fin. Officer & Exec. V.P.--Brown-Forman Corporation, Louisville, KY; *U.S. Public*, pg. 261

Rau Reist, Susanne, Chief Exec. Officer & Exec. V.P.--WRH Walter Reist Holding AG, Zurich, Switzerland; *Int'l*, pg. 1484

Rauchle, Craig W., Exec. V.P.--Inter-Tel, Incorporated, Phoenix, AZ; *U.S. Public*, pg. 888

Rauwerdink, William J., Chief Fin. Officer, Exec. V.P., Treas. & Sec.--Lason, Inc., Troy, MI; *U.S. Public*, pg. 979

Ravine, Harris, Chief Admin. Officer & Exec. V.P.--Storage Technology Corporation, Louisville, CO; *U.S. Public*, pg. 1522

Rawls, S. Waite, III, Exec. V.P.--ABN AMRO Chicago Corp., Chicago, IL; *Int'l*, pg. 10

Raxter, Alan, Chief Fin. Officer, Exec. V.P. & Treas.--Younkers, Inc., Des Moines, IA; *U.S. Public*, pg. 1334

Ray, David, Exec. V.P.--Bill Ray Nissan, Inc., Longwood, FL; *U.S. Private*, pg. 911

Ray, Gary J., Exec. V.P.-Opers.--Hormel Foods Corp., Austin, MN; *U.S. Public*, pg. 840

Ray, Harold B., Exec. V.P.-Gen. Bus. Unit--Southern California Edison Company, Rosemead, CA; *U.S. Public*, pg. 564

Ray, Michael, Exec. V.P.--American Bankers Insurance Group, Inc., Miami, FL; *U.S. Public*, pg. 67

Ray, Michael T., Exec. V.P.-Info. Svcs.--American Bankers Insurance Co. of Florida, Miami, FL; *U.S. Public*, pg. 67

Ray, Michael T., Exec. V.P.-Information Systems--American Bankers Life Assurance Co. of Florida, Miami, FL; *U.S. Public*, pg. 67

Ray, William D., III, Exec. V.P.--Bill Ray Nissan, Inc., Longwood, FL; *U.S. Private*, pg. 911

Raybuck, Roger, Chief Fin. Officer & Exec. V.P.--Boyer Candy Company Inc., Altoona, PA; *U.S. Private*, pg. 162

Rayfield, Michael R.P., Exec. V.P.-Corp. Banking--Bank of Montreal, Toronto, Canada; *Int'l*, pg. 153

Raymond, Mike, Exec. V.P. & Client Service Dir.--DMB&B St. Louis, Saint Louis, MO; *U.S. Private*, pg. 303

Razon, Jacob, Exec. V.P.--The Israel Electric Corporation Ltd., Haifa, Israel; *Int'l*, pg. 690

Reagan, Larry, Chief Fin. Officer & Exec. V.P.--Pascoe Building Systems, Inc., Columbus, GA; *U.S. Private*, pg. 842

Reagor, Craig, Exec. V.P.--QST Industries, Inc., Chicago, IL; *U.S. Private*, pg. 897

Reaman, John, Exec. V.P.-Logistics--Eastern Fine Paper, Brewer, ME; *U.S. Private*, pg. 357

Reardon, J. Michael, Exec. V.P.-Opers. & Pres.-Home Shopping Club Outlet, Inc.--Home Shopping Network, Inc., Saint Petersburg, FL; *U.S. Public*, pg. 1685

Reardon, Joseph M., Chief Fin. Officer, Exec. V.P. & Treas.--B.M.J. Financial Corp., Bordentown, NJ; *U.S. Public*, pg. 1528

Reardon, Michael J., Exec. V.P.--United States Filter Corporation, Palm Desert, CA; *U.S. Public*, pg. 1681

Reaser, Thomas J., Exec. V.P.--U.S. Office Products Company, Washington, DC; *U.S. Public*, pg. 1686

Reasoner, Chris J., Exec. V.P.--Sysco/Louisville Food Services Co., Louisville, KY; *U.S. Public*, pg. 1552

Rebeille, Jean-Claude, Exec. V.P.--Elf Atochem North America, Inc., Philadelphia, PA; *Int'l*, pg. 445

Reber, Ron, Chief Oper. Officer & Exec. V.P.--SkyWest Inc., Saint George, UT; *U.S. Public*, pg. 1476

Rebmann, Emil, Exec. V.P.-Fin. & Controller--Sika Finanz AG, Baar, Switzerland; *Int'l*, pg. 1248

Recchia, Richard D., Chief Oper. Officer & Exec. V.P.--Mitsubishi Motor Sales of America, Inc., Cypress, CA; *Int'l*, pg. 875

Recchia, Richard D., Exec. V.P.--Diamond Star Motors, Normal, IL; *Int'l*, pg. 875

Receveur, R.F.P.M., Exec. V.P.--ABN-AMRO Holding N.V., Amsterdam, Netherlands; *Int'l*, pg. 8

Reddin, Don, Exec. V.P. & Mng. Dir.-West Coast--Alcone Marketing Group, Irvine, CA; *U.S. Public*, pg. 1223

Redding, P.S., Exec. V.P. & Chief Oper. Officer--Document Management Division, Dayton, OH; *U.S. Public*, pg. 1505

Reddinger, James M., Exec. V.P.-Admin.--Buffalo Rock Company, Birmingham, AL; *U.S. Private*, pg. 179

Reddy, Sena C., Exec. V.P.-Opers.--MMC Networks, Inc., Sunnyvale, CA; *U.S. Public*, pg. 1027

Reding, Nicholas L., Vice Chm.--Monsanto Company, Saint Louis, MO; *U.S. Public*, pg. 1124

Redman, Dale E., Chief Fin. Officer & Exec. V.P.--United Companies Financial Corporation, Baton Rouge, LA; *U.S. Public*, pg. 1675

Redmon, John W., Exec. V.P.-Engrng. & Construction--Brown & Root Inc., Alhambra, CA; *U.S. Public*, pg. 775

Redmond, Donald P., Exec. V.P.--GMAC Insurance Holdings, Detroit, MI; *U.S. Public*, pg. 719

Redmond, Marlin W., Exec. V.P.--Young Supply Company, Detroit, MI; *U.S. Private*, pg. 1202

Reduzzi, Dave, Pres.-JM&A Grp. & Exec. V.P.-JM Family--JM Family Enterprises Inc., Deerfield Beach, FL; *U.S. Private*, pg. 577

Reed, A. Ralph, Exec. V.P.-Opers.--Barrett Resources Corporation, Denver, CO; *U.S. Public*, pg. 191

Reed, Carl W., Jr., Exec. V.P.--Nevada State Bank, Las Vegas, NV; *U.S. Public*, pg. 1793

Reed, Clyde A., Jr., Chief Oper. Officer & Exec. V.P.--Kevco, Inc., Fort Worth, TX; *U.S. Public*, pg. 952

Reed, Fred, Exec. V.P.-Fin.--Smith-Edwards-Dunlap Company, Philadelphia, PA; *U.S. Private*, pg. 1007

Reed, Frederick, Chief Fin. Officer, Exec. V.P. & Gen. Counsel--Wendy's International Inc., Dublin, OH; *U.S. Public*, pg. 1754

Reed, James C., Jr., Exec. V.P., Gen. Counsel & Sec.--Tesoro Petroleum Corporation, San Antonio, TX; *U.S. Public*, pg. 1581

Reed, Robert P., Exec. V.P.--Advanced Forming Technology, Inc., Longmont, CO; *U.S. Public*, pg. 1320

Reed, Scott E., Chief Fin. Officer & Sr. Exec. V.P.--BB&T Corporation, Winston Salem, NC; *U.S. Public*, pg. 159

Reed, Stewart B., Exec. V.P.--Mestek, Inc., Westfield, MA; *U.S. Public*, pg. 1099

Reed, W. Earl, III, Chief Fin. Officer & Exec. V.P.--Vencor, Inc., Louisville, KY; *U.S. Public*, pg. 1711

Reed, William R., Jr., Vice Chm. & Exec. V.P.--National Commerce Bancorporation, Memphis, TN; *U.S. Public*, pg. 1154

Reen, John G., Chief Fin. Officer & Exec. V.P.-Fin.--Caldor, Inc., Norwalk, CT; *U.S. Public*, pg. 292

Reene, Jeffrey C., Exec. V.P. & Gen. Mgr.--Cerner Corporation, Kansas City, MO; *U.S. Public*, pg. 331

Rees, Rick S., Exec. V.P.--Halter Marine Group, Inc., Gulfport, MS; *U.S. Public*, pg. 778

Reese, Ann N., Chief Fin. Officer & Exec. V.P.--ITT Corporation, New York, NY; *U.S. Public*, pg. 1512

Reese, Thomas J., Exec. V.P.-Commercial Div.--Continental General Tire, Inc., Charlotte, NC; *Int'l*, pg. 327

Reeth, George P., Jr., Exec. V.P. & Chief Exec. Officer-Marine, Aviation & Intl. Div.--Willis Faber North America, Inc.-New York, New York, NY; *Int'l*, pg. 1503

Reeves, Dennis G., Sr. V.P. & Chief Auditor--First Security Corporation, Salt Lake City, UT; *U.S. Public*, pg. 637

Reeves, Derril W., Exec. V.P.-Devel.--Phycor, Inc., Nashville, TN; *U.S. Public*, pg. 1293

Reeves, G. Stuart, Exec. V.P.--Electronic Data Systems Corporation, Plano, TX; *U.S. Public*, pg. 569

Reeves, Michael S., Exec. V.P.--Peoples Energy Corporation, Chicago, IL; *U.S. Public*, pg. 1274

Reeves, Randall R., Sr. Exec. V.P.--Riggs National Corporation, Washington, DC; *U.S. Public*, pg. 1389

Reeves, Randall R., Exec. V.P.-Sr. Credit Officer--Riggs Bank N.A., Washington, DC; *U.S. Public*, pg. 1390

Reeves, Stuart, Exec. V.P.--EDS, Government Systems Group, Bethesda, MD; *U.S. Public*, pg. 570

Refvem, Trygve, Exec. V.P.--Norsk Hydro a.s, Oslo, Norway; *Int'l*, pg. 959

Regan, Howard, Exec. V.P.--Nadel Architects, Inc., Los Angeles, CA; *U.S. Private*, pg. 773

Regan, Peter, Exec. V.P., Gen. Mgr. & Media Dir.--Cliff Freeman & Partners, New York, NY; *U.S. Public*, pg. 1422

Regan, Thomas J., Exec. V.P.--PCS Phosphate - Raleigh, Raleigh, NC; *Int'l*, pg. 1064

Regan, Thomas J., Jr., Exec. V.P.-Phosphate--Potash Corporation of Saskatchewan Inc., Saskatoon, Canada; *Int'l*, pg. 1064

Reghitto, William M., Exec. V.P.--State Street Corporation, Boston, MA; *U.S. Public*, pg. 1513

Regis, Jacques, Exec. V.P.-Customers & Distr.--Hydro-Quebec, Montreal, Canada; *Int'l*, pg. 640

Rehg, Robert, Exec. V.P.--Edelman Worldwide, Inc., Washington, DC; *U.S. Private*, pg. 362

Reichard, Sandy, Exec. V.P.--D.L. Blair Inc., Garden City, NY; *U.S. Private*, pg. 148

Reichow, Jim, Exec. V.P.--J & R Film / Moviola Digital Co., Hollywood, CA; *U.S. Private*, pg. 576

Reichwald, William H., Exec. V.P.-Mktg.--Lutheran Brotherhood, Minneapolis, MN; *U.S. Private*, pg. 681

Reid, George, Exec. V.P.-Opers.--American Freightways Corporation, Harrison, AR; *U.S. Public*, pg. 75

Reid, Jack R., Exec. V.P.-Refining--Holly Corporation, Dallas, TX; *U.S. Public*, pg. 830

Reid, James, Exec. V.P.-Opers. & Gen. Mngmt.--Thomas J. Lipton Company, Englewood Cliffs, NJ; *Int'l*, pg. 1435

Reid, John, Chief Fin. Officer & Exec. V.P.-Fin.--BC Gas Inc., Vancouver, Canada; *Int'l*, pg. 114

Reiker, Karl, Exec. V.P.--euroflamm GmbH, Bremen, Germany; *Int'l*, pg. 400

Reiker, Karl, Exec. V.P.--PTG Plasma-Oberflachentechnik GmbH, Horb am Neckar, Germany; *Int'l*, pg. 400

Reilly, Thomas V., Exec. V.P.--Trak Auto Corporation, Landover, MD; *U.S. Public*, pg. 484

Reimers, T.E., Chief Oper. Officer & Exec. V.P.--Mitsubishi Fuso Truck of America, Inc., Bridgeport, NJ; *Int'l*, pg. 875

Rein, Catherine A., Exec. V.P.-Corp. Services--Metropolitan Life Insurance Co., New York, NY; *U.S. Private*, pg. 737

Reiner, Terry, Exec. V.P. & Client Services Dir.--Grey Direct, New York, NY; *U.S. Public*, pg. 764

Reinhard, J. Pedro, Chief Fin. Officer & Exec. V.P.-Fin.--The Dow Chemical Company, Midland, MI; *U.S. Public*, pg. 522

Reinhardt, J. Alec, Chief Fin. Officer & Exec. V.P.--Cooper Tire & Rubber Company, Findlay, OH; *U.S. Public*, pg. 445

Reinhart, Thomas, Exec. V.P.--Production Operators Inc., Houston, TX; *U.S. Public*, pg. 298

Reis, C. Dale, Exec. V.P.--Raytheon Systems Company, Arlington, VA; *U.S. Public*, pg. 1364

Reis, R.J., Exec. V.P.--Serigraph, Inc., West Bend, WI; *U.S. Private*, pg. 985

Reisberg, Alan, Exec. V.P. & Acct. Dir.--Trahan, Burden & Charles, Inc., Baltimore, MD; *U.S. Private*, pg. 1095

Reisch, Marc L., Grp. Pres.-Sls., Chief Oper. Officer & Exec. V.P.--World Color Press, Inc., Greenwich, CT; *U.S. Public*, pg. 1778

Reiser, Herbert, Exec. V.P.--International Shoe Machine Corp., Nashua, NH; *U.S. Private*, pg. 572

Reiser, Richard S., Exec. V.P. & Gen. Counsel--Werner Enterprises, Inc., Omaha, NE; *U.S. Public*, pg. 1754

Reiss, Steven M., Exec. V.P.--HNTB Corporation, Kansas City, MO; *U.S. Private*, pg. 492

Reitman, Morton L., Exec. V.P.--The Tranzonic Companies, Pepper Pike, OH; *U.S. Public*, pg. 1632

Reitman, Stephen F., Exec. V.P.--Reitmans (Canada) Limited, Montreal, Canada; *Int'l*, pg. 1102

Releyea, Robert, Exec. V.P.-Production--Metro-Goldwyn-Mayer Pictures, Inc., Santa Monica, CA; *U.S. Public*, pg. 1102

Relph, Brian P., Exec. V.P.-Ontario Central--Shoppers Drug Mart, Ltd., Toronto, Canada; *Int'l*, pg. 112

Remedios, Robert T., Sr. V.P. & Cashier--San Jose National Bank, San Jose, CA; *U.S. Public*, pg. 1418

Remick, James S., Exec. V.P. & Gen. Mgr.-TRW Occupant Restraint Systems Grp.--TRW Inc., Cleveland, OH; *U.S. Public*, pg. 1558

Remick, James S., Exec. V.P. & Gen. Mgr.--TRW Occupant Restraints Systems, Cleveland, OH; *U.S. Public*, pg. 1558

Rempel, E., Exec. V.P.--Spindelfabrik Suessen, Suessen, Germany; *Int'l*, pg. 1290

Remsing, Dennis, Exec. V.P. & Gen. Mgr.--Rubin Postaer & Associates, Santa Monica, CA; *U.S. Private*, pg. 949

Remsing, Dennis, Exec. V.P. & Gen. Mgr.--RP alpha, Santa Monica, CA; *U.S. Private*, pg. 950

Renalda, Roy, Exec. V.P.-Sls. & Mktg.--The Faxon Company, Inc., Westwood, MA; *Int'l*, pg. 385

Rende, M.J., Exec. V.P.--Hartford Insurance Group of Canada, Willowdale, Canada; *U.S. Public*, pg. 794

Renna, Eugene A., Exec. V.P.--Mobil Oil Corporation, Fairfax, VA; *U.S. Public*, pg. 1118

Renne, Paul F., Chief Fin. Officer & Exec. V.P.--H.J. Heinz Company, Pittsburgh, PA; *U.S. Public*, pg. 805

Renschler, C. Arnold, Exec. V.P.--Beverly Enterprises, Inc., Fort Smith, AR; *U.S. Public*, pg. 227

Rensi, E. Samuel, Exec. V.P.-Mfg.--Remington Arms Company, Inc., Madison, NC; *U.S. Private*, pg. 921

Rentsch, Heinz-Jurgen, Sr. Exec. V.P. & Treas.--Landesbank Rheinland-Pfalz, Mainz, Germany; *Int'l*, pg. 799

Rentschler, Peter R., Exec. V.P. & Grp. Dir.--Young & Rubicam Detroit, Detroit, MI; *U.S. Private*, pg. 1198

Reny, Timothy G., Exec. V.P.--Standard Duplicating Machines Corp., Andover, MA; *U.S. Private*, pg. 1031

Reser, Edward J., Exec. V.P.--United Missouri Bank of Jefferson City, Jefferson City, MO; *U.S. Public*, pg. 1655

Resnik, Jaime, Exec. V.P.--Jean Philippe Fragrances, Inc., New York, NY; *U.S. Public*, pg. 924

Retat, Bernard, Sr. Exec. V.P.--Thomson S.A., Paris, France; *Int'l*, pg. 1381

Retat, Bernard, Sr. Exec. V.P.--Thomson-CSF S.A., Paris, France; *Int'l*, pg. 1383

Rettinger, Dale G., Chief Fin. Officer & Exec. V.P.--Petroleum Development Corporation, Bridgeport, WV; *U.S. Public*, pg. 1280

Reuther, John W., Chief Fin. Officer & Sr. Exec. V.P.--Pioneer American Holding Company, Carbondale, PA; *U.S. Public*, pg. 1298

Revenaud, Pierre, Exec. V.P.-Europe--Schneider Electric S.A., Boulogne-Billancourt, France; *Int'l*, pg. 1207

Reveniaud, Pierre, Exec. V.P.-European Div./Schneider Electric--Schneider S.A., Boulogne-Billancourt, France; *Int'l*, pg. 1207

Revhaug, Omund, Exec. V.P.-Corp. Devel.--Norske Skogindustrier A.S, Skogn, Norway; *Int'l*, pg. 965

Reyners, Thierry, Exec. V.P.-European Grp.--United States Filter Corporation, Palm Desert, CA; *U.S. Public*, pg. 1681

Reynolds, Craig A., Chief Fin. Officer, Exec. V.P. & Sec.--American Homestar Corporation, League City, TX; *U.S. Public*, pg. 83

Reynolds, Fred, Chief Fin. Officer & Exec. V.P.--CBS, New York, NY; *U.S. Public*, pg. 273

Reynolds, Fredric G., Chief Fin. Officer & Exec. V.P.--CBS Corporation, Pittsburgh, PA; *U.S. Public*, pg. 273

Reynolds, James G., Chief Fin. Officer & Exec. V.P.--Health Care Property Investors, Inc., Newport Beach, CA; *U.S. Public*, pg. 801

Reynolds, Randall, Exec. V.P.-Retail Investment Sls.--Compass Bank, Birmingham, AL; *U.S. Public*, pg. 418

Reynolds, Richard I., Chief Oper. Officer & Exec. V.P.--Libbey Owens Ford Co., Toledo, OH; *Int'l*, pg. 1056

Rhe, Dong, Exec. V.P.--Pohang Iron & Steel Co., Ltd., Kyongbuk, Korea; *Int'l*, pg. 1061

Rhee, Taeyoung, Exec. V.P.--Oricom Inc., Seoul, Korea; *Int'l*, pg. 1008

Rhoades, Ann, Exec. V.P.-Human Resources--Doubletree Corporation, Memphis, TN; *U.S. Public*, pg. 1335

Rhoades, Shirrel, Exec. V.P.-Publishing--Marvel Entertainment Group, New York, NY; *U.S. Public*, pg. 1052
Rhoads, Michael A., Chief Fin. Officer & Exec. V.P.--Blue Cross and Blue Shield of Oklahoma, Tulsa, OK; *U.S. Private*, pg. 151
Rhulen, Harry W., Chief Oper. Officer & Exec. V.P.--Frontier Insurance Group, Inc., Rock Hill, NY; *U.S. Public*, pg. 684
Ribohn, Lennart, Sr. Exec. V.P.--Electrolux, AB, Stockholm, Sweden; *Int'l*, pg. 438
Ribolla, Luigi, Exec. V.P. & Pres.-Heinz Europe--H.J. Heinz Company, Pittsburgh, PA; *U.S. Public*, pg. 805
Ricca, Gregory, Exec. V.P.-Bus. Affairs--Viacom Broadcasting Inc., New York, NY; *U.S. Private*, pg. 778
Riccio, Janet, Exec. V.P.--Arnold Communications, Inc., Boston, MA; *U.S. Private*, pg. 83
Rice, C. Thomas, Exec. V.P.--Bank One, Ohio Trust Company, N.A., Columbus, OH; *U.S. Public*, pg. 173
Rice, Glen E., Exec. V.P.--Blue Grass Quality Meats, Crescent Springs, KY; *U.S. Private*, pg. 152
Rice, John, Exec. V.P.-Opers.--Miles Kimball Company, Oshkosh, WI; *U.S. Private*, pg. 745
Rice, Patricia A., Exec. V.P.-Clinical Opers.--Continental Medical Systems, Inc., Mechanicsburg, PA; *U.S. Public*, pg. 839
Rice, William, Exec. V.P.--General Automation, Inc., Irvine, CA; *U.S. Public*, pg. 706
Rich, Bradford R., Chief Fin. Officer, Exec. V.P. & Treas.--SkyWest Inc., Saint George, UT; *U.S. Public*, pg. 1476
Rich, Harold, Exec. V.P. & Chief Oper. Officer--Instinet Corporation, New York, NY; *Int'l*, pg. 1106
Rich, Harry E., Chief Fin. Officer & Exec. V.P.--Brown Group, Inc., Saint Louis, MO; *U.S. Public*, pg. 262
Rich, Marvin P., Exec. V.P.-Strategic Plng., Fin. & Admin.--Kmart Corporation, Troy, MI; *U.S. Public*, pg. 963
Rich, Michael D., Exec. V.P.--RAND, Santa Monica, CA; *U.S. Private*, pg. 908
Rich, Robert C., Exec. V.P.-Opers. & Fin., Controller & Asst. Sec.--Master Lock Company, Milwaukee, WI; *U.S. Public*, *pg. 675*
Richard, Duayne F., Exec. V.P.--The First National Bank of Lafayette, Lafayette, LA; *U.S. Public*, pg. 630
Richard, Ralph S., Exec. V.P.--Johnston, Lemon & Co. Inc., Washington, DC; *U.S. Private*, pg. 595
Richards, Barbara, Exec. V.P.-Mktg.--Chicago Mercantile Exchange, Chicago, IL; *U.S. Private*, pg. 235
Richards, Clarence A., Exec. V.P.-Pre-Construction Devel.--McCrory Construction Co., Inc., Columbia, SC; *U.S. Private*, pg. 720
Richards, Joel, III, Exec. V.P.-Human Resources--El Paso Natural Gas Co., Houston, TX; *U.S. Public*, pg. 567
Richards, John, Exec. V.P.-Mktg.--Four Seasons Hotels Inc., Don Mills, Canada; *Int'l*, pg. 502
Richards, John, Chief Creative Officer & Exec. V.P.--Jack Levy Associates, Chicago, IL; *U.S. Private*, pg. 664
Richards, Scott, Exec. V.P.-Mdsg.--HomeBase, Inc., Irvine, CA; *U.S. Public*, pg. 832
Richards, Thomas E., Exec. V.P.-Communications & Information Prods.--Ameritech Corporation, Chicago, IL; *U.S. Public*, pg. 97
Richardson, F D, Exec. Dir.--WF Corroon-Thatcham, Thatcham, United Kingdom,; *Int'l*, pg. 1502
Richardson, Gerald, Exec. V.P.-Converting Oper.--Green Bay Packaging Inc., Green Bay, WI; *U.S. Private*, pg. 476
Richardson, John, Exec. V.P.--Willis Corroon International/Americas, Nashville, TN; *Int'l*, pg. 1508
Richardson, M. Monte, Chief Oper. Officer & Exec. V.P.--Willis Corroon Corp. of Eugene, Eugene, OR; *Int'l*, pg. 1505
Richardson, Paul, Exec. V.P.--Cott Corporation, Pointe-Claire, Canada; *Int'l*, pg. 337
Richardson, Paul, Exec. V.P.--Cott Corporation International Operations, Burlingame, CA; *Int'l*, pg. 338
Richardson, William, Exec. V.P.-Construction--Circus Circus Hotel Casinos, Inc., Las Vegas, NV; *U.S. Public*, pg. 374
Richey, Ellen, Exec. V.P., Gen. Counsel & Sec.--Providian Financial Corporation, San Francisco, CA; *U.S. Public*, pg. 1338
Richling, Larry, Exec. V.P.--First Mortgage Corporation, Omaha, NE; *U.S. Public*, pg. 501
Richman, Bruce, Exec. V.P.--S.D. Richman Sons, Inc., Philadelphia, PA; *U.S. Private*, pg. 929
Richman, Herbert J., Exec. V.P.--Republic National Bank of New York, New York, NY; *U.S. Public*, pg. 1380
Richmon, Wayne M., Chief Fin. Officer, Exec. V.P. & Treas.--The Flight International Group, Inc., Newport News, VA; *U.S. Public*, pg. 654
Richmond, Charles R., Exec. V.P. & Sec.--Washington Federal Savings, Seattle, WA; *U.S. Public*, pg. 1740
Richmond, Patrick, Exec. V.P.-Corp. Devel.--Primark Corporation, Waltham, MA; *U.S. Public*, pg. 1325
Richter, Joseph M., Chief Fin. Officer, Exec. V.P. & Treas.--The Somerset Group, Inc., Indianapolis, IN; *U.S. Public*, pg. 1484
Richters, J.W.H., Exec. V.P.--ING North America Insurance Company, Atlanta, GA; *Int'l*, pg. 648
Rickey, Mark J., Exec. V.P. & Chief Oper. Officer--Markel Service, Inc., Glen Allen, VA; *U.S. Public*, pg. 1046
Rickey, Mark J., Exec. V.P. & Chief Oper. Officer--Markel American Insurance Co., Glen Allen, VA; *U.S. Public*, pg. 1046
Ricordi, Carlo, Exec. V.P.-Corp. Fin.--Istituto Bancario San Paolo Di Torino S.p.A., Turin, Italy; *Int'l*, pg. 691
Riddle, James R., Exec. V.P.-Mktg.--Heilig-Meyers Company, Richmond, VA; *U.S. Public*, pg. 804
Ridenour, Mark, Exec. V.P. & Treas.--Heidtman Steel Products, Inc., Toledo, OH; *U.S. Private*, pg. 519
Ridenour, Mark, Exec. V.P. & Treas.--H.S. Processing, Toledo, OH; *U.S. Private*, pg. 519
Ridhisilpa, Damrong, Exec. V.P.-Foreign Grp.--Nakornthon Bank Public Company Limited, Bangkok, Thailand; *Int'l*, pg. 904
Ridout, Leslie P., Jr., Exec. V.P.--Huntington Bancshares Inc., Columbus, OH; *U.S. Public*, pg. 849
Ridux, Paul, Exec. V.P.-Fin., Opers. & Admin.--Sega of America Inc., Redwood City, CA; *Int'l*, pg. 1218
Riedel, Hans, Exec. V.P.-Sls. & Mktg.--Porsche AG, Stuttgart, Germany; *Int'l*, pg. 1063
Riegel, David L., Chief Oper. Officer & Exec. V.P.--Exabyte Corporation, Boulder, CO; *U.S. Public*, pg. 597
Riegel, Larry, Exec. Grp. Dir.--Avrett, Free & Ginsberg, Inc., New York, NY; *U.S. Private*, pg. 103
Riegert, Theodore, Exec. V.P.--Plastic Suppliers, Inc., Columbus, OH; *U.S. Private*, pg. 871
Riesch, John, Exec. V.P.-Opers.--Edwards Baking Co., Norcross, GA; *U.S. Private*, pg. 365
Rieske, Gordon, Exec. V.P. & Chief Fin. Officer--Ventura Foods LLC, City of Industry, CA; *Int'l*, pg. 879
Rietz, Ake, Chief Fin. Officer & Exec. V.P.--Svenska Cellulosa Aktiebolaget (SCA), Stockholm, Sweden; *Int'l*, pg. 1326
Rifkin, Richard S., Exec. V.P. & Sec.--Omnisource Corporation, Fort Wayne, IN; *U.S. Private*, pg. 817
Riggs, Larry, Exec. V.P.--Warmington Homes, Costa Mesa, CA; *U.S. Private*, pg. 1150
Rigoni, Robert J., Exec. V.P.--Bacco Construction Co., Iron Mountain, MI; *U.S. Private*, pg. 109
Riley, Dale, Chief Oper. Officer & Exec. V.P.--Lund Food Holdings, Inc., Edina, MN; *U.S. Private*, pg. 680
Riley, Daniel J., Exec. V.P.--Building Plastics, Inc., Memphis, TN; *U.S. Private*, pg. 180
Riley, Daniel P., Grp. Exec. V.P.-Support Services--Bank of America NT&SA, San Francisco, CA; *U.S. Public*, pg. 180
Riley, James B., Chief Fin. Officer & Exec. V.P.--Republic Engineered Steels, Inc., Massillon, OH; *U.S. Public*, pg. 1378
Riley, Kevin T., Exec. V.P. & Dir.-Natl. Treaty Prod.--Willis Faber North America, Inc.-New York, New York, NY; *Int'l*, pg. 1503
Riley, Richard, Exec. V.P., Media Dir. & Pub. Rels. Dir.--Sawyer Riley Compton Inc., Atlanta, GA; *U.S. Private*, pg. 969
Riley, William F., III, Chief Fin. Officer & Exec V.P.--Swift Transportation Co., Sparks, NV; *U.S. Public*, pg. 1543
Rinderknecht, Urs, Exec. V.P. & Pres.-Exec. Board Switzerland--Union Bank of Switzerland, Zurich, Switzerland; *Int'l*, pg. 1439
Rines, John R., Exec. V.P.-Global Mkts.--Citicorp, New York, NY; *U.S. Public*, pg. 376
Ringel, Jordan, Exec. V.P.-Bus. Affairs--SFM Entertainment, New York, NY; *U.S. Private*, pg. 957
Ringwald, Arthur D., Grp. Exec. V.P.-BankAmerica Mortgage--Bank of America NT&SA, San Francisco, CA; *U.S. Public*, pg. 180
Rink, Robert J., Chief Oper. Officer & Exec. V.P.--Prestige Stamping, Inc., Warren, MI; *U.S. Private*, pg. 882
Rinn, Russ, Exec. V.P.-Sls./CMC Steel Grp.--Structural Metals, Inc., Seguin, TX; *U.S. Public*, pg. 412
Rinner, Richard, Exec. V.P.-Admin. & Publ.--American Automobile Association, Heathrow, FL; *U.S. Private*, pg. 50
Riordan, John F., Exec. V.P.--Occidental Petroleum Corporation, Los Angeles, CA; *U.S. Public*, pg. 1210
Riordan, Rip, Chief Oper. Officer & Exec. V.P.--Clear Channel Television, Inc., Minneapolis, MN; *U.S. Public*, pg. 383
Riordan, Rip, Chief Oper. Officer & Exec. V.P.--WFTC-TV, Minneapolis, MN; *U.S. Public*, pg. 385
Rios Montero, Ernesto, Exec. V.P.--Bufete Industrial S.A. de C.V., Mexico, Mexico; *Int'l*, pg. 232
Ripich, John R., Exec. V.P.--American Tank & Fabricating Co., Cleveland, OH; *U.S. Private*, pg. 63
Ripp, Robert M., Exec. V.P.--AMP Incorporated, Harrisburg, PA; *U.S. Public*, pg. 7
Rippee, Doyle A., Exec. V.P. & Gen. Mgr.--NationsBank of Tennessee, Nashville, TN; *U.S. Public*, pg. 1163
Rischke, R.E., Exec. V.P.--ABN-AMRO Holding N.V., Amsterdam, Netherlands; *Int'l*, pg. 8
Risdall, William, Exec V.P.--Smith System Manufacturing Company, Plano, TX; *U.S. Private*, pg. 1009
Risley, Phillip L., Chief Admin. Officer, Exec. V.P. & Cashier--Brenton Banks, Inc., Des Moines, IA; *U.S. Public*, pg. 251
Risser, Thomas, Exec. V.P.--U.S. Bottlers Machinery Co., Charlotte, NC; *U.S. Private*, pg. 1124
Risser, Timothy, Exec. V.P.-Sls. & Admin.--U.S. Bottlers Machinery Co., Charlotte, NC; *U.S. Private*, pg. 1124
Ristimaki, Matti, Exec. V.P.--Stockmann Automotive Sales Div., Helsinki, Finland; *Int'l*, pg. 1301
Ritch, David, Chief Fin. Officer & Exec. V.P.--Republic Beverage Company, Houston, TX; *U.S. Private*, pg. 149
Ritch, David, Chief Fin. Officer & Exec. V.P.--Republic Beverage Co., Dallas, TX; *U.S. Private*, pg. 150
Ritchie, Lewis, Chief Fin. Officer & Exec. V.P.-Fin. & Admin.--Cinram Ltd., Scarborough, Canada; *Int'l*, pg. 293
Ritchie, Timothy, Chief Oper. Officer & Exec. V.P.--Kirby Building Systems, Inc., Portland, TN; *Int'l*, pg. 699
Ritter, Alfred F., Jr., Chief Fin. Officer & Exec. V.P.--Landmark Communications, Inc., Norfolk, VA; *U.S. Private*, pg. 647
Rittinghaus, Erhard, Exec. V.P. & Pres.-Agfa Division--Bayer Corporation, Pittsburgh, PA; *Int'l*, pg. 172
Rittinghaus, Erhard, Pres.-AGFA Div. & Exec. V.P.--Bayer Corporation, Pittsburgh, PA; *Int'l*, pg. 172
Rittinghaus, Erhard, Exec. V.P. & Pres.-Agfa Div.--Bayer Corporation, Parsippany, NJ; *Int'l*, pg. 172
Rivard, Michael, Exec. V.P.-Mktg.--Miracle Recreation Equipment Company, Monett, MO; *U.S. Private*, pg. 752
Rivers, J. Calvin, Jr., Exec. V.P.--Sterling Capital Management Company, Charlotte, NC; *U.S. Public*, pg. 1674
Rivest, Jeffrey A., Chief Oper. Officer & Exec. V.P.--The Children's Hospital of Philadelphia, Philadelphia, PA; *U.S. Private*, pg. 236
Rivet, Jeannine M., Exec. V.P.-Health Care Svcs.--United HealthCare Corporation, Minnetonka, MN; *U.S. Public*, pg. 1677
Rizzo, J., Exec. V.P.--GAB Robins North America, Inc., Parsippany, NJ; *Int'l*, pg. 1153
Rizzo, Richard J., Exec. V.P.-Bldg. Construction--Perini Corporation, Framingham, MA; *U.S. Public*, pg. 1278
Roach, Alfred R., Jr., Exec. V.P.-Mktg., Sls. & Prod. Support--Group Maintenance America Corp., Houston, TX; *U.S. Public*, pg. 766
Roach, Barrett B., Exec. V.P.-Strategic Devel.--Fair, Isaac and Company, Inc., San Rafael, CA; *U.S. Public*, pg. 609
Roach, Ed, Chief Fin. Officer, Exec. V.P. & Treas.--Dominion Resources, Inc., Richmond, VA; *U.S. Public*, pg. 516
Roark, D. Michael, Exec. V.P.-H.R.--Mellon Bank Corporation, Pittsburgh, PA; *U.S. Public*, pg. 1084
Roark, Dennis, Exec. V.P.-Engrng.--Power-One, Inc., Camarillo, CA; *U.S. Private*, pg. 878
Robards, Thomas F., Exec. V.P.--Republic National Bank of New York, New York, NY; *U.S. Public*, pg. 1380
Robataille, Pierre, Chief Fin. Officer & Exec. V.P.--SNC-Lavalin Group Inc., Montreal, Canada; *Int'l*, pg. 1161
Robb, Michael S., Exec. V.P.-Real Estate Investments--Pacific Life Insurance Company, Newport Beach, CA; *U.S. Private*, pg. 831
Robbe, Chris, Exec. V.P.--JL Media Inc., Miami, FL; *U.S. Private*, pg. 577
Robbin, Jim, Exec. V.P. & Gen. Mgr.--K & R Express Systems Inc., Hinsdale, IL; *U.S. Private*, pg. 602
Robbins, Bruce E., Exec. V.P.-Corp. Banking--PNC Bank Corp., Pittsburgh, PA; *U.S. Public*, pg. 1242
Robbins, David, Exec. V.P.--Ha-Lo Industries, Inc., Niles, IL; *U.S. Public*, pg. 773
Robbins, Kim D., Exec. V.P.-Gen. Mdsg. Mgr.--House of Fabrics, Inc., Sherman Oaks, CA; *U.S. Public*, pg. 842
Robbins, Paul, Chief Oper. Officer & Exec. V.P.--Christianity Today, Inc., Carol Stream, IL; *U.S. Private*, pg. 238
Roberts, Dan, Exec. V.P.-Sls. & Mktg.--Wellington Industries Inc., Madison, GA; *U.S. Private*, pg. 1161
Roberts, Douglas D., Exec. V.P.--Gemtron Corporation, Sweetwater, TN; *Int'l*, pg. 1523
Roberts, Francine Pareles, Exec. V.P. & Reg. Brdcst. Dir.--Western International Media Corporation, Los Angeles, CA; *U.S. Private*, pg. 1165
Roberts, Francine Pareles, Exec. V.P. & Reg. Brdcst. Dir.--Western International Media Corporation, San Francisco, CA; *U.S. Private*, pg. 1167
Roberts, Gary, Pres. & Chief Oper. Officer--Greenstone Roberts Advertising, Melville, NY; *U.S. Public*, pg. 763
Roberts, Hugh, Exec. V.P.-Central & Eastern Europe, Middle East & Africa--Kraft Foods International, Rye Brook, NY; *U.S. Public*, pg. 1288
Roberts, Hugh, Sr. V.P.-Efficient Consumer Response--Kraft Foods Inc., Glenview, IL; *U.S. Public*, pg. 1288
Roberts, Keith C., Sr. V.P., Exec. V.P.--Riedel Environmental Services Inc.--Smith Technologies Corp., Portland, OR; *U.S. Public*, pg. 1478
Roberts, Richard B., Exec. V.P. & Treas.--Wachovia Corporation, Winston Salem, NC; *U.S. Public*, pg. 1730
Roberts, Ted, Exec. V.P.-Sls.--Dean Operations Inc., Kansas City, MO; *U.S. Private*, pg. 318
Roberts, Wyman, Exec. V.P.--Red Lobster USA, Orlando, FL; *U.S. Public*, pg. 484
Robertson, David L., Exec. V.P.-Human Resources & Corp. Law--Weirton Steel Corporation, Weirton, WV; *U.S. Public*, pg. 1751
Robertson, Dennis, Chief Exec. Officer & Exec. V.P.--Arkansas Farm Bureau Federation, Little Rock, AR; *U.S. Private*, pg. 82
Robertson, John, Exec. V.P.-Wireless Opers.--Glentel Inc., Burnaby, Canada; *Int'l*, pg. 1336
Robertson, Joseph W., Chief Fin. Officer & Exec. V.P.--Weingarten Realty Investors, Houston, TX; *U.S. Public*, pg. 1751
Robertson, P.J., Exec. V.P.--Chevron U.S.A. Inc., San Francisco, CA; *U.S. Public*, pg. 348
Robertson, P.J., Exec. V.P.--Chevron USA Production Co., Houston, TX; *U.S. Public*, pg. 348
Robertson, Richard S., Exec. V.P. & Corp. Risk Officer--Lincoln National Corporation, Fort Wayne, IN; *U.S. Public*, pg. 997
Robertson, Thomas E., Exec. V.P. & Treas.--C-Line Products, Inc., Des Plaines, IL; *U.S. Private*, pg. 192
Robertson, William, Exec. V.P.-Mfg. Housing Lending--Resource Mortgage Capital, Inc., Glen Allen, VA; *U.S. Public*, pg. 1382
Robertson, William M., Exec. V.P.--Hamilton, Allen & Associates, Inc, Atlanta, GA; *U.S. Public*, pg. 1673
Robie, Richard S., III, Exec. V.P.--UAM Retirement Plan Services, Inc., New York, NY; *U.S. Public*, pg. 1674
Robinowitz, Joe, Exec. V.P.--News America Publishing Inc., New York, NY; *Int'l*, pg. 925
Robinson, Bill, Exec. V.P.-Annuities--Pacific Life Insurance Company, Newport Beach, CA; *U.S. Private*, pg. 831
Robinson, C.J., Exec. V.P.--Filtrona Richmond Company, Richmond, VA; *Int'l*, pg. 232
Robinson, Carol, Exec. V.P.--Presto Food Stores, Inc., Plant City, FL; *U.S. Private*, pg. 882
Robinson, Charles T., Exec. V.P.--Cannon Equipment, Chattanooga, TN; *Int'l*, pg. 646
Robinson, David F., Exec. V.P.--CTX Mortgage Co., Inc., Dallas, TX; *U.S. Public*, pg. 323
Robinson, David L., Exec. V.P.--Weston Paper & Manufacturing Co., Terre Haute, IN; *U.S. Private*, pg. 1169
Robinson, Jim, Exec. V.P.--Balkamp, Inc., Indianapolis, IN; *U.S. Public*, pg. 732
Robinson, Wilburn, Chief Fin. Officer & Exec. V.P.--Omniflight, Inc., Dallas, TX; *U.S. Private*, pg. 816
Robinson, Wilburn, Chief Fin. Officer & Exec. V.P.--Omniflight Helicopters, Inc., Dallas, TX; *U.S. Private*, pg. 817

Robitaille, Pierre, Exec. V.P.-Fin. & Plng.--SNC-Lavalin Inc., Montreal, Canada; *Int'l*, pg. 1162
Robson, William E., Exec. V.P.-Opers.--Luby's Cafeterias, Inc., San Antonio, TX; *U.S. Public*, pg. 1017
Rocca, Rino, Exec. V.P.-Intl. Rels.--Istituto Bancario San Paolo Di Torino S.p.A., Turin, Italy; *Int'l*, pg. 691
Rocchio, Frederick J., Jr., Exec. V.P.-Devel. & Tech.--Birmingham Steel Corporation, Birmingham, AL; *U.S. Public*, pg. 232
Roche, Alexander, Exec. V.P.-Sls. & Mktg.--Fishery Products International Ltd., Saint Johns, Canada; *Int'l*, pg. 492
Roche, Arthur D., Chief Fin. Officer & Exec. V.P.--Vicon Industries, Inc., Hauppauge, NY; *U.S. Public*, pg. 1719
Roche, Terence P., Exec. V.P., Asst. Treas. & Asst. Sec.--Binks Sames Corporation, Franklin Park, IL; *U.S. Public*, pg. 229
Rocheleau, Michael, Chief Fin. Officer & Exec. V.P.--PTA Corporation, Oxford, CT; *U.S. Private*, pg. 828
Rochet, Pierre Louis, Exec. V.P.--Systra-Sofretu-Sofrerail, Paris, France; *Int'l*, pg. 1165
Rockafellow, Gordon G., Corp. Exec. V.P.-First Trust Grp.--Fiserv, Inc., Brookfield, WI; *U.S. Public*, pg. 647
Roddick, Gary D., Exec. V.P.-Admin.--The Franklin Life Insurance Company, Springfield, IL; *U.S. Public*, pg. 76
Roden, Thomas E., Exec. V.P.-Field Opers. & Subsidiaries--Harleysville Group, Harleysville, PA; *U.S. Public*, pg. 786
Rodenberg, Jim, Exec. V.P.--San Angelo National Bank, San Angelo, TX; *U.S. Public*, pg. 633
Rodgers, Bruce W., Exec. V.P.-Opers.--Newbridge Networks Corporation, Kanata, Canada; *Int'l*, pg. 923
Rodloytuk, Komkai, Exec. V.P.--Bangkok Bank Public Company Limited, Bangkok, Thailand; *Int'l*, pg. 146
Rodrigues, Joseph, Chief Fin. Officer, Exec. V.P. & Treas.--Seaboard Corporation, Shawnee Mission, KS; *U.S. Public*, pg. 1448
Rodrigues, Michael A., Exec. V.P.--Priority Finishing Corp., Fall River, MA; *U.S. Private*, pg. 887
Rodriguez, Hector, Exec. V.P.-Logistics--URS Logistics, Atlanta, GA; *U.S. Private*, pg. 1114
Rodriguez, Jorge, Exec. V.P.--Avantel, S.A., Mexico, Mexico; *Int'l*, pg. 574
Roe, Lisa, Exec. V.P.--Salon & Fitness Systems, Brooklyn, NY; *U.S. Private*, pg. 962
Roehrenbeck, William G., Exec. V.P.--First Commercial Mortgage Co., Little Rock, AR; *U.S. Public*, pg. 630
Roewe, John, Exec. V.P.--First National Bank of Magnolia, Magnolia, AR; *U.S. Public*, pg. 641
Roffey, Robert C., Exec. V.P.--Commercial Union Corporation, Boston, MA; *Int'l*, pg. 308
Rogan, R. Eric, Chief Fin. Officer & Exec. V.P.--Stelco Inc., Hamilton, Canada; *Int'l*, pg. 1299
Rogers, Candice W., Sr. Exec. V.P.-Consumer Banking & Mktg. Div.--AmSouth Bancorporation, Birmingham, AL; *U.S. Public*, pg. 105
Rogers, Douglas C., Exec. V.P.-Mktg.--Whitehall-Robins Healthcare, Madison, NJ; *U.S. Public*, pg. 80
Rogers, Earl W., Jr., Exec. V.P.--John H. Harland Company, Decatur, GA; *U.S. Public*, pg. 785
Rogers, G.R., Chief Fin. Officer, Exec. V.P. & Treas.--Alexander & Baldwin, Inc., Honolulu, HI; *U.S. Public*, pg. 39
Rogers, Glenn, Exec. V.P.--Advanstar Communications, Cleveland, OH; *U.S. Private*, pg. 22
Rogers, John M., Exec. V.P.--Douglas Steel Fabricating Corporation, Lansing, MI; *U.S. Private*, pg. 341
Rogers, Ken, Exec. V.P.-Mktg. & Sls. (Canada)--Intertape Polymer Group, Green Bay, WI; *Int'l*, pg. 685
Rogers, Kris, Exec. V.P. & Gen. Mgr.-U.S. Opers.--Micro Warehouse, Inc., Norwalk, CT; *U.S. Public*, pg. 1104
Rogers, Randall K., Exec. V.P.-Opers.--TCA Management Company, Tyler, TX; *U.S. Public*, pg. 1553
Rogers, Warren, Exec. V.P. & Treas.--Mississippi Valley Gas Co., Jackson, MS; *U.S. Private*, pg. 753
Rogge, Patrick, Exec. V.P. & New Bus. Contact--Friedland Jacobs Communications, Burbank, CA; *U.S. Private*, pg. 428
Rohm, C.E., Exec. V.P.--The Principal Financial Group, Des Moines, IA; *U.S. Private*, pg. 885
Rohm, C.E., Exec. V.P.--Principal Mutual Life Insurance Co., Des Moines, IA; *U.S. Private*, pg. 886
Rohn, Charles, Exec. V.P.--Darling's, Bangor, ME; *U.S. Private*, pg. 311
Rohnberg, Karl, Dr., Exec. V.P.--Hochtief AG, Essen, Germany; *Int'l*, pg. 623
Rohr, Daniel C., Exec. V.P.--Comml. Banking Grp.--U.S. Bancorp, Minneapolis, MN; *U.S. Public*, pg. 1680
Rohrbasser, Markus, Chief Exec. Officer & Exec. V.P.-N. America--Union Bank of Switzerland, Zurich, Switzerland; *Int'l*, pg. 1439
Rohrbasser, Markus, Exec. V.P.--Zurich Insurance Company, Zurich, Switzerland; *Int'l*, pg. 1529
Roid, Hahns, Exec. V.P.-Sls. & Mktg.--Premier Cruises, Miami, FL; *U.S. Private*, pg. 293
Roisman, Joseph, Exec. V.P.--Supreme International Corp., Miami, FL; *U.S. Public*, pg. 1542
Rolla, Peter M., Exec. V.P.--American Specialties Inc., Yonkers, NY; *U.S. Private*, pg. 62
Rollins, Edward, Exec. V.P. & Gen. Mgr.-Pub. Affairs--Edelman Worldwide, Inc., New York, NY; *U.S. Private*, pg. 362
Rollins, Fred H., III, Exec. V.P. & Pub. Rels. Dir.--EvansGroup, Salt Lake City, UT; *U.S. Private*, pg. 385
Rollins, O.R., Exec. V.P. & Gen. Counsel--Tultex Corporation, Martinsville, VA; *U.S. Public*, pg. 1644
Rolls, D., Exec. V.P.-Mktg. & Sls.--The Chamberlain Group, Inc., Elmhurst, IL; *U.S. Private*, pg. 344
Rolnick, Ronald, Esq., Exec. V.P. & Gen. Counsel--Pacesetter Inc., Sylmar, CA; *U.S. Public*, pg. 1428
Rom, Carlos, Jr., Exec. V.P.-Caribbean & Latin American Expansion--Banco Popular de Puerto Rico, San Juan, PR; *U.S. Public*, pg. 175
Rom, Carlos, Jr., Exec. V.P.--BanPonce Corporation, Hato Rey, PR; *U.S. Public*, pg. 176
Romanaux, Dan, Exec. V.P. & Gen. Mgr.--Paper Corporation of United States, New York, NY; *U.S. Public*, pg. 1671
Romano, Gary M., Chief Oper. Officer & Exec. V.P.--Equis Financial Group, Boston, MA; *U.S. Private*, pg. 379
Romanok, David, Exec. V.P.--L&R Manufacturing Co., Kearny, NJ; *U.S. Private*, pg. 638
Romeo, Carmen V., Exec. V.P.--SEI Investments, Oaks, PA; *U.S. Public*, pg. 1417
Romeo, Charles, Exec. V.P.--EFS Service Corporation, Chicago, IL; *U.S. Public*, pg. 1428
Romer, Richard, Exec. V.P.--The CIT Group/Commercial Services, New York, NY; *Int'l*, pg. 360
Romeril, Barry D., Chief Fin. Officer & Exec. V.P.--Xerox Corporation, Stamford, CT; *U.S. Public*, pg. 1783
Ronco, Al, Exec. V.P. & Sec.--Keystone Automotive Industries, Inc., Pomona, CA; *U.S. Public*, pg. 955
Rongione, Donald, Exec. V.P.--Bollman Hat Co., Adamstown, PA; *U.S. Private*, pg. 155
Roome, Hugh, Exec. V.P.-Promotion & Sls./Scholastic School Grp.--Scholastic Corporation, New York, NY; *U.S.* Public, pg. 1440
Rooney, Thomas S., Chief Oper. Officer & Exec. V.P.--Versar Inc., Springfield, VA; *U.S. Public*, pg. 1717
Roos, Burkard, Exec. V.P.-Sls.--Koenig & Bauer-Albert AG, Wurzburg, Germany; *Int'l*, pg. 742
Root, Brad I., Exec. V.P.--A.I. Root Company, Medina, OH; *U.S. Private*, pg. 944
Root, Charles A., Exec. V.P.--Safeguard Scientifics, Inc., Wayne, PA; *U.S. Public*, pg. 1424
Root, Douglas W., Chief Oper. Officer & Exec. V.P.--Successful Money Management Seminars, Inc., Tualatin, OR; *U.S. Public*, pg. 1376
Roper, David A., Deputy Chief Exec.--Wassall Plc, London, United Kingdom; *Int'l*, pg. 1486
Roper, Hartwell H., Chief Fin. Officer & Exec. V.P.--Universal Leaf Tobacco Company, Inc., Richmond, VA; *U.S. Public*, pg. 1694
Roper, John L., IV, Exec. V.P.-Opers. & Sec.--Norfolk Shipbuilding & Drydock Corporation, Norfolk, VA; *U.S. Private*, pg. 802
Ropponen, Veli-Matti, Exec. V.P. & Deputy Chief Oper. Officer--Neste Oy, Espoo, Finland; *Int'l*, pg. 912
Rorke, Kevin, Exec. V.P.--Time Warner Cable, Stamford, CT; *U.S. Public*, pg. 1610
Rosa, Scott, Exec. V.P.-Sls. & Mktg.--Cannon Equipment, Chattanooga, TN; *Int'l*, pg. 646
Rosakamp, J.W., Exec. V.P.--ABN-AMRO Holding N.V., Amsterdam, Netherlands; *Int'l*, pg. 8
Roscitt, Richard R., Pres.-AT&T Solutions & Exec. V.P.--AT&T Corporation, Basking Ridge, NJ; *U.S. Public*, pg. 10
Rose, D.N., Exec. V.P.--Questar Corporation, Salt Lake City, UT; *U.S. Public*, pg. 1352
Rose, Dan, Exec. V.P., Client Services Dir. & Integrated Services Dir.--Frankel & Company, Chicago, IL; *U.S. Private*, pg. 424
Rose, Elliot, Exec. V.P.--Prudential Real Estate Affiliates Inc., Costa Mesa, CA; *U.S. Private*, pg. 892
Rose, Jack, Exec. V.P.--Kao Infosystems Company (MA), Plymouth, MA; *Int'l*, pg. 717
Rose, Kenneth L., Exec. V.P.-Opers. Services--IBP, Inc., Dakota City, NE; *U.S. Public*, pg. 852
Rose, Michel, Sr. Exec. V.P.--Lafarge S.A., Paris, France; *Int'l*, pg. 788
Rosemore, Andrew S., Chief Oper. Officer, Exec. V.P., Treas. & Asst. Sec.--PMC Capital Inc., Dallas, TX; *U.S. Public*, pg. 1242
Rosen, Elaine D., Exec. V.P.--Options and Choices, Inc., Cheyenne, WY; *U.S. Public*, pg. 1699
Rosen, Florence, Exec. V.P.--Rosen Associates Management Corp., Jericho, NY; *U.S. Private*, pg. 945
Rosen, Harold, Exec. V.P. & Creative Dir.--North Castle Partners Advertising, Inc., Stamford, CT; *U.S. Private*, pg. 804
Rosen, James, Exec. V.P.--The Pace Collection, Long Island City, NY; *U.S. Private*, pg. 829
Rosen, Les B., M.D., Exec. V.P. & Medical Dir.--AmeriPath, Inc., Riviera Beach, FL; *U.S. Public*, pg. 96
Rosen, Mike, Chief Exec. Officer & Exec. V.P.-Corp Devel Mktg.--Herbalife International of America, Inc., Century City, CA; *U.S. Public*, pg. 809
Rosenbaum, Robert, Exec. V.P.--Bruckner Machine & Tool Corp., Port Washington, NY; *U.S. Private*, pg. 175
Rosenberg, Edward L., Exec. V.P.-Supply & Transportation--Crown Central Petroleum Corporation, Baltimore, MD; *U.S. Public*, pg. 462
Rosenberg, Ervin, Exec. V.P.-Large Corps. & Opers.--Banque Nationale de Paris, Paris, France; *Int'l*, pg. 163
Rosenberg, Michael, Exec. V.P.-Imagine--Imagine Entertainment, Los Angeles, CA; *U.S. Private*, pg. 558
Rosenberg, Philip G., Chief Fin. Officer, Exec. V.P. & Asst. Sec.--Casual Male, Inc., Hyde Park, MA; *U.S. Public*, pg. 168
Rosenberg, R.A., Exec. V.P.-Washington Opers.--Science Applications International Corp., San Diego, CA; *U.S. Private*, pg. 975
Rosenberg, Ronald E., Exec. V.P.--Anthem, Inc., Indianapolis, IN; *U.S. Private*, pg. 76
Rosenberg, Steve, Exec. V.P.-Universal Television Enterprises--Universal Studios TV, Universal City, CA; *Int'l*, pg. 1215
Rosenberger, Howard, Exec. V.P.-Sls.--Ellen Tracy Inc., New York, NY; *U.S. Private*, pg. 372
Rosenblatt, Robert J., Chief Fin. Officer & Exec. V.P.--USA Networks, Inc., Saint Petersburg, FL; *U.S. Public*, pg. 1685
Rosenfeld, H.J., Exec. V.P.--John Brown E & C Corporate Offices (U.S.), Houston, TX; *Int'l*, pg. 774
Rosenfeld, Irene, Exec. V.P. & Gen. Mgr.-Desserts & Snacks Div.--Kraft Foods Inc., Glenview, IL; *U.S. Public*, pg. 1288
Rosenswig, Deanna, Exec. V.P.-Corp. Electronic Banking Services--Bank of Montreal, Toronto, Canada; *Int'l*, pg. 153
Rosenswig, Deanna, Exec. V.P.-Corp Electronic Fin. Svcs.--Corporate & Institutional Financial Services - Montreal, Toronto, Canada; *Int'l*, pg. 153
Rosenzweig, Richard S., Exec. V.P.--Playboy Enterprises, Inc., Chicago, IL; *U.S. Public*, pg. 1309
Rosenzweig, Richard S., Exec. V.P.--Special Editions, Ltd., Chicago, IL; *U.S. Public*, pg. 1310
Rosenzwog, Harvey, Exec. V.P.--Monumental Millwork, Inc., Westminster, MD; *U.S. Private*, pg. 759
Rosetti, Richard, Exec. V.P.--Alta Loma Productions, Inc., Beverly Hills, CA; *U.S. Public*, pg. 1310
Rosetti, Richard, Exec. V.P.--After Dark Video, Inc., Beverly Hills, CA; *U.S. Public*, pg. 1310
Rosetti, Richard P., Exec. V.P.-Production--Playboy Entertainment Group, Inc., Beverly Hills, CA; *U.S. Public*, pg. 1310
Rosiek, Robert A., Exec. V.P. & Fin. Dir.-Ford WW AFD--Young & Rubicam Detroit, Detroit, MI; *U.S. Private*, pg. 1198
Ross, Alex, Exec. V.P.-Creative Services--Jordan, McGrath, Case & Taylor Inc., New York, NY; *U.S. Private*, pg. 598
Ross, Anthony J., Exec. V.P.--The Cafaro Co., Youngstown, OH; *U.S. Private*, pg. 198
Ross, Donald L., Chief Oper. Officer & Sr. Exec. V.P.--Enterprise Rent-A-Car Company, Saint Louis, MO; *U.S. Private*, pg. 377
Ross, Elliot B., Chief Oper. Officer & Exec. V.P.--Essef Corporation, Chardon, OH; *U.S. Public*, pg. 592
Ross, H.G., Exec. V.P.--Gas Equipment Company, Inc., Dallas, TX; *U.S. Private*, pg. 440
Ross, J., Exec. V.P.-Human Resources--Labatt Breweries of Canada, Toronto, Canada; *Int'l*, pg. 679
Ross, James M., Exec. V.P.--Worldwide Telecommunications--SHL Systemhouse, Ottawa, Canada; *Int'l*, pg. 1154
Ross, Joseph E., Exec. V.P.--Baker Engineering, Inc., Chicago, IL; *U.S. Public*, pg. 168
Ross, Matthew, Exec. V.P. & Dir.-Stores--Fedco, Inc., Santa Fe Springs, CA; *U.S. Private*, pg. 398
Ross, Michael, Exec. V.P.--Vance Publishing Corporation, Lincolnshire, IL; *U.S. Private*, pg. 1133
Ross, Stuart B., Chm. & Chief Exec. Officer-Xerox Fin. Services Inc. & Exec. V.P.--Xerox Corporation, Stamford, CT; *U.S. Public*, pg. 1783
Rossetti, Pamela A., Exec. V.P. & Chief Fin. Officer-Ferguson Communications Grp.--CommonHealth USA, Parsippany, NJ; *Int'l*, pg. 1483
Rossi, Jerome, Exec. V.P.--T.J. Maxx, Framingham, MA; *U.S. Public*, pg. 1557
Rossi, Jerome, Exec. V.P.--The Marmax Group, Framingham, MA; *U.S. Public*, pg. 1557
Rossi, Steve, Exec. V.P. & Gen Mgr.--Philadelphia Daily News, Philadelphia, PA; *U.S. Public*, pg. 964
Rossi, Ugo Marchesa, Exec. V.P.-Org. Assistance--Istituto Bancario San Paolo Di Torino S.p.A., Turin, Italy; *Int'l*, pg. 691
Rossler, John, Exec. V.P.-Fin. & Treas.--Shonac Corporation, Columbus, OH; *U.S. Private*, pg. 996
Rost Onnes, J.J.N., Exec. V.P.--ABN-AMRO Holding N.V., Amsterdam, Netherlands; *Int'l*, pg. 8
Rostollan, Jean C., Exec. V.P.-Pur. & Asst. Sec.--Buffets, Inc., Eden Prairie, MN; *U.S. Public*, pg. 267
Rosuck, Jordan I., Exec. V.P. & Grp. Dir.--Grey Advertising Inc., New York, NY; *U.S. Public*, pg. 764
Rotaecke, Jose Ramon, Exec. V.P.-Fin.--Banco Provincial S.A. Banco Universal, Caracas, Venezuela; *Int'l*, pg. 142
Rotchford, Caitlin, Exec. V.P.--Higher Education Division, Upper Saddle River, NJ; *U.S. Private*, pg. 778
Roth, Daniel, Exec. V.P. & Chief Strategic Officer--Western International Media Corporation, Los Angeles, CA; *U.S. Private*, pg. 1165
Roth, Gerald, Exec. V.P.--Fenton Hill American Limited, Valley Stream, NY; *Int'l*, pg. 103
Roth, L. Jack, Exec. V.P.-Buying--Universal International, Inc., New Hope, MN; *U.S. Public*, pg. 1697
Roth, Mel, Exec. V.P.--Harris Drury Cohen, Fort Lauderdale, FL; *U.S. Private*, pg. 505
Roth, Nancy, Exec. V.P.-USA--Ketchum Directory Advertising/Chicago, Chicago, IL; *U.S. Private*, pg. 616
Roth, Petra, Exec. V.P.--Frankfurter Sparkasse, Frankfurt, Germany; *Int'l*, pg. 504
Roth, Steven F., Exec. V.P.--World Oil Corp., South Gate, CA; *U.S. Private*, pg. 1190
Rother, Doug C., Chief Oper. Officer & Exec. V.P.--Columbine JDS Systems, Inc., Denver, CO; *U.S. Public*, pg. 228
Rothermich, John, Exec. V.P.--Phoenix Learning Resources, New York, NY; *U.S. Private*, pg. 863
Rothschild, John, Exec. V.P.--Cometals, New York, NY; *U.S. Public*, pg. 412
Rothstein, Harvey, Sr. Exec. V.P.-Real Estate & Devel.--Davco Restaurants Inc., Crofton, MD; *U.S. Public*, pg. 488
Rouanne, Guy, Exec. V.P. & Mng. Dir.-Terminals & Telecommunications Div.--Societe d'Applications Generales d'Electricite et de Mechanique, Paris, France; *Int'l*, pg. 1273
Rountree, W. Dekle, Jr., Chief Oper. Officer & Exec. V.P.--Ohmeda, Inc., Liberty Corner, NJ; *Int'l*, pg. 121
Rountreee, Robert, Exec. V.P. & Gen. Mgr.--Subaru of New England, Inc., Norwood, MA; *Int'l*, pg. 523
Rouse, Richard S., Exec. V.P.-Corp. Devel. & Admin.--Group Maintenance America Corp., Houston, TX; *U.S. Public*, pg. 766
Roush, Peggy O., Exec. V.P.--Norwest Bank Minnesota N.A., Minneapolis, MN; *U.S. Public*, pg. 1202
Routson, Donald E., Exec. V.P. & Sr. Loan Officer--Dubois County Bank, Jasper, IN; *U.S. Public*, pg. 1217
Roux, David, Exec. V.P.-Corp. Devel.--Oracle Corporation, Redwood City, CA; *U.S. Public*, pg. 1227

Rowe, J. Paul, Exec. V.P. & Chief Admin. Officer--The McClure Group, Wayne, PA; *U.S. Private*, pg. 719
Rowe, Joe, Exec. Dir.-Womenswear--Marks & Spencer PLC, London, United Kingdom; *Int'l*, pg. 842
Rowe, Kevin S., Exec. V.P.-Pacific--The Bank of Nova Scotia, Toronto, Canada; *Int'l*, pg. 155
Rowell, David, Exec. V.P.--Foss Manufacturing Company Incorporated, Hampton, NH; *U.S. Private*, pg. 420
Rowell, Harry B., Jr., Exec. V.P.--Hubbell Incorporated, Orange, CT; *U.S. Public*, pg. 844
Rowland, Thomas H., Exec. V.P. & Pres.-Home Prods. Div.--First Brands Corporation, Danbury, CT; *U.S. Public*, pg. 626
Rowlenson, Richard C., Exec. V.P. & Gen. Counsel--Vanguard Cellular Systems, Inc., Greensboro, NC; *U.S. Public*, pg. 1707
Rowley, John F., Exec. V.P.-Opers. & Logistics--Fort James Corporation, Richmond, VA; *U.S. Public*, pg. 670
Rowley, Philip, Chief Fin. Officer & Exec. V.P.--Golden Books Family Entertainment Inc., New York, NY; *U.S. Public*, pg. 749
Rowley, Steven R., Exec. V.P.--Illinois Cement Co., La Salle, IL; *U.S. Public*, pg. 322
Rowny, Michael, Exec. V.P.-Alliances & Ventures--MCI Communications Corp., Atlanta, GA; *U.S. Public*, pg. 1023
Roxburgh, C.D., Exec. V.P.--Exxon Company International, Florham Park, NJ; *U.S. Public*, pg. 601
Roy, Francois R., Chief Fin. Officer & Exec. V.P.--Avenor, Inc., Montreal, Canada; *Int'l*, pg. 101
Royer, Donald E., Exec. V.P. & Gen. Counsel--Downey Financial Corp., Newport Beach, CA; *U.S. Public*, pg. 525
Royer, Donald E., Exec. V.P., Gen. Counsel & Sec.--Downey Savings & Loan Association, F.A., Newport Beach, CA; *U.S. Public*, pg. 526
Rozenberg, Mark A., Chief Admin. Officer & Exec. V.P.--Shand, Morahan & Co., Inc., Evanston, IL; *U.S. Public*, pg. 1046
Rozzano, Michael J., Exec. V.P.-Opers. & Processed Meats--Thorn Apple Valley, Inc., Southfield, MI; *U.S. Public*, pg. 1602
Rubel, Darrell D., Chief Fin. Officer, Exec. V.P., Treas. & Asst. Sec.--Marten Transport, Ltd., Mondovi, WI; *U.S. Public*, pg. 1052
Ruben, Dennis L., Exec. V.P. & Gen. Counsel--Franchise Finance Corp. of America, Scottsdale, AZ; *U.S. Public*, pg. 679
Ruberto, James M., Exec. V.P.-Admin.--Rexene Corporation, Dallas, TX; *U.S. Private*, pg. 549
Rubin, A. Louis, Exec. V.P. & Mktg. Planner Dir.--Doremus & Company, New York, NY; *U.S. Public*, pg. 1223
Rubin, Andrew, Exec. Dir.--Pentland Group PLC, London, United Kingdom; *Int'l*, pg. 1035
Rubin, Ben, Exec. V.P.--Stevens-Lee Company, Minneapolis, MN; *U.S. Private*, pg. 1042
Rubin, Bruce, Exec. V.P.--Weber Public Relations Worldwide, Cambridge, MA; *U.S. Private*, pg. 1157
Rubin, Harry M., Exec. V.P. & Gen. Mgr.-Intl. Div. & Bus. Affairs--GT Interactive Software Corp., New York, NY; *U.S. Public*, pg. 696
Rubin, Howard, Exec. V.P.--Shogyo International Corporation, Plainview, NY; *U.S. Private*, pg. 996
Rubin, Mark S., Exec. V.P.--Superior Bank, Chicago, IL; *U.S. Private*, pg. 1054
Rubin, Samuel, Exec. V.P.--Prime Tanning Co., Inc., Rochester, NH; *U.S. Private*, pg. 884
Rubright, James A., Exec. V.P., Gen. Counsel & Sec.--Sonat Exploration Company, Houston, TX; *U.S. Public*, pg. 1485
Rubright, James A., Exec. V.P. & Gen. Counsel--Sonat Energy Services Company, Birmingham, AL; *U.S. Public*, pg. 1485
Rucci, Peter P., Exec. V.P.--Weichert Realtors, Inc., Bethesda, MD; *U.S. Private*, pg. 1159
Rucci, Tony, Exec. V.P.-H.R. & Admin.--Sears, Roebuck and Co., Hoffman Estates, IL; *U.S. Public*, pg. 1452
Ruch, Mike, Chief Fin. Officer& Exec. V.P.--Feld Productions, Vienna, VA; *U.S. Private*, pg. 399
Rucker, Peter, Exec. V.P.--Bayerische Hypotheken-und Wechsel-Bank Aktiengesellschaft, Munich, Germany; *Int'l*, pg. 175
Rude, Antone J., Chief Exec. Officer, Exec. V.P. & Gen. Mgr.--United Power Association, Elk River, MN; *U.S. Private*, pg. 1123
Rude, Lillie L., Exec. V.P.-EB Trust--AMCORE Trust Company, Rockford, IL; *U.S. Public*, pg. 65
Ruder, Brian, Exec. V.P.-Global Mktg.--Citibank N.A., Long Island City, NY; *U.S. Public*, pg. 377
Rudis, James, Exec. V.P.--Polyphase Corporation, Dallas, TX; *U.S. Public*, pg. 1315
Rudisi, John, Exec. V.P.-Trust Grp.--First Security Bank of New Mexico, Albuquerque, NM; *U.S. Public*, pg. 637
Rudnik, Robert J., Exec. V.P., Gen. Counsel & Sec.--Prime Group Realty Trust, Chicago, IL; *U.S. Public*, pg. 1326
Rudolph, Richard M., Exec. V.P.-Sls. & Mktg.--Rudolph Foods Company, Lima, OH; *U.S. Private*, pg. 950
Rudovsky, Paul, Chief Fin. Officer & Exec. V.P.-Fin. & Plng.--Atlantis Plastic, Inc., Atlanta, GA; *U.S. Public*, pg. 145
Ruff, Gary F., Chief Tech. Officer & Exec. V.P.--CMI International Inc., Southfield, MI; *U.S. Private*, pg. 195
Ruffat, Didier, Exec. V.P.--Bull S.A., Louveciennes, France; *Int'l*, pg. 315
Ruffer, Michael R., Exec. V.P. & Gen. Mgr.--Residence Inn, Washington, DC; *U.S. Public*, pg. 1048
Ruffolo, Joseph E., Exec. V.P.-H.R.--Peregrine Incorporated, Southfield, MI; *U.S. Private*, pg. 852
Rugg, Kenneth L., Exec. V.P.-Fragrance--Florasynth Inc., Teterboro, NJ; *Int'l*, pg. 173
Ruggeri, Dennis, Chief Oper. Officer & Exec. V.P.--Hutchins/Young & Rubicam, Rochester, NY; *U.S. Private*, pg. 1197
Ruhl, Barry L., Exec. V.P.--The Spanos Companies, Stockton, CA; *U.S. Private*, pg. 1020
Ruhl, Douglas L., Exec. V.P.--Liberty Bank & Trust Company of Oklahoma City, Oklahoma City, OK; *U.S. Public*, pg. 174
Ruhle, Robert E., Chief Fin. Officer, Exec. V.P., Treas. & Sec.--Ruhle Companies, Inc., Valhalla, NY; *U.S. Private*, pg. 950
Ruhlman, Richard M., Exec. V.P. & Exec. Creative Dir.--Liggett-Stashower, Inc., Cleveland, OH; *U.S. Private*, pg. 667
Ruhstorfer, Bob, Exec. V.P.--Aquion, Elk Grove Village, IL; *U.S. Private*, pg. 78
Ruiz, Hector, Exec. V.P. & Gen. Mgr.-Messaging Systems Prods. Grp.--Motorola, Inc., Schaumburg, IL; *U.S. Public*, pg. 1136
Ruiz, Oscar, Exec. V.P-Fin.--Sol Melia, Palma de Mallorca, Spain; *Int'l*, pg. 1277
Rumble, Gregory W., Exec. V.P.--Contrans Corporation, Woodstock, Canada; *Int'l*, pg. 328
Rundorff, William J., Exec. V.P.--F.N.B. Corporation, Hermitage, PA; *U.S. Public*, pg. 607
Runger, Donald R., Exec. V.P.--Mercantile Bank of Iowa, Des Moines, IA; *U.S. Public*, pg. 1087
Runk, Robert, Exec. V.P.--Willis Corroon Aerospace, New York, NY; *Int'l*, pg. 1505
Rupert, Timothy G., Chief Fin. Officer & Exec. V.P.--RMI Titanium Company, Niles, OH; *U.S. Public*, pg. 1662
Ruppelli, Todd P., Exec. V.P. & Gen. Mgr.-Indus. Div.--Plasti-Kote Company Inc., Medina, OH; *U.S. Private*, pg. 870
Rusch, Jack C., Exec. V.P. & Treas.--First Federal Capital Corp., La Crosse, WI; *U.S. Public*, pg. 632
Ruschak, William S., Exec. V.P.-Mktg. & Company Rels.--Willis Corroon Corp. of Michigan, Livonia, MI; *Int'l*, pg. 1506
Ruscheinski, Nancy, Exec. V.P. & Gen. Mgr.-Creative Services--Edelman Public Relations Worldwide, Chicago, IL; *U.S. Private*, pg. 362
Rusgis, Warren J., Exec. V.P.--Lapham-Hickey Steel Corp., Chicago, IL; *U.S. Private*, pg. 651
Ruslander, Harold L., Exec. V.P.--The Jewett Refrigerator Co., Inc., Buffalo, NY; *U.S. Private*, pg. 952
Russ, Charles P., III, Exec. V.P.-Law & Human Resources, Gen. Counsel & Sec.--U S West Inc., Englewood, CO; *U.S. Public*, pg. 1688
Russell, Donald G., Vice Chm. & Exec. V.P.--Sonat Inc., Birmingham, AL; *U.S. Public*, pg. 1484
Russell, Ed, Exec. V.P.-Worldwide Publicity--Columbia Pictures, Culver City, CA; *Int'l*, pg. 1281
Russell, Lawrence, Exec. V.P. & Pres.-Info. Services--Unisys Corporation, Blue Bell, PA; *U.S. Public*, pg. 1671
Russell, Richard, Exec. V.P.--Russell Chevrolet Company, Sherwood, AR; *U.S. Private*, pg. 952
Russo, John, Exec. V.P. & Exec. Creative Dir.--Pedone & Partners Adv., Inc., New York, NY; *U.S. Private*, pg. 846
Russo, Richard, Exec. V.P. & Chief Creative Officer--Tierney & Partners, Philadelphia, PA; *U.S. Public*, pg. 1641
Russo, Richard A., Exec. V.P.--Middlesex Water Company, Iselin, NJ; *U.S. Public*, pg. 1110
Russo, Richard A., Exec. V.P.--Utility Service Affiliates, Inc., Iselin, NJ; *U.S. Public*, pg. 1110
Russo, Robert, Exec. V.P. & Gen. Mgr.--Madison Square Garden Center Inc., New York, NY; *U.S. Public*, pg. 288
Russo, Robert, Exec. V.P.--Electro-Optical Systems Group, Oakland, NJ; *U.S. Public*, pg. 474
Rustin, Anthony, Exec. V.P.--SNC-Lavalin Group Inc., Montreal, Canada; *Int'l*, pg. 1161
Ruston, James R., Exec. V.P.-Employee Benefits--Willis Corroon Corp. of Illinois, Chicago, IL; *Int'l*, pg. 1506
Rutgers, H.J., Exec. V.P.--ABN-AMRO Holding N.V., Amsterdam, Netherlands; *Int'l*, pg. 8
Ruth, Jon, Exec. V.P.--North Star Steel Co., Wayzata, MN; *U.S. Private*, pg. 210
Ruthenburg, J.C. (Pete), Exec. V.P.--Red Spot Paint & Varnish Co., Evansville, IN; *U.S. Private*, pg. 915
Rutherford, Alan, Chief Fin. Officer & Exec. V.P.--Crown Cork & Seal Company, Inc., Philadelphia, PA; *U.S. Public*, pg. 462
Rutherford, Skip, Exec. V.P. & Pub. Policy Dir.--Cranford Johnson Robinson Woods, Little Rock, AR; *U.S. Private*, pg. 286
Rutledge, E. Peter, Exec. V.P.--Brown-Forman Beverages Worldwide, Louisville, KY; *U.S. Public*, pg. 261
Ruttenberg, Don-Allen, Exec. V.P.-New Store Devel.--Just For Feet, Inc., Pelham, AL; *U.S. Public*, pg. 935
Ruybal, Jim, Exec. V.P.-New Bus. Dept.--United Artists Theatre Circuits Incorporated, Englewood, CO; *U.S. Private*, pg. 1120
Ruzic, Ronald M., Exec. V.P.--Borg Warner Automotive, Inc., Chicago, IL; *U.S. Public*, pg. 245
Ryan, Ashton J., Jr., Sr. Exec. V.P.--First Commerce Corporation, New Orleans, LA; *U.S. Public*, pg. 629
Ryan, David, Exec. Dir.--Industrial Equity Limited, Sydney, Australia; *Int'l*, pg. 676
Ryan, Joseph, Exec. V.P. & Gen. Counsel--Marriott International, Inc., Washington, DC; *U.S. Public*, pg. 1047
Ryan, Kathleen, Exec. V.P. & Gen. Mgr.--Greenstone Roberts Public Relations, Coconut Creek, FL; *U.S. Public*, pg. 763
Ryan, Kathryn, Exec. V.P. & Grp. Dir.-Acct. Svcs.--Jordan, McGrath, Case & Taylor Inc., New York, NY; *U.S. Private*, pg. 598
Ryan, Kenneth, Exec. V.P.--The Van Metres Companies, Burke, VA; *U.S. Private*, pg. 1132
Ryan, Michael J., Exec. V.P. & Acct. Dir.--Campbell-Ewald Advertising, Warren, MI; *U.S. Public*, pg. 908
Ryan, Richard K., Exec. V.P.--Buehler, Limited, Lake Bluff, IL; *U.S. Public*, pg. 574
Ryan, Terry, Exec. V.P.--Minnesota Twins Baseball Club, Minneapolis, MN; *U.S. Private*, pg. 750
Ryan, Thomas D., Exec. V.P.-LaserMaster Tech. & LaserMaster Corp.--LaserMaster Technologies, Inc., Eden Prairie, MN; *U.S. Public*, pg. 979
Ryan, Tom, Exec. V.P.-Opers.--URS Logistics, Atlanta, GA; *U.S. Private*, pg. 1114
Rydin, Anders, Exec. V.P.-Admin., Control & Fin.--Investor AB, Stockholm, Sweden; *Int'l*, pg. 686
Ryerson, Jay, Chief Oper. Officer & Exec. V.P.--Analysis & Technology, Inc., North Stonington, CT; *U.S. Public*, pg. 109
Rygh, Tom Vidar, Exec. V.P. & Mng. Dir. Fin. Investments--Orkla A.S.A., Oslo, Norway; *Int'l*, pg. 1010
Ryman, R.L., Exec. V.P.--TBAC - Prince Gardner, Inc., Arlington, TX; *U.S. Public*, pg. 1560
Rynne, David, Chief Fin. Officer & Exec. V.P.--Bay Networks, Inc., Santa Clara, CA; *U.S. Public*, pg. 196
Ryoke, Norio, Exec. Dir.--Isuzu Motors Limited, Tokyo, Japan; *Int'l*, pg. 692
Rzasnicki, Peter, Exec. V.P.-Global Trust Svcs.--Mellon Bank Corporation, Pittsburgh, PA; *U.S. Public*, pg. 1084
Saal, Elias, Exec. V.P.--Republic National Bank of New York, New York, NY; *U.S. Public*, pg. 1380
Saarinen, Aulis, Exec. V.P.-Res. & Devel.--Rautaruukki Oy, Helsinki, Finland; *Int'l*, pg. 1088
Sabatalo, John, Exec. V.P.-Sls.--Planes Moving And Storage, Inc., Cincinnati, OH; *U.S. Private*, pg. 869
Sabatalo, John, Exec. V.P.--Planes Moving & Storage Company Of Columbus, Columbus, OH; *U.S. Private*, pg. 869
Sabin, Bruce D., Chief Oper. Officer & Exec. V.P.--Civic Center Corporation, Saint Louis, MO; *U.S. Public*, pg. 114
Sabin, Edward, Exec. V.P.--Fresh America Corp., Dallas, TX; *U.S. Public*, pg. 681
Sabl, John J., Exec. V.P., Gen. Counsel & Sec.--Conseco Inc., Carmel, IN; *U.S. Public*, pg. 432
Sablosky, Larry, Exec. V.P.--Finish Line, Inc., Indianapolis, IN; *U.S. Public*, pg. 623
Sabol, Albert T., Chief Fin. Officer & Exec. V.P.-Fin. & Admin.--Central Sprinkler Corporation, Lansdale, PA; *U.S. Public*, pg. 327
Sabol, Albert T., Exec. V.P.-Fin. & Admin.--Central Sprinkler Company, Lansdale, PA; *U.S. Public*, pg. 327
Sabourin, Richard, Chief Fin. Officer & Exec. V.P.--Vicorp Restaurants, Inc., Denver, CO; *U.S. Public*, pg. 1719
Sacasa, Frederico, Grp. Exec. V.P.-Europe, Middle East & Africa Grp.--Bank of America NT&SA, San Francisco, CA; *U.S. Public*, pg. 180
Sacharin, Ken, Exec. V.P. & Media Dir.--Young & Rubicam San Francisco, San Francisco, CA; *U.S. Private*, pg. 1198
Sacher, John, Exec. Dir.-IT & Physical Distr.--Marks & Spencer PLC, London, United Kingdom; *Int'l*, pg. 842
Sachs, Alan, Exec. V.P., Gen. Counsel & Sec.--Edison Brothers Stores, Inc., Saint Louis, MO; *U.S. Public*, pg. 563
Sachse, Robert G., Chief Oper. Officer & Exec. V.P.--Mapco Inc., Tulsa, OK; *U.S. Public*, pg. 1042
Sack, Burton M., Exec. V.P.-New Bus. Devel.--Applebee's International, Inc., Overland Park, KS; *U.S. Public*, pg. 122
Sackett, David, Chief Oper. Officer & Exec. V.P.--PAID Prescriptions, Inc., Fair Lawn, NJ; *U.S. Public*, pg. 1091
Sadakata, Mitsuo, Exec. V.P.--Dai-Ichi Kikaku Co. Ltd., Tokyo, Japan; *Int'l*, pg. 357
Sadler, Catherine, Exec. V.P.-Mktg.--AnnTaylor, Inc., New York, NY; *U.S. Public*, pg. 116
Sadler, Ed, Exec. V.P.-Stores--Caldor, Inc., Norwalk, CT; *U.S. Public*, pg. 292
Saeger, Bob, Exec. V.P.-Mktg. & Adv. Services--Visa U.S.A. Inc., San Francisco, CA; *U.S. Private*, pg. 1141
Saeki, Haruo, Exec. Mng. Dir.--Tokuyama Corporation, Tokyo, Japan; *Int'l*, pg. 1393
Saenger, Eugene L., Jr., Chief Fin. Officer & Exec. V.P.--Avon Workshop Ficks Reed, Cincinnati, OH; *U.S. Private*, pg. 102
Saey, Paul, Exec. V.P.--Maison Mathieu, S.A., Antwerp, Belgium; *Int'l*, pg. 846
Sage, Gordon H., Exec. Dir.--Rio Tinto PLC, London, United Kingdom; *Int'l*, pg. 1118
Sager, Harry C., Exec. V.P.-Exploration & Production--Conoco Inc., Houston, TX; *U.S. Public*, pg. 531
Saggese, Joseph M., Exec. V.P.--Borden, Inc., Columbus, OH; *U.S. Private*, pg. 157
Sahlman, Seppo, Chief Fin. Officer & Exec. V.P.-Treas.--Rautaruukki Oy, Helsinki, Finland; *Int'l*, pg. 1088
Saigusa, Shigeo, Exec. Dir.--Isuzu Motors Limited, Tokyo, Japan; *Int'l*, pg. 692
Saik, Clifton J., Exec. V.P.--First National Bank of Commerce, New Orleans, LA; *U.S. Public*, pg. 629
Saiki, Toshio, Exec. V.P.--The Daishi Bank, Ltd., Niigata, Japan; *Int'l*, pg. 372
Saito, Koji, Exec. V.P.--Fanuc Ltd., Yamanashi, Japan; *Int'l*, pg. 477
Saji, Nobutado, Exec. V.P.-Mktg. Tokyo--Suntory Ltd., Osaka, Japan; *Int'l*, pg. 1321
Sajovic, Frank, Exec. V.P.-Mktg.--Pharmavite Corp., Mission Hills, CA; *U.S. Private*, pg. 860
Sajus, Lucien, Sr. Exec. V.P.--Technip, Paris, France; *Int'l*, pg. 1360
Sakai, Kiyoshi, Exec. V.P.--Mycal, Corp., Osaka, Japan; *Int'l*, pg. 897
Sakaino, Kozo, Exec. Dir.--Isuzu Motors Limited, Tokyo, Japan; *Int'l*, pg. 692
Sakairi, Tatsuo, Exec. V.P.--NEC Corporation, Tokyo, Japan; *Int'l*, pg. 899
Sakakura, Shogo, Exec. V.P.--Pasco Corporation, Tokyo, Japan; *Int'l*, pg. 1024
Sakamoto, Shuzo, Exec. V.P.--OYO Corporation, Tokyo, Japan; *Int'l*, pg. 1019
Sakata, Noboru, Exec. V.P.--Nippon Yusen K.K., Tokyo, Japan; *Int'l*, pg. 941
Saklad, Daniel A., Exec. V.P.-Community Banking--Norwest Corporation, Minneapolis, MN; *U.S. Public*, pg. 1201
Sakornratanakul, Sirichai, Sr. Exec. V.P.--The Industrial Finance Corporation of Thailand, Bangkok, Thailand; *Int'l*, pg. 677

Sakurai, George S., Exec. V.P.-Retail Auto Opers.--Servco Pacific Inc., Honolulu, HI; *U.S. Private*, pg. 986
Salcher, Anton, Exec. V.P.-Portfolio Mgnmt. & Res.--Bayerische Landesbank, Munich, Germany; *Int'l*, pg. 176
Saldin, Thomas R., Exec V.P.-Admin. & Gen. Counsel--Albertson's, Inc., Boise, ID; *U.S. Public*, pg. 38
Salentine, Thomas J., Chief Fin. Officer & Exec. V.P.--Bindley Western Industries, Inc., Indianapolis, IN; *U.S. Public*, pg. 228
Salerno, Frederic V., Chief Fin. Officer & Sr. Exec. V.P.--Bell Atlantic Corporation, New York, NY; *U.S. Public*, pg. 201
Saless, Bijan S., Exec. V.P.-Sls. & Mktg.--EA Engineering, Science & Technology, Inc., Hunt Valley, MD; *U.S. Public*, pg. 540
Saliba, Antonio Carlos, Exec. V.P. & Gen. Mgr.--Janssen Cilag Brazil, Sao Paulo, Brazil; *U.S. Public*, pg. 929
Saliba, Naseeb M., Exec. V.P.--Tutor-Saliba Corporation, Sylmar, CA; *U.S. Private*, pg. 1111
Salinger, Robert M., Exec. V.P., Gen. Counsel & Sec.--First Financial Bank, FSB, Stevens Point, WI; *U.S. Public*, pg. 140
Salisbury, Charles H., Exec. V.P. & Dir.-Mktg. & Service Strategies--United Asset Management Corporation, Boston, MA; *U.S. Public*, pg. 1672
Salisbury, Phil, Exec. V.P.--Dekko Technical Center, Laotto, IN; *U.S. Private*, pg. 484
Salisbury, Robert C., Chief Fin. Officer & Exec. V.P.-Fin. & Admin.--Pharmacia & Upjohn, Inc., Windsor, United Kingdom; *Int'l*, pg. 1047
Salisbury, Ronald C., Chief Fin. Officer & Exec. V.P.--Pharmacia & Upjohn, Kalamazoo, MI; *Int'l*, pg. 1048
Salit, Jan F., Chief Investment Officer & Exec. V.P.--PMC Capital Inc., Dallas, TX; *U.S. Public*, pg. 1242
Salomon, Bernard, Exec. V.P. & Gen. Mgr.-Mavic--Salomon S.A., Annecy, France; *Int'l*, pg. 1181
Salonen, Timo, Grp. V.P. & Controller--Leaf Group B.V., Espoo, Finland,; *Int'l*, pg. 638
Salsbury, Michael H., Exec. V.P. & Gen. Counsel--MCI Communications Corp., Atlanta, GA; *U.S. Public*, pg. 1023
Salt, G.A., Exec. V.P.--Haeger Potteries of Macomb, Inc., Macomb, IL; *U.S. Private*, pg. 493
Salter, William E., Exec. V.P.--Intergraph Corporation, Huntsville, AL; *U.S. Public*, pg. 890
Salto, Leon, Sr. Exec. V.P.-Bus. Devel.--Promodes SA, Mondeville, France; *Int'l*, pg. 1071
Saltwell, Susan, Exec. V.P.-Client Services--Jack Levy Associates, Chicago, IL; *U.S. Private*, pg. 664
Salvoch Oncins, Manuel, Exec. V.P.--Empresas ICA Sociedad Controladora S.A.C.V., Mexico, Mexico; *Int'l*, pg. 454
Salwasser, Leslie, Exec. V.P.--Salwasser Manufacturing Company, Inc., Reedley, CA; *U.S. Private*, pg. 963
Salway, Roger A., Chief Oper. Officer & Exec. V.P.--Paper Calmenson & Co., Saint Paul, MN; *U.S. Private*, pg. 837
Salzano, Joseph V., Sr. Exec. V.P.--AMBAC Financial Group, Inc., New York, NY; *U.S. Public*, pg. 62
Samartini, James R., Chief Admin. Officer & Exec. V.P.--Whirlpool Corporation, Benton Harbor, MI; *U.S. Public*, pg. 1764
Samet, Michael, Exec. V.P. & Global Media Dir.--Young & Rubicam Inc., New York, NY; *U.S. Private*, pg. 1196
Samet, Mike, Exec. V.P. & Global Media Dir.-Y&R Adv.--Young & Rubicam New York, New York, NY; *U.S. Private*, pg. 1198
Samford, Ron E., Jr., Exec. V.P. & Controller--Hibernia Corporation, New Orleans, LA; *U.S. Public*, pg. 825
Samoff, Pete W., Chief Oper. Officer & Exec. V.P.--T.D. Williamson, Inc., Tulsa, OK; *U.S. Private*, pg. 1179
Sampson, Michael, Exec. V.P. & Gen. Mgr.--Goldenberg Group, Inc., Lynwood, CA; *U.S. Public*, pg. 1193
Samra, Hisham, Sr. Exec. V.P.-North & Latin America--Ares-Serono S.A., Geneva, Switzerland; *Int'l*, pg. 80
Samson, Claire, Chief Oper. Officer & Exec. V.P.--Reseau de Television Quatre Saisons Inc., Montreal, Canada; *Int'l*, pg. 241
Samson, Marc, Exec. V.P.-Chemical Grp.--Degussa Corporation, Ridgefield Park, NJ; *Int'l*, pg. 388
Samson, Roger, Exec. V.P.-Personnel--Sterling Supply Company, Inc., Lisle, IL; *U.S. Private*, pg. 1041
Samuels, Howard J., Exec. V.P.-Natl. Accts.--The Mills Corporation, Arlington, VA; *U.S. Public*, pg. 1113
Samuta, Joe, Exec. V.P.-Aerospace--Japan Aviation Electronics Industry, Ltd., Tokyo, Japan; *Int'l*, pg. 701
Sanahuja, Victor, Dr., Head-MB/P&A--Clariant International Ltd., Muttenz, Switzerland; *Int'l*, pg. 624
Sanchez, Ernesto, Exec. V.P.--Hylsa S.A.-North Plant, Apodaca, Mexico; *Int'l*, pg. 56
Sanchez, Evagrio, Exec. V.P.-N&S America--Sol Melia, Palma de Mallorca, Spain; *Int'l*, pg. 1277
Sanchez, Fernando, Exec. V.P.-Admin. Mktg.--Leather Center, Inc., Carrollton, TX; *U.S. Private*, pg. 656
Sandberg, Hakan, Exec. V.P.-Reg. Bank, Southern Norrland--Svenska Handelsbanken, Stockholm, Sweden; *Int'l*, pg. 1327
Sandefur, Jennifer Shiley, Exec. V.P. & Treas.--Countrywide Home Loans Inc., Pasadena, CA; *U.S. Public*, pg. 452
Sander, Jack, Exec. V.P.-Television Grp.--A.H. Belo Corporation, Dallas, TX; *U.S. Public*, pg. 209
Sanderson, Robin, Exec. V.P.--MarketSource Corporation, Cranbury, NJ; *U.S. Private*, pg. 705
Sandford, E. Halsey, Exec. V.P.-Devel.--Res-Care Incorporated, Louisville, KY; *U.S. Public*, pg. 1382
Sandi, Francisco Rubio, Sr. Exec. V.P.-Europe--Ares-Serono S.A., Geneva, Switzerland; *Int'l*, pg. 80
Sandler, Arthur, Exec. V.P.--L.M. Sandler & Sons, Virginia Beach, VA; *U.S. Private*, pg. 964
Sandler, Robert M., Exec. V.P.-Sr. Actuary & Sr. Claims Officer--American International Group, Inc., New York, NY; *U.S. Public*, pg. 83
Sandlund, C. Per-Erik, Exec. V.P.-Fin. & Admin.--Pharmacia & Upjohn Biotech AB, Uppsala, Sweden; *Int'l*, pg. 1047
Sandman, John B., Chief Oper. Officer & Exec. V.P.--A. Teichert & Son, Inc., Sacramento, CA; *U.S. Private*, pg. 1072
Sandnes, Ludvik, Chief Fin. Officer & Grp. Exec. V.P.--Christiania Bank og Kreditkasse ASA, Oslo, Norway; *Int'l*, pg. 289
Sands, Paul T., Jr., Exec. V.P. & Gen. Counsel--Chicago Title Insurance Co., Chicago, IL; *U.S. Public*, pg. 42
Sands, Paul, Jr., Exec. V.P., Gen. Counsel & Sec.--Chicago Title & Trust Co., Chicago, IL; *U.S. Public*, pg. 42
Sands, Robert, Exec. V.P., Gen. Counsel & Sec.--Canandaigua Wine Company, Inc., Canandaigua, NY; *U.S. Public*, pg. 300
Sandvig, Dave, Exec. V.P.-Mktg.--Fort Dodge Animal Health, Overland Park, KS; *U.S. Public*, pg. 79
Sanford, William, Exec. V.P.-Airgas Direct Indus.--Airgas, Inc., Radnor, PA; *U.S. Public*, pg. 33
Sanguinetti, L. David, Chief Oper. Officer & Exec. V.P.--Florsheim Group Inc., Chicago, IL; *U.S. Public*, pg. 656
Sans, Jose, Exec. V.P.--Medieval Times Dinner & Tournament, Inc., Buena Park, CA; *U.S. Private*, pg. 728
Sant, Stephen R., Chief Oper. Officer & Exec. V.P.--First Western Bancorp, Inc., New Castle, PA; *U.S. Public*, pg. 642
Santangelo, C.E., Jr., Exec. V.P.--D.A. Stuart Company, Warrenville, IL; *U.S. Private*, pg. 1048
Santini, Francesco, Exec. V.P.--Merloni Elettrodomestici S.P.A., Fabriano, Italy; *Int'l*, pg. 860
Santos, Everaldo N., Exec. V.P.-Fabricated Prods.--Alcan Aluminium Limited, Montreal, Canada; *Int'l*, pg. 50
Saper, Ronald L., Chief Fin. Officer & Exec. V.P.--Washington Federal Savings, Seattle, WA; *U.S. Public*, pg. 1740
Sapienza, Tony, Exec. V.P. & Gen. Mgr.-Boston--Miller Shandwick Technologies, Boston, MA; *Int'l*, pg. 1227
Sardina, Eduardo M., Exec. V.P.-N.A. Region--Bacardi Limited, Pembroke, Bermuda; *Int'l*, pg. 131
Sargent, Phillip B., Exec. V.P.--Todd & Sargent, Inc., Ames, IA; *U.S. Private*, pg. 1089
Sarkisian, Alex, Exec. V.P. & Sec.--Schawk, Inc., Des Plaines, IL; *U.S. Public*, pg. 1437
Sarrey, Joseph W., Exec. V.P. & Dir.-Sls.--Willis Corroon Corp. of Massachusetts, Boston, MA; *Int'l*, pg. 1506
Sarrica, Lewis F., Chief Investment Officer & Exec. V.P.--BankAtlantic Bancorp, Inc., Fort Lauderdale, FL; *U.S. Public*, pg. 183
Sartor, Rod, Exec. V.P.--Swift Transportation Co., Sparks, NV; *U.S. Public*, pg. 1543
Sasaki, Hajime, Sr. Exec. V.P.--NEC Corporation, Tokyo, Japan; *Int'l*, pg. 899
Sasaki, Kazuo, Exec. Advisor--Nippon Paint Company Ltd., Osaka, Japan; *Int'l*, pg. 937
Sasaki, Sumiaki, Exec. V.P.--Kao Corporation, Tokyo, Japan; *Int'l*, pg. 717
Sasaki, Yoshiro, Exec. V.P.--Nippon Steel Corporation, Tokyo, Japan; *Int'l*, pg. 939
Sasao, Keizo, Exec. V.P.--Asahi Chemical Industry Co., Ltd., Tokyo, Japan; *Int'l*, pg. 83
Sase, Yoichiro, Exec. V.P.--Dai-ichi Life Insurance Agency (U.S.A.), Inc.-Los Angeles, Los Angeles, CA; *Int'l*, pg. 362
Sastre, Eugenio Vela, Exec. V.P.--Amper, S.A., Madrid, Spain; *Int'l*, pg. 1372
Satin, Dick, Principal Exec. V.P.--Bradford Industries, Inc., Lowell, MA; *U.S. Private*, pg. 163
Sato, Hideo, Exec. V.P.--Nishimatsu Construction Co., Ltd., Tokyo, Japan; *Int'l*, pg. 942
Sato, Hirosuke, Exec. V.P.--Nichiro Corporation, Tokyo, Japan; *Int'l*, pg. 928
Sato, Masumi, Exec. V.P.--Kobe Steel, Ltd., Kobe, Japan; *Int'l*, pg. 740
Sato, Motohide, Exec. V.P.--Chubu Electric Power Company, Inc., Nagoya, Japan; *Int'l*, pg. 290
Sato, Nobutake, Exec. V.P.-Plng.--Ito-Yokado Co., Ltd., Tokyo, Japan; *Int'l*, pg. 693
Sato, S., Exec. V.P.-Corp. Office--Kawasaki Motors Corp., U.S.A., Irvine, CA; *Int'l*, pg. 725
Sattizahn, Ed, Exec. V.P.-Mktg.--The Learning Co., Inc., Cambridge, MA; *U.S. Public*, pg. 982
Satz, Joseph R., Exec. V.P., Gen. Counsel & Sec.--Price Enterprises, Inc., San Diego, CA; *U.S. Public*, pg. 1324
Sauder, Clair, Chief Fin. Officer & Exec. V.P.--Huffman Koos, River Edge, NJ; *U.S. Private*, pg. 546
Saul, Stephen R., Chief Fin. Officer & Exec. V.P.--Glenborough Realty Trust Incorporated, San Mateo, CA; *U.S. Public*, pg. 747
Saunders, Gary, Chief Fin. Officer & Exec. V.P.--Robert Bosch Corporation, Broadview, IL; *Int'l*, pg. 204
Saunders, Gregory S., Chief Fin. Officer, Exec. V.P. & Treas.--National Insurance Group, South San Francisco, CA; *U.S. Public*, pg. 1157
Saunders, Gregory S., Chief Fin. Officer & Exec. V.P.--Great Pacific Insurance Company, San Bruno, CA; *U.S. Public*, pg. 1158
Saunders, Gregory S., Chief Fin. Officer & Exec. V.P.--FASTRAC Systems, Inc., San Bruno, CA; *U.S. Public*, pg. 1158
Saunders, Gregory S., Chief Fin. Officer & Exec. V.P.--Pinnacle Data Corporation, San Bruno, CA; *U.S. Public*, pg. 1158
Saunders, Gregory S., Chief Fin. Officer & Exec. V.P.--FASTRAC Systems, Inc.-Insurance Agent & Broker, South San Francisco, CA; *U.S. Public*, pg. 1158
Saunders, Keith C., Chief Fin. Officer, Exec. V.P. & Sec.--Zions Co-operative Mercantile Institution, Salt Lake City, UT; *U.S. Public*, pg. 1793
Saure, Hans-Friedrich, Exec. V.P.--Norddeutsche Landesbank (NORD/LB), Hannover, Germany; *Int'l*, pg. 957
Sautter, Edouard, Exec. V.P.-Risk Policy & Indus. Res.--Banque Nationale de Paris, Paris, France; *Int'l*, pg. 163
Sauvageot, Claude, Exec. V.P.--Saint Dominique Participations, Paris, France; *Int'l*, pg. 344
Savage, Thomas F., Exec. V.P.--Mellon First Business Bank, Los Angeles, CA; *U.S. Public*, pg. 1085
Savage, Tom, Exec. V.P.--Trafalgar Ghurka Ltd., Norwalk, CT; *U.S. Private*, pg. 1095
Savary, Jean-Jacques, Exec. V.P.--Esselte AB, Solna, Sweden; *Int'l*, pg. 459
Savedge, Henry S., Jr., Chief Fin. Officer & Exec. V.P.--Reynolds Metals Company, Richmond, VA; *U.S. Public*, pg. 1385
Savey, Dominique, Exec. V.P.-Auto Div. Dep.--PSA Peugeot Citroen, Paris, France; *Int'l*, pg. 1020
Saville, Ian, Exec. V.P.-Toronto--Cossette Communication Marketing, Quebec, Canada; *Int'l*, pg. 335
Saville, Ian, Exec. V.P.--Cossette Communication-Marketing (Toronto) Inc., Toronto, Canada; *Int'l*, pg. 336
Saville, Ian, Exec. V.P.--Promotion Blitz Inc., Toronto, Canada; *Int'l*, pg. 336
Savitt, David, Exec. V.P. & Treas.--Pace Press, Inc., Moonachie, NJ; *U.S. Private*, pg. 829
Sawa, Kunihiko, Exec. V.P.--Fuji Electric Co., Ltd., Tokyo, Japan; *Int'l*, pg. 522
Sawada, Masahiro, Exec.V.P.--Heller International Corporation, Chicago, IL; *Int'l*, pg. 519
Sawada, Tsutomu, Exec. V.P.--Nissan Motor Co., Ltd., Tokyo, Japan; *Int'l*, pg. 943
Sawdei, Milan A., Exec. V.P., Chief Legal Officer & Sec.--Bergen Brunswig Corporation, Orange, CA; *U.S. Public*, pg. 213
Sawruk, Donald, Chief Oper. Officer & Exec. V.P.--ESELCO, Inc., Sault Sainte Marie, MI; *U.S. Public*, pg. 591
Sawyer, Bill, Exec. V.P.-Opers.--PSDI, Bedford, MA; *U.S. Private*, pg. 828
Sawyer, Charles W., Chief Oper. Officer & Exec. V.P.--Colonial Gas Company, Lowell, MA; *U.S. Public*, pg. 400
Sawyer, Louis, Exec. V.P.-Strategic Mktg.--Sawyer Riley Compton Inc., Atlanta, GA; *U.S. Private*, pg. 969
Sawyer, Wayne L., EXec. V.P.--American Security Group, Atlanta, GA; *Int'l*, pg. 499
Saxby, Hal, Exec. V.P.--Sysco Food Services of Virginia, Inc., Harrisonburg, VA; *U.S. Public*, pg. 1552
Saxton, Craig, M.D., V.P. & Exec. V.P.-Central Research--Pfizer Inc., New York, NY; *U.S. Public*, pg. 1281
Saynor, John B., Exec. V.P.--Arch Communications Group, Inc., Westborough, MA; *U.S. Public*, pg. 127
Sayre, Robert H., Exec. V.P.-Human Resources--U.S. Bancorp, Minneapolis, MN; *U.S. Public*, pg. 1680
Sayre, William H., Vice Chm.--National Penn Bank, Boyertown, PA; *U.S. Public*, pg. 1159
Sbarro, Joseph, Sr. Exec. V.P. & Sec.--Sbarro, Inc., Commack, NY; *U.S. Public*, pg. 1435
Scalca, Rob, Exec. V.P.-Strategic Plng.--Hill, Holliday, Connors, Cosmopulos, Inc., Boston, MA; *U.S. Private*, pg. 529
Scalerandi, Piero, Exec. V.P.-Risk Mngmt.--Istituto Bancario San Paolo Di Torino S.p.A., Turin, Italy; *Int'l*, pg. 691
Scalley, John J., Exec. V.P.--Genuine Parts Company, Atlanta, GA; *U.S. Public*, pg. 732
Scangamor, Joseph A., Chief Fin. Officer & Exec. V.P.--Carat MBS, New York, NY; *U.S. Private*, pg. 208
Scangas, Christopher A., Exec. V.P. & Treas.--Scangas Brothers Holdings, Inc., Lynn, MA; *U.S. Private*, pg. 969
Scangas, Nicholas A., Exec. V.P.-Mktg. & Sls.--Scangas Brothers Holdings, Inc., Lynn, MA; *U.S. Private*, pg. 969
Scanlan, Charles R., Jr., Exec. V.P.--Lockheed Martin Missiles & Space, Sunnyvale, CA; *U.S. Public*, pg. 1008
Scanlan, Robert, Exec. V.P.--Kaufman and Broad-Antelope Valley Regional Office, Palmdale, CA; *U.S. Public*, pg. 945
Scanlon, David, Exec. V.P. & Acct. Services Dir.--Arnold Advertising, Mc Lean, VA; *U.S. Private*, pg. 84
Scanlon, John M., Exec. V.P. & Gen. Mgr.-Cellular Infrastructure Grp.--Motorola, Inc., Schaumburg, IL; *U.S. Public*, pg. 1136
Scarbo, Clifford K., Exec. V.P. & Chief Credit Officer--Seafirst Corporation, Seattle, WA; *U.S. Public*, pg. 181
Scardino, Mike, Exec. V.P. & Co-Creative Dir.--The Lord Group, New York, NY; *U.S. Private*, pg. 325
Scarpinato, Joseph N., Exec. V.P.-Credit Card--Associates First Capital Corporation, Dallas, TX; *U.S. Public*, pg. 662
Schaaf, Edward M., III, Exec. V.P. & Dir.-Opers.--Universal Leaf Tobacco Company, Inc., Richmond, VA; *U.S. Public*, pg. 1694
Schadeck, Barry W., Exec. V.P.-Western Regional Opers.--Corrpro Companies, Inc., Medina, OH; *U.S. Public*, pg. 451
Schaefer, B.P., Exec. V.P.--Braas GmbH, Oberursell, Germany; *Int'l*, pg. 1091
Schaefer, Rohn, Exec. V.P.--Diebel Manufacturing Co., Morton Grove, IL; *U.S. Private*, pg. 331
Schaefer, Thomas C., Chief Fin. Officer & Exec. V.P.--United Planners' Financial Services of America, Scottsdale, AZ; *U.S. Private*, pg. 831
Schaeffer, David H., Exec. V.P.--First National Bank of Naples, Naples, FL; *U.S. Public*, pg. 607
Schaeffer, Joe K., Exec. V.P.--ADT Security Systems, Inc., Carmel, IN; *U.S. Public*, pg. 1649
Schaeffer, Wayne G., Exec. V.P.--Citizens Banking Corporation, Flint, MI; *U.S. Public*, pg. 379
Schaftlien, Mark, Exec. V.P.--Westmark Group Holdings Inc., Delray Beach, FL; *U.S. Public*, pg. 1761
Schall, Valeria, Exec. V.P.--All Star Gas Corporation, Lebanon, MO; *U.S. Private*, pg. 35
Schantz, James D., Exec. V.P.--Hagler, Mastrovita & Hewitt, Inc., Boston, MA; *U.S. Public*, pg. 1673
Scharf, Charles, Chief Fin. Officer & Exec. V.P.--Salomon Smith Barney Holdings, Inc., New York, NY; *U.S. Public*, pg. 1633
Schartz, Daniel M., Exec. V.P.--Republic National Bank of New York, New York, NY; *U.S. Public*, pg. 1380
Schatz, Olivier, Exec. V.P.-Acctg. Fin. Control & Securities--Credit Nationale, Paris, France; *Int'l*, pg. 344
Schauf, Lawrence E., Exec. V.P. & Sec.--Foodmaker, Inc., San Diego, CA; *U.S. Public*, pg. 661

Schaus, David W., Exec. V.P.--Unigas, Calgary, Canada; *Int'l*, pg. 1492

Schauss, Ralph, Grp. Exec. V.P.-Europe, Middle East & Africa Grp.--Bank of America NT&SA, San Francisco, CA; *U.S. Public*, pg. 180

Schautz, Carol A., Chief Oper. Officer & Exec. V.P.--Wunderman Cato Johnson, New York, NY; *U.S. Private*, pg. 1197

Schechter, Saul, Exec. V.P.--Superior Surgical Mfg. Co., Inc., Seminole, FL; *U.S. Public*, pg. 1539

Scheeffer, H.M., Exec. V.P.--ABN-AMRO Holding N.V., Amsterdam, Netherlands; *Int'l*, pg. 8

Scheffer, Stephen J., Exec. V.P.-Film Programming & Home Video--Home Box Office, Inc., New York, NY; *U.S. Public*, pg. 1612

Scheflen, John W., Sr. Exec. V.P., Gen. Counsel & Sec.--MBNA Corporation, Wilmington, DE; *U.S. Public*, pg. 1023

Scheid, Steven L., Chief Fin. Officer & Exec. V.P.--The Charles Schwab Corporation, San Francisco, CA; *U.S. Public*, pg. 1442

Scheinman, Tom, Exec. V.P.--Shepaug Corporation, New York, NY; *U.S. Private*, pg. 993

Schemmann, Gert, Dr., Exec. V.P.--DG Bank, Frankfurt/Main, Germany; *Int'l*, pg. 351

Schenck, A. William, III, Exec. V.P.-Retail Banking--PNC Bank Corp., Pittsburgh, PA; *U.S. Public*, pg. 1242

Schengili, Veerle, Exec. V.P.-Opers.--Numetrix Ltd., Toronto, Canada; *Int'l*, pg. 990

Schenk, Douglas R., Exec. V.P.-Pineapple--Maui Land & Pineapple Co., Inc., Kahului, HI; *U.S. Public*, pg. 1060

Schenker, Leo, Sr. Exec. V.P.--Central National-Gottesman Inc., Purchase, NY; *U.S. Private*, pg. 224

Scheper, Fran, Exec. V.P.-Human Resources--CPI Corp., Saint Louis, MO; *U.S. Public*, pg. 283

Schepler, Charles, Exec. V.P. & Chief Oper. Officer--Manhattan National Life Insurance Company, Cincinnati, OH; *U.S. Public*, pg. 434

Scher, Norman A., Chief Fin. Officer & Exec. V.P.--Tredegar Industries Inc., Richmond, VA; *U.S. Public*, pg. 1633

Schereck, William, Exec. V.P.-Intl.--QVC, Inc., West Chester, PA; *U.S. Private*, pg. 897

Scherer, George F., Chief Fin. Officer, Exec. V.P. & Treas.--McCarthy Building Companies, Saint Louis, MO; *U.S. Private*, pg. 719

Scherer, Peter R., Exec. V.P.--Tom Brown, Inc., Midland, TX; *U.S. Public*, pg. 262

Scherman, Carol, Exec. V.P.-Human Resources--Bergen Brunswig Corporation, Orange, CA; *U.S. Public*, pg. 213

Scherr, Walter, Exec. V.P. & Gen. Mgr.--Veeco Instruments, Inc., Plainview, NY; *U.S. Public*, pg. 1711

Scherrer, Urs, Exec. V.P.-Sulzer Winterthur Group--Sulzer Ltd., Winterthur, Switzerland; *Int'l*, pg. 1305

Scherrer, Urs, Exec. V.P.--Sulzer-Winterthur Group, Winterthur, Switzerland; *Int'l*, pg. 1307

Scherwinski, Darrell, Exec. V.P.-Mdsg.--The Copps Corp., Stevens Point, WI; *U.S. Private*, pg. 275

Schick, Thomas, Exec. V.P.-Corp. Affairs & Communications--American Express Company, New York, NY; *U.S. Public*, pg. 73

Schick, Tom, Exec. V.P. & Deputy to BCAG Pres.--Boeing Commercial Airplane Group, Renton, WA; *U.S. Public*, pg. 240

Schiefer, Ware F., Exec. V.P.--Piedmont Natural Gas Co., Inc., Charlotte, NC; *U.S. Public*, pg. 1295

Schiek, Fred A., Chief Oper. Officer & Exec. V.P.--EMC Insurance Companies, Des Moines, IA; *U.S. Public*, pg. 545

Schiek, Frederick A., Chief Oper. Officer & Exec. V.P.--EMC Insurance Group, Inc., Des Moines, IA; *U.S. Public*, pg. 545

Schievelbein, T.C., Exec. V.P.--Newport News Shipbuilding, Inc., Newport News, VA; *U.S. Public*, pg. 1179

Schilling, William J., Exec. V.P.-Opers.-Magnet Wire Division--Rea Magnet Wire Company, Inc., Fort Wayne, IN; *U.S. Private*, pg. 913

Schilt, Paul U., Exec. V.P.--Switzerland Cheese Association, Inc., Valley Cottage, NY; *Int'l*, pg. 1211

Schimpf, John J., Exec. V.P.--Hovnanian Enterprises, Inc., Red Bank, NJ; *U.S. Public*, pg. 843

Schinder, Rainer, Chief Oper. Officer & Exec. V.P.--Ragold, Inc., Chicago, IL; *Int'l*, pg. 1084

Schindler, Gary N., Exec. V.P. & Gen. Mgr.-Northern Calif.--AirTouch Cellular, Walnut Creek, CA; *U.S. Public*, pg. 34

Schindler, Paul R., Sr. V.P.-Intl. Opers.--AlliedSignal Inc., Morristown, NJ; *U.S. Public*, pg. 49

Schinsky, Larry, Exec. V.P.-Sls.--Computer Sales International Inc., Saint Louis, MO; *U.S. Private*, pg. 260

Schissler, Gerald J., Exec. V.P.-Law--Burlington Resources Inc., Houston, TX; *U.S. Public*, pg. 269

Schissler, Gerald J., Exec. V.P.-Law & Corp. Affairs--Meridian Oil Holding Inc., Houston, TX; *U.S. Public*, pg. 269

Schivley, William W., Exec. V.P. & Chief Oper. Officer-CMS Marketing--Consumers Energy, Jackson, MI; *U.S. Public*, pg. 280

Schlanger, Marvin O., Chief Oper. Officer & Exec. V.P.--ARCO Chemical Co., Newtown Square, PA; *U.S. Public*, pg. 144

Schlegel, Bill, Pres. & Chief Exec. Officer, Medical Economics Data--Medical Economics Company Inc., Montvale, NJ; *U.S. Public*, pg. 1601

Schleif, Gerhard, Exec. V.P.-Trading Div.--Deutsche Girozentrale-Deutsche Kommunalbank, Frankfurt/Main, Germany; *Int'l*, pg. 406

Schleiter, James, Exec. V.P.--Vance Industries, Inc., Chicago, IL; *U.S. Private*, pg. 1133

Schlesinger, Vicki, Sr. Partner & Exec. V.P.--Fleishman-Hillard Inc., Saint Louis, MO; *U.S. Private*, pg. 411

Schlomann, James M., Chief Fin. Officer & Sr. Exec. V.P.--USLIFE Corporation, New York, NY; *U.S. Public*, pg. 77

Schlosberg, Richard T., III, Exec. V.P.--The Times Mirror Company, Los Angeles, CA; *U.S. Public*, pg. 1615

Schlosberg, Richard T., III, Exec. V.P.--Times Mirror Magazines, Inc., New York, NY; *U.S. Public*, pg. 1616

Schlossberg, Alan, Exec. V.P. & Opers. & Media Devel. Dir.--Kelly, Scott And Madison, Inc., Chicago, IL; *U.S. Private*, pg. 613

Schmale, Neal E., Chief Fin. Officer & Exec. V.P.--Pacific Enterprises, Los Angeles, CA; *U.S. Public*, pg. 1249

Schmale, Neal E., Chief Fin. Officer & Exec. V.P.--Southern California Gas Co., Los Angeles, CA; *U.S. Public*, pg. 1249

Schmelzer, Wilhelm A., Exec. V.P.-Sealing Sys.--Federal-Mogul Corporation, Southfield, MI; *U.S. Public*, pg. 615

Schmid, Peter, Exec. V.P.-Domestic Distribution--Saban Entertainment, Los Angeles, CA; *U.S. Private*, pg. 959

Schmid, Ronald J., Exec. V.P.-Hawaii Market--Bank of Hawaii, Honolulu, HI; *U.S. Public*, pg. 1248

Schmidt Bies, Susan, Exec. V.P.-Risk Mngmt.--First Tennessee Bank National Association, Memphis, TN; *U.S. Public*, pg. 639

Schmidt, Fred, Exec. V.P. & Acct. Mngmt. Dir.--Romann & Tannenholz Advertising, Inc., New York, NY; *U.S. Private*, pg. 942

Schmidt, Glenn W., Exec. V.P.--Market Facts, Inc., Arlington Heights, IL; *U.S. Public*, pg. 1046

Schmidt, Jim, Exec. V.P. & Creative Dir.--McConnaughy Stein Schmidt Brown, Chicago, IL; *U.S. Private*, pg. 720

Schmidt, Mark F., Exec. V.P.-Govt. Affairs--American Waste Services, Inc., Warren, OH; *U.S. Public*, pg. 94

Schmit, John B., Exec. V.P.-Prod.--Boeing Defense & Space Group, Kent, WA; *U.S. Public*, pg. 240

Schmitz, Clarence T., Chief Fin. Officer & Exec. V.P.--Jefferies Group, Inc., Los Angeles, CA; *U.S. Public*, pg. 924

Schmitz, Clarence T., Exec. V.P.--Jefferies & Company, Inc., Los Angeles, CA; *U.S. Public*, pg. 925

Schmitz, Michael J., Exec. V.P.--Firstar Corporation, Milwaukee, WI; *U.S. Public*, pg. 642

Schmitz, Stephen G., Chief Investment Officer & Exec. V.P.--Franchise Finance Corp. of America, Scottsdale, AZ; *U.S. Public*, pg. 679

Schmitz, Walter, Dr., Exec. V.P.--Bayerische Landesbank Girozentrale - Dusseldorf Branch, Dusseldorf, Germany; *Int'l*, pg. 176

Schnabel, Richard F., Exec. V.P.--Book of the Month Club, New York, NY; *U.S. Public*, pg. 1612

Schnack, Uwe, Chief Oper. Officer & Exec. V.P.--TSC Shannock Corporation, Burnaby, Canada; *Int'l*, pg. 1343

Schnaidt, Kay E., Chief Exec. Officer & Exec. V.P.--American Barmag Co., Charlotte, NC; *U.S. Private*, pg. 51

Schneck, Edward N., Exec. V.P.--Wahlstrom & Company, Stamford, CT; *U.S. Public*, pg. 1641

Schneider, David, Exec. V.P.--Plastag Corporation, Elk Grove Village, IL; *U.S. Private*, pg. 870

Schneider, H., Exec V.P. & Creative Dir.--Brierley & Partners, Dallas, TX; *U.S. Private*, pg. 168

Schneider, Robert E., Chief Fin. Officer & Exec. V.P.--The New England, Boston, MA; *U.S. Private*, pg. 737

Schneider, Robert F., Chief Fin. Officer, Exec. V.P. & Asst. Treas.--Kimball International, Inc., Jasper, IN; *U.S. Public*, pg. 956

Schneider, Thomas C., Exec. V.P. & Chief Strategic & Admin. Officer--Morgan Stanley Dean Witter & Co., New York, NY; *U.S. Public*, pg. 1132

Schneider, Thomas C., Chief Fin. Officer & Exec. V.P.--Dean Witter, Discover & Co., New York, NY; *U.S. Public*, *pg. 1132*

Schneider, Thomas J., Exec. V.P.--Goodman Equipment Corp., Bedford Park, IL; *U.S. Private*, pg. 464

Schnewlin, Frank, Exec. V.P.--Zurich Insurance Company, Zurich, Switzerland; *Int'l*, pg. 1529

Schnieders, Bob, Exec. V.P.-Sls. & Mktg.--Universal Studios, Inc., Universal City, CA; *Int'l*, pg. 1215

Schnitler, Didenk, Exec. V.P.-Shipbuilding & Dir.-Mktg.--Kvaerner a.s.a., Lysaker, Norway; *Int'l*, pg. 766

Schnitzer, Gary, Exec. V.P.--Schnitzer Steel Industries, Inc., Portland, OR; *U.S. Public*, pg. 1439

Schochet, Barry P., Exec. V.P.-Opers.--Tenet Healthcare Corporation, Santa Barbara, CA; *U.S. Public*, pg. 1576

Schoenbachler, C.L., Chief Fin. Officer & Exec. V.P.--Brown & Williamson Tobacco Corp., Louisville, KY; *Int'l*, pg. 111

Schoenfeld, Richard, Exec. V.P. & Treas.--Tomco Auto Products, Inc., Los Angeles, CA; *U.S. Private*, pg. 1090

Schoenke, Richard W., Sr. Exec. V.P.--Firstar Corporation, Milwaukee, WI; *U.S. Public*, pg. 642

Schoff, James A., Chief Oper. Officer & Exec. V.P.--Developers Diversified Realty Corporation, Moreland Hills, OH; *U.S. Public*, pg. 502

Schoffstall, David W., Exec. V.P.--CoreStates Bank, N.A., Philadelphia, PA; *U.S. Public*, pg. 446

Scholten, E.G., Exec. V.P.--ABN-AMRO Holding N.V., Amsterdam, Netherlands; *Int'l*, pg. 8

Schomer, Richard F., Exec. V.P.-Service--Peregrine Incorporated, Southfield, MI; *U.S. Private*, pg. 852

Schoonenberg, Donald S., Exec. V.P.--Simplicity Manufacturing, Inc., Port Washington, WI; *U.S. Private*, pg. 1002

Schopp, Alryn A., Chief Fin. Officer & Exec. V.P.--T-NETIX, Inc., Englewood, CO; *U.S. Public*, pg. 1553

Schorderet, Georges, Exec. V.P.-Corp. Fin. & Devel.--The Swissair Group, Zurich, Switzerland; *Int'l*, pg. 1333

Schorr, Brian L., Exec. V.P. & Gen. Counsel--Triarc Companies, Inc., New York, NY; *U.S. Public*, pg. 1634

Schott, Birgitta, Dir.-Savings Bank Zone North--Swedbank, Stockholm, Sweden; *Int'l*, pg. 1328

Schott, Gerhard, Dr., Sr. Exec. V.P.-Treas.--Bayerische Landesbank, Munich, Germany; *Int'l*, pg. 176

Schour, Avi, Exec. V.P.--H.H. Brown Shoe Company, Inc., Greenwich, CT; *U.S. Public*, pg. 217

Schrader, Richard A., Exec. V.P. & Asst. Sec.--Parsons Brinckerhoff Inc., New York, NY; *U.S. Private*, pg. 841

Schrage, Klaus, Exec. V.P.-Chemicals--Huls America Inc., Somerset, NJ; *Int'l*, pg. 1455

Schreiber, Alfred L., Exec. V.P. & Gen. Mgr.--Graham Gregory Bozell, Inc., New York, NY; *U.S. Public*, pg. 1642

Schreiber, George A., Jr., Chief Fin. Officer & Exec. V.P.--Pinnacle West Capital Corporation, Phoenix, AZ; *U.S. Public*, pg. 1297

Schreiber, George A., Jr., Chief Fin. Officer & Exec. V.P.--APS, Phoenix, AZ; *U.S. Public*, pg. 1297

Schreiner, Daniel, Exec. V.P.--Texas Homestead Mortgage Co., San Antonio, TX; *U.S. Public*, pg. 945

Schreyer, John Y., Chief Fin. Officer & Exec. V.P.--Amerada Hess Corporation, New York, NY; *U.S. Public*, pg. 65

Schrick, Ben, Chief Oper. Officer & Exec. V.P.--Petroleum Helicopters, Inc., Metairie, LA; *U.S. Public*, pg. 1281

Schrickel, Patrick D., Exec. V.P.--WPS Resources Corp., Green Bay, WI; *U.S. Public*, pg. 1728

Schrifer, Gregory, Exec. V.P.-Bldg. & Industrial Wire--Essex International, Inc., Fort Wayne, IN; *U.S. Public*, pg. 593

Schriver, Donald, Chief Exec. Officer & Exec. V.P.--Milk Marketing Inc., Strongsville, OH; *U.S. Private*, pg. 745

Schroder, Bernie, Exec. V.P.-Multinational Banking--Royal Bank of Canada, Toronto, Canada; *Int'l*, pg. 1131

Schrodt, Daniel, Exec. V.P.--Jiffy Products of America, Inc., Batavia, IL; *Int'l*, pg. 706

Schroeder, James, Exec. V.P.--MSC Industrial Supply Co., Plainview, NY; *U.S. Private*, pg. 998

Schroeder, John, Exec. V.P.-Environmental Prods. & Services--Sybron Chemicals Inc., Birmingham, NJ; *U.S. Public*, pg. 1544

Schucet, Phillip, Exec. V.P.-Environmental--Michael Baker Corporation, Pittsburgh, PA; *U.S. Public*, pg. 168

Schuck, Terry, Chief Information Officer & Exec. V.P.--Allegiant Physician Services, Atlanta, GA; *U.S. Public*, pg. 45

Schuck, Timothy B., Exec. V.P. & Chief Oper. Officer--Barclays American/Mortgage Corp., Charlotte, NC; *Int'l*, pg. 165

Schueler, John, Exec. V.P. & Gen. Mgr.--The Orange County Register, Santa Ana, CA; *U.S. Private*, pg. 425

Schueler, S., Exec. V.P.--Richard Hirschmann of America, Inc., Riverdale, NJ; *Int'l*, pg. 1108

Schueppert, George L., Chief Fin. Officer & Exec. V.P.--Outboard Marine Corporation, Waukegan, IL; *U.S. Private*, pg. 478

Schuette, Thomas, Chief Info. Officer & V.P.-Opers. & Matls.--Wausau Homes, Inc., Rothschild, WI; *U.S. Private*, pg. 1154

Schuh, Ronald C., Exec. V.P.-Petrochemicals--Occidental Chemical Corporation, Dallas, TX; *U.S. Public*, pg. 1210

Schull, Lester, Exec. V.P.--Building Products Inc., Watertown, SD; *U.S. Private*, pg. 180

Schultz, Alan F., Chief Oper. Officer & Exec. V.P.--Valassis Communications, Inc., Livonia, MI; *U.S. Public*, pg. 1704

Schultz, Bob, Exec. V.P.-Mktg.--Marine World Africa USA, Vallejo, CA; *U.S. Private*, pg. 703

Schultz, Charles G., Exec. V.P.--Sanwa Business Credit Corporation, Chicago, IL; *Int'l*, pg. 1189

Schultz, Randy, Chief Oper. Officer & Exec. V.P.--IGI Resources, Inc., Boise, ID; *U.S. Private*, pg. 568

Schumacher, Norbert, Exec. V.P.-Publication Services--The Physician and Sportsmedicine, Minneapolis, MN; *U.S. Public*, pg. 1071

Schun, A., Exec. V.P.--Elf Atochem S.A., Paris, France; *Int'l*, *pg. 445*

Schurheck, Robert J., Chief Fin. Officer & Exec. V.P.--CVB Financial Corp., Ontario, CA; *U.S. Public*, pg. 286

Schuster, Carol, Exec. V.P. & Mng. Dir.--DMB&B New York, New York, NY; *U.S. Private*, pg. 302

Schut, Bragi F., Exec. V.P.--The Alpine Group, Inc., New York, NY; *U.S. Public*, pg. 58

Schut, N.A., Exec. V.P.--ABN-AMRO Holding N.V., Amsterdam, Netherlands; *Int'l*, pg. 8

Schute, E. Alan, Exec. V.P., Chief Fin. Officer-HLS Corp.--CommonHealth USA, Parsippany, NJ; *Int'l*, pg. 1483

Schutz, John, Exec. V.P.-Sls. & Mktg.--Strombecker Corporation, Chicago, IL; *U.S. Private*, pg. 1047

Schutzbank, Stanley G., Ph.D., Exec. V.P.--Interferon Sciences, Inc., New Brunswick, NJ; *U.S. Public*, pg. 694

Schwab, Leonard C., Exec. V.P.--S. Schwab Company, Cumberland, MD; *U.S. Private*, pg. 974

Schwach, Barry, Chief Fin. Officer & Exec. V.P.--Sunrise Leasing Corporation, Golden Valley, MN; *U.S. Public*, pg. 1535

Schwach, Matthew, Exec. V.P. & Plng. Dir.--The Media Edge, New York, NY; *U.S. Private*, pg. 1079

Schwartz, Alan D., Exec. V.P. & Sr. Mng. Dir.--The Bear Stearns Companies Inc., New York, NY; *U.S. Public*, pg. 197

Schwartz, Alan V., Chief Oper. & Fin. Officer & Exec. V.P.--Bernard Hodes Group, New York, NY; *U.S. Public*, pg. 1224

Schwartz, Arthur J., Ph.D., Exec. V.P.-Tech.--Aura Systems, Inc., El Segundo, CA; *U.S. Public*, pg. 147

Schwartz, Bob, Exec. V.P. & Corp. Sec.--Bozell Retail, Toronto, Canada; *Int'l*, pg. 209

Schwartz, Curtis, Exec. V.P.-Fin.--Hartz Mountain Industries, Secaucus, NJ; *U.S. Private*, pg. 508

Schwartz, Curtis B., Vice Chm. & Exec. V.P.--The Hartz Mountain Corp., Secaucus, NJ; *U.S. Private*, pg. 508

Schwartz, Donald P., Exec. V.P. & Gen. Mgr.-Small Bus. Banking--The Dime Savings Bank of New York, New York, NY; *U.S. Public*, pg. 509

Schwartz, Gary W., Chief Information Officer & Exec. V.P.--Kimball International, Inc., Jasper, IN; *U.S. Public*, pg. 956

Schwartz, Helmut, Exec. V.P. & Pres.-Automotive Grp.--Robert Bosch Corporation, Broadview, IL; *Int'l*, pg. 204

Schwartz, Kenneth, Exec. V.P.--K & F Industries Inc., New York, NY; *U.S. Private*, pg. 602

Schwartz, Larry, V.P.-Fin. & Admin.--RTG Furniture Corp., Seffner, FL; *U.S. Private*, pg. 905

Schwartz, Larry, Exec. V.P.--Jack Schwartz Shoes, Inc., New York, NY; *U.S. Private*, pg. 974

Schwartz, Paul, Exec. V.P. & Sr. Creative Dir.--N.W. Ayer & Partners New York, New York, NY; *U.S. Private*, pg. 104
Schwartz, Perry, Chief Fin. Officer & Exec. V.P.--Baldwin Piano & Organ Company, Loveland, OH; *U.S. Public*, pg. 169
Schwartz, Phil, Exec. V.P.--St. Martins Press, Inc., New York, NY; *Int'l*, pg. 1479
Schwartz, Robert, Exec. V.P.--Red Apple Companies, New York, NY; *U.S. Private*, pg. 914
Schwartz, Robert, Exec. V.P.--Republic National Bank of New York, New York, NY; *U.S. Public*, pg. 1380
Schwartz, Robert J., Exec. V.P.--Tokyo-Mitsubishi Derivative Products (USA), Inc., New York, NY; *Int'l*, pg. 157
Schwartz, Sanford M., Dr., Exec. V.P. & Pres.-Market Facts-New York--Market Facts, Inc., Arlington Heights, IL; *U.S. Public*, pg. 1046
Schwartz, Stanley, Exec. V.P.--Rosco Laboratories, Inc., Stamford, CT; *U.S. Private*, pg. 944
Schwartzbeck, Tom, Pres., Chief Oper. Officer & Exec. V.P.--Duron, Inc., Beltsville, MD; *U.S. Private*, pg. 349
Schwarz, John H., Exec. V.P.-Fin. & Admin.--Perini Corporation, Framingham, MA; *U.S. Public*, pg. 1278
Schwarz, Manfred, Exec. V.P.-Fin.--Stihl Inc., Virginia Beach, VA; *Int'l*, pg. 1301
Schwarz, Robert, Exec. V.P.--Peter Pan Bus Lines, Inc., Springfield, MA; *U.S. Private*, pg. 856
Schwarz, Steven R., Exec. V.P.--United Stationers Inc., Des Plaines, IL; *U.S. Public*, pg. 1689
Schwass, Gary, Chief Fin. Officer & Exec. V.P.--DQE Inc., Coraopolis, PA; *U.S. Public*, pg. 474
Schwatka, Mark A., Exec. V.P. & Sr. Creative Dir.--Grey Advertising Inc., New York, NY; *U.S. Public*, pg. 764
Schweiger, Frederick, Exec. V.P.--Old World Industries, Inc., Northbrook, IL; *U.S. Private*, pg. 814
Schweitzer, George, Exec. V.P.-Mktg. Communications--CBS, New York, NY; *U.S. Public*, pg. 273
Schweitzer, George, Exec. V.P.-Mktg. & Communications--CBS Television Network, New York, NY; *U.S. Public*, pg. 274
Schweitzer, Mike, Exec. V.P. & Mng. Dir.--Western International Media Corporation, Orlando, FL; *U.S. Private*, pg. 1167
Schweitzer, Rudolf, Exec. V.P.-Fin.--Careal Holding AG, Zurich, Switzerland; *Int'l*, pg. 271
Schweizer, Leslie, Exec. V.P.-Engrng.--Schweizer Aircraft Corporation, Big Flats, NY; *U.S. Private*, pg. 975
Schweizer, Paul H., Exec. V.P.-Fin.--Schweizer Aircraft Corporation, Big Flats, NY; *U.S. Private*, pg. 975
Schwertly, Gary, Chief Fin. Officer & Exec. V.P.--The Woodfin Suite Hotels, San Diego, CA; *U.S. Private*, pg. 1187
Schyborger, Gert, Exec. V.P. & Gen. Mgr.--Saab AB, Linkoping, Sweden; *Int'l*, pg. 686
Scicutella, John V., Exec. V.P.-Opers. & Systems--The Prudential Insurance Company of America, Newark, NJ; *U.S. Private*, pg. 892
Scisson, Brenda, Exec. V.P. & Pub. Rels. Dir.--Cranford Johnson Robinson Woods, Little Rock, AR; *U.S. Private*, *pg. 286*
Sclafani, Joseph L., Exec. V.P. & Controller--The Chase Manhattan Corporation, New York, NY; *U.S. Public*, pg. 337
Scocks, Chuck, Exec. V.P.--Helm, Inc., Detroit, MI; *U.S. Private*, pg. 520
Scodari, Joseph C., Exec. V.P.-Pharmaceutical Div.--Centocor Pharmaceutical Division, Malvern, PA; *U.S. Public*, pg. 323
Sconyers, Richard L., Exec. V.P.--Centex Real Estate Corp./Centex Homes, Dallas, TX; *U.S. Public*, pg. 323
Scopaz, John M., Exec. V.P.--Republic National Bank of New York, New York, NY; *U.S. Public*, pg. 1380
Scott, C. Wes, Exec. V.P.-Corp.--Northern Telecom Limited, Brampton, Canada; *Int'l*, pg. 968
Scott, David, Exec. V.P.--Georgia Duck & Cordage Mills, Scottdale, GA; *U.S. Private*, pg. 448
Scott, E.Michael D., Principal & Exec. V.P.--Vox Medica Corporation, Philadelphia, PA; *U.S. Private*, pg. 1143
Scott, Gail, Exec. V.P. & Reg. Brdcst. Dir.--Western International Media Corporation, Los Angeles, CA; *U.S. Private*, pg. 1165
Scott, Gail, Exec. V.P. & Reg. Media Dir.--Western International Media Corporation, Atlanta, GA; *U.S. Private*, pg. 1167
Scott, H. Lee, Jr., Exec. V.P.-Mdsg.--Wal-Mart Stores, Inc., Bentonville, AR; *U.S. Public*, pg. 1732
Scott, James, Exec. V.P.-Opers./N. America--FCA International Ltd., Westmount, Canada; *Int'l*, pg. 470
Scott, Jerry S., Exec. V.P.-Fresh Meats Opers.--IBP, Inc., Dakota City, NE; *U.S. Public*, pg. 852
Scott, Lary R., Exec. V.P.--Arkansas Best Corporation, Fort Smith, AR; *U.S. Public*, pg. 130
Scott, Richard W., Chief Investment Officer & Exec. V.P.--American General Corporation, Houston, TX; *U.S. Public*, *pg. 76*
Scott, Robert, Chief Fin. Officer & Exec. V.P.--Morgan Stanley Dean Witter & Co., New York, NY; *U.S. Public*, pg. 1132
Scott, Robert H., Exec. V.P.--TCF Bank Minnesota FSB, Minneapolis, MN; *U.S. Public*, pg. 1554
Scott, Terry, Exec. V.P.-Rollins Leasing--Rollins Leasing Corp., Wilmington, DE; *U.S. Public*, pg. 1405
Scotti, Benjamin J., Sr. Exec. V.P. & Exec. V.P.-All American Music Grp.--All American Communications, Inc., Santa Monica, CA; *U.S. Public*, pg. 41
Scotti, Enrico, Sr. Exec. V.P.-Credit Mngmt.--Istituto Bancario San Paolo Di Torino S.p.A., Turin, Italy; *Int'l*, pg. 691
Scricco, Francis M., Chief Oper. Officer & Exec. V.P.--Arrow Electronics, Inc., Melville, NY; *U.S. Public*, pg. 133
Scrivani, Francine, Exec. V.P.--Futter Lumber Corporation, Rockville Center, NY; *U.S. Private*, pg. 432
Seagal, Alvin, Chief Oper. Officer & Exec. V.P.--Perry H. Koplik & Sons, New York, NY; *U.S. Private*, pg. 632
Seager, F. Ronald, Exec. V.P.--Illinois Tool Works Inc., Glenview, IL; *U.S. Public*, pg. 865
Seaman, John T., Jr., Exec. V.P.-Opers.--Hickman, Williams & Co. Inc., Cincinnati, OH; *U.S. Private*, pg. 525
Sear, T.R.G., Exec. V.P.-Intl.--Alcon Laboratories, Inc., Fort Worth, TX; *Int'l*, pg. 916
Sear, T.R.G., Exec. V.P.--Alcon Pharma, Inc., Fort Worth, TX; *Int'l*, pg. 916
Searer, Rick, Exec. V.P. & Gen. Mgr.-Oscar Mayer Foods Corp.--Kraft Foods Inc., Glenview, IL; *U.S. Public*, pg. 1288
Searfoss, David W., Chief Fin. Officer & Exec. V.P.--Phoenix Home Life Mutual Insurance Company, Hartford, CT; *U.S. Private*, pg. 863
Searfoss, David W., Chief Fin. Officer & Exec. V.P.--Phoenix Home Life Mutual Insurance Co., Hartford, CT; *U.S. Private*, pg. 863
Seaver, James M., Exec. V.P.-Sls. & Mktg. Grp.--AGCO Corporation, Duluth, GA; *U.S. Public*, pg. 28
Seaward, Michael, Exec. V.P.--Rio Minerales, San Jose, Costa Rica; *Int'l*, pg. 1498
Seay, J. Rodney, Exec. V.P.-Mergers & Acq.--Medpartners Inc., Birmingham, AL; *U.S. Public*, pg. 1082
Seck, Gregory, Exec. V.P.--Studley Products Co., Inwood, NY; *U.S. Public*, pg. 1193
Seckel, M.F., Exec. V.P.--ABN-AMRO Holding N.V., Amsterdam, Netherlands; *Int'l*, pg. 8
Secrist, Rich, Jr., Exec. V.P.--The George E. Failing Company, Enid, OK; *U.S. Private*, pg. 153
Sedler, Jordan B., Exec. V.P., Sec. & Treas.--Paper Enterprises, Inc., Bronx, NY; *U.S. Private*, pg. 837
Sedlmeier, M.E., Exec. V.P.--Ziegler Medical Equipment Group, Inc., Omaha, NE; *U.S. Public*, pg. 1792
See, Bernard, Exec. V.P. Data Processing--Credit Nationale, Paris, France; *Int'l*, pg. 344
Seefried, Renee P., Exec. V.P.-H.R.--Webster Financial Corporation, Waterbury, CT; *U.S. Public*, pg. 1751
Seegers, Gary, Exec. V.P. & Dir.-Fin.--Driv-Lok, Inc., Sycamore, IL; *U.S. Private*, pg. 343
Seelbach, Kurt H., Exec. V.P.--Florists' Mutual Insurance Co., Edwardsville, IL; *U.S. Private*, pg. 415
Seeley, Donald L., Chief Fin. Officer & Exec. V.P.-True North Communications Inc.--True North Communications Inc., Chicago, IL; *U.S. Public*, pg. 1641
Segal, Brian, Exec. V.P. & Publr.-Maclean's--Maclean Hunter Publishing Ltd., Toronto, Canada; *Int'l*, pg. 1123
Segal, Isaac, Exec. V.P.-Creative--RBT/Strum, Cherry Hill, NJ; *U.S. Private*, pg. 902
Segel, Walter, Exec. V.P.-Sls.--Hampshire Hosiery, Inc., Spruce Pine, NC; *U.S. Public*, pg. 778
Segner, Edmund P., III, Exec. V.P.--Enron Corp., Houston, TX; *U.S. Public*, pg. 584
Seguin, Claude, Exec. V.P.-Fin. & Chief Fin. Officer--Teleglobe, Inc., Montreal, Canada; *Int'l*, pg. 1373
Seibel, Ron, Exec. V.P. & Chief Oper. Officer--Preferred Health Network, Long Beach, CA; *U.S. Public*, pg. 678
Seibel, William A., Exec. V.P.-Americas--Cambridge Technology Partners, Cambridge, MA; *U.S. Public*, pg. 1424
Seidel, Andrew D., Exec. V.P.-Wastewater Grp.--United States Filter Corporation, Palm Desert, CA; *U.S. Public*, pg. 1681
Seidel, Thomas E., Chief Tech. Officer & Exec. V.P.--Genus Inc., Sunnyvale, CA; *U.S. Public*, pg. 732
Seidner, Edward B., Exec. V.P.--Jennifer Convertibles Inc., Woodbury, NY; *U.S. Public*, pg. 926
Seiffert, Ronald J., Exec. V.P.--Huntington National Bank, Columbus, OH; *U.S. Public*, pg. 850
Seigner, Maurice, Exec. Dir. & Sec.--France Telecom, Paris, France; *Int'l*, pg. 503
Seiler, Melvin, Chief Oper. Officer & Exec. V.P.--Micro Warehouse, Inc., Norwalk, CT; *U.S. Public*, pg. 1104
Seiler, Stephen R., Exec. V.P.-Plng., Investment & Devel.--Elan Corporation Plc, Dublin, Ireland; *Int'l*, pg. 435
Seip, Tom Decker, Exec. V.P.-Retail Brokerage--The Charles Schwab Corporation, San Francisco, CA; *U.S. Public*, pg. 1442
Seitz, H.A., Exec. V.P.--Loblaw Companies Limited, North York, Canada; *Int'l*, pg. 1495
Seitz, James K., Exec. V.P.--United Missouri Bank of Carthage, Carthage, MO; *U.S. Public*, pg. 1654
Seitz, John N., Exec. V.P.-Exploration & Production--Anadarko Petroleum Corporation, Houston, TX; *U.S. Public*, pg. 107
Seki, Atsushi, Exec. V.P.--Kajima Corporation, Tokyo, Japan; *Int'l*, pg. 721
Seki, Hirotada, Exec. V.P.--Hakuhodo Incorporated, Tokyo, Japan; *Int'l*, pg. 587
Sekiguchi, Matt, Chief Oper. Officer & Exec. V.P.--Johnson Yokogawa Corporation, Newnan, GA; *Int'l*, pg. 1521
Sekiya, Iwao, Exec. Dir.--Disco Corporation, Tokyo, Japan; *Int'l*, pg. 413
Sekiya, Shinji, Exec. V.P.--Disco Corporation, Tokyo, Japan; *Int'l*, pg. 413
Selfridge, Steven G., Chief Oper. Officer & Exec. V.P.--Checkpoint Systems Inc., Thorofare, NJ; *U.S. Public*, pg. 343
Selig, Jeff, Exec. V.P.-Sls./CMC Steel Grp.--Structural Metals, Inc., Seguin, TX; *U.S. Public*, pg. 412
Selland, Howard M., Exec. V.P. & Pres.-Aeroquip Corp.--Aeroquip-Vickers, Inc., Maumee, OH; *U.S. Public*, pg. 24
Seltzer, David S., Chief Oper. Officer, Exec. V.P., Treas. & Sec.--Hi-Tech Pharmacal Co., Inc., Amityville, NY; *U.S. Public*, pg. 825
Seltzer, William, Exec. V.P.-MIS--Office Depot Inc., Delray Beach, FL; *U.S. Public*, pg. 1212
Semel, Scott N., Exec. V.P., Gen. Counsel & Sec.--Designs, Inc., Needham, MA; *U.S. Public*, pg. 501
Seminew, John, Exec. V.P.--Abbey Etna Machine Company, Perrysburg, OH; *U.S. Private*, pg. 9
Sen, Laura J., Exec. V.P.-Merchandising--BJ's Wholesale Club, Inc., Natick, MA; *U.S. Public*, pg. 162
Sennott, Michael, Exec. V.P. & Reg. Dir.-Europe--McCann-Erickson Worldwide, New York, NY; *U.S. Public*, pg. 909
Seo, Kazuya, Exec. V.P.--Kanematsu Corporation, Tokyo, Japan; *Int'l*, pg. 722
Sepulveda, Joaquin Guzman, Exec. V.P.--Hylsa S.A.-Tubular Division, San Nicolas, Mexico; *Int'l*, pg. 56
Serafini, William A., Chief Oper. Officer & Exec. V.P.--Countrywide Partnership Investments, Inc., Pasadena, CA; *U.S. Public*, pg. 453
Seregny, Jeffrey T., Exec. V.P. & Plng./Devel. Dir.--Campbell-Ewald Advertising, Warren, MI; *U.S. Public*, pg. 908
Sergel, Richard P., Chm. Bd.--Narragansett Electric Co., Providence, RI; *U.S. Public*, pg. 1171
Sergio, George, Chief Fin. Officer & Exec. V.P.--WWF Paper Corporation, Bala Cynwyd, PA; *U.S. Private*, pg. 1145
Serpico, Donald D., Exec. V.P.-Opers.--Chicago Mercantile Exchange, Chicago, IL; *U.S. Private*, pg. 235
Serruya, Aaron, Exec. V.P.--Yogen Fruz Worldwide Inc., Markham, Canada; *Int'l*, pg. 1520
Serruya, Simon, Exec. V.P.--Yogen Fruz Worldwide Inc., Markham, Canada; *Int'l*, pg. 1520
Servison, Roger T., Exec. V.P.--Fidelity Investments (FMR Corp.), Boston, MA; *U.S. Private*, pg. 402
Sevenet, Eric, Exec. V.P.--Club Mediterranee SA, Paris, France; *Int'l*, pg. 298
Seward, James R., CFA, Chief Fin. Officer & Exec. V.P.--Seafield Capital Corporation, Kansas City, MO; *U.S. Public*, pg. 1449
Seward, R. Lee, Exec. V.P.--Heska Corporation, Fort Collins, CO; *U.S. Public*, pg. 812
Sexton, Carol, Exec. V.P.-Corp. Rels.--Chicago Mercantile Exchange, Chicago, IL; *U.S. Private*, pg. 235
Sexton, David J., Exec. V.P.--State Street Corporation, Boston, MA; *U.S. Public*, pg. 1513
Sexton, Rod, Exec. V.P.-Mktg.--ICEE-USA Corp., Ontario, CA; *U.S. Public*, pg. 916
Seyadi, Yousef A., Exec. V.P.--Medical Supplies Division, Dammam, Saudi Arabia; *Int'l*, pg. 502
Seyferth, Stephen Y., Exec. V.P. & Client Services Dir.--Young & Rubicam Detroit, Detroit, MI; *U.S. Private*, pg. 1198
Sferra, James P., Exec. V.P.-Mfg.--LSI Industries, Inc., Cincinnati, OH; *U.S. Public*, pg. 971
Sganga, John B., Chief Fin. Officer & Exec. V.P.--Consolidated Furniture Corporation, Wilmington, DE; *U.S. Private*, pg. 265
Shadduck, John, Exec. V.P.--Heska Corporation, Fort Collins, CO; *U.S. Public*, pg. 812
Shadid, George D., Chief Fin. Officer & Exec. V.P.--Applebee's International, Inc., Overland Park, KS; *U.S. Public*, pg. 122
Shaffer, Norman, Exec. V.P.-Media Services--Jordan, McGrath, Case & Taylor Inc., New York, NY; *U.S. Private*, pg. 598
Shaffer, Oren G., Chief Fin. Officer & Exec. V.P.--Ameritech Corp., Chicago, IL; *U.S. Public*, pg. 98
Shaheen, Gabriel L., Exec. V.P.--The Lincoln National Life Insurance Co., Fort Wayne, IN; *U.S. Public*, pg. 998
Shailer, Barry L., Exec. V.P.-Retail Banking & Admin.--The Bank of Bermuda Limited, Hamilton, Bermuda; *Int'l*, pg. 150
Shannon, Patrick J., Exec. V.P.--Communications Diversified, New York, NY; *U.S. Private*, pg. 259
Shannon, Paul B., Exec. V.P.--First Maryland Bancorp, Baltimore, MD; *Int'l*, pg. 64
Shapell, David, Exec. V.P.--Shapell Industries, Inc., Beverly Hills, CA; *U.S. Private*, pg. 990
Shapiro, Arthur, Exec. V.P.-Mktg.--Seagram Chateau & Estate Wines Co., New York, NY; *Int'l*, pg. 1215
Shapiro, Arthur, Exec. V.P.- Mktg.--The House of Seagram, New York, NY; *Int'l*, pg. 1217
Shapiro, Bennett M., Exec. V.P.-Worldwide Basic Res.--Merck Research Laboratories, Rahway, NJ; *U.S. Public*, pg. 1091
Shapiro, Harold D., Exec. V.P.--Commander Oil Corporation, Oyster Bay, NY; *U.S. Private*, pg. 257
Shapiro, Jeffrey M., Exec. V.P. & Sec.--Michael Foods, Inc., Minneapolis, MN; *U.S. Public*, pg. 1103
Share, Kenneth, Exec. V.P.--Fairchild Publications, New York, NY; *U.S. Public*, pg. 513
Sharff, John S., Exec. V.P.--Baltimore Stationery Co./Total Office, Baltimore, MD; *U.S. Private*, pg. 113
Sharland, T.T., Exec. Dir.-Corp. Strategy--English China Clays Plc, Theale, United Kingdom; *Int'l*, pg. 455
Sharma, Anil, Chief Fin. Officer & Exec. V.P.--Raleigh Enterprises, Inc., Santa Monica, CA; *U.S. Private*, pg. 907
Sharp, Howard W., Exec. V.P.--ONBANCorp, Inc., Syracuse, NY; *U.S. Public*, pg. 631
Sharp, Roger L., Exec. V.P. & Chief-Global Opers.--Witco Corporation, Greenwich, CT; *U.S. Public*, pg. 1773
Sharp, Terry, Exec. V.P.-H.R.--Dart Group Corporation, Landover, MD; *U.S. Public*, pg. 484
Shatzer, Warren, Exec. V.P.-Mdsg.--Discount Auto Parts, Inc., Lakeland, FL; *U.S. Public*, pg. 510
Shaw, Bruce C., Exec. V.P.--Cleveland Shiprepair Company, Cleveland, OH; *U.S. Public*, pg. 1041
Shaw, Catherine, Exec. V.P.--Carson Pirie Scott & Co., Milwaukee, WI; *U.S. Public*, pg. 309
Shaw, Frederick J., Exec. V.P.-Sls.--Bloomsburg Mills Inc., New York, NY; *U.S. Private*, pg. 150
Shaw, Howard A., Exec. V.P.--Penguin Industries, Inc., Coatesville, PA; *U.S. Private*, pg. 849
Shaw, James M., Exec. V.P.--MTV Networks, New York, NY; *U.S. Private*, pg. 779
Shaw, John C., Jr., Exec. V.P. & Asst. Mgr.-Natl. Sls.--Jefferies & Company, Inc., Los Angeles, CA; *U.S. Public*, *pg. 925*
Shaw, Mark, Chief Oper. Officer & Exec. V.P.--Plenum Publishing Corporation, New York, NY; *U.S. Public*, pg. 1311
Shaw, Norman, Vice Chm. & Exec. V.P.--Collin Street Bakery, Corsicana, TX; *U.S. Private*, pg. 252

Shaw, Robert C., Chief Fin. Officer & Exec. V.P.-Opers.--ELXSI Corporation, Orlando, FL; *U.S. Public*, pg. 545
Shaw, Thomas S., Exec. V.P.--Delmarva Power & Light Company, Wilmington, DE; *U.S. Public*, pg. 430
Shaw, William J., Pres.-Marriott Service Grp. & Exec. V.P.--Fairfield Inn, Washington, DC; *U.S. Public*, pg. 1048
Shay, Dewey K., Sr. Exec. V.P. & Chief Admin. Officer--Donna Karan, New York, NY; *U.S. Public*, pg. 517
Shay, William M., Exec. V.P.--CILCORP Inc., Peoria, IL; *U.S. Public*, pg. 367
Shea, Michael J., Chief Fin. Officer, Exec V.P. & Treas.--Grossman's, Inc., Stoughton, MA; *U.S. Private*, pg. 585
Shea, Tom, Exec. V.P. & Mng. Dir.--Shorewood Packaging Corporation of Canada, Ltd., Scarborough, Canada; *U.S. Public*, pg. 1468
Shea, William H., Jr., Exec. V.P.--Buckeye Partners, L.P., Allentown, PA; *U.S. Public*, pg. 266
Shea, William J., Jr., Exec. V.P.--Buckeye Pipe Line Company, L.P., Allentown, PA; *U.S. Public*, pg. 266
Sheehan, Kevin, Chief Fin. Officer & Exec. V.P.--Avis Rent A Car System, Inc., Garden City, NY; *U.S. Public*, pg. 321
Sheehan, Michael, Exec. V.P. & Grp. Creative Dir.--Hill, Holliday, Connors, Cosmopulos, Inc., Boston, MA; *U.S. Private*, pg. 529
Sheehan, Robert, Exec. V.P.-Bus. Affairs & Fin.--Paramount Pictures Corporation, Los Angeles, CA; *U.S. Private*, pg. 776
Sheets, Kenneth E., Exec. V.P.--Rapid Industries, Inc., Louisville, KY; *U.S. Private*, pg. 910
Sheetz, Charles H., Exec. V.P.-H.R.--Sheetz, Inc., Altoona, PA; *U.S. Private*, pg. 991
Sheetz, Joseph M., Exec. V.P.-Store Devel.--Sheetz, Inc., Altoona, PA; *U.S. Private*, pg. 991
Sheetz, Randall A., Exec. V.P.-Mktg.--Sheetz, Inc., Altoona, PA; *U.S. Private*, pg. 991
Sheingold, Richard, Exec. V.P.--CBS Television Stations Div., New York, NY; *U.S. Public*, pg. 275
Sheldon, Mike, Exec. V.P. & Gen. Mgr.-L.A.--Deutsch LA, Santa Monica, CA; *U.S. Private*, pg. 328
Sheldon, Mike, Exec. V.P.--Fattal & Collins (F&C), Marina Del Rey, CA; *U.S. Public*, pg. 765
Shelton, James D., Chief Fin. Officer, Exec. V.P. & Sec.--PharMerica, Inc., Tampa, FL; *U.S. Public*, pg. 1286
Shelton, Stanley W., Exec. V.P.--State Street Corporation, Boston, MA; *U.S. Public*, pg. 1513
Shemesh, Jacob, Exec. V.P.-Sls.--IIS Intelligent Information Systems Ltd., Yokneam, Israel; *Int'l*, pg. 645
Shepard, Rachelle, Exec. V.P.--Highway Equipment Company, Cedar Rapids, IA; *U.S. Private*, pg. 529
Shepelak, Timothy D., Exec. Dir.-America--Halma p.l.c., Amersham, United Kingdom; *Int'l*, pg. 589
Shepharson, John, Exec. V.P.--Rockbottom Stores, Inc., Lake Success, NY; *U.S. Private*, pg. 938
Shepley, Lewis B., Chief Fin. Officer & Exec. V.P.--The Reliable Life Insurance Company, Webster Groves, MO; *U.S. Public*, pg. 1374
Sheppard, Jim, Exec. V.P.--Cousins Submarines, Menomonee Falls, WI; *U.S. Private*, pg. 280
Sheppard, Scott, Exec. V.P. & Grp. Publisher--Southern Progress Corporation, Birmingham, AL; *U.S. Public*, pg. 1612
Sheppard, Vern E., Exec. V.P.--Tong Yang SHL Corp., Seoul, Korea; *Int'l*, pg. 1154
Sherak, Tom, Exec. V.P.--Twentieth Century Fox Film Corp., Los Angeles, CA; *Int'l*, pg. 926
Sheridan, Patrick M., Chief Fin. Officer & Exec. V.P.--Anthem, Inc., Indianapolis, IN; *U.S. Private*, pg. 76
Sheridan, Rosemary, Asst. Exec. Dir.-Mktg. & Commun.--NJ Transit, Newark, NJ; *U.S. Private*, pg. 794
Sherman, Roger H., Exec. V.P.--Bank of America Illinois, Chicago, IL; *U.S. Public*, pg. 180
Sherman, Thomas W., Chief Fin. Officer, Exec. V.P. & Treas.--Bay State Gas Company, Westborough, MA; *U.S. Public*, pg. 196
Sherwin, J.T., Chief Fin. Officer & Exec. V.P.--Hunter Douglas N.V., Rotterdam, Netherlands; *Int'l*, pg. 639
Sherwood, R.C., Chief Fin. Officer & Exec. V.P.--L.B. Smith, Inc., Camp Hill, PA; *U.S. Private*, pg. 1009
Shetler, H.L., Exec. V.P.--Interstate Bakeries Corporation, Kansas City, MO; *U.S. Public*, pg. 909
Shetler, H.L., Exec. V.P.-Corp.--Interstate Brands Corporation, Kansas City, MO; *U.S. Public*, pg. 909
Shetty, Ajit, Dr., Exec. V.P.--Janssen Pharmaceutica N.V., Beersel, Belgium; *U.S. Public*, pg. 930
Shibuya, Teiji, Exec. V.P.-Tech.--NKK Corporation, Tokyo, Japan; *Int'l*, pg. 902
Shields, Alden K., Exec. V.P.--Hawk Management Corporation, Overland Park, KS; *U.S. Private*, pg. 511
Shields, H. Jay, Exec. V.P. & New Bus. Contact--Austin Kelley Advertising, Inc., Atlanta, GA; *U.S. Private*, pg. 100
Shier, Barry A., Exec. V.P.-Mktg. & Hotel Opers.--Mirage Resorts Incorporated, Las Vegas, NV; *U.S. Public*, pg. 1116
Shiffman, Roger, Exec. V.P.--Tiger Electronics, Inc., Vernon Hills, IL; *U.S. Private*, pg. 1086
Shiflett, Pendleton H., III, Exec. Dir.--AON Advisors, Inc., Chicago, IL; *U.S. Public*, pg. 117
Shiga, Yu, Exec. Dir.--Isuzu Motors Limited, Tokyo, Japan; *Int'l*, pg. 692
Shigefuchi, Masatoshi, Exec. V.P.--Toto Ltd., Kitakyushu, Japan; *Int'l*, pg. 1410
Shih, T.M., Exec. V.P.--Fubon Insurance Co. Ltd., Taipei, Taiwan; *Int'l*, pg. 60
Shiina, Susumu, Exec. V.P.--Mikuni Corporation, Tokyo, Japan; *Int'l*, pg. 867
Shim, Yi Taek, Exec. V.P.-Aerospace--Korean Airlines Co., Ltd., Seoul, Korea; *Int'l*, pg. 758
Shimayama, Hiroaki, Exec. V.P.--NEC Corporation, Tokyo, Japan; *Int'l*, pg. 899
Shimizu, Kenji, Exec. V.P.--Candela Corporation, Wayland, MA; *U.S. Public*, pg. 300
Shimizu, Norikatsu, Exec. Dir.--Minolta Co., Ltd., Osaka, Japan; *Int'l*, pg. 869
Shimizu, Reiichiro, Exec. V.P.--Sato Kogyo Co., Ltd., Tokyo, Japan; *Int'l*, pg. 1197
Shimizu, Scott E., Exec. V.P.-Sls.--Pillowtex Corporation, Dallas, TX; *U.S. Public*, pg. 1296
Shimizu, Tamotsu, Exec. V.P.--Brother Industries, Ltd., Nagoya, Japan; *Int'l*, pg. 229
Shimizu, Yasukazu, Exec. V.P.--Meitsu Inc., Tokyo, Japan; *Int'l*, pg. 856
Shimogaichi, Yoichi, Exec. V.P.-Steel Div.--NKK Corporation, Tokyo, Japan; *Int'l*, pg. 902
Shimono, Kikuo, Exec. V.P.--Duskin Co., Ltd., Osaka, Japan; *Int'l*, pg. 422
Shimotani, Masahisa, Exec. V.P.--Osaka Gas Co., Ltd., Osaka, Japan; *Int'l*, pg. 1011
Shimozuma, Hiroshi, Exec. V.P.--Sumitomo Metal Industries, Ltd., Tokyo, Japan; *Int'l*, pg. 1315
Shimura, Shigeshi, Exec. V.P. & Chief Officer-Import & Export & Industrial Mktg. Div--Japan Energy Corporation, Tokyo, Japan; *Int'l*, pg. 702
Shin, Jai P., Exec. V.P.-Bus. Devel.--Aspec Technology, Inc., Sunnyvale, CA; *U.S. Private*, pg. 89
Shinohara, Kunio, Exec. V.P.--Kumagai Gumi Co., Ltd., Tokyo, Japan; *Int'l*, pg. 763
Shinozaki, Masami, Exec. V.P.--NEC Corporation, Tokyo, Japan; *Int'l*, pg. 899
Shioiri, Akira, Exec. V.P.--Oji Paper Co., Ltd., Tokyo, Japan; *Int'l*, pg. 998
Shiotsu, Seiji, Sr. Exec. Dir. & Grp. Gen. Mgr.-Human Resources--Sharp Corporation, Osaka, Japan; *Int'l*, pg. 1228
Shipley, Graham, Exec. Dir.--AIS Media, Surrey Hills, Australia; *Int'l*, pg. 15
Shipley, Larry, Exec. V.P.-Corp. Devel.--IBP, Inc., Dakota City, NE; *U.S. Public*, pg. 852
Shircliff, Wayne J., Exec. V.P. Commercial Banking--Starbanc Corporation, Cincinnati, OH; *U.S. Public*, pg. 1510
Shirley, Clifford J., Exec. V.P.-Support Services Individual Bank, CIBC--Canadian Imperial Bank of Commerce, Toronto, Canada; *Int'l*, pg. 256
Shirley, Marvin, Exec. V.P.-CBS Enterprises--CBS Enterprises Division, New York, NY; *U.S. Public*, pg. 274
Shiroishi, Takeshi, Exec. V.P.--Shimizu Corporation, Tokyo, Japan; *Int'l*, pg. 1233
Shively, Bill, Exec. V.P.-Worldwide Sls.--Gelco Information Network, Inc., Eden Prairie, MN; *U.S. Private*, pg. 442
Shnycer, William, Pres.--Aamco Transmissions, Inc., Bala Cynwyd, PA; *U.S. Private*, pg. 9
Shoemaker, Edwin J., Vice Chm. & Exec. V.P.--La-Z-Boy Incorporated, Monroe, MI; *U.S. Public*, pg. 972
Shoen, Jim, Exec. V.P.--U-Haul International, Inc., Phoenix, AZ; *U.S. Private*, pg. 49
Shoji, Keijiro, Exec. V.P. & Gen. Mgr.-Information & Communications Grp.--Mitsubishi Electric Corporation, Tokyo, Japan; *Int'l*, pg. 872
Sholakh, Marwan, Chief Oper. Officer & Exec. V.P.--Nexus Plastics, Inc., Hawthorne, NJ; *U.S. Private*, pg. 797
Sholley, Adam, Exec. V.P.--Arnold Communications, Inc., Boston, MA; *U.S. Private*, pg. 83
Shonk-Simmons, Georgia, Exec. V.P.-Mdsg. & Mktg.--Newport News, Inc., New York, NY; *U.S. Public*, pg. 1499
Shoquist, Debora C., Exec. V.P.-HDD Opers.--Quantum Corporation, Milpitas, CA; *U.S. Public*, pg. 1350
Shor, Alan, Chief Admin. Officer, Exec. V.P. & Gen. Counsel--Zale Corporation, Irving, TX; *U.S. Public*, pg. 1789
Shore, Harvey, Exec. V.P.--Concord Assets Group, Boca Raton, FL; *U.S. Private*, pg. 261
Shoreman, Terence C., Chief Oper. Officer & Exec. V.P.--Unitog Company, Kansas City, MO; *U.S. Public*, pg. 1693
Shortlidge, Thomas A., Exec. V.P. & Exec. Creative Dir.--Young & Rubicam Chicago, Chicago, IL; *U.S. Private*, pg. 1198
Shrader, K. Michael, Exec. V.P.-Human Resources--Buffets, Inc., Eden Prairie, MN; *U.S. Public*, pg. 267
Shrigley, David A., Exec. V.P.-Sls., Service & Mktg.--Bay Networks, Inc., Santa Clara, CA; *U.S. Public*, pg. 196
Shriver, Don, Exec. V.P.--Dairy Farmers of America, Inc., Arlington, TX; *U.S. Private*, pg. 307
Shropshire, William S., Jr., Chief Fin. Officer, Exec. V.P., Treas. & Sec.--Dyersburg Corporation, Dyersburg, TN; *U.S. Public*, pg. 538
Shugart, Wade, Exec. V.P.--Carolina First Bank, Greenville, SC; *U.S. Public*, pg. 306
Shulman, Mark, Chief Oper. & Mdsg. Officer & Exec. V.P.--Talbots, Inc., Hingham, MA; *Int'l*, pg. 28
Shultz, Stephen, Exec. V.P.--Schultz Steel Company, South Gate, CA; *U.S. Private*, pg. 973
Shumacher, Norbert, Exec. V.P.--Science & Technology Group, New York, NY; *U.S. Public*, pg. 1071
Shumejda, John M., Exec. V.P.-Mfg. & Tech.--AGCO Corporation, Duluth, GA; *U.S. Public*, pg. 28
Shur, Walter, Exec. V.P.--New York Life Insurance Company, New York, NY; *U.S. Private*, pg. 794
Shyrock, Larry L., Exec. V.P.-Comml. Banking--Texas Commerce Bank, Houston, TX; *U.S. Public*, pg. 339
Sia, David, Exec. V.P., Chm., Chief Exec. Officer, Asia/Pacific & Dir.--BBDO Worldwide Inc., New York, NY; *U.S. Public*, pg. 1223
Sibley, Gerry, Exec. V.P.--Eclipse Inc., Rockford, IL; *U.S. Private*, pg. 360
Sica, Heather A., C.P.A., Exec. V.P. & Treas.--Litchfield Financial Corporation, Williamstown, MA; *U.S. Public*, pg. 1001
Siddiqui, A. Sami, Exec. V.P.-Unsecured Spread Bus.--AEGON USA, Inc., Louisville, KY; *Int'l*, pg. 26
Siddle, C. Warriner, Exec. V.P. & Dir.-Devel.--Piccadilly Cafeterias, Inc., Baton Rouge, LA; *U.S. Public*, pg. 1294
Siddons, Ernest G., Chief Oper. Officer & Exec. V.P.--Ampco-Pittsburgh Corporation, Pittsburgh, PA; *U.S. Public*, pg. 103
Sider, Thomas M., Chief Fin. Officer & Exec. V.P.--Erie Family Life Insurance Company, Erie, PA; *U.S. Public*, pg. 590
Sidorsky, Arthur, Exec. V.P.--Standard Microsystems Corp., Hauppauge, NY; *U.S. Public*, pg. 1502
Sidsworth, Howard, Exec. V.P. & Gen. Mgr.--Shorewood Packaging Corporation of Canada, Ltd., Scarborough, Canada; *U.S. Public*, pg. 1468
Siebenmorgen, Paul S., Exec. V.P.--Lakeland Financial Corporation, Warsaw, IN; *U.S. Public*, pg. 975
Sieber, Norbert J., Exec. V.P. & Gen. Mgr.--MARC, Pittsburgh, PA; *U.S. Private*, pg. 701
Siebert, Thomas R., Chief Fin. Officer & Exec. V.P.--Hoxan America Incorporated, Piscataway, NJ; *Int'l*, pg. 363
Sieff, David, The Hon., Exec. Dir.-Corp. & External Affairs--Marks & Spencer PLC, London, United Kingdom; *Int'l*, pg. 842
Siegel, Bernard, Exec. V.P.-Risk Mngmnt.--Waterhouse Investor Services, New York, NY; *Int'l*, pg. 1401
Siegel, Clifford A., Exec. V.P.--Jefferies & Company, Inc., Los Angeles, CA; *U.S. Public*, pg. 925
Siegel, Jeff, Exec. V.P.-Sls. & Mktg.--Lifetime Hoan Corp., Westbury, NY; *U.S. Public*, pg. 992
Siegel, Randy, Partner, Exec. V.P. & Gen. Mgr.--Fleishman-Hillard, Inc., Atlanta, GA; *U.S. Private*, pg. 411
Siegel, Richard E., Exec. V.P.-Pub. Rels.--Supertex, Inc., Sunnyvale, CA; *U.S. Public*, pg. 1539
Sieghart, Josef J., Exec. V.P.--Voest-Alpine Services and Technologies Corp., New York, NY; *Int'l*, pg. 1471
Siegmann, Charles E., Exec. V.P.--Mercantile-Safe Deposit & Trust Co., Baltimore, MD; *U.S. Public*, pg. 1089
Siek, Rainer, Exec. V.P.--CBS Enterprises Division, New York, NY; *U.S. Public*, pg. 274
Sienkiewicz, Richard, Jr., Exec. V.P.-Opers.--Davidson Printing Company, Duluth, MN; *U.S. Private*, pg. 314
Sieracki, Eric P., Exec. V.P.-Corp. Fin. & Investor Rels.--Countrywide Funding Corporation, Pasadena, CA; *U.S. Public*, pg. 453
Sierro, Jean Francis, Exec. V.P.--Union Bank of Switzerland, Zurich, Switzerland; *Int'l*, pg. 1439
Sievers, James W., Chief Fin. Officer & Exec. V.P.--Spiegel, Inc., Downers Grove, IL; *U.S. Public*, pg. 1498
Signorini, John E., Chief Fin. Officer, Exec. V.P. & Treas.--The F.A. Bartlett Tree Expert Co., Stamford, CT; *U.S. Private*, pg. 119
Sikora, W.A., Exec. V.P.--TransMontaigne Oil Company, Denver, CO; *U.S. Public*, pg. 1631
Silberman, Steve V., Exec. V.P.--Framesi USA, Inc./Roffler Industries, Inc./Casa di Colore, Inc., Coraopolis, PA; *U.S. Private*, pg. 419
Silhasek, James, Exec. V.P. & Gen. Counsel--Reinalt-Thomas Corp., Ann Arbor, MI; *U.S. Private*, pg. 919
Silva, Ageo, Exec. V.P.--Banco Bradesco S.A., Sao Paulo, Brazil; *Int'l*, pg. 139
Silva, William L., Exec. V.P.--Mercury Air Group Inc., Los Angeles, CA; *U.S. Public*, pg. 1092
Silver, Alvin M., Exec. V.P.--Alarm Device Manufacturing Company, Syosset, NY; *U.S. Public*, pg. 1306
Silver, Jack, Exec. V.P. & Acct Services Dir.--Western International Media Corporation, Los Angeles, CA; *U.S. Private*, pg. 1165
Silver, Joe, Exec. V.P. & Gen. Counsel--Sterling Vision, Inc., East Meadow, NY; *U.S. Public*, pg. 1516
Silver, Michael, Exec. V.P. & Mng. Partner-Acct.--Wells BDDP, Inc., New York, NY; *Int'l*, pg. 117
Silver, Richard V., Sr. V.P. & Deputy Gen. Counsel--The Equitable Companies Incorporated, New York, NY; *U.S. Public*, pg. 588
Silver, Sandy, Exec. V.P.-Global Mktg.--Simon Marketing, Inc., Oak Brook Terrace, IL; *U.S. Private*, pg. 1001
Silverman, S.W., Chief Oper. Officer & Exec. V.P.--PQ Corporation, Berwyn, PA; *U.S. Private*, pg. 827
Silvestro, Frank B., Exec. V.P.--Ecology and Environment, Inc., Lancaster, NY; *U.S. Public*, pg. 562
Simi, Louis W., Jr., Exec. V.P.--Atrium Companies, Inc., Dallas, TX; *U.S. Private*, pg. 98
Simi, Louis W., Jr., Exec. V.P.--Atrium Companies, Inc., Irving, TX; *U.S. Private*, pg. 98
Simkins, Richard C., Chief Fin. Officer, Exec. V.P., Treas. & Sec.--Knape & Vogt Mfg. Co., Grand Rapids, MI; *U.S. Public*, pg. 963
Simmerman, Gary F., Exec. V.P.--Summit Bancorp, Princeton, NJ; *U.S. Public*, pg. 1527
Simmers, John, Exec. V.P.--Financial Network Investment Corp, Torrance, CA; *U.S. Private*, pg. 404
Simmons, Brian, Exec. V.P. & Sec.--M. Kamenstein, Inc., Elmsford, NY; *U.S. Private*, pg. 606
Simmons, John M., Chm. Bd. & Exec. V.P.--Elberta Crate & Box Company, Bainbridge, GA; *U.S. Private*, pg. 367
Simmons, Martin E., Exec. V.P.-Admin., Gen. Counsel & Sec.--First American Corporation, Nashville, TN; *U.S. Public*, pg. 624
Simmons, Pam, Exec. V.P.--Affiliated Computer Services, Inc., Dallas, TX; *U.S. Public*, pg. 27
Simmons, Sam, Exec. V.P.-Mdsg.--Grossman's, Inc., Stoughton, MA; *U.S. Private*, pg. 585
Simon, Jean-Marc, Exec. V.P.-Travel Agencies & Pub. Restaurants--Accor S.A., Evry, France; *Int'l*, pg. 20
Simon, Richard M., Exec. V.P.-Professional Practice--GZA GeoEnvironmental Technologies, Inc., Newton, MA; *U.S. Public*, pg. 697
Simon, Richard M., Exec. V.P.-Professional Practice--GZA GeoEnvironmental, Inc., Newton, MA; *U.S. Public*, pg. 697
Simon, Steve, Exec. V.P.--Riccobon & Company, Inc., Santa Fe Springs, CA; *U.S. Private*, pg. 927
Simon, Ted, Exec. V.P.--Standard Publishing, Cincinnati, OH; *U.S. Public*, pg. 1506
Simonson, Claes R., Exec. V.P.-Extrusions--Granges AB, Stockholm, Sweden; *Int'l*, pg. 439
Simpson, Dale, Exec. V.P. & Exec. Dir.-Food Grp.--EvansGroup, Seattle, WA; *U.S. Private*, pg. 385

Simpson, Kevin, Chief Fin. Officer & Partner--Friedman, Eisenstein, Raemer and Schwartz, LLP, Chicago, IL; *U.S. Private*, pg. 428
Simpson, L. Donald, Exec. V.P.--Great Lakes Chemical Corporation, West Lafayette, IN; *U.S. Public*, pg. 760
Sindzingre, Michel, Exec. V.P.-Indus. Minerals--Imetal, Paris, France; *Int'l*, pg. 661
Singer, W. Douglas, Exec. V.P. & Treas.--Long Island Bancorp, Inc., Melville, NY; *U.S. Public*, pg. 1013
Singleton, J. Matthew, Exec. V.P.--Canadian Imperial Bank of Commerce, Toronto, Canada; *Int'l*, pg. 256
Sipe, Gene H., Exec. V.P. & Grp. Pres.--Bremer Financial Corporation, Saint Paul, MN; *U.S. Private*, pg. 167
Sipe, Mary E., Exec. V.P.--TCF Financial Corp., Minneapolis, MN; *U.S. Public*, pg. 1554
Siracusa, Paul J., Chief Fin. Officer & Exec. V.P.--The Hertz Corporation, Park Ridge, NJ; *U.S. Public*, pg. 664
Sirmons, James F., Exec. V.P.-Indus. Rels.--CBS, New York, NY; *U.S. Public*, pg. 273
Sirulnick, Dave, Exec. V.P.-News & Prod.--MTV: Music Television, New York, NY; *U.S. Private*, pg. 779
Sisson, R.H., Exec. V.P.-Ophthalmic & Vision Care--Alcon Laboratories, Inc., Fort Worth, TX; *Int'l*, pg. 916
Sisson, Thomas W., Exec. V.P.-Strategic Plng.--Associates First Capital Corporation, Dallas, TX; *U.S. Public*, pg. 662
Sistermans, Joop F., Exec. V.P.-Strategy & Tech.--Akzo Nobel N.V., Arnhem, Netherlands; *Int'l*, pg. 42
Sisul, John T., Exec. V.P.-Human Resources--Wilton Corporation, Palatine, IL; *U.S. Private*, pg. 1181
Sizenando Silva, Cesar Augusto, Exec. V.P.--Uniao de Bancos Brasileiros S.A. (Unibanco), Sao Paulo, Brazil; *Int'l*, pg. 1431
Sjogren, Christer, Exec. V.P.--Quipp Systems, Inc., Hialeah, FL; *U.S. Public*, pg. 1353
Sjostedt, Lennart, Chief Oper. Officer & Exec. V.P.--SAB WABCO N.V., Zaventem, Belgium; *Int'l*, pg. 271
Skaaning, Gunnar, Exec. V.P.--Royal Copenhagen A/S, Frederiksberg, Denmark; *Int'l*, pg. 1134
Skaggs, Don L., Exec. V.P. & Gen. Mgr.-STS--American Stores Company, Salt Lake City, UT; *U.S. Public*, pg. 92
Skaggs, Don L., Exec. V.P. & Gen. Mgr.--Skaggs Telecommunications Services, Inc., Murray, UT; *U.S. Public*, pg. 93
Skaggs, R.C. Jr., Exec. V.P.--Columbia Gas Distribution Companies, Columbus, OH; *U.S. Public*, pg. 402
Skelton, John D., II, Exec. V.P. & Gen. Mgr.-Plastic Packaging Div.--Rock-Tenn Company, Norcross, GA; *U.S. Public*, pg. 1396
Skilling, Raymond I., Exec. V.P. & Gen. Counsel--AON Corporation, Chicago, IL; *U.S. Public*, pg. 117
Skinner, James E., Chief Fin. Officer, Exec. V.P., Treas. & Asst. Sec.--CompUSA, Dallas, TX; *U.S. Public*, pg. 420
Skipp, Andrew K., Exec. V.P.--Hubbard Hall Inc., Waterbury, CT; *U.S. Private*, pg. 544
Skitka, Jack, Exec. V.P.--Dorr-Oliver Incorporated, Milford, CT; *Int'l*, pg. 839
Skollar, Robert, Exec. V.P. & Exec. Creative Dir.--Grey Advertising Inc., New York, NY; *U.S. Public*, pg. 764
Skorge, Ralph, Exec. V.P. & Creative Dir.--Cline, Davis & Mann, Inc., New York, NY; *U.S. Private*, pg. 246
Skumlien, Glen A., Exec. V.P.-Opers.--Glacier Water Services Inc., Carlsbad, CA; *U.S. Public*, pg. 745
Sladek, Keith, Exec. V.P.--L & D Group, Aurora, IL; *U.S. Private*, pg. 638
Slager, Don, Exec. V.P.--National Waste Services Inc., Chicago, IL; *U.S. Public*, pg. 49
Slaney, Gordon, Jr., Exec. V.P.--HNTB Corporation, Kansas City, MO; *U.S. Private*, pg. 492
Slater, Alan, Exec. V.P. & Gen. Mgr.-Electronic Document Systems--Group 1 Software, Inc., Lanham, MD; *U.S. Public*, pg. 417
Slattery, William H., Exec. V.P. & Gen. Counsel--Republic Bank for Savings, New York, NY; *U.S. Public*, pg. 1380
Slaughter, Russ, Exec. V.P. & Creative Dir.--Tinsley Advertising, Miami, FL; *U.S. Private*, pg. 1088
Slayton, John W., Jr., Sr. V.P.-Supply Chain Mngmt.--W.W. Grainger, Inc., Lincolnshire, IL; *U.S. Public*, pg. 758
Sleeper, Gordon C., III, Exec. V.P.--Grace & Rothschild, New York, NY; *U.S. Private*, pg. 468
Slezak, Robert, Exec. V.P.-Tech. & Mktg.--Comverse Network Systems, Wakefield, MA; *U.S. Public*, pg. 425
Sliva, Catherine L., Exec. V.P.--Domain Energy Corporation, Houston, TX; *U.S. Public*, pg. 515
Sliwinski, Alfred J., Exec. V.P.-Community Banking--D & N Financial Corporation, Hancock, MI; *U.S. Public*, pg. 472
Sliwinski, Alfred J., Exec. V.P.-Community Banking--D & N Bank, Hancock, MI; *U.S. Public*, pg. 472
Sloan, David J., Chief Oper. Officer & Exec. V.P.--Bankers Security Life Insurance Society, Woodbury, NY; *U.S. Public*, pg. 1375
Sloan, Kenneth H., Chief Exec. Officer & Sr. Exec. V.P.-Fin., Plng.--Shoppers Drug Mart, Ltd., Toronto, Canada; *Int'l*, pg. 112
Sloan, L. Lawrence, Exec. V.P.--Price Stern Sloan Inc., Los Angeles, CA; *Int'l*, pg. 1215
Sloan, William E. II, Exec. V.P., Treas. & Sec.--Sloan Valve Company, Franklin Park, IL; *U.S. Private*, pg. 1006
Sloane, Elliot, Exec. V.P. & Corp. Fin. Dir.--Edelman Worldwide, Inc., New York, NY; *U.S. Private*, pg. 362
Sloane, G. Michael, Exec. V.P. & Chief Mktg. Officer--American Reliable Insurance Company, Scottsdale, AZ; *U.S. Public*, pg. 67
Slonaker, Jack, Exec. V.P. & Opers. Dir.--Cline, Davis & Mann, Inc., New York, NY; *U.S. Private*, pg. 246
Slone, Thomas R., Exec. V.P.-Consumer Branch Opers.--Associates First Capital Corporation, Dallas, TX; *U.S. Public*, pg. 662
Slotnick, Ilene, Exec. V.P.--Fattal & Collins (F&C), Marina Del Rey, CA; *U.S. Public*, pg. 765
Slott, Michael P., Exec. V.P.--Columbian Advertising Inc., Chicago, IL; *U.S. Private*, pg. 256
Slotta, Mark R., Exec. V.P.-Env., Health & Safety--Peregrine Incorporated, Southfield, MI; *U.S. Private*, pg. 852
Slotten, Nancy, Exec. V.P. & Treas.--Border States Paving, Inc., Fargo, ND; *U.S. Private*, pg. 160
Slowey, Thomas A., Exec. V.P.-Sls.--Platinum Technology, Inc., Oak Brook Terrace, IL; *U.S. Public*, pg. 1309
Slusarski, Don, Exec. V.P.-Field Opers.--Lawson Software, Minneapolis, MN; *U.S. Private*, pg. 654
Slutzky, Elliot, Exec. V.P.-Sls.--LIVE Film & Mediaworks, Van Nuys, CA; *U.S. Private*, pg. 671
Small, Michael J., Chief Fin. Officer & Exec. V.P.--360 Degrees Communications Company, Chicago, IL; *U.S. Public*, pg. 1607
Smalley, Robert A., Jr., Chief Oper. Officer & Exec. V.P.--Cruise America, Inc., Mesa, AZ; *U.S. Private*, pg. 178
Smart, James L., Exec. V.P.--Novo Nordisk Pharmaceuticals, Inc., Princeton, NJ; *Int'l*, pg. 987
Smarto, Michael G., Chief Fin. Officer & Exec. V.P.-Fin.--Tippins Incorporated, Pittsburgh, PA; *U.S. Private*, pg. 1088
Smelas, William A., Exec. V.P.--Horsehead Resource Development Company, Inc., Palmerton, PA; *U.S. Private*, pg. 540
Smelas, William A., Exec. V.P. of HRD & Acting Pres.--Zinc Corporation of America, Monaca, PA; *U.S. Private*, pg. 540
Smelcer, Wilma J., Exec. V.P.--Bank of America Illinois, Chicago, IL; *U.S. Public*, pg. 180
Smend, Axel, Dr., Exec. V.P.--DG Bank, Frankfurt/Main, Germany; *Int'l*, pg. 351
Smerge, Raymond G., Exec. V.P , Gen. Counsel & Sec.--Centex Corporation, Dallas, TX; *U.S. Public*, pg. 322
Smetts, Stewart, Exec. V.P.-Mktg.--La Rosa's, Inc., Cincinnati, OH; *U.S. Private*, pg. 640
Smisek, Jeffrey A., Exec. V.P., Gen. Counsel & Sec.--Continental Airlines, Houston, TX; *U.S. Public*, pg. 439
Smith, Alford L., Exec. V.P. & Gen. Mgr.-Paperboard Prods. Div.--Rock-Tenn Company, Norcross, GA; *U.S. Public*, pg. 1396
Smith, Alton, Exec. V.P. & Controller--Furr's/Bishops, Inc., Lubbock, TX; *U.S. Public*, pg. 689
Smith, Arvin H., Exec. V.P.--Thermo Electron Corporation, Waltham, MA; *U.S. Public*, pg. 1591
Smith, Brian J., Exec. V.P. & Pres.-BLP Sls. Support Div.--Boron LePore Group, Fair Lawn, NJ; *U.S. Public*, pg. 246
Smith, Brian J., Chief Fin. Officer & Exec. V.P.--IMC Global, Bannockburn, IL; *U.S. Public*, pg. 856
Smith, C. Thomas, III, Exec. V.P. & Client Services Dir.--FGI Inc., Chapel Hill, NC; *U.S. Private*, pg. 389
Smith, C. Wesley, Exec. V.P.-Printing Papers--International Paper Company, Purchase, NY; *U.S. Public*, pg. 901
Smith, Calvin C., Exec. V.P.--David A. Bramble, Inc., Chestertown, MD; *U.S. Private*, pg. 165
Smith, Craig R., Chief Oper. Officer & Exec. V.P.--Owens & Minor Inc., Glen Allen, VA; *U.S. Public*, pg. 1236
Smith, D.V., Exec. V.P.--Equifax Inc., Atlanta, GA; *U.S. Public*, pg. 588
Smith, Darrell H., Exec. V.P. & Acct. Services Dir.--EURO RSCG Dahlin Smith White, LLC, Salt Lake City, UT; *U.S. Private*, pg. 384
Smith, Daryl, Pres.-World Omni Financial Corp. & Exec. V.P.--JM Family Enterprises Inc., Deerfield Beach, FL; *U.S. Private*, pg. 577
Smith, David B., Exec. V.P.-Unsecured Spread Opers.--AEGON USA, Inc., Louisville, KY; *Int'l*, pg. 26
Smith, David B., Exec. V.P.--Providian Financial Corporation, San Francisco, CA; *U.S. Public*, pg. 1338
Smith, David C., Exec. V.P.--Trenwick America Reinsurance Corporation, Stamford, CT; *U.S. Public*, pg. 1634
Smith, David M., Exec. V.P.--H.J. Baker & Bro., Inc., Stamford, CT; *U.S. Private*, pg. 112
Smith, Dennis, Chief Oper. Officer & Exec. V.P.--Mednet, MPC Corporation, Las Vegas, NV; *U.S. Public*, pg. 1082
Smith, Dennis, Exec. V.P.-Sls.--Hobart Corporation, Troy, OH; *U.S. Public*, pg. 1322
Smith, Derek, Exec. V.P.--The Dialog Corporation plc, London, United Kingdom; *Int'l*, pg. 412
Smith, Derek, Exec. V.P.--Penguin Putnam Inc., New York, NY; *Int'l*, pg. 1027
Smith, Douglas A., Exec. V.P.--Borden, Inc., Columbus, OH; *U.S. Private*, pg. 157
Smith, Eric M., Exec. V.P.--Indiana Lawrence Bank, North Manchester, IN; *U.S. Public*, pg. 633
Smith, Ernest B., Exec. V.P.--CoreStates Bank, N.A., Philadelphia, PA; *U.S. Public*, pg. 446
Smith, G. Andrews, Exec. V.P. & Gen. Mgr.--The L & B Group, Dallas, TX; *U.S. Public*, pg. 1673
Smith, G.H., Exec. V.P.--Equity Residential Properties Trust, Chicago, IL; *U.S. Public*, pg. 590
Smith, Gary V., Exec. V.P., Treas. & Sec.--Hughes Construction, Inc., North Salt Lake, UT; *U.S. Private*, pg. 546
Smith, George, Exec. V.P.--Okla Homer Smith Furniture Co., Fort Smith, AR; *U.S. Private*, pg. 226
Smith, George B., Exec. V.P. & Chief Oper. Officer-Textile & Apparel Grp.--The Dixie Group, Inc., Chattanooga, TN; *U.S. Public*, pg. 514
Smith, Gibbert, Chief Oper. Officer & Exec. V.P.--Helene Curtis Industries, Inc., Chicago, IL; *Int'l*, pg. 1434
Smith, H. Pete, Chief Fin. Officer & Exec. V.P.--Ultramar Diamond Shamrock Corporation, San Antonio, TX; *U.S. Public*, pg. 1663
Smith, Howard I., Chief Fin. Officer, Exec. V.P. & Comptroller--American International Group, Inc., New York, NY; *U.S. Public*, pg. 83
Smith, James N., Exec. V.P.--Wyle Electronics, Irvine, CA; *Int'l*, pg. 1457
Smith, Jason R., O.D., Exec. V.P.--40 Fort Eye Associates, Forty Fort, PA; *U.S. Private*, pg. 420
Smith, Jay H., Exec. V.P.-Corp. Exploration & Production Opers.--Sonat Exploration Company, Houston, TX; *U.S. Public*, pg. 1485
Smith, Jim, Exec. V.P.-Mktg.--Shadow Broadcast Services, Bala Cynwyd, PA; *U.S. Public*, pg. 1763
Smith, Joe, Exec. V.P.-Worldwide Opers.--SyQuest Technology, Inc., Fremont, CA; *U.S. Public*, pg. 1550
Smith, John E., Exec. V.P.-Retail Banking--Hibernia Corporation, New Orleans, LA; *U.S. Public*, pg. 825
Smith, John E., Exec. V.P.-Securitization & Wholesale--United Companies Financial Corporation, Baton Rouge, LA; *U.S. Public*, pg. 1675
Smith, John M., Exec. V.P.-Equities Prods.--The Guardian Life Insurance Company of America, New York, NY; *U.S. Private*, pg. 486
Smith, June, Exec. V.P.-College Div.--Houghton Mifflin Company, Boston, MA; *U.S. Public*, pg. 841
Smith, June, Exec. V.P.--Houghton Mifflin College Div., Boston, MA; *U.S. Public*, pg. 841
Smith, Karen M., Exec. V.P.- Proxy Solicitation--Allen Nelson & Co., Seattle, WA; *U.S. Private*, pg. 790
Smith, Kent D., Exec. V.P.-Customer Opers.--Legato Systems, Inc., Palo Alto, CA; *U.S. Public*, pg. 984
Smith, Kermit C., CPCU, Sr. Exec. V.P.--Atlantic Mutual Companies, New York, NY; *U.S. Private*, pg. 95
Smith, Lawrence C., Exec. V.P.--Comcast Corporation, Philadelphia, PA; *U.S. Public*, pg. 406
Smith, Ley S., Exec. V.P.--Pharmacia & Upjohn, Inc., Windsor, United Kingdom; *Int'l*, pg. 1047
Smith, Ley S., Exec. V.P.--Pharmacia & Upjohn, Kalamazoo, MI; *Int'l*, pg. 1048
Smith, Liz, Exec. V.P. & Mng. Dir.-Peer Med--Lally, McFarland & Pantello Inc., New York, NY; *Int'l*, pg. 601
Smith, Lonnie L., Exec. V.P.--L. Perrigo Company, Allegan, MI; *U.S. Public*, pg. 1280
Smith, Marc, Exec. V.P.-Sls. & Mktg.--The Stop & Shop Companies, Inc., Quincy, MA; *Int'l*, pg. 750
Smith, Marville, Exec. V.P.-South--Right Management Consultants, Inc., Philadelphia, PA; *U.S. Public*, pg. 1390
Smith, Michael E., Exec. V.P.--Checkpoint Systems Inc., Thorofare, NJ; *U.S. Public*, pg. 343
Smith, Mike, Exec. V.P.--Blue Seal Feeds, Inc., Londonderry, NH; *U.S. Private*, pg. 1134
Smith, Nancy, Exec. V.P.-Sls.--Electronic Arts, San Mateo, CA; *U.S. Public*, pg. 569
Smith, Norman W., Exec. V.P.-Consumer Banking--BOK Financial Corp., Tulsa, OK; *U.S. Public*, pg. 163
Smith, Norman W., Exec. V.P.-Consumer Banking--Bank of Oklahoma, N.A., Tulsa, OK; *U.S. Public*, pg. 163
Smith, Paul, Exec. Dir.-Retail Opers., Far East--Marks & Spencer PLC, London, United Kingdom; *Int'l*, pg. 842
Smith, Phillip J., Exec. V.P.--United Missouri Bank N.A., Brookfield, MO; *U.S. Public*, pg. 1654
Smith, Pierce R., Exec. V.P. & Treas.--PaineWebber Incorporated, New York, NY; *U.S. Public*, pg. 1252
Smith, R. Scott, Jr., Exec. V.P.--Fulton Financial Corp., Lancaster, PA; *U.S. Public*, pg. 687
Smith, Randall, Exec. V.P. & Gen. Mgr.--WPHL-TV, Inc., Philadelphia, PA; *U.S. Public*, pg. 1636
Smith, Ray, Exec. V.P.-Sls.--U.N.A. Corporation, Elk Grove Village, IL; *Int'l*, pg. 1001
Smith, Richard, Chief Oper. Officer & Exec. V.P.--Providian Auto & Home Insurance Group, Saint Louis, MO; *Int'l*, pg. 27
Smith, Richard, Chief Fin. Officer & Exec. V.P.--Long John Silver's, Inc., Lexington, KY; *U.S. Private*, pg. 674
Smith, Richard F., Exec. V.P.--The Climatic Corp., Columbia, SC; *U.S. Private*, pg. 246
Smith, Richard G., III, Exec. V.P.-Opers.--Executive Jet Aviation, Inc., Columbus, OH; *U.S. Private*, pg. 388
Smith, Robert A., Exec. V.P.--Smith & Sons Foods, Inc., Macon, GA; *U.S. Private*, pg. 1006
Smith, Robert A., Exec. V.P.-Consumer Fin.--Oakwood Homes Corporation, Greensboro, NC; *U.S. Public*, pg. 1209
Smith, Robert A., Exec. V.P.-Consumer Fin.--Oakwood Acceptance Corp., Greensboro, NC; *U.S. Public*, pg. 1209
Smith, Robert H., Chief Fin. Officer & Exec. V.P.-Fin. & Admin.--Novellus Systems, Inc., San Jose, CA; *U.S. Public*, pg. 1204
Smith, Roy C., Exec. V.P.-Store Opers.--Cache, Inc., New York, NY; *U.S. Public*, pg. 289
Smith, S.A., Exec. V.P.-Worldwide Finance & Admin.--Occidental Oil & Gas Corporation, Bakersfield, CA; *U.S. Public*, pg. 1210
Smith, Stephen C., Exec. V.P. & Client Services Dir.--Laughlin/Constable, Inc., Milwaukee, WI; *U.S. Private*, pg. 653
Smith, Stephen E., Exec. V.P. & Dir.-Human Resources--Starbanc Corporation, Cincinnati, OH; *U.S. Public*, pg. 1510
Smith, Stephen R., Exec. V.P.-Mktg.--Excel Communications, Inc., Dallas, TX; *U.S. Public*, pg. 598
Smith, Terry D., Chief Fin. Officer, Exec. V.P. & Sec.--Easco Inc., Girard, OH; *U.S. Public*, pg. 548
Smith, Thomas M., Exec. V.P.-Mktg. & Sales--CPS Direct, Inc., Woburn, MA; *U.S. Private*, pg. 196
Smith, W. Randolph, Exec. V.P.-Eastern Opers.--Tenet Healthcare Corporation, Santa Barbara, CA; *U.S. Public*, pg. 1576
Smith, Wayne A., Exec. V.P.--George & Lynch, Inc., New Castle, DE; *U.S. Private*, pg. 448
Smith, Wes, Exec. V.P.--Hammermill Papers, Memphis, TN; *U.S. Public*, pg. 902
Smith, William A., Exec. V.P.--Sonat Inc., Birmingham, AL; *U.S. Public*, pg. 1484
Smith, William D., Exec. V.P.-Domestic General-Brokerage--American International Group, Inc., New York, NY; *U.S. Public*, pg. 83
Smith, William L., Exec. V.P.--Gusher Pumps, Inc., Dry Ridge, KY; *U.S. Private*, pg. 488
Smith, William, Jr., Exec. V.P.--Brown & Bigelow, Inc., Saint Paul, MN; *U.S. Private*, pg. 172
Smith, Winthrop H., Jr., Exec. V.P.-Intl.--Merrill Lynch & Co., Inc., New York, NY; *U.S. Public*, pg. 1097
Smithart, Debra L., Chief Fin. Officer & Exec. V.P.--Brinker International, Inc., Dallas, TX; *U.S. Public*, pg. 253

Smits, Richard, Chief Oper. Officer & Exec. V.P.--First Northern Capital Corp., Green Bay, WI; *U.S. Public*, pg. 636
Smoot, E. Philip, Exec. V.P.--Park Electrochemical Corporation, Lake Success, NY; *U.S. Public*, pg. 1258
Smoulder, Blair T., Exec. V.P.--Blair Corporation, Warren, PA; *U.S. Public*, pg. 236
Smurfit, D.F., Deputy Chm. & Exec. V.P.-Worldwide Sls. & Mktg.--Jefferson Smurfit Group p.l.c., Dublin, Ireland; *Int'l*, pg. 1269
Smutny, Chuck, Exec. V.P.-Sls. & Mktg.--Agripac Inc., Salem, OR; *U.S. Private*, pg. 26
Smyre, Calvin, Exec. V.P.-Corp. Affairs--Synovus Financial Corp., Columbus, GA; *U.S. Public*, pg. 1548
Snediker, R.R., Jr., Exec. V.P.-Sls.--Chicago Show Printing Co., Morton Grove, IL; *U.S. Private*, pg. 235
Sneed, Jan, Exec. V.P. & Corp. Communications Dir.--BDDP North America, Inc., New York, NY; *Int'l*, pg. 117
Snell, Christopher J., Sr. Creative Partner & Exec. V.P.--Gerbig, Snell/Weisheimer & Assoc., Inc., Columbus, OH; *U.S. Private*, pg. 449
Snell, Luther, Exec. V.P.--First State Bank N.A., Abilene, Abilene, TX; *U.S. Public*, pg. 874
Sniady, Karl, Exec. V.P.-Fin. & Opers.--Trend-Lines Inc., Revere, MA; *U.S. Private*, pg. 1099
Snider, Ronald, Exec. V.P.--Slane Hosiery Mills, Inc., High Point, NC; *U.S. Private*, pg. 1005
Snow, David, Jr., Exec. V.P.-Govt. Programs--Oxford Health Plans Inc., Norwalk, CT; *U.S. Public*, pg. 1238
Snyder, Art, III, Exec. V.P.--A.M. Best Company, Oldwick, NJ; *U.S. Private*, pg. 139
Snyder, Byron R., Exec. V.P. & Chief Oper. Officer--Pioneer/Eclipse Corp., Sparta, NC; *Int'l*, pg. 71
Snyder, David L., Exec. V.P.--Robert Orr-Sysco Food Services Co., Nashville, TN; *U.S. Public*, pg. 1551
Snyder, Gerald C., Exec. V.P.--G.E. Johnson Construction Co., Inc., Colorado Springs, CO; *U.S. Private*, pg. 591
Snyder, Isadore, Exec. V.P.-Ontario West--Shoppers Drug Mart, Ltd., Toronto, Canada; *Int'l*, pg. 112
Snyder, James M., Chief Investment Officer & Exec. V.P.--Northern Trust Corporation, Chicago, IL; *U.S. Public*, pg. 1195
Snyder, John, Exec. V.P.--A.M. Best Company, Oldwick, NJ; *U.S. Private*, pg. 139
Snyder, Kathryn D., Exec. V.P. & Treas.--Glendale Federal Bank, F.S.B., Glendale, CA; *U.S. Public*, pg. 747
Snyder, Marcia K., Exec. V.P.-Corp. Lending--BankAtlantic Bancorp, Inc., Fort Lauderdale, FL; *U.S. Public*, pg. 183
Snyder, Richard, Exec. V.P.-Engrng.--Cognex Corporation, Natick, MA; *U.S. Public*, pg. 394
Snyder, Robert, Exec. V.P.-Opers.--American Manufacturing Company, Chattanooga, TN; *U.S. Private*, pg. 58
Sobey, John R., Chief Oper. Officer & Exec. V.P.--Sobey Inc., Stellarton, Canada; *Int'l*, pg. 454
Sobol, Yehiel, Exec. V.P.--Kao Infosystems Company (MA), Plymouth, MA; *Int'l*, pg. 717
Socks, Lyn, Exec. V.P.--Modern Equipment Co., Inc., Port Washington, WI; *U.S. Private*, pg. 33
Soderberg, Kathleen, Exec. V.P.--National Bank of Alaska, Anchorage, AK; *U.S. Public*, pg. 1153
Soh, N., Exec. V.P.--Pacific Fuel Trading Corporation, Long Beach, CA; *Int'l*, pg. 700
Sokol, John, Exec. V.P.--Bancinsurance Corp., Columbus, OH; *U.S. Public*, pg. 175
Sokolow, Steve, Exec. V.P.--Leviton Mfg. Co., Inc., Little Neck, NY; *U.S. Private*, pg. 663
Solberg, Elizabeth T., Sr. Partner, Exec. V.P. & Gen. Mgr.--Fleishman-Hillard, Inc., Kansas City, MO; *U.S. Private*, pg. 411
Soldo, Marie H., Exec. V.P.-Govt. Affairs & Special Projects--Sierra Health Services, Inc., Las Vegas, NV; *U.S. Public*, *pg. 1469*
Sole, Shlomo, Exec. V.P.-Res.--Sapiens USA, Inc., Durham, NC; *Int'l*, pg. 1193
Solente, Pierre, Exec. V.P.--Air Liquide S.A., Paris, France; *Int'l*, pg. 37
Solheim, Allan, Exec. V.P.--Karsten Manufacturing Corporation, Phoenix, AZ; *U.S. Private*, pg. 608
Sollenberger, Mark L., Exec. V.P. & Treas.--Laurel Bank, Johnstown, PA; *U.S. Public*, pg. 164
Solley, L.W., Exec. V.P.--Emerson Electric Co., Saint Louis, MO; *U.S. Public*, pg. 572
Solomon, Max, Exec. V.P.-Claims--Greater New York Mutual Insurance Company, New York, NY; *U.S. Private*, *pg. 476*
Solomon, Robert, Exec. V.P., Mng. & Mktg. Dir.--Ammirati, Puris & Lintas, Inc., New York, NY; *U.S. Private*, pg. 66
Solomon, Stephen, Pres.--ABB Lummus Global Inc., Bloomfield, NJ; *Int'l*, pg. 4
Solt, Russell, Exec. V.P.-Fin. & Admin. & Sec.--Venture Stores, Inc., O Fallon, MO; *U.S. Public*, pg. 1716
Soltys, George J., Jr., Exec. V.P.--Summit Bancorp, Princeton, NJ; *U.S. Public*, pg. 1527
Somers, Daniel E., Chief Fin. Officer & Sr. Exec. V.P.--AT&T Corporation, Basking Ridge, NJ; *U.S. Public*, pg. 10
Somers, Frank A., Grp. Exec. V.P.-Special Assets--Bank of America NT&SA, San Francisco, CA; *U.S. Public*, pg. 180
Somers, John A., Exec. V.P.-TIAA Investments--Teachers Insurance and Annuity Association, New York, NY; *U.S. Private*, pg. 1071
Somers, K. Brent, Chief Fin. Officer & Sr. Exec. V.P.--Keycorp, Cleveland, OH; *U.S. Public*, pg. 954
Sometani, Morihiko, Sr. Exec. V.P.--Japan Tobacco Inc., Tokyo, Japan; *Int'l*, pg. 703
Sommer, Barbara, Exec. V.P.-Mktg.--Letraset Nielsen & Bainbridge, Paramus, NJ; *Int'l*, pg. 460
Sommer, John, Exec. V.P.-Sls. & Mktg.--Kidron Inc., Kidron, OH; *U.S. Private*, pg. 619
Sommers, Bettina, Exec. V.P.--Allied Printing Services, Inc., Manchester, CT; *U.S. Private*, pg. 40
Sommers, Gerald, Exec. V.P.-Sls. & Mktg.--Allied Printing Services, Inc., Manchester, CT; *U.S. Private*, pg. 40
Song, Doik, Exec. V.P.--Seoul DMB&B, Inc., Seoul, Korea; *Int'l*, pg. 1223
Song, In-Hee, Exec. V.P.--Jinwoong Inc., Seoul, Korea; *Int'l*, *pg. 706*
Song, Seung-Hyo, Exec. V.P. & Dir.--Cho Hung Bank, Seoul, Korea; *Int'l*, pg. 287
Sonksen, John, Chief Fin. Officer & Sr. V.P.--J.H. Baxter & Company, San Mateo, CA; *U.S. Private*, pg. 124
Sonnabend, Jacqueline, Exec. V.P.-Human Resources--Sonesta International Hotels Corporation, Boston, MA; *U.S. Public*, pg. 1485
Sonnabend, Volker, Exec. V.P.--Glens Falls Cement Co., Glens Falls, NY; *Int'l*, pg. 423
Sonner, Sandy, Exec. V.P.--Lightalarms Electronics Corporation, Baldwin, NY; *Int'l*, pg. 725
Soo Kim, Chang, Exec. V.P.--LG Group, Seoul, Korea; *Int'l*, pg. 778
Soo-Kang, Lee, Exec. V.P.-Production & Indus. Machinery--Korea Heavy Industries & Construction Co., Ltd., Seoul, Korea; *Int'l*, pg. 758
Soon, Soh Kim, Sr. Exec. V.P.-Banking, Data Resources, Systems & Trade Service--DBS Bank Ltd., Singapore, Singapore; *Int'l*, pg. 350
Soper, Michael R., M.D., Exec. V.P.-Physician Integration--Advocate Health Care, Oak Brook, IL; *U.S. Private*, pg. 23
Sophonpanich, Chatri, Exec. V.P.--Bel (Cayman) Limited, Georgetown, Cayman Islands; *Int'l*, pg. 146
Sorbets, Pierre, Exec. V.P.-Intl. Fin.--Credit Commercial de France, Paris, France; *Int'l*, pg. 341
Sorden, James, Exec. V.P.-Comml. Sys.--Trimble Navigation Limited, Sunnyvale, CA; *U.S. Public*, pg. 1638
Sordo, Art, Exec. V.P.-North American Opers.--MiTek, Inc., Chesterfield, MO; *Int'l*, pg. 1106
Sorensen, Stuart L., Exec. V.P., Chief Actuary & Sec.--Security American Financial Enterprises, Inc., Minnetonka, MN; *U.S. Private*, pg. 980
Sorokin, Cheryl A., Exec. V.P. & Corp. Sec.--BankAmerica Corporation, San Francisco, CA; *U.S. Public*, pg. 179
Sortwell, Christopher, Chief Fin. Officer & Exec. V.P.-Intl.--The Stroh Brewery Company, Detroit, MI; *U.S. Private*, pg. 1047
Sosa, Enrique J., Exec. V.P.-Chemicals--Amoco Corporation, Chicago, IL; *U.S. Public*, pg. 101
Sosa, Enrique J., Exec. V.P.-Chemicals--Amoco Chemicals, Chicago, IL; *U.S. Public*, pg. 102
Sosiak, Jack J., Exec. V.P.-Human Resources--Exide Corporation, Reading, PA; *U.S. Public*, pg. 600
Sosnoski, Richard, Exec. V.P.-Admin. & Supply Chain--Castleberry/Snow's Brands Inc., Augusta, GA; *U.S. Private*, pg. 219
Sotani, Yuzo, Deputy Pres.--ORIX Computer Systems Corporation, Tokyo, Japan; *Int'l*, pg. 1008
Soto, Raul, Chief Fin. Officer & Exec. V.P.--Carrafiello, Diehl & Associates, Inc., Irvington, NY; *U.S. Private*, pg. 215
Sousa, Thomas, Exec. V.P.--National Programs Division, Tampa, FL; *U.S. Public*, pg. 1312
Southerland, Michael, Exec. V.P.-Mktg.--Automobile Protection Corporation-APCO, Atlanta, GA; *U.S. Public*, pg. 150
Southern, William S., Jr., Exec. V.P.--Krause Plow Corp., Hutchinson, KS; *U.S. Private*, pg. 635
Southers, Dewey, Exec. V.P.--Young Refining Corp., Douglasville, GA; *U.S. Private*, pg. 1202
Southway, Peter, Vice Chm. & Exec. V.P.--Valley National Bancorp, Wayne, NJ; *U.S. Public*, pg. 1705
Southwell, Leonard, Chief Exec. Officer & Exec. V.P.--Prairie Farms Dairy, Inc., Carlinville, IL; *U.S. Private*, pg. 878
Sowerby, Ronald E., Chief Fin. Officer, Exec. V.P.-Fin., & Sec.--TCG International Inc., Burnaby, Canada; *Int'l*, pg. 1336
Sowers, Joel H., Exec. V.P.--Centex Real Estate Corp./Centex Homes, Dallas, TX; *U.S. Public*, pg. 323
Sowinski, Frank S., Exec. V.P.--Dun & Bradstreet, Murray Hill, NJ; *U.S. Public*, pg. 535
Spangenberg, David R., Chief Oper. Officer & Exec. V.P.--Liberty National Life Insurance Co., Birmingham, AL; *U.S. Public*, pg. 1622
Spaniac, Pamela M., Exec. V.P.-Fin. & Admin.--Res-Care Incorporated, Louisville, KY; *U.S. Public*, pg. 1382
Spano, Eduardo, Exec. V.P.--Metropolitana Milanese S.P.A., Milan, Italy; *Int'l*, pg. 863
Spanos, Michael A., Exec. V.P.--The Spanos Companies, Stockton, CA; *U.S. Private*, pg. 1020
Sparks, Michael, Exec. V.P.--Brooks Brothers, New York, NY; *Int'l*, pg. 843
Sparks, W. Alvon, Jr., Chief Fin. Officer & Exec. V.P.--GEICO Corporation, Washington, DC; *U.S. Public*, pg. 219
Spaulding, Richard M., Exec. V.P.-Scholastic, Inc.--Scholastic Inc., New York, NY; *U.S. Public*, pg. 1440
Spear, Cecil C., Jr., Exec. V.P.--Trinity-Structural Steel, Montgomery, AL; *U.S. Public*, pg. 1639
Spears, Richard R., Exec. V.P.-Retail Division--First of America Bank Corporation, Kalamazoo, MI; *U.S. Public*, pg. 636
Spears, Willie E., Exec. V.P.-Retail Banking--Hibernia Corporation, New Orleans, LA; *U.S. Public*, pg. 825
Specht, Ilon, Exec. V.P.-Creative Services--Jordan, McGrath, Case & Taylor Inc., New York, NY; *U.S. Private*, pg. 598
Specht, Uwe, Dr., Exec. V.P.-Cosmetics & Toiletries--Henkel KGaA, Dusseldorf, Germany; *Int'l*, pg. 609
Specter, Eric M., Chief Fin. Officer & Exec. V.P.--Charming Shoppes, Inc., Bensalem, PA; *U.S. Public*, pg. 335
Spector, David A., Exec. V.P. & Head Trader--Countrywide Home Loans Inc., Pasadena, CA; *U.S. Public*, pg. 452
Spector, G.A., Chief Oper. Officer & Exec. V.P.--Equity Residential Properties Trust, Chicago, IL; *U.S. Public*, pg. 590
Spector, Janice, Exec. V.P.--Grey Advertising Inc., New York, NY; *U.S. Public*, pg. 764
Spector, Warren J., Exec. V.P. & Sr. Mng. Dir.--The Bear Stearns Companies Inc., New York, NY; *U.S. Public*, pg. 197
Speer, David B., Exec. V.P.--Illinois Tool Works Inc., Glenview, IL; *U.S. Public*, pg. 865
Speidel, Doug, Exec. V.P. & Exec. Creative Dir.--Lowe Direct, New York, NY; *U.S. Private*, pg. 678
Speiser, Robert D., Exec. V.P.--Health-Chem Corporation, New York, NY; *U.S. Public*, pg. 802
Spell, David T., Jr., Exec. V.P.--First National Bank of Commerce, New Orleans, LA; *U.S. Public*, pg. 629
Spellman, Robert, Exec. V.P.-Admin. & Fin.--Star Markets Company, Inc., Cambridge, MA; *U.S. Private*, pg. 1035
Spence, Mike, Exec. V.P.--TU Services, Dallas, TX; *U.S. Public*, pg. 1588
Spence, William F., Exec. V.P.-Western Canada, Asia & Australasia, Corp. Bank CIBC--Canadian Imperial Bank of Commerce, Toronto, Canada; *Int'l*, pg. 256
Spencer, Diane, Exec. V.P. & Media Plng. Dir.--Young & Rubicam New York, New York, NY; *U.S. Private*, pg. 1198
Spencer, Rodney, Exec. V.P. & Gen. Mgr.--Leonard & Harral Packing Co., San Antonio, TX; *U.S. Private*, pg. 660
Spencer, Terry S., Exec. V.P.-Devel.--First American Corporation, Nashville, TN; *U.S. Public*, pg. 624
Speranzella, Charles J., Jr., Exec. V.P., Gen. Counsel & Sec.--Breed Technologies, Inc., Lakeland, FL; *U.S. Public*, pg. 251
Sperry, James K., Exec. V.P.--Fulton Financial Corp., Lancaster, PA; *U.S. Public*, pg. 687
Sperry, Michael W., Sr. Exec. V.P.--BB&T Corporation, Winston Salem, NC; *U.S. Public*, pg. 159
Spetrino, John, Exec. V.P. & Exec. Creative Dir.--Thomas G. Ferguson Associates, Inc., Parsippany, NJ; *Int'l*, pg. 1483
Spetz, Lennart, Exec. V.P.--Svenska Handelsbanken, Stockholm, Sweden; *Int'l*, pg. 1327
Spicknall, Charles G., III, Exec. V.P.--First Virginia Bank, Falls Church, VA; *U.S. Public*, pg. 641
Spiess, Sarah P., Exec. V.P.--Analysts International Corporation, Minneapolis, MN; *U.S. Public*, pg. 110
Spiess, Sarah S., Exec. V.P.--AIC-FSS Advertising, Minneapolis, MN; *U.S. Private*, pg. 5
Spiesshoefer, Peter, Dr., Exec. V.P.-Adv. & Intl. Sls.--Burda Holding GmbH & Co., KG, Munich, Germany; *Int'l*, pg. 233
Spiker, J. Scott, Sr. Exec. V.P.-Bus. Svcs. Grp.--Dain Rauscher Corporation, Minneapolis, MN; *U.S. Public*, pg. 476
Spikerman, Richard C., Exec. V.P.--Republic National Bank of New York, New York, NY; *U.S. Public*, pg. 1380
Spilsbury, Michael A.C., Exec. V.P.-Opers. & Services Grp.--Union Bank of California, San Francisco, CA; *Int'l*, pg. 157
Spitz, Arnold J., Exec. V.P., Treas. & Sec.--International Seaway Trading Corporation, Boca Raton, FL; *U.S. Private*, pg. 572
Spivak, Helayne, Exec. V.P., Creative Dir.--Ammirati, Puris & Lintas, Inc., New York, NY; *U.S. Private*, pg. 66
Spivak, Herb, Exec. V.P.-Opers.--New Balance Athletic Shoe, Inc., Boston, MA; *U.S. Private*, pg. 792
Spivak, Joan, Exec. V.P. & Gen. Mgr.-Healthcare--Edelman Worldwide, Inc., New York, NY; *U.S. Private*, pg. 362
Spivey, J. Harrell, Exec. V.P.--Cameron Ashley Building Products, Inc, Dallas, TX; *U.S. Public*, pg. 298
Spletzer, Richard J., Exec. & V.P. Chief Investment Officer--Duff & Phelps Utilities Income Inc., Chicago, IL; *U.S. Public*, pg. 534
Spohn, George W., III, Exec. V.P.--ColeJon Corporation, Cleveland, OH; *U.S. Private*, pg. 251
Spolane, David A., Exec. V.P.--Sterling Electronics Corporation, Houston, TX; *U.S. Public*, pg. 1051
Sprackman, Mel, Exec. V.P. & Mgr.-Vancouver--Canadian Broadcast Sales, Toronto, Canada; *Int'l*, pg. 1482
Spragg, Gregory, Exec. V.P.-Sls. & Mdsg.--FINAST, Maple Heights, OH; *Int'l*, pg. 750
Sprague, Charles W., Exec. V.P., Gen. Counsel & Sec.--Fiserv, Inc., Brookfield, WI; *U.S. Public*, pg. 647
Spray, Ed, Exec. V.P.--Home & Garden Television, Knoxville, TN; *U.S. Public*, pg. 1447
Spreng, Douglas C., Exec. V.P.-Client Access/Interface Prods. Grp.--3Com Corporation, Santa Clara, CA; *U.S. Public*, pg. 1603
Sprimont, Roger, Exec. V.P.-Mktg.--Celsius AB, Stockholm, Sweden; *Int'l*, pg. 276
Springer, Glen, Exec. V.P.--Viking Pump, Inc., Cedar Falls, IA; *U.S. Public*, pg. 862
Springer, James L., Jr., Exec. V.P.--NationsBank of Tennessee, Nashville, TN; *U.S. Public*, pg. 1163
Springer, William C., Exec. V.P.-The Americas--H.J. Heinz Company, Pittsburgh, PA; *U.S. Public*, pg. 805
Sproule, Michael Edward, Chief Fin. Officer & Exec. V.P.--American Mutual Life Holding Co., Des Moines, IA; *U.S. Private*, pg. 59
Spruill, John, Chm. Bd. & Exec. V.P.--Alcon Systems, Inc., Fort Worth, TX; *Int'l*, pg. 916
Spruill, John R., Chief Fin. Officer & Exec. V.P.--CNB Bancshares, Inc., Evansville, IN; *U.S. Public*, pg. 280
Spur, R., Exec. V.P.--Azcon Corp., Chicago, IL; *U.S. Private*, *pg. 153*
Spurr, Lori, Exec. V.P.--Johnson Moving & Storage, Boulder/Longmont, Longmont, CO; *U.S. Private*, pg. 594
Spurrell, Eldon H.N., Exec. V.P.-North American Distr. Grp.--Aluma Systems Corp., Toronto, Canada; *Int'l*, pg. 1423
Squires, Robert, Exec. V.P.-Admin.--Scott Specialty Gases, Plumsteadville, PA; *U.S. Private*, pg. 977
Squires, Stanley, Chief Oper. Officer & Exec. V.P.--Anorad Corporation, Hauppauge, NY; *U.S. Private*, pg. 75
St. George, Lucy, Exec. V.P. & Client Svcs. Dir.-DR--Western International Media Corporation, Los Angeles, CA; *U.S. Private*, pg. 1165
St. John, Norbert, Exec. V.P.-Mktg.--Richey Electronics, Inc., Garden Grove, CA; *U.S. Public*, pg. 1388

St. Martin, Charlotte, Exec. V.P.-Loews Hotels--Loews Hotels, New York, NY; *U.S. Public*, pg. 1011
St. Onge, Vincent A., Exec. V.P.-Components--Osram Sylvania Inc., Malvern, PA; *Int'l*, pg. 1245
Stacey, Ronald L., Exec. V.P.--Western Group, Sherman Oaks, CA; *U.S. Public*, pg. 650
Stachura, Robert D., V.P. & Exec. Mgr.--Douglas & Lomason Company, Marianna, AR; *Int'l*, pg. 830
Stack, Richard, Exec. V.P.--Jack Levy Associates, Chicago, IL; *U.S. Private*, pg. 664
Stacy, Don, Exec. V.P.--Inland Detroit Diesel Allison Co., Butler, WI; *U.S. Private*, pg. 564
Stafford, Thomas, Exec. V. P. & Gen. Mgr.-Mfg.--Gilman Paper Co., Saint Marys, GA; *U.S. Private*, pg. 454
Stahl, Kirk, Chief Oper. Officer, Exec. V.P. & Acct. Exec.--Caldwell VanRiper, Inc., Indianapolis, IN; *U.S. Private*, pg. 200
Stai, Harlan C., Exec. V.P.-Opers.--Owen Health Care, Inc., Houston, TX; *U.S. Public*, pg. 304
Staiano, Edward F., Exec. V.P. & Pres. & Gen. Mgr.-General Systems--Motorola, Inc., Schaumburg, IL; *U.S. Public*, pg. 1136
Staib, Michel, Exec. V.P. & V.P.-Corp. Communications--Schneider S.A., Boulogne-Billancourt, France; *Int'l*, pg. 1207
Staikopoulos, Joanne, Exec. V.P.- Worldwide Fin. & Admin.--Quantum Media International, Inc., New York, NY; *U.S. Private*, pg. 899
Stainrook, Harry R., Exec. V.P.--First Empire State Corporation, Buffalo, NY; *U.S. Public*, pg. 631
Stainrook, Harry R., Exec. V.P.--Manufacturers & Traders Trust Company, Buffalo, NY; *U.S. Public*, pg. 631
Stairs, Harriet, Exec. V.P.-H.R.--Bank of Montreal, Toronto, Canada; *Int'l*, pg. 153
Stallard, Larry, Exec. V.P.--Feed Service Corp., Ohiowa, NE; *U.S. Private*, pg. 399
Stallkamp, William J., Exec. V.P.--Mellon Bank Corporation, Pittsburgh, PA; *U.S. Public*, pg. 1084
Stamm, Charles H., Exec. V.P. & Gen. Counsel--Teachers Insurance and Annuity Association, New York, NY; *U.S. Private*, pg. 1071
Stamp, Robert, Chief Oper. Officer & Exec. V.P.--Hold-E-Zee, Ltd., Meadville, PA; *U.S. Private*, pg. 229
Stamper, Michael K., Exec. V.P.-Risk Mngmt.--Federal Home Loan Mortgage Corporation, Mc Lean, VA; *U.S. Public*, pg. 615
Stanbrook, Steven P., Exec. V.P. & Reg. Dir.-Consumer Products, Europe--S.C. Johnson & Son, Inc., Racine, WI; *U.S. Private*, pg. 592
Stanford, Arlyn, Exec. V.P.--Anderson Lithograph Company, Los Angeles, CA; *U.S. Private*, pg. 72
Stanford, Paul, Exec. V.P.-Admin., Gen. Counsel & Sec.--CalMat Co., Los Angeles, CA; *U.S. Public*, pg. 295
Stangler, Kevin J., Chief Fin. Officer & Exec. V.P.--Security American Financial Enterprises, Inc., Minnetonka, MN; *U.S. Private*, pg. 980
Stankovic, Jovan, Exec. V.P.--Jugobanka Banking Group, Belgrade, Serbia; *Int'l*, pg. 716
Stansoucy, R.J., Exec. V.P.--The Presmet Corp., Worcester, MA; *U.S. Private*, pg. 882
Stanton, Margaret P., Exec. V.P. & Corp. Sec.--Jazzercise, Inc., Carlsbad, CA; *U.S. Private*, pg. 584
Stanton, Victoria, Exec. V.P., Gen. Counsel & Sec.--Farm Family Casualty Insurance Co., Glenmont, NY; *U.S. Private*, pg. 394
Stanzione, Dan, Chief Oper. Officer & Exec. V.P.--Lucent Technologies Inc., Murray Hill, NJ; *U.S. Public*, pg. 1017
Stark, Daniel J., Exec. V.P.--Kinney System, Inc., New York, NY; *U.S. Private*, pg. 622
Stark, Edward, Exec. V.P. & Mgr.-Sls.--Dixie Dairy Company, Gary, IN; *U.S. Private*, pg. 337
Starkweather, Ken, Chief Fin. Officer & Exec. V.P.-Fin.--Copley Pharmaceuticals, Inc., Canton, MA; *U.S. Public*, pg. 446
Starr, Marion, Exec. V.P.--Bernard Hodes Group, New York, NY; *U.S. Public*, pg. 1224
Starr, Michael D., Chief Exec. Officer & Sr. Exec. V.P.-Government Managed Care--PHP Healthcare Corporation, Reston, VA; *U.S. Public*, pg. 1241
Stasik, Robert W., Exec. V.P.-Global Cash Mngmt.--Mellon Bank Corporation, Pittsburgh, PA; *U.S. Public*, pg. 1084
Staton, Daniel C., Chief Oper. Officer & Exec. V.P.--Duke Realty Investments, Inc., Indianapolis, IN; *U.S. Public*, pg. 535
Stavropoulos, Nickolas, Chief Fin. Officer & Exec. V.P.-Fin. & Mktg.--Colonial Gas Company, Lowell, MA; *U.S. Public*, pg. 400
Stearns, David, Exec V.P.--The Coleman Company, Inc., Golden, CO; *U.S. Private*, pg. 690
Stearns, David P., Chief Oper. Officer & Exec. V.P.--J.H. Routh Packing Co., Sandusky, OH; *U.S. Private*, pg. 948
Steed, Richard E., Exec. V.P. & Gen. Mgr.-Partition Div.--Rock-Tenn Company, Norcross, GA; *U.S. Public*, pg. 1396
Steele, Jeffrey D., Exec. V.P.--Bucilla Corporation, Hazleton, PA; *U.S. Private*, pg. 352
Steele, Tommy D., Exec. V.P.--Intergraph Corporation, Huntsville, AL; *U.S. Public*, pg. 890
Steets, Richard J., Exec. V.P.-Corp. Devel.--TrizecHahn Corporation, Toronto, Canada; *Int'l*, pg. 1424
Stefan, William, Exec. V.P.--Key Handling Systems, Inc., Moonachie, NJ; *U.S. Private*, pg. 618
Stefanelli, Joseph B., Exec. V.P.-Derivative Securities--The American Stock Exchange, New York, NY; *U.S. Private*, pg. 62
Stefanski, Stan, Exec. V.P. & Chief Fin. Officer--Young & Rubicam Inc., New York, NY; *U.S. Private*, pg. 1196
Steffen, Cennert, Exec. V.P.-Mfg. & Engrng.--The Eureka Company, Bloomington, IL; *Int'l*, pg. 440
Steffons, John L., Exec. V.P.-Private Client--Merrill Lynch & Co., Inc., New York, NY; *U.S. Public*, pg. 1097
Steigerwald, Karl A., Exec. V.P.-Admin.--Spiegel, Inc., Downers Grove, IL; *U.S. Public*, pg. 1498
Stein, C. Jeffrey, Exec. V.P. & Mngmt. Rep.--Grey Advertising Inc., New York, NY; *U.S. Public*, pg. 764
Stein, Michael A., Chief Fin. Officer & Exec. V.P.--Marriott International, Inc., Washington, DC; *U.S. Public*, pg. 1047
Stein, Michael A., Chief Fin. Officer & Exec. V.P.--Fairfield Inn, Washington, DC; *U.S. Public*, pg. 1048
Stein, Stanley R., Exec. V.P.--McDonald's Corporation, Oak Brook, IL; *U.S. Public*, pg. 1068
Steinbach, Gordon H., Exec. V.P.-Affordable Housing--Mortgage Guaranty Insurance Corporation, Milwaukee, WI; *U.S. Public*, pg. 1026
Steiner, Detlef, Exec. V.P.--Zurich Insurance Company, Zurich, Switzerland; *Int'l*, pg. 1529
Steiner, John E., Exec. V.P.--MagneTek, Inc., Nashville, TN; *U.S. Public*, pg. 1037
Steingard, Nancy, Exec. V.P.-Universal Cartoon Studios--Universal Studios TV, Universal City, CA; *Int'l*, pg. 1215
Steinhafel, Gregg, Exec. V.P.-Mdsg.--Target Stores, Minneapolis, MN; *U.S. Public*, pg. 489
Steinhart, Donald L., Exec. V.P.--Snavely Forest Products, Inc., Pittsburgh, PA; *U.S. Private*, pg. 1010
Steinhauer, Chuck, Exec. V.P.--Madison Dairy Produce Company, Madison, WI; *U.S. Private*, pg. 694
Steinour, Stephen D., Exec. V.P. & Dir.-Credit Policy & Admin.--Citizens Financial Group, Inc., Providence, RI; *Int'l*, pg. 1132
Steinwandel, A. Charles, Exec. V.P.--Ross Island Sand & Gravel Co., Inc., Portland, OR; *U.S. Private*, pg. 836
Stelmach, Leigh S., Exec. V.P.-Opers.--Dollar General Corporation, Nashville, TN; *U.S. Public*, pg. 515
Stelzel, Walter T., Chief Fin. Officer & Sr. Exec. V.P.--American National Can Company, Chicago, IL; *Int'l*, pg. 1029
Stempler, Mark, Exec. V.P.-Sls.--Craftmatic Organization, Inc., Trevose, PA; *U.S. Private*, pg. 284
Stenbit, John P., Acting Exec. V.P. & Gen. Mgr.-TRW Systems Integration Grp.--TRW Inc., Cleveland, OH; *U.S.* Public, pg. 1558
Stenbit, John P., Acting Exec. V.P. & Gen. Mgr.--TRW Systems Integration Group, Fairfax, VA; *U.S. Public*, pg. 1558
Stenstadvold, Halvor, Exec. V.P.--Orkla A.S.A., Oslo, Norway; *Int'l*, pg. 1010
Stephens, Bobby W., Exec. V.P.-Asset Mngmt.--Beverly Enterprises, Inc., Fort Smith, AR; *U.S. Public*, pg. 227
Stephens, David, Exec. V.P.-Private Banking--Comerica Incorporated, Detroit, MI; *U.S. Public*, pg. 408
Stephens, John R., Exec. V.P.--Gas Tech, Newark, CA; *U.S. Public*, pg. 1593
Stephenson, E.W., Jr., Sr. Exec. V.P. & Chm. & Chief Exec. Officer-AmSouth Bank FL--AmSouth Bancorporation, Birmingham, AL; *U.S. Public*, pg. 105
Stephenson, Tom, Exec. V.P.-Asset Mngmnt.--Crown American Realty Trust, Johnstown, PA; *U.S. Public*, pg. 461
Stephenson, William A., Exec. V.P.--Uniroyal Chemical Corporation, Middlebury, CT; *U.S. Public*, pg. 459
Stephenson, William A., Exec. V.P.--Uniroyal Chemical Company, Inc., Middlebury, CT; *U.S. Public*, pg. 460
Stepp, J. Michael, Chief Fin. Officer & Exec. V.P.--Collins & Aikman Corporation, Charlotte, NC; *U.S. Public*, pg. 399
Sterenberg, J. William, Exec. V.P.--J.E. Baker Co., York, PA; *U.S. Private*, pg. 112
Sterling, Clyde E., Exec. V.P.-Alaska Production--Peter Pan Seafoods, Inc., Seattle, WA; *Int'l*, pg. 928
Stern, Andrew, Exec. V.P.-Strategic Corp. Plng.--USF&G Corporation, Baltimore, MD; *U.S. Public*, pg. 1659
Stern, Edward J., Exec. V.P.--The Hartz Mountain Corp., Secaucus, NJ; *U.S. Private*, pg. 508
Steuterman, James M., Exec. V.P.--New Plan Realty Trust, New York, NY; *U.S. Public*, pg. 1172
Stevens, Donald W., Chief Fin. Officer, Exec. V.P. & Treas.--Mikohn Gaming Corporation, Las Vegas, NV; *U.S. Public*, pg. 1111
Stevens, Edward A., Chief Fin. Officer, Exec. V.P. & Sec.--Peak Technologies Group, Inc., New York, NY; *Int'l*, pg. 890
Stevens, Jane, Exec. V.P. & Exec. Media Dir.--Bernstein-Rein Advertising, Inc., Kansas City, MO; *U.S. Private*, pg. 137
Stevens, Kathie S., Exec. V.P. & Sr. Lending Officer--UST Corporation, Boston, MA; *U.S. Public*, pg. 1660
Stevens, Ken, Exec. V.P.--Taco Bell Corp., Irvine, CA; *U.S. Public*, pg. 1637
Stevens, Leroy, Exec. V.P.--Pacific Hide & Fur Depot, Great Falls, MT; *U.S. Private*, pg. 831
Stevens, Mark, Exec. V.P.-Personal Fin. Services--Northern Trust Corporation, Chicago, IL; *U.S. Public*, pg. 1195
Stevens, R., Chief Fin. Officer & Exec. V.P.--Robertson-Ceco Corporation, San Ramon, CA; *U.S. Public*, pg. 1394
Stevens, Robert D., Exec. V.P.--MK Centennial, Arvada, CO; *U.S. Public*, pg. 1134
Stevens, Thomas C., Exec. V.P., Gen. Counsel & Sec.--Keycorp, Cleveland, OH; *U.S. Public*, pg. 954
Stevenson, Robert W., Chief Fin. Officer, Exec. V.P. & Sec.--Esterline Technologies Corporation, Bellevue, WA; *U.S. Public*, pg. 594
Steves, Tom, Chief Oper. Officer & Exec. V.P.--Cranford Johnson Robinson Woods, Little Rock, AR; *U.S. Private, pg. 286*
Stewart, Barry D., Exec. V.P.-Resources Group--Suncor Inc., Calgary, Canada; *Int'l*, pg. 1320
Stewart, Barry D., Exec. V.P.--Suncor Exploration & Production Group, Calgary, Canada; *Int'l*, pg. 1320
Stewart, Bernard F., Exec. V.P., Gen. Counsel & Sec.--Exide Corporation, Reading, PA; *U.S. Public*, pg. 600
Stewart, Edward D., Exec. V.P.--G.E. Capital Commercial Real Estate Financing, Stamford, CT; *U.S. Public*, pg. 712
Stewart, Guthrie, Exec. V.P.-Corp. Devel. & Sec.--Teleglobe, Inc., Montreal, Canada; *Int'l*, pg. 1373
Stewart, James G., Chief Fin. Officer & Exec. V.P.--Cigna Corp., Philadelphia, PA; *U.S. Public*, pg. 356
Stewart, Robert, Chief Fin. Officer & Exec. V.P.--Lois/EJL New York, New York, NY; *U.S. Public*, pg. 1011
Stewart, Robert, Exec. V.P.-Fin. & Admin--Lois/EJL Chicago, Chicago, IL; *U.S. Public*, pg. 1011
Stewart, Robert K., Chief Fin. Officer & Exec. V.P.--Lois/USA Inc., New York, NY; *U.S. Public*, pg. 1011
Stewart, William L., Exec. V.P.-Generation--APS, Phoenix, AZ; *U.S. Public*, pg. 1297
Stidham, J. Michael, Exec. V.P.-Sls.--Oakwood Homes Corporation, Greensboro, NC; *U.S. Public*, pg. 1209
Stiehl, Robert J., Jr., Chief Fin. Officer, Exec. V.P.-Opers. & Treas.--Hampton Industries, Inc., Kinston, NC; *U.S. Public*, pg. 779
Stifel, Richard Q., Exec. V.P.-Commercial Banking--1st Source Bank Consolidated, South Bend, IN; *U.S. Public*, pg. 638
Stillman, John C., Exec. V.P. & Sec.--Stillman & Hoag, Inc., Englewood, NJ; *U.S. Private*, pg. 1043
Stillwagon, Leon, Exec. V.P.-Opers.--Hitchiner Manufacturing Company, Inc., Milford, NH; *U.S. Private*, pg. 531
Stilson, Peter, Exec. V.P. & Gen. Mgr.-Norstan Southern--Norstan, Inc., Plymouth, MN; *U.S. Public*, pg. 1192
Stimpert, M.A., Chief Exec. Officer & Exec. V.P.--Golden Peanut Company, Alpharetta, GA; *U.S. Private*, pg. 459
Stine, James O., Exec. V.P. & Gen. Mgr.--Aeronca, Inc., Middletown, OH; *Int'l*, pg. 829
Stinson, Kenneth E., Exec. V.P.--Peter Kiewit Sons Inc., Omaha, NE; *U.S. Private*, pg. 619
Stipp, D.C., Principal--Richards, Brock, Miller, Mitchell & Assoc. Inc., Dallas, TX; *U.S. Private*, pg. 929
Stockmann, Karl W., Exec. V.P.-Buying & Intl. Opers.--Stockmann Department Store Div., Helsinki, Finland; *Int'l*, pg. 1301
Stoewsand, Robert J., Exec. V.P.--Alaron Inc., Auburn Hills, MI; *U.S. Private*, pg. 31
Stoffaes, Christian, Chief Inspector Gen. & Exec. V.P.--Electricite de France, Paris, France; *Int'l*, pg. 437
Stoll, Matthew, Exec. V.P.--Sunflower Carriers, York, NE; *U.S. Private*, pg. 289
Stolworthy, R. Randy, Chief Oper. Officer & Exec. V.P.--New Mexico & Arizona Land Co., Phoenix, AZ; *U.S. Public*, pg. 1172
Stolzer, Ernest, Chief Oper. Officer & Exec. V.P.--Quality Bakers of America Cooperative, Inc., Greenwich, CT; *U.S. Private*, pg. 898
Stombaugh, Paul, Exec. V.P.--York Barbell Co., Inc., York, PA; *U.S. Private*, pg. 1196
Stone, B.H., Exec. V.P.--Greate Bay Casino Corporation, Atlantic City, NJ; *U.S. Public*, pg. 760
Stone, Bruce W., Exec. V.P.--Ogden Energy Group, Inc., Fairfield, NJ; *U.S. Public*, pg. 1213
Stone, Colleen, Exec. V.P.--Merle Norman Cosmetics, Inc., Los Angeles, CA; *U.S. Private*, pg. 733
Stone, David B., Exec. V.P.-Sls. & Mktg.--Merit Behavioral Care Corp., Park Ridge, NJ; *U.S. Public*, pg. 1036
Stone, E. C., Exec. V.P.-Corp. Banking--Regions Financial Corporation, Birmingham, AL; *U.S. Public*, pg. 1371
Stone, G. Ray, Sr. Exec. V.P. & Chief Credit Officer--Compass Bank, Birmingham, AL; *U.S. Public*, pg. 418
Stone, Larry, Sr. Exec. V.P.-Production--Bestform Foundations, Inc., Long Island City, NY; *U.S. Private*, pg. 140
Stone, Larry D., Exec. V.P.-Store Opers.--Lowe's Companies, Inc., North Wilkesboro, NC; *U.S. Public*, pg. 1015
Stone, Patrick F., Exec. V.P.--Fidelity National Financial, Inc., Irvine, CA; *U.S. Public*, pg. 620
Stone, Robert, Exec. V.P.--Wasserstrom Company, Columbus, OH; *U.S. Private*, pg. 1152
Stone, Robert E., V.P. & Exec. V.P.-DTCA--American Healthcorp Inc., Nashville, TN; *U.S. Public*, pg. 78
Stone, Ronald, Exec. V.P.-Fin., & Dir.--Pioneer Electronics (USA) Inc., Long Beach, CA; *Int'l*, pg. 1058
Stone, Ronald A., Exec. V.P. & Chief Creative Officer--EvansGroup, Salt Lake City, UT; *U.S. Private*, pg. 385
Stoneman, Gordon C., Exec. V.P., Reg. Mgr. & Branch Mgr.-Toronto--Willis Corroon Melling Inc., Toronto, Canada; *Int'l*, pg. 1509
Stonich, Timothy W., Chief Fin. Officer & Exec. V.P.--U.S. Can Company, Oak Brook, IL; *U.S. Public*, pg. 1681
Stooksbury, Walter E., Exec. V.P.-Alternate Distributor--Horace Mann Educators Corporation, Springfield, IL; *U.S. Public*, pg. 835
Storch, Wendy, Exec. V.P. & Mng. Dir.--Promotion House, San Francisco, CA; *U.S. Private*, pg. 1166
Stork, Detlef, Exec. V.P.-Sls.--Koenig & Bauer-Albert AG, Wurzburg, Germany; *Int'l*, pg. 742
Storkebaum, Christoph, Exec. V.P.--BTE Brauerel-Technik Essen GmbH, Essen, Germany; *Int'l*, pg. 400
Stormes, Charles, Exec. V.P.--The Wickman Corp., Oak Park, MI; *U.S. Private*, pg. 1175
Storrier, John, Chief Oper. Officer & Exec. V.P.--All American Television, Inc., New York, NY; *U.S. Public*, pg. 41
Story, Leslie J., Exec. V.P.-Specialty Bus.--Occidental Chemical Corporation, Dallas, TX; *U.S. Public*, pg. 1210
Stover, Richard, Exec. V.P. & Chief Lending Officer--First Western Bancorp, Inc., New Castle, PA; *U.S. Public*, pg. 642
Stowe, Donald, Exec. V.P.-Sls. & Technology--Dravo Lime Company, Pittsburgh, PA; *U.S. Public*, pg. 527
Stowe, Donald H., Jr., V.P.-Sls. & Tech.--Dravo Corporation, Pittsburgh, PA; *U.S. Public*, pg. 527
Stowe, Jon H., Exec. V.P.--Firstar Corporation, Milwaukee, WI; *U.S. Public*, pg. 642
Stowe, Leonard, Exec. V.P.--Gibraltar Corp. of America, New York, NY; *U.S. Public*, pg. 1528
Strain, Robert D., Exec. V.P. & Gen. Mgr.-Electronics & Sensor Systems Grp.--Orbital Sciences Corporation, Dulles, VA; *U.S. Public*, pg. 1229
Strait, Rick E., Exec. V.P.--Netzsch Incorporated, Exton, PA; *U.S. Private*, pg. 792

Strand, James W., Exec. V.P.-Mktg. & Customer Service--Aliant Communications Co., Lincoln, NE; *U.S. Public*, pg. 40

Strand, Ron, Exec. V.P.-Banking Grp.--Community First Bankshares, Inc., Fargo, ND; *U.S. Public*, pg. 416

Strange, Michael R., Exec. V.P.--Franklin Electronic Publishers, Inc., Burlington, NJ; *U.S. Public*, pg. 679

Stratton, Earl D., Exec. V.P.--TCF Financial Corp., Minneapolis, MN; *U.S. Public*, pg. 1554

Straub, Gerard, Chief Fin. Officer & Exec. V.P.--Viking Yacht Co., New Gretna, NJ; *U.S. Private*, pg. 1140

Strauch, Carol J., Exec. V.P.--First Security Bank of Oregon, Salem, OR; *U.S. Public*, pg. 637

Straus, Peter, Exec. V.P.--Superba, Inc., Los Angeles, CA; *U.S. Private*, pg. 1054

Straus, Steven C., Sr. V.P.--Columbia/H.C.A., Dallas, TX; *U.S. Public*, pg. 404

Strauss, Philip E., Jr., Exec. V.P.--Central Group, Chicago, IL; *U.S. Public*, pg. 649

Strecker, Ian, Exec. V.P.-Tech., Health, Safety & Environ.--Schlumberger Limited, New York, NY; *U.S. Public*, pg. 1439

Street, Andrew, Exec. Dir.--Tokyo-Mitsubishi International plc, London, United Kingdom; *Int'l*, pg. 158

Street, James E., Exec. V.P.--UMB Financial Corporation, Kansas City, MO; *U.S. Public*, pg. 1653

Strewler, Joan, Exec. V.P.-North Central--Right Management Consultants, Inc., Philadelphia, PA; *U.S. Public*, pg. 1390

Strickland, J.E., Exec. Dir.-Services--HSBC Holdings plc, London, United Kingdom; *Int'l*, pg. 579

Strickland, Ross M., Exec. V.P.-Mortgage Banking--Webster Financial Corporation, Waterbury, CT; *U.S. Public*, pg. 1751

Stricklin, John C., Exec. V.P.--Tarragon Realty Investors, Dallas, TX; *U.S. Public*, pg. 1561

Stringer, Christopher J., Exec. V.P.-Trust Services--Canada Trustco Mortgage Company, London, Canada; *Int'l*, pg. 112

Stringer, John R., Exec. V.P.-Support Svcs.--Network Associates, Inc., Santa Clara, CA; *U.S. Public*, pg. 1168

Stringfellow, Stu, Exec. V.P.-Domestic Television Sls.--King World Productions, Inc., New York, NY; *U.S. Public*, pg. 961

Strobel, Gerald A., P.E., Exec. V.P.-Technical Services--Ecology and Environment, Inc., Lancaster, NY; *U.S. Public*, pg. 562

Strohm, B.C., Exec. V.P., Gen. Counsel & Sec.--Equity Residential Properties Trust, Chicago, IL; *U.S. Public*, pg. 590

Stropki, John M., Exec. V.P.-Sls. & Mfg.--The Lincoln Electric Company, Cleveland, OH; *U.S. Public*, pg. 996

Strothman, Wendy, Exec. V.P.-Trade & Reference Publ.--Houghton Mifflin Company, Boston, MA; *U.S. Public*, pg. 841

Stroucken, Albert P.L., Exec. V.P. & Pres.-Indus. Chemicals Div.--Bayer Corporation, Parsippany, NJ; *Int'l*, pg. 172

Stroud, Russell, Exec. V.P.--Thyssen Inc., Detroit, MI; *Int'l*, pg. 1389

Strouken, Albert P.L., Pres.-Industrial Chemicals Div. & Exec. V.P.--Bayer Corporation, Pittsburgh, PA; *Int'l*, pg. 172

Stroup, Stanley S., Exec. V.P. & Gen. Counsel--Norwest Corporation, Minneapolis, MN; *U.S. Public*, pg. 1201

Strunk, Carl A., Exec. V.P.--Fidelity National Financial, Inc., Irvine, CA; *U.S. Public*, pg. 620

Struxness, Ronald E., Exec. V.P.-North Regional Opers.--Advocate Health Care, Oak Brook, IL; *U.S. Private*, pg. 23

Stuart, William, Exec. V.P.-Opers. & Fin.--Visa U.S.A. Inc., San Francisco, CA; *U.S. Private*, pg. 1141

Stubblefield, Jerry W., Chief Fin. Officer, Exec. V.P. & Treas.--nVIEW Corporation, Newport News, VA; *U.S. Public*, pg. 1206

Stulc, Dennis, Exec. V.P.--Outdoor Technologies Group, Spirit Lake, IA; *U.S. Private*, pg. 822

Stull, Pam, Exec. V.P.-Corp. Devel.--Market Place Print, Inc., Pittsburgh, PA; *U.S. Private*, pg. 701

Stults, G. Ray, Chief Oper. Officer & Exec. V.P.--Shelter Components Corporation, Elkhart, IN; *U.S. Public*, pg. 952

Stupey, Rebecca, Exec. V.P.--Harris Ford, Inc., Lynnwood, WA; *U.S. Private*, pg. 506

Sturgeon, John A., Exec. V.P. & Gen. Comptroller--United of Omaha Life Insurance Company, Omaha, NE; *U.S. Private*, pg. 770

Sturgis, William T., Exec. V.P.--Peninsula Bank, Princess Anne, MD; *U.S. Public*, pg. 1089

Sturm, Klaus, Exec. V.P.-Treas.--Bayerische Landesbank, Munich, Germany; *Int'l*, pg. 176

Stylianidis, Roulis, Exec. V.P.-Creative--Leo Burnett Athens, Athens, Greece; *U.S. Private*, pg. 184

Styring, Albert F., Exec. V.P.--VAW of America, Inc., Ellenville, NY; *Int'l*, pg. 1466

Suarez, Alfonso F., Corp. V.P.-Control--Grupo Iberia, Madrid, Spain; *Int'l*, pg. 574

Suarino, Francis C., Exec. V.P.--Associates Commercial Corporation, Dallas, TX; *U.S. Public*, pg. 663

Subasic, Richard T., Exec. V.P. & Gen. Mgr.--Susquehanna Division, Sayre, PA; *U.S. Public*, pg. 439

Subasic, Richard T., Exec. V.P. & Gen. Mgr.--Roaring Creek Division, Shamokin, PA; *U.S. Public*, pg. 439

Subotnick, Stuart, Exec. V.P.--Metromedia Company, East Rutherford, NJ; *U.S. Private*, pg. 736

Suchik, Martin S., Exec. V.P.--VSI Holdings, Inc., Bloomfield Hills, MI; *U.S. Public*, pg. 1703

Sudo, Paul, Sr. Exec. V.P.--Chugai Boyeki (America) Corp., New York, NY; *Int'l*, pg. 290

Sugar, Ronald D., Exec. V.P. & Gen. Mgr.-TRW Auto Elec. Grp.--TRW Inc., Cleveland, OH; *U.S. Public*, pg. 1558

Sugar, Ronald D., Exec. V.P. & Gen. Mgr.--TRW Automotive Electronics Group, Cleveland, OH; *U.S. Public*, pg. 1558

Sugimoto, Hiroshi, Exec. V.P.--Kobe Steel, Ltd., Kobe, Japan; *Int'l*, pg. 740

Sugimoto, Michio, Exec. V.P.--Nishimatsu Construction Co., Ltd., Tokyo, Japan; *Int'l*, pg. 942

Sugita, Satoshi, Exec. V.P.--Prap Japan, Inc., Tokyo, Japan; *U.S. Private*, pg. 617

Sugiura, Yasuhiko, Exec. V.P.--SIA Co., Ltd., Tokyo, Japan; *Int'l*, pg. 1189

Sugiyama, Kazuhiko, Exec. V.P.--Matsushita Electric Industrial Co., Ltd., Kadoma, Japan; *Int'l*, pg. 846

Sugrue, Charles J., Exec. V.P.--Divane Bros. Electric Co., Franklin Park, IL; *U.S. Private*, pg. 336

Suila, Keijo, Vice Chm. & Exec. V.P.--Huhtamaki Oy, Espoo, Finland; *Int'l*, pg. 638

Suk-Chun, Suh, Exec. V.P.-Power Plant, Civil & Construction Bus.--Korea Heavy Industries & Construction Co., Ltd., Seoul, Korea; *Int'l*, pg. 758

Sullivan, Bill, Sr. Exec. V.P.--Black Rogers Sullivan Goodnight, Inc., Houston, TX; *U.S. Private*, pg. 147

Sullivan, Bill, Chief Oper. Officer & Exec. V.P.--Optical Radiation Corporation, Azusa, CA; *U.S. Public*, pg. 160

Sullivan, David C., Chief Oper. Officer & Exec. V.P.--Promus Hotel Corporation, Memphis, TN; *U.S. Public*, pg. 1335

Sullivan, Dennis W., Exec. V.P.--Parker Hannifin Corporation, Cleveland, OH; *U.S. Public*, pg. 1259

Sullivan, Gary, Exec. V.P.-Sls. & Mktg.--EMPI, Inc., Saint Paul, MN; *U.S. Public*, pg. 545

Sullivan, Gregory W., Chief Fin. Officer & Exec. V.P.--TrizecHahn Corporation, Toronto, Canada; *Int'l*, pg. 1424

Sullivan, J. Emmett, Exec. V.P.--Jackpot Enterprises, Inc., Las Vegas, NV; *U.S. Public*, pg. 920

Sullivan, James M., Exec. V.P.-Devel./Marriott Lodging--Marriott International, Inc., Washington, DC; *U.S. Public*, pg. 1047

Sullivan, Jerry, Exec. V.P.--Rosendin Electric, Inc., San Jose, CA; *U.S. Private*, pg. 945

Sullivan, Patty, Exec. V.P. & Publr.-Children's Publ. Grp.--Golden Books Family Entertainment Inc., New York, NY; *U.S. Public*, pg. 749

Sullivan, Richard, Sr. Partner, Exec. V.P. & Gen. Mgr.--Fleishman-Hillard, Inc., Washington, DC; *U.S. Private*, pg. 411

Sullivan, Robert P., Exec. V.P.--Jaymark, Inc., San Diego, CA; *U.S. Private*, pg. 584

Sullivan, Robert W., Exec. V.P.--Eastern Fine Paper, Brewer, ME; *U.S. Private*, pg. 357

Sullivan, Shawn, Chief Oper. Officer & Exec V.P.--Van Cleef & Arpels, Inc., New York, NY; *U.S. Private*, pg. 1132

Sumas, John, Exec. V.P.--Village Super Market Inc., Springfield, NJ; *U.S. Public*, pg. 1721

Sumas, Robert, Exec. V.P. & Sec.--Village Super Market Inc., Springfield, NJ; *U.S. Public*, pg. 1721

Sumas, William, Exec. V.P.--Village Super Market Inc., Springfield, NJ; *U.S. Public*, pg. 1721

Sumerel, William M., Exec. V.P.--Davis Electrical Constructors, Inc., Greenville, SC; *U.S. Private*, pg. 315

Sumi, Yoshihiko, Exec. V.P.--The Kansai Electric Power Co., Inc., Osaka, Japan; *Int'l*, pg. 722

Sumida, Sheila M., Sr. Exec. V.P.-H.R. Div.--First Hawaiian Bank, Honolulu, HI; *U.S. Public*, pg. 634

Summerhayes, Clive Q., Exec. Dir.-Environmental Control--Halma p.l.c., Amersham, United Kingdom; *Int'l*, pg. 589

Summers, William E., Exec. V.P. & Trust Officer--United Southwest Bank, Washington, IN; *U.S. Public*, pg. 1217

Sumner, David, Exec. V.P.--American Radio Relay League, Newington, CT; *U.S. Private*, pg. 60

Sumner, Ronald H., Exec. V.P.-Fin.--Alcell Technologies Inc., Newcastle, Canada; *Int'l*, pg. 1104

Sundback, V., Exec. V.P.--Oy Nokia Ab/Nokia Group, Helsinki, Finland; *Int'l*, pg. 951

Sundermeyer, Ron, Exec. V.P.--S.A.S.I. Corporation, Collinsville, IL; *U.S. Private*, pg. 955

Sundstrom, Goran, Exec. V.P.-Special Customers--Nordbanken AB, Stockholm, Sweden; *Int'l*, pg. 957

Sung-Soo, Kim, Exec. Mng. Dir.-Plng. & Admin.--Korea Heavy Industries & Construction Co., Ltd., Seoul, Korea; *Int'l*, pg. 758

Sunnermalm, Leif, Exec. V.P. & Chief Fin. Officer--Sandvik AB, Sandviken, Sweden; *Int'l*, pg. 1185

Suomela, Juhani, Exec. V.P.-Human Resources & Quality--FinnAir Oy, Helsinki, Finland; *Int'l*, pg. 485

Suquet, Jose, Exec. V.P. & Chief Agency Officer--The Equitable Companies Incorporated, New York, NY; *U.S. Public*, pg. 588

Sureda, Miguel, Exec. V.P.-Europe Resort Hotels--Sol Melia, Palma de Mallorca, Spain; *Int'l*, pg. 1277

Surowiec, R.H., Exec. V.P.-Central Div.--Interstate Brands Corporation, Kansas City, MO; *U.S. Public*, pg. 909

Sutherland, Fred, Chief Fin. Officer & Exec. V.P.--Aramark Corp., Philadelphia, PA; *U.S. Private*, pg. 78

Sutin, David E., Exec. V.P.--Harrowston Corporation, Toronto, Canada; *Int'l*, pg. 599

Suto, Yoshietsu, Exec. V.P.--Tohoku Electric Power Co., Ltd., Sendai, Japan; *Int'l*, pg. 1390

Sutter, Blanche M., Chief Fin. Officer, Exec. V.P. & Sec.--Caere Corporation, Los Gatos, CA; *U.S. Public*, pg. 291

Sutter, Suzanne, Exec. V.P.--Things Remembered, Inc., Highland Heights, OH; *U.S. Public*, pg. 397

Sutton, V.P.-Admin. & Sec.--K & R Express Systems Inc., Hinsdale, IL; *U.S. Private*, pg. 602

Sutton, Kelso F., Exec. V.P.--Time Inc., New York, NY; *U.S. Public*, pg. 1612

Suzuki, Akira, Exec. V.P.--Sony Trans Com Systems Inc., Costa Mesa, CA; *Int'l*, pg. 1281

Suzuki, Masanobu, Exec. V.P.--Nippon Telegraph and Telephone Corporation, Tokyo, Japan; *Int'l*, pg. 940

Suzuki, Teiji, Exec. V.P.-Parts Grp.--Nissan Motor Co., Ltd., Tokyo, Japan; *Int'l*, pg. 943

Suzuki, Yoshihiro, Sr. Exec. V.P.--NEC Corporation, Tokyo, Japan; *Int'l*, pg. 899

Svendsen, Steve, Chief Fin. Officer & Sr. V.P.--Edward Hines Lumber Co., Itasca, IL; *U.S. Private*, pg. 530

Svoboda, Jeffrey A., Exec. V.P.-Opers.--Moen Incorporated, North Olmsted, OH; *U.S. Public*, pg. 675

Swaim, Donald C., Exec. V.P., Cashier & Trust Officer--Rockville National Bank, Rockville, IN; *U.S. Public*, pg. 1217

Swam, Robert L., Exec. V.P., Chm. Bd. & Chief Exec. Officer-Raytheon Appliances--Raytheon Company, Lexington, MA; *U.S. Public*, pg. 1364

Swan, Alfred W., Jr., Sr. Exec. V.P. & Pres. & Head-Commercial Banking-AmSouth Bank FL--AmSouth Bancorporation, Birmingham, AL; *U.S. Public*, pg. 105

Swanson, Alvin, Exec. V.P.-Govt. Affairs--Johnson Storage Moving Co, Denver, CO; *U.S. Private*, pg. 594

Swanson, Brenda, Exec. V.P. & Gen. Mgr.--Haworth Group Inc., Minneapolis, MN; *U.S. Private*, pg. 511

Swanson, Douglas J., Exec. V.P.--Carolina Biological Supply Co., Burlington, NC; *U.S. Private*, pg. 213

Swanson, Michael H., Exec. V.P.-Mark VII Transportation Co., Inc.--Mark VII, Inc., Memphis, TN; *U.S. Public*, pg. 1046

Swanson, Michael H., Exec. V.P.--Mark VII Transportation Company, Inc., Greenwood, IN; *U.S. Public*, pg. 1046

Swanson, Robert O., Exec. V.P.--International Marketing & Refining Division, Fairfax, VA; *U.S. Public*, pg. 1118

Swanson, William H., Exec. V.P. & Gen. Mgr.--Raytheon Electronics Systems, Marlborough, MA; *U.S. Public*, pg. 1364

Swanzey, Robert, Exec. V.P.--Century Data Services, Inc., New York, NY; *U.S. Private*, pg. 226

Swartz, Jeffrey B., Chief Oper. Officer & Exec. V.P.--The Timberland Company, Stratham, NH; *U.S. Public*, pg. 1609

Swartz, Mark H., Chief Fin. Officer & Exec. V.P.--Tyco International Ltd., Exeter, NH; *U.S. Public*, pg. 1647

Sweatt, Blaine, III, Exec. V.P. & Pres.-New Bus. Devel.--Darden Restaurants, Inc., Orlando, FL; *U.S. Public*, pg. 483

Sweeney, Kevin R., Exec. V.P.-Water Prod. Div.--Watts Industries, Inc., North Andover, MA; *U.S. Public*, pg. 1746

Sweeney, Michael L., Exec. V.P.--U.S. Aviation Underwriters, Inc., New York, NY; *U.S. Public*, pg. 726

Sweeney, Ron, Exec. V.P.-Black Music--Sony Music Entertainment, Inc., New York, NY; *Int'l*, pg. 1281

Sweeney, William E., Exec. V.P.--BDM International, Inc., Mc Lean, VA; *U.S. Public*, pg. 1558

Sweeney, William J., Exec. V.P.-Corrugated Prods. Div.--Tenneco Packaging, Evanston, IL; *U.S. Public*, pg. 1579

Swenson, Alan D., Exec. V.P.--Dart Transit Company, Eagan, MN; *U.S. Private*, pg. 311

Swette, Brian, Exec. V.P.-Mktg.--Pepsi-Cola Company, Somers, NY; *U.S. Public*, pg. 1277

Swift, Robert P., Exec. V.P. & Treas.--Chuck Swift Sales & Leasing, Davis, CA; *U.S. Private*, pg. 1058

Swindells, William, Exec. V.P.--Northeast Group, Glastonbury, CT; *U.S. Public*, pg. 649

Swinden, David, Exec. V.P.--Imperial Schrade Corp., Ellenville, NY; *U.S. Private*, pg. 559

Swinehart, Robert E., Exec. V.P. & Chief Oper. Officer--McGill Manufacturing Company, Inc., Valparaiso, IN; *U.S. Public*, pg. 573

Swistowicz, Donald J., Chief Fin. & Acctg. Officer & Exec. V.P.--First Midwest Bancorp, Inc., Itasca, IL; *U.S. Public*, pg. 636

Swithenbank, Gene W., Exec. V.P.-Sls. & Mktg.--CommScope, Inc., Hickory, NC; *U.S. Public*, pg. 415

Sword, Ian, Sr. Exec. V.P.--SGS Societe Generale de Surveillance Holding S.A., Geneva, Switzerland; *Int'l*, pg. 1153

Sylvetsky, Barry, Chief Oper. Officer & Exec. V.P.--Goodman Knitting Company, Brockton, MA; *U.S. Public*, pg. 948

Sylvia, B. Ralph, Exec. V.P.-Electric Generation & Chief Nuclear Officer--Niagara Mohawk Power Corporation, Syracuse, NY; *U.S. Public*, pg. 1181

Sylvia, Joseph, Chief Fin. Officer & Exec. V.P.--Simonds Industries Inc., Fitchburg, MA; *U.S. Private*, pg. 1001

Symonds, Curtis N., Exec. V.P.-Affiliate Sls. & Mktg.--Black Entertainment Television Holdings Inc., Washington, DC; *U.S. Public*, pg. 235

Symons, Al P., Exec. V.P. & Dir.-Canadian Div.--The Canada Life Assurance Company, Toronto, Canada; *Int'l*, *pg. 254*

Symons, Gregory K., Exec. V.P.-Services--Bank of Oklahoma, N.A., Tulsa, OK; *U.S. Public*, pg. 163

Symons, Jeanette, Chief Tech. Officer & Exec. V.P.--Ascend Communications, Inc., Alameda, CA; *U.S. Public*, *pg. 138*

Synowicki, Robert E., Jr., Chief Oper. Officer & Exec. V.P.--Werner Enterprises, Inc., Omaha, NE; *U.S. Public*, pg. 1754

Syrjamaki, Maxine, Chief Fin. Officer & Exec. V.P.--Jefferies & Company, Inc., Los Angeles, CA; *U.S. Public*, pg. 925

Szathmary, Ivan K., Chief Services Officer & Exec. V.P.--The Great Atlantic & Pacific Tea Company, Inc., Montvale, NJ; *Int'l*, pg. 1375

Szesny, Kurt, Exec. V.P.--Bayerische Hypotheken-und Wechsel-Bank Aktiengesellschaft, Munich, Germany; *Int'l*, pg. 175

Szews, Charles, Chief Fin. Officer & Exec. V.P.--Oshkosh Truck Corporation, Oshkosh, WI; *U.S. Public*, pg. 1233

Szwec, Terry W., Exec. V.P.-Canada--Right Management Consultants, Inc., Philadelphia, PA; *U.S. Public*, pg. 1390

Tabakin, Scott M., Chief Fin. Officer & Exec. V.P.--Beverly Enterprises, Inc., Fort Smith, AR; *U.S. Public*, pg. 227

Taber, Edward A., III, Sr. Exec. V.P.--Legg Mason, Inc., Baltimore, MD; *U.S. Public*, pg. 984

Tabin, David, Exec. V.P. & Media Plng. Dir.--SFM Media Corporation, New York, NY; *U.S. Private*, pg. 956

Taffet, Bruce, Exec. V.P.-Concessions--United Artists Theatre Circuits Incorporated, Englewood, CO; *U.S. Private*, pg. 1120

Tagliarino, Scott, Pres., Exec. V.P. & Gen. Mgr.-New York Corp. & Fin.--Edelman Worldwide, Inc., New York, NY; *U.S. Private*, pg. 362

Taguchi, Mitsuo, Exec. Dir.--Dentsu Inc., Tokyo, Japan; *Int'l*, pg. 392

Tahara, Hisao, Exec. V.P.--Matsushita Electric Industrial Co., Ltd., Kadoma, Japan; *Int'l*, pg. 846

Tahara, Sadaaki, Sr. Exec. Dir.--Shiseido Company Ltd., Tokyo, Japan; *Int'l*, pg. 1235

Tai, Henry H.B., Exec. V.P.--The International Commercial Bank of China, Taipei, Taiwan; *Int'l*, pg. 683

Tait, Clifford W., Jr., Exec. V.P.--Highline Financial Services, Inc., Boulder, CO; *U.S. Public*, pg. 1785

Tait, David C., Exec. V.P.--Mercantile-Safe Deposit & Trust Co., Baltimore, MD; *U.S. Public*, pg. 1089

Tajima, Hitoshi, Exec. V.P.--Nippon Telegraph and Telephone Corporation, Tokyo, Japan; *Int'l*, pg. 940

Tajima, Kisuke, Exec. V.P.--Asahi Glass Co., Ltd., Tokyo, Japan; *Int'l*, pg. 84

Takada, Keizo, Exec. V.P.--Daishowa Paper Mfg. Co., Ltd., Fuji, Japan; *Int'l*, pg. 373

Takagi, Seiji, Exec. V.P.--Sanyo Electric Co., Ltd., Osaka, Japan; *Int'l*, pg. 1190

Takahashi, Atsuo, Sr. Exec. Dir.--The Japan Development Bank, Tokyo, Japan; *Int'l*, pg. 701

Takahashi, Atsushi, Exec. V.P.--Nippon Paint Company Ltd., Osaka, Japan; *Int'l*, pg. 937

Takahashi, Masaki, Chief Fin. Officer & Exec. V.P.--Mitsubishi Motor Sales of America, Inc., Cypress, CA; *Int'l*, pg. 875

Takahashi, Masao, Exec. V.P.--The Fuji Bank & Trust Co., New York, NY; *Int'l*, pg. 519

Takahashi, Shigemitsu, Exec. V.P.--JGC Corporation, Tokyo, Japan; *Int'l*, pg. 697

Takata, Osamu, Exec. V.P.--Kobe Steel, Ltd., Kobe, Japan; *Int'l*, pg. 740

Takato, Tetsuo, Exec. V.P.--Sankyo Company Limited, Tokyo, Japan; *Int'l*, pg. 1189

Takayama, Tadaomi, Exec. Dir.--Isuzu Motors Limited, Tokyo, Japan; *Int'l*, pg. 692

Takayama, Takuya, Exec. V.P.--Toray Industries, Inc., Tokyo, Japan; *Int'l*, pg. 1399

Takayama, Tsuyoshi, Sr. Mng. Dir.--Daido Steel Co., Ltd., Nagoya, Japan; *Int'l*, pg. 364

Takayanagi, Itaru, Exec. Dir.--Isuzu Motors Limited, Tokyo, Japan; *Int'l*, pg. 692

Takebayashi, Mamoru, Exec. V.P.-Personnel, Admin. & Pub. Affairs--Mazda Motor Corporation, Hiroshima, Japan; *Int'l*, pg. 849

Takei, Tadao, Exec. V.P.--Nissan Motor Co., Ltd., Tokyo, Japan; *Int'l*, pg. 943

Takemura, Hisashi, Exec. V.P.--Tomen Corporation, Osaka, Japan; *Int'l*, pg. 1395

Takeshita, Shinpei, Exec. V.P.--Advantest Corporation, Tokyo, Japan; *Int'l*, pg. 25

Takeuchi, I., Exec. V.P.--Nippon Kaiji Kyokai, Tokyo, Japan; *Int'l*, pg. 934

Takiss, Peter, Exec. V.P.-Admin.--Polygram Records, Inc., New York, NY; *Int'l*, pg. 1052

Takizawa, Kiyotaka, Exec. V.P.--Mitsubishi Motors Corporation, Tokyo, Japan; *Int'l*, pg. 875

Talamantes, Alfred, Chief Oper. Officer & Exec. V.P.--Mid Atlantic Medical Services, Inc., Rockville, MD; *U.S. Public*, pg. 1109

Talbert, William L., Exec. V.P.-Mktg.--Clark Construction Group, Inc., Bethesda, MD; *U.S. Private*, pg. 242

Talbot, John, Exec. V.P.--A. Epstein and Sons, Intl., Inc., Chicago, IL; *U.S. Private*, pg. 379

Talbott, Fenton R., Exec. V.P.-Community Banking--Comerica Incorporated, Detroit, MI; *U.S. Public*, pg. 408

Taliaferro, Mike, Exec. V.P.-Consumer Mkts. Div./Sls. & Mktg.--Countrywide Home Loans Inc., Pasadena, CA; *U.S. Public*, pg. 452

Tall, Craig E., Exec. V.P.-Corp. Devel. & Commercial Banking--Washington Mutual Inc., Seattle, WA; *U.S. Public*, pg. 1741

Tallis, Alan, Exec. V.P.-Corp. Devel.--Red Roof Inns, Inc., Hilliard, OH; *U.S. Public*, pg. 1369

Tallman, John F., Exec. V.P. & Dir.-Scientific--Neurogen Corporation, Branford, CT; *U.S. Public*, pg. 1169

Tallman, Wesley C., Exec. V.P.--Visa U.S.A. Inc., San Francisco, CA; *U.S. Private*, pg. 1141

Tamberlane, John, Exec. V.P.--Republic National Bank of New York, New York, NY; *U.S. Public*, pg. 1380

Tamblyn, Ken C., Chief Fin. Officer & Exec. V.P.--Tidewater Inc., New Orleans, LA; *U.S. Public*, pg. 1608

Tamburrini, Vincent, Exec. V.P.--Dryvit Systems, Inc., West Warwick, RI; *U.S. Public*, pg. 1357

Tamura, Masaaki, Exec. V.P.--Eisai Co., Ltd., Tokyo, Japan; *Int'l*, pg. 435

Tan, John, Exec. V.P.--Fuji Bank Canada, Toronto, Canada; *Int'l*, pg. 521

Tan, Oliver, Sr. Exec. V.P.--DBS Bank Ltd., Singapore, Singapore; *Int'l*, pg. 350

Tanaka, Francis, Exec. V.P.--Haseko (Hawaii) Inc., Honolulu, HI; *Int'l*, pg. 600

Tanaka, Kazumasa, Exec. V.P.--Nippon Oil Company, Limited (NiSSEKI), Tokyo, Japan; *Int'l*, pg. 936

Tanaka, Kenichiro, Exec. V.P.--Heller International Corporation, Chicago, IL; *Int'l*, pg. 519

Tanaka, Masuru, Exec. V.P.--Toyota Motor Corporation, Tokyo, Japan; *Int'l*, pg. 1411

Tanaka, Minoru, Exec. V.P.--Nippon Steel Corporation, Tokyo, Japan; *Int'l*, pg. 939

Tanaka, Nobuo, Sr. Exec. V.P.--Asahi Glass Co., Ltd., Tokyo, Japan; *Int'l*, pg. 84

Tanaka, Susumu, Exec. V.P.--Kyushu Electric Power Co., Inc., Fukuoka, Japan; *Int'l*, pg. 778

Tanaka, Susumu, Exec. V.P.--Meiji Milk Products Co., Ltd., Tokyo, Japan; *Int'l*, pg. 855

Tanaka, Teruhiko, Exec. V.P.--Sekisui House, Ltd., Osaka, Japan; *Int'l*, pg. 1219

Taneichi, Takeshi, Exec. V.P.--The Tokyo Electric Power Co., Inc., Tokyo, Japan; *Int'l*, pg. 1394

Tanenbaum, Ellen, Exec. V.P. & Co-op Dir.--The Media Edge, New York, NY; *U.S. Private*, pg. 1079

Tanguay, Normand, Exec. V.P.-Spartech Canada--Spartech Corporation, Clayton, MO; *U.S. Public*, pg. 1495

Tanhuanpaa, Kalle, Exec. V.P.--Leaf Group B.V., Espoo, Finland,; *Int'l*, pg. 638

Tani, Tsunehiko, Exec. V.P.--Teijin America, Inc., New York, NY; *Int'l*, pg. 1362

Taniguchi, Fumihiko, Exec. V.P.-Health Care--Japan Aviation Electronics Industry, Ltd., Tokyo, Japan; *Int'l*, pg. 701

Taniguchi, Yugi, Exec. V.P.-Pacific Rim Corporate Group--Union Bank of California, San Francisco, CA; *Int'l*, pg. 157

Tanikoshi, Toshihiko, Exec. V.P.--Hitachi Zosen Corporation, Osaka, Japan; *Int'l*, pg. 622

Tanimoto, Toshiaki, Exec. V.P.--Nissho Iwai Corporation, Tokyo, Japan; *Int'l*, pg. 946

Tanner, Michael S., Exec. V.P.--Tanner Co., Rutherfordton, NC; *U.S. Private*, pg. 1068

Tanner, Scott, Exec. V.P. & Cashier--Chelsea State Bank, Chelsea, MI; *U.S. Private*, pg. 231

Tansey, Thomas F., Chief Oper., Exec. V.P. & Treas.--Raritan Bancorp Inc., Bridgewater, NJ; *U.S. Public*, pg. 1361

Taphorn, Robert J., Exec. V.P.--S & K Famous Brands, Inc., Glen Allen, VA; *U.S. Public*, pg. 1414

Taragen, R.J., Exec. V.P.-Mktg.--Nielsen Media Research, New York, NY; *U.S. Public*, pg. 395

Taratunio, Jim, Exec. V.P.-Field Services--MarketSource Corporation, Cranbury, NJ; *U.S. Private*, pg. 705

Tarbell, Joseph W., Exec. V.P. & Dir.-Mktg.--Willis Corroon Corp. of Massachusetts, Boston, MA; *Int'l*, pg. 1506

Taricani, Leon V., Exec. V.P.--Wahlstrom & Company, Stamford, CT; *U.S. Public*, pg. 1641

Tarman, Robert, Exec. V.P. & Gen. Mgr.--Aircraft Service International, Miami, FL; *U.S. Public*, pg. 1719

Tarman, Robert, Exec. V.P. & Gen. Mgr.--Dispatch Services, Inc., Miami, FL; *U.S. Public*, pg. 1719

Tarman, Robert, Exec. V.P. & Gen. Mgr.--Aircraft Service International Group, Miami, FL; *U.S. Public*, pg. 1719

Tarpley, Richard, Exec.V.P.-Mfg.--CPI Corp., Saint Louis, MO; *U.S. Public*, pg. 283

Tashima, Norio, Exec. Dir.--Minolta Co., Ltd., Osaka, Japan; *Int'l*, pg. 869

Tasker, Bill, Exec. V.P.--INX International, Milwaukee, WI; *Int'l*, pg. 1311

Tatro, Paul A., Exec. V.P.-Intl. Opers.--Platinum Technology, Inc., Oak Brook Terrace, IL; *U.S. Public*, pg. 1309

Tatum, Rick, Exec. V.P.--Tatum Farms Int., Inc., Dawsonville, GA; *U.S. Private*, pg. 1069

Tatzin, Donald, Exec. V.P.--Showboat, Incorporated, Las Vegas, NV; *U.S. Public*, pg. 1469

Taube, Stanley M., Exec. V.P.--Grand Casinos, Inc., Minnetonka, MN; *U.S. Public*, pg. 758

Tauber, David, Exec. V.P.--Tauber Oil Company, Houston, TX; *U.S. Private*, pg. 1069

Tauber, Richard, Exec. V.P.--Tauber Oil Company, Houston, TX; *U.S. Private*, pg. 1069

Taubitz, Fredricka, Chief Fin. Officer & Exec. V.P.--Zenith National Insurance Corp., Woodland Hills, CA; *U.S. Public*, pg. 1790

Taubman, William S., Exec. V.P.-Acq. & Devel.--Taubman Centers, Inc., Bloomfield Hills, MI; *U.S. Public*, pg. 1561

Tauder, Arthur, Exec. V.P.--McCann-Erickson Worldwide, New York, NY; *U.S. Public*, pg. 909

Taukojarvi, Jouko, Exec. V.P.--Enso Oyj, Helsinki, Finland; *Int'l*, pg. 455

Tausche, Kurt, Exec. V.P. & Creative Services Dir.--Tausche Martin Lonsdorf, Atlanta, GA; *U.S. Private*, pg. 1069

Tawil, Isaac, Exec. V.P.--Tawil Associates Inc., Carteret, NJ; *U.S. Private*, pg. 1070

Tawil, Moise, Exec. V.P.--Republic National Bank of New York, New York, NY; *U.S. Public*, pg. 1380

Tawil, Moise, Exec. V.P.--Republic National Bank of New York (U.K.), London, United Kingdom; *U.S. Public*, pg. 1381

Tayaputch, Vim, Exec. V.P.--The Industrial Finance Corporation of Thailand, Bangkok, Thailand; *Int'l*, pg. 677

Taylor, Barry M., Exec. V.P.--Jefferies Group, Inc., Los Angeles, CA; *U.S. Public*, pg. 924

Taylor, Dan, Exec V.P.-New Bus. Devel.--Communications Instruments Inc., Fairview, NC; *U.S. Private*, pg. 259

Taylor, David H., Chief Fin. Officer, Exec. V.P.-Fin. & Sec.--JPS Textile Group, Inc., Greenville, SC; *U.S. Private*, pg. 578

Taylor, Eileen, Exec. V.P. & Mktg. Dir.--The McClure Group, Wayne, PA; *U.S. Private*, pg. 719

Taylor, Frances, Exec. V.P. & Mng. Dir.--BA Asia Ltd., Hong Kong, Hong Kong; *U.S. Public*, pg. 182

Taylor, Guy D., Exec. V.P.--Southern Electric Supply Co., Inc., Meridian, MS; *Int'l*, pg. 1107

Taylor, Henry H., Exec. V.P. & Gen. Counsel--Laidlaw Environmental Services, Inc., Columbia, SC; *U.S. Public*, pg. 975

Taylor, James F., Jr., Exec. V.P.--Intergraph Corporation, Huntsville, AL; *U.S. Public*, pg. 890

Taylor, Jeff, Pres. & Exec. V.P.-Interactive, TMPW--TMP Worldwide/Interactive Division, Framingham, MA; *U.S. Private*, pg. 1065

Taylor, John C., Exec. V.P.-Sls. & Mktg.--John B. Sanfilippo & Son, Inc., Elk Grove Village, IL; *U.S. Public*, pg. 1431

Taylor, Mary Alice, Exec. V.P.-Opers.--Citicorp, New York, NY; *U.S. Public*, pg. 376

Taylor, Perry, Exec. V.P. & Corp. Counsel--ABN AMRO Chicago Corp., Chicago, IL; *Int'l*, pg. 10

Taylor, Perry L., Exec. V.P.--ABN AMRO Chicago Corporation, Chicago, IL; *Int'l*, pg. 10

Taylor, Ray N., Exec. V.P.--Textile Rubber & Chemical Company, Dalton, GA; *U.S. Private*, pg. 1079

Taylor, Stephen E., Exec. V.P.--Globe Newspaper Company, Boston, MA; *U.S. Public*, pg. 1175

Taylor, Steve, Exec. V.P.--John B. Sanfilippo & Son, Inc., Elk Grove Village, IL; *U.S. Public*, pg. 1431

Taylor, W.M., Exec. V.P.--TU Electric, Dallas, TX; *U.S. Public*, pg. 1588

Te Pastte, Joel R., Exec. V.P.--Sysco Food Services of Grand Rapids, Inc., Grand Rapids, MI; *U.S. Public*, pg. 1551

Teare, A.H., Exec. Dir.--English China Clays Plc, Theale, United Kingdom; *Int'l*, pg. 455

Tecca, James E., Exec. V.P.-Comml. Banking Grp.--Western Financial Bank, Irvine, CA; *U.S. Public*, pg. 1757

Techamontrikul, Anothai, Sr. Exec. V.P.--The Industrial Finance Corporation of Thailand, Bangkok, Thailand; *Int'l*, pg. 677

Tefft, John L., Exec. V.P.--Shaklee Corporation, San Francisco, CA; *Int'l*, pg. 1518

Tehrami, Julliette S., Chief Fin. Officer & Exec. V.P.--MBIA Inc., Armonk, NY; *U.S. Public*, pg. 1023

Teiwes, William M., Exec. V.P. & Treas.--UMB Financial Corporation, Kansas City, MO; *U.S. Public*, pg. 1653

Tejon, Jose, Exec. V.P.--Banco Santander, Madrid, Spain; *Int'l*, pg. 143

Tell, Martin T., Chief Fin. Officer & V.P. & Treas.--JJI Lighting Group Inc., Greenwich, CT; *Int'l*, pg. 821

Tellegrene, John, Exec. V.P.-Mktg.--Dayton Hudson Corporation, Minneapolis, MN; *U.S. Public*, pg. 489

Temares, Steven H., Chief Oper. Officer & Exec. V.P.--Bed Bath & Beyond Inc., Union, NJ; *U.S. Public*, pg. 200

Temling, Peter, Chief Fin. Officer & Exec. V.P.--Carnival Hotels & Casinos, Miami, FL; *U.S. Public*, pg. 1265

Temple, John M., Exec. V.P.--Memphis Group, Inc., Memphis, TN; *U.S. Private*, pg. 730

Temple, John M., Exec. V.P.--Aero Electronics Incorporated, Memphis, TN; *U.S. Private*, pg. 731

Temple, Larry D., Chief Oper. Officer & Exec. V.P.--CMC Kalamazoo Inc., Kalamazoo, MI; *U.S. Private*, pg. 1030

Templeton, Richard K., Exec. V.P.--Texas Instruments Incorporated, Dallas, TX; *U.S. Public*, pg. 1585

ten Cate, J.C., Exec. V.P.--ABN-AMRO Holding N.V., Amsterdam, Netherlands; *Int'l*, pg. 8

Tench, Hal, Exec. V.P. & Grp. Creative Dir.--The Martin Agency, Richmond, VA; *U.S. Public*, pg. 909

Tener, Jim, Exec. V.P.-Store Opers.--OfficeMax, Shaker Heights, OH; *U.S. Public*, pg. 1212

Teo, Ronnie, Exec. Dir.--DBS Asset Management Ltd., Singapore, Singapore; *Int'l*, pg. 350

Tepperman, Fred L., Sr. Exec. V.P. & Chief Fin. Officer--Andrews Group, Incorporated, New York, NY; *U.S. Private*, pg. 689

Terade, Toraji, Exec. V.P.--Wacoal Corporation, Kyoto, Japan; *Int'l*, pg. 1484

Terhune, David N., Chief Oper. Officer & Exec. V.P.--Applied Extrusion Technologies, Inc., Peabody, MA; *U.S.* Public, pg. 122

Terlep, Michael R., Exec. V.P.--Coachmen Recreational Vehicle Company, Middlebury, IN; *U.S. Public*, pg. 388

Terrano, Bob, Chief Fin. Officer & Exec. V.P.--Del Taco, Inc., Laguna Hills, CA; *U.S. Private*, pg. 321

Terrazas Villarreal, J. Manuel, Sr. Exec. V.P.-Mngmt. & Opers.--Grupo Casa Autrey, Mexico, Mexico; *Int'l*, pg. 573

Terrazzoni, Claude, Corp. Exec. V.P.-Aircraft Bus.--Aerospatiale, Paris, France; *Int'l*, pg. 28

Terrien, Jean-Francois, Exec. V.P.-Mechanical Engrng.--Framatome SA, Paris, France; *Int'l*, pg. 502

Terrill, James E., Exec. V.P.--United States Sugar Corporation, Clewiston, FL; *U.S. Private*, pg. 1126

Tesch, Mike, Partner, Exec. V.P. & Co-Creative Dir.--Harris Drury Cohen, Fort Lauderdale, FL; *U.S. Private*, pg. 505

Teschner, Jorg, Exec. V.P.--Chema Balcke-Durr Verfahrenstechnik GmbH Rudisleben, Rudisleben, Germany; *Int'l*, pg. 399

Tesi, Aldo, Chief Oper. Officer & Exec. V.P.--First Data Resources, Omaha, NE; *U.S. Public*, pg. 631

Tessensohn, Joseph, Chief Fin. Officer & Sr. Exec. V.P.--F. J. Benjamin Holdings Ltd., Singapore, Singapore; *Int'l*, pg. 187

Tett, Peter A., Exec. Dir.-Security--Halma p.l.c., Amersham, United Kingdom; *Int'l*, pg. 589

Tewhill, Janet, Exec. V.P.--CMG Health, Owings Mills, MD; *U.S. Public*, pg. 1036

Thaiprasittiporn, Pensri, Exec. V.P.--The Industrial Finance Corporation of Thailand, Bangkok, Thailand; *Int'l*, pg. 677

Thaler, Arnold, Exec. V.P.-Prod. Dev., Engineering & Manufacturing--Windmere-Durable Holdings, Hialeah, FL; *U.S. Public*, pg. 1771

Thaler, Horst, Exec. V.P.--Stora Feldmuhle AG, Dusseldorf, Germany; *Int'l*, pg. 1303

Thansathit, Suwarn, Exec. V.P.--Bangkok Bank Public Company Limited, Bangkok, Thailand; *Int'l*, pg. 146

Theler, John L., Chief Fin. Officer, Exec. V.P. & Treas.--Franklin Covey, Salt Lake City, UT; *U.S. Public*, pg. 679

Theophilos, Theodore, Exec. V.P. & Corp. Gen. Counsel--True North Communications Inc.--True North Communications Inc., Chicago, IL; *U.S. Public*, pg. 1641

Therrien, Michel, Exec. V.P.-Installations--Hydro-Quebec, Montreal, Canada; *Int'l*, pg. 640

Thexton, Kent P., Chief Oper. Officer & Exec. V.P.--Rogers Cantel Mobile Communications Inc., Saint-Laurent, Canada; *Int'l*, pg. 1122

Thielen, Gunter, Dr., Mng. Dir.--Bertelsmann AG, Gutersloh, Germany; *Int'l*, pg. 189

Tholan, Kenneth M., Chief Oper. Officer & Exec. V.P.--Team, Inc., Alvin, TX; *U.S. Public*, pg. 1562

Tholen, J. David, Exec. V.P.-Sls. & Mktg.--Hycor Biomedical, Inc., Irvine, CA; *U.S. Public*, pg. 851

Thoma, Ronald R., Exec. V.P.-Procurement & Traffic--Crown Cork & Seal Company, Inc., Philadelphia, PA; *U.S. Public*, pg. 462

Thomas, Allen, Exec. V.P. & Worldwide Creative Dir.--J. Walter Thompson Company, New York, NY; *Int'l*, pg. 1483

Thomas, Christopher R., Exec. V.P.--Sizzler International, Inc., Los Angeles, CA; *U.S. Public*, pg. 1475

Thomas, Elbert L., Jr., Chief Fin. Officer & Exec. V.P.--First Tennessee National Corporation, Memphis, TN; *U.S. Public*, pg. 638
Thomas, Gary, Exec. V.P.-Human Resources--JM Family Enterprises Inc., Deerfield Beach, FL; *U.S. Private*, pg. 577
Thomas, J. Grover, Exec. V.P.--Fortis, Inc., New York, NY; *Int'l*, pg. 499
Thomas, Janis P., Exec. V.P.-Mktg. & Mdse.--Black Entertainment Television Holdings Inc., Washington, DC; *U.S. Public*, pg. 235
Thomas, Jeffrey S., Chief Investment Officer, Exec. V.P., Mng. Dir.--Pell, Rudman & Company, Boston, MA; *U.S. Public*, pg. 1673
Thomas, Jeffrey S., Chief Investment Officer & Exec. V.P.--Rothschild/Pell, Rudman & Co., Inc., Baltimore, MD; *U.S. Public*, pg. 1674
Thomas, Joseph R., Exec. V.P.--Gage Marketing Group, Minneapolis, MN; *U.S. Private*, pg. 437
Thomas, L.B., Sr. V.P. & Sec.--ConAgra, Inc., Omaha, NE; *U.S. Public*, pg. 425
Thomas, Leo J., Exec. V.P.--Eastman Kodak Company, Rochester, NY; *U.S. Public*, pg. 550
Thomas, Leo J., Exec. V.P. & Pres.-Imaging Grp.--Scientific Imaging Systems, New Haven, CT; *U.S. Public*, pg. 550
Thomas, Mark W., Exec. V.P.-Prod. Devel.--National Cattlemen's Beef Association, Chicago, IL; *U.S. Private*, pg. 780
Thomas, Mary M., Chief Fin. Officer & Exec. V.P.--IRT Property Company, Atlanta, GA; *U.S. Public*, pg. 858
Thomas, Patrick L., Exec. V.P. & Chief Oper. Officer-Industry--Sundstrand Corporation, Rockford, IL; *U.S. Public*, pg. 1533
Thomas, Roald, Exec. V.P.-Bus. Devel.--Palmer Jarvis Communications, Vancouver, Canada; *Int'l*, pg. 1022
Thomas, Robert B., Jr., Exec. V.P.-Insurance--United Companies Financial Corporation, Baton Rouge, LA; *U.S. Public*, pg. 1675
Thomas, Scott S., Exec. V.P.--UMB First National Bank, Collinsville, IL; *U.S. Public*, pg. 1654
Thomas, Stanley A., Sr. Exec. V.P.-Mktg.--Shoppers Drug Mart, Ltd., Toronto, Canada; *Int'l*, pg. 112
Thomason, Donald W., Exec. V.P.-Corp. Services & Tech.--Kellogg Company, Battle Creek, MI; *U.S. Public*, pg. 947
Thomason, June C., Exec. V.P.--ICI Paints, Cleveland, OH; *Int'l*, pg. 664
Thomasson, Jeffrey, Exec. V.P.--Syndicate Systems, Inc., Middlebury, IN; *U.S. Private*, pg. 1060
Thomazeau, Jean, Exec. V.P.-Banks & Risks--Banque Nationale de Paris, Paris, France; *Int'l*, pg. 163
Thome, James J., Exec. V.P.--BHA Group Holdings Inc., Kansas City, MO; *U.S. Public*, pg. 161
Thompson, Bruce, Exec V.P.--North Carolina Equipment Co., Raleigh, NC; *U.S. Private*, pg. 804
Thompson, Derek, Exec. V.P.-Worldwide Field Opers.--Storage Technology Corporation, Louisville, CO; *U.S. Public*, pg. 1522
Thompson, E. Graham, Chief Credit Policy Officer & Exec. V.P.--First Commerce Corporation, New Orleans, LA; *U.S. Public*, pg. 629
Thompson, Geoff, Exec. V.P. & Exec. Creative Dir.--Chicago--FCB, New York, NY; *U.S. Private*, pg. 389
Thompson, J.W., Exec. V.P.--Loblaw Companies Limited, North York, Canada; *Int'l*, pg. 1495
Thompson, Jack B., Exec. V.P.--Athletic Attic Retail Company, Gainesville, FL; *U.S. Public*, pg. 936
Thompson, James, Exec. V.P.--Jackson Paper Company, Jackson, MS; *U.S. Private*, pg. 579
Thompson, James C., Exec. V.P. & Mgr.--United Missouri Bank of St. Louis, Saint Louis, MO; *U.S. Public*, pg. 1655
Thompson, James R., Exec. V.P. & Gen. Mgr.-Launch Sys. Grp.--Orbital Sciences Corporation, Dulles, VA; *U.S. Public*, pg. 1229
Thompson, Jeffrey L., Chief Oper. Officer & Exec. V.P.--Edelbrock Corp., Torrance, CA; *U.S. Public*, pg. 563
Thompson, John, Exec. V.P. & Treas.--Toastmaster, Inc., Columbia, MO; *U.S. Public*, pg. 1619
Thompson, Keith, Exec. V.P.--Letraset Nielsen & Bainbridge, Paramus, NJ; *Int'l*, pg. 460
Thompson, Kenneth, Exec. V.P.-Supply Chain Prods.--Manugistics Group, Inc., Rockville, MD; *U.S. Public*, pg. 1042
Thompson, Mark D., Chief Fin. Officer & Exec. V.P.--Lexford Residential Trust, Columbus, OH; *U.S. Public*, pg. 991
Thompson, Michael, Chief Oper. Officer & Exec. V.P.--Merry Land & Investment Company, Inc., Augusta, GA; *U.S. Public*, pg. 1098
Thompson, Murray, Exec. V.P.--Cole, Sherman & Associates Ltd., Thornhill, Canada; *U.S. Public*, pg. 1657
Thompson, R. Bruce, Chief Fin. Officer & Exec. V.P.--Circon Corporation, Santa Barbara, CA; *U.S. Public*, pg. 373
Thompson, Robert D., Chief Fin. Officer & Exec. V.P.--Lab One, Lenexa, KS; *U.S. Public*, pg. 1449
Thompson, Robert E., Exec. V.P.-Admin.--Kelly Services, Inc., Troy, MI; *U.S. Public*, pg. 949
Thompson, Tommie D., Exec. V.P. & Corp. Controller--United of Omaha Life Insurance Company, Omaha, NE; *U.S. Private*, pg. 770
Thomsen, Aage Nyholm, Exec. V.P.--Chr. Hansen Holding A/S, Horsholm, Denmark; *Int'l*, pg. 288
Thomson, Kenneth C., Exec. V.P.--DiscWasher, Lake Mary, FL; *U.S. Public*, pg. 1369
Thomson, L. Barry, Exec. V.P.--Tridel Enterprises Inc., Downsview, Canada; *Int'l*, pg. 1423
Thomson, Roger F., Exec. V.P., Gen. Counsel & Sec.--Brinker International, Inc., Dallas, TX; *U.S. Public*, pg. 253
Thore, Thom, Exec. Dir.-Publicity & Promo.--Allied Advertising Agency, Public Relations, Washington, DC; *U.S. Private*, pg. 38
Thorell, C. Scott, Exec. V.P. & Sec.--Integrated Systems Analysts, Inc., Arlington, VA; *U.S. Private*, pg. 566
Thornburgh, Robert W., Jr., Exec. V.P.--Fiduciary Management Associates, Inc., Chicago, IL; *U.S. Public*, pg. 1673
Thorne, Oakleigh B., Pres. & Chief Exec. Officer--CCH Incorporated, Riverwoods, IL; *Int'l*, pg. 1513
Thornes, Reginald R., Exec. V.P.--ESPN, Inc., Bristol, CT; *U.S. Public*, pg. 512
Thornhill, Barbara, Chief Admin. Officer & Exec. V.P.--The Martin Agency, Richmond, VA; *U.S. Private*, pg. 678
Thornhill, Barbara, Chief Admin. Officer & Exec. V.P.--The Martin Agency, Richmond, VA; *U.S. Public*, pg. 909
Thornhill, William C., Exec. V.P.-Prods.--CT Financial Services, Inc., Toronto, Canada; *Int'l*, pg. 112
Thornley, Anthony S., Chief Fin. Officer & Exec. V.P.--QUALCOMM, San Diego, CA; *U.S. Public*, pg. 1348
Thornton, George A., III, Exec. V.P.--Rhodes, Inc., Atlanta, GA; *U.S. Public*, pg. 805
Thornton, John T., Chief Fin. Officer & Exec. V.P.--Norwest Corporation, Minneapolis, MN; *U.S. Public*, pg. 1201
Thostrup, Peter, Exec. V.P.-Fin.--Bang & Olufsen A/S, Struer, Denmark; *Int'l*, pg. 145
Thrailkill, Larry, Chief Oper. Officer & Exec. V.P.--The Edward J. DeBartolo Corporation, Youngstown, OH; *U.S.* Private, pg. 319
Thrasher, Kenneth, Exec. V.P.--Fred Meyer Incorporated, Portland, OR; *U.S. Public*, pg. 1103
Thrasher, Kenneth, Exec. V.P.--Fred Meyer Stores, Portland, OR; *U.S. Public*, pg. 1103
Thrasher, Tracy P., Exec. V.P.-Admin. & Corp. Sec.--Medpartners Inc., Birmingham, AL; *U.S. Public*, pg. 1082
Thum, Denny, Exec. V.P. & Asst. Mgr.--Kansas City Chiefs Football Club, Inc., Kansas City, MO; *U.S. Private*, pg. 607
Thung, Roy T.K., Chief Fin. Officer, Exec. V.P. & Treas.--Independence Holding Company, Stamford, CT; *U.S. Private*, pg. 446
Thurber, Robert E., Exec. V.P.--Intergraph Corporation, Huntsville, AL; *U.S. Public*, pg. 890
Thurston, George R., Exec. V.P.-Fin., Intl.--North Pacific Lumber Company, Portland, OR; *U.S. Private*, pg. 805
Thyen, John, Sr. Exec. V.P.-Mktg. & Sls.--Kimball International, Inc., Jasper, IN; *U.S. Public*, pg. 956
Thyen, Ronald J., Sr. Exec. V.P. & Opers. Officer, Furniture & Cabinets--Kimball International, Inc., Jasper, IN; *U.S. Public*, pg. 956
Thys, Patrice J., Exec. V.P.-Asian Opers.--Interbrew S.A., Leuven, Belgium; *Int'l*, pg. 679
Tice, Gary L., Chief Oper. Officer & Exec. V.P.--F.N.B. Corporation, Hermitage, PA; *U.S. Public*, pg. 607
Tidwell, James M., Chief Fin. Officer & Exec. V.P.--Daniel Industries, Inc., Houston, TX; *U.S. Public*, pg. 482
Tiefel, William R., Exec. V.P. & Pres.-Marriott Lodging Grp.--Marriott International, Inc., Washington, DC; *U.S. Public*, pg. 1047
Tiefel, William R., Pres.-Marriott Lodging Grp. & Exec. V.P.--Fairfield Inn, Washington, DC; *U.S. Public*, pg. 1048
Tieken, Robert W., Chief Fin. Officer & Exec. V.P.--The Goodyear Tire & Rubber Company, Akron, OH; *U.S. Public*, pg. 752
Tiernan, John M., Exec. V.P.--Central Steel & Wire Company, Chicago, IL; *U.S. Public*, pg. 327
Tierno, Anthony F., Chief Oper. Officer & Exec. V.P.--MediaNews Group Inc., Denver, CO; *U.S. Private*, pg. 727
Tierno, Anthony F., Chief Oper. Officer & Exec. V.P.--Garden State Newspapers, Inc., Denver, CO; *U.S. Private*, pg. 727
Tighe, Larry, Exec. V.P.-Mktg.--Grand Holdings, Inc., Edina, MN; *U.S. Private*, pg. 468
Tikka, Kalevi, Exec. V.P.--Stockmann Automotive Sales Div., Helsinki, Finland; *Int'l*, pg. 1301
Tilton, Kenneth L., Exec. V.P. & Controller--Texas Commerce Bank, Houston, TX; *U.S. Public*, pg. 339
Tindel, Terry A., Exec. V.P. & Gen. Mgr.-Great Lakes--AirTouch Cellular, Walnut Creek, CA; *U.S. Public*, pg. 34
Tinsley, Stephen, Exec. V.P.--CB Commercial Real Estate Group, Inc., Los Angeles, CA; *U.S. Public*, pg. 272
Tirkkonen, Esa, Exec. V.P.--Kemira Oy, Helsinki, Finland; *Int'l*, pg. 727
Tirouflet, Jean-Pierre, Chief Fin. Officer & Exec. V.P.-Fin.--Rhone-Poulenc S.A., Courbevoie, France; *Int'l*, pg. 1108
Tisdale, Thomas P., Exec. V.P.--Sangamon Industries, Taylorville, IL; *U.S. Private*, pg. 965
Tishman, Daniel R., Exec. V.P.--Tishman Realty & Construction Co., Inc., New York, NY; *U.S. Private*, pg. 1089
Titzel, Carol, Exec. V.P.--Delchester Oil Co. Inc., West Chester, PA; *U.S. Private*, pg. 518
Tober, Stephen J., Exec. V.P.-Fin. & Bus. Devel.--SPR, Inc., Oak Brook, IL; *U.S. Public*, pg. 1419
Tobia, Alphonso J., Exec. V.P.--VIMRx Pharmaceuticals, Inc., Wilmington, DE; *U.S. Public*, pg. 1702
Tobin, Timothy P., Sr. Exec. V.P.--Fairfax Lumber & Millwork Company Inc., Springfield, VA; *U.S. Private*, pg. 391
Tobita, Eiichi, Exec. V.P.--Tostem Corporation, Tokyo, Japan; *Int'l*, pg. 1408
Tobler, D. Lee, Chief Fin. Officer & Exec. V.P.--The B.F. Goodrich Company, Richfield, OH; *U.S. Public*, pg. 751
Tocci, Robert S., Exec. V.P.--International Recovery Corp., Miami Springs, FL; *U.S. Public*, pg. 906
Tocklin, Adrian M., Sr. V.P.--The Continental Corporation, New York, NY; *U.S. Public*, pg. 1011
Toda, Isao, Exec. V.P.--Hitachi Zosen Corporation, Osaka, Japan; *Int'l*, pg. 622
Toda, Takashi, Exec. V.P.--Shimizu Corporation, Tokyo, Japan; *Int'l*, pg. 1233
Todd, Harold B., Jr., Exec. V.P.-Institutional Trust--National City Corporation, Cleveland, OH; *U.S. Public*, pg. 1154
Todd, James S., Exec. V.P.--A.M. Todd Company, Kalamazoo, MI; *U.S. Private*, pg. 1089
Todd, Madeliene K.E., Exec. Dir.--Bermuda Trust (Jersey) Limited, Saint Helier, United Kingdom; *Int'l*, pg. 151
Todd, William R., Exec. V.P.--Hubbard Farms, Inc., Walpole, NH; *U.S. Public*, pg. 1092
Todd, William R., Exec. V.P.--Hubbard Farms, Inc., Walpole, NH; *Int'l*, pg. 1114
Togo, Takeshi, Exec. V.P.--Daiwa House Industry Co., Ltd., Osaka, Japan; *Int'l*, pg. 374
Toigo, Peter R., Sr. Exec. V.P.--Shato Holdings Ltd., Vancouver, Canada; *Int'l*, pg. 1230
Tokuue, Kazuhiro, Exec. V.P.--Meiji Seika Kaisha, Ltd., Tokyo, Japan; *Int'l*, pg. 855
Tolar, Thomas, Exec. V.P.--Sarkes Tarzian, Bloomington, IN; *U.S. Private*, pg. 966
Tolari, Geno P., Chief Oper. Officer & Exec. V.P.--Sterling Software, Inc., Dallas, TX; *U.S. Public*, pg. 1516
Toledano, Salomon, Exec. V.P.-Devel., Mergers & Aquisitions--Club Mediterranee SA, Paris, France; *Int'l*, pg. 298
Tollefson, James C., Exec. V.P.-Asset Recovery Division--Pacific Century Financial Corporation, Honolulu, HI; *U.S. Public*, pg. 1248
Tollefson, James C., Exec. V.P.-Asset Recovery Division--Bank of Hawaii, Honolulu, HI; *U.S. Public*, pg. 1248
Tollenaar, Jan C., Exec. V.P.--Philips International B.V., Eindhoven, Netherlands; *Int'l*, pg. 1051
Tollinger, Jane, Exec. V.P.-Admin.--Lifetime Television/ABC, New York, NY; *U.S. Public*, pg. 512
Tollinger, Jane, Exec. V.P.-Admin.--Lifetime Television/ABC, New York, NY; *U.S. Private*, pg. 516
Tolonen, Jim, Chief Fin. Officer & Exec. V.P.--Novell, Inc., Orem, UT; *U.S. Public*, pg. 1203
Tolstedt, Brad L., Exec. V.P. & Managing Officer--First National Bank of Ohio, Akron, OH; *U.S. Public*, pg. 646
Tolstedt, Carrie L., Exec. V.P.--FirstMerit Corporation, Akron, OH; *U.S. Public*, pg. 646
Tolworthy, Thomas A., Pres.-Barnes & Noble Superstores, Inc.& Exec. V.P.--Barnes & Noble Inc., New York, NY; *U.S. Public*, pg. 189
Tomai, Thomas, Exec. V.P.-Consumer Div.--Fleet Bank NH, Manchester, NH; *U.S. Public*, pg. 649
Tomber, Barbara S., Exec. V.P.-Wholesale Grp.--First Hawaiian Bank, Honolulu, HI; *U.S. Public*, pg. 634
Tomczyk, Philip W., Exec. V.P.--Gal Corp., Ann Arbor, MI; *Int'l*, pg. 1249
Tomes, Frank, Exec. V.P.-Gen. Prods.--Federal-Mogul Corporation, Southfield, MI; *U.S. Public*, pg. 615
Tomita, Katsuzo, Exec. V.P. & Represent. Dir.--Kubota Corp., Osaka, Japan; *Int'l*, pg. 762
Tomizawa, Hiroshi, Sr. Exec. V.P.--Japan Tobacco Inc., Tokyo, Japan; *Int'l*, pg. 703
Tomlin, Merrell, Sr. V.P.-Sls.--RAYOVAC Corporation, Madison, WI; *U.S. Private*, pg. 912
Tomlinson, John P., III, Exec. V.P.--First Farmers & Merchants National Bank, Columbia, TN; *U.S. Private*, pg. 407
Tompkins, J. Bruce, Exec. V.P.-Cement Grp.--Southdown, Inc., Houston, TX; *U.S. Public*, pg. 1488
Tong, Tan Mong, Exec. V.P.-Treasury--DBS Bank Ltd., Singapore, Singapore; *Int'l*, pg. 350
Tonge, C.R., Exec. V.P.-Community Banking--Harris Bankcorp, Inc., Chicago, IL; *Int'l*, pg. 154
Tonini, Emilio, Sr. Exec. V.P.-Intl. Affairs & Treas.--Banca Monte dei Paschi di Siena S.p.A., Siena, Italy; *Int'l*, pg. 136
Tonoike, Tohru, Sr. Exec. V.P.--The CIT Group Holdings, Inc., New York, NY; *Int'l*, pg. 360
Tonoike, Tohru, Sr. Exec. V.P.--The CIT Group/Equipment Financing, Livingston, NJ; *Int'l*, pg. 360
Toolan, James, Exec. V.P.--Reitman Division, West Caldwell, NJ; *U.S. Private*, pg. 902
Toopes, James A., Jr., Exec. V.P.-Fin., Admin. & Corp. Devel.--Big V Supermarkets, Inc., Florida, NY; *U.S. Private*, pg. 143
Toorenvliet, R., Exec. V.P.--ABN-AMRO Holding N.V., Amsterdam, Netherlands; *Int'l*, pg. 8
Top, Franklin H., Jr., Exec. V.P. & Dir.-Medical--MedImmune, Inc., Gaithersburg, MD; *U.S. Public*, pg. 1081
Toppeta, William J., Exec. V.P.-Individual Bus.--Metropolitan Life Insurance Co., New York, NY; *U.S. Private*, pg. 737
Torcivia, Benedict, Jr., Exec. V.P.--Torcon, Inc., Westfield, NJ; *U.S. Private*, pg. 1092
Torcivia, Joseph A., Exec. V.P.--Torcon, Inc., Westfield, NJ; *U.S. Private*, pg. 1092
Torey, Donald W., Chief Fin. Officer & Exec. V.P.-Fin. & Admin.--General Electric Investment Corp., Stamford, CT; *U.S. Public*, pg. 712
Torgersen, Donald B., Exec. V.P.--Rich Products Corp., Buffalo, NY; *U.S. Private*, pg. 928
Tornek, Terry, Exec. V.P.--Haseko (California) Inc., Los Angeles, CA; *Int'l*, pg. 600
Torrence, Samuel L., Exec. V.P.-Admin.--Mack Trucks, Inc., Allentown, PA; *Int'l*, pg. 1102
Torres, William, Exec. V.P. & Chief Fin. Officer--Gibbs Wire & Steel Company, Inc., Southington, CT; *U.S. Private*, pg. 451
Toscanini, Arthur M., Chief Fin. Officer, Exec. V.P.-Fin. & Treas.--Cambridge Technology Partners, Cambridge, MA; *U.S. Public*, pg. 1424
Tostrud, Jerrol, Exec. V.P.--West Information Publishing Group, Saint Paul, MN; *U.S. Public*, pg. 1602
Totaro, David J., Chief Mktg. Officer & Exec. V.P.--The Dime Savings Bank of New York, New York, NY; *U.S. Public*, pg. 509
Toth, Steve, Jr., Chm. Bd., Pres. & Exec. V.P.--VSI Holdings, Inc., Bloomfield Hills, MI; *U.S. Public*, pg. 1703
Toth, Susan, Exec. V.P.--Toth Design, Concord, MA; *U.S. Private*, pg. 1093
Touchet, Donovan B., Exec. V.P. & Dir.-Info. Sys.--Piccadilly Cafeterias, Inc., Baton Rouge, LA; *U.S. Public*, pg. 1294
Touhill, Tom, Exec. V.P. & Mng. Dir.--CheckMark Communications, Saint Louis, MO; *U.S. Private*, pg. 231
Toulantis, Marie, Exec. V.P.-Fin.--Barnes & Noble Inc., New York, NY; *U.S. Public*, pg. 189

Tourtoulou, Pierre, Exec. V.P. Real Estate & Equipment--Credit Nationale, Paris, France; *Int'l*, pg. 344
Tovin, Hal R., Exec. V.P. & Dir.-Mktg. & Alternative Delivery--Citizens Financial Group, Inc., Providence, RI; *Int'l*, pg. 1132
Towne, William, Chief Fin. Officer & Exec. V.P.-Fin.--Leiner Health Products, Inc., Carson, CA; *U.S. Private*, pg. 659
Townsend, Charles, Exec. V.P.--The Conde Nast Publications Inc., New York, NY; *U.S. Private*, pg. 20
Townsend, J. Alan, Exec. V.P.--Equitable Resources Energy Company, Pittsburgh, PA; *U.S. Public*, pg. 589
Townsend, Joe, Exec. V.P.--Ranir Corporation/DCP, Grand Rapids, MI; *U.S. Private*, pg. 909
Toyoda, Ryuzo, Exec. V.P.--Marubeni Corporation, Osaka, Japan; *Int'l*, pg. 844
Toyoda, Shinobu, Chief Fin. Officer, Exec. V.P. & Sec.--Sega of America Inc., Redwood City, CA; *Int'l*, pg. 1218
Trabulsi, Judy, Exec. V.P. & Media Dir.--GSD&M, Austin, TX; *U.S. Private*, pg. 436
Tracey, Peter, Exec. V.P.-Corp. Devel.--Cambrex Corporation, East Rutherford, NJ; *U.S. Public*, pg. 297
Trachtenberg, Michael, Chief Fin. Officer, Chief Acctg. Officer, Exec. V.P. & Sec.--York Research Corporation, New York, NY; *U.S. Public*, pg. 1789
Trafford, William F., Exec. V.P.-Sales--Strategic Technology Services, Cerritos, CA; *Int'l*, pg. 1154
Trakanpaskun, Mali, Exec. V.P.--SCF Finance & Securities Co., Ltd., Bangkok, Thailand; *Int'l*, pg. 1239
Trangmar, Don, Exec. Dir.-Menswear & Gen. Merchandise Tech.--Marks & Spencer PLC, London, United Kingdom; *Int'l*, pg. 842
Trant, John T., Exec. V.P.--All American Homes, Inc., Decatur, IN; *U.S. Public*, pg. 388
Trapani, Cosmo S., Chief Fin. Officer, Exec. V.P. & Treas.--Unitrode Corporation, Merrimack, NH; *U.S. Public*, pg. 1694
Trapp, Kenneth A., Exec. V.P.--Cullen/Frost Bankers, Inc., San Antonio, TX; *U.S. Public*, pg. 467
Traub, Wayne, Exec. V.P. & Mngmt. Supvr.--Sudler & Hennessey, New York, NY; *U.S. Private*, pg. 1197
Trausch, Dan, Exec. V.P. & Gen. Mgr.--Sea World of Ohio, Aurora, OH; *U.S. Public*, pg. 114
Travatello, Lisa, Exec. V.P.--Edelman Worldwide, Inc., New York, NY; *U.S. Private*, pg. 362
Travis, Peggy S., Exec. V.P.-Human Resources--Siecor Corporation, Hickory, NC; *U.S. Public*, pg. 449
Travis, Peggy S., Exec. V.P.-Human Resources--Siecor Corporation, Hickory, NC; *Int'l*, pg. 1245
Treacy, Edward, Exec. V.P. & Gen. Mgr.--Bank of Ireland (U.S.A.), New York, NY; *Int'l*, pg. 152
Treadway, Stephen J., Exec. V.P.--PIMCO Advisors L.P., Newport Beach, CA; *U.S. Private*, pg. 832
Trebing, Robert T., Chief Fin. Officer & Exec. V.P.--Family Restaurants, Inc., Irvine, CA; *U.S. Private*, pg. 393
Trecroci, Ernie, Exec. V.P. & Chief Creative Officer--The McClure Group, Wayne, PA; *U.S. Private*, pg. 719
Trego, Charles, Jr., Chief Fin. Officer & Exec. V.P.--Rich Products Corp., Buffalo, NY; *U.S. Private*, pg. 928
Treharne, William H., PE, Exec. V.P.--Broad, Vogt & Conant, Inc., Detroit, MI; *U.S. Private*, pg. 170
Tremblay, Daniel, Exec. V.P.-Opers. & Mdsg.--Provigo Inc., Montreal, Canada; *Int'l*, pg. 1072
Tremblay, Daniel, Exec. V.P.-Opers./Provigo Supermarkets & Loeb--Provigo Distribution, Montreal, Canada; *Int'l*, pg. 1073
Tremblay, John F., Exec. V.P. & Pres.-Bank of Mid-Jersey--B.M.J. Financial Corp., Bordentown, NJ; *U.S. Public*, pg. 1528
Tremblay, Michel, Exec. V.P.-Distr. Grp.--Provigo Inc., Montreal, Canada; *Int'l*, pg. 1072
Trembly, Randall M., Exec. V.P.--Crown Central Petroleum Corporation, Baltimore, MD; *U.S. Public*, pg. 462
Trevenen, Harold E., Exec. V.P.--Laurel Bank, Johnstown, PA; *U.S. Public*, pg. 164
Trexler, Tom, Chief Fin. Officer & Exec. V.P.--Nobility Homes, Inc., Ocala, FL; *U.S. Public*, pg. 1186
Trice, W.H., Exec. V.P.--Union Camp Corporation, Wayne, NJ; *U.S. Public*, pg. 1665
Trilling, Morton, Exec. V.P. & Treas.--NationsBank/Miami, Miami, FL; *U.S. Public*, pg. 1162
Tringali, Donald J., Exec. V.P.--Telemundo Group, Inc., Hialeah, FL; *U.S. Public*, pg. 1570
Tripp, Montie, Exec. V.P.--Garney Holding Company, Inc., Kansas City, MO; *U.S. Private*, pg. 440
Tripple, David D., Exec. V.P.--The Pioneer Group, Inc., Boston, MA; *U.S. Public*, pg. 1298
Tropeano, A., Chief Fin. Officer & Exec. V.P.--Italimpianti of America, Incorporated, Coraopolis, PA; *Int'l*, pg. 655
Trosch, Hans G., Deputy Exec. V.P.--Von Roll AG, Gerlafingen, Switzerland; *Int'l*, pg. 1480
Trosino, Vincent J., Chief Oper. Officer & Exec. V.P.--State Farm Mutual Automobile Insurance Company, Bloomington, IL; *U.S. Private*, pg. 1036
Trotman, Alexander J., Exec. V.P.--Ford North American Automotive Operation, Dearborn, MI; *U.S. Public*, pg. 662
Trotta, Thomas A., Sr. V.P.--Connecticut Energy Corporation, Bridgeport, CT; *U.S. Public*, pg. 431
Trotter, Mike, Exec. V.P.--Quintana Petroleum Corp., Houston, TX; *U.S. Private*, pg. 901
Troup, Diana, Exec. V.P.-Prod. Design--Mattel, Inc., El Segundo, CA; *U.S. Public*, pg. 1057
Troup, Gordon A., Exec. V.P.-Eastern Grp.--Cardinal Distribution, Dublin, OH; *U.S. Public*, pg. 304
Troy, Edward G., Exec. V.P.--Liberty Mutual Insurance Co., Boston, MA; *U.S. Private*, pg. 666
Trujillo, Robert R., Exec. V.P. & Dir.-Franchise Mngmt.--Glendale Federal Bank, F.S.B., Glendale, CA; *U.S. Public*, pg. 747
Trumbull, R. Scott, Exec. V.P.-Intl. Opers.--Owens-Illinois, Inc., Toledo, OH; *U.S. Public*, pg. 1238
Trusk, John, Exec. V.P. & Exec. Creative Dir.--N.W. Ayer & Partners Chicago, Chicago, IL; *U.S. Private*, pg. 104
Truta, Joseph M., Exec. V.P.--Petroleum & Resources Corp., Baltimore, MD; *U.S. Public*, pg. 1280
Tschetter, Ronald A., Sr. Exec. V.P.-Private Client Grp.--Dain Rauscher Corporation, Minneapolis, MN; *U.S. Public*, pg. 476
Tschetter, Ronald A., Exec. V.P.--Dain Rauscher Incorporated, Minneapolis, MN; *U.S. Public*, pg. 476
Tsuboi, Kiyoshi, Exec. V.P.--Hitachi Zosen Corporation, Osaka, Japan; *Int'l*, pg. 622
Tsuboshima, Masami, Exec. V.P.-Central Pharmaceutical Res. Institute--Japan Tobacco Inc., Tokyo, Japan; *Int'l*, pg. 703
Tsuchikawa, Takeo, Exec. V.P.--Mitsui & Co., Ltd., Tokyo, Japan; *Int'l*, pg. 877
Tsujimoto, Hirokazu, Chief Oper. Officer & Exec. V.P.--Kintetsu World Express (U.S.A.), Inc., Roslyn Heights, NY; *Int'l*, pg. 734
Tsujioka, Dan, Exec. V.P.-Mdsg. & Sec.--White Cap Industries, Inc., Costa Mesa, CA; *U.S. Public*, pg. 1765
Tsuruta, Tadao, Exec. V.P.-Tech. & New Enterprises--Nikon Corporation, Tokyo, Japan; *Int'l*, pg. 931
Tsusaka, John, Sr. Exec. V.P.--MIC-USA Inc., New York, NY; *Int'l*, pg. 867
Tucci, James, Exec. V.P.--Associated Global Systems, New Hyde Park, NY; *U.S. Private*, pg. 90
Tuchner, Marcel, Exec. V.P.-Mfg. & Engrng.--Cinram Ltd., Scarborough, Canada; *Int'l*, pg. 293
Tucker, Bradford, Exec. V.P. & Gen. Counsel--Mustang Tractor & Equip. Co., Houston, TX; *U.S. Private*, pg. 768
Tucker, Frederick T., Exec. V.P. & Gen. Mgr.-Auto., Energy & Controls--Motorola, Inc., Schaumburg, IL; *U.S. Public*, pg. 1136
Tucker, Richard B.C., Jr., Pres.-Unifoam Div. & Exec. V.P.--Wm. T. Burnett & Co., Inc., Baltimore, MD; *U.S. Private*, pg. 186
Tucker, Thomas J., Exec. V.P., Chief Credit Officer-Corp Loan Admin.& Special Serv.--AmSouth Bancorporation, Birmingham, AL; *U.S. Public*, pg. 105
Tuckey, R.D., Exec. V.P.-Opers.--MacMillan Bloedel Limited, Vancouver, Canada; *Int'l*, pg. 828
Tudor-Foley, Rebecca, Exec. V.P. & Worldwide Creative Dir.--Doremus & Company, New York, NY; *U.S. Public*, pg. 1223
Tuffy Joao, Carmo, Exec. V.P.--Uniao de Bancos Brasileiros S.A. (Unibanco), Sao Paulo, Brazil; *Int'l*, pg. 1431
Tufo, Henry, M.D., Exec. V.P.--IDX Systems Corporation, Burlington, VT; *U.S. Public*, pg. 854
Tuite, James E., Exec. V.P.--TCF Financial Corp., Minneapolis, MN; *U.S. Public*, pg. 1554
Tulananda, Deja, Sr. Exec. V.P.--Bangkok Bank Public Company Limited, Bangkok, Thailand; *Int'l*, pg. 146
Tully, Tom, Exec. V.P.--Marketing Support, Incorporated, Chicago, IL; *U.S. Private*, pg. 705
Tumpowsky, Ira, Exec. V.P. & Media Dir.--FerrellCalvillo Communications, Inc., New York, NY; *U.S. Private*, pg. 401
Tumy, Julie, Exec. V.P. & Chief Mktg. Officer--Noble & Associates, Springfield, MO; *U.S. Private*, pg. 800
Tunchumrus, Boonsom, Exec. V.P.--Siam City Bank Public Company Limited, Bangkok, Thailand; *Int'l*, pg. 1239
Tuner, Mats, Exec. V.P.-Fin.--Perstorp AB, Perstorp, Sweden; *Int'l*, pg. 1036
Tuomi, F.C., Exec. V.P.--Equity Residential Properties Trust, Chicago, IL; *U.S. Public*, pg. 590
Tuppak, Fritz, Prof., Exec. V.P.--Ruhrgas AG, Essen, Germany; *Int'l*, pg. 1149
Turchin, Carol, Exec. V.P.--Box Hill Systems Corporation, New York, NY; *U.S. Public*, pg. 249
Turcotte, Glenn W., Exec. V.P.--Katy Industries, Inc., Englewood, CO; *U.S. Public*, pg. 944
Turiano, Vincent C., Chief Oper. Officer & Exec. V.P.--Hollidaysburg Trust Company, Hollidaysburg, PA; *U.S. Public*, pg. 1222
Turk, Milan J., Exec. V.P.-Specialty Bus.--International Paper Company, Purchase, NY; *U.S. Public*, pg. 901
Turkin, Todd, Exec. V.P., Sec. & Dir.-Telecomm.--Broder Bros. Co., Plymouth, MI; *U.S. Private*, pg. 170
Turmel, Jean, Sr. Exec. V.P.-Treas., Brokerage & Corp. Banking--National Bank of Canada, Montreal, Canada; *Int'l*, pg. 907
Turnbull, D.M., Exec. Dir.--Swire Pacific Limited, Central, Hong Kong; *Int'l*, pg. 1328
Turnbull, Joan, Exec. V.P.--Provident Mutual Life Insurance Co., Berwyn, PA; *U.S. Private*, pg. 891
Turner, Ed, Exec. V.P.--CNN (Cable News Network), Atlanta, GA; *U.S. Public*, pg. 1614
Turner, Gavin N.S., Exec. Dir.-Saftey & Services--Halma p.l.c., Amersham, United Kingdom; *Int'l*, pg. 589
Turner, Jimmie L., Chief Oper. Officer & Exec. V.P.--Gamma Biologicals Inc., Houston, TX; *U.S. Public*, pg. 698
Turner, John L., Exec. V.P. & Chief Oper. Officer--Allied Mineral Products, Inc., Columbus, OH; *U.S. Private*, pg. 39
Turner, Keith, Exec. V.P.--JTC LLC, Fort Wayne, IN; *U.S. Private*, pg. 579
Turner, Lee, Exec. V.P.--BTI Americas, Inc., Northbrook, IL; *U.S. Private*, pg. 108
Turner, Philip G., Deputy Chief Exec.--Wassall Plc, London, United Kingdom; *Int'l*, pg. 1486
Turner, Ronald L., Exec. V.P.-Opers.--Ceridian Corporation, Bloomington, MN; *U.S. Public*, pg. 330
Tuthill, Dewayne, Exec. V.P.-Mfg.--WHX Corporation, New York, NY; *U.S. Public*, pg. 1726
Tuthill, John, Exec. V.P. & Sec.--Hallwood Commercial Real Estate, Inc., Dallas, TX; *U.S. Public*, pg. 778
Tuzcu, Ertugnul, Exec. V.P.-Store Opers.--The Department Store Division of Dayton Hudson Corporation, Minneapolis, MN; *U.S. Public*, pg. 489
Tweedie, John H., Exec. V.P.-Individual Life Insurance--Metropolitan Life Insurance Co., New York, NY; *U.S. Private*, pg. 737
Twiddy, David A., Sr. Exec. V.P.-Tech. & Engrng.--The PBS&J Corporation, Miami, FL; *U.S. Private*, pg. 825
Twiss, Wesley R., Exec. V.P.--Petro-Canada, Calgary, Canada; *Int'l*, pg. 1041
Twomey, Kevin M., Vice Chm., Chief Fin. Officer & Sr. Exec. V.P.--H.F. Ahmanson & Co., Irwindale, CA; *U.S. Public*, pg. 29
Tyler, W. Ed, Exec. V.P. & Sector Pres.--R.R. Donnelley & Sons Company, Chicago, IL; *U.S. Public*, pg. 517
Tyson, Michael H., Exec. V.P.-Trust--Texas Commerce Bank, Houston, TX; *U.S. Public*, pg. 339
Tyson, Ron, Exec. V.P., Treas. & Sec.--Miracle Recreation Equipment Company, Monett, MO; *U.S. Private*, pg. 752
Ubell, Robert, Exec. V.P.-New Media--Marcel Dekker, Inc., New York, NY; *U.S. Private*, pg. 321
Uchida, Mutsubu, Exec. V.P.--Mitsui & Co., Ltd., Tokyo, Japan; *Int'l*, pg. 877
Uchida, Toshihisa, Exec. V.P.--Chubu Electric Power Company, Inc., Nagoya, Japan; *Int'l*, pg. 290
Uchikoshi, Shiro, Exec. V.P.--Nippon Paper Industries Company Limited, Tokyo, Japan; *Int'l*, pg. 937
Uchiyama, Atsumi, Sr. Exec. V.P.--Toshiba Corporation, Tokyo, Japan; *Int'l*, pg. 1402
Ueda, Hirozo, Exec. V.P.--Fuji Photo Film Co., Ltd., Tokyo, Japan; *Int'l*, pg. 523
Ueda, Kozo, Exec. V.P.--Osaka Gas Co., Ltd., Osaka, Japan; *Int'l*, pg. 1011
Ueda, Takahiko, Exec. V.P.--Krung Thai IBJ Leasing Co., Bangkok, Thailand; *Int'l*, pg. 676
Ueland, J. Ronald, Exec. V.P.--United Agri Products Co., Greeley, CO; *U.S. Public*, pg. 426
Uesawa, Nobuhiko, Exec. V.P.--Calsonic Yorozu Corporation, Morrison, TN; *Int'l*, pg. 944
Uesugi, M., Exec. V.P.--Nichimen America, Inc., New York, NY; *Int'l*, pg. 927
Uggla, Magnus, Exec. V.P.-Reg. Bank, Svenska Handelsbanken--Svenska Handelsbanken, Stockholm, Sweden; *Int'l*, pg. 1327
Ugoretz, Beth A., Exec. V.P.--KinderCare Learning Centers, Inc., Portland, OR; *U.S. Public*, pg. 961
Uhlmann, Rainer, Exec. V.P.--WABAG Leipzig GmbH Wassertechnische Anlagen, Markkleeberg, Germany; *Int'l*, pg. 399
Uhrich, Carole, Exec. V.P. & Pres.-Commercial Imaging Grp.--Polaroid Corporation, Cambridge, MA; *U.S. Public*, pg. 1313
Ukegawa, Miromi, Exec. V.P.--Nikko Securities Co., Chicago, Chicago, IL; *Int'l*, pg. 930
Ulbrich, Scott C., Chief Fin. Officer & Exec. V.P.--First Security Corporation, Salt Lake City, UT; *U.S. Public*, pg. 637
Ulizio, Louis H., Jr., Exec. V.P.-Comm. Banking Div.--People's Bank, Bridgeport, CT; *U.S. Public*, pg. 1274
Ulsh, Gordon, Exec. V.P.-Opers.--Cooper Industries, Inc., Houston, TX; *U.S. Public*, pg. 442
Umbach, Wilfried, Dr., Exec. V.P.-Res. & Tech.--Henkel KGaA, Dusseldorf, Germany; *Int'l*, pg. 609
Umeda, Masaru, Exec. Dir. & Grp. Gen. Mgr.-Law--Sharp Corporation, Osaka, Japan; *Int'l*, pg. 1228
Umphlette, Edward, Exec. V.P., Treas., Gen. Counsel & Gen. Mgr.--Stainless Incorporated, Deerfield Beach, FL; *U.S. Private*, pg. 1029
Unbekant, Donald E., Exec. V.P.-Civil & Environ. Construction--Perini Corporation, Framingham, MA; *U.S. Public*, pg. 1278
Underwood, Michael W., Exec. V.P.-Corp. Loan Admin. Div.--AmSouth Bancorporation, Birmingham, AL; *U.S. Public*, pg. 105
Ungern-Sternberg, Christoph V., Exec. V.P.--Bayerische Hypotheken-und Wechsel-Bank Aktiengesellschaft, Munich, Germany; *Int'l*, pg. 175
Updike, Malon S., Chief Information Officer & Exec. V.P.--Wachovia Bank, Charlottesville, VA; *U.S. Public*, pg. 1730
Upson, Dick, Exec. V.P. & Acct. Mng. Dir.--Young & Rubicam New York, New York, NY; *U.S. Private*, pg. 1198
Urakami, Akio, Exec. V.P.--Ryobi Ltd., Tokyo, Japan; *Int'l*, pg. 1151
Urkowitz, Michael, Exec. V.P.-Credit Cards--The Chase Manhattan Corporation, New York, NY; *U.S. Public*, pg. 337
Usaba, Hisashi, Sr. Mng. Dir.--Asahi Breweries Ltd., Tokyo, Japan; *Int'l*, pg. 83
Ushioda, Yoichiro, Exec. V.P.--Tostem Corporation, Tokyo, Japan; *Int'l*, pg. 1408
Usui, Hidetsugu, Exec. Dir.--Isuzu Motors Limited, Tokyo, Japan; *Int'l*, pg. 692
Uthaisangchai, Prasong, Exec. V.P.--Bangkok Bank Public Company Limited, Bangkok, Thailand; *Int'l*, pg. 146
Utley, Keith A., Exec. V.P.--Farmers Bank & Trust Co., Henderson, KY; *U.S. Public*, pg. 1217
Utne, Anders, Exec. V.P.-Commercial Div.--Saga Petroleum ASA, Sandvika, Norway; *Int'l*, pg. 1169
Uzzi, Donald R., Exec. V.P.-Consumer Prods. Worldwide--Sunbeam Corporation, Delray Beach, FL; *U.S. Public*, pg. 1533
Vaartimo, Olli, Exec. V.P.--Rauma Ltd., Helsinki, Finland; *Int'l*, pg. 1428
Vacca, Thomas A., Exec. V.P.-Mktg.--Midland Title Security, Inc., Cleveland, OH; *U.S. Public*, pg. 626
Vaccari, Gian Carlo, Exec. V.P.--SASIB SpA, Bologna, Italy; *Int'l*, pg. 1194
Vadala, Nicholas A., Chief Fin. Officer & Exec. V.P.-Opers.--CPS Direct, Inc., Woburn, MA; *U.S. Private*, pg. 196
Vadell, Pablo Vallbona, Vice Chm.--Banca March S.A., Palma de Mallorca, Spain; *Int'l*, pg. 136
Vaez, Joseph E., Exec. V.P. & Dir.-Credit Examination Services--BankAmerica Corporation, San Francisco, CA; *U.S. Public*, pg. 179
Vaez, Joseph E., Grp. Exec. V.P. & Dir.-Corp. Credit Examination Services--Bank of America NT&SA, San Francisco, CA; *U.S. Public*, pg. 180
Vagner, Kaare, Exec. V.P.-Transportation--ABB Asea Brown Boveri (Holding) Ltd., Zurich, Switzerland; *Int'l*, pg. 1

Vaillancourt, Marcel, Exec. V.P. & Gen. Mgr.--B.A. Bank Note, Ottawa, Canada; *Int'l*, pg. 1077
Vainisi, Julie T., Exec. V.P.-Gas. Div.--Torco Oil Co., Chicago, IL; *U.S. Private*, pg. 1092
Vaisto, Pekka, Exec. V.P.--Stockmann Automotive Sales Div., Helsinki, Finland; *Int'l*, pg. 1301
Valade, Gary C., Chief Fin. Officer & Exec. V.P.-Fin.--Chrysler Corporation, Auburn Hills, MI; *U.S. Public*, pg. 352
Valaisathien, Suvarn, Dr., Exec. V.P.--Finance One Public Company Limited, Bangkok, Thailand; *Int'l*, pg. 484
Valandra, Kent, Exec. V.P. & New Media Dir.--Western International Media Corporation, Los Angeles, CA; *U.S. Private*, pg. 1165
Valdivia, Jose F., Jr., Exec. V.P.--Atlantic Sugar Association, Inc., Belle Glade, FL; *U.S. Private*, pg. 95
Valencia, Luis E., Chief Admin. Oficer & Exec. V.P.--The Charles Schwab Corporation, San Francisco, CA; *U.S. Public*, pg. 1442
Valencia, Oscar, Exec. Sr. V.P.--Etienne Aigner, New York, NY; *U.S. Private*, pg. 384
Valentine, Mark, Exec. V.P.--Cole Vision Corporation, Cleveland, OH; *U.S. Public*, pg. 396
Valeriola, Jean-Pierre, Dir.-Corp. Communications & Public Rels.--L'Oreal S.A., Clichy, France; *Int'l*, pg. 818
Valesio, Joseph V., Exec. V.P.-Card & Member Services--MEDCO Containment Services, Inc., Montvale, NJ; *U.S. Public*, pg. 1091
Valiant, Jonathan J., Exec. V.P.-Real Estate--O&Y Properties Corporation, Toronto, Canada; *Int'l*, pg. 993
Vallet, Dominnique, Exec. V.P.-Research & Corp. Advisory Services--Credit Nationale, Paris, France; *Int'l*, pg. 344
Vallone, Tom, Exec. V.P.-Fin. Mng.--Comdisco, Inc., Rosemont, IL; *U.S. Public*, pg. 407
Valpey, Willard A., Exec. V.P.-Michigan Reg. Banking--First Chicago NBD Corporation, Chicago, IL; *U.S. Public*, pg. 627
Van Beusekom, Roger D., Exec. V.P.-Fin. Svcs.--Norstan, Inc., Plymouth, MN; *U.S. Public*, pg. 1192
Van Bokkelen, James, Exec. V.P.--FTP Software Inc., Andover, MA; *U.S. Public*, pg. 609
Van Borkulo-Nuzzo, D. Lynn, Exec. V.P. & Corp. Sec.--Hubco, Inc., Mahwah, NJ; *U.S. Public*, pg. 845
Van Brunt, Gary, Exec. V.P.-Pur.--Reinalt-Thomas Corp., Ann Arbor, MI; *U.S. Private*, pg. 919
Van Bruwaene, Raymond T., Exec. V.P.-Field Svcs.--Airborne Freight Corporation, Seattle, WA; *U.S. Public*, pg. 32
Van de Bunt, Ben, Exec. V.P.--Guthy-Renker Corp., Palm Desert, CA; *U.S. Private*, pg. 488
van de Winkel, Jack M.M., Vice Chm. & Exec. V.P.--N.V. Deli-Universal, Rotterdam, Netherlands; *U.S. Public*, pg. 1695
van den Brink, Hendrikus, Exec. V.P.--Grupo Tribasa S.A. de C.V., Mexico, Mexico; *Int'l*, pg. 577
van den Ende, J., Exec. V.P.--Albert Heijn B.V., Zaandam, Netherlands; *Int'l*, pg. 749
van der Heyden, Andre, Exec. Dir.--Union Miniere, Brussels, Belgium; *Int'l*, pg. 1441
van der Horst, R.J.M., Exec. V.P.--ABN-AMRO Holding N.V., Amsterdam, Netherlands; *Int'l*, pg. 8
van der Kaay, Erik H., Exec. V.P.--Allen Telecom, Inc., Beachwood, OH; *U.S. Public*, pg. 45
Van Der Kamp, Jerry, Chief Exec. Officer & Exec. V.P.--American Grain & Related Industries, West Des Moines, IA; *U.S. Private*, pg. 55
Van Devender, James, Chief Fin. Officer & Exec. V.P.--Champion HealthCare Corporation, Houston, TX; *U.S. Public*, pg. 333
van Dijk, E.J., Exec. V.P.--ABN-AMRO Holding N.V., Amsterdam, Netherlands; *Int'l*, pg. 8
Van Dine, Jim, Exec. V.P.-Sls., Mktg. & Customer Services--Deckers Outdoor Corporation, Goleta, CA; *U.S. Public*, pg. 491
van Dun, Peter, Exec. V.P.--Koninklijke Ahold NV, Zaandam, Netherlands; *Int'l*, pg. 749
Van Eck, A. Dale, Exec. V.P.--Merchants Publishing Co., Kalamazoo, MI; *U.S. Private*, pg. 732
van Epp, Daniel C., Exec. V.P.-Summerlin Div.--Howard Hughes Corporation, Las Vegas, NV; *U.S. Public*, pg. 1407
van Gemert, Lo, Exec. V.P.-PCS, Paging & Data--Rogers Cantel Mobile Communications Inc., Saint-Laurent, Canada; *Int'l*, pg. 1122
van Gemert, Marnix, Exec.-Sls.--Rogers Cantel Mobile Communications Inc., Saint-Laurent, Canada; *Int'l*, pg. 1122
van Gessel, C.J.M., Exec. V.P.--ABN-AMRO Holding N.V., Amsterdam, Netherlands; *Int'l*, pg. 8
Van Gilder, George T., Exec. V.P.--Chubb & Son, Inc., Warren, NJ; *U.S. Public*, pg. 355
Van Gorder, Jan R., Sr. Exec. V.P., Gen. Counsel & Sec.--Erie Family Life Insurance Company, Erie, PA; *U.S. Public*, pg. 590
Van Horn, Bob, Exec. V.P. & Client Services Dir.--Crispin Porter & Bogusky, Miami, FL; *U.S. Private*, pg. 290
Van Horn, Bob, Exec. V.P. & Strategic Plng. Dir.--Crispin Porter & Bogusky Advertising, Miami, FL; *U.S. Private*, pg. 290
Van Horne, Dave, Exec. V.P.--Norcraft Companies, Inc., Saint Paul, MN; *U.S. Private*, pg. 801
van Joolen, H.A., Exec. V.P.--ABN-AMRO Holding N.V., Amsterdam, Netherlands; *Int'l*, pg. 8
Van Kampem, Paul L., Exec. Dir.--AON Advisors, Inc., Chicago, IL; *U.S. Public*, pg. 117
Van Kerkove, Jim, Exec. V.P.-Opers.--Mitsubishi Silicon America, Salem, OR; *Int'l*, pg. 875
Van Kleef, William T., Exec. V.P.-Opers.--Tesoro Petroleum Corporation, San Antonio, TX; *U.S. Public*, pg. 1581
van Luyk, A.B., Exec. V.P.-Passenger Sls. & Service Div.--KLM Royal Dutch Airlines, Amstelveen, Netherlands; *Int'l*, pg. 719
Van Niekerk, Louis, Exec. Dir.-Fin.--Iscor, Pretoria, South Africa; *Int'l*, pg. 688
Van Patten, Robert M., Exec. V.P.--The Vigoro Corporation, Chicago, IL; *U.S. Public*, pg. 856
Van Pelt, John, Exec. V.P.-Treasury Mngmt. Mktg.--Northern Trust Corporation, Chicago, IL; *U.S. Public*, pg. 1195
van Saur, Bruce, Chief Fin. Officer & Exec. V.P.--The Bank of New York Company, Inc., New York, NY; *U.S. Public*, pg. 178
Van Sickle, Paul B., Exec. V.P.--Tupperware Corporation, Orlando, FL; *U.S. Public*, pg. 1644
Van Skilling, D., Exec. V.P. & Gen. Mgr.--TRW Information Systems & Services, Orange, CA; *Int'l*, pg. 557
van Slobbe, R.P.M., Exec. V.P.-Logistics & Procurement--Nedlloyd Lines B.V., Rotterdam, Netherlands; *Int'l*, pg. 1145
Van Slyke, Peter, Exec. V.P.--Stephen Gould Paper Co., Inc., Whippany, NJ; *U.S. Private*, pg. 467
van Veen, E.F., Exec. V.P.-Fin. & Admin.--Nutricia BV, Zoetermeer, Netherlands; *Int'l*, pg. 991
Van Vleet, W.B., Exec. V.P.--Pioneer Life Insurance Co. of Illinois, Rockford, IL; *U.S. Public*, pg. 434
van Wensen, H.P.A., Exec. V.P. & Sec.--ABN-AMRO Holding N.V., Amsterdam, Netherlands; *Int'l*, pg. 8
van Woudenberg, C., Exec. V.P.-Opers.--KLM Royal Dutch Airlines, Amstelveen, Netherlands; *Int'l*, pg. 719
van Zandt, Pamela, Exec. V.P.--The Conde Nast Publications Inc., New York, NY; *U.S. Private*, pg. 20
Van Zandt, William, Exec. V.P.-Global Health Care Div.--Total Research Corporation, Princeton, NJ; *U.S. Public*, pg. 1625
Vanavit, Somchai, Exec. V.P.--Siam City Bank Public Company Limited, Bangkok, Thailand; *Int'l*, pg. 1239
Vandegrift, Richard, Exec. V.P.--McCarthy Building Companies, Saint Louis, MO; *U.S. Private*, pg. 719
Vandenberghe, James, Chief Fin. Officer & Exec. V.P.-Fin.--Lear Corporation, Southfield, MI; *U.S. Public*, pg. 981
Vander Pol, Daryl L., Chief Fin. Officer, Exec. V.P., Treas. & Sec.--Vitamilk Dairy, Inc., Seattle, WA; *U.S. Private*, pg. 1142
VanderKloot, Barbara, Exec. V.P.--Carstens Inc., Chicago, IL; *U.S. Private*, pg. 216
Vanijyanonda, Somrong, Sr. Exec. V.P.--Bangkok Bank of Commerce Ltd., Bangkok, Thailand; *Int'l*, pg. 146
Vannatta, M. Jack, Exec. V.P., Controller & Treas.--First American Corporation, Nashville, TN; *U.S. Public*, pg. 624
Vareberg, Terje, Grp. Exec. V.P.--Statoil, Stavanger, Norway; *Int'l*, pg. 1297
Vargas, Eduardo, Exec. V.P. & Chm., Chief Exec. Officer-Latin America & Dir.--BBDO Worldwide Inc., New York, NY; *U.S. Public*, pg. 1223
Vargo, Geoffrey, Exec. V.P.--Sarkes Tarzian, Bloomington, IN; *U.S. Private*, pg. 966
Varnadore, Lon, Exec. V.P.--Western Reinsurance Brokers, Inc., Los Angeles, CA; *U.S. Private*, pg. 1168
Varnell, Henry D., III, Exec. V.P.--Sysco Food Services of Central Florida, Inc., Ocoee, FL; *U.S. Public*, pg. 1551
Vasconcellos, Carlos, Exec. V.P.--Dun & Bradstreet Portugal Lda., Lisbon, Portugal; *U.S. Public*, pg. 536
Vasques, Gary, Exec. V.P.-Mktg.--Kohl's Corporation, Menomonee Falls, WI; *U.S. Public*, pg. 965
Vass, William H., Exec. V.P.--Publix Supermarkets Inc., Lakeland, FL; *U.S. Private*, pg. 893
Vasvari, Hal A., Chief Oper. Officer & Exec. V.P.--Federal Realty Investment Trust, Rockville, MD; *U.S. Public*, pg. 616
Vaswig, Donald, Exec. V.P., Treas. & Dir.-Fin.--Harmony Foods Corporation, Santa Cruz, CA; *U.S. Private*, pg. 503
Vaughan, George C., Chief Oper. Officer & Exec. V.P.--Vaughan & Sons, Inc., San Antonio, TX; *U.S. Private*, pg. 1134
Vaughan, Richard, Chief Fin. Officer & Exec. V.P.--Lincoln National Corporation, Fort Wayne, IN; *U.S. Public*, pg. 997
Vaughan, Robert L., Chief Fin. Officer & Exec. V.P.--Vaughan & Sons, Inc., San Antonio, TX; *U.S. Private*, pg. 1134
Vaughan, William, Jr., Exec. V.P.--nexAir, Memphis, TN; *U.S. Private*, pg. 797
Vaughn, Barry S., Exec. V.P.--The Suddath Companies, Jacksonville, FL; *U.S. Private*, pg. 1049
Vaughn, David, Exec. V.P.-Bus. Devel.--Trimble Navigation Limited, Sunnyvale, CA; *U.S. Public*, pg. 1638
Vaughn, William M., III, Exec. V.P.-Human Resources & Support Services--The Stop & Shop Companies, Inc., Quincy, MA; *Int'l*, pg. 750
Vaupen, Hy, Chief Fin. Officer, Exec. V.P. & Sec.--Beverage Canners International Corp., Miami, FL; *U.S. Private*, pg. 106
Vazquez, Carlos J., Exec. V.P.--Banco Popular de Puerto Rico, San Juan, PR; *U.S. Public*, pg. 175
Vecci, Raymond, Exec. V.P.-Customer Svcs.--Northwest Airlines, Inc., Saint Paul, MN; *U.S. Public*, pg. 1200
Veil, Lynne C., Partner & Exec. V.P.--Media That Works, Cincinnati, OH; *U.S. Private*, pg. 727
Veilleux, Martin J., Chief Fin. Officer, Exec. V.P.-Fin., Treas. & Sec.--Boron LePore Group, Fair Lawn, NJ; *U.S. Public*, pg. 246
Velli, Joseph M., Exec. V.P.-Worldwide Securities & Processing Services--The Bank of New York Company, Inc., New York, NY; *U.S. Public*, pg. 178
Venturi, Guiseppi, Exec. V.P.-US Opers.--G.D. Packaging Machinery Inc., Richmond, VA; *Int'l*, pg. 531
Verdoorn, Ronald D., Exec. V.P.-Mfg.--Seagate Technology Inc., Scotts Valley, CA; *U.S. Public*, pg. 1449
Verdurme, Philippe, Exec. V.P.-Sls. & Mktg.--Rail Europe Inc., Harrison, NY; *Int'l*, pg. 1165
Vereen, H.B., Exec. V.P.--Riverside Manufacturing Co., Moultrie, GA; *U.S. Private*, pg. 934
Verhassel, Jean-Pierre, Sr.Exec. V.P.-Mfg. & Opers.--Ares-Serono S.A., Geneva, Switzerland; *Int'l*, pg. 80
Verheij, Richard H., Exec. V.P.--UST Inc., Greenwich, CT; *U.S. Public*, pg. 1660
Verklin, David, Exec. V.P. & Mng. Dir.--Hal Riney & Partners, Inc., San Francisco, CA; *U.S. Private*, pg. 931
Vermeulen, H., Exec. V.P.--ABN-AMRO Holding N.V., Amsterdam, Netherlands; *Int'l*, pg. 8
Vermeulen, Jean-Luc, Exec. V.P.-Exploration & Production--Elf Aquitane, Paris, France; *Int'l*, pg. 444
Vermillion, Ursula, Exec. V.P.--Wasserstrom Company, Columbus, OH; *U.S. Private*, pg. 1152
Vernon, Chris, Exec. V.P.-Mktg. & Sls.--The Vernon Company, Newton, IA; *U.S. Private*, pg. 1137
Vernon, Paul, Exec. V.P., Gen. Mgr.--EJL Advertising/Houston, Houston, TX; *U.S. Private*, pg. 673
Verrecchia, Alfred J., Exec. V.P. & Pres.-Global Opers.--Hasbro, Inc., Pawtucket, RI; *U.S. Public*, pg. 797
Verrill, Peter J., Chief Oper. Officer, Exec. V.P. & Treas.--Peoples Heritage Financial Group, Inc., Portland, ME; *U.S. Public*, pg. 1275
Vert, Paul A., Exec. V.P. & Asst. to Pres.--Young's Holdings Inc., Orange, CA; *U.S. Private*, pg. 1202
Vertrees, Scott, Exec. V.P.--American White Cross, Dayville, CT; *U.S. Public*, pg. 694
Vertucci, Lawrence, Exec. V.P. & Capital Reg. Pres.--Marine Midland Bank, Buffalo, NY; *Int'l*, pg. 581
Vesey, Michael T., Exec. V.P.-Project Mngmt.--FPA Corporation, Bensalem, PA; *U.S. Public*, pg. 608
Vessey, Thomas E., Exec. V.P. & Sr. Credit Officer--California State Bank, West Covina, CA; *U.S. Public*, pg. 294
Veyrines, Jacques, Exec. V.P.-Loans & Credits--Credit Nationale, Paris, France; *Int'l*, pg. 344
Vezina, G. Robert, Exec. V.P.-Personnel--First Tennessee National Corporation, Memphis, TN; *U.S. Public*, pg. 638
Via, George, Exec. V.P.--Bellcore, Morristown, NJ; *U.S. Private*, pg. 976
Viar, David, Exec. V.P.--CNB Bancshares, Inc., Evansville, IN; *U.S. Public*, pg. 280
Viars, E. Leon, Exec. V.P.--Arvin Industries, Inc., Columbus, IN; *U.S. Public*, pg. 136
Vicens, Joseph, Exec. V.P. & Gen. Mgr.--Dial A Mattress USA, Long Island City, NY; *U.S. Private*, pg. 330
Vickers, John A., Exec. V.P.--Tishman Realty & Construction Co., Inc., New York, NY; *U.S. Private*, pg. 1089
Viertel, Thomas, Chief Fin. Officer & Exec. V.P.--Presidential Realty Corporation, White Plains, NY; *U.S. Public*, pg. 1323
Viertel, Thomas, Chief Fin. Officer & Exec. V.P.--PDL, Inc., White Plains, NY; *U.S. Public*, pg. 1323
Viertel, Thomas, Chief Fin. Officer & Exec. V.P.--Presidential Realty of Iowa, Inc., White Plains, NY; *U.S. Public*, pg. 1324
Vierzba, Mike, Exec. V.P.-Asia & Australia--Fiskars Oy AB, Helsinki, Finland; *Int'l*, pg. 492
Vigh, Donald A., Chief Oper. Officer & Exec. V.P.--Kimble Glass Inc., Vineland, NJ; *Int'l*, pg. 1464
Vighetto, Marco, Exec. V.P.-Credit--Istituto Bancario San Paolo Di Torino S.p.A., Turin, Italy; *Int'l*, pg. 691
Vigmostad, Odd, Exec. V.P.--Orkla A.S.A., Oslo, Norway; *Int'l*, pg. 1010
Vignale, Mike, Exec. V.P.--Duferco Steel Inc., Laurence Harbor, NJ; *U.S. Private*, pg. 345
Vijayan, Uday, Exec. V.P.-Bangalore Branch--MAA Communications Bozell, Bangalore, India; *U.S. Public*, pg. 1642
Vike, Floyd, Exec. V.P.-Building Matls. Grp.--Willamette Industries, Inc., Portland, OR; *U.S. Public*, pg. 1768
Vikner, Paul L., Exec. V.P.-Sls. & Mktg.--Mack Trucks, Inc., Allentown, PA; *Int'l*, pg. 1102
Vilches, Luis, Exec. V.P.-Intl.--Grupo Iberia, Madrid, Spain; *Int'l*, pg. 574
Viles, Donald L., Chief Fin. Officer & Exec. V.P.--Anacomp, Inc., Indianapolis, IN; *U.S. Public*, pg. 106
Villani, Kevin E., Chief Fin. Officer & Exec. V.P.--Imperial Credit Industries, Inc., Torrance, CA; *U.S. Public*, pg. 872
Villarreal, Carlos C., Sr., Exec. V.P.--Wilbur Smith Associates, Columbia, SC; *U.S. Private*, pg. 1009
Villegas, Eduardo Mateos, Exec. V.P.-Corp. Mgmt. Design & Dev.--Sepi, Madrid, Spain; *Int'l*, pg. 1224
Villiger, Daniel, Exec. V.P.--Zurich Insurance Company, Zurich, Switzerland; *Int'l*, pg. 1529
Vincent, Daniel L., Chief Oper. Officer & Exec. V.P.--Pacific Coast Producers, Lodi, CA; *U.S. Private*, pg. 830
Vincent, Jacques, Sr. Exec. V.P.-Asia--Danone Group, Paris, France; *Int'l*, pg. 379
Vine, Mitchell J., Exec. V.P.--Legacy Storage Systems Corp., Markham, Canada; *Int'l*, pg. 805
Vinje, Ronald, Exec. V.P.--Psomas & Associates, Santa Monica, CA; *U.S. Private*, pg. 893
Vinson, Charles, Exec. V.P.--Transicoil, Inc., Valley Forge, PA; *U.S. Private*, pg. 538
Vinson, W. Jarrell, Exec. V.P.-Loan Admin.--Wachovia Bank, Charlottesville, VA; *U.S. Public*, pg. 1730
Vinton, Bob, Exec. V.P.--Comlinear Corporation, Fort Collins, CO; *U.S. Public*, pg. 1160
Vipperman, Joseph H., Exec. V.P.-Corp. Svcs.--American Electric Power Company, Inc., Columbus, OH; *U.S. Public*, pg. 71
Vipperman, Joseph H., Exec. V.P.-Corp. Svcs.--American Electric Power Service Corp., Columbus, OH; *U.S. Public*, pg. 72
Virene, Peter, Exec. V.P. & Dir.-Sls. & Mktg.--American Modular Technologies, Liberty, NC; *U.S. Public*, pg. 69
Virgulak, Christopher, Chief Fin. Officer & Exec. V.P.--General Cable Corporation, Highland Heights, KY; *Int'l*, pg. 1486
Visosky, Leonard M., Chief Fin. Officer & Exec. V.P. & Sec.--Tapco International Corporation, Plymouth, MI; *U.S. Private*, pg. 1068
Visserman, D., Exec. V.P.--ABN-AMRO Holding N.V., Amsterdam, Netherlands; *Int'l*, pg. 8
Vita, Alfiero, Exec. V.P.--American Appraisal Associates, Inc., Milwaukee, WI; *U.S. Private*, pg. 49
Vittor, Kenneth M., Sr. Exec. V.P.--The McGraw-Hill Companies, New York, NY; *U.S. Public*, pg. 1069

Vlamis, Betty, Exec. V.P.--Continental American Corp., Wichita, KS; *U.S. Private*, pg. 267
Voelker, Frank C., Chief Exec. Officer & Exec. V.P.--Celegec Automation Projects Inc., Macon, GA; *Int'l*, pg. 53
Voet, Paul C., Exec. V.P.--Chemed Corporation, Cincinnati, OH; *U.S. Public*, pg. 343
Vogel, Guillermo F., Exec. V.P.--Tubos de Acero de Mexico, S.A., Mexico, Mexico; *Int'l*, pg. 1426
Voglimacci, J.P., Exec. V.P.-Opers.--Compagnie Generale de Geophysique, Massy, France; *Int'l*, pg. 241
Vojnovic, Zoran, Exec. V.P.--Jugobanka Banking Group, Belgrade, Serbia; *Int'l*, pg. 716
Volk, Christopher H., Chief Oper. Officer & Exec. V.P.--Franchise Finance Corp. of America, Scottsdale, AZ; *U.S. Public*, pg. 679
Volk, Kristin, Exec. V.P. & Consumer Insight Dir.--Arnold Communications, Inc., Boston, MA; *U.S. Private*, pg. 83
Volk, Robert T., Exec. V.P. & Dir.-Consumer Banking--Long Island Bancorp, Inc., Melville, NY; *U.S. Public*, pg. 1013
Voll, Keith A., Chief Information Officer & Exec. V.P.--Downey Savings & Loan Association, F.A., Newport Beach, CA; *U.S. Public*, pg. 526
Vollbrecht, Heinz-Ruediger, Dr., Mngmt. Bd.--SKW Trostberg Aktiengesellschaft, Trostberg, Germany; *Int'l*, pg. 1464
Volonino, Richard A., Exec. V.P.--United Waste Systems, Inc., Houston, TX; *U.S. Public*, pg. 1691
Volpentesta, Frank, Chief Oper. Officer & V.P.--Bearing Headquarters Co., Broadview, IL; *U.S. Private*, pg. 127
von Borstel, George, Exec. V.P.--Mrs. Smith's Bakeries, Inc., Thomasville, GA; *U.S. Public*, pg. 657
von Frenckell, Mikael, Exec. V.P.--Merita Bank Ltd., Helsinki, Finland; *Int'l*, pg. 858
Von Gruben, Brian G., Exec. V.P. & Dir.-Admin. Svcs.--Piccadilly Cafeterias, Inc., Baton Rouge, LA; *U.S. Public*, pg. 1294
von Hallwyl, Michael Graf, Exec. V.P.-International Fin. & Credit--Bayerische Landesbank, Munich, Germany; *Int'l*, pg. 176
von Koerber, Dr. Eberhard, Exec. V.P.-Germany, Austria, Italy, E. Europe & Greece--ABB Asea Brown Boveri (Holding) Ltd., Zurich, Switzerland; *Int'l*, pg. 1
von Luhrte, Richard L., Exec. V.P., Sec. & Dir.--RNL Facilities Corporation, Denver, CO; *U.S. Private*, pg. 905
von Natzmer, Helmut, Exec. V.P. & Gen. Mgr.--Deutsche Bank AG (New York Branch), New York, NY; *Int'l*, pg. 403
von Ruedorffer, Axel Frhr., Mng. Dir.-Credit Risk Mngmt., Auditing, Compliance & Security--Commerzbank AG, Frankfurt, Germany; *Int'l*, pg. 308
von Waldthausen, Gottfried Wilhelm, Exec. V.P.-H.R.--Commerzbank AG, Frankfurt, Germany; *Int'l*, pg. 308
Vongruamlarp, Visit, Exec. V.P.--The Industrial Finance Corporation of Thailand, Bangkok, Thailand; *Int'l*, pg. 677
Vonnahme, Neil, Exec. V.P.-Rollins Logistics Inc.--Rollins Leasing Corp., Wilmington, DE; *U.S. Public*, pg. 1405
Vonnahme, Neil, Exec. V.P.--Rollins Logistics Inc., Wilmington, DE; *U.S. Public*, pg. 1405
Vosicky, John J., Chief Fin. Officer & Exec. V.P.--Comdisco, Inc., Rosemont, IL; *U.S. Public*, pg. 407
Voss, James M., Exec. V.P.--First Midwest Bank, N.A., Itasca, IL; *U.S. Public*, pg. 636
Voss, Jeffrey, Chief Fin. Officer, Exec. V.P. & Treas.--Beverly Bancorporation Inc., Chicago, IL; *U.S. Public*, pg. 227
Voss, Steve, Exec. V.P. & H.R.--Golden West Financial Corporation, Oakland, CA; *U.S. Public*, pg. 750
Voss, William, Exec. V.P.--Crown Cork & Seal Company, Inc., Philadelphia, PA; *U.S. Public*, pg. 462
Voth, Richard A., Exec. V.P.--Brent Transportation Co., Greenville, MS; *U.S. Public*, pg. 961
Vouvakis, Jim, Exec. V.P.-Yellow Pages--Western International Media Corporation, Los Angeles, CA; *U.S. Private*, pg. 1165
Vouvakis, Jim, Exec. V.P.--U.S. Yellow Pages, Los Angeles, CA; *U.S. Private*, pg. 1168
Vroegop, J., Exec. V.P.--ABN-AMRO Holding N.V., Amsterdam, Netherlands; *Int'l*, pg. 8
Vuneo, Ngaire, Exec. V.P.--Conseco Capital Partners II, L.P., New York, NY; *U.S. Public*, pg. 432
Wabler, Robert C., Chief Fin. Officer & Exec. V.P.--Just For Feet, Inc., Pelham, AL; *U.S. Public*, pg. 935
Wachalter, Terry, Exec. V.P.-Admin.--Robert A. Becker, New York, NY; *Int'l*, pg. 601
Wachtel, M.D., Exec. V.P. & Chief Oper. Officer--Domestic Wholesale, Oshkosh, WI; *U.S. Public*, pg. 1233
Wachtel, Michael P., Chief Oper. Officer & Exec. V.P.--OshKosh B'Gosh, Inc., Oshkosh, WI; *U.S. Public*, pg. 1232
Wackerlin, Jim, Exec. V.P.--American Seating Company, Grand Rapids, MI; *U.S. Private*, pg. 61
Wada, Fujio, Sr. Exec. Dir.--Minolta Co., Ltd., Osaka, Japan; *Int'l*, pg. 869
Wada, Minoru, Exec. V.P.--Mitsubishi Motors Corporation, Tokyo, Japan; *Int'l*, pg. 875
Wada, Norio, Exec. V.P.-Tire Mfg. Opers.--Bridgestone/Firestone, Inc., Nashville, TN; *Int'l*, pg. 213
Wada, Norio, Exec. V.P.-Mfg.--Bridgestone/Firestone Tire Manufacturing Operations, Nashville, TN; *Int'l*, pg. 213
Wada, Norio, Exec. V.P.--Nippon Telegraph and Telephone Corporation, Tokyo, Japan; *Int'l*, pg. 940
Waddell, James S., Chief Admin. Officer, Exec. V.P. & Sec.--Amcore Financial, Inc., Rockford, IL; *U.S. Public*, pg. 64
Waddell, James S., Chief Admin. Officer & Exec. V.P.--AMCORE Bank N.A., Rockford, Rockford, IL; *U.S. Public*, pg. 64
Wade, Frederick E., Exec. V.P.--Centex-Rooney Construction Co., Inc., Fort Lauderdale, FL; *U.S. Public*, pg. 322
Wade, Jeffrey L., Exec. V.P.-Affiliate Rels.--QVC, Inc., West Chester, PA; *U.S. Private*, pg. 897
Wade, Thomas, Exec. V.P. & Controller--Jamison Bedding, Inc., Franklin, TN; *U.S. Private*, pg. 581
Wade, William E., Exec. V.P.-Upstream--Atlantic Richfield Company, Los Angeles, CA; *U.S. Public*, pg. 144
Wadensten, Karl, Exec. V.P.--Vibco Inc., Wyoming, RI; *U.S. Private*, pg. 1138
Wagenhals, Tod J., Exec. V.P. & Sec.--Action Performance Companies, Inc., Phoenix, AZ; *U.S. Public*, pg. 17
Wager, Deidra, Exec. V.P.-Retail Mktg. & Opers.--Starbucks Coffee Company, Seattle, WA; *U.S. Public*, pg. 1510
Waggoner, David W., Exec. V.P.--Firstbank of Illinois Co., Springfield, IL; *U.S. Public*, pg. 643
Wagman, Lee H., Exec. V.P.-Retail--TrizecHahn Corporation, Toronto, Canada; *Int'l*, pg. 1424
Wagner, Chris, Exec. V.P.--Vilter Manufacturing Corporation, Cudahy, WI; *U.S. Private*, pg. 1140
Wagner, Erick, Exec. V.P.--Progress West Corporation, Omaha, NE; *U.S. Private*, pg. 890
Wagner, Fernand, Exec. V.P.-Iron & Steelmaking, Flat Products--Arbed S.A., Luxembourg, Luxembourg; *Int'l*, pg. 78
Wagner, Gary, Chief Fin. Officer, Sr. V.P. & Treas.--Ameron International Corporation, Pasadena, CA; *U.S. Public*, pg. 98
Wagner, James Allen, Exec. V.P.--City Machine Tool & Die Company, Inc., Muncie, IN; *U.S. Private*, pg. 241
Wagner, James E., Exec. V.P.--Sullivan Paper Company, West Springfield, MA; *U.S. Private*, pg. 1050
Wagner, K.E., Exec. V.P.--Vilter Manufacturing Corporation, Cudahy, WI; *U.S. Private*, pg. 1140
Wagner, Reinhold, Exec. V.P.-Rolled Prods., Europe--Alcan Aluminium Limited, Montreal, Canada; *Int'l*, pg. 50
Wagner, Thomas J., Exec. V.P. & Gen. Counsel--Cigna Corp., Philadelphia, PA; *U.S. Public*, pg. 356
Wagoner, G. Richard, Jr., Exec. V.P. & Pres. N. American Opers.--General Motors Corporation, Detroit, MI; *U.S. Public*, pg. 718
Waguespack, Hickley M., Exec. V.P.-Customer Svcs. & Retention--RehabCare Group, Inc., Saint Louis, MO; *U.S. Public*, pg. 1373
Wahbe, Albert E., Exec. V.P.-Opers.--The Bank of Nova Scotia, Toronto, Canada; *Int'l*, pg. 155
Wahlstrom, Mats, Exec. V.P.--Gambro AB, Lund, Sweden; *Int'l*, pg. 666
Wahtola, Charles H., Exec. V.P.-Bus. Devel--Woodward-Clyde Group, Inc., Denver, CO; *U.S. Public*, pg. 1655
Wainberg, Alan, Exec. V.P.--VKO, Inc., Taunton, MA; *U.S. Private*, pg. 1130
Waite, Donald L., Chief Fin. Officer, Exec. V.P.-Fin. & Sec.--Seagate Technology Inc., Scotts Valley, CA; *U.S. Public*, pg. 1449
Waite, Peter G., Exec. V.P.--Precision Castparts Corp., Portland, OR; *U.S. Public*, pg. 1320
Waitman, Barbara, Exec. V.P. & Gen. Counsel--Slim-Fast Foods Company, West Palm Beach, FL; *U.S. Private*, pg. 1006
Waiwood, Michael F., Exec. V.P., Gen. Cousel & Sec.--Midland Title Security, Inc., Cleveland, OH; *U.S. Public*, pg. 626
Wakabayashi, Toshio, Exec. V.P.--Tokyu Agency Inc., Tokyo, Japan; *Int'l*, pg. 1394
Wakai, Masao, Exec. V.P.--Fuji Securities Inc.-New York, New York, NY; *Int'l*, pg. 519
Wakeen, Stephen, Exec. V.P. & Gen. Mgr.--Emmerling Post, Inc., New York, NY; *U.S. Private*, pg. 374
Wakefield, David, Exec. V.P.-United Kingdom Hospital Div.--Community Psychiatric Centers of London (Unlimited), London, United Kingdom; *U.S. Public*, pg. 1716
Wakerly, John F., Chief Tech. Officer & Exec. V.P.--Alantec Corp., San Jose, CA; *U.S. Public*, pg. 667
Wald, Donna, Exec. V.P.-Acct. Services--Western International Media Corporation, Los Angeles, CA; *U.S. Private*, pg. 1165
Waldeland, Donald, Exec. V.P.--Colwell Industries, Inc., Minneapolis, MN; *U.S. Private*, pg. 257
Waldemarson, Bo, Exec. V.P.--L E Lundbergforetagen AB, Stockholm, Sweden; *Int'l*, pg. 820
Waldron, W. Daniel, Exec. V.P.--FirstMerit Corporation, Akron, OH; *U.S. Public*, pg. 646
Wales, Don, Exec. V.P.--ConAgra Poultry Co., Duluth, GA; *U.S. Public*, pg. 427
Walford, Brian G., Exec. V.P., Chief Fin. Officer & Sec.--Exel Insurance Co. Ltd., Hamilton, Bermuda; *Int'l*, pg. 467
Walgenbach, Ewald, Deputy Chief Exec. Officer & Exec. V.P.-TV--CLT-UFA, Luxembourg, Luxembourg; *Int'l*, pg. 561
Walk, Ronald D., Exec. V.P.-Retail Opers.--Albertson's, Inc., Boise, ID; *U.S. Public*, pg. 38
Walker, Cory, Exec. V.P.--Poe & Brown of California, San Francisco, CA; *U.S. Public*, pg. 1312
Walker, David, Exec. V.P.--Countrywide Home Loans Inc., Pasadena, CA; *U.S. Public*, pg. 452
Walker, Don W., Exec. V.P.-Investigations & Consulting--Pinkerton's Inc., Encino, CA; *U.S. Public*, pg. 1296
Walker, Donald R., Chief Info. Officer & Exec. V.P.--USAA (United Services Automobile Association), San Antonio, TX; *U.S. Private*, pg. 1114
Walker, Haywood, III, Exec. V.P.--Trinity Construction Products, Dallas, TX; *U.S. Public*, pg. 1639
Walker, James C., Exec. V.P.-Sls.--Ernst W. Dorn Co., Inc., Gardena, CA; *U.S. Private*, pg. 340
Walker, James E., Exec. V.P.--Cassens Transport Company, Edwardsville, IL; *U.S. Private*, pg. 219
Walker, John, Chief Fin. Officer & Exec. V.P.--Emerson Radio Corp., Parsippany, NJ; *U.S. Public*, pg. 578
Walker, John P., Chief Fin. Officer & Exec. V.P.--Sport Supply Group, Inc., Dallas, TX; *U.S. Public*, pg. 1499
Walker, Larry M., Exec. V.P.-Mfg.--Oakwood Homes Corporation, Greensboro, NC; *U.S. Public*, pg. 1209
Walker, Norman C., Exec. V.P. & Pres.-Intl.--Hasbro, Inc., Pawtucket, RI; *U.S. Public*, pg. 797
Walker, Richard A., Chief Admin. Officer, Exec. V.P., Gen. Counsel & Sec.--Kuhlman Corporation, Savannah, GA; *U.S. Public*, pg. 968
Walker, Steven C., Exec. V.P.--Deposit Guaranty Corp., Jackson, MS; *U.S. Public*, pg. 500
Walker, Steven C., Exec. V.P.--Deposit Guaranty National Bank, Jackson, MS; *U.S. Public*, pg. 500
Walker, Thomas M., Chief Fin. Officer & Exec. V.P.--IES Industries Inc., Cedar Rapids, IA; *U.S. Public*, pg. 855
Wall, Anthony J., Exec. V.P.-Bus. Affairs, Gen. Counsel & Sec.--Big Dog Holdings Inc., Santa Barbara, CA; *U.S. Public*, pg. 227
Wall, John L., Exec. V.P.-Enviro. & Natural Resources--Al Larson Boat Shop, Inc., Terminal Island, CA; *U.S. Private*, pg. 652
Wallace, Chris, Exec. V.P. & Gen. Mgr.-Basketball Subsidiary Partnership--Boston Celtics Limited Partnership, Boston, MA; *U.S. Public*, pg. 246
Wallace, Merl A., Exec. V.P.-Opers.--Apria Healthcare Group Inc., Costa Mesa, CA; *U.S. Public*, pg. 125
Wallace, Theodore, Chief Oper. Officer & Exec. V.P.--PriceSmart Inc., San Diego, CA; *U.S. Public*, pg. 1324
Wallach, Abe, Exec. V.P.--Trump Organization, New York, NY; *U.S. Private*, pg. 1108
Wallach, Barry, Exec. V.P.-Syndication--CBS Enterprises Division, New York, NY; *U.S. Public*, pg. 274
Wallach, Diane, Exec. V.P. & Treas.--Cody Company, Denver, CO; *U.S. Private*, pg. 249
Wallach, Kenneth L., Exec. V.P.--Central National-Gottesman Inc., Purchase, NY; *U.S. Private*, pg. 224
Wallenburg, Marcus, Exec. V.P.-Bus. Devel.--Investor AB, Stockholm, Sweden; *Int'l*, pg. 686
Waller, Debra S., Exec. V.P. & Asst. to Pres.--Jockey International, Inc., Kenosha, WI; *U.S. Private*, pg. 588
Waller, Stephen L., Sr. V.P.-Network Transportation & Plng.--DHL Airways, Inc., Redwood City, CA; *U.S. Private*, pg. 302
Wallis, Christopher, Exec. V.P.-Design & Construction--Four Seasons Hotels Inc., Don Mills, Canada; *Int'l*, pg. 502
Wallis, Ken, Exec. V.P.-Opers.--Alfa Corporation, Montgomery, AL; *U.S. Public*, pg. 40
Wallock, Terrence J., Exec. V.P., General Counsel & Sec.--The Vons Companies, Inc., Arcadia, CA; *U.S. Public*, pg. 1426
Wallrabe, Horst K. D., Exec. V.P. & Pres.-Pharmaceutical Div.--Bayer Corporation/Consumer Care Division, Morristown, NJ; *Int'l*, pg. 173
Walrod, David J., Exec. V.P.-Opers.--Seaway Food Town, Inc., Maumee, OH; *U.S. Public*, pg. 1452
Walser, William A., Exec. V.P.--ABN AMRO Chicago Corp., Chicago, IL; *Int'l*, pg. 10
Walsh, Donald, Exec. V.P.-IIS Division--Brite Voice Systems, Inc., Heathrow, FL; *U.S. Public*, pg. 257
Walsh, Gerald C., Exec. V.P.--V-Band Corporation, Elmsford, NY; *U.S. Public*, pg. 1701
Walsh, James K., Exec. V.P. & Gen. Counsel--Ardent Software, Inc., Westborough, MA; *U.S. Public*, pg. 129
Walsh, Jerome K., Sr. V.P.--American Steamship Company, Williamsville, NY; *U.S. Public*, pg. 690
Walsh, John, Pres. & Exec. V.P.-Shaving Prods. Grp.--Warner-Lambert Shaving Products Group, Milford, CT; *U.S. Public*, pg. 1739
Walsh, John F., Pres.-Consumer Prods. Sector & Exec. V.P.--Warner-Lambert Company, Morris Plains, NJ; *U.S. Public*, pg. 1738
Walsh, John F., Pres.-Consumer Products Sector & Exec. V.P.--Warner-Lambert Consumer Healthcare, Morris Plains, NJ; *U.S. Public*, pg. 1739
Walsh, Kelly, Exec. V.P. & Gen. Counsel--Ameritech Corp., Chicago, IL; *U.S. Public*, pg. 98
Walsh, Kenneth G., Exec. V.P.--U.S. Trust Corporation, New York, NY; *U.S. Public*, pg. 1688
Walsh, Kevin J., Exec. V.P.--Mercury Air Group Inc., Los Angeles, CA; *U.S. Public*, pg. 1092
Walsh, Thomas G., Exec. V.P.--First Data Corporation, Englewood, CO; *U.S. Public*, pg. 631
Walsh, Thomas G., Exec. V.P.-Insurance Services--Teachers Insurance and Annuity Association, New York, NY; *U.S. Private*, pg. 1071
Walsh, William J., Jr., Chief Oper. Officer, Exec. V.P. & Sec.--Consumers Financial Corporation, Camp Hill, PA; *U.S. Public*, pg. 437
Walsworth, Edgar, Exec. V.P.-Mfg. & Comml. Sls.--Walsworth Publishing Company, Inc., Marceline, MO; *U.S. Private*, pg. 1148
Walter, John C., Exec. V.P.-Admin., Fin. & H.R.--Western Gas Resources, Inc., Denver, CO; *U.S. Public*, pg. 1758
Walters, James, Exec. V.P.--La Mesa R V Center, Inc., San Diego, CA; *U.S. Private*, pg. 640
Walters, Jess M., Exec. V.P.--Hall Contracting Corp., Louisville, KY; *U.S. Private*, pg. 495
Walther, William M., Exec. V.P.-Mngmt. & Tech.--Albany International Corp., Albany, NY; *U.S. Public*, pg. 36
Walton, E.C., Exec. V.P.--Unisource, Doraville, GA; *U.S. Public*, pg. 1671
Walton, Jerry W., Chief Fin. Officer & Exec. V.P.-Fin.--J.B. Hunt Transport Services, Inc., Lowell, AR; *U.S. Public*, pg. 849
Walton, Kent R., Sr. Exec. V.P.-Sls. Promo.--Rexair, Inc., Troy, MI; *U.S. Public*, pg. 1684
Waltzer, Julius, V.P., Treas. & Sec.--Jack Young Associates, Hazleton, PA; *U.S. Private*, pg. 1201
Walz, Judith T., Exec. V.P.--First Midwest Bank, N.A., Itasca, IL; *U.S. Public*, pg. 636
Wambold, Richard L., Exec. V.P.-Specialty & Consumer Prods.--Tenneco Packaging, Evanston, IL; *U.S. Public*, pg. 1579
Wambsganss, Dick, Exec. V.P.-Trust--Regions Financial Corporation, Birmingham, AL; *U.S. Public*, pg. 1371
Wan, David, Exec. V.P.-Strategic Plng. & Devel.--Simon & Schuster, New York, NY; *U.S. Private*, pg. 777
Wangprakobsook, Sumalee, Exec. V.P.--Bangkok Bank Public Company Limited, Bangkok, Thailand; *Int'l*, pg. 146

Wannamaker, Gerald R., Exec. V.P.-Opers.--Kit Manufacturing Company, Long Beach, CA; *U.S. Public*, pg. 962

Wannamaker, Jeffrey R., Exec. V.P.-Opers.--The Coast Distribution System, San Jose, CA; *U.S. Public*, pg. 388

Wansik, R.E., Exec. V.P.-Chemical Logistics America--Royal Pakhoed NV, Rotterdam, Netherlands; *Int'l*, pg. 1147

Ward-Burns, J. Robert, Chief Oper. Officer & Exec. V.P.--BeautiControl Cosmetics, Inc., Carrollton, TX; *U.S. Public*, pg. 198

Ward, Bruce C., Exec. V.P.--BRE Properties, Inc., San Francisco, CA; *U.S. Public*, pg. 163

Ward, David, Exec. V.P.--Namico, Inc., Philadelphia, PA; *U.S. Private*, pg. 773

Ward, Jeff, Publisher & Exec. V.P.--Weight Watchers Magazine, Birmingham, AL; *U.S. Public*, pg. 1612

Ward, Lloyd, Exec. V.P. & Pres.-N.A. Appliance--Maytag Corporation, Newton, IA; *U.S. Public*, pg. 1064

Ward, Michael E., Exec. V.P.--Ward Trucking Corp., Altoona, PA; *U.S. Private*, pg. 1149

Ward, Richard S., Exec. V.P., Gen. Counsel & Sec.--ITT Corporation, New York, NY; *U.S. Public*, pg. 1512

Ward, Robert A., Exec. V.P.--Unifi Inc., Greensboro, NC; *U.S. Public*, pg. 1665

Wardell, Kevin S., Exec. V.P.-South Regional Opers.--Advocate Health Care, Oak Brook, IL; *U.S. Private*, pg. 23

Warden, William C., Jr., Chief Admin. Officer, Exec. V.P., Gen. Counsel & Sec.--Lowe's Companies, Inc., North Wilkesboro, NC; *U.S. Public*, pg. 1015

Warfel, Daniel L., Chief Fin. Officer & Exec. V.P.--Omega Financial Corporation, State College, PA; *U.S. Public*, pg. 1222

Warga, John E., Chief Fin. Officer & Exec. V.P.--Dynalectric Company, Mc Lean, VA; *U.S. Public*, pg. 571

Warner, Bradford H., Exec. V.P.--BankBoston Corporation, Boston, MA; *U.S. Public*, pg. 183

Warner, Greg, Chief Oper. Officer & Exec. V.P.--Kia Motors America, Inc., Irvine, CA; *Int'l*, pg. 733

Warner, Jeffrey D., Exec. V.P.- Fin.--Environetx, Itasca, IL; *U.S. Private*, pg. 378

Warner, John, Exec. V.P.--Science Applications International Corp., San Diego, CA; *U.S. Private*, pg. 975

Warner, Robin, Exec. V.P.-Golden Books/Mass Market Div.--Golden Books Publishing, New York, NY; *U.S. Public*, pg. 749

Warren, Anthony J., Exec. V.P. & Chief Oper. Officer--Illinois National Insurance Co., Manchester, NH; *U.S. Public*, pg. 84

Warren, R. Conner, Chief Fin. Officer, & Exec. V.P.-Fin. & Admin.--Citation Corporation, Birmingham, AL; *U.S. Public*, pg. 376

Warrington, Robert H., Exec. V.P.--Old Kent Financial Corporation, Grand Rapids, MI; *U.S. Public*, pg. 1216

Washburn, Don, Exec. V.P.-Flight Opers. & Pres./Northwest Cargo--Northwest Airlines, Inc., Saint Paul, MN; *U.S. Public*, pg. 1200

Washburn, Donald A., Exec. V.P.-Customer Svcs. & Opers.--Northwest Airlines Corp., Saint Paul, MN; *U.S. Public*, pg. 1199

Washburn, Frank A., Chief Oper. Officer, Exec. V.P. & Sec.--Pamida Holdings Corporation, Omaha, NE; *U.S. Public*, pg. 1255

Washburn, Richard V., Exec. V.P.-H.R. & Sec.--First of America Bank Corporation, Kalamazoo, MI; *U.S. Public*, pg. 636

Washizuka, Isamu, Sr. Exec. Dir.-Info., Communication & Printing Systems--Sharp Corporation, Osaka, Japan; *Int'l, pg. 1228*

Washow, Lawrence E., Chief Oper. Officer & Exec. V.P.--AMCOL International Corp., Arlington Heights, IL; *U.S. Public*, pg. 63

Wason, Robert A., IV, Exec. V.P.-Performance Systems--Vulcan Chemicals, Birmingham, AL; *U.S. Public*, pg. 1725

Wassell, James T., Exec. V.P.--ABR Information Services, Inc., Palm Harbor, FL; *U.S. Public*, pg. 2

Wassenaar, John, Exec. V.P. & Treas.--Fareway Stores, Inc., Boone, IA; *U.S. Private*, pg. 393

Wasserman, Leonard, Exec. V.P.--Today's Man, Inc., Moorestown, NJ; *U.S. Public*, pg. 1619

Wasulko, William, V.P.-America's--Atotech U.S.A. Inc., Rock Hill, SC; *U.S. Private*, pg. 97

Watanabe, August M., M.D., Exec. V.P.-Science & Tech.--Eli Lilly and Company, Indianapolis, IN; *U.S. Public*, pg. 992

Watanabe, Goro, Exec. V.P.--Mitsui & Co., Ltd., Tokyo, Japan; *Int'l*, pg. 877

Watanabe, Kenji, Exec. V.P.-Engrng. & Tech.--Mitsubishi Silicon America, Salem, OR; *Int'l*, pg. 875

Watanabe, Shotaro, Exec. V.P.--Kao Corporation, Tokyo, Japan; *Int'l*, pg. 717

Watanabe, Suzuo, Exec. V.P.--Meiji Seika Kaisha, Ltd., Tokyo, Japan; *Int'l*, pg. 855

Watanabe, Takeji, Exec. Dir.--Dentsu Inc., Tokyo, Japan; *Int'l*, pg. 392

Watchmaker, Ken, Exec. V.P.-Fin. & Systems(Reebok Brand)--Reebok International Ltd., Stoughton, MA; *U.S. Public*, pg. 1369

Waterkotte, Michael, Exec. V.P. & Co-Creative Dir.--Lois/EJL Chicago, Chicago, IL; *U.S. Public*, pg. 1011

Watjen, Thomas R., Chief Fin. Officer & Exec. V.P.--Provident Companies, Inc., Chattanooga, TN; *U.S. Public*, pg. 1337

Watkins, Tim, Exec. V.P. & Controller--The Acorn, Kalamazoo, MI; *U.S. Private*, pg. 454

Watkins, William, Jr., Exec. V.P.--Narragansett Energy Resources Company, Providence, RI; *U.S. Public*, pg. 1171

Watson, A.M. Bruce, Exec. V.P.--The Loewen Group, Inc., Burnaby, Canada; *Int'l*, pg. 814

Watson, Christopher M., Exec. V.P.--Pacific Gateway Properties, San Francisco, CA; *U.S. Public*, pg. 1250

Watson, David, Grp. Pres.-ICF Kaiser Engineers & Constructors Grp. & Exec. V.P.--ICF Kaiser International Inc., Fairfax, VA; *U.S. Public*, pg. 852

Watson, David E., Chief Fin. Officer & Exec. V.P.--American Italian Pasta Company, Excelsior Springs, MO; *U.S. Public*, pg. 85

Watson, Edward A., Chief Oper. Officer & Exec. V.P.--International Dairy Queen, Inc., Minneapolis, MN; *U.S. Public*, pg. 220

Watson, Kenneth, Chief Fin. Officer & Exec. V.P.--MBL Life Assurance Corporation, Newark, NJ; *U.S. Private*, pg. 685

Watson, Molly, Sr. V.P. & Media Services Dir.--Tierney & Partners, Philadelphia, PA; *U.S. Public*, pg. 1641

Watson, Richard P., Chief Oper. Officer & Exec. V.P.--H & H Tube & Manufacturing Co., Vanderbilt, MI; *U.S. Private*, pg. 489

Watson, Robert A., Exec. V.P.-Consumer & Comml. Lending Opers.--Transamerica Corporation, San Francisco, CA; *U.S. Public*, pg. 1629

Watson, William M., Jr., Exec. V.P. & Gen. Counsel--Wachovia Bank, Charlottesville, VA; *U.S. Public*, pg. 1730

Watt, David C., Exec. V.P., Gen. Counsel & Sec.--ICN Pharmaceuticals, Inc., Costa Mesa, CA; *U.S. Public*, pg. 853

Watt, Robert, Exec. V.P.--Golden Cat Corporation, Saint Louis, MO; *U.S. Public*, pg. 1360

Watt, William F., Exec. V.P. & Dir.-Mktg./Retail Banking--FirstFed Financial Corp., Santa Monica, CA; *U.S. Public*, pg. 645

Wattanakasaem, Indhira, Exec. V.P.-Chief Policy Grp.--Nakornthon Bank Public Company Limited, Bangkok, Thailand; *Int'l*, pg. 904

Wattel, Bob, Exec. V.P.-Mktg.--Lettuce Entertain You Enterprises, Inc., Chicago, IL; *U.S. Private*, pg. 661

Watters, Ginger, Exec. V.P. & Acct. Mngmt. Dir.--Fahlgren, Tampa, FL; *U.S. Private*, pg. 391

Watts, James B., Exec. V.P.-Human Resources, Education & Training--Associates First Capital Corporation, Dallas, TX; *U.S. Public*, pg. 662

Watts, James B., Exec. V.P.-Human Resources--Associates Financial Services Corporation, Dallas, TX; *U.S. Public*, pg. 663

Watts, James O., III, Exec. V.P.--American Security Group, Atlanta, GA; *Int'l*, pg. 499

Waugh, R.E., Exec. V.P.--The Bank of Nova Scotia, New York, NY; *Int'l*, pg. 156

Waxenberg, Alan M., Exec. V.P. & Publr.--Victoria, New York, NY; *U.S. Private*, pg. 517

Waxman, Jeffrey H., Exec. V.P.-Applications Group--Novell, Inc., Orem, UT; *U.S. Public*, pg. 1203

Waxman, Melvin, Chief Exec. Officer--CWI International China, Ltd., Fujian, China; *U.S. Public*, pg. 1749

Waxman, Norman, Exec. V.P.--Schnadig Corporation, Des Plaines, IL; *U.S. Private*, pg. 971

Wayman, Robert P., Chief Fin. Officer & Exec. V.P.-Fin. & Admin.--Hewlett-Packard Company, Palo Alto, CA; *U.S. Public*, pg. 813

Wayne, Joel, Exec. V.P.-Worldwide Creative Adv. Projects--Warner Bros. Studios, Inc., Burbank, CA; *U.S. Public*, pg. 1611

Wayvon, Paul, Exec. V.P.--Fleming Packaging Corp., Peoria, IL; *U.S. Private*, pg. 411

Weatherford, Timothy, Exec. V.P.-Sls.--SofTECH, Inc., Grand Rapids, MI; *U.S. Public*, pg. 1482

Weathers, D. Lee, Exec. V.P.-Trust Div.--AmSouth Bancorporation, Birmingham, AL; *U.S. Public*, pg. 105

Weaver, B. H., Chief Oper. Officer & Exec. V.P.--Westco Products, Inc., Pico Rivera, CA; *Int'l*, pg. 244

Weaver, David F., Exec. V.P.--First Banks America, Inc., Clayton, MO; *U.S. Public*, pg. 626

Weaver, John, Exec. V.P. & Pres.-Newsprint Opers. & Sls.--Abitibi-Consolidated Inc., Montreal, Canada; *Int'l*, pg. 19

Weaver, John C., Exec. V.P. & Chm. Bd. & Chief Exec. Officer-Raytheon Intl., Inc.--Raytheon Company, Lexington, MA; *U.S. Public*, pg. 1364

Webb, E. Lynn, Exec. V.P. & Treas.--Dualite Sales & Service, Inc., Williamsburg, OH; *U.S. Private*, pg. 344

Webb, Kyle, Exec. V.P.--Mayfield Building Supply Co., Arlington, TX; *U.S. Private*, pg. 686

Webb, Lewis, Jr., Exec. V.P.--Webb Automotive Group, Cerritos, CA; *U.S. Private*, pg. 1156

Webb, Ronald L., Exec. V.P.-Edelbrock Foundry Corp.--Edelbrock Corp., Torrance, CA; *U.S. Public*, pg. 563

Weber, Andrew, Exec. V.P.-Mfg. & New Prod. Info.--Reed Elsevier Business Information, Newton, MA; *Int'l*, pg. 1095

Weber, Jacques, Exec. V.P.--Bull S.A., Louveciennes, France; *Int'l*, pg. 315

Weber, John H., Exec. V.P. & Pres.-Vickers, Incorporated--Aeroquip-Vickers, Inc., Maumee, OH; *U.S. Public*, pg. 24

Weber, Ronald G., Exec. V.P.-Tech. & Engrng.--Lowrance Electronics, Inc., Tulsa, OK; *U.S. Public*, pg. 1015

Webking, Rick, Exec. V.P.--BTI Americas, Inc., Northbrook, IL; *U.S. Private*, pg. 108

Webster, G. Alfred, Exec. V.P.--Unifi Inc., Greensboro, NC; *U.S. Public*, pg. 1665

Webster, Michael, Exec. V.P. & Service Line Dir.--Ross Roy Communications, Inc., Bloomfield Hills, MI; *U.S. Private*, pg. 946

Webster, Vic, Exec. V.P.--Laidlaw Transit, Inc, Van Nuys, CA; *Int'l*, pg. 259

Weckworth, Rodney R., Exec. V.P.--Rex Moore Electrical Contractors & Engineers, West Sacramento, CA; *U.S. Private*, pg. 760

Wedaman, David H., Chief Oper. Officer, Exec. V.P. & Pres.-Mark VII Transportation--Mark VII, Inc., Memphis, TN; *U.S. Public*, pg. 1046

Wedel, Jorgen, Exec. V.P.-Intl. Grp.--The Gillette Company, Boston, MA; *U.S. Public*, pg. 743

Wedge, Michael T., Exec. V.P.-Sls. Opers.--BJ's Wholesale Club, Inc., Natick, MA; *U.S. Public*, pg. 162

Wee, Sung Bok, Exec. V.P. & Dir.--Cho Hung Bank, Seoul, Korea; *Int'l*, pg. 287

Weeber, W. Steven, Exec. V.P.-Opers. Staff--Nalco Chemical Company, Naperville, IL; *U.S. Public*, pg. 1150

Weeden, James E., Exec. V.P.--American Felt & Filter, Newburgh, NY; *U.S. Private*, pg. 54

Weedon, Michael, Chief Admin. Officer & Exec. V.P.--The Loewen Group, Inc., Burnaby, Canada; *Int'l*, pg. 814

Weg, Kenneth E., Exec. V.P. & Pres.-Worldwide Medicines Grp.--Bristol-Myers Squibb Company, New York, NY; *U.S. Public*, pg. 253

Wegner, Arthur E., Exec. V.P., Chm. Bd. & Chief Exec. Officer-Raytheon Aircraft Co.--Raytheon Company, Lexington, MA; *U.S. Public*, pg. 1364

Weibley, Vance, Exec. V.P.--Sun City Industries, Inc., Fort Lauderdale, FL; *U.S. Public*, pg. 1529

Weicht, Scott, Exec. V.P.--Adolfson & Peterson, Inc., Minneapolis, MN; *U.S. Private*, pg. 17

Weidner, Wayne R., Exec. V.P.--National Penn Bancshares, Inc., Boyertown, PA; *U.S. Public*, pg. 1158

Weikel, M. Keith, Chief Oper. Officer & Sr. Exec. V.P.--Health Care & Retirement Corporation, Toledo, OH; *U.S.* Public, pg. 801

Weimer, Jerry, Exec. V.P.-Records & Music--Word, Incorporated, Dallas, TX; *U.S. Public*, pg. 704

Weimer, Jerry W., Chief Oper. Officer & Exec. V.P.--Integrity Incorporated, Mobile, AL; *U.S. Public*, pg. 886

Weinberg, Richard A., Exec. V.P., Gen. Counsel & Sec.--GAF Materials Corporation, Wayne, NJ; *U.S. Private*, pg. 433

Weinberg, Robert W., Chief Fin. Officer, Sr. Exec. V.P. & Treas.--K-Tron International, Inc., Pitman, NJ; *U.S. Public*, pg. 938

Weinberg, Thomas A., Chief Oper. Officer-Los Angeles, Exec. V.P. & Dir.--EvansGroup, Salt Lake City, UT; *U.S. Private*, pg. 385

Weiner, Eugene L., Exec. V.P., Sec. & Treas.--Paradise, Inc., Plant City, FL; *U.S. Public*, pg. 1256

Weiner, Gerald, Exec. V.P.--Republic National Bank of New York, New York, NY; *U.S. Public*, pg. 1380

Weiner, Jurgen M., Vice Chm. & Exec. V.P.--Nezel S.A., Barcelona, Spain; *Int'l*, pg. 1279

Weiner, Steven, Exec. V.P.--Intercontinental Branded Apparel, Buffalo, NY; *U.S. Public*, pg. 796

Weiner, Warren, Exec. V.P., Treas. & Sec.--Deb Shops, Inc., Philadelphia, PA; *U.S. Public*, pg. 491

Weinfeld, Lewis A., Chief Fin. Officer & Exec. V.P.--Starrett HRH, New York, NY; *U.S. Private*, pg. 1035

Weinhart, Martin, Chm. Bd. & Treas.--Master Molded Products Corporation, Elgin, IL; *U.S. Private*, pg. 714

Weinhold, Joachim, Exec. V.P.-Intl. Securities--Bayerische Landesbank, Munich, Germany; *Int'l*, pg. 176

Weinhuff, Jeffry K., Exec. V.P. & Dir.-Corp. Fin.--Jefferies & Company, Inc., Los Angeles, CA; *U.S. Public*, pg. 925

Weinstein, Alan I., Chief Fin. & Admin. Officer, Sr. Exec. V.P. & Sec.--Morse Shoe, Inc., Canton, MA; *U.S. Public*, pg. 168

Weinstein, Marta, Exec. V.P.--Logistix, Fremont, CA; *U.S. Private*, pg. 673

Weinstein, Walter, Exec. V.P.--Levlad, Inc., Chatsworth, CA; *U.S. Private*, pg. 663

Weinstock, Milton, Exec. V.P.--Grey Advertising Inc., New York, NY; *U.S. Public*, pg. 764

Weir, Kevin, Co-Mng. Dir. & Exec. V.P.--Fort Pitt Acquisitions, Inc., Coraopolis, PA; *U.S. Private*, pg. 419

Weir, Stephen J., Chief Fin. Officer & Exec. V.P.--Telemedia Inc., Montreal, Canada; *Int'l*, pg. 1373

Weirsoe, Steen, Exec. V.P.--Danisco A/S, Copenhagen, Denmark; *Int'l*, pg. 378

Weis, Peter, Dr., Exec. V.P.--Bayerische Hypotheken-und Wechsel-Bank Aktiengesellschaft, Munich, Germany; *Int'l*, pg. 175

Weise, Theodore L., Exec. V.P.-Worldwide Opers.--FDX Corporation, Memphis, TN; *U.S. Public*, pg. 603

Weiseman, James M., Exec. V.P.--Citizens First State Bank, Hartford City, IN; *U.S. Public*, pg. 632

Weisfeld, Marty, Exec. V.P. & Mgr.-Promo Sls.--MUDD Jeans, Inc., New York, NY; *U.S. Private*, pg. 766

Weisheimer, Richard A., Exec. V.P.--Gerbig, Snell/Weisheimer & Assoc., Inc., Columbus, OH; *U.S. Private*, pg. 449

Weisman, Steve, Chief Oper. Officer & Exec. V.P.--Gulf Coast Food Service Inc., Port Richey, FL; *U.S. Public*, pg. 1529

Weiss, Andrew J., Exec. V.P.--Stebbins Engineering & Mfg. Co., Watertown, NY; *U.S. Private*, pg. 1037

Weiss, Edmund C., Jr., Exec. V.P. & Auditor--Summit Bancorp, Princeton, NJ; *U.S. Public*, pg. 1527

Weiss, Eric, Exec. V.P. & Gen. Counsel--Active International, Pearl River, NY; *U.S. Private*, pg. 15

Weiss, Martin, Sr. Exec. V.P.-Sls.--Bestform Foundations, Inc., Long Island City, NY; *U.S. Private*, pg. 140

Weiss, Martin, Sr. Exec. V.P.-Sls.--Lily of France, Inc., New York, NY; *U.S. Private*, pg. 140

Weiss, Robert S., Chief Fin. Officer & Exec. V.P.--The Cooper Companies, Inc., Irvine, CA; *U.S. Public*, pg. 442

Weisser, Sidney, Exec. V.P.--Cine Magnetics, Inc., Armonk, NY; *U.S. Private*, pg. 240

Weisshappel, Robert N., Exec. V.P. & Gen. Mgr.-Cellular Subscriber Grp.--Motorola, Inc., Schaumburg, IL; *U.S. Public*, pg. 1136

Weisz, Stephen P., Exec. V.P.-Marriott Lodging & Pres.-Marriott Vacation Club Intl.--Marriott International, Inc., Washington, DC; *U.S. Public*, pg. 1047

Weitz, Eric, Exec. V.P.--Apparel America, Inc., New Haven, CT; *U.S. Public*, pg. 120

Weitzel, John, Exec. V.P.-Seattle--J.W. Messner, Inc., Grand Rapids, MI; *U.S. Private*, pg. 734

Weitzel, John A., Exec. V.P.--Premium Budget Plan, Inc., Winston Salem, NC; *U.S. Public*, pg. 1453

Weitzel, John A., Exec. V.P.--The Innovative Company, Winston Salem, NC; *U.S. Public*, pg. 1454

Weitzel, John A., Exec. V.P.--Universal Insurance Co., Winston Salem, NC; *U.S. Public*, pg. 1454

Weitzen, Jeffrey, Exec. V.P.-Bus. Markets Div.--AT&T Corporation, Basking Ridge, NJ; *U.S. Public*, pg. 10

Weitzman, Howard L., Exec. V.P.-Corp. Opers.--Universal Studios, Inc., Universal City, CA; *Int'l*, pg. 1215

Weixel, Kenneth, Exec. V.P.-Health Care Fin. Bus. Strategy--PHP Healthcare Corporation, Reston, VA; *U.S. Public*, pg. 1241

Welch, James, Exec. V.P.-Bistro Suppa Brand--Restaurants Unlimited, Seattle, WA; *U.S. Private*, pg. 925

Welch, Laurel, Exec. V.P.--JL Media Inc., Miami, FL; *U.S. Private*, pg. 577

Welch, R.J., Exec. V.P. & Chief Actuary--American National Insurance Company, Galveston, TX; *U.S. Public*, pg. 87

Welchman, Gary P., Exec. V.P.--Burlington Industries, Inc., Greensboro, NC; *U.S. Public*, pg. 268

Welge, Michael W., Exec. V.P., Treas., Sec. & Comptroller--Gilster Mary Lee Corp., Chester, IL; *U.S. Private*, pg. 455

Welin, Per, Exec. V.P.--L E Lundbergforetagen AB, Stockholm, Sweden; *Int'l*, pg. 820

Wellard, Charles L., Exec. V.P.--Communication Cable, Inc., Sanford, NC; *U.S. Public*, pg. 968

Weller, Andrew M., Chief Fin. Officer, Exec. V.P., Dir. & Sec--Johnstown America Industries, Chicago, IL; *U.S. Public*, pg. 933

Wellington, Donna, Chief Oper. Officer & Exec. V.P.--Ronco, Inventions. LLC, Chatsworth, CA; *U.S. Private*, pg. 943

Wells Robert, Exec. V.P. & WW Human Resources Dir.--Young & Rubicam New York, New York, NY; *U.S. Private*, pg. 1198

Wells, Don S., Exec. V.P.-Strategic Investments--Royal Bank of Canada, Toronto, Canada; *Int'l*, pg. 1131

Wells, J.M., III, Exec. V.P. & Sec.--The Homer Laughlin China Company, Newell, WV; *U.S. Private*, pg. 653

Wells, J.M., III, Exec. V.P. & Sec.--The Newell Company, Newell, WV; *U.S. Private*, pg. 653

Wells, J.M., III, Exec. V.P. & Sec.--Newell Bridge & Railway Company, Newell, WV; *U.S. Private*, pg. 653

Wells, Randall S., Exec. V.P. & Gen. Mgr.--Wells-Gardner Electronics Corp., Chicago, IL; *U.S. Public*, pg. 1753

Wells, Robert B., Chief Fin. Officer & Exec. V.P.--Bank of Montreal, Toronto, Canada; *Int'l*, pg. 153

Welp, David W., Exec. V.P.--Raytheon Systems Company, Arlington, VA; *U.S. Public*, pg. 1364

Welp, David W., Exec. V.P.--Texas Instruments Incorporated, Dallas, TX; *U.S. Public*, pg. 1585

Welsh, Kelly R., Exec. V.P. & Gen. Counsel--Ameritech Corporation, Chicago, IL; *U.S. Public*, pg. 97

Welts, Rick, Exec. V.P.--National Basketball Association, New York, NY; *U.S. Private*, pg. 780

Wendell, Peter H., Exec. V.P.--ABN AMRO Chicago Corp., Chicago, IL; *Int'l*, pg. 10

Wender, Ira T., Chm. Bd.--Perry Ellis, New York, NY; *U.S. Public*, pg. 1429

Wendlandt, Gary E., Chief Investment Officer & Exec. V.P.--Massachusetts Mutual Life Insurance Co., Springfield, MA; *U.S. Private*, pg. 712

Wendler, George, Exec. V.P. & Sr. Credit Officer--Republic National Bank of New York, New York, NY; *U.S. Public*, pg. 1380

Wendler, George T., Exec. V.P.--Republic New York Corporation, New York, NY; *U.S. Public*, pg. 1380

Wendler, George T., Exec. V.P.--Republic Bank for Savings, New York, NY; *U.S. Public*, pg. 1380

Wendling, Erhard, Exec. V.P.--Lester B. Knight & Associates, Inc., Chicago, IL; *U.S. Private*, pg. 626

Weng, Simon, Exec. V.P.-Sls., Asia--Tippins Incorporated, Pittsburgh, PA; *U.S. Private*, pg. 1088

Wenger, Jurg E., Chief Fin. Officer & Exec. V.P.--Mikron Holding AG, Biel, Switzerland; *Int'l*, pg. 866

Wenk, Robert, Exec. V.P.--Pacific Handy Cutter, Inc., Costa Mesa, CA; *U.S. Private*, pg. 831

Wenk, Robert B., Exec. V.P.--Spectrum Razor Tools, Costa Mesa, CA; *U.S. Private*, pg. 831

Wentworth, John, Exec. V.P.-Mktg. Paramount T.V. Div.--Paramount Pictures Corporation, Los Angeles, CA; *U.S. Private*, pg. 776

Werber, Elliott, Exec. V.P.-W. Region--Bergen Brunswig Corporation, Orange, CA; *U.S. Public*, pg. 213

Werhahn-Mees, Kai, Dr., Exec. V.P.--Bayerische Vereinsbank AG, Hong Kong, Hong Kong; *Int'l*, pg. 180

Werhane, John, Exec. V.P. & Dir.-Engrng.--Sargent & Lundy, Chicago, IL; *U.S. Private*, pg. 965

Werle, Wolfgang, Exec. V.P.-Catering--The Swissair Group, Zurich, Switzerland; *Int'l*, pg. 1333

Wernecke, Daniel R., Exec. V.P.--Sparks State Bank, Sparks, MD; *U.S. Public*, pg. 1089

Werner, David, Chief Fin. Officer & Exec. V.P.--KTI, Orange, CA; *U.S. Public*, pg. 939

Werner, Hermann R., Exec. V.P. & Pres.-Fibers, Organics & Rubber Div.--Bayer Corporation, Parsippany, NJ; *Int'l*, pg. 172

Werner, Klaus, Dr., Exec. V.P.--H. Krantz-TKT GmbH, Bergisch Gladbach, Germany; *Int'l*, pg. 399

Werner, Nina, Chief Fin. Officer & Exec. V.P.--Zenith Media Services, Inc., New York, NY; *U.S. Private*, pg. 1204

Wernick, Jeffrey, Exec. V.P.-Opers.--DIC Entertainment, Burbank, CA; *U.S. Public*, pg. 513

Wernick, Justin, Dr., Exec. V.P. & Sec.--The Langer Biomechanics Group, Inc., Deer Park, NY; *U.S. Public*, pg. 978

Wertheimer, Merrill J., Exec. V.P.-Fin. & Admin.--Zale Corporation, Irving, TX; *U.S. Public*, pg. 1789

Wertheimer, Robert E., Exec. V.P.--Longview Fibre Company, Longview, WA; *U.S. Public*, pg. 1013

Wertz, Larry J., Exec. V.P. & Chief Fin. Officer-First Union Nat'l Bank of FL--First Union Corporation, Charlotte, NC; *U.S. Public*, pg. 639

Wertz, Larry J., Chief Fin. Officer & Exec. V.P.--First Union National Bank of Florida, Jacksonville, FL; *U.S. Public*, pg. 640

Wessel, Jay, Exec. V.P.--Christie Design, Chatsworth, CA; *U.S. Public*, pg. 1369

Wessel, Jeffrey H., Exec. V.P.-Corp., Institutional & Investment Services--Northern Trust Corporation, Chicago, IL; *U.S. Public*, pg. 1195

Wessels, D., Exec. V.P.--ABN-AMRO Holding N.V., Amsterdam, Netherlands; *Int'l*, pg. 8

West, Kevin, Exec. V.P.--Southwest Recreational Industries Inc., Leander, TX; *U.S. Private*, pg. 1018

West, Neil S., Exec. Officer--First Commercial Corporation, Little Rock, AR; *U.S. Public*, pg. 630

West, Richard E., Exec. V.P.-Wholesale Banking--D & N Financial Corporation, Hancock, MI; *U.S. Public*, pg. 472

West, Steven H., V.P.--Delagra Corporation, Bridgeville, DE; *U.S. Private*, pg. 321

West, William H., Jr., Exec. V.P.-Portfolio Management--Resource Mortgage Capital, Inc., Glen Allen, VA; *U.S. Public*, pg. 1382

Westerhoff, Garret P., Exec. V.P.--Malcolm Pirnie, Inc., White Plains, NY; *U.S. Private*, pg. 867

Westerman, Frank G., Exec. V.P.--Select Canfield, Chicago, IL; *U.S. Private*, pg. 982

Westermeyer, A. Neal, Chief Oper. Officer & Exec. V.P.--National Health Enhancement Systems, Inc., Phoenix, AZ; *U.S. Public*, pg. 1157

Westfall, Bill, Exec. V.P.--Westfall GMC Truck Inc., Kansas City, MO; *U.S. Private*, pg. 1169

Westfall, Dave, Exec. V.P.--RE/MAX International, Inc., Englewood, CO; *U.S. Private*, pg. 912

Westlund, Per, Exec. V.P.-Grp. Devel.--Skanska AB, Danderyd, Sweden; *Int'l*, pg. 1260

Weston, Paul J., Exec. V.P.-Mutual Funds--Gradison Division, Cincinnati, OH; *U.S. Public*, pg. 1068

Wettlaufer, Keith, Chief Fin. Officer & Exec. V.P.--A.G. Simpson Co. Limited, Scarborough, Canada; *Int'l*, pg. 1252

Wetzel, Gilbert, Exec. V.P.--Right Management Consultants, Inc., Philadelphia, PA; *U.S. Public*, pg. 1390

Wexler, Howard B., Exec. V.P.--American Security Group, Atlanta, GA; *Int'l*, pg. 499

Wexler, Philip M., Exec. V.P.-Specialized Lending--Union Bank of California, San Francisco, CA; *Int'l*, pg. 157

Wexler, Steve, Exec. V.P. & Gen. Mgr.-Northern Area--Norstan, Inc., Plymouth, MN; *U.S. Public*, pg. 1192

Weyant, Donald E., Exec. V.P.--Bank of the West, Walnut Creek, CA; *Int'l*, pg. 163

Weymarn, Rabbe V., Exec. V.P.--Leiras Oy, Turku, Finland; *Int'l*, pg. 639

Weymarn, Tom, Exec. V.P.-Cultor Grp.--Cultor Ltd., Helsinki, Finland; *Int'l*, pg. 349

Whalen, James W., Chief Fin. Officer, Sr. Exec. V.P. & Treas.--Tejas Gas Corporation, Houston, TX; *Int'l*, pg. 1136

Wheaton, Robert E., Exec. V.P.--CKE Restaurants Inc., Anaheim, CA; *U.S. Public*, pg. 278

Wheeler, John E., Chief Fin. Officer, Exec. V.P. & Treas.--Crown Central Petroleum Corporation, Baltimore, MD; *U.S. Public*, pg. 462

Wheeler, Jonathan R., Exec. V.P. & Pres.-CT Film--Rexene Corporation, Dallas, TX; *U.S. Private*, pg. 549

Whelan, John, Exec. V.P.--Bright of America, Inc., Summersville, WV; *U.S. Public*, pg. 223

Whelan, Nancy, Exec. V.P.--Baldi, Bloom & Whelan Advertising, New York, NY; *U.S. Private*, pg. 112

Whelehan, Kathleen, Exec. V.P. & Rochester Reg. Pres.--Marine Midland Bank, Buffalo, NY; *Int'l*, pg. 581

Whelpton, P., Exec. V.P.--Royal Caribbean Cruises Ltd., Miami, FL; *U.S. Public*, pg. 1410

Whiddon, Thomas E., Chief Fin. Officer & Exec. V.P.--Lowe's Companies, Inc., North Wilkesboro, NC; *U.S. Public*, pg. 1015

Whipple, Kenneth, Exec. V.P.--Ford Motor Company, Dearborn, MI; *U.S. Public*, pg. 661

Whipple, Richard, Exec. V.P.--Kingsbury Corporation, Keene, NH; *U.S. Private*, pg. 621

White, Britton, Jr., Exec. V.P.-Govt. Affairs & Gen. Counsel--El Paso Natural Gas Co., Houston, TX; *U.S. Public*, pg. 567

White, Charles R., Exec. V.P. & Chief Exec. Officer--Fastec Industrial, Elkhart, IN; *U.S. Private*, pg. 397

White, Connie, Chief Oper. Officer, Sr. V.P. & Media Dir.--EvansGroup, Salt Lake City, UT; *U.S. Private*, pg. 385

White, Dewey A., III, Exec. V.P.-Correspondent & Investment Services--Compass Bank, Birmingham, AL; *U.S. Public*, pg. 418

White, J. Robert, Chief Fin. Officer, Exec. V.P. & Treas.--Michael Baker Corporation, Pittsburgh, PA; *U.S. Public*, pg. 168

White, James A., Chief Fin. Officer & Exec. V.P.--BOK Financial Corp., Tulsa, OK; *U.S. Public*, pg. 163

White, James A., Chief Fin. Officer & Exec. V.P.--Bank of Oklahoma, N.A., Tulsa, OK; *U.S. Public*, pg. 163

White, Lawrence A., Exec. V.P.-Corp. Devel.--Versar Inc., Springfield, VA; *U.S. Public*, pg. 1717

White, Lawrence D., Exec. V.P.-Mktg.--NFO Research, Inc., Greenwich, CT; *U.S. Public*, pg. 1146

White, Lawrence E., Chief Fin. Officer & Exec. V.P.--El Chico Restaurants, Inc., Dallas, TX; *U.S. Private*, pg. 283

White, Michael J., Sr. V.P.-Corporate & Chief Investment Officer--Confederation Life Insurance Company, Toronto, Canada; *Int'l*, pg. 325

White, Nick, Exec V.P.-Supercenter Div.--Wal-Mart Stores, Inc., Bentonville, AR; *U.S. Public*, pg. 1732

White, Nick, Exec. V.P.-Super Center Div.--Hypermart USA, Bentonville, AR; *U.S. Public*, pg. 1733

White, Paul H., Exec. V.P.--M.L. Stern & Company, Inc., Beverly Hills, CA; *U.S. Private*, pg. 1041

White, Ph. D., Richard L., Exec. V.P. & Pres.-Fibers, Organics & Rubber Division--Bayer Corporation, Pittsburgh, PA; *Int'l*, pg. 172

White, Richard H., Exec. V.P.--First Maryland Bancorp, Baltimore, MD; *Int'l*, pg. 64

White, Richard L., Pres.-Fibers, Organics & Rubber Div. & Exec. V.P.--Bayer Corporation, Pittsburgh, PA; *Int'l*, pg. 172

White, Ronald R., Exec. V.P.--West Coast Bancorp, Newport Beach, CA; *U.S. Public*, pg. 1755

White, Scott, Exec. V.P.-Corp. Devel.--Budget Rent A Car Corporation, Lisle, IL; *U.S. Private*, pg. 178

White, Sherman, Exec. V.P.-Credit Recovery--Mellon Bank Corporation, Pittsburgh, PA; *U.S. Public*, pg. 1084

White, Tommi A., Exec. V.P.-Service, Quality & Info. Tech.--Kelly Services, Inc., Troy, MI; *U.S. Public*, pg. 949

White, Turner, Exec. V.P.-Corp. Devel.--Kansas City Power & Light Company, Kansas City, MO; *U.S. Public*, pg. 943

White, Utah, Exec. V.P.-Opers.--Fabwel Inc., Elkhart, IN; *U.S. Private*, pg. 390

White, W. Donald, Exec. V.P.-Interactive Media--Trone Advertising, Inc., Greensboro, NC; *U.S. Private*, pg. 1104

White, Walter, Chief Fin. Officer & Exec. V.P.--Lumbermen's Mutual Casualty Company, Long Grove, IL; *U.S. Private*, pg. 614

White, Walter, Chief Fin. Officer & Exec. V.P.--American Manufacturers Mutual Insurance Company, Long Grove, IL; *U.S. Private*, pg. 614

White, Walter L., Chief Fin. Officer & Exec. V.P.--Kemper Insurance Companies, Long Grove, IL; *U.S. Private*, pg. 614

Whitehouse, Neil I., Exec. V.P.--TCF Bank Minnesota FSB, Minneapolis, MN; *U.S. Public*, pg. 1554

Whiteman, Michael B., Exec. V.P.--Sheldon Good & Co., Chicago, IL; *U.S. Private*, pg. 463

Whitenack, William, Exec. V.P.--Dun & Bradstreet, Murray Hill, NJ; *U.S. Public*, pg. 535

Whitesell, Terry, Exec. V.P.-Sls. & Mktg.--Carpenter Industries, Inc., Richmond, IN; *U.S. Private*, pg. 215

Whitham, J., Exec. V.P. & Mng. Dir.--BBDO Canada, Toronto, Canada; *U.S. Private*, pg. 104

Whitman, Bruce N., Exec. V.P.--FlightSafety International Inc., Flushing, NY; *U.S. Public*, pg. 218

Whitman, William E., Chief Fin. Officer, Exec. V.P. & Treas.--Ogden Energy Group, Inc., Fairfield, NJ; *U.S. Public*, pg. 1213

Whitmore, Donald A., Exec. V.P.-Corp. Affairs--Willis Corroon Melling Inc., Toronto, Canada; *Int'l*, pg. 1509

Whitson, James N., Chief Oper. Officer & Exec. V.P.--Sammons Enterprises, Inc., Dallas, TX; *U.S. Private*, pg. 963

Whittaker, Andrew R., Exec. V.P. & Dir.-Fin.--Jefferies & Company, Inc., Los Angeles, CA; *U.S. Public*, pg. 925

Whittaker, Paul, Exec. V.P.--Oberdorfer Industries, Inc., Syracuse, NY; *U.S. Private*, pg. 810

Whittam, James, Exec. V.P.--Shaklee Corporation, San Francisco, CA; *Int'l*, pg. 1518

Whittington, M.J., Exec. V.P.--Philips Electronics Ltd., Scarborough, Canada; *Int'l*, pg. 1055

Whittle, Rob, Exec. V.P. & Gen. Mgr.--Palmer Jarvis Communications, Vancouver, Canada; *Int'l*, pg. 1022

Whyte, Robert, Exec. V.P.--Commercial Union Assurance Company of Canada, Toronto, Canada; *Int'l*, pg. 308

Wichmann, William J., Exec. V.P.--Noville, South Hackensack, NJ; *U.S. Private*, pg. 808

Wickenmann, John, Exec. V.P.--Edelman Worldwide, Inc., New York, NY; *U.S. Private*, pg. 362

Wickett, Richard A., Chief Fin. Officer & Exec. V.P.--The PBS&J Corporation, Miami, FL; *U.S. Private*, pg. 825

Widerberg, M. Johan, Exec. V.P.-Reg. Bank, Western Sweden--Svenska Handelsbanken, Stockholm, Sweden; *Int'l*, pg. 1327

Widerschein, Neil, Chief Oper. Officer & Exec. V.P.--SBC Advertising, Columbus, OH; *U.S. Private*, pg. 955

Widgodsky, John, Exec. V.P.-Sls. & Mktg.--Fruit of the Loom, Inc., Chicago, IL; *U.S. Public*, pg. 685

Widler, James R., Exec. V.P.-Eastern Div.--Interstate Brands Corporation, Kansas City, MO; *U.S. Public*, pg. 909

Wiedelmann, Heinz-Ludwig, Exec. V.P.-Private Banking--Commerzbank AG, Frankfurt, Germany; *Int'l*, pg. 308

Wienkoop, Glenn, Exec. V.P.-Engrng. & Mktg./Independant Sys. Grp.--Honeywell-Measurex Corporation, Cupertino, CA; *U.S. Public*, pg. 833

Wier, James A., Exec. V.P.-Opers.--Briggs & Stratton Corporation, Wauwatosa, WI; *U.S. Public*, pg. 252

Wigan, Gareth P., Exec. V.P.-Production--Columbia Pictures, Culver City, CA; *Int'l*, pg. 1281

Wigdor, Lawrence A., Exec. V.P.--NL Industries, Inc., Houston, TX; *U.S. Private*, pg. 270

Wiggins, Dwight L., Exec. V.P. & Pres.-Tosco Refining Co.--Tosco Corporation, Stamford, CT; *U.S. Public*, pg. 1624

Wigglesworth, Kenneth B., Chief Fin. Officer & V.P.--Newbridge Networks Corporation, Kanata, Canada; *Int'l*, pg. 923

Wight, John W., Jr., Exec. V.P.--HNTB Corporation, Kansas City, MO; *U.S. Private*, pg. 492

Wigodsky, John, Exec. V.P.-Mktg. & Sls.--Delta Apparel, Duluth, GA; *U.S. Public*, pg. 498

Wigodsky, John, Exec. V.P.-Mktg. & Sls.--Union Underwear Co., Inc., Bowling Green, KY; *U.S. Public*, pg. 686

Wiking, Wolf, Exec. V.P.-Haderslev--Scan-Ad Gruppen A/S, Arhus, Denmark; *Int'l*, pg. 1198

Wiklund, J. Thomas P., Exec. V.P.--Norwest Bank Minnesota N.A., Minneapolis, MN; *U.S. Public*, pg. 1202

Wilcott, Scott J., Exec. V.P.--River Vista Development Co., Los Angeles, CA; *U.S. Public*, pg. 296

Wilcott, Scott J., Exec. V.P.--Rio Norte Este Co., Los Angeles, CA; *U.S. Public*, pg. 296

Wilder, Michael, Exec. V.P.--Arnold Communications, Inc., Boston, MA; *U.S. Private*, pg. 83

Wilder, Robert D., Chief Fin. Officer & Exec. V.P.--John Wiley & Sons, Inc., New York, NY; *U.S. Public*, pg. 1768

Wilen, Tom V., Exec. V.P.-Worldwide Sls. & Mktg.--JBB Worldwide, Inc., Deerfield, IL; *U.S. Public*, pg. 675

Wiley, Alan E., Chief Fin. & Admin. Officer, Sr. Exec. V.P. & Sec.--The Cato Corporation, Charlotte, NC; *U.S. Public*, pg. 318

Wiley, Edward L., Exec. V.P.-Civil--Michael Baker Corporation, Pittsburgh, PA; *U.S. Public*, pg. 168

Wiley, Edward L., Exec. V.P.--Michael Baker, Jr., Inc., Beaver, PA; *U.S. Public*, pg. 168

Wiley, Michael E., Exec. V.P.--Atlantic Richfield Company, Los Angeles, CA; *U.S. Public*, pg. 144

Wilhelmsson, Claes, Exec. V.P.--Astra AB, Sodertalje, Sweden; *Int'l*, pg. 93

Wilhoit, William H., Exec. V.P.--Skyway Luggage Co., Seattle, WA; *U.S. Private*, pg. 1005

Wilke, George, Exec. V.P.-Pharmaceutical Opers.--Meridian Medical Tech., Saint Louis, MO; *U.S. Public*, pg. 1095

Wilkes, Roy, Exec. V.P.--Mining Group, San Antonio, TX; *U.S. Public*, pg. 1134

Wilkins, Patrick, Exec. V.P. & Chief Oper. Officer--CH & A Corporation, Kingwood, TX; *Int'l*, pg. 1153

Wilkinson, Edward A., Exec. V.P.--Intergraph Corporation, Huntsville, AL; *U.S. Public*, pg. 890

Wilkinson, Frank S., Exec. V.P.--E.W. Blanch Holdings, Inc., Minneapolis, MN; *U.S. Public*, pg. 236

Wilkinson, John E., Exec. V.P.-Mktg.--Track 'n Trail, El Dorado Hills, CA; *U.S. Public*, pg. 1626

Wilkison, Terry L., Exec. V.P.--Owens-Illinois, Inc., Toledo, OH; *U.S. Public*, pg. 1238

Wilkolak, Thomas N., Exec. V.P.--Carlson Marketing Group, Inc., Minneapolis, MN; *U.S. Private*, pg. 212

Willey, Frank P., Exec. V.P.--Fidelity National Title Insurance Company, Irvine, CA; *U.S. Public*, pg. 620

Willey, Frank P., Exec. V.P.--Fidelity National Title Insurance Company of Tennessee, Knoxville, TN; *U.S. Public*, pg. 621

Williams, A.S., III, Exec. V.P.--Protective Life Corporation, Birmingham, AL; *U.S. Public*, pg. 1336

Williams, Anthony R., Chief Fin. & Acctg. Officer & Exec. V.P.--Acclaim Entertainment, Inc., Glen Cove, NY; *U.S. Public*, pg. 15

Williams, Byrd, Exec. V.P.--Compass Bancshares, Inc., Birmingham, AL; *U.S. Public*, pg. 418

Williams, Byrd, Grp. Exec. V.P.--Compass Bank, Birmingham, AL; *U.S. Public*, pg. 418

Williams, Byrd, Exec. V.P.--Compass Bank, Plano, TX; *U.S. Public*, pg. 419

Williams, C.E., Chief Oper. Officer & Exec. V.P.--Security Pacific Financial Services Inc., San Diego, CA; *U.S. Public*, pg. 181

Williams, Cynthia L., Executive V.P.--Forest City Capital Corporation, Cleveland, OH; *U.S. Public*, pg. 668

Williams, D. Richard, Chief Fin. Officer & Exec. V.P.--Primerica Financial Services, Duluth, GA; *U.S. Public*, pg. 1633

Williams, D.M., Exec. V.P.--Loblaw Companies Limited, North York, Canada; *Int'l*, pg. 1495

Williams, David K., Exec. V.P., Controller & Sec.--Killearn Properties, Inc., Stockbridge, GA; *U.S. Public*, pg. 956

Williams, David M., Exec. V.P.--George Weston Limited, Toronto, Canada; *Int'l*, pg. 1494

Williams, Derek, Chief Oper. Officer & Exec. V.P.--Pall Europe Ltd., Portsmouth, United Kingdom; *U.S. Public*, pg. 1254

Williams, Derek T.D., Chief Oper. Officer & Exec. V.P.--Pall Corporation, Greenvale, NY; *U.S. Public*, pg. 1253

Williams, Doris, Exec. V.P. & Sec.--Jay Jacobs, Inc., Seattle, WA; *U.S. Public*, pg. 922

Williams, Eldridge M., Chief Oper. Officer & Exec. V.P.--Universal Life Insurance Company, Memphis, TN; *U.S. Private*, pg. 1127

Williams, Elizabeth, Exec. V.P.-Mdsg.--Charming Shoppes, Inc., Bensalem, PA; *U.S. Public*, pg. 335

Williams, G. Bretnell, Exec. V.P.-Indus. Process--Morrison Knudsen Corp.-Engineering & Construction, Cleveland, OH; *U.S. Public*, pg. 1134

Williams, G. Bretnell, Exec. V.P.--Industrial/Process Division, Cleveland, OH; *U.S. Public*, pg. 1134

Williams, Gerald, Chief Fin. Officer & Exec. V.P.--Huntington Bancshares Inc., Columbus, OH; *U.S. Public*, pg. 849

Williams, Glen E., Jr., Chief Fin. Officer & Exec. V.P.--Dodson Group, Kansas City, MO; *U.S. Private*, pg. 338

Williams, James A., Exec. V.P.--Unicover Corporation, Cheyenne, WY; *U.S. Private*, pg. 1117

Williams, James H., Exec. V.P. & Chief Acctg. Officer--BankAmerica Corporation, San Francisco, CA; *U.S. Public*, pg. 179

Williams, James H., Grp. Exec. V.P. & Chief Acctg. Officer--Bank of America NT&SA, San Francisco, CA; *U.S. Public*, pg. 180

Williams, Jay, Exec. V.P.--Arnold Communications, Inc., Boston, MA; *U.S. Private*, pg. 83

Williams, Jimmie D., Chief Fin. Officer, Exec. V.P., Treas. & Sec.--Belz Enterprises, Memphis, TN; *U.S. Private*, pg. 132

Williams, Jimmy O., Exec. V.P.--SunTrust, Orlando, FL; *U.S. Public*, pg. 1537

Williams, John C., Jr., Exec. V.P.-Commercial Banking--National City Bank, Pennsylvania, Pittsburgh, PA; *U.S. Public*, pg. 1154

Williams, John V., Exec. V.P.-Worldwide Field Opers.--Storage Technology Corporation, Louisville, CO; *U.S. Public*, pg. 1522

Williams, Kenneth R., Exec. V.P.-Mktg. & Opers.--Foodmaker, Inc., San Diego, CA; *U.S. Public*, pg. 661

Williams, Kenneth S., Exec. V.P.--Sony Pictures Entertainment, Culver City, CA; *Int'l*, pg. 1281

Williams, Lewis T., Sr. V.P.--Chiron Corporation, Emeryville, CA; *U.S. Public*, pg. 349

Williams, Miles A., Exec. V.P.--Anschutz Corporation, Denver, CO; *U.S. Private*, pg. 75

Williams, Nicole S., Chief Fin. Officer, Exec. V.P.-Fin. & Sec.--R.P. Scherer Corporation, Troy, MI; *U.S. Public*, pg. 1437

Williams, Robert, Chief Fin. Officer & Exec. V.P.--Keyes Martin, East Hanover, NJ; *U.S. Private*, pg. 618

Williams, Roger D., Exec. V.P.-Food Products, Mktg., Pur., & Tech. Services--Bob Evans Farms, Inc., Columbus, OH; *U.S. Public*, pg. 596

Williams, Roger D., Exec. V.P.-Mktg.-Food Products--Bob Evans Farms, Inc. Sausage Division, Columbus, OH; *U.S. Public*, pg. 596

Williams, Stephen T., Exec. V.P.-Mktg. Dir.--American Bankers Insurance Co. of Florida, Miami, FL; *U.S. Public*, *pg. 67*

Williams, Stephen T., Exec. V.P.--American Bankers Life Assurance Co. of Florida, Miami, FL; *U.S. Public*, pg. 67

Williams, Steve, Exec. V.P.--American Bankers Insurance Group, Inc., Miami, FL; *U.S. Public*, pg. 67

Williams, Steven C., Chief Exec. Officer & Exec. V.P.--State Volunteer Mutual Insurance Co., Brentwood, TN; *U.S. Private*, pg. 1037

Williams, Steven T., Exec. V.P.--Bankers American Life Assurance Company, Pearl River, NY; *U.S. Public*, pg. 68

Williams, Sykes S., Exec. V.P.-Ontario & West Indies, Individual Bank CIBC--Canadian Imperial Bank of Commerce, Toronto, Canada; *Int'l*, pg. 256

Williams, T. E., Exec. V.P.--First Citizens Banc Shares, Inc., Raleigh, NC; *U.S. Public*, pg. 628

Williams, Timothy V., Chief Fin. Officer & Exec. V.P.--Policy Management Systems Corporation, Blythewood, SC; *U.S. Public*, pg. 1314

Williams, Tom, Exec V.P.-Division Opers.--Associated Wholesale Grocers, Inc., Kansas City, KS; *U.S. Private*, pg. 93

Williamson, Charles D., Exec. V.P.-Capital Markets--BOK Financial Corp., Tulsa, OK; *U.S. Public*, pg. 163

Williamson, Charles D., Exec. V.P.-Capital Markets--Bank of Oklahoma, N.A., Tulsa, OK; *U.S. Public*, pg. 163

Williamson, Dan, Exec. V.P.-Retail Div.--Tampa Retail Division, Tampa, FL; *U.S. Public*, pg. 1312

Williamson, John W., Chief Admin. Officer & Exec. V.P.--Gibraltar Savings, Simi Valley, CA; *U.S. Public*, pg. 181

Williamson, Scott, Chief Fin. Officer & Exec. V.P.--Plasti-Kote Company Inc., Medina, OH; *U.S. Private*, pg. 870

Willingham IV, Edward L., Exec. V.P.--First Citizens Banc Shares, Inc., Raleigh, NC; *U.S. Public*, pg. 628

Willingham, Jack W., Exec. V.P.-Restaurant Devel.--Perkins Family Restaurants, Memphis, TN; *U.S. Private*, pg. 925

Willis, Richard, Chief Fin. Officer & Exec. V.P.--Petersen Publishing Company, L.L.C., Los Angeles, CA; *U.S. Private*, pg. 856

Willke, Joe, Exec. V.P. & Gen. Mgr.-BASES PM&D--BASES Worldwide, Covington, KY; *U.S. Private*, pg. 120

Willkie, Hall, Exec. V.P.--Brown, Harris, Stevens, Inc., New York, NY; *U.S. Private*, pg. 174

Willmann, James B., Exec. V.P.--XL Vision Inc., Sebastian, FL; *U.S. Public*, pg. 1424

Willox, Randy, Exec. V.P.-Consumer Mkts. Prod./Western Div.--Countrywide Home Loans Inc., Pasadena, CA; *U.S. Public*, pg. 452

Wills, Travers H., Chief Oper. Officer & Sr. Exec. V.P.--United HealthCare Corporation, Minnetonka, MN; *U.S. Public*, pg. 1677

Wills, William L., Exec. V.P.-Opers.--Cummins Mid-South, Inc., Memphis, TN; *U.S. Private*, pg. 295

Wilmot, Gunnar, Exec. V.P.--McCann-Erickson Worldwide, New York, NY; *U.S. Public*, pg. 909

Wilmoth, Gene, Exec. V.P.--Peterson Farms, Decatur, AR; *U.S. Private*, pg. 857

Wilnai, Amos, Chm. Bd. & Exec. V.P.-Bus. Devel.--MMC Networks, Inc., Sunnyvale, CA; *U.S. Public*, pg. 1027

Wilson-Gray, Sheri, Exec. V.P.--Saks Fifth Avenue, New York, NY; *U.S. Public*, pg. 1429

Wilson, Allan B., Exec. V.P.-Corp. Mktg.--Intergraph Corporation, Huntsville, AL; *U.S. Public*, pg. 890

Wilson, Bruce A., Exec. V.P.--Bank of Boston Connecticut, Hartford, CT; *U.S. Public*, pg. 184

Wilson, Dave, Exec. V.P.--NWS Inc., Chicago, IL; *U.S. Private*, pg. 772

Wilson, David E., Exec. V.P.--Shipley Companies, York, PA; *U.S. Private*, pg. 994

Wilson, David G., Jr., Grp. Exec. V.P.-Cadmus Prof Commun.--Cadmus Communications Corporation, Richmond, VA; *U.S. Public*, pg. 290

Wilson, David R., Exec. V.P. & Mgr.-Capital Markets Div.--First Security Corporation, Salt Lake City, UT; *U.S. Public*, pg. 637

Wilson, Don M., III, Exec. V.P.-Global Trading--The Chase Manhattan Corporation, New York, NY; *U.S. Public*, pg. 337

Wilson, Glenn L., Exec. V.P.--The Citizens National Bank, Laurel, MD; *U.S. Public*, pg. 1089

Wilson, Graham M., Chief Fin. Officer & Exec. V.P.--Westcoast Energy Inc., Vancouver, Canada; *Int'l*, pg. 1492

Wilson, H. James, Exec. V.P. & Gen. Counsel--The New England, Boston, MA; *U.S. Private*, pg. 737

Wilson, James T., Chief Fin. Officer & Exec. V.P.-Opers. & Fin.--Gibson Greetings, Inc., Cincinnati, OH; *U.S. Public*, pg. 742

Wilson, James W., III, Exec. V.P.--Jim Wilson & Associates, Inc., Montgomery, AL; *U.S. Private*, pg. 1181

Wilson, Joe L., Exec. V.P.--United Bankshares, Inc., Parkersburg, WV; *U.S. Public*, pg. 1674

Wilson, John B., Chief Admin. Officer & Exec. V.P.--The Gap, Inc., San Francisco, CA; *U.S. Public*, pg. 702

Wilson, Jonathan D., Exec. V.P.-Consumer & Customer Engagement--Kellogg Company, Battle Creek, MI; *U.S. Public*, pg. 947

Wilson, Jonathan D., Exec. V.P.--Kellogg North America Division, Battle Creek, MI; *U.S. Public*, pg. 947

Wilson, Jonathon D., Exec. V.P. & Gen. Mgr.-Convenience Foods Div.--Kellogg USA Convenience Foods Division, Battle Creek, MI; *U.S. Public*, pg. 947

Wilson, Joseph V. III, Sr. Exec. V.P.--First Commerce Corporation, New Orleans, LA; *U.S. Public*, pg. 629

Wilson, Kemmons, Jr., Exec. V.P.--Kemmons Wilson, Inc., Memphis, TN; *U.S. Private*, pg. 613

Wilson, Malcomb C., Exec. V.P.--Mercantile-Safe Deposit & Trust Co., Baltimore, MD; *U.S. Public*, pg. 1089

Wilson, Matt, Sr. V.P. & Gen. Mgr.--SBC Advertising, Columbus, OH; *U.S. Private*, pg. 955

Wilson, Michael M., Exec. V.P.-Global Mktg. & Logistics--Methanex Corporation, Vancouver, Canada; *Int'l*, pg. 862

Wilson, P. Rodney, Exec. V.P.-Sls.--Potash Corporation of Saskatchewan Inc., Saskatoon, Canada; *Int'l*, pg. 1064

Wilson, Ralph, Exec. V.P.-Risk Mngmt. Services--Willis Corroon Corp. of Illinois, Chicago, IL; *Int'l*, pg. 1506

Wilson, Robert, Exec. V.P.--Kemmons Wilson, Inc., Memphis, TN; *U.S. Private*, pg. 613

Wilson, Robert K., Chief Fin. Officer & Exec. V.P.--Woodward-Clyde Group, Inc., Denver, CO; *U.S. Public*, pg. 1655

Wilson, Robert M., Chief Fin. Officer, Exec. V.P., Gen. Counsel & Sec.--Roberds, Inc., Carrollton, OH; *U.S. Public*, pg. 1393

Wilson, Robert W., Chief Fin. Officer, Exec. V.P., Controller, Treas. & Asst. Sec.--Supreme Industries, Inc., Goshen, IN; *U.S. Public*, pg. 1541

Wilson, S. Liane, Exec. V.P.-Corp. Opers.--Washington Mutual Inc., Seattle, WA; *U.S. Public*, pg. 1741

Wilson, Stephen R., Chief Fin. Officer & Sr. V.P.--CF Industries, Inc., Long Grove, IL; *U.S. Private*, pg. 193

Wilson, Steven E., Chief Fin. Officer, Exec. V.P., Treas. & Sec.--United Bankshares, Inc., Parkersburg, WV; *U.S. Public*, pg. 1674

Wiltshire, Dennis, Chief Oper. Officer & Exec. V.P.--Klosterman Baking Company, Inc., Cincinnati, OH; *U.S. Private*, pg. 626

Wimer, Charles, Exec. V.P.--Fidelity National Title Insurance Company of New York, New York, NY; *U.S. Public*, pg. 620

Winer, Warren J., Exec. V.P.-Grp. Life & Health--General American Life Insurance Co., Saint Louis, MO; *U.S. Private*, pg. 443

Wines, Leland E., Chief Fin. Officer & Exec. V.P.--BWC Financial Corp., Walnut Creek, CA; *U.S. Private*, pg. 108

Winiger, Rolf, Exec. V.P.-Services--The Swissair Group, Zurich, Switzerland; *Int'l*, pg. 1333

Winkler, Joe, Chief Fin. Officer, Exec. V.P. & Treas.--Tuboscope Incorporated, Houston, TX; *U.S. Public*, pg. 1643

Winkler, Thomas R., Chief Oper. Officer & Exec. V.P.--BioWhittaker, Inc., Walkersville, MD; *U.S. Public*, pg. 297

Winn, Harry L., Chief Fin. Officer & Exec. V.P.--Fleming Companies, Inc., Oklahoma City, OK; *U.S. Public*, pg. 652

Winninghoff, Albert C.M., Chm. & Chief Exec. Officer--Noordervliet & Winninghoff/Leo Burnett B.V., Amsterdam, Netherlands; *U.S. Private*, pg. 186

Winocur, Peter, Exec. V.P.--Graham-Field Health Products, Inc., Hauppauge, NY; *U.S. Public*, pg. 757

Winslow, James E., Chief Fin. Officer, Exec. V.P. & Sec.--Home Products International, Inc., Chicago, IL; *U.S. Public*, pg. 832

Winslow, Jim, Chief Fin. Officer & Exec. V.P.--Selfix, Inc., Chicago, IL; *U.S. Public*, pg. 832

Winter, Irwin W., Chief Fin. Officer & Exec. V.P.--Phillips-Van Heusen Corporation, New York, NY; *U.S. Public*, pg. 1291

Wirt, David B., Exec. V.P.-Admin. Support Div.--First of America Bank Corporation, Kalamazoo, MI; *U.S. Public*, pg. 636

Wirt, Donald E., Exec. V.P.--First Virginia Bank-Blue Ridge, Staunton, VA; *U.S. Public*, pg. 641

Wise, Ed, Exec. V.P. & Creative Dir.--Cline, Davis & Mann, Inc., New York, NY; *U.S. Private*, pg. 246

Wise, Jerry L., Exec. V.P.--Tom Johnson Investment Management, Inc., Oklahoma City, OK; *U.S. Public*, pg. 1673

Wise, Ted, Exec. V.P.--O'Reilly Automotive Inc., Springfield, MO; *U.S. Public*, pg. 1230

Wisely, Robert W., Exec. V.P.-Mktg.--CKE Restaurants Inc., Anaheim, CA; *U.S. Public*, pg. 278

Wiseman, Eric, Exec. V.P.--JanSport, Appleton, WI; *U.S. Public*, pg. 1702

Wish, Peter, Exec. V.P.-Admin.--Recoton Corporation, Lake Mary, FL; *U.S. Public*, pg. 1369

Wisneski, William J., Exec. V.P.--Houghton Mifflin School Division, Boston, MA; *U.S. Public*, pg. 841

Wisnom, Thomas D., Exec. V.P.--Old Kent Financial Corporation, Grand Rapids, MI; *U.S. Public*, pg. 1216

Wissen, Pehr, Exec. V.P.-Treasury--Svenska Handelsbanken, Stockholm, Sweden; *Int'l*, pg. 1327

Witaszak, Richard B., Chief Fin. Officer & Exec. V.P.--Fred's Inc., Memphis, TN; *U.S. Public*, pg. 680

Withall, Gary A., Exec. V.P.--Miner Enterprises Inc., Geneva, IL; *U.S. Private*, pg. 749

Witherspoon, Gregory J., Chief Fin. Officer & Exec. V.P.-Fin.--Aames Financial Corporation, Los Angeles, CA; *U.S. Public*, pg. 12

Witkin, Kenneth, Exec. V.P.--Business Credit Div., Providence, RI; *U.S. Public*, pg. 650

Witte, Harald O., Dr., Exec. V.P.-Fin. Institutions--Landesbank Rheinland-Pfalz, Mainz, Germany; *Int'l*, pg. 799

Wittler, Manfred, Exec. V.P.-Worldwide Sls.--Intergraph Corporation, Huntsville, AL; *U.S. Public*, pg. 890

Wittman, Peter, Exec. V.P.-New Bus. Devel.--WWF Paper Corporation, Bala Cynwyd, PA; *U.S. Private*, pg. 1145

Wittnam, Donald W., Exec. V.P.--United Agri Products Co., Greeley, CO; *U.S. Public*, pg. 426

Wittwer, John W., Exec. V.P.--Alpnet Inc., Salt Lake City, UT; *U.S. Public*, pg. 58

Wohl, Richard H., Sr. Exec. V.P., Gen. Counsel & Sec.--INMC Mortgage Holdings, Inc., Pasadena, CA; *U.S. Public*, pg. 857

Wohler, Jon E., Exec. V.P.-Tech.--Pratt & Whitney Operations, East Hartford, CT; *U.S. Public*, pg. 1690

Wohnsen, Joraen, Exec. V.P. & Sec.--Nykredit, Copenhagen, Denmark; *Int'l*, pg. 993

Wohrer, Michel, Exec. V.P.-Intl. Fin.--Credit Commercial de France, Paris, France; *Int'l*, pg. 341

Wolchonok, Jane M., Exec. V.P.-Retail Banking--Citizens Bank of Massachusetts, Fairhaven, MA; *Int'l*, pg. 1132

Wolcott, Harold R., Exec. V.P. & Gen. Mgr.--Ballard Medical Products, Draper, UT; *U.S. Public*, pg. 171

Wold, Casey R., Exec. V.P.-Office--TrizecHahn Corporation, Toronto, Canada; *Int'l*, pg. 1424
Woldrich, John D., Chief Oper. Officer & Exec. V.P.--Fair, Isaac and Company, Inc., San Rafael, CA; *U.S. Public*, pg. 609
Wolf, Henry C., Exec. V.P.-Fin.--Norfolk Southern Corporation, Norfolk, VA; *U.S. Public*, pg. 1190
Wolf, Jeffrey, Exec. V.P. & Acct. Plng. Dir.--Deutsch, Inc., New York, NY; *U.S. Private*, pg. 328
Wolf, Kevin M., Exec. V.P.--Leonard Wholesale, Inc., Springfield, NJ; *U.S. Private*, pg. 660
Wolf, Richard, Exec. V.P.-Opers.--Beverage Canners International Corp., Miami, FL; *U.S. Private*, pg. 106
Wolfe, Lawrence A., Exec. V.P. & Sec.--Production Tool Supply Co., Warren, MI; *U.S. Private*, pg. 889
Wolfe, R. Dean, Exec. V.P.-Acquisitions & Real Estate--The May Department Stores Company, Saint Louis, MO; *U.S. Public*, pg. 1063
Wolff, David, Exec. V.P.-Trading & Asset Mngmnt. & Real Estate--El Camino Resources, Ltd., Woodland Hills, CA; *U.S. Private*, pg. 366
Wolff, Gary, Chief Fin. Officer & Exec. V.P.--Fenn Manufacturing Co., Newington, CT; *U.S. Public*, pg. 1676
Wolff, Kenneth K., Chief Fin. Officer & Exec. V.P.--Amtran, Inc., Indianapolis, IN; *U.S. Public*, pg. 106
Wolkenmuth, Edward F., Exec. V.P. & Gen. Mgr.--BASES Services & Durables Division, San Ramon, CA; *U.S. Private*, pg. 120
Wolniak, Donald E., Exec. V.P. & Dir.-Power Generation Systems--Sargent & Lundy, Chicago, IL; *U.S. Private*, pg. 965
Wolski, Lawrence G., Chief Exec. Officer--Joslyn Corporation, Chicago, IL; *U.S. Public*, pg. 481
Wolzenski, Ben, Exec. V.P.-Individual--General American Life Insurance Co., Saint Louis, MO; *U.S. Private*, pg. 443
Womble, James T., Exec. V.P.-Alliances Grp.--Acxiom Corporation, Conway, AR; *U.S. Public*, pg. 18
Wong, Michael, Exec. Dir.-Corp. Plng. & Investments--Sun Hung Kai Properties Ltd., Wan Chai, Hong Kong; *Int'l*, pg. 1318
Wongphayak, Rangsan, Exec. V.P.--Bangkok Bank Public Company Limited, Bangkok, Thailand; *Int'l*, pg. 146
Wongtrakool, Pojanee, Exec. V.P.--The Industrial Finance Corporation of Thailand, Bangkok, Thailand; *Int'l*, pg. 677
Wood, Ben, Exec. V.P.-Building Products--Gilman Paper Co., Saint Marys, GA; *U.S. Private*, pg. 454
Wood, David R., Chief Fin. Officer, Exec. V.P.-Admin. & Treas.--The Sands Regent, Reno, NV; *U.S. Public*, pg. 1431
Wood, E. Jenner, III, Exec. V.P.-Trust & Investment Services--SunTrust Banks, Inc., Atlanta, GA; *U.S. Public*, *pg. 1537*
Wood, Jerry W., Exec. V.P.--Tandy Brands Accessories, Inc., Arlington, TX; *U.S. Public*, pg. 1560
Wood, Peter Anthony, Exec. Dir.--Standard Chartered Bank PLC, London, United Kingdom; *Int'l*, pg. 1294
Wood, Robert E., Exec. V.P. & Gen. Mgr.-Novus Brands--NOVUS Services, Inc., Riverwoods, IL; *U.S. Public*, pg. 1132
Wood, Robert E., II, Exec. V.P. & Gen. Mgr.-Novus Services--Dean Witter, Discover & Co., New York, NY; *U.S. Public*, pg. 1132
Woodall, Graham, Exec. V.P. & Grp. Creative Dir.--DMB&B New York, New York, NY; *U.S. Private*, pg. 302
Woodall, Michael A., Exec. V.P.--Beneficial Corporation, Wilmington, DE; *U.S. Public*, pg. 211
Woodall, Michael A., Exec. V.P.-Intl.--Beneficial Management Corporation, Peapack, NJ; *U.S. Public*, pg. 211
Woodall, Michael A., Exec. V.P.--Beneficial Management Corporation of America & Affiliated Corps., Wilmington, DE; *U.S. Public*, pg. 211
Woodard, William M., Exec. V.P.-Sls.--I.V. One, Altamonte Springs, FL; *U.S. Public*, pg. 229
Woodbeck, Thomas M., Exec. V.P.--Overhead Conveyor Co., Ferndale, MI; *U.S. Private*, pg. 822
Woodburn, Connie R., Exec. V.P.-Corp. Sls.--Cardinal Health Inc., Dublin, OH; *U.S. Public*, pg. 304
Woodgate, John, Exec. Dir.--Oxford Instruments plc, Witney, United Kingdom; *Int'l*, pg. 1018
Woodhouse, Michael, Chief Fin. Officer & Exec. V.P.--Metromedia Steakhouses, Inc., Vandalia, OH; *U.S. Private*, pg. 736
Woodring, A. Greig, Exec. V.P.-Reinsurance--General American Life Insurance Co., Saint Louis, MO; *U.S. Private*, pg. 443
Woodring, Kenneth G., Exec. V.P.-Mining Opers.--Arch Coal, Inc., Saint Louis, MO; *U.S. Public*, pg. 139
Woods, James W., III, Exec. V.P. & Acct. Service Dir.--Long Haymes Carr, Inc., Winston Salem, NC; *U.S. Public*, pg. 909
Woods, M. Troy, Exec. V.P.--Total System Services, Inc., Columbus, GA; *U.S. Public*, pg. 1550
Woods, V. Lehman, Chief Fin. Officer & Exec. V.P.--Analysis & Technology International Corporation, North Stonington, CT; *U.S. Public*, pg. 109
Woods, Wayne, Exec. V.P. & Travel/Tourism Dir.--Cranford Johnson Robinson Woods, Little Rock, AR; *U.S. Private*, *pg. 286*
Woodwark, Chris, Exec. Dir.--Vickers PLC, London, United Kingdom; *Int'l*, pg. 1466
Woodword, Allan, Exec. V.P.--First Citizens Banc Shares, Inc., Raleigh, NC; *U.S. Public*, pg. 628
Woodworth, James, Exec. V.P.--AAI/ACL Technologies, Santa Ana, CA; *U.S. Public*, pg. 1679
Woody, C.O., Sr. V.P.-Power Generation--Florida Power & Light Company, North Palm Beach, FL; *U.S. Public*, pg. 608
Woolbert, Richard E., Chief Admin. Officer & Exec. V.P.--McDermott International, Inc., New Orleans, LA; *U.S. Public*, pg. 1067
Woollatt, Paul G., Exec. V.P. & Dir.-Retail Banking--Downey Savings & Loan Association, F.A., Newport Beach, CA; *U.S. Public*, pg. 526
Woolmington, Paul, Exec. V.P. & Worldwide Strategic Media Dir.--Ammirati Puris Lintas Worldwide, New York, NY; *U.S. Public*, pg. 908
Woolsey, James C., Exec. V.P. & Treas.--Emigrant Savings Bank, New York, NY; *U.S. Private*, pg. 373
Woolworth, Andrew B., Exec. V.P.--Woodstream Corporation, Lititz, PA; *U.S. Public*, pg. 566
Wooten, Marvin, V.P. & Gen. Mgr.--Southco Distributing Company, Goldsboro, NC; *U.S. Private*, pg. 1014
Wooten, Rosalie, Exec. V.P.--O'Reilly Automotive Inc., Springfield, MO; *U.S. Public*, pg. 1230
Workman, John, Exec. V.P.-Corp. Restructuring--Montgomery Ward & Co., Inc., Chicago, IL; *U.S. Private*, pg. 758
World, John P., Exec. V.P. & Gen. Mgr.--Carver Corporation, Lynnwood, WA; *U.S. Public*, pg. 310
Wortel, T.M., Chm. Bd. & Exec. V.P.--Esso N.V./S.A., Maasmechelen, Belgium; *U.S. Public*, pg. 602
Wortley, Mark D., Exec. V.P.--Beverly Enterprises, Inc., Fort Smith, AR; *U.S. Public*, pg. 227
Woudstra, F. Robert, Exec. V.P. & Treas.--Foremost Corporation of America, Caledonia, MI; *U.S. Public*, pg. 667
Wray, Dick, Exec. V.P., Chief Oper. Officer & Gen. Mgr.--J. Brown & Associates Minneapolis/St. Paul, Minneapolis, MN; *U.S. Public*, pg. 764
Wright, David B., Exec. V.P.-Enterprise Computing Grp.--Amdahl Corporation, Sunnyvale, CA; *Int'l*, pg. 527
Wright, David N., Exec. V.P. & Sr. Mgr.-Small Bus. & Mortgage Banking--Compass Bank, Birmingham, AL; *U.S. Public*, pg. 418
Wright, David P., Exec. V.P.-Sls. & Mktg.--MedImmune, Inc., Gaithersburg, MD; *U.S. Public*, pg. 1081
Wright, Donald S., Exec. V.P.--Ilco Unican Corp., Rocky Mount, NC; *Int'l*, pg. 1432
Wright, Gary K., Exec. V.P.-Corp. Banking--Texas Commerce Bank, Houston, TX; *U.S. Public*, pg. 339
Wright, James O., Chm. Bd.--Badger Meter, Inc., Milwaukee, WI; *U.S. Public*, pg. 164
Wright, Norman B., Exec. V.P. & Corp. Sec.--Alias Wavefront, Toronto, Canada; *U.S. Public*, pg. 1474
Wright, Richard D., Exec. V.P.-Opers.--Phycor, Inc., Nashville, TN; *U.S. Public*, pg. 1293
Wright, Richard G., Sr. Exec. V.P.-Credit Quality--Hibernia Corporation, New Orleans, LA; *U.S. Public*, pg. 825
Wright, Ron, Chief Oper. Officer & Exec. V.P.--C & S Wholesale Grocery Inc., Brattleboro, VT; *U.S. Private*, pg. 192
Wright, Vernon H.C., Sr. Exec. V.P. & Treas.--MBNA Corporation, Wilmington, DE; *U.S. Public*, pg. 1023
Wristen, Edward L., Exec. V.P.-Risk Prods.--First Health Group Corp., Downers Grove, IL; *U.S. Public*, pg. 635
Wroten, Richad W., Chief Fin. Officer & Exec. V.P.--Old Kent Financial Corporation, Grand Rapids, MI; *U.S. Public*, pg. 1216
Wu, Tsung-Ching, Exec. V.P.-Tech--Atmel Corporation, San Jose, CA; *U.S. Public*, pg. 145
Wuestefeld, Norman H., Exec. V.P.--Wilbur Smith Associates, Columbia, SC; *U.S. Private*, pg. 1009
Wunderlich, John D., Chief Fin. Officer & Exec. V.P.--Fred Weber, Inc., Maryland Heights, MO; *U.S. Private*, pg. 424
Wurst, B.J., Exec. V.P.--Camelot Communications, Inc., Dallas, TX; *U.S. Private*, pg. 203
Wurster, Hans C., Exec. V.P.-Mktg. & Sls.--Bel/Kaukauna USA, Little Chute, WI; *U.S. Private*, pg. 130
Wyant, Clyde, Chief Fin. Officer & Exec. V.P.--Lennox International Inc., Richardson, TX; *U.S. Private*, pg. 659
Wyatt, James V., Exec. V.P.--McAnally Enterprises, Inc., Yucaipa, CA; *U.S. Private*, pg. 718
Wyness, Tom, Exec. V.P.-Transportation--Barton Beers, Ltd., Chicago, IL; *U.S. Public*, pg. 300
Wynn, Robert P., Chief Fin. Officer, Exec. V.P. & Sec.--AmeriPath, Inc., Riviera Beach, FL; *U.S. Public*, pg. 96
Wynne, Scott C., Exec. V.P.-Opers. & Sec.--Just For Feet, Inc., Pelham, AL; *U.S. Public*, pg. 935
Wyszomierski, Jack L., Chief Fin. Officer & Exec. V.P.--Schering-Plough Corporation, Madison, NJ; *U.S. Public*, pg. 1438
Xanders, Roy, Exec. V.P.-Engrng. & Quality Assurance--Airtex Products, Fairfield, IL; *U.S. Private*, pg. 1113
Yablon, Leonard H., Chief Fin. Officer & Exec. V.P.--Forbes, Inc., New York, NY; *U.S. Private*, pg. 417
Yacenda, Michael, Exec. V.P.--Executone Information Systems, Inc., Milford, CT; *U.S. Public*, pg. 599
Yada, Sei-ichi, Exec. V.P.--Kyowa Hakko Kogyo Company, Ltd., Tokyo, Japan; *Int'l*, pg. 778
Yahn, Chuck, Exec. V.P.--Kenco, Middlebury, IN; *U.S. Public*, pg. 1769
Yakir, David, Pres. & Exec. V.P.--Blue Marble Advanced Communications Group, New York, NY; *U.S. Private*, pg. 104
Yaku, Takahiro, Exec. V.P.--Asahi Breweries Ltd., Tokyo, Japan; *Int'l*, pg. 83
Yam, Colin, Chief Fin. Officer & Exec. V.P.--Times Publishing Limited, Singapore, Singapore; *Int'l*, pg. 1390
Yamada, Albert M., Chief Fin. Officer & Exec. V.P.--First Hawaiian Bank, Honolulu, HI; *U.S. Public*, pg. 634
Yamada, Eddie, Exec. V.P.--Chemoil, San Francisco, CA; *U.S. Private*, pg. 233
Yamada, Michio, Exec. V.P.--Nikkei Advertising Co., Tokyo, Japan; *Int'l*, pg. 930
Yamada, Yasuhisa, Exec. V.P.--Takeda Chemical Industries, Ltd., Osaka, Japan; *Int'l*, pg. 1350
Yamaga, Motoo, Exec. V.P.-Engrng. Div.--NKK Corporation, Tokyo, Japan; *Int'l*, pg. 902
Yamagami, K., Exec. V.P.--Fujitsu Ten Corp. of America, Torrance, CA; *Int'l*, pg. 526
Yamagata, Norimoto, Exec. V.P.--Mercian Corporation, Tokyo, Japan; *Int'l*, pg. 858
Yamagata, T., Exec. V.P.--Mitsubishi Cable America, Inc., New York, NY; *Int'l*, pg. 870
Yamaguchi, Kazunori, Exec. V.P.--Dai-ichi Life Insurance Agency (U.S.A.) Inc., New York, NY; *Int'l*, pg. 362
Yamaji, Hiroki, Exec. V.P.--G-Net Corporation, Osaka, Japan; *Int'l*, pg. 531
Yamamoto, Osamu, Sr. Mng. Dir.--Asahi Breweries Ltd., Tokyo, Japan; *Int'l*, pg. 83
Yamamoto, Shuji, Exec. V.P.--Daido Steel Co., Ltd., Nagoya, Japan; *Int'l*, pg. 364
Yamamoto, Tetsuya, Sr. Exec. V.P.--Toshiba Corporation, Tokyo, Japan; *Int'l*, pg. 1402
Yamamura, Takashi, Exec. V.P.--Itochu Corporation, Tokyo, Japan; *Int'l*, pg. 694
Yamamura, Takehiko, Chief Fin. Officer, Exec. V.P. & Dir.-Inv. Rels.--Haseko Corporation, Tokyo, Japan; *Int'l*, pg. 599
Yamashita, Kazuhiko, Exec. V.P. & Gen. Mgr.-Dentsu Inc. Kansai (Osaka)--Dentsu Inc., Tokyo, Japan; *Int'l*, pg. 392
Yamashita, Kenichi, Exec. V.P.--Obayashi Corporation, Tokyo, Japan; *Int'l*, pg. 995
Yamashita, Takuji, Exec. V.P.--Mitsubishi Estate Co., Ltd., Tokyo, Japan; *Int'l*, pg. 873
Yamazaki, Masao, Sr. Exec. V.P.--Japan Tobacco Inc., Tokyo, Japan; *Int'l*, pg. 703
Yan, Peter Tan Keh, Exec. Dir.--DBS Finance Ltd., Singapore, Singapore; *Int'l*, pg. 350
Yanagisawa, Yukitoshi, Exec. V.P.--Nishimatsu Construction Co., Ltd., Tokyo, Japan; *Int'l*, pg. 942
Yanase, Takeshi, Exec. V.P.--Kansai Paint Co., Ltd., Osaka, Japan; *Int'l*, pg. 723
Yano, Masami, Exec. V.P.--Kanematsu Corporation, Tokyo, Japan; *Int'l*, pg. 722
Yantis, J. Mike, Exec. V.P. & Treas.--Yantis Corporation, San Antonio, TX; *U.S. Private*, pg. 1195
Yanuklis, John, Exec. V.P.--The Strober Organization, Inc., Brooklyn, NY; *U.S. Private*, pg. 403
Yarberry, Lawrence C., V.P.-Fin.--Southern Pacific Rail Corporation, San Francisco, CA; *U.S. Public*, pg. 1668
Yarmark, Martin J., Exec. V.P.--Triboro Electric Co., Doylestown, PA; *U.S. Private*, pg. 1102
Yarnoff, Alan, Exec. V.P.--Partners & Shevack, Inc., New York, NY; *U.S. Private*, pg. 842
Yarom, Artzi, Exec. V.P.--Elscint Ltd., Haifa, Israel; *Int'l*, pg. 450
Yastine, Barbara A., Exec. V.P.-Fin. & Insurance--Commercial Credit Company, Baltimore, MD; *U.S. Public*, *pg. 1633*
Yastow, Shelby, Exec. V.P., Gen. Counsel & Sec.--McDonald's Corporation, Oak Brook, IL; *U.S. Public*, pg. 1068
Yasuda, Junichi, Sr. Exec. V.P.--Meiji Seika Kaisha, Ltd., Tokyo, Japan; *Int'l*, pg. 855
Yasui, Tomomasa, Exec. V.P.--Brother Industries, Ltd., Nagoya, Japan; *Int'l*, pg. 229
Yazgi, Abdo, Exec. V.P. & Sec.--Continental Can Co., Norwalk, CT; *U.S. Public*, pg. 439
Yazgi, Rogih, Exec. V.P.--Chemtex International, Inc., New York, NY; *Int'l*, pg. 872
Yee, Winnie Wang Wing, Vice Chm. & Exec. V.P.--Johnson Electric Holdings Limited, Tai No, Hong Kong; *Int'l*, pg. 712
Yeld, Piers, Exec. V.P.-Client Services-Europe, Middle East & Africa--Grey Europe/Brussels, Brussels, Belgium; *U.S. Public*, pg. 765
Yellin, Melvin, Exec. V.P. & Gen. Counsel--Bankers Trust New York Corporation, New York, NY; *U.S. Public*, pg. 185
Yiakas, C.D., Exec. V.P.--Wyle Laboratories, Inc., El Segundo, CA; *U.S. Private*, pg. 1193
Yoder, Edward L., Exec. V.P.-Lending--The State Bank and Trust Company, Defiance, OH; *U.S. Public*, pg. 1413
Yoder, Stephen A., Exec. V.P. & Gen. Counsel--AmSouth Bancorporation, Birmingham, AL; *U.S. Public*, pg. 105
Yokoshige, Takahisa, Exec. V.P.--The Chugoku Electric Power Co., Inc., Hiroshima, Japan; *Int'l*, pg. 291
Yokota, Sunao, Exec. V.P.-Domestic Mktg. & Sls. & Parts & Accessories--Mazda Motor Corporation, Hiroshima, Japan; *Int'l*, pg. 849
Yokoyama, Seijiro, Sr. Exec. V.P.--NEC Corporation, Tokyo, Japan; *Int'l*, pg. 899
Yollich, Lester, Exec. V.P.--Production Tool Supply Co., Warren, MI; *U.S. Private*, pg. 889
Yonezu, Takehiko, Exec. V.P. & Treas.--Sumitomo Corporation, Tokyo, Japan; *Int'l*, pg. 1312
Yongkittikul, Chatjai, Exec. V.P.--Bangkok Bank Berhad, Kuala Lumpur, Malaysia; *Int'l*, pg. 146
Yoo, Paul J., Chief Fin. Officer, Exec. V.P. & Sec.--Jockey International, Inc., Kenosha, WI; *U.S. Private*, pg. 588
Yoshida, Hisayasu, Exec. Dir.--Isuzu Motors Limited, Tokyo, Japan; *Int'l*, pg. 692
Yoshida, Kozo, Exec. V.P.-Life-Style Bus. Devel.--East Japan Railway Company, Tokyo, Japan; *Int'l*, pg. 431
Yoshida, Seiji, Exec. V.P.--Kyushu Electric Power Co., Inc., Fukuoka, Japan; *Int'l*, pg. 778
Yoshida, Seiji, Exec. V.P.--Meiji Milk Products Co., Ltd., Tokyo, Japan; *Int'l*, pg. 855
Yoshida, Takahisa, Exec. V.P.--YKK Corporation, Tokyo, Japan; *Int'l*, pg. 1514
Yoshida, Takashi, Exec. V.P.--Fuji Securities Inc.-New York, New York, NY; *Int'l*, pg. 519
Yoshimoto, Takanori, Exec. V.P.-Opers.--Benihana, Inc., Miami, FL; *U.S. Public*, pg. 211
Yoshimura, Yoshimi, Exec. V.P.--The Kyoei Mutual Fire & Marine Insurance Company, Tokyo, Japan; *Int'l*, pg. 777
Yoshinashi, Taka, Exec. V.P.--Fuji Heavy Industries, Ltd., Tokyo, Japan; *Int'l*, pg. 522
Yoshino, Hiroyuki, Exec. V.P. & Rep. Dir.--Honda Motor Co., Ltd., Tokyo, Japan; *Int'l*, pg. 634
Yoshino, Tohru, Exec. V.P.--Oji Paper Co., Ltd., Tokyo, Japan; *Int'l*, pg. 998
Yoshioka, Shigeyuki, Exec. V.P.--Asahi Breweries U.S.A., Inc., Los Angeles, CA; *Int'l*, pg. 83
Yoskowitz, Irving B., Exec. V.P. & Gen. Counsel--United Technologies Corporation, Hartford, CT; *U.S. Public*, pg. 1689

Youdelman, Robert A., Chief Fin. Officer & Exec. V.P.--Allen Telecom, Inc., Beachwood, OH; *U.S. Public*, pg. 45
Youmans, Andrew, Exec. V.P.--Connecticut Spring & Stamping Corporation, Farmington, CT; *U.S. Private*, pg. 263
Young, Dona D., Exec. V.P.-Individual Insurance Counsel--Phoenix Home Life Mutual Insurance Company, Hartford, CT; *U.S. Private*, pg. 863
Young, Dona D., Exec. V.P.-Individual Insurance Counsel--Phoenix Home Life Mutual Insurance Co., Hartford, CT; *U.S. Private*, pg. 863
Young, Donald A., Exec. V.P.-Resort--Maui Land & Pineapple Co., Inc., Kahului, HI; *U.S. Public*, pg. 1060
Young, George, Exec. V.P.--Williams Foods Inc., Lenexa, KS; *U.S. Private*, pg. 1178
Young, Helene, Exec. V.P. & Chief Science Officer--Harrison & Star, Inc., New York, NY; *U.S. Private*, pg. 506
Young, James H., Chief Oper. Officer & Exec. V.P.--Reactive Metals & Alloys Corporation (REMACOR), West Pittsburg, PA; *U.S. Private*, pg. 913
Young, James T., Exec. V.P.--Young Refining Corp., Douglasville, GA; *U.S. Private*, pg. 1202
Young, Matthew, Exec. V.P.--Murry's, Inc., Upper Marlboro, MD; *U.S. Private*, pg. 768
Young, Neil, Exec. V.P.--Grubb & Ellis Management Services, Inc., Northbrook, IL; *U.S. Public*, pg. 767
Young, Nigel J., Exec. Dir.-Safety Interlock--Halma p.l.c., Amersham, United Kingdom; *Int'l*, pg. 589
Young, Paul, Exec. V.P.--Young Electric Sign Company, Salt Lake City, UT; *U.S. Private*, pg. 1201
Young, Peter A., Exec. V.P. & Sec.--Burd & Fletcher Company, Kansas City, MO; *U.S. Private*, pg. 181
Young, Robert H., Chief Fin. Officer, Exec. V.P., Treas. & Corp. Sec.--First Western Bancorp, Inc., New Castle, PA; *U.S. Public*, pg. 642
Young, Scott, Exec. V.P. & Creative Dir.--Evans, Hardy & Young, Inc., Santa Barbara, CA; *U.S. Private*, pg. 384
Young, Stan, Exec. V.P.--Poly Pak America, Inc., Los Angeles, CA; *U.S. Private*, pg. 875
Young, T.E., Exec. V.P.--General Sekiyu K.K., Tokyo, Japan; *U.S. Public*, pg. 602
Young, Thomas J., Exec. V.P.--Church Mutual Insurance Co., Merrill, WI; *U.S. Private*, pg. 239
Young, Thomas L., Exec. V.P.-Admin., Gen. Counsel & Sec.--Owens-Illinois, Inc., Toledo, OH; *U.S. Public*, pg. 1238
Youngclaus, Bill, Exec. V.P.-Bus. Devel.--Noble & Associates, Springfield, MO; *U.S. Private*, pg. 800
Younts, Richard W., Exec. V.P. & Corp. Exec. Dir.-Intl./Asia & Americas--Motorola, Inc., Schaumburg, IL; *U.S. Public*, pg. 1136
Yowell, John B., Exec. V.P.--Old Dominion Freight Line, Inc., High Point, NC; *U.S. Public*, pg. 1216
Yu, Lawrence W., Exec. V.P.--Edison Capital, Irvine, CA; *U.S. Public*, pg. 564
Yuan, James Teh-Tai, Exec. V.P.--The International Commercial Bank of China, Taipei, Taiwan; *Int'l*, pg. 683
Yudonarpodo, Sunarto, Exec. V.P.--P.T. Freeport Indonesia Co., New Orleans, LA; *U.S. Public*, pg. 681
Yuge, Yutaka, Exec. V.P. & Gen. Mgr.-Corp. Plng. & Coordination Grp.--Japan Energy Corporation, Tokyo, Japan; *Int'l*, pg. 702
Yui, Daizaburo, Sr. Mng. Dir.--Asahi Breweries Ltd., Tokyo, Japan; *Int'l*, pg. 83
Yun, Tyron, Chief Information Officer & Exec. V.P.--National Insurance Group, South San Francisco, CA; *U.S. Public*, pg. 1157
Yundt, Jeffrey W., Exec. V.P.--NIPSCO Industries, Inc., Hammond, IN; *U.S. Public*, pg. 1185
Yundt, Jeffrey W., Exec. V.P.--Northern Indiana Public Service Company, Hammond, IN; *U.S. Public*, pg. 1185
Yustein, Mark, Exec. V.P., Creative Dir. & Art Dir.--Jerry & Ketchum, New York, NY; *U.S. Private*, pg. 616
Yuyama, Korehira, Exec. V.P.--Snow Brand Milk Products Co. Ltd., Tokyo, Japan; *Int'l*, pg. 1271
Yuzawa, Mikio, Exec. V.P., Domestic--Chuo Senko Advertising Co., Ltd., Tokyo, Japan; *Int'l*, pg. 291
Zacharias, Antoine, Exec. V.P.--Compagnie Generale Des Eaux, Paris, France; *Int'l*, pg. 321
Zaharna, M. N., Grp. Exec. V.P.--ELSAG Bailey Process Automation N.V., Schiphol, Netherlands; *Int'l*, pg. 449
Zahorsky, Karen A., Exec. V.P.--Diversified Agency Services, New York, NY; *U.S. Public*, pg. 1223
Zaiac, Joanne, Exec. V.P. & Client Services Dir.--Wunderman Cato Johnson, New York, NY; *U.S. Private*, pg. 1197
Zaizen, Hiroshi, Exec. V.P.-Foods & Textiles & Gen. Mdse.--Mitsubishi Corporation, Tokyo, Japan; *Int'l*, pg. 871
Zakarin, Mark, Exec. V.P.-Original Programming--Showtime Networks Inc., New York, NY; *U.S. Private*, pg. 779
Zako, Toshisuke, Exec. V.P.--Asahi Breweries U.S.A., Inc., Los Angeles, CA; *Int'l*, pg. 83
Zambano, Laura L., Exec. V.P.-Mdsg.--Lillian Vernon Corporation, New Rochelle, NY; *U.S. Public*, pg. 1716
Zambrano, Lorenzo H., Chm. Bd. & Chief Exec. Officer--Cemex, S.A. de C.V., Monterrey, Mexico; *Int'l*, pg. 278
Zammit, Val, Exec. V.P.--True North Diversified Companies, New York, NY; *U.S. Public*, pg. 1642
Zank, Dennis, Exec. V.P.--Raymond James Financial, Inc., Saint Petersburg, FL; *U.S. Public*, pg. 923
Zannino, Richard, Chief Fin. Officer & Exec. V.P.--Saks Fifth Avenue, New York, NY; *U.S. Public*, pg. 1429
Zarate, Ricardo R., Exec. V.P.-Network Services--Philippine Long Distance Telephone Company, Manila, Philippines; *Int'l*, pg. 1051
Zarembra, Michael, Exec. V.P.--GSP Marketing Services, Inc., Chicago, IL; *U.S. Private*, pg. 436
Zarenkim, Lior, Exec. V.P.-Mktg. & Customer Rels.--The Israel Electric Corporation Ltd., Haifa, Israel; *Int'l*, pg. 690
Zaret, Jerry, Exec. V.P.--Grey Advertising Inc., New York, NY; *U.S. Public*, pg. 764
Zarett, Martin, Exec. V.P.-Private Label Pharmaceuticals--Queens Group, Inc., Long Island City, NY; *U.S. Private*, pg. 900
Zarick, Robert S., Exec. V.P.-Admin.--Central Reserve Life Corporation, Strongsville, OH; *U.S. Public*, pg. 326
Zarrow, Jack, Exec. V.P.--Sooner Pipe & Supply Corp., Tulsa, OK; *U.S. Private*, pg. 1014
Zatina, Thomas, Chief Oper. Officer, Exec. V.P. & Asst. Sec.--Bozzuto's Inc., Cheshire, CT; *U.S. Public*, pg. 249
Zaunders, Per, Chief Fin. Officer & Exec. V.P.--BT Industries AB, Mjolby, Sweden; *Int'l*, pg. 123
Zavadsky, Tom, Exec. V.P.-Sls. & Mktg.--Noel Olson Group, Stevens Point, WI; *U.S. Private*, pg. 800
Zee, Teddy, Exec. V.P.-Production--Columbia Pictures, Culver City, CA; *Int'l*, pg. 1281
Zeigon, James W., Exec. V.P.-Global Services--The Chase Manhattan Corporation, New York, NY; *U.S. Public*, pg. 337
Zeikel, Arthur, Exec. V.P.-Asset Mngnt.--Merrill Lynch & Co., Inc., New York, NY; *U.S. Public*, pg. 1097
Zeitman, Steven S., Exec. V.P. & Chief Underwriting Officer--United Capitol Insurance Company, Atlanta, GA; *U.S. Public*, pg. 303
Zekaria, Leon, Exec. V.P.--Windsor Fashions, Los Angeles, CA; *U.S. Private*, pg. 1182
Zelin, Jerome, Exec. V.P.--Masters, Inc., Westbury, NY; *U.S. Private*, pg. 714
Zell, Keith D., Exec. V.P.--MTS Systems Corporation, Eden Prairie, MN; *U.S. Public*, pg. 1028
Zeller, K.W., Exec. V.P.--Zeller Corp., Defiance, OH; *U.S. Private*, pg. 1204
Zellmer, Wallace A., Exec. V.P.--Nelson, Benson & Zellmer, Inc., Denver, CO; *U.S. Public*, pg. 1673
Zendt, Charles H., Jr., Exec. V.P.--Omega Bank, N.A., State College, PA; *U.S. Public*, pg. 1222
Zentmyer, Hugh J., Exec. V.P.--Illinois Tool Works Inc., Glenview, IL; *U.S. Public*, pg. 865
Zeratsky, A.A., Exec. V.P.--National Rivet & Manufacturing Company, Waupun, WI; *U.S. Private*, pg. 786
Zerbe, Mark A., Exec. V.P.--Kent Electronics Corp., Houston, TX; *U.S. Public*, pg. 951
Zettek, Chris R., Chief Fin. Officer & Exec. V.P.--Firstbank of Illinois Co., Springfield, IL; *U.S. Public*, pg. 643
Zetterstein, Rolf, Exec. V.P. & Publr.-Thomas Nelson Books--Thomas Nelson Inc., Nashville, TN; *U.S. Public*, pg. 1167
Zettle, Larry, Exec. V.P.--Golub Corporation, Schenectady, NY; *U.S. Private*, pg. 463
Ziegler, Patti, Exec. V.P.-Integrated Opers.--HMS Partners, Columbus, OH; *U.S. Private*, pg. 491
Ziegler, Patti, Exec. V.P.-Integrated Opers.--HMS Partners-Columbus, Columbus, OH; *U.S. Private*, pg. 492
Ziegler, R.B., Sr. V.P.-Intl. Opers.--Geraghty & Miller, Inc., Denver, CO; *Int'l*, pg. 607
Ziegler, Victor E., Exec. V.P.--Paco Pharmaceutical Services, Inc., Lakewood, NJ; *U.S. Public*, pg. 1755
Ziel, C.D., Exec. V.P.--Roessing Bronze Co., Mars, PA; *U.S. Private*, pg. 939
Ziereis, Leopold, Exec. V.P. & Creative Dir.--Demner, Merlicek & Bergmann Werbegesellschaft mbH, Vienna, Austria; *Int'l*, pg. 392
Zikmund, Donald R., Exec. V.P.--Stonhard, Inc., Maple Shade, NJ; *U.S. Public*, pg. 1358
Zilovic, Alexandra, Exec. V.P.--Language Institute for English (L.I.F.E.), Madison, NJ; *U.S. Public*, pg. 221
Zimmer, William W., Exec. V.P.--Chicago Asset Management Company, Chicago, IL; *U.S. Public*, pg. 1672
Zimmerman, Michael, Exec. V.P.--Watt, Roop & Co., Cleveland, OH; *U.S. Private*, pg. 1154
Zimmermann, Frederick K., Exec. V.P. & Chief Investment Officer--The New England, Boston, MA; *U.S. Private*, pg. 737
Zimmermann, Keith, Exec. V.P.--Whitney Blake Company of Vermont, Inc., Bellows Falls, VT; *U.S. Private*, pg. 148
Zink, Darell E., Jr., Chief Fin. Officer, Exec. V.P. & Asst. Sec.--Duke Realty Investments, Inc., Indianapolis, IN; *U.S. Public*, pg. 535
Zinn, Harry B., Exec. V.P.--Calvert Bank & Trust Co., Prince Frederick, MD; *U.S. Public*, pg. 1088
Zinser, Gerhard, Exec. V.P. & Chocolate Business--Kraft Jacobs Suchard AG, Zurich, Switzerland; *U.S. Public*, pg. 1288
Zint, Erna, Exec. V.P.-Sourcing--Charming Shoppes, Inc., Bensalem, PA; *U.S. Public*, pg. 335
Zipko, Ray, Exec. V.P. & Mngmt. Supvr.--Doremus & Company, New York, NY; *U.S. Public*, pg. 1223
Zirkel, Klaus, Exec. V.P.-Intl Trade--Bayerische Landesbank, Munich, Germany; *Int'l*, pg. 176
Zisman, Michael D., Exec. V.P.-Strategy--Lotus Development Corporation, Cambridge, MA; *U.S. Public*, pg. 896
Zisman, Michael D., Chief Exec. Officer & Exec. V.P.--Lotus Business Products Div., Cambridge, MA; *U.S. Public*, pg. 896
Zitman, Th. L.J., Exec. V.P.--FGH Bank N.V., Utrecht, Netherlands; *Int'l*, pg. 26
Zoga, Chris, Exec. V.P.-Mfg.--Premier Mill Corp., Reading, PA; *U.S. Private*, pg. 881
Zoga, Chris, Exec. V.P.-Mfg.--Integrated Press Systems, Reading, PA; *U.S. Private*, pg. 881
Zook, Dennis R., Chief Oper. Officer & Exec. V.P.-S. Div. & Mexico--Costco Wholesale, Issaquah, WA; *U.S. Public*, pg. 451
Zore, Edward J., Chief Fin. Officer & Exec. V.P.--Northwestern Mutual Life Insurance Co., Milwaukee, WI; *U.S. Private*, pg. 807
Zubiria, Jose M., Exec. V.P.--Avantel, S.A., Mexico, Mexico; *Int'l*, pg. 574
Zuckerman, Alan M., Exec. V.P.--Chi Systems Division, Ann Arbor, MI; *U.S. Public*, pg. 1539
Zuerker, Jack A., Exec. V.P.--Sivalls, Inc., Odessa, TX; *U.S. Private*, pg. 1004
Zugaro, Umberto Galli, Intl. V.P.--FCA!BMZ, Milan, Italy; *Int'l*, pg. 470
Zumbach, Felix, Chief Exec. Officer & Exec. V.P.--Union Bank of Switzerland, Zurich, Switzerland; *Int'l*, pg. 1439
Zumbiel, Thomas J., Exec. V.P. & Sec.--C.W. Zumbiel Company, Norwood, OH; *U.S. Private*, pg. 1207
Zumbuehl, Paul, Exec. V.P.-Plastics Technology--Mikron Holding AG, Biel, Switzerland; *Int'l*, pg. 866
Zumwalt, John B, III, Chief Oper. Officer & Exec. V.P--The PBS&J Corporation, Miami, FL; *U.S. Private*, pg. 825
Zuqi, Jiang, Vice Chm. & Exec. V.P.--Bank of China, Beijing, China; *Int'l*, pg. 152
Zuver, Chuck, Exec. V.P. & Dir.-Govt. Affairs--Credit Union National Association, Madison, WI; *U.S. Private*, pg. 288
Zvesper, Joseph P., Chief Fin. Officer, Exec. V.P., Treas. & Sec.--American Appraisal Associates, Inc., Milwaukee, WI; *U.S. Private*, pg. 49
Zwartendijk, Rob, Exec. V.P.--Koninklijke Ahold NV, Zaandam, Netherlands; *Int'l*, pg. 749
Zweegers, J.J.W., Exec. V.P.--ABN-AMRO Holding N.V., Amsterdam, Netherlands; *Int'l*, pg. 8
Zweifel, James A., Chief Fin. Officer & Exec. V.P.--President Casinos, Inc., Saint Louis, MO; *U.S. Public*, pg. 1323
Zweig, Stephen A., Exec. V.P.-Integrated Services--Meldrum & Fewsmith Communications Inc., Cleveland, OH; *U.S. Private*, pg. 730
Zwierzina, T.F., Exec. V.P.--ABN-AMRO Holding N.V., Amsterdam, Netherlands; *Int'l*, pg. 8

EXPORT

Abel, James J., Chief Fin. Officer, Exec. V.P., Treas. & Sec.--The Lamson & Sessions Co., Cleveland, OH; *U.S. Public*, pg. 976
Abraham, Andrea, Dir.-Traffic--Swiss Army Brands, Inc., Shelton, CT; *U.S. Public*, pg. 1544
Aguiar, Carlos, Mgr.-Export & Admin.--Cervejarias Kaiser Brasil Ltda., Campinas, Brazil; *Int'l*, pg. 279
Allaman, Jim, Mgr.-Sls.--Wire Rope Corporation of America, Inc., Saint Joseph, MO; *U.S. Private*, pg. 1184
Allred, Dustin, Mgr.-Export--Wm. Wrigley Jr. Company, Chicago, IL; *U.S. Public*, pg. 1781
Altman, Barry, Mgr.-Export Sls.--Melitta U.S.A., Inc., Clearwater, FL; *Int'l*, pg. 857
Amado, Jose, Dir.-Exports--BS Continental S.A. Utilidades Domesticas, Sao Paulo, Brazil; *Int'l*, pg. 123
Amundsen, David, Corp. Mgr.-Customer Service & Exports--Pabst Brewing Co., San Antonio, TX; *U.S. Private*, pg. 954
Andersson, Roland, Dir.-Pur. & Export Control--ABB Asea Brown Boveri (Holding) Ltd., Zurich, Switzerland; *Int'l*, pg. 1
Anlauf, Dick, Mgr.-Export--BJ's Wholesale Club, Inc., Natick, MA; *U.S. Public*, pg. 162
Archer, L.F., Export Mgr.--ITT Jabsco, Costa Mesa, CA; *U.S. Public*, pg. 860
Arnon, Ehud, Sr. V.P.-Foreign Trade--Bank Hapoalim, Tel Aviv, Israel; *Int'l*, pg. 149
Artaiz, Vic, Mgr.-Intl. Sls.--Ulbrich Stainless Steels & Special Metals, Inc., North Haven, CT; *U.S. Private*, pg. 1115
Austin, Ed, Mgr.-Export--Circle International, Saint Rose, LA; *U.S. Public*, pg. 371
Aycock, John, Mgr.-Export & Mktg.--Kennedy Manufacturing Company, Van Wert, OH; *U.S. Private*, pg. 614
Bagrie, J., Mgr.-Export--Quality Bakers New Zealand Ltd., Auckland, New Zealand; *Int'l*, pg. 556
Baguer, Ihena, Mgr.-Import--Bernard Chaus, Inc., New York, NY; *U.S. Public*, pg. 342
Bailey, Richard, Dir.-Exports--Beauty Enterprises Inc., Hartford, CT; *U.S. Private*, pg. 128
Baker, Al, Mgr.-Export--Norpac Foods, Inc., Stayton, OR; *U.S. Private*, pg. 802
Balter, Stuart M., V.P.-Trade Rels.--The Jaydor Corporation, Millburn, NJ; *U.S. Private*, pg. 584
Banazak, Mark, Mgr.-Export--Parker Hannifin Corporation, Cleveland, OH; *U.S. Public*, pg. 1259
Bandy, Janell, Sls. & Export Rep.--Gibson Wine Company, Sanger, CA; *U.S. Private*, pg. 452
Barko, David G., Mgr.-Export Sls.--Hickman, Williams & Co. Inc., Cincinnati, OH; *U.S. Private*, pg. 525
Barreto, Al, Mgr.-Export--Esselte Corporation, Garden City, NY; *Int'l*, pg. 459
Barta, Z., Mgr.-Export--Semikron International, GmbH & Co. KG, Nuremberg, Germany; *Int'l*, pg. 1220
Bartner, L. Scott, Mgr.-Corp. Traffic--P.H. Glatfelter Company, Spring Grove, PA; *U.S. Public*, pg. 746
Beams, Chris, Mgr.-Export--Ilco Unican Corp., Rocky Mount, NC; *Int'l*, pg. 1432
Becherer, Hans W., Chm. Bd. & Chief Exec. Officer--Deere & Company, Moline, IL; *U.S. Public*, pg. 491
Begani, R.F., Mgr.-Export--La-Co Industries Markal Company, Elk Grove Village, IL; *U.S. Private*, pg. 640
Bell, Bill, Mgr.-Export--Symons Corporation, Des Plaines, IL; *U.S. Private*, pg. 932
Berg, David, Chief Oper. Officer & Exec. V.P.-Sls.--PremiumWear, Inc., Minneapolis, MN; *U.S. Public*, pg. 1323
Bergmann, Richard, Mgr.-Distr. & Customer Service--Ato-Findley, Inc., Wauwatosa, WI; *Int'l*, pg. 445
Berman, Bernard, Gen. Mgr.--Butler Ventamatic Corp., Mineral Wells, TX; *U.S. Private*, pg. 190
Berrutti, Martin, Export Mgr.--Sudamtex de Uruguay, S.A., Montevideo, Uruguay; *Int'l*, pg. 1304
Bertsch, Dave, Mgr.-Export--Harris Calorific Co., Gainesville, GA; *U.S. Public*, pg. 996
Beyer, Angelika, First V.P.-Export, Trade & Aircraft Financing--Deutsche Girozentrale-Deutsche Kommunalbank, Frankfurt/Main, Germany; *Int'l*, pg. 406
Bires, Beverly, Mgr.-Export--Courtaulds Aerospace, Glendale, CA; *Int'l*, pg. 339
Bjornefeldt, Thorbjorn, Dir.-Export--Atlet AB, Molnlycke, Sweden; *Int'l*, pg. 97

Blackmur, Peter, Mgr.-Export--Clemco Industries Corp., Washington, MO; *U.S. Private*, pg. 24
Blair, J.S., Mgr.-Intl. Sls.--Trion, Inc., Sanford, NC; *U.S. Public*, pg. 1639
Blair, Joan, Dir.-Export--Tekelec, Calabasas, CA; *U.S. Public*, pg. 1566
Blanckaert, Jan, Mgr.-Export & Pur.--Digital Equipment N.V./S.A., Brussels, Belgium; *U.S. Public*, pg. 508
Blum, Richard, Sr. V.P.-Intl.--Swank, Inc., Attleboro, MA; *U.S. Public*, pg. 1543
Boege, Steen, Mgr.-Export--GN Netcom A/S, Copenhagen, Denmark; *Int'l*, pg. 537
Boehm, Dan, Mgr.-Export--AP North American Aftermarket Division, Goldsboro, NC; *U.S. Private*, pg. 230
Borell, Mark, Mgr.-Transportation & Distr.--Titan International, Inc., Quincy, IL; *U.S. Public*, pg. 1618
Borggren, Lennart, Mgr.-Projects--Fastighetsaktiebolaget Hufvudstaden, Stockholm, Sweden; *Int'l*, pg. 478
Bosch, Larry, Dir.-Intl. Sls.--Celestial Seasonings, Boulder, CO; *U.S. Public*, pg. 319
Bostick, Don, Mgr.-Export--Correct Craft, Inc., Orlando, FL; *U.S. Private*, pg. 276
Boulas, Sami, Mgr.-Export--Alkota Cleaning Systems, Inc., Alcester, SD; *U.S. Private*, pg. 34
Brack, Allan F., V.P.-Intl.--Criticare Systems, Inc., Waukesha, WI; *U.S. Public*, pg. 459
Bramman, Alys, Dir.-Intl.--Invacare Health Care Furnishings, Chesterfield, MO; *U.S. Public*, pg. 911
Branz, Adele, Sls. Admin.--Miss Elaine Inc., Saint Louis, MO; *U.S. Private*, pg. 752
Brehm, Rodney, Sr. V.P.-Distr.--7-Eleven Stores, Dallas, TX; *Int'l*, pg. 693
Brink, Donald L., Dir.-Export--General Mills, Inc., Minneapolis, MN; *U.S. Public*, pg. 717
Brinker, Kenneth J., Dir.-Pur. & World Trade--Warner-Lambert Company, Morris Plains, NJ; *U.S. Public*, pg. 1738
Brinninstool, Bill, Export Mgr.--Heil Environmental Industries, Chattanooga, TN; *U.S. Public*, pg. 520
Brizzolara, Yvonne Monique, V.P.-Intl. Sls.--Eversharp Pen Co., Franklin Park, IL; *U.S. Private*, pg. 386
Brocker, Paul, Mgr.-Intl. Sls.--FMC FoodTech/Fran Rica, Stockton, CA; *U.S. Public*, pg. 605
Brothers, Carl W., Sr. V.P.-Intl. Rice & Partnership--Riceland Foods, Inc., Stuttgart, AR; *U.S. Private*, pg. 928
Brown, Anneliese, Mgr.-Intl. Mktg.--Armor All Products Group, Oakland, CA; *U.S. Public*, pg. 387
Bruckdorfer, Lenora, Mgr.-Export--Circle International, Houston, TX; *U.S. Public*, pg. 371
Bufford, Terry, Dir.-Intl.--Inter-Tel, Incorporated, Phoenix, AZ; *U.S. Public*, pg. 888
Buland, M., Admin.-Export--Swish Products Ltd., Tamworth, United Kingdom; *Int'l*, pg. 925
Bunting, Paul, Mgr.-Import/Export--Wyeth Australia Pty. Ltd., Baulkham Hills, Australia; *U.S. Public*, pg. 82
Burchfield, Lisa, Mgr.-Export--Bunn-O-Matic Corporation, Springfield, IL; *U.S. Private*, pg. 180
Burgos, Lori, Mgr.-Import & Export--Deerskin Trading Post, Inc., North Bergen, NJ; *U.S. Public*, pg. 879
Burnham, Duane L., Chm. & Chief Exec. Officer--Abbott Laboratories, Abbott Park, IL; *U.S. Public*, pg. 12
Burns, Ed, Mgr.-Import/Export--Marquette Coppersmithing Co., Inc., Philadelphia, PA; *U.S. Private*, pg. 706
Burnstein, Elyse, Mgr.-Sls./Export--The W.E. Bassett Company, Shelton, CT; *U.S. Private*, pg. 122
Burstein, Arnold, V.P.-Intl. Sls. & Mktg.--Inverness Corp., Fair Lawn, NJ; *U.S. Private*, pg. 574
Burt, Donna, Mgr.-Export--IMI Cash Valve, Inc., Cullman, AL; *Int'l*, pg. 646
Bury, Jefrey D., V.P.-Bus. Devel.--Wyandot Inc., Marion, OH; *U.S. Private*, pg. 1193
Bustamante, Tony, Mgr.-Export--DEECO Industries, Hillside, NJ; *U.S. Private*, pg. 320
Butensky, Martin, Dir.-Mktg.--Vernitron Sensor Systems, Saint Petersburg, FL; *U.S. Public*, pg. 157
Cabrera, Richard, Mgr.-Export--American International Container, Inc., Miami, FL; *U.S. Private*, pg. 57
Callahan, Chris, V.P.-New Bus. Devel.--American Pad and Paper Company, Dallas, TX; *U.S. Public*, pg. 88
Callander, Douglas, Dir.-Export Sls.--Campbell Distillers Limited, Brentford, United Kingdom; *Int'l*, pg. 567
Cameron, Julie, Mgr.-Intl. Sls.--Elixir Industries, Gardena, CA; *U.S. Private*, pg. 371
Cameron, Stuart, Mgr.-Export--A. Schulman, Inc., Akron, OH; *U.S. Public*, pg. 1441
Carpenter, Scott R., V.P.-Sls.--Bachman Company, Reading, PA; *U.S. Private*, pg. 109
Carr, Brig, Dir.-Export--Invacare Corporation, Elyria, OH; *U.S. Public*, pg. 911
Carter, Stephen P., Chief Fin. Officer, V.P. & Treas.--Woodward Governor Company, Rockford, IL; *U.S. Public*, pg. 1776
Cash, David, Mgr.-Export--Conwood Company L.P., Memphis, TN; *U.S. Private*, pg. 272
Catita, Jose, Dir.-Internal Trade--Giant Food Inc., Landover, MD; *U.S. Public*, pg. 741
Cavanaugh, Leo, V.P. & Gen. Mgr.-Trade Rels. & Special Projects--Fuji Photo Film U.S.A., Inc., Elmsford, NY; *Int'l, pg. 524*
Cavellini, Luissa, Commercial Mgr.-Italy & Export--Gedy S.p.A., Senago, Italy; *Int'l*, pg. 542
Ce Ra Boma, Vito, Mgr.-Export--Caleffi S.p.A., Viadana, Italy; *Int'l*, pg. 252
Cellier, Cecile, Mgr.-Mktg. & Export--BG SAS, Le Tholy, France; *Int'l*, pg. 201
Chan, Sunday, Gen. Mgr.-Export Opers.--Kintetsu World Express (H.K.) Ltd., Kowloon, Hong Kong; *Int'l*, pg. 735
Chapman, P., Dir.-Export Sls.--Addison Tube Forming Limited, Preston, United Kingdom; *Int'l*, pg. 448
Chase, Peter R., Pres. & Chief Exec. Officer--Chase Corporation, Braintree, MA; *U.S. Public*, pg. 337
Cheney, Joy, Mgr.-Export--Hutchinson Technology Inc., Hutchinson, MN; *U.S. Public*, pg. 850
Ching, A.K., Mgr.-Exports--Peters & Brownes Foods Ltd., Balcatta, Australia; *Int'l*, pg. 1040
Chong-Sung, Lee, Exec. Mng. Dir.-Motor Vehicles Export--Daewoo Corporation, Seoul, Korea; *Int'l*, pg. 357
Ciquier, Jean Paul, Mgr.-Export--Tefal S.A., Rumilly, France; *Int'l*, pg. 569
Clark, George A., Chm. Bd., Pres. & Chief Exec. Officer--Snap-Tite, Inc., Erie, PA; *U.S. Private*, pg. 1010
Clark, George P., V.P.--Snap-Tite, Inc., Erie, PA; *U.S. Private*, pg. 1010
Clarke, Chris, Mng. Dir.-Import & Export--Hunt-Wesson, Inc., Fullerton, CA; *U.S. Public*, pg. 428
Clary, Luke, Export Mgr.--CertainTeed Corporation, Valley Forge, PA; *Int'l*, pg. 1170
Clawson, Marci, Mgr.-Matls.--Utah Medical Products, Inc., Midvale, UT; *U.S. Public*, pg. 1700
Clemmer, Jake, Mgr.-Direct Export Sls.--Hatfield Quality Meats, Hatfield, PA; *U.S. Private*, pg. 510
Cloet, Paul, Mgr.-Export--Posso S.A., Paris, France; *Int'l*, pg. 1064
Cobb, Carl, Supvr.-Export--F.X. Coughlin Co., Taylor, MI; *U.S. Private*, pg. 278
Cobb, Neil, Dir.-Intl. Tent Sls.--Anchor Industries Inc., Evansville, IN; *U.S. Private*, pg. 71
Cole, Wes, Traffic Coord.--BJ Services Company, Houston, TX; *U.S. Public*, pg. 161
Colenun, Brue, Mgr.-Export--M K Diamond Products, Inc., Torrance, CA; *U.S. Private*, pg. 684
Colson, Peter, Mgr.-Export--Smith & Wesson Corp., Springfield, MA; *Int'l*, pg. 1397
Coonan, Joseph, Mgr.-Export--Generation Metals Corp., Hauppauge, NY; *U.S. Private*, pg. 446
Cooper, Bob, Dir.-Mktg.--Tomco Auto Products, Inc., Los Angeles, CA; *U.S. Private*, pg. 1090
Cooper, Kris, Mgr.-Export--Union Special Corp., Huntley, IL; *Int'l*, pg. 716
Coughenour, J.L., Mgr.-Export--Danisco Ingredients USA, Inc., New Century, KS; *Int'l*, pg. 378
Coughlin, Neil P., V.P.-Sls. & Mktg.--Kingsbury Corporation, Keene, NH; *U.S. Private*, pg. 621
Coutinho, Carlos, Mgr.-Export--Souza Cruz, S.A., Rio de Janeiro, Brazil; *Int'l*, pg. 112
Cowan, David, Mgr.-Pur.--Pride International, Inc., Houston, TX; *U.S. Public*, pg. 1324
Cram, James, Mgr.-Export--Deck House Inc., Acton, MA; *U.S. Private*, pg. 320
Cram, James, Mgr.-Export--Acorn Structures, Acton, MA; *U.S. Private*, pg. 320
Craze, John, Mgr.-Export--Chattem, Inc., Chattanooga, TN; *U.S. Public*, pg. 341
Cristo, Gus, Exec. V.P. & Dir.-Sls. & Mktg.--Ferguson International, Inc., Dallas, TX; *U.S. Private*, pg. 401
Crosier, Thelma, Mgr.-Export & Customer Svcs.--The Keller Manufacturing Co., Inc., Corydon, IN; *U.S. Private*, pg. 612
Cyriacks, Anne, Mgr.-Export--Dow Jones Markets, Jersey City, NJ; *U.S. Public*, pg. 525
D'Amico, Paul, Intl.--Dahlberg, Inc., Golden Valley, MN; *U.S.* Public, pg. 194
Dahlin, Ross A., Mgr.-Intl. Div.--Andersen Corporation, Bayport, MN; *U.S. Private*, pg. 71
Daniel, Jose, Gen. Mgr.-Pharmaceutical Prods. & Cosmetics--Nestle S.A., Vevey, Switzerland; *Int'l*, pg. 915
Dau, J., Mgr.-Export--Agfa-Gevaert N.V., Antwerp, Belgium; *Int'l*, pg. 174
David, John, Mgr.-Export--Salem Carpet Mills, Inc., Winston Salem, NC; *U.S. Public*, pg. 1464
Davis, Jim, Mgr.-Export--GSC Enterprises, Inc., Sulphur Springs, TX; *U.S. Private*, pg. 436
de Moraes, Antonio, Mgr.-Export--Cia. Agro Industrial Igarassu, Recife, Brazil; *Int'l*, pg. 677
de Moraes, Antonio Ermirio, Mgr.-Export--S.A. Industrias Votorantim, Sao Paulo, Brazil; *Int'l*, pg. 677
de Souza, Aristides Jose, Mgr.-Export--3M Do Brasil Ltda., Sao Paulo, Brazil; *U.S. Public*, pg. 1606
DeCastro, Amelia, Mgr.-Export--Cole of California, Los Angeles, CA; *U.S. Public*, pg. 148
Desai, Rasik, Mgr.-Export--New Brunswick Scientific Co., Inc., Edison, NJ; *U.S. Public*, pg. 1169
Diamant, J.R., V.P.-Intl. Div.--Victaulic Company of America, Easton, PA; *U.S. Private*, pg. 1138
Diaz, Miguel, V.P.-Intl. Opers.--Duro-Test Corporation, Fairfield, NJ; *U.S. Private*, pg. 349
Dilschneider, Ray, Pres.-Ing. Div.--Tree Top, Inc., Selah, WA; *U.S. Private*, pg. 1098
DiMichele, Rose, Supvr.-Orders--AGR International, Inc., Butler, PA; *U.S. Private*, pg. 5
Docherty, D., Mgr.-Export--British Gypsum Ltd., Loughborough, United Kingdom; *Int'l*, pg. 122
Donma, Robert, Mgr.-Export--Spiegel Meats, Inc., Miami, FL; *U.S. Private*, pg. 1025
Dorfman, Robert, Pres.--King Wire Inc., North Chicago, IL; *U.S. Private*, pg. 621
Dourthe, P., Dir.-Export--Grands Terroirs Associes BV, Nieuw-Vennep, Netherlands; *Int'l*, pg. 751
Dourthe, P., Dir.-Export--Consortium Vinicole de Bordeaux et de la Gironde SA, Parempuyre, France; *Int'l*, pg. 752
Dowell, Neville, Chief Fin. Officer--Union City Body Company, L.P., Union City, IN; *U.S. Private*, pg. 1118
Doyle, Gary, Dir.-Contracts & Matls.--Xicor, Inc., Milpitas, CA; *U.S. Public*, pg. 1785
Draughon, Terry, V.P.-Intl. Export Publishing Sls.--Thomas Nelson Inc., Nashville, TN; *U.S. Public*, pg. 1167
Drilling, Mike, V.P.-Gateway--DHL Worldwide Express, Redwood City, CA; *U.S. Private*, pg. 301
Drummond, Paul, V.P.-Sls.--Great Plains Manufacturing, Inc., Salina, KS; *U.S. Private*, pg. 475
Duarte, Mirta, V.P.--Mason Distributors, Inc., Hialeah, FL; *U.S. Private*, pg. 712
Duff, J., Grp. Mgr.-Export--Kiwi Brands Pty. Ltd., Clayton, Australia; *U.S. Public*, pg. 1434
Duffy, Peter A., V.P.-Sls. & Mktg.--Haskel International, Inc., Burbank, CA; *U.S. Public*, pg. 798
Dummer, Glen, V.P.-Quality--Red Wing Shoe Co., Inc., Red Wing, MN; *U.S. Private*, pg. 915
Duncan, Sharon, Mgr.-Export--DIT-MCO Intl., Kansas City, MO; *U.S. Private*, pg. 1194
Dunn, Mark, Mgr.-Export--Star Fine Foods, Inc., Fresno, CA; *U.S. Private*, pg. 1034
Duvall, William R., Sr. V.P.-Opers.--LoJack Corporation, Dedham, MA; *U.S. Public*, pg. 1012
Dytko, Greg, Mgr.-Wholesale--Sun Electric, Lincolnshire, IL; *U.S. Public*, pg. 1480
Eckert, Randy, Mgr.-Export Sls.--Stadelman Fruit L.L.C., Yakima, WA; *U.S. Private*, pg. 1028
Edelsbacher, Willibald, Mng. Dir.-Export--Julius Meinl AG, Vienna, Austria; *Int'l*, pg. 856
Edmonds, Dennis, Mgr.-Traffic--Jefferson Mills, Inc., Pulaski, VA; *U.S. Private*, pg. 584
Egner, Ernst, Mgr.-Export--Klafs Saunabau GmbH & Co. KG Medizinische Technik, Schwabisch Hall, Germany; *Int'l*, pg. 736
Eickhoff, Dietrich, Div. Mgr.--Durkopp Adler AG, Bielefeld, Germany; *Int'l*, pg. 468
Elain, William, Mgr.-Export--Milton Bradley Company, East Longmeadow, MA; *U.S. Public*, pg. 797
Elison, Mike, Intl. Sls. Mgr.--Belshaw Brothers, Inc., Seattle, WA; *Int'l*, pg. 188
Ell, Paul C., Mgr.-Export--Crown Holdings, Inc., Roseville, MN; *U.S. Private*, pg. 293
Ellickson, Sam, Export Mgr.--Gilbert Paper, Menasha, WI; *U.S. Public*, pg. 1074
Ellsworth, Pam, Dir.-Import & Export--S. Schwab Company, Cumberland, MD; *U.S. Private*, pg. 974
English, Floyd L., Chm. Bd., Pres. & Chief Exec. Officer--Andrew Corporation, Orland Park, IL; *U.S. Public*, pg. 112
Epstein, Phil, Div. Exec. V.P.--KTI, Inc., Guttenberg, NJ; *U.S. Public*, pg. 939
Etzweiler, Thomas I., Dir.-Intl. Sls.--WWF Paper Corporation, Bala Cynwyd, PA; *U.S. Private*, pg. 1145
Faase, Karen, Mgr.-Export--Ziebart International Corporation, Troy, MI; *U.S. Private*, pg. 1205
Fairey, Laurence Y., V.P.-Intl. Mktg.--Danek Medical Inc., Memphis, TN; *U.S. Public*, pg. 1482
Farmer, David, Mgr.-Treas. Svcs.--The Will-Burt Company, Orrville, OH; *U.S. Private*, pg. 1177
Fernandes, Manny, Mgr.-Export--Amprobe Instrument, Lynbrook, NY; *U.S. Public*, pg. 1676
Fillion, Roger, Mgr.-Export--Auto Driveaway Co., Chicago, IL; *U.S. Private*, pg. 100
Findlay, Koni, Mgr.-Export--Conso Products Company, Union, SC; *U.S. Public*, pg. 434
Finie, Paul, Gen. Mgr.--Trend Offset Printing Services, Los Alamitos, CA; *U.S. Private*, pg. 1099
Fischer, Werner F., V.P.-Export Intl. Div.--Brother International Corporation, Somerset, NJ; *Int'l*, pg. 229
Fisher, John, Mgr.-Export, Aerospace--Lord Corporation, Mechanical Products Division, Erie, PA; *U.S. Private*, pg. 676
Fleming, Robert, Dir.-Import & Export--QMS, Inc., Mobile, AL; *U.S. Public*, pg. 1346
Flood, Peter E., Pres. & Chief Exec. Officer--The Flood Company, Hudson, OH; *U.S. Private*, pg. 414
Forcelle, Joyce, Mgr.-Intl. Sls.--WINCO, Le Center, MN; *U.S. Private*, pg. 350
Forsans, Pierre, Dir.-Exporting--Yves Saint Laurent Parfums S.A., Neuilly-sur-Seine, France; *Int'l*, pg. 445
Forsyth, Stephen C., Gen. Mgr.-Resins/Exports--Hexcel Corporation, Pleasanton, CA; *U.S. Public*, pg. 824
Foster, George, Dir.-Mktg.--Pacific Coast Building Products Inc., Sacramento, CA; *U.S. Private*, pg. 830
Fraser, Mike, Mgr.-Intl. Bus.--James Hardie Industries Ltd., Sydney, Australia; *Int'l*, pg. 596
Fratino, Constantino, Mgr.-Import/Export--Nestle Industrial e Commercial Ltda., Sao Paulo, Brazil; *Int'l*, pg. 921
French, John, Mgr.-Export & Sls.--Thomas Equipment Limited, Centreville, Canada; *Int'l*, pg. 850
Frengle, Doug, Mgr.-Export--Agripac Inc., Salem, OR; *U.S. Private*, pg. 26
Fritz, Charles, Mgr.-Export--Magnetic Metals Corp., Camden, NJ; *U.S. Private*, pg. 560
Funston, Mark D., V.P.-Fin.--COMSAT RSI, Inc., Sterling, VA; *U.S. Public*, pg. 424
Fusco, Tom, Mgr.-Export--Dixon Ticonderoga Company, Heathrow, FL; *U.S. Public*, pg. 514
Gagliardi, Micheal, Mgr.-Export--West Chemical Products, Inc., Princeton, NJ; *U.S. Private*, pg. 1158
Gallagher, Richard, V.P.-International Div.--Sonic Couriers of Arizona, Inc., Scottsdale, AZ; *U.S. Private*, pg. 1123
Gallaher, Edward W., Sr., Pres., Chief Exec. Officer & Treas.--Phoenix Medical Technology, Inc., Andrews, SC; *U.S. Public*, pg. 1292
Ganz-Haseloff, Hendrik, Mgr.-Export--Apollinaris & Schweppes Gmbh & Co., Hamburg, Germany; *Int'l*, pg. 78
Gargano, Joe, Mgr.-Export--Duro-Test Corporation, Fairfield, NJ; *U.S. Private*, pg. 349
Garsley, J.K., Admin.-Export--Swish Products Ltd., Tamworth, United Kingdom; *Int'l*, pg. 925
Garten, Toby, Dir.-OEM & New Prod. Devel.--Nady Systems, Inc., Emeryville, CA; *U.S. Private*, pg. 773
Gaudrault, Donna, Mgr.-Export--Texon Materials Inc., Russell, MA; *U.S. Private*, pg. 1079
Gawith, Robert, Export Coord.--Fuller, Smith & Turner Plc, London, United Kingdom; *Int'l*, pg. 529
Gellert, Robert, Mgr.-Export--Atalanta Corporation, Elizabeth, NJ; *U.S. Private*, pg. 93
Gentile, Dominic, V.P.-Sls. & Export--The Eureka Company, Bloomington, IL; *Int'l*, pg. 440
Gerber, Yves, Dir.-Export--Bongard, Holtzheim, France; *Int'l, pg. 570*
Gibbs, Michael F., Mgr.-Export--Sleepeezee Limited, London, United Kingdom; *Int'l*, pg. 1263
Gille, Lori-Jean, J.D., Sr. V.P., Gen. Counsel & Sec.--MGI PHARMA INC., Minneapolis, MN; *U.S. Public*, pg. 1026

Goergen, Greg, Mgr.-Export--Osmose Wood Preserving, Inc., Buffalo, NY; *U.S. Private*, pg. 821
Goldberg, Charlotte, Mgr.-Export--All-Luminum Products, Inc., Philadelphia, PA; *U.S. Private*, pg. 34
Gomez, Ricardo, Mgr.-Export--Vitromex, S.A., Saltillo, Mexico; *Int'l*, pg. 1469
Goranlindglad, Nils, Mgr.-Export--Royal Copenhagen A/S, Frederiksberg, Denmark; *Int'l*, pg. 1134
Gordon, Marquart, Mgr.-Export--Nasco, Fort Atkinson, WI; *U.S. Private*, pg. 446
Gracie, J.S., V.P. & Pres.-First Brands Intl.--First Brands Corporation, Danbury, CT; *U.S. Public*, pg. 626
Graham, Chuck, Mgr.-Intl. Sls.--Rudolph Foods Company, Lima, OH; *U.S. Private*, pg. 950
Graney, John, Mgr.-Export--Barouh Eaton Allen Corporation, Brooklyn, NY; *U.S. Private*, pg. 117
Gray, Brian, Mgr.-Sls./Intl. Sls. & Exports--United Aluminum Corporation, North Haven, CT; *U.S. Private*, pg. 1120
Greco, Natalie O., Mgr.-Opers.--Nelson Westerberg, Inc., Elk Grove Village, IL; *U.S. Private*, pg. 1163
Green, Lorraine, Mgr.-Intl. Customer Svc.--Merit Medical Systems, Inc., South Jordan, UT; *U.S. Public*, pg. 1096
Gronfors, Antti, Mgr.-Export--Meijeriosuuskunta/ Mejeriandelslaget Milka, Helsinki, Finland; *Int'l*, pg. 854
Gruaz, Bruno, V.P.-Intl. Sls.--DOALL Company, Des Plaines, IL; *U.S. Private*, pg. 337
Guareschi, Giulio, Mgr.-Export--I.B.I.S.-S.p.A., Busseto, Italy; *Int'l*, pg. 642
Gun-Woo, Park, Exec. Mng. Dir.-Motor Vehicles Export Plng.--Daewoo Corporation, Seoul, Korea; *Int'l*, pg. 357
Ha, Shita, Dir.-Import & Export Adv.--Lotte Shopping Co. Ltd., Seoul, Korea; *Int'l*, pg. 819
Habermann, Reiner, Mgr.-Export Sls.--Kermi GmbH, Plattling, Germany; *Int'l*, pg. 1069
Hagen, Dennis, Mgr.-Export--Viking Pump, Inc., Cedar Falls, IA; *U.S. Public*, pg. 862
Hahn, Stan, Mgr.-Export--State Industries Inc., Ashland City, TN; *U.S. Private*, pg. 1036
Hall, Don, Mgr.-Export--MTS Systems Corporation, Eden Prairie, MN; *U.S. Public*, pg. 1028
Hall, Peter, Dir.-Export Sls. & Mktg.--Gaylord Container Corporation, Deerfield, IL; *U.S. Public*, pg. 704
Hanono, Salomon, Dir.-Export--Carfel, Inc., Miami, FL; *U.S. Private*, pg. 210
Hardmeyer, Bob, Admin. Mgr.-Indus. Export--Rice Growers Association of California, West Sacramento, CA; *U.S. Private*, pg. 927
Hardy, Donal B., V.P.-Export--Bruce Oakley, Inc., North Little Rock, AR; *U.S. Private*, pg. 809
Harp, Milford B., Exec. V.P.-Opers.--Nalco Chemical Company, Naperville, IL; *U.S. Public*, pg. 1150
Harper, Georgie, V.P.-Sls.--Dakotah, Inc., Webster, SD; *U.S. Public*, pg. 477
Harris, B. Joe, Mgr.-Transportation--Republic Gypsum Co.-Gypsum Wallboard Plant, Duke, OK; *U.S. Public*, pg. 1378
Harris, David, Mgr.-Export--Christensen Products, Salt Lake City, UT; *U.S. Public*, pg. 981
Harrison, Walter, Mgr.-Mktg.--Delta Pride Catfish, Inc., Indianola, MS; *U.S. Private*, pg. 322
Hart, Charles R., Sr. V.P.-Intl. Opers.--Marine Construction & Design Co., Seattle, WA; *U.S. Private*, pg. 703
Hauca, Gregory J., V.P.-Mktg.--Distribution America, Des Plaines, IL; *U.S. Private*, pg. 335
Hausjell, Alois, Mgr.-Exporting--Agrolinz Melamin GmbH, Lienz, Austria; *Int'l*, pg. 356
Haversat, Robert, Jr., Dir.-Export--Essex Industries, Inc., New Haven, CT; *Int'l*, pg. 18
Haverstock, Marilyn, Dir.-Export--General Automation, Inc., Irvine, CA; *U.S. Public*, pg. 706
Hawk, Robert, Exec. V.P.--Northland Cranberries, Inc., Wisconsin Rapids, WI; *U.S. Public*, pg. 1197
Hawley, F.J., Mgr.-Export & Eastern Sls.--Sloan Valve Company, Franklin Park, IL; *U.S. Private*, pg. 1006
Headley, Steve, Mng. Dir.-Export--Brown & Haley, Tacoma, WA; *U.S. Private*, pg. 173
Heider, Herbert, Dir.-Export--Lux GmbH & Co. KG, Wermelskirchen, Germany; *Int'l*, pg. 993
Helms, Beverly, Export Mgr.--Micromatic Textron, Holland, MI; *U.S. Public*, pg. 1589
Henderson, David, V.P. & Gen. Mgr.--American Locker Group, Inc., Jamestown, NY; *U.S. Public*, pg. 85
Henderson, Denis N., Dir.-Export--Irish Biscuits Ltd., Dublin, Ireland; *Int'l*, pg. 688
Henkels, Jan Peter, Mgr.-Export--Stocko Metallwaren Fabriken Henkels & Sohn, Wuppertal, Germany; *Int'l*, pg. 1301
Henning, Robert V., Pres.--Belmont Metals, Inc., Brooklyn, NY; *U.S. Private*, pg. 132
Henrotte, Jean-Marie, Mgr.-Export--Cockerill Sambre, Brussels, Belgium; *Int'l*, pg. 301
Herboth, Veronica, Mgr.-Export--Purity Products Inc., Miami, FL; *U.S. Private*, pg. 896
Hernandez, Mirna, Mgr.-Export--Monico Alloys, Inc., Los Angeles, CA; *U.S. Private*, pg. 757
Hessel, Tom, Mgr.-Export Sls.--J.D. Streett & Co., Inc., Maryland Heights, MO; *U.S. Private*, pg. 1047
Hetherwick, Gilbert, Sr. V.P.-Intl. Mktg., Sony Classical--Sony Music Entertainment, Inc., New York, NY; *Int'l*, pg. 1281
Hienrich, Andreas J., Prod. Mgr.--Inka Paletten GmbH, Hoehenkirchen, Germany; *Int'l*, pg. 678
Hillard, Michael, V.P.-Intl. Sls.--Fieldcrest Cannon, Inc., Kannapolis, NC; *U.S. Public*, pg. 1296
Hinajosa, Arnold, Mgr.-Export--The Kent Company, Elkhart, IN; *Int'l*, pg. 440
Hirose, Mario, Mgr.-Export--General Motors do Brasil Ltda., Sao Caetano do Sul, Brazil; *U.S. Public*, pg. 722
Hirshberg, Louis, Mgr.-Intl. Opers.--Milgray Electronics, Inc., Farmingdale, NY; *U.S. Public*, pg. 205
Hoben, James, Dir.-Export Sls.--WLR Foods, Inc., Timberville, VA; *U.S. Public*, pg. 1727
Hodapp, Don J., Chief Fin. Officer & Exec. V.P.--Hormel Foods Corp., Austin, MN; *U.S. Public*, pg. 840
Hodgekinson, R., Mgr.-Export--Weiser Inc., Burnaby, Canada; *U.S. Public*, pg. 1055
Hoelter, Timothy, V.P.-Intl. Trade & Regulatory Affairs--Harley-Davidson, Inc., Milwaukee, WI; *U.S. Public*, pg. 786
Hoey, Jane, Mgr.-Import--M.S. Walker, Inc., Somerville, MA; *U.S. Private*, pg. 1147
Hogue, Bill, Dir.-Export--IRD Mechanalysis, Inc. (U.S.A.), Columbus, OH; *U.S. Public*, pg. 789
Hollingsworth, G.B., Mgr.-Import & Export--E. & E. Kaye Limited, Enfield, United Kingdom; *Int'l*, pg. 727
Hosoda, Yuji, Mng. Dir.--Toyo Tire & Rubber Co., Ltd., Osaka, Japan; *Int'l*, pg. 1411
Hotta, Takeshi, Mgr.-Import & Export--Narumi China Corporation, Nagoya, Japan; *Int'l*, pg. 906
Hout, Claer, Mgr.-Export--Vandemoortele N.V., Izegem, Belgium; *Int'l*, pg. 1451
Howe, Janel, Mgr.-Export--Brush Research Manufacturing Company, Los Angeles, CA; *U.S. Private*, pg. 176
Hudson, Clive, V.P.-Europe, Middle East & Africa Opers.--3Com Personal Communications Div., Skokie, IL; *U.S. Public*, pg. 1604
Huether, Richard D., Pres. & Chief Exec. Officer--Independent Can Company, Belcamp, MD; *U.S. Private*, pg. 559
Husband, Kenneth W., V.P.-Pur.--R&B, Inc., Colmar, PA; *U.S. Public*, pg. 1354
Irez, Nuri, Mgr.-Export--Arcelik A.S., Istanbul, Turkey; *Int'l*, pg. 741
Issar, Christina, Intl. Sls. Rep.--GTCO Corporation, Columbia, MD; *U.S. Private*, pg. 436
Jackson, Jim, Mgr.-Export Sls.--Scotch Premium Meat, Gorgie, United Kingdom; *U.S. Public*, pg. 607
Jahagirdar, S., Asst. Mgr.-Exports--Precision Fasteners Ltd., Thane, India; *U.S. Public*, pg. 1420
James, Graham, Mgr.-Intl.--Anchor Continental Incorporated, Columbia, SC; *U.S. Private*, pg. 70
Jaskoviak, James, V.P.-Sls. & Mktg.--Winnebago Industries, Inc., Forest City, IA; *U.S. Public*, pg. 1772
Jaudenes, Jose, Gen. Mgr.-Olympia Intl.--Olympic Steel Inc., Cleveland, OH; *U.S. Public*, pg. 1221
Jex, Brady, Mgr.-Export--Nature's Sunshine Products, Inc., Provo, UT; *U.S. Public*, pg. 1166
Johnson, Barry, V.P.-Exports--Castex Incorporated, Holland, MI; *U.S. Public*, pg. 1577
Johnson, Harold R., Sr. V.P.-Bus. Devel.--The Fairchild Corporation, Chantilly, VA; *U.S. Public*, pg. 610
Johnson, J.B., Jr., Sr. V.P.--Birdsong Corporation, Suffolk, VA; *U.S. Private*, pg. 145
Johnston, Jeffrey D., V.P.-Intl. Sls. & Mktg.--Ruslander & Sons, Inc., Buffalo, NY; *U.S. Private*, pg. 952
Jones, Ronald V., Mgr.-Intl. Sls. & Svc. Center--Lukens Inc., Coatesville, PA; *U.S. Public*, pg. 1019
Jordan, Mike, Mgr.-Export--Beltone Electronics Corporation, Chicago, IL; *U.S. Private*, pg. 132
Joyce, Bill, Mgr.-Traffic--Bird Machine Company, South Walpole, MA; *U.S. Public*, pg. 166
Kagan, Ilanit, Mgr.-Export--IIS Intelligent Information Systems Ltd., Yokneam, Israel; *Int'l*, pg. 645
Kampff, Julio, Mgr.-Export--Henkel S/A. Industrias Quimicas, Sao Paulo, Brazil; *Int'l*, pg. 613
Kampken, Wolfgang, V.P.-Export, Trade & Aircraft Financing--Deutsche Girozentrale-Deutsche Kommunalbank, Frankfurt/Main, Germany; *Int'l*, pg. 406
Kan, Michael, Mgr.-Export--Branson Ultrasonics, Danbury, CT; *U.S. Public*, pg. 574
Kanabar, Anil, Mgr.-Export Sls.--Conestoga Wood Specialties Corp., East Earl, PA; *U.S. Private*, pg. 262
Kaplan, Joseph, Mgr.-Export Sls.--Pitco Frialator Inc., Bow, NH; *U.S. Public*, pg. 1065
Karper, Donald J., Exec. V.P.--Alva/Amco Pharmacal Companies, Inc., Chicago, IL; *U.S. Private*, pg. 47
Kates, Jon, Dir.-Export--Guilford Mills, Inc., Greensboro, NC; *U.S. Public*, pg. 768
Kats, Mrs., Mgr.-Export--Orlane, Paris, France; *Int'l*, pg. 1011
Kaufman, Jay, V.P.-Pur.--Crown Andersen Inc., Peachtree City, GA; *U.S. Public*, pg. 462
Kaufman, Marcia, Mgr.-Export--B&G Foods, Inc., Roseland, NJ; *U.S. Private*, pg. 105
Kawaguchi, Yasuhiro, Deputy Sr. Mgr.-Export--Mizuno Corporation, Osaka, Japan; *Int'l*, pg. 884
Kearney, Mike, Mgr.-Export--Dexion Group plc, Hemel Hempstead, United Kingdom; *U.S. Public*, pg. 893
Keaveney, W.J., Mgr.-Global Sls./Steel Div.--Carpenter Technology Corporation, Reading, PA; *U.S. Public*, pg. 307
Keegan, John, Mgr.-Intl. Bus. Devel.--Clayton Corporation, Fenton, MO; *U.S. Private*, pg. 244
Keegan, R., Mgr.-Projects--Australian Oil & Gas Corporation Limited, Sydney, Australia; *Int'l*, pg. 101
Keller, Dick, Mgr.-Export--Burns Philp Company of San Francisco, San Francisco, CA; *Int'l*, pg. 236
Kellersman, John, Mgr.-Export--Cooper Instrument Corp., Middlefield, CT; *U.S. Private*, pg. 274
Kelly, Joe, Mgr.-Export--Bel-Art Products, Pequannock, NJ; *U.S. Private*, pg. 130
Keltz, Hugo A., V.P.-Intl.--Briggs & Stratton Corporation, Wauwatosa, WI; *U.S. Public*, pg. 252
Kemp, Jon, Mgr.-Export--Mohawk Finishing Products, Inc., Amsterdam, NY; *U.S. Public*, pg. 1357
Kessel, Ulrich, Mgr.-Export--O&K Orenstein & Koppel Aktiengesellschaft, Dortmund, Germany; *Int'l*, pg. 516
Kettunen, Jouni, Export Mgr.--Koltek Oy, Vantaa, Finland; *Int'l*, pg. 1379
Keuffel, Gerd, V.P.-Intl. Sls.--Durakon Industries, Inc., Lapeer, MI; *U.S. Public*, pg. 537
Khan, M. Anwar, Mgr.-Matls.--Parke-Davis & Company, Limited, Karachi, Pakistan; *U.S. Public*, pg. 1739
Khawaja, Shahid Waheed, Sr. Mgr.-Supply--National Refinery Limited, Karachi, Pakistan; *Int'l*, pg. 909
Kiernan, Paul E., Dir.-Corp. Mktg.--Thermo Fibertek, Inc., Waltham, MA; *U.S. Public*, pg. 1593
Kimosh, Joe, Mgr.-Export--GoodMark Foods, Inc., Raleigh, NC; *U.S. Public*, pg. 751
Kindlund, Newton C., Chm. Bd., Pres., Chief Exec. & Chief Oper. Officer--Holiday RV Superstores, Inc., Orlando, FL; *U.S. Public*, pg. 829
King, James, Treas.--Kulicke & Soffa Industries, Inc., Willow Grove, PA; *U.S. Public*, pg. 968
Kinik, Steve, Mgr.-Export--JJI Lighting Group Inc., Greenwich, CT; *Int'l*, pg. 821
Kinsley, P.H., Chm. Bd., Chief Exec. Officer & Chief Oper. Officer--Permark International (Pty.) Ltd., Johannesburg, South Africa; *Int'l*, pg. 1036
Kirwin, Maridee, Mgr.-Govt. Procurement--Geo-Centers, Inc., Newton, MA; *U.S. Private*, pg. 447
Klein, Jim, Mgr.-Pur.--Voyager Emblems, Inc., Sanborn, NY; *U.S. Private*, pg. 1143
Klint, Douglas E., V.P., Gen. Counsel & Sec.--Gatefield Corporation, Fremont, CA; *U.S. Public*, pg. 703
Koot, Fon, Mgr.-Intl. Sls.--Utility Trailer Manufacturing Co., City of Industry, CA; *U.S. Private*, pg. 1130
Kopshever, John, Dir.-Export--Circle International Group, Inc., San Francisco, CA; *U.S. Public*, pg. 370
Kramer, Dennis, Dir.-Export--Supertex, Inc., Sunnyvale, CA; *U.S. Public*, pg. 1539
Krant, Robert, Sr. V.P.-Intl. Fin.--City National Corporation, Beverly Hills, CA; *U.S. Public*, pg. 380
Krejca, Jack E., Chief Fin. Officer, Treas. & Controller--Curran Group, Inc., Crystal Lake, IL; *U.S. Private*, pg. 297
Krochmal, Walt, Mgr.-Intl. Sls.--Simpson Industries, Inc., Plymouth, MI; *U.S. Public*, pg. 1474
Kumpf, Dale, Mgr.-Export--Fleischer Manufacturing, Inc., Columbus, NE; *U.S. Private*, pg. 410
Kurz, Alyson, Mgr.-Export--George Kovacs Lighting, Inc., Glendale, NY; *U.S. Private*, pg. 634
Labas, James, Mgr.-Intl. Sls.--Weaver Popcorn Company, Inc., Van Buren, IN; *U.S. Private*, pg. 1156
Lacob, Dave, Mgr.-Export--Henry Lee Company, Miami, FL; *U.S. Private*, pg. 657
Laird, Larrie W., Pres. & Chief Exec. Officer--Laird & Company, Eatontown, NJ; *U.S. Private*, pg. 642
Lamas, John, Dir.-Intl. Support--BioChem ImmunoSystems, Inc., Allentown, PA; *Int'l*, pg. 196
Lamond, Dennis, V.P.-Export--Briggs Industries, Inc., Tampa, FL; *U.S. Private*, pg. 168
Lane, Charles, Mgr.-Export--Lonza Inc., Fair Lawn, NJ; *Int'l*, pg. 67
Lane, Curly, Dir.-Corp. Logistics--Falcon Products, Inc., Saint Louis, MO; *U.S. Public*, pg. 611
Lang, Christian, Dr. Ing., Mgr.-Export--Traub AG, Reichenbach, Germany; *Int'l*, pg. 1419
Lang, Richard J., V.P.-Intl. Sls. & Mktg.--DeVlieg-Bullard Inc., Westport, CT; *U.S. Public*, pg. 502
Langel, Bernhard H., V.P.-Kohler Plumbing Far East & Export--Kohler Company, Kohler, WI; *U.S. Private*, pg. 630
Lanigir, Joanne, Dir.-Personnel--Cubix Corporation, Carson City, NV; *U.S. Private*, pg. 294
Lannen, Jack, Mgr.-Export--Hubbard Hall Inc., Waterbury, CT; *U.S. Private*, pg. 544
Larsen, Trond, Mgr.-Export--Stabburet A/S, Skien, Norway; *Int'l*, pg. 1011
Larson, John, Mgr.-Export--Siemens Corporation, New York, NY; *Int'l*, pg. 1245
Lawrence, Ken, Mgr.-Program--Cincinnati Gear Company, Cincinnati, OH; *U.S. Private*, pg. 240
Lawrence, Ralph, Pres. & Chief Oper. Officer--Hyde Manufacturing Co., Southbridge, MA; *U.S. Private*, pg. 551
Lawrie, R.E., Dir.-Export Sls.--Sunkist Growers, Inc., Sherman Oaks, CA; *U.S. Private*, pg. 1052
LeBed, Orest, V.P.-Sls. & Mktg.--John Dusenbery Co., Inc., Randolph, NJ; *U.S. Private*, pg. 349
Lee, Jimmy, Export Mgr.--Southwest Recreational Industries Inc., Leander, TX; *U.S. Private*, pg. 1018
Lee, Kyu B., Mgr.-Import/Export--Crown Confectionery Co., Ltd., Seoul, Korea; *Int'l*, pg. 348
Leeto, Sandra, Dir.-Import--Alfin, Inc., New York, NY; *U.S. Public*, pg. 40
Legezynski, Stephanie, Mgr.-Export--Cortland Line Co., Inc., Cortland, NY; *U.S. Private*, pg. 277
Legler, Timothy J., Mgr.-Import & Export--Kansas City Southern Industries, Inc., Kansas City, MO; *U.S. Public*, pg. 943
LeGrande, E. David, Mng. Dir.-Export Division & Treas.--Gudebrod, Inc., Pottstown, PA; *U.S. Private*, pg. 486
Leineu, Hermann, Mgr.-Export--Bitburger Brauerei Th. Simon GmbH, Bitburg, Germany; *Int'l*, pg. 197
Lembo, Dick, Mgr.-Intl. Sls.--B.A. Ballou & Co. Inc., East Providence, RI; *U.S. Private*, pg. 112
Lenk, Edward, V.P.--Unisystems, Inc., New York, NY; *U.S. Private*, pg. 1120
Lenton, R.J., Dir.-Export & Intl.--Stafford-Miller Limited, Welwyn Garden City, United Kingdom; *U.S. Public*, pg. 237
Lenz, Gunny, Mgr.-Export--Interpoint, Redmond, WA; *U.S. Public*, pg. 457
Leone, Lucas J., Chm. Bd.--Eggland's Best, Inc., King of Prussia, PA; *U.S. Private*, pg. 366
Leu, Meg, Mgr.-Intl. Sls.--Seika Electric Co., Ltd., Taipei, Taiwan; *Int'l*, pg. 1218
Leuenberger, John, V.P.--Koh-I-Noor, Inc., Bloomsbury, NJ; *U.S. Private*, pg. 629
Levey, Peter, Mgr.-Import--Sport Obermeyer Ltd., USA, Aspen, CO; *U.S. Private*, pg. 1026
Lewis, Edie, Mgr.-Export Control--Tandem Computers Inc., Cupertino, CA; *U.S. Public*, pg. 417
Limay, Luis A., Gen. Mgr.-El Salvadoran Opers.--Commerce Group Corp., Milwaukee, WI; *U.S. Public*, pg. 410
Lin, Jia-Shyong, V.P.-Mktg./Sls., Sec. & Gen. Mgr.--Amspec Chemical Corporation, Gloucester City, NJ; *U.S. Private*, pg. 67
Lindsay, Lynn I., Mgr.-Export--Lubriplate Div. of Fiske Bros. Refining Co., Newark, NJ; *U.S. Private*, pg. 409

Lineberry, Jerry, Supvr.-Materials--The Flight International Group, Inc., Newport News, VA; *U.S. Public*, pg. 654
Lippitt, A.J., Mgr.-Export Promos.--The General Electric Company, p.l.c., London, United Kingdom; *Int'l*, pg. 543
Livingstone, Eugenie, Mgr.-Export--Weslock National, Inc., Los Angeles, CA; *U.S. Private*, pg. 1163
Lockner, Alex, Mgr.-Certified Intl.--Certified Grocers of California, Los Angeles, CA; *U.S. Private*, pg. 226
Lopez, Orpha, Mgr.-Export--Arch Aluminium & Glass L.C., Tamarac, FL; *U.S. Private*, pg. 79
Low, Linda, Mgr.-Export Sls.--Kwe-Kintetsu World Express(S)Pte Ltd., Singapore, Singapore; *Int'l*, pg. 735
Lowder, Mark, Dir.-Export--International Dairy Queen, Inc., Minneapolis, MN; *U.S. Public*, pg. 220
Lowry, Ken, Mgr.-Export Sls.--BGF Industries Inc., Greensboro, NC; *U.S. Private*, pg. 106
Luchetta, Rodolfo, Div. Mgr.-Mktg.--Y.P.F., S.A., Buenos Aires, Argentina; *Int'l*, pg. 1515
Luevano, Maria, Dir.-Intl. Sls.--Berryman Products, Inc., Arlington, TX; *U.S. Private*, pg. 138
Lunde, Jeff, Coord.-Intl. Sls.--Ciprico, Inc., Plymouth, MN; *U.S. Public*, pg. 370
Lupone, Luigi, Mgr.-Import & Export--Agusta S.P.A., Varese, Italy; *Int'l*, pg. 32
Lynch, John, Dir-Exports--TST/Impreso, Inc., Coppell, TX; *U.S. Private*, pg. 1066
Macarthur, Fil Castello, Mgr.-Export--Asahi/America, Inc., Malden, MA; *U.S. Public*, pg. 137
Maginot, John, V.P.-Intl.--AMCOL International Corp., Arlington Heights, IL; *U.S. Public*, pg. 63
Maglione, Jose, Mgr.-Export--Jacuzzi Bros., Jacuzzi, Inc., Little Rock, AR; *U.S. Public*, pg. 1684
Maguire, Peter F., Dir.-Intl. Sls.--Millennium Petrochemicals, Inc., Cincinnati, OH; *Int'l*, pg. 594
Maile, John, V.P.-Sls., Import & Export--Cold Spring Granite Company, Cold Spring, MN; *U.S. Private*, pg. 250
Malehorn, Rodger A., V.P.-Comml. Opers.--Bayou Steel Corporation, La Place, LA; *U.S. Public*, pg. 197
Malespin, Carlos E., V.P.-Intl. Sls.--McIlhenny Company, Avery Island, LA; *U.S. Private*, pg. 722
Malik, Sohail, Mgr.-Import & Export--Unitech Industries, Inc., Tempe, AZ; *U.S. Public*, pg. 1672
Malmstrom, Kari, Dir.-Export--Kone Corporation, Helsinki, Finland; *Int'l*, pg. 746
Malone, Thomas J., V.P.-Intl. Bus. Devel.--Wolverine Tube Inc., Huntsville, AL; *U.S. Public*, pg. 1774
Manitta, Randy, Mgr.-Natl. Sls.--Hope's Architectural Products Inc., Jamestown, NY; *U.S. Private*, pg. 538
Manzano, A., Mgr.-Export--Meret Communications, San Diego, CA; *U.S. Public*, pg. 1233
Mariasis, Saul, Mgr.-Export--Simpson Electric Co., Elgin, IL; *U.S. Private*, pg. 1002
Marion, Will, Mgr.-Export--Roller Derby Skate Corp., Litchfield, IL; *U.S. Private*, pg. 941
Martin, Jim, Gen. Mgr.-Lubes--J.D. Streett & Co., Inc., Maryland Heights, MO; *U.S. Private*, pg. 1047
Martins-Boyte, Sandra, Mgr.-Exports--Action Instruments, Inc., San Diego, CA; *U.S. Private*, pg. 15
Mascarenhas, J.L., Mgr.-Export--Nestle Portugal, S.A., Carnaxide, Portugal; *Int'l*, pg. 921
Mastropolo, Richard, V.P.-Intl. Sls.--Telsmith, Inc., Mequon, WI; *U.S. Public*, pg. 141
Matheu, Edgardo, Mgr.-Export--Bagley S.A., Buenos Aires, Argentina; *Int'l*, pg. 379
Matsuoka, Jiro, Mgr.-Import Terminal--Kintetsu World Express Inc., Inglewood, CA; *Int'l*, pg. 734
Matthews, Charles, Mgr.-Export--Carolina Biological Supply Co., Burlington, NC; *U.S. Private*, pg. 213
May, Joan, Mgr.-Export--Danaher Tool Group, Lancaster, PA; *U.S. Public*, pg. 480
Mayer, Gary, Dir.-Intl. Sls. & Mktg.--RHC/Spacemaster Corporation, Melrose Park, IL; *U.S. Private*, pg. 904
Mazoff, Stanley S., V.P.-Intl.--Unican Security Systems Ltd., Montreal, Canada; *Int'l*, pg. 1432
Mazoni, Gabriela, Mgr.-Export--Opticos S.r.l., Brembate di Sopra, Italy; *Int'l*, pg. 1007
Mazur, Jack, V.P.-Sls. & Mktg.--Johnstown Corporation, Johnstown, PA; *U.S. Private*, pg. 595
McClusky, Tom, Mgr.-Export--Alta-Dena Certified Dairy, City of Industry, CA; *Int'l*, pg. 201
McConnaughy, Dolores F., V.P.-Natl. Accts. & Export Sls.--The Fuller Brush Company, Great Bend, KS; *U.S. Public*, *pg. 282*
McCoy, Michael, Dir.-Pur.--LeaRonal, Inc., Freeport, NY; *U.S. Public*, pg. 982
McCray, A.A., Mgr.-Overseas & Corp. Devel.--Q.U.F. Industries Ltd., Brisbane, Australia; *Int'l*, pg. 1074
McDonough, Phil S., Gen. Mgr.-Export & Plng.--International Division, Melbourne, Australia; *Int'l*, pg. 226
McGovern, Joseph P., Chief Tech. Advisor--White Rock Distilleries Inc., Lewiston, ME; *U.S. Private*, pg. 1173
McHale, J.W., V.P.-Trading--Texaco Oil Trading & Supply Company, White Plains, NY; *U.S. Public*, pg. 1583
McIndoe, J., Dir.-Works--Energizer Eveready Ltd., London, United Kingdom; *U.S. Public*, pg. 1360
McKeague, Marsha A., Mgr.-Woodlands--Great Northern Paper, Inc., Millinocket, ME; *U.S. Public*, pg. 248
McKenzie, Gil, Mgr.-Export--Carter Products, Canada, Mississauga, Canada; *U.S. Public*, pg. 310
McMillan, Tom, Mgr.-Export--J.E. Higgins Lumber Co., Concord, CA; *U.S. Private*, pg. 527
McMillin, G.T., Gen. Dir.-IPC Opers.--General Motors of Canada Ltd., Oshawa, Canada; *U.S. Public*, pg. 722
Mcnamara, Jack, Dir.-Co-Pack & Export--Cains Foods, L.P., Ayer, MA; *U.S. Private*, pg. 199
McQueen, Edwin D., V.P.-Sls. & Mktg.--Steelox Systems Inc., Mason, OH; *U.S. Private*, pg. 1038
Meddock, Larry, V.P.-Mktg.--Correct Craft, Inc., Orlando, FL; *U.S. Private*, pg. 276
Meili, Hans, Dir.-Export--Migros, Zurich, Switzerland; *Int'l*, pg. 865
Meinicke, Chris, Mgr.-Export--Sequent Computer Systems, Inc., Beaverton, OR; *U.S. Public*, pg. 1459
Melhuish, Nicolas B., Mgr.-Industrial Sls.--Algood Food Company, Louisville, KY; *U.S. Private*, pg. 34
Melnick, Norman, Chm. Bd. & Chief Exec. Officer--Pentech International, Inc., Edison, NJ; *U.S. Public*, pg. 1274
Mentzingen, Angela Maria, Mgr.-Import & Export--SmithKline Beecham Laboratorios Ltda., Rio de Janeiro, Brazil; *Int'l*, pg. 1266
Messinger, Steven, V.P.-Mktg.--Simi Winery, Healdsburg, CA; *Int'l*, pg. 781
Metros, Robert, Mgr.-Export--Uniflow Manufacturing Co., Erie, PA; *U.S. Private*, pg. 1117
Meyer, Craig, Mgr.-Intl. & Export--HON Industries Inc., Muscatine, IA; *U.S. Public*, pg. 772
Micheletti, George, Dir.-U.S. Export--Associated Merchandising Corp. (AMC), New York, NY; *U.S. Private*, *pg. 91*
Miller, Anita, Coord.-Export--MacDermid Incorporated, Waterbury, CT; *U.S. Public*, pg. 1029
Miller, Derek, Mgr.-Intl. Sls.--Northland Aluminum Products, Inc., Minneapolis, MN; *U.S. Private*, pg. 805
Miller, Wayne, Mgr.-Sls.--Astrex, Inc., Plainview, NY; *U.S. Public*, pg. 141
Mirsepahi, J.A., V.P.-Intl. Opers.--Mack Trucks, Inc., Allentown, PA; *Int'l*, pg. 1102
Misconis, Lenn, Dir.-Personnel--Associated Grocers of the South, Inc., Birmingham, AL; *U.S. Private*, pg. 91
Mitchell, Steve, Dir.-Sls. Admin.--Iomega Corporation, Roy, UT; *U.S. Public*, pg. 912
Mix, Tom, Dir.-Export--Aeroglide Corporation, Cary, NC; *U.S.* Private, pg. 24
Mix, Tom, Dir.-Export Sls.--Aeroglide Americas International, Inc., Raleigh, NC; *U.S. Private*, pg. 24
Molnau, Mark, Dir.-Intl. Sls & Mktg.--Fender Musical Instruments, Scottsdale, AZ; *U.S. Private*, pg. 400
Mongelluzzo, John A., Gen. Counsel & Sec.--Structural Dynamics Research Corp., Milford, OH; *U.S. Public*, pg. 1525
Montmeny, Ted, Branch Mgr.-Import/Export--Circle International, Wilder, KY; *U.S. Public*, pg. 371
Mooney, Matilda, Mgr.-Export--Ko-Rec-Type, Brooklyn, NY; *U.S. Private*, pg. 117
Moran, D., Mgr.-Product--The U.S. Baird Corporation, Stratford, CT; *U.S. Private*, pg. 1124
Moran, Dennis, Mgr.-Export--The A.H. Nilson Machine Co., Stratford, CT; *U.S. Private*, pg. 1124
Morley, Erwin, Mgr.-Export--Philip Morris Limited, Moorabbin, Australia; *U.S. Public*, pg. 1290
Morris, Scott, Mgr.-Intl. Bus.--The Brulin Corporation, Indianapolis, IN; *U.S. Private*, pg. 176
Morroni, Alex, Mgr.-Export Sls.--Indiana Glass Company, Cincinnati, OH; *U.S. Public*, pg. 976
Moses, Robert, Dir.-Export Sls.--Power & Telephone Supply Company, Memphis, TN; *U.S. Private*, pg. 877
Mosey, Bill, V.P.-Sls. & Mktg.--K-D Lamp Company, Cincinnati, OH; *U.S. Private*, pg. 603
Moure, Jose Antonio, Mgr.-Export--General Motors Chile S.A., Industria Automotriz, Santiago, Chile; *U.S. Public*, pg. 721
Murphy, Suzie, Dir.-Export--Culp, Inc., High Point, NC; *U.S. Public*, pg. 467
Murray, David, Mgr.-Export--Trumpf Inc., Farmington, CT; *U.S. Private*, pg. 1108
Murray, O.W., V.P.-Intl. Sls. & Export--Doron Precision Systems, Inc., Binghamton, NY; *U.S. Private*, pg. 341
Muskat, Dan, V.P.-Opers.--Jac Pac Foods, Ltd., Manchester, NH; *U.S. Private*, pg. 579
Myers, Lilo, Mgr.-Intl. Sls.--Hobart Corporation, Troy, OH; *U.S. Public*, pg. 1322
Myung-Chi, Kim, Gen. Mgr.--Korea Heavy Industries & Construction Co., Ltd., Seoul, Korea; *Int'l*, pg. 758
Nachby, Alan, Mgr.-Export--Zoeller Co., Louisville, KY; *U.S. Private*, pg. 1207
Nagel, Reinhard, Mgr.-Import, Export--Bierbrauerei Fohrenburg, Bludenz, Austria; *Int'l*, pg. 194
Narayan, Badri, Dir.-Export--Unistrut Corporation, Wayne, MI; *U.S. Public*, pg. 1651
Navarro, Carmen E., Mgr.-Sls. & Export Mktg.--Benguet Corporation, Manila, Philippines; *Int'l*, pg. 186
Neri, John, Dir.-Export--Nordyne Inc., Saint Louis, MO; *U.S. Public*, pg. 1193
Neuhaus, Elfriede, Mgr.-Export--Life-Like Products, Inc., Baltimore, MD; *U.S. Private*, pg. 666
Neumann, Mark C., V.P.-Sls.--Badger Paper Mills, Inc., Peshtigo, WI; *U.S. Public*, pg. 165
Niederst, James E., Mgr.-Natl. & Export Sls.--Glastic Corporation, Cleveland, OH; *Int'l*, pg. 740
Niemier, Charles, Sr. V.P.-Intl. Opers.--Biomet, Inc., Warsaw, IN; *U.S. Public*, pg. 231
Nightingale, G., Mgr.-Export--BBA Friction LTD., Cleckheaton, United Kingdom; *Int'l*, pg. 112
Niki, Yasuhiko, Mng. Dir.--Kayaba Industry Co., Ltd., Tokyo, Japan; *Int'l*, pg. 727
Niklason, Donna, Mgr.-Mktg.--Butler Automatic, Inc., Canton, MA; *U.S. Private*, pg. 189
Norris, Robert, Sr. V.P.-Fin. & Admin.--Calcot, Ltd., Bakersfield, CA; *U.S. Private*, pg. 200
Nunez, Olga M., Sec.--Northwestern Meats Inc., Miami, FL; *U.S. Private*, pg. 807
Nuno, R. Ricardo, Mgr.-Export--C.A. Cigarrera Bigott, Sucs., Caracas, Venezuela; *Int'l*, pg. 111
O'Connor, Tim, V.P.-Investor Rels. & Treas.--ICF Kaiser International Inc., Fairfax, VA; *U.S. Public*, pg. 852
Obarski, Mary, Mgr.-Export--Lockformer Company, Lisle, IL; *U.S. Public*, pg. 1100
Oestlien, Bredo, Pres.-Seagram Asia Pacific/Global Duty Free Div.--Joseph E. Seagram & Sons, Inc., New York, NY; *Int'l*, pg. 1215
Ohga, Taizo, Dir. & Gen. Mgr.--Cosmo Oil Co., Ltd., Tokyo, Japan; *Int'l*, pg. 335
Omuro, Tsuyoshi, V.P.-Export & Import--The Hokkaido Takushoku Bank, Ltd., New York Branch, New York, NY; *Int'l*, pg. 626
Osio, James, Mgr.-Export--International Division, Oneida, NY; *U.S. Public*, pg. 1226
Owen, Robert E., Chm. Bd. & Pres.--Owen Industries, Inc., Carter Lake, IA; *U.S. Private*, pg. 824
Ownby, Paul, V.P.-Contracts--Tecstar Inc., City of Industry, CA; *U.S. Private*, pg. 1072
Pacoe, Cindy, Export Specialist--Brush Wellman Inc., Cleveland, OH; *U.S. Public*, pg. 266
Paden, Mark, Dir.-Intl. Fin. & Export--NationsBank Corporation, Charlotte, NC; *U.S. Public*, pg. 1162
Pailas, Evelyn, Mgr.-Export Sls.--C.R. Gibson Co., Norwalk, CT; *U.S. Public*, pg. 1168
Paja, Gene, Mgr.-Export--Multi-Clean Inc., Shoreview, MN; *Int'l*, pg. 587
Palafox, Salvador O., V.P.-Intl. Sls.--S & C Electric Company, Chicago, IL; *U.S. Private*, pg. 954
Palmer, Guy, Mgr.-Import & Export--Applied Materials, Inc., Santa Clara, CA; *U.S. Public*, pg. 123
Palucci, Sergio, Mgr.-Intl. Sls.--Pass & Seymour/Legrand, Syracuse, NY; *Int'l*, pg. 806
Paris, Andy, Mgr.--LubeCon Systems, Inc., White Cloud, MI; *U.S. Private*, pg. 679
Pasquali, Guglielmo, Mgr.-Export--Candy S.p.A., Brugherio, Italy; *Int'l*, pg. 259
Peeters, Peter W., Dir.-Intl. Bus.--Marsh Company, Belleville, IL; *U.S. Private*, pg. 707
Peiffer, Carl, Mgr.-Intl. Sls.--Hull Corporation, Hatboro, PA; *U.S. Private*, pg. 547
Pelych, Andy, Mgr.-Export--Empire Berol U.S.A., Brentwood, TN; *U.S. Public*, pg. 1178
Perez, Hank, Mgr.-Export--Chr. Hansen, Inc., Milwaukee, WI; *Int'l*, pg. 288
Perez, John L., Mgr.-Sls.--Vilter Manufacturing Corporation, Cudahy, WI; *U.S. Private*, pg. 1140
Peters, John, Dir.-Export--Ames Company, Parkersburg, WV; *U.S. Public*, pg. 1683
Peterson, Vicki, Mgr.-Exporting--Scotchman Industries, Inc., Philip, SD; *U.S. Private*, pg. 636
Petke, Mary, Mgr.-Export--Spotnails, Rolling Meadows, IL; *U.S. Private*, pg. 845
Petkus, Barbara, Mgr.-Intl. Sls. & Mktg.--Portec, Inc., Lake Forest, IL; *U.S. Public*, pg. 1317
Pillart, B., Mgr.-Export--Spadel SA, Brussels, Belgium; *Int'l*, pg. 1287
Plematia, E., Mgr.-Export--Karelia Tobacco Company Inc., Kalamata, Greece; *Int'l*, pg. 724
Ploix, Arnaud, Dir.-Exporting--Yves Saint Laurent Parfums S.A., Neuilly-sur-Seine, France; *Int'l*, pg. 445
Poll, Bill, V.P.-Fin. & Pricing--Warner-Chilcott Laboratories, Inc., Rockaway, NJ; *Int'l*, pg. 436
Presley, Rick, V.P.-Sls.--Cook Manufacturing Corporation, Duncan, OK; *U.S. Private*, pg. 272
Price, A. David, Dir.-Export--Mesa Laboratories, Inc., Wheat Ridge, CO; *U.S. Public*, pg. 1099
Prosapio, Christy, Mgr.-Export Sls.--Trippe Mfg. Co., Chicago, IL; *U.S. Private*, pg. 1104
Prothet, R., Export Mgr.--Rossignol S.A., Voiron, France; *Int'l*, pg. 1127
Przybylek, G.P., Dir.-Intl. Sls.--Duraco Products, Inc., Streamwood, IL; *U.S. Private*, pg. 348
Purdy, S., Mgr.--Menley & James Laboratories, Inc., Horsham, PA; *U.S. Public*, pg. 1086
Quaassdorf, Gerrardo, Mgr.-Export--Holstein Association USA, Inc., Brattleboro, VT; *U.S. Private*, pg. 536
Quirino, Sylvia P., V.P.-Intl. Bus. Opers.--La Tondena Distillers, Inc., Manila, Philippines; *Int'l*, pg. 785
Ramos, Joselin, Mgr.-Import & Export--Caribe Express, Aguadilla, PR; *U.S. Private*, pg. 211
Ramsey, K.C., Pres.--United States Bronze Powders, Inc., Flemington, NJ; *U.S. Private*, pg. 1124
Randazzo, B., Dir.-Export Sls.--W.W. Grainger, Inc., Lincolnshire, IL; *U.S. Public*, pg. 758
Ranshaw, John R., V.P.-Bus. Devel., Dir.-Export & Intl. Mgr.--E & A Industries, Inc., Indianapolis, IN; *U.S. Private*, pg. 352
Rapp, Larry T., V.P. & Corp. Sec.--Electro Scientific Industries, Inc., Portland, OR; *U.S. Public*, pg. 568
Rargel, Pedro, Mgr.-Import & Export--Procter & Gamble Venezuela, C.A., Caracas, Venezuela; *U.S. Public*, pg. 1332
Rasimas, Ken, Mgr.-Export Sls.--Okuma America Corporation, Charlotte, NC; *Int'l*, pg. 1001
Rau, Peter, Mgr.-Exports--Porsche AG, Stuttgart, Germany; *Int'l*, pg. 1063
Rauchwerger, Jerry, V.P.-Intl. Sls. & Mktg.--Inverness Corp., Fair Lawn, NJ; *U.S. Private*, pg. 574
Ravinowich, Eric, Mgr.-Export, Industrial--Lord Corporation, Mechanical Products Division, Erie, PA; *U.S. Private*, pg. 676
Readal, Tom, V.P.-Export Sls.--Penreco, Karns City, PA; *U.S. Public*, pg. 1273
Recabarren, Alberto, Mgr.-Export--Fate S.A., San Fernando, Argentina; *Int'l*, pg. 478
Reda, Frank, Mgr.-Export--The Jel Sert Co., West Chicago, IL; *U.S. Private*, pg. 585
Reddington, John, Mgr.-Import/Export--LeaRonal, Inc., Freeport, NY; *U.S. Public*, pg. 982
Reid, John C., Mgr.-Export Sls.--Cashco, Inc., Ellsworth, KS; *U.S. Private*, pg. 218
Reneau, Robert L., V.P.-Intl. Trade & Mngmt. Information Systems--Bourns, Inc., Riverside, CA; *U.S. Private*, pg. 161
Renner, H., Mgr.-Export--H.A. Schlatter AG, Schlieren, Switzerland; *Int'l*, pg. 1205
Retuerto, Jorge, Mgr.-Intl. Sls.--Theochem Labs., Inc., Tampa, FL; *U.S. Private*, pg. 1079
Retzlaff, Robert Z., Pres. & Chief Fin. Officer--Retzlaff Incorporated, San Rafael, CA; *U.S. Private*, pg. 925
Rheem, Richard, Dir.-Plng. & Business Devel.--Freedom Forge Corporation, Burnham, PA; *U.S. Private*, pg. 425
Richards, H. Lee, Chm. Bd. & Chief Exec. Officer--Hygeia Dairy Co., Inc., Harlingen, TX; *U.S. Private*, pg. 552
Riedel, James F., V.P.-Mktg. & Sls.--Webster Industries Inc., Tiffin, OH; *U.S. Private*, pg. 1157
Ring, Randy, V.P.-Mfg.--Network Computing Devices, Inc., Mountain View, CA; *U.S. Public*, pg. 1168

Rizol, Tom, Dir.-Traffic--Ensoniq, Malvern, PA; *U.S. Private*, pg. 377
Roberson, Donald, Dir.-Mktg. & Sls.--Theradyne Corporation, Jordan, MN; *U.S. Private*, pg. 637
Roberts, Mary, Mgr.-Export--Griffin Transport Services, Inc., Sparks, NV; *U.S. Private*, pg. 481
Robichaud, Richard, Mgr.-Export Services--Hercules Incorporated, Wilmington, DE; *U.S. Public*, pg. 809
Roche, Edward, Dir.-Intl. Sls.--H.J. Baker & Bro., Inc., Stamford, CT; *U.S. Private*, pg. 112
Rodriguez, Xoe, Mgr.-Export--Chicago Lock Company, Pleasant Prairie, WI; *U.S. Private*, pg. 235
Rogato, Elza, Mgr.-Export--Johnson & Johnson Ltda., Sao Paulo, Brazil; *U.S. Public*, pg. 931
Rollo, Jim, Dir.-Intl. Bus. Devel.--PAXAR Corporation, White Plains, NY; *U.S. Public*, pg. 1266
Rondeau, Andre, V.P.-Export & Sls.--Uniboard Canada Inc., Laval, Canada; *Int'l*, pg. 1431
Root, John, Mgr.-Credit--Airflex Div. Eaton Corp., Cleveland, OH; *U.S. Public*, pg. 556
Rosenstreich, Howard, Mgr.-Import & Export--Cardinal Inc., Rahway, NJ; *U.S. Private*, pg. 208
Roser, Peter, Mgr.-Export--Brauerei AG, Zurich, Switzerland; *Int'l*, pg. 479
Ross, Julie, Mgr.-Export--General Housewares Corp., Terre Haute, IN; *U.S. Public*, pg. 715
Ross, Julie, Mgr.-Export--Chicago Cutlery, Inc., Terre Haute, IN; *U.S. Public*, pg. 716
Rowan, Sheryl, Mgr.-Import & Export--Sanyo Fisher Company, Chatsworth, CA; *Int'l*, pg. 1191
Ruehle, Joan, Mgr.-Credit--Seneca Foods Corporation, Pittsford, NY; *U.S. Public*, pg. 1456
Rupp, Steve, Mgr.-Export--Lambda Electronics Inc., Melville, NY; *Int'l*, pg. 1241
Russman, Robert, V.P.-New Bus. & Intl. Devel.--StarSight Telecast, Inc., Fremont, CA; *U.S. Public*, pg. 705
Ruxton, David, Dir.-Export--Atlet AB, Molnlycke, Sweden; *Int'l*, pg. 97
Ryan, Tom, Mgr.-N.W. Territory--Pickering Inc., Tacoma, WA; *U.S. Private*, pg. 864
Saak, Robert, Mgr.-Sls.--Gilster Mary Lee Corp., Chester, IL; *U.S. Private*, pg. 455
Sabal, Marian, Mgr.-Export--Alpha Industries, Inc., Woburn, MA; *U.S. Public*, pg. 57
Sanfilippo, Charles, Mgr.-Export--Allomatic Products Company, Sullivan, IN; *U.S. Public*, pg. 1363
Santana, Joe, Intl. Sls.--Propper Manufacturing Co., Inc., Long Island City, NY; *U.S. Private*, pg. 891
Santangelo, John, Mgr.-Export--Stanback Company, Salisbury, NC; *U.S. Private*, pg. 1030
Santiso, Tony, Export Mgr.--Safway Steel Products Inc., Waukesha, WI; *Int'l*, pg. 1389
Sarabia, Jose Ramon, Mgr.-Export--Vicente Puig Oliver S.A., Crevillente, Spain; *Int'l*, pg. 1001
Sarrazin, B., V.P.-Export Devel.--Robin Hood Multifoods Inc., Markham, Canada; *U.S. Public*, pg. 901
Sasdella Z.Z.I., Ferse, Mgr.-Export--D. Lazzaroni & C. S.p.A., Saronno, Italy; *Int'l*, pg. 804
Saslow, Seymour, Dir.-Sls. & Engrng.--Espey Mfg. & Electronics Corp., Saratoga Springs, NY; *U.S. Public*, pg. 592
Sault, Dennis, Mgr.-Dist. & Transportation--Kawasaki Motors Corp., U.S.A., Irvine, CA; *Int'l*, pg. 725
Savage, Bob, V.P.-Sls. & Mktg.- Thermal Prods.--The Bergquist Company, Minneapolis, MN; *U.S. Private*, pg. 135
Savolainen, Toini, Export Mgr.--Koltek Oy, Vantaa, Finland; *Int'l*, pg. 1379
Scadding, Ailene, Mgr.-Import & Export--Ferrofluidics Corporation, Nashua, NH; *U.S. Public*, pg. 620
Schaefer, Terry, Export Supvr.--Bou-Matic, Madison, WI; *U.S. Private*, pg. 301
Schluter, Dieter, V.P.-Dealer Sls.--Brinkmann Instruments, Inc., Westbury, NY; *U.S. Private*, pg. 169
Schmidt, Marie, Mgr.-Export--Gehl Company, West Bend, WI; *U.S. Public*, pg. 704
Schneider, David, Dir.-Export--Oshkosh Truck Corporation, Oshkosh, WI; *U.S. Public*, pg. 1233
Schneiderman, Stephanie, Mgr.-Export Sls.--Thermador, Los Angeles, CA; *U.S. Public*, pg. 1053
Schoepe, Rick, Mgr.-Export--Gougler Industries, Inc., Kent, OH; *U.S. Private*, pg. 466
Schultz, R., Dir.-Import & Export--Dataproducts Corporation, Simi Valley, CA; *Int'l*, pg. 620
Sedler, Jordan B., Exec. V.P., Sec. & Treas.--Paper Enterprises, Inc., Bronx, NY; *U.S. Private*, pg. 837
Shafer, Randall J., V.P.-Import & Export--Shafer Commercial Seating Inc., Denver, CO; *U.S. Private*, pg. 988
Shapiro, Jeffrey M., Exec. V.P. & Sec.--Michael Foods, Inc., Minneapolis, MN; *U.S. Public*, pg. 1103
Shatney, Kristin, Mgr.-Export--Oil-Dri Corporation of America, Chicago, IL; *U.S. Public*, pg. 1214
Sheffey, K.L., Mgr.-Export--Neapco, Inc., Pottstown, PA; *U.S. Private*, pg. 1113
Sherman, Ron, Mgr.-Export--Music Sales Corporation, New York, NY; *U.S. Private*, pg. 768
Shimizu, Shunsuke, Mgr.-Trading Dept.--Nemic-Lambda KK, Tokyo, Japan; *Int'l*, pg. 1242
Shlomm, Alexander, V.P.-Import/Export--Amicale Industries, Inc., New York, NY; *U.S. Private*, pg. 66
Shukla, Eric, Mgr.-Export--Weigh-Tronix, Inc., Fairmont, MN; *Int'l*, pg. 1299
Shurman, John, Pres.--Beverage Canners International Corp., Miami, FL; *U.S. Private*, pg. 106
Sibley, Cathy, Mgr.-Export--World Dryer Corp., Berkeley, IL; *U.S. Public*, pg. 1497
Silver, William H., V.P.--Akrochem Corporation, Akron, OH; *U.S. Private*, pg. 30
Simone, Carl, Mgr.-Export--Pennaco Hosiery, New York, NY; *U.S. Public*, pg. 483
Simonsen, K., Dir.-Export & Fin.--Simonsen & Sons Limited, Nykobing, Denmark; *Int'l*, pg. 894
Simpson, Neville, Mgr.-Export--Macwhyte Co., Kenosha, WI; *U.S. Private*, pg. 68
Sio, Fernando, Mgr.-Import & Export--Zenith Electronics Corp., Glenview, IL; *U.S. Public*, pg. 1790
Sjoberg, Bo, Mgr.-Export--Esab AB, Goteborg, Sweden; *Int'l*, pg. 281
Skelton, James, Dir.-Sls.--Caddock Electronics, Inc., Riverside, CA; *U.S. Private*, pg. 198
Sloane, Steven, V.P.-Intl. Sls.--Chyron Corp., Melville, NY; *Int'l*, pg. 1372
Smith, A.R.J., Dir.-Export--Seven Seas Limited, Hull, United Kingdom; *Int'l*, pg. 593
Smith, Gina, Mgr.-Export--Kleer-Vu Plastics Corp., Compton, CA; *U.S. Public*, pg. 962
Smith, Kevin, Mgr.-Export--Linear Technology Corp., Milpitas, CA; *U.S. Public*, pg. 1000
Smith, Thomas, Mgr.-Export Mktg.--CiMatrix L.L.C., Canton, MA; *U.S. Public*, pg. 1395
Snively, Bob, Mgr.-Export--F.E. Myers, Ashland, OH; *U.S. Public*, pg. 1273
Soulmiac, Phillippe, Mgr.-Export/Import Opers.--Kintetsu World Express (France) S.A., Roissy, France; *Int'l*, pg. 735
South, John R., Pres. & Chief Exec. Officer--Staodyn Inc., Longmont, CO; *U.S. Public*, pg. 1509
Souza, John, Chief Intl. Officer--Karsten Manufacturing Corporation, Phoenix, AZ; *U.S. Private*, pg. 608
Sparvero, Robert P., Dir.-NAAO Export Sls.--NAAO Marketing, Dearborn, MI; *U.S. Public*, pg. 662
Specter, James, Mgr.-Export--International Research & Evaluation, Eagan, MN; *U.S. Private*, pg. 571
Spivey, Doug, V.P.-Mktg.--Packerland Packing Co., Green Bay, WI; *U.S. Private*, pg. 833
Springer, Andrew, Pres. & Chief Exec. Officer--Lee Grocery Company, Everett, WA; *U.S. Private*, pg. 657
Stackhouse, Richard, Mgr.-Export--Raytheon Systems Co., Kirkwood, NY; *U.S. Public*, pg. 1364
Stafford, Dave, V.P.-Export Sls.--Kysor/Warren, Conyers, GA; *U.S. Public*, pg. 1445
Stanley, Karen, Mgr.-Export--Dermik Laboratories, Inc., Collegeville, PA; *Int'l*, pg. 1110
Steele, D., Mgr.- Export/Home Sls.--James Walker & Co. Limited, Woking, United Kingdom; *Int'l*, pg. 1485
Steiner, Robin, Mgr.-Import/Export--Electro Scientific Industries, Inc., Portland, OR; *U.S. Public*, pg. 568
Stephenson, Roger, V.P.-Export--The Pfaltzgraff Co., York, PA; *U.S. Private*, pg. 860
Stevenson, Edward T., Mgr.-Import, Export & Admin.--Ludlow Textiles Co., Inc., Ludlow, MA; *U.S. Private*, pg. 680
Stevenson, Wade, Pres.-Eastman Export--Eastman Worldwide, Buffalo, NY; *U.S. Private*, pg. 358
Stimpple, Werner, Mgr.-Export--Temca Chemische Union GmbH, Nuremberg, Germany; *U.S. Public*, pg. 1333
Stokes, John, Dir.-Export Sls.--Georgia/Durango Boot Company, Franklin, TN; *U.S. Public*, pg. 1684
Stucki, Connie, Mgr.-Mktg. & Export--U.S. Safety, Lenexa, KS; *U.S. Private*, pg. 1125
Stuttaford, Richard, Dir.-Export Div.--Genesco Inc., Nashville, TN; *U.S. Public*, pg. 728
Suda, Shunichiro, Mng. Dir.--Sakata Seed Corporation, Yokohama, Japan; *Int'l*, pg. 1178
Sugihara, Yoshinori, Mgr.-Exporting--Takagi Chokoku Co., Ltd., Wakayama, Japan; *Int'l*, pg. 1349
Sullivan, Marion, V.P.-Mktg.--Roundy's, Inc., Pewaukee, WI; *U.S. Private*, pg. 948
Suwanchindachai, Somporn, Mgr.-Intl.--Bangkok Athletic Co., Ltd., Bangkok, Thailand; *Int'l*, pg. 146
Suzuki, Isao, Sr. Mgr.-Export, Import & Remittance Opers. Ctr.--The Chiba Bank, Ltd.-International Divison, Tokyo, Japan; *Int'l*, pg. 283
T'Joens, Frans, Mgr.-Bekaert Intl. Trade--N.V. Bekaert S.A., Kortrijk, Belgium; *Int'l*, pg. 183
Taillante, Francis, Dir. Gen.-Exports--SNCF, Paris, France; *Int'l*, pg. 1163
Takano, Jay, Mgr.-Export--Ventura Foods LLC, City of Industry, CA; *Int'l*, pg. 879
Takeda, Masaaki, Gen. Mgr.-Export/Import--Cosmo Oil Co., Ltd., Tokyo, Japan; *Int'l*, pg. 335
Tal, Peter, Mgr.-Export--Slant/Fin Corporation, Greenvale, NY; *U.S. Private*, pg. 1005
Tal, Sender, Mgr.-Export--Keter Plastic Ltd., Herzliyya, Israel; *Int'l*, pg. 732
Tamer, George, V.P.-Auto--Marson/Creative Fastener, Inc., Stoughton, MA; *U.S. Private*, pg. 708
Taylor, Paul, Mgr.-Sls.(Export)--S.A. Durco Europe N.V., Brussels, Belgium; *U.S. Public*, pg. 659
Taylor, Walter, Dir.-Bus. Devel./Export--Bestfoods, Englewood Cliffs, NJ; *U.S. Public*, pg. 223
Tevez, Hernan, Mgr.-Export & Import--Sancor Cooperativas Unidas Limitadas, Buenos Aires, Argentina; *Int'l*, pg. 1183
Theodore, Michael, V.P.-Mfg. Opers--SouthCo. Inc., Concordville, PA; *U.S. Private*, pg. 1014
Theriot, Scott, V.P.-Production--Bollinger Shipyards, Inc., Lockport, LA; *U.S. Private*, pg. 155
Thiry, Steve, Mgr.-Export--Knape & Vogt Mfg. Co., Grand Rapids, MI; *U.S. Public*, pg. 963
Thomas, Chuck, Mgr.-Intl. Sls.--Chattanooga Group, Inc., Hixson, TN; *U.S. Private*, pg. 231
Thompson, Henry, Export Sls. Mgr.--Castelazo & Associates, Los Angeles, CA; *U.S. Public*, pg. 1071
Tikkanen, Kari, Mgr.-Import & Export--FINNAIR, New York, NY; *Int'l*, pg. 485
Tomiyama, Joji, Export Terminal Mgr.--Kintetsu World Express Inc., Burlingame, CA; *Int'l*, pg. 735
Torresan, Rafaelli, Dir.-Export--Lotto S.p.A., Montebelluna, Italy; *Int'l*, pg. 819
Tosto, N., Dir.-Intl. Sls.--Fairmont Tamper, West Columbia, SC; *U.S. Public*, pg. 793
Toussaint, John-Charles, Chief Oper. Officer & V.P.--Propper Manufacturing Co., Inc., Long Island City, NY; *U.S. Private*, pg. 891
Tracy, Larry, Pres.-Intl. Radionics, Inc.--Detection Systems, Inc., Fairport, NY; *U.S. Public*, pg. 501
Tripp, Kathy, Mgr.-Export--Aspen Imaging International, Inc., Cleveland, OH; *U.S. Public*, pg. 1339
Truter, Douglas, Mgr.-Import/Export--Framesi USA, Inc./Roffler Industries, Inc./Casa di Colore, Inc., Coraopolis, PA; *U.S. Private*, pg. 419
Truxton, Louis, Dir.-Import & Export--Emulex Corporation, Costa Mesa, CA; *U.S. Public*, pg. 579
Turnage, John A., V.P.-Mfg. & Sourcing--Kellwood Company, Chesterfield, MO; *U.S. Public*, pg. 948
Upegui, Jose, V.P.-Intl. Sls.--Montgomery KONE Inc., Moline, IL; *Int'l*, pg. 746
Utterson, Diane, Mgr.-Intl. Export--Lynx Golf, Inc., City of Industry, CA; *U.S. Private*, pg. 684
van der Westhuizen, Etienne, Mgr.-Export--Sasol Fertilizers, Randburg, South Africa; *Int'l*, pg. 1196
van Heerden, Vaughn, Mgr.-Export--Sasol Solvents, Rosebank, South Africa; *Int'l*, pg. 1196
Varona, Edward, Mgr.-Export--Spiegel Meats, Inc., Miami, FL; *U.S. Private*, pg. 1025
Vaslin, Barnard, Mgr.-Export--Alcatel Cit (S.A.), Velizy-Villacoublay, France; *Int'l*, pg. 56
Verkauf, S., Mgr.-Export--Technic Incorporated, Cranston, RI; *U.S. Private*, pg. 1071
Viljoem, I., Mgr.-Export--CIBA-GEIGY (Pty.) Ltd., Isando, South Africa; *Int'l*, pg. 978
Wagner, Jeanette, Mgr.-Export--Polyloom Corp. of America, Dayton, TN; *U.S. Private*, pg. 875
Walker, Gary, Mgr.-Export--Champion Laboratories, Inc., Albion, IL; *U.S. Private*, pg. 1113
Walker, Ken, Mgr.-Import & Export--DuBois Chemicals, Cincinnati, OH; *Int'l*, pg. 1437
Walther, Lee, Dir.-Intl. Sls.--The New Piper Aircraft, Inc., Vero Beach, FL; *U.S. Private*, pg. 794
Wang, William, Dir.-Intl. Sls.--Interface Electronics Corporation, Hopkinton, MA; *U.S. Private*, pg. 567
Wangprakobsook, Sumalee, Exec. V.P.--Bangkok Bank Public Company Limited, Bangkok, Thailand; *Int'l*, pg. 146
Waters, Carter, Mgr.-Export--Wilton Corporation, Palatine, IL; *U.S. Private*, pg. 1181
Watson, Brian, V.P.-Mktg./Patterson Dental Supply, Inc.--Patterson Dental Company, Saint Paul, MN; *U.S. Public*, pg. 1265
Weaver, John H., V.P.-Export Sls.--The Lincoln Electric Company, Cleveland, OH; *U.S. Public*, pg. 996
Web, Charles, Mgr.-Export & Intl. Mktg.--Battenfeld Gloucester Engineering Co. Inc., Gloucester, MA; *U.S. Private*, pg. 123
Webb, Liz, Mgr.-Export--JSB Electrical PLC, Crewe, United Kingdom; *Int'l*, pg. 453
Weeks, Carl, Mgr.-Export--Continental Conveyor & Equipment Company, Winfield, AL; *U.S. Private*, pg. 791
Wesley, Charles, V.P.-Sls. & Mktg.--Hyer Industries Inc./Thayer Scale, Pembroke, MA; *U.S. Private*, pg. 552
Wharf, Peter D., V.P.-Intl. Opers.--Daisytek International Corporation, Plano, TX; *U.S. Public*, pg. 477
Wilcox, Linda, Mgr.-Export--U.S. Electrical Motor Division, Saint Louis, MO; *U.S. Public*, pg. 573
Wilensky, Ron, V.P.-Bus. Devel.--TCI International Inc., Sunnyvale, CA; *U.S. Public*, pg. 1555
Williams, Cheryl, Mgr.-Client Services--Jack Lenor Larsen, Inc., New York, NY; *U.S. Private*, pg. 652
Wilson, Barrett, V.P.--Whitney Holding Corporation, New Orleans, LA; *U.S. Public*, pg. 1766
Winkle, K.T., Dir.-Export--Seven Seas Limited, Hull, United Kingdom; *Int'l*, pg. 593
Wisidwuyikul, Tawisak, Sr. V.P.--Siam City Bank Public Company Limited, Bangkok, Thailand; *Int'l*, pg. 1239
Wolf, Georg, Mgr.-Foreign Subsidiaries--Knurr AG, Munich, Germany; *Int'l*, pg. 739
Wolf, Joyce, Mgr.-Export--Cooper Instrument Corp., Middlefield, CT; *U.S. Private*, pg. 274
Wolkenbrod, Lynn, Mgr.-Export Sls.--I. Spiewak & Sons, Inc., New York, NY; *U.S. Private*, pg. 1025
Wong, Michael, Mgr.-Sls.--Kewaunee Scientific Corporation, Statesville, NC; *U.S. Public*, pg. 953
Woolfson, Donna, Mgr.-Export--Vicon Industries, Inc., Hauppauge, NY; *U.S. Public*, pg. 1719
Wright, G.J., V.P., Gen. Counsel & Sec.--ABB Lummus Global Inc., Bloomfield, NJ; *Int'l*, pg. 4
Wu, C.C., Mgr.-Export--Taiwan Glass Industry Corp., Taipei, Taiwan; *Int'l*, pg. 1348
Yamamoto, Kuni, V.P.-Asia & Pacific Area--Genetics Institute, Inc., Cambridge, MA; *U.S. Public*, pg. 79
Yamamoto, Toshiya, V.P.-World Trade--John O. Butler Co., Chicago, IL; *Int'l*, pg. 1320
Yarrish, Al, V.P.-Intl. Sls.--Macrotech Plyseal, Inc., Salt Lake City, UT; *U.S. Private*, pg. 693
Yeager, Lana, Mgr.-Export--Convex Technology Center - Hewlett-Packard, Richardson, TX; *U.S. Public*, pg. 815
Yoshioka, Mitch, Mgr.-Import & Export--The Vendo Company, Fresno, CA; *Int'l*, pg. 1184
Young, Michael R., Chief Fin. Officer & V.P.-Intl. Div.--Allen & Hoshall, Inc., Memphis, TN; *U.S. Private*, pg. 36
Zakheim, Dor, V.P.--System Planning Corp., Arlington, VA; *U.S. Private*, pg. 1061
Zeigle, Stacie, Mgr.-Export--The Blodgett Oven Co., Inc., Burlington, VT; *U.S. Public*, pg. 1064
Zieger, Ari, Dir.-Sls. & Mdsg.--Interbath, Inc., City of Industry, CA; *U.S. Private*, pg. 566
Zirkel, Klaus, Exec. V.P.-Intl Trade--Bayerische Landesbank, Munich, Germany; *Int'l*, pg. 176
Zlotnik, Arnold, Pres.--Surco Products, Inc., Pittsburgh, PA; *U.S. Private*, pg. 1056
Zobel, Mike, Dir.-Sls. & Mktg.--Vacu-Dry Company, Sebastopol, CA; *U.S. Public*, pg. 1704
Zobell, Isabel, Mgr.-Import & Export--LogEtronics Corporation, Springfield, VA; *U.S. Public*, pg. 6

GENERAL COUNSEL

Aaron, Marcus, II, Pres. & Treas.--The Homer Laughlin China Company, Newell, WV; *U.S. Private*, pg. 653
Abbott, Henry J., Sec. & Gen. Counsel--Central Parking Corp., Nashville, TN; *U.S. Public*, pg. 326
Abbott, Sharon, V.P., Gen. Counsel & Sec.--UniCARE Financial Corp., Irvine, CA; *U.S. Private*, pg. 152
Ables, Clinton E., V.P. & Gen. Counsel--Dresser Industries, Inc., Dallas, TX; *U.S. Public*, pg. 528
Abramson, David M., Sr. V.P. & Gen. Counsel--JP Foodservice, Inc., Columbia, MD; *U.S. Public*, pg. 918
Abramson, Stephanie W., Exec. V.P. & Gen. Counsel--Young & Rubicam Inc., New York, NY; *U.S. Private*, pg. 1196
Acerra, Valerie, Gen. Counsel--Associated Merchandising Corp. (AMC), New York, NY; *U.S. Private*, pg. 91
Achterkirchen, David M., Legal Officer--Siliconix, Inc., Santa Clara, CA; *Int'l*, pg. 367
Ackman, Roger S., V.P., Gen. Counsel & Sec.--Imperial Tobacco Limited, Montreal, Canada; *Int'l*, pg. 112
Adamo, Charles D., Exec. V.P.-Corp. Devel. & Gen. Counsel--Sun International Hotels Limited, Fort Lauderdale, FL; *U.S. Public*, pg. 1531
Adams, J. Phillip, V.P. & Gen. Counsel-Tax--CBS Corporation, Pittsburgh, PA; *U.S. Public*, pg. 273
Adams, John M., Jr., Asst. Gen. Counsel & Asst. Sec.--American Electric Power Service Corp., Columbus, OH; *U.S. Public*, pg. 72
Adams, Larry L., V.P. & Gen. Counsel--Tanning Research Labs., Inc., Ormond Beach, FL; *U.S. Private*, pg. 1068
Adams, Nat, Gen. Counsel--MWCA, Rexburg, ID; *U.S. Public*, pg. 804
Adams, Thomas J., V.P. & Gen. Corp. Counsel--Chicago Title & Trust Co., Chicago, IL; *U.S. Public*, pg. 42
Addis, David R., Gen. Counsel--Herbalife International of America, Inc., Century City, CA; *U.S. Public*, pg. 809
Addy, George, Exec. V.P. & Chief Gen. Counsel--Telus Corporation, Edmonton, Canada; *Int'l*, pg. 1374
Adelberg, Arthur W., V.P.-Law & Power Supply--Central Maine Power Company, Augusta, ME; *U.S. Public*, pg. 325
Adelman, Graham, Sr. V.P., Gen. Counsel & Sec.--Global Industrial Technologies, Dallas, TX; *U.S. Public*, pg. 747
Adikes, Robert K., V.P., Sec. & Gen. Counsel--Spalding & Evenflo Companies, Inc., Chicopee, MA; *U.S. Private*, pg. 629
Adler, Jack P., Esq., V.P., Gen. Counsel & Sec.--EA Engineering, Science & Technology, Inc., Hunt Valley, MD; *U.S. Public*, pg. 540
Afrow, Allan, Gen. Counsel--Uno Restaurant Corporation, West Roxbury, MA; *U.S. Public*, pg. 1698
Agger, James H., Sr. V.P., Gen. Counsel & Sec.--Air Products and Chemicals, Inc., Allentown, PA; *U.S. Public*, pg. 30
Agnich, Richard J., Sr. V.P., Gen. Counsel & Sec.--Texas Instruments Incorporated, Dallas, TX; *U.S. Public*, pg. 1585
Agranoff, Gerald N., V.P.-Gen. Counsel & Corp Sec.--Datapoint Corporation, Paris, France; *Int'l*, pg. 384
Agress, Ellen, V.P.-Legal Policy & Plng.--National Broadcasting Co., Inc., New York, NY; *U.S. Public*, pg. 712
Ahlbin, Frank, V.P. & Sec.--Atlantic Guest, Inc., Meriden, CT; *U.S. Public*, pg. 1705
Ahles, Dave, V.P. & Gen. Counsel--American International Airways, Ypsilanti, MI; *U.S. Private*, pg. 57
Ailstock, Janet, V.P. & Gen. Counsel--Catalina Lighting, Inc., Miami, FL; *U.S. Public*, pg. 314
Aiuvalasit, Anthony G., Jr., V.P.-Law--Block Drug Company, Inc., Jersey City, NJ; *U.S. Public*, pg. 236
Alberg, James, V.P. & Gen. Counsel--Dun & Bradstreet Software Services, Atlanta, GA; *Int'l*, pg. 532
Alcantara, Maria Emilia M., Mgr.-Legal--Acos Villares S.A., Sao Paulo, Brazil; *Int'l*, pg. 23
Alesso, Dominick, Gen. Counsel & Sec.--A-P-A Transport Corp., North Bergen, NJ; *U.S. Private*, pg. 2
Alexander, Anthony J., Exec. V.P. & Gen. Counsel--FirstEnergy Corp., Akron, OH; *U.S. Public*, pg. 644
Alexander, Nicholas Z., Sr. V.P.-Gen. Counsel & Sec.--ACCEL International Corporation, Dublin, OH; *U.S. Public*, pg. 14
Alfano, J.D., Mgr.-Law Services--Salt River Project Agricultural Improvement and Power District, Tempe, AZ; *U.S. Private*, pg. 962
Alford, Walter H., Exec. V.P. & Sr. Gen. Counsel--BellSouth Corporation, Atlanta, GA; *U.S. Public*, pg. 207
Aliff, Debbie, Gen. Counsel & Sec.--Washington Homes, Inc., Landover, MD; *U.S. Public*, pg. 1741
Alix, Patrick, V.P.-Fin. & Legal Affairs--Lafarge Materiaux de Specialites, Montrouge, France; *Int'l*, pg. 789
Allen, Clive V., Sr. V.P. & Gen. Counsel--Northern Telecom Limited, Brampton, Canada; *Int'l*, pg. 968
Allen, John C., V.P.-Human Resources, Corp. Counsel & Sec.--Energy West Inc., Great Falls, MT; *U.S. Public*, pg. 581
Allen, Kay-Dawn, Gen. Counsel--Gerald H. Phipps, Inc., Denver, CO; *U.S. Private*, pg. 862
Allen, Wayne, Gen. Counsel--Monico Alloys, Inc., Los Angeles, CA; *U.S. Private*, pg. 757
Allgood, Joan U., V.P. & Gen. Counsel--Developers Diversified Realty Corporation, Moreland Hills, OH; *U.S. Public*, pg. 502
Allison, Charles, V.P., Gen. Counsel & Sec.--Gulf States Paper Corporation, Tuscaloosa, AL; *U.S. Private*, pg. 487
Allison, W.T., II, Gen. Counsel--GSC Enterprises, Inc., Sulphur Springs, TX; *U.S. Private*, pg. 436
Almase, Teodoro, V.P.-Legal & Corp Sec.--Atlas Consolidated Mining & Development Corporation, Manila, Philippines; *Int'l*, pg. 95
Almond, David R., Sr. V.P., Gen. Counsel & Sec.--Fleming Companies, Inc., Oklahoma City, OK; *U.S. Public*, pg. 652
Alogna, J.A., Sr. V.P. & Gen. Counsel--Fuller Company, Bethlehem, PA; *Int'l*, pg. 475
Alper, Harvey M., Gen. Counsel--Holiday RV Superstores, Inc., Orlando, FL; *U.S. Public*, pg. 829
Alphson, Howard C., Gen. Counsel & Sec.--M.C. Gill Corporation, El Monte, CA; *U.S. Private*, pg. 453
Althoff, John J., V.P., Gen. Counsel & Sec.--Ekco Group, Inc., Nashua, NH; *U.S. Public*, pg. 566
Altman, Steven R., Exec. V.P. & Gen. Counsel--QUALCOMM, San Diego, CA; *U.S. Public*, pg. 1348
Alvarado, Don, Gen. Counsel--Henry Lee Company, Miami, FL; *U.S. Private*, pg. 657
Alvarado, Donald G., V.P. & Gen. Counsel--Smart & Final, Vernon, CA; *Int'l*, pg. 563
Amas, Gus J., Exec. V.P. & Gen. Counsel--Eagle Industries, Inc., Chicago, IL; *U.S. Private*, pg. 473
Ambler, Michael M., Gen. Tax Counsel--Texaco Inc., White Plains, NY; *U.S. Public*, pg. 1582
Ambrusko, Therese, V.P. & Gen. Counsel--Atkinson, San Bruno, CA; *U.S. Public*, pg. 143
Ames, Richard S., Chm. Bd., Pres. & Chief Exec. Officer--Command Plastic Corporation, Akron, OH; *U.S. Private*, pg. 257
Amhowitz, Harris J., Deputy Chm. & Gen. Counsel--Coopers & Lybrand, New York, NY; *U.S. Private*, pg. 274
Anastasio, Curt, V.P., Gen. Counsel & Corp. Sec.--Ultramar Diamond Shamrock Corporation, San Antonio, TX; *U.S. Public*, pg. 1663
Anastos, Peter C., Assoc. Gen. Counsel--Nashua Corporation, Nashua, NH; *U.S. Public*, pg. 1152
Ancarrow, N. Hopper, V.P., Sec. & Gen. Counsel--Southern States Cooperative, Inc., Richmond, VA; *U.S. Private*, pg. 1017
Andereck, Eugene, Gen. Counsel--Associated Electric Co-op Inc., Springfield, MO; *U.S. Private*, pg. 89
Andersen, Darian B., Corp. Sec. & Dir.-Law Dept.--Foodbrands America, Inc., Oklahoma City, OK; *U.S. Public*, pg. 852
Andersen, Michael P., V.P., Gen. Counsel & Sec.--John Alden Financial Corporation, Miami, FL; *U.S. Public*, pg. 39
Anderson, Barbara C., V.P., Gen. Counsel & Corp. Sec.--Executone Information Systems, Inc., Milford, CT; *U.S. Public*, pg. 599
Anderson, C.R., Gen. Counsel--States, Inc., Breckenridge, TX; *U.S. Private*, pg. 1037
Anderson, David B., V.P.-Corp. Devel., Gen. Counsel & Sec.--GATX Corporation, Chicago, IL; *U.S. Public*, pg. 690
Anderson, David C., Gen. Counsel & Corp. Sec.--Airborne Freight Corporation, Seattle, WA; *U.S. Public*, pg. 32
Anderson, Douglas L., Asst. Gen. Counsel & Asst. Sec.--CalEnergy Co., Omaha, NE; *U.S. Public*, pg. 292
Anderson, Edwyna, Gen. Counsel--Duquesne Light Company, Pittsburgh, PA; *U.S. Public*, pg. 474
Anderson, Gregory W., Corp. Counsel & Sec.--Martin Color-Fi, Edgefield, SC; *U.S. Public*, pg. 1052
Anderson, James, Legal Officer--Prairie Farms Dairy, Inc., Carlinville, IL; *U.S. Private*, pg. 878
Anderson, James, Gen. Counsel--Ingram Micro Inc., Santa Ana, CA; *U.S. Public*, pg. 878
Anderson, Kim E., V.P. & Asst. Gen. Counsel--Magellan Health Services, Inc., Atlanta, GA; *U.S. Public*, pg. 1033
Anderson, Peer L., V.P. & Gen. Counsel--Citgo Petroleum Corporation, Tulsa, OK; *Int'l*, pg. 1045
Anderson, R.D., Gen. Counsel & Sec.--Procter & Gamble Inc., North York, Canada; *U.S. Public*, pg. 1332
Anderson, Vincent P., Sr. V.P. & Legal Officer--Wawa, Inc., Media, PA; *U.S. Private*, pg. 1155
Anderson, William E., Gen. Counsel--WorldCom, Inc., Jackson, MS; *U.S. Public*, pg. 1779
Anderson, William E., II, Sr. V.P., Sec. & Gen. Counsel--Long John Silver's, Inc., Lexington, KY; *U.S. Private*, pg. 674
Andreas, G. Allen, Pres. & Chief Exec. Officer--Archer Daniels Midland Company (ADM), Decatur, IL; *U.S. Public*, pg. 127
Andreopoulos, Konstantin, Dir.-Legal Affairs--European Investment Bank, Luxembourg, Luxembourg; *Int'l*, pg. 465
Andreozzi, Lou, Chief Legal Counsel--LEXIS-NEXIS, Miamisburg, OH; *Int'l*, pg. 1096
Andrews, Donald, V.P.-Legal Affairs--Weyerhaeuser Canada Ltd., Vancouver, Canada; *U.S. Public*, pg. 1764
Andrews, Roger L., Gen. Counsel & Risk Mngmt. Dir.--E.D. Bullard Company, Cynthiana, KY; *U.S. Private*, pg. 180
Andrews, Steven R., V.P., Gen. Counsel & Sec.--Multigraphics Inc., Mount Prospect, IL; *U.S. Public*, pg. 1141
Annes, Michael D., V.P.-Bus. Devel./Counsel Law--The Quaker Oats Company, Chicago, IL; *U.S. Public*, pg. 1347
Annesi, P., Dir.-Legal Affairs & Personnel--Sigma-Tau Finanziaria S.p.A., Rome, Italy; *Int'l*, pg. 1248
Annis, Michael, V.P., Gen. Counsel & Sec.--Del Taco, Inc., Laguna Hills, CA; *U.S. Private*, pg. 321
Answorth, Louis L., Sr. V.P. & Gen. Counsel--Pentair, Inc., Saint Paul, MN; *U.S. Public*, pg. 1273
Anthony, Aubra, Jr., Gen. Counsel, Treas. & Sec.--Anthony Forest Products Co., Inc., El Dorado, AR; *U.S. Private*, pg. 76
Anthony, Frank S., V.P., Gen. Counsel & Sec.--Bird Incorporated, Norwood, MA; *Int'l*, pg. 1170
Apgar, Robert F., V.P. & Gen. Counsel--Consolidated-Tomoka Land Co., Daytona Beach, FL; *U.S. Public*, pg. 437
Appel, R. Jan, Gen. Counsel--Sparton Corporation, Jackson, MI; *U.S. Public*, pg. 1496
Appell, Jochen, Gen. Counsel--Commerzbank AG, Frankfurt, Germany; *Int'l*, pg. 308
Appenzeller, Rebecca H., Gen. Counsel & Corp. Sec.--The Standard Register Company, Dayton, OH; *U.S. Public*, pg. 1505
Apple, Robert, V.P. & Gen. Counsel--Progressive Bank, Inc., Fishkill, NY; *U.S. Public*, pg. 1334
Applebaum, Martin I., Sr. V.P. & Gen. Counsel--Tridel Enterprises Inc., Downsview, Canada; *Int'l*, pg. 1423
Appling, Dana, Gen. Counsel & Sec.--Sacramento Municipal Utility District, Sacramento, CA; *U.S. Private*, pg. 959
Aquilino, Vincent, Gen. Counsel & Sec.--Graymills Corp., Chicago, IL; *U.S. Private*, pg. 473
Arai, Junichi, Mng. Dir.-Publications, Pub. Rels. & Legal Affairs--Nihon Keizai Shimbun, Inc., Tokyo, Japan; *Int'l*, pg. 929
Arakas, Peter, Gen. Counsel--LEGO Systems, Inc., Enfield, CT; *Int'l*, pg. 805
Arbitman, William A., V.P., Sec. & Assoc. Gen. Counsel--The Dial Corporation, Phoenix, AZ; *U.S. Public*, pg. 505
Arbour, Peter W., V.P. & Gen. Counsel--Brown & Root Inc., Alhambra, CA; *U.S. Public*, pg. 775
Archibald, David D., V.P. & Dep. Gen. Counsel--Northern Telecom Limited, Brampton, Canada; *Int'l*, pg. 968
Arditti, Elliot, V.P. & Gen. Counsel--Dart Group Corporation, Landover, MD; *U.S. Public*, pg. 484
Argila, Raymond P., Sr. V.P., Legal & Asst. Sec.--Urstadt Biddle Properties, Inc., Greenwich, CT; *U.S. Public*, pg. 1700
Argilla, Luke, Corp. Counsel--Swinerton Inc., San Francisco, CA; *U.S. Private*, pg. 1059
Arjaluoto, Ilkka, V.P.-Fin. & Legal Admin.--Rautaruukki Oy, Helsinki, Finland; *Int'l*, pg. 1088
Arkell, Robert B., V.P.-Industrial Rels. & Gen. Counsel--Longview Fibre Company, Longview, WA; *U.S. Public*, pg. 1013
Armitage, Rod, Sec. & Dir.-Legal Dept.--Staveley Industries PLC, Croydon, United Kingdom; *Int'l*, pg. 1298
Arms, G. Geoffrey, V.P., Gen. Counsel & Sec.--Pool Energy Services Co., Houston, TX; *U.S. Public*, pg. 1316
Armstrong, J.P., Gen. Counsel--Esso UK plc, London, United Kingdom; *U.S. Public*, pg. 602
Armstrong, Kenneth E., V.P. & Gen. Counsel--Florida Progress Corporation, Saint Petersburg, FL; *U.S. Public*, pg. 655
Armstrong, Kenneth E., V.P. & Gen. Counsel--Florida Power Corporation, Saint Petersburg, FL; *U.S. Public*, pg. 655
Arnerup, Tord, Chief Legal Advisor--Nordbanken AB, Stockholm, Sweden; *Int'l*, pg. 957
Arnold, William, V.P.-Real Estate Law--Albertson's, Inc., Boise, ID; *U.S. Public*, pg. 38
Aron, Mark G., Exec. V.P.-Law & Pub. Affairs--CSX Corporation, Richmond, VA; *U.S. Public*, pg. 284
Arraj, David, V.P. & Gen. Counsel--Bally's Grand Inc. (Las Vegas), Las Vegas, NV; *U.S. Public*, pg. 829
Arthur, H. Thomas, II, V.P., Gen. Counsel & Asst. Sec.--SCANA Corporation, Columbia, SC; *U.S. Public*, pg. 1436
Arthur, Magaret K., Sr. V.P. & Gen. Counsel--National Life Insurance Company, Montpelier, VT; *U.S. Private*, pg. 785
Asciutto, Valerie, V.P. & Gen. Counsel--AMREP Corporation, New York, NY; *U.S. Public*, pg. 104
Ash, Michael S., Gen. Counsel--Pinnacle West Capital Corporation, Phoenix, AZ; *U.S. Public*, pg. 1297
Ashworth, Brent F., V.P., Gen. Counsel & Sec.--Nature's Sunshine Products, Inc., Provo, UT; *U.S. Public*, pg. 1166
Assini, Frederick, Gen. Counsel & Corp. Sec.--Plasti-Kote Company Inc., Medina, OH; *U.S. Private*, pg. 870
Astrue, Michael J., Esq., V.P., Gen. Counsel & Sec.--Biogen, Inc., Cambridge, MA; *U.S. Public*, pg. 230
Athos, Gus J., Sr. V.P., Gen. Counsel & Sec.--Eagle Industries, Inc., Chicago, IL; *U.S. Private*, pg. 473
Atkinson, Jerome, Sr. V.P., Gen. Counsel & Sec.--Fortis, Inc., New York, NY; *Int'l*, pg. 499
Atkinson, Jerome A., Sr. V.P., Gen. Counsel & Sec.--American Security Group, Atlanta, GA; *Int'l*, pg. 499
Atkinson, Peter Y., V.P. & Gen. Counsel--Hollinger Inc., Vancouver, Canada; *Int'l*, pg. 630
Attaway, John, Corp. Counsel--Publix Supermarkets Inc., Lakeland, FL; *U.S. Private*, pg. 893
Atterbury, Robert Rennie, III, V.P., Gen. Counsel & Sec.--Caterpillar Inc., Peoria, IL; *U.S. Public*, pg. 315
Aufox, Jerry M., Legal Counsel & Sec.--A.M. Castle & Co., Franklin Park, IL; *U.S. Public*, pg. 312
Augenbraun, Barry S., Exec. V.P. & Gen. Counsel--Home Shopping Network, Inc., Saint Petersburg, FL; *U.S. Public*, pg. 1685
Austin, Bill, Mgr.-Mktg. & Sls.--Industra Inc., Portland, OR; *Int'l*, pg. 74
Austin, Brock, Legal Counsel--G.E. Capital Fleet Services, Fort Wayne, IN; *U.S. Public*, pg. 710
Austin, Frank E., Sr. V.P., Gen. Counsel & Corp. Sec.--Glenborough Realty Trust Incorporated, San Mateo, CA; *U.S. Public*, pg. 747
Austin, Neil D., V.P.-Gen. Counsel & Sec.--Checkpoint Systems Inc., Thorofare, NJ; *U.S. Public*, pg. 343
Austin, Toby J., Gen. Counsel--TransAlta Energy Corporation, Calgary, Canada; *Int'l*, pg. 1416
Austin, Toby J., Gen. Counsel--TransAlta Enterprises Corporation, Calgary, Canada; *Int'l*, pg. 1416
Avera, Stephen R., Asst. Gen. Counsel--Flowers Industries, Inc., Thomasville, GA; *U.S. Public*, pg. 656
Avis, James C., Exec. V.P., Gen. Counsel & Sec.--Newbridge Networks Corporation, Kanata, Canada; *Int'l*, pg. 924
Avram, G.A., Gen. Counsel--Pioneer/Eclipse Corp., Sparta, NC; *Int'l*, pg. 71
Axley, Frederick, Gen. Counsel--Chicago Tube & Iron Co., Chicago, IL; *U.S. Private*, pg. 235
Aydon, Richard, Sec. & Dir.-Legal--Christies International plc, London, United Kingdom; *Int'l*, pg. 289
Azar, Michael C., Gen. Counsel & Sec.--Noble International Ltd., Bloomfield Hills, MI; *U.S. Public*, pg. 1187
Babbin, Fred, Gen. Counsel--Orleans International, Inc., Bloomfield Hills, MI; *U.S. Private*, pg. 820

Babcock, Reginald, V.P.-Corp. Services, Gen. Counsel & Sec.--Connecticut Natural Gas Corporation, Hartford, CT; *U.S. Public*, pg. 285
Babcock, Reginald L., V.P., Gen. Counsel & Sec.--CTG Resources, Inc., Hartford, CT; *U.S. Public*, pg. 285
Babcock, Reginald L., V.P., Gen. Counsel & Sec.--Energy Networks, Inc. (ENI), Hartford, CT; *U.S. Public*, pg. 285
Babilla, Terrence, Gen. Counsel & Sec.--Sport Supply Group, Inc., Dallas, TX; *U.S. Public*, pg. 1499
Babin, Mara, Sec. & Gen. Counsel--Sifco Industries, Inc., Cleveland, OH; *U.S. Public*, pg. 1470
Babineau, Anne S., V.P., Gen. Counsel & Sec.--Bell Atlantic-NJ, Newark, NJ; *U.S. Public*, pg. 202
Bach, Dieter, Legal--Braun AG, Kronberg, Germany; *U.S. Public*, pg. 744
Bachand, Jean-Paul, Exec. V.P., Gen. Counsel & Corp. Sec.--Montreal Trustco, Montreal, Canada; *Int'l*, pg. 155
Bachinger, Konrad, Dr., Exec. V.P.-Commercial Banking & Legal Affairs--Liechtenstein Global Trust Limited, Vaduz, Liechtenstein; *Int'l*, pg. 809
Backofen, Richard, V.P. & Assc. Gen. Counsel--Republic National Bank of New York, New York, NY; *U.S. Public*, pg. 1380
Bacon, Donna L., V.P., Gen. Counsel & Sec.--JPE, Inc., Ann Arbor, MI; *U.S. Public*, pg. 919
Bacon, Richard A., Sr. V.P. & Gen. Counsel--John Wieland Homes Inc., Atlanta, GA; *U.S. Private*, pg. 1175
Baddeley, D. Jeffrey, V.P., Gen. Counsel & Sec.--Outboard Marine Corporation, Waukegan, IL; *U.S. Private*, pg. 478
Bae, Shinhan, Consultant--Oricom Inc., Seoul, Korea; *Int'l*, pg. 1008
Baer, Luke, V.P., Gen. Counsel & Sec.--Robert Bosch Corporation, Broadview, IL; *Int'l*, pg. 204
Baer, Susan, Gen. Counsel--Haarmann & Reimer Corp., Springfield, NJ; *Int'l*, pg. 173
Bagan, Kenneth M., Gen. Counsel & Sec.--Nowsco Well Service Ltd., Calgary, Canada; *Int'l*, pg. 989
Bagerdjian, Haig, V.P., Gen. Counsel & Sec.--Syncor International Corporation, Woodland Hills, CA; *U.S. Public*, pg. 1548
Bahler, Gary M., V.P., Gen. Counsel & Sec.--Woolworth Corporation, New York, NY; *U.S. Public*, pg. 1777
Bahlmann, Jerome R., Sr. V.P. & Gen. Counsel--Battelle Memorial Institute, Columbus, OH; *U.S. Private*, pg. 123
Bail, Clifford A., V.P.-Legal Affairs & Gen. Counsel--Century Communications Corp., New Canaan, CT; *U.S. Public*, pg. 329
Bailas, David, Gen. Counsel--First Data Corporation, Hackensack, NJ; *U.S. Public*, pg. 630
Bailey, Mark, V.P., Gen. Counsel & Sec.--SENCORP, Newport, KY; *U.S. Private*, pg. 983
Bailey, Richard A., V.P.-Gen. Counsel & Sec.--Kraft Canada Inc., Don Mills, Canada; *U.S. Public*, pg. 1288
Baillargeon, Marie, Asst. Gen. Counsel & Asst. Sec.--The Ivaco Group, Montreal, Canada; *Int'l*, pg. 695
Bain, Doug, V.P. & Gen. Counsel--Boeing Commercial Airplane Group, Renton, WA; *U.S. Public*, pg. 240
Bain, Irwin A., Gen. Counsel & Sec.--Schottenstein Stores Corporation, Columbus, OH; *U.S. Private*, pg. 972
Baines, Harry F., Gen. Counsel & Sec.--T & N Plc, Manchester, United Kingdom; *Int'l*, pg. 1334
Bair, Jack, Staff Counsel--San Francisco Giants Baseball Club, San Francisco, CA; *U.S. Private*, pg. 964
Bair, Stephen L., V.P., Corp. Counsel & Sec.--Time-Life, Inc., Alexandria, VA; *U.S. Public*, pg. 1613
Baird, John N., Sec. & Gen. Counsel--Air Liquide America Corporation, Houston, TX; *Int'l*, pg. 37
Baisley, James M., Sr. V.P., Gen. Counsel & Sec.--W.W. Grainger, Inc., Lincolnshire, IL; *U.S. Public*, pg. 758
Baker, Brian, Gen. Counsel--Rolls-Royce plc, London, United Kingdom; *Int'l*, pg. 1126
Baker, David, V.P. & Gen. Counsel--CENEX, Inc., Inver Grove Heights, MN; *U.S. Private*, pg. 221
Baker, John, V.P. & Gen. Counsel--Air Canada, Saint-Laurent, Canada; *Int'l*, pg. 36
Baker, Martin R., V.P. & Gen. Counsel--Lattice Semiconductor Corporation, Hillsboro, OR; *U.S. Public*, pg. 979
Baker, Richard C., V.P., Gen. Counsel & Sec.--H.B. Fuller Company, Saint Paul, MN; *U.S. Public*, pg. 686
Baker, Richard M., Sr. V.P. & Gen. Counsel--Imperial Bank, Inglewood, CA; *U.S. Public*, pg. 871
Baker, Robert, V.P., Gen. Counsel & Sec.--IDX Systems Corporation, Burlington, VT; *U.S. Public*, pg. 854
Baker, Roger, Gen. Counsel--Freeport-McMoRan Inc., New Orleans, LA; *U.S. Public*, pg. 680
Baker, Susan D., V.P., Sec. & Gen. Counsel-Mngmt. Services--The ServiceMaster Company, Downers Grove, IL; *U.S. Public*, pg. 1461
Balasiano, Steve, V.P. & Gen. Counsel--The Children's Place Retail Stores, Inc., West Caldwell, NJ; *U.S. Private*, pg. 237
Baldauf, David, V.P., Sec. & Gen. Counsel--Benderson Development Co., Inc., Buffalo, NY; *U.S. Private*, pg. 132
Bales, Thomas, V.P.-Property Mngmt. & Gen. Counsel--Seligman & Associates, Inc., Southfield, MI; *U.S. Private*, *pg. 982*
Balius, Louis M., Assoc. Gen. Counsel & Asst. Sec.--Champion Enterprises, Inc., Auburn Hills, MI; *U.S. Public*, *pg. 332*
Balka, Sigmound, Gen. Counsel--Krasdale Foods Inc., White Plains, NY; *U.S. Private*, pg. 635
Ball, James H., Sr. V.P., Sec. & Gen. Counsel--Nestle Holdings, Inc., Stamford, CT; *Int'l*, pg. 916
Ballantyne, Richard L., V.P., Gen. Counsel & Sec.--Harris Corporation, Melbourne, FL; *U.S. Public*, pg. 791
Ballard, Richard, Gen. Counsel--Taylor Machine Works, Inc., Louisville, MS; *U.S. Private*, pg. 1070
Ballentine, Richard O., V.P., Gen. Counsel & Sec.--Butler Manufacturing Company, Kansas City, MO; *U.S. Public*, pg. 271
Ballway, Joseph H., Jr., V.P. & Gen. Counsel--Cleveland-Cliffs Inc, Cleveland, OH; *U.S. Public*, pg. 386
Balzano, John, Gen. Counsel--C. Weaver Chevrolet, Inc., New York Mills, NY; *U.S. Private*, pg. 1156
Bandler, Beth M., V.P., Gen. Counsel & Sec.--Hawker Siddeley Canada Inc., Mississauga, Canada; *Int'l*, pg. 604
Bangs, Nelson A., V.P., Gen Counsel & Sec.--Dr Pepper/Seven Up No. America, Dallas, TX; *Int'l*, pg. 248
Bankston, Archie M., Sec. & Assoc. Gen. Counsel--Consolidated Edison Company of New York, Inc., New York, NY; *U.S. Public*, pg. 434
Bannerman, Martha G., V.P. & Gen. Counsel--NAC Re Corp., Greenwich, CT; *U.S. Public*, pg. 1144
Bannerman, Martha G., Exec. V.P., Gen. Counsel & Sec.--Greenwich Insurance Company, Greenwich, CT; *U.S. Public*, pg. 1144
Bannerman, Martha G., Exec. V.P., Gen. Counsel & Sec.--Indian Harbor Insurance Company, Greenwich, CT; *U.S. Public*, pg. 1144
Banstetter, Robert J., V.P., Gen. Counsel & Sec.--General American Life Insurance Co., Saint Louis, MO; *U.S. Private*, pg. 443
Banta, Michael G., V.P. & Asst. Gen. Counsel--Indianapolis Power & Light Company, Indianapolis, IN; *U.S. Public*, pg. 913
Barash, Anthony H., Sr. V.P.-Corp. Affairs & Gen. Counsel--Bowater Incorporated, Greenville, SC; *U.S. Public*, pg. 247
Barbarowicz, Robert P., Exec. V.P., Gen. Counsel & Sec.--National Insurance Group, South San Francisco, CA; *U.S. Public*, pg. 1157
Barberi, Robert O., Gen. Counsel--MB America, Inc., Westport, CT; *Int'l*, pg. 267
Barbour, Rodney, Chief Fin. Officer & Gen. Counsel--Lawson Mechanical Contractors, Sacramento, CA; *U.S. Private*, pg. 654
Barclay, Bruce, Gen. Counsel & Sec.--Guidant Corporation-Vascular Intervention Group, Santa Clara, CA; *U.S. Public*, pg. 768
Barclay, David A., V.P. & Assoc. Gen. Counsel--Republic Industries, Inc., Fort Lauderdale, FL; *U.S. Public*, pg. 1378
Bardenwerper, Walter, V.P. & Gen. Counsel--Watson Wyatt Worldwide, Bethesda, MD; *U.S. Private*, pg. 1154
Barkai, Judith, Gen. Counsel, Sec. & Dir.-Investor Rels.--American Israeli Paper Mills Ltd., Hadera, Israel; *Int'l*, pg. 74
Barkan, Lee, Sr. V.P, Sec. & Gen. Counsel--AVC/Nu-Vision, Inc., Flint, MI; *U.S. Private*, pg. 9
Barkley, Jim, Gen. Counsel & Sec.--Simon DeBartolo Group, Inc., Indianapolis, IN; *U.S. Public*, pg. 1474
Barlett, Lee, V.P., Gen. Counsel & Sec.--Torchmark Corporation, Birmingham, AL; *U.S. Public*, pg. 1622
Barlow, Thomas J., Reg. Counsel & Asst. Sec.--OHM Remediation Services Corp., Findlay, OH; *U.S. Public*, pg. 1208
Barmeier, William G., V.P., Gen. Counsel & Sec.--VeriFone, Inc., Redwood City, CA; *U.S. Public*, pg. 815
Barnard, Douglas C., V.P., Gen. Counsel & Sec.--Furnishings International, Inc., Thomasville, NC; *U.S. Private*, pg. 431
Barnard, Douglas C., V.P., Gen. Counsel & Sec.--LifeStyle Furnishings International, Ltd., Thomasville, NC; *U.S. Private*, pg. 431
Barnes, Robert M., V.P., Gen. Counsel & Sec.--Unitog Company, Kansas City, MO; *U.S. Public*, pg. 1693
Barnett, Charlie, Gen. Counsel--Kenny Rogers Roasters, Fort Lauderdale, FL; *U.S. Private*, pg. 939
Barnett, James, Assoc. Gen. Counsel & Asst. Sec.--MidAmerican Capital Company, Des Moines, IA; *U.S. Public*, pg. 1109
Barnett, Robert G., Gen. Counsel & Sec.--Deposit Guaranty Corp., Jackson, MS; *U.S. Public*, pg. 500
Barnett, Steve, Sec. & Corp. Counsel--Global Industrial Technologies, Dallas, TX; *U.S. Public*, pg. 747
Barnickol, Karl R., Sr. V.P., Gen. Counsel & Sec.--Solutia Inc., Saint Louis, MO; *U.S. Public*, pg. 1483
Barnum, Cathy, Gen. Counsel--United Design Corporation, Noble, OK; *U.S. Private*, pg. 1121
Barnum, James, Gen. Counsel--Hubbard Broadcasting, Inc., Saint Paul, MN; *U.S. Private*, pg. 543
Barr, Charles F., V.P., Gen. Counsel & Sec.--General Re Corporation, Stamford, CT; *U.S. Public*, pg. 725
Barr, William P., Sr. V.P. & Gen. Counsel--GTE Corporation, Stamford, CT; *U.S. Public*, pg. 696
Barratt, Paul, V.P., Gen. Counsel & Sec.--Triangle Pacific Corporation, Dallas, TX; *U.S. Public*, pg. 1634
Barratt, Paul, V.P. & Gen. Counsel--Bruce Hardwood Floors, Dallas, TX; *U.S. Public*, pg. 1634
Barrett, William A., V.P. & Asst. Gen. Counsel--Tenet Healthcare Corporation, Santa Barbara, CA; *U.S. Public*, pg. 1576
Barron, Harold S., Sr. V.P., Gen. Counsel & Sec.--Unisys Corporation, Blue Bell, PA; *U.S. Public*, pg. 1671
Bartel, Charles, Gen. Counsel--Masters, Inc., Westbury, NY; *U.S. Private*, pg. 714
Barth, Peter H., V.P., Corp. Counsel & Asst. Sec.--Smith's Food & Drug Centers, Inc., Salt Lake City, UT; *U.S. Public*, pg. 1103
Bartl, James F., Sec.--National Presto Industries, Inc., Eau Claire, WI; *U.S. Public*, pg. 1159
Bartlett, Jeffrey W., V.P.-Regulatory Affairs--Stepan Company, Northfield, IL; *U.S. Public*, pg. 1514
Bartlett, John B., Sr. V.P., Gen. Counsel & Sec.--Rhone-Poulenc Rorer - U.S., Collegeville, PA; *Int'l*, pg. 1110
Barton, Greg, V.P.-Corp. & Legal Affairs & Gen. Counsel--Alliance Semiconductor Corp., San Jose, CA; *U.S. Public*, pg. 47
Barton, Greg, Gen. Counsel--Alliance Semiconductor Corp., San Jose, CA; *U.S. Public*, pg. 47
Barton, Nancy E., Sr. V.P., Gen. Counsel & Sec.--General Electric Capital Services, Inc., Stamford, CT; *U.S. Public*, *pg. 711*
Bartony, Diane, Corp. Gen. Counsel--Medrad, Inc., Indianola, PA; *Int'l*, pg. 1204
Basdevant, Francois, V.P.-Legal Affairs--Financiere Saint Dominique, Paris, France; *Int'l*, pg. 344
Bashoff, K.H., Sr. V.P.-Gen. Counsel & Sec.--Fidelity Mutual Life Insurance Co., Radnor, PA; *U.S. Private*, pg. 403
Baskett, William D., III, Chief Legal Officer & Gen. Counsel--Cincinnati Bell Telephone, Cincinnati, OH; *U.S. Public*, pg. 367
Baskins, Ann O., Mng. Counsel & Asst. Sec.--Hewlett-Packard Company, Palo Alto, CA; *U.S. Public*, pg. 813
Bassham, Terry, Gen. Counsel--El Paso Electric Company, El Paso, TX; *U.S. Public*, pg. 567
Bateman, William E., Corp. Sec. & Gen. Counsel--FTI Foodtech International Inc., Don Mills, Canada; *Int'l*, pg. 476
Batenhorst, Gary, V.P. & Gen. Counsel--Godfather's Pizza, Inc., Omaha, NE; *U.S. Private*, pg. 458
Bates, Carolyn, Gen. Counsel & Sec.--Imation Corporation, Oakdale, MN; *U.S. Public*, pg. 870
Batow, David P., Gen. Counsel--Williams Natural Gas Company, Tulsa, OK; *U.S. Public*, pg. 1769
Battaglia, Tim, Sr. V.P. & Gen. Counsel--Enron Acess, Dublin, OH; *U.S. Public*, pg. 584
Battle, Thomas P., Sr. V.P., Gen. Counsel & Sec.--Mitchell Energy & Development Corp., Spring, TX; *U.S. Public*, pg. 1117
Baty, Lee, Gen. Counsel--Wahl Clipper Corp., Sterling, IL; *U.S. Private*, pg. 1146
Bauer, Douglas F., Gen. Counsel & Sec.--Bowne & Co., Inc., New York, NY; *U.S. Public*, pg. 248
Bauer, Joseph W., V.P. & Gen. Counsel--The Lubrizol Corporation, Wickliffe, OH; *U.S. Public*, pg. 1016
Bauer, Michael, Exec. V.P., Sec. & Treas.--Al & Ed's Auto Sound Center, Monterey Park, CA; *U.S. Private*, pg. 30
Baum, Robert H., Vice Chm. & Gen. Counsel--The Inland Group, Inc., Oak Brook, IL; *U.S. Private*, pg. 564
Baum, Rubin, Gen. Counsel--Alfin, Inc., New York, NY; *U.S. Public*, pg. 40
Bauman, Bryan, Gen. Counsel--Aqua Care Systems Inc., Coral Springs, FL; *U.S. Public*, pg. 126
Bauman, Wallace, Gen. Counsel--Aqua Care Systems Inc., Coral Springs, FL; *U.S. Public*, pg. 126
Baumgarten, Herbert J., Sr. V.P., Gen. Counsel & Sec.--Unilever United States Inc., New York, NY; *Int'l*, pg. 1435
Baxter, David, Gen. Counsel--Concorp, Inc., Nitro, WV; *U.S. Private*, pg. 262
Bays, S.C., V.P. & Chief Legal Officer--Siebe plc, Windsor, United Kingdom; *Int'l*, pg. 1240
Beal, Karen, Sec. & Treas.--Crane Creek Cedar, Kent, WA; *Int'l*, pg. 1071
Bean, Christopher V., Gen. Counsel--D.D. Bean & Sons Co., Jaffrey, NH; *U.S. Private*, pg. 126
Beard, Pat, Gen. Counsel--Artco-Bell Corporation, Temple, TX; *U.S. Private*, pg. 86
Beardsley, Mary Louise, Asst. Gen. Counsel & Asst. Sec.--Barnes Group Inc., Bristol, CT; *U.S. Public*, pg. 189
Bearmon, Lee, V.P., Gen. Counsel & Sec.--Carlson Companies, Inc., Minnetonka, MN; *U.S. Private*, pg. 211
Beasley, Mark V., V.P., Gen. Counsel & Sec.--Michaels Stores, Inc., Irving, TX; *U.S. Public*, pg. 1104
Beatt, Bruce H., V.P., Gen. Counsel & Sec.--The Dexter Corporation, Windsor Locks, CT; *U.S. Public*, pg. 504
Beatty, Michael L., Exec. V.P. & Gen. Counsel--The Coastal Corporation, Houston, TX; *U.S. Public*, pg. 389
Beauchemin, Manon, Gen. Counsel & Sec.--Sico Inc., Longueuil, Canada; *Int'l*, pg. 1239
Beaud, Roland, Sr. V.P. & Legal Advisor--Ferrier Lullin & Cie SA, Geneva, Switzerland; *Int'l*, pg. 480
Beaudouin, Mark T., 1st Sr. V.P. & Gen. Counsel--J. Baker, Inc., Canton, MA; *U.S. Public*, pg. 167
Beaudouin, Mark T., Sr. V.P., Gen. Counsel & Asst. Sec.--Morse Shoe, Inc., Canton, MA; *U.S. Public*, pg. 168
Beaudouin, Mark T., 1st Sr. V.P., Gen. Counsel & Asst. Sec.--Casual Male, Inc., Hyde Park, MA; *U.S. Public*, pg. 168
Beaver, Kelly, V.P. Legal & General Counsel--Hilti Inc., Tulsa, OK; *Int'l*, pg. 620
Beber, Robert H., Exec. V.P. & Gen. Counsel--W.R. Grace & Co., Boca Raton, FL; *U.S. Public*, pg. 754
Beck, Edward W., Sr. V.P., Gen. Counsel & Sec.--Shaklee Corporation, San Francisco, CA; *Int'l*, pg. 1518
Becker, Mark, Sr. V.P. & Assoc. Gen Counsel--Showtime Networks Inc., New York, NY; *U.S. Private*, pg. 779
Becker, Paul, V.P., Treas., Gen. Counsel & Sec.--Cosco Industries, Spring Valley, NY; *U.S. Private*, pg. 277
Beckerlegge, Bernard R., Sr. V.P. & Gen. Counsel--Keyport Life Insurance Company, Boston, MA; *U.S. Private*, pg. 666
Beckerlegge, Bob, Gen. Counsel--Keyport Life Insurance Company, Boston, MA; *U.S. Private*, pg. 666
Bedell, Richard S., Gen. Counsel & Mgr.-Contracts--Greenhorne & O'Mara, Inc., Greenbelt, MD; *U.S. Private*, *pg. 477*
Bedewi, Elizabeth M., Sr. V.P, Sec. & Treas.--New Mexico & Arizona Land Co., Phoenix, AZ; *U.S. Public*, pg. 1172
Beebe, Raymond M., V.P., Gen. Counsel & Sec.--Winnebago Industries, Inc., Forest City, IA; *U.S. Public*, pg. 1772
Beeby, Kenneth J., V.P., Gen. Counsel & Sec.--Ocean Spray Cranberries, Inc., Middleboro, MA; *U.S. Private*, pg. 811
Beerman, Joel I., V.P., Gen. Counsel & Sec.--Georgia Gulf Corporation, Atlanta, GA; *U.S. Public*, pg. 734
Beery, James, Gen. Counsel & Sec.--SmithKline Beecham plc, Brentford, United Kingdom; *Int'l*, pg. 1264
Beeson, Donald L., Gen. Counsel--Peerless Lighting Corp., Berkeley, CA; *U.S. Private*, pg. 847
Beha, Ralph W., Gen. Counsel & Sec.--Control Data Systems, Inc., Arden Hills, MN; *U.S. Public*, pg. 441
Behm, Per, Legal--Preem Petroleum AB, Stockholm, Sweden; *Int'l*, pg. 1066
Beilly, Bradford J., V.P. & Gen. Counsel--Health Professionals, Inc., Fort Lauderdale, FL; *U.S. Public*, pg. 802

Beine, David, Gen. Counsel--Regal Ware, Inc., Kewaskum, WI; *U.S. Private*, pg. 917

Belair, Jacques, V.P.-Legal Affairs--Assurance vie Desjardins-Laurentienne, Levis, Canada; *Int'l*, pg. 396

Beland, Michel, Gen. Counsel & Sec.--Societe Generale de Financement du Quebec, Montreal, Canada; *Int'l*, pg. 1274

Belich, Mel F., Sr. V.P., Gen. Counsel & Sec.--IPL Energy Inc., Calgary, Canada; *Int'l*, pg. 651

Beliveau, Daniele, Gen. Counsel & Sec.--Domco Inc., Farnham, Canada; *Int'l*, pg. 415

Bell, Albert J., Sr. V.P., Gen. Counsel & Sec.--Consolidated Stores Corp., Columbus, OH; *U.S. Public*, pg. 437

Bell, Carmela Leone, V.P., Gen. Counsel & Corp. Sec.--Reliable Stores Inc., Columbia, MD; *U.S. Private*, pg. 920

Bell, Marc N., V.P., Gen. Counsel & Sec.--Brooke Group Ltd., Miami, FL; *U.S. Public*, pg. 259

Bell, Marc N., V.P. & Gen. Counsel--BGLS Inc., Miami, FL; *U.S. Public*, pg. 259

Beller, Gary A., Exec. V.P. & Gen. Counsel--Metropolitan Life Insurance Co., New York, NY; *U.S. Private*, pg. 737

Bellis, F.A., Gen. Counsel--Tech-Tran Corporation, Rancocas, NJ; *U.S. Private*, pg. 560

Belsky, Ira, V.P. & Gen. Counsel--Six Flags Theme Parks Inc., Parsippany, NJ; *U.S. Public*, pg. 1611

Bender, James J., Asst. Gen. Counsel--NRG Energy, Inc., Minneapolis, MN; *U.S. Public*, pg. 1195

Bender, Roberta, Acting Gen. Counsel--MTA Long Island Rail Road, Jamaica, NY; *U.S. Private*, pg. 739

Benik, Tina, V.P., Gen. Counsel & Sec.--A.T. Cross Co., Lincoln, RI; *U.S. Public*, pg. 460

Benjamin, Jeff, V.P.-Legal--Ciba Specialty Chemicals, Tarrytown, NY; *Int'l*, pg. 291

Benjamin, Michael S., Sr. V.P., Gen. Counsel & Sec.--Meditrust Corporation, Needham, MA; *U.S. Public*, pg. 1081

Benjamin, Robert M., Sec. & Gen. Counsel--E.W. Blanch Holdings, Inc., Minneapolis, MN; *U.S. Public*, pg. 236

Benjamin, Scott, Sec. & Mgr.-Legal Opers.--Bumble Bee Seafoods Inc., San Diego, CA; *U.S. Private*, pg. 526

Bennett, George H., Jr., Exec. V.P., Gen. Counsel & Sec.--Cardinal Health Inc., Dublin, OH; *U.S. Public*, pg. 304

Bennett, Kevin D., Sr. Corp. Counsel & Asst. Sec.--Lowe's Companies, Inc., North Wilkesboro, NC; *U.S. Public*, pg. 1015

Bennett, R.E.T., Head-Legal & Compliance--The Hongkong and Shanghai Banking Corporation Limited (HongkongBank), Central, Hong Kong; *Int'l*, pg. 583

Bennett, Scott L., V.P. & Assoc. Gen. Counsel--The McGraw-Hill Companies, New York, NY; *U.S. Public*, pg. 1069

Bennett, Steven A., Gen. Counsel & Sec.--Banc One Corporation, Columbus, OH; *U.S. Public*, pg. 172

Bennett, Terryn, Gen. Counsel--Lazy Days R V Center, Inc., Seffner, FL; *U.S. Private*, pg. 655

Bennett, Thomas F., Legal Counsel--Veda Incorporated, Alexandria, VA; *U.S. Private*, pg. 1136

Benoliel, Joel, Sr. V.P.-Real Estate & Law, Gen. Counsel & Corp. Sec.--Costco Wholesale, Issaquah, WA; *U.S. Public*, pg. 451

Bensignor, Laurence, Gen. Counsel--Rosen Associates Management Corp., Jericho, NY; *U.S. Private*, pg. 945

Benson, Reed L., Gen. Counsel & Corp. Sec.--Data Broadcasting Corporation, Jackson, WY; *U.S. Public*, pg. 484

Bent, B.P., V.P.-Latin America & Legal Admin.--Mead Packaging, Atlanta, GA; *U.S. Public*, pg. 1074

Bentley, Antoinette C., Sr. V.P., Sec. & Assoc. Gen. Counsel--Talegen Corporation, Seattle, WA; *U.S. Public*, pg. 1784

Berg, Egon E., V.P. & Assoc. Gen. Counsel--American Home Products Corporation, Madison, NJ; *U.S. Public*, pg. 79

Berg, Mark S., Sr. V.P. & Gen. Counsel--American General Corporation, Houston, TX; *U.S. Public*, pg. 76

Berg, Thomas C., V.P.-Personnel, Gen. Counsel & Sec.--Amsted Industries Incorporated, Chicago, IL; *U.S. Private*, pg. 68

Bergant, Paul R., Exec. V.P.-Mktg.--J.B. Hunt Transport Services, Inc., Lowell, AR; *U.S. Public*, pg. 849

Bergen, Robert, Gen. Counsel--Metropolitan Transportation Authority, New York, NY; *U.S. Private*, pg. 739

Bergendorf, H.W., Gen. Counsel--UOP, Des Plaines, IL; *U.S. Public*, pg. 52

Berger, Edward S., V.P., Gen. Counsel & Sec.--Information Resources, Inc., Chicago, IL; *U.S. Public*, pg. 875

Berger, Helmuth, Legal Officer--VARTA AG, Hannover, Germany; *Int'l*, pg. 1451

Berger, Nol, Sr. V.P.-Legal Affairs & Corp. Sec.--Koninklijke Ahold NV, Zaandam, Netherlands; *Int'l*, pg. 749

Bergere, Del, V.P., Gen. Counsel & Sec.--Altera Corporation, San Jose, CA; *U.S. Public*, pg. 59

Bergeron, Claude, V.P.-Legal Affairs--Caisse de depot et placement du Quebec, Montreal, Canada; *Int'l*, pg. 249

Bergeron, Maurice A., Gen. Counsel--Perini Corporation, Framingham, MA; *U.S. Public*, pg. 1278

Bergh, Marcus B., Jr., V.P. & Gen. Counsel--American General Life & Accident Insurance Co., Nashville, TN; *U.S. Public*, pg. 76

Bergreen, Bernard, Gen. Counsel--Gilman Paper Co., Saint Marys, GA; *U.S. Private*, pg. 454

Berkelhamer, Les, Gen. Counsel--Koh-I-Noor, Inc., Bloomsbury, NJ; *U.S. Private*, pg. 629

Berman, Ira, V.P., Gen. Counsel & Sec.--Gulfstream Aerospace Corporation, Savannah, GA; *U.S. Private*, pg. 419

Bernadino, Joseph, Sr. Exec. V.P. & Gen. Counsel--Prime Hospitality Corp., Fairfield, NJ; *U.S. Public*, pg. 1326

Berndt, Chris, Gen. Counsel--Great Plains Companies, Inc., Roseville, MN; *U.S. Private*, pg. 475

Berndt, Gary B., Grp. Legal Advisor--Barlow Ltd., Sandton, South Africa; *Int'l*, pg. 167

Bernfeld, Jeffrey A., V.P. & Gen. Counsel--American Science & Engineering, Inc., Billerica, MA; *U.S. Public*, pg. 90

Bernhardson, Ivy S., V.P., Assoc. Gen. Counsel. & Asst. Sec.--General Mills, Inc., Minneapolis, MN; *U.S. Public*, pg. 717

Bernik, Joseph M., Asst. Sec.--Abbott Laboratories, Abbott Park, IL; *U.S. Public*, pg. 12

Bernstein, Harold L., Gen. Counsel & Sec.--Hi-Shear Industries Inc., New Hyde Park, NY; *U.S. Public*, pg. 824

Bernstein, Harvey N., V.P. & Deputy Gen. Counsel--Computer Sciences Corporation, El Segundo, CA; *U.S. Public*, pg. 422

Berritt, Harold E., Gen. Counsel & Sec.--Claire's Stores Inc., Pembroke Pines, FL; *U.S. Public*, pg. 381

Berry, Jim, Sec. & Gen. Counsel--SmithKline Beecham Corporation, Philadelphia, PA; *Int'l*, pg. 1264

Berson, Joel, Sec. & Gen. Counsel--Tork, Inc., Mount Vernon, NY; *U.S. Private*, pg. 1092

Bertelsen, Mark, Sec. & Attorney--Atmel Corporation, San Jose, CA; *U.S. Public*, pg. 145

Bertorp, Michael, Sr. V.P. & Gen. Counsel--Svenska Cellulosa Aktiebolaget (SCA), Stockholm, Sweden; *Int'l*, pg. 1326

Berwart, Pablo, Chief Counsel--El Teniente Division, Rancagua, Chile; *Int'l*, pg. 302

Beshears, Paul R., V.P. & Corp. Counsel--John H. Harland Company, Decatur, GA; *U.S. Public*, pg. 785

Bessozzi, John F., Jr., Gen. Counsel--Summit Corporation of America, Thomaston, CT; *U.S. Private*, pg. 1050

Best, Michael, Gen. Counsel--Spartech Plastics, Portage, WI; *U.S. Public*, pg. 1496

Bethea, Richard W., Jr., V.P., Corp. Counsel & Sec.--Astec Industries, Inc., Chattanooga, TN; *U.S. Public*, pg. 141

Bethel, D. Wyatt, Gen. Counsel--The Van Metres Companies, Burke, VA; *U.S. Private*, pg. 1132

Bethurun, Shirley A., V.P., Treas. & Sec.--Bushwhacker Associates, Inc., Texas City, TX; *U.S. Private*, pg. 141

Beveridge, R.E., Gen. Counsel & Sec.--Marley PLC, Sevenoaks, United Kingdom; *Int'l*, pg. 843

Beverly, Michael D., Assoc. Gen. Counsel--Chesapeake Corporation, Richmond, VA; *U.S. Public*, pg. 346

Bewley, Peter D., Sr. V.P., Gen. Counsel & Sec.--NovaCare Inc., King of Prussia, PA; *U.S. Public*, pg. 1203

Bexhed, Jan-Mikael, Gen. Counsel & Sec.--Skandia Insurance Company Limited, Stockholm, Sweden; *Int'l*, pg. 1256

Beyer, Michael K., Sr. V.P., Gen. Counsel & Sec.--Robert Mondavi Winery, Inc., Oakville, CA; *U.S. Public*, pg. 1393

Bianchi, Richard, Gen. Counsel--Transamerican Natural Gas Corporation, Houston, TX; *U.S. Private*, pg. 1096

Bich-Dufour, Marie-Aimee, Exec. V.P., Gen. Counsel & Sec.--Societe BIC S.A., Clichy, France; *Int'l*, pg. 1272

Bichara Talamas, Patricio, Dir.-Legal--Copamex Industrias S.A. de C.V., Garza Garcia, Mexico; *Int'l*, pg. 330

Bidwell, Michael, V.P. & Gen. Counsel--Arizona Cardinals, Phoenix, AZ; *U.S. Private*, pg. 81

Biegel, Joseph D., V.P. & Deputy Gen. Counsel--Federal National Mortgage Association (Fannie Mae), Washington, DC; *U.S. Public*, pg. 615

Bielsky, Hyman, Sr. V.P. & Gen. Counsel--Safety-Kleen Corp., Elgin, IL; *U.S. Public*, pg. 1425

Biggart, Robert K., V.P. & Intl. Counsel--PepsiCo, Inc., Purchase, NY; *U.S. Public*, pg. 1276

Bilawsky, Mark A., V.P., Gen. Counsel & Sec.--Church & Dwight Co., Inc., Princeton, NJ; *U.S. Public*, pg. 355

Billecard, Georges, Dir.-Pub. Affairs & Legal--3M France, Cergy-Pontoise, France; *U.S. Public*, pg. 1606

Biller, Joel, Sr. V.P. & Gen. Counsel--Manpower Inc., Milwaukee, WI; *U.S. Public*, pg. 1042

Biller, Odd I., Gen. Counsel & Sec.--Norsk Hydro a.s, Oslo, Norway; *Int'l*, pg. 959

Billingslea, William, Jr., Corp. Counsel & Asst. Sec.--Rohr, Inc., Chula Vista, CA; *U.S. Public*, pg. 751

Bilstrom, Jon W., Gen. Counsel & Sec.--Mercantile Bancorporation Inc., Saint Louis, MO; *U.S. Public*, pg. 1087

Bindelglass, Richard, Gen. Counsel--The Genlyte Group Incorporated, Union, NJ; *U.S. Public*, pg. 729

Biolchini, Robert R., Gen. Counsel & Sec.--Lowrance Electronics, Inc., Tulsa, OK; *U.S. Public*, pg. 1015

Bird, Thomas J., Jr., Exec. V.P., Gen. Counsel & Sec.--IMO Industries Inc., Lawrenceville, NJ; *U.S. Public*, pg. 856

Birk, David R., Sr. V.P., Gen. Counsel & Sec.--Avnet, Inc., Great Neck, NY; *U.S. Public*, pg. 155

Birkhahn, Jonathan, Sr. V.P.-Bus. Affairs & Gen. Counsel--King World Productions, Inc., New York, NY; *U.S. Public*, pg. 961

Birmingham, Hobart, V.P. & Gen. Counsel--Borland International, Inc., Scotts Valley, CA; *U.S. Public*, pg. 246

Birn, S.R., Sr. V.P. & Assoc. Gen. Counsel--Auto-Owners Insurance, Lansing, MI; *U.S. Private*, pg. 100

Birndorf, B., Gen. Counsel--Donlen Corp., Northbrook, IL; *U.S. Private*, pg. 340

Bisaro, Paul, Sr. V.P., Gen. Counsel & Sec.--Barr Laboratories Inc., Pomona, NY; *U.S. Public*, pg. 191

Bishop, Daniel S., V.P., Gen. Counsel & Sec.--PAXAR Corporation, White Plains, NY; *U.S. Public*, pg. 1266

Bishop, Daniel S., V.P. & Assoc. Gen. Counsel--Western Atlas Inc., Houston, TX; *U.S. Public*, pg. 1757

Bishop, E. Liston, III, Deputy Gen. Counsel, Dir.-Acquisitions & Asst. Sec.--Coca-Cola Enterprises Inc., Atlanta, GA; *U.S. Public*, pg. 393

Bishop, James C., Jr., Exec. V.P.-Law--Norfolk Southern Corporation, Norfolk, VA; *U.S. Public*, pg. 1190

Bissey, Brian P., Gen. Counsel--Victaulic Company of America, Easton, PA; *U.S. Private*, pg. 1138

Bittenbender, Charles A., V.P., Gen. Counsel & Sec.--NACCO Industries, Inc., Cleveland, OH; *U.S. Public*, pg. 1149

Bitting, Bill, Exec. V.P. & Gen. Counsel--Pabst Brewing Co., San Antonio, TX; *U.S. Private*, pg. 954

Bitting, Bill, Exec. V.P. & Gen. Counsel--Pabst Brewing Co./ Tumwater, Tumwater, WA; *U.S. Private*, pg. 954

Bitting, Cynthia N., Gen. Counsel & Sec.--Allied Industrial Group, Inc., Saint Louis, MO; *U.S. Private*, pg. 39

Bitting, Cynthia N., Gen. Counsel & Sec.--Chemtech Products Inc., Saint Louis, MO; *U.S. Private*, pg. 39

Bitting, William M., Gen. Counsel--General Brewing Company, Vancouver, WA; *U.S. Private*, pg. 954

Black, Barrie H., Gen. Counsel & Sec.--Bruncor, Inc., Saint John, Canada; *Int'l*, pg. 230

Black, David, Exec. V.P., Sec. & Gen. Counsel--Affiliated Computer Services, Inc., Dallas, TX; *U.S. Public*, pg. 27

Black, Jonathan R., V.P. & Gen. Counsel--Clean Harbors, Inc., Braintree, MA; *U.S. Public*, pg. 383

Black, Natalie A., V.P. & Gen. Counsel--Kohler Company, Kohler, WI; *U.S. Private*, pg. 630

Blackburn, Barry J., V.P. & Chief Legal Advisor--Sun Life Assurance Company of Canada (U.K.) Limited, Basingstoke, United Kingdom; *Int'l*, pg. 1319

Blackburn, G. Templeton, II, V.P.-Real Estate, Gen. Counsel & Sec.--Rose's Stores, Inc., Henderson, NC; *U.S. Public*, pg. 1405

Blackstone, Franklin, Jr., Gen. Counsel & Sec.--Bearing Service Company, Pittsburgh, PA; *U.S. Private*, pg. 127

Blackwell, Katrina, V.P. & Gen. Mgr.--Red Ball Forwarders, Inc., Indianapolis, IN; *U.S. Private*, pg. 97

Blackwell, Richard M., Sr. V.P.--Metropolitan Life Insurance Co., New York, NY; *U.S. Private*, pg. 737

Bladel, F. Van, Gen. Counsel--Sidmar N.V., Gent, Belgium; *Int'l*, pg. 79

Blair, James B., Gen. Counsel--Tyson Foods, Inc., Springdale, AR; *U.S. Public*, pg. 1652

Blake, Francis S., V.P.-Bus. Devel. & Gen. Counsel--G.E. Power Systems, Schenectady, NY; *U.S. Public*, pg. 711

Blanchard, Eric A., V.P., Sec. & Gen. Counsel--Dean Foods Company, Franklin Park, IL; *U.S. Public*, pg. 489

Blanchard, Michael D., V.P. & Gen. Counsel--TNP Enterprises, Inc., Fort Worth, TX; *U.S. Public*, pg. 1557

Blanscet, Glen A., V.P., Gen. Counsel & Sec.--Atmos Energy Corporation, Dallas, TX; *U.S. Public*, pg. 145

Blaxter, H. Vaughan, III, V.P. & Gen. Counsel--The Hillman Company, Pittsburgh, PA; *U.S. Private*, pg. 530

Bleier, Michael E., Sr. V.P. & Gen. Counsel--Mellon Bank Corporation, Pittsburgh, PA; *U.S. Public*, pg. 1084

Blettgen, Hans Gerd, Legal--Rhenania Schiffahrts-und Speditions-Gesellschaft mbH, Mannheim, Germany; *Int'l*, pg. 1033

Blixt, Charles A., Exec. V.P., Sec. & Gen. Counsel--R.J. Reynolds Tobacco Company, Winston Salem, NC; *U.S. Public*, pg. 1355

Bloch, Ron, Gen. Counsel--Shurfine International, Inc., Northlake, IL; *U.S. Private*, pg. 997

Block, Arthur R., V.P. & Sr. Deputy Gen. Counsel--Comcast Corporation, Philadelphia, PA; *U.S. Public*, pg. 406

Block, Ira, V.P., Gen. Counsel & Sec.--Wechsler Coffee Corp., Moonachie, NJ; *U.S. Private*, pg. 1158

Block, Richard, Corp. Counsel--Nissin Foods (U.S.A.) Co. Ltd., Gardena, CA; *Int'l*, pg. 949

Block, Stephen A., V.P.-Law & Sec.--International Flavors & Fragrances, Inc., New York, NY; *U.S. Public*, pg. 898

Blodgett, William A., Jr., V.P. & Deputy Gen. Counsel--Brown-Forman Corporation, Louisville, KY; *U.S. Public*, pg. 261

Blohowiak, Bruce, Chief Oper. Officer, Sr. V.P. & Gen. Counsel--Metropolitan Mortgage & Securities Co., Inc., Spokane, WA; *U.S. Private*, pg. 738

Blomme, Erling, Sr. V.P.-Legal Affairs & Gen. Counsel--Telefonaktiebolaget LM Ericsson, Stockholm, Sweden; *Int'l*, pg. 1363

Blomrosen, J.R., Gen. Counsel--Plains Cotton Co-op Association, Lubbock, TX; *U.S. Private*, pg. 868

Bloom, Alan, Sr. V.P., Gen. Counsel & Sec.--Maxicare Health Plans, Inc., Los Angeles, CA; *U.S. Public*, pg. 1061

Bloom, Arnold, V.P., Gen. Counsel & Sec.--Russ Berrie and Company, Inc., Oakland, NJ; *U.S. Public*, pg. 222

Bloomfield, Kevin L., V.P., Gen. Counsel & Sec.--Belden Inc., Saint Louis, MO; *U.S. Public*, pg. 200

Blum, Eva T., Sr. V.P. & Mng. Gen. Counsel--PNC Bank Corp., Pittsburgh, PA; *U.S. Public*, pg. 1242

Blum, Herbert M., Chief Legal Officer--Geraghty & Miller, Inc., Denver, CO; *Int'l*, pg. 607

Blumenthal, Richard A., Sr. V.P., Gen. Counsel & Sec.--Systems & Computer Technology Corporation, Malvern, PA; *U.S. Public*, pg. 1552

Blunk, Richard, Exec. V.P., Gen. Counsel & Sec.--ShowBiz Pizza Time, Inc., Irving, TX; *U.S. Public*, pg. 1468

Bluth, Lawrence N., V.P., Gen. Counsel & Sec.--Penske Corporation, Detroit, MI; *U.S. Private*, pg. 850

Boardman, Harold F., V.P., Gen. Counsel & Sec.--Hoffmann-La Roche Inc., Nutley, NJ; *Int'l*, pg. 1120

Boardman, Robert A., Sr. V.P. & Gen. Counsel--Navistar International Corporation, Chicago, IL; *U.S. Public*, pg. 1167

Bober, Joanne L., Sr. V.P., Gen. Counsel & Sec.--General Signal Corporation, Stamford, CT; *U.S. Public*, pg. 726

Bodager, Brian R., Sr. V.P., Gen. Counsel & Sec.--Associated Banc-Corp, Green Bay, WI; *U.S. Public*, pg. 140

Bodnar, Andrew G., M.D., V.P.-Medical & Legal Affairs--Bristol-Myers Squibb Company, New York, NY; *U.S. Public*, pg. 253

Bogan, Charles E., V.P. & Gen. Counsel--Duckwall-Alco Stores, Inc., Abilene, KS; *U.S. Public*, pg. 533

Bogatz, I. Scott, V.P., Gen. Counsel & Sec.--Rio Hotel & Casino Inc., Las Vegas, NV; *U.S. Public*, pg. 1390

Bogomolny, Robert L., V.P., Gen. Counsel & Sec.--Searle Laboratories, Skokie, IL; *U.S. Public*, pg. 1125

Bokat, Steve, V.P.-Gen. Counsel--Nation's Business, Washington, DC; *U.S. Private*, pg. 788

Bollington, John R., Sr. V.P., Gen. Counsel & Sec.--20th Century Industries, Woodland Hills, CA; *U.S. Public*, pg. 1646

Bonaros, Thomas P., V.P. & Gen. Counsel--Utica Mutual Insurance Company, New Hartford, NY; *U.S. Private*, pg. 1129

Bonavia, Paul, Gen. Counsel--New Century Energies, Inc., Denver, CO; *U.S. Public*, pg. 1170
Bond, Richard, V.P. & Gen. Counsel--Holiday Rambler, Wakarusa, IN; *U.S. Public*, pg. 1123
Bond, Richard E., V.P., Gen. Counsel & Sec.--Monaco Coach Corporation, Coburg, OR; *U.S. Public*, pg. 1123
Bonekamp, A.J., Mgr.-Tech., Registration & Patents--Corporate New Business Development Div., Delft, Netherlands; *Int'l*, pg. 1142
Bonfiglio, Kristi S., Corp. Counsel--Inter-Tel, Incorporated, Phoenix, AZ; *U.S. Public*, pg. 888
Bonnes, Charles A., V.P. & Gen. Counsel--Ohmeda, Inc., Liberty Corner, NJ; *Int'l*, pg. 121
Bonney, Henry, Gen. Counsel--Duncan Equipment Company, Oklahoma City, OK; *U.S. Private*, pg. 346
Bontoux, Bernard, Sr. Exec. V.P.-Legal--Promodes SA, Mondeville, France; *Int'l*, pg. 1071
Bonvino, Frank W., V.P., Gen. Counsel & Sec.--International Multifoods Corporation, Minneapolis, MN; *U.S. Public*, pg. 900
Booker, Lewis, Gen. Counsel--Christian Children's Fund, Inc., Richmond, VA; *U.S. Private*, pg. 238
Boon, Y.M., Gen. Counsel--Phillips Petroleum Chemicals S.A., Overijse, Belgium; *U.S. Public*, pg. 1291
Booth, Richard H., Corp. Counsel & Sec.--Standex International Corporation, Salem, NH; *U.S. Public*, pg. 1505
Boranyak, Mark, V.P.-State Affairs--Anheuser-Busch Companies, Inc., Saint Louis, MO; *U.S. Public*, pg. 113
Borg, John W., V.P. & Asst. Gen. Counsel--Medtronic, Inc., Minneapolis, MN; *U.S. Public*, pg. 1082
Borgerding, Bruce J., Deputy Gen. Counsel & Sec.--Tennant Company, Minneapolis, MN; *U.S. Public*, pg. 1577
Borgeson, Steven E., Sr. V.P., Gen. Counsel, Sec., Treas. & Clerk--ChemDesign Corporation, Fitchburg, MA; *Int'l*, pg. 173
Borgvardt, Jack, Gen. Counsel--Fraser Papers, Inc., Stamford, CT; *Int'l*, pg. 434
Boring, Gary, Gen. Counsel--Countrymark Cooperative, Inc., Indianapolis, IN; *U.S. Private*, pg. 279
Boris, Fran, Exec. V.P., Sr. Corp. Counsel & Sec.--Blimpie International, Inc., Atlanta, GA; *U.S. Public*, pg. 236
Boris, Howard, Gen. Counsel--Lefrak Organization Inc., Rego Park, NY; *U.S. Private*, pg. 658
Borish, Arnold P., V.P., Gen. Counsel & Sec.--Roy F. Weston, Inc., West Chester, PA; *U.S. Public*, pg. 1761
Bormann, Verna Kay, Legal Svcs. Specialist--United HealthCare Corporation, Minnetonka, MN; *U.S. Public*, pg. 1677
Born, Dawn S., V.P. & Gen. Counsel--The GNI Group, Inc., Deer Park, TX; *U.S. Public*, pg. 693
Boschwitz, Kenneth S., V.P.-Bus. Devel. & Gen. Counsel--Faroudja, Inc., Sunnyvale, CA; *U.S. Public*, pg. 613
Bosser, M. Alain, Gen. Counsel & Sec.--SNECMA - Societe Nationale d'Etude et de Construction de Moteurs d'Aviation, Paris, France; *Int'l*, pg. 1165
Boswell, William P., V.P.-Gen. Counsel & Sec.--The Peoples Natural Gas Co., Pittsburgh, PA; *U.S. Public*, pg. 435
Boudreau, Tom, Sr. V.P. & Gen. Counsel--Express Scripts, Inc., Maryland Heights, MO; *U.S. Public*, pg. 600
Bourgeault, Jean-Jacques, Sr. Exec. V.P.-Fin., Gen. Counsel, & Information Tech.--Air Canada, Saint-Laurent, Canada; *Int'l*, pg. 36
Bovaird, Brendan P., V.P. & Gen. Counsel--UGI Corporation, King of Prussia, PA; *U.S. Public*, pg. 1653
Bovaird, Brendan P., V.P. & Gen. Counsel--AmeriGas Partners, L.P., Valley Forge, PA; *U.S. Public*, pg. 1653
Bowe, William J., Exec. V.P., Gen. Counsel & Sec.--Encyclopaedia Britannica, Inc., Chicago, IL; *U.S. Private*, pg. 375
Bowen, Bill, V.P. & Gen. Counsel--Super 8 Motels, Inc., Aberdeen, SD; *U.S. Public*, pg. 322
Bowers, Jotce, Counsel--New Plan Realty Trust, New York, NY; *U.S. Public*, pg. 1172
Bowers, Richard, Sr. Exec. V.P., Gen. Counsel & Sec.--Jan Bell Marketing Inc., Sunrise, FL; *U.S. Public*, pg. 207
Bowers, Roger, Gen. Counsel--Southeastern Pennsylvania Transportation Authority, Philadelphia, PA; *U.S. Private*, pg. 1015
Bowman, David W., Sr. V.P., Gen. Counsel & Sec.--Mapco Inc., Tulsa, OK; *U.S. Public*, pg. 1042
Bowman, Katie-Pat, V.P. & Gen. Counsel--Daniel Industries, Inc., Houston, TX; *U.S. Public*, pg. 482
Boxer, Robert L., V.P., Gen. Counsel & Sec.--Moscom Corporation, Pittsford, NY; *U.S. Public*, pg. 1136
Boyazis, James, V.P. & Sec.--The Goodyear Tire & Rubber Company, Akron, OH; *U.S. Public*, pg. 752
Boyd, Jeffery, Exec. V.P. & Gen. Counsel--Oxford Health Plans Inc., Norwalk, CT; *U.S. Public*, pg. 1238
Boyd, Larry, Gen. Counsel--Dallas Gold & Silver Exchange, Inc., Dallas, TX; *U.S. Public*, pg. 478
Boyd, Michael A., Sr. V.P. & Gen. Counsel--Donaldson, Lufkin, & Jenrette, Inc., New York, NY; *U.S. Public*, pg. 589
Boyd, R.T., Sec. & Corp. Counsel--The Torrington Co., Torrington, CT; *U.S. Public*, pg. 877
Boyd, William F., V.P., Sec. & Corp. Counsel--Coeur D'Alene Mines Corporation, Coeur D'Alene, ID; *U.S. Public*, pg. 394
Boyer, Tamara, Gen. Counsel & Asst. Sec.--Clayton Homes, Inc., Knoxville, TN; *U.S. Public*, pg. 382
Boyle, Matthew A., Sr. V.P.-Corp. Counsel--Dassault Falcon Jet Corp., South Hackensack, NJ; *Int'l*, pg. 383
Boyle, Michael W.P., Gen. Counsel & Asst. Sec.--Trans Mountain Pipeline Company Ltd., Vancouver, Canada; *Int'l*, pg. 114
Bracke, Walter, Gen. Counsel--Union Carbide (Europe) S.A., Meyrin, Switzerland; *U.S. Public*, pg. 1667
Bradford, David, Sr. V.P., Gen. Counsel & Corp. Sec.--Novell, Inc., Orem, UT; *U.S. Public*, pg. 1203
Bradford, Kent, Gen. Counsel--Central Mutual Insurance Co., Van Wert, OH; *U.S. Private*, pg. 223
Bradford, Koger, Legal Officer--Zima Corporation, Spartanburg, SC; *U.S. Private*, pg. 637
Bradley, Andrea, V.P. & Gen. Counsel--CarrAmerica Realty, Washington, DC; *U.S. Public*, pg. 308
Bradley, Donald D., Gen. Counsel & Sec.--Furon Company, Laguna Niguel, CA; *U.S. Public*, pg. 688
Bradley, J.S., Gen. Counsel & Sec.--The RTZ Corporation PLC, London, United Kingdom; *Int'l*, pg. 1118
Brady, Julie C., V.P., Gen. Counsel & Sec.--Apertus Technologies Incorporated, Eden Prairie, MN; *U.S. Public*, pg. 119
Brady, Pat, Gen. Counsel--Wausau Homes, Inc., Rothschild, WI; *U.S. Private*, pg. 1154
Brafman, Howard, Gen. Counsel--J.I. Kislak Inc., Hialeah, FL; *U.S. Private*, pg. 624
Braga, Jose Luiz, Gen. Counsel--Aracruz Celulose S.A., Rio de Janeiro, Brazil; *Int'l*, pg. 78
Brandes, JoAnne, V.P. & Gen. Counsel-SC Johnson Comml. Markets--S.C. Johnson & Son, Inc., Racine, WI; *U.S. Private*, pg. 592
Brandt, Joel, Gen. Counsel--Whitehall-Robins Healthcare, Madison, NJ; *U.S. Public*, pg. 80
Branhaggen, Darrel, Gen. Counsel--ElectroCom Automation L.P., Arlington, TX; *Int'l*, pg. 1244
Brasher, James E., Sec. & Gen. Counsel--Western Atlas International, Inc., Houston, TX; *U.S. Public*, pg. 1757
Braswell, Pam, Gen. Counsel--Starving Students, Inc., Los Angeles, CA; *U.S. Private*, pg. 1035
Braswell, Walter M., V.P., Gen. Counsel & Sec.--E'Town Corporation, Westfield, NJ; *U.S. Public*, pg. 540
Braund, Peter, Gen. Counsel--Yamaha Motor Canada Ltd., North York, Canada; *Int'l*, pg. 1516
Braverman, Alan N., V.P. & Gen. Counsel--ABC, Inc, New York, NY; *U.S. Public*, pg. 511
Braybrooks, Colin S., Sr. V.P., Gen. Counsel & Sec.--United Family Life Insurance Co., Atlanta, GA; *Int'l*, pg. 499
Breaux, Melvin, V.P. & Gen. Counsel--DVI, Inc., Doylestown, PA; *U.S. Public*, pg. 476
Breed, Joseph, V.P. & Gen. Counsel--Simpson Investment Co., Seattle, WA; *U.S. Private*, pg. 1003
Brehm, James G., Mng. Dir.-Corp. Counsel--American Automobile Association, Heathrow, FL; *U.S. Private*, pg. 50
Bremer, John M., Sr. V.P., Gen. Counsel & Sec.--Northwestern Mutual Life Insurance Co., Milwaukee, WI; *U.S. Private*, pg. 807
Bremer, Thomas R., Sr. V.P. & Gen. Counsel--U.S. Surgical Corp., Norwalk, CT; *U.S. Public*, pg. 1687
Brenes, Norbert, Gen. Counsel--S.A. Cimenteries CBR, Brussels, Belgium; *Int'l*, pg. 605
Brennan, Herbert J., V.P.-Legal Affairs--Sandoz Pharmaceuticals Corp., East Hanover, NJ; *Int'l*, pg. 974
Brennan, Richard S., Gen. Counsel & Sec.--Case Corporation, Racine, WI; *U.S. Public*, pg. 311
Brenner, Michael, Gen. Counsel--MasTec, Inc., Miami, FL; *U.S. Public*, pg. 1055
Brenner, Stephen, Chief Oper. Officer, Exec. V.P.-Bus. Affairs. & Gen. Counsel--USA Networks, New York, NY; *U.S. Public*, pg. 1686
Brett, Stephen M., Exec. V.P. & Sec.--TCI Communications, Inc., Englewood, CO; *U.S. Public*, pg. 1554
Brewer, Michael C., Corp. Legal Counsel--National Computer Systems, Eden Prairie, MN; *U.S. Public*, pg. 1155
Brewer, Scott E., V.P., Gen. Counsel & Sec.--International Total Services, Independence, OH; *U.S. Public*, pg. 908
Breyer, Karl J., Sr. V.P.-Corp. Affairs & Gen. Counsel--American Express Financial Advisor, Minneapolis, MN; *U.S. Public*, pg. 73
Brickman, David R., V.P. & Gen. Counsel--Capital Senior Living, Inc., Dallas, TX; *U.S. Public*, pg. 302
Brickner, Lynne, V.P., Gen. Counsel & Sec.--Whittaker Corporation, Simi Valley, CA; *U.S. Public*, pg. 1766
Brickson, Richard A., V.P., Sec. & Gen. Counsel--The May Department Stores Company, Saint Louis, MO; *U.S. Public*, pg. 1063
Bridge, John B., V.P., Gen. Counsel & Sec.--Brougher Agency, Inc., Indianapolis, IN; *Int'l*, pg. 464
Bridgford, R.K., Gen. Counsel--Bridgford Foods Corporation, Anaheim, CA; *U.S. Public*, pg. 252
Brier, Bonnie S., Gen. Counsel--The Children's Hospital of Philadelphia, Philadelphia, PA; *U.S. Private*, pg. 236
Brigham, S.T. Jack, III, Sr. V.P.-Corp. Affairs & Gen. Counsel--Hewlett-Packard Company, Palo Alto, CA; *U.S. Public*, pg. 813
Brill, Robert M., V.P., Gen. Counsel & Sec.--Stokely USA, Inc., Oconomowoc, WI; *U.S. Public*, pg. 1518
Brill, W.A., Asst. Gen. Counsel--Delta Air Lines, Inc., Atlanta, GA; *U.S. Public*, pg. 497
Brinberg, Simeon, Gen. Counsel--Gould Investors, L.P., Great Neck, NY; *U.S. Private*, pg. 466
Bring, Murray H., Exec. V.P.-External Affairs & Gen. Counsel--Philip Morris Companies Inc., New York, NY; *U.S. Public*, pg. 1287
Brinkley, Linster E., Gen. Counsel--Payless Car Rental System, Inc., Saint Petersburg, FL; *U.S. Private*, pg. 844
Brinkman, Dale T., Gen. Counsel--Worthington Industries, Inc., Columbus, OH; *U.S. Public*, pg. 1780
Brisban, G., Gen. Counsel--Onan Corporation, Minneapolis, MN; *U.S. Public*, pg. 468
Briskman, Louis J., Sr. V.P. & Gen. Counsel--CBS Corporation, Pittsburgh, PA; *U.S. Public*, pg. 273
Brissy, Yves, Grp. V.P.-Legal--Rhone-Poulenc S.A., Courbevoie, France; *Int'l*, pg. 1108
Britton, Patricia, Sec. & Gen. Counsel--Porsche Cars North America, Inc., Reno, NV; *Int'l*, pg. 1063
Broderick, Dennis J., Sr. V.P., Gen. Counsel & Sec.--Federated Department Stores, Inc., Cincinnati, OH; *U.S. Public*, pg. 617
Broderick, James, V.P. & Gen. Counsel--RAYOVAC Corporation, Madison, WI; *U.S. Private*, pg. 912
Brodkey, Andrew A., V.P., Gen. Counsel & Sec.--BHP Copper North America, Tucson, AZ; *Int'l*, pg. 224
Bromfield, Wayne A., Gen. Counsel & Sec.--The JPM Company, Lewisburg, PA; *U.S. Public*, pg. 919
Broodryk, D. J., Gen. Counsel--South African Breweries, Ltd., Johannesburg, South Africa; *Int'l*, pg. 1286
Brooks, Gene C., Gen. Counsel--The Dime Savings Bank of New York, New York, NY; *U.S. Public*, pg. 509
Brooks, George S., II, Gen. Counsel & Sec.--KU Energy, Lexington, KY; *U.S. Public*, pg. 940
Brooks, George S., II, Gen. Counsel & Corp. Sec.--KU Capital Corporation, Lexington, KY; *U.S. Public*, pg. 941
Brooks, Randy, Legal Dept. Admin.--Family Inns of America, Inc., Pigeon Forge, TN; *U.S. Private*, pg. 392
Brooks, Ronald J., Gen. Counsel--Blair Television, New York, NY; *U.S. Private*, pg. 148
Brookshire, Alexandra, V.P., Gen. Counsel & Sec.--Wall Data Incorporated, Kirkland, WA; *U.S. Public*, pg. 1734
Brosche, W., Legal Officer--Deminex-Deutsche GmbH, Essen, Germany; *Int'l*, pg. 1460
Brower, Sam R., General Counsel--Owen Industries, Inc., Carter Lake, IA; *U.S. Private*, pg. 824
Brown, Colin, Chief Oper. Officer & Gen. Counsel--JM Family Enterprises Inc., Deerfield Beach, FL; *U.S. Private*, pg. 577
Brown, D.H., V.P. & Gen. Counsel--Rheem Manufacturing Co., New York, NY; *Int'l*, pg. 1022
Brown, David, Esq., Sec.--Kao Corporation of America (DE), Wilmington, DE; *Int'l*, pg. 717
Brown, Eric B., V.P., Gen. Counsel & Sec.--Transocean Offshore, Inc., Houston, TX; *U.S. Public*, pg. 1631
Brown, Frank C., V.P., Gen. Counsel & Corp. Sec.--Rexam Inc., Charlotte, NC; *Int'l*, pg. 1106
Brown, Franklin C., Vice Chm., Exec. V.P. & Gen. Counsel--Rite Aid Corporation, Camp Hill, PA; *U.S. Public*, pg. 1390
Brown, Henry E., V.P. & Gen. Counsel--CNG Transmission Corporation, Clarksburg, WV; *U.S. Public*, pg. 435
Brown, Jeffrey W., Gen. Counsel--TCA Cable TV, Inc., Tyler, TX; *U.S. Public*, pg. 1553
Brown, Jeffrey W., Gen. Counsel--TCA Management Company, Tyler, TX; *U.S. Public*, pg. 1553
Brown, Kenneth J., V.P. & Chief Counsel--Boeing Defense & Space Group, Kent, WA; *U.S. Public*, pg. 240
Brown, Larry G., Sr. V.P., Gen. Counsel & Sec.--AEGON USA, Inc., Baltimore, MD; *Int'l*, pg. 26
Brown, Larry R., V.P. & Gen. Counsel--The Timken Company, Canton, OH; *U.S. Public*, pg. 1617
Brown, Melinda, V.P. & Gen. Counsel--Lotus Development Corporation, Cambridge, MA; *U.S. Public*, pg. 896
Brown, Nancy G., Asst. Gen. Counsel--Borden, Inc., Columbus, OH; *U.S. Private*, pg. 157
Brown, Nancy G., V.P. & Gen. Counsel--Borden Foods Corporation, Columbus, OH; *U.S. Private*, pg. 157
Brown, R. C., Sec. & Gen. Counsel--BTR plc, London, United Kingdom; *Int'l*, pg. 124
Brown, Roger A., Sr. V.P., Sec. & Gen. Counsel--Harleysville Group, Harleysville, PA; *U.S. Public*, pg. 786
Brown, Ronald A., V.P.-Legal & Gen. Counsel--First Pacific Company Limited, Hong Kong, Hong Kong; *Int'l*, pg. 487
Brown, Scott M., Sr. V.P., Gen. Counsel & Sec.--Tenet Healthcare Corporation, Santa Barbara, CA; *U.S. Public*, pg. 1576
Brown, Timothy N., Corp. Counsel & Sec.--J.E. Higgins Lumber Co., Concord, CA; *U.S. Private*, pg. 527
Brown, William R., Gen. Counsel & Sec.--American United Life Insurance Company, Indianapolis, IN; *U.S. Private*, pg. 64
Browne, John, Gen. Counsel--Nikon Inc., Melville, NY; *Int'l*, pg. 931
Browning, David S., Gen. Counsel & Sec.--Schlumberger Limited, New York, NY; *U.S. Public*, pg. 1439
Browning, Walter G., V.P. & Gen. Counsel--Rust International Inc., Birmingham, AL; *U.S. Public*, pg. 1366
Brownley, William L. Prieur, V.P., Gen. Counsel & Sec.--Telos Corporation, Ashburn, VA; *U.S. Public*, pg. 1573
Brozyna, Jeffry H., V.P. & Gen. Counsel--Lehigh Portland Cement Company, Allentown, PA; *Int'l*, pg. 605
Bruening, R.P., Sr. V.P. & Gen. Counsel--The Kansas City Southern Railway Co., Kansas City, MO; *U.S. Public*, pg. 944
Bruening, Richard P., V.P. & Gen. Counsel--Kansas City Southern Industries, Inc., Kansas City, MO; *U.S. Public*, pg. 943
Brumm, James E., Exec. V.P., Sec. & Gen. Counsel--Mitsubishi International Corporation, New York, NY; *Int'l*, pg. 871
Bruning, Rolf, Dr., V.P.-Patents--The Braas Group, Oberursell, Germany; *Int'l*, pg. 1091
Bruno, Robert A., V.P., Gen. Counsel & Sec.--First Medical Group Inc., Stamford, CT; *U.S. Public*, pg. 636
Brunt, George, V.P., Gen. Counsel & Sec.--DSC Communications Corporation, Plano, TX; *U.S. Public*, pg. 475
Bruntrager, Edward C., V.P. & Gen. Counsel--General Dynamics Corporation, Falls Church, VA; *U.S. Public*, pg. 708
Bruton, Beth, Gen. Counsel--H.G. Fenton Material Company, San Diego, CA; *U.S. Private*, pg. 400
Bryan, Kerry R., Gen. Counsel--IGT-(Australia), Pty. Limited, Rosebery, Australia; *U.S. Public*, pg. 900
Bryan, Michelle V., V.P. & Dep. Gen Counsel & Sec.--US Airways, Inc., Arlington, VA; *U.S. Public*, pg. 1680
Bryant, Randolph W., Sr. V.P., Gen. Counsel & Sec.--Group Maintenance America Corp., Houston, TX; *U.S. Public*, pg. 766
Buchanan, John D., Sr. V.P.-Legal--SouthTrust Corporation, Birmingham, AL; *U.S. Public*, pg. 1491
Buckey, Alan, Chief Fin. Officer, Treas. & Legal Officer--Pease Industries, Inc., Fairfield, OH; *U.S. Private*, pg. 845
Buckingham, E.J., V.P.-Legal Services--Solvay America Inc., Houston, TX; *Int'l*, pg. 1278
Buckingham, N.J., Legal--Acco-Rexel Group Services PLC, West Drayton, United Kingdom; *U.S. Public*, pg. 674
Buckley, Dennis, Gen. Counsel--Vulcan International Corporation, Wilmington, DE; *U.S. Public*, pg. 1725

Buckly, Ronald W., Gen. Counsel & Sec.--Tekelec, Calabasas, CA; *U.S. Public*, pg. 1566

Buckman Davis, Katherine, Esq., Gen. Counsel--Buckman Laboratories Inc., Memphis, TN; *U.S. Private*, pg. 180

Buckman, James E., Sr. Exec. V.P., Gen. Counsel & Asst. Sec.--HFS, Incorporated, Parsippany, NJ; *U.S. Public*, pg. 321

Bucknum, Thomas J., Chief Corp. Counsel & Assoc. Gen. Counsel--Biogen, Inc., Cambridge, MA; *U.S. Public*, pg. 230

Buda, T.J., Sr. V.P., Sec. & Gen. Counsel--Auto-Owners Insurance, Lansing, MI; *U.S. Private*, pg. 100

Buecken, Lutz, Dr., Gen Counsel--Heidelberger Druckmaschinen A.G., Heidelberg, Germany; *Int'l*, pg. 604

Buekman, Duncan, Mgr.-Gen. Counsel--Wholesale Electronic Supply, Dallas, TX; *U.S. Private*, pg. 1174

Buettner, Bob, Sr. V.P. & Corp. Counsel--Alabama Power Co., Birmingham, AL; *U.S. Public*, pg. 1489

Buffum, Paul, V.P., Gen. Counsel & Sec.--Nashua Corporation, Nashua, NH; *U.S. Public*, pg. 1152

Bugge, Robert G., Gen. Counsel & Dir.-Contracts--RJO Enterprises, Inc., Lanham, MD; *U.S. Private*, pg. 904

Buker, Robert H., Jr., Sr. V.P.-Corp. Affairs--United States Sugar Corporation, Clewiston, FL; *U.S. Private*, pg. 1126

Bukowski, Gerry, V.P. & Gen. Counsel--Burns & McDonnell Engineers-Architects-Consultants, Kansas City, MO; *U.S. Private*, pg. 187

Bullard, Patrick, V.P. & Gen. Counsel--Southdown, Inc., Houston, TX; *U.S. Public*, pg. 1488

Bulliner, P. Alan, V.P., Gen. Counsel & Sec.--Bell Atlantic Corporation, New York, NY; *U.S. Public*, pg. 201

Bullwinkel, George, Gen. Counsel--World's Finest Chocolate, Inc., Chicago, IL; *U.S. Private*, pg. 1191

Bump, Mark, Corp. Attorney--The Timken Company, Canton, OH; *U.S. Public*, pg. 1617

Bumstead, R. Glenn, Sr. V.P. & Gen. Counsel--The Toronto Dominion Bank, Toronto, Canada; *Int'l*, pg. 1401

Burak Melchione, Janet, Sr. V.P., Gen. Counsel & Sec.--Everest Reinsurance Holdings, Liberty Corner, NJ; *U.S. Public*, pg. 597

Burak Melchione, Janet, Sr. V.P. & Gen. Counsel--Everest Reinsurance Co., Liberty Corner, NJ; *U.S. Public*, pg. 597

Burgess, Lynne, V.P. & Gen. Counsel--Entex Information Services, Rye Brook, NY; *U.S. Private*, pg. 378

Burgon, Barre G., V.P., Corp. Counsel & Sec.--Flying J. Inc., Brigham City, UT; *U.S. Private*, pg. 415

Burish, Mark D., Gen. Counsel--Badger Paper Mills, Inc., Peshtigo, WI; *U.S. Public*, pg. 165

Burke, Edward O., Gen. Counsel--Double AA Builders, Ltd., Scottsdale, AZ; *U.S. Private*, pg. 341

Burke, F.A., V.P.-Law & Gen. Counsel--Brown & Williamson Tobacco Corp., Louisville, KY; *Int'l*, pg. 111

Burke, J. Terence, Gen. Counsel & Sec.--Realty One, Cleveland, OH; *U.S. Private*, pg. 914

Burke, Linda B., Tax Counsel--Aluminum Company of America, Pittsburgh, PA; *U.S. Public*, pg. 60

Burkett, Lawrence V., Exec. V.P. & Gen. Counsel--Massachusetts Mutual Life Insurance Co., Springfield, MA; *U.S. Private*, pg. 712

Burkey, J. Brent, Sr. V.P., Gen. Counsel & Sec.--Matria Healthcare, Inc., Marietta, GA; *U.S. Public*, pg. 1057

Burks, Ashby Q., V.P., Gen. Counsel & Corp. Sec.--Quorum Health Group, Inc., Brentwood, TN; *U.S. Public*, pg. 1353

Burns, Arthur L., Gen. Counsel & Sec.--Interpool, Inc., Princeton, NJ; *U.S. Public*, pg. 908

Burns, B. Bernard, Jr., Sr. V.P., Gen. Counsel & Sec.--United Dominion Industries, Ltd., Charlotte, NC; *U.S. Public*, pg. 1675

Burns, Bob, V.P.-Gen. Counsel--Eby Corporation, Wichita, KS; *U.S. Private*, pg. 359

Burns, Daniel T., Sr. V.P. & Gen. Counsel--TruServ Corporation, Chicago, IL; *U.S. Private*, pg. 1108

Burns, Gerald, V.P.-Gen. Counsel--North American Van Lines, Inc., Fort Wayne, IN; *U.S. Public*, pg. 1191

Burns, Patrick, Sr. Exec. V.P. & Gen. Counsel--Mutual of America Life Insurance Company, New York, NY; *U.S. Private*, pg. 769

Burns, Patrick, Sr. Exec. V.P. & Gen. Counsel--American Life Insurance Company of New York, New York, NY; *U.S. Private*, pg. 769

Burns, Stephen F., Chm. Bd. & Chief Exec. Officer--Wheaton Van Lines, Inc., Indianapolis, IN; *U.S. Private*, pg. 1171

Bursley, Kathleen A., V.P. & Deputy Chief Council--Harcourt Brace & Company - Elementary Div., Orlando, FL; *U.S. Public*, pg. 783

Burt, Richard, V.P., Gen. Counsel & Sec.--ABB Inc., Norwalk, CT; *Int'l*, pg. 3

Burton, Amanda J., Grp. Sec. & Legal Advisor--Meyer International PLC, London, United Kingdom; *Int'l*, pg. 864

Burton, Steven, Gen. Counsel & Sec.--Sithe Energies, Inc., New York, NY; *U.S. Private*, pg. 1004

Busby, D.J., Sec. & Legal--Tioxide Group Limited, London, United Kingdom; *Int'l*, pg. 663

Busch, Richard, Asst. V.P.-Legal--Amwest Insurance Group, Inc., Calabasas, CA; *U.S. Public*, pg. 106

Busch, Richard, V.P. & Corp. Counsel--Amwest Surety Insurance Company, Calabasas, CA; *U.S. Public*, pg. 106

Busch, William R., Jr., Sec. & Gen. Counsel--Cowles Media Company, Minneapolis, MN; *U.S. Private*, pg. 280

Buschmann, Raymond P., V.P.-Legal Affairs & Gen. Counsel--Morton International Inc., Chicago, IL; *U.S. Public*, pg. 1134

Bush, Donald, Sr. V.P. & Gen. Labor Counsel--Quebecor Printing (USA) Corp., Boston, MA; *Int'l*, pg. 1076

Bush, Edwin F., Sec. & Gen. Counsel--Appleton Papers Inc., Appleton, WI; *Int'l*, pg. 567

Bush, John A.H., V.P., Gen. Counsel & Sec.--Rio Algom Limited, Toronto, Canada; *Int'l*, pg. 1118

Butenas, John P., Asst. Gen. Counsel & Asst. Sec.--Manor Care, Inc., Gaithersburg, MD; *U.S. Public*, pg. 1041

Butler, Bill, Gen. Counsel--Van Waters & Rogers, Kirkland, WA; *Int'l*, pg. 1147

Butt, P. Lawrence, V.P., Gen. Counsel & Sec.--Marsh Supermarkets, Inc., Indianapolis, IN; *U.S. Public*, pg. 1049

Butterfield, Benjamin P., Sec. & Gen. Counsel--Hughes Supply, Inc., Orlando, FL; *U.S. Public*, pg. 846

Butts, Edward A., V.P.-Gen. Counsel & Sec.--Ameritech, Chicago, IL; *U.S. Public*, pg. 97

Cabello, David, Sr. V.P., Gen. Counsel & Sec.--COMPAQ Computer Corporation, Houston, TX; *U.S. Public*, pg. 417

Caflisch, Christian, Corp. Counsel--Hilti AG, Schaan, Liechtenstein; *Int'l*, pg. 619

Cagampang-De Castro, Soledad M., V.P.-Legal & Audit & Sec.--Benguet Corporation, Manila, Philippines; *Int'l*, pg. 186

Cahill, Richard M., V.P. & Gen. Counsel--GTE North Incorporated, Irving, TX; *U.S. Public*, pg. 696

Cahill, Richard M., V.P. & Gen. Counsel--GTE South Incorporated, Irving, TX; *U.S. Public*, pg. 697

Cain, David P., Sr. V.P., Gen. Counsel & Sec.--International Comfort Products, Franklin, TN; *U.S. Public*, pg. 898

Cairns, Ivan R., Sr. V.P. & Gen. Counsel--Laidlaw Inc., Burlington, Canada; *Int'l*, pg. 259

Calfas, William, Exec. V.P., Gen. Counsel & Sec.--Courtaulds Aerospace, Glendale, CA; *Int'l*, pg. 339

Calhoun, John H., V.P.-Intl. Law & Assoc. Gen. Corp. Counsel--The Quaker Oats Company, Chicago, IL; *U.S. Public*, pg. 1347

Calianese, Elizabeth J., Deputy Gen. Counsel--Emerson Radio Corp., Parsippany, NJ; *U.S. Public*, pg. 578

Caliendo, G.D., Sr. V.P., Gen. Counsel & Sec.--Orange and Rockland Utilities, Inc., Pearl River, NY; *U.S. Public*, pg. 1229

Calise, William J., Jr., Sr. V.P., Gen. Counsel & Sec.--Rockwell International Corporation, Costa Mesa, CA; *U.S. Public*, pg. 1397

Call, Kevin, Assoc. Gen. Counsel--The West Company, Incorporated, Lionville, PA; *U.S. Public*, pg. 1755

Calvocoressi, Thomas J., Gen. Counsel--Aetna Inc., Hartford, CT; *U.S. Public*, pg. 26

Camargo Chalita, Luis Rosendo, Gen. Counsel--Grupo Comercial Chedraui S.A. de C.V., Veracruz, Mexico; *Int'l*, pg. 573

Camargo Chalita, Luis Rosendo, Gen. Counsel--Tiendas Chedraui S.A. de C.V., Veracruz, Mexico; *Int'l*, pg. 573

Camera, Nicholas J., V.P., Gen. Counsel & Sec.--The Interpublic Group of Companies, Inc., New York, NY; *U.S. Public*, pg. 908

Cammaker, Sheldon I., Exec. V.P. & Gen. Counsel--EMCOR Group, Inc., Norwalk, CT; *U.S. Public*, pg. 571

Camp, Tom, V.P., Treas., Gen. Counsel & Sec.--The Apogee Companies, Inc., Lake Oswego, OR; *U.S. Private*, pg. 77

Campbell, Allan R., Sr. V.P. & Gen. Counsel--Unitrode Corporation, Merrimack, NH; *U.S. Public*, pg. 1694

Campbell, G. Anthony, Gen. Counsel & Sec.--Flowers Industries, Inc., Thomasville, GA; *U.S. Public*, pg. 656

Campbell, Michael, V.P. & Gen. Counsel--McCain Foods Limited, Florenceville, Canada; *Int'l*, pg. 850

Campbell, Robin A., Sr. V.P. & Gen. Counsel--TrizecHahn Corporation, Toronto, Canada; *Int'l*, pg. 1424

Cannady, Cynthia, V.P.-Law, Devel. & Mfg.--Apple Computer, Inc., Cupertino, CA; *U.S. Public*, pg. 121

Canning, John B., Corp. Sec. & Assoc. Gen. Counsel--Rayonier Inc., Stamford, CT; *U.S. Public*, pg. 1363

Cannon, W. Stephen, Sr. V.P. & Gen. Counsel--Circuit City Stores, Inc., Richmond, VA; *U.S. Public*, pg. 374

Caparros, Ann M., V.P., Gen. Counsel & Sec.--Horace Mann Educators Corporation, Springfield, IL; *U.S. Public*, pg. 835

Capps, Rae A., V.P., Gen. Counsel & Sec.--Hawaiian Airlines, Inc., Honolulu, HI; *U.S. Public*, pg. 799

Caputo, Lawrence, Corp. Counsel--Duty Free International, Inc., Ridgefield, CT; *Int'l*, pg. 103

Carabillo, Joseph, Chief Legal Officer & V.P.--ULLICO Inc., Washington, DC; *U.S. Private*, pg. 1115

Carbonell, Joaquin R., V.P. & Gen. Counsel-Mobile Systems--BellSouth Enterprises, Inc., Atlanta, GA; *U.S. Public*, pg. 208

Cardman, Philip N., V.P., Gen. Counsel & Sec.--Objective Systems Integrators, Inc., Folsom, CA; *U.S. Public*, pg. 1209

Cardman, Phillip N., V.P., Gen. Counsel & Sec.--Convex Technology Center - Hewlett-Packard, Richardson, TX; *U.S. Public*, pg. 815

Carles, Robert S., Sec.--Lance, Inc., Charlotte, NC; *U.S. Public*, pg. 977

Carlsen, David R., Chm. Bd., Sec. & Legal Counsel--Upper Midwest Industries, Incorporated, Minneapolis, MN; *U.S. Private*, pg. 1129

Carlson, Jennie P., Sr. V.P., Deputy Gen. Counsel & Asst. Sec.--Starbanc Corporation, Cincinnati, OH; *U.S. Public*, pg. 1510

Carlson, Stanley A., Sr. V.P., Gen. Counsel & Corp. Sec.--Seafirst Corporation, Seattle, WA; *U.S. Public*, pg. 181

Carlson, Tim, Gen. Counsel--In Focus Systems, Inc., Wilsonville, OR; *U.S. Public*, pg. 873

Carmichael, David R., Sr. V.P. & Gen. Counsel--Pacific Life Insurance Company, Newport Beach, CA; *U.S. Private*, pg. 831

Carneal, Drew St. J., Sr. V.P., Corp. Counsel & Sec.--Owens & Minor Inc., Glen Allen, VA; *U.S. Public*, pg. 1236

Carney, Thomas D., V.P. & Gen. Counsel--Borders Group, Inc., Ann Arbor, MI; *U.S. Public*, pg. 245

Carney, Valerie, Sr. V.P. & Gen. Counsel--Sarkes Tarzian, Bloomington, IN; *U.S. Private*, pg. 966

Carpenter, Bob R., Chief Admin. Officer, V.P. & Gen. Counsel--Dollar General Corporation, Nashville, TN; *U.S. Public*, pg. 515

Carpenter, Ernest A., V.P.-Admin. & Gen. Counsel--Tippins Incorporated, Pittsburgh, PA; *U.S. Private*, pg. 1088

Carpenter, James W., V.P. & Sr. Counsel--The Western and Southern Life Insurance Company, Cincinnati, OH; *U.S. Private*, pg. 1164

Carpenter, W. Geoffrey, Asst. Sec. & Assoc. Gen. Counsel--McCormick & Company, Incorporated, Sparks, MD; *U.S. Public*, pg. 1066

Carr, C., Gen. Mgr. & Grp. Legal Adviser--HSBC Holdings plc, London, United Kingdom; *Int'l*, pg. 579

Carr, Stephen R., Exec. Dir.-Legal Svcs.--Growmark, Inc., Bloomington, IL; *U.S. Private*, pg. 484

Carrara, John J., Asst. Gen. Counsel & Asst. Sec.--Westvaco Corporation, New York, NY; *U.S. Public*, pg. 1762

Carrell, Nancy J., V.P., Gen. Counsel & Sec.--Celanese Canada, Inc., Montreal, Canada; *Int'l*, pg. 625

Carretta, Thomas, Gen. Counsel--Control Systems Inc., Saint Paul, MN; *U.S. Private*, pg. 271

Carriere, Jean-Philippe, V.P.-Legal--SEITA, Societe Nationale D'Exploitation Industrielle des Tabacs et des Allumettes, Paris, France; *Int'l*, pg. 1219

Carroll, David, Gen. Counsel--American Express Credit Corporation, Wilmington, DE; *U.S. Public*, pg. 74

Carroll, Kathleen M., V.P., Gen. Counsel & Sec.--Chartwell Re Corporation, Stamford, CT; *U.S. Public*, pg. 336

Carroll, Kenneth P., Sr. V.P. & Gen. Counsel--United Retail Group, Inc., Rochelle Park, NJ; *U.S. Public*, pg. 1679

Carson, Daniel M., V.P., Gen. Counsel & Sec.--Sweetheart Cup Company Inc., Owings Mills, MD; *U.S. Private*, pg. 1058

Carson, Steve, Gen. Counsel--Wallace Computer Services, Inc., Lisle, IL; *U.S. Public*, pg. 1735

Carter, C. Michael, Exec. V.P., Gen. Counsel & Sec.--Pinkerton's Inc., Encino, CA; *U.S. Public*, pg. 1296

Carton, Sydney, V.P. & Gen. Counsel--CD Products, Inc., New Providence, NJ; *U.S. Public*, pg. 276

Caruso, John A., V.P.-Legal Affairs & Sec.--Enzon, Inc., Piscataway, NJ; *U.S. Public*, pg. 587

Casal, Eileen, V.P. & Gen. Counsel--Stratus Computer, Inc., Marlborough, MA; *U.S. Public*, pg. 1524

Casciano, Frank, Exec. V.P. & Gen. Counsel--MBL Life Assurance Corporation, Newark, NJ; *U.S. Private*, pg. 685

Case, C. Wayne, V.P., Corp. Counsel & Sec.--Gundle/SLT Environmental, Inc., Houston, TX; *U.S. Public*, pg. 769

Case, Robert O., Gen. Counsel & Sec.--Hach Company, Loveland, CO; *U.S. Public*, pg. 773

Casey, Gerard W., V.P. & Assoc. Gen. Counsel--PepsiCo, Inc., Purchase, NY; *U.S. Public*, pg. 1276

Casey, John J., Gen. Counsel--TSC Shannock Corporation, Burnaby, Canada; *Int'l*, pg. 1343

Casmere, Vicki L., V.P., Gen. Counsel & Sec.--Varlen Corporation, Naperville, IL; *U.S. Public*, pg. 1710

Cason, Marilynn, V.P., Gen. Counsel & Sec.--DeVry Institutes, Oak Brook Terrace, IL; *U.S. Public*, pg. 503

Cassetty, Fred, Chm. Bd., Pres. & Chief Exec. Officer--Alley-Cassetty Coal Co., Nashville, TN; *U.S. Private*, pg. 37

Cassey, Woodrow, Chief Counsel--Fedco, Inc., Santa Fe Springs, CA; *U.S. Private*, pg. 398

Cassibba, Vincenzo, Dir.-Legal Service--Olivetti SpA, Turin, Italy; *Int'l*, pg. 1002

Castens, Christopher C., Sec.--International Thoroughbred Breeders, Inc., Cherry Hill, NJ; *U.S. Public*, pg. 908

Castres Saint-Martin, Pascal, V.P.-Admin. & Fin.--L'Oreal S.A., Clichy, France; *Int'l*, pg. 818

Castro, Jose Antonio Alfaro, Dr., Legal Counsel--Mineral San Sebastian S.A., San Salvador, El Salvador; *U.S. Public*, pg. 410

Catano, Hector Zires, Dir.-Legal Affairs--Grupo Synkro, S.A. de C.V., Mexico, Mexico; *Int'l*, pg. 576

Catron, William G., Chief Admin. Officer, Exec. V.P. & Gen. Counsel--Galoob Toys, Inc., South San Francisco, CA; *U.S. Public*, pg. 698

Cattani, Maryellen, Exec. V.P., Gen. Counsel & Sec.--APL Limited, Oakland, CA; *Int'l*, pg. 912

Caudill, Douglas, V.P. & Gen. Counsel--Nobel Insurance Limited, Hamilton, Bermuda; *Int'l*, pg. 951

Causey, J.P., Jr., Sr. V.P., Gen. Counsel & Sec.--Chesapeake Corporation, Richmond, VA; *U.S. Public*, pg. 346

Cave, Bryan, Gen. Counsel--Essex County Gas Company, Amesbury, MA; *U.S. Public*, pg. 593

Cave, Bryan, Gen. Counsel--Tenera, Inc., San Francisco, CA; *U.S. Public*, pg. 1576

Cawen, Klaus, Sr. V.P.-Acquisions & Gen. Counsel--Kone Corporation, Helsinki, Finland; *Int'l*, pg. 746

Cella, Christopher L., V.P., Gen. Counsel & Sec.--Holly Corporation, Dallas, TX; *U.S. Public*, pg. 830

Cerutti, P.B., Gen. Counsel--URM Stores, Inc., Spokane, WA; *U.S. Private*, pg. 1114

Chabora, Robert, V.P.-& Gen. Counsel--Schering Berlin Inc., Cedar Knolls, NJ; *Int'l*, pg. 1204

Chaffart, Ferdinand, Chm.-Exec. Committee & Mng. Dir.--Generale de Banque S.A., Brussels, Belgium; *Int'l*, pg. 546

Chaifetz, David H., V.P., Gen. Counsel & Sec.--Praxair Inc., Danbury, CT; *U.S. Public*, pg. 1319

Chalifoux, Charles, V.P.-Mfg.--Bradley Printing Company, Des Plaines, IL; *U.S. Public*, pg. 1778

Challis, Georgina, Sr. V.P.-Corp. Communications & Legal Counsel--BPI Communications Inc., New York, NY; *Int'l*, pg. 1446

Chance, Steven K., V.P., Gen. Counsel & Sec.--Teleflex Incorporated, Plymouth Meeting, PA; *U.S. Public*, pg. 1569

Chandley, Cynthia M., Gen. Counsel & Mgr.-Land & Water Resources--Phelps Dodge Corporation, Phoenix, AZ; *U.S. Public*, pg. 1286

Chant, M.E.A., Gen. Counsel--Redland PLC, Reigate, United Kingdom; *Int'l*, pg. 1090

Chapline, Edward S., III, Gen. Counsel & Sec.--TIC United Corporation, Dallas, TX; *U.S. Private*, pg. 1063

Chapman, Kathryn A., V.P.-Legal--Comdisco, Inc., Rosemont, IL; *U.S. Public*, pg. 407

Chapple, Thomas L., Sr. V.P., Gen. Counsel & Sec.--Gannett Company, Inc., Arlington, VA; *U.S. Public*, pg. 698
Chasey, Jackie, Gen. Counsel--Bertelsmann Inc., New York, NY; *Int'l*, pg. 191
Chateauneuf, Pierre-Marie, V.P.-Admin. & Legal Affairs--Groupe Pernod Ricard, Paris, France; *Int'l*, pg. 566
Chatfield, David Blake, Gen. Counsel--Pac Rim Holding Corporation, Woodland Hills, CA; *U.S. Public*, pg. 1246
Chatfield, David Blake, Gen. Counsel--The Pacific Rim Assurance Company, Woodland Hills, CA; *U.S. Public*, pg. 1246
Chatroo, Art, Gen. Counsel--Mycogen Corporation, San Diego, CA; *U.S. Public*, pg. 1142
Chattin, Phillip K., Gen. Counsel & Sec.--American Ecology Corporation, Boise, ID; *U.S. Public*, pg. 71
Chaykin, Arthur A., V.P.-Law, Gen. Bus. & Intellectual Property--Sprint Corporation, Westwood, KS; *U.S. Public*, *pg. 1500*
Chell, Beverly C., Vice Chm., Gen. Counsel & Sec.--Primedia Inc., New York, NY; *U.S. Public*, pg. 1327
Chenard, Pierre D., V.P.-Corp. Devel. & Gen. Counsel--Cambior Inc., Montreal, Canada; *Int'l*, pg. 253
Cheney, Jeff, Sr. V.P., & Gen. Counsel--Atari Games Corporation, Milpitas, CA; *U.S. Public*, pg. 1727
Chenoweth, Nick, V.P. & Gen. Counsel--Empire Airlines, Coeur D'Alene, ID; *U.S. Private*, pg. 374
Chero, Thomas H., Sr. V.P.-Legal & Sec.--Avemco Corporation, Frederick, MD; *U.S. Public*, pg. 151
Cherry, J.R., V.P. & Deputy Gen. Counsel--Lorillard Tobacco Company, Greensboro, NC; *U.S. Public*, pg. 1011
Chester, Lawrence, V.P.-Sec. & Gen. Counsel--Northern Telecom Inc., Rochester, NY; *Int'l*, pg. 970
Chibesakunda, G., Gen. Counsel--National Bank of Malawi, Blantyre, Malawi; *Int'l*, pg. 1296
Chilibeck, Peter, Sr. V.P.-Legal Affairs--Imax Corporation, Mississauga, Canada; *Int'l*, pg. 661
Chilibeck, Peter J., Asst. Gen. Counsel & Sec.--Northern Telecom Limited, Brampton, Canada; *Int'l*, pg. 968
Chilton, Charles, Gen. Counsel--Colorado Boxed Beef Co., Auburndale, FL; *U.S. Private*, pg. 254
Chipperfield, Lynn, V.P., Gen. Counsel & Sec.--Furniture Brands International Inc., Saint Louis, MO; *U.S. Public*, pg. 688
Choate, A.G., V.P.-Law, Gen. Counsel & Sec.--American Trading and Production Corporation, Baltimore, MD; *U.S. Private*, pg. 63
Choate, Chris A., Sr. V.P., Gen. Counsel & Sec.--AmeriCredit Corp., Fort Worth, TX; *U.S. Public*, pg. 96
Chod, Edward, Gen. Counsel--Jones Medical Industries Inc., Saint Louis, MO; *U.S. Public*, pg. 933
Chozen, Richard, Gen. Counsel--Pumpelly Oil, Inc., Westlake, LA; *U.S. Private*, pg. 895
Christenbury, Edward S., Sr. V.P. & Gen. Counsel--Tennessee Valley Authority, Knoxville, TN; *U.S. Public*, pg. 1580
Christensen, Edward, V.P., Gen. Counsel & Sec.--Culligan International Company, Northbrook, IL; *U.S. Public*, pg. 467
Christenson, James E., V.P. & Gen. Counsel & Sec.--Herman Miller, Inc., Zeeland, MI; *U.S. Public*, pg. 1111
Christian, Betty S., Chm. Bd., Pres. & Chief Exec. Officer--Central Coca-Cola Bottling Company, Inc., Richmond, VA; *U.S. Private*, pg. 222
Christian, Ronald E., Gen. Counsel & Sec.--Indiana Energy, Inc., Indianapolis, IN; *U.S. Public*, pg. 874
Christian, Ronald E., Gen. Counsel & Sec.--Indiana Gas Company, Inc., Indianapolis, IN; *U.S. Public*, pg. 875
Christie, E.H., Sec. & Legal Counsel--Cyanamid Canada Inc., Markham, Canada; *U.S. Public*, pg. 80
Chubb, Thomas C., Assoc. Gen. Counsel & Asst. Sec.--Oxford Industries, Inc., Atlanta, GA; *U.S. Public*, pg. 1239
Chun, Thomas Lyman, V.P. & Gen. Counsel--SyQuest Technology, Inc., Fremont, CA; *U.S. Public*, pg. 1550
Church, Marla, Corp. Counsel-Patents & Intellectual Property--Elan Corporation Plc, Dublin, Ireland; *Int'l*, pg. 435
Church, R. Dean, V.P.-Contracts & Legal--Avondale Industries, Inc., Avondale, LA; *U.S. Public*, pg. 156
Church, Richard O., Gen. Counsel--DSM Engineering Plastic Products, Reading, PA; *Int'l*, pg. 354
Churchill, Jim, Gen. Council--Ventura Foods LLC, City of Industry, CA; *Int'l*, pg. 879
Churma, Vic, Gen. Counsel--Dombrowski & Holmes, Inc., Hammond, IN; *U.S. Private*, pg. 338
Chustz, J. Steve, Gen. Counsel--ChemFirst Inc., Jackson, MS; *U.S. Public*, pg. 344
Cianciusi, Diana, Gen. Counsel & Sec.--Gandalf Technologies Inc., Nepean, Canada; *Int'l*, pg. 540
Cibsner, Joel, Esq., Gen. Counsel--The Solender Group, Inc., Los Angeles, CA; *U.S. Private*, pg. 1012
Ciccotelli, Teresa T., Esq., V.P., Legal Counsel & Sec.--AmeriSource Health Corp., Malvern, PA; *U.S. Public*, pg. 96
Ciocca, Henry G., Gen. Counsel--Thomson U.S. Inc., Stamford, CT; *U.S. Public*, pg. 1601
Cioffi, Michael L., V.P. & Asst. Gen Counsel--American Financial Group, Cincinnati, OH; *U.S. Public*, pg. 75
Ciotti, Martin, Gen. Counsel--Speedy Muffler King, Inc., Toronto, Canada; *U.S. Public*, pg. 1578
Ciotti, Martin J., V.P. & Legal Counsel--Speedy Car-X, Inc., Chicago, IL; *U.S. Public*, pg. 1578
Ciprich, Paula M., Gen. Counsel & Asst. Sec.--National Fuel Gas Distribution Corp., Buffalo, NY; *U.S. Public*, pg. 1156
Claiborne, Herbert, III, Legal Counsel & Sec.--Carpenter Co., Richmond, VA; *U.S. Private*, pg. 214
Clark, B. Keith, V.P. & Gen. Counsel--Pizza Inn, Inc., Dallas, TX; *U.S. Public*, pg. 1307
Clark, David R., Asst. Gen. Counsel--San Diego Gas & Electric Company, San Diego, CA; *U.S. Public*, pg. 584
Clark, J. Patrick, V.P., Gen. Counsel & Sec.--Dentsply International Inc., York, PA; *U.S. Public*, pg. 498
Clark, Jacquel K., Asst. Treas. & Asst. Sec.--Hughes Supply, Inc., Orlando, FL; *U.S. Public*, pg. 846
Clark, John C., III, Gen. Counsel--Crestar Financial Corporation, Richmond, VA; *U.S. Public*, pg. 458
Clark, John C., III, Gen. Counsel--Crestar Bank, Richmond, VA; *U.S. Public*, pg. 458
Clark, John M., III, Sr. V.P., Gen. Counsel & Sec.--National Semiconductor Corporation, Santa Clara, CA; *U.S. Public*, pg. 1159
Clark, John R., III, V.P. & Gen. Counsel--Steuart Investment Company, Chevy Chase, MD; *U.S. Private*, pg. 1042
Clark, Jonathan M., Gen. Counsel & Sec.--Morgan Stanley Group Inc., New York, NY; *U.S. Public*, pg. 1132
Clark, Peter, Gen. Counsel--OGE Energy Corp., Oklahoma City, OK; *U.S. Public*, pg. 1207
Clark, Richard M., Sr. V.P., Gen. Counsel & Sec.--Kellogg Company, Battle Creek, MI; *U.S. Public*, pg. 947
Clark, Tim, Gen. Counsel--Colonial Gas Company, Lowell, MA; *U.S. Public*, pg. 400
Clarkson, Charles, Sec. & Counsel--TLC Beatrice International Holdings Inc., New York, NY; *U.S. Private*, pg. 1064
Clarkson, S.B., V.P., Gen. Counsel & Sec.--Newport News Shipbuilding, Inc., Newport News, VA; *U.S. Public*, pg. 1179
Clayman, Raymond, Gen. Counsel--The Elder-Beerman Stores Corp., Dayton, OH; *U.S. Private*, pg. 367
Clayton, D. Michael, Gen. Counsel--Samsonite Corporation, Denver, CO; *U.S. Public*, pg. 1430
Clayton, Mark Anthony, V.P. & Gen. Counsel--Showboat, Incorporated, Las Vegas, NV; *U.S. Public*, pg. 1469
Cleary, James J., V.P. & Gen. Counsel--Southern Natural Gas Company, Birmingham, AL; *U.S. Public*, pg. 1485
Clem, Terje, Gen. Counsel--Jotun A/S, Sandefjord, Norway; *Int'l*, pg. 714
Cline, Geoffrey, Legal Officer--Lost Arrow Corporation, Ventura, CA; *U.S. Private*, pg. 676
Cloues, Edward B., Gen. Counsel--K-Tron International, Inc., Pitman, NJ; *U.S. Public*, pg. 938
Cloutier, N. Paul, V.P., Gen. Counsel & Sec.--Gendis Inc., Winnipeg, Canada; *Int'l*, pg. 542
Coates, Roberta, V.P.-Corp. Affairs & Gen. Counsel--Taco John's International, Inc., Cheyenne, WY; *U.S. Private*, pg. 1066
Cochrane, E.G., II, V.P.-Sec. & Gen. Counsel--Mount Vernon Mills, Inc., Greenville, SC; *U.S. Private*, pg. 835
Cochrane, Laura J., Gen. Counsel & Sec.--TSI Incorporated, Shoreview, MN; *U.S. Public*, pg. 1559
Coe, Keith, Gen. Counsel--Omni Hotels, Irving, TX; *U.S. Private*, pg. 1065
Cofer, David T., V.P., Gen. Counsel & Sec.--Kennametal Inc., Latrobe, PA; *U.S. Public*, pg. 950
Cogliano, Michael G., V.P.-Legal--Shopping Centre Group, Toronto, Canada; *Int'l*, pg. 253
Cohan, Leon S., Sr. V.P. & Gen. Counsel--DTE Energy Company, Detroit, MI; *U.S. Public*, pg. 475
Cohen, Dana Klapper, Mgr.-Strategic & Legal Affairs--Grease Monkey International Inc., Denver, CO; *U.S. Public*, pg. 759
Cohen, Robert, Gen. Counsel & Sec.--Hall Financial Group, Inc., Dallas, TX; *U.S. Private*, pg. 495
Cohen, Roger, Gen. Counsel--Famous Restaurants Inc., Scottsdale, AZ; *U.S. Private*, pg. 393
Cohen, Theodore, V.P. Legal--U.S. Operations Div., Hato Rey, PR; *U.S. Public*, pg. 176
Cohen, Victor, V.P. & Gen. Counsel--Polo/Ralph Lauren Corporation, New York, NY; *U.S. Private*, pg. 874
Cohen, Victor, Gen. Counsel--Ralph Lauren Womenswear Co., L.P., New York, NY; *U.S. Private*, pg. 875
Cohen, William N., V.P., Gen. Counsel, & Sec.--Environmental Industries, Inc., Calabasas, CA; *U.S. Private*, pg. 378
Coin, Kerry W., Sr. V.P. & Gen. Mgr.-Boston Pacific--Carl Karcher Enterprises, Inc., Anaheim, CA; *U.S. Public*, pg. 278
Coit, Lynde H., Sr. V.P. & Gen. Counsel--Ogden Corporation, New York, NY; *U.S. Public*, pg. 1213
Colburn, J. Brian, Exec. V.P.-Special Projects & Sec.--Magna International Inc., Markham, Canada; *Int'l*, pg. 829
Cole, Charles F., V.P.-Legal & Asst. Gen. Counsel--Albertson's, Inc., Boise, ID; *U.S. Public*, pg. 38
Cole, Robert B., Sec.--Lennar Corporation, Miami, FL; *U.S. Public*, pg. 987
Cole, Robert B., Gen. Counsel--Lennar Homes Inc., Miami, FL; *U.S. Public*, pg. 988
Cole, Rosser, Gen. Counsel--Executive Software, Glendale, CA; *U.S. Private*, pg. 388
Cole, Vincent J., V.P., Gen. Counsel & Sec.--Lexmark International Group, Inc., Lexington, KY; *U.S. Public*, pg. 991
Cole, Vincent J., V.P., Gen. Counsel & Sec.--Lexmark International, Inc., Lexington, KY; *U.S. Public*, pg. 991
Coleman, John M., Sr. V.P.-Law & Pub. Affairs--Campbell Soup Company, Camden, NJ; *U.S. Public*, pg. 298
Coleman, Lester L., Exec. V.P. & Gen. Counsel--Halliburton Company, Dallas, TX; *U.S. Public*, pg. 775
Coleman, Lester L., Exec. V.P. & Gen. Counsel--Halliburton Energy Services, Inc., Dallas, TX; *U.S. Public*, pg. 776
Collier, T. Harris, III, Gen. Counsel--Trustmark Corporation, Jackson, MS; *U.S. Public*, pg. 1643
Collier, T. Harris, III, Gen. Counsel--Trustmark National Bank, Jackson, MS; *U.S. Public*, pg. 1643
Collins, Dave, Gen. Counsel--The Saturn Corporation, Troy, MI; *U.S. Public*, pg. 721
Collins, Frank E., Exec. V.P., Gen. Counsel & Sec.--Sierra Health Services, Inc., Las Vegas, NV; *U.S. Public*, pg. 1469
Collins, Henry, V.P.-Admin. & Gen. Counsel--TrustCo Bank Corp., NY, Schenectady, NY; *U.S. Public*, pg. 1643
Collins, J. Barclay II, Exec. V.P. & Gen. Counsel--Amerada Hess Corporation, New York, NY; *U.S. Public*, pg. 65
Collins, John J., Jr., V.P., Gen. Counsel & Sec.--Champion Enterprises, Inc., Auburn Hills, MI; *U.S. Public*, pg. 332
Collins, Patricia M., V.P., Assoc. Gen. Counsel & Asst. Sec.--Ogden Energy Group, Inc., Fairfield, NJ; *U.S. Public*, pg. 1213
Collins, Richard S., Assoc. Gen. Counsel--American Express Company, New York, NY; *U.S. Public*, pg. 73
Collins, Theodore J., V.P. & Gen. Counsel--The Boeing Company, Seattle, WA; *U.S. Public*, pg. 239
Collins, Thomas P., V.P.-Legal & Sec.--Wilmington Trust Corporation, Wilmington, DE; *U.S. Public*, pg. 1770
Collis, Foster J., V.P. & Gen. Counsel--East Kentucky Power Co-op, Winchester, KY; *U.S. Private*, pg. 356
Colton, Edward, Sr. V.P. & Gen. Counsel--Alpha Therapeutic Corp., Los Angeles, CA; *Int'l*, pg. 558
Colville, William W., Sr. V.P., Gen. Counsel & Acting Sec.--Owens Corning, Toledo, OH; *U.S. Public*, pg. 1236
Compton, Gregory A., Sr. V.P., Sec. & Gen. Counsel--NTS Development Company, Louisville, KY; *U.S. Private*, pg. 772
Conklin, Randall R., Gen. Counsel--Transcontinental Gas Pipe Line Corp., Houston, TX; *U.S. Public*, pg. 1769
Connely, Peter, Sr. V.P. & Gen. Counsel--Hyatt Hotels Corporation, Chicago, IL; *U.S. Private*, pg. 551
Connolly, James P., Deputy Gen. Counsel--The Gillette Company, Boston, MA; *U.S. Public*, pg. 743
Connors, James, Gen. Counsel--Universal Builders Supply, Inc., Mount Vernon, NY; *U.S. Private*, pg. 1126
Connors, Joseph C., Exec. V.P. & Gen. Counsel--Schering-Plough Corporation, Madison, NJ; *U.S. Public*, pg. 1438
Connors, K.B., V.P.-Human Resources & Division Counsel--Patent Construction Systems, Paramus, NJ; *U.S. Public*, pg. 793
Constant, Richard, Gen. Counsel--Polygram N.V., Baarn, Netherlands; *Int'l*, pg. 1051
Conway, John, Gen. Counsel--Kemper Insurance Companies, Long Grove, IL; *U.S. Private*, pg. 614
Cook, Terry, Sr. V.P., Gen. Counsel & Sec.--Kaiser Ventures, Inc., Ontario, CA; *U.S. Public*, pg. 941
Cooke, Roger, Sr. V.P., Gen. Counsel & Sec.--Smith's Food & Drug Centers, Inc., Salt Lake City, UT; *U.S. Public*, pg. 1103
Cooke, Roger A., Sr. V.P., Gen. Counsel & Sec.--Fred Meyer Incorporated, Portland, OR; *U.S. Public*, pg. 1103
Cooke, Roger A., Sr. V.P., Gen. Counsel & Sec.--Fred Meyer Stores, Portland, OR; *U.S. Public*, pg. 1103
Cooke, Stephen D., Sr. V.P., Gen. Counsel & Sec.-AMBAC Assurance Corp.--AMBAC Financial Group, Inc., New York, NY; *U.S. Public*, pg. 62
Cookerly, Ernest S., Gen. Counsel--David A. Bramble, Inc., Chestertown, MD; *U.S. Private*, pg. 165
Cookman, Jill D., Attorney--W.R. Berkley Corporation, Greenwich, CT; *U.S. Public*, pg. 215
Coonan, Liam S., Sr. V.P. & Asst. Gen. Counsel--SBC Communications Inc., San Antonio, TX; *U.S. Public*, pg. 1415
Cooney, Michael B., Sr. V.P.-Law & Admin. & Sec.--A.P. Green Industries, Inc., Mexico, MO; *U.S. Public*, pg. 761
Coons, Ann M., Assoc. Gen. Counsel & Asst. Sec.--The Times Mirror Company, Los Angeles, CA; *U.S. Public*, pg. 1615
Cooper, Douglas K., Exec. V.P. & Gen. Counsel--Peregrine Incorporated, Southfield, MI; *U.S. Private*, pg. 852
Cooper, Ian, Gen. Counsel--GEC Plessey Semiconductors, Swindon, United Kingdom; *Int'l*, pg. 544
Cooper, James H., Sr. V.P.-Legal--MEDCO Containment Services, Inc., Montvale, NJ; *U.S. Public*, pg. 1091
Cooper, Linda G., V.P.-Legal Affairs--Corrections Corporation of America, Nashville, TN; *U.S. Public*, pg. 450
Cooper, Richard F., V.P.-Admin, Gen. Counsel & Sec.--Arkansas Best Corporation, Fort Smith, AR; *U.S. Public*, pg. 130
Cooper, Sheila, Sr. V.P., Gen. Counsel & Sec.--Mary Kay, Inc., Dallas, TX; *U.S. Private*, pg. 711
Cooper, Steven D., Sr. V.P.-Plng., Gen. Counsel & Sec.--Electrolux Corporation, Atlanta, GA; *U.S. Private*, pg. 369
Copeland, Donald F., Gen. Counsel--Land O'Lakes, Inc., Southampton, PA; *U.S. Private*, pg. 646
Copeland, Donald F., Gen. Counsel--Resco Products, Inc., Conshohocken, PA; *U.S. Private*, pg. 924
Copeland, James N., V.P.-Legal & Personnel--Murphy Eastern Oil Co., London, United Kingdom; *U.S. Public*, pg. 1142
Coppock, Paul C., Chief Admin. Officer, Sr. V.P., Gen. Counsel & Sec.--Harsco Corporation, Camp Hill, PA; *U.S. Public*, pg. 792
Coragem, Almeida, Dr., Legal Counsel--Portuguese Railways (CP), Lisbon, Portugal; *Int'l*, pg. 1063
Corasanti, Joseph, V.P.-Legal Affairs & Corp. Counsel--Conmed Corporation, Utica, NY; *U.S. Public*, pg. 431
Corhan, Ken P., Gen. Counsel--Lewis Homes Management Corp., Upland, CA; *U.S. Private*, pg. 665
Corn, Amy C., Sec. & Assoc. Gen. Counsel--Pitney Bowes Inc., Stamford, CT; *U.S. Public*, pg. 1303
Corrallo, Carl, Sr. V.P. & Gen. Counsel--The Coastal Corporation, Houston, TX; *U.S. Public*, pg. 389
Correia, Jose, Gen. Mgr.-Legal Dept.--Banco Totta & Acores, Lisbon, Portugal; *Int'l*, pg. 144
Cortese, Greg, V.P., Gen. Counsel & Sec.--PAR Technology Corporation, New Hartford, NY; *U.S. Public*, pg. 1256
Cortez, R. Michael, V.P. & Gen. Counsel--Sheetz, Inc., Altoona, PA; *U.S. Private*, pg. 991
Corwin, Laura J., Sec. & Corp. Counsel--The New York Times Company, New York, NY; *U.S. Public*, pg. 1173
Corwine, David B., V.P., Gen. Counsel & Corp. Sec.--Allied Products Corporation, Chicago, IL; *U.S. Public*, pg. 48
Cosgrove, Barry C., Esq., V.P. & Gen. Counsel--Total Renal Care Holdings, Inc., Torrance, CA; *U.S. Public*, pg. 1625
Cosse, Steven A., Sr. V.P. & Gen. Counsel--Murphy Oil Corporation, El Dorado, AR; *U.S. Public*, pg. 1141
Costantini, William P., Sr. V.P. & Gen. Counsel--Olsten Corporation, Melville, NY; *U.S. Public*, pg. 1220
Costanza, Nicholas J., Chief Admin. Officer, V.P. & Gen. Counsel--Exide Electronics Group, Inc., Raleigh, NC; *Int'l*, pg. 126

Costello, Thomas, Gen. Counsel--Compuware Corporation, Farmington Hills, MI; *U.S. Public*, pg. 423
Costigan, John M., Sr. V.P., Gen. Counsel & Sec.--Premark International, Inc., Deerfield, IL; *U.S. Public*, pg. 1321
Cotanda, Francisco Carballo, Dir.-Legal Affairs & Sec.--Repsol S.A., Madrid, Spain; *Int'l*, pg. 1104
Cothran, Jack T., Corp. Counsel & Asst. Sec.--Abrams Industries, Inc., Atlanta, GA; *U.S. Public*, pg. 14
Coton, Daniel, Gen. Counsel--Presto Food Stores, Inc., Plant City, FL; *U.S. Private*, pg. 882
Cotter, William, V.P. & Gen. Counsel--American Optical Corporation, Greenwich, CT; *U.S. Private*, pg. 60
Cottick, William R., Sec. & Assoc. Gen. Counsel--Laidlaw Inc., Burlington, Canada; *Int'l*, pg. 259
Cottle, Karen, V.P., Gen. Counsel & Sec.--Raychem Corporation, Menlo Park, CA; *U.S. Public*, pg. 1362
Cotton, David S., V.P. & Gen. Counsel--Phelps Dodge Exploration Corporation, Phoenix, AZ; *U.S. Public*, pg. 1287
Cotton, Richard, Exec. V.P. & Gen. Counsel--National Broadcasting Co., Inc., New York, NY; *U.S. Public*, pg. 712
Cottrell, Frank S., V.P., Gen. Counsel & Sec.--Deere & Company, Moline, IL; *U.S. Public*, pg. 491
Cottrell, Jane R., Assoc. Gen. Counsel--Group W Satellite Communications, Stamford, CT; *U.S. Public*, pg. 275
Coulter, Chad W., V.P., Gen. Counsel & Sec.--Reliance Standard Life Insurance Company, Philadelphia, PA; *U.S. Public*, pg. 496
Coulter, Chail, Sr. V.P. & Gen. Counsel--National Life Insurance Company, Montpelier, VT; *U.S. Private*, pg. 785
Courtade, Arturo Perez, Gen. Counsel & Sec.--Grupo Sidek, S.A. de C.V., Guadalajara, Mexico; *Int'l*, pg. 576
Covell, Andrea M., V.P. & Legislative Counsel--GEICO Corporation, Washington, DC; *U.S. Public*, pg. 219
Covez, R.A., Gen. Counsel & Sec.--Foster-Miller, Inc., Waltham, MA; *U.S. Private*, pg. 421
Covington, Christopher, Sr. V.P. & Gen. Counsel--Vanstar Corporation, Pleasanton, CA; *U.S. Public*, pg. 1708
Covino, Susan T., V.P. & Gen. Counsel--KCS Energy Marketing Inc., Edison, NJ; *U.S. Public*, pg. 938
Cowell, Marion A., Jr., Exec. V.P., Gen. Counsel & Sec.--First Union Corporation, Charlotte, NC; *U.S. Public*, pg. 639
Cowper-Smith, G. Blair, Corp. Sec. & Special Counsel--Stelco Inc., Hamilton, Canada; *Int'l*, pg. 1299
Cox, Willaim S., V.P., Gen. Counsel & Sec.--Smith Technologies Corp., Portland, OR; *U.S. Public*, pg. 1478
Cox, Garen, Gen. Counsel--Medicalodges, Inc., Coffeyville, KS; *U.S. Private*, pg. 728
Cox, Garen, V.P. & Gen. Counsel--Medicalodges, Inc., Coffeyville, KS; *U.S. Private*, pg. 728
Cox, Robert T., V.P. & Gen. Counsel--Shelter Mutual Insurance Company, Columbia, MO; *U.S. Private*, pg. 992
Coyle, Dennis P., Gen. Counsel & Sec.--FPL Group, Inc., North Palm Beach, FL; *U.S. Public*, pg. 608
Cozean, Ronald J., Gen. Counsel & Sec.--Park-Ohio Industries, Inc., Cleveland, OH; *U.S. Public*, pg. 1258
Cozzi, Paul D.J., V.P. & Assoc. Gen. Counsel--Sun Life Assurance Company of Canada, Toronto, Canada; *Int'l*, pg. 1318
Craig, Barton J., Sr. V.P. & Gen. Counsel--Morgan's Foods, Inc., Beachwood, OH; *U.S. Public*, pg. 1133
Crain, A.R., V.P. & Gen. Counsel--Union Texas Petroleum Holdings, Houston, TX; *U.S. Public*, pg. 1669
Craine, Katherine G., V.P. & Gen. Counsel--Kettle Restaurants, Houston, TX; *U.S. Private*, pg. 617
Cram, Douglas M., V.P. & Asst. Gen. Counsel--PepsiCo, Inc., Purchase, NY; *U.S. Public*, pg. 1276
Cramblit, Miggie, V.P. & Gen. Counsel--Minnegasco, Minneapolis, MN; *U.S. Public*, pg. 843
Cramer, Michael J., V.P., Gen. Counsel & Sec.--The Morning Star Group, Dallas, TX; *U.S. Public*, pg. 1527
Crane, Don, Gen. Counsel--UniHealth, Burbank, CA; *U.S. Private*, pg. 1117
Crane, Richard A., Gen. Counsel--Samuel Bingham Co, Bloomingdale, IL; *U.S. Private*, pg. 144
Craugh, Joseph P., Jr., Sr. V.P. & Govt. Affairs Counsel--Harleysville Group, Harleysville, PA; *U.S. Public*, pg. 786
Craun, Todd R., Gen. Counsel & Sec.--Airgas, Inc., Radnor, PA; *U.S. Public*, pg. 33
Cravatte, Ernest, Dir.-Loans, Legal Affairs, Acctg. & Operational Control--Banque Generale du Luxembourg SA, Luxembourg, Luxembourg; *Int'l*, pg. 161
Crawford, Christine, Sec. & Legal Officer--Henkels & McCoy, Inc., Blue Bell, PA; *U.S. Private*, pg. 522
Crawford, Kenneth, Legal Officer--General Physics Corporation, Columbia, MD; *U.S. Public*, pg. 694
Creasman, William P., Sr. V.P., Gen. Counsel & Sec.--TCBY Enterprises Inc., Little Rock, AR; *U.S. Public*, pg. 1553
Creese, Sen, V.P. & Gen. Counsel--Comalco Limited, Brisbane, Australia; *Int'l*, pg. 307
Cremins, William T., Exec. V.P., Gen. Counsel & Sec.--Naugatuck Glass Company, Naugatuck, CT; *U.S. Private*, pg. 789
Crews, Donald R., Sr. V.P., Legal & Sec.--Harte-Hanks Communications, Inc., San Antonio, TX; *U.S. Public*, pg. 793
Crider, Karen K., Gen. Counsel & Sec.--The Stride Rite Corporation, Lexington, MA; *U.S. Public*, pg. 1524
Croke, Jerome P., Exec. V.P., Sec. & Legal Counsel--LaSalle-Talman Bank, Chicago, IL; *Int'l*, pg. 11
Cronkhite, John, Exec. V.P. & Gen. Counsel--Sea Ray, Knoxville, TN; *U.S. Public*, pg. 266
Crouch, Keith M., Sr. V.P. & Gen. Counsel--Patina Oil & Gas Corp., Denver, CO; *U.S. Public*, pg. 1264
Croushore, Bruce J., Sec. & Gen. Counsel--Bender Shipbuilding & Repair Company, Inc., Mobile, AL; *U.S. Private*, pg. 132
Crowl, Richard R., Sr. V.P. & Gen. Counsel--ReliaStar Financial Corp., Minneapolis, MN; *U.S. Public*, pg. 1375
Crowley, Francis L., Jr., V.P. & Assoc. Gen. Counsel--Western Atlas Inc., Houston, TX; *U.S. Public*, pg. 1757
Crowley, R. Terrence, Gen. Counsel--Sunstone Hotel Investors, Inc., San Clemente, CA; *U.S. Public*, pg. 1536
Crozier, Scott A., V.P. & Gen. Counsel--Phelps Dodge Corporation, Phoenix, AZ; *U.S. Public*, pg. 1286
Crutcher, Michael B., Sr. V.P., Gen. Counsel & Sec.--Brown-Forman Corporation, Louisville, KY; *U.S. Public*, pg. 261
Crystal, Joel F., Sr. Counsel & Asst. Sec.--New Plan Realty Trust, New York, NY; *U.S. Public*, pg. 1172
Cstellano, John, Gen. Counsel--YKK (U.S.A.), Marietta, GA; *Int'l*, pg. 1515
Cuellar, John, Sr. V.P. & Gen. Counsel--El Chico Restaurants, Inc., Dallas, TX; *U.S. Private*, pg. 283
Cull, William, V.P. & Gen. Counsel--Picker International, Inc., Cleveland, OH; *Int'l*, pg. 545
Cullen, Karen M., Exec. V.P. & Gen. Counsel--Long Island Bancorp, Inc., Melville, NY; *U.S. Public*, pg. 1013
Cullers, Zelkowitz Barry, Gen. Counsel--Ariel Corporation, Mount Vernon, OH; *U.S. Private*, pg. 81
Culp, Robert H., Gen. Counsel--Raytheon Systems Co., Kirkwood, NY; *U.S. Public*, pg. 1364
Cummings, Candace S., V.P.-Admin. & Gen. Counsel--VF Corporation, Wyomissing, PA; *U.S. Public*, pg. 1702
Cummings, Larry E., V.P., Gen. Counsel & Sec.--Harken Energy Corporation, Irving, TX; *U.S. Public*, pg. 785
Cummings, R.C., Gen. Counsel & Sec.--Smith-Lee Co., Inc., Oneida, NY; *U.S. Private*, pg. 1009
Cundiff, James N., Gen. Counsel-New Ventures & Corp. Services & Asst. Sec.--Mapco Inc., Tulsa, OK; *U.S. Public*, pg. 1042
Cunningham, Bob, Gen. Counsel & Sec.--Tennessee Farmers Co-op, La Vergne, TN; *U.S. Private*, pg. 1076
Cunningham, Dale, Sr. V.P. & Gen. Counsel--Sunkist Growers, Inc., Sherman Oaks, CA; *U.S. Private*, pg. 1052
Cunningham, David, Corp. Counsel--Sequent Computer Systems, Inc., Beaverton, OR; *U.S. Public*, pg. 1459
Cunningham, N.J., Treas. & Sec.--Atlantic Generation, Inc., Pleasantville, NJ; *U.S. Public*, pg. 430
Cunningham, N.J., Pres. & Sec.--Atlantic Energy Technology, Inc., Pleasantville, NJ; *U.S. Public*, pg. 430
Curp, John H., Gen. Counsel & Sec.--CitFed Bancorp, Inc., Dayton, OH; *U.S. Public*, pg. 376
Curran, Kevin J., Sr. V.P., Gen. Counsel & Sec.--Parsons Brinckerhoff Inc., New York, NY; *U.S. Private*, pg. 841
Curran, Timothy J., Exec. V.P. & Gen. Counsel--Curran Group, Inc., Crystal Lake, IL; *U.S. Private*, pg. 297
Currie, R.M., Gen. Counsel & Sec.--Detrex Corporation, Southfield, MI; *U.S. Public*, pg. 501
Curtin, James B., V.P. & Gen. Counsel--The Southern New England Telephone Company, New Haven, CT; *U.S. Public*, pg. 1491
Curtin, Mary E., V.P., Gen. Counsel & Sec.--Innovex, Inc., Hopkins, MN; *U.S. Public*, pg. 880
Curtis, Brian, Gen. Counsel--Oil-Dri Corporation of America, Chicago, IL; *U.S. Public*, pg. 1214
Cutchins, Clifford A., IV, Sr. V.P. & Gen. Counsel--Fort James Corporation, Richmond, VA; *U.S. Public*, pg. 670
Cutler, Richard J., Sr. V.P. & Gen. Counsel--TBG Services, Inc., New York, NY; *Int'l*, pg. 1335
Cutter, Edward A., Sr. V.P., Gen. Counsel & Sec.--The Clorox Company, Oakland, CA; *U.S. Public*, pg. 386
Cyrus, Kenneth M., Sr. V.P., Gen. Counsel & Sec.--Pharmacia & Upjohn, Inc., Windsor, United Kingdom; *Int'l*, pg. 1047
Cyrus, Kenneth M., Exec. V.P., Gen. Counsel & Sec.--Pharmacia & Upjohn, Kalamazoo, MI; *Int'l*, pg. 1048
D'Atri, Justin, Gen. Counsel & Sec.--John Boos & Company, Effingham, IL; *U.S. Private*, pg. 156
da Silva Amaro, Luciano, Legal Consultant--Banco Itau S.A., Sao Paulo, Brazil; *Int'l*, pg. 142
Dacier, Paul T., V.P. & Gen. Counsel--EMC Corporation, Hopkinton, MA; *U.S. Public*, pg. 545
Dadourian, Elise, Gen. Counsel & Sec.--Deluxe Storage Systems, Inc., Warren, PA; *U.S. Private*, pg. 323
Dahlen, Richard G., V.P. & Gen. Counsel--Hercules Incorporated, Wilmington, DE; *U.S. Public*, pg. 809
Dailey, Ed, Chief Legal Officer & Gen. Counsel--Blue Cross and Blue Shield of Massachusetts, Boston, MA; *U.S. Private*, pg. 151
Daley, Pamela, V.P. & Senior Counsel-Transactions--General Electric Company, Fairfield, CT; *U.S. Public*, pg. 709
Dallob, Naomi C., V.P. & Sec.--Chemed Corporation, Cincinnati, OH; *U.S. Public*, pg. 343
Dalton, James F., V.P. & Gen. Counsel--Tektronix, Inc., Wilsonville, OR; *U.S. Public*, pg. 1567
Daly, Denis G., Chief Legal Officer, V.P., Gen. Counsel & Sec.--Amcast Industrial Corporation, Dayton, OH; *U.S. Public*, pg. 63
Daly, James, Gen. Counsel--Software AG Americas, Inc., Reston, VA; *U.S. Public*, pg. 1482
Dance, J. Christopher, V.P.-Legal Affairs & Corp. Sec.--Excel Communications, Inc., Dallas, TX; *U.S. Public*, pg. 598
Daneri, Roxanne, Gen. Counsel & Sec.--Chuck Swift Sales & Leasing, Davis, CA; *U.S. Private*, pg. 1058
Dangeau, Jeffrey L., Gen. Counsel--Southwestern Energy Company, Fayetteville, AR; *U.S. Public*, pg. 1494
Daniels, Diana M., V.P., Gen. Counsel & Sec.--The Washington Post Company, Washington, DC; *U.S. Public*, pg. 1742
Daniels, R.M., Gen. Counsel & Corp. Sec.--H.P. Bulmer Holdings Plc, Hereford, United Kingdom; *Int'l*, pg. 232
Dankmeyer, T. R., Sr. V.P. & Gen. Counsel--New Business Development, San Francisco, CA; *Int'l*, pg. 224
Danner, Bryant C., Exec. V.P. & Gen. Counsel--Edison International, Rosemead, CA; *U.S. Public*, pg. 564
Dansky, Ira, Gen. Counsel--Jones Apparel Group, Inc., Bristol, PA; *U.S. Public*, pg. 933
Dapier, Mark E., Gen. Counsel--Mercury Finance Co., Lake Forest, IL; *U.S. Public*, pg. 1093
Darr, James E., Jr., Sr. V.P., Gen. Counsel & Sec.--Dillard's, Inc., Little Rock, AR; *U.S. Public*, pg. 509
Dauman, Philippe, Dep. Chm., Chief Admin. Officer, Exec. V.P. & Gen. Counsel--Viacom Inc., New York, NY; *U.S. Private*, pg. 775
Davenport, Colleen M., Assoc. Gen. Counsel & Asst. Sec.--Analysts International Corporation, Minneapolis, MN; *U.S. Public*, pg. 110
Davenport, Fred B., Jr., Gen. Counsel & Corp. Sec.--Pharmaceutical Product Development, Inc., Wilmington, NC; *U.S. Public*, pg. 1285
Davenport, Marian, V.P., Gen. Counsel & Sec.--Destec Energy, Inc., Houston, TX; *U.S. Public*, pg. 1146
David, Orna Bar, Gen. Counsel & Sec.--Elscint Ltd., Haifa, Israel; *Int'l*, pg. 450
Davidson, Karla, Sr. V.P. & Gen. Counsel-Entertainment--MGM Entertainment Company, Culver City, CA; *U.S. Public*, pg. 1614
Davies, Charles R., V.P. & Gen. Counsel--GEICO Corporation, Washington, DC; *U.S. Public*, pg. 219
Davies, Charles R., Gen. Counsel--GEICO Casualty Company, Washington, DC; *U.S. Public*, pg. 219
Davies, Richard W., Jr., Gen. Counsel & Sec.--Hubbell Incorporated, Orange, CT; *U.S. Public*, pg. 844
Davis, Bonni G., Gen. Counsel & Sec.--Finlay Enterprises, Inc., New York, NY; *U.S. Public*, pg. 623
Davis, Don E., Sec. & Gen. Counsel--Acceptance Insurance Co., Inc., Omaha, NE; *U.S. Public*, pg. 14
Davis, Florence A., V.P. & Gen Counsel--American International Group, Inc., New York, NY; *U.S. Public*, pg. 83
Davis, G. Gervaise III, V.P., Legal Counsel & Sec.--American Recreation Centers, Inc., Sacramento, CA; *U.S. Public*, pg. 90
Davis, Jane G., V.P., Gen. Counsel & Sec.--Joy Mining Machinery, Warrendale, PA; *U.S. Public*, pg. 789
Davis, Jeannine M., V.P., Gen. Counsel & Sec.--CTS Corporation, Elkhart, IN; *U.S. Public*, pg. 285
Davis, John M., V.P., Gen. Counsel & Sec.--IWC Resources Corporation, Indianapolis, IN; *U.S. Public*, pg. 1185
Davis, John M., V.P., Gen. Counsel & Sec.--Indianapolis Water Company, Indianapolis, IN; *U.S. Public*, pg. 1185
Davis, John S., V.P., Gen. Counsel & Sec.--Cameron Ashley Building Products, Inc, Dallas, TX; *U.S. Public*, pg. 298
Davis, M.A., Gen. Counsel & Sec.--Sterling Pulp Chemicals, Ltd., Etobicoke, Canada; *U.S. Public*, pg. 1580
Davis, Mark F., Gen. Counsel--Dewberry & Davis, Fairfax, VA; *U.S. Private*, pg. 329
Davis, Robert L., Gen. Counsel & Sec.--Provident Bankshares Corporation, Baltimore, MD; *U.S. Public*, pg. 1337
Davis, Steve J., Chief Admin. Officer, Gen. Counsel & Asst. Sec.--Magellan Health Services, Inc., Atlanta, GA; *U.S. Public*, pg. 1033
Davis, Thomas F., Admin. V.P. & Gen. Counsel--Ashland Chemical, Dublin, OH; *U.S. Public*, pg. 139
Davis, W. William, V.P., Sec. & Gen. Counsel--NationsBank of Tennessee, Nashville, TN; *U.S. Public*, pg. 1163
Davis, Walter S., V.P. & Gen. Counsel--Grede Foundries, Inc., Milwaukee, WI; *U.S. Private*, pg. 476
Davisson, Ralph M., V.P. & Gen. Counsel--Potlatch Corporation, Spokane, WA; *U.S. Public*, pg. 1318
Davisson, Richard F., Gen. Counsel & Sec.--Pay Less Super Markets, Inc., Anderson, IN; *U.S. Private*, pg. 844
Dawahare, Joe, Dir.-Govt. Affairs & Gen. Counsel--Dawahares, Inc., Lexington, KY; *U.S. Private*, pg. 316
Dawson, Grant, Gen. Counsel & Company Sec.--Centrica Plc, Slough, United Kingdom; *Int'l*, pg. 279
Dawson, Richard, Sr. V.P.-Law & Admin., Gen. Counsel & Sec.--Harvard Industries, Inc., Tampa, FL; *U.S. Public*, pg. 796
Day, Kerry, Assoc. Gen. Counsel & Sec.--Telus Corporation, Edmonton, Canada; *Int'l*, pg. 1374
Day, Larry, Sr. V.P. & Gen. Counsel--Forecast Group, Rancho Cucamonga, CA; *U.S. Private*, pg. 418
Day, Robert L., Corp. Sec. & Asst. Gen. Counsel--FMC Corporation, Chicago, IL; *U.S. Public*, pg. 604
Daymond, Ian C., Gen. Counsel & Sec.--Delta Gold N.L., Sydney, Australia; *Int'l*, pg. 389
de Baenst, Eric, Head-Legal & Fiscal Affairs--Bank Brussels Lambert, Brussels, Belgium; *Int'l*, pg. 146
De Fao, Michael E., V.P. & Gen. Counsel--UAM Fund Services Inc., Boston, MA; *U.S. Public*, pg. 1674
De Golia, Jim, V.P. & Gen. Counsel--Network Equipment Technologies, Inc., Redwood City, CA; *U.S. Public*, pg. 1168
de Lagausie, Patrice, Exec. V.P.-Legal Affairs--PSA Peugeot Citroen, Paris, France; *Int'l*, pg. 1020
de LaPasse, Patrice, Mgr.-Legal Affairs--Banque de France, Paris, France; *Int'l*, pg. 160
de Lasa, Jose M., Sr. V.P., Gen. Counsel & Sec.--Abbott Laboratories, Abbott Park, IL; *U.S. Public*, pg. 12
de Lasa, Jose M., Sr. V.P., Sec. & Gen. Counsel--Abbott Laboratories, Abbott Park, IL; *U.S. Public*, pg. 13
de Losa, Jose M., V.P. & Legal Officer--Bristol-Myers Squibb Pharmaceutical & Nutritional Group, New York, NY; *U.S. Public*, pg. 254
De Majistre, Robert, V.P. & Sec.--Seton Company, Norristown, PA; *U.S. Private*, pg. 987
de Noronha, Joao Otavio, Gen. Counsel--Banco do Brasil, Brasilia, Brazil; *Int'l*, pg. 141
de Parada, Rodolfo Garcia Gomez, Dir.-Legal--Controladora Comercial Mexicana, S.A. de C.V., Mexico, Mexico; *Int'l*, pg. 328
de Paredes Castillo, Vicente Santamaria, Gen. Counsel & Dep. Sec.--Tabacalera, S.A., Madrid, Spain; *Int'l*, pg. 1345
de Vaca, Ignacio Benjumea Cabeza, Gen. Counsel-Sec.--Banco Santander de Negocios, Madrid, Spain; *Int'l*, pg. 143
de Verdiere, Jean-Francois Colin, Gen. Counsel, Sec. & Dir.-Medium & Long Term Export Credits Div.--Banque Francaise du Commerce Exterieur, Paris, France; *Int'l*, pg. 160

Dean, Edwin, Gen. Counsel--Pennaco Hosiery, New York, NY; *U.S. Public*, pg. 483
Dean, Edwin W., Vice Chm., Gen. Counsel & Sec.--Danskin Inc., New York, NY; *U.S. Public*, pg. 483
Deane, James R., Sec. & Gen. Counsel--Fiduciary Trust Company International, New York, NY; *U.S. Public*, pg. 621
Dearborn, Charles H., V.P., Gen. Counsel & Sec.--Acuson Corporation, Mountain View, CA; *U.S. Public*, pg. 18
Deaton, Michael F., Gen. Counsel--Valvoline Instant Oil Change, Inc., Lexington, KY; *U.S. Public*, pg. 139
DeBolt, Bruce R., Chief Fin. Officer & Sr. V.P.--Northwest Natural Gas Company, Portland, OR; *U.S. Public*, pg. 1200
deBrier, Donald P., Exec. V.P., Sr. Gen. Counsel & Corp. Sec.--Occidental Petroleum Corporation, Los Angeles, CA; *U.S. Public*, pg. 1210
DeBuono, Laureen, Exec. V.P.-H.R., Gen Counsel & Sec.--Nellcor Puritan Bennett Incorporated, Pleasanton, CA; *U.S. Public*, pg. 1039
Decker, Mark R., V.P. & Gen. Counsel--Connell Co., Westfield, NJ; *U.S. Private*, pg. 264
Decker, Thomas A., V.P., Gen. Counsel & Sec.--Vetrotex CertainTeed Corporation, Wichita Falls, TX; *Int'l*, pg. 1171
Decker, Thomas A., V.P. & Gen. Counsel--CertainTeed Manatee Insulation Ltd., Montreal, Canada; *Int'l*, pg. 1176
Dederer, James W., Exec. V.P.& Gen. Counsel--Transamerica Life Companies, Los Angeles, CA; *U.S. Public*, pg. 1630
Dee, James, V.P., Gen. Counsel & Sec.--SPS Technologies, Inc., Jenkintown, PA; *U.S. Public*, pg. 1419
Deeming, Nick, Dir.-Legal & Corp. Sec.--PPP hc, Tunbridge Wells, United Kingdom; *Int'l*, pg. 1020
Deerson, Bruce A., General Counsel--Martin Marietta Materials, Inc., Raleigh, NC; *U.S. Public*, pg. 1007
Degnan, John J., Vice Chm. & Gen. Counsel--Chubb & Son, Inc., Warren, NJ; *U.S. Public*, pg. 355
Degnan, Martin J., V.P., Assoc. Gen. Counsel & Asst. Sec.--Rubbermaid Incorporated, Wooster, OH; *U.S. Public*, pg. 1411
del Campo Rodriguez, Miguel, Dir., Gen. Mgr., Legal Counsel & Sec.--Asland S.A., Madrid, Spain; *Int'l*, pg. 790
Delaby, L., Gen. Counsel--Danone Group, Paris, France; *Int'l*, pg. 379
Delaney, Patricia C., Gen. Counsel--Smithtown Bancorp, Inc., Smithtown, NY; *U.S. Public*, pg. 1479
Delaney, Patrick, Gen. Counsel & Sec.--MTS Systems Corporation, Eden Prairie, MN; *U.S. Public*, pg. 1028
Delany, Francis E., Jr., V.P. & Corp. Rate Counsel--Public Service Electric & Gas Co., Newark, NJ; *U.S. Public*, pg. 1340
Delany, G., Gen. Mgr.-Legal & Compliance--Pearl Group Plc, Peterborough, United Kingdom; *Int'l*, pg. 100
DelCol, John V., V.P., Gen. Counsel & Sec.--Chartwell Re Corporation, Stamford, CT; *U.S. Public*, pg. 336
DeMatteo, Madelyn M., V.P., Gen. Counsel & Sec.--Southern New England Telecommunications Corporation, New Haven, CT; *U.S. Public*, pg. 1490
Demonth, Robin, Gen. Counsel--Sandoz Agro, Inc., Des Plaines, IL; *Int'l*, pg. 974
DeMoss, Ronald, Corp. Counsel--Rent-Way, Inc., Erie, PA; *U.S. Public*, pg. 1377
Dempsey, Timothy M., V.P., Gen. Counsel & Sec.--Oshkosh Truck Corporation, Oshkosh, WI; *U.S. Public*, pg. 1233
den Dulk, J.L., Mgr.-Legal--Clyde Petroleum - Netherlands, Hague, Netherlands; *Int'l*, pg. 578
Dennis, Joel I., Corp. Counsel--Dennis Chemical Co., Inc., Saint Louis, MO; *U.S. Private*, pg. 324
Dennis, Richard, Gen. Counsel--Oshman's Sporting Goods, Inc., Houston, TX; *U.S. Public*, pg. 1233
Denniston, John, Gen. Counsel & Sec.--Bobit Publishing Company, Torrance, CA; *U.S. Private*, pg. 154
Derounian, Paul, Gen. Counsel--Reliable Automatic Sprinkler Co., Inc., Mount Vernon, NY; *U.S. Private*, pg. 920
DeRoy, Craig I., Exec. V.P. & Gen. Counsel--The First American Financial Corporation, Santa Ana, CA; *U.S. Public*, pg. 624
Derrick, James V., Jr., Sr. V.P. & Gen. Counsel--Enron Corp., Houston, TX; *U.S. Public*, pg. 584
Desch, Theodore E., Sr. V.P.-Law & Corp. Affairs--Blue Cross & Blue Shield of Illinois, Chicago, IL; *U.S. Private*, pg. 151
Deshaw, Nancy S., Gen. Counsel/Canada--Royal Oak Mines Inc., Kirkland, WA; *U.S. Public*, pg. 1410
Despres, Monique, V.P., Gen. Counsel & Sec.--Telemedia Inc., Montreal, Canada; *Int'l*, pg. 1373
Desy, Luc O., Gen. Counsel & Sec.--Rolland Inc., Saint-Jerome, Canada; *Int'l*, pg. 273
Detjen, David W., Legal Officer--Beiersdorf, Inc., Norwalk, CT; *Int'l*, pg. 182
Dettinger, Warren W., V.P. & Gen. Counsel--Diebold, Incorporated, Canton, OH; *U.S. Public*, pg. 506
Devlin, J. Richard, Exec. V.P.-Law & External Affairs--Sprint Corporation, Westwood, KS; *U.S. Public*, pg. 1500
Devlin, Terry, Gen. Counsel--Laser Systems, Apopka, FL; *U.S. Public*, pg. 1002
Dewey, R. Bruce, Sr. V.P. & Gen. Counsel--Mestek, Inc., Westfield, MA; *U.S. Public*, pg. 1099
Dewey, Richardson, III, Gen. Counsel--McKinney & McKinney Advertising, Redondo Beach, CA; *U.S. Private*, pg. 723
Dewez, Brigitte M., Deputy Gen. Counsel & Corp. Sec.--Unocal Corporation, El Segundo, CA; *U.S. Public*, pg. 1698
DeWitt, Thomas H., Exec. V.P.-Admin. & Gen. Counsel--Standex International Corporation, Salem, NH; *U.S. Public*, pg. 1505
Diaz-Ambrona, Juan Antonio Ortega, Dir.-Corp. Affairs--Repsol S.A., Madrid, Spain; *Int'l*, pg. 1104
Dibb, Bruce, Gen. Counsel--Granite Furniture Co., Salt Lake City, UT; *U.S. Private*, pg. 469
Dickerson, L.C., III, Gen. Counsel--Bollinger Shipyards, Inc., Lockport, LA; *U.S. Private*, pg. 155
Dickerson, Mark S., V.P., Gen. Counsel & Sec.--Talley Industries, Inc., Phoenix, AZ; *U.S. Public*, pg. 307
Dickie, Lawrence F., V.P., Assoc. Gen. Counsel & Asst. Sec.--PepsiCo, Inc., Purchase, NY; *U.S. Public*, pg. 1276
Didonato, Ann, Gen. Counsel--Country Home Magazine, Des Moines, IA; *U.S. Public*, pg. 1094
Dieker, Lawrence L., Asst. Gen. Counsel--Borden, Inc., Columbus, OH; *U.S. Private*, pg. 157
Diemer, Klaus, Dr., Legal Officer--Boehringer Mannheim GmbH, Mannheim, Germany; *Int'l*, pg. 331
Dietrich, Alan D., V.P.-Admin. & Sec.--Northwestern Public Service, Huron, SD; *U.S. Public*, pg. 1200
Diggs, James C., Sr. V.P. & Gen. Counsel--PPG Industries, Inc., Pittsburgh, PA; *U.S. Public*, pg. 1245
DiGioia, Victor, Gen. Counsel--Digital Solutions, Inc., Somerset, NJ; *U.S. Public*, pg. 508
Dillmann, Todd A., Corp. Counsel & Sec.--Giddings & Lewis, Inc., Fond Du Lac, WI; *Int'l*, pg. 1389
DiNicola, John W., V.P. & Gen. Counsel--Gilbane Building Company, Providence, RI; *U.S. Private*, pg. 452
DiNovi, Fiore, Corp. Counsel & Res. Dir.--Creative Marketing International Corp., West Chicago, IL; *U.S. Private*, pg. 287
Director, Mark D., Chief Admin. Officer & Gen. Counsel--U.S. Office Products Company, Washington, DC; *U.S. Public*, pg. 1686
Ditto, Michael E., V.P., Gen. Counsel & Sec.--Republic Financial Services, Inc., Dallas, TX; *Int'l*, pg. 346
Ditto, Michael E., V.P. & Corp. Sec.--Republic Underwriters Insurance Co., Dallas, TX; *Int'l*, pg. 346
Ditto, Michael E., V.P. & Corp. Sec.--Republic-Vanguard Life Insurance Co., Dallas, TX; *Int'l*, pg. 346
Ditto, Michael E., V.P. & Sec.--Southern County Mutual Insurance Company, Dallas, TX; *Int'l*, pg. 346
Dittrich, Reinhard, Gen. Counsel & Mng. Dir.-Insurance--Julius Meinl AG, Vienna, Austria; *Int'l*, pg. 856
Dix, William, V.P. & Gen. Counsel--Jenny Craig, Inc., La Jolla, CA; *U.S. Public*, pg. 926
Dixon, Paul E., V.P., Gen. Counsel & Sec.--Handy & Harman, New York, NY; *U.S. Public*, pg. 780
Dobbs, James C., V.P., Gen. Counsel & Sec.--Versar Inc., Springfield, VA; *U.S. Public*, pg. 1717
Dobran, James, Chief Litigation & Devel. Counsel--The Cafaro Co., Youngstown, OH; *U.S. Private*, pg. 198
Dobson, Jon A., Dir.-Legal Services--BMC Industries, Inc., Minneapolis, MN; *U.S. Public*, pg. 162
Dockery, Daniel P., Asst. Gen. Counsel & Asst. Sec.--Miller Brewing Company, Milwaukee, WI; *U.S. Public*, pg. 1289
Dodd, Martin H., Sr. V.P., Gen. Counsel & Sec.--TRC Companies, Inc., Windsor, CT; *U.S. Public*, pg. 1557
Dohnal, D.E., Sec. & Counsel--The Kelly-Springfield Tire Company, Cumberland, MD; *U.S. Public*, pg. 753
Dolan, James V., V.P.-Law--Union Pacific Railroad Company, Omaha, NE; *U.S. Public*, pg. 1668
Dolan, Richard, Sr. V.P.-Legal Affairs & Gen. Counsel--SNC-Lavalin Group Inc., Montreal, Canada; *Int'l*, pg. 1161
Dolan, Timothy, V.P., Sec. & Gen. Attorney--Robertshaw Controls Company, Richmond, VA; *Int'l*, pg. 1243
Domeniconi, Reto F., Gen. Mgr.-Fin., Control, Legal, Taxes, Admin.--Nestle S.A., Vevey, Switzerland; *Int'l*, pg. 915
Donadio, Mark C., Gen. Counsel & Sec.--Barrister Information Systems Corporation, Buffalo, NY; *U.S. Public*, pg. 192
Donnellan, Andrew B. Jr., V.P. & Litigation Counsel--Reliance Group Holdings, Inc., New York, NY; *U.S. Public*, pg. 1374
Donnelly, Kevin W., V.P., Gen. Counsel & Sec.--Nortek, Inc., Providence, RI; *U.S. Public*, pg. 1192
Donohue, Peter, Counsel--New Plan Realty Trust, New York, NY; *U.S. Public*, pg. 1172
Donohue, Robert F., V.P. & Chief Legal Officer--Cirrus Logic, Inc., Fremont, CA; *U.S. Public*, pg. 375
Donovan, John S., Exec. V.P. & Gen. Counsel--Cives Corporation, Roswell, GA; *U.S. Private*, pg. 241
Doppelt, Earl H., Exec. V.P. & Gen. Counsel.--A.C. Nielsen, Stamford, CT; *U.S. Public*, pg. 1183
Doran, Sandra J., V.P., Gen. Counsel & Sec.--Shaw's Supermarkets, Inc., East Bridgewater, MA; *Int'l*, pg. 1170
Dorflinger, Peter G., V.P., Gen. Counsel & Corp. Sec.--Sulzermedica USA Inc., Angleton, TX; *Int'l*, pg. 1307
Dornbusch, Arthur A., II, V.P., Gen. Counsel & Sec.--Engelhard Corporation, Iselin, NJ; *U.S. Public*, pg. 582
Dorsen, Hariette, Sr. V.P., Sec. & Gen. Counsel--Bantam Doubleday Dell Publishing Group, Inc., New York, NY; *Int'l*, pg. 191
Dorsett, C. Powers, Sr. V.P., Gen. Counsel & Sec.--Springs Industries, Inc., Fort Mill, SC; *U.S. Public*, pg. 1499
Dorsey, Patrick B., Sr. V.P., Gen. Counsel & Sec.--Tiffany & Co., New York, NY; *U.S. Public*, pg. 1608
Dorson, Patricia Freeman, V.P. & Gen. Counsel--VASA Brougher, Inc., Indianapolis, IN; *Int'l*, pg. 464
Dorwart, Frederic, Gen. Counsel & Sec.--BOK Financial Corp., Tulsa, OK; *U.S. Public*, pg. 163
Dougherty, James T., Sr. V.P., Gen. Counsel & Sec.--Lone Star Technologies, Inc., Dallas, TX; *U.S. Public*, pg. 1012
Douglas, Gene, V.P.-Legal & Admin. & Corp. Sec.--Hvide Marine Incorporated, Fort Lauderdale, FL; *U.S. Public*, pg. 851
Douglas, J. Paul, V.P., Corp. Counsel & Sec.--Public Service Company of North Carolina, Inc., Gastonia, NC; *U.S. Public*, pg. 1340
Dowd, Thomas F., V.P., Gen. Counsel & Sec.--Graybar Electric Company, Inc., Clayton, MO; *U.S. Private*, pg. 472
Dowdy, Robert A., V.P. & Gen. Counsel--Weyerhaeuser Company, Federal Way, WA; *U.S. Public*, pg. 1764
Downing, G. Edgar, V.P., Sec. & Gen. Counsel--Mobile Gas Service Corp., Mobile, AL; *U.S. Public*, pg. 1120
Downing, Walt, Gen. Counsel--RK Mechanical, Inc., Denver, CO; *U.S. Private*, pg. 904
Downs, Kenneth E., Gen. Legal Counsel--Staple Cotton Cooperative Association, Greenwood, MS; *U.S. Private*, pg. 1033
Doyle, Charles A., V.P., Gen. Counsel & Sec.--Burns & Roe Enterprises, Inc., Oradell, NJ; *U.S. Private*, pg. 187
Draetta, Ugo R., V.P. & Sr. Counsel--General Electric International Operations, London, United Kingdom; *U.S. Public*, pg. 713
Drake, William F., Jr., Vice Chm. & Gen. Counsel--Ikon Office Solutions, Inc., Malvern, PA; *U.S. Public*, pg. 862
Drakeman, Donald L., V.P. & Gen. Counsel--Essex Chemical Corporation, Clifton, NJ; *U.S. Public*, pg. 523
Draper, John M., Sr. V.P. & Gen. Counsel--Liberty Media Corporation, Englewood, CO; *U.S. Public*, pg. 1555
Dropkin, Philip, Sec. & Gen. Counsel--Time Warner Cable Liberty Division, Ferndale, NY; *U.S. Public*, pg. 1611
Drouin, Sylvie, V.P.-Legal Affairs & Corp. Sec.--Cadim, Montreal, Canada; *Int'l*, pg. 249
Drushel, W.H., Jr., Gen. Counsel--Quintana Petroleum Corp., Houston, TX; *U.S. Private*, pg. 901
Du Bois, Guy, Gen. Counsel--Bank Brussels Lambert, Brussels, Belgium; *Int'l*, pg. 146
Duane, Joseph M., V.P. & Gen. Counsel--Moore Corporation Limited, Toronto, Canada; *Int'l*, pg. 888
Dubin, Stephen V., Sr. V.P., Gen. Counsel & Sec.--CSS Industries, Inc., Philadelphia, PA; *U.S. Public*, pg. 283
Dubow, R., V.P. & Gen. Counsel--Quality Bakers of America Cooperative, Inc., Greenwich, CT; *U.S. Private*, pg. 898
Dubrule, Raphael, Gen. Counsel & Dir.-Investor Rels.--Sodexho S.A., Montigny-le-Bretonneux, France; *Int'l*, pg. 1274
DuChene, Todd, V.P., Gen. Counsel & Sec.--Fisher Scientific International, Hampton, NH; *U.S. Private*, pg. 658
Dudas, J., Gen. Counsel--Hesco, Inc., Teterboro, NJ; *U.S. Private*, pg. 524
Dudognon, Marc, Gen. Counsel--LeGrand S.A., Limoges, France; *Int'l*, pg. 805
Duenser, M.W., Gen. Counsel--Friendswood Development Company, Houston, TX; *U.S. Public*, pg. 988
Duerr, Richard E., Jr., V.P., Gen. Counsel & Sec.--Sofamor Danek Group, Inc., Memphis, TN; *U.S. Public*, pg. 1482
Duffield, Anne E., V.P., Div. Counsel & Sec.--ContiMortgage Corporation, Horsham, PA; *U.S. Public*, pg. 439
Duffy, James F., Exec. V.P. & Gen. Counsel--The American Stock Exchange, New York, NY; *U.S. Private*, pg. 62
Duffy, Tom, Gen. Counsel--Fujitsu Computer Products of America, Inc., San Jose, CA; *Int'l*, pg. 526
DuFresne, Marc, Mgr.-Legal Opers.-France--European Investment Bank, Luxembourg, Luxembourg; *Int'l*, pg. 465
Dugan, David A., Controller & Sec.--Georgia-Bonded Fibers, Inc., Newark, NJ; *U.S. Public*, pg. 734
Dugan, H.J.A., Legal--Tate & Lyle PLC, London, United Kingdom; *Int'l*, pg. 1356
Dugan, Lawrence, Gen. Counsel--FPA Corporation, Bensalem, PA; *U.S. Public*, pg. 608
Duggan, Thomas E., Gen. Counsel & Sec.--OppenheimerFunds Distributor, Inc., New York, NY; *U.S. Private*, pg. 818
Duggin, Sarah, Gen. Counsel--Amtrak-National Railroad Passenger Corp., Washington, DC; *U.S. Private*, pg. 68
Dumeny, Marcel J., Sr. V.P., Chief Gen. Counsel & Corp. Sec.--Fairfield Communities, Inc., Little Rock, AR; *U.S. Public*, pg. 610
Dun, David, Gen. Counsel & Sec.--Sierra Pacific Industries, Anderson, CA; *U.S. Private*, pg. 998
Dunlap, F. Thomas, Jr., V.P., Gen. Counsel & Sec.--Intel Corporation, Santa Clara, CA; *U.S. Public*, pg. 886
Dunn, G.J., Sr. V.P. & Gen. Counsel--BP America Inc., Cleveland, OH; *Int'l*, pg. 220
Dunn, Leslie, Sr. V.P., Gen. Counsel & Sec.--Cole National Corporation, Cleveland, OH; *U.S. Public*, pg. 396
Dunn, Nina Laserson, Exec. V.P., Gen. Counsel & Sec.--DRS Technologies, Inc., Parsippany, NJ; *U.S. Public*, pg. 474
Dunn, Robert V., Sr. V.P.-Law & Admin.--General Nutrition, Inc., Pittsburgh, PA; *U.S. Public*, pg. 725
Dunne, Timothy R., V.P., Gen. Counsel & Sec.--CRSS Inc., Houston, TX; *Int'l*, pg. 1415
Dunnett, Roderick, Mgr.-Legal Opers./Ireland & U.K.--European Investment Bank, Luxembourg, Luxembourg; *Int'l*, pg. 465
duPont, Augustus I., V.P., Gen. Counsel & Sec.--Crane Co., Stamford, CT; *U.S. Public*, pg. 456
duPont, Augustus I., V.P. & Gen. Counsel--Reeves Brothers, Inc., Spartanburg, SC; *U.S. Private*, pg. 507
Dupre, Durward D., V.P. & Assoc. Gen. Counsel--Southwestern Bell Telephone Co., Saint Louis, MO; *U.S. Public*, pg. 1416
Durant, Charles, V.P.-Legal & Sec.--Interactive Technologies, Inc., Saint Paul, MN; *U.S. Public*, pg. 888
Durant, Richard K., Asst. Gen. Counsel--Edison International, Rosemead, CA; *U.S. Public*, pg. 564
Durcan, Martha, V.P.-Admin. & Gen. Counsel--Parametric Technology Corporation, Waltham, MA; *U.S. Public*, pg. 1257
Durden, M. Frances, Sr. V.P., Gen. Counsel & Sec.--Michael Anthony Jewelers, Inc., Mount Vernon, NY; *U.S. Public*, pg. 1103
Durham, James W., Sr. V.P.-Legal & Gen. Counsel--PECO Energy Company, Philadelphia, PA; *U.S. Public*, pg. 1268
Durham, Joan Drake, Gen. Counsel--Moto Photo, Inc., Dayton, OH; *U.S. Public*, pg. 1136
Durning, Peter F., Asst. Gen. Counsel & Asst. Sec.--Stone & Webster, Incorporated, Boston, MA; *U.S. Public*, pg. 1519
Durso, Edwin M., Exec. V.P.-Admin.--ESPN, Inc., Bristol, CT; *U.S. Public*, pg. 512
Dwyer, Gregg A., Sr. V.P., Gen. Counsel & Sec.--Duracell International Inc., Bethel, CT; *U.S. Public*, pg. 743

Dye, Edward R., Sec. & Asst. Gen. Counsel--GenCorp Inc., Fairlawn, OH; *U.S. Public*, pg. 705
Dyen, Randall, Sr. V.P., Gen. Counsel & Sec.--General Accident Insurance, Philadelphia, PA; *Int'l*, pg. 543
Dykeman, Peter J., Gen. Counsel & Corp. Sec.--New Brunswick Power Corporation, Fredericton, Canada; *Int'l, pg. 923*
Dynek, Sigrid, V.P. & Gen. Counsel--Kohl's Corporation, Menomonee Falls, WI; *U.S. Public*, pg. 965
Dynner, Alan R., V.P. & Gen. Counsel--Eaton Vance Corp., Boston, MA; *U.S. Public*, pg. 559
Eason, William E., Jr., Sr. V.P., Gen. Counsel & Sec.--Scientific-Atlanta, Inc., Norcross, GA; *U.S. Public*, pg. 1443
East, Ernest E., V.P., Gen. Counsel & Sec.--Artisoft, Inc., Tucson, AZ; *U.S. Public*, pg. 136
Easter, R. Bruce, Jr., V.P., Gen. Counsel & Sec.--Nextlink Communications Inc., Bellevue, WA; *U.S. Public*, pg. 1181
Eastman, Joel M., V.P., Gen. Counsel & Sec.--Bristol Hotels & Resorts, Dallas, TX; *U.S. Public*, pg. 253
Easton, Reed W., Gen. Counsel--Mona Industries, Inc., Paterson, NJ; *U.S. Private*, pg. 756
Ebbeler, Jon, Gen. Counsel--Ericsson, Inc., Richardson, TX; *Int'l*, pg. 1364
Eberhardt, M.C., V.P., Gen. Counsel & Sec.--Raytheon E-Systems, Greenville, TX; *U.S. Public*, pg. 1365
Eckberg, David, Gen. Counsel & Sec.--Hart Crowser, Inc., Seattle, WA; *U.S. Private*, pg. 507
Eddins, Heidi J., General Counsel & Sec.--Providence and Worcester Railroad Company, Worcester, MA; *U.S. Public*, pg. 1336
Edelson, James I., Exec. V.P., Gen. Counsel & Sec.--PEC Israel Economic Corporation, New York, NY; *Int'l*, pg. 644
Edelstein, Stuart, Gen. Counsel--Commercial Light Company, Hillside, IL; *U.S. Private*, pg. 258
Eder, James A., V.P., Gen. Counsel & Sec.--Kollmorgen Corporation, Waltham, MA; *U.S. Public*, pg. 965
Edidin, Orrin J., V.P., Sec. & Gen. Counsel--WMS Industries Inc., Chicago, IL; *U.S. Public*, pg. 1727
Edwards, Carl, Jr., Exec. V.P., Gen. Counsel & Sec.--Lennox International Inc., Richardson, TX; *U.S. Private*, pg. 659
Edwards, Christine, Exec. V.P. & Chief Legal Officer--Morgan Stanley Dean Witter & Co., New York, NY; *U.S. Public*, pg. 1132
Edwards, Christine A., Exec. V.P. & Chief Legal Officer--Dean Witter, Discover & Co., New York, NY; *U.S. Public, pg. 1132*
Edwards, Daniel P., Gen. Counsel--Analytical Surveys, Inc., Colorado Springs, CO; *U.S. Public*, pg. 110
Edwards, David, V.P., Legal Counsel & Sec.--Bombardier, Learjet Inc., Wichita, KS; *Int'l*, pg. 200
Edwards, Robert N., V.P. & Gen. Counsel--Fedders Corp., Liberty Corner, NJ; *U.S. Public*, pg. 614
Eells, Gwen J., Sr. V.P. & Asst. Gen. Counsel--Countrywide Funding Corporation, Pasadena, CA; *U.S. Public*, pg. 453
Eells, Gwen J., Sr. V.P. & Gen. Counsel-Secondary Mktg.--INMC Mortgage Holdings, Inc., Pasadena, CA; *U.S. Public*, pg. 857
Egan, Charles J., Jr., V.P., Gen. Counsel & Sec.--Hallmark Cards, Inc., Kansas City, MO; *U.S. Private*, pg. 495
Egan, Thomas P., Jr., V.P., Gen. Counsel & Sec.--Valmont Industries, Inc., Valley, NE; *U.S. Public*, pg. 1706
Ege, Karl J., Gen. Counsel--Frank Russell Company, Tacoma, WA; *U.S. Private*, pg. 952
Eggenschwiler, James, Asst. Gen. Counsel & Asst. Sec.--Consolidated Stores Corp., Columbus, OH; *U.S. Public*, pg. 437
Eggleston, Alan P., Sr. V.P. & Gen. Counsel--Astoria Financial Corporation, Lake Success, NY; *U.S. Public*, pg. 141
Ehrhardt, Samuel, Gen. Counsel--Alusuisse-Lonza Holding Ltd., Zurich, Switzerland; *Int'l*, pg. 66
Eichel, Roger, Sec. & Legal--Hampton Industries, Inc., Kinston, NC; *U.S. Public*, pg. 779
Eid, Gordon L., Sr. V.P. & Deputy Gen. Counsel--American Express Financial Advisor, Minneapolis, MN; *U.S. Public, pg. 73*
Einhorn, Alan S., Gen. Counsel--MEDIQ Incorporated, Pennsauken, NJ; *U.S. Public*, pg. 1081
Eisele, Tom, V.P. & Gen. Counsel--NIBCO, Inc., Elkhart, IN; *U.S. Private*, pg. 798
Eisen, Alan, Mgr.--SouthCo. Inc., Concordville, PA; *U.S. Private*, pg. 1014
Eisen, Bruce M., V.P. & Chief Patent Counsel--Genetics Institute, Inc., Cambridge, MA; *U.S. Public*, pg. 79
Eisenberg, Barbara K., V.P., Assoc. Gen. Counsel & Corp. Sec.--Burlington Industries, Inc., Greensboro, NC; *U.S. Public*, pg. 268
Eisenberg, David M., V.P.-Law, Mktg. & Sls.--Sprint Corporation, Westwood, KS; *U.S. Public*, pg. 1500
Eisenstaedt, Richard M., Group Counsel--Ikon Office Solutions, Inc., Malvern, PA; *U.S. Public*, pg. 862
Eisner, William, V.P., Sec. & Gen. Counsel--ITT Federal Services Corporation, Colorado Springs, CO; *U.S. Public, pg. 859*
Ekdahl, Jon N., Gen. Counsel--Andersen Worldwide, New York, NY; *U.S. Private*, pg. 72
Ekdahl, Mikael, Gen. Counsel & Sec.--Skanska AB, Danderyd, Sweden; *Int'l*, pg. 1260
Ekker, Erik, Dir.-Legal, Amsterdam--Reed Elsevier plc, London, United Kingdom; *Int'l*, pg. 1093
Eksten, Ronald C., V.P., Gen. Counsel & Sec.--Hamilton Beach/Proctor-Silex, Inc., Glen Allen, VA; *U.S. Public*, pg. 1149
Eldridge, James F., Exec. V.P.-Corp. Legal & Sec.--American Family Mutual Insurance Co., Madison, WI; *U.S. Private*, pg. 53
Elefante, Jeffrey P., Exec. V.P., Gen. Counsel & Sec.--CACI International Inc, Arlington, VA; *U.S. Public*, pg. 272
Eliasberg, James A., Exec V.P. & Gen. Counsel--Taco Cabana, San Antonio, TX; *U.S. Public*, pg. 1559
Eliot, Judy, Corp. Counsel--T.D. Williamson, Inc., Tulsa, OK; *U.S. Private*, pg. 1179
Elizondo, Jose Eduardo Ancira, Gen. Counsel--Altos Hornos de Mexico, S.A., Monclova, Mexico; *Int'l*, pg. 66
Elkins, David G., V.P., Gen. Counsel & Sec.--Sterling Chemicals Holdings, Inc., Houston, TX; *U.S. Public*, pg. 1515
Elkins, Marshall A., Exec. V.P. & Gen. Counsel--Integrated Health Services, Inc., Owings Mills, MD; *U.S. Public*, pg. 884
Ellcessor, Steven J., V.P.-Admin., Gen. Counsel & Sec.--J.M. Smucker Company, Orrville, OH; *U.S. Public*, pg. 1480
Ellingson, Dave, V.P. & Assoc. Gen. Counsel--The Principal Financial Group, Des Moines, IA; *U.S. Private*, pg. 885
Ellingson, Dave, V.P. & Assoc. Gen. Counsel--Principal Mutual Life Insurance Co., Des Moines, IA; *U.S. Private*, pg. 886
Elliot, William, Sr. V.P., Gen. Counsel & Asst. Sec.--Gateway 2000, North Sioux City, SD; *U.S. Public*, pg. 703
Elliott, Daniel R., Jr., Sr. V.P., Gen. Counsel & Sec.--White Consolidated Industries, Inc., Cleveland, OH; *Int'l*, pg. 439
Elliott, Deirdre C., V.P., Corp. Counsel & Sec.--Badger Meter, Inc., Milwaukee, WI; *U.S. Public*, pg. 164
Elliott, James V., Sr. V.P., Gen. Counsel & Sec.--AEGON USA, Inc., Louisville, KY; *Int'l*, pg. 26
Elliott, M.B., Asst. Gen. Counsel & Asst. Sec.--Union Camp Corporation, Wayne, NJ; *U.S. Public*, pg. 1665
Elliott, P.M., Sec. & Solicitor--English China Clays Plc, Theale, United Kingdom; *Int'l*, pg. 455
Ellis, James D., Sr. Exec. V.P. & Gen. Counsel--SBC Communications Inc., San Antonio, TX; *U.S. Public*, pg. 1415
Ellwein, Michael D., V.P.-Corp. Devel. & Assoc. Gen. Counsel--Medtronic, Inc., Minneapolis, MN; *U.S. Public*, pg. 1082
Elmore, E. Whitehead, Sr. V.P., Gen. Counsel & Sec.--Albemarle Corporation, Richmond, VA; *U.S. Public*, pg. 37
Elwood, Clark D., V.P., Gen. Counsel & Sec.--ITT Educational Services, Inc., Indianapolis, IN; *U.S. Public*, pg. 1512
Elwood, Harrison, Mgr.-Legal--Shoppers Drug Mart, Ltd., London, Canada; *Int'l*, pg. 112
Emch, Thomas, Dr., Gen. Counsel--Landis & Staefa AG, Zug, Switzerland; *Int'l*, pg. 800
Emmens, David P., Corp. Counsel--The Gorman-Rupp Company, Mansfield, OH; *U.S. Public*, pg. 754
End, Ralph P., V.P. & Gen. Counsel--Keystone Consolidated Industries, Inc., Dallas, TX; *U.S. Public*, pg. 955
Engdahl, Walter A., V.P.-Corp. Counsel & Sec.--Sensormatic Electronics Corporation, Boca Raton, FL; *U.S. Public*, pg. 1457
Engelhart, Kenneth G., V.P.-Regulatory Law--Rogers Communications, Inc., Toronto, Canada; *Int'l*, pg. 1122
Engelmann, Glen, Gen. Counsel & Corp. Sec.--Zeneca Inc., Wilmington, DE; *Int'l*, pg. 1525
Englar, John D., Sr. V.P.-Corp. Devel. & Law--Burlington Industries, Inc., Greensboro, NC; *U.S. Public*, pg. 268
Engler, W. Joseph, Jr., V.P. & Gen. Counsel--Rochester & Pittsburgh Coal Company, Indiana, PA; *U.S. Public*, pg. 1395
Engstrom, Mark W., Assoc. Gen. Counsel-Labor--CBS, New York, NY; *U.S. Public*, pg. 273
Eno, Woodrow E., Sr. V.P.-Law & Govt. Rels., Sec. & Gen. Counsel--Aid Association for Lutherans, Appleton, WI; *U.S. Private*, pg. 27
Ensign, Gregory M., V.P., Gen. Counsel & Sec.--Kirkwood Industries, Inc., Cleveland, OH; *U.S. Private*, pg. 623
Epps, Michael, V.P. & Gen. Counsel--Helm Resources Inc., Greenwich, CT; *U.S. Public*, pg. 808
Epps, Michael R., Gen. Counsel--Unapix Entertainment Inc., New York, NY; *U.S. Public*, pg. 1664
Erbasol, Hasan Cihat, Dir.-Legal--Sabanci Holding A.S., Istanbul, Turkey; *Int'l*, pg. 1167
Ereckson, Stanley, Jr., Sr. V.P., Gen. Counsel & Sec.--Vicorp Restaurants, Inc., Denver, CO; *U.S. Public*, pg. 1719
Erickson, Gordon R., Gen. Counsel--Bolt Technology Corporation, Norwalk, CT; *U.S. Public*, pg. 244
Erickson, Grant D., Gen. Counsel & Sec.--Nelson Westerberg, Inc., Elk Grove Village, IL; *U.S. Private*, pg. 1163
Erickson, Jackie M., V.P.-Gen. Counsel & Govt. Rels.--Hawaiian Electric Company, Inc., Honolulu, HI; *U.S. Public*, pg. 800
Erickson, Phillip A., Gen. Counsel & Sec.--IMI Cornelius Inc. (MN), Anoka, MN; *Int'l*, pg. 646
Erikson, George W., Chm. Bd. & Gen. Counsel--CERBCO, Inc., Landover, MD; *U.S. Public*, pg. 330
Erikson, J. Lance, Exec. V.P., Sec. & Gen Counsel--Great Western Financial Corporation, Chatsworth, CA; *U.S. Public*, pg. 1741
Erlandsson, Per, Sec. & Legal--Saab AB, Linkoping, Sweden; *Int'l*, pg. 686
Ershammar, John, Gen. Counsel--Celsius AB, Stockholm, Sweden; *Int'l*, pg. 276
Erwin, Robert P., Jr., Gen. Counsel & Sec.--Bartlett and Company, Kansas City, MO; *U.S. Private*, pg. 118
Esau, Steven, V.P., Gen. Counsel & Sec.--Asymetrix Learning Systems, Inc., Bellevue, WA; *U.S. Private*, pg. 93
Estes, Royce J., V.P. & Gen. Counsel--Anheuser-Busch Companies, Inc., Saint Louis, MO; *U.S. Public*, pg. 113
Etter, Greg V., Gen. Counsel & Sec.--Battle Mountain Gold Company, Houston, TX; *U.S. Public*, pg. 193
Evanoff, Michael, V.P.-Devel. & Gen. Counsel--Hyatt International Corporation, Chicago, IL; *U.S. Private*, pg. 551
Evans, F. Maxwell, V.P., Gen. Counsel & Sec.--Sterling Chemicals, Inc., Houston, TX; *U.S. Public*, pg. 1515
Evans, Hank, Gen. Counsel--Blue Anchor, Inc., Dinuba, CA; *U.S. Private*, pg. 150
Evans, James E., Sr. V.P. & Gen. Counsel--American Financial Group, Cincinnati, OH; *U.S. Public*, pg. 74
Evans, Mark, V.P. & Gen. Counsel--Nestle Chocolate & Confection, Glendale, CA; *Int'l*, pg. 917
Evans, Ross, V.P. & Gen. Counsel--Otis Elevator Company, Farmington, CT; *U.S. Public*, pg. 1690
Everakes, Howard C., Exec. V.P. & Gen. Counsel--Glendale Federal Bank, F.S.B., Glendale, CA; *U.S. Public*, pg. 747
Everingham, J. Theodore, V.P. & Gen. Counsel--General Host Corporation, Stamford, CT; *U.S. Public*, pg. 715
Evers, Bradley W., V.P., Gen. Counsel & Sec.--Price Brothers Co., Dayton, OH; *U.S. Private*, pg. 883
Ewert, Darrell, Sec. & Gen. Counsel--The Oshawa Group Limited, Etobicoke, Canada; *Int'l*, pg. 1012
Ewing-Ladd, Christina, Gen. Counsel--Warrantech Corporation, Stamford, CT; *U.S. Public*, pg. 1740
Eyster, Franklin S., II, Sr. V.P., Gen. Counsel & Sec.--Atlantic Aviation Corp., New Castle, DE; *U.S. Private*, pg. 94
Ezer, Shaul I., Asst. Gen. Counsel--BCE Inc., Montreal, Canada; *Int'l*, pg. 114
Ezra, Robert, Gen. Counsel--Gilrichco, Inc., Oxnard, CA; *U.S. Private*, pg. 454
Facciolo, Jay, Gen. Counsel--Delcal Enterprises, Inc., New York, NY; *U.S. Private*, pg. 322
Fagan, Christopher, Gen. Counsel--The Florists Assn. of Greater Cleveland, Inc., Cleveland, OH; *U.S. Private*, pg. 415
Fagan, J. Gregory, V.P. & Gen. Counsel--The Cato Corporation, Charlotte, NC; *U.S. Public*, pg. 318
Fagerlund, Mats, Sr. V.P. & Gen. Counsel--Vattenfall AB, Stockholm, Sweden; *Int'l*, pg. 1452
Faigin, Alan W., Gen. Counsel & Sec.--Fremont General Corporation, Santa Monica, CA; *U.S. Public*, pg. 681
Falick, Paul, V.P. & Gen. Counsel--ICC Industries, Inc., New York, NY; *U.S. Private*, pg. 553
Falik, Joseph L., Gen. Counsel--GMAC Insurance Holdings, Detroit, MI; *U.S. Public*, pg. 719
Falkman, Malcolm, Dir.-Legal Affairs--Sandvik AB, Sandviken, Sweden; *Int'l*, pg. 1185
Fannin, David C., Exec. V.P., Gen. Counsel & Sec.--Sunbeam Corporation, Delray Beach, FL; *U.S. Public*, pg. 1533
Fantin, Louis A., V.P., Gen. Counsel & Sec.--Lenox, Incorporated, Lawrenceville, NJ; *U.S. Public*, pg. 261
Farr, Thomas, Gen. Counsel--Preferred Risk Mutual Insurance, West Des Moines, IA; *U.S. Private*, pg. 880
Farrell, Catherine, V.P., Corp. Counsel & Sec.--Fluor Daniel GTI, Inc., Norwood, MA; *U.S. Public*, pg. 660
Farris, John, Gen. Counsel--Conley Frog/Switch & Forge Co., Memphis, TN; *U.S. Private*, pg. 263
Faulkner, Harry F., III, V.P.-Legal & Sec.--North American Royalties, Inc., Chattanooga, TN; *U.S. Private*, pg. 803
Feather, William L., Sr. V.P., Gen. Counsel & Sec.--Allegiance Healthcare Corp., McGaw Park, IL; *U.S. Public*, pg. 44
Feazell, Thomas L., Sr. V.P., Gen. Counsel & Sec.--Ashland, Inc., Russell, KY; *U.S. Public*, pg. 138
Feibel, James B., Sec. & Gen. Counsel--Electric Power Equipment Co., Columbus, OH; *U.S. Private*, pg. 368
Feiner, Stuart F., Exec. V.P., Gen. Counsel & Sec.--Inco Limited, Toronto, Canada; *Int'l*, pg. 672
Feinsand, Howard L., Sr. V.P.-Bus. & Legal Affairs--General Electric Capital Aviation Services, San Francisco, CA; *U.S. Public*, pg. 712
Feirstein, Michael, Sr. V.P. & Chief Legal Counsel--Reed Elsevier Business Information, Newton, MA; *Int'l*, pg. 1095
Feller, Harriet Burns, Exec. V.P., Sec. & Gen Counsel--Westcorp, Irvine, CA; *U.S. Public*, pg. 1756
Feller, Harriet Burns, Sr. V.P., Gen. Counsel & Sec.--Western Financial Bank, Irvine, CA; *U.S. Public*, pg. 1757
Femal, Mike, Gen. Counsel--Schneider Automation, Inc., North Andover, MA; *Int'l*, pg. 1208
Femsler, John, House Counsel--Weis Markets, Inc., Sunbury, PA; *U.S. Public*, pg. 1751
Fenton, Charles E., Sr. V.P. & Gen. Counsel--The Black & Decker Corporation, Towson, MD; *U.S. Public*, pg. 233
Ferguson, John T., II, Gen. Counsel & Sec.--Crompton & Knowles Corporation, Stamford, CT; *U.S. Public*, pg. 459
Ferguson, Terrence J., Gen. Counsel & Sec.--MFS WorldCom, Inc., Omaha, NE; *U.S. Public*, pg. 1779
Fernandez, D. Gabriel Barrasa, General Counsel--Hispasat, S.A., Madrid, Spain; *Int'l*, pg. 1372
Fernstrom, Petri, Sr. V.P. & Gen. Counsel--Outokumpu Oyj, Espoo, Finland; *Int'l*, pg. 1015
Ferrando, Jonathan P., V.P. & Gen. Counsel--Republic Industries, Inc., Fort Lauderdale, FL; *U.S. Public*, pg. 1378
Ferraro, Peter, Gen. Counsel & Sec.--Parmalat Canada Ltd., Etobicoke, Canada; *Int'l*, pg. 1023
Ferri, Robert, Sec. & Assoc. Gen. Counsel--Asarco Incorporated, New York, NY; *U.S. Public*, pg. 137
Ferrin, Mark A., Gen. Counsel--Defense & Launch Vehicles Division, Brigham City, UT; *U.S. Public*, pg. 1597
Ferris, Brian W., Asst. Gen. Counsel & Asst. Sec.--CalMat Co., Los Angeles, CA; *U.S. Public*, pg. 295
Festinger, Jonathan, Gen. Counsel & Sec.--WIC Western International Communications Ltd., Vancouver, Canada; *Int'l*, pg. 1481
Festinger, Jonathan B., Sec. & Gen. Counsel--Canadian Satellite Communications Inc., Mississauga, Canada; *Int'l*, pg. 1481
Ficarro, John R., V.P., Gen. Counsel & Sec.--Phar-Mor, Inc., Youngstown, OH; *U.S. Public*, pg. 1284
Fickenscher, Donald A., V.P., Gen. Counsel & Sec.--Virginia Natural Gas, Inc., Norfolk, VA; *U.S. Public*, pg. 436
Fiedler, William L., V.P., Gen. Counsel & Sec.--Philip Industrial Services Group, Houston, TX; *Int'l*, pg. 1050
Fielden, Barbara, Corp. Counsel--Active Voice Corporation, Seattle, WA; *U.S. Public*, pg. 17

Fields, Gary I., Sr. V.P. & Gen. Counsel--Medical Resources Inc., Hackensack, NJ; *U.S. Public*, pg. 1080
Fife, Lorin M., Sr. V.P. & Gen. Counsel--SunAmerica Inc., Los Angeles, CA; *U.S. Public*, pg. 1532
Finamore, Karyn, Gen. Counsel--PAREXEL International Corporation, Waltham, MA; *U.S. Public*, pg. 1257
Fine, Howard, Gen. Counsel--Tiger Electronics, Inc., Vernon Hills, IL; *U.S. Private*, pg. 1086
Fine, Roger S., V.P. & Gen. Counsel-Exec. Committee--Johnson & Johnson, New Brunswick, NJ; *U.S. Public*, pg. 927
Fingarson, John L., V.P., Sec. & Gen. Counsel--Trans Mountain Pipeline Company Ltd., Vancouver, Canada; *Int'l*, pg. 114
Finie, Paul, Gen. Mgr.--Trend Offset Printing Services, Los Alamitos, CA; *U.S. Private*, pg. 1099
Fink, Karen G., V.P., Gen. Counsel & Sec.--Concurrent Computer Corporation, Fort Lauderdale, FL; *U.S. Public*, pg. 430
Finley, Paul C., Gen. Counsel & Sec.--Algoma Steel Inc., Sault Sainte Marie, Canada; *Int'l*, pg. 56
Finn, Thomas W., V.P., Gen. Counsel & Sec.--DataCard Corporation, Minnetonka, MN; *U.S. Private*, pg. 312
Finneran, John G., Jr., Sr. V.P., Gen. Counsel & Sec.--Capital One Financial Corporation, Falls Church, VA; *U.S. Public*, pg. 302
Firth, John, Gen. Counsel & Sec.--Quality Dining Inc., Mishawaka, IN; *U.S. Public*, pg. 1349
Fischer, Daniel J., Pres., Chief Exec. Officer & Gen. Counsel--Manhattan Life Insurance Company, Cincinnati, OH; *U.S. Private*, pg. 1118
Fischer, Eric R., Exec. V.P.& Gen. Counsel--UST Corporation, Boston, MA; *U.S. Public*, pg. 1660
Fischer, Eric R., Exec. V.P., Gen. Counsel & Sec.--United States Trust Company, Boston, MA; *U.S. Public*, pg. 1660
Fischer, Eric R., Exec. V.P., Gen. Counsel & Sec.--USTrust, Boston, MA; *U.S. Public*, pg. 1660
Fischer, Klaus P., V.P., Gen. Counsel & Sec.--Elliott Company, Jeannette, PA; *U.S. Private*, pg. 373
Fischer, Michael S., V.P., Gen. Counsel & Sec.--Washington Square Securities, Minneapolis, MN; *U.S. Public*, pg. 1376
Fischette, Joseph A., V.P., Gen. Counsel & Sec.--Calgon Carbon Corporation, Pittsburgh, PA; *U.S. Public*, pg. 292
Fish, Eugene C., Dir.-Corp. Counsel--Hull Corporation, Hatboro, PA; *U.S. Private*, pg. 547
Fisher, David F., V.P., Gen. Counsel & Corp. Sec.--ADC Telecommunications, Inc., Minnetonka, MN; *U.S. Public*, pg. 4
Fisher, Douglas A., V.P., Gen. Counsel & Dir.-Bus. Svcs.--AgriBioTech, Inc., Las Vegas, NV; *U.S. Public*, pg. 28
Fisher, MaryAnn, V.P., Sec. & Gen. Counsel--Condea Vista Company, Houston, TX; *Int'l*, pg. 325
Fishman, Lawrence, Asst. Gen. Counsel--Forest City Enterprises, Inc., Cleveland, OH; *U.S. Public*, pg. 667
Fisk, Hayward D., Gen. Counsel & Sec.--Computer Sciences Corporation, El Segundo, CA; *U.S. Public*, pg. 422
Fiske, Terry N., V.P. & Gen. Counsel-U.S. Opers.--Echo Bay Mines Ltd., Englewood, CO; *U.S. Public*, pg. 561
FitzGerald, C. F., Gen. Counsel--National Westminster Bank PLC, London, United Kingdom; *Int'l*, pg. 910
Fitzgerald, Jeremiah M., V.P. & Gen. Counsel--Comdisco, Inc., Rosemont, IL; *U.S. Public*, pg. 407
Fitzgerald, Robert M., Esq., Legal Officer--Son Chief Electrics, Inc., Winsted, CT; *U.S. Private*, pg. 1014
Fitzpatrick, Nora, Legal Asst. & H.R. Mngmt.--Tandycrafts, Inc., Fort Worth, TX; *U.S. Public*, pg. 1561
FitzRoy, Forrest S., Sr. V.P. & Gen. Counsel--NationsBank West, Saint Louis, MO; *U.S. Public*, pg. 1164
Fitzsimons, John H., Gen. Counsel & Sec.--The Dyson-Kissner-Moran Corporation, New York, NY; *U.S. Private*, pg. 351
Flacks, D. M., Gen. Counsel & Sec.--Carter Holt Harvey Limited, Auckland, New Zealand; *U.S. Public*, pg. 904
Flanagan, Mary Jo, V.P. & Gen. Counsel--Brink's, Inc., Darien, CT; *U.S. Public*, pg. 1305
Flannery, M.E., V.P. & Gen. Counsel--Duchossois Industries, Inc., Elmhurst, IL; *U.S. Private*, pg. 344
Flanzraich Neil W., Sr. V.P. & Co-Gen. Counsel--Syntex, Palo Alto, CA; *Int'l*, pg. 1120
Flax, Robert J., Exec. V.P., Gen. Counsel & Sec.--Bay View Capital Corporation, San Mateo, CA; *U.S. Public*, pg. 197
Fleishaker, Aaron, Gen. Counsel--Henry Modell & Company, Inc., New York, NY; *U.S. Private*, pg. 754
Fleishman, Robert S., Gen. Counsel--Baltimore Gas and Electric Company, Baltimore, MD; *U.S. Public*, pg. 172
Fleming, Gordon, Treas. & Sec.--Brach & Brock Confections Inc., Chattanooga, TN; *U.S. Private*, pg. 163
Fletcher-Rogers, H., Mgr.-Legal & Corp. Rels.--Kodak Limited, Hemel Hempstead, United Kingdom; *U.S. Public*, pg. 553
Fletcher, Anne J., Gen. Counsel--ITC Learning Corp., Herndon, VA; *U.S. Public*, pg. 859
Fletcher, F. Alan, V.P., Gen. Counsel & Sec.--Pegasus Gold Corporation, Spokane, WA; *U.S. Public*, pg. 1269
Fletcher, J.E., V.P.-Legal & Corp. Affairs & Sec.--Ranger Oil Limited, Calgary, Canada; *Int'l*, pg. 1086
Fletcher, L. John, V.P. & Asst. Gen. Counsel--Premark International, Inc., Deerfield, IL; *U.S. Public*, pg. 1321
Flickinger, Catherine, V.P. & Gen. Counsel--Hachette Filipacchi Magazines Inc., New York, NY; *Int'l*, pg. 794
Flink, Richard A., V.P., Gen. Counsel & Sec.--C.R. Bard, Inc., Murray Hill, NJ; *U.S. Public*, pg. 189
Flinn, Gloria J., Gen. Counsel--Dwight Asset Management Company, Burlington, VT; *U.S. Public*, pg. 1673
Flodstrom, Johan, Gen. Counsel & Sec.--Mo och Domsjo AB, Stockholm, Sweden; *Int'l*, pg. 885
Florence, Faye A., V.P., Gen. Counsel & Sec.--Syratech Corporation, East Boston, MA; *U.S. Private*, pg. 1060
Florio, Mary Jo, Gen. Counsel--Competitive Media Reporting, New York, NY; *Int'l*, pg. 1447
Flowers, Michael L., V.P., Asst. Sec. & Chief In-House Counsel--The Midland Company, Cincinnati, OH; *U.S. Public*, pg. 1110
Floyd, Israel J., Sec. & Asst. Gen. Counsel--Hercules Incorporated, Wilmington, DE; *U.S. Public*, pg. 809
Flynn, Brian, Gen. Counsel--Nanometrics Incorporated, Sunnyvale, CA; *U.S. Public*, pg. 1151
Flynn, Joseph P., Gen. Counsel--Advantage Companies, Inc., Wichita, KS; *U.S. Private*, pg. 22
Fogarty, Michael, Gen. Counsel--Tempel Steel Company, Skokie, IL; *U.S. Private*, pg. 1075
Fohrman, Monica, V.P., Asst. Gen. Counsel & Corp. Sec.--R.R. Donnelley & Sons Company, Chicago, IL; *U.S. Public*, pg. 517
Folan, McDara P., III, V.P., Sec. & Gen. Counsel--Allen Telecom, Inc., Beachwood, OH; *U.S. Public*, pg. 45
Foley, Cheryl M., V.P., Gen. Counsel & Sec.--Cinergy Corp., Cincinnati, OH; *U.S. Public*, pg. 368
Foley, Cheryl M., V.P., Gen. Counsel & Corp. Sec.--CINergy Services, Inc., Cincinnati, OH; *U.S. Public*, pg. 369
Foley, Patrick J., V.P. & Assoc. Gen. Counsel--American International Group, Inc., New York, NY; *U.S. Public*, pg. 83
Foltz, Jack L., V.P. & Gen. Counsel--Sun Company, Inc., Philadelphia, PA; *U.S. Public*, pg. 1530
Foong Lan, Helen Chong nee Chia, Sec. & Legal Counsel--Singapore Petroleum Company Ltd., Singapore, Singapore; *U.S. Public*, pg. 102
Force, Jill L., Sr. V.P., Gen. Counsel & Sec.--Vencor, Inc., Louisville, KY; *U.S. Public*, pg. 1711
Ford, Gary, V.P., Gen. Counsel & Sec.--Axent Technologies, Rockville, MD; *U.S. Public*, pg. 157
Ford, Peggy, V.P., Gen. Counsel & Sec.--La Petite Academy Inc., Overland Park, KS; *U.S. Private*, pg. 640
Ford, Steven J., V.P., Gen. Counsel & Sec.--Carlisle Companies Incorporated, Syracuse, NY; *U.S. Public*, pg. 305
Forehand, N. Carolyn, V.P. & Gen. Counsel--Phycor, Inc., Nashville, TN; *U.S. Public*, pg. 1293
Foremny, Brian, Gen. Counsel & Sec.--CyberGuard Corporation, Fort Lauderdale, FL; *U.S. Public*, pg. 470
Forman, Thomas M., V.P. & Gen. Counsel--Sealy Corporation, Cleveland, OH; *U.S. Private*, pg. 978
Forsstedt, Kurt-Erik, V.P. & Gen. Counsel--Fiskars Oy AB, Helsinki, Finland; *Int'l*, pg. 492
Forte, Wesley E., Exec. V.P. & Gen. Counsel--USLIFE Corporation, New York, NY; *U.S. Public*, pg. 77
Fortenbaugh, Samuel B., III, Gen. Counsel--Goodman Equipment Corp., Bedford Park, IL; *U.S. Private*, pg. 464
Fortin, Raymond D., Sr. V.P. & Sec.--SunTrust Banks, Inc., Atlanta, GA; *U.S. Public*, pg. 1537
Fortin, Waldo, V.P.-Legal Affairs--CODELCO Chile (Corporacion Nacional Del Cobre De Chile), Santiago, Chile; *Int'l*, pg. 302
Fortun, Jay, Gen. Counsel--Wickland Corporation, Sacramento, CA; *U.S. Private*, pg. 1174
Foster, Roger L., V.P. & Gen. Counsel--Mylan Laboratories, Inc., Pittsburgh, PA; *U.S. Public*, pg. 1143
Fountain, John E., V.P., Gen. Counsel & Sec.--Morrison Health Care Inc., Smyrna, GA; *U.S. Public*, pg. 1133
Fourniadis, Robert A., Sr. V.P., Gen. Counsel & Sec.--Calton, Inc., Manalapan, NJ; *U.S. Public*, pg. 296
Fowler, J. Edward, Gen. Counsel--Mobil Oil Corporation, Fairfax, VA; *U.S. Public*, pg. 1118
Fox, Catherine, Gen. Counsel--Alcatel Cit (S.A.), Velizy-Villacoublay, France; *Int'l*, pg. 56
Fox, D. V., Gen. Counsel--Ferolie Group, Montvale, NJ; *U.S. Private*, pg. 401
Fox, Deborah, V.P. & Gen. Counsel--BTG, Inc., Fairfax, VA; *U.S. Public*, pg. 164
Fox, Robert, Sr. V.P.-Fin. & Admin., Treas. & Sec.--Rocor Transportation Companies Inc., Oklahoma City, OK; *U.S. Private*, pg. 938
Fox, Stacy, Gen. Counsel--Johnson Controls, Inc., Plymouth, MI; *U.S. Public*, pg. 932
Fox, Stephen, V.P., Gen. Counsel & Sec.--Amperif Corporation, Chatsworth, CA; *U.S. Public*, pg. 1523
Fraedrich, Michael, Dir.-Legal Dept.--IKB Deutsche Industriebank AG, Dusseldorf, Germany; *Int'l*, pg. 645
Franchi, Cristina, Gen. Counsel--Benetton Group S.p.A., Ponzano Veneto, Italy; *Int'l*, pg. 186
Francis, Kathleen C., Assoc. Counsel & Asst. Sec.--Interpool, Inc., Princeton, NJ; *U.S. Public*, pg. 908
Francis, William, Chief Fin. Officer, Treas. & Controller--Captive-Aire Systems, Inc., Youngsville, NC; *U.S. Private*, pg. 207
Frank, Alan, Sr. V.P. & Gen. Counsel--Olympia & York Developments Ltd., Toronto, Canada; *Int'l*, pg. 1004
Frank, Bernie, Gen. Counsel & Sec.--Williams Patent Crusher and Pulverizer Co., Saint Louis, MO; *U.S. Private*, pg. 1178
Frank, Jacob, V.P. & Gen. Counsel--Data General Corporation, Westborough, MA; *U.S. Public*, pg. 485
Frank, Lloyd, Gen. Counsel & Sec.--Esquire Radio & Electronics Inc., Brooklyn, NY; *U.S. Private*, pg. 383
Frank, Sanford B., Gen. Counsel & Sec.--Toymax International Inc., Plainview, NY; *U.S. Public*, pg. 1626
Frank, Steven N., V.P., Assoc. Gen. Counsel & Sec.--McDonnell Aircraft & Missile Systems Div., Berkeley, MO; *U.S. Public*, pg. 241
Frankel, Edward M., Chief Fin. Officer, V.P. & Gen. Counsel--Standard Textile Co., Inc., Cincinnati, OH; *U.S. Private*, pg. 1032
Frankel, Jeffrey A.H., V.P.-Legal & Asst. Sec.--MicroAge, Inc., Tempe, AZ; *U.S. Public*, pg. 1104
Frankel, Sam, Chief Gen. Counsel--AFC Enterprises, Atlanta, GA; *U.S. Private*, pg. 5
Franken, Paul, Dr., Chief Legal Advisor--Dresdner Bank AG, Frankfurt/Main, Germany; *Int'l*, pg. 417
Franklin, Earl R., Sec. & Assoc. Gen. Counsel--Eaton Corporation, Cleveland, OH; *U.S. Public*, pg. 555
Franklin, J.E., II, Sec. & Gen. Counsel--Atlantic Electric Co., Pleasantville, NJ; *U.S. Public*, pg. 430
Franklin, Malcolm G., Asst. V.P. & Corp. Counsel--Selective Insurance Group, Inc, Branchville, NJ; *U.S. Public*, pg. 1455
Franklin, Malcolm G., V.P. & Gen. Counsel--Selective Technical Administrative Services, Inc., Branchville, NJ; *U.S. Public*, pg. 1456
Frankovich, George, Sec. & Gen. Counsel--Sterling Inc., Akron, OH; *Int'l*, pg. 1248
Frantz, Francis X., Sr. V.P.-External Affairs, Gen Counsel & Sec.--ALLTEL Corporation, Little Rock, AR; *U.S. Public*, pg. 55
Frasco, Robert A., Esq., V.P., Gen. Counsel & Sec.--Devon Group, Inc., Stamford, CT; *U.S. Public*, pg. 503
Fraser, Brian G., V.P.-Admin. & Gen. Counsel--Clark Foodservice, Inc., Elk Grove Village, IL; *U.S. Private*, pg. 242
Frasier, Ralph K., Gen. Counsel & Sec.--Huntington Bancshares Inc., Columbus, OH; *U.S. Public*, pg. 849
Frasier, Ralph K., Exec. V.P., Gen. Counsel, Sec. & Cashier--Huntington National Bank, Columbus, OH; *U.S. Public*, pg. 850
Frawley, Frederic, Sec. & Sr. Attorney--Central and South West Corporation, Dallas, TX; *U.S. Public*, pg. 324
Fray, Jennifer H., Gen. Counsel & Sec.--Hart Holding Company, Inc., Norwalk, CT; *U.S. Private*, pg. 507
Frazer, Miriam K., Chief Fin. Officer & V.P.--Software Publishing Corporation, Fairfield, NJ; *U.S. Public*, pg. 1483
Frazer, Robert H., Esq., V.P., Gen. Counsel & Sec.--ACMAT Corporation, New Britain, CT; *U.S. Public*, pg. 16
Frazer, Robert H., Esq., V.P., Gen. Counsel & Sec.--United Coastal Insurance Company, New Britain, CT; *U.S. Public*, pg. 16
Frederickson, John S., V.P.-Admin. & Gen. Counsel--Mesaba Holdings, Inc., Minneapolis, MN; *U.S. Public*, pg. 1099
Fredinburg, Wes, Sr. V.P. & Gen. Counsel--National Car Rental System, Inc., Minneapolis, MN; *U.S. Public*, pg. 1379
Free, William J., V.P. & Asst. Gen. Counsel--SBC Communications Inc., San Antonio, TX; *U.S. Public*, pg. 1415
Freed, Dean, Gen. Counsel--Mentor Graphics Corporation, Wilsonville, OR; *U.S. Public*, pg. 1086
Freed, Sharon V., V.P., Bank Counsel & Sec.--The Trustcompany Bancorporation, Jersey City, NJ; *U.S. Public*, pg. 1643
Freedman, James, Gen. Counsel--Cavco Industries, Inc., Phoenix, AZ; *U.S. Public*, pg. 323
Freedman, James D., Gen. Counsel--Progress Software Corporation, Bedford, MA; *U.S. Public*, pg. 1334
Freedman, Larry S., Sr. V.P., Gen. Counsel & Sec.--Platinum Technology, Inc., Oak Brook Terrace, IL; *U.S. Public*, pg. 1309
Freedman, Sanford, Exec. V.P. & Gen. Counsel--Tollman/Hundley Hotels, Hopewell Junction, NY; *U.S. Private*, pg. 1090
Frelinghuysen, Peter, Legal Counsel--KOA Holdings, New York, NY; *U.S. Private*, pg. 603
Freund, Allan G., V.P.-Gen. Counsel--Mercedes-Benz of North America, Inc., Montvale, NJ; *Int'l*, pg. 368
Frey, J.J., Gen. Counsel--Kraft Jacobs Suchard, Velizy-Villacoublay, France; *U.S. Public*, pg. 1290
Fricklas, Michael D., Sr. V.P.-Legal & Deputy Gen. Counsel--Viacom Inc., New York, NY; *U.S. Private*, pg. 775
Fridman, Josef J., Sr. V.P.-Law, Corp. Services & Sec.--BCE Inc., Montreal, Canada; *Int'l*, pg. 114
Fried, Samuel P., V.P. & Gen. Counsel--The Limited, Inc., Columbus, OH; *U.S. Public*, pg. 995
Friedlander, Bruce, Gen. Counsel--The Keyes Company Realtors, Miami, FL; *U.S. Private*, pg. 618
Friedman, Arnold M., V.P. & Deputy Gen. Counsel--Textron Inc., Providence, RI; *U.S. Public*, pg. 1588
Friedman, Charlene Andros, Gen. Counsel & Asst. Sec.--Collagen Corporation, Palo Alto, CA; *U.S. Public*, pg. 399
Friedman, Gary E., Corp. V.P. & Gen. Counsel--Agouron Pharmaceuticals, Inc., La Jolla, CA; *U.S. Public*, pg. 28
Friedman, Gerry, Gen. Counsel--Fox Television Stations Inc., Los Angeles, CA; *Int'l*, pg. 926
Friedman, Samuel, V.P. & Gen. Counsel--Millennium Inorganic Chemicals, Hunt Valley, MD; *Int'l*, pg. 593
Friend, Paul S., V.P.-Legal--Federal Home Loan Bank of New York, New York, NY; *U.S. Private*, pg. 399
Friend, William K., V.P., Sec. & Counsel--Hills Stores Co., Canton, MA; *U.S. Public*, pg. 828
Frierson, Robert W., V.P. & Asst. Sec.--Southern County Mutual Insurance Company, Dallas, TX; *Int'l*, pg. 346
Frierson, Robert W., V.P. & Asst. Sec.--Allied Premium Finance, Dallas, TX; *Int'l*, pg. 346
Frising, Roland, Gen. Mgr.-Legal Engrng.--Banque Generale du Luxembourg SA, Luxembourg, Luxembourg; *Int'l*, pg. 161
Frith, Barbara, Gen. Counsel--Phoenix Medical Technology, Inc., Andrews, SC; *U.S. Public*, pg. 1292
Fritz, David, Group Counsel--Sony Electronics, Park Ridge, NJ; *Int'l*, pg. 1281
Fritz, Jerald N., V.P. & Gen. Counsel--Allbritton Communications Company, Washington, DC; *U.S. Private*, pg. 854
Froberg, James, Sr. V.P. & Gen. Counsel--LINC Capital Group, Chicago, IL; *U.S. Public*, pg. 996
Froberg, Tom, V.P. & Gen. Counsel--Sophus Berendsen A/S, Soeborg, Denmark; *Int'l*, pg. 1284
Froga, Jose Roberto N., Gen. Counsel--3M Do Brasil Ltda., Sao Paulo, Brazil; *U.S. Public*, pg. 1606
Fromm, Charles B., V.P. & Gen. Counsel--Cable Design Technologies Corporation, Pittsburgh, PA; *U.S. Public*, pg. 287
Fromm, Frederick A., Jr., Gen. Counsel--Delco Electronics Overseas Corporation, Detroit, MI; *U.S. Public*, pg. 721
Frost, Thomas E., Sr. V.P. & Gen. Counsel--The Mills Corporation, Arlington, VA; *U.S. Public*, pg. 1113

Fujikawa, Helio Shiguenobu, Dir.-Legal Affairs--Petrobras - Petroleo Brasileiro S.A., Rio de Janeiro, Brazil; *Int'l*, pg. 1041
Fuller, Glenn, Corp. Counsel--Freedom Communication Inc., Irvine, CA; *U.S. Private*, pg. 425
Fullerton, Jon O., V.P. & Gen. Counsel--Rexel, Inc., Coral Gables, FL; *Int'l*, pg. 1107
Fulton, Anita, Grp. Dir.-Legal--Dorling Kindersley Holdings plc, London, United Kingdom; *Int'l*, pg. 416
Fulton, Steven P., V.P.-H.R. & Gen. Counsel--Respironics, Inc., Pittsburgh, PA; *U.S. Public*, pg. 1383
Funke, R., V.P.-Admin. & Gen. Counsel--Princess Hotels International Inc., New York, NY; *Int'l*, pg. 818
Furey, John J., Gen. Counsel & Sec.--Campbell Soup Company, Camden, NJ; *U.S. Public*, pg. 298
Furlow, Brenda, Sr. V.P. & Gen. Counsel--Credit Union National Association, Madison, WI; *U.S. Private*, pg. 288
Furman, Jack, Gen. Counsel--BankAtlantic Bancorp, Inc., Fort Lauderdale, FL; *U.S. Public*, pg. 183
Furman, John, Gen. Counsel--Cerprobe Corporation, Gilbert, AZ; *U.S. Public*, pg. 332
Fuson, Harold W., Jr., Sec. & Chief Legal Officer--The Copley Press, Inc., La Jolla, CA; *U.S. Private*, pg. 275
Futch, Michael, V.P., Gen. Counsel & Sec.--Granite Construction Incorporated, Watsonville, CA; *U.S. Public*, pg. 759
Fynn, David H., V.P.-Compliance--National City Corporation, Cleveland, OH; *U.S. Public*, pg. 1154
Gaan, Cary A., Sr. V.P. & Gen. Counsel--Bally Total Fitness Holdings Corporation, Chicago, IL; *U.S. Public*, pg. 171
Gaan, Cary A., Sr. V.P. & Gen. Counsel--Bally Total Fitness Corporation, Chicago, IL; *U.S. Public*, pg. 171
Gaba, Charles, Gen. Counsel--British Aerospace Holdings Inc., Chantilly, VA; *Int'l*, pg. 218
Gadbaw, R. Michael, V.P. & Sr. Counsel-Intl. Law & Policy--General Electric Company, Fairfield, CT; *U.S. Public*, pg. 709
Gaggella, Vito, Mgr.-Legal Affairs.--Banco Ambrosiano Veneto S.p.A., Milan, Italy; *Int'l*, pg. 138
Gagnon, Lawrence J., V.P., Gen. Counsel & Sec.--Southeastern Michigan Gas Enterprises, Inc., Port Huron, MI; *U.S. Public*, pg. 1489
Gagnon, Louis Gilles, V.P., Gen. Counsel & Sec.--Donohue Inc., Quebec, Canada; *Int'l*, pg. 1075
Gagnon, Louis Gilles, V.P., Gen. Counsel &Sec.--Westburne Inc., Montreal, Canada; *Int'l*, pg. 1491
Gahwilers, Urs, Dr., V.P.-Legal Affairs--Liechtenstein Global Trust Limited, Vaduz, Liechtenstein; *Int'l*, pg. 809
Gail, Dan, Exec. V.P., Sec. & Gen. Counsel--Southwestern Financial Services Corp., Dallas, TX; *U.S. Private*, pg. 1018
Gail, Daniel B., Exec. V.P., Gen. Counsel & Sec.--Constitution Life Insurance Co., Dallas, TX; *U.S. Private*, pg. 1018
Gail, John, Asst. Sec.--Schlosser Forge Company, Rancho Cucamonga, CA; *U.S. Private*, pg. 970
Gailey, John R., III, V.P., Gen. Counsel & Sec.--The West Company, Incorporated, Lionville, PA; *U.S. Public*, pg. 1755
Gaither, Michael, Sr. V.P. & Gen. Counsel--J.H. Heafner Co. Inc., Lincolnton, NC; *U.S. Private*, pg. 514
Galanes, Philip, V.P., Gen. Counsel & Sec.--Golden Books Family Entertainment Inc., New York, NY; *U.S. Public*, pg. 749
Gale, Connie, V.P., Gen. Counsel & Sec.--Frontier Communications Services, Bingham Farms, MI; *U.S. Public*, pg. 684
Galiardo, John W., Vice Chm. & Gen. Counsel--Becton Dickinson & Company, Franklin Lakes, NJ; *U.S. Public*, pg. 199
Gallagher, Dennis V., Gen. Counsel--Power House Technologies, Inc., Bozeman, MT; *U.S. Public*, pg. 1319
Gallagher, Frann M., Asst. Gen. Counsel & Asst. Sec.--International Game Technology, Reno, NV; *U.S. Public*, pg. 900
Gallagher, James G., V.P., Gen. Counsel & Sec.--USA Networks, Inc., Saint Petersburg, FL; *U.S. Public*, pg. 1685
Gallagher, Kevin C., Sr. V.P., Gen. Counsel & Sec.--360 Degrees Communications Company, Chicago, IL; *U.S. Public*, pg. 1607
Gallagher, Thomas E., Exec. V.P. & Gen. Counsel--Hilton Hotels Corporation, Beverly Hills, CA; *U.S. Public*, pg. 828
Gallagher, Thomas W., Sr. V.P., Gen. Counsel & Sec.--Citizens Banking Corporation, Flint, MI; *U.S. Public*, pg. 379
Gallagher, William T., Asst. Corp. Sec. & Asst. Gen. Counsel--Crown Cork & Seal Company, Inc., Philadelphia, PA; *U.S. Public*, pg. 462
Gallagher, Willkie Farry, Gen. Counsel--Menley & James Laboratories, Inc., Horsham, PA; *U.S. Public*, pg. 1086
Galle, R., Gen. Counsel--Campina Melkunie BV, Zaltbommel, Netherlands; *Int'l*, pg. 254
Gallivan, Sarah M., V.P. & Chief Legal Counsel--BJ's Wholesale Club, Inc., Natick, MA; *U.S. Public*, pg. 162
Gallo, Samuel J., Sr. V.P., Gen. Counsel & Sec.--Arthur D. Little, Inc., Cambridge, MA; *U.S. Private*, pg. 670
Gallucci, Sheila, V.P. & Gen. Counsel--Subaru of America, Inc., Cherry Hill, NJ; *Int'l*, pg. 523
Galowich, Ronald H., Exec. V.P., Sec. & Gen. Counsel--First Health Group Corp., Downers Grove, IL; *U.S. Public*, pg. 635
Gamoran, Saul, Exec. V.P., Gen. Counsel & Sec.--Play by Play Toys & Novelties, Inc., San Antonio, TX; *U.S. Public*, pg. 1309
Gannon, Christopher, Gen. Counsel--The Blodgett Oven Co., Inc., Burlington, VT; *U.S. Public*, pg. 1064
Gannon, Christopher R., Gen. Counsel--G.S. Blodgett Corporation, Burlington, VT; *U.S. Public*, pg. 1064
Gans, Robert M., Exec. V.P., Gen. Counsel & Sec.--PriceSmart Inc., San Diego, CA; *U.S. Public*, pg. 1324
Gans, Walter G., V.P. & Gen. Counsel--Siemens Corporation, New York, NY; *Int'l*, pg. 1245
Ganzi, Victor F., Chief Fin. Officer, Exec. V.P. & Legal Officer--The Hearst Corporation, New York, NY; *U.S. Private*, pg. 515
Garay, Joseph P., V.P., Sec. & Gen. Counsel--Bailey, Fischer & Porter Company, Warminster, PA; *Int'l*, pg. 449
Garbade, Nancy C., Sec. & Gen. Counsel--Arrhythmia Research Technology, Inc., Austin, TX; *U.S. Public*, pg. 133
Garber, Robert E., Exec. V.P. & Gen. Counsel--The Equitable Companies Incorporated, New York, NY; *U.S. Public*, pg. 588
Garber, Ronald D., Gen. Counsel & Sec.--Koo Koo Roo, Inc., Los Angeles, CA; *U.S. Public*, pg. 966
Garber, Samuel B., V.P., Gen. Counsel & Sec.--Evans, Inc., Chicago, IL; *U.S. Public*, pg. 596
Gardener, Bruce D., Gen. Counsel, Dir.-Legal Opers. & Sec.--Hartford Life & Accident Insurance Company, Hartford, CT; *U.S. Public*, pg. 795
Gardener, Marvin, Gen. Counsel & Sec.--Loehmann's, Inc., Bronx, NY; *U.S. Public*, pg. 1010
Gardner, James L., Sr. V.P. & Gen. Counsel--A.T. Massey Coal Company, Inc., Richmond, VA; *U.S. Public*, pg. 660
Gardner, John, Gen. Counsel--Inter-Tel, Incorporated, Phoenix, AZ; *U.S. Public*, pg. 888
Gardner, Kathleen D., V.P. & Gen. Counsel--Arkla, Little Rock, AR; *U.S. Public*, pg. 843
Garner, William S., Jr., V.P. & Gen. Counsel--K N Energy, Inc., Lakewood, CO; *U.S. Public*, pg. 937
Garone, Giovanni, Gen. Mgr. & Dir.-Legal--Banca Nazionale del Lavoro Sj.A., Rome, Italy; *Int'l*, pg. 136
Garonzik, Arnon E., Gen. Counsel & Sec.--Environmental Resources Management, Exton, PA; *U.S. Private*, pg. 378
Garr, Louis J., Jr., Exec. V.P. & Gen. Counsel--The May Department Stores Company, Saint Louis, MO; *U.S. Public*, pg. 1063
Garrison, Joanne K., V.P. & Assoc. Gen. Counsel--The Gap, Inc., San Francisco, CA; *U.S. Public*, pg. 702
Garson, Gary, V.P., Deputy Gen. Counsel & Asst. Sec.--Loews Corporation, New York, NY; *U.S. Public*, pg. 1010
Garten, David B., V.P., Gen. Counsel & Sec.--NL Industries, Inc., Houston, TX; *U.S. Private*, pg. 270
Gartenberg, Irving L., Gen. Counsel--Inner Secrets, Inc., Harrison, NJ; *U.S. Private*, pg. 564
Garver, Patrick J., Exec. V.P. & Gen. Counsel--Barrick Gold Corporation, Toronto, Canada; *Int'l*, pg. 168
Gary, Kenneth J., V.P. & Gen. Counsel--Toll Brothers, Inc., Huntingdon Valley, PA; *U.S. Public*, pg. 1620
Garza, Mario M., Reg. Counsel--Anadarko Petroleum Corporation, Houston, TX; *U.S. Public*, pg. 107
Gaskin, George C., Sr. V.P. & Gen. Counsel--Anacomp, Inc., Indianapolis, IN; *U.S. Public*, pg. 106
Gaskin, John R., V.P., Gen. Counsel & Sec.--Duke Realty Investments, Inc., Indianapolis, IN; *U.S. Public*, pg. 535
Gates, Nancy, In-House Council--Exolon-Esk Company, Tonawanda, NY; *U.S. Public*, pg. 600
Gates, Signe S., V.P., Gen. Counsel & Sec.--Axel Johnson Inc., Stamford, CT; *Int'l*, pg. 709
Gates, Stephen F., V.P. & Gen. Counsel--Amoco Corporation, Chicago, IL; *U.S. Public*, pg. 101
Gatewood, Robert C., Sr. Exec. V.P.-Legal Affairs, Sec. & Treas.--Dairy Queen Corporate Store, Louisville, KY; *U.S. Public*, pg. 220
Gattchel, Dave, Lawyer--Graphic Technology, Inc., New Century, KS; *Int'l*, pg. 950
Gatzek, Deborah R., Sr. V.P., Gen. Counsel & Asst. Sec.--Franklin Resources, Inc., San Mateo, CA; *U.S. Public*, pg. 679
Gauck, Charles H., Sec. & Assoc. Gen. Counsel--Alliant Techsystems, Hopkins, MN; *U.S. Public*, pg. 47
Gaudin, Claude, Gen. Counsel & Board Sec.--Lyonnaise des Eaux S.A., Nanterre, France; *Int'l*, pg. 822
Gauthier, P. Wilbrod, V.P.-Legislation & Govt. Relations--Donohue Inc., Quebec, Canada; *Int'l*, pg. 1075
Gavin, Carol Coghlan, V.P, Gen. Counsel. & Asst. Sec.--Tellabs Operations, Inc., Lisle, IL; *U.S. Public*, pg. 1572
Gay, R. Norwood, III, Sr. V.P., Gen. Counsel & Sec.--Attorneys' Title Insurance Fund, Orlando, FL; *U.S. Private*, pg. 98
Gaynor, Mitchell L., V.P., Gen. Counsel & Sec.--Sybase, Inc., Emeryville, CA; *U.S. Public*, pg. 1544
Geckle, Timothy, Corp. Counsel--The Ryland Group, Inc., Columbia, MD; *U.S. Public*, pg. 1414
Geddie, Rowland H., III, V.P., Gen. Counsel & Sec.--O'Sullivan Industries Holdings, Lamar, MO; *U.S. Public*, pg. 1234
Gee, Gregory W., Sr. V.P., Gen. Counsel & Sec.--Sun Life Assurance Company of Canada, Toronto, Canada; *Int'l*, pg. 1318
Geissler, Dietfried, Dr., Mgr.-Law & Patents--DSM Chemie Linz GmbH, Lienz, Austria; *Int'l*, pg. 356
Geizhals, Benjamin, V.P. & Gen. Counsel--Continental Health Affiliates, Inc., Englewood Cliffs, NJ; *U.S. Public*, pg. 440
Geller, Edward, Asst. Gen. Counsel--First Union Real Estate Investments, Cleveland, OH; *U.S. Public*, pg. 640
Geller, Eric P., Sr. V.P., Gen. Counsel & Sec.--Harcourt General, Inc., Chestnut Hill, MA; *U.S. Public*, pg. 782
Gellert, Stephen, Gen. Counsel--James Hardie Industries Ltd., Sydney, Australia; *Int'l*, pg. 596
Gelman, I. Lawrence, V.P., Sec. & Assoc. Counsel--Rite Aid Corporation, Camp Hill, PA; *U.S. Public*, pg. 1390
Gentile, Robert N., V.P.-Law, Gen. Counsel & Sec.--Transtar Holdings, L.P., Monroeville, PA; *U.S. Private*, pg. 1097
Gentry, Hubert, Jr., Sr. V.P., Gen. Counsel & Sec.--NorAm Energy Corp., Houston, TX; *U.S. Public*, pg. 843
Genzer, Marvin D., V.P., Gen. Counsel & Sec.--EDO Corporation, New York, NY; *U.S. Public*, pg. 541
Geoghan, Joseph E., V.P., Gen. Counsel & Sec.--Union Carbide Corporation, Danbury, CT; *U.S. Public*, pg. 1666
Geoghegan, Andrew P., Sr. V.P., Gen. Counsel & Sec.--Hannaford Bros. Co., Scarborough, ME; *U.S. Public*, pg. 781
Geogino, Damian C., V.P., Gen. Counsel & Sec.--United States Filter Corporation, Palm Desert, CA; *U.S. Public*, pg. 1681
George, Armen S., Legal Officer--Up-Right, Inc., Selma, CA; *U.S. Private*, pg. 1128
George, D.C., V.P. & Sr. Land Attorney--Wilshire Oil Co. of Texas, Jersey City, NJ; *U.S. Public*, pg. 1770
Geraldino, Pedro, Gen. Mgr. & Sr. V.P.--Chilton Research Services, Radnor, PA; *Int'l*, pg. 1096
Gernander, Kent, Gen. Counsel--Fastenal Company, Winona, MN; *U.S. Public*, pg. 614
Gerrard, Bob, Gen. Counsel--Home & Garden Television, Knoxville, TN; *U.S. Public*, pg. 1447
Gerson, Elliot S., Sr. V.P. & Asst. Chief Legal Counsel--Rite Aid Corporation, Camp Hill, PA; *U.S. Public*, pg. 1390
Gerstman, George, Legal Officer--JS&A Group, Inc., Las Vegas, NV; *U.S. Private*, pg. 578
Gervais, Steven, V.P.-Gen. Counsel--Suncor Development Company, Phoenix, AZ; *U.S. Public*, pg. 1298
Gestman, Peter, Sr. V.P. & Gen. Counsel--Robson Communities, Sun Lakes, AZ; *U.S. Private*, pg. 937
Getman, Dennis J., Exec. V.P. & Gen. Counsel--Avatar Holdings Inc., Coral Gables, FL; *U.S. Public*, pg. 151
Getz, Herbert, Sr. V.P., Gen. Counsel & Sec.--Waste Management, Inc., Oak Brook, IL; *U.S. Public*, pg. 1744
Getzler, Michael J., V.P. & Attorney--The Dime Savings Bank of New York, New York, NY; *U.S. Public*, pg. 509
Gherlein, Gerald L., Exec. V.P. & Gen. Counsel--Eaton Corporation, Cleveland, OH; *U.S. Public*, pg. 555
Gianetti, Marisa, Coord.-Legal Affairs--SITQ Immobilier, Montreal, Canada; *Int'l*, pg. 249
Giard, A., V.P.-Law & Sec.--Canadian National Railway Company, Montreal, Canada; *Int'l*, pg. 258
Giarla, Pamela, Gen. Counsel--Chicago Holdings, Inc., Pittsburgh, PA; *U.S. Private*, pg. 234
Gibbons, Gregg M., V.P.-Corp. Affairs, Gen. Counsel & Sec.--Wynn's International, Inc., Orange, CA; *U.S. Public*, pg. 1782
Gibbs, Gary, Gen. Counsel--Cinemark USA, Inc., Dallas, TX; *U.S. Private*, pg. 240
Giblin, Pat, Legal Officer--Kampgrounds of America, Inc., Billings, MT; *U.S. Private*, pg. 603
Gibson, Janet, Counsel--The W.W. Williams Company, Columbus, OH; *U.S. Private*, pg. 1178
Gilbert, Bruce, Gen. Counsel--Universal Health Services, Inc., King of Prussia, PA; *U.S. Public*, pg. 1696
Gilbert, James F., Gen. Counsel & Sec.--PrimeEnergy Corporation, Stamford, CT; *U.S. Public*, pg. 1328
Gilbert, Martin G., Asst. Gen. Counsel & Asst Sec.--Wal-Mart Stores, Inc., Bentonville, AR; *U.S. Public*, pg. 1732
Gill, John J., Gen. Counsel--The American Bankers Association, Washington, DC; *U.S. Private*, pg. 51
Gille, Lori-Jean, J.D., Sr. V.P., Gen. Counsel & Sec.--MGI PHARMA INC., Minneapolis, MN; *U.S. Public*, pg. 1026
Gillen, James R., Sr. V.P. & Gen. Counsel--The Prudential Insurance Company of America, Newark, NJ; *U.S. Private*, pg. 892
Gillen, James R., Sr. V.P. & Gen. Counsel--The Prudential Investment Corp., Newark, NJ; *U.S. Private*, pg. 892
Gillespie, Carol J., V.P., Gen. Counsel & Sec.--The Liposome Company, Inc., Princeton, NJ; *U.S. Public*, pg. 1000
Gillespie, Samuel H., III, V.P. & Gen. Counsel--Mobil Oil Corporation, Fairfax, VA; *U.S. Public*, pg. 1118
Gilliam, James H., Jr., Exec. V.P. & Gen. Counsel--Beneficial Corporation, Wilmington, DE; *U.S. Public*, pg. 211
Gimple, Ron, Sr. V.P. & Gen. Counsel--CBL & Associates Properties, Inc., Chattanooga, TN; *U.S. Public*, pg. 273
Gimson, Curtis S., Sr. V.P. & Gen. Counsel--Triarc Restaurant Group, Fort Lauderdale, FL; *U.S. Public*, pg. 1635
Gindin, Peter J., Sr. V.P. & Litigation Counsel--Summit Bancorp, Princeton, NJ; *U.S. Public*, pg. 1527
Ginn, David K., Gen. Counsel & Sec.--Oxford Industries, Inc., Atlanta, GA; *U.S. Public*, pg. 1239
Ginsberg, Lambert L., Esq., Gen. Counsel--The Troy Savings Bank, Troy, NY; *U.S. Private*, pg. 1106
Ginsky, Marvin H., Sr. V.P. & Gen. Counsel--Champion International Corp., Stamford, CT; *U.S. Public*, pg. 333
Giresi, Mark, Worldwide General Counsel--Burger King Corporation, Miami, FL; *Int'l*, pg. 411
Gladden, Joseph R., Jr., Sr. V.P. & Gen. Counsel--The Coca-Cola Company, Atlanta, GA; *U.S. Public*, pg. 392
Glantz, Miles M., Gen. Counsel & Sec.--Wechco, Inc., Princeton, NJ; *U.S. Private*, pg. 1158
Glass, Susan J., Asst. Sec. & Asst. Gen. Counsel--Allergan, Inc., Irvine, CA; *U.S. Public*, pg. 46
Glasscock, Edward, Gen. Counsel--DMI Furniture Inc., Louisville, KY; *U.S. Public*, pg. 473
Gleason, George L., Sr. V.P. & Gen. Counsel--Tetra Tech NUS, Inc., Gaithersburg, MD; *U.S. Public*, pg. 1582
Gleason, Owen, Gen. Counsel--C.H. Robinson Co., Eden Prairie, MN; *U.S. Public*, pg. 1394
Gleberman, Ellen, V.P. & Gen. Counsel--Mitsubishi Motor Sales of America, Inc., Cypress, CA; *Int'l*, pg. 875
Gleiner, Richard, Sr. V.P. & Gen. Counsel--Marcus Cable Company, L.P., Dallas, TX; *U.S. Private*, pg. 702
Glendening, R. Bradley, Sr. V.P., Sec. & Gen. Counsel--Mary Kay Corporation, Dallas, TX; *U.S. Private*, pg. 710
Glenn, John M., V.P., Gen. Counsel & Sec.--Roadway Express, Inc., Akron, OH; *U.S. Public*, pg. 1392
Glover, Reynaldo, Exec. V.P. & Gen. Counsel--TLC Beatrice International Holdings Inc., New York, NY; *U.S. Private*, pg. 1064
Godfrey, Cullen M., Sr. V.P., Gen. Counsel & Sec.--Fina, Inc., Dallas, TX; *Int'l*, pg. 1044
Godiner, Donald L., Sr. V.P., Gen. Counsel & Sec.--Laclede Gas Company, Saint Louis, MO; *U.S. Public*, pg. 973
Godinho, Flavio, V.P.-Legal, South America--TVX Gold Inc., Toronto, Canada; *Int'l*, pg. 1345

Goeller, Michael C., Sec. & Gen. Counsel--Hatzel & Buehler, Inc., Wilmington, DE; *U.S. Private*, pg. 266
Goetsch, Richard J., Mng. Counsel--BP Oil Co., Cleveland, OH; *Int'l*, pg. 220
Goff, Anita R., V.P.-Legal Affairs--Salick Health Care, Inc., Los Angeles, CA; *Int'l*, pg. 1524
Goh, Derek, Gen. Counsel & Sec.--Hai Sun Hup Group Ltd., Singapore, Singapore; *Int'l*, pg. 586
Gold, Peter S., Sr. V.P. & Gen. Counsel--Akzo Nobel Inc., Chicago, IL; *Int'l*, pg. 47
Goldberg, Bryna, V.P. & Gen. Counsel--Shoppers Drug Mart, Ltd., Toronto, Canada; *Int'l*, pg. 112
Goldberg, David S., V.P., Gen. Counsel & Sec.--InterTAN Inc., Fort Worth, TX; *U.S. Public*, pg. 910
Goldberg, Larry, Gen. Counsel & Sec.--Gemstar International Group Limited, Pasadena, CA; *U.S. Public*, pg. 705
Goldberg, Lena G., Sr. V.P. & Gen. Counsel--Fidelity Investments (FMR Corp.), Boston, MA; *U.S. Private*, pg. 402
Goldberg, Marvin A., Sr. Exec. V.P.-Legal & Corp. Affairs & Sec.--Shoppers Drug Mart, Ltd., Toronto, Canada; *Int'l*, pg. 112
Goldberg, Sherman I., Exec. V.P., Gen. Counsel & Sec.--First Chicago NBD Corporation, Chicago, IL; *U.S. Public*, pg. 627
Goldblatt, Jay A., Assoc. Gen. Counsel & Asst. Sec.--Pubco Corporation, Cleveland, OH; *U.S. Public*, pg. 1339
Goldblatt, Stanford J., Gen. Counsel--US ServVis, West Orange, NJ; *U.S. Public*, pg. 1687
Goldenring, Peter, Gen. Counsel--Advance Business Graphics, Mira Loma, CA; *U.S. Private*, pg. 18
Goldin, Edward S., Legal Officer--Union Industries, Inc., Providence, RI; *U.S. Private*, pg. 1119
Golding, A.C., Gen. Counsel--LASMO plc, London, United Kingdom; *Int'l*, pg. 803
Golding, H., Legal Counsel--Burns, Philp & Company Limited, Sydney, Australia; *Int'l*, pg. 236
Goldings, Morris, Gen. Counsel & Sec.--Jet Spray Corp., Norwood, MA; *U.S. Private*, pg. 586
Goldner, Leonard H., Sr. V.P. & Gen. Counsel--Symbol Technologies, Inc., Holtsville, NY; *U.S. Public*, pg. 1546
Goldsmith, Harry L., Gen. Counsel & Sec.--AutoZone, Inc., Memphis, TN; *U.S. Public*, pg. 150
Goldstein, Ned, Sr. V.P. & Gen. Counsel--Ticketmaster Corporation, West Hollywood, CA; *U.S. Private*, pg. 1084
Gonzales, Ignacio, Gen. Counsel & Dir.-Data Processing--Cash & Carry Grocer Inc., Chicago, IL; *U.S. Private*, pg. 218
Gonzalez Gonzalez, Enrique, Legal Counsel--Grupo IMSA S.A. de C.V., Garza Garcia, Mexico; *Int'l*, pg. 575
Gonzalez, Richard J., Chief Fin. Officer, V.P., Treas. & Sec.--Bayou Steel Corporation, La Place, LA; *U.S. Public*, pg. 197
Goodkin, Richard P., Corp. Counsel--Thinking Machines Corporation, Burlington, MA; *U.S. Private*, pg. 1081
Goodman, James A., Gen. Counsel & Sec.--Day & Zimmermann, Inc., Philadelphia, PA; *U.S. Private*, pg. 316
Goodman, Roy B., Sr. V.P.-Fin., Sec. & Treas.--Heilig-Meyers Company, Richmond, VA; *U.S. Public*, pg. 804
Goodrich, H.L., Sec. & Gen. Counsel--Dan River Inc., Danville, VA; *U.S. Public*, pg. 478
Goodwin, Mark B., V.P. & Gen. Counsel--Overnite Transportation Co., Richmond, VA; *U.S. Public*, pg. 1668
Goody, Alycia, Gen Counsel & Sec.--Providence Energy Corporation, Providence, RI; *U.S. Public*, pg. 1337
Goonrey, Charles W., V.P. & Gen. Counsel--AMP Incorporated, Harrisburg, PA; *U.S. Public*, pg. 7
Gordan, Cynthia, V.P.-Human Resources & Legal Counsel--Quaker Fabric Corporation, Fall River, MA; *U.S. Public*, pg. 1347
Gordon, Dale, Gen. Counsel--Golden Books Publishing, New York, NY; *U.S. Public*, pg. 749
Gordon, Gail J., Corp. Counsel/U.S.A.--Royal Oak Mines Inc., Kirkland, WA; *U.S. Public*, pg. 1410
Gordon, George D., Asst. Gen. Counsel--Falconbridge Limited, Toronto, Canada; *Int'l*, pg. 433
Gordon, Lawrence M., V.P. & Gen. Counsel--GP Strategies Corporation, New York, NY; *U.S. Public*, pg. 694
Gordon, Mark, Counsel--Amcel Corp., Watertown, MA; *U.S. Private*, pg. 48
Gordon, S. Amber, Sec.--Hadron, Inc., Alexandria, VA; *U.S. Public*, pg. 773
Gordon, Sherwood, Gen. Counsel--Lightalarms Electronics Corporation, Baldwin, NY; *Int'l*, pg. 725
Gordonsmith, John A., Exec. V.P.-Treasury, Legal & Corp. Sec.--FCA International Ltd., Westmount, Canada; *Int'l*, pg. 470
Gorham, William, Gen. Counsel & Sec.--Zoll Medical Corporation, Burlington, MA; *U.S. Private*, pg. 1207
Gorin, Robert S., Sr. V.P., Gen. Counsel & Sec.--W.R. Berkley Corporation, Greenwich, CT; *U.S. Public*, pg. 215
Gorlin, Robert H., V.P. & Gen. Counsel--Guardian Industries Corp., Auburn Hills, MI; *U.S. Private*, pg. 485
Gorman, Hal V., V.P. & Gen. Counsel--IDV North America, Fort Lee, NJ; *Int'l*, pg. 411
Gorman, Jeff, V.P. & Gen. Counsel--Adventure Tours USA, Inc., Dallas, TX; *U.S. Private*, pg. 22
Goss, Rebecca O., V.P. & Gen. Counsel--Eli Lilly and Company, Indianapolis, IN; *U.S. Public*, pg. 992
Gotkin, Michael S., Sr. V.P. & Gen. Counsel--Farley Candy Company, Chicago, IL; *U.S. Private*, pg. 397
Gotlieb, Heidi, Gen. Counsel--Grandy's, Inc., Lewisville, TX; *U.S. Private*, pg. 61
Gotte, Dennis, V.P. & Gen. Counsel--Armour Swift Eckrich, Downers Grove, IL; *U.S. Public*, pg. 426
Gottesman, Joel, Sr. V.P, Gen. Counsel & Sec.--Green Tree Financial Corporation, Saint Paul, MN; *U.S. Public*, pg. 761
Gottesman, M., Legal Officer--Antwerp Diamond Distributors Inc., New York, NY; *U.S. Private*, pg. 76
Gowland, Karen, V.P., Corp. Sec. & Asst. Gen. Counsel--Boise Cascade Corporation, Boise, ID; *U.S. Public*, pg. 242
Gozo, Sara J., V.P. & Corp. Sec.--The Turner Corporation, New York, NY; *U.S. Public*, pg. 1645
Graass, James H., V.P. & Gen. Counsel--CTX Mortgage Co., Inc., Dallas, TX; *U.S. Public*, pg. 323
Grabell, Neil S., Sr. V.P., Gen. Counsel & Sec.--QVC, Inc., West Chester, PA; *U.S. Private*, pg. 897
Graf, George H., Gen. Patent Counsel--Alcatel N.V., Amsterdam, Netherlands; *Int'l*, pg. 55
Grafstrom, Nils, Exec. V.P. & Gen. Counsel--Stora Kopparbergs Bergslags AB, Falun, Sweden; *Int'l*, pg. 1302
Graham, Alma, Gen. Counsel--UHP Healthcare, Inglewood, CA; *U.S. Private*, pg. 1113
Graham, Edward H., V.P. & Gen. Counsel--Maytag Corporation, Newton, IA; *U.S. Public*, pg. 1064
Graham, Lawrence E., Sr. V.P. & Counsel--USLIFE Corporation, New York, NY; *U.S. Public*, pg. 77
Graham, William H., V.P., Gen. Counsel & Sec.--Bethlehem Steel Corporation, Bethlehem, PA; *U.S. Public*, pg. 226
Granat, Peter M., Sr. V.P. & Legal Counsel--United Missouri Bank N.A., Kansas City, MO; *U.S. Public*, pg. 1654
Grandis, Leslie A., Gen. Counsel--Markel Corporation, Glen Allen, VA; *U.S. Public*, pg. 1046
Grant, Philip J., Co. Sec. & Legal Counsel--Skandia UK Insurance plc, London, United Kingdom; *Int'l*, pg. 1258
Grantner, Francis J., Gen. Counsel & Sec.--Rieth-Riley Construction Co. Inc., Goshen, IN; *U.S. Private*, pg. 930
Granzier, Paul A., V.P., Gen. Counsel & Sec.--RPM, Inc., Medina, OH; *U.S. Public*, pg. 1356
Graves, James T., Vice Chm., Gen. Counsel & Sec.--Mark VII, Inc., Memphis, TN; *U.S. Public*, pg. 1046
Graves, James T., Gen. Counsel & Sec.--Mark VII Transportation Company, Inc., Greenwood, IN; *U.S. Public*, pg. 1046
Graves, John, Sr. V.P.-Legal Affairs & Bus. Ventures--Earl G. Graves, Ltd., New York, NY; *U.S. Private*, pg. 471
Graves, Kathy, Contracts Counsel--The Cerplex Group, Inc., Tustin, CA; *U.S. Public*, pg. 332
Graves, Ronald N., V.P., Gen. Counsel & Sec.--J.R. Simplot Company, Boise, ID; *U.S. Private*, pg. 1002
Gray, Jeffrey E., Sr. Corp. Counsel & Asst. Sec.--Lowe's Companies, Inc., North Wilkesboro, NC; *U.S. Public*, pg. 1015
Gray, S. Garrett, Gen. Counsel & Sec.--Minerals Technologies, Inc., New York, NY; *U.S. Public*, pg. 1115
Grayson, Edward D., V.P. & Gen. Counsel--Honeywell Inc., Minneapolis, MN; *U.S. Public*, pg. 833
Graziano, Anthony W., Jr., V.P., Gen. Counsel & Sec.--Stant Corporation, Denver, CO; *Int'l*, pg. 1396
Green, D.J., V.P. & Assoc. Gen. Counsel--Emerson Electric Co., Saint Louis, MO; *U.S. Public*, pg. 572
Green, Jack, Sr. V.P. & Gen. Counsel--Converse Inc., North Reading, MA; *U.S. Public*, pg. 441
Green, Joseph T., V.P., Gen. Counsel & Sec.--TCF Bank Minnesota FSB, Minneapolis, MN; *U.S. Public*, pg. 1554
Green, Kenneth, V.P.-Human Resources, Real Estate & Gen. Counsel--Gantos Inc., Stamford, CT; *U.S. Public*, pg. 702
Green, Michael, Gen. Counsel--Sizzler International, Inc., Los Angeles, CA; *U.S. Public*, pg. 1475
Green, Robert, Gen. Counsel--Empress International Ltd., Port Washington, NY; *U.S. Private*, pg. 375
Green, Stewart E., V.P., Gen. Counsel & Sec.--George Weston Limited, Toronto, Canada; *Int'l*, pg. 1494
Green, Thomas B., Gen. Counsel & Sec.--Dell Computer Corporation, Round Rock, TX; *U.S. Public*, pg. 495
Green, William G., Esq., Sr. V.P., Gen. Counsel & Sec.--Chiron Corporation, Emeryville, CA; *U.S. Public*, pg. 349
Greenberg, Howard, Gen. Counsel--Ruetgers-Nease Corporation, State College, PA; *Int'l*, pg. 1148
Greenberg, Marc L., Asst. Gen. Counsel--Eagle-Picher Industries, Inc., Cincinnati, OH; *U.S. Private*, pg. 355
Greenberger, Joseph, Gen. Counsel & Sec.--Moore Medical Corp., New Britain, CT; *U.S. Public*, pg. 1128
Greene, James, Gen. Counsel--Gary-Williams Energy Corporation, Denver, CO; *U.S. Private*, pg. 440
Greene, Joe, Gen. Counsel--O'Reilly Automotive Inc., Springfield, MO; *U.S. Public*, pg. 1230
Greene, Margaret H., V.P. & Gen. Counsel--BellSouth Telecommunications, Inc., Atlanta, GA; *U.S. Public*, pg. 209
Greene, Stephen R., Gen. Counsel--Credit Suisse First Boston, Inc., New York, NY; *Int'l*, pg. 345
Gregory, George, Gen. Counsel--Home Savings of America, FSB, Irwindale, CA; *U.S. Public*, pg. 29
Greve, Jan M., Sr. V.P. & Gen. Counsel--Kvaerner a.s.a., Lysaker, Norway; *Int'l*, pg. 766
Grey, R.W., Company Solicitor--George Wimpey PLC, London, United Kingdom; *Int'l*, pg. 1510
Grey, Robert J., Sr. V.P., Gen. Counsel & Sec.--PP&L Resources, Allentown, PA; *U.S. Public*, pg. 1244
Grey, Robert J., Sr. V.P., Gen. Counsel & Sec.--Pennsylvania Power & Light Company-Lehigh Div., Allentown, PA; *U.S. Public*, pg. 1244
Griffith, Brian, Sec. & Gen. Counsel--MFA Incorporated, Columbia, MO; *U.S. Private*, pg. 686
Griffith, G. Sanders, III, Sr. Exec. V.P., Gen. Counsel & Sec.--Synovus Financial Corp., Columbus, GA; *U.S. Public*, pg. 1548
Grigsby, Lonnie O., Exec. V.P. & Gen. Counsel--IBP, Inc., Dakota City, NE; *U.S. Public*, pg. 852
Grimm, Kurt R., V.P. & Gen. Counsel--Galderma Laboratories, Inc., Fort Worth, TX; *Int'l*, pg. 819
Grimstad, John A., Gen. Counsel & Sec.--Waters Instruments, Inc., Rochester, MN; *U.S. Public*, pg. 1745
Grinstein, Jeffrey M., Exec. V.P., Gen. Counsel, & Sec.--American Waste Services, Inc., Warren, OH; *U.S. Public*, pg. 94
Grisham, R.B., V.P.-Legal--Halliburton Energy Services, Carrollton, TX; *U.S. Public*, pg. 776
Gritchen, Lyle S., Sr. V.P., Gen. Counsel & Sec.--Qual-Med, Inc., Pueblo, CO; *U.S. Public*, pg. 678
Grocock, J. Bennet, Gen. Counsel--Spray-Tech, Inc., Longwood, FL; *U.S. Private*, pg. 1026
Groen, Keith C., V.P.-Legal & Sec.--Aaron Rents, Inc., Atlanta, GA; *U.S. Public*, pg. 12
Groetzinger, Jon, Jr., Sr. V.P., Gen. Counsel & Sec.--American Greetings Corporation, Cleveland, OH; *U.S. Public*, pg. 77
Grommers, L.E.R., Dir.-Legal Affairs--Koninklijke Hoogovens N.V., Ijmuiden, Netherlands; *Int'l*, pg. 753
Grommers, L.E.R., Dir.-Legal Affairs--Hoogovens Groep B.V., Ijmuiden, Netherlands; *Int'l*, pg. 753
Groninger, Donald L., Exec. V.P., Gen. Counsel & Sr. Compliance Officer--Bridgestone/Firestone, Inc., Nashville, TN; *Int'l*, pg. 213
Gronningsaeter, Marius H., Sr. V.P.-Legal, Gen. Counsel & Sec.--Elkem ASA, Oslo, Norway; *Int'l*, pg. 446
Gross, Bennett S., V.P., Gen. Counsel & Sec.--Caldor, Inc., Norwalk, CT; *U.S. Public*, pg. 292
Gross, Bert M., Sr. V.P. & Gen. Counsel--Regis Corporation, Minneapolis, MN; *U.S. Public*, pg. 1373
Gross, Douglas H., V.P., Gen. Counsel & Sec.--Computer Language Research, Inc., Carrollton, TX; *U.S. Public*, pg. 421
Gross, Lawrence A., V.P., Gen. Counsel & Sec.--SunGard Data Systems Inc., Wayne, PA; *U.S. Public*, pg. 1534
Gross, Murray, Sr. V.P., Gen. Counsel & Clerk--EG & G, Inc., Wellesley, MA; *U.S. Public*, pg. 542
Gross, Richard B., Sr. V.P., Gen. Counsel & Sec.--AMBAC Financial Group, Inc., New York, NY; *U.S. Public*, pg. 62
Grossman, Carole, Corp. Counsel--Lund International Holdings, Inc., Anoka, MN; *U.S. Public*, pg. 1020
Grossman, Mitchell, V.P.-Legal Compliance/U.S.A.--FCA International Ltd., Westmount, Canada; *Int'l*, pg. 470
Grossmann, Ralph L., Sec.--The Reliable Life Insurance Company, Webster Groves, MO; *U.S. Public*, pg. 1374
Grover, James R., Jr., Esq., Gen. Counsel--TII Industries, Inc., Copiague, NY; *U.S. Public*, pg. 1556
Groves, Vaughn R., V.P. & Gen. Counsel--Pittston Minerals Group, Inc., Lebanon, VA; *U.S. Public*, pg. 1305
Grube, T., Sr. V.P., Gen Counsel & Sec.--Mack Trucks, Inc., Allentown, PA; *Int'l*, pg. 1102
Guarriello, Joseph L., Exec. V.P., Gen. Counsel & Sec.--Mid Atlantic Medical Services, Inc., Rockville, MD; *U.S. Public*, pg. 1109
Gubman, Irwin L., Gen. Counsel & Sec.--Imperial Credit Industries, Inc., Torrance, CA; *U.S. Public*, pg. 872
Gudgel, Thomas H., Grp. V.P. & Gen. Counsel--Blue Cross and Blue Shield of Oklahoma, Tulsa, OK; *U.S. Private*, pg. 151
Guerin, Stephan, Gen. Counsel--Alcatel N.V., Amsterdam, Netherlands; *Int'l*, pg. 55
Guerra, Michael, V.P.-Legal Services--Chi-Chi's Inc., Louisville, KY; *U.S. Private*, pg. 393
Guerriero, Tim, Gen. Counsel--T & N Industries, Inc., Ann Arbor, MI; *Int'l*, pg. 1334
Guinn, Donald E., Asst. Gen. Counsel--Aluminum Company of America, Pittsburgh, PA; *U.S. Public*, pg. 60
Gullace, Dante, Gen. Counsel--Travel Ports of America Inc., Rochester, NY; *U.S. Public*, pg. 1632
Gundersen, Mark, Gen. Counsel--DCV Inc., Wilmington, DE; *U.S. Private*, pg. 301
Gunter, Joe T., Sr. V.P. & Special Counsel--Fairfield Communities, Inc., Little Rock, AR; *U.S. Public*, pg. 610
Gunther, Robert A., Sr. V.P. & Assoc. Counsel--Summit Bancorp, Princeton, NJ; *U.S. Public*, pg. 1527
Gura, Philip P., Corp. Counsel--LaRoche Industries Inc., Atlanta, GA; *U.S. Private*, pg. 651
Gurion, Henry B., V.P. & Corp. Counsel--MI-Jack Products, Inc., Hazel Crest, IL; *U.S. Private*, pg. 740
Gust, Anne B. ., Sr. V.P. & Gen. Counsel--The Gap, Inc., San Francisco, CA; *U.S. Public*, pg. 702
Gust, Morgan M., V.P.-Admin., Gen. Counsel & Sec.--Giant Industries Inc., Scottsdale, AZ; *U.S. Public*, pg. 741
Gustafson, Bengt, Sr. V.P. & Chief Legal Counsel--Svedala Industri AB, Malmo, Sweden; *Int'l*, pg. 1323
Gutierrez, Jorge Barrera, Gen. Counsel--Empressa La Moderna SA de CV, Monterrey, Mexico; *Int'l*, pg. 454
Gyselinck, Rodolphe, Gen. Counsel--Cockerill Sambre, Brussels, Belgium; *Int'l*, pg. 301
Haarer, G. Donald, Sec. & Legal Officer--ITT Cannon Sealectro, New Britain, CT; *U.S. Public*, pg. 859
Hackler, Don, Gen. Counsel--N.B.M. Corp., McAlester, OK; *U.S. Private*, pg. 771
Haesler, Pierre F., Dir.-Legal Affairs--Holderbank Financiere Glaris Ltd., Glaris, Switzerland; *Int'l*, pg. 628
Hafer, Thomas F., Sr. V.P., Gen. Counsel & Sec.--Salient 3 Communications, Inc., Reading, PA; *U.S. Public*, pg. 1429
Hafner, T.M., V.P. & Gen. Counsel--Philips Consumer Electronics, Knoxville, TN; *Int'l*, pg. 1054
Hagan, Julia P., Sec. & Corp. Counsel--Vermont American Tool Corp., Louisville, KY; *U.S. Public*, pg. 575
Hagan, R.R., Gen. Counsel--LaSalle Partners, Chicago, IL; *U.S. Public*, pg. 978
Hageman, Douglas L., Sr. V.P. & Gen. Counsel--TrizecHahn Centers Inc., San Diego, CA; *Int'l*, pg. 1425
Hageman, John A., Sr. V.P. & Gen. Counsel--Metals USA, Inc., Houston, TX; *U.S. Public*, pg. 1100
Hageman, John A., Sr. V.P.-Legal Affairs, Gen. Counsel & Sec.--Physician Corporation of America, Miami, FL; *U.S. Public*, pg. 1293
Hagorrt, Thomas H., Gen. Counsel & Sec.--Albany International Corp., Albany, NY; *U.S. Public*, pg. 36
Hahn, David, Sr. V.P., Gen. Counsel & Sec.--The Titan Corporation, San Diego, CA; *U.S. Public*, pg. 1618
Hailey, J.M., Legal Counsel--Williams International, Walled Lake, MI; *U.S. Private*, pg. 1178
Hain, Mark, V.P., Gen. Counsel & Sec.--Norrell Corporation, Atlanta, GA; *U.S. Public*, pg. 1192
Haines, Dennis, Gen Counsel & Sec.--Zurn Industries, Inc., Erie, PA; *U.S. Public*, pg. 1794

Haines, Gerald A., III, Sec. & Gen. Counsel--Applied Extrusion Technologies, Inc., Peabody, MA; *U.S. Public*, pg. 122
Haist, Dave, V.P.-Corp. Affairs--Hardware Wholesalers, Inc., Fort Wayne, IN; *U.S. Private*, pg. 502
Haist, Dennis P., V.P., Gen. Counsel & Sec.--Dillingham Construction Corporation, Pleasanton, CA; *U.S. Private*, pg. 333
Haje, Peter R., Exec. V.P., Gen. Counsel & Treas.--Time Warner Inc., New York, NY; *U.S. Public*, pg. 1610
Halas, Paul J., Sr. V.P., Gen. Counsel & Sec.--Oak Industries Inc., Waltham, MA; *U.S. Public*, pg. 1209
Halbritter, M.A., Gen. Counsel & Sec.--Hope Gas, Inc., Clarksburg, WV; *U.S. Public*, pg. 435
Hale, James R., Gen. Counsel & Sec.--Luby's Cafeterias, Inc., San Antonio, TX; *U.S. Public*, pg. 1017
Hale, James T., Sr. V.P., Gen. Counsel & Sec.--Dayton Hudson Corporation, Minneapolis, MN; *U.S. Public*, pg. 489
Halhigian, Jay, Gen. Counsel--SEEQ Technology Inc., Fremont, CA; *U.S. Public*, pg. 1417
Hall, Curtis E., Gen. Counsel--Stryker Corporation, Kalamazoo, MI; *U.S. Public*, pg. 1525
Hall, David K., V.P., Gen. Counsel & Sec.--Bell Atlantic-WV, Charleston, WV; *U.S. Public*, pg. 203
Hall, Ralph, Gen. Counsel--Guidant Corporation-Cardiac Rhythm Management Group, Saint Paul, MN; *U.S. Public*, pg. 768
Hall, Robert, V.P.-Legal Affairs & Sec.--The Cascades Group, Kingsey Falls, Canada; *Int'l*, pg. 273
Hall, Robert F., V.P.-Legal Affairs & Sec.--Cascades, Inc., Kingsey Falls, Canada; *Int'l*, pg. 273
Hall, Stewart K., Gen. Counsel & Sec.--Howtek, Inc., Hudson, NH; *U.S. Public*, pg. 844
Halladay, Angela, V.P. & Gen. Counsel--Fairfield Communities, Inc., Little Rock, AR; *U.S. Public*, pg. 610
Hallagan, Kevin, Sr. V.P. & Corp. Counsel--Bank of America Illinois, Chicago, IL; *U.S. Public*, pg. 180
Halleen, Otis H., V.P., Gen. Counsel & Sec.--United Stationers Inc., Des Plaines, IL; *U.S. Public*, pg. 1689
Hallemeesch, Willy, Sec. & Gen. Counsel--N.V. Bekaert S.A., Kortrijk, Belgium; *Int'l*, pg. 183
Hallemeier, Ulrich, Legal Officer--Battenfeld GmbH, Meinerzhagen, Germany; *Int'l*, pg. 825
Haller, A., V.P. & Gen. Counsel--John Brown E & C Corporate Offices (U.S.), Houston, TX; *Int'l*, pg. 774
Hallinan, William J., Sr. V.P., Gen. Counsel & Sec.--The FINOVA Group Inc., Phoenix, AZ; *U.S. Public*, pg. 624
Halloran, Michael, Exec. V.P. & Gen. Counsel--BankAmerica Corporation, San Francisco, CA; *U.S. Public*, pg. 179
Hallquist, Scott G., Sr. V.P., Gen. Counsel & Sec.--Immunex Corporation, Seattle, WA; *U.S. Public*, pg. 871
Halpern, M. Ronald, V.P. & Gen. Counsel--Hampton Inns, Inc., Memphis, TN; *U.S. Public*, pg. 1335
Halverson, Philip R., V.P., Gen. Counsel & Sec.--Minnesota Power, Duluth, MN; *U.S. Public*, pg. 1116
Hamasaki, James S., V.P. & Gen. Counsel--Pacific Telesis Group, San Francisco, CA; *U.S. Public*, pg. 1415
Hambly, Gail, Gen. Counsel & Company Sec.--John Fairfax Holdings Limited, Sydney, Australia; *Int'l*, pg. 477
Hamilton, Nancy E., Sr. Counsel & Sec.--Ralston Purina Company, Saint Louis, MO; *U.S. Public*, pg. 1359
Hamilton, Sally, Mgr.-Legal Services--Printronix, Inc., Irvine, CA; *U.S. Public*, pg. 1329
Hamilton, Stephen G., Sr. V.P., Gen. Counsel & Sec.--Computer Sales International Inc., Saint Louis, MO; *U.S. Private*, pg. 260
Hamilton, Steven, V.P.-Legal & Gen. Counsel--Alaska Air Group, Inc., Seattle, WA; *U.S. Public*, pg. 35
Hammerman, Stephen L., Vice Chm. & Gen. Counsel--Merrill Lynch & Co., Inc., New York, NY; *U.S. Public*, pg. 1097
Hammond, Frederic G., Gen. Counsel & Sec.--Avid Technology, Inc., Tewksbury, MA; *U.S. Public*, pg. 154
Hampton, John L.M., Sr. V.P., Gen. Counsel & Sec.--Potash Corporation of Saskatchewan Inc., Saskatoon, Canada; *Int'l*, pg. 1064
Hamric, Laurence M., Gen. Counsel-Corp. & Securities--Entergy Corporation, New Orleans, LA; *U.S. Public*, pg. 585
Hance, Charles E., Sr. V.P. & Gen. Counsel--Beneficial Management Corporation, Peapack, NJ; *U.S. Public*, pg. 211
Hance, Charles E., Sr. V.P. & Gen. Counsel--Beneficial Management Corporation of America & Affiliated Corps., Wilmington, DE; *U.S. Public*, pg. 211
Handelsman, Harold, Sr. V.P. & Gen. Counsel--Hyatt Corporation, Chicago, IL; *U.S. Private*, pg. 551
Handler, Janice, V.P.-Gen. Counsel--Elizabeth Arden Company, New York, NY; *Int'l*, pg. 1435
Handley, Richard L., Sr. V.P. & Gen. Counsel--Florida Panthers Holdings, Inc., Fort Lauderdale, FL; *U.S. Public*, pg. 654
Handley, Richard L., Sr. V.P., Gen. Counsel & Sec.--Republic Industries, Inc., Fort Lauderdale, FL; *U.S. Public*, pg. 1378
Hands, Harold P., Exec. V.P.-Legal & Sec.--Mackenzie Financial Corporation, Toronto, Canada; *Int'l*, pg. 828
Handschuh, Gregory, V.P.-Legal Affairs, Gen. Counsel & Asst. Sec.--Amdahl Corporation, Sunnyvale, CA; *Int'l*, pg. 527
Hann, Daniel P., V.P., Gen. Counsel & Sec.--Biomet, Inc., Warsaw, IN; *U.S. Public*, pg. 231
Hannesson, John D., V.P., Gen. Counsel & Sec.--Flowserve Corporation, Long Beach, CA; *U.S. Public*, pg. 658
Hans, Allen, Sr. V.P. & Gen. Counsel--Minolta Corporation, Ramsey, NJ; *Int'l*, pg. 869
Hans, Peter E., V.P. & Gen. Counsel--Capitol Indemnity Corporation, Madison, WI; *U.S. Public*, pg. 302
Hans, Peter E., V.P. & Gen. Counsel--Capitol Specialty Insurance Corporation, Madison, WI; *U.S. Public*, pg. 302
Hansen, Dr. A., Gen. Counsel--Kuehne & Nagel International AG, Schindellegi, Switzerland; *Int'l*, pg. 763
Hansen, Linda, Dir.-Legal & Admin.--BRC Holdings, Dallas, TX; *U.S. Public*, pg. 163
Hansen, Linda, V.P., Gen. Counsel & Sec.--BetzDearborn Inc., Trevose, PA; *U.S. Public*, pg. 226
Hanson, Grant, Gen. Counsel--Cole-Haan, Yarmouth, ME; *U.S. Public*, pg. 1184
Hanssen, John, Gen. Counsel--Du Pont (Australia) Ltd., Sydney, Australia; *U.S. Public*, pg. 532
Hantman, Lawrence, Gen. Counsel--Dunkin' Donuts Incorporated, Randolph, MA; *Int'l*, pg. 63
Hapke, Daniel S., Jr., V.P. & Gen. Counsel--Thiokol Corporation, Ogden, UT; *U.S. Public*, pg. 1596
Haran, Douglas S., Gen. Counsel--Harbor Electric Energy Company, Boston, MA; *U.S. Public*, pg. 247
Harbeke, Christof, Gen. Counsel & Dir.--Frankfurter Sparkasse, Frankfurt, Germany; *Int'l*, pg. 504
Harbour, Ted I., Gen. Counsel--D.R. Horton, Inc., Arlington, TX; *U.S. Public*, pg. 840
Harden, Oleta J., Sr. V.P., Gen. Counsel & Corp. Sec.--New Jersey Resources Corporation, Wall, NJ; *U.S. Public*, pg. 1172
Harder, William E., V.P.-Law, Gen. Counsel & Asst. Sec.--Dayton Hudson Corporation, Minneapolis, MN; *U.S. Public*, pg. 489
Hardy, Brad D., Exec. V.P.-Corp. Svcs. & Gen. Counsel--First Security Corporation, Salt Lake City, UT; *U.S. Public*, pg. 637
Hardy, Gene, Exec. V.P., Sec. & Gen. Counsel--United Artists Theatre Circuits Incorporated, Englewood, CO; *U.S. Private*, pg. 1120
Hardy, Robert M., Jr., Gen. Counsel--Kentucky Investors, Inc., Frankfort, KY; *U.S. Public*, pg. 951
Harkey, Robert S., Sr. V.P., Gen. Counsel & Sec.--Delta Air Lines, Inc., Atlanta, GA; *U.S. Public*, pg. 497
Harmon, Paul M., Gen. Counsel--Country Life Insurance Company, Bloomington, IL; *U.S. Private*, pg. 278
Harner, Timothy, Gen. Counsel--Upstate Milk Cooperatives Inc., Le Roy, NY; *U.S. Private*, pg. 1129
Haroche, Philippe, V.P. & Gen. Counsel--Chargeurs, Paris, France; *Int'l*, pg. 280
Harper, Ralph E., V.P., Gen. Counsel & Sec.--Gleason Corporation, Rochester, NY; *U.S. Public*, pg. 746
Harrington, Chris, Gen. Counsel--Knape & Vogt Mfg. Co., Grand Rapids, MI; *U.S. Public*, pg. 963
Harris, A.D., Gen. Counsel--Powerscreen International Plc, Dungannon, United Kingdom; *Int'l*, pg. 1066
Harris, Jon M., Gen. Counsel & Sec.--Wheat First Butcher Singer, Inc., Richmond, VA; *U.S. Public*, pg. 640
Harris, Lee A., Sr. V.P., Gen. Counsel & Sec.--IRT Property Company, Atlanta, GA; *U.S. Public*, pg. 858
Harris, R. Jeffrey, V.P., Gen. Counsel & Sec.--Sybron International Corporation, Milwaukee, WI; *U.S. Public*, pg. 1544
Harris, Susan L., Sr. V.P., Gen. Counsel & Sec.--SunAmerica Inc., Los Angeles, CA; *U.S. Public*, pg. 1532
Harrison, Dave, Gen. Counsel--Quantum Corporation, Milpitas, CA; *U.S. Public*, pg. 1350
Harrison, Dean W., Sr. V.P., Gen. Counsel & Sec.--Gibraltar Savings, Simi Valley, CA; *U.S. Public*, pg. 181
Harrison, Donald, Chm. Bd. & Gen. Counsel--PVS Chemicals, Inc., Detroit, MI; *U.S. Private*, pg. 828
Harrison, M.M., Gen. Counsel--Esso Sekiyu Kabushiki Kaisha, Tokyo, Japan; *U.S. Public*, pg. 602
Hart, Robert M., Sr. V.P., Gen. Counsel & Sec.--Alleghany Corporation, New York, NY; *U.S. Public*, pg. 42
Harter, Robert J., Jr., Sr. V.P.-Admin. & Gen. Counsel--Rykoff-Sexton, Inc., Wilkes-Barre, PA; *U.S. Public*, pg. 918
Hartman, James O., Gen. Counsel & Sec.--Up-Right Work Platforms Division, Selma, CA; *U.S. Private*, pg. 1128
Hartmann, Richard J., Sec. & Treas.--ALLTEL Answering Service, Inc., Export, PA; *U.S. Public*, pg. 55
Hartwig, Eugene L., Sr. V.P., Gen. Counsel & Sec.--Kelly Services, Inc., Troy, MI; *U.S. Public*, pg. 949
Harvey, Cannon Y., Exec. V.P.-Fin. & Law & Gen. Counsel--Southern Pacific Rail Corporation, San Francisco, CA; *U.S. Public*, pg. 1668
Harvey, Gerald, V.P., Gen. Counsel & Sec.--TransTechnology Corporation, Liberty Corner, NJ; *U.S. Public*, pg. 1632
Harvey, H. Scott, V.P., Assoc. Gen. Counsel & Asst. Sec.--Comdisco, Inc., Rosemont, IL; *U.S. Public*, pg. 407
Harvey, Jr., A. Mosby, V.P., General Counsel & Sec.--HON Industries Inc., Muscatine, IA; *U.S. Public*, pg. 772
Harvey, Mo, Gen. Counsel--The HON Co., Muscatine, IA; *U.S. Public*, pg. 772
Harvey, Tom, Gen. Counsel--Southwestern/Great American Inc., Nashville, TN; *U.S. Private*, pg. 1018
Harvie, C. Thomas, V.P. & Gen. Counsel--The Goodyear Tire & Rubber Company, Akron, OH; *U.S. Public*, pg. 752
Harwood, Dennis W., Legal Officer--Label-Aire Inc., Fullerton, CA; *U.S. Private*, pg. 641
Hasbrouck, Albert, III, Sr. Dir.-Corp. Affairs--NJ Transit, Newark, NJ; *U.S. Private*, pg. 794
Haskin, Robert W., Jr., V.P., Gen. Counsel & Sec.--Remington Arms Company, Inc., Madison, NC; *U.S. Private*, pg. 921
Hatch, Brian, Gen. Counsel--Continental Promotion Group, Tempe, AZ; *U.S. Private*, pg. 269
Hatzler, Dale, V.P.-Legal Affairs--Solvay Pharmaceuticals, Inc., Marietta, GA; *Int'l*, pg. 1278
Haubenreich, George R., Jr., V.P., Gen. Counsel & Sec.--Oceaneering International, Inc., Houston, TX; *U.S. Public*, pg. 1211
Haubenreich, George R., Jr., V.P., Gen. Counsel & Sec.--Oceaneering International, Inc., Morgan City, LA; *U.S. Public*, pg. 1211
Hauser, Warren J., V.P. & Gen. Counsel--Pharmaceutical Marketing Services Inc., Phoenix, AZ; *U.S. Public*, pg. 1284
Hawkins, Thomas W., Sr. V.P., Gen. Counsel & Sec.--Blockbuster Entertainment Group, Dallas, TX; *U.S. Private*, pg. 775
Hawryluk, Allan A., Gen. Counsel & Sec.--Atomic Energy of Canada Ltd., Mississauga, Canada; *Int'l*, pg. 97
Hay, William H., V.P., Gen. Counsel & Sec.--Beckman Instruments, Inc., Fullerton, CA; *U.S. Public*, pg. 199
Hayes, Albert H., Attorney-in-Fact--Chubb Lloyds Insurance Co. of TX, Dallas, TX; *U.S. Public*, pg. 355
Hayes, Chester F., Sec. & Gen. Counsel--ARGOSystems, Inc., Sunnyvale, CA; *U.S. Public*, pg. 240
Hayes, David, Corp. Counsel--Sodexho USA, Waltham, MA; *Int'l*, pg. 1274
Hayes, David M., Sr. V.P., Gen. Counsel & Sec.--Agway, Inc., De Witt, NY; *U.S. Private*, pg. 27
Hayes, James W., III, Gen. Counsel & Sec.--Brown & Sharpe Manufacturing Company, North Kingstown, RI; *U.S. Public*, pg. 260
Hayes, Patricia, Gen. Counsel & Sec.--Centimark Corporation, Canonsburg, PA; *U.S. Private*, pg. 222
Haynie, Louis M., Gen. Counsel--Baxter Research Medical, Inc., Midvale, UT; *U.S. Public*, pg. 196
Head, Christopher A., Exec. V.P., Gen. Counsel & Sec.--Comptek Research, Inc., Buffalo, NY; *U.S. Public*, pg. 419
Head, Patrick J., V.P. & Gen. Counsel--FMC Corporation, Chicago, IL; *U.S. Public*, pg. 604
Healey, Mary J., V.P., Gen. Counsel & Sec.--Yankee Energy System, Inc., Meriden, CT; *U.S. Public*, pg. 1787
Hearn, Michael D., Gen. Counsel & Sec.--Interstate/Johnson Lane, Inc., Charlotte, NC; *U.S. Public*, pg. 909
Hearn, Michael D., Sr. Mng. Dir., Gen. Counsel & Sec.--Interstate/Johnson Lane Corporation, Charlotte, NC; *U.S. Public*, pg. 910
Hearnburg, William V., Exec. V.P.-Legal--Southwire Company, Carrollton, GA; *U.S. Private*, pg. 1019
Heath, Charles D., V.P.-Northern Reg. Counsel--Century Telephone Enterprises, Inc., Monroe, LA; *U.S. Public*, pg. 329
Heaton, Mary Margaret, Corp. Counsel & Asst. Sec.--Oxford Industries, Inc., Atlanta, GA; *U.S. Public*, pg. 1239
Hebbeler, Regis J., Gen. Counsel--Goody's Family Clothing, Inc., Knoxville, TN; *U.S. Public*, pg. 753
Hecht, Louis A., Sec. & Gen. Counsel--Molex Incorporated, Lisle, IL; *U.S. Public*, pg. 1121
Hecker, David, Sr. V.P., Sec. & Gen. Counsel--S.C. Johnson & Son, Inc., Racine, WI; *U.S. Private*, pg. 592
Hedemann, G.C., Gen. Counsel--Black & Veatch, Kansas City, MO; *U.S. Private*, pg. 146
Hedlund, Karen J., Sr. V.P. & Gen. Counsel--SunAmerica Inc., Los Angeles, CA; *U.S. Public*, pg. 1532
Heekin, W. Michael, Sr. V.P. & Gen. Counsel & Sec.--American Heritage Life Insurance Co., Jacksonville, FL; *U.S. Public*, pg. 79
Heffernan, Brian, Corp. Counsel--Comverse Network Systems, Wakefield, MA; *U.S. Public*, pg. 425
Heggland, Roy T., Sr. V.P., Gen. Counsel & Sec.--Cincinnati Bell Information Systems Inc., Cincinnati, OH; *U.S. Public*, pg. 367
Heiden, E. P., Gen. Counsel--DSM N.V., Heerlen, Netherlands; *Int'l*, pg. 352
Heidmeier, Heiner, Dr., Gen. Counsel--Degussa AG, Frankfurt/Main, Germany; *Int'l*, pg. 388
Heidorn, Robert E., Deputy Gen. Counsel & Asst. Sec.--Indiana Energy, Inc., Indianapolis, IN; *U.S. Public*, pg. 874
Heine, Spencer H., Exec. V.P. & Gen. Counsel--Montgomery Ward & Co., Inc., Chicago, IL; *U.S. Private*, pg. 758
Heininger, Dan, Sr. V.P. & Gen. Counsel--Renaissance International Hotels, Cleveland, OH; *U.S. Public*, pg. 1048
Heinrich, Robert, V.P. & Gen. Counsel--Fender Musical Instruments, Scottsdale, AZ; *U.S. Private*, pg. 400
Heiser, James S., Chief Fin. Officer, V.P., Gen. Counsel, Sec. & Treas.--Ducommun Incorporated, Carson, CA; *U.S. Public*, pg. 533
Hekker, Maria, Gen. Counsel--Barra, Inc., Berkeley, CA; *U.S. Public*, pg. 191
Held, John H., V.P., Gen. Mgr. & Corp. Legal Counsel--LGC Management, Englewood, CO; *U.S. Private*, pg. 639
Heldman, Paul W., Sr. V.P., Gen. Counsel & Sec.--The Kroger Co., Cincinnati, OH; *U.S. Public*, pg. 967
Heller, Hanes A., V.P.-Legal Affairs--Bestfoods, Englewood Cliffs, NJ; *U.S. Public*, pg. 223
Hellrung, Stephen A., Sr. V.P. & Gen. Counsel--The Pillsbury Company, Minneapolis, MN; *Int'l*, pg. 411
Helsten, David L., V.P.-Corp. Counsel--Restaura, Inc., Phoenix, AZ; *U.S. Public*, pg. 1718
Hempstead, George H., III, V.P, Gen. Counsel & Sec.--Hanson North America, Woodbridge, NJ; *Int'l*, pg. 593
Hendee, Susan B., Gen. Counsel--Big O Tires Incorporated, Englewood, CO; *U.S. Public*, pg. 1553
Henderson, Harold L., Sr. V.P. & Gen. Counsel--Eastman Chemical Company, Kingsport, TN; *U.S. Public*, pg. 550
Henderson, Thomas K., V.P.-Legal--Allegheny Power System, Inc., Hagerstown, MD; *U.S. Public*, pg. 42
Hendon, Robert C., Jr., V.P., Gen. Counsel & Sec.--Berlitz International, Inc., Princeton, NJ; *U.S. Public*, pg. 221
Hendry, Andrew D., Sr. V.P., Gen. Counsel & Sec.--Colgate-Palmolive Company, New York, NY; *U.S. Public*, pg. 397
Hendry, Lloyd G., Gen. Counsel--Alico, Inc., La Belle, FL; *U.S. Public*, pg. 41
Henning, Edward J., Sr. V.P., Gen. Counsel & Sec.--Health Care Property Investors, Inc., Newport Beach, CA; *U.S. Public*, pg. 801
Henry, Bob J., V.P., Gen. Counsel & Sec.--Allied Van Lines, Inc., Naperville, IL; *Int'l*, pg. 901
Henry, Don, Sr. V.P. & Gen. Counsel--First Commercial Bank, N.A., Little Rock, AR; *U.S. Public*, pg. 630
Henry, John, Gen. Counsel--American Consumers, Inc., Fort Oglethorpe, GA; *U.S. Public*, pg. 70
Henry, Nancy L., Sr. V.P. & Gen. Counsel--The Dun & Bradstreet Corporation, Murray Hill, NJ; *U.S. Public*, pg. 535
Hensley, J. Murray, Gen. Counsel--Plains Co-op Oil Mill, Lubbock, TX; *U.S. Private*, pg. 868

Hensley, William H., V.P.-Gen. Counsel & Sec.--Mueller Industries, Inc., Memphis, TN; *U.S. Public*, pg. 1141

Herbel, Peter, V.P. & Gen. Counsel/Refining & Mktg.--Elf Aquitane, Paris, France; *Int'l*, pg. 444

Herbers, John, Attorney--Times Printing Company, Inc., Random Lake, WI; *U.S. Private*, pg. 1087

Herbert, David, Legal Officer--3i Group plc, London, United Kingdom; *Int'l*, pg. 1386

Herbert, John, Gen. Counsel & Sec.--Ace Doran Hauling & Rigging Company, Cincinnati, OH; *U.S. Private*, pg. 340

Herbert, John, Gen. Counsel & Sec.--Ace Doran Brokerage, Cincinnati, OH; *U.S. Private*, pg. 340

Herlihy, Michael, Gen. Counsel--Imperial Chemical Industries PLC, London, United Kingdom; *Int'l*, pg. 662

Herman, Robin A., Sr. V.P., Gen. Counsel & Sec.--Western Staff Services, Walnut Creek, CA; *U.S. Public*, pg. 1760

Herner, Donald A., Gen. Counsel & Sec.--JJI Lighting Group Inc., Greenwich, CT; *Int'l*, pg. 821

Herrera, Margarita, Esq., 2nd V.P.-Legal & Compliance--Banco Popular de Puerto Rico, San Juan, PR; *U.S. Public*, pg. 175

Herwitz, Tom, V.P.-Corp. & Legal Affairs-Washington--Fox Television Stations Inc., Los Angeles, CA; *Int'l*, pg. 926

Hess, Barry J., Gen. Counsel--ACI International Ltd., Melbourne, Australia; *Int'l*, pg. 128

Hess, Beat, Dr., Dir.-Legal Affairs--ABB Asea Brown Boveri (Holding) Ltd., Zurich, Switzerland; *Int'l*, pg. 1

Hess, Jerry, V.P. & Legal Counsel--Pony Express Delivery Services, Inc., Atlanta, GA; *U.S. Public*, pg. 245

Hess, P.Gregory, Legal Counsel & Sec.--Barr & Barr, Inc., New York, NY; *U.S. Private*, pg. 117

Hess, Paul W., Gen. Counsel--Ballard Medical Products, Draper, UT; *U.S. Public*, pg. 171

Hess, Peter L., Gen. Counsel & Sec.--Farrel Corporation, Ansonia, CT; *U.S. Public*, pg. 614

Hetherington, Edwin S., Gen. Counsel & Sec.--Sea Containers Ltd., Hamilton, Bermuda; *Int'l*, pg. 1213

Hetherington, Edwin S., Gen. Counsel & Sec.--Orient-Express Hotels Inc., New York, NY; *Int'l*, pg. 1213

Heyd, Ulrich, Bd. Member, Legal Affairs--Puma AG Rudolf Dassler Sport, Herzogenaurach, Germany; *Int'l*, pg. 1072

Heyman, Ralph, Gen. Counsel--The Sportsman's Guide, Inc., Saint Paul, MN; *U.S. Public*, pg. 1499

Hickey, John E., V.P., Sec. & Asst. Gen. Counsel--International Business Machines Corporation, Armonk, NY; *U.S. Public*, pg. 895

Hickey, Thomas, Asst. Gen. Counsel--Nextel Communications, Mc Lean, VA; *U.S. Public*, pg. 1180

Hickey, Thomas J., V.P. & Gen. Counsel--Malcolm Pirnie, Inc., White Plains, NY; *U.S. Private*, pg. 867

Hicks, David L., V.P.- Law & Gen. Counsel--Santa Fe Energy Resources, Inc., Houston, TX; *U.S. Public*, pg. 1431

Hicks, Lawrence E., V.P.-Law & Admin.--Thomas J. Lipton Company, Englewood Cliffs, NJ; *Int'l*, pg. 1435

Hilborne, Rebecca H., Asst. Gen. Counsel--The Williams Companies, Inc., Tulsa, OK; *U.S. Public*, pg. 1769

Hildebrandt, Stephen A., V.P. & Gen. Counsel--CBS Radio, New York, NY; *U.S. Public*, pg. 274

Hildreth, Gary R., V.P., Gen. Counsel & Sec.--Armco Inc., Pittsburgh, PA; *U.S. Public*, pg. 131

Hill, Bruce G., V.P., Gen. Counsel & Sec.--INSO Corporation, Boston, MA; *U.S. Public*, pg. 882

Hill, Elizabeth Holden, V.P. & Gen. Counsel--Berkley Administrators, Minneapolis, MN; *U.S. Public*, pg. 216

Hill, Mark, V.P. & Gen. Counsel--Tandy Corporation, Fort Worth, TX; *U.S. Public*, pg. 1560

Hill, R.D., Sr. V.P.-General Counsel--Holiday Inn Worldwide, Atlanta, GA; *Int'l*, pg. 170

Hiller, Theodore, Gen. Counsel--Kepner-Tregoe, Inc., Skillman, NJ; *U.S. Public*, pg. 1659

Hillin, W.K., Sr. V.P., Gen. Counsel & Sec.--Reading & Bates Corporation, Houston, TX; *U.S. Public*, pg. 1354

Hiltgen, Bill, Gen. Mgr.--TIC Investment Corp., Dallas, TX; *U.S. Private*, pg. 1064

Hinchliff, James T., Sr. V.P. & Gen. Counsel--Peoples Energy Corporation, Chicago, IL; *U.S. Public*, pg. 1274

Hinchliff, James T., Sr. V.P. & Gen. Counsel--Peoples District Energy Corporation, Chicago, IL; *U.S. Public*, pg. 1275

Hinchliff, James T., Sr. V.P. & Gen. Counsel--Peoples Energy Services Corporation, Chicago, IL; *U.S. Public*, pg. 1275

Hinchliff, James T., Sr. V.P. & Gen. Counsel--Peoples NGV Corp., Chicago, IL; *U.S. Public*, pg. 1275

Hinderer, Amy, Corp. Counsel--Tacony Corporation, Fenton, MO; *U.S. Private*, pg. 1066

Hindman, Don J., Chm. Bd., Pres. & Chief Exec. Officer--Clark Foodservice, Inc., Elk Grove Village, IL; *U.S. Private*, pg. 242

Hine, Thompson, Gen. Counsel--Hercules Engine Company, Canton, OH; *U.S. Private*, pg. 523

Hinkley, Richard L., V.P., Chief Counsel & Sec.--Nevada Power Company, Las Vegas, NV; *U.S. Public*, pg. 1169

Hinman, Harvey D., V.P. & Gen. Counsel--Chevron Corporation, San Francisco, CA; *U.S. Public*, pg. 347

Hinman, Michael, Gen. Counsel--Basin Electric Power Cooperative, Bismarck, ND; *U.S. Private*, pg. 121

Hipolit, J.E., V.P. & Gen. Counsel--Irex Corporation, Lancaster, PA; *U.S. Public*, pg. 913

Hipwell, Arthur P., Sr. V.P. & Gen. Counsel--Humana Inc., Louisville, KY; *U.S. Public*, pg. 847

Hirsch, Barry, Sr. V.P., Gen. Counsel & Sec.--Loews Corporation, New York, NY; *U.S. Public*, pg. 1010

Hirsch, D.L., V.P. & Sr. Counsel--NI Industries, Inc., Seal Beach, CA; *U.S. Public*, pg. 1054

Hislip, Daniel, Sr. V.P. & Legal Counsel--Cerberus Pyrotronics Inc., Cedar Knolls, NJ; *Int'l*, pg. 1246

Hitchens, Glenn, Gen. Counsel--Metal Masters Foodservice Equipment, Clayton, DE; *U.S. Private*, pg. 734

Hoak, Jonathon S., Sr. V.P. & Gen. Counsel--NCR Corporation, Dayton, OH; *U.S. Public*, pg. 1146

Hoard, Heidi, V.P., Gen. Counsel & Sec.--Musicland Group Inc., Minnetonka, MN; *U.S. Public*, pg. 1142

Hobbs, George D., V.P., Gen. Counsel & Sec.--Centocor, Inc., Malvern, PA; *U.S. Public*, pg. 323

Hobbs, Kenneth, Gen. Counsel--Bush Brothers & Company, Knoxville, TN; *U.S. Private*, pg. 189

Hodge, Linda J., Assoc. Gen. Counsel & Asst. Sec.--Amgen Inc., Thousand Oaks, CA; *U.S. Public*, pg. 100

Hoehn, Richard, Gen. Counsel--Kingsbury Corporation, Keene, NH; *U.S. Private*, pg. 621

Hoel, Richard A., Legal Advisor--Aero Systems Engineering Inc., Saint Paul, MN; *Int'l*, pg. 276

Hoellering, Michael F., Gen. Counsel--American Arbitration Association, New York, NY; *U.S. Private*, pg. 50

Hofer, Mark A., Sr. V.P. & Gen. Counsel--Genzyme Corporation, Cambridge, MA; *U.S. Public*, pg. 733

Hoffman, Barry P., Grp. V.P., Gen. Counsel & Sec.--Valassis Communications, Inc., Livonia, MI; *U.S. Public*, pg. 1704

Hoffman, Gary K., V.P., Assoc. Gen. Counsel & Asst. Sec.--Old American Insurance Co., Kansas City, MO; *U.S. Public*, pg. 943

Hoffman, James F., V.P. & Assoc. Gen. Counsel--Prime Group Realty Trust, Chicago, IL; *U.S. Public*, pg. 1326

Hoffmann, Christoph L., Exec. V.P.-Law & Corp. Admin. & Sec.--Raytheon Company, Lexington, MA; *U.S. Public*, pg. 1364

Hoffmann, Richard W., Gen. Counsel--EMC Insurance Group, Inc., Des Moines, IA; *U.S. Public*, pg. 545

Hohn, Richard G., Sr. V.P., Sec. & Gen. Counsel--USLIFE Corporation, New York, NY; *U.S. Public*, pg. 77

Holcombe, Paul A., Jr., V.P., Gen. Counsel & Sec.--Glaxo Wellcome PLC, Research Triangle Park, NC; *Int'l*, pg. 553

Holcombe, Robert S., Sr. V.P.,Gen. Counsel & Sec.--Apria Healthcare Group Inc., Costa Mesa, CA; *U.S. Public*, pg. 125

Holder, James T., Exec. V.P., Gen. Counsel & Sec.--Checkers Drive-In Restaurants, Inc., Clearwater, FL; *U.S.* Public, pg. 342

Holder, Randy, Exec. V.P. & Gen. Counsel--Thrifty Rent-a-Car System, Inc., Tulsa, OK; *U.S. Public*, pg. 354

Holderness, Kevin J., Assoc. Gen. Counsel--Heavy Civil Construction, Boise, ID; *U.S. Public*, pg. 1134

Holdorf, Paul, Gen. Counsel--Polymer Composites Inc., Winona, MN; *Int'l*, pg. 624

Holland, G. Edison, Jr., V.P. & Corp. Counsel--Gulf Power Company, Pensacola, FL; *U.S. Public*, pg. 1490

Holland, Robert B., III, Sr. V.P., Gen. Counsel & Sec.--Triton Energy Limited, Dallas, TX; *U.S. Public*, pg. 1640

Holleran, John W., Sr. V.P. & Gen. Counsel--Boise Cascade Corporation, Boise, ID; *U.S. Public*, pg. 242

Holley, Cheri, Gen. Counsel & Sec.--Titan International, Inc., Quincy, IL; *U.S. Public*, pg. 1618

Holliday, Susan J., Sr. V.P. & Gen. Counsel--CBS, New York, NY; *U.S. Public*, pg. 273

Hollings, David, Gen. Counsel & Sec.--Tano Automation, Inc., Harahan, LA; *U.S. Public*, pg. 1763

Hollingsworth, John Mark, Sr. Legal Counsel & Asst. Sec.--Valhi, Inc., Dallas, TX; *U.S. Private*, pg. 270

Hollingsworth, Mark, Gen. Counsel--Contran Corporation, Dallas, TX; *U.S. Private*, pg. 270

Hollister, John, Corp. Counsel--SunTrust Banks of Georgia, Inc., Atlanta, GA; *U.S. Public*, pg. 1538

Holloway, Eugene, Gen. Counsel--Brother International Corporation, Somerset, NJ; *Int'l*, pg. 229

Holloway, Eugene C., V.P., Gen. Counsel & Sec.--Thomas & Betts/Amerace, Brooksville, FL; *U.S. Public*, pg. 1598

Holschuh, Laurel A., Sr. V.P., Asst. Gen. Counsel & Sec.--Norwest Corporation, Minneapolis, MN; *U.S. Public*, pg. 1201

Holsenbeck, G. Penn, V.P., Assoc. Gen. Counsel & Sec.--Philip Morris Companies Inc., New York, NY; *U.S. Public*, *pg. 1287*

Holt, Wayne G., Gen. Counsel--Alberta Energy Company, Ltd., Calgary, Canada; *Int'l*, pg. 48

Holton, T., Gen. Counsel--Dimco-Gray Company, Centerville, OH; *U.S. Private*, pg. 333

Holzman, Donald J., Gen. Counsel & Sec.--Dinaire Corp., Buffalo, NY; *U.S. Private*, pg. 334

Honda, James, Gen. Counsel--Aromat Corporation, New Providence, NJ; *Int'l*, pg. 847

Hook, Kenneth, V.P. & Legal Counsel--Rexair, Inc., Troy, MI; *U.S. Public*, pg. 1684

Hoolihan, Thomas, V.P. & Gen. Counsel--DBT Online, Inc., Las Vegas, NV; *U.S. Public*, pg. 472

Hooper, Lawrence L., Jr., Gen. Counsel & Sec.--Petroleum & Resources Corp., Baltimore, MD; *U.S. Public*, pg. 1280

Hopkins, Jacques, Gen. Counsel--American Mathematical Society, Inc., Providence, RI; *U.S. Private*, pg. 59

Hopkins, Jim, Gen. Counsel--Lee Grocery Company, Everett, WA; *U.S. Private*, pg. 657

Hopkins, John D., Sr. V.P. & Gen. Counsel--Jefferson-Pilot Corporation, Greensboro, NC; *U.S. Public*, pg. 925

Hopkins, R. Howard, Sr. V.P., Gen. Counsel & Sec.--SGS North America Inc., New York, NY; *Int'l*, pg. 1153

Hopp, Daniel F., V.P., Gen. Counsel & Sec.--Whirlpool Corporation, Benton Harbor, MI; *U.S. Public*, pg. 1764

Hopwood, Howard H., III, Sr. V.P. & Gen. Counsel--Firstar Corporation, Milwaukee, WI; *U.S. Public*, pg. 642

Hopwood, Terry, V.P., Gen. Counsel & Sec.--Suncor Inc., Calgary, Canada; *Int'l*, pg. 1320

Horan, Douglas S., Sr. V.P. & Gen. Counsel--Boston Edison Company, Boston, MA; *U.S. Public*, pg. 247

Horbaczewski, Henry, Gen. Counsel--Reed Elsevier Inc., New York, NY; *Int'l*, pg. 1095

Horiszny, Laurene H., V.P., Gen. Counsel & Sec.--Borg Warner Automotive, Inc., Chicago, IL; *U.S. Public*, pg. 245

Horn, Richard P., V.P., Gen. Counsel & Asst. Sec.--HealthAmerica Pennsylvania, Inc., Pittsburgh, PA; *U.S. Public*, pg. 454

Horner, Robert W., III, Sr. V.P., Gen. Counsel & Sec.--Vitalink Pharmacy Services, Inc., Naperville, IL; *U.S. Public*, pg. 1041

Horner, Russell G., Jr., Sr. V.P., Gen. Counsel & Sec.--Kerr-McGee Corporation, Oklahoma City, OK; *U.S. Public*, pg. 952

Horowitz, Ira, Gen. Counsel--Webcraft Technologies, Inc., North Brunswick, NJ; *U.S. Public*, pg. 228

Horowitz, Jeffrey R., Sr. V.P., Gen. Counsel & Sec.--Ogden Energy Group, Inc., Fairfield, NJ; *U.S. Public*, pg. 1213

Horvath, Robert, Gen. Counsel & Asst. Sec.--National Electronics Warranty Corporation, Sterling, VA; *U.S. Private*, pg. 782

Hoskins, William K., V.P. & Gen. Counsel--Hoechst Marion Roussel North America, Kansas City, MO; *Int'l*, pg. 625

Hougen, H. Monty, V.P., Sec. & Deputy Gen. Counsel--DynCorp, Reston, VA; *U.S. Private*, pg. 351

Houston, Tom, Gen. Counsel & Sec.--Scottish Widows' Fund & Life Assurance Society, Edinburgh, United Kingdom; *Int'l*, pg. 1212

Hover-Smoot, Scott R., Gen. Counsel & Sec.--California Micro Devices, Milpitas, CA; *U.S. Public*, pg. 293

Howaldt, Jens P., Dr., Dir.-Fin., Controlling & Law--Continental AG, Hannover, Germany; *Int'l*, pg. 327

Howard, Heather, Gen. Counsel & Sec.--The Boeing Company, Seattle, WA; *U.S. Public*, pg. 239

Howard, J.L., Q.C., V.P. & Gen. Counsel--MacMillan Bloedel Limited, Vancouver, Canada; *Int'l*, pg. 828

Howard, Patricia J., V.P., Asst. Gen. Counsel & Deputy Sec.--Republic New York Corporation, New York, NY; *U.S. Public*, pg. 1380

Howell, Dean, V.P. & Corp. Counsel--InterVoice, Inc., Dallas, TX; *U.S. Public*, pg. 910

Howell, Hilton, Gen. Counsel--Atlantic American Corporation, Atlanta, GA; *U.S. Public*, pg. 143

Howie, P.R.S., Gen. Counsel & Sec.--Burmah Castrol plc, Swindon, United Kingdom; *Int'l*, pg. 234

Howley, Thomas, V.P. & Gen. Counsel--Au Bon Pain Co., Inc., Boston, MA; *U.S. Public*, pg. 146

Hoynes, Louis L. Jr., Sr. V.P. & Gen. Counsel--American Home Products Corporation, Madison, NJ; *U.S. Public*, pg. 79

Hretzay, Eugene, Gen. Counsel & Sec.--Acklands Limited, Toronto, Canada; *Int'l*, pg. 23

Hritz, John G., V.P. & Gen. Counsel--AK Steel Corporation, Middletown, OH; *U.S. Public*, pg. 7

Hron, Michael G., Gen. Counsel & Sec.--Telephone and Data Systems, Inc., Chicago, IL; *U.S. Public*, pg. 1570

Hrusoff, Ronald, Gen. Counsel--John Burnham & Co., San Diego, CA; *U.S. Private*, pg. 186

Huben, Christina E., Gen. Counsel & Sec.--EnviroSource, Inc., Horsham, PA; *U.S. Public*, pg. 587

Huber, Thomas P., Exec. V.P., Gen. Counsel & Asst. Sec.--First Hawaiian Bank, Honolulu, HI; *U.S. Public*, pg. 634

Hubler, James T., Sr. V.P.-Industrial Rels., Gen. Counsel & Sec.--Freightliner Corp., Portland, OR; *Int'l*, pg. 368

Hubschman, Henry A., V.P.-Bus. Devel. & Gen. Counsel--G.E. Aircraft Engines, Cincinnati, OH; *U.S. Public*, pg. 710

Hudnut, Stewart S., Sr. V.P., Sec. & Gen. Counsel--Illinois Tool Works Inc., Glenview, IL; *U.S. Public*, pg. 865

Hudry, Robert, Mgr.-Fin. & Legal Affairs--Groupe Usinor, Paris, France; *Int'l*, pg. 570

Huff, Charles E., V.P., Gen. Counsel & Sec.--Boyd Gaming Corporation, Las Vegas, NV; *U.S. Public*, pg. 249

Huffman, H.V., Assoc. Counsel--Citizens Gas & Coke Utility, Indianapolis, IN; *U.S. Private*, pg. 241

Hufham, Barbara, V.P. & Gen. Counsel--HarperCollins Publishers, New York, NY; *Int'l*, pg. 926

Hughes, Catherine L., Gen. Counsel & Sec.--Acxiom Corporation, Conway, AR; *U.S. Public*, pg. 18

Huibregtsen, A.H., Legal Officer--KTI Group B.V., Zoetermeer, Netherlands; *Int'l*, pg. 837

Hull, Allan, V.P. & Gen. Counsel--Greif Brothers Corporation, Delaware, OH; *U.S. Public*, pg. 763

Hulme, Michael E., Jr., Asst. Gen. Counsel & Asst. Sec.--United States Filter Corporation, Palm Desert, CA; *U.S. Public*, pg. 1681

Humphries, M. Clayton, Jr., Gen. Counsel--WestPoint Stevens Inc., West Point, GA; *U.S. Public*, pg. 1762

Hunt, Brian, Gen. Counsel--Amtran, Inc., Indianapolis, IN; *U.S. Public*, pg. 106

Hunt, Philip G., Sr. V.P., Gen. Counsel & Sec.--Ruby Tuesday, Inc., Mobile, AL; *U.S. Public*, pg. 1411

Hunt, Samuel P., III, V.P. & Gen. Counsel--PerSeptive Biosystems, Inc., Framingham, MA; *U.S. Public*, pg. 1279

Hunter, Amy, Gen. Counsel--Uni-Marts, Inc., State College, PA; *U.S. Public*, pg. 1664

Hunter, Jack D., Exec. V.P. & Gen. Counsel--Lincoln National Corporation, Fort Wayne, IN; *U.S. Public*, pg. 997

Hunter, Jack D., Exec. V.P. & Gen. Counsel--The Lincoln National Life Insurance Co., Fort Wayne, IN; *U.S. Public*, *pg. 998*

Huppi, Rolf, Chm. Bd. & Chief Exec. Officer--Zurich Insurance Company, Zurich, Switzerland; *Int'l*, pg. 1529

Hurley, Maureen O., V.P. & Gen. Counsel--Rich Products Corp., Buffalo, NY; *U.S. Private*, pg. 928

Hurley, Melissa M., Sr. V.P., Gen. Counsel & Sec.--Northstar Investment Management Corporation, Greenwich, CT; *U.S. Public*, pg. 1375

Hurwich, Robert A., V.P.-Admin., Sec. & Gen. Counsel--Lynch Corporation, Greenwich, CT; *U.S. Public*, pg. 1021

Hurwitz, Laurence, Gen. Counsel--Ambac International Corp., Columbia, SC; *U.S. Private*, pg. 48

Husson, Christian, V.P. & Gen. Counsel--Renault, Boulogne-Billancourt, France; *Int'l*, pg. 1102

Huston, Steven, Gen. Counsel--Wm. Wrigley Jr. Company, Chicago, IL; *U.S. Public*, pg. 1781

Hutcheson, N., Gen. Counsel & Asst. Sec.--The Budd Company, Troy, MI; *Int'l*, pg. 1388

Hutchison, Larry M., V.P. & Gen. Counsel--Torchmark Corporation, Birmingham, AL; *U.S. Public*, pg. 1622

Hyde, Thomas D., Sr. V.P. & Gen. Counsel--Raytheon Company, Lexington, MA; *U.S. Public*, pg. 1364

Hyman, Frank, Gen. Counsel--Astre Corporate Group, Alexandria, VA; *U.S. Private*, pg. 93

Hyndman, Peter S., V.P.-Law, Gen. Counsel & Sec.--The Loewen Group, Inc., Burnaby, Canada; *Int'l*, pg. 814
Hynes, Mary Ann, V.P. & Gen. Counsel--CCH Incorporated, Riverwoods, IL; *Int'l*, pg. 1513
Hyvnar, John K., Gen. Counsel--Interleaf, Inc., Waltham, MA; *U.S. Public*, pg. 893
Ibach, Wynn, Gen. Counsel--Swift Energy Company, Houston, TX; *U.S. Public*, pg. 1543
Ide, R. William, III, Sr. V.P., Gen. Counsel & Sec.--Monsanto Company, Saint Louis, MO; *U.S. Public*, pg. 1124
Ieki, Hirotaka, Dir. & Legal Officer--Ishihara Sangyo Kaisha, Ltd., Osaka, Japan; *Int'l*, pg. 689
Imbeau, Claude, Gen. Counsel & Sec.--Tembec Inc., Montreal, Canada; *Int'l*, pg. 1374
Imbriaco, James, Assoc. Gen. Counsel & Asst. Sec.--The Times Mirror Company, Los Angeles, CA; *U.S. Public*, pg. 1615
Imhoff, Herbert F., Jr., Pres., Chief Oper. Officer & Gen. Counsel--General Employment Enterprises, Inc., Oak Brook Terrace, IL; *U.S. Public*, pg. 714
Infante, Bernardo, Chief Counsel--CODELCO Chile (Corporacion Nacional Del Cobre De Chile), Santiago, Chile; *Int'l*, pg. 302
Ingram, E. Michael, Sr. V.P., Gen. Counsel & Sec.--National Data Corporation, Atlanta, GA; *U.S. Public*, pg. 1155
Ingram, W. Ronald, Gen. Counsel & Sec.--Chronicle Publishing Co. Inc., San Francisco, CA; *U.S. Private*, pg. 239
Innanen, L., Exec. V.P.-Legal & Gen. Counsel--Labatt Breweries of Canada, Toronto, Canada; *Int'l*, pg. 679
Innarone, David, Gen. Counsel--CRIIMI MAE, Rockville, MD; *U.S. Public*, pg. 459
Ireland, Timothy G., Gen. Counsel--The Chardon Rubber Co., Chardon, OH; *U.S. Private*, pg. 229
Irissou, A.M., Gen. Counsel--Total S.A., Paris, France; *Int'l*, pg. 1408
Irving, J., Dir.-Legal Affairs--Iveco-Ford Truck Ltd., Watford, United Kingdom; *Int'l*, pg. 484
Irving, Richard H., III, Sr. V.P. & Gen. Counsel--Blount International, Inc., Montgomery, AL; *U.S. Public*, pg. 237
Irving, Richard H., III, Sr. V.P. & Gen. Counsel--Blount, Inc., Montgomery, AL; *U.S. Public*, pg. 238
Irwin, Henry, Gen. Counsel--Benjamin Obdyke, Inc., Warminster, PA; *U.S. Private*, pg. 810
Isaac, Bob, Gen. Counsel--Ensco International Incorporated (ENSCO), Dallas, TX; *U.S. Public*, pg. 585
Isaacson, Erin, Corp. Counsel--Velsicol Chemical Corporation, Rosemont, IL; *U.S. Private*, pg. 1135
Isaacson, Kirk, Gen. Counsel--System Software Associates, Inc., Chicago, IL; *U.S. Public*, pg. 1552
Isakoff, Louis A., Sr. V.P., Gen. Counsel & Sec.--International Family Entertainment, Inc., Virginia Beach, VA; *Int'l*, pg. 927
Ivey, Reef C., III, Gen. Counsel--Nutri/System Inc., Horsham, PA; *U.S. Private*, pg. 859
Ivey, Robert, V.P. & Gen. Counsel--Reeves International, Spartanburg, SC; *U.S. Private*, pg. 507
Jaccard, Walter B., V.P.- Gen. Counsel & Sec.--U.S. Trails, Dallas, TX; *U.S. Public*, pg. 1688
Jackman, Edward F., V.P., Gen. Counsel & Sec.--Cytec Industries Inc., West Paterson, NJ; *U.S. Public*, pg. 471
Jacks, Ethan E., V.P. & Gen. Counsel--Molten Metal Technology, Inc., Fall River, MA; *U.S. Public*, pg. 1123
Jackson, Andrew, Gen. Counsel--Peace River Electric Cooperative, Inc., Wauchula, FL; *U.S. Private*, pg. 845
Jackson, Greg, Gen. Counsel--Taylor Corporation, Mankato, MN; *U.S. Private*, pg. 1070
Jackson, Johnnie M., Jr., V.P., Gen. Counsel & Sec.--Olin Corporation, Norwalk, CT; *U.S. Public*, pg. 1218
Jackson, Rex S., V.P., Gen. Counsel & Sec.--Read-Rite Corporation, Milpitas, CA; *U.S. Public*, pg. 1366
Jackson, Richard M., Jr., V.P. & Gen. Counsel--G.E. Lighting Division, Cleveland, OH; *U.S. Public*, pg. 710
Jacobi, Ronald N., Exec. V.P & Gen. Counsel--Sony Pictures Entertainment, Culver City, CA; *Int'l*, pg. 1281
Jacobs, Curtis M., Sr. V.P., Chief Counsel & Sec.--National City Bank, Kentucky, Louisville, KY; *U.S. Public*, pg. 1154
Jacobs, Mark N., V.P., Sec. & Deputy Gen. Counsel--The Dreyfus Corporation, New York, NY; *U.S. Public*, pg. 1085
Jacobs, Michael, Deputy Gen. Counsel--Reed Elsevier Inc., New York, NY; *Int'l*, pg. 1095
Jacobs, Michael, V.P. & Gen. Counsel--LEXIS-NEXIS, Miamisburg, OH; *Int'l*, pg. 1096
Jacobs, Seth, Sr. V.P. & Gen. Counsel--Blue Shield of California, San Francisco, CA; *U.S. Private*, pg. 153
Jacobson, L.H., Exec. V.P. & Gen. Counsel--Nuburn Capital, Calgary, Canada; *Int'l*, pg. 990
Jacobson, Richard N., Gen. Counsel & Sec.--The Standard Products Company, Dearborn, MI; *U.S. Public*, pg. 1504
Jacoy, Catherine E., Gen. Counsel & Sec.--Unigard Insurance Co., Bellevue, WA; *Int'l*, pg. 345
Jacoy, Catherine E., Gen. Counsel & Sec.--Unigard Indemnity Co., Bellevue, WA; *Int'l*, pg. 345
Jaeckel, Howard F., Assoc. Gen. Counsel-Licensing--CBS, New York, NY; *U.S. Public*, pg. 273
Jaeger, Mark S., V.P., Gen. Counsel & Asst. Sec.--Jockey International, Inc., Kenosha, WI; *U.S. Private*, pg. 588
Jali, Jim, Esq., Gen. Counsel--Computer Power Incorporated, High Bridge, NJ; *U.S. Public*, pg. 421
James, John, V.P. & Gen. Counsel--Gerber Products Company, Fremont, MI; *Int'l*, pg. 973
James, Jyrl, V.P.-H.R. & Gen. Counsel--The Beacon Journal Publishing Company, Akron, OH; *U.S. Public*, pg. 963
Jameson, Kelly J., V.P., Gen. Counsel & Sec.--Cornerstone Natural Gas, Inc., Dallas, TX; *U.S. Public*, pg. 567
Janger, Jerome, Sec. & Legal--Kennington Ltd., Inc., Van Nuys, CA; *U.S. Private*, pg. 615
Jankowski, Tad, V.P. & Gen. Counsel--National Amusements, Inc., Dedham, MA; *U.S. Private*, pg. 775
Janney, Oliver J., V.P., Gen. Counsel & Sec.--Uniroyal Technology Corporation, Sarasota, FL; *U.S. Public*, pg. 1670
Janosky, Arnold, V.P., Gen. Counsel & Sec.--Precision Tune Autocare Inc., Leesburg, VA; *U.S. Public*, pg. 1321
Janus, Paul, Actuary--Certified Life Insurance, Chicago, IL; *U.S. Public*, pg. 433
Jany, Marc, Gen. Counsel--Alcatel Business Systems (France), Colombes, France; *Int'l*, pg. 55
Japha, Daniel S., Gen. Counsel-Corp., Sec. & Dir.-Investor Rels.--M.D.C. Holdings, Inc., Denver, CO; *U.S. Public*, pg. 1025
Jardine, Jim, Gen. Counsel--Zions Co-operative Mercantile Institution, Salt Lake City, UT; *U.S. Public*, pg. 1793
Jartz, John G., Sr. V.P.-Law & Bus. Devel./Corp. Sec.--The Quaker Oats Company, Chicago, IL; *U.S. Public*, pg. 1347
Jarvi, K.T., Sr. V.P. & Gen. Counsel--MidCon Corp., Lombard, IL; *U.S. Public*, pg. 1210
Jaske, John B., Sr. V.P.-Labor Rels. & Asst. Gen. Counsel--Gannett Company, Inc., Arlington, VA; *U.S. Public*, pg. 698
Jaudes, William E., V.P. & Gen. Counsel--AmerenUE, Saint Louis, MO; *U.S. Public*, pg. 66
Jaudes, William E., V.P. & Gen. Counsel--Union Electric Development Corporation, Saint Louis, MO; *U.S. Public*, pg. 66
Jay, Dan, Pres., Chief Exec. Officer & Chief Fin. Officer--Campmor Inc., Upper Saddle River, NJ; *U.S. Private*, pg. 204
Jay, Morton, Chm. Bd.--Campmor Inc., Upper Saddle River, NJ; *U.S. Private*, pg. 204
Jaye, Steven A., Sr. V.P., Gen. Counsel & Corp. Sec.--Sunrise Medical, Inc., Carlsbad, CA; *U.S. Public*, pg. 1535
Jeannot, Louis D., Dir.-Industrial Contracts & Opers.--Arianespace SA, Evry, France; *Int'l*, pg. 81
Jeffers, William, Corp. Counsel--Trimble Navigation Limited, Sunnyvale, CA; *U.S. Public*, pg. 1638
Jekel, Louis G., Legal Officer--Rural Metro Corporation, Scottsdale, AZ; *U.S. Public*, pg. 1412
Jenkins, J., V.P., Gen. Counsel & Sec.--Dow Corning Corporation, Midland, MI; *U.S. Public*, pg. 523
Jenko, Jerry, Gen. Counsel--Pillsbury Co., Minneapolis, MN; *Int'l*, pg. 411
Jenks, Rodney P., V.P., Gen. Counsel & Sec.--Hexcel Corporation, Pleasanton, CA; *U.S. Public*, pg. 824
Jennings, Ann, V.P. & Gen. Counsel--Nissan Motor Corporation in U.S.A., Gardena, CA; *Int'l*, pg. 945
Jennings, Thomas P., Sr. V.P., Gen. Counsel & Sec.--First Virginia Banks, Inc., Falls Church, VA; *U.S. Public*, pg. 641
Jeremiah, Barbara S., Sec. & Asst. Gen. Counsel--Aluminum Company of America, Pittsburgh, PA; *U.S. Public*, pg. 60
Jewels, Fran, Gen. Counsel--Ascend Communications, Inc., Alameda, CA; *U.S. Public*, pg. 138
Jewett, Robert William, Sr. V.P., Gen. Counsel & Sec.--Hooper Holmes Corporation, Basking Ridge, NJ; *U.S. Public*, pg. 835
Jibilian, Gerald A., V.P. & Assoc. Gen. Counsel--American Home Products Corporation, Madison, NJ; *U.S. Public*, pg. 79
Joffe, Carl H., Gen. Counsel & Sec.--Purcell Co., Inc., Diamondhead, MS; *U.S. Private*, pg. 895
Johns, D. Malcolm, Jr., V.P., Gen. Counsel & Sec.--CNG Producing Co., New Orleans, LA; *U.S. Public*, pg. 435
Johnsen, Ken C., V.P., Gen. Counsel & Sec.--Geneva Steel, Vineyard, UT; *U.S. Public*, pg. 729
Johnson, B. S., Gen. Counsel & Corp. Sec.--Qantas Airways Ltd., Mascot, Australia; *Int'l*, pg. 1074
Johnson, Bonnie L., V.P. & Gen. Counsel--DAP Inc., Tipp City, OH; *Int'l*, pg. 1486
Johnson, Craig W., Gen. Counsel & Sec.--Laserscope Surgical Systems, San Jose, CA; *U.S. Public*, pg. 979
Johnson, Curtis, U.S. Counsel--Counsel Corporation, Toronto, Canada; *Int'l*, pg. 338
Johnson, Daniel R., Sr. V.P., Gen. Counsel & Sec.--Combe Incorporated, White Plains, NY; *U.S. Private*, pg. 257
Johnson, David G., Sr. Exec. V.P. & Gen. Counsel--Metro-Goldwyn-Mayer Inc., Santa Monica, CA; *U.S. Public*, pg. 1101
Johnson, Douglas A., V.P., Gen. Counsel & Sec.--Pettibone Corporation, Lisle, IL; *U.S. Private*, pg. 859
Johnson, E. Peter, Sr. V.P. & Gen. Counsel--Sundt Corp., Tucson, AZ; *U.S. Private*, pg. 1051
Johnson, Elizabeth Pringle, Sr. V.P., Gen. Counsel & Sec.--Camden Property Trust, Houston, TX; *U.S. Public*, pg. 298
Johnson, Gary R., V.P., Gen. Counsel & Sec.--Northern States Power Company, Minneapolis, MN; *U.S. Public*, pg. 1195
Johnson, Greg, Gen. Counsel--Warner-Lambert Consumer Healthcare, Morris Plains, NJ; *U.S. Public*, pg. 1739
Johnson, Greg, V.P. & Gen. Counsel--Adams U.S.A., Morris Plains, NJ; *U.S. Public*, pg. 1739
Johnson, Gregory L., V.P. & Gen. Counsel--Warner-Lambert Company, Morris Plains, NJ; *U.S. Public*, pg. 1738
Johnson, Harry A., III, Exec. V.P. & Gen. Counsel--First Tennessee National Corporation, Memphis, TN; *U.S. Public*, pg. 638
Johnson, Harry A., III, Exec. V.P. & Gen. Counsel--First Tennessee Bank National Association, Memphis, TN; *U.S. Public*, pg. 639
Johnson, J. Brooke, Jr., Sr. V.P. & Gen. Counsel--Medpartners Inc., Birmingham, AL; *U.S. Public*, pg. 1082
Johnson, James J., Sr. V.P. & Gen. Counsel--The Procter & Gamble Company, Cincinnati, OH; *U.S. Public*, pg. 1330
Johnson, Joia, Gen. Counsel--H.J. Russell & Co., Atlanta, GA; *U.S. Private*, pg. 952
Johnson, Justin, Esq., V.P., Gen. Counsel & Sec.--Atlanta Life Insurance Company, Atlanta, GA; *U.S. Private*, pg. 94
Johnson, Lawrence, Chm. Bd., Pres., Chief Exec. Officer & Gen. Counsel--Kelley Company, Inc., Milwaukee, WI; *U.S. Private*, pg. 612
Johnson, Lawrence, Chm. Bd., Pres., Chief Exec. Officer & Gen Counsel--Kelley Dock Systems, Milwaukee, WI; *U.S. Private*, pg. 612
Johnson, Mark W., Assoc. Gen. Counsel-Washington--CBS, New York, NY; *U.S. Public*, pg. 273
Johnson, Robert A., V.P., Gen. Counsel & Sec.--Bonneville International Corp., Salt Lake City, UT; *U.S. Private*, pg. 327
Johnson, Ronald, V.P.-Corp. Counsel--Bankers Systems Incorporated, Saint Cloud, MN; *U.S. Private*, pg. 114
Johnson, Scott W., Sr. V.P., Gen. Counsel & Sec.--Bemis Company, Inc., Minneapolis, MN; *U.S. Public*, pg. 210
Johnson, Stephen L., Sr. V.P.-Legal Affairs & Gen. Counsel--America West Airlines, Inc., Phoenix, AZ; *U.S. Public*, pg. 67
Johnson, Steven, Gen. Counsel & Dir.-Legal & Admin. Svcs.--Norbest, Inc., Midvale, UT; *U.S. Private*, pg. 801
Johnson, Steven A., V.P.-Customer Svc., Gen. Counsel & Sec.--Maine Public Service Company, Presque Isle, ME; *U.S. Public*, pg. 1038
Johnson, Susan Glatthorn, V.P.-Legal Svcs. & Admin.--Echelon International Corporation, Saint Petersburg, FL; *U.S. Public*, pg. 560
Johnson, William D., V.P.-Legal, Sr. Counsel & Asst. Sec.--Carolina Power & Light Company, Raleigh, NC; *U.S. Public*, pg. 306
Johnston, Carl, Gen. Counsel--Hitachi Home Electronics, Norcross, GA; *Int'l*, pg. 621
Johnston, Murray, V.P., Gen. Counsel & Sec.--H.B. Zachry, San Antonio, TX; *U.S. Private*, pg. 1203
Jolles, Ira H., Sr. V.P. & Gen. Counsel--GPU, Inc., Morristown, NJ; *U.S. Public*, pg. 695
Jolly, Elizabeth B., Gen. Counsel--Microtek Medical, Inc., Columbus, MS; *U.S. Public*, pg. 914
Jollymore, Nick, Gen. Counsel--People, New York, NY; *U.S. Public*, pg. 1613
Jones Kane, M'Liss, Sr. V.P., Gen. Counsel & Corp. Sec.--Fidelity National Financial, Inc., Irvine, CA; *U.S. Public*, pg. 620
Jones, Colin D., Gen. Counsel & Sec.--Cambridge Shopping Centres Limited, Toronto, Canada; *Int'l*, pg. 253
Jones, D. Michael, V.P.-Gen. Counsel--Reynolds Metals Company, Richmond, VA; *U.S. Public*, pg. 1385
Jones, David, Sr. Gen. Counsel--Hubbard Broadcasting, Inc., Saint Paul, MN; *U.S. Private*, pg. 543
Jones, David, Legal Counsel--KSTP-TV, Saint Paul, MN; *U.S. Private*, pg. 544
Jones, Dereck M., Sr. V.P. & Gen. Counsel--Bank of Montreal, Toronto, Canada; *Int'l*, pg. 153
Jones, Graham, Grp. Sec. & Head of Legal Services--Norwich Union Life Insurance, Norwich, United Kingdom; *Int'l*, pg. 970
Jones, Gregory R., V.P.-Human Resources, Gen. Counsel & Sec.--OMS, Inc., Mobile, AL; *U.S. Public*, pg. 1346
Jones, James E., Chief Fin. Officer, Treas. & Sec.--Modern Welding Co., Inc., Owensboro, KY; *U.S. Private*, pg. 755
Jones, James P., V.P., Gen. Counsel & Sec.--Stone & Webster, Incorporated, Boston, MA; *U.S. Public*, pg. 1519
Jones, K., Gen. Counsel & Sec.--Colonial Pipeline Company, Atlanta, GA; *U.S. Private*, pg. 254
Jones, O. Steve, Gen. Counsel--Sylvan Learning Systems Inc., Baltimore, MD; *U.S. Public*, pg. 1545
Jones, Orlo D., Sr. V.P.-Properties & Sec.--Longs Drug Stores Corporation, Walnut Creek, CA; *U.S. Public*, pg. 1013
Jones, Richard, V.P. & Gen. Counsel--Anschutz Corporation, Denver, CO; *U.S. Private*, pg. 75
Jones, Robert E., V.P. & Gen. Counsel--Mississippi Chemical Corporation, Yazoo City, MS; *U.S. Public*, pg. 1117
Jones, Robertson C., V.P. & Gen. Counsel--Del Webb Corporation, Phoenix, AZ; *U.S. Public*, pg. 494
Jones, Samuel, V.P. & Legal Officer--Getty Petroleum Marketing Inc., Jericho, NY; *U.S. Public*, pg. 740
Jongleux, Lynn B., Gen. Counsel & Sec.--United Farm Family Life Insurance Co., Indianapolis, IN; *U.S. Private*, pg. 1122
Jordan, Russell W., III, Sr. V.P., Gen. Counsel & Sec.--Lawyers Title Insurance Corporation, Richmond, VA; *U.S. Public*, pg. 981
Jorgensen, Julie A., V.P. & Gen. Counsel--NRG Energy, Inc., Minneapolis, MN; *U.S. Public*, pg. 1195
Josenhans, Paul J., Assoc. Gen. Counsel & Sec.--Borden, Inc., Columbus, OH; *U.S. Private*, pg. 157
Joseph, Anne, Dir.-Legal, London--Reed Elsevier plc, London, United Kingdom; *Int'l*, pg. 1093
Joseph, Marc, V.P. & Gen. Counsel--Haggar Corporation, Dallas, TX; *U.S. Public*, pg. 774
Joubert, Nereus, Dr., Gen. Mgr., Gen. Counsel & Sec.--Sasol Limited, Johannesburg, South Africa; *Int'l*, pg. 1196
Joyce, Edward J., V.P. & Gen. Counsel--Connell Limited Partnership, Boston, MA; *U.S. Private*, pg. 264
Joyce, Joseph, V.P.-Human Resources & Legal Counsel--Best Buy Co., Inc., Eden Prairie, MN; *U.S. Public*, pg. 223
Joyce, Joseph J., V.P. & Asst. Gen. Counsel--PepsiCo, Inc., Purchase, NY; *U.S. Public*, pg. 1276
Jozefek, Jane M., V.P., Gen. Counsel & Asst. Sec.--Porta Systems Corp., Syosset, NY; *U.S. Public*, pg. 1317
Juchatz, Wayne W., Exec. V.P. & Gen. Counsel--Textron Inc., Providence, RI; *U.S. Public*, pg. 1588
Judd, Ardon, B., Jr., V.P.-Washington Counsel--Dresser Industries, Inc., Dallas, TX; *U.S. Public*, pg. 528
Judd, Peter, Gen. Counsel--Superior Reprographics, Seattle, WA; *U.S. Private*, pg. 418
Juelsgaard, Stephen, V.P., Gen. Counsel & Asst. Sec.--Genentech, Inc., South San Francisco, CA; *Int'l*, pg. 1120

June, Roy, Gen. Counsel--Knight Equipment International Inc., Costa Mesa, CA; *U.S. Public*, pg. 862
Juno, Gary, Gen. Counsel & Dir.-Environ. Affairs--Columbian Chemicals Company, Atlanta, GA; *U.S. Public*, pg. 1286
Jussup, W. John, V.P., Gen. Counsel & Sec.--Cognos Inc., Ottawa, Canada; *Int'l*, pg. 305
Just, Lawrence E., Asst. Sec. & Gen. Counsel--Bradley Printing Company, Des Plaines, IL; *U.S. Public*, pg. 1778
Justesen, Wayne, V.P., Gen. Counsel & Sec.--Greenwood Mills, Inc., Greenwood, SC; *U.S. Private*, pg. 479
Kabak, Edward M., V.P. & Gen. Counsel--Grolier Inc., Danbury, CT; *Int'l*, pg. 794
Kabak, Wayne, Gen. Counsel--ICM Holdings Inc., New York, NY; *U.S. Private*, pg. 554
Kaden, Ellen O., Exec. V.P., Gen. Counsel & Sec.--CBS, New York, NY; *U.S. Public*, pg. 273
Kadish, David A., Sec. & Gen. Counsel--Integral Systems, Inc., Walnut Creek, CA; *Int'l*, pg. 242
Kadow, Joe, V.P., Gen. Counsel & Sec.--Outback Steakhouse Inc., Tampa, FL; *U.S. Public*, pg. 1235
Kahen, Harold I., Gen. Counsel & Sec.--Standard Microsystems Corp., Hauppauge, NY; *U.S. Public*, pg. 1502
Kahle, John H., Exec. V.P., Gen. Counsel & Asst. Sec.--Kimball International, Inc., Jasper, IN; *U.S. Public*, pg. 956
Kahn, Harry H., V.P., Gen. Counsel & Sec.--ABM Industries, San Francisco, CA; *U.S. Public*, pg. 2
Kahn, Todd, Exec. V.P., Gen. Counsel & Sec.--Salant Corporation, New York, NY; *U.S. Public*, pg. 1429
Kaiser, Robert, V.P. & Gen. Counsel--Durex Consumer Products, Norcross, GA; *Int'l*, pg. 815
Kalaher, Richard A., V.P., Gen. Counsel & Sec.--American Standard Inc., Piscataway, NJ; *U.S. Public*, pg. 91
Kaleta, Paul J., V.P.-Law & Gen. Counsel--Niagara Mohawk Power Corporation, Syracuse, NY; *U.S. Public*, pg. 1181
Kalette, Stephen R., V.P.-Admin. & Gen. Counsel--Pubco Corporation, Cleveland, OH; *U.S. Public*, pg. 1339
Kalib, David L., V.P., Gen. Counsel & Sec.--Berkshire Life Insurance Company, Pittsfield, MA; *U.S. Private*, pg. 136
Kalin, Richard S., Gen. Counsel & Sec.--Pentech International, Inc., Edison, NJ; *U.S. Public*, pg. 1274
Kalitte, Stephen R., V.P., Gen. Counsel & Sec.--Kroy Inc., Scottsdale, AZ; *U.S. Public*, pg. 1339
Kalnins-Ghafari, Mara, Gen. Counsel--Ghafari Associates, Inc., Dearborn, MI; *U.S. Private*, pg. 450
Kambara, T., Gen. Counsel--Tonen Corporation, Tokyo, Japan; *Int'l*, pg. 1398
Kamins, Howard, V.P., Gen. Counsel & Corp. Sec.--EA Industries, West Long Branch, NJ; *U.S. Public*, pg. 541
Kaminsky, Judy, Gen. Counsel--International Apparel Marketing Corp., New York, NY; *U.S. Public*, pg. 498
Kane, Alice T., Exec. V.P.-Asset Mngmnt. & Investment Prods. & Gen. Counsel--New York Life Insurance Company, New York, NY; *U.S. Private*, pg. 794
Kane, Kathleen G., Sr. V.P.-Head Counsel--World Financial Properties, Inc., New York, NY; *Int'l*, pg. 1004
Kantner, John, Gen. Counsel--Bob Evans Farms, Inc., Columbus, OH; *U.S. Public*, pg. 596
Kantner, John, Gen. Counsel--Bob Evans Farms, Inc. Restaurant Division, Columbus, OH; *U.S. Public*, pg. 596
Kantor, Andrea D., Assoc. Gen. Counsel--GP Strategies Corporation, New York, NY; *U.S. Public*, pg. 694
Kantor, Jonathan, Sr. V.P., Gen. Counsel & Sec.--Continental Assurance Company, Chicago, IL; *U.S. Private*, pg. 267
Kaplan, Elliot S., Gen. Counsel & Sec.--Best Buy Co., Inc., Eden Prairie, MN; *U.S. Public*, pg. 223
Kaplan, Lawrence, Sr. V.P.-Business & Legal Affairs--Buena Vista Pictures Distribution Inc., Burbank, CA; *U.S. Public*, pg. 513
Kaplan, Theodore S., Sr. V.P. & Gen. Counsel--Legg Mason, Inc., Baltimore, MD; *U.S. Public*, pg. 984
Kareh, Guillermo, V.P.-H.R. & Insurance & Gen. Counsel--Consorcio G. Grupo Dina, S.A. de C.V., Mexico, Mexico; *Int'l*, pg. 326
Kareh, Guillermo, V.P. & Gen. Counsel--Motor Coach Industries International, Inc., Phoenix, AZ; *Int'l*, pg. 326
Karel, Steven, V.P., Gen. Counsel & Sec.--Robert Half International Inc., Menlo Park, CA; *U.S. Public*, pg. 774
Kargula, Michael R., Exec. V.P., Gen. Counsel & Sec.--Primark Corporation, Waltham, MA; *U.S. Public*, pg. 1325
Karl, Frederick B., Jr., V.P., Gen. Counsel & Sec.--Medical Manager Corporation, Tampa, FL; *U.S. Public*, pg. 1080
Karlshausen, Robert, Gen. Counsel & Sec.--Herstal S.A., Herstal, Belgium; *Int'l*, pg. 617
Karniel, Uzi, Corp. Counsel & Sec.--Teva Pharmaceutical Industries Ltd., Petah Tiqwa, Israel; *Int'l*, pg. 1380
Karp, Roberta S., V.P.-Corp. Affairs & Gen. Counsel--Liz Claiborne, Inc., New York, NY; *U.S. Public*, pg. 1005
Karsky, Gloria J., Gen. Counsel & Sec.--TCF Bank Illinois, Oak Brook, IL; *U.S. Public*, pg. 1554
Kasak, Robert, Gen. Counsel--MTL Inc., Plant City, FL; *U.S. Public*, pg. 1028
Kasak, Robert, Gen. Counsel--Montgomery Tank Lines, Inc., Plant City, FL; *U.S. Public*, pg. 1028
Katter, William F., V.P.-Gen. Counsel--TAD Resources International, Inc., Cambridge, MA; *U.S. Private*, pg. 1062
Katz, Jason L., V.P. & Gen. Counsel--Farmers Group, Inc., Los Angeles, CA; *Int'l*, pg. 110
Katz, Melvin, Dir.-Legal--PharmHouse, Inc., New York, NY; *U.S. Public*, pg. 1286
Kauf, Thomas, Gen. Counsel--Wilcox Electric, Inc., Kansas City, MO; *Int'l*, pg. 1384
Kaufman, Alan, V.P. & Gen. Counsel--Penguin Putnam Inc., New York, NY; *Int'l*, pg. 1027
Kaufman, Alan J., Treas. & Gen. Counsel--H.W. Kaufman Financial Group, Inc., Farmington, MI; *U.S. Private*, pg. 609
Kaufman, Joseph Q., Gen. Counsel--American Vanguard Corporation, Newport Beach, CA; *U.S. Public*, pg. 94
Kaufman, Steven J., V.P. & Gen. Counsel--Arrow Shirt Company, New York, NY; *Int'l*, pg. 194
Kawahara, Hisashi, Dir. & Sr. Adviser--UBS Phillips & Drew Intl. Ltd., Tokyo, Japan; *Int'l*, pg. 1440
Kawalick, Steven, Gen. Counsel & Asst. Sec.--Intelligent Electronics, Inc., Exton, PA; *U.S. Public*, pg. 887
Kaye, Diane L., V.P., Gen. Counsel & Sec.--Federal-Mogul Corporation, Southfield, MI; *U.S. Public*, pg. 615
Keane, John K., Jr., Sr. V.P. & Gen. Counsel--Washington Gas Light Co., Springfield, VA; *U.S. Public*, pg. 1740
Keanrs, Virginia, V.P. & Gen. Counsel--Tenneco Automotive, Deerfield, IL; *U.S. Public*, pg. 1577
Kear, F.E., Grp. Attorney--Solar Turbines Incorporated, San Diego, CA; *U.S. Public*, pg. 316
Kearney, Christopher J., V.P., Gen. Counsel & Sec.--SPX Corporation, Muskegon, MI; *U.S. Public*, pg. 1420
Keating, Michael K., Exec. V.P. & Gen. Counsel--Fifth Third Bancorp, Cincinnati, OH; *U.S. Public*, pg. 621
Keating, Pamela A., Gen. Counsel & Clerk--LTX Corporation, Westwood, MA; *U.S. Public*, pg. 972
Keefe, Mary Patricia, Grp. V.P. & Gen. Counsel--Elizabethtown Gas Co., Union, NJ; *U.S. Public*, pg. 1147
Keen, Paul R., Gen. Counsel & Sec.--Argo-Tech Corporation, Cleveland, OH; *U.S. Private*, pg. 81
Keeshan, Larry, Gen. Counsel--Price Waterhouse L.L.P. - U.S., New York, NY; *U.S. Private*, pg. 883
Keith, Susan S., V.P., Corp. Counsel & Sec.--Halliburton Company, Dallas, TX; *U.S. Public*, pg. 775
Keithley, Jay C., V.P.-Law & External Affairs--Sprint Corporation, Westwood, KS; *U.S. Public*, pg. 1500
Keler, Marianne M., Sr. V.P. & Gen. Counsel--SLM Holding Corp., Washington, DC; *U.S. Public*, pg. 1419
Kelleher, Harry B., Gen. Counsel & Sec.--Reagan Equipment Company, Inc., Gretna, LA; *U.S. Private*, pg. 913
Keller, Bryan, V.P., Gen. Counsel & Sec.--Delaware North Companies, Inc., Buffalo, NY; *U.S. Private*, pg. 321
Keller, Roger, V.P. & Gen. Counsel--Mallinckrodt Inc., Saint Louis, MO; *U.S. Public*, pg. 1039
Keller, Roger A., V.P., Gen. Counsel & Sec.--Mallinckrodt Inc., Saint Louis, MO; *U.S. Public*, pg. 1039
Kelley, James F., Sr. V.P.-Law & Gen. Counsel--Georgia-Pacific Corporation, Atlanta, GA; *U.S. Public*, pg. 735
Kelley, Janet G., V.P. & Assoc. Gen. Counsel--Sunbeam Corporation, Delray Beach, FL; *U.S. Public*, pg. 1533
Kelley, Robert L., Sr. V.P. & Gen. Counsel--Insituform Technologies, Inc., Chesterfield, MO; *U.S. Public*, pg. 881
Kelley, W. Michael, Gen. Counsel--New Mexico & Arizona Land Co., Phoenix, AZ; *U.S. Public*, pg. 1172
Kelliher, Daniel J., Jr., Sr. V.P. & Assoc. Gen. Counsel-Investments--The New England, Boston, MA; *U.S. Private*, pg. 737
Kellogg, Martin N., Pres. & Chief Exec. Officer--UFE Incorporated, Stillwater, MN; *U.S. Private*, pg. 1112
Kelly, Anastasia D., Sr. V.P. & Deputy Gen. Counsel--Federal National Mortgage Association (Fannie Mae), Washington, DC; *U.S. Public*, pg. 615
Kelly, Brian C., Gen. Counsel & Sec.--Chris-Craft Industries, Inc., New York, NY; *U.S. Public*, pg. 351
Kelly, Brian C., Gen. Counsel & Sec.--BHC Communications, Inc., New York, NY; *U.S. Public*, pg. 352
Kelly, Clive R., Gen. Counsel--Pentland Group PLC, London, United Kingdom; *Int'l*, pg. 1035
Kelly, Harold V., Exec. V.P. & Gen. Counsel--Republic Engineered Steels, Inc., Massillon, OH; *U.S. Public*, pg. 1378
Kelly, Hugh Rice, Exec. V.P. & Gen. Counsel--Houston Industries Incorporated, Houston, TX; *U.S. Public*, pg. 842
Kelly, Janet Langford, Sr. V.P., Gen. Counsel & Sec.--Sara Lee Corporation, Chicago, IL; *U.S. Public*, pg. 1432
Kelly, John F., V.P., Gen. Counsel & Asst. Sec.--Allmerica Financial Corporation, Worcester, MA; *U.S. Public*, pg. 54
Kelly, Laura, Gen. Counsel--Converse Inc., North Reading, MA; *U.S. Public*, pg. 441
Kelly, Michael T., Sr. V.P. & Gen Counsel--Schieffelin & Somerset Co., New York, NY; *Int'l*, pg. 412
Kempner, Brian, V.P. & Gen. Counsel--Shepaug Corporation, New York, NY; *U.S. Private*, pg. 993
Kenagy, Robert T., Assoc. Gen. Counsel--Whirlpool Corporation, Benton Harbor, MI; *U.S. Public*, pg. 1764
Kenduck, Neil G., Gen. Counsel--Amplicon, Inc., Santa Ana, CA; *U.S. Public*, pg. 104
Kendy, Joseph S., V.P.-Legal--Zotos International, Darien, CT; *Int'l*, pg. 1236
Kenneally, William, Sr. V.P., Gen. Counsel & Sec.--Golub Corporation, Schenectady, NY; *U.S. Private*, pg. 463
Kennedy-Good, John, Gen. Counsel--New Zealand Dairy Board, Wellington, New Zealand; *Int'l*, pg. 923
Kennedy, Bernard D., Pres. & Chief Oper. Officer--King Kullen Grocery Co., Inc., Westbury, NY; *U.S. Private*, pg. 621
Kennedy, Christopher, Gen. Cousel--Chemoil, San Francisco, CA; *U.S. Private*, pg. 233
Kennedy, James C., V.P. & Gen. Counsel--Spelling Entertainment Group, Inc., Los Angeles, CA; *U.S. Private*, pg. 776
Kennedy, John P., V.P., Gen. Counsel & Sec.--Johnson Controls, Inc., Milwaukee, WI; *U.S. Public*, pg. 932
Kennedy, Quentin J., Exec. V.P. & Sec.--Imperial Bondware Corp., Montvale, NJ; *U.S. Public*, pg. 903
Kennedy, R. Michael, Sr. V.P. & Gen. Counsel--Tyco Toys, Inc., Mount Laurel, NJ; *U.S. Public*, pg. 1058
Kennedy, Ruth A., Sr. V.P., Gen. Counsel & Sec.--Electronic Arts, San Mateo, CA; *U.S. Public*, pg. 569
Kenney, Crane H., V.P., Gen. Counsel & Sec.--Tribune Company, Chicago, IL; *U.S. Public*, pg. 1635
Kenney, Thomas J., Gen. Counsel--McKenzies of Vermont, Inc., Burlington, VT; *U.S. Private*, pg. 723
Kennis, Robert H., V.P. & Gen. Counsel--Circle International Group, Inc., San Francisco, CA; *U.S. Public*, pg. 370
Kensing, Henry V., V.P., Gen. Counsel & Sec.--Dynamics Corporation of America, Greenwich, CT; *U.S. Public*, pg. 286
Kent, Andrew G., V.P. & Assoc. Gen. Counsel--Franchise Finance Corp. of America, Scottsdale, AZ; *U.S. Public*, pg. 679
Kent, Kristin H., V.P., Sr. Legal Counsel & Asst. Sec.--Gannett Company, Inc., Arlington, VA; *U.S. Public*, pg. 698
Kent, Richard E., V.P., Sec. & Gen. Counsel--Grossman's, Inc., Stoughton, MA; *U.S. Private*, pg. 585
Kenward, A.T., V.P.-Winery Communications--Wine World Estates Company, Saint Helena, CA; *Int'l*, pg. 917
Kerber, Ken, Attorney--Victory Financial Group, Inc., Metairie, LA; *U.S. Private*, pg. 1139
Kerjouan, Jean-Pierre, V.P. & Gen. Counsel--Elf Aquitane, Paris, France; *Int'l*, pg. 444
Kerr, Henry V., Gen. Counsel--McDonald & Company Investments, Inc., Cleveland, OH; *U.S. Public*, pg. 1068
Kershner, Rodger A., Sr. V.P. & Gen. Counsel--CMS Energy Corporation, Dearborn, MI; *U.S. Public*, pg. 279
Kershner, Rodger A., Gen. Counsel--CMS Generation Co., Dearborn, MI; *U.S. Public*, pg. 280
Kesner, Harvey J., Esq., Sr. V.P., Gen. Counsel & Sec.--American Banknote Corp., New York, NY; *U.S. Public*, pg. 68
Kessel, Roger H., Gen. Counsel & Sec.--Tampa Electric Co., Tampa, FL; *U.S. Public*, pg. 1565
Kessler, John L., Senior Counsel--Ikon Office Solutions, Inc., Malvern, PA; *U.S. Public*, pg. 862
Kessler, Leonard, Sr. V.P. & Gen. Counsel--Morse Diesel International, Inc., New York, NY; *U.S. Private*, pg. 762
Kettig, David T., V.P.-Legal & Sec.--Independence Holding Company, Stamford, CT; *U.S. Private*, pg. 446
Kevorkian, Corinne, Gen. Counsel--F. Schumacher & Co., New York, NY; *U.S. Private*, pg. 973
Keyes, Bryan F., Treas., Sec. & Dir.-Legal & Fin.--STB Systems, Inc., Richardson, TX; *U.S. Public*, pg. 1421
Keysor, Gus, Gen. Counsel--Linotype-Hell Company, Hauppauge, NY; *Int'l*, pg. 604
Khazarian, Roxanne, Gen. Counsel--Ethan Allen Interiors Inc., Danbury, CT; *U.S. Public*, pg. 595
Khazarian, Roxanne, Gen. Counsel & Sec.--Ethan Allen, Inc., Danbury, CT; *U.S. Public*, pg. 595
Kiefer, Joseph T., Exec. V.P. & Gen. Counsel--Pacific Century Financial Corporation, Honolulu, HI; *U.S. Public*, pg. 1248
Kiefer, Joseph T., Exec. V.P.-Legal Division--Bank of Hawaii, Honolulu, HI; *U.S. Public*, pg. 1248
Kiefer, William R., V.P.-Law & Sec.--Weirton Steel Corporation, Weirton, WV; *U.S. Public*, pg. 1751
Kinander, Lars, Legal Officer--Svenska Handelsbanken, Stockholm, Sweden; *Int'l*, pg. 1327
Kindler, Jeffrey B., Exec. V.P. & Gen. Counsel--McDonald's Corporation, Oak Brook, IL; *U.S. Public*, pg. 1068
King, J.B., V.P., Gen. Counsel & Sec.--Guidant Corporation, Indianapolis, IN; *U.S. Public*, pg. 768
King, James A., Jr., Asst. Gen. Counsel--Borden, Inc., Columbus, OH; *U.S. Private*, pg. 157
King, Jeffrey J., V.P. & Gen. Counsel--Expeditors International of Washington, Inc., Seattle, WA; *U.S. Public*, pg. 600
King, John L., Legal Officer--F.B. Wright Co., Dearborn, MI; *U.S. Private*, pg. 1192
King, Kevan S., Gen. Counsel & Sec.--Poco Petroleums Ltd., Calgary, Canada; *Int'l*, pg. 1061
King, Lawrence E., V.P., Gen. Counsel & Sec.--Flint Ink Corp., Detroit, MI; *U.S. Private*, pg. 413
King, Stephen, Sec.--Datron Incorporated, Windsor, CT; *U.S. Private*, pg. 313
King, Thomas R., Gen. Counsel & Sec.--First Team Sports Inc., Anoka, MN; *U.S. Public*, pg. 638
King, W. Gary, Gen. Counsel & Sec.--Frisch's Restaurants, Inc., Cincinnati, OH; *U.S. Public*, pg. 682
King, William B., Gen. Counsel & Sec.--Bradley Real Estate, Inc., Northbrook, IL; *U.S. Public*, pg. 250
Kinnard, Michael B., V.P., Gen. Counsel & Sec.--Matlack Systems, Inc., Wilmington, DE; *U.S. Public*, pg. 1057
Kinnard, Michael B., V.P., Gen. Counsel & Sec.--Rollins Truck Leasing Corp., Wilmington, DE; *U.S. Public*, pg. 1405
Kinney, Karin M., Corp. Counsel & Sec.--Ikon Office Solutions, Inc., Malvern, PA; *U.S. Public*, pg. 862
Kinney, Patrick J., Gen. Counsel & Sec.--All-Phase Electric Supply Co., Benton Harbor, MI; *U.S. Private*, pg. 35
Kinoshita, Hajime, Mgr.-Inv. Rels., Legal & Admin. Div.--NEC Corporation, Tokyo, Japan; *Int'l*, pg. 899
Kinsolving, Augustus B., V.P. & Gen. Counsel--Asarco Incorporated, New York, NY; *U.S. Public*, pg. 137
Kirby, Dan L., Co.-Chm. Bd., Exec. V.P., Gen. Counsel & Sec.--Western Surety Company, Sioux Falls, SD; *U.S. Public*, pg. 303
Kirchhof, Anton C., Gen. Counsel & Sec.--Louisiana Pacific Corporation, Portland, OR; *U.S. Public*, pg. 1015
Kirk, James G., V.P., Gen. Counsel & Sec.--International Technology Corporation, Monroeville, PA; *U.S. Public*, pg. 907
Kirk, Timothy W., V.P., Gen. Counsel & Sec.--ROHN Industries, Inc., Peoria, IL; *U.S. Public*, pg. 1404
Kirk, Wayne, V.P., Gen. Counsel, & Sec.--Homestake Mining Company, San Francisco, CA; *U.S. Public*, pg. 832
Kirkman, Carol, V.P. & Asst. Gen. Counsel--Brinker International, Inc., Dallas, TX; *U.S. Public*, pg. 253
Kirkman, James A., III, Exec. V.P., Gen. Counsel & Sec.--Nabisco Inc., Parsippany, NJ; *U.S. Public*, pg. 1355
Kirkpatrick, Douglas, Gen. Counsel & Sec.--Miken Companies, Inc., Cheektowaga, NY; *U.S. Private*, pg. 745
Kirsch, Daniel A., Gen. Counsel--Interbath, Inc., City of Industry, CA; *U.S. Private*, pg. 566
Kirsch, Nancy, Gen. Counsel--Cranston Print Works Company, Cranston, RI; *U.S. Private*, pg. 286

Kirschbaum, Gerald S., V.P. & Gen. Counsel--The Hartz Mountain Corp., Secaucus, NJ; *U.S. Private,* pg. 508

Kirscher, Ian, Gen. Counsel & Sec.--Danielson Holding Corporation, New York, NY; *U.S. Public,* pg. 483

Kish, David, V.P.-Admin. & Gen. Counsel--American Classic Voyagers Company, New Orleans, LA; *U.S. Private,* pg. 380

Kish, Timothy E., Esq., Exec. V.P. & Gen. Counsel--Capital Factors, Inc., Fort Lauderdale, FL; *U.S. Public,* pg. 1669

Kissam, Roger H., V.P. & Gen. Counsel--Welbilt Corporation, Stamford, CT; *Int'l,* pg. 188

Kissane, Michael, V.P., Gen. Counsel & Sec.--CTB International Corp., Milford, IN; *U.S. Public,* pg. 284

Kissinger, Thomas, Gen. Counsel & Sec.--The Marcus Corporation, Milwaukee, WI; *U.S. Public,* pg. 1044

Kitay, Harvey, Gen. Counsel--Ruhle Companies, Inc., Valhalla, NY; *U.S. Private,* pg. 950

Kittleman, Wes, Gen. Counsel--Jones & Jones, Inc., McAllen, TX; *U.S. Private,* pg. 596

Kittner, Marc R., Sr. V.P. & Corp. Counsel--Washington Mutual Inc., Seattle, WA; *U.S. Public,* pg. 1741

Klarr, James P., Asst. Sec. & Tax Counsel--La-Z-Boy Incorporated, Monroe, MI; *U.S. Public,* pg. 972

Klausman, C. William, Gen. Counsel--Form-You-3 International, Inc., Akron, OH; *U.S. Private,* pg. 418

Klausman, C. William, Gen. Counsel--Physicians Weight Loss Centers, Inc., Akron, OH; *U.S. Private,* pg. 864

Klausman, William, Gen. Counsel--Diet Center Worldwide, Inc., Akron, OH; *U.S. Private,* pg. 864

Klausner, Jack, Gen. Counsel--Hunter Contracting Company, Gilbert, AZ; *U.S. Private,* pg. 549

Kleban, Albert J., Gen. Counsel & Sec.--Chessco Industries, Inc., Westport, CT; *U.S. Private,* pg. 234

Klein, Eric G., Gen. Counsel & Corp. Sec.--Kyocera International, Inc., San Diego, CA; *Int'l,* pg. 775

Klein, Peter W., V.P., Sec. & Gen. Counsel--Atlantis Plastic, Inc., Atlanta, GA; *U.S. Public,* pg. 145

Klein, Peter W., V.P., Gen. Counsel & Sec.--Biscayne Apparel Inc., Clifton, NJ; *U.S. Public,* pg. 232

Klein, Stanley, Gen. Counsel--Crystal Clear Industries, Ridgefield Park, NJ; *U.S. Private,* pg. 293

Klein, Stephen, Pres. & Gen. Counsel--Encore Marketing International, Inc., Lanham, MD; *U.S. Public,* pg. 580

Klein, Stephen, Pres. & Gen. Counsel--Encore Clubs, Inc., Lanham, MD; *U.S. Public,* pg. 580

Klein, Stephen, Pres. & Gen. Counsel--E.M.I. Travel Center, Inc., Lanham, MD; *U.S. Public,* pg. 580

Klein, Stephen, Pres. & Gen. Counsel--Encore Group, Inc., Lanham, MD; *U.S. Public,* pg. 580

Klein, Stephen, Pres. & Gen. Counsel--Quality Services International, Inc., Lanham, MD; *U.S. Public,* pg. 580

Kleiner, Madeline, Exec. V.P.-Admin., Gen. Counsel & Sec.--H.F. Ahmanson & Co., Irwindale, CA; *U.S. Public,* pg. 29

Kleinman, Robert D., Exec. V.P., Sec. & Gen. Counsel--AFA Protective Systems, Inc., Syosset, NY; *U.S. Public,* pg. 5

Kleva, Gregory, Exec. V.P. & Deputy Gen. Counsel--American Life Insurance Company of New York, New York, NY; *U.S. Private,* pg. 769

Kleva, Gregory A., Jr., Exec. V.P. & Deputy Gen. Counsel--Mutual of America Life Insurance Company, New York, NY; *U.S. Private,* pg. 769

Kline, James E., V.P. & Gen. Counsel--Aeroquip-Vickers, Inc., Maumee, OH; *U.S. Public,* pg. 24

Kline, Lowry F., Sr. V.P. & Gen. Counsel--Coca-Cola Enterprises Inc., Atlanta, GA; *U.S. Public,* pg. 393

Kline, Sidney D., Jr., Dir.--Bachman Company, Reading, PA; *U.S. Private,* pg. 109

Klinefelter, Gary V., Sec. & Gen. Counsel--Amerco, Reno, NV; *U.S. Private,* pg. 48

Klinefelter, Gary V., Gen. Counsel--U-Haul International, Inc., Phoenix, AZ; *U.S. Private,* pg. 49

Klinger, Jeffery L., V.P., Chief Legal Officer & Sec.--Peabody Holding Company, Inc., Saint Louis, MO; *Int'l,* pg. 594

Klint, Douglas E., V.P., Gen. Counsel & Sec.--Gatefield Corporation, Fremont, CA; *U.S. Public,* pg. 703

Klitgaard, Thomas, Sr. V.P. & Gen. Counsel--Sega of America Inc., Redwood City, CA; *Int'l,* pg. 1218

Kloster, Burton J. Jr., Sr. V.P., Gen. Counsel & Sec.--General Electric Capital Services, Inc., Stamford, CT; *U.S. Public,* pg. 711

Kluger, Allan, Gen. Counsel--The Lion Brewery, Inc., Wilkes-Barre, PA; *U.S. Public,* pg. 1000

Knack, Gaylen L., V.P. & Gen. Counsel--Grow Biz International, Inc., Minneapolis, MN; *U.S. Public,* pg. 767

Knauss, Robert H., V.P.-Law, Sec. & Assoc. Gen. Counsel--AmeriGas Partners, L.P., Valley Forge, PA; *U.S. Public,* pg. 1653

Kneezel, Ronald D., V.P., Gen. Counsel & Sec.--Banta Corporation, Menasha, WI; *U.S. Public,* pg. 187

Knight, Jeffrey L., Gen. Counsel & Sec.--Old National Bancorp, Evansville, IN; *U.S. Public,* pg. 1217

Knopf, Matthew, V.P. & Gen. Counsel--County Seat Stores, Inc., Dallas, TX; *U.S. Private,* pg. 279

Knouse, Mark S., V.P.-Govt. Rels. & Pub. Affairs--Union Pacific Resources Company (UPRC), Fort Worth, TX; *U.S. Public,* pg. 1668

Knox, James E., Sr. V.P., Gen. Counsel & Sec.--Anixter International, Chicago, IL; *U.S. Public,* pg. 115

Knox, James E., Gen. Counsel--The Antec Corporation, Rolling Meadows, IL; *U.S. Public,* pg. 116

Kobiashvili, Zurab S., V.P., Gen. Counsel & Sec.--Apache Corporation, Houston, TX; *U.S. Public,* pg. 119

Koch, Christopher L., V.P. & Gen. Counsel--Sea-Land Service, Inc., Charlotte, NC; *U.S. Public,* pg. 284

Koch, Richard J., V.P., Sec. & Gen. Counsel--American City Business Journals, Inc., Charlotte, NC; *U.S. Private,* pg. 19

Kocher, Walter W., V.P. & Gen. Counsel--Borden, Inc., Columbus, OH; *U.S. Private,* pg. 157

Koelbl, James A., Asst. V.P. & Gen. Counsel--National Guardian Life Insurance Company, Madison, WI; *U.S. Private,* pg. 784

Koelling, Demetra, V.P. & Corp. Counsel--Clear Channel Communications, Inc., San Antonio, TX; *U.S. Public,* pg. 383

Koester, Robert, Gen. Counsel--HBE Corporation/Design Build Divisions, Saint Louis, MO; *U.S. Private,* pg. 489

Koivuniemi, Paul, Gen. Counsel--Amgen Boulder, Inc., Boulder, CO; *U.S. Public,* pg. 101

Koken, Diane, V.P. & Gen. Counsel--Provident Mutual Life Insurance Co., Berwyn, PA; *U.S. Private,* pg. 891

Kolbe, William F., Gen. Counsel & Sec.--Color Arts, Inc., Racine, WI; *U.S. Private,* pg. 254

Kolleng, John L., Gen. Counsel--American National Bank & Trust Co. of Chicago, Chicago, IL; *U.S. Public,* pg. 628

Kolodney, Richard S., V.P. & Gen. Counsel--Graham-Field Health Products, Inc., Hauppauge, NY; *U.S. Public,* pg. 757

Konney, Paul E., Sr. V.P., Gen. Counsel & Sec.--Quaker State Corporation, Irving, TX; *U.S. Public,* pg. 1348

Konopko, Elliot, V.P., Gen. Counsel & Sec.--Axsys Technologies, Inc., New York, NY; *U.S. Public,* pg. 157

Konowiecki, Joseph S., Gen. Counsel & Sec.--PacifiCare Health Systems, Inc., Cypress, CA; *U.S. Public,* pg. 1250

Koonce, Neil, V.P. & Gen. Counsel--Cone Mills Corporation, Greensboro, NC; *U.S. Public,* pg. 430

Kopf, R.S., Gen. Counsel & Sec.--The Fremont Group, San Francisco, CA; *U.S. Private,* pg. 427

Koprowski, D., V.P., Gen. Counsel & Sec.--Kawasaki Motors Corp., U.S.A., Irvine, CA; *Int'l,* pg. 725

Koprowski, Wayne M., V.P., Gen. Counsel & Sec.--Joslyn Corporation, Chicago, IL; *U.S. Public,* pg. 481

Korchek, Jeffrey A., Exec. V.P.-Legal & Business Affairs--Universal Pictures, Universal City, CA; *Int'l,* pg. 1216

Korn, Stephen, V.P., Gen. Counsel & Clerk--Ionics, Incorporated, Watertown, MA; *U.S. Public,* pg. 912

Kosato, H., Exec. V.P.-Legal--Kawasaki Motors Corp., U.S.A., Irvine, CA; *Int'l,* pg. 725

Koskie, J.S., Gen. Counsel--Litton Systems Canada Ltd., Etobicoke, Canada; *U.S. Public,* pg. 1005

Kosturko, William T., Exec. V.P.-Legal Dept. & Gen. Counsel--People's Bank, Bridgeport, CT; *U.S. Public,* pg. 1274

Kosugi, Soichiro, Counsel--Kosugi Sangyo Co., Ltd., Tokyo, Japan; *Int'l,* pg. 759

Kotler, Norman, Sr. Legal Advisor & Sec.--ECI Telecom Ltd., Petah Tiqwa, Israel; *Int'l,* pg. 643

Koutsogiane, Wallis, Staff Counsel--Valley Resources, Inc., Cumberland, RI; *U.S. Public,* pg. 1706

Kovacs, Attila, Gen. Counsel & Mgr.--Malev Hungarian Airlines, Plc., Budapest, Hungary; *Int'l,* pg. 833

Koza, Thomas Andrew, V.P. & Sec.-Law Admin.--The North American Coal Corporation, Dallas, TX; *U.S. Public,* pg. 1149

Koziar, Stephen F., Jr., Grp. V.P., Gen. Counsel & Sec.--DPL Inc., Dayton, OH; *U.S. Public,* pg. 473

Kraft, James A., V.P.-Law & Corp. Affairs--Plum Creek Timber Co., L.P., Seattle, WA; *U.S. Public,* pg. 1311

Krakauer, Albert A., Sr. Exec. V.P.-Legal & Corp. Affairs & Sec.--Shoppers Drug Mart, Ltd., Toronto, Canada; *Int'l,* pg. 112

Kramer, Peter J., Gen. Counsel--Consumers Financial Corporation, Camp Hill, PA; *U.S. Public,* pg. 437

Kramp, J.B., Gen. Counsel--WESCO Distribution, Inc., Pittsburgh, PA; *U.S. Private,* pg. 244

Kranzow, Ron, Sr. V.P. & Legal Counsel--Frito-Lay Company, Plano, TX; *U.S. Public,* pg. 1277

Krasnostein, D., Grp. Gen. Counsel--National Australia Bank Limited, Melbourne, Australia; *Int'l,* pg. 906

Kraus, Frederick H., Exec. V.P. & Gen. Counsel--Greate Bay Casino Corporation, Atlantic City, NJ; *U.S. Public,* pg. 760

Kraus, Joseph M., V.P., Gen. Counsel & Sec.--Central Vermont Public Service Corporation, Rutland, VT; *U.S. Public,* pg. 327

Kraus, William J., Gen. Counsel--Restaurant Developers Corp., Independence, OH; *U.S. Private,* pg. 925

Kream, Deborah A., Gen. Counsel--Plymouth Rubber Company, Inc., Canton, MA; *U.S. Public,* pg. 1311

Kreindler, Peter M., Sr. V.P., Gen. Counsel & Sec.--AlliedSignal Inc., Morristown, NJ; *U.S. Public,* pg. 49

Kreiter, Fredric J., Chief Fin. Officer & Legal Counsel--Castcraft Industries, Inc., Skokie, IL; *U.S. Private,* pg. 219

Krieger, Bruce D., V.P., Gen. Counsel & Sec.--Blyth Industries, Greenwich, CT; *U.S. Public,* pg. 239

Krieger, Philip S., Gen. Counsel--DDB Needham Worldwide Inc., New York, NY; *Int'l,* pg. 357

Krieger, Philip S., Gen. Counsel--DDB Needham Worldwide Inc., New York, NY; *U.S. Public,* pg. 1223

Krinsly, S.Z., Sr. Exec. V.P. & Gen. Counsel--Sequa Corporation, New York, NY; *U.S. Public,* pg. 1458

Kripalani, Eva, V.P., Gen. Counsel & Sec.--KinderCare Learning Centers, Inc., Portland, OR; *U.S. Public,* pg. 961

Kriscunas, Robert A., V.P. & Gen. Counsel--IP Timberlands, Ltd., Purchase, NY; *U.S. Public,* pg. 904

Kriss, Leonard, Gen. Counsel. & Sec.--Mobile Telecommunications Technologies Corp., Jackson, MS; *U.S. Public,* pg. 1120

Kritzer, Paul, Gen. Counsel & Sec.--Journal Communications Inc., Milwaukee, WI; *U.S. Private,* pg. 601

Krivosha, Norman M., Judge, Exec. V.P., Sec. & Gen. Counsel--Ameritas Life Insurance Corp., Lincoln, NE; *U.S. Private,* pg. 65

Krivoshia, E., Jr., V.P., Gen. Counsel & Sec.--National Steel Corporation, Mishawaka, IN; *Int'l,* pg. 902

Kronenberg, Jerry, V.P. & Gen. Counsel--Thomas & Betts Corporation, Memphis, TN; *U.S. Public,* pg. 1597

Kroppel, Gunther, Dir.-Personnel & Legal Affairs--VP-Schickedanz AG, Nuremberg, Germany; *U.S. Public,* pg. 1333

Krueger, Blake, Exec. V.P., Gen. Counsel & Sec.--Wolverine World Wide, Inc., Rockford, MI; *U.S. Public,* pg. 1775

Kruger, Horst, Legal Counsel--Schering AG, Berlin, Germany; *Int'l,* pg. 1203

Krugman, James, Gen. Counsel--Hayward Industries, Inc., Elizabeth, NJ; *U.S. Private,* pg. 513

Krupnick, L.A., Sec. & Legal Officer--Inductotherm Industries, Inc., Rancocas, NJ; *U.S. Private,* pg. 560

Krupnick, Laurence, Gen. Counsel--Inductotherm Corp., Rancocas, NJ; *U.S. Private,* pg. 560

Kruse, Kay, V.P.-Tax & Legal--Kraft Jacobs Suchard AG, Zurich, Switzerland; *U.S. Public,* pg. 1288

Kruth, Harold, Gen. Counsel & Sec.--SRI International, Menlo Park, CA; *U.S. Private,* pg. 958

Kruys, B.Th., Gen. Counsel & Sec.--Van Leeuwen Pipe and Tube Group B.V., Zwijndrecht, Netherlands; *Int'l,* pg. 1449

Kryle, Sanford I., Assoc. Gen. Counsel-Contracts & Rights Devel.--CBS, New York, NY; *U.S. Public,* pg. 273

Krzyzanowski, Richard L., Exec. V.P., Gen. Counsel & Sec.--Crown Cork & Seal Company, Inc., Philadelphia, PA; *U.S. Public,* pg. 462

Kubacki, Robert W., Sr. Counsel & Corp. Sec.--Bourns, Inc., Riverside, CA; *U.S. Private,* pg. 161

Kucera, Philip E., Deputy Gen. Counsel & Asst. Sec.--The Times Mirror Company, Los Angeles, CA; *U.S. Public,* pg. 1615

Kuck, Timothy W., Gen. Counsel & Sec.--EBP Life Insurnace Co., Minneapolis, MN; *U.S. Public,* pg. 635

Kuckro, Lee G., Sr. V.P., Gen. Counsel & Sec.--The Advest Group, Inc., Hartford, CT; *U.S. Public,* pg. 23

Kuehn, George E., Exec. V.P. & Gen. Counsel--The Stroh Brewery Company, Detroit, MI; *U.S. Private,* pg. 1047

Kuemmerlein, Marc L., V.P. & Gen. Counsel--Houlihan's Restaurant Group, Kansas City, MO; *U.S. Public,* pg. 841

Kugle, J. Alan, Exec. V.P. & Gen. Counsel--C. Brewer & Company, Limited, Honolulu, HI; *U.S. Private,* pg. 190

Kuha, Jan, Gen. Counsel--William Brojack Lumber Company, Olyphant, PA; *U.S. Private,* pg. 171

Kuhbach, Robert G., V.P., Gen. Counsel & Sec.--Dover Corporation, New York, NY; *U.S. Public,* pg. 520

Kuhlmann, F. Mark, Sr. V.P.-Admin. & Gen. Counsel--McDonnell Aircraft & Missile Systems Div., Berkeley, MO; *U.S. Public,* pg. 241

Kuhn, Humberto G., Gen. Counsel & Sec.--Wilson Industries Inc., Houston, TX; *U.S. Private,* pg. 1181

Kuhnmuenchijr, John, V.P., Gen. Counsel & Sec.--HK Systems, Inc., New Berlin, WI; *U.S. Private,* pg. 491

Kulla, Raymond, V.P., Gen. Counsel & Sec.--General Housewares Corp., Terre Haute, IN; *U.S. Public,* pg. 715

Kuramoto, Toyohisa, Mng. Dir.-Prod., Procurement, Quality Control & Prod. Liability--Nikon Corporation, Tokyo, Japan; *Int'l,* pg. 931

Kurczewski, Walter W., V.P., Gen. Counsel & Sec.--Square D Company, Palatine, IL; *Int'l,* pg. 1208

Kurkinen, J., Dir.-Legal Affairs--Enso Oyj, Helsinki, Finland; *Int'l,* pg. 455

Kurkinen, Juha, Gen. Counsel--Cultor Ltd., Helsinki, Finland; *Int'l,* pg. 349

Kurren, Faye W., V.P. & Gen. Counsel--Gasco, Inc., Honolulu, HI; *Int'l,* pg. 225

Kurtz, Melvin H., V.P., Gen. Counsel & Sec.--Chesebrough-Pond's USA Co., Greenwich, CT; *Int'l,* pg. 1435

Kurtz, Michael, V.P., Legal & Asst. Sec.--Oracle Corporation, Redwood City, CA; *U.S. Public,* pg. 1227

Kurz, Thomas P., Gen. Counsel--Sysco Corporation, Houston, TX; *U.S. Public,* pg. 1550

Kutyla, Elizabeth, V.P. & Gen. Counsel--Barton Incorporated, Chicago, IL; *U.S. Public,* pg. 300

Kuwano, Fumio, Mng. Dir. & Sr. V.P.-Information Sys.--Japan Airlines Company, Ltd., Tokyo, Japan; *Int'l,* pg. 699

Kvist, Lars-Erik, Chief Credit & Legal Affairs Officer--Swedbank, Stockholm, Sweden; *Int'l,* pg. 1328

Kwok, Helen, Legal Advisor--Sun Hung Kai Properties Ltd., Wan Chai, Hong Kong; *Int'l,* pg. 1318

Laborde, Clifford, Sr. V.P., Gen. Counsel & Sec.--Tidewater Inc., New Orleans, LA; *U.S. Public,* pg. 1608

Lacci, John, V.P. & Chief Counsel--Great Lakes Chemical Corporation, West Lafayette, IN; *U.S. Public,* pg. 760

Lachmann, W.R., Gen. Counsel--Esso Aktiengesellschaft, Hamburg, Germany; *U.S. Public,* pg. 601

Lackey, Robert E.T., V.P., Gen. Counsel & Corp. Sec.--Borg-Warner Security Corporation, Chicago, IL; *U.S. Public,* pg. 245

Lackey, S.A., V.P. & Gen. Counsel--Shell Oil Company, Houston, TX; *Int'l,* pg. 1136

Lackman, James S., Gen. Counsel--Camp Dresser & McKee Inc., Cambridge, MA; *U.S. Private,* pg. 203

LaCour, Barry, Gen. Counsel & Sec.--The Laitram Corporation, Harahan, LA; *U.S. Private,* pg. 643

Lafleur, Anthony J., V.P., Assoc. Gen. Counsel & Asst. Sec.--Northern Telecom Limited, Brampton, Canada; *Int'l,* pg. 968

LaFleur, Cheryl A., V.P., Gen. Counsel & Sec.--New England Electric System, Westborough, MA; *U.S. Public, pg. 1171*

Lafon, Rene Armando, Gen. Mgr.--Keystone Automotive Industries, Inc.-Tijuana, Tijuana, Mexico; *U.S. Public,* pg. 955

Lahey, Edward V., Jr., Sr. V.P., Gen. Counsel & Sec.--PepsiCo, Inc., Purchase, NY; *U.S. Public,* pg. 1276

Lajoie, James R., V.P., Gen. Counsel & Sec.--Xtra Corporation, Boston, MA; *U.S. Public,* pg. 1786

Lake, Ralph B., Sr. V.P., Gen. Counsel & Sec.--Promus Hotel Corporation, Memphis, TN; *U.S. Public,* pg. 1335

Lakin, Thomas J., Exec. V.P., Sec. & Gen. Counsel--Starbanc Corporation, Cincinnati, OH; *U.S. Public,* pg. 1510

Lamade, Barbara S., Gen. Counsel--Advanced Marine Enterprises, Inc., Arlington, VA; *U.S. Public,* pg. 1182

Lambert, H. Ed, V.P.-Legal--E-Z Serve Corp., Houston, TX; *U.S. Public,* pg. 540

Lambert, Paul M., V.P. & Assoc. Gen. Counsel--Franchise Finance Corp. of America, Scottsdale, AZ; *U.S. Public,* pg. 679

Lammert, Richard A., Sr. V.P., Gen. Counsel & Sec.--First Empire State Corporation, Buffalo, NY; *U.S. Public*, pg. 631
Lampen, Richard J., Exec. V.P. & Gen. Counsel--New Valley Corporation, Miami, FL; *U.S. Public*, pg. 1173
Lanam, Linda, Gen. Counsel--The Life Insurance Co. of Virginia, Richmond, VA; *U.S. Public*, pg. 712
Land, Thornton R., Exec. V.P.-Admin. & Gen. Counsel--Selective Insurance Group, Inc, Branchville, NJ; *U.S. Public*, pg. 1455
Land, Thornton R., V.P., Gen. Counsel & Asst. Sec.--Charleston Insurance Company, Buffalo, NY; *U.S. Public*, *pg. 1455*
Land, Thornton R., V.P. & Gen. Counsel--Niagara Exchange Corporation, Buffalo, NY; *U.S. Public*, pg. 1455
Land, Thornton R., Gen. Counsel--Selective Insurance Company of the Southeast, Charlotte, NC; *U.S. Public*, pg. 1456
Landau, Harriet, Gen. Counsel--Racetrac Petroleum, Inc., Smyrna, GA; *U.S. Private*, pg. 906
Landau, Yvette, Gen. Counsel--Circus Circus Hotel Casinos, Inc., Las Vegas, NV; *U.S. Public*, pg. 374
Landergan, Walter L., Jr., Gen. Counsel & Sec.--Components Corporation Of America, Dallas, TX; *U.S. Private*, pg. 259
Lane, Jeffrey H., Sr. V.P., Gen. Counsel & Sec.--MGIC Investment Corporation, Milwaukee, WI; *U.S. Public*, pg. 1026
Lane, Jeffrey H., Sr. V.P., Gen. Counsel & Sec.--Mortgage Guaranty Insurance Corporation, Milwaukee, WI; *U.S. Public*, pg. 1026
Lane, Ronald E., Sr. V.P., Legal Counsel & Sec.--Illinois Central Corporation, Chicago, IL; *U.S. Public*, pg. 864
Lane, Steve, Dir.-Legal--U.S. Home Corporation, Houston, TX; *U.S. Public*, pg. 1682
Laney, S. David, Gen. Counsel--Johnston Industries, Inc., Columbus, GA; *U.S. Public*, pg. 933
Lang, Eugene A., Jr., Sr. V.P. & Gen. Counsel--Barrett Resources Corporation, Denver, CO; *U.S. Public*, pg. 191
Lang, Stephen R., V.P., Gen. Counsel & Sec.--Carter-Wallace, Inc., New York, NY; *U.S. Public*, pg. 309
Langham, James W., V.P., Gen. Counsel & Sec.--Lone Star Industries, Inc., Stamford, CT; *U.S. Public*, pg. 1012
Langley, Marcia, V.P., Gen. Counsel & Sec.--Atlantic Gulf Communities Corporation, Miami, FL; *U.S. Public*, pg. 144
Langus, Alan L., Chief Counsel, V.P. & Sec.--ContiFinancial Corporation, New York, NY; *U.S. Public*, pg. 439
Lankowsky, Zenon, V.P. & Gen. Counsel--CVS Corp., Woonsocket, RI; *U.S. Public*, pg. 287
Lannie, P. Anthony, Sr. V.P., Gen. Counsel & Sec.--Tejas Gas Corporation, Houston, TX; *Int'l*, pg. 1136
Lano, James D., V.P. & Assoc. Gen. Counsel--Rouse Legal Div., Columbia, MD; *U.S. Public*, pg. 1407
Lansing, Andrew, Pres.-Opers. & Gen. Counsel--The Levy Organization, Chicago, IL; *U.S. Private*, pg. 664
Lanza, Shelley B., Sr. V.P.-Law & Corp. Affairs & Gen. Counsel--Starbucks Coffee Company, Seattle, WA; *U.S. Public*, pg. 1510
Lapine, Jay M., Sr. V.P., Gen. Counel & Asst. Sec.--HBOC, Atlanta, GA; *U.S. Public*, pg. 770
Larkins, Thomas F., Sr. V.P., Gen. Counsel & Sec.--L.A. Gear, Inc., Santa Monica, CA; *U.S. Public*, pg. 969
LaRocque, James, Gen. Counsel & Sec.--James McHugh Construction Co., Chicago, IL; *U.S. Private*, pg. 721
Larsen, Paul A., Gen. Counsel--United Power Association, Elk River, MN; *U.S. Private*, pg. 1123
Larson, Brian A., V.P.-Devel. & Assoc. Gen. Counsel--Boyd Gaming Corporation, Las Vegas, NV; *U.S. Public*, pg. 249
Larson, David J., Sr. V.P., Gen. Counsel & Sec.--Lutheran Brotherhood, Minneapolis, MN; *U.S. Private*, pg. 681
Larson, Michelle, Gen. Counsel--OmniQuip International, Inc., Port Washington, WI; *U.S. Private*, pg. 500
Laserson, Lillian, V.P. & Gen. Counsel--DC Comics, Inc., New York, NY; *U.S. Public*, pg. 1614
Lasker, Joel M., V.P. & Gen. Counsel--Bristol-Myers Squibb U.S. Pharmaceutical Group, Plainsboro, NJ; *U.S. Public*, pg. 255
Lasker, Judith O., Gen. Counsel & Sec.--Krause's Furniture Inc., Brea, CA; *U.S. Public*, pg. 967
Lassiter, Joe, Jr., Gen. Counsel--One Price Clothing Stores, Inc., Duncan, SC; *U.S. Public*, pg. 1225
Lassiter, John, V.P. & Gen. Counsel--Belk Stores Services Inc., Charlotte, NC; *U.S. Private*, pg. 131
Lassonde, Richard, V.P.-Legal Services--Gaz Metropolitain & Company, Montreal, Canada; *Int'l*, pg. 541
Latham, David C., Gen. Counsel & Corp. Sec.--Citrus World Inc., Lake Wales, FL; *U.S. Private*, pg. 241
Latham, James D., Sr. V.P., Sec. & Gen. Counsel--ITT Sheraton Corporation, Boston, MA; *U.S. Public*, pg. 1512
LaTourette, Brainerd W., Jr., Gen. Counsel--UniGroup, Inc., Fenton, MO; *U.S. Private*, pg. 1117
Latz, Jeanie Sell, Chief Legal Officer & Sr. V.P.-Corp. Services--Kansas City Power & Light Company, Kansas City, MO; *U.S. Public*, pg. 943
Laughead, G. Ross, V.P., Gen. Counsel, & Corp. Sec.--Datapoint Corporation, Paris, France; *Int'l*, pg. 384
Laughter, Bennie M., V.P., Sec. & Gen. Counsel--Shaw Industries, Inc., Dalton, GA; *U.S. Public*, pg. 1464
Laurin, Diane Marcelin, V.P.-Gen. Counsel & Sec.--Steinberg Inc., Montreal, Canada; *Int'l*, pg. 1272
Lauver, E. Eugene, V.P., Gen. Counsel & Sec.--APS Holding Corporation, Houston, TX; *U.S. Public*, pg. 10
Lauver, E. Eugene, Sr. V.P., Gen. Counsel & Sec.--A.P.S., Inc., Houston, TX; *U.S. Public*, pg. 10
Lauver, E. Eugene, V.P.- Real Estate, Gen. Counsel & Sec.--A.P.S., Memphis, TN; *U.S. Public*, pg. 10
Laveissiere, Jean, Sec. & Legal--Forasol S.A., Velizy-Villacoublay, France; *Int'l*, pg. 496
Lavelle, Michael, V.P.--Eversharp Pen Co., Franklin Park, IL; *U.S. Private*, pg. 386
Lavine, Gary J., Sr. V.P.-Legal & Corp. Rels.--Niagara Mohawk Power Corporation, Syracuse, NY; *U.S. Public*, pg. 1181
Law, L. William, Jr., Sr. V.P., Gen. Counsel & Sec.--Eastern Enterprises, Weston, MA; *U.S. Public*, pg. 548
Law, Robert, Gen. Counsel & Sec.--Canadian Tire Corporation Limited, Toronto, Canada; *Int'l*, pg. 259
Lawing, Jack L., V.P.-Law & Sec.--Gold Kist, Inc., Atlanta, GA; *U.S. Private*, pg. 459
Lawn, Aloysius T., IV, Gen. Counsel & Sec.--Tel-Save Holdings, Inc., New Hope, PA; *U.S. Public*, pg. 1568
Lawrence, George J., V.P. & Assoc. Gen. Counsel--OHM Remediation Services Corp., Findlay, OH; *U.S. Public*, pg. 1208
Lawrence, J. Rodney, Sr. V.P.-Legal Affairs & Corp. Sec.--Pier 1 Imports, Inc., Fort Worth, TX; *U.S. Public*, pg. 1295
Lawrence, William B., Exec. V.P.-Corp. Devel. & Intl. & Govt. Rels., Gen. Counsel & Sec--TRW Inc., Cleveland, OH; *U.S. Public*, pg. 1558
Laws, D.M., Gen. Counsel--U.S. Steel International, Inc., Pittsburgh, PA; *U.S. Public*, pg. 1661
Lawson, P.B., Gen. Counsel--Lloyds TSB Group PLC, London, United Kingdom; *Int'l*, pg. 812
Lawson, Peter, Sr. V.P. & Gen. Counsel--Motorola, Inc., Schaumburg, IL; *U.S. Public*, pg. 1136
Lawson, R.L., Sr. Legal Counsel--Email Limited, Waterloo, Australia; *Int'l*, pg. 450
Layne, David W., V.P. & Assoc. Gen. Counsel--Tenet Healthcare Corporation, Santa Barbara, CA; *U.S. Public*, pg. 1576
Le Goff, Sophie, Gen. Counsel--Leclerc, Issy-les-Moulineaux, France; *Int'l*, pg. 805
League, David W., V.P., Gen. Counsel & Sec.--Ace Hardware Corporation, Oak Brook, IL; *U.S. Private*, pg. 12
Lear, William H., V.P., Gen. Counsel & Sec.--Fleetwood Enterprises, Inc., Riverside, CA; *U.S. Public*, pg. 650
Leberman, Peter, Gen. Counsel--Jac Pac Foods, Ltd., Manchester, NH; *U.S. Private*, pg. 579
Lebovitz, James A., Sr. V.P., Gen. Counsel & Sec.--FPA Medical Management, Inc., San Diego, CA; *U.S. Public*, pg. 608
Leckerling, Jon P., Exec. V.P.-Admin., Gen. Counsel & Corp. Sec.--Echlin Inc., Branford, CT; *U.S. Public*, pg. 560
Ledbetter, Bureon E., V.P. & Gen. Counsel--Chick-fil-A, Inc., Atlanta, GA; *U.S. Private*, pg. 236
Lederer, Ann E., Sr. V.P., Gen. Counsel & Sec.--FirstFed Financial Corp., Santa Monica, CA; *U.S. Public*, pg. 645
Lederer, Leslie T., V.P., Gen. Counsel & Sec.--Stone Container Corporation, Chicago, IL; *U.S. Public*, pg. 1520
Lederman, Ira S., Sr. V.P., Asst. Gen. Counsel & Asst. Sec.--W.R. Berkley Corporation, Greenwich, CT; *U.S. Public*, pg. 215
Ledesma, Manuel, Asst. Mgr.--Caixa d'Estalvis de Catalunya, Barcelona, Spain; *Int'l*, pg. 249
Lee, Cheryl L., Chief Admin. Officer & Gen. Counsel--Image Entertainment, Inc., Chatsworth, CA; *U.S. Public*, pg. 870
Lee, Debra, V.P.-Gen.Counsel--Black Entertainment Television Holdings Inc., Washington, DC; *U.S. Public*, pg. 235
Lee, Lewis, Legal Counsel--Florida Rock Industries, Inc., Jacksonville, FL; *U.S. Public*, pg. 655
Lee, Paul L., Exec. V.P. & Gen. Counsel--Republic New York Corporation, New York, NY; *U.S. Public*, pg. 1380
Lee, Tae Hee, Gen. Counsel--Korean Airlines Co., Ltd., Seoul, Korea; *Int'l*, pg. 758
Lee, Theresa K., Gen. Counsel & Sec.--Eastman Chemical Company, Kingsport, TN; *U.S. Public*, pg. 550
Leekley, John R., V.P. & Gen. Counsel--Masco Corporation, Taylor, MI; *U.S. Public*, pg. 1052
Leff, Todd, Gen. Counsel--Cottman Transmission Systems, Inc., Fort Washington, PA; *U.S. Private*, pg. 278
Legg, James S., Gen. Counsel & Asst. Sec.--Griffith Laboratories Worldwide, Inc., Alsip, IL; *U.S. Private*, pg. 481
Lehfeldt, Richard, Asst. Gen. Counsel & Asst. Sec.--Edison Mission Energy, Irvine, CA; *U.S. Public*, pg. 564
Lehman, Mark E., Exec. V.P. & Sr. Mng. Dir.--The Bear Stearns Companies Inc., New York, NY; *U.S. Public*, pg. 197
Lehr, Meredith L., Asst. V.P. & Dir.-Corp. Legal Affairs--Unigard Insurance Co., Bellevue, WA; *Int'l*, pg. 345
Lehr, Meredith L., Asst. V.P. & Dir.-Corp. Legal Affairs--Unigard Indemnity Co., Bellevue, WA; *Int'l*, pg. 345
Lehrman, Jerry P., V.P. & Gen. Counsel--Norstan, Inc., Plymouth, MN; *U.S. Public*, pg. 1192
Lehtinen, Veikko, Deputy Pres.-Legal Affairs, Human Resources & Corp. Communication--Outokumpu Oyj, Espoo, Finland; *Int'l*, pg. 1015
Lehto, Timo, Sr. V.P. & Gen. Counsel--Metra Corporation, Helsinki, Finland; *Int'l*, pg. 862
Leisten, Arthur G., Sr. V.P. & Gen. Counsel--USG Corporation, Chicago, IL; *U.S. Public*, pg. 1660
Leka, Donald, Gen. Counsel--Teradyne, Inc., Boston, MA; *U.S. Public*, pg. 1580
LeMarier, John, Sr. V.P.-Legal--International Plastics Company, New York, NY; *U.S. Private*, pg. 571
Lemberg, Thomas M., Sr. V.P., Gen. Counsel & Sec.--Polaroid Corporation, Cambridge, MA; *U.S. Public*, pg. 1313
Lemke, John R., Gen. Counsel & Sec.--The Amalgamated Sugar Company LLC, Ogden, UT; *U.S. Private*, pg. 48
Lemle, Robert S., Sr. V.P., Gen. Counsel & Sec.--Cablevision Systems Corporation, Woodbury, NY; *U.S. Public*, pg. 288
Lemmer, Peter L., Sr. V.P. & Gen. Counsel--D & N Financial Corporation, Hancock, MI; *U.S. Public*, pg. 472
Lemmer, William C., V.P., Gen. Counsel & Sec.--Oryx Energy, Dallas, TX; *U.S. Public*, pg. 1232
Lemoyne, Stewart, Gen. Counsel & Sec.--Management Dynamics, New Providence, NJ; *U.S. Public*, pg. 1040
Lenar, Jeffrey J., V.P. & Gen. Counsel--ADT Automotive, Inc., Nashville, TN; *U.S. Public*, pg. 1648
Lence, Robert, V.P.-Legal--Huntsman Corporation, Salt Lake City, UT; *U.S. Private*, pg. 549
Leness, John S., Gen. Counsel & Sec.--Flow International Corporation, Kent, WA; *U.S. Public*, pg. 656
Lenfestey, Laurel J., V.P., Gen. Counsel & Sec.--Poe & Brown, Inc., Daytona Beach, FL; *U.S. Public*, pg. 1312
Lenhard, John E., Assoc. Gen. Counsel & Sec.--Cleveland-Cliffs Inc, Cleveland, OH; *U.S. Public*, pg. 386
Lenhart, Jeff, Gen. Counsel--ComSonics, Inc., Harrisonburg, VA; *U.S. Private*, pg. 260
Lennox, D. Craig, V.P., Gen. Counsel & Sec.--The Great-West Life Assurance Company, Winnipeg, Canada; *Int'l*, pg. 557
Lents, Don, Sec.--Miss Elaine Inc., Saint Louis, MO; *U.S. Private*, pg. 752
Lenzi, Louis G., Gen. Counsel & Sec.--MBIA Inc., Armonk, NY; *U.S. Public*, pg. 1023
Leo, M.S., Chief Admin. Officer, Sr. V.P. & Gen. Counsel--Rhone-Poulenc Inc., Princeton, NJ; *Int'l*, pg. 1112
Leonard, David A., V.P. & Gen. Counsel--Philadelphia American Life Insurance Company, Houston, TX; *U.S. Public*, pg. 853
Leonard, David A., V.P., Assoc. Gen. Counsel & Asst. Sec.--Southwestern Life Insurance Company, Dallas, TX; *U.S.* Private, pg. 1018
Leonard, James, V.P. & Gen. Counsel--Foster Wheeler Environmental Corporation, Livingston, NJ; *U.S. Public*, pg. 677
Leonoff, Lawrence, Sr. V.P., Gen. Counsel & Sec.--Ontario Hydro, Toronto, Canada; *Int'l*, pg. 1007
Lerch, Andreas P., Gen. Counsel--Forbo Holding SA, Eglisau, Switzerland; *Int'l*, pg. 496
Lerenius, Goran, Dir.-Legal Affairs--Astra AB, Sodertalje, Sweden; *Int'l*, pg. 93
Lerner, Martin, Gen. Counsel--Universal Photonics, Inc., Hicksville, NY; *U.S. Private*, pg. 1127
LeRoy, Pierre, Gen. Counsel & Sec.--Lagardere Groupe, Paris, France; *Int'l*, pg. 791
LeRoy, Spencer, III, Sr. V.P., Gen. Counsel & Sec.--Old Republic International Corporation, Chicago, IL; *U.S. Public*, pg. 1218
LeSage, Jim, Mgr.-Import--Outboard Marine Corporation, Waukegan, IL; *U.S. Private*, pg. 478
Lesher, Frank, Exec. V.P. & Gen. Counsel--Sony Electronics, Park Ridge, NJ; *Int'l*, pg. 1281
Lester, Dick, Corp. Counsel--Riddell Sports, Inc., New York, NY; *U.S. Public*, pg. 1389
Letica, Mara, Gen. Counsel--Letica Corporation, Rochester, MI; *U.S. Private*, pg. 661
Leunig, Mark W., V.P., Gen. Counsel & Sec.--Genesee Corporation, Rochester, NY; *U.S. Public*, pg. 728
Lev, Bruce L., V.P., Gen. Counsel & Sec.--Micro Warehouse, Inc., Norwalk, CT; *U.S. Public*, pg. 1104
LeVander, Harold, Jr., Gen. Counsel--Dakota Electric Association, Farmington, MN; *U.S. Private*, pg. 308
Leventhal, Thierry, Gen. Counsel--Compagnie Laitiere BESNIER, Laval, France; *Int'l*, pg. 322
Levesque, Marc, Sec. & Gen. Counsel--Dominion Textile Inc., Montreal, Canada; *Int'l*, pg. 415
Levin, Bruce A., V.P., Gen. Counsel & Sec.--Mirage Resorts Incorporated, Las Vegas, NV; *U.S. Public*, pg. 1116
Levin, Michael D., Sr. V.P., Gen. Counsel & Sec.--Sears, Roebuck and Co., Hoffman Estates, IL; *U.S. Public*, pg. 1452
Levin, Paul F., Sr. V.P., Gen. Counsel & Sec.--First Union Real Estate Investments, Cleveland, OH; *U.S. Public*, pg. 640
Levin, Steve, Sr. V.P. & Gen. Counsel--The Kaempfer Company, Investment Builders, Washington, DC; *U.S. Private*, pg. 604
Levine, Theodore, Gen. Counsel & Sec.--PaineWebber Group Incorporated, New York, NY; *U.S. Public*, pg. 1252
Levinson, Lawrence M., Gen. Counsel & Sec.--Arrow Automotive Industries, Inc., Framingham, MA; *U.S. Public*, pg. 133
Levitan, Paul L., V.P. & Assoc. Gen. Counsel--The Gap, Inc., San Francisco, CA; *U.S. Public*, pg. 702
Levitt, Edward J., Gen. Counsel & Sec.--Gelman Sciences, Inc., Ann Arbor, MI; *U.S. Public*, pg. 1253
Levitt, Matthew, Gen. Counsel--Patterson Dental Company, Saint Paul, MN; *U.S. Public*, pg. 1265
Levy, David, Exec. V.P.-Admin. & Counsel--National Service Industries, Inc., Atlanta, GA; *U.S. Public*, pg. 1160
Levy, Ivan, Gen. Counsel--Interplastic Corp., Saint Paul, MN; *U.S. Private*, pg. 572
LeWine, Jerome M., Attorney--Sensormatic Electronics Corporation, Boca Raton, FL; *U.S. Public*, pg. 1457
Lewis, David, Exec. V.P.-Corp. & Legal Affairs--Alias Wavefront, Toronto, Canada; *U.S. Public*, pg. 1474
Lewis, Donald C., Gen. Counsel & Asst. Corp. Sec.--Ball Corporation, Muncie, IN; *U.S. Public*, pg. 170
Lewis, Robert, V.P. & Gen. Counsel--Eckerd Corporation, Largo, FL; *U.S. Public*, pg. 917
Lewis, Robert L., Gen. Counsel--Lone Star Equities Inc., Lynbrook, NY; *U.S. Private*, pg. 674
Lewis, Roderic W., V.P.-Legal Affairs, Gen. Counsel & Corp. Sec.--Micron Technology Inc., Boise, ID; *U.S. Public*, pg. 1105
Lichter, Leonard, Gen. Counsel--Nord Resources Corporation, Albuquerque, NM; *U.S. Public*, pg. 1188
Lieb, Fred, V.P. & Gen. Counsel--ANGUS Chemical Company, Buffalo Grove, IL; *U.S. Private*, pg. 75
Lieberman, Kathleen H., Esq., V.P., Assoc. Gen. Counsel & Asst. Sec.--Charming Shoppes, Inc., Bensalem, PA; *U.S. Public*, pg. 335
Liebman, Seymour, V.P.-Credit, Contract & Legal Admin.--Canon U.S.A., Inc., Lake Success, NY; *Int'l*, pg. 262
Lifflander, Matthew, Gen. Counsel--Queens Group, Inc., Long Island City, NY; *U.S. Private*, pg. 900

Lightfoot, Mark F., V.P. & Gen. Counsel & Sec.--American Home Shield Corporation, Memphis, TN; *U.S. Public*, pg. 1461
Ligon, Duke R., V.P. & Gen. Counsel--Devon Energy Corporation, Oklahoma City, OK; *U.S. Public*, pg. 503
Lijestrom, Gunnar, Dir.-Personnel & Legal Affairs--NCC AB, Solna, Sweden; *Int'l*, pg. 898
Liles, Curtis, Gen. Counsel--National Computer Print, Inc., Birmingham, AL; *U.S. Private*, pg. 780
Liljstrom, Gunnar, Sr. V.P.-Admin. & Head-Legal Affairs & Personnel--NCC AB, Solna, Sweden; *Int'l*, pg. 898
Lillycrop, David P., Gen. Counsel & Sec.--TI Group plc, Abingdon, United Kingdom; *Int'l*, pg. 1337
Lincoln, E.W., V.P. & Gen. Counsel--Tetley USA Inc., Shelton, CT; *Int'l*, pg. 1377
Linden, Ray, V.P., Gen. Counsel & Sec.--The Canada Life Assurance Company, Toronto, Canada; *Int'l*, pg. 254
Lindenmeyer, Mark R., V.P., Gen. Counsel & Sec.--Hillenbrand Industries, Inc., Batesville, IN; *U.S. Public*, pg. 828
Lindig, Robert, Gen. Counsel--Arcon Construction Co., Inc., Harris, MN; *U.S. Private*, pg. 80
Lindsay, Ronald T., V.P., Gen. Counsel & Sec.--Collins & Aikman Corporation, Charlotte, NC; *U.S. Public*, pg. 399
Lines, Jim, Chief Fin. Officer, Gen. Counsel & Sec.--ITI Marketing Services, Inc., Omaha, NE; *U.S. Private*, pg. 555
Ling, Robert M., Jr., V.P., Gen. Councel & Sec.--Certified Grocers of California, Los Angeles, CA; *U.S. Private*, pg. 226
Ling, W.S., Gen. Counsel--Tainan Spinning Co., Ltd., Tainan, Taiwan; *Int'l*, pg. 1347
Linge, H. Kennedy, V.P., Sec. & Assoc. Gen. Counsel--PPG Industries, Inc., Pittsburgh, PA; *U.S. Public*, pg. 1245
Linn, Thomas F., Gen. Counsel--ARCO Coal Company, Denver, CO; *U.S. Public*, pg. 144
Linnat, Terrence G., Sr. V.P. & Gen. Counsel--The B.F. Goodrich Company, Richfield, OH; *U.S. Public*, pg. 751
Linne, R. Steven, Gen. Counsel & Sec.--Haynes International, Inc., Kokomo, IN; *U.S. Public*, pg. 801
Linnell, Norman C., Gen. Counsel & Sec.--Donaldson Company, Inc., Minneapolis, MN; *U.S. Public*, pg. 517
Linton, John, V.P. & Gen. Counsel--RE/MAX International, Inc., Englewood, CO; *U.S. Private*, pg. 912
Lione, Gail, V.P., Gen. Counsel & Sec.--Harley-Davidson, Inc., Milwaukee, WI; *U.S. Public*, pg. 786
Lione, Gail A., Gen. Counsel--U.S. News & World Report, New York, NY; *U.S. Private*, pg. 1125
Lipani, John F., V.P. & Gen. Counsel--Boh Bros. Construction Co., LLC, New Orleans, LA; *U.S. Private*, pg. 154
Lippart, Thomas E., Sr. V.P.-Fin. & Admin. & Gen. Counsel--Tube City Inc., Glassport, PA; *U.S. Private*, pg. 1108
Lippes, Gerald S., Gen. Counsel & Sec.--Mark IV Industries Inc., Amherst, NY; *U.S. Public*, pg. 1044
Lipson, Allen, V.P. & Gen. Counsel--Remington Products Company, L.L.C., Bridgeport, CT; *U.S. Private*, pg. 921
Lipton, Amy N., Sr. V.P. & Gen. Counsel--CUC International, Inc., Stamford, CT; *U.S. Public*, pg. 320
Lissy, David H., Sr. V.P., Gen. Counsel & Corp. Sec.--Ames Department Stores, Inc., Rocky Hill, CT; *U.S. Public*, pg. 99
Litman, Peter, Exec. V.P. & Gen. Counsel--Summit Technology, Inc., Waltham, MA; *U.S. Public*, pg. 1528
Little, Silas, Gen. Counsel--East Coast Steel, Inc., Claremont, NH; *U.S. Private*, pg. 356
Litwin, H., Gen. Counsel--Traub-Hermle Corporation, Menomonee Falls, WI; *Int'l*, pg. 1419
Livingston, Calvin J., V.P. & Gen. Counsel--A. Duda & Sons Inc., Oviedo, FL; *U.S. Private*, pg. 344
Lloveras, Ramon, V.P., Gen. Counsel & Sec.--Pueblo Xtra International, Inc., Pompano Beach, FL; *U.S. Private*, pg. 894
Lloyd, Marcea Bland, V.P. & Asst. Gen. Counsel--Medtronic, Inc., Minneapolis, MN; *U.S. Public*, pg. 1082
Lloyd, Rjay, Vice Chm. & Chief Fin. Officer--Forever Living Products International, Inc., Scottsdale, AZ; *U.S. Private*, *pg. 418*
Lloyd, T.R., Gen. Counsel & Sec.--Pitt-Des Moines, Inc., Pittsburgh, PA; *U.S. Public*, pg. 1304
LoBaugh, Leslie E., V.P. & Gen. Counsel--Pacific Enterprises, Los Angeles, CA; *U.S. Public*, pg. 1249
Loble, Lester H., II, Gen. Counsel & Sec.--MDU Resources Group, Inc., Bismarck, ND; *U.S. Public*, pg. 1025
Lochelt, Dieter, Dr., Gen. Counsel--Bayerische Motoren Werke Aktiengesellschaft, Munich, Germany; *Int'l*, pg. 177
Lockwood, Michael P., V.P.-Fin. & Legal Services--El Camino Resources, Ltd., Woodland Hills, CA; *U.S. Private*, pg. 366
Lockwood, Robert W., V.P., Gen. Counsel & Sec.--Ralcorp Holdings Inc., Saint Louis, MO; *U.S. Public*, pg. 1359
Loehr, Robert A., Gen. Counsel--SJW Corp., San Jose, CA; *U.S. Public*, pg. 1418
Loftin, Nancy C., Chief Legal Counsel, V.P. & Sec.--APS, Phoenix, AZ; *U.S. Public*, pg. 1297
Loftin, Valerie, V.P. & Attorney--Jefferson-Pilot Property Insurance Company, Greensboro, NC; *U.S. Public*, pg. 926
Logas, George P., V.P., Sec. & Gen. Counsel--New Hampshire Insurance Group, New York, NY; *U.S. Public*, *pg. 84*
Logue, Larry, Legal Counsel--International Lottery & Totalizator Systems, Inc., Carlsbad, CA; *U.S. Public*, pg. 900
Lombard, Richard, Sec.--Lombard Company, Alsip, IL; *U.S. Private*, pg. 673
Lombardozzi, Micahel E., Sr. V.P. & Gen. Counsel--Signet Star Reinsurance Company, Florham Park, NJ; *U.S. Public*, pg. 216
Lombardozzi, Michael E., V.P. & Gen. Counsel--Signet Star Holdings, Inc., Stamford, CT; *U.S. Public*, pg. 216
London, Fredric S., Sr. V.P., Gen. Counsel & Sec.--OMI Corp., New York, NY; *U.S. Public*, pg. 1208
Long, Deborah J., Sr. V.P. & Gen. Counsel--Protective Life Corporation, Birmingham, AL; *U.S. Public*, pg. 1336
Long, Deborah J., Sr. V.P. & Gen. Counsel--Protective Life Insurance Co., Birmingham, AL; *U.S. Public*, pg. 1336
Long, Lucinda P., Sr. V.P. & Gen. Counsel--Valley National Bank, Parsippany, NJ; *U.S. Public*, pg. 1705
Long, W. Audie, Sr., Sr. V.P., Gen. Counsel & Sec.--USLD Communications Corp., San Antonio, TX; *U.S. Public*, pg. 969
Long, William B., V.P. & Gen. Counsel--Drummond Company, Inc., Jasper, AL; *U.S. Private*, pg. 343
Longenecker, Chester D., Exec. V.P. & Gen. Counsel--Associates First Capital Corporation, Dallas, TX; *U.S. Public*, pg. 662
Longes, Richard A., Gen. Counsel--Lend Lease Corporation Limited, Sydney, Australia; *Int'l*, pg. 806
Longnecker, Chester D., Exec. V.P. & Gen. Counsel--Associates Financial Services Corporation, Dallas, TX; *U.S. Public*, pg. 663
Loomis, John, Gen. Counsel--Salwasser Manufacturing Company, Inc., Reedley, CA; *U.S. Private*, pg. 963
Lopez M., Jose Antonio, Pres.-Legal, Pub. & Banking Rels. Div.--Vitro, Sociedad Anonima, Garza Garcia, Mexico; *Int'l*, pg. 1469
Lopez, Alicia, V.P., Sec. & Gen. Counsel--Haemonetics Corporation, Braintree, MA; *U.S. Public*, pg. 773
Lopez, David B., Sr. V.P-Legal Counsel--Clopay Corporation, Cincinnati, OH; *U.S. Public*, pg. 766
Lord, Christopher J., Gen. Counsel--Intermagnetics General Corporation, Latham, NY; *U.S. Public*, pg. 893
Loree, James H., Gen. Counsel & Sec.--Zantop International Airlines, Inc., Ypsilanti, MI; *U.S. Private*, pg. 1204
Lorenz, Terry, Dir.-Bus. & Legal Affairs--Westwood One, Inc., New York, NY; *U.S. Public*, pg. 1763
Lorenzen, Peter E., V.P. & Gen. Counsel--Snyder Oil Corporation, Fort Worth, TX; *U.S. Public*, pg. 1481
Loritz, Richard, Gen. Counsel--C.J. Vitner Co., Chicago, IL; *U.S. Private*, pg. 1142
Lotter, Charles R., Exec. V.P., Gen. Counsel & Sec.--JC Penney Company, Inc., Plano, TX; *U.S. Public*, pg. 916
Loudermilk, Joey M., Sr. V.P., Gen. Counsel, & Corp. Sec.--AFLAC Incorporated, Columbus, GA; *U.S. Public*, pg. 28
Louis, J.V., Gen. Counsel.--Banque Nationale de Belgique, Brussels, Belgium; *Int'l*, pg. 162
Loureiro, Hernani Costa, Sr. Mgr.-Legal Dept.--Caixa Geral de Depositos, Lisbon, Portugal; *Int'l*, pg. 250
Lourens, H., Mgr.-Legal Affairs--Corporate New Business Development Div., Delft, Netherlands; *Int'l*, pg. 1142
Louttit, Gordon J., Sr. V.P., Gen. Counsel & Sec.--Aerospace Corporation, El Segundo, CA; *U.S. Private*, pg. 24
Love, Alison T., Sec. & Assoc. Gen. Counsel--Transcanada Pipelines Limited, Calgary, Canada; *Int'l*, pg. 1416
Love, D.A., V.P., Gen. Counsel & Sec.--The Molson Companies Limited, Toronto, Canada; *Int'l*, pg. 887
Lovejoy, Jerry, V.P. & Gen. Counsel--Baskin-Robbins Incorporated, Glendale, CA; *Int'l*, pg. 63
Loveless, Keith, Corp. Sec. & Assoc. Gen. Counsel--Alaska Air Group, Inc., Seattle, WA; *U.S. Public*, pg. 35
Loveridge, Gary, Sr. V.P.-Admin. Services & Gen. Counsel--Sutter Health, Sacramento, CA; *U.S. Private*, pg. 1057
Lovgren, Richard, Acting Gen. Counsel--Advanced Micro Devices, Inc., Sunnyvale, CA; *U.S. Public*, pg. 21
Low, Harold W., V.P. & Gen. Counsel--Publishers Clearing House, Port Washington, NY; *U.S. Private*, pg. 893
Lowenfels, Fred M., Sr. V.P. & Gen. Counsel--Transammonia Inc., New York, NY; *U.S. Private*, pg. 1096
Lowrance, George, V.P.--United Auto Group, Inc., New York, NY; *U.S. Private*, pg. 1095
Lowry, Donald M., Sr. V.P., Gen. Counsel & Sec.--Continental Assurance Company, Chicago, IL; *U.S. Private*, pg. 267
Lowther, John, V.P., Sec. & Gen. Counsel--State Automobile Mutual Insurance Co., Columbus, OH; *U.S. Private*, pg. 1036
Lowy, Susanna M., Assoc. Gen. Counsel-Litigation--CBS, New York, NY; *U.S. Public*, pg. 273
Lu, Jimmy, Asst. V.P.--Acer Incorporated, Taipei, Taiwan; *Int'l*, pg. 22
Lubben, David J., Gen. Counsel & Sec.--United HealthCare Corporation, Minnetonka, MN; *U.S. Public*, pg. 1677
Lucas, Lourdes, Dir.-Legal Affairs--Centennial Cellular Corp., New Canaan, CT; *U.S. Public*, pg. 329
Lucas, William R., Jr., Exec. V.P.-Admin. & Gen. Counsel--Birmingham Steel Corporation, Birmingham, AL; *U.S. Public*, pg. 232
Luchsinger, John F., Jr., JD., V.P., Gen. Counsel & Sec.--Farmers and Traders Life Insurance Co., Syracuse, NY; *U.S. Private*, pg. 394
Ludwig, Michael, Gen. Counsel--Spar Handels AG, Schenefeld, Germany; *Int'l*, pg. 1288
Lukas, David, V.P.-H.R. & Corp. Counsel--Northland Cranberries, Inc., Wisconsin Rapids, WI; *U.S. Public*, pg. 1197
Luke, J., V.P. & Gen. Counsel--Nana Regional Corporation, Inc., Anchorage, AK; *U.S. Private*, pg. 774
Luke, Kathleen Allen, V.P. & Corp. Div. Counsel--PepsiCo, Inc., Purchase, NY; *U.S. Public*, pg. 1276
Lund, Ronald E., Sr. V.P., Gen. Counsel & Sec.--Medtronic, Inc., Minneapolis, MN; *U.S. Public*, pg. 1082
Lundberg, G. Ulf, Gen. Counsel--Pharmacia & Upjohn Biotech AB, Uppsala, Sweden; *Int'l*, pg. 1047
Lundgren, Alan, Assoc. Gen. Counsel--Tenet Healthcare Corporation, Santa Barbara, CA; *U.S. Public*, pg. 1576
Lunt, Jack R., Sr. V.P., Asst. Gen. Counsel & Sec.--American Stores Company, Salt Lake City, UT; *U.S. Public*, pg. 92
Luraschi, William R., Gen. Counsel & Sec.--AES Corporation, Arlington, VA; *U.S. Public*, pg. 5
Luria-Cohen, Nancy, V.P. & Gen. Counsel--L. Luria & Son, Inc., Medley, FL; *U.S. Public*, pg. 1020
Lustbader, Brian G., Exec. V.P., Gen. Counsel & Sec.--The P.J. Carlin Construction Company, New Rochelle, NY; *U.S. Private*, pg. 211
Lutynski, Adam M., Gen. Counsel & Sec.--The Reynolds and Reynolds Company, Dayton, OH; *U.S. Public*, pg. 1384
Lyford, Bob, Gen. Counsel--Arkansas Electric Cooperatives Inc., Little Rock, AR; *U.S. Private*, pg. 82
Lyman, Chris, Gen. Counsel--CML Group, Inc., Acton, MA; *U.S. Public*, pg. 279
Lyman, Daniel F., Assoc. Gen. Counsel--Nashua Corporation, Nashua, NH; *U.S. Public*, pg. 1152
Lyman, Patricia A., V.P., Asst. Gen. Counsel & Asst. Sec.--Edison Mission Energy, Irvine, CA; *U.S. Public*, pg. 564
Lynch, Corrine, Gen. Counsel--Northland Aluminum Products, Inc., Minneapolis, MN; *U.S. Private*, pg. 805
Lynch, John E., Jr., V.P. & Gen. Counsel--Augat, Inc., Mansfield, MA; *U.S. Public*, pg. 1597
Lynch, Mary Ann, Gen. Counsel--Maine Yankee, Brunswick, ME; *U.S. Public*, pg. 325
Lynch, Steve, Gen. Counsel--World Acceptance Corporation, Greenville, SC; *U.S. Public*, pg. 1778
Lynch, T. Stephen, Sr. V.P. & Gen. Counsel--South Carolina National Corporation, Columbia, SC; *U.S. Public*, pg. 1730
Lyon, Clarke, Gen. Counsel--Hazen Paper Company, Holyoke, MA; *U.S. Private*, pg. 514
Lyons, Gary, V.P. & Gen. Counsel--Triarc Beverage Group, White Plains, NY; *U.S. Public*, pg. 1635
Lyons, Ray, Gen. Counsel--Tri-K Industries, Inc., Northvale, NJ; *U.S. Private*, pg. 1100
Lytton, William B., V.P & Gen. Counsel--International Paper Company, Purchase, NY; *U.S. Public*, pg. 901
Lyvense, S., Gen. Counsel--Courtaulds Coatings Inc., Louisville, KY; *Int'l*, pg. 338
Ma, Y.A., Dir.-Legal Affairs Div.--Chinese Petroleum Corporation, Taipei, Taiwan; *Int'l*, pg. 286
MacColl, John A., Exec. V.P.-Human Resources & Gen. Counsel--USF&G Corporation, Baltimore, MD; *U.S. Public*, pg. 1659
MacDougall, Thomas R., V.P. & Gen. Counsel--AM General Corporation, South Bend, IN; *U.S. Private*, pg. 922
MacGill, Kent, Corp. Legal Counsel--Layne Christenson Co., Mission Woods, KS; *U.S. Public*, pg. 981
MacGillivray, William D., Corp. Counsel & Asst. Clerk--Bay State Gas Company, Westborough, MA; *U.S. Public*, pg. 196
Machesney, Lisa A., Gen. Counsel & Sec.--Cabot Oil & Gas Corporation, Houston, TX; *U.S. Public*, pg. 289
Machov, Steven J., V.P., Gen. Counsel & Sec.--Merrill Corporation, Saint Paul, MN; *U.S. Public*, pg. 1097
Machulak, John E., Gen. Counsel--Commerce Group Corp., Milwaukee, WI; *U.S. Public*, pg. 410
MacIver, Robertson, Gen. Counsel & Sec.--PNC Bank, Philadelphia, PA; *U.S. Public*, pg. 1243
Mack, Catherine R., V.P., Gen. Counsel & Sec.--Federal Realty Investment Trust, Rockville, MD; *U.S. Public*, pg. 616
MacKenzie, Harold, Gen. Counsel & Sec.--Overton Gear & Tool Corp., Addison, IL; *U.S. Private*, pg. 823
MacKenzie, J. Blair, V.P., Gen. Counsel & Sec.--Southam Inc., Don Mills, Canada; *Int'l*, pg. 631
Mackey, Steven, V.P.-Gen. Counsel & Sec.--Helmerich & Payne, Inc., Tulsa, OK; *U.S. Public*, pg. 808
Mackie, David L., V.P.-Legal & Real Estate--Nordstrom, Inc., Seattle, WA; *U.S. Public*, pg. 1190
Mackie, Howard, Gen. Counsel--Calgary Flames Hockey Club, Calgary, Canada; *Int'l*, pg. 252
Mackiw, Christine I., V.P. & Assoc. Gen. Counsel--Sun Life Assurance Company of Canada, Toronto, Canada; *Int'l*, pg. 1318
Mackness, Richard, Sec.--Meristem plc, Wetherby, United Kingdom; *Int'l*, pg. 858
Maclean, Daniel C., III, V.P. & Gen. Counsel--The Dreyfus Corporation, New York, NY; *U.S. Public*, pg. 1085
MacLean, George H., Sr. V.P., Gen. Counsel & Sec.--U.S. Industries, Inc., Iselin, NJ; *U.S. Public*, pg. 1683
Maclin, Joan, Gen. Counsel--The Scoular Company, Omaha, NE; *U.S. Private*, pg. 977
Macomber, Gary, Gen. Counsel--Hubbard Broadcasting, Inc., Saint Paul, MN; *U.S. Private*, pg. 543
Macomber, Mary, Gen. Counsel--Encore Computer Corporation, Fort Lauderdale, FL; *U.S. Public*, pg. 580
Madans, Elliot, V.P.-Taxes--Tyco Toys, Inc., Mount Laurel, NJ; *U.S. Public*, pg. 1058
Maddox, Thomas E., Sr. V.P. & Deputy Gen. Counsel--American Stores Company, Salt Lake City, UT; *U.S. Public*, pg. 92
Madge, Betty J., Sec.--Laurentian Financial Services, Toronto, Canada; *Int'l*, pg. 396
Madison, George W., Exec. V.P., Gen. Counsel & Corp. Sec.--Comerica Incorporated, Detroit, MI; *U.S. Public*, pg. 408
Madoff, Steven, Sr. V.P.-Bus. Affairs & Legal--Paramount Pictures Corporation, Los Angeles, CA; *U.S. Private*, pg. 776
Madsen, Richard W., V.P., Gen. Counsel & Sec.--Rohr, Inc., Chula Vista, CA; *U.S. Public*, pg. 751
Maffeo, Vincent A., Sr. V.P. & Gen. Counsel--ITT Industries, Inc., White Plains, NY; *U.S. Public*, pg. 859
Maffeo, Vincent A., V.P., Gen. Counsel & Sec.--ITT Automotive, Inc., Auburn Hills, MI; *U.S. Public*, pg. 859
Magee, Cecil G., Gen. Counsel--Southwestern Electric Service Co., Dallas, TX; *U.S. Public*, pg. 1588
Magee, Mark E., Sr. V.P., Gen. Counsel & Sec.--Provident Financial Group, Inc., Cincinnati, OH; *U.S. Public*, pg. 1338
Maggs, Kelly, General Counsel--International Home Foods Inc., Parsippany, NJ; *U.S. Private*, pg. 526
Maggs, Kelly, V.P. & Gen. Counsel--Stella Foods, Inc., Green Bay, WI; *U.S. Private*, pg. 1040
Maglivy, David, Gen. Counsel--SRS Technologies, Newport Beach, CA; *U.S. Private*, pg. 958

Magnuson, G.E., Sec. & Legal Counsel--Sheldahl, Inc., Northfield, MN; *U.S. Public*, pg. 1465
Magnuson, Mark G., V.P. & Asst. Gen. Counsel--Consolidated Natural Gas Company, Pittsburgh, PA; *U.S. Public*, pg. 435
Magnuson, Mark G., V.P. & Asst. Gen. Counsel--Consolidated Natural Gas Service Co., Inc., Pittsburgh, PA; *U.S. Public*, pg. 435
Magnusson, Ingmar, Sec. & Gen. Counsel--Gambro AB, Lund, Sweden; *Int'l*, pg. 666
Magnusson, Ulf, Gen. Counsel & Corp. Sec.--Electrolux, AB, Stockholm, Sweden; *Int'l*, pg. 438
Magram, Saul H., Sr. V.P., Gen. Counsel & Sec.--Estee Lauder Companies Inc., New York, NY; *U.S. Public*, pg. 594
Maher, Francesca M., V.P., Gen. Counsel & Sec.--UAL Corporation, Elk Grove Village, IL; *U.S. Public*, pg. 1652
Maher, Francesca M., V.P., Gen. Counsel & Sec.--United Air Lines, Inc., Elk Grove Village, IL; *U.S. Public*, pg. 1653
Maher, Tom, Gen. Counsel--Bull HN Information Systems Inc., Billerica, MA; *Int'l*, pg. 316
Mahler, Dirk, Dr., Gen. Counsel--Freudenberg & Company, Weinheim, Germany; *Int'l*, pg. 505
Mahler, Thomas R., Sec. & Gen. Counsel--Analysts International Corporation, Minneapolis, MN; *U.S. Public*, pg. 110
Mahler, Tom, Gen. Counsel & Sec.--AIC-FSS Advertising, Minneapolis, MN; *U.S. Private*, pg. 5
Mahoney, George, Sec. & Gen. Counsel--Media General, Inc., Richmond, VA; *U.S. Public*, pg. 1077
Mahoney, George R., Jr., Exec. V.P., Gen. Counsel & Sec.--Family Dollar Stores, Inc., Matthews, NC; *U.S. Public*, pg. 612
Mai, Elizabeth, V.P., Gen. Counsel & Sec.--Advanta Corp., Spring House, PA; *U.S. Public*, pg. 22
Mainardi, Francesco, Mgr.-Legal Services--Coop Switzerland, Basel, Switzerland; *Int'l*, pg. 329
Maine, Cliff, Corp. Counsel--Prime Technology, Inc., Grand Rapids, MI; *U.S. Private*, pg. 884
Maitland, William T., Exec. Mng. Dir. & Chief Legal Officer--Nomura Securities International, Inc., New York, NY; *Int'l*, pg. 956
Makowski, Joseph G., V.P., Gen. Counsel & Sec.--Computer Task Group, Inc. (CTG), Buffalo, NY; *U.S. Public*, pg. 423
Malacarne, C. John, V.P., Gen. Counsel & Sec.--Kansas City Life Insurance Co., Kansas City, MO; *U.S. Public*, pg. 942
Mallams, Rodney, Gen. Counsel--Atwood Oceanics, Inc., Houston, TX; *U.S. Public*, pg. 146
Malley, Robert J., Sr. V.P. & Gen. Counsel--State Street Corporation, Boston, MA; *U.S. Public*, pg. 1513
Malmgren, Mr., Gen. Counsel--Taisei America Corp., New York, NY; *Int'l*, pg. 1347
Maloney, Michael, Gen. Counsel--Orion Capital Companies, Inc., Farmington, CT; *U.S. Public*, pg. 1231
Maloney, Michael P., V.P., Gen. Counsel & Sec.--Orion Capital Corporation, New York, NY; *U.S. Public*, pg. 1231
Maloney, Robert, Gen. Counsel--Killearn Properties, Inc., Stockbridge, GA; *U.S. Public*, pg. 956
Maltzman, Marvin S., Sr. V.P.-Admin., Sec. & Gen. Counsel--House of Fabrics, Inc., Sherman Oaks, CA; *U.S. Public*, pg. 842
Malysheff, George, Gen. Counsel & Sec.--Telus Corporation, Edmonton, Canada; *Int'l*, pg. 1374
Manchester, Gilbert M., V.P. & Gen. Counsel--Commercial Intertech Corp., Youngstown, OH; *U.S. Public*, pg. 411
Mancino, Peter B., V.P., Gen. Counsel & Sec.--UCAR International Inc., Danbury, CT; *U.S. Public*, pg. 1662
Mancuso, John H., Sr. V.P. & Deputy Gen. Counsel--Keycorp, Cleveland, OH; *U.S. Public*, pg. 954
Mancuso, Tommy, Gen. Counsel--Whitfield Foods, Inc., Montgomery, AL; *U.S. Private*, pg. 1173
Mandel, James, Gen. Counsel--Vail Resorts, Inc., Vail, CO; *U.S. Public*, pg. 1704
Mangel, Steven E., Exec. V.P.-Legal & Bus. Affairs & Gen. Counsel--LIVE Film & Mediaworks, Van Nuys, CA; *U.S. Private*, pg. 671
Mann, Gail S., V.P., Sec., Asst. Gen. Counsel & Clerk--Digital Equipment Corporation, Maynard, MA; *U.S. Public*, pg. 507
Manning, Laurence R., Pres. & Gen. Counsel--The Racal Corporation, Sunrise, FL; *Int'l*, pg. 1082
Manning, Martha E., Sr. V.P., Gen. Counsel & Sec.--U.S. Bioscience, Inc., Conshohocken, PA; *U.S. Public*, pg. 1681
Manning, Ronald B., V.P. & Gen. Counsel--Pogo Producing Company, Houston, TX; *U.S. Public*, pg. 1312
Mannis, Bob, V.P. & Gen. Counsel--Sanofi Pharmaceuticals, Inc., New York, NY; *Int'l*, pg. 445
Mansell, Thomas S., Sr. V.P., Legal Counsel & Asst. Sec.--First Western Bancorp, Inc., New Castle, PA; *U.S. Public*, pg. 642
Mansfield, Christopher C., Sr. V.P. & Gen. Counsel--Liberty Mutual Insurance Co., Boston, MA; *U.S. Private*, pg. 666
Manuel, G. Leonard, Gen. Counsel & Sec.--Cominco, Ltd., Vancouver, Canada; *Int'l*, pg. 307
Marafioti, Robert, V.P. & Gen. Counsel--CMP Media, Inc., Manhasset, NY; *U.S. Public*, pg. 279
Marchand, Gilles, Gen. Counsel--Hydro-Quebec, Montreal, Canada; *Int'l*, pg. 640
Marchand, Jim, Pres.--Carter Chambers Supply, Inc., Baton Rouge, LA; *U.S. Private*, pg. 216
Marchegiani, Giannangelo, Dir.-Gen. Legal Policy--European Investment Bank, Luxembourg, Luxembourg; *Int'l*, pg. 465
Marchisott, Alan, Sec. & Gen. Counsel--Moran Bulk Corporation, Greenwich, CT; *U.S. Private*, pg. 760
Marchisotto, Alan, Gen. Counsel & Sec.--Moran Towing Of Delaware, Inc, Greenwich, CT; *U.S. Private*, pg. 760
Marchisotto, Alan, Sec. & Gen. Counsel--Jakobson Shipyard, Inc, Greenwich, CT; *U.S. Private*, pg. 760
Marchisotto, Alan, Sec & Gen. Counsel--Hampton Roads Land Co., Ltd, Greenwich, CT; *U.S. Private*, pg. 760
Marchisotto, Alan, Sec. & Gen. Counsel--Seaboard Barge Corporation, Greenwich, CT; *U.S. Private*, pg. 761
Marchisotto, Alan, Sec. & Gen. Counsel--Petroleum Transportation Corporation, Greenwich, CT; *U.S. Private*, *pg. 761*
Marchisotto, Alan, Sec. & Gen. Counsel--Moran Shipyard Corporation, Greenwich, CT; *U.S. Private*, pg. 761
Marchisotto, Alan, Sec. & Gen. Counsel--Portsmouth Navigation Corporation, Greenwich, CT; *U.S. Private*, pg. 761
Marchisotto, Alan L., Gen. Counsel & Sec.--Moran Transporation Company, Greenwich, CT; *U.S. Private*, pg. 760
Marchisotto, Alan L., Gen. Counsel & Sec.--Moran Towing Corporation, Greenwich, CT; *U.S. Private*, pg. 760
Marcus, Gwen, Exec. V.P., Gen. Counsel & Admin.--Showtime Networks Inc., New York, NY; *U.S. Private*, pg. 779
Marcus, Thomas L., V.P.-Bus Devel., Gen. Counsel & Sec.--Broderbund Software, Inc., Novato, CA; *U.S. Public*, pg. 258
Marella, Philip, Sr. V.P.-Legal & Bus. Affairs--Worldvision Enterprises, New York, NY; *U.S. Private*, pg. 776
Margetts, W. Thomas, Sr. V.P.-Human Resources, Gen. Counsel & Sec.--Stant Corporation, Denver, CO; *Int'l*, pg. 1396
Margolin, Christopher J., V.P., Gen. Counsel & Sec.--XOMA Corporation, Berkeley, CA; *U.S. Public*, pg. 1786
Margue, Jean-Louis, Gen. Mgr.-Loans & Legal Affairs--Banque Generale du Luxembourg SA, Luxembourg, Luxembourg; *Int'l*, pg. 161
Margulies, Richard A., V.P.-Legal--Conair Corporation, Stamford, CT; *U.S. Private*, pg. 261
Marino, Frances, Vice Chm. & Gen. Counsel--Ideon Group, Inc., Jacksonville, FL; *U.S. Public*, pg. 320
Marks, Michael J., V.P., Gen. Counsel & Sec.--Alexander & Baldwin, Inc., Honolulu, HI; *U.S. Public*, pg. 39
Maroney, James, V.P., Gen. Counsel & Sec.--Tuboscope Incorporated, Houston, TX; *U.S. Public*, pg. 1643
Marquaire, Jean-Francois, Sr. V.P.-Legal & Human Resources--Compagnie Generale de Geophysique, Massy, France; *Int'l*, pg. 241
Marquard, Henry F., Gen. Counsel & Asst. Sec.--Stanley Consultants, Inc., Muscatine, IA; *U.S. Private*, pg. 1033
Marra, Anthony F., Sr. V.P. & Deputy Gen. Counsel--Federal National Mortgage Association (Fannie Mae), Washington, DC; *U.S. Public*, pg. 615
Marrinan, Susan F., V.P., Sec. & Gen. Counsel--Snap-On Tools Corporation, Kenosha, WI; *U.S. Public*, pg. 1480
Marsh, Michael G., Gen. Counsel, Sec. & Mgr.-Human Resources--Todd Pacific Shipyards Corp., Seattle, WA; *U.S. Public*, pg. 1619
Marsh, Norman J., Jr., V.P.-Legal Affairs--Sanders, A Lockheed Martin Company, Nashua, NH; *U.S. Public*, pg. 1008
Marsh, R. Bruce, Gen. Tax Counsel--Chevron Corporation, San Francisco, CA; *U.S. Public*, pg. 347
Marsh, William A., V.P., Gen. Counsel & Sec.--Spang & Company, Butler, PA; *U.S. Private*, pg. 1020
Marshal, Douglas, V.P.-Pub. Affairs, Gen. Counsel & Sec.--Darigold, Inc., Seattle, WA; *U.S. Private*, pg. 311
Marshall, Frank C., Jr., V.P. & Assoc. Gen. Counsel--Litton Industries, Inc., Woodland Hills, CA; *U.S. Public*, pg. 1002
Marshall, R., Gen. Counsel--Horsehead Resource Development Company, Inc., Palmerton, PA; *U.S. Private*, pg. 540
Marshall, Sharon, Assoc. Gen. Counsel--Active International, Pearl River, NY; *U.S. Private*, pg. 15
Marshall, Siri S., Sr. V.P. & Gen. Counsel--General Mills, Inc., Minneapolis, MN; *U.S. Public*, pg. 717
Marsilius, Richard A., Exec. V.P. & Sec.--Moore Tool Company, Inc., Bridgeport, CT; *U.S. Private*, pg. 889
Martell, Michael, Gen. Counsel--Hasselblad USA, Inc., Fairfield, NJ; *Int'l*, pg. 1468
Martens, Hans Ditlef, Jr., Dir.-Legal--Bergesen d.y. A.S., Oslo, Norway; *Int'l*, pg. 188
Martha, J. Paul, Exec. V.P. & Gen. Counsel-Civic Arena--The Edward J. DeBartolo Corporation, Youngstown, OH; *U.S. Private*, pg. 319
Martin, Brian J., Sr. V.P.-Human Resources & Gen. Counsel--Proffitt's, Inc., Alcoa, TN; *U.S. Public*, pg. 1333
Martin, Derek C., V.P., Gen. Counsel & Sec.--Precision Drilling Corporation, Calgary, Canada; *Int'l*, pg. 1066
Martin, G.G., Gen. Counsel & Sec.--Coats & Clark Inc., Greenville, SC; *Int'l*, pg. 300
Martin, Harry D., Esq., Gen. Counsel & Sec.--Snap-Tite, Inc., Erie, PA; *U.S. Private*, pg. 1010
Martin, J. Stephen, V.P. & Gen. Counsel--Anadarko Petroleum Corporation, Houston, TX; *U.S. Public*, pg. 107
Martin, John W., Jr., V.P. & Gen. Counsel--Ford Motor Company, Dearborn, MI; *U.S. Public*, pg. 661
Martin, William F., Jr., Sr. V.P.-Legal & Corp. Sec.--Yellow Corporation, Overland Park, KS; *U.S. Public*, pg. 1788
Marullo, Lori, Gen. Counsel--MarketSource Corporation, Cranbury, NJ; *U.S. Private*, pg. 705
Marx, Max, V.P. & Gen. Counsel--Sunkyong America, Inc., New York, NY; *Int'l*, pg. 1320
Masket, Steven N., Sr. V.P. & Gen. Counsel--Maidenform Worldwide, New York, NY; *U.S. Private*, pg. 697
Mason, Thomas, Gen. Counsel & Sec.--Freeway Corporation, Cleveland, OH; *U.S. Private*, pg. 426
Massanet, Francisco Ramallo, Chief Legal Counsel--Banca March S.A., Palma de Mallorca, Spain; *Int'l*, pg. 136
Massaro, Patti L., Corp. Counsel & Sec.--Landmark Graphics Corporation, Houston, TX; *U.S. Public*, pg. 776
Massicotte, Guy-Paul, V.P., Gen. Counsel & Sec.--The Ivaco Group, Montreal, Canada; *Int'l*, pg. 695
Massing, Bertram K., Sec.--Light Signatures, Inc., Los Angeles, CA; *U.S. Public*, pg. 588
Masters, Joseph, V.P. & Gen. Counsel--URS Corporation, San Francisco, CA; *U.S. Public*, pg. 1655
Masterson, Karen, V.P., Gen. Counsel & Sec.--ADAC Laboratories Inc., Milpitas, CA; *U.S. Public*, pg. 3
Masterson, Kenneth R., Exec. V.P., Gen. Counsel & Sec.--FDX Corporation, Memphis, TN; *U.S. Public*, pg. 603
Masuhara, David M., V.P.-Legal & Regulatory Affairs--BC Gas Utility, Vancouver, Canada; *Int'l*, pg. 114
Matecki, Paul, Gen. Counsel--Raymond James Financial, Inc., Saint Petersburg, FL; *U.S. Public*, pg. 923
Matejka, Regina A., Gen. Counsel--MTI/The Image Group, Inc., New York, NY; *U.S. Private*, pg. 688
Matejka, Rick, Gen. Counsel--Venture Stores, Inc., O Fallon, MO; *U.S. Public*, pg. 1716
Mater, Maud, Sr. V.P., Gen. Counsel & Sec.--Federal Home Loan Mortgage Corporation, Mc Lean, VA; *U.S. Public*, pg. 615
Mathews, Robert, Gen. Counsel--Clothestime Stores, Inc., Anaheim, CA; *U.S. Public*, pg. 387
Matlock, Ron, V.P., Gen. Counsel & Sec.--Sonic Corporation, Oklahoma City, OK; *U.S. Public*, pg. 1485
Matschullat, Dale L., V.P. & Gen. Counsel--Newell Co., Freeport, IL; *U.S. Public*, pg. 1176
Mattison, Robert M., V.P., Gen. Counsel & Sec.--Graco Inc., Golden Valley, MN; *U.S. Public*, pg. 756
Maulding, B.C., V.P., Gen. Counsel & Sec.--PrimeSource Corporation, Pennsauken, NJ; *U.S. Public*, pg. 1329
May, Allan W., V.P.-Strategic Devel., Gen. Counsel & Sec.--OEC Medical Systems, Inc., Salt Lake City, UT; *U.S. Public*, pg. 1207
May, J. Michael, Gen. Counsel & Sec.--Ameritruck Distribution Corporation, Fort Worth, TX; *U.S. Private*, pg. 65
Mayer, Steven M., V.P. & Gen. Counsel--Ethyl Corporation, Richmond, VA; *U.S. Public*, pg. 595
Mayhew, Mary Ann, Exec. V.P.-Contracts & Legal Services--Computer Data Systems, Inc., Rockville, MD; *U.S. Public*, pg. 28
Mayle, Dave, Legal Officer--Miracle Recreation Equipment Company, Monett, MO; *U.S. Private*, pg. 752
Mayo, G.M., Asst. Gen. Counsel--Delta Air Lines, Inc., Atlanta, GA; *U.S. Public*, pg. 497
Mayton, Kathleen, V.P. & Gen. Counsel--Rollins, Inc., Atlanta, GA; *U.S. Public*, pg. 1404
McAlister, Daniel K., Sr. V.P., Gen. Counsel & Sec.--Jefferson-Pilot Communications Company, Greensboro, NC; *U.S. Public*, pg. 925
McAllister, Kenneth W., Exec. V.P. & Gen. Counsel--Wachovia Corporation, Winston Salem, NC; *U.S. Public*, pg. 1730
McArdle, Maureen, Asst. Gen. Counsel--Grow Group, Inc., Cleveland, OH; *Int'l*, pg. 663
McArthur, Steven A., Sr. V.P., Gen. Counsel & Sec.--CalEnergy Co., Omaha, NE; *U.S. Public*, pg. 292
McAuliffe, Joan, Chief Fin. Officer & Gen. Counsel--Compendium Systems Corporation, Greenwich, CT; *U.S. Private*, pg. 259
McBride, Beverly, V.P., Gen. Counsel & Sec.--The Andersons Incorporated, Maumee, OH; *U.S. Public*, pg. 111
McBride, H. Colin, V.P., Asst. Gen. Counsel & Asst. Sec.--RJR Nabisco Holdings Corp., New York, NY; *U.S. Public*, *pg. 1354*
McBride, Michael F., V.P. & Gen. Counsel--SAFECO Credit Company, Inc., Seattle, WA; *U.S. Public*, pg. 1423
McBride, Terry W., V.P., Gen. Counsel & Sec.--Repap Enterprises Inc., Montreal, Canada; *Int'l*, pg. 1104
McBride, Terry W., V.P., Gen. Counsel & Sec.--Repap New Brunswick Inc., Montreal, Canada; *Int'l*, pg. 1104
McCabe, John F., Corp. V.P., Gen. Counsel & Sec.--BDM International, Inc., Mc Lean, VA; *U.S. Public*, pg. 1558
McCabe, Lawrence J., Sr. V.P. & Gen. Counsel--H.J. Heinz Company, Pittsburgh, PA; *U.S. Public*, pg. 805
McCabe, Thomas E., Sr. V.P., Gen. Counsel & Sec.--GRC International, Inc., Vienna, VA; *U.S. Public*, pg. 695
McCall, Bruce, V.P.-Legal & Gen. Counsel--Sun Data Inc., Norcross, GA; *U.S. Private*, pg. 1050
McCall, John R., Exec. V.P., Gen. Counsel & Sec.--LG & E Energy Corp., Louisville, KY; *U.S. Public*, pg. 970
McCallie, S. Wyatt, Gen. Counsel--CH2M Hill, Inc., Greenwood Village, CO; *U.S. Private*, pg. 195
McCallum, W.S., Legal Advisor--Exxon Chemical Olefins Inc., Fareham, United Kingdom; *U.S. Public*, pg. 602
McCanless, Bill, Sr. V.P.-Admin. & Gen. Counsel--Food Lion, Inc., Salisbury, NC; *Int'l*, pg. 463
McCann, Gregory L., V.P., Gen. Counsel & Sec.--The Danis Companies, Dayton, OH; *U.S. Private*, pg. 310
McCarthy, David J., Asst. Gen. Counsel--Ipalco Enterprises, Inc., Indianapolis, IN; *U.S. Public*, pg. 912
McCarthy, David J., Asst. Gen. Counsel--Indianapolis Power & Light Company, Indianapolis, IN; *U.S. Public*, pg. 913
McCarthy, Frank, Exec. V.P. & Gen. Counsel--North Central Life Insurance Company, Saint Paul, MN; *U.S. Private*, pg. 404
McCarthy, Jim, Sr. V.P., Gen. Counsel & Sec.--Ponderosa Steakhouse, Dallas, TX; *U.S. Private*, pg. 736
McCarthy, Jim, V.P.-Gen. Counsel--Bennigan's, Dallas, TX; *U.S. Private*, pg. 736
McCarthy, Joseph F., V.P., Gen. Counsel & Sec.--Lear Corporation, Southfield, MI; *U.S. Public*, pg. 981
McCarthy, Kenneth W., Jr., Sr. V.P. & Gen. Counsel--T&W Financial Corporation, Tacoma, WA; *U.S. Public*, pg. 1552
McCarthy, Michael J., Sr. V.P., Gen. Counsel & Sec.--A.H. Belo Corporation, Dallas, TX; *U.S. Public*, pg. 209
McCarthy, Robert E., Sr. V.P. & Gen. Counsel--Time Inc., New York, NY; *U.S. Public*, pg. 1612
McCarthy, Timothy, Gen. Counsel & Sec.--Western Regional Off Track Betting, Batavia, NY; *U.S. Private*, pg. 1168
McCarty, Joel, Sr. V.P., Gen. Counsel & Sec.--Old Dominion Freight Line, Inc., High Point, NC; *U.S. Public*, pg. 1216
McCarty, Joel B., Jr., Legal Counsel--Old Dominion Freight Line, Inc., High Point, NC; *U.S. Public*, pg. 1216

McCauley, Ann, V.P.-Legal--The TJX Companies, Inc., Framingham, MA; *U.S. Public*, pg. 1556
McCauley, Daniel, V.P., Gen. Counsel & Sec.--Air Express International Corporation, Darien, CT; *U.S. Public*, pg. 30
McCaw, Ken, Jr., V.P. & Gen. Counsel--Esco Corporation, Portland, OR; *U.S. Private*, pg. 382
McClaine, Doug, Gen. Counsel--Mine Safety Appliances Co., Pittsburgh, PA; *U.S. Public*, pg. 1114
McClave, Wilkes, III, Sr. V.P., Gen. Counsel & Sec.--Tosco Corporation, Stamford, CT; *U.S. Public*, pg. 1624
McClendon, Joe N., V.P.-Gen. Counsel & Sec.--Lone Star Gas Co., Dallas, TX; *U.S. Public*, pg. 1587
McClure, Terry N., V.P.-Legal & Gen. Counsel--American Cometra, Inc., Fort Worth, TX; *Int'l*, pg. 562
McColley, John, Gen. Counsel--Service Supply Co. Inc. of Indiana, Indianapolis, IN; *U.S. Private*, pg. 987
McConnell, Mary, V.P., Gen. Counsel & Sec.--Genmar Holdings, Inc., Minneapolis, MN; *U.S. Private*, pg. 447
McConomy, John W., V.P. & Assoc. Gen. Counsel--Harrah's Entertainment, Inc., Memphis, TN; *U.S. Public*, pg. 790
McCorkell, Peter L., Sr. V.P., Gen. Counsel & Sec.--Fair, Isaac and Company, Inc., San Rafael, CA; *U.S. Public*, pg. 609
McCormick, Michael D., Exec. V.P., Legal Counsel & Sec.--Bindley Western Industries, Inc., Indianapolis, IN; *U.S. Public*, pg. 228
McCormick, Neil, Gen. Counsel & Sec.--Morrison Petroleums Ltd., Calgary, Canada; *Int'l*, pg. 895
McCotter, James, V.P. & Deputy Gen. Counsel--El Paso Natural Gas Co., Houston, TX; *U.S. Public*, pg. 567
McCoy, Bob F., Assoc. Gen. Counsel--The Williams Companies, Inc., Tulsa, OK; *U.S. Public*, pg. 1769
McCoy, Bob F., Gen. Counsel--Williams Pipe Line Co., Tulsa, OK; *U.S. Public*, pg. 1769
McCoy, Carol A., Sec. & Assoc. Counsel--Torchmark Corporation, Birmingham, AL; *U.S. Public*, pg. 1622
McCoy, Dustan E., Sr. V.P., Gen. Counsel & Corp. Sec.--Witco Corporation, Greenwich, CT; *U.S. Public*, pg. 1773
McCracken, Ellis W., Jr., V.P. & Gen. Counsel--Anheuser-Busch Companies, Inc., Saint Louis, MO; *U.S. Public*, pg. 113
McCrary, William, Gen. Counsel--The Colonial BancGroup, Inc., Montgomery, AL; *U.S. Public*, pg. 400
McCrea, Charles, Jr., Exec. V.P., Gen. Counsel & Sec.--Mikohn Gaming Corporation, Las Vegas, NV; *U.S. Public*, pg. 1111
McCulloch, James L., V.P.-Litigation & Risk Mngmt.--Global Marine Inc., Houston, TX; *U.S. Public*, pg. 748
McCurrie, J.A., Legal Officer--Morgan Grenfell Group PLC, London, United Kingdom; *Int'l*, pg. 405
McCusker, Thomas J., Exec. V.P. & Gen. Counsel--Mutual of Omaha Insurance Company, Omaha, NE; *U.S. Private*, pg. 769
McCutchan, Gordon E., Exec. V.P., Law & Corp. Services--Nationwide Insurance Enterprise, Columbus, OH; *U.S. Private*, pg. 788
McCutchan, Gordon E., Exec. V.P., Gen. Counsel & Sec.--Nationwide Mutual Insurance Co., Columbus, OH; *U.S. Private*, pg. 789
McDaniel, Charles B., Gen. Counsel & Sec.--Hondo Oil & Gas Company, Roswell, NM; *Int'l*, pg. 818
McDaniel, R., Gen. Counsel--Presstek, Inc., Hudson, NH; *U.S. Public*, pg. 1324
McDavid, William H., Exec. V.P. & Gen. Counsel--The Chase Manhattan Corporation, New York, NY; *U.S. Public*, pg. 337
McDermett, Don J., Jr., Sr. V.P. & Gen. Counsel--Sterling Software, Inc., Dallas, TX; *U.S. Public*, pg. 1516
McDermott, Frank X., Gen. Counsel--Peerless Tube Company, Bloomfield, NJ; *U.S. Public*, pg. 1269
McDermott, Kathleen E., Chief Legal Officer & Asst. Sec.--American Stores Company, Salt Lake City, UT; *U.S. Public*, pg. 92
McDole, Keith C., Sr. V.P. & Gen. Counsel--Occidental Chemical Corporation, Dallas, TX; *U.S. Public*, pg. 1210
McDonald, Daniel R., V.P. & Corp. Counsel--Hahn Automotive Warehouse, Inc., Rochester, NY; *U.S. Public*, pg. 774
McDonald, Daryl P., Corp. Counsel & Sec.--Tecumseh Products Company, Tecumseh, MI; *U.S. Public*, pg. 1565
McDonald, Mary M., Sr. V.P. & Gen. Counsel--Merck & Co., Inc., Whitehouse Station, NJ; *U.S. Public*, pg. 1090
McDonald, William F., V.P. & Corp. Counsel--Emery Worldwide, Redwood City, CA; *U.S. Public*, pg. 281
McDougall, Gerald, Gen. Counsel--Customedix Corporation, Wallingford, CT; *U.S. Private*, pg. 298
McDowell, John, Corp. Attorney--Lewis Drug, Inc., Sioux Falls, SD; *U.S. Private*, pg. 665
McElroy, Pender, Gen. Counsel & Sec.--Burke Mills, Inc., Valdese, NC; *U.S. Public*, pg. 267
McFarland, Patricia J., V.P., Gen. Counsel & Sec.--Norwest Financial, Inc., Des Moines, IA; *U.S. Public*, pg. 1202
McGauley, Matthew P., V.P. & Assoc. Gen. Counsel--General American Life Insurance Co., Saint Louis, MO; *U.S. Private*, pg. 443
McGee, F.D., Gen. Counsel & Sec.--National Sea Products Limited, Lunenburg, Canada; *Int'l*, pg. 909
McGenee, Robert B., Sr. V.P. & Gen. Counsel-Pub. & Corp. Rels.--Carolina Power & Light Company, Raleigh, NC; *U.S. Public*, pg. 306
McGhee, W. Thomas, Gen. Counsel & Sec.--Berg Electronics, Saint Louis, MO; *U.S. Public*, pg. 212
McGlockton, Joan R., Sec. & Asst. Gen. Counsel--Marriott International, Inc., Washington, DC; *U.S. Public*, pg. 1047
McGlynn, Dan, Corp. Attorney--Symbol Technologies, Inc., Holtsville, NY; *U.S. Public*, pg. 1546
McGlynn, Richard B., V.P. & Gen. Counsel--United Water Resources, Harrington Park, NJ; *U.S. Public*, pg. 1691
McGlynn, Richard B., V.P. & Gen. Counsel--United Water Management & Services, Harrington Park, NJ; *U.S. Public*, pg. 1692
McGoldrick, John L., Sr. V.P. & Gen. Counsel--Bristol-Myers Squibb Company, New York, NY; *U.S. Public*, pg. 253
McGrath, J. Paul, Sr. V.P. & Gen. Counsel--FMC Corporation, Chicago, IL; *U.S. Public*, pg. 604
McGraw, John, V.P., Gen. Counsel & Sec.--Ciba Specialty Chemicals, Tarrytown, NY; *Int'l*, pg. 291
McGuiness, Robert E., V.P. & Counsel--Sun Life Assurance Company of Canada (U.S.), Wellesley Hills, MA; *Int'l*, pg. 1319
McGuinness, Kathleen G., V.P., Gen. Counsel & Sec.--The Times Mirror Company, Los Angeles, CA; *U.S. Public*, pg. 1615
McHale, Judith, Sr. V.P.-Admin. & Gen. Counsel--Discovery Networks, Inc., Bethesda, MD; *U.S. Private*, pg. 334
McInnes, A. Kell, III, V.P. & Corp. Counsel--Cajun Electric Power Co-op, Baton Rouge, LA; *U.S. Private*, pg. 199
McIntyre, Edward A., Gen. Counsel--The Foxboro Company, Foxboro, MA; *Int'l*, pg. 1243
McIntyre, Donald G., V.P.-Human Resources, General Counsel & Sec.--Mitel Corporation, Kanata, Canada; *Int'l*, pg. 870
McIntyre, J. Lawrence, V.P., Gen. Counsel & Sec.--The Toro Company, Bloomington, MN; *U.S. Public*, pg. 1623
McIntyre, John F., V.P., Sec. & Gen. Counsel--Alcon Laboratories, Inc., Fort Worth, TX; *Int'l*, pg. 916
McIver, Angus, Deputy Gen. Counsel-Europe--Alcatel N.V., Amsterdam, Netherlands; *Int'l*, pg. 55
McKaig, Richard G., V.P.-Govt. Business & Legal--BMY-Wheeled Vehicles, Marysville, OH; *U.S. Public*, pg. 793
McKay, Brian, V.P., General Counsel & Sec.--International Game Technology, Reno, NV; *U.S. Public*, pg. 900
McKee, David, V.P., Sec. & Deputy Gen. Counsel--Baxter International Inc., Deerfield, IL; *U.S. Public*, pg. 196
McKee, Kenneth A., Chief Fin. Officer, Treas. & Gen. Counsel--Johnson Storage Moving Co, Denver, CO; *U.S. Private*, pg. 594
McKeithen, Smith, V.P., Gen. Counsel & Sec.--Cadence Design Systems, Inc., San Jose, CA; *U.S. Public*, pg. 290
McKenzie, James D., Pres.-Petroleum Coke Grp.--Great Lakes Carbon Corp., Houston, TX; *U.S. Private*, pg. 540
McKeough, Thomas R., V.P.-Mergers & Acquisitions & Assoc. Gen. Counsel--Bell Atlantic Corporation, New York, NY; *U.S. Public*, pg. 201
McKinlay, J., Counsel--United Technologies, Chemical Systems Div., San Jose, CA; *U.S. Public*, pg. 1690
McKinzie, J. Mark, Sr. V.P., Sec. & Gen. Counsel--Meridian Insurance Group, Inc., Indianapolis, IN; *U.S. Public*, pg. 1095
McKnight, Douglas G., V.P., Gen. Counsel & Sec.--Fluke Corporation, Everett, WA; *U.S. Public*, pg. 659
McKnight, H. James, V.P., Gen. Counsel & Sec.--Michael Baker Corporation, Pittsburgh, PA; *U.S. Public*, pg. 168
McLain, Christopher M., Sr. V.P., General Counsel & Sec.--Crown Vantage Inc., Oakland, CA; *U.S. Public*, pg. 465
McLaughlin, Charles M., V.P. & Asst. Gen. Counsel--Kelly Services, Inc., Troy, MI; *U.S. Public*, pg. 949
McLaughlin, Mark, Gen. Counsel.--Caere Corporation, Los Gatos, CA; *U.S. Public*, pg. 291
McLaughlin, Michael J., Sr. V.P. & Gen. Counsel--New York Life Insurance Company, New York, NY; *U.S. Private*, pg. 794
McLaughlin, Norris, Gen. Counsel--New Brunswick Scientific Co., Inc., Edison, NJ; *U.S. Public*, pg. 1169
McLaughlin, Stephen, Sec. & Gen. Counsel--Martin Exploration Management Company, Alsip, IL; *U.S. Private*, pg. 709
McLeod, Donald J., V.P. & Gen. Counsel--Agra Inc., Calgary, Canada; *Int'l*, pg. 30
McManigal, Robert M., Gen. Counsel & Sec.--Adams Rite Manufacturing Co., City of Industry, CA; *U.S. Private*, pg. 17
McMillan, Michael K., Gen. Counsel & Sec.--Helian Health Group, Inc., Monterey, CA; *U.S. Public*, pg. 1715
McNally, Mark K., Gen. Counsel & Sec.--Aristech Chemical Corporation, Pittsburgh, PA; *Int'l*, pg. 872
McNamara, Anne H., Sr. V.P. & Gen. Counsel--AMR Corporation, Fort Worth, TX; *U.S. Public*, pg. 9
McNamara, Anne H., Sr. V.P.-Admin. & Gen. Counsel--American Airlines, Inc., Fort Worth, TX; *U.S. Public*, pg. 9
McNamara, Dennis, Sr. V.P. & Gen. Counsel--Plaid Clothing Company, New York, NY; *U.S. Public*, pg. 796
McNamee, Bernard J., Exec. V.P., Gen. Counsel & Sec.--Rexene Corporation, Dallas, TX; *U.S. Private*, pg. 549
McNaney, Robert T., Gen. Counsel--Brunswick Corporation, Lake Forest, IL; *U.S. Public*, pg. 265
McNeely, Milinda, Sr. V.P.-Legal--Paramount Pictures Corporation, Los Angeles, CA; *U.S. Private*, pg. 776
McNish, Susan K., V.P. & Gen. Counsel--MichCon, Detroit, MI; *U.S. Public*, pg. 1025
McPhail, John R., Gen. Counsel--Nebraska Public Power District, Columbus, NE; *U.S. Private*, pg. 789
McQueston, James K., Counsel & Sec.--National Life Insurance Company, Montpelier, VT; *U.S. Private*, pg. 785
McRobie, Fred S., V.P. & Asst. Gen. Counsel--PepsiCo, Inc., Purchase, NY; *U.S. Public*, pg. 1276
McSweeney, Maurice J., Gen. Counsel & Sec.--Hein-Werner Corporation, Waukesha, WI; *U.S. Public*, pg. 805
McWilliams, John B., Sr. V.P., Gen. Counsel & Sec.--Canadian Occidental Petroleum Ltd., Calgary, Canada; *U.S. Public*, pg. 1210
Mead, Wayland M., Gen. Counsel--American International Group, Inc., New York, NY; *U.S. Public*, pg. 83
Meadvin, Michael, Sr. V.P. & Gen. Counsel--Castle Oil Corporation, Harrison, NY; *U.S. Private*, pg. 219
Mean, J.P., Sr. V.P.-Legal--SGS Societe Generale de Surveillance Holding S.A., Geneva, Switzerland; *Int'l*, pg. 1153
Meaney, Daniel J. Jr., V.P., Sec. & Gen. Counsel--Circon Video Div., Santa Barbara, CA; *U.S. Public*, pg. 373
Meckler, Lawrence M., Gen. Counsel--Niagara Frontier Transportation Authority, Buffalo, NY; *U.S. Private*, pg. 798
Medford, Cecil, V.P., Sec. & Gen. Counsel--The Scott Fetzer Company, Westlake, OH; *U.S. Public*, pg. 217
Medina Noriega, Sergio F., Dir.-Legal--Telefonos de Mexico S.A. de C.V., Mexico, Mexico; *Int'l*, pg. 1373
Mehnert, Thomas P., V.P.-Legal--Cincinnati Bell Telephone, Cincinnati, OH; *U.S. Public*, pg. 367
Meier, Jeannette P., Exec. V.P., Gen. Counsel & Sec.--Sterling Commerce, Inc., Dublin, OH; *U.S. Public*, pg. 1515
Meisler, Joanne, Sr. V.P., Gen. Counsel & Sec.--Bellemead Development Corp., Roseland, NJ; *U.S. Public*, pg. 355
Mejia Pericas, Heladio, Dir.-Legal--Transportacion Maritima Mexicana S.A. de C.V., Mexico, Mexico; *Int'l*, pg. 1418
Mele, Charles A., Exec. V.P. & Gen. Counsel--MEDCO Containment Services, Inc., Montvale, NJ; *U.S. Public*, pg. 1091
Melendrez, Thomas R., V.P.-Legal Affairs & Gen. Counsel--EXAR Corporation, Fremont, CA; *U.S. Public*, pg. 597
Melican, James P., Exec. V.P.-Legal & External Affairs--International Paper Company, Purchase, NY; *U.S. Public*, pg. 901
Melton, Elizabeth, Gen. Counsel--I.C. System, Inc., Vadnais Heights, MN; *U.S. Private*, pg. 553
Meltzer, Jay H., Sr. V.P., Gen. Counsel & Sec.--The TJX Companies, Inc., Framingham, MA; *U.S. Public*, pg. 1556
Melvin, Bob, Legal Officer--Information Systems & Network Corporation, Bethesda, MD; *U.S. Private*, pg. 561
Menache, Jack, V.P., Gen. Counsel & Sec.--Integrated Device Technology, Inc., Santa Clara, CA; *U.S. Public*, pg. 884
Menaker, Frank H., Jr., Sr. V.P. & Gen. Counsel--Lockheed Martin Corporation, Bethesda, MD; *U.S. Public*, pg. 1006
Menashe, Gerald, Gen. Counsel--First National Bank Holdings Limited, Johannesburg, South Africa; *Int'l*, pg. 487
Mendelson, Alan C., Gen. Counsel & Sec.--PETsMART, Inc., Phoenix, AZ; *U.S. Public*, pg. 1281
Mendelson, Morley, Gen. Counsel--National R.V., Inc., Perris, CA; *U.S. Public*, pg. 1159
Mendes, Robert, V.P. & Gen. Counsel--PMA Reinsurance Corporation, Philadelphia, PA; *U.S. Public*, pg. 1272
Mendoza, Christina, V.P. & Gen. Counsel--Knight-Ridder, Inc., Miami, FL; *U.S. Public*, pg. 963
Menu, Gerard, Gen. Counsel, Dir.-Fin. & Mgr.-Info Sys.--Lipha Chemicals S.A., Lyon, France; *Int'l*, pg. 812
Mercier, Monique, Asst. Gen. Counsel--BCE Inc., Montreal, Canada; *Int'l*, pg. 114
Merck, Robert M., V.P., Gen. Counsel & Secretary--Mercedes-Benz Credit Corp., Norwalk, CT; *Int'l*, pg. 368
Mercurio, Bob, Gen. Counsel--Pyramid Handbags Inc., New York, NY; *U.S. Private*, pg. 896
Mercurio, S.L., Gen. Counsel--Procter & Gamble Pharmaceuticals, Inc., Cincinnati, OH; *U.S. Public*, pg. 1331
Merdek, Andrew A., V.P.-Legal Affairs & Sec.--Cox Enterprises, Inc., Atlanta, GA; *U.S. Private*, pg. 281
Meredith, Frank, Chief Fin. Officer, Gen. Counsel & Sec.--Harman International Industries, Inc., Woodbury, NY; *U.S. Public*, pg. 787
Meriam, Harold, Esq., Gen. Counsel--Helmsley Enterprises, Inc., New York, NY; *U.S. Private*, pg. 521
Meringer, Patricia C., Sr. V.P., Corp. Counsel & Sec.--Hibernia Corporation, New Orleans, LA; *U.S. Public*, pg. 825
Merli, Gian Oddone, Gen. Counsel--Merloni Elettrodomestici S.P.A., Fabriano, Italy; *Int'l*, pg. 860
Merritt, Ray, Gen. Counsel--Cowen & Company, New York, NY; *U.S. Private*, pg. 280
Merryman, Gregory K., Corp. Sec. & Asst. Gen. Counsel--General Motors Acceptance Corporation (GMAC), Detroit, MI; *U.S. Public*, pg. 719
Mesher, John R., V.P. & Sec. & Gen. Counsel--CertainTeed Corporation, Valley Forge, PA; *Int'l*, pg. 1170
Messemer, Glenn M., V.P., Sec. & Gen. Counsel--Kaman Corporation, Bloomfield, CT; *U.S. Public*, pg. 941
Messinger, Martin P., Sr. V.P. & Gen. Counsel--CBS, New York, NY; *U.S. Public*, pg. 273
Metz, Lawrence A., Sr. V.P. & Deputy Gen. Counsel--American Stores Company, Salt Lake City, UT; *U.S. Public*, pg. 92
Metzger, Barry, Gen. Counsel--Asian Development Bank, Manila, Philippines; *Int'l*, pg. 88
Meyer, A. David, Gen. Counsel & Sec.--R.O. Whitesell & Associates, Inc, Indianapolis, IN; *U.S. Private*, pg. 1173
Meyer, Donald, Sr. V.P. & Gen. Counsel--Union Bank of California, San Francisco, CA; *Int'l*, pg. 157
Meyer, Fred C., Jr., Sr. V.P. & Gen. Counsel--Central and South West Corporation, Dallas, TX; *U.S. Public*, pg. 324
Meyer, James R., V.P. & Gen. Counsel--W.S. Badcock Corporation, Mulberry, FL; *U.S. Private*, pg. 109
Meyer, Jeffrey D., Assoc. Gen. Counsel--Lexford Residential Trust, Columbus, OH; *U.S. Public*, pg. 991
Meyer, Thomas J., V.P.-Legal--Jackson National Life Insurance Company, Lansing, MI; *Int'l*, pg. 1073
Meyering, Chris, Assoc. Gen. Counsel--The Pittston Company, Glen Allen, VA; *U.S. Public*, pg. 1305
Meyerson, Ivan D., V.P. & Gen. Counsel--McKesson Corporation, San Francisco, CA; *U.S. Public*, pg. 1072
Michael, Mark D., Sr. V.P., Gen. Counsel & Sec.--3Com Corporation, Santa Clara, CA; *U.S. Public*, pg. 1603
Michaud, Nancy A., V.P., Gen. Counsel & Sec.--Huffy Corporation, Miamisburg, OH; *U.S. Public*, pg. 846
Michno, Timothy, Corp. Sec. & Gen. Counsel--Movado Group, Inc., Lyndhurst, NJ; *U.S. Public*, pg. 1140
Middlebrook, Stephen B., Sr. V.P. & Exec. Counsel--Aetna Inc., Hartford, CT; *U.S. Public*, pg. 26
Miears, James L., Exec. V.P. & Gen. Mgr.-Cedar Point--Cedar Fair, L.P., Sandusky, OH; *U.S. Public*, pg. 319
Mikelonis, David A., Sr. V.P. & Gen. Counsel-Consumers--CMS Energy Corporation, Dearborn, MI; *U.S. Public*, pg. 279
Mikelonis, David A., Sr. V.P. & Gen. Counsel--Consumers Energy, Jackson, MI; *U.S. Public*, pg. 280

Mikesell, David, Dir.-H.R. & Attorney--Horizon Enterprises Group LLC, Taylor, MI; *U.S. Private,* pg. 539

Miklich, Thomas R., Chief Fin. Officer, Treas., Gen. Counsel & Sec.--Invacare Corporation, Elyria, OH; *U.S. Public,* pg. 911

Milano, Sandra C., Legal Asst.--W.R. Berkley Corporation, Greenwich, CT; *U.S. Public,* pg. 215

Mildwaters, Ken, Dr., Dir.-Grp. Legal Srvcs.--Guinness Plc, London, United Kingdom; *Int'l,* pg. 412

Mileaf, Howard, V.P.-Special Counsel--WHX Corporation, New York, NY; *U.S. Public,* pg. 1726

Miley, Samuel A., V.P., Gen. Counsel & Sec.--MagneTek, Inc., Nashville, TN; *U.S. Public,* pg. 1037

Milich, Herb, Dir.-Finance & Svcs.--Datapro Information Services Grp., Delran, NJ; *U.S. Public,* pg. 1070

Miller, Arthur R., Gen. Counsel & Sec.--Katy Industries, Inc., Englewood, CO; *U.S. Public,* pg. 944

Miller, Charlotte L., Sr. V.P., Gen. Counsel & Sec.--Summit Family Restaurants, Inc., Salt Lake City, UT; *U.S. Public, pg. 278*

Miller, D., Legal Officer--Johnson Matthey Inc., Wayne, PA; *Int'l,* pg. 713

Miller, David, V.P.--National Income Realty Trust, New York, NY; *U.S. Public,* pg. 1157

Miller, David P., V.P. & Gen. Counsel--Rogers Communications, Inc., Toronto, Canada; *Int'l,* pg. 1122

Miller, David P., V.P. & Gen. Counsel--Maclean Hunter Publishing Ltd., Toronto, Canada; *Int'l,* pg. 1123

Miller, Donald E., Sr. V.P., Gen. Counsel & Sec.--The Fairchild Corporation, Chantilly, VA; *U.S. Public,* pg. 610

Miller, Eugene F., V.P., Sec. & Corp. Gen. Counsel--Loctite Corporation, Rocky Hill, CT; *Int'l,* pg. 611

Miller, James, Gen. Counsel--Pacesetter Corporation, Omaha, NE; *U.S. Private,* pg. 830

Miller, Jay J., Gen. Counsel--Westbrae Natural, Inc., Carson, CA; *U.S. Public,* pg. 774

Miller, Jeffrey J., Gen. Counsel & Sec.--NeoRx Corporation, Seattle, WA; *U.S. Private,* pg. 791

Miller, Kirk, Sr. V.P., Sec. & Gen. Counsel--Kaiser Permanente, Oakland, CA; *U.S. Private,* pg. 605

Miller, Neil, Gen. Counsel--Apex Oil Company, Inc., Saint Louis, MO; *U.S. Private,* pg. 77

Miller, Paul S., Sr. V.P. & Gen. Counsel--Pfizer Inc., New York, NY; *U.S. Public,* pg. 1281

Miller, Peter D., V.P., Gen. Counsel & Sec.--National Auto Credit Inc., Solon, OH; *U.S. Public,* pg. 1152

Miller, Phebe C., Chief Legal Officer & Sec.--The Bank of New York Company, Inc., New York, NY; *U.S. Public,* pg. 178

Miller, Richard L., Gen. Counsel & Sec.--American Institute of C.P.A.'s Inc., New York, NY; *U.S. Private,* pg. 57

Miller, Robert A., Jr., V.P.-Law--Plains Petroleum Operating Co., Lakewood, CO; *U.S. Public,* pg. 191

Miller, Robert M., V.P.-Law & Sec.--FKI Industries. Inc., Fairfield, CT; *Int'l,* pg. 472

Miller, Scott, Sr. V.P., Gen. Counsel & Asst. Sec.--Coherent, Inc., Santa Clara, CA; *U.S. Public,* pg. 395

Miller, Steve, Gen. Counsel--P/A Industries, Inc., Bloomfield, CT; *U.S. Private,* pg. 825

Miller, Tom, Sr. Counsel--Nortel, Nashville, TN; *Int'l,* pg. 970

Miller, Ward M., Jr., Sr. V.P., Gen. Counsel & Sec.--Avon Products, Inc., New York, NY; *U.S. Public,* pg. 155

Miller, Yvette, Gen. Counsel--Parents Magazine, New York, NY; *Int'l,* pg. 191

Millinger, Don, V.P.-Law--Wells Fargo Alarm Services, Inc., King of Prussia, PA; *U.S. Public,* pg. 246

Millisor, William P., Reg. Counsel & Asst. Sec.--OHM Remediation Services Corp., Findlay, OH; *U.S. Public,* pg. 1208

Millman, Linda R., Assoc. Gen. Counsel & Asst. Sec.--Ekco Group, Inc., Nashua, NH; *U.S. Public,* pg. 566

Mills, Michael R., Asst. Gen. Counsel--Vulcan Materials Company, Birmingham, AL; *U.S. Public,* pg. 1725

Mills, Robert, Gen. Counsel--Virco Mfg. Corporation, Torrance, CA; *U.S. Public,* pg. 1721

Millstein, David J., Sr. V.P.--Millstein Industries, Youngwood, PA; *U.S. Private,* pg. 749

Milner, David, Esq., Sec.--Commercial Travelers Mutual Insurance Company, Utica, NY; *U.S. Private,* pg. 258

Milstein, Ronald S., V.P. & Gen. Counsel--Del Laboratories, Inc., Farmingdale, NY; *U.S. Public,* pg. 494

Minnick, David, Gen. Counsel--Morgan Keegan, Inc., Memphis, TN; *U.S. Public,* pg. 1131

Minnot, Debra F., Sr. V.P. & Gen. Counsel--Essex International, Inc., Fort Wayne, IN; *U.S. Public,* pg. 593

Miotto, Robert, V.P.-Gen. Counsel--New Holland Ltd., Brentford, United Kingdom; *Int'l,* pg. 484

Miroela, Todd, Gen. Counsel--Fosters Freeze International, Inc., San Luis Obispo, CA; *U.S. Public,* pg. 677

Miruiss, Israel, Gen. Counsel--Dynamic Homes, Inc., Detroit Lakes, MN; *U.S. Public,* pg. 538

Mistretta, F. David, V.P., Gen. Counsel & Sec.--Security Mutual Life Insurance Co. of New York, Binghamton, NY; *U.S. Private,* pg. 981

Mistretta, Susan E., Second V.P. & Assoc. Gen. Counsel--Security Mutual Life Insurance Co. of New York, Binghamton, NY; *U.S. Private,* pg. 981

Mitau, Lee R., Exec. V.P., Gen. Counsel & Sec.--U.S. Bancorp, Minneapolis, MN; *U.S. Public,* pg. 1680

Mitchell, Daniel R., V.P. & Gen. Tax Counsel--Amoco Corporation, Chicago, IL; *U.S. Public,* pg. 101

Mitchell, E. Benjamin, Jr., V.P., Sec. & Gen. Counsel--Logicon, Inc., Torrance, CA; *U.S. Public,* pg. 1198

Mitchell, H. Thomas, V.P., Gen. Counsel & Sec.--Buffets, Inc., Eden Prairie, MN; *U.S. Public,* pg. 267

Mitchell, Thompson, Gen. Counsel--Tober Industries, Inc., Saint Louis, MO; *U.S. Private,* pg. 1089

Mitten, L. Russell, II, V.P. & Gen. Counsel--Citizens Utilities Company, Stamford, CT; *U.S. Public,* pg. 379

Miyazawa, Ishio, Auditor--Japan Energy Corporation, Tokyo, Japan; *Int'l,* pg. 702

Mlotek, Mark, V.P. & Gen. Counsel--Henry Schein, Inc., Melville, NY; *U.S. Public,* pg. 1437

Moates, Kathleen, Sr. V.P. & Deputy Gen. Counsel--Synovus Financial Corp., Columbus, GA; *U.S. Public,* pg. 1548

Mocniak, Michael J., V.P., Gen. Counsel & Sec.--Fansteel, Inc., North Chicago, IL; *U.S. Public,* pg. 612

Moderow, Joseph, Sr. V.P. & Sec.--United Parcel Service of America, Inc., Atlanta, GA; *U.S. Private,* pg. 1123

Moderow, Mark, Gen. Counsel--General Communication, Inc., Anchorage, AK; *U.S. Public,* pg. 708

Moe, James D., V.P., Gen. Counsel & Sec.--Cargill, Wayzata, MN; *U.S. Private,* pg. 210

Moen, Richard, Exec. V.P.-Admin., Gen. Counsel & Sec.--Golden Valley Microwave Foods, Inc., Edina, MN; *U.S. Public,* pg. 427

Moffett, Robert T., V.P., Gen. Counsel & Sec.--Howell Corporation, Houston, TX; *U.S. Public,* pg. 843

Mohan, Patrick, Exec. V.P., Gen. Counsel & Sec.--A.E. Staley Manufacturing Co., Decatur, IL; *Int'l,* pg. 1356

Mohr, C. Donald, Gen. Counsel--LVMH Moet Hennessy Louis Vuitton, New York, NY; *Int'l,* pg. 781

Moir, R.J., V.P., Sec. & Gen. Counsel--Holnam Inc. (West Division), Lakewood, CO; *Int'l,* pg. 628

Mokris, Paul, Gen. Counsel--Signature Flight Support, Orlando, FL; *Int'l,* pg. 114

Molino, Virginia L., Gen. Counsel--McKinsey & Company, Inc., New York, NY; *U.S. Private,* pg. 723

Molleur, E. Claude, V.P.-Legal & Public Affairs--Ivanhoe, Montreal, Canada; *Int'l,* pg. 249

Molleur, Richard R., V.P. & Gen. Counsel--Northrop Grumman Corporation, Los Angeles, CA; *U.S. Public,* pg. 1197

Momboisse, R. Michael, Chief Fin. Officer, V.P.-Legal & Sec.--EMCON, San Mateo, CA; *U.S. Public,* pg. 571

Moncada, L. Patricia, Gen. Counsel & Asst. Sec.--Oracle Corporation, Redwood City, CA; *U.S. Public,* pg. 1227

Mondius, E., Legal & Trademark Dept.--Bols Royal Distilleries, Nieuw-Vennep, Netherlands; *Int'l,* pg. 751

Monfort, Myra H., V.P., Sec. & Gen. Counsel--Monfort, Inc., Greeley, CO; *U.S. Public,* pg. 427

Mongan, Tod V., Sr. V.P., Gen. Counsel, & Sec.--BancTec, Inc., Dallas, TX; *U.S. Public,* pg. 176

Mongelluzzo, John A., Gen. Counsel & Sec.--Structural Dynamics Research Corp., Milford, OH; *U.S. Public,* pg. 1525

Monk, Thomas, Gen. Counsel & Sec.--Lotus Cars USA, Inc., Lawrenceville, GA; *Int'l,* pg. 1071

Monson, Scott G., Gen. Counsel & Asst. Corp. Sec.--JB Oxford Holdings Inc., Beverly Hills, CA; *U.S. Public,* pg. 916

Montgomery, William, V.P. & Gen. Counsel--State Farm Mutual Automobile Insurance Company, Bloomington, IL; *U.S. Private,* pg. 1036

Montjoy, John, V.P. & Gen. Counsel--GTE Internetworking, Cambridge, MA; *U.S. Public,* pg. 696

Moodispaw, Leonard, Gen. Counsel & Sec.--Essex Corporation, Columbia, MD; *U.S. Public,* pg. 593

Moomjian, Cary A., V.P., Gen. Counsel & Sec.--Santa Fe International Corporation, Dallas, TX; *Int'l,* pg. 765

Moonan, Jeffrey P., Sr. V.P.-Gen. Counsel & Sec.--Photronics, Inc., Brookfield, CT; *U.S. Public,* pg. 1293

Moore, C. Steven, V.P., Mng. Attorney & Sec.--Service Merchandise Company, Inc., Brentwood, TN; *U.S. Public, pg. 1461*

Moore, Jeff, Gen. Counsel--Kulicke & Soffa Industries, Inc., Willow Grove, PA; *U.S. Public,* pg. 968

Moore, John P., Jr., Sec. & Gen. Counsel--Northern States Power Co. (Wis.), Eau Claire, WI; *U.S. Public,* pg. 1195

Moore, R., V.P. & Gen. Counsel--The Richman Brothers Co., Fall River, MA; *U.S. Public,* pg. 1777

Moore, Robert C., V.P., Gen. Counsel & Sec.--Texas Industries, Inc., Dallas, TX; *U.S. Public,* pg. 1585

Moore, Roni, Counselor--Golin/Harris Communications, Inc., Chicago, IL; *Int'l,* pg. 1226

Moore, Tom, General Counsel--Pic'n Pay Stores, Inc., Matthews, NC; *U.S. Private,* pg. 864

Moore, William B., V.P., Gen. Counsel & Sec.--Whitman Corporation, Rolling Meadows, IL; *U.S. Public,* pg. 1766

Moorhead, Thomas L., V.P.-Law & Asst. Sec.--Nordson Corporation, Westlake, OH; *U.S. Public,* pg. 1188

Mooyaart, L.W., Legal Officer--KLM Royal Dutch Airlines, Amstelveen, Netherlands; *Int'l,* pg. 719

Mora, R.N., Gen. Counsel & Sec.--The HOH Organizations, Chicago, IL; *U.S. Private,* pg. 492

Moran, David E., V.P.-Law & Deputy Gen. Counsel--Dow Jones & Company, Inc., New York, NY; *U.S. Public,* pg. 524

Moran, Glenn, Sr. V.P., Gen. Counsel & Sec.--The LTV Corporation, Cleveland, OH; *U.S. Public,* pg. 971

Moran, John, Gen. Counsel--Corrpro Companies, Inc., Medina, OH; *U.S. Public,* pg. 451

Moran, Michael R., Exec. V.P., Gen. Counsel & Sec.--Spiegel, Inc., Downers Grove, IL; *U.S. Public,* pg. 1498

Moran, Ronald, V.P. & Gen. Counsel--Medical Meadow Gold Dairies, Inc., Ogden, UT; *U.S. Private,* pg. 1016

Moran, Ronald P., Asst. Gen. Counsel--Borden, Inc., Columbus, OH; *U.S. Private,* pg. 157

Morbilli, Alessandro, Dir. Gen.-Legal--European Investment Bank, Luxembourg, Luxembourg; *Int'l,* pg. 465

Moreira, Manuel, Gen. Counsel--Bagley S.A., Buenos Aires, Argentina; *Int'l,* pg. 379

Moreland, Jeffrey R., Sr. V.P.-Law & Gen. Counsel--Burlington Northern Santa Fe Corporation, Fort Worth, TX; *U.S. Public,* pg. 268

Morelli, William P., V.P. & Gen. Counsel--Ingram Industries Inc., Nashville, TN; *U.S. Private,* pg. 562

Morello, Steve, Gen. Counsel--ASC Incorporated, Southgate, MI; *U.S. Private,* pg. 8

Moreno, Albert, Sr. V.P. & Gen. Counsel--Levi Strauss & Co., San Francisco, CA; *U.S. Private,* pg. 662

Moretzsohn, Dianne G., Senior Counsel--Ikon Office Solutions, Inc., Malvern, PA; *U.S. Public,* pg. 862

Morgan-Prager, Karole, Gen. Counsel & Corp. Sec.--McClatchy Newspapers Inc., Sacramento, CA; *U.S. Public,* pg. 1065

Morgan, Charles R., Exec. V.P. & Gen. Counsel--BellSouth Corporation, Atlanta, GA; *U.S. Public,* pg. 207

Morgan, D. Russell, Gen. Counsel--Equity Services, Inc., Montpelier, VT; *U.S. Private,* pg. 785

Morgan, James A., Sr. V.P., Gen. Counsel & Sec.--Rubbermaid Incorporated, Wooster, OH; *U.S. Public,* pg. 1411

Morie, G. Glen, V.P. & Gen. Counsel--Paccar Inc., Bellevue, WA; *U.S. Public,* pg. 1246

Morledge, W. Frank, Gen. Counsel--GES Inc., Marianna, AR; *U.S. Private,* pg. 434

Morley, Bruce E., V.P.-Legal Services--Clearly Canadian Beverage Corp., Vancouver, Canada; *Int'l,* pg. 297

Moroz, Robin, Gen. Counsel & Sec.--Ground Round Inc., Braintree, MA; *U.S. Public,* pg. 766

Morozuk, John J., V.P., Gen. Counsel & Sec.--Enogex Inc., Oklahoma City, OK; *U.S. Public,* pg. 1207

Morreale, Justin P., Gen. Counsel--All Seasons Services, Inc., Braintree, MA; *U.S. Private,* pg. 35

Morril, Mark C., Sr. V.P. & Gen. Counsel--Simon & Schuster, New York, NY; *U.S. Private,* pg. 777

Morris, Gregory D., V.P., Gen. Counsel & Sec.--Pioneer Mutual Life Insurance Company, Fargo, ND; *U.S. Private, pg. 866*

Morris, Kenneth, Gen. Counsel--AgrEvo USA Company, Wilmington, DE; *Int'l,* pg. 1203

Morris, L. Daniel, Jr., V.P.-Legal Svcs.--Blount, Inc., Montgomery, AL; *U.S. Public,* pg. 238

Morris, Margaret M., Dir.-Corp. & Legal Admin. & Asst. Sec.--Transus Intermodal L.L.C., Atlanta, GA; *U.S. Private,* pg. 1097

Morris, Michael H., V.P., Gen. Counsel & Sec.--Sun Microsystems, Inc., Palo Alto, CA; *U.S. Public,* pg. 1531

Morris, Ralph K., Gen. Counsel & Sec.--American Crystal Sugar Company, Moorhead, MN; *U.S. Private,* pg. 52

Morris, Rebecca R., V.P., Corp. Counsel & Sec.--Dresser Industries, Inc., Dallas, TX; *U.S. Public,* pg. 528

Morris, T., Gen. Counsel--Armstrong International, Inc., Three Rivers, MI; *U.S. Private,* pg. 83

Morris, T.N., Jr., Chm., Pres. & Chief Exec. Officer--Calcasieu Lumber Company, Austin, TX; *U.S. Private,* pg. 200

Morrison, M.R., Gen. Counsel & Sec.--Woodside Petroleum Ltd., Melbourne, Australia; *Int'l,* pg. 1137

Morrison, P.A., Attorney--Colonial Pipeline Company, Atlanta, GA; *U.S. Private,* pg. 254

Morrison, Stephen D., V.P., Gen. Counsel & Sec.--Norwest Mortgage, Inc., Des Moines, IA; *U.S. Public,* pg. 1202

Morrison, Stephen G., Chief Admin. Officer, Exec. V.P., Gen. Counsel & Sec.--Policy Management Systems Corporation, Blythewood, SC; *U.S. Public,* pg. 1314

Morrisson, A.S., Sr. V.P., Gen. Counsel & Sec.--Sverdrup Corporation, Maryland Heights, MO; *U.S. Private,* pg. 1057

Morse, M. Brinkley, V.P., Gen. Counsel & Sec.--BMC Software, Inc., Houston, TX; *U.S. Public,* pg. 162

Morton, James, Gen. Counsel--Pickering Inc., Tacoma, WA; *U.S. Private,* pg. 864

Moseley, Joe, V.P.& Gen. Counsel--Shelter Mutual Insurance Company, Columbia, MO; *U.S. Private,* pg. 992

Moseley, Valerie, Gen. Counsel--Martin Lawrence Limited Editions, Inc., North Hollywood, CA; *U.S. Private,* pg. 709

Moskowitz, Jules, V.P., Sec. & Gen. Counsel--DST Systems, Inc., Kansas City, MO; *U.S. Public,* pg. 943

Moskowitz, Robert, Sr. V.P. & Gen. Counsel--Shamrock Holdings, Inc., Burbank, CA; *U.S. Private,* pg. 989

Mosli, Stefan, Gen. Counsel & Sec.--Sika Finanz AG, Baar, Switzerland; *Int'l,* pg. 1248

Moss, Sare E., V.P. & Gen. Counsel--Pitney Bowes Inc., Stamford, CT; *U.S. Public,* pg. 1303

Motchan, Brent L., V.P., Gen. Counsel & Sec.--Zeigler Coal Holding Company, Fairview Heights, IL; *U.S. Public,* pg. 1790

Motsko, Don, Gen. Counsel--U.S. Repeating Arms Company, New Haven, CT; *U.S. Private,* pg. 1125

Moulopoulos, Rena J., V.P. & Deputy Gen. Counsel--Sotheby's Holdings Inc., New York, NY; *U.S. Public,* pg. 1487

Mount, Larry C., V.P. & Gen. Counsel--Edison Capital, Irvine, CA; *U.S. Public,* pg. 564

Mountain, Robert P., Jr., Counsel--Time Life International do Brazil Ltda., Rio de Janeiro, Brazil; *U.S. Public,* pg. 1615

Mouton, Edgar, Jr., Gen. Counsel--Louisiana Gaming Management, Inc., Metairie, LA; *U.S. Private,* pg. 677

Mouw, John, Gen. Counsel--Bacco Construction Co., Iron Mountain, MI; *U.S. Private,* pg. 109

Moyer, Terry, V.P. & Legal Counsel--Milliken & Company, Spartanburg, SC; *U.S. Private,* pg. 748

Muchin, A., Gen. Counsel--Heresite Protective Coatings Inc., Manitowoc, WI; *U.S. Private,* pg. 523

Mudrow, Michael, V.P., Gen. Counsel & Sec.--Regence BlueCross BlueShield of Oregon, Portland, OR; *U.S. Private,* pg. 917

Muelker, Ruth, Gen. Counsel--RMT, Inc., Madison, WI; *U.S. Public,* pg. 1728

Mueller-Gebel, Klaus, Mng. Dir.-H.R. & Legal Svcs.--Commerzbank AG, Frankfurt, Germany; *Int'l,* pg. 308

Mueller, Mary, Gen. Counsel & Asst. Sec.--Steak 'n Shake, Inc., Indianapolis, IN; *U.S. Public,* pg. 437

Mueller, Mary H., Gen. Counsel & Asst. Sec.--Consolidated Products, Inc., Indianapolis, IN; *U.S. Public,* pg. 436

Mueller, Mary H., Gen. Counsel & Asst. Sec.--Consolidated Specialty Restaurant, Indianapolis, IN; *U.S. Public,* pg. 436

Mueller, Mary H., Gen. Counsel & Asst. Sec.--SNS Investment Company, Indianapolis, IN; *U.S. Public,* pg. 436

Mukai, Don, Gen. Counsel--AirTouch Cellular - Western Region, Bellevue, WA; *U.S. Public,* pg. 34

Mulcahy, M.J., V.P., Gen. Counsel & Sec.--Gehl Company, West Bend, WI; *U.S. Public,* pg. 704

Mulholland, E., Head-Legal Services--John Menzies plc, Edinburgh, United Kingdom; *Int'l*, pg. 707

Mullarkey, Kathleen, Gen. Counsel & Corp. Sec.--Federal Farm Credit Banks Funding Corporation, Jersey City, NJ; *U.S. Private*, pg. 398

Mullen, Mary A., V.P. & Asst. Counsel--Fiduciary Trust Company International, New York, NY; *U.S. Public*, pg. 621

Mulligan, James J., Gen. Counsel & Sec.--Krug International Corp., Houston, TX; *U.S. Public*, pg. 967

Mulliken, W.D., V.P., Gen. Counsel & Sec.--CHEMCENTRAL Corporation, Bedford Park, IL; *U.S. Private*, pg. 231

Mullins, Dennis, V.P.-Pub. Affairs, Sec. & Gen. Counsel--Tejon Ranch Company, Lebec, CA; *U.S. Public*, pg. 1566

Mullman, Mike, Gen. Counsel--Furniture Consultants, New York, NY; *U.S. Public*, pg. 1686

Mulroy, Richard, Sr. V.P. & Gen. Counsel--The Mutual Life Insurance Company of New York, New York, NY; *U.S. Private*, pg. 769

Mulvaney, Thomas, V.P., Gen. Counsel, & Sec.--VLSI Technology, Inc., San Jose, CA; *U.S. Public*, pg. 1703

Mumford, Jim, Gen. Counsel--Equitable of Iowa Companies, Des Moines, IA; *Int'l*, pg. 647

Munn, David, Gen. Counsel--Pella Corporation, Pella, IA; *U.S. Private*, pg. 848

Munro, D.M., Gen. Counsel & Sec.--M.I.M. Holdings Ltd., Brisbane, Australia; *Int'l*, pg. 827

Munro, K. Doug, Gen. Counsel & Sec.--Manitoba Hydro, Winnipeg, Canada; *Int'l*, pg. 834

Munzer, Patrick, Gen. Counsel--Symons Corporation, Des Plaines, IL; *U.S. Private*, pg. 932

Muraro, Bob, Gen. Counsel--United States Sugar Corporation, Clewiston, FL; *U.S. Private*, pg. 1126

Murdock, Viola, Corp. Counsel--PAR Technology Corporation, New Hartford, NY; *U.S. Public*, pg. 1256

Murphy, Finbarr, Gen. Counsel--Bank of Ireland, Dublin, Ireland; *Int'l*, pg. 152

Murphy, Jeffrey J., Sr. V.P.-Law & Human Resources, Sec. & Gen. Counsel--Aviall, Inc., Dallas, TX; *U.S. Public*, pg. 154

Murphy, Jesse, Gen. Counsel--Kaufman and Broad of Texas, Ltd., San Antonio, TX; *U.S. Public*, pg. 945

Murphy, Kenyon W., V.P., Sec. & Assoc. Counsel--National Service Industries, Inc., Atlanta, GA; *U.S. Public*, pg. 1160

Murphy, Lisabeth F., V.P. & Gen. Counsel--Elan Corporation Plc, Dublin, Ireland; *Int'l*, pg. 435

Murphy, Robert, Sr. V.P. & Gen. Counsel--Sun Healthcare Group Inc., Albuquerque, NM; *U.S. Public*, pg. 1530

Murphy, S. Wayne, Sr. V.P., Gen. Counsel & Sec.--McDermott International, Inc., New Orleans, LA; *U.S. Public*, pg. 1067

Murphy, S. Wayne, V.P., Gen. Counsel & Corp. Sec.--McDermott International, Inc., New Orleans, LA; *U.S. Public*, pg. 1067

Murray, Cheryl, Gen. Counsel--PMC Capital Inc., Dallas, TX; *U.S. Public*, pg. 1242

Murray, Graham, Gen. Counsel--Air UK Ltd., Stansted, United Kingdom; *Int'l*, pg. 38

Murray, Mike, V.P. & Gen. Counsel--Gator Freightways, Inc., Wilmington, OH; *U.S. Private*, pg. 441

Murrayd, William J., V.P. & Asst. Gen. Counsel--Chubb & Son, Inc., Warren, NJ; *U.S. Public*, pg. 355

Murrell, Jack O., V.P., Gen. Counsel & Sec.--ITT Defense & Electronics, Inc., Mc Lean, VA; *U.S. Public*, pg. 859

Musacchia, Mary, Gen. Counsel--SAS Institute Inc., Cary, NC; *U.S. Private*, pg. 966

Muse, Albert C., Pres. & Chief Exec. Officer--Crown Coal & Coke Co. Inc., Pittsburgh, PA; *U.S. Private*, pg. 292

Musgraves, Robert E., V.P., Gen. Counsel & Sec.--Tremont Corporation, Denver, CO; *U.S. Private*, pg. 270

Musgraves, Robert E., V.P., Sec. & Gen. Counsel--Titanium Metals Corporation, Denver, CO; *U.S. Private*, pg. 270

Mustoe, Jack S., Sr. V.P., Gen. Counsel & Eniron. Officer--Nova Corporation, Calgary, Canada; *Int'l*, pg. 971

Muther, Stephen C., Sr. V.P.-Admin., Gen. Counsel & Sec.--Buckeye Partners, L.P., Allentown, PA; *U.S. Public*, pg. 266

Muto, Tony, V.P. & Gen. Counsel--Senco Products, Inc., Cincinnati, OH; *U.S. Private*, pg. 984

Mutterperl, William C., Sr. V.P., Gen. Counsel & Sec.--Fleet Financial Group, Inc., Boston, MA; *U.S. Public*, pg. 648

Myddelton, Roger H., Sec. & Grp. Dir.-Legal--Grand Metropolitan Plc, London, United Kingdom; *Int'l*, pg. 408

Myers, Barry D., V.P., Gen. Counsel & Asst. Sec.--R&B, Inc., Colmar, PA; *U.S. Public*, pg. 1354

Myers, G. William, Sr. V.P. & Legal Counsel--L. Robert Kimball & Associates, Ebensburg, PA; *U.S. Private*, pg. 619

Myers, Gary L., V.P., Gen. Counsel & Sec.--St. Joseph Light & Power Co., Saint Joseph, MO; *U.S. Public*, pg. 1427

Myers, Gary L., Gen. Counsel & Sec.--SJLP Inc., Saint Joseph, MO; *U.S. Public*, pg. 1427

Myers, Howard B., Gen. Counsel & Sec.--RSR Corporation, Dallas, TX; *U.S. Private*, pg. 900

Myers, Thomas D., V.P. & Assoc. Counsel--Urstadt Biddle Properties, Inc., Greenwich, CT; *U.S. Public*, pg. 1700

Nacht, Wendy, Gen. Counsel--Gitano Fashions Ltd., Bowling Green, KY; *U.S. Public*, pg. 686

Nachtigal, Patricia, V.P. & Gen. Counsel--Ingersoll-Rand Company, Woodcliff Lake, NJ; *U.S. Public*, pg. 876

Nadeau, Peter, V.P. & Gen. Counsel--Newbridge Networks Corporation, Kanata, Canada; *Int'l*, pg. 923

Nagin, Lawrence M., Exec. V.P.-Corp. Affairs & Gen. Counsel--US Airways Group, Inc., Arlington, VA; *U.S. Public*, pg. 1680

Nagler, Barry, V.P. & Gen. Counsel--Reebok International Ltd., Stoughton, MA; *U.S. Public*, pg. 1369

Nagy, Louis, V.P. & Gen. Counsel--Chubb & Son, Inc., Warren, NJ; *U.S. Public*, pg. 355

Nakagawa, Kenshi, Sr. V.P.-Legal & Sec.--DIC Trading (USA) Inc., Fort Lee, NJ; *Int'l*, pg. 369

Nakashima, Katrin, Sec. & Counsel--Imasco Limited, Montreal, Canada; *Int'l*, pg. 112

Nalley, Elliot, Gen. Counsel--Oki Telecom Group, Suwanee, GA; *Int'l*, pg. 1000

Narber, Gregg, Sr. V.P. & Gen. Counsel--The Principal Financial Group, Des Moines, IA; *U.S. Private*, pg. 885

Narber, Gregg, Sr. V.P. & Gen. Counsel--Principal Mutual Life Insurance Co., Des Moines, IA; *U.S. Private*, pg. 886

Narie, Agathe, Gen. Counsel--GEODIS, Paris, France; *Int'l*, pg. 549

Nash, Peter, Corp. Counsel--Viewlogic Systems Group, Marlborough, MA; *U.S. Public*, pg. 1548

Naslin, Jean, Gen. Counsel--The Eurotunnel Group, London, United Kingdom; *Int'l*, pg. 466

Nastasia, Helen A., Gen. Counsel--Manugistics Group, Inc., Rockville, MD; *U.S. Public*, pg. 1042

Natcher, Stephen, Sr. V.P.-Admin., Gen. Counsel, & Sec.--Wyle Electronics, Irvine, CA; *Int'l*, pg. 1457

Nathan, Thomas R., V.P. & Gen. Counsel--Comcast Cable Communications, Inc., Philadelphia, PA; *U.S. Public*, pg. 407

Natsumeda, Tsuneyoshi, Exec. V.P.-Affiliate Rels., Property & Legal Affairs--Nihon Keizai Shimbun, Inc., Tokyo, Japan; *Int'l*, pg. 929

Nault, Robert P., Gen. Counsel & Asst. Sec.--The Pioneer Group, Inc., Boston, MA; *U.S. Public*, pg. 1298

Navas Oloriz, D. Javier, General Counsel--Seguros De Vida Y Pensiones Antares, S.A., Madrid, Spain; *Int'l*, pg. 1371

Neale, Charles A., V.P. & Gen. Counsel--National Commerce Bancorporation, Memphis, TN; *U.S. Public*, pg. 1154

Neatl, Francis, Gen. Counsel--Schroders PLC, London, United Kingdom; *Int'l*, pg. 1210

Nebel, Mary Beth, V.P. & Gen. Counsel--RLI Corp., Peoria, IL; *U.S. Public*, pg. 1356

Nebergall, Cynthia A., Gen. Counsel & Corp. Sec.--GTECH Corporation, West Greenwich, RI; *U.S. Public*, pg. 767

Neely, Walter E., V.P., Assoc. Gen. Counsel & Asst. Sec.--Humana Inc., Louisville, KY; *U.S. Public*, pg. 847

Neely, Walter E., V.P., Assoc. Gen. Counsel & Asst. Sec.--Humana Health Insurance of Nevada, Inc., Las Vegas, NV; *U.S. Public*, pg. 847

Neely, Walter E., V.P., Assoc. Gen. Counsel & Asst. Sec.--Humana Health Chicago, Inc., Chicago, IL; *U.S. Public*, pg. 847

Neely, Walter E., V.P., Assoc. Gen. Counsel & Asst. Sec.--Employers Health Insurance Company, Green Bay, WI; *U.S. Public*, pg. 847

Neely, Walter E., V.P., Assoc. Gen. Counsel & Asst. Sec.--Humana Health Plan of Texas, Inc., San Antonio, TX; *U.S. Public*, pg. 848

Neely, Walter E., V.P., Assoc. Gen. Counsel & Asst. Sec.--Humana Medical Plan Inc.-Miami, Miramar, FL; *U.S. Public*, pg. 848

Neely, Walter E., V.P., Assoc. Gen. Counsel & Asst. Sec.--Humana Health Plan of Georgia, Inc., Louisville, KY; *U.S. Public*, pg. 848

Neely, Walter E., V.P., Assoc. Gen. Counsel & Asst. Sec.--Humana Health Plan of Louisiana, Inc., Louisville, KY; *U.S. Public*, pg. 848

Neely, Walter E., V.P., Assoc. Gen. Counsel & Asst. Sec.--Humana Insurance Company, Kansas City, MO; *U.S. Public*, pg. 848

Neely, Walter E., V.P., Assoc. Gen. Counsel & Asst. Sec.--Humana Health Plan of Ohio, Inc., Cincinnati, OH; *U.S. Public*, pg. 848

Neely, Walter E., V.P., Assoc. Gen. Counsel & Asst. Sec.--Humana Health Plan of Utah, Inc., Salt Lake City, UT; *U.S. Public*, pg. 848

Neely, Walter E., V.P., Assoc. Gen. Counsel & Asst. Sec.--Humana Health Plan, Inc., Louisville, KY; *U.S. Public*, pg. 848

Neely, Walter E., V.P., Assoc. Gen. Counsel & Asst. Sec.--Humana Health Plan of Alabama, Inc., Montgomery, AL; *U.S. Public*, pg. 848

Neely, Walter E., V.P., Assoc. Gen. Counsel & Asst. Sec.--Humana Wisconsin Health Organization Insurance Corporation, Milwaukee, WI; *U.S. Public*, pg. 848

Neely, Walter E., V.P., Assoc Gen. Counsel & Asst. Sec.--Network EPO, Inc., Milwaukee, WI; *U.S. Public*, pg. 848

Neeman, E., V.P.-Legal Services & Sec.--Confederation Trust Company, Toronto, Canada; *Int'l*, pg. 326

Neff, Wheeler K., V.P., Asst. Gen. Counsel & Asst. Sec.--Beneficial Corporation, Wilmington, DE; *U.S. Public*, pg. 211

Nehrkorn, William H., V.P., Gen. Counsel & Sec.--Heil Environmental Industries, Chattanooga, TN; *U.S. Public*, pg. 520

Neilsson, Douglas, Gen. Counsel--Leasing Solutions, Inc., San Jose, CA; *U.S. Public*, pg. 982

Nelman, Richard, Exec. V.P. & Gen. Counsel--Waterhouse Investor Services, New York, NY; *Int'l*, pg. 1401

Nelson, Byron D., Sr. V.P., Sec. & Gen. Counsel--MYR Group Inc., Rolling Meadows, IL; *U.S. Public*, pg. 1029

Nelson, Dennis R., V.P., Gen. Counsel & Sec.--UniSource Energy Corporation, Tucson, AZ; *U.S. Public*, pg. 1670

Nelson, Dennis R., V.P., Gen. Counsel & Corp. Sec.--Tucson Electric Power Company, Tucson, AZ; *U.S. Public*, pg. 1670

Nelson, Elaine, Gen. Counsel & Sec.--Austin Industries, Inc., Dallas, TX; *U.S. Private*, pg. 99

Nelson, Gary M., V.P. & Gen. Counsel--Ceridian Corporation, Bloomington, MN; *U.S. Public*, pg. 330

Nelson, James E., Asst. Treas., Asst. Gen. Counsel & Asst. Sec.--Washington Square Securities, Minneapolis, MN; *U.S. Public*, pg. 1376

Nelson, Jane E., Gen. Counsel & Sec.--CPI Corp., Saint Louis, MO; *U.S. Public*, pg. 283

Nelson, Mike, V.P., Gen. Counsel & Sec.--Beverage America, Inc., Holland, MI; *U.S. Private*, pg. 141

Nelson, Ralph S., Sr. V.P., Gen. Counsel & Sec.--Burlington Motor Holdings Inc., Daleville, IN; *U.S. Private*, pg. 183

Nelson, Susan, Gen. Counsel--Sulzer Bingham Pumps Inc., Portland, OR; *Int'l*, pg. 1305

Nelson, Wilfrid D., Gen. Counsel & Sec.--Smith Environmental Technologies Corp., Plymouth Meeting, PA; *U.S. Public*, pg. 1477

Nelson, William, Gen. Counsel--Atlapac Trading Company, Inc., Los Angeles, CA; *U.S. Private*, pg. 96

Nemeth, Kathleen, Sr. Corp. Counsel--Key Tronic Corporation, Spokane, WA; *U.S. Public*, pg. 953

Nern, Christopher C., V.P. & Assoc. Gen. Counsel--DTE Energy Company, Detroit, MI; *U.S. Public*, pg. 475

Nesser, Anita, V.P. & Gen. Counsel--Yogen Fruz Worldwide Inc., Markham, Canada; *Int'l*, pg. 1520

Neto, Albilio, Mgr.-Legal--Central de Cervejas, S.A., Lisbon, Portugal; *Int'l*, pg. 279

Neuman, Clifford L., Gen. Counsel & Sec.--American Educational Products, Boulder, CO; *U.S. Public*, pg. 71

Neumann, Jens, Dr., Mgr.-Grp. Strategy, Treas. & Legal--Volkswagen AG, Wolfsburg, Germany; *Int'l*, pg. 1473

Neville, James M., V.P., Gen. Counsel & Asst. Sec.--Ralston Purina Company, Saint Louis, MO; *U.S. Public*, pg. 1359

Newcomb, Verne W., Gen. Counsel--Cascade Corporation, Troutdale, OR; *U.S. Public*, pg. 310

Newman, Eric H., Exec. V.P. & Legal Counsel--Bojangles' Restaraunts, Inc., Charlotte, NC; *U.S. Private*, pg. 154

Newman, John H., V.P.-Legal Affairs, Gen. Counsel & Sec.--Scios Inc., Mountain View, CA; *U.S. Public*, pg. 1444

Newman, John M., Gen. Counsel--The Metropolitan Savings Bank of Ohio, Youngstown, OH; *U.S. Public*, pg. 608

Newman, William B., Jr., V.P. & Washington Counsel--Conrail, Inc., Philadelphia, PA; *U.S. Public*, pg. 431

Newton, Jon P., Vice Chm. & Gen. Counsel--American General Corporation, Houston, TX; *U.S. Public*, pg. 76

Niarchos, Michael C., Sr. V.P., Gen. Counsel & Sec.--Howard Hughes Corporation, Las Vegas, NV; *U.S. Public*, pg. 1407

Nichols, Georgia, Legal Officer--O.F. Mossberg & Sons, Inc., North Haven, CT; *U.S. Private*, pg. 764

Nichols, John C., Sr. V.P.-Admin., Gen. Counsel & Sec.--Environmental Elements Corporation, Baltimore, MD; *U.S. Public*, pg. 586

Nichols, Stuart J., V.P., Gen. Counsel & Sec.--Phoenix Technologies Ltd., San Jose, CA; *U.S. Public*, pg. 1292

Nicholson, James E., Gen. Counsel--Digi International Inc., Minnetonka, MN; *U.S. Public*, pg. 506

Nicoll, John, Sr. V.P., Corp Counsel & Sec.--Colorado National Bank, Denver, CO; *U.S. Public*, pg. 1680

Nicoll, Peter, Sec. & Legal Services--Costain Group PLC, London, United Kingdom; *Int'l*, pg. 336

Niese, William A., Sr. V.P.-Law & Human Resources--Los Angeles Times, Los Angeles, CA; *U.S. Public*, pg. 1616

Nietzel, Warren, Gen. Counsel & Corp. Sec.--Bulova Corporation, Woodside, NY; *U.S. Public*, pg. 1010

Nikonovich-Kahn, Richard, Legal Officer--Heery International, Inc., Atlanta, GA; *U.S. Private*, pg. 519

Nishikawa, Wendy K.K., Asst. Gen. Counsel & Asst. Sec.--Wynn's International, Inc., Orange, CA; *U.S. Public*, pg. 1782

Noble, Herbert B., V.P. & Intl. Counsel--Tridel Enterprises Inc., Downsview, Canada; *Int'l*, pg. 1423

Noble, Richard, Gen. Counsel--Delta Pride Catfish, Inc., Indianola, MS; *U.S. Private*, pg. 322

Noblia, Norberto, V.P.-Legal Affairs--Y.P.F., S.A., Buenos Aires, Argentina; *Int'l*, pg. 1515

Noelker, Joe, V.P., Gen. Counsel & Sec.--The Earthgrains Company, Clayton, MO; *U.S. Public*, pg. 547

Noelle, B. Dr., Legal Officer--William Prym GmbH & Co. KG, Stolberg, Germany; *Int'l*, pg. 1499

Nolan, J. Michael, Sr. V.P., Sec. & Gen. Counsel--Argonaut Co., Menlo Park, CA; *U.S. Public*, pg. 129

Nolan, Michael, Gen. Counsel--Red Devil Inc., Union, NJ; *U.S. Private*, pg. 915

Nolan, Michael, Gen. Counsel--Rocky Shoes & Boots, Inc., Nelsonville, OH; *U.S. Public*, pg. 1402

Nolan, Peter F., V.P. & Counsel--The Walt Disney Company, Burbank, CA; *U.S. Public*, pg. 511

Noland, Michael, Gen. Counsel--Metra Commuter Rail, Chicago, IL; *U.S. Private*, pg. 919

Noll, Dennis E., V.P., Gen. Counsel & Sec.--Kinetic Concepts, Inc., San Antonio, TX; *U.S. Private*, pg. 620

Nord, Thomas C., V.P., Gen. Counsel & Sec.--GATX Capital Corporation, San Francisco, CA; *U.S. Public*, pg. 690

Nordholm, Edwin B., V.P. & Gen. Counsel--Brookfield Properties Corporation, Toronto, Canada; *Int'l*, pg. 228

Nordlund, D. Craig, Assoc. Gen. Counsel & Sec.--Hewlett-Packard Company, Palo Alto, CA; *U.S. Public*, pg. 813

Nordvaller, Thomas, Gen. Counsel--AB Industrivarden, Stockholm, Sweden; *Int'l*, pg. 678

Norgren, P.W., Gen. Counsel & Asst. Sec.--Lakehead Pipe Line Co., Inc., Superior, WI; *Int'l*, pg. 652

Norlander, Anders, Gen. Counsel--Axel Johnson AB, Stockholm, Sweden; *Int'l*, pg. 707

Norman, Barbara, V.P., Corp. Counsel & Sec.--WHG Resorts & Casinos, Carolina, PR; *U.S. Public*, pg. 1265

Norman, David J., Gen. Counsel & Sec.--Davco Restaurants Inc., Crofton, MD; *U.S. Public*, pg. 488

Norman, E.J., V.P.-Admin., Gen. Counsel & Sec.--Trico Products Corporation, Buffalo, NY; *Int'l*, pg. 1397

Normandeau, Andrew, Gen. Counsel--Guest Services, Inc., Fairfax, VA; *U.S. Private*, pg. 486

Norris, Jerry, Gen. Counsel--Leo A. Daly Company, Omaha, NE; *U.S. Private*, pg. 309

Norris, Michael, Sr. V.P., Gen. Counsel & Sec.--National Financial Insurance Company, Fort Worth, TX; *U.S. Private*, pg. 782

Northey, Randy, Sr. V.P., Gen. Counsel & Sec.--O&Y Properties Corporation, Toronto, Canada; *Int'l*, pg. 993

Norton, J., Gen. Counsel--Brach & Brock Confections, Inc., Chicago, IL; *U.S. Private*, pg. 163

Norton, Robert, Sr. V.P. & Gen. Counsel--Mastercard International, Inc., Purchase, NY; *U.S. Private*, pg. 714

Norwood, R. Bredt, Gen. Counsel--HD Vest Financial Services, Irving, TX; *U.S. Public*, pg. 770

Notini, Albert A., Sr. V.P., Gen. Counsel & Sec.--Wang Laboratories, Inc., Billerica, MA; *U.S. Public*, pg. 1737

Novak, Karen, Gen. Counsel--Milk Marketing Inc., Strongsville, OH; *U.S. Private*, pg. 745
Novak, Peter J., V.P. & Gen. Counsel--Viad Corp, Phoenix, AZ; *U.S. Public*, pg. 1718
Novello, Leonard P., Sr. V.P. & Gen. Counsel--Long Island Lighting Company, Hicksville, NY; *U.S. Public*, pg. 1013
Novick, Jeffery, Legal Officer--I. Spiewak & Sons, Inc., New York, NY; *U.S. Private*, pg. 1025
Nowe, Kevin G., Asst. Sec. & Asst. Gen. Counsel--Kennametal Inc., Latrobe, PA; *U.S. Public*, pg. 950
Nuernberg, Robert A., V.P.-Corp. Rels. & Sec.--Wisconsin Gas Company, Milwaukee, WI; *U.S. Public*, pg. 1767
Nugent, Brian M., V.P. & Gen. Counsel--Outsource International, Deerfield Beach, FL; *U.S. Public*, pg. 1236
Nunes, Melbourne, Sr. V.P., Dep. Counsel & Sec.--New York Life Insurance Company, New York, NY; *U.S. Private*, pg. 794
Nunlist, Hans, Mng. Dir.-Corp. Intellectual Property Rights--Landis & Staefa AG, Zug, Switzerland; *Int'l*, pg. 800
Nuortila, Olli, Sr. V.P. & Gen. Counsel--Metsa-Serla Corporation, Espoo, Finland; *Int'l*, pg. 863
Nute, Lee F., Sr. V.P., Gen. Counsel & Sec.--Bayer Corporation, Pittsburgh, PA; *Int'l*, pg. 172
Nute, Leslie, Gen. Counsel & Sec.--Bayer Corporation, Pittsburgh, PA; *Int'l*, pg. 172
O'Brien, James G., Gen. Tax Counsel--Bankers Trust New York Corporation, New York, NY; *U.S. Public*, pg. 185
O'Brien, Neil J., Gen. Counsel--Tyler Corporation, Dallas, TX; *U.S. Public*, pg. 1651
O'Brien, Paul T., Gen. Counsel & Sec.--Huls America Inc., Somerset, NJ; *Int'l*, pg. 1455
O'Brien, T. Michael, V.P. & Deputy Gen. Counsel--Waste Management, Inc., Oak Brook, IL; *U.S. Public*, pg. 1744
O'Brien, Thomas R., Sr. V.P. & Gen. Counsel--Foster Wheeler Corporation, Clinton, NJ; *U.S. Public*, pg. 676
O'Brien, W.D., V.P. & Gen. Tax Counsel--Exxon Corporation, Irving, TX; *U.S. Public*, pg. 601
O'Connor, John, V.P. & Gen. Counsel--Esselte Corporation, Garden City, NY; *Int'l*, pg. 459
O'Donnell, Lawrence, III, V.P. & Gen. Counsel--Baker Hughes Incorporated, Houston, TX; *U.S. Public*, pg. 165
O'Hara, Michael A., Corp. Counsel--Brookstone Company, Inc., Nashua, NH; *U.S. Public*, pg. 259
O'Hare, James P., Sr. V.P. & Gen. Counsel--Cambridge Technology Partners, Cambridge, MA; *U.S. Public*, pg. 1424
O'Leary, Robert L., V.P. & Corp. Counsel--Comarco, Inc., Yorba Linda, CA; *U.S. Public*, pg. 406
O'Leary, Thomas M., Chief Fin. Officer & Gen. Counsel--The Pepper Companies, Inc., Chicago, IL; *U.S. Private*, pg. 851
O'Loughlin, Johanna G., V.P. & Gen. Counsel--Equitable Resources, Inc., Pittsburgh, PA; *U.S. Public*, pg. 589
O'Malia, David T., Exec. V.P. & Gen. Counsel--O'Malia Food Markets Inc., Carmel, IN; *U.S. Private*, pg. 816
O'Malley, Kevin T., V.P. & Gen. Counsel--St. Jude Medical, Inc., Saint Paul, MN; *U.S. Public*, pg. 1427
O'Meara, S.C., Sr. V.P. & Gen. Counsel--The Ziegler Companies, Inc., West Bend, WI; *U.S. Public*, pg. 1791
O'Meara, Vicki A., Exec. V.P. & Gen. Counsel--Ryder System, Inc., Miami, FL; *U.S. Public*, pg. 1413
O'Neil, Jack, Gen. Counsel & Sec.--The Western Group, Saint Louis, MO; *U.S. Private*, pg. 1165
O'Neil, Tim, Gen. Counsel--Automatic Equipment Mfg. Co., Pender, NE; *U.S. Private*, pg. 101
O'Neill, Finbarr, Sr. V.P. & Gen. Counsel--Hyundai Motor America, Fountain Valley, CA; *Int'l*, pg. 641
O'Neill, Michael J., Jr., V.P. & Gen. Counsel--The Chubb Corporation, Warren, NJ; *U.S. Public*, pg. 354
O'Neill, Robert B., V.P., Gen. Counsel & Sec.--Capitol Industries-EMI Inc., Hollywood, CA; *Int'l*, pg. 427
O'Reilly, Terrence M., V.P., Gen. Counsel & Sec.--Universal Foods Corporation, Milwaukee, WI; *U.S. Public*, pg. 1695
O'Reilly, William, V.P., Gen. Counsel & Corp. Sec.--Sentry Insurance, A Mutual Company, Stevens Point, WI; *U.S. Private*, pg. 984
O'Rourke, Kevin C. C., Sr. V.P. & Gen. Counsel--Matson Navigation Company, Inc., San Francisco, CA; *U.S. Public*, pg. 39
O'Rourke, William J., Patent Counsel--Aluminum Company of America, Pittsburgh, PA; *U.S. Public*, pg. 60
O'Shea, Peter J., Jr., Sr. V.P. & Gen. Counsel--Consolidated Edison Company of New York, Inc., New York, NY; *U.S. Public*, pg. 434
O'Toole, Timothy T., Sr. V.P.-Law & Govt. Affairs--Conrail, Inc., Philadelphia, PA; *U.S. Public*, pg. 431
Oathout, James M., Assoc. Gen. Counsel & Sec.--Aeroquip-Vickers, Inc., Maumee, OH; *U.S. Public*, pg. 24
Ober, Richard F., Jr., Exec. V.P., Gen. Counsel & Sec.--Summit Bancorp, Princeton, NJ; *U.S. Public*, pg. 1527
Oberly, Kathryn A., Vice Chm. & Gen. Counsel--Ernst & Young, LLP, New York, NY; *U.S. Private*, pg. 381
Obert, Paul R., V.P., Gen. Counsel & Sec.--CF Industries, Inc., Long Grove, IL; *U.S. Private*, pg. 193
Ocampo, Antonio V., Sr. V.P., Gen. Counsel & Sec.--Philippine Airlines, Inc., Manila, Philippines; *Int'l*, pg. 1050
Ocampo, Raymond L., Jr., Sr. V.P., Gen Counsel & Sec.--Oracle Corporation, Redwood City, CA; *U.S. Public*, pg. 1227
Odelberg, Carl, Sr. V.P.-Legal Affairs & Sec.--Esselte AB, Solna, Sweden; *Int'l*, pg. 459
Odgers, Richard W., Exec. V.P., Gen. Counsel & Sec.--Pacific Telesis Group, San Francisco, CA; *U.S. Public*, pg. 1415
Odre, Steven M., V.P.-Intellectual Property & Assoc. Gen. Counsel--Amgen Inc., Thousand Oaks, CA; *U.S. Public*, pg. 100
Oettinger, Julian A., V.P., Gen. Counsel & Corp. Sec.--Walgreen Co., Deerfield, IL; *U.S. Public*, pg. 1733
Offer, Mary Ellen, V.P., Senior Counsel & Asst. Corp. Sec.--The Great Atlantic & Pacific Tea Company, Inc., Montvale, NJ; *Int'l*, pg. 1375
Ogden, Jean H., Sec. & Gen. Counsel--Werner & Pfleiderer Corporation, Ramsey, NJ; *Int'l*, pg. 511
Ogden, Robert S., Jr., V.P. & Counsel-Consumer Prods. Div.--The Walt Disney Company, Burbank, CA; *U.S. Public*, pg. 511
Ohsawa, Satoru, Gen. Counsel--Murata Machinery, Ltd., Kyoto, Japan; *Int'l*, pg. 897
Okarma, Jerome D., Asst. Sec. & Asst. Gen. Counsel--Johnson Controls, Inc., Milwaukee, WI; *U.S. Public*, pg. 932
Okun, Wendi, Gen. Counsel--Wind River Systems, Inc., Alameda, CA; *U.S. Public*, pg. 1770
Olander, Donald E., V.P. & Gen. Counsel--People's Choice TV Corp., Shelton, CT; *U.S. Public*, pg. 1274
Oldfield, Russell M., V.P.-Legal & Corp. Sec.--Rogers Group Inc., Nashville, TN; *U.S. Private*, pg. 939
Oldham, S., Sec. & Gen. Counsel--Boehringer Mannheim Pharmaceuticals Corp., Rockville, MD; *Int'l*, pg. 331
Oldham, Steve A., V.P. & Gen. Counsel--Corange U.S. Holdings, Inc, Indianapolis, IN; *Int'l*, pg. 331
Oleson, George T., Sec. & Legal Officer--Allied Mutual Insurance Company, Des Moines, IA; *U.S. Private*, pg. 39
Olin, Richard J., V.P.-Real Estate & Law & Asst. Gen. Counsel--Costco Wholesale, Issaquah, WA; *U.S. Public*, pg. 451
Oliphant, John H., Sec. & Gen. Counsel--Technicolor, Inc., North Hollywood, CA; *Int'l*, pg. 272
Ollendorff, Steven, Gen. Counsel--Computer Products, Inc., Boca Raton, FL; *U.S. Public*, pg. 422
Olmsted, Daniel, V.P.-Corp. Legal Sec.--Atlantic Mutual Companies, New York, NY; *U.S. Private*, pg. 95
Olon, Lawrence P., V.P.-Legal Affairs--SmithKline Beecham Laboratories, Bristol, TN; *Int'l*, pg. 1264
Olsen, Geoffrey G., Sr. V.P.-Legal--Coast Savings Financial, Inc., Los Angeles, CA; *U.S. Public*, pg. 388
Olson, D. Joseph, V.P., Gen. Counsel & Sec.--Citizens Insurance Company of America, Howell, MI; *U.S. Public*, pg. 54
Olson, Robert W., Sr. V.P., Gen. Counsel & Sec.--American Financial Group, Cincinnati, OH; *U.S. Public*, pg. 75
Olson, Robert W., V.P., Gen. Counsel & Sec.--Chiquita Brands International, Inc., Cincinnati, OH; *U.S. Public*, pg. 349
Opazo, Manuel, Chief Counsel--Salvador Division, El Salvador, Chile; *Int'l*, pg. 302
Opsomer, Ann, Mgr.-Legal Dept.--Groupe Bruxelles Lambert S.A., Brussels, Belgium; *Int'l*, pg. 561
Oreck, Bruce, V.P. & Gen. Counsel--Oreck Corporation, New Orleans, LA; *U.S. Private*, pg. 819
Orellana, Nemesio, Chief Counsel & Legal Services--Chuquicamata Division, Chuquicamata, Chile; *Int'l*, pg. 302
Orenstein, John B., V.P., Deputy Gen. Counsel & Asst. Sec.--Dain Rauscher Corporation, Minneapolis, MN; *U.S.* Public, pg. 476
Orie, James G., Gen. Counsel--F.N.B. Corporation, Hermitage, PA; *U.S. Public*, pg. 607
Orlick, Jonathan, V.P.-Intellectual Property & Gen. Counsel--StarSight Telecast, Inc., Fremont, CA; *U.S. Public*, pg. 705
Orme, Jed, Sr. V.P. & Gen. Counsel--DHL Worldwide Express, Redwood City, CA; *U.S. Private*, pg. 301
Ornstein, Warren K., Asst. Gen. Counsel--Forest City Enterprises, Inc., Cleveland, OH; *U.S. Public*, pg. 667
Ortiz, Carlos, Gen. Counsel--Goya Foods, Inc., Secaucus, NJ; *U.S. Private*, pg. 468
Ortiz, Patrick T., Sr. V.P., Gen. Counsel & Sec.--Public Service Company of New Mexico, Albuquerque, NM; *U.S. Public*, pg. 1339
Oshel, David B., Mgr.-Legal--Louis Dreyfus Natural Gas Corp., Oklahoma City, OK; *U.S. Private*, pg. 342
Osme, Jed, Gen. Counsel--DHL Airways, Inc., Redwood City, CA; *U.S. Private*, pg. 302
Osten, Judd, Sr. V.P., Gen. Counsel & Sec.--Crawford & Company, Atlanta, GA; *U.S. Public*, pg. 458
Oster, Helen P., Sec.--Baldwin Technology Company, Inc., Norwalk, CT; *U.S. Public*, pg. 169
Osterhouse, Donald, Gen. Counsel & Sec.--King Milling Company, Lowell, MI; *U.S. Private*, pg. 621
Otamura-Kester, Judith K., Sr. V.P., Asst. Gen. Counsel & Asst. Sec.--Jefferies & Company, Inc., Los Angeles, CA; *U.S. Public*, pg. 925
Otis, Thomas, V.P., Sec. & Legal--Eaton Vance Corp., Boston, MA; *U.S. Public*, pg. 559
Ott, Charles W., Gen. Counsel--Vivra Incorporated, San Mateo, CA; *U.S. Public*, pg. 1723
Otto, Jeffrey W., Gen. Counsel & Sec.--Safety National Casualty Corp., Saint Louis, MO; *U.S. Public*, pg. 496
Ounsworth, James A., Sr. V.P., Gen. Counsel & Sec.--Safeguard Scientifics, Inc., Wayne, PA; *U.S. Public*, pg. 1424
Overbey, Terry, Sec. & Corp. Counsel--The Procter & Gamble Company, Cincinnati, OH; *U.S. Public*, pg. 1330
Ovrut, Barnett D., Assoc. Gen. Counsel & Sec.--The Hanover Insurance Company, Worcester, MA; *U.S. Public*, pg. 54
Owen, Rebecca, Gen. Counsel--Clark Enterprises, Inc., Bethesda, MD; *U.S. Private*, pg. 242
Owens, Jane, Sr. V.P. & Gen. Counsel--The Dial Corporation, Phoenix, AZ; *U.S. Public*, pg. 505
Owens, Jane E., V.P., Gen. Counsel & Asst. Sec.--The Timberland Company, Stratham, NH; *U.S. Public*, pg. 1609
Owsley, Thomas L., V.P.-Legal--Crown Central Petroleum Corporation, Baltimore, MD; *U.S. Public*, pg. 462
Paalborg, Andrew M., V.P. & Gen. Counsel--WorldCorp, Inc., Herndon, VA; *U.S. Public*, pg. 1779
Pachino, Barton P., Sr. V.P. & Gen. Counsel--Kaufman and Broad Home Corporation, Los Angeles, CA; *U.S. Public*, pg. 944
Pacholder, Robin E., Sr. V.P. & Gen. Counsel--ICO, Inc., Houston, TX; *U.S. Public*, pg. 853
Paddon, Patrick E., Chm. Bd., Pres. & Chief Exec. Officer--Amplicon, Inc., Santa Ana, CA; *U.S. Public*, pg. 104
Padron Amare, Carlos E., Gen. Counsel--Petroleos de Venezuela S.A., Caracas, Venezuela; *Int'l*, pg. 1045
Paige, Stephen, V.P. & General Counsel--The NutraSweet Company, Deerfield, IL; *U.S. Public*, pg. 1125
Pain, George H., V.P., Gen. Counsel & Sec.--Primex Technologies, Inc., Saint Petersburg, FL; *U.S. Public*, pg. 1329
Painton, Russell E., V.P., Gen. Counsel & Sec.--Tracor, Inc., Austin, TX; *U.S. Public*, pg. 1627
Palabrica, Raul J., V.P.-Legal--Philippine Long Distance Telephone Company, Manila, Philippines; *Int'l*, pg. 1051
Paladino, Daniel R., Exec. V.P.-Legal & Environmental Affairs--The Seagram Company Ltd., Montreal, Canada; *Int'l*, pg. 1214
Palimeri, Nicola, Grp. V.P. & Gen. Counsel--Montedison S.p.A., Milan, Italy; *Int'l*, pg. 324
Palizzi, Anthony N., Exec. V.P. & Gen. Counsel--Kmart Corporation, Troy, MI; *U.S. Public*, pg. 963
Pallam, John J., V.P. & Gen. Counsel--Brush Wellman Inc., Cleveland, OH; *U.S. Public*, pg. 266
Pallasen, Mike, Corp. Counsel--American Business Information, Inc., Omaha, NE; *U.S. Public*, pg. 69
Palleschi, John, V.P. & Gen. Counsel--Telex Communications, Inc., Minneapolis, MN; *U.S. Private*, pg. 1074
Palmarella, Ernest D., Gen. Counsel--Investors Insurance Group, Inc., Boca Raton, FL; *U.S. Public*, pg. 911
Palmariello, Joan, Gen. Counsel--Servico, Inc., West Palm Beach, FL; *U.S. Public*, pg. 1462
Palmer, John, Gen. Counsel & Sec.--Dunham's Athleisure Corporation, Waterford, MI; *U.S. Private*, pg. 346
Palmer, Peter J., V.P.-Labor Rels. & Asst. Gen. Counsel--Kmart Corporation, Troy, MI; *U.S. Public*, pg. 963
Palmer, Ronald J., Sr. V.P. & Gen. Counsel--Standard Federal Bank, Troy, MI; *Int'l*, pg. 10
Palmer, Thomas E., V.P., Gen. Counsel & Sec.--The Mead Corporation, Dayton, OH; *U.S. Public*, pg. 1074
Palmore, Roderick A., V.P. & Deputy Gen. Counsel--Sara Lee Corporation, Chicago, IL; *U.S. Public*, pg. 1432
Palumbo, Lisa M., V.P. & Gen. Counsel--Rayonier Inc., Stamford, CT; *U.S. Public*, pg. 1363
Paquet, Marc, Legal Counsel & Asst. Sec.--Societe Generale de Financement du Quebec, Montreal, Canada; *Int'l*, pg. 1274
Parent, Louise M., Exec. V.P. & Gen. Counsel--American Express Company, New York, NY; *U.S. Public*, pg. 73
Paris, Luis, Dir.-Legal--Banco Quilmes, Buenos Aires, Argentina; *Int'l*, pg. 142
Paris, R. Stephen, Sr. V.P. & Trust Counsel--United Missouri Bank N.A., Kansas City, MO; *U.S. Public*, pg. 1654
Parish, Rhonda J., Sr. V.P., Gen. Counsel & Sec.--Advantica Restaurant Group, Inc., Spartanburg, SC; *U.S.* Public, pg. 22
Parker, Ed W., II, V.P. & Gen. Counsel--BHP Petroleum (Americas) Inc., Houston, TX; *Int'l*, pg. 225
Parker, James F., V.P. & Gen. Counsel--Southwest Airlines Co., Dallas, TX; *U.S. Public*, pg. 1493
Parks, Cynthia E., V.P. & Gen. Counsel--Phoenix American Incorporated, San Rafael, CA; *U.S. Private*, pg. 862
Parlmutter, J.A., V.P. & Gen. Counsel--Kayser-Roth Corporation, Inc., Greensboro, NC; *Int'l*, pg. 576
Parnass, Geoffrey, V.P. & Gen. Counsel--Hunter Douglas, Inc., Upper Saddle River, NJ; *Int'l*, pg. 639
Parr, David W., V.P., Gen. Counsel & Clerk--Chancellor Corporation, Boston, MA; *U.S. Public*, pg. 335
Parr, Royse M., Gen. Counsel & Sec.--Mapco Natural Gas Liquids Inc., Tulsa, OK; *U.S. Public*, pg. 1042
Parr, W. Scott, Gen. Counsel & Dir.--LaserMaster Technologies, Inc., Eden Prairie, MN; *U.S. Public*, pg. 979
Parrott, Charles, Sec.& Gen. Counsel--Fred V. Fowler Company, Inc., Newton, MA; *U.S. Private*, pg. 422
Parry, Timothy, V.P. & Gen. Counsel--Health Management Associates, Inc., Naples, FL; *U.S. Public*, pg. 802
Parry, William E., V.P. & Gen. Counsel--Nalco Chemical Company, Naperville, IL; *U.S. Public*, pg. 1150
Parsons, John, Gen. Counsel--Radix Corporation, Salt Lake City, UT; *U.S. Private*, pg. 906
Parsons, Jon R., Gen. Counsel--Esprit Systems, Inc., San Jose, CA; *U.S. Private*, pg. 383
Partington, Donald E., Sr. V.P. & Gen. Counsel--Fidelity National Title Insurance Company, Irvine, CA; *U.S. Public*, pg. 620
Pascoe, Christopher J.C., Counsel & Corp. Sec.--Pratt & Whitney Canada Inc., Longueuil, Canada; *U.S. Public*, pg. 1690
Pasquarello, Theodore, Pres. & Chief Exec. Officer--Chiswick Trading Inc., Sudbury, MA; *U.S. Private*, pg. 237
Pasternak, Bart, V.P.-Corp. Devel.--Angelo Brothers Co., Philadelphia, PA; *U.S. Private*, pg. 74
Paterson, Robert, Gen. Counsel--Australia & New Zealand Banking Group Limited, Melbourne, Australia; *Int'l*, pg. 98
Patterson, Douglas, V.P. & Gen. Counsel--Ivex Packaging Corporation, Lincolnshire, IL; *U.S. Public*, pg. 915
Patterson, Michael R., V.P., Gen. Counsel & Sec.--Plains Resources Inc., Houston, TX; *U.S. Public*, pg. 1307
Patterson, W. Lin, Gen. Counsel & Sec.--Mapco Petroleum Inc., Tulsa, OK; *U.S. Public*, pg. 1042
Patton, John J., Gen. Counsel--OPICOIL Houston, Inc., Houston, TX; *Int'l*, pg. 286
Patton, Neal, Gen. Counsel & Sec.--AMC, Inc., Atlanta, GA; *U.S. Private*, pg. 6
Pattusch, Gunter, Exec. Dir.-Counsel--Schering AG, Berlin, Germany; *Int'l*, pg. 1203
Patz, Thomas L., Gen. Counsel--Micros Systems Inc., Beltsville, MD; *U.S. Public*, pg. 1106
Patzke, Pamela, Gen. Counsel & Asst. Sec.--Lands' End, Inc., Dodgeville, WI; *U.S. Public*, pg. 977

Paul, Richard S., Sr. V.P. & Gen. Counsel--Xerox Corporation, Stamford, CT; *U.S. Public*, pg. 1783

Paulson, Stuart M., V.P.-Claims, Gen. Counsel & Sec.--Blue Ridge Insurance Co., Simsbury, CT; *Int'l*, pg. 345

Paulson, Stuart M., V.P.-Claims, Gen. Counsel & Sec.--Blue Ridge Indemnity Co., Simsbury, CT; *Int'l*, pg. 345

Paulson, Stuart M., V.P.-Claims, Gen. Counsel & Sec.--MassWest Insurance Company, West Springfield, MA; *Int'l*, pg. 345

Paver, Robert L., Gen. Counsel & Sec.--Jabil Circuit, Inc., Saint Petersburg, FL; *U.S. Public*, pg. 919

Pavlick, W.E., Sr. V.P., Gen. Counsel & Sec.--Modine Manufacturing Company, Racine, WI; *U.S. Public*, pg. 1121

Payne, James P., V.P. & Sec.--National Western Life Insurance Company, Austin, TX; *U.S. Public*, pg. 1161

Payne, Robert J., Corp. Counsel--Harmon Industries, Inc., Blue Springs, MO; *U.S. Public*, pg. 788

Payne, Ron, Div. Counsel--Amecom Div., College Park, MD; *U.S. Public*, pg. 1002

Payne, Stanley J., V.P., Gen. Counsel & Sec.--Bassett Furniture Industries, Incorporated, Bassett, VA; *U.S. Public*, pg. 193

Payne, T. Michael, V.P. & Assoc. Gen. Counsel-Opers.--Southwestern Bell Telephone Co., Saint Louis, MO; *U.S. Public*, pg. 1416

Payne, William J., V.P., Gen. Counsel & Sec.--Rinker Materials Corp., West Palm Beach, FL; *Int'l*, pg. 246

Payson, Martin D., Exec. V.P. & Gen. Counsel--Warner Communications Inc., New York, NY; *U.S. Public*, pg. 1611

Peace, John C., V.P., Gen. Counsel & Sec.--Shenandoah Life Insurance Company, Roanoke, VA; *U.S. Private*, pg. 992

Pearson, Thomas L., Gen. Counsel & Sec.--Mapco Coal Inc., Tulsa, OK; *U.S. Public*, pg. 1042

Peary, Stephen, Sr. V.P., Sec. & Gen. Counsel--PLM International, Inc., San Francisco, CA; *U.S. Public*, pg. 1241

Peck, David R., Gen. Counsel & Treas.--Centennial Technologies, Inc., Wilmington, MA; *U.S. Public*, pg. 322

Peck, Douglas E., Pres. & Gen. Counsel--Renosol Corp., Saline, MI; *U.S. Private*, pg. 922

Pedro, Geronimo M., Gen. Counsel--AGP Industrial Corporation, Manila, Philippines; *Int'l*, pg. 14

Peet, Carlisle, Gen. Counsel--Rollins Leasing Corp., Wilmington, DE; *U.S. Public*, pg. 1405

Peil, Krister, Gen. Counsel--AB SKF, Goteborg, Sweden; *Int'l*, pg. 1156

Peltz, Ernest, Gen. Counsel--Clark Specialty Co., Inc., Hammondsport, NY; *U.S. Private*, pg. 243

Peluso, John, V.P. & Gen. Counsel--The Guardian Life Insurance Company of America, New York, NY; *U.S. Private*, pg. 486

Pendergraft, Jeffrey R., Chief Admin. Officer & Sr. V.P.--Lyondell Petrochemical Company, Houston, TX; *U.S. Public*, pg. 1022

Penny, Brenda J., Gen. Counsel--Golden State Mutual Life Insurance Company, Los Angeles, CA; *U.S. Private*, pg. 461

Pentz, William H., Sr. Assoc. Gen. Counsel & Asst. Sec.--The Penn Mutual Life Insurance Company, Philadelphia, PA; *U.S. Private*, pg. 849

Perez, Arnaldo, Gen. Counsel--Carnival Corporation, Miami, FL; *U.S. Public*, pg. 306

Perez, Enrique, Chief Oper. Officer, Sr. Exec. V.P., Gen. Counsel & Sec.--Philippine Long Distance Telephone Company, Manila, Philippines; *Int'l*, pg. 1051

Perillo, Sal, Gen. Counsel--Mohawk Industries, Inc., Calhoun, GA; *U.S. Public*, pg. 1121

Perlman, Charles H., Gen. Counsel & Sec.--Grist Mill Company, Lakeville, MN; *U.S. Public*, pg. 766

Perlowitz, Marc, Gen. Counsel--Barneys Inc., New York, NY; *U.S. Private*, pg. 116

Perron, Ed, Gen. Counsel--Sanyo Fisher Company, Chatsworth, CA; *Int'l*, pg. 1191

Perrone, Dee, Gen. Counsel & Sec.--Newport Electronics, Inc., Santa Ana, CA; *U.S. Private*, pg. 816

Perry, Harvey P., Sr. V.P., Gen. Counsel & Sec.--Century Telephone Enterprises, Inc., Monroe, LA; *U.S. Public*, pg. 329

Perry, Samuel, V.P. & Gen. Counsel--American Kennel Club, Inc., New York, NY; *U.S. Private*, pg. 58

Perskie, Steven P., Exec. V.P. & Gen. Counsel--Players International, Inc., Atlantic City, NJ; *U.S. Public*, pg. 1310

Persson, Eva, Chief-Corp. Legal & Sec.--AB Volvo, Goteborg, Sweden; *Int'l*, pg. 1476

Pessia, Michael, Gen. Counsel--James Ferrera & Sons, Inc., Canton, MA; *U.S. Private*, pg. 401

Pestronk, Mark, Gen. Counsel--Omega World Travel, Inc., Fairfax, VA; *U.S. Private*, pg. 816

Petelle, James F., Corp. Sec. & Gen. Attorney--Andrew Corporation, Orland Park, IL; *U.S. Public*, pg. 112

Peterman, Tom, Sr. V.P. & Gen. Counsel--MGM Grand Hotel, Inc., Las Vegas, NV; *U.S. Public*, pg. 1027

Peters, John E., Sr. V.P., Gen. Counsel & Sec.--Block Drug Company, Inc., Jersey City, NJ; *U.S. Public*, pg. 236

Peters, Roger J., Gen. Counsel--Dick Corporation, Large, PA; *U.S. Private*, pg. 331

Peters, Roger J., V.P. & Gen. Counsel--Pacific Gas & Electric Company, San Francisco, CA; *U.S. Public*, pg. 1241

Peterson, Craig D., Gen. Counsel & Sec.--Xerxes Corporation, Minneapolis, MN; *U.S. Private*, pg. 1194

Peterson, Paul R., Sr. V.P., Gen. Counsel & Sec.--Technology Solutions Company (TSC), Chicago, IL; *U.S. Public*, pg. 1564

Peterson, Paul R., Sec. & Gen. Counsel--Technology Solutions Company (TSC), Chicago, IL; *U.S. Public*, pg. 1564

Peterson, William E., Sr. V.P. & Gen. Counsel--Sierra Pacific Resources, Reno, NV; *U.S. Public*, pg. 1470

Pfaff, Robert E., Chief Legal Counsel & Sec.--Anchor Tool & Die Company, Cleveland, OH; *U.S. Private*, pg. 71

Phair, Joseph B., V.P., Gen. Counsel & Sec.--Varian Associates, Inc., Palo Alto, CA; *U.S. Public*, pg. 1710

Pharand, Gilles, Sr. V.P.-Corp. Affairs, Gen. Counsel & Sec.--Domtar Inc., Montreal, Canada; *Int'l*, pg. 416

Philipp, Elizabeth R., Exec. V.P., Gen. Counsel & Sec.--Collins & Aikman Corporation, Charlotte, NC; *U.S. Public*, pg. 399

Philips, Ian, Legal Officer--SGD International Corp., Riverdale, NY; *U.S. Private*, pg. 957

Phillips, Leo H., Jr., V.P., Asst. Gen. Counsel & Asst. Sec.--Manor Care, Inc., Gaithersburg, MD; *U.S. Public*, pg. 1041

Phillips, Peter, Exec. V.P. -Admin. & Gen. Counsel--The Stop & Shop Companies, Inc., Quincy, MA; *Int'l*, pg. 750

Phillips, Steve, Exec. V.P. & Gen. Counsel--Intergraph Corporation, Huntsville, AL; *U.S. Public*, pg. 890

Phillips, William, Sr. V.P.-Law & Gen. Counsel--GenCorp Inc., Fairlawn, OH; *U.S. Public*, pg. 705

Piazza, George B., Gen. Counsel--Pioneer Concrete of America, Houston, TX; *Int'l*, pg. 1058

Pickens, T.H., V.P.-Legal & Gen. Counsel--Chevron Chemical Co., San Ramon, CA; *U.S. Public*, pg. 348

Pickett, Stephen E., Asst. Gen. Counsel--Edison International, Rosemead, CA; *U.S. Public*, pg. 564

Pickle, Robert D., V.P., Gen. Counsel & Sec.--Brown Group, Inc., Saint Louis, MO; *U.S. Public*, pg. 262

Pienaar, A.V., Grp. Legal Adviser--Standard Bank Investment Corporation Limited, Johannesburg, South Africa; *Int'l*, pg. 1293

Pierson, Greg, Corp. Counsel.--Pioneer New Media Technologies, Long Beach, CA; *U.S. Private*, pg. 866

Pierson, Greg, Gen. Counsel--Pioneer Electronics (USA) Inc., Long Beach, CA; *Int'l*, pg. 1058

Pietroski, Joseph J., Sr. V.P., Gen. Counsel & Sec.--Manulife Financial (The Manufacturers Life Insurance Company), Toronto, Canada; *Int'l*, pg. 840

Pietroski, Joseph J., Sr. V.P. & Gen. Counsel--Manulife Financial, Toronto, Canada; *Int'l*, pg. 840

Pike, Robert W., Sr. V.P., Sec. & Gen. Counsel--The Allstate Corporation, Northbrook, IL; *U.S. Public*, pg. 55

Pingstore, Joseph J., Jr., V.P. & Gen. Counsel--MSI Insurance Companies, Arden Hills, MN; *U.S. Private*, pg. 688

Pinkston, Arnie, V.P. & Gen. Counsel--PCS Health Systems, Inc., Scottsdale, AZ; *U.S. Public*, pg. 993

Pinney, J., Sec. & Gen. Counsel--Courtaulds Aerospace, Littleborough, United Kingdom; *Int'l*, pg. 338

Pisaruk, George, Assoc. Gen. Counsel--Three-Five Systems, Tempe, AZ; *U.S. Public*, pg. 1604

Pitcock, Charles L., Asst. Gen. Counsel--Forest City Enterprises, Inc., Cleveland, OH; *U.S. Public*, pg. 667

Pitler, Barry, Gen. Counsel & Sec.--Rapid Mounting & Finishing Co., Chicago, IL; *U.S. Private*, pg. 910

Pittenger, Bradford, Gen. Counsel--V.T. Inc., Merriam, KS; *U.S. Private*, pg. 1131

Place, John, Gen. Counsel--Yahoo!, Inc., Santa Clara, CA; *U.S. Public*, pg. 1787

Plaeger, Frederick J., II, V.P., Gen. Counsel & Corp. Sec.--The Louisiana Land and Exploration Company, New Orleans, LA; *U.S. Public*, pg. 269

Plamondon, Luc, V.P. & Assoc. Gen. Counsel--Sun Life Assurance Company of Canada, Toronto, Canada; *Int'l*, pg. 1318

Platt, Joel, V.P.-Legal--Bradford Exchange Ltd., Niles, IL; *U.S. Private*, pg. 163

Platt, Thomas C., III, V.P., Gen. Counsel & Sec.--Chemfab Corporation, Merrimack, NH; *U.S. Public*, pg. 344

Plitch, Lawrence W., V.P. & Gen. Counsel--Wheelabrator Technologies Inc., Hampton, NH; *U.S. Public*, pg. 1745

Plubell, Ann Marie P., V.P., Sec. & Assoc. Gen. Counsel--SLM Holding Corp., Washington, DC; *U.S. Public*, pg. 1419

Plumbly, Daniel, Chm. Bd. & Corp. Counsel--The Will-Burt Company, Orrville, OH; *U.S. Private*, pg. 1177

Plunket, Paul W., III, V.P. & Gen. Counsel--Entex, Houston, TX; *U.S. Public*, pg. 843

Poe, Sheena E., V.P., Gen. Counsel & Sec.--Integon Corporation, Winston Salem, NC; *U.S. Public*, pg. 719

Poero, Edgardo, Exec. V.P.-Legal--Istituto Bancario San Paolo Di Torino S.p.A., Turin, Italy; *Int'l*, pg. 691

Poetker, J., Gen. Counsel--Calgary Flames Hockey Club, Calgary, Canada; *Int'l*, pg. 252

Pohl, W. Timothy, Gen. Counsel & Sec.--American Water Works Company, Inc., Voorhees, NJ; *U.S. Public*, pg. 95

Poinssot, Alain, Dir. Gen.-Legal--SNCF, Paris, France; *Int'l*, pg. 1163

Poirier, Pierre, V.P.-Legal Affairs & Corp. Sec.--Provigo Inc., Montreal, Canada; *Int'l*, pg. 1072

Pokross, David R., Jr., Gen. Counsel & Sec.--Tech/Ops Sevcon, Inc., Boston, MA; *U.S. Public*, pg. 1563

Polack, Robert, V.P., Corp. Counsel & Sec.--Reilly Industries, Inc., Indianapolis, IN; *U.S. Private*, pg. 919

Polan, Steven M., Gen. Counsel--Fischbach Corporation, Englewood, CO; *U.S. Public*, pg. 84

Polansky, Sheldon, V.P., Legal Counsel & Sec.--Spar Aerospace Limited, Toronto, Canada; *Int'l*, pg. 1287

Polasek, Ron, Gen. Counsel--Recon/Optical, Inc., Barrington, IL; *U.S. Private*, pg. 914

Polking, Paul J., Gen. Counsel--NationsBank Corporation, Charlotte, NC; *U.S. Public*, pg. 1162

Pollan, Lynn, V.P., Gen. Counsel & Corp. Sec.--Williamhouse-Regency, Inc., New York, NY; *U.S. Public*, pg. 89

Pollard, K., Mgr.-Legal--Kiwi Brands Pty. Ltd., Clayton, Australia; *U.S. Public*, pg. 1434

Pollihan, Thomas H., V.P., Gen. Counsel & Sec.--Kellwood Company, Chesterfield, MO; *U.S. Public*, pg. 948

Pollock, Ross, V.P., Gen. Counsel & Sec.--OfficeMax, Shaker Heights, OH; *U.S. Public*, pg. 1212

Polsky, Barbara S., Sr. V.P. & Gen. Counsel--Aames Financial Corporation, Los Angeles, CA; *U.S. Public*, pg. 12

Polucki, Robert, Gen. Counsel--Ricoh Corporation, West Caldwell, NJ; *Int'l*, pg. 1114

Pomerantz, Sanford E., Legal Counsel--NES Holdings, Inc., Raleigh, NC; *U.S. Private*, pg. 771

Pomeranz, Harold, Gen. Counsel--Movie Star, Inc., New York, NY; *U.S. Public*, pg. 1140

Pomeroy, John J., V.P., Gen. Counsel & Sec.--Allendale Mutual Insurance Co., Johnston, RI; *U.S. Private*, pg. 37

Pomeroy, Joseph, V.P.-Legal & Indus. Affairs--Mercury Marine, Fond Du Lac, WI; *U.S. Public*, pg. 265

Pommerville, Robert W., Exec. V.P., Gen. Counsel & Sec.--Beverly Enterprises, Inc., Fort Smith, AR; *U.S. Public*, pg. 227

Ponitz, J.A., Gen. Counsel, Asst. Sec.--Grand Trunk Western Railroad, Inc., Detroit, MI; *Int'l*, pg. 258

Ponitz, P.A., Gen. Counsel--Grand Trunk Corporation (GTC), Detroit, MI; *Int'l*, pg. 258

Pope, James Arthur, Chief Fin. Officer, Exec. V.P. & Gen. Counsel--Variety Wholesalers, Incorporated, Raleigh, NC; *U.S. Private*, pg. 1134

Popov, Peter N., V.P., Gen. Counsel & Sec.--Marine Transport Lines, Inc., Weehawken, NJ; *U.S. Private*, pg. 703

Porento, Gerald J., Gen. Counsel--Unicom Corporation, Chicago, IL; *U.S. Public*, pg. 1664

Port, Larry N., Asst. Gen. Counsel--Texaco Inc., White Plains, NY; *U.S. Public*, pg. 1582

Porter, Edward A., V.P.-Admin., Gen. Counsel & Sec.--National Gypsum Company, Charlotte, NC; *Int'l*, pg. 790

Porter, Edward A., V.P., Gen. Counsel & Sec.--Walter Industries, Inc., Tampa, FL; *U.S. Public*, pg. 1736

Porter, Russell W., Asst. Gen. Counsel--Aluminum Company of America, Pittsburgh, PA; *U.S. Public*, pg. 60

Posch, Robert, Gen. Counsel--Doubleday Direct, Garden City, NY; *Int'l*, pg. 191

Positan, Wayne C., Gen. Counsel--Marotta Scientific Controls, Inc., Montville, NJ; *U.S. Private*, pg. 706

Posner, E.G., V.P., Gen. Counsel & Sec.--PQ Corporation, Berwyn, PA; *U.S. Private*, pg. 827

Posner, J., V.P. & Legal Counsel--Bristol-Myers Products, New York, NY; *U.S. Public*, pg. 254

Post, G. Roger, V.P., Gen. Counsel & Sec.--White Castle System, Inc., Columbus, OH; *U.S. Private*, pg. 1171

Pottash, Bruce, Sr. V.P.-Business Affairs & Legal--Paramount Pictures Corporation, Los Angeles, CA; *U.S. Private*, pg. 776

Potter, Thomas A., V.P. & Gen. Counsel--The Titan Industrial Corp., New York, NY; *U.S. Private*, pg. 1089

Potter, William C., Gen. Counsel--DBA Systems, Inc., Melbourne, FL; *U.S. Public*, pg. 472

Potthoff, M. Elizabeth, Dir. & Corp. Counsel--Bytex Corporation, Westborough, MA; *U.S. Public*, pg. 1522

Pouliot, Colleen M., V.P., Gen. Counsel & Sec.--Adobe Systems Incorporated, San Jose, CA; *U.S. Public*, pg. 20

Povich, Ilissa, Sr. V.P. & Gen. Counsel--Interactive Data Corporation, Lexington, MA; *Int'l*, pg. 1025

Powell, D.B., Gen. Counsel--Midland Bank PLC, London, United Kingdom; *Int'l*, pg. 580

Powell, Jerry, Gen. Counsel & Sec.--Compass Bancshares, Inc., Birmingham, AL; *U.S. Public*, pg. 418

Powell, Robert J., V.P.-Intl. Licensing, Sec. & Gen. Counsel--Signal Apparel Company, Inc., Chattanooga, TN; *U.S. Public*, pg. 1472

Powers Barr, Eve, General Counsel & Asst. Sec.--Atotech U.S.A. Inc., Rock Hill, SC; *U.S. Private*, pg. 97

Prentice, F. Sheldon, Sr. V.P., Gen. Counsel & Sec.--Chittenden Corporation, Burlington, VT; *U.S. Public*, pg. 350

Prentice, Rebecca, Sr. V.P. & Gen. Counsel--Paramount Pictures Corporation, Los Angeles, CA; *U.S. Private*, pg. 776

Preston, John E., Sr. V.P. & Gen. Counsel--Litton Industries, Inc., Woodland Hills, CA; *U.S. Public*, pg. 1002

Preussner, Joachim, Dr., Grp. Mgr.-Legal Dept.--Bankgesellschaft Berlin, Berlin, Germany; *Int'l*, pg. 159

Pribisko, Patricia W., V.P., Gen. Counsel & Sec.--Lesco, Inc., Rocky River, OH; *U.S. Public*, pg. 989

Price, Francis D., Jr., V.P. & Gen. Counsel--The Penn Traffic Company, Syracuse, NY; *U.S. Public*, pg. 1270

Price, Russell L., V.P., Gen. Counsel & Sec.--Tandycrafts, Inc., Fort Worth, TX; *U.S. Public*, pg. 1561

Pridgen, Eugen, Sr. V.P. & Gen. Counsel--Glenayre Technologies, Inc., Charlotte, NC; *U.S. Public*, pg. 746

Priest, Gordon W., Asst. Sec. & Asst. Gen. Counsel--PHH Corporation, Hunt Valley, MD; *U.S. Public*, pg. 321

Prifti, William M., Gen. Counsel & Sec.--Pax World Fund Family, Portsmouth, NH; *U.S. Public*, pg. 1266

Prince, Charles O., III, Exec. V.P., Gen. Counsel & Sec.--Travelers Group, New York, NY; *U.S. Public*, pg. 1632

Printz, Peter E., Dir.-Safety, Health & Environmental & Chief Labor Counsel--Vulcan Materials Company, Birmingham, AL; *U.S. Public*, pg. 1725

Proctor, Timothy D., Sr. V.P., Gen. Counsel & Sec.--Glaxo Wellcome Inc., Research Triangle Park, NC; *Int'l*, pg. 552

Profaci, Joseph R., V.P. & Gen. Counsel--Colivita USA, Inc., Linden, NJ; *U.S. Private*, pg. 252

Prohofsky, Dennis, V.P., Gen. Counsel & Sec.--The Minnesota Mutual Life Insurance Company, Saint Paul, MN; *U.S. Private*, pg. 750

Prosser, Raymond L., V.P. & Gen. Counsel--Lincoln National Administrative Services Corp., Fort Wayne, IN; *U.S. Public*, pg. 998

Pruett, Leo M., Dir.-Environ. Svcs. & Asst. Gen. Counsel--Phelps Dodge Corporation, Phoenix, AZ; *U.S. Public*, pg. 1286

Pryor, Joe, Gen. Counsel & Dir.-Tech. Affairs--Alamo Group, Inc., Seguin, TX; *U.S. Public*, pg. 34

Puck, Steve, V.P. & Gen. Counsel--National Group Marketing Corp., Irving, TX; *U.S. Public*, pg. 433

Pudlin, Helen P., Sr. V.P. & Gen. Counsel--PNC Bank Corp., Pittsburgh, PA; *U.S. Public*, pg. 1242

Pugh, Lowell E., II, Gen. Counsel & Asst. Sec.--United Foods, Inc., Bells, TN; *U.S. Public*, pg. 1677

Pugh, Richard, Sr. V.P. & Gen. Counsel--Fremont Financial Corporation, Santa Monica, CA; *U.S. Public*, pg. 681

Puhala, James J., V.P., Gen. Counsel & Sec.--Dravo Corporation, Pittsburgh, PA; *U.S. Public*, pg. 527
Puhl, Frances Pellegrino, V.P. & Gen. Counsel--Associated Wholesale Grocers, Inc., Kansas City, KS; *U.S. Private*, pg. 93
Pulkrabek, Larry A., Sr. V.P., Sec. & Gen. Counsel--Armstrong World Industries, Inc., Lancaster, PA; *U.S. Public*, pg. 131
Pulsifer, Howard A., V.P., Gen. Counsel & Sec.--AAR Corp., Wood Dale, IL; *U.S. Public*, pg. 1
Pultz, George S., V.P., Sec. & Gen. Counsel--Robertson-Ceco Corporation, San Ramon, CA; *U.S. Public*, pg. 1394
Purcell, Terri L., Deputy Gen. Counsel & Asst. Sec.--Coca-Cola Enterprises Inc., Atlanta, GA; *U.S. Public*, pg. 393
Purtell, Lawrence R., Sr. V.P., Gen. Counsel & Sec.--McDermott International, Inc., New Orleans, LA; *U.S. Public*, pg. 1067
Purvines, Verne E., V.P., Gen. Counsel & Sec.--National General Insurance Co., Earth City, MO; *U.S. Public*, pg. 721
Purycar, Michael P., V.P. & Gen. Counsel--McLane Company, Inc., Temple, TX; *U.S. Public*, pg. 1733
Puryear, Michael P., Gen. Counsel--McLane Company, Inc., Temple, TX; *U.S. Public*, pg. 1733
Pusey, N. Woody, General Counsel--BASF Corporation Fiber Products Division, Charlotte, NC; *Int'l*, pg. 105
Puthoff, Frank M., V.P., Gen. Counsel & Sec.--Miami Subs Corporation, Fort Lauderdale, FL; *U.S. Public*, pg. 1103
Pyke, John S., Jr., V.P., Sec. & Legal--M.A. Hanna Company, Cleveland, OH; *U.S. Public*, pg. 780
Querejeta, Alfonso, Mgr.-Legal Opers./Spain & Portugal--European Investment Bank, Luxembourg, Luxembourg; *Int'l*, pg. 465
Quevedo, Rolando, V.P. & Legal Counsel--Firstbank Puerto Rico, Santurce, PR; *U.S. Public*, pg. 644
Quiner, Paul, Sr. V.P. & Gen. Counsel--Coram Healthcare Corporation, Denver, CO; *U.S. Public*, pg. 446
Quinn, Jeffry N., Sr. V.P.-Law & Human Resources, Gen. Counsel & Sec.--Arch Coal, Inc., Saint Louis, MO; *U.S. Public*, pg. 139
Quinn, Robert, Sr. V.P.-Legal--LaSalle National Bank, Chicago, IL; *Int'l*, pg. 10
Quinney-Nebeker, Ray, Gen. Counsel--Daw Technologies, Inc., Salt Lake City, UT; *U.S. Public*, pg. 489
Quintanilla Ochoa, Raul, Sr. Exec. V.P., Gen. Counsel & Sec.--Grupo Casa Autrey, Mexico, Mexico; *Int'l*, pg. 573
Quirk, Kathryn L., Gen. Counsel--Scudder Kemper Investments, Inc., New York, NY; *Int'l*, pg. 1530
Quitmeyer, John, Gen. Counsel--Breed Technologies, Sterling Heights, MI; *U.S. Public*, pg. 251
Rabinowitz, Alan, V.P. & Gen. Counsel--Motel 6 Operating L.P., Dallas, TX; *Int'l*, pg. 21
Rabkin, Alan B., Gen. Counsel--Sierra West Bancorp, Truckee, CA; *U.S. Public*, pg. 1470
Rackwitz, Ulrich, Mgr.-Fin. & Legal Affairs--Melitta Unternehmensgruppe Bentz KG, Minden, Germany; *Int'l*, *pg. 856*
Rader, Larry, Gen. Counsel & Sec.--Marine Travelift, Inc., Sturgeon Bay, WI; *U.S. Private*, pg. 703
Raggio, William J., V.P., Gen. Counsel & Sec.--Santa Fe Gaming Corporation, Las Vegas, NV; *U.S. Public*, pg. 1432
Ragsdale, Kent M., Gen. Counsel--Interstate Power Company, Dubuque, IA; *U.S. Public*, pg. 910
Raiden, Norman H., Exec. V.P.-Legal & Subsidiaries--Coast Savings Financial, Inc., Los Angeles, CA; *U.S. Public*, pg. 388
Raimondi, Josephine A., Gen. Counsel & Sec.--Midwest Employer's Casualty Company, Maryland Heights, MO; *U.S. Public*, pg. 215
Rainwater, Jay Earl, Gen. Counsel & Sec.--Wm. S. Trimble Company, Inc., Knoxville, TN; *U.S. Private*, pg. 1103
Ralston, James A., V.P., Gen. Counsel & Sec.--Eagle-Picher Industries, Inc., Cincinnati, OH; *U.S. Private*, pg. 355
Ramirez, Ivonne, Dir.-Legal--Puerto Rico Tourism Company, San Juan, PR; *U.S. Private*, pg. 894
Ramirez, Joseph L., Gen. Counsel & Corp. Sec.--Network Computing Devices, Inc., Mountain View, CA; *U.S. Public*, pg. 1168
Rampacek, Anne, Gen. Counsel--Primerica Financial Services, Duluth, GA; *U.S. Public*, pg. 1633
Ramrath, Joseph R., Sr. V.P. & Gen. Counsel--United Asset Management Corporation, Boston, MA; *U.S. Public*, pg. 1672
Randall, Karen, Sr. V.P. & Gen. Counsel--Universal Studios, Inc., Universal City, CA; *Int'l*, pg. 1215
Randall, Robert W., V.P., Gen. Counsel & Sec.--Pride International, Inc., Houston, TX; *U.S. Public*, pg. 1324
Randall, Ron, V.P., Sec. & Gen. Counsel--Camco International Inc., Houston, TX; *U.S. Public*, pg. 298
Randall, Ronald R., V.P., Gen. Counsel & Sec.--Camco International Inc., Houston, TX; *U.S. Public*, pg. 297
Randi, G., Legal, Admin. & Fin.--Electrolux San Jose, Pordenone, Italy; *Int'l*, pg. 442
Randolph, Kenneth, Sr. V.P. & Gen. Counsel--NGC Corporation, Houston, TX; *U.S. Public*, pg. 1146
Raney, Kenneth C., Jr., V.P. & Asst. Gen. Counsel--Central and South West Corporation, Dallas, TX; *U.S. Public*, pg. 324
Raney, Kenneth C., Jr., V.P.-Asst. Gen. Counsel--Central and South West Services, Inc., Dallas, TX; *U.S. Public*, pg. 324
Ranin, Ursula, Gen. Counsel--Oy Nokia Ab/Nokia Group, Helsinki, Finland; *Int'l*, pg. 951
Rankin, W., Gen. Counsel--Clariant Corporation, Charlotte, NC; *Int'l*, pg. 624
Rapuano, Robert A., V.P. & Corp. Counsel--Kinney System, Inc., New York, NY; *U.S. Private*, pg. 622
Rascio, Anthony, V.P., Gen. Counsel & Sec.--Roberts Pharmaceutical Corporation, Eatontown, NJ; *U.S. Public*, *pg. 1393*
Rasmussen, John, Sr. V.P. & Gen. Counsel--MidAmerican Energy Holdings, Des Moines, IA; *U.S. Public*, pg. 1109
Rathlisberger, Arnold, Exec. V.P. & Gen. Counsel--Western Waste Industries, Torrance, CA; *U.S. Public*, pg. 1686
Ratner, Hank J., Sr. V.P.-Legal & Bus. Affairs--Rainbow Programming Holdings, Inc., Woodbury, NY; *U.S. Public*, pg. 288
Rauch, Allan, Gen. Counsel--Bed Bath & Beyond Inc., Union, NJ; *U.S. Public*, pg. 200
Rawson, Jerry, Gen. Counsel--North Shore Movers, Northbrook, IL; *U.S. Private*, pg. 805
Rawson, Rich, Sr. V.P. & Gen. Counsel--Lucent Technologies Inc., Murray Hill, NJ; *U.S. Public*, pg. 1017
Ray, William C., V.P., Gen. Counsel & Sec.--Guilford Mills, Inc., Greensboro, NC; *U.S. Public*, pg. 768
Raznick, Carol, Gen. Counsel-Real Estate--M.D.C. Holdings, Inc., Denver, CO; *U.S. Public*, pg. 1025
Raznick, Carol, Gen. Counsel & Real Estate--Richmond Homes, Inc. I, Denver, CO; *U.S. Public*, pg. 1025
Reagan, Paul, Gen. Counsel--Harris Bankcorp, Inc., Chicago, IL; *Int'l*, pg. 154
Ream, Christopher, Esq., Gen. Counsel--McGrath RentCorp, Livermore, CA; *U.S. Public*, pg. 1069
Rebane, John, V.P. & Gen. Counsel--Land O'Lakes, Inc., Arden Hills, MN; *U.S. Private*, pg. 645
Redepenning, Charles W., Jr., Sr. V.P., Gen. Counsel & Sec.--Unique Casual Restaurants, inc., Danvers, MA; *Int'l*, pg. 324
Redpath, John S. Jr., Sr. V.P., Gen. Counsel & Sec.--Home Box Office, Inc., New York, NY; *U.S. Public*, pg. 1612
Reed, Austin F., V.P., Gen. Counsel & Sec.--The Pittston Company, Glen Allen, VA; *U.S. Public*, pg. 1305
Reed, Cynthia S., Sr. V.P. & Gen. Counsel--Hasbro, Inc., Pawtucket, RI; *U.S. Public*, pg. 797
Reed, Frederick, Chief Fin. Officer, Exec. V.P. & Gen. Counsel--Wendy's International Inc., Dublin, OH; *U.S. Public*, pg. 1754
Reed, James C., Jr., Exec. V.P., Gen. Counsel & Sec.--Tesoro Petroleum Corporation, San Antonio, TX; *U.S. Public*, pg. 1581
Reed, Kenneth D., Gen. Counsel--Hammond Group Inc., Hammond, IN; *U.S. Private*, pg. 498
Reese, Robert M., V.P., Gen. Counsel & Sec.--Hershey Foods Corporation, Hershey, PA; *U.S. Public*, pg. 811
Refinski, Elizabeth, Associate V.P.--Edwards and Kelcey, Inc., Boston, MA; *U.S. Private*, pg. 364
Regez, Rudolph, V.P.-Legal Council & H.R.--The Swiss Colony, Inc, Monroe, WI; *U.S. Private*, pg. 1059
Regnier, Marc, Sr. V.P. & Gen. Counsel--Avenor, Inc., Montreal, Canada; *Int'l*, pg. 101
Reichardt, David L., Sr. V.P. & Gen. Counsel--DynCorp, Reston, VA; *U.S. Private*, pg. 351
Reichenberger, John F., Asst. Gen. Counsel & Dir.-Risk Mngmt. & Claims--Kerr-McGee Corporation, Oklahoma City, OK; *U.S. Public*, pg. 952
Reichler, Richard, V.P.-Tax & Benefits Plng. & Deputy Gen. Counsel--Long Island Lighting Company, Hicksville, NY; *U.S. Public*, pg. 1013
Reichman, N., Gen. Counsel & Sec.--Airport Group International, Inc., Glendale, CA; *U.S. Public*, pg. 1009
Reid, Malcolm D., V.P., Gen. Counsel & Sec.--Network Systems Corporation, Minneapolis, MN; *U.S. Public*, pg. 1522
Reilly, Sally, Corp. Attorney--Southern Progress Corporation, Birmingham, AL; *U.S. Public*, pg. 1612
Reines, Larry B., Gen. Counsel & Dir.-Pur.--Vivian & Elliette, Inc., Vernon, CA; *U.S. Private*, pg. 1142
Reinhardt, Dr. Dietrich, General Counsel--Saarbergwerke Aktiengesellschaft, Saarbruecken, Germany; *Int'l*, pg. 1166
Reinhart, Peter S., Sr. V.P. & Gen. Counsel--Hovnanian Enterprises, Inc., Red Bank, NJ; *U.S. Public*, pg. 843
Reiser, Richard S., Exec. V.P. & Gen. Counsel--Werner Enterprises, Inc., Omaha, NE; *U.S. Public*, pg. 1754
Reisman, Kenneth, V.P., Gen. Counsel & Sec.--Technical Aid Corporation, Newton, MA; *U.S. Private*, pg. 1072
Remine, Debra B., First V.P. & Gen. Counsel--Federated Mutual Insurance Company, Owatonna, MN; *U.S. Private*, pg. 399
Rempe, James H., Sr. V.P., Gen. Counsel & Sec.--Manor Care, Inc., Gaithersburg, MD; *U.S. Public*, pg. 1041
Renard, Bruce W., V.P.-Regulatory Compliance & Gen. Counsel--Peoples Telephone Company, Inc., Miami, FL; *U.S. Public*, pg. 1275
Renbarger, Larry D., Pres. & Chief Exec. Officer--Shelter Components Corporation, Elkhart, IN; *U.S. Public*, pg. 952
Render, Ann, V.P.-Admin. & Employee Rels. Counsel--Mason & Hanger Corporation, Inc., Lexington, KY; *U.S. Private*, pg. 711
Renegar, Greg, Attorney--Griffin Manufacturing Co., Muskogee, OK; *U.S. Private*, pg. 481
Rennert, Chuck, Gen. Counsel--Sterling Healthcare Group, Inc., Miami, FL; *U.S. Public*, pg. 608
Rennie, A. Marie, Corp. Sec.--Royal LePage Limited, Don Mills, Canada; *Int'l*, pg. 1143
Renton, David, Dir.-Contracts & Legal Services--Wyse Technology Inc., San Jose, CA; *U.S. Private*, pg. 1194
Rentsch, Hanspeter, Dir.-Legal Affairs, H.R., Real Estate & Licensing--SMH Swiss Corporation for Micro Electronics & Watchmaking Indus. Ltd., Bienne, Switzerland; *Int'l*, pg. 1160
Repp, Sheldon D., V.P. & Assoc. Gen. Counsel--SLM Holding Corp., Washington, DC; *U.S. Public*, pg. 1419
Resler, Ed, Corp. Counsel--Northrup King Co., Golden Valley, MN; *Int'l*, pg. 974
Resnick, Gina, Exec. V.P.-Legal Affairs--Columbia Tri-Star Home Video, Burbank, CA; *Int'l*, pg. 1282
Rethorn, Dietrich, Gen. Counsel--Landesbank Hessen-Thuringen Girozentrale, Frankfurt/Main, Germany; *Int'l*, pg. 798
Reuterfors, Robert, Dir.-Legal--Woodward Governor Company, Rockford, IL; *U.S. Public*, pg. 1776
Rewoldt, Dana, Gen. Counsel--Garst Seed Company, Slater, IA; *Int'l*, pg. 1524
Reynolds, Dudley C., Gen. Counsel & Sec.--Energen Corporation, Birmingham, AL; *U.S. Public*, pg. 581
Reynolds, Jonathan P., V.P. & Gen. Counsel--Cosco, Inc., Columbus, IN; *U.S. Private*, pg. 277
Rheinhardt, Roger, Gen. Counsel & Sec.--Panneaux Malette-OSB Inc., Saint-Georges, Canada; *Int'l*, pg. 833
Rhinehart, June A., V.P. & Gen. Counsel--Johnson Publishing Company, Inc., Chicago, IL; *U.S. Private*, pg. 591
Rhoads, Robert K., Sr. V.P., Gen. Counsel & Sec.--Wal-Mart Stores, Inc., Bentonville, AR; *U.S. Public*, pg. 1732
Rhoads, Robert K., Gen. Counsel & Sec.--Wal-Mart Stores, Inc., Bentonville, AR; *U.S. Public*, pg. 1732
Ricciardi, Lawrence R., Sr. V.P. & Gen. Counsel--International Business Machines Corporation, Armonk, NY; *U.S. Public*, pg. 895
Rich, Bradford W., Gen. Counsel & Sec.--USAA (United Services Automobile Association), San Antonio, TX; *U.S. Private*, pg. 1114
Rich, Carsten, Gen. Counsel & Sec.--ISS-International Service System A/S, Holte, Denmark; *Int'l*, pg. 656
Rich, Craig R., Gen. Counsel--Williams Field Services, Tulsa, OK; *U.S. Public*, pg. 1769
Rich, Marvin, Gen. Counsel--Valentine Radford, Inc., Kansas City, MO; *U.S. Private*, pg. 1131
Richards, B.S., V.P. & Gen. Counsel--Equifax Inc., Atlanta, GA; *U.S. Public*, pg. 588
Richards, G. Robert, V.P. & Gen. Counsel--The Flxible Corp., Delaware, OH; *U.S. Private*, pg. 444
Richards, Maureen, Gen. Counsel & Sec.--Footstar Inc., Mahwah, NJ; *U.S. Public*, pg. 661
Richards, Stanley, Sr. V.P. & Gen. Counsel--General Growth Properties Inc., Chicago, IL; *U.S. Public*, pg. 715
Richards, Stephen D., Sr. V.P. & Gen. Counsel--Consolidated Freightways Corp., Menlo Park, CA; *U.S. Public*, pg. 435
Richenthal, Arthur, Gen. Counsel & Corp. Sec.--Carrafiello, Diehl & Associates, Inc., Irvington, NY; *U.S. Private*, pg. 215
Richenthal, Arthur, Gen. Counsel--Espey Mfg. & Electronics Corp., Saratoga Springs, NY; *U.S. Public*, pg. 592
Richey, Ellen, Exec. V.P., Gen. Counsel & Sec.--Providian Financial Corporation, San Francisco, CA; *U.S. Public*, pg. 1338
Richman, Arlene, Gen. Counsel--Landau & Heyman Inc., Chicago, IL; *U.S. Private*, pg. 646
Richter, Alfred G., Jr., V.P. & Gen. Counsel-Missouri--Southwestern Bell Telephone Co., Saint Louis, MO; *U.S. Public*, pg. 1416
Richter, David, Gen. Counsel--Hill International Inc., Willingboro, NJ; *U.S. Private*, pg. 529
Richterich, Guido, Dr., Mng. Dir.-Law & Communications--F. Hoffmann-La Roche Ltd., Basel, Switzerland; *Int'l*, pg. 1119
Rick, James, Gen. Counsel--International Research & Evaluation, Eagan, MN; *U.S. Private*, pg. 571
Riden, Tom, Gen. Counsel--Nutmeg Mills Inc., Tampa, FL; *U.S. Public*, pg. 1702
Rieck, Kim A., Sr. V.P., Gen. Counsel & Sec.--The Edward J. DeBartolo Corporation, Youngstown, OH; *U.S. Private*, *pg. 319*
Riecke, Robert J., V.P.-Admin., Gen. Counsel & Sec.--WTD Industries, Inc., Portland, OR; *U.S. Public*, pg. 1729
Riegel, J. Kent, Pres. & Gen. Counsel--ICI Americas, Inc., Wilmington, DE; *Int'l*, pg. 663
Riesenbach, E. Gerald, Sec.--Kleinert's, Inc., Plymouth Meeting, PA; *U.S. Private*, pg. 625
Riganelli, Paul E., V.P.-Admin., Sec. & Gen. Counsel--TecSyn International, Inc., Saint Catharines, Canada; *Int'l*, pg. 1361
Riggs, G.L., Asst. Gen. Counsel--Delta Air Lines, Inc., Atlanta, GA; *U.S. Public*, pg. 497
Rigot, Joseph M., Gen. Counsel & Sec.--Robbins & Myers, Inc., Dayton, OH; *U.S. Public*, pg. 1393
Riley, Frank A., Gen. Counsel--Bancorp South Inc., Tupelo, MS; *U.S. Public*, pg. 176
Riley, Joan R., Gen. Counsel, Sec. & Dir.-Investor Rels.--Quixote Corporation, Chicago, IL; *U.S. Public*, pg. 1353
Riley, Robert, V.P. & Gen. Counsel--Meijer, Inc., Grand Rapids, MI; *U.S. Private*, pg. 729
Rines, Robert, V.P. & Gen. Counsel--Megapulse, Inc., Bedford, MA; *U.S. Private*, pg. 729
Ringleb, Henrik-Michael, Gen. Counsel--Fried. Krupp AG, Essen, Germany; *Int'l*, pg. 507
Ringswald, Michael A., First V.P., Gen. Counsel & Sec.--The Fifth Third Bank of Kentucky, Louisville, Louisville, KY; *U.S. Public*, pg. 621
Rinner, Richard, Exec. V.P.-Admin. & Publ.--American Automobile Association, Heathrow, FL; *U.S. Private*, pg. 50
Risley, Gary E., Chief Legal Officer & Sec.--Mesa Air Group, Las Vegas, NV; *U.S. Public*, pg. 1098
Rivera-Soto, Roberto, Sr. V.P. & Gen. Counsel--Caesars World, Inc., Las Vegas, NV; *U.S. Public*, pg. 1512
Roach, Edgar M., Jr., V.P.-Regulation & Gen. Counsel--Virginia Electric and Power Company, Richmond, VA; *U.S. Public*, pg. 516
Roach, Walter, Gen. Counsel--Petro-Hunt Corporation, Dallas, TX; *U.S. Private*, pg. 858
Robbins, Al, Gen. Counsel--New York Law Journal, New York, NY; *Int'l*, pg. 956
Robbins, Donald M., Sr. V.P., Gen. Counsel & Sec.--Hasbro, Inc., Pawtucket, RI; *U.S. Public*, pg. 797
Robbins, Rachel F., Gen. Counsel--J.P. Morgan Co. Incorporated, New York, NY; *U.S. Public*, pg. 1129
Roberts, C.K., V.P. & Gen. Counsel--Exxon Corporation, Irving, TX; *U.S. Public*, pg. 601
Roberts, Donald M., Gen. Counsel & Sec.--Maxwell Technologies, Inc., San Diego, CA; *U.S. Public*, pg. 1061
Roberts, June E., Gen. Counsel--Acordia Northeast, Boston, MA; *Int'l*, pg. 671
Roberts, Norman L., Sr. V.P. & Gen. Counsel--Western Atlas Inc., Houston, TX; *U.S. Public*, pg. 1757

Roberts, Rex H., V.P., Assoc. Gen. Counsel & Sec.--American General Life & Accident Insurance Co., Nashville, TN; *U.S. Public*, pg. 76

Roberts, Russell H., Gen. Counsel--The Free Lance-Star Publishing Co., Fredericksburg, VA; *U.S. Private*, pg. 424

Roberts, Scott A., Asst. Gen. Counsel & Asst. Sec.--Archer Daniels Midland Company (ADM), Decatur, IL; *U.S. Public*, pg. 127

Robertson, David, Sr. V.P. & Gen. Mgr.-U.S.A.--Royal Bank of Canada, New York, NY; *Int'l*, pg. 1131

Robertson, Jonathan M., Assoc. Gen. Counsel--Morrison Knudsen Corporation, Boise, ID; *U.S. Public*, pg. 1133

Robin, Kenneth, Sr. V.P. & Gen. Counsel--Household International, Inc., Prospect Heights, IL; *U.S. Public*, pg. 842

Robins, Kevin, Esq., Gen. Counsel--SEI Investments, Oaks, PA; *U.S. Public*, pg. 1417

Robins, Martin, V.P. & Gen. Counsel--Meridian Technology Leasing Services, Deerfield, IL; *U.S. Private*, pg. 732

Robinson, Billy J., V.P. & Gen. Counsel--Curtis Mathes Holding Corp., Dallas, TX; *U.S. Public*, pg. 1057

Robinson, Billy J., Gen. Counsel--Curtis Mathes Corporation, Dallas, TX; *U.S. Public*, pg. 1057

Robinson, Ed, Sr. V.P. & Gen. Counsel--Harrah's Entertainment, Inc., Memphis, TN; *U.S. Public*, pg. 790

Robinson, Leroy, Gen. Counsel & Consultant--Belk Stores Services Inc., Charlotte, NC; *U.S. Private*, pg. 131

Robinson, Marvin S., V.P., Gen. Counsel & Sec.--Garan, Incorporated, New York, NY; *U.S. Public*, pg. 703

Robinson, Otto P., Jr., Pres. & Gen. Counsel--Penn Security Bank and Trust Co., Scranton, PA; *U.S. Public*, pg. 1270

Robinson, Ron, Of Counsel--Cranford Johnson Robinson Woods, Little Rock, AR; *U.S. Private*, pg. 286

Roces, Manuel Basteiro, Gen. Counsel--Hulleras Del Norte, S.A. (HUNOSA), Asturias, Spain; *Int'l*, pg. 639

Roche, Jack, Gen. Counsel--Citibank N.A., Long Island City, NY; *U.S. Public*, pg. 377

Roche, John J., Exec. V.P.-Legal Affairs--Citicorp, New York, NY; *U.S. Public*, pg. 376

Roche, Mark A., V.P. & Gen. Counsel--Fortune Brands, Inc., Old Greenwich, CT; *U.S. Public*, pg. 674

Roche, Sandra L., Esq., Corp. Sec.--Roche Constructors, Inc., Greeley, CO; *U.S. Private*, pg. 937

Rochette, Bermanrd, Sec. & Dir.-Legal Affairs--The Jean Coutu Group (PJC) Inc., Longueuil, Canada; *Int'l*, pg. 340

Rockowitz, Noah E., V.P., Gen. Counsel & Sec.--Hudson General Corporation, Great Neck, NY; *U.S. Public*, pg. 845

Rod, Einer M., Gen. Counsel--First Brands Corporation, Danbury, CT; *U.S. Public*, pg. 626

Rodgers, Thomas H., V.P.-Gen. Counsel--Hobart Corporation, Troy, OH; *U.S. Public*, pg. 1322

Rodrigues, Bettencourt, Dr., Dir.-Legal--Transportes Aereos Portugueses, Lisbon, Portugal; *Int'l*, pg. 1418

Roehlk, Thomas, Sr. V.P., Gen. Counsel & Sec.--Tupperware Corporation, Orlando, FL; *U.S. Public*, pg. 1644

Roelke, Norman L., V.P. & Gen. Counsel--Tokheim Corporation, Fort Wayne, IN; *U.S. Public*, pg. 1620

Roge, Paul E., Asst. Sec.--Abbott Laboratories, Abbott Park, IL; *U.S. Public*, pg. 12

Rogers, Shelby R., Sr. V.P. & Gen. Counsel--Texas Commerce Bank, Houston, TX; *U.S. Public*, pg. 339

Rogers, Yandell, Jr., Pres., Chief Exec. Officer & Gen. Counsel--YRJ Corporation, Houston, TX; *U.S. Private*, pg. 1176

Roiter, Eric D., V.P. & Gen. Counsel--FMR Corp., Boston, MA; *U.S. Private*, pg. 403

Rollins, O.R., Exec. V.P. & Gen. Counsel--Tultex Corporation, Martinsville, VA; *U.S. Public*, pg. 1644

Rollins, Robert, Treas. & Legal Officer--Nashville Wire Product Co., Nashville, TN; *U.S. Private*, pg. 775

Rolnick, Ronald, Esq., Exec. V.P. & Gen. Counsel--Pacesetter Inc., Sylmar, CA; *U.S. Public*, pg. 1428

Roloff, Jeffrey J., Chm. Bd. & Chief Exec. Officer--Central Data Corporation, Champaign, IL; *U.S. Private*, pg. 223

Romano, Robert S., Asst. Gen. Counsel & Asst. Sec.--Outboard Marine Corporation, Waukegan, IL; *U.S. Private*, pg. 478

Romita, Carla L., V.P. & Assoc. Gen. Counsel--Castle Oil Corporation, Harrison, NY; *U.S. Private*, pg. 219

Romoser, W. David, V.P., Gen. Counsel & Sec.--A.O. Smith Corporation, Milwaukee, WI; *U.S. Public*, pg. 1476

Ronquillo, Allan L., V.P. & Gen. Counsel--Chrysler Financial Corporation, Southfield, MI; *U.S. Public*, pg. 354

Rooke, Ben G., Exec. V.P., Gen. Counsel & Sec.--Keystone Financial Inc., Harrisburg, PA; *U.S. Public*, pg. 956

Roome, Katherine D., V.P. & Assoc. Gen. Counsel--The McGraw-Hill Companies, New York, NY; *U.S. Public*, pg. 1069

Roquefeuil, Andre, V.P. & Gen. Counsel--Schneider S.A., Boulogne-Billancourt, France; *Int'l*, pg. 1207

Rosard, Steven J., V.P. & Sr. Corp. Counsel--Safeguard Scientifics, Inc., Wayne, PA; *U.S. Public*, pg. 1424

Rose, Donald, V.P., Gen. Counsel & Sec.--Placer Dome Inc., Vancouver, Canada; *Int'l*, pg. 1060

Rose, Joanne, Sr. V.P. & Gen. Counsel-Standard & Poor's--The McGraw-Hill Companies, New York, NY; *U.S. Public, pg. 1069*

Rose, Proskauer, Gen. Counsel--Comtech Telecommunications Corp., Melville, NY; *U.S. Public*, pg. 425

Rosedahl, David Evans, Gen. Counsel & Sec.--Piper Jaffray Companies, Inc., Minneapolis, MN; *U.S. Public*, pg. 1300

Rosen, Calvin, V.P. & Legal Counsel--Mita Copystar America Inc., Fairfield, NJ; *Int'l*, pg. 870

Rosen, Deborah A., Asst. Gen. Counsel & Asst. Sec.--Standex International Corporation, Salem, NH; *U.S. Public*, pg. 1505

Rosen, Joel, V.P.-Admin. & Gen. Counsel--Nutri/System Inc., Horsham, PA; *U.S. Private*, pg. 859

Rosen, Stuart I., V.P., Assoc. Gen. Counsel & Sec.--Triarc Companies, Inc., New York, NY; *U.S. Public*, pg. 1634

Rosenbaum, III, Ben, Gen. Counsel & Sec.--PHP Healthcare Corporation, Reston, VA; *U.S. Public*, pg. 1241

Rosenberg, Barnett, Sr. V.P., Gen. Counsel & Sec.--Mattel, Inc., El Segundo, CA; *U.S. Public*, pg. 1057

Rosenberg, Bruce, V.P. & Gen. Counsel--Mail Boxes Etc., San Diego, CA; *U.S. Public*, pg. 1687

Rosenberg, Channa, Deputy Mng. Dir. & Chief Legal Adviser--Bank Hapoalim, Tel Aviv, Israel; *Int'l*, pg. 149

Rosenberg, Ira S., V.P., Gen. Counsel & Sec.--Lechters, Inc., Harrison, NJ; *U.S. Public*, pg. 983

Rosenberg, John K., Exec. V.P. & Gen. Counsel--Western Resources, Inc., Topeka, KS; *U.S. Public*, pg. 1759

Rosenberg, Marvin B., Sr. V.P. & Gen. Counsel--Terex Corporation, Westport, CT; *U.S. Public*, pg. 1581

Rosenblum, William F., Sr. V.P., Deputy Gen. Counsel & Corp. Sec.--Republic New York Corporation, New York, NY; *U.S. Public*, pg. 1380

Rosengren, John C., V.P. & Gen. Counsel--Arthur J. Gallagher & Co., Itasca, IL; *U.S. Public*, pg. 698

Rosengren, William R., Sr. V.P.-Law & Gen. Counsel--Ecolab Inc., Saint Paul, MN; *U.S. Public*, pg. 562

Rosenthal, David, Corp. Counsel--F & W Publications, Inc., Cincinnati, OH; *U.S. Private*, pg. 388

Rosenthal, Mark, Chief. Oper. Officer, V.P. & Gen. Counsel--Raleigh Enterprises, Inc., Santa Monica, CA; *U.S. Private*, pg. 907

Rosenzweig, Dena, Gen. Counsel--Republic Industries, Inc., Fort Lauderdale, FL; *U.S. Public*, pg. 1378

Rosoff, William L., Sr. V.P. & Gen. Counsel--RJR Nabisco Holdings Corp., New York, NY; *U.S. Public*, pg. 1354

Ross, Charles, Dir.-Legal Div.--Wyeth-Ayerst Laboratories, Inc., Philadelphia, PA; *U.S. Public*, pg. 80

Ross, John B., V.P. & Gen. Counsel--Williams Scotsman, Inc., Baltimore, MD; *U.S. Private*, pg. 976

Ross, John H. III, Sr. V.P. & Gen. Counsel--Ash Grove Cement Company, Shawnee Mission, KS; *U.S. Private*, pg. 87

Ross, Michael C., Sr. V.P., Gen. Counsel & Sec.--Safeway Inc., Pleasanton, CA; *U.S. Public*, pg. 1426

Ross, Mike, V.P., Gen. Counsel & Asst. Sec.--Atmel Corporation, San Jose, CA; *U.S. Public*, pg. 145

Ross, Ronald J., Chief Real Estate Counsel--The Cafaro Co., Youngstown, OH; *U.S. Private*, pg. 198

Rossini, Edwin R., V.P., Deputy Gen. Counsel & Asst. Sec.--S.C. Johnson & Son, Inc., Racine, WI; *U.S. Private*, pg. 592

Rossiter, Peter L., Exec. V.P., Gen. Counsel & Sec.--Northern Trust Corporation, Chicago, IL; *U.S. Public*, pg. 1195

Roth, Peter, Gen. Counsel--Lucky Winner, Inc., New York, NY; *U.S. Private*, pg. 679

Rothberg, Robert, V.P. & Gen. Counsel--Cabot Corporation, Boston, MA; *U.S. Public*, pg. 288

Rothschild, Bruce I., V.P., Gen. Counsel & Sec.--The Rouse Company, Columbia, MD; *U.S. Public*, pg. 1407

Rothschild, Bruce I., V.P., Gen. Counsel & Sec.--Rouse Legal Div., Columbia, MD; *U.S. Public*, pg. 1407

Roti, Thomas, V.P. & Gen. Counsel--Dominick's Finer Foods, Northlake, IL; *U.S. Private*, pg. 1202

Rotzien, William A., Gen. Counsel & Asst. Sec.--John Deere Credit Company, Moline, IL; *U.S. Public*, pg. 492

Rounsaville, Guy, Jr., Gen. Counsel & Sec.--Wells Fargo & Company, San Francisco, CA; *U.S. Public*, pg. 1753

Rountree, Steve, Esq., Gen. Counsel--M K Diamond Products, Inc., Torrance, CA; *U.S. Private*, pg. 684

Rowan, James P., V.P., Assoc. Gen. Counsel & Asst. Sec.--The Wackenhut Corporation, Palm Beach Gardens, FL; *U.S. Public*, pg. 1731

Rowe, W. Bayless, Gen. Counsel & Sec.--Deltic Timber Corporation, El Dorado, AR; *U.S. Public*, pg. 498

Rowland, Tom, Gen. Counsel--Stimson Lane Ltd., Woodinville, WA; *U.S. Public*, pg. 1661

Rowlenson, Richard C., Exec. V.P. & Gen. Counsel--Vanguard Cellular Systems, Inc., Greensboro, NC; *U.S. Public*, pg. 1707

Rowley, Dave, V.P. & Gen. Counsel--Bell Sports Corp., San Jose, CA; *U.S. Public*, pg. 207

Rowsey, Paul, III, Pres. & Gen. Counsel--Rosewood Property Company, Dallas, TX; *U.S. Private*, pg. 946

Roy, Harold, Gen. Counsel & Sec.--Bayer Clothing Group, New York, NY; *U.S. Private*, pg. 124

Royal, Robert, Gen. Counsel--Plant Maintenance Service Corporation, Memphis, TN; *U.S. Private*, pg. 869

Royer, Donald E., Exec. V.P. & Gen. Counsel--Downey Financial Corp., Newport Beach, CA; *U.S. Public*, pg. 525

Royer, Donald E., Exec. V.P., Gen. Counsel & Sec.--Downey Savings & Loan Association, F.A., Newport Beach, CA; *U.S. Public*, pg. 526

Rozee, Peter C., Gen. Counsel & Sec.--Inmet Mining Corporation, Toronto, Canada; *Int'l*, pg. 678

Rozee, Peter C., Gen. Counsel--Metall Mining Corporation, Toronto, Canada; *Int'l*, pg. 862

Rozel, Samuel J., Chief Legal Officer, Sr. V.P., Gen. Counsel & Sec.--Philips Electronics North America Corporation, New York, NY; *Int'l*, pg. 1053

Ruben, Dennis L., Exec. V.P. & Gen. Counsel--Franchise Finance Corp. of America, Scottsdale, AZ; *U.S. Public*, pg. 679

Rubin, Audrey, Gen. Counsel--Grant Thornton LLP, Chicago, IL; *U.S. Private*, pg. 470

Rubin, David M., Gen. Counsel & Sec.--CC Industries, Inc., Chicago, IL; *U.S. Private*, pg. 192

Rubin, Eric, Gen. Counsel--The Ackerley Group, Seattle, WA; *U.S. Public*, pg. 15

Rubin, Milton, Sec. & Gen. Counsel--Argo International Corp., New York, NY; *U.S. Private*, pg. 322

Rubin, Steven, V.P., Gen. Counsel & Sec.--General Binding Corporation, Northbrook, IL; *U.S. Public*, pg. 707

Rubinfeld, Abraham N., Gen. Counsel & Sec.--CSA Management Inc., Toronto, Canada; *Int'l*, pg. 243

Rubinfeld, Abraham N., Corp. Counsel & Sec.--Wharf Resources Ltd., Lead, SD; *Int'l*, pg. 243

Rubinfeld, Abraham N., Gen. Counsel & Sec.--Lexam Explorations Inc., Toronto, Canada; *Int'l*, pg. 243

Rubino, Pauli, Gen. Counsel--DeVault Foods, Devault, PA; *U.S. Private*, pg. 329

Rubinstein, Marc, Sr. V.P. & Gen. Counsel--Caesars Palace, Las Vegas, NV; *U.S. Public*, pg. 1512

Ruble, Joseph, V.P. & Gen. Counsel--CSG Systems International, Inc., Englewood, CO; *U.S. Public*, pg. 283

Rubright, James A., Exec. V.P., Gen. Counsel & Sec.--Sonat Exploration Company, Houston, TX; *U.S. Public*, pg. 1485

Rubright, James A., Exec. V.P. & Gen. Counsel--Sonat Energy Services Company, Birmingham, AL; *U.S. Public*, pg. 1485

Ruby, G. Mary, V.P.-Legal Affairs, Gen. Counsel & Sec.--Imax Corporation, Mississauga, Canada; *Int'l*, pg. 661

Ruddy, James, Sr. V.P. & Gen. Counsel--SAFECO Corporation, Seattle, WA; *U.S. Public*, pg. 1423

Rudge, Howard J., Sr. V.P. & Gen. Counsel--Du Pont (E.I. Du Pont De Nemours & Co.), Wilmington, DE; *U.S. Public*, pg. 530

Rudick, Richard S., Sr. V.P. & Gen. Counsel--John Wiley & Sons, Inc., New York, NY; *U.S. Public*, pg. 1768

Rudin, Jeffrey, V.P. & Gen. Counsel--Millipore Corporation, Bedford, MA; *U.S. Public*, pg. 1112

Rudnick, Alan A., V.P., Gen. Counsel & Corp. Sec.--CSX Corporation, Richmond, VA; *U.S. Public*, pg. 284

Rudnik, Robert J., Exec. V.P., Gen. Counsel & Sec.--Prime Group Realty Trust, Chicago, IL; *U.S. Public*, pg. 1326

Rudolph, Karen, Corp. Counsel--Rudolph and Sletten, Inc., Foster City, CA; *U.S. Private*, pg. 950

Ruegsegger, Martin C., V.P., Corp. Counsel & Sec--Piedmont Natural Gas Co., Inc., Charlotte, NC; *U.S. Public*, pg. 1295

Ruff, Ellen T., Sec. & Dep. Gen. Counsel--Duke Energy Corporation, Charlotte, NC; *U.S. Public*, pg. 534

Ruffner, Ernest L., Gen. Counsel & Sec.--Halifax Corporation, Alexandria, VA; *U.S. Public*, pg. 775

Ruppert, John L., Gen. Counsel & Corp. Sec.--Brothers Gourmet Coffees, Inc., Boca Raton, FL; *U.S. Public*, pg. 259

Rush, Curt S., Gen. Counsel & Sec.--Global Direct Mail Corp, Port Washington, NY; *U.S. Public*, pg. 747

Rusinak, Ronald, V.P., Gen. Counsel & Sec.--Crown American Realty Trust, Johnstown, PA; *U.S. Public*, pg. 461

Rusis, Robert, Sr. V.P. & Gen. Counsel--The Chubb Corporation, Warren, NJ; *U.S. Public*, pg. 354

Russ, Charles P., III, Exec. V.P.-Law & Human Resources, Gen. Counsel & Sec.--U S West Inc., Englewood, CO; *U.S. Public*, pg. 1688

Russell, Cliff G., Esq., Gen. Counsel--Environmental Tectonics Corporation (ETC), Southampton, PA; *U.S. Public*, pg. 587

Russell, David, Assoc. Gen. Counsel & Asst. Sec.--Grow Group, Inc., Cleveland, OH; *Int'l*, pg. 663

Russell, Donald S., Jr., Gen. Counsel--NationsBank South Carolina, N.A., Columbia, SC; *U.S. Public*, pg. 1163

Russell, Joyce M., Sr. V.P. & Gen. Counsel--Fruit of the Loom, Inc., Chicago, IL; *U.S. Public*, pg. 685

Russell, L. Michael, V.P., Gen. Counsel & Sec.--International Rectifier Corporation, El Segundo, CA; *U.S.* Public, pg. 906

Russell, Ronald J., V.P., Gen. Counsel & Sec.--Methanex Corporation, Vancouver, Canada; *Int'l*, pg. 862

Rutenberg, Sara, Sr. V.P.-Legal & Bus. Affairs--Universal Studios TV, Universal City, CA; *Int'l*, pg. 1215

Rutgers, J.A., Dir.-Legal & Gen Sec.--Philips Electronics N.V., Eindhoven, Netherlands; *Int'l*, pg. 1051

Ruth, James C., V.P. & Gen. Counsel--TEPPCO Partners L.P., Houston, TX; *U.S. Public*, pg. 534

Ruth, James C., V.P., Gen. Counsel & Asst. Sec.--Texas Eastern Products Pipeline Company, L.P., Houston, TX; *U.S. Public*, pg. 535

Rutman, Gregory, V.P., Sec. & Gen. Counsel--The Geon Company, Avon Lake, OH; *U.S. Public*, pg. 733

Rutstein, David W., Sr. V.P. & Gen. Counsel--Giant Food Inc., Landover, MD; *U.S. Public*, pg. 741

Ruxmin, Robert, V.P. & Gen. Counsel--Pony U.S.A., Nashville, TN; *Int'l*, pg. 1036

Ryan, Edwin, Gen. Counsel & Sec.--Tomkins Industries Inc., Dayton, OH; *Int'l*, pg. 1397

Ryan, Gary L., Sr. V.P. & Corp. Counsel--Hibernia Corporation, New Orleans, LA; *U.S. Public*, pg. 825

Ryan, Jim, Gen. Counsel--Hale-Halsell Company, Tulsa, OK; *U.S. Private*, pg. 494

Ryan, Joseph, Exec. V.P. & Gen. Counsel--Marriott International, Inc., Washington, DC; *U.S. Public*, pg. 1047

Ryan, Louis F., Exec. V.P., Gen. Counsel & Sec.--Landmark Communications, Inc., Norfolk, VA; *U.S. Private*, pg. 647

Ryan, Marc J., Gen. Counsel--BCE Inc., Montreal, Canada; *Int'l*, pg. 114

Ryan, Patrick, Sr. V.P., Sec. & Gen. Counsel--Hunt-Wesson, Inc., Fullerton, CA; *U.S. Public*, pg. 428

Ryan, Tom, General Counsel--Tropicana Dole Beverages North America, Bradenton, FL; *Int'l*, pg. 1217

Ryba, John W., V.P. & Gen. Counsel--Sulcus Computer Corp., Greensburg, PA; *U.S. Public*, pg. 1527

Ryder, John, Gen. Counsel--Metro Foods, Inc., Olive Branch, MS; *U.S. Private*, pg. 736

Ryea, Jack, Gen. Counsel--Lodgistix, Inc., Phoenix, AZ; *U.S. Public*, pg. 1527

Ryser, Philip R., V.P.-Franchising, Gen. Counsel & Sec.--Stanley Steemer International, Inc., Dublin, OH; *U.S. Private*, pg. 1033

Sabatine, Jeffrey P., Gen. Counsel--Riser Foods, Inc., Bedford, OH; *U.S. Private*, pg. 450

Sabl, John J., Exec. V.P., Gen. Counsel & Sec.--Conseco Inc., Carmel, IN; *U.S. Public*, pg. 432

Sabourin, John, Gen. Counsel--Maryland & Virginia Milk Producers Cooperative Association, Inc., Reston, VA; *U.S. Private*, pg. 711

Sachs, Alan, Exec. V.P., Gen. Counsel & Sec.--Edison Brothers Stores, Inc., Saint Louis, MO; *U.S. Public*, pg. 563

Sack, James M., V.P., Gen. Counsel & Sec.--NVR, Inc., Mc Lean, VA; *U.S. Public*, pg. 1148

Sackett, Gary G., V.P. & Gen. Counsel--Questar Corporation, Salt Lake City, UT; *U.S. Public*, pg. 1352

Sackman, Julie I., V.P. & Gen. Counsel--International Lease Finance Corporation, Los Angeles, CA; *U.S. Public*, pg. 85

Sacks, Michael B., V.P., Sec. & Gen. Counsel--ADT Security Services, Inc., Aurora, CO; *U.S. Public*, pg. 1649

Safier, Kerry D., V.P. & Gen. Counsel--Engle Homes, Inc., Boca Raton, FL; *U.S. Public*, pg. 583

Sagara, Kevin C., Asst. Gen. Counsel--Enova Corp, San Diego, CA; *U.S. Public*, pg. 583

Sagner, Dianne, Gen. Counsel--Peak Technologies Group, Inc., New York, NY; *Int'l*, pg. 890

Sahlman, Seppo, Chief Fin. Officer & Exec. V.P.-Treas.--Rautaruukki Oy, Helsinki, Finland; *Int'l*, pg. 1088

Sahn, John G., V.P., Gen. Counsel & Sec.--CILCORP Inc., Peoria, IL; *U.S. Public*, pg. 367

Sainsbury, Colin, Corp. Counsel-Commercial--Elan Corporation Plc, Dublin, Ireland; *Int'l*, pg. 435

Saint-Arnaud, Louis, V.P.-Legal Services & Sec.--Quebecor Inc., Montreal, Canada; *Int'l*, pg. 1075

Saint-Arnaud, Louis, V.P-Legal Affairs & Sec.--Quebecor Communications, Inc., Montreal, Canada; *Int'l*, pg. 1076

Saint-Arnaud, Louis, V.P.-Legal Services & Sec.--Quebecor Multimedia Inc., Montreal, Canada; *Int'l*, pg. 1076

Sajor, Donald J., Gen. Counsel--J.M. Peters Co., Newport Beach, CA; *U.S. Public*, pg. 302

Salamon, Diane, Treas., Sec. & Legal Counsel--Pic N'Pay Supermarkets, Inc., Dania, FL; *U.S. Private*, pg. 864

Saldin, Thomas R., Exec V.P.-Admin. & Gen. Counsel--Albertson's, Inc., Boise, ID; *U.S. Public*, pg. 38

Salinger, Robert M., Gen. Counsel & Sec.--First Financial Corporation, Stevens Point, WI; *U.S. Public*, pg. 140

Salinger, Robert M., Exec. V.P., Gen. Counsel & Sec.--First Financial Bank, FSB, Stevens Point, WI; *U.S. Public*, pg. 140

Salisbury, Kevin M., Staff V.P. & Assoc. Gen. Counsel--AlliedSignal Inc., Engineered Materials, Morristown, NJ; *U.S. Public*, pg. 51

Salit, Gary, Gen. Counsel & Sec.--Bell & Howell Holdings, Skokie, IL; *U.S. Public*, pg. 201

Sallet, Jonathan B., Chief Policy Council--MCI Communications Corp., Atlanta, GA; *U.S. Public*, pg. 1023

Salowitz, Charles B., Sec. & Assoc. Gen. Counsel--Inland Steel Industries, Inc., Chicago, IL; *U.S. Public*, pg. 879

Salsbury, Michael H., Exec. V.P. & Gen. Counsel--MCI Communications Corp., Atlanta, GA; *U.S. Public*, pg. 1023

Salter, M.A.W., Dir.-Pur., Legal & Estates--Britvic Soft Drinks Ltd., Chelmsford, United Kingdom; *Int'l*, pg. 170

Saltzman, Nancy B., V.P. & Assoc. Counsel--Chartwell Re Corporation, Stamford, CT; *U.S. Public*, pg. 336

Salup, Stephen, V.P. & Gen. Counsel--Starrett HRH, New York, NY; *U.S. Private*, pg. 1035

Samet, Andrew B., V.P. & Assoc. Gen. Counsel--AlliedSignal Inc., Morristown, NJ; *U.S. Public*, pg. 49

Samp, Frederick, Gen. Counsel & Corp. Clerk--Bangor Hydro-Electric Company, Bangor, ME; *U.S. Public*, pg. 178

Samson, Bruce, Sr. V.P.-Regulatory Affairs & Gen. Counsel--Northwest Natural Gas Company, Portland, OR; *U.S. Public*, pg. 1200

Samuels, John M., V.P. & Sr. Counsel-Taxes--General Electric Company, Fairfield, CT; *U.S. Public*, pg. 709

Samuels, Sandor E., Mng. Dir.-Legal, Gen. Counsel & Sec.--Countrywide Home Loans Inc., Pasadena, CA; *U.S. Public*, pg. 452

San Sebastian Flechoso, Federico, Gen. Counsel--Iberdrola, S.A., Bilbao, Spain; *Int'l*, pg. 657

Sanchez, Eduardo, Legal Counsel--CPC Europe Consumer Foods Division, Brussels, Belgium; *U.S. Public*, pg. 224

Sanchez, Luis Felipe Castresana, Sec. & Legal Counsel--SEPI, Madrid, Spain; *Int'l*, pg. 1223

Sandberg, Daniel, V.P.-Intl. & Gen. Counsel--Hayes Wheels International, Inc., Romulus, MI; *U.S. Private*, pg. 513

Sandberg, Hans, Sr. V.P. & Gen. Counsel--Atlas Copco AB, Stockholm, Sweden; *Int'l*, pg. 95

Sandberg, Steven A., Sr. Dir. & Gen. Counsel--Cushman & Wakefield, Inc., New York, NY; *Int'l*, pg. 873

Sander, James M., V.P.-Law & Sec.--General Nutrition, Inc., Pittsburgh, PA; *U.S. Public*, pg. 725

Sanders, David E., V.P., Gen. Counsel & Sec.--LSI Logic Corp., Milpitas, CA; *U.S. Public*, pg. 971

Sanders, John, Legal Officer--Customedix Corporation, Wallingford, CT; *U.S. Private*, pg. 298

Sanderson, Lisa, Corp. Counsel--Buck Knives, Inc., El Cajon, CA; *U.S. Private*, pg. 177

Sandgrund, David M., V.P., Gen. Counsel & Sec.--Goody Products, Inc., Peachtree City, GA; *U.S. Public*, pg. 1177

Sandifer, Thomas N., Chm. & Chief Exec. Officer--Cain & Bultman, Jacksonville, FL; *U.S. Private*, pg. 199

Sandman, Dan B., Gen. Counsel & Sec.--USX Corporation, Pittsburgh, PA; *U.S. Public*, pg. 1661

Sandman, Paul, Sr. V.P., Gen. Counsel & Sec.--Boston Scientific Corp., Natick, MA; *U.S. Public*, pg. 247

Sands, Paul T., Jr., Exec. V.P. & Gen. Counsel--Chicago Title Insurance Co., Chicago, IL; *U.S. Public*, pg. 42

Sands, Paul, Jr., Exec. V.P., Gen. Counsel & Sec.--Chicago Title & Trust Co., Chicago, IL; *U.S. Public*, pg. 42

Sands, Robert, Exec. V.P., Gen. Counsel & Sec.--Canandaigua Wine Company, Inc., Canandaigua, NY; *U.S. Public*, pg. 300

Sands, Robert-John H., V.P. & Gen. Counsel--The Acacia Group - Acacia Life Insurance Co., Bethesda, MD; *U.S. Private*, pg. 10

Sandusky, Sandy, Gen. Counsel--Peavey Electronics Corp., Meridian, MS; *U.S. Private*, pg. 845

Sanetti, Steven, Legal Counsel--Sturm, Ruger & Co., Inc., Southport, CT; *U.S. Public*, pg. 1526

Sanford, Larry, Sr. V.P.-Legal--The Coleman Company, Inc., Golden, CO; *U.S. Private*, pg. 690

Sanner, Paul, Gen. Counsel--Woodward-Clyde Group, Inc., Denver, CO; *U.S. Public*, pg. 1655

Santaniello, Joseph M., V.P. & Counsel--The Walt Disney Company, Burbank, CA; *U.S. Public*, pg. 511

Santillana Del Barrio, D. Ignacio, General Counsel--Telefonica Internacional De Espana S.A., Madrid, Spain; *Int'l*, pg. 1372

Santo, Mark V., Grp. V.P. & Gen. Counsel--ELSAG Bailey Process Automation N.V., Schiphol, Netherlands; *Int'l*, pg. 449

Sariego, Jose M., Sr. V.P. & Gen. Counsel--MasTec, Inc., Miami, FL; *U.S. Public*, pg. 1055

Sarkisian, Lisa A., Gen. Counsel & Asst. Sec.--Marketing Displays International, Farmington Hills, MI; *U.S. Private*, pg. 705

Sarnecki, Tom, V.P.-Legal Counsel--Sunclipse, Inc., Buena Park, CA; *Int'l*, pg. 72

Sarosiek, James J., V.P., Gen. Counsel & Sec.--Menasha Corporation, Neenah, WI; *U.S. Private*, pg. 731

Sarver, J. William, V.P., Gen. Counsel & Sec.--Bell Atlantic-MD, Baltimore, MD; *U.S. Public*, pg. 202

Saslow, Richard P., V.P. & Gen. Counsel--Superior Consultant Holdings Corp., Southfield, MI; *U.S. Public*, pg. 1538

Sasseville, Kati, Gen. Counsel & Fed. Liaison--Otter Tail Power Company, Fergus Falls, MN; *U.S. Public*, pg. 1234

Satz, Joseph R., Exec. V.P., Gen. Counsel & Sec.--Price Enterprises, Inc., San Diego, CA; *U.S. Public*, pg. 1324

Satzger, Doug, Sr. V.P., Gen. Counsel & Sec.--Air & Water Technologies Corporation, Branchburg, NJ; *U.S. Public*, pg. 29

Sauder, Scot, V.P. & Gen. Counsel--Horizon/CMS Healthcare Corporation, Albuquerque, NM; *U.S. Public*, pg. 836

Sauder, Scot, V.P., Gen. Counsel & Sec.--Continental Medical Systems, Inc., Mechanicsburg, PA; *U.S. Public*, pg. 839

Saunders, Beulah, Sec. & Treas.--Dakco Distributors, Inc., Minot, ND; *U.S. Private*, pg. 308

Saunders, Harry, Corp. Counsel--NationsBank South, Atlanta, GA; *U.S. Public*, pg. 1163

Saunders, Stuart D., Sr. V.P. & Gen. Counsel--Prime Bancshares Inc., Houston, TX; *U.S. Public*, pg. 1326

Sauro, Frank, Gen. Counsel--Village Super Market Inc., Springfield, NJ; *U.S. Public*, pg. 1721

Sauvey, Marian Weilert, V.P.-Law & Corp. Sec.--Atlas Van Lines, Inc., Evansville, IN; *U.S. Private*, pg. 97

Savage, Thomas R., V.P. & Gen. Counsel--Briggs & Stratton Corporation, Wauwatosa, WI; *U.S. Public*, pg. 252

Sawch, William B., V.P., Gen. Counsel & Sec.--The Perkin-Elmer Corporation, Norwalk, CT; *U.S. Public*, pg. 1279

Sawdei, Milan A., Exec. V.P., Chief Legal Officer & Sec.--Bergen Brunswig Corporation, Orange, CA; *U.S. Public*, pg. 213

Sawyers, William R., V.P.-Legal Affairs--Del Monte Foods, San Francisco, CA; *U.S. Private*, pg. 321

Scallon, Jim, Sr. V.P. & Gen. Councel--Citibank, Federal Savings Bank (Illinois), Chicago, IL; *U.S. Public*, pg. 378

Scanlon, Elizabeth A., Gen. Counsel & Sec.--The Wella Corporation, Montvale, NJ; *Int'l*, pg. 1489

Scarfone, Anthony, Sec. & Gen. Counsel--Dahlberg, Inc., Golden Valley, MN; *U.S. Public*, pg. 194

Schad, Meinrad, Legal Counsel--J.M. Voith, GmbH, Heidenheim, Germany; *Int'l*, pg. 1472

Schaeffer, Becky, Corp. Counsel & Sec.--The PBS&J Corporation, Miami, FL; *U.S. Private*, pg. 825

Schaller, Barbara L., Corp. Counsel--Key Production Company, Inc., Denver, CO; *U.S. Public*, pg. 953

Schatz, David, Gen. Counsel--Marsh Company, Belleville, IL; *U.S. Private*, pg. 707

Schauf, Lawrence E., Exec. V.P. & Sec.--Foodmaker, Inc., San Diego, CA; *U.S. Public*, pg. 661

Scheerer, R. Penelope, V.P. & Asst. Gen. Counsel--Harcourt General, Inc., Chestnut Hill, MA; *U.S. Public*, pg. 782

Scheflen, John W., Sr. Exec. V.P., Gen. Counsel & Sec.--MBNA Corporation, Wilmington, DE; *U.S. Public*, pg. 1023

Schell, Ivan, Gen. Counsel & Sec.--Roll Forming Corporation, Shelbyville, KY; *U.S. Private*, pg. 941

Schell, Mark E., Gen. Counsel & Sec.--Unit Corporation, Tulsa, OK; *U.S. Public*, pg. 1672

Scher, Meyer, Gen. Counsel--Byer California, San Francisco, CA; *U.S. Private*, pg. 191

Scherer, J. Peter, Sr. V.P.-Legal Svcs.--Taubman Centers, Inc., Bloomfield Hills, MI; *U.S. Public*, pg. 1561

Schermer, Gregory P., Gen. Counsel--Lee Enterprises, Incorporated, Davenport, IA; *U.S. Public*, pg. 983

Schett, N.B., Gen. Counsel & Sec.--PIMCO Advisors, Stamford, CT; *U.S. Public*, pg. 1296

Scheuer, Thomas, Legal Counsel & Asst. Sec.--Louis Dreyfus Corporation, Wilton, CT; *U.S. Private*, pg. 342

Schieren, George A., Sr. V.P. & Gen. Counsel--Merrill Lynch, Pierce, Fenner & Smith, Inc., New York, NY; *U.S. Public*, pg. 1098

Schiffer, Daniel L., Sr. V.P., Gen. Counsel & Sec.--MCN Energy Group, Inc., Detroit, MI; *U.S. Public*, pg. 1024

Schiffer, Daniel L., V.P., Gen. Counsel & Sec.--MCN Investment, Detroit, MI; *U.S. Public*, pg. 1025

Schiller, Arthur J., V.P., Gen. Counsel & Sec.--Lane Industries, Inc., Northbrook, IL; *U.S. Private*, pg. 649

Schilling, Richard M., V.P., Gen. Counsel & Sec.--Sundstrand Corporation, Rockford, IL; *U.S. Public*, pg. 1533

Schissler, Gerald J., Exec. V.P.-Law--Burlington Resources Inc., Houston, TX; *U.S. Public*, pg. 269

Schissler, Gerald J., Exec. V.P.-Law & Corp. Affairs--Meridian Oil Holding Inc., Houston, TX; *U.S. Public*, pg. 269

Schlack, David A., Legal Officer--Levy Security Corp., Chicago, IL; *U.S. Private*, pg. 664

Schlain, Barbara E., V.P. & Assoc. Gen. Counsel--The McGraw-Hill Companies, New York, NY; *U.S. Public*, pg. 1069

Schlatter, Donald A., Pres., Chief Exec. Officer & Gen. Counsel--Art Iron, Inc., Toledo, OH; *U.S. Private*, pg. 86

Schloss, Bruce M., V.P., Gen. Counsel & Sec.--Health-Chem Corporation, New York, NY; *U.S. Public*, pg. 802

Schloss, Martin E., V.P. & Gen. Counsel--Autotote Corporation, Newark, DE; *U.S. Public*, pg. 150

Schlyer, Lyle, Gen. Counsel--USA Petroleum Corporation, Agoura Hills, CA; *U.S. Private*, pg. 1125

Schmalz, Richard L., V.P. & Asst. Gen. Counsel--Westvaco Corporation, New York, NY; *U.S. Public*, pg. 1762

Schmatz, Robert L., Gen. Counsel--Wilbur-Ellis Company & Connell Brothers Company, San Francisco, CA; *U.S. Private*, pg. 1175

Schmid, James A., Chief Exec. Officer--Crescent Electric Supply Co., East Dubuque, IL; *U.S. Private*, pg. 289

Schmidt, Gary, V.P. & Gen. Counsel--Fujisawa U.S.A., Deerfield, IL; *Int'l*, pg. 525

Schmidt, Gary P., V.P. & Gen. Counsel--Alberto-Culver Company, Melrose Park, IL; *U.S. Public*, pg. 37

Schmidt, Thomas, V.P., Gen. Counsel & Sec.--Midland Enterprises Inc., Cincinnati, OH; *U.S. Public*, pg. 549

Schmidtman, Scott, Gen. Counsel & Sec.--Olsy North America Inc., Liberty Lake, WA; *Int'l*, pg. 1002

Schmit, James, Gen. Counsel & Sec.--Robert James Sales Inc., Buffalo, NY; *U.S. Private*, pg. 935

Schmitt, David L., Sr. V.P.-Admin., Gen. Counsel & Sec.--Bradlees Inc., Braintree, MA; *U.S. Public*, pg. 249

Schmitt, Timothy J., V.P., Sec., & Asst. Gen. Counsel--Newmont Mining Corporation, Denver, CO; *U.S. Public*, pg. 1178

Schmoller, Eberhard G.H., Sr. V.P., Gen. Counsel & Sec.--CNF Transportation Inc., Palo Alto, CA; *U.S. Public*, pg. 281

Schmutz, John F., V.P., Gen. Counsel & Sec.--La Quinta Inns, Inc., San Antonio, TX; *U.S. Public*, pg. 972

Schnaekel, John, Gen. Counsel--Precision Systems, Inc., Saint Petersburg, FL; *U.S. Public*, pg. 1321

Schneider, Bernard, Chm. Bd. & Gen. Counsel--Swisscom, Bern, Switzerland; *Int'l*, pg. 1334

Schneider, David M., Chief Legal Officer & Sec.--The Progressive Corporation, Cleveland, OH; *U.S. Public*, pg. 1334

Schneider, Eric N., V.P., Gen. Counsel & Sec.--Schneider Corp., Kitchener, Canada; *Int'l*, pg. 1207

Schneider, Mahlon C., V.P. & Gen. Counsel--Hormel Foods Corp., Austin, MN; *U.S. Public*, pg. 840

Schneider, Thomas A., Chief Legal Counsel--Safeguard Business Systems, Inc., Fort Washington, PA; *U.S. Private*, pg. 960

Schneiderman, Arthur F., Gen. Counsel--Linear Technology Corp., Milpitas, CA; *U.S. Public*, pg. 1000

Schneier, Charldene, Attorney--Regal-Beloit Corporation, Beloit, WI; *U.S. Public*, pg. 1370

Schnuck, Terry, Gen. Counsel & Sec.--Schnuck Markets, Inc., Saint Louis, MO; *U.S. Private*, pg. 971

Schnur, Daniel R., Sr. V.P., Gen. Counsel & Sec.--Richfood Holdings, Inc., Glen Allen, VA; *U.S. Public*, pg. 1388

Schochet, William, V.P., Gen. Counsel & Sec.--Overhead Door Corporation, Dallas, TX; *U.S. Private*, pg. 822

Schoenbeck, Lee, Sec.--Dakotah, Inc., Webster, SD; *U.S. Public*, pg. 477

Schoenfeld, Joel M., Sr. V.P. & General Counsel--Bertelsmann Music Group, Wilmington, DE; *Int'l*, pg. 191

Schoeniger, Terrence, Pres., Gen. Counsel & Asst. Treas.--Safety National Casualty Corp., Saint Louis, MO; *U.S. Public*, pg. 496

Schonwald, Gary A., Sec. & Legal Officer--General Felt Industries, Inc., Linwood, PA; *U.S. Private*, pg. 1094

Schorr, Brian L., Exec. V.P. & Gen. Counsel--Triarc Companies, Inc., New York, NY; *U.S. Public*, pg. 1634

Schotz, Cole, Gen. Counsel--Sharon Concepts, Millburn, NJ; *U.S. Private*, pg. 990

Schoyer, E., Gen. Counsel--Munroe, Inc., Pittsburgh, PA; *U.S. Private*, pg. 767

Schrager, Marvin L., Gen. Counsel--Don E. Williams Co., Rock Island, IL; *U.S. Private*, pg. 1177

Schraven, J.H., Coordinator-Legal--Royal Dutch/Shell Group of Companies, Hague, Netherlands; *Int'l*, pg. 1135

Schroeder, Stephen K., Gen. Counsel--Williams Telecommunications Systems, Inc., Houston, TX; *U.S. Public*, pg. 1769

Schroter, Jurgen, Div. Head-Legal Affairs--BHF-BANK AG, Frankfurt, Germany; *Int'l*, pg. 119

Schuback, Marc G., Asst. Gen. Counsel & Asst. Sec.--Footstar Inc., Mahwah, NJ; *U.S. Public*, pg. 661

Schulman, Robert P., Sr. V.P. & Gen. Counsel--Kimco Realty Corporation, New Hyde Park, NY; *U.S. Public*, pg. 960

Schultz, Ed, Gen. Counsel--Western International Media Corporation, Los Angeles, CA; *U.S. Private*, pg. 1165

Schultz, Robert, Dir.-New Bus.--The Sharper Image, San Francisco, CA; *U.S. Public*, pg. 1464

Schultz, Robert F., V.P.-Indus. Rels. & Sr. Counsel--Ampco-Pittsburgh Corporation, Pittsburgh, PA; *U.S. Public*, pg. 103

Schulze, Max H., V.P., Treas., Gen. Counsel & Sec.--MCRB Service Bureau, Inc., Chatsworth, CA; *U.S. Private*, pg. 686

Schumacher, Diane Kosmach, Sr. V.P., Gen. Counsel & Sec.--Cooper Industries, Inc., Houston, TX; *U.S. Public*, pg. 442

Schuman, Marion, Gen. Counsel--Propper Manufacturing Co., Inc., Long Island City, NY; *U.S. Private*, pg. 891

Schuman, Thomas R., V.P., Gen. Counsel & Sec.--Caremark International Inc, Northbrook, IL; *U.S. Public*, pg. 1082

Schums, William G., V.P., Gen. Counsel & Sec.--Miller Brewing Company, Milwaukee, WI; *U.S. Public*, pg. 1289
Schuster, Karl, Gen. Counsel--Christian Memorial Cultural Center, Rochester Hills, MI; *U.S. Private*, pg. 238
Schuster, Stephen M., V.P., Gen. Counsel & Sec.--Envirodyne Industries, Inc., Oak Brook, IL; *U.S. Public*, pg. 586
Schwab, Christine, V.P.-Human Resources & Legal--Software AG, Darmstadt, Germany; *Int'l*, pg. 1276
Schwappach, Nancy S., Gen. Counsel--Kaufman and Broad Home Corporation, Los Angeles, CA; *U.S. Public*, pg. 944
Schwark, Dawn, Esq., Corp. Counsel--Rust Environment & Infrastructure, Inc., Greenville, SC; *U.S. Public*, pg. 1745
Schwartz, Barry F., V.P. & Chief Counsel-Litigation--Mafco Worldwide Corp., Camden, NJ; *U.S. Private*, pg. 690
Schwartz, Bart, Legal Officer--Werthan Packaging, Inc., Nashville, TN; *U.S. Private*, pg. 1162
Schwartz, Mel, Gen. Counsel & Sec.--Honeywell Limited, North York, Canada; *U.S. Public*, pg. 835
Schwarzenbach, Peter M., V.P. & Gen. Counsel--Staples, Inc., Westborough, MA; *U.S. Public*, pg. 1509
Schweizer, Robert, Gen. Counsel--Burda GmbH, Offenburg, Germany; *Int'l*, pg. 233
Schwer, W.F., Sr. V.P., Gen. Counsel & Sec.--Imperial Holly Corporation, Sugar Land, TX; *U.S. Public*, pg. 872
Schwertfeger, Kathy, Gen. Counsel--Mercury Air Group Inc., Los Angeles, CA; *U.S. Public*, pg. 1092
Schwertz, Joseph D., Jr., Gen. Counsel & Sec.--Whitney Holding Corporation, New Orleans, LA; *U.S. Public*, pg. 1766
Schwind, William F., Jr., Gen. Counsel & Sec.--Marathon Oil Company, Houston, TX; *U.S. Public*, pg. 1661
Schwolsky, Peter M., Chief Legal Officer & Sr. V.P.--Columbia Energy Group, Reston, VA; *U.S. Public*, pg. 402
Scipione, Richard S., Gen. Counsel--John Hancock Mutual Life Insurance Company, Boston, MA; *U.S. Private*, pg. 589
Scola, Richard J., V.P.-Real Estate Law & Asst. Gen. Counsel--The Great Atlantic & Pacific Tea Company, Inc., Montvale, NJ; *Int'l*, pg. 1375
Scopp, Kathy, Gen. Counsel--Time Warner Cable of New York City, New York, NY; *U.S. Public*, pg. 1611
Scott, D.E., Sr. V.P. & Gen. Counsel--Science Applications International Corp., San Diego, CA; *U.S. Private*, pg. 975
Scott, Edwin W., V.P. & Deputy Gen. Counsel--Consolidated Edison Company of New York, Inc., New York, NY; *U.S. Public*, pg. 434
Scott, John R., V.P., Gen. Counsel & Sec.--Hunt Oil Company, Dallas, TX; *U.S. Private*, pg. 548
Scott, Michael, Gen. Counsel--Mooney Chemicals, Cleveland, OH; *U.S. Public*, pg. 1208
Scott, R., V.P. & Deputy Gen. Counsel--Houston Industries Incorporated, Houston, TX; *U.S. Public*, pg. 842
Scotton, William P., Pres.--Custom Decor, Inc., Smyrna, DE; *U.S. Private*, pg. 298
Sears, Alan, Gen. Counsel--Dow Chemical Canada, Inc., Sarnia, Canada; *U.S. Public*, pg. 523
Searson, Greg, Gen. Counsel--Future Foam, Inc., Council Bluffs, IA; *U.S. Private*, pg. 433
See, Tan Ai, Gen. Counsel--Scotts Holdings Limited, Singapore, Singapore; *Int'l*, pg. 1212
Seeliger, Hans-Jurgen, Mgr.-Legal Opers./Germany & Austria--European Investment Bank, Luxembourg, Luxembourg; *Int'l*, pg. 465
Seely, John J., V.P. & Gen. Counsel--Newly Weds Foods Inc., Chicago, IL; *U.S. Private*, pg. 796
Seeman, Leslie C., Sr. V.P. & Gen. Counsel--Orbital Sciences Corporation, Dulles, VA; *U.S. Public*, pg. 1229
Seibert, Kail, V.P.-H.R. & Gen. Counsel--GTI Corporation, San Diego, CA; *U.S. Public*, pg. 767
Seidl, Gerald D., Gen. Counsel--United Fire & Casualty Company, Cedar Rapids, IA; *U.S. Public*, pg. 1677
Seigfried, John P., V.P., Gen. Counsel, Sec. & Dir.-Investor Rels.--Medusa Corporation, Cleveland, OH; *U.S. Public*, pg. 1084
Seiler, Bill, Gen. Counsel--Vanguard Plastics, Inc., Mc Pherson, KS; *U.S. Private*, pg. 1134
Seils, William G., Sr. V.P., Gen. Counsel & Corp. Sec.--Richardson Electronics, Ltd., Lafox, IL; *U.S. Public*, pg. 1387
Seller, Victor P., Gen. Counsel--Scoville Press, Inc., Minneapolis, MN; *U.S. Private*, pg. 977
Semel, Scott N., Exec. V.P., Gen. Counsel & Sec.--Designs, Inc., Needham, MA; *U.S. Public*, pg. 501
Sepulveda Amor, Bernardo, Gen. Counsel--Empresas ICA Sociedad Controladora S.A.C.V., Mexico, Mexico; *Int'l*, pg. 454
Serr, Erik, Gen. Counsel & Sec.--R & B Machine Tool Co., Saline, MI; *U.S. Private*, pg. 901
Serwin, Bradley K., Sr. V.P., Gen. Counsel & Sec.--PAULA Financial, Pasadena, CA; *U.S. Public*, pg. 1266
Seth, E. Anthony, V.P., Gen. Counsel & Sec.--Falconbridge Limited, Toronto, Canada; *Int'l*, pg. 433
Seton, G., Gen. Counsel--Master International Corp., Santa Monica, CA; *U.S. Private*, pg. 713
Settles, G. Patrick, V.P. & Asst. Gen. Counsel--Avatar Holdings Inc., Coral Gables, FL; *U.S. Public*, pg. 151
Sevilla, Stanley, Gen. Counsel--TCI Aluminum, Gardena, CA; *U.S. Private*, pg. 1063
Seymour, Christopher H., Gen. Counsel--American Express Bank Ltd., New York, NY; *U.S. Public*, pg. 73
Sgambellone, James J., Asst. Sec. & Corp. Dir.-Taxes--The Sherwin-Williams Company, Cleveland, OH; *U.S. Public*, pg. 1465
Shaddix, James W., Gen. Counsel--Pennzoil Company, Houston, TX; *U.S. Public*, pg. 1272
Shaff, Karen, Assoc. Gen. Counsel--Principal Mutual Life Insurance Co., Des Moines, IA; *U.S. Private*, pg. 886
Shaffer, R.J., V.P., Gen. Counsel & Sec.--NI Industries, Inc., Seal Beach, CA; *U.S. Public*, pg. 1054
Shafran, Grace B., V.P. & Gen. Counsel--Baton Broadcasting Incorporated, Scarborough, Canada; *Int'l*, pg. 170
Shames, Eric, Gen. Counsel--Fahnestock & Co., Inc., New York, NY; *Int'l*, pg. 476
Shanahan, Lauri M., V.P. & Assoc. Gen. Counsel--The Gap, Inc., San Francisco, CA; *U.S. Public*, pg. 702
Shannon, James, Sr. V.P.-Admin. & Gen. Counsel--National Fire Protection Association, Quincy, MA; *U.S. Private*, pg. 782
Shannon, L. Jean, Senior Counsel--Ikon Office Solutions, Inc., Malvern, PA; *U.S. Public*, pg. 862
Shannon, Margaret B., V.P., Gen. Counsel & Sec.--BJ Services Company, Houston, TX; *U.S. Public*, pg. 161
Shannon, Patrick J., Gen. Counsel--Ed Miniat, Inc., Chicago, IL; *U.S. Private*, pg. 750
Shapiro, Amy M., Sr. V.P., Gen. Counsel & Sec.--CommNet Cellular Inc., Englewood, CO; *U.S. Public*, pg. 414
Shapiro, Howard, Exec. V.P.-Law & Admin., Gen. Counsel & Sec.--Playboy Enterprises, Inc., Chicago, IL; *U.S. Public*, pg. 1309
Shapiro, Louis, Gen. Counsel--Triton Industries, Inc., Chicago, IL; *U.S. Private*, pg. 1104
Shaw, William J., Gen. Counsel & Sec.--Bently Nevada Corporation, Minden, NV; *U.S. Private*, pg. 134
Shay, Paul R., Sec. & Asst. Gen. Counsel--Household International, Inc., Prospect Heights, IL; *U.S. Public*, pg. 842
Shea, Kevin, V.P. & Sr. Corp. Counsel--Provident Financial Group, Inc., Cincinnati, OH; *U.S. Public*, pg. 1338
Shea, Richard, Gen. Counsel--Icon International, Stamford, CT; *U.S. Private*, pg. 556
Sheehan, Richard H., Jr., Gen. Counsel & Sec.--City National Corporation, Beverly Hills, CA; *U.S. Public*, pg. 380
Sheets, Thomas R., V.P. & Gen. Counsel--Southwest Gas Corporation, Las Vegas, NV; *U.S. Public*, pg. 1493
Sheffer, Sandra, Gen. Counsel--Mosler Inc., Hamilton, OH; *U.S. Private*, pg. 763
Sheidlower, Arnold M., V.P., Assoc. Gen. Counsel & Asst. Sec.--Harvard Industries, Inc., Tampa, FL; *U.S. Public*, pg. 796
Sheikh, M. Jamil, Gen. Counsel--National Bank of Pakistan, Karachi, Pakistan; *Int'l*, pg. 907
Shelger, James M., Sr. V.P., Gen. Counsel & Sec.--Service Corporation International, Houston, TX; *U.S. Public*, pg. 1460
Shelley, James H., Staff V.P.-Employee Rels. & Gen. Counsel--Sonoco Products Company, Hartsville, SC; *U.S. Public*, pg. 1485
Shellman, Jolene L., Asst. Gen. Counsel & Asst. Sec.--A.O. Smith Corporation, Milwaukee, WI; *U.S. Public*, pg. 1476
Shender, Lewis, Corp. Counsel--Computer Network Technology Corporation, Minneapolis, MN; *U.S. Public*, pg. 421
Sheppard, M. Jackie, V.P.-Legal, Corp. Projects & Corp. Sec.--Talisman Energy Inc., Calgary, Canada; *Int'l*, pg. 1352
Sherer, F., V.P. & Gen. Counsel--Timex Corporation, Middlebury, CT; *U.S. Private*, pg. 1088
Sheridan, Bryan, Grp. Legal Counsel--Allied Irish Banks, p.l.c., Dublin, Ireland; *Int'l*, pg. 64
Sheridan, Daphne, Gen. Counsel--Giorgio Beverly Hills, Santa Monica, CA; *U.S. Public*, pg. 1331
Sheridan, Robin, Corp. Counsel--Quad/Graphics, Inc., Pewaukee, WI; *U.S. Private*, pg. 897
Sherman, Michael, Sr. V.P.-Bus. Devel., Gen. Counsel & Sec.--Fingerhut Corp., Minnetonka, MN; *U.S. Public*, pg. 623
Sherman, Pauline, V.P., Sec. & Assoc. Gen. Counsel--The Equitable Companies Incorporated, New York, NY; *U.S. Public*, pg. 588
Shiba, Wendy C., V.P., Sec. & Asst. Gen. Counsel--Bowater Incorporated, Greenville, SC; *U.S. Public*, pg. 247
Shields, Craig, Esq., Gen. Counsel--Triangle Marketing Corp., New York, NY; *U.S. Private*, pg. 1102
Shihata, Ibrahim F.I., Sr. V.P. & Gen. Counsel--The World Bank, Washington, DC; *U.S. Private*, pg. 1188
Shimizu, Hiroharu, Dir.--Chiyoda Mutual Life Insurance Company, Tokyo, Japan; *Int'l*, pg. 286
Shinnock, John B., Asst. Gen. Counsel & Asst. Sec.--American Electric Power Service Corp., Columbus, OH; *U.S. Public*, pg. 72
Shipley, P.L., V.P. & Assoc. Gen. Counsel--Guarantee Life Insurance Co., Omaha, NE; *U.S. Public*, pg. 768
Shoemaker, James M., Jr., Gen. Counsel--Ryan's Family Steak Houses, Inc., Greer, SC; *U.S. Public*, pg. 1413
Sholander, Mark C., Gen. Counsel--Kansas City Power & Light Company, Kansas City, MO; *U.S. Public*, pg. 943
Shor, Alan, Chief Admin. Officer, Exec. V.P. & Gen. Counsel--Zale Corporation, Irving, TX; *U.S. Public*, pg. 1789
Shor, Alan, Sr. V.P., Gen. Counsel & Sec.--Zale Corporation, Irving, TX; *U.S. Public*, pg. 1789
Shore, Andrew N., Esq., V.P. & Gen. Counsel--Shorewood Packaging Corporation, New York, NY; *U.S. Public*, pg. 1468
Short, David G., V.P.-Legal & Sec.--NPC International, Inc., Pittsburg, KS; *U.S. Public*, pg. 1146
Shrot, David, V.P.-Legal & Gen. Counsel--Romacorp, Inc., Dallas, TX; *U.S. Public*, pg. 1147
Shudtz, Peter J., Gen. Counsel--CSX Corporation, Richmond, VA; *U.S. Public*, pg. 284
Shuff, Ronald F., V.P., Gen. Counsel & Sec.--Flowserve Corporation, Dayton, OH; *U.S. Public*, pg. 658
Shuman, Bonnie L., V.P., Gen. Counsel & Asst. Sec.--Shared Medical Systems Corporation, Malvern, PA; *U.S. Public*, pg. 1463
Shutts, Kenneth R., Sr. V.P., Gen. Counsel & Sec.--Penn National Insurance, Harrisburg, PA; *U.S. Private*, pg. 850
Sibold, Stephen P., Sr. V.P., Gen. Counsel & Corp. Sec.--Canadian Airlines Corporation, Calgary, Canada; *Int'l*, pg. 255
Sicks, J.N., Gen. Counsel & Asst. Sec.--Berwind Corporation, Philadelphia, PA; *U.S. Private*, pg. 138
Sidman, Thomas J., Gen. Counsel--Nextel Communications, Mc Lean, VA; *U.S. Public*, pg. 1180
Sidran, Mark, City Attorney--Seattle City Light, Seattle, WA; *U.S. Private*, pg. 979
Siebels, Scott A., V.P., Sec. & Assoc. Counsel--Beneficial Corporation, Wilmington, DE; *U.S. Public*, pg. 211
Siegal, Don, Gen. Counsel--Dawson Construction Co., Inc., Gadsden, AL; *U.S. Private*, pg. 316
Siegel Steven F., Gen. Counsel & Sec.--New Plan Realty Trust, New York, NY; *U.S. Public*, pg. 1172
Siegel, David B., V.P. & Deputy Gen. Counsel--W.R. Grace & Co., Boca Raton, FL; *U.S. Public*, pg. 754
Siegel, Harold Aryai, V.P.-Office of Law--COMSAT RSI, Inc., Sterling, VA; *U.S. Public*, pg. 424
Siegel, Kenneth S., Sr. V.P., Gen. Counsel & Corp. Sec.--Cognizant Corporation, Westport, CT; *U.S. Public*, pg. 395
Siegel, Paul B., Sr. V.P.-Legal--Pennzoil Products Co., Houston, TX; *U.S. Public*, pg. 1272
Siegel, Richard D., Sec.--Comair Holdings, Inc., Erlanger, KY; *U.S. Public*, pg. 406
Siegel, Steven, Chief Fin. Officer & Gen. Counsel--Filene's Basement, Inc., Wellesley, MA; *U.S. Public*, pg. 622
Siegfried, Peter, V.P., Gen. Counsel & Sec.--Central National-Gottesman Inc., Purchase, NY; *U.S. Private*, pg. 224
Siekman, Thomas C., V.P. & Gen. Counsel--Digital Equipment Corporation, Maynard, MA; *U.S. Public*, pg. 507
Siemers, Frank, Pres. & Gen. Counsel--Norddeutsche Landesbank (NORD/LB), Hannover, Germany; *Int'l*, pg. 957
Silbey, William J., Staff V.P., Sec. & Assoc. Gen. Counsel--Schering-Plough Corporation, Madison, NJ; *U.S. Public*, pg. 1438
Sileo, Michael A., Jr., Gen. Counsel--Microsemi Corporation, Santa Ana, CA; *U.S. Public*, pg. 1107
Silhasek, James, Exec. V.P. & Gen. Counsel--Reinalt-Thomas Corp., Ann Arbor, MI; *U.S. Private*, pg. 919
Sills, John D., V.P. & Gen. Counsel--Don Massey Cadillac Inc., Plymouth, MI; *U.S. Private*, pg. 712
Silva, Charles J., Jr., Asst. Gen. Counsel & Asst. Sec.--Albany International Corp., Albany, NY; *U.S. Public*, pg. 36
Silva, Fernando L.V, Cabral, V.P.-Legal--Compania Nacional de Mineracao, Rio de Janeiro, Brazil; *Int'l*, pg. 1345
Silver, Joe, Exec. V.P. & Gen. Counsel--Sterling Vision, Inc., East Meadow, NY; *U.S. Public*, pg. 1516
Silver, Renee, V.P. & Gen. Counsel--Staff Builders Inc., Lake Success, NY; *U.S. Public*, pg. 1501
Silver, Richard B., V.P. & Assoc. Gen. Counsel--Tenet Healthcare Corporation, Santa Barbara, CA; *U.S. Public*, pg. 1576
Silverman, Barry J., V.P. & Assoc. Gen. Counsel--Masco Corporation, Taylor, MI; *U.S. Public*, pg. 1052
Silverman, Marvin, House Counsel--Computer Horizons Corp., Mountain Lakes, NJ; *U.S. Public*, pg. 421
Silverman, Scott D., Sr. V.P., Gen. Counsel & Sec.--PennCorp Financial Group, Inc., New York, NY; *U.S. Public*, pg. 1271
Silverstein, Scott, V.P. & Gen. Counsel--The Topps Company, Inc., New York, NY; *U.S. Public*, pg. 1621
Silverstein, Stanley P., V.P., Gen. Counsel & Sec.--Warnaco Inc., New York, NY; *U.S. Public*, pg. 1738
Silverthorn, Richard W., Gen. Counsel & Sec.--Koss Corporation, Milwaukee, WI; *U.S. Public*, pg. 966
Simandl, Robert, Gen. Counsel & Sec.--Bel Fuse Inc., Jersey City, NJ; *U.S. Public*, pg. 200
Simmons, Harvey O., III, Gen. Counsel & Sec.--Crucible Materials Corp., Solvay, NY; *U.S. Private*, pg. 293
Simmons, Jay B., Sr. V.P., Gen. Counsel & Sec.--Trans Financial, Inc., Bowling Green, KY; *U.S. Public*, pg. 1628
Simmons, Martin E., Exec. V.P.-Admin., Gen. Counsel & Sec.--First American Corporation, Nashville, TN; *U.S. Public*, pg. 624
Simon, Andrea, Sr. V.P. & Deputy Gen. Counsel--Showtime Networks Inc., New York, NY; *U.S. Private*, pg. 779
Simon, David F., Sr. V.P.-Corp. Counsel--U.S. Healthcare, Inc., Blue Bell, PA; *U.S. Public*, pg. 26
Simonett, Mark J., Sec.--Photo Control Corporation, Minneapolis, MN; *U.S. Public*, pg. 1292
Simons, Drew, V.P., Sec. & Gen. Counsel--Circon Corporation, Santa Barbara, CA; *U.S. Public*, pg. 373
Simpson, D.L., III, Gen. Counsel & Sec.--Conwood Company L.P., Memphis, TN; *U.S. Private*, pg. 272
Simpson, Hugh A., Sr. V.P., Gen. Counsel & Sec.--Cash America International, Inc., Fort Worth, TX; *U.S. Public*, pg. 312
Simpson, James R., Legal Counsel--WSMP, Inc., Claremont, NC; *U.S. Public*, pg. 1729
Simpson, Timothy J., V.P., Assoc. Gen. Counsel & Asst. Sec.--Ogden Energy Group, Inc., Fairfield, NJ; *U.S. Public*, pg. 1213
Sims, John R., V.P. & Deputy Gen. Counsel--Federated Department Stores, Inc., Cincinnati, OH; *U.S. Public*, pg. 617
Sims, Steven K., Gen. Counsel--U.S. Can Company, Oak Brook, IL; *U.S. Public*, pg. 1681
Sinclair, Wayne, Sr. V.P., Gen. Counsel & Sec.--MMI Companies, Inc., Deerfield, IL; *U.S. Public*, pg. 1027
Singer, Robert W., Gen. Counsel--Bearing Headquarters Co., Broadview, IL; *U.S. Private*, pg. 127
Singer, Thomas D., V.P. & Gen. Counsel--JLG Industries, Inc., McConnellsburg, PA; *U.S. Public*, pg. 918
Sirota, Bohdan I., Gen. Counsel & Asst. Sec.--CCL Industries, Inc., Willowdale, Canada; *Int'l*, pg. 238
Sirpson, Tom, Gen. Counsel--Ziebart International Corporation, Troy, MI; *U.S. Private*, pg. 1205
Siskind, Arthur, Gen. Counsel--The News Corporation Limited, Sydney, Australia; *Int'l*, pg. 925
Siskind, David A., Sec. & Asst. Gen. Counsel--The Kendall Company, Mansfield, MA; *U.S. Public*, pg. 1647

Sisler, David G., V.P., Gen. Counsel & Sec.--Elcor Corporation, Dallas, TX; *U.S. Public*, pg. 567

Sisley, G. William, Gen. Counsel & Sec.--Smith Corona Corp., Cortland, NY; *U.S. Private*, pg. 1007

Sisson, Jill B.W., Gen. Counsel & Sec.--ACX Technologies Inc., Golden, CO; *U.S. Public*, pg. 3

Sisson, Roger G., Gen. Counsel & Sec.--Genesco Inc., Nashville, TN; *U.S. Public*, pg. 728

Siverd, Robert J., Sec. & Gen. Counsel--General Cable Corporation, Highland Heights, KY; *Int'l*, pg. 1486

Siwek, Reuben M., Chm. Bd. & Gen. Counsel--Puroflow Incorporated, Van Nuys, CA; *U.S. Public*, pg. 1345

Skelsey, Roger, Gen. Counsel--Mirror Group plc, London, United Kingdom; *Int'l*, pg. 869

Skelton, Robert W., V.P., Gen. Counsel & Sec.--McCormick & Company, Incorporated, Sparks, MD; *U.S. Public*, pg. 1066

Skilling, Raymond I., Exec. V.P. & Gen. Counsel--AON Corporation, Chicago, IL; *U.S. Public*, pg. 117

Skinner, Peter, Gen. Counsel--Barron's The Dow Jones Business & Financial Weekly, New York, NY; *U.S. Public*, pg. 524

Skinner, Peter G., Sr. V.P., Gen. Counsel, Sec. & Pres.-Television--Dow Jones & Company, Inc., New York, NY; *U.S. Public*, pg. 524

Skobin, Alan J., Gen. Counsel--Galpin Motors, North Hills, CA; *U.S. Private*, pg. 438

Skornicka, Carol N., V.P., Gen. Counsel & Sec.--Midwest Express Holdings, Inc., Oak Creek, WI; *U.S. Public*, pg. 1111

Skornicka, Carol N., V.P., Sec. & Gen. Counsel--Midwest Express Airlines, Inc., Oak Creek, WI; *U.S. Public*, pg. 1111

Skrine, Bruce E., V.P., Gen. Counsel & Sec.--John Hancock Mutual Life Insurance Company, Boston, MA; *U.S. Private*, pg. 589

Slaby, James J., Gen. Counsel--National Technical Systems, Inc., Calabasas, CA; *U.S. Public*, pg. 1161

Sladnick, Clifford, Sr. V.P., Gen. Counsel & Sec.--St. Paul Bancorp, Inc., Chicago, IL; *U.S. Public*, pg. 1428

Slattery, James, Gen. Counsel & Sec.--Paradyne, Largo, FL; *U.S. Private*, pg. 838

Slattery, William H., Sr. V.P. & Gen. Counsel--Republic National Bank of New York, New York, NY; *U.S. Public*, pg. 1380

Slattery, William H., Exec. V.P. & Gen. Counsel--Republic Bank for Savings, New York, NY; *U.S. Public*, pg. 1380

Slaughter, Thomas L., V.P., Gen. Counsel & Sec.--Meredith Corporation, Des Moines, IA; *U.S. Public*, pg. 1094

Slezak, David G., Sec. & Dir.-Legal Affairs--Oglebay Norton Company, Cleveland, OH; *U.S. Public*, pg. 1213

Slichter, Donald A., Gen. Counsel & Sec.--Applied Materials, Inc., Santa Clara, CA; *U.S. Public*, pg. 123

Sloan, Mike, V.P., Gen. Counsel & Sec.--Circus Circus - Las Vegas, Las Vegas, NV; *U.S. Public*, pg. 374

Slobodien, David J., Sr. V.P. & Gen. Counsel--Dun & Bradstreet, Murray Hill, NJ; *U.S. Public*, pg. 535

Small, Clay, V.P. & Gen. Counsel--Pizza Hut, Inc., Dallas, TX; *U.S. Public*, pg. 1636

Smalley, Kathleen, Sr. V.P., Gen. Counsel & Sec.--Catellus Development Corporation, San Francisco, CA; *U.S. Public*, pg. 314

Smedira, Nicholas A., V.P. & Corp. Counsel--E.J. Footwear Corp., Endicott, NY; *U.S. Public*, pg. 1684

Smerge, Raymond G., Exec. V.P , Gen. Counsel & Sec.--Centex Corporation, Dallas, TX; *U.S. Public*, pg. 322

Smisek, Jeffrey A., Exec. V.P., Gen. Counsel & Sec.--Continental Airlines, Houston, TX; *U.S. Public*, pg. 439

Smith Jr., William A., Gen. Counsel--Graham Corporation, Batavia, NY; *U.S. Public*, pg. 757

Smith, Anne, Gen. Counsel & Sec.--General Casualty Company of Wisconsin, Sun Prairie, WI; *Int'l*, pg. 345

Smith, Anne, Gen. Counsel & Sec.--General Casualty Company of Illinois, Freeport, IL; *Int'l*, pg. 346

Smith, Anne, Gen. Counsel & Sec.--Hoosier Insurance Company, Indianapolis, IN; *Int'l*, pg. 346

Smith, Bob, Corp. Counsel--Vermeer Manufacturing Company, Pella, IA; *U.S. Private*, pg. 1137

Smith, Brian, Gen. Counsel--The Southland Corporation, Dallas, TX; *Int'l*, pg. 693

Smith, Carla J., Sr. V.P., Gen. Counsel & Sec.--Dain Rauscher Corporation, Minneapolis, MN; *U.S. Public*, pg. 476

Smith, Christine, Gen. Counsel--AEA Investors Inc., New York, NY; *U.S. Private*, pg. 4

Smith, Daniel C., V.P. & Deputy Gen. Counsel--Federal National Mortgage Association (Fannie Mae), Washington, DC; *U.S. Public*, pg. 615

Smith, David J., V.P., Gen. Counsel & Sec.--Archer Daniels Midland Company (ADM), Decatur, IL; *U.S. Public*, pg. 127

Smith, David W., Sr. V.P. & Gen. Counsel--Transatlantic Holdings Inc., New York, NY; *U.S. Public*, pg. 84

Smith, Emery W., Asst. Gen. Counsel & Asst. Sec.--Cleveland-Cliffs Inc, Cleveland, OH; *U.S. Public*, pg. 386

Smith, Gary, V.P.-Legal Affairs--Alabama Electric Cooperative, Inc., Andalusia, AL; *U.S. Private*, pg. 30

Smith, Jeffrey E., V.P. & Gen. Counsel--Comcast Cellular Communications, Inc., Wayne, PA; *U.S. Public*, pg. 407

Smith, John B., Sr. V.P., Gen. Counsel & Sec.--Interim Services Inc., Fort Lauderdale, FL; *U.S. Public*, pg. 892

Smith, John C., Sec. & Gen. Counsel--Arinc Inc. (Consolidated), Annapolis, MD; *U.S. Private*, pg. 81

Smith, Lawrence A., V.P.-Legal--The Home Depot, Inc., Atlanta, GA; *U.S. Public*, pg. 831

Smith, Marschall I., Sr. V.P., Gen. Counsel & Asst. Sec.--IMC Global, Bannockburn, IL; *U.S. Public*, pg. 856

Smith, Philip N., Sr. V.P. & Gen. Counsel--Trace International Holdings, Inc., New York, NY; *U.S. Private*, pg. 1094

Smith, Richard, Gen. Counsel--Taco Bell Corp., Irvine, CA; *U.S. Public*, pg. 1637

Smith, Richard H., Sr. V.P., Gen. Counsel & Sec.--Cooper Communities, Inc., Bella Vista, AR; *U.S. Private*, pg. 273

Smith, Richard H., V.P., Gen. Counsel & Sec.--Cooper Ventures, Inc., Bella Vista, AR; *U.S. Private*, pg. 274

Smith, Rick, Gen. Counsel & Sec.--Nova Scotia Power Inc., Halifax, Canada; *Int'l*, pg. 971

Smith, Robert C., Sr. V.P., Gen. Counsel & Sec.--White Hen Pantry, Inc., Elmhurst, IL; *U.S. Private*, pg. 1172

Smith, Robert W., V.P. & Gen. Counsel--DEC International, Inc., Madison, WI; *U.S. Private*, pg. 301

Smith, Seymour, Exec. V.P. & Gen. Counsel--Loews Theatre Management Corp., New York, NY; *Int'l*, pg. 1282

Smith, Shirley R., V.P., Gen. Counsel & Sec.--Coventry Corporation, Nashville, TN; *U.S. Public*, pg. 454

Smith, Stephen R., V.P., Gen. Counsel & Sec.--The Interlake Corporation, Lisle, IL; *U.S. Public*, pg. 892

Smith, Steve, Gen. Counsel--Exabyte Corporation, Boulder, CO; *U.S. Public*, pg. 597

Smith, Walter L., V.P., Gen. Counsel & Asst. Sec.--Hilb, Rogal and Hamilton Company, Glen Allen, VA; *U.S. Public*, pg. 826

Snarr, Steve W., Gen. Counsel--Northwest Pipeline Corp., Salt Lake City, UT; *U.S. Public*, pg. 1769

Snider, Debra H., Gen. Counsel--Heller International, Chicago, IL; *U.S. Private*, pg. 520

Snitzer, Isadore, Gen. Counsel & Sec.--C.H. Heist Corp., Clearwater, FL; *U.S. Public*, pg. 807

Snow, R.M., Jr., V.P. & Counsel--Oliver Rubber Co., Athens, GA; *U.S. Public*, pg. 1504

Snowiss, Howard, Esq., Legal Officer--Foodarama Supermarkets, Inc., Freehold, NJ; *U.S. Public*, pg. 661

Snyder, Laura Lee, Gen. Counsel--Canisco Resources, Inc., Wilmington, DE; *U.S. Public*, pg. 301

Snyder, Ronald R., V.P. & Gen Counsel, Sec.--Arvin Industries, Inc., Columbus, IN; *U.S. Public*, pg. 136

Sobol, Lawrence R., Principal & Gen. Counsel--Edward Jones, Saint Louis, MO; *U.S. Private*, pg. 597

Sogard, David, Gen. Counsel--Minnkota Power Cooperative, Inc., Grand Forks, ND; *U.S. Private*, pg. 751

Soikkanen, Kalle, Dir.-Legal Affairs--AMER TOBACCO Ltd., Tuusula, Finland; *Int'l*, pg. 72

Soland, Norman R., V.P., Gen. Counsel & Sec.--Nash Finch Company, Edina, MN; *U.S. Public*, pg. 1151

Soled, Kathleen A., Assoc. Gen. Counsel & Sec.--Trans World Airlines, Inc., Saint Louis, MO; *U.S. Public*, pg. 1629

Solis, Javier, Sr. V.P.-Admin., Gen. Counsel & Sec.--Ameron International Corporation, Pasadena, CA; *U.S. Public*, pg. 98

Solomon, Deryck J., Sec.--Glynwed International PLC, Birmingham, United Kingdom; *Int'l*, pg. 554

Solomon, Hadar, Esq., V.P., Gen. Counsel & Sec.--Laser Industries Ltd., Tel Aviv, Israel; *Int'l*, pg. 429

Solomon, Mike, Sr. V.P.-Legal--Tower Records, West Sacramento, CA; *U.S. Private*, pg. 688

Solomon, Paul F., Sr. V.P. & Gen. Counsel--Jacor Communications, Inc., Covington, KY; *U.S. Public*, pg. 922

Sondag, Robert H., Chief Admin. Officer--Gage Marketing Group, Minneapolis, MN; *U.S. Private*, pg. 437

Sonderman, Andy, Gen. Counsel & Sec.--Columbia Gas Distribution Companies, Columbus, OH; *U.S. Public*, pg. 402

Sonnabend, Peter J., Gen. Counsel & Sec.--Sonesta International Hotels Corporation, Boston, MA; *U.S. Public*, pg. 1485

Soshnick, Julian, V.P. & Gen. Counsel--Analogic Corporation, Peabody, MA; *U.S. Public*, pg. 109

Soutendijk, D.R., V.P., Gen. Counsel & Sec.--Union Camp Corporation, Wayne, NJ; *U.S. Public*, pg. 1665

Southerst, Mark, V.P., Gen. Counsel & Sec.--Greyhound Lines, Inc., Dallas, TX; *U.S. Public*, pg. 765

Southerst, Mark, Sr. V.P., Gen. Counsel & Sec.--Greyhound Lines, Inc., Dallas, TX; *U.S. Public*, pg. 765

Southwick, Stephen W., V.P., Gen. Counsel & Sec.--IES Industries Inc., Cedar Rapids, IA; *U.S. Public*, pg. 855

Southwick, Stephen W., V.P., Gen. Counsel & Sec.--IES Utilities Inc., Cedar Rapids, IA; *U.S. Public*, pg. 855

Spackman, Randall P., Sr. V.P. & Gen. Counsel--Opal Concepts, Inc., Anaheim, CA; *U.S. Private*, pg. 817

Spalding, Leonard A., Deputy Gen. Counsel--The Gillette Company, Boston, MA; *U.S. Public*, pg. 743

Spangler, David B., Pres. & Chief Exec. Officer--Jefferson Mills, Inc., Pulaski, VA; *U.S. Private*, pg. 584

Spanos, George G., Legal Counsel--The Spanos Companies, Stockton, CA; *U.S. Private*, pg. 1020

Speaker, Mark D., V.P. & Sr. Counsel--Bristol-Myers Squibb U.S. Pharmaceutical Group, Plainsboro, NJ; *U.S. Public*, pg. 255

Spears, Robert, V.P. & Gen. Counsel--Lone Star Technologies, Inc., Dallas, TX; *U.S. Public*, pg. 1012

Spector, Martin W., Exec. V.P. & Gen. Counsel--Aramark Corp., Philadelphia, PA; *U.S. Private*, pg. 78

Spellman, Richard A., Sr. V.P., Gen. Counsel & Sec.--Guarantee Life Insurance Co., Omaha, NE; *U.S. Public*, pg. 768

Spencer, Cliff, Attorney--Buffalo Rock Company, Birmingham, AL; *U.S. Private*, pg. 179

Speranza, Paul S., Gen. Counsel & Sec.--Wegmans Food Markets, Inc., Rochester, NY; *U.S. Private*, pg. 1158

Speranzella, Charles J., Jr., Exec. V.P., Gen. Counsel & Sec.--Breed Technologies, Inc., Lakeland, FL; *U.S. Public*, pg. 251

Spetze, Eric, M.L., Sec. & Legal--Pharmacia & Upjohn Biosystems AB, Uppsala, Sweden; *Int'l*, pg. 1047

Spicq, Francois, Gen. Counsel--Iveco-Unic S.A., Trappes, France; *Int'l*, pg. 484

Spies, Robert, Gen. Counsel--Empire Berol U.S.A., Brentwood, TN; *U.S. Public*, pg. 1178

Spiess, Gary A., Gen. Counsel & Clerk--BankBoston Corporation, Boston, MA; *U.S. Public*, pg. 183

Spiller, Scott, Gen. Counsel & Sec.--Raytheon Appliances, Ripon, WI; *U.S. Public*, pg. 1366

Spindler, George S., Sr. V.P.-Law & Corp. Affairs & Gen. Counsel--Amoco Corporation, Chicago, IL; *U.S. Public*, pg. 101

Spitzberg, Marian, V.P. & Gen. Counsel--A.H. Belo Corporation, Dallas, TX; *U.S. Public*, pg. 209

Spool, James, Gen. Counsel--North Safety Products, Charleston, SC; *Int'l*, pg. 1243

Sporn, Benjamin T., V.P.-Legal & Sec.--AMBI Inc., Tarrytown, NY; *U.S. Public*, pg. 7

Spors, Karen, V.P., Gen. Counsel & Sec.--Sta-Rite Industries, Inc., Delavan, WI; *U.S. Public*, pg. 1767

Spors, Karen, Gen. Counsel--Sta-Rite Water Systems, Delavan, WI; *U.S. Public*, pg. 1767

Sprague, Charles W., Exec. V.P., Gen. Counsel & Sec.--Fiserv, Inc., Brookfield, WI; *U.S. Public*, pg. 647

Sprague, Donald, Legal Officer--Giles & Ransome, Inc., Bensalem, PA; *U.S. Private*, pg. 453

Sprague, William D., V.P. & Gen. Counsel--Lukens Inc., Coatesville, PA; *U.S. Public*, pg. 1019

Spransy, Joseph W., Corp. Counsel & Asst. Sec.--United States Pipe & Foundry Company, Inc., Birmingham, AL; *U.S. Public*, pg. 1736

Springer, Paul, Sr. V.P. & Asst. Gen. Counsel--Paramount Pictures Corporation, Los Angeles, CA; *U.S. Private*, pg. 776

Squires, Vernon T., Sr. V.P. & Gen. Counsel--The ServiceMaster Company, Downers Grove, IL; *U.S. Public*, pg. 1461

St. John, R.A., Gen. Counsel--The Broken Hill Proprietary Company Limited, Melbourne, Australia; *Int'l*, pg. 223

Stables, Jane, Grp. Legal Advisor--United News & Media plc, London, United Kingdom; *Int'l*, pg. 1443

Staff, Kenneth, V.P. & Gen. Counsel--WWF Paper Corporation, Bala Cynwyd, PA; *U.S. Private*, pg. 1145

Stagg, Dard F., V.P., Gen. Counsel & Sec.--Greenwich Air Services, Miami, FL; *U.S. Public*, pg. 710

Stahl, Roy H., Esq., Sr. V.P. & Gen. Counsel--Philadelphia Suburban Corporation, Bryn Mawr, PA; *U.S. Public*, pg. 1287

Stahman, Robert W., V.P., Gen. Counsel & Sec.--Idaho Power Company, Boise, ID; *U.S. Public*, pg. 861

Stamm, Charles H., Exec. V.P. & Gen. Counsel--Teachers Insurance and Annuity Association, New York, NY; *U.S. Private*, pg. 1071

Stammer, William, Assoc. Gen. Counsel--Playtex Products Inc., Westport, CT; *U.S. Public*, pg. 1310

Standish, Linda S., Gen. Counsel & Corp. Sec.--Central Reserve Life Corporation, Strongsville, OH; *U.S. Public*, pg. 326

Standish, Myles E., Sr. V.P. & Gen. Counsel--Oakwood Homes Corporation, Greensboro, NC; *U.S. Public*, pg. 1209

Standlee, Christopher, Gen. Counsel--High Plains Corporation, Wichita, KS; *U.S. Public*, pg. 825

Stanford, Paul, Exec. V.P.-Admin., Gen. Counsel & Sec.--CalMat Co., Los Angeles, CA; *U.S. Public*, pg. 295

Stanley, David H., V.P.-Legal, Gen. Counsel & Sec.--Informix Software, Menlo Park, CA; *U.S. Public*, pg. 876

Stanton, Victoria, Exec. V.P., Gen. Counsel & Sec.--Farm Family Casualty Insurance Co., Glenmont, NY; *U.S. Private*, pg. 394

Staple, Peter, Sr. V.P. & Gen. Counsel--Alza Corporation, Palo Alto, CA; *U.S. Public*, pg. 62

Staples, F. Dudley, Jr., Sec. & Gen. Counsel--BioWhittaker, Inc., Walkersville, MD; *U.S. Public*, pg. 297

Stapleton, Richard, Exec. V.P.-Fin. & Admin., Gen. Counsel & Sec.--The Lane Construction Corp., Meriden, CT; *U.S. Private*, pg. 649

Stark, Gary E., V.P. & Gen. Counsel--Nationwide Health Properties Inc., Newport Beach, CA; *U.S. Public*, pg. 1166

Stark, Patrick V., Gen. Counsel--Intellicall, Inc., Carrollton, TX; *U.S. Public*, pg. 887

Stark, W., Sr. V.P., Gen. Counsel & Sec.--ESCO Electronics Corporation, Saint Louis, MO; *U.S. Public*, pg. 546

Staskiel, James, V.P., Legal Counsel & Sec.--McCarthy Building Companies, Saint Louis, MO; *U.S. Private*, pg. 719

Stasz, Peter J., Gen. Counsel--H.B. Smith Co., Inc., Westfield, MA; *U.S. Private*, pg. 1008

Stathman, Charles O., Sr. Deputy Gen. Counsel--Unocal Corporation, El Segundo, CA; *U.S. Public*, pg. 1698

Staubitz, Arthur, Sr. V.P. & Gen. Counsel--Baxter International Inc., Deerfield, IL; *U.S. Public*, pg. 196

Staubitz, Arthur F., Sr. V.P. & Gen. Counsel--Baxter Healthcare Corporation, Deerfield, IL; *U.S. Public*, pg. 196

Stauton, Marshal, V.P. & Counsel--United Refining Company, Warren, PA; *U.S. Private*, pg. 915

Stavely, Richard W., V.P., Sec. & Gen. Counsel--Misco Industries, Wichita, KS; *U.S. Private*, pg. 752

Stecher, Jamie, Gen. Counsel--Florasynth Inc., Teterboro, NJ; *Int'l*, pg. 173

Steele, Elizabeth M., V.P., Gen. Counsel & Sec.--Jones Intercable, Inc., Englewood, CO; *U.S. Private*, pg. 597

Steenland, Douglas, Sr. V.P. & Gen. Counsel--Northwest Airlines Corp., Saint Paul, MN; *U.S. Public*, pg. 1199

Steffan, Frederick V., Division Counsel--Intermec Technologies Corporation, Everett, WA; *U.S. Public*, pg. 1699

Stein, Ernest D., Gen. Counsel--The CIT Group Holdings, Inc., New York, NY; *Int'l*, pg. 360

Stein, Kenneth, Gen. Counsel--LeaRonal, Inc., Freeport, NY; *U.S. Public*, pg. 982

Steinberg, Howard E., Sr. V.P., Sec. & Gen. Counsel--Reliance Group Holdings, Inc., New York, NY; *U.S. Public*, pg. 1374

Steinkamp, Robert, V.P., Sec. & Gen. Counsel--Applebee's International, Inc., Overland Park, KS; *U.S. Public*, pg. 122

Stellato, Louis E, V.P., Gen. Counsel & Sec.--The Sherwin-Williams Company, Cleveland, OH; *U.S. Public*, pg. 1465

Stensman, Lars, Head-Grp. Staff Law & Corp. Sec.--BTL AB, Goteborg, Sweden; *Int'l*, pg. 123

Stephen, K.G., Mng. Counsel--Mobil Oil Company, Ltd., Milton Keynes, United Kingdom; *U.S. Public*, pg. 1119
Stephens, Tom, Gen. Counsel--Celestial Seasonings, Boulder, CO; *U.S. Public*, pg. 319
Stephenson, Jack, Gen. Counsel--Medical Assurance, Inc., Birmingham, AL; *U.S. Public*, pg. 1079
Sterkel, Alice V., Gen. Counsel--Mississippi River Transmission, Saint Louis, MO; *U.S. Public*, pg. 843
Sterken, Thomas A., V.P. & Gen. Counsel--Associated Grocers, Inc., Seattle, WA; *U.S. Private*, pg. 90
Sterling, Donald R., V.P.-Legal Affairs & Sec.--Iomega Corporation, Roy, UT; *U.S. Public*, pg. 912
Sterling, Marcia, V.P.-Bus. Devel. & Gen. Counsel--Autodesk, Inc., San Rafael, CA; *U.S. Public*, pg. 148
Stern, Bruce E., Gen. Counsel & Sec.--Financial Security Assurance Holdings Ltd., New York, NY; *U.S. Public*, pg. 622
Stern, Colin D., Esq., Exec. V.P. & Gen. Counsel--Charming Shoppes, Inc., Bensalem, PA; *U.S. Public*, pg. 335
Stern, Robert E., V.P., Gen. Counsel & Sec.--The Bon Ton Stores, Inc., York, PA; *U.S. Public*, pg. 244
Sternberg, Paul J., V.P., Gen. Counsel & Sec.--The Raymond Corporation, Greene, NY; *Int'l*, pg. 123
Stetzner, Leah Manning, Gen. Counsel & Corp. Sec.--Illinova Inc., Decatur, IL; *U.S. Public*, pg. 869
Stetzner, Leah Manning, V.P., Gen. Counsel & Sec.--Illinois Power Company, Decatur, IL; *U.S. Public*, pg. 869
Steuber, Frederick G., Sr. V.P., Gen. Counsel & Sec.--The Lincoln Electric Company, Cleveland, OH; *U.S. Public*, pg. 996
Stevens, A.J., Sr. V.P. & Gen. Counsel--Lorillard Tobacco Company, Greensboro, NC; *U.S. Public*, pg. 1011
Stevens, Glenn H., V.P., Gen. Counsel & Sec.--Maxtor Corporation, Milpitas, CA; *Int'l*, pg. 641
Stevens, M.A.G., Grp. Soliciter--Ladbroke Group Plc, London, United Kingdom; *Int'l*, pg. 787
Stevens, Thomas C., Exec. V.P., Gen. Counsel & Sec.--Keycorp, Cleveland, OH; *U.S. Public*, pg. 954
Stevenson, Bernard A., V.P.-Admin. & Legal Affairs--Harlequin Enterprises Ltd., Don Mills, Canada; *Int'l*, pg. 1402
Stewart, Bernard F., Exec. V.P., Gen. Counsel & Sec.--Exide Corporation, Reading, PA; *U.S. Public*, pg. 600
Stewart, Lever, Gen. Counsel & Asst. Sec.--Rock-Tenn Company, Norcross, GA; *U.S. Public*, pg. 1396
Stewart, William C., Jr., V.P., Gen. Counsel & Sec.--Cubic Corporation, San Diego, CA; *U.S. Public*, pg. 466
Stibich, Paul, Gen. Counsel--Perlmuter Printing Company, Cleveland, OH; *Int'l*, pg. 1177
Stidham, Gregory R., Gen. Counsel--Sharpe Dry Goods Co., Inc., Checotah, OK; *U.S. Private*, pg. 990
Stigler, David M., Sr. V.P.-Legal & Pub. Affairs, Gen. Counsel & Sec.--ADVO, Inc., Windsor, CT; *U.S. Public*, pg. 23
Still, Stephen H., V.P. & Assoc. Gen. Counsel--Torchmark Corporation, Birmingham, AL; *U.S. Public*, pg. 1622
Stinchfield, John E., Gen. Counsel & Sec.--The Donohoe Companies, Inc., Washington, DC; *U.S. Private*, pg. 340
Stinnett, J. Daniel, V.P., Sec. & Gen. Counsel--Commerce Bancshares, Inc., Kansas City, MO; *U.S. Public*, pg. 409
Stinson, Robert C., V.P.-Admin. & H.R., Gen. Counsel & Sec.--Applied Industrial Technologies, Cleveland, OH; *U.S. Public*, pg. 122
Stitzer, H. Todd, V.P., Gen. Counsel & Sec.--Cadbury Beverages North America, Stamford, CT; *Int'l*, pg. 248
Stokes, David, Chief Counsel--Applied Communications, Inc., Omaha, NE; *U.S. Public*, pg. 1629
Stokes, George Ann, Sr. V.P. & Gen. Counsel--The Minute Maid Company, Houston, TX; *U.S. Public*, pg. 392
Stolar, Henry, Sr. V.P. & Gen. Counsel--Maritz Inc., Fenton, MO; *U.S. Private*, pg. 703
Stoll, William F., Sr. V.P. & Gen. Counsel--Borden, Inc., Columbus, OH; *U.S. Private*, pg. 157
Stoller, John R., V.P., Gen. Counsel & Sec.--Pulte Corporation, Bloomfield Hills, MI; *U.S. Public*, pg. 1344
Stone, Gary L., Sr. V.P., Gen. Counsel & Sec.--Parsons Corporation, Pasadena, CA; *U.S. Private*, pg. 841
Stone, Marc J., V.P.-Corp. Plng. & Devel., Gen. Counsel & Sec.--Omega Research Inc., Miami, FL; *U.S. Public*, pg. 1222
Stone, Meredith, V.P.-Legal--Konica Business Machines USA, Inc., Windsor, CT; *Int'l*, pg. 748
Stone, Robert H., V.P., Gen. Counsel & Sec.--Avatex Corporation, Dallas, TX; *U.S. Public*, pg. 151
Stonebraker, Kelly L., V.P. & Gen. Counsel--Capsure Holdings Corp., Chicago, IL; *U.S. Public*, pg. 303
Storms, Clifford B., Sr. V.P. & Gen. Counsel--Bestfoods, Englewood Cliffs, NJ; *U.S. Public*, pg. 223
Storus, T.E., V.P. & Gen. Counsel--National Trustco Inc., Toronto, Canada; *Int'l*, pg. 909
Story, Jacqualee, Gen. Counsel--Nintendo of America, Redmond, WA; *Int'l*, pg. 932
Stracham, Jeremy, Exec. Dir.-Legal & Corp. Affairs--Glaxo Wellcome plc, London, United Kingdom; *Int'l*, pg. 552
Straghan, H., Gen. Counsel--Eveready Battery Co., Saint Louis, MO; *U.S. Public*, pg. 1360
Straka, Angeline C., V.P., Sec. & Assoc. Gen. Counsel--CBS Corporation, Pittsburgh, PA; *U.S. Public*, pg. 273
Stramman, John, V.P. & Gen. Counsel--North American Refractories Company, Cleveland, OH; *U.S. Private*, pg. 803
Strasburg, Sari Ann, Gen. Counsel & Sec--Velcro Industries N.V., Willemstad, Netherlands Antilles; *Int'l*, pg. 1462
Strassler, Marc, Gen. Counsel & Sec--Pathmark Stores Incorporated, Woodbridge, NJ; *U.S. Private*, pg. 843
Stratton, Jane, Gen. Counsel--Chiron Corporation, Emeryville, CA; *U.S. Public*, pg. 349
Straub, Donald A., Gen. Counsel & Sec.--NT Dor-omatic, Harwood Heights, IL; *U.S. Private*, pg. 771
Strauss, Jonathon, V.P. & Gen. Counsel--Century America Corporation, Chicago, IL; *U.S. Private*, pg. 225
Straw, Ralph L., Jr., V.P., Gen. Cousel & Sec.--United National Bancorp, Bridgewater, NJ; *U.S. Public*, pg. 1679
Streisinger, Cory, Gen. Counsel--Port of Portland, Portland, OR; *U.S. Private*, pg. 876
Strickland, Barbara S., Gen. Counsel--The Suddath Companies, Jacksonville, FL; *U.S. Private*, pg. 1049
Strobel, Martin J., V.P., Gen. Counsel & Sec.--Dana Corporation, Toledo, OH; *U.S. Public*, pg. 479
Strobel, Pamela B., V.P. & Gen. Counsel--ComEd, Chicago, IL; *U.S. Public*, pg. 1664
Strohm, B.C., Exec. V.P., Gen. Counsel & Sec.--Equity Residential Properties Trust, Chicago, IL; *U.S. Public*, pg. 590
Strome, William F., Sr. V.P. & Deputy Gen. Counsel--PNC Bank Corp., Pittsburgh, PA; *U.S. Public*, pg. 1242
Strong, Barry P., Gen. Counsel & Sec.--The National Mutual Life Association of Australia Limited, Melbourne, Australia; *Int'l*, pg. 909
Stroud, D. Michael, V.P., Gen. Counsel & Sec.--Bell Atlantic-PA, Philadelphia, PA; *U.S. Public*, pg. 203
Stroup, Stanley S., Exec. V.P. & Gen. Counsel--Norwest Corporation, Minneapolis, MN; *U.S. Public*, pg. 1201
Strutt, David, Chief Fin. Officer, Gen. Counsel & Sec.--The Weitz Company, Inc., Des Moines, IA; *U.S. Private*, pg. 1160
Stuart, Gloria, Grp. Dir.-Legal Affairs & Sec.--The BOC Group plc, Windlesham, United Kingdom; *Int'l*, pg. 121
Stubblefield, William, Legal Counsel--Dunavant Enterprises, Inc., Memphis, TN; *U.S. Private*, pg. 346
Styer, Paul A., Sr. V.P., Gen. Counsel & Sec.--Copart, Inc., Benicia, CA; *U.S. Public*, pg. 446
Sudbury, David M., V.P., Gen. Counsel & Sec.--Commercial Metals Company, Dallas, TX; *U.S. Public*, pg. 411
Suenner, Eckart, Dr., Div. Head-Legal, Taxes & Insurance--BASF AG, Ludwigshafen, Germany; *Int'l*, pg. 103
Sullivan, Dennis G., V.P., Gen. Counsel, Asst. Treas. & Asst. Sec.--Middlesex Water Company, Iselin, NJ; *U.S. Public*, pg. 1110
Sullivan, John, Gen. Counsel--Silicon Graphics, Inc., Mountain View, CA; *U.S. Public*, pg. 1473
Sullivan, John L., Gen. Counsel & Corp. Sec.--Cray Research, Eagan, MN; *U.S. Public*, pg. 1473
Sullivan, Judith A., Gen. Counsel & Sec.--Citizens Financial Group, Inc., Providence, RI; *Int'l*, pg. 1132
Sullivan, Kevin T., V.P. & Asst. Gen. Counsel--The Allstate Corporation, Northbrook, IL; *U.S. Public*, pg. 55
Sullivan, Mark, Gen. Counsel--Bose Corporation, Framingham, MA; *U.S. Private*, pg. 160
Sullivan, Maureen O., Sr. V.P. & Gen. Counsel--Halter Marine Group, Inc., Gulfport, MS; *U.S. Public*, pg. 778
Sullivan, Michael P., V.P., Gen. Counsel & Sec.--Commonwealth Energy System, Cambridge, MA; *U.S. Public*, pg. 414
Sullivan, Michael P., V.P.-Clerk & Gen. Counsel--Hopkinton LNG Corp., Cambridge, MA; *U.S. Public*, pg. 415
Sullivan, Robert J., Sr. V.P. & Gen. Counsel--Talegen Corporation, Seattle, WA; *U.S. Public*, pg. 1784
Sulzbach, Christi R., Sr. V.P.-Pub. Affairs & Assoc. Gen. Counsel--Tenet Healthcare Corporation, Santa Barbara, CA; *U.S. Public*, pg. 1576
Sumner, Gordon H., V.P. & Gen. Auditor--Northern Telecom Limited, Brampton, Canada; *Int'l*, pg. 968
Sunday, Jeffery H., House Counsel--Pennsylvania Enterprises Inc., Wilkes-Barre, PA; *U.S. Public*, pg. 1271
Sunkin, David, V.P.-Legal, Gen. Counsel & Sec.--Earl Scheib, Inc., Beverly Hills, CA; *U.S. Public*, pg. 1437
Surface, Katheryn E., Sec. & Gen. Counsel--United Dominion Realty Trust, Inc., Richmond, VA; *U.S. Public*, pg. 1677
Sussman, Harvey A., V.P. & Gen. Counsel--Westwood-Squibb Pharmaceuticals Inc., Buffalo, NY; *U.S. Public*, pg. 255
Sutter, Larry, Legal Officer--General Media International Inc., New York, NY; *U.S. Private*, pg. 444
Suttmeier, Catherine H., V.P., Gen. Counsel & Sec.--Oneida Ltd., Oneida, NY; *U.S. Public*, pg. 1225
Sutton, Neal, Sr. V.P., Gen. Counsel & Sec.--Smith International, Inc., Houston, TX; *U.S. Public*, pg. 1478
Sutton, Ray Sandy, V.P.-Corp. Sec. & Gen. Counsel--Interstate Bakeries Corporation, Kansas City, MO; *U.S. Public*, pg. 909
Sveinsson, Pal, Gen. Counsel--Den norske Bank ASA, Oslo, Norway; *Int'l*, pg. 392
Sverdlov, Eli, Dr., Auditor--The Israel Electric Corporation Ltd., Haifa, Israel; *Int'l*, pg. 690
Swan, Barbara J., V.P. & Gen. Counsel--Wisconsin Power & Light Company, Madison, WI; *U.S. Public*, pg. 1728
Swan, Neil, Sec. & Gen. Counsel--London International Group plc, London, United Kingdom; *Int'l*, pg. 815
Sweatt, Millard E., Sr. V.P.-Opers. Analysis, Pur. & Legal & Gen. Counsel--Federal Reserve Bank of Dallas, Dallas, TX; *U.S. Private*, pg. 399
Sweeney, David, Legal Counsel--NESCO, Inc., Cleveland, OH; *U.S. Private*, pg. 791
Sweeney, Thomas, Gen. Counsel & Sec.--HDS Services, Farmington Hills, MI; *U.S. Private*, pg. 490
Swick, Michael F., V.P., Gen. Counsel & Corp. Sec.--AGCO Corporation, Duluth, GA; *U.S. Public*, pg. 28
Swift, Dean A., V.P., Gen. Counsel & Asst. Sec.--Belden & Blake Corporation, Canton, OH; *U.S. Private*, pg. 1078
Swirsky, Barry, Gen. Counsel--Nobel Education Dynamics, Inc., Media, PA; *U.S. Public*, pg. 1185
Switalski, Gillian, Gen. Counsel & Sec.--Proudfoot USA Company, West Palm Beach, FL; *Int'l*, pg. 1072
Switalski, Gillian E., Gen. Counsel & Sec.--Proudfoot plc, Richmond, United Kingdom; *Int'l*, pg. 1071
Sydnor, E. Starke, Asst. Gen. Counsel & Dir.-Chemicals & Environmental--Vulcan Materials Company, Birmingham, AL; *U.S. Public*, pg. 1725
Sygenda, Susan M., V.P. & Gen. Counsel--Binswanger, Philadelphia, PA; *U.S. Private*, pg. 144
Syrrist, Baard, Gen. Counsel--Christiania Bank og Kreditkasse ASA, Oslo, Norway; *Int'l*, pg. 289
Szoke, E.G., V.P. & Gen. Counsel--Henkel Corporation, King of Prussia, PA; *Int'l*, pg. 610
Taaffe, George A., Jr., V.P. & Asst. Gen. Counsel--Consolidated Natural Gas Company, Pittsburgh, PA; *U.S. Public*, pg. 435
Taaffe, George A., Jr., V.P. & Asst. Gen. Counsel--Consolidated Natural Gas Service Co., Inc., Pittsburgh, PA; *U.S. Public*, pg. 435
Tabernilla, Armando A., V.P.-Legal Affairs, Gen. Counsel & Sec.--IVAX Corporation, Miami, FL; *U.S. Public*, pg. 914
Tabler, Bryan G., V.P., Gen. Counsel & Sec.--Ipalco Enterprises, Inc., Indianapolis, IN; *U.S. Public*, pg. 912
Taithe, Andre Gilles, V.P.-Legal Affairs--Lafarge S.A., Paris, France; *Int'l*, pg. 788
Takahashi, Tetsuro, Gen. Counsel--Toyo Tire & Rubber Co., Ltd., Osaka, Japan; *Int'l*, pg. 1411
Tamburo, Vincent A., Gen. Counsel & Sec.--1st Source Corporation, South Bend, IN; *U.S. Public*, pg. 638
Tamburo, Vincent A., Sr. V.P., Gen. Counsel & Sec.--1st Source Bank Consolidated, South Bend, IN; *U.S. Public*, pg. 638
Tanaka, Akira, Mngmt. Counselor--Dentsu, Sudler & Hennessey Inc., Tokyo, Japan; *U.S. Private*, pg. 325
Tanaka, David F., V.P., Gen. Counsel & Sec.--Gaylord Container Corporation, Deerfield, IL; *U.S. Public*, pg. 704
Tanaka, Seiichi, Couns. & Rep. Dir.--Central Japan Railway Company, Nagoya, Japan; *Int'l*, pg. 279
Tandstad, Ola Petter, Lawyer--Tiedemanns - Joh.H.Andresen ANS, Oslo, Norway; *Int'l*, pg. 1389
Tandy, Bradley J., Asst. Gen. Counsel--Biomet, Inc., Warsaw, IN; *U.S. Public*, pg. 231
Tang, Paul, V.P., Gen. Counsel & Asst. Sec.--Burlington Coat Factory Warehouse Corporation, Burlington, NJ; *U.S. Public*, pg. 268
Tang, Rick, Grp. Legal Advisor--Hong Kong Telephone Company Ltd., Wan Chai, Hong Kong; *Int'l*, pg. 247
Taniguchi, Sadao, Chief Fin Officer, Legal Officer & Dir.-Personnel & Inv. Rels.--Kosugi Sangyo Co., Ltd., Tokyo, Japan; *Int'l*, pg. 759
Tantlinger, William A., Gen. Counsel--Persingers, Inc., Charleston, WV; *U.S. Private*, pg. 855
Tapp, Richard, Sec. & Chief Legal Advisor--Blue Circle Industries PLC, London, United Kingdom; *Int'l*, pg. 197
Tarajano, Jose, Gen. Counsel & Mgr.-Personnel--Pala Group, Inc., Baton Rouge, LA; *U.S. Private*, pg. 834
Tarma, Tiina, Gen. Counsel--OY Stockmann AB, Helsinki, Finland; *Int'l*, pg. 1301
Taronji, Jaime Jr., V.P. & Gen. Counsel--Tenneco Packaging, Evanston, IL; *U.S. Public*, pg. 1579
Tarr, Alan, Gen. Counsel--Friendship Dairies, Inc., Friendship, NY; *U.S. Private*, pg. 429
Tarvainen, Veli-Matti, Corp. Counsel--Partek Corporation, Helsinki, Finland; *Int'l*, pg. 1024
Tasher, Steven A., V.P.-Environmental Affairs & Assoc. Gen. Counsel-Environment--American Home Products Corporation, Madison, NJ; *U.S. Public*, pg. 79
Tassone, Joe, V.P. & Gen. Counsel--Dayco Products Inc., Miamisburg, OH; *U.S. Public*, pg. 1045
Tatum, Jeffery Anne, V.P. & Gen. Counsel--Chips and Technologies, Inc., San Jose, CA; *U.S. Public*, pg. 349
Taylor, C., Gen. Counsel--Northern Rock PLC, Newcastle upon Tyne, United Kingdom; *Int'l*, pg. 968
Taylor, Craig, Assoc. Gen. Counsel--Morrison Knudsen Corporation, Boise, ID; *U.S. Public*, pg. 1133
Taylor, Dana, Gen. Counsel & Sec.--Curtiss-Wright Corp., Lyndhurst, NJ; *U.S. Public*, pg. 469
Taylor, Dennis J., Gen. Counsel--Degussa Corporation, Ridgefield Park, NJ; *Int'l*, pg. 388
Taylor, Henry H., Exec. V.P. & Gen. Counsel--Laidlaw Environmental Services, Inc., Columbia, SC; *U.S. Public*, pg. 975
Taylor, James, Gen. Counsel, Loeb & Loeb--DKB & Partners, Inc., Morristown, NJ; *U.S. Private*, pg. 302
Taylor, James, V.P., Gen. Counsel & Sec.--Southwestern Bell Telephone Co., Saint Louis, MO; *U.S. Public*, pg. 1416
Taylor, Kathleen, Sr. V.P. & Gen. Counsel--Four Seasons Hotels Inc., Don Mills, Canada; *Int'l*, pg. 502
Taylor, L.E., Gen. Counsel--Commonwealth Bank Group, Sydney, Australia; *Int'l*, pg. 312
Taylor, Nancy M., Corp. Counsel & Sec.--Tredegar Industries Inc., Richmond, VA; *U.S. Public*, pg. 1633
Taylor, Perry, Exec. V.P. & Corp. Counsel--ABN AMRO Chicago Corp., Chicago, IL; *Int'l*, pg. 10
Taylor, Terry, Sr. V.P., Gen. Counsel & Sec.--Club Corporation International, Dallas, TX; *U.S. Private*, pg. 247
Taylor, Thomas E., Sr. V.P. & Gen. Counsel--Cincinnati Bell Telephone Company, Cincinnati, OH; *U.S. Public*, pg. 367
Taylor, Wayne F., V.P., Gen. Counsel & Sec.--Cincinnati Milacron Inc., Cincinnati, OH; *U.S. Public*, pg. 368
Teeple, R.D., V.P. & Gen. Counsel--Cooper Tire & Rubber Company, Findlay, OH; *U.S. Public*, pg. 445
Teigen, Philip J., V.P., Gen. Counsel & Sec.--Capital Associates, Inc., Lakewood, CO; *U.S. Public*, pg. 302
Tennyson, Peter, Gen. Counsel--Hycor Biomedical, Inc., Irvine, CA; *U.S. Public*, pg. 851
Terilli, Sam, Gen. Counsel--The Miami Herald, Miami, FL; *U.S. Public*, pg. 964
Terlato, John, V.P. & Asst. Legal Counsel--Paterno Imports Limited, Lake Bluff, IL; *U.S. Private*, pg. 843
Terrell, James, Deputy Gen. Counsel-US--Alcatel N.V., Amsterdam, Netherlands; *Int'l*, pg. 55
Terrill, Richard D., Sec. & Assoc. Gen. Counsel--Western Resources, Inc., Topeka, KS; *U.S. Public*, pg. 1759
Terry, Gregory J., Legal Counsel--Jardine Matheson Holdings Limited, Hamilton, Bermuda; *Int'l*, pg. 703
Terry, Robert, V.P. & Gen. Counsel--Farmland Industries, Inc., Kansas City, MO; *U.S. Private*, pg. 395
Terry, W. Burks, V.P. & Asst. Gen. Counsel--Northrop Grumman Corporation, Los Angeles, CA; *U.S. Public*, pg. 1197
Tertaut, Jean-Louis, V.P.-Admin. & Legal Services--Tembec Inc., Montreal, Canada; *Int'l*, pg. 1374

Tessier, Charles A., V.P.-Legal Affairs & Sec.--BioChem Pharma Inc., Laval, Canada; *Int'l*, pg. 196
Tetsujiro, Nakamura, Gen. Counsel--Mutual Trading Co., Inc., Los Angeles, CA; *U.S. Private*, pg. 770
Tetzlaff, Thoedore R., Gen. Counsel--Tenneco Inc., Greenwich, CT; *U.S. Public*, pg. 1577
Teytaud, Cecile, Sr. V.P.-Legal & Tax Affairs--Credit Commercial de France, Paris, France; *Int'l*, pg. 341
Thackeray, Jonathan E., V.P. & Gen. Counsel--The Hearst Corporation, New York, NY; *U.S. Private*, pg. 515
Thauer, Peter E., V.P.-Law & Environment, Gen. Counsel, & Sec.--Cambrex Corporation, East Rutherford, NJ; *U.S. Public*, pg. 297
Theobald, John O., Gen. Counsel--Gosnell Builders, Phoenix, AZ; *U.S. Private*, pg. 873
Theophilos, Theodore, Exec. V.P. & Corp. Gen. Counsel-True North Communications Inc.--True North Communications Inc., Chicago, IL; *U.S. Public*, pg. 1641
Thibert, Bertrand, Dir.-Legal Affairs--Quebecor Multimedia Inc., Montreal, Canada; *Int'l*, pg. 1076
Thiessen, Mike, Gen. Counsel--Jenkins & Associates, Shawnee Mission, KS; *U.S. Private*, pg. 585
Thomas, Arthur E., V.P.-Legal--Horizon Air Industries, Seattle, WA; *U.S. Public*, pg. 35
Thomas, Benjamin E., Jr., Corp. Sec. & Assoc. Gen. Counsel--H.J. Heinz Company, Pittsburgh, PA; *U.S. Public*, pg. 805
Thomas, Bruce V., Chief Fin. Officer, Sr. V.P. & Gen. Counsel--Cadmus Communications Corporation, Richmond, VA; *U.S. Public*, pg. 290
Thomas, Curt, Gen. Counsel--Sunclipse, Inc., Buena Park, CA; *Int'l*, pg. 72
Thomas, Eugene C., Gen. Counsel & Sec.--Intermountain Industries, Inc., Boise, ID; *U.S. Private*, pg. 568
Thomas, George S., V.P. & Deputy Gen. Counsel--Anheuser-Busch European Trade Ltd., London, United Kingdom; *U.S. Public*, pg. 115
Thomas, H. Suzanne, Sr. V.P., Gen. Counsel & Sec.--Weatherford Enterra Incorporated, Houston, TX; *U.S. Public*, pg. 1749
Thomas, James S., Jr., V.P.-Legal--AGL Resources, Atlanta, GA; *U.S. Public*, pg. 6
Thomas, Jeanette M., V.P., Sec. & Asst. Gen. Counsel--Litton Industries, Inc., Woodland Hills, CA; *U.S. Public*, pg. 1002
Thomas, Timothy R., Sr. Deputy Gen. Counsel--Unocal Corporation, El Segundo, CA; *U.S. Public*, pg. 1698
Thomas, W. Lee, Gen. Counsel--The Ward Machinery Company, Hunt Valley, MD; *U.S. Private*, pg. 1149
Thomay, Mark L., V.P. & Assoc. Legal Counsel--FirstMerit Corporation, Akron, OH; *U.S. Public*, pg. 646
Thompkins, Kelly P., Asst. Gen. Counsel--RPM, Inc., Medina, OH; *U.S. Public*, pg. 1356
Thompson, Ann, Gen. Counsel--The Rival Company, Kansas City, MO; *U.S. Public*, pg. 1391
Thompson, Bruce, V., Sr. V.P.-Admin. Mktg. & Gen. Counsel--Forest Oil Corporation, Denver, CO; *U.S. Public*, pg. 670
Thompson, Daniel J., V.P. & Gen. Counsel-Adv. & Publ.--BellSouth Enterprises, Inc., Atlanta, GA; *U.S. Public*, pg. 208
Thompson, Frederick, Gen. Counsel--Ag Processing Inc., A Cooperative, Omaha, NE; *U.S. Private*, pg. 26
Thompson, Kevin N., V.P., Sec. & Gen. Counsel--Noranda Inc., Toronto, Canada; *Int'l*, pg. 433
Thompson, Lily, Gen. Counsel--Johnson Products Co., Inc., Chicago, IL; *U.S. Public*, pg. 915
Thompson, Michael G., Sr. V.P., Gen. Counsel & Sec.--Entergy Corporation, New Orleans, LA; *U.S. Public*, pg. 585
Thompson, Toby, V.P. & Corp. Legal Counsel--Midland Life Insurance Co., Columbus, OH; *U.S. Private*, pg. 744
Thomson, Roger F., Exec. V.P., Gen. Counsel & Sec.--Brinker International, Inc., Dallas, TX; *U.S. Public*, pg. 253
Thoresen, Trygve M., V.P., Gen. Counsel & Sec.--Summa Industries, Torrance, CA; *U.S. Public*, pg. 1527
Thornander, Ulf, Grp. Legal Counsel--Skandinaviska Enskilda Banken, Stockholm, Sweden; *Int'l*, pg. 1258
Thorne, Oakleigh B., Pres. & Chief Exec. Officer--CCH Incorporated, Riverwoods, IL; *Int'l*, pg. 1513
Thornton, Debra, V.P. & Gen. Counsel--Harvest States Cooperatives, Saint Paul, MN; *U.S. Private*, pg. 508
Thorpe, Janet C., Gen. Counsel--SunTrust, Orlando, FL; *U.S. Public*, pg. 1537
Thrubis, Anthony P., Gen. Counsel--AC Rochester Overseas Corporation, Detroit, MI; *U.S. Public*, pg. 722
Thumann, Richard K., V.P. & Gen. Counsel--Sierra On-Line, Inc., Bellevue, WA; *U.S. Public*, pg. 321
Tiano, J. Richard, V.P., Gen. Counsel & Sec.--Connecticut Energy Corporation, Bridgeport, CT; *U.S. Public*, pg. 431
Tibbitts, J. Brett, V.P. & Gen. Counsel--Dole Food Company, Inc., Westlake Village, CA; *U.S. Public*, pg. 515
Tierney, Kevin J., Sr. V.P., Gen. Counsel & Sec.--UNUM Corporation, Portland, ME; *U.S. Public*, pg. 1699
Tierney, Michael, V.P. & Gen. Counsel--Jefferson Smurfit Corporation, Saint Louis, MO; *Int'l*, pg. 1269
Tilis, Harry, Gen. Counsel--ADI (Ademco Distribution, Inc.), Syosset, NY; *U.S. Public*, pg. 1306
Timm, Theodore, Gen. Counsel & Sec.--DOALL Company, Des Plaines, IL; *U.S. Private*, pg. 337
Timmons, S.D., V.P.-Bus. Affairs & Legal--National Steel & Shipbuilding Company, San Diego, CA; *U.S. Private*, pg. 787
Timmons, Tim, V.P. & Gen. Counsel--Hiram Walker, Southfield, MI; *Int'l*, pg. 63
Tippins, J. Rankin, Gen. Counsel & Sec.--Tech-Sym Corporation, Houston, TX; *U.S. Public*, pg. 1563
Tjedeski, Jim, Gen. Counsel--Kvaerner Davy, Pittsburgh, PA; *Int'l*, pg. 774
Toal, John H., Gen. Counsel--Phonetics, Inc., Aston, PA; *U.S. Private*, pg. 863
Tobin, Frederick M., Gen. Counsel--The F.A. Bartlett Tree Expert Co., Stamford, CT; *U.S. Private*, pg. 119
Tobin, Jay, V.P. & Asst. Gen. Counsel--Brinker International, Inc., Dallas, TX; *U.S. Public*, pg. 253
Tobin, Paul, Gen. Counsel--CDB Infotec Inc., Santa Ana, CA; *U.S. Private*, pg. 193
Tobin, Thomas M., V.P., Gen. Counsel & Sec.--Hudson Insurance Company, New York, NY; *Int'l*, pg. 1258
Tobin, Thomas M., Sr. V.P., Gen. Counsel & Corp. Sec.--Odyssey Reinsurance Corporation, New York, NY; *Int'l*, pg. 1258
Toler, Gene, Gen. Counsel--Pabst Brewing Co., San Antonio, TX; *U.S. Private*, pg. 954
Tomas, Antonio Condal, Dir.-Legal, Pur. & Personnel--Agropecuaria de Guissona, S. Coop. Ltda., Guisona, Spain; *Int'l*, pg. 31
Tomassi, Stephen J., Asst. Gen. Counsel--Sybron International Corporation, Milwaukee, WI; *U.S. Public*, pg. 1544
Toner, Gerard, V.P., Gen. Counsel & Sec.--Doubleday Publishing Company, New York, NY; *Int'l*, pg. 191
Tonkin, William H., Treas. & Sec.--Pennsylvania Power & Light Company-Northeast Div., Wilkes-Barre, PA; *U.S. Public*, pg. 1244
Toohey, Philip S., Exec. V.P., Gen. Counsel & Sec.--HSBC Americas, Buffalo, NY; *Int'l*, pg. 580
Toole, Edward D., V.P., Assoc. Gen. Counsel & Asst. Sec.--Echlin Inc., Branford, CT; *U.S. Public*, pg. 560
Topham, Verl R., Sr. V.P. & Gen. Counsel--PacifiCorp, Portland, OR; *U.S. Public*, pg. 1251
Torgerson, Robert, Gen. Counsel & Sec.--Jewelers Mutual Insurance Company, Neenah, WI; *U.S. Private*, pg. 587
Torgerson, William T., Sr. V.P.-External Affairs & Gen. Counsel--Potomac Electric Power Company, Washington, DC; *U.S. Public*, pg. 1318
Tormey, Diane R., V.P. & Gen. Counsel--Marcam Solutions, Inc., Newton, MA; *U.S. Public*, pg. 1042
Torres, Dr. Abelardo, Legal Counsel--Mineral San Sebastian S.A., San Salvador, El Salvador; *U.S. Public*, pg. 410
Torres, Osvaldo F., Asst. Gen. Counsel & Sec.--Telemundo Group, Inc., Hialeah, FL; *U.S. Public*, pg. 1570
Tortorello, Robert J., V.P., Gen. Counsel & Sec.--Woodhead Industries, Inc., Buffalo Grove, IL; *U.S. Public*, pg. 1776
Toshimitsu, Matsuo, Counsellor--Japan Airlines Company, Ltd., Tokyo, Japan; *Int'l*, pg. 699
Totman, Pat, Counsel--Furr's Supermarkets, Albuquerque, NM; *U.S. Private*, pg. 432
Touff, Michael, V.P. & Gen. Counsel--M.D.C. Holdings, Inc., Denver, CO; *U.S. Public*, pg. 1025
Touse, James L., V.P., Gen. Counsel & Sec.--Group Health Plan, Inc., Saint Louis, MO; *U.S. Public*, pg. 454
Towers, John R., Sr. V.P., Gen. Counsel & Sec.--State Street Bank & Trust Co., Boston, MA; *U.S. Public*, pg. 1513
Townsend, Christopher G., Sr. V.P. & Gen. Counsel--Host Marriott Corporation, Bethesda, MD; *U.S. Public*, pg. 841
Trabbuco, John E., Gen. Counsel & Sec.--Beckwith Machinery Company, Murrysville, PA; *U.S. Private*, pg. 129
Tracey, William, Gen. Counsel--Dorr-Oliver Incorporated, Milford, CT; *Int'l*, pg. 839
Trachimovsky, S., Gen. Counsel & Corp. Sec.--Du Pont Canada Inc., Mississauga, Canada; *U.S. Public*, pg. 532
Trachsel, William H., V.P., Gen. Counsel & Sec.--United Technologies Corporation, Hartford, CT; *U.S. Public*, pg. 1689
Traill, P.G., Gen. Counsel--Australian Mutual Provident, Sydney, Australia; *Int'l*, pg. 100
Trank, Burgess N., V.P. & Gen. Counsel--Centex Real Estate Corp./Centex Homes, Dallas, TX; *U.S. Public*, pg. 323
Travers, Bernard F., III, Dir.-Law & Tax & Asst. Sec.--Andersen Group, Inc., Bloomfield, CT; *U.S. Public*, pg. 111
Travers, Bernard F., III, Esq., Asst. Sec.--The J.M. Ney Company, Bloomfield, CT; *U.S. Public*, pg. 111
Travis, Andrew D., V.P. & Legal Counsel--Allright Corporation, Houston, TX; *U.S. Private*, pg. 42
Treacy, Richard F., Jr., Sec. & Gen. Counsel--Gerber Scientific, Inc., South Windsor, CT; *U.S. Public*, pg. 740
Tremaine, Davis Wright, Gen. Counsel--AirSensors, Inc., Seattle, WA; *U.S. Public*, pg. 33
Tremallo, Mark V.B., V.P. & Gen. Counsel--Dynatech Corporation, Burlington, MA; *U.S. Public*, pg. 539
Tremayne, F.A.M., V.P., Gen. Counsel & Sec.--BFC Construction Corporation, Scarborough, Canada; *Int'l*, pg. 118
Trembath, Peter H., Esq., V.P., Gen. Counsel & Sec.--BEC Group, Inc., Rye, NY; *U.S. Public*, pg. 160
Tremblax, Mary, Gen. Counsel & Sec.--Lydall, Inc., Manchester, CT; *U.S. Public*, pg. 1020
Trevino, Jorge, Gen. Counsel--Hylsamex, S.A. de C.V., San Nicolas, Mexico; *Int'l*, pg. 56
Trigg, Donald C., Sr. V.P.-Sec. & Gen. Counsel--Anthem, Inc., Indianapolis, IN; *U.S. Private*, pg. 76
Trillo, Jesus, Mng. Dir.-Legal--Iberdrola, S.A., Bilbao, Spain; *Int'l*, pg. 657
Trimble, B.W., Asst. Gen. Counsel--Union Camp Corporation, Wayne, NJ; *U.S. Public*, pg. 1665
Trimboli, Michael, Gen. Counsel--Leach & Garner Company, North Attleboro, MA; *U.S. Private*, pg. 655
Trump, Arthur, Sec. & Gen. Counsel--Atlantic Builders Group Inc., Baltimore, MD; *U.S. Private*, pg. 95
Tschirhart, Paul M., Sr. V.P., Gen. Counsel & Sec.--The Hertz Corporation, Park Ridge, NJ; *U.S. Public*, pg. 664
Tseng, V., V.P. & Gen. Counsel--Welch Foods Inc., A Cooperative, Concord, MA; *U.S. Private*, pg. 784
Tubbs, Robert J., Exec. V.P., Gen. Counsel & Sec.--Coltec Holdings Inc, Charlotte, NC; *U.S. Public*, pg. 401
Tubbs, Robert J., Sr. V.P. & Gen. Counsel--Coltec Industries Inc., Charlotte, NC; *U.S. Public*, pg. 401
Tucker, Bradford, Exec. V.P. & Gen. Counsel--Mustang Tractor & Equip. Co., Houston, TX; *U.S. Private*, pg. 768
Tucker, Brian H., V.P. & Deputy Gen. Counsel--Harsco Corporation, Camp Hill, PA; *U.S. Public*, pg. 792
Tucker, Jeffrey, Gen. Counsel--Weingarten Realty Investors, Houston, TX; *U.S. Public*, pg. 1751
Tufnell, John F.D., Gen. Counsel & Sec.--Air Products Europe, Inc., Allentown, PA; *U.S. Public*, pg. 30
Tulli, Pierre-Marie, Dir.-Legal Affairs--Banque Francaise du Commerce Exterieur, Paris, France; *Int'l*, pg. 160
Tumminello, Theodore, Sr. V.P., Gen. Counsel & Sec.--Pan-American Life Insurance Company, New Orleans, LA; *U.S. Private*, pg. 836
Tunney, Francis R., Jr., Corp. V.P., Gen. Counsel & Sec.--Allergan, Inc., Irvine, CA; *U.S. Public*, pg. 46
Tuot, Thierry, Corp. V.P.-Legal Affairs & Gen. Counsel--Aerospatiale, Paris, France; *Int'l*, pg. 28
Turgeon, Nancy, Sec.--Robertson's Auto Salvage, Wareham, MA; *U.S. Private*, pg. 936
Turleque, Clotilde, Dir.-Legal & Patent Rights--Salomon S.A., Annecy, France; *Int'l*, pg. 1181
Turnbaugh, Charles W., Sr. V.P. & Gen. Counsel--Riggs National Corporation, Washington, DC; *U.S. Public*, pg. 1389
Turner, Keith M., Sec. & Dir.-Legal & Bus. Affairs--Really Useful Holdings Limited, London, United Kingdom; *Int'l*, pg. 1089
Turner, M. Caroline, Sr. V.P., Gen. Counsel & Asst. Sec.--Adolph Coors Company, Golden, CO; *U.S. Public*, pg. 445
Turner, M. Caroline, Sr. V.P., Gen. Counsel & Asst. Sec.--Coors Brewing Company, Golden, CO; *U.S. Public*, pg. 445
Turner, Peter J., Exec. Dir.-Legal Affairs--Foster's Brewing Group Limited, Southbank, Australia; *Int'l*, pg. 500
Turner, Stephen M., Sr. V.P. & Gen. Counsel--Texaco Inc., White Plains, NY; *U.S. Public*, pg. 1582
Turpin, Francois, Gen. Counsel & Mgr.-Admin. & Opers.--Credit Mutuel, Paris, France; *Int'l*, pg. 344
Tuura, Doris K., Gen. Counsel & Asst. Sec.--International Multifoods Corporation, Minneapolis, MN; *U.S. Public*, pg. 900
Tyacke, Steven W., Asst. Gen. Counsel--Minnesota Power, Duluth, MN; *U.S. Public*, pg. 1116
Ucles, Jose Ignacio, Sr. V.P. & Legal Counsel--Banco Santander, Madrid, Spain; *Int'l*, pg. 143
Udow, Hank, V.P. & Counsel--Cadbury Beverages North America, Stamford, CT; *Int'l*, pg. 248
Ueda, Koji, Dir.-Legal--Maruzen Company Limited, Tokyo, Japan; *Int'l*, pg. 845
Ughetta, William C., Sr. V.P. & Gen. Counsel--Corning Incorporated, Corning, NY; *U.S. Public*, pg. 448
Uhr, Stanley A., V.P.-Real Estate & Corp. Counsel--Deb Shops, Inc., Philadelphia, PA; *U.S. Public*, pg. 491
Ulery, Shari L., V.P. & Gen. Counsel--Government Employees Financial Corporation, Washington, DC; *U.S. Public*, pg. 220
Ulrich, Robert G., Sr. V.P. & Gen. Counsel--The Great Atlantic & Pacific Tea Company, Inc., Montvale, NJ; *Int'l*, *pg. 1375*
Umeda, Masaru, Exec. Dir. & Grp. Gen. Mgr.-Law--Sharp Corporation, Osaka, Japan; *Int'l*, pg. 1228
Umphlette, Edward, Exec. V.P., Treas., Gen. Counsel & Gen. Mgr.--Stainless Incorporated, Deerfield Beach, FL; *U.S. Private*, pg. 1029
Underwood, Edmund H., III, Gen. Counsel--Offshore Logistics, Inc., Lafayette, LA; *U.S. Public*, pg. 1212
Underwood, William E., Jr., Sec. & Gen. Counsel--Republic Automotive-AEA Division, Charlotte, NC; *U.S. Public*, pg. 1377
Ungerland, Thomas J., Assoc. Gen. Counsel--Crane Co., Stamford, CT; *U.S. Public*, pg. 456
Upchurch, Samuel E., Jr., Gen. Counsel & Corp. Sec.--Regions Financial Corporation, Birmingham, AL; *U.S. Public*, pg. 1371
Ursel, Dale, V.P. & Gen. Counsel--Sandwell Inc., Vancouver, Canada; *Int'l*, pg. 1188
Ursu, John J., Sr. V.P.-Legal Affairs & Gen. Counsel--3M, Saint Paul, MN; *U.S. Public*, pg. 1604
Uteau de Vos, Sergio, Chief Counsel--Andina Division, Los Andes, Chile; *Int'l*, pg. 302
Utecht, Andrea, Sr. V.P., Gen. Counsel & Sec.--Elf Atochem North America, Inc., Philadelphia, PA; *Int'l*, pg. 445
Uvena, Frank J., Sr. V.P.-Law & Corp. Staffs--R.R. Donnelley & Sons Company, Chicago, IL; *U.S. Public*, pg. 517
Vail, Charles, Corp. Sec.--Fred's Inc., Memphis, TN; *U.S. Public*, pg. 680
Valentine, Catherine L., V.P., Gen. Counsel & Sec.--Intuit, Inc., Mountain View, CA; *U.S. Public*, pg. 911
Valentine, Stephen K., Jr., Gen. Counsel--Paul Inman Associates Inc., Farmington, MI; *U.S. Private*, pg. 564
Van Allen, Moore, Gen. Counsel--Long MFG. NC Inc., Tarboro, NC; *U.S. Private*, pg. 674
Van Auken, Bradley A., Sr. V.P., Gen. Counsel & Sec.--Lexford Residential Trust, Columbus, OH; *U.S. Public*, pg. 991
Van Brunt, William A., V.P. & Gen. Counsel-Foods--General Mills, Inc., Minneapolis, MN; *U.S. Public*, pg. 717
Van Caenegem, Jettie, Dir.-Legal Dept.--UCB, S.A., Brussels, Belgium; *Int'l*, pg. 1427
Van den Eynde, Alain, Mng. Dir. & Legal Dir.--Garbarski EURO RSCG, Brussels, Belgium; *Int'l*, pg. 603
van den Vlist, R., Gen. Counsel--Royal Dutch/Shell Group of Companies, Hague, Netherlands; *Int'l*, pg. 1135
van der Klaauw, J.W.E., Gen. Counsel & Sec.--CSM N.V., Diemen, Netherlands; *Int'l*, pg. 243
van der Velden, Jan M.M., Gen. Counsel & Sec.--Oce-van der Grinten N.V., Venlo, Netherlands; *Int'l*, pg. 993
van der Wal, W.H., Sec. & Gen. Counsel--Ballast Nedam NV, Amstelveen, Netherlands; *Int'l*, pg. 133
van der Zwan, Arie Jacobs James, Exec. Dir. & Dir.-Legal, Mktg., Human Res., Tax Services & Plng.--The Southern Life Association Limited, Cape Town, South Africa; *Int'l*, pg. 77

Van Duzer, Charles B., Sec.--Reunion Industries, Inc., Stamford, CT; *U.S. Public*, pg. 1383

Van Gorder, Jan R., Sr. Exec. V.P., Gen. Counsel & Sec.--Erie Family Life Insurance Company, Erie, PA; *U.S. Public*, pg. 590

Van Graafeiland, Gary P., Sr. V.P. & Gen. Counsel--Eastman Kodak Company, Rochester, NY; *U.S. Public*, pg. 550

Van Horn, James R., V.P., Gen. Counsel & Sec.--NUI Corporation, Bedminster, NJ; *U.S. Public*, pg. 1147

Van Lare, Wendell J., V.P.-Labor Counsel--Gannett Company, Inc., Arlington, VA; *U.S. Public*, pg. 698

Van Orden, Charles, V.P., Gen. Counsel & Sec.--Honeywell-Measurex Corporation, Cupertino, CA; *U.S. Public*, pg. 833

van Schoonenberg, Robert G., Sr. V.P., Gen. Counsel & Sec.--Avery Dennison Corporation, Pasadena, CA; *U.S. Public*, pg. 152

Van Vlierbergen, Brian R., V.P., Gen. Counsel & Sec.--Blue Cross & Blue Shield of Illinois, Chicago, IL; *U.S. Private*, pg. 151

Van Woerkman, Jack, Gen. Counsel--A.W. Chesterton Company, Stoneham, MA; *U.S. Private*, pg. 234

Vana, Robert J., Chief Corp. Counsel & Sec.--Charter One Financial, Inc., Cleveland, OH; *U.S. Public*, pg. 336

Vanairsdale, Carol M., V.P. & Asst. Gen. Counsel--Grubb & Ellis Company, Northbrook, IL; *U.S. Public*, pg. 767

Vandeman, George A., Sr. V.P., Gen. Counsel & Sec.--Amgen Inc., Thousand Oaks, CA; *U.S. Public*, pg. 100

Vandenberg, Tom, Gen. Counsel--Schneider National, Inc., Green Bay, WI; *U.S. Private*, pg. 971

Vanderberry, James G., Gen. Counsel & Sec.--Wachovia Bank of North Carolina, N.A., Winston Salem, NC; *U.S. Public*, pg. 1730

Vane, Robert J., Gen. Counsel & Sec.--Charter One Bank, Cleveland, OH; *U.S. Public*, pg. 336

VanGundy, Gregory F., Gen. Counsel--Marsh & McLennan Companies, Inc., New York, NY; *U.S. Public*, pg. 1048

Vanleuven, Joseph, Gen. Counsel--Fone America, Inc., Portland, OR; *U.S. Public*, pg. 661

Varner, Sally Stroud, Asst. Gen. Counsel--Wal-Mart Stores, Inc., Bentonville, AR; *U.S. Public*, pg. 1732

Vasconcelos, J.A., Dir.-Legal--Eli Lilly do Brasil Limitada, Sao Paulo, Brazil; *U.S. Public*, pg. 993

Vaughan, Bernard, Sr. V.P. & Gen. Counsel--Flexi-Van Leasing, Inc., Kenilworth, NJ; *U.S. Private*, pg. 413

Vaupshas, R.A., Treas. & Sec.--Henry Birks & Sons (1993) Inc., Montreal, Canada; *Int'l*, pg. 196

Vautier, N.J., Sec. & Legal Counsel--Feltrax International, Inc., Auckland, New Zealand; *Int'l*, pg. 130

Vecsler, Robert, Esq., Gen. Counsel & Sec.--Geotek Communications, Montvale, NJ; *U.S. Public*, pg. 739

Veitenheimer, Michael, V.P., Gen. Counsel & Sec.--The Bombay Company, Inc., Fort Worth, TX; *U.S. Public*, pg. 244

Veitenheimer, Mike, V.P., Gen. Counsel & Sec.--The Bombay Company, Fort Worth, TX; *U.S. Public*, pg. 244

Velasco, Jose A., Sr. V.P., Gen. Counsel & Sec.--Centris Group Inc., Costa Mesa, CA; *U.S. Public*, pg. 328

Ventre, Frank Jr., Gen. Counsel--Ventre Packing Company, Inc., Syracuse, NY; *U.S. Private*, pg. 1135

Verdon, William, Sr. V.P. & Gen. Counsel--Crowley Maritime Corporation, Oakland, CA; *U.S. Private*, pg. 292

Verheij, Richard H., Gen. Counsel--UST Inc., Greenwich, CT; *U.S. Public*, pg. 1660

Vestner, Eliot N. Jr., Exec. Counsel--BankBoston Corporation, Boston, MA; *U.S. Public*, pg. 183

Vetter, David, V.P. & Gen. Counsel--Tech Data Corporation, Clearwater, FL; *U.S. Public*, pg. 1562

Veysey, Michael C., Sr. V.P. & Gen. Counsel--Gould Electronics Inc., Eastlake, OH; *U.S. Public*, pg. 1591

Vickruck, J.M., V.P. & Gen. Counsel--Canadian Kenworth Co., Mississauga, Canada; *U.S. Public*, pg. 1247

Villadolid, David, Corp. Counsel--Empire Southwest Co., Mesa, AZ; *U.S. Private*, pg. 374

Villaruz, Francisco H., Jr., V.P & Gen. Counsel--La Tondena Distillers, Inc., Manila, Philippines; *Int'l*, pg. 785

Vincent, Kirk F., V.P.-Fin. & Law--J & L Specialty Products Corp., Pittsburgh, PA; *Int'l*, pg. 572

Vincke, Francois, Sec. Gen.--Petrofina S.A., Brussels, Belgium; *Int'l*, pg. 1043

Vinocur, Peter, Gen. Counsel--Master Builders Inc., Cleveland, OH; *Int'l*, pg. 1465

Vinson, William T., V.P. & Chief Counsel--Lockheed Martin Corporation, Bethesda, MD; *U.S. Public*, pg. 1006

Violet, Timothy, V.P.-Legal--Hubbard Feeds Inc., Mankato, MN; *Int'l*, pg. 1116

Viricelle, R., Dir.-Legal Affairs--SNCF, Paris, France; *Int'l*, pg. 1163

Vitale, Joseph M., Sr. V.P., Gen. Counsel & Sec.--Belden & Blake Corporation, Canton, OH; *U.S. Private*, pg. 1078

Vitkus, Richard F., Sr. V.P., Gen. Counsel & Sec.--Zenith Electronics Corp., Glenview, IL; *U.S. Public*, pg. 1790

Vix, Carol A., Sr. Attorney & Asst. Sec.--Premark International, Inc., Deerfield, IL; *U.S. Public*, pg. 1321

Vlach, Robert, V.P., Gen. Sec. & Gen. Counsel--The Chesapeake Life Insurance Co., Oklahoma City, OK; *U.S. Public*, pg. 1679

Vlach, Robert B., V.P., Gen. Counsel & Sec.--United Insurance Companies, Inc., Dallas, TX; *U.S. Public*, pg. 1679

Voet, Martin A., Asst. Sec. & Assoc. Gen. Counsel--Allergan, Inc., Irvine, CA; *U.S. Public*, pg. 46

Vogel, Robert P., V.P. & Gen. Counsel--Rohm and Haas Company, Philadelphia, PA; *U.S. Public*, pg. 1403

Volpi, Walter M., V.P., Sec. & Gen. Counsel--Lever Brothers Co., New York, NY; *Int'l*, pg. 1435

Voltz, David L., V.P., Gen. Counsel & Sec.--L.B. Foster Company, Pittsburgh, PA; *U.S. Public*, pg. 675

von Bernuth, Carl W., Sr. V.P. & Gen. Counsel--Union Pacific Corporation, Dallas, TX; *U.S. Public*, pg. 1667

Von Glahn, William G., Sr. V.P. & Gen. Counsel--The Williams Companies, Inc., Tulsa, OK; *U.S. Public*, pg. 1769

von Gruben, Robert, V.P. & Gen. Counsel--TruGreen-ChemLawn, Memphis, TN; *U.S. Public*, pg. 1461

Von Wald, Richard B., Sr. V.P., Gen. Counsel & Sec.--Johns Manville Corporation, Denver, CO; *U.S. Public*, pg. 927

Von Wrangel, Christine, V.P. & Gen. Counsel--Candle Corporation, Santa Monica, CA; *U.S. Private*, pg. 204

Vorbach, Joseph, V.P., Gen. Counsel & Sec.--American Bureau of Shipping, New York, NY; *U.S. Private*, pg. 51

Vorpahl, George S., V.P. & Gen. Counsel--Temple-Inland Forest Products Corporation, Diboll, TX; *U.S. Public*, pg. 1575

Vorsanger, Robert, Gen. Counsel--Domino Sugar Corporation, New York, NY; *Int'l*, pg. 1356

Voss, Theodore R., Gen. Counsel & Asst. Sec.--Starter Corp., New Haven, CT; *U.S. Public*, pg. 1511

Vossel, Herbert, Dr., Legal Counsel--Deutz AG, Cologne, Germany; *Int'l*, pg. 407

Voysey, Peter, Gen. Counsel & Sec.--Comdata Corporation, Brentwood, TN; *U.S. Public*, pg. 331

Vradenburg, George, Sr. V.P. & Gen. Counsel--America Online Incorporated, Dulles, VA; *U.S. Public*, pg. 66

Vulleau, Richard, Gen. Counsel--Beechmont Investments Inc., Cincinnati, OH; *U.S. Private*, pg. 129

Waak, Richard, Gen. Counsel--National Safety Associates, Memphis, TN; *U.S. Private*, pg. 786

Wachterman, Richard M., Sr. V.P., Gen. Counsel & Sec.--Gradison Division, Cincinnati, OH; *U.S. Public*, pg. 1068

Wade, Byron, Chief Legal Officer & Sr. V.P.--The Pacific Lumber Company, Scotia, CA; *U.S. Public*, pg. 1062

Wade, Byron L., Chief Legal Officer & Sr. V.P.--Maxxam Inc., Houston, TX; *U.S. Public*, pg. 1062

Wade, Byron L., Chief Legal Officer & Sr. V.P.--MAXXAM Property Company, Houston, TX; *U.S. Public*, pg. 1062

Wade, Mike, Corp. Attorney--Tech Mold, Tempe, AZ; *U.S. Private*, pg. 1071

Wadler, Arnold, Sr. V.P., Gen. Counsel & Sec.--Metromedia Company, East Rutherford, NJ; *U.S. Private*, pg. 736

Wadler, Arnold L., Sr. V.P., Gen. Counsel & Sec.--Metromedia International Group, Inc., East Rutherford, NJ; *U.S. Public*, pg. 1102

Wadler, Sanford S., Gen. Counsel & Sec.--Bio-Rad Laboratories, Inc., Hercules, CA; *U.S. Public*, pg. 230

Wadsworth, Edward N., Sr. V.P. & Assoc. Gen. Counsel--The New England, Boston, MA; *U.S. Private*, pg. 737

Wagar, Harvey, Gen. Counsel & Sec.--Lundy Enterprises, Inc., New Orleans, LA; *U.S. Private*, pg. 681

Wagener, Robert, Mgr.-Belgium, Denmark, Greece, Finland Legal Affairs--European Investment Bank, Luxembourg, Luxembourg; *Int'l*, pg. 465

Waggoner, John M., Chief Legal Officer--CUNA Mutual Insurance Society, Madison, WI; *U.S. Private*, pg. 296

Wagner, Barry J., Gen. Counsel & Sec.--Omnicom Group Inc., New York, NY; *U.S. Public*, pg. 1223

Wagner, Jay H., Reg. Counsel & Asst. Sec.--OHM Remediation Services Corp., Findlay, OH; *U.S. Public*, pg. 1208

Wagner, Richard B., Gen. Counsel--General Motors Acceptance Corporation (GMAC), Detroit, MI; *U.S. Public*, pg. 719

Wagner, Thomas J., Exec. V.P. & Gen. Counsel--Cigna Corp., Philadelphia, PA; *U.S. Public*, pg. 356

Wahrsager, Stewart H., Sr. V.P., Gen. Counsel & Sec.--The Alpine Group, Inc., New York, NY; *U.S. Public*, pg. 58

Waite, Edward J., III, V.P. & Gen. Counsel--General Chemical Corporation, Parsippany, NJ; *U.S. Public*, pg. 707

Waitman, Barbara, Exec. V.P. & Gen. Counsel--Slim-Fast Foods Company, West Palm Beach, FL; *U.S. Private*, pg. 1006

Waiwood, Michael F., Exec. V.P., Gen. Cousel & Sec.--Midland Title Security, Inc., Cleveland, OH; *U.S. Public*, pg. 626

Wakefield, Tom, V.P. & Gen. Counsel--The Cessna Aircraft Co., Wichita, KS; *U.S. Public*, pg. 1589

Walder, Ken, Sec. & Dir.-Legal--British Airways PLC, London, United Kingdom; *Int'l*, pg. 218

Waldis, Markus, Dr., Gen. Counsel--Oerlikon-Buhrle Holding AG, Zurich, Switzerland; *Int'l*, pg. 996

Waldman, Robert A., Sr. V.P. & Gen. Counsel--Continental Mortgage and Equity Trust, Dallas, TX; *U.S. Public*, pg. 441

Waldman, Robert A., Sr. V.P. & Gen. Counsel--Transcontinental Realty Investors, Inc., Dallas, TX; *U.S. Public*, pg. 1630

Waldoks, Phillip H., Sr. V.P.-Legal Affairs--Hasbro, Inc., Pawtucket, RI; *U.S. Public*, pg. 797

Waldon, John, Gen. Counsel--Distributed Systems Division, Lisle, IL; *U.S. Public*, pg. 1522

Waldrop, Alexander M., V.P.-Admin., Gen. Counsel & Sec.--Churchill Downs, Inc., Louisville, KY; *U.S. Public*, pg. 356

Walk, Frank H., Jr., Legal Officer--Walk, Haydel & Associates, Inc., New Orleans, LA; *Int'l*, pg. 624

Walker, Catherine, Sr. V.P. & Gen. Counsel--Westin Hotels & Resorts, Seattle, WA; *U.S. Public*, pg. 1512

Walker, Diane E., Sr. V.P., Gen. Counsel & Sec.--CT Financial Services, Inc., Toronto, Canada; *Int'l*, pg. 112

Walker, Ken, V.P., Gen. Counsel & Copr. Sec.--Sealy Corporation, Cleveland, OH; *U.S. Private*, pg. 978

Walker, Mark R., V.P.-Gen. Counsel & Sec.--CompUSA, Dallas, TX; *U.S. Public*, pg. 420

Walker, Myron D., V.P. & Deputy Gen. Counsel--Marriott International, Inc., Washington, DC; *U.S. Public*, pg. 1047

Walker, R.C., Gen. Counsel--Imperial Oil Limited, Toronto, Canada; *U.S. Public*, pg. 602

Walker, Richard A., Chief Admin. Officer, Exec. V.P., Gen. Counsel & Sec.--Kuhlman Corporation, Savannah, GA; *U.S. Public*, pg. 968

Walker, Robert C., Sr. V.P. & Gen. Counsel--The Hartford Steam Boiler Inspection & Insurance Co., Hartford, CT; *U.S. Public*, pg. 795

Wall, Anthony J., Exec. V.P.-Bus. Affairs, Gen. Counsel & Sec.--Big Dog Holdings Inc., Santa Barbara, CA; *U.S. Public*, pg. 227

Wall, Hugh, III, Gen. Counsel--Gosiger Inc., Dayton, OH; *U.S. Private*, pg. 466

Wall, Richard J. Jr., V.P., Gen. Counsel & Sec.--Cerner Corporation, Kansas City, MO; *U.S. Public*, pg. 331

Wallace, Bass C., Jr., Corp. Counsel & Sec.--Tetra Technologies, Woodlands, TX; *U.S. Public*, pg. 1582

Wallace, M., Gen. Counsel--Crestbrook Forest Industries Ltd., Cranbrook, Canada; *Int'l*, pg. 348

Wallace, Sally J., V.P. & Gen. Counsel--Kronos Incorporated, Waltham, MA; *U.S. Public*, pg. 967

Wallace, Wayne, V.P.-Gen. Counsel & Corp. Sec.--Raytheon Aircraft Company, Wichita, KS; *U.S. Public*, pg. 1365

Wallenberg, Lars, Sr. V.P.-Grp. Counsel--Trelleborg AB, Trelleborg, Sweden; *Int'l*, pg. 1419

Waller, William A., Sr. V.P., Gen. Counsel & Sec.--Petty Company, Inc., Effingham, IL; *U.S. Private*, pg. 860

Wallin, R.E., Gen. Counsel--Kemmons Wilson, Inc., Memphis, TN; *U.S. Private*, pg. 613

Wallin, Ulf, Gen. Counsel--NCC AB, Solna, Sweden; *Int'l*, pg. 898

Wallingford, Rufus, Sr. V.P. & Gen. Counsel--Browning-Ferris Industries, Inc., Houston, TX; *U.S. Public*, pg. 262

Wallock, Terrence, Sr. V.P., Sec. & Gen. Counsel--Ralphs Grocery Company, Compton, CA; *U.S. Private*, pg. 1202

Wallock, Terrence J., Exec. V.P., General Counsel & Sec.--The Vons Companies, Inc., Arcadia, CA; *U.S. Public*, pg. 1426

Walner, Robert J., Sr. V.P., Gen. Counsel & Corp. Sec.--Grubb & Ellis Company, Northbrook, IL; *U.S. Public*, pg. 767

Walseth, Daniel G., V.P., Dir.-Legal Opers. & Sec.--ITT Hartford Life & Annuity Insurance Corporation, Minneapolis, MN; *U.S. Public*, pg. 795

Walsh, David J., Gen. Counsel-State Regulatory Affairs, Domestic Brokerage Group--American International Group, Inc., New York, NY; *U.S. Public*, pg. 83

Walsh, James K., Exec. V.P. & Gen. Counsel--Ardent Software, Inc., Westborough, MA; *U.S. Public*, pg. 129

Walsh, Kelly, Exec. V.P. & Gen. Counsel--Ameritech Corp., Chicago, IL; *U.S. Public*, pg. 98

Walter, John C., Exec. V.P.-Admin., Fin. & H.R.--Western Gas Resources, Inc., Denver, CO; *U.S. Public*, pg. 1758

Walters, Bette J., V.P. & Gen. Counsel--Alco Industries, Inc., Valley Forge, PA; *U.S. Private*, pg. 32

Walters, John C., Sr. V.P. & Gen. Counsel--John H. Harland Company, Decatur, GA; *U.S. Public*, pg. 785

Walters, Leigh, Gen. Counsel--Valcor Engineering Corp., Springfield, NJ; *U.S. Private*, pg. 1131

Walton, H. Steven, V.P.-Govt. Affairs, Gen. Counsel & Sec.--Sanifill, Inc., Houston, TX; *U.S. Public*, pg. 1686

Walton, Jon D., Sr. V.P., Gen. Counsel & Sec.--Allegheny Teledyne Incorporated, Pittsburgh, PA; *U.S. Public*, pg. 43

Wamhoff, Fredrick, V.P., Gn. Counsel & Sec.--Rawson-Koenig, Inc., Houston, TX; *U.S. Public*, pg. 1362

Wandell, Linda, Gen. Counsel--R.W. Beck, Inc., Seattle, WA; *U.S. Private*, pg. 128

Wander, Herb, Gen. Counsel--Northwestern Steel & Wire Co., Sterling, IL; *U.S. Public*, pg. 1201

Wang, Stanley L., Sr. V.P., Gen. Counsel & Sec.--Comcast Corporation, Philadelphia, PA; *U.S. Public*, pg. 406

Ward, Bill, Sr. V.P., Gen. Counsel & Sec.--NW Transport Service, Inc., Denver, CO; *U.S. Private*, pg. 772

Ward, David L. Jr., Gen. Counsel--First Citizens Banc Shares, Inc., Raleigh, NC; *U.S. Public*, pg. 628

Ward, James J. Jr., Gen. Attorney--Anadarko Petroleum Corporation, Houston, TX; *U.S. Public*, pg. 107

Ward, Jeff, Gen. Counsel--Sugar Cane Growers Cooperative of Florida, Belle Glade, FL; *U.S. Private*, pg. 1049

Ward, Michael, Sr. V.P. & Deputy Gen. Counsel--Showtime Networks Inc., New York, NY; *U.S. Private*, pg. 779

Ward, Richard S., Exec. V.P., Gen. Counsel & Sec.--ITT Corporation, New York, NY; *U.S. Public*, pg. 1512

Warden, William C., Jr., Chief Admin. Officer, Exec. V.P., Gen. Counsel & Sec.--Lowe's Companies, Inc., North Wilkesboro, NC; *U.S. Public*, pg. 1015

Wardlow, Anne V., V.P., Gen. Counsel & Sec.--John Alden Life Insurance Company, Miami, FL; *U.S. Public*, pg. 39

Ware, David, V.P. & Counsel--United Technologies Automotive, Dearborn, MI; *U.S. Public*, pg. 1691

Warner, M. Richard, V.P., Gen. Counsel & Sec.--Temple-Inland Inc., Diboll, TX; *U.S. Public*, pg. 1574

Warren, E.T., Gen. Counsel--Molded Fiber Glass Companies, Ashtabula, OH; *U.S. Private*, pg. 755

Warren, William M., Sr. V.P., Gen. Counsel & Asst. Sec.--Forest City Enterprises, Inc., Cleveland, OH; *U.S. Public*, pg. 667

Wartman, C.H., Gen. Counsel & Sec.--Consolidated Papers, Inc., Wisconsin Rapids, WI; *U.S. Public*, pg. 436

Washburn, John H., Sr. V.P.-Legal & Gen. Counsel--Sammons Enterprises, Inc., Dallas, TX; *U.S. Private*, pg. 963

Wassong, Dwight, Gen Counsel & Dir.-Taxes & Legal Services--Butterick Company, Inc., New York, NY; *U.S. Private*, pg. 190

Waterman, Robert, Gen. Counsel--Columbia/HCA Healthcare Corporation, Nashville, TN; *U.S. Public*, pg. 403

Watkin, Nancy, Gen. Counsel & Sec.--Tiger Direct, Inc., Miami, FL; *U.S. Public*, pg. 747

Watkins, James, Dir.-Legal--Trafalgar House PLC, London, United Kingdom; *Int'l*, pg. 772

Watkins, James B., V.P. & Counsel--Centex Real Estate Corp./Centex Homes, Dallas, TX; *U.S. Public*, pg. 323

Watkins, L. Earl, Jr., Gen. Counsel & Sec.--Sunflower Electric Power Corporation, Hays, KS; *U.S. Private*, pg. 1052

Watkins, Latham, Gen. Counsel--Ernst W. Dorn Co., Inc., Gardena, CA; *U.S. Private*, pg. 340

Watkins, Latham, Gen. Counsel--Union City Body Company, L.P., Union City, IN; *U.S. Private*, pg. 1118

Watkinson, D.J., V.P. & Gen. Counsel--Pembina Pipeline Corporation, Calgary, Canada; *Int'l*, pg. 1032
Watson, C. David, Sr. V.P.-Admin. & Gen. Counsel--National Propane Corp., Cedar Rapids, IA; *U.S. Public*, pg. 1635
Watson, James, Gen. Counsel--Wakefern Food Corporation, Elizabeth, NJ; *U.S. Private*, pg. 1146
Watson, L.G., Sec. & Grp. Legal Counsel--London & Edinburgh Insurance Group Limited, Worthing, United Kingdom; *U.S. Public*, pg. 795
Watson, Solomon B., IV, V.P. & Gen. Counsel--The New York Times Company, New York NY; *U.S. Public*, pg. 1173
Watson, William M., Jr., Exec. V.P. & Gen. Counsel--Wachovia Bank, Charlottesville, VA; *U.S. Public*, pg. 1730
Watt, David C., Exec. V.P., Gen. Counsel & Sec.--ICN Pharmaceuticals, Inc., Costa Mesa, CA; *U.S. Public*, pg. 853
Watters, Charles P., Grp. Sec. & Gen. Counsel--Allied Colloids Group Plc., Bradford, United Kingdom; *Int'l*, pg. 62
Wax, Robert P., V.P., Gen. Counsel & Sec.--Northeast Utilities, Berlin, CT; *U.S. Public*, pg. 1194
Wax, Robert P., V.P. & Gen. Counsel--Public Service Company of New Hampshire, Manchester, NH; *U.S. Public*, pg. 1195
Wayman, W. Russell, Corp. V.P., Gen. Counsel & Sec.--Storage Technology Corporation, Louisville, CO; *U.S. Public*, pg. 1522
Weatherbie, Shelley, Gen. Counsel--The Dwyer Group, Inc., Waco, TX; *U.S. Public*, pg. 537
Weaver, Joseph R., Jr., Gen. Counsel & Sec.--Darling International, Inc, Irving, TX; *U.S. Public*, pg. 484
Weaver, Kennard, Gen. Counsel--Jayco Inc., Middlebury, IN; *U.S. Private*, pg. 583
Weaver, Paul D., Sr. V.P., Clerk, Sec. & Gen. Counsel--Houghton Mifflin Company, Boston, MA; *U.S. Public*, pg. 841
Weaver, Steven, V.P.-Legal--Specialty Restaurants Corporation, Anaheim, CA; *U.S. Private*, pg. 1022
Webb, Brainard T., Jr., V.P. & Gen. Counsel--Genuine Parts Company, Atlanta, GA; *U.S. Public*, pg. 732
Webb, Chris, V.P. & Gen. Counsel--Jervis B. Webb Company, Farmington Hills, MI; *U.S. Private*, pg. 1156
Webb, Henley R., V.P. & Gen. Counsel--Millennium Petrochemicals, Inc., Cincinnati, OH; *Int'l*, pg. 594
Webb, Horrison, Jr., V.P. & Gen. Counsel--Bell Atlantic New England, Boston, MA; *U.S. Public*, pg. 202
Webb, Robert, V.P. & Gen. Counsel--The Marmon Group, Inc., Chicago, IL; *U.S. Private*, pg. 706
Webber, Robert N., V.P., Gen. Counsel & Asst. Sec.--Seaman Furniture Company, Inc., Woodbury, NY; *U.S. Public*, pg. 1452
Weber, Edward D. Jr., V.P., Gen. Counsel & Sec.--Acme Metals Incorporated, Riverdale, IL; *U.S. Public*, pg. 16
Webster, Mark, Chief Exec. Officer, Chief Fin. Officer & Gen. Counsel--Heritage Co-op, Rushville, IN; *U.S. Private*, pg. 524
Weddle, Stephen S., V.P., Sec. & Gen. Counsel--The Stanley Works, New Britain, CT; *U.S. Public*, pg. 1508
Weeks, Bill, Gen. Counsel--Aiken Electric Cooperative Inc., Aiken, SC; *U.S. Private*, pg. 28
Weeks, Bill, Gen. Counsel.--Aiken Electric Satellite, Aiken, SC; *U.S. Private*, pg. 28
Weeks, Paul, II, Sr. V.P., Gen. Counsel & Sec.--ICF Kaiser International Inc., Fairfax, VA; *U.S. Public*, pg. 852
Weglarz, Stephen J., Gen. Counsel & Dir.-Labor Rels.--C&D Charter Power Systems, Blue Bell, PA; *U.S. Public*, pg. 271
Weglarz, Stephen J., V.P.-Corp. Services & Counsel--C & D Technologies, Inc., Blue Bell, PA; *U.S. Public*, pg. 272
Wehrenberg, Kim A., V.P.-Gen. Counsel & Sec.--Federal Signal Corporation, Oak Brook, IL; *U.S. Public*, pg. 616
Weicher, Richard E., V.P. & Gen. Counsel--Burlington Northern Santa Fe Corporation, Fort Worth, TX; *U.S. Public*, pg. 268
Weil, Gary, V.P. & Sr. Corp. Counsel--RE/MAX International, Inc., Englewood, CO; *U.S. Private*, pg. 912
Weinberg, Herschel M., Gen. Counsel & Sec.--Milgray Electronics, Inc., Farmingdale, NY; *U.S. Public*, pg. 205
Weinberg, Richard A., Exec. V.P., Gen. Counsel & Sec.--GAF Materials Corporation, Wayne, NJ; *U.S. Private*, pg. 433
Weinberg, Richard G., Sr. V.P., Gen. Counsel & Sec.--GAF Corporation, Wayne, NJ; *U.S. Private*, pg. 433
Weinberg, Robert, V.P. & Gen. Counsel--GAF Premium Products, Inc., Wayne, NJ; *U.S. Private*, pg. 433
Weiner, Ronald, V.P., Gen. Counsel & Sec.--Radiator Specialty Company, Charlotte, NC; *U.S. Private*, pg. 906
Weinman, Glenn, Gen. Counsel--Guess ?, Inc., Los Angeles, CA; *U.S. Public*, pg. 768
Weinreich, Howard B., Gen. Counsel--Volt Information Sciences, Inc., New York, NY; *U.S. Public*, pg. 1724
Weinstein, G., Gen. Counsel--The Biltrite Corporation, Waltham, MA; *U.S. Private*, pg. 144
Weinstein, Gerald H., Legal Officer--Alliance America, Norcross, GA; *U.S. Private*, pg. 37
Weinstock, Michael, Sr. V.P. & Gen. Counsel--Pacificare Health Systems, Santa Ana, CA; *U.S. Public*, pg. 1251
Weir, M.A., Gen. Counsel & Sec.--Australian National Industries Limited, Pyrmont, Australia; *Int'l*, pg. 100
Weir, R. Harold, V.P., Gen. Counsel & Sec.--Jannock Limited, Toronto, Canada; *Int'l*, pg. 698
Weisberger, Glenn, V.P.-Legal & Bus. Affairs--Universal Studios TV, Universal City, CA; *Int'l*, pg. 1215
Weisberger, Mark, V.P., Sec. & Gen. Counsel--IHOP Corp., Glendale, CA; *U.S. Public*, pg. 862
Weiser, Paul D., Sr. V.P., Sec. & Corp. Counsel--Dataproducts Corporation, Simi Valley, CA; *Int'l*, pg. 620
Weiss, Andre, Sec. & Gen. Counsel--Toys "R" Us, Inc., Paramus, NJ; *U.S. Public*, pg. 1626
Weiss, Ed, Gen. Counsel & Sec.--Group 1 Software, Inc., Lanham, MD; *U.S. Public*, pg. 417
Weiss, Edward, Gen. Counsel & Sec.--COMNET Corporation, Lanham, MD; *U.S. Public*, pg. 416
Weiss, Eric, Exec. V.P. & Gen. Counsel--Active International, Pearl River, NY; *U.S. Private*, pg. 15
Weiss, Paul, Legal Counsel & Corp. Sec.--Gandalf Systems Corporation, Delran, NJ; *Int'l*, pg. 540
Weiss, Stephen, Sr. V.P. & Deputy Gen. Counsel--Union Bank of California, San Francisco, CA; *Int'l*, pg. 157
Weiss, Steven, Sr. V.P. & Gen. Counsel--Sanwa Bank California, Los Angeles, CA; *Int'l*, pg. 1189
Weiss, William L., Gen. Counsel--Craftmatic Industries, Inc., Trevose, PA; *U.S. Private*, pg. 284
Weiss, William L., Gen. Counsel--Craftmatic Organization, Inc., Trevose, PA; *U.S. Private*, pg. 284
Weiss, William L., Sec. & Gen. Counsel--Jetronic Industries, Inc., Philadelphia, PA; *U.S. Public*, pg. 926
Weissglass, Joel, Gen. Counsel--Magruder Color Company, Inc., Elizabeth, NJ; *U.S. Private*, pg. 696
Weiswasser, Stephen A., Pres.-Capital Cities/ABC Media Grp., Sr. V.P. & Gen. Counsel--ABC, Inc, New York, NY; *U.S. Public*, pg. 511
Welch, Charles, Gen. Counsel--Smart Modular Technologies, Fremont, CA; *U.S. Public*, pg. 1476
Welch, Jim, Gen. Counsel--Correct Craft, Inc., Orlando, FL; *U.S. Private*, pg. 276
Welge, Tom, Mgr.--Gilster Mary Lee Corp., Chester, IL; *U.S. Private*, pg. 455
Weller, Mark, Gen. Counsel--AGA Gas, Inc., Independence, OH; *Int'l*, pg. 13
Welsh, Kelly R., Exec. V.P. & Gen. Counsel--Ameritech Corporation, Chicago, IL; *U.S. Public*, pg. 97
Welty, John R., V.P., Gen. Counsel & Sec.--Carpenter Technology Corporation, Reading, PA; *U.S. Public*, pg. 307
Wendt, T.M., V.P., Div. Counsel & Asst. Sec.--Zimmer, Inc., Warsaw, IN; *U.S. Public*, pg. 254
Wenegrat, Eileen, Dir.-Legal Matters--Alfa Laval Inc., Kenosha, WI; *Int'l*, pg. 1378
Wennett, Richard W., Sec.--Blauer Manufacturing Co., Inc., Boston, MA; *U.S. Private*, pg. 149
Wentworth, Francis M., Jr., Sr. V.P., Sec. & General Counsel--Gaylord Entertainment Co., Nashville, TN; *U.S. Public*, pg. 704
Wentworth, Frank, Gen. Counsel--Gaylord Entertainment/ Opryland USA, Nashville, TN; *U.S. Public*, pg. 704
Weppler, Lawrence G., V.P. & Gen. Counsel--Continental Grain Company, New York, NY; *U.S. Private*, pg. 268
Werber, Richard, V.P.-Legal Affairs, Gen. Counsel & Sec.--Rexall Sundown Inc., Boca Raton, FL; *U.S. Public*, pg. 1384
Wertheimer, Robert, V.P., Gen. Counsel & Sec.--American Mail-Well Envelope, Englewood, CO; *U.S. Public*, pg. 1038
Wertheimer, Roger, V.P. & Gen. Counsel--Mail-Well Inc., Englewood, CO; *U.S. Public*, pg. 1037
West, Stephen A., Sr. V.P. & Gen. Counsel--Fairfield Inn, Washington, DC; *U.S. Public*, pg. 1048
Westberg, Anders, Chief Fin. Officer--Morgardshammar AB, Smedjebacken, Sweden; *Int'l*, pg. 378
Westen, B. Curtis, Sr. V.P., Gen. Counsel & Sec.--Foundation Health Systems, Inc., Pueblo, CO; *U.S. Public*, pg. 678
Westerbeck, Daniel J., V.P. & Gen. Tax Counsel--Burlington Northern Santa Fe Corporation, Fort Worth, TX; *U.S. Public*, pg. 268
Westerbeck, David F., Sr. V.P., Gen. Counsel & Sec.--The Union Central Life Insurance Co., Cincinnati, OH; *U.S. Private*, pg. 1118
Westfall, Timothy C., V.P. & Gen. Counsel--Continental Homes Holding Corp., Scottsdale, AZ; *U.S. Public*, pg. 440
Westmark, David L., V.P. & Gen. Counsel--Security American Financial Enterprises, Inc., Minnetonka, MN; *U.S. Private*, pg. 980
Wetherald, David, Gen. Counsel & Sec.--Torstar Corporation, Toronto, Canada; *Int'l*, pg. 1402
Wetmore, Edward C., Sec. & Gen. Counsel--Amphenol Corporation, Wallingford, CT; *U.S. Private*, pg. 629
Wetzel, Douglas, Gen. Counsel--Modern Welding Co., Inc., Owensboro, KY; *U.S. Private*, pg. 755
Wetzel, Robert, Gen. Counsel & Sec.--KTI, Inc., Guttenberg, NJ; *U.S. Public*, pg. 939
Wexler, Gene, V.P.--Genovese Drug Stores, Inc., Melville, NY; *U.S. Public*, pg. 730
Whaley, John A., V.P., Gen. Counsel & Sec.--CT Financial Services, Inc., Toronto, Canada; *Int'l*, pg. 112
Whare, W.S., Gen. Counsel--Irex Corporation, Lancaster, PA; *U.S. Public*, pg. 913
Wharton, Garry, Corp. Counsel & Sec.--Motorists Mutual Insurance Co., Columbus, OH; *U.S. Private*, pg. 764
Wharton, Garry L., Gen. Counsel & Sec.--American Hardware Mutual Insurance Co., Columbus, OH; *U.S. Private*, pg. 764
Wheeler, Joyce, Gen. Counsel & Sec.--Royal Insurance, Charlotte, NC; *Int'l*, pg. 1130
Whisman, John Michael, V.P. & Assoc. Gen. Counsel--The Gap, Inc., San Francisco, CA; *U.S. Public*, pg. 702
White, Britton, Jr., Exec. V.P.-Govt. Affairs & Gen. Counsel--El Paso Natural Gas Co., Houston, TX; *U.S. Public*, pg. 567
White, H. Katherine, Sec. & Asst. Gen. Counsel--Sealed Air Corporation, Saddle Brook, NJ; *U.S. Public*, pg. 1450
White, James B., Gen. Counsel--Papa Gino's Inc., Dedham, MA; *U.S. Private*, pg. 837
White, James M., III, Gen. Counsel & Sec.--Universal Corporation, Richmond, VA; *U.S. Public*, pg. 1694
White, Michael B., V.P., Gen. Counsel & Corp. Sec.--Hecla Mining Company, Coeur D'Alene, ID; *U.S. Public*, pg. 803
White, Paul, V.P. & Gen. Counsel--Pacific Telesis Group, San Francisco, CA; *U.S. Public*, pg. 1415
White, Paul H., Gen. Counsel & Asst. Sec.--AirTouch Communications, Inc., San Francisco, CA; *U.S. Public*, pg. 34
Whitehill, Clifford L., Sr. V.P. & Gen. Counsel--Darden Restaurants, Inc., Orlando, FL; *U.S. Public*, pg. 483
Whiteman, Joseph D., V.P., Gen. Counsel & Sec.--Parker Hannifin Corporation, Cleveland, OH; *U.S. Public*, pg. 1259
Whitfield, Alan, Solicitor--British Telecommunications plc, London, United Kingdom; *Int'l*, pg. 222
Whitmore, Bruce G., Sr. V.P., Gen. Counsel & Sec.--Atlantic Richfield Company, Los Angeles, CA; *U.S. Public*, pg. 144
Whitney, Wallace F., V.P.-Legal, Gen. Counsel & Clerk--Wyman-Gordon, North Grafton, MA; *U.S. Public*, pg. 1782
Whittaker, D., Gen. Counsel & Sec.--Racal Electronics Plc, Bracknell, United Kingdom; *Int'l*, pg. 1082
Whittle, Susan Thomas, V.P., Gen. Counsel & Sec.--Paragon Health Network, Inc., Atlanta, GA; *U.S. Public*, pg. 1256
Whitworth, J. Bryan, Sr. V.P. & Gen. Counsel--Phillips Petroleum Company, Bartlesville, OK; *U.S. Public*, pg. 1290
Wick, Randy, V.P. & Gen. Counsel--AST Research Inc., Irvine, CA; *Int'l*, pg. 1181
Wicker, Robert A., V.P. & Gen. Counsel--Burlington Industries, Inc., Greensboro, NC; *U.S. Public*, pg. 268
Wiener, Jude B., Corp. Counsel--Lone Star Equities Inc., Lynbrook, NY; *U.S. Private*, pg. 674
Wienke, Robert O., Sr. V.P.-Law & Gen. Counsel--The Loewen Group, Inc., Burnaby, Canada; *Int'l*, pg. 814
Wigley, Spencer, Sec. & Dir.-, Legal, Internal Audit & Risk Mngmt.--Bass PLC, London, United Kingdom; *Int'l*, pg. 169
Wilcher, Larry, Gen. Counsel--Dollar General Corporation, Nashville, TN; *U.S. Public*, pg. 515
Wilder, Michael S., Sr. V.P. & Gen. Counsel--The Hartford Financial Services Group Inc., Hartford, CT; *U.S. Public*, pg. 794
Wilder, Michael S., Sec. & Gen. Counsel--Hartford International Insurance Company, Hartford, CT; *U.S. Public*, pg. 795
Williams, Roy C., Gen. Counsel & Sec.--Inchcape PLC, London, United Kingdom; *Int'l*, pg. 671
Wilkie, Ian C., Sr. V.P.-Strategic Devel., Gen. Counsel & Sec.--Cara Operations Limited, Toronto, Canada; *Int'l*, pg. 266
Wilkins, P.D., Dir.-Legal Affairs--Morgan Crucible Co. Plc, Windsor, United Kingdom; *Int'l*, pg. 890
Wilkinson, James, Gen. Counsel--Meritcare, Inc., Sewickley, PA; *U.S. Private*, pg. 733
Wilkman, Nina, Gen. Counsel--Huhtamaki Oy, Espoo, Finland; *Int'l*, pg. 638
Wilkoc, A. Ronald, Counsel--Clupak, Inc., New York, NY; *U.S. Public*, pg. 1762
Wilks, Marylaurel E., V.P.-Commun., Gen. Counsel & Sec.--Speedway Motorsports, Inc., Concord, NC; *U.S. Public*, pg. 1498
Willems, Ilse P., Assoc. Gen. Counsel & Asst. Sec.--Alleghany Corporation, New York, NY; *U.S. Public*, pg. 42
Williams, Frank J., Jr., V.P.-Pub. Affairs & Sr. Counsel--The May Department Stores Company, Saint Louis, MO; *U.S. Public*, pg. 1063
Williams, John H., Gen. Counsel--Mack Molding Company Inc., Arlington, VT; *U.S. Private*, pg. 691
Williams, Martha G., V.P., Sec. & Legal--Liberty Corporation, Greenville, SC; *U.S. Public*, pg. 991
Williams, Martha T., Gen. Counsel--Port of Houston Authority, Houston, TX; *U.S. Private*, pg. 876
Williams, Richard John, Legal Officer--Handgards Inc., Northbrook, IL; *U.S. Private*, pg. 499
Williams, Robert I., Reg. Counsel & Asst. Sec.--OHM Remediation Services Corp., Findlay, OH; *U.S. Public*, pg. 1208
Williams, Ronald A., Asst. Gen. Counsel--Wal-Mart Stores, Inc., Bentonville, AR; *U.S. Public*, pg. 1732
Williams, S. Linn, Sr. V.P. & Gen. Counsel--Edison Mission Energy, Irvine, CA; *U.S. Public*, pg. 564
Williams, Stephen E., Sr. V.P. & Gen. Counsel--Consolidated Natural Gas Company, Pittsburgh, PA; *U.S. Public*, pg. 435
Williams, Thomas J., Assoc. Gen. Counsel & Asst. Sec.--The Stanley Works, New Britain, CT; *U.S. Public*, pg. 1508
Williams, Warren, Gen.Counsel--Gottschalks Inc., Fresno, CA; *U.S. Public*, pg. 754
Willing, Ulla, Mgr.-Legal Dept.--Dun & Bradstreet Deutschland GmbH, Frankfurt/Main, Germany; *U.S. Public*, pg. 536
Willis, Albert, Legal Counsel--North Carolina Mutual Life Insurance Co., Durham, NC; *U.S. Private*, pg. 804
Willkie, Wendell L., II, Sr. V.P. & Gen. Counsel--Westvaco Corporation, New York, NY; *U.S. Public*, pg. 1762
Willoch, Raymond S., V.P., Gen. Counsel & Sec.--Interface Inc., Atlanta, GA; *U.S. Public*, pg. 889
Wilson, Alan A., Grp. Mng. Dir.--Skandia Life Assurance Co. Ltd., Southampton, United Kingdom; *Int'l*, pg. 1258
Wilson, David D., Asst. Sec. & Assoc. Gen. Counsel-Legal Affairs--Armstrong World Industries, Inc., Lancaster, PA; *U.S. Public*, pg. 131
Wilson, Donna M.P., Gen. Counsel--Goodwill Industries International, Bethesda, MD; *U.S. Private*, pg. 464
Wilson, Frederick, Asst. V.P.-Legal--Bacardi-Martini, USA, Inc., Miami, FL; *U.S. Private*, pg. 109
Wilson, H. James, Exec. V.P. & Gen. Counsel--The New England, Boston, MA; *U.S. Private*, pg. 737
Wilson, John M., Asst. Gen. Counsel--Aluminum Company of America, Pittsburgh, PA; *U.S. Public*, pg. 60
Wilson, Logan J., V.P.-Legal Affairs & Sec.--Fike Corporation, Blue Springs, MO; *U.S. Private*, pg. 404
Wilson, N.W., III, V.P.-Americas--Union Texas Petroleum Holdings, Houston, TX; *U.S. Public*, pg. 1669
Wilson, Robert M., Chief Fin. Officer, Exec. V.P., Gen. Counsel & Sec.--Roberds, Inc., Carrollton, OH; *U.S. Public*, pg. 1393

Wilson, Roger, Gen. Counsel--Blue Cross and Blue Shield Association, Chicago, IL; *U.S. Private*, pg. 151

Wiltshire, J.M., Jr., V.P., Gen. Counsel & Sec.--Home Beneficial Corporation, Richmond, VA; *U.S. Public*, pg. 76

Winebarger, Paige, Sr. V.P. & Gen. Counsel--Marquette Bancshares Inc., Minneapolis, MN; *U.S. Private*, pg. 706

Winnick, Burton, Gen. Counsel--Asahi/America, Inc., Malden, MA; *U.S. Public*, pg. 137

Winquist, Donna F., V.P., Gen. Counsel & Sec.--AMETEK, Inc., Paoli, PA; *U.S. Public*, pg. 99

Winsor, Alan, Gen. Counsel--Stolt-Nielsen S.A., London, United Kingdom; *Int'l*, pg. 1301

Winter, Richard, Gen. Counsel--Bass PLC, London, United Kingdom; *Int'l*, pg. 169

Wirtz, Eli, Legal Officer--Casey's General Stores, Inc., Ankeny, IA; *U.S. Public*, pg. 312

Wise, Richard, Sec. & Gen. Counsel--Mississippi Valley Gas Co., Jackson, MS; *U.S. Private*, pg. 753

Wise, William, Asst. Gen. Counsel--Analog Devices, Inc., Norwood, MA; *U.S. Public*, pg. 107

Wiseman, Donald F., V.P., Gen. Counsel & Sec.--Perkins Family Restaurants, Memphis, TN; *U.S. Private*, pg. 925

Withers, W.W., Sr. V.P., Gen. Counsel & Sec.--Emerson Electric Co., Saint Louis, MO; *U.S. Public*, pg. 572

Witmer, John H., Jr., Sr. V.P., Gen. Counsel & Sec.--Dekalb Genetics Corporation, De Kalb, IL; *U.S. Public*, pg. 493

Witte, Derek, V.P. & Gen. Counsel--Symantec Corporation, Cupertino, CA; *U.S. Public*, pg. 1545

Witter, Jill, V.P., Sec. & Gen. Counsel--Angelica Corporation, Chesterfield, MO; *U.S. Public*, pg. 113

Wnorowski, A.K., Sr. V.P.-Admin. & Gen. Counsel--Comverse Network Systems, Wakefield, MA; *U.S. Public*, pg. 425

Woessner, Ron, Gen. Counsel & Sec.--Amtech Corporation, Dallas, TX; *U.S. Public*, pg. 105

Wohl, Richard H., Sr. Exec. V.P., Gen. Counsel & Sec.--INMC Mortgage Holdings, Inc., Pasadena, CA; *U.S. Public*, pg. 857

Wohlman, Herbert, Dr., Gen. Counsel, Sec. & Head-Legal Dept.--Clariant International Ltd., Muttenz, Switzerland; *Int'l*, pg. 624

Wohlschlaeger, Frederick G., Sr. V.P. & Gen. Counsel--Hartmarx Corporation, Chicago, IL; *U.S. Public*, pg. 795

Wolf, Philip C., Sr. V.P., Gen. Counsel & Sec.--Cyprus Amax Minerals Company, Englewood, CO; *U.S. Public*, pg. 470

Wolf, Robert P., Sr. V.P. & Gen. Counsel--Alumax Inc., Atlanta, GA; *U.S. Public*, pg. 59

Wolfcale, A.D., V.P., Deputy Gen. Counsel & Sec.--The Edward J. DeBartolo Corporation, Youngstown, OH; *U.S. Private*, pg. 319

Wolfe, J.H., V.P., Gen. Counsel & Sec.--Raytheon Engineers & Constructors International, Inc., Lexington, MA; *U.S. Public*, pg. 1366

Wolff, Richard H., Sec. & Assoc. Gen. Counsel--Newell Co., Freeport, IL; *U.S. Public*, pg. 1176

Wollaston, Scott, V.P. & Gen. Counsel--Siemens Business Communication Systems, Inc., Santa Clara, CA; *Int'l*, pg. 1245

Wollen, A. Ross, Sr. V.P., Gen. Counsel & Sec.--General Cigar Holdings Inc, New York, NY; *U.S. Public*, pg. 707

Wood, David, V.P. & Gen. Counsel--Safelite AutoGlass, Columbus, OH; *U.S. Private*, pg. 960

Wood, George N., V.P., Gen. Counsel & Sec.--Celotex Corporation, Tampa, FL; *U.S. Private*, pg. 221

Wood, Richard A., Jr., Gen. Counsel & Asst. Sec--Wellco Enterprises, Inc., Waynesville, NC; *U.S. Public*, pg. 1752

Woodard, Elizabeth B., V.P., Gen. Counsel & Sec.--Riviana Foods Inc., Houston, TX; *U.S. Public*, pg. 1392

Woodbury, A.T., V.P., Sec. & Assoc. Counsel--Fidelity Mutual Life Insurance Co., Radnor, PA; *U.S. Private*, pg. 403

Woodbury, T. Bowring, II, Sr. V.P. & Gen. Counsel--Consolidated Edison Company of New York, Inc., New York, NY; *U.S. Public*, pg. 434

Woodruff, J. David, Jr., V.P.-Legal & Corp. Devel. & Asst. Sec.--Energen Corporation, Birmingham, AL; *U.S. Public*, pg. 581

Woodward, A. Davis, V.P.-Legal, Sec., Asst. Gen. Counsel & Dir.-Tax Plng.--Surgical Laser Technologies, Inc., Montgomeryville, PA; *U.S. Public*, pg. 1542

Woodward, K., Chief Legal Officer & Sec.--John Mowlem & Company plc, Isleworth, United Kingdom; *Int'l*, pg. 896

Wooters, Thoams A., Sec. & Gen. Counsel--LoJack Corporation, Dedham, MA; *U.S. Public*, pg. 1012

Worcester, Theodore E., Sr. V.P.-Law & Admin. & Gen. Counsel--Westmoreland Coal Co., Colorado Springs, CO; *U.S. Public*, pg. 1761

Worden, Bill, V.P.-Legal & Admin.--Beaver Lumber Company Limited, Markham, Canada; *Int'l*, pg. 887

Worthing, Robert, V.P. & Gen. Counsel--United Industrial Corporation, New York, NY; *U.S. Public*, pg. 1679

Worthing, Robert W., V.P., Gen. Counsel & Sec.--AAI Corporation, Hunt Valley, MD; *U.S. Public*, pg. 1679

Worthington, Bruce R., Sr. V.P. & Gen. Counsel--PG&E Corporation, San Francisco, CA; *U.S. Public*, pg. 1240

Wozniak, Gregory, V.P. & Gen. Counsel--Dairy Mart Convenience Stores, Inc., Cuyahoga Falls, OH; *U.S. Public*, pg. 476

Wright, G.J., V.P., Gen. Counsel & Sec.--ABB Lummus Global Inc., Bloomfield, NJ; *Int'l*, pg. 4

Wright, James W., V.P.-Legal Affairs & Sec.--Lord Corporation, Cary, NC; *U.S. Private*, pg. 675

Wright, John K., V.P., Sr. Assoc. Counsel & Sec.--Protective Life Insurance Co., Birmingham, AL; *U.S. Public*, pg. 1336

Wright, Joseph, Gen. Counsel--Kentucky Medical Insurance Company (KMIC), Louisville, KY; *U.S. Private*, pg. 741

Wright, Timothy C., Gen. Counsel & Sec.--National-Standard Co., Niles, MI; *U.S. Public*, pg. 1160

Wuebbling, Donald J., V.P. & Gen. Counsel--The Western and Southern Life Insurance Company, Cincinnati, OH; *U.S. Private*, pg. 1164

Wuestner, Joseph A., Assoc. Gen. Counsel & Asst. Sec.--Mallinckrodt Inc., Saint Louis, MO; *U.S. Public*, pg. 1039

Wurtzel, Paul, Attorney--Inverness Corp., Fair Lawn, NJ; *U.S. Private*, pg. 574

Wushinske, Robert P., V.P., Treas., Gen. Counsel & Sec.--Pennsylvania Power Co., New Castle, PA; *U.S. Public*, pg. 645

Wyatt, Bruce H., V.P., Gen. Counsel, Sec. & Clerk--Stanhome Inc., Westfield, MA; *U.S. Public*, pg. 1508

Wyckoff, Thomas C., Sr. V.P., Gen. Counsel & Asst. Sec.--Artistic Greetings, Inc., Elmira, NY; *U.S. Public*, pg. 136

Wyker, Kenneth, Sr. V.P.-Legal Affairs--Clear Channel Communications, Inc., San Antonio, TX; *U.S. Public*, pg. 383

Wynn, John R., Gen. Counsel--Nichols Research Corporation, Huntsville, AL; *U.S. Public*, pg. 1182

Wyrsch, Martha B., V.P., Deputy Gen. Counsel & Sec.--K N Energy, Inc., Lakewood, CO; *U.S. Public*, pg. 937

Yahav, David, Gen. Counsel & Sec.--The Israel Electric Corporation Ltd., Haifa, Israel; *Int'l*, pg. 690

Yamazaki, Masao, Sr. Exec. V.P.--Japan Tobacco Inc., Tokyo, Japan; *Int'l*, pg. 703

Yanes, Clementina, Gen. Counsel & Sec.--Corporacion Grupo Quimico, S.A.C.A., Caracas, Venezuela; *Int'l*, pg. 331

Yared, Paul D., Sr. V.P., Gen. Counsel & Sec.--Foremost Corporation of America, Caledonia, MI; *U.S. Public*, pg. 667

Yastow, Shelby, Exec. V.P., Gen. Counsel & Sec.--McDonald's Corporation, Oak Brook, IL; *U.S. Public*, pg. 1068

Yeagley, Laurence A., V.P.-Sulphur & Gen. Counsel--International Chemical Company, Tulsa, OK; *U.S. Private*, pg. 568

Yellin, Melvin, Exec. V.P. & Gen. Counsel--Bankers Trust New York Corporation, New York, NY; *U.S. Public*, pg. 185

Yellin, Sue, Gen. Counsel--Lambda Electronics Inc., Melville, NY; *Int'l*, pg. 1241

Yestrumskas, Paul E., V.P., Gen. Counsel & Sec.--Playtex Products Inc., Westport, CT; *U.S. Public*, pg. 1310

Ylitalo, Joe A., Gen. Counsel & Asst. Sec.--Vertex Communications Corporation, Kilgore, TX; *U.S. Public*, pg. 1717

Yoder, Stephen A., Exec. V.P. & Gen. Counsel--AmSouth Bancorporation, Birmingham, AL; *U.S. Public*, pg. 105

Yon, Charles, Chief Legal Officer--Astra USA, Inc., Westborough, MA; *Int'l*, pg. 93

Yoskowitz, Irving B., Exec. V.P. & Gen. Counsel--United Technologies Corporation, Hartford, CT; *U.S. Public*, pg. 1689

Yosowitz, Sanford, V.P., Gen. Counsel & Sec.--Alcan Aluminum Corporation, Cleveland, OH; *Int'l*, pg. 50

Young, Carl, Sr. V.P. & Gen. Counsel--Anchor Glass Container Corporation, Tampa, FL; *Int'l*, pg. 327

Young, Carl H., Gen. Counsel--HMI Industries, Cleveland, OH; *U.S. Public*, pg. 771

Young, Dona D., Exec. V.P.-Individual Insurance Counsel--Phoenix Home Life Mutual Insurance Company, Hartford, CT; *U.S. Private*, pg. 863

Young, Dona D., Exec. V.P.-Individual Insurance Counsel--Phoenix Home Life Mutual Insurance Co., Hartford, CT; *U.S. Private*, pg. 863

Young, James R., V.P. & Gen. Counsel--Bell Atlantic Corporation, New York, NY; *U.S. Public*, pg. 201

Young, LeGrande L., V.P., Gen. Counsel & Sec.--Raytech Corporation, Shelton, CT; *U.S. Public*, pg. 1363

Young, Merne, Gen. Counsel--Amelco Corporation, Gardena, CA; *U.S. Public*, pg. 65

Young, Michael D., V.P. & Gen. Counsel--Phibro Division of Salomon Inc., Westport, CT; *U.S. Public*, pg. 1633

Young, Robert A.M., Sr. V.P.-Law--Transcanada Pipelines Limited, Calgary, Canada; *Int'l*, pg. 1416

Young, Stewart, V.P.-Legal Affairs--United Broadcasting L.P., Bethesda, MD; *U.S. Private*, pg. 1121

Young, Thomas L., Exec. V.P.-Admin., Gen. Counsel & Sec.--Owens-Illinois, Inc., Toledo, OH; *U.S. Public*, pg. 1238

Yslas, Stephen D., V.P. & Asst. Gen. Counsel--Northrop Grumman Corporation, Los Angeles, CA; *U.S. Public*, pg. 1197

Yudell, Carl, General Counsel--Midco International Inc., Chicago, IL; *U.S. Private*, pg. 744

Zabitchuck, Suzanne, Asst. Gen. Counsel--The Stride Rite Corporation, Lexington, MA; *U.S. Public*, pg. 1524

Zabitchuck, Suzanne M., Corp. Counsel & Asst. Sec.--Watts Industries, Inc., North Andover, MA; *U.S. Public*, pg. 1746

Zackin, Martha, Corp. Counsel--Keane, Inc., Boston, MA; *U.S. Public*, pg. 946

Zahler, Eric J., V.P., Gen. Counsel & Sec.--Loral Space & Communications, New York, NY; *U.S. Public*, pg. 1014

Zahra, E. Ellis, V.P., Gen. Counsel & Sec.--Winn-Dixie Stores, Inc., Jacksonville, FL; *U.S. Public*, pg. 1771

Zak, S. Arieh, Esq., V.P.-Regulatory Affairs, Corp. Counsel & Asst. Sec.--Datascope Corp., Montvale, NJ; *U.S. Public*, pg. 487

Zakos, Dean R., Assoc. Gen. Counsel & Asst. Sec.--Modine Manufacturing Company, Racine, WI; *U.S. Public*, pg. 1121

Zambri, Robert R., Sr. V.P., Gen. Counsel & Sec.--Fortis Benefits Insurance Company, Kansas City, MO; *Int'l*, pg. 499

Zamore, Peter H., Gen. Counsel--Green Mountain Power Corporation, South Burlington, VT; *U.S. Public*, pg. 761

Zanetti, Dario, Gen. Counsel--Cassa di Risparmio delle Provincie Lombarde SpA (CARIPLO), Milan, Italy; *Int'l*, pg. 274

Zar, Keith A., V.P. & Gen. Counsel--General Instrument Corporation, Horsham, PA; *U.S. Public*, pg. 716

Zato, D. Carlos Jomenez, General Counsel--Estrategias Telefonicas, S.A. (Estratel), Madrid, Spain; *Int'l*, pg. 1371

Zawel, Susan Fein, V.P.-Corp. Commun., Sec. & Assoc. Gen. Counsel--United Industrial Corporation, New York, NY; *U.S. Public*, pg. 1679

Zeger, Warren Y., V.P., Gen. Counsel & Sec.--COMSAT Corporation, Bethesda, MD; *U.S. Public*, pg. 424

Zeller, Paul W., V.P., Deputy Gen. Counsel & Asst. Sec.--Reliance Group Holdings, Inc., New York, NY; *U.S. Public*, pg. 1374

Zeller, Randi E., Assoc. Gen. Counsel--McKinsey & Company, Inc., New York, NY; *U.S. Private*, pg. 723

Zermati, Paul, Mgr.-Contracts & Legal Affairs--Arianespace SA, Evry, France; *Int'l*, pg. 81

Zigel, James M., Gen. Counsel & Sec.--LucasVarity Inc., Buffalo, NY; *Int'l*, pg. 820

Ziino, Joseph J., Jr., V.P., Assoc. Gen. Counsel & Asst. Sec.--Mortgage Guaranty Insurance Corporation, Milwaukee, WI; *U.S. Public*, pg. 1026

Zimmer, Daryl L., V.P. & Gen. Counsel--Alliant Techsystems, Hopkins, MN; *U.S. Public*, pg. 47

Zimmer, Edward, Sr. V.P., Sec. & Gen. Counsel--Levitz Furniture Incorporated, Boca Raton, FL; *U.S. Public*, pg. 990

Zimmer, Herbert J., Gen. Counsel--Reeds Jewelers, Inc., Wilmington, NC; *U.S. Public*, pg. 1370

Zimmerman, Bill J., V.P. & Gen. Counsel--Union Pacific Resources Company (UPRC), Fort Worth, TX; *U.S. Public*, pg. 1668

Zimmerman, Doug, Legal Officer--Best Western International, Inc., Phoenix, AZ; *U.S. Private*, pg. 140

Zimmerman, Michael, V.P. & Gen. Counsel--Montana Power Company, Butte, MT; *U.S. Public*, pg. 1126

Zink, Robert L., V.P.-Litigation--Hilti Inc., Tulsa, OK; *Int'l*, pg. 620

Zinn, Frank K., Gen. Counsel & Sec.--Simpson Industries, Inc., Plymouth, MI; *U.S. Public*, pg. 1474

Zirkman, Joseph A., V.P., Gen. Counsel & Sec.--Carrols Corporation, Syracuse, NY; *U.S. Private*, pg. 216

Zisowitz, Terry S., V.P.-Legal & Regulatory & Gen. Counsel--E-Z-Em, Inc., Westbury, NY; *U.S. Public*, pg. 540

Zkedata, Hideo, Mng. Dir.-Intellectual Property--Nikon Corporation, Tokyo, Japan; *Int'l*, pg. 931

Zoeller, David L., Sr. V.P., Gen. Counsel & Sec.--National City Corporation, Cleveland, OH; *U.S. Public*, pg. 1154

Zoellick, Robert B., Exec. V.P., Gen. Counsel & Sec.--Federal National Mortgage Association (Fannie Mae), Washington, DC; *U.S. Public*, pg. 615

Zoobkoff, Anthony A., Sr. Counsel & Asst. Sec.--Cominco, Ltd., Vancouver, Canada; *Int'l*, pg. 307

Zopp, E. Frederick, Sr. V.P., Sec. & Gen. Counsel--PNC Bank, Louisville, KY; *U.S. Public*, pg. 1242

Zucco, William C., V.P.-Legal--International Dairy Queen, Inc., Minneapolis, MN; *U.S. Public*, pg. 220

Zuk, Nicholas W., Legal Officer--White Castle System, Inc., Columbus, OH; *U.S. Private*, pg. 1171

Zumstein, Christophe, Gen. Counsel--BBA Group plc, London, United Kingdom; *Int'l*, pg. 112

Zussman, Ephraim, Dir.-Legal Affairs--El Al Airlines Ltd., Lod, Israel; *Int'l*, pg. 435

Zussman, Milton, Treas. & Gen. Counsel--Norman Levy Associates, Inc., Southfield, MI; *U.S. Private*, pg. 664

Zwicky, Elisabeth, Sr. V.P.-Legal Affairs & Special Projects--Liechtenstein Global Trust Limited, Vaduz, Liechtenstein; *Int'l*, pg. 809

Zwicky, Elisabeth, Deputy Mng. Dir.-Legal & Projects--LGT Bank in Liechtenstein Aktiengesellschaft, Vaduz, Liechtenstein; *Int'l*, pg. 809

Zwolsman, P.V.B., Mgr.-Legal Affairs--Royal Nedlloyd Group N.V., Rotterdam, Netherlands; *Int'l*, pg. 1143

Zylstra, Michael, Corp. Sec. & Gen. Counsel--Cracker Barrel Old Country Store, Inc., Lebanon, TN; *U.S. Public*, pg. 455

GROUP VICE PRESIDENT

Abernathy, Robert E., Grp. Pres.-Health, Non-Woven, Tech., Aviation & World Support--Kimberly-Clark Corporation, Dallas, TX; *U.S. Public*, pg. 958

Adams, Rick, Grp. V.P.--MicroAge, Inc., Tempe, AZ; *U.S. Public*, pg. 1104

Agdern, R.D., Grp. V.P.--Amoco Production Company, Chicago, IL; *U.S. Public*, pg. 102

Agrawal, Satish C., Grp. V.P.--Polaroid Corporation, Cambridge, MA; *U.S. Public*, pg. 1313

Albright, Steve, V.P. Prod. Mktg.--The Check Store, Lakewood, CO; *U.S. Public*, pg. 785

Alderson, David P., II, Grp. V.P.-Fin. & Acctg.--Pennzoil Company, Houston, TX; *U.S. Public*, pg. 1272

Aldridge, J. Mac, Div. Mgr.--Huntington Division, Huntington, WV; *U.S. Public*, pg. 333

Aldridge, J. Mac, Div. Mgr.--Stationers, Inc., Huntington, WV; *U.S. Public*, pg. 333

Alepian, Taro, Grp. V.P.-Industrial--SNC-Lavalin Inc., Montreal, Canada; *Int'l*, pg. 1162

Allen, Dean, Reg. V.P.-Western Reg.--Scott Forseman/Addison Wesley, Glenview, IL; *Int'l*, pg. 927

Allen, William, Reg. V.P.-Orlando Reg. Distr. Ctr. (RDC)--Bergen Brunswig Drug Company, Orange, CA; *U.S. Public*, pg. 213

Allspach, Eugene R., Grp. V.P.-Tech. & Mfg.--Millennium Petrochemicals, Inc., Cincinnati, OH; *Int'l*, pg. 594

Anderson, Daniel L., Grp. V.P.--DST Systems, Inc., Kansas City, MO; *U.S. Public*, pg. 943

Anderson, Thomas, V.P.-Construction-San Diego--Bergelectric Corporation, Los Angeles, CA; *U.S. Private*, pg. 135

Angiolini, Guido, Sr. Grp. V.P.-Admin.--Montedison S.p.A., Milan, Italy; *Int'l*, pg. 324

Aoki, Tsuneo, Mng. Dir. & Gen. Mgr.--Ashikaga Finance (H.K.) Limited, Hong Kong, Hong Kong; *Int'l*, pg. 88

Apostolopoulos, Alexander A., V.P. & Grp. Exec.-Plumbing Prods./Americas Intl.--American Standard Inc., Piscataway, NJ; *U.S. Public*, pg. 91

Arnesen, Christer, Grp. V.P.-Pulp & Paper--Canfor Corporation, Vancouver, Canada; *Int'l*, pg. 260

Ash, David, Reg. V.P.--Payless Cashways, Inc., Kansas City, MO; *U.S. Public*, pg. 1267

Ashcraft, David L., Grp. V.P.-Bleached Paperboard--Temple-Inland Forest Products Corporation, Diboll, TX; *U.S. Public*, pg. 1575

Ausfahl, William R., Chief Fin. Officer & Grp. V.P.--The Clorox Company, Oakland, CA; *U.S. Public*, pg. 386

Avery, Robert L., V.P. & Grp. V.P.-Maintenance, Repair & Overhaul--The B.F. Goodrich Company, Richfield, OH; *U.S. Public*, pg. 751

Aymar, Michael, V.P. & Gen. Mgr.-Santa Clara--Intel Microcomputer Group, Santa Clara, CA; *U.S. Public*, pg. 887

Ayoub, Sam, Grp. V.P.-Services--B/E Aerospace, Inc., Wellington, FL; *U.S. Public*, pg. 159

Azieres, Claude, Grp. V.P. & Gen. Mgr.-Engineered Materials--Engelhard Corporation, Iselin, NJ; *U.S. Public*, pg. 582

Baars, C., Grp. V.P.-Dairy Europe--Koninklijke BolsWessanen nv, Amstelveen, Netherlands; *Int'l*, pg. 750

Bailey, Robert D., Grp. Exec.-Institutional Bank-Caribbean, Central & S. America--Citicorp, New York, NY; *U.S. Public*, pg. 376

Baker, M. Gerald, Grp. V.P.-Distributed Prods.--Modine Manufacturing Company, Racine, WI; *U.S. Public*, pg. 1121

Baker, T.F., Chief Fin. Officer, Grp. V.P.-Fin. & Treas.--Harvest States Cooperatives, Saint Paul, MN; *U.S. Private*, pg. 508

Baker, William G., Grp. V.P.-Admin. Services--HarperCollins Publishers, New York, NY; *Int'l*, pg. 926

Baldrige, Ronald E., Reg. V.P.-Corona RDC--Bergen Brunswig Drug Company, Orange, CA; *U.S. Public*, pg. 213

Bangs, Lawrence N., Grp. Exec.-Private Label, UK, Canada, Insurance--Household International, Inc., Prospect Heights, IL; *U.S. Public*, pg. 842

Banks, Robert K., Grp. V.P.-Real Estate--Albertson's, Inc., Boise, ID; *U.S. Public*, pg. 38

Bardeen, Bette, V.P.-Business Practices--Rockwell International Corporation, Costa Mesa, CA; *U.S. Public*, pg. 1397

Barneby, David G., V.P.-Power Delivery Division--Nevada Power Company, Las Vegas, NV; *U.S. Public*, pg. 1169

Barrett, Kein, Grp. V.P.--Beloit Corporation, Beloit, WI; *U.S. Public*, pg. 789

Barron, Arnold S., Sr. V.P. & Grp. Exec.--The TJX Companies, Inc., Framingham, MA; *U.S. Public*, pg. 1556

Bartelt, Linda L., Grp. Pres.--Kimberly-Clark Corporation, Dallas, TX; *U.S. Public*, pg. 958

Barthelmes, Richard B., Dir.-Exec. Grp. Publishing--American Express Publishing Corporation, New York, NY; *U.S. Public*, pg. 74

Batchelder, Lewis W., Grp. V.P.--Archer Daniels Midland Company (ADM), Decatur, IL; *U.S. Public*, pg. 127

Bates, Arlene, V.P. Human Resources--The Check Store, Lakewood, CO; *U.S. Public*, pg. 785

Bates, Garth C., Jr., Grp. V.P.-Distr.--Stewart & Stevenson Services, Inc., Houston, TX; *U.S. Public*, pg. 1517

Beahm, Clyde W., Grp. V.P.-Prods. & Mktg.--Pennzoil Company, Houston, TX; *U.S. Public*, pg. 1272

Bealmear, Keith A., Grp. V.P.--Genuine Parts Company, Atlanta, GA; *U.S. Public*, pg. 732

Bear, J.E., Grp. V.P.--Industrial Electronics Group, Torrance, CA; *U.S. Public*, pg. 1364

Becky, Walter W., II, Grp. V.P.-Salt--Morton International Inc., Chicago, IL; *U.S. Public*, pg. 1134

Behrendt, John M., Regional V.P.--The Lincoln National Life Insurance Co., Fort Wayne, IN; *U.S. Public*, pg. 998

Bellerdine, Anthony J., Grp. V.P.--CORT Business Services Corporation, Fairfax, VA; *U.S. Public*, pg. 451

Belton, John P., Grp. V.P.-Sls.--American & Efird, Inc., Mount Holly, NC; *U.S. Public*, pg. 1412

Bendik, John F., Grp. V.P.--U.S. Industries, Inc., Iselin, NJ; *U.S. Public*, pg. 1683

Benham, Helen V., Corp. V.P. & Early Childhood Advisor--Scholastic Corporation, New York, NY; *U.S. Public*, pg. 1440

Benson, John, Grp. V.P.-Indus. Markets Grp.--3M, Saint Paul, MN; *U.S. Public*, pg. 1604

Beracha, Barry H., V.P. & Grp. Exec.--Anheuser-Busch Companies, Inc., Saint Louis, MO; *U.S. Public*, pg. 113

Bergeland, Michael, Grp. V.P.-Grain & Agriculture Services--Harvest States Cooperatives, Saint Paul, MN; *U.S. Private*, pg. 508

Bernado, Allen J., Dept. Mgr.-Corp. Trust--Bank of Bermuda (Cayman) Limited, Georgetown, Cayman Islands; *Int'l*, pg. 151

Bernstein, Carol L., V.P. & Group Dir. of Stores, Northern Div.--Elder-Beerman Stores Div., Dayton, OH; *U.S. Private*, pg. 367

Berr, Vera, Grp. Dir.--The Dartnell Corporation, Chicago, IL; *U.S. Private*, pg. 312

Berrey, Howard J., Grp. V.P.-Real Estate & Construction--Bob Evans Farms, Inc., Columbus, OH; *U.S. Public*, pg. 596

Berrey, Howard J., Grp. V.P.-Real Estate & Construction--Bob Evans Farms, Inc. Restaurant Division, Columbus, OH; *U.S. Public*, pg. 596

Billig, Ed, V.P.-Construction-L.A.--Bergelectric Corporation, Los Angeles, CA; *U.S. Private*, pg. 135

Bjorkqvist, Krister, Grp. V.P.-Bus. Controller--Polarcup Group Headquarters, Espoo, Finland; *Int'l*, pg. 638

Blackshire, Gary A., Div. Mgr.--Charleston Division, Charleston, WV; *U.S. Public*, pg. 333

Blackwell, M.A., V.P.-Atlantic Region--Canadian National Railway Company, Montreal, Canada; *Int'l*, pg. 258

Blair, Jack, Grp. Dir.-North America--Smith & Nephew PLC, London, United Kingdom; *Int'l*, pg. 1263

Blanchard, Robert T., Grp. V.P. & Pres.-Beauty Care Prods./North America--The Procter & Gamble Company, Cincinnati, OH; *U.S. Public*, pg. 1330

Blumenthal, Lowell, V.P.-Intl.--Duro Dyne Corporation, Farmingdale, NY; *U.S. Private*, pg. 349

Bokach, Peter M., Grp. V.P.-Distr.--Ashland Chemical, Dublin, OH; *U.S. Public*, pg. 139

Bongiorno, John J., Grp. V.P. & Gen. Mgr.-Fin. Services--Navistar International Corporation, Chicago, IL; *U.S. Public*, pg. 1167

Boone, John T., Grp. V.P.-Domestic Consumer Prods.--Alberto-Culver USA, Inc., Melrose Park, IL; *U.S. Public*, pg. 38

Bosco, Carmine, Grp. V.P. & Gen. Mgr.-Measure & Control Grp.--Giddings & Lewis, Inc., Fond Du Lac, WI; *Int'l*, pg. 1389

Bourgeois, David, Div. Mgr.--Pride Offshore, Inc., Houma, LA; *U.S. Public*, pg. 1325

Bourke, Thomas J., Grp. V.P.-Directories--BCE Inc., Montreal, Canada; *Int'l*, pg. 114

Boutwell, Donald J., Grp. V.P.-Field Svcs.--Jacobs Engineering Group Inc., Pasadena, CA; *U.S. Public*, pg. 921

Bowersox, Robert, V.P.-Transportaion--Casey's General Stores, Inc., Ankeny, IA; *U.S. Public*, pg. 312

Bowick, Christopher J., Chief Tech. Officer & Grp. V.P.-Tech.--Jones Intercable, Inc., Englewood, CO; *U.S. Private*, pg. 597

Bowman, Donald R., Reg. V.P.--Payless Cashways, Inc., Kansas City, MO; *U.S. Public*, pg. 1267

Boynton, Bob, Reg. V.P.-Northeast Reg.--Scott Forseman/Addison Wesley, Glenview, IL; *Int'l*, pg. 927

Brace, Robert P., Dir.-Grp. Fin.--British Telecommunications plc, London, United Kingdom; *Int'l*, pg. 222

Brannon, George M., Grp. V.P. & Pres.-Nalco Pacific--Nalco Chemical Company, Naperville, IL; *U.S. Public*, pg. 1150

Brautigam, Dale, Grp. V.P.--LubeCon Systems, Inc., White Cloud, MI; *U.S. Private*, pg. 679

Breci, Robert J., Grp. V.P.--Genuine Parts Company, Atlanta, GA; *U.S. Public*, pg. 732

Brennan, Vin, V.P.-Community Mkts.Sls.--The Check Store, Lakewood, CO; *U.S. Public*, pg. 785

Brevig, Christian, Grp. V.P.-CTC--Jotun A/S, Sandefjord, Norway; *Int'l*, pg. 714

Bricklin, Mark, Grp. V.P.--Rodale Press, Inc., Emmaus, PA; *U.S. Private*, pg. 939

Britton, Robert A., Grp. Pres.--Kimberly-Clark Corporation, Dallas, TX; *U.S. Public*, pg. 958

Broderick, Matthew, Grp. V.P.-Mktg.--Turtle Wax, Inc., Chicago, IL; *U.S. Private*, pg. 1110

Brody, Carolyn P., Regional V.P.--The Lincoln National Life Insurance Co., Fort Wayne, IN; *U.S. Public*, pg. 998

Brogoch, Gary A., V.P. & Grp. Exec.--American Standard Inc., Piscataway, NJ; *U.S. Public*, pg. 91

Bronson, Joseph R., Grp. V.P.-Worldwide Mfg. Opers.--Applied Materials, Inc., Santa Clara, CA; *U.S. Public*, pg. 123

Brown, Eric, Grp. V.P.-Grocery Prods.--Hormel Grocery Prods. Div., Austin, MN; *U.S. Public*, pg. 840

Brown, Eric A., Grp. V.P.-Prepared Foods--Hormel Foods Corp., Austin, MN; *U.S. Public*, pg. 840

Brown, J.M., Grp. V.P.--Amoco Production Company, Chicago, IL; *U.S. Public*, pg. 102

Brown, Michael D., Grp. V.P.-Metallurgical Opers.--Pittston Minerals Group, Inc., Lebanon, VA; *U.S. Public*, pg. 1305

Bruck, Terry E., Grp. V.P.-Transmission & Distribution--CINergy Services, Inc., Cincinnati, OH; *U.S. Public*, pg. 369

Brunelli, Massimo S., Chief Fin. Officer & Grp. V.P.--ELSAG Bailey Process Automation N.V., Schiphol, Netherlands; *Int'l*, pg. 449

Brunetti, Franco, Grp. V.P.-H.R. & Corp. Commun.--Montedison S.p.A., Milan, Italy; *Int'l*, pg. 324

Brunton, Ellis, Grp. V.P.-Res. & Quality Assurance--Tyson Foods, Inc., Springdale, AR; *U.S. Public*, pg. 1652

Bryant, Thomas L., Corp. V.P.--Bryant Electric Supply Company, Inc., Lowell, NC; *U.S. Private*, pg. 177

Bryson, Jon H., Grp. V.P.-Natl. Sys. Grp.--Aerospace Corporation, El Segundo, CA; *U.S. Private*, pg. 24

Bucci, James, Grp. V.P.-Corp. Personnel--First Citizens Banc Shares, Inc., Raleigh, NC; *U.S. Public*, pg. 628

Buckley, Thomas J., Grp. V.P.-Standard Prods.--Invacare Corporation, Elyria, OH; *U.S. Public*, pg. 911

Bungert, David M., V.P.-Group Sls.--Security American Financial Enterprises, Inc., Minnetonka, MN; *U.S. Private*, pg. 980

Buoy, Howard E., Grp. V.P.--Archer Daniels Midland Company (ADM), Decatur, IL; *U.S. Public*, pg. 127

Burch, Larry E., Reg. V.P.-Southwest Reg.--Bergen Brunswig Drug Company, Orange, CA; *U.S. Public*, pg. 213

Burdakin, David C., Grp. V.P.-Seating--The HON Co., Muscatine, IA; *U.S. Public*, pg. 772

Burke, William R., Grp. Mgr.-White Cap Closures, USA--Schmalbach-Lubeca AG, Braunschweig, Germany; *Int'l*, pg. 1206

Burnett, Joe, V.P.-Southeastern--YKK (U.S.A.), Marietta, GA; *Int'l*, pg. 1515

Burns, Ross F., V.P.-Exploration--Royal Oak Mines Inc., Kirkland, WA; *U.S. Public*, pg. 1410

Burton, J.C., Grp. V.P.-Intl. Opers.--Amoco Corporation, Chicago, IL; *U.S. Public*, pg. 101

Burton, J.C., Grp. V.P.--Amoco Production Company, Chicago, IL; *U.S. Public*, pg. 102

Burtscher, Peter, Grp. V.P.--U.S. Surgical Corp., Norwalk, CT; *U.S. Public*, pg. 1687

Butcher, Preston, Reg. Partner--Lincoln Property Company, Dallas, TX; *U.S. Private*, pg. 668

Butynski, Donald L., Grp. V.P.--Zurn Industries, Inc., Erie, PA; *U.S. Public*, pg. 1794

Butzko, Tracy, Grp. Dir.--The Dartnell Corporation, Chicago, IL; *U.S. Private*, pg. 312

Byrne, Tim, Reg. Partner--Lincoln Property Company, Dallas, TX; *U.S. Private*, pg. 668

Byrnes, Bruce L., Grp. V.P. & Pres.-Health Care Prods./North America--The Procter & Gamble Company, Cincinnati, OH; *U.S. Public*, pg. 1330

Cady, Al, Grp. V.P.--TMP Worldwide, Inc., Minneapolis, MN; *U.S. Private*, pg. 1064

Cady, Al, Grp. V.P.--TMP Worldwide, Inc., Skokie, IL; *U.S. Private*, pg. 1064

Cady, Al, Grp. V.P.--TMP Worldwide, Inc., Cincinnati, OH; *U.S. Private*, pg. 1065

Cain, Richard, Chm. Bd. & Corp. V.P.--West Hudson, Inc. (Healthcare Consulting Services), Dallas, TX; *U.S. Public*, pg. 45

Calcagni, Robert, Mng. Dir. & Group V.P.--Astron S.A.R.L., Vincennes, France; *U.S. Public*, pg. 411

Calcagni, Robert A., Grp. V.P.-Building Sys. & Metal Prods.--Commercial Intertech Corp., Youngstown, OH; *U.S. Public*, pg. 411

Campbell, Bill, Div. Mgr.--Parkersburg Division, Parkersburg, WV; *U.S. Public*, pg. 333

Campbell, John, V.P.-Sls. Svcs.--Diagraph Corporation, Earth City, MO; *U.S. Private*, pg. 330

Cappeline, Gary A., Grp. V.P.-Drew Businesses--Ashland Chemical, Dublin, OH; *U.S. Public*, pg. 139

Cappicelle, Chuck, Grp. V.P.-Bank Mkt.--Computer Language Research, Inc., Carrollton, TX; *U.S. Public*, pg. 421

Carpenter, Charles, Reg. V.P.-Pine Brook RDC--Bergen Brunswig Drug Company, Orange, CA; *U.S. Public*, pg. 213

Carpenter, Vic, V.P.-Opers.-Memphis Branch--Pemko Manufacturing Company, Ventura, CA; *U.S. Private*, pg. 848

Carr, David, Reg. V.P.--First Cash, Inc., Arlington, TX; *U.S. Public*, pg. 627

Carroll, Patti, Reg. V.P.--Eli's Cheese Cake Company, Chicago, IL; *U.S. Private*, pg. 371

Carruth, L. Brent, V.P.-Opers.--Maynard Oil Co., Dallas, TX; *U.S. Public*, pg. 1064

Carson, Ralph, Reg. V.P.-Strategic Plng. & Implementation, Team 1--Scott Forseman/Addison Wesley, Glenview, IL; *Int'l*, pg. 927

Cathcart, William J., Grp. V.P.-Trust--First Citizens Banc Shares, Inc., Raleigh, NC; *U.S. Public*, pg. 628

Caverzan, I., Dir.-Cooling Appl.--Zanussi Elettrodomestici S.p.A., Pordenone, Italy; *Int'l*, pg. 442

Cavo, Antonio, Grp. V.P.-Eastern Europe, Africa & Middle East--ELSAG Bailey Process Automation N.V., Schiphol, Netherlands; *Int'l*, pg. 449

Chagnon, Pierre J., Grp. V.P.-Human Resources--Bell Canada, Montreal, Canada; *Int'l*, pg. 115

Chan, Allan, V.P. & Gen. Mgr.-Precision Products Div.--Innovex, Inc., Hopkins, MN; *U.S. Public*, pg. 880

Chancellor, Glenn A., Grp. V.P.-Forests--Temple-Inland Forest Products Corporation, Diboll, TX; *U.S. Public*, pg. 1575

Chao, Charles S., V.P.-Feed Div.--McAnally Enterprises, Inc., Yucaipa, CA; *U.S. Private*, pg. 718

Charles, James J., Grp. V.P.-Core Tech.--Computer Language Research, Inc., Carrollton, TX; *U.S. Public*, pg. 421

Charlton, Thomas E., Grp. V.P.-Communication Prds.--Andrew Corporation, Orland Park, IL; *U.S. Public*, pg. 112

Cheylan, Jacques, Grp. V.P.-Industrialization--Rhone-Poulenc S.A., Courbevoie, France; *Int'l*, pg. 1108

Chickarello, James J., Grp. V.P.-Worldwide Opers.--Alberto-Culver Company, Melrose Park, IL; *U.S. Public*, pg. 37

Christ, Philip T., Grp. V.P.--CTS Corporation, Elkhart, IN; *U.S. Public*, pg. 285

Christie, Robert S., Grp. V.P.-Equity Services--McGraw-Hill Financial Information Services Group, New York, NY; *U.S. Public*, pg. 1071

Church, Richard E., V.P.-Exploration--Apache International, Inc., Houston, TX; *U.S. Public*, pg. 119

Clark, David, Pres. & Chief Oper. Officer--WSMP, Inc., Claremont, NC; *U.S. Public*, pg. 1729

Clark, Paul N., Sr. V.P.-Pharmaceutical Opers.--Abbott Laboratories, Abbott Park, IL; *U.S. Public*, pg. 12

Clark, R. Kerry, Grp. V.P. & Pres.-Laundry & Cleaning Prods./North America--The Procter & Gamble Company, Cincinnati, OH; *U.S. Public*, pg. 1330

Clark, Tim, Exec. V.P. & Mng. Dir.-Europe/Middle East/Africa--Holiday Inn Worldwide, Atlanta, GA; *Int'l*, pg. 170

Clasper, M., Reg. V.P.-Laundry & Cleaning Prods.--Procter & Gamble Ltd., Newcastle upon Tyne, United Kingdom; *U.S. Public*, pg. 1332

Clay, O. Perry, Sr. V.P.-Consumer Electronics Grp.--Sharp Electronics Corporation, Mahwah, NJ; *Int'l*, pg. 1228

Cloninger, Tim, Reg. V.P.-Chicago--Leon Shaffer Golnick Advertising, Inc., Fort Lauderdale, FL; *U.S. Private*, pg. 463

Cogels, Axel, Reg. V.P.--Interbrew S.A., Leuven, Belgium; *Int'l*, pg. 679

Cohen, Flo, Grp. V.P.--Shandwick Minneapolis, Minneapolis, MN; *Int'l*, pg. 1227

Cole, James W., Grp. V.P.-Foodservice--Hormel Foods Corp., Austin, MN; *U.S. Public*, pg. 840

Cole, James W., Grp. V.P.--Hormel Foodservice Division, Austin, MN; *U.S. Public*, pg. 840

Collins, Paul J., Grp. Exec.-Europe, Middle East--Citicorp, New York, NY; *U.S. Public*, pg. 376

Conant, Douglas R., Pres.-Sales & Integrated Logistics Company & Grp. Exec. V.P.--Nabisco Inc., Parsippany, NJ; *U.S. Public*, pg. 1355

Cordaro, C. Roberto, Grp. Pres.-Automotive & Exec. V.P.--Cummins Engine Company, Inc., Columbus, IN; *U.S. Public*, pg. 467

Corti, Robert J., Grp. V.P.-Fin.--Avon Products, Inc., New York, NY; *U.S. Public*, pg. 155

Cotter, Stephen, Grp. Dir.-Retailing--Laura Ashley Holdings Plc, Maidenhead, United Kingdom; *Int'l*, pg. 804

Coulter, Alan, V.P.-Equipment--Rogers Group Inc., Nashville, TN; *U.S. Private*, pg. 939

Courtois, Bernard, Grp. V.P.-Law--Bell Canada, Montreal, Canada; *Int'l*, pg. 115

Cowie, Donald J., Grp. V.P.-Original Equip. Mfg.--Recoton Auto Corporation, Lincolnshire, IL; *U.S. Public*, pg. 1369

Cox, Ronald O., Grp. V.P.--Wm. Wrigley Jr. Company, Chicago, IL; *U.S. Public*, pg. 1781
Coyle, Kevin P., Chief Fin. Officer & Grp. V.P.-Fin.--Jones Intercable, Inc., Englewood, CO; *U.S. Private*, pg. 597
Crane, Paul, Grp. V.P.-Info. Systems Grp.--Sharp Electronics Corporation, Mahwah, NJ; *Int'l*, pg. 1228
Crawford, David, Dir.-DistribuTech--Haas Publishing Companies, Inc., Norcross, GA; *U.S. Public*, pg. 1327
Crawshaw, John, Area V.P.-Pacific Rim--H.J. Heinz Company, Pittsburgh, PA; *U.S. Public*, pg. 805
Creekman, James E., Grp. V.P.-Legal Services--First Citizens Banc Shares, Inc., Raleigh, NC; *U.S. Public*, pg. 628
Cross, Bill, Grp. V.P.-Adv--Service Merchandise Company, Inc., Brentwood, TN; *U.S. Public*, pg. 1461
Crowe, James F., Grp. V.P.--United Illuminating Company, New Haven, CT; *U.S. Public*, pg. 1678
Culbertson, Michael A., Grp. V.P.--South Carolina Insurance Company, Columbia, SC; *U.S. Public*, pg. 1453
Cunningham, Larry H., Grp. V.P.--Archer Daniels Midland Company (ADM), Decatur, IL; *U.S. Public*, pg. 127
Dabringhausen, Peter, Grp. V.P. & Pres.-Process Chemicals Div.--Nalco Chemical Company, Naperville, IL; *U.S. Public*, pg. 1150
Dagley, Robert C., Grp. V.P.-Mfg.--American & Efird, Inc., Mount Holly, NC; *U.S. Public*, pg. 1412
Daily, Curtis E., Grp. V.P.--Flowserve Corporation, Dayton, OH; *U.S. Public*, pg. 658
Daily, Curtis E., Pres. & Grp. V.P.--Flowserve Corporation, Rotating Equipment Grp., Dayton, OH; *U.S. Public*, pg. 658
Dale, F.J., Grp. V.P.-Fin.--Safeway Inc., Pleasanton, CA; *U.S. Public*, pg. 1426
Dales, Allen, V.P. & Tech Services--Omniflight, Inc., Dallas, TX; *U.S. Private*, pg. 816
Daly, Tom, Grp. V.P.--TMP Worldwide, Inc., Saint Louis, MO; *U.S. Private*, pg. 1064
Dane, John, III, Grp. V.P.--Trinity Industries Inc., Dallas, TX; *U.S. Public*, pg. 1638
Dare, Larry G., Grp. V.P. & Pres.-Paper & Beverage Prods./Europe--The Procter & Gamble Company, Cincinnati, OH; *U.S. Public*, pg. 1330
Davenport, Joe, V.P.-Supply--Johnson Acoustical & Supply Co., Portland, OR; *U.S. Private*, pg. 590
Davis, Eddie, Grp. V.P.--Taylor Impression, Inc., Nashville, TN; *U.S. Private*, pg. 1070
Davis, Gerald L., Div. V.P.-Electronic Contracting--Baldwin Piano & Organ Company, Loveland, OH; *U.S. Public*, pg. 169
Davis, J. Lynn, Grp. V.P.-Cement Prod.--Texas Industries, Inc., Dallas, TX; *U.S. Public*, pg. 1585
Davis, Jeff, V.P.-Rhode Island Div.--Hubbard Hall Inc., Waterbury, CT; *U.S. Private*, pg. 544
Davis, Jim, Grp. V.P.--B.A.S.S., Inc., Montgomery, AL; *U.S. Private*, pg. 105
De Benedetti, Franco, Grp. V.P.-European Opers.--ELSAG Bailey Process Automation N.V., Schiphol, Netherlands; *Int'l*, pg. 449
Dean, David G., Grp. V.P.-Procurement--Albertson's, Inc., Boise, ID; *U.S. Public*, pg. 38
Dean, Warren M., Grp. V.P.-Bldgs. & Infrastructure--Jacobs Engineering Group Inc., Pasadena, CA; *U.S. Public*, pg. 921
Deering, Joseph W., Grp. V.P. & Pres.-Food Equipment Grp.--Premark International, Inc., Deerfield, IL; *U.S. Public*, pg. 1321
Degnan, Thomas J., Grp. V.P.--Universal Foods Corporation, Milwaukee, WI; *U.S. Public*, pg. 1695
Deininger, Lawrence R., Grp. V.P.-Vickers Aerospace Marine Defense--Aeroquip-Vickers, Inc., Maumee, OH; *U.S. Public*, pg. 24
Delker, Wilfried, V.P. & Grp. Exec.-Plumbing Prods.--American Standard Inc., Piscataway, NJ; *U.S. Public*, pg. 91
Dellinger, Kenneth S., Grp. V.P.-Mfg.--American & Efird, Inc., Mount Holly, NC; *U.S. Public*, pg. 1412
Delsol, Sheryl, Grp. V.P.-Human Resources--Servco Pacific Inc., Honolulu, HI; *U.S. Private*, pg. 986
Diaddezzio, Fred, Grp. V.P.-Mktg.--First Citizens Banc Shares, Inc., Raleigh, NC; *U.S. Public*, pg. 628
Dickerson, Gary E., Grp. V.P.--KLA Tencor Corporation, San Jose, CA; *U.S. Public*, pg. 939
Dickson, David N., Grp. V.P.-Intl. & Corp. Devel.--Hormel Foods Corp., Austin, MN; *U.S. Public*, pg. 840
Dickson, David N., Grp. V.P.--Hormel International Corporation, Austin, MN; *U.S. Public*, pg. 840
Dimling, David S., Grp. V.P.-Comunication Papers--Georgia-Pacific Corporation, Atlanta, GA; *U.S. Public*, pg. 735
Dodd, John C., Grp. Pres.--Kimberly-Clark Corporation, Dallas, TX; *U.S. Public*, pg. 958
Dolan, Arnold, Sr. V.P., Publisher-Plume--Penguin Putnam Inc., New York, NY; *Int'l*, pg. 1027
Dominguez, Robert, Reg. V.P.-North Pacific & Rockies Reg.--Bergen Brunswig Drug Company, Orange, CA; *U.S. Public*, pg. 213
Donnelly, William P., Grp. V.P. & Controller--ELSAG Bailey Process Automation N.V., Schiphol, Netherlands; *Int'l*, pg. 449
Donnon, Albert T., Jr., Grp. V.P.--Genuine Parts Company, Atlanta, GA; *U.S. Public*, pg. 732
Donovan, Stephen P., Jr., Grp. V.P. & Pres.-Food & Beverage Prods./North America--The Procter & Gamble Company, Cincinnati, OH; *U.S. Public*, pg. 1330
Drum, James R., Grp. V.P.-Systems Furniture--The HON Co. Systems Furniture Plant, Muscatine, IA; *U.S. Public*, pg. 772
Duke, Willie L., Grp. V.P.-Softwood Lumber--Georgia-Pacific Corporation, Atlanta, GA; *U.S. Public*, pg. 735
Dulek, Clarence L., Grp. V.P.-Beef--BeefAmerica Operating Co., Inc., Omaha, NE; *U.S. Private*, pg. 130
Duncan, Edward, Sr. V.P.-Residential Business Grp.--Mannington Resilient Floors, Salem, NJ; *U.S. Private*, pg. 700
Dupont, Charles, Grp. V.P.--Cegelec, Levallois-Perret, France; *Int'l*, pg. 52
Duquin, J.A., Grp. V.P.-Specialty Chemicals--Ashland Chemical, Dublin, OH; *U.S. Public*, pg. 139
Eastman, Ronald E., Grp. V.P.-Lodging Devel.--Marriott International, Inc., Washington, DC; *U.S. Public*, pg. 1047
Eb, Robert N., Group V.P.-Opers.--ChemDesign Corporation, Fitchburg, MA; *Int'l*, pg. 173
Eckert, Robert A., Grp. V.P.--Kraft Foods, Inc., Northfield, IL; *U.S. Public*, pg. 1287
Edge, Kenneth E., Grp. V.P.-Banking--Amcore Financial, Inc., Rockford, IL; *U.S. Public*, pg. 64
Edwards, John K., Grp. Pres.-Power Generation & Exec. V.P.--Cummins Engine Company, Inc., Columbus, IN; *U.S. Public*, pg. 467
Ekstrom, John, Grp. V.P.-Fluid Systems--Norton Performance Plastics, Wayne, NJ; *Int'l*, pg. 1174
Emmert, Arlan C., Grp. V.P.-Western Reg.--Jacobs Engineering Group Inc., Pasadena, CA; *U.S. Public*, pg. 921
English, Hugh, V.P.-Citrus Div.--A. Duda & Sons Inc., Oviedo, FL; *U.S. Private*, pg. 344
Erdahl, Steven L., V.P.-Industrial Coatings Grp.--The Valspar Corporation, Minneapolis, MN; *U.S. Public*, pg. 1707
Espegard, Duaine C., Grp. Pres. & Exec. V.P.--Bremer Financial Services, Inc., Saint Paul, MN; *U.S. Private*, pg. 167
Eulberg, Joe, V.P.-Human Resources--Motel 6 Operating L.P., Dallas, TX; *Int'l*, pg. 21
Facey, Duncan B., Grp. V.P.-Distrib.--Georgia-Pacific Corporation, Atlanta, GA; *U.S. Public*, pg. 735
Faciane, Emile L., Grp. V.P.-Engrng. & V.P.-Environ.--Texas Industries, Inc., Dallas, TX; *U.S. Public*, pg. 1585
Faig, Harold J., Grp. V.P.-Plastics Machinery--Cincinnati Milacron Inc., Cincinnati, OH; *U.S. Public*, pg. 368
Fairbanks, Walter, Grp. V.P.-Defense--Cubic Corporation, San Diego, CA; *U.S. Public*, pg. 466
Fairbanks, Walter, Grp. V.P.--Cubic Defense Systems, San Diego, CA; *U.S. Public*, pg. 466
Falk, Thomas J., Grp. Pres.-North American Tissue, Pulp & Paper--Kimberly-Clark Corporation, Dallas, TX; *U.S. Public*, pg. 958
Feder, Steve, Grp. V.P.-Sls.--Fleischmann's Yeast, Fenton, MO; *Int'l*, pg. 237
Feinberg, Daniel D., Grp. V.P.-Electronic Matls.--Morton International Inc., Chicago, IL; *U.S. Public*, pg. 1134
Feinstein, Sumner S., Grp. V.P.-Worldwide Decorative Prods.--Borden, Inc., Columbus, OH; *U.S. Private*, pg. 157
Ferkany, Edward A., Grp. V.P.-Processed Steel--Worthington Industries, Inc., Columbus, OH; *U.S. Public*, pg. 1780
Feurholzer, James J., Grp. V.P.-Adhesives & Chemical Specialties--Morton International Inc., Chicago, IL; *U.S. Public*, pg. 1134
Fields, Jack, Grp. V.P.-Resort Fin.--The FINOVA Group Inc., Phoenix, AZ; *U.S. Public*, pg. 624
Fischlin, Josef, V.P.--Feintool U.S. Operations Inc., White Plains, NY; *Int'l*, pg. 479
Fitzpatrick, Nancy, V.P. & Editor-in-Chief, Oxmoor House--Southern Progress Corporation, Birmingham, AL; *U.S. Public*, pg. 1612
Fitzsimmons, Tom, Grp. V.P.--TMP Worldwide/Recruitment Division, Denver, CO; *U.S. Private*, pg. 1065
Flanagan, Kerrie R., V.P.-Mdsg. Payables--The Home Depot, Inc., Atlanta, GA; *U.S. Public*, pg. 831
Flannaghan, Jim, Reg. V.P.-Seattle--Leon Shaffer Golnick Advertising, Inc., Fort Lauderdale, FL; *U.S. Private*, pg. 463
Floyd, James E., Grp. V.P.--American Consumers, Inc., Fort Oglethorpe, GA; *U.S. Public*, pg. 70
Fontas, Jordi, First Vice Chm.--Caixa d'Estalvis de Catalunya, Barcelona, Spain; *Int'l*, pg. 249
Foos, Gerry, Reg. V.P.-Midwest Reg.--Scott Forseman/Addison Wesley, Glenview, IL; *Int'l*, pg. 927
Forde, Richard B., Grp. V.P.-Filtration Prods.--Dana Corporation, Toledo, OH; *U.S. Public*, pg. 479
Forrester, Jim, V.P.-Chemical Prods. & Custom Prods.--Plastics Manufacturing Company, Dallas, TX; *U.S. Public*, pg. 1530
Forssman, Peter, V.P.-SAS Airline Sweden--SAS Airline, Stockholm, Sweden; *Int'l*, pg. 1201
Frangopoulos, Victor S., Grp. V.P.-Off-Highway Prods.--Modine Manufacturing Company, Racine, WI; *U.S. Public*, pg. 1121
Frank, Ken, Jr., Reg. V.P.--Payless Cashways, Inc., Kansas City, MO; *U.S. Public*, pg. 1267
Frederick, Donald A., Grp. V.P.-Oil & Gas--Pennzoil Company, Houston, TX; *U.S. Public*, pg. 1272
French, John R., V.P. & Reg. Dir.-Region 1--Ames Department Stores, Inc., Rocky Hill, CT; *U.S. Public*, pg. 99
Frere, Jean, Grp. V.P.--Cegelec, Levallois-Perret, France; *Int'l*, pg. 52
Frohman, Dov, V.P. & Gen. Mgr.-Intel Israel--Intel Microcomputer Group, Santa Clara, CA; *U.S. Public*, pg. 887
Frohnmayer, William G., Grp. V.P.-Fiber Products Div.--Pope & Talbot, Inc., Portland, OR; *U.S. Public*, pg. 1316
Fryer, Alan, Grp. Dir.-UK, Europe & S. Africa--Smith & Nephew PLC, London, United Kingdom; *Int'l*, pg. 1263
Fujimoto, Shiro, V.P.-Mktg.--Mutoh America Inc., Phoenix, AZ; *Int'l*, pg. 897
Gagnon, Andre, Grp. V.P.-Power--SNC-Lavalin Inc., Montreal, Canada; *Int'l*, pg. 1162
Gallio, Richard M., Grp. V.P. & Gen. Mgr.--Toyota Motor Sales, U.S.A., Inc., Torrance, CA; *Int'l*, pg. 1412
Ganz, Isaac, V.P.--Villaume Industries, Inc., Saint Paul, MN; *U.S. Private*, pg. 1140
Garfinkel, Lori, Grp. V.P.--Young Stuff Apparel Group, Inc., New York, NY; *U.S. Private*, pg. 1202
Garuzzo, Giorgio, Vice Chm. & Grp. V.P.--Olivetti SpA, Turin, Italy; *Int'l*, pg. 1002
Gava, P., Dir.-Dishwashers--Zanussi Elettrodomestici S.p.A., Pordenone, Italy; *Int'l*, pg. 442
Geisler, Paul S., Grp. Pres.-Asia/Pacific--Kimberly-Clark Corporation, Dallas, TX; *U.S. Public*, pg. 958
Gentges, Heinz, V.P.--Feintool U.S. Operations Inc., White Plains, NY; *Int'l*, pg. 479
Gentry, Monroe, Grp. V.P.--Environmental Air Systems, Inc., Greensboro, NC; *U.S. Private*, pg. 378
Gerow, Stephen A., Grp. V.P.-Coatings--Morton International Inc., Chicago, IL; *U.S. Public*, pg. 1134
Giberson, Carolyn J., Grp. V.P.-Retail Lending--B.M.J. Financial Corp., Bordentown, NJ; *U.S. Public*, pg. 1528
Gibson, David E., Grp. Exec.-Individual Bank-Private Banking--Citicorp, New York, NY; *U.S. Public*, pg. 376
Gilchrist, John, Grp. V.P.-Hydraulic Prods.--Commercial Intertech Corp., Youngstown, OH; *U.S. Public*, pg. 411
Giordano, J.A., Div. V.P.--Electronic Products Division, Austin, TX; *U.S. Public*, pg. 1605
Goldberg, Jeffrey A., V.P.-Enterprise Systems Grp.--EMC Corporation, Hopkinton, MA; *U.S. Public*, pg. 545
Goldberg, Wayne B., Grp. V.P.-Opers.--Red Roof Inns, Inc., Hilliard, OH; *U.S. Public*, pg. 1369
Golner, Jerold J., Grp. V.P.-North American Plastic Opers.--Borden, Inc., Columbus, OH; *U.S. Private*, pg. 157
Golubock, Harvey L., Grp. V.P.-Lubricants--Witco Corporation, Greenwich, CT; *U.S. Public*, pg. 1773
Gonnella, Joseph E., Grp. V.P. & Gen. Mgr.-Automotive Emisson Systems--Engelhard Corporation, Iselin, NJ; *U.S. Public*, pg. 582
Gonnella, Joseph E., Grp. V.P.--Automotive Emission Systems, Iselin, NJ; *U.S. Public*, pg. 582
Gonzalez, Claudio X., Grp. Pres.--Kimberly-Clark Corporation, Dallas, TX; *U.S. Public*, pg. 958
Goodman, Roy, Grp. V.P.-Industrial Chemicals--Aceto Corporation, Lake Success, NY; *U.S. Public*, pg. 15
Goodwin, W.M., Grp. V.P.-Intl.--WESCO Distribution, Inc., Pittsburgh, PA; *U.S. Private*, pg. 244
Gordon, H. Bruce, V.P.-U.S. Group--ManuLife Investment Holdings Limited, Toronto, Canada; *Int'l*, pg. 840
Gorman, Robert W., V.P.-Professional Prods.--Windmere-Durable Holdings, Hialeah, FL; *U.S. Public*, pg. 1771
Grava, Alfred H., Grp. V.P.--Masco Corporation, Taylor, MI; *U.S. Public*, pg. 1052
Green, Daniel E., Grp. V.P.-Specialty Dairy Div.--Dean Foods Company, Franklin Park, IL; *U.S. Public*, pg. 489
Gregorini, E., Dir.-Bus. Units--Zanussi Grandi Impianti S.p.A., Pordenone, Italy; *Int'l*, pg. 442
Greiner, Guenther, Grp. Exec. Investment Bank-Europe/Middle East/Africa--Citicorp, New York, NY; *U.S. Public*, pg. 376
Greisinger, James R., Grp. V.P. & Pres.-Dean Pickle & Specialty Products Co.--Dean Foods Company, Franklin Park, IL; *U.S. Public*, pg. 489
Grilli, Michael R., V.P.-Europe--EMC Corporation, Hopkinton, MA; *U.S. Public*, pg. 545
Grisik, John, V.P. & Grp. V.P.-Safety Systems--The B.F. Goodrich Company, Richfield, OH; *U.S. Public*, pg. 751
Groot, Jacobus, Grp. V.P. & Pres.-Asia/North--The Procter & Gamble Company, Cincinnati, OH; *U.S. Public*, pg. 1330
Grossman, Barbara, Sr. V.P., Publisher-Viking--Penguin Putnam Inc., New York, NY; *Int'l*, pg. 1027
Grossman, Janice, V.P. & Grp. Publr.--Seventeen Magazine, New York, NY; *U.S. Public*, pg. 1328
Grossman, Janice, Grp. Publr.--Soap Opera Weekly, New York, NY; *U.S. Public*, pg. 1328
Grossman, Janice, Grp. Publr.--Chicago Magazine, Chicago, IL; *U.S. Public*, pg. 1328
Grubbe, K.S., Chief Fin. Officer, Grp. V.P.-Fin. & Asst. Sec.--Ag Processing Inc., A Cooperative, Omaha, NE; *U.S. Private*, pg. 26
Gudgel, Thomas H., Grp. V.P. & Gen. Counsel--Blue Cross and Blue Shield of Oklahoma, Tulsa, OK; *U.S. Private*, pg. 151
Guittar, Lee J., V.P. & Grp. Exec.-Hearst Newspapers--The Hearst Corporation, New York, NY; *U.S. Private*, pg. 515
Gurney, John R., Reg. V.P.-Australia--Mentholatum Pty. Ltd., Scoresby, Australia; *Int'l*, pg. 1126
Gustafson, William R., Grp. V.P. & Gen. Mgr.-Automotive Emisson Systems--Engelhard Corporation, Iselin, NJ; *U.S. Public*, pg. 582
Gustafson, William R., Grp. V.P. & Gen. Mgr.--Petroleum Catalysts, Iselin, NJ; *U.S. Public*, pg. 582
Haan, Thomas E., Grp. V.P.-Fluid Sealing Group--Flowserve Corporation, Dayton, OH; *U.S. Public*, pg. 658
Haeffner, Alexandre, Area Grp. V.P.--CAP Gemini Austria, Vienna, Austria; *Int'l*, pg. 264
Hale, Ronald G., Grp. V.P.-Intl. Opers.--Pool Energy Services Co., Houston, TX; *U.S. Public*, pg. 1316
Hall, Chris, Chief Acctg. Officer & Grp. V.P.--Ralphs Grocery Company, Compton, CA; *U.S. Private*, pg. 1202
Hall, David A., Grp. V.P.--Great Lakes Chemical Corporation, West Lafayette, IN; *U.S. Public*, pg. 760
Hall, W. Reginald, V.P. & Gen. Mgr.-Specialty Chemicals Group--FMC Corporation, Chicago, IL; *U.S. Public*, pg. 604
Hamilton Harding, Robin A., Grp. V.P-Startegic Issues--Bell Canada, Montreal, Canada; *Int'l*, pg. 115
Hamlin, Craig L., Grp. V.P.--Archer Daniels Midland Company (ADM), Decatur, IL; *U.S. Public*, pg. 127
Hammer, C. LaRoy, Grp. V.P.-Tactical Vehicles--Stewart & Stevenson Services, Inc., Houston, TX; *U.S. Public*, pg. 1517
Hammond, Thomas R., Grp. V.P.-Central Reg.--Jacobs Engineering Group Inc., Pasadena, CA; *U.S. Public*, pg. 921
Hanna, Nequita, Grp. V.P.-Benefits Admin.--Blue Cross and Blue Shield of Oklahoma, Tulsa, OK; *U.S. Private*, pg. 151
Hanson, Brian L., Grp. V.P.-Loan Admin.--CRIIMI MAE, Rockville, MD; *U.S. Public*, pg. 459
Hanson, J. Roy, Div. V.P.-Electronic Musical Prods.--Baldwin Piano & Organ Company, Loveland, OH; *U.S. Public*, pg. 169

Hardin, Richard V., Grp. V.P.-Tech.--Oil-Dri Corporation of America, Chicago, IL; *U.S. Public*, pg. 1214
Harrell, E. W., V.P.-Nuclear Engineering--Virginia Electric and Power Company, Richmond, VA; *U.S. Public*, pg. 516
Harris, Allen, Grp. V.P.-Corp. Mkt.--Computer Language Research, Inc., Carrollton, TX; *U.S. Public*, pg. 421
Harris, Bob, Grp. V.P.-Technical Opers.--Polarcup Group Headquarters, Espoo, Finland; *Int'l*, pg. 638
Hassell, Aarno A., V.P.-Electronic Matls. Grp.--Rogers Corporation, Rogers, CT; *U.S. Public*, pg. 1402
Hauck, Richard E., Grp. V.P.--Astronics Corporation, Buffalo, NY; *U.S. Public*, pg. 142
Havet, Jean Pierre, Grp. V.P.--Cegelec, Levallois-Perret, France; *Int'l*, pg. 52
Hawkins, Thomas E., Dir.-Partner Services--Jones, Day, Reavis & Pogue, Cleveland, OH; *U.S. Private*, pg. 596
Healy, M. Brian, Chief Fin. Officer & Grp. V.P.-Fin. & Admin.--Computer Language Research, Inc., Carrollton, TX; *U.S. Public*, pg. 421
Heiman, David G., Grp. Coord.-Bus. Practice--Jones, Day, Reavis & Pogue, Cleveland, OH; *U.S. Private*, pg. 596
Helene, Claude, Grp. V.P.-Scientific Affairs--Rhone-Poulenc S.A., Courbevoie, France; *Int'l*, pg. 1108
Hemm, Kenneth W., Grp. V.P.--CORT Business Services Corporation, Fairfax, VA; *U.S. Public*, pg. 451
Hemmerich, Larry D., V.P.-CLARiiON Business Unit--Data General Corporation, Westborough, MA; *U.S. Public*, pg. 485
Henderson, Kevin, Div. Pres.--Fifth Quarter, Nashville, TN; *U.S. Public*, pg. 1467
Hendricks, Richard C., V.P. & Dir.-Corp. Business Devel.--Kennametal Inc., Latrobe, PA; *U.S. Public*, pg. 950
Hendrix, Calvin R., V.P.-N. America--Culligan International Company, Northbrook, IL; *U.S. Public*, pg. 467
Hennigan, Ned M., Grp. Pres.-Southwest Grp.--Beneficial Corporation, Wilmington, DE; *U.S. Public*, pg. 211
Henninger, Suzanne T., Grp. V.P.-Corp. Devel.--Healthsouth Corporation, Birmingham, AL; *U.S. Public*, pg. 803
Henricksen, Albert H., Grp. V.P.-Support Services--United Illuminating Company, New Haven, CT; *U.S. Public*, pg. 1678
Henry, Patrick, Grp. V.P.--Cegelec, Levallois-Perret, France; *Int'l*, pg. 52
Herran, Wayne L., V.P.-Hallmark/Opers.--Hallmark Cards, Inc., Kansas City, MO; *U.S. Private*, pg. 495
Hesse, Selwyn, Vice Chm., Exec. V.P. & Sec.--Automatic Equipment Mfg. Co., Pender, NE; *U.S. Private*, pg. 101
Higgins, Frank M. (Pete), Grp. V.P.-Interactive Media--Microsoft Corporation, Redmond, WA; *U.S. Public*, pg. 1107
Hill, Jim, Div. Mgr.--Carolina Cut Sheets, Timmonsville, SC; *U.S. Public*, pg. 333
Hill, Larry, Sr. V.P. & Dir.-Stores/NY--Saks Fifth Avenue, New York, NY; *U.S. Public*, pg. 1429
Hill, Matt, Grp. V.P.--American Eco Corporation, Toronto, Canada; *Int'l*, pg. 73
Hislop, Barbara R., Grp. V.P.-Coastal Opers.--Canfor Corporation, Vancouver, Canada; *Int'l*, pg. 260
Hodge, Robin H., V.P.-Assembly & Test Opers.--Integrated Device Technology, Inc., Santa Clara, CA; *U.S. Public*, pg. 884
Hodges, John E., Jr., V.P.-Customer Service & Div. Opers.--Gulf Power Company, Pensacola, FL; *U.S. Public*, pg. 1490
Hoffman, Barry P., Grp. V.P., Gen. Counsel & Sec.--Valassis Communications, Inc., Livonia, MI; *U.S. Public*, pg. 1704
Hoffman, George W., Grp. V.P.--Varlen Corporation, Naperville, IL; *U.S. Public*, pg. 1710
Hojland, Peter, V.P.-SAS Airline Denmark--SAS Airline, Stockholm, Sweden; *Int'l*, pg. 1201
Holsinger, John, V.P.-Intl.--Kaepa Inc., Greenville, SC; *U.S. Private*, pg. 604
Holtshouse, James, Grp. V.P.--DowBrands, L.P., Indianapolis, IN; *U.S. Public*, pg. 523
Hooley, Peter, Grp. Dir.-Fin.--Smith & Nephew PLC, London, United Kingdom; *Int'l*, pg. 1263
Horn, Lee, V.P.-Underwriting--Garden State Life Insurance Company, League City, TX; *U.S. Public*, pg. 88
House, Steve, Reg. V.P.-Chicago--Leon Shaffer Golnick Advertising, Inc., Fort Lauderdale, FL; *U.S. Private*, pg. 463
Howard, John A., Grp. V.P.--J.M. Schneider Inc., Kitchener, Canada; *Int'l*, pg. 1207
Howard, L. Dean, Grp. V.P.-Europe--Modine Manufacturing Company, Racine, WI; *U.S. Public*, pg. 1121
Howes, Brian J., Grp. Pres.--Kimberly-Clark Corporation, Dallas, TX; *U.S. Public*, pg. 958
Hoyle, John, Grp. V.P.-Sls.--American & Efird, Inc., Mount Holly, NC; *U.S. Public*, pg. 1412
Hoylman, Donald L., Grp. V.P.-Coal Processing--Salem Corporation, Pittsburgh, PA; *U.S. Private*, pg. 961
Hubbard, Alice P., Grp. V.P.-Hospitality & Real Estate--Kohler Company, Kohler, WI; *U.S. Private*, pg. 630
Hubbard, Walter W., Grp. V.P.-Carpet & Textile Fiber Prods.--BASF Corporation Fiber Products Division, Charlotte, NC; *Int'l*, pg. 105
Hudson, Michael J., Corp. V.P.--Convertors/Custom Sterile, McGaw Park, IL; *U.S. Public*, pg. 44
Huebner, George C., V.P.-Keyboard Acceptance Corp.--Baldwin Piano & Organ Company, Loveland, OH; *U.S. Public*, pg. 169
Huey, Rodney, MD, Grp. V.P. & Dir.-Medical--Blue Cross and Blue Shield of Oklahoma, Tulsa, OK; *U.S. Private*, pg. 151
Hughes, J. Celtyn, Grp. V.P.-Package Prods.--Texas Industries, Inc., Dallas, TX; *U.S. Public*, pg. 1585
Hulce, Terry, Grp. V.P.--CMI International Inc., Southfield, MI; *U.S. Private*, pg. 195
Hutchings, Clifton S., Grp. V.P.-Fluid Power Opers.--Pall Corporation, Greenvale, NY; *U.S. Public*, pg. 1253
Hyland, James, Grp. V.P.--Super Fresh Company, Florence, NJ; *Int'l*, pg. 1375
Ielase, James C., Grp. V.P.--Archer Daniels Midland Company (ADM), Decatur, IL; *U.S. Public*, pg. 127
Irish, George, V.P. & Grp. Exec.-Hearst Newspapers--The Hearst Corporation, New York, NY; *U.S. Private*, pg. 515
Irvine, Albert L., Jr., Grp. V.P.-Sls.--American & Efird, Inc., Mount Holly, NC; *U.S. Public*, pg. 1412
Irving, Robert V., Grp. V.P.--Kreonite, Inc., Wichita, KS; *U.S. Private*, pg. 635
Irwin, Clark, Grp. V.P.-Distr. & Commodity Pur.--Tyson Foods, Inc., Springdale, AR; *U.S. Public*, pg. 1652
Isaac, Steven R., Grp. V.P.-Cadmus Mktg. Commun. Grp., Inc.--Cadmus Communications Corporation, Richmond, VA; *U.S. Public*, pg. 290
Jain, Nirmal, Grp. V.P.-Polymer Chemicals--Witco Corporation, Greenwich, CT; *U.S. Public*, pg. 1773
Jain, Nirmal, Grp. V.P.--Polymer Chemicals Group, Greenwich, CT; *U.S. Public*, pg. 1774
James, Tom, Exec. Grp. Dir.--Avrett, Free & Ginsberg, Inc., New York, NY; *U.S. Private*, pg. 103
Jastrow, Kenneth M., II, Chief Fin. Officer & Grp. V.P.--Temple-Inland Inc., Diboll, TX; *U.S. Public*, pg. 1574
Jenkins, Robert G., Grp. V.P.-Worldwide Resins--Borden, Inc., Columbus, OH; *U.S. Private*, pg. 157
Jenkins, Thomas M., Chief Fin. Officer & Grp. V.P.--Dayton Power & Light Co., Dayton, OH; *U.S. Public*, pg. 473
Jewell, G. Bernard, Grp. V.P. & Gen. Mgr.-Seating--B/E Aerospace, Inc., Wellington, FL; *U.S. Public*, pg. 159
Jewell, G. Bernard, Grp. V.P. & Gen. Mgr.--B/E Aerospace Seating Products, Winston Salem, NC; *U.S. Public*, pg. 159
Johanneson, David J., Grp. V.P.-Truck Bus.--Navistar International Corporation, Chicago, IL; *U.S. Public*, pg. 1167
Johanneson, David J., Grp. V.P.-Truck Businesses--Navistar International Transportation Corp., Chicago, IL; *U.S. Public*, pg. 1167
John, Jerry, V.P.-Regulatory Compliance--Fleischli Oil Company, Inc., Cheyenne, WY; *U.S. Private*, pg. 410
Johnson, Carl, Grp. V.P.-Risk Mngmt.--Tyson Foods, Inc., Springdale, AR; *U.S. Public*, pg. 1652
Johnson, David E., Grp. V.P.-Agronomy, CENEX/Land O'Lakes--CENEX, Inc., Inver Grove Heights, MN; *U.S. Private*, pg. 221
Johnson, James B., V.P. & Gen. Mgr.-PC Enhancement Div.--Intel Systems Group, Santa Clara, CA; *U.S. Public*, pg. 887
Johnston, Gerald E., Grp. V.P.--The Clorox Company, Oakland, CA; *U.S. Public*, pg. 386
Jones, Jeffrey D., Grp. V.P. & Pres.-Latin America/South--The Procter & Gamble Company, Cincinnati, OH; *U.S. Public*, pg. 1330
Jones, Peggy Jo, Grp. V.P.-Employee Devel. & Communications--Albertson's, Inc., Boise, ID; *U.S. Public*, pg. 38
Jones, Susan, Grp. V.P. & Acct. Dir.--Northlich Stolley LaWarre, Cincinnati, OH; *U.S. Private*, pg. 806
Jones, William F., V.P.-Southern Grp.--Weston Paper & Manufacturing Co., Terre Haute, IN; *U.S. Private*, pg. 1169
Jones, William R., Grp. V.P.-North Central Grp.--Beneficial Corporation, Wilmington, DE; *U.S. Public*, pg. 211
Joslin, Raymond E., V.P. & Grp. Head--Hearst Entertainment & Syndication, New York, NY; *U.S. Private*, pg. 516
Kalmanson, Steven R., Grp. Pres.--Kimberly-Clark Corporation, Dallas, TX; *U.S. Public*, pg. 958
Kanner, Edwin, Grp. V.P.-Wire & Cable--Leviton Mfg. Co., Inc., Little Neck, NY; *U.S. Private*, pg. 663
Katz, Gerald, Grp. V.P.-Performance Chemicals--Witco Corporation, Greenwich, CT; *U.S. Public*, pg. 1773
Katz, Gerald, Grp. V.P.--Petroleum Specialties Group, Greenwich, CT; *U.S. Public*, pg. 1774
Kawashima, William, Grp. V.P.-Mktg. & Adv.--Servco Pacific Inc., Honolulu, HI; *U.S. Private*, pg. 986
Kazmi, Iftikhar H., Grp. V.P.-Midwest Div.--Superior Industries International, Inc., Van Nuys, CA; *U.S. Public*, pg. 1539
Keller, Richard D., Grp. V.P.--Energy & Transportation--Florida Progress Corporation, Saint Petersburg, FL; *U.S. Public*, pg. 655
Kelley, Robert, Reg. V.P.-Southwest Reg.--Scott Forseman/Addison Wesley, Glenview, IL; *Int'l*, pg. 927
Kellogg, C.B., Grp. V.P.--A.M. Best Company, Oldwick, NJ; *U.S. Private*, pg. 139
Kennebeck, Alan W., Grp. V.P.-Diversified Financial Services Group--Amcore Financial, Inc., Rockford, IL; *U.S. Public*, pg. 64
Kennedy, Cathryn I., Grp. V.P.--Shandwick Minneapolis, Minneapolis, MN; *Int'l*, pg. 1227
Keough, M.E., Grp. V.P.-Prod. Mgmt. & Supply--WESCO Distribution, Inc., Pittsburgh, PA; *U.S. Private*, pg. 244
Kerber, Stanley E., Grp. V.P.-Meat Prods.--Hormel Foods Corp., Austin, MN; *U.S. Public*, pg. 840
Kerber, Stanley E., Grp. V.P.--Hormel Meat Products Div., Austin, MN; *U.S. Public*, pg. 840
Kerr, James, Grp. V.P.--European American Bank & Trust Co., Uniondale, NY; *Int'l*, pg. 9
Kerrison, Dennis J., Grp. V.P.--Great Lakes Chemical Corporation, West Lafayette, IN; *U.S. Public*, pg. 760
Kerwin, Joseph P., M.D., Pres.-Krug Life Sciences, Inc.--Krug International Corp., Houston, TX; *U.S. Public*, pg. 967
Kesman, Anthony K., Corp. V.P.--Distribution, McGaw Park, IL; *U.S. Public*, pg. 44
Kessellman, Ronald C., Grp. V.P.-Foodservice & Seafood Prods./North American Foods--Borden, Inc., Columbus, OH; *U.S. Private*, pg. 157
Ketchum, Mark D., Grp. V.P. & Pres.-Paper Prods./North America--The Procter & Gamble Company, Cincinnati, OH; *U.S. Public*, pg. 1330
Kimmet, Daniel E., Grp. V.P.-Aeroquip Automotive Grp.--Aeroquip-Vickers, Inc., Maumee, OH; *U.S. Public*, pg. 24
Kinnamon, Terry E., Grp. Pres.--Kimberly-Clark Corporation, Dallas, TX; *U.S. Public*, pg. 958
Kipp, Robert, V.P.-Hallmark/Corp., Commun. & Svcs.--Hallmark Cards, Inc., Kansas City, MO; *U.S. Private*, pg. 495
Kipperman, Edward O., V.P.-Tax--Citizens Utilities Company, Stamford, CT; *U.S. Public*, pg. 379
Kissel, W. Craig, V.P. & Grp. Exec.--American Standard Inc., Piscataway, NJ; *U.S. Public*, pg. 91
Kissel, W. Craig, V.P. & Grp. Exec.--The Trane Company, Unitary Products Group, Tyler, TX; *U.S. Public*, pg. 92
Kitchen, Marc, Div. Mgr.--Dallas Printing, Jackson, MS; *U.S. Public*, pg. 333
Kline, Peter C., Grp. V.P.-North American Snacks--Borden, Inc., Columbus, OH; *U.S. Private*, pg. 157
Klug, William A., V.P. & Grp. Exec.-Air Conditioning Prods./Intl.--American Standard Inc., Piscataway, NJ; *U.S. Public*, pg. 91
Knez, Brian J., Grp. V.P. & Pres.-Harcourt Brace & Company--Harcourt General, Inc., Chestnut Hill, MA; *U.S. Public*, pg. 782
Knight, Benjamin H., Grp. V.P.--Kimberly-Clark Corporation, Dallas, TX; *U.S. Public*, pg. 958
Knight, Jeffrey A., Grp. V.P.--Guardian Industries Corp., Auburn Hills, MI; *U.S. Private*, pg. 485
Knight, Scott, V.P.-Fulfillment Div.--MCRB Service Bureau, Inc., Chatsworth, CA; *U.S. Private*, pg. 686
Koeller, David, Pres.-Grp. Practice--HBO & Company/Cycare Business Group, Scottsdale, AZ; *U.S. Public*, pg. 770
Kohut, Andrew J., Grp. V.P.-Specialty Pkgng. & Mdsg. Services--Chesapeake Corporation, Richmond, VA; *U.S. Public*, pg. 346
Konerko, Henry W., Grp. Exec.--Phelps Dodge Mining Company, Phoenix, AZ; *U.S. Public*, pg. 1286
Koonce, Joel, Chief Fin. Officer & Grp. V.P.-Fin.--CENEX, Inc., Inver Grove Heights, MN; *U.S. Private*, pg. 221
Kopf, Robert, V.P. & Gen. Mgr.-Window Coverings--Hunter Douglas, Inc., Upper Saddle River, NJ; *Int'l*, pg. 639
Koster, Elaine, Sr. V.P., Publisher-Dutton/Signet--Penguin Putnam Inc., New York, NY; *Int'l*, pg. 1027
Koziar, Stephen F., Jr., Grp. V.P., Gen. Counsel & Sec.--DPL Inc., Dayton, OH; *U.S. Public*, pg. 473
Koziar, Stephen F., Jr., Grp. V.P. & Sec.--Dayton Power & Light Co., Dayton, OH; *U.S. Public*, pg. 473
Kozinski, Allen A., Grp. V.P.--Amoco Corporation, Chicago, IL; *U.S. Public*, pg. 101
Kraft, Burnell D., Grp. V.P.--Archer Daniels Midland Company (ADM), Decatur, IL; *U.S. Public*, pg. 127
Kraus, William, Grp. Pres.-Specialty Chemicals--Elf Atochem North America, Inc., Philadelphia, PA; *Int'l*, pg. 445
Kring, Larry A., Grp. V.P.--Esterline Technologies Corporation, Bellevue, WA; *U.S. Public*, pg. 594
Kringel, John G., Sr. V.P.-Hospital Prods.--Abbott Laboratories, Abbott Park, IL; *U.S. Public*, pg. 12
Kronfeld, Andrew S., Grp. V.P.-Sls.--Spirite Industries, Inc., Englewood, NJ; *U.S. Private*, pg. 1026
Krumbholz, David, Reg. V.P.--Payless Cashways, Inc., Kansas City, MO; *U.S. Public*, pg. 1267
Kujawa, John R., Grp. V.P.--Atchison Casting Corporation, Atchison, KS; *U.S. Public*, pg. 142
Kupper, William P., Publr.-Health--Time Inc., New York, NY; *U.S. Public*, pg. 1612
Kuraytim, Fuad O., Grp. V.P. & Pres.-Middle East, Africa & Gen. Export--The Procter & Gamble Company, Cincinnati, OH; *U.S. Public*, pg. 1330
La Grouw, J.C., Grp. V.P. & Dir.-Wines & Spirits--Bols Royal Distilleries, Nieuw-Vennep, Netherlands; *Int'l*, pg. 751
Labrum, Ron K., Corp. & Grp. V.P.-Reg. Cos. & Health Sys.--Allegiance Healthcare Corp., McGaw Park, IL; *U.S. Public*, pg. 44
Lacerda, Flavio T., Grp. V.P.-Latin America--Avery Dennison Corporation, Pasadena, CA; *U.S. Public*, pg. 152
Lackey, Jay, Reg. V.P.-Strategic Plng. & Implementation, Team 2--Scott Forseman/Addison Wesley, Glenview, IL; *Int'l*, pg. 927
Lai, Pin Yong, V.P. & Gen. Mgr.-Penang Oper.--Intel Microcomputer Group, Santa Clara, CA; *U.S. Public*, pg. 887
Laisure, Mike, Grp. V.P.-Modular Systems--Dana Corporation, Toledo, OH; *U.S. Public*, pg. 479
Lamarre, Jacques, Grp. V.P.-Transportation Systems & Construction--SNC-Lavalin Inc., Montreal, Canada; *Int'l*, pg. 1162
Lambright, Stephen K., V.P. & Grp. Exec.--Anheuser-Busch Companies, Inc., Saint Louis, MO; *U.S. Public*, pg. 113
Lane, Wendell, Dir.-Engrng.--Breed Technologies, Sterling Heights, MI; *U.S. Public*, pg. 251
Lang, Jan, Grp. V.P.-Opers.--Leaf Group B.V., Espoo, Finland,; *Int'l*, pg. 638
Lang, Paul E., Grp. V.P.--J.M. Schneider Inc., Kitchener, Canada; *Int'l*, pg. 1207
Langert, Andrew, Grp. V.P.--Alberto-Culver Company, Melrose Park, IL; *U.S. Public*, pg. 37
Langert, Andrew C., Grp. V.P.--Alberto-Culver USA, Inc., Melrose Park, IL; *U.S. Public*, pg. 38
Lansaw, Judy W., Grp. V.P.--DPL Inc., Dayton, OH; *U.S. Public*, pg. 473
Lapp, J. Parker, Grp. V.P.-Specialty Fin.--The FINOVA Group Inc., Phoenix, AZ; *U.S. Public*, pg. 624
Larson, Steven R., Grp. V.P.--Esterline Technologies Corporation, Bellevue, WA; *U.S. Public*, pg. 594
Lauchert, F.H., Grp. Pres.-Industrial Chemicals--Elf Atochem North America, Inc., Philadelphia, PA; *Int'l*, pg. 445
Lauer, John E., Grp. V.P.--J.M. Schneider Inc., Kitchener, Canada; *Int'l*, pg. 1207
Lawrence, James, Grp. V.P.-Opers.--Del Laboratories, Inc., Farmingdale, NY; *U.S. Public*, pg. 494
Lawrence, James, Grp. V.P.-Opers.--Sally Hansen, Farmingdale, NY; *U.S. Public*, pg. 494
Lawson, Gregory M., Grp. V.P.-Publication Inks--Flint Ink Corp., Detroit, MI; *U.S. Private*, pg. 413
Lehman, Timothy J., Grp. Pres.--Kimberly-Clark Corporation, Dallas, TX; *U.S. Public*, pg. 958
Lehman, W. Dudley, Grp. Pres.--Kimberly-Clark Corporation, Dallas, TX; *U.S. Public*, pg. 958

Leinonen, John, Grp. V.P.--The Failure Group, Inc., Menlo Park, CA; *U.S. Public*, pg. 609
Lenson, Lloyd, Grp. V.P.--CORT Business Services Corporation, Fairfax, VA; *U.S. Public*, pg. 451
Light, Steve, V.P.-Steel Div.--Pacific Hide & Fur Depot, Great Falls, MT; *U.S. Private*, pg. 831
Liguori, Ralph, Grp. V.P.-Mfg.--Del Laboratories, Inc., Farmingdale, NY; *U.S. Public*, pg. 494
Lincoln, John, Grp. V.P.-Revenue Collection--Cubic Corporation, San Diego, CA; *U.S. Public*, pg. 466
Lipscomb, Anne, Grp. V.P.-Mktg.--The Mills Corporation, Arlington, VA; *U.S. Public*, pg. 1113
Lipton, Arthur, Grp. V.P.-In Flight Entertainment--B/E Aerospace, Inc., Wellington, FL; *U.S. Public*, pg. 159
Lipton, Arthur, Grp. V.P. & Gen. Mgr.--B/E Aerospace, Inc./In Flight Entertainment Group, Irvine, CA; *U.S. Public*, pg. 159
Lister, Gerald W., Grp. V.P.--Amcore Financial, Inc., Rockford, IL; *U.S. Public*, pg. 64
Littleton, Ed, Dir.-Opers.--The Bartell Drug Company, Seattle, WA; *U.S. Private*, pg. 118
Lohrengel, Alfred, Grp. Mgr.-White Cap Closures, Europe--Schmalbach-Lubeca AG, Braunschweig, Germany; *Int'l*, pg. 1206
Loibl, Dipl.-Ing., Chief of Telecom Grp. & Deputy Gen. Dir.--Austrian Postal & Telegraph Administration, Vienna, Austria; *Int'l*, pg. 101
Loomis, Peter, Grp. V.P.-Customer & Oper. Services--The Southern Connecticut Gas Company, Bridgeport, CT; *U.S. Public*, pg. 431
Loughrey, F. Joseph, Grp. Pres.-Indus. & Exec. V.P.--Cummins Engine Company, Inc., Columbus, IN; *U.S. Public*, pg. 467
Lounsbury, Charles, Grp. V.P. & Pres.--The Toro Company, Bloomington, MN; *U.S. Public*, pg. 1623
Louras, Peter N., Jr., Grp. V.P.--The Clorox Company, Oakland, CA; *U.S. Public*, pg. 386
Lucas, Scott, V.P.-Sls. & Mktg.--Dorner Manufacturing Corp., Hartland, WI; *U.S. Private*, pg. 340
Lucas, Thomas J., Grp. V.P.-Commercial & Packaging Inks--Flint Ink Corp., Detroit, MI; *U.S. Private*, pg. 413
Lundevall, Brent, Grp. V.P.-Projects--Daw Technologies, Inc., Salt Lake City, UT; *U.S. Public*, pg. 489
Lynch, William T., Grp. V.P.-Acctg. Tax Market--Computer Language Research, Inc., Carrollton, TX; *U.S. Public*, pg. 421
MacAllister, Bruce, Grp. V.P.-Southern & Western Reg. & Corp. V.P.--Owens & Minor Inc., Glen Allen, VA; *U.S. Public*, pg. 1236
Macapagal, Norman K., Grp. Mgr.-Mktg.--EEI Corporation, Manila, Philippines; *Int'l*, pg. 425
MacDonald, Alan S., Grp. Exec.-Investment Bank-North America--Citicorp, New York, NY; *U.S. Public*, pg. 376
Madden, Michael J., Grp. V.P.-Store Opers.--Toys "R" Us United States, Paramus, NJ; *U.S. Public*, pg. 1626
Madill, Darrell S., Grp. V.P.-Wood Prods.--Canfor Corporation, Vancouver, Canada; *Int'l*, pg. 260
Maher, Michael, Reg. V.P.-Houston--Leon Shaffer Golnick Advertising, Inc., Fort Lauderdale, FL; *U.S. Private*, pg. 463
Malecek, Chris, Grp. V.P.--Shandwick Minneapolis, Minneapolis, MN; *Int'l*, pg. 1227
Maloney, Michael M., Reg. V.P.--American Mail-Well Envelope, Englewood, CO; *U.S. Public*, pg. 1038
Mandia, Joseph, Group V.P.-Opers.--NESCO, Inc., Cleveland, OH; *U.S. Private*, pg. 791
Manoogian, Linda A., Grp. V.P.--TriMas Corporation, Ann Arbor, MI; *U.S. Public*, pg. 1054
Mansfield, William L., V.P.-Packaging Coatings Grp.--The Valspar Corporation, Minneapolis, MN; *U.S. Public*, pg. 1707
Mantzavinos, Anthony G., Grp. Exec.-Institutional Bank-Europe/Middle East-Africa Banking--Citicorp, New York, NY; *U.S. Public*, pg. 376
Marcum, James A., Grp. V.P.--D.A. Stuart Company, Warrenville, IL; *U.S. Private*, pg. 1048
Maritz, Paul A., Grp. V.P.-Platforms & Applications--Microsoft Corporation, Redmond, WA; *U.S. Public*, pg. 1107
Marlborough, Donald J., Grp. V.P.--Atchison Casting Corporation, Atchison, KS; *U.S. Public*, pg. 142
Marshall, Bert, Grp. V.P.-P&C--Blue Cross and Blue Shield of Oklahoma, Tulsa, OK; *U.S. Private*, pg. 151
Marshall, Jon A., Grp. V.P.--Global Marine Inc., Houston, TX; *U.S. Public*, pg. 748
Martini, Frank, Grp. V.P.--CORT Business Services Corporation, Fairfax, VA; *U.S. Public*, pg. 451
Martinsen, Robert, Grp. Exec.-Institutional Bank-Asia Pacific--Citicorp, New York, NY; *U.S. Public*, pg. 376
Mastalski, Leo, V.P.-Mfg.--Freeway Corporation, Cleveland, OH; *U.S. Private*, pg. 426
Mastroianni, Dave, V.P.-Product Devel.--Weider Nutrition Intl., Salt Lake City, UT; *U.S. Private*, pg. 1159
Mata, Pedro, Grp. V.P.--Primedia Inc., New York, NY; *U.S. Public*, pg. 1327
Maxwell, Harold C., Grp. V.P.--Temple-Inland Inc., Diboll, TX; *U.S. Public*, pg. 1574
Maxwell, Harold C., Grp. V.P.-Building Prods.--Temple-Inland Forest Products Corporation, Diboll, TX; *U.S. Public*, pg. 1575
Mayfield, Stephen D., Grp. V.P.-Cement Mktg.--Texas Industries, Inc., Dallas, TX; *U.S. Public*, pg. 1585
McCann, Anthony F., Grp. V.P.--Magnetic Metals Corp., Camden, NJ; *U.S. Private*, pg. 560
McClurkin, David K., Dir.-Fin. Services--Jones, Day, Reavis & Pogue, Cleveland, OH; *U.S. Private*, pg. 596
McDonald, Rebecca A., Grp. V.P.--Amoco Corporation, Chicago, IL; *U.S. Public*, pg. 101
McGee, J. Brad, Grp. V.P.-Tyco Specialty Products & V.P.--Tyco International Ltd., Exeter, NH; *U.S. Public*, pg. 1647
McGee, Millard L., Jr., Grp. V.P.-Sls.--American & Efird, Inc., Mount Holly, NC; *U.S. Public*, pg. 1412
McIntosh, David, Grp. V.P. & Pres.--The Toro Company, Bloomington, MN; *U.S. Public*, pg. 1623
McIntyre, Sharon R., Dir.-New Matter Services--Jones, Day, Reavis & Pogue, Cleveland, OH; *U.S. Private*, pg. 596
McKinney, Blaine, Sr. V.P.-Consumer Bus. Grp.--The Scotts Company, Marysville, OH; *U.S. Public*, pg. 1446
McLachlan, John, Grp. V.P.-Northern Reg.--Jacobs Engineering Group Inc., Pasadena, CA; *U.S. Public*, pg. 921
McLachlan, John, Grp. V.P.-Northern Region--Jacobs Engineering Group Inc., Cincinnati, OH; *U.S. Public*, pg. 921
McLaughlin, Martin J., V.P.-Corp. Affairs--WTTW (Channel 11), Chicago, IL; *U.S. Private*, pg. 1145
McLeod, Scott, Reg. V.P.-Dallas--Leon Shaffer Golnick Advertising, Inc., Fort Lauderdale, FL; *U.S. Private*, pg. 463
McMillan, Mike, V.P.-Sls.--Superior Auctioneers & Marketing, Inc., San Antonio, TX; *U.S. Private*, pg. 1054
McMullen, James, Asst. Gen. Mgr. & Asst. Sec.--Tillamook County Creamery Assn., Tillamook, OR; *U.S. Private*, pg. 1086
McNally, Thomas M., Sr. V.P.-Ross Products--Abbott Laboratories, Abbott Park, IL; *U.S. Public*, pg. 12
McNamara, John D., Grp. V.P.--Archer Daniels Midland Company (ADM), Decatur, IL; *U.S. Public*, pg. 127
McNeel, Richard L., Grp. V.P.--Amoco Corporation, Chicago, IL; *U.S. Public*, pg. 101
McVicker, John R., V.P. & Gen. Mgr.--Nelsen Steel & Wire Co., Franklin Park, IL; *U.S. Private*, pg. 790
Mebane, Bern, Sr. Grp. Pres.-Gannett Piedmont Newspaper Grp.--Gannett Company, Inc., Arlington, VA; *U.S. Public*, pg. 698
Mellow, James L., Grp. V.P.--TriMas Corporation, Ann Arbor, MI; *U.S. Public*, pg. 1054
Meloni, Stefano, Sr. Grp. V.P.-Fin.--Montedison S.p.A., Milan, Italy; *Int'l*, pg. 324
Mercer, James B., V.P.-Enmark Stations, Inc.--Colonial Oil Industries, Savannah, GA; *U.S. Private*, pg. 253
Merta, Thomas, Reg. V.P.-Dallas--Leon Shaffer Golnick Advertising, Inc., Fort Lauderdale, FL; *U.S. Private*, pg. 463
Metz, John S., Grp. Pres.--Kimberly-Clark Corporation, Dallas, TX; *U.S. Public*, pg. 958
Meyer, Claude L., Grp. V.P. & Pres.-Laundry & Cleaning Prods./Europe--The Procter & Gamble Company, Cincinnati, OH; *U.S. Public*, pg. 1330
Meyer, Joseph, Grp. V.P.-Vegetable Oils, Pet Foods & Ag. Environ. Prod.--Ag Processing Inc., A Cooperative, Omaha, NE; *U.S. Private*, pg. 26
Meyers, Eric, Grp. V.P.-Corp. Restructuring/Implementation--Witco Corporation, Greenwich, CT; *U.S. Public*, pg. 1773
Middleton, A. Duncan, Sr. V.P.-European Opers.--Dexter Nonwovens Division, Windsor Locks, CT; *U.S. Public*, pg. 504
Miller, Edwin F., V.P.-Corp. Facilities Mngmt.--PHH Corporation, Hunt Valley, MD; *U.S. Public*, pg. 321
Millsaps, Kenneth, Sr. V.P.-Central Region Opers.--Rogers Group Inc., Nashville, TN; *U.S. Private*, pg. 939
Miran, Yvou, Grp. V.P.--Cegelec, Levallois-Perret, France; *Int'l*, pg. 52
Miranda, Matthias K., Grp. Mgr.-Beverage Packaging--Schmalbach-Lubeca AG, Braunschweig, Germany; *Int'l*, pg. 1206
Mistretta, John A., Grp. V.P.--U.S. Industries, Inc., Iselin, NJ; *U.S. Public*, pg. 1683
Moe, Daryl, Reg. V.P.-Minneapolis/St. Paul--Leon Shaffer Golnick Advertising, Inc., Fort Lauderdale, FL; *U.S. Private*, pg. 463
Moe, Keith, Grp. V.P.-Electro & Commun. Markets Grp.--3M, Saint Paul, MN; *U.S. Public*, pg. 1604
Moeller, Bill, Grp. V.P.-Swine Div.--Tyson Foods, Inc., Springdale, AR; *U.S. Public*, pg. 1652
Montag, Alfred C., Grp. V.P. & Gen. Mgr.-Cross Huller--Giddings & Lewis, Inc., Fond Du Lac, WI; *Int'l*, pg. 1389
Mooney, Barbara, Grp. V.P.--Vision Financial Corporation, Keene, NH; *U.S. Private*, pg. 1141
Moore, George T., Grp. Mgr.-PET Packaging--Schmalbach-Lubeca AG, Braunschweig, Germany; *Int'l*, pg. 1206
Moore, James M., Grp. V.P.--Guardian Industries Corp., Auburn Hills, MI; *U.S. Private*, pg. 485
Moore, S.I., Grp. V.P.--Raytheon Support Systems, Long Beach, CA; *U.S. Public*, pg. 1364
Morgan, Wayne F., V.P.-New Mexico Div.--McAnally Enterprises, Inc., Yucaipa, CA; *U.S. Private*, pg. 718
Morin, Normand, Grp. V.P.-Gen. Engrng. & Environment--SNC-Lavalin Inc., Montreal, Canada; *Int'l*, pg. 1162
Morrissey, Michael W., Grp. V.P.--KLA Tencor Corporation, San Jose, CA; *U.S. Public*, pg. 939
Morrow, George, Grp. V.P.-U.S. Comml. Opers.--Glaxo Wellcome plc, London, United Kingdom; *Int'l*, pg. 552
Morrow, George J., Grp. V.P.-Commercial Opers.--Glaxo Wellcome Inc., Research Triangle Park, NC; *Int'l*, pg. 552
Mrozek, Ernest, Grp. Pres.--ServiceMaster Consumer Services Company, Memphis, TN; *U.S. Public*, pg. 1461
Mulhollem, Paul, Grp. V.P.--Archer Daniels Midland Company (ADM), Decatur, IL; *U.S. Public*, pg. 127
Muller, Thomas, Grp. V.P.--Binney & Smith Inc., Easton, PA; *U.S. Private*, pg. 496
Muller, Tom, Grp. V.P.--Crayola Products Div., Easton, PA; *U.S. Private*, pg. 496
Murphy, Barbara K., Dir.-Relocation--Jones, Day, Reavis & Pogue, Cleveland, OH; *U.S. Private*, pg. 596
Murray, David R., Grp. Pres.--Kimberly-Clark Corporation, Dallas, TX; *U.S. Public*, pg. 958
Murray, Donald C., Grp. V.P.--The Clorox Company, Oakland, CA; *U.S. Public*, pg. 386
Mussallem, Mike, Grp. V.P.-Cardiovascular--Baxter International Inc., Deerfield, IL; *U.S. Public*, pg. 196
Myers, William J., Grp. V.P.-U.S. Opers.--Pool Energy Services Co., Houston, TX; *U.S. Public*, pg. 1316
Myhrvold, Nathan P., Chief Tech. Officer & Grp. V.P.--Microsoft Corporation, Redmond, WA; *U.S. Public*, pg. 1107
Nammari, Kelly M., Grp. V.P. & Gen. Mgr.--Pre Finish Metals Incorporated, Elk Grove Village, IL; *U.S. Public*, pg. 1056
Naquet-Radiguet, Michel, Reg. V.P.--Interbrew S.A., Leuven, Belgium; *Int'l*, pg. 679
Nardin, Theodore, Grp. V.P.--Professional Book Group, New York, NY; *U.S. Public*, pg. 1071
Navarro, Richard J., Grp. V.P. & Controller--Albertson's, Inc., Boise, ID; *U.S. Public*, pg. 38
Neethling, P., Grp. Dir.-Australia & Asia--Smith & Nephew PLC, London, United Kingdom; *Int'l*, pg. 1263
Neiheisel, Edward J., Grp. V.P.-Vickers Indus.--Aeroquip-Vickers, Inc., Maumee, OH; *U.S. Public*, pg. 24
Neilson, Martin F., Exec. V.P. & Mgr.-Consumer Assets Div.--Seafirst Corporation, Seattle, WA; *U.S. Public*, pg. 181
Nelson, Kenneth P., Grp. Pres. & Exec. V.P.--Bremer Financial Services, Inc., Saint Paul, MN; *U.S. Private*, pg. 167
Newby, Thomas A., Jr., Grp. V.P.--Kimberly-Clark Corporation, Dallas, TX; *U.S. Public*, pg. 958
Newman, E. Davis, Grp. V.P.-Amoco Energy, N. America--Amoco Corporation, Chicago, IL; *U.S. Public*, pg. 101
Newmann, Paul, V.P.-Industrial Group--Vermont American Tool Corp., Louisville, KY; *U.S. Public*, pg. 575
Neyer, John, V.P.-Construction--Al Neyer, Inc., Cincinnati, OH; *U.S. Private*, pg. 797
Ng, Anita, Reg. V.P.-North Asia--Mentholatum Co. (Hong Kong) Ltd., Sha Tin, Hong Kong; *Int'l*, pg. 1126
Nicodemus, Dieter L., Grp. V.P.-Europe--General Motors Acceptance Corporation (GMAC), Detroit, MI; *U.S. Public*, pg. 719
Nishi, Masatu, Grp. V.P.--G-Net Corporation, Osaka, Japan; *Int'l*, pg. 531
Noetzel, Mark L., Grp. V.P.-Chemical Feedstocks--Amoco Corporation, Chicago, IL; *U.S. Public*, pg. 101
Norgaard, Ole, Grp. V.P.- Dairy Intl./Intl. Foods--Borden, Inc., Columbus, OH; *U.S. Private*, pg. 157
Norgard, David W., Grp. V.P.-Human Resources--ELSAG Bailey Process Automation N.V., Schiphol, Netherlands; *Int'l*, pg. 449
Norton, Ed, Grp. V.P.--Mail-Well Inc., Englewood, CO; *U.S. Public*, pg. 1037
Novak, Michael, Grp. V.P.--SNC-Lavalin Group Inc., Montreal, Canada; *Int'l*, pg. 1161
Novak, Tom, Reg. V.P.-Gainesville, FL--Leon Shaffer Golnick Advertising, Inc., Fort Lauderdale, FL; *U.S. Private*, pg. 463
Nozari, Moe S., Grp. V.P.-Consumer & Office Markets Grp.--3M, Saint Paul, MN; *U.S. Public*, pg. 1604
Nuccetelli, Nick, V.P. & Reg. Dir.-Region 4--Ames Department Stores, Inc., Rocky Hill, CT; *U.S. Public*, pg. 99
Nuechtern, Martin J., Grp. V.P. & Pres.-ASEAN & Australasia--The Procter & Gamble Company, Cincinnati, OH; *U.S. Public*, pg. 1330
Nunally, Denise, Reg. V.P.-Denver--Leon Shaffer Golnick Advertising, Inc., Fort Lauderdale, FL; *U.S. Private*, pg. 463
Nutter, G. Eric, V.P. & Grp. Exec.-Plumbing Prods.--American Standard Inc., Piscataway, NJ; *U.S. Public*, pg. 91
O'Brien, Phyllis A., Grp. V.P.-Acctg., Regulatory & Customer Rels.--The Southern Connecticut Gas Company, Bridgeport, CT; *U.S. Public*, pg. 431
O'Brien, Robert L., V.P.-Regulatory Affairs--Citizens Utilities Company, Stamford, CT; *U.S. Public*, pg. 379
O'Dare, James T., Jr., Grp. V.P.-Sls. & Distr.--Navistar International Corporation, Chicago, IL; *U.S. Public*, pg. 1167
O'Fill, R.J., Div. V.P.--Ameron Protective Linings Division, Brea, CA; *U.S. Public*, pg. 99
O'Hara, James T., Grp. Coord.-Tax--Jones, Day, Reavis & Pogue, Cleveland, OH; *U.S. Private*, pg. 596
O'Keefe, James, Grp. V.P. & Pres.-Health & Beauty Care Prods./Europe--The Procter & Gamble Company, Cincinnati, OH; *U.S. Public*, pg. 1330
O'Neil, T. J., V.P.-Energy Efficiency--Virginia Electric and Power Company, Richmond, VA; *U.S. Public*, pg. 516
O'Riordan, Dan, Sr. Grp. V.P. & Pres.-Intl. Foods--Borden, Inc., Columbus, OH; *U.S. Private*, pg. 157
Oldford, John S., Grp. V.P.--Hanson North America, Woodbridge, NJ; *Int'l*, pg. 593
Oldford, John S., Grp. V.P.--U.S. Industries, Inc., Iselin, NJ; *U.S. Public*, pg. 1683
Olsen, Paul, Grp. V.P.--Rite-Hite Corporation (WI), Milwaukee, WI; *U.S. Private*, pg. 933
Olsen, Paul S., Grp. V.P.--Rite-Hite Corporation, Milwaukee, WI; *U.S. Private*, pg. 933
Olson, Bruce, Grp. V.P.--Marcus Restaurants Inc., Milwaukee, WI; *U.S. Public*, pg. 1044
Olson, Robert G., Grp. V.P.--PVS Chemicals, Inc., Detroit, MI; *U.S. Private*, pg. 828
Orbam, Christina, Grp. V.P.--TMP Worldwide, Inc., Milwaukee, WI; *U.S. Private*, pg. 1064
Orban, Christina, Grp. V.P.--TMP Worldwide/Recruitment Division, Chicago, IL; *U.S. Private*, pg. 1065
Orban, Christina, Grp. V.P.--TMP Worldwide, Inc., Chicago, IL; *U.S. Private*, pg. 1065
Ormes, Kevin, Grp. V.P.-Sls. & Mktg.--Mitsubishi Motor Sales of America, Inc., Cypress, CA; *Int'l*, pg. 875
Orrby, Per-Johan, V.P.-SAS Cargo--SAS Airline, Stockholm, Sweden; *Int'l*, pg. 1201
Ortega, Jacinto F., Jr., V.P.-Safety & Security--Philippine Airlines, Inc., Manila, Philippines; *Int'l*, pg. 1050
Ortwein, Henry M., Jr., Grp. V.P.-Rail Mfg. Prods.--L.B. Foster Company, Pittsburgh, PA; *U.S. Public*, pg. 675
Osborne, W., V.P.--Electrovert, Grand Prairie, TX; *Int'l*, pg. 328
Ostby, Ron, Chief Fin. Officer & Grp. V.P.--Land O'Lakes, Inc., Arden Hills, MN; *U.S. Private*, pg. 645
Otto, Robert, V.P.-Corp. Opers.--Cousins Submarines, Menomonee Falls, WI; *U.S. Private*, pg. 280

Overton, Michael, Grp. Dir.-Logistics--Laura Ashley Holdings Plc, Maidenhead, United Kingdom; *Int'l*, pg. 804
Owens, Stewart K., Grp. V.P.-Food Prod.--Bob Evans Farms, Inc. Restaurant Division, Columbus, OH; *U.S. Public*, pg. 596
Owens, T.A., Grp. V.P.-Containerboard Div.--Inland Container Corporation, Indianapolis, IN; *U.S. Public*, pg. 1575
Owens, Ted A., Grp. V.P.--Temple-Inland Inc., Diboll, TX; *U.S. Public*, pg. 1574
Owens, Ted A., Grp. V.P.--Inland Container-Containerboard Division, Indianapolis, IN; *U.S. Public*, pg. 1575
Owens, William T., Grp. V.P.-Fin. & Controller--Healthsouth Corporation, Birmingham, AL; *U.S. Public*, pg. 803
Page, Robert E., Grp. V.P.--Beloit Corporation, Beloit, WI; *U.S. Public*, pg. 789
Pagoni, G., Dir.-Spare Parts--Zanussi Elettrodomestici S.p.A., Pordenone, Italy; *Int'l*, pg. 442
Paisner, Bruce L., V.P. & Deputy Grp. Head--Hearst Entertainment & Syndication, New York, NY; *U.S. Private*, pg. 516
Palazzo, Dorothy M., Dir.-Continuing Legal Education--Jones, Day, Reavis & Pogue, Cleveland, OH; *U.S. Private*, pg. 596
Palimeri, Nicola, Grp. V.P. & Gen. Counsel--Montedison S.p.A., Milan, Italy; *Int'l*, pg. 324
Panayotopoulos, Dimitri, Grp. V.P. & Pres.-China/Proctor & Gamble Asia--The Procter & Gamble Company, Cincinnati, OH; *U.S. Public*, pg. 1330
Parry-Jones, Richard, Grp. V.P.-Prod. Devel.--Ford Motor Company, Dearborn, MI; *U.S. Public*, pg. 661
Partridge, Jack W., Grp. V.P.-Corp. Affairs--The Kroger Co., Cincinnati, OH; *U.S. Public*, pg. 967
Patrick, Scotty B., Grp. V.P.-Petrochemical & Tech.--Ashland Chemical, Dublin, OH; *U.S. Public*, pg. 139
Paul, Steven M., Grp. V.P. & Controller-Pipe Sys. Grp.--Price Brothers Co., Dayton, OH; *U.S. Private*, pg. 883
Pearcy, Robert, Grp. V.P.-Health Indus. Rels. & Blue Lines--Blue Cross and Blue Shield of Oklahoma, Tulsa, OK; *U.S. Private*, pg. 151
Pecnard, Antoine, Grp. V.P.--Crehalet Pouget Poussielgues, Paris, France; *U.S. Private*, pg. 1152
Pelon, William D., Reg. V.P.--Lowe's Companies, Inc., North Wilkesboro, NC; *U.S. Public*, pg. 1015
Perkins, Michel E., Grp. V.P.-North Texas Ready-Mix--Texas Industries, Inc., Dallas, TX; *U.S. Public*, pg. 1585
Perry, Barry W., Grp. V.P. & Gen. Mgr.-Paper Pigments & Chemicals--Engelhard Corporation, Iselin, NJ; *U.S. Public*, pg. 582
Perry, Barry W., Grp. V.P. & Gen. Mgr.--Pigments & Additives, Iselin, NJ; *U.S. Public*, pg. 582
Petersen, Merritt E., Grp. V.P.-Grain & Food Processing--Harvest States Cooperatives, Saint Paul, MN; *U.S. Private*, pg. 508
Peterson, Stephen M., Grp. V.P. & Gen. Mgr.-Fadal Engineering--Giddings & Lewis, Inc., Fond Du Lac, WI; *Int'l*, pg. 1389
Phillips, Mark, Reg. V.P.--Taco Cabana, San Antonio, TX; *U.S. Public*, pg. 1559
Pickett, Cecil, Dr., V.P.-Merck Frosst Centre for Therapeutic Research--Merck Frosst Canada Inc., Kirkland, Canada; *U.S. Public*, pg. 1092
Pietinen, Markku, Grp. V.P.-Commun.--Polarcup Group Headquarters, Espoo, Finland; *Int'l*, pg. 638
Pinon, Shawn, Reg. V.P.--Medical Meadow Gold Dairies, Inc., Ogden, UT; *U.S. Private*, pg. 1016
Pinzon, Gilberto, Grp. V.P. & Pres.-Nalco Latin America--Nalco Chemical Company, Naperville, IL; *U.S. Public*, pg. 1150
Pistoria, Gary A., Grp. V.P.-Amber Milling--Harvest States Cooperatives, Saint Paul, MN; *U.S. Private*, pg. 508
Pitney, Garvin, Grp. V.P.--Beloit Corporation, Beloit, WI; *U.S. Public*, pg. 789
Pittard, Daniel E., Grp. V.P.--Amoco Corporation, Chicago, IL; *U.S. Public*, pg. 101
Pitts, Shannon, Grp. V.P.-Acct. Services--LVL Advertising, Palo Alto, CA; *U.S. Private*, pg. 640
Piva, S., Dir.-Cooking Appl.--Zanussi Elettrodomestici S.p.A., Pordenone, Italy; *Int'l*, pg. 442
Pluff, Thomas H., Grp. V.P.--Hubbell Incorporated, Orange, CT; *U.S. Public*, pg. 844
Plyler, James C., Jr., Reg. V.P.--Hughes Supply, Inc., Orlando, FL; *U.S. Public*, pg. 846
Porter, Anthony, Grp. V.P.-Soybean Processing & Corn Opers. & Transportation--Ag Processing Inc., A Cooperative, Omaha, NE; *U.S. Private*, pg. 26
Pottenger, Charles R., Grp. V.P.-Pulp & Paperboard--Potlatch Corporation, Spokane, WA; *U.S. Public*, pg. 1318
Pratt, Norris, Grp. V.P.-Sls.--Fleischmann's Yeast, Fenton, MO; *Int'l*, pg. 237
Preiksaitis, Raymond V., Grp. V.P.--Archer Daniels Midland Company (ADM), Decatur, IL; *U.S. Public*, pg. 127
Price, John B., V.P.-Sourcing--Kaepa Inc., Greenville, SC; *U.S. Private*, pg. 604
Proger, Phillip A., Grp. Coord.-Govt. Relations--Jones, Day, Reavis & Pogue, Cleveland, OH; *U.S. Private*, pg. 596
Pulcini, Charles C., V.P.-Returns & Retail Opers.--QVC, Inc., West Chester, PA; *U.S. Private*, pg. 897
Quast, P.M., Grp. V.P.--Raytheon Support Systems, Long Beach, CA; *U.S. Public*, pg. 1364
Quick, Dennis M., Reg. V.P.-Vaencia RDC--Bergen Brunswig Drug Company, Orange, CA; *U.S. Public*, pg. 213
Raaths, William A., Grp. V.P.-Tissue Prods.--Chesapeake Corporation, Richmond, VA; *U.S. Public*, pg. 346
Radebaugh, James B., Grp. V.P.-Admin. & Human Resources--Bob Evans Farms, Inc., Columbus, OH; *U.S. Public*, pg. 596
Radebaugh, Jim, Grp. V.P.-Personnel Trng. & Devel.--Bob Evans Farms, Inc. Restaurant Division, Columbus, OH; *U.S. Public*, pg. 596
Radkoski, Donald J., Chief Fin. Officer, Grp. V.P.-Fin. & Treas.--Bob Evans Farms, Inc., Columbus, OH; *U.S. Public*, pg. 596
Rahilly, John F., Grp. Pres.--Kimberly-Clark Corporation, Dallas, TX; *U.S. Public*, pg. 958
Raikes, Jeffrey S., Grp. V.P.-Sls. & Mktg.--Microsoft Corporation, Redmond, WA; *U.S. Public*, pg. 1107
Ramos, Raul, Reg. V.P.--First Cash, Inc., Arlington, TX; *U.S. Public*, pg. 627
Randolph, Rodger L., V.P. & Treas.--Kentucky-Tennessee Clay Co., Mayfield, KY; *U.S. Public*, pg. 804
Rayburn, David B., Grp. V.P.-Highway Prods.--Modine Manufacturing Company, Racine, WI; *U.S. Public*, pg. 1121
Reagan, Martin, Grp. V.P.-Grain--Ag Processing Inc., A Cooperative, Omaha, NE; *U.S. Private*, pg. 26
Redding, Mark, Grp. V.P.--Beloit Corporation, Beloit, WI; *U.S. Public*, pg. 789
Reese, J. Barrett, Grp. V.P.-Sls. & Mktg./Expanded Shale & Clay--Texas Industries, Inc., Dallas, TX; *U.S. Public*, pg. 1585
Reid, James T., Grp. V.P.--Century America Corporation, Chicago, IL; *U.S. Private*, pg. 225
Reid, Virgil C., Jr., Grp. V.P.-Medium Volume Grp.--Citation Corporation, Birmingham, AL; *U.S. Public*, pg. 376
Reilly, Thomas, Grp. V.P.-OPers.--King Kullen Grocery Co., Inc., Westbury, NY; *U.S. Private*, pg. 621
Reinas, Jan, V.P.-SAS Airline Norway--SAS Airline, Stockholm, Sweden; *Int'l*, pg. 1201
Reustle, Dennis, V.P.-Sls. & Prod. Planning--QVC, Inc., West Chester, PA; *U.S. Private*, pg. 897
Rewey, Robert L., Jr., Grp. V.P.-Mktg., Sls. & Service--Ford Motor Company, Dearborn, MI; *U.S. Public*, pg. 661
Rhodes, C. Douglas, Grp. V.P.-H.R.--Harris Teeter, Inc., Charlotte, NC; *U.S. Public*, pg. 1412
Ricci, Osvaldo, V.P.-Distr. Services--Ames Department Stores, Inc., Rocky Hill, CT; *U.S. Public*, pg. 99
Rice, Deris, Reg. V.P.-Salt Lake City--Leon Shaffer Golnick Advertising, Inc., Fort Lauderdale, FL; *U.S. Private*, pg. 463
Rich, Richard P., Asst. Mgr.-Private Banking--Bank of Bermuda (Cayman) Limited, Georgetown, Cayman Islands; *Int'l*, pg. 151
Richardson, Joseph H., Grp. V.P.-Utilities--Florida Progress Corporation, Saint Petersburg, FL; *U.S. Public*, pg. 655
Richelsen, R.C., Grp. V.P.-Traffic & Personal Safety Markets Grp.--3M, Saint Paul, MN; *U.S. Public*, pg. 1604
Richmond, Jane N., Dir.-Writing Program--Jones, Day, Reavis & Pogue, Cleveland, OH; *U.S. Private*, pg. 596
Riegel, Larry, Exec. Grp. Dir.--Avrett, Free & Ginsberg, Inc., New York, NY; *U.S. Private*, pg. 103
Robb, William M., Grp. V.P.-Prods. Mfg.--Pennzoil Company, Houston, TX; *U.S. Public*, pg. 1272
Roberts, James, Grp. V.P.-Mktg.--Blue Cross and Blue Shield of Oklahoma, Tulsa, OK; *U.S. Private*, pg. 151
Roberts, Timothy L., Grp. V.P.-Special Foundry Grp.--Citation Corporation, Birmingham, AL; *U.S. Public*, pg. 376
Robins, Alan, Grp. V.P.-Quality Control--Daw Technologies, Inc., Salt Lake City, UT; *U.S. Public*, pg. 489
Robotti, Dorene E., V.P.-Legal--Ames Department Stores, Inc., Rocky Hill, CT; *U.S. Public*, pg. 99
Rosenbloom, Harvey, Sr. V.P. & Dir.-Stores/W. Region--Saks Fifth Avenue, New York, NY; *U.S. Public*, pg. 1429
Roseski, Michael J., Grp. Pres.-Southern Grp.--Beneficial Corporation, Wilmington, DE; *U.S. Public*, pg. 211
Routhier, B., Grp. V.P.-Paper & Pkgng.--Kruger Inc., Montreal, Canada; *Int'l*, pg. 761
Routhier, Bernard, Grp. V.P.--Ville LaSalle Plant, La Salle, Canada; *Int'l*, pg. 761
Roxo, Tony, Grp. V.P.--Beloit Corporation, Beloit, WI; *U.S. Public*, pg. 789
Rudy, Rex E., Grp. Pres.-Gulf Coast Grp.--Beneficial Corporation, Wilmington, DE; *U.S. Public*, pg. 211
Rumpza, Bob, Grp. V.P.--Shandwick Minneapolis, Minneapolis, MN; *Int'l*, pg. 1227
Russo, S., Grp. V.P.-Basic Chemicals--Rhone-Poulenc Inc., Princeton, NJ; *Int'l*, pg. 1112
Rutherford, F.N., Grp. Pres.-Fine Chemicals--Elf Atochem North America, Inc., Philadelphia, PA; *Int'l*, pg. 445
Sabol, Joseph J., Dir.-Production Services--Jones, Day, Reavis & Pogue, Cleveland, OH; *U.S. Private*, pg. 596
Sachinis, Harry, Grp. V.P.-CIS--Commodity Information Services Group, New York, NY; *U.S. Public*, pg. 1071
Saito, Moriya, Grp. V.P.--Mitsui Fudosan Co., Ltd., Tokyo, Japan; *Int'l*, pg. 882
Salay, Stephen G., Grp. V.P.-Power Opers.--Cinergy, Plainfield, IN; *U.S. Public*, pg. 369
Salay, Stephen G., Grp. V.P.-Power Opers.--CINergy Services, Inc., Cincinnati, OH; *U.S. Public*, pg. 369
Salay, Stephen G., Grp. V.P.-Power Opers.--Cinergy Corp., Cincinnati, OH; *U.S. Public*, pg. 369
Saliminen, Hannele, Grp. V.P.-H.R.--Polarcup Group Headquarters, Espoo, Finland; *Int'l*, pg. 638
Salminen, Hannele, Grp. V.P.-H.R.--Leaf Group B.V., Espoo, Finland,; *Int'l*, pg. 638
Salvati, Vincent W., Chief Fin. Officer & Grp. V.P.--Bell Canada, Montreal, Canada; *Int'l*, pg. 115
Sanelli, Steven G., Grp. V.P.--The Eastern Company, Naugatuck, CT; *U.S. Public*, pg. 548
Santo, Mark V., Grp. V.P. & Gen. Counsel--ELSAG Bailey Process Automation N.V., Schiphol, Netherlands; *Int'l*, pg. 449
Satterfield, Jack W., Grp. V.P.-Asia/Pacific Opers.--ELSAG Bailey Process Automation N.V., Schiphol, Netherlands; *Int'l*, pg. 449
Savage, Stanley D., Vice Chm. & Mgr.-Commercial Markets Grp.--Seafirst Corporation, Seattle, WA; *U.S. Public*, pg. 181
Scancarella, Neil D., Grp. V.P. & Chief Scientific Officer--Avon Products, Inc., New York, NY; *U.S. Public*, pg. 155
Scarborough, Dean A., Grp. V.P.-Fasson Roll/North America & Europe--Avery Dennison Corporation, Pasadena, CA; *U.S. Public*, pg. 152
Schanck, John W., Grp. V.P. & Pres.-Spirit Energy 76--Unocal Corporation, El Segundo, CA; *U.S. Public*, pg. 1698
Schaub, Ernest F., V.P. & Grp. V.P.-Landing Sys.--The B.F. Goodrich Company, Richfield, OH; *U.S. Public*, pg. 751
Schillings, Barry, Grp. V.P.--Regal-Beloit Corporation, Beloit, WI; *U.S. Public*, pg. 1370
Schlauch, Walter F., Grp. V.P.-Resins Div.--National Starch and Chemical Company, Bridgewater, NJ; *Int'l*, pg. 1435
Schlumberger, Allan A., Grp. V.P.--PVS Chemicals, Inc., Detroit, MI; *U.S. Private*, pg. 828
Schmidt, Fritz, Grp. V.P.--Wurzner Dauerbackwaren GmbH, Wurzen, Germany; *Int'l*, pg. 1514
Schmidt, Klaus-Dieter, Grp. Mgr.-Metal Packaging--Schmalbach-Lubeca AG, Braunschweig, Germany; *Int'l*, pg. 1206
Schmidt, Steve, Grp. V.P.--TMP Worldwide, Inc., North Hollywood, CA; *U.S. Private*, pg. 1064
Schmidt, Steve, Grp. V.P.--TMP Worldwide, Inc., Seattle, WA; *U.S. Private*, pg. 1064
Schmidt, Steve, Grp. V.P.--TMP Worldwide, Inc., Westlake Village, CA; *U.S. Private*, pg. 1064
Schmidt, Steve, Grp. V.P.--TMP Worldwide/Recruitment Division, Orange, CA; *U.S. Private*, pg. 1065
Schmitt, John, Group V.P.-Thermography Imprinting Div.--Taylor Corporation, Mankato, MN; *U.S. Private*, pg. 1070
Schmitz, Herbert, Grp. V.P. & Pres.-Central & Eastern Europe--The Procter & Gamble Company, Cincinnati, OH; *U.S. Public*, pg. 1330
Schnitzer, Arthur P., Grp. V.P.--KLA Tencor Corporation, San Jose, CA; *U.S. Public*, pg. 939
Schoch, Walter, Area Grp. V.P.--CAP Gemini Austria, Vienna, Austria; *Int'l*, pg. 264
Schramm, Karen, Group V.P.--Friendly Holidays Inc., Lake Success, NY; *U.S. Private*, pg. 428
Schultz, James H., V.P. & Grp. Exec.-Air Conditioning Prods./N. America--American Standard Inc., Piscataway, NJ; *U.S. Public*, pg. 91
Schultz, James H., V.P. & Grp. Exec.--The Trane Company North American Commercial Group, La Crosse, WI; *U.S. Public*, pg. 92
Schwab, Stephen C., Grp. V.P.-Aeroquip Engineered Sys. Grp.--Aeroquip-Vickers, Inc., Maumee, OH; *U.S. Public*, pg. 24
Schwartz, E. Ernest, Grp. V.P.-Galley Prod.--B/E Aerospace, Inc., Wellington, FL; *U.S. Public*, pg. 159
Schwartz, E. Ernest, Grp. V.P. & Gen. Mgr.--Aircraft Products Company, Delray Beach, FL; *U.S. Public*, pg. 159
Scott, John B., Grp. V.P.-Corp. Mktg. & Research & Devel.--Andrew Corporation, Orland Park, IL; *U.S. Public*, pg. 112
Scott, L. E. (Ed), Grp. V.P.-Diversified Bus. Grp.--Unocal Corporation, El Segundo, CA; *U.S. Public*, pg. 1698
See, Gary H., Grp. V.P.-Mktg.--International Dairy Queen, Inc., Minneapolis, MN; *U.S. Public*, pg. 220
Segatto, L., Dir.-Washing Appl.--Zanussi Elettrodomestici S.p.A., Pordenone, Italy; *Int'l*, pg. 442
Seifert, Kathi P., Grp. Pres.--Kimberly-Clark Corporation, Dallas, TX; *U.S. Public*, pg. 958
Semmann, Ronald L., Grp. V.P.--Madison Gas and Electric Company, Madison, WI; *U.S. Public*, pg. 1032
Senion, Gerald, Grp. V.P.-Fedders North America--Fedders Corp., Liberty Corner, NJ; *U.S. Public*, pg. 614
Senior, Gerry, V.P. & Gen. Mgr.--Frigidaire Home Products-Home Comfort Products, Edison, NJ; *Int'l*, pg. 440
Serre, Pierre, Dir.-Ready-Mixed Concrete Grp.--Ciments Francais, Paris, France; *Int'l*, pg. 292
Seta, Frank E., Div. V.P.-Acoustic Piano--Baldwin Piano & Organ Company, Loveland, OH; *U.S. Public*, pg. 169
Seufert, Walter, Grp. V.P.-Mktg Fiber Prods.--BASF Corporation Fiber Products Division, Charlotte, NC; *Int'l*, pg. 105
Shaffer, Alan L., Grp. V.P.-Indus. Prods.--Cincinnati Milacron Inc., Cincinnati, OH; *U.S. Public*, pg. 368
Shaw, Jeffrey P., Grp. V.P. & Pres.-Dean Foods Vegetable Co.--Dean Foods Company, Franklin Park, IL; *U.S. Public*, pg. 489
Shaw, M. Bane, Jr., Grp. V.P.-Mfg.--American & Efird, Inc., Mount Holly, NC; *U.S. Public*, pg. 1412
Shedlarski, George A., Grp. V.P.-Rotating Equipment Group--Flowserve Corporation, Dayton, OH; *U.S. Public*, pg. 658
Sheeder, Frank E., Grp. V.P.--Zurn Industries, Inc., Erie, PA; *U.S. Public*, pg. 1794
Sherbin, Robert, Grp. V.P.-Corp. Commun.--First Pacific Company Limited, Hong Kong, Hong Kong; *Int'l*, pg. 487
Shinners, Frederick, Grp. V.P.-Europe--Witco Corporation, Greenwich, CT; *U.S. Public*, pg. 1773
Shoults, Martin G., Grp. Mgr.-Plastic Packaging/Thermoformable Sheet--Schmalbach-Lubeca AG, Braunschweig, Germany; *Int'l*, pg. 1206
Shumaker, William A., V.P. & Gen. Mgr.-LPG--Kewaunee Scientific Corporation, Statesville, NC; *U.S. Public*, pg. 953
Silverstone, Edwin, Grp. V.P.--Hanson North America, Woodbridge, NJ; *Int'l*, pg. 593
Simms, Steven E., V.P. & Grp. Exec.--Danaher Corporation, Washington, DC; *U.S. Public*, pg. 480
Simon, James B., Grp. V.P. & Gen. Mgr.-Automation Tech.--Giddings & Lewis, Inc., Fond Du Lac, WI; *Int'l*, pg. 1389
Simon, Susie, Grp. V.P.--TMP Worldwide, Inc., Memphis, TN; *U.S. Private*, pg. 1064
Simon, Susie, Grp. V.P.--TMP Worldwide, Inc., Fort Wayne, IN; *U.S. Private*, pg. 1064
Sipe, Gene H., Grp. Pres. & Exec. V.P.--Bremer Financial Services, Inc., Saint Paul, MN; *U.S. Private*, pg. 167
Sjogren, Bengt, Grp. V.P.--Beloit Corporation, Beloit, WI; *U.S. Public*, pg. 789
Slapke, Philip C., Grp. V.P.-Engine Grp.--AAR Corp., Wood Dale, IL; *U.S. Public*, pg. 1
Slater, Richard J., Grp. V.P.-Suropean Reg.--Jacobs Engineering Group Inc., Pasadena, CA; *U.S. Public*, pg. 921

Slavin, Joe, Grp. V.P.--TMP Worldwide, Inc., Holliston, MA; *U.S. Private*, pg. 1064
Slavin, Joe, Grp. V.P.--TMP Worldwide, Inc., Hoboken, NJ; *U.S. Private*, pg. 1064
Slavin, Joe, Grp. V.P.--TMP Worldwide/Recruitment Division, New York, NY; *U.S. Private*, pg. 1065
Smalis, Gregroy C., Grp. V.P.-Portfolio Mngmt.--The FINOVA Group Inc., Phoenix, AZ; *U.S. Public*, pg. 624
Smith, E.T., Grp. V.P.-Aeroquip Indus. Grp.--Aeroquip-Vickers, Inc., Maumee, OH; *U.S. Public*, pg. 24
Smith, E.T., Grp. V.P.--International Group, Hayes, United Kingdom; *U.S. Public*, pg. 24
Smith, Eddie, Grp. V.P.-Perishable Div.--Ralphs Grocery Company, Compton, CA; *U.S. Private*, pg. 1202
Smith, Edward D., Grp. V.P.--Calsonic International, Inc., Irvine, CA; *Int'l*, pg. 944
Smith, James D., V.P.-Grp. Opers.--Shenandoah Life Insurance Company, Roanoke, VA; *U.S. Private*, pg. 992
Smith, Robert A., Grp. V.P.--Harcourt General, Inc., Chestnut Hill, MA; *U.S. Public*, pg. 782
Smrekar, Thomas J., Grp. V.P.-Wood Prods.--Potlatch Corporation, Spokane, WA; *U.S. Public*, pg. 1318
Snow, David L., Grp. V.P.-Analytics--ELSAG Bailey Process Automation N.V., Schiphol, Netherlands; *Int'l*, pg. 449
Sorensen, Vagn, V.P.-SAS Airline Intl.--SAS Airline, Stockholm, Sweden; *Int'l*, pg. 1201
Spiess, Dale H., Grp. V.P.-Polyolefins & Performance Polymers--Millennium Petrochemicals, Inc., Cincinnati, OH; *Int'l*, pg. 594
Sprague, Cheryl M., Grp. V.P.-H.R.--Jones Intercable, Inc., Englewood, CO; *U.S. Private*, pg. 597
Standeven, Joseph D., Pres.-Kelvinator & Philco--WCI International Company, Pittsburgh, PA; *Int'l*, pg. 440
Stanhope, John E., Grp. V.P.--Amoco Corporation, Chicago, IL; *U.S. Public*, pg. 101
Stans, Rick, V.P.--Hitachi Home Electronics, Norcross, GA; *Int'l*, pg. 621
Starkey, Thomas J., V.P.-Feed--H.J. Baker & Bro., Inc., Stamford, CT; *U.S. Private*, pg. 112
Staron, William L., Grp. V.P. & Gen. Mgr.-Chemical Catalysts, Pigments & Additives--Engelhard Corporation, Iselin, NJ; *U.S. Public*, pg. 582
Steele, John, Dir.-Personnel--British Telecommunications plc, London, United Kingdom; *Int'l*, pg. 222
Steever, Daniel J., Grp. V.P. & Gen. Mgr.-Sls.--Broderbund Software, Inc., Novato, CA; *U.S. Public*, pg. 258
Steffen, James R., Grp. Pres.--Kimberly-Clark Corporation, Dallas, TX; *U.S. Public*, pg. 958
Steiger, Josef, Grp. V.P.--Saurer AG, Arbon, Switzerland; *Int'l*, pg. 1198
Stellhorn, Stephen J., Group Sr. V.P.-Investment Svcs.--European American Bank & Trust Co., Uniondale, NY; *Int'l*, pg. 9
Stephens, Ricky, V.P.-Distr.--Merisel, Inc., El Segundo, CA; *U.S. Public*, pg. 1095
Stevenson, John R., V.P.-Special Products Grp. & Admin.--The Valspar Corporation, Minneapolis, MN; *U.S. Public*, pg. 1707
Steward, Jerry N., Grp. V.P.--Poultry Group, Atlanta, GA; *U.S. Private*, pg. 459
Stiles, Mark W., Grp. V.P.--Trinity Industries Inc., Dallas, TX; *U.S. Public*, pg. 1638
Stoilen, Sheldon T., Grp. V.P.-Corp. Services & Plng. & Public Affairs--Canfor Corporation, Vancouver, Canada; *Int'l*, pg. 260
Stoker, Lindell G., Grp. V.P.-Mfg.--American & Efird, Inc., Mount Holly, NC; *U.S. Public*, pg. 1412
Stokes, Patrick T., V.P. & Grp. Exec.--Anheuser-Busch Companies, Inc., Saint Louis, MO; *U.S. Public*, pg. 113
Stott, James, Grp. V.P.--Atchison Casting Corporation, Atchison, KS; *U.S. Public*, pg. 142
Stoutenburgh, Dennis J., Pres.-Communications Grp.--Intellicall, Inc., Carrollton, TX; *U.S. Public*, pg. 887
Stovall, Bill, Grp. V.P.--Koh-I-Noor, Inc., Bloomsbury, NJ; *U.S. Private*, pg. 629
Strauch, John L., Grp. Coord.-Litigation--Jones, Day, Reavis & Pogue, Cleveland, OH; *U.S. Private*, pg. 596
Streeter, Stephanie A., Grp. V.P.-Worldwide Office Prods.--Avery Dennison Corporation, Pasadena, CA; *U.S. Public*, *pg. 152*
Streich, Mark A., Grp. Pres.--Kimberly-Clark Corporation, Dallas, TX; *U.S. Public*, pg. 958
Strutz, Henri, Grp. V.P.--CAP Sesa Industrie, Paris, France; *Int'l*, pg. 263
Stucky, Michael L., Reg. V.P.--Payless Cashways, Inc., Kansas City, MO; *U.S. Public*, pg. 1267
Student, Roy, V.P.-Gaming Operations--Sulcus Computer Corp., Greensburg, PA; *U.S. Public*, pg. 1527
Sturken, Craig, Grp. V.P.-Michigan--Farmer Jack Supermarkets, Detroit, MI; *Int'l*, pg. 1375
Sturm, William L., Grp. V.P. & Gen. Mgr.--Chemical Catalysts, Iselin, NJ; *U.S. Public*, pg. 582
Sturtz, Henri, Grp. V.P.--CAP Sesa Hoskyns, Paris, France; *Int'l*, pg. 263
Suggett, A., Grp. Dir.-Res. & devel.--Smith & Nephew PLC, London, United Kingdom; *Int'l*, pg. 1263
Surbaugh, Gary, V.P.-Natl. Sls.--Tension Envelope Corp., Kansas City, MO; *U.S. Private*, pg. 1077
Swed, P.M., Grp. V.P.-Industrial--WESCO Distribution, Inc., Pittsburgh, PA; *U.S. Private*, pg. 244
Sweeny, Jack C., Grp. V.P.--Temple-Inland Inc., Diboll, TX; *U.S. Public*, pg. 1574
Sweeny, Jack C., Grp. V.P.--Temple-Inland Forest Products Corporation, Diboll, TX; *U.S. Public*, pg. 1575
Szuluk, Charles W., Grp. V.P.--Ford Motor Company, Dearborn, MI; *U.S. Public*, pg. 661
Tabickman, M. Louis, Grp. V.P.-Rehab Prods.--Invacare Corporation, Elyria, OH; *U.S. Public*, pg. 911
Tang, Tracy, V.P., Publisher-Puffin--Penguin Putnam Inc., New York, NY; *Int'l*, pg. 1027
Tarbutton, Allen J., Jr., Sr. V.P. & Pres.-Gas Services Div.--Mitchell Energy & Development Corp., Spring, TX; *U.S. Public*, pg. 1117
Taylor, Mark, V.P.-Corp. Services--BMC Software, Inc., Houston, TX; *U.S. Public*, pg. 162
Taylor, Ron, Div. Mgr.--Lexington Division, Lexington, KY; *U.S. Public*, pg. 333
Taylor, Russell C., Grp. Pres.--Kimberly-Clark Corporation, Dallas, TX; *U.S. Public*, pg. 958
Temple, Larry, Group V.P.--Checker Motors Corporation, Kalamazoo, MI; *U.S. Private*, pg. 1029
Templeton, Ronald R., V.P. & Reg. Dir.-Region 3--Ames Department Stores, Inc., Rocky Hill, CT; *U.S. Public*, pg. 99
Terrenzi, John T., Sr. V.P.-Grp.--Security Mutual Life Insurance Co. of New York, Binghamton, NY; *U.S. Private*, pg. 981
Thibault, Robert D., Grp. Pres.--Kimberly-Clark Corporation, Dallas, TX; *U.S. Public*, pg. 958
Thiele, Henry J., Grp. Pres.--MascoTech, Inc., Taylor, MI; *U.S. Public*, pg. 1055
Thimjon, D.H., Grp. V.P.-Utility--WESCO Distribution, Inc., Pittsburgh, PA; *U.S. Private*, pg. 244
Thomas, Larry E., Grp. V.P. & Chief Transformation Officer--Cinergy Corp., Cincinnati, OH; *U.S. Public*, pg. 368
Thompson, Anthony, Grp. V.P.-Mktg.--Proudfoot USA Company, West Palm Beach, FL; *Int'l*, pg. 1072
Thorkilsen, Eric, Publr.-Martha Stewart Living--Time Inc., New York, NY; *U.S. Public*, pg. 1612
Thornton, William T., Group Sr. V.P.-Admin.--European American Bank & Trust Co., Uniondale, NY; *Int'l*, pg. 9
Tibbets, Jim, Grp. V.P.--Honeymead Products Co., Mankato, MN; *U.S. Private*, pg. 537
Tiedens, George R., Grp. V.P.-Power Sys.--Kohler Company, Kohler, WI; *U.S. Private*, pg. 630
Tinsley, J. David, Grp. V.P. & Pres.-Water & Waste Treatment Div.--Nalco Chemical Company, Naperville, IL; *U.S. Public*, pg. 1150
Tipple, H. Douglas, Grp. V.P.-Logistics--Bell Canada, Montreal, Canada; *Int'l*, pg. 115
Tipton, Dave, Grp. V.P.-Sls.--Fleischmann's Yeast, Fenton, MO; *Int'l*, pg. 237
Todd, Carl, Reg. V.P.--Medical Meadow Gold Dairies, Inc., Ogden, UT; *U.S. Private*, pg. 1016
Toney, Glen O., Grp. V.P.-Global Human Resources--Applied Materials, Inc., Santa Clara, CA; *U.S. Public*, pg. 123
Toombs, H. Dean, V.P.-Sematech--Intel Components Technology & Manufacturing Group, Santa Clara, CA; *U.S. Public*, pg. 886
Torres, Ramon, Reg. V.P.--Taco Cabana, San Antonio, TX; *U.S. Public*, pg. 1559
Townsley, Boyd T., V.P.-Kauai Electric Division--Citizens Utilities Company, Stamford, CT; *U.S. Public*, pg. 379
Transou, Robert H., Grp. V.P.-Mfg.--Ford Motor Company, Dearborn, MI; *U.S. Public*, pg. 661
Tribe, Robert, Grp. V.P.--SNC-Lavalin Group Inc., Montreal, Canada; *Int'l*, pg. 1161
Triozon, Henri, Grp. V.P.--Cegelec, Levallois-Perret, France; *Int'l*, pg. 52
Tritt, Robert L., Grp. V.P.--DST Systems, Inc., Kansas City, MO; *U.S. Public*, pg. 943
Turk, Joseph E., Grp. V.P.--Temple-Inland Inc., Diboll, TX; *U.S. Public*, pg. 1574
Turk, Joseph E., Grp. V.P.--Inland Container-Container Division, Indianapolis, IN; *U.S. Public*, pg. 1575
Twyford, Walt, Director--Tridon Inc., Lawrenceburg, TN; *U.S. Public*, pg. 11
Urban, G., Grp. V.P.-Oleochemeals & Derivatives--Witco Corporation, Greenwich, CT; *U.S. Public*, pg. 1773
Urban, Georg, Grp. V.P.--Oleochemicals & Derivatives Group, Greenwich, CT; *U.S. Public*, pg. 1774
Urban, Scott D., Grp. V.P.-Exploration--Amoco Corporation, Chicago, IL; *U.S. Public*, pg. 101
Ustian, Daniel C., Grp. V.P. & Gen. Mgr.-Engine & Foundry--Navistar International Corporation, Chicago, IL; *U.S. Public*, pg. 1167
Utsunomiya, Takaharu, Grp. V.P.-Fin., Treas. & Asst. Sec.--Sega of America Inc., Redwood City, CA; *Int'l*, pg. 1218
Valentine, B.J., Grp. V.P.--Raytheon Support Systems, Long Beach, CA; *U.S. Public*, pg. 1364
Vallillo, Anthony J., Grp. V.P.-Client Services--United Illuminating Company, New Haven, CT; *U.S. Public*, pg. 1678
van de Werken, Jan, Grp. V.P.-Automotive & Chemical Markets Grp.--3M, Saint Paul, MN; *U.S. Public*, pg. 1604
van der Meer, Marten, Div. V.P. & Gen. Mgr.--Ameron B.V., Protective Coatings Division-Europe, Geldermalsen, Netherlands; *U.S. Public*, pg. 99
van der Merwe, Robert P., Grp. Pres.--Kimberly-Clark Corporation, Dallas, TX; *U.S. Public*, pg. 958
Van Driest, Richard C., Grp. V.P.--Kimberly-Clark Corporation, Dallas, TX; *U.S. Public*, pg. 958
van Ogtrop, R.J.A.M., Grp. V.P.-Convenience Food--Koninklijke BolsWessanen nv, Amstelveen, Netherlands; *Int'l*, pg. 750
van Os, A., V.P.-Gas Processing--Tidelands Oil Production Co., Long Beach, CA; *U.S. Private*, pg. 1084
Van Steenberg, John A., Grp. Pres.--Kimberly-Clark Corporation, Dallas, TX; *U.S. Public*, pg. 958
Vanderhoff, R.E., Grp. V.P.-Mfg. Structure--WESCO Distribution, Inc., Pittsburgh, PA; *U.S. Private*, pg. 244
Vaughn, Jeff, Grp. V.P.-Sls.--Turtle Wax, Inc., Chicago, IL; *U.S. Private*, pg. 1110
Verner, David, Grp. V.P.-Organo Silicones--Witco Corporation, Greenwich, CT; *U.S. Public*, pg. 1773
Verner, David, Grp. V.P.--Organo Silicones Group, Greenwich, CT; *U.S. Public*, pg. 1774
Vernon, Mark E., Grp. V.P.-Industrial Products Group--Flowserve Corporation, Dayton, OH; *U.S. Public*, pg. 658
Vodicka, Hermann, Div. Head-Polymers--Novartis, Basel, Switzerland; *Int'l*, pg. 972
Vogel, Carl E., Grp. V.P.--Jones Spacelink, Ltd., Englewood, CO; *U.S. Private*, pg. 597
Voss, Wolfgang, V.P. & Grp. Exec.-Plumbing Prods. Europe--American Standard Inc., Piscataway, NJ; *U.S. Public*, pg. 91
Wade, Robert, Grp. Exec.-Asia Pacific Banking Grp.--Citicorp, New York, NY; *U.S. Public*, pg. 376
Walbridge, Thomas C., Grp. V.P.--Auto Glass Products--Libbey Owens Ford Co., Toledo, OH; *Int'l*, pg. 1056
Waldrep, George C., Jr., Grp. V.P.--Burlington Industries, Inc., Greensboro, NC; *U.S. Public*, pg. 268
Walker, Robert L., Chief Fin. Officer & Sr. V.P.-Fin.--AEGON USA, Inc., Louisville, KY; *Int'l*, pg. 26
Wallace, Timothy R., Grp. V.P.--Trinity Industries Inc., Dallas, TX; *U.S. Public*, pg. 1638
Walters, Peter S., Grp. V.P.--Guardian Industries Corp., Auburn Hills, MI; *U.S. Private*, pg. 485
Warden, Richard, Sr. V.P.-Southen Region Opers.--Rogers Group Inc., Nashville, TN; *U.S. Private*, pg. 939
Waterford, Michael A., Grp. V.P.--DST Systems, Inc., Kansas City, MO; *U.S. Public*, pg. 943
Watson, John P., V.P. & Grp. Exec.--Danaher Corporation, Washington, DC; *U.S. Public*, pg. 480
Watson, Richard A., Grp. V.P.--Textron Inc., Providence, RI; *U.S. Public*, pg. 1588
Weaver, John A., V.P. & Grp. V.P.-Specialty Additives--The B.F. Goodrich Company, Richfield, OH; *U.S. Public*, pg. 751
Weber, Alan, Grp. Exec.-Intl. Fin. Institutions Grp.--Citicorp, New York, NY; *U.S. Public*, pg. 376
Weber, John H., Grp. V.P.--Vickers Industrial, Maumee, OH; *U.S. Public*, pg. 24
Weber, Stefan, Grp. V.P.--Beloit Corporation, Beloit, WI; *U.S. Public*, pg. 789
Weich, Gerhard, Grp. V.P.--Pall Corporation, Greenvale, NY; *U.S. Public*, pg. 1253
Weiner, Arnold, Grp. V.P.-Asian Opers.--Pall Corporation, Greenvale, NY; *U.S. Public*, pg. 1253
Welke, Karen E., Grp. V.P.-Medical Markets Grp.--3M, Saint Paul, MN; *U.S. Public*, pg. 1604
Wellman, K. Michael, Grp. V.P.--Sturm, Ruger & Co., Inc., Southport, CT; *U.S. Public*, pg. 1526
Wells, Thomas M., Grp. V.P. & Controller--GEICO Corporation, Washington, DC; *U.S. Public*, pg. 219
Westbrock, Leon, Grp. V.P.-Petroleum Mktg.--Cenex/Land O'Lakes, Inc., Inver Grove Heights, MN; *U.S. Private*, pg. 222
Westerberg, L. John, Grp. V.P. & Pres.-North Amer. Pasta Prods.--Borden, Inc., Columbus, OH; *U.S. Private*, pg. 157
Wheat, James M., Grp. V.P.-Franchise Opers.--Pennzoil Company, Houston, TX; *U.S. Public*, pg. 1272
Wheeler, James R., V.P.-Residential--The Newhall Land And Farming Company, Valencia, CA; *U.S. Public*, pg. 1178
Whitcraft, Charles O., Grp. V.P.-Product Group--Cerner Corporation, Kansas City, MO; *U.S. Public*, pg. 331
Whitmire, Kenneth N., Grp. V.P.-Poultry Grp.--Gold Kist, Inc., Atlanta, GA; *U.S. Private*, pg. 459
Wicks, Laurie D., Grp. V.P.--Beloit Corporation, Beloit, WI; *U.S. Public*, pg. 789
Wikler, Janet, Grp. V.P. & Dir. Advanced Media--HarperCollins Publishers, New York, NY; *Int'l*, pg. 926
Wilks, Charles E., Grp. V.P.--Amoco Corporation, Chicago, IL; *U.S. Public*, pg. 101
Williams, Richard J., Ph.D., Grp. V.P.--Ultratech Stepper, Inc., San Jose, CA; *U.S. Public*, pg. 1663
Williams, Roger L., Grp. V.P.-Southern Reg.--Jacobs Engineering Group Inc., Pasadena, CA; *U.S. Public*, pg. 921
Williamson, Bruce, Reg. V.P.--Medical Meadow Gold Dairies, Inc., Ogden, UT; *U.S. Private*, pg. 1016
Williamson, Charles R., Grp. V.P.-Intl. Opers.--Unocal Corporation, El Segundo, CA; *U.S. Public*, pg. 1698
Williamson, Donald R., Sr. V.P.-Fin. & Kentucky Region--Rogers Group Inc., Nashville, TN; *U.S. Private*, pg. 939
Wilson, Thomas E., Grp. Pres.--Kimberly-Clark Corporation, Dallas, TX; *U.S. Public*, pg. 958
Wiltz, James W., Pres.-Patterson Dental Supply, Inc.--Patterson Dental Company, Saint Paul, MN; *U.S. Public*, pg. 1265
Wimberly, John H., Grp. V.P.--Hanson North America, Woodbridge, NJ; *Int'l*, pg. 593
Winland, Virgil, Grp. V.P.--Worthington Cylinder Corporation, Columbus, OH; *U.S. Public*, pg. 1780
Winning, Cynthia A., Grp. V.P.-Mktg.--Jones Intercable, Inc., Englewood, CO; *U.S. Private*, pg. 597
Winstead, George W., Grp. V.P.-Ag Bus. Unit--Southern States Cooperative, Inc., Richmond, VA; *U.S. Private*, pg. 1017
Wiskind, M., Pres.-Myers Tire Supply Div.--Myers Industries, Inc., Akron, OH; *U.S. Public*, pg. 1143
Witt, F. William, Grp. V.P.--Morse Controls, Hudson, OH; *U.S. Public*, pg. 857
Wolfe, Myron J., Grp. V.P.-Food Service & Produce Companies--The Oshawa Group Limited, Etobicoke, Canada; *Int'l*, pg. 1012
Woolf, Blair, Dir.-Pharmacy--Smith's Food & Drug Centers, Inc., Salt Lake City, UT; *U.S. Public*, pg. 1103
Work, D.F., Grp. V.P.--Amoco Production Company, Chicago, IL; *U.S. Public*, pg. 102
Wortham, Claude, Reg. V.P.-West Texas--Leon Shaffer Golnick Advertising, Inc., Fort Lauderdale, FL; *U.S. Private*, pg. 463
Wortham, Samuel T., Grp. V.P.-Biomedical Prods.--Pall Corporation, Greenvale, NY; *U.S. Public*, pg. 1253
Wright, Raymond L., Grp. V.P.--The Eastern Company, Naugatuck, CT; *U.S. Public*, pg. 548
Wylie, Richard, Grp. V.P.--CMI International Inc., Southfield, MI; *U.S. Private*, pg. 195
Wyrwas, Margaret E., V.P.-Corp. Communications & Investor Relations--Ames Department Stores, Inc., Rocky Hill, CT; *U.S. Public*, pg. 99
Yalen, Richard, V.P.-Intl. Business Devel.--Cable & Wireless Communications Inc., Vienna, VA; *Int'l*, pg. 247
Yates, W.A., Grp. V.P.--Raytheon Support Systems, Long Beach, CA; *U.S. Public*, pg. 1364
Yoli, Albert H., V.P.-Preferred Engrng.--Preferred Utilities Manufacturing Corp., Danbury, CT; *U.S. Private*, pg. 881

Yon, Gene T., Grp. V.P.--ELSAG Bailey Process Automation N.V., Schiphol, Netherlands; *Int'l*, pg. 449
Yorke, Paul, Grp. V.P.-Human Resources--Hickson International Plc, Castleford, United Kingdom; *Int'l*, pg. 618
Yuen, Tony M., Grp. V.P.-Public Switching--Bell-Northern Research Ltd., Nepean, Canada; *Int'l*, pg. 116
Zahler, Kevin, Grp. V.P.--Deltak Inc., Plymouth, MN; *U.S. Public*, pg. 924
Zarrella, Ronald L., V.P. & Grp. Exec.-North American Sls., Svc. & Mktg.--General Motors Corporation, Detroit, MI; *U.S. Public*, pg. 718
Zboyovsky, J.F., Grp. V.P.--Hapco/American Div., Abingdon, VA; *U.S. Private*, pg. 351
Zollars, Robert J., Grp. Pres.-Pharmacy Automation & Mngmt.--Cardinal Health Inc., Dublin, OH; *U.S. Public*, pg. 304
Zoss, Joseph L., Grp. V.P.--HMI Industries, Cleveland, OH; *U.S. Public*, pg. 771
Zuniga, Marco, Grp. V.P., Grp. Dir. & New Bus. Contact--Young & Rubicam, S.A. de C.V., Mexico, Mexico; *U.S. Private*, pg. 1200
Zwisler, Ronald R., Grp. Pres.--Kimberly-Clark Corporation, Dallas, TX; *U.S. Public*, pg. 958

HUMAN RESOURCES

Aarseth, Geir, Sr. V.P.-Personnel/Organization--Orkla A.S.A., Oslo, Norway; *Int'l*, pg. 1010
Aasheim, Hilde, Sr. V.P.-Personnel/Health, Safety & Environment--Elkem ASA, Oslo, Norway; *Int'l*, pg. 446
Abbott, Susan A., V.P.-Human Resources--Community Bank N.A., De Witt, NY; *U.S. Public*, pg. 416
Abell, Julia, H.R. Dir.--Media That Works, Cincinnati, OH; *U.S. Private*, pg. 727
Abels, Debbie, V.P.-Human Resources--The Knight Publishing Co., Charlotte, NC; *U.S. Public*, pg. 964
Abendanon, G., Dir.-Human Resources--VNU Verenigde Nederlandse Uitgeversbedrijven B.V., Haarlem, Netherlands; *Int'l*, pg. 1445
Aber, William T., Dir.-Human Resources--BEI Technologies, Inc., San Francisco, CA; *U.S. Public*, pg. 160
Abernathy, Penelope Muse, Sr. V.P.-Plng. & Human Resources--The New York Times, New York, NY; *U.S. Public*, pg. 1174
Abhe, Brad, V.P.-H.R.--Canton Drop Forge, Canton, OH; *U.S. Private*, pg. 205
Aboud, Jennifer, V.P.-Human Resources--EAC-Embraer Aircraft Corporation, Fort Lauderdale, FL; *Int'l*, pg. 452
Abram, Drew, V.P.-Human Resources--Appleton Electric Co., Chicago, IL; *U.S. Public*, pg. 572
Abrams, Claudia, V.P.-Human Resources--Williams-Sonoma, Inc., San Francisco, CA; *U.S. Public*, pg. 1770
Abramson, Betty, Dir.-Personnel & Acctg.--Starcrest Products of California, Perris, CA; *U.S. Private*, pg. 1035
Abreu, Robert, Dir.-H.R.--Triangle Services, Inc., Valley Stream, NY; *U.S. Private*, pg. 1102
Achatz, Harvey H., V.P.-Admin. & Sec.--Daisytek International Corporation, Plano, TX; *U.S. Public*, pg. 477
Ackermann, Martin, Mgr.-Personnel--Oerlikon-Contraves AG, Zurich, Switzerland; *Int'l*, pg. 998
Acosta, Jose, Mgr.-H.R.--de la Cruz & Associates, San Juan, PR; *U.S. Private*, pg. 318
Acquilina, Michelle, Mgr.-Corp. Human Resources--Mark IV Industries Inc., Amherst, NY; *U.S. Public*, pg. 1044
Acton, Maureen, Dir.-Human Resources--Monier Inc., Irvine, CA; *Int'l*, pg. 1091
Adamov, Robert M., V.P.-Human Resources & Investor Rels.--Corrpro Companies, Inc., Medina, OH; *U.S. Public*, *pg. 451*
Adams, Albert, V.P.-Human Resources--Lincoln Industrial, Saint Louis, MO; *U.S. Public*, pg. 1273
Adams, Anita, V.P.-Human Resources--Digitron Tool Co., Inc., Miamisburg, OH; *U.S. Private*, pg. 332
Adams, Beth, V.P. & Dir.-Personnel--The Times-Picayune Publishing Corp., New Orleans, LA; *U.S. Private*, pg. 1087
Adams, Carol, Dir.-Human Resources--Holstein Association USA, Inc., Brattleboro, VT; *U.S. Private*, pg. 536
Adams, David E., Mgr.-Human Resources--A.P. Green Industries, Inc., Mexico, MO; *U.S. Public*, pg. 761
Adams, Freida G., Mgr.-Personnel--Transus Intermodal L.L.C., Atlanta, GA; *U.S. Private*, pg. 1097
Adams, Gary, Dir.-Personnel--Diamond Chain Company, Indianapolis, IN; *U.S. Private*, pg. 68
Adams, J.R., Staff Coord.--Swire Pacific Limited, Central, Hong Kong; *Int'l*, pg. 1328
Adams, John, Dir.-H.R.--Nationwide Homes, Inc., Martinsville, VA; *U.S. Private*, pg. 788
Adams, Kathie, Mgr.-Corp. Services--Bumble Bee Seafoods Inc., San Diego, CA; *U.S. Private*, pg. 526
Adams, Larry M., V.P.-Info. Systems & Sec.--Carmike Cinemas, Inc., Columbus, GA; *U.S. Public*, pg. 305
Adams, Michael, Mgr.-Human Resources--Southwest Marine, Inc., San Diego, CA; *U.S. Private*, pg. 213
Adams, Michael, Dir.-H.R.--Chesapeake Utilities Corporation, Dover, DE; *U.S. Public*, pg. 347
Adams, R.G., Sr. V.P.-Personnel Services--Delta Air Lines, Inc., Atlanta, GA; *U.S. Public*, pg. 497
Adams, Rex D., V.P.-Admin.--Mobil Oil Corporation, Fairfax, VA; *U.S. Public*, pg. 1118
Adams, Rob, Dir.-H.R.--Trus Joist MacMillan, Boise, ID; *Int'l*, *pg. 829*
Adams, Rob, Dir.-H.R.--TJ International, Inc., Boise, ID; *U.S. Public*, pg. 1556
Adams, Rob, Dir.-H.R.--Trus Joist MacMillan, Boise, ID; *U.S. Public*, pg. 1556
Adams, Robert, Dir.-Personnel--MTD Products Limited, Kitchener, Canada; *U.S. Private*, pg. 688
Adams, Robert, Mgr.-Human Resources--Wickes Inc., Vernon Hills, IL; *U.S. Public*, pg. 1391
Adams, Shirley, Mgr.-H.R.--Correct Craft, Inc., Orlando, FL; *U.S. Private*, pg. 276
Adams, Suzie, Mgr.--Commemorative Brands, Inc., Austin, TX; *U.S. Private*, pg. 258
Adams, Thomas H., Exec. V.P.-Human Resources--American National Bank & Trust Co. of Chicago, Chicago, IL; *U.S. Public*, pg. 628
Adashek, Anne, Human Resources Dir.--Carat ICG, Los Angeles, CA; *U.S. Private*, pg. 207
Adaway, Kerrie, Dir.-H.R.--Dun & Bradstreet (Australia) Pty. Ltd., Melbourne, Australia; *U.S. Public*, pg. 536
Aden, Kevin, Dir.-Human Resources--Fresh America Corp., Dallas, TX; *U.S. Public*, pg. 681
Adkins, Bronda, Mgr.-Human Resources--Payless Car Rental System, Inc., Saint Petersburg, FL; *U.S. Private*, pg. 844
Adkins, Deborah S., V.P.-Fin. & Human Resources--Calibron, Inc., Lake Mary, FL; *U.S. Public*, pg. 1369
Adler, Stephen, V.P.-Human Resources--Sybron Chemicals Inc., Birmingham, NJ; *U.S. Public*, pg. 1544
Ador, Hans, Dir.-Personnel--Sodra Cell AB, Vaxjo, Sweden; *Int'l*, pg. 1275
Adshead, John E., Dir.-Personnel--J. Sainsbury plc, London, United Kingdom; *Int'l*, pg. 1169
Affeldt, Kathleen J., V.P.-H.R.--Lexmark International Group, Inc., Lexington, KY; *U.S. Public*, pg. 991
Affeldt, Kathleen J., V.P.-H.R.--Lexmark International, Inc., Lexington, KY; *U.S. Public*, pg. 991
Agaard, Henrik, V.P.-H.R.--Novo Nordisk A/S, Bagsvaerd, Denmark; *Int'l*, pg. 987
Agar, Jane, Mgr.-H.R.--Oakland Tool & Manufacturing Company, Fraser, MI; *U.S. Private*, pg. 809
Agase, Mike, Mgr.-H.R.--D.A. Stuart Company, Warrenville, IL; *U.S. Private*, pg. 1048
Agren, Christer, Sr. V.P.-Personnel--Stora Kopparbergs Bergslags AB, Falun, Sweden; *Int'l*, pg. 1302
Agruso, Victor, III, V.P.-Org. Devel. & H.R.--Humana Inc., Louisville, KY; *U.S. Public*, pg. 847
Aguire, Marc, Personnel Trng. & Devel. Dir.--Alpha One Exchange, New Providence, NJ; *U.S. Private*, pg. 45
Ahles, Dave, V.P. & Gen. Counsel--American International Airways, Ypsilanti, MI; *U.S. Private*, pg. 57
Ahlfinger, R.E., Dir.-H.R.--Colonial Pipeline Company, Atlanta, GA; *U.S. Private*, pg. 254
Ahner, Gene, Dir.-Human Resources--Wells-Gardner Electronics Corp., Chicago, IL; *U.S. Public*, pg. 1753
Aho, Jukka, V.P.-Human Resources--Valmet Corporation, Helsinki, Finland; *Int'l*, pg. 1447
Ahola, Olli, V.P.-Personnel--Metra Corporation, Helsinki, Finland; *Int'l*, pg. 862
Ahrens, Robert, Dir.-H.R.--Tekni-Plex, Inc., Somerville, NJ; *U.S. Private*, pg. 1073
Ahsmann, Lee, V.P.-Human Resources--Superior Coffee and Foods, Bensenville, IL; *U.S. Public*, pg. 1434
Aiken, Barry H., Dir.-Human Resources & Pub. Affairs--S.C. Johnson, Camberley, United Kingdom; *U.S. Private*, pg. 593
Aiosa, Dick, V.P.-Human Resources--AVX Corporation, Myrtle Beach, SC; *Int'l*, pg. 775
Aker, David, V.P.-Worldwide Human Resources--Unisys Corporation, Blue Bell, PA; *U.S. Public*, pg. 1671
Akins, Barbara, Dept. Head-Human Resources--Metra Commuter Rail, Chicago, IL; *U.S. Private*, pg. 919
Akins, Joe, Dir.-H.R.--Holly Corporation, Dallas, TX; *U.S. Public*, pg. 830
Aksamit, LaVern V., Dir.-Human Resources--Isco Separation Instruments Division, Lincoln, NE; *U.S. Public*, pg. 914
Albanese, Michael, Dir.-H.R.--Number Nine Visual Technology, Lexington, MA; *U.S. Public*, pg. 1206
Alberghini, Dolores, Dir.-H.R. & Asst. Treas.--Cains Foods, L.P., Ayer, MA; *U.S. Private*, pg. 199
Alberto, John, V.P.-Human Resources--ADT Security Services, Inc., Aurora, CO; *U.S. Public*, pg. 1649
Albrecht, George B., Div. Dir.-Human Resources--Delphi Energy & Engine Management Systems, Flint, MI; *U.S. Public*, pg. 719
Albrecht, Nancy, Dir.-H.R.--First Federal FSB, Hutchinson, MN; *U.S. Public*, pg. 608
Albrecht, Rebecca A., V.P.-Human Resources--Hutchinson Technology Inc., Hutchinson, MN; *U.S. Public*, pg. 850
Albregts, Robert, V.P.-Human Resources--Pay Less Super Markets, Inc., Anderson, IN; *U.S. Private*, pg. 844
Albright, Mary Ann, Dir.-Personnel--Connelly Containers, Inc., Bala Cynwyd, PA; *U.S. Private*, pg. 264
Alcott, V., Mgr.-Industrial Design & Mktg. Communications--G.E. Appliances, Louisville, KY; *U.S. Public*, pg. 710
Alden, Alison, Sr. V.P.-Sls., Service & Human Resources--Boston Edison Company, Boston, MA; *U.S. Public*, pg. 247
Alderman, Betty, Mgr.-H.R.--W.A. Roosevelt Co., La Crosse, WI; *U.S. Private*, pg. 943
Aldrich, Mike, Mgr.-Personnel--Amurol Confections Co., Yorkville, IL; *U.S. Public*, pg. 1781
Aldworth, Patrick J., Mgr.-Human Resources--Humphrey Products Company, Kalamazoo, MI; *U.S. Private*, pg. 547
Aleman, John S., V.P.-H.R.--Angelica Corporation, Chesterfield, MO; *U.S. Public*, pg. 113
Alesio, Dennis, V.P.-Personnel--Duckwall-Alco Stores, Inc., Abilene, KS; *U.S. Public*, pg. 533
Alexander, Barbara C., Mgr.-H.R.--Potomac Electric Power Company, Washington, DC; *U.S. Public*, pg. 1318
Alexander, Donna, Dir.-Human Resources--Advance Seed Co., Fulton, KY; *Int'l*, pg. 566
Alexander, Howard, Dir.-Personnel--Elgin Watch Company, Long Island City, NY; *U.S. Private*, pg. 371
Alexander, Jack, V.P.-Human Resources--MidAmerican Energy Holdings, Des Moines, IA; *U.S. Public*, pg. 1109
Alexander, Steve, Mgr.-H.R.--AMCOL International Corp., Arlington Heights, IL; *U.S. Public*, pg. 63
Alexander, Susan, Sr. V.P.-Human Resources--Sotheby's Holdings Inc., New York, NY; *U.S. Public*, pg. 1487
Alexander, Willard A., Vice Chm., Chief Credit Officer, Human Res. & Specialized Lending--NationsBank South, Atlanta, GA; *U.S. Public*, pg. 1163
Alfano, Attilio A., V.P.-H.R.--International Plastics Company, New York, NY; *U.S. Private*, pg. 571
Alizart, Robert, V.P.-Corp. Commun.--Airbus Industrie, Blagnac, France; *Int'l*, pg. 39
Allard, Ann, V.P.-Human Resources--The Thompson-Minwax Company, Upper Saddle River, NJ; *U.S. Public*, pg. 1466
Alleman, James B., V.P.-H.R.--Global Industrial Technologies, Dallas, TX; *U.S. Public*, pg. 747
Allen, Barbara, Asst. V.P.-H.R.--Amwest Insurance Group, Inc., Calabasas, CA; *U.S. Public*, pg. 106
Allen, Barbara, Asst. V.P.-H.R.--Amwest Surety Insurance Company, Calabasas, CA; *U.S. Public*, pg. 106
Allen, Cathy C., Human Resources Dir.--Coyne Beahm Inc., Colfax, NC; *U.S. Private*, pg. 283
Allen, Charlene, Principal-H.R.--Camp Dresser & McKee Inc., Cambridge, MA; *U.S. Private*, pg. 203
Allen, Charles E., Sr. V.P.-Human Resources--The Lamson & Sessions Co., Cleveland, OH; *U.S. Public*, pg. 976
Allen, J., Sec.--Babcock International Group PLC, Amersham, United Kingdom; *Int'l*, pg. 130
Allen, Jim, Dir.-Human Resources--Appleton Electric Co., Chicago, IL; *U.S. Public*, pg. 572
Allen, Jim, Mgr.-Personnel--Appleton Electric Co., Chicago, IL; *U.S. Public*, pg. 572
Allen, John C., V.P.-Human Resources, Corp. Counsel & Sec.--Energy West Inc., Great Falls, MT; *U.S. Public*, pg. 581
Allen, Mark, Dir.-Personnel--The Vendo Company, Fresno, CA; *Int'l*, pg. 1184
Allen, Sally, V.P.-Admin. & Govt. Affairs--Gary-Williams Energy Corporation, Denver, CO; *U.S. Private*, pg. 440
Allen, Valerie, Dir.-H.R.--Azon Corporation, Johnson City, NY; *U.S. Private*, pg. 104
Allenbach, Brian, Mgr.-H.R.--Nobel Education Dynamics, Inc., Media, PA; *U.S. Public*, pg. 1185
Allers, Patricia A., Mgr.-H.R.--Tarlton Corporation, Saint Louis, MO; *U.S. Private*, pg. 1069
Alletag, Prentess, V.P.-Human Resources--Homeland Stores, Inc., Oklahoma City, OK; *U.S. Public*, pg. 832
Alletag, Pretess E., Jr., V.P.-H.R.--Homeland Holding Corp., Oklahoma City, OK; *U.S. Public*, pg. 832
Alley, Nancy, Human Resources Dir.--TBWA Chiat/Day Los Angeles, Venice, CA; *U.S. Private*, pg. 1062
Allison, A. Jaynne, V.P.-Human Resources--American Airlines, Inc., Fort Worth, TX; *U.S. Public*, pg. 9
Allison, A.J., V.P.-Human Resources--AMR Corporation, Fort Worth, TX; *U.S. Public*, pg. 9
Allor, Marilyn, Sr. V.P.-Human Resources--Citizens Banking Corporation, Flint, MI; *U.S. Public*, pg. 379
Alluza, Manuel, Dir.-Human Resources--Kalifarma S.A., Barcelona, Spain; *Int'l*, pg. 1279
Almeida, E.M., III, Dir.-Personnel--Colonial Oil Industries, Savannah, GA; *U.S. Private*, pg. 253
Alotbell, Lawrence, V.P.-Human Resources--Air Liquide America Corporation, Houston, TX; *Int'l*, pg. 37
Altiere, Daniel J., Sr. V.P.--Blonder-Tongue Laboratories, Inc., Old Bridge, NJ; *U.S. Public*, pg. 237
Altmann, Rick, Asst. V.P.-Human Resources--Avemco Corporation, Frederick, MD; *U.S. Public*, pg. 151
Altuch, Peter, Dir.-Personnel--Samsung Electronics America, Inc., Ridgefield Park, NJ; *Int'l*, pg. 1183
Alvares, Kenneth M., V.P.-H.R.--Sun Microsystems, Inc., Palo Alto, CA; *U.S. Public*, pg. 1531
Alvarez, Martha, Mgr.-Personnel--Lee Pharmaceuticals, South El Monte, CA; *U.S. Public*, pg. 984
Alvarez, Vicente Blanco, V.P.-Human Resources--Asland S.A., Madrid, Spain; *Int'l*, pg. 788
Alves, Luiz Cristiano de Lima, Exec. Dir.-Human Resources & Admin.--Banco Itau S.A., Sao Paulo, Brazil; *Int'l*, pg. 142
Alves, Michelle, Admin.-H.R.--Yale/Chase Materials Handling, Inc., City of Industry, CA; *U.S. Private*, pg. 1195
Amalfitano, Sharon, Dir.-H.R.--Sunroc Corporation, Dover, DE; *U.S. Private*, pg. 1053
Amato, Linda, Mgr.-Human Resources--CSX Corporation, Richmond, VA; *U.S. Public*, pg. 284
Ambrosio, Anthony, V.P.-Personnel Benefits--CBS, New York, NY; *U.S. Public*, pg. 273
Amburn, P., Mgr.-Human Resources--Consumer Products Company, Muncie, IN; *U.S. Public*, pg. 56
Amerman, Tom, Sr. V.P.-Human Resources--Younkers, Inc., Des Moines, IA; *U.S. Public*, pg. 1334
Ames, Lorne M., V.P.-Human Resources--Inco Limited, Toronto, Canada; *Int'l*, pg. 672
Ammons, Dora M., Asst. Sec.--Hickory Construction Company, Hickory, NC; *U.S. Private*, pg. 525
Amoroso, Gina, Mgr.-Human Resources--The H.W. Wilson Co., Bronx, NY; *U.S. Private*, pg. 1180
Amos, Betsy, Dir.-Personnel--Omega World Travel, Inc., Fairfax, VA; *U.S. Private*, pg. 816
Amos, Donald, Exec. V.P.-Admin. & Human Resources--Magna International Inc., Markham, Canada; *Int'l*, pg. 829
Anand, Anil, Chief Fin. Officer--Andrew Sports Club Inc., Secaucus, NJ; *U.S. Private*, pg. 73
Anconelli, Giuseppe, Dir.-Human Resources--SASIB SpA, Bologna, Italy; *Int'l*, pg. 1194
Andersen, Helge, Mgr.-Personnel--K/S Kaldnes de Groot A/S, Tonsberg, Norway; *Int'l*, pg. 965
Anderson, Barbara, Dir.-Personnel--Byers Portland Willamette, Portland, OR; *U.S. Private*, pg. 191
Anderson, Belinda, Dir.-Human Resources--Acrometal Companies, Inc., Plymouth, MN; *U.S. Private*, pg. 14
Anderson, Bruce C., V.P.-Human Resources--First Allmerica Financial Life Insurance Company, Worcester, MA; *U.S. Public*, pg. 54
Anderson, Charles, V.P.-Human Resources--TRC Companies, Inc., Windsor, CT; *U.S. Public*, pg. 1557
Anderson, Charles S., V.P.-Corp. Rels. & Human Resources--Encore Computer Corporation, Fort Lauderdale, FL; *U.S. Public*, pg. 580

Anderson, Dee, Dir.-Personnel--Rogers N.K. Seed Co., Boise, ID; *Int'l*, pg. 974
Anderson, Dick, Dir.-H.R.--Bio-Rad Laboratories, Inc., Hercules, CA; *U.S. Public*, pg. 230
Anderson, Donald E., V.P.-H.R.--L & D Group, Aurora, IL; *U.S. Private*, pg. 638
Anderson, Gail Philip, Sr. V.P.-H.R.--Raytheon Company, Lexington, MA; *U.S. Public*, pg. 1364
Anderson, Georgene, V.P.-Personnel--Airco Mechanical Inc., Sacramento, CA; *U.S. Private*, pg. 29
Anderson, Gregory S., V.P.-Human Resources--Cascade Corporation, Troutdale, OR; *U.S. Public*, pg. 310
Anderson, James, Sr. V.P.-Labor Rels. & Personnel Admin.--Hilton Hotels Corporation, Beverly Hills, CA; *U.S. Public*, pg. 828
Anderson, James M., Sr. V.P.-Labor Rels. & Corp. Admin.--Hilton Hotels Div., Beverly Hills, CA; *U.S. Public*, pg. 829
Anderson, Janet, Dir.-Employee Rels.--Periphonics Corp., Bohemia, NY; *U.S. Public*, pg. 1278
Anderson, Jeannette, Dir.-Personnel--Dallas Peterbilt, Inc., Irving, TX; *U.S. Private*, pg. 309
Anderson, Judy, V.P.-H.R.--Snyder's Drug Stores, Inc., Minnetonka, MN; *U.S. Private*, pg. 1011
Anderson, Katherine, Dir.-Personnel--CRSS Inc., Houston, TX; *Int'l*, pg. 1415
Anderson, Ken, Mgr.-Personnel--Alcoa of Australia Limited, Melbourne, Australia; *U.S. Public*, pg. 62
Anderson, Ken, Mgr.-H.R.--Foss Maritime Co., Portland, OR; *U.S. Private*, pg. 1092
Anderson, L.C., V.P.-Personnel--Longs Drug Stores California, Inc., Walnut Creek, CA; *U.S. Public*, pg. 1013
Anderson, Laurel, Mgr.-H.R.--The Children's Place Retail Stores, Inc., West Caldwell, NJ; *U.S. Private*, pg. 237
Anderson, Les C., V.P.-Personnel--Longs Drug Stores Corporation, Walnut Creek, CA; *U.S. Public*, pg. 1013
Anderson, R. Wayne, Sr. V.P.-H.R.--Amoco Corporation, Chicago, IL; *U.S. Public*, pg. 101
Anderson, Rob, Dir.-Human Resources--Tone Brothers Inc., Ankeny, IA; *Int'l*, pg. 237
Anderson, Sharon, Dir.-Human Resources--Irwin Toy Ltd., Toronto, Canada; *Int'l*, pg. 688
Anderson, Shirley, Mgr.-Human Resources--MGI PHARMA INC., Minneapolis, MN; *U.S. Public*, pg. 1026
Anderson, Steve, Dir.-Personnel--Adventure Lands of America, Inc., Des Moines, IA; *U.S. Private*, pg. 22
Andrejezyk, Donald, Dir.-Human Rels.--Plymouth Rubber Company, Inc., Canton, MA; *U.S. Public*, pg. 1311
Andresen, Yvette, Mgr.-H.R.--Faribault Woolen Mill Co., Faribault, MN; *U.S. Private*, pg. 394
Andrews, D., Mgr.-Personnel--Spartan Tool, Mendota, IL; *U.S. Private*, pg. 860
Andrews, Dick, V.P.-Human Resources--Color Tile, Inc., Fort Worth, TX; *Int'l*, pg. 686
Anesta, Michael, Dir.-H.R.--Steinway Musical Instruments, Inc., Waltham, MA; *U.S. Public*, pg. 1514
Anesta, Michael, Dir.-Human Resources--Steinway & Sons, Long Island City, NY; *U.S. Public*, pg. 1514
Angelone, Jane, Mgr.-Human Resources--Haydon Switch & Instrument, Inc., Waterbury, CT; *U.S. Private*, pg. 513
Angers, Thomas, Sr. V.P.-Personnel--The Bank of New York Company, Inc., New York, NY; *U.S. Public*, pg. 178
Angowitz, David I., Sr. V.P.-Human Resources & Admin.--RJR Nabisco Holdings Corp., New York, NY; *U.S. Public*, pg. 1354
Angus, William R., V.P.-Human Resources--Canada Malting Co. Limited, Mississauga, Canada; *U.S. Public*, pg. 428
Annasagasti, Joe, Mgr.-H.R.--Buck Knives, Inc., El Cajon, CA; *U.S. Private*, pg. 177
Anscombe, M., Group Dir.-Human Resources--Kraft Jacobs Suchard, Cheltenham, United Kingdom; *U.S. Public*, pg. 1290
Ansieau, Jerome, Mgr.-H.R.--Banque Bruxelles Lambert France, Paris, France; *Int'l*, pg. 148
Ansted, James P., Chief Fin. Officer, Treas., & Sec.--Plastic Suppliers, Inc., Columbus, OH; *U.S. Private*, pg. 871
Anthes, Mike, Dir.-Human Resources--Louis Padnos Iron & Metal Co., Holland, MI; *U.S. Private*, pg. 834
Anthony, Judy, Dir.-Personnel--American Furniture Company, Incorporated, Martinsville, VA; *U.S. Public*, pg. 974
Anthony, Lynda, Mgr.-Human Resources--Anthony Forest Products Co., Inc., El Dorado, AR; *U.S. Private*, pg. 76
Antieau, L.E., Mgr.-Personnel--Oldsmobile Div. General Motors Corp., Lansing, MI; *U.S. Public*, pg. 720
Antoniazzi, Cheri, V.P.-Human Resources--Everest & Jennings, Inc., Earth City, MO; *U.S. Public*, pg. 758
Anzalone, Bob, Dir.-Personnel--Technical Aid Corporation, Newton, MA; *U.S. Private*, pg. 1072
Apitz, Karin, V.P.-Human Resources--JanSport, Appleton, WI; *U.S. Public*, pg. 1702
Apple, Rodger, V.P.-Human Resources--Handleman Company, Troy, MI; *U.S. Public*, pg. 779
Applegate, Jerry, Mgr.-Personnel--Coleman Powermate, Inc., Omaha, NE; *U.S. Private*, pg. 691
Aquilina, Gerald, V.P.-Personnel--Victoria Packing Corporation, Brooklyn, NY; *U.S. Private*, pg. 1139
Arai, F., Mgr.-Personnel--Fujitsu Ten Corp. of America, Torrance, CA; *Int'l*, pg. 526
Aramony, Diane, Sr. V.P.-Human Resources--Mutual of America Life Insurance Company, New York, NY; *U.S. Private*, pg. 769
Araps, Tim, V.P.-Human Resources--Royal Appliance Mfg. Co., Cleveland, OH; *U.S. Public*, pg. 1410
Arcangeli, Paule, Mgr.-H.R. & Personnel Trng. & Devel.--Credit Mutuel, Paris, France; *Int'l*, pg. 344
Archbold, Cecil A., V.P.-H.R.--Hershey Pasta and Grocery Group, Hershey, PA; *U.S. Public*, pg. 812
Ard, Anthony E., Sr. V.P.-Corp. Affairs--Indiana Gas Company, Inc., Indianapolis, IN; *U.S. Public*, pg. 875
Aregger, Anton, Dir.-Personnel--Von Roll AG, Gerlafingen, Switzerland; *Int'l*, pg. 1480
Arendt, William, V.P.-H.R.--Scoville Press, Inc., Minneapolis, MN; *U.S. Private*, pg. 977
Argenziano, Carmen, Dir.-Pur. & Personnel Trng. & Devel.--BR Associates, Inc., Jasper, IN; *U.S. Private*, pg. 107
Argile, J., Dir.-Human Resources--Seven Seas Limited, Hull, United Kingdom; *Int'l*, pg. 593
Arlea, Michael N., Controller & Mgr.-Personnel--Cardinal Inc., Rahway, NJ; *U.S. Private*, pg. 208
Arlington, William J., Sr. V.P.-H.R.--John Wiley & Sons, Inc., New York, NY; *U.S. Public*, pg. 1768
Armer, Heidi, Mgr.-Human Resources--Hydraulics International, Inc., Chatsworth, CA; *U.S. Private*, pg. 551
Armitage, Rob, V.P.-Human Resources--Penn-Daniels, Inc., Quincy, IL; *U.S. Public*, pg. 1467
Armstrong, Connie, Dir.-Personnel--SJL of Kansas Corp., Wichita, KS; *U.S. Public*, pg. 984
Armstrong, Guy, Mgr.-Customer Service--GSW Thermoplastics Company, Barrie, Canada; *Int'l*, pg. 538
Armstrong, Joan, Mgr.-Human Resources--Broan Limited, Mississauga, Canada; *U.S. Public*, pg. 1194
Armstrong, Steve, V.P.-Human Resources--Wise Foods, Inc., Parsippany, NJ; *U.S. Private*, pg. 157
Armstrong, Sylvia, Dir.-H.R.--Heavy Machines, Inc., Memphis, TN; *U.S. Private*, pg. 518
Armstrong, Ted W., Asst. V.P.-Human Resources--Rite Aid Corporation, Camp Hill, PA; *U.S. Public*, pg. 1390
Armstrong, William A., V.P.-Admin. & Human Resources--McKesson Corporation, San Francisco, CA; *U.S. Public*, pg. 1072
Arnoff, Jolen, Dir.-Human Resources--Charter-Provo School, Inc., Provo, UT; *U.S. Public*, pg. 1035
Arnold, Douglas S., V.P.-Human Resources--United States Cellular Corporation, Chicago, IL; *U.S. Public*, pg. 1572
Arnold, Linda, V.P.-H.R. & Sec.--Toastmaster, Inc., Columbia, MO; *U.S. Public*, pg. 1619
Aronson, Gerrit O., Grp. Dir.-H.R.--TI Group plc, Abingdon, United Kingdom; *Int'l*, pg. 1337
Arrington, David J., Sr. V.P.-Human Resources--Niagara Mohawk Power Corporation, Syracuse, NY; *U.S. Public*, pg. 1181
Arrison, Mike, V.P.-H.R.--Allen & Ohara, Inc., Memphis, TN; *U.S. Private*, pg. 36
Arseneau, George, Exec. V.P.-Human Resources--Alliant Foodservice, Inc., Deerfield, IL; *U.S. Private*, pg. 244
Arsoy, Kaya, Mgr.-Human Resources--Sabanci Holding A.S., Istanbul, Turkey; *Int'l*, pg. 1167
Arteaga, George, Dir.-H.R.--Juno Lighting, Inc., Des Plaines, IL; *U.S. Public*, pg. 935
Artis, Curt, Sr. V.P.-Human Resources--Lucent Technologies Inc., Murray Hill, NJ; *U.S. Public*, pg. 1017
Artuz, Edwin, Asst. V.P.-Corp. Svcs.--Federal Home Loan Bank of New York, New York, NY; *U.S. Private*, pg. 399
Aruffo, Carol, Dir.-Personnel--Zenith Products Corp., New Castle, DE; *U.S. Public*, pg. 1054
Asaro, Janice, Dir.-Personnel--Innovative Plastics Corporation, Orangeburg, NY; *U.S. Private*, pg. 565
Ash, Barbara, Mgr.-H.R.--O'Malia Food Markets Inc., Carmel, IN; *U.S. Private*, pg. 816
Ash, Basil H., Mgr.-Human Resources & Employee Benefits--Southeastern Michigan Gas Enterprises, Inc., Port Huron, MI; *U.S. Public*, pg. 1489
Ashenhurst, Harry, Exec. V.P.-Human Resources--Lennox International Inc., Richardson, TX; *U.S. Private*, pg. 659
Ashton, R., Mgr.-Personnel--Kelco International Ltd., London, United Kingdom; *U.S. Public*, pg. 1091
Aspengren, Ann, V.P.-H.R.--Dart Transit Company, Eagan, MN; *U.S. Private*, pg. 311
Asselin, Patrice, Dir.-Human Resources--Imprimerie Quebecor Montreal, Montreal, Canada; *Int'l*, pg. 1077
Assis, Jane, Dir.-Personnel--Ceras Johnson Ltda., Rio de Janeiro, Brazil; *U.S. Private*, pg. 593
Ataka, Tomio, Dir.-Human Resources--Matsushita Electric Works, Ltd., Osaka, Japan; *Int'l*, pg. 847
Atchley, Barbara, Mgr.-Human Resources--Alco Chemical, Chattanooga, TN; *Int'l*, pg. 1435
Athy, Charles W., V.P.-Human Resources--Delavan Gas Turbine Products Division, West Des Moines, IA; *U.S. Public*, pg. 401
Atkins-Patterson, Wendy, Sr. V.P. & Human Resources Dir.--Ketchum Advertising/San Francisco, San Francisco, CA; *U.S. Private*, pg. 616
Atkins, Mike, V.P.-H.R.--Daniel Industries, Inc., Houston, TX; *U.S. Public*, pg. 482
Atkinson, Barbara, Mgr.-H.R. & Admin.--Ranger Oil Limited, Calgary, Canada; *Int'l*, pg. 1086
Atkinson, Connie, Dir.-H.R.--Advertising Checking Bureau Incorporated, New York, NY; *U.S. Private*, pg. 23
Atkinson, Linda, Dir.-H.R.--RHC/Spacemaster Corporation, Melrose Park, IL; *U.S. Private*, pg. 904
Attiken, Chandva, V.P.-Human Resources--Warner Cable Communications, Inc., Columbus, OH; *U.S. Public*, pg. 1611
Atzinger, Tim, Sr. Mgr.-Human Resources--Philips Components, Jupiter, FL; *Int'l*, pg. 1054
Aubrey, Gary, V.P.-Human Resources--Komatsu America International Company, Vernon Hills, IL; *Int'l*, pg. 744
Aumiller, Gerald E., Sr. V.P. & Dir.-Human Resources--Keystone Financial Inc., Harrisburg, PA; *U.S. Public*, pg. 956
Austin, Andy, Dir.-H.R.--Conley Frog/Switch & Forge Co., Memphis, TN; *U.S. Private*, pg. 263
Austin, Diane, Dir.-Personnel--Gress Foods Inc., Gainesville, GA; *U.S. Private*, pg. 480
Austin, Kareen, V.P.-H.R.--North Pacific Lumber Company, Portland, OR; *U.S. Private*, pg. 805
Austin, Kathryn M., Human Resources Officer--Community National Bank, Derby, VT; *U.S. Public*, pg. 416
Austin, Kathryn M., Human Resources Officer--Community National Bank, Saint Johnsbury, VT; *U.S. Public*, pg. 416
Austin, Patrick M., Mgr.-H.R.--STV Group, Inc., Douglassville, PA; *U.S. Public*, pg. 1421
Austin, Paul N., V.P.-Personnel--Norfolk Southern Corporation, Norfolk, VA; *U.S. Public*, pg. 1190
Austin, Robin L., V.P.-Human Resources--PLM International, Inc., San Francisco, CA; *U.S. Public*, pg. 1241
Auteri, Enrico, Sr. V.P.-H.R.--Fiat Auto SpA, Turin, Italy; *Int'l*, pg. 480
Authehent, Charles, Dir.-H.R.--Bollinger Shipyards, Inc., Lockport, LA; *U.S. Private*, pg. 155
Autrey, William, Mgr.-Human Resources--Steelox Systems Inc., Mason, OH; *U.S. Private*, pg. 1038
Avant, Roy, Dir.-Personnel--Burgess Pigment Co., Sandersville, GA; *U.S. Private*, pg. 182
Avery, Warren, V.P.-Human Resources--Baker Hughes INTEQ, Houston, TX; *U.S. Public*, pg. 166
Aviles, Hernando, V.P.-H.R.--Gorges/Quik-To-Fix Foods, Dallas, TX; *U.S. Private*, pg. 465
Avis, Joe, Sr. V.P.--Riggs National Corporation, Washington, DC; *U.S. Public*, pg. 1389
Avner, Brett, V.P.-Human Resources--Victoria's Secret Stores, Reynoldsburg, OH; *U.S. Public*, pg. 995
Awad, Carmen, Dir.-Personnel--Zack Electronics/Tele-Com Products, Inc., Duarte, CA; *U.S. Private*, pg. 1203
Awtry, Glenn, V.P.-H.R.--Flint Ink Corp., Detroit, MI; *U.S. Private*, pg. 413
Axelrode, Julia, V.P.-Human Resources--Management Dynamics, New Providence, NJ; *U.S. Public*, pg. 1040
Axson, Pearl, Dir.-Personnel--W.W. Norton & Company, Inc., New York, NY; *U.S. Private*, pg. 807
Ayala, Olivia, V.P.-Artist Devel.--The Guber Peters Entertainment Company, Los Angeles, CA; *Int'l*, pg. 1283
Aydelotte, Julie, Mgr.-H.R.--Icicle Seafoods, Inc., Seattle, WA; *U.S. Private*, pg. 556
Ayers, Nancy, Dir.-Human Resources--Clipper Belt Lacer Company, Grand Rapids, MI; *U.S. Private*, pg. 413
Ayers, Richard, Dir.-H.R.--Hyde Manufacturing Co., Southbridge, MA; *U.S. Private*, pg. 551
Ayers, Tom P., Dir.-Human Resources--Cyro Industries, Rockaway, NJ; *Int'l*, pg. 1454
Ayles, Bill, Dir.-Personnel--Alimak Elevator Company, Bridgeport, CT; *U.S. Private*, pg. 34
Aylward, Patricia M., Dir.-Personnel--William Blair & Company L.L.C., Chicago, IL; *U.S. Private*, pg. 148
Baade, Roberta C., Ph.D., V.P.-H./R.--Sunrise Medical, Inc., Carlsbad, CA; *U.S. Public*, pg. 1535
Baar, John, Dir.-H.R.--Michigan Wheel Corporation, Grand Rapids, MI; *U.S. Private*, pg. 741
Babcock, Paul, Dir.-H.R.--Nemschoff Chairs, Inc., Sheboygan, WI; *U.S. Private*, pg. 791
Bachand, Paul, V.P.-H.R. & Indus. Rels.--Cara Operations Limited, Toronto, Canada; *Int'l*, pg. 266
Bacher, Philip J., Exec. V.P. & DMB&B Worldwide Human Resources Dir.--DMB&B Communications, New York, NY; *U.S. Private*, pg. 302
Bachman, Ardella, Mgr.-H.R.--Hopple Plastics, Inc., Florence, KY; *U.S. Private*, pg. 538
Bachman, John, V.P.-Human Resources, Flexograph--Walle Corporation, Harahan, LA; *U.S. Private*, pg. 1148
Back, John, Sr. V.P.-H.R.--Fingerhut Corp., Minnetonka, MN; *U.S. Public*, pg. 623
Backes, Robert J., Sr. V.P.-H.R.--United HealthCare Corporation, Minnetonka, MN; *U.S. Public*, pg. 1677
Bacon, Larry S., Sr. V.P.-H.R.--Berg Electronics, Saint Louis, MO; *U.S. Public*, pg. 212
Badgett, Peyton, Mgr.-H.R.--Steel Technologies Inc., Louisville, KY; *U.S. Public*, pg. 1513
Baen, Dee Dee, Dir.-Human Resources--Thermon Manufacturing Company, San Marcos, TX; *U.S. Private*, pg. 1080
Baer, Bill, V.P.-H.R.--Associated Merchandising Corp. (AMC), New York, NY; *U.S. Private*, pg. 91
Baffa, Cheryl, Mgr.-Human Resources--Rainbow Technologies, Inc., Irvine, CA; *U.S. Public*, pg. 1359
Baggio, Bruce L., V.P.-Human Resources--Mississippi Lime Co., Alton, IL; *U.S. Private*, pg. 753
Baggott, Tim, Dir.-Human Resources--Willis Corroon Group PLC, London, United Kingdom; *Int'l*, pg. 1501
Bailey, Cindee, V.P.-H.R.--The Climatic Corp., Columbia, SC; *U.S. Private*, pg. 246
Bailey, Leon, Sr. V.P. & Dir.-Store Opers.--AVC/Nu-Vision, Inc., Flint, MI; *U.S. Private*, pg. 9
Bailey, Lydia J., Dir.-Personnel--Erving Paper Mills, Inc., Erving, MA; *U.S. Private*, pg. 382
Bailey, Richard T., V.P.-H.R.--The Ward Machinery Company, Hunt Valley, MD; *U.S. Private*, pg. 1149
Bailey, Rose, V.P.-Corp. Human Relations--County Seat Stores, Inc., Dallas, TX; *U.S. Private*, pg. 279
Bailey, William D., Dir.-H.R.--National Forge Company, Irvine, PA; *U.S. Private*, pg. 783
Baileys, C. Neal, V.P.-Human Resources--Hobart Corporation, Troy, OH; *U.S. Public*, pg. 1322
Baker, Carol S., Dir.-Human Resources--Day & Zimmermann International, Inc., Philadelphia, PA; *U.S. Private*, pg. 317
Baker, David, Mgr.-H.R.--Labelon Corporation, Canandaigua, NY; *U.S. Private*, pg. 641
Baker, Dennis, V.P.-Human Resources--CertainTeed Corporation, Valley Forge, PA; *Int'l*, pg. 1170
Baker, Dennis J., V.P.-Human Resources-Abrasives--Norton Company, Worcester, MA; *Int'l*, pg. 1173
Baker, Diane, Mgr.-H.R.--J.W. Allen & Company, Wheeling, IL; *U.S. Private*, pg. 37
Baker, Gary, Dir.-Personnel--Standard Candy Co., Inc., Nashville, TN; *U.S. Private*, pg. 1030
Baker, Ingrid, Mgr.-H.R.--L.R. Nelson Corporation, Peoria, IL; *U.S. Private*, pg. 790
Baker, Larry, V.P.-Corp. Services & Human Resources--Kinetic Concepts, Inc., San Antonio, TX; *U.S. Private*, pg. 620
Baker, Larry, V.P.-Human Resources--National Machinery, Tiffin, OH; *U.S. Private*, pg. 785
Baker, Laurie L., V.P.-Employer Rels.--Paccar Inc., Bellevue, WA; *U.S. Public*, pg. 1246
Baker, Lew, Human Resources--Cracker Jack Division, Northbrook, IL; *U.S. Private*, pg. 157
Baker, Michael, Gen. Mgr.-H.R. & Office Svcs.--Sun Life and Provincial Holdings plc, London, United Kingdom; *Int'l*, pg. 1318

Baker, Patricia, Mgr.-H.R.--Planning Systems Inc., Mc Lean, VA; *U.S. Private*, pg. 869
Baker, Randy, V.P.-Human Resources--Resort Condominiums International, Indianapolis, IN; *U.S. Public*, pg. 322
Baker, Reid, Dir.-Personnel--Parkdale Mills, Gastonia, NC; *U.S. Private*, pg. 840
Baker, Russ, Dir.-Personnel--Interstate Bakeries Corporation, Kansas City, MO; *U.S. Public*, pg. 909
Baker, Sam, Mgr.-H.R.--Norfolk Shipbuilding & Drydock Corporation, Norfolk, VA; *U.S. Private*, pg. 802
Baker, William D., Dir.-H.R.--E Z Loader Corporate, Airway Heights, WA; *U.S. Private*, pg. 352
Bakken, Lisa, Mgr.-Human Resources--The Rottlund Company, Inc., Roseville, MN; *U.S. Public*, pg. 1406
Baldwin, Richard, Dir.-H.R.--CENEX, Inc., Inver Grove Heights, MN; *U.S. Private*, pg. 221
Balestrino, Earlene P., V.P. & Mgr.-Human Resources--FirstMerit Corporation, Akron, OH; *U.S. Public*, pg. 646
Ball, Jo Ann, Dir.-H.R.--Magellan Aerospace Corporation, Mississauga, Canada; *Int'l*, pg. 829
Ballantyne, John, Mgr.-Human Resources--Fenn Manufacturing Co., Newington, CT; *U.S. Public*, pg. 1676
Ballard, Calvin A., Sr. V.P.-Human Resources--Citizens Savings Bank, Providence, RI; *Int'l*, pg. 1132
Ballard, Georganne, Dir.-Human Resources--Semtech Corporation, Newbury Park, CA; *U.S. Public*, pg. 1456
Balog, Pamela, Mgr.-Personnel--The Hilsinger Co. L.P., Plainville, MA; *U.S. Private*, pg. 530
Balser, Bobbi, Personnel--The National Super Service Co., Toledo, OH; *U.S. Private*, pg. 787
Banbury, Gary, V.P.-H.R.--Coeur D'Alene Mines Corporation, Coeur D'Alene, ID; *U.S. Public*, pg. 394
Bankowski, Dennis R., Sr. V.P.-Human Resources--American National Can Company, Chicago, IL; *Int'l*, pg. 1029
Bankowski, Elizabeth, Sr. Dir.-Social Mission--Ben & Jerry's Homemade Inc., South Burlington, VT; *U.S. Public*, pg. 210
Banks, Arthur, Sr. V.P.-H.R.--Blue Cross and Blue Shield of Massachusetts, Boston, MA; *U.S. Private*, pg. 151
Banks, Bob D., Dir.-Employee Benefits--Florida Rock Industries, Inc., Jacksonville, FL; *U.S. Public*, pg. 655
Banks, Glen B., V.P. & Dir.-H.R./Risk Mngmt.--Forever Living Products International, Inc., Scottsdale, AZ; *U.S. Private*, pg. 418
Banks, Jerry, Dir.-H.R.--Ingles Markets, Incorporated, Black Mountain, NC; *U.S. Public*, pg. 878
Banner, Darrell, Mgr.-Personnel--Garst Seed Company, Slater, IA; *Int'l*, pg. 1524
Bannister, M.A., Dir.-Human Resources--Sonoco Ltd., Brantford, Canada; *U.S. Public*, pg. 1487
Banucci, Phyllis, Mgr.-Human Resources--ATMI, Inc., Danbury, CT; *U.S. Public*, pg. 12
Banyon, Hilda, First V.P. & Dir.-Personnel--Shoreline Financial Corp., Benton Harbor, MI; *U.S. Public*, pg. 1467
Banyon, Hilda L., First V.P. & Dir.-Personnel--Shoreline Bank, Benton Harbor, MI; *U.S. Public*, pg. 1468
Baranello, Alane, V.P.-H.R.--Ogden Corporation, New York, NY; *U.S. Public*, pg. 1213
Baravik, Andrew W., V.P.-Human Resources--Quality Stores Inc., Muskegon, MI; *U.S. Private*, pg. 899
Barawed, Mark A., V.P. & Mgr.-Human Resources--Stockton Savings Bank, Stockton, CA; *U.S. Public*, pg. 1575
Barber, Cheryl, V.P.-Human Resources--Saskatchewan Government Insurance, SGI, Regina, Canada; *Int'l*, pg. 1195
Barber, Debbie, V.P. & Sec.--Denver Wholesale Florists Company, Denver, CO; *U.S. Private*, pg. 326
Barber, Deborah, V.P.-Human Resources--Quantum Corporation, Milpitas, CA; *U.S. Public*, pg. 1350
Barclay, Don, Dir.-H.R.--Affiliated Foods, Inc., Amarillo, TX; *U.S. Private*, pg. 25
Barclay, Gerald, Mgr.-Human Resources--Transamerican Natural Gas Corporation, Houston, TX; *U.S. Private*, pg. 1096
Bard, Dennis, Dir.-H.R.--James Austin Co., Mars, PA; *U.S. Private*, pg. 99
Bareilles, Nancy M., V.P.-Worldwide Real Estate & Workplace Resources--Cisco Systems, Inc., San Jose, CA; *U.S. Public*, pg. 375
Barger, James F., Personnel Mgr.--Koppel Steel Corp., Beaver Falls, PA; *U.S. Public*, pg. 1147
Barker, Dan, Dir.-H.R.--Akzo Nobel Inc., Chicago, IL; *Int'l*, pg. 47
Barker, James, Mgr.-H.R.--Office Products Division, Brattleboro, VT; *U.S. Public*, pg. 620
Barker, Ray, V.P.-H.R.--The Georgia Marble Company, Kennesaw, GA; *U.S. Private*, pg. 448
Barkley, Richard, Dir.-Human Resources--Imperial Bancorp, Inglewood, CA; *U.S. Public*, pg. 871
Barlow, Sally, Mgr.-H.R.--Right Management Consultants, Inc., Philadelphia, PA; *U.S. Public*, pg. 1390
Barnard, John G., Dir.-Human Resources--Harrisons & Crosfield plc, London, United Kingdom; *Int'l*, pg. 598
Barnes, Deborah, Dir.-H.R.--George Lithograph, Brisbane, CA; *U.S. Private*, pg. 448
Barnes, Dick, Dir.-Human Resources--Boeing Aerospace Operations, Cocoa Beach, FL; *U.S. Public*, pg. 241
Barnes, Jesse, Dir.-Corp. Personnel--Commercial Metals Company, Dallas, TX; *U.S. Public*, pg. 411
Barnes, JoAnne, Mgr.-H.R.--Rent-Way, Inc., Erie, PA; *U.S. Public*, pg. 1377
Barnett, F.M., V.P.-Personnel--SmithKline Beecham Laboratories, Bristol, TN; *Int'l*, pg. 1264
Barnett, Sharon, Mgr.-H.R.--Package Service Company, LLC., Kansas City, MO; *U.S. Private*, pg. 833
Barnett, Todd, V.P.-Admin.--PAXAR Corporation, White Plains, NY; *U.S. Public*, pg. 1266
Barney, Roger, V.P.-Human Res.--Network Equipment Technologies, Inc., Redwood City, CA; *U.S. Public*, pg. 1168
Barnick, Florence C., Dir.-H.R.--The Free Lance-Star Publishing Co., Fredericksburg, VA; *U.S. Private*, pg. 424
Baron, Peter L., V.P.-Human Resources--Searle & Co., Skokie, IL; *U.S. Public*, pg. 1125
Baron, Sandra, V.P.-Human Resources--E-Z-Em, Inc., Westbury, NY; *U.S. Public*, pg. 540
Barr, Arthur, Dir.-Human Resources--NDS, Columbus, OH; *Int'l*, pg. 918
Barr, Daniel C., Exec. V.P.-Human Resources--First USA, Inc., Dallas, TX; *U.S. Public*, pg. 174
Barr, Ian, Mgr.-Human Resources--Scholl Plc, Newton, United Kingdom; *Int'l*, pg. 1209
Barr, L., Dir.-Human Resources--American Cast Iron Pipe Co., Birmingham, AL; *U.S. Private*, pg. 51
Barr, Roy S., V.P.-Human Resources--Chandler Evans Control Systems Division, West Hartford, CT; *U.S. Public*, pg. 401
Barrenchea, Linda, Dir.-Human Resources--Porsche Cars North America, Inc., Reno, NV; *Int'l*, pg. 1063
Barrera, Sylvia, Dir.-H.R.--Academy Corporation, Katy, TX; *U.S. Private*, pg. 11
Barret, Hilary, Dir.-Human Resources--Media 100, Inc., Marlborough, MA; *U.S. Public*, pg. 1079
Barrett, Elisabeth H., V.P.- Human Resources & Mngmt. Information Systems--Ikon Office Solutions, Inc., Malvern, PA; *U.S. Public*, pg. 862
Barrett, William W., V.P. & Dir.-Employee Rels.--ITT Gilfillan, Van Nuys, CA; *U.S. Public*, pg. 859
Barrington, Kelly, Dir.-Human Resources--McKesson U.S. Health Care, San Francisco, CA; *U.S. Public*, pg. 1073
Barron, Mabel, Admin.-Human Resources--WJZ-TV, Baltimore, MD; *U.S. Public*, pg. 275
Barry, David, Dir.-Human Resources--Syratech Corporation, East Boston, MA; *U.S. Private*, pg. 1060
Barry, Doug, V.P.-Human Resources--Rinker Materials Corp., West Palm Beach, FL; *Int'l*, pg. 246
Barry, June B., V.P.-H.R. & Admin.--BetzDearborn Inc., Trevose, PA; *U.S. Public*, pg. 226
Barry, Wes, Dir.-Human Resources--ELX Group, Wichita Falls, TX; *Int'l*, pg. 439
Barsalou, Gerry, V.P.-H.R.--Agra Inc., Calgary, Canada; *Int'l*, *pg. 30*
Barsilay, N., Dir.-Personnel--Elbit Computers Ltd., Haifa, Israel; *Int'l*, pg. 644
Barson, Janice, Dir.-Human Resources--Baxter Research Medical, Inc., Midvale, UT; *U.S. Public*, pg. 196
Bartels, Debbie, V.P.-Personnel & Admin.--Seigle's Home & Building Centers, Elgin, IL; *U.S. Private*, pg. 981
Barthel, Dale R., Mgr.-Human Resources--Frigidaire Home Products-Freezer Products, Saint Cloud, MN; *Int'l*, pg. 440
Barthlow, A.C., Mgr.-Matl.--Lancaster Glass Corporation, Lancaster, OH; *U.S. Public*, pg. 977
Bartholomew, Leonard W., Sec. & Dir.-Personnel--Frozen Food Express Industries, Inc., Dallas, TX; *U.S. Public*, pg. 685
Bartlett, Mary, Mgr.-H.R.--Enidine Incorporated, Orchard Park, NY; *U.S. Private*, pg. 377
Bartley, Joyce, Mgr.-Human Resources--South Bend Plastics, Inc., Mishawaka, IN; *U.S. Private*, pg. 1014
Bartnett, John C., V.P.-H.R. & Labor Rels.--J.S. Alberici Construction Co., Inc., Saint Louis, MO; *U.S. Private*, pg. 32
Barto, Chris, Mgr.-H.R.--Colad Group Inc., Buffalo, NY; *U.S. Private*, pg. 250
Barton, Charlotte, Dir.-H.R.--Barton Malow Enterprises, Inc., Southfield, MI; *U.S. Private*, pg. 120
Barton, Mike, V.P.-H.R. & Admin.--NGC Corporation, Houston, TX; *U.S. Public*, pg. 1146
Barton, Paul, Dir.-Human Resources--The Geon Company, Avon Lake, OH; *U.S. Public*, pg. 733
Barton, R.K., Sr. V.P.-Human Resources--Simmons Company, Atlanta, GA; *Int'l*, pg. 686
Barz, Peter, Dir.-Personnel--Deutsche Unilever Gmbh, Hamburg, Germany; *Int'l*, pg. 1436
Baseman, Jerrie, Dir.-Personnel--Sutter Auburn Faith Community Hospital, Auburn, CA; *U.S. Private*, pg. 1057
Baskerville, Lark, V.P. & Human Resources Dir.--Rubin Postaer & Associates, Santa Monica, CA; *U.S. Private*, pg. 949
Baskerville, Theresa J., Dir.-Personnel--American Systems Corporation, Chantilly, VA; *U.S. Private*, pg. 63
Baskey, Jim, V.P.-Employee Rels.--Climate & Industrial Controls Group, Cleveland, OH; *U.S. Public*, pg. 1260
Basso, Robert A., V.P.-Personnel--Dassault Falcon Jet Corp., South Hackensack, NJ; *Int'l*, pg. 383
Bastiannelli, Ann, V.P.-Trng. & Devel.--Ikon Office Solutions-Indiana, Indianapolis, IN; *U.S. Public*, pg. 863
Batal, Ann P. Larkin, Dir.-Human Resource Devel.--Biogen, Inc., Cambridge, MA; *U.S. Public*, pg. 230
Bates, Arlene, V.P.-Human Resources--John H. Harland Company, Decatur, GA; *U.S. Public*, pg. 785
Bates, Arlene, V.P. Human Resources--The Check Store, Lakewood, CO; *U.S. Public*, pg. 785
Bates, Bonnie, Mgr.-Human Resources--Columbus Show Case Company, Columbus, OH; *U.S. Private*, pg. 257
Bates, Mike, Dir.-Personnel--Remmele Engineering, Inc., New Brighton, MN; *U.S. Private*, pg. 921
Bateson, S.L., Mgr.-Personnel--Salford Electrical Instruments Ltd., Heywood, United Kingdom; *Int'l*, pg. 545
Batista, Carlos, Mgr.-H.R.--Central de Cervejas, S.A., Lisbon, Portugal; *Int'l*, pg. 279
Battersby, George, Dir.-Human Resources--Laporte plc, Luton, United Kingdom; *Int'l*, pg. 801
Battino, Jesse, V.P.-H.R.--Sequa Corporation, New York, NY; *U.S. Public*, pg. 1458
Battista, R., Dir.-Personnel--Stebbins Engineering & Mfg. Co., Watertown, NY; *U.S. Private*, pg. 1037
Battle, Dick E., V.P.-Human Resources--Nissan Motor Corporation in U.S.A., Gardena, CA; *Int'l*, pg. 945
Baucom, Ed, V.P.-H.R.--Stewart Enterprises, Inc., Metairie, LA; *U.S. Public*, pg. 1518
Baudoin, Jean, Sr. V.P.-H.R.--Credit Commercial de France, Paris, France; *Int'l*, pg. 341
Bauer, Patti, Dir.-Human Resources--Penn Champ, East Butler, PA; *U.S. Private*, pg. 145
Baughman, Robert M., V.P.-H.R.--Tektronix, Inc., Wilsonville, OR; *U.S. Public*, pg. 1567
Bauman, Marnie, Exec. Dir.-Human Resources--Careers USA Inc., Philadelphia, PA; *U.S. Private*, pg. 209
Baumgartner, Chuck, V.P.-Human Resources--Seaway Food Town, Inc., Maumee, OH; *U.S. Public*, pg. 1452
Baxter, Beverly, Mgr.-Personnel--IGI, Inc., Buena, NJ; *U.S. Public*, pg. 855
Baxter, Maureen, Mgr.-Human Resources--FINNAIR, New York, NY; *Int'l*, pg. 485
Bays, Barry, Dir.-Human Resources--Xomed Surgical Products, Jacksonville, FL; *U.S. Public*, pg. 253
Bazelides, Philip J., V.P.-Human Resources--Enron Corp., Houston, TX; *U.S. Public*, pg. 584
Bazemore, Edward F., V.P.-Human Resources--CalEnergy Co., Omaha, NE; *U.S. Public*, pg. 292
Beach, Lani L., V.P.-Human Resources--M.A. Hanna Company, Cleveland, OH; *U.S. Public*, pg. 780
Beach, Nancy, V.P.-Human Resources--Bel Air Markets, West Sacramento, CA; *U.S. Private*, pg. 908
Beadles, Jane, V.P.-Human Resources--Mosby-Year Book, Inc., Saint Louis, MO; *U.S. Public*, pg. 1616
Beagle, Fred, Dir.-Personnel--Progressive Tool & Industries Co., Southfield, MI; *U.S. Private*, pg. 890
Beal, David, V.P.-Human Resources--Renfro Corp., Mount Airy, NC; *U.S. Private*, pg. 922
Beale, R. Michelle, Sr. V.P.-H.R., Pub. Affairs & Admin. Svcs.--The Minute Maid Company, Houston, TX; *U.S. Public*, pg. 392
Beall, Katherine, V.P.-Human Resources--VeriFone, Inc., Redwood City, CA; *U.S. Public*, pg. 815
Beam, Diane S., Dir.-H.R.--The Commercial Bank, Delphos, OH; *U.S. Public*, pg. 410
Beasley, Deborah, Dir.-H.R.--Sunrise Medical, Inc., Carlsbad, CA; *U.S. Public*, pg. 1535
Beasley, Gary, Asst. V.P.--E.C. Barton & Company, Jonesboro, AR; *U.S. Private*, pg. 119
Beasley, John H., Sr. V.P.-Personnel & Admin.--The Pepper Companies, Inc., Chicago, IL; *U.S. Private*, pg. 851
Beath, Cathy, V.P. & Human Resources Dir.--Moroch & Assoc., Inc., Dallas, TX; *U.S. Private*, pg. 762
Beaton, William T., V.P.-H.R. & Customer Svcs.--Essex County Gas Company, Amesbury, MA; *U.S. Public*, pg. 593
Beattie, Don, Chief Exec.-Personnel--The BOC Group plc, Windlesham, United Kingdom; *Int'l*, pg. 121
Beauchamp, Bill, Dir.-H.R.--Shivers Trading & Operating Co., Augusta, GA; *U.S. Private*, pg. 994
Beauchamp, Bill, Dir.-Human Resources--Morris Communications Corporation, Augusta, GA; *U.S. Private*, *pg. 995*
Beauchamp, Carol, V.P.-Human Resources--Datawatch Corporation, Wilmington, MA; *U.S. Public*, pg. 488
Beaudoin, Ken, Dir.-Personnel--World Carpets, Inc., Dalton, GA; *U.S. Private*, pg. 1190
Beaudry, Jackie, Dir.-H.R.--Chr. Hansen, Inc., Milwaukee, WI; *Int'l*, pg. 288
Beavais, Robert, Chief Fin. Officer--Austin Group, Flint, MI; *U.S. Private*, pg. 99
Beberus, John, Dir.-Personnel--Pennsylvania Enterprises Inc., Wilkes-Barre, PA; *U.S. Public*, pg. 1271
Beccaro, Barbara, Mgr.-Pub. Rels.--The Swiss Life/ Rentenanstalt Group, Zurich, Switzerland; *Int'l*, pg. 1332
Becella, Joyce, Dir.-H.R.--J.H. Roberts Industries Inc., Des Plaines, IL; *U.S. Private*, pg. 935
Bechtel, Barrie, V.P.-Human Resources--Rapistan Demag Corp., Grand Rapids, MI; *Int'l*, pg. 837
Beck, Barbara, V.P.-Human Resources--Cisco Systems, Inc., San Jose, CA; *U.S. Public*, pg. 375
Beck, Jo Ann, V.P.-H.R.--Lyondell Petrochemical Company, Houston, TX; *U.S. Public*, pg. 1022
Beck, Robert N., Sr. V.P.-Corp. Human Resources--Gateway 2000, North Sioux City, SD; *U.S. Public*, pg. 703
Becker, H.S., V.P.-Human Resources--American Meter Company, Horsham, PA; *Int'l*, pg. 1149
Becker, Hugh E., Dir.-Corp. Communications--Robbins & Myers, Inc., Dayton, OH; *U.S. Public*, pg. 1393
Becker, Hugo, V.P.-Personnel--Union Underwear Co., Inc., Bowling Green, KY; *U.S. Public*, pg. 686
Becker, Linda, Dir.-H.R.--Pedus Services, Inc., Los Angeles, CA; *U.S. Private*, pg. 846
Beckett, Marcia, Personnel--Cassano's Inc., Dayton, OH; *U.S. Private*, pg. 218
Beckman, Erik, Sr. V.P.-Human Resources--Nykredit, Copenhagen, Denmark; *Int'l*, pg. 993
Beckman, Jerry, Dir.-Human Resources--Flying J. Inc., Brigham City, UT; *U.S. Private*, pg. 415
Beckman, Judy, Dir.-Human Resources--Houck Industries, Inc., Visalia, CA; *U.S. Private*, pg. 541
Beckstett, Douglas, V.P.-Human Resources--A.P.S., Memphis, TN; *U.S. Public*, pg. 10
Beckwith, Margaret, Dir.-Personnel--J.L. Hammett Company, Braintree, MA; *U.S. Private*, pg. 498
Bedard, Normand, V.P.-H.R.--Cambior Inc., Montreal, Canada; *Int'l*, pg. 253
Bedard, Steven A., V.P.-Human Resources--The May Department Stores Company, Saint Louis, MO; *U.S. Public*, pg. 1063
Bedford, A., Dir.-Personnel--Magnetek Motors & Generators, Saint Louis, MO; *U.S. Public*, pg. 1037
Bedford, Steve, Dir.-Human Resources--BHS Plc, London, United Kingdom; *Int'l*, pg. 1304
Beecher, R., Dir.-Personnel--L.B. Smith, Inc., Camp Hill, PA; *U.S. Private*, pg. 1009
Beelen, Caryn, Mgr.-H.R.--Arrington Travel Center Inc., Chicago, IL; *U.S. Private*, pg. 85
Beer, Susan, V.P.-H.R.--Skyway Freight Systems, Inc., Watsonville, CA; *U.S. Private*, pg. 1005

Begert, Jane, V.P.-Human Rels.--Guy Gannett Communications, Portland, ME; *U.S. Private*, pg. 439
Begley, Carol, Dir.-Human Resources--Four-S Baking Company, Los Angeles, CA; *U.S. Private*, pg. 422
Beglinger, Viktor, Exec. V.P.-Sulzer Infra Group--Sulzer Ltd., Winterthur, Switzerland; *Int'l*, pg. 1305
Behan, John, Dir.-H.R.--Aer Lingus, Dublin, Ireland; *Int'l*, pg. 28
Behr, Cynthia, Mgr.-Human Resources & Admin.--Time Systems, Inc., Phoenix, AZ; *U.S. Private*, pg. 1086
Behrens, Mike, Dir.-Human Resources--Pulp & Paper Div., Mosinee, WI; *U.S. Public*, pg. 1747
Beilfuss, Bob, V.P.-H.R. & Admin.--Transilwrap Company, Inc., Chicago, IL; *U.S. Private*, pg. 1097
Beker, R. E., V.P.-Human Resources-Cub & Intl.--Carlton & United Breweries Ltd., Southbank, Australia; *Int'l*, pg. 500
Bekes, Michael J., Chief Oper. Officer & V.P.--Badger Paper Mills, Inc., Peshtigo, WI; *U.S. Public*, pg. 165
Beland, Randy, Mgr.-H.R.--New England Frozen Foods, Inc., Southborough, MA; *U.S. Private*, pg. 793
Belcher, Debbie, Human Resources Dir.--American Television Time, Inc., Austin, TX; *U.S. Private*, pg. 63
Belford, Kim, Dir.-H.R.--PharMerica, Inc., Tampa, FL; *U.S. Public*, pg. 1286
Beliunas, Linda, Mgr.-H.R.--GHM Industries, Inc., Worcester, MA; *U.S. Private*, pg. 435
Bell, Allen W., Sr. V.P.-H.R.--The Toronto Dominion Bank, Toronto, Canada; *Int'l*, pg. 1401
Bell, Donna M., V.P. & Dir.-Human Resources--ABM Industries, San Francisco, CA; *U.S. Public*, pg. 2
Bell, Ernie, V.P.-H.R.--Wakefern Food Corporation, Elizabeth, NJ; *U.S. Private*, pg. 1146
Bell, Judy, Dir.-Personnel--George S. May International Company, Park Ridge, IL; *U.S. Private*, pg. 717
Bell, L., Mgr.-Human Resources--Beaird Industries, Inc., Shreveport, LA; *U.S. Public*, pg. 1639
Bell, Peter J., Mgr.-Human Resources--BHP Manganese, Melbourne, Australia; *Int'l*, pg. 224
Bell, Steven F., V.P.-Human Resources & Organizational Devel.--COMSAT Corporation, Bethesda, MD; *U.S. Public*, pg. 424
Bell, Vilma M., V.P.-H.R.--S & C Electric Company, Chicago, IL; *U.S. Private*, pg. 954
Bellatti, Charles, V.P.-Human Resources--Le Tourneau, Inc., Longview, TX; *U.S. Public*, pg. 1410
Bellemare, Kathleen, Dir.-H.R.--Connecticut Spring & Stamping Corporation, Farmington, CT; *U.S. Private*, pg. 263
Belton, Nancy, Dir.-Human Resources--Radionics, Inc., Salinas, CA; *U.S. Public*, pg. 501
Ben-Asher, Ze'ev, Sr. Deputy Mng. Dir.-H.R.--Bank Hapoalim, Tel Aviv, Israel; *Int'l*, pg. 149
Benard, Sue, V.P.-Admin. & Human Resources--National Energy Group, Inc., Dallas, TX; *U.S. Public*, pg. 1156
Benedict, D., Mgr.-Indus. Rels.--Organon Inc., West Orange, NJ; *Int'l*, pg. 48
Benedict, Judy, Dir.-Personnel--A&M Records, Hollywood, CA; *Int'l*, pg. 1052
Benedict, Vincent P.A., Sr. Dir.-Personnel--Henkels & McCoy, Inc., Blue Bell, PA; *U.S. Private*, pg. 522
Benish, Clayton, Mgr.-H.R.--Lake Region Manufacturing, Inc., Chaska, MN; *U.S. Private*, pg. 643
Benjamin, F.L., V.P.-Pur., Opers., Personnel & Data Processing--Morris Kirschman & Company, Inc., New Orleans, LA; *U.S. Private*, pg. 623
Benjamin, Gerry, Sr. V.P.-H.R. & Admin.--Henry Schein, Inc., Melville, NY; *U.S. Public*, pg. 1437
Benjamini, Haim, V.P.-Human Resources--Teva Pharmaceutical Industries Ltd., Petah Tiqwa, Israel; *Int'l*, pg. 1380
Benn, Jerry, Dir.-H.R.--Brother International Corporation, Somerset, NJ; *Int'l*, pg. 229
Bennett, Arthur C., Chief Human Res. Officer & Exec. V.P.--The Dime Savings Bank of New York, New York, NY; *U.S. Public*, pg. 509
Bennett, Barbara, Mgr.-H.R.--Arizona Wholesale Supply Company, Phoenix, AZ; *U.S. Private*, pg. 82
Bennett, Dan, Asst. Controller--Levlad, Inc., Chatsworth, CA; *U.S. Private*, pg. 663
Bennett, John, V.P.-Human Resources--Crown Vantage Inc., Oakland, CA; *U.S. Public*, pg. 465
Bennett, Monty C., V.P.-Employee Rels. & Corp. Sec.--Hastings Manufacturing Company, Hastings, MI; *U.S. Public*, pg. 798
Bennett, Sondra, Dir.-Human Resources--Amos-Hill Associates, Inc., Edinburgh, IN; *U.S. Private*, pg. 67
Benninger, Patricia A., Sr. V.P.-Human Resources--Great Western Bank, Chatsworth, CA; *U.S. Public*, pg. 1741
Bennyhoff, George R., Sr. V.P.-Human Resources & Pub. Affairs--The West Company, Incorporated, Lionville, PA; *U.S. Public*, pg. 1755
Bensel, Norbert, Dr., Dir.-Personnel--Daimler-Benz Aerospace AG, Munich, Germany; *Int'l*, pg. 367
Bensimon, Raquel, Pres. & Chief Fin. Officer--Dearden's, Los Angeles, CA; *U.S. Private*, pg. 319
Benson, Bonnie, Dir.-Human Resources--Bachman's, Inc., Minneapolis, MN; *U.S. Private*, pg. 109
Benson, Donald T., V.P.-Human Resources & Admin.--Coventry Corporation, Nashville, TN; *U.S. Public*, pg. 454
Benson, Gary, Mgr.-Personnel--Pendleton Woolen Mills, Inc., Portland, OR; *U.S. Private*, pg. 848
Benson, J., Mgr.-Human Resources--Pilkington Plc, Saint Helens, United Kingdom; *Int'l*, pg. 1056
Benson, Jean, Dir.-H.R.--Cannondale Corporation, Bethel, CT; *U.S. Public*, pg. 301
Benson, Ramona, Dir.-H.R.--Automobile Protection Corporation-APCO, Atlanta, GA; *U.S. Public*, pg. 150
Benson, Shirley, Mgr.-Personnel--Duro-Test Corporation, Fairfield, NJ; *U.S. Private*, pg. 349
Bensyl, William, Sr. V.P.-Personnel--PepsiCo, Inc., Purchase, NY; *U.S. Public*, pg. 1276
Bentley, Brian, Grp. Dir.-Global H.R.--Reckitt & Colman plc, London, United Kingdom; *Int'l*, pg. 1089
Bentley, Larry, V.P.-Human Resources--Recoton Auto Corporation, Lincolnshire, IL; *U.S. Public*, pg. 1369
Benton, Murray, Treas. & Dir.-Personnel--Mid South Sales, Helena, AR; *U.S. Private*, pg. 744
Berard, Deborah W., V.P.-H.R. & Admin. Services--Collagen Corporation, Palo Alto, CA; *U.S. Public*, pg. 399
Berchelmann, Kevin, Dir.-H.R.--Gundle/SLT Environmental, Inc., Houston, TX; *U.S. Public*, pg. 769
Berdusco, John, V.P.-Admin.--St. Jude Medical, Inc., Saint Paul, MN; *U.S. Public*, pg. 1427
Berg, Deborah L., V.P.-Human Resources--Union Insurance Company, Lincoln, NE; *U.S. Public*, pg. 216
Berg, Erik, V.P.-H.R.--BT Industries AB, Mjolby, Sweden; *Int'l*, pg. 123
Berg, Jennifer N., V.P.-H.R.--Al Neyer, Inc., Cincinnati, OH; *U.S. Private*, pg. 797
Berg, Robert M., V.P.-H.R.--HNTB Corporation, Kansas City, MO; *U.S. Private*, pg. 492
Berg, Steven L., V.P.-Investments & Human Resources--Millers Mutual Insurance Assn., Alton, IL; *U.S. Private*, pg. 748
Berg, Thomas C., V.P.-Personnel, Gen. Counsel & Sec.--Amsted Industries Incorporated, Chicago, IL; *U.S. Private*, pg. 68
Berge, Nils, Mgr.-Personnel--Kaldnes Heavy Lift Trucks, Tonsberg, Norway; *Int'l*, pg. 965
Berge, W.M., Dir.-Indus. Rels.--The Kerite Company, Seymour, CT; *U.S. Public*, pg. 844
Bergeman, Richard P., Sr. V.P.-Human Resources--Bestfoods, Englewood Cliffs, NJ; *U.S. Public*, pg. 223
Berger, George, V.P.-H.R.--Tandy Corporation, Fort Worth, TX; *U.S. Public*, pg. 1560
Bergeron, Paul D., Sr. V.P. & Dir.-Human Resources--Whitney Holding Corporation, New Orleans, LA; *U.S. Public*, pg. 1766
Bergeson, Margo R., Corp. Sec.--Alta Gold Co., Henderson, NV; *U.S. Public*, pg. 58
Bergeson, Scott, Sr. V.P.-Human Resources--American Stores Company, Salt Lake City, UT; *U.S. Public*, pg. 92
Berggren, Debra, Mgr.-H.R.--Oriel Instruments Corporation, Stratford, CT; *U.S. Private*, pg. 819
Bergholtz-Widell, Curt, Sr. V.P.-Human Resources & Security--Vattenfall AB, Stockholm, Sweden; *Int'l*, pg. 1452
Bergougnoux, G., Coord.-H.R.--Danone Group, Paris, France; *Int'l*, pg. 379
Bergstedt, Lennart, Sr. V.P.-Personnel--Trelleborg AB, Trelleborg, Sweden; *Int'l*, pg. 1419
Bergsteinsson, Bryan, V.P.-Human Resources--Toyota Motor Sales, U.S.A., Inc., Torrance, CA; *Int'l*, pg. 1412
Berke, Richard, V.P.-Human Resources--Automatic Data Processing, Inc., Roseland, NJ; *U.S. Public*, pg. 150
Berker, Teri, Dir.-H.R.--Ronco, Inventions. LLC, Chatsworth, CA; *U.S. Private*, pg. 943
Berkes, Judith, Mgr.-H.R.--Deck House Inc., Acton, MA; *U.S. Private*, pg. 320
Berkes, Judith, Mgr.-Human Resources--Acorn Structures, Acton, MA; *U.S. Private*, pg. 320
Berkovitz, Lesley M., V.P.-Human Resources--Sunglass Hut International, Coral Gables, FL; *U.S. Public*, pg. 1535
Berkovitz, Lewis, Mgr.-Human Resources--Interactive Technologies, Inc., Saint Paul, MN; *U.S. Public*, pg. 888
Bernard, Jean A., V.P.-Personnel--Bell Canada, Montreal, Canada; *Int'l*, pg. 115
Bernath, Donna, Mgr.-H.R.--Colonial Beef Co., Philadelphia, PA; *U.S. Private*, pg. 253
Berridge, Steve, Mgr.-Personnel--Kruger Inc., Montreal, Canada; *Int'l*, pg. 761
Berry, Dana, Dir.-H.R.--Solon Manufacturing Company, Solon, ME; *U.S. Private*, pg. 1013
Berry, Dorothy Hamachi, V.P.-Human Resouces--The World Bank, Washington, DC; *U.S. Private*, pg. 1188
Berry, Sandra W., Mgr.-H.R. & Office Admin.--Kentucky Medical Insurance Company (KMIC), Louisville, KY; *U.S. Private*, pg. 741
Berry, Susan D., Sec.--Arizona Instrument Corporation, Phoenix, AZ; *U.S. Public*, pg. 129
Berryhill, Dennis G., V.P.-H.R.--Galveston-Houston Company, Houston, TX; *U.S. Private*, pg. 438
Berryman, Erin, Mgr.-Trng.--Grease Monkey International Inc., Denver, CO; *U.S. Public*, pg. 759
Bertsch, Don, Dir.-Personnel & Office Admin.--Ludlow Composites Corporation, Fremont, OH; *U.S. Private*, pg. 680
Bertuccini, John A., V.P.-Human Resources--Quebecor Printing, Inc., Montreal, Canada; *Int'l*, pg. 1076
Berube, Alain, Dir.-Personnel--Aliments Flamingo, Iberville, Canada; *Int'l*, pg. 57
Berwald, Joanne, Dir.-Personnel--DHP Limited Partnership, Chicopee, MA; *U.S. Private*, pg. 302
Besch, William, Chief Learning & Resource Officer & V.P.--Crawford & Company, Atlanta, GA; *U.S. Public*, pg. 458
Bessant, Thomas A., Jr., Chief Fin. Officer, Sr. V.P. & Treas.--Cash America International, Inc., Fort Worth, TX; *U.S. Public*, pg. 312
Bethell, Benjamin L., Sr. V.P.-Human Resources--The Procter & Gamble Company, Cincinnati, OH; *U.S. Public*, pg. 1330
Betts, Murray, Jr., Dir.-Personnel--STRAFCO, Inc., San Antonio, TX; *U.S. Private*, pg. 1046
Bevilagua, D., Mgr.-Human Resources--American Welding & Manufacturing Co., Warren, OH; *U.S. Private*, pg. 425
Bey, David, Mgr.-Human Resources--McCauley Propeller Systems, Vandalia, OH; *U.S. Public*, pg. 1589
Beyerl, Bill, Dir.-Human Resources--Today's Man, Inc., Moorestown, NJ; *U.S. Public*, pg. 1619
Bezalel, Yohaman, Exec. V.P.-Human Resources--The Israel Electric Corporation Ltd., Haifa, Israel; *Int'l*, pg. 690
Biale, Patricia, Mgr.-Personnel Services--Bestfoods, Englewood Cliffs, NJ; *U.S. Public*, pg. 223
Bianchi, Frank C., Sr. V.P.-Human Resources--Mac Frugal's Bargains Close-Outs Inc., Rancho Dominguez, CA; *U.S. Public*, pg. 437
Bias-Purdy, June, Mgr.-Recruiting--Brite Voice Systems, Inc., Heathrow, FL; *U.S. Public*, pg. 257
Bibby, Douglas M., Sr. V.P.-Human Resources--Federal National Mortgage Association (Fannie Mae), Washington, DC; *U.S. Public*, pg. 615
Biber, Robert, Dir.-Employee Rels.--Providence Energy Corporation, Providence, RI; *U.S. Public*, pg. 1337
Bickford, Dick, Mgr.-Human Resources--Hitchiner Manufacturing Company, Inc., Milford, NH; *U.S. Private*, pg. 531
Bide, R.W., Mng. Dir.-Human Resources--Tate & Lyle PLC, London, United Kingdom; *Int'l*, pg. 1356
Bide, Richard, Dir.-H.R.--Centrica Plc, Slough, United Kingdom; *Int'l*, pg. 279
Bidese, John, V.P.-Human Resources--Rieter Automotive North America Inc, Farmington Hills, MI; *Int'l*, pg. 1117
Biel, Walter, Div. Mgr.-Personnel--Migros, Zurich, Switzerland; *Int'l*, pg. 865
Bieler, Mark, Exec. V.P.-Human Resources--Bankers Trust New York Corporation, New York, NY; *U.S. Public*, pg. 185
Bieniek, Linda, Dir.-H.R.--CLTV News, Oak Brook, IL; *U.S. Public*, pg. 1635
Biggs, R.G., Sr. V.P. & Dir.-H.R.--Fedco, Inc., Santa Fe Springs, CA; *U.S. Private*, pg. 398
Bigler, Patsy, Mgr.-Personnel Admin.--Tighe Industries, Inc., York, PA; *U.S. Private*, pg. 1086
Bikowsky, Nancy, Controller--Stapo Hollander Industries, Lakewood, NJ; *U.S. Private*, pg. 1033
Bilcliff, C., Mgr.-H.R.--Bespak plc, Norfolk, United Kingdom; *Int'l*, pg. 193
Bilgrami, M.A. Rehman, Mgr.-Personnel & Admin.--National Refinery Limited, Karachi, Pakistan; *Int'l*, pg. 909
Bilich, Joseph T., V.P.-H.R.--Drummond Company, Inc., Jasper, AL; *U.S. Private*, pg. 343
Billings, Gene P., Dir.-Personnel--Ash Grove Cement Company, Shawnee Mission, KS; *U.S. Private*, pg. 87
Bilmes, Barry, V.P.-Fin. & Admin.--Brothers Gourmet Coffees, Inc., Boca Raton, FL; *U.S. Public*, pg. 259
Bilt, Matthew, Mgr.-Human Resources--Rheometric Scientific, Piscataway, NJ; *U.S. Public*, pg. 1387
Bindelglass, Denise, V.P.-H.R.--Playboy Enterprises, Inc., Chicago, IL; *U.S. Public*, pg. 1309
Binger, Rhonda L., Dir.-Human Resources--Noland Company, Newport News, VA; *U.S. Public*, pg. 1187
Binkerd, Edward G., V.P.-H.R.--Republic Industries, Inc., Fort Lauderdale, FL; *U.S. Public*, pg. 1378
Biondollilo, Michael A., Sr. V.P.-H.R.--The Penn Mutual Life Insurance Company, Philadelphia, PA; *U.S. Private*, pg. 849
Birch, David, Dir.-Personnel--Fiat Auto Ireland Ltd., Dublin, Ireland; *Int'l*, pg. 481
Bircher, Christoph, Mgr.-Personnel--Ringier AG, Zurich, Switzerland; *Int'l*, pg. 1118
Bird, Graeme, Mgr.-Personnel--Australian Guarantee Corporation Limited, Sydney, Australia; *Int'l*, pg. 1496
Bird, Karen, Dir.-Human Resources--Blue Coral Systems, Tucson, AZ; *U.S. Public*, pg. 1348
Bireley, Don, V.P.-Human Resources--Moen Incorporated, North Olmsted, OH; *U.S. Public*, pg. 675
Birkner, Christine, V.P.-Human Resources--Alpha Wire Company, Elizabeth, NJ; *U.S. Public*, pg. 201
Birmingham, Karen, Mgr.-H.R.--Florafax International, Inc., Vero Beach, FL; *U.S. Public*, pg. 654
Birney, Donald M., V.P.-Personnel--American Bureau of Shipping, New York, NY; *U.S. Private*, pg. 51
Bishop, Robert, Dir.-MIS--Key Food Stores Co-operative, Inc., Brooklyn, NY; *U.S. Private*, pg. 617
Bishop, Sherril, Dir.-Personnel--Corcom, Inc., Libertyville, IL; *U.S. Public*, pg. 446
Bismuth, Pierre E., V.P.-Personnel--Schlumberger Limited, New York, NY; *U.S. Public*, pg. 1439
Bissey, Rayna, Mgr.-Personnel--John Boos & Company, Effingham, IL; *U.S. Private*, pg. 156
Bithell, Thomas C., Sr. V.P.-H.R. & Admin.--Taubman Centers, Inc., Bloomfield Hills, MI; *U.S. Public*, pg. 1561
Bizal, Janet, Corp. Acctg. & Personnel--Aloette Cosmetics, Inc., West Chester, PA; *U.S. Public*, pg. 57
Black, Clyde, Sr. V.P.-Human Resources--Mitchell Energy & Development Corp., Spring, TX; *U.S. Public*, pg. 1117
Black, Dale, Dir.-Human Resources--Jacuzzi Bros., Jacuzzi, Inc., Little Rock, AR; *U.S. Public*, pg. 1684
Black, Javene, Dir.-Personnel--Zero Corporation, Los Angeles, CA; *U.S. Public*, pg. 1791
Black, Jim, Mgr.-Human Resources & Credit--Warner-Chilcott Laboratories, Inc., Rockaway, NJ; *Int'l*, pg. 436
Black, Jim, Mgr.-Personnel--Ross Technology Corp., Leola, PA; *U.S. Private*, pg. 946
Black, Ralph, Dir.-Human Resources--Christian Children's Fund, Inc., Richmond, VA; *U.S. Private*, pg. 238
Blackburn, Varon, V.P.-Personnel--AgriNorthwest, Inc., Pasco, WA; *U.S. Private*, pg. 26
Blain, Marielle T., V.P.-Human Resources--Publicis BCP Montreal Inc., Montreal, Canada; *Int'l*, pg. 116
Blair, Brantley, Dir.-H.R.--Craddock-Terry Inc., Lynchburg, VA; *U.S. Private*, pg. 284
Blair, Judy D., V.P.-H.R.--American Management Systems, Inc., Fairfax, VA; *U.S. Public*, pg. 86
Blais, M.A., V.P.-Human Resources--U.S. Borax Inc., Valencia, CA; *Int'l*, pg. 1119
Blake, Julia S., Dir.-Human Resources--Bailey, Fischer & Porter Company, Warminster, PA; *Int'l*, pg. 449
Blanc, Mia, Mgr.-H.R.--Mercury Interactive Corp., Sunnyvale, CA; *U.S. Public*, pg. 1093
Blanchard, Jacqueline M., V.P.-Human Resources--The Bureau of National Affairs, Inc., Washington, DC; *U.S. Private*, pg. 181
Bland, Louis T., Jr., V.P.-H.R. & Sec.--Oil-Dri Corporation of America, Chicago, IL; *U.S. Public*, pg. 1214
Blandford, Teresa, Dir.-Human Resources--COBE Laboratories, Inc., Lakewood, CO; *Int'l*, pg. 667
Blaquiere, Gillet, Dir.-Human Resources--Purdel, Cooperative Agro-Alimentaire, Bic, Canada; *Int'l*, pg. 1073

Blauner, Audrey, Human Resources Dir. & Admin.--Quantum Media International, Inc., New York, NY; *U.S. Private*, pg. 899

Blaylock, Lou Ann, V.P.-Corp. Rels.--Tandy Corporation, Fort Worth, TX; *U.S. Public*, pg. 1560

Blickens, George, Dir.-Personnel--Haddon Craftsmen, Inc., Scranton, PA; *U.S. Public*, pg. 518

Blignaut, Alan, Dir.-Human Resources--Henkel Canada Ltd., Mississauga, Canada; *Int'l*, pg. 612

Blizzard, Doug, Mgr.-Personnel--Channel Master, Smithfield, NC; *U.S. Private*, pg. 228

Bloch, Harold, Dir.-Personnel--Allen Organ Company, Macungie, PA; *U.S. Public*, pg. 45

Blocher, Terry, V.P.-Human Resources--The Southland Corporation, Dallas, TX; *Int'l*, pg. 693

Block, Philip W., Sr. V.P.-H.R.--Ashland, Inc., Russell, KY; *U.S. Public*, pg. 138

Blockett, Bridgett, Dir.-Human Resources--Bing Steel Inc., Detroit, MI; *U.S. Private*, pg. 144

Blokland, C., Sr. Dir.-Corp. Personnel & Org.--Koninklijke Hoogovens N.V., Ijmuiden, Netherlands; *Int'l*, pg. 753

Blokland, C., Sr. Dir.-Grp. Personnel & Org.--Hoogovens Groep B.V., Ijmuiden, Netherlands; *Int'l*, pg. 753

Blomberg, Joe, Dir.-H.R.--KTI, Orange, CA; *U.S. Public*, pg. 939

Blondel, Bernard, Dir.-H.R.--Banque Francaise du Commerce Exterieur, Paris, France; *Int'l*, pg. 160

Bloodworth, Leda, Office Mgr.--Apex Broach & Machine Co., Detroit, MI; *U.S. Private*, pg. 77

Bloomfield, Steve, Dir.-H.R.--Beltone Electronics Corporation, Chicago, IL; *U.S. Private*, pg. 132

Blount, Terry, V.P.-Human Resources--Arctic Cat Inc., Thief River Falls, MN; *U.S. Public*, pg. 128

Blum, Jeffrey R., V.P.-Admin. & H.R.--Xtra Corporation, Boston, MA; *U.S. Public*, pg. 1786

Blum, Reto, Mng. Dir.-Human Resources--Landis & Staefa AG, Zug, Switzerland; *Int'l*, pg. 800

Bly, Nate, Supvr.-H.R.--Tucson Electric Power Company, Tucson, AZ; *U.S. Public*, pg. 1670

Blystone, Bev, Dir.-Pur. & Personnel--Union City Chair Co., Union City, PA; *U.S. Private*, pg. 170

Boan, Edward E., Exec. V.P.-Fresh Pork & Human Resources--Thorn Apple Valley, Inc., Southfield, MI; *U.S.* Public, pg. 1602

Boas, Hilda H., Sr. V.P. & Dir.-Human Resources & Corp. Admin.--Municipal Bond Investors Assurance Corporation, Armonk, NY; *U.S. Public*, pg. 1023

Bobel, Peggy, Mgr.-H.R.--Harley Ellington Design, Southfield, MI; *U.S. Private*, pg. 503

Bocco, Claudio, Exec. V.P.-Personnel--Istituto Bancario San Paolo Di Torino S.p.A., Turin, Italy; *Int'l*, pg. 691

Boden, William D., V.P. & Dir.-H.R. & Admin. Svcs.--The Rouse Company, Columbia, MD; *U.S. Public*, pg. 1407

Boehm, Richard, Dir.-Human Resources--Precision Twist Drill Co., Crystal Lake, IL; *Int'l*, pg. 1185

Boelman, Bob, Dir.-H.R.--Ag Services of America, Inc., Cedar Falls, IA; *U.S. Public*, pg. 6

Boes, Paul, Mgr.-Employee Relations--Kia Motors America, Inc., Irvine, CA; *Int'l*, pg. 733

Bogart, Robert B., Exec. V.P.-Human Resources--Mutual of Omaha Insurance Company, Omaha, NE; *U.S. Private*, pg. 769

Bohlender, P. Edward, V.P.-Personnel--Lever Brothers Co., New York, NY; *Int'l*, pg. 1435

Bohlin, Peder, Grp. V.P.-Human Resources--Jotun A/S, Sandefjord, Norway; *Int'l*, pg. 714

Bohne, Chris, Dir.-Personnel--Sentinel Technologies Inc., Downers Grove, IL; *U.S. Private*, pg. 984

Bohneman, Barbara A., V.P.-Human Resources--Royal Doulton USA Inc., Somerset, NJ; *Int'l*, pg. 1135

Bohnenkemp, Don, Mgr.-Personnel--Mautz Paint Co., Madison, WI; *U.S. Private*, pg. 715

Bohrofen, Judy, Sr. V.P. & Dir.-H.R.--Brenton Banks, Inc., Des Moines, IA; *U.S. Public*, pg. 251

Boisseranc, Patricia S., V.P.-H.R.--Centris Group Inc., Costa Mesa, CA; *U.S. Public*, pg. 328

Boisvert, Daniel, V.P.-Customer Service--Thomas & Betts Ltd., Iberville, Canada; *U.S. Public*, pg. 1598

Boldt, Ronald, V.P.-Human Resources--Teleflex Incorporated, Plymouth Meeting, PA; *U.S. Public*, pg. 1569

Boldt, Wendy J., Asst. Controller--Mathews & Boucher, Rochester, NY; *U.S. Private*, pg. 714

Bolen, Steve, Dir.-Human Resources--Wangner Systems Corporation, Greenville, SC; *Int'l*, pg. 1418

Boles, Doug, Sr. V.P.-Human Resources--Armstrong World Industries, Inc., Lancaster, PA; *U.S. Public*, pg. 131

Boles, Vincent, Dir.-Human Resources--Royal Consumer Business Products, Bridgewater, NJ; *Int'l*, pg. 1002

Bolger, Michael, Dir.-Human Resources--Texaco (Ireland) Ltd., Dublin, Ireland; *U.S. Public*, pg. 1584

Bolger, Susan, V.P.-Human Resources--Arrow Industries, Inc., Carrollton, TX; *U.S. Public*, pg. 426

Bolger, Susan R., Sr. V.P.-Human Resources--Starwood Hotels & Resorts, Phoenix, AZ; *U.S. Public*, pg. 1512

Bolivar, Dercy, Mgr.-Human Resources--Bundy Venezolana C.A., Valencia, Venezuela; *Int'l*, pg. 1342

Bolivar, Mary, Dir.-Personnel--Injectron Corporation, Plainfield, NJ; *U.S. Private*, pg. 563

Bombardi, Eleutrio, Mgr.-Personnel--Cassa di Risparmio delle Provincie Lombarde SpA (CARIPLO), Milan, Italy; *Int'l*, pg. 274

Bomze, Glenda, Dir.-H.R.--Niches, Inc., San Diego, CA; *U.S.* Public, pg. 1181

Bondoc, Evelyn, Controller, Computer Opers. & Personnel--GWP, Inc., Los Angeles, CA; *U.S. Private*, pg. 437

Bondy, Susan, V.P.-Human Resources--Schwarz Paper Company, Morton Grove, IL; *U.S. Private*, pg. 974

Bondy, Susan, Dir.-Human Resources--John O. Butler Co., Chicago, IL; *Int'l*, pg. 1320

Bonen, James J., Chief Fin. Officer--Sonic Couriers of Arizona, Inc., Scottsdale, AZ; *U.S. Private*, pg. 1123

Boneta, Carol, Mgr.-Personnel & Pub. Rels.--Lectrodryer Div., Ajax Magnethermic Corp., Richmond, KY; *Int'l*, pg. 113

Bonfigio, Adriane, Mgr.-Personnel--Ain Plastics, Inc., Mount Vernon, NY; *Int'l*, pg. 1388

Bongardt, Joachim, Dir.-Personnel--Warsteiner Brauerei Haus Cramer GmbH & Co., Warstein, Germany; *Int'l*, pg. 1486

Bonhard, Charlotte, Personnel & Office Admin. Dir.--Einson Freeman Inc., Paramus, NJ; *Int'l*, pg. 1483

Bonhoff, Ali, Mgr.-Personnel--Mike Daugherty's Chevrolet Geo, Inc., Sacramento, CA; *U.S. Private*, pg. 313

Bonn, Patricia, Mgr.-Admin. & Employee Rels.--Bobst Group Inc., Roseland, NJ; *Int'l*, pg. 198

Bonnadonna, A.F., V.P.-Human Resources--U.S. Can Company, Oak Brook, IL; *U.S. Public*, pg. 1681

Bonnell, William E., V.P.-Human Resources--Talley Industries, Inc., Phoenix, AZ; *U.S. Public*, pg. 307

Bonner, J. Joseph, Dir.-Human Resources--Kao Corporation of America (DE), Wilmington, DE; *Int'l*, pg. 717

Bonsignore, Francis N., Sr. V.P.-Human Resources & Admin.--Marsh & McLennan Companies, Inc., New York, NY; *U.S. Public*, pg. 1048

Bontron, Robert, Mgr.-Personnel--Tefal S.A., Rumilly, France; *Int'l*, pg. 569

Booher, Gary, V.P.-Human Resources--Miller Brewing Company, Milwaukee, WI; *U.S. Public*, pg. 1289

Booker, Gail, Dir.-H.R.--Sanderson Plumbing Products Inc., Columbus, MS; *U.S. Private*, pg. 964

Booker, Lawson, III, V.P.-Human Resources--Glen-Gery Corporation, Wyomissing, PA; *Int'l*, pg. 658

Booms, Esther, Dir.-Human Resources--American Express Service Europe Ltd., Amsterdam, Netherlands; *U.S. Public*, pg. 74

Boone, Richard, V.P.-Human Resources--Rutt Custom Cabinetry, Goodville, PA; *U.S. Private*, pg. 507

Borba, Mary P., Sr. V.P.-Human Resources--News America Marketing, Norwalk, CT; *Int'l*, pg. 925

Borchers, Ann, V.P.-H.R.--Inacom Corp., Omaha, NE; *U.S. Public*, pg. 873

Borchers, Richard H., Exec. V.P.-H.R.--Davco Restaurants Inc., Crofton, MD; *U.S. Public*, pg. 488

Bordeleau, Lise, Sr. Dir.-Human Resources Devel.--Assurance vie Desjardins-Laurentienne, Levis, Canada; *Int'l*, pg. 396

Bordelon, Clarence J., V.P.-Sls. & Admin.--Tyler Elevator Products, Inc., Valley View, OH; *U.S. Private*, pg. 1112

Borenbos, Lynn, Mgr.-Personnel--L&J Technologies, Hillside, IL; *U.S. Private*, pg. 638

Borges, Lynne M., Sr. V.P.-H.R.--London Fog Industries, Inc., New York, NY; *U.S. Private*, pg. 673

Borgeson, Roger, Sr. V.P.-Human Resources--Alexander's, Inc., Saddle Brook, NJ; *U.S. Public*, pg. 1725

Borgia, John, Exec. V.P.-Human Resources--The Seagram Company Ltd., Montreal, Canada; *Int'l*, pg. 1214

Borgia, John, V.P.-Human Resources--Joseph E. Seagram & Sons, Inc., New York, NY; *Int'l*, pg. 1215

Borgia, Philip, Dir.-H.R.--Rockbestos-Suprenant Cable Corp., Clinton, MA; *U.S. Private*, pg. 938

Boright, I., Section Mgr.-Personnel--Firestone Textiles Company, Woodstock, Canada; *Int'l*, pg. 214

Borin, Michael, V.P.-H.R.--Xyvision, Inc., Wakefield, MA; *U.S. Public*, pg. 1787

Bornemann, Mark, Mgr.-Human Resources--LoJack Corporation, Dedham, MA; *U.S. Public*, pg. 1012

Bornstein, Lawrence M., V.P.-Human Resources--PictureTel, Andover, MA; *U.S. Public*, pg. 1294

Borseso, Donna, Sr. V.P. & Human Resources Dir.--McCann-Erickson Worldwide, New York, NY; *U.S. Public*, *pg. 909*

Borzi, Peggy, V.P.-H.R.--Martino's Bakery, Inc., Burbank, CA; *U.S. Private*, pg. 710

Bosco, Rose Ann, Sr. V.P.-Human Resources--Michael Anthony Jewelers, Inc., Mount Vernon, NY; *U.S. Public*, pg. 1103

Boser, Marcel, Mgr.-Training & Devel.--Oerlikon-Buhrle Holding AG, Zurich, Switzerland; *Int'l*, pg. 996

Bosma, R., Mgr.-Personnel & Organization--CSM Sugar Division, Diemen, Netherlands; *Int'l*, pg. 243

Bossaller, Steve, Mgr.-Human Resources--Six Flags St. Louis, Eureka, MO; *U.S. Public*, pg. 1612

Bostian, Eric, Dir.-H.R.--Superior Label Systems, Inc., Mason, OH; *U.S. Private*, pg. 1055

Bostick, Gerri Feemster, Sr. V.P.-Human Resources--AnnTaylor, Inc., New York, NY; *U.S. Public*, pg. 116

Boston, Terry P., V.P.-Human Resources--BHP Petroleum Ltd., London, United Kingdom; *Int'l*, pg. 225

Boswell, Robert H., V.P.-Corp. Human Resources--Moyer Packing Company, Souderton, PA; *U.S. Private*, pg. 765

Boswell, S.M., Sr., Dir.-Employee Rels.--United States Pipe & Foundry Company, Inc., Birmingham, AL; *U.S. Public*, pg. 1736

Both, Michael, V.P.-H.R.--Georg Fischer Ltd., Schaffhausen, Switzerland; *Int'l*, pg. 488

Bothe, Brooke, Sec.--H.W. Kaufman Financial Group, Inc., Farmington, MI; *U.S. Private*, pg. 609

Bottino, Hugo C., V.P.-H.R.--New Jersey Natural Gas Co., Wall, NJ; *U.S. Public*, pg. 1172

Bottomley, C. R., Dir.-Human Resources--NatWest U.K., London, United Kingdom; *Int'l*, pg. 910

Bottorff, John, V.P.-Human Resources--Fairbanks Morse Engine Division, Beloit, WI; *U.S. Public*, pg. 401

Botwins, Rita, Dir.-Personnel--Winkelman Stores, Inc., Plymouth, MI; *U.S. Private*, pg. 858

Bouchard, Clifford, Asst. V.P.-Human Rels.--Mohawk Paper Mills, Inc., Cohoes, NY; *U.S. Private*, pg. 755

Bouchard, E.M., Dir.-Labor Rels.--Grand Trunk Corporation (GTC), Detroit, MI; *Int'l*, pg. 258

Bouchard, J. Thomas, Sr. V.P.-Human Resources--International Business Machines Corporation, Armonk, NY; *U.S. Public*, pg. 895

Boucher-Krickl, Celeste, V.P.-Human Resources--Cobra Electronics Corporation, Chicago, IL; *U.S. Public*, pg. 391

Boucher, Sandra, Mgr.-H.R.--Felton Brush Inc., Manchester, NH; *U.S. Private*, pg. 400

Boudreau, Karen, Dir.-Human Resources--Marcam Solutions, Inc., Newton, MA; *U.S. Public*, pg. 1042

Boudreau, Patrick V., V.P.-H.R.--Cirrus Logic, Inc., Fremont, CA; *U.S. Public*, pg. 375

Boulanger, Alain, V.P.-Human Resources--SEITA, Societe Nationale D'Exploitation Industrielle des Tabacs et des Allumettes, Paris, France; *Int'l*, pg. 1219

Bouldin, T. Michael, Asst. V.P.-Human Resources--Allied Clinical Laboratories, Inc., Nashville, TN; *U.S. Public*, pg. 973

Boulerice, Daniel, Dir.-Personnel--Alcan Cable Division, Atlanta, GA; *Int'l*, pg. 50

Boure, Don, Mgr.-Human Resources--Safway Steel Products Inc., Waukesha, WI; *Int'l*, pg. 1389

Bourgault, Carole, Admin. Dir.-H.R.--The Jean Coutu Group (PJC) Inc., Longueuil, Canada; *Int'l*, pg. 340

Bourgon, George M., V.P.--Charter One Financial, Inc., Cleveland, OH; *U.S. Public*, pg. 336

Bourgon, George M., Jr., Sr. V.P. & Dir.-Personnel--First Federal of Michigan, Detroit, MI; *U.S. Public*, pg. 336

Boutonnat, Pierre-Louis, Gen. Sec.--Entreprise Miniere et Chimique, Paris, France; *Int'l*, pg. 458

Bouverot, Georges, Sr. V.P.-Corp. Human Resources--Renault, Boulogne-Billancourt, France; *Int'l*, pg. 1102

Bove, Eileen, Dir.-Human Resources--Universal Health Services, Inc., King of Prussia, PA; *U.S. Public*, pg. 1696

Bowden, June, Mgr.-Personnel--Aromat Corporation, New Providence, NJ; *Int'l*, pg. 847

Bower, Audrey, Dir.-Human Resources--Ground Round Inc., Braintree, MA; *U.S. Public*, pg. 766

Bowers, Elizabeth, Dir.-Personnel--Conmed Corporation, Utica, NY; *U.S. Public*, pg. 431

Bowick, Susan D., V.P.-H.R.--Hewlett-Packard Company, Palo Alto, CA; *U.S. Public*, pg. 813

Bowland, Wanda L., Mgr.-Human Resources--Cyber Systems, Inc., Anaheim, CA; *U.S. Private*, pg. 299

Bowling, Virginia, Mgr.-Personnel--Educational Insights, Inc., Carson, CA; *U.S. Public*, pg. 565

Bowman, Joan, V.P.-H.R.--Swiss Army Brands, Inc., Shelton, CT; *U.S. Public*, pg. 1544

Bowman, Judy, Mgr.-Personnel--ITT Jabsco, Costa Mesa, CA; *U.S. Public*, pg. 860

Bowman, Rod, Sr. V.P.-Human Resource--White Consolidated Industries, Inc., Cleveland, OH; *Int'l*, pg. 439

Boxell, David E., V.P.-Personnel--Wm. Wrigley Jr. Company, Chicago, IL; *U.S. Public*, pg. 1781

Boxleitner, Paul, Dir.-H.R.--Itron Inc., Spokane, WA; *U.S. Public*, pg. 914

Boyce, Pat, Dir.-Human Resources--Ramada Express, Laughlin, NV; *U.S. Public*, pg. 158

Boyd, Joe E., V.P.-Human Resources--Santa Fe International Corporation, Dallas, TX; *Int'l*, pg. 765

Boyd, R., Dir.-Human Resources--Britvic Soft Drinks Ltd., Chelmsford, United Kingdom; *Int'l*, pg. 170

Boyes, Pamela, Human Resources Mgr.--Citron Haligman Bedecarre, San Francisco, CA; *U.S. Private*, pg. 241

Boykin, C.L., Mgr.-Personnel--MelloButtercup Ice Cream Inc., Wilson, NC; *U.S. Private*, pg. 730

Boyle, P., Dir.-Human Resources--Carter Holt Harvey Limited, Auckland, New Zealand; *U.S. Public*, pg. 904

Bozell, Jerry M., Dir.-H.R.--Maxon Corporation, Muncie, IN; *U.S. Private*, pg. 716

Bradford, Claire V., V.P.-Sls. & Staff Services--The Arnold Palmer Golf Company, Ooltewah, TN; *U.S. Public*, pg. 132

Bradford, Richard, V.P.-Human Resources--Siebe plc, Windsor, United Kingdom; *Int'l*, pg. 1240

Bradley, Charles F., Mgr.-Personnel--Summit Corporation of America, Thomaston, CT; *U.S. Private*, pg. 1050

Bradley, Charles J., V.P.-H.R. & Admin.--Fluor Corporation, Irvine, CA; *U.S. Public*, pg. 659

Bradley, Connie, V.P.-Human Resources--Kalmbach Publishing Co., Waukesha, WI; *U.S. Private*, pg. 606

Bradley, Patric, Mgr.-H.R.--River Ranch Northeast, Inc., Buffalo, NY; *U.S. Private*, pg. 934

Bradshaw, Karen, Controller--Amspec Chemical Corporation, Gloucester City, NJ; *U.S. Private*, pg. 67

Bradt, Robert, Personnel Dir.--Sun Chemical Pigments Div., Cincinnati, OH; *Int'l*, pg. 370

Brady, David, Grp. Personnel Exec.--Trafalgar House PLC, London, United Kingdom; *Int'l*, pg. 772

Brady, Janet, V.P.-Human Resources--The Clorox Company, Oakland, CA; *U.S. Public*, pg. 386

Brady, Patricia, Mgr.-Human Resources--Trans World Entertainment Corporation, Albany, NY; *U.S. Public*, pg. 1629

Brady, Walter J., V.P.-Admin.--Middlesex Water Company, Iselin, NJ; *U.S. Public*, pg. 1110

Bragdon, Scott, Dir.-Human Resources--Bank of Boston Connecticut, Hartford, CT; *U.S. Public*, pg. 184

Bragg, David C., V.P.-Employee Relations--Van Dorn Demag Corporation, Strongsville, OH; *Int'l*, pg. 837

Bragg, J. Richard, Dir.-H.R.--Bunzl Extrusion, Richmond, VA; *Int'l*, pg. 232

Brain, Carol, Dir.-H.R.--Pac Paper Inc., Vancouver, WA; *U.S.* Private, pg. 828

Brainard, Donald W., V.P.-Human Resources--Refined Sugars, Inc., Yonkers, NY; *Int'l*, pg. 699

Bramblett, Ronald L., V.P.-Human Resources--A.P. Green Industries, Inc., Mexico, MO; *U.S. Public*, pg. 761

Bramson, Ruth, V.P.-Human Resources--Shaw's Supermarkets, Inc., East Bridgewater, MA; *Int'l*, pg. 1170

Branch, John D., Chief Fin. Officer & Sr. V.P.-Fin.--Earl Scheib, Inc., Beverly Hills, CA; *U.S. Public*, pg. 1437

Brandmahl, John C., V.P.-Human Resources--The Standard Products Company, Dearborn, MI; *U.S. Public*, pg. 1504

Brandt, Gerard R., Sr. V.P.-Human Resources--Georgia-Pacific Corporation, Atlanta, GA; *U.S. Public*, pg. 735

Brandt, Judy, V.P.-H.R.--Ogden Aviation Services, New York, NY; *U.S. Public*, pg. 1213

Brandt, Terry, Dir.-H.R.-Magnetic Data, MN--Magnetics Data Inc., Goleta, CA; *U.S. Private*, pg. 695

Brang, Barry, Mgr.-Personnel--Genova Products, Inc., Davison, MI; *U.S. Private*, pg. 447

Bras, Barbara, Dir.-H.R.--Wisconsin Energy Corporation, Milwaukee, WI; *U.S. Public*, pg. 1773

Brassel, Heinz, Mgr.-H.R.--Jelmoli AG, Zurich, Switzerland; *Int'l*, pg. 705

Brastrup, Frances, Mgr.-H.R.--Advanced Input Devices, Inc., Coeur D'Alene, ID; *U.S. Private*, pg. 21

Braun, Gene, Mgr.-Personnel--The Metal Ware Corp., Two Rivers, WI; *U.S. Private*, pg. 734

Braunstein, Mark, Dir.-Mfg. & Personnel--Whiting Manufacturing Co., Inc., Cincinnati, OH; *U.S. Private*, pg. 1174

Brechet, Giorgio, Dir.-Human Resources--Istituto Mobiliare Italiano, Rome, Italy; *Int'l*, pg. 692

Breeden, Bruce, Dir.-H.R. (Indianapolis)--Tultex Corporation, Martinsville, VA; *U.S. Public*, pg. 1644

Breeger, Jalene, Mgr.-Human Resources--The Flight International Group, Inc., Newport News, VA; *U.S. Public*, pg. 654

Breese, Kevin, V.P.-H.R.--Turtle Wax, Inc., Chicago, IL; *U.S. Private*, pg. 1110

Breeze, Kathy, Dir.-H.R.--Reliable Castings Corporation, Cincinnati, OH; *U.S. Private*, pg. 920

Breintenbach, Peggy, Mgr.-H.R.--Blue Grass Quality Meats, Crescent Springs, KY; *U.S. Private*, pg. 152

Breland, Dan, Mgr.-Personnel--Family Smacks, Inc., Liberty, MO; *U.S. Private*, pg. 393

Brennan, Amy, Dir.-Human Resources--Trippe Mfg. Co., Chicago, IL; *U.S. Private*, pg. 1104

Brennan, John, Dir.-Human Resources--Coppus Murray Group, Tuthill Corporation, Millbury, MA; *U.S. Private*, pg. 1110

Brenner, Susan, Dir.-Personnel--The Disney Channel, Burbank, CA; *U.S. Public*, pg. 513

Brenny, Mike, V.P.-H.R.--Outdoor Technologies Group, Spirit Lake, IA; *U.S. Private*, pg. 822

Breshears, Ronald G., V.P.-Human Resources--Harmon Industries, Inc., Blue Springs, MO; *U.S. Public*, pg. 788

Breski, Debra, Div. Mgr.-Human Resources--Seal Products Incorporated, Naugatuck, CT; *U.S. Public*, pg. 849

Breslin, Mike, Vice Chm.-Law & H.R. Worldwide--Leo Burnett Company, Inc., Chicago, IL; *U.S. Private*, pg. 183

Brett, Edward J., Asst. V.P.-Human Resources--Circuit City Stores, Inc., Richmond, VA; *U.S. Public*, pg. 374

Brett, Theresa, V.P.-H.R.--Realty One, Cleveland, OH; *U.S. Private*, pg. 914

Breuer, Sandra, Mgr.-Human Resources--Boise Cascade Paper Div., Boise, ID; *U.S. Public*, pg. 243

Brewer, Brooke E., V.P.-H.R.--Texas Industries, Inc., Dallas, TX; *U.S. Public*, pg. 1585

Brewer, Rob, Mgr.-Human Resources--Austin Industries, Inc., Dallas, TX; *U.S. Private*, pg. 99

Brewington, Edward, V.P.-Human Resources--KinderCare Learning Centers, Inc., Portland, OR; *U.S. Public*, pg. 961

Brewton, Gerald, Controller & Mgr.-Cash Mngmt., Employee Ben. & Human Resources--Jerry Hamm Chevrolet Inc., Jacksonville, FL; *U.S. Private*, pg. 497

Breza, Barb, Mgr.-Human Relations--Lucas Body Systems - North America, Winona, MN; *Int'l*, pg. 820

Brick, Marcy, Mgr.-Human Resources--Snyder Berlin, Berlin, PA; *U.S. Private*, pg. 887

Bridge, E.R., Asst. Dir.-H.R.--Northern Rock PLC, Newcastle upon Tyne, United Kingdom; *Int'l*, pg. 968

Bridger, Barbara, V.P.-Human Resources--Butler Manufacturing Company, Kansas City, MO; *U.S. Public*, pg. 271

Bridges, Thomas, Mgr.-Human Resources--Frigidaire Company Dishwasher Products, Kinston, NC; *Int'l*, pg. 439

Bridges, Trisha, Mgr.-H.R.--Marsh Company, Belleville, IL; *U.S. Private*, pg. 707

Brier, Deb, Mgr.-Human Resources--Stark Candy Company, Pewaukee, WI; *U.S. Private*, pg. 1113

Brigham, Sarah, V.P.-H.R. & Intl.--Diagraph Corporation, Earth City, MO; *U.S. Private*, pg. 330

Brinkerhoff, Bette J., V.P.-H.R.--Arthur J. Gallagher & Co., Itasca, IL; *U.S. Public*, pg. 698

Brinkman, Arne, Deputy-Personnel--Stora Kopparbergs Bergslags AB, Falun, Sweden; *Int'l*, pg. 1302

Brinkman, Wayne, V.P.-Opers. & Human Resources--D.C.I., Inc., Saint Cloud, MN; *U.S. Private*, pg. 301

Briqolime, Garry, V.P.-Human Resources--Kamax-G.B. DuPont L.P., Troy, MI; *U.S. Private*, pg. 606

Broadwell, John, Dir.-H.R.--AGCO Corporation, Duluth, GA; *U.S. Public*, pg. 28

Brock, Cecelia, Dir.-Human Resources--L3 Communications Telemetry & Instrumentation Div., San Diego, CA; *U.S. Private*, pg. 639

Brock, John, Mgr.-Human Resources--Revell-Monogram Inc., Morton Grove, IL; *U.S. Private*, pg. 926

Brock, Stephen, Dr., Mgr.-Trng. & Devel.--Ryobi Motor Products, Anderson, SC; *Int'l*, pg. 1151

Brockelman, Phil, Mgr.-Human Resources--The Barden Corporation, Danbury, CT; *Int'l*, pg. 468

Brockman, Rob, Exec. V.P.-Admin.--Cash America International, Inc., Fort Worth, TX; *U.S. Public*, pg. 312

Broderick, Mike, Dir.-Personnel--Ed Miniat, Inc., Chicago, IL; *U.S. Private*, pg. 750

Broderick, Thomas F., Principal Attorney-Central Illinois Light Co.--CILCORP Inc., Peoria, IL; *U.S. Public*, pg. 367

Brody, Dennis, V.P.-Human Resources--Nice-Pak Products, Inc., Orangeburg, NY; *U.S. Private*, pg. 798

Broedling, Laurie A., Sr. V.P.-Human Resources & Quality--McDonnell Aircraft & Missile Systems Div., Berkeley, MO; *U.S. Public*, pg. 241

Broekman, E. van Mourik, Coordinator-Human Resources & Organization--Royal Dutch/Shell Group of Companies, Hague, Netherlands; *Int'l*, pg. 1135

Brogan, Richard, V.P.-Human Resources--Kearney Company, Tucker, GA; *U.S. Public*, pg. 444

Brooks, B.J., Human Resources Dir.--WPP Group plc, London, United Kingdom; *Int'l*, pg. 1482

Brooks, Richard, Dir.-H.R.--Ocean Spray Cranberries, Inc., Middleboro, MA; *U.S. Private*, pg. 811

Brooks, Tim, Dir.-Human Resources--Fila USA, Sparks, MD; *Int'l*, pg. 484

Brookshire, Jane T., V.P.-Human Resources--WLR Foods, Inc., Timberville, VA; *U.S. Public*, pg. 1727

Brookshire, Tim, Exec. V.P.-H.R.--Brookshire Grocery, Tyler, TX; *U.S. Private*, pg. 172

Broom, Geoffrey R., V.P.-H.R.--Century Communications Corp., New Canaan, CT; *U.S. Public*, pg. 329

Broome, Lisa, Dir.-H.R.--SFA, Inc., Hyattsville, MD; *U.S. Private*, pg. 956

Broome, Monnie L., V.P.-H.R.--JPS Textile Group, Inc., Greenville, SC; *U.S. Private*, pg. 578

Broome, Nigel, Dir.-Retail Personnel--J. Sainsbury plc, London, United Kingdom; *Int'l*, pg. 1169

Brothers, Ruth H., V.P.-Human Resources--CAE Inc., Toronto, Canada; *Int'l*, pg. 237

Brouilette, Alan, Exec. V.P.--Strombecker Corporation, Chicago, IL; *U.S. Private*, pg. 1047

Brouwer, Arthur, V.P.-Mngmt. Devel. & Organizations--Koninklijke Ahold NV, Zaandam, Netherlands; *Int'l*, pg. 749

Brown, Celia R., V.P., Mgr.-H.R. & Asst. Sec.--NAC Reinsurance Corporation, Greenwich, CT; *U.S. Public*, pg. 1144

Brown, Claire M., Mgr.-Human Resources--Caere Corporation, Los Gatos, CA; *U.S. Public*, pg. 291

Brown, Don, V.P.-Human Resources--InterVoice, Inc., Dallas, TX; *U.S. Public*, pg. 910

Brown, Donald C., V.P.-Human Resources--Caliber System, Inc., Akron, OH; *U.S. Public*, pg. 604

Brown, Donna, Dir.-Personnel--Corporate Express Delivery Systems Southwest, Inc., Houston, TX; *U.S. Public*, pg. 449

Brown, Fran, Dir.-Personnel--Inductotherm Industries, Inc., Rancocas, NJ; *U.S. Private*, pg. 560

Brown, Francis C., V.P.-H.R.--AutoZone, Inc., Memphis, TN; *U.S. Public*, pg. 150

Brown, Geoff, Dir.-Human Resources--Applied Communications, Inc., Omaha, NE; *U.S. Public*, pg. 1629

Brown, George, V.P.-Dir. Of H.R.--Paul Inman Associates Inc., Farmington, MI; *U.S. Private*, pg. 564

Brown, Grady, Human Resource Adm.--Cerprobe Corporation, Gilbert, AZ; *U.S. Public*, pg. 332

Brown, Joan, Dir.-H.R. & Employee Benefits--Control Systems Inc., Saint Paul, MN; *U.S. Private*, pg. 271

Brown, John, Dir.-Human Resources--The H.T. Hackney Co., Knoxville, TN; *U.S. Private*, pg. 493

Brown, John, Mgr.-Personnel--Habisat Globe Inc., Buffalo, NY; *Int'l*, pg. 585

Brown, John W., V.P.-Human Resources--Zinc Corporation of America, Monaca, PA; *U.S. Private*, pg. 540

Brown, Karen, Dir.-Human Resources--Nathan's Famous Inc., Westbury, NY; *U.S. Public*, pg. 1152

Brown, Kelsey, Mgr.-Human Resources--American Meter Company, Horsham, PA; *Int'l*, pg. 1149

Brown, Larry, Dir.-H.R.--Weldun International, Inc., Bridgman, MI; *Int'l*, pg. 205

Brown, Larry, V.P.-Human Resources Services--High Industries, Inc., Lancaster, PA; *U.S. Private*, pg. 528

Brown, Linda, Dir.-Human Resources--Pioneer-Standard Electronics, Inc., Cleveland, OH; *U.S. Public*, pg. 1300

Brown, Meghan, Dir.-H.R.--Tapemark, Saint Paul, MN; *U.S. Private*, pg. 1068

Brown, Parker, Dir.-Personnel--The Blodgett Oven Co., Inc., Burlington, VT; *U.S. Public*, pg. 1064

Brown, Radine, Mgr.-Human Resources--Master Builders Inc., Cleveland, OH; *Int'l*, pg. 1465

Brown, Rayna, V.P.-Human Resources--Capitol Records, Inc., Hollywood, CA; *Int'l*, pg. 428

Brown, Richard, V.P.-H.R.--Medusa Corporation, Cleveland, OH; *U.S. Public*, pg. 1084

Brown, Robert, Dir.-Personnel--Y & S Candies, Farmington, NM; *U.S. Public*, pg. 812

Brown, Robert K., V.P.-H.R.--Spang & Company, Butler, PA; *U.S. Private*, pg. 1020

Brown, Robin, Second V.P.-H.R.--Columbian Mutual Life Insurance Co., Binghamton, NY; *U.S. Private*, pg. 256

Brown, Ross, V.P.-Human Resources--Analog Devices, Inc., Norwood, MA; *U.S. Public*, pg. 107

Brown, Ross S., V.P.-Human Resources--TVX Gold Inc., Toronto, Canada; *Int'l*, pg. 1345

Brown, Sandra, Mgr.-Human Resources--Atari Games Corporation, Milpitas, CA; *U.S. Public*, pg. 1727

Brown, Steve, Dir.-Human Resources--Wine World Estates Company, Saint Helena, CA; *Int'l*, pg. 917

Brownlee, Kathy, Dir.-Employee Benefits--Valhi, Inc., Dallas, TX; *U.S. Private*, pg. 270

BrownWebb, Vicky, V.P. & Human Resources Dir.--Western International Media Corporation, Los Angeles, CA; *U.S. Private*, pg. 1165

Brozovich, Tim, V.P.-Labor Rels. & Human Resources--Metz Baking Company, Deerfield, IL; *U.S. Private*, pg. 1022

Bruce, Doug, Dir.-Personnel Programs--Red Roof Inns, Inc., Hilliard, OH; *U.S. Public*, pg. 1369

Bruce, Gail, V.P.-Human Resources--The Eureka Company, Bloomington, IL; *Int'l*, pg. 440

Bruce, Peter W., Exec. V.P.--Northwestern Mutual Life Insurance Co., Milwaukee, WI; *U.S. Private*, pg. 807

Bruce, Twyla, Dir.-Human Resources--US SerVis, West Orange, NJ; *U.S. Public*, pg. 1687

Bruegger, Tim, Dir.-Human Resources--Reed Tool Company, Houston, TX; *U.S. Public*, pg. 298

Bruggeman, Douglas, V.P.-Fin. & Treas.--Rex Stores Corp., Dayton, OH; *U.S. Public*, pg. 1384

Bruggeman, Mike, Sr. V.P.-H.R.--Commercial Federal Corporation, Omaha, NE; *U.S. Public*, pg. 411

Brulot, Theodoor P.J.W., Mng. Dir.-Human Resources--Schmalbach-Lubeca AG, Braunschweig, Germany; *Int'l*, pg. 1206

Brumbaugh, Beverly M., V.P.-Human Resources & Corp. Excellence--Sheldahl, Inc., Northfield, MN; *U.S. Public*, pg. 1465

Brumfield, Byron, V.P.-Human Resources--American Buildings Co., Eufaula, AL; *U.S. Public*, pg. 69

Brumfield, Paul, V.P.-H.R., Safety, Health & Environ.--C.H. Heist Corp., Clearwater, FL; *U.S. Public*, pg. 807

Brumm, Bob, V.P.-H.R.--CarrAmerica Realty, Washington, DC; *U.S. Public*, pg. 308

Brunelle, Paul E., V.P.-Personnel--Tennant Company, Minneapolis, MN; *U.S. Public*, pg. 1577

Brunetti, Franco, Grp. V.P.-H.R. & Corp. Commun.--Montedison S.p.A., Milan, Italy; *Int'l*, pg. 324

Bruno, Frank, V.P.-H.R.--Bucyrus International, South Milwaukee, WI; *U.S. Private*, pg. 177

Brunson, Calvin, Dir.-H.R.--Overhead Door Corporation, Dallas, TX; *U.S. Private*, pg. 822

Bruscas, Angelo, V.P.-H.R.--Associated Grocers, Inc., Seattle, WA; *U.S. Private*, pg. 90

Bruser, T., Dir.-Personnel--Myers Industries, Inc., Akron, OH; *U.S. Public*, pg. 1143

Bruser, Thomas A., V.P.-Human Resources--Buckhorn Material Handling Group Inc., Milford, OH; *U.S. Public*, pg. 1143

Brusher, Paul, V.P.-Human Resources--Pneumafil Corporation, Charlotte, NC; *U.S. Private*, pg. 873

Brutoux, Ph., Dir.-Human Resources--Spadel SA, Brussels, Belgium; *Int'l*, pg. 1287

Bryan, C.J., Dir.-Admin.--Coastal Lumber Company, Weldon, NC; *U.S. Private*, pg. 248

Bryant, Galina, V.P.--Beverly Bancorporation Inc., Chicago, IL; *U.S. Public*, pg. 227

Bryant, Paul M., V.P.-Human Resources--Dresser Industries, Inc., Dallas, TX; *U.S. Public*, pg. 528

Bryant, Regina D., Dir.-Human Resources--Serologicals Corporation, Clarkston, GA; *U.S. Public*, pg. 1460

Bryant, T. Harrison, Dir.-H.R.--Digi International Inc., Minnetonka, MN; *U.S. Public*, pg. 506

Bryant, Tom, Dir.-Human Resources--Aladdin Industries, Incorporated, Nashville, TN; *U.S. Private*, pg. 30

Bucalo, Jack P., Sr. V.P.-Corp. Human Resources--Fiserv, Inc., Brookfield, WI; *U.S. Public*, pg. 647

Bucci, James, Grp. V.P.-Corp. Personnel--First Citizens Banc Shares, Inc., Raleigh, NC; *U.S. Public*, pg. 628

Bucciarelli, Gary, V.P.-Human Resources & Treas.--Medrad, Inc., Indianola, PA; *Int'l*, pg. 1204

Buck, Beverly, Human Resources Mgr.--Rockett, Burkhead, Lewis & Winslow, Raleigh, NC; *U.S. Private*, pg. 938

Buck, Douglas, V.P.-Personnel--Stemco Truck Products Division, Longview, TX; *U.S. Public*, pg. 402

Buck, M. Pamela, Dir.-Human Resources--Izod, New York, NY; *U.S. Public*, pg. 1292

Buck, N. S., V.P.-H.R.--Tree Top, Inc., Selah, WA; *U.S. Private*, pg. 1098

Buckles, Robert, Mgr.-Personnel--A & S Tribal Industries, Poplar, MT; *U.S. Private*, pg. 1

Bucknall, William L. Jr., Sr. V.P.-Human Resources & Organization--United Technologies Corporation, Hartford, CT; *U.S. Public*, pg. 1689

Buckner, Susan, Dir.-Personnel--Monroe Forgings Inc., Rochester, NY; *Int'l*, pg. 488

Buckovich, Thomas J., Dir.-Employee Rels.--P.H. Glatfelter Company, Spring Grove, PA; *U.S. Public*, pg. 746

Bucur, John, V.P.-Human Resources--PHP Healthcare Corporation, Reston, VA; *U.S. Public*, pg. 1241

Budge, Dave, Mgr.-Personnel--Bangor & Aroostook Railroad Co., Bangor, ME; *U.S. Private*, pg. 575

Budge, Scott, Sr. V.P.--SEI Investments, Oaks, PA; *U.S. Public*, pg. 1417

Buedenbender, Ulrich, Dr., Dir.-Central Personnel Div.--RWE AG, Essen, Germany; *Int'l*, pg. 1081

Buehler, Sarah, Dir.-Human Resources--Jazzercise, Inc., Carlsbad, CA; *U.S. Private*, pg. 584

Buford, Lucie, V.P.-H.R.--Comdisco, Inc., Rosemont, IL; *U.S. Public*, pg. 407

Bugbee, Jody, V.P.-Human Resources--Yankee Publishing Incorporated, Dublin, NH; *U.S. Private*, pg. 1195

Buhl, James W., Dir.-Human Resources--Outlook Group Corporation, Neenah, WI; *U.S. Public*, pg. 1235

Buisson, Jean-Rene, Sr. V.P.-H.R.--Danone Group, Paris, France; *Int'l*, pg. 379

Buitenhuis, Theresa, Sec. & Mgr.-H.R.--Dover Industries Limited, Burlington, Canada; *Int'l*, pg. 417

Buitron, Fernando, V.P. & Dir.-Human Resources--Mexicana de Aviacion S.A. de C.V., Mexico, Mexico; *Int'l*, pg. 332

Bulle, Ralph, Sr. V.P.-Human Resources--Hanover Direct, Inc., Weehawken, NJ; *U.S. Public*, pg. 782

Bunce, Robert, Dir.-Human Resources--The Cerplex Group, Inc., Tustin, CA; *U.S. Public*, pg. 332

Bundy, Phillip, V.P.-Personnel & Labor Rels.--Morgan Foods, Inc., Austin, IN; *U.S. Private*, pg. 761

Bunn, Michael, Dir.-Admin. Services--Monroc, Inc., Salt Lake City, UT; *U.S. Public*, pg. 1124

Bunten, Anita, Dir.-H.R.--United Farm Family Life Insurance Co., Indianapolis, IN; *U.S. Private*, pg. 1122

Burch-DeLuca, Kerrie, V.P.-Corp. Communication--USF&G Corporation, Baltimore, MD; *U.S. Public*, pg. 1659

Burch, Janet E., V.P.-Human Resources--Firstar Corporation-Iowa, Des Moines, IA; *U.S. Public*, pg. 643

Burch, Lisa, Mgr.-Personnel--Hays Fluid Controls-Division of Romac Industries, Dallas, NC; *U.S. Private*, pg. 942

Burchstead, Dick, Dir.-Human Resources--The Weetabix Company, Inc., Clinton, MA; *Int'l*, pg. 1488

Burden, Brad, V.P.-Human Resources--Parisian, Inc., Birmingham, AL; *U.S. Public*, pg. 1333

Burett, Valerie, Dir.-H.R.--New Plan Realty Trust, New York, NY; *U.S. Public*, pg. 1172

Burger, Fred, Dir.-Human Resources--Von Roll AG, Gerlafingen, Switzerland; *Int'l*, pg. 1480

Burgess, Chris, Mgr.-Human Resources--Paramount Carowinds, Charlotte, NC; *U.S. Private*, pg. 776

Burgess, Gary L., V.P.-H.R. & Indus. Rels.--Crown Cork & Seal Company, Inc., Philadelphia, PA; *U.S. Public*, pg. 462

Burgess, Kevin, V.P.-Human Resource--Mack Trucks, Inc., Allentown, PA; *Int'l*, pg. 1102
Burhoe, Brian W., Sr. V.P.-Human Resources--Midas-International Corp., Chicago, IL; *U.S. Public*, pg. 1766
Burian, Robert J., Sr. V.P.-H.R.--Safety-Kleen Corp., Elgin, IL; *U.S. Public*, pg. 1425
Burie, Hilde, Exec. V.P.-Human Resources--Sabena, Zaventem, Belgium; *Int'l*, pg. 1168
Buring, Volker, Grp. V.P.-H.R. & Organization--Accor S.A., Evry, France; *Int'l*, pg. 20
Burke, Deborah, Dir.-H.R.--EG & G, Inc., Wellesley, MA; *U.S. Public*, pg. 542
Burke, Frank A. Jr., V.P.-Human Resources--Biogen, Inc., Cambridge, MA; *U.S. Public*, pg. 230
Burke, Geralyn, Dir.-H.R.--PAREXEL International Corporation, Waltham, MA; *U.S. Public*, pg. 1257
Burke, Holly, Dir.-H.R.--Guest Services, Inc., Fairfax, VA; *U.S. Private*, pg. 486
Burke, John M., V.P.-Pur. & H.R.--Osco Industries Inc., Portsmouth, OH; *U.S. Private*, pg. 820
Burke, Kathleen J., Vice Chm. & Personnel Rel. Officer--BankAmerica Corporation, San Francisco, CA; *U.S. Public*, pg. 179
Burke, Morgan J., V.P.-H.R.--Inland Steel Industries, Inc., Chicago, IL; *U.S. Public*, pg. 879
Burke, Sally, V.P.-Human Resources--Ardent Software, Inc., Westborough, MA; *U.S. Public*, pg. 129
Burkett, J.M., Dir.-Human Resources--Fostoria Industries, Inc., Fostoria, OH; *U.S. Private*, pg. 421
Burkhard, Mark, V.P.-H.R.--Eaton Vance Corp., Boston, MA; *U.S. Public*, pg. 559
Burkhardt, George, Dir.-Human Resources--Aesculap, Inc., South San Francisco, CA; *Int'l*, pg. 29
Burkhart, Glenda K., Sr. V.P.-Strategic Plng. & H.R.--The Reader's Digest Association, Inc., Pleasantville, NY; *U.S. Public*, pg. 1367
Burkhart, Richard, Chief Fin. Officer & Controller--Mid-Continent Screw Products Co., Lincolnwood, IL; *U.S. Private*, pg. 743
Burklund, Clayton L., V.P.-Personnel & Admin.--Amvestors Financial Corporation, Topeka, KS; *U.S. Private*, pg. 59
Burlingame, Barry, Dir.-H.R.--Kaiser Aerospace & Electronics Corp., Foster City, CA; *U.S. Private*, pg. 605
Burlingame, Harold W., Exec. V.P.-Human Resources--AT&T Corporation, Basking Ridge, NJ; *U.S. Public*, pg. 10
Burlington, Walter, Mgr.-H.R.--Rocco Quality Foods, Inc., Saint Pauls, NC; *U.S. Private*, pg. 937
Burman, Richard, V.P. & Controller--CRN International, Inc., Hamden, CT; *U.S. Private*, pg. 197
Burnette, Jim, Dir.-Human Resources--Qualex Inc., Durham, NC; *U.S. Public*, pg. 551
Burnette, Rob, V.P.-Employee Services--W.S. Badcock Corporation, Mulberry, FL; *U.S. Private*, pg. 109
Burney, Muriel, Dir.-Human Resources--Go-Video, Inc., Scottsdale, AZ; *U.S. Public*, pg. 748
Burns, Cindy, Dir.-H.R.--ICN Pharmaceuticals, Inc., Costa Mesa, CA; *U.S. Public*, pg. 853
Burns, James T., Dir.-H.R.--Wickland Corporation, Sacramento, CA; *U.S. Private*, pg. 1174
Burns, Karla, Mgr.-Personnel--Wicks 'n Sticks, Ltd, Houston, TX; *U.S. Private*, pg. 1175
Burns, Mike L., V.P.-Human Resources & Total Quality Culture--The Goodyear Tire & Rubber Company, Akron, OH; *U.S. Public*, pg. 752
Burns, Sandi, Mgr.-Human Resources--Ardmore Farms, De Land, FL; *U.S. Public*, pg. 1348
Buron, Ed, Sr. V.P.-Human Resources--Jewel-Osco, Melrose Park, IL; *U.S. Public*, pg. 93
Burone, Maureen, Mgr.-Personnel--Lady Marlene Sales Corp., New York, NY; *U.S. Private*, pg. 642
Burr, Jonathan, V.P. & Dir.-Human Resources--Instron Corporation, Canton, MA; *U.S. Public*, pg. 882
Burrows, Donald F., V.P.-Personnel--AGA Gas, Inc., Independence, OH; *Int'l*, pg. 13
Busa, Kathryn, Mgr.-Personnel--Benthos, Inc., North Falmouth, MA; *U.S. Public*, pg. 212
Busby, Sue, Exec. Admin. & Mgr.-Human Resources--Distribution America, Des Plaines, IL; *U.S. Private*, pg. 335
Busch, David C., V.P.-Admin.--Roundy's, Inc., Pewaukee, WI; *U.S. Private*, pg. 948
Bush, Bill, Controller & Mgr.-H.R.--Woodbury Business Forms, Inc., La Grange, GA; *U.S. Private*, pg. 1186
Buss, William, Dir.-H.R.--Victaulic Company of America, Easton, PA; *U.S. Private*, pg. 1138
Butler, Clinton, Dir.-Personnel & Recruitment--Continental Conveyor & Equipment Company, Winfield, AL; *U.S. Private*, pg. 791
Butler, Clive, Dir.-Personnel & Reg. Dir.-Europe--Unilever Plc, London, United Kingdom; *Int'l*, pg. 1433
Butler, Jack, Mgr.-Human Resources--Quebecor Printing Hazleton Inc., Hazleton, PA; *Int'l*, pg. 1076
Butler, John D., Exec. V.P.-Admin. & H.R.--Textron Inc., Providence, RI; *U.S. Public*, pg. 1588
Butler, Larry, V.P.-Human Resources--PeopleSoft, Inc., Pleasanton, CA; *U.S. Public*, pg. 1276
Butler, Leslie R., Chief Human Resources Officer--CoreStates Financial Corp., Philadelphia, PA; *U.S. Public*, pg. 446
Butler, Sheila, Mgr.-Personnel--The Rival Company, Kansas City, MO; *U.S. Public*, pg. 1391
Butner, Beverly B., V.P.-Admin. & Sec.--Proto Systems of Atlanta, Alpharetta, GA; *U.S. Private*, pg. 891
Butner, James S., V.P.-Indus. & Pub. Rels.--Cone Mills Corporation, Greensboro, NC; *U.S. Public*, pg. 430
Butorac, Terry, V.P.-Human Resources--Carlson Companies, Inc., Minnetonka, MN; *U.S. Private*, pg. 211
Butryn, John, Dir.-Human Resources--Gary Steel Co., Inc., Long Beach, CA; *U.S. Private*, pg. 884
Butschle, Ron, V.P.-Human Resources--Varity Dayton Walther, Dayton, OH; *Int'l*, pg. 820
Butts, Grady P., V.P.-Human Resources--Northern States Power Company, Minneapolis, MN; *U.S. Public*, pg. 1195
Buxton, Mark, V.P.-Corp. Personnel--Del Monte Foods, San Francisco, CA; *U.S. Private*, pg. 321
Buzzard, Maura, Mgr.-Payroll & Benefits--Triarc Companies, Inc., New York, NY; *U.S. Public*, pg. 1634
Buzzell, Lynn J., Mgr.-H.R.--Independent Metals, Germantown, WI; *U.S. Private*, pg. 559
Bygrave, Charlotte, V.P.-Personnel--Hoffmann-La Roche Ltd., Mississauga, Canada; *Int'l*, pg. 1121
Bynoe, Margie, V.P.-Human Resources--Chadwick's of Boston, West Bridgewater, MA; *U.S. Public*, pg. 996
Byrd, Caleta, Mgr.-Human Resources--Production Operators Inc., Houston, TX; *U.S. Public*, pg. 298
Byrd, Marion E., Sr. V.P.-Human Resources--Government Employees Insurance Co. (GEICO), Washington, DC; *U.S. Public*, pg. 220
Byrd, R. Bryant, V.P.-Human Resources--GTE Information Services Incorporated, Dallas-Fort Worth Airport, TX; *U.S. Public*, pg. 696
Byrd, Trapinisse, Dir.-Personnel--Rauch Industries, Inc., Gastonia, NC; *U.S. Private*, pg. 1061
Byrne, Donald T., V.P.-Human Resources--Martin Marietta Space Group, Bethesda, MD; *U.S. Public*, pg. 1007
Byrnes, Robert M., Sr. V.P.-Human Resources--International Paper Company, Purchase, NY; *U.S. Public*, pg. 901
Byron, Patrice, V.P.-H.R.--The Cosmetic Center Inc., Columbia, MD; *U.S. Private*, pg. 689
Cabrelli, P.P., Dir.-Personnel--Pearson plc, London, United Kingdom; *Int'l*, pg. 1025
Cada, Dennis, Mgr.-Personnel--Radiometer America Inc., Westlake, OH; *Int'l*, pg. 1083
Cadieux, Michel, V.P.-H.R.--Telemedia Inc., Montreal, Canada; *Int'l*, pg. 1373
Cahill, Pauline, Dir.-Personnel--ITW Switches, Chicago, IL; *U.S. Public*, pg. 867
Caillier, Ed, V.P.-H.R.--Piper Jaffray Companies, Inc., Minneapolis, MN; *U.S. Public*, pg. 1300
Cain, Martin, V.P.-H.R.--American Fuel Cell & Coated Fabrics Co. (Amfuel), Magnolia, AR; *U.S. Private*, pg. 55
Cain, Susan S., Sr. V.P.-Human Resources--Deposit Guaranty Corp., Jackson, MS; *U.S. Public*, pg. 500
Cairns, Robert, Dir.-Human Resources--Boeing Fabrication Division, Auburn, WA; *U.S. Public*, pg. 240
Cajacob, Peter, V.P.-Human Resources--McClatchy Newspapers Inc., Sacramento, CA; *U.S. Public*, pg. 1065
Calabres, Debbie, Dir.-Human Resources--Amgen Boulder, Inc., Boulder, CO; *U.S. Public*, pg. 101
Calandra, Paul, Mgr.-Human Rels.--Thomson S.A., Paris, France; *Int'l*, pg. 1381
Calandra, Paul, Mgr.-Human Rels.--Thomson-CSF S.A., Paris, France; *Int'l*, pg. 1383
Calandra, Tom, V.P.-Human Resources--CommNet Cellular Inc., Englewood, CO; *U.S. Public*, pg. 414
Calanni, Patty, Mgr.-Personnel Svcs.--American Locker Group, Inc., Jamestown, NY; *U.S. Public*, pg. 85
Caldas, Dr. Gustavo, Dir.-Technical Opers.--CIBA-GEIGY Colombiana S.A., Bogota, Colombia; *Int'l*, pg. 976
Caley, Susan A., Sr. V.P. & Human Resources Dir.--Creswell, Munsell, Fultz & Zirbel, L.P., Cedar Rapids, IA; *U.S. Private*, pg. 1197
Calhoun, Gerald, V.P.-Human Resources--Telos Corporation, Ashburn, VA; *U.S. Public*, pg. 1573
Calhoun, James P., V.P.-H.R.--Quest Medical, Inc., Allen, TX; *U.S. Public*, pg. 1352
Calhoun, Jim, V.P.-Human Resources--Enterprise Service Solutions, Carrollton, TX; *U.S. Public*, pg. 729
Califar, Max, V.P.-Human Resources--Indianapolis Power & Light Company, Indianapolis, IN; *U.S. Public*, pg. 913
Callahan, Maureen, Dir.-H.R.--Zoll Medical Corporation, Burlington, MA; *U.S. Private*, pg. 1207
Callahan, Patricia R., Dir.-Personnel--Wells Fargo & Company, San Francisco, CA; *U.S. Public*, pg. 1753
Callan, Pete, Mgr.-Human Resources--McInnes Steel Company, Corry, PA; *U.S. Private*, pg. 722
Calo, Thomas, Sr. V.P.-Human Resources--Midlantic Bank, N.A., Edison, NJ; *U.S. Public*, pg. 1242
Calvente, Kathy, Dir.-Personnel--Allou Health & Beauty Care, Inc., Brentwood, NY; *U.S. Public*, pg. 55
Calvert, Marilyn, Dir.-Human Resources--SENCORP, Newport, KY; *U.S. Private*, pg. 983
Cameron, James, Dir.-Personnel--Bangor Hydro-Electric Company, Bangor, ME; *U.S. Public*, pg. 178
Cameron, Keith, Dir.-Grp. Personnel--The Burton Group PLC, London, United Kingdom; *Int'l*, pg. 237
Camire, Viateur, V.P.-H.R.--Donohue Inc., Quebec, Canada; *Int'l*, pg. 1075
Camp, Richard O., Dir.-H.R.--Freeman Decorating Co., Dallas, TX; *U.S. Private*, pg. 426
Campa, Rolando, Dir.-Human Resoces--Vitromex, S.A., Saltillo, Mexico; *Int'l*, pg. 1469
Campanile, Connie, Dir.-Personnel--SRS Technologies, Newport Beach, CA; *U.S. Private*, pg. 958
Campbell, Eric, V.P.-H.R.--International Flavors & Fragrances, Inc., New York, NY; *U.S. Public*, pg. 898
Campbell, George, V.P.-Human Resources--Edwards High Vacuum International, Wilmington, MA; *Int'l*, pg. 121
Campbell, Hilary, Mgr.-Personnel--United Utilities plc, Warrington, United Kingdom; *Int'l*, pg. 1444
Campbell, Jeanneen, Mgr.-Personnel--Misco Industries, Wichita, KS; *U.S. Private*, pg. 752
Campbell, Jim, Dir.-Personnel--Tom's Foods, Inc., Columbus, GA; *U.S. Private*, pg. 1090
Campbell, Judy, Mgr.-Human Resources--Mary Maxim, Inc., Port Huron, MI; *U.S. Private*, pg. 716
Campbell, Keith M., V.P.-H.R. & Mngmt. Svcs.--The Minnesota Mutual Life Insurance Company, Saint Paul, MN; *U.S. Private*, pg. 750
Campbell, L. Ross, V.P.-Human Resources & Admin.--Bell-Northern Research Ltd., Nepean, Canada; *Int'l*, pg. 116
Campbell, Marshall A., V.P.-H.R.--BHP Copper North America, Tucson, AZ; *Int'l*, pg. 224
Campbell, Michael H., Sr. V.P.-H.R.--Continental Airlines, Houston, TX; *U.S. Public*, pg. 439
Campbell, Norton C., V.P.-Human Resources--London Life Insurance Group, London, Canada; *Int'l*, pg. 435
Campbell, R.H., Mgr.-Personnel--British Chrome & Chemicals Ltd., Stockton on Tees, United Kingdom; *Int'l*, pg. 598
Campbell, Raymond, V.P.-H.R.--Sugar Cane Growers Cooperative of Florida, Belle Glade, FL; *U.S. Private*, pg. 1049
Campoy, Robert, Dir.-H.R.--American Water Works Association, Denver, CO; *U.S. Public*, pg. 94
Camuso, K.L., Mgr.-Human Resources--General Electric Investment Corp., Stamford, CT; *U.S. Public*, pg. 712
Canada, John, Dir.-H.R.--Gemtron Corporation, Sweetwater, TN; *Int'l*, pg. 1523
Canavan, I., Mgr.-Personnel--Arnotts plc, Dublin, Ireland; *Int'l*, pg. 81
Canfield, Charles F., V.P.-Human Resources--Moore Corporation Limited, Toronto, Canada; *Int'l*, pg. 888
Canino, Leonard, V.P.-H.R. & Admin.--CC Industries, Inc., Chicago, IL; *U.S. Private*, pg. 192
Cantreau, Eugene, Dir.-Personnel--Sierracin Corporation, Sylmar, CA; *U.S. Private*, pg. 999
Canzi, Clara, Dir.-Human Resources & Mgr.-Pub. Rels.--Johnson Wax S.p.A., Milan, Italy; *U.S. Private*, pg. 593
Capdeville, Ralph, Dir.-Personnel--Production Management Companies, Inc., Harvey, LA; *U.S. Private*, pg. 888
Capezzuti, Nancy M., Sr. V.P.- Human Resources--Southern Union Company, Austin, TX; *U.S. Public*, pg. 1491
Caplan, Deb, Mgr.-Human Resources--Harcourt General, Inc., Chestnut Hill, MA; *U.S. Public*, pg. 782
Caple, Dorry, Dir.-H.R. & Pub. Rels.--Fischer Packing Co., Louisville, KY; *Int'l*, pg. 201
Capone, Joe, V.P.-H.R. & Pub. Rels.--Canac Kitchens Ltd, Thornhill, Canada; *U.S. Private*, pg. 630
Caponigro, Leonard, V.P.-Opers.--Tork, Inc., Mount Vernon, NY; *U.S. Private*, pg. 1092
Capozio, Mary, Mgr.-H.R.--The U.S. Baird Corporation, Stratford, CT; *U.S. Private*, pg. 1124
Caprano, Marilyn, Mgr.-Human Resources--Cranston Print Works Company, Cranston, RI; *U.S. Private*, pg. 286
Caputo, Louise, V.P. & Dir.-H.R.--Central National-Gottesman Inc., Purchase, NY; *U.S. Private*, pg. 224
Caputo, Tony, V.P.-H.R.--Wherehouse Entertainment, Inc., Torrance, CA; *U.S. Private*, pg. 1171
Carabetta, John, Comptroller & Dir.-Personnel & Investor Rels.--Beauty Enterprises Inc., Hartford, CT; *U.S. Private*, pg. 128
Carballosa, Maria, Dir.-Corp. Communications--CRSS Inc., Houston, TX; *Int'l*, pg. 1415
Carboneau, Matt, Dir.-H.R.--Fabwel Inc., Elkhart, IN; *U.S. Private*, pg. 390
Carder, Gerry, V.P.-Human Resources--Shimadzu Scientific Instruments, Inc., Columbia, MD; *Int'l*, pg. 1232
Cardin, Anne, Dir.-Human Resources--Plan International USA, Inc., Warwick, RI; *U.S. Private*, pg. 869
Cardone, Sophie, V.P.-Human Resources--Lumex Medical Products, Bay Shore, NY; *U.S. Public*, pg. 758
Cardoso, Clotario Francisco, Dir.-Human Resources--Petrobras - Petroleo Brasileiro S.A., Rio de Janeiro, Brazil; *Int'l*, pg. 1041
Carew, Jane, Mgr.-Human Resources--Fred Usinger, Inc., Milwaukee, WI; *U.S. Private*, pg. 1129
Carew, Rita, Mgr.-H.R.--Merrimac Industries, Inc., West Caldwell, NJ; *U.S. Public*, pg. 1098
Carey, Kevin, Sr. V.P.-Human Resources--Avis Rent A Car System, Inc., Garden City, NY; *U.S. Public*, pg. 321
Carey, Kevin, Dir.-Human Resources--World Color-Chicago Div., Elk Grove Village, IL; *U.S. Public*, pg. 1778
Carey, Yvonne, Mgr.-Personnel--Danaher Tool Group, Lancaster, PA; *U.S. Public*, pg. 480
Carhart, George, Dir.-Human Resources--Paul Stuart, Inc., New York, NY; *U.S. Private*, pg. 844
Carioscia, Raymond, Dir.-Personnel--J.A. Sexauer, Inc., Scarsdale, NY; *U.S. Private*, pg. 352
Carius, J.R., Asst. V.P.-Employee Rels. Chief Employee Council--Emerson Electric Co., Saint Louis, MO; *U.S. Public*, pg. 572
Carl, James, Mgr.-Safety & H.R.--Cable Constructors, Inc., Iron Mountain, MI; *U.S. Private*, pg. 197
Carlquist, Robert, V.P.-Admin.--Houston Chronicle, Houston, TX; *U.S. Private*, pg. 517
Carlson, Donald M., V.P.-Human Resources--OshKosh B'Gosh, Inc., Oshkosh, WI; *U.S. Public*, pg. 1232
Carlson, Hans, Sr. V.P.-Human Resources--Pharmacia & Upjohn, Inc., Windsor, United Kingdom; *Int'l*, pg. 1047
Carlson, John, V.P.-Human Resources--INX International, Milwaukee, WI; *Int'l*, pg. 1311
Carlson, Larue, Sec.--AXIA Incorporated, Lombard, IL; *U.S. Private*, pg. 103
Carlson, Linda, Dir.-Personnel--Swinerton Inc., San Francisco, CA; *U.S. Private*, pg. 1059
Carlsson, Jan-Eric, Dir.-Personnel Devel.--SAS Trading, Stockholm, Sweden; *Int'l*, pg. 1202
Carlstone, Lawrence R., V.P.-H.R.--Waterloo Industries, Inc., Waterloo, IA; *U.S. Public*, pg. 675
Carmin, Monica, Mgr.-Personnel--Wausau Homes, Inc., Rothschild, WI; *U.S. Private*, pg. 1154
Carnahan, M.L., V.P.-Human Resources--California & Hawaiian Sugar Company Inc., Crockett, CA; *U.S. Public*, pg. 39
Carne, Francis, Dir.-Personnel & Human Resources--Weyco Group, Inc., Milwaukee, WI; *U.S. Public*, pg. 1763
Carneiro, Amalio, V.P.-H.R.--The Miami Herald, Miami, FL; *U.S. Public*, pg. 964
Carney, Dale, H.R.-Specialist--Barton Malow Enterprises, Inc., Southfield, MI; *U.S. Private*, pg. 120
Carney, James P., Asst. V.P.-Human Resources--Valley Resources, Inc., Cumberland, RI; *U.S. Public*, pg. 1706
Carolfi, Bernie, Supvr.-H.R.--Advantage Learning Systems, Inc., Wisconsin Rapids, WI; *U.S. Public*, pg. 22
Carpenter, Ernest A., V.P.-Admin. & Gen. Counsel--Tippins Incorporated, Pittsburgh, PA; *U.S. Private*, pg. 1088
Carpiaux, Michael M., Dir.-Human Resources--Wausau-Mosinee Papers Specialty Papers Group, Rhinelander, WI; *U.S. Public*, pg. 1747

Carr, Cassandra C., Sr. V.P.-Human Resources--SBC Communications Inc., San Antonio, TX; *U.S. Public*, pg. 1415
Carr, Jo, Dir.-H.R.--North American Capacitor Co., Indianapolis, IN; *U.S. Private*, pg. 803
Carr, Kathy, Dir.-H.R.--General Communication, Inc., Anchorage, AK; *U.S. Public*, pg. 708
Carr, Ruth, Mgr.-Personnel--The Hercules Tire & Rubber Company, Findlay, OH; *U.S. Private*, pg. 523
Carr, Tina, V.P.-Human Resources & Sec.--First Northern Capital Corp., Green Bay, WI; *U.S. Public*, pg. 636
Carrier, Martin, Dir.-Personnel--Waterville TG Inc., Waterville, Canada; *Int'l*, pg. 1487
Carrigan, Maureen, Mgr.-H.R.--Alimed, Inc., Dedham, MA; *U.S. Private*, pg. 34
Carrillo, Regla, Asst. V.P.-H.R.--Bacardi-Martini, USA, Inc., Miami, FL; *U.S. Private*, pg. 109
Carrington, Edward V., V.P.-Human Resources--Hercules Incorporated, Wilmington, DE; *U.S. Public*, pg. 809
Carrington, John, Mgr.-Employee Rels.--Brunswick Plant, Brunswick, ME; *U.S. Public*, pg. 444
Carrington, Maggie, Mgr.-Personnel--Chattanooga Group, Inc., Hixson, TN; *U.S. Private*, pg. 231
Carroccio, Joanne F., Mgr.-Personnel--Thermo Electric Co., Inc., Saddle Brook, NJ; *U.S. Private*, pg. 1080
Carroll, Don, V.P.-H.R.--EnviroSource-International Mill Service, Inc., Horsham, PA; *U.S. Public*, pg. 587
Carroll, Janet, Dir.-Personnel--ScotiaMocatta, New York, NY; *Int'l*, pg. 156
Carroll, John, Dir.-Personnel--Kemps Foods, Inc., Lancaster, PA; *Int'l*, pg. 752
Cartacci, Giorgio, Dir.-Human Resources--Mazzucchelli 1849 S.p.a., Castiglione Olona, Italy; *Int'l*, pg. 849
Carte, Jessie M., Mgr.-H.R.--Sherms Thunderbird Market, Medford, OR; *U.S. Private*, pg. 993
Carter, Debra, V.P. & Dir.-Human Resources--Selective Insurance Group, Inc, Branchville, NJ; *U.S. Public*, pg. 1455
Carter, Diane L., V.P.-H.R.--AmeriGas Partners, L.P., Valley Forge, PA; *U.S. Public*, pg. 1653
Carter, Guy, V.P.-Human Resources--QMS, Inc., Mobile, AL; *U.S. Public*, pg. 1346
Carter, Jack, Dir.-Personnel--John Zink Co., Tulsa, OK; *U.S. Private*, pg. 628
Carter, Jerry N, Sr. V.P.-Human Resources--Union Camp Corporation, Wayne, NJ; *U.S. Public*, pg. 1665
Carter, Richard L., Sr. V.P.-Human Resources--Ames Department Stores, Inc., Rocky Hill, CT; *U.S. Public*, pg. 99
Carter, Robert, V.P.-Personnel--Penske Corporation, Detroit, MI; *U.S. Private*, pg. 850
Carter, Robert L., V.P.-Human Resources--ABX Air, Inc., Wilmington, OH; *U.S. Public*, pg. 33
Carter, Selwym, Mgr.-H.R.--Riley Creek Lumber Company, Laclede, ID; *U.S. Private*, pg. 931
Carter, Theresa, Dir.-Human Resources--Ensoniq, Malvern, PA; *U.S. Private*, pg. 377
Cartus, Kathleen, Dir.-Personnel--Cannon, Grand Island, NY; *U.S. Private*, pg. 205
Cartwright, Jack, Dir.-Personnel--Atotech U.S.A. Inc., Rock Hill, SC; *U.S. Private*, pg. 97
Cartwright, Kathleen, V.P.-H.R.--Cinram Ltd., Scarborough, Canada; *Int'l*, pg. 293
Carty, Brian, Mng. Dir.-Fin. Svcs. & Exec. V.P.-New Bus./ Human Resources--Hill, Holliday, Connors, Cosmopulos, Inc., Boston, MA; *U.S. Private*, pg. 529
Caruso, J.A., V.P. & Dir.-Human Resources--PQ Corporation, Berwyn, PA; *U.S. Private*, pg. 827
Carver, John, Mgr.-H.R.--LSB Industries, Inc., Oklahoma City, OK; *U.S. Public*, pg. 970
Casagrande, Angela, Dir.-H.R.--Dugan & Meyers Interests, Inc., Cincinnati, OH; *U.S. Private*, pg. 345
Casalle, Iris, Mgr.-Human Resources--Power Conversion, Inc., Elmwood Park, NJ; *Int'l*, pg. 127
Casamento, Joseph, V.P.-H.R.--Twin County Grocers, Inc., Edison, NJ; *U.S. Private*, pg. 1111
Cascardo, Priscila, Mgr.-H.R.--Carfel, Inc., Miami, FL; *U.S. Private*, pg. 210
Cascardo, Priscilla, Mgr.-Human Resources--Supreme International Corp., Miami, FL; *U.S. Public*, pg. 1542
Case, Joan, Mgr.-H.R.--The Spencer Turbine Co., Windsor, CT; *U.S. Private*, pg. 1025
Casey, Beverly, Mgr.-H.R.--Towne Properties, Cincinnati, OH; *U.S. Private*, pg. 1093
Casey, Kathleen, V.P.-Human Resources--Times Mirror Magazines, Inc., New York, NY; *U.S. Public*, pg. 1616
Cash, D.R., V.P.-Human Resources & Communications--Texas-New Mexico Power Co., Fort Worth, TX; *U.S. Public*, pg. 1557
Cash, Dennis, V.P.-H.R.--TNP Enterprises, Inc., Fort Worth, TX; *U.S. Public*, pg. 1557
Cash, Ethlyn B., Mgr.-H.R.--Computer Corporation of America, Framingham, MA; *U.S. Private*, pg. 260
Cash, Glenn, Dir.-Personnel--American Fast Print, Limited, Spartanburg, SC; *U.S. Private*, pg. 53
Cashion, Don, V.P.-Human Resources--Glaxo Wellcome Inc., Research Triangle Park, NC; *Int'l*, pg. 552
Caskey, Carol, Dir.-Employee Rels.--Long John Silver's, Inc., Lexington, KY; *U.S. Private*, pg. 674
Cassidy, Al, Dir.-Human Resources--Alliant Foodservice, Bensenville, IL; *U.S. Private*, pg. 244
Cassidy, John J., Mgr.-Personnel--Franklin Sports, Inc., Stoughton, MA; *U.S. Private*, pg. 424
Cassidy, Rita, Mgr.-Personnel--Frutarom Meer Corporation, North Bergen, NJ; *U.S. Private*, pg. 554
Casson, Helen, Dir.-Personnel--Saratoga Equine Sports Center, Saratoga Springs, NY; *U.S. Private*, pg. 965
Castaignet, Christian, Dir.-Personnel--Compagnie Generale Des Eaux, Paris, France; *Int'l*, pg. 321
Castain, Esther K., Corp. Sec. & Mgr.-Employee Rels.--Vacu-Dry Company, Sebastopol, CA; *U.S. Public*, pg. 1704
Castanon, Louie, Mgr.-Human Resources--Agromac International, Inc., Gering, NE; *U.S. Private*, pg. 27
Castellano, Peggy, V.P.-Human Resources--The Orange County Register, Santa Ana, CA; *U.S. Private*, pg. 425
Castonguay, Brenda, V.P.-H.R.--Carolina Power & Light Company, Raleigh, NC; *U.S. Public*, pg. 306
Castor, Marc, V.P.-Human Resources--Case Corporation, Racine, WI; *U.S. Public*, pg. 311
Castor, Marc J., V.P.-Human Resources--Agricultural Equipment Div., J.I. Case, Racine, WI; *U.S. Public*, pg. 311
Caswell, Pat, Mgr.-Personnel--Cablewave Systems, North Haven, CT; *U.S. Private*, pg. 197
Cataldi, Rose, Office Mgr.--Cedar Farms Company, Inc., Philadelphia, PA; *U.S. Private*, pg. 221
Catalino, Ken, Dir.-H.R.--ASCG, Inc., Anchorage, AK; *U.S. Private*, pg. 80
Catt, Randall L., Exec. V.P.-Human Resources--Kimball International, Inc., Jasper, IN; *U.S. Public*, pg. 956
Catteau, Paul, Mng. Dir.-H.R., Corp. & Investment Banking--Generale de Banque S.A., Brussels, Belgium; *Int'l*, pg. 546
Cauley, Kathleen P., Dir.-Personnel--United McGill Corp., Groveport, OH; *U.S. Private*, pg. 1122
Cavanagh, Sean Frank, Dir.-Human Resources--Editions du Juris-Classeur, Paris, France; *Int'l*, pg. 1095
Cavanaugh, Andrew J., Sr. V.P.-H.R.--Estee Lauder Companies Inc., New York, NY; *U.S. Public*, pg. 594
Cavanaugh, Mike, V.P.-Admin.--OMRON Systems, Inc., Schaumburg, IL; *Int'l*, pg. 1005
Cavanna, C., Mgr.-H.R.--Presstek, Inc., Hudson, NH; *U.S. Public*, pg. 1324
Cawsey, D.R., Mgr.-H.R. & Asst. Corp. Sec.--ATCO Group Co., Calgary, Canada; *Int'l*, pg. 95
Cawthon, A. Alexander, Exec. V.P. & Dir.-H.R.--Thiele Kaolin Co., Sandersville, GA; *U.S. Private*, pg. 1081
Cazals, Bernard, V.P.-Human Resources--Groupe Pernod Ricard, Paris, France; *Int'l*, pg. 566
Celentano, Doris, Treas. & Sec.--Celentano Bros. Inc., Verona, NJ; *U.S. Private*, pg. 221
Cella, John, Dir.-Personnel--Value Line, Inc., New York, NY; *U.S. Private*, pg. 137
Cendrick, Tom, Mgr.-Adv. & Opers.--Carter Chambers Supply, Inc., Baton Rouge, LA; *U.S. Private*, pg. 216
Cenek, Robert, Exec. Mgr.-Personnel Rels.--Montana Power Company, Butte, MT; *U.S. Public*, pg. 1126
Cercone, Joseph A., Dir.-Personnel--Besser Company, Alpena, MI; *U.S. Private*, pg. 139
Cervantes, Don, Dir.-Human Resources--CCH Incorporated, Riverwoods, IL; *Int'l*, pg. 1513
Cesario, Lauretta, Dir.-H.R.--Scios Inc., Mountain View, CA; *U.S. Public*, pg. 1444
Chabod, Rene, Corp. V.P.-H.R.--Aerospatiale, Paris, France; *Int'l*, pg. 28
Chacana, Kathryn, Dir.-Human Resources--William Morrow & Co., Inc., New York, NY; *U.S. Private*, pg. 515
Chacon, Leovigildo, Dir.-Personnel--CIBA-GEIGY Colombiana S.A., Bogota, Colombia; *Int'l*, pg. 976
Chadburn, Carl T., Exec. V.P.-H.R.--Phoenix Home Life Mutual Insurance Company, Hartford, CT; *U.S. Private*, pg. 863
Chadburn, Carl T., Sr. V.P.-Human Resources--Phoenix Home Life Mutual Insurance Co., Hartford, CT; *U.S. Private*, pg. 863
Chadwell, Danny, Dir.-Corp. Affairs--Executive Software, Glendale, CA; *U.S. Private*, pg. 388
Chadwick, Everett, Chief Fin. Officer & Treas.--Chase Corporation, Braintree, MA; *U.S. Public*, pg. 337
Chaffetz, Jason, Dir.-Mktg. & Personal Care--Nu Skin International, Provo, UT; *U.S. Private*, pg. 808
Chafin, Jack, Dir.-H.R.--CFA Holding Company, Charlotte, MI; *U.S. Private*, pg. 194
Chagnon, Pierre J., Grp. V.P.-Human Resources--Bell Canada, Montreal, Canada; *Int'l*, pg. 115
Chaguri, Reinaldo, Mgr.-Personnel--LPC Industrias Alimenticias S.A., Vila Jaguara, Brazil; *Int'l*, pg. 380
Chakraborty, S.C., Exec. Dir.-Human Resources--Head Office, New Delhi, India; *Int'l*, pg. 673
Chalfin, William D., V.P.-Human Resources--Wabash Alloys Division, Wabash, IN; *U.S. Private*, pg. 264
Chalifoux, Gail, Mgr.-Human Resources--Premier Coatings, Inc., Elk Grove Village, IL; *Int'l*, pg. 1488
Chalmers, Richard, V.P.-H.R.--Red Wing Shoe Co., Inc., Red Wing, MN; *U.S. Private*, pg. 915
Chalnick, Bruce, V.P.-Human Resources--Konica Imaging USA, Inc., Glen Cove, NY; *Int'l*, pg. 749
Chamberlain, Paul, V.P.-Personnel & Admin.--Entex, Houston, TX; *U.S. Public*, pg. 843
Chambers, William L., V.P.-Human Resources--GATX Corporation, Chicago, IL; *U.S. Public*, pg. 690
Chan, Clara, Asst. Mgr.-Personnel--Sun Hung Kai Properties Ltd., Wan Chai, Hong Kong; *Int'l*, pg. 1318
Chance, Ron, Dir.-H.R.--Camping World, Inc., Bowling Green, KY; *U.S. Private*, pg. 204
Chancellor, Fred, V.P.-H.R. & Admin.--Wyse Technology Inc., San Jose, CA; *U.S. Private*, pg. 1194
Chandler, Corine M., Dir.-Personnel--Gas Tech, Newark, CA; *U.S. Public*, pg. 1593
Chandler, Howard, J., Sr. V.P. & Chief Admin. Officer--LucasVarity Inc., Buffalo, NY; *Int'l*, pg. 820
Chandler, J.H., Mgr.-Human Resources--LucasVarity plc, London, United Kingdom; *Int'l*, pg. 819
Chandler, John, Dir.-Personnel--Venchurs Packaging, Inc., Adrian, MI; *U.S. Private*, pg. 1135
Chandler, John, Dir.-Human Resources--AmTran Corporation, Conway, AR; *U.S. Public*, pg. 1167
Chandler, W.S., Jr., V.P.-Devel.--Glen Raven Mills, Inc., Glen Raven, NC; *U.S. Private*, pg. 456
Chang, Rita, Mgr.-Exec. Svcs.--Grafton Fraser Inc., Willowdale, Canada; *Int'l*, pg. 556
Channell, Lee, V.P.-People Svcs.--AFC Enterprises, Atlanta, GA; *U.S. Private*, pg. 5
Chapman, William, V.P.-Human Resources--Huntsman Corporation, Salt Lake City, UT; *U.S. Private*, pg. 549
Chappell, Sheila, Mgr.-Personnel--A.L. Hansen Manufacturing Co., Waukegan, IL; *U.S. Private*, pg. 500
Chaput, Barbara, Personnel Administrator--The Berkshire Gas Company, Pittsfield, MA; *U.S. Public*, pg. 216
Charles, Gary, Mgr.-H.R.--Littelfuse, Inc., Des Plaines, IL; *U.S. Public*, pg. 1001
Charlesworth, Dennis, Dir.-Personnel--Continental Eagle Corporation, Prattville, AL; *U.S. Private*, pg. 267
Charron, Jacques, V.P.-H.R. & Commun.--Gaz Metropolitain & Company, Montreal, Canada; *Int'l*, pg. 541
Chartrand, Jolee, V.P. & Dir.-H.R.--The Brulin Corporation, Indianapolis, IN; *U.S. Private*, pg. 176
Charts, Denise, Mgr.-Personnel--Outboard Marine Corporation, Waukegan, IL; *U.S. Private*, pg. 478
Chase, Robert, Dir.-Human Resources--Comark Communications, Inc., Chalfont, PA; *Int'l*, pg. 1383
Chase, Tom, Mgr.-Personnel--Simpson Electric Co., Elgin, IL; *U.S. Private*, pg. 1002
Chastain, Donna, Dir.-Personnel--Seabrook Wallcoverings, Inc., Memphis, TN; *U.S. Private*, pg. 978
Chatham, Joanne, Dir.-Human Resources--Worldvision Enterprises, New York, NY; *U.S. Private*, pg. 776
Chatman, Linda, V.P.-Legal Affairs & Human Resources--World's Finest Chocolate, Inc., Chicago, IL; *U.S. Private*, pg. 1191
Chattertan, Ava, V.P.-H.R. & Dir.-Admin.--Fortune Fashion Inc., City of Commerce, CA; *U.S. Private*, pg. 419
Chaumeil, George, Dir.-Personnel--Sciaky S.A., Vitry-sur-Seine, France; *Int'l*, pg. 1211
Chavance, Roberta, V.P.-Human Resources--Strouds, Inc., City of Industry, CA; *U.S. Public*, pg. 1525
Chavez, T., Mgr.-Human Resources--Hitachi Instruments, Inc., San Jose, CA; *Int'l*, pg. 622
Chavez, Teresa, Mgr.-H.R.--American Vanguard Corporation, Newport Beach, CA; *U.S. Public*, pg. 94
Cheatham, Ollie V., V.P.-Human Resources--Magna Lomason Corp., Farmington Hills, MI; *Int'l*, pg. 830
Cheatham, Sharon, Mgr.-Human Resources--O.I. Corporation, College Station, TX; *U.S. Public*, pg. 1208
Cheeks, Michael, Mgr.-Human Resources--Dermik Laboratories, Inc., Collegeville, PA; *Int'l*, pg. 1110
Chelgren, William, Benefits Administrator--ComSonics, Inc., Harrisonburg, VA; *U.S. Private*, pg. 260
Chenail, Patricia, Mgr.-H.R.--Spirol International Corp., Danielson, CT; *U.S. Private*, pg. 1026
Chenell, Mary Ann, V.P. & Dir.-Human Resources--Designs, Inc., Needham, MA; *U.S. Public*, pg. 501
Chenette, John, V.P.-Human Resources--UB Networks, Santa Clara, CA; *Int'l*, pg. 924
Chenoweth, Joe, Mgr.-Personnel--Flambeau Plastics Co., Baraboo, WI; *U.S. Private*, pg. 409
Chernack, Lee Ann, Dir.-H.R.--Esprit de Corp., San Francisco, CA; *U.S. Private*, pg. 383
Chess, Bob, Dir.-H.R.--Roadway Express, Inc., Akron, OH; *U.S. Public*, pg. 1392
Chew, Albert, V.P.-Human Resources--Club Corporation International, Dallas, TX; *U.S. Private*, pg. 247
Chiappetta, Susan, V.P.-H.R.--National Life Insurance Company, Montpelier, VT; *U.S. Private*, pg. 785
Chiaro, Joseph, Dir.-H.R.--Red Devil Inc., Union, NJ; *U.S. Private*, pg. 915
Childers, Mark V., Sr. V.P.-Organizational Devel. & Human Resources--Champion International Corp., Stamford, CT; *U.S. Public*, pg. 333
Childers, Ron, Mgr.-Personnel--Golden State Foods, Irvine, CA; *U.S. Private*, pg. 460
Childs, Edwin, V.P.-H.R.--C-COR Electronics, Inc., State College, PA; *U.S. Public*, pg. 272
Childs, Kay, V.P.-Personnel--Shaklee Corporation, San Francisco, CA; *Int'l*, pg. 1518
Chimbel, LaVonne M., V.P.-Human Resources--Orthofix Inc., Richardson, TX; *Int'l*, pg. 1011
Chin, Julie, Sr. Mgr.-Resources & Training--Standard Chartered Bank Malaysia Berhad, Kuala Lumpur, Malaysia; *Int'l*, pg. 1295
Ching, Ruby, Admin. & Personnel Mgr.--EURO RSCG Partnership, Quarry Bay, Hong Kong; *Int'l*, pg. 602
Chinni, R., V.P.-Indus. Rels.--Davis Standard Corporation, Pawcatuck, CT; *U.S. Public*, pg. 459
Chiocca, Enrico, Sr. Exec. V.P.-Personnel & Org. Div.--Istituto Bancario San Paolo Di Torino S.p.A., Turin, Italy; *Int'l*, pg. 691
Chirico, Michael, Personnel--Freeman Cosmetic Corp., Los Angeles, CA; *U.S. Private*, pg. 426
Chitty, JoAnne, Dir.-Personnel--The Shidler Group, Honolulu, HI; *U.S. Private*, pg. 994
Chizek, Roger, Dir.-Personnel--NK Lawn & Garden, Golden Valley, MN; *Int'l*, pg. 974
Chmara, Diane, Mgr.-Personnel--Kenwal Products Corp., Dearborn, MI; *U.S. Private*, pg. 615
Choenling, Sue, Dir.-Communications--Bigg's Hyper Shoppes, Inc., Milford, OH; *U.S. Public*, pg. 1541
Chohon, Doris, Mgr.-H.R. & Credit--Fleischer Manufacturing, Inc., Columbus, NE; *U.S. Private*, pg. 410
Chonko, A.T., V.P.-Human Resources--Columbia Gas Distribution Companies, Columbus, OH; *U.S. Public*, pg. 402
Chouzenoux, Pierre, Dir. Gen.-H.R.--Dassault Aviation Group, Vaucresson, France; *Int'l*, pg. 383
Chrisman, Valerie A., Sr. V.P.-Customer & Employee Services--Horace Mann Educators Corporation, Springfield, IL; *U.S. Public*, pg. 835
Chrismon, Eddie, Dir.-H.R.--Carolina Biological Supply Co., Burlington, NC; *U.S. Private*, pg. 213
Christen, Joe, V.P.-Human Resource Devel.--The Andersons Incorporated, Maumee, OH; *U.S. Public*, pg. 111
Christensen, Donald, V.P.-Human Resources--Dexter Electronic Materials Division, City of Industry, CA; *U.S. Public*, pg. 504
Christensen, Ebba, Dir.-Personnel--SAS Park Royal Hotel, Lysaker, Norway; *Int'l*, pg. 1202
Christensen, Erik Bogh, Sr. Gen. Mgr.-H.R.--The East Asiatic Company Ltd. A/S, Copenhagen, Denmark; *Int'l*, pg. 430

Christensen, Ralph, V.P.-Hallmark/H.R.--Hallmark Cards, Inc., Kansas City, MO; *U.S. Private*, pg. 495

Christian, Chip, V.P.-Human Resources--Rocco Inc., Harrisonburg, VA; *U.S. Private*, pg. 937

Christian, Dennis, Dir.-Human Resources--Thilmany Division, Kaukauna, WI; *U.S. Public*, pg. 903

Christian, Jenny, Dir.-H.R.--Pullman Industries, Inc., Pullman, MI; *U.S. Private*, pg. 894

Christian, Robert, V.P.-H.R.--Johnston Industries, Inc., Columbus, GA; *U.S. Public*, pg. 933

Christiani, Gunnar, Dir.-H.R. Grp.--Astra AB, Sodertalje, Sweden; *Int'l*, pg. 93

Christler, Mike, Mgr.-Human Resources--Bayou Steel Corporation, La Place, LA; *U.S. Public*, pg. 197

Chromey, Rosemary, Mgr.-H.R.--Sandvik Steel Co., Scranton, PA; *Int'l*, pg. 1185

Chrominska, Sylvia D., Exec. V.P.-H.R.--The Bank of Nova Scotia, Toronto, Canada; *Int'l*, pg. 155

Chung, William G., V.P.-Personnel & Indus. Rels.--Young Brothers, Ltd., Honolulu, HI; *U.S. Public*, pg. 800

Church, Kathy, Asst. V.P.-H.R.--Kansas City Life Insurance Co., Kansas City, MO; *U.S. Public*, pg. 942

Churchill, Stuart W., Mgr.-Human Resources--Menard Electric Cooperative, Petersburg, IL; *U.S. Private*, pg. 731

Chvala, Vicki, V.P.-Human Resources--American Family Mutual Insurance Co., Madison, WI; *U.S. Private*, pg. 53

Ciangiulli, Helen Sands, Asst. Sec.--International Thoroughbred Breeders, Inc., Cherry Hill, NJ; *U.S. Public*, pg. 908

Cierins, Nora, Mgr.-Personnel--Seradyn, Inc., Indianapolis, IN; *Int'l*, pg. 871

Cieslak, Daniel, Mng. Dir.-H.R.--Dunham's Athleisure Corporation, Waterford, MI; *U.S. Private*, pg. 346

Ciha T.P., Mgr.-Human Resources--Diamonite Plant, Shreve, OH; *U.S. Public*, pg. 618

Cilio, Leatrice, Dir.-Human Resources--Carillon Importers, Ltd., Fort Lee, NJ; *Int'l*, pg. 409

Cimino, Robert C., Dir.-Human Resources--Electro Scientific Industries, Inc., Portland, OR; *U.S. Public*, pg. 568

Cioffi, Ann Marie, V.P.-H.R.--Conair Corporation, Stamford, CT; *U.S. Private*, pg. 261

Cioffi, Mary, Human Resources Dir.--Griffin Bacal Inc., New York, NY; *U.S. Private*, pg. 480

Cipullo, Mitch, Mgr.-Personnel--Interform Corporation, Bridgeville, PA; *U.S. Public*, pg. 333

Civelek, Mehmet, Asst. Gen. Coord.-Human Resources--Sabanci Holding A.S., Istanbul, Turkey; *Int'l*, pg. 1167

Clair, Michel, Mgr.-Personnel--Compagnie Bancaire, Paris, France; *Int'l*, pg. 319

Clancy, Bob, Dir.-Human Resources--PSDI, Bedford, MA; *U.S. Private*, pg. 828

Clancy, Martin, Dir.-Human Resources--Itam Tech Italimplianti, Inc., Coraopolis, PA; *Int'l*, pg. 655

Clandy, Tom, Sr. V.P.-Human Resources--QVC, Inc., West Chester, PA; *U.S. Private*, pg. 897

Clansnitzer, Suzanne, Dir.-Personnel--Malloy Lithographing Inc., Ann Arbor, MI; *U.S. Private*, pg. 698

Clapp, Richard, Sr. V.P.-Personnel--Gannett Company, Inc., Arlington, VA; *U.S. Public*, pg. 698

Clardy, Thomas A., V.P.-Human Resources--Wheaton Inc., Millville, NJ; *Int'l*, pg. 67

Clarice, Alison D., Grp. Mgr.-Personnel--Sea Containers Ltd., Hamilton, Bermuda; *Int'l*, pg. 1213

Clark, Brenda, Mgr.-H.R.--Georgia-Bonded Fibers, Inc., Newark, NJ; *U.S. Public*, pg. 734

Clark, Carolyn, Mgr.-H.R.--Dana Corporation, Toledo, OH; *U.S. Public*, pg. 479

Clark, Cindy, Dir.-H.R.--Broadmoor Hotel, Inc., Colorado Springs, CO; *U.S. Private*, pg. 170

Clark, Eileen, Esq., V.P.-H.R.--AmeriSource Health Corp., Malvern, PA; *U.S. Public*, pg. 96

Clark, Gary L., Chief Admin. Officer & V.P.--Snap-Tite, Inc., Erie, PA; *U.S. Private*, pg. 1010

Clark, Jim, V.P.-Fin. & Human Resources--Bussmann Division, Ellisville, MO; *U.S. Public*, pg. 443

Clark, Kenneth L., V.P.-Indus. Rels.--Potlatch Corporation, Spokane, WA; *U.S. Public*, pg. 1318

Clark, Major L., III, Corp. Sr. V.P.-Corp. Dev. & Admin.--The Maxima Corporation, Lanham, MD; *U.S. Private*, pg. 716

Clark, Pamela D., Dir.-Human Resources--PLM International, Inc., San Francisco, CA; *U.S. Public*, pg. 1241

Clark, Steven R., Sr. V.P.-Human Resources--The Cato Corporation, Charlotte, NC; *U.S. Public*, pg. 318

Clark, William, Mgr.-Personnel--Spangler Candy Company, Bryan, OH; *U.S. Private*, pg. 1020

Clark, Winston, Dir.-Human Resources--Air Nova, Bedford, Canada; *Int'l*, pg. 36

Claus, Sherrill, Dir.-H.R.--Paradyne, Largo, FL; *U.S. Private*, pg. 838

Clay, Kenneth, Dir.-H.R.--Armstrong International, Inc., Three Rivers, MI; *U.S. Private*, pg. 83

Clay, Wendy F., V.P.-Admin.--CPAC, Inc., Leicester, NY; *U.S. Public*, pg. 282

Claypool, Jeffrey C., V.P.-H.R.--Sealy Corporation, Cleveland, OH; *U.S. Private*, pg. 978

Clayton, Robin, Mgr.-Human Resources--Galderma Laboratories, Inc., Fort Worth, TX; *Int'l*, pg. 819

Cleaver, Lynn, Acctg. Admin.--Beacon Container Corporation, Birdsboro, PA; *U.S. Private*, pg. 125

Clemens, John P., Mgr.-H.R.--St. Joseph Light & Power Co., Saint Joseph, MO; *U.S. Public*, pg. 1427

Clement, Debbie, Chief Fin. Officer--Quality Foods Inc., Little Rock, AR; *U.S. Private*, pg. 898

Clement, Ken, Dir.-Human Resources--Key Tronic Corporation, Spokane, WA; *U.S. Public*, pg. 953

Clements, Larry, Dir.-H.R.--Orr Safety Company, Louisville, KY; *U.S. Private*, pg. 820

Clements, Tambra, V.P.-Human Resources--Acxiom Corporation, Conway, AR; *U.S. Public*, pg. 18

Cleveland, Kathy, Dir.-Human Resources--Televideo, Inc., San Jose, CA; *U.S. Public*, pg. 1572

Clevidence, Thomas G., Mgr.-Human Resources--McDonald & Company Investments, Inc., Cleveland, OH; *U.S. Public*, pg. 1068

Clewes, Brian, V.P.-Human Resources--Transalta Corporation, Calgary, Canada; *Int'l*, pg. 1416

Click, Judy, Dir.-Personnel--Wheaton Van Lines, Inc., Indianapolis, IN; *U.S. Private*, pg. 1171

Clifford, Frank, V.P.-Human Resources & Admin.--Raytheon Aircraft Company, Wichita, KS; *U.S. Public*, pg. 1365

Clifford, John, Dir.-Human Resources--GEC Plessey Semiconductors, Swindon, United Kingdom; *Int'l*, pg. 544

Clink, Donald, Mgr.-Mfg. & Human Resources--Amot Controls Corporation, Richmond, CA; *U.S. Public*, pg. 1405

Clinnin, Ted, V.P.-H.R.--Certified Grocers Midwest, Inc., Hodgkins, IL; *U.S. Private*, pg. 226

Clinton, Daniel J., V.P.-Human Resources--Lear Corporation, Rochester Hills, MI; *U.S. Public*, pg. 982

Clinton, Mark, Dir.-Personnel--Gemtron Corporation, Sweetwater, TN; *Int'l*, pg. 1523

Cloer, Jim, V.P.-Employee Rels.--Cooper Power Tools Division, Lexington, SC; *U.S. Public*, pg. 444

Cloud, Corene, Dir.-Personnel--Howell Instruments Inc., Fort Worth, TX; *U.S. Private*, pg. 543

Cloverdale, David G., V.P.-H.R.--Vilter Manufacturing Corporation, Cudahy, WI; *U.S. Private*, pg. 1140

Clutter, Stephen, Mgr.-Employee Rels.--Cooper Tools, Statesboro, GA; *U.S. Public*, pg. 444

Coatney, Betty, Dir.-Personnel--International Chemical Company, Tulsa, OK; *U.S. Private*, pg. 568

Cobb, Jim, Grp. Dir.-H.R.--Specialty Textile Products, Talladega, AL; *U.S. Private*, pg. 1023

Cobb, Vivian, Dir.-H.R.--Chattanooga Choo-Choo Holiday Inn, Chattanooga, TN; *U.S. Private*, pg. 231

Coblin, James, Mgr.-Personnel Services--Nucor Corporation, Charlotte, NC; *U.S. Public*, pg. 1205

Cocchiola, Anne, Dir.-Human Resources--Suprema Specialties, Inc., Paterson, NJ; *U.S. Public*, pg. 1541

Cocchiola, Anne, Dir.-Human Resources--Suprema Specialties Northeast, Inc., Ogdensburg, NY; *U.S. Public*, *pg. 1541*

Coceo, Cecily A., V.P.-H.R.--Blue Shield of California, San Francisco, CA; *U.S. Private*, pg. 153

Cochran, Carol, Dir.-Human Resources--Hondo Oil & Gas Company, Roswell, NM; *Int'l*, pg. 818

Cochran, Mark A., V.P.-H.R. & Org. Strategy--Systems & Computer Technology Corporation, Malvern, PA; *U.S. Public*, pg. 1552

Cochran, Sherry, Gen. Mgr.--Professional/First Travelcorp, Dalton, GA; *U.S. Private*, pg. 408

Cochrane, Rod, Dir.-Personnel--Unigate PLC, London, United Kingdom; *Int'l*, pg. 1433

Cockerham, Haven, V.P.-H.R.--DTE Energy Company, Detroit, MI; *U.S. Public*, pg. 475

Cocking, Lori, Dir.-Personnel--Apertus Technologies Incorporated, Eden Prairie, MN; *U.S. Public*, pg. 119

Cocking, Lori, Mgr.-Pension Admin. & Human Resources--Apertus Technologies Incorporated, Eden Prairie, MN; *U.S. Public*, pg. 119

Cocquyt, L., Mgr.-Personnel--Agfa-Gevaert N.V., Antwerp, Belgium; *Int'l*, pg. 174

Cody, Thomas G., Exec. V.P.-Legal & Human Resources--Federated Department Stores, Inc., Cincinnati, OH; *U.S. Public*, pg. 617

Coelho, Peres, Dr., Dir.-Human Resources--Petrogal, s.a., Lisbon, Portugal; *Int'l*, pg. 1044

Coffee, Richard P., V.P.-Human Resources--National Steel Corporation, Mishawaka, IN; *Int'l*, pg. 902

Coffey, Brian, V.P.-Human Resources--Beiersdorf, Inc., Norwalk, CT; *Int'l*, pg. 182

Coffey, Brian M., Dir.-Personnel--Ragu Foods, Inc., Trumbull, CT; *Int'l*, pg. 1436

Coffey, John, V.P.-Personnel--State Farm Mutual Automobile Insurance Company, Bloomington, IL; *U.S. Private*, pg. 1036

Coffin, Dwight, V.P.-Human Resources--Continental Grain Company, New York, NY; *U.S. Private*, pg. 268

Coffman, Barbara J., Mgr.-Personnel--American Technical Publishers, Inc., Homewood, IL; *U.S. Private*, pg. 63

Cofsky, Karen Jaffee, Mgr.-Human Resources--Oil-Dri Corporation of America, Chicago, IL; *U.S. Public*, pg. 1214

Coggins, Dot, Dir.-Personnel--Swiss-M-Tex, L.P., Travelers Rest, SC; *U.S. Private*, pg. 1059

Cohen, Candice, Mgr.-H.R.--Summit Technology, Inc., Waltham, MA; *U.S. Public*, pg. 1528

Cohen, Leonard, V.P.-Human Resources--Arbor Drugs, Inc., Troy, MI; *U.S. Public*, pg. 126

Cohen, Leonard, V.P.-Human Resources--Frank's Nursery & Crafts, Inc., Detroit, MI; *U.S. Public*, pg. 715

Cohen, Robin, Dir.-Human Resources--Homeowners Group, Inc., Sunrise, FL; *U.S. Public*, pg. 832

Cohn, Stuart, V.P.-Human Resources & Admin.--Scott Forseman/Addison Wesley, Glenview, IL; *Int'l*, pg. 927

Coker, Charles D., Mgr.-Human Resources--AC Corporation, Greensboro, NC; *U.S. Private*, pg. 3

Colalillo, Claudia, Sr. V.P.-Organizational Devel.--May & Speh, Inc., Downers Grove, IL; *U.S. Public*, pg. 1063

Colaut, Jean, Head-H.R.--Bank Brussels Lambert, Brussels, Belgium; *Int'l*, pg. 146

Colbourn, Bill, Exec. Dir.-H.R. & Admin.--Blue Cross and Blue Shield Association, Chicago, IL; *U.S. Private*, pg. 151

Colclough, George, V.P.-Human Resources--Smith & Wesson Corp., Springfield, MA; *Int'l*, pg. 1397

Cole, Janice M., V.P.-Trng. & Devel.--Computer Task Group, Inc. (CTG), Buffalo, NY; *U.S. Public*, pg. 423

Cole, Jay, Dir.-Personnel--Marine World Africa USA, Vallejo, CA; *U.S. Private*, pg. 703

Cole, Terry P., V.P.-Human Resources--Foster & Gallagher, Inc., Peoria, IL; *U.S. Private*, pg. 420

Cole, Tracey, Mgr.-Human Resources--First Team Sports Inc., Anoka, MN; *U.S. Public*, pg. 638

Coleman, Barry, Dir.-H.R.--Dexter Packaging Products, Waukegan, IL; *U.S. Public*, pg. 504

Coleman, James C., Sr. V.P.-Human Resources--Premark International, Inc., Deerfield, IL; *U.S. Public*, pg. 1321

Coleman, Jon W., V.P.-Human Resources--Industrial Dielectrics, Inc., Noblesville, IN; *U.S. Private*, pg. 560

Coleman, Nancy, V.P.-H.R. & Admin.--LIVE Entertainment Inc., Van Nuys, CA; *U.S. Private*, pg. 671

Coleman, Nancy, V.P.-H.R.--LIVE Film & Mediaworks, Van Nuys, CA; *U.S. Private*, pg. 671

Coleman, Wesley A., V.P.-H.R./North American Consumer Prods.--S.C. Johnson & Son, Inc., Racine, WI; *U.S. Private*, pg. 592

Colemenares, Linda, Mgr.-Personnel--Dataram Corporation, Princeton, NJ; *U.S. Public*, pg. 487

Colgan, Celeste, V.P.-Human Resources--Halliburton Company, Dallas, TX; *U.S. Public*, pg. 775

Colgan, Celeste, V.P.-Human Resources--Halliburton Energy Services, Inc., Dallas, TX; *U.S. Public*, pg. 776

Coll, Zahira, Dir.-Personnel--Sonoma Mission Inn & Spa, Sonoma, CA; *U.S. Private*, pg. 1014

Collett, Robert, Dir.-H.R.--E.D. Bullard Company, Cynthiana, KY; *U.S. Private*, pg. 180

Collevechio, Bob, Dir.-Human Resources--Carrier Corporation, Indianapolis, IN; *U.S. Public*, pg. 1689

Collevechio, Bob, Dir.-Human Resources--Carrier Corp., Indianapolis, IN; *U.S. Public*, pg. 1690

Collevechio, Robert C., Chief H.R. Officer & V.P.--Amcast Industrial Corporation, Dayton, OH; *U.S. Public*, pg. 63

Collier, George, Chief Fin. Officer, V.P.-Fin. & Mgr.-Personnel--Streamlight Inc., Norristown, PA; *U.S. Private*, *pg. 1047*

Collier, Susan, Dir.-Personnel--Douglas/Quikut, Walnut Ridge, AR; *U.S. Public*, pg. 217

Collin, Richard, Dir.-H.R.--Bass Leisure, Burton on Trent, United Kingdom; *Int'l*, pg. 170

Collingwood, Richard J., V.P.-Gen. Services--Cedar Fair, L.P., Sandusky, OH; *U.S. Public*, pg. 319

Collins, Davis, Mgr.-Personnel--Air BC, Richmond, Canada; *Int'l*, pg. 36

Collins, Donald, V.P.-Benefits & Compensation--Foremost Corporation of America, Caledonia, MI; *U.S. Public*, pg. 667

Collins, Jean, Dir.-Personnel--Physician Sales and Services Inc., Jacksonville, FL; *U.S. Public*, pg. 1293

Collins, Joseph A., V.P.-H.R.--Collins Electric Company, Inc., Chicopee, MA; *U.S. Private*, pg. 253

Collins, Lonnie E., V.P.-Personnel--M. Bruenger & Co., Inc., Wichita, KS; *U.S. Private*, pg. 175

Collins, Mary, Dir.-H.R.--The Gazette Company, Cedar Rapids, IA; *U.S. Private*, pg. 442

Collis, Denise, Dir.-Human Resources--Proudfoot plc, Richmond, United Kingdom; *Int'l*, pg. 1071

Collister, Richard A., Exec. V.P. & Chief H.R. Officer--Comerica Incorporated, Detroit, MI; *U.S. Public*, pg. 408

Colloc'h, Francoise, Sr. Exec. V.P.-Grp. Human Resources & Communications--AXA-UAP, Paris, France; *Int'l*, pg. 18

Collum, Audrey, Dir.-H.R.--Robson Communities, Sun Lakes, AZ; *U.S. Private*, pg. 937

Colman, Robert L., V.P.-Human Resources--G.E. Aircraft Engines, Cincinnati, OH; *U.S. Public*, pg. 710

Colo, Ann, Dir.-Personnel--BEC Inc., Richmond, MI; *U.S. Private*, pg. 106

Colo, Ann, Dir.-Personnel--Brencal Contractors Inc., Detroit, MI; *U.S. Private*, pg. 106

Colon, Mercedes, Human Resources Dir.--The Lord Group, New York, NY; *U.S. Private*, pg. 325

Colon, Rosario, Dir.-Human Resources--Sein Mendez Laboratories, Inc., Rio Piedras, PR; *U.S. Public*, pg. 670

Colwell, Ann, V.P.-H.R.--The First Years Inc., Avon, MA; *U.S. Public*, pg. 642

Comeau, Susan, Exec. V.P.-Human Resources--State Street Corporation, Boston, MA; *U.S. Public*, pg. 1513

Comeau, Susan, Exec. V.P.--State Street Bank & Trust Co., Boston, MA; *U.S. Public*, pg. 1513

Comer, E. Talmon, Dir.-Human Resources--Owens & Minor Inc., Glen Allen, VA; *U.S. Public*, pg. 1236

Comesana, Juan J., Mgr.-Personnel--La Nacion S.A., Buenos Aires, Argentina; *Int'l*, pg. 785

Comilla, Alla Marie, Mgr.-Human Resources--W.R. Case & Sons Cutlery Company, Bradford, PA; *U.S. Private*, pg. 1207

Comins, Ric, Exec. V.P.-Human Resources--OfficeMax, Shaker Heights, OH; *U.S. Public*, pg. 1212

Commens, Diane, Mgr.-H.R.--Diagraph Corporation, Earth City, MO; *U.S. Private*, pg. 330

Commins, Julie, Mgr.-Personnel--J.E. Higgins Lumber Co., Concord, CA; *U.S. Private*, pg. 527

Comparin, John L., V.P.-H.R. & Admin.--ALLTEL Corporation, Little Rock, AR; *U.S. Public*, pg. 55

Compitello, Linda, Mgr.-Human Resources--Comtech Telecommunications Corp., Melville, NY; *U.S. Public*, pg. 425

Compton, Rich, Mgr.-H.R.--Ameriwood Industries International Inc., Grand Rapids, MI; *U.S. Public*, pg. 98

Comstock, Roland W., Mgr.-Human Resources--Kansas City Southern Industries, Inc., Kansas City, MO; *U.S. Public*, pg. 943

Comtet, Maurice, V.P.-Human Resources--Elf Aquitane, Paris, France; *Int'l*, pg. 444

Conant, June, Dir.-Personnel--Delta Education, Inc., Hudson, NH; *Int'l*, pg. 1402

Conaty, William J., Sr. V.P.-Human Resources--General Electric Company, Fairfield, CT; *U.S. Public*, pg. 709

Condit, Richard, Sr. V.P.-Personnel--Sundt Corp., Tucson, AZ; *U.S. Private*, pg. 1051

Condon, R.P., Dir.-Human Resources--Pluess-Staufer Industries, Inc., Proctor, VT; *Int'l*, pg. 1061

Condry, Michael, V.P.-Client Services & Human Resources--National Computer Print, Inc., Birmingham, AL; *U.S. Private*, pg. 780

Cone, D.F., V.P.-Human Resources--Amoco Oil Company, Chicago, IL; *U.S. Public*, pg. 102

Cone, David F., V.P.-H.R.--Amoco Corporation, Chicago, IL; *U.S. Public*, pg. 101
Conforti, Joanne, Exec. V.P.-H.R.--Bozell Worldwide, Inc., New York, NY; *U.S. Public*, pg. 1642
Conger, Kenneth W., Sr. V.P.-H.R.--Kohler Company, Kohler, WI; *U.S. Private*, pg. 630
Conklyn, Elizabeth D., Sr. V.P.-Human Resources--General Signal Corporation, Stamford, CT; *U.S. Public*, pg. 726
Conley, Linda, V.P.-Human Resources--Resource Mortgage Capital, Inc., Glen Allen, VA; *U.S. Public*, pg. 1382
Conlon, Cathleen, Dir.-Human Resources--Little Switzerland, Inc., Charlotte Amalie, VI; *U.S. Public*, pg. 1001
Conn, David, Dir.-Personnel--Anchor Industries Inc., Evansville, IN; *U.S. Private*, pg. 71
Conn, Mike, Dir.-Human Resources--National-Standard Co., Niles, MI; *U.S. Public*, pg. 1160
Connally, James, V.P.-H.R.--AGL Resources, Atlanta, GA; *U.S. Public*, pg. 6
Connell, Cleveland E., Dir.-Customer Services--Universal Leaf Tobacco Company, Inc., Richmond, VA; *U.S. Public*, pg. 1694
Connell, Gordon E., Sr. V.P.--Standard Federal Bank, Troy, MI; *Int'l*, pg. 10
Connelly, Elizabeth K., Sr. V.P., Corp. Sec., Human Resources & Office Mngmt.--Adler Boschetto Peebles & Partners, Inc., New York, NY; *U.S. Private*, pg. 17
Conner, Cherylle, Mgr.-Personnel--Cattleman's, Inc., Detroit, MI; *U.S. Public*, pg. 318
Conner, Kevin P., V.P.-H.R.--Westinghouse Air Brake Company, Wilmerding, PA; *U.S. Public*, pg. 1760
Conner, Richard, Mgr.-Personnel--New Hampshire Ball Bearings, Inc., Peterborough, NH; *Int'l*, pg. 868
Connors, K.B., V.P.-Human Resources & Division Counsel--Patent Construction Systems, Paramus, NJ; *U.S. Public*, pg. 793
Connors, Mary Jean, Sr. V.P.-H.R.--Knight-Ridder, Inc., Miami, FL; *U.S. Public*, pg. 963
Constanza, Joan, Mgr.-Personnel--Guest Supply, Inc., Monmouth Junction, NJ; *U.S. Public*, pg. 768
Conte, Michael, Dir.-Human Resources--General Cigar Company, Inc., Bloomfield, CT; *U.S. Public*, pg. 708
Conte, Steven A., V.P.-Human Resources--Newmont Gold Company, Denver, CO; *U.S. Public*, pg. 1179
Conti, Barbara J., Sr. V.P.--Andover Bancorp, Inc., Andover, MA; *U.S. Public*, pg. 111
Contino, Terri, Mgr.-Human Resources--Barry Controls, Brighton, MA; *U.S. Public*, pg. 124
Contois, Leo L., Sr. V.P.-Human Resources--Syntex, Palo Alto, CA; *Int'l*, pg. 1120
Cook, Barbara, V.P.-H.R.--UniHealth, Burbank, CA; *U.S. Private*, pg. 1117
Cook, Julie, Mgr.-H.R.--Samtec Inc., New Albany, IN; *U.S. Private*, pg. 963
Cook, Kathy, Supvr.-H.R.--Bliss-Salem, Inc., Salem, OH; *U.S. Private*, pg. 149
Cook, Marlene, Mgr.-Human Resources--Meridian Diagnostics, Inc., Cincinnati, OH; *U.S. Public*, pg. 1094
Cook, Mary, Dir.-Human Resources & Personnel Training & Devel.--M.D.C. Holdings, Inc., Denver, CO; *U.S. Public*, pg. 1025
Cook, Stephen, Exec. V.P.-Export--Genfoot Inc., Montreal, Canada; *Int'l*, pg. 549
Cook, Susan J., V.P.-Human Resources--Eaton Corporation, Cleveland, OH; *U.S. Public*, pg. 555
Cool, Judd R., Sr. V.P.-H.R.--Allegheny Teledyne Incorporated, Pittsburgh, PA; *U.S. Public*, pg. 43
Cooley, Charles, Dir.-Human Resources--NationsBank Corporation, Charlotte, NC; *U.S. Public*, pg. 1162
Cooley, Harold E., V.P.--G B Stores, Columbus, OH; *U.S. Private*, pg. 972
Coombs, Kevin, V.P.-Corp. Affairs--Fishery Products International Ltd., Saint Johns, Canada; *Int'l*, pg. 492
Cooney, Ed, Sr. V.P.-Personnel--The Bon Marche, Inc., Seattle, WA; *U.S. Public*, pg. 617
Coop, Sheila, V.P.-H.R.--Syncor International Corporation, Woodland Hills, CA; *U.S. Public*, pg. 1548
Cooper, Angela, Dir.-Personnel--Datapoint Corporation, San Antonio, TX; *Int'l*, pg. 384
Cooper, B., Mgr.-H.R.--P/A Industries, Inc., Bloomfield, CT; *U.S. Private*, pg. 825
Cooper, Ed, Mgr.-Personnel--Reagan Equipment Company, Inc., Gretna, LA; *U.S. Private*, pg. 913
Cooper, Jack, Mgr.-Personnel--Rollins Leasing Corp., Wilmington, DE; *U.S. Public*, pg. 1405
Cooper, James R., Mgr.-Human Resources--Faribault Foods Inc., Minneapolis, MN; *U.S. Private*, pg. 393
Cooper, Jerry D., V.P.-Human Resources--HCBeck, Dallas, TX; *U.S. Private*, pg. 490
Cooper, Kay, Dir.-H.R.--Lance, Inc., Charlotte, NC; *U.S. Public*, pg. 977
Cooper, Robert, Mgr.-Personnel--Marotta Scientific Controls, Inc., Montville, NJ; *U.S. Private*, pg. 706
Cooper, Sandy, Dir.-H.R.--Nellcor Puritan Bennett Incorporated, Pleasanton, CA; *U.S. Public*, pg. 1039
Cooper, Susan K., Sr. Human Resources Exec.--BellSouth Corporation, Atlanta, GA; *U.S. Public*, pg. 207
Cooper, Susan L., V.P.-Human Resources--The Gap, Inc., San Francisco, CA; *U.S. Public*, pg. 702
Cooper, Warren, Exec. V.P.-Human Resources & Admin.--Kmart Corporation, Troy, MI; *U.S. Public*, pg. 963
Copeland, James N., V.P.-Legal & Personnel--Murphy Eastern Oil Co., London, United Kingdom; *U.S. Public*, pg. 1142
Copeland, Sue, Mgr.-Human Resources--Manna Pro Corporation, Saint Louis, MO; *U.S. Private*, pg. 700
Coq, Raoul, Dir.-Personnel Mngmt.--Credit Agricole, Bonvin, France; *Int'l*, pg. 341
Coraci-McCann, Catherine, Sr. V.P. & Human Resources Dir.--Young & Rubicam Detroit, Detroit, MI; *U.S. Private*, pg. 1198
Corbin, Ginger, Mgr.-H.R.--Metal Trades, Inc., Hollywood, SC; *U.S. Private*, pg. 734
Corcoran, Allan, Dir.-Employee Rels.--Weis Markets, Inc., Sunbury, PA; *U.S. Public*, pg. 1751
Cordes, Linus, V.P.-H.R.--Novellus Systems, Inc., San Jose, CA; *U.S. Public*, pg. 1204
Cordes, Sue, Mgr.-Personnel--Grist Mill Company, Danville, IL; *U.S. Public*, pg. 766
Cormack, I.D., V.P.-Human Resources--Kiwi Brands Pty. Ltd., Clayton, Australia; *U.S. Public*, pg. 1434
Corman, Joan, Dir.-H.R.--W. Braun Company, Chicago, IL; *U.S. Private*, pg. 166
Corn, Fran, V.P.-H.R. & Office Mngmt.--CPM, Inc., Chicago, IL; *U.S. Private*, pg. 196
Cornbleu, Shirley, Dir.-H.R.--Simplicity Holdings Inc., New York, NY; *U.S. Private*, pg. 1002
Cornett, Robert C., V.P.-Human Resources Benefits--UNUM Corporation, Portland, ME; *U.S. Public*, pg. 1699
Cornish, Al, V.P.-Human Resources--Central Parking Corp., Nashville, TN; *U.S. Public*, pg. 326
Corona, Eduardo, Dir.-H.R.--Taca International Airlines, S. A., San Salvador, El Salvador; *Int'l*, pg. 1346
Corriveau, Roger, Dir.-Human Resources--Prism Integrated Sanitation Management, Inc., Miami, FL; *U.S. Private*, pg. 592
Cortez, Vicki, V.P.-H.R.--Tropical Sportswear International, Tampa, FL; *U.S. Private*, pg. 1105
Cortise, Vicky L., V.P.-Personnel & Risk Mngmt.--Federal Compress & Warehouse Company, Inc., Memphis, TN; *U.S. Private*, pg. 398
Costa, Juan D., Mgr.-Human Resources--Neumaticos Goodyear SA, Buenos Aires, Argentina; *U.S. Public*, pg. 753
Costello, RoseMary, Human Resources Dir.--Anderson & Lembke Inc., New York, NY; *U.S. Private*, pg. 72
Cote, Martin, Dir.-H.R.--Uniboard Division Sayabec, Sayabec, Canada; *Int'l*, pg. 1431
Cote, Richard, V.P.-Human Resources--Sico Inc., Longueuil, Canada; *Int'l*, pg. 1239
Cotton, J.W.G., Dir.-Personnel--Barclays Bank PLC, London, United Kingdom; *Int'l*, pg. 164
Coughlin, Deborah, Sr. V.P.-Personnel--Computer Associates International, Inc., Islandia, NY; *U.S. Public*, pg. 420
Coulter, Molly, Mgr.-Human Resources--Pico Products, Inc., Lake View Terrace, CA; *U.S. Public*, pg. 1294
Coulton, David R., Dir.-H.R.--NewAge Industries Inc., Willow Grove, PA; *U.S. Private*, pg. 796
Council, Ivy D., V.P.-Human Resources--Ross Stores, Inc., Newark, CA; *U.S. Public*, pg. 1405
Counen, Paul, Chief Personnel Officer--Degussa AG, Frankfurt/Main, Germany; *Int'l*, pg. 388
Coupey, P., V.P.-Human Resources--Versa Services Ltd., Etobicoke, Canada; *U.S. Private*, pg. 79
Courcelle, Jean-Pierre, V.P.-Personnel & Labor Rels.--COGEMA - Compagnie Generale des Matieres Nucleaires, Velizy-Villacoublay, France; *Int'l*, pg. 304
Courcy, Denis, V.P.-H.R.--The Jean Coutu Group (PJC) Inc., Longueuil, Canada; *Int'l*, pg. 340
Courson, Robert W., Dir.-Personnel--Calgon Carbon Corporation, Pittsburgh, PA; *U.S. Public*, pg. 292
Courtney, Caren, Dir.-Personnel & Office Mgr.--Capitol Metals Company, Torrance, CA; *U.S. Private*, pg. 206
Coute, Joe, V.P.-H.R.--Western Staff Services, Walnut Creek, CA; *U.S. Public*, pg. 1760
Cover, Fred, V.P.-H.R.--Southwest Gas Corporation, Las Vegas, NV; *U.S. Public*, pg. 1493
Covert, Pat, V.P. & Dir.-Human Resources--Rice Growers Association of California, West Sacramento, CA; *U.S. Private*, pg. 927
Cowden, Jack, V.P.-Human Resources--Collins Industries, Inc., Hutchinson, KS; *U.S. Public*, pg. 399
Cowen, Ann, V.P.-Human Resources--Phoenix Home Life Mutual Insurance Company, Hartford, CT; *U.S. Private*, pg. 863
Cowen, Ann, V.P.-Human Resources--Phoenix Home Life Mutual Insurance Co., Hartford, CT; *U.S. Private*, pg. 863
Cowen, Nancy, Mgr.-H.R.--Celebrity Incorporated, Tyler, TX; *U.S. Public*, pg. 319
Cowling, Susan, Mgr.-H.R.--Inmet Mining Corporation, Toronto, Canada; *Int'l*, pg. 678
Cox, Andrew J., V.P.-Human Resources--Walbar Inc., Peabody, MA; *U.S. Public*, pg. 402
Cox, Beverley, Sr. V.P.-H.R.--Glenayre Technologies, Inc., Charlotte, NC; *U.S. Public*, pg. 746
Cox, Carolyn, Mgr.-H.R.--Lowrance Electronics, Inc., Tulsa, OK; *U.S. Public*, pg. 1015
Cox, Christeen H., Corp. Sec. & Dir.-Human Resources--American Cometra, Inc., Fort Worth, TX; *Int'l*, pg. 562
Cox, Henry, Mgr.-H.R.--Butler Ventamatic Corp., Mineral Wells, TX; *U.S. Private*, pg. 190
Cox, Larry, V.P.-H.R.--Advanced Telemarketing Corp., Irving, TX; *U.S. Public*, pg. 11
Cox, M., Dir.-Human Resources--Van Leer Containers, Inc., Alsip, IL; *Int'l*, pg. 1146
Cox, Peter, Dir.-Grp. Personnel--Dixons Group plc, Hemel Hempstead, United Kingdom,; *Int'l*, pg. 413
Cox, Ronald, Dir.-H.R. (Martinsville)--Tultex Corporation, Martinsville, VA; *U.S. Public*, pg. 1644
Cox, Sadie, Mgr.-Personnel--Carolina Steel Corporation, Greensboro, NC; *U.S. Private*, pg. 214
Cox, Susan, Dir.-Personnel--Schroders PLC, London, United Kingdom; *Int'l*, pg. 1210
Cox, Yvonne, Mgr.-Employee Rels.--Brudi, Inc., Ridgefield, WA; *U.S. Private*, pg. 675
Cozort, Terry A., V.P.-Human Resources--Family Dollar Stores, Inc., Matthews, NC; *U.S. Public*, pg. 612
Crabtree, Howard R., V.P.-Org. & H.R.--Minerals Technologies, Inc., New York, NY; *U.S. Public*, pg. 1115
Craft, Daniel L., Sr. V.P.-Human Resources--1st Source Bank Consolidated, South Bend, IN; *U.S. Public*, pg. 638
Craft, Fred, Jr., Mgr.-H.R.--Cheraw Yarn Mills, Inc., Cheraw, SC; *U.S. Private*, pg. 233
Craig, Floyd, V.P.-H.R.--SCT Yarns, Inc., Chattanooga, TN; *U.S. Private*, pg. 956
Craig, Robert, Dir.-Personnel--Universal Flavors-U.S.A., Indianapolis, IN; *U.S. Public*, pg. 1696
Crain, Linda, Dir.-H.R.--Darling International, Inc, Irving, TX; *U.S. Public*, pg. 484
Cramer, Charles, V.P.-Personnel--Baldor Electric Company, Fort Smith, AR; *U.S. Public*, pg. 168
Cramer, Patty, Dir.-Human Resources--Ultrak Inc., Lewisville, TX; *U.S. Public*, pg. 1663
Crane, Arthur E., Dir.-Admin. & Human Resources--Odyssey Reinsurance Corporation, New York, NY; *Int'l*, pg. 1258
Crane, Basil, Mgr.-Personnel--Cape Breton Development Corporation, Glace Bay, Canada; *Int'l*, pg. 265
Crane, Russell L., Sr. V.P.-Human Resources & Admin.--PPG Industries, Inc., Pittsburgh, PA; *U.S. Public*, pg. 1245
Cranford, Aileen, V.P.-H.R.--Surgical Specialties, Reading, PA; *U.S. Private*, pg. 1056
Crater, Beth, Dir.-Human Resources--Middleby Marshall/CTX, Elgin, IL; *U.S. Public*, pg. 1110
Crawford, Bruce, Mgr.-Human Resources--Building & Industrial Products Division, Sydney, Australia; *Int'l*, pg. 225
Crawford, Ellen, Office Mgr.--Cottman Transmission Systems, Inc., Fort Washington, PA; *U.S. Private*, pg. 278
Crawford, James, V.P.-Human Resources--The Chas. Levy Company, Chicago, IL; *U.S. Private*, pg. 664
Crawford, Jim, V.P.-Human Resources--Fujisawa U.S.A., Deerfield, IL; *Int'l*, pg. 525
Crawford, Rob J., Mgr.-H.R.--Long Products Division, Whyalla, Australia; *Int'l*, pg. 227
Crawford, Sandra, V.P.-Personnel--Ellicott Machine Corporation International, Baltimore, MD; *U.S. Private*, pg. 372
Creager, Dan, V.P.-Human Resources--Alantec Corp., San Jose, CA; *U.S. Public*, pg. 667
Cree, Donna, Mgr.-H.R.--Ward Trucking Corp., Altoona, PA; *U.S. Private*, pg. 1149
Creek, Phyllis, V.P.-Human Resources--SRDS, Des Plaines, IL; *U.S. Private*, pg. 958
Creveling, Allen C., Sr. V.P.-Human Resources--Symbol Technologies, Inc., Holtsville, NY; *U.S. Public*, pg. 1546
Creviston, Robert L., Sr. V.P.-Human Resources--Kellogg Company, Battle Creek, MI; *U.S. Public*, pg. 947
Crey, Russell, Dir.-Personnel--Smith Frozen Foods, Inc., Weston, OR; *U.S. Private*, pg. 1008
Crickmore, Sue, V.P.-Human Resources--Genovese Drug Stores, Inc., Melville, NY; *U.S. Public*, pg. 730
Crisp, David, V.P.-Human Resources--Hudson's Bay Company, Toronto, Canada; *Int'l*, pg. 637
Crisp, Linda, Dir.-Admin. & Asst. Sec.--Consolidated-Tomoka Land Co., Daytona Beach, FL; *U.S. Public*, pg. 437
Crist, Elmer, V.P.-Human Resources--Ryobi Motor Products, Anderson, SC; *Int'l*, pg. 1151
Crist, Gretchen, Dir.-H.R.--Playtex Products Inc., Westport, CT; *U.S. Public*, pg. 1310
Critchlow, Don, Mgr.-H.R.--Jofco Inc., Jasper, IN; *U.S. Private*, pg. 588
Crockett, Bruce, V.P.-Human Resources--Mallinckrodt Inc., Saint Louis, MO; *U.S. Public*, pg. 1039
Crockett, Joan M., Sr. V.P.-Human Resources--The Allstate Corporation, Northbrook, IL; *U.S. Public*, pg. 55
Croft, Rob, Mgr.-Personnel--North Limited, Melbourne, Australia; *Int'l*, pg. 967
Croissant, Dorie, Human Resources & Office Mgr.--Larkin Meeder & Schweidel, Dallas, TX; *U.S. Private*, pg. 651
Crompton, Richard, Dir.-Human Resources--McCain Foods Limited, Florenceville, Canada; *Int'l*, pg. 850
Crook, Steve, Dir.-Road Driver Personnel--American Freightways Corporation, Harrison, AR; *U.S. Public*, pg. 75
Crosbie, Clay, Mgr.-Human Resources--Missiles & Space Division, Huntsville, AL; *U.S. Public*, pg. 241
Crosby, Liz, Mgr.-H.R.--Diversified Communications, Portland, ME; *U.S. Private*, pg. 336
Crosby, Roxanne, V.P.-Human Resources--Borden Foods Corporation, Columbus, OH; *U.S. Private*, pg. 157
Cross, C. Allen, Sr. V.P.-Human Resources--First American Federal Savings Bank, Bristol, VA; *U.S. Public*, pg. 624
Cross, Gar, Mgr.-Human Res.--Wiltron Company, Morgan Hill, CA; *Int'l*, pg. 77
Cross, Graeme F., Mgr.-Personnel--Bristile Clay Tiles, Ltd., Caversham, Australia; *Int'l*, pg. 216
Cross, Karen, V.P.-H.R.--Harmony House Records & Tapes, Troy, MI; *U.S. Private*, pg. 503
Crow, David C., V.P.-Human Resources--Arkla, Little Rock, AR; *U.S. Public*, pg. 843
Crowder, Graeme, Mgr.-Admin. & Personnel--Kintetsu World Express (U.K.) Ltd., Slough, United Kingdom; *Int'l*, pg. 735
Crowe, Barbara L., V.P.-Human Resources--Plum Creek Timber Co., L.P., Seattle, WA; *U.S. Public*, pg. 1311
Crowell, Carole, Dir.-Human Resources--Foster & Gallagher, Inc., Peoria, IL; *U.S. Private*, pg. 420
Crowell, Edward F., V.P.-Human Resources & Admin.--Miltope Corporation, Montgomery, AL; *U.S. Public*, pg. 1114
Crowl, Chris L., Dir.-Org. Svcs.--Cyprus Amax Minerals Company, Englewood, CO; *U.S. Public*, pg. 470
Crowley, Diane N., Corp. Sec.--Superior Auctioneers & Marketing, Inc., San Antonio, TX; *U.S. Private*, pg. 1054
Crowley, Donald, Sr. V.P.-Human Resources--First Data Corporation, Hackensack, NJ; *U.S. Public*, pg. 630
Cruea, Ruth, Admin. Asst.--Covington Foods, Inc., Covington, IN; *U.S. Private*, pg. 280
Crumley, Robert W., Sr. V.P.-Personnel--Boddie-Noell Enterprises Inc., Rocky Mount, NC; *U.S. Private*, pg. 154
Crumling, R.T., III, Pres.-Macco Adhesives & V.P.-Human Resources--ICI Paints, Cleveland, OH; *Int'l*, pg. 664
Cruz, Thomas A., V.P.-Human Resources & Admin.--Cincinnati Bell Telephone, Cincinnati, OH; *U.S. Public*, pg. 367
Csimma, Zoltan A., V.P.-Human Resources & Opers.--Genetics Institute, Inc., Cambridge, MA; *U.S. Public*, pg. 79

Cuff, Dennis, Sr. V.P.-Human Resources--Eckerd Corporation, Largo, FL; *U.S. Public*, pg. 917
Culbreth, Michael G., V.P.-Employee Rels.--Federal Paper Board Company, Inc., Montvale, NJ; *U.S. Public*, pg. 903
Culbreth, Michael G., V.P.-Employee Rels.--Imperial Bondware Corp., Montvale, NJ; *U.S. Public*, pg. 903
Culich, Nick, Chief Oper. Officer--Union City Body Company, L.P., Union City, IN; *U.S. Private*, pg. 1118
Cullen, Jeanne, Mgr.-Human Resources--Britrail Travel International Inc., New York, NY; *Int'l*, pg. 1165
Culshaw, Bill, Dir.-H.R.--Bass Taverns Ltd., Birmingham, United Kingdom; *Int'l*, pg. 170
Culverhouse, John, Dir.-Personnel & Admn.--Thorntons PLC, Darbyshire, United Kingdom; *Int'l*, pg. 1386
Cummin, I.R., Exec. Gen. Mgr.-Human Resources--Southcorp Holdings Ltd., Adelaide, Australia; *Int'l*, pg. 1287
Cummings-Frain, Mary Jo, Supervisor-Employee Benefits--S.A.S.I. Corporation, Collinsville, IL; *U.S. Private*, pg. 955
Cummins, James L., V.P.-Human Resources--CTS Corporation, Elkhart, IN; *U.S. Public*, pg. 285
Cummins, Kimberly, Recruiting Coord.--ATCOM, Inc., Research Triangle Park, NC; *U.S. Private*, pg. 94
Cummins, Robert, V.P.-H.R.--Robert Bosch Corporation, Broadview, IL; *Int'l*, pg. 204
Cunningham, Deborah M., Coord.-Pers. Rels.--Ohio Edison Co.-Akron Div., Akron, OH; *U.S. Public*, pg. 645
Cunningham, G.K., Exec. Gen. Mgr.-Corp. Affairs--Southcorp Holdings Ltd., Adelaide, Australia; *Int'l*, pg. 1287
Cunningham, J. Roger, V.P.-H.R. & Corp. Services--Confederation Life Insurance Company, Toronto, Canada; *Int'l*, pg. 325
Cunningham, Jack, Jr., V.P.--Trinity Industries Inc., Dallas, TX; *U.S. Public*, pg. 1638
Cunningham, James M., V.P.-H.R.--Argo-Tech Corporation, Cleveland, OH; *U.S. Private*, pg. 81
Cunningham, M., Dir.-Personnel--Inco Alloys International, Inc., Huntington, WV; *Int'l*, pg. 672
Cunningham, Pat, Controller & Dir.-Personnel--I. Spiewak & Sons, Inc., New York, NY; *U.S. Private*, pg. 1025
Cunningham, Patsy, Human Resources Reprentative--Software Publishing Corporation, Fairfield, NJ; *U.S. Public*, pg. 1483
Cuppett, Dona Kaye, Mgr.-H.R.--Accu-Sort Systems, Inc., Telford, PA; *U.S. Private*, pg. 11
Curcio, Peter, Dir.-Human Resources--CMI International Inc., Southfield, MI; *U.S. Private*, pg. 195
Cure, Kaye, Dir.-Human Resources--Griffin Manufacturing Co., Muskogee, OK; *U.S. Private*, pg. 481
Curia, Chris, Mgr.-H.R.--Jiffy Lube International, Inc., Houston, TX; *U.S. Public*, pg. 1272
Curless, Michael A., Sr. V.P. & Tech. & Trng. Dir.--Creswell, Munsell, Fultz & Zirbel, L.P., Cedar Rapids, IA; *U.S. Private*, pg. 1197
Curley, Robert, Dir.-Human Resources--Boeing Helicopters, Ridley Park, PA; *U.S. Public*, pg. 241
Curran, Kathy, V.P.-Human Resources--Telex Communications, Inc., Minneapolis, MN; *U.S. Private*, pg. 1074
Curry, Levy, V.P.-Human Resources--Paging Network, Inc., Plano, TX; *U.S. Public*, pg. 1252
Curry, Rita, V.P.-Personnel--U.S. Clearing Corp., New York, NY; *U.S. Public*, pg. 650
Curtin, Thomas F., Jr., V.P.-H.R.--Tridex Corporation, Westport, CT; *U.S. Public*, pg. 1637
Curtis, Ann B., Sr. V.P.--Calpine Corporation, San Jose, CA; *U.S. Public*, pg. 296
Curtis, Faith, Dir.-Personnel--Bio-Logic Systems Corp., Mundelein, IL; *U.S. Public*, pg. 230
Cusey, Francois, Dir.-Human Resources--Automobiles Citroen, Neuilly, France; *Int'l*, pg. 1020
Custadio, Eva, Dir.-Personnel--Quaker Fabric Corporation, Fall River, MA; *U.S. Public*, pg. 1347
Cutler, Stephen, Dir.-Human Resources--Polk Audio, Inc., Baltimore, MD; *U.S. Public*, pg. 1315
Cytter, Jacob, V.P.-Human Resources--Elscint Ltd., Haifa, Israel; *Int'l*, pg. 450
Czaja, Darlene E., Sec.--PC Quote, Inc., Chicago, IL; *U.S. Public*, pg. 1240
Czudak, Tracy, Dir.-Personnel--Carder Concrete Products Co., Littleton, CO; *U.S. Private*, pg. 208
D'Alesandro, Richard, Asst. V.P.--Hooper Holmes Corporation, Basking Ridge, NJ; *U.S. Public*, pg. 835
D'Ambrosio, Charles, Treas. & Dir.-Human Resources--Intermetrics, Inc., Burlington, MA; *U.S. Private*, pg. 567
D'Arcangelo, Carol, V.P.-H.R.--Broad National Bancorporation, Newark, NJ; *U.S. Public*, pg. 257
D'Arcy, Katherine McKenzie, Exec. V.P. & Dir.-Human Resources--Citizens Financial Group, Inc., Providence, RI; *Int'l*, pg. 1132
D'Arcy, Kathy A., Sr. V.P. & Dir.-Human Resources--Riggs Bank N.A., Washington, DC; *U.S. Public*, pg. 1390
D'Augusta, Alfred M., Exec. V.P.-Human Resources--Summit Bancorp, Princeton, NJ; *U.S. Public*, pg. 1527
D'Avilla, Nydia, Mgr.-Personnel--Farmland Dairies, Wallington, NJ; *U.S. Private*, pg. 395
D'Elia, Vivian, V.P.-Human Resources--Polychrome Corp. Div., Fort Lee, NJ; *Int'l*, pg. 370
D'Elia, Vivian, Sr. V.P.-Human Resources--Movado Group, Inc., Lyndhurst, NJ; *U.S. Public*, pg. 1140
D'Orazio, Gene, V.P.-Human Resources, CBNA--Cadbury Beverages North America, Stamford, CT; *Int'l*, pg. 248
Dacey, Margaret, V.P.-Corp. H.R.--Cognos Inc., Ottawa, Canada; *Int'l*, pg. 305
Daeppen, Hans-Ulrich, Mng. Dir.-Human Resources--Landis & Staefa AG, Zug, Switzerland; *Int'l*, pg. 800
Dagneau, Marius, V.P.-Human Resources--Imperial Tobacco Limited, Montreal, Canada; *Int'l*, pg. 112
Dahl, Lone, Mgr.-Personnel--GN Great Nordic Ltd., Copenhagen, Denmark; *Int'l*, pg. 536
Dahlstrand, Harold S., Exec. V.P.-H.R.--Spiegel, Inc., Downers Grove, IL; *U.S. Public*, pg. 1498
Dahlstrom, Nancy A., V.P.-Admin. & H.R.--Alva/Amco Pharmacal Companies, Inc., Chicago, IL; *U.S. Private*, pg. 47
Daily, James A., V.P.-Admin. Svcs.--Cajun Electric Power Co-op, Baton Rouge, LA; *U.S. Private*, pg. 199
Dainton, Ronald F., V.P.-Human Resources--First Brands Corporation, Danbury, CT; *U.S. Public*, pg. 626
Dajer, Antonio, V.P.-Human Resources & Asst. Sec.--Pueblo International, Inc.-P.R. Div., Carolina, PR; *U.S. Private*, pg. 894
Dale, Jean, Dir.-Personnel--Vertical Products Div., City of Industry, CA; *U.S. Public*, pg. 861
Daley, Dan, Dir.-Personnel--Kohl's Food Stores, Wauwatosa, WI; *Int'l*, pg. 1375
Daley, Patrick, Dir.-Human Resources, Employee Benefits & Pension Admin.--Lindsay Manufacturing Company, Lindsay, NE; *U.S. Public*, pg. 999
Dallacqua, John, Chief Fin. Officer, V.P.-Fin., Treas. & Sec.--Crowley, Milner & Company, Detroit, MI; *U.S. Public*, pg. 461
Dallal, Elias, V.P.-Personnel & Admin.--El Al Airlines Ltd., Lod, Israel; *Int'l*, pg. 435
Dalloy, Pierre, Exec. V.P.-H.R.--Credit Nationale, Paris, France; *Int'l*, pg. 344
Dalrymple, Tammy, Mgr.-Human Resources--Holt Hosiery Mills, Inc., Burlington, NC; *U.S. Private*, pg. 536
Damewood, Tom, V.P.-H.R.--Tollman/Hundley Hotels, Hopewell Junction, NY; *U.S. Private*, pg. 1090
Damian, Walter E., V.P.-H.R.--The Carbide/Graphite Group, Inc., Pittsburgh, PA; *U.S. Public*, pg. 304
Dando, Stephen, Dir.-Personnel--United Distillers UK Plc, Perth, United Kingdom; *Int'l*, pg. 412
Daniel, Teresa A., V.P.-Human Resources--Arch Coal, Inc., Saint Louis, MO; *U.S. Public*, pg. 139
Daniels, Aline, Dir.-Personnel--Welsco Inc., North Little Rock, AR; *U.S. Private*, pg. 1161
Daniels, Bud, Mgr.-Personnel--Kleinert's, Inc., Plymouth Meeting, PA; *U.S. Private*, pg. 625
Daniels, Patricia, Dir.-Intl. H.R.--K-Tron International, Inc., Pitman, NJ; *U.S. Public*, pg. 938
Daniels, W.D., V.P.-H.R.--Canfor Corporation, Vancouver, Canada; *Int'l*, pg. 260
Dank, Denise, V.P.-Human Resources--Duke Realty Investments, Inc., Indianapolis, IN; *U.S. Public*, pg. 535
Danner, Hazel, Sec.--Electronic Tele-Communications, Inc., Waukesha, WI; *U.S. Public*, pg. 570
Danshy, Terry, Supvr.-Human Resources--Tropicana Dole Beverages North America, Bradenton, FL; *Int'l*, pg. 1217
Dany, Daniel, Dir.-Human Resources--Augat, Inc., Automotive Division, Mount Clemens, MI; *U.S. Public*, pg. 1598
Darrow, Katharine P., Sr. V.P.-Brdcst., Corp. Devel. & H.R.--The New York Times Company, New York, NY; *U.S. Public*, pg. 1173
Das, S.L., Gen. Mgr.-Human Resources & Pipelines--Head Office, New Delhi, India; *Int'l*, pg. 673
Dathe, Robert F., Chief Fin. Officer, Sr. V.P.-Fin., & Corp. Sec.--Marotta Scientific Controls, Inc., Montville, NJ; *U.S. Private*, pg. 706
Dauer, Robert J., Gen. Mgr.-H.R.--National Fuel Gas Company, Buffalo, NY; *U.S. Public*, pg. 1156
Dauska, John B., Dir.-Personnel--Green Bay Packaging Inc., Green Bay, WI; *U.S. Private*, pg. 476
Dauterman, Kurt, Dir.-Personnel--Roppe Corp., Fostoria, OH; *U.S. Private*, pg. 944
Daver, Ed, Mgr.-Personnel--Alcan Powders & Pigments Division, Union, NJ; *Int'l*, pg. 50
David, Daryl, V.P.-H.R.--MagneTek, Inc., Nashville, TN; *U.S. Public*, pg. 1037
David, Daryl D., Sr. V.P.-Human Resources & Admin.--MagneTek, Inc., Nashville, TN; *U.S. Public*, pg. 1037
David, Gilbert, Mgr.-Personnel--Avions de Transport Regional - ATR, Blagnac, France; *Int'l*, pg. 654
David, Len, V.P.-Pub. Rels.--Henry Schein, Inc., Melville, NY; *U.S. Public*, pg. 1437
Davidson, Brad, Mgr.-Employee Rels.--Statesboro Plant, Statesboro, GA; *U.S. Public*, pg. 444
Davidson, Tom, V.P.-Human Resources--Wisconsin Tissue Mills, Inc., Menasha, WI; *U.S. Public*, pg. 347
Davie, Andrew, Chief Oper. Officer, Sec. & Mgr.-Personnel--Campbell Distillers Limited, Brentford, United Kingdom; *Int'l*, pg. 567
Davies, B.S., Mgr.-H.R.--Pembina Pipeline Corporation, Calgary, Canada; *Int'l*, pg. 1032
Davies, John, Gen. Mgr.-H.R.--Yorkshire Building Society, Bradford, United Kingdom; *Int'l*, pg. 1522
Davies, R. J., Dir.-Human Resources--South African Breweries, Ltd., Johannesburg, South Africa; *Int'l*, pg. 1286
Davies, Tom R., Dir.-Personnel--Ames Company, Parkersburg, WV; *U.S. Public*, pg. 1683
Davis, Angela, V.P.-Human Resources--Columbus Mills, Inc., Columbus, GA; *U.S. Private*, pg. 256
Davis, Ann B., V.P.-Human Resources--Hilb, Rogal and Hamilton Company, Glen Allen, VA; *U.S. Public*, pg. 826
Davis, Bill, Dir.-Personnel--SuperValu, Inc.-Keene Div., Keene, NH; *U.S. Public*, pg. 1540
Davis, Charise D., V.P.--Market Facts, Inc., Arlington Heights, IL; *U.S. Public*, pg. 1046
Davis, Dan, Mgr.-Personnel--Conbraco Industries Inc., Matthews, NC; *U.S. Private*, pg. 261
Davis, David J., Dir.-Personnel--Rochester & Pittsburgh Coal Company, Indiana, PA; *U.S. Public*, pg. 1395
Davis, Diane L., Dir.-Human Resources--Killington Limited, Killington, VT; *U.S. Private*, pg. 61
Davis, Donald D., Sr. V.P.-Employee Rels.--CSX Transportation, Inc., Jacksonville, FL; *U.S. Public*, pg. 284
Davis, Donald R., V.P.-Corp. Rels.--Gate Petroleum Company, Jacksonville, FL; *U.S. Private*, pg. 441
Davis, Donna, Dir.-Human Resources--Fisher Pierce Division, Weymouth, MA; *U.S. Public*, pg. 1250
Davis, Gary, Mgr.-Personnel--Barksdale, Inc., Los Angeles, CA; *U.S. Public*, pg. 457
Davis, Gary L., Sr. V.P.-Admin. & Personnel--JC Penney Company, Inc., Plano, TX; *U.S. Public*, pg. 916
Davis, George E., Sr. V.P.-Human Resources--Lincoln National Corporation, Fort Wayne, IN; *U.S. Public*, pg. 997
Davis, Hillel, Exec. V.P.-Personnel--Republic New York Corporation, New York, NY; *U.S. Public*, pg. 1380
Davis, James E., Dir.-H.R.--American Ecology Corporation, Boise, ID; *U.S. Public*, pg. 71
Davis, Kathy, H. R. Dir.--LVL Advertising, Palo Alto, CA; *U.S. Private*, pg. 640
Davis, Kathy, Mgr.-Personnel--Forest Oil Corporation, Denver, CO; *U.S. Public*, pg. 670
Davis, Kim, Mgr.-Personnel--Skeeter Products, Inc., Kilgore, TX; *U.S. Private*, pg. 689
Davis, Lee, V.P.-H.R.--Packerland Packing Co., Green Bay, WI; *U.S. Private*, pg. 833
Davis, Melvyn R., V.P.-Intl. Human Resources--Rockwell International Corporation, Costa Mesa, CA; *U.S. Public*, pg. 1397
Davis, Mindy, Mgr.-Human Resources--Fisher Broadcasting Inc., Seattle, WA; *U.S. Public*, pg. 648
Davis, Penny L., Dir.-Human Resources Devel.--Consolidated Stores Corp., Columbus, OH; *U.S. Public*, pg. 437
Davis, Rebecca, Mgr.-Human Resources--Timec Company, Vallejo, CA; *U.S. Private*, pg. 1087
Davis, Robert, V.P.-H.R.--Kemper Insurance Companies, Long Grove, IL; *U.S. Private*, pg. 614
Davis, Roberta, Dir.-Personnel--Rogers Markets Inc., Fort Wayne, IN; *U.S. Private*, pg. 940
Davis, Stanley H., V.P.-H.R. & Org. Devel.--Huffy Corporation, Miamisburg, OH; *U.S. Public*, pg. 846
Davis, Susan, V.P.-Human Resources--Johnson Controls, Inc., Controls Group, Milwaukee, WI; *U.S. Public*, pg. 932
Davis, Susan F., V.P.-Human Resources--Johnson Controls, Inc., Milwaukee, WI; *U.S. Public*, pg. 932
Davis, Thomas, III, V.P.-Human Resources--BJ's Wholesale Club, Inc., Natick, MA; *U.S. Public*, pg. 162
Davis, Valerie, Dir.-Personnel--Cornerstone Natural Gas, Inc., Dallas, TX; *U.S. Public*, pg. 567
Davis, W. Derek, V.P.-H.R.--The Dixie Group, Inc., Chattanooga, TN; *U.S. Public*, pg. 514
Davis, W. Stewart Jr., V.P.-H.R. & Info. Sys.--Grede Foundries, Inc., Milwaukee, WI; *U.S. Private*, pg. 476
Davis, W. Stewart, Jr., V.P.-H.R. & Info. Sys.--Grede-Pryor, Inc., Pryor, OK; *U.S. Private*, pg. 476
Davitt, Charles, Dir.-Personnel--Gibraltar Steel Corp., Buffalo, NY; *U.S. Public*, pg. 742
Dawson, Beccie, Dir.-Admin. & H.R.--Wonderware Corporation, Irvine, CA; *U.S. Public*, pg. 1775
Dawson, C.M., Grp. Gen. Mgr.-Personnel--LASMO plc, London, United Kingdom; *Int'l*, pg. 803
Dawson, R.D., V.P.-Human Resources--ABB Lummus Global Inc., Bloomfield, NJ; *Int'l*, pg. 4
Day, Jonathan C., Dir.-Human Resources--Central Vermont Public Service Corporation, Rutland, VT; *U.S. Public*, pg. 327
Day, Wendy, V.P., Personnel Mgr.--Ammirati, Puris & Lintas, Inc., New York, NY; *U.S. Private*, pg. 66
de Berail, Arnaud, V.P.-Human Resources--Lafarge PlatresInternational, Sorges, France; *Int'l*, pg. 789
De Bruin, Wayne, Dir.-Indus. Rels.--Crenlo, Inc., Rochester, MN; *U.S. Private*, pg. 288
de Camargo, Joao Batista, Dir.-H.R.--Banco do Brasil, Brasilia, Brazil; *Int'l*, pg. 141
de Dietrich, Bertrand, Dir.-Human Resources--Dumez-GTM, Nanterre, France; *Int'l*, pg. 823
de Jesus, Roland P., Mgr.-Personnel--Benguet Corporation, Manila, Philippines; *Int'l*, pg. 186
de Kerchove, Andre, Chief Mgr.-Human Resources--Bank Brussels Lambert, Brussels, Belgium; *Int'l*, pg. 146
de Lalour, Grace, Sr. V.P.-Employee Rels.--TCI Communications, Inc., Englewood, CO; *U.S. Public*, pg. 1554
de Leeuw, John, Grp. H.R. Dir.--Diageo Plc, London, United Kingdom; *Int'l*, pg. 408
De Leeuw, John, Dir.-H.R.--Guinness Plc, London, United Kingdom; *Int'l*, pg. 412
De Luca, Alejandro, Mgr.-Personnel--Fate S.A., San Fernando, Argentina; *Int'l*, pg. 478
De Marco, Patricia, Dir.-Personnel--Bradley Printing Company, Des Plaines, IL; *U.S. Public*, pg. 1778
de Moraes, Sergio, Dir.-Human Resources--CPC Latin American Consumer Foods Division, Englewood Cliffs, NJ; *U.S. Public*, pg. 447
de Ocejo, Lou J., Sr. V.P.-H.R.--The Pillsbury Company, Minneapolis, MN; *Int'l*, pg. 411
de Olivera Flores, Elvio, Dir.-Quality & Human Resources--Sadia Group, Barueri, Brazil; *Int'l*, pg. 1168
de Poret, Pierre, Sr. V.P.-Personnel & H.R.--Compagnie de Suez, Paris, France; *Int'l*, pg. 313
de Ridder, C., Mgr.-H.R.--Campina Melkunie BV, Zaltbommel, Netherlands; *Int'l*, pg. 254
De Rijke, Marianne, Office Mgr.--Wieden & Kennedy-Amsterdam, Amsterdam, Netherlands; *U.S. Private*, pg. 1175
de Souza, Graham, Mgr.-H.R.--BHP Copper, San Francisco, CA; *Int'l*, pg. 227
de St. Germain, Herve, Dir.-Human Resources & Communications--Arjo Wiggins Appleton plc, Basingstoke, United Kingdom; *Int'l*, pg. 567
De Vos, Erik, Corp. V.P.-Human Resources--Sodexho S.A., Montigny-le-Bretonneux, France; *Int'l*, pg. 1274
Deacy, John S., V.P.-Human Resources--Dresher, Inc., Carthage, MO; *U.S. Public*, pg. 986
Dean, N., Advisor-Human Resources, Pub. Rels. & Communications--British Aerospace Defence Limited (Military Aircraft), Preston, United Kingdom; *Int'l*, pg. 217
Dean, Stanley, Dir.-Tax & Employee Benefits--Flexible Products Company, Marietta, GA; *U.S. Private*, pg. 412
DeAngelo, Joseph A., Treas.--Moran Transporation Company, Greenwich, CT; *U.S. Private*, pg. 760

DeAngelo, Joseph A., Treas.--Moran Towing Corporation, Greenwich, CT; *U.S. Private*, pg. 760
DeAngelo, Thomas J., Chief Fin. Officer, Treas. & Sec.--Isomedix Inc., Whippany, NJ; *U.S. Public*, pg. 1515
Dear, Theresa, Mgr.-H.R.--SPSS Inc., Chicago, IL; *U.S. Public*, pg. 1420
Dearden, Douglas E., Chief Exec. Officer--Dearden's, Los Angeles, CA; *U.S. Private*, pg. 319
Dease, William, Mgr.-H.R.--ENStar, Inc., Eden Prairie, MN; *U.S. Public*, pg. 585
DeBaun, Robert B., Corp. V.P.-H.R.--Allegiance Healthcare Corp., McGaw Park, IL; *U.S. Public*, pg. 44
DeBell, David, Dir.-H.R.--Western Gas Resources, Inc., Denver, CO; *U.S. Public*, pg. 1758
Debiasi, Glenn, V.P.-H.R.--Alex Lee, Inc., Hickory, NC; *U.S. Private*, pg. 657
DeBoer, Rhonda S., Mgr.-Human Resources--Autocam Corporation, Grand Rapids, MI; *U.S. Public*, pg. 148
DeBruin, Robert J., Mgr.-Human Resources--Svedala Industries Inc., Appleton, WI; *Int'l*, pg. 1325
DeBuono, Laureen, Exec. V.P.-H.R., Gen Counsel & Sec.--Nellcor Puritan Bennett Incorporated, Pleasanton, CA; *U.S. Public*, pg. 1039
DeCamp, Kathi, Mgr.-Human Resources--Comlinear Corporation, Fort Collins, CO; *U.S. Public*, pg. 1160
DeCarolis, Donna, Gen. Mgr.-Corp. Commun. & H.R.--National Fuel Gas Company, Buffalo, NY; *U.S. Public*, pg. 1156
DeCarolis, Donna, Gen. Mgr.-Corp. Commun. & H.R.--National Fuel Gas Distribution Corp., Buffalo, NY; *U.S. Public*, pg. 1156
DeChello, Kim, Dir.-H.R.--Essex Corporation, Columbia, MD; *U.S. Public*, pg. 593
Decker, Kim, Mgr.-H.R.--Computerized Medical Systems, Inc., Saint Louis, MO; *U.S. Private*, pg. 260
Decker, William, Dir.-H.R.--Respironics, Inc., Pittsburgh, PA; *U.S. Public*, pg. 1383
Decressac, Anne, Exec. V.P.-Personnel & Communication--Technip, Paris, France; *Int'l*, pg. 1360
Dedrick, Greg, Sr. V.P.-Human Resources--Kentucky Fried Chicken Corporation (KFC), Louisville, KY; *U.S. Public*, pg. 1636
Dedrick, Gregg, Chief People Officer--Tricon Global Restaurants, Inc., Louisville, KY; *U.S. Public*, pg. 1636
DeFayes, Isabelle, Mgr.-Human Resources--La Metaire Clinic, Nyon, Switzerland; *U.S. Public*, pg. 1036
Defruscio, Lisa, Mgr.-H.R.--American Power Conversion Corporation, West Kingston, RI; *U.S. Public*, pg. 89
Degee, F., Exec. V.P.-Personnel--Cockerill Sambre, Brussels, Belgium; *Int'l*, pg. 301
DeGenarro, Joseph, V.P.--Gemini Consulting, Morristown, NJ; *Int'l*, pg. 264
Degnan, T.E., Dir.-Personnel--Wacker Silicones Corporation, Adrian, MI; *Int'l*, pg. 625
Dehmel, Hans-Hermann, Dr., Div. Head-H.R.--BASF AG, Ludwigshafen, Germany; *Int'l*, pg. 103
DeJesus, Maritza, Mgr.-EEO/AAP--M.A. Mortenson Company, Minneapolis, MN; *U.S. Private*, pg. 763
DeJonghe, Johan, Dir.-Sls.--Haco N.V., Roeselare, Belgium; *Int'l*, pg. 585
Del Amo, Pablo, V.P.-H.R.--Y.P.F., S.A., Buenos Aires, Argentina; *Int'l*, pg. 1515
del Strother, Jeremy, Dir.-H.R.--Nationwide Building Society, Swindon, United Kingdom; *Int'l*, pg. 912
Del Vacario, Anthony, Mgr.-Wholesale Mktg.--Geneva Pharmaceuticals, Inc., Broomfield, CO; *Int'l*, pg. 973
DeLallo, Eugene, V.P.-H.R.--Brooks Instrument, Hatfield, PA; *U.S. Public*, pg. 574
Delaney, James K., V.P.-Personnel--Jacobson Stores Inc., Jackson, MI; *U.S. Public*, pg. 922
Delanoy, Mario C., Dir.-Personnel--Alcon (Puerto Rico) Inc., Humacao, PR; *Int'l*, pg. 916
Delduchetto, Thomas R., V.P.-Human Resources--ONBANCorp, Inc., Syracuse, NY; *U.S. Public*, pg. 631
Delevoy, Marc E., Dir.-Human Resources--Moore Europe, Lausanne, Switzerland; *Int'l*, pg. 889
Delgado, Elizabeth, Controller & Treas.--Presidential Realty Corporation, White Plains, NY; *U.S. Public*, pg. 1323
Dellamono, Stacie, Mgr.-H.R.--Alliance Construction Solutions, Inc., Fort Collins, CO; *U.S. Private*, pg. 38
DellaTorre, Susan, Dir.-Employee Services--Noville, South Hackensack, NJ; *U.S. Private*, pg. 808
Dellplain, Kathy, Dir.-H.R.--IDX Systems Corporation, Burlington, VT; *U.S. Public*, pg. 854
Delmenhorst, H. Fred, V.P.-H.R.--The Marcus Corporation, Milwaukee, WI; *U.S. Public*, pg. 1044
Delnegro, Anthony, V.P.-Human Resources--Empire Berol U.S.A., Brentwood, TN; *U.S. Public*, pg. 1178
DelNegro, Anthony T., V.P.-Human Resources--Berol Corporation, Brentwood, TN; *U.S. Public*, pg. 1178
DeLong, David, Mgr.-Human Resources--Homestake Canada Inc., Vancouver, Canada; *U.S. Public*, pg. 833
Delozier, J., Mgr.-H.R.--Dale Industries Inc., Dearborn, MI; *U.S. Private*, pg. 308
Delsol, Sheryl, Grp. V.P.-Human Resources--Servco Pacific Inc., Honolulu, HI; *U.S. Private*, pg. 986
Delson, Richard, Mgr.-Employee Benefits--Delicato Vineyards, Manteca, CA; *U.S. Private*, pg. 322
DeMarco, Pat, Dir.-H.R.--The Spring Air Company, Des Plaines, IL; *U.S. Private*, pg. 1027
DeMarco, William, Chief Fin. Officer & V.P.--PrimeSource Corporation, Pennsauken, NJ; *U.S. Public*, pg. 1329
Demarest, Mary, V.P.-Personnel--Camerican International, Paramus, NJ; *U.S. Public*, pg. 426
DeMaria, Benedict, V.P.-H.R. & Corp. Commun.--Mine Safety Appliances Co., Pittsburgh, PA; *U.S. Public*, pg. 1114
DeMaria, Terry, Mgr.-Personnel--Mentor Corporation, Santa Barbara, CA; *U.S. Public*, pg. 1086
DeMars, Virginia J., V.P.-Human Resources--KLA Tencor Corporation, San Jose, CA; *U.S. Public*, pg. 939
Demarte, Joseph V., V.P.-Personnel--Nordstrom, Inc., Seattle, WA; *U.S. Public*, pg. 1190
Demers, D., V.P.-H.R. & Admin. & Corp. Sec.--F.W. Myers & Co., Inc., Rouses Point, NY; *U.S. Private*, pg. 770
Demers, Fred, Mgr.-Human Resources--Hunt Valley Plant, Hunt Valley, MD; *U.S. Public*, pg. 1066
Demick, Stephen, Human Resources Gen. Mgr.--MarketSource Corporation, Cranbury, NJ; *U.S. Private*, pg. 705
Demont, David A., V.P.-H.R.--Unocal Corporation, El Segundo, CA; *U.S. Public*, pg. 1698
Dempsey, Jack, Mgr.-Personnel--Texon Materials Inc., Russell, MA; *U.S. Private*, pg. 1079
Dempsey, Yvette D., Mgr.-H.R. & Admin. Svcs.--Fay, Spofford & Thorndike, Inc., Burlington, MA; *U.S. Private*, pg. 397
Demuth, Carol, Human Resources Dir.--Creative Alliance, Inc., Louisville, KY; *U.S. Private*, pg. 287
den Haan, Aad, Mgr.-Human Resources--Varco BJ Oil Tools B.V., Etten-Leur, Netherlands; *U.S. Public*, pg. 1709
DeNicola, Nick, V.P.-H.R.--Damark International, Inc., Minneapolis, MN; *U.S. Public*, pg. 478
Denison, Ann W., V.P. & Dir.-Human Resources--SRA International Inc., Arlington, VA; *U.S. Private*, pg. 957
Denison, John B., V.P. & Sec.--National Gas & Oil Company, Newark, OH; *U.S. Public*, pg. 1156
Denning, Robert, Dir.-H.R.--Perry's Ice Cream Co., Inc., Akron, NY; *U.S. Private*, pg. 855
Dennis, Marlene, Gen. Mgr.-H.R.--Aerospace Corporation, El Segundo, CA; *U.S. Private*, pg. 24
Denny, Jim, V.P.-H.R.--QuikTrip Corporation, Tulsa, OK; *U.S. Private*, pg. 901
DeNome, Lou, V.P.-Human Resources & Process Improvement--Sawhill Tubular Div., Sharon, PA; *U.S. Public*, pg. 131
Dentz, Jeffrey, Sr. V.P.-Human Resources--Horace Small Apparel Company, Nashville, TN; *Int'l*, pg. 635
Denz, Deb, V.P.-Human Resources--Medtronic Europe S.A./N.V., Lausanne, Switzerland; *U.S. Public*, pg. 1083
DePalma, Gerald, Sr. V.P.-H.R.--Schieffelin & Somerset Co., New York, NY; *Int'l*, pg. 412
DeParde, Charlie, Dir.-Personnel--Water Technologies Group, Seneca Falls, NY; *U.S. Public*, pg. 861
DePedro, Cynthia, Mgr.-Human Resources--GZA GeoEnvironmental Technologies, Inc., Newton, MA; *U.S. Public*, pg. 697
DeRan, Tim, Human Resources Mgr.--UTA Sheridan Mfg. Plant, Wauseon, OH; *U.S. Public*, pg. 1691
Derck, Jerry N., V.P.-H.R.--IDEX Corporation, Northbrook, IL; *U.S. Public*, pg. 862
Derderian, Ruben, V.P. Milcare Customer Centers--Milcare, Inc., Grandville, MI; *U.S. Public*, pg. 1112
Derinta, David, Dir.-H.R.--Recon/Optical, Inc., Barrington, IL; *U.S. Private*, pg. 914
DeRoy, L., Mgr.-Personnel--Union Carbide (Europe) S.A., Meyrin, Switzerland; *U.S. Public*, pg. 1667
Derrick, T.C., Jr., V.P.-Labor Rels.--Emerson Electric Co., Saint Louis, MO; *U.S. Public*, pg. 572
Dertz, Susan, V.P.-Human Resources & Sec.--Louis Allis Company, Milwaukee, WI; *U.S. Private*, pg. 677
DeSabato, Anthony A., Esq., Exec. V.P. & Corp. Dir.-Human Resources--Charming Shoppes, Inc., Bensalem, PA; *U.S. Public*, pg. 335
Desautard, Jean-Marie, Dir.-Personnel--Ferembal S.A., Clichy, France; *U.S. Public*, pg. 440
Descamps, Jacques, Dir.-Human Resources--Salomon S.A., Annecy, France; *Int'l*, pg. 1181
Deschenes, Maureen, Dir.-Personnel--Wasco Products, Inc., Sanford, ME; *U.S. Private*, pg. 1152
Deshotel, Adrian B., V.P.-H.R.--American Standard Inc., Piscataway, NJ; *U.S. Public*, pg. 91
DeSmidt, Michael, Mgr.-Industrial Rels.--UTA Morganfield Plant, Morganfield, KY; *U.S. Public*, pg. 1691
DeSouza, Beverly, Mgr.-Personnel--Tasco Sales Inc., Miramar, FL; *U.S. Private*, pg. 928
Desrochers, Gisele, Sr. V.P.-Human Resources & Admin.--National Bank of Canada, Montreal, Canada; *Int'l*, pg. 907
DeThomasis, Susan J., V.P.-Human Resources--United Capital Corp., Great Neck, NY; *U.S. Public*, pg. 1674
Detrick, Miller, Dir.-Human Resources--Catalina Marketing Corporation, Saint Petersburg, FL; *U.S. Public*, pg. 314
Dettori, Vincenzo, Mgr.-Human Resources--IRI Istituto Ricostruzione Industriale, Rome, Italy; *Int'l*, pg. 652
Detwiler, D.L., Coord.-Pers. Rels.--Ohio Edison Co.-Springfield Div., Springfield, OH; *U.S. Public*, pg. 645
Deuser, Edward, Dir.-Human Resources--Ohio Machinery Co., Cleveland, OH; *U.S. Private*, pg. 812
Devaney, A.J., Dir.-Fin. & Personnel--Stafford-Miller Limited, Welwyn Garden City, United Kingdom; *U.S. Public*, pg. 237
Devaney, Bill, Dir.-Player Personnel--San Diego Chargers, San Diego, CA; *U.S. Private*, pg. 964
Devany, Ken, Mgr.-Personnel--Kennedy Valve, Elmira, NY; *U.S. Private*, pg. 725
Devine, Chuck, Sr. V.P.-Human Resources--G.E. Capital Fleet Services, Fort Wayne, IN; *U.S. Public*, pg. 710
DeVirgilio, Joseph J., Jr., V.P.-H.R. & Admin.--Central Hudson Gas & Electric Corporation, Poughkeepsie, NY; *U.S. Public*, pg. 324
DeVita, Frances, Mgr.-H.R.--Phototype Color Graphics, Inc., Pennsauken, NJ; *U.S. Private*, pg. 864
Devlin, Art, V.P.-Corp. Affairs & H.R.--Parmalat Canada Ltd., Etobicoke, Canada; *Int'l*, pg. 1023
DeVore, Bruce, V.P.-Human Resources--Philips Consumer Electronics, Knoxville, TN; *Int'l*, pg. 1054
DeVries, Chantry, Mgr.-Employee Benefits--The Weitz Company, Inc., Des Moines, IA; *U.S. Private*, pg. 1160
Dew, C. Eugene, Mgr.-Human Resources--Allied Mineral Products, Inc., Columbus, OH; *U.S. Private*, pg. 39
Dewalt, Diana, Consultant--Mitek Systems, Inc., San Diego, CA; *U.S. Public*, pg. 1117
Dewan, Vikram, Chief Human Resources Officer--CoreStates Financial Corp., Philadelphia, PA; *U.S. Public*, pg. 446
Dewitt, M., Dir.-Personnel--Fleet Engineers, Inc., Muskegon, MI; *U.S. Private*, pg. 410
DeWolf, Cathy, Mgr.-Investor Rels.--Aydin Displays (East), Horsham, PA; *U.S. Public*, pg. 158
Dexter, Cathy, Mgr.-H.R.--KTI, Inc., Guttenberg, NJ; *U.S. Public*, pg. 939
Dholakia, B.R., Gen. Mgr.-Human Resources--Head Office, New Delhi, India; *Int'l*, pg. 673
Diacont, Steven, Dir.-Human Resources--The Magee Carpet Company, Bloomsburg, PA; *U.S. Private*, pg. 694
Diano, Robert, Dir.-Human Resources--Equitrac Corporation, Coral Gables, FL; *U.S. Public*, pg. 590
Diaz, Luz P., Mgr.-Personnel--Medtronic Med Rel, Inc., Humacao, PR; *U.S. Public*, pg. 1083
Diaz, Naomi, Mgr.-Personnel--UMI Data Courier, Louisville, KY; *U.S. Public*, pg. 201
Dicandia, Juan C., Mgr.-Personnel--Banco de la Nacion Argentina, Buenos Aires, Argentina; *Int'l*, pg. 140
DiCarlo, Charlotte, Mgr.-H.R.--The North American Manufacturing Co., Cleveland, OH; *U.S. Private*, pg. 803
DiCenso, Robert E., Sr. V.P.-Personnel & Admin.--The Gillette Company, Boston, MA; *U.S. Public*, pg. 743
Dichiana, Shannon, Dir.-Human Resources--Ramsay Health Care, Inc., Coral Gables, FL; *U.S. Public*, pg. 1360
Dicke, Howard W., V.P.-Human Resources & Corp. Devel. & Treas.--Osmonics, Inc., Minnetonka, MN; *U.S. Public*, pg. 1233
Dickerson, Donna, Mgr.-Personnel--Kleer-Vu Plastics Corp., Compton, CA; *U.S. Public*, pg. 962
Dickerson, Mason O., V.P.-H.R.--CalMat Co., Los Angeles, CA; *U.S. Public*, pg. 295
Dickie, John W., Sec. & Dir.-Human Resources--ComSonics, Inc., Harrisonburg, VA; *U.S. Private*, pg. 260
Dickson, William P., Jr., V.P.-Human Resources--Russell Corporation, Alexander City, AL; *U.S. Public*, pg. 1413
Didier, D'Arcy, Dir.-H.R.--Fellowes Manufacturing Co., Itasca, IL; *U.S. Private*, pg. 400
Didrikson, Barbara J., V.P.-Human Resources--Green Tree Financial Corporation, Saint Paul, MN; *U.S. Public*, pg. 761
Diebold, John F., Dir.-Human Resources--Florsheim Group Inc., Chicago, IL; *U.S. Public*, pg. 656
Diehl, Karman, Mgr.-Payroll--Eby Corporation, Wichita, KS; *U.S. Private*, pg. 359
Diem, Ruth A., V.P. & Dir.-Human Resources--Hearst Magazines Division, New York, NY; *U.S. Private*, pg. 516
Diercks, Karen J., V.P. & Dir.-H.R.--Stanley Consultants, Inc., Muscatine, IA; *U.S. Private*, pg. 1033
Dieser, Peter M., V.P.-Human Resources--Secomerica, Inc., Newport Beach, CA; *Int'l*, pg. 1217
Dietz, Tiffany, Mgr.-Human Resources--Wisconsin Machine and Tool Corporation, Milwaukee, WI; *U.S. Private*, pg. 1185
DiGiovani, L.J., V.P.-Human Resources--Alliant Techsystems (Aerospace Division), Wilmington, DE; *U.S. Public*, pg. 47
Dilbeck, Gloria, Mgr.-H.R.--UVP, Inc., Upland, CA; *U.S. Private*, pg. 1115
Dill, Cindy, Dir.-Personnel--J.I. Kislak Inc., Hialeah, FL; *U.S. Private*, pg. 624
Dillon, Roger, Reg. Mgr.-Human Resources--Sermatech Southwest, Sugar Land, TX; *U.S. Public*, pg. 1570
DiMascio, Linda M., V.P.-H.R.--Kentucky Utilities Company, Lexington, KY; *U.S. Public*, pg. 941
DiMiglio, Lucile, Dir.-Personnel & Pur.--Norwalk Powdered Metals, Inc., Norwalk, CT; *U.S. Private*, pg. 808
Dimon, Gerry, V.P.-Corp. Resources--Ameritas Life Insurance Corp., Lincoln, NE; *U.S. Private*, pg. 65
Dingle, Larr, Mgr.-Human Resources--G.E. Superabrasives, Worthington, OH; *U.S. Public*, pg. 711
Dingman, C.E., Sr. V.P.-Human Resources--National Trustco Inc., Toronto, Canada; *Int'l*, pg. 909
Diorio, Ellen, Dir.-H.R. & Office Admin.--Binswanger, Philadelphia, PA; *U.S. Private*, pg. 144
Dirks, Tricia, Sr. V.P.-Human Resources--The Department Store Division of Dayton Hudson Corporation, Minneapolis, MN; *U.S. Public*, pg. 489
DiRubbo, Lee, Dir.-Personnel--Construction Specialties, Inc., Cranford, NJ; *U.S. Private*, pg. 266
Disbro, Eva Lynne, Dir.-H.R.--McKee Foods Corporation, Collegedale, TN; *U.S. Private*, pg. 723
Disbrow, Nancy M., V.P.-Human Resources & Corp. Sec.--Liggett-Stashower, Inc., Cleveland, OH; *U.S. Private*, pg. 667
Discepolo, Michaelanne, V.P.-Human Resources--Primedia Inc., New York, NY; *U.S. Public*, pg. 1327
Dittmar, Richard, V.P.-Employee Rels.--Kerr Group, Inc., Lancaster, PA; *U.S. Public*, pg. 952
Dix, Ronald H., V.P.-Admin. & H.R.--Badger Meter, Inc., Milwaukee, WI; *U.S. Public*, pg. 164
Dixon, David J., V.P.-H.R.--Pancho's Mexican Buffet, Inc., Fort Worth, TX; *U.S. Public*, pg. 1255
Dixon, Greg, Dir.-H.R.--J.D. Edwards & Company, Denver, CO; *U.S. Private*, pg. 365
Dixon, Maureen, Mgr.-H.R.--National Amusements, Inc., Dedham, MA; *U.S. Private*, pg. 775
Doane, Doug, V.P.-Human Resources--Hickory Farms, Inc., Maumee, OH; *U.S. Private*, pg. 525
Dobbins, Mark, V.P.-Human Resources--RBX Corporation, Roanoke, VA; *U.S. Private*, pg. 56
Dobbins, Mark, V.P.-Human Resources--Rubatex Corporation, Roanoke, VA; *U.S. Private*, pg. 56
Dobie, B.J., Dir.-Human Resources & Org. Effectiveness--Navistar International Corporation Canada, Hamilton, Canada; *U.S. Public*, pg. 1167
Dobkowski, F., V.P.-Customer Rels.--Ascom Hasler Mailing Systems, Inc., Shelton, CT; *Int'l*, pg. 86
Dobmeier, Shelly, Mgr.-H.R.--Interphase Corporation, Dallas, TX; *U.S. Public*, pg. 908
Dobson, Joanne, Mgr.-H.R.--Au Bon Pain Co., Inc., Boston, MA; *U.S. Public*, pg. 146
Dobson, Roger, Dir.-H.R.--Bradford & Bingley Building Society, Bingley, United Kingdom; *Int'l*, pg. 210

doCarmo, Winston, V.P.-Personnel--Giant Food Inc., Landover, MD; *U.S. Public*, pg. 741
Dockery, K.L., Mgr.-Human Resources--Fuller Company, Bethlehem, PA; *Int'l*, pg. 475
Dodge, Edward T., Dir.-H.R.--Giffels Associates, Inc., Southfield, MI; *U.S. Private*, pg. 452
Dodge, Judy M., V.P. & Sr. Human Resources Officer--Horizon Bancorp, Michigan City, IN; *U.S. Private*, pg. 538
Doellstedt, Jon, Dir.-Quality & Customer Support--Activision, Santa Monica, CA; *U.S. Public*, pg. 17
Dohler, D. Gary, Chief Fin. Officer, V.P. & Treas.--Atlantic Builders Group Inc., Baltimore, MD; *U.S. Private*, pg. 95
Dohr, Ronald M., V.P.-Human Resources--UTILX Corporation, Kent, WA; *U.S. Public*, pg. 1701
Dohrer, Trisha, V.P.-Human Resources--Etec Systems, Inc., Hayward, CA; *U.S. Public*, pg. 594
Dohse, Knuth, Dir.-Gen. Personnel & Social Services--Schering AG, Berlin, Germany; *Int'l*, pg. 1203
Dolan, Diane, V.P.-Human Resources--Sonic Corporation, Oklahoma City, OK; *U.S. Public*, pg. 1485
Dolan, Diane, V.P.-Admin. & Corp. Human Resources--Sonic Industries, Inc., Oklahoma City, OK; *U.S. Public*, pg. 1485
Doll, Hans Wilhelm, Mgr.-Personnel--Triumph International Gruppe Deutschland, Munich, Germany; *Int'l*, pg. 1424
Dolliver, Richard, Personnel Dir.--General Physics Corporation, Columbia, MD; *U.S. Public*, pg. 694
Doly, J.P., V.P.-Human Resources--Bagley S.A., Buenos Aires, Argentina; *Int'l*, pg. 379
Doman, Frank, V.P.-Human Resources--Bridgestone/Firestone, Inc., Nashville, TN; *Int'l*, pg. 213
Dombek, Debbie, Dir.-H.R.--Metal Seal & Products, Inc., Willoughby, OH; *U.S. Private*, pg. 734
Dombroski, George, Dir.-H.R.--Church & Dwight Co., Inc., Princeton, NJ; *U.S. Public*, pg. 355
Donahue, Mary Ann, V.P.-Human Devel.--Medtronic, Inc., Minneapolis, MN; *U.S. Public*, pg. 1082
Donaldson, M'Leah, Dir.-H.R.--TCBY Enterprises Inc., Little Rock, AR; *U.S. Public*, pg. 1553
Donaldson, Margie, Dir.-Human Resources--Tanning Research Labs., Inc., Ormond Beach, FL; *U.S. Private*, pg. 1068
Donatell, Dawn, Dir.-Human Resources--Lund International Holdings, Inc., Anoka, MN; *U.S. Public*, pg. 1020
Donnatien, Jeanette, V.P.-Human Resources--Girgenti, Hughes, Butler & McDowell, New York, NY; *U.S. Private*, *pg. 455*
Donnelly, Tom, V.P.-H.R.--Everbrite, Inc., Greenfield, WI; *U.S. Private*, pg. 386
Donovan, Dennis M., V.P.-Human Resources--G.E. Power Systems, Schenectady, NY; *U.S. Public*, pg. 711
Donovan, Gary L., V.P.-Human Resources--Makino Inc., Mason, OH; *Int'l*, pg. 831
Donsbach, Don, Mgr.-Employment & Placement--Growmark, Inc., Bloomington, IL; *U.S. Private*, pg. 484
Doolan, Laurie, Gen. Mgr.-Corp. Affairs & H.R.--Air New Zealand Ltd., Auckland, New Zealand; *Int'l*, pg. 38
Dooley, Laura, Mgr.-H.R.--D.C. Taylor Co., Cedar Rapids, IA; *U.S. Private*, pg. 1070
Doolittle, Richard A., V.P.-Human Resources--Busch Entertainment Corp., Clayton, MO; *U.S. Public*, pg. 114
Dooper, M.M.W., V.P.-Human Resources--AEGON Nederland N.V., Hague, Netherlands; *Int'l*, pg. 26
Doppstadt, William K., V.P.-Personnel Rels.--Newell Co., Freeport, IL; *U.S. Public*, pg. 1176
Doran, Diehard, Sr. Dir.-Human Resources--Ben & Jerry's Homemade Inc., South Burlington, VT; *U.S. Public*, pg. 210
Doran, John, Mgr.-Personnel--Process Equipment, Manchester, United Kingdom; *Int'l*, pg. 1444
Dore, G., Human Resources Trng. & Devel.--Kiwi Brands Pty. Ltd., Clayton, Australia; *U.S. Public*, pg. 1434
Dorf, Ira H., V.P.-Human Resources--Informix Software, Menlo Park, CA; *U.S. Public*, pg. 876
Dorff, Gordon, Sr. V.P.-Human Resources--Ag Processing Inc., A Cooperative, Omaha, NE; *U.S. Private*, pg. 26
Dorion, Robert H., Jr., V.P.-Human Resources--General Datacomm Industries, Inc., Middlebury, CT; *U.S. Public*, pg. 708
Dorman, Paul, Dir.-Personnel--Mayfair Mills, Inc., Arcadia, SC; *U.S. Private*, pg. 718
Dormann, Rudolph, Dir.-Personnel--DSM Chemie Linz GmbH, Lienz, Austria; *Int'l*, pg. 356
Dorn, James P., V.P.-Human Resources--Paragon Health Network, Inc., Atlanta, GA; *U.S. Public*, pg. 1256
Dorn, Raenell, Mgr.-H.R.--Minnesota Twins Baseball Club, Minneapolis, MN; *U.S. Private*, pg. 750
Dorr, Chris, Dir.-H.R.--Brown and Caldwell, Pleasant Hill, CA; *U.S. Private*, pg. 173
Dorsey, Bill, V.P.-Human Resources--Supreme Industries, Inc., Goshen, IN; *U.S. Public*, pg. 1541
Dorsey, Owen, Sr. V.P.-Human Resources--Saks Fifth Avenue, New York, NY; *U.S. Public*, pg. 1429
Dorsey, Tia, V.P.-H.R.--Regence BlueCross BlueShield of Oregon, Portland, OR; *U.S. Private*, pg. 917
Dotson, Marty, V.P.-Admin. & H.R.--Pioneer Aluminum, Inc., Los Angeles, CA; *U.S. Private*, pg. 866
Dotson, S., Dir.-Personnel--Webster Industries Inc., Tiffin, OH; *U.S. Private*, pg. 1157
Doucet, Edward, Dir.-Personnel--Gaz Metropolitain & Company, Montreal, Canada; *Int'l*, pg. 541
Doucette, Bill, V.P.-H.R.--Edward Don & Company, North Riverside, IL; *U.S. Private*, pg. 339
Dougherty, Thomas, Dir.-Personnel--Smith-Edwards-Dunlap Company, Philadelphia, PA; *U.S. Private*, pg. 1007
Douglas, Patricia, Mgr.-Human Resources--Mizuno USA, Inc., Norcross, GA; *Int'l*, pg. 885
Douglas, Sharon, Mgr.-H.R.--Collegeville Flag & Mfg. Company, Collegeville, PA; *U.S. Private*, pg. 252
Doutre, R., V.P.-Human Resources--Henry Birks & Sons (1993) Inc., Montreal, Canada; *Int'l*, pg. 196
Dowe, Sherry, Dir.-Human Resources--Interstate Electronics Corp., Anaheim, CA; *U.S. Public*, pg. 622
Dowling, Harry E., V.P.-Human Resources & Customer Service--Pennsylvania Enterprises Inc., Wilkes-Barre, PA; *U.S. Public*, pg. 1271
Downey, J. Patrick, V.P.-H.R.--Commercial Intertech Corp., Youngstown, OH; *U.S. Public*, pg. 411
Downs, Jon, Dir.-Human Resources--Toll Brothers, Inc., Huntingdon Valley, PA; *U.S. Public*, pg. 1620
Downs, Robert, Corp. Mgr.-HRIS--Barnes Group Inc., Bristol, CT; *U.S. Public*, pg. 189
Doyle, J., Controller--Asahi Glass America, Inc., New York, NY; *Int'l*, pg. 84
Doyon, Rose, Mgr.-Human Resources--CSP Inc., Billerica, MA; *U.S. Public*, pg. 283
Dragon, A., Dir.-Personnel--Gebr. Eickhoff Maschinenfabrik und Eisengiesserei mbH, Bochum, Germany; *Int'l*, pg. 542
Drainville, Gary P., Exec. V.P.-H.R. & Trust Asset Mngmt.--Citizens Banking Corporation, Flint, MI; *U.S. Public*, pg. 379
Dray, B.G., Dir.-Personnel--Cyanamid of Great Britain Ltd., Gosport, United Kingdom; *U.S. Public*, pg. 81
Drdek, Frank J., V.P.-Human Resources--Proxima Corporation, San Diego, CA; *U.S. Public*, pg. 1339
Dressing, Julie Stumpe, Dir.-Human Resources--Jones, Day, Reavis & Pogue, Cleveland, OH; *U.S. Private*, pg. 596
Drew, Robert E., Dir.-Personnel--Schawk, Inc., Des Plaines, IL; *U.S. Public*, pg. 1437
Drinan, Helen G., Exec. V.P. & Dir.-H.R.--BankBoston Corporation, Boston, MA; *U.S. Public*, pg. 183
Drinkwater, Cindy, Dir.-H.R.--Organizational Dynamics Inc., Burlington, MA; *U.S. Private*, pg. 819
Driscoll, Denis, Sr. V.P.-H.R.--Prime Hospitality Corp., Fairfield, NJ; *U.S. Public*, pg. 1326
Driscoll, Mike, Mgr.-Human Resources--Stafford-Miller Limited, Welwyn Garden City, United Kingdom; *U.S. Public*, pg. 237
Droege, John, V.P.-Human Relations--Green Bay Packaging Inc., Green Bay, WI; *U.S. Private*, pg. 476
Droessler, Carol, Mng. Dir.-Human Resources--American Automobile Association, Heathrow, FL; *U.S. Private*, pg. 50
Droppert, Marc, Exec. V.P.-Legal, H.R. & Corp. Affairs--Physio-Control Corporation, Redmond, WA; *U.S. Public*, pg. 1294
Drudy, Carole, Mgr.-Personnel--Haviland Enterprises, Grand Rapids, MI; *U.S. Private*, pg. 511
Drury, Tom, V.P.-H.R./Quality--TriEnda Corporation, Portage, WI; *U.S. Private*, pg. 1103
Drydyk, Joe, Dir.-Personnel--Bou-Matic, Madison, WI; *U.S. Private*, pg. 301
Drydyk, John, Dir.-Personnel--DEC International, Inc., Madison, WI; *U.S. Private*, pg. 301
Du Quette, Ernest A., V.P.-Human Resources & Admin.--American Optical Corporation, Greenwich, CT; *U.S. Private*, pg. 60
Duarte, Mirta, V.P.--Mason Distributors, Inc., Hialeah, FL; *U.S. Private*, pg. 712
Dubin, Stephen V., Sr. V.P., Gen. Counsel & Sec.--CSS Industries, Inc., Philadelphia, PA; *U.S. Public*, pg. 283
Dubnicki, Carol, V.P.-H.R. Consulting Svcs.--Amoco Corporation, Chicago, IL; *U.S. Public*, pg. 101
Dubur, Ghislaine, Dir.-Human Resources--Editions Scientifiques et Medicales Elsevier, Paris, France; *Int'l*, pg. 1099
Duchaine, Jean-Guy, V.P.-Human Resources & Communications--Provigo Inc., Montreal, Canada; *Int'l*, pg. 1072
Ducharme, C., Mgr.-Personnel--Eriez Magnetics, Erie, PA; *U.S. Private*, pg. 381
Duckworth, K., V.P.-Admin--Hyundai Motor America, Fountain Valley, CA; *Int'l*, pg. 641
Duckworth, Norman E., V.P.-Human Resources & Corp. Sec.--ONEOK Inc., Tulsa, OK; *U.S. Public*, pg. 1226
Duda, Andy, Personnel--Kraus-Anderson, Incorporated, Minneapolis, MN; *U.S. Private*, pg. 635
Dudley, Diane M., Chief Personnel Officer & V.P.--Maxxam Inc., Houston, TX; *U.S. Public*, pg. 1062
Duff, Vickie, Mgr.-Human Resources--RAM Golf Corporation, Melrose Park, IL; *U.S. Private*, pg. 908
Duffy, Barbara, V.P.-Human Resources--ComputerLand Canada, Brampton, Canada; *Int'l*, pg. 1154
Duffy, Brian F., V.P.-Human Resources--Pratt & Whitney Canada Inc., Longueuil, Canada; *U.S. Public*, pg. 1690
Duffy, Mark, H.R. Admin.--Samtec Inc., New Albany, IN; *U.S. Private*, pg. 963
Dufore, Thomas, V.P.-H.R.--Easco Inc., Girard, OH; *U.S. Public*, pg. 548
Dufort, D., Mgr.-Personnel--Maple Leaf Meats, Winnipeg, Canada; *Int'l*, pg. 841
Dufourmantelle, Henry, Mgr.-Personnel--Lafarge Ciments, Saint Cloud, France; *Int'l*, pg. 788
Dugan, Mark, Dir.-Personnel--American Fluorescent Corporation, Waukegan, IL; *U.S. Private*, pg. 54
Duggan, John, V.P.-H.R.--Continental Medical Systems, Inc., Mechanicsburg, PA; *U.S. Public*, pg. 839
Duggan, John P., Chief H.R. Officer & V.P.--Horizon/CMS Healthcare Corporation, Albuquerque, NM; *U.S. Public*, pg. 836
Duggan, Pamela J., Dir.-Human Resources--Zymark Corporation, Hopkinton, MA; *U.S. Private*, pg. 139
Duggau, John, Dir.-Human Resources--Qual-Med, Inc., Pueblo, CO; *U.S. Public*, pg. 678
Dugle, William M., V.P.-Human Resources--Engelhard Corporation, Iselin, NJ; *U.S. Public*, pg. 582
Duke, Lonnie, Dir.-Human Resources--Wing Industries, Inc., Greenville, TX; *U.S. Private*, pg. 1183
Duloc, Andrea, Dir.-H.R.--S L C Graphics, LP, Pittston, PA; *U.S. Private*, pg. 955
Dulude, G., V.P.-Human Resources--La Brasserie Labatt Limitee, La Salle, Canada; *Int'l*, pg. 679
Dumas, Debbie, Mgr.-H.R.--I.C. System, Inc., Vadnais Heights, MN; *U.S. Private*, pg. 553
Dumas, Isabelle, Mgr.-H.R.--Compagnie Generale Maritime et Financiere, Suresnes, France; *Int'l*, pg. 322
Duncan, Brenda, Dir.-H.R.--Regional Transportation Authority (RTA), Chicago, IL; *U.S. Private*, pg. 918
Duncan, Dan, Mgr.-Personnel--Pennzoil Products Co., Houston, TX; *U.S. Public*, pg. 1272
Duncan, Karen, Mgr.-Human Resources--Market Facts, Inc., Arlington Heights, IL; *U.S. Public*, pg. 1046
Duncan, Max, Dir.-H.R.--Southern Belle Dairy Company, Somerset, KY; *U.S. Private*, pg. 1015
Duncan, Milne J., Sr. V.P.--First Federal Capital Corp., La Crosse, WI; *U.S. Public*, pg. 632
Duncan, Philip C., V.P.-Human Resources--SyQuest Technology, Inc., Fremont, CA; *U.S. Public*, pg. 1550
Duncan, Sam, E., Dir.-Personnel--J.H. Fletcher & Co., Huntington, WV; *U.S. Private*, pg. 412
Dunlap, Joanne, V.P.-Admin. Services & Sec.--Logicon Geodynamic, Torrance, CA; *U.S. Public*, pg. 1199
Dunlap, Rosemary, Human Resources & Training Dir.--Hutchins/Young & Rubicam, Rochester, NY; *U.S. Private*, pg. 1197
Dunn, Barbara, Dir.-Human Resources--Colgate Oral Pharmaceutical, Canton, MA; *U.S. Public*, pg. 397
Dunn, Betty, Mgr.-Personnel--Jones Blair Company, Dallas, TX; *U.S. Private*, pg. 596
Dunn, E.R., V.P.-Human Resources & Asst. Sec.--Whirlpool Corporation, Benton Harbor, MI; *U.S. Public*, pg. 1764
Dunn, Jack, Dir.-Human Resources--Sabreliner Corporation, Saint Louis, MO; *U.S. Private*, pg. 959
Dunn, Jeff, Mgr.-Personnel--NESLAB Instruments, Inc., Newington, NH; *U.S. Public*, pg. 1595
Dunn, John, V.P.-Human Resources, Flushing--Time Warner Cable of New York City, New York, NY; *U.S. Public*, pg. 1611
Dunn, Katherine, Mgr.-Human Resources--Six Flags Over Georgia, Austell, GA; *U.S. Public*, pg. 1612
Dunn, Patty, Dir.-Human Resources--Team, Inc., Alvin, TX; *U.S. Public*, pg. 1562
Dunn, Rebecca M., V.P.-Human Resources & Corp. Services--BellSouth Telecommunications, Inc., Atlanta, GA; *U.S. Public*, pg. 209
Dunn, Robert, V.P.-H.R.--American Pad and Paper Company, Dallas, TX; *U.S. Public*, pg. 88
Dunn, Roger A., V.P.-Human Resources--TECO Energy, Inc., Tampa, FL; *U.S. Public*, pg. 1565
Dunphy, A., Mgr.-Personnel--Park Air Electronics Ltd., Peterborough, United Kingdom; *U.S. Public*, pg. 1198
Dupell, Maureen D., V.P.-H.R.--Greenhorne & O'Mara, Inc., Greenbelt, MD; *U.S. Private*, pg. 477
Duplessis, Carol, Sec. & Mgr.-Personnel--Cooper Instrument Corp., Middlefield, CT; *U.S. Private*, pg. 274
Dupre, Louis E., V.P.-Human Resources--Pool Energy Services Co., Houston, TX; *U.S. Public*, pg. 1316
Dupre, Werner, Dir.-Fin. & Personnel--Herberts GmbH, Wuppertal, Germany; *Int'l*, pg. 625
Dupuis, Rachel A., Mgr.-Human Resources & Personnel Training & Devel.--Candela Corporation, Wayland, MA; *U.S. Public*, pg. 300
Durbin, Steven L., V.P.-Human Resources--Columbia/HCA Healthcare Corporation, Nashville, TN; *U.S. Public*, pg. 403
Durbin, William J., V.P.-H.R.--Zurn Industries, Inc., Erie, PA; *U.S. Public*, pg. 1794
Durcanin, Joseph, Dir.-H.R.--J.E. Berkowitz, LP, Westville, NJ; *U.S. Private*, pg. 135
Dusharm, Pam, Mgr.-H.R.--Ginsberg's Institutional Foods, Inc., Hudson, NY; *U.S. Private*, pg. 455
Dutrisac, Maurice, V.P.-Human Resources--Domtar Inc., Montreal, Canada; *Int'l*, pg. 416
Duval, Philip, V.P.-Human Resources & Communications--Uniboard Canada Inc., Laval, Canada; *Int'l*, pg. 1431
Duxbury, Crystal, V.P.-H.R.--Henry Lee Company, Miami, FL; *U.S. Private*, pg. 657
Dweck, Leah, V.P.-Admin. & H.R.--A&E Stores, Inc., Teterboro, NJ; *U.S. Private*, pg. 1
Dwyer, Kate, Sr. V.P.-H.R.--City National Corporation, Beverly Hills, CA; *U.S. Public*, pg. 380
Dwyer, R., Mgr.-Human Resources--London International Group plc, London, United Kingdom; *Int'l*, pg. 815
Dyar, Bill, Dir.-Personnel--Davis Electrical Constructors, Inc., Greenville, SC; *U.S. Private*, pg. 315
Dyer, J.R., Gen. Mgr.-Personnel--Burns, Philp & Company Limited, Sydney, Australia; *Int'l*, pg. 236
Dyer, Liza, Human Resources Dir.--Ingalls Moranville Advertising, San Francisco, CA; *U.S. Private*, pg. 316
Dyer, Victor D., V.P.-H.R.--Ladd Furniture, Inc., Greensboro, NC; *U.S. Public*, pg. 974
Dyjak, Carol A., Mgr.-Bus. Admin. & Human Resources--Springborn Testing & Research, Inc., Enfield, CT; *U.S. Private*, pg. 1027
Dykman, Susan, Exec. Asst.-Investor Rels.--Allegiant Physician Services, Atlanta, GA; *U.S. Public*, pg. 45
Dykman, Terry, Dir.-Human Resources--Claris Corporation, Santa Clara, CA; *U.S. Public*, pg. 121
Dyson, F. Branson, V.P.-H.R. & Admin.--Phycor, Inc., Nashville, TN; *U.S. Public*, pg. 1293
Dziewisz, M.S., Dir.-Human Resources--WESCO Distribution, Inc., Pittsburgh, PA; *U.S. Private*, pg. 244
Eade, Dennis, V.P.-H.R.--Beverage America, Inc., Holland, MI; *U.S. Private*, pg. 141
Eagan, Trudy, V.P.-Corp. Affairs & H.R.--Sun Media Corporation, Toronto, Canada; *Int'l*, pg. 1320
Earl Jones, W., V.P.-Pur.--Shealy Electrical Wholesalers, Greenville, SC; *U.S. Private*, pg. 991
Early, Debra, Dir.-H.R.--Angelo Brothers Co., Philadelphia, PA; *U.S. Private*, pg. 74
Earp, Harlon, V.P.-H.R.--Harp's Food Stores, Inc., Springdale, AR; *U.S. Private*, pg. 504
Easler, Oliver, Mgr.-H.R.--The Felters Company, Roebuck, SC; *U.S. Private*, pg. 400
Easter, William, V.P.-Human Resources--Alpha Metals, Inc., Jersey City, NJ; *Int'l*, pg. 328
Eastman, Joseph F., V.P.-Human Resources--A.T. Cross Co., Lincoln, RI; *U.S. Public*, pg. 460
Easton, Howard, Dir.-H.R.--Penco Products, Oaks, PA; *U.S. Private*, pg. 848

Easton, Robert, Mgr.-Personnel--Republic Storage Systems Company Inc., Canton, OH; *U.S. Private*, pg. 924
Ebel, Gregory L., V.P.-Human Resources--The E.W. Scripps Company, Cincinnati, OH; *U.S. Public*, pg. 1447
Eberly, Connie, Dir.-H.R.--Ranir Corporation/DCP, Grand Rapids, MI; *U.S. Private*, pg. 909
Ebert, K.A., Dir.-Human Resources--Consolidated Papers, Inc., Wisconsin Rapids, WI; *U.S. Public*, pg. 436
Ebling, Chris L., V.P.-H.R.--True Temper Hardware Company, Camp Hill, PA; *U.S. Public*, pg. 846
Eby, Mike, Dir.-Human Resources--Discount Drug Mart Inc., Medina, OH; *U.S. Private*, pg. 334
Eck, Helen, Dir.-Personnel--Trimtex Co. Inc., Williamsport, PA; *U.S. Private*, pg. 1103
Eckel, James A., Sr. V.P.-Personnel--Cullen/Frost Bankers, Inc., San Antonio, TX; *U.S. Public*, pg. 467
Eckhoff-Stickle, Diane, Dir.-Personnel--Jaco Electronics, Inc., Hauppauge, NY; *U.S. Public*, pg. 920
Eckman, Michael, V.P.-Employee Rels.--Armour Swift Eckrich, Downers Grove, IL; *U.S. Public*, pg. 426
Edelin, Joan, Human Resources Dir.--ADWORKS, Inc., Washington, DC; *U.S. Private*, pg. 23
Edelman, Heather E., V.P.-Human Resources--Lifeline Systems, Inc., Cambridge, MA; *U.S. Public*, pg. 992
Edelman, John, V.P.-Human Resources--Edelman Public Relations Worldwide, Chicago, IL; *U.S. Private*, pg. 362
Eder, Tom, Dir.-Personnel--A-Dec, Inc., Newberg, OR; *U.S. Private*, pg. 2
Edmonds, David B., Exec. V.P.-Human Resources--AmSouth Bancorporation, Birmingham, AL; *U.S. Public*, pg. 105
Edmondson, Lisa, Human Resources Dir.--Team One Advertising, El Segundo, CA; *U.S. Public*, pg. 1422
Edmonson, Denise, Mgr.-H.R.--Builder Marts of America, Inc., Greenville, SC; *U.S. Private*, pg. 179
Edsinga, Elsie, Mgr.-H.R.--Calavo Growers of California, Santa Ana, CA; *U.S. Private*, pg. 199
Edwards, Brenda, Dir.-Personnel & Employee Benefits--Peirce-Phelps, Inc., Philadelphia, PA; *U.S. Private*, pg. 847
Edwards, Dorothy, Mgr.-Personnel--T & N Plc, Manchester, United Kingdom; *Int'l*, pg. 1334
Edwards, Elizabeth, Sr. V.P.-Personnel--Marquis Investments, New Orleans, LA; *U.S. Public*, pg. 629
Edwards, Henry, Exec. V.P.-Human Resources--FINAST, Maple Heights, OH; *Int'l*, pg. 750
Edwards, John, Sr. V.P.-Corp. Rels.--Texas-New Mexico Power Co., Fort Worth, TX; *U.S. Public*, pg. 1557
Edwards, Julian A., Jr., V.P.-Human Resources--General Motors Acceptance Corporation (GMAC), Detroit, MI; *U.S. Public*, pg. 719
Edwards, Kent M., V.P.-H.R. & Asst. Sec.--Vallen Corporation, Houston, TX; *U.S. Public*, pg. 1705
Edwards, P., Dir.-Human Resources--Metro Brewery, Etobicoke, Canada; *Int'l*, pg. 679
Edwards, Robert W., V.P.-H.R.--American & Efird, Inc., Mount Holly, NC; *U.S. Public*, pg. 1412
Edwards, Susie, Mgr.-Human Resources--NPC International, Inc., Pittsburg, KS; *U.S. Public*, pg. 1146
Edwards, Tim, Dir.-Human Resources--Amecom Div., College Park, MD; *U.S. Public*, pg. 1002
Egan, K.C., Dir.-H.R.--Hambrecht & Quist LLC., San Francisco, CA; *U.S. Public*, pg. 778
Egan, Sally G., V.P.-Human Resources--Martin Marietta Information Group, Bethesda, MD; *U.S. Public*, pg. 1007
Egan, Thomas J., Sr. V.P. & Sr. Admin. Deputy--Freeport-McMoRan Inc., New Orleans, LA; *U.S. Public*, pg. 680
Egede-Nissen, Thor, V.P.-Indus. Rels.--Great Dane Trailers, Inc., Savannah, GA; *U.S. Private*, pg. 1030
Egland, Sandra L., V.P.-H.R.--Excel Communications, Inc., Dallas, TX; *U.S. Public*, pg. 598
Ehlinger, Peter, Sr. V.P.-Human Resources--Johnny Carson Apparel, Inc., Buffalo, NY; *U.S. Public*, pg. 796
Ehly, Milt, Dir.-H.R.--Chief Industries, Inc., Grand Island, NE; *U.S. Private*, pg. 236
Ehret, Bob, Sr. V.P.-H.R. & Commun.--Adolph Coors Company, Golden, CO; *U.S. Public*, pg. 445
Ehret, Robert W., Sr. V.P.-Human Resources--Coors Brewing Company, Golden, CO; *U.S. Public*, pg. 445
Ehrman, Susan, V.P.-Human Resources--San Antonio Express News, San Antonio, TX; *U.S. Private*, pg. 517
Eichhold, Louis B., V.P.-H.R. & Indus.--The United States Playing Card Company, Cincinnati, OH; *U.S. Private*, pg. 1125
Einav, M., Mgr.-Personnel--El Al Israel Airlines, Ltd., New York, NY; *Int'l*, pg. 435
Eisenberg, Jamie, V.P.-H.R.--Vienna Sausage Mfg. Co., Chicago, IL; *U.S. Private*, pg. 1139
Eisennagel, John J., Dir.-Personnel--Magnetic Metals Corp., Camden, NJ; *U.S. Private*, pg. 560
Eisman, Bernard, Mgr.-Personnel--Lasko Metal Products, Inc., West Chester, PA; *U.S. Private*, pg. 652
Ekberg, Willy, Chief Info. Officer (MIS) & Dir.-Personnel--Akzo Nobel AB, Stockholm, Sweden; *Int'l*, pg. 48
Eklof, Al, V.P.-H.R.--Anoka Electric Cooperative, Ramsey, MN; *U.S. Private*, pg. 75
Ekman, Olof, Dir.-Personnel--Scandinavian Airlines System (SAS), Solna, Sweden; *Int'l*, pg. 1201
Ekstrom, Dean E., V.P.-Admin.--IES Industries Inc., Cedar Rapids, IA; *U.S. Public*, pg. 855
Eldridge, Rick, V.P.-H.R.--Ruby Tuesday, Inc., Mobile, AL; *U.S. Public*, pg. 1411
Elgie, E., Dir.-Human Resources--Oland Breweries Limited, Halifax, Canada; *Int'l*, pg. 679
Elias, Jeffrey A., Sr. V.P.-H.R. & Admin.--RemedyTemp, Inc., San Juan Capistrano, CA; *U.S. Public*, pg. 1376
Elizondo, Juanita, Dir.-H.R.--Fiesta Mart Inc., Houston, TX; *U.S. Private*, pg. 403
Elkin, Marvin, Chief Admin. Officer, Chief Human Resources Officer & V.P.--Northrop Grumman Corporation, Los Angeles, CA; *U.S. Public*, pg. 1197
Elliott, David, Mgr.-Pub. Rels.--Brooklyn Union, Brooklyn, NY; *U.S. Public*, pg. 259
Elliott, Rosemary T., V.P.-Global Human Resources--Applied Materials, Inc., Santa Clara, CA; *U.S. Public*, pg. 123
Elliott, Sharon, Sr. V.P.-Human Resources--Starbucks Coffee Company, Seattle, WA; *U.S. Public*, pg. 1510
Ellis, Jeff, V.P.-Personal Lines--VASA North Atlantic Insurance Company, Indianapolis, IN; *Int'l*, pg. 464
Ellis, Kay, Dir.-H.R.--Kitchell Corporation, Phoenix, AZ; *U.S. Private*, pg. 624
Ellis, Laura, Dir.-H.R.--Awrey Bakeries, Inc., Livonia, MI; *U.S. Private*, pg. 103
Ellis, O. L., Mgr.-Human Resources--Wire Rope Corporation of America, Inc., Saint Joseph, MO; *U.S. Private*, pg. 1184
Ellis, Robert, V.P.-Human Resources--J.M. Smucker Company, Orrville, OH; *U.S. Public*, pg. 1480
Elnberg, Eric, Mgr.-H.R.--Blitz USA, Inc., Miami, OK; *U.S. Private*, pg. 149
Elrod, Gene, Dir.-Personnel--Lewis Drug, Inc., Sioux Falls, SD; *U.S. Private*, pg. 665
Elzerman, John C., V.P.-Human Resources--MCN Energy Group, Inc., Detroit, MI; *U.S. Public*, pg. 1024
Emanuelson, Marianna, V.P.-Human Resources--Scan-Optics, Inc., Manchester, CT; *U.S. Public*, pg. 1436
Embury, Kathy M., Mgr.-Human Resources--Rayrock Yellowknife Resources Inc., Toronto, Canada; *Int'l*, pg. 1089
Emig, Camille, Dir.-Employee Devel. & Communications--Anheuser-Busch Companies, Inc., Saint Louis, MO; *U.S. Public*, pg. 113
Emig, Tom, Mgr.-Corp. Personnel--Penn Engineering & Manufacturing Corp., Danboro, PA; *U.S. Public*, pg. 1269
Emmick, Gary K., Sr. V.P.-Employee Rels.--Corning Incorporated, Corning, NY; *U.S. Public*, pg. 448
Emondts, M.H.P.J., Dir.-Personnel & Organization--BolsWessanen Nederland BV, Amstelveen, Netherlands; *Int'l*, pg. 751
Engel, Hank, Dir.-Personnel--Mooney Aircraft Corporation, Kerrville, TX; *U.S. Private*, pg. 759
Engel, Leslie J., Sr. V.P. & Human Resources Dir.-NY--DMB&B New York, New York, NY; *U.S. Private*, pg. 302
Engelmann, B., Mgr.-Human Resources--Deminex-Deutsche GmbH, Essen, Germany; *Int'l*, pg. 1460
Engle, Charlene, V.P.-H.R.--Atlas Electric Devices Co., Chicago, IL; *U.S. Private*, pg. 96
Engler, Carol Franklin, Dir.-Human Resources--Swiss Reinsurance Company, Zurich, Switzerland; *Int'l*, pg. 1332
English, Roderick, Sr. V.P.-Human Resources & Communications--Delco Remy America, Inc., Anderson, IN; *U.S. Public*, pg. 495
Engman, Gosta, Exec. V.P.-Personnel & Admin.--Rautaruukki Oy, Helsinki, Finland; *Int'l*, pg. 1088
Enright, Kathy, Mgr.-H.R.--Mitel Corporation, Kanata, Canada; *Int'l*, pg. 870
Enright, Patty, Sr. Partner & Human Resources Dir.--Ogilvy & Mather Worldwide, Inc., New York, NY; *Int'l*, pg. 1483
Enright, Stephen J., V.P.-Human Resources--Overnite Transportation Co., Richmond, VA; *U.S. Public*, pg. 1668
Ensslin, Richard, Dir.-Personnel--Milwaukee Electric Tool Corp., Brookfield, WI; *Int'l*, pg. 96
Entrekin, Robert L., V.P. & Sec.--Murata Electronics North America, Inc., Smyrna, GA; *Int'l*, pg. 897
Eppel, W.G., V.P.-Human Resources--CF Industries, Inc., Long Grove, IL; *U.S. Private*, pg. 193
Epperson, Charlie, V.P.-H.R.--West Union Corporation, Memphis, TN; *U.S. Private*, pg. 1163
Epperson, William A., V.P.-H.R.--Gold Kist, Inc., Atlanta, GA; *U.S. Private*, pg. 459
Epstein, Jill, Dir.-Human Resources--McCall Oil & Chemical Corp., Portland, OR; *U.S. Private*, pg. 719
Erban, Tomas, V.P.-H.R--Bacardi-Martini, USA, Inc., Miami, FL; *U.S. Private*, pg. 109
Erdei, Martin, V.P.-H.R.--The Jewett Refrigerator Co., Inc., Buffalo, NY; *U.S. Private*, pg. 952
Erdei, Martin J., V.P.-H.R. & Mfg.--Ruslander & Sons, Inc., Buffalo, NY; *U.S. Private*, pg. 952
Erdmann, Richard, Sr. V.P.-Human Resources--Serigraph, Inc., West Bend, WI; *U.S. Private*, pg. 985
Erickson, Tom, V.P.-Human Resources--Elgar Corporation, San Diego, CA; *U.S. Public*, pg. 789
Eriks, Mark, V.P.-H.R.--Waste Management, Inc., Oak Brook, IL; *U.S. Public*, pg. 1744
Erikson, Lucy, V.P. & Dir.-Human Resources--Edelman Public Relations Worldwide, Chicago, IL; *U.S. Private*, pg. 362
Erlen, Hubertus, Dr., Exec. Dir.-Personnel, Production & Environmental Protection--Schering AG, Berlin, Germany; *Int'l*, pg. 1203
Erney, Charles, Dir.-Human Resources--Latrobe Brewing Co., Latrobe, PA; *Int'l*, pg. 680
Ernst, Mark, V.P.-H.R.--Freedom Communication Inc., Irvine, CA; *U.S. Private*, pg. 425
Ernst, Paul, Mgr.-Personnel--Goodman Equipment Corp., Bedford Park, IL; *U.S. Private*, pg. 464
Ernst, Scott, Dir.-Personnel--Dialight Corporation, Manasquan, NJ; *Int'l*, pg. 1130
Erskine, T.M., V.P.-Personnel Relations--Delta Air Lines, Inc., Atlanta, GA; *U.S. Public*, pg. 497
Ertle, Christine, V.P.-H.R.--MBL Life Assurance Corporation, Newark, NJ; *U.S. Private*, pg. 685
Ertz, Caroline, Mgr.-H.R.--Amana Society, Inc., Amana, IA; *U.S. Private*, pg. 48
Erven, Jim, V.P.-Human Resources--Garlock Sealing Technologies, Palmyra, NY; *U.S. Public*, pg. 402
Erzen, Robert, V.P.-Human Resources--Mercedes-Benz of North America, Inc., Montvale, NJ; *Int'l*, pg. 368
Escarrer, Maria Antonia, Exec. V.P.-Human Resources--Sol Melia, Palma de Mallorca, Spain; *Int'l*, pg. 1277
Eschelman, Becky, Mgr.-Employee Benefits--Jamison Plastic Corporation, Allentown, PA; *U.S. Private*, pg. 581
Eshleman, Bob, Dir.-Personnel--Reading Body Works, Inc., Reading, PA; *U.S. Private*, pg. 913
Espeland, Richard A., Mgr.-Human Resources--MDU Resources Group, Inc., Bismarck, ND; *U.S. Public*, pg. 1025
Espi, Jose Maria, Exec. V.P.-Human Resources, Systems & Opers.--Banco Santander, Madrid, Spain; *Int'l*, pg. 143
Espinosa, Tania, Dir.-Human Resources--Parlux Fragrances Inc., Fort Lauderdale, FL; *U.S. Public*, pg. 1264
Espinoza, Judy, Mgr.-Human Resources--Advantage Companies, Inc., Wichita, KS; *U.S. Private*, pg. 22
Essex, Katheen, V.P.-Human Resources--Hunt Corporation, Philadelphia, PA; *U.S. Public*, pg. 848
Estes, Sylvia, V.P.-Human Resources--Grizzard, Atlanta, GA; *U.S. Private*, pg. 482
Estey, Mona, Mgr.-H.R. & Employee Benefits--Lydall, Inc., Manchester, CT; *U.S. Public*, pg. 1020
Estrada, Eve, Human Resources/Office Services Dir.--EURO RSCG Tatham, Chicago, IL; *Int'l*, pg. 601
Etienne, Tom S., Dir.-H.R.--Brutger Equities, Inc., Saint Cloud, MN; *U.S. Private*, pg. 176
Etsler, Philip R., V.P.-H.R.--Keithley Instruments, Inc., Cleveland, OH; *U.S. Public*, pg. 946
Ettie, Suzie, Office Mgr. & Human Resources--TargetCom, Inc., Chicago, IL; *U.S. Private*, pg. 1069
Euler, Rich, Dir.-H.R.--Prime Tanning Co., Inc., Rochester, NH; *U.S. Private*, pg. 884
Euritt, Robert L., V.P.-H.R.--Remington Arms Company, Inc., Madison, NC; *U.S. Private*, pg. 921
Evans, Dave, V.P.-Human Resources--Ponderosa Steakhouse, Dallas, TX; *U.S. Private*, pg. 736
Evans, Ed, Personnel Admin.--Chartwell Partners, Los Angeles, CA; *U.S. Private*, pg. 230
Evans, Eileen, Mgr.-Personnel--Advance Business Graphics, Mira Loma, CA; *U.S. Private*, pg. 18
Evans, Evan L., Chief Human Resources Officer--Bank of America Illinois, Chicago, IL; *U.S. Public*, pg. 180
Evans, Gayle, Asst. V.P.-H.R.--Standard Insurance Co., Portland, OR; *U.S. Private*, pg. 1031
Evans, Janice, Mgr.-Human Resources--Active Voice Corporation, Seattle, WA; *U.S. Public*, pg. 17
Evans, Jim, Mgr.-H. R.--The Laitram Corporation, Harahan, LA; *U.S. Private*, pg. 643
Evans, Judith, Dir.-Corp. Personnel--J. Sainsbury plc, London, United Kingdom; *Int'l*, pg. 1169
Evans, Mark, Dir.-H.R.--Eva-Tone Inc., Clearwater, FL; *U.S. Private*, pg. 384
Evans, Mark A., V.P.-H.R.--The Dispatch Printing Company, Columbus, OH; *U.S. Private*, pg. 334
Evans, Meg, Dir.-H.R.--Manufacturers' News, Inc., Evanston, IL; *U.S. Private*, pg. 700
Evans, Peggy, Dir.-Personnel & Corp. Video Systems--GES Inc., Marianna, AR; *U.S. Private*, pg. 434
Evans, Richard H., Chief Strategy Officer & Sr. V.P.-Global Human Resources--NCR Corporation, Dayton, OH; *U.S. Public*, pg. 1146
Evans, Sheila, Mgr.-Personnel--The Acorn, Kalamazoo, MI; *U.S. Private*, pg. 454
Evans, W. King, V.P.-H.R.--Rosser International, Inc., Atlanta, GA; *U.S. Private*, pg. 946
Everitt, Thomas W., V.P.-Human Resources--Camco International Inc., Houston, TX; *U.S. Public*, pg. 297
Everitt, Tom, V.P.-Human Resources--Camco International Inc., Houston, TX; *U.S. Public*, pg. 298
Evers, Mark, Dir.-Human Resources--Curries Company, Mason City, IA; *Int'l*, pg. 18
Evitt, Scott, Dir.-Personnel--Freightliner Corp., Portland, OR; *Int'l*, pg. 368
Ewalt, Alan R., Sr. V.P.-H.R.--Tenet Healthcare Corporation, Santa Barbara, CA; *U.S. Public*, pg. 1576
Ewen, Tim, Dir.-H.R. & Pur.--Applied Magnetics Corporation, Goleta, CA; *U.S. Public*, pg. 123
Ewing, James C., V.P.-H.R.--Belden & Blake Corporation, Canton, OH; *U.S. Private*, pg. 1078
Eyster, Franklin S., II, Sr. V.P., Gen. Counsel & Sec.--Atlantic Aviation Corp., New Castle, DE; *U.S. Private*, pg. 94
Faas, Andrew J., Sr. V.P.-Human Resources--George Weston Limited, Toronto, Canada; *Int'l*, pg. 1494
Fabian, David L., Sr. V.P.-Corp. Services--Capital Associates, Inc., Lakewood, CO; *U.S. Public*, pg. 302
Fabian, Mary Ann, Dir.-Personnel--Hybrid Products, Pearl River, NY; *Int'l*, pg. 1283
Fabre, Susan, V.P.-H.R.--Houston Industries Incorporated, Houston, TX; *U.S. Public*, pg. 842
Fahlen, Lars, Sr. V.P.-H.R.--Incentive AB, Stockholm, Sweden; *Int'l*, pg. 666
Fairbairn, Kelly, Dir.-Employment Services--The Seibels Bruce Group, Inc., Columbia, SC; *U.S. Public*, pg. 1453
Fairbairn, Ursula, Exec. V.P.-Quality & Human Resources--American Express Company, New York, NY; *U.S. Public*, pg. 73
Faircloth, Kathy, Mgr.-Human Resources--Hanna Corporation, Chicago, IL; *U.S. Private*, pg. 231
Fairweather, Henry, Grp. Dir.-Personnel & Services--Scottish & Newcastle plc, Edinburgh, United Kingdom; *Int'l*, pg. 1211
Falk, Eric, V.P.-Personnel--E.A. Miller Company, Hyrum, UT; *U.S. Public*, pg. 428
Falkner, James, Mgr.-Human Resources--Schlegel Corporation, Rochester, NY; *Int'l*, pg. 128
Faller, Patrick, Dir.-Personnel & Employee Benefits--The New Piper Aircraft, Inc., Vero Beach, FL; *U.S. Private*, pg. 794
Fallon, Murial, Dir.-Personnel--Mount Snow Resort, Mount Snow, VT; *U.S. Private*, pg. 61
Falzareno, Cathryn, Sr. V.P.-Human Resources--Builders Square, Inc., San Antonio, TX; *U.S. Private*, pg. 477
Fama, Maureen C., Mgr.-Communications--Uniroyal Chemical Corporation, Middlebury, CT; *U.S. Public*, pg. 459
Fanara, Brenda, Mgr.-Human Resources--Oak Industries Inc., Waltham, MA; *U.S. Public*, pg. 1209
Fangmann, Ronald G., Dir.-Human Resources--Product Support Division, Wichita, KS; *U.S. Public*, pg. 241

Farallo, Mary, Dir.-H.R.--New Era Cap. Co., Derby, NY; *U.S. Private*, pg. 793
Farber, Donna, Dir.-Personnel--Petroleum Marketers, Inc., Roanoke, VA; *U.S. Private*, pg. 859
Farkel, Nancy, Dir.-H.R.--Black Hills Corporation, Rapid City, SD; *U.S. Public*, pg. 235
Farley, Jeffrey T., V.P.-Admin. & Human Resources--Castrol North America, Wayne, NJ; *Int'l*, pg. 235
Farley, Roger B., V.P.-Human Resources--Greenfield Industries Inc., Evans, GA; *U.S. Public*, pg. 950
Farley, Tom, Controller & Mgr.-Daily Opers.--Norman Levy Associates, Inc., Southfield, MI; *U.S. Private*, pg. 664
Farmer, Bryce E., Sr. V.P.-Admin.--ACCEL International Corporation, Dublin, OH; *U.S. Public*, pg. 14
Farmer, Dennis, V.P.-H.R.--Imation Corporation, Oakdale, MN; *U.S. Public*, pg. 870
Farr, J.J., Dir.-Personnel--Black & Veatch, Kansas City, MO; *U.S. Private*, pg. 146
Farr, Pam, Sr. V.P.-Human Resources--Fairfield Inn, Washington, DC; *U.S. Public*, pg. 1048
Farrahar, Richard M., V.P.-Exec. Opers.--PerSeptive Biosystems, Inc., Framingham, MA; *U.S. Public*, pg. 1279
Farrand, Christopher G., V.P.-Corp. Affairs--Peabody Holding Company, Inc., Saint Louis, MO; *Int'l*, pg. 594
Farrar, Eileen C., Sr. V.P.-Human Resources--UNUM Corporation, Portland, ME; *U.S. Public*, pg. 1699
Farrell, Carol, V.P.-H.R.--Sechrist Industries, Inc., Anaheim, CA; *U.S. Private*, pg. 980
Farrell, Jim, Sr. V.P.-H.R.--The M/A/R/C Group, Irving, TX; *U.S. Public*, pg. 1022
Farrell, John J., Exec. V.P.-Human Resources--The Chase Manhattan Corporation, New York, NY; *U.S. Public*, pg. 337
Farren, J., V.P.-Human Resources--Dataproducts Corporation, Simi Valley, CA; *Int'l*, pg. 620
Farrin, Gwen, Personnel Asst.-Pub. Rels.--Betacom Plc, Brentwood, United Kingdom; *Int'l*, pg. 193
Farrington, Ronda, Dir.-H.R.--PC Connection, Inc., Milford, MA; *U.S. Private*, pg. 826
Farrugia, Joseph P., Grp. Head-H.R.--Air Malta Co. Ltd., Luqa, Malta; *Int'l*, pg. 37
Faulkner, Laurie, Mgr.-Human Resources--The Pilot Pen Corp. of America, Trumbull, CT; *Int'l*, pg. 1057
Faulks, Rusty, Dir.-Human Resources--Thomas Nelson Inc., Nashville, TN; *U.S. Public*, pg. 1167
Fausher, Duane, Sr. V.P.-H.R.--Marvin Lumber & Cedar Company, Warroad, MN; *U.S. Private*, pg. 710
Faust, James M., V.P.-MIS & H.R.--McCarthy Building Companies, Saint Louis, MO; *U.S. Private*, pg. 719
Faust, Tammy, Dir.-Adv.--Dairy Queen Corporate Store, Louisville, KY; *U.S. Public*, pg. 220
Favero, G., Dir.-Personnel & Organization--Zanussi Grandi Impianti S.p.A., Pordenone, Italy; *Int'l*, pg. 442
Feagans, Chris, V.P.-H.R.--Keller Crescent Co., Evansville, IN; *U.S. Private*, pg. 612
Fears, Barbara, V.P.-Human Resources--Dexter Magnetic Materials, Fremont, CA; *U.S. Public*, pg. 504
Fechter, Maxine, V.P.-Human Resources--Coach, New York, NY; *U.S. Public*, pg. 1433
Federici, Anne, Mgr.-H.R.--Clear Channel Radio, Inc., Hamden, CT; *U.S. Public*, pg. 383
Federspiel, Dan, Mgr.-Personnel--Hardware Wholesalers, Inc., Fort Wayne, IN; *U.S. Private*, pg. 502
Fee, Candida M., V.P.-Indus. Rels.--Reliable Automatic Sprinkler Co., Inc., Mount Vernon, NY; *U.S. Private*, pg. 920
Feekin, Duane D., Exec. V.P.-H.R. Division--Pacific Century Financial Corporation, Honolulu, HI; *U.S. Public*, pg. 1248
Feekin, Duane D., Exec. V.P.-H.R.--Bank of Hawaii, Honolulu, HI; *U.S. Public*, pg. 1248
Fegen, Chris, Mgr.-H.R.--Urban Shopping Centers, Inc., Chicago, IL; *U.S. Public*, pg. 1700
Fehn, Tammie, Mgr.-Human Resources--Precor, Inc., Bothell, WA; *U.S. Public*, pg. 1322
Feightner, Charles M., V.P.-Consumer Lending--Southwest National Bank of Pennsylvania, Greensburg, PA; *U.S. Public*, pg. 1493
Feild, Suzan J., Dir.-Human Resources--AAI Corporation, Hunt Valley, MD; *U.S. Public*, pg. 1679
Felago, Ernest M., V.P.-H.R.--Varian Associates, Inc., Palo Alto, CA; *U.S. Public*, pg. 1710
Feldman, B., V.P.-Indus. Rels.--NI Industries, Inc., Seal Beach, CA; *U.S. Public*, pg. 1054
Feldman, Benny, V.P.-H.R.--Check Point Software Technologies Ltd., Redwood City, CA; *U.S. Public*, pg. 342
Feldman, Ken, V.P.-Human Resources--Bernard Hodes Group, New York, NY; *U.S. Public*, pg. 1224
Feldman, Rudy, Dir.-Pro Personnel--San Diego Chargers, San Diego, CA; *U.S. Private*, pg. 964
Feldman, Sheila B., V.P.-H.R.--Solutia Inc., Saint Louis, MO; *U.S. Public*, pg. 1483
Feliciano, Gloria, V.P.-Human Resources--Polygram Records, Inc., New York, NY; *Int'l*, pg. 1052
Felix, Deborah, V.P.-Human Resources--Filene's Basement, Inc., Wellesley, MA; *U.S. Public*, pg. 622
Feller, Dieter, Mgr.-Personnel--Bally Management AG, Schonenwerd, Switzerland; *Int'l*, pg. 996
Fellin, Kathryn, V.P.-Fin.--A&W Restaurants, Inc., Livonia, MI; *U.S. Private*, pg. 1
Felts, William H., Jr., V.P. & Dir-Personnel & Investor Rels.--American Indemnity Financial Corp., Galveston, TX; *U.S. Public*, pg. 83
Fenoglio, Edmundo, Mgr.-Personnel--Sancor Cooperativas Unidas Limitadas, Buenos Aires, Argentina; *Int'l*, pg. 1183
Ferber, James D., V.P.-Human Resources--Sunshine Biscuits, Inc., Woodbridge, NJ; *U.S. Private*, pg. 434
Ferber, James D., V.P.-Human Resources--Sunshine Biscuits, Inc., Woodbridge, NJ; *U.S. Public*, pg. 657
Ferch, Burt, Industry Rels.-N. America--Redland Ohio Inc., Woodville, OH; *Int'l*, pg. 1091
Ferdig, Coleen, Admin. Asst.--Miracle Recreation Equipment Company, Monett, MO; *U.S. Private*, pg. 752
Ferguson, Charles, V.P.-Human Resources--Arrow Shirt Company, New York, NY; *Int'l*, pg. 194
Ferguson, Linda, Dir.-Human Resources--American Pacific Corporation, Las Vegas, NV; *U.S. Public*, pg. 88
Ferguson, Patricia, V.P.-Human Resources--Hampton Inns, Inc., Memphis, TN; *U.S. Public*, pg. 1335
Ferguson, William, V.P.-Personnel--Midland Enterprises Inc., Cincinnati, OH; *U.S. Public*, pg. 549
Fermier, Alan M., V.P.-Human Resources & Organizational Devel.--Medex Inc., Hilliard, OH; *U.S. Public*, pg. 689
Fernandez, Jane A., V.P.-Human Resources--Long Island Lighting Company, Hicksville, NY; *U.S. Public*, pg. 1013
Ferrales, Savino R., V.P.-Worldwide Human Resources--Digital Equipment Corporation, Maynard, MA; *U.S. Public*, pg. 507
Ferrara, Kim, Personnel Admin. Services Mgr.--Quantum Media International, Inc., New York, NY; *U.S. Private*, pg. 899
Ferrari, Debra L., Sr. V.P.-H.R.--360 Degrees Communications Company, Chicago, IL; *U.S. Public*, pg. 1607
Ferreira, Jorge T., Gen. Mgr.-Personnel--Banco Totta & Acores, Lisbon, Portugal; *Int'l*, pg. 144
Ferrentino, Dawn, Asst. Controller--Karnak Corporation, Clark, NJ; *U.S. Private*, pg. 607
Ferrera, Diane, Dir.-Personnel--James Ferrera & Sons, Inc., Canton, MA; *U.S. Private*, pg. 401
Ferrero, Maryann, Coord.-Personnel--Sentry Technology Corp., Hauppauge, NY; *U.S. Public*, pg. 1458
Ferri, Hank, Dir.-H.R.--Tech Industries, Inc., Woonsocket, RI; *U.S. Private*, pg. 1071
Ferris, Dean, Sr. V.P.-Employee Rels.--Twentieth Century Fox Film Corp., Los Angeles, CA; *Int'l*, pg. 926
Festo, Michael J., V.P.-Human Resources--ContiFinancial Corporation, New York, NY; *U.S. Public*, pg. 439
Fethe, Harold, V.P.-Human Resources--Alza Corporation, Palo Alto, CA; *U.S. Public*, pg. 62
Fetters, Buck, V.P.-H.R.--Central States Diversified, Inc., Saint Louis, MO; *U.S. Private*, pg. 224
Fetters, Buck, Corp. Dir.-H.R. & Safety--Insituform Technologies, Inc., Chesterfield, MO; *U.S. Public*, pg. 881
Feucht, Kenneth, Mgr.-H.R.--Gehl Company, West Bend, WI; *U.S. Public*, pg. 704
Ficks, Ronald, V.P.-Human Resources & Admin. Services--Topco Associates, Inc., Skokie, IL; *U.S. Private*, pg. 1091
Fidalgo, Juan Rodriguez, Dir.--Compania Espanola de Petroleos, S.A. (CEPSA), Madrid, Spain; *Int'l*, pg. 323
Field, Barbara A., V.P.-Human Resources--Colonial Gas Company, Lowell, MA; *U.S. Public*, pg. 400
Field, K. L., Exec. Gen. Mgr.-Human Resources--M.I.M. Holdings Ltd., Brisbane, Australia; *Int'l*, pg. 827
Fields, Alan R., V.P.-Human Resources--Jefferson-Pilot Life Insurance Co., Greensboro, NC; *U.S. Public*, pg. 926
Fields, Bruce H., V.P.-H.R.--Nordson Corporation, Westlake, OH; *U.S. Public*, pg. 1188
Fierke, William, Dir.-H.R.--Wenger Corporation, Owatonna, MN; *U.S. Private*, pg. 1162
Figueredo, Jorge L., Sr. V.P.-H.R.--Liz Claiborne, Inc., New York, NY; *U.S. Public*, pg. 1005
Fikes, Howard, Dir.-Personnel--Orbit Valve Co., Little Rock, AR; *U.S. Private*, pg. 819
Fila, Joan, Dir.-Personnel & Admin.--Woman's Day, New York, NY; *Int'l*, pg. 795
Filipovic, Sabina, V.P.-Human Rels.--Ha-Lo Industries, Inc., Niles, IL; *U.S. Public*, pg. 773
Filipovitz, Frank E., Gen. Mgr.-H.R.--The LTV Corporation, Cleveland, OH; *U.S. Public*, pg. 971
Finch, Geff, V.P.-H.R.--Harriet & Henderson Yarns, Inc., Henderson, NC; *U.S. Private*, pg. 504
Findlay, Linda, V.P.-Human Resources--Danzas Corporation, Bellevue, WA; *Int'l*, pg. 382
Fine, Karen, Sr. V.P.-Human Resources--Primerica Financial Services, Duluth, GA; *U.S. Public*, pg. 1633
Fine, Robert H., V.P.-H.R.--Lord Corporation, Cary, NC; *U.S. Private*, pg. 675
Finger, Van, Dir.-H.R.--R.W. Beck, Inc., Seattle, WA; *U.S. Private*, pg. 128
Finie, Paul, Gen. Mgr.--Trend Offset Printing Services, Los Alamitos, CA; *U.S. Private*, pg. 1099
Fink, K.W., V.P.-H.R.--Roquette America Inc., Keokuk, IA; *U.S. Private*, pg. 944
Fink, Lisa, Mgr.-H.R.--Asahi/America, Inc., Malden, MA; *U.S. Public*, pg. 137
Fink, Robert, Mgr.-Quality Control & Human Resources--Allomatic Products Company, Sullivan, IN; *U.S. Public*, pg. 1363
Finkle, Judith Tavano, Mgr.-Human Resources--INSO Corporation, Boston, MA; *U.S. Public*, pg. 882
Finley, David, Sr. V.P.-Human Resources--Ingram Micro Inc., Santa Ana, CA; *U.S. Public*, pg. 878
Finley, G. Stephen, Chief Admin. Officer & Sr. V.P.--Baker Hughes Incorporated, Houston, TX; *U.S. Public*, pg. 165
Finn, Heidi, Mgr.-Personnel--American Passage Media Corporation, Seattle, WA; *U.S. Private*, pg. 60
Finnerty, Neil, V.P.-H.R.--Dean Foods Company, Franklin Park, IL; *U.S. Public*, pg. 489
Finney, Ray B., V.P.-Human Resources--Century Telephone Enterprises, Inc., Monroe, LA; *U.S. Public*, pg. 329
Fino, Raymond M., V.P.-Human Resources--Warner-Lambert Company, Morris Plains, NJ; *U.S. Public*, pg. 1738
Fiola, Janet S., Sr. V.P.-Human Resources--Medtronic, Inc., Minneapolis, MN; *U.S. Public*, pg. 1082
Fiore, Donald A., Treas. & Mgr.-Personnel--Palmer Manufacturing Company, Malden, MA; *U.S. Private*, pg. 835
Fiorillo, E. Frances, V.P.-H.R.--Canadian Airlines Corporation, Calgary, Canada; *Int'l*, pg. 255
Fiorini, Jo Ann M., Asst. to Pres.--Leader Instruments Corporation, Hauppauge, NY; *U.S. Private*, pg. 655
Fiorini, P., Mgr.-Human Resources--Marcegaglia SpA, Mantova, Italy; *Int'l*, pg. 841
Firlotte, Charles V., V.P.-Admin. & Human Resources--Aquarion Company, Bridgeport, CT; *U.S. Public*, pg. 126
Firth, Richard, Dir.-H.R.--MTL Inc., Plant City, FL; *U.S. Public*, pg. 1028
Fischel, Shelley D., Sr. V.P.-Human Resources--Home Box Office, Inc., New York, NY; *U.S. Public*, pg. 1612
Fischer, George, Sr. V.P. -H.R.--Ameron International Corporation, Pasadena, CA; *U.S. Public*, pg. 98
Fischer, John C., V.P.-Human Resources--The Williams Companies, Inc., Tulsa, OK; *U.S. Public*, pg. 1769
Fischer, Robert, V.P.-Human Resources--Hiram Walker, Southfield, MI; *Int'l*, pg. 63
Fischer, Tom, Mgr.-H.R.--Basin Electric Power Cooperative, Bismarck, ND; *U.S. Private*, pg. 121
Fischer, Wanda, Dir.-H.R.--Lawson Software, Minneapolis, MN; *U.S. Private*, pg. 654
Fisher, Adrienne L., V.P.-Personnel--CD Products, Inc., New Providence, NJ; *U.S. Public*, pg. 276
Fisher, Dan, Chief Information Officer--Watson Wyatt Worldwide, Bethesda, MD; *U.S. Private*, pg. 1154
Fisher, Foy F., V.P.-Human Resources--WestPoint Stevens Inc., West Point, GA; *U.S. Public*, pg. 1762
Fisher, Hugh, Mgr.-Human Resources--AGA Gas, Inc., Independence, OH; *Int'l*, pg. 13
Fisher, John, Dir.-Personnel--Milk Marketing Inc., Strongsville, OH; *U.S. Private*, pg. 745
Fisher, Martin, Grp. Dir.-Personnel--Varity Perkins, Peterborough, United Kingdom; *Int'l*, pg. 820
Fisher, Nancy, Dir.-Personnel--The Kiplinger Washington Editors, Inc., Washington, DC; *U.S. Private*, pg. 623
Fisher, Norman B., V.P.-Indus. Rels. & H.R.--Gwaltney of Smithfield, Ltd., Smithfield, VA; *U.S. Public*, pg. 1479
Fisher, Rodger, V.P.-Personnel--Furr's/Bishops, Inc., Lubbock, TX; *U.S. Public*, pg. 689
Fisk, Deb, V.P.-Human Resources--E.H. Titchener & Company, Binghamton, NY; *U.S. Private*, pg. 1089
Fitzgerald, Anne, Dir.-H.R.--Westcorp, Irvine, CA; *U.S. Public*, pg. 1756
Fitzgerald, Bill, V.P.-Organ. Devel. & Human Resouces--Comstock Michigan Fruit, Rochester, NY; *U.S. Private*, pg. 887
Fitzgerald, Carole, Mgr.-Personnel--Remington Products Company, L.L.C., Bridgeport, CT; *U.S. Private*, pg. 921
Fitzgerald, Regina, V.P.-H.R.--Taco John's International, Inc., Cheyenne, WY; *U.S. Private*, pg. 1066
Fitzhenry, Jack, V.P.-Human Resources--Altera Corporation, San Jose, CA; *U.S. Public*, pg. 59
Fitzon, Herb, V.P.--ElectroCom Automation L.P., Arlington, TX; *Int'l*, pg. 1244
Fitzpatrick, Nora, Legal Asst. & H.R. Mngmt.--Tandycrafts, Inc., Fort Worth, TX; *U.S. Public*, pg. 1561
Fixmer, Susan M., Mgr.-Personnel--Andros Incorporated, Berkeley, CA; *U.S. Private*, pg. 74
Fixter, D.G., Sr. V.P.-Org. & Bus. Devel.--GSW Inc., Guelph, Canada,; *Int'l*, pg. 538
Flam, Deborah, V.P.-H.R.--Cowen & Company, New York, NY; *U.S. Private*, pg. 280
Flanary, Bill, V.P.-Personnel--Tuscarora Yarns Inc., Mount Pleasant, NC; *U.S. Private*, pg. 1110
Flasher, Jennifer, Mgr.-H.R.--Carhartt, Inc., Dearborn, MI; *U.S. Private*, pg. 210
Flateley, Carmel, V.P.-Human Resources--McDonald's Hamburgers Limited, London, United Kingdom; *U.S. Public*, pg. 1069
Flavin, Mike, Dir.-Human Resources--G.I. Plastek, Elyria, OH; *U.S. Private*, pg. 435
Fleck, Victor B., V.P.-H.R.--The F.A. Bartlett Tree Expert Co., Stamford, CT; *U.S. Private*, pg. 119
Fleetham, R., V.P.-Human Resources--Camco Inc., Mississauga, Canada; *U.S. Public*, pg. 713
Fleming, Ann, Mgr.-Personnel--Synchro-Start Products, Inc., Niles, IL; *U.S. Private*, pg. 627
Fleming, Richard D., Gen. Dir.-Personnel & Pub. Rels., Locomotive Grp.--Electro-Motive Division, La Grange, IL; *U.S. Public*, pg. 719
Flewellen, Lorene, V.P.-H.R.--Interlake Material Handling Div., Naperville, IL; *U.S. Public*, pg. 893
Flood, Hal, Dir.-H.R.--SouthCo. Inc., Concordville, PA; *U.S. Private*, pg. 1014
Flood, Patricia, Mgr.-Human Resources--Cache, Inc., New York, NY; *U.S. Public*, pg. 289
Flores, Armando B., Sr. V.P.-Human Resources & Corp. Services--APS, Phoenix, AZ; *U.S. Public*, pg. 1297
Flosi, Daryl, Dir.-H.R.--Interstate Van Lines, Inc., Springfield, VA; *U.S. Private*, pg. 573
Flowers, Jack, V.P.-Human Resources--Northern Illinois Gas Company, Naperville, IL; *U.S. Public*, pg. 1183
Flowers, John C., V.P.-Human Resources--NICOR Inc., Naperville, IL; *U.S. Public*, pg. 1182
Floyd, Dorris, Mgr.-Personnel--Nocona Boot Co., Nocona, TX; *U.S. Public*, pg. 937
Flynn, Dermot, Sr. V.P.-Human Resources--Cosmair, Inc., New York, NY; *Int'l*, pg. 818
Flynn, Jack D., V.P. & Mgr.-Personnel--Westvaco Corporation, New York, NY; *U.S. Public*, pg. 1762
Flynn, Leo C., Dir.-Human Resources--COMSAT RSI, Inc., Sterling, VA; *U.S. Public*, pg. 424
Flynn, Paul, Mgr.-Personnel--Mallinckrodt Medical, Athlone, Ireland; *U.S. Public*, pg. 1040
Flynn, Rita, V.P. & Mgr.-H.R.--Central Pacific Bank, Honolulu, HI; *U.S. Public*, pg. 283
Flynn, Steve, Mgr.-Personnel--Pace Industries, Inc., Fayetteville, AR; *U.S. Public*, pg. 986
Flyntz, Robert, V.P.-H.R.--The Miller Company, Meriden, CT; *U.S. Private*, pg. 746
Fodor, W.S., V.P.-Human Resources & Risk Mngmt.--Harwick Standard Distribution Corporation, Akron, OH; *U.S. Private*, pg. 509
Foehr, Horst, Dr., Dir.-Personnel--Deutsche Bahn, Frankfurt/Main, Germany; *Int'l*, pg. 401
Fogelman, Rodney, V.P.-Human Resources--WGM Safety Corporation, Reading, PA; *Int'l*, pg. 462

Fohrd, Cynthia L., Mgr.-Human Resources--Seneca Foods Corporation, Pittsford, NY; *U.S. Public*, pg. 1456
Foley, Daniel R., V.P.-Human Resources--Masco Corporation, Taylor, MI; *U.S. Public*, pg. 1052
Foley, John F., Sr. V.P.-Human Resources--CFX Bank, Keene, NH; *U.S. Public*, pg. 277
Follis, Russ, V.P.-Human Resources--Comdata Corporation, Brentwood, TN; *U.S. Public*, pg. 331
Foltz, Kimberly, V.P. & Dir.-Human Resources--Michael Baker Corporation, Pittsburgh, PA; *U.S. Public*, pg. 168
Fonda, Arline, V.P.-Human Resources--Washington Federal Savings, Seattle, WA; *U.S. Public*, pg. 1740
Foran, Steve, Mgr.-Employee Benefits--Nalco Chemical Company, Naperville, IL; *U.S. Public*, pg. 1150
Forberg, Jerry L., Mgr.-Human Resources--Woodward Governor Company, Rockford, IL; *U.S. Public*, pg. 1776
Forbes, C.G., Dir.-Personnel--Christies International plc, London, United Kingdom; *Int'l*, pg. 289
Forcht, William R., V.P.-Human Resources--F.W. Woolworth Co., New York, NY; *U.S. Public*, pg. 1777
Ford, Charles, H., V.P.-H.R.--U.S. Bioscience, Inc., Conshohocken, PA; *U.S. Public*, pg. 1681
Ford, Henry, V.P.-H.R.--Commonwealth Industries, Inc., Louisville, KY; *U.S. Public*, pg. 415
Ford, J., V.P.-H.R.--Comdial Corporation, Charlottesville, VA; *U.S. Public*, pg. 407
Ford, Judy, Dir.-Personnel & Labor Rels.--Ag Processing Inc., A Cooperative, Omaha, NE; *U.S. Private*, pg. 26
Ford, Terry, Dir.-Personnel--Eckerd Drug Co., Clearwater, FL; *U.S. Public*, pg. 917
Ford, Thomas A., V.P.-Human Resources--Rio Algom Limited, Toronto, Canada; *Int'l*, pg. 1118
Foreman, Gisela, Dir.-H.R.--Guardian Alarm Co., Southfield, MI; *U.S. Private*, pg. 485
Forget, Gary, Grp. Dir.-Human Resources--Imprimeries Quebecor Canada, Richmond Hill, Canada; *Int'l*, pg. 1077
Forgione, William S., V.P.-Human Resources--Perkins Family Restaurants, Memphis, TN; *U.S. Private*, pg. 925
Forness, Colleen, Supvr.-H.R.--Central Coca-Cola Bottling Company, Inc., Richmond, VA; *U.S. Private*, pg. 222
Forni, Kathleen, Dir.-H.R.--Syar Industries, Inc., Napa, CA; *U.S. Private*, pg. 1059
Forsell, John, Mgr.-Personnel & Info.--Esab AB, Goteborg, Sweden; *Int'l*, pg. 281
Forsman, Terry, V.P.-Personnel--A&W Restaurants, Inc.-Carousel Div., Minneapolis, MN; *U.S. Private*, pg. 2
Forsythe, Suzanne, V.P.-Human Resources--Things Remembered, Inc., Highland Heights, OH; *U.S. Public*, pg. 397
Fortes, Juan Blanco, Mgr.-H.R.--Controladora Comercial Mexicana, S.A. de C.V., Mexico, Mexico; *Int'l*, pg. 328
Fortier, Camille, Sr. V.P.-Fin., Human Resources & Tech.--Assurance vie Desjardins-Laurentienne, Levis, Canada; *Int'l*, pg. 396
Fortin, Dominique, Mgr.-Human Resources--Lyonnaise des Eaux S.A., Nanterre, France; *Int'l*, pg. 822
Fortin, Jean, Mgr.-Personnel--Rolland Inc., Fine Papers Division, Saint-Jerome, Canada; *Int'l*, pg. 274
Fortin, Raymond D., Sr. V.P. & Sec.--SunTrust Banks, Inc., Atlanta, GA; *U.S. Public*, pg. 1537
Fortin, Sophie, Gen. Mgr.-H.R. & Communications--Agropur, Granby, Canada; *Int'l*, pg. 31
Fortpied, Pierre, Gen. Mgr.-Human Resources--Solvay S.A., Brussels, Belgium; *Int'l*, pg. 1277
Fortune, Rosalee, V.P.-H.R.--The Fairmont Hotels, San Francisco, CA; *U.S. Private*, pg. 391
Fortune, Venita, Mgr.-Personnel--Carefree of Colorado, Broomfield, CO; *U.S. Public*, pg. 217
Foss, Deb, Sr. V.P.-Human Resources--Fortis Financial Group, Woodbury, MN; *Int'l*, pg. 499
Foster, Carol, Mgr.-Personnel--Brooks Instrument, Hatfield, PA; *U.S. Public*, pg. 574
Foster, Jack, Dir.-Human Resources--Augat, Inc., Wiring Systems, Montgomery, AL; *U.S. Public*, pg. 1598
Foster, Richard D., V.P.-Human Resources--Springs Industries, Inc., Fort Mill, SC; *U.S. Public*, pg. 1499
Foster, Robert D., Mgr.-H.R.--Dunn Industries Inc., Kansas City, MO; *U.S. Private*, pg. 347
Foster, Sara E., Sr. V.P.-H.R.--Commerce Bancshares, Inc., Kansas City, MO; *U.S. Public*, pg. 409
Foti, Frances, Sec. & Dir.-Personnel--ICC Industries, Inc., New York, NY; *U.S. Private*, pg. 553
Foulkes, Ninsome, Dir.-Pers.--Telephonics Corp., Farmington, NY; *U.S. Public*, pg. 766
Found, Larry, V.P.-Human Resources/Americas--Medtronic, Inc., Minneapolis, MN; *U.S. Public*, pg. 1082
Fournier, Peter, V.P.-Human Resources & Admin.--Loews Theatre Management Corp., New York, NY; *Int'l*, pg. 1282
Foushee, Smith, V.P.-Human Resources--Indian Head Industries Inc., Charlotte, NC; *U.S. Private*, pg. 559
Fouts, James, Dir.-H.R.--Transnational Motors Inc., Grand Rapids, MI; *U.S. Private*, pg. 1097
Fowler, David S., Chief Admin. Officer & Sr. V.P.--The Chubb Corporation, Warren, NJ; *U.S. Public*, pg. 354
Fowler, Debbie, Dir.-Human Resources--Gerber Garment Technology, Inc., Richardson, TX; *U.S. Public*, pg. 740
Fowler, Peggy, Dir.-Personnel--Federal Realty Investment Trust, Rockville, MD; *U.S. Public*, pg. 616
Fowler, S. Craig, Mgr.-H.R.--Xtek, Inc., Cincinnati, OH; *U.S. Private*, pg. 1194
Fowler, Susan, Exec. V.P. & Dir.-Human Resources--Sanwa Bank California, Los Angeles, CA; *Int'l*, pg. 1189
Fox, Diann D., Sr. V.P.--Scott & Stringfellow Financial, Inc., Richmond, VA; *U.S. Public*, pg. 1445
Fox, Pamela, Dir.-Human Resources--Rolling Stone Magazine, New York, NY; *U.S. Private*, pg. 1162
Fox, Pamela, Mgr.-Human Resources--Us Magazine, New York, NY; *U.S. Private*, pg. 1162
Foxworthy, James C., Sr. V.P.-Human Resources--Inland Container Corporation, Indianapolis, IN; *U.S. Public*, pg. 1575
Foyad, Vince, Dir.-Human Resources--Sulzer Bingham Pumps Inc., Portland, OR; *Int'l*, pg. 1305
Frahm, James R., V.P.-Personnel--Coachmen Industries, Inc., Elkhart, IN; *U.S. Public*, pg. 387
France, Richard E., V.P.-H.R. & Pub. Rels.--Caraustar Industries, Inc., Austell, GA; *U.S. Public*, pg. 303
France, Woodrow, Dir.-Human Resources--North American Royalties, Inc., Chattanooga, TN; *U.S. Private*, pg. 803
Franceschini, Susan, V.P. & Human Resources Dir.--DavisElen Advertising, Inc., Los Angeles, CA; *U.S. Private*, pg. 316
Francesco, Anne De, Human Resources Officer--New Hampshire Insurance Group, New York, NY; *U.S. Public*, pg. 84
Francis, Bette, Dir.-Human Resources--Pentax Precision Instrument Corp., Orangeburg, NY; *Int'l*, pg. 85
Francis, Coleen, Mgr.-Benefits--Brite Voice Systems, Inc., Heathrow, FL; *U.S. Public*, pg. 257
Francis, John, Dir.-Personnel/Dixons Grp.--Dixons Group plc, Hemel Hempstead, United Kingdom,; *Int'l*, pg. 413
Frank, D.K., Dir.-Personnel--Idaho Forest Industry, Inc., Coeur D'Alene, ID; *U.S. Private*, pg. 556
Frank, Iris, Dir.-Personnel--Longevity International, Ltd., New York, NY; *U.S. Private*, pg. 444
Franklin, Laura M., Chief Acctg. Officer & V.P.--Washington Real Estate Investment Trust, Kensington, MD; *U.S. Public*, pg. 1743
Franklin, Marla, V.P.-H.R.--Allied Mutual Insurance Company, Des Moines, IA; *U.S. Private*, pg. 39
Franks, Richard, V.P.-H.R.--Avatar Holdings Inc., Coral Gables, FL; *U.S. Public*, pg. 151
Franks, Richard B., V.P.-Human Resources--Avatar Properties Inc., Miami, FL; *U.S. Public*, pg. 151
Fransen van de Putte, J. J., Mgr.-Personnel & Organization--DSM N.V., Heerlen, Netherlands; *Int'l*, pg. 352
Fransen, Darla A., V.P.-Human Resources & Sec.--Tri-State Insurance Company of Minnesota, Luverne, MN; *U.S. Public*, pg. 215
Fransson, Nils-Erik, Dir.-Personnel--Sodra Cell AB, Vaxjo, Sweden; *Int'l*, pg. 1275
Frantz, John F., Dir.-H.R.--Altec Industries, Inc., Birmingham, AL; *U.S. Private*, pg. 47
Franz, Ron, V.P.-Human Resources--Amperif Corporation, Chatsworth, CA; *U.S. Public*, pg. 1523
Fraser, Brian G., V.P.-Admin. & Gen. Counsel--Clark Foodservice, Inc., Elk Grove Village, IL; *U.S. Private*, pg. 242
Fraser, Karen L., V.P.-Human Resources--Axel Johnson Inc., Stamford, CT; *Int'l*, pg. 709
Frasse, Ed, Dir.-Human Resources--Transkrit Corporation, Roanoke, VA; *U.S. Private*, pg. 782
Frassi, Will, Mgr.-Human Resources--Hamilton Co., Inc., Reno, NV; *U.S. Private*, pg. 497
Fratte, Fred, V.P.-Human Resources--Goody Products, Inc., Peachtree City, GA; *U.S. Public*, pg. 1177
Frautschi, Deanna L., V.P.-Commun. & H.R.--Country Life Insurance Company, Bloomington, IL; *U.S. Private*, pg. 278
Frayne, Kathy, Dir.-H.R.--Craftmatic Industries, Inc., Trevose, PA; *U.S. Private*, pg. 284
Frazier, Edward F., V.P.--Scientific Software-Intercomp, Inc., Denver, CO; *U.S. Public*, pg. 1443
Frechette, John D., V.P. & Dir.-H.R.--Owens-Illinois, Inc., Toledo, OH; *U.S. Public*, pg. 1238
Freddi, Rita, Dir.-Personnel--Caleffi S.p.A., Viadana, Italy; *Int'l*, pg. 252
Frederickson, Millie, Dir.-Personnel--Betac International Corporation, Alexandria, VA; *U.S. Private*, pg. 140
Frederickson, Robert P., Dir.-Personnel--Flambeau Mill, Park Falls, WI; *Int'l*, pg. 434
Fredette, Thomas, Mgr.-Human Resources--Sheffield Steel Corporation-Joliet, Joliet, IL; *U.S. Private*, pg. 991
Fredianelli, Ronald E., Dir.-H.R.--ILC Technology, Inc., Sunnyvale, CA; *U.S. Public*, pg. 856
Freearis, Mike, Dir.-H.R.--National Safety Associates, Memphis, TN; *U.S. Private*, pg. 786
Freedman, Bob, Dir.-H.R., North America--Caradon Plc, Weybridge, United Kingdom; *Int'l*, pg. 266
Freedman, Charles M., V.P.-Corp. Excellence--Hawaiian Electric Company, Inc., Honolulu, HI; *U.S. Public*, pg. 800
Freedman, Leslie E., Mgr.-Internal Communications--Quorum Health Group, Inc., Brentwood, TN; *U.S. Public*, pg. 1353
Freeman, Clara, Exec. Dir.-Personnel--Marks & Spencer PLC, London, United Kingdom; *Int'l*, pg. 842
Freeman, Jean E., Benefits Coord.--Chi Systems Division, Ann Arbor, MI; *U.S. Public*, pg. 1539
Freeman, Linda, Dir.-Human Resources--National Technical Systems, Inc., Calabasas, CA; *U.S. Public*, pg. 1161
Freer, Glad, Dir.-Personnel & Corp. Travel Planner--The Canadian Coleman Co., Ltd., Toronto, Canada; *U.S. Private*, pg. 691
Freesmeier, Eric, Exec. V.P.--Edison Brothers Stores, Inc., Saint Louis, MO; *U.S. Public*, pg. 563
Freiburghaus, Jean-Robert, First V.P.--Ferrier Lullin & Cie SA, Geneva, Switzerland; *Int'l*, pg. 480
French, Larry, Mgr.-Human Resources--Frigidaire Home Products-Refrigerator Products, Greenville, MI; *Int'l*, pg. 440
French, Milford B., V.P.-Human Resources--Intergraph Corporation, Huntsville, AL; *U.S. Public*, pg. 890
Frenette, Jean, Dir.-Personnel, Head Office & Distr. Ctr.--The Jean Coutu Group (PJC) Inc., Longueuil, Canada; *Int'l*, pg. 340
Freudmann, Axel I., Sr. V.P.-Human Resources--American International Group, Inc., New York, NY; *U.S. Public*, pg. 83
Frey, Marilyn, Dir.-Personnel--Basler Electric Company, Highland, IL; *U.S. Private*, pg. 121
Frick, H.C., Jr., V.P.-Human Resources--Brown & Williamson Tobacco Corp., Louisville, KY; *Int'l*, pg. 111
Fricke, David, Mgr.-Personnel--Watkins Incorporated, Winona, MN; *U.S. Private*, pg. 1153
Friday, Peggy, Dir.-Personnel--Angelo Brothers Co., Philadelphia, PA; *U.S. Private*, pg. 74
Frideres, Ken, Dir.-Personnel--Advance Machine Company, Plymouth, MN; *Int'l*, pg. 932
Friedberg, Toy, Dir.-Human Resources, N.A.--A. Schulman, Inc., Akron, OH; *U.S. Public*, pg. 1441
Friedberg, Toy, Dir.-Human Resources--A. Schulman, Inc., Fort Wayne, IN; *U.S. Public*, pg. 1441
Friedland, A., V.P.-Human Resources--Lambda Electronics Inc., Melville, NY; *Int'l*, pg. 1241
Friedland, Klaus, Dir.-Personnel--Continental AG, Hannover, Germany; *Int'l*, pg. 327
Friedman, Alan, Sr. V.P. & Dir.-H.R.--Arthur D. Little, Inc., Cambridge, MA; *U.S. Private*, pg. 670
Friedman, Lenard, Dir.-Human Resources--EIS Brake Parts Div., Berlin, CT; *U.S. Public*, pg. 1503
Friedman, Terri, Dir.-H.R.--Friedman, Eisenstein, Raemer and Schwartz, LLP, Chicago, IL; *U.S. Private*, pg. 428
Friedrich, Carla M., V.P.-H.R.--Lawrence Savings Bank, North Andover, MA; *U.S. Public*, pg. 980
Friedrich, Hubert, Dir.-Personnel--Battenfeld GmbH, Meinerzhagen, Germany; *Int'l*, pg. 825
Friend, Andrea, Human Resource Mgr.--Chicago Creative Partnership, Chicago, IL; *U.S. Private*, pg. 234
Friesen, Eugene K., Chief Fin. Officer, Sr. V.P. & Treas.--Howard B. Wolf, Inc., Dallas, TX; *U.S. Public*, pg. 1774
Frigeni, Ermanno, Dir.-Personnel--Opticos S.r.l., Brembate di Sopra, Italy; *Int'l*, pg. 1007
Frisch, D., V.P.-Human Resources--Alumax Mill Products, Inc., Morris, IL; *U.S. Public*, pg. 59
Frisch, Richard F., V.P.-H.R. & Admin--Bowater Incorporated, Greenville, SC; *U.S. Public*, pg. 247
Fritz, G.B., Dir.-Personnel--AmerenCIPS, Springfield, IL; *U.S. Public*, pg. 65
Fritz, Ron, Mgr.-Human Resources--Norpac Foods, Inc., Stayton, OR; *U.S. Private*, pg. 802
Froggatt, Kirk, V.P.-H.R.--Silicon Graphics, Inc., Mountain View, CA; *U.S. Public*, pg. 1473
Frye, Darrell, V.P.-Fin. & Sec.--Harriss & Covington Hosiery Mills, High Point, NC; *U.S. Private*, pg. 506
Fuchigama, Yuzo, Mgr.-Personnel--Takagi Chokoku Co., Ltd., Wakayama, Japan; *Int'l*, pg. 1349
Fuerman, Evelyn, Dir.-Personnel--Starrett HRH, New York, NY; *U.S. Private*, pg. 1035
Fujii, M., Dir.-Personnel & Pub. Rels.--Otto Sumisho Inc., Tokyo, Japan; *Int'l*, pg. 1015
Fujii, Osamu, Gen. Mgr.-Human Resources--Tosoh Corporation, Tokyo, Japan; *Int'l*, pg. 1407
Fulkosky, Marriane, Dir.-Human Res.--Sierra On-Line, Inc., Bellevue, WA; *U.S. Public*, pg. 321
Fuller, Patti, Mgr.-H.R.--E & A Industries, Inc., Indianapolis, IN; *U.S. Private*, pg. 352
Fuller, Stephen V., V.P.-H.R.--AmeriPath, Inc., Riviera Beach, FL; *U.S. Public*, pg. 96
Fuller, Sue, Dir.-Personnel & Pub. Rels.--Litton Systems, Inc. Advanced Circuitry Div., Springfield, MO; *U.S. Public*, pg. 1003
Fullerton, George, Mgr.-Personnel--Denison Hydraulics, Inc., Marysville, OH; *U.S. Private*, pg. 324
Fulton, Steven P., V.P.-H.R. & Gen. Counsel--Respironics, Inc., Pittsburgh, PA; *U.S. Public*, pg. 1383
Fulwider, Gail M., V.P.-Human Resources--Smith Environmental Technologies Corp., Plymouth Meeting, PA; *U.S. Public*, pg. 1477
Fumagalli, Douglas A., Sr. V.P.-Human Resources--SHL Systemhouse, Ottawa, Canada; *Int'l*, pg. 1154
Funck-Bretano, Thierry, Exec. V.P.-Communications & Human Resources--Lagardere Groupe, Paris, France; *Int'l*, pg. 791
Funk, Roger, Dr., V.P.-Human & Technical Resources--The Davey Tree Expert Company, Kent, OH; *U.S. Private*, pg. 314
Funk, Warren C., Dir.-Personnel--Memphis Publishing Co., Memphis, TN; *U.S. Public*, pg. 1448
Furbee, Eric, Mgr.-H.R.--The Homer Laughlin China Company, Newell, WV; *U.S. Private*, pg. 653
Furfar, Ricardo, V.P.-Human Resources & Legal Afairs--Johnson & Johnson de Argentina, S.A., Buenos Aires, Argentina; *U.S. Public*, pg. 930
Furlong, Richie, Dir.-Personnel--Birds Eye Walls Ltd., Walton-on-Thames, United Kingdom; *Int'l*, pg. 1434
Furnas, Walt, Sr. V.P.-Human Resources--Red Roof Inns, Inc., Hilliard, OH; *U.S. Public*, pg. 1369
Furry, Diane, Mgr.-Human Resources--Schnadig Corporation, Des Plaines, IL; *U.S. Private*, pg. 971
Fuse, Keigo, Dir.-H.R.--G-Net Corporation, Osaka, Japan; *Int'l*, pg. 531
Fushitani, H., Dir.-Human Resources--Avon Products Co., Ltd., Tokyo, Japan; *U.S. Public*, pg. 156
Gabriel, S.G., Dir.-Personnel--Stonecutter Mills Corp., Spindale, NC; *U.S. Private*, pg. 1044
Gadsden, Edward N., Jr., Dir.-Employment & Diversity--Texaco Inc., White Plains, NY; *U.S. Public*, pg. 1582
Gaeth, W.A., V.P.-H.R.--Daubert Industries, Inc., Westchester, IL; *U.S. Private*, pg. 313
Gafney, Richard, Dir.-Human Resources--New England Confectionery Co., Cambridge, MA; *U.S. Private*, pg. 1113
Gage, Melinda, Dir.-H.R.--Span-America Medical Systems Inc., Greenville, SC; *U.S. Public*, pg. 1495
Gage, Tim, Dir.-H.R.--Brodart Company, Williamsport, PA; *U.S. Private*, pg. 170
Gagliardi, Richard J., V.P.-Admin.--Allegheny Power System, Inc., Hagerstown, MD; *U.S. Public*, pg. 42
Gagne, Christian, Mgr.-Personnel & Finance--Atlet France S.A., Cergy-Pontoise, France; *Int'l*, pg. 97
Gagnon, Rodrigue, V.P.-H.R.--G.T.C. Transcontinental Group Ltd., Montreal, Canada; *Int'l*, pg. 538
Gailey, Kim, Dir.-Human Resources--Crested Butte Mountain Resort, Inc., Crested Butte, CO; *U.S. Private*, pg. 289
Gailitano, Frances, V.P.-Human Resources--Sodexho USA, Waltham, MA; *Int'l*, pg. 1274

Gale, D.J., Dir.-Personnel--Austin Reed Limited, London, United Kingdom; *U.S. Public*, pg. 796
Galla, Patrick, V.P.-Human Resources--Crown American Realty Trust, Johnstown, PA; *U.S. Public*, pg. 461
Gallagher, Chuck, V.P.-Personnel--The Andersons Incorporated, Maumee, OH; *U.S. Public*, pg. 111
Gallagher, Marilyn, V.P.-Human Resources--Pepsi-Cola Bottling Company of Charlotte Inc., Charlotte, NC; *U.S. Private*, pg. 852
Gallagher, Thomas S., V.P.-Employee Rels.--Chrysler Corporation, Auburn Hills, MI; *U.S. Public*, pg. 352
Gallaspy, Rhonda, V.P.-H.R.--Outsource International, Deerfield Beach, FL; *U.S. Public*, pg. 1236
Gallegos, Pat, Dir.-Human Resources--Evans & Sutherland Computer Corporation, Salt Lake City, UT; *U.S. Public*, pg. 595
Gallina, Larry, Mgr.-Human Resources--Aquion, Elk Grove Village, IL; *U.S. Private*, pg. 78
Gallo, Maria, Dir.-Personnel--Injection Footwear Corp., Miami, FL; *U.S. Private*, pg. 563
Gallogly, Paul A., Dir.-Human Resources--Ark-Les Corporation, Stoughton, MA; *U.S. Private*, pg. 82
Gallow, D.J., Mgr.-Personnel--Distillers Corporation S.A., Stellenbosch, South Africa; *Int'l*, pg. 1129
Galovan, James W., V.P. & Dir.-H.R. & Mktg.--General Mills, Inc., Minneapolis, MN; *U.S. Public*, pg. 717
Galvin, Susan M., Administrator--New England Coffee Company, Malden, MA; *U.S. Private*, pg. 792
Gamba, John F., Sr. V.P.-Corp. Resources & Performance Assurance--Bell Atlantic Corporation, New York, NY; *U.S. Public*, pg. 201
Gambill, Michael, Dir.-Total Compensation & Human Resource Info.--Aluminum Company of America, Pittsburgh, PA; *U.S. Public*, pg. 60
Gamble, Kevin, Dir.-Personnel--Weir Group PLC, Glasgow, United Kingdom; *Int'l*, pg. 1488
Gambon, Marie, V.P.-H.R.--Celestial Seasonings, Boulder, CO; *U.S. Public*, pg. 319
Gambrell, Al, V.P.-Human Resources--Stella Foods Inc., Lincolnshire, IL; *U.S. Private*, pg. 1040
Gameson, Ray, Sr. V.P.-Human Resources--Pilgrim's Pride Corporation, Pittsburg, TX; *U.S. Public*, pg. 1296
Gammon, Jeanne, Admin.-Corp. Affairs--Alaska Air Group, Inc., Seattle, WA; *U.S. Public*, pg. 35
Gannon, Patrick, Dir.-Human Resources Devel.--Brunswick Corporation, Lake Forest, IL; *U.S. Public*, pg. 265
Gantou, Yves, Dir.-Human Resources--Telediffusion de France, Paris, France; *Int'l*, pg. 503
Gantz, Stacey, Mgr.-H.R.--Bachman Company, Reading, PA; *U.S. Private*, pg. 109
Garabed, Maida, Mgr.-Personnel--Olin Microelectronic Materials, Inc., Norwalk, CT; *U.S. Public*, pg. 1219
Garber, Samuel B., V.P., Gen. Counsel & Sec.--Evans, Inc., Chicago, IL; *U.S. Public*, pg. 596
Garcia, Aida M., Sr. V.P.-H.R.--Firstbank Puerto Rico, Santurce, PR; *U.S. Public*, pg. 644
Garcia, Benjamin R., Dir.-Human Resources--SmithKline Beecham Research Limited, Pasig, Philippines; *Int'l*, pg. 1266
Garcia, David, Dir.-Personnel--Paul Ecke Ranch, Encinitas, CA; *U.S. Private*, pg. 359
Garcia, Sonia, Personnel--Rums of Puerto Rico, New York, NY; *U.S. Private*, pg. 951
Garcia, Suzanne, Mgr.-Human Resources, Personnel Training & Devel.--Electronic Arts, San Mateo, CA; *U.S. Public*, pg. 569
Gardiner, Craig O., Dir.-H.R.--Stepan Company, Northfield, IL; *U.S. Public*, pg. 1514
Gardner, Gary E., V.P.-Human Res. & Public Affairs--The Valspar Corporation, Minneapolis, MN; *U.S. Public*, pg. 1707
Gardner, Howard, V.P.-Human Reources--Medical Meadow Gold Dairies, Inc., Ogden, UT; *U.S. Private*, pg. 1016
Gardner, Nolan, Dir.-H.R.--C.H. Heist Corp., Clearwater, FL; *U.S. Public*, pg. 807
Gardner, Ricci, V.P.-H.R.--Burlington Northern Santa Fe Corporation, Fort Worth, TX; *U.S. Public*, pg. 268
Gardner, Scott, V.P.-H.R.--Tekelec, Calabasas, CA; *U.S. Public*, pg. 1566
Garelli, Susan B., V.P.-H.R.--Avery Dennison Corporation, Pasadena, CA; *U.S. Public*, pg. 152
Garey, Daniel T., V.P.-H.R.--Parker Hannifin Corporation, Cleveland, OH; *U.S. Public*, pg. 1259
Garfield, P.B., Grp. Personnel Controller--Johnson Matthey Public Limited Company, London, United Kingdom; *Int'l*, pg. 713
Garlock, Janice O., V.P.-Human Resources--Elliott Company, Jeannette, PA; *U.S. Private*, pg. 373
Garner, Donna, Mgr.-H.R.--Klipsch, Inc., Hope, AR; *U.S. Private*, pg. 626
Garner, Fran, Dir.-H.R.--AM Cosmetics Inc., Nyack, NY; *U.S. Private*, pg. 6
Garner, Fran, Dir.-H.R.--General Bearing Corp., West Nyack, NY; *U.S. Public*, pg. 706
Garner, R.W., Dir.-Human Resources--H.P. Bulmer Holdings Plc, Hereford, United Kingdom; *Int'l*, pg. 232
Garner, Richard, Sr. V.P.-Human Resources--Pic'n Pay Stores, Inc., Matthews, NC; *U.S. Private*, pg. 864
Garner, Trevor A., Mgr.-H.R.--Burke Engineering Company, South El Monte, CA; *U.S. Private*, pg. 183
Garnett, Edward F., V.P.-Human Resources--Amgen Inc., Thousand Oaks, CA; *U.S. Public*, pg. 100
Garofalo, Angela, V.P.-Human Resources--Willis Corroon Corp. of Illinois, Chicago, IL; *Int'l*, pg. 1506
Garratt, Paul R., V.P.-H.R.--Air Canada, Saint-Laurent, Canada; *Int'l*, pg. 36
Garrett, Harry L., Dir.-Human Resources--NationsBank South, Atlanta, GA; *U.S. Public*, pg. 1163
Garrett, Tammy, Dir.-Personnel--Jake Sweeney Auto Leasing, Inc., Cincinnati, OH; *U.S. Private*, pg. 1058
Garrido Manzano, Feliciando, Asst. Dir.-Personnel--Banca March S.A., Palma de Mallorca, Spain; *Int'l*, pg. 136
Garrison, Peggy, Dir.-Admin. Svcs.--Burgess & Niple, Limited, Columbus, OH; *U.S. Private*, pg. 182
Gartland, Timothy C., Sr. V.P.-Human Resources--Provident Companies, Inc., Chattanooga, TN; *U.S. Public*, pg. 1337
Garwood, Geof, Dir.-Human Resources--British Printing Company Ltd., London, United Kingdom; *Int'l*, pg. 220
Garza, Abraham, Dir.-H.R.--Cabot Oil & Gas Corporation, Houston, TX; *U.S. Public*, pg. 289
Garza, Raul, Dir.-Personnel--Hygeia Dairy Co., Inc., Harlingen, TX; *U.S. Private*, pg. 552
Gaskill, Robin, V.P.-H.R.--Wells Aluminum Corp., Baltimore, MD; *U.S. Private*, pg. 1161
Gaspar, David, Dir.-H.R.--Auto Glass Specialists, Madison, WI; *U.S. Private*, pg. 100
Gasparini, Claudia, V.P.-H.R.--WPIX, Inc., New York, NY; *U.S. Public*, pg. 1636
Gaston, Roger, Exec. V.P.-Human Resources--Carson Pirie Scott & Co., Milwaukee, WI; *U.S. Public*, pg. 309
Gaston, Roger C., Sr. V.P.-Human Resources--Toys "R" Us, Inc., Paramus, NJ; *U.S. Public*, pg. 1626
Gately, Arthur T., Jr., Sr. V.P.-Admin.--Swank, Inc., Attleboro, MA; *U.S. Public*, pg. 1543
Gatesmith, Jeffrey R., V.P.-Retail Store Opers. & H.R.--Funco, Inc., Eden Prairie, MN; *U.S. Public*, pg. 688
Gatewood, Char, Dir.-Personnel--Crystal Cabinet Works, Inc., Princeton, MN; *U.S. Private*, pg. 293
Gathers, Thomas W., Sr. V.P.-H.R.--Uno Restaurant Corporation, West Roxbury, MA; *U.S. Public*, pg. 1698
Gatti, Bill, V.P.-H.R.--Doubleday Direct, Garden City, NY; *Int'l*, pg. 191
Gattuso, Orysia, Mgr.-Personnel--Weldotron Corporation, Piscataway, NJ; *U.S. Public*, pg. 1752
Gatzke, Carla, Dir.-H.R.--Daktronics, Inc., Brookings, SD; *U.S. Public*, pg. 478
Gaufin, Shirley, V.P. & Mgr.-Human Resources--Parsons Corporation, Pasadena, CA; *U.S. Private*, pg. 841
Gaugler, William, V.P.-H.R.--Hanover Foods Corporation, Hanover, PA; *U.S. Private*, pg. 499
Gaullier, J.P., Deputy Mgr.-Human Resources--Groupe GAN, Paris, France; *Int'l*, pg. 563
Gausman, Joseph, Mgr.-H.R.--Plastek Group, Erie, PA; *U.S. Private*, pg. 870
Gauthier, D., V.P.-Human Resources--ITT Cannon Sealectro, New Britain, CT; *U.S. Public*, pg. 859
Gavic, Stan, Mgr.-H.R.--Weinbrenner Shoe Company, Inc., Merrill, WI; *U.S. Private*, pg. 1160
Gavin, Gregg, Dir.-Human Resources--Quebecor Printing Semline Inc., Braintree, MA; *Int'l*, pg. 1078
Gay, Garry, V.P.-Human Resources--Spaghetti Warehouse, Inc., Garland, TX; *U.S. Public*, pg. 1495
Gaymon, Nancy L., V.P.-H.R.--Litton Industries, Inc., Woodland Hills, CA; *U.S. Public*, pg. 1002
Gazes, Jerry P., V.P.-H.R.--First Financial Holdings, Inc., Charleston, SC; *U.S. Public*, pg. 634
Gazzano, Tina, Mgr.-Personnel--Otari Corporation, Foster City, CA; *Int'l*, pg. 1013
Gearhart, Pearl H., V.P.-H.R.--Shenandoah Life Insurance Company, Roanoke, VA; *U.S. Private*, pg. 992
Geary, Verna, Dir.-H.R.--Franchise Finance Corp. of America, Scottsdale, AZ; *U.S. Public*, pg. 679
Gebhardt, Erwin, Mgr.-Employee Rels.--Midland Enterprises Inc., Cincinnati, OH; *U.S. Public*, pg. 549
Geczy, Paul C., V.P.-Admin.--Jayco Inc., Middlebury, IN; *U.S. Private*, pg. 583
Geesey, Beverly, Supvr.-Human Resources--John Copes Food Products, Inc., Rheems, PA; *U.S. Private*, pg. 274
Gehrke, Norbert, Dir.-Personnel--Braun AG, Kronberg, Germany; *U.S. Public*, pg. 744
Geier, James A., V.P.-H.R.--Quaker Chemical Corporation, Conshohocken, PA; *U.S. Public*, pg. 1346
Geis, Walter, V.P.-Human Devel. & Personnel Services--The Copps Corp., Stevens Point, WI; *U.S. Private*, pg. 275
Gelfand, Neal, Sr. V.P.-Human Resources--Amerada Hess Corporation, New York, NY; *U.S. Public*, pg. 65
Gelven, Arthur E., V.P.-Human Resources, Contracts & Admin.--COMSAT Mobile Communications, Clarksburg, MD; *U.S. Public*, pg. 424
Gembitsky, Nancy, V.P.-Human Resources--Zee Medical, Inc., Irvine, CA; *U.S. Public*, pg. 1073
Gendron, Kathy, Mgr.-Human Resources--The Dometic Corporation, Elkhart, IN; *Int'l*, pg. 440
Genschou, P. Arne, V.P.-Human Resources Intl.--Pharmacia & Upjohn Biotech AB, Uppsala, Sweden; *Int'l*, pg. 1047
Gentry, Steve, Dir.-H.R.--Uniblend Spinners, Inc., Conway, SC; *U.S. Private*, pg. 1117
Gentz, Manfred, Chief Fin. Officer--Daimler-Benz Aktiengesellschaft, Stuttgart, Germany; *Int'l*, pg. 366
Genuardi, Gerlando, Mgr.-Personnel Admin.--European Investment Bank, Luxembourg, Luxembourg; *Int'l*, pg. 465
George, Herbert J., V.P.-Human Resources--Temple-Inland Forest Products Corporation, Diboll, TX; *U.S. Public*, pg. 1575
Georgia, Frank, Mgr.-H.R.--Mycogen Corporation, San Diego, CA; *U.S. Public*, pg. 1142
Gephart, Mary, Dir.-Human Resources--Manatron, Inc., Kalamazoo, MI; *U.S. Public*, pg. 1040
Geraghty, S.J., Dir.-Customer Engagement--National & Provincial Building Society, Bradford, United Kingdom; *Int'l*, pg. 906
Geran, D.B., Mgr.-Personnel--Los Alamos Technical Associates, Inc., Los Alamos, NM; *U.S. Private*, pg. 676
Gerard, Antonia, Chief Oper. & Chief Fin. Officer, Exec. V.P., Sec. & Controller--Bolliger, Inc., Stamford, CT; *U.S. Private*, pg. 155
Gerard, Ivan, V.P.-H.R.--Pacesetter Corporation, Omaha, NE; *U.S. Private*, pg. 830
Gerard, J. Michael, V.P.-Human Resources--F.E. Myers, Ashland, OH; *U.S. Public*, pg. 1273
Gerardo, Alexander M., V.P.-Human Resources--Troy Corporation, Florham Park, NJ; *U.S. Private*, pg. 1105
Gerhart, Doug, V.P.-Corp. Devel.--Trimble Navigation Limited, Sunnyvale, CA; *U.S. Public*, pg. 1638
Gerlach, Karen, V.P.-Human Resources--Chemical Leaman Tank Lines, Inc., Exton, PA; *U.S. Private*, pg. 233
Gerner, David W., Dir.-Personnel--Ripon Foods, Inc., Ripon, WI; *U.S. Private*, pg. 931
Gerold, Roger, Mgr.-Personnel Rels.--Teleflex Automotive, Van Wert, OH; *U.S. Public*, pg. 1569
Gerow, Janet, Dir.-Personnel--RTG Furniture Corp., Seffner, FL; *U.S. Private*, pg. 905
Gerson, Gail, Human Resources Mgr.--Jack Levy Associates, Chicago, IL; *U.S. Private*, pg. 664
Gertmenian, Jaime, V.P.-H.R. & Admin.--Catellus Development Corporation, San Francisco, CA; *U.S. Public*, pg. 314
Gerwe, Rick, Mgr.-Personnel--Senco Products, Inc., Cincinnati, OH; *U.S. Private*, pg. 984
Geslison, Daniel, Dir.-Human Resources--Nature's Sunshine Products, Inc., Provo, UT; *U.S. Public*, pg. 1166
Gettig, T.E., V.P.-H.R.--Welch Foods Inc., A Cooperative, Concord, MA; *U.S. Private*, pg. 784
Gettys, Robert M., V.P.-Human Resources--Freeport-McMoRan Inc., New Orleans, LA; *U.S. Public*, pg. 680
Getzlaff, Darryll J., V.P.-Human Resources--Quidel Corporation, San Diego, CA; *U.S. Public*, pg. 1352
Ghanam, Jenny, Mgr.-Human Resources--Charter Medical of England Ltd., London, United Kingdom; *U.S. Public*, pg. 1036
Gholston, Julie, Human Resources Admin.--Karakas, VanSickle, Ouellette Advertising & Public Relations, Portland, OR; *U.S. Private*, pg. 607
Ghuzal Tahir, Encik Ahmad, Sr. Mgr.-Industrial Rels. & Comp./Human Resources--Standard Chartered Bank Malaysia Berhad, Kuala Lumpur, Malaysia; *Int'l*, pg. 1295
Giachardi, David, Dir.-H.R., Health, Safety & Environment--Courtaulds plc, London, United Kingdom; *Int'l*, pg. 338
Giallanzo, Judy, Mgr.-Personnel--HCI Chemtech, Chesterfield, MO; *U.S. Private*, pg. 490
Giardina, Carol Ann T., V.P.-Human Resources Plng.--Automated Wagering, Hackensack, NJ; *U.S. Public*, pg. 1319
Gibaldi, Lori, Dir.-Human Resources--Six Flags Great Adventure Theme Park & Wild Safari Animal Park, Jackson, NJ; *U.S. Public*, pg. 1611
Gibbs, Larry, Dir.-Personnel--Schwan's Sales Enterprises, Marshall, MN; *U.S. Private*, pg. 974
Gibson, B.R., Dir.-Human Resources & Insurance--Sea Island Company, Sea Island, GA; *U.S. Private*, pg. 977
Gibson, Charles E., V.P.-Human Resources--Public Service Company of North Carolina, Inc., Gastonia, NC; *U.S. Public*, pg. 1340
Gibson, Charles, Jr., Mgr.-Admin. Services--Bovaird Supply Co., Tulsa, OK; *U.S. Private*, pg. 162
Gibson, Chuck, V.P.-Human Res.--Jacobsen Textron, Racine, WI; *U.S. Public*, pg. 1589
Gibson, Gloria S., Dir.-Human Resources--Interstate/Johnson Lane, Inc., Charlotte, NC; *U.S. Public*, pg. 909
Gibson, J.C., Mgr.-Human Resources--Great Lakes Confectionery, Cleveland, OH; *Int'l*, pg. 865
Gibson, Paul, Dir.-Human Resource--Fleck Manufacturing Inc., Tillsonburg, Canada; *Int'l*, pg. 955
Gibson, Sandra, V.P.-H.R.--Corel Corporation, Ottawa, Canada; *Int'l*, pg. 331
Giddings, Lois, Mgr.-Employee Rels.--Mark IV Automotive Canada Inc., Weston, Canada; *U.S. Public*, pg. 1045
Giegerich, Robert, V.P.-Service--XRE Corporation, Littleton, MA; *U.S. Public*, pg. 1595
Gienko, Glenn A., Sr. V.P. & Dir.-Human Resources--Motorola, Inc., Schaumburg, IL; *U.S. Public*, pg. 1136
Giese, Margaret, Mgr.-Personnel--Frederick Wildman & Sons Ltd., New York, NY; *U.S. Private*, pg. 1176
Giesen, L.J.A., Dir.-Employee Benefits--Oce-van der Grinten N.V., Venlo, Netherlands; *Int'l*, pg. 993
Gieske, Geoff, V.P.-Human Resources--John Crane North America, Morton Grove, IL; *Int'l*, pg. 1339
Giffen, G., Dir.-Personnel--Hilton Canada Inc., Montreal, Canada; *Int'l*, pg. 788
Gifford, Patricia L., Sr. V.P.-Human Resources--The Elder-Beerman Stores Corp., Dayton, OH; *U.S. Private*, pg. 367
Giffvne, Dr. Kenneth, V.P.-H.R.--PAR Technology Corporation, New Hartford, NY; *U.S. Public*, pg. 1256
Gilbert, Dean B., V.P.-H.R.--Newsprint South, Inc., Jackson, MS; *U.S. Private*, pg. 797
Gilbert, Fay, Dir.-H.R.--Ansell International, Glen Waverley, Australia; *Int'l*, pg. 1021
Gilbert, Pauline, V.P.-Human Resources--Grocery Division, Montreal, Canada; *Int'l*, pg. 348
Gilchrist, Anne, Personnel Officer--Rigby-Maryland (Stainless) Ltd., Liversedge, United Kingdom; *U.S. Public*, pg. 780
Gilead, Marilyn, Mgr.-Human Resources--Ark Restaurants Corp., New York, NY; *U.S. Public*, pg. 129
Giles, Douglas J., Sr. V.P.-Human Resources--The May Department Stores Company, Saint Louis, MO; *U.S. Public*, pg. 1063
Giles, Harold G., V.P.-Human Resources--General Electric Canada Inc., Mississauga, Canada; *U.S. Public*, pg. 713
Gill, Paris, Mgr.-H.R.--Westgate Inc., Port Allen, LA; *U.S. Private*, pg. 1169
Gillen, Bunny, Mgr.-Personnel--Harbor Financial Mortgage Corp., Houston, TX; *U.S. Public*, pg. 644
Gilles, Donald L., V.P.-Human Resources--Lockheed Martin Electronics Group, Bethesda, MD; *U.S. Public*, pg. 1006
Gilles, James W., V.P.-H.R.--Leupold & Stevens, Inc., Beaverton, OR; *U.S. Private*, pg. 662
Gillespie, John F., Sr. V.P.-Human Resources--Woolworth Corporation, New York, NY; *U.S. Public*, pg. 1777
Gillespie, Ruth, Dir.-Human Resources--Reed Business Information, Sutton, United Kingdom; *Int'l*, pg. 1094
Gillette, Fred, V.P.-H.R.--Park Foods L.P., Barrington, IL; *U.S. Private*, pg. 839
Gilligan, Janice, Dir.-Personnel--H.O. Penn Machinery Co. Inc., Poughkeepsie, NY; *U.S. Private*, pg. 849
Gilliland, Harold, Safety Coord.--Plant Maintenance Service Corporation, Memphis, TN; *U.S. Private*, pg. 869
Gillis, Daniel F., Sr. V.P.-Human Resources--PNC Bank Corp., Pittsburgh, PA; *U.S. Public*, pg. 1242

Gillson, G. Thomas, Dir.-Human Resources--Paragon Health Network, Inc., Atlanta, GA; *U.S. Public*, pg. 1256

Gilman, Thomas J., Mgr.-Human Resources--Rodney Hunt Company, Orange, MA; *U.S. Private*, pg. 549

Gilman, Valerie H., V.P.-Human Resources--Comverse Network Systems, Wakefield, MA; *U.S. Public*, pg. 425

Gilmas, Yves, Grp. Dir.-H.R. & Admin.--Bouygues, Saint Quentin-en-Yvelines, France; *Int'l*, pg. 206

Gilmore, William E., Asst. Sec. & Plan Admin.--Maryland & Virginia Milk Producers Cooperative Association, Inc., Reston, VA; *U.S. Private*, pg. 711

Gilpin, Kathleen, Dir.-Personnel & Mngmt. Information Systems--Bio-Tek Instruments, Inc., Winooski, VT; *U.S. Private*, pg. 144

Gilreath, G.L., Gen. Mgr.-Admin.--Murphy Oil Corporation, El Dorado, AR; *U.S. Public*, pg. 1141

Ginn, Evan, V.P.-H.R.--Baker Petrolite Corporation, Houston, TX; *U.S. Public*, pg. 166

Ginnetti, Tom, Dir.-H.R.--Reptron Electronics, Inc., Tampa, FL; *U.S. Public*, pg. 1377

Girard, Andre, Dir.-H.R. (Quebec)--Synergistics Industries Limited, Mississauga, Canada; *U.S. Public*, pg. 734

Girvan, Daniel J., Sr. V.P.-H.R. & Admin.--Fort James Corporation, Richmond, VA; *U.S. Public*, pg. 670

Girvin, Larry M., V.P.-Human Resources--Virginia Electric and Power Company, Richmond, VA; *U.S. Public*, pg. 516

Gittleson, Gail, V.P.-Human Resources--Barnes & Noble Inc., New York, NY; *U.S. Public*, pg. 189

Giveble, Mehnet, Asst. Gen. Coord.-Human Resources--Sabanci Holding A.S., Istanbul, Turkey; *Int'l*, pg. 1167

Gladstone, Myles, Dir.-Personnel--Miller & Long Co. Inc., Bethesda, MD; *U.S. Private*, pg. 746

Gladt, Karl, Dir.-Human Resourcees--Henkel Austria Group, Vienna, Austria; *Int'l*, pg. 611

Glasberg, Larry, Chief Fin. Officer--MacDonald Communications, New York, NY; *U.S. Private*, pg. 691

Glascock, J.J., Dir.-Human Resources--El Camino Resources, Ltd., Woodland Hills, CA; *U.S. Private*, pg. 366

Glass, Geogia, Mgr.-Human Resources--The Scoular Company, Omaha, NE; *U.S. Private*, pg. 977

Glass, Gerbert, Mgr.-Human Resources--National Fruit Product Company, Winchester, VA; *U.S. Private*, pg. 783

Glaudel, Robert H., V.P.-H.R.--New England Business Service, Inc., Groton, MA; *U.S. Public*, pg. 1170

Gleasman, Phyllis, Dir.-Personnel--Trout-Blue Cheliau, Inc., Chelan, WA; *U.S. Private*, pg. 1105

Glennan, Mike, V.P.-Admin.--Six Flags Theme Parks Inc., Parsippany, NJ; *U.S. Public*, pg. 1611

Glenny, James P., V.P.-Personnel--Frederick's of Hollywood, Inc., Hollywood, CA; *U.S. Private*, pg. 424

Glotfelty, Phillip E., Dir.-Human Resources--First Midwest Bancorp, Inc., Itasca, IL; *U.S. Public*, pg. 636

Glover, Richard, Dir.-Personnel Services--IRPC Hinton Limited, Hinckley, United Kingdom; *Int'l*, pg. 1502

Glueck, Dorothy, Dir.-Personnel--Karsten Manufacturing Corporation, Phoenix, AZ; *U.S. Private*, pg. 608

Gmur, Beat, Sr. V.P.-Personnel--Liechtenstein Global Trust Limited, Vaduz, Liechtenstein; *Int'l*, pg. 809

Gmur, Beat, Deputy Mng. Dir.-Personnel--LGT Bank in Liechtenstein Aktiengesellschaft, Vaduz, Liechtenstein; *Int'l*, pg. 809

Gnibus, Robert, V.P.-Human Resources--Bacardi Corporation, San Juan, PR; *Int'l*, pg. 131

Goberville, Gary J., V.P.-H.R.--W.W. Grainger, Inc., Lincolnshire, IL; *U.S. Public*, pg. 758

Goddard, Linda, Corp. Sec. & Human Resources Dir.--Griffin Bacal Volny, Toronto, Canada; *U.S. Private*, pg. 480

Godomski, Richard, Chm. Bd., Pres. & Chief Exec. Officer--Process Systems Inc., Memphis, TN; *U.S. Private*, pg. 888

Godsell, David, V.P.-Personnel--Alcan Aluminum Corporation, Cleveland, OH; *Int'l*, pg. 50

Godsell, R.M., Dir. Public Affairs & Indus. Rels.--Anglo American Corporation of South Africa Limited, Johannesburg, South Africa; *Int'l*, pg. 76

Godwin, Diane, Mgr.-Personnel--Forms & Supply, Inc., Charlotte, NC; *U.S. Private*, pg. 419

Goebels, Joseph, Dir.-H.R.--Pharmakinetics Laboratories, Inc., Baltimore, MD; *U.S. Public*, pg. 1285

Goettel, Lisa, V.P.-Human Resources--Duty Free International, Inc., Ridgefield, CT; *Int'l*, pg. 103

Goff, Barb, Mgr.-H.R.--K-D Lamp Company, Cincinnati, OH; *U.S. Private*, pg. 603

Goff, Leah, Dir.-Human Resources--Grow Biz International, Inc., Minneapolis, MN; *U.S. Public*, pg. 767

Goh, Lily, Mgr.-H.R.--GB Holdings, Jurong, Singapore; *Int'l*, pg. 531

Goins, Stephen, Dir.-H.R.--Kocolene Oil Corp., Seymour, IN; *U.S. Private*, pg. 629

Gold, Edward M., Sr. V.P.-H.R.--The Ryland Group, Inc., Columbia, MD; *U.S. Public*, pg. 1414

Gold, Jaques, Dir.-H.R.--S.A. Cimenteries CBR, Brussels, Belgium; *Int'l*, pg. 605

Goldberg, Frank, Controller & Dir.-Human Resources--Electro-Science Laboratories, Inc., King of Prussia, PA; *U.S. Private*, pg. 369

Goldberg, George, Dir.-Personnel--Addison-Wesley Longman, Inc., Reading, MA; *Int'l*, pg. 1026

Goldberg, Lila, Mgr.-H.R.--Information Builders, New York, NY; *U.S. Private*, pg. 561

Goldberg, Louis S., Sr. V.P.-Human Resources--GAF Corporation, Wayne, NJ; *U.S. Private*, pg. 433

Goldberg, Stanton H., V.P.-Human Resources--Ciba Specialty Chemicals, Tarrytown, NY; *Int'l*, pg. 291

Goldberg, Yolaine, Mgr.-Human Resources--Movie Star, Inc., New York, NY; *U.S. Public*, pg. 1140

Goldblatt, Jay A., Assoc. Gen. Counsel & Asst. Sec.--Pubco Corporation, Cleveland, OH; *U.S. Public*, pg. 1339

Goldfein, Iris, Vice Chm.-H.R.--Coopers & Lybrand, New York, NY; *U.S. Private*, pg. 274

Goldman, Ann, Dir.-H.R.--Paul Arpin Vanlines, Inc., West Warwick, RI; *U.S. Private*, pg. 85

Goldman, Florence, Dir.-Personnel--Lippincott-Raven Publishing, New York, NY; *Int'l*, pg. 1513

Goldthorp, B., Dir.-Personnel--Trafalgar House Engineering, London, United Kingdom; *Int'l*, pg. 773

Golomski, Russell, Dir.-Human Resources--Western States Envelope Co., Milwaukee, WI; *U.S. Private*, pg. 1168

Gombos, Rich, Dir.-Human Resources--ADT Automotive, Inc., Nashville, TN; *U.S. Public*, pg. 1648

Gomez, Richard, Dir.-H.R.--Beverage Canners International Corp., Miami, FL; *U.S. Private*, pg. 106

Goncalves, Nelson, Dir.-Personnel--C.A. Cigarrera Bigott, Sucs., Caracas, Venezuela; *Int'l*, pg. 111

Gondek, Michael, Mgr.-Opers.--Minnesota Brewing Company, Saint Paul, MN; *U.S. Public*, pg. 1115

Gonthier, Jean-Marie, Exec. V.P.-Quality & Human Resources--Hydro-Quebec, Montreal, Canada; *Int'l*, pg. 640

Gonzales, Dick W., Sr. V.P.- Human Resources--The Vons Companies, Inc., Arcadia, CA; *U.S. Public*, pg. 1426

Gonzales, Luz E., V.P.-H.R.--Glacier Water Services Inc., Carlsbad, CA; *U.S. Public*, pg. 745

Gonzales, Victorino R., V.P.-Human Resources--La Tondena Distillers, Inc., Manila, Philippines; *Int'l*, pg. 785

Gonzalez Schiavon, Alfonso, Dir.-H.R.--Transportacion Maritima Mexicana S.A. de C.V., Mexico, Mexico; *Int'l*, pg. 1418

Gonzalez, Antonio, Mgr.-H.R.--Groupe GTM, Nanterre, France; *Int'l*, pg. 823

Gonzalez, Donna, Office Mgr.--P & F Industries, Inc., Farmingdale, NY; *U.S. Public*, pg. 1239

Gonzalez, Mario Garza, Pres.-Human Rels. & Plng. Div.--Vitro, Sociedad Anonima, Garza Garcia, Mexico; *Int'l*, pg. 1469

Gonzalez, Roberto L., Mgr.-Human Resources--Bundy Argentina SA, Victoria, Argentina; *Int'l*, pg. 1342

Gonzalez, Rocio, Mgr.-Human Resources--McGraw-Hill/ Interamericana de Mexico, S.A. de CV, Mexico, Mexico; *U.S. Public*, pg. 1072

Good, Douglas, Mgr.-Human Resources--Dayton Superior Corporation, Miamisburg, OH; *U.S. Private*, pg. 931

Good, I., Dir.-Human Resources--Cincinnati Milacron U.K. Limited, Birmingham, United Kingdom; *U.S. Public*, pg. 368

Goodall, Robert, Grp.-Dir.-Personnel--Inchcape PLC, London, United Kingdom; *Int'l*, pg. 671

Goode, Dan, Mgr.-Personnel--Temco Fireplace Products, Inc., Nashville, TN; *U.S. Public*, pg. 1576

Goode, William C., V.P.-Human Resources--Star-Kist Foods, Inc., Newport, KY; *U.S. Public*, pg. 806

Goodman, Clifford, Dir.-Human Resources--West Mill Clothes, Inc., Woodside, NY; *U.S. Private*, pg. 1163

Goodrow, Mary Ellen, Dir.-H.R.--Copper & Brass Sales, Inc., Eastpointe, MI; *Int'l*, pg. 1389

Goodsell, Lynn, Dir.-Human Resources--Clear Shield National, Inc., Wheeling, IL; *U.S. Public*, pg. 586

Goodwin, Richard G., Sr. V.P.-H.R.--Airborne Freight Corporation, Seattle, WA; *U.S. Public*, pg. 32

Gooselaw, Carolann, Dir.-Human Resources--EMC Corporation, Hopkinton, MA; *U.S. Public*, pg. 545

Gordan, Cynthia, V.P.-Human Resources & Legal Counsel--Quaker Fabric Corporation, Fall River, MA; *U.S. Public*, pg. 1347

Gordon, Ellen, Dir.-H.R.--HMI Industries, Cleveland, OH; *U.S. Public*, pg. 771

Gordon, Ellen, Liaison Officer--HMI Industries, Cleveland, OH; *U.S. Public*, pg. 771

Gordon, James M., Dir.-Human Resources--Stockham Valves & Fittings, Inc., Birmingham, AL; *U.S. Private*, pg. 1043

Gordon, John, V.P.-Human Resources & Corp. Affairs--Methanex Corporation, Vancouver, Canada; *Int'l*, pg. 862

Gordon, Robert R., Jr., Exec. V.P.-Human Resources--R.J. Reynolds Tobacco Company, Winston Salem, NC; *U.S. Public*, pg. 1355

Gordon, Sue, V.P.-Human Resources--Radisson Hotel Corporation, Minneapolis, MN; *U.S. Private*, pg. 212

Gordonsmith, John A., Exec. V.P.-Treasury, Legal & Corp. Sec.--FCA International Ltd., Westmount, Canada; *Int'l*, pg. 470

Gorell, Randy, V.P.-H.R.--USCS International, Inc., Rancho Cordova, CA; *U.S. Public*, pg. 1659

Goresh, Andrew, Mng.Dir.-H.R.--T. Rowe Price Associates, Inc., Baltimore, MD; *U.S. Public*, pg. 1324

Gorham, Karen, Dir.-Human Resources--Familian Corp., Van Nuys, CA; *Int'l*, pg. 1512

Goring, Terry, V.P.-H.R.--Maritz Inc., Fenton, MO; *U.S. Private*, pg. 703

Gorman, Lilian R., V.P.-Human Resources--Southern California Edison Company, Rosemead, CA; *U.S. Public*, pg. 564

Gorman, Lillian R., V.P.-Human Resources--Edison International, Rosemead, CA; *U.S. Public*, pg. 564

Gorres, Chuck, Dir.-Admin., Opers. & Human Resources--Cold Spring Granite Company, Cold Spring, MN; *U.S. Private*, pg. 250

Gorwas, Paul, V.P.-H.R.--Robbins, Inc., Cincinnati, OH; *U.S. Private*, pg. 934

Gossard, Thomas A., Mgr.-H.R.--Union Pump Company, Battle Creek, MI; *U.S. Private*, pg. 1119

Gosset, Gerard, V.P.-H.R. & Commun.--Ciments Francais, Paris, France; *Int'l*, pg. 292

Goswami, Bindu, Dir.-Human Resources--Voest-Alpine International Corporation, New York, NY; *Int'l*, pg. 1470

Goto, Keith A., V.P.-Labor Rels.--A & B-Hawaii, Inc., Honolulu, HI; *U.S. Public*, pg. 39

Gotsch, Steve, V.P.-Human Resources--The Medical Protective Company, Fort Wayne, IN; *U.S. Private*, pg. 728

Gottberg, Barbo, Mgr.-Personnel--Morgardshammar AB, Smedjebacken, Sweden; *Int'l*, pg. 378

Gottler, Jurgen, Dir.-Personnel--J.M. Voith, GmbH, Heidenheim, Germany; *Int'l*, pg. 1472

Gottlieb, Carole, Human Resources Dir.--Lyons Lavey Nickel Swift, Inc., New York, NY; *U.S. Public*, pg. 1224

Goudchaux, Herve, Dir.-Human Resources--Moulinex S.A., Bagnolet, France; *Int'l*, pg. 896

Gourdie, Karen H., Mgr.-Human Resources--WCI International Company, Pittsburgh, PA; *Int'l*, pg. 440

Gowaty, Nina L., Sr. V.P.-Human Resources--B.M.J. Financial Corp., Bordentown, NJ; *U.S. Public*, pg. 1528

Gowen, Lana, Dir.-Personnel--Landauer, Inc., Glenwood, IL; *U.S. Public*, pg. 977

Gower, Pam, Mgr.-Human Resources--Blimpie International, Inc., Atlanta, GA; *U.S. Public*, pg. 236

Goya, Donna, Sr. V.P.-H.R.--Levi Strauss & Co., San Francisco, CA; *U.S. Private*, pg. 662

Goyet, Jean Marie, V.P.-Human Resources--UAP, Inc., Montreal, Canada; *Int'l*, pg. 1426

Graauwmans, A.F., Dir.-Personnel--Internatio-Muller N.V., Rotterdam, Netherlands; *Int'l*, pg. 680

Grabel, William G., Chief Fin. Officer & Sr. V.P.-Fin., Human Resources & Admin.--TDS Telecommunications Corporation, Madison, WI; *U.S. Public*, pg. 1570

Grace, Richard C., Sr. V.P.-Human Resources--PNC Bank Corp., Pittsburgh, PA; *U.S. Public*, pg. 1242

Grady, Dan, V.P.-Human Resources--American Metal Products, Olive Branch, MS; *U.S. Public*, pg. 1053

Grady, Gilbert R., Jr., V.P.-Corp. H.R.--Thomas Industries Inc., Louisville, KY; *U.S. Public*, pg. 1598

Graf, Robin, Dir.-Personnel--Carpeteria, Inc., Valencia, CA; *U.S. Private*, pg. 215

Graff, Patricia, Dir.-Human Resources--ACO Inc., Farmington Hills, MI; *U.S. Private*, pg. 3

Graff, Rod, Mgr.-Human Resources--Haines Kibblehouse, Skippack, PA; *U.S. Private*, pg. 494

Graham, Baxter J., Sr. V.P.-H.R.--The Chubb Corporation, Warren, NJ; *U.S. Public*, pg. 354

Graham, Dorothy, Dir.-Human Resources--Puget Sound Energy, Inc., Bellevue, WA; *U.S. Public*, pg. 1342

Graham, Douglas W., Sr. V.P. & Dir.-Corp. Personnel--Regions Financial Corporation, Birmingham, AL; *U.S. Public*, pg. 1371

Graham, Richard A., Dir.-Human Resources--C.R. Gibson Co., Norwalk, CT; *U.S. Public*, pg. 1168

Graham, Robert W., V.P.-Admin. & Human Resources--Fleetwood Enterprises, Inc., Riverside, CA; *U.S. Public*, pg. 650

Gramm, Cheryl, Mgr.-Human Resources--Hycor Biomedical, Inc., Irvine, CA; *U.S. Public*, pg. 851

Granadillo, Pedro P., V.P.-Human Resources--Eli Lilly and Company, Indianapolis, IN; *U.S. Public*, pg. 992

Granado, Deborah L., V.P.-Personnel--Continental Homes Holding Corp., Scottsdale, AZ; *U.S. Public*, pg. 440

Grandin, Elliott, Mgr.--Merry Land & Investment Company, Inc., Augusta, GA; *U.S. Public*, pg. 1098

Grandstaff, Roy, Dir.-H.R.--Reliance Medical Products, Inc., Mason, OH; *U.S. Private*, pg. 921

Grandy, David, Dir.-Personnel--Henkel Surface Technologies, Madison Heights, MI; *Int'l*, pg. 610

Grant, Carol J., V.P.-H.R.--Textron Inc., Providence, RI; *U.S. Public*, pg. 1588

Grant, Craig A., V.P.-H.R.--The Interlake Corporation, Lisle, IL; *U.S. Public*, pg. 892

Grant, Edward L., Sr. V.P.--MasTec, Inc., Miami, FL; *U.S. Public*, pg. 1055

Grant, Eleanor L., Dir.-H.R.--Boston Mutual Life Insurance Co., Canton, MA; *U.S. Private*, pg. 161

Granville, Fred J., V.P.-Human Resources--Chapters Inc., Etobicoke, Canada; *Int'l*, pg. 280

Graske, Theodore, V.P.-Human Resources--Ricoh Corporation, West Caldwell, NJ; *Int'l*, pg. 1114

Grassi, Tony, V.P.-H.R.--Field Container Company, L.P., Elk Grove Village, IL; *U.S. Private*, pg. 403

Grassman, Len, Dir.-Personnel--Emerson Motor Company, Sturgeon Bay, WI; *U.S. Public*, pg. 573

Grasso, Anthony, Dir.-Human Resources--Allied Waste Industries, Scottsdale, AZ; *U.S. Public*, pg. 49

Graves, Laura A., Personnel Officer--San Jose National Bank, San Jose, CA; *U.S. Public*, pg. 1418

Gray, Bob, Dir.-Personnel--Republic Automotive-AEA Division, Charlotte, NC; *U.S. Public*, pg. 1377

Gray, C. William, V.P.-Human Resources--Harley-Davidson, Inc., Milwaukee, WI; *U.S. Public*, pg. 786

Gray, Christie, Mgr.-Benefits & Compensation--Gorges/ Quik-To-Fix Foods, Dallas, TX; *U.S. Private*, pg. 465

Gray, Crystal, Dir.-Human Resources--First Southwest Company, Dallas, TX; *U.S. Private*, pg. 407

Gray, Elizabeth Ann, Dir.-Personnel--Wilson Industries Inc., Houston, TX; *U.S. Private*, pg. 1181

Gray, Herbert, V.P.-Human Resources--Cranston Print Works Company, Cranston, RI; *U.S. Private*, pg. 286

Gray, John, Mgr.-Personnel--Varian X-Ray Tube Products, Salt Lake City, UT; *U.S. Public*, pg. 1710

Grayson, Christine, V.P.-H.R. & Asst. Treas.--Folger Nolan Fleming Douglas, Washington, DC; *U.S. Private*, pg. 416

Greabe, Raymond R., V.P.-Personnel--Grainger, Lincolnshire, IL; *U.S. Public*, pg. 758

Greathouse, G.B., Coord.-Pers. Rels.--Ohio Edison Co.-Youngstown Div., Youngstown, OH; *U.S. Public*, pg. 645

Greaves, Kristin, Sr. V.P. & H.R./Devel. Dir.--Deutsch, Inc., New York, NY; *U.S. Private*, pg. 328

Greaves, Kristin, Sr. V.P. & H.R./Devel. Dir.--Deutsch LA, Santa Monica, CA; *U.S. Private*, pg. 328

Greeley, Kevin, H.R.-Admin.--Eller Media Company, Phoenix, AZ; *U.S. Public*, pg. 383

Green, Barbara J., Dir.-Personnel--Superior Dairy, Inc., Canton, OH; *U.S. Private*, pg. 1054

Green, David E., Asst. V.P.-Human Resources--Western National Corporation, Houston, TX; *U.S. Public*, pg. 76

Green, David E., Asst. V.P.-Human Resources--Western National Life Insurance Co., Houston, TX; *U.S. Public*, pg. 76

Green, Fred, V.P.-Human Resources--American Rehability Services, Inc., Brentwood, TN; *U.S. Public*, pg. 1257

Green, Kenneth, V.P.-Human Resources, Real Estate & Gen. Counsel--Gantos Inc., Stamford, CT; *U.S. Public*, pg. 702
Green, Lorraine, V.P.-Personnel--Amtrak-National Railroad Passenger Corp., Washington, DC; *U.S. Private*, pg. 68
Green, Michael, Mgr.-Personnel & Human Resources--Dey Laboratories Inc., Napa, CA; *Int'l*, pg. 812
Green, Pat, Mgr.-Human Resources--CiMatrix L.L.C., Canton, MA; *U.S. Public*, pg. 1395
Green, Robert G., V.P.-Human Resources--Metal Container Corporation, Saint Louis, MO; *U.S. Public*, pg. 114
Greenberg, Ken, Mgr.-Human Resources--Crescent Genlyte, Barrington, NJ; *U.S. Public*, pg. 730
Greenberg, Marcia, V.P.-H.R.--Esterline Technologies Corporation, Bellevue, WA; *U.S. Public*, pg. 594
Greenburg, Elizabeth, Dir.-Human Resources--Vital Signs, Inc., Totowa, NJ; *U.S. Public*, pg. 1723
Greene, Cyndi, H.R. Admin.--Prime Medical Services, Inc., Austin, TX; *U.S. Public*, pg. 1327
Greene, Lucy G., V.P.-Human Resources--Sun Life Assurance Company of Canada, Toronto, Canada; *Int'l*, pg. 1318
Greene, Nancy, Exec. Sec.-Human Resources--ConAgra Frozen Food Company, Omaha, NE; *U.S. Public*, pg. 427
Greenfield, Ann, V.P.-H.R.--Lewis Brothers Bakeries, Inc., Evansville, IN; *U.S. Private*, pg. 665
Greenfield, Hope, V.P.-Human Resources--C.R. Bard, Inc., Murray Hill, NJ; *U.S. Public*, pg. 189
Greenway, Mark, V.P.-H.R.--J.B. Hunt Transport Services, Inc., Lowell, AR; *U.S. Public*, pg. 849
Greenwell, Sue, Dir.-H.R.--The Van Metres Companies, Burke, VA; *U.S. Private*, pg. 1132
Greer, Michael D., V.P.-Human Resources & Corp. Rels.--CNG Transmission Corporation, Clarksburg, WV; *U.S. Public*, pg. 435
Gregg, Gloria, V.P.-Admin.--WWF Paper Corporation, Bala Cynwyd, PA; *U.S. Private*, pg. 1145
Gregory, Robert, Dir.-H.R.--3i Group plc, London, United Kingdom; *Int'l*, pg. 1386
Gregory, Roger, Dir.-H.R.--North Carolina Mutual Life Insurance Co., Durham, NC; *U.S. Private*, pg. 804
Grenier, Stella M., V.P.-Human Resources--Somerset Savings Bank, Somerville, MA; *U.S. Public*, pg. 1484
Grete, Ulrich, Dr., Exec. V.P.-Resources & Mngmt. Support--Union Bank of Switzerland, Zurich, Switzerland; *Int'l*, pg. 1439
Grier, Anne M., Mgr.-Human Resources & Admin.--Dominion Rescurces, Inc., Richmond, VA; *U.S. Public*, pg. 516
Grier, Boyd, Dir.-H.R.--Gulf States Manufacturers, Inc., Starkville, MS; *Int'l*, pg. 699
Griesse, Dan, Dir.-Personnel--ABF Freight System, Inc., Fort Smith, AR; *U.S. Public*, pg. 130
Griffey, J.I., Mgr.-Human Resources--HPM Corporation, Mount Gilead, OH; *U.S. Private*, pg. 492
Griffin, Al, V.P.-Human Resources--Blaw-Knox Construction Equipment Corporation, Mattoon, IL; *U.S. Public*, pg. 877
Griffin, Carolyn, Mgr.-Human Resources--The Osterneck Co. Inc., Lumberton, NC; *U.S. Private*, pg. 821
Griffin, Ernest F., V.P.-Human Resources--Avondale Industries, Inc., Avondale, LA; *U.S. Public*, pg. 156
Griffin, J., Dir.-Personnel--Laser Systems, Apopka, FL; *U.S. Public*, pg. 1002
Griffin, Raymond J., V.P. & Mgr.-H.R.--Roy F. Weston, Inc., West Chester, PA; *U.S. Public*, pg. 1761
Griffin, S., Mgr.-Human Resources--LaSalle Bristol Corp., Elkhart, IN; *Int'l*, pg. 618
Griffith, Jo Ann, V.P.-Human Resources--American General Corporation, Houston, TX; *U.S. Public*, pg. 76
Griffith, Thomas I., Dir.-H.R.--Pacific Scientific Company, Newport Beach, CA; *U.S. Public*, pg. 1250
Grigaliunas, Ben, Ph.D., Sr. V.P.-H.R.--Advocate Health Care, Oak Brook, IL; *U.S. Private*, pg. 23
Grigalunas, A.J., Dir.-Human Rels.--American Steel Foundries, Chicago, IL; *U.S. Private*, pg. 68
Grigg, N.E., Mgr.-Personnel--Hussmann Store Equipment Limited, Brantford, Canada; *U.S. Public*, pg. 1766
Grill, Joseph, V.P.-H.R.--Richardson Electronics, Ltd., Lafox, IL; *U.S. Public*, pg. 1387
Grill, Shirley, V.P.-H.R.--Atlantic Mutual Companies, New York, NY; *U.S. Private*, pg. 95
Grillo, Joanna, V.P.-Human Resources--Christian Dior Perfumes Inc., New York, NY; *Int'l*, pg. 781
Grim, Bud, V.P.-Human Resources--Laser Systems, Apopka, FL; *U.S. Public*, pg. 1002
Grimaldi, D.G., Dir.-Human Resources--Duraco Products, Inc., Streamwood, IL; *U.S. Private*, pg. 348
Grimm, Robert L., V.P.--Consolidated Products, Inc., Indianapolis, IN; *U.S. Public*, pg. 436
Grimone, Frank W., Chief Fin. Officer & Sr. Exec. V.P.--Central Reserve Life Corporation, Strongsville, OH; *U.S. Public*, pg. 326
Grindstead, Roger, V.P.-Human Resources--Copeland Corporation, Sidney, OH; *U.S. Public*, pg. 573
Grisham, Sher, Mgr.-H.R.--Novellus Systems, Inc., San Jose, CA; *U.S. Public*, pg. 1204
Grissom, Tom, Mgr.-Personnel--County Seat Stores, Inc., Dallas, TX; *U.S. Private*, pg. 279
Grom, Gary C., Sr. V.P.-Human Resources--Sara Lee Corporation, Chicago, IL; *U.S. Public*, pg. 1432
Gronquist, Robert, Mgr.-H.R.--Dimensional Merchandising, Inc., Wharton, NJ; *U.S. Private*, pg. 333
Gross, Joe, V.P.-Admin.--NIBCO, Inc., Elkhart, IN; *U.S. Private*, pg. 798
Gross, John, V.P.-Human Resources--Steel, Inc., Commerce City, CO; *U.S. Private*, pg. 1037
Gross, John E., V.P.-Personnel--Broan Mfg. Co., Inc., Hartford, WI; *U.S. Public*, pg. 1193
Grossberg, Ellen, V.P.-H.R.--Lovejoy Inc., Downers Grove, IL; *U.S. Private*, pg. 677
Grout, James M., Exec. V.P.--Sholodge, Inc., Hendersonville, TN; *U.S. Public*, pg. 1467
Grove, R., Dir.-Human Resources--Verbatim Tape Corporation, San Diego, CA; *Int'l*, pg. 872
Grow, Steven A., V.P.-Human Resources--Corange U.S. Holdings, Inc, Indianapolis, IN; *Int'l*, pg. 331
Grubb, Laura, Dir.-H.R.--TelCom Semiconductor, Inc., Mountain View, CA; *U.S. Public*, pg. 1569
Grubbs, Renee, Asst. V.P.-Trng. & Devel.--Nomura Securities International, Inc., New York, NY; *Int'l*, pg. 956
Gruber, R.M., V.P.-Human Resources--MacMillan Bathurst Inc., Mississauga, Canada; *Int'l*, pg. 20
Gruden, Charles, Dir.-Human Resources--White Cap Industries, Inc., Costa Mesa, CA; *U.S. Public*, pg. 1765
Gruenhut, Steven M., Mgr.-H.R. & Admin.--Banque Indosuez, New York, NY; *Int'l*, pg. 313
Grundy, C., Dir.-H.R.--Compass Group plc, Chertsey, United Kingdom,; *Int'l*, pg. 324
Grvez, Nikki, Chief Oper. Officer--Lee Grocery Company, Everett, WA; *U.S. Private*, pg. 657
Gualtiere, Ann, V.P.-Human Resources--Searle & Co., Skokie, IL; *U.S. Public*, pg. 1125
Guarascio, Nancy, Dir.-Human Resources--Cherry Electrical Products Corporation, Waukegan, IL; *U.S. Public*, pg. 346
Guarneschelli, Philip G., V.P.-Human Resources--AMP Incorporated, Harrisburg, PA; *U.S. Public*, pg. 7
Guastaferro, Cecilia, Dir.-Human Resources--Insight Health Services Corp., Newport Beach, CA; *U.S. Public*, pg. 880
Gueguen, Franck, V.P.-H.R.--Club Mediterranee SA, Paris, France; *Int'l*, pg. 298
Guenter, C.E., V.P.-Human Resources--ABB Air Preheater Inc., Wellsville, NY; *Int'l*, pg. 3
Guenther, Richard, Mgr.-H.R.--Centimark Corporation, Canonsburg, PA; *U.S. Private*, pg. 222
Guerin, Marisa, V.P. & Dir.-H.R.--Rohm and Haas Company, Philadelphia, PA; *U.S. Public*, pg. 1403
Guerra, Juan, Superintendent-H.R.--Salvador Division, El Salvador, Chile; *Int'l*, pg. 302
Guerra, Rebecca, Dir.-H.R.--Adobe Systems Incorporated, San Jose, CA; *U.S. Public*, pg. 20
Guevarra, Robert, Human Resources Dir.--Heil-Brice Retail Advertising, Newport Beach, CA; *U.S. Private*, pg. 519
Guibert, Yolanda, V.P.-H.R.--Case-Swayne Co. Inc., Corona, CA; *U.S. Private*, pg. 218
Guidice, Jim, V.P.-Human Resources--The Apparel Group, Ltd., Louisville, KY; *U.S. Private*, pg. 78
Guillory, R. Lynn, V.P.-H.R. & Admin.--Coho Energy, Inc., Dallas, TX; *U.S. Public*, pg. 396
Guilmette, J., Mgr.-Human Resources--Litton Solid State, Santa Clara, CA; *U.S. Public*, pg. 1003
Guin, James M., V.P.-H.R. & Pub. Rels.--Burlington Industries, Inc., Greensboro, NC; *U.S. Public*, pg. 268
Guiney, Alice, V.P.-H.R.--Dairy Mart Convenience Stores, Inc., Cuyahoga Falls, OH; *U.S. Public*, pg. 476
Guinta, R., V.P.-H.R.--Kruger Inc., Montreal, Canada; *Int'l*, pg. 761
Guiot de la Garza, Eduardo, Dir.-Personnel--Grupo Comercial Chedraui S.A. de C.V., Veracruz, Mexico; *Int'l*, *pg. 573*
Guiot de la Garza, Eduardo, Dir.-Personnel--Tiendas Chedraui S.A. de C.V., Veracruz, Mexico; *Int'l*, pg. 573
Gunderson, Fred G., Sr. Dir.-Human Resources--White Castle System, Inc., Columbus, OH; *U.S. Private*, pg. 1171
Gunderson, Kathy, Mgr.-H.R.--Alra Laboratories, Inc., Gurnee, IL; *U.S. Private*, pg. 45
Gundrum, Raymond M., V.P.-Fin.--Planes Moving And Storage, Inc., Cincinnati, OH; *U.S. Private*, pg. 869
Gunnarsson, Kjell, Dir.-Personnel--ICA Handlarnas AB, Solna, Sweden; *Int'l*, pg. 642
Gunning, Barbara L., Corp. Dir.-H.R.--Solar Communications, Inc., Naperville, IL; *U.S. Private*, pg. 1012
Gurka, Jane, Mgr.-Personnel & Sec.--M. Swift & Sons Inc., Hartford, CT; *U.S. Private*, pg. 1059
Gurrola, Marleen, Dir.-Human Resources--Big Flower Press Holdings, Inc., New York, NY; *U.S. Public*, pg. 228
Gurski, Carrie D., Admin.-Benefits--Portec, Inc., Lake Forest, IL; *U.S. Public*, pg. 1317
Gurtler, Henrik, V.P.-H.R. Devel.--Novo Nordisk A/S, Bagsvaerd, Denmark; *Int'l*, pg. 987
Gurton, Lenora, Corp. Sec.--Benchmark Electronics Inc., Angleton, TX; *U.S. Public*, pg. 210
Gustafson, Sara, Admin.-Personnel--Modern Controls, Inc., Minneapolis, MN; *U.S. Public*, pg. 1120
Gustafson, Victoria, Dir.-H.R.--New Brunswick Scientific Co., Inc., Edison, NJ; *U.S. Public*, pg. 1169
Gutfreund, Martin J., V.P.-H.R. & Admin.--Uniroyal Technology Corporation, Sarasota, FL; *U.S. Public*, pg. 1670
Guthrie, Laura D., Mgr.-Human Resources--BHP Petroleum (Americas) Inc., Houston, TX; *Int'l*, pg. 225
Guthrie, Terry, Dir.-H.R.--Century Furniture Industries, Hickory, NC; *U.S. Private*, pg. 226
Gutierrez, Esperanza, Dir.-Personnel--Tomco Auto Products, Inc., Los Angeles, CA; *U.S. Private*, pg. 1090
Gutknecht, Lori, Pub. Rels. Specialist--IDB WorldCom, Inc., Culver City, CA; *U.S. Public*, pg. 1779
Gutzdorf, Sue, Mgr.-Personnel--Joern's Sunrise Medical, Stevens Point, WI; *U.S. Public*, pg. 1536
Guy, Mark L., Mgr.-Employee Rels.--Trim Division, Kalkaska, MI; *U.S. Private*, pg. 355
Guzzi, Carlos, Mgr.-Personnel--Nuevo Federal S.A., Buenos Aires, Argentina; *Int'l*, pg. 990
Gwartney, J. Michael, V.P.-H.R.--Boise Cascade Corporation, Boise, ID; *U.S. Public*, pg. 242
Haagensen, Vagn, V.P.-Personnel--SAS Service Partner A/S, Copenhagen, Denmark; *Int'l*, pg. 1202
Haake, K.I., Mgr.-Human Resources--Salt River Project Agricultural Improvement and Power District, Tempe, AZ; *U.S. Private*, pg. 962
Haarbrink, Sue, Dir.-H.R.--Fleischmann's Yeast, Fenton, MO; *Int'l*, pg. 237
Haas, Michael, Mgr.-Human Resources--Trauth Dairy Inc., Newport, KY; *U.S. Private*, pg. 1098
Haas, S.H., V.P.-Personnel--Bud Industries, Inc., Willoughby, OH; *U.S. Private*, pg. 178
Haase, Barbara S., Sr. V.P.-H.R.--General Alum & Chemical, Holland, OH; *U.S. Private*, pg. 443
Haba, Beth, Mgr.-H.R.--Yahoo!, Inc., Santa Clara, CA; *U.S. Public*, pg. 1787
Habeggar, Gary L., V.P.-H.R.--The B.F. Goodrich Company, Richfield, OH; *U.S. Public*, pg. 751
Habighorst, Dan W., V.P.-H.R.--Patrick Cudahy Inc., Cudahy, WI; *U.S. Public*, pg. 1479
Hacker, David, V.P.-H.R.--Erickson's Diversified Corp., Hudson, WI; *U.S. Private*, pg. 381
Hackett, Pat, Mgr.-Personnel--Fansteel VR/Wesson-Plantsville, Plantsville, CT; *U.S. Public*, pg. 612
Hackfeld, Sally, Mgr.-Personnel--Bates Container, Inc., North Richland Hills, TX; *U.S. Private*, pg. 122
Hadala, Trudy, Mgr.-Human Resources--Western Data Systems, Calabasas, CA; *U.S. Private*, pg. 1165
Haderlein, Kathleen A., V.P.-Human Resources--Argonaut Co., Menlo Park, CA; *U.S. Public*, pg. 129
Haessig, Herbert, V.P.-Human Resources--Hilti Inc., Tulsa, OK; *Int'l*, pg. 620
Hagemann, Reiner, Dr., Dir.-Personnel--Allianz Aktiengesellschaft, Munich, Germany; *Int'l*, pg. 58
Hagemann, Reiner, Dr., Dir.-Personnel--Allianz Versicherungs-AG, Munich, Germany; *Int'l*, pg. 58
Hagen, Cecilia A., Mgr.-Human Resources--Vencor, Inc., Louisville, KY; *U.S. Public*, pg. 1711
Hagenlocker, Matt, Mgr.-H.R.--Bibler Brothers, Inc., Russellville, AR; *U.S. Private*, pg. 142
Hager, Michael W., Chief H.R. Officer--Banc One Corporation, Columbus, OH; *U.S. Public*, pg. 172
Haggerty, Marie, V.P.-H.R.--Resorts Casino Hotel, Atlantic City, NJ; *U.S. Public*, pg. 1531
Haggerty, Robert, Sr. V.P.-Human Resources & Training--Grossman's, Inc., Stoughton, MA; *U.S. Private*, pg. 585
Hagihara, Masashi, Exec. Dir.-Personnel & Labor Relations--Japan Tobacco Inc., Tokyo, Japan; *Int'l*, pg. 703
Hagmann, P., Mgr.-H.R.--H.A. Schlatter AG, Schlieren, Switzerland; *Int'l*, pg. 1205
Hague, Wendy, Dir.-H.R.--Veeco Instruments, Inc., Plainview, NY; *U.S. Public*, pg. 1711
Haig, Ann Kramer, Dir.-Personnel--Zilber, Ltd., Milwaukee, WI; *U.S. Private*, pg. 1206
Hain, Charles G., V.P.-Human & Data Resources--Santa Fe Energy Resources, Inc., Houston, TX; *U.S. Public*, pg. 1431
Hains, Gaetane, Dir.-Human Resources--Shirmax Leasing Ltd., Montreal, Canada; *Int'l*, pg. 1235
Hairston, Peyton T., Sr. V.P.-Labor Relations & Safety--Tennessee Valley Authority, Knoxville, TN; *U.S. Public*, pg. 1580
Hake, Randall, Dr., V.P.-Admin. & H.R.--TIE/Communications, Inc., Overland Park, KS; *U.S. Private*, pg. 1085
Halat, Hank, Dir.-Human Resources--Physician Computer Network, Inc., Morris Plains, NJ; *U.S. Public*, pg. 1293
Hale, Brandon O., V.P.-Human Resources--Healthsouth Corporation, Birmingham, AL; *U.S. Public*, pg. 803
Hale, Denise, V.P.-H.R.--Kleinert's, Inc., Plymouth Meeting, PA; *U.S. Private*, pg. 625
Hale, John, V.P.-Human Resources--Leggett & Platt, Incorporated, Carthage, MO; *U.S. Public*, pg. 985
Hale, Michael, Dir.-H.R.--Tootsie Roll Industries, Inc., Chicago, IL; *U.S. Public*, pg. 1621
Hale, Michael, Mgr.-Personell--World Trade & Marketing, LTD., Chicago, IL; *U.S. Public*, pg. 1621
Haley, Monica, V.P.-H.R.--AMETEK, Inc., Paoli, PA; *U.S. Public*, pg. 99
Haley, Monica, V.P.-Human Resources--Subaru of America, Inc., Cherry Hill, NJ; *Int'l*, pg. 523
Haley, Stanley M., V.P.-H.R.--Battle Mountain Gold Company, Houston, TX; *U.S. Public*, pg. 193
Hall, Colleen, Dir.-Employee Relations--Edwards Brothers, Inc., Ann Arbor, MI; *U.S. Private*, pg. 365
Hall, E. Wayne, V.P.-Human Resources--Southwestern Electric Service Co., Dallas, TX; *U.S. Public*, pg. 1588
Hall, Eddie, Mgr.-Human Resources--Copperweld Bimetallics Products Co., Fayetteville, TN; *Int'l*, pg. 662
Hall, Glenn, Dir.-Fin. & Admin.--Vibro-Meter Corp., Long Beach, CA; *U.S. Private*, pg. 1138
Hallam, Thomas F., V.P.-Human Resources--Arrow Electronics, Inc., Melville, NY; *U.S. Public*, pg. 133
Hallett, R.A., Sr. V.P.-Human Resources--Shoppers Drug Mart, Ltd., Toronto, Canada; *Int'l*, pg. 112
Halley, Jim, Mgr.-Personnel--Fuller, Smith & Turner Plc, London, United Kingdom; *Int'l*, pg. 529
Halliburton, Renee, Dir.-Human Resources--Putt Putt Golf Courses of America, Inc., Fayetteville, NC; *U.S. Private*, pg. 896
Hallin, Liz, V.P.-Human Resources--Koll Co., Newport Beach, CA; *U.S. Private*, pg. 631
Hallman, Stanley P., V.P.-Human Resources--Baldwin Hardware Corporation, Reading, PA; *U.S. Public*, pg. 1053
Hallmark, Chris, Mgr.-H.R.--Thermalloy, Inc., Farmers Branch, TX; *Int'l*, pg. 208
Hallock, Richard W., Exec. V.P.-H.R.--Occidental Petroleum Corporation, Los Angeles, CA; *U.S. Public*, pg. 1210
Hallor, Mary M., Mgr.-H.R.--Teledyne Laars/Jandy Products, Novato, CA; *U.S. Public*, pg. 43
Halloran, Jim, Dir.-Employee Benefits & H.R.--K & R Express Systems Inc., Hinsdale, IL; *U.S. Private*, pg. 602
Hallquist, Dee, Dir.-Human Resources--San Diego Division, San Diego, CA; *U.S. Public*, pg. 27
Hallquist, Donald E., V.P.-H.R.--First Federal Savings, East Hartford, CT; *U.S. Public*, pg. 632
Halnon, William G., V.P.-Enterprise Systems--DIMON, Incorporated, Danville, VA; *U.S. Public*, pg. 509
Halphen, Ed, Dir.-Human Resources--McIlhenny Company, Avery Island, LA; *U.S. Private*, pg. 722
Halsted, Scott, Dir.-Personnel--Bike Athletic Co., Knoxville, TN; *U.S. Private*, pg. 143
Halverson, Elvin, Mgr.-Human Resources--Owatonna Canning Company, Owatonna, MN; *U.S. Public*, pg. 349

Hamacher, L. Fred, V.P.-Compensation & Benefits--Dayton Hudson Corporation, Minneapolis, MN; *U.S. Public*, pg. 489
Hamada, Mamoru, Mng. Dir. & Dir.-Gen. Affairs, Personnel & Legal--Showa Denko K.K., Tokyo, Japan; *Int'l*, pg. 1236
Hambleton, Mike, V.P.-Human Resources--Gould Electronics Inc., Shawmut Circuit Protection Division, Newburyport, MA; *U.S. Public*, pg. 1592
Hambley, David C., V.P.-Human Resources--Noranda Inc., Toronto, Canada; *Int'l*, pg. 433
Hamel, Dennis, Staff V.P.-Employee Services--Alaska Air Group, Inc., Seattle, WA; *U.S. Public*, pg. 35
Hamel, Dennis, V.P.-Employee Services--Alaska Airlines, Inc., Seattle, WA; *U.S. Public*, pg. 35
Hamel, Dennis M., Dir.-H.R.--Roney & Co., Detroit, MI; *U.S. Private*, pg. 943
Hamer, Eileen, Mgr.-Personnel--Kepner-Tregoe, Inc., Skillman, NJ; *U.S. Public*, pg. 1659
Hamer, J. William, Jr., V.P.-Human Resources--Protective Life Corporation, Birmingham, AL; *U.S. Public*, pg. 1336
Hamers, J. Th., Mgr.-Personnel, Training & Devel.--Wavin Bv, Zwolle, Netherlands; *Int'l*, pg. 1135
Hamill, Don, V.P.-Human Resources--Cole-Haan, Yarmouth, ME; *U.S. Public*, pg. 1184
Hamill, Randy A., Sr. V.P.-Mfg. & Resources--Square Two Golf Incorporated, Fairfield, NJ; *U.S. Public*, pg. 1501
Hamilton, James P., V.P.-H.R.--General Re Corporation, Stamford, CT; *U.S. Public*, pg. 725
Hamilton, Larry, Mgr.-Human Resources--Metz Baking Co., Chicago, IL; *U.S. Private*, pg. 1022
Hamilton, Lawrence W., Sr. V.P.-Human Resources--Tech Data Corporation, Clearwater, FL; *U.S. Public*, pg. 1562
Hamilton, Libby, Dir.-H.R.--Byer California, San Francisco, CA; *U.S. Private*, pg. 191
Hamilton, Pamela J., Sr. V.P.-Human Resources, Environment, Health & Safety--W.R. Grace & Co., Boca Raton, FL; *U.S. Public*, pg. 754
Hammar, D. Bertil, Sr. V.P.-Human Resources--Pharmacia & Upjohn Biotech AB, Uppsala, Sweden; *Int'l*, pg. 1047
Hammarberg, Gunila, Mgr.-Personnel--Swedish Match S.A., Nyon, Switzerland; *Int'l*, pg. 1328
Hamme, Elizabeth I., V.P.-Human Resources--Accuride Corp., Henderson, KY; *U.S. Public*, pg. 1286
Hammett, John B., Sr. V.P.-Employee Rels.--San Jose Mercury News, San Jose, CA; *U.S. Public*, pg. 964
Hammett, Sandy, Mgr.-H.R.--Header Products Inc., Romulus, MI; *U.S. Private*, pg. 514
Hammond, Gilbert P., Jr., V.P.-H.R. & Corp. Sec.--Geupel DeMars, Inc., Indianapolis, IN; *U.S. Private*, pg. 449
Hammond, Kathy, Dir.-Human Resources--Kao Infosystems Company (MA), Plymouth, MA; *Int'l*, pg. 717
Hammond, Teresa, Mgr.-Personnel & Human Resources--Quarterdeck Corp., Marina Del Rey, CA; *U.S. Public*, pg. 1350
Hammons, Gloria, Mgr.-Admin. Services--Bettis Corporation, Waller, TX; *U.S. Public*, pg. 482
Hammons, Lori, Mgr.-H.R.--Sport Supply Group, Inc., Dallas, TX; *U.S. Public*, pg. 1499
Hammons, Ron L., Sr. V.P.-Human Resources & Pur.--Johns Manville Corporation, Denver, CO; *U.S. Public*, pg. 927
Hampton, Claudette, V.P.-H.R.--Baker & Taylor, Inc., Charlotte, NC; *U.S. Private*, pg. 111
Hanak, John M., V.P.-Human Resources--Inland Steel Products Company, East Chicago, IN; *U.S. Public*, pg. 879
Hancook, Ben, Mgr.-H.R.--PHB Die Casting, Fairview, PA; *U.S. Private*, pg. 826
Hand, Steve, Asst. V.P.-H. R.--Lackman Food Service, Woodbury, NY; *U.S. Private*, pg. 642
Handing, Donna R., Dir.-Human Resources--Amlings Flowerland, Hinsdale, IL; *U.S. Private*, pg. 66
Handler, Bruce J., Mgr.-Human Resources--GATX Corporation, Chicago, IL; *U.S. Public*, pg. 690
Hanemann, Louis L., V.P.-H.R.--North Carolina Natural Gas Corporation, Fayetteville, NC; *U.S. Public*, pg. 1194
Hanigosky, Don, Dir.-Opers.--VWS, Inc., Cleveland, OH; *Int'l*, pg. 440
Hanley, Sarah, Dir.-Human Resources & Benefits--Renosol Corp., Saline, MI; *U.S. Private*, pg. 922
Hannah, Mike, Mgr.-Human Resources, Quality Control & Govt. Affairs--National R.V., Inc., Perris, CA; *U.S. Public*, pg. 1159
Hannan, Pete, Mgr.-H.R.--CH2M Hill, Inc., Greenwood Village, CO; *U.S. Private*, pg. 195
Hannay, Lori, V.P.-Human Resources--GenRad, Inc., Westford, MA; *U.S. Public*, pg. 731
Hannis, Jean M., V.P.-H.R.--AmerenUE, Saint Louis, MO; *U.S. Public*, pg. 66
Hanquiez, Bernard, V.P.-H.R.--Docks de France S.A., Tours, France; *Int'l*, pg. 98
Hanscom, Kathi, Dir.-Personnel--Nelson & Small Inc., Portland, ME; *U.S. Private*, pg. 790
Hansell, Joseph, V.P.-Human Resources--Millhouse Group, Glendora, CA; *U.S. Private*, pg. 748
Hansen, Art, V.P.-H.R.--Edwards Baking Co., Norcross, GA; *U.S. Private*, pg. 365
Hansen, Clyde, V.P.-Human Resources--Graco Inc., Golden Valley, MN; *U.S. Public*, pg. 756
Hansen, J. Ronald, Chief Fin. Officer & V.P.-Fin. & Admin.--Graham Corporation, Batavia, NY; *U.S. Public*, pg. 757
Hansen, Jennifer, Mgr.-Human Resources--Hall Sign, Inc., Bloomington, IN; *U.S. Private*, pg. 495
Hansen, Julien R., V.P.-Human Resources--Dillingham Construction Corporation, Pleasanton, CA; *U.S. Private*, pg. 333
Hansen, Linda, Dir.-Legal & Admin.--BRC Holdings, Dallas, TX; *U.S. Public*, pg. 163
Hansen, M.L., Dir.-Employee Rels.--Kinney Vacuum Company, Canton, MA; *U.S. Private*, pg. 1110
Hansen, Nancy S., V.P.-Admin. & Sec.--Pennsylvania Crusher Corp., Broomall, PA; *U.S. Private*, pg. 850
Hansen, Stephen W., Exec. V.P. & Dir.-Human Resources--Norwest Corporation, Minneapolis, MN; *U.S. Public*, pg. 1201
Hansen, Steve, Mgr.-Human Resources--Snyder Industries, Inc., Lincoln, NE; *U.S. Private*, pg. 1011
Hanson, Al, Dir.-H.R.--International Research & Evaluation, Eagan, MN; *U.S. Private*, pg. 571
Hanson, Cheri, Personnel--Unitech Industries, Inc., Tempe, AZ; *U.S. Public*, pg. 1672
Hanson, Dennis, Dir.-H.R.--Peterson American Corp., Southfield, MI; *U.S. Private*, pg. 857
Hanson, John, V.P.-Human Resources--Minnegasco, Minneapolis, MN; *U.S. Public*, pg. 843
Hanson, Kathy, Dir.-Admin.--SpeedFan International, Inc., Chandler, AZ; *U.S. Public*, pg. 1497
Hanson, Paul N., Chief Fin. Officer--Communications Systems, Inc., Hector, MN; *U.S. Public*, pg. 415
Hanss, Ted, Dir.-H.R.--Crescive Die & Tool, Inc., Saline, MI; *U.S. Private*, pg. 289
Happel, Marvin, V.P.-Human Resources--Uniroyal Chemical Company, Inc., Middlebury, CT; *U.S. Public*, pg. 460
Happert, Harold, V.P.-Human Resources--Pirelli Armstrong Tire Corporation, New Haven, CT; *Int'l*, pg. 1058
Haputpong, Sittisak, Corp. Planning & Human Res. Dir.--Avon Cosmetics (Thailand) Ltd., Bangkok, Thailand; *U.S. Public*, pg. 156
Hara, Nobumichi, Asst. V.P.--Metropolitan Mortgage & Securities Co., Inc., Spokane, WA; *U.S. Private*, pg. 738
Harcharek, Janice, Dir.-Human Resources & Corp. Sec.--Universal Dynamics, Inc., Woodbridge, VA; *Int'l*, pg. 484
Harcourt, D., V.P.-H.R.--Perry Equipment Corporation, Mineral Wells, TX; *U.S. Private*, pg. 855
Harder, Angela, Mgr.-Human Resources--Theochem Labs., Inc., Tampa, FL; *U.S. Private*, pg. 1079
Hardin, J.W., V.P.-Human Resources--Contech Construction Products Inc., Middletown, OH; *U.S. Private*, pg. 267
Harding, Jacalyn W., Dir.-H.R.--Woolpert, Dayton, OH; *U.S. Private*, pg. 1188
Harding, Robert A., Sr. V.P.-Human Resources, Corp. Plng. & Trng. Grp.--First Security Service Company, Salt Lake City, UT; *U.S. Public*, pg. 638
Hardman, Marcy, Human Resource Recruiter--Cyborg Systems, Inc., Chicago, IL; *U.S. Private*, pg. 299
Hardouin, Daniel, Mgr.-Human Resources--Credit Commercial de France, Paris, France; *Int'l*, pg. 341
Hardwick, Ron, V.P.-H.R.--Miniature Precision Components, Walworth, WI; *U.S. Private*, pg. 750
Hardy, Mark, Dir.-Human Resources--Medeva PLC, London, United Kingdom; *Int'l*, pg. 852
Harloe, Bob, V.P. & Dir-Human Resources--Lechters, Inc., Harrison, NJ; *U.S. Public*, pg. 983
Harman, William, Dir.-Personnel--Integrated Device Technology, Inc., Santa Clara, CA; *U.S. Public*, pg. 884
Harmel, Harro, V.P.-Human Resources--Porsche AG, Stuttgart, Germany; *Int'l*, pg. 1063
Harmon, Celeste, Personnel Admin.--Ruscon Corp., Charleston, SC; *U.S. Private*, pg. 952
Harmon, Larry A., V.P.-Human Resources--Cintas Corporation, Mason, OH; *U.S. Public*, pg. 370
Harmon, Mark A., V.P.-Human Resources--Twin City Die Castings Co., Minneapolis, MN; *U.S. Private*, pg. 1111
Harmon, Samuel W., Sr. V.P.-H.R.--GenCorp Inc., Fairlawn, OH; *U.S. Public*, pg. 705
Harmsen, Dan, V.P.-H.R.--Journal Communications Inc., Milwaukee, WI; *U.S. Private*, pg. 601
Harned, David, Dir.-H.R.--Carpenter Co., Richmond, VA; *U.S. Private*, pg. 214
Harper, Brooks, Dir.-H.R.--Broughton Foods Company, Marietta, OH; *U.S. Public*, pg. 259
Harper, Judy, Admin.-Human Resources--Peabody TecTank, Inc., Parsons, KS; *U.S. Public*, pg. 1477
Harr, Dennis B., Mgr.-Human Resources Devel.--Kennametal Inc., Latrobe, PA; *U.S. Public*, pg. 950
Harrell, James M., V.P.-Human Resources--Illinois Central Corporation, Chicago, IL; *U.S. Public*, pg. 864
Harren, Owen, V.P.-Human Resources--Pollak Division, Boston, MA; *U.S. Private*, pg. 1045
Harrigan, Myles, V.P.-Human Resources--Glaxo Wellcome Inc., Mississauga, Canada; *Int'l*, pg. 553
Harrington, Karalyn J., V.P.-Human Resources--Cray Research, Eagan, MN; *U.S. Public*, pg. 1473
Harrington, Marguerite, Dir.-H.R.--Transammonia Inc., New York, NY; *U.S. Private*, pg. 1096
Harrington, Michael, V.P.-Personnel--Jefferson Smurfit Corporation, Saint Louis, MO; *Int'l*, pg. 1269
Harrington, Payson L., V.P.-Personnel--McDonald's Corporation, Oak Brook, IL; *U.S. Public*, pg. 1068
Harris, Ann P., V.P.-H.R.--International Technology Corporation, Monroeville, PA; *U.S. Public*, pg. 907
Harris, Barbara R., V.P.-Human Resources--Praxair Inc., Danbury, CT; *U.S. Public*, pg. 1319
Harris, David, Chief Fin. Officer, Sr. V.P. & Dir.-Human Resources--Whitin Roberts Co., Sanford, NC; *U.S. Private*, pg. 309
Harris, Duane, V.P.-H.R.-ING.--Tree Top, Inc., Selah, WA; *U.S. Private*, pg. 1098
Harris, E. Lee, Jr., Exec. V.P.-Human Resources--Compass Bank, Birmingham, AL; *U.S. Public*, pg. 418
Harris, F. Malcolm, V.P.-H.R.--Spiegel, Inc., Downers Grove, IL; *U.S. Public*, pg. 1498
Harris, James, Dir.-Human Resources--Paslode, Vernon Hills, IL; *U.S. Public*, pg. 867
Harris, Karen K., V.P.-H.R.--MainStreet BankGroup Incorporated, Martinsville, VA; *U.S. Public*, pg. 1038
Harris, Kristine, Rep.-H.R.--The Failure Group, Inc., Menlo Park, CA; *U.S. Public*, pg. 609
Harris, Lynn, Human Resources Dir.--TMP Worldwide Recruitment Division, New York, NY; *U.S. Private*, pg. 1065
Harris, R., Dir.-Human Resources--Labatt Breweries of Canada - Prairie Region, Edmonton, Canada; *Int'l*, pg. 679
Harris, W.N., V.P.-Personnel--Transus Intermodal L.L.C., Atlanta, GA; *U.S. Private*, pg. 1097
Harrison, Steve, V.P.-Human Resources--Bush Brothers & Company, Knoxville, TN; *U.S. Private*, pg. 189
Harrison, Sue, Mgr.-Personnel--Pentel of America, Ltd., Torrance, CA; *Int'l*, pg. 1035
Harsanyi, Fruzsina M., V.P.-Pub. Affairs & Corp. Communications--ABB Inc., Norwalk, CT; *Int'l*, pg. 3
Hart, Angela B., Mgr.-H.R.--AFLAC Incorporated, Columbus, GA; *U.S. Public*, pg. 28
Hart, Chuck, V.P.-Human Resources--EVCON Industries, Wichita, KS; *U.S. Public*, pg. 1788
Hart, James R., V.P.-H.R.--Ryan's Family Steak Houses, Inc., Greer, SC; *U.S. Public*, pg. 1413
Hart, Janet, Dir.-Human Resources--3Com Corporation, Southborough, MA; *U.S. Public*, pg. 1604
Hart, Larry, V.P.-H.R.--Carl Zeiss, Inc., Thornwood, NY; *Int'l*, pg. 1523
Harte, Sharon, H.R.--CM Partners, Inc., Rolling Meadows, IL; *U.S. Private*, pg. 195
Hartle, P.S., V.P.-Fin. & Personnel--Nestaway, Cleveland, OH; *U.S. Private*, pg. 103
Hartley, Cynthia A., V.P.-H.R.--Sonoco Products Company, Hartsville, SC; *U.S. Public*, pg. 1485
Hartman, Judy, Mgr.-H.R.--Continental Circuits Corp., Phoenix, AZ; *U.S. Public*, pg. 440
Hartman, Karan, Mgr.-H.R.--Aerco International Inc., Northvale, NJ; *U.S. Private*, pg. 23
Hartman, P.F., Exec. V.P.-Personnel & Organization--KLM Royal Dutch Airlines, Amstelveen, Netherlands; *Int'l*, pg. 719
Hartmann, Jackie, Mgr.-Personnel--Six Flags Magic Mountain & Six Flags Hurricane Harbor, Valencia, CA; *U.S. Public*, pg. 1611
Hartnett, D., Dir.-Human Resources--ICI Americas, Inc., Wilmington, DE; *Int'l*, pg. 663
Hartsog, Catherine, Dir.-Corp. Communications--Quantum Corporation, Milpitas, CA; *U.S. Public*, pg. 1350
Hartwig, Jeanne, Dir.-Employee Benefits & H.R.--Acme Foundry, Inc., Coffeyville, KS; *U.S. Private*, pg. 13
Hartz, Peter, Dir.-H.R.--Volkswagen AG, Wolfsburg, Germany; *Int'l*, pg. 1473
Harvey, Dan, Mgr.-H.R.--F.X. Coughlin Co., Taylor, MI; *U.S. Private*, pg. 278
Harwin, Cindy, V.P.-Human Resources--Korey, Kay & Partners, New York, NY; *U.S. Private*, pg. 632
Harwood, Russ, Internal Opers. Dir. & Human Resources Dir.--Rhea & Kaiser Marketing Communications, Naperville, IL; *U.S. Private*, pg. 927
Hasenbank, Gary, V.P.-Human Resources--Pinkerton's Inc., Encino, CA; *U.S. Public*, pg. 1296
Haskell, John R., Dir.-Personnel--Cabot Corporation, Boston, MA; *U.S. Public*, pg. 288
Haskell, Pat, Dir.-Personnel & Benefits--Witt Company, Cincinnati, OH; *U.S. Private*, pg. 1185
Haslam, William E., Pres.--Pilot Corporation, Knoxville, TN; *U.S. Private*, pg. 865
Hassan, Barbara A., V.P.-H.R.--Eastern Utilities Associates, Boston, MA; *U.S. Public*, pg. 549
Hassan, Barbara A., V.P.-H.R.--EUA Service Corporation, West Bridgewater, MA; *U.S. Public*, pg. 549
Hasson, Eibert, Sr. V.P.-Human Resources--Perstorp AB, Perstorp, Sweden; *Int'l*, pg. 1036
Hatch, Suzanne, Human Resources--Highway One Communications, Integrated Marketing Services, San Francisco, CA; *U.S. Private*, pg. 303
Hatches, Barrett, V.P.-Human Resources--Southeastern Michigan Gas Enterprises, Inc., Port Huron, MI; *U.S. Public*, pg. 1489
Hateley, J. Michael, V.P.-Human Resources & Admin.--Aircraft Division, Hawthorne, CA; *U.S. Public*, pg. 1198
Hatfield, Sara, Coord.-Employee Rels.--Centex Corporation, Dallas, TX; *U.S. Public*, pg. 322
Hathcock, Bonnie, V.P.-Human Resources--US Airways, Inc., Arlington, VA; *U.S. Public*, pg. 1680
Hatlen, Erich, Dir.-H.R.--MNP Corp., Utica, MI; *U.S. Private*, pg. 687
Hatley, Harold, Dir.-Employee Benefits--TIC United Corporation, Dallas, TX; *U.S. Private*, pg. 1063
Hatt, Joyce M., V.P.-Human Resources--SHL Systemhouse - Canada/Asia, Ottawa, Canada; *Int'l*, pg. 1154
Hatton, Keith, Dir.-H.R.--IXC Communications, Inc., Austin, TX; *U.S. Private*, pg. 556
Hatton, Ray, Mgr.-Human Resources--Gear Products Inc., Tulsa, OK; *U.S. Public*, pg. 238
Haunschild, Harold E., V.P.-Human Resources--Burlington Resources Inc., Houston, TX; *U.S. Public*, pg. 269
Haunschild, Harold E., Exec. V.P.-Human Resources & Admin.--Meridian Oil Holding Inc., Houston, TX; *U.S. Public*, pg. 269
Hausmann, Audrey, Dir.-H.R.--Associated Wholesalers Inc., Robesonia, PA; *U.S. Private*, pg. 93
Hauster, Robert, Dir.-Fin. & Acctg.--Sheldon Good & Co., Chicago, IL; *U.S. Private*, pg. 463
Havener, Ron, Mgr.-H.R.--All-Luminum Products, Inc., Philadelphia, PA; *U.S. Private*, pg. 34
Havlicek, Frank, V.P.-Industrial Rels.--The Washington Post, Washington, DC; *U.S. Public*, pg. 1743
Haw, Kathy, Dir.-H.R.--Joe E. Woods, Inc., Mesa, AZ; *U.S. Private*, pg. 1187
Hawkey, Loyd, Dir.-Human Resources--Rhone-Poulenc Performance Resins & Coatings, Kennesaw, GA; *Int'l*, pg. 1110
Hawkins, Cecilia G., Supvr.-Employment & EEO--Indianapolis Power & Light Company, Indianapolis, IN; *U.S. Public*, pg. 913
Hawkins, D. Hunt, Sr. V.P.-Human Resources--Stein Mart, Inc., Jacksonville, FL; *U.S. Public*, pg. 1514
Hawkins, F. Ray, Dir.-Human Resources--Daw Technologies, Inc., Salt Lake City, UT; *U.S. Public*, pg. 489
Hawkins, J., Dir.-H.R.--Highway Equipment Company, Cedar Rapids, IA; *U.S. Private*, pg. 529
Hawkins, John, V.P. & Treas.--Dillard's, Inc., Little Rock, AR; *U.S. Public*, pg. 509

Hawkins, Lydia, Mgr.-Human Resources--W.G. Thompson & Sons Ltd., Blenheim, Canada; *Int'l*, pg. 1381

Hawkins, Richard C., V.P.-Human Resources--Harsco Corporation, Camp Hill, PA; *U.S. Public*, pg. 792

Hawkins, William, Sr. V.P.-Human Resources--Paramount Pictures Corporation, Los Angeles, CA; *U.S. Private*, pg. 776

Hawks, Aleen, Human Resources Supvr.--JPE Canada Inc., Peterborough, Canada; *U.S. Public*, pg. 919

Hayashi, Terry, Associate Mgr.-Human Resources--Fujisawa Pharmaceutical Co. Ltd., Osaka, Japan; *Int'l*, pg. 525

Hayden, Anne E., Sr. V.P.-Corp. H.R.--Metropolitan Life Insurance Co., New York, NY; *U.S. Private*, pg. 737

Hayden, Laura, Sr. V.P.-H.R.--Bruno's Inc., Birmingham, AL; *U.S. Public*, pg. 265

Hayes, Cecilia A., V.P.-Human Resources--S3 Incorporated, Santa Clara, CA; *U.S. Public*, pg. 1415

Hayes, Jon, Mgr.-Personnel--East Moline Metal Products Company, East Moline, IL; *U.S. Private*, pg. 357

Hayes, Noreen J., V.P.-H.R.--The Western and Southern Life Insurance Company, Cincinnati, OH; *U.S. Private*, pg. 1164

Hayes, Sally J., Mgr.-H.R.--Lomak Petroleum Inc., Fort Worth, TX; *U.S. Public*, pg. 1012

Haynes, Rick, Mgr.-H.R.--GF Office Furniture Ltd., Gallatin, TN; *U.S. Private*, pg. 434

Haynes, Ronney L., Mgr.-Personnel--Ruffin Building Systems, Inc., Oak Grove, LA; *U.S. Private*, pg. 950

Hays, Randy K., Treas. & Sec.--Masek Distributing Inc., Gering, NE; *U.S. Private*, pg. 711

Hayton, Martin, Dir.-Personnel & Admin.--Hong Kong Telecommunications Limited, Quarry Bay, Hong Kong; *Int'l*, pg. 247

Hayward, Andrea, Dir.-Human Resources--DRS Technologies, Inc., Parsippany, NJ; *U.S. Public*, pg. 474

Hayward, Maria, Mgr.-Human Resources--Poly-Seal Corporation, Baltimore, MD; *U.S. Private*, pg. 875

Hazelton, Donna, Dir.-H.R.--The Barbers, Hairstyling for Men & Women, Inc., Minneapolis, MN; *U.S. Private*, pg. 115

Head, Ann, Dir.-Personnel--Americo Manufacturing Co., Inc., Acworth, GA; *U.S. Private*, pg. 64

Head, Michael, V.P.-Human Resources--Ingram Industries Inc., Nashville, TN; *U.S. Private*, pg. 562

Head, Robert, Mgr.-Personnel--Pearson plc, London, United Kingdom; *Int'l*, pg. 1025

Headey, R.M., Mgr.-Human Resources--Gestetner Holdings PLC, London, United Kingdom; *Int'l*, pg. 1114

Heald, Rachel, Dir.-H.R.--TMP Worldwide Pty Limited, Sydney, Australia; *Int'l*, pg. 1342

Healy, George, Head-Employee Rels.--The Financial Times Ltd., London, United Kingdom; *Int'l*, pg. 1025

Heape, Byron, Dir.-Human Resources--National Steel Corp., Granite City Division, Granite City, IL; *Int'l*, pg. 902

Heard, L. Wayne, V.P.-Human Resources & Corp. Affairs--The Quaker Oats Co. of Canada Ltd., Peterborough, Canada; *U.S. Public*, pg. 1348

Heartwell, Dick, Mgr.-Employee Services--Oryx Energy, Dallas, TX; *U.S. Public*, pg. 1232

Heartwell, Frances G., V.P.-Human Resources & Admin.--Oryx Energy, Dallas, TX; *U.S. Public*, pg. 1232

Heator, J., Dir.-Personnel--Ideal Homes Holdings Plc, Woking, United Kingdom; *Int'l*, pg. 773

Heavlier, Laurie, Dir.-Personnel--J.H. Heafner Co. Inc., Lincolnton, NC; *U.S. Private*, pg. 514

Hebelsen, Bruce, Mgr.-Personnel--MTS Systems Corporation, Eden Prairie, MN; *U.S. Public*, pg. 1028

Heber, Tom, V.P.-Human Resources--United States Sugar Corporation, Clewiston, FL; *U.S. Private*, pg. 1126

Heberling, David, V.P.-H.R.--Manor Care, Inc., Gaithersburg, MD; *U.S. Public*, pg. 1041

Heberling, David, V.P.-Human Resources--Manor Healthcare Corp., Gaithersburg, MD; *U.S. Public*, pg. 1041

Hecker, Peter, Dr., Mng. Dir.-Personnel--Dyckerhoff & Widmann AG, Munich, Germany; *Int'l*, pg. 423

Hecks, Trudy, Exec. Admin.-Mktg.--Crabar Business Systems, Dayton, OH; *U.S. Private*, pg. 283

Hedwall, Elmyra, Human Resources Rep.--National General Insurance Co., Earth City, MO; *U.S. Public*, pg. 721

Heffernan, Myra, Mgr.-Personnel--Bank Brussels Lambert, London Branch, London, United Kingdom; *Int'l*, pg. 147

Heffner, Landon, V.P.-H.R.--Monrovia Nursery Co., Azusa, CA; *U.S. Private*, pg. 757

Hefke, Herbert J., V.P.-Human Resources--J.P. Morgan Co. Incorporated, New York, NY; *U.S. Public*, pg. 1129

Heggenes, Per, Mng. Dir.-Human Resources Worldwide (New York)--Burson-Marsteller, New York, NY; *U.S. Private*, pg. 1197

Hein, John P., Dir.-Personnel--Dale Electronics, Inc., Columbus, NE; *U.S. Public*, pg. 1722

Heineman, Ronald E., V.P.-Human Resources--Frisch's Restaurants, Inc., Cincinnati, OH; *U.S. Public*, pg. 682

Heitmann, Donald, Mgr.-Corp. Personnel--Twin City Foods, Inc., Stanwood, WA; *U.S. Private*, pg. 1111

Helderman, Carolyn, Dir.-Personnel--T & S Brass & Bronze Works, Inc., Travelers Rest, SC; *U.S. Private*, pg. 1061

Heldreth, Nick E., V.P.-H.R. & Corp. Rels.--Harris Corporation, Melbourne, FL; *U.S. Public*, pg. 791

Helfrich, Thomas E., Exec. V.P.-Human Resources--Keycorp, Cleveland, OH; *U.S. Public*, pg. 954

Heller, Maurice R., V.P.-Human Resources--Connell Limited Partnership, Boston, MA; *U.S. Private*, pg. 264

Helms, Cheryl, Dir.-Personnel--Plastigage Corporation, Jackson, MI; *U.S. Private*, pg. 871

Helms, Jerry, V.P.-Human Resources--Paramount Carowinds, Charlotte, NC; *U.S. Private*, pg. 776

Helzer, Hank, Dir.-Human Resources--SASIB Packaging North America, Skokie, IL; *Int'l*, pg. 1194

Hemels, Jan, Dir.-Human Resources, Amsterdam--Reed Elsevier plc, London, United Kingdom; *Int'l*, pg. 1093

Hempel, Stewart, Dir.-Personnel--Upstate Milk Cooperatives Inc., Le Roy, NY; *U.S. Private*, pg. 1129

Hemphill, Neil D., Sr. V.P.-Human Resources & Admin.--Columbia/HCA Healthcare Corporation, Nashville, TN; *U.S. Public*, pg. 403

Hemrich, Charles, V.P.-H.R.--Fender Musical Instruments, Scottsdale, AZ; *U.S. Private*, pg. 400

Henderson, Alvia L., V.P.-H.R.--Morrison Knudsen Corporation, Boise, ID; *U.S. Public*, pg. 1133

Henderson, Amy, Mgr.-Human Resources--KLAS, Inc., Las Vegas, NV; *U.S. Private*, pg. 647

Henderson, D.R., Dir.-Human Resources & Communications--Du Pont Canada Inc., Mississauga, Canada; *U.S. Public*, pg. 532

Hendrix, R.L., Dir.-Indus. Rels.--Griffin Pipe Products Co., Downers Grove, IL; *U.S. Private*, pg. 68

Heney, Jim, Dir.-Human Resources--Universal Flavors-U.S.A., Indianapolis, IN; *U.S. Public*, pg. 1696

Henke, Judy A., V.P.-Human Resources--Cox Communications, Inc., Atlanta, GA; *U.S. Public*, pg. 454

Henkel, Peter, Dir.-Personnel & Admin.--AgrEvo GmbH, Berlin, Germany; *Int'l*, pg. 624

Henkle, Bruce, Dir.-H.R.--EDO Corporation, New York, NY; *U.S. Public*, pg. 541

Henley, Terry E., Sr. V.P.-H.R.--Provident Financial Group, Inc., Cincinnati, OH; *U.S. Public*, pg. 1338

Henley, Terry E., V.P.-Human Resources--The Provident Bank, Cincinnati, OH; *U.S. Public*, pg. 1338

Hennen, Anne Y., Mgr.-H.R.--The Cincinnati Cordage & Paper Company, Cincinnati, OH; *U.S. Private*, pg. 239

Hennesey, Dale, Dir.-H.R.--OGE Energy Corp., Oklahoma City, OK; *U.S. Public*, pg. 1207

Hennessey, Jack, V.P.-Human Resources--Modern Drop Forge Co., Blue Island, IL; *U.S. Private*, pg. 754

Hennessey, Jim, Dir.-H.R.--Varian Associates, Inc., Palo Alto, CA; *U.S. Public*, pg. 1710

Hennessy, Robert B., V.P.-Human Resources--National Starch and Chemical Company, Bridgewater, NJ; *Int'l*, pg. 1435

Hennigan, Michael, V.P.-H.R.--Millhouse Group, Glendora, CA; *U.S. Private*, pg. 748

Henning, Christine, Mgr.-H.R.--Rudolph/Libbe, Inc., Walbridge, OH; *U.S. Private*, pg. 950

Henning, David A., V.P.-Personnel--R.P. Adams Company, Inc., Tonawanda, NY; *U.S. Public*, pg. 19

Hennings, Sigrid, Wage & Benefits Admin. & Dir.-Human Resources--McWilliams Forge Co., Rockaway, NJ; *U.S. Private*, pg. 725

Henningsen, Robert C., Sr. V.P.-H.R. & Admin.--International Comfort Products, Franklin, TN; *U.S. Public*, *pg. 898*

Henningsen, Robert C., V.P.-Human Resources & Admin.--International Comfort Products Corp., Lewisburg, TN; *U.S. Public*, pg. 898

Henry, Daniel, Mgr.-Human Resources--Iomega Corporation, Roy, UT; *U.S. Public*, pg. 912

Henry, Danroy, V.P.-H.R./Staples Contract & Comml.--Staples, Inc., Westborough, MA; *U.S. Public*, pg. 1509

Henry, Francis x., V.P.-Personnel--SCI Systems, Inc., Huntsville, AL; *U.S. Public*, pg. 1416

Henry, Jack, V.P.-Employee & Labor Rels.--P & C Food Markets, Inc., Syracuse, NY; *U.S. Public*, pg. 1270

Henry, John C., V.P.-Personnel & Manpower Devel.--Quality Markets, Inc., Jamestown, NY; *U.S. Public*, pg. 1270

Henry, Karen, Dir.-Admin. Services--Linear Dynamics Inc., Parsippany, NJ; *U.S. Private*, pg. 668

Henry, Kim, V.P.-Human Resources--Lark Luggage Company, Inc., Denver, CO; *U.S. Public*, pg. 1430

Henry, Roni, Mgr.-Admin. & Human Resources & Asst. Sec.--Waters Instruments, Inc., Rochester, MN; *U.S. Public*, pg. 1745

Hensel, Bryan, Mgr.-Corp. H.R.--Wyandot Inc., Marion, OH; *U.S. Private*, pg. 1193

Hensley, Robert, Sr. V.P.-Human Resources--Venture Stores, Inc., O Fallon, MO; *U.S. Public*, pg. 1716

Hensley, S.M., Coord.-Pers. Rels.--Ohio Edison Co.-Stark Div., Massillon, OH; *U.S. Public*, pg. 645

Henson, Frona, Mgr.-Employee Benefits--Barrett Resources Corporation, Denver, CO; *U.S. Public*, pg. 191

Henson, Robert W., V.P.-Human Resources--Atlantis Plastic, Inc., Atlanta, GA; *U.S. Public*, pg. 145

Heostinelli, Gus, V.P.-H.R.--Dal-Tile International, Dallas, TX; *U.S. Private*, pg. 308

Hepler, Merrilee, Sr. V.P.-H.R.--MMI Companies, Inc., Deerfield, IL; *U.S. Public*, pg. 1027

Herbert, C. Theodore, V.P.-Human Resources--Telephone and Data Systems, Inc., Chicago, IL; *U.S. Public*, pg. 1570

Herbert, Dean R., Mgr.-H.R.--Numac Energy Inc., Calgary, Canada; *Int'l*, pg. 990

Herbert, Francois, Dir.-H.R.--Bazar de L'Hotel de Ville, Paris, France; *Int'l*, pg. 181

Herbold, Sandra, Dir.-Human Resources--Analytical Surveys, Inc., Colorado Springs, CO; *U.S. Public*, pg. 110

Hercules, Dennis, V.P.-Human Resources Div.--Cook Composites & Polymers Inc., Kansas City, MO; *Int'l*, pg. 1409

Herman, Debra K., Mgr.-H.R.--Northland Cranberries, Inc., Wisconsin Rapids, WI; *U.S. Public*, pg. 1197

Herman, Don, V.P.-H.R.--TelCom Semiconductor, Inc., Mountain View, CA; *U.S. Public*, pg. 1569

Hermanns, Peter, Div. Mgr.--Durkopp Adler AG, Bielefeld, Germany; *Int'l*, pg. 468

Hermes, Mike, Dir.-Personnel--Intercounty Title Co. of Illinois, Chicago, IL; *U.S. Private*, pg. 567

Hernandez, Barbara, Admin.-Payroll & Benefits--Bradley Real Estate, Inc., Northbrook, IL; *U.S. Public*, pg. 250

Hernandez, Ruben Escoria, Dir.-Human Resources--Altos Hornos de Mexico, S.A., Monclova, Mexico; *Int'l*, pg. 66

Herrera, Sadie, Dir.-Human Resources--Emulex Corporation, Costa Mesa, CA; *U.S. Public*, pg. 579

Herrera, Sadie A., V.P.-H.R.--Emulex Corporation, Costa Mesa, CA; *U.S. Public*, pg. 579

Herrett, Michael P., V.P.-H.R.--BHP Petroleum Pty Ltd., Melbourne, Australia; *Int'l*, pg. 225

Herrin, Lucynda, Asst. Controller--Domain Energy Corporation, Houston, TX; *U.S. Public*, pg. 515

Herring, Bobby, V.P.-Personnel--D.P. Fitness, Opelika, AL; *U.S. Public*, pg. 1354

Herring, Bobby, Dir.-Human Resources--Techsonic Industries, Inc., Eufaula, AL; *U.S. Public*, pg. 1570

Herring, Kevin, Mgr.-Human Resources--EnviroTech PumpSystems, Salt Lake City, UT; *Int'l*, pg. 1489

Herring, Paula, Dir.-H.R.--T.A. Loving Company, Goldsboro, NC; *U.S. Private*, pg. 677

Herringer, Alan, Gen. Mgr.-Human Res.--The Southern Life Association Limited, Cape Town, South Africa; *Int'l*, pg. 77

Herrlin, Rosemary, Dir.-Human Resources & Communications--Fiatallis North America, Inc., Carol Stream, IL; *Int'l*, pg. 483

Herron, Mary Ann, V.P.-Human Resources--Tyco Toys, Inc., Mount Laurel, NJ; *U.S. Public*, pg. 1058

Heslet, Fred, Dr., Exec. V.P.-Quality & H.R.--Genus Inc., Sunnyvale, CA; *U.S. Public*, pg. 732

Heslin, Barbara, Mgr.-Personnel--Spectronics Corporation, Westbury, NY; *U.S. Private*, pg. 1024

Hess, Barbara, Mgr.-H.R.--Brooks Resources Corporation, Bend, OR; *U.S. Private*, pg. 172

Hess, Deanna, V.P.-H.R.--Northwest Airlines, Inc., Saint Paul, MN; *U.S. Public*, pg. 1200

Hess, Hans-Jurgen, Personnel Dir.--Berlitz Schools of Languages GmbH, Frankfurt/Main, Germany; *U.S. Public*, pg. 222

Hess, Josef, Dir.-Personnel--Stadtsparkasse Munchen, Munich, Germany; *Int'l*, pg. 1293

Hess, Karen, Dir.-H.R.--Ultra Tool & Plastics, Inc., Amherst, NY; *U.S. Private*, pg. 1116

Hess, Paul, Mgr.-Human Resources--Frigidaire Home Products-Laundry Products, Webster City, IA; *Int'l*, pg. 440

Hesselberth, Jerry, Mgr.-H.R.--Multi-Ad Services, Incorporated, Peoria, IL; *U.S. Private*, pg. 766

Hessey, P., Asst. Gen. Mgr.-Grp. H.R.--General Accident Fire and Life Assurance Corporation p.l.c., Perth, United Kingdom; *Int'l*, pg. 542

Hetrick, Roger L., V.P.-Human Resources--Modine Manufacturing Company, Racine, WI; *U.S. Public*, pg. 1121

Hetrick, Victor, Mgr.-Personnel--New Standard Corporation, Mount Joy, PA; *U.S. Private*, pg. 794

Hettlinger, Bob, Human Resources Dir.--Colle & McVoy Marketing Communications, Minneapolis, MN; *U.S. Private*, pg. 252

Heusdens, J.J., Mng. Dir.-Personnel, Environment & Physical Plng.--Hoogovens Ijmuiden, Ijmuiden, Netherlands; *Int'l*, pg. 753

Hewitt, Nancy B., Mgr.-Human Resources--Prima Energy Corporation, Denver, CO; *U.S. Public*, pg. 1325

Hewlett, Linda, Dir.-Personnel--First Gibraltar Bank, Irving, TX; *U.S. Public*, pg. 181

Heyboer, Judy, Sr. V.P.-Human Resources--Genentech, Inc., South San Francisco, CA; *Int'l*, pg. 1120

Heyman, Jerry, V.P.-Human Resources--Colorado Boxed Beef Co., Auburndale, FL; *U.S. Private*, pg. 254

Hezelton, William, Mgr.-Personnel--Central Maine Power Company, Augusta, ME; *U.S. Public*, pg. 325

Hibbs, Linda, Dir.-Human Resources--GEC Precision Corp., Wellington, KS; *Int'l*, pg. 545

Hickam, Clara, Mgr.-Personnel--Wilson Products Co., Salt Lake City, UT; *U.S. Private*, pg. 1181

Hickey, Sylvia, Dir.-Human Resources--Air New Zealand Ltd. (U.S.A.), El Segundo, CA; *Int'l*, pg. 38

Hickman, Laura, Mgr.-Risk--Staffing Solutions, Boulder, CO; *U.S. Private*, pg. 1028

Hickman, Sue, Dir.-H.R.--American Wyott Corporation, Cheyenne, WY; *U.S. Private*, pg. 1193

Hickok, Dee, Dir.-H.R.--Recoton Corporation, Lake Mary, FL; *U.S. Public*, pg. 1369

Hicks, Don, V.P.-H.R.--Daisy Manufacturing Company, Inc., Rogers, AR; *U.S. Private*, pg. 308

Hicks, Donald, Dir.-Personnel--Reeves Southeastern Corporation, Tampa, FL; *U.S. Private*, pg. 916

Hicks, Randy W., Mgr.-Personnel--Horton Homes, Inc., Eatonton, GA; *U.S. Private*, pg. 540

Higgins, Barbara, Mgr.-Pub. Rels. & Personnel Training & Devel.--Bata Shoe Co., Inc., Belcamp, MD; *U.S. Private*, pg. 195

Higgins, Catherine F., V.P.-Human Resources--Barr Laboratories Inc., Pomona, NY; *U.S. Public*, pg. 191

Higgins, John J., Sr. V.P.-Human Resources--Boston Edison Company, Boston, MA; *U.S. Public*, pg. 247

Higgins, Kate, Dir.-Personnel--Tingley Rubber Corporation, South Plainfield, NJ; *U.S. Private*, pg. 1088

Higgins, Kathie E., Sr. V.P. & Dir.-H.R.--Nevada State Bank, Las Vegas, NV; *U.S. Public*, pg. 1793

Higgins, Mary Alyce, V.P.-Human Resources--Guilford of Maine, Inc., Guilford, ME; *U.S. Public*, pg. 889

Higgins, P., Dir.-H.R.--Treibacher Schleifmittel Corp., Niagara Falls, NY; *U.S. Private*, pg. 1099

Higgins, William X., Dir.-Human Resources--Morgan Stanley Group Inc., New York, NY; *U.S. Public*, pg. 1132

Hight, Jean, Mgr.-Personnel--Microtel International Inc., Ontario, CA; *U.S. Public*, pg. 1108

Hilbink, Ron, Dir.-H.R.--BC-USA, New Holland, PA; *Int'l*, pg. 201

Hilbrands, Vicki, V.P.-H.R.--Shonac Corporation, Columbus, OH; *U.S. Private*, pg. 996

Hilburn, Julius, V.P.-Human Resources--Kerr-McGee Corporation, Oklahoma City, OK; *U.S. Public*, pg. 952

Hildebrand, Janet, Sr. V.P.-Human Resources--Richfood Holdings, Inc., Glen Allen, VA; *U.S. Public*, pg. 1388

Hildreth, Burgess, V.P.-Admin.--Anchor Continental Incorporated, Columbia, SC; *U.S. Private*, pg. 70

Hile, Dan, V.P.-Human Resources--Ransomes-Cushman-Ryan, Lincoln, NE; *Int'l*, pg. 1088

Hilgers, Harald, Mgr.-Personnel--Melitta Unternehmensgruppe Bentz KG, Minden, Germany; *Int'l*, *pg. 856*

Hill, Bruce A., V.P. & Asst. Dir.-Personnel--JC Penney Company, Inc., Plano, TX; *U.S. Public*, pg. 916
Hill, Charlie W., V.P.-H.R.--Landmark Communications, Inc., Norfolk, VA; *U.S. Private*, pg. 647
Hill, Dave, Mgr.-Personnel--Markem Corporation, Keene, NH; *U.S. Private*, pg. 704
Hill, Joan, Chief Oper. Officer & V.P.-H.R.--Jami, Inc., Shawnee Mission, KS; *U.S. Private*, pg. 581
Hill, Joseph G., Chief Fin. Officer, V.P.-Fin., Treas. & Sec.--DMI Furniture Inc., Louisville, KY; *U.S. Public*, pg. 473
Hill, Linda, Mgr.-H.R.--Bedford Industries, Inc., Worthington, MN; *U.S. Private*, pg. 129
Hill, Merna, Mgr.-Personnel--MacDermid Incorporated, Waterbury, CT; *U.S. Public*, pg. 1029
Hill, Monica L., Dir.-Human Resources--Pepper, Hamilton & Scheetz, Philadelphia, PA; *U.S. Private*, pg. 851
Hill, Norman J., Sr. V.P.-Human Resources--Cracker Barrel Old Country Store, Inc., Lebanon, TN; *U.S. Public*, pg. 455
Hill, Roger, Dir.-Oper. & Trng.--Tuffy Associates Corp., Toledo, OH; *U.S. Private*, pg. 1109
Hill, Steven, Sr. V.P.-H.R.--Weyerhaeuser Company, Federal Way, WA; *U.S. Public*, pg. 1764
Hill, Wendi A., V.P.-H.R.--Tab Products Co., Palo Alto, CA; *U.S. Public*, pg. 1559
Hiller, Bruce, V.P.-H.R.--Rural Metro Corporation, Scottsdale, AZ; *U.S. Public*, pg. 1412
Hiller, Nick, Dir.-Personnel--Sun Chemical General Printing Inc., Northlake, IL; *Int'l*, pg. 370
Hilles, Richard J., Corp. V.P.-Human Resources--Allergan, Inc., Irvine, CA; *U.S. Public*, pg. 46
Hilliard, Clifford, Dir.-H.R.--CRH, plc, Dublin, Ireland; *Int'l*, pg. 242
Hillman, James C., V.P.-Human Resources--O'Sullivan Industries Holdings, Lamar, MO; *U.S. Public*, pg. 1234
Hills, E.P., Dir.-Personnel--Hofmann Industries, Inc., Sinking Spring, PA; *U.S. Private*, pg. 533
Himel, Steve, Dir.-H.R.--William B. Reily & Co., Inc., New Orleans, LA; *U.S. Private*, pg. 919
Hinckley, Clark B., Sr. V.P.-Human Resources--Zions Bancorporation, Salt Lake City, UT; *U.S. Public*, pg. 1792
Hinderliter, Mark, Asst. V.P.-Human Resources--CPI Corp., Saint Louis, MO; *U.S. Public*, pg. 283
Hindmarch, Derek, Mgr.-Personnel--Raleigh Industries Ltd., Nottingham, United Kingdom; *Int'l*, pg. 394
Hinds, Phil H., Dir.-Personnel--Gateway Press, Inc., Louisville, KY; *U.S. Private*, pg. 441
Hines, Kimberly, Dir.-Human Resources--Nomaco, Inc., Zebulon, NC; *U.S. Private*, pg. 801
Hines, Robby, Dir.-Personnel--Collier-Keyworth, Inc., Liberty, NC; *U.S. Public*, pg. 985
Hines, Steve, Mgr.-Human Resources & Risk Mngmnt.--Stewart & Stevenson Services, Inc., Houston, TX; *U.S. Public*, pg. 1517
Hinkle, Anne, Mgr.-Human Resources--American Educational Products, Boulder, CO; *U.S. Public*, pg. 71
Hinson-Zane, Lisa, Dir.-H.R.--Leasing Solutions, Inc., San Jose, CA; *U.S. Public*, pg. 982
Hinthorn, Jim, Dir.-H.R.--F. Schumacher & Co., New York, NY; *U.S. Private*, pg. 973
Hinton, Ellen, Mgr.-H.R.--Sonoma Mission Inn & Spa, Sonoma, CA; *U.S. Private*, pg. 1014
Hinton, Ray H., Corp. Exec.-Human Resources--NationsBank Virginia, Richmond, VA; *U.S. Public*, pg. 1163
Hinton, Ray H., Exec. V.P. & Dir. Human Resources--Nationsbank/Tennessee, Nashville, TN; *U.S. Public*, pg. 1163
Hintz, Rosemary, Dir.-Human Resources--L.A. Gear, Inc., Santa Monica, CA; *U.S. Public*, pg. 969
Hirai, Norio, Sr. Mng. Dir.-Human Resources--Omron Corporation, Kyoto, Japan; *Int'l*, pg. 1005
Hirata, Hideyuki, Chief Mgr.-Personnel--Showa Denko K.K., Tokyo, Japan; *Int'l*, pg. 1236
Hirata, Shigeru, Gen. Mgr.-Personnel--Meiji Life Insurance Company, Tokyo, Japan; *Int'l*, pg. 854
Hitch, John L., Mgr.-Mktg. Communications--Belden Inc., Saint Louis, MO; *U.S. Public*, pg. 200
Hitch, John L., Mgr.-Mktg. Communications--Belden Wire & Cable Company, Richmond, IN; *U.S. Public*, pg. 201
Hitchcock, April, Admin.-H.R.--North Central Life Insurance Company, Saint Paul, MN; *U.S. Private*, pg. 404
Hite, Brenda, Mgr.-Personnel--The Homestead L.C., Hot Springs, VA; *U.S. Private*, pg. 247
Hite, C.L., V.P.-Human Resources & Admin.--Square D Company, Palatine, IL; *Int'l*, pg. 1208
Hittman, S.K., Dir.-Human Resources--The Ziegler Companies, Inc., West Bend, WI; *U.S. Public*, pg. 1791
Hittman, S.K., V.P.-Personnel--B.C. Ziegler & Co., West Bend, WI; *U.S. Public*, pg. 1792
Hitzgrath, Carol, Mgr.-Personnel--Edwin B. Stimpson Company, Inc., Bayport, NY; *U.S. Private*, pg. 1043
Ho, H.M., V.P.-Human Resources--Fedmet International Inc., Mississauga, Canada; *Int'l*, pg. 1150
Hoalt, Carol, Exec. V.P.-Human Resources--Edwards Super Food Stores, Carlisle, PA; *Int'l*, pg. 749
Hobgood, William P., Sr. V.P.-People--UAL Corporation, Elk Grove Village, IL; *U.S. Public*, pg. 1652
Hockman, Thomas L., V.P.-Personnel--Worthington Industries, Inc., Columbus, OH; *U.S. Public*, pg. 1780
Hodge, Brenda, V.P. & Human Resources Dir.--Gleason/Calise/Associates, Inc., Dallas, TX; *U.S. Private*, pg. 455
Hodge, Robert C., V.P.-Human Resources--Ohmeda, Inc., Liberty Corner, NJ; *Int'l*, pg. 121
Hodge, Tommy, V.P.-Human Resources--Milliken & Company, Spartanburg, SC; *U.S. Private*, pg. 748
Hodges, June Jenkins, Asst. Treas.--SL Industries, Inc., Mount Laurel, NJ; *U.S. Public*, pg. 1418
Hodgkinson, D.H., Head-Human Resources--The Hongkong and Shanghai Banking Corporation Limited (HongkongBank), Central, Hong Kong; *Int'l*, pg. 583
Hoech, Steve, V.P.-Employee Rels.--H.B. Zachry, San Antonio, TX; *U.S. Private*, pg. 1203
Hoffer, Walt, V.P.-Human Resources--Chase & Sanborn Coffee, Inc., San Francisco, CA; *Int'l*, pg. 917
Hoffhein, Kathleen, Dir.-H.R.--Legacy Marketing Group, Petaluma, CA; *U.S. Private*, pg. 658
Hoffman, Cheryl, Mgr.-Human Resources--Heurikon Corporation, Madison, WI; *U.S. Public*, pg. 422
Hoffman, Dustan, V.P.-H.R.--Crown Prince, Inc. (CA), City of Industry, CA; *U.S. Private*, pg. 293
Hoffman, Garth, V.P.-Human Resources--Yorktowne, Inc., Red Lion, PA; *U.S. Private*, pg. 1196
Hoffman, Patti, Pres.-U.S. Reg. Offices & H.R.--Total Research Corporation, Princeton, NJ; *U.S. Public*, pg. 1625
Hoffman, Ronald R., Exec. V.P.-Human Resources, Quality & Communications--Aluminum Company of America, Pittsburgh, PA; *U.S. Public*, pg. 60
Hoffpauir, Gary, Dir.-Human Resources--Allright Corporation, Houston, TX; *U.S. Private*, pg. 42
Hofman, Charles, Treas.--Shopsmith, Inc., Dayton, OH; *U.S. Public*, pg. 1467
Hogenmiller, Jeffrey N., V.P.-Human Resources--Abbott Chemical & Agricultural Products Division, Abbott Park, IL; *U.S. Public*, pg. 13
Hokka, Jorma, Mgr.-Personnel--Raisio Group, Raisio, Finland; *Int'l*, pg. 1085
Holbert, Rick, Dir.-H.R.--Thomas Built Buses, Inc., High Point, NC; *U.S. Private*, pg. 1082
Holdeman, Dick, Mgr.-H.R.--Accra Pac Group, Elkhart, IN; *U.S. Private*, pg. 11
Holden, Richard, V.P.-Human Resources--Scotsman Industries, Inc., Vernon Hills, IL; *U.S. Public*, pg. 1444
Holland, Donna M., V.P.-H.R.--Eastern Fine Paper, Brewer, ME; *U.S. Private*, pg. 357
Holland, Larry V., V.P.-Corp. H.R. & Employee Svcs.--Scholastic Corporation, New York, NY; *U.S. Public*, pg. 1440
Holland, Steve, V.P.-Human Resources--Sermatech International, Inc., Limerick, PA; *U.S. Public*, pg. 1569
Holland, Sue, Human Resources Dir.--Eisner & Associates, Inc., Baltimore, MD; *U.S. Private*, pg. 366
Hollenbach, Fritz, V.P.-H.R.--Regal-Beloit Corporation, Beloit, WI; *U.S. Public*, pg. 1370
Hollins, Leon Z., Jr., V.P.-Human Resources--Federal National Mortgage Association (Fannie Mae), Washington, DC; *U.S. Public*, pg. 615
Hollis, Deborah D., Exec. V.P.-Human Resources & Govt. Rels.--Shoney's, Inc., Nashville, TN; *U.S. Public*, pg. 1467
Hollis, Wilburn J., V.P.-H.R.--United Fire & Casualty Company, Cedar Rapids, IA; *U.S. Public*, pg. 1677
Hollnagel, Daryl, V.P.-Human Resources, Legal--Continental General Tire, Inc., Charlotte, NC; *Int'l*, pg. 327
Hollnagel, Daryl, Dir.-Human Resources & Pur.--Continental General Tire, Inc., Charlotte, NC; *Int'l*, pg. 327
Holloway, Cecelia, V.P.-Human Resources & Admin.--Viacom Entertainment, New York, NY; *U.S. Private*, pg. 779
Holm, Judy, V.P.-Human Resources--Southern Pacific Rail Corporation, San Francisco, CA; *U.S. Public*, pg. 1668
Holmes, Graeme, Mgr.-Grp. H.R.--National Consolidated, Melbourne, Australia; *Int'l*, pg. 908
Holmes, Meg, Mgr.-H.R.--Midwest Industries, Inc., Ida Grove, IA; *U.S. Private*, pg. 744
Holms, Robin, Dir.-Personnel--Scottish & Courage Beer Div., Edinburgh, United Kingdom; *Int'l*, pg. 1212
Holstein, Hartwig, V.P.-Human Resources--The Braas Group, Oberursell, Germany; *Int'l*, pg. 1091
Holzhauser, Glenn, Dir.-H.R.--Sandusky International Inc., Sandusky, OH; *U.S. Private*, pg. 964
Honda, Masayoshi, Mgr.-Human Resources--Rohto Pharmaceutical Co., Osaka, Japan; *Int'l*, pg. 1126
Hondras, Sylvia, Dir.-Human Resources--Johnson Products Co., Inc., Chicago, IL; *U.S. Public*, pg. 915
Hood, Dennis C., V.P.-H.R.--Morgan Products Ltd., Williamsburg, VA; *U.S. Public*, pg. 1132
Hood, Graeme T., Div. Mgr.-H.R.--International Division, Melbourne, Australia; *Int'l*, pg. 226
Hood, Linda, Dir.-Human Resources--Athey Products Corporation, Wake Forest, NC; *U.S. Public*, pg. 142
Hooker, J.R., V.P.-Employee Rels.--Crouse-Hinds, Syracuse, NY; *U.S. Public*, pg. 444
Hooper, Brad, Grp. Mgr.-H.R.--John Fairfax Holdings Limited, Sydney, Australia; *Int'l*, pg. 477
Hooper, Harry, Controller & Dir.-H.R.--Trailer Wheel & Frame Company, Houston, TX; *U.S. Private*, pg. 1095
Hooper, Steven E., V.P.-Human Resources--Terex Corporation, Westport, CT; *U.S. Public*, pg. 1581
Hoops, Barry, Dir.-Personnel--Jones Dairy Farm, Fort Atkinson, WI; *U.S. Private*, pg. 596
Hoose, James W., Dir.-H.R.--Krug International Corp., Houston, TX; *U.S. Public*, pg. 967
Hoose, James W., Dir.-Human Resources--Krug Life Sciences Inc., San Antonio, TX; *U.S. Public*, pg. 968
Hoose, James W., Sr., Dir.-Human Resources--Krug Life Sciences Inc., Houston, TX; *U.S. Public*, pg. 968
Hope, Theresa M., Dir.-Human Resources--Varco International, Inc., Orange, CA; *U.S. Public*, pg. 1709
Hopkins, Curt, V.P.-H.R.--Golub Corporation, Schenectady, NY; *U.S. Private*, pg. 463
Hopwood, Dennis, V.P.-Human Resources--PSC Inc., Webster, NY; *U.S. Public*, pg. 1245
Horn, Scott, Dir.-Human Resources--Jackson Hole Ski Resort, Teton Village, WY; *U.S. Private*, pg. 579
Hornaday, Renee, Controller--Warren Distributing Corp., Raleigh, NC; *U.S. Private*, pg. 1151
Hornberger, William E., V.P.-Human Resources--Rouge Steel Company, Dearborn, MI; *U.S. Public*, pg. 1406
Hornbuckle, Mertoe B., V.P.-Human Resources--Deere & Company, Moline, IL; *U.S. Public*, pg. 491
Horne, David S., V.P.-H.R.--USLD Communications Corp., San Antonio, TX; *U.S. Public*, pg. 969
Horne, George R., V.P.-H.R.--Dole Food Company, Inc., Westlake Village, CA; *U.S. Public*, pg. 515
Horner, Matina S., Exec. V.P.-Human Resources--Teachers Insurance and Annuity Association, New York, NY; *U.S. Private*, pg. 1071
Hornstein, Donald A., V.P.-H.R.--Channellock, Inc., Meadville, PA; *U.S. Private*, pg. 229
Horslev, Dave, Dir.-Human Resources--Culligan International Company, Northbrook, IL; *U.S. Public*, pg. 467
Horton, Alyson, Dir.-H.R.--Riverside Group, Inc., Jacksonville, FL; *U.S. Public*, pg. 1391
Horton, George, Dir.-Safety & Personnel--Cliffs Drilling Co., Broussard, LA; *U.S. Public*, pg. 386
Horton, Virdie, Human Resources Dir.--Berry-Brown Advertising, Inc., Dallas, TX; *U.S. Private*, pg. 137
Horwath, E.I., Sr. H.R. Strategy Consultant--Orange and Rockland Utilities, Inc., Pearl River, NY; *U.S. Public*, pg. 1229
Horwood, Jody, Dir.-Personnel--W.M. Grace Development, Phoenix, AZ; *U.S. Private*, pg. 468
Hoseus, Robert, Dir.-Human Resources--Borden Italian Foods, Columbus, OH; *U.S. Private*, pg. 158
Hosking, Peter, Dir.-Personnel--Coles Myer Ltd., Tooronga, Australia; *Int'l*, pg. 306
Hosoya, Eiji, Mng. Dir.-Fin. & Health & Welfare--East Japan Railway Company, Tokyo, Japan; *Int'l*, pg. 431
Hossley, Dan, Mgr.-Staff Grp. & Mdse.--Southland Corporation, Brea, CA; *Int'l*, pg. 694
Houchens, D., Mgr.-Employee Rels.--Comdial Corporation, Charlottesville, VA; *U.S. Public*, pg. 407
Hough, G. Thomas, Vice Chm.-Human Resources--Ernst & Young, LLP, New York, NY; *U.S. Private*, pg. 381
Houle, Leo, Mgr.-H.R.--Alusuisse-Lonza Holding Ltd., Zurich, Switzerland; *Int'l*, pg. 66
Houser, Michael E., V.P.-Human Resources & Quality Assurance--Treasure Chest Advertising Co., Inc., Glendora, CA; *U.S. Public*, pg. 228
Houser, William R., V.P.-Human Resources--Guilford Mills, Inc., Greensboro, NC; *U.S. Public*, pg. 768
Houston, Farley, Mgr.-Personnel--ITT A-C Pump/ITT Marlow, Cincinnati, OH; *U.S. Public*, pg. 860
Houston, Paula, Mgr.-H.R.--Hart Crowser, Inc., Seattle, WA; *U.S. Private*, pg. 507
Hove, Brenda, Dir.-H.R.--Demco Inc., Madison, WI; *U.S. Private*, pg. 323
Howard, Brian P., V.P.-Human Resources--The Ingersoll Milling Machine Co., Rockford, IL; *U.S. Private*, pg. 562
Howard, Donald L., V.P.-Human Resources--National Data Corporation, Atlanta, GA; *U.S. Public*, pg. 1155
Howard, Irene C., V.P.-Human Resources & Risk Mngmt.--KLLM Transport Services, Inc., Jackson, MS; *U.S. Public*, pg. 939
Howard, Jerry, V.P.-Human Resources & Environment--Marathon Oil Company, Houston, TX; *U.S. Public*, pg. 1661
Howard, Karen, V.P.-Human Resources--National Computer Systems, Eden Prairie, MN; *U.S. Public*, pg. 1155
Howard, Tom, Human Resources--Wang's International, Inc., Memphis, TN; *U.S. Private*, pg. 1149
Howard, William, V.P.-H.R.--Bernhardt Furniture Co., Lenoir, NC; *U.S. Private*, pg. 137
Howatt, Neels, Gen. Mgr.-Human Resources & Pub. Relations--Iscor, Pretoria, South Africa; *Int'l*, pg. 688
Howatt, Terry, Dir.-Human Resources--Encore Computer Corporation, Fort Lauderdale, FL; *U.S. Public*, pg. 580
Howe, Anne, Dir.-H.R.--Burke Industries, Inc., San Jose, CA; *U.S. Private*, pg. 183
Howell, Arden, V.P.-H.R.--Lyon's Restaurants, Inc., Foster City, CA; *U.S. Private*, pg. 684
Howell, William M., Gen. Mgr.-H.R.--Goodman Fielder Limited, Sydney, Australia; *Int'l*, pg. 555
Howes, Banning, Dir.-Human Resources--Hipotronics, Inc., Brewster, NY; *U.S. Public*, pg. 844
Howey, William, V.P.-Admin. Services & Human Resources--Waddell & Reed, Inc., Shawnee Mission, KS; *U.S. Public*, pg. 1623
Howley, Colleen, Mgr.-Human Resources--Versar Inc., Springfield, VA; *U.S. Public*, pg. 1717
Hoyle, John, Mgr.-Personnel--Nissan Forklift Corporation, North America, Marengo, IL; *Int'l*, pg. 944
Hoysted, D.C.F., Dir.-Personnel--Morgan Grenfell Group PLC, London, United Kingdom; *Int'l*, pg. 405
Hoyt, Susan, Exec. V.P.-H.R.--Staples, Inc., Westborough, MA; *U.S. Public*, pg. 1509
Hritsuk, Elaine, Dir.-H.R.--The Middleby Corporation, Rolling Meadows, IL; *U.S. Public*, pg. 1109
Hromin, Nancy, Mgr.-Human Resources--Reed Business Information Pty. Limited, Chatswood, Australia; *Int'l*, pg. 1094
Hrudecky, Cheryl, Mgr.-Human Resources--Mail Boxes Etc., San Diego, CA; *U.S. Public*, pg. 1687
Hubacek, Sherry, Mgr.-Human Resources & Employee Benefits--General Employment Enterprises, Inc., Oak Brook Terrace, IL; *U.S. Public*, pg. 714
Hubbard, James, V.P.-Human Resources--Mercury Marine, Fond Du Lac, WI; *U.S. Public*, pg. 265
Hubbard, James W., Pres. & Chief Exec. Officer--Herff Jones Inc., Indianapolis, IN; *U.S. Private*, pg. 523
Hubbard, Jean A., V.P. & Dir.-H.R.--Rurban Financial Corp., Defiance, OH; *U.S. Public*, pg. 1412
Huber, Ray, V.P.-Personnel & Labor Rels.--Giant Eagle, Inc., Pittsburgh, PA; *U.S. Private*, pg. 450
Huber, Richard L., Dir.-Personnel--GM Powertrain Group, Pontiac, MI; *U.S. Public*, pg. 719
Hubler, Celine, Human Resources--Hampel/Stefanides, New York, NY; *U.S. Private*, pg. 498
Hubley, Rose, Gen. Mgr.-H.R.--Bruncor, Inc., Saint John, Canada; *Int'l*, pg. 230
Hubschman, Robyn, Dir.-Human Resources--Vornado Realty Trust, Saddle Brook, NJ; *U.S. Public*, pg. 1725
Hucklenbroich, Michel, Mgr.-Personnel & Admin.--Groupe Bruxelles Lambert S.A., Brussels, Belgium; *Int'l*, pg. 561
Hudak, Bill, Dir.-H.R.--Hirschfeld, Inc., San Angelo, TX; *U.S. Private*, pg. 530

Hudnall, Jim, Dir.-Human Resources--Charter Hospital of Mobile, Inc., Mobile, AL; *U.S. Public*, pg. 1034
Hudson, John, V.P.-Human Resources--M.S. Carriers, Inc., Memphis, TN; *U.S. Public*, pg. 1027
Hudson, Keith H., Dir.-H.R.--Robertson-Ceco Corporation, San Ramon, CA; *U.S. Public*, pg. 1394
Hudson, R., Mgr.-H.R.--Blue Bird Corporation, Macon, GA; *U.S. Private*, pg. 151
Hudson, Rhonda, Dir.-Personnel--The Law Company, Inc., Wichita, KS; *U.S. Private*, pg. 653
Huebner, Bryan J., Sr. V.P.-Hartford Region & Human Resources--People's Bank, Bridgeport, CT; *U.S. Public*, pg. 1274
Huebner, Margaret A., V.P.-Human Resources & Labor Rels.--Certified Grocers of California, Los Angeles, CA; *U.S. Private*, pg. 226
Hueston, Brock, Dir.-Human Resources--Electrohome Ltd., Kitchener, Canada; *Int'l*, pg. 438
Huey, Burkett W., Jr., V.P.-Benefits--PepsiCo, Inc., Purchase, NY; *U.S. Public*, pg. 1276
Huffman, Pam, V.P.-Human Resources--Kent Electronics Corp., Houston, TX; *U.S. Public*, pg. 951
Huffman, Todd, Dir.-Personnel--Polka Dot Dairy/Tom Thumb Food Markets, Hastings, MN; *U.S. Private*, pg. 874
Hug, Caroline, Dir.-Personnel--Ohse Foods Inc., Topeka, KS; *U.S. Private*, pg. 396
Hughes, Donald, Dir.-Human Resources--The Tetley Group Limited, Greenford, United Kingdom; *Int'l*, pg. 1377
Hughes, Gerald T., V.P.-Human Resources--Harcourt General, Inc., Chestnut Hill, MA; *U.S. Public*, pg. 782
Hughes, James, Dir.-Personnel--Barnhill Contracting Company, Tarboro, NC; *U.S. Private*, pg. 117
Hughes, Maggie, V.P.-Human Resources--Burke Mills, Inc., Valdese, NC; *U.S. Public*, pg. 267
Hughes, Roger, Mgr.-Production--Phoenix Medical Technology, Inc., Andrews, SC; *U.S. Public*, pg. 1292
Hughes, S.J., Jr., V.P.--Barnhill Contracting Company, Tarboro, NC; *U.S. Private*, pg. 117
Hughes, Valery, Mgr.-Personnel--Suspa, Inc., Grand Rapids, MI; *Int'l*, pg. 1322
Huisinga, Darrel, Pres. & Chief Exec. Officer--J.D. Streett & Co., Inc., Maryland Heights, MO; *U.S. Private*, pg. 1047
Hulett, Michael, Exec. Partner--MeritCare Health System, Fargo, ND; *U.S. Private*, pg. 733
Hull, Phyllis, Dir.-Personnel--Megapulse, Inc., Bedford, MA; *U.S. Private*, pg. 729
Huls, Klaus, Dir.-Personnel--Saarbergwerke Aktiengesellschaft, Saarbruecken, Germany; *Int'l*, pg. 1166
Hulst, Evert, Mgr.-Personnel--Banque Paribas Nederland N.V., Amsterdam, Netherlands; *Int'l*, pg. 320
Hulst, Les, V.P.-Opers.--Dickinson Press, Inc., Grand Rapids, MI; *U.S. Private*, pg. 331
Humenesky, Greg, Sr. V.P.-Human Resources--Zale Corporation, Irving, TX; *U.S. Public*, pg. 1789
Humphrey, Colleen, Dir.-H.R.--Thinking Machines Corporation, Burlington, MA; *U.S. Private*, pg. 1081
Hundley, Jay F., V.P.-Personnel--JC Penney Company, Inc., Plano, TX; *U.S. Public*, pg. 916
Hunt, Colin Edward, Gen. Mgr.-H.R.--First National Bank Holdings Limited, Johannesburg, South Africa; *Int'l*, pg. 487
Hunt, Connie, Dir.-Human Resources--Empire of Carolina, Inc., Delray Beach, FL; *U.S. Public*, pg. 579
Hunt, Pat, Mgr.-Personnel--Shell Pipe Line Corp., Houston, TX; *Int'l*, pg. 1136
Hunter, Joe, Exec. Dir.-H.R.--The Swiss Colony, Inc, Monroe, WI; *U.S. Private*, pg. 1059
Huntley, Bridget, Coord.-H.R.--Sonoma Mission Inn & Spa, Sonoma, CA; *U.S. Private*, pg. 1014
Huntley, R.T., Dir.-Human Resources--Raytheon E-Systems, Greenville, TX; *U.S. Public*, pg. 1365
Hurelbrink, Gene, Dir.-Personnel--Sangamon Industries, Taylorville, IL; *U.S. Private*, pg. 965
Hurley, Shirley, V.P.-Human Resources--Weber Marking Systems, Inc., Arlington Heights, IL; *U.S. Private*, pg. 1157
Hurwitz-Schwab, Betsy, 22r.-H.R.--S. Schwab Company, Cumberland, MD; *U.S. Private*, pg. 974
Huss, L. Joseph, V.P.-Human Resources--Gould Electronics Inc., Eastlake, OH; *U.S. Public*, pg. 1591
Hussey, Ron, V.P.-Human Resources--Lasco Bathware, Anaheim, CA; *Int'l*, pg. 1397
Hustin, Kathy, V.P.-Human Resources--National Card Control, Inc., Crozier, VA; *U.S. Public*, pg. 321
Hutcheson, H. Ian, Mgr.-Plng. & Admin.--Ocelot Energy Inc., Calgary, Canada; *Int'l*, pg. 996
Hutchison, P.A., Sr. V.P.-H.R. & Admin.--ESCO Electronics Corporation, Saint Louis, MO; *U.S. Public*, pg. 546
Hutto, Barb, Dir.-Human Resources--EMPI, Inc., Saint Paul, MN; *U.S. Public*, pg. 545
Hutzler, Larry, V.P.-Mfg.--David White, L.L.C., Germantown, WI; *U.S. Public*, pg. 1765
Hutzler, Larry, V.P.-Mfg.--David White, L.L.C., Germantown, WI; *U.S. Private*, pg. 1765
Hwang, B.C., Mgr.-Personnel--Kodak Korea Ltd., Seoul, Korea; *U.S. Public*, pg. 555
Hyde, Don, Dir.-Opers. & Personnel--Battey Machinery Company, Rome, GA; *U.S. Private*, pg. 123
Hyde, Gerald, Jr., V.P.-Personnel & Labor Relations--Lone Star Industries, Inc., Stamford, CT; *U.S. Public*, pg. 1012
Hyde, Joanne, Dir.-Human Resources--Summa Four, Inc., Manchester, NH; *U.S. Public*, pg. 1527
Hyde, Marcia, V.P.-Corp. H.R.--Valassis Communications, Inc., Livonia, MI; *U.S. Public*, pg. 1704
Hyman, Gladys, Mgr.-Employee Benefits--Harkins Builders, Inc., Silver Spring, MD; *U.S. Private*, pg. 502
Hyndham, Ruth, Dir.-Personnel--Entertainment UK Ltd., Hayes, United Kingdom; *Int'l*, pg. 733
Hysop, Gary, V.P.-Human Resources--Sterling Pulp Chemicals, Ltd., Etobicoke, Canada; *U.S. Public*, pg. 1580
Ibach, John C., V.P.-Human Resources--Peoples Energy Corporation, Chicago, IL; *U.S. Public*, pg. 1274
Ibach, John C., V.P.-Human Resources--North Shore Gas Co., Waukegan, IL; *U.S. Public*, pg. 1275
Ibach, John C., V.P.-Human Resources--The Peoples Gas Light & Coke Co., Chicago, IL; *U.S. Public*, pg. 1275
Ibach, Kathy, Dir.-H.R.--Bank Of North Dakota, Bismarck, ND; *U.S. Private*, pg. 114
Ichiki, Yutaka, Sr. Mng. Dir.-Gen. Affairs, Personnel, & Broadcasting & Telecommu--Nihon Keizai Shimbun, Inc., Tokyo, Japan; *Int'l*, pg. 929
Idles, Cinnamon, Human Resources Mgr.--Italia/Gal Advertising, Los Angeles, CA; *U.S. Private*, pg. 576
Ieraci, Meridith, Personnel Asst.--Lyman Products Corporation, Middletown, CT; *U.S. Private*, pg. 683
Igyarto, Mia F., Dir.-Human Resources & Quality--McWhorter Technologies, Inc., Carpentersville, IL; *U.S. Public*, pg. 1074
Ikeda, Donna S., V.P.-H.R.--Franklin Resources, Inc., San Mateo, CA; *U.S. Public*, pg. 679
Iker, T. Denny, V.P.-Human Resources--General Electric Capital Railcar Services, Chicago, IL; *U.S. Public*, pg. 712
Imamura, S., Mgr.-Personnel & Admin./Opers.--Japan Airlines, Zurich, Switzerland; *Int'l*, pg. 700
Imbs, Robert, Chief Fin. Officer & V.P.-Fin.--Louis P. Ciminelli Construction Co. Inc., Buffalo, NY; *U.S. Private*, pg. 239
Imeson, Tom, V.P.-Communications--Utah Power & Light, Salt Lake City, UT; *U.S. Public*, pg. 1251
Ince, Mary, Dir.-Human Resources--UETA, Inc., Laredo, TX; *Int'l*, pg. 103
Indeck, Pamela, V.P.-Human Resources--Reed Elsevier Business Information, Newton, MA; *Int'l*, pg. 1095
Indgjer, Lisa, Dir.-H.R.--ABC Supply Company, Inc., Beloit, WI; *U.S. Private*, pg. 3
Indivero, Mike, Gen. Mgr.-Human Resources--Sunkyong America, Inc., New York, NY; *Int'l*, pg. 1320
Infante, Maria, Dir.-Human Resources--Seaman Furniture Company, Inc., Woodbury, NY; *U.S. Public*, pg. 1452
Ingalls, Rick, Dir.-Personnel--Schlumberger Industries, Owenton, KY; *U.S. Public*, pg. 1439
Ingelhuber, James E., Grp. V.P.-Mfg. Opers. & Human Resources--Metal Container Corporation, Saint Louis, MO; *U.S. Public*, pg. 114
Ingram-Hasall, Rebecca, Dir.-H.R.--EAC Corporation, Saint Louis, MO; *U.S. Private*, pg. 353
Ingram, Barbara, V.P.-Human Resources--Tiffany & Co., New York, NY; *U.S. Public*, pg. 1608
Ingram, Clark, V.P.-H.R.--Team, Inc., Alvin, TX; *U.S. Public*, pg. 1562
Ingram, Kathy, Dir.-Personnel--Cain & Bultman, Jacksonville, FL; *U.S. Private*, pg. 199
Ingram, Sharon D., Dir.-Corp. H.R.--Comcast Corporation, Philadelphia, PA; *U.S. Public*, pg. 406
Ingrassia, Rita, Mgr.-Personnel--Dunhill Personnel System, Inc., Hauppauge, NY; *U.S. Public*, pg. 1746
Insch, Brian D., Dir.-H.R.--GKN plc, Redditch, United Kingdom; *Int'l*, pg. 534
Isaac, Kim J., Dir.-Personnel--McJunkin Corporation, Charleston, WV; *U.S. Private*, pg. 722
Isenstein, Joe, Sr. V.P.-Employee Rels.--Bertelsmann Music Group, Wilmington, DE; *Int'l*, pg. 191
Ishoj, Ole K., Mgr.-Personnel--Royal Copenhagen A/S, Frederiksberg, Denmark; *Int'l*, pg. 1134
Isola, Thomas, V.P.-Mktg. & Pub. Rels.--Silver State Disposal Service, Inc., Las Vegas, NV; *U.S. Public*, pg. 1380
Itavuori, Jussi, Sr. V.P.-H.R.--Kone Corporation, Helsinki, Finland; *Int'l*, pg. 746
Ito, Hisashi, Exec. Mng. Dir.--Sankyo Company Limited, Tokyo, Japan; *Int'l*, pg. 1189
Ito, Osamu, Exec. V.P.-Human Resources & Gen. Affairs--Diamond Star Motors, Normal, IL; *Int'l*, pg. 875
Ito, Yasuhisa, Sr. Mng. Dir.-Store Opers.--Ito-Yokado Co., Ltd., Tokyo, Japan; *Int'l*, pg. 693
Itta-Lee, Brenda, Dir.-H.R.--Arctic Slope Regional Corporation, Barrow, AK; *U.S. Private*, pg. 80
Ivins, Lori, V.P.-Human Resources--American Woodmark Corporation, Winchester, VA; *U.S. Public*, pg. 96
Iwaisaki, Takayoshi, Mgr.-Personnel--Nippon Oil Company, Limited (NiSSEKI), Tokyo, Japan; *Int'l*, pg. 936
Iwanaga, Mitsuo, Mng. Dir.--Kubota Corp., Osaka, Japan; *Int'l*, pg. 762
Iwanowitsch, Jakob, Dir.-H.R.--Freudenberg & Company, Weinheim, Germany; *Int'l*, pg. 505
Izewski, Ron, V.P.-Fin.--Just Born, Inc., Bethlehem, PA; *U.S. Private*, pg. 602
Izumiya, Seizaburo, Gen. Mgr.-Human Resources--Kawasho Corporation, Tokyo, Japan; *Int'l*, pg. 726
Jackman, Neil W., V.P.-Sls. & Human Resources--Pease Industries, Inc., Fairfield, OH; *U.S. Private*, pg. 845
Jackson, Carol, V.P.-H.R.--National Western Life Insurance Company, Austin, TX; *U.S. Public*, pg. 1161
Jackson, D., V.P.-H.R.--Marley Mouldings Inc., Marion, VA; *Int'l*, pg. 843
Jackson, Dale R., V.P.-Human Resources--XOMA Corporation, Berkeley, CA; *U.S. Public*, pg. 1786
Jackson, Dominick, Mgr.-Personnel--Meco Corporation, Greeneville, TN; *U.S. Private*, pg. 726
Jackson, James, V.P.-Human Resources--Berkshire Realty Company, Inc., Boston, MA; *U.S. Public*, pg. 221
Jackson, Jeffrey L., V.P.-Human Resources--TransPro, Inc., New Haven, CT; *U.S. Public*, pg. 1631
Jackson, Jennifer, Dir.-H.R.--Cheesecake Factory Incorporated, Calabasas Hills, CA; *U.S. Public*, pg. 343
Jackson, Joseph L., V.P.-H.R.--Tenet Healthcare Corporation, Santa Barbara, CA; *U.S. Public*, pg. 1576
Jackson, Leo, Dir.-Personnel--Nabholz Construction Corp., Conway, AR; *U.S. Private*, pg. 772
Jackson, Roger A., Sr. V.P.-Human Resources & Corp. Rels.--Lear Corporation, Southfield, MI; *U.S. Public*, pg. 981
Jackson, Steven P., V.P.--Johnson Bros. Corporation, Litchfield, MN; *U.S. Private*, pg. 590
Jackson, Sue, Dir.-Personnel--Racetrac Petroleum, Inc., Smyrna, GA; *U.S. Private*, pg. 906
Jackson, Yvonne, Worldwide H.R.--Burger King Corporation, Miami, FL; *Int'l*, pg. 411
Jacobs, Les, Dir.-Human Resources--Insilco Corporation, Dublin, OH; *U.S. Public*, pg. 881
Jacobs, Nancy, Mgr.-Admin. Svcs.--The Hennegan Company, Florence, KY; *U.S. Private*, pg. 522
Jacobs, Verna, Mgr.-Personnel--UDT Sensors, Inc., Hawthorne, CA; *U.S. Private*, pg. 1112
Jacobsen, Bjorn-Frode, V.P.-H.R.--Norske Skogindustrier A.S, Skogn, Norway; *Int'l*, pg. 965
Jacobsen, Pat, Sr. V.P.-Human Resources & Corp. Services--Manulife Financial, Toronto, Canada; *Int'l*, pg. 840
Jacobson, L.M., Mgr.-Personnel--Joslyn Corporation, Chicago, IL; *U.S. Public*, pg. 481
Jacobson, Mark O., V.P.-Human Services--The TJX Companies, Inc., Framingham, MA; *U.S. Public*, pg. 1556
Jacobson, Steve, Mgr.-H.R.--Chance Industries, Inc., Wichita, KS; *U.S. Private*, pg. 228
Jacques, Serge A., V.P.-Human Resources & Communications--St. Lawrence Cement Inc., Montreal, Canada; *Int'l*, pg. 628
Jadwin, Linda J., V.P.-H.R.--Ceridian Corporation, Bloomington, MN; *U.S. Public*, pg. 330
Jaeb, Michael, V.P.-Corp. Admin.--Aetrium Inc., Saint Paul, MN; *U.S. Public*, pg. 27
Jaeger, Connie, V.P. & Dir.-Human Resources--High Point Financial Corp., Branchville, NJ; *U.S. Public*, pg. 826
Jaen Tortajada, Ruben, Mgr.-H.R.--Grupo Cementos de Chihuahua S.A. de C.V., Chihuahua, Mexico; *Int'l*, pg. 573
Jaenel, Sharon, V.P.-Human Resources--Barton Incorporated, Chicago, IL; *U.S. Public*, pg. 300
Jahnke, Tim, V.P.-Human Resources--Sanford Corporation, Bellwood, IL; *U.S. Public*, pg. 1178
Jais, Bernard, Exec. Dir.-Human Resources--France Telecom, Paris, France; *Int'l*, pg. 503
Jakobs, Nancy, V.P.-Human Resources--Orange and Rockland Utilities, Inc., Pearl River, NY; *U.S. Public*, pg. 1229
James, Donna A., V.P.-Human Resources--Nationwide Insurance Enterprise, Columbus, OH; *U.S. Private*, pg. 788
James, Jyrl, V.P.-H.R. & Gen. Counsel--The Beacon Journal Publishing Company, Akron, OH; *U.S. Public*, pg. 963
James, Lesley, Dir.-H.R.--Tesco PLC, Cheshunt, United Kingdom; *Int'l*, pg. 1376
James, Ross N., Sr. V.P. & Grp. Gen. Mgr.--The BHP Copper Group, San Francisco, CA; *Int'l*, pg. 224
James, Susan, Govt. Affairs Admin.--Octagon Process Inc., Edgewater, NJ; *U.S. Private*, pg. 811
Janczak, Mike, Mgr.-Human Resources--Curtis Lumber Company, Ballston Spa, NY; *U.S. Private*, pg. 297
Janies, Lee, Dir.-Personnel--Schwegmann Giant Super Markets, New Orleans, LA; *U.S. Private*, pg. 629
Janke, Patricia, Mgr.-H.R.--Henley Paper Company, Greensboro, NC; *U.S. Private*, pg. 522
Jantzen, Jean, V.P.-H.R. & Public Affairs--CENEX, Inc., Inver Grove Heights, MN; *U.S. Private*, pg. 221
Janzer, Terry, V.P.-Human Resources--Thermotron Industries, Holland, MI; *U.S. Private*, pg. 1136
Jaramillo, Carol, Dir.-Personnel--Casio Phone-Mate, Inc., Torrance, CA; *Int'l*, pg. 274
Jardim, Jean, Dir.-H.R.--The Harodite Finishing Company Inc., North Dighton, MA; *U.S. Private*, pg. 503
Jarjour, Lynn, V.P.-H.R.--Apple Canada Ltd., Markham, Canada; *U.S. Public*, pg. 121
Jarnigan, LuAnn, Dir.-Human Resources--Sea Ray, Knoxville, TN; *U.S. Public*, pg. 266
Jaubert, Pierre, Dir.-Human Resources--Air Canada Vacations Inc., Montreal, Canada; *Int'l*, pg. 36
Jaworski, Pauline, V.P.-Personnel--Miken Companies, Inc., Cheektowaga, NY; *U.S. Private*, pg. 745
Jaycox, William, Sr. V.P.-Human Resources--Tyson Foods, Inc., Springdale, AR; *U.S. Public*, pg. 1652
Jeavons, Elaina L., Dir.-Personnel & Data Processing--Danisco Ingredients USA, Inc., New Century, KS; *Int'l*, pg. 378
Jefferson, Larry, Dir.-Human Resources--CIS Technologies, Inc., Tulsa, OK; *U.S. Public*, pg. 1155
Jeffries, Larry, Mgr.-Personnel--Sunshine Mining And Refining Company, Boise, ID; *U.S. Public*, pg. 1536
Jenkins, James, Mgr.-Human Resources--Frigidaire Home Products, Conway, AR; *Int'l*, pg. 439
Jenkins, Lillian, Dir.-Human Resources--Aladdin Synergetics, Inc., Nashville, TN; *U.S. Private*, pg. 31
Jenkins, Lillian B., V.P.-Human Resources--Aladdin Industries, Incorporated, Nashville, TN; *U.S. Private*, pg. 30
Jenkins, Norman, Dir.-H.R.--Ogden Entertainment, Inc., New York, NY; *U.S. Public*, pg. 1213
Jenkins, Tiny, Dir.-H.R.--Process Systems Inc., Memphis, TN; *U.S. Private*, pg. 888
Jenks, Diana, V.P.-H.R.--La Petite Academy Inc., Overland Park, KS; *U.S. Private*, pg. 640
Jenks, Karen, Sr. V.P.-H.R.--George W. Park Seed Co., Inc., Greenwood, SC; *U.S. Private*, pg. 839
Jennings-Galla, Marlene, V.P.-H.R.--Delaware North Companies, Inc., Buffalo, NY; *U.S. Private*, pg. 321
Jennings, Charles W., Jr., Sr. V.P.-Human Resources--Old Kent Financial Corporation, Grand Rapids, MI; *U.S. Public*, pg. 1216
Jennings, Donna, V.P.-Human Resources & Communication--Velsicol Chemical Corporation, Rosemont, IL; *U.S. Private*, pg. 1135
Jennings, Gary, Dir.-H.R.--Cummings Inc., Nashville, TN; *U.S. Private*, pg. 295
Jennings, Ray, Dir.-Human Resources--Dowty Aerospace, Abingdon, United Kingdom; *Int'l*, pg. 1337

Jennison, Pat, Mgr.-Personnel--Robotic Vision Systems, Inc., Hauppauge, NY; *U.S. Public*, pg. 1395

Jentges, Vicki, Dir.-Human Resources--Adaptive Information Systems, Mission Viejo, CA; *Int'l*, pg. 946

Jeppesen, K. Tad, Sr. V.P.-Human Resources Div.--First Security Service Company, Salt Lake City, UT; *U.S. Public*, pg. 638

Jesse, Hunter, Dir.-H.R.--ICO, Inc., Houston, TX; *U.S. Public*, pg. 853

Jevotovsky, Ira D., V.P.-Human Resources--Hahn Automotive Warehouse, Inc., Rochester, NY; *U.S. Public*, pg. 774

Jewell, Betty, Dir.-H.R.--Dualite Inc., Williamsburg, OH; *U.S. Private*, pg. 344

Jimenez, M. A., Dir.-Personnel--Revlon, S.A., Madrid, Spain; *U.S. Private*, pg. 690

Jimenez, Sara, Supr.-H.R.--Aetna Bearing Company, Chicago, IL; *U.S. Private*, pg. 25

Jo, Duck H., Mgr.-Personnel--Crown Engineering Co., Ltd., Seoul, Korea; *Int'l*, pg. 348

Jo, Kyung J., Mgr.-Personnel--Crown Confectionery Co., Ltd., Seoul, Korea; *Int'l*, pg. 348

Joachim, Yvette, Dir.-H.R.--Mikohn Gaming Corporation, Las Vegas, NV; *U.S. Public*, pg. 1111

Jock, Jim, Mgr.-Human Resources--Johnstown Corporation, Johnstown, PA; *U.S. Private*, pg. 595

Johannson, Jim, Mgr.-Personnel--SJW Corp., San Jose, CA; *U.S. Public*, pg. 1418

Johansen, Carol, Sr. V.P.-Human Resources--Beverly Enterprises, Inc., Fort Smith, AR; *U.S. Public*, pg. 227

Johansson, Barbro, Exec. V.P.-Personnel--Svenska Handelsbanken, Stockholm, Sweden; *Int'l*, pg. 1327

Johansson, Kent, Exec. V.P.-Information, Admin. & Personnel--Celsius AB, Stockholm, Sweden; *Int'l*, pg. 276

Johansson, Magnus, Dir.-Personnel--AB SKF, Goteborg, Sweden; *Int'l*, pg. 1156

John, E. Lynn, Sr. V.P.-Human Resources--Bristol-Myers Health Care Group, New York, NY; *U.S. Public*, pg. 253

John, Jerry, V.P.-Regulatory Compliance--Fleischli Oil Company, Inc., Cheyenne, WY; *U.S. Private*, pg. 410

Johncox, G.H., V.P.-H.R.--MacMillan Bloedel Limited, Vancouver, Canada; *Int'l*, pg. 828

Johns, Adrienne M., Sr. V.P.-Human Resources--The Gap, Inc., San Francisco, CA; *U.S. Public*, pg. 702

Johnson, Alvin, Mgr.-Human Resources--FKI Industries, Inc., Fairfield, CT; *Int'l*, pg. 472

Johnson, Anne, Dir.-H.R.--Reuter Manufacturing Inc., Hopkins, MN; *U.S. Public*, pg. 1383

Johnson, Betty, Mgr.-Personnel & Pension--Kaiser Cement Corporation, Pleasanton, CA; *Int'l*, pg. 593

Johnson, Brad, Asst. V.P.-Fin.--Owen Industries, Inc., Carter Lake, IA; *U.S. Private*, pg. 824

Johnson, Darrell, Dir.-Human Resources Admin. & Compensation--Food Lion, Inc., Salisbury, NC; *Int'l*, pg. 463

Johnson, Diana J., V.P.-Human Resources & Admin. Services--Northwest Natural Gas Company, Portland, OR; *U.S. Public*, pg. 1200

Johnson, Don R., Sr. V.P.-Human Resources--First Union Corporation, Charlotte, NC; *U.S. Public*, pg. 639

Johnson, Frances, V.P.-Human Resources--CUC International, Inc., Stamford, CT; *U.S. Public*, pg. 320

Johnson, Fred, V.P.-Human Resources--Sara Lee Sock Company, High Point, NC; *U.S. Public*, pg. 1434

Johnson, Harold, Mgr.-Personnel--Narrow Fabric Industries, Inc., Reading, PA; *U.S. Private*, pg. 774

Johnson, J. Larry, V.P.-Human Res. & Admin.--Kysor Cooling Systems, Cadillac, MI; *U.S. Public*, pg. 968

Johnson, J.E., Dir.-Human Resources--Symbol Technologies, Portable Systems Division, Costa Mesa, CA; *U.S. Public*, pg. 1546

Johnson, J.L., V.P.-Personnel & Indus. Rels.--General Dynamics Land Systems Div., Muskegon, MI; *U.S. Public*, pg. 709

Johnson, James R., Exec. V.P. & Sec.--Johnson Storage Moving Co, Denver, CO; *U.S. Private*, pg. 594

Johnson, Jerald, Second V.P.-H.R.--National Life Insurance Company, Montpelier, VT; *U.S. Private*, pg. 785

Johnson, John, Dir.-Human Resources--Sub-Zero Freezer Co., Inc., Madison, WI; *U.S. Private*, pg. 1048

Johnson, Keith, Dir.-Employee Benefits--Valhi, Inc., Dallas, TX; *U.S. Private*, pg. 270

Johnson, Keith, Dir.-Human Resources--Svedala Pumps & Process, Colorado Springs, CO; *Int'l*, pg. 1325

Johnson, Kim, Mgr.-H.R.--Murphy Family Farms, Rose Hill, NC; *U.S. Private*, pg. 768

Johnson, LeRoy, Sr. V.P.-Admin. & H.R.--Pioneer Aluminum, Inc., Los Angeles, CA; *U.S. Private*, pg. 866

Johnson, Linda, Mgr.-H.R.--Kennedy Tank & Manufacturing Co., Inc., Indianapolis, IN; *U.S. Private*, pg. 614

Johnson, Maggie, Dir.-H.R.--Heald Colleges, San Francisco, CA; *U.S. Private*, pg. 514

Johnson, Max, V.P.-H.R.--The Principal Financial Group, Des Moines, IA; *U.S. Private*, pg. 885

Johnson, Max, V.P.-Human Resources--Principal Mutual Life Insurance Co., Des Moines, IA; *U.S. Private*, pg. 886

Johnson, Michelle, People Resources--Action Instruments, Inc., San Diego, CA; *U.S. Private*, pg. 15

Johnson, Norma, Mgr.-Personnel--World Pacific Ullenberg Corp., Chattanooga, TN; *U.S. Public*, pg. 861

Johnson, Owen C., Jr., V.P.-Human Resources--NIPSCO Industries, Inc., Hammond, IN; *U.S. Public*, pg. 1185

Johnson, Phil, V.P.-Human Resources--Tandem Computers Inc., Cupertino, CA; *U.S. Public*, pg. 417

Johnson, Philip, Sr. V.P.-Human Resources--Entex Information Services, Rye Brook, NY; *U.S. Private*, pg. 378

Johnson, Richard, V.P.-H.R. & Opers.--Mason Shoe Mfg. Co., Chippewa Falls, WI; *U.S. Private*, pg. 712

Johnson, Stephen B., V.P.-Mktg. & Customer Services--Minnegasco, Minneapolis, MN; *U.S. Public*, pg. 843

Johnson, Steve, Dir.-Training--Sylvan Learning Systems Inc., Baltimore, MD; *U.S. Public*, pg. 1545

Johnson, Theodore C., Sr. V.P.-Human Resources--The Bon Ton Stores, Inc., York, PA; *U.S. Public*, pg. 244

Johnson, Tina, Mgr.-Human Resources--Datasouth Computer Corporation, Charlotte, NC; *U.S. Public*, pg. 267

Johnson, Todd T., Treas. & Sec.--Industrial Construction, Inc., Idaho Falls, ID; *U.S. Private*, pg. 560

Johnson, Wayne, Dir.-Personnel--C. B. Fleet Co., Inc., Lynchburg, VA; *U.S. Private*, pg. 410

Johnson, Wiley, V.P.-Personnel--Orders Distributing Co., Greenville, SC; *U.S. Private*, pg. 819

Johnston, Bonnie, Dir.-H.R.--Computer Language Research, Inc., Carrollton, TX; *U.S. Public*, pg. 421

Johnston, Lee, V.P.-Human Resources--Holder Corporation, Atlanta, GA; *U.S. Private*, pg. 533

Johnston, Patrick, V.P.-Human Resources--Osco Drug, Salt Lake City, UT; *U.S. Public*, pg. 93

Johnston, Peter B., Gen. Mgr.-Human Resources--Western Mining Corporation Holdings Limited, Southbank, Australia; *Int'l*, pg. 1494

Johnston, Stephen E., Sr. V.P.-H.R.--Analysis & Technology, Inc., North Stonington, CT; *U.S. Public*, pg. 109

Johnston, Stephen K., V.P.-Human Resources--The Union Central Life Insurance Co., Cincinnati, OH; *U.S. Private*, pg. 1118

Johnston, Vern, Dir.-Personnel--Allsups Convenience Stores Inc., Clovis, NM; *U.S. Private*, pg. 44

Jolly, Al, Sr. V.P.-Human Resources--CVS Corp., Woonsocket, RI; *U.S. Public*, pg. 287

Jolly, Ernest, V.P.-Human Resources--Atlantic Electric Co., Pleasantville, NJ; *U.S. Public*, pg. 430

Jones, A., Sr. V.P.-Admin. & Human Resources--GAB Robins North America, Inc., Parsippany, NJ; *Int'l*, pg. 1153

Jones, Bonnie, V.P.-Human Resources--Laserscope Surgical Systems, San Jose, CA; *U.S. Public*, pg. 979

Jones, Cathy, Mgr.-Personnel--Allen-Edmonds Shoe Corp., Port Washington, WI; *U.S. Private*, pg. 36

Jones, Clare, Head-Human Resources--BBC Magazines, London, United Kingdom; *Int'l*, pg. 114

Jones, Craig R., Chief Fin. Officer & V.P.--Electro Rent Corporation, Van Nuys, CA; *U.S. Public*, pg. 568

Jones, Deborah L., Mgr.-Human Resources--Peter Pan Seafoods, Inc., Seattle, WA; *Int'l*, pg. 928

Jones, Donna, Mgr.-Human Resources--Axent Technologies, Rockville, MD; *U.S. Public*, pg. 157

Jones, Ellen M., Asst. V.P.-Human Resources--CFX Bank, Keene, NH; *U.S. Public*, pg. 277

Jones, Faith, Dir.-H.R.--MDIS Group plc, Hemel Hempstead, United Kingdom; *Int'l*, pg. 826

Jones, Graceanna, Dir.-Human Resources--Dresser Industries, Inc., Dallas, TX; *U.S. Public*, pg. 528

Jones, Gregory R., V.P.-Human Resources, Gen. Counsel & Sec.--QMS, Inc., Mobile, AL; *U.S. Public*, pg. 1346

Jones, Jarratt H., V.P.-Human Resources--Coca-Cola Enterprises Inc., Atlanta, GA; *U.S. Public*, pg. 393

Jones, Jim, Mgr.-Human Resources--Great Plains Manufacturing, Inc., Salina, KS; *U.S. Private*, pg. 475

Jones, Jim, Dir.-Human Resources--The Standard Register Company, Dayton, OH; *U.S. Public*, pg. 1505

Jones, Les, Dir.-Human Resources--Marshall Industries, El Monte, CA; *U.S. Public*, pg. 1051

Jones, Lisa, Dir.-Personnel--Standard Communications Corp., Torrance, CA; *Int'l*, pg. 841

Jones, Myrna, Dir.-H.R.--Mason & Hanger Corporation, Inc., Lexington, KY; *U.S. Private*, pg. 711

Jones, Patricia, Sr. V.P. & Dir.-HR--AmeriCredit Corp., Fort Worth, TX; *U.S. Public*, pg. 96

Jones, Paul, V.P.-Human Resources--COMSAT World Systems, Bethesda, MD; *U.S. Public*, pg. 424

Jones, Peggy Jo, Grp. V.P.-Employee Devel. & Communications--Albertson's, Inc., Boise, ID; *U.S. Public*, pg. 38

Jones, Richard, Grp. Mgr.-Personnel--Lex Service PLC, Bourne, United Kingdom; *Int'l*, pg. 806

Jones, Robert, V.P.-H.R.--Rally's Hamburgers, Inc., Louisville, KY; *U.S. Public*, pg. 1359

Jones, W.O., Dir.-Personnel--Bank of Mississippi, Tupelo, MS; *U.S. Public*, pg. 176

Jones, William, V.P.-H.R.--Schnuck Markets, Inc., Saint Louis, MO; *U.S. Private*, pg. 971

Jonson, Wayne, V.P.-Human Resources--Maple Leaf Foods Inc., Toronto, Canada; *Int'l*, pg. 841

Jordan, Betty, Dir.-Personnel--Better Brands Of Atlanta, Inc., Atlanta, GA; *U.S. Private*, pg. 141

Jordan, Elizabeth S., V.P.-Human Resources--Kids "R" Us, Paramus, NJ; *U.S. Public*, pg. 1626

Jordan, Nicholas, V.P.-Human Resources--Beatrice Cheese Co., Waukesha, WI; *U.S. Public*, pg. 426

Jordan, Pat, Dir.-H.R.--Conap Inc., Olean, NY; *U.S. Private*, pg. 261

Jordan, Rodney W., Sr. V.P.-Human Resources--Jostens, Minneapolis, MN; *U.S. Public*, pg. 934

Jorgenson, James A., V.P.-H.R.--Hormel Foods Corp., Austin, MN; *U.S. Public*, pg. 840

Joseph, K.C., Gen. Mgr.-Human Resources--Indian Oil Corporation Limited, New Delhi, India; *Int'l*, pg. 673

Joskey, K. M., Mgr.-Personnel--Taunton Cider Company P.L.C., Taunton, United Kingdom; *Int'l*, pg. 849

Joslin, Donald E., V.P.-Personnel--Commercial Travelers Mutual Insurance Company, Utica, NY; *U.S. Private*, pg. 258

Joy, Robert, V.P.-Global Human Resources--Colgate-Palmolive Company, New York, NY; *U.S. Public*, pg. 397

Joyce, Frank E., V.P.-Human Resources--Joy Mining Machinery, Warrendale, PA; *U.S. Public*, pg. 789

Joyce, Joseph, V.P.-Human Resources & Legal Counsel--Best Buy Co., Inc., Eden Prairie, MN; *U.S. Public*, pg. 223

Joyce, Julie, Mng. Dir.-Human Resources--Wheat First Butcher Singer, Inc., Richmond, VA; *U.S. Public*, pg. 640

Joyce, Stephen F., Sr. V.P.-Human Resources--Ross Stores, Inc., Newark, CA; *U.S. Public*, pg. 1405

Joyce, William, V.P.-Admin.--The H.W. Wilson Co., Bronx, NY; *U.S. Private*, pg. 1180

Juarez, Irma, Mgr.-Human Resources--Cowden Metal Specialties, Inc., Chino, CA; *U.S. Private*, pg. 280

Judd, Barbara, Dir.-Personnel--TIC, Steamboat Springs, CO; *U.S. Private*, pg. 1064

Judge, Leigh Ann, V.P.-Human Resources--Salick Health Care, Inc., Los Angeles, CA; *Int'l*, pg. 1524

Juliao, Claudio, Mgr.-Human Resources--Costa Cruise Lines, N.V., Miami, FL; *U.S. Private*, pg. 278

Julsrud, Christopher K., V.P.-H.R.--Morton International Inc., Chicago, IL; *U.S. Public*, pg. 1134

Jund, Bernard, Dir.-Personnel--Lilly France S.A., Saint Cloud, France; *U.S. Public*, pg. 994

Jung, Marikay, V.P.-Human Resources--Delta International Machinery Corp., Pittsburgh, PA; *U.S. Public*, pg. 1273

Junger, Helmut, Mgr.-Personnel--Gebr. Eickhoff Maschinenfabrik und Eisengiesserei mbH, Bochum, Germany; *Int'l*, pg. 542

Junque, Nelson, Jr., Dir.-Human Resources--Johnson & Johnson Ltda., Sao Paulo, Brazil; *U.S. Public*, pg. 931

Junso, Gary, V.P.-H.R.--John Morrell & Co., Cincinnati, OH; *U.S. Public*, pg. 1479

Jurek, Noreen, Sr. Mgr.-Mktg. Commun.--Tekelec, Calabasas, CA; *U.S. Public*, pg. 1566

Jurgens, Richard, Chief Admin. Officer & Sr. V.P.--Hy-Vee Food Stores Incorporated, West Des Moines, IA; *U.S. Private*, pg. 550

Jurgens, Sharon, Mgr.-H.R.--Dakotah, Inc., Webster, SD; *U.S. Public*, pg. 477

Kabellis, Fran, Mgr.-H.R.--KineticSystems Corporation, Lockport, IL; *U.S. Private*, pg. 620

Kaczmarek, Bob, V.P.-Human Resources--Zippo Manufacturing Company, Bradford, PA; *U.S. Private*, pg. 1207

Kadoyama, Tetsuo, Mng. Dir.-Personnel & Pur.--UBE Industries Ltd., Tokyo, Japan; *Int'l*, pg. 1426

Kafafian, Lori, Partner-Global H.R.--Ketchum Public Relations Worldwide, New York, NY; *U.S. Private*, pg. 617

Kahane, Benjamin B., Sr. V.P.-Indus. Rels.--MGM Entertainment Company, Culver City, CA; *U.S. Public*, pg. 1614

Kahlstrom, Deborah, V.P.-Human Resources--BPI Communications Inc., New York, NY; *Int'l*, pg. 1446

Kahmeyer, Heinrich, Dir.-Personnel & Social Policy--Fried. Krupp AG, Essen, Germany; *Int'l*, pg. 507

Kain, Alice, Dir.-Human Resources--El Chico Restaurants, Inc., Dallas, TX; *U.S. Private*, pg. 283

Kairts, Dennis, V.P.-Human Resources--IRD Mechanalysis, Inc. (U.S.A.), Columbus, OH; *U.S. Public*, pg. 789

Kaiser, W.H., Dir.-Human Resources--Becton Dickinson Canada Inc., Mississauga, Canada; *U.S. Public*, pg. 200

Kajian, Linda, Human Resources Mgr.--Lewis Gace Bozell Healthcare Worldwide, Fort Lee, NJ; *U.S. Public*, pg. 1642

Kalleberg, Arnfinn, Dir.-H.R.--Christiania Bank og Kreditkasse ASA, Oslo, Norway; *Int'l*, pg. 289

Kamer, Conard, Dir.-H.R.--The Dartnell Corporation, Chicago, IL; *U.S. Private*, pg. 312

Kaminski, L., Asst. Dir.-Personnel--Zim-American Israeli Shipping Co., New York, NY; *U.S. Private*, pg. 1206

Kamka, Patrick, Mgr.-Personnel--Konami Corporation of America Inc., Buffalo Grove, IL; *Int'l*, pg. 746

Kammer, Bob, Gen. Mgr.-Human Resources--Sanden International (U.S.A.), Inc., Wylie, TX; *Int'l*, pg. 1184

Kamp, J.J., Sr. Exec. V.P.-Personnel--ABN-AMRO Holding N.V., Amsterdam, Netherlands; *Int'l*, pg. 8

Kana, Kiane, Dir.-H.R.--Desco Corporation, Columbus, OH; *U.S. Private*, pg. 326

Kanarick, Arnold F., Exec. V.P. & Dir.-Human Resources--The Limited, Inc., Columbus, OH; *U.S. Public*, pg. 995

Kane, Bill, Mgr.-Human Resources--Frigidaire Home Products-Home Comfort Products, Edison, NJ; *Int'l*, pg. 440

Kane, Brett, Mgr.-Personnel--Aydin Displays (East), Horsham, PA; *U.S. Public*, pg. 158

Kane, John, Mgr.-Personnel--Gardner Abrasives, South Beloit, IL; *U.S. Public*, pg. 1699

Kane, Linden, Dir.-Personnel--Apex Oil Company, Inc., Saint Louis, MO; *U.S. Private*, pg. 77

Kanning, Myron, V.P.-Human Resources--Batesville Casket Company, Inc., Batesville, IN; *U.S. Public*, pg. 828

Kantasewi, Utai, Sr. Mgr.-Human Resources--The Siam Cement Public Company Limited, Bangkok, Thailand; *Int'l*, pg. 1237

Kanton, Peter G., V.P.-Human Resources--PETsMART, Inc., Phoenix, AZ; *U.S. Public*, pg. 1281

Kantor, Helen, Mgr.-Human Resources--Galileo Corp., Sturbridge, MA; *U.S. Public*, pg. 698

Kapitanoff, Art, Mgr.-Corp. H.R.--Regal-Beloit Corporation, Beloit, WI; *U.S. Public*, pg. 1370

Kaplan, Andrew J., Sr. V.P.-Production, Fin. & Admin.--Columbia TriStar Television, Culver City, CA; *Int'l*, pg. 1282

Kaplan, Carol, Dir.-Intl. Compensation & Benefits--Donnelly Corporation, Holland, MI; *U.S. Public*, pg. 519

Kaplan, Maxine, Human Resources--Propper Manufacturing Co., Inc., Long Island City, NY; *U.S. Private*, pg. 891

Karalus, Jo-Ann B., V.P.-Human Resources--Brookstone Company, Inc., Nashua, NH; *U.S. Public*, pg. 259

Karapetian, David, V.P.-Human Resources--HomeTown Communications Network, Inc., Livonia, MI; *U.S. Private*, pg. 537

Kareh, Guillermo, V.P.-H.R. & Insurance & Gen. Counsel--Consorcio G. Grupo Dina, S.A. de C.V., Mexico, Mexico; *Int'l*, pg. 326

Karl, Nitsche, Mgr.-Personnel & Admin.--Agrolinz Melamin GmbH, Lienz, Austria; *Int'l*, pg. 356

Karlin, Richard, Mgr.-Personnel--Arvey Paper & Office Products, Chicago, IL; *U.S. Public*, pg. 903

Karlsson, Sven, Sr. V.P.-Personnel--Nordbanken AB, Stockholm, Sweden; *Int'l*, pg. 957

Karno, Pamela, Mgr.-Human Resources--Haskel International, Inc., Burbank, CA; *U.S. Public*, pg. 798
Karpan, John, Sr. V.P.-Human Resources--Illinois Tool Works Inc., Glenview, IL; *U.S. Public*, pg. 865
Karpinski, John, Mgr.-Indus. Rels.--Mafco Worldwide Corp., Camden, NJ; *U.S. Private*, pg. 690
Karrenbauer, Mark, Dir.-Human Resources--Anchor Glass Container Corporation, Tampa, FL; *Int'l*, pg. 327
Kasamatsu, Hideo, Assoc. Dir. & Gen. Mgr.--Cosmo Oil Co., Ltd., Tokyo, Japan; *Int'l*, pg. 335
Kaschub, William J., Sr. V.P.-Human Resources--PECO Energy Company, Philadelphia, PA; *U.S. Public*, pg. 1268
Kasenter, Robert A., Exec. V.P.-H.R.--Montgomery Ward & Co., Inc., Chicago, IL; *U.S. Private*, pg. 758
Kaslow, Andrew J., V.P.-Human Resources--Becton Dickinson & Company, Franklin Lakes, NJ; *U.S. Public*, pg. 199
Kaslow, Andrew J., V.P.-Human Resources--PepsiCo, Inc., Purchase, NY; *U.S. Public*, pg. 1276
Kass, Deborah, Sr. V.P.-H.R.--Yellow Corporation, Overland Park, KS; *U.S. Public*, pg. 1788
Kass, Deborah, Sr. V.P.-H.R.--Yellow Freight System, Inc., Overland Park, KS; *U.S. Public*, pg. 1788
Kass, Linda, Mgr.-H.R.--Ryan Herco Products Corp., Burbank, CA; *U.S. Private*, pg. 953
Kather, Christine, Coord.-Personnel--Detection Systems, Inc., Fairport, NY; *U.S. Public*, pg. 501
Katner, Terri, Mgr.-H.R.--Graymills Corp., Chicago, IL; *U.S. Private*, pg. 473
Kato-Ujihara, Linda, Dir.-H.R.--Consilium, Inc., Mountain View, CA; *U.S. Public*, pg. 434
Katz, Meredith, Office Mgr.--Pyramid Handbags Inc., New York, NY; *U.S. Private*, pg. 896
Katz, Neil, Dir.-H.R. & Investor Rels.--Curtis Mathes Holding Corp., Dallas, TX; *U.S. Public*, pg. 1057
Katzes, Alan, Dir.-H.R.--AJC International, Inc., Atlanta, GA; *U.S. Private*, pg. 6
Kaufman, Sandy, Mgr.-H.R.--Lander Co., Inc., Englewood, NJ; *U.S. Private*, pg. 647
Kaufmann, Alex, V.P.-Human Resources--The Swissair Group, Zurich, Switzerland; *Int'l*, pg. 1333
Kaul, M.L., Gen. Mgr.-Personnel--Precision Fasteners Ltd., Thane, India; *U.S. Public*, pg. 1420
Kaul, Rajendera, Exec. V.P.--F. J. Benjamin Holdings Ltd., Singapore, Singapore; *Int'l*, pg. 187
Kavcic, Louis, V.P.-Human Resources--Fuddruckers, Inc., Danvers, MA; *Int'l*, pg. 325
Kawakubo, Hiroshi, Dir.--Sakata Seed Corporation, Yokohama, Japan; *Int'l*, pg. 1178
Kay, Dwight, Dir.-Admin. Services--Cassens Transport Company, Edwardsville, IL; *U.S. Private*, pg. 219
Kay, Sanford, V.P.-Human Resources & Sec.--Standard Motor Products Inc., Long Island City, NY; *U.S. Public*, pg. 1503
Kaye, Aimee, Sr. V.P.-Human Resources--Madison Square Garden Corporation, New York, NY; *U.S. Public*, pg. 288
Kaye, Alan, Sr. V.P.-H.R. & Admin.--Mattel, Inc., El Segundo, CA; *U.S. Public*, pg. 1057
Keal, Gary, Dir.-Human Resources--Dixieland Food Stores Inc., Geneva, AL; *U.S. Private*, pg. 337
Keane, Joan, Dir.-Personnel--Unicorp American Corporation, New York, NY; *Int'l*, pg. 1433
Kearns, Richard P., Vice Chm.-Partnership Affairs & Human Resources--Price Waterhouse L.L.P. - U.S., New York, NY; *U.S. Private*, pg. 883
Keat, Starr, Dir.-H.R.--UGI Corporation, King of Prussia, PA; *U.S. Public*, pg. 1653
Keates, Barry, Grp. Personnel Advisor--Smith & Nephew PLC, London, United Kingdom; *Int'l*, pg. 1263
Keating, Edah, Sec.--Newpark Resources, Inc., Metairie, LA; *U.S. Public*, pg. 1179
Keating, Michael, Dir.-Human Resources--Hanson North America, Woodbridge, NJ; *Int'l*, pg. 593
Keaton, Daniel C., V.P.-H.R.--WHX Corporation, New York, NY; *U.S. Public*, pg. 1726
Keats, Jeanne A., V.P.-H.R.--Churchill Downs, Inc., Louisville, KY; *U.S. Public*, pg. 356
Keebler, Jack, Mgr.-H.R.--Moog Incorporated, East Aurora, NY; *U.S. Public*, pg. 1127
Keefe, Daniel M., V.P.-H.R.--Fifth Third Bancorp, Cincinnati, OH; *U.S. Public*, pg. 621
Keefer, Francine P., Supvr.-Personnel--AGR International, Inc., Butler, PA; *U.S. Private*, pg. 5
Keegan, Brendan M., Sr. V.P.-Human Resources--Marriott International, Inc., Washington, DC; *U.S. Public*, pg. 1047
Keegan, Fran, Dir.-Personnel--Electroglas, Inc., Santa Clara, CA; *U.S. Public*, pg. 727
Keegan, Wayne, V.P.-Personnel--Durex Consumer Products, Norcross, GA; *Int'l*, pg. 815
Keegan, Wayne, V.P.-H.R.--Vanstar Corporation, Pleasanton, CA; *U.S. Public*, pg. 1708
Keenan, John F., V.P.-Human Resource--Falconbridge Limited, Toronto, Canada; *Int'l*, pg. 433
Keenan, Julie, Mgr.-H.R.--Dann Dee Display Fixtures, Niles, IL; *U.S. Private*, pg. 310
Keenan, Mike, Personnel--Radio Direct Response, Broomall, PA; *U.S. Private*, pg. 906
Keenoy, Nancy, Dir.-H.R.--Arizona Cardinals, Phoenix, AZ; *U.S. Private*, pg. 81
Keever, F.J., Mgr.-H.R.--Plastic Packaging Company, Muncie, IN; *U.S. Public*, pg. 57
Kehl, Kim, V.P.-Fin. & Controller--Electro Brand, Inc., Chicago, IL; *U.S. Private*, pg. 368
Keil, Beverly, V.P.-Human Resources--The Washington Post Company, Washington, DC; *U.S. Public*, pg. 1742
Keinberger, Joe, Dir.-Human Resources--Winthrop-Atkins Co., Inc., Middleboro, MA; *U.S. Private*, pg. 1183
Keith, Pamela J., Mgr.-H.R. & Insurance--The Converse Professional Group, Inc., Monrovia, CA; *U.S. Private*, pg. 271
Kelleher, Lawrence J., V.P.-H.R.--FPL Group, Inc., North Palm Beach, FL; *U.S. Public*, pg. 608
Kelleher, Robert X., Sr. V.P.-Human Resources--Long Island Lighting Company, Hicksville, NY; *U.S. Public*, pg. 1013
Keller, Craig, V.P.-Human Resources--American Classic Voyagers Company, New Orleans, LA; *U.S. Private*, pg. 380
Keller, Debbie, Mgr.-Personnel--Sommer Metalcraft Corporation, Crawfordsville, IN; *U.S. Private*, pg. 1013
Keller, George, V.P.-H.R.--Wayne Dalton Corporation, Mount Hope, OH; *U.S. Private*, pg. 1155
Keller, Joseph J., Jr., Sr. V.P.-Admin. & Opers.--PharmHouse, Inc., New York, NY; *U.S. Public*, pg. 1286
Keller, Linda, Dir.-H.R.--WGN-TV, Chicago, IL; *U.S. Public*, pg. 1636
Keller, Robert E., Dir.-Exec. Staffing--General Dynamics Corporation, Falls Church, VA; *U.S. Public*, pg. 708
Kelley, Dee, Dir.-Human Resources--Patrick Industries Inc., Elkhart, IN; *U.S. Public*, pg. 1264
Kelley, Dwight, Dir.-Personnel--Worthington Industries, Inc., Columbus, OH; *U.S. Public*, pg. 1780
Kelley, James J., Grp. Exec. V.P.-Mngmt. Resources Grp. & Dir.-Human Resources--Crestar Financial Corporation, Richmond, VA; *U.S. Public*, pg. 458
Kelley, James J., Grp. Exec. V.P. & Dir.-Human Resources--Crestar Bank, Richmond, VA; *U.S. Public*, pg. 458
Kelley, Leslie, Exec. Dir.-H.R.--National Cattlemen's Beef Association, Chicago, IL; *U.S. Private*, pg. 780
Kelley, William G., V.P.-H.R.--Florida Progress Corporation, Saint Petersburg, FL; *U.S. Public*, pg. 655
Kelley, William G., V.P.-H.R.--Florida Power Corporation, Saint Petersburg, FL; *U.S. Public*, pg. 655
Kellogg, Fred, Dir.-Personnel--Acorn Engineering Company, City of Industry, CA; *U.S. Private*, pg. 14
Kellogg, Richard L., V.P.-Employee Rels.--Coors Brewing Company, Golden, CO; *U.S. Public*, pg. 445
Kelly, C.T., V.P.-Human Resources--Emerson Electric Co., Saint Louis, MO; *U.S. Public*, pg. 572
Kelly, Colin P., Sr. V.P.-Human Resources--Household International, Inc., Prospect Heights, IL; *U.S. Public*, pg. 842
Kelly, Dan M., V.P.-H.R.--Gilbane Building Company, Providence, RI; *U.S. Private*, pg. 452
Kelly, G., Mgr.-Personnel--Iveco-Ford Truck Ltd., Watford, United Kingdom; *Int'l*, pg. 484
Kelly, Helen, Dir.-Personnel--Sunniland Corporation, Sanford, FL; *U.S. Private*, pg. 1053
Kelly, Henry, V.P.-Human Resources--U-Haul International, Inc., Phoenix, AZ; *U.S. Private*, pg. 49
Kelly, Janice, Dir.-H.R.--Heald Colleges, San Francisco, CA; *U.S. Private*, pg. 514
Kelly, JoAnn, Dir.-H.R.--Foxworth-Galbraith Lumber Co., Dallas, TX; *U.S. Private*, pg. 423
Kelly, Joe, Dir.-H.R.--Guideposts Associates, Inc., Carmel, NY; *U.S. Private*, pg. 487
Kelly, John H., Sr. V.P.-H.R.--Atlantic Richfield Company, Los Angeles, CA; *U.S. Public*, pg. 144
Kelly, Kathleen, Mgr.-Human Resources & Personnel Admin.--Rapid Mounting & Finishing Co., Chicago, IL; *U.S. Private*, pg. 910
Kelly, M. Lyn, Mgr.-Personnel--La Victoria Foods, Inc., City of Industry, CA; *U.S. Private*, pg. 641
Kelly, R.J., Mgr.-Human Resources--LaSalle Steel Company, Hammond, IN; *U.S. Public*, pg. 1181
Kelly, Thomas J., Dir.-Human Resources--ABT Building Products Corporation, Neenah, WI; *Int'l*, pg. 20
Kelm, S.E., Dir.-Indus. Rels.--Burgess-Norton Mfg. Co., Geneva, IL; *U.S. Private*, pg. 68
Kelsay, Ron, Dir.-H.R.--Keith Smith Company, Hot Springs National Park, AR; *U.S. Private*, pg. 1008
Kelso, Jennifer, Mgr.-Employee Rels. & Devel.--Cognos Inc., Ottawa, Canada; *Int'l*, pg. 305
Kemp, Ruth J., V.P.-Human Resources--Harlequin Enterprises Ltd., Don Mills, Canada; *Int'l*, pg. 1402
Kemp, William B., V.P.-H.R.--ChemFirst Inc., Jackson, MS; *U.S. Public*, pg. 344
Kenan, H.D., V.P.-Human Resources--Kayser-Roth Corporation, Inc., Greensboro, NC; *Int'l*, pg. 576
Kennedy, Dave, V.P.-Human Resources--New England Electric System, Westborough, MA; *U.S. Public*, pg. 1171
Kennedy, Helen T., V.P.-Personnel--Torco Oil Co., Chicago, IL; *U.S. Private*, pg. 1092
Kennedy, James F., Mgr.-Personnel--Kennedy Manufacturing Company, Van Wert, OH; *U.S. Private*, pg. 614
Kennedy, Pam, Dir.-Personnel--Kern's Bakeries, Incorporated, Knoxville, TN; *U.S. Public*, pg. 547
Kennedy, Richard, V.P.-H.R.--Soft Sheen Products, Inc., Chicago, IL; *U.S. Private*, pg. 1012
Kennedy, Wayne, V.P.-Human Resources--York International Corporation, York, PA; *U.S. Public*, pg. 1789
Kennedy, Wayne J., V.P.-Human Resources--York International Corporation, York, PA; *U.S. Public*, pg. 1788
Kenney, Mary J., V.P.-Human Resources--Converse Inc., North Reading, MA; *U.S. Public*, pg. 441
Kennon, Mary, Dir.-Customer Care & H.R.--Tel-Save Holdings, Inc., New Hope, PA; *U.S. Public*, pg. 1568
Kenny, Philip, V.P.-H.R.--Coca-Cola Bottling Co. Consolidated, Charlotte, NC; *U.S. Public*, pg. 391
Kensel, Elizabeth, Mgr.-Human Resources--Stone & Webster Engineering & Constructors Corp., Boston, MA; *U.S. Public*, pg. 1519
Keogh, Steve M., Mgr.-Human Resources--New Business Development, San Francisco, CA; *Int'l*, pg. 224
Kephart, Kelly G., V.P.-Fin. & Admin.--Marketing Communications, Lenexa, KS; *U.S. Public*, pg. 794
Kerin, Meg, Asst.-H.R.--Robert F. Driver Co., Inc., San Diego, CA; *U.S. Private*, pg. 343
Kerlik, Andrew J., V.P.-Personnel & Safety--Arnold Industries, Inc., Lebanon, PA; *U.S. Public*, pg. 132
Kern, Jane, Mgr.-Personnel--Reading Tube Corp., Reading, PA; *U.S. Private*, pg. 202
Kerns, Jo, Dir.-Human Resources--Toledo Blade Co., Toledo, OH; *U.S. Private*, pg. 147
Kerns, Steve, V.P.-Human Resources--Dayco Products Inc., Miamisburg, OH; *U.S. Public*, pg. 1045
Kerr, Aven A., Sr. V.P.-H.R.--NovaCare Inc., King of Prussia, PA; *U.S. Public*, pg. 1203
Kerr, Barbara, Dir.-Personnel--Chiron Corporation, Emeryville, CA; *U.S. Public*, pg. 349
Kerr, D., Mgr.-Human Resources--Australian Oil & Gas Corporation Limited, Sydney, Australia; *Int'l*, pg. 101
Kerr, Mary Ann, Dir.-Mktg.--US SerVis, West Orange, NJ; *U.S. Public*, pg. 1687
Kerry, Dale H., V.P.-Human Resources--Jannock Limited, Toronto, Canada; *Int'l*, pg. 698
Kersey, Cindy, V.P.-H.R.--Hull Corporation, Hatboro, PA; *U.S. Private*, pg. 547
Kerwin, Diane, Mgr.-H.R.--Rapid Power Technologies, Inc., Brookfield, CT; *U.S. Private*, pg. 910
Kessinger, Malcolm A., V.P.-H.R.--Union Carbide Corporation, Danbury, CT; *U.S. Public*, pg. 1666
Kessler, Eugene D., Mgr.-Human Resources--Phillips-Van Heusen Corporation, New York, NY; *U.S. Public*, pg. 1291
Kessler, Roberta R., Dir.-H.R.--Air Conditioning Co., Inc., Glendale, CA; *U.S. Private*, pg. 28
Ketron, David, Mgr.-Personnel--Hoffco/Comet Industries, Inc., Richmond, IN; *U.S. Private*, pg. 532
Kettler, William H., Jr., V.P.-H.R. & Facility Svcs.--Kaneb Services, Inc., Richardson, TX; *U.S. Public*, pg. 942
Keyser, John, V.P.-Customer Support Services--Memorex Telex Corp., Irving, TX; *Int'l*, pg. 857
Khan, Ismael G., Jr., V.P.-Human Resources--Philippine Airlines, Inc., Manila, Philippines; *Int'l*, pg. 1050
Khisty, C.H., Dir.-Personnel--Bharat Coking Coal Limited, Dhanbad, India; *Int'l*, pg. 298
Khumalo, B.A., Exec. Dir.-Human Resources--Eskom, Sandton, South Africa; *Int'l*, pg. 459
Kibbey, Jane, Dir.-Personnel--Prudential Corporation PLC, London, United Kingdom; *Int'l*, pg. 1073
Kidd, Al, Dir.-Human Resources--Canandaigua Wine Company, Inc., Canandaigua, NY; *U.S. Public*, pg. 300
Kidd, Marvin R., Dir.-H.R.--Caddock Electronics, Inc., Riverside, CA; *U.S. Private*, pg. 198
Kietzmann, Ellen, V.P.-H.R.--Automatic Equipment Mfg. Co., Pender, NE; *U.S. Private*, pg. 101
Kika, Hiroshi, Sr. Mgr.-Human Resources--Nissin Foods (U.S.A.) Co. Ltd., Gardena, CA; *Int'l*, pg. 949
Kilby, Jack, Dir.-H.R.--Innovex, Inc., Hopkins, MN; *U.S. Public*, pg. 880
Kiley, Eileen M., V.P.-Human Resources & Admin.--Spaulding & Slye, Boston, MA; *U.S. Private*, pg. 1021
Kiley, Kristina, Dir.-Human Resources--Gerber Products Company, Fremont, MI; *Int'l*, pg. 973
Kill, Stephen, V.P.-Human Resources--The Minster Machine Company, Minster, OH; *U.S. Private*, pg. 751
Killingback, Moira, Mgr.-Personnel--Saft Nife Ltd., Hampton, United Kingdom; *Int'l*, pg. 55
Kilpatrick, Patricia, Mgr.-Indus. Rels.--Met-Coil Systems Corp., Cedar Rapids, IA; *U.S. Public*, pg. 1099
Kilton, Wayne N., V.P.-Personnel--Central Mutual Insurance Co., Van Wert, OH; *U.S. Private*, pg. 223
Kim, Dong Yong, Exec. V.P. & Dir.-Personnel--Cho Hung Bank, Seoul, Korea; *Int'l*, pg. 287
Kim, Eun-Sik, Dir.-Human Resources--Grand Hyatt Seoul, Seoul, Korea; *U.S. Private*, pg. 551
Kim, Man S., Chief Fin. Officer & Mng. Dir.--Crown Confectionery Co., Ltd., Seoul, Korea; *Int'l*, pg. 348
Kimball, James, Dir.-H.R.--Geo-Centers, Inc., Newton, MA; *U.S. Private*, pg. 447
Kimball, Richard T., Dir.-Personnel--Exide Corporation, Reading, PA; *U.S. Public*, pg. 600
Kimbro, Kenneth J., V.P.-Human Resources--IBP, Inc., Dakota City, NE; *U.S. Public*, pg. 852
Kimmet, Michelle, Dir.-Human Resources--Crescent Manufacturing Company, Fremont, OH; *U.S. Private*, pg. 289
Kimpel, Sherrell, Mgr.-H.R.--The Ohio Art Company, Inc., Bryan, OH; *U.S. Public*, pg. 1214
Kimura, Kanji, Mng. Dir.--All Nippon Airways Co. Ltd., Tokyo, Japan; *Int'l*, pg. 57
Kincaid, Bob, Mgr.-H.R.--Delta Industries, East Granby, CT; *U.S. Private*, pg. 322
Kind, Josef, Dir.-Personnel Policy--Daimler-Benz Aerospace AG, Munich, Germany; *Int'l*, pg. 367
Kinder, Susan D., Sr. V.P.-Human Resources--American Express Financial Advisor, Minneapolis, MN; *U.S. Public*, pg. 73
King, D.A., Dir.-Personnel--Wilbur Smith Associates, Columbia, SC; *U.S. Private*, pg. 1009
King, Don, Dir.-Human Resources--Producers Rice Mill Inc., Stuttgart, AR; *U.S. Private*, pg. 888
King, Richard, Dir.-H.R.--Concord Litho Co., Inc., Concord, NH; *U.S. Private*, pg. 261
King, Roger, Sr. V.P.-Human Resources--Frito-Lay Company, Plano, TX; *U.S. Public*, pg. 1277
King, Sheila, Mgr.-Personnel--MCRB Service Bureau, Inc., Chatsworth, CA; *U.S. Private*, pg. 686
King, Stephen, Dir.-H.R.--American Bible Society, New York, NY; *U.S. Private*, pg. 51
Kingman, Daniel, V.P.-Human Resources--MDL Information Systems, Inc., San Leandro, CA; *Int'l*, pg. 1100
Kinney, Bernie, V.P.-H.R. Laser Grp.--Coherent, Inc., Santa Clara, CA; *U.S. Public*, pg. 395
Kinney, Paul, Mgr.-Human Resources--Copley Pharmaceuticals, Inc., Canton, MA; *U.S. Public*, pg. 446
Kinoshita, Kenichi, Dir.--Sumikin Bussan Corporation, Osaka, Japan; *Int'l*, pg. 1308
Kinsella, Geraldine, V.P.-Human Resources--Borg Warner Automotive, Inc., Chicago, IL; *U.S. Public*, pg. 245
Kinsey, Susan, V.P.-Human Resources--Atlantic Gulf Communities Corporation, Miami, FL; *U.S. Public*, pg. 144
Kirby, John W., V.P.-H.R.--Analogic Corporation, Peabody, MA; *U.S. Public*, pg. 109

Kirk, Karen, V.P.--Prime Bancshares Inc., Houston, TX; *U.S. Public*, pg. 1326
Kirk, Melanie, Mgr.-Human Resources--Urban Outfitters, Inc., Philadelphia, PA; *U.S. Public*, pg. 1700
Kirk, Tom, Dir.-H.R. & Adv.--Crestbrook Forest Industries Ltd., Cranbrook, Canada; *Int'l*, pg. 348
Kirkman, Carol, V.P. & Asst. Gen. Counsel--Brinker International, Inc., Dallas, TX; *U.S. Public*, pg. 253
Kirkman, Mike, Mgr.-Human Resources--BICC plc, London, United Kingdom; *Int'l*, pg. 120
Kirley, James, V.P.-Human Resources & Admin. Services--Southern Company Services, Inc., Atlanta, GA; *U.S. Public*, pg. 1490
Kiryluk, Carol, Sr. V.P.-H.R.--Tupperware Corporation, Orlando, FL; *U.S. Public*, pg. 1644
Kisela, James F., V.P.-H.R.--The Vanguard Group, Inc., Valley Forge, PA; *U.S. Private*, pg. 1133
Kiskis, Ronald, V.P.-Human Resources--Chevron Corporation, San Francisco, CA; *U.S. Public*, pg. 347
Kist, E.K.M., V.P.-Human Resources--Koninklijke BolsWessanen nv, Amstelveen, Netherlands; *Int'l*, pg. 750
Kitagawa, Katsuya, Gen. Mgr.--Okuma Corporation, Niwa, Japan; *Int'l*, pg. 1000
Kitchell, Pamela, Dir.-H.R. & Mgr.-Pension Admin.--Carrington Laboratories, Inc., Irving, TX; *U.S. Public*, pg. 309
Kitchens, Marlys, Human Resources Mgr.--Grizzard, Atlanta, GA; *U.S. Private*, pg. 482
Kitchens, Marlys, Human Resources Mgr.--TABS Direct (Operating Div.), Stafford, TX; *U.S. Private*, pg. 482
Kittaka, Jacqueline Y., Sr. V.P.-H.R.--FirstFed Financial Corp., Santa Monica, CA; *U.S. Public*, pg. 645
Kives, Sharon, Dir.-Human Resources--LWI Holdings Inc., Cleveland, OH; *U.S. Public*, pg. 782
Kjellman, Rune, Sr. V.P.-Personnel--Skanska AB, Danderyd, Sweden; *Int'l*, pg. 1260
Klabunde, Hyla, Mgr.--Warner Press, Inc., Anderson, IN; *U.S. Private*, pg. 1150
Klammert, Mike, Dir.-Personnel--Maynard Steel Casting Company, Milwaukee, WI; *U.S. Private*, pg. 718
Klapper, Steve, Mgr.-Personnel--American TV & Appliance of Madison, Inc., Madison, WI; *U.S. Private*, pg. 64
Klar, Henry, Sr. V.P.-Personnel--Riverside Manufacturing Co., Moultrie, GA; *U.S. Private*, pg. 934
Klecha, Maureen, Dir.-Human Resources--Philips Electronics Instruments Company, Mahwah, NJ; *Int'l*, pg. 1054
Kleckner, Delmar B., V.P.-Human Resources--Mauna Loa Macadamia Nut Corporation, Hilo, HI; *U.S. Private*, pg. 190
Klegner, Christie, Dir.-Human Resources--Four Media Companies, Burbank, CA; *U.S. Private*, pg. 422
Kleiman, David, Dir.-H.R.--La-Co Industries Markal Company, Elk Grove Village, IL; *U.S. Private*, pg. 640
Klein, Greg, V.P.-Human Resources--Harding Lawson Associates Group, Inc., Novato, CA; *U.S. Public*, pg. 785
Klein, J., Dir.-Personnel--Kawasaki Motors Corp., U.S.A., Irvine, CA; *Int'l*, pg. 725
Klein, James E., Sr. V.P.-Human Resources--Fiduciary Trust Company International, New York, NY; *U.S. Public*, pg. 621
Kleine-Weischede, Klaus, Mgr.-H.R.--Bayer AG, Leverkusen, Germany; *Int'l*, pg. 171
Kleinman, Linda, Mgr.-Personnel & Admin.--Silhouette Books, New York, NY; *Int'l*, pg. 1402
Kleman, Oscar D., Jr., V.P.-H.R.--Anderson Trucking Service Inc., Saint Cloud, MN; *U.S. Private*, pg. 72
Kleypas, Larry, Dir.-Personnel--Weiners Stores, Inc., Houston, TX; *U.S. Private*, pg. 1160
Kliche, Trudy, Human Resource Mgr.--Select Communications, L.P., New York, NY; *U.S. Private*, pg. 982
Klick, Winnie, V.P.-Employee Resources--United Power Association, Elk River, MN; *U.S. Private*, pg. 1123
Kline, Ed, Mgr.-Personnel--Schlosser Forge Company, Rancho Cucamonga, CA; *U.S. Private*, pg. 970
Kline, Philip, Human Resources Officer--Royal Insurance, Charlotte, NC; *Int'l*, pg. 1130
Kline, Richard A., Mgr.-Human Resources--Glastic Corporation, Cleveland, OH; *Int'l*, pg. 740
Kling, Gen, Mgr.-Human Resources--Dunmore Corporation, Newtown, PA; *U.S. Private*, pg. 346
Kling, Judy, Mgr.-Personnel--Fujitsu Computer Products of America, Inc., San Jose, CA; *Int'l*, pg. 526
Klingelhofer, Dr., Dir.-Personnel--Linde AG, Wiesbaden, Germany; *Int'l*, pg. 810
Klinkhammer, Heinz, Dr., Head-Personnel & Legal Affairs--Deutsche Telekom AG, Bonn, Germany; *Int'l*, pg. 407
Klint, Douglas E., V.P., Gen. Counsel & Sec.--Gatefield Corporation, Fremont, CA; *U.S. Public*, pg. 703
Klippel, S., Asst. Dir.-Personnel--Deutsche Bahn, Frankfurt/Main, Germany; *Int'l*, pg. 401
Klomp, Robert, Dir.-Human Resources--Frequency Electronics, Inc., Uniondale, NY; *U.S. Public*, pg. 681
Kloosterboer, Jay, Dir.-Human Resources--AlliedSignal, Automotive Aftermarket, Rumford, RI; *U.S. Public*, pg. 51
Klouthis, W.G., V.P.-Admin.--Pioneer Plastics Corporation, Auburn, ME; *U.S. Private*, pg. 867
Kluckhohn, Larry, Mgr.-Personnel & Employee Rels.--Winnebago Industries, Inc., Forest City, IA; *U.S. Public*, pg. 1772
Kluft, Phil, Dir.-Human Resources--Knoll Pharmaceutical Company, Whippany, NJ; *Int'l*, pg. 105
Klumpp, Brian, Sr. V.P.-H.R.--Brite Voice Systems, Inc., Heathrow, FL; *U.S. Public*, pg. 257
Knapp, Bryan, Dir.-Human Resources--Lehman Brothers, Inc., New York, NY; *U.S. Public*, pg. 987
Knapp, David, Dir.-H.R.--Metropolitan Transportation Authority, New York, NY; *U.S. Private*, pg. 739
Knauss, Kelli A., Admin.-Personnel--Namco Controls Corporation, Highland Heights, OH; *U.S. Public*, pg. 482
Knebel, Bethanne, Mgr.-Human Resources--Flow International Corporation, Kent, WA; *U.S. Public*, pg. 656
Knechtel, Gerald A., V.P.-Personnel-North American Opers.--General Motors Corporation, Detroit, MI; *U.S. Public*, pg. 718
Knese, Suzan, Human Resources Dir.--DMB&B St. Louis, Saint Louis, MO; *U.S. Private*, pg. 303
Knez, Ronald, Corp. V.P.-Human Resources--National Car Rental System, Inc., Minneapolis, MN; *U.S. Public*, pg. 1379
Knight, Dawn, V.P.-H.R.--Gilbert Paper, Menasha, WI; *U.S. Public*, pg. 1074
Knight, Jeanne, Mgr.-Human Resources--The Faxon Company, Inc., Westwood, MA; *Int'l*, pg. 385
Knight, Robert B., Sr. V.P.-Admin. & Treas.--White Hen Pantry, Inc., Elmhurst, IL; *U.S. Private*, pg. 1172
Kniskern, Gary D., V.P.-Admin. & Sec.--Insteel Industries, Inc., Mount Airy, NC; *U.S. Public*, pg. 882
Knitter, Hartwig, Dr., Dir.-Personnel--Daimler-Benz Aerospace AG, Munich, Germany; *Int'l*, pg. 367
Knoernschild, Connie, Mgr.-H.R.--S.T. Research, Newington, VA; *U.S. Private*, pg. 958
Knopp, Arthur, Dir.-Human Resources--Case France S.A., Paris, France; *U.S. Public*, pg. 1579
Knorrek, Robert, Mgr.-Corp. Personnel--A.J. Gerrard and Company, Des Plaines, IL; *U.S. Private*, pg. 449
Knors, Joe, Mgr.-Personnel, Office, Credit & Systems Admin.--Master Appliance Corp., Racine, WI; *U.S. Private*, pg. 713
Knox, K.B., Grp. Personnel Control--De La Rue plc, London, United Kingdom; *Int'l*, pg. 386
Knupp, Ralph, Dir.-Human Resources, USA--Reed Elsevier plc, London, United Kingdom; *Int'l*, pg. 1093
Knutson, David T., Dir.-Personnel--Hubbard Feeds Inc., Mankato, MN; *Int'l*, pg. 1116
Knutson, Deb S., V.P.-H.R.--Pentair, Inc., Saint Paul, MN; *U.S. Public*, pg. 1273
Knutson, Jim, Dir.-H.R. & Mgr.-Risk--Rockford Acromatic Product Co., Rockford, IL; *U.S. Private*, pg. 938
Knutson, Paul, V.P.-Human Resources--Pamida Holdings Corporation, Omaha, NE; *U.S. Public*, pg. 1255
Kobori, Teruo, Mng. Dir. & Gen. Mgr.-Personnel--Mitsubishi Chemical Corporation, Tokyo, Japan; *Int'l*, pg. 870
Koci, Dennis, Sr. V.P.-Opers. Support--Hilton Hotels Div., Beverly Hills, CA; *U.S. Public*, pg. 829
Kock, H., Dir.-Personnel--N.V. Kodak S.A., Vilvoorde, Belgium; *U.S. Public*, pg. 554
Kodweis, John B., V.P.-H.R. & Admin.--Gleason Corporation, Rochester, NY; *U.S. Public*, pg. 746
Koehler, Lloyd, Dir.-Human Resources--Hackney and Sons, Inc., Washington, NC; *U.S. Private*, pg. 1097
Koenig, Brian C., Sr. V.P.-Human Resources--Scientific-Atlanta, Inc., Norcross, GA; *U.S. Public*, pg. 1443
Koep, Donna, V.P.-H.R.--Power-One, Inc., Camarillo, CA; *U.S. Private*, pg. 878
Koerner, Sydney, Dir.-Human Resources--Hovnanian Enterprises, Inc., Red Bank, NJ; *U.S. Public*, pg. 843
Koesser, Susan, Dir.-H.R.--Liquid Controls LLC, Lake Bluff, IL; *U.S. Private*, pg. 669
Koestner, Marcia, V.P.-Human Resources--CMC Kalamazoo Inc., Kalamazoo, MI; *U.S. Private*, pg. 1030
Koevoets, Peter, Dir.-H.R.--Lips United B.V., Drunen, Netherlands; *Int'l*, pg. 812
Kogutek, Susan, Dir.-Human Resources--Comptek Research, Inc., Buffalo, NY; *U.S. Public*, pg. 419
Kohl, Jennifer A., Mgr.-H.R.--Harza Engineering Co., Chicago, IL; *U.S. Private*, pg. 509
Kohlberger, Richard A., Sr. V.P.--UST Inc., Greenwich, CT; *U.S. Public*, pg. 1660
Kohsaka, Youji, Dir.-Personnel--Anritsu Corporation, Tokyo, Japan; *Int'l*, pg. 77
Koll, Traci, Dir.-H.R.--Special Devices, Incorporated, Newhall, CA; *U.S. Public*, pg. 1496
Kollenz, Wolfgang, Mgr.-Personnel--AGA Ges.m.b.H., Vienna, Austria; *Int'l*, pg. 13
Kombrinck, Edwin B., V.P.-Human Resources--LSI Industries, Inc., Cincinnati, OH; *U.S. Public*, pg. 971
Komidar, Frank, Dir.-H.R.--Uni-Marts, Inc., State College, PA; *U.S. Public*, pg. 1664
Komulainen, Marilyn, Mgr.-H.R.--Muro Pharmaceutical, Inc., Tewksbury, MA; *U.S. Private*, pg. 767
Konkel, Diane, Mgr.-H.R.--Waukesha Foundry Inc., Waukesha, WI; *U.S. Private*, pg. 1154
Konvalinka, David W., V.P.-Human Resources--Trans Canada Credit Corporation, Etobicoke, Canada; *U.S. Public*, pg. 1202
Koo, K.C., Head-Human Resources--The Hongkong and Shanghai Banking Corporation Limited (HongkongBank), Central, Hong Kong; *Int'l*, pg. 583
Koonmee, Kalayanee, Dr., V.P.-Human Resources--Nakornthon Bank Public Company Limited, Bangkok, Thailand; *Int'l*, pg. 904
Koons, Michael J., V.P.-H.R.--Hein-Werner Corporation, Waukesha, WI; *U.S. Public*, pg. 805
Koper, Chris, V.P.-H.R.--Cineplex Odeon Corporation, Toronto, Canada; *Int'l*, pg. 292
Kopp, Marvin J., Sr. V.P.-Human Resources--Hardee's Food Systems, Inc., Rocky Mount, NC; *U.S. Public*, pg. 278
Koppekin, Stephen, Sr. V.P.-Indus. Rels--Paramount Pictures Corporation, Los Angeles, CA; *U.S. Private*, pg. 776
Korda, William, V.P.-Human Resources--Ryerson Tull, Chicago, IL; *U.S. Public*, pg. 879
Kosch, Mary L., V.P.-H.R.--Andis Company, Sturtevant, WI; *U.S. Private*, pg. 73
Kosciusko, Robert A., V.P.-H.R.--Continental Circuits Corp., Phoenix, AZ; *U.S. Public*, pg. 440
Koskiniemi, Mark, V.P.-Human Resources--Buckman Laboratories Inc., Memphis, TN; *U.S. Private*, pg. 180
Kostenbauer, John, Mgr.-Human Resources--Atlas Cylinder, Eugene, OR; *U.S. Public*, pg. 1261
Kosterman, Gayle P., Sr. V.P.-Worldwide H.R.--S.C. Johnson & Son, Inc., Racine, WI; *U.S. Private*, pg. 592
Kotake, Akio, Exec. Dir.-Personnel & Labor Rels.--Japan Tobacco Inc., Tokyo, Japan; *Int'l*, pg. 703
Kotilainen, Pii, V.P.-Human Resources--Oy Nokia Ab/Nokia Group, Helsinki, Finland; *Int'l*, pg. 951
Kou, C.Y., Mgr.-Personnel--China Steel Chemical Corp., Kao-hsiung, Taiwan; *Int'l*, pg. 286
Kouenhoven, George, Dir.-H.R./Central Europe--S.A. Cimenteries CBR, Brussels, Belgium; *Int'l*, pg. 605
Kounelias, Christina, Sr. V.P.-Publicity & Promotions--New Line Cinema Corporation, New York, NY; *U.S. Public*, pg. 1614
Kovacs, Geza, Dr., Dir.-H.R.--Malev Hungarian Airlines, Plc., Budapest, Hungary; *Int'l*, pg. 833
Kovar, Nancy, Dir.-Personnel--Asoma Corporation, White Plains, NY; *U.S. Private*, pg. 89
Kozeny, JoAnn, V.P.-Human Resources--Omaha Steaks, Omaha, NE; *U.S. Private*, pg. 815
Kraft, Herb, Dir.-Personnel--Oxford Industries, Inc., Atlanta, GA; *U.S. Public*, pg. 1239
Kramer, Debbie, Mgr.-H.R.--Grindmaster Corporation, Louisville, KY; *U.S. Private*, pg. 482
Kramer, Douglas, Sr. V.P.-Human Resources--The Guardian Life Insurance Company of America, New York, NY; *U.S. Private*, pg. 486
Kramer, Louis, Dir.-Human Resources & Admin.--Ajinomoto U.S.A., Inc., Teaneck, NJ; *Int'l*, pg. 40
Kramer, Maria, Dir.-Human Resources--Presidential Life Corporation, Nyack, NY; *U.S. Public*, pg. 1323
Kramer, Michael, Dir.-Publicity--New Line Cinema Corporation, New York, NY; *U.S. Public*, pg. 1614
Kramer, Nancy, Mgr.-H.R.--Chemoil, San Francisco, CA; *U.S. Private*, pg. 233
Kramer, Richard, V.P.--Trans-Lux Corporation, Norwalk, CT; *U.S. Public*, pg. 1628
Kramer, Robert O., V.P.-H.R.--Ford Motor Company, Dearborn, MI; *U.S. Public*, pg. 661
Krammer, Kenneth, V.P.-Personnel--Nickerson Lumber Company, Orleans, MA; *U.S. Private*, pg. 798
Kramolc, Mary, Dir.-Fin. & Human Resources--Western Broadcast Sales Ltd., Toronto, Canada; *Int'l*, pg. 1482
Krannich, Beverley T., V.P.-H.R. & Sec.--Sonat Inc., Birmingham, AL; *U.S. Public*, pg. 1484
Krannich, Beverley T., V.P.-Human Resources--Southern Natural Gas Company, Birmingham, AL; *U.S. Public*, pg. 1485
Krannich, Beverly T., V.P.-Human Resources--Sonat Exploration Company, Houston, TX; *U.S. Public*, pg. 1485
Kraudy, Ken, Dir.-Human Resources--Zions Co-operative Mercantile Institution, Salt Lake City, UT; *U.S. Public*, pg. 1793
Kraun, Michele, Dir.-Human Resources--Continental Web Press, Inc., Itasca, IL; *U.S. Private*, pg. 269
Kraunellis, Al, Dir.-Personnel--Malden Mills Industries, Inc., Lawrence, MA; *U.S. Private*, pg. 698
Kraus, Norma J., V.P.-Human Resources & Investor Rels.--Volt Information Sciences, Inc., New York, NY; *U.S. Public*, pg. 1724
Krause-Stetson, Diane, V.P.-H.R.--Duchossois Industries, Inc., Elmhurst, IL; *U.S. Private*, pg. 344
Krause, Don, Mgr.-Data Processing--Ajay Leisure Products, Inc., Delavan, WI; *U.S. Public*, pg. 34
Kravitz, Irving, Asst. V.P.-Human Resources--The Edward J. DeBartolo Corporation, Youngstown, OH; *U.S. Private*, pg. 319
Krejca, Jack E., Chief Fin. Officer, Treas. & Controller--Curran Group, Inc., Crystal Lake, IL; *U.S. Private*, pg. 297
Krieger, Richard, V.P.-Human Resources--Lafarge Materiaux de Specialites, Montrouge, France; *Int'l*, pg. 789
Krieps, Neil, Dir.-H.R.--Geneva Steel, Vineyard, UT; *U.S. Public*, pg. 729
Kriever, Shelly, Dir.-Personnel--Cortland Line Co., Inc., Cortland, NY; *U.S. Private*, pg. 277
Krippel, Joseph W., V.P.-Human Resources--Menasco Aerosystems Division, Euless, TX; *U.S. Public*, pg. 402
Krische, Marilyn, Gen. Mgr.--Hollymatic Corporation, Countryside, IL; *U.S. Private*, pg. 535
Krivacek, Steven M., V.P.-Human Resources--Gardner Denver Machinery Inc., Quincy, IL; *U.S. Public*, pg. 703
Krizman, Michael, Dir.-Human Resources--Union Special Corp., Huntley, IL; *Int'l*, pg. 716
Krocak, W.M., V.P.-Human Resources--Imperial Holly Corporation, Sugar Land, TX; *U.S. Public*, pg. 872
Kroebel, Harold, Dir.-H.R.--Dan's Supreme Super Markets Inc., Hempstead, NY; *U.S. Private*, pg. 310
Kroeber, C. Kent, Sr. V.P.-Human Resources--The Interpublic Group of Companies, Inc., New York, NY; *U.S. Public*, pg. 908
Kroeger, Thomas, Exec. V.P.-H.R.--Office Depot Inc., Delray Beach, FL; *U.S. Public*, pg. 1212
Krogman, Sheila, Mgr.-H.R.--Woodcraft Industries, Inc., Saint Cloud, MN; *U.S. Private*, pg. 1187
Kroh, James E., V.P.-H.R.--Frontier Insurance Group, Inc., Rock Hill, NY; *U.S. Public*, pg. 684
Kroppel, Gunther, Dir.-Personnel & Legal Affairs--VP-Schickedanz AG, Nuremberg, Germany; *U.S. Public*, pg. 1333
Krovic, John E., V.P.-Human Resources & Safety--Kenan Transport Company, Chapel Hill, NC; *U.S. Public*, pg. 949
Krueger, Donna, Mgr.-H.R.--Vinyl Plastics Incorporated, Sheboygan, WI; *U.S. Private*, pg. 1141
Krueger, Lyn, Mgr.-Human Resources--Continental Mortgage and Equity Trust, Dallas, TX; *U.S. Public*, pg. 441
Kruell, Roy, Dir.-H.R.--Tony Downs Foods Company, Saint James, MN; *U.S. Private*, pg. 342
Kruger, Dan, Mgr.-Div. Human Resources--Intermec Technologies Corporation, Everett, WA; *U.S. Public*, pg. 1699
Kruttek, K., Dir.-Human Resources--Andres Wines Ltd., Winona, Canada; *Int'l*, pg. 75
Kubalic, J., Mgr.-Personnel--Cochrane, Inc., King of Prussia, PA; *U.S. Public*, pg. 456

Kubas, David S., Dir.-Personnel--Hynes Industries Inc., Youngstown, OH; *U.S. Private*, pg. 552

Kuchenburg, Leigh Ann, Mgr.-Human Resources--Hubert Company, Harrison, OH; *U.S. Private*, pg. 545

Kuchof, Rennie, Mgr.-Human Resources--Weibel Winery, Lodi, CA; *U.S. Private*, pg. 1159

Kuck, Tim, V.P.-Quality & H.R.--Regal Marine Industries Inc., Orlando, FL; *U.S. Private*, pg. 917

Kuebler, Karl-Heinz, Mgr.-Personnel--Hermann Pfauter GmbH & Co., Ludwigsburg, Germany; *Int'l*, pg. 617

Kuehne, Carol, Mgr.-Admin.--Calton, Inc., Manalapan, NJ; *U.S. Public*, pg. 296

Kuhn, Roberta, Dir.-H.R.--Packard BioScience Company, Meriden, CT; *U.S. Private*, pg. 833

Kunkle, Tom, Mgr.-Indus. Rels.--Dexter Company, Fairfield, IA; *U.S. Private*, pg. 329

Kunkomoeller, Paul, Mgr.-H.R.--Gaymar Industries, Inc., Orchard Park, NY; *U.S. Private*, pg. 442

Kuntz, Carla, Mgr.-Human Resources--Indiana Glass Company, Cincinnati, OH; *U.S. Public*, pg. 976

Kuntz, Thorton, V.P.-H.R.--Matria Healthcare, Inc., Marietta, GA; *U.S. Public*, pg. 1057

Kupps, Angela, V.P.-Human Resources--Alliance Semiconductor Corp., San Jose, CA; *U.S. Public*, pg. 47

Kupris, Eleanor M., V.P.-Admin. & Sec.--Bowles Fluidics Corporation, Columbia, MD; *U.S. Public*, pg. 248

Kuraitis, Vito, V.P.-H.R.--Lee Enterprises, Incorporated, Davenport, IA; *U.S. Public*, pg. 983

Kurihara, Shogo, Gen. Mgr.--Chiyoda Mutual Life Insurance Company, Tokyo, Japan; *Int'l*, pg. 286

Kurten, George W., Sec. & Dir.-H.R.--Walsworth Publishing Company, Inc., Marceline, MO; *U.S. Private*, pg. 1148

Kurtz, Michael J., V.P.-Human Resources--Micro Warehouse, Inc., Norwalk, CT; *U.S. Public*, pg. 1104

Kutcha, William, V.P.-Organizational Devel.--Paychex, Inc., Rochester, NY; *U.S. Public*, pg. 1267

Kutty, T. Madhavan, Dir.-H.R.--Air India, Mumbai, India; *Int'l*, *pg. 37*

Kuzniarek, Jim, Human Resources--Varco BJ Oil Tools, Houston, TX; *U.S. Public*, pg. 1709

Kuzsma, Dick, Mgr.-Human Resources--Amano Cincinnati, Inc., Roseland, NJ; *Int'l*, pg. 70

Kyd, Margot A., V.P.-Human Resources--Enova Corp, San Diego, CA; *U.S. Public*, pg. 583

Kyd, Margot A., V.P.-Human Resources--San Diego Gas & Electric Company, San Diego, CA; *U.S. Public*, pg. 584

Kyle, Wayne, Exec. V.P.-Human Resources--Waterhouse Investor Services, New York, NY; *Int'l*, pg. 1401

La Malfa, Anthony, Mgr.-Corp. Personnel--J.J. Keller & Associates, Inc., Neenah, WI; *U.S. Private*, pg. 612

Labas, Sara, Dir.-Corp. Commun.--Brunschwig & Fils, Inc., White Plains, NY; *U.S. Private*, pg. 176

LaBenne, Jim, Dir.-H.R.--Chemi-Trol Chemical Co., Gibsonburg, OH; *U.S. Public*, pg. 345

Laberee, S., Dir.-Human Resources--Labatt Breweries British Columbia, New Westminster, Canada; *Int'l*, pg. 679

Labraca, Lehilany, Mgr.-H.R.--Alexander Doll Company, Inc., New York, NY; *U.S. Private*, pg. 33

Labrecque, M., Dir.-Human Resources--La Brasserie Labatt Limitee, La Salle, Canada; *Int'l*, pg. 679

Labrom, R., Asst. V.P.-H.R.--Canadian Pacific Limited, Calgary, Canada; *Int'l*, pg. 258

Lackey, Charles, V.P.-H.R.--The Sportsman's Guide, Inc., Saint Paul, MN; *U.S. Public*, pg. 1499

Lacross, Lisa, Dir.-H.R. & Pub. Rels.--Nor-Cal Beverage Co., Inc., West Sacramento, CA; *U.S. Private*, pg. 801

Ladota, J., Mgr.-H.R.--National Restaurant Management, Inc., New York, NY; *U.S. Private*, pg. 786

Ladzinski, Greg, Dir.-Personnel & Indus. Rels.--Macwhyte Co., Kenosha, WI; *U.S. Private*, pg. 68

Ladzinski, Terri, Dir.-Personnel--Golden Books Publishing, New York, NY; *U.S. Public*, pg. 749

LaFauci, Peter, Chief Fin. Officer--Jay Advertising, Inc., Rochester, NY; *U.S. Private*, pg. 583

Lafevre, J., V.P.-Human Resources-Alcon Building Prods.--The Stolle Corporation, Sidney, OH; *U.S. Public*, pg. 61

Laflin, Jack, V.P.-H.R.--Kulicke & Soffa Industries, Inc., Willow Grove, PA; *U.S. Public*, pg. 968

Lagergren, Bo, Sr. V.P.-H.R.--Trygg-Hansa, Stockholm, Sweden; *Int'l*, pg. 1425

Lagna, Jane, Mgr.-Personnel--Campbell Distillers Limited, Brentford, United Kingdom; *Int'l*, pg. 567

Lagno, Fred, Mgr.-H.R.--Friendly Holidays Inc., Lake Success, NY; *U.S. Private*, pg. 428

Laidlaw, Richard, Mgr.-Human Rels.--Active Tool & Manufacturing Co., Inc., Roseville, MI; *U.S. Private*, pg. 16

Lair, Jeane, Mgr.-Personnel--Jones Blair Company, Dallas, TX; *U.S. Private*, pg. 596

Laird, Keith, Dir.-H.R.--The Times Publishing Co., Saint Petersburg, FL; *U.S. Private*, pg. 1087

Lale, Annette, Dir.-Personnel--Scholl U.S.A., Memphis, TN; *U.S. Public*, pg. 1438

Lalonde-Bard, Jeanette, V.P.-Human Resources--BCE Mobile Communications Inc., Saint-Laurent, Canada; *Int'l*, pg. 115

Lalonde-Bard, Jeannette, V.P.-Human Resources--CFCF Inc., Montreal, Canada; *Int'l*, pg. 240

Lam, Maisie, V.P.-Personnel--First Pacific Company Limited, Hong Kong, Hong Kong; *Int'l*, pg. 487

LaMarre, Robert, Mgr.-Personnel--Nichols-Homeshield, Davenport, IA; *U.S. Public*, pg. 1350

LaMaster, Larry D., V.P.-Human Resources--Union Insurance Company, Lincoln, NE; *U.S. Public*, pg. 216

Lamb, Betsy, V.P.-H.R.--Komag, Incorporated, San Jose, CA; *U.S. Public*, pg. 966

Lamb, Russell W., V.P.-Human Resources--Utilities Construction Co., Inc. Of South Carolina, Charleston, SC; *U.S. Private*, pg. 1130

Lambe, James F., Sr. V.P.-Human Resources--Nalco Chemical Company, Naperville, IL; *U.S. Public*, pg. 1150

Lambert, Lou Ann, Mgr.-H.R.--The Flood Company, Hudson, OH; *U.S. Private*, pg. 414

Lambillotte, Dana, Mgr.-Personnel--Brush Wellman Inc., Cleveland, OH; *U.S. Public*, pg. 266

Lambly, Sharon A., V.P.-H.R.--Hershey Foods Corporation, Hershey, PA; *U.S. Public*, pg. 811

Lambrecht, Lynn, V.P.-Human Resources/Training--Kohl's Corporation, Menomonee Falls, WI; *U.S. Public*, pg. 965

Lamelas, Virginia, Mgr.-Personnel--Edmund Scientific Company, Barrington, NJ; *U.S. Private*, pg. 364

Lametta, Marti, V.P. & Dir. -Human Resources--Chartwell Re Corporation, Stamford, CT; *U.S. Public*, pg. 336

Lamie, Theresa, Dir.-Personnel--Griffin Corporation, Valdosta, GA; *U.S. Private*, pg. 480

LaMotte, Louise, Mgr.-H.R.--RE/MAX International, Inc., Englewood, CO; *U.S. Private*, pg. 912

Lampkin, Ellen, Mgr.-Human Resources--Christian Children's Fund, Inc., Richmond, VA; *U.S. Private*, pg. 238

Lamprecht, Andre J., Dir.-Human Resources & Social Investment--Barlow Ltd., Sandton, South Africa; *Int'l*, pg. 167

Lance, Ron, V.P.-Human Resources--Signature Flight Support, Orlando, FL; *Int'l*, pg. 114

Lanciaux, Concetta, V.P.-Human Resources--LVMH Moet Hennessy Louis Vuitton, Paris, France; *Int'l*, pg. 779

Landauer, Jay, V.P.-Human Resources--Musicland Group Inc., Minnetonka, MN; *U.S. Public*, pg. 1142

Landen, Kay, V.P.-Human Resources--Integrated Marketing Services, Omaha, NE; *U.S. Public*, pg. 631

Lander, Jim, V.P.-Human Resources--Intertec Publishing, Overland Park, KS; *U.S. Public*, pg. 1327

Landers, Jan, Dir.-H.R.--Keeneland Assoc., Inc., Lexington, KY; *U.S. Private*, pg. 611

Landfors, Ingalill, V.P.-Personnel--Mo och Domsjo AB, Stockholm, Sweden; *Int'l*, pg. 885

Landis, Drew W., V.P.-Human Resources--Binney & Smith Inc., Easton, PA; *U.S. Private*, pg. 496

Landon, William, Dir.-Personnel--Pridgeon & Clay, Inc., Grand Rapids, MI; *U.S. Private*, pg. 883

Landress, Ben S., Chief Info. Officer & Exec. V.P.--CBL & Associates Properties, Inc., Chattanooga, TN; *U.S. Public*, pg. 273

Lane, Beth, Mgr.-Personnel--Xentek, Inc., San Marcos, CA; *Int'l*, pg. 1349

Lane, David, Dir.-Personnel--SIFCO Custom Machining, Minneapolis, MN; *U.S. Public*, pg. 1471

Lane, Jim, Gen. Mgr.-Human Resources--Smorgon A.R.C., Sunshine, Australia; *Int'l*, pg. 1269

Lane, John T., Dir.-Personnel--Lennar Corporation, Miami, FL; *U.S. Public*, pg. 987

Lane, Jon, Div. V.P.-Human Resources--Data General Corporation, Westborough, MA; *U.S. Public*, pg. 485

Lang, Cheryl L., V.P.-H.R.--Unigard Insurance Co., Bellevue, WA; *Int'l*, pg. 345

Lang, Cheryl L., V.P.-H.R.--Unigard Indemnity Co., Bellevue, WA; *Int'l*, pg. 345

Lang, Larry, Mgr.-Personnel--Svedala Industries-Universal Engineering, Cedar Rapids, IA; *Int'l*, pg. 1326

Lang, Leonard, Dir.-Personnel & Controller--Kaz, Inc., New York, NY; *U.S. Private*, pg. 610

Langdon, P.H., V.P.-Human Resources & Asst. Sec.--Shaw Industries Ltd., Etobicoke, Canada; *Int'l*, pg. 1231

Lange, Eric, V.P.-Human Resources--Competitive Media Reporting, New York, NY; *Int'l*, pg. 1447

Lange, Heiko, Dr., Dir.-Personnel--Deutsche Lufthansa AG, Cologne, Germany; *Int'l*, pg. 407

Langford, Alyce, Mgr.-H.R.--Thomas L. Green & Co., Inc., Indianapolis, IN; *U.S. Private*, pg. 477

Langford, R. Brent, V.P.-Human Resources--Heilig-Meyers Company, Richmond, VA; *U.S. Public*, pg. 804

Langlais, Jackie, Dir.-Personnel--Edelbrock Corp., Torrance, CA; *U.S. Public*, pg. 563

Langley, Glenn C., Sr. V.P.-H.R.--American National Insurance Company, Galveston, TX; *U.S. Public*, pg. 87

Langlois, Paul, Dir.-H.R.--Uniboard Division Val d'Or, Val d'Or, Canada; *Int'l*, pg. 1431

Langnois, Paul, Dir.-H.R.--Uniboard Division Unires, Val d'Or, Canada; *Int'l*, pg. 1431

Langsam, Donna, Dir.-Human Resources--Signal Apparel Company, Inc., Chattanooga, TN; *U.S. Public*, pg. 1472

Langstaff, Jon T., V.P.-H.R.--Hecla Mining Company, Coeur D'Alene, ID; *U.S. Public*, pg. 803

Lanigir, Joanne, Dir.-Personnel--Cubix Corporation, Carson City, NV; *U.S. Private*, pg. 294

Lankester, G.E., Dir.-Personnel--Imperial Tobacco Group, Ltd., Bristol, United Kingdom; *Int'l*, pg. 666

Lannan, Roxanne, Dir.-H.R. & Employee Benefits--Dynamic Metal Products Company, Manchester, CT; *U.S. Private*, pg. 350

Lanzaro, Tom, Mgr.-H.R.--Minarik Corp, Glendale, CA; *U.S. Private*, pg. 749

Lanzi Gillespie, Donna, Mng. Partner-Media & Human Resources--Gillespie, Lawrenceville, NJ; *U.S. Private*, pg. 453

Lanzilloti, Dom, Dir.-Personnel--Crystal Oil Company, Shreveport, LA; *U.S. Public*, pg. 466

Lapoint, Richard D., Dir.-Human Resources--Wausau Papers of New Hampshire, Inc., Groveton, NH; *U.S. Public*, pg. 1748

Lapointe, Jean B., V.P.-H.R.--Chiquita Brands International, Inc., Cincinnati, OH; *U.S. Public*, pg. 349

Larkin, Kathleen A., V.P.-Human Resources--Merrill Corporation, Saint Paul, MN; *U.S. Public*, pg. 1097

Laroche, Valerie, Mgr.-Personnel--Banque Continentale Du Luxembourg, Luxembourg, Luxembourg; *Int'l*, pg. 319

LaRosa, Frank J., V.P.-H.R. & Info. Tech.--Haynes International, Inc., Kokomo, IN; *U.S. Public*, pg. 801

Larrabee, Ray, Dir.-Human Resources--Papa Gino's Inc., Dedham, MA; *U.S. Private*, pg. 837

Larsen, Pamela J., Asst. V.P. & Asst. Sec.--Mercantile Bank of Iowa, Des Moines, IA; *U.S. Public*, pg. 1087

Larson, Ken, V.P.-Admin. & H.R.--Candle Corporation, Santa Monica, CA; *U.S. Private*, pg. 204

Larson, Richard D., V.P.-Human Resources/European Grp.--Coca-Cola Enterprises Inc., Atlanta, GA; *U.S. Public*, pg. 393

Larson, Ron, Dir.-Human Resources--777 Program, Everett, WA; *U.S. Public*, pg. 240

Larson, Wayne, V.P.-Human Resources--Binkley Company, Warrenton, MO; *U.S. Private*, pg. 534

Lary, Karen, Mgr.-H.R.--Heat & Control, Inc., Hayward, CA; *U.S. Private*, pg. 518

Lasalle, Jean, Dir.-Personnel--Panneaux Malette-OSB Inc., Saint-Georges, Canada; *Int'l*, pg. 833

Lash, Gary, Mgr.-Personnel--DeVault Foods, Devault, PA; *U.S. Private*, pg. 329

Laska, Tamara, V.P.-Human Resources--Byerly's Inc., Edina, MN; *U.S. Private*, pg. 680

Lasorich, Laurie, Dir.-Employee Communications/Training & Devel.--Moore Corporation Limited, Toronto, Canada; *Int'l*, pg. 888

Lasrich, Karen, V.P.-H.R.--Dairy Mart Convenience Stores, Inc., Cuyahoga Falls, OH; *U.S. Public*, pg. 476

Laterra, Jacqueline, V.P.-H.R.--Valley Bank & Trust, Brighton, CO; *U.S. Private*, pg. 1132

Latham, T.E., V.P.-Human Resources--Alcatel Telecom, Richardson, TX; *Int'l*, pg. 55

LaTour, Barbara J., V.P.-Quality & Human Resources--Adecco S.A., Lausanne, Switzerland; *Int'l*, pg. 23

LaTour, D., Mgr.-H.R.--HEI, Inc., Victoria, MN; *U.S. Public*, pg. 770

Latz, Karl-Heinz, Mgr.-Personnel--Villeroy & Boch AG, Mettlach, Germany; *Int'l*, pg. 1468

Laughlin, Linda, Dir.-Human Resources Admin.--Sheldahl, Inc., Northfield, MN; *U.S. Public*, pg. 1465

Laukhuff, R.E., Mgr.-H.R. & Sec.--Universal Composites-U.S.C., Manheim, PA; *U.S. Private*, pg. 1126

LaVecchia, Jean M., V.P.-Human Resources--The Southern New England Telephone Company, New Haven, CT; *U.S. Public*, pg. 1491

Lavery, Diane, Mgr.-Personnel--The Body Shop, Cedar Knolls, NJ; *Int'l*, pg. 199

Lavorata, Mary Jo, Mgr.-Personnel--Biospherics Incorporated, Beltsville, MD; *U.S. Public*, pg. 232

Lavter, Tally, Dir.-H.R. & Devel.--Cole Hersee Company, Boston, MA; *U.S. Private*, pg. 251

Lawrence, Jerry, V.P.-H.R.--Ivex Packaging Corporation, Lincolnshire, IL; *U.S. Public*, pg. 915

Lawrence, Robert, Dir.-Compensation & Benefits--The Genlyte Group Incorporated, Union, NJ; *U.S. Public*, pg. 729

Lawson, John K., Sr. V.P.-Engrng., Tech. & H.R.--Deere & Company, Moline, IL; *U.S. Public*, pg. 491

Lawson, Rhonda Piar, V.P.-H.R.--Lesco, Inc., Rocky River, OH; *U.S. Public*, pg. 989

Lawson, Scott, Dir.-Personnel--Pegasus Gold Corporation, Spokane, WA; *U.S. Public*, pg. 1269

Lay, Connie, Mgr.-Personnel--CMI Corporation, Oklahoma City, OK; *U.S. Public*, pg. 278

Lay, W. Carl, V.P.-Corp. Rels.--Ambrake Corporation, Elizabethtown, KY; *U.S. Public*, pg. 721

Lazatte, Chris, Mgr.-H.R.--Hudson Valley Paper Company, Albany, NY; *U.S. Private*, pg. 546

Lazowski, Frank J., V.P.-Human Resources--Material Sciences Corporation, Elk Grove Village, IL; *U.S. Public*, pg. 1056

Leach, Linda, Mgr.-Personnel--Capsonic Group, Inc., Elgin, IL; *U.S. Private*, pg. 207

Leach, Myron E., Dir.-Admin--Intermagnetics General Corporation, Latham, NY; *U.S. Public*, pg. 893

Leach, William, Dir.-Human Resources--Boeing Military Airplanes Division, Seattle, WA; *U.S. Public*, pg. 241

Leake, Earl. D., V.P.--Lance, Inc., Charlotte, NC; *U.S. Public*, pg. 977

Leamer, Marybeth H., V.P.-Human Resources--Cox Enterprises, Inc., Atlanta, GA; *U.S. Private*, pg. 281

Leamon, G.F., Dir.-H.R.--Doron Precision Systems, Inc., Binghamton, NY; *U.S. Private*, pg. 341

Leamy, Brenda, Mgr.-H.R.--Eastern Air Devices, Inc., Dover, NH; *U.S. Private*, pg. 357

Lebel, Ernie, V.P.-H.R.--Emery Waterhouse Company, Portland, ME; *U.S. Private*, pg. 373

Lebetsamer, Jenni, Human Resources Mgr.--Suissa Miller Advertising, Inc., Los Angeles, CA; *U.S. Private*, pg. 1049

LeBlanc, Francis, Dir.-Human Resources--Applied Extrusion Technologies, Inc., Peabody, MA; *U.S. Public*, pg. 122

Lebo, Mike, Dir.-Human Resources--Lowe's Food Stores, Inc., Winston Salem, NC; *U.S. Private*, pg. 657

Lebra, Nicholas L., V.P. & Dir.-H.R.--Garden State Newspapers, Inc., Denver, CO; *U.S. Private*, pg. 727

Lechner, Hartmut, Mng. Dir.-Admin. & Human Resources--Bausparkasse Gemeinschaft der Freunde Wuestenrot gem.GmbH, Ludwigsburg, Germany; *Int'l*, pg. 1514

Leclerc, J.P., V.P.-Gen. Affairs & Human Resources--SNCF, Paris, France; *Int'l*, pg. 1163

Ledbetter, Bill, Mgr.-Personnel--Justin Boot Company, Fort Worth, TX; *U.S. Public*, pg. 937

Ledbetter, Rickey, Dir.-H.R.--Mrs. Smith's Bakeries, Inc., Thomasville, GA; *U.S. Public*, pg. 657

Lee, Charles, Dir.-Human Resources--Maclean Hunter Publishing Ltd., Toronto, Canada; *Int'l*, pg. 1123

Lee, Cheryl L., Chief Admin. Officer & Gen. Counsel--Image Entertainment, Inc., Chatsworth, CA; *U.S. Public*, pg. 870

Lee, Chris, Dir.-Personnel--Singapore Airlines, Los Angeles, CA; *Int'l*, pg. 1374

Lee, Colin, Human Resources Devel.--Wyeth Australia Pty. Ltd., Baulkham Hills, Australia; *U.S. Public*, pg. 82

Lee, Dennis M., Exec. V.P.-Human Resources--Caldor, Inc., Norwalk, CT; *U.S. Public*, pg. 292

Lee, Gary, V.P.-H.R.--Grey Wolf, Inc., Houston, TX; *U.S. Public*, pg. 765

Lee, H., Gen. Mgr.-Human Resources--China Steel Corporation, Kao-hsiung, Taiwan; *Int'l*, pg. 285

Lee, J.T., Dir.--Taiwan Power Company, Taipei, Taiwan; *Int'l*, pg. 1348

Lee, James B., Dir.-H.R.--Alabama Electric Cooperative, Inc., Andalusia, AL; *U.S. Private*, pg. 30
Lee, Jesse, Chief Fin. Officer, Sr. V.P. & Sec.--The IDI Group Companies, Arlington, VA; *U.S. Private*, pg. 554
Lee, Kyung-Kyoon, Exec. V.P.-Human Resources--Korean Airlines Co., Ltd., Seoul, Korea; *Int'l*, pg. 758
Lee, Larry, V.P. & H.R. Dir.--Bernstein-Rein Advertising, Inc., Kansas City, MO; *U.S. Private*, pg. 137
Lee, Ofelia U., Dir.-Personnel--Wilbur-Ellis Company & Connell Brothers Company, San Francisco, CA; *U.S. Private*, pg. 1175
Lee, Sue, Sr. V.P.-Human Resources & Communications--Suncor Inc., Calgary, Canada; *Int'l*, pg. 1320
Lee, Susan, Mgr.-Human Resources--Environmental Resources Management, Exton, PA; *U.S. Private*, pg. 378
Lee, Wanda, Sr. V.P.-H.R.--PacifiCare Health Systems, Inc., Cypress, CA; *U.S. Public*, pg. 1250
Lee, Won Soon, Exec. V.P. & Dir.-Personnel--Cho Hung Bank, Seoul, Korea; *Int'l*, pg. 287
Leeper, Denise, Dir.-Human Resoures--Penn-Daniels, Inc., Quincy, IL; *U.S. Public*, pg. 1467
LeFauve, Richard G., Sr. V.P.-Global Leadership Devel. & H.R.--General Motors Corporation, Detroit, MI; *U.S. Public*, pg. 718
Lefevre, Russ, V.P.-Employee Rels.--RAYOVAC Corporation, Madison, WI; *U.S. Private*, pg. 912
Leffler, Dennis, Mgr.-Personnel--The Keller Manufacturing Co., Inc., Corydon, IN; *U.S. Private*, pg. 612
Lefko, Ken, Dir.-H.R.--Mark III Industries, Ocala, FL; *U.S. Private*, pg. 704
Lefko, Marsha, Controller--Sierra Coating Technologies, De Pere, WI; *U.S. Private*, pg. 998
LeForestier, Michele, V.P.-Human Resources--Imetal, Paris, France; *Int'l*, pg. 661
Legaspi, Maria C., Mgr.-Human Resources--Rhone-Poulenc Rorer Philippines Inc., Manila, Philippines; *Int'l*, pg. 1111
LeGrand, Bernard, Mgr.-Human Resources--Poliet, Courbevoie, France; *Int'l*, pg. 1177
LeGrow, Walter D., V.P.-Human Resources--Emco Limited, London, Canada; *Int'l*, pg. 452
Lehnert, Mary, Mgr.-Benefits--Apogee Enterprises, Inc., Minneapolis, MN; *U.S. Public*, pg. 120
Lehni, Markus, Dr., Mng. Dir.-Corp. Environment--Landis & Staefa AG, Zug, Switzerland; *Int'l*, pg. 800
Lehtinen, Veikko, Deputy Pres.-Legal Affairs, Human Resources & Corp. Communication--Outokumpu Oyj, Espoo, Finland; *Int'l*, pg. 1015
Leibold, Uli, Mgr.-Human Resources--Traub AG, Reichenbach, Germany; *Int'l*, pg. 1419
Leidelmeyer, Loius, V.P.-H.R.--Bugle Boy Industries, Inc., Simi Valley, CA; *U.S. Private*, pg. 179
Leigl, Kathy, Mgr.-Personnel--Scientific Protein Laboratories, Inc., Waunakee, WI; *U.S. Public*, pg. 80
Leimsieder, Barbara B., Mgr.-Compensation & Benefits--Eastern Enterprises, Weston, MA; *U.S. Public*, pg. 548
Lemaire, Michel, Mgr.-H.R.--Alcatel Cit (S.A.), Velizy-Villacoublay, France; *Int'l*, pg. 56
Lemaitre, Nadine, Gen. Mgr.-H.R.--Generale de Banque S.A., Brussels, Belgium; *Int'l*, pg. 546
Lemay, Nicole, Sr. V.P.-Human Resources--SNC-Lavalin Group Inc., Montreal, Canada; *Int'l*, pg. 1161
Lemec, Bernard, Exec. V.P.-H.R.--Banque Nationale de Paris, Paris, France; *Int'l*, pg. 163
Lemeiux, Nancy, Mgr.-Personnel--Mulberry Metal Products, Inc., Union, NJ; *U.S. Private*, pg. 766
Lemieux, Paul, Mgr.-Employee Rels.--The Amalgamated Sugar Company LLC, Ogden, UT; *U.S. Private*, pg. 48
Lemieux, Paul, Dir.-Personnel--Peter Pan Bus Lines, Inc., Springfield, MA; *U.S. Private*, pg. 856
LeMire, Deidred, Mgr.-Employee Assistance--H.S. Crocker Co., Inc., Huntley, IL; *U.S. Private*, pg. 290
Lemmer, Carole, Dir.-H. R.--Shurfine International, Inc., Northlake, IL; *U.S. Private*, pg. 997
Lemons, Mary, Dir.-Human Resources--Truevision, Inc., Santa Clara, CA; *U.S. Public*, pg. 1642
Leneweaver, Gerry, V.P.-Human Resources--Ground Round Inc., Braintree, MA; *U.S. Public*, pg. 766
Lenhart, Vaughn, Dir.-Human Resources--Lyman Lumber Company, Excelsior, MN; *U.S. Private*, pg. 683
Lennertz, Tina, Mgr.-H.R.--Lawter International, Inc., Kenosha, WI; *U.S. Public*, pg. 980
Lennon, Frank T., V.P.-H.R. & Admin.--The Pittston Company, Glen Allen, VA; *U.S. Public*, pg. 1305
Lent, Steve, V.P.-Exec. Personnel Admin.--Alexander's, Inc., Saddle Brook, NJ; *U.S. Public*, pg. 1725
Leoncavallo, Phyllis A., Mgr.-Personnel--Lithograph Printing Company, Inc., Memphis, TN; *U.S. Private*, pg. 713
Leone, Susan L., Dir.-Admin.--Dominguez Services Corporation, Long Beach, CA; *U.S. Public*, pg. 516
Leongnarktongdee, Matana, Mgr.-Pub. Rels.--The Siam Cement Public Company Limited, Bangkok, Thailand; *Int'l*, pg. 1237
Leopold, Michael, V.P.-H.R.--Walbro Corporation, Cass City, MI; *U.S. Public*, pg. 1733
Lerner, Bennett, Sr. V.P.-Personnel--Gateway Apparel, Inc., Saint Louis, MO; *U.S. Private*, pg. 441
Lerner, Linda J., Sr. V.P.-Human Resources--UST Corporation, Boston, MA; *U.S. Public*, pg. 1660
Lerner, Linda J., Sr. V.P.-Human Resources--USTrust, Boston, MA; *U.S. Public*, pg. 1660
Lerner, Phillip, Dir.-Human Resources--Union Industries, Inc., Providence, RI; *U.S. Private*, pg. 1119
LeRoux, Philip, V.P.-Human Resources--Pass & Seymour/Legrand, Syracuse, NY; *Int'l*, pg. 806
Lery, Susan, Dir.-H.R.--Rockford Products Corp., Rockford, IL; *U.S. Private*, pg. 938
Leslie, Mary, Mgr.-Personnel--Admiration Hosiery Mills, Inc., Charlotte, NC; *U.S. Private*, pg. 528
Lessard, Paul, Dir.-Personnel--Savage Arms Inc., Westfield, MA; *U.S. Private*, pg. 968
Lessig, Rickeia Ally, Mgr.-Human Resources--Trans Leasing International Inc., Northbrook, IL; *U.S. Public*, pg. 1628
Lester, Karen, Human Resources Mgr.--UTA Thompson Plant, Thomson, GA; *U.S. Public*, pg. 1691
Lester, Keith, Mgr.-Pub. Rels.--Broan Mfg. Co., Inc., Hartford, WI; *U.S. Public*, pg. 1193
Lester, Mark, Dir.-Personnel--Kingsley Machine Co., Downers Grove, IL; *U.S. Public*, pg. 866
Letcavage, Steve, Dir.-Human Resources--Craftex Mills Inc. of Pennsylvania, Blue Bell, PA; *U.S. Private*, pg. 284
Letemendia, Ignacio, Mgr.-H.R.--Maxus Energy Corporation, Dallas, TX; *Int'l*, pg. 1515
Letizio, Lisa, V.P.-Human Resources--The Timberland Company, Stratham, NH; *U.S. Public*, pg. 1609
Letourneau, Louise, Dir.-H.R.--MDF La Baie Inc., La Baie, Canada; *Int'l*, pg. 1432
Lette, Richard, Dir.-Human Resources--Iams Company, Dayton, OH; *U.S. Private*, pg. 556
Lettl, Jill, Mgr.-Personnel--Olympic Steel Inc., Cleveland, OH; *U.S. Public*, pg. 1221
Letts, David, Dir.-Personnel--Raytheon Systems Co., Kirkwood, NY; *U.S. Public*, pg. 1364
Leung, Violet, Dir.-Personnel--Barnhardt Manufacturing Co., Charlotte, NC; *U.S. Private*, pg. 116
Levan, B.W., V.P.-Human Resources--Shell Oil Company, Houston, TX; *Int'l*, pg. 1136
LeVan, George, Mgr.-H.R.--Alpha Industries, Inc., Woburn, MA; *U.S. Public*, pg. 57
Levenson, Andrea, V.P.-H.R. Svcs.--Office Depot Inc., Delray Beach, FL; *U.S. Public*, pg. 1212
Leventry-Jeffers, Anne, V.P.-Human Resources--Ball Horticultural Company, West Chicago, IL; *U.S. Private*, pg. 112
Levi, M. Suellen, V.P.-Human Resources--CT Financial Services, Inc., Toronto, Canada; *Int'l*, pg. 112
Levin, Harvey, Sr. V.P.-Human Resources--American Greetings Corporation, Cleveland, OH; *U.S. Public*, pg. 77
Levine, Richard, V.P. & Dir.-H.R.--The New Yorker Magazine, New York, NY; *U.S. Private*, pg. 795
Levinson, Donald M., Exec. V.P.-H.R.--Cigna Corp., Philadelphia, PA; *U.S. Public*, pg. 356
Levinson, Jody, Dir.-H.R.--Johnson & Johnson, New Brunswick, NJ; *U.S. Public*, pg. 927
Levoy, Lynn, Mgr.-Personnel--Wynn Oil Company, Azusa, CA; *U.S. Public*, pg. 1782
Levy, Gilles-Pierre, Exec. V.P.-Human Resources--Pechiney S.A., Courbevoie, France; *Int'l*, pg. 1027
Lewaller, Shelly, Admin.-Employee Benefits--Guardian Industries Corp., Auburn Hills, MI; *U.S. Private*, pg. 485
Leweller, Joan, Mgr.-H.R.--Regal Ware, Inc., Jacksonville, AR; *U.S. Private*, pg. 917
Lewin, Luis E., V.P.-H.R.--Tribune Company, Chicago, IL; *U.S. Public*, pg. 1635
Lewin, Margareta, Sr. V.P.-Human Resources--Esselte AB, Solna, Sweden; *Int'l*, pg. 459
Lewin, Rene, V.P.-Human Resources--American Home Products Corporation, Madison, NJ; *U.S. Public*, pg. 79
Lewis, Bill, Dir.-Admin.--E.A. Sween Company, Eden Prairie, MN; *U.S. Private*, pg. 1058
Lewis, Diana, V.P.-H.R.--Ecolab Inc., Saint Paul, MN; *U.S. Public*, pg. 562
Lewis, H. Nelson, Sr. V.P.-Human Resources--The Great Atlantic & Pacific Tea Company, Inc., Montvale, NJ; *Int'l*, *pg. 1375*
Lewis, Joan, V.P.-H.R.--Select Restaurants, Inc., Cleveland, OH; *U.S. Private*, pg. 982
Lewis, Jodi, Mgr.-Personnel--Valvoline Instant Oil Change, Inc., Lexington, KY; *U.S. Public*, pg. 139
Lewis, John, Dir.-Personnel--Wurzburg, Inc., Memphis, TN; *U.S. Private*, pg. 1192
Lewis, Judith, Dir.-Personnel--Esselte Corporation, Garden City, NY; *Int'l*, pg. 459
Lewis, Mike, Grp. Head-H.R.--Allied Irish Banks, p.l.c., Dublin, Ireland; *Int'l*, pg. 64
Lewis, Peter C., V.P.-Admin.--Hawaiian Electric Industries, Inc., Honolulu, HI; *U.S. Public*, pg. 799
Lewis, Richard A., V.P.-Human Resources--Anadarko Petroleum Corporation, Houston, TX; *U.S. Public*, pg. 107
Lewis, Shirley, Mgr.-Personnel Svcs.--Sacramento Municipal Utility District, Sacramento, CA; *U.S. Private*, pg. 959
Lewison, John, Dir.-H.R.--American Institute of C.P.A.'s Inc., New York, NY; *U.S. Private*, pg. 57
Liang, C.C., Dir.-Personnel--China Steel Structure Co., Ltd., Kao-hsiung, Taiwan; *Int'l*, pg. 286
Licon, George, Dir.-Personnel--Clayton Industries Co., El Monte, CA; *U.S. Private*, pg. 245
Lidstad, Richard A., V.P.-H.R.--3M, Saint Paul, MN; *U.S. Public*, pg. 1604
Liebscher, Klaus, Dr., Dir.-Gen. Mngmt.--Raiffeisen Zentralbank Osterreich, Vienna, Austria; *Int'l*, pg. 1084
Liggett, Jerry W., V.P.-Human Resources Strategy--Cinergy Corp., Cincinnati, OH; *U.S. Public*, pg. 368
Lijestrom, Gunnar, Dir.-Personnel & Legal Affairs--NCC AB, Solna, Sweden; *Int'l*, pg. 898
Lilak, David, V.P.-Personnel--Yoplait USA, Minneapolis, MN; *U.S. Public*, pg. 718
Liljstrom, Gunnar, Sr. V.P.-Admin. & Head-Legal Affairs & Personnel--NCC AB, Solna, Sweden; *Int'l*, pg. 898
Lilla, John D., V.P.-Human Resources & Risk Mngmt.--PCC Flow Technologies, Inc., Houston, TX; *U.S. Public*, pg. 1320
Lim, Sylvia, Asst. Mgr.-Personnel & Admin.--Orchard Parade Holdings Limited, Singapore, Singapore; *Int'l*, pg. 1007
Lim, Wendy, Mgr.-Personnel & Admin.--Singapore Land Limited, Singapore, Singapore; *Int'l*, pg. 1252
Limone, Vona, Dir.-Personnel--Norwalk Co., Inc., Norwalk, CT; *U.S. Private*, pg. 807
Linch, Martha, Dir.-Human Resources/Conway--Virco Mfg. Corporation, Torrance, CA; *U.S. Public*, pg. 1721
Lincoln, William O., Mgr.-H.R.--Thompson Steel Co., Inc., Canton, MA; *U.S. Private*, pg. 1083
Lindaman, Christine, Sr. V.P.--Raymond James Financial, Inc., Saint Petersburg, FL; *U.S. Public*, pg. 923
Lindemans, Jan, Gen. Mgr.-Personnel--Kredietbank N.V., Brussels, Belgium; *Int'l*, pg. 760
Linder, Per, Dir.-Human Resources & Organization--Electrolux, AB, Stockholm, Sweden; *Int'l*, pg. 438
Lindquist, Richard, Mgr.-Personnel--G. Leblanc Corporation, Kenosha, WI; *U.S. Private*, pg. 656
Lindsay, Richard C., V.P.-Human Resources--Blount, Inc. Oregon Cutting Systems Division, Portland, OR; *U.S. Public*, pg. 238
Lindsey, Donette, Mgr.-Personnel--PACCAR Winch Division, Broken Arrow, OK; *U.S. Public*, pg. 1246
Lindsey, Patricia, Dir.-Personnel--Danka Business Systems, La Grange, IL; *Int'l*, pg. 379
Lindsey, Vicky, V.P.-H.R.--Stuart Entertainment Inc., Council Bluffs, IA; *U.S. Public*, pg. 1526
Linford, Richard, Dir.-H.R.--Gulf States, Inc., Freeport, TX; *U.S. Private*, pg. 487
Linn, Don, Dir.-Human Resources--Scherer Bros. Lumber Company, Minneapolis, MN; *U.S. Private*, pg. 970
Linsdau, Anne C., V.P.-H.R.--Fortune Brands, Inc., Old Greenwich, CT; *U.S. Public*, pg. 674
Linville, Richard A., V.P.-H.R.--Piedmont Natural Gas Co., Inc., Charlotte, NC; *U.S. Public*, pg. 1295
Lipcomb, Balfour, Mgr.-Human Resources--Kellwood Lingerie/Active Group, Summit, MS; *U.S. Public*, pg. 948
Lipinski, Ken, Dir.-Human Resources--Danaher Tool Group, Chicago, IL; *U.S. Public*, pg. 481
Lipman, Judy, Mgr.-Personnel--AEP Industries, Inc., South Hackensack, NJ; *U.S. Public*, pg. 4
Lippens, G., Dir.-Human Resources--Sidmar N.V., Gent, Belgium; *Int'l*, pg. 79
Lippert, D., Dir.-Human Resources--Dare Foods Limited, Kitchener, Canada; *Int'l*, pg. 383
Lippert, Roger, V.P.-H.R.--GSW Water Heating Company, Fergus, Canada; *Int'l*, pg. 538
Lippi, Cristina, Dir.-H.R.--Candy S.p.A., Brugherio, Italy; *Int'l*, *pg. 259*
Lipscomb, Robert, Mgr.-Human Resources--Frigidaire Home Products-Range Products, Springfield, TN; *Int'l*, pg. 440
Lipsetz, Alvin, V.P.-Human Resources--Midland Life Insurance Co., Columbus, OH; *U.S. Private*, pg. 744
Lipton, Wanda, V.P.-Human Resources--Amcore Financial, Inc., Rockford, IL; *U.S. Public*, pg. 64
Lishinsky, Bernard J., Dir.--Handy & Harman, New York, NY; *U.S. Public*, pg. 780
Lison, Stephen A., V.P.-H.R.--SPX Corporation, Muskegon, MI; *U.S. Public*, pg. 1420
Litrerini, George, Dir.-Human Resources--Dataproducts Corporation, Simi Valley, CA; *Int'l*, pg. 620
Little, Alfred, Jr., V.P.-H.R.--Newport News Shipbuilding, Inc., Newport News, VA; *U.S. Public*, pg. 1179
Little, C. Lyn, Mgr.-Human Resources--Spire Corporation, Bedford, MA; *U.S. Public*, pg. 1499
Littrell, James, Dir.-H.R.--Tecstar Inc., City of Industry, CA; *U.S. Private*, pg. 1072
Litvack, Sanford M., Chief Oper. Officer & Sr. Exec. V.P.--The Walt Disney Company, Burbank, CA; *U.S. Public*, pg. 511
Litz, Terry, V.P.-Human Resources--Rite-Hite Corporation (WI), Milwaukee, WI; *U.S. Private*, pg. 933
Litz, W., Dir.-Human Res.--Yuasa-Exide, Inc., Reading, PA; *Int'l*, pg. 1522
Lloyd, Jackie, Grp. Gen. Mgr.-H.R.--New Zealand Dairy Board, Wellington, New Zealand; *Int'l*, pg. 923
Lloyd, Patricia, Mgr.-Human Resources--Premark International, Inc., Deerfield, IL; *U.S. Public*, pg. 1321
Lobo, Pat, Dir.-Personnel & Employee Benefits--Petro-Hunt Corporation, Dallas, TX; *U.S. Private*, pg. 858
Loch, A.A., V.P.-Human Resources--White Cap, Inc., Downers Grove, IL; *Int'l*, pg. 1207
Lochman, William H., Jr., Sr. V.P.-Human Resources--PNC Bank, Camp Hill, PA; *U.S. Public*, pg. 1243
Locibento, Arthur T., Jr., Sr. V.P.-H.R.--NovaCare Employee Services, Inc., Norristown, PA; *U.S. Public*, pg. 1203
Lock, Dawn, Dir.-Human Resources--Shelter Components Corporation, Elkhart, IN; *U.S. Public*, pg. 952
Lockard, Paul, V.P.-Human Resources--The Sports Authority Inc., Fort Lauderdale, FL; *U.S. Public*, pg. 1499
Lockhart, Debi, Sr. V.P., Human Resources Dir. & Office Facilities Dir.--Publicis/Bloom Inc., New York, NY; *Int'l*, pg. 470
Lockridge, B. Russell, Sr. V.P.-H.R.--IMC Global, Bannockburn, IL; *U.S. Public*, pg. 856
Lodeweges, H.F., Sr. V.P.-Customer Service & Processing--UBO Verzekeringen, Utrecht, Netherlands; *Int'l*, pg. 26
Lodge, Robert W., V.P.-H.R.--Carpenter Technology Corporation, Reading, PA; *U.S. Public*, pg. 307
Loeffler, Allyson, Asst. H.R. Mgr.--Kulite Semiconductor Products, Inc., Leonia, NJ; *U.S. Private*, pg. 636
Loesch, R.E., V.P.-Human Resources--Lafarge Construction Materials, Canfield, OH; *Int'l*, pg. 788
Loeser, David, Sr. V.P.-H.R.--Quaker State Corporation, Irving, TX; *U.S. Public*, pg. 1348
Lofgren, Candace, Dir.-Personnel--Reed & Barton Corporation, Taunton, MA; *U.S. Private*, pg. 916
Logan, John, V.P.-Human Resources--Master Builders Inc., Cleveland, OH; *Int'l*, pg. 1465
Logan, Michelle, Dir.-Personnel--Beutler Heating & Air Conditioning Inc., Sacramento, CA; *U.S. Private*, pg. 141
Loggans, D. Bradford, V.P.-Human Resources--Sanders, A Lockheed Martin Company, Nashua, NH; *U.S. Public*, pg. 1008
Logsdon, Jani, Mgr.-H.R.--F. Korbel Bros. Inc., Guerneville, CA; *U.S. Private*, pg. 632
Logue, F. Andrew, Staff V.P.-Human Resources--National Service Industries, Inc., Atlanta, GA; *U.S. Public*, pg. 1160
Loker, Susan J., Sr. V.P.-Human Resources--Cambridge Technology Partners, Cambridge, MA; *U.S. Public*, pg. 1424
Lombardo, Rosa, V.P.-Human Resources--Sudler & Hennessey, New York, NY; *U.S. Private*, pg. 1197

Lonca, Donna L., Dir.-Human Resources--Barrister Information Systems Corporation, Buffalo, NY; *U.S. Public*, pg. 192
Long, Betsy, Mgr.-H.R.--Heath Consultants Incorporated, Houston, TX; *U.S. Private*, pg. 518
Long, Beverly, Dir.-H.R.--Paddock Publications, Inc., Arlington Heights, IL; *U.S. Private*, pg. 833
Long, George E., Dir.-Admin. Svcs.--Unitil Corporation, Hampton, NH; *U.S. Public*, pg. 1692
Long, John R., III, Exec. V.P.-Human Resources--US Airways Group, Inc., Arlington, VA; *U.S. Public*, pg. 1680
Long, Liz, Dir.- H.R.--U.S. Divers Co., Inc., Santa Ana, CA; *U.S. Private*, pg. 1125
Long, Ron, Dir.-Human Resources--M.C. Gill Corporation, El Monte, CA; *U.S. Private*, pg. 453
Long, Ronald, Dir.-Personnel--4C Foods Corporation, Brooklyn, NY; *U.S. Private*, pg. 421
Longbottom, David, Dir.-Grp. H.R.--Dixons Group plc, Hemel Hempstead, United Kingdom,; *Int'l*, pg. 413
Longenecker, Kathie, V.P.-Human Resources--Apple Computer, Inc., Cupertino, CA; *U.S. Public*, pg. 121
Longhorn, Anne, Personnel Administrator--Air UK Ltd., Stansted, United Kingdom; *Int'l*, pg. 38
Longstreet, John, V.P.-Employee Svcs.--Bristol Hotels & Resorts, Dallas, TX; *U.S. Public*, pg. 253
Longworth, Stuart, V.P.-H.R.--A. Duda & Sons Inc., Oviedo, FL; *U.S. Private*, pg. 344
Lonnroth-Laaksonen, Merja, Dir.-Personnel--OY Stockmann AB, Helsinki, Finland; *Int'l*, pg. 1301
Looby, Mary Ann, Sr. V.P.-Human Resources--First Data Corporation, Englewood, CO; *U.S. Public*, pg. 631
Lopater, David, Dir.-H.R.--Clayton Homes, Inc., Knoxville, TN; *U.S. Public*, pg. 382
Lopez, Irma, V.P.-Human Resources--TII Industries, Inc., Copiague, NY; *U.S. Public*, pg. 1556
Lopez, Mary, Mgr.-H.R.--International Lottery & Totalizator Systems, Inc., Carlsbad, CA; *U.S. Public*, pg. 900
Lopez, Pernilla, Dir.-H.R.--Ikea North America, Inc., Plymouth Meeting, PA; *Int'l*, pg. 660
Lopienski, Tom, Exec. Dir.-H.R.--Roadway Express, Inc., Akron, OH; *U.S. Public*, pg. 1392
Loppinet, Claude, V.P.-Human Resources--SNECMA - Societe Nationale d'Etude et de Construction de Moteurs d'Aviation, Paris, France; *Int'l*, pg. 1165
Loquan, Patricia, Dir.-Personnel & Corp. Affairs--Lever Brothers West Indies Ltd., Champs Fleurs, Trinidad & Tobago; *Int'l*, pg. 1437
Lorenz, Nancy J., Sr. V.P.-H.R., Mngmt. & Org. Devel.--Magna Group, Inc., Saint Louis, MO; *U.S. Public*, pg. 1037
Loria, Clara, Mgr.-Human Resources--Crowley, Milner & Company, Detroit, MI; *U.S. Public*, pg. 461
Loria, Clara, Dir.-Human Resources--Steinbach Stores, Inc., Detroit, MI; *U.S. Public*, pg. 461
Lotochinski, G.J., V.P.-Human Resources--BC Gas Inc., Vancouver, Canada; *Int'l*, pg. 114
Lotochinski, Gary J., V.P.-Human Resources--BC Gas Utility, Vancouver, Canada; *Int'l*, pg. 114
Loughlin, L., V.P.-Personnel--United Refining Company, Warren, PA; *U.S. Private*, pg. 915
Louzeiro, Paula, Mgr.-H.R.--Bank Brussels Lambert, New York Branch, New York, NY; *Int'l*, pg. 147
Love, John, V.P.-H.R.--Boise Cascade Office Products Corporation, Itasca, IL; *U.S. Public*, pg. 243
Love, John, Dir.-Personnel--Gilman Paper Co., Saint Marys, GA; *U.S. Private*, pg. 454
Lovelace, Linda, Mgr.-H.R.--Saladmaster, Inc., Arlington, TX; *U.S. Private*, pg. 917
Lovelace, Linda, Mgr.-H.R.--Nationwide Acceptance, Arlington, TX; *U.S. Private*, pg. 917
Lovelace, Linda, Mgr.-Personnel--Saladmaster, Arlington, TX; *U.S. Private*, pg. 961
Lovelady, Ron E., Sr. V.P.-Human Resources--Longs Drug Stores Corporation, Walnut Creek, CA; *U.S. Public*, pg. 1013
Lovett, Keith, Sr. V.P.-Human Resources--Fred Meyer Stores, Portland, OR; *U.S. Public*, pg. 1103
Loving, Richard J., V.P.-H.R.--Texaco Worldwide Exploration & Production, Scroggins, TX; *U.S. Public*, pg. 1583
Lowe, Challis, Sr. V.P.-H.R.--Beneficial Corporation, Wilmington, DE; *U.S. Public*, pg. 211
Lowe, Challis, Sr. V.P.-H.R., Admin. & Special Projects--Beneficial Management Corporation, Peapack, NJ; *U.S. Public*, pg. 211
Lowe, Charlene B., H.R. Admin.--Consumers Water Company, Portland, ME; *U.S. Public*, pg. 438
Lowe, Michael A., V.P.-Human Resources--Royal Insurance Company of Canada, Toronto, Canada; *Int'l*, pg. 1131
Lowe, Michael B., Sr. V.P.-H.R.--Corporate & Institutional Financial Services - Montreal, Toronto, Canada; *Int'l*, pg. 153
Lowrey, J.S., Gen. Mgr.-Human Resources--Australian Mutual Provident, Sydney, Australia; *Int'l*, pg. 100
Lowrimore, Lawrence, V.P.-H.R.--AptarGroup, Inc., Crystal Lake, IL; *U.S. Public*, pg. 125
Lowy, Patricia K., Dir.-Human Resources--Pall Corporation, Greenvale, NY; *U.S. Public*, pg. 1253
Loy, H. Steven, V.P.-Human Resources--Motorists Mutual Insurance Co., Columbus, OH; *U.S. Private*, pg. 764
Loy, H. Steven, V.P.-Human Resources, Motorists Insurance Cos.--American Hardware Mutual Insurance Co., Columbus, OH; *U.S. Private*, pg. 764
Loyola, Eduardo, V.P.-H.R.--CODELCO Chile (Corporacion Nacional Del Cobre De Chile), Santiago, Chile; *Int'l*, pg. 302
Lozano, Jairo, Mgr.-Human Resources--Bundy Colombia S.A., Bogota, Colombia; *Int'l*, pg. 1342
Lu, Terry, Asst. V.P.--Acer Incorporated, Taipei, Taiwan; *Int'l*, pg. 22
Lua, Clifford, Mgr.-Admin.--Showpla Asia Limited, Singapore, Singapore; *Int'l*, pg. 1237
Luca, Albert, Dir.-Pur. & Personnel--AFA Protective Systems, Inc., Syosset, NY; *U.S. Public*, pg. 5
Lucas, Frank, Dir.-Personnel & Dir.-Intl. Rels.--VAW of America, Inc., Ellenville, NY; *Int'l*, pg. 1466
Lucas, William R., Jr., Exec. V.P.-Admin. & Gen. Counsel--Birmingham Steel Corporation, Birmingham, AL; *U.S. Public*, pg. 232
Lucchesi, Christine, Dir.-Personnel--Gingiss International, Addison, IL; *U.S. Private*, pg. 455
Lucenta, Dominic, Sr. V.P.-H.R.--Essex International, Inc., Fort Wayne, IN; *U.S. Public*, pg. 593
Luci, James, V.P.-Human Resources--Harvard Industries, Inc., Tampa, FL; *U.S. Public*, pg. 796
Lucia, Kathleen A., Mgr.-H.R.--CCL Custom Manufacturing, Niles, IL; *Int'l*, pg. 238
Ludeman, Cindy, Mgr.-Personnel--Nasco Modesto, Modesto, CA; *U.S. Private*, pg. 446
Ludeman, Cynthia, Dir.-Personnel--Nasco, Fort Atkinson, WI; *U.S. Private*, pg. 446
Ludvigsen, Gary, Mgr.-H.R.--Toter Incorporated, Statesville, NC; *U.S. Private*, pg. 1092
Ludwick, John D., V.P.-Human Resources--Mortgage Guaranty Insurance Corporation, Milwaukee, WI; *U.S. Public*, pg. 1026
Ludwig, Kenneth M., Sr. V.P.-H.R.--Culp, Inc., High Point, NC; *U.S. Public*, pg. 467
Lueger, Susan A., V.P.-Human Resources--Northwestern Mutual Life Insurance Co., Milwaukee, WI; *U.S. Private*, pg. 807
Lukas, David, V.P.-H.R. & Corp. Counsel--Northland Cranberries, Inc., Wisconsin Rapids, WI; *U.S. Public*, pg. 1197
Lunbeck, Arlene B., Mgr.-H.R.--Speakman Company, Wilmington, DE; *U.S. Private*, pg. 1021
Lundell, Bob, Dir.-Personnel--IMI Cornelius Inc. (MN), Anoka, MN; *Int'l*, pg. 646
Lundell, Byron, V.P.-H.R.--U.S. Pharmaceuticals, Baltimore, MD; *U.S. Public*, pg. 58
Lunn, Evanline K., Exec. V.P.--First Farmers & Merchants National Bank, Columbia, TN; *U.S. Private*, pg. 407
Lunt, Terry, V.P.-Human Resources--Moorman's Inc., Quincy, IL; *U.S. Private*, pg. 760
Luongoi, Laura, Dir.-H.R.--Bel-Art Products, Pequannock, NJ; *U.S. Private*, pg. 130
Lupica, Thomas J., Sr. Dir.-Human Resources--Ball Packaging Holdings Corp., Westminster, CO; *U.S. Public*, pg. 171
Lupo, Terry, Mgr.-H.R.--Superior Surgical Mfg. Co., Inc., Seminole, FL; *U.S. Public*, pg. 1539
Lurie, Eileen, V.P.-H.R.--Financial World Partners, New York, NY; *U.S. Private*, pg. 404
Lusk, Rhonda, Mgr.-Human Resources--Thermador, Los Angeles, CA; *U.S. Public*, pg. 1053
Lutgen, Robert M., Dir.-H.R.--Mercury Finance Co., Lake Forest, IL; *U.S. Public*, pg. 1093
Luther, Michael C., V.P.-H.R.--Briggs Industries, Inc., Tampa, FL; *U.S. Private*, pg. 168
Luther, Warren, Mgr.-Personnel--Jaguar Cars, Mahwah, NJ; *U.S. Public*, pg. 664
Lutz, Emil, Mgr.-Human Resources--Sulzer Ltd., Winterthur, Switzerland; *Int'l*, pg. 1305
Luxon, Pam, Mgr.-Personnel--Smith Enterprises, Rock Hill, SC; *U.S. Private*, pg. 1007
Luyten, Ben, Exec. V.P.-Human Resources--Interbrew S.A., Leuven, Belgium; *Int'l*, pg. 679
Luzier, Patricia, Sr. V.P.-H.R.--Vicorp Restaurants, Inc., Denver, CO; *U.S. Public*, pg. 1719
Luzzi, Jane, Mgr.-Personnel--McCourt Label Co., Lewis Run, PA; *U.S. Private*, pg. 720
Luzzi, Robert D., V.P.-H.R.--Lukens Inc., Coatesville, PA; *U.S. Public*, pg. 1019
Lyle, Stuart, Dir.-Human Resources--Dahlberg, Inc., Golden Valley, MN; *U.S. Public*, pg. 194
Lyman, Sandra, Mgr.-Human Resources--American Mathematical Society, Inc., Providence, RI; *U.S. Private*, pg. 59
Lynch, Mary, Dir.-Human Resources--Husqvarna Forest & Garden Products, Charlotte, NC; *Int'l*, pg. 440
Lynch, Pat, Dir.-Personnel--McWane Cast Iron Pipe Co., Birmingham, AL; *U.S. Private*, pg. 725
Lynch, Paul, V.P.-Human Resources--Lipton, Toronto, Canada; *Int'l*, pg. 1438
Lynn, Judith A., Dir.-H.R.--Arrow Gear Company, Downers Grove, IL; *U.S. Private*, pg. 85
Lynn, Patrick J., Dir.-H.R.--Bioproducts, Inc., Fairlawn, OH; *U.S. Private*, pg. 145
Lynn, Richard C., V.P.-Labor Rels.--Fleming Companies, Inc., Oklahoma City, OK; *U.S. Public*, pg. 652
Lyon, Bob, V.P.-Human Resources--Anthem Electronics Inc., San Jose, CA; *U.S. Public*, pg. 134
Lyon, David, Dir.-H.R.--Cheltenham & Gloucester plc, Gloucester, United Kingdom; *Int'l*, pg. 283
Lyon, William, V.P.-H.R.--The W.E. Bassett Company, Shelton, CT; *U.S. Private*, pg. 122
Lyons, Dana, Mgr.-Human Resources--Greenwich Air Services, Miami, FL; *U.S. Public*, pg. 710
Lyons, Daniel M., Sr. V.P.-Personnel--Darden Restaurants, Inc., Orlando, FL; *U.S. Public*, pg. 483
Lyons, Kimberly, Mgr.-Human Resources--West Penetone Corporation, Tenafly, NJ; *U.S. Private*, pg. 1158
Lyons, Kimberly A., Dir.-Human Resources--West Chemical Products, Inc., Princeton, NJ; *U.S. Private*, pg. 1158
Lyons, Suzanne, V.P.-Human Resources--Keyport Life Insurance Company, Boston, MA; *U.S. Public*, pg. 666
Lyphout, Dan, Mgr.-Quality Process--Don E. Williams Co., Rock Island, IL; *U.S. Private*, pg. 1177
Lytle, Bill, V.P.-Org. Devel.--Durakon Industries, Inc., Lapeer, MI; *U.S. Public*, pg. 537
Mabe, D., Dir.-Personnel--Dimco-Gray Company, Centerville, OH; *U.S. Private*, pg. 333
Mabille, Guy, Dir.-Personnel--Bacardi-Martini Belgium, Brussels, Belgium; *U.S. Private*, pg. 109
Mabry, Carlis, Dir.-Personnel--Spencer's Inc., Mount Airy, NC; *U.S. Private*, pg. 1025
Macbeth, Charles, Dir.-Human Resources--Bourns, Inc., Riverside, CA; *U.S. Private*, pg. 161
MacBride, Tim, V.P.-Human Resources--Allders International (Canada) Limited, Mississauga, Canada; *Int'l*, pg. 30
MacColl, John A., Exec. V.P.-Human Resources & Gen. Counsel--USF&G Corporation, Baltimore, MD; *U.S. Public*, pg. 1659
MacDonald, J. Randall, Sr. V.P.-Human Resources & Admin.--GTE Corporation, Stamford, CT; *U.S. Public*, pg. 696
MacDonald, Wayne K., Mgr.-H.R.--Empire Company Limited, Stellarton, Canada; *Int'l*, pg. 453
Mace, Mike E., Mgr.-Human Resources--APAC/Ballenger Paving Company, Inc., Taylors, SC; *U.S. Public*, pg. 139
Macfarland, Alan, Dir.-Human Resources--Peoples Telephone Company, Inc., Miami, FL; *U.S. Public*, pg. 1275
Macfarland, Molly, V.P.-Human Resources--Boeing Commercial Airplane Group, Renton, WA; *U.S. Public*, pg. 240
Macgillis, A. Roy, V.P.-Personnel--London International, U.S. Holdings Inc., Norcross, GA; *Int'l*, pg. 815
Macguire, Carrie, Admin.-Human Resources--Acceptance Insurance Companies, Inc., Omaha, NE; *U.S. Public*, pg. 15
Macgurie, Carrie, Admin.-Human Resources--Acceptance Insurance Co., Inc., Omaha, NE; *U.S. Public*, pg. 14
Machin, Robert, V.P.-Human Resources--Rhone-Poulenc Inc., Princeton, NJ; *Int'l*, pg. 1112
Maciak, Walter, V.P.-H.R.--Klein Tools Inc., Skokie, IL; *U.S. Private*, pg. 625
Maciejewski, Elizabeth, Mgr.-Human Resources--Ohmite Manufacturing Company, Skokie, IL; *U.S. Private*, pg. 813
Macik, Mike, V.P.-Human Resources-Kmart Stores--Kmart Corporation, Troy, MI; *U.S. Public*, pg. 963
Macintyre, Alasdair, Dir.-H.R.--Scottish Widows' Fund & Life Assurance Society, Edinburgh, United Kingdom; *Int'l*, pg. 1212
Mack, Raymond P., V.P.-Human Resources--Arvin Industries, Inc., Columbus, IN; *U.S. Public*, pg. 136
Mackesy, Jerome C., V.P.-Human Resources--Risdon Corporation, Naugatuck, CT; *U.S. Public*, pg. 463
Mackin, James, V.P.-H.R. & Admin.--DynCorp, Reston, VA; *U.S. Private*, pg. 351
MacLean, Robert, V.P.-Human Resources--National Semiconductor Corporation, Santa Clara, CA; *U.S. Public*, pg. 1159
MacNeil, Bonnie, Dir.-Corp. H.R.--Candle Corporation, Santa Monica, CA; *U.S. Private*, pg. 204
MacWilliams, Marcia, Rep.-Human Resources--Sipex Corporation, Billerica, MA; *Int'l*, pg. 1415
Madden, Christopher J., V.P.-H.R.--Helix Technology Corp., Mansfield, MA; *U.S. Public*, pg. 808
Madden, Denis, Grp. Dir.-Personnel--John Laing PLC, London, United Kingdom; *Int'l*, pg. 796
Madden, Terry, V.P.-Industrial Rels. & Personnel--Alfred Nickles Bakery, Inc., Navarre, OH; *U.S. Private*, pg. 799
Madden, Terry, V.P.-Indus. Rels. & Personnel--Nickles Bakery, Inc., Martins Ferry, OH; *U.S. Private*, pg. 799
Maddock, Barbara M., Sr. V.P.-Human Resources--The McGraw-Hill Companies, New York, NY; *U.S. Public*, pg. 1069
Maddona, Nancy D., Dir.-Personnel--Gudebrod, Inc., Pottstown, PA; *U.S. Private*, pg. 486
Madriz, Magda, V.P.-Human Resources--Xicor, Inc., Milpitas, CA; *U.S. Public*, pg. 1785
Madsen, Marci, Dir.-Human Resources--Gottschalks Inc., Fresno, CA; *U.S. Public*, pg. 754
Maeda, Faye, Dir.-Human Resource Devel.--Hawaiian Electric Company, Inc., Honolulu, HI; *U.S. Public*, pg. 800
Maffa, Kim, Dir.-Human Resources--Cytogen Corporation, Princeton, NJ; *U.S. Public*, pg. 471
Magary, Richard, Sr. V.P.-Admin. & Asst. Sec.--American Shared Hospital Services, San Francisco, CA; *U.S. Public*, pg. 91
Magistris, De, Dir.-H.R.--Olivetti SpA, Turin, Italy; *Int'l*, pg. 1002
Magness, Michael L., Mgr.-Personnel--Memphis Light, Gas & Water, Memphis, TN; *U.S. Private*, pg. 731
Magnus-Jackson, Judy, Sr. V.P. & Human Resources Dir.--Wunderman Cato Johnson, New York, NY; *U.S. Private*, pg. 1197
Magruder, Jack, Dir.-H.R.--The Coca-Cola Bottling Co. of New York, Inc., Hawthorne, NY; *U.S. Public*, pg. 393
Maharam, Stephen, Exec. V.P.-Fin. & Personnel--Maharam, Hauppauge, NY; *U.S. Private*, pg. 696
Maher, Carol A., V.P.-Human Resources--DM Management Company, Hingham, MA; *U.S. Public*, pg. 473
Maher, Marlene, V.P.-H.R.--Maxwell Technologies, Inc., San Diego, CA; *U.S. Public*, pg. 1061
Maher, Michael, Dir.-H.R.--Dalgety Plc, London, United Kingdom; *Int'l*, pg. 376
Mahler, Thomas R., Sec. & Gen. Counsel--Analysts International Corporation, Minneapolis, MN; *U.S. Public*, pg. 110
Mahon, Barb, Mgr.-H.R.--Buck Knives, Inc., El Cajon, CA; *U.S. Private*, pg. 177
Mahoney, Janet H., V.P.-Worldwide H.R.--Sybase, Inc., Emeryville, CA; *U.S. Public*, pg. 1544
Mahoney, W.E., V.P.-Human Resources--Tasty Baking Company, Philadelphia, PA; *U.S. Public*, pg. 1561
Mahoney, William, Mgr.-Human Resources--Norton Performance Plastics, Wayne, NJ; *Int'l*, pg. 1174
Maialetti, Sheila, Mgr.-Human Resources--American Travellers Corporation, Bensalem, PA; *U.S. Public*, pg. 433
Maidel, Jacquie R., V.P.-Human Resources--Geraghty & Miller, Inc., Denver, CO; *Int'l*, pg. 607
Major, David, V.P.-H.R.--Townsends, Inc., Wilmington, DE; *U.S. Private*, pg. 1094
Makahilahila, Bill, V.P.-Human Resources--SGS-Thomson Microelectronics, Inc., Carrollton, TX; *Int'l*, pg. 1153

Maki, Hisashi, Mng. Dir.-Personnel & Gen. Mgr.-Gen. Affairs Bureau, Tokyo--Nihon Keizai Shimbun, Inc., Tokyo, Japan; *Int'l*, pg. 929
Makoski, Milton J., V.P.-H.R.--Echlin Inc., Branford, CT; *U.S. Public*, pg. 560
Malarik, Edward F., V.P.-Human Resources--Best Foods, Englewood Cliffs, NJ; *U.S. Public*, pg. 224
Malenfant, Jacques, V.P.-Human Resources--Caisse de depot et placement du Quebec, Montreal, Canada; *Int'l*, pg. 249
Malivert, Daniel, Mgr.-Personnel--Laboratoire LaChartre S.A., Blois, France; *U.S. Public*, pg. 1331
Mallarkey, Nancy, Dir.-Human Resources & Office Admin.--Borg-Warner Security Corporation, Chicago, IL; *U.S. Public*, pg. 245
Mallet, Rosalyn T., V.P.-Human Resources--Applebee's International, Inc., Overland Park, KS; *U.S. Public*, pg. 122
Mallon, Charlie, V.P.-Fin.--Right Management Consultants, Inc., Philadelphia, PA; *U.S. Public*, pg. 1390
Malone, Celeste, Dir.-Personnel--Misener Marine Construction, Tampa, FL; *U.S. Private*, pg. 752
Malone, Charles, V.P.-Human Resources--Electrolux Corporation, Atlanta, GA; *U.S. Private*, pg. 369
Malone, Steve, Mgr.-Employee Commun. & Library--Burr-Brown Corporation, Tucson, AZ; *U.S. Public*, pg. 270
Maloney, W., Dir.-Personnel--Elizabethtown Gas Co., Union, NJ; *U.S. Public*, pg. 1147
Malta, Debra, Dir.-H.R.--The Will-Burt Company, Orrville, OH; *U.S. Private*, pg. 1177
Maltby, JoAnn, Mgr.-Human Resources & Office Mgr.--Taracorp, Inc., Atlanta, GA; *U.S. Private*, pg. 1068
Mandia, Dick, Dir.-Human Devel.--Black Box Corporation of PA, Lawrence, PA; *U.S. Public*, pg. 235
Mandis, Marcia, Mgr.-Human Resources--Millipore Tylan Products, San Diego, CA; *U.S. Public*, pg. 1112
Mandracchia, Robert, Mgr.-H.R.--Dettra Flag Company, Oaks, PA; *U.S. Private*, pg. 328
Manes, Eunice C., V.P.-Human Resources--Blue Cross & Blue Shield of Texas, Inc., Richardson, TX; *U.S. Private*, pg. 152
Manes, Nancy, Dir.-Personnel--Central Maine Newspapers, Augusta, ME; *U.S. Private*, pg. 439
Mangerson, Debbie, Mgr.-H.R.--Hammond Group Inc., Hammond, IN; *U.S. Private*, pg. 498
Manigold, Robert E., V.P.-H.R.--Arinc Inc. (Consolidated), Annapolis, MD; *U.S. Private*, pg. 81
Manis, Jon, Acting Dir.-Human Resources--Sterling Healthcare Group, Inc., Miami, FL; *U.S. Public*, pg. 608
Mank, Karen L., V.P.-Compensation & Benefits--Hannaford Bros. Co., Scarborough, ME; *U.S. Public*, pg. 781
Mankus, Cynthia, Mgr.-H.R.--Speedway Motorsports, Inc., Concord, NC; *U.S. Public*, pg. 1498
Manley, Robert, Dir.-Human Resources--Savin Corporation, Stamford, CT; *Int'l*, pg. 1114
Manly, Marylyn, Mgr.-Human Resources--Harmony Engineering Corporation, Minneapolis, MN; *U.S. Private*, pg. 503
Mann, Bruce, Dir.-Human Resources--Parametric Technology Corporation, Waltham, MA; *U.S. Public*, pg. 1257
Mann, Donald C., Sr. V.P.-Human Resources--The Prudential Investment Corp., Newark, NJ; *U.S. Private*, pg. 892
Mann, Katie, Mgr.-H.R.--Genesee Metal Stampings, Inc., West Henrietta, NY; *U.S. Private*, pg. 446
Mann, Morris, V.P.-Personnel Opers.--UMI, Ann Arbor, MI; *U.S. Public*, pg. 201
Mannelli, Romain, Dir.-Personnel--CLT-UFA, Luxembourg, Luxembourg; *Int'l*, pg. 561
Mannes, Barry L., Sr. V.P.-H.R.--Travelers Group, New York, NY; *U.S. Public*, pg. 1632
Mannes, Cindy, V.P.-H.R. & Admin.--Marcus Cable Company, L.P., Dallas, TX; *U.S. Private*, pg. 702
Manning-Dutko, Debra, Mgr.-Human Resources--ESA, Inc., Chelmsford, MA; *U.S. Private*, pg. 354
Manning, James D., V.P.-H.R.--Crane & Co., Inc., Dalton, MA; *U.S. Private*, pg. 286
Mannschreck, Stephen L., Chief Human Resources Officer--American Stores Company, Salt Lake City, UT; *U.S. Public*, pg. 92
Mansfield, James, Dir.-Human Resources--Keystone Powdered Metal Company, Saint Marys, PA; *U.S. Private*, pg. 619
Mansfield, Jeff, Dir.-Personnel--East Coast Steel, Inc., Claremont, NH; *U.S. Private*, pg. 356
Manske, Joyce, Dir.-H.R.--Southwest Recreational Industries Inc., Leander, TX; *U.S. Private*, pg. 1018
Manson, Janet, Dir.-Human Res.--Pearle Inc., Dallas, TX; *U.S. Public*, pg. 396
Manson, Joan, Dir.-Human Resources--Pearle Vision Express, Dallas, TX; *U.S. Public*, pg. 397
Mansson, Ola, Pres.--Skanska Teknik AB, Malmo, Sweden; *Int'l*, pg. 1261
Manyon, Mary Kay, Mgr.-Human Resources--U.S. Safety, Lenexa, KS; *U.S. Private*, pg. 1125
Manzon-Winsser, Marianne, Dir.-Personnel--Ionics, Incorporated, Watertown, MA; *U.S. Public*, pg. 912
Maples, Susan, Mgr.-H.R.--American Kennel Club, Inc., New York, NY; *U.S. Private*, pg. 58
Marcello, Christine, Mgr.-H.R.--Tropar Mfg. Co., Inc., Florham Park, NJ; *U.S. Private*, pg. 1105
Marcello, Joan, Dir.-Pub. Rels.--Northville Industries Corp., Melville, NY; *U.S. Private*, pg. 806
Marchal, Andre, Gen. Mgr.-H.R. & Info.--Electrabel S.A., Brussels, Belgium; *Int'l*, pg. 436
Marchant, James R., V.P.-Human Resources--Avenor, Inc., Montreal, Canada; *Int'l*, pg. 101
Marchildren, Christine, Sr. V.P.-Corp. Services--Federation des caisses populaires Desjardins, Montreal, Canada; *Int'l*, pg. 479
Marchio, Cathy, V.P. & Human Resources & Admin. Dir.--Miller Meester Advertising Inc., Minneapolis, MN; *U.S. Private*, pg. 747
Marcolina, Peter, Mgr.-Personnel--Reeds Jewelers, Inc., Wilmington, NC; *U.S. Public*, pg. 1370
Marcus, Matt, Dir.-Human Resources--Inverness Corp., Fair Lawn, NJ; *U.S. Private*, pg. 574
Marcus, Stuart L., V.P.-H.R.--Phelps Dodge Corporation, Phoenix, AZ; *U.S. Public*, pg. 1286
Mardenborough, Leslie, V.P.-H.R.--The New York Times Company, New York, NY; *U.S. Public*, pg. 1173
Marek, John J., V.P. & Controller--Huffy Sports Company, Sussex, WI; *U.S. Public*, pg. 846
Marek, Steve I., Dir.-Human Resources--Living Centers of America, Houston, TX; *U.S. Public*, pg. 1257
Mares, Fidencio M., V.P.-Human Resources--Beckman Instruments, Inc., Fullerton, CA; *U.S. Public*, pg. 199
Maresh, Richard, Dir.-Personnel--Ennis Business Forms, Inc., Ennis, TX; *U.S. Public*, pg. 583
Margerum, Marie, Payroll Mgr. & Human Resources Admin.--Gillespie Public Relations, Princeton, NJ; *U.S. Private*, pg. 454
Margetts, R.J., Grp. Dir.-Personnel & Engrng.--Imperial Chemical Industries PLC, London, United Kingdom; *Int'l*, pg. 662
Margetts, W. Thomas, Sr. V.P.-Human Resources, Gen. Counsel & Sec.--Stant Corporation, Denver, CO; *Int'l*, pg. 1396
Margolis, Bruce, Sr. V.P. & Dir.-Human Services/The Marmaxx Grp.--The TJX Companies, Inc., Framingham, MA; *U.S. Public*, pg. 1556
Margolis, Bruce, Sr. V.P.-Human Resources--T.J. Maxx, Framingham, MA; *U.S. Public*, pg. 1557
Maring, Faye L., V.P. & Dir.-Human Resources--Omega Financial Corporation, State College, PA; *U.S. Public*, pg. 1222
Marinho de Castro, Antonio, Sr. Mgr.-Human Resources & Training--Caixa Geral de Depositos, Lisbon, Portugal; *Int'l*, pg. 250
Marino, G., Mgr.-Personnel--Zanussi Elettrodomestici S.p.A., Pordenone, Italy; *Int'l*, pg. 442
Mark, Rick, V.P.-Human Resources--Drexel Heritage Furnishings Inc., Drexel, NC; *U.S. Private*, pg. 432
Markis, William G., Mgr.-Personnel--Maxon Industries, Inc., Huntington Park, CA; *U.S. Private*, pg. 717
Markle, Garold L., V.P.-Human Resources--Columbian Chemicals Company, Atlanta, GA; *U.S. Public*, pg. 1286
Markow, Alan, V.P.-Corp. Communications--National Semiconductor Corporation, Santa Clara, CA; *U.S. Public*, pg. 1159
Marks, Amy P., Sr. V.P.-Human Resources--USF&G Corporation, Baltimore, MD; *U.S. Public*, pg. 1659
Marmash, Bohdan V., V.P.-Human Resources--Royal LePage Limited, Don Mills, Canada; *Int'l*, pg. 1143
Marnich, Gayvaughn, Mgr.-Human Resources--Amgen Boulder, Inc., Boulder, CO; *U.S. Public*, pg. 101
Marold, Allen D., V.P.-Human Resources & Admin.--Bowne & Co., Inc., New York, NY; *U.S. Public*, pg. 248
Marold, Louis, Sec. & Mgr.-H.R.--Maxcor Manufacturing, Inc., Colorado Springs, CO; *U.S. Private*, pg. 716
Maron, Annerose E., V.P. & Human Resource Officer--Horizon Bancorp, Michigan City, IN; *U.S. Private*, pg. 538
Marquaire, Jean-Francois, Sr. V.P.-Legal & Human Resources--Compagnie Generale de Geophysique, Massy, France; *Int'l*, pg. 241
Marquette, Jennifer, Mgr.-Personnel--The Garber Company, Ashland, OH; *U.S. Public*, pg. 303
Marquez, Susan, Dir.-Human Resources--Press Enterprise Company, Riverside, CA; *U.S. Public*, pg. 209
Marquis-Moore, Freida, V.P.-H.R.--Domco Inc., Farnham, Canada; *Int'l*, pg. 415
Marr, Diane, Dir.-Personnel--Seattle Post-Intelligencer, Seattle, WA; *U.S. Private*, pg. 517
Marre, Roger, Sr. V.P.-Personnel & Safety--Compagnie Generale de Geophysique, Massy, France; *Int'l*, pg. 241
Marrese, Thomas, V.P.-Human Resources--Consolidated Cigar Corp., Fort Lauderdale, FL; *U.S. Private*, pg. 690
Marsden, Janet, Dir.-Personnel--Iceland Frozen Foods plc., Deeside, United Kingdom; *Int'l*, pg. 658
Marsey, Steve, Dir.-Human Resources--Linear Technology Corp., Milpitas, CA; *U.S. Public*, pg. 1000
Marsh, Michael G., Gen. Counsel, Sec. & Mgr.-Human Resources--Todd Pacific Shipyards Corp., Seattle, WA; *U.S. Public*, pg. 1619
Marsh, Miriam, Dir.-Human Resources--Authentic Fitness Corp., Los Angeles, CA; *U.S. Public*, pg. 147
Marsh, Pamela, Sr. V.P. & Dir.-H.R.--INMC Mortgage Holdings, Inc., Pasadena, CA; *U.S. Public*, pg. 857
Marshall, Don, Dir.-H.R.--Sound Advice, Inc., Dania, FL; *U.S. Public*, pg. 1488
Marshall, Ed, Mgr.-Pub. Rels.--First National Bank of Commerce, New Orleans, LA; *U.S. Public*, pg. 629
Marshall, Harold, Dir.-Employment & Benefits--Yellow Corporation, Overland Park, KS; *U.S. Public*, pg. 1788
Marshall, Madria, Dir.-Personnel--UHP Healthcare, Inglewood, CA; *U.S. Private*, pg. 1113
Marshall, Mike, Controller-Employee Rels.--Qantas Airways Ltd., London, United Kingdom; *Int'l*, pg. 1075
Marshall, Richard, Dir.-Human Resources--Pollo Tropical, Inc., Miami, FL; *U.S. Public*, pg. 1315
Marshall, Tom, V.P.-H.R.--Castleberry/Snow's Brands Inc., Augusta, GA; *U.S. Private*, pg. 219
Marsilio, Dale, Dir.-Personnel--Great Scott Advertising Co. Inc., New York, NY; *U.S. Private*, pg. 475
Marston, Richard, Mgr.-Human Resources--Fraser Papers, Inc., Stamford, CT; *Int'l*, pg. 434
Martell, Sandy, Dir.-H.R.--Imperial Hotels, El Segundo, CA; *U.S. Private*, pg. 558
Martels, Fred, Dir.-Personnel--Dierbergs Markets Inc., Chesterfield, MO; *U.S. Private*, pg. 332
Martin, Betty, Dir.-Human Resources--Duff-Norton, Charlotte, NC; *U.S. Public*, pg. 406
Martin, Brent, Dir.-H.R.--PST Vans, Inc., Salt Lake City, UT; *U.S. Public*, pg. 1246
Martin, Brian J., Sr. V.P.-Human Resources & Gen. Counsel--Proffitt's, Inc., Alcoa, TN; *U.S. Public*, pg. 1333
Martin, Christine, Human Resources Dir.--Jordan, McGrath, Case & Taylor Inc., New York, NY; *U.S. Private*, pg. 598
Martin, Dawn, Dir.-Employee Benefits & Svcs.--WD-40 Company, San Diego, CA; *U.S. Public*, pg. 1726
Martin, Delaine, Mgr.-H.R.--Fournier Furniture, Saint Paul, VA; *U.S. Private*, pg. 422
Martin, Diane, Mgr.-Human Resources & Benefits--A.G. Simpson Co. Limited, Scarborough, Canada; *Int'l*, pg. 1252
Martin, Dixie, Mgr.-Personnel--Gem-Dandy, Inc., Madison, NC; *U.S. Private*, pg. 442
Martin, Don R., V.P. & Grp. Exec.-Human Resources--Ball Aerospace & Technologies Corp., Broomfield, CO; *U.S. Public*, pg. 171
Martin, Ed, Exec. V.P.-Human Resources--Showboat, Incorporated, Las Vegas, NV; *U.S. Public*, pg. 1469
Martin, Jack, V.P.-H.R.--Land O'Lakes, Inc., Arden Hills, MN; *U.S. Private*, pg. 645
Martin, Jack, V.P.-Human Resources--Hospital Staffing Services, Inc., Fort Lauderdale, FL; *U.S. Public*, pg. 840
Martin, Jerry C., Chief Fin. Officer & Sr. V.P.--Global Marine Inc., Houston, TX; *U.S. Public*, pg. 748
Martin, Kay, Dir.-Human Resources--McRae Industries, Inc., Mount Gilead, NC; *U.S. Public*, pg. 1073
Martin, M. Retta, Mgr.-Human Resources--Ruetgers-Nease Corporation, State College, PA; *Int'l*, pg. 1148
Martin, Marcia P., Sr. V.P.-Personnel--Alfa Corporation, Montgomery, AL; *U.S. Public*, pg. 40
Martin, Matthew T., Dir.-Personnel--Coltec Holdings Inc, Charlotte, NC; *U.S. Public*, pg. 401
Martin, Pierre, Dir.-Human Resources--Steelcase Strafor, Strasbourg, France; *Int'l*, pg. 569
Martin, Rebecca, Dir.-Human Resources--Argo Instruments Inc., Winchester, VA; *Int'l*, pg. 839
Martin, Rocine, Dir.-H.R.--Nulaid Foods, Ripon, CA; *U.S. Private*, pg. 809
Martinez, Doris, Dir.-H.R.--RIU International Pan American Ocean Resort Hotel, Miami Beach, FL; *U.S. Private*, pg. 904
Martinez, Estefania, Gen. Sec.-H.R.--Monsanto Argentina S.A.I.C., Buenos Aires, Argentina; *U.S. Public*, pg. 1125
Martinez, Gustavo, Mgr.-Personnel--A.C. Nielsen Company S.A., Madrid, Spain; *U.S. Public*, pg. 1183
Martinez, Miriam, Dir.-Personnel--Bel Fuse Inc., Jersey City, NJ; *U.S. Public*, pg. 200
Martinez, Yvonne, Mgr.-Human Resources--The Dwyer Group, Inc., Waco, TX; *U.S. Public*, pg. 537
Martins, Mary H., Dir.-Human Resources--Patterson Dental Company, Saint Paul, MN; *U.S. Public*, pg. 1265
Martisch, Peggy, Mgr.-H.R.--Tuscan/Lehigh Dairies LP, Union, NJ; *U.S. Private*, pg. 1110
Martucci, Joseph, Dir.-H.R.--LaRoche Industries Inc., Atlanta, GA; *U.S. Private*, pg. 651
Martyn, Simon A., Sr. V.P.-Grp. Human Resources-USA--HSBC Americas, Buffalo, NY; *Int'l*, pg. 580
Martyn, Simon A., Exec. V.P.-Grp. Human Resources-USA--Marine Midland Bank, Buffalo, NY; *Int'l*, pg. 581
Marvin, Mary, V.P.-Personnel--Minyard Food Stores, Inc., Coppell, TX; *U.S. Private*, pg. 752
Marx, Jurg, Exec. V.P.-Human Resources--The Swissair Group, Zurich, Switzerland; *Int'l*, pg. 1333
Mascari, Thomas A., Mgr.-Employee Rels.--Reeves Division, Columbus, IN; *U.S. Public*, pg. 1398
Mascia, Frank, Mgr.-H.R.--United Aluminum Corporation, North Haven, CT; *U.S. Private*, pg. 1120
Mask, Gary, V.P.-Human Resources--Sunbeam Corporation, Delray Beach, FL; *U.S. Public*, pg. 1533
Mason, Charles, V.P.-H.R.--Sunclipse, Inc., Buena Park, CA; *Int'l*, pg. 72
Mason, Chellie, Mgr.-H.R.--Divi Hotels, Inc., Chapel Hill, NC; *U.S. Private*, pg. 336
Mason, Clive, Dir.-Personnel--Ploof Truck Lines, Inc., Jacksonville, FL; *U.S. Private*, pg. 872
Mason, Dan, V.P.-Opers. & Dir.-Personnel--Capitol Group, Springfield, IL; *U.S. Private*, pg. 206
Mason, Kenneth, V.P.-H.R.--Sonoco Engraph, Inc., Atlanta, GA; *U.S. Public*, pg. 1486
Mason, Laura, Personnel Asst.--MBI Inc., Norwalk, CT; *U.S. Private*, pg. 685
Mason, Robert J., Mgr.-Indus. Rels. & Payroll--Western Atlas International, Inc., Houston, TX; *U.S. Public*, pg. 1757
Mason, Robert W., Dir.-Human Resources--Selas Corporation of America, Dresher, PA; *U.S. Public*, pg. 1454
Masoud, Keith, Dir.-Personnel--Beach Mold & Tool Inc., New Albany, IN; *U.S. Private*, pg. 125
Mass, Jackie, V.P.-H.R.--American Business Information, Inc., Omaha, NE; *U.S. Public*, pg. 69
Massey, James P., V.P.-Human Resources & Quality--Osborn Manufacturing, Cleveland, OH; *U.S. Public*, pg. 924
Masson, D.C., Dir.-Personnel--BTU International, Inc., North Billerica, MA; *U.S. Public*, pg. 164
Massucco, R., Mgr.-Personnel--Bryant Grinder Corp., Springfield, VT; *U.S. Private*, pg. 461
Mast, Julia K., Mgr.-Human Resources--Tiger Direct, Inc., Miami, FL; *U.S. Public*, pg. 747
Mastilock, Dianne, V.P.-H.R.--Digital Link Corporation, Sunnyvale, CA; *U.S. Public*, pg. 508
Masukawa, Hitoei, Exec. V.P.-Personnel--Ito-Yokado Co., Ltd., Tokyo, Japan; *Int'l*, pg. 693
Masulli, Denise, Coord.-Personnel--Bridgeport Machines, Inc., Bridgeport, CT; *U.S. Public*, pg. 251
Masullo, Nick, V.P.-Human Resources--Levitz Furniture Incorporated, Boca Raton, FL; *U.S. Public*, pg. 990
Masumoto, Hideo, Dir.-Human Resources--Henkel S/A Industrias Quimicas, Sao Paulo, Brazil; *Int'l*, pg. 613
Mata, Doris, Personnel Admin.--California Panel & Veneer Company, Cerritos, CA; *U.S. Private*, pg. 201
Mata, Rhonda, Mgr.-Personnel--California Hardware Company, Ontario, CA; *U.S. Private*, pg. 335
Matejka, Glen, V.P.-H.R.--Actron Manufacturing Company, Cleveland, OH; *U.S. Private*, pg. 16

Matheny, Joy, Human Resources Mgr.--GSD&M, Austin, TX; *U.S. Private*, pg. 436
Matheny, Steve, V.P.-Human Resources--Highlights for Children, Inc., Columbus, OH; *U.S. Private*, pg. 528
Matheson, Glenn D., V.P.-Human Resources--Weyerhaeuser Canada Ltd., Vancouver, Canada; *U.S. Public*, pg. 1764
Matheson, James A., V.P.-Fin.--Advanced Magnetics, Inc., Cambridge, MA; *U.S. Public*, pg. 20
Mathews, Juli A., V.P.-Human Resources--Printronix, Inc., Irvine, CA; *U.S. Public*, pg. 1329
Mathews, Nick, Mgr.-H.R.--Performance Contracting Group, Lenexa, KS; *U.S. Private*, pg. 853
Mathews, Sharon, Dir.-Human Resources--Pip Printing, Agoura Hills, CA; *U.S. Private*, pg. 423
Mathewson, Robert W., Sr. V.P.-Human Resources--Schuller International, Inc., Denver, CO; *U.S. Public*, pg. 927
Mathias, Jean-Louis, Exec. V.P. & Head-Human Resources-Electricite de France, Paris, France; *Int'l*, pg. 437
Mathias, Jean-Louis, Exec. V.P.-H.R.--Gaz de France, Paris, France; *Int'l*, pg. 541
Mathias, Lawrence L., V.P.-H.R. & Pub. Rels.--American Crystal Sugar Company, Moorhead, MN; *U.S. Private*, pg. 52
Mathieson, T. Stuart, V.P.-H.R.--Cominco, Ltd., Vancouver, Canada; *Int'l*, pg. 307
Mathieu, Francis, Dir.-Human Resources & Training--Promodes SA, Mondeville, France; *Int'l*, pg. 1071
Mathieu, Mark, V.P.-H.R.--The Stanley Works, New Britain, CT; *U.S. Public*, pg. 1508
Mathieu, Y., Mgr.-Human Resources--ANTEA SA, Orleans, France; *Int'l*, pg. 607
Mathis, Laurie, Dir.-Personnel--Republic Automotive Parts, Inc., Brentwood, TN; *U.S. Public*, pg. 1377
Mathis, T. C., Dir.-Human Resources--Benzonia Manufacturing, Benzonia, MI; *U.S. Private*, pg. 753
Mathis, T. C., Dir.-Human Resources--Mitchell Corporation, Clare Div., Clare, MI; *U.S. Private*, pg. 753
Mathis, Tom, Dir.-H.R.--Mitchell Corporation of Owosso, Owosso, MI; *U.S. Private*, pg. 753
Mathwich, Lyle, Dir.-Human Resources Admin.--Stokely USA, Inc., Oconomowoc, WI; *U.S. Public*, pg. 1518
Matiya, Mary, Mgr.-Human Resources Services--A.E. Staley Manufacturing Co., Decatur, IL; *Int'l*, pg. 1356
Matson, Paul, V.P.-Human Resources--Moore Document Solutions, Lake Forest, IL; *Int'l*, pg. 890
Matsuda, Yoshifumi, Dir.-Gen. Affairs & Personnel--Tokuyama Corporation, Tokyo, Japan; *Int'l*, pg. 1393
Matsumoto, Iris, Dir.-H.R.--Maui Land & Pineapple Co., Inc., Kahului, HI; *U.S. Public*, pg. 1060
Mattern, James, V.P.-Admin.--Black Hills Corporation, Rapid City, SD; *U.S. Public*, pg. 235
Matteuzzi, Karen, Mgr.-H.R.--Express Scripts, Inc., Maryland Heights, MO; *U.S. Public*, pg. 600
Matthews, Frank, V.P.-H.R.--U.S. Home Corporation, Houston, TX; *U.S. Public*, pg. 1682
Matthews, John, Sr. V.P.-Human Resources & Risk Mngmt.-Costco Wholesale, Issaquah, WA; *U.S. Public*, pg. 451
Matthews, Robert, Sr. V.P.-Employee Rels.--Philips Electronics North America Corporation, New York, NY; *Int'l*, pg. 1053
Matthiesen, JoAnn, V.P.-Pub. Rels. & Organizational Devel. & Asst. to Chm. Bd.--The Washington Water Power Company, Spokane, WA; *U.S. Public*, pg. 1744
Mattox, Kathleen, Mgr.-Human Resources--McDougal/Littell, Evanston, IL; *U.S. Public*, pg. 841
Mattson, Esther J., Dir.-Human Resources--Crompton & Knowles Corporation, Stamford, CT; *U.S. Public*, pg. 459
Matyas, Burke, Dir.-H.R.--American Decal & Mfg. Co., Chicago, IL; *U.S. Private*, pg. 53
Matzko, Michael M., Dir.-Human Resources--The Danis Companies, Dayton, OH; *U.S. Private*, pg. 310
Mauceri, Susan, V.P.-Human Resources--K-III Media Group, New York, NY; *U.S. Public*, pg. 1328
Maudlin, Gwen, Personnel Administrator--Eager Beaver, Lake Wales, FL; *U.S. Private*, pg. 354
Maul, Karen, V.P.-H.R.--L. Robert Kimball & Associates, Ebensburg, PA; *U.S. Private*, pg. 619
Maunders, Don, Dir.-People Potential--A&W Food Services of Canada Inc., North Vancouver, Canada; *Int'l*, pg. 1
Maurer, Christopher, Sr. V.P.-Human Resources--FirstMerit Corporation, Akron, OH; *U.S. Public*, pg. 646
Mauser, Theodore, V.P.-Human Resources--Cincinnati Milacron Inc., Cincinnati, OH; *U.S. Public*, pg. 368
Maxwell, Evelyn, Mgr.-Personnel--Triplett Corporation, Bluffton, OH; *U.S. Private*, pg. 1104
Maxwell, Hosie L., Chief Information Officer & Sr. V.P.-Opers.--Virginia First Savings Bank, F.S.B., Petersburg, VA; *U.S. Public*, pg. 1721
Maxwell, Robert, V.P.-Human Resources--Edwards Systems Tech, Cheshire, CT; *U.S. Public*, pg. 726
May, Janet, Dir.-Personnel--Texas Refinery Corp., Fort Worth, TX; *U.S. Private*, pg. 1078
May, L.H., V.P. & Dir.-Assoc. Rels. & Benefits--Winn-Dixie Stores, Inc., Jacksonville, FL; *U.S. Public*, pg. 1771
May, Linda, Chief Fin. Officer--Bam Media, Pleasant Hill, CA; *U.S. Private*, pg. 113
May, Nancy, V.P.-H.R.--Rexall Sundown Inc., Boca Raton, FL; *U.S. Public*, pg. 1384
Mayer, Bill, V.P.-Human Resources--OCE-U.S.A., Itasca, IL; *Int'l*, pg. 994
Mayer, Donna, Dir.-Human Resources--The Sorg Paper Co., Middletown, OH; *U.S. Public*, pg. 1747
Mayer, Steve, Mgr.-H.R.--United States Bakery, Portland, OR; *U.S. Private*, pg. 1124
Mayes, Michelle, V.P.-Human Resources--Colgate U.S.A., New York, NY; *U.S. Public*, pg. 397
Mayger, John, Mgr.-H.R.--Monaco Coach Corporation, Coburg, OR; *U.S. Public*, pg. 1123
Mayne, Carol, V.P.-H.R.--Burnham, Atlanta, GA; *Int'l*, pg. 686
Mays, Ted, V.P.-Personnel--Mays Chemical Company, Indianapolis, IN; *U.S. Private*, pg. 718
Mazarella, Linda L., V.P. & Dir.-Human Resources--Santa Monica Bank, Santa Monica, CA; *U.S. Public*, pg. 1757
Mazza, Maxine, Dir.-H.R.--Gray Printing Co., Fostoria, OH; *U.S. Private*, pg. 472
McAlister, Robert O., V.P.-H.R. & Admin.--Sterling Chemicals Holdings, Inc., Houston, TX; *U.S. Public*, pg. 1515
McAlister, Robert O., V.P.-Human Resources & Admin.--Sterling Chemicals, Inc., Houston, TX; *U.S. Public*, pg. 1515
McAllister, Irene F., Mgr.-Human Resources--Tuscarora Incorporated, New Brighton, PA; *U.S. Public*, pg. 1646
McAndrew, Joseph P., V.P.-H.R.--Air Products and Chemicals, Inc., Allentown, PA; *U.S. Public*, pg. 30
McAtee, James, Dir.-H.R.--SmithGroup, Inc., Detroit, MI; *U.S. Private*, pg. 1010
McAvoy, John, V.P.-Employee Rels.--Cooper Hand Tools, Raleigh, NC; *U.S. Public*, pg. 444
McBride, Beverly, Coord.-H. R.--Sooner Pipe & Supply Corp., Tulsa, OK; *U.S. Private*, pg. 1014
McCabe, Lisa, Mgr.-Human Resources--Castrol North America, Wayne, NJ; *Int'l*, pg. 235
McCain, Andrea, Mgr.-Pension Admin. & Human Resources--The Colonial BancGroup, Inc., Montgomery, AL; *U.S. Public*, pg. 400
McCall, James W., V.P.-Personnel & Public Affairs--Chesebrough-Pond's USA Co., Greenwich, CT; *Int'l*, pg. 1435
McCall, Mel, Sr. V.P.-Human Resources--CompUSA, Dallas, TX; *U.S. Public*, pg. 420
McCallion, Anne D., Exec. V.P. & Dir.-H.R.--Countrywide Home Loans Inc., Pasadena, CA; *U.S. Public*, pg. 452
McCambridge, John, Dir.-Human Resources--Voith Hydro, Inc., York, PA; *Int'l*, pg. 1473
McCammon, David, Dir.-Personnel--Air UK Ltd., Stansted, United Kingdom; *Int'l*, pg. 38
McCandless, Carolyn K., V.P.-Human Resources--Time Warner Inc., New York, NY; *U.S. Public*, pg. 1610
McCann, M.J., Mgr.-Employee & Pub. Rels.--Babcock & Wilcox Co., Barberton, OH; *U.S. Public*, pg. 1068
McCarter, Ken J., V.P.-Human Resources--Chrysler Canada Ltd., Windsor, Canada; *U.S. Public*, pg. 354
McCarthy, Al, V.P.-H.R.--Simplex Time Recorder Co., Gardner, MA; *U.S. Private*, pg. 1002
McCarthy, Jean S., Asst. V.P.-H.R.--CTG Resources, Inc., Hartford, CT; *U.S. Public*, pg. 285
McCarthy, Jean S., Asst. V.P.-H.R.--Connecticut Natural Gas Corporation, Hartford, CT; *U.S. Public*, pg. 285
McCarthy, Jean S., Asst. V.P.-H.R.--Energy Networks, Inc. (ENI), Hartford, CT; *U.S. Public*, pg. 285
McCarthy, Robyn, Mgr.-Personnel & H.R.--Illinois Tool Works Inc., Glenview, IL; *U.S. Public*, pg. 865
McCartt, Richard D., Human Resources Mgr.--UTA Iowa City Plant, Iowa City, IA; *U.S. Public*, pg. 1691
McCaslin, Teresa, Sr. V.P.-H.R.--Continental Grain Company, New York, NY; *U.S. Private*, pg. 268
McCaul, Harriette S., Sr. V.P.-Human Resources--Community First Bankshares, Inc., Fargo, ND; *U.S. Public*, pg. 416
McCauley, Leslie, Dir.-Human Resources--Wechsler Coffee Corp., Moonachie, NJ; *U.S. Private*, pg. 1158
McCellon-Allen, Venita, Sr. V.P.-Corp. Devel.--Central and South West Corporation, Dallas, TX; *U.S. Public*, pg. 324
McClendon, Karen E., V.P.-H.R.--Comcast Cellular Communications, Inc., Wayne, PA; *U.S. Public*, pg. 407
McCloskey, C. Brock, V.P.-Human Resources--Moog Automotive, Inc., Saint Louis, MO; *U.S. Public*, pg. 443
McClure, Lawerence D., V.P.-H.R.--The Dexter Corporation, Windsor Locks, CT; *U.S. Public*, pg. 504
McCluskey, M., Mgr.-Personnel--Monarch Luggage Co. Inc., Brooklyn, NY; *U.S. Private*, pg. 757
McConkey, Toni, Mgr.-Personnel--Reliability Incorporated, Houston, TX; *U.S. Public*, pg. 1373
McConnaughay, James T., V.P.-Opers. & Human Resources--Golden Grain Company, Pleasanton, CA; *U.S. Public*, pg. 1348
McCormack, Dave, Dir.-H.R.--Oasis Corp., Columbus, OH; *U.S. Private*, pg. 810
McCormack, Tom, Mgr.-Human Resources--GH Hensley Industries, Inc., Dallas, TX; *U.S. Private*, pg. 439
McCoy, Holly D., V.P.-H.R.--Farmland Industries, Inc., Kansas City, MO; *U.S. Private*, pg. 395
McCoy, John O., Jr., Chief Admin. Officer & V.P.--Pogo Producing Company, Houston, TX; *U.S. Public*, pg. 1312
McCracken, Thomas F., V.P.-Human Resources--Cogentrix Incorporated, Charlotte, NC; *U.S. Private*, pg. 249
McCreesh, Donald S., Sr. V.P.-H.R.--Northern Telecom Limited, Brampton, Canada; *Int'l*, pg. 968
McCreight, Deb, V.P.-Human Resources--Gage Marketing Group, Minneapolis, MN; *U.S. Private*, pg. 437
McCuaig, Susan M., V.P.-Human Resources--The Stride Rite Corporation, Lexington, MA; *U.S. Public*, pg. 1524
McCudden, Walter T., Dir.-Employee Rels.--WTD Industries, Inc., Portland, OR; *U.S. Public*, pg. 1729
McCue, C., Dir.-Personnel--Armatron International, Inc., Melrose, MA; *U.S. Public*, pg. 131
McCullough, Carleen, Asst. V.P. & Mgr.-Personnel--SouthTrust Bank of Charleston, Charleston, SC; *U.S. Public*, pg. 1492
McCullum, David W., V.P.-Human Resources--Mackenzie Financial Corporation, Toronto, Canada; *Int'l*, pg. 828
McCune, Dale, Dir.-H.R.--DeSoto Inc., Joliet, IL; *U.S. Public*, pg. 956
McDaneil, Donna, Mgr.-Human Resources--Mark Andy, Inc., Chesterfield, MO; *U.S. Public*, pg. 521
McDaniel, Michael K., V.P.-Human Resources--Standard Commercial Corporation, Wilson, NC; *U.S. Public*, pg. 1501
McDermott, Michael P., V.P.-H.R.--Jockey International, Inc., Kenosha, WI; *U.S. Private*, pg. 588
McDermott, Peggy, Dir.-Human Resources--Alfin, Inc., New York, NY; *U.S. Public*, pg. 40
McDonald, Barrie C., V.P.-Human Resources--Petro-Canada, Calgary, Canada; *Int'l*, pg. 1041
McDonald, Douglas J., Dir.-H.R.--PTA Corporation, Oxford, CT; *U.S. Private*, pg. 828
McDonald, Kevin, Dir.-Human Resources--Foster Wheeler Environmental Corporation, Livingston, NJ; *U.S. Public*, pg. 677
McDonald, Michael L., V.P.-Human Resources--Mead Publishing Paper, Escanaba, MI; *U.S. Public*, pg. 1074
McDonald, Philip, Mgr.-Human Resources--Hazen Paper Company, Holyoke, MA; *U.S. Private*, pg. 514
McDonald, Scott, Mgr.-Personnel--The Binkley Co., Dumas Plant, Dumas, AR; *U.S. Private*, pg. 534
McDonnell, Amy, Dir.-H.R.--RCB Baking Company, Fargo, ND; *U.S. Public*, pg. 1354
McDonough, Jeffrey, V.P.-Human Resources--Bank of the Hudson, Poughkeepsie, NY; *U.S. Public*, pg. 1319
McDougall, Ed, Dir.-H.R.--Jac Pac Foods, Ltd., Manchester, NH; *U.S. Private*, pg. 579
McDowell, Gary D., V.P.-Admin. & Human Resources--Alumax Inc., Atlanta, GA; *U.S. Public*, pg. 59
McDowell, Gloria A., Dir.-Human Resources & Sec.--Golden State Mutual Life Insurance Company, Los Angeles, CA; *U.S. Private*, pg. 461
McElfresh, Jim, Mgr.-Personnel--Behlen Mfg. Co., Columbus, NE; *U.S. Private*, pg. 130
McElfresh, Stephen B., V.P.-H.R.--SRI International, Menlo Park, CA; *U.S. Private*, pg. 958
McEllen, Linda, Dir.-H.R.--Broder Bros. Co., Plymouth, MI; *U.S. Private*, pg. 170
McElroy, John, Dir.-Human Resources & Admin.--Mitsubishi Motor Sales of America, Inc., Cypress, CA; *Int'l*, pg. 875
McEnery, Jack, Sr. V.P.-Human Resources--Budget Rent A Car Corporation, Lisle, IL; *U.S. Private*, pg. 178
McEwen, Patti, Sr. Dir.-Human Resources--DHL Worldwide Express, Redwood City, CA; *U.S. Private*, pg. 301
McFadden, Lou, Dir.-Personnel--Tropicana Casino & Resort, Atlantic City, NJ; *U.S. Public*, pg. 159
McFadden, M.L., Mgr.-Personnel--ITW Ramset/Red Head, Wood Dale, IL; *U.S. Public*, pg. 867
Mcfall, Carlyn, Dir.-Personnel--Barber Dairies, Inc., Birmingham, AL; *U.S. Private*, pg. 115
McFall, Carlyn, Dir.-Personnel--Barber Ice Cream Company, Birmingham, AL; *U.S. Private*, pg. 115
McFalls, Joan M., Dir.-H.R.--Berkshire Life Insurance Company, Pittsfield, MA; *U.S. Private*, pg. 136
McFarland, Kathy, Dir.-Human Resources--Circle International Group, Inc., San Francisco, CA; *U.S. Public*, pg. 370
McFarlane, Christine, V.P.-Human Rels.--California Water Service Co., San Jose, CA; *U.S. Public*, pg. 294
McGagin, Nancy, Mgr.-Pub. Affairs--Raley's & Bel Air, West Sacramento, CA; *U.S. Private*, pg. 907
McGee, Dave, Dir.-H.R.--Morton's of Chicago, Inc., Chicago, IL; *U.S. Public*, pg. 1136
McGee, Thomas, Human Resources--Scanforms, Inc., Bristol, PA; *U.S. Public*, pg. 228
McGee, Thomas, V.P.-Human Resources--Peterson's Guides, Inc., Princeton, NJ; *U.S. Private*, pg. 858
McGhee, Mary Ellen, H.R.--Smith Management Co., Inc., Shreveport, LA; *U.S. Private*, pg. 1009
McGillicuddy, Thomas, Dir.-Human Resources--Skyline Corporation, Elkhart, IN; *U.S. Public*, pg. 1476
McGillis, Linda, Dir.-Personnel--Guarantee Electrical Company, Saint Louis, MO; *U.S. Private*, pg. 485
McGinn, Verna, Mgr.-Human Resources--Arnolds Interiors, Inc., San Diego, CA; *U.S. Private*, pg. 546
McGinnis, Kathleen, Sr. V.P.-Human Resources--Wendy's International Inc., Dublin, OH; *U.S. Public*, pg. 1754
McGirr, Kathy, V.P.-Employee Rels.--Bull HN Information Systems Inc., Billerica, MA; *Int'l*, pg. 316
McGoey, Linda, Dir.-Human Resources--Altec Lansing Technologies, Inc., Milford, PA; *U.S. Private*, pg. 479
McGonagle, Patrick J., Pres. & Chief Exec. Officer--National Gas & Oil Company, Newark, OH; *U.S. Public*, pg. 1156
McGonnell, Trish, Dir.-Human Resources--Sentinel Consumer Products, Inc., Mentor, OH; *U.S. Private*, pg. 984
McGoogan, Charles, V.P.-Human Resources--BGF Industries Inc., Greensboro, NC; *U.S. Private*, pg. 106
McGoogan, Tom, Dir.-Personnel--QMS, Inc., Mobile, AL; *U.S. Public*, pg. 1346
McGough, John, V.P.-Human Resources--Kiwi Brands, Douglassville, PA; *U.S. Public*, pg. 1433
McGovern, John R., Dir.-Employee Benefits & Human Resources--Sunkist Growers, Inc., Sherman Oaks, CA; *U.S. Private*, pg. 1052
McGowan, Bill, V.P.-H.R.--Software AG Americas, Inc., Reston, VA; *U.S. Public*, pg. 1482
McGowan, Gay, Human Resources--Paradigm Communications, Tampa, FL; *U.S. Private*, pg. 838
McGowan, Tim, Dir.-H.R.--Bird Machine Company, South Walpole, MA; *U.S. Public*, pg. 166
McGraw, Kay, Dir.-Human Resources--The Virginian-Pilot, Norfolk, VA; *U.S. Private*, pg. 649
McGraw, M.J., Sr. V.P.- Law, Human Resources & Pub. Affairs--Brown & Williamson Tobacco Corp., Louisville, KY; *Int'l*, pg. 111
McGregor, Bob, Dir.-Human Resources--Grandy's, Inc., Lewisville, TX; *U.S. Private*, pg. 61
McGregor, D.K., V.P.-Human Resources--Wrigley Canada Inc., Don Mills, Canada; *U.S. Public*, pg. 1781
McGregor, Robert E., V.P.-Human Resources--OHM Remediation Services Corp., Findlay, OH; *U.S. Public*, pg. 1208
McGregor, Susan, Sr. V.P.-H.R.--BankAtlantic Bancorp, Inc., Fort Lauderdale, FL; *U.S. Public*, pg. 183
McGregor, Wynn D., V.P.-Human Resources--Atmos Energy Corporation, Dallas, TX; *U.S. Public*, pg. 145
McGrew, Stan, Mgr.-Human Resources--Bergen Brunswig Medical Corporation, Orange, CA; *U.S. Public*, pg. 214
McGuigan, Jane, Personnel Admin. & Corp. Travel Planner-Mitsui Foods, Inc., Norwood, NJ; *Int'l*, pg. 879
McGuigan, Kathryn T., V.P.-H.R.--Sizzler International, Inc., Los Angeles, CA; *U.S. Public*, pg. 1475

McGuigan, Thomas J., V.P.-H.R.--Freedom Forge Corporation, Burnham, PA; *U.S. Private*, pg. 425

McGuin, Dennis, Dir.-Personnel--AGI Inc., Melrose Park, IL; *U.S. Private*, pg. 5

McGuinn, Bart, Dir.-Personnel--Farm Progress Publications, Carol Stream, IL; *U.S. Public*, pg. 513

McGuire, Jim, Dir.-Human Resources--Air Express International Corporation, Darien, CT; *U.S. Public*, pg. 30

McGurl, Maureen K., Sr. V.P.-H.R.--Olsten Corporation, Melville, NY; *U.S. Public*, pg. 1220

McHale, Judith, Sr. V.P.-Admin. & Gen. Counsel--Discovery Networks, Inc., Bethesda, MD; *U.S. Private*, pg. 334

McHale, Theresa, Mgr.-Personnel--Checkpoint Systems Inc., Thorofare, NJ; *U.S. Public*, pg. 343

McHenry, Edith, Dir.-Admin. Svcs.--Sealaska Corporation, Juneau, AK; *U.S. Private*, pg. 978

McIndoe, Robert W., Dir.-H.R.--Kinross Gold Corporation, Toronto, Canada; *Int'l*, pg. 734

McInerney, Tom, Dir.-Human Resources--Bissell Inc., Grand Rapids, MI; *U.S. Private*, pg. 145

McInnes, D. Joseph, Chief Admin. Officer, Exec. V.P.-Admin. & Corp. Sec.--Blount International, Inc., Montgomery, AL; *U.S. Public*, pg. 237

McIntire, Don L., V.P.-Human Resources--Reading & Bates Corporation, Houston, TX; *U.S. Public*, pg. 1354

McIntosh, A., Dir.-Personnel--Morgan Crucible Co. Plc, Windsor, United Kingdom; *Int'l*, pg. 890

McIntyre, Donald G., V.P.-Human Resources, General Counsel & Sec.--Mitel Corporation, Kanata, Canada; *Int'l*, *pg. 870*

McKamey, Carol, Mgr.-Human Resource--Ausco Products, Inc., Benton Harbor, MI; *U.S. Private*, pg. 299

McKean, Bruce, Dir.-Human Resources--Ventura Foods LLC, City of Industry, CA; *Int'l*, pg. 879

McKean, Larry G., Sr. V.P.-H.R.--The Boeing Company, Seattle, WA; *U.S. Public*, pg. 239

McKeen, David, Dir.-Human Resources--Arjo Wiggins Appleton plc, Basingstoke, United Kingdom; *Int'l*, pg. 567

McKeever, Thomas P., V.P.-Corp. Affairs & H.R.--Blair Corporation, Warren, PA; *U.S. Public*, pg. 236

McKelvey, Doug, Mgr.-H.R.--Southwire Company, Carrollton, GA; *U.S. Private*, pg. 1019

McKelvey, John, Dir.-H.R.--WinCup, Phoenix, AZ; *U.S. Private*, pg. 1182

McKenna, Joe, Dir.-Personnel--Medical Laboratory Automation, Inc., Pleasantville, NY; *U.S. Private*, pg. 727

McKenna, Robert, V.P.-H.R.--Spectrum Control, Inc., Erie, PA; *U.S. Public*, pg. 1497

McKenzie, Donald J., V.P.-Industrial Rels.--Ford Motor Co. of Canada Ltd, Oakville, Canada; *U.S. Public*, pg. 666

McKenzie, Mary, V.P.-Human Resources--The Sharper Image, San Francisco, CA; *U.S. Public*, pg. 1464

McKenzie, Richard C., Dir.-H.R.--National Beverage Corp., Plantation, FL; *U.S. Public*, pg. 1153

McKevitt, Frank, V.P.-Human Resources--Solvay America Inc., Houston, TX; *Int'l*, pg. 1278

McKiernon, Tommy, Dir.-Personnel & Svcs.--Mississippi Chemical Corporation, Yazoo City, MS; *U.S. Public*, pg. 1117

McKinley, Eugene, V.P.-Human Resources--Food Lion, Inc., Salisbury, NC; *Int'l*, pg. 463

McKinley, Nancy, Dir.-Human Resources--Excalibur Technologies Corporation, Vienna, VA; *U.S. Public*, pg. 598

McKinney, Aida, V.P.-Admin.--AFP Imaging Corporation, Elmsford, NY; *U.S. Public*, pg. 6

McKinney, Michael, Dir.-H.R.--UniFirst Corporation, Wilmington, MA; *U.S. Public*, pg. 1665

McKinnon, Thomas E., Exec. V.P.-Human Resources--Ryder System, Inc., Miami, FL; *U.S. Public*, pg. 1413

McKnight, William, V.P.-H.R.--Marquette Bancshares Inc., Minneapolis, MN; *U.S. Private*, pg. 706

McLachlin, Daniel, V.P. & Sec.--Nabors Industries, Inc., Houston, TX; *U.S. Public*, pg. 1148

McLamb, Norma, Mgr.-H.R.--Global Software, Inc., Raleigh, NC; *U.S. Private*, pg. 457

McLane, Charles, II, V.P.-Human Resources--La Quinta Inns, Inc., San Antonio, TX; *U.S. Public*, pg. 972

McLaren, K. Louise, V.P.-Human Resources--Sun Life of Canada, Toronto, Canada; *Int'l*, pg. 1319

McLaughlin, F. Christopher, Exec. V.P.-Human Resources--Marine Midland Bank, Buffalo, NY; *Int'l*, pg. 581

McLaughlin, Maureen, Dir.-Human Resources--The Food Emporium, Bronx, NY; *Int'l*, pg. 1375

McLean, Arlis, V.P.-H.R.--Fel-Pro Incorporated, Skokie, IL; *U.S. Private*, pg. 399

McLean, Dan, Dir.-Personnel--Hampton Industries, Inc., Kinston, NC; *U.S. Public*, pg. 779

McLean, Stephen H., V.P.-Employee Rels.--Public Service Company of North Carolina, Inc., Gastonia, NC; *U.S. Public*, pg. 1340

McLean, Steve, Mgr.-H.R.--Kauffman Products, Inc., Carmel, IN; *U.S. Private*, pg. 609

McLeod, D. A., Mgr.-H.R.--Rod & Bar Products Division, Port Waratah, Australia; *Int'l*, pg. 227

McLeod, Howard, V.P.-H.R.--J.H. Harvey Company, Nashville, GA; *U.S. Private*, pg. 508

McLeod, John G., Jr., Sr. V.P.-Human Resources & Sec.--Apple South, Inc., Madison, GA; *U.S. Public*, pg. 121

McLeod, Neil A., Jr., V.P.-H.R.--Glassmaster Company, Lexington, SC; *U.S. Public*, pg. 745

McLeod, Norrie, Gen. Mgr.-Personnel--Standard Life Assurance, Edinburgh, United Kingdom; *Int'l*, pg. 1297

McMahon, Margaret, Mgr.-H.R.--Shonac Corporation, Columbus, OH; *U.S. Private*, pg. 996

McMahon, Steve, V.P.-Human Resources--Autodesk, Inc., San Rafael, CA; *U.S. Public*, pg. 148

McMath, Steve, V.P.-Human Resources--American Freightways Corporation, Harrison, AR; *U.S. Public*, pg. 75

McMillan, Maureen, V.P.-H.R.--Pacific Crest Capital, Inc., Agoura Hills, CA; *U.S. Public*, pg. 1248

McMillan, Michael, V.P.-Human Resources--Merisel, Inc., El Segundo, CA; *U.S. Public*, pg. 1095

McMillian, Marcia S., V.P.-H.R.--General American Life Insurance Co., Saint Louis, MO; *U.S. Private*, pg. 443

McMullen, Arthur, Dir.-Human Resources--Tribune Review Publishing Co., Greensburg, PA; *U.S. Private*, pg. 1102

McMullen, Chet, Mgr.-Human Resources--Airtex Products, Fairfield, IL; *U.S. Private*, pg. 1113

McMullin-Lawton, Bonnie, Dir.-H.R.--Persoft, Inc., Madison, WI; *U.S. Private*, pg. 856

McMurray, Dennis, Mgr.-Employee Rels.--National Cooperative Refinery Association, Mc Pherson, KS; *U.S. Private*, pg. 781

McNally, Michael, Sr. V.P.-Corp. & Human Resources--Rogers Group Inc., Nashville, TN; *U.S. Private*, pg. 939

McNamara, Thomas, V.P.-Human Resources--Block Drug Company, Inc., Jersey City, NJ; *U.S. Public*, pg. 236

McNeal, Cheryl D., V.P.-Human Resources--Flowserve Corporation, Dayton, OH; *U.S. Public*, pg. 658

McNeely, Joyce, Dir.-H.R.--Galpin Motors, North Hills, CA; *U.S. Private*, pg. 438

McNish, Russ, Personnel Mgr.--First American Metro Corp., Mc Lean, VA; *U.S. Public*, pg. 640

McNulty, James E., Exec. V.P.-Human Resources & Admin.--Thiokol Corporation, Ogden, UT; *U.S. Public*, pg. 1596

McOllough, Julie, Mgr.-H.R.--Hagie Manufacturing Co., Clarion, IA; *U.S. Private*, pg. 493

McPartland, Michael J., V.P.-Human Resources--The Perkin-Elmer Corporation, Norwalk, CT; *U.S. Public*, pg. 1279

McPherson, Sam, V.P.-Human Resources--Raley's & Bel Air, West Sacramento, CA; *U.S. Private*, pg. 907

McQueen, B., Mgr.-Personnel--Canon (U.K.) Ltd., Wallington, United Kingdom; *Int'l*, pg. 263

McQueen, James R., V.P.-Customer Service & Govt. Affairs--Connecticut Water Service, Inc., Clinton, CT; *U.S. Public*, pg. 431

McQuirter, Don, Mgr.-Human Resources--Volkswagen Canada, Inc., Ajax, Canada; *Int'l*, pg. 1475

McTyre, Elaine, Asst. Sec.--Electronic Tele-Communications, Inc., Waukesha, WI; *U.S. Public*, pg. 570

McVeigh, Rod, Dir.-Human Resources--Minolta Corporation, Ramsey, NJ; *Int'l*, pg. 869

McVicar, Sherry F., V.P.-Human Resources--Read-Rite Corporation, Milpitas, CA; *U.S. Public*, pg. 1366

McWhite, Leon M., V.P.-H.R.--Kellwood Company, Chesterfield, MO; *U.S. Public*, pg. 948

Mead, David, Dir.-Communications--Utah Power & Light, Salt Lake City, UT; *U.S. Public*, pg. 1251

Mead, Sarah, Sr. V.P.-H.R.--Durham Transportation, Inc., Austin, TX; *U.S. Private*, pg. 348

Meade, Debra, Dir.-Human Resources--The Roanoke Times, Roanoke, VA; *U.S. Private*, pg. 649

Meagher, Neil, V.P.-Tech. & Human Resources--Assurance vie Desjardins-Laurentienne, Levis, Canada; *Int'l*, pg. 396

Meakin, Rob, Dir.-Personnel--British Aerospace p.l.c., Farnborough, United Kingdom; *Int'l*, pg. 217

Mearns, Robert, Dir.-H.R.--GaSonics International, San Jose, CA; *U.S. Public*, pg. 703

Mease, Bill, V.P.-H.R.--Gencor Industries, Inc., Orlando, FL; *U.S. Public*, pg. 705

Medley, Gloria J., V.P.-Human Resources--Mead Specialty Paper, South Lee, MA; *U.S. Public*, pg. 1074

Meek, Donna, Mgr.-H.R.--Duncan Equipment Company, Oklahoma City, OK; *U.S. Private*, pg. 346

Mehrhoff, Malinda, Dir.-H.R.--Dakota Electric Association, Farmington, MN; *U.S. Private*, pg. 308

Mehrtens, Leslie R., Sr. V.P.-H.R.--Magna Group, Inc., Saint Louis, MO; *U.S. Public*, pg. 1037

Meier, Heiner, Head-H.R.--Clariant International Ltd., Muttenz, Switzerland; *Int'l*, pg. 624

Meier, Paul G., V.P.-Human Resources--Appleton Papers Inc., Appleton, WI; *Int'l*, pg. 567

Meineke, Susan, Mgr.-H.R.--Agouron Pharmaceuticals, Inc., La Jolla, CA; *U.S. Public*, pg. 28

Meister, Mark W., V.P.-H.R.--The Lubrizol Corporation, Wickliffe, OH; *U.S. Public*, pg. 1016

Mejer, Bruce, V.P.-H.R.--Hayes Microcomputer Products, Inc., Norcross, GA; *U.S. Public*, pg. 801

Mejia, Carlos, Dir.-Human Resources--Analog Devices, Santa Clara, CA; *U.S. Public*, pg. 108

Melbourne, Barbara, Dir.-Personnel--Conair Corporation, Stamford, CT; *U.S. Private*, pg. 261

Mele, Sheila E., Dir.-H.R.--TCI International Inc., Sunnyvale, CA; *U.S. Public*, pg. 1555

Meliker, Gary, V.P.-H.R.--Textilease Corporation, Beltsville, MD; *U.S. Private*, pg. 1079

Mellett, M.P., V.P.-H.R.--Public Service Electric & Gas Co., Newark, NJ; *U.S. Public*, pg. 1340

Mellies, Marla, Dir.-Human Resources--3Com Personal Communications Div., Skokie, IL; *U.S. Public*, pg. 1604

Mellies, Marla D., V.P.-H.R./Client Accesss--3Com Corporation, Santa Clara, CA; *U.S. Public*, pg. 1603

Melnick, Dean, Dir.-Personnel--Ingram Paper Company, City of Industry, CA; *U.S. Public*, pg. 904

Melo, John, Dir.-Personnel--A.T. Cross Co., Lincoln, RI; *U.S. Public*, pg. 460

Melore, Michael, Dir.-Human Resources--Centocor, Inc., Malvern, PA; *U.S. Public*, pg. 323

Melton, Jerry, V.P.-Human Resources--Mohawk Industries, Inc., Calhoun, GA; *U.S. Public*, pg. 1121

Melton, Lou Ann, Mgr.-Payroll & Benefits--Electrical Insulation Suppliers, Atlanta, GA; *U.S. Private*, pg. 368

Melvin, Martyn, Dir.-Human Resources--Matthew Clark Brands, Bristol, United Kingdom; *Int'l*, pg. 848

Meminger, D. Mitchell, Mgr.-Employee Rels.--Crescent/Xcelite, Sumter, SC; *U.S. Public*, pg. 444

Menager, Valerie, Dir.-H.R.--Atmel Corporation, San Jose, CA; *U.S. Public*, pg. 145

Mendenhall, Candice, Sr. V.P.-H.R.--Federal Home Loan Mortgage Corporation, Mc Lean, VA; *U.S. Public*, pg. 615

Mendenhall, Steven C., Chief Admin. Officer & Sr. V.P.--Fortune Brands, Inc., Old Greenwich, CT; *U.S. Public*, pg. 674

Meneely, Douglas E., V.P.-H.R.--Alberto-Culver Company, Melrose Park, IL; *U.S. Public*, pg. 37

Mengezberg, O.W.A.H.M., Dir.-Human Resources--Wavin Bv, Zwolle, Netherlands; *Int'l*, pg. 1135

Menke, Gerald T., Treas. & Sec.--The F.D. Lawrence Electric Co., Cincinnati, OH; *U.S. Private*, pg. 654

Mercado, Charlene, Mgr.-Personnel--Shugart Corporation, Mission Viejo, CA; *U.S. Private*, pg. 997

Mercado, Nancy, Human Resources Dir.--Icon International, Stamford, CT; *U.S. Private*, pg. 556

Mercer, Brian, Dir.-Human Resources--Cambridge Shopping Centres Limited, Toronto, Canada; *Int'l*, pg. 253

Meredith, Suzanne, Dir.-Human Resources--United Asset Management Corporation, Boston, MA; *U.S. Public*, pg. 1672

Mergele, Cyndi, Mgr.-H.R.--Signtech USA, Ltd., San Antonio, TX; *U.S. Private*, pg. 999

Merkel, Millie, Dir.-Personnel--Baldwin Piano & Organ Company, Loveland, OH; *U.S. Public*, pg. 169

Merrell, James, V.P.-Human Resources--Gulf States Paper Corporation, Tuscaloosa, AL; *U.S. Private*, pg. 487

Merrell, Pamela K., V.P.-Human Resources & Sec.--Montana Power Company, Butte, MT; *U.S. Public*, pg. 1126

Merrill, Diane, V.P.-Human Resources--Bil Mar Foods, Inc., Zeeland, MI; *U.S. Public*, pg. 1433

Merrill, R. Dale, V.P.-Human Resources--SkyWest Inc., Saint George, UT; *U.S. Public*, pg. 1476

Merrill, R. Dale, V.P.-Human Resources--SkyWest Airlines, Inc., Saint George, UT; *U.S. Public*, pg. 1476

Merritt, John, Dir.-Employee Rels.--CC Industries, Inc., Chicago, IL; *U.S. Private*, pg. 192

Merritt, Lisa, Mgr.-Human Resources--AGA Gas, Inc., Independence, OH; *Int'l*, pg. 13

Merritt, Sara P., Sr. V.P. & Dir.-H.R.--Chittenden Corporation, Burlington, VT; *U.S. Public*, pg. 350

Merritt, Terry, Corp. Sec. & Dir.-H.R.--Walbridge Aldinger Company, Detroit, MI; *U.S. Private*, pg. 1146

Merriweather, Donna, Dir.-H.R.--Mountain Valley Spring Company, Hot Springs National Park, AR; *U.S. Private*, pg. 963

Mersed, Debra, Dir.-H.R.--Lincoln Electric Systems, Lincoln, NE; *U.S. Private*, pg. 668

Merten, Lisa, Human Resources Mgr.--Kragie/Newell, Des Moines, IA; *U.S. Private*, pg. 634

Meserve, R.P., Dir.-H.R.--Bodine Electric Company, Chicago, IL; *U.S. Private*, pg. 154

Meske, Arthur M., Dir.-Personnel--Amsted Industries Incorporated, Chicago, IL; *U.S. Private*, pg. 68

Messana, Steve, Sr. V.P.-Human Resources--The Home Depot, Inc., Atlanta, GA; *U.S. Public*, pg. 831

Messick, Kathryn S., V.P.-Human Resources--Bindley Western Industries, Inc., Indianapolis, IN; *U.S. Public*, pg. 228

Messier, Mike, V.P.-H.R.--Open Market, Inc., Burlington, MA; *U.S. Public*, pg. 1226

Messner, Ronald E., V.P.-Human Resources--Philip Metals Inc., Cleveland, OH; *Int'l*, pg. 1050

Mettling, James L., Dir.-Indus. Rels. & Employee Benefits--Standex International Corporation, Salem, NH; *U.S. Public*, pg. 1505

Metts, James A., V.P.-Human Resources--H.B. Fuller Company, Saint Paul, MN; *U.S. Public*, pg. 686

Metz, J.G., Dir.-Personnel--Conwood Company L.P., Memphis, TN; *U.S. Private*, pg. 272

Metzger, George, V.P.- Human Resources--AlliedSignal Aerospace, Stratford, CT; *U.S. Public*, pg. 50

Metzger, George, V.P.-H.R.--Bell Helicopter Textron, Hurst, TX; *U.S. Public*, pg. 1588

Metzler, Gayle, V.P.-Human Resources--Armor All Products Group, Oakland, CA; *U.S. Public*, pg. 387

Meuchel, Gary, V.P.-H.R.--Prescolite Moldcast Lighting Company, San Leandro, CA; *U.S. Public*, pg. 1684

Meyer, Bill, Mgr.-Human Resources--PACCAR Automotive Inc., Renton, WA; *U.S. Public*, pg. 1247

Meyer, Bruce, V.P.-Human Resources--Genicom Corporation, Chantilly, VA; *U.S. Public*, pg. 729

Meyer, Jane, V.P.-Human Resources--Fortis, Inc., New York, NY; *Int'l*, pg. 499

Meyer, Karen M., V.P.-Human Resources & Admin. Services--The Toro Company, Bloomington, MN; *U.S. Public*, pg. 1623

Meyer, Kathy, Dir.-Personnel--KTI Fish, Houston, TX; *U.S. Private*, pg. 604

Meyer, Liz, Mgr.-H.R.--Environment/One Corporation, Niskayuna, NY; *U.S. Public*, pg. 586

Meyer, Richard W., Jr., V.P.-Human Resources--Amtran, Inc., Indianapolis, IN; *U.S. Public*, pg. 106

Meyers, Ronald, Dir.-H.R.--Exolon-Esk Company, Tonawanda, NY; *U.S. Public*, pg. 600

Miarecki, Arcelia, Dir.-Admin.--S. Bent & Brothers, Inc., Gardner, MA; *U.S. Private*, pg. 134

Micelotti, Sandra, V.P.-H.R.--Jet Spray Corp., Norwood, MA; *U.S. Private*, pg. 586

Michael, C. Kim, Sr. V.P.-H.R.--Southwest National Corporation, Greensburg, PA; *U.S. Public*, pg. 1493

Michael, Katie, Mgr.-Human Resources--Iowa Precision Industries, Cedar Rapids, IA; *U.S. Public*, pg. 1100

Michalak, Norbert, V.P. & Dir.-H.R.--Baird & Warner Inc., Chicago, IL; *U.S. Private*, pg. 111

Michel, Charles, Mgr.-H.R.--Southern Ohio Fabricators, Inc., Batavia, OH; *U.S. Private*, pg. 1017

Michelland-Bidegain, Martine, Dir.-Human Resources--Groupe Air France, Roissy, France; *Int'l*, pg. 559

Michener, Sally R., Sec. & Dir.-Personnel & Pub. Rels.--Scott Specialty Gases, Plumsteadville, PA; *U.S. Private*, pg. 977

Michlitsch, Barbara, V.P.-Human Resources--Super 8 Motels, Inc., Aberdeen, SD; *U.S. Public*, pg. 322

Middelmann, Thomas, Mgr.-H.R.--Knurr AG, Munich, Germany; *Int'l*, pg. 739

Middelschulte, Achim, Dir.-Personnel--Ruhrgas Aktiengesellschaft, Essen, Germany; *Int'l*, pg. 1148

Miele, Donna, V.P.-Human Resources--The New York Times, New York, NY; *U.S. Public*, pg. 1174
Mietus, Becky, Mgr.-H.R.--Anchor Tool & Die Company, Cleveland, OH; *U.S. Private*, pg. 71
Miglietta, Julie, Mgr.-H.R.--Litecontrol Corporation, Hanson, MA; *U.S. Private*, pg. 669
Miguelena, Rosy, Dir.-Personnel--The Keyes Company Realtors, Miami, FL; *U.S. Private*, pg. 618
Mihm, Curt, Dir.-Human Resources--Peerless Chain Company, Winona, MN; *U.S. Public*, pg. 1268
Miiro, Karl, V.P.-Staff Rels.--SAS Airline, Stockholm, Sweden; *Int'l*, pg. 1201
Mike, Cheryl, Dir.-Human Resources--Koss Corporation, Milwaukee, WI; *U.S. Public*, pg. 966
Mikesell, David, Dir.-H.R. & Attorney--Horizon Enterprises Group LLC, Taylor, MI; *U.S. Private*, pg. 539
Mikesell, David, Dir.-H.R.--Horizon Technology Group LLC, Taylor, MI; *U.S. Private*, pg. 539
Mikuta, John, Dir.-Personnel--Mitchel & Scott Machine Co., Inc., Indianapolis, IN; *U.S. Private*, pg. 753
Milack, Brian, Mgr.-H.R.--Acclaim Entertainment, Inc., Glen Cove, NY; *U.S. Public*, pg. 15
Milam, David, V.P.-Human Resources--Salem Carpet Mills, Inc., Winston Salem, NC; *U.S. Public*, pg. 1464
Milam, Mark, Dir.-Human Resources--John Roberts Company, Minneapolis, MN; *U.S. Private*, pg. 935
Milana, Susan, V.P.-H.R.--Dollar General Corporation, Nashville, TN; *U.S. Public*, pg. 515
Milburn, Paula, Dir.-H.R.--Towne Square Furniture, Inc., Hillsboro, TX; *U.S. Private*, pg. 1093
Milcent, Jean-Claude, Exec. V.P.-H.R.--PSA Peugeot Citroen, Paris, France; *Int'l*, pg. 1020
Milcent, Jean-Claude, Dir.-Human Resources--Peugeot S.A., Paris, France; *Int'l*, pg. 1020
Milch, Donna, V.P. & Human Resources Dir.--N.W. Ayer & Partners, New York, NY; *U.S. Private*, pg. 103
Miles, Diane, Human Resources Dir.--SicolaMartin Inc., Austin, TX; *U.S. Private*, pg. 998
Miles, Paula, Personnel--Hall Contracting Corp., Louisville, KY; *U.S. Private*, pg. 495
Miller, Adrianne, V.P.-Human Resources--VWR Scientific Products, West Chester, PA; *U.S. Public*, pg. 1703
Miller, Alan H., Dir.-Human Resources--Detroit Stoker Co., Monroe, MI; *U.S. Public*, pg. 1679
Miller, Barbara, Sr. V.P. & Dir.-H.R.--Bremer Financial Services, Inc., Saint Paul, MN; *U.S. Private*, pg. 167
Miller, Barbara, Dir.-Human Resources--Shady Brook Farms, Dayton, VA; *U.S. Private*, pg. 937
Miller, Barbara E., Sr. V.P. & Dir.-Human Resources--Bremer Financial Corporation, Saint Paul, MN; *U.S. Private*, pg. 167
Miller, Carolyn M., Dir.-Personnel--Scott's Liquid Gold-Inc., Denver, CO; *U.S. Public*, pg. 1447
Miller, Christian, V.P.-H.R.--Hostmark Management Group, Rolling Meadows, IL; *U.S. Private*, pg. 541
Miller, Dave, Mgr.-Human Rels.--Schilling Plant, Salinas, CA; *U.S. Public*, pg. 1066
Miller, David R., V.P.-H.R.--T.D. Williamson, Inc., Tulsa, OK; *U.S. Private*, pg. 1179
Miller, Dean, Mgr.-Human Resources & Employee Benefits--BeefAmerica Operating Co., Inc., Omaha, NE; *U.S. Private*, pg. 130
Miller, Donald O., V.P.-Human Resources & Admin.--Getchell Gold Corp., Englewood, CO; *U.S. Public*, pg. 740
Miller, Dr. W., Mgr.-Personnel--Fuji Photo Film (U.K.), Ltd., London, United Kingdom; *Int'l*, pg. 524
Miller, Edward R., V.P.-Human Resources--Bombardier, Learjet Inc., Wichita, KS; *Int'l*, pg. 200
Miller, Geoff L., V.P.-Human Resources--Varco-Pruden Buildings, Memphis, TN; *U.S. Public*, pg. 1677
Miller, Gregg P., V.P.-Human Resources--Dwyer Instruments Inc., Michigan City, IN; *U.S. Private*, pg. 350
Miller, Gregory, Dir.-Human Resources--Automotive Rentals, Inc. (ARI), Mount Laurel, NJ; *U.S. Private*, pg. 535
Miller, Harry, V.P.-Human Resources--R.G. Barry Corporation, Pickerington, OH; *U.S. Public*, pg. 192
Miller, Irene, Dir.-H.R.--Roman, Inc., Roselle, IL; *U.S. Private*, pg. 942
Miller, J. Lee, V.P.-Human Resources--Entergy Gulf States, Inc., Beaumont, TX; *U.S. Public*, pg. 586
Miller, James, Dir.-H.R.--Glenshaw Glass Co. Inc., Allison Park, PA; *U.S. Private*, pg. 457
Miller, Jean, Mgr.-Employee Relations--Sunnen Products Company, Saint Louis, MO; *U.S. Private*, pg. 1053
Miller, Katrina, Mgr.-Personnel--Ederer Inc., Seattle, WA; *U.S. Private*, pg. 363
Miller, Kenneth I., Chief Fin. Officer, Treas., Sr. V.P. & Sec.--Johnston, Lemon & Co. Inc., Washington, DC; *U.S. Private*, pg. 595
Miller, Kent, Dir.-Commun.--Farmway Co-Op Inc., Beloit, KS; *U.S. Private*, pg. 396
Miller, Kim, V.P.-Human Resources--Trimac Transportation System, Calgary, Canada; *Int'l*, pg. 1424
Miller, Linda, Mgr.-Human Resources--Liqui-Box Corporation, Worthington, OH; *U.S. Public*, pg. 1000
Miller, Linda J., V.P.-H.R.--Dodson Group, Kansas City, MO; *U.S. Private*, pg. 338
Miller, Liz, Mgr.-Human Resources--Custom Cheques of Canada, North York, Canada; *Int'l*, pg. 1077
Miller, Patricia, V.P.-Admin. Svcs.--Dietrich's Milk Products, Inc., Reading, PA; *U.S. Private*, pg. 332
Miller, Peter, V.P.-Human Resources--Aristokraft, Inc., Jasper, IN; *U.S. Public*, pg. 675
Miller, Peter D., V.P.-H.R.--Hickory Printing Group, Inc., Conover, NC; *U.S. Private*, pg. 525
Miller, Rose, V.P.-Human Resources--Cambridge Shopping Centres Limited, Toronto, Canada; *Int'l*, pg. 253
Miller, Ruth Ann, Dir.-Personnel Trng. & Devel.--Wilton Industries, Inc., Woodridge, IL; *U.S. Private*, pg. 1181
Miller, Samuel M., Mgr.-H.R.--Roanoke Electric Steel Corporation, Roanoke, VA; *U.S. Public*, pg. 1392
Miller, Stacy, Supvr.-H.R.--Trion, Inc., Sanford, NC; *U.S. Public*, pg. 1639
Miller, Sue, Dir.-Human Resources--Clover Club Foods, Inc., Kaysville, UT; *U.S. Private*, pg. 469
Miller, Sue, Head-Corp. Communications--T & N Plc, Manchester, United Kingdom; *Int'l*, pg. 1334
Miller, Thomas, Mgr.-Personnel--Berger Transfer & Storage, Inc., Saint Paul, MN; *U.S. Private*, pg. 135
Miller, Thomas R., V.P.-H.R.--Cameron Ashley Building Products, Inc, Dallas, TX; *U.S. Public*, pg. 298
Miller, Tom, Dir.-Human Resources--Mannington Resilient Floors, Salem, NJ; *U.S. Private*, pg. 700
Miller, Vi, Dir.-H.R.--Wigwam Mills, Inc., Sheboygan, WI; *U.S. Private*, pg. 1175
Milliman, Susan, Dir.-Human Resources--Pizza Inn, Inc., Dallas, TX; *U.S. Public*, pg. 1307
Mills, Charles A., V.P.-H.R.--Hunt Oil Company, Dallas, TX; *U.S. Private*, pg. 548
Mills, John, Grp. Dir.-Personnel--BAA plc, London, United Kingdom; *Int'l*, pg. 103
Mills, Monica, Mgr.-Human Resources--Stihl Inc., Virginia Beach, VA; *Int'l*, pg. 1301
Mills, Nancy, Dir.-H.R.--Stanco Metal Products, Inc., Grand Haven, MI; *U.S. Private*, pg. 1030
Mills, Sarah, Sr. Dir.-H.R.--Checkers Drive-In Restaurants, Inc., Clearwater, FL; *U.S. Public*, pg. 342
Milos, V.P.-Bus. Devel. & Human Resources--Schering Berlin Inc., Cedar Knolls, NJ; *Int'l*, pg. 1204
Milslagle, James, V.P.-Human Resources--Fox River Paper Company, Appleton, WI; *U.S. Private*, pg. 422
Miltier, Thomas W., Jr., Dir.-Human Resources--Sentrol Controls Group, Hickory, NC; *U.S. Private*, pg. 139
Mims, J. Michael, V.P.-H.R.--Crown Central Petroleum Corporation, Baltimore, MD; *U.S. Public*, pg. 462
Mims, Louis, Dir.-Human Resources--Suitt Construction Company, Inc., Greenville, SC; *U.S. Private*, pg. 106
Min, Wong Wai, Dir.-H.R.--CAM International Holdings Ltd., Singapore, Singapore; *Int'l*, pg. 238
Minella, Nancy J., Dir.-H.R.--Worthington Foods Inc., Worthington, OH; *U.S. Public*, pg. 1780
Minichbauer, Rick, V.P.-H.R.--Stanley Furniture Co. Inc., Stanleytown, VA; *U.S. Public*, pg. 1508
Mink, Susan, Dir.-Personnel--Liberty Corporation, Greenville, SC; *U.S. Public*, pg. 991
Minor, Dan, Mgr.-Human Resources--Idaho Power Company, Boise, ID; *U.S. Public*, pg. 861
Minor, Janlaw, V.P.-Human Relations--Hamilton Standard, Windsor Locks, CT; *U.S. Public*, pg. 1690
Minora, Vince, Dir.-Personnel--Wyeth-Ayerst Laboratories, Inc., Philadelphia, PA; *U.S. Public*, pg. 80
Minors, B., Mgr.-Personnel--British Steel Seamless Tubes-Wednesfield Works, Wolverhampton, United Kingdom; *Int'l*, pg. 220
Miraben, George, Sr. V.P.-Policy & H.R.--Tucson Electric Power Company, Tucson, AZ; *U.S. Public*, pg. 1670
Miracle, Linda, Dir.-Human Resources--Gas Equipment Company, Inc., Dallas, TX; *U.S. Private*, pg. 440
Mirsky, Susan, Sr. Partner & Intl. Human Resources Dir.--J. Walter Thompson Company, New York, NY; *Int'l*, pg. 1483
Misconis, Lenn, Dir.-Personnel--Associated Grocers of the South, Inc., Birmingham, AL; *U.S. Private*, pg. 91
Misialek, Kurt A., Chief Fin. Officer & V.P.--Eggland's Best, Inc., King of Prussia, PA; *U.S. Private*, pg. 366
Mistry, Kal, V.P.-Human Resources--FPA Medical Management, Inc., San Diego, CA; *U.S. Public*, pg. 608
Mitchell, Bobby, Controller--J.L. Lester & Son, Inc., Rockmart, GA; *U.S. Private*, pg. 660
Mitchell, E. G., Exec V.P.-Human Resources--Royal Bank of Canada, Toronto, Canada; *Int'l*, pg. 1131
Mitchell, Greg, V.P.-Human Resources--Philip Laser Magnetic Storage, Colorado Springs, CO; *Int'l*, pg. 1054
Mitchell, Helen, Dir.-Human Resources--Baldwin Technology Company, Inc., Norwalk, CT; *U.S. Public*, pg. 169
Mitchell, Helen M., Mgr.-Benefits & Personnel--Baldwin Graphic Systems, Inc., Shelton, CT; *U.S. Public*, pg. 170
Mitchell, Peter K., V.P.-Human Resources--JJI Lighting Group Inc., Greenwich, CT; *Int'l*, pg. 821
Mitchell, Rhonda, Mgr.-H.R.--Regency Associates Limited Partnership, Champaign, IL; *U.S. Private*, pg. 918
Mitchell, Robert, V.P.-Human Resources--Central Parking Corp., Nashville, TN; *U.S. Public*, pg. 326
Mitson, R.E., Mgr.-Personnel--Pauls plc, Ipswich, United Kingdom; *Int'l*, pg. 598
Mixon, John A., V.P.-Human Resources--Dynatech Corporation, Burlington, MA; *U.S. Public*, pg. 539
Mizeras, Vincent, Dir.-Human Resources--High Industries, Inc., Lancaster, PA; *U.S. Private*, pg. 528
Moberg, Jim R., Exec. V.P.-Human Resources--Pacific Telesis Group, San Francisco, CA; *U.S. Public*, pg. 1415
Mocetti, Jorge, Dir.-Human Resources--Banco Quilmes, Buenos Aires, Argentina; *Int'l*, pg. 142
Mochizuki, Ellen F., Controller--K2 Inc., Los Angeles, CA; *U.S. Public*, pg. 940
Moellering, Meg, Mgr.-Human Resources--H & H Distributing Company, Inc., West Union, IA; *U.S. Private*, pg. 489
Moen, Timothy P., Exec. V.P.-Human Resources--First Chicago NBD Corporation, Chicago, IL; *U.S. Public*, pg. 627
Moffat, Kenneth M., Sr. V.P.-Personnel--Amica Mutual Insurance Co., Lincoln, RI; *U.S. Private*, pg. 66
Mohr, Christy, Dir.-Personnel--Modern Equipment Co., Inc., Port Washington, WI; *U.S. Private*, pg. 33
Mohta, Zareen, Mgr.-Human Resources--California Micro Devices, Milpitas, CA; *U.S. Public*, pg. 293
Moiana, Louise, Mgr.-Human Resources--Methode Electronics Inc., Chicago, IL; *U.S. Public*, pg. 1101
Molaison, William H., Jr., V.P.-Personnel/Admin. Services--Santa Fe Minerals Inc., Dallas, TX; *Int'l*, pg. 765
Moley, M.J., V.P.-Human Resources--Dunlop Tire Corporation, Buffalo, NY; *Int'l*, pg. 1317
Molina Duque, Estanislao, V.P.-H.R.--Grupo Continental S.A., Tampico, Mexico; *Int'l*, pg. 573
Molina, Bruno, Sr. H.R. Rep.--Security Plastics, Inc., Hialeah, FL; *U.S. Private*, pg. 981
Moline, Doug, V.P.-Human Resources--Wells Fargo Alarm Services, Inc., King of Prussia, PA; *U.S. Public*, pg. 246
Moll, Jane, Mgr.-Human Resources--Knoll Pharmaceutical Company, Whippany, NJ; *Int'l*, pg. 105
Mollaun, Dan, V.P.-Human Resources--Roto-Rooter, Cincinnati, OH; *U.S. Public*, pg. 344
Moller, Larry, Mgr.-Personnel--Service Corporation International, Houston, TX; *U.S. Public*, pg. 1460
Molloy, Michelle, Dir.-Human Resources--Marcel Dekker, Inc., New York, NY; *U.S. Private*, pg. 321
Molnar, Vera, Mgr.-Personnel Admin.--Roussel Corporation, Montvale, NJ; *Int'l*, pg. 625
Molnar, Yvonne, V.P.-H.R.--MAG Innovision Co., Inc., Santa Ana, CA; *U.S. Private*, pg. 694
Molofsky, Ivy, Dir.-Personnel--Thomas Publishing Company, New York, NY; *U.S. Private*, pg. 1082
Molofsky, Ivy, Dir.-Human Resources--Industrial Equipment News, New York, NY; *U.S. Private*, pg. 1082
Moloney, Maggie, Mgr.-Personnel--Club Med Sales, Inc., New York, NY; *Int'l*, pg. 298
Moloney, Theresa, Mgr.-H.R.--M. Kamenstein, Inc., Elmsford, NY; *U.S. Private*, pg. 606
Momchilov, Thomas J., V.P.-Human Resources--The Reynolds and Reynolds Company, Dayton, OH; *U.S. Public*, pg. 1384
Momeyer, Alan, V.P.-Human Resources--Loews Corporation, New York, NY; *U.S. Public*, pg. 1010
Momeyer, Alan, V.P.-Human Resources--Loews Hotels, New York, NY; *U.S. Public*, pg. 1011
Monaghan, Gail, Mgr.-Human Resources--Interstate Steel Supply Company, Philadelphia, PA; *U.S. Public*, pg. 1100
Monaghan, John, Dir.-Personnel--North West Water Limited, Warrington, United Kingdom; *Int'l*, pg. 1444
Monchein, Minta A., V.P.-Human Resources--Forest City Enterprises, Inc., Cleveland, OH; *U.S. Public*, pg. 667
Monk, Stephanie, Dir.-H.R.--Granada Group PLC, London, United Kingdom; *Int'l*, pg. 556
Monoscalco, L., Dir.-Human Resources--Follett Corporation, River Grove, IL; *U.S. Private*, pg. 416
Monroe, William M., V.P.-Human Resources--W.R. Grace & Co., Boca Raton, FL; *U.S. Public*, pg. 754
Monson, Michael, Staff V.P. & Dir.-Human Resources--Meredith Corporation, Des Moines, IA; *U.S. Public*, pg. 1094
Montgomery, Gary, Dir.-Human Resources--Ropak Corporation, Fullerton, CA; *Int'l*, pg. 811
Montgomery, R. Lawrence, Vice Chm.--Kohl's Corporation, Menomonee Falls, WI; *U.S. Public*, pg. 965
Montieth, David, V.P.-H.R.--The Dress Barn, Inc., Suffern, NY; *U.S. Public*, pg. 528
Moody, Betty, Mgr.-Personnel--Advanced Circuit Technology, Nashua, NH; *U.S. Private*, pg. 21
Moog, Jeanne M., Dir.-H.R.--Colorado MEDtech, Inc., Boulder, CO; *U.S. Public*, pg. 401
Moon, Bobby, Dir.-Personnel--Acme Brick Co., Fort Worth, TX; *U.S. Public*, pg. 936
Mooney, John, V.P.- Human Resources--Drake Bakeries, Inc., Wayne, NJ; *Int'l*, pg. 349
Mooney, Kristen, Dir.-H.R.--Schieffelin & Somerset Co., New York, NY; *Int'l*, pg. 412
Moore, Andrew R., V.P.-Human Resources--Northwestern Steel & Wire Co., Sterling, IL; *U.S. Public*, pg. 1201
Moore, Bill, Risk Mngmt.--Buffalo Rock Company, Birmingham, AL; *U.S. Private*, pg. 179
Moore, Ian, Gen. Mgr.-Human Resources--James Hardie Industries Ltd., Sydney, Australia; *Int'l*, pg. 596
Moore, J. Michael, V.P.-H.R.--J. Alexanders Corporation, Nashville, TN; *U.S. Public*, pg. 40
Moore, James, Dir.-Human Resources--Gaston County Dyeing Machine Co., Mount Holly, NC; *U.S. Private*, pg. 441
Moore, Joe, Dir.-H.R.--Weber-Stephen Products Co., Palatine, IL; *U.S. Private*, pg. 1157
Moore, John E., Sr. V.P.-Personnel & Community Rels.--The Cessna Aircraft Co., Wichita, KS; *U.S. Public*, pg. 1589
Moore, Kathy, Sr. V.P.-Human Resources--Caesars World, Inc., Las Vegas, NV; *U.S. Public*, pg. 1512
Moore, Kay, Human Resources--Barkley & Evergreen Advertising, Inc., Kansas City, MO; *U.S. Private*, pg. 116
Moore, Mary, Mgr.-Human Resources, Admin.--Nobel Insurance Limited, Hamilton, Bermuda; *Int'l*, pg. 951
Moore, P., Personnel--R.T. Vanderbilt Company, Inc., Norwalk, CT; *U.S. Private*, pg. 1133
Moore, Robert A., V.P.-H.R. & Sec.--Dead River Company, Portland, ME; *U.S. Private*, pg. 318
Moore, T.J., V.P.-Human Resources--Alberta Power Limited, Edmonton, Canada; *Int'l*, pg. 95
Moore, Terry J., V.P.-Human Resources--The Yukon Electrical Co. Ltd., Whitehorse, Canada; *Int'l*, pg. 95
Moorer, Lew, V.P.-Human Resources--Hennessy Industries, Inc., La Vergne, TN; *U.S. Public*, pg. 481
Moorhead, Thomas B., V.P.-Human Resources--Carter-Wallace, Inc., New York, NY; *U.S. Public*, pg. 309
Mooten, R., Mgr.-Personnel--Fokker Aircraft Services B.V., Hoogerheyde, Netherlands; *Int'l*, pg. 1304
Moquin, Patrick, V.P.-Human Resources--Unitrode Corporation, Merrimack, NH; *U.S. Public*, pg. 1694
Morales, Teri, Mgr.-H.R.--M K Diamond Products, Inc., Torrance, CA; *U.S. Private*, pg. 684
Moran, Hugh, V.P.--Mid American Elevator Co., Inc., Chicago, IL; *U.S. Private*, pg. 743
Moran, James G., Sr. V.P.-Corp. Admin.--Regal Ware, Inc., Kewaskum, WI; *U.S. Private*, pg. 917
Moran, Michael, Mgr.-Personnel--Moore Products Co., Spring House, PA; *U.S. Public*, pg. 1128
Moran, Theresa, Mgr.-H.R.--Hawkins Chemical, Inc., Minneapolis, MN; *U.S. Public*, pg. 800
Morchison, Gloria, Sr. V.P.-Personnel--Auto-Owners Insurance, Lansing, MI; *U.S. Private*, pg. 100
Morden, Larry, Sr. V.P.-H.R. & Corp. Affairs--Parmalat Canada Ltd., Etobicoke, Canada; *Int'l*, pg. 1023
Moreau, Leslie, Corp. Sec.--Elixir Industries, Gardena, CA; *U.S. Private*, pg. 371

Moreno, Ernest, V.P.-H.R.--Orval Kent Food Co., Wheeling, IL; *U.S. Private*, pg. 820

Moreno, Linda, Dir.-H.R.--Continental/Midland, Inc., Park Forest, IL; *U.S. Private*, pg. 268

Moreno, William, Dir.-Personnel Services--LEGO Systems, Inc., Enfield, CT; *Int'l*, pg. 805

Morgan, Charly, Dir.-Personnel--Daniel Valve Company, Houston, TX; *U.S. Public*, pg. 483

Morgan, Debbie, Mgr.-H.R.--Video Products Distributors, Inc., Sacramento, CA; *U.S. Private*, pg. 1139

Morgan, Kenneth L., V.P.-Personnel--Stone & Thomas, Wheeling, WV; *U.S. Private*, pg. 1044

Morgan, Linda, Dir.-Human Resources--Computer Power Incorporated, High Bridge, NJ; *U.S. Public*, pg. 421

Morgan, Michael A.J., Dir.-Personnel--Northern Foods plc, Hull, United Kingdom; *Int'l*, pg. 967

Morgan, Richard E., V.P.-Human Resources--C.P. Clare Corporation, Beverly, MA; *U.S. Public*, pg. 382

Morgan, Richard G., V.P.-Human Resources--Canadian Tire Acceptance Ltd., Welland, Canada; *Int'l*, pg. 259

Morgan, Rochelle, Dir.-H.R.--Merit Medical Systems, Inc., South Jordan, UT; *U.S. Public*, pg. 1096

Morgan, Susan, Mgr.-Human Resources--Intellicall, Inc., Carrollton, TX; *U.S. Public*, pg. 887

Morgenstern, Barbara, Exec. V.P.--Nuarc Company, Inc., Niles, IL; *U.S. Private*, pg. 808

Moriarty, Brian D., Sr. V.P.-Human Resources--First Financial Bancorp, Hamilton, OH; *U.S. Public*, pg. 632

Moribe, Hideo, Dir.-Acctg., Systems & Personnel--Mitsumi Electric Co., Ltd., Tokyo, Japan; *Int'l*, pg. 884

Morin, Maria, Mgr.-Human Resources--Interpoint, Redmond, WA; *U.S. Public*, pg. 457

Mork, Nancy, Mgr.-H.R.--Corporate Travel Services, San Francisco, CA; *U.S. Private*, pg. 276

Morley, Michael P., Sr. V.P. & Dir.-Human Resources--Eastman Kodak Company, Rochester, NY; *U.S. Public*, pg. 550

Moroishi, Mitsuhiro, Mng. Dir.-Legal & Personnel--Sumitomo Chemical Company, Ltd., Tokyo, Japan; *Int'l*, pg. 1310

Morokuma, Hajime, Sr. Exec. Dir.-Admin. & H.R.--Seiko Corporation, Tokyo, Japan; *Int'l*, pg. 1218

Morr, Thomas, Mgr.-Personnel--Delphi Packard Electric Systems, Beachwood, OH; *U.S. Public*, pg. 719

Morris, Carole, V.P.-Human Resources--California State Bank-La Habra, La Habra, CA; *U.S. Public*, pg. 294

Morris, Daniel T., V.P.-Risk Mngmt. & Safety--The ServiceMaster Company, Downers Grove, IL; *U.S. Public*, pg. 1461

Morris, Denise, Dir.-Human Resources--Philips Speech Processing, Atlanta, GA; *Int'l*, pg. 1055

Morris, Evelyn A., V.P. & Dir.-H.R.--The Troy Savings Bank, Troy, NY; *U.S. Private*, pg. 1106

Morris, Kathryn J., V.P.-H.R.--Amurcon Equities, Southfield, MI; *U.S. Private*, pg. 69

Morris, Phillip, V.P. & Dir.-Human Resources & Safety--Heckethorn Mfg. Company, Inc., Dyersburg, TN; *U.S. Private*, pg. 519

Morris, Sandi, Dir.-Personnel--Weiser Lock, Tucson, AZ; *U.S. Public*, pg. 1053

Morris, William L., Sr. Assoc. & Dir.--Hayes, Seay, Mattern & Mattern, Inc., Roanoke, VA; *U.S. Private*, pg. 513

Morris, William L., V.P.-Indus. Rels.--Universal-Rundle Corp., New Castle, PA; *U.S. Public*, pg. 1193

Morrison, D., Mgr.-Human Resources--Stanford Telecommunications, Sunnyvale, CA; *U.S. Public*, pg. 1508

Morrison, David F., V.P.-H.R. Devel.--The Toronto Dominion Bank, Toronto, Canada; *Int'l*, pg. 1401

Morrison, L. Bryan, V.P.-H.R.--Universal Cooperatives, Inc., Minneapolis, MN; *U.S. Private*, pg. 1127

Morrison, Randy, Dir.-Personnel & Safety--McCrory Construction Co., Inc., Columbia, SC; *U.S. Private*, pg. 720

Morrison, Sara, Hon., Dir.-Employee Rels.--The General Electric Company, p.l.c., London, United Kingdom; *Int'l*, pg. 543

Morrissey, John, V.P.-Human Resources--A.G. Simpson Co. Limited, Scarborough, Canada; *Int'l*, pg. 1252

Morrow, Robert, V.P.-Corp. Communications--Stone & Webster Engineering & Constructors Corp., Boston, MA; *U.S. Public*, pg. 1519

Morse, Barbara, V.P.-Corp. Communications--Copley Pharmaceuticals, Inc., Canton, MA; *U.S. Public*, pg. 446

Morse, Robert, V.P.-H.R.--Spartan Stores Inc., Grand Rapids, MI; *U.S. Private*, pg. 1021

Morthland, David W., V.P.-Personnel & Indus. Rels.--Willamette Industries, Inc., Portland, OR; *U.S. Public*, pg. 1768

Morton, Jack, V.P.-Human Resources--Jimmy Dean Foods, Cordova, TN; *U.S. Public*, pg. 1433

Morton, Leo E., Sr. V.P.-Human Resources & Opers. Support--UtiliCorp United Inc., Kansas City, MO; *U.S. Public*, pg. 1700

Morton, Roy, V.P.-Human Resources--Old America Stores, Howe, TX; *U.S. Public*, pg. 1215

Moschel, Marilyn, Dir.-H.R.--Metro Information Services, Virginia Beach, VA; *U.S. Public*, pg. 1102

Moses, Patricia, Dir.-H.R.--Agouron Pharmaceuticals, Inc., La Jolla, CA; *U.S. Public*, pg. 28

Mosher, Fran, Dir.-Human Resources--Pro-Log Corporation, Monterey, CA; *U.S. Private*, pg. 887

Moshinsky, Arthur, Dir.-Human Resources--Sanyo Fisher Company, Chatsworth, CA; *Int'l*, pg. 1191

Moss, J., Dir.-Personnel--Fredestein Banden, Enschede, Netherlands; *Int'l*, pg. 504

Moss, John, Dir.-Human Resources--BancTec, Inc., Dallas, TX; *U.S. Public*, pg. 176

Moss, Kenneth, Mgr.-H.R.--Grant Thornton LLP, Chicago, IL; *U.S. Private*, pg. 470

Moss, Sylvia, V.P.--The Blackstone Group, New York, NY; *U.S. Private*, pg. 147

Mostaccio, Jean, Human Resource Dir.--Greenstone Roberts Advertising, Melville, NY; *U.S. Public*, pg. 763

Mostyn, Steve, Mgr.-Personnel- Europe--Astec International Limited, Wan Chai, Hong Kong; *Int'l*, pg. 92

Mote, Shirley, Mgr.-Personnel--Hill & Griffith Company, Cincinnati, OH; *U.S. Private*, pg. 529

Mott, Betty, Dir.-Admin. & Human Resources--McBride and Associates, Inc., Albuquerque, NM; *U.S. Private*, pg. 719

Moulds, Kelly, H.R. Specialist--Open Market, Inc., Burlington, MA; *U.S. Public*, pg. 1226

Moulie, Pierre, Sr. Exec. V.P.-Human Resources--Electricite de France, Paris, France; *Int'l*, pg. 437

Moulton, Robert A., V.P.-H.R.--Woodhead Industries, Inc., Buffalo Grove, IL; *U.S. Public*, pg. 1776

Mount, Lee, V.P.-Human Resources--Thorn Apple Valley, Inc., Southfield, MI; *U.S. Public*, pg. 1602

Mountcastle, Elizabeth, Mgr.-Human Resources--Stainless Incorporated, Deerfield Beach, FL; *U.S. Private*, pg. 1029

Mouren, Henri, Dir.-Communications & Personnel--Compagnie des Machines Bull, Louveciennes, France; *Int'l*, pg. 315

Moutier, Bernard, Dir.-Human Resources--Bongard, Holtzheim, France; *Int'l*, pg. 570

Mouw, Daniel, V.P.-H.R. & Admin.--Color Arts, Inc., Racine, WI; *U.S. Private*, pg. 254

Mowrer, Gale, Mgr.-H.R.--Applied Microsystems Corporation, Redmond, WA; *U.S. Public*, pg. 123

Moxom, Peter, Dir.-Human Resources--Rexam PLC, London, United Kingdom; *Int'l*, pg. 1106

Moyer, Gregory, V.P.-H.R. & Quality--Cadmus Communications Corporation, Richmond, VA; *U.S. Public*, pg. 290

Moyer, Steven K., V.P.-Human Resources--Hatfield Quality Meats, Hatfield, PA; *U.S. Private*, pg. 510

Moyers, Thomas R., V.P.-Human Resources--Perdue Farms Incorporated, Salisbury, MD; *U.S. Private*, pg. 852

Moylan, John, V.P.-Human Resources--Dayton Rogers Mfg. Co., Blaine, MN; *U.S. Private*, pg. 318

Mozingo, Dave, Dir.-H.R.--AP North American Aftermarket Division, Goldsboro, NC; *U.S. Private*, pg. 230

Mrachek, William, Dir.-H.R.--Programart Corporation, Cambridge, MA; *U.S. Private*, pg. 890

Mraz, Michael L., Asst. V.P.-H.R. Devel.--CUNA Mutual Insurance Society, Madison, WI; *U.S. Private*, pg. 296

Mucha, Joseph R., V.P.-H.R./Opers.--General Mills, Inc., Minneapolis, MN; *U.S. Public*, pg. 717

Mudge, C.W., Gen. Mgr.-H.R.--The Broken Hill Proprietary Company Limited, Melbourne, Australia; *Int'l*, pg. 223

Muehlberger, Edward F., V.P.-Personnnel--Blue Circle America Inc., Marietta, GA; *Int'l*, pg. 197

Mueller-Gebel, Klaus, Mng. Dir.-H.R. & Legal Svcs.--Commerzbank AG, Frankfurt, Germany; *Int'l*, pg. 308

Mueller, Laurie, Dir.-Government Affairs--Perlmuter Printing Company, Cleveland, OH; *Int'l*, pg. 1177

Muellman, Susie, Mgr.-Human Resources--Euromarket Designs, Inc., Northbrook, IL; *U.S. Private*, pg. 384

Muench, Cheryl, Dir.-H.R.--Dynamic Materials Corporation, Lafayette, CO; *U.S. Public*, pg. 539

Muggli, Jacques, V.P.-H.R.--Bobst S.A., Lausanne, Switzerland; *Int'l*, pg. 198

Mullen, James R., V.P.-H.R.--Sweetheart Cup Company Inc., Owings Mills, MD; *U.S. Private*, pg. 1058

Muller, Jorg-Viggo, Member-Mngmt. Bd.--Hugo Boss AG, Metzingen, Germany; *Int'l*, pg. 637

Mullet, Bob, V.P.-Personnel--Excel Industries, Inc., Hesston, KS; *U.S. Private*, pg. 387

Mullins, B., V.P.-Personnel--Princess Hotels International Inc., New York, NY; *Int'l*, pg. 818

Mullins, James L., Dir.-Personnel--Southwestern Energy Company, Fayetteville, AR; *U.S. Public*, pg. 1494

Mulroy, Barry, Dir.-Human Resources--First Commerce Corporation, New Orleans, LA; *U.S. Public*, pg. 629

Mulvaney, Brian, V.P.-H.R.--Aramark Corp., Philadelphia, PA; *U.S. Private*, pg. 78

Mulvey, John, Dir.-Human Resources--Bill Communications, Inc., New York, NY; *Int'l*, pg. 1446

Mumford, Ayliffe B., V.P.-Human Resources--The Gap, Inc., San Francisco, CA; *U.S. Public*, pg. 702

Mumma, Madolyn, Dir.-Human Resources--Dayton Newspapers, Inc., Dayton, OH; *U.S. Private*, pg. 281

Muncy, Julie, Sec. & H.R. Dir.--Caldwell VanRiper, Inc., Indianapolis, IN; *U.S. Private*, pg. 200

Munger, D.W., V.P. & Dir.-Personnel--General Motors of Canada Ltd., Oshawa, Canada; *U.S. Public*, pg. 722

Munji, Divinia F., Asst. V.P.-Human Resources--EEI Corporation, Manila, Philippines; *Int'l*, pg. 425

Munoz, Ellen, Mgr.-H.R.--Inter-Tel, Incorporated, Phoenix, AZ; *U.S. Public*, pg. 888

Munoz, Marilu, Mgr.-Personnel--International Electronic Research Corp., Burbank, CA; *U.S. Public*, pg. 286

Murakami, K., V.P.-Human Resources--Warner-Lambert K.K., Tokyo, Japan; *U.S. Public*, pg. 1739

Murase, Makoto, Mng. Dir.-Human Resources--Oji Paper Co., Ltd., Tokyo, Japan; *Int'l*, pg. 998

Murawski, Hank, Mgr.-H.R.--Beckwith Machinery Company, Murrysville, PA; *U.S. Private*, pg. 129

Murdock, Michelle, Mgr.-Human Resources--Corel Corporation, Orem, UT; *Int'l*, pg. 331

Mure, Douglas V., V.P.-H.R. & Risk Mngmt.--Perini Corporation, Framingham, MA; *U.S. Public*, pg. 1278

Murgel, Michele, Dir.-Human Resources--Alias Wavefront, Toronto, Canada; *U.S. Public*, pg. 1474

Murphey, Cynthia Kiser, Sr. V.P.-Human Resources & Admin.--MGM Grand Hotel, Inc., Las Vegas, NV; *U.S. Public*, pg. 1027

Murphey, Jim, Dir.-H.R.--Quintana Petroleum Corp., Houston, TX; *U.S. Private*, pg. 901

Murphy, Brian, Dir.-Regional Communications & Pub. Affairs--Nortel, Nashville, TN; *Int'l*, pg. 970

Murphy, Brian J., Sr. V.P.-H.R.--Brink's, Inc., Darien, CT; *U.S. Public*, pg. 1305

Murphy, David L., Jr., V.P.-Retail Human Resources--John Hancock Mutual Life Insurance Company, Boston, MA; *U.S. Private*, pg. 589

Murphy, James D., V.P.-Staff--EMCOR Group, Inc., Norwalk, CT; *U.S. Public*, pg. 571

Murphy, John, V.P.-H.R.--Foremost Farms USA Cooperative, Baraboo, WI; *U.S. Private*, pg. 418

Murphy, Kathy, Asst. Dir.-H.R.--Franchise Finance Corp. of America, Scottsdale, AZ; *U.S. Public*, pg. 679

Murphy, Patricia A., V.P.-H.R.--Broderbund Software, Inc., Novato, CA; *U.S. Public*, pg. 258

Murphy, Patrick, V.P.-Human Resources--LEGO Systems, Inc., Enfield, CT; *Int'l*, pg. 805

Murphy, Robert H., Sr. V.P.-Organization & Human Resources--Rockwell International Corporation, Costa Mesa, CA; *U.S. Public*, pg. 1397

Murphy, Robert J., Dir.-Human Resources--Powell Industries, Inc., Houston, TX; *U.S. Public*, pg. 1319

Murphy, Tama, Mgr.-H.R.--Tetko, Inc., Briarcliff Manor, NY; *U.S. Private*, pg. 1078

Murray, Cathy M., Dir.-Personnel/Insurance--McAnally Enterprises, Inc., Yucaipa, CA; *U.S. Private*, pg. 718

Murray, George, Chief Human Resources Officer & Sr. V.P.--Canandaigua Wine Company, Inc., Canandaigua, NY; *U.S. Public*, pg. 300

Murray, Gerald P., V.P.-HR--Kay-Bee Toy & Hobby Shops, Inc., Pittsfield, MA; *U.S. Public*, pg. 437

Murray, Judy, Mgr.-Personnel--Penobscot Shoe Company, Old Town, ME; *U.S. Public*, pg. 1273

Murray, M., Dir.-Human Resources--L3 Communications Narda-Microwave Div., Hauppauge, NY; *U.S. Private*, pg. 638

Murray, Marilyn, V.P. & Mgr.-Employee Rels.--CVB Financial Corp., Ontario, CA; *U.S. Public*, pg. 286

Murray, Michael R., V.P.-H.R. & Admin.--Microsoft Corporation, Redmond, WA; *U.S. Public*, pg. 1107

Murray, Michael W., V.P.-Human Resources--FMC Corporation, Chicago, IL; *U.S. Public*, pg. 604

Murray, Paul M., Dir.-Human Resources--Pratt & Lambert United, Inc., Cleveland, OH; *U.S. Public*, pg. 1466

Murray, Susan, Mgr.-H.R.--H.O. Penn Machinery Co. Inc., Poughkeepsie, NY; *U.S. Private*, pg. 849

Murray, Sylvia, V.P.-Fin. & Human Resources--Tech Spray, Inc., Amarillo, TX; *U.S. Private*, pg. 1071

Murrill, Tom, V.P.-Human Resources--Royal Caribbean Cruises Ltd., Miami, FL; *U.S. Public*, pg. 1410

Murro, John M., V.P.-Strategic Plng.--Lebhar-Friedman, Inc., New York, NY; *U.S. Private*, pg. 656

Muscato, Gregory C., Dir.-Personnel--Astronics Corporation, Buffalo, NY; *U.S. Public*, pg. 142

Musetti, Umberto, Dir.-Personnel--Istituto Mobiliare Italiano, Rome, Italy; *Int'l*, pg. 692

Musial, Tom, V.P.-Human Rels.--The Manitowoc Company, Inc., Manitowoc, WI; *U.S. Public*, pg. 1040

Musick, Jeff, Dir.-Human Resources--Jumping Jacks, Monett, MO; *U.S. Private*, pg. 767

Muskievicz, Mike, V.P.-Human Resources--Elco Textron, Rockford, IL; *U.S. Public*, pg. 1590

Musseau, Joseph, Head-Personnel--Credit Lyonnais S.A., Paris, France; *Int'l*, pg. 343

Musson, George, Dir.-Indus. Rels.--Superior Industries International, Inc., Van Nuys, CA; *U.S. Public*, pg. 1539

Muszynski, Bruce, V.P.-Personnel--EZ Paintr Corp., Saint Francis, WI; *U.S. Public*, pg. 1177

Muth, Jane, Mgr.-Personnel--Andes Candies Inc., Delavan, WI; *U.S. Private*, pg. 163

Muto, Takamitsu, Dir.-Admin., H.R. & Gen. Affairs--Seiko Corporation, Tokyo, Japan; *Int'l*, pg. 1218

Mutter, Peter, Dir.-Personnel--Blue Circle Industries PLC, London, United Kingdom; *Int'l*, pg. 197

Myers, Brenda, Human Resources Mgr. & Office Mgr.--Hadeler Sullivan Ewing, Dallas, TX; *U.S. Private*, pg. 493

Myers, George, V.P.-Human Resources--ABF Freight System, Inc., Fort Smith, AR; *U.S. Public*, pg. 13C

Myers, John, V.P.-Human Resources--Eclipse Inc., Rockford, IL; *U.S. Private*, pg. 360

Myers, Robert, Dir.-Human Resources--Mylan Laboratories, Inc., Pittsburgh, PA; *U.S. Public*, pg. 1143

Myers, Shelly, Asst. V.P.-H.R.--Wasserstrom Company, Columbus, OH; *U.S. Private*, pg. 1152

Myers, Tom, V.P.-Assoc. Support--Baker's Supermarkets, Inc., Omaha, NE; *U.S. Public*, pg. 652

Myles, Debra W., Dir.-Human Resources--Coca-Cola Bottling Co. United, Inc., Birmingham, AL; *U.S. Private*, pg. 248

Myoda, Vicki, Sr. V.P.-H.R.--WSFS Financial Corporation, Wilmington, DE; *U.S. Public*, pg. 1728

Mysliewicz, Mike, Dir.-Personnel--Tenneco Specialty Products, Deerfield, IL; *U.S. Public*, pg. 1579

Nadeau, Marie-Jose, Exec. V.P.-Human Resources--Hydro-Quebec, Montreal, Canada; *Int'l*, pg. 640

Nagel, Friedrich, Dir.-Human Resources--Pittler Maschinenfabrik AG, Langen, Germany; *Int'l*, pg. 1128

Nagle, Thomas, Dir.-Personnel & Labor Rels.--King Kullen Grocery Co., Inc., Westbury, NY; *U.S. Private*, pg. 621

Nagy, Joan S., V.P.-Human Resources--Haverty Furniture Companies, Inc., Atlanta, GA; *U.S. Public*, pg. 799

Nail, Bethany, Dir.-Human Resources--Motown Record Company, J.P., New York, NY; *Int'l*, pg. 1052

Nakaji, Sandra, Dir.-Human Resources--Integral Systems, Inc., Walnut Creek, CA; *Int'l*, pg. 242

Nakamatsu, M., Dir.-Mktg. & Mgr.-Personnel--Takagi Chokoku Co., Ltd.-Hamamatsu Factory, Hamamatsu, Japan; *Int'l*, pg. 1349

Nakamura, Masakatsu, Mng. Dir.-Personnel--Ajinomoto Company Inc., Tokyo, Japan; *Int'l*, pg. 40

Nakamura, Tomonori, Dir.-Personnel & Labor Rels. Div.--Kokusai Electric Co., Ltd., Tokyo, Japan; *Int'l*, pg. 743

Nalette, Robert, Mgr.-Human Resources--ASC Incorporated, Southgate, MI; *U.S. Private*, pg. 8

Nambu, Hirohi, Gen. Mgr.-Human Resources--Tekken Corporation, Tokyo, Japan; *Int'l*, pg. 1362

Names, Christine, V.P.-H.R.--Random House, Inc., New York, NY; *U.S. Private*, pg. 20

Nandkeolyar, K.C., Dir.-Personnel--South Eastern Coalfields Limited, Bilaspur, India; *Int'l*, pg. 299

Napier, Iain, Dir.-Personnel--Bass PLC, London, United Kingdom; *Int'l*, pg. 169

Napolitano, Susan, V.P.-Human Resources--American Media, Inc., Lake Worth, FL; *U.S. Public*, pg. 87
Napper, Stacy B., V.P.-Human Resources--GTE Government Systems Corporation, Needham, MA; *U.S. Public*, pg. 696
Nardone, Richard J., V.P.-Human Resources--Telco Systems, Inc., Norwood, MA; *U.S. Public*, pg. 1568
Narnio, Jean-Pierre, Gen. Mgr.-H.R.--Compagnie UAP, Paris, France; *Int'l*, pg. 323
Nash Merker, Linda, V.P.-Human Resources--Loehmann's, Inc., Bronx, NY; *U.S. Public*, pg. 1010
Natale, Anthony G., V.P.-Human Resources--Day & Zimmermann, Inc., Philadelphia, PA; *U.S. Private*, pg. 316
Nathan, Arte, V.P.-Human Resources--Mirage Resorts Incorporated, Las Vegas, NV; *U.S. Public*, pg. 1116
Natsumeda, Tsuneyoshi, Exec. V.P.-Affiliate Rels., Property & Legal Affairs--Nihon Keizai Shimbun, Inc., Tokyo, Japan; *Int'l*, pg. 929
Naughton, Robert J., Dir.-Personnel--AAR Corp., Wood Dale, IL; *U.S. Public*, pg. 1
Naugo, Sandra, Mgr.-Human Resources--CMI International Inc., Southfield, MI; *U.S. Private*, pg. 195
Nauman, Richard, Dir.-Personnel & Mgr.-Employee Benefits & Risk--National Presto Industries, Inc., Eau Claire, WI; *U.S. Public*, pg. 1159
Naumann, Reiner, Dir.-H.R.--Dun & Bradstreet Deutschland GmbH, Frankfurt/Main, Germany; *U.S. Public*, pg. 536
Neal, Clinton H., Jr., Dir.-Human Resources--GoodMark Foods, Inc., Raleigh, NC; *U.S. Public*, pg. 751
Neal, Dawn, Dir.-Internal Communications--Eli Lilly and Company, Indianapolis, IN; *U.S. Public*, pg. 992
Neal, Jane, Sr. V.P.-H.R.--NBT Bancorp Inc., Norwich, NY; *U.S. Public*, pg. 1144
Neenan, Lisa, Mgr.-H.R.--Stamco Industries Inc., Euclid, OH; *U.S. Private*, pg. 1029
Neer, Fred J., V.P.-Human Resources--Ace Hardware Corporation, Oak Brook, IL; *U.S. Private*, pg. 12
Negoro, Takashi, Sr. Mng. Dir.-Personnel, Gen. Affairs & Paperboard--Settsu Corporation, Amagasaki, Japan; *Int'l*, pg. 1225
Nehls, Robert, Mgr.-Human Resources--Kewaunee Scientific Corporation, Statesville, NC; *U.S. Public*, pg. 953
Neibert, Bob, Dir.-H.R.--Port of Portland, Portland, OR; *U.S. Private*, pg. 876
Neill, C. Thomas, V.P.-Corp. Services--Quorum Health Group, Inc., Brentwood, TN; *U.S. Public*, pg. 1353
Neilson, Kathy, Human Resources--Philadelphia Daily News, Philadelphia, PA; *U.S. Public*, pg. 964
Neilson, William A., V.P.-H.R.--Genesee Corporation, Rochester, NY; *U.S. Public*, pg. 728
Neligan, Patrick F., Dir.-Employee Rels.--Lonza Inc., Fair Lawn, NJ; *Int'l*, pg. 67
Nelson, Eileen, V.P.-H.R./Enterprise Sys.--3Com Corporation, Santa Clara, CA; *U.S. Public*, pg. 1603
Nelson, Jim, Dir.-H.R.--Marcal Paper Mills, Inc., Elmwood Park, NJ; *U.S. Private*, pg. 701
Nelson, Joanne, Dir.-Personnel--Novell Inc., San Jose, CA; *U.S. Public*, pg. 1203
Nelson, Josie, Supvr.-H.R.--Herberts-O'Brien Inc., Houston, TX; *Int'l*, pg. 626
Nelson, Larry, Mgr.-Human Resources & Safety--TVX Gold Inc., Toronto, Canada; *Int'l*, pg. 1345
Nelson, Marc, Coord.-Personnel Programs--Kawasaki Motors Corp., U.S.A., Irvine, CA; *Int'l*, pg. 725
Nelson, Paul, V.P.-Continuous Improvement--YSI Incorporated, Yellow Springs, OH; *U.S. Private*, pg. 1195
Nelson, Scott, Dir.-Human Resources--Sloan Valve Company, Franklin Park, IL; *U.S. Private*, pg. 1006
Nelson, Steve, Mgr.-H.R.--Davis Industries Inc., Plymouth, MI; *U.S. Private*, pg. 315
Nelson, Terri, Dir.-Staffing & Human Capital--International Multifoods Corporation, Minneapolis, MN; *U.S. Public*, pg. 900
Nelson, Thomas, Mgr.-H.R.--TimeMed Labeling Systems, Inc., Burr Ridge, IL; *U.S. Private*, pg. 1087
Nenner, Amy, V.P.-Human Resources--Labatt U.S.A., Darien, CT; *Int'l*, pg. 679
Neppl, Beth B., V.P.-H.R.--Equitable of Iowa Companies, Des Moines, IA; *Int'l*, pg. 647
Nesbit, Warren, V.P.-Human Resources--Alba-Waldensian, Inc., Valdese, NC; *U.S. Public*, pg. 35
Nesler, Robert, V.P.-Human Resources--The Crown Group, Inc., Warren, MI; *U.S. Private*, pg. 292
Ness, Barbara, Dir.-Employee Benefits--Michael Foods, Inc., Minneapolis, MN; *U.S. Public*, pg. 1103
Nesvig, Dianne, Dir.-Human Resources--King Company, Owatonna, MN; *U.S. Public*, pg. 1676
Neve, Laurinda M., V.P. & Human Resources Officer--Independent Bank Corporation, Ionia, MI; *U.S. Public*, pg. 874
Nevers, Bruce, V.P.-Human Resources--Newly Weds Foods Inc., Chicago, IL; *U.S. Private*, pg. 796
Neville, Roseanne, Exec. Dir.-Human Res.--MTA Long Island Rail Road, Jamaica, NY; *U.S. Private*, pg. 739
New, Michael J., Mng. Dir-H.R.--Banknorth Group Inc., Burlington, VT; *U.S. Public*, pg. 186
Newberg, Nancy, Mgr.-H.R.--American Louver Co., Skokie, IL; *U.S. Private*, pg. 58
Newburg, Frances, Dir.-Personnel--Scientific American, Inc., New York, NY; *Int'l*, pg. 1479
Newcomb, Patricia, Dir.-Personnel--Fulton Industries Inc., Wauseon, OH; *U.S. Private*, pg. 431
Newell, Terry F., Dir.Personnel Opers.--TSB Bank Scotland Plc, Edinburgh, United Kingdom; *Int'l*, pg. 813
Newlin, Joan, Dir.-Employee Benefits--Porta Systems Corp., Syosset, NY; *U.S. Public*, pg. 1317
Newman, F. Robert, V.P.-Human Resources--Reynolds Metals Company, Richmond, VA; *U.S. Public*, pg. 1385
Newman, Gary, Exec. V.P.-Human Resources--Information Resources, Inc., Chicago, IL; *U.S. Public*, pg. 875
Newman, Kathleen, V.P.-H.R.--Phoenix Technologies Ltd., San Jose, CA; *U.S. Public*, pg. 1292
Newsom, Kirk W., Dir.-H.R.--Buckeye Partners, L.P., Allentown, PA; *U.S. Public*, pg. 266
Newton, David, Dir.-Human Resources--Accor North America, Scarsdale, NY; *Int'l*, pg. 21
Newton, Pat, Dir.-Personnel--Stanley Steemer International, Inc., Dublin, OH; *U.S. Private*, pg. 1033
Newton, Vicki, Controller--LGC Management, Englewood, CO; *U.S. Private*, pg. 639
Niacaris, Jeannine, Sr. Dir.-Human Resources--Sequus Pharmaceuticals, Inc., Menlo Park, CA; *U.S. Public*, pg. 1460
Nibling, Ken, V.P.-Human Resources & Admin.--Tuboscope Incorporated, Houston, TX; *U.S. Public*, pg. 1643
Nichol, Gretchen, V.P.-Employee Benefits & Dir.-H.R.--American Furniture Company, Albuquerque, NM; *U.S. Private*, pg. 55
Nicholas, Nan, Asst. Dir.-Human Resources--Artistic Greetings, Inc., Elmira, NY; *U.S. Public*, pg. 136
Nichols, Connie L., Dir.-Human Resources--Blount, Inc. Forestry & Industrial Equipment Division, Zebulon, NC; *U.S. Public*, pg. 238
Nichols, Michael C., V.P.-Mngmt. Devel. & Human Resources--Sysco Corporation, Houston, TX; *U.S. Public*, pg. 1550
Nichols, Rick, Mgr.-Personnel--Hampshire Hosiery, Inc., Spruce Pine, NC; *U.S. Public*, pg. 778
Nichols, Robin, Mgr.-H.R.--Meridian Insurance Group, Inc., Indianapolis, IN; *U.S. Public*, pg. 1095
Nicholson, Jon, V.P.-H.R.--Weatherford Enterra Incorporated, Houston, TX; *U.S. Public*, pg. 1749
Nicholson, Peter, Dir.-H.R.--Smith International, Inc., Houston, TX; *U.S. Public*, pg. 1478
Nichting, Richard, Dir.-Personnel--Western States Machine Company, Hamilton, OH; *U.S. Private*, pg. 1168
Nickolds, Clive, Dir.-European Store Opers. & Personnel--Marks & Spencer PLC, London, United Kingdom; *Int'l*, pg. 842
Nicol, Roger, V.P.-H.R.--Countrymark Cooperative, Inc., Indianapolis, IN; *U.S. Private*, pg. 279
Niederer, Charles, V.P.-Human Resources--Ohmeda, Liberty Corner, NJ; *Int'l*, pg. 121
Niedzielski, Robert, Dir.-H.R.--Tighe Industries, Inc., York, PA; *U.S. Private*, pg. 1086
Nielsen, Kurt Anker, Chief Fin. Officer--Novo Nordisk A/S, Bagsvaerd, Denmark; *Int'l*, pg. 987
Nientemp, Thomas I., V.P.-Human Resources--Northern Telecom Inc., Rochester, NY; *Int'l*, pg. 970
Nientimp, Tom, V.P.-Human Resources--Nalge Company, Rochester, NY; *U.S. Public*, pg. 1545
Niese, William A., Sr. V.P.-Law & Human Resources--Los Angeles Times, Los Angeles, CA; *U.S. Public*, pg. 1616
Niesen, Gil, V.P.-Employee Rels.--Mirro Company, Manitowoc, WI; *U.S. Public*, pg. 1177
Nikka, David, V.P.-Human Resources--IG Laboratories, Inc., Framingham, MA; *U.S. Public*, pg. 733
Niman, Catherine, Mgr.-Opers.--Ocean Bio-Chem Inc., Fort Lauderdale, FL; *U.S. Public*, pg. 1211
Nimtz, Kim, Human Resources & Fin. Mgr.--N.W. Ayer & Partners Chicago, Chicago, IL; *U.S. Private*, pg. 104
Nino, Rick, V.P.-Human Resources--Laidlaw Carriers Inc., Woodstock, Canada; *Int'l*, pg. 328
Nippins, R., Mgr.-Personnel--Tech-Tran Corporation, Rancocas, NJ; *U.S. Private*, pg. 560
Nivens, Ken, V.P.-H.P.--Shelter Mutual Insurance Company, Columbia, MO; *U.S. Private*, pg. 992
Nivert, Marianne, Exec. V.P.-Corp. Network Services--Telia AB, Farsta, Sweden; *Int'l*, pg. 1373
Nix, Judy, V.P.-Human Resources--Mitsubishi Silicon America, Salem, OR; *Int'l*, pg. 875
Nizard, Isabelle, Mgr.-Personnel--Merinos, Saint Quentin-en-Yvelines, France; *Int'l*, pg. 858
Noble, Linda, V.P.-Human Resources--Comair Holdings, Inc., Erlanger, KY; *U.S. Public*, pg. 406
Noble, Stan, V.P.-Human Resources--Greenlee Textron, Rockford, IL; *U.S. Public*, pg. 1589
Noel, Al, Dir.-Human Resources--Middlesex Insurance, Westford, MA; *U.S. Private*, pg. 985
Noel, Alfred C., Sr. V.P.-H.R.--Sentry Insurance, A Mutual Company, Stevens Point, WI; *U.S. Private*, pg. 984
Noel, Cherryl, Mgr.-Office & H.R.--Joshua L. Baily Co., Inc., Hoboken, NJ; *U.S. Private*, pg. 110
Noel, Kathy, Mgr.-Human Resources--Lucas Body Systems - North America, Winona, MN; *Int'l*, pg. 820
Nogue, Francois, Dir.-H.R. & Commun.--Framatome SA, Paris, France; *Int'l*, pg. 502
Nola, Elizabeth Ann, Dir.-Personnel--Martin Electronics, Inc., Perry, FL; *U.S. Private*, pg. 709
Nolan, Anne, Dir.-Human Resources--Fluor Daniel GTI, Inc., Norwood, MA; *U.S. Public*, pg. 660
Nolan, Pat, V.P.-H.R.--Binks Sames Corporation, Franklin Park, IL; *U.S. Public*, pg. 229
Nolan, William H., Dir.-Personnel--Hanovia Colight, Union, NJ; *Int'l*, pg. 17
Nolen, Susan C., V.P.--General Accident Insurance, Philadelphia, PA; *Int'l*, pg. 543
Nomura, Takashi, Gen. Mgr.-Personnel--Sumitomo Corporation, Tokyo, Japan; *Int'l*, pg. 1312
Noordin Hassan, Tan Sri Dato'Mohd, Dr., V.P.-Human Resource Mngmt.--Petroliam Nasional Berhad (Petronas), Kuala Lumpur, Malaysia; *Int'l*, pg. 1046
Nordfors, Raimo, Dir.-Human Resources--Nokia Telecommunications, Espoo, Finland; *Int'l*, pg. 952
Nordick, Dori, Mgr.-Benefits--Tri-City Electrical Contractors Inc., Altamonte Springs, FL; *U.S. Private*, pg. 1100
Nordin, Wanda K., Mgr.-Personnel--Hickok Incorporated, Cleveland, OH; *U.S. Public*, pg. 825
Noreau, Joel, Mgr.-Personnel--Banque Paribas (Luxembourg) S.A., Luxembourg, Luxembourg; *Int'l*, pg. 320
Norgard, David W., Grp. V.P.-Human Resources--ELSAG Bailey Process Automation N.V., Schiphol, Netherlands; *Int'l*, pg. 449
Noriega, Janie, Human Resources Mgr.--Bromley, Aguilar & Associates, San Antonio, TX; *U.S. Private*, pg. 692
Noriega, Ruth, Mgr.-Human Resources--Punch Press Products, Inc., Los Angeles, CA; *U.S. Private*, pg. 895
Norman, Bryan, Dir.-Human Resources--George Koch Sons, Inc., Evansville, IN; *U.S. Private*, pg. 628
Norman, Marita, Mgr.-Human Resources--Jagenberg, Inc., Enfield, CT; *Int'l*, pg. 1108
Norman, Richard, V.P.-Human Resources--Coats North America, Charlotte, NC; *Int'l*, pg. 300
Norman, Stan, Mgr.- H.R.--Braid Electric Company, Nashville, TN; *U.S. Private*, pg. 165
Norris, Becca, Human Resources Dir.--FGI Inc., Chapel Hill, NC; *U.S. Private*, pg. 389
Norris, Christopher, Mgr.-Indus. Rels.--Isemoto Contracting Co. Ltd., Hilo, HI; *U.S. Private*, pg. 575
Norris, Tim, Mgr.-H.R. & Safety--Stanback Company, Salisbury, NC; *U.S. Private*, pg. 1030
Northcut, Jim, Dir.-Human Resources--American Manufacturing Company, Chattanooga, TN; *U.S. Private*, pg. 58
Norton, David, Mgr.-H.R.--Macrotech Plyseal, Inc., Salt Lake City, UT; *U.S. Private*, pg. 693
Norton, Nicole, Mgr.-Personnel--Orlane, Inc., New York, NY; *Int'l*, pg. 1011
Norwood, Ellyn M., Sr. V.P.-Human Resources--The Foothill Group, Inc., Los Angeles, CA; *U.S. Public*, pg. 1201
Nosset, Larry, Mgr.-H.R.--Vermeer Manufacturing Company, Pella, IA; *U.S. Private*, pg. 1137
Nott, Patricia, Dir.-Human Resources--Grow Biz International, Inc., Minneapolis, MN; *U.S. Public*, pg. 767
Novacek, Pavel, Dr., Dir.-Human Resources--SKODA, Automobilova a.s., Mlada Boleslav, Czech Republic; *Int'l*, pg. 1475
Novak, John, Mgr.-Human Resources--Copperweld Chicago Division, Chicago, IL; *Int'l*, pg. 662
Novak, Richard E., V.P.-Human Resources--Guilford Mills, Inc., Greensboro, NC; *U.S. Public*, pg. 768
Novak, Richard F., V.P.-Human Resources--Cleveland-Cliffs Inc, Cleveland, OH; *U.S. Public*, pg. 386
Nugent, Bernard P., Dir.-Workplace Rels.--Wisconsin Power & Light Company, Madison, WI; *U.S. Public*, pg. 1728
Nugent, Helen, Dir.-Strategy & Communication--Westpac Banking Corporation, Sydney, Australia; *Int'l*, pg. 1495
Nunes, Jose Luiz, V.P.-H.R.--Cervejarias Kaiser Brasil Ltda., Campinas, Brazil; *Int'l*, pg. 279
Nunnally, Robert, Dir.-H.R.--The Empire District Electric Company, Joplin, MO; *U.S. Public*, pg. 579
Nursey, Les, V.P.-Personnel & Human Resources--Bundy North America, Warren, MI; *Int'l*, pg. 1340
Nusbaum, Sandra, V.P.-H.R.--The Wackenhut Corporation, Palm Beach Gardens, FL; *U.S. Public*, pg. 1731
Nyberg, Rune, Mgr.-Personnel--Sandvik AB, Sandviken, Sweden; *Int'l*, pg. 1185
O'Brian, Wade B., V.P. & Dir.-Human Resources & Labor Rels.--Health Care & Retirement Corporation, Toledo, OH; *U.S. Public*, pg. 801
O'Brien, Barbara, Dir.-Human Resources--Sylvan Learning Systems Inc., Baltimore, MD; *U.S. Public*, pg. 1545
O'Brien, Bonnie, V.P.-Human Resources--Huitt-Zollars, Inc., Dallas, TX; *U.S. Private*, pg. 547
O'Brien, Gordon, Sr. V.P.-Human Resources--Schering-Plough Corporation, Madison, NJ; *U.S. Public*, pg. 1438
O'Brien, Michael A., Sr. V.P.-Human Resources--Pulte Corporation, Bloomfield Hills, MI; *U.S. Public*, pg. 1344
O'Brien, Richard F., V.P.-Corp. Personnel--General Motors Corporation, Detroit, MI; *U.S. Public*, pg. 718
O'Brien, Sheila, Sr. V.P.-H.R.--Nova Corporation, Calgary, Canada; *Int'l*, pg. 971
O'Brien, Tim, Dir.-H.R.--HD Vest Financial Services, Irving, TX; *U.S. Public*, pg. 770
O'Connell, Brian P., V.P.-Human Resources--EMC Corporation, Hopkinton, MA; *U.S. Public*, pg. 545
O'Connell, Dee, Mgr.-Personnel--Electronics Div., San Diego, CA; *U.S. Public*, pg. 396
O'Connell, Leonard D., V.P.-H.R.--SK Hand Tool Corp., Chicago, IL; *Int'l*, pg. 570
O'Connell, Liz, Personnel--Audiovox Corporation, Hauppauge, NY; *U.S. Public*, pg. 147
O'Connell, Mary C., Mgr.-Personnel--Schweizer Aircraft Corporation, Big Flats, NY; *U.S. Private*, pg. 975
O'Connor, Edward J., V.P.-Human Resources & Public Affairs--A.O. Smith Corporation, Milwaukee, WI; *U.S. Public*, pg. 1476
O'Connor, Nancy, Dir.-Personnel--Oxford University Press, Inc., New York, NY; *Int'l*, pg. 1019
O'Connor, Patrick, V.P.-H.R.--Blue Cross & Blue Shield of Illinois, Chicago, IL; *U.S. Private*, pg. 151
O'Connor, Valerie, Mgr.-Human Resources--Dudek & Bock Spring Manufacturing Company, Chicago, IL; *U.S. Private*, pg. 344
O'Connor, Virginia, Dir.-Personnel--Four Seasons Solar Products Corp., Holbrook, NY; *U.S. Private*, pg. 422
O'Connor, William, V.P.-H.R.--Clean Harbors, Inc., Braintree, MA; *U.S. Public*, pg. 383
O'Connor, William G., V.P.-Admin.--The Topps Company, Inc., New York, NY; *U.S. Public*, pg. 1621
O'Dea, Marita, Sr. V.P.-Human Resources--Neiman Marcus Co., Dallas, TX; *U.S. Public*, pg. 785
O'Dell, Sharon, Mgr.-Personnel--Conso Products Company, Union, SC; *U.S. Public*, pg. 434
O'Donnell, John, Dir.-Human Resources--Fairfax Lumber & Millwork Company Inc., Springfield, VA; *U.S. Private*, pg. 391
O'Dwyer, J. Purcell, Personnel Exec.--BPB Industries PLC, Slough, United Kingdom; *Int'l*, pg. 122
O'Grady, Barbara, Mgr.-H.R.--Precision Systems, Inc., Saint Petersburg, FL; *U.S. Public*, pg. 1321
O'Hara, Liisa A., V.P.-Human Resources & Regulatory Affairs--Trans Mountain Pipeline Company Ltd., Vancouver, Canada; *Int'l*, pg. 114
O'Hara, Patrick J., V.P.-Human Resources/Facilities--Fluke Corporation, Everett, WA; *U.S. Public*, pg. 659
O'Hare, Sally, Dir.-Human Resources/Taren--Cole of California, Los Angeles, CA; *U.S. Public*, pg. 148

O'Hern, Elizabeth, V.P.-Human Resources--The Quick & Reilly Group Inc., Palm Beach, FL; *U.S. Public*, pg. 650
O'Hern, Mary E., V.P.-Human Resources--Quick & Reilly, Inc., New York, NY; *U.S. Public*, pg. 650
O'Keefe, Jane, Asst. V.P.-Human Resources--Roanoke Gas Company, Roanoke, VA; *U.S. Public*, pg. 1392
O'Kelly, Eugene, V.P.-H.R.--Maynard Steel Casting Company, Milwaukee, WI; *U.S. Private*, pg. 718
O'Laughlin, John, V.P.-Human Resources--Corporate Express, Inc., Broomfield, CO; *U.S. Public*, pg. 449
O'Leary, Cindy, Mgr.-H.R.--Phoenix Technologies Ltd., San Jose, CA; *U.S. Public*, pg. 1292
O'Leary, David C., Mng. Dir.-Human Resources--Credit Suisse First Boston, Inc., New York, NY; *Int'l*, pg. 345
O'Leary, Holly, Dir.-Human Resources--Chancellor Corporation, Boston, MA; *U.S. Public*, pg. 335
O'Leary, Ken, Dir.-Human Resources--Eckerd Corporation, Largo, FL; *U.S. Public*, pg. 917
O'Loughlin, John P., V.P.-Human Resources--Convex Technology Center - Hewlett-Packard, Richardson, TX; *U.S. Public*, pg. 815
O'Malley, John, V.P.-Human Resources--Clopay Corporation, Cincinnati, OH; *U.S. Public*, pg. 766
O'Mara, Diane M., Mgr.-Human Resources--Ceco Door Products, Brentwood, TN; *U.S. Public*, pg. 1676
O'Mara, Karen, Dir.-Human Resources--Bally Management, New Rochelle, NY; *Int'l*, pg. 998
O'Mea, Elizabeth, V.P.-Human Resources--Callaway Golf Company, Carlsbad, CA; *U.S. Public*, pg. 294
O'Neal, Leeann, H.R.--The Stephenz Group, Inc., San Jose, CA; *U.S. Private*, pg. 1040
O'Neal, Patrick, Dir.-H.R. & Personnel--The Chardon Rubber Co., Chardon, OH; *U.S. Private*, pg. 229
O'Neil, Charles E., Sr. V.P.-Human Resources--Coast Savings Financial, Inc., Los Angeles, CA; *U.S. Public*, pg. 388
O'Neil, John P., V.P.-Personnel--Digital Microwave Corporation, San Jose, CA; *U.S. Public*, pg. 508
O'Neil, Ruth, Dir.-Human Resources & Asst. Sec.--The Somerset Group, Inc., Indianapolis, IN; *U.S. Public*, pg. 1484
O'Neill, C., Mgr.-Personnel--Fortnum & Mason PLC, London, United Kingdom; *Int'l*, pg. 500
O'Neill, John T., Dir.-Personnel--Malcolm Pirnie, Inc., White Plains, NY; *U.S. Private*, pg. 867
O'Neill, Joyce, V.P.-Human Resources--Data Dimensions, Inc., Culver City, CA; *U.S. Public*, pg. 485
O'Neill, Richard J., V.P.-Human Resources--NUI Corporation, Bedminster, NJ; *U.S. Public*, pg. 1147
O'Neill, Shirley, Dir.-Personnel--BIW Cable Systems, Inc., Franklin, MA; *Int'l*, pg. 417
O'Reardon, Steven P., Dir.-Human Resources--Ranger Oil (U.K.) Ltd., Guildford, United Kingdom; *Int'l*, pg. 1086
O'Reilly, Richard D., Sr. V.P.-Human Resources--DIMON, Incorporated, Danville, VA; *U.S. Public*, pg. 509
O'Rourke, Karen, V.P.-H.R.--Research, Incorporated, Eden Prairie, MN; *U.S. Public*, pg. 1382
O'Rourke, Patricia, Officer-Human Res.--United Missouri Bank of St. Louis, Saint Louis, MO; *U.S. Public*, pg. 1655
O'Shana, Ramina, Dir.-Human Resources & Employee Benefits--Western Waste Industries, Torrance, CA; *U.S. Public*, pg. 1686
O'Shea, James M., V.P.-Human Resources--Sbarro, Inc., Commack, NY; *U.S. Public*, pg. 1435
O'Shields, Brent, Mgr.-Human Resources--Hollingsworth Saco Lowell Corporation, Inc., Easley, SC; *U.S. Private*, pg. 535
Oakes, John, Sr. V.P.--Union Planters Corporation, Cordova, TN; *U.S. Public*, pg. 1668
Oakes, John, Sr. V.P.-Human Resources Div.--Union Planters Bank, Memphis, TN; *U.S. Public*, pg. 1669
Oakes, Philip, V.P.-Human Resources--Birmingham Steel Corporation, Birmingham, AL; *U.S. Public*, pg. 232
Oates, Bud, Dir.-H.R.--Tanner Co., Rutherfordton, NC; *U.S. Private*, pg. 1068
Oatman, Carolyn, Dir.-Information Services--Harte-Hanks Communications, Inc., San Antonio, TX; *U.S. Public*, pg. 793
Obana, Yuji, Mng. Dir.-Admin., Personnel, Safety, Sls., Adv. & Customer Serv.--Nikon Corporation, Tokyo, Japan; *Int'l*, pg. 931
Obele, Gary, Dir.-Human Resources--Acrometal Companies, Inc., Plymouth, MN; *U.S. Private*, pg. 14
Obenhoff, Bill, Mgr.-Personnel--The Grandoe Corp., Gloversville, NY; *U.S. Private*, pg. 469
Oberg, Gail, Mgr.-Human Resources & Admin.--Buss (America) Inc., Bloomingdale, IL; *Int'l*, pg. 490
Oberhelman, John M., Sr. V.P.-Human Resources--CNB Bancshares, Inc., Evansville, IN; *U.S. Public*, pg. 280
Oberman, Alice, Human Resources Mgr.--Kirshenbaum, Bond & Partners, New York, NY; *U.S. Private*, pg. 624
Obrecht, Dean, Dir.-Human Resources--Evans, Inc., Chicago, IL; *U.S. Public*, pg. 596
Obrzut, Linda, Dir.-Personnel--McBee Systems, Inc., Parsippany, NJ; *U.S. Private*, pg. 718
Obst, Robert, Dir.-Human Resources--MedImmune, Inc., Gaithersburg, MD; *U.S. Public*, pg. 1081
Ochi, M., Gen. Affairs & Personnel Mngmt. Dir.--Man Nen Sha Inc., Osaka, Japan; *Int'l*, pg. 834
Ochoa, Joaquin, Mng. Dir.-Human Resources--Iberdrola, S.A., Bilbao, Spain; *Int'l*, pg. 657
Ochsenwald, Ron, Dir.-Human Resources--Pueblo Xtra International, Inc., Pompano Beach, FL; *U.S. Private*, pg. 894
Ochu, Kristine, Mgr.-Human Resources--Computer Network Technology Corporation, Minneapolis, MN; *U.S. Public*, pg. 421
Ockerbloom, Carl, V.P.-H.R.--Parametric Technology Corporation, Waltham, MA; *U.S. Public*, pg. 1257
Oder, Kenneth W., Exec. V.P.-Labor Rels., Human Resources, Law & Pub. Affairs--Safeway Inc., Pleasanton, CA; *U.S. Public*, pg. 1406
Odhall, Tomas, Dir.-Personnel--BTL AB, Goteborg, Sweden; *Int'l*, pg. 123
Odier, Claude, Dir.-Human Resources--Yves Saint Laurent Parfums S.A., Neuilly-sur-Seine, France; *Int'l*, pg. 445
Odillard, Martine, V.P.-Corp. Commun. & H.R.--Chargeurs, Paris, France; *Int'l*, pg. 280
Odle, Sally J., V.P.-Human Resources--Exide Electronics Group, Inc., Raleigh, NC; *Int'l*, pg. 126
Oeberst, Kimberly, Mgr.-Human Resources--Sun TV & Appliances, Inc., Groveport, OH; *U.S. Public*, pg. 1532
Oechsner, Kenneth E., Dir.-Human Resources--Mayville Metal Products Division, Mayville, WI; *U.S. Private*, pg. 264
Oetzel, Brian K., V.P.-Personnel--Hart Graphics Inc., Austin, TX; *U.S. Private*, pg. 507
Ogan, Debby, V.P.-HR--Sterling Financial Corporation, Spokane, WA; *U.S. Public*, pg. 1516
Ogburn, Emily, Mgr.-Marcom--Oliver Rubber Co., Athens, GA; *U.S. Public*, pg. 1504
Ogg, Larry B., Exec. V.P. & Mgr.-Human Resources Grp.--Seafirst Corporation, Seattle, WA; *U.S. Public*, pg. 181
Ogle, Bonnie, Dir.-Human Resources--The Fifth Third Bank of Kentucky, Louisville, Louisville, KY; *U.S. Public*, pg. 621
Ogren, Hugh, Dir.-Human Resources--Utilimaster Corp., Wakarusa, IN; *U.S. Private*, pg. 1130
Ohly, Jeffrey W., Sr. V.P., Treas. & Sec.--World Acceptance Corporation, Greenville, SC; *U.S. Public*, pg. 1778
Ohme, Barbara, Dir.-Human Resources--Raven Industries, Inc., Sioux Falls, SD; *U.S. Public*, pg. 1361
Ohr, Bill, Dir.-Human Resources--Cincom Systems, Inc., Cincinnati, OH; *U.S. Private*, pg. 240
Okazaki, Sharon, Dir.-Human Resources/Torrance--Virco Mfg. Corporation, Torrance, CA; *U.S. Public*, pg. 1721
Oksa, Niilo, V.P.-Human Resources--Neste Oy, Espoo, Finland; *Int'l*, pg. 912
Oksnevad, Haakon, Mgr.-Human Resources & Employee Benefits--TSI Incorporated, Shoreview, MN; *U.S. Public*, pg. 1559
Okun, Patricia, Office Mgr.--Deb Shops, Inc., Philadelphia, PA; *U.S. Public*, pg. 491
Olawaiye, Dayo, Dir.-Personnel--Cadbury Nigeria PLC, Ikeja, Nigeria; *Int'l*, pg. 248
Oldenzeel, C. Vlaanderen, Sr. Dir.-Personnel & Gen. Affairs--Hoogovens Aluminium BV, Amstelveen, Netherlands; *Int'l*, pg. 753
Oldman, Linda, Dir.-Human Resources--Plews/Edelmann, Buffalo Grove, IL; *Int'l*, pg. 1396
Oleszek, Kristen, Mgr.-Personnel--Security Van Lines, Kenner, LA; *U.S. Private*, pg. 594
Oleszek, Kristine, Mgr.-Personnel--Johnson Storage & Moving, Aurora, Aurora, CO; *U.S. Private*, pg. 594
Oleszek, Kristine, Mgr.-Personnel--Johnson Moving & Storage, Boulder/Longmont, Longmont, CO; *U.S. Private*, pg. 594
Oleszek, Kristine, Mgr.-Personnel--Johnson Storage & Moving, Cheyenne, Cheyenne, WY; *U.S. Private*, pg. 594
Oleszek, Kristine, Mgr.-Personnel--Johnson Storage & Moving, Cleburne, Arlington, TX; *U.S. Private*, pg. 594
Oleszek, Kristine, Mgr.-Personnel--Johnson Storage & Moving, Colorado Springs, Colorado Springs, CO; *U.S. Private*, pg. 594
Oleszek, Kristine, Mgr.-Personnel--Johnson Storage & Moving, Englewood, Englewood, CO; *U.S. Private*, pg. 594
Oleszek, Kristine, Mgr.-Personnel--Johnson Storage & Moving, San Diego, Poway, CA; *U.S. Private*, pg. 594
Oleszek, Kristine, Mgr.-Personnel--Johnson Storage & Moving, Santa Fe, Santa Fe, NM; *U.S. Private*, pg. 594
Oleszek, Kristine, Mgr.-Personnel--Johnson Moving & Storage, Naperville, IL; *U.S. Private*, pg. 594
Oliver, Donald, V.P.-Human Resources--Dorr-Oliver Incorporated, Milford, CT; *Int'l*, pg. 839
Oliver, Doug, V.P.-Human Resources--East Kentucky Power Co-op, Winchester, KY; *U.S. Private*, pg. 356
Oliver, Michael, V.P.-H.R.--W.H. Brady Co., Milwaukee, WI; *U.S. Public*, pg. 250
Oliver, Walter M., Sr. V.P.-Human Resources--Ameritech Corporation, Chicago, IL; *U.S. Public*, pg. 97
Oliver, Walter M., Sr. V.P.-Human Resources--Ameritech Corp., Chicago, IL; *U.S. Public*, pg. 98
Oliveras, Gasper, Dir.-H.R.--Puerto Rico Tourism Company, San Juan, PR; *U.S. Private*, pg. 894
Oliverre, Grace, Dir.-Personnel--Whaling Industries, Inc., Fall River, MA; *U.S. Private*, pg. 1170
Ollinick, Susan, Dir.-Pub. Rels.--People, New York, NY; *U.S. Public*, pg. 1613
Olmedillo, Nelson E., Mgr.-Human Resources--Petroleos de Venezuela S.A., Caracas, Venezuela; *Int'l*, pg. 1045
Olney, Dick, Dir.-Human Resources--APAC/Ballenger Paving Company, Inc., Taylors, SC; *U.S. Public*, pg. 139
Olsen, Joan, Mgr.-Personnel--Multi-Clean Inc., Shoreview, MN; *Int'l*, pg. 587
Olson, Bruce J., V.P.-Corp. Services--Kimberly-Clark Corporation, Dallas, TX; *U.S. Public*, pg. 958
Olson, Darrell J., V.P.-Human Resources--Twin Disc, Incorporated, Racine, WI; *U.S. Public*, pg. 1646
Olson, Elisabeth, Mgr.-Personnel--Atlet AB, Molnlycke, Sweden; *Int'l*, pg. 97
Olson, James M., V.P.-Human Resources--Ag-Chem Equipment Co., Inc., Minnetonka, MN; *U.S. Public*, pg. 6
Olson, Linda, V.P.-Human Resources--Hyatt Corporation, Chicago, IL; *U.S. Private*, pg. 551
Olson, Roger D., Sr. V.P.-Labor Rels. & Personnel--Giant Food Inc., Landover, MD; *U.S. Public*, pg. 741
Olson, Tina, V.P.-H.R.--Calvin Klein, Inc., New York, NY; *U.S. Private*, pg. 202
Olson, Vern, Dir.-Staffing--Electronic Data Systems Corporation, Plano, TX; *U.S. Public*, pg. 569
Olsson, Arne, Dir.-Mngmt. Resources--ABB Asea Brown Boveri (Holding) Ltd., Zurich, Switzerland; *Int'l*, pg. 1
Olszowka, Corinne, Dir.-H.R.--Quest Medical, Inc., Allen, TX; *U.S. Public*, pg. 1352
Ondrias, Paul, Mgr.-Personnel--Adams Extract Co., Inc., Austin, TX; *U.S. Private*, pg. 16
Oosthuizen, G.J., Dir.-Human Resources--Pretoria Portland Cement Co. Ltd., Johannesburg, South Africa; *Int'l*, pg. 167
Oosthuizen, G.J., Mgr.-Human Resources--Reunert Ltd., Sandton, South Africa; *Int'l*, pg. 1105
Opel, Peter, V.P.-Human Resources--Whataburger, Inc., Corpus Christi, TX; *U.S. Private*, pg. 1170
Orbst, Richard C., Sr., Sr. V.P.-Personnel--M & I Thunderbird Bank, Phoenix, AZ; *U.S. Public*, pg. 1050
Orf, Dave, Dir.-H.R.--Clayton Corporation, Fenton, MO; *U.S. Private*, pg. 244
Ormond, Neil, Dir.-Personnel--Irish Biscuits Ltd., Dublin, Ireland; *Int'l*, pg. 688
Orozco Arreola, Mario, V.P.-H.R.--Grupo Casa Autrey, Mexico, Mexico; *Int'l*, pg. 573
Orozco, Dan R., Dir.-Admin.--The Macneal-Schwendler Corp., Los Angeles, CA; *U.S. Public*, pg. 1030
Orr, David, Dir.-Personnel--Process Instrumentation, Manchester, United Kingdom; *Int'l*, pg. 1444
Orrell, Shirley, Dir.-H.R.--Shuford Mills, Inc., Hickory, NC; *U.S. Private*, pg. 996
Ortega, Gabriela, Mgr.-Human Resources--Sony Corporation of Panama, Panama, Panama; *Int'l*, pg. 1284
Orth, Al, Dir.-Human Resources--Toronto Star Newspapers Ltd., Toronto, Canada; *Int'l*, pg. 1402
Osborn, Shari, Rep.-H.R.--Datametrics Corporation, Calabasas, CA; *U.S. Public*, pg. 487
Osborne, Terry, Sr. V.P.-Human Resources--SunTrust, Orlando, FL; *U.S. Public*, pg. 1537
Osdieck, Bob, V.P.-Human Resources--Swingster Company, Kansas City, MO; *U.S. Private*, pg. 58
Osdiecke, Robert, V.P.-H.R.--American Marketing Industries, Inc., Kansas City, MO; *U.S. Private*, pg. 58
Osman, Datuk, Dir.-H.R.--Sime Darby Berhad, Kuala Lumpur, Malaysia; *Int'l*, pg. 1249
Osmer, Susan, Mgr.-Personnel--SBE, Inc., San Ramon, CA; *U.S. Public*, pg. 1416
Ossolinski, John, Sr. V.P.-H.R.--Kolmar Laboratories, Inc., Port Jervis, NY; *Int'l*, pg. 239
Ostan, William S., V.P.-Human Resources--Rheem Manufacturing Co., New York, NY; *Int'l*, pg. 1022
Ostanek, Ray, Personnel Mgr.--Mayfran International, Inc., Cleveland, OH; *Int'l*, pg. 1397
Oster, Lynsey, Mgr.-Human Resources--Preferred Risk Mutual Insurance, West Des Moines, IA; *U.S. Private*, pg. 880
Ostergaard, Ian, Sr. V.P.-Human Resources--Citibank, Federal Savings Bank (Illinois), Chicago, IL; *U.S. Public*, pg. 378
Osthushenrich, Hans, Mgr.-Personnel--Atlet Flurforderzuege GmbH, Willich, Germany; *Int'l*, pg. 97
Ostroff, Arthur J., Controller & Treas.--Standard Medical Imaging, Inc., Columbia, MD; *U.S. Private*, pg. 1032
Ostrom, W. M., Dir.-Compensation & Benefits--The Canada Life Assurance Company, Toronto, Canada; *Int'l*, pg. 254
Ostrov, Rob, Sr. V.P.-H.R.--TruServ Corporation, Chicago, IL; *U.S. Private*, pg. 1108
Oswald, Kathleen M., V.P.-Corp. Personnel--Chrysler Corporation, Auburn Hills, MI; *U.S. Public*, pg. 352
Otero, Gilberto, Mgr.-Personnel--Goya Foods, Inc., Secaucus, NJ; *U.S. Private*, pg. 468
Otis, Robert, V.P.-Human Resources--The Holland Hitch Company, Holland, MI; *U.S. Private*, pg. 534
Otsuka, Mutsutake, Exec. V.P.-Corp. Plng. & Personnel--East Japan Railway Company, Tokyo, Japan; *Int'l*, pg. 431
Ott, John, Dir.-Human Resources--Apollo Colors Inc., Northbrook, IL; *U.S. Private*, pg. 77
Otto, James, Mgr.-Human Resources--Wrought Washer Mfg., Inc., Milwaukee, WI; *U.S. Private*, pg. 1192
Otto, Larry, Dir.-Personnel--Spelling Entertainment Group, Inc., Los Angeles, CA; *U.S. Private*, pg. 776
Otto, Lawrence J., Mgr.-Human Resources--American Financial Group, Cincinnati, OH; *U.S. Public*, pg. 74
Ouellet, Gaston, V.P.-Human Resources--Alcan Aluminium Limited, Montreal, Canada; *Int'l*, pg. 50
Ouellet, Yves, Mgr.-Personnel--Sulphite Pulp, Temiscaming, Canada; *Int'l*, pg. 1375
Ouimet, Joyce, Human Resources Dir.--Laughlin/Constable, Inc., Milwaukee, WI; *U.S. Private*, pg. 653
Outram, Murray, Mgr.-H.R.--Research, Melbourne, Australia; *Int'l*, pg. 227
Ovellette, Paula, Dir.-Personnel--Holiday RV Superstores, Inc., Orlando, FL; *U.S. Public*, pg. 829
Overby, Ed, Dir.-Personnel--Bill's Dollar Stores, Inc., Ridgeland, MS; *U.S. Private*, pg. 144
Overstreet, Jim, V.P.-Business Devel.--One Price Clothing Stores, Inc., Duncan, SC; *U.S. Public*, pg. 1225
Owen, Judy, Mgr.-Personnel--The Pierce Co., Inc., Upland, IN; *U.S. Private*, pg. 102
Owen, Laura, V.P.-H.R.--ADC Telecommunications, Inc., Minnetonka, MN; *U.S. Public*, pg. 4
Owens, Jim, Dir.-Human Rels.--Leach International, Buena Park, CA; *U.S. Private*, pg. 655
Owens, LaSandra, Dir.-Personnel--Pressure Systems, Inc., Hampton, VA; *Int'l*, pg. 1130
Owens, Robert, Dir.-Human Resources--Unison Industries, Jacksonville, FL; *U.S. Private*, pg. 1120
Oxford, W. Cliff, Sr. V.P.-Corp. & Human Devel.--Lowe's Companies, Inc., North Wilkesboro, NC; *U.S. Public*, pg. 1015
Oyanedel, Alfredo, Asst. Mgr.-Personnel--CODELCO Chile (Corporacion Nacional Del Cobre De Chile), Santiago, Chile; *Int'l*, pg. 302
Oyler, Allen L., V.P.-H.R. & Admin.--Protocol Systems, Inc., Beaverton, OR; *U.S. Public*, pg. 1336
Ozaki, Naoya, Dir.-Personnel--Nikon Corporation, Tokyo, Japan; *Int'l*, pg. 931
Paananen, Tom, Dir.-H.R.--Walter Industries, Inc., Tampa, FL; *U.S. Public*, pg. 1736
Paccione, Christine, Mgr.-H.R.--Flying Food Fare, Inc., Chicago, IL; *U.S. Private*, pg. 415
Pack, Eileen, Dir.-Personnel--Donnkenny, Inc., New York, NY; *U.S. Public*, pg. 519

Packer, James, Dir.-Personnel--Werthan Packaging, Inc., Nashville, TN; *U.S. Private*, pg. 1162
Page, Arthur L., V.P.-Human Resources--The Lincoln National Life Insurance Co., Fort Wayne, IN; *U.S. Public*, pg. 998
Page, D., V.P.-Human Resources--SGS Societe Generale de Surveillance Holding S.A., Geneva, Switzerland; *Int'l*, pg. 1153
Page, David C., Mgr.-Human Resources--Dixon Industries, Inc., Coffeyville, KS; *U.S. Public*, pg. 238
Page, Henry C., Jr., V.P.-H.R. & External Affairs--Ethyl Corporation, Richmond, VA; *U.S. Public*, pg. 595
Page, Holly, Mgr.-Human Resources--Industrial Plastics Company, Fort Smith, AR; *U.S. Public*, pg. 56
Page, Michelle, Mgr.-Personnel--Air Alliance, Sainte-Foy, Canada; *Int'l*, pg. 36
Page, Thomas, Mgr.-Human Resources--Auburn Hosiery Mills, Inc., Auburn, KY; *U.S. Private*, pg. 98
Pagel, Signe, V.P.-Human Resources, Meeting & Travel Svcs.--International Dairy Queen, Inc., Minneapolis, MN; *U.S. Public*, pg. 220
Pagliuco, Anthony R., Dir.-Personnel--Gerber Scientific, Inc., South Windsor, CT; *U.S. Public*, pg. 740
Pahl, John, Dir.-Personnel--Storz Instrument Co., Saint Louis, MO; *U.S. Public*, pg. 79
Palmer, A. Page, Second V.P.-Human Resources--John Hancock Mutual Life Insurance Company, Boston, MA; *U.S. Private*, pg. 589
Palmer, Cass, Dir.-H.R.--Bally's Grand Inc. (Las Vegas), Las Vegas, NV; *U.S. Public*, pg. 829
Palmer, Charlotte, Mgr.-Adv.--Wheeling Corrugating Co., Wheeling, WV; *U.S. Public*, pg. 1727
Palmer, Dennis, Dir.-Admin. Svcs.--Alexander Doll Company, Inc., New York, NY; *U.S. Private*, pg. 33
Palmer, Mike, Mgr.-Human Resources--The Wooster Brush Company, Wooster, OH; *U.S. Private*, pg. 1188
Palo, R., V.P.-Personnel--Coca-Cola Bottling Co. of Chicago, Niles, IL; *U.S. Private*, pg. 248
Palumbo, Thomas, Dir.-Personnel--Warren Equities Inc., Providence, RI; *U.S. Private*, pg. 1151
Panico, Jennie, Dir.-Human Resources--Orion Research Inc., Boston, MA; *U.S. Public*, pg. 1592
Panke, Helmut, Dr., Dir.-Personnel & Admin.--Bayerische Motoren Werke Aktiengesellschaft, Munich, Germany; *Int'l*, pg. 177
Pankey, Barbara, Dir.-Human Resources--Newspapers First, New York, NY; *U.S. Public*, pg. 964
Pannell, Brenda, Dir.-Human Resources--WSMP, Inc., Claremont, NC; *U.S. Public*, pg. 1729
Panocha, Bernice, Dir.-Human Resources--Farley Candy Company, Chicago, IL; *U.S. Private*, pg. 397
Panyik, Rod C., V.P.-H.R.--Horizon/CMS Healthcare Corporation, Albuquerque, NM; *U.S. Public*, pg. 836
Papallia, Sherrill, V.P.-H.R.--Maguire Group Inc., Foxboro, MA; *U.S. Private*, pg. 696
Papke, Robert, Dir.-Personnel--Marine Travelift, Inc., Sturgeon Bay, WI; *U.S. Private*, pg. 703
Paquette, Jeanne S., V.P.--Androscoggin Savings Bank, Lewiston, ME; *U.S. Private*, pg. 74
Paquette, Kap, Mgr.-H.R.--Alloy Products Corp, Waukesha, WI; *U.S. Private*, pg. 42
Paquette, Michael, V.P.-Corp. H.R. Officer--Excel Industries, Inc., Elkhart, IN; *U.S. Public*, pg. 598
Paradise, Kevin J., V.P.-Human Resources--Tambrands Inc., Cincinnati, OH; *U.S. Public*, pg. 1331
Paradiso, Greg, Dir.-Human Resources--Tubed Products, Inc., Easthampton, MA; *U.S. Public*, pg. 1066
Paramio, V., Mgr.-Human Resources--Hispano Olivetti Office, Barcelona, Spain; *Int'l*, pg. 1003
Pardue, Linda, Mgr.-Personnel Services--Speedling Incorporated, Sun City, FL; *U.S. Private*, pg. 1024
Parham, Joseph, Jr., V.P.-Human Resources--Polaroid Corporation, Cambridge, MA; *U.S. Public*, pg. 1313
Parham, Kenneth A., V.P.-Personnel--General Shale Products Corp., Johnson City, TN; *Int'l*, pg. 843
Parham, Kenneth A., V.P.-Personnel--General Shale Products Corp., Elizabethton, TN; *Int'l*, pg. 843
Paris, Emmanuel, Mgr.-H.R.--Compagnie Laitiere BESNIER, Laval, France; *Int'l*, pg. 322
Parker, Don, Exec. V.P. & Chief H.R. Officer--Ammirati Puris Lintas Worldwide, New York, NY; *U.S. Public*, pg. 908
Parker, Gail E., V.P.-Human Resources & Sec.--The Failure Group, Inc., Menlo Park, CA; *U.S. Public*, pg. 609
Parker, Marianne, Dir.-Human Resources--Flambeau Products-Columbus, Columbus, IN; *U.S. Private*, pg. 410
Parker, Ronald C., V.P.-Corp. Human Resources--PepsiCo, Inc., Purchase, NY; *U.S. Public*, pg. 1276
Parker, Ross, Mgr.-Human Resources--Quality Bakers Australia Ltd., Eastwood, Australia; *Int'l*, pg. 555
Parker, S. Victoria, Sr. V.P.--John Wieland Homes Inc., Atlanta, GA; *U.S. Private*, pg. 1175
Parker, Scott, Dir.-H.R.--Nichols Research Corporation, Huntsville, AL; *U.S. Public*, pg. 1182
Parker, Thomas D., V.P.-Human Resources--Newcor, Inc., Bloomfield Hills, MI; *U.S. Public*, pg. 1176
Parks, Greg A., Dir.-Human Resources--Interstate Power Company, Dubuque, IA; *U.S. Public*, pg. 910
Parnell, Michael, Mgr.-Human Resources--Oneida Rostone Corporation, Oneida, NY; *U.S. Public*, pg. 1383
Parpan, Donald, Dir.-Human Resources--Troy Mills, Inc., Troy, NH; *U.S. Private*, pg. 1106
Parr, Jeanette, Dir.-H.R.--Cal-Air Inc., Whittier, CA; *U.S. Private*, pg. 199
Parris, Sarah, Dir.-H.R.--Sternheimer Brothers Inc., Sandston, VA; *U.S. Private*, pg. 1042
Parrish, Robert G., V.P.-H.R.--California Microwave, Inc., Sunnyvale, CA; *U.S. Public*, pg. 293
Parske, Mike, Dir.-Quality & Indus. Rels.--A. Finkl & Sons Co., Chicago, IL; *U.S. Private*, pg. 405
Parsley, Sandy, Dir.-Personnel--Hammel, Green & Abrahamson, Inc., Minneapolis, MN; *U.S. Private*, pg. 497
Parson, Larry, Mgr.-Employee Rels.--Apex Operation, Dayton, OH; *U.S. Public*, pg. 444
Parsons, A.C., Dir.-Personnel--British Gypsum Ltd., Loughborough, United Kingdom; *Int'l*, pg. 122
Parsons, Joseph, V.P.-H.R.--ABC Rail Products Corp., Chicago, IL; *U.S. Public*, pg. 2
Partridge, N.J., Dir.-Personnel--Hepworth Heating Ltd., Belper, United Kingdom; *Int'l*, pg. 615
Pasbrig, Dave, V.P.-Personnel & Insurance--Mayville Engineering Co., Inc., Mayville, WI; *U.S. Private*, pg. 718
Pascal, Diane, Corp. Communications Dir.--Cramer-Krasselt, Chicago, IL; *U.S. Private*, pg. 285
Pascual, Hidelito S., Asst. V.P.-Human Resources Mngmt.--Atlas Consolidated Mining & Development Corporation, Manila, Philippines; *Int'l*, pg. 95
Pasek, Mary Jo, Asst. V.P.-Admin. & Personnel--Calcot, Ltd., Bakersfield, CA; *U.S. Private*, pg. 200
Pasker, Barbara, V.P.-Human Resources--EvansGroup, Salt Lake City, UT; *U.S. Private*, pg. 385
Passante, John, V.P.-H.R.--Monet Jewelers, New York, NY; *U.S. Private*, pg. 757
Pasteris, Donna G., V.P.-H.R. & Admin.--Atomic Energy of Canada Ltd., Mississauga, Canada; *Int'l*, pg. 97
Pate, Ann, Dir.-Personnel & Insurance--USA Petroleum Corporation, Agoura Hills, CA; *U.S. Private*, pg. 1125
Pate, Derrell L., V.P.-Human Resources--Mead Coated Board, Atlanta, GA; *U.S. Public*, pg. 1074
Patrick, Andrew, Grp. Dir.-H.R.--Allied Domecq PLC, London, United Kingdom; *Int'l*, pg. 62
Patten, D., Dir.-Human Resources--S & C Electric Canada Ltd., Toronto, Canada; *U.S. Private*, pg. 954
Patterson, Kimber, Admin. Dir. & Human Resources Dir.--Cohn & Wells, San Francisco, CA; *Int'l*, pg. 601
Patterson, Nate, Dir.-Personnel--Shelby Williams Industries, Inc., Morristown, TN; *U.S. Public*, pg. 1464
Patterson, Theresa, Mgr.-H.R. & Risk Mngmt.--GSC Enterprises, Inc., Sulphur Springs, TX; *U.S. Private*, pg. 436
Pattison, Albert J., V.P.-H.R.--Aloha Airgroup, Inc., Honolulu, HI; *U.S. Private*, pg. 44
Pattison, Albert J., V.P.-H.R.--Aloha Airlines, Inc., Honolulu, HI; *U.S. Private*, pg. 44
Patton, Greg, Mgr.-H.R.--Pre-Paid Legal Services, Inc., Ada, OK; *U.S. Public*, pg. 1320
Patton, John, Dir.-Human Resources--Metrologic Instruments, Inc., Blackwood, NJ; *U.S. Public*, pg. 1102
Paty, JoAnne, V.P.-H.R.--The Paty Company, Piney Flats, TN; *U.S. Private*, pg. 844
Paul, John A., V.P.-Human Resources & Admin.--Norcen Energy Resources Limited, Calgary, Canada; *Int'l*, pg. 434
Paul, Pete, Mgr.-Admin. Svcs.--Standco Industries, Inc., Houston, TX; *U.S. Private*, pg. 1032
Paul, Robert, Sr. V.P.-H.R.--NVR, Inc., Mc Lean, VA; *U.S. Public*, pg. 1148
Paulison, Wayne, V.P.-Human Resourcees--Zebco, Tulsa, OK; *U.S. Public*, pg. 265
Paull, David Z., Dir.-Human Resources--RMI Titanium Company, Niles, OH; *U.S. Public*, pg. 1662
Paulos, Michele, Dir.-H.R.--Tru-Weld Grating, Inc., Wexford, PA; *U.S. Private*, pg. 1107
Pausig, Ralph W., Sr. V.P.-Human Resources--ITT Corporation, New York, NY; *U.S. Public*, pg. 1512
Pavel, Mary, Mgr.-Human Resources--Zack Electronics, San Jose, CA; *U.S. Private*, pg. 1203
Pavlik, Mark J., Mgr.-Bus. Rels.--GAI Consultants, Inc., Monroeville, PA; *U.S. Private*, pg. 433
Paxson, Linda, Asst.-Human Resources--Fiatallis North America, Inc., Carol Stream, IL; *Int'l*, pg. 483
Payne, Diana, Asst. V.P.-Human Resources--Koger Equity Inc., Jacksonville, FL; *U.S. Public*, pg. 965
Payne, Elizabeth, Dir.-Personnel--Oklahoma Publishing Company, Oklahoma City, OK; *U.S. Private*, pg. 813
Payson, Richard, V.P.-Human Resources--Sea World of Florida, Orlando, FL; *U.S. Public*, pg. 114
Peacock, T.G., Mgr.-Personnel--Rothmans (UK) Ltd., Aylesbury, United Kingdom; *Int'l*, pg. 1130
Pearson, Kenneth R., V.P.-H.R.--Ducommun Incorporated, Carson, CA; *U.S. Public*, pg. 533
Pearson, Patricia, Mgr.-Human Resources--Amano Cincinnati, Inc., Roseland, NJ; *Int'l*, pg. 70
Peck, Diane, Sr. V.P.-Human Resources--Safeway Inc., Pleasanton, CA; *U.S. Public*, pg. 1426
Peck, Katy, Dir.-Human Resources--International Envelope Company, Exton, PA; *U.S. Public*, pg. 70
Peck, Patricia A., V.P.-Human Resources--Woolworth Corporation, New York, NY; *U.S. Public*, pg. 1777
Peck, Stephen E., V.P.-H.R.--Rugg Manufacturing Company, Greenfield, MA; *U.S. Private*, pg. 950
Peddle, Elizabeth A., Dir.-Personnel--Spire Corporation, Bedford, MA; *U.S. Public*, pg. 1499
Peddrick, Allen R., V.P.-H.R.--Comcast Cable Communications, Inc., Philadelphia, PA; *U.S. Public*, pg. 407
Pede, Richard, Sr. Leader-H.R.--Crown International, Inc., Elkhart, IN; *U.S. Private*, pg. 293
Peden, Keith, V.P. & Deputy Dir.-H.R.--Raytheon Company, Lexington, MA; *U.S. Public*, pg. 1364
Pedersen, Douglas A., Dir.-H.R.--Werner Enterprises, Inc., Omaha, NE; *U.S. Public*, pg. 1754
Pedrett, R.J., Dir.-Personnel--Rowan Companies, Inc., Houston, TX; *U.S. Public*, pg. 1409
Pedrick, Donna J., V.P.-H.R.--SunGard Data Systems Inc., Wayne, PA; *U.S. Public*, pg. 1534
Pedroza, Laurie, Mgr.-Human Res.--Bancomm, Anaheim, CA; *U.S. Public*, pg. 488
Peek, Henk, Mng. Dir. & Mgr.-Human Resources--Kelly Uitzendburo, Hague, Netherlands; *U.S. Public*, pg. 949
Peel, Michael A., Sr. V.P.-Personnel--General Mills, Inc., Minneapolis, MN; *U.S. Public*, pg. 717
Peery, J.K., V.P.-H.R.--Quanex Corporation, Houston, TX; *U.S. Public*, pg. 1349
Peet, Jan, Dir.-Personnel--Farr Company, El Segundo, CA; *U.S. Public*, pg. 613
Pehrson, Rona King, V.P.-H.R.--Transamerica Corporation, San Francisco, CA; *U.S. Public*, pg. 1629
Peipman, Fred, Dir.-Personnel--Fonar Corporation, Melville, NY; *U.S. Public*, pg. 661
Peixotto, Bob, V.P.-H.R.--L.L. Bean, Inc., Freeport, ME; *U.S. Private*, pg. 639
Pelletier, Elise, V.P.-Human Resources--The Cascades Group, Kingsey Falls, Canada; *Int'l*, pg. 273
Pelletier, Elise, V.P.-H.R.--Cascades, Inc., Kingsey Falls, Canada; *Int'l*, pg. 273
Pelliciari, Robert, V.P.-Human Resources--Elf Atochem North America, Inc., Philadelphia, PA; *Int'l*, pg. 445
Pelsa, Ronald, Dir.-H.R.--Teledyne Fluid Systems, Brecksville, OH; *U.S. Public*, pg. 43
Pena, Mardella, Sr. V.P.-H.R.--ADVO, Inc., Windsor, CT; *U.S. Public*, pg. 23
Pendel, Marc, Mgr.-H.R.--Modernfold, Inc., New Castle, IN; *U.S. Private*, pg. 755
Pendexter, Harold E., Jr., Chief Admin. Officer & Sr. V.P.--USG Corporation, Chicago, IL; *U.S. Public*, pg. 1660
Penfield, Rodney C., Dir.-Human Resources--SIGCORP, Inc., Evansville, IN; *U.S. Public*, pg. 1471
Penfield, Rodney C., Dir.-Human Resources--Southern Indiana Gas & Electric Co., Evansville, IN; *U.S. Public*, pg. 1471
Penisson, Rene, Grp. Sr. V.P.-Human Resources--Rhone-Poulenc S.A., Courbevoie, France; *Int'l*, pg. 1108
Pennachio, Joseph M., Asst. V.P.-Human Resources--W.R. Berkley Corporation, Greenwich, CT; *U.S. Public*, pg. 215
Penner, Richard A., Dir.-H.R.--Dewberry & Davis, Fairfax, VA; *U.S. Private*, pg. 329
Pennington, Kevin P., V.P.-Human Resources--Bell Atlantic Corporation, New York, NY; *U.S. Public*, pg. 201
Penrose, Dianna, Dir.-H.R.--Nady Systems, Inc., Emeryville, CA; *U.S. Private*, pg. 773
Pepin, Barbara, Admin.-Human Resources--Carver Corporation, Lynnwood, WA; *U.S. Public*, pg. 310
Percival, Robert, Dir.-Human Resources--Cegelec AEG Automation Systems Corp., Canonsburg, PA; *Int'l*, pg. 52
Perea, Dave, Mgr.-Human Resources--Rosemount Analytical, Uniloc Div., Irvine, CA; *U.S. Public*, pg. 574
Peredia, Mary, Mgr.-H.R.--PharmChem Laboratories, Inc., Menlo Park, CA; *U.S. Public*, pg. 1285
Perez, Mario, Dir.-Human Resources--Interbath, Inc., City of Industry, CA; *U.S. Private*, pg. 566
Perez, Pat, Dir.-H.R.--Juno Lighting, Inc., Des Plaines, IL; *U.S. Public*, pg. 935
Perez, Rudolfo, Mgr.-Personnel--Aero Peru Corporation, Coral Gables, FL; *U.S. Private*, pg. 24
Perich, Cile K., V.P.-Human Rels.--McCormick Flavor Division-U.S.A., Hunt Valley, MD; *U.S. Public*, pg. 1066
Perish, J., V.P.-Human Resources--Verson Division, Chicago, IL; *U.S. Public*, pg. 48
Perkins, James A., Chief Personnel Officer & Sr. V.P.--FDX Corporation, Memphis, TN; *U.S. Public*, pg. 603
Perkinson, Myra J., V.P.-Human Resources & Communications--Millennium Petrochemicals, Inc., Cincinnati, OH; *Int'l*, pg. 594
Pero, Charles J., V.P.-H.R.--Terra Nitrogen Company, L.P., Tulsa, OK; *U.S. Public*, pg. 1581
Perossio, Susanna, Mgr.-Personnel--Anaheim Manufacturing Company, Anaheim, CA; *U.S. Private*, pg. 70
Perot-Tripp, Rebecca, Mgr.-Human Resources--Louis Dreyfus Natural Gas Corp., Oklahoma City, OK; *U.S. Private*, pg. 342
Perrault, Denise, V.P.-Human Resource Plng.--Imasco Limited, Montreal, Canada; *Int'l*, pg. 112
Perreault, Mark S.P., Sr. V.P.-H.R.--The Bank of Bermuda Limited, Hamilton, Bermuda; *Int'l*, pg. 150
Perrin, Ellen, Dir.-Human Resources--Stuart Circle Hospital Corporation, Atlanta, GA; *U.S. Public*, pg. 1036
Perrott, Pam, Dir.-Human Resources--Markel Corporation, Glen Allen, VA; *U.S. Public*, pg. 1046
Perry, Alan R., V.P.-H.R.--Knowles Electronics, Inc., Itasca, IL; *U.S. Private*, pg. 627
Perry, Bill, Dir.-Personnel--Furman Lumber Company, Inc., Billerica, MA; *U.S. Private*, pg. 431
Perry, Ellie J., V.P.-H.R.--LaBarge, Inc., Saint Louis, MO; *U.S. Public*, pg. 973
Perry, Fran, Mgr.-Human Resources--Network Long Distance, Inc., Baton Rouge, LA; *U.S. Public*, pg. 1169
Perry, Ron, Dir.-Personnel--The Tog Shop, Americus, GA; *U.S. Private*, pg. 1090
Perry, Stephen A., V.P.-H.R. & Logistics--The Timken Company, Canton, OH; *U.S. Public*, pg. 1617
Persky, James L., Exec. V.P.-Admin. & Fin.--Southdown, Inc., Houston, TX; *U.S. Public*, pg. 1488
Persson, Ingrid, Dir.-Personnel--Swedbank, Stockholm, Sweden; *Int'l*, pg. 1328
Persson, Sven-Erik, Exec. V.P. & Head-Group Staff--Cardo AB, Malmo, Sweden; *Int'l*, pg. 268
Perzow, Carrie, V.P.-H.R.--Centigram Communications Corporation, San Jose, CA; *U.S. Public*, pg. 323
Pesce, Peter, V.P.-H.R.--Andersen Worldwide, New York, NY; *U.S. Private*, pg. 72
Pessetti, Melanie A., Mgr.-H.R.--A.M. Todd Company, Kalamazoo, MI; *U.S. Private*, pg. 1089
Peterman, Joyce, V.P.-Human Resources--Biggs Gilmore Communications, Kalamazoo, MI; *U.S. Private*, pg. 143
Peternell, Ben C., Sr. V.P.-Human Resources & Corp. Rels.--Harrah's Entertainment, Inc., Memphis, TN; *U.S. Public*, pg. 790
Peters, Colleen J., V.P. & Fin. Administrator--Annabelle Candy Company, Inc., Hayward, CA; *U.S. Private*, pg. 75
Peters, Elizabeth, Dir.-H.R.--The Vermont Teddy Bear Company, Inc., Shelburne, VT; *U.S. Public*, pg. 1716
Peters, Mary O., V.P.-Admin. & Human Resources--Plains Resources Inc., Houston, TX; *U.S. Public*, pg. 1307
Peters, Renee, Mgr.-Personnel--Moscom Corporation, Pittsford, NY; *U.S. Public*, pg. 1136
Peters, Sheila S., V.P.-Human Resources--The Gap, Inc., San Francisco, CA; *U.S. Public*, pg. 702
Petersen, Randall A., V.P.-Human Resources--Hach Company, Loveland, CO; *U.S. Public*, pg. 773
Petersen, Rod, Dir.-H.R.--Harker's Distribution, Inc., Le Mars, IA; *U.S. Private*, pg. 502

Peterson, Adaire C., V.P.-Human Resources--ReliaStar Financial Corp., Minneapolis, MN; *U.S. Public,* pg. 1375
Peterson, Adaire C., V.P.-Human Resources--Northwestern National Life Insurance Co., Minneapolis, MN; *U.S. Public,* pg. 1375
Peterson, Byron, V.P.-H.R.--Branson Ultrasonics Corp.-Plastics Joining Div., Danbury, CT; *U.S. Public,* pg. 574
Peterson, Byron, V.P.-Human Resources--Branson Ultrasonics, Danbury, CT; *U.S. Public,* pg. 574
Peterson, Carol, Dir.-Human Resources--Comshare, Incorporated, Ann Arbor, MI; *U.S. Public,* pg. 425
Peterson, Clarke, V.P.-H.R.--Utica Mutual Insurance Company, New Hartford, NY; *U.S. Private,* pg. 1129
Peterson, Coleman, Sr. V.P.-Human Resources--Wal-Mart Stores, Inc., Bentonville, AR; *U.S. Public,* pg. 1732
Peterson, Craig, V.P.-Admin.--Gelco Information Network, Inc., Eden Prairie, MN; *U.S. Private,* pg. 442
Peterson, Dave, Mgr.-Human Resources & Pub. Rels.--Southern Minnesota Beet Sugar Cooperative, Renville, MN; *U.S. Private,* pg. 1016
Peterson, Jan, V.P.-Human Resources--DonTech, Chicago, IL; *U.S. Public,* pg. 98
Peterson, Jim, Mgr.-Human Resources--Duck Head Apparel, Winder, GA; *U.S. Public,* pg. 498
Peterson, Kim, Sr. V.P.-Human Resources--C. Brewer & Company, Limited, Honolulu, HI; *U.S. Private,* pg. 190
Peterson, Kim L., V.P.-H.R.--Buyco, Inc., Honolulu, HI; *U.S. Private,* pg. 190
Peterson, Pete, V.P.-H.R.--Quadion Corporation, Minneapolis, MN; *U.S. Private,* pg. 898
Peterson, Phillip E., V.P.-Human Resources--Honeywell-Measurex Corporation, Cupertino, CA; *U.S. Public,* pg. 833
Peterson, Richard P., V.P.-Human Resources--Mead School & Office Products, Dayton, OH; *U.S. Public,* pg. 1074
Peterson, Sarah, Mgr.--Hennells, Inc., Ferndale, MI; *U.S. Private,* pg. 522
Peterson, Stefan, Dir.-Benefits & Compensation--BMC Industries, Inc., Minneapolis, MN; *U.S. Public,* pg. 162
Peterson, Steven W., Chief Fin. Officer, V.P.-Fin. & Sec.--Mesa Laboratories, Inc., Wheat Ridge, CO; *U.S. Public,* pg. 1099
Peterson, Susan, Mgr.-Personnel--D.D. Bean & Sons Co., Jaffrey, NH; *U.S. Private,* pg. 126
Petrauskas, Eleanore, Dir.-Personnel--Anemostat Products, Scranton, PA; *U.S. Public,* pg. 286
Petrino, Richard A., V.P.-H.R. & Plng. & Devel.--Comcast Corporation, Philadelphia, PA; *U.S. Public,* pg. 406
Petro, Mike, Dir.-Human Resources--Ulbrich Stainless Steels & Special Metals, Inc., North Haven, CT; *U.S. Private,* pg. 1115
Pettie, Chris, V.P.-Human Resources & Training--Monterey's Acquisition Corp., Houston, TX; *U.S. Private,* pg. 758
Pettus, Robert, V.P.-Human Resources--Coca-Cola Consolidated, Charlotte, NC; *U.S. Public,* pg. 392
Pfeffer, Susan, V.P.-Human Resources--Sherwood-Davis & Geck, Saint Louis, MO; *U.S. Public,* pg. 80
Pfeiffer, Gerard, Dir.-H.R.--Generale Sucriere SNC, Paris, France; *Int'l,* pg. 548
Pfeiffer, Robert N., Sr. V.P.-H.R. & Customer Opers.--St. Paul Bancorp, Inc., Chicago, IL; *U.S. Public,* pg. 1428
Pfeiffer, Wally, V.P.-Human Resources Devel.--Fred Meyer Stores, Portland, OR; *U.S. Public,* pg. 1103
Pfeuffer, Eberhard, Mgr.-H.R.--Landesbank Hessen-Thuringen Girozentrale, Frankfurt/Main, Germany; *Int'l,* pg. 798
Pfistner, Stephen, V.P.-H.R. & Org. Devel.--FiberMark Inc., Brattleboro, VT; *U.S. Public,* pg. 620
Phelan, Dan, V.P.-Personnel--SmithKline Beecham Corporation, Philadelphia, PA; *Int'l,* pg. 1264
Phelps, David, V.P.-H.R.--RELTEC Corporation, Cleveland, OH; *U.S. Private,* pg. 921
Phelps, Ed, Dir.-Human Resources--Tombstone Pizza Corporation, Northfield, IL; *U.S. Public,* pg. 1288
Phelps, Sally, Mgr.-Human Resources--The Wm. Powell Company, Cincinnati, OH; *U.S. Private,* pg. 877
Phelps, Sherry, Dir.-Employment--Southwest Airlines Co., Dallas, TX; *U.S. Public,* pg. 1493
Phenix, Lee, Dir.-Personnel--Plains Cotton Co-op Association, Lubbock, TX; *U.S. Private,* pg. 868
Phifer, Karen, Mgr.-H.R.--Oil-Dri Corporation of America, Chicago, IL; *U.S. Public,* pg. 1214
Phillips, Aaron, V.P.-Human Resources--UOP, Des Plaines, IL; *U.S. Public,* pg. 52
Phillips, Carla, Dir.-Human Resources--Oregon Metallurgical Corporation, Albany, OR; *U.S. Public,* pg. 43
Phillips, Craig S., Dir.-Personnel--The Greenbrier, White Sulphur Springs, WV; *U.S. Public,* pg. 284
Phillips, Dave, Mgr.-Personnel--The Vernon Company, Newton, IA; *U.S. Private,* pg. 1137
Phillips, E.L., Dir.-Personnel--Del Mar Avionics, Irvine, CA; *U.S. Private,* pg. 321
Phillips, Gary, Dir.-Human Resources--Robertshaw Tennessee, Knoxville, TN; *Int'l,* pg. 1243
Phillips, Hoyt J., Sr. V.P.-H.R.--Jefferson-Pilot Corporation, Greensboro, NC; *U.S. Public,* pg. 925
Phillips, Hoyt J., Sr. V.P.-Human Resources--Jefferson-Pilot Life Insurance Co., Greensboro, NC; *U.S. Public,* pg. 926
Phillips, Lawrence, Sr. H.R. Officer--Citicorp, New York, NY; *U.S. Public,* pg. 376
Phillips, Richard B., V.P.-Human Resources--Crane Co., Stamford, CT; *U.S. Public,* pg. 456
Phillips, Sheryl, V.P.-Human Resources--Andrew Corporation (Austin), Austin, TX; *U.S. Public,* pg. 112
Philp, J.R., V.P.-Admin. & H.R.--The Hillman Company, Pittsburgh, PA; *U.S. Private,* pg. 530
Philpott, Jim, V.P. & Dir.-Employee Rels.--Bassett Furniture Industries, Incorporated, Bassett, VA; *U.S. Public,* pg. 193
Piazzolla, R., Gen. Mgr.-H.R.--Nuovo Pignone S.p.a., Florence, Italy; *Int'l,* pg. 990
Picard, Roland, Dir.-Personnel--Son Chief Electrics, Inc., Winsted, CT; *U.S. Private,* pg. 1014
Picker, Jackson C., V.P.-H.R. & Admin.--Primex Technologies, Inc., Saint Petersburg, FL; *U.S. Public,* pg. 1329
Pickering, Jim L., Dir.-Personnel--Santa Fe Drilling Co., Alhambra, CA; *Int'l,* pg. 765
Pickett, J.B., Corp. Gen. Mgr.-Personnel--Email Limited, Waterloo, Australia; *Int'l,* pg. 450
Pienaar, Jane, Dir.-Human Resources--Morgan Keegan, Inc., Memphis, TN; *U.S. Public,* pg. 1131
Pieper, Jurgen, Dir.-Personnel--Mercedes-Benz AG, Stuttgart, Germany; *Int'l,* pg. 368
Pierce, Daniel, V.P.-H.R.--Aetna Industries, Inc., Center Line, MI; *U.S. Private,* pg. 25
Pierce, Gerard, Dir.-H.R.--Wegmans Food Markets, Inc., Rochester, NY; *U.S. Private,* pg. 1158
Pierce, Jon P., Exec. V.P.-Human Resources--Mercantile Bancorporation Inc., Saint Louis, MO; *U.S. Public,* pg. 1087
Pierce, Norh, V.P.-H.R.--RJO Enterprises, Inc., Lanham, MD; *U.S. Private,* pg. 904
Pieroni, Gina, Dir.-Personnel--Fannie May Candy Shops, Inc., Chicago, IL; *U.S. Private,* pg. 598
Pieschacon, Jamie, V.P.-Human Resources--Warner-Lambert Consumer Healthcare, Morris Plains, NJ; *U.S. Public,* pg. 1739
Pietrzak, Leonard W., Chief Fin. Officer & V.P.-Fin.--Jetronic Industries, Inc., Philadelphia, PA; *U.S. Public,* pg. 926
Pietsch, K., Dir.-Personnel--Kuehne & Nagel International AG, Schindellegi, Switzerland; *Int'l,* pg. 763
Pigg, Carol, Personnel Admin.--Data Transmission Network Corporation, Omaha, NE; *U.S. Public,* pg. 486
Pike, Bob, Sr. V.P.-Mtel H.R.--Mobile Telecommunications Technologies Corp., Jackson, MS; *U.S. Public,* pg. 1120
Pike, D.R., Corp. V.P.-Human Resources--Scott Paper Limited, Mississauga, Canada; *Int'l,* pg. 762
Pike, Jagoda, V.P.-Opers. & Human Resources--Toronto Star Newspapers Ltd., Toronto, Canada; *Int'l,* pg. 1402
Pike, John C., Dir.-Human Resources--Heluva Good Cheese Inc., Sodus, NY; *Int'l,* pg. 752
Pilliard, Jean Francois, V.P.-H.R.--Schneider S.A., Boulogne-Billancourt, France; *Int'l,* pg. 1207
Pilon, Lawrence J., Sr. V.P.-Human Resources--Whitman Corporation, Rolling Meadows, IL; *U.S. Public,* pg. 1766
Pimentel, Rocha, Dr., Gen. Mgr.-Personnel--Transportes Aereos Portugueses, Lisbon, Portugal; *Int'l,* pg. 1418
Pimentel, Rocha, Dr., Dir.-Personnel--Transportes Aereos Portugueses, Lisbon, Portugal; *Int'l,* pg. 1418
Pin, Christian, Gen. Mgr.-Human Resources--Groupe SEB, Ecueille, France; *Int'l,* pg. 568
Pineau, Chuck, V.P.-Human Resources--Falcon Products, Inc., Saint Louis, MO; *U.S. Public,* pg. 611
Pinto, Charles P., V.P.-Human Resources--PP&L Resources, Allentown, PA; *U.S. Public,* pg. 1244
Pion, Robert, Mgr.-Personnel--Smith & Wesson Corp., Springfield, MA; *Int'l,* pg. 1397
Piotter, Robert, Dir.-Personnel--The Cafaro Co., Youngstown, OH; *U.S. Private,* pg. 198
Pippen, Mann, Dir.-Pub. Rels.--Coastal Lumber Company, Weldon, NC; *U.S. Private,* pg. 248
Piquet, Gerard, Mgr.-Personnel--Iveco France S.A., Trappes, France; *Int'l,* pg. 696
Pisano, S., Dir.-Personnel--Eli Lilly Italia, S.p.A., Sesto Fiorentino, Italy; *U.S. Public,* pg. 994
Pisarek, Sue, Mgr.-Human Resources--Varco BJ Drilling Systems, Orange, CA; *U.S. Public,* pg. 1709
Piston, Vija, Mgr.-Human Resources--American Modular Technologies, Liberty, NC; *U.S. Public,* pg. 69
Pitaro, Veronica, Dir.-Human Resources--Louis Dreyfus Corporation, Wilton, CT; *U.S. Private,* pg. 342
Pitishov, Valerie, Coord.-H.R.--Consumers Packaging Inc., Etobicoke, Canada; *Int'l,* pg. 326
Pitkaniemi, Arto, Mgr.-Personnel--Atlet AB, Molnlycke, Sweden; *Int'l,* pg. 97
Pittman, Helen, Mgr.-H.R.--Wholesale Electronic Supply, Dallas, TX; *U.S. Private,* pg. 1174
Pittman, Michael J., V.P.-Human Resources--PacifiCorp, Portland, OR; *U.S. Public,* pg. 1251
Pittman, Pitt, Personnel--Texas Utilities Company, Dallas, TX; *U.S. Public,* pg. 1586
Pitts, Virginia M., 1st Sr. V.P. & Dir.-Human Resources--J. Baker, Inc., Canton, MA; *U.S. Public,* pg. 167
Pitzer, Brian, V.P.-Human Resources--Intertek Testing Services, Andover, MA; *Int'l,* pg. 672
Playfair, Scott, V.P.-Personnel--CSR America Inc., Atlanta, GA; *Int'l,* pg. 245
Plaza, Susan, Dir.-Human Resources--The Strober Organization, Inc., Brooklyn, NY; *U.S. Private,* pg. 403
Pledger, Lee, V.P.-Human Resources--Jackson National Life Insurance Company, Lansing, MI; *Int'l,* pg. 1073
Plesnicher, Carl J., Jr., Sr. V.P.-Human Resources--Cooper Industries, Inc., Houston, TX; *U.S. Public,* pg. 442
Plimpton, Rodney B., Sr. V.P.-H.R.--American Electric Power Service Corp., Columbus, OH; *U.S. Public,* pg. 72
Ploetz, Richard A., V.P.-Corp. H.R.--Medtronic, Inc., Minneapolis, MN; *U.S. Public,* pg. 1082
Ploude, Alice, Dir.-Human Resources & Security--L3 Communications Hycor Div., Woburn, MA; *U.S. Private,* pg. 638
Plummer, Gary, Mgr.-H.R.--Modernfold, Inc., New Castle, IN; *U.S. Private,* pg. 755
Plummer, Jerry L., Sr. V.P.-Human Resources & Corp. Support--American United Life Insurance Company, Indianapolis, IN; *U.S. Private,* pg. 64
Plunkett, Tony, Mgr.-Human Resources--Avonmore Waterford Group plc, Killkenny, Ireland; *Int'l,* pg. 102
Po, Mario, Dir.-Personnel & Organization--Agusta S.P.A., Varese, Italy; *Int'l,* pg. 32
Pocci, Eugene R., V.P.-Human Resources--Copperweld Fayetteville Division, Fayetteville, TN; *Int'l,* pg. 662
Podawiltz, Joseph A., V.P.-H.R.--Harnischfeger Industries, Inc., Saint Francis, WI; *U.S. Public,* pg. 788
Podraza, Bill, V.P.-H.R. & External Affairs--Nebraska Public Power District, Columbus, NE; *U.S. Private,* pg. 789
Podwell, Ann, Dir.-Personnel--Industrial Towel & Uniform, New Berlin, WI; *U.S. Private,* pg. 561
Poinsette, Cheryl, V.P.-Human Resources--McKesson Corporation, San Francisco, CA; *U.S. Public,* pg. 1072
Pol, Anne, Sr. V.P.-H.R.--Trex Medical Corporation, Danbury, CT; *U.S. Public,* pg. 1595
Polhs Andrade, Guillermo, Dir.-H.R.--Grupo SYR, S.A. de C.V., Mexico, Mexico; *Int'l,* pg. 576
Poll, Eric, Mgr.-Human Resources--Leica A.G., Saint Gallen, Switzerland; *Int'l,* pg. 806
Pollard, Ward, Mgr.-Human Resources--BHP Coal, Brisbane, Australia; *Int'l,* pg. 223
Pollarollo, Juan Carlos, Asst. Mgr.-H.R.--El Teniente Division, Rancagua, Chile; *Int'l,* pg. 302
Pollin, Mary Ellen, V.P.-Human Resources--USA Networks, Inc., Saint Petersburg, FL; *U.S. Public,* pg. 1685
Polmery, Rich K., Mgr.-H.R.--O'Sullivan Corporation, Winchester, VA; *U.S. Public,* pg. 1234
Pomares, Jim, Treas., Sec. & Mgr.-Personnel--Sacramento Jaguar, Inc., Sacramento, CA; *U.S. Private,* pg. 1143
Pondaco, Aldo, Mgr.-Personnel--Nestle Industrial e Commercial Ltda., Sao Paulo, Brazil; *Int'l,* pg. 921
Pong-Aree, Kantima, Mgr.-Personnel--Benetone Land & Houses Co., Ltd., Bangkok, Thailand; *Int'l,* pg. 186
Ponzi, Guido, Dir.-Personnel & Admin.--Metropolitana Milanese S.P.A., Milan, Italy; *Int'l,* pg. 863
Ponzio, Vito, V.P.-Human Resources--Coram Healthcare Corporation, Denver, CO; *U.S. Public,* pg. 446
Poole, Darren W., Mgr.-Gen. Affairs & Personnel--Pioneer/Eclipse Corp., Sparta, NC; *Int'l,* pg. 71
Popaditch, Suzanne, Dir.-Personnel--Kelsey Construction, Inc., Orlando, FL; *U.S. Private,* pg. 613
Pope, Steve, V.P.-H.R.--O'Reilly Automotive Inc., Springfield, MO; *U.S. Public,* pg. 1230
Pophema, Gerard, Mgr.-Trng., Devel. & Pub. Rels.--Elsevier Bedrijfinformatie B.V., Doetinchem, Netherlands; *Int'l,* pg. 1099
Popp, Susan, Mgr.-H.R.--J.F. Ahern Co., Fond Du Lac, WI; *U.S. Private,* pg. 27
Poppe, Dean, Mgr.-Personnel--Dutton-Lainson Co., Hastings, NE; *U.S. Private,* pg. 350
Porter, James E., V.P.-H.R.--Honeywell Inc., Minneapolis, MN; *U.S. Public,* pg. 833
Porter, Nancy, Mgr.-H.R.--Kolmar Laboratories, Inc., Port Jervis, NY; *Int'l,* pg. 239
Porter, Robert, V.P.-Human Resources--Faultless Caster, Evansville, IN; *Int'l,* pg. 473
Posner, Barbara G., V.P.-Corp. Rels.--Tenneco Automotive, Deerfield, IL; *U.S. Public,* pg. 1577
Poss, Richard L., Sr. V.P.-Organization & Mngmt. Devel.--National Computer Systems, Eden Prairie, MN; *U.S. Public,* pg. 1155
Postweiler, R. J., Mgr.-Human Resources--GPU, Inc., Morristown, NJ; *U.S. Public,* pg. 695
Postweiler, Richard J., V.P.-Human Resources--GPU Service Corp., Parsippany, NJ; *U.S. Public,* pg. 695
Potasnak, Betty, V.P.-Human Resources--Pharmacia & Upjohn Deltec, Inc., Arden Hills, MN; *Int'l,* pg. 1049
Potter, Judy, Dir.-Human Resources--SLJ Retail LLC, Smyrna, GA; *U.S. Private,* pg. 957
Pouch, Ronnie, Mgr.-Human Resources--Advertising Display Co., Englewood Cliffs, NJ; *U.S. Private,* pg. 23
Poulin, Monika, Mgr.-Human Resources--Jan-Co., Inc., Cranston, RI; *U.S. Private,* pg. 581
Poulin, Poul, Personnel Mgr.--ISS Scandinavia A/S, Copenhagen, Denmark; *Int'l,* pg. 656
Powell, Annabelle, Dir.-Personnel Trng. & Devel.--UniCARE Financial Corp., Irvine, CA; *U.S. Private,* pg. 152
Powell, Brad, Mgr.-H.R.--Centrex Corporation, Findlay, OH; *U.S. Private,* pg. 225
Powell, Catherine C., Sr. V.P.-Employee Svcs.--Central Louisiana Electric Company, Inc., Pineville, LA; *U.S. Public,* pg. 325
Powell, Charles, Personnel Dir.--American Trouser, Inc., Columbus, MS; *U.S. Private,* pg. 64
Powell, Deborah, V.P.-H.R.--Huffy Service First, Inc., Miamisburg, OH; *U.S. Public,* pg. 846
Powell, Denise, Mgr.-Payroll & Benefits--Miracle Feeds Inc., London, Canada; *U.S. Private,* pg. 432
Powell, Don, Dir.-Human Resources--Melitta U.S.A., Inc., Clearwater, FL; *Int'l,* pg. 857
Powell, Jennifer, V.P.-H. R.--The Weather Channel, Atlanta, GA; *U.S. Private,* pg. 647
Powell, Lanee, Dir.-H.R.--Artichoke Industries, Inc., Castroville, CA; *U.S. Private,* pg. 86
Powell, Roger, Mgr.-Human Resources--Danfoss Fluid Power, Easley, SC; *Int'l,* pg. 377
Powell, T.F., Dir.-Human Resources--Lockheed Aeronautical Systems Company, Marietta, GA; *U.S. Public,* pg. 1007
Power, Donna, Mgr.-H.R.--First Marathon Inc., Toronto, Canada; *Int'l,* pg. 486
Powers, Betsy, Dir.-Human Resources--Public Service Company of Oklahoma, Tulsa, OK; *U.S. Public,* pg. 324
Powers, Marcy, Mgr.-Admin. & H.R.--Intelligent Systems Corp., Norcross, GA; *U.S. Public,* pg. 888
Powers, Ron, Dir.-Personnel & Pub. Rels.--Ward Leonard Electric Company, Inc., Mount Vernon, NY; *U.S. Private,* pg. 1118
Poyfair, Paul B., Exec. V.P.-Svcs.--CompUSA, Dallas, TX; *U.S. Public,* pg. 420
Pozos, Anthony M., Sr. V.P.-Human Resources & Corp. Services--Amdahl Corporation, Sunnyvale, CA; *Int'l,* pg. 527
Pradier, Jean-Pierre, Dir.-H.R.--UCB, S.A., Brussels, Belgium; *Int'l,* pg. 1427
Prange, John, Dir.-H.R.--Miles Kimball Company, Oshkosh, WI; *U.S. Private,* pg. 745
Prater-Harvey, Peggy, V.P.-Human Resources--Memphis Light, Gas & Water, Memphis, TN; *U.S. Private,* pg. 731
Pratt, Larry, Dir.-Personnel--Akers Packaging Service Inc., Middletown, OH; *U.S. Private,* pg. 29
Preedy, Anthony, V.P.-Personnel--Polygram N.V., Baarn, Netherlands; *Int'l,* pg. 1051

Prendergast, Albert, Sr. V.P.-Human Resources--Mastercard International, Inc., Purchase, NY; *U.S. Private*, pg. 714
Prendeville, Mark, Dir.-Personnel--Republic Die & Tool Company, Belleville, MI; *U.S. Private*, pg. 923
Prentice, John, Dr., Mgr.-Human Resources--Maritime Telegraph & Telephone Company, Ltd., Halifax, Canada; *Int'l*, pg. 116
Pressnail, Patsy, Mgr.-Human Resources--BAT Office Products, Zion, IL; *U.S. Public*, pg. 1686
Preston, Gary, Exec. V.P.-Human Resources--BI-LO Inc., Greenville, SC; *Int'l*, pg. 749
Preston, Simon, Dir.-Personnel--International Water Limited, Manchester, United Kingdom; *Int'l*, pg. 1444
Prevost, Mary, Dir.-Human Resources--Orange Julius of America, Edina, MN; *U.S. Public*, pg. 220
Pribilla, Peter, Dir.-H.R.--Siemens AG, Munich, Germany; *Int'l*, pg. 1244
Price, C.J., Dir.-H.R.--Pitt-Des Moines, Inc., Pittsburgh, PA; *U.S. Public*, pg. 1304
Price, Carol, Mgr.-Human Resources--Fountain Powerboat Industries, Inc., Washington, NC; *U.S. Public*, pg. 678
Price, Dan, Mgr.-Personnel--Bassick by Kaspar, Shiner, TX; *U.S. Private*, pg. 122
Price, Dan A., Mgr.-Personnel--Kaspar Wire Works, Inc., Shiner, TX; *U.S. Private*, pg. 608
Price, Gerald M., Mgr.-H.R.--Acme United Corporation, Fairfield, CT; *U.S. Public*, pg. 17
Price, Janet, V.P.-H.R.--GSC Enterprises, Inc., Sulphur Springs, TX; *U.S. Private*, pg. 436
Price, Jesse W., Mgr.-Employee Services--Illinois Power Company, Decatur, IL; *U.S. Public*, pg. 869
Price, Linden, Mgr.-H.R.--Tetra Technologies, Woodlands, TX; *U.S. Public*, pg. 1582
Price, Richard, Dir.-Personnel--American Felt & Filter, Newburgh, NY; *U.S. Private*, pg. 54
Price, Sandra, Dir.-H.R.--Key Industries, Inc., Fort Scott, KS; *U.S. Private*, pg. 618
Prickett, Elena, Personnel Spec.--Empire Electric Association, Cortez, CO; *U.S. Private*, pg. 374
Pride, Pamela, V.P.-H.R.--Wall Data Incorporated, Kirkland, WA; *U.S. Public*, pg. 1734
Priede, Ernesto, Asst. V.P. & Mgr.-Personnel--Atlantic Sugar Association, Inc., Belle Glade, FL; *U.S. Private*, pg. 95
Pries, William, Dir.-Human Resources--Knape & Vogt Mfg. Co., Grand Rapids, MI; *U.S. Public*, pg. 963
Prifrel, Bob, Mgr.-Trng. & Devel.--Dahlberg, Inc., Golden Valley, MN; *U.S. Public*, pg. 194
Pringle, Denise, Mgr.-H.R.--Trimble Navigation Limited, Sunnyvale, CA; *U.S. Public*, pg. 1638
Printz, Peter E., Dir.-Safety, Health & Environmental & Chief Labor Counsel--Vulcan Materials Company, Birmingham, AL; *U.S. Public*, pg. 1725
Pritchard, Jackie, Mgr.-H.R.--Physio-Control Corporation, Redmond, WA; *U.S. Public*, pg. 1294
Pritsker, Robert, Dir.-Personnel & Prod. Mgr.--Marquette Coppersmithing Co., Inc., Philadelphia, PA; *U.S. Private*, pg. 706
Proksch, Fritz, Controller--Osterreichischen Bundesbahnen GmbH, Vienna, Austria; *Int'l*, pg. 1012
Proudlock, W., Dir.-Human Resources--Glaxo Pharmaceuticals UK Ltd., Uxbridge, United Kingdom; *Int'l*, pg. 552
Provo, Frank G., V.P.-Human Resources--Hoover Company, Canton, OH; *U.S. Public*, pg. 1065
Pruett, John, Dir.-Personnel--Community Cash Stores, Spartanburg, SC; *U.S. Private*, pg. 259
Pruitt, Lott L., Sr. V.P. & Dir.-Personnel--NBSC Corporation, Columbia, SC; *U.S. Public*, pg. 1549
Pryor, John, V.P.-Human Rels. & Pub. Rels.--Builders Transport, Incorporated, Camden, SC; *U.S. Public*, pg. 267
Psaros, Cathy Wells, V.P.-H.R. Devel.--Staples, Inc., Westborough, MA; *U.S. Public*, pg. 1509
Puech, Bertrand, Deputy Mng. Dir.-Human Resources--Hermes International, Paris, France; *Int'l*, pg. 617
Puggin, Michelle, V.P.-Human Resources & Admin.--Alpha Microsystems, Santa Ana, CA; *U.S. Public*, pg. 57
Pulido, Carmen, Mgr.-Human Resources--Catalina Lighting, Inc., Miami, FL; *U.S. Public*, pg. 314
Pulliam, Marv, V.P.-Human Resources--Computer Sciences Corporation, El Segundo, CA; *U.S. Public*, pg. 422
Pupkes, Sheryl, Mgr.-Human Resources--Ramsey Technology, Inc., Minneapolis, MN; *U.S. Public*, pg. 1592
Purcell, Dennis, V.P.-H.R.--The Hennegan Company, Florence, KY; *U.S. Private*, pg. 522
Purdy, David, Mgr.-Communications--The Wyco Tool Co., Racine, WI; *U.S. Private*, pg. 906
Purelis, Eileen, V.P.-Human Resources--R.R. Bowker, New Providence, NJ; *Int'l*, pg. 1096
Purelis, Eileen, V.P.-Human Resources--Martindale-Hubbell, New Providence, NJ; *Int'l*, pg. 1096
Purelis, Eileen, V.P.-Human Resources--National Register Publishing, New Providence, NJ; *Int'l*, pg. 1096
Purelis, Eileen, V.P.-Human Resources--Marquis Who's Who, New Providence, NJ; *Int'l*, pg. 1096
Purtell, Ronald, Dir.-Human Resources--Westwood-Squibb Pharmaceuticals Inc., Buffalo, NY; *U.S. Public*, pg. 255
Pusateri, Gloria, Dir.-H.R.--Boehringer Ingelheim Animal Health Inc., Saint Joseph, MO; *Int'l*, pg. 199
Putman, Gerald H., Sr. V.P.-H.R.--Raytheon Systems Company, Arlington, VA; *U.S. Public*, pg. 1364
Putman, John, Dir.-Personnel--Philips Components, Jupiter, FL; *Int'l*, pg. 1054
Putman, Roseann, H.R.--Whitney Blake Company of Vermont, Inc., Bellows Falls, VT; *U.S. Private*, pg. 148
Py, Alain, Dir.-Human Res.--Societe Generale, Paris, France; *Int'l*, pg. 1273
Pyle, P., Dir.-Personnel--Interkal, Inc., Kalamazoo, MI; *Int'l*, pg. 759
Qian, C.Y., Dir.-Personnel--Shanghai Morgan Carbon Company Limited, Shanghai, China; *Int'l*, pg. 892
Quagliana, Pete, Dir.-Human Resources--Boler Company, Itasca, IL; *U.S. Private*, pg. 155
Quail, Don, Mgr.-Admin.--Aerostar International, Sioux Falls, SD; *U.S. Public*, pg. 1361
Quandt, Byron D., V.P.-TQM & Human Resources--Libbey Owens Ford Co., Toledo, OH; *Int'l*, pg. 1056
Quay, Sharon R., Exec. V.P. & Dir.-Human Resources--Dain Rauscher Corporation, Minneapolis, MN; *U.S. Public*, pg. 476
Querol, Josep, Asst. Mgr.--Caixa d'Estalvis de Catalunya, Barcelona, Spain; *Int'l*, pg. 249
Quevedo, Frank J., V.P.-Equal Opportunity--Southern California Edison Company, Rosemead, CA; *U.S. Public*, pg. 564
Quick, Cheryl, Dir.-H.R.--The Chicago Faucet Co., Des Plaines, IL; *U.S. Private*, pg. 234
Quigley, Debbie, Mgr.-H.R.--M & C Specialties Company, Southampton, PA; *U.S. Private*, pg. 684
Quigley, Jack, Dir.-Personnel--Thetford Corporation, Ann Arbor, MI; *U.S. Private*, pg. 352
Quillien, Jenny, Mgr.-Personnel Policy--European Investment Bank, Luxembourg, Luxembourg; *Int'l*, pg. 465
Quinlan, Joyce, Dir.-Employee Benefits--Curtiss-Wright Corp., Lyndhurst, NJ; *U.S. Public*, pg. 469
Quinn, Bette, Mgr.-Human Resources--Pfaudler, Inc., Rochester, NY; *U.S. Public*, pg. 1393
Quintal, Julie, V.P.-Customer Support Services--Computer Network Technology Corporation, Minneapolis, MN; *U.S.* Public, pg. 421
Rabasca, A., V.P.-Human Resources--Mosler Inc., Hamilton, OH; *U.S. Private*, pg. 763
Raber, James A., Corp. Sec.--Star Bronze Company, Alliance, OH; *U.S. Private*, pg. 1034
Rachie, Ed, V.P.-H.R.--Cosco, Inc., Columbus, IN; *U.S. Private*, pg. 277
Rack, Larry, Dir.-Human Resources--Institute For Scientific Information, Philadelphia, PA; *U.S. Public*, pg. 1600
Radder, Jeffrey J., Dir.-Personnel--Curt G. Joa, Inc., Sheboygan Falls, WI; *U.S. Private*, pg. 588
Radebaugh, James B., Grp. V.P.-Admin. & Human Resources--Bob Evans Farms, Inc., Columbus, OH; *U.S. Public*, pg. 596
Rader, John, V.P.-H.R.--Neenah Foundry Company, Neenah, WI; *U.S. Private*, pg. 790
Radigonda, Sondra, V.P.-H.R.--Capstead Mortgage Corporation, Dallas, TX; *U.S. Public*, pg. 303
Raffaele, Al, Dir.-H.R.--Photronics, Inc., Brookfield, CT; *U.S.* Public, pg. 1293
Rager, Gary G., Dir.-Personnel--ACF Industries, Inc., Saint Charles, MO; *U.S. Private*, pg. 556
Ragonesi, Karin, Dir.-Human Resources--Ullo International, Inc., Altamonte Springs, FL; *U.S. Private*, pg. 1116
Rahn, Deb, Mgr.-Personnel--Boyer Candy Company Inc., Altoona, PA; *U.S. Private*, pg. 162
Raimann, Ginny, Partner-H.R. Mgr. & Admin. Svcs.--Dugan/Farley Communications, Upper Saddle River, NJ; *U.S. Public*, pg. 1642
Rainey, Mary, Dir.-H.R.--Bobit Publishing Company, Torrance, CA; *U.S. Private*, pg. 154
Rajoppe, Richard, Dir.-Personnel & Admin. Services--Russ Berrie and Company, Inc., Oakland, NJ; *U.S. Public*, pg. 222
Rakov, Ange, Human Resources Mng. Supvr.--Williams Worldwide, Santa Monica, CA; *U.S. Private*, pg. 1179
Rakow, May T., Sr. V.P.-Personnel & Sec.--IHC Group, Inc., South Elgin, IL; *U.S. Private*, pg. 555
Rall-Koepke, Katja, Dir.-Human Resources--Cedar Point, Sandusky, OH; *U.S. Public*, pg. 319
Ralph, Bruce, Dir.-Human Resources--Videojet Systems International, Inc., Wood Dale, IL; *Int'l*, pg. 545
Ralston, Douglas J., Sr. V.P.-H.R.--The Quaker Oats Company, Chicago, IL; *U.S. Public*, pg. 1347
Ralston, Sarah, Dir.-Human Resources--Circus Circus Hotel Casinos, Inc., Las Vegas, NV; *U.S. Public*, pg. 374
Ramacciotti, Michelle, Mgr.-H.R.--Amtech Corporation, Dallas, TX; *U.S. Public*, pg. 105
Ramirez, Rosie, Dir.-H.R.--International Bancshares Corp, Laredo, TX; *U.S. Private*, pg. 568
Ramirez, Suzette, Sr. V.P. & Human Resources Dir.--DMB&B Detroit, Troy, MI; *U.S. Private*, pg. 302
Ramis, Linda, Dir.-Personnel--Olga Div., Bridgeport, CT; *U.S. Public*, pg. 1738
Rammes, William L., V.P.-Corp. Human Resources--Anheuser-Busch Companies, Inc., Saint Louis, MO; *U.S. Public*, pg. 113
Ramnitz, Carl E., V.P.-H.R.--Geneva Steel, Vineyard, UT; *U.S. Public*, pg. 729
Ramon, Licia, Dir.-H.R.--Rain Bird Sprinklers Manufacturing Corp., Glendora, CA; *U.S. Private*, pg. 907
Ramos, Ana, Dir.-Human Resources--Benihana, Inc., Miami, FL; *U.S. Public*, pg. 211
Ramsay, David A., V.P.-H.R.--Rohr, Inc., Chula Vista, CA; *U.S. Public*, pg. 751
Ramsey, Beth, Mgr.-H.R.--Urban Shopping Centers, Inc., Chicago, IL; *U.S. Public*, pg. 1700
Ramsey, David W., Sr. V.P., Dir.-Admin. & Asst. Sec.--Federated Mutual Insurance Company, Owatonna, MN; *U.S. Private*, pg. 399
Ramsey, Donald, V.P.-Human Resources--Staff Builders Inc., Lake Success, NY; *U.S. Public*, pg. 1501
Ramstedt, Ola, Exec. V.P.--Skandia Insurance Company Limited, Stockholm, Sweden; *Int'l*, pg. 1256
Ramzy, Mary, Dir.-Human Resources Plng. & Devel.--American Mutual Life Holding Co., Des Moines, IA; *U.S. Private*, pg. 59
Randall, Phillip M., V.P.-H.R.--Northeast Utilities, Berlin, CT; *U.S. Public*, pg. 1194
Randazzo, Richard P., V.P.-H.R.--Federal-Mogul Corporation, Southfield, MI; *U.S. Public*, pg. 615
Randerson, Camilla, Mgr.-Human Resources--Sophus Berendsen A/S, Soeborg, Denmark; *Int'l*, pg. 1284
Randle, Frances, V.P.-Human Resources--Noma Industries Limited, North York, Canada; *Int'l*, pg. 954
Randles, Douglas, Asst. V.P.-Admin. & Human Resources--Halifax Corporation, Alexandria, VA; *U.S. Public*, pg. 775
Ranieri, Robert, V.P.-H.R.--Chorus Line Corporation, Vernon, CA; *U.S. Private*, pg. 238
Rank-Smith, Connie, Asst. V.P.-H.R.--Jewelers Mutual Insurance Company, Neenah, WI; *U.S. Private*, pg. 587
Rankin, John J., V.P.-Human Resources--Canadian Tire Corporation Limited, Toronto, Canada; *Int'l*, pg. 259
Ransom, Patti, Human Resources Dir. & Opers. Dir.--Gotham Incorporated, New York, NY; *U.S. Private*, pg. 677
Raphnel, Sheryl, Dir.-H.R.--Medical Graphics Corp., Saint Paul, MN; *U.S. Public*, pg. 1080
Rarey, Ray, Dir.-H.R.--Berg Electronics, Saint Louis, MO; *U.S. Public*, pg. 212
Rasicot, Michael D., Dir.-Human Resources & Personnel--FMC-Crosby Valve, Inc., Wrentham, MA; *U.S. Public*, pg. 605
Rasmus, Jim, V.P.-Human Resources--The Coleman Company, Inc., Golden, CO; *U.S. Private*, pg. 690
Rasntale, Ken, Mgr.-H.R.--Towers Perrin, New York, NY; *U.S. Private*, pg. 1093
Ratcliffe, Lawrence A., V.P. & Dir.-Indus. Rels.--Greif Brothers Corporation, Delaware, OH; *U.S. Public*, pg. 763
Rathbun, James, Mgr.-Personnel--Castle Rubber Co., East Butler, PA; *U.S. Public*, pg. 1258
Rathbun, Kathy, V.P. & Dir.-H.R.--Telescope Casual Furniture, Inc., Granville, NY; *U.S. Private*, pg. 1074
Rau, Dr. M., Dir.-Personnel--Riedel-de Haen AG, Seelze, Germany; *Int'l*, pg. 625
Rauman, Jouko, Dir.-Personnel & Admin.--Amer Group Ltd., Helsinki, Finland; *Int'l*, pg. 72
Rausch, Jennifer, V.P.-Human Resources--Holland Mark Martin, Boston, MA; *U.S. Private*, pg. 534
Rausch, Richard L., V.P.-H.R.--First Western Bancorp, Inc., New Castle, PA; *U.S. Public*, pg. 642
Rawlings, Gray A., V.P.-Admin.--S & K Famous Brands, Inc., Glen Allen, VA; *U.S. Public*, pg. 1414
Rawlings, James W., Sr. V.P. & Dir.-Human Resources--UMB Financial Corporation, Kansas City, MO; *U.S. Public*, pg. 1653
Rawlins, R.E, Dir.-Human Resources--Permacel, New Brunswick, NJ; *Int'l*, pg. 950
Ray, Allan, V.P.-H.R.--Southern Mills, Inc., Union City, GA; *U.S. Private*, pg. 1016
Ray, Gary A., Sr. V.P.-H.R.--Kaufman and Broad Home Corporation, Los Angeles, CA; *U.S. Public*, pg. 944
Ray, I., Dir.-Personnel--Trafalgar House Construction Ltd., Croydon, United Kingdom; *Int'l*, pg. 773
Ray, Windell, V.P.-Personnel--Meijer, Inc., Grand Rapids, MI; *U.S. Private*, pg. 729
Rayfield, Elizabeth, Mgr.-Personnel--Mauney Hosiery Mills, Inc., Kings Mountain, NC; *U.S. Private*, pg. 715
Rayman, J., Dir.-Grp. H.R.--Thorn plc, Chertsey, United Kingdom; *Int'l*, pg. 1385
Raymond, Dennis M., V.P.-H.R.--The Austin Company, Cleveland, OH; *U.S. Private*, pg. 99
Raynaud, Gilles, V.P.-H.R.--Rexel, S.A., Paris, France; *Int'l*, pg. 1107
Razum, Eugene, Mgr.-Human Resources & Personnel--Reactive Metals & Alloys Corporation (REMACOR), West Pittsburg, PA; *U.S. Private*, pg. 913
Ready, James, Dir.-Personnel--Barclay Furniture Company, Sherman, MS; *U.S. Public*, pg. 974
Reardon, Barbara, Mgr.-Personnel--Kevex Instruments, Valencia, CA; *U.S. Public*, pg. 1594
Reardon, John, Dir.-Human Resources--Imperial Schrade Corp., Ellenville, NY; *U.S. Private*, pg. 559
Reardon, N.A., Sr. V.P.-H.R. & Corp. Affairs--Borden, Inc., Columbus, OH; *U.S. Private*, pg. 157
Reardon, Nancy A., Sr. V.P.-Human Resources--Duracell International Inc., Bethel, CT; *U.S. Public*, pg. 743
Reardon, Thomas E., V.P.-H.R. & Environmental--Tesoro Petroleum Corporation, San Antonio, TX; *U.S. Public*, pg. 1581
Reath, Penny, V.P.-Human Rels.--Gilroy Foods, Inc., Gilroy, CA; *U.S. Public*, pg. 428
Reavis, Neva J., V.P.-H.R. & Quality Devel.--Vanguard Cellular Systems, Inc., Greensboro, NC; *U.S. Public*, pg. 1707
Rebata, Virginia, Sr. V.P.-Human Resources--Fortis, Inc., New York, NY; *Int'l*, pg. 499
Recht, Richard, Dir.-Personnel--Eaton Corporation, Pressure Sensors Division, Bethel, CT; *U.S. Public*, pg. 557
Reck, Kate, V.P.-Human Resources--The Todd-AO Corporation, Hollywood, CA; *U.S. Public*, pg. 1619
Redden, David M., Sr. V.P.-Human Resources--Marsh Supermarkets, Inc., Indianapolis, IN; *U.S. Public*, pg. 1049
Redding, D.H., Dir.-Personnel--Rolls-Royce Power Engineering plc, Newcastle upon Tyne, United Kingdom; *Int'l*, pg. 1127
Redgate, R.M., V.P.-Human Resources & Corp. Svcs.--Talisman Energy Inc., Calgary, Canada; *Int'l*, pg. 1352
Redling, Buddy, V.P.-H.R.--Krause Publications, Inc., Iola, WI; *U.S. Private*, pg. 635
Redlinger, Donald J., Sr. V.P.-Human Resources & Communications--AlliedSignal Inc., Morristown, NJ; *U.S. Public*, pg. 49
Redman, Paula, V.P.-Personnel--B-Line Systems, Inc., Highland, IL; *U.S. Public*, pg. 1471
Redman, Stephanie, V.P.-H.R.--NTH Consultants, Ltd., Farmington, MI; *U.S. Private*, pg. 772
Redmond, Mike, Mgr-Human Resources--The American Companies, Inc., Topeka, KS; *U.S. Private*, pg. 52
Redpath, Peter A., V.P.-Personnel--Hitchcock Industries, Inc., Bloomington, MN; *U.S. Private*, pg. 531
Reece, Mark, Controller, Treas & Sec.--Young-Phillips Sales Co., Clemmons, NC; *U.S. Private*, pg. 1201
Reed, Brian, Dir.-Personnel--Kova Fertilizer Inc., Greensburg, IN; *U.S. Private*, pg. 634
Reed, Carl, V.P.-Human Resources--Techalloy Co., Inc., Mahwah, NJ; *Int'l*, pg. 572
Reed, Debbie, Mgr.-Human Resources--Madison Newspapers, Inc., Madison, WI; *U.S. Public*, pg. 984

Reed, Howard W., Sr. V.P.-Human Resources--Bayer Corporation, Pittsburgh, PA; *Int'l*, pg. 172

Reed, Maria Y., Human Resources Dir.--Don Coleman Advertising, Inc., Southfield, MI; *U.S. Private*, pg. 251

Reed, Natalie, Mgr.-H.R.--Arch Aluminium & Glass L.C., Tamarac, FL; *U.S. Private*, pg. 79

Reed, Sue, Dir.-Personnel--Pine State Trading Company, Augusta, ME; *U.S. Private*, pg. 865

Reedy, June, Dir.-H.R.--United Receptical, Inc., Pottsville, PA; *U.S. Private*, pg. 1123

Reeher, Larry, V.P.-Human Resources--Krystal Company, Chattanooga, TN; *U.S. Private*, pg. 636

Reese, Dick, V.P.-Human Resources--Fieldcrest Cannon, Inc., Kannapolis, NC; *U.S. Public*, pg. 1296

Reese, Tom, Mgr.-Personnel--MBI Inc., Norwalk, CT; *U.S. Private*, pg. 685

Reese, Tom, Mgr.-Personnel--Danbury Mint, Norwalk, CT; *U.S. Private*, pg. 685

Reeser, Ralph, V.P.-Human Resources--Florida Tile Industries, Inc., Lakeland, FL; *U.S. Public*, pg. 1322

Reeves, Connie, H.R. Mgr.--Sawyer Riley Compton Inc., Atlanta, GA; *U.S. Private*, pg. 969

Reeves, Joni, Coord. H.R.--Downey Designs International, Indianapolis, IN; *U.S. Private*, pg. 342

Reeves, Michael F., V.P.-H.R.--Deluxe Corporation, Shoreview, MN; *U.S. Public*, pg. 498

Reffel, Lois, V.P.-Human Resources--Colorado National Bankshares, Inc., Denver, CO; *U.S. Public*, pg. 1680

Reffner, Bob, Exec.-H.R.--Hardwick Clothes Inc., Cleveland, TN; *U.S. Private*, pg. 502

Regalado, Oscar, Mgr.-Human Resources--Plastag Corporation, Elk Grove Village, IL; *U.S. Private*, pg. 870

Regan, Timothy J., V.P. & Treas.--The Scoular Company, Omaha, NE; *U.S. Private*, pg. 977

Regas, Kathi M., V.P.-H.R.--Molex Incorporated, Lisle, IL; *U.S. Public*, pg. 1121

Regehr, R., Mgr.-Personnel--Weiser Inc., Burnaby, Canada; *U.S. Public*, pg. 1055

Regez, Rudolph, V.P.-Legal Council & H.R.--The Swiss Colony, Inc, Monroe, WI; *U.S. Private*, pg. 1059

Rehnback, Roland, V.P.-Communications--Alfa Laval AB, Lund, Sweden; *Int'l*, pg. 1378

Reices, Jan, V.P.-H.R. & Info. Svcs.--Graphic Controls Corporation, Buffalo, NY; *U.S. Private*, pg. 470

Reich, Joni J., Asst. V.P.-Human Resources Opers.--SLM Holding Corp., Washington, DC; *U.S. Public*, pg. 1419

Reichard, Gail, Dir.-Human Resources--Legg Mason, Inc., Baltimore, MD; *U.S. Public*, pg. 984

Reid, I.D., Dir.-Human Resources--ACI International Ltd., Melbourne, Australia; *Int'l*, pg. 128

Reid, Mark, Mgr.-H.R.--Lukens Inc., Coatesville, PA; *U.S. Public*, pg. 1019

Reid, Murray, Grp. Staff Mgr.--N.G. Bailey & Co. Ltd., Ilkley, United Kingdom; *Int'l*, pg. 132

Reider, Paula, Mgr.-Human Resources--Leblanc Communications, Inc., Richardson, TX; *U.S. Private*, pg. 656

Reigle, Bill, Dir.-Human Resources--Skyline Chili, Inc., Fairfield, OH; *U.S. Public*, pg. 1475

Reigo, Britt, Sr. V.P.-Human Resources & Organization--Telefonaktiebolaget LM Ericsson, Stockholm, Sweden; *Int'l*, pg. 1363

Reilley, Walter, V.P.-H.R. & Corp. Svcs.--Elkay Manufacturing Company, Oak Brook, IL; *U.S. Private*, pg. 372

Reilly, Thomas E., Dir.-Human Resources--Lakeside Foods, Inc., Manitowoc, WI; *U.S. Private*, pg. 643

Reimer, Carol J., V.P.-H.R.--Midwest Express Holdings, Inc., Oak Creek, WI; *U.S. Public*, pg. 1111

Reimer, Carol J., V.P.-Human Resources--Midwest Express Airlines, Inc., Oak Creek, WI; *U.S. Public*, pg. 1111

Reinhartsen, John R., Mgr.-Human Resources--Florida Public Utilities Company, West Palm Beach, FL; *U.S. Public*, pg. 655

Reis, Tom, Dir.-Human Resources--Saab Cars USA, Inc., Norcross, GA; *Int'l*, pg. 687

Reiss, John, V.P.-Human Resources--Renaissance International Hotels, Cleveland, OH; *U.S. Public*, pg. 1048

Reitman, Jeff, Sr. V.P.-Human Resources--Texas Commerce Bank, Houston, TX; *U.S. Public*, pg. 339

Reivitz, Leon C., V.P.-H.R.--Viad Corp, Phoenix, AZ; *U.S. Public*, pg. 1718

Reks, Jenny, Dir.-Human Resources--Thermo Jarrell Ash Corporation, Franklin, MA; *U.S. Public*, pg. 1594

Renaudin, Louis-Pascal, V.P.-Human Resources--Gie ETEX Gestion, Vernouillet, France; *Int'l*, pg. 430

Renault, Pierre, Dir.-H.R.--Davie Industries Inc., Levis, Canada; *Int'l*, pg. 385

Renaux, Luiz Carlos, Mgr.-Human Resources--Swedish Match do Brasil S/A, Rio de Janeiro, Brazil; *Int'l*, pg. 1328

Rendin, Roger A., V.P.-Human Resources--The Pep Boys-Manny, Moe & Jack, Philadelphia, PA; *U.S. Public*, pg. 1276

Rene, Joe, Dir.-H.R.--Plastipak Packaging Inc., Plymouth, MI; *U.S. Private*, pg. 872

Renker, David, Sr. Dir.-Human Resources--U.S. Surgical Corp., Norwalk, CT; *U.S. Public*, pg. 1687

Rennie, Robert P., V.P.-Human Resources--Phelps Dodge Magnet Wire Co., Fort Wayne, IN; *U.S. Public*, pg. 1286

Reno, Patricia, Mgr.-Human Resources--SEEQ Technology Inc., Fremont, CA; *U.S. Public*, pg. 1417

Reno, Peter, Dir.-H.R.--Alpha Shirt Co., Inc., Philadelphia, PA; *U.S. Private*, pg. 45

Renouf, John W., V.P.-Human Resources--Raytheon Engineers & Constructors International, Inc., Lexington, MA; *U.S. Public*, pg. 1366

Rensel, Kathleen S., V.P.-Human Resources--Micros Systems Inc., Beltsville, MD; *U.S. Public*, pg. 1106

Renton, George, V.P.-H.R.--The Liposome Company, Inc., Princeton, NJ; *U.S. Public*, pg. 1000

Rentsch, Hanspeter, Dir.-Legal Affairs, H.R., Real Estate & Licensing--SMH Swiss Corporation for Micro Electronics & Watchmaking Indus. Ltd., Bienne, Switzerland; *Int'l*, pg. 1160

Rettberg, Roy, Dir.-H.R.--Ascend Communications, Inc., Alameda, CA; *U.S. Public*, pg. 138

Reuss, Anita, Dir.-Human Resources--Central Research Laboratories, Red Wing, MN; *U.S. Public*, pg. 521

Reusswig, Michael, V.P.-Personnel--Maytag Company, Newton, IA; *U.S. Public*, pg. 1064

Reveman, Lars, Sr. V.P.-Personnel--Svedala Industri AB, Malmo, Sweden; *Int'l*, pg. 1323

Rexroad, Kelly, V.P.-H.R.--Reflectone, Inc., Tampa, FL; *Int'l*, pg. 218

Reynolds, William, Dir.-H.R.--Christy's Markets, Inc., Brockton, MA; *U.S. Private*, pg. 238

Rhoades, Ann, Exec. V.P.-Human Resources--Doubletree Corporation, Memphis, TN; *U.S. Public*, pg. 1335

Rhodes, C. Douglas, Grp. V.P.-H.R.--Harris Teeter, Inc., Charlotte, NC; *U.S. Public*, pg. 1412

Rhodes, Jim, V.P.-H.R. & Dir.-Pub. Rels.--Publix Supermarkets Inc., Lakeland, FL; *U.S. Private*, pg. 893

Rhodes, Sheila, Mgr.-Human Resources--B.T. Mancini Co., Inc., Milpitas, CA; *U.S. Private*, pg. 699

Rhude Viteo, Penelope, V.P.-H.R.--Ultramar Diamond Shamrock Corporation, San Antonio, TX; *U.S. Public*, pg. 1663

Riale, Patti L., Mgr.-H.R.--Artesian Resources Corporation, Newark, DE; *U.S. Public*, pg. 135

Riale, Patti L., Mgr.-Human Resources--Artesian Water Company, Inc., Newark, DE; *U.S. Public*, pg. 135

Ricca, Jim, Mgr.-H.R.--Perkasie Industries Corporation, Perkasie, PA; *U.S. Private*, pg. 854

Ricci, Miriam E., Office Mgr.--Marie Brizard Wines & Spirits USA, North Miami, FL; *U.S. Private*, pg. 702

Ricci, Salvatore, Dir.-Personnel--Merloni Elettrodomestici S.P.A., Fabriano, Italy; *Int'l*, pg. 860

Rice, Jeffrey R., Dir.-Human Resources--Dollar General Corporation, Nashville, TN; *U.S. Public*, pg. 515

Rice, Roger B., V.P.-Human Resources--Snyder Oil Corporation, Fort Worth, TX; *U.S. Public*, pg. 1481

Rice, Sue, Sr. V.P.-Human Resources--Reed Elsevier Business Information, Newton, MA; *Int'l*, pg. 1095

Rice, Tom, Dir.-Human Resources--OmniQuip International, Inc., Port Washington, WI; *U.S. Private*, pg. 500

Ricewig, Michael, Sr. V.P.-Human Resources--Maytag Corporation, Newton, IA; *U.S. Public*, pg. 1064

Rich, B. Scott, Dir.-H.R.--Flowers Industries, Inc., Thomasville, GA; *U.S. Public*, pg. 656

Rich, G. Andrew, Sr. V.P.-Human Resources--Williams-Sonoma, Inc., San Francisco, CA; *U.S. Public*, pg. 1770

Rich, Gary S., Sr. V.P.-Global Human Resources--A.C. Nielsen, Stamford, CT; *U.S. Public*, pg. 1183

Rich, Ruth, V.P.-Admin. & Human Resources--Control Data Systems, Inc., Arden Hills, MN; *U.S. Public*, pg. 441

Richard, Denis, Mgr.-H.R.--Fisher Gauge Limited, Peterborough, Canada; *Int'l*, pg. 491

Richard, Jean, V.P.-H.R.--Celanese Canada, Inc., Montreal, Canada; *Int'l*, pg. 625

Richards, Barbara, Admin.-H.R.--Future Foam, Inc., Council Bluffs, IA; *U.S. Private*, pg. 433

Richards, Joel, III, Exec. V.P.-Human Resources--El Paso Natural Gas Co., Houston, TX; *U.S. Public*, pg. 567

Richards, Larry, Mgr.-H.R.--Allied Plywood Corp., Alexandria, VA; *U.S. Private*, pg. 40

Richards, Mark L., V.P.-Human Resources--Union Standard Insurance Company, Irving, TX; *U.S. Public*, pg. 216

Richards, Mary, V.P.-Human Resources--Epsilon, Burlington, MA; *U.S. Public*, pg. 74

Richardson, John, Dir.-H.R.--Directory Distributing Associates, Inc., Saint Louis, MO; *U.S. Private*, pg. 334

Richardson, John D., Sr. V.P.-Human Resources--Oak Industries Inc., Waltham, MA; *U.S. Public*, pg. 1209

Richardson, Sandra, Mgr.-Corp. Affairs--Cape Breton Development Corporation, Glace Bay, Canada; *Int'l*, pg. 265

Richcreek, M.J., V.P.-Human Resources--Citizens Gas & Coke Utility, Indianapolis, IN; *U.S. Private*, pg. 241

Riches, Karen, Mgr.-H.R.--Titan Wheel Corporation, Walcott, IA; *U.S. Public*, pg. 1618

Richie, John A., V.P.-H.R.--Rogers Corporation, Rogers, CT; *U.S. Public*, pg. 1402

Richins, Paul O., Chief Admin. Officer, V.P. & Treas.--Utah Medical Products, Inc., Midvale, UT; *U.S. Public*, pg. 1700

Richman, Fran, V.P.-Personnel--Carter Companies, Kansas City, MO; *U.S. Private*, pg. 216

Richter, Catherine, V.P.-H.R.--National Bank of Alaska, Anchorage, AK; *U.S. Public*, pg. 1153

Rickabaugh, Paul E., V.P.-H.R.--Lava World International/Haggerty Enterprises, Inc., Chicago, IL; *U.S. Private*, pg. 653

Rickard, David W., Dir.-Personnel--The Foxboro Company, Foxboro, MA; *Int'l*, pg. 1243

Ricker, Natt, Mgr.-Trainer & Adv.--Alamo Group, Inc., La Grange, IL; *U.S. Public*, pg. 35

Rickert, Michael, V.P.-Fin. & H.R.--Marsh Company, Belleville, IL; *U.S. Private*, pg. 707

Rickert, Rick, Dir.-Personnel--Bob Montgomery Chevrolet/Honda, Louisville, KY; *U.S. Private*, pg. 758

Rickett, Cheryl, Mgr.-Human Resources--Kenco, Middlebury, IN; *U.S. Public*, pg. 1769

Rideout, DeWayne, Dir.-Human Resources--Gateway 2000, North Sioux City, SD; *U.S. Public*, pg. 703

Rieck, Karen, Mgr.-Human Resources--Marketing Communications, Lenexa, KS; *U.S. Public*, pg. 794

Riefler, Laurel, Mgr.-Personnel--CEM South, Leesburg, FL; *U.S. Private*, pg. 1009

Riel, Brenda L., Corp. Dir.-Employee Relations--Universal Leaf Tobacco Company, Inc., Richmond, VA; *U.S. Public*, pg. 1694

Riemer, Kenneth, V.P.-Human Resources--Aramark Educational Resources Inc. Inc., Golden, CO; *U.S. Private*, pg. 79

Rien, Cathy, V.P.-Human Resources--TMP Worldwide, Inc., New York, NY; *U.S. Private*, pg. 1064

Riffe, Thomas J., Dir.-Human Resources--FlightSafety International Inc., Flushing, NY; *U.S. Public*, pg. 218

Rifkin, Judy, Dir.-H.R.--Banfi Vintners, Old Brookville, NY; *U.S. Private*, pg. 113

Riggs, Lorita, Dir.-Personnel--Champion Industries, Huntington, WV; *U.S. Public*, pg. 333

Rightmer, Connie, Admin.-Human Resources--Pinnacle West Capital Corporation, Phoenix, AZ; *U.S. Public*, pg. 1297

Rikardsen, Bernhard, Sr. V.P.-Human Resources--Scandinavian Airlines System (SAS), Solna, Sweden; *Int'l*, pg. 1201

Riley, Alice, Mgr.-Personnel--Pabst Brewing Co./Tumwater, Tumwater, WA; *U.S. Private*, pg. 954

Riley, Judy, Dir.-Human Resources--Deltak Inc., Plymouth, MN; *U.S. Public*, pg. 924

Riley, Marcia B., Asst. V.P.-Training & Organizational Devel.--SLM Holding Corp., Washington, DC; *U.S. Public*, pg. 1419

Riley, Saundra, Dir.-Personnel--Poly Pak America, Inc., Los Angeles, CA; *U.S. Private*, pg. 875

Rindom, David E., Dir.-H.R.--Midwest Grain Products, Inc., Atchison, KS; *U.S. Public*, pg. 1111

Rindskopf, Steven, V.P.-H.R.--Bassett Furniture Industries, Incorporated, Bassett, VA; *U.S. Public*, pg. 193

Rios, Irene, Mgr.-H.R.--Advanced Logic Research, Inc., Irvine, CA; *U.S. Public*, pg. 703

Rios, Roberto L. C., Dir.-Human Resources--3M Do Brasil Ltda., Sao Paulo, Brazil; *U.S. Public*, pg. 1606

Ripley, Lou, Dir.-Personnel--Mercantile Stores Company, Inc., Fairfield, OH; *U.S. Public*, pg. 1089

Ripley, Samme L., Mgr.-Corp. H.R.--Kelly-Moore Paint Company, Inc., San Carlos, CA; *U.S. Private*, pg. 613

Rippinger, Marcel, Mgr.-Human Resources--Herstal S.A., Herstal, Belgium; *Int'l*, pg. 617

Risenberg, Jack, V.P.-H.R.--Specialty Foods Corporation, Deerfield, IL; *U.S. Private*, pg. 1022

Rist, Vaughn, V.P.-Employee Rels.--Spalding Sports Worldwide, Chicopee, MA; *U.S. Private*, pg. 630

Ristucci, Vince, V.P.-Human Resources--Grubb & Ellis Company, Northbrook, IL; *U.S. Public*, pg. 767

Ristucci, Vince, Dir.-H.R.--Grubb & Ellis Company, Northbrook, IL; *U.S. Public*, pg. 767

Ritner, Joanne, Dir.-Personnel--Restaurant Developers Corp., Independence, OH; *U.S. Private*, pg. 925

Riva, Fabio Dalla, Dir.-H.R.--Dun & Bradstreet Kosmos Spa, Milan, Italy; *U.S. Public*, pg. 536

Rivens, J.R., Dir.-H.R.--Rolls-Royce plc, London, United Kingdom; *Int'l*, pg. 1126

Rivera, Joanne P., Mgr.-Human Resources--Tidelands Oil Production Co., Long Beach, CA; *U.S. Private*, pg. 1084

Rivers, Geri, Dir.-H.R.--Viking Office Products, Torrance, CA; *U.S. Public*, pg. 1720

Rizzo, Marianna, Mgr.-Personnel--Bachmann Industries, Inc., Philadelphia, PA; *U.S. Private*, pg. 109

Rizzo, Vincent, Personnel--The Texwipe Co., Inc., Upper Saddle River, NJ; *U.S. Private*, pg. 1079

Roach, James G., Mgr.-H.R.--The C.P. Hall Company, Chicago, IL; *U.S. Private*, pg. 495

Roach, Kim, Mgr.-Employee Rels.--Downey Printing, Waukee, IA; *U.S. Private*, pg. 342

Roane, Michael L., V.P.-Human Resources--Owens & Minor Inc., Glen Allen, VA; *U.S. Public*, pg. 1236

Roark, D. Michael, Exec. V.P.-H.R.--Mellon Bank Corporation, Pittsburgh, PA; *U.S. Public*, pg. 1084

Roarty, Carroll, Dir.-H.R.--Best Western International, Inc., Phoenix, AZ; *U.S. Private*, pg. 140

Robb, Dee, Dir.-H.R.--Empire Southwest Co., Mesa, AZ; *U.S. Private*, pg. 374

Robbins, Stanley, Mgr.-Human Resources--Mrs. Giles Country Kitchens, Inc., Lynchburg, VA; *U.S. Public*, pg. 596

Robellotto, Vince A., V.P.-Human Resources--E-Z-GO Textron, Augusta, GA; *U.S. Public*, pg. 1589

Roberts, Ben L., Mgr.-H.R.--Wolverine Tube Inc., Huntsville, AL; *U.S. Public*, pg. 1774

Roberts, Charles, V.P.-H.R.--Shamrock Foods Company, Phoenix, AZ; *U.S. Private*, pg. 989

Roberts, Holly, Dir.-H.R.--Duo-Fast Corporation, Huntley, IL; *U.S. Private*, pg. 347

Roberts, James A., V.P.-Corp. Rels.--Minnesota Power, Duluth, MN; *U.S. Public*, pg. 1116

Roberts, Kent L., V.P.-Human Resources--Nalleys Fine Foods, Tacoma, WA; *U.S. Private*, pg. 887

Robertson, David L., Sr. V.P.-H.R.--Rubbermaid Incorporated, Wooster, OH; *U.S. Public*, pg. 1411

Robertson, David L., Exec. V.P.-Human Resources & Corp. Law--Weirton Steel Corporation, Weirton, WV; *U.S. Public*, pg. 1751

Robertson, G.L., V.P.-Human Resources--Wyman-Gordon, North Grafton, MA; *U.S. Public*, pg. 1782

Robertson, Jack M., V.P.-H.R.--Seagull Energy Corporation, Houston, TX; *U.S. Public*, pg. 1450

Robinson, Alice, Coord.-Personnel--House of White Birches, Inc., Berne, IN; *U.S. Private*, pg. 542

Robinson, Brenda, Dir.-Personnel--United Distributors, Inc., Smyrna, GA; *U.S. Private*, pg. 1121

Robinson, Daryl, V.P.-Human Resources--Zellerbach Division, Miamisburg, OH; *U.S. Public*, pg. 1074

Robinson, Dennis, Mgr.-Personnel--Teleflex Marine, Limerick, PA; *U.S. Public*, pg. 1569

Robinson, Dick, Dir.-Personnel--Cook Communication Ministries, Colorado Springs, CO; *U.S. Private*, pg. 272

Robinson, James, V.P.-Human Resources--Sandoz Corporation, New York, NY; *Int'l*, pg. 974

Robinson, Janet, Mgr.-Human Resources--SmithKline Beecham Clinical Laboratories, Nashville, TN; *Int'l*, pg. 1265

Robinson, Jim, V.P.-Human Resources--Smart & Final, Vernon, CA; *Int'l*, pg. 563

Robinson, Joanne, V.P.-Human Resources--Okidata Group, Mount Laurel, NJ; *Int'l*, pg. 1000

Robinson, Kay, Dir.-Human Resources--Omniflight, Inc., Dallas, TX; *U.S. Private*, pg. 816

Robinson, Kay, Dir.-Human Resources--Omniflight Helicopters, Inc., Dallas, TX; *U.S. Private*, pg. 817

Robinson, Michael H., Mng. Dir.-Personnel--Henderson Administration Group PLC, London, United Kingdom; *Int'l*, pg. 609

Robinson, Monica, Sec. & Dir.-Personnel--Fritz Industries Inc., Mesquite, TX; *U.S. Private*, pg. 429

Robinson, Robin, Mgr.-H.R.--Sanderson Farms, Inc., Laurel, MS; *U.S. Public*, pg. 1430

Robinson, Ronnie, V.P.-Human Resources--Hart Schaffner & Marx Clothes, Chicago, IL; *U.S. Public*, pg. 795

Robison, William J., Sr. V.P.-Employee Resources--Pfizer Inc., New York, NY; *U.S. Public*, pg. 1281

Roble, Bill, Dir.-Communications--Goodwill Industries International, Bethesda, MD; *U.S. Private*, pg. 464

Robles, Gene, Mgr.-Human Resources--EXAR Corporation, Fremont, CA; *U.S. Public*, pg. 597

Robson, Diane, Mgr.-H.R.--Primark Corporation, Waltham, MA; *U.S. Public*, pg. 1325

Robson, M.W., Grp. Mgr.-Personnel--Q.U.F. Industries Ltd., Brisbane, Australia; *Int'l*, pg. 1074

Roca, Enrique, Dir.-Human Resources--Leather Center, Inc., Carrollton, TX; *U.S. Private*, pg. 656

Rocchi, Augusto, Assoc. Mgr.-Human Resources--IRI Istituto Ricostruzione Industriale, Rome, Italy; *Int'l*, pg. 652

Rocha, Celso, Dir.-Human Resources--Souza Cruz, S.A., Rio de Janeiro, Brazil; *Int'l*, pg. 112

Roche, Susan, Sr. V.P. & Human Resources Dir.--Arnold Communications, Inc., Boston, MA; *U.S. Private*, pg. 83

Roche, William C., Sr. V.P.-Human Resources & Facilities Plng.--The FINOVA Group Inc., Phoenix, AZ; *U.S. Public*, pg. 624

Rockstad, Bruce, V.P.-Human Resources--Hancock Fabrics, Inc., Tupelo, MS; *U.S. Public*, pg. 779

Rodenhuis, Tjeerd, Gen. Mgr.-Grp. H.R.--Sasol Limited, Johannesburg, South Africa; *Int'l*, pg. 1196

Rodgers, James H., V.P.-Human Resources--Federal Cartridge Co., Anoka, MN; *U.S. Public*, pg. 239

Rodgers, Richard, Dir.-Human Resources--Advance Circuits, Inc., Minnetonka, MN; *Int'l*, pg. 713

Rodgers, Sharon, V.P.-Human Resources--Avondale Incorporated, Monroe, GA; *U.S. Private*, pg. 102

Rodgers, Susan, V.P.-H.R.--Crowley Maritime Corporation, Oakland, CA; *U.S. Private*, pg. 292

Rodgers, Thomas J., V.P.-Human Resources--Thiokol Space Operations, Brigham City, UT; *U.S. Public*, pg. 1597

Rodlong, Thomas, Dir.-H.R.--The Hall China Company, East Liverpool, OH; *U.S. Private*, pg. 494

Rodloytuk, Komkai, Exec. V.P.--Bangkok Bank Public Company Limited, Bangkok, Thailand; *Int'l*, pg. 146

Rodrigues, Carlos, Dr., Dir.-Personnel--Portuguese Railways (CP), Lisbon, Portugal; *Int'l*, pg. 1063

Rodriguez, Betty, Mgr.-Personnel--Apparel Ventures, Inc., Gardena, CA; *U.S. Private*, pg. 78

Rodriguez, Eduardo, Sr. V.P.-Human Resources--Banco Popular de Puerto Rico, San Juan, PR; *U.S. Public*, pg. 175

Rodriguez, Michael A., V.P.-Human Resources--Pacific Bell, San Ramon, CA; *U.S. Public*, pg. 1416

Rodriguez, Robert, Dir.-Human Resources--Setco, Inc., Anaheim, CA; *U.S. Public*, pg. 1066

Rodriguez, Ruben, V.P.-H.R.--Sun City Redi-Mix Inc., El Paso, TX; *Int'l*, pg. 573

Rodriguez, Stella, Dir.-Personnel--Label-Aire Inc., Fullerton, CA; *U.S. Private*, pg. 641

Roedl, Suzanne, V.P.-Fin.--Condor D.C. Power Supplies Inc., Oxnard, CA; *U.S. Public*, pg. 1419

Rogers, Arthur A., V.P.-Mngmt. Resources--LucasVarity Inc., Buffalo, NY; *Int'l*, pg. 820

Rogers, Becky, Dir.-Human Resources--Eatelcorp Inc., Gonzales, LA; *U.S. Private*, pg. 358

Rogers, James S., V.P.-Human Resources--AmeriSteel, Tampa, FL; *U.S. Private*, pg. 65

Rogers, JoAnn, V.P.-H.R.--Network Computing Devices, Inc., Mountain View, CA; *U.S. Public*, pg. 1168

Rogers, Terry, V.P.-Corp. Admin., Benefits & Human Resources--Herff Jones Inc., Indianapolis, IN; *U.S. Private*, pg. 523

Rogna, Lawrence G., Sr. V.P.--Gaylord Container Corporation, Deerfield, IL; *U.S. Public*, pg. 704

Rogoff, Ellen, Sr. V.P.-Personnel--Broad National Bank, Newark, NJ; *U.S. Public*, pg. 257

Rogoff, Ellen K., Sr. V.P.-Human Resources--Broad National Bancorporation, Newark, NJ; *U.S. Public*, pg. 257

Rohleder, Claus, Dr., Dir.-Corp. Bd.-Indus. Div.-H.R. & Special Prods.--Boehringer Ingelheim GmbH, Ingelheim, Germany; *Int'l*, pg. 199

Rohmann, Walter, V.P.-Human Resources--Novartis Nutrition Corporation, Saint Louis Park, MN; *Int'l*, pg. 974

Rojo, Jose L., Dir.-Human Resources--Bundy Mexico SA, Tultitlan, Mexico; *Int'l*, pg. 1342

Roldan, Simeon Y., Chief Fin. Officer & Controller--King Wire Inc., North Chicago, IL; *U.S. Private*, pg. 621

Rolek, Gary, V.P.-Human Resources--Coleman Powermate Compressors, Springfield, MN; *U.S. Private*, pg. 691

Roles, Kirk, Dir.-Human Resources--Cavco Industries, Inc., Phoenix, AZ; *U.S. Public*, pg. 323

Rolfsmeyer, Jerry, Dir.-H.R.--Walbridge Aldinger Company, Detroit, MI; *U.S. Private*, pg. 1146

Rolland, Andre, Dir.-Rels. Sociales & Human Resources--Kodak Pathe S.A., Paris, France; *U.S. Public*, pg. 554

Rolle, Ilse, Mgr.-Staff Support--Coop Switzerland, Basel, Switzerland; *Int'l*, pg. 329

Roller, Robert, Mgr.-Human Resources--Overton Gear & Tool Corp., Addison, IL; *U.S. Private*, pg. 823

Rollins, Morag R., V.P.-H.R.--American Arbitration Association, New York, NY; *U.S. Private*, pg. 50

Rolston, B.F., V.P.-H.R., Health, Safety, Environ. & Security--Eastman Chemical Company, Kingsport, TN; *U.S. Public*, pg. 550

Romano, Fran, Mgr.--H.J. Baker & Bro., Inc., Stamford, CT; *U.S. Private*, pg. 112

Romero, C., Dir.-H.R. & Personnel Trng.--Gator Industries Inc., Hialeah, FL; *U.S. Private*, pg. 441

Romero, Carlos, Dir.-Personnel--Praxair Espania S.A., Madrid, Spain; *U.S. Public*, pg. 1320

Rominiecki, Carol, V.P.-Opers. & Human Resources--Vox Medica Corporation, Philadelphia, PA; *U.S. Private*, pg. 1143

Romm, Adria Alpert, V.P.-Employee Rels.--CNBC, Fort Lee, NJ; *U.S. Public*, pg. 712

Romm, Marcy A., Sr. V.P. & Dir.-H.R.--ICF Kaiser International Inc., Fairfax, VA; *U.S. Public*, pg. 852

Roncing, Tom, Dir.-H.R.--Jake Sweeney Automotive Inc., Cincinnati, OH; *U.S. Private*, pg. 1058

Roney, Jo, V.P.-Human Resoources--Consolidated Stores Corp., Columbus, OH; *U.S. Public*, pg. 437

Ronning, Arne, Dir.-Personnel--Courtaulds Aerospace, Glendale, CA; *Int'l*, pg. 339

Ronningen, Hans Jorn, Dir.-Human Resources--Norsk Hydro a.s, Oslo, Norway; *Int'l*, pg. 959

Ronzheimer, Jan, V.P.-Human Resources & Admin.--Jantzen, Portland, OR; *U.S. Public*, pg. 1702

Roper, Ted E., V.P.-Human Resources--J.R. Simplot Company, Boise, ID; *U.S. Private*, pg. 1002

Rosa, Steve, Dir.-Personnel--Camellia Food Stores, Inc., Norfolk, VA; *U.S. Private*, pg. 203

Rosa, Steve, Mgr.-Human Resources--Be-Lo Markets Inc., Norfolk, VA; *U.S. Private*, pg. 203

Rosales, Bertha, Dir.-H.R.--Aladdin Hotel & Casino, Las Vegas, NV; *U.S. Private*, pg. 30

Rosales, Manuel Gutierrez, Deputy Mng. Dir.-Human Resources--Caja de Madrid Group, Madrid, Spain; *Int'l*, pg. 251

Rose, Janet, Mgr.-Human Resources--Alsons Corporation, Hillsdale, MI; *U.S. Public*, pg. 1053

Rose, Thomas C., V.P.-Human Resources--Moore Medical Corp., New Britain, CT; *U.S. Public*, pg. 1128

Rosen, Florence, Exec. V.P.--Rosen Associates Management Corp., Jericho, NY; *U.S. Private*, pg. 945

Rosen, Jeffrey, Sr. V.P.-Human Resources--SGS North America Inc., New York, NY; *Int'l*, pg. 1153

Rosen, Peter, V.P.-H.R.--Norrell Corporation, Atlanta, GA; *U.S. Public*, pg. 1192

Rosenberg, Charles, V.P.-H.R.--Tops Appliance City, Edison, NJ; *U.S. Public*, pg. 1622

Rosenberg, Donald, Sr. V.P.-Human Resources--IMO Industries Inc., Lawrenceville, NJ; *U.S. Public*, pg. 856

Rosenberger, A.R., V.P.-H.R.--The Mead Corporation, Dayton, OH; *U.S. Public*, pg. 1074

Rosenberger, Robert, V.P.-Human Resources--Mead Packaging, Atlanta, GA; *U.S. Public*, pg. 1074

Rosenkotter, Mike, Dir.-Res. & Devel. & Mgr.-H.R.--Long MFG. NC, Inc., Tarboro, NC; *U.S. Private*, pg. 674

Rosenkranz, Ken, Controller & Dir.-Personnel--Spirite Industries, Inc., Englewood, NJ; *U.S. Private*, pg. 1026

Rosenthal, W., Dir.-Human Resources--Semikron International, GmbH & Co. KG, Nuremberg, Germany; *Int'l*, pg. 1220

Rosich, Jose, Dir.-Personnel--Ponce Cement Div., Ponce, PR; *U.S. Public*, pg. 1342

Rosich, Jose E., Dir.-Personnel--Puerto Rican Cement Co., Inc., Guaynabo, PR; *U.S. Public*, pg. 1341

Rosier, Marlene, Mgr.-H.R.--Buffelen Woodworking Company, Tacoma, WA; *U.S. Private*, pg. 179

Rosnak, Emily, Dir.-H.R.--Rock Bottom Restaurants, Louisville, CO; *U.S. Public*, pg. 1396

Rosok, Larry, V.P.-H.R. & Corp. Sec.--Cascade Natural Gas Corporation, Seattle, WA; *U.S. Public*, pg. 311

Ross, Alessandro V., V.P.-H.R.--Citizens Utilities Company, Stamford, CT; *U.S. Public*, pg. 379

Ross, Donna, V.P.-Human Resources--Pharmacia & Upjohn Biotech Inc., Piscataway, NJ; *Int'l*, pg. 1047

Ross, J., Exec. V.P.-Human Resources--Labatt Breweries of Canada, Toronto, Canada; *Int'l*, pg. 679

Ross, Jack, Mgr.-Human Resources--Encore Marketing International, Inc., Lanham, MD; *U.S. Public*, pg. 580

Ross, Kevin, V.P.-Personnel--Charles Curtain Company, Inc., Dallas, TX; *U.S. Private*, pg. 229

Ross, Michael, V.P.-Human Resources--Mother's Cake & Cookie Co., Oakland, CA; *U.S. Private*, pg. 1022

Ross, Peter, Sr. V.P.-H.R.--The Dun & Bradstreet Corporation, Murray Hill, NJ; *U.S. Public*, pg. 535

Ross, Peter J., Sr. V.P.-H.R.--Dun & Bradstreet, Murray Hill, NJ; *U.S. Public*, pg. 535

Ross, Ron, V.P.-Personnel & Corp. Grants Contact--Battenfeld Gloucester Engineering Co. Inc., Gloucester, MA; *U.S. Private*, pg. 123

Ross, Thomas, V.P.-H.R.--The Smithfield Packing Co., Inc., Smithfield, VA; *U.S. Public*, pg. 1479

Rosselet, Thomas, Chief Oper. Officer--Milprint Inc., Oshkosh, WI; *U.S. Public*, pg. 210

Rossi, James J., V.P.-Human Resources--Kewaunee Scientific Corporation, Statesville, NC; *U.S. Public*, pg. 953

Rossi, Jerome, Exec. V.P.--The Marmax Group, Framingham, MA; *U.S. Public*, pg. 1557

Rossi, Marie, Mgr.-Personnel--Vicon Industries, Inc., Hauppauge, NY; *U.S. Public*, pg. 1719

Rossi, Richard, Recruitment Dir.--Al Paul Lefton Co., Inc., Philadelphia, PA; *U.S. Private*, pg. 658

Rossi, Richard P., V.P. & Dir.-Human Resources--Penn Security Bank and Trust Co., Scranton, PA; *U.S. Public*, pg. 1270

Rossman, Hans G., Mgr.-Personnel & Legal Affairs--Lufthansa Cargo AG, Frankfurt, Germany; *Int'l*, pg. 407

Roth, David E., V.P.-Human Resources--Western Resources, Inc., Topeka, KS; *U.S. Public*, pg. 1759

Roth, Ivan, Treas.--National Income Realty Trust, New York, NY; *U.S. Public*, pg. 1157

Roth, Joanne M., Mgr.-Personnel--Staodyn Inc., Longmont, CO; *U.S. Public*, pg. 1509

Roth, John, Mgr.-Personnel--Photo-Me International plc, Bookham, United Kingdom; *Int'l*, pg. 1055

Roth, Malou, V.P.-H.R., Trng. & Devel.--Molex Incorporated, Lisle, IL; *U.S. Public*, pg. 1121

Roth, Tom, V.P.-Human Resources--Pony Express Delivery Services, Inc, Atlanta, GA; *U.S. Public*, pg. 245

Rothlind, Allan, V.P.-Personnel--Saab Automobile AB, Nykoping, Sweden; *Int'l*, pg. 687

Rothlind, Allan, V.P.-Personnel--Saab Automobile AB, Nykoping, Sweden; *U.S. Public*, pg. 725

Rothwax, Joel H., V.P.-Human Resources--Reliance Group Holdings, Inc., New York, NY; *U.S. Public*, pg. 1374

Routhe, Louise T., V.P.-Human Resources & Admin.--NRG Energy, Inc., Minneapolis, MN; *U.S. Public*, pg. 1195

Rowden, Pat, Mgr.-Personnel--Grocers Baking Co., Grand Rapids, MI; *U.S. Private*, pg. 482

Rowe, Victoria V., Mgr.-Human Resources--Ruhle Companies, Inc., Valhalla, NY; *U.S. Private*, pg. 950

Rowie, Sheryl, V.P.-H.R.--Atlanta Life Insurance Company, Atlanta, GA; *U.S. Private*, pg. 94

Rowland, Bill, Dir.-Personnel--Wix Div., Gastonia, NC; *U.S. Public*, pg. 479

Rowland, G. Joyce, V.P.-H.R.--Pacific Enterprises, Los Angeles, CA; *U.S. Public*, pg. 1249

Rowland, Keith, V.P.-Personnel--Thomas J. Lipton Company, Englewood Cliffs, NJ; *Int'l*, pg. 1435

Rowland, Mike, V.P.-H.R.--Bass Pro Shops, Inc., Springfield, MO; *U.S. Private*, pg. 122

Rowland, Susan E., Sec.--Griffon Corp., Jericho, NY; *U.S. Public*, pg. 766

Rowland, T. Keith, V.P.-Human Resources--Unilever United States Inc., New York, NY; *Int'l*, pg. 1435

Roy, Andre, V.P.-Corp. Affairs--Societe Generale de Financement du Quebec, Montreal, Canada; *Int'l*, pg. 1274

Roy, Maria, Dir.-Human Resources--Bodine Assembly and Test Systems, Bridgeport, CT; *U.S. Private*, pg. 154

Roy, S.S., Dir.-Personnel--Central Coalfields Limited, Ranchi, India; *Int'l*, pg. 298

Rozenek, Aliana, V.P.-Human Resources--The Oshawa Group Limited, Etobicoke, Canada; *Int'l*, pg. 1012

Rubin, Allen F., V.P.-Human Resources & Corp. Services--Reitmans (Canada) Limited, Montreal, Canada; *Int'l*, pg. 1102

Rubin, Gayle, Mgr.-H.R.--Au Bon Pain Co., Inc., Boston, MA; *U.S. Public*, pg. 146

Rubino, John A., Sr. V.P.-Human Resources--Walgreen Co., Deerfield, IL; *U.S. Public*, pg. 1733

Rubottom, Jim, Mgr.-Personnel--The Knapheide Mfg. Co., Quincy, IL; *U.S. Private*, pg. 626

Rudich, Gerald, V.P.-H.R.--Monroe Systems For Business, Inc., Morris Plains, NJ; *U.S. Private*, pg. 757

Rudiwitz, Irv, V.P.-H.R.--British Airways, Flushing, NY; *Int'l*, pg. 219

Rudman, R. Michael, V.P.-H.R.--Hit or Miss, Inc., Stoughton, MA; *U.S. Private*, pg. 531

Rudolph, Ronald A., V.P.-H.R. Opers.--3Com Corporation, Santa Clara, CA; *U.S. Public*, pg. 1603

Rue, Sandra, Dir.-H.R.--Columbine JDS Systems, Inc., Denver, CO; *U.S. Public*, pg. 228

Ruete, Joan, Admin. Asst.--Preferred Utilities Manufacturing Corp., Danbury, CT; *U.S. Private*, pg. 881

Ruf, H. William, V.P.-Admin. & Legal Affairs--Oglebay Norton Company, Cleveland, OH; *U.S. Public*, pg. 1213

Ruffin, Robert, V.P.-Human Resources & Sec.--Servico, Inc., West Palm Beach, FL; *U.S. Public*, pg. 1462

Ruffle, Keith H.C., Dir.-Personnel--British Alcan Aluminium plc, Gerrards Cross, United Kingdom; *Int'l*, pg. 51

Ruffolo, Joseph E., Exec. V.P.-H.R.--Peregrine Incorporated, Southfield, MI; *U.S. Private*, pg. 852

Ruggieri, Thomas F., Asst. V.P.-Human Resources--The Pep Boys-Manny, Moe & Jack, Philadelphia, PA; *U.S. Public*, pg. 1276

Ruggiero, Albert V., Mgr.-H.R.--South Jersey Industries, Inc., Folsom, NJ; *U.S. Public*, pg. 1488

Ruggiero, Albert V., V.P.--South Jersey Gas Co., Folsom, NJ; *U.S. Public*, pg. 1488

Ruhlo, Tina, V.P.-Human Resources--VLSI Technology, Inc., San Jose, CA; *U.S. Public*, pg. 1703

Ruikkie, Ellen, Dir.-Human Resources--Technology Research Corporation, Clearwater, FL; *U.S. Public*, pg. 1564

Ruiz, Carlos, Mgr.-Personnel & Admin. Svcs.--Banca Serfin, S.A., New York Agency, New York, NY; *Int'l*, pg. 137

Rulli, John, Sr. V.P.-H.R. & Corp. Opers.--Simon DeBartolo Group, Inc., Indianapolis, IN; *U.S. Public*, pg. 1474

Ruman, Jane, Mgr.-Human Resources--Effective Management Systems, Milwaukee, WI; *U.S. Public*, pg. 565

Rumke, M.J., Sr. V.P.-H.R.--Holiday Inn Worldwide, Atlanta, GA; *Int'l*, pg. 170

Rumpel, Hans Peter, Mgr.-Personnel--Coop Switzerland, Basel, Switzerland; *Int'l*, pg. 329

Rumschlag, Linda R., V.P.-Human Resources & Admin.--Chrysler Financial Corporation, Southfield, MI; *U.S. Public*, pg. 354

Rumsey, E. Christine, Sr. V.P.-H.R.--HBOC, Atlanta, GA; *U.S. Public*, pg. 770

Runchey, Jim, V.P.-Human Resources--ALARIS Medical Systems, Inc., San Diego, CA; *U.S. Public*, pg. 35

Runk, Sandra, Dir.-H.R. (Ontario)--Synergistics Industries Limited, Mississauga, Canada; *U.S. Public*, pg. 734

Ruotolo, Dottie, Mgr.-Personnel--O.F. Mossberg & Sons, Inc., North Haven, CT; *U.S. Private*, pg. 764

Rupert, Wim G.M., Dir.-Human Resources--Heidemij N.V., Arnhem, Netherlands; *Int'l*, pg. 606

Rurly, Mary, Dir.-H.R.--WD-40 Company, San Diego, CA; *U.S. Public*, pg. 1726

Rusak, William K., Chief Admin. Officer & Sr. V.P.--Dominion Textile Inc., Montreal, Canada; *Int'l*, pg. 415

Rush, Libby, Admin.-Human Resources--Capital Controls Company Inc., Colmar, PA; *Int'l*, pg. 1226

Rushin, Kelley, Sr. Dir.-H.R.--Jones Medical Industries Inc., Saint Louis, MO; *U.S. Public*, pg. 933
Rushing, Barbara, Dir.-H.R.--Advanced Accessories Systems, LLC., Sterling Heights, MI; *U.S. Private*, pg. 21
Rushkewicz, Robert M., V.P.-Human Resources--Brunswick Indoor Recreation Group, Lake Forest, IL; *U.S. Public*, pg. 265
Rusin, Juanita E., Mgr.-H.R.--Salton/Maxim Housewares, Inc., Mount Prospect, IL; *U.S. Public*, pg. 1430
Russ, Charles P., III, Exec. V.P.-Law & Human Resources, Gen. Counsel & Sec.--U S West Inc., Englewood, CO; *U.S. Public*, pg. 1688
Russek, H., V.P.-Employee Rels.--Astronautics Corporation of America, Milwaukee, WI; *U.S. Private*, pg. 93
Russell, David, Dir.-Human Resources--Gateway 2000, North Sioux City, SD; *U.S. Public*, pg. 703
Russell, Juanita, Dir.-Human Resources--Kvaerner Davy, Pittsburgh, PA; *Int'l*, pg. 774
Russell, Robin, Mgr.-H.R.--The Robert E. Morris Company, Farmington, CT; *U.S. Private*, pg. 762
Russo, Blaise, V.P.-Human Resources--Kearfott Guidance & Navigation Corp., Wayne, NJ; *U.S. Private*, pg. 93
Russo, David, Dir.-H.R.--SAS Institute Inc., Cary, NC; *U.S. Private*, pg. 966
Rust, David, V.P.-H.R.--Menasha Corporation, Neenah, WI; *U.S. Private*, pg. 731
Ruth, Richard J., V.P.-Human Resources--Nordyne Inc., Saint Louis, MO; *U.S. Public*, pg. 1193
Rutherford, Kevin, V.P.-Human Resources--Borders Group, Inc., Ann Arbor, MI; *U.S. Public*, pg. 245
Rutkowski, Dave, Dir.-H.R.--Rawlings Sporting Goods Company, Fenton, MO; *U.S. Public*, pg. 1361
Ruttman, David C., V.P.-H.R.--Blue Cross and Blue Shield of Oklahoma, Tulsa, OK; *U.S. Private*, pg. 151
Ryan, Elizabeth, Dir.-Personnel--Cone-Blanchard Machine Company, Windsor, VT; *U.S. Private*, pg. 262
Ryan, Ethel, Mgr.-H.R.--Better Baked Foods, Inc., North East, PA; *U.S. Private*, pg. 141
Ryan, J.T., V.P.-Human Resources--Freeman Energy Corporation, Springfield, IL; *U.S. Public*, pg. 709
Ryan, Jan, Mgr.-Employee Rels.--Boye Needle, Chicago, IL; *U.S. Private*, pg. 1192
Ryan, John J., Dir.-H.R.--Parsons Brinckerhoff Inc., New York, NY; *U.S. Private*, pg. 841
Ryan, Linda, Human Resources--Enzon, Inc., Piscataway, NJ; *U.S. Public*, pg. 587
Ryan, Mary, V.P.-Human Resources--Lamonts Apparel, Inc., Kirkland, WA; *U.S. Public*, pg. 975
Ryan, Paige, Dir.-H.R.--American Science & Engineering, Inc., Billerica, MA; *U.S. Public*, pg. 90
Ryan, S.L., V.P.-Human Resources & Admin.--Guarantee Life Insurance Co., Omaha, NE; *U.S. Public*, pg. 768
Rydel, James W., V.P.-Admin. & Sec.--Intermet Corporation, Troy, MI; *U.S. Public*, pg. 894
Ryder, Lynn, Sr. V.P.-Human Resources--Washington Mutual Inc., Seattle, WA; *U.S. Public*, pg. 1741
Saah, Cindy, Mgr.-H.R.--ANSER (Analytic Services Inc.), Arlington, VA; *U.S. Private*, pg. 75
Sabatino, Bill, Sr. V.P.-Employee Rels.--Philadelphia Daily News, Philadelphia, PA; *U.S. Public*, pg. 964
Sabin, Darryl R., V.P.-Personnel--SAFECO Corporation, Seattle, WA; *U.S. Public*, pg. 1423
Sabino, Lyn, Mgr.-Human Resources--Graphic Enterprises of Ohio, Inc., Canton, OH; *U.S. Private*, pg. 471
Sackett, Julie A., V.P.-H.R.--Dell Computer Corporation, Round Rock, TX; *U.S. Public*, pg. 495
Sackett, Les C., V.P. & Dir.-Human Resources--ITT Aerospace/Communications Div., Fort Wayne, IN; *U.S. Public*, pg. 859
Sacks, Lewis, V.P.-H.R.--URS Logistics, Atlanta, GA; *U.S. Private*, pg. 1114
Saez, Carlos Sanchez, Dir.-Human Resources--Amper, S.A., Madrid, Spain; *Int'l*, pg. 1372
Sage, Peter J., V.P.-Human Resources--Lonza Inc., Fair Lawn, NJ; *Int'l*, pg. 67
Sager, Harlin, V.P.-Human Resources--Ouachita Coca-Cola Bottling Company, Monroe, LA; *U.S. Public*, pg. 393
Sahara, K., Dir.-Personnel--Miyata Industry Co., Ltd., Chigasaki, Japan; *Int'l*, pg. 884
Sahinbas, Tamer, V.P.-Human Resources Mngmt.--Koc Holding A.S., Istanbul, Turkey; *Int'l*, pg. 741
Sahler, F. Bruce, Mgr.-H.R.--Everest Reinsurance Holdings, Liberty Corner, NJ; *U.S. Public*, pg. 597
Sakai, Shoji, Exec. V.P.-Human Resources--Diamond Star Motors, Normal, IL; *Int'l*, pg. 875
Sakata, Masayuki, Gen. Mgr.-Personnel--West Japan Railway Company, Osaka, Japan; *Int'l*, pg. 1490
Salach, Michael, V.P.-Human Resources--Schneider Automation, Inc., North Andover, MA; *Int'l*, pg. 1208
Salazar, Susan, Sr. V.P.--Westin Hotels & Resorts, Seattle, WA; *U.S. Public*, pg. 1512
Sale, K. Lyn, Asst. Treas.--DMI Furniture Inc., Louisville, KY; *U.S. Public*, pg. 473
Saleh, Muhammad, V.P.-H.R.--Timex Corporation, Middlebury, CT; *U.S. Private*, pg. 1088
Salem, Staci, Dir.-H.R.--Reinalt-Thomas Corp., Ann Arbor, MI; *U.S. Private*, pg. 919
Saliminen, Hannele, Grp. V.P.-H.R.--Polarcup Group Headquarters, Espoo, Finland; *Int'l*, pg. 638
Saline, Craig, Dir.-H.R.--Reckitt & Colman Inc., Montvale, NJ; *Int'l*, pg. 1090
Salinero, Alejandro, Asst. Mgr.-H.R.--Chuquicamata Division, Chuquicamata, Chile; *Int'l*, pg. 302
Salk, Steve, Dir.-Human Resources--American Retail Group, New York, NY; *U.S. Private*, pg. 61
Salminen, Hannele, V.P.-H.R.--Huhtamaki Oy, Espoo, Finland; *Int'l*, pg. 638
Salminen, Hannele, Grp. V.P.-H.R.--Leaf Group B.V., Espoo, Finland,; *Int'l*, pg. 638
Salmon, E., Dir.-Personnel-Pretty Products Inc.--Lancaster Colony Automotive Group, Dublin, OH; *U.S. Public*, pg. 977
Saloom, David, Dir.-Personnel--Walgreen Co., Deerfield, IL; *U.S. Public*, pg. 1733
Salsberg, Eric P., V.P.-Corp. Affairs--Fairfax Financial Holdings Limited, Toronto, Canada; *Int'l*, pg. 476
Salsbury, Peter, Joint Mng. Dir.-Grp. Estates, Personnel, Store Opers. & Devel.--Marks & Spencer PLC, London, United Kingdom; *Int'l*, pg. 842
Salter, J., Mgr.-Personnel--Durham Chemicals Ltd., Chester le Street, United Kingdom; *Int'l*, pg. 598
Salter, Sandy, Admin. Asst.-Human Resources--American Financial Group, Cincinnati, OH; *U.S. Public*, pg. 75
Salvagnac, Claude, Mng. Dir.-Human Resources--Nestle France, Courbevoie, France; *Int'l*, pg. 921
Sampaio, Mario Roberto L., Mgr.-Human Resources--Acos Villares S.A., Sao Paulo, Brazil; *Int'l*, pg. 23
Sampson, C.P., Asst. V.P.-Human Resources--Canadian Pacific Railway, Minneapolis, MN; *Int'l*, pg. 259
Samson, Roger, Exec. V.P.-Personnel--Sterling Supply Company, Inc., Lisle, IL; *U.S. Private*, pg. 1041
Samuelsen, David, Dir.-Human Resources--Danly Die Set Division, Cicero, IL; *U.S. Private*, pg. 264
Samways, Sandy, V.P.-H.R.--Southern Pump & Tank Company, Charlotte, NC; *U.S. Private*, pg. 1017
Sanchez, Frank, V.P.-Human Resources--Playtex Beauty Care, Inc., Westport, CT; *U.S. Public*, pg. 1311
Sanchez, Frank M., V.P.-H.R.--Playtex Products Inc., Westport, CT; *U.S. Public*, pg. 1310
Sanders, Anthony O., Dir.-Human Resources--X-Rite, Incorporated, Grandville, MI; *U.S. Public*, pg. 1783
Sanders, D.S., V.P.-Human Resources--Exxon Corporation, Irving, TX; *U.S. Public*, pg. 601
Sanders, Jerry, Mgr.-Human Resources--Woodward-Clyde Group, Inc., Denver, CO; *U.S. Public*, pg. 1655
Sanders, M.H., Dir.-Personnel & Organization--Wolters Kluwer N.V., Amsterdam, Netherlands; *Int'l*, pg. 1512
Sanders, Zink, Mgr.-Personnel--Hinckley & Schmitt, Inc., Chicago, IL; *Int'l*, pg. 1322
Sanderson, James E., Reg. Dir.-Organizational Services--Cyprus Foote Mineral Co., Kings Mountain, NC; *U.S. Public*, pg. 471
Sandhu, Harmit, Coord.-H.R.--Numetrix Ltd., Toronto, Canada; *Int'l*, pg. 990
Sandmal, Jerry, Dir. Human Resources--Allen Foods, Inc., Saint Louis, MO; *U.S. Private*, pg. 37
Sands, Karen, Dir.-Benefits--Sithe Energies, Inc., New York, NY; *U.S. Private*, pg. 1004
Sands, Linda, V.P.-H.R.--Candle Corporation of America, Des Plaines, IL; *U.S. Public*, pg. 239
Sanglier, Lynn, Mgr.-H.R.--Tenera, Inc., San Francisco, CA; *U.S. Public*, pg. 1576
Sankey, Cindy, Dir.-H.R.--The Bartell Drug Company, Seattle, WA; *U.S. Private*, pg. 118
Sansone, Janet F., V.P.-Human Resources--Frontier Corporation, Rochester, NY; *U.S. Public*, pg. 683
Santa Maria, Pablo, Dir. Gen.-H.R.--Grupo Elektra S.A. de C.V., Mexico, Mexico; *Int'l*, pg. 573
Santelia, Robin, Mgr.-H.R.--Bernard Chaus, Inc., New York, NY; *U.S. Public*, pg. 342
Santelia, Robin, Mgr.-Human Resources--Bernard Chaus, Inc., Secaucus, NJ; *U.S. Public*, pg. 342
Santella, Gene, V.P.-Human Resources--Sanofi Pharmaceuticals, Inc., New York, NY; *Int'l*, pg. 445
Santiago, Marcelo R., Mgr.-Human Resources--TI Brazil Industria E Comerico Ltda., Sao Jose dos Campos, Brazil; *Int'l*, pg. 1342
Santiago, Rosane, Mgr.-Personnel--SmithKline Beecham Laboratorios Ltda., Rio de Janeiro, Brazil; *Int'l*, pg. 1266
Santillan, Eva, Mgr.-H.R.--Zitel Corporation, Fremont, CA; *U.S. Public*, pg. 1793
Santora, James, V.P.-H.R.--Burns & Roe Enterprises, Inc., Oradell, NJ; *U.S. Private*, pg. 187
Santoro, Katharyn F., V.P.-Human Resources--Molten Metal Technology, Inc., Fall River, MA; *U.S. Public*, pg. 1123
Santos, Hugo, Dir.-Human Resources--Applied Biosystems, Foster City, CA; *U.S. Public*, pg. 1279
Sanz, Jesus Fernandez De La Vega, Dir.-Human Resources--Repsol S.A., Madrid, Spain; *Int'l*, pg. 1104
Saranczak, Mary, Mgr.-H.R.--Magnetrol International, Downers Grove, IL; *U.S. Private*, pg. 696
Sarjoo, Priya, Asst. Treas. & Asst. Sec.--Astrex, Inc., Plainview, NY; *U.S. Public*, pg. 141
Sartain, Elizabeth P., V.P.-People--Southwest Airlines Co., Dallas, TX; *U.S. Public*, pg. 1493
Sartori, Paul H., Sr. V.P.-Human Resources--Novartis Pharmaceuticals, East Hanover, NJ; *Int'l*, pg. 973
Sass, Diane, Mgr.-Personnel--Trumpf Inc., Farmington, CT; *U.S. Private*, pg. 1108
Sasso, John R., Chief Admin. Officer & V.P.--Fisher Scientific International, Hampton, NH; *U.S. Private*, pg. 658
Sastre, Angel, Gen. Mgr.-Human Resources--Tabacalera, S.A., Madrid, Spain; *Int'l*, pg. 1345
Saternus, Robert, Dir.-Personnel--Bessin Corporation, Chicago, IL; *U.S. Public*, pg. 1433
Saternus, Robert, V.P.-Human Resources--Best Kosher Sausage Co., Chicago, IL; *U.S. Public*, pg. 1433
Satkiewicz, Marilyn, Mgr.-H.R.--U.S.S. Seko Worldwide, Elk Grove Village, IL; *U.S. Private*, pg. 1115
Sato, Masaru, Gen. Mgr.-Personnel--Maruha Corporation, Tokyo, Japan; *Int'l*, pg. 845
Satoji, Ichita, Mng. Dir.-Human Resources--Nippon Shinpan Co., Ltd., Tokyo, Japan; *Int'l*, pg. 939
Saulpaugh, Don, V.P.-Human Resources--Giant Food Stores Inc., Carlisle, PA; *Int'l*, pg. 750
Saunders, D.P., Dir.-Personnel & Indus. Rels.--Carolina Tractor & Equipment Co., Charlotte, NC; *U.S. Private*, pg. 214
Savage, Jack, Dir.-Personnel--Commercial Intertech Corp., Youngstown, OH; *U.S. Public*, pg. 411
Savage, Martha, Mgr.-Personnel--Abdalla's Lafayette, Inc., Lafayette, LA; *U.S. Private*, pg. 10
Sawahn, Jochen W., Grp. Mgr.-Human Resources--Bankgesellschaft Berlin, Berlin, Germany; *Int'l*, pg. 159
Sawtelle, Don, V.P.-H.R.--Swift Textiles, Inc., Atlanta, GA; *Int'l*, pg. 415
Sawyer, Dave, Dir.-H.R.--Howard Miller, Zeeland, MI; *U.S. Private*, pg. 747
Sawyer, Dwight A., V.P.-Human Resources--Amway Corporation, Ada, MI; *U.S. Private*, pg. 69
Sawyer, Kenny, V.P.-Human Resources--Dorsey Trailers, Inc., Atlanta, GA; *U.S. Public*, pg. 520
Saxon, Lee, Dir.-Human Resources--Micromatic Textron, Holland, MI; *U.S. Public*, pg. 1589
Sayin, Serhat, Mgr.-Human Resources--Arcelik A.S., Istanbul, Turkey; *Int'l*, pg. 741
Sayles, Helen, Sr. V.P. & Mgr.-H.R.--Liberty Mutual Insurance Co., Boston, MA; *U.S. Private*, pg. 666
Sayre, Robert H., Exec. V.P.-Human Resources--U.S. Bancorp, Minneapolis, MN; *U.S. Public*, pg. 1680
Scaduto, James A., V.P.-Employee Rels.--Dow Jones & Company, Inc., New York, NY; *U.S. Public*, pg. 524
Scalise, J., Mgr.-H.R.--Econolite Control Products, Inc., Anaheim, CA; *U.S. Private*, pg. 361
Scanlan, Melissa, Dir.-Human. Rels.--Comdisco, Inc., Rosemont, IL; *U.S. Public*, pg. 407
Scanlan, Steve, Dir.-Personnel--Brown Group, Inc., Saint Louis, MO; *U.S. Public*, pg. 262
Scanlon, Edward, Exec. V.P.-Employee Rels.--National Broadcasting Co., Inc., New York, NY; *U.S. Public*, pg. 712
Scanlon, Jaime, Human Resources--The Arnold Agency, Richmond, VA; *U.S. Private*, pg. 84
Scanlon, Thomas M., V.P.-Employee Rels.--The Okonite Company, Ramsey, NJ; *U.S. Private*, pg. 813
Scardelleffi, Donna, Human Resources Dir.--Gillespie, Lawrenceville, NJ; *U.S. Private*, pg. 453
Scardina, Betty, V.P.-H.R.--Gendis Inc., Winnipeg, Canada; *Int'l*, pg. 542
Scarlett, Robert P., V.P.-H.R.--Dukane Corporation, Saint Charles, IL; *U.S. Private*, pg. 345
Scarpato, George, Dir.-Pub. Rels. & Communications--Industrial Indemnity Company, San Francisco, CA; *U.S. Public*, pg. 681
Scarpelli, J.E., V.P.-Human Resources--The Standard Register Company, Dayton, OH; *U.S. Public*, pg. 1505
Scartezina, Stan, Sr. V.P.-Human Resources--Kennecott Holdings Corporation, Magna, UT; *Int'l*, pg. 1119
Schaaf, Eileen, Mgr.-Personnel--ASICS Tiger Corporation, Fountain Valley, CA; *U.S. Private*, pg. 89
Schaal, Rene, Dir.-Human Resources--Clestra Hauserman, Strasbourg, France; *Int'l*, pg. 569
Schachtel, Lyn-Marie, Human Resources Dir.--Avrett, Free & Ginsberg, Inc., New York, NY; *U.S. Private*, pg. 103
Schadeberg, Joseph, V.P.-H.R.--IEC Electronics Corp., Newark, NY; *U.S. Public*, pg. 854
Schaefer, Barbara W., V.P.-Human Resources--Union Pacific Railroad Company, Omaha, NE; *U.S. Public*, pg. 1668
Schaefer, Debra G., V.P.-H.R. & Commun., Aeroquip--Aeroquip-Vickers, Inc., Maumee, OH; *U.S. Public*, pg. 24
Schaeffer, Audrey N., V.P.-Human Resources--FileNet Corporation, Costa Mesa, CA; *U.S. Public*, pg. 622
Schaeffer, Daniel L., V.P.-Human Resources--Apache Corporation, Houston, TX; *U.S. Public*, pg. 119
Schaeffer, Patti, Mgr.-Human Resources--Advanced Marine Enterprises, Inc., Arlington, VA; *U.S. Public*, pg. 1182
Schafer, Margaret E., Mgr.-Personnel--Electrospace Systems, Inc., Richardson, TX; *U.S. Public*, pg. 1365
Schaffer, Shirley, Mgr.-Payroll--Charlie Thomas Dealerships, Houston, TX; *U.S. Private*, pg. 1082
Schanzmeyer, Babs, Mgr.-Human Resources--Kwal-Howells, Inc.(Denver), Denver, CO; *Int'l*, pg. 1501
Scharfenberger, R.N., V.P.-Human Resources-Bed Fashions--Home Furnishings Segment, Fort Mill, SC; *U.S. Public*, pg. 1500
Schatt, J.F., V.P.-Admin.--Detrex Corporation, Southfield, MI; *U.S. Public*, pg. 501
Schauffler, Pamela J., V.P.-Human Resource Devel.--Jacobson Stores Inc., Jackson, MI; *U.S. Public*, pg. 922
Schaulin, Richard L., V.P.-Human Resources--GTE South Incorporated, Irving, TX; *U.S. Public*, pg. 697
Schaumburg, Ronald G., V.P.-H.R.--National Cooperative Refinery Association, Mc Pherson, KS; *U.S. Private*, pg. 781
Schefflan, Beth, Admin. Dir. & Human Resources--Serino Coyne Inc., New York, NY; *U.S. Private*, pg. 985
Scheick, Don, Dir.-H.R.--Huffy Corporation, Miamisburg, OH; *U.S. Public*, pg. 846
Schell, Susan, V.P.-H.R. & Corp. Quality--Advanced Energy Industry, Fort Collins, CO; *U.S. Public*, pg. 20
Schelshaudt, Janice, Mgr.-H.R.--IDEA Corporation, Bedford, MA; *U.S. Private*, pg. 557
Schemmel, Don, V.P.-Personnel--Dyna Technology Incorporated, Le Center, MN; *U.S. Private*, pg. 350
Schemmel, Don, V.P.-Personnel--WINCO, Le Center, MN; *U.S. Private*, pg. 350
Schenkel, Tom, Mgr.-H.R.--Weaver Popcorn Company, Inc., Van Buren, IN; *U.S. Private*, pg. 1156
Scheper, Fran, Exec. V.P.-Human Resources--CPI Corp., Saint Louis, MO; *U.S. Public*, pg. 283
Scherer, Heidi, Mgr.-H.R.--CORS, Itasca, IL; *U.S. Private*, pg. 196
Schergen, Sharon K., V.P.-Human Resources--Peabody Holding Company, Inc., Saint Louis, MO; *Int'l*, pg. 594
Scherman, Carol, Exec. V.P.-Human Resources--Bergen Brunswig Corporation, Orange, CA; *U.S. Public*, pg. 213
Scherpenzeel, B.G., Mgr.-Personnel & Org.--Blydenstein-Willink N.V., Hengelo, Netherlands; *Int'l*, pg. 198
Schessler, James E., V.P.-H.R. & Admin.--Foster Wheeler Corporation, Clinton, NJ; *U.S. Public*, pg. 676
Scheuermann, June, Dir.-Personnel--Holcomb & Hoke Mfg. Company, Inc., Indianapolis, IN; *U.S. Private*, pg. 533
Scheurer, Charles B., V.P.-Human Resources--Diebold, Incorporated, Canton, OH; *U.S. Public*, pg. 506
Schick, Donna, Mgr.-Human Resources--LeaRonal, Inc., Freeport, NY; *U.S. Public*, pg. 982
Schiefer, Marianne, Mgr.-Human Resources--Worzalla Publishing Co., Inc., Stevens Point, WI; *U.S. Private*, pg. 1191

Schiff, Peggy, V.P.-Controller, Personnel Admin.--The Washington Post, Washington, DC; *U.S. Public*, pg. 1743
Schimberg, Darlene, Admin.-H.R.--Sybron International Corporation, Milwaukee, WI; *U.S. Public*, pg. 1544
Schimelman, Joan K., Sr. V.P.-H.R. & Mktg./Adv.--Republic Security Financial Corporation, West Palm Beach, FL; *U.S. Public*, pg. 1381
Schimelman, Joan K., V.P.-Human Resources--Republic Security Bank, West Palm Beach, FL; *U.S. Public*, pg. 1382
Schittone, John P., Jr., V.P.-Human Resources--Associated Grocers, Inc., Baton Rouge, LA; *U.S. Private*, pg. 90
Schlapp, Henry T., Dir.-Personnel--Marine Construction & Design Co., Seattle, WA; *U.S. Private*, pg. 703
Schleef, Andreas, Dir.-Human Resources--Audi AG, Ingolstadt, Germany; *Int'l*, pg. 1473
Schlocker, David, Dir.-H.R.--CSE Insurance Group, San Francisco, CA; *U.S. Private*, pg. 197
Schmalz, Greg, Mgr.-Employee Rels.--Melroe Company, Fargo, ND; *U.S. Public*, pg. 877
Schmeelk, John, Mgr.-H.R.--Apex Supply Co., Inc., Atlanta, GA; *U.S. Private*, pg. 77
Schmeichel, Scott, V.P.-Human Resources--Whitehall-Robins Healthcare, Madison, NJ; *U.S. Public*, pg. 80
Schmeider, Steve, Mgr.-Human Resources--Barnstead/Thermolyne Corporation, Dubuque, IA; *U.S. Public*, pg. 1545
Schmid, Dietmar, Mng. Dir. & Div. Head-Personnel & Admin.--BHF-BANK AG, Frankfurt, Germany; *Int'l*, pg. 119
Schmid, James, Dir.-H.R.--Bently Nevada Corporation, Minden, NV; *U.S. Private*, pg. 134
Schmidt, Curtis R., Dir.-Human Resources--Wausau Papers - Printing & Writing Div., Brokaw, WI; *U.S. Public*, pg. 1747
Schmidt, Fred L., Sr. V.P.-Human Resources--Public Service Company of North Carolina, Inc., Gastonia, NC; *U.S. Public*, pg. 1340
Schmidt, Janet L., Sr. V.P.-H.R.--The Acacia Group - Acacia Life Insurance Co., Bethesda, MD; *U.S. Private*, pg. 10
Schmidt, Jim, V.P.-H.R.--Borland International, Inc., Scotts Valley, CA; *U.S. Public*, pg. 246
Schmidt, Joseph, V.P.-H.R.--Mylex Corporation, Fremont, CA; *U.S. Public*, pg. 1143
Schmidt, Linda G., V.P.-Human Resources--Totes Incorporated, Loveland, OH; *U.S. Private*, pg. 111
Schmidt, Paul, V.P.-Human Resources--Hinderliter Heat Treating, Inc., Dallas, TX; *U.S. Private*, pg. 530
Schmidt, Pauline, Mgr.-Employee Benefits & Corp. Admin.--Agra Inc., Calgary, Canada; *Int'l*, pg. 30
Schmidt, W., Dir.-Human Resources--TA Triumph-Adler Vertriebs GmbH, Nuremberg, Germany; *Int'l*, pg. 1004
Schmitz, Jean-Marie, Exec. V.P.-Human Resources--Lafarge S.A., Paris, France; *Int'l*, pg. 788
Schmitz, Paul, Mgr.-Personnel--Ato-Findley, Inc., Wauwatosa, WI; *Int'l*, pg. 445
Schneck, Charles, Dir.-Personnel--Del Laboratories, Inc., Farmingdale, NY; *U.S. Public*, pg. 494
Schneck, Charles, Dir.-Human Resources--Sally Hansen, Farmingdale, NY; *U.S. Public*, pg. 494
Schneider, Kathy, Dir.-Personnel--F & W Publications, Inc., Cincinnati, OH; *U.S. Private*, pg. 388
Schneider, Leon J., Dir.-Personnel--Winchester Division-Defense & Ammunition, East Alton, IL; *U.S. Public*, pg. 1219
Schneider, Pamela C., V.P.-H.R. & Diversity Officer--Corning Incorporated, Corning, NY; *U.S. Public*, pg. 448
Schnepp, Dale, Mgr.-H.R.--Williams International, Walled Lake, MI; *U.S. Private*, pg. 1178
Schnur, Alan E., Sr. V.P.-H.R.--Robert Mondavi Winery, Inc., Oakville, CA; *U.S. Public*, pg. 1393
Schober, Jim, Dir.-Personnel--San Jose Mercury News, San Jose, CA; *U.S. Public*, pg. 964
Schoening, Allan, Mgr.-Human Resources--Barrick Gold Corporation, Toronto, Canada; *Int'l*, pg. 168
Schoettner, Manfred, Dir.-Bus. Devel. & Personnel--Cherry Mikroschalter GmbH, Auerbach, Germany; *U.S. Public*, pg. 346
Schonberg, Nanette, Dir.-H.R.--John G. Shedd Aquarium, Chicago, IL; *U.S. Private*, pg. 991
Schope, Gerald J., V.P.-Employee Rels.--Acme Metals Incorporated, Riverdale, IL; *U.S. Public*, pg. 16
Schoy, Jean, Mgr.-Human Resources--Sigma Designs, Inc., Fremont, CA; *U.S. Public*, pg. 1472
Schrader, Joseph, Human Resources Mgr.--UTA Holland Plant, Holland, MI; *U.S. Public*, pg. 1691
Schraeder, Marsha, Dir.-Customer Service--G.E. Capital Fleet Services, Eden Prairie, MN; *U.S. Public*, pg. 712
Schramek, Brad, V.P.-Human Resources--Monro Muffler/Brake, Inc., Rochester, NY; *U.S. Public*, pg. 1124
Schramek, Brad, Dir.-Human Resources--Tractor Supply Co., Nashville, TN; *U.S. Public*, pg. 1627
Schrank, Harris, V.P.-Human Resources--The Equitable Companies Incorporated, New York, NY; *U.S. Public*, pg. 588
Schrank, Leslyi, Dir.-Human Resources--ITC Learning Corp., Herndon, VA; *U.S. Public*, pg. 859
Schreiweis, Michael, Dir.-H.R.--Robinson Nugent, Inc., New Albany, IN; *U.S. Public*, pg. 1394
Schriener, Lynn, Human Resources & Admin.--Ney Dental International, Bloomfield, CT; *Int'l*, pg. 388
Schroeder, Gordon, V.P.-H.R.--GE Capital/IT Solutions, Minneapolis, MN; *U.S. Public*, pg. 711
Schroeter, S., Mgr.-Personnel--Land Instruments International Ltd., Dronfield, United Kingdom; *Int'l*, pg. 798
Schrum, Nancy, Dir.-H.R.--Carolina Mills, Inc., Maiden, NC; *U.S. Private*, pg. 214
Schuba, Mary T., Dir.-Human Resources--Homestake Mining Company, San Francisco, CA; *U.S. Public*, pg. 832
Schuett, Amy, Dir.-H.R.--Office Electronics, Inc., Itasca, IL; *U.S. Private*, pg. 812
Schugar, Phil, Mgr.-H.R.--Allied Security, Inc., Pittsburgh, PA; *U.S. Private*, pg. 40
Schulaner, Felice, Sr. V.P.-Human Resources--Salant Corporation, New York, NY; *U.S. Public*, pg. 1429
Schuler, Deborah K., Dir.-Human Resources--Tension Envelope Corp., Kansas City, MO; *U.S. Private*, pg. 1077
Schuller, Jorge, Dir.-Personnel--Gillette Argentina S.A., Buenos Aires, Argentina; *U.S. Public*, pg. 744
Schulman, Pamela, Dir.-Human Resources--Carolina Builders Corporation, Marietta, GA; *Int'l*, pg. 1512
Schulte, Virgiline M., V.P.-Human Resources & Sec.--Capitol Indemnity Corporation, Madison, WI; *U.S. Public*, pg. 302
Schulte, Virgiline M., V.P.-Human Resources & Sec.--Capitol Specialty Insurance Corporation, Madison, WI; *U.S. Public*, pg. 302
Schultz, Darcy, Mgr.-Human Resources--Barber-Colman Company, Rockford, IL; *Int'l*, pg. 1242
Schultz, Henry G., Gen. Mgr.-Human Resources--AutoAlliance International Inc., Flat Rock, MI; *Int'l*, pg. 849
Schultz, Joy, H.R.--Curtis C. Gunn, Inc., San Antonio, TX; *U.S. Private*, pg. 488
Schultz, Steve, Mgr.-Human Resources--Newport Steel Corporation, Newport, KY; *U.S. Public*, pg. 1147
Schultz, William, Dir.-Human Resources--Freudenberg Nonwovens, Durham, NC; *Int'l*, pg. 505
Schulz, Lemoin, V.P.-Personnel--Farmers & Merchants Bank of Central California, Lodi, CA; *U.S. Private*, pg. 394
Schulz, Patricia L., Dir.-Human Resources--Tower Group International, New York, NY; *U.S. Public*, pg. 1071
Schulz, Roland, Exec. V.P.-Personnel--Henkel KGaA, Dusseldorf, Germany; *Int'l*, pg. 609
Schulze, Donald W., Sr. V.P.-H.R.--D & N Financial Corporation, Hancock, MI; *U.S. Public*, pg. 472
Schulze, Donald W., Sr. V.P.-H.R.--D & N Bank, Hancock, MI; *U.S. Public*, pg. 472
Schumacher, Phil, V.P.-Human Resources--Kraft Canada Inc., Don Mills, Canada; *U.S. Public*, pg. 1288
Schuman, Barry R., Sr. V.P.-Human Resources--Tenneco Inc., Greenwich, CT; *U.S. Public*, pg. 1577
Schumann, Tom, V.P.-Human Resources--Sta-Rite Industries, Inc., Delavan, WI; *U.S. Public*, pg. 1767
Schumann, Tom, V.P.-Human Resources--Sta-Rite Water Systems, Delavan, WI; *U.S. Public*, pg. 1767
Schumm, Jochen, Dir.-Human Resources--SEAT, S.A., Barcelona, Spain; *Int'l*, pg. 1475
Schupp, Carl F., Dir.-Human Resources--Dowty Aerospace Aviation Services, Sterling, VA; *Int'l*, pg. 1337
Schutte, Earlene, Mgr.-Human Resources--Willis Corroon Corp. of Nashville, Nashville, TN; *Int'l*, pg. 1506
Schutte, Thierry, V.P.-H.R.--Airbus Industrie, Blagnac, France; *Int'l*, pg. 39
Schuttenberg, M. Lynn, V.P.-H.R.--Del Webb Corporation, Phoenix, AZ; *U.S. Public*, pg. 494
Schutz, Diane, Dir.-Human Resources--Cooker Restaurant Corporation, West Palm Beach, FL; *U.S. Public*, pg. 442
Schutz, Pierre, V.P.-H.R.--De Dietrich & Co., Niederbronn-les-Bains, France; *Int'l*, pg. 386
Schwab, Christine, V.P.-Human Resources & Legal--Software AG, Darmstadt, Germany; *Int'l*, pg. 1276
Schwab, Karin, Human Resources Dir.--AGA Catalog Marketing & Design, New York, NY; *U.S. Private*, pg. 5
Schwab, Ramona, Dir.-Human Resources--Mentor Corporation, Santa Barbara, CA; *U.S. Public*, pg. 1086
Schwanke, Dean, Dir.-H.R.--Smead Manufacturing Company, Hastings, MN; *U.S. Private*, pg. 1006
Schwanke, Lawrence E., V.P.-H.R.--Bemis Company, Inc., Minneapolis, MN; *U.S. Public*, pg. 210
Schwartz, Barbara, V.P.-H.R.--Sid Tool Co. Inc., Plainview, NY; *U.S. Private*, pg. 998
Schwartz, Barbara, V.P.-H.R.--MSC Industrial Supply Co., Plainview, NY; *U.S. Private*, pg. 998
Schwartz, Chuck, Chief Fin. Officer & Sr. V.P.--People's Choice TV Corp., Shelton, CT; *U.S. Public*, pg. 1274
Schwartz, Helene, Sr. V.P.-H.R.--The American Stock Exchange, New York, NY; *U.S. Private*, pg. 62
Schwartz, Ingrid, Dir.-Personnel--Ladies' Home Journal, New York, NY; *U.S. Public*, pg. 1094
Schwartz, Meline, Dir.-H.R.--Eateries, Inc., Oklahoma City, OK; *U.S. Public*, pg. 555
Schwartz, Meline, Dir.-H.R.--Pepperoni Grill, Oklahoma City, OK; *U.S. Public*, pg. 555
Schweers, Yolanda, Dir.-Human Resources--Anorad Corporation, Hauppauge, NY; *U.S. Private*, pg. 75
Schweickardt, James, Dir.-Human Resources--Pacific Coast Producers, Lodi, CA; *U.S. Private*, pg. 830
Schwery, Wes, Mgr.-Personnel--AAI/ACL Technologies, Santa Ana, CA; *U.S. Public*, pg. 1679
Scifres, C., Asst. V.P.-H.R.--National Fire Protection Association, Quincy, MA; *U.S. Private*, pg. 782
Sciortino, Tom, Sr. V.P.-Admin. & Human Resources--Congoleum Corporation, Mercerville, NJ; *U.S. Public*, pg. 69
Scipione, Jane, Dir.-Human Resources--Provident Mutual Life Insurance Co., Berwyn, PA; *U.S. Private*, pg. 891
Scogin, Gary, Dir.-Human Resources--Eagle Window & Door, Inc., Dubuque, IA; *U.S. Public*, pg. 67
Scott, Cheryl, Mgr.-Personnel--Wood Industries, Indianapolis, IN; *U.S. Public*, pg. 944
Scott, Colleen, Dir.-MIS--Reinalt-Thomas Corp., Ann Arbor, MI; *U.S. Private*, pg. 919
Scott, Denny, Mgr.-H.R.--Burns & McDonnell Engineers-Architects-Consultants, Kansas City, MO; *U.S. Private*, pg. 187
Scott, Dianne, V.P.-Human Resources--The Titan Corporation, San Diego, CA; *U.S. Public*, pg. 1618
Scott, Eileen, Dir.-Human Resources--General Nutrition, Inc., Pittsburgh, PA; *U.S. Public*, pg. 725
Scott, Frances, Dir.-Personnel--Crain Communications, Inc., Chicago, IL; *U.S. Private*, pg. 284
Scott, James, V.P.-Field H.R.--Staples, Inc., Westborough, MA; *U.S. Public*, pg. 1509
Scott, James B., Dir.-Personnel--Agripac Inc., Salem, OR; *U.S. Private*, pg. 26
Scott, Jeanne, V.P.-H.R.--Koo Koo Roo, Inc., Los Angeles, CA; *U.S. Public*, pg. 966
Scott, Jeffrey R., Sr. V.P.-Human Resources--South Carolina National Corporation, Columbia, SC; *U.S. Public*, pg. 1730
Scott, Lawrence, Mgr.-H.R.--Tippins Incorporated, Pittsburgh, PA; *U.S. Private*, pg. 1088
Scott, Robert E., Sr. V.P.-Real Estate & Human Resources--Silcorp Limited, Scarborough, Canada; *Int'l*, pg. 1249
Scott, Toni, Dir.-H.R.--Lindal Cedar Homes, Inc., Seattle, WA; *U.S. Public*, pg. 998
Scotti, Fred, V.P.-Human Resources--All American Communications, Inc., Santa Monica, CA; *U.S. Public*, pg. 41
Scotto, Kathy, Mgr.-Human Resources & Payroll--Bestform Foundations, Inc., Long Island City, NY; *U.S. Private*, pg. 140
Scruggs, Julian, Dir.-Human Resources--Piedmont Mechanical, Inc., Spartanburg, SC; *U.S. Private*, pg. 865
Scully, John, Sr. V.P.-Human Resources--LaSalle National Bank, Chicago, IL; *Int'l*, pg. 10
Seale, Julie, Mgr.-H.R.--Globe Furniture Rentals, Cincinnati, OH; *U.S. Private*, pg. 458
Seaman, Dana, Dir.-Human Resources--Snorkel, Saint Joseph, MO; *U.S. Private*, pg. 500
Sears, Lewis N., V.P.-Human Resources--AlliedSignal Inc., Engineered Materials, Morristown, NJ; *U.S. Public*, pg. 51
Sears, Richard G., V.P.-Employee Rels.--Masland, Carlisle, PA; *U.S. Public*, pg. 981
Sechovek, Kirby, Mgr.-Human Resources--Platinum Solutions, Inglewood, CA; *U.S. Public*, pg. 1309
Sechrist, Gail M., Mgr.-Employee Svcs.--Marietta Corporation, Cortland, NY; *U.S. Private*, pg. 702
Sedgwick, Ava, Mgr.-Human Resources--Aurora Electronics, Inc., Irvine, CA; *U.S. Public*, pg. 147
Sedgwick, P., Mgr.-Personnel--Halfords, Ltd., Redditch, United Kingdom; *Int'l*, pg. 203
Sedrowski, Robert J., V.P.-Human Resources--Wolverine World Wide, Inc., Rockford, MI; *U.S. Public*, pg. 1775
Sedwin, Susan, Dir.-H.R.--Roberts Pharmaceutical Corporation, Eatontown, NJ; *U.S. Public*, pg. 1393
See, Loh Meng, Dir.-Personnel--Keppel Corporation Limited, Singapore, Singapore; *Int'l*, pg. 731
Seefried, Renee P., Exec. V.P.-H.R.--Webster Financial Corporation, Waterbury, CT; *U.S. Public*, pg. 1751
Seeger, Geri, Mgr.-H.R.--Industrial Electronic Engineers, Inc., Van Nuys, CA; *U.S. Private*, pg. 561
Seelig, Karen, Sr. V.P.-Human Resources--North Fork Bancorporation, Inc., Melville, NY; *U.S. Public*, pg. 1194
Seibel, Nelda, Mgr.-Personnel--Emcee Broadcast Products, Inc., White Haven, PA; *U.S. Public*, pg. 570
Seibert, Kail, V.P.-H.R. & Gen. Counsel--GTI Corporation, San Diego, CA; *U.S. Public*, pg. 767
Seid, Rick, Dir.-Compensation & Benefits--Watson Wyatt Worldwide, Bethesda, MD; *U.S. Private*, pg. 1154
Seifert, Shelley J., Sr. V.P.-H.R.--National City Corporation, Cleveland, OH; *U.S. Public*, pg. 1154
Seino, Satoshi, Dir.-Personnel--East Japan Railway Company, Tokyo, Japan; *Int'l*, pg. 431
Sejero-DeColli, Aida, Mgr.-H.R.--Jones Apparel Group, Inc., Bristol, PA; *U.S. Public*, pg. 933
Selander, Jo, V.P.-Human Resources--Christianity Today, Inc., Carol Stream, IL; *U.S. Private*, pg. 238
Self, Dan, Dir.-H.R.--Cavalier Corporation, Chattanooga, TN; *U.S. Private*, pg. 220
Self, W. David, V.P.-Human Resources & Admin.--Energen Corporation, Birmingham, AL; *U.S. Public*, pg. 581
Self, W. David, V.P.-Human Resources & Admin.--Alabama Gas Corporation, Birmingham, AL; *U.S. Public*, pg. 581
Sellers, Danny C., V.P.-Mfg. Support--Bender Shipbuilding & Repair Company, Inc., Mobile, AL; *U.S. Private*, pg. 132
Sellers, Garry, Sr. V.P.-Human Resources--DHL Worldwide Express, Redwood City, CA; *U.S. Private*, pg. 301
Selman, T. C., II, V.P.-Human Resouces & Admin.--Sulzermedica USA Inc., Angleton, TX; *Int'l*, pg. 1307
Semmann, Ronald L., Grp. V.P.--Madison Gas and Electric Company, Madison, WI; *U.S. Public*, pg. 1032
Semtner, Patrick, Dir.-Recruiting--Cracker Barrel Old Country Store, Inc., Lebanon, TN; *U.S. Public*, pg. 455
Senecal, Madeleine, Dir.-Human Resources--Imprimerie Quebecor Lasalle, La Salle, Canada; *Int'l*, pg. 1077
Senker, Mitch, V.P.-Corp. Human Resources--Siemens Corporation, New York, NY; *Int'l*, pg. 1245
Seo, Yoom S., Mgr.-Personnel--Crown Snack Co., Ltd., Chung Nam, Korea; *Int'l*, pg. 348
Seok keng, Lim-Yeow, Mgr.-Personnel & Admin.--Kwe-Kintetsu World Express(S)Pte Ltd., Singapore, Singapore; *Int'l*, pg. 735
Seper, Robert, Sr. V.P. & H.R. Dir.--Campbell Mithun Esty, Minneapolis, MN; *U.S. Private*, pg. 204
Sepesy, Ron, Dir.-Personnel--Hubbard Construction Co., Winter Park, FL; *U.S. Private*, pg. 544
Serafino, Helio Loureiro, Dir.-Human Resources Devel.--Sao Paulo Alpargatas S.A., Sao Paulo, Brazil; *Int'l*, pg. 1193
Seres, William, Sr. Dir.-H.R.--NJ Transit, Newark, NJ; *U.S. Private*, pg. 794
Serff, Paul, Sr. V.P.-Human Resources--Tom's Foods, Inc., Columbus, GA; *U.S. Private*, pg. 1090
Sergent, Gerald, Jr., Dir.-Human Resources--Vitramon, Incorporated, Monroe, CT; *U.S. Public*, pg. 1722
Seritchfield, C., Dir.-Personnel--American Foundry Group, Inc., Bixby, OK; *U.S. Private*, pg. 54
Serne, Marlene, Dir.-H.R.--Trendway Corporation, Holland, MI; *U.S. Private*, pg. 1099
Serpico, Sharon, Mgr.-Personnel--Universal Coach Parts, Inc., Des Plaines, IL; *Int'l*, pg. 326
Sessler, Andrea, Sr. V.P., Human Resources & Pub. Rels. Dir.--Ammirati, Puris & Lintas, Inc., New York, NY; *U.S. Private*, pg. 66

Sesterhenn, Steve, Dir.-Human Resources--HBO & Company/Cycare Business Group, Scottsdale, AZ; *U.S. Public*, pg. 770

Sestito, Stephanie, Dir.-H.R.--Safety 1st, Inc., Chestnut Hill, MA; *U.S. Public*, pg. 1425

Setterstrom, William N., Sr. V.P.-Human Resources--Northern Trust Corporation, Chicago, IL; *U.S. Public*, pg. 1195

Severn, Dan, Mgr.-Personnel--Furman Foods, Inc., Northumberland, PA; *U.S. Private*, pg. 431

Severson, Ron, Dir.-Personnel--True Companies, Casper, WY; *U.S. Private*, pg. 1107

Sexton, Beth B., V.P.-H.R.--Ikon Office Solutions, Inc., Malvern, PA; *U.S. Public*, pg. 862

Seybold, Scott, Mgr.-Pension Admin.--Harman International Industries, Inc., Woodbury, NY; *U.S. Public*, pg. 787

Seymour, John, Mgr.-Human Resources--Champ/Pik-A-Nut Service Line, Edwardsville, KS; *U.S. Public*, pg. 1503

Seymour, Patti, Dir.-Human Resources Devel.--Food Lion, Inc., Salisbury, NC; *Int'l*, pg. 463

Seywert, Jean, Sr. V.P.-H.R.--Banque Internationale a Luxembourg S.A., Luxembourg, Luxembourg; *Int'l*, pg. 162

Shaddix, Sue, Mgr.-Personnel--Atlantic Southeast Airlines Inc., Atlanta, GA; *U.S. Public*, pg. 144

Shadwick, Peggy, Dir.-Personnel--Communications International (NY), New York, NY; *U.S. Private*, pg. 259

Shaffer, Reuben, V.P.-H.R.--The Kroger Co., Cincinnati, OH; *U.S. Public*, pg. 967

Shah, Kumar, Dir.-Plng., Bus. Devel. & Investor Rels.--Cytec Industries Inc., West Paterson, NJ; *U.S. Public*, pg. 471

Shanklin, Catherine A., V.P.-H.R.--Boyd Gaming Corporation, Las Vegas, NV; *U.S. Public*, pg. 249

Shanks, David C., V.P.-Human Resources--Sun Company, Inc., Philadelphia, PA; *U.S. Public*, pg. 1530

Shanks, David C., V.P.-Human Resources--Sun Company, Inc. (R&M), Philadelphia, PA; *U.S. Public*, pg. 1530

Shanks, David C., V.P.-Human Resources--Sun Refining & Marketing Co. Lubes Div., Philadelphia, PA; *U.S. Public*, pg. 1530

Shardlow, Bill, Grp. Dir.-Personnel--Coats Viyella plc, Manchester, United Kingdom; *Int'l*, pg. 299

Sharkey, John G., V.P.-Fin., Controller & Sec.--TSR Inc., Hauppauge, NY; *U.S. Public*, pg. 1559

Sharkey, Phillip, V.P.-H.R.--American Bankers Insurance Group, Inc., Miami, FL; *U.S. Public*, pg. 67

Sharkey, Phillip J., Sr. V.P.-Human Resources--American Bankers Life Assurance Co. of Florida, Miami, FL; *U.S. Public*, pg. 67

Sharkey, William L., Jr., V.P.-Human Resources--Lillian Vernon Corporation, New Rochelle, NY; *U.S. Public*, pg. 1716

Sharkley, Philip J., Sr. V.P.-Human Resources--American Bankers Insurance Co. of Florida, Miami, FL; *U.S. Public*, *pg. 67*

Sharp, Cal, Sr. V.P.-Admin.--Detroit Diesel Corp., Detroit, MI; *U.S. Private*, pg. 850

Sharp, D. W., Exec. V.P.-Personnel--Foster's Brewing Group, Toronto, Canada; *Int'l*, pg. 501

Sharp, Jane, Mgr.-Human Resources--News & Record, Greensboro, NC; *U.S. Private*, pg. 649

Sharp, Liz, V.P.-Corp. Rels.--Three-Five Systems, Tempe, AZ; *U.S. Public*, pg. 1604

Sharp, Patricia, Sr. V.P.-Human Resources--Apple Computer, Inc., Cupertino, CA; *U.S. Public*, pg. 121

Sharp, Terry, Exec. V.P.-H.R.--Dart Group Corporation, Landover, MD; *U.S. Public*, pg. 484

Sharry, Paul, Mgr.-Human Resources--Evening Post Publishing Co., Charleston, SC; *U.S. Private*, pg. 385

Shasteen, Julie, Mgr.-Personnel--Ferolie Group, Montvale, NJ; *U.S. Private*, pg. 401

Shatteen, Sherrilyn, Dir.-Human Resources--Florida Residential Treatment Centers, Inc., West Palm Beach, FL; *U.S. Public*, pg. 1035

Shaughnessy, Joel, Dir.-Personnel--The L.S. Starrett Company, Athol, MA; *U.S. Public*, pg. 1511

Shaver, Greg, Mgr.-Personnel--Service Supply Co. Inc. of Indiana, Indianapolis, IN; *U.S. Private*, pg. 987

Shaver, Harold, Dir.-Human Resources--Augat, Inc., Communications Division, Seattle, WA; *U.S. Public*, pg. 1598

Shaw, Bonnie, Mgr.-HR--Jan Bell Marketing Inc., Sunrise, FL; *U.S. Public*, pg. 207

Shaw, Brad, Dir.-Human Resources--Kelly Services (Ltd.), Sydney, Australia; *U.S. Public*, pg. 949

Shaw, Margaret, Mgr.-Personnel--The Hartstone Group PLC, London, United Kingdom; *Int'l*, pg. 599

Shaw, Steve, V.P.-H.R.--Metro-Goldwyn-Mayer Inc., Santa Monica, CA; *U.S. Public*, pg. 1101

Shawvan, I.E., V.P.-Human Resources--Columbus McKinnon Corp., Amherst, NY; *U.S. Public*, pg. 405

Shea, Deborah, V.P.-Human Resources--Poppe Tyson, New York, NY; *U.S. Public*, pg. 1642

Shea, J., V.P.-Personnel--Shure Brothers Incorporated, Evanston, IL; *U.S. Private*, pg. 997

Sheahin, John M., Sr. V.P.-Employee Rels. & Admin.--Navistar International Corporation, Chicago, IL; *U.S. Public*, pg. 1167

Sheban, R.K., Dir.-Human Resources--Eveready Battery Co., Saint Louis, MO; *U.S. Public*, pg. 1360

Sheehan, Dan F., Dir.-Admin. & Human Resources--Mesaba Holdings, Inc., Minneapolis, MN; *U.S. Public*, pg. 1099

Sheehy, M. Elaine, V.P.-Human Resources--Nautilus Insurance Company, Scottsdale, AZ; *U.S. Public*, pg. 216

Sheen, Tony, Dir.-Human Resources, London--Reed Elsevier plc, London, United Kingdom; *Int'l*, pg. 1093

Sheer, S., V.P.-Human Resources & Admin.--Penguin Putnam Inc., New York, NY; *Int'l*, pg. 1027

Sheets, Roger, V.P.-Human Resources--Woolrich, Inc., Woolrich, PA; *U.S. Private*, pg. 1188

Sheetz, Charles H., Exec. V.P.-H.R.--Sheetz, Inc., Altoona, PA; *U.S. Private*, pg. 991

Sheffer, Keith, Dir.-Human Resources--Consumers Financial Corporation, Camp Hill, PA; *U.S. Public*, pg. 437

Sheil, David R., V.P.-Personnel--Cooper Industries, Inc., Houston, TX; *U.S. Public*, pg. 442

Shelor, Mike, V.P.-Depot Opers.--Genicom Corporation, Chantilly, VA; *U.S. Public*, pg. 729

Shelton, Daniel L., Sr. V.P. & Dir.-Human Resources--Liberty Bancorp, Inc., Oklahoma City, OK; *U.S. Public*, pg. 174

Shen, Hunter, Dir.--Acer Incorporated, Taipei, Taiwan; *Int'l*, pg. 22

Shengdai, Ma, Gen. Mgr.-Personnel--Bank of China, Beijing, China; *Int'l*, pg. 152

Shepard, Homer J., Jr., Dir.-Personnel--Stern-Leach Company, Attleboro, MA; *Int'l*, pg. 329

Shepela, Joe, V.P.-Human Resources--Symantec Corporation, Cupertino, CA; *U.S. Public*, pg. 1545

Sheridan, Chris, Dir.-Personnel--Alta-Dena Certified Dairy, City of Industry, CA; *Int'l*, pg. 201

Sheridan, Tom, V.P.-H.R.--National Welders Supply Co. Inc., Charlotte, NC; *U.S. Private*, pg. 788

Sherman, Finda B., Sec. & Dir.-Personnel--MacNeal-Schwendler Corp., Costa Mesa, CA; *U.S. Public*, pg. 1031

Sherman, Melaine A., Mgr.-H.R.--Port of Houston Authority, Houston, TX; *U.S. Private*, pg. 876

Sherman, Richard, V.P.-Human Resources--Southern States Cooperative, Inc., Richmond, VA; *U.S. Private*, pg. 1017

Sherrill, Houston, V.P.-Human Relations--MEMC Electronic Materials, Inc., Saint Peters, MO; *Int'l*, pg. 1455

Sherwin, R. Lawrence, Asst. V.P.-Human Resources--Laclede Gas Company, Saint Louis, MO; *U.S. Public*, pg. 973

Shevchenko, Larisa, V.P.-H.R.--Brinkmann Instruments, Inc., Westbury, NY; *U.S. Private*, pg. 169

Shew-a-Tjon, Ivan, Dir.-H.R.--Kenny Rogers Roasters, Fort Lauderdale, FL; *U.S. Private*, pg. 939

Shibata, Shichinohyoe, Sr. Mng. Dir.-Personnel--Ishihara Sangyo Kaisha, Ltd., Osaka, Japan; *Int'l*, pg. 689

Shick, Sandy, Mgr.-Personnel--Eastman Worldwide, Buffalo, NY; *U.S. Private*, pg. 358

Shillam, Paul L., Chief Fin. Officer--Diadora America, Inc., Kent, WA; *U.S. Private*, pg. 330

Shimono, Carolyn, Dir.-Human Resources--Fremont General Corporation, Santa Monica, CA; *U.S. Public*, pg. 681

Shindo, Josuke, Gen. Mgr.--The Tokio Marine & Fire Insurance Company, Ltd., Tokyo, Japan; *Int'l*, pg. 1391

Shiner, Margaret, Mgr.-H.R.--Marinette Marine Corporation, Marinette, WI; *U.S. Private*, pg. 703

Shinn, Kenneth, Mgr.-H.R.--Bearden Lumber Company, Inc., Bearden, AR; *U.S. Private*, pg. 127

Shinnick, Dee, Dir.-H.R., Personnel Trng. & Devel.--Dawahares, Inc., Lexington, KY; *U.S. Private*, pg. 316

Shinton, Richard, Dir.-Human Resources--Exabyte Corporation, Boulder, CO; *U.S. Public*, pg. 597

Shiotsu, Seiji, Sr. Exec. Dir. & Grp. Gen. Mgr.-Human Resources--Sharp Corporation, Osaka, Japan; *Int'l*, pg. 1228

Shiplett, Susan G., Human Resources Specialist--Sunshine Mining And Refining Company, Boise, ID; *U.S. Public*, pg. 1536

Shippar, Donald J., Dir.-Human Resources--Minnesota Power, Duluth, MN; *U.S. Public*, pg. 1116

Shirley, Debbie, Mgr.-Personnel--Mar-Mac Manufacturing Company, Inc., McBee, SC; *U.S. Private*, pg. 701

Shives, E. Wayne, V.P.-Employee Rels.--SuperValu, Inc., Eden Prairie, MN; *U.S. Public*, pg. 1540

Shoemaker, Joseph C., Mgr.-H.R. & Pub. Rels.--Zoeller Co., Louisville, KY; *U.S. Private*, pg. 1207

Shoemaker, Mark, Dir.-Fin. & Dir.-Human Resources--PPG Canada Inc., Mississauga, Canada; *U.S. Public*, pg. 1245

Sholakh, Kariman, Mgr.-Human Resources--Nexus Plastics, Inc., Hawthorne, NJ; *U.S. Private*, pg. 797

Sholl, Jack, Sr. V.P.-H.R.--ICN Pharmaceuticals, Inc., Costa Mesa, CA; *U.S. Public*, pg. 853

Shone, Rick, Dir.-H.R. & Sec.--Underground Construction Co., Inc., Benicia, CA; *U.S. Private*, pg. 1116

Shook, Gregory R., Sr. V.P.-Admin. & Sec.--Branford Savings Bank, Branford, CT; *U.S. Public*, pg. 250

Shore, Bernice, Dir.-Personnel--Dovatech, Ltd., Beecher, IL; *U.S. Public*, pg. 520

Short, David, Dir.-Human Resources, JCPE--John Crane Polymer Division, Abingdon, United Kingdom; *Int'l*, pg. 1338

Short, Donna, Mgr.-Human Resources--Frequency and Time Systems, Inc., Beverly, MA; *U.S. Public*, pg. 488

Short, Eileen A., Dir.-H.R.--Sybron International Corporation, Milwaukee, WI; *U.S. Public*, pg. 1544

Short, Robert, Mgr.-Personnel & Corp. Sec.--Pacific Hide & Fur Depot, Great Falls, MT; *U.S. Private*, pg. 831

Showalter, Joan, Sr. V.P.-Human Resources--CBS, New York, NY; *U.S. Public*, pg. 273

Shrader, Debbie, Admin.-Personnel--Brown & Haley, Tacoma, WA; *U.S. Private*, pg. 173

Shrader, K. Michael, Exec. V.P.-Human Resources--Buffets, Inc., Eden Prairie, MN; *U.S. Public*, pg. 267

Shrimpton, Patricia, Mgr.-Personnel & Sec.--A.I. Root Company, Medina, OH; *U.S. Private*, pg. 944

Shriver, Diane, Mgr.-H.R.--Parfums International Ltd., New York, NY; *Int'l*, pg. 1435

Shuda, Sandra, Mgr.-Human Resources--Watkins Manufacturing Corp./Hot Spring Portable Spas, Vista, CA; *U.S. Public*, pg. 1054

Shue, Donna, Mgr.-Communication--Wilcox Electric, Inc., Kansas City, MO; *Int'l*, pg. 1384

Shuerman, Janice, V.P.-Admin. & Personnel--MFA Incorporated, Columbia, MO; *U.S. Private*, pg. 686

Shultz, Joan, Dir.-Human Resources--ITA Group Inc., West Des Moines, IA; *U.S. Private*, pg. 555

Shuman, Mary Kay, Mgr.-Human Resources--Gulfmark Offshore Inc., Houston, TX; *U.S. Public*, pg. 769

Shumate, James R., V.P.-H.R.--Luwa Bahnson, Inc., Winston Salem, NC; *U.S. Private*, pg. 682

Shute, M., Dir.-Human Resources--Whitbread PLC, London, United Kingdom; *Int'l*, pg. 1498

Sibbernsen, Richard D., V.P.-H.R.--BellSouth Corporation, Atlanta, GA; *U.S. Public*, pg. 207

Sibbersen, R. D., Grp. Gen. Mgr.-Human Resources--TNT Limited, Redfern, Australia; *Int'l*, pg. 1342

Sicheri, Dick, Dir.-Human Resources--Snap-Tite, Inc., Erie, PA; *U.S. Private*, pg. 1010

Sichko, W., V.P.-H.R.--North American Salt Company, Overland Park, KS; *U.S. Private*, pg. 505

Sickels, Linda, V.P.-Pub. Rels.--Trinity Industries Inc., Dallas, TX; *U.S. Public*, pg. 1638

Sickle, Dennis, V.P.-Human Resources--WorldCom, Inc., Jackson, MS; *U.S. Public*, pg. 1779

Sickles, Sue, Asst. V.P.--El Paso Electric Company, El Paso, TX; *U.S. Public*, pg. 567

Sickman, William J., V.P.-Corp. Rels.--Figgie International Inc., Cleveland, OH; *U.S. Public*, pg. 622

Sides, Barbara B., Asst. V.P. & Dir.-H.R.--Atlantic American Corporation, Atlanta, GA; *U.S. Public*, pg. 143

Sidor, Kathleen M., Dir.-Personnel--Facemate Corporation, Chicopee, MA; *U.S. Private*, pg. 391

Siebert, Scott, Mgr.-Personnel--Tecumseh Products Co. Engine & Transmission Group, Grafton, WI; *U.S. Public*, pg. 1566

Sieck, Keith R., V.P.-Personnel--General Mills, Consumer Foods Sales Div., Minneapolis, MN; *U.S. Public*, pg. 718

Siegenthaler, Andre, Dir.-H.R.--Hilti AG, Schaan, Liechtenstein; *Int'l*, pg. 619

Sierro, Jean Francis, Exec. V.P.--Union Bank of Switzerland, Zurich, Switzerland; *Int'l*, pg. 1439

Sievers, Sandi, Mgr.-H.R.--Van Dyne-Crotty, Inc., Dayton, OH; *U.S. Private*, pg. 1132

Siff, Barry, V.P.-H.R.--ITI Marketing Services, Inc., Omaha, NE; *U.S. Private*, pg. 555

Sigler, Kelly, V.P.-H.R.--The National Latex Products Co., Ashland, OH; *U.S. Private*, pg. 785

Sigona, Michael, Dir.-H.R.--Rome Cable Corporation, Rome, NY; *U.S. Private*, pg. 942

Sijersen, Susan, Dir.-Personnel--Milk Specialties Company, Dundee, IL; *U.S. Private*, pg. 746

Silas, Rick, V.P.-H.R.--ULLICO Inc., Washington, DC; *U.S. Private*, pg. 1115

Silberman, Elinor, V.P.-Human Resources--Home Box Office, Inc., New York, NY; *U.S. Public*, pg. 1612

Silva Wilson, Ellen, V.P.-Human Resources--A.H. Belo Corporation, Dallas, TX; *U.S. Public*, pg. 209

Silva, Alfredo, Mgr.-Personnel--Nestle Portugal, S.A., Carnaxide, Portugal; *Int'l*, pg. 921

Silva, Celeste, Dir.-Human Resources--Galoob Toys, Inc., South San Francisco, CA; *U.S. Public*, pg. 698

Silva, Kevin D., Sr. V.P & Dir.-Human Resources--MBIA Inc., Armonk, NY; *U.S. Public*, pg. 1023

Silva, Pat, Dir.-Personnel--Ferry-Morse Seed Company, Modesto, CA; *Int'l*, pg. 566

Silva, Patricio, Asst. Mgr.-H.R.--Andina Division, Los Andes, Chile; *Int'l*, pg. 302

Silver, Renee, V.P. & Gen. Counsel--Staff Builders Inc., Lake Success, NY; *U.S. Public*, pg. 1501

Silver, Robert C., Sr. V.P. & Dir.-H.R.--Sierra West Bancorp, Truckee, CA; *U.S. Public*, pg. 1470

Silvestri, Charlie, Dir.-Consumer & Community Rels.--Southwest Gas Corporation, Las Vegas, NV; *U.S. Public*, *pg. 1493*

Silvey, Ray, V.P.-H.R.--Mid-America Dairymen, Inc., Springfield, MO; *U.S. Private*, pg. 743

Siminske, Patti, Mgr.-Human Resources--Kal Grafx, Kentwood, MI; *U.S. Private*, pg. 387

Simmermeyer, Leo, Dir.-Human Resources--Bush Hog Division, Selma, AL; *U.S. Public*, pg. 48

Simmonds, Louise, Dir.-Human Resources--Messier-Dowty Ltd., Gloucester, United Kingdom; *Int'l*, pg. 1340

Simmons, Caroline, Mgr.-Human Resources--Charter Clinic Nightingale, London, United Kingdom; *U.S. Public*, pg. 1036

Simmons, George, Dir.-Personnel--Aberdeen Mfg. Corporation, New York, NY; *U.S. Private*, pg. 1094

Simmons, Gwen, Dir.-Human Resources--Learning International, Stamford, CT; *U.S. Public*, pg. 1617

Simmons, Jeff, Dir.-H.R.--Interphase Corporation, Dallas, TX; *U.S. Public*, pg. 908

Simmons, Larry, Chief Oper. Officer-Personnel Lines--Royal Insurance, Charlotte, NC; *Int'l*, pg. 1130

Simmons, Tom, Controller--Bongards Creameries Inc., Norwood, MN; *U.S. Private*, pg. 156

Simms, Denise, Mgr.-Human Resources--Grubb & Ellis Company, Northbrook, IL; *U.S. Public*, pg. 767

Simms, Janice C., Mgr.-H.R.--DBA Systems, Inc., Melbourne, FL; *U.S. Public*, pg. 472

Simonett, Mark J., Sec.--Photo Control Corporation, Minneapolis, MN; *U.S. Public*, pg. 1292

Simons, Deb, Mgr.-Human Resources--Spartech Plastics, Portage, WI; *U.S. Public*, pg. 1496

Simons, Michael, Chief Fin. Officer--Blauer Manufacturing Co., Inc., Boston, MA; *U.S. Private*, pg. 149

Simpson, H.S., Mgr.-Personnel--Flexible Technologies Inc., Abbeville, SC; *Int'l*, pg. 1267

Simpson, James R., Sr. V.P.-Human Resources--The Times Mirror Company, Los Angeles, CA; *U.S. Public*, pg. 1615

Simpson, Larry, Sr. V.P.-Human Resources--Svenska Cellulosa Aktiebolaget (SCA), Stockholm, Sweden; *Int'l*, pg. 1326

Simpson, Lynda, Corp. Sec.--Liuski International, Inc., Norcross, GA; *U.S. Public*, pg. 1005

Sims, Don, Dir.-Human Resources--Citrus World Inc., Lake Wales, FL; *U.S. Private*, pg. 241

Sims, L. Ed, V.P.-Human Resources--Degussa Corporation, Ridgefield Park, NJ; *Int'l*, pg. 388

Sims, Nina, Dir.-Personnel--Hamilton Stores, Inc., Bozeman, MT; *U.S. Private*, pg. 497

Sims, Sam, Mgr.-Personnel--Rochester Gauges Inc. Of Texas, Dallas, TX; *U.S. Private*, pg. 440

Sinclair, Desmond, Chm. Bd. & Pres.--DEECO Industries, Hillside, NJ; *U.S. Private*, pg. 320

Sinclair, I. Paul, Dir.-Human Resources--Microdyne Corporation, Alexandria, VA; *U.S. Public*, pg. 1105

Sinclair, K.A., Dir.-Human Res.--Federal Industries Industrial Group, Inc., Winnipeg, Canada; *Int'l*, pg. 1150

Sinclair, Mel, Sr. V.P. & Dir.-Human Resources--Carolina First Corporation, Greenville, SC; *U.S. Public*, pg. 306

Sindall, Reg, Dir.-H.R.--Bass PLC, London, United Kingdom; *Int'l*, pg. 169

Singh, R.A.P., Dir.-Personnel & Indus. Rels.--Coal India Limited, Calcutta, India; *Int'l*, pg. 298

Singletary, Don, V.P.-Human Resources--The Home Depot, Inc., Atlanta, GA; *U.S. Public*, pg. 831

Singleton, Cindy, Mgr.-Personnel--Columbus Mills, Inc., Columbus, GA; *U.S. Private*, pg. 256

Singleton, R. Keith, Mgr.-Indus. Rels.--The Crystal Tissue Co., Middletown, OH; *U.S. Private*, pg. 294

Sinha, A.N., Gen. Mgr.-Human Resources--Indian Oil Corporation Limited, New Delhi, India; *Int'l*, pg. 673

Sink, Diane, Dir.-Human Resources--Binning's Building Products, Inc., Lexington, NC; *U.S. Public*, pg. 67

Sipila, Eero, Dir.-Personnel--Kemira Oy, Helsinki, Finland; *Int'l*, pg. 727

Sirkia, S., Dir.-H.R.--Enso Oyj, Helsinki, Finland; *Int'l*, pg. 455

Sirney, William, Dir.-Human Resources--NCC Industries, Inc., Cortland, NY; *U.S. Private*, pg. 697

Sirois, Bonnie, Mgr.-Human Resources--NAPCO, Inc., Terryville, CT; *U.S. Public*, pg. 1592

Sisbarro, P.R., Dir.-H.R.--EBSCO Industries, Inc., Birmingham, AL; *U.S. Private*, pg. 358

Sisomvang, Phitsona, Supvr.-Human Resources--Clothestime Stores, Inc., Anaheim, CA; *U.S. Public*, pg. 387

Sisson, Kim, Mgr.-Personnel--Bead Industries Inc., Bridgeport, CT; *U.S. Private*, pg. 126

Sisti, Carlo, Dir.-Human Resources--Fiamm S.p.A., Montecchio Maggiore, Italy; *Int'l*, pg. 480

Sisul, John T., Exec. V.P.-Human Resources--Wilton Corporation, Palatine, IL; *U.S. Private*, pg. 1181

Siveira, Mike, V.P.-H.R. & Law--Save Mart Supermarkets, Modesto, CA; *U.S. Private*, pg. 968

Skara, Susan, Sr. V.P.-H.R.--Apria Healthcare Group Inc., Costa Mesa, CA; *U.S. Public*, pg. 125

Skelley, William, V.P.-Human Resources--Greenwich Air Services, Miami, FL; *U.S. Public*, pg. 710

Skinner, Cyndi, Mgr.-H.R.--Grease Monkey International Inc., Denver, CO; *U.S. Public*, pg. 759

Skjervem, Harley, V.P.-H.R.--Credit Union National Association, Madison, WI; *U.S. Private*, pg. 288

Skoch, Daniel, V.P.-H.R.--Brush Wellman Inc., Cleveland, OH; *U.S. Public*, pg. 266

Skomp, Jim, Dir.-Human Resources--Nutmeg Mills Inc., Tampa, FL; *U.S. Public*, pg. 1702

Skondahl, Gunnar, Mgr.-Personnel--Iggesund Paperboard AB, Iggesund, Sweden; *Int'l*, pg. 886

Skrobisch, Elizabeth, Dir.-Human Resources--Nomura Securities International, Inc., New York, NY; *Int'l*, pg. 956

Skuba, Kenneth J., V.P.-Human Resources--Eastern Environmental Services, Inc., Drums, PA; *U.S. Public*, pg. 549

Slade, Jennifer, Mgr.-H.R.--The Airolite Company, Marietta, OH; *U.S. Private*, pg. 29

Slade, Mike, Human Resources Mgr.--Eric Mower and Associates, Inc., Syracuse, NY; *U.S. Private*, pg. 765

Slagle, Jack, Dir.-H.R.--Dunn-Edwards Corporation, Los Angeles, CA; *U.S. Private*, pg. 347

Slash, Joseph A., V.P.-Community & Corp. Effectiveness--Indianapolis Power & Light Company, Indianapolis, IN; *U.S. Public*, pg. 913

Slater, Scott, Dir.-H.R.--Desa International, Bowling Green, KY; *U.S. Private*, pg. 326

Slaton, Jeanita K., V.P.-Employee Benefits--Piccadilly Cafeterias, Inc., Baton Rouge, LA; *U.S. Public*, pg. 1294

Slaughter, Seth, Dir.-Human Rels.--Burr-Brown Corporation, Tucson, AZ; *U.S. Public*, pg. 270

Slay, Leland, V.P.-H.R.--Associated Grocers of the South, Inc., Birmingham, AL; *U.S. Private*, pg. 91

Slay, V. Jane, Office Mgr.--Columbus Pipe & Equipment Company, Columbus, OH; *U.S. Private*, pg. 257

Slaybaugh, Nina, Mgr.-Personnel--Neapco, Inc., Pottstown, PA; *U.S. Private*, pg. 1113

Slazyk, Dianne H., V.P.-H.R.--Anchor Financial Corporation, Myrtle Beach, SC; *U.S. Public*, pg. 111

Sleek, Sewell, V.P.-Human Resources--Storage Technology Corporation, Louisville, CO; *U.S. Public*, pg. 1522

Sleeva, Jim, Mgr.-Staff Grp.--Ito-Yokado Capitol Division, Alexandria, VA; *Int'l*, pg. 694

Sleggs, Sandra, Mgr.-Human Resources--Acme Electric Corporation, East Aurora, NY; *U.S. Public*, pg. 16

Slein, Karen, V.P.-Human Resources--Cybex International, Inc., Medway, MA; *U.S. Private*, pg. 1114

Slenn, J.R., V.P.-H.R.--SPD Technologies, Philadelphia, PA; *U.S. Private*, pg. 957

Slingerland, Stan, Mgr.-Personnel--Anaren Microwave Inc., East Syracuse, NY; *U.S. Public*, pg. 110

Slinkard, John, Mgr.-Human Resources--Sun-Maid Growers of California, Kingsburg, CA; *U.S. Private*, pg. 1051

Sloan, Willaim, Dir.-Personnel--R.C.A. Rubber Company, Akron, OH; *U.S. Private*, pg. 902

Slocum, Cynthia, Mgr.-H.R.--Shur-Lok Corporation, Irvine, CA; *U.S. Private*, pg. 997

Slocumbe, Elaine, Coord.-Personnel--Atlanta Beverage Co., Atlanta, GA; *U.S. Private*, pg. 94

Smalley, John G., V.P. & Dir.-Human Resources--The Canada Life Assurance Company, Toronto, Canada; *Int'l*, *pg. 254*

Smallwood, Donald E., Mgr.-H.R.--Alberta Energy Company, Ltd., Calgary, Canada; *Int'l*, pg. 48

Smead, Nick, V.P.-H.R.--Intesys Technologies, Gilbert, AZ; *U.S. Private*, pg. 574

Smeester, Charles A., Sr. V.P.-Opers.--Old Kent Bank, Grand Rapids, MI; *U.S. Public*, pg. 1216

Smethurst, Ron, Dir.-Personnel & Mngmt. Devel.--Costain Group PLC, London, United Kingdom; *Int'l*, pg. 336

Smiley, Dorothy, Dir.-H.R.--Seattle City Light, Seattle, WA; *U.S. Private*, pg. 979

Smith-Linehan, Ellen, Mgr.-Personnel--Flexfab Horizons International, Inc., Hastings, MI; *U.S. Private*, pg. 412

Smith, A., Dir.-H.R.--Bass Brewers Ltd., Burton on Trent, United Kingdom; *Int'l*, pg. 170

Smith, Allan, Dir.-Personnel--Salz Leathers, Inc., Santa Cruz, CA; *U.S. Private*, pg. 963

Smith, Betty Lou, Dir.-Human Resources--Hunter Douglas, Inc., Upper Saddle River, NJ; *Int'l*, pg. 639

Smith, Brian, Dir.-Personnel--Jordan's Meats, Portland, ME; *U.S. Private*, pg. 599

Smith, Brian, Dir.-Human Resources, B.C./Alberta region--Imprimeries Quebecor Canada, Richmond Hill, Canada; *Int'l*, pg. 1077

Smith, Charmaine, Mgr.-H.R.--Del Taco, Inc., Laguna Hills, CA; *U.S. Private*, pg. 321

Smith, Craig R., Pres. & Chief Exec. Officer--Raytech Corporation, Shelton, CT; *U.S. Public*, pg. 1363

Smith, D.J., Dir.-Personnel--Rolls-Royce-Commercial Aero Engines Ltd., Derby, United Kingdom; *Int'l*, pg. 1127

Smith, David, Dir.-Human Resources--Yuba Heat Transfer Division, Tulsa, OK; *U.S. Private*, pg. 264

Smith, David, Dir.-H.R.--North American Products Corp., Jasper, IN; *U.S. Private*, pg. 803

Smith, Deborah K., Sr. V.P.-Human Resources--Merck & Co., Inc., Whitehouse Station, NJ; *U.S. Public*, pg. 1090

Smith, Edith, Mgr.-H.R.--Fike Corporation, Blue Springs, MO; *U.S. Private*, pg. 404

Smith, Eleanor, V.P.-Human Resources--Bulova Corporation, Woodside, NY; *U.S. Public*, pg. 1010

Smith, Felicia, V.P.-H.R.--Modern Group Ltd., Bristol, PA; *U.S. Private*, pg. 754

Smith, Gary, Dir.-Human Resources--General Binding Corporation, Northbrook, IL; *U.S. Public*, pg. 707

Smith, Gloria, Mgr.-Human Resources--Keithley Instruments, Inc., Cleveland, OH; *U.S. Public*, pg. 946

Smith, Gordon, Sr. V.P.-Human Resources--Olsten Health Services, Melville, NY; *U.S. Public*, pg. 1221

Smith, Hepsie, Mgr.-Human Resources--Evans Rule Co., Inc., Charleston, SC; *U.S. Public*, pg. 1511

Smith, J.E., Dir.-Personnel--Franklin Baking Co., Inc., Goldsboro, NC; *U.S. Private*, pg. 424

Smith, J.H., V.P.-Indus. Affairs--Schlumberger Oilfield Services, Houston, TX; *U.S. Public*, pg. 1439

Smith, James J., V.P.-H.R.--Lawson Products, Inc., Des Plaines, IL; *U.S. Public*, pg. 980

Smith, James P., Jr., Sr. V.P.-Human Resources--ITT Industries, Inc., White Plains, NY; *U.S. Public*, pg. 859

Smith, Jeanie, Dir.-H.R.--Elias Brothers Restaurants, Inc., Warren, MI; *U.S. Private*, pg. 371

Smith, Jennifer H., Sr. V.P.-H.R.--Lutheran Brotherhood, Minneapolis, MN; *U.S. Private*, pg. 681

Smith, Joan, Dir.-Human Resources--Toyota Motor Sales, U.S.A., Inc., Torrance, CA; *Int'l*, pg. 1412

Smith, Joe, Dir.-H.R.--Esco Corporation, Portland, OR; *U.S. Private*, pg. 382

Smith, John, Mgr.-Personnel--Standard Chartered Bank PLC, London, United Kingdom; *Int'l*, pg. 1294

Smith, Karen, Mgr.-Personnel/Office--Rolled Steel Products Corporation, Los Angeles, CA; *U.S. Private*, pg. 941

Smith, Kathy, V.P.-Human Resources--The Coleman Company, Inc., Golden, CO; *U.S. Private*, pg. 690

Smith, Lauren, V.P.-Human Resources--Winston Tire Company, Burbank, CA; *U.S. Private*, pg. 514

Smith, Linda S., Dir.-Human Resources--UMB First National Bank, Collinsville, IL; *U.S. Public*, pg. 1654

Smith, Lu-Ann, Asst. V.P.-H.R.--Quincy Mutual Fire Insurance Company, Quincy, MA; *U.S. Private*, pg. 901

Smith, Marcia, V.P.-Personnel & Admin.--The Wheatley Group, Inc., Stamford, CT; *U.S. Public*, pg. 152

Smith, Maurice, Dir.-Personnel Training & Devel.--Warner-Jenkinson Co., Saint Louis, MO; *U.S. Public*, pg. 1696

Smith, Mike, V.P.-Human Resources--The Bombay Company, Inc., Fort Worth, TX; *U.S. Public*, pg. 244

Smith, Mike, V.P.-H.R.--The Bombay Company, Fort Worth, TX; *U.S. Public*, pg. 244

Smith, Pam, Dir.-H.R.--Industrial Ceramics, Inc., Lima, NY; *U.S. Private*, pg. 560

Smith, Pamela, Mgr.-Human Resources--Rocco Farm Foods, Inc., Edinburg, VA; *U.S. Private*, pg. 937

Smith, Patricia, Dir.-H.R.--Westat Inc., Rockville, MD; *U.S. Private*, pg. 1163

Smith, Randy, V.P.-Human Resoures--Eagle Food Centers, Inc., Milan, IL; *U.S. Public*, pg. 547

Smith, Richard, Mgr.-Data Processing--Hughes-Peters, Inc., Cincinnati, OH; *U.S. Private*, pg. 546

Smith, Rick, Mgr.-Human Resources--Giles & Ransome, Inc., Bensalem, PA; *U.S. Private*, pg. 453

Smith, Robert W., Jr., Sr. V.P.-H.R.--Battelle Memorial Institute, Columbus, OH; *U.S. Private*, pg. 123

Smith, Robin, Mgr.-H.R.--KCL Corporation, Shelbyville, IN; *U.S. Private*, pg. 603

Smith, Ron, Dir.-Personnel--Batson-Cook Company, West Point, GA; *U.S. Private*, pg. 123

Smith, Rosemary, V.P.-H.R.--The Scotts Company, Marysville, OH; *U.S. Public*, pg. 1446

Smith, Shawn, V.P.-H.R.--O'Neal Steel Inc., Birmingham, AL; *U.S. Private*, pg. 817

Smith, Shirley R., V.P., Gen. Counsel & Sec.--Coventry Corporation, Nashville, TN; *U.S. Public*, pg. 454

Smith, Stephen E., Exec. V.P. & Dir.-Human Resources--Starbanc Corporation, Cincinnati, OH; *U.S. Public*, pg. 1510

Smith, Stephen J., V.P.-Human Resources--Tenneco Inc., Greenwich, CT; *U.S. Public*, pg. 1577

Smith, Stephen W., V.P.--EnergyNorth, Inc., Manchester, NH; *U.S. Public*, pg. 581

Smith, Steve, Dir.-Personnel--Hampshire Chemical Corp., Lexington, MA; *U.S. Private*, pg. 498

Smith, Susan, H.R. Sec.--Sierra West Bancorp, Truckee, CA; *U.S. Public*, pg. 1470

Smith, Suzanne E., V.P.-H.R.--A.H. Hoffman, Inc., Landisville, PA; *U.S. Private*, pg. 532

Smith, Thomas, V.P. & Dir.-Personnel--HarperCollins Publishers, New York, NY; *Int'l*, pg. 926

Smith, Thomas A., V.P.-H.R.--Chesapeake Corporation, Richmond, VA; *U.S. Public*, pg. 346

Smith, Vickie, V.P.-H.R.--Bojangles' Restaraunts, Inc., Charlotte, NC; *U.S. Private*, pg. 154

Smith, William, V.P.-Personnel--Viking Pump, Inc., Cedar Falls, IA; *U.S. Public*, pg. 862

Smith, William T., Dir.-Human Resources--Noland Company, Newport News, VA; *U.S. Public*, pg. 1187

Smithwick, John W., Exec. V.P.-Human Resources--First American Corporation, Nashville, TN; *U.S. Public*, pg. 624

Smyth, Lyn, Gen. Affairs Administrator--Harrington Hoists, Inc., Manheim, PA; *U.S. Private*, pg. 504

Sniskac, Mike, Dir.-Personnel--Information Systems & Network Corporation, Bethesda, MD; *U.S. Private*, pg. 561

Snodgrass, Michael, V.P.-Human Resources--International Aluminum Corporation, Monterey Park, CA; *U.S. Public*, pg. 894

Snodgrass, S. Gary, V.P.-Human Resources & Opers.--USG Corporation, Chicago, IL; *U.S. Public*, pg. 1660

Snow, Dean J., V.P.-Personnel & Employee Benefits--Albertson's, Inc., Boise, ID; *U.S. Public*, pg. 38

Snyder, D.E., Dir.-Human Resources--Seco Warwick Corporation, Meadville, PA; *U.S. Private*, pg. 980

Snyder, Lance, Controller--McLaughlin Manufacturing Company, Greenville, SC; *U.S. Private*, pg. 724

Snyder, Mariana, Mgr.-Employment--Borden Decorative Products, Saint Louis, MO; *U.S. Private*, pg. 158

Sober, David W., V.P.-Human Resources & Sec.--Performance Food Group Company, Richmond, VA; *U.S. Public*, pg. 1278

Soberon, Sue E., V.P.-Human Resources--National Insurance Group, South San Francisco, CA; *U.S. Public*, pg. 1157

Soberon, Sue E., V.P.-Human Resources--FASTRAC Systems, Inc.-Insurance Agent & Broker, South San Francisco, CA; *U.S. Public*, pg. 1158

Sobol, Irene, Mgr.-Personnel--Midco International Inc., Chicago, IL; *U.S. Private*, pg. 744

Sobyak, Larry, V.P.-Fin., Treas. & Mgr.-Personnel--Demco Inc., Madison, WI; *U.S. Private*, pg. 323

Socolofsky, Richard C., V.P.-Personnel--Anheuser-Busch Companies, Inc., Saint Louis, MO; *U.S. Public*, pg. 113

Sohl, Marvel, Controller & Treas.--Bluewater, Mora, MN; *U.S. Private*, pg. 153

Sokolove, Angela, Dir.-H.R.--Goldwell Cosmetics (USA) Inc., Linthicum Heights, MD; *Int'l*, pg. 718

Soliani, Carol, V.P.-H.R.--The Turner & Seymour Mfg. Company, Torrington, CT; *U.S. Private*, pg. 1109

Soligon, Peter, V.P.-Human Resources--Olsy North America Inc., Liberty Lake, WA; *Int'l*, pg. 1002

Solis, Javier Elguea, Dir.-Human Resources--Telefonos de Mexico S.A. de C.V., Mexico, Mexico; *Int'l*, pg. 1373

Sollitto, Paul, V.P. & Corp. H.R. Dir.-True North Communications Inc.--True North Communications Inc., Chicago, IL; *U.S. Public*, pg. 1641

Sollom, Michael C., V.P.-Human Resources--Sun Life Assurance Company of Canada (U.K.) Limited, Basingstoke, United Kingdom; *Int'l*, pg. 1319

Sollomen, Teresa, Mgr.-Personnel--Polyloom Corp. of America, Dayton, TN; *U.S. Private*, pg. 875

Solonica, M., Mgr.-Personnel--Prestige Stamping, Inc., Warren, MI; *U.S. Private*, pg. 882

Solowey, Andrew, Dir.-Human Resources--Standard Microsystems Corp., Hauppauge, NY; *U.S. Public*, pg. 1502

Soltis, William T., Mgr.-Indus. Rels. & Sls.--Consolidated Industries, Inc., Cheshire, CT; *U.S. Private*, pg. 265

Sompolski, Timothy A., Sr. V.P.-Human Resources & Admin.--Philip Morris Companies Inc., New York, NY; *U.S. Public*, pg. 1287

Sonnabend, Jacqueline, Exec. V.P.-Human Resources--Sonesta International Hotels Corporation, Boston, MA; *U.S. Public*, pg. 1485

Sonner, Sunny, V.P.-Human Resources--Trader Publishing Company, Norfolk, VA; *U.S. Private*, pg. 649

Soongsukdi, Pensri, Mgr.-Personnel--Bangkok Athletic Co., Ltd., Bangkok, Thailand; *Int'l*, pg. 146

Sopata, Ron, Office Mgr.-Human Resources--Freeway Corporation, Cleveland, OH; *U.S. Private*, pg. 426

Soper, Thomas, III, Sr. V.P.-Human Resources--Tambrands Inc., Cincinnati, OH; *U.S. Public*, pg. 1331

Sorensen, Tore Wiggo, Dir.-H.R.--Den norske Bank ASA, Oslo, Norway; *Int'l*, pg. 392

Sorenson, Roger, Div. Mgr.-Human Resources--Omaha Public Power District, Omaha, NE; *U.S. Private*, pg. 815

Sorheim, Dennis R., Treas. & Sec.--Peoples Electric Contractor, Inc., Saint Paul, MN; *U.S. Private*, pg. 851

Soriano, Randee, Mgr.-Personnel--Dominick & Dominick, Incorporated, New York, NY; *U.S. Private*, pg. 338

Sosiak, Jack J., Exec. V.P.-Human Resources--Exide Corporation, Reading, PA; *U.S. Public*, pg. 600

Souder, Robert, Sr. V.P.-Labor Rels.--Rite Aid Corporation, Camp Hill, PA; *U.S. Public*, pg. 1390

Southard, Mike, V.P.-Personnel--Wesley-Jessen, Des Plaines, IL; *U.S. Private*, pg. 111

Southard, Renee, V.P.-H.R.--Keane, Inc., Boston, MA; *U.S. Public*, pg. 946

Southern, Robert E., Dir.-Personnel--Affiliated Foods Southwest, Little Rock, AR; *U.S. Private*, pg. 26

Southgate-Fox, Susie, V.P.-H.R.--Lettuce Entertain You Enterprises, Inc., Chicago, IL; *U.S. Private*, pg. 661

Southwood, Kevin, Mng. Dir.-Personnel & Fin. Services--Alliance & Leicester Building Society, London, United Kingdom; *Int'l*, pg. 57

Souza, Frances, V.P.-Human Resources--McLane Company, Inc., Temple, TX; *U.S. Public*, pg. 1733

Sowards, Doris, Mgr.-Personnel--Clark Grave Vault Co., Columbus, OH; *U.S. Private*, pg. 243

Soza, Rita, Mgr.-Personnel--Astec America Inc., Carlsbad, CA; *Int'l*, pg. 93

Spadoni, Anna, Dir.-Human Resources--Cassina, Milan, Italy; *Int'l*, pg. 570

Spadoni, George, Mgr.-H.R. & Labor Rels.--Chicago Lock Company, Pleasant Prairie, WI; *U.S. Private*, pg. 235

Spampanato, Frank, V.P.-Human Resources--Harris Corp., RF Communications Group Marketing Division, Rochester, NY; *U.S. Public*, pg. 792

Spangler, Gaynelle C., Dir.-Personnel--Jefferson Mills, Inc., Pulaski, VA; *U.S. Private*, pg. 584

Spann, William S., Jr., Sr. V.P.-Human Resources--United Companies Financial Corporation, Baton Rouge, LA; *U.S. Public*, pg. 1675

Sparber, Joan, H.R. & Facilities Mgr.--DCA Advertising, Inc., New York, NY; *Int'l*, pg. 393

Spearman, Vivian, V.P.-Sls. Opers.--Weider Publications, Inc., Woodland Hills, CA; *U.S. Private*, pg. 1159

Spechts, Frances A., Dir.-Human Resources--Parlex Corporation, Methuen, MA; *U.S. Public*, pg. 1264

Spector, James A., Sr. V.P.-Human Resources--Catherines Stores Corporation, Memphis, TN; *U.S. Public*, pg. 317

Spector, Jerome B., Asst. V.P. & Dir.-H.R.--Enterprise Rent-A-Car Company, Saint Louis, MO; *U.S. Private*, pg. 377

Spedale, Ann, Mgr.--Koh-I-Noor, Inc., Bloomsbury, NJ; *U.S. Private*, pg. 629

Speer, Eileen, Dir.-Personnel--States, Inc., Breckenridge, TX; *U.S. Private*, pg. 1037

Spena, Flavia, Exec. Dir.-Corp. Human Rels.--Bulgari SPA, Rome, Italy; *Int'l*, pg. 232

Spence, Richard, Mgr.-H.R.--United Air Specialists, Inc., Cincinnati, OH; *U.S. Public*, pg. 382

Spencer, David M., Dir.-Human Resources--Smiths Industries plc, London, United Kingdom; *Int'l*, pg. 1266

Spencer, Kathy, V.P.-H.R.--Immunex Corporation, Seattle, WA; *U.S. Public*, pg. 871

Speranza, Nickolas, V.P.-Human Resources--Time Warner Cable Liberty Division, Ferndale, NY; *U.S. Public*, pg. 1611

Spicer, Roberta, Chief Fin. Officer--Shillcraft, Inc., Baltimore, MD; *U.S. Private*, pg. 994

Spindel, Barbara A., Dir.-Human Resources--Butler International, Inc., Montvale, NJ; *U.S. Public*, pg. 270

Spires, Robert, Sr. V.P.-Human Resources--Foodarama Supermarkets, Inc., Freehold, NJ; *U.S. Public*, pg. 661

Spires, William J., V.P.-Indus. Rels. & Sec.--Vishay Intertechnology, Inc., Malvern, PA; *U.S. Public*, pg. 1721

Spitalnik, Paul, Dir.-Trade Rels. & Managed Healthcare--Knoll Pharmaceutical Company, Whippany, NJ; *Int'l*, pg. 105

Spitzer, Jan, Dir.-Human Resources--American Buildings Co., Eufaula, AL; *U.S. Public*, pg. 69

Spizzica, J., Human Resources Team Leader--KDI Precision Products, Inc., Cincinnati, OH; *U.S. Private*, pg. 603

Sponseller, Ben, Dir.-Personnel--Abbott Laboratories/ Ashland, Ashland, OH; *U.S. Public*, pg. 13

Spor, Tammy, Mgr.-Personnel--United Design Corporation, Noble, OK; *U.S. Private*, pg. 1121

Spradley, Elizabeth, V.P.-H.R.--The Suddath Companies, Jacksonville, FL; *U.S. Private*, pg. 1049

Spradling, Steve, Dir.-Human Resources--CEM Corporation, Matthews, NC; *U.S. Public*, pg. 277

Sprague, Cherie, Dir.-Human Resources--Dixon Paper Co., Denver, CO; *U.S. Public*, pg. 902

Sprague, Cheryl, Dir.-Human Resources--Westmoreland Coal Co., Colorado Springs, CO; *U.S. Public*, pg. 1761

Sprague, Cheryl M., Grp. V.P.-H.R.--Jones Intercable, Inc., Englewood, CO; *U.S. Private*, pg. 597

Sprague, Todd, Dir.-H.R.--Helmerich & Payne, Inc., Tulsa, OK; *U.S. Public*, pg. 808

Sprague, Walter, V.P.-Human Resources--Cliftex, New Bedford, MA; *U.S. Public*, pg. 1777

Spratt, Richard D., Mgr.-Human Resources & Quality Control--Airflex Div. Eaton Corp., Cleveland, OH; *U.S. Public*, pg. 556

Sprayberry, Betty, Mgr.-Personnel--Barbour Thread, Inc., Blue Mountain, AL; *Int'l*, pg. 618

Sprouls, John, V.P.-Human Resources--The Seagram Spirits and Wine Group, New York, NY; *Int'l*, pg. 1217

Spurlock, Rick L., Sr. V.P.-Human Resources & Admin. Services--NorAm Energy Corp., Houston, TX; *U.S. Public*, pg. 843

St. Amand, Brenda, V.P.-H.R.--The Erin Company, Bangor, ME; *U.S. Private*, pg. 381

St. Clair, Jon, V.P.-Human Resources--Circon Corporation, Santa Barbara, CA; *U.S. Public*, pg. 373

St. Clair, Jon, V.P.-Human Resources--Circon Video Div., Santa Barbara, CA; *U.S. Public*, pg. 373

St. Pierre, Gary, Dir.-Human Resources--MacDermid Incorporated, Waterbury, CT; *U.S. Public*, pg. 1029

Staby, Kathleen M., V.P.-Human Resources--Pacing Business Unit, Minneapolis, MN; *U.S. Public*, pg. 1083

Staby, Ludger W., Chm. Bd.-Mngmt.--Reemtsma Cigarettenfabriken GmbH, Hamburg, Hamburg, Germany; *Int'l*, pg. 1100

Stacey, Angel, Dir.-Personnel--Matrix Service Company, Tulsa, OK; *U.S. Public*, pg. 1057

Stack, Charlie, Mgr.-H.R.--Nebraska Public Power District, Columbus, NE; *U.S. Private*, pg. 789

Stack, Katie, Mgr.-Human Resources--Corrpro Companies, Inc., Medina, OH; *U.S. Public*, pg. 451

Stack, Robert J., Dir.-Grp. H.R.--Cadbury Schweppes p.l.c., London, United Kingdom; *Int'l*, pg. 247

Stacke, Mary, V.P.-H.R.--Augsburg Fortress, Publishers, Minneapolis, MN; *U.S. Private*, pg. 98

Stacy, Karen, V.P.-H.R. & Support Plng.--ANSER (Analytic Services Inc.), Arlington, VA; *U.S. Private*, pg. 75

Stairs, Harriet, Exec. V.P.-H.R.--Bank of Montreal, Toronto, Canada; *Int'l*, pg. 153

Stambaugh, William, Mgr.-Human Resources--Bay West Paper Corp. Towel & Tissue Div., Middletown, OH; *U.S. Public*, pg. 1747

Stamper, Steve, Reg. Dir.-Claims--Country Mutual Insurance Company, Bloomington, IL; *U.S. Private*, pg. 279

Standlee, Christopher, Gen. Counsel--High Plains Corporation, Wichita, KS; *U.S. Public*, pg. 825

Standring, J., Dir.-Human Resources--ABB Kent Plc, Luton, United Kingdom; *Int'l*, pg. 2

Stanford, Mark, Mgr.-Production--United Farm Tools, Inc., Glasgow, KY; *U.S. Private*, pg. 1122

Stang, J.C., Dir. & Gen. Mgr.-Human Resources--Solar Turbines Incorporated, San Diego, CA; *U.S. Public*, pg. 316

Stange, Rainer, Mgr.-Human Resources--Apollinaris & Schweppes Gmbh & Co., Hamburg, Germany; *Int'l*, pg. 78

Stanger, Winn, Mgr.-Employee Rels.--Elgin Sweeper Company, Elgin, IL; *U.S. Public*, pg. 617

Stangler, Kevin J., Chief Fin. Officer & Exec. V.P.--Security American Financial Enterprises, Inc., Minnetonka, MN; *U.S. Private*, pg. 980

Stanley, Bob, Dir.-H.R.--Del Taco, Inc., Laguna Hills, CA; *U.S. Private*, pg. 321

Stanley, G. Brent, Sr. V.P.-H.R.--PG&E Corporation, San Francisco, CA; *U.S. Public*, pg. 1240

Stanley, John, Jr., Mgr.-Human Resources--Transamerican Natural Gas Corporation, Houston, TX; *U.S. Private*, pg. 1096

Stanley, S.A., Mgr.-H.R.--Unimark Plastics Company, Greer, SC; *U.S. Public*, pg. 57

Stansel, Eugene A., Jr., V.P.-H.R. & Sec.--Staple Cotton Cooperative Association, Greenwood, MS; *U.S. Private*, pg. 1033

Stanton, Jeffrey A., V.P.-H.R.--Central Tractor Farm & Country, Inc., Des Moines, IA; *U.S. Private*, pg. 237

Stanton, John J., Dir.-Indus. Rels.--Utility Trailer Manufacturing Co., City of Industry, CA; *U.S. Private*, pg. 1130

Stanworth, Tony, Dir.-H.R.--Kingfisher plc, London, United Kingdom; *Int'l*, pg. 733

Staples, Cathy, Dir.-Human Resources--Belden Inc., Saint Louis, MO; *U.S. Public*, pg. 200

Staples, Cathy, Dir.-Human Resources--Belden Wire & Cable Company, Richmond, IN; *U.S. Public*, pg. 201

Staples, Robert R., Dir.-Human Resources--Eskimo Pie Corporation, Richmond, VA; *U.S. Public*, pg. 592

Stapleton, Robyn, Dir.-Human Resources--Finish Line, Inc., Indianapolis, IN; *U.S. Public*, pg. 623

Starr, Gary D., Mgr.-Human Resources--UTA Niles Plant, Niles, MI; *U.S. Public*, pg. 1691

Starr, Robert A., V.P.-H.R.--ADAC Laboratories Inc., Milpitas, CA; *U.S. Public*, pg. 3

Stathis, Melba, Dir.-Human Resources--Supertex, Inc., Sunnyvale, CA; *U.S. Public*, pg. 1539

Statz, Ronald G., V.P.-H.R.--Western Industries, Inc., Milwaukee, WI; *U.S. Private*, pg. 1165

Staudohar, J.E., Sec. & Dir.-Corp. Services--Lakehead Pipe Line Co., Inc., Superior, WI; *Int'l*, pg. 652

Stavish, Mark, V.P.-H.R.--America Online Incorporated, Dulles, VA; *U.S. Public*, pg. 66

Stawarky, John C., V.P.-Human Resources--Moore Tool Company, Inc., Bridgeport, CT; *U.S. Private*, pg. 889

Stawnwczy, Diana, V.P.-H.R. & Admin.--Sun Data Inc., Norcross, GA; *U.S. Private*, pg. 1050

Stearns, Chuck, Dir.-Personnel--Capital Industries, Inc., Seattle, WA; *U.S. Private*, pg. 206

Steed, Bob, V.P.-H.R.--Huffy Bicycle Company, Celina, OH; *U.S. Public*, pg. 846

Steeg, Rhonda, H.R. Mgr.--Merkley Newman Harty, New York, NY; *U.S. Public*, pg. 1224

Steel, E.G., Grp. Gen. Mgr.-Grp. Human Resources--National Australia Bank Limited, Melbourne, Australia; *Int'l*, pg. 906

Steele, Andrea, Dir.-H.R.--Duron, Inc., Beltsville, MD; *U.S. Private*, pg. 349

Steele, Donald F., Sr. V.P.-Employee Rels.--The Hertz Corporation, Park Ridge, NJ; *U.S. Public*, pg. 664

Steele, Jackie, V.P.-Human Resources--Mead Containerboard, Atlanta, GA; *U.S. Public*, pg. 1074

Steele, John, Dir.-Personnel--British Telecommunications plc, London, United Kingdom; *Int'l*, pg. 222

Steele, Mark, Mgr.-Human Resources--Farnam Companies, Inc., Phoenix, AZ; *U.S. Private*, pg. 396

Steele, William, Dir.-Employee Rels.--American Recreation Products, Inc., Saint Louis, MO; *U.S. Public*, pg. 948

Stefani, Xavier, V.P.-H.R.--CAP Gemini S.A., Paris, France; *Int'l*, pg. 263

Steger, Cathy, Mgr.-Assoc. Rels.--Odetics Inc., Anaheim, CA; *U.S. Public*, pg. 1212

Stegman, Deborah, Dir.-Human Resources--DC Comics, Inc., New York, NY; *U.S. Public*, pg. 1614

Stein, C., V.P.-Human Resources--Krause's Furniture Inc., Brea, CA; *U.S. Public*, pg. 967

Stein, Stanley R., Exec. V.P.--McDonald's Corporation, Oak Brook, IL; *U.S. Public*, pg. 1068

Steinbacher, Cheryl, Dir.-Human Resources--Elo TouchSystems, Inc., Fremont, CA; *U.S. Public*, pg. 1362

Steinberg, Karl, V.P.-Human Resources--Encyclopaedia Britannica, Inc., Chicago, IL; *U.S. Private*, pg. 375

Steinberg, Terry, V.P.-Admin.--Aceto Corporation, Lake Success, NY; *U.S. Public*, pg. 15

Steiner, Don, Dir.-H.R.--Star Lumber & Supply Company, Inc., Wichita, KS; *U.S. Private*, pg. 1034

Steinkirchner, William, Dir.-Human Resources--Eaton Corporation, Hydraulics Division, Eden Prairie, MN; *U.S. Public*, pg. 557

Steinman, Marjorie, Mgr.-Office Admin.--Jack Schwartz Shoes, Inc., New York, NY; *U.S. Private*, pg. 974

Stelling, Geri, Dir.-Personnel--Ballard Medical Products, Draper, UT; *U.S. Public*, pg. 171

Stem, Gloria, Sr. Dir.-Human Resources--Mid Atlantic Medical Services, Inc., Rockville, MD; *U.S. Public*, pg. 1109

Stembridge, Julie, Mgr.-Personnel--Robinson Helicopter Company, Torrance, CA; *U.S. Private*, pg. 936

Stempson, Susan, V.P.-H.R.--Excite, Inc., Redwood City, CA; *U.S. Public*, pg. 599

Stenzel, R., Dir.-Human Resources--Honeywell Defense Avionics Systems, Albuquerque, NM; *U.S. Public*, pg. 834

Stephany, Edward, Mgr.-Human Resources--Kingsbury, Inc., Philadelphia, PA; *U.S. Private*, pg. 622

Stephens, Dan, Asst. Dir.-Personnel--Viking Pump, Inc., Cedar Falls, IA; *U.S. Public*, pg. 862

Stephens, J. Michael, Div. Dir.-Admin. Services & Personnel--Goodwill Industries International, Bethesda, MD; *U.S. Private*, pg. 464

Stephenson, Dorothy L., V.P.-Human Resources--Bethlehem Steel Corporation, Bethlehem, PA; *U.S. Public*, pg. 226

Stepien, Barbara E., Dir.-H.R.--Farmers and Traders Life Insurance Co., Syracuse, NY; *U.S. Private*, pg. 394

Sterling, T.W., III, V.P.-Employee Rels.--U.S. Steel International, Inc., Pittsburgh, PA; *U.S. Public*, pg. 1661

Stern, Ingrid, Dir.-H.R.--Newport Corporation, Irvine, CA; *U.S. Public*, pg. 1179

Stern, John, V.P.-Opers.--Jackson MSC, Nashville, TN; *U.S. Private*, pg. 579

Sterrett, Frank, Dir.-Human Resources--British Aerospace Holdings Inc., Chantilly, VA; *Int'l*, pg. 218

Stevens, Bill, Mgr.-Personnel--J-Star Industries, Inc., Fort Atkinson, WI; *U.S. Private*, pg. 576

Stevens, Brad, Dir.-Personnel--Samsill Corporation, Fort Worth, TX; *U.S. Private*, pg. 963

Stevens, Deb, V.P.-Human Resources--Robert A. Becker, New York, NY; *Int'l*, pg. 601

Stevens, Elizabeth, V.P.-Human Resources & Pub. Rels.--The Chase Manhattan Bank of Canada, Toronto, Canada; *U.S. Public*, pg. 340

Stevens, Phyllis A., Dir.-H.R.--Rama Group of Companies, Cheektowaga, NY; *U.S. Private*, pg. 908

Stevens, Ralph W., Gen. Mgr.-H.R.--BHP Petroleum, Melbourne, Australia; *Int'l*, pg. 224

Stevens, Sandra K., Sr. V.P.-Human Resources--Haggar Corporation, Dallas, TX; *U.S. Public*, pg. 774

Stevens, Stanley, V.P.-Human Resources--Xomed Surgical Products, Jacksonville, FL; *U.S. Public*, pg. 253

Stevenson, Gary, Dir.-Human Resources--Doehler-Jarvis, Inc., Toledo, OH; *U.S. Public*, pg. 796

Stevenson, Sherry, Dir.-Personnel--Crown Holdings, Inc., Roseville, MN; *U.S. Private*, pg. 293

Stewart, Bonnie, Dir-Human Resources--White River Corporation, White Plains, NY; *U.S. Public*, pg. 1765

Stewart, Delia, Mgr.-Personnel--Multilin, Markham, Canada; *U.S. Public*, pg. 713

Stewart, John F., Chief Acctg. Officer & Controller--The Penn Traffic Company, Syracuse, NY; *U.S. Public*, pg. 1270

Stewart, Jonathan T., V.P.-Human Resources--Martin Marietta Materials, Inc., Raleigh, NC; *U.S. Public*, pg. 1007

Stewart, Larry, II, V.P.-H.R.--Invacare Corporation, Elyria, OH; *U.S. Public*, pg. 911

Stewart, Marsha, Mgr.-Human Resources--Premarc Corporation, Durand, MI; *U.S. Private*, pg. 881

Stewart, Michael, V.P.-H.R.--Mrs. Baird's Bakeries, Inc., Fort Worth, TX; *U.S. Private*, pg. 765

Stewart, Shirley, Dir.-Personnel & Mktg.--Modern Concrete Septic Tank Company, Ottsville, PA; *U.S. Private*, pg. 754

Stewart, Ted, Dir.-H.R.--Haarmann & Reimer Corp., Springfield, NJ; *Int'l*, pg. 173

Stier, Mark H., V.P.-Human Resources--Worthington Industries, Inc., Columbus, OH; *U.S. Public*, pg. 1780

Stier, Robert, V.P.-H.R.--Racetrac Petroleum, Inc., Smyrna, GA; *U.S. Private*, pg. 906

Stiles, Victoria L., V.P.-Human Resources & Corp. Risk Mngmt.--CORT Business Services Corporation, Fairfax, VA; *U.S. Public*, pg. 451

Stillings, Robert, V.P.-Opers., Sls., Mktg. & Dir.-Personnel--Presto Food Stores, Inc., Plant City, FL; *U.S. Private*, pg. 882

Stillman, Jedd B., V.P., Treas & Dir.-Personnel--David Michael & Co. Inc., Philadelphia, PA; *U.S. Private*, pg. 740

Stillson, Beverly, Dir.-Personnel--Farmer Brothers Company, Torrance, CA; *U.S. Public*, pg. 613

Stinson, Cathy, Dir.-Human Resources--Florida Health Facilities, Inc., Lutz, FL; *U.S. Public*, pg. 1035

Stinson, Robert C., V.P.-Admin. & H.R., Gen. Counsel & Sec.--Applied Industrial Technologies, Cleveland, OH; *U.S. Public*, pg. 122

Stinson, Ruth Ann, Treas. & Dir.-Personnel--Young Supply Company, Detroit, MI; *U.S. Private*, pg. 1202

Stock, T.D., Dir.-Human Resources--Cookson Matthey Ceramics, West Chester, PA; *Int'l*, pg. 714

Stockden, Jeff M., Mgr.-H.R.--BHP Iron Ore, Perth, Australia; *Int'l*, pg. 224

Stocker, Dr. H. F., Dir.-Personnel--Credit Suisse, Zurich, Switzerland; *Int'l*, pg. 345

Stocker, Phil, V.P.-H.R.--Advanstar Communications, Cleveland, OH; *U.S. Private*, pg. 22

Stoddard, Brian, V.P.-Safety & Personnel--Old Dominion Freight Line, Inc., High Point, NC; *U.S. Public*, pg. 1216

Stoehr, Douglas E., V.P.-Quality & Human Resources--Philips Automotive Electronics, Cheshire, CT; *Int'l*, pg. 1054

Stokes, Darryl A., Mgr.-Employee Svcs.--Baltimore Gas and Electric Company, Baltimore, MD; *U.S. Public*, pg. 172

Stokes, Jack, Mgr.-Human Resources--United Bankshares, Inc., Parkersburg, WV; *U.S. Public*, pg. 1674

Stokes, Linda C., V.P.-Human Resources--Dexter Aerospace Materials Division, Pittsburg, CA; *U.S. Public*, pg. 504

Stokking, Jacques, Dir.-Personnel--Forasol S.A., Velizy-Villacoublay, France; *Int'l*, pg. 496

Stolberg, Cathy S., Mgr.-Employee Benefits--Penn Virginia Corporation, Radnor, PA; *U.S. Public*, pg. 1271

Stolper, Stuart, V.P.-Human Resources--Talbots, Inc., Hingham, MA; *Int'l*, pg. 28

Stoltz, Richard, V.P.-H.R.--Phillips Plastics Corporation, Phillips, WI; *U.S. Private*, pg. 862

Stoneback, Heather, Dir.-H.R.--Rodale Press, Inc., Emmaus, PA; *U.S. Private*, pg. 939

Stoner, Janet L., Pres.-H.R. Div. & V.P.--Texaco Inc., White Plains, NY; *U.S. Public*, pg. 1582

Storasli, Knut, Mgr.-Personnel--Ford Motor Norge A/S, Kolbotn, Norway; *U.S. Public*, pg. 666
Storberget, Roald A., V.P.-Personnel--Helly-Hansen A/S, Moss, Norway; *Int'l*, pg. 1010
Stoues, Cathy, Dir.-H.R.--Equitable Savings & Loan Association, Wauwatosa, WI; *U.S. Private*, pg. 380
Stout, Elisabeth, Treas.--Burlington Coat Factory Warehouse Corporation, Burlington, NJ; *U.S. Public*, pg. 268
Stowell, Calvin S., Jr., Human Resources Dept. Exec.--Harris & Bank, Chicago, IL; *Int'l*, pg. 154
Strachan, Wendy, V.P.-Human Resources--Hyatt International Corporation, Chicago, IL; *U.S. Private*, pg. 551
Strahley, James T., V.P.-H.R.--Simpson Industries, Inc., Plymouth, MI; *U.S. Public*, pg. 1474
Strange, Jeanne, Dir.-Mktg. & Adv.--First Southwest Company, Dallas, TX; *U.S. Private*, pg. 407
Strassel, Gary, V.P.-Fin. & Dir.-Admin.--Carlisle Equipment Company, Wilder, KY; *U.S. Private*, pg. 211
Strater, Felix F., V.P.-Human Resources--BP North America Petroleum Inc., Cleveland, OH; *Int'l*, pg. 220
Strater, Felix F., V.P.-H.R.--BP Oil Co., Cleveland, OH; *Int'l*, pg. 220
Stratton, S.M., Mgr.-Mktg. Communications--Solar Turbines Incorporated, San Diego, CA; *U.S. Public*, pg. 316
Straub, Helmut, Mng. Dir.-Human Resources--Landis & Staefa AG, Zug, Switzerland; *Int'l*, pg. 800
Strauss, Catherine B., V.P.-Human Resources--Harleysville Group, Harleysville, PA; *U.S. Public*, pg. 786
Street, James E., Sr. V.P.-Human Resources--Tejas Gas Corporation, Houston, TX; *Int'l*, pg. 1136
Strelow, G.D., Sr. V.P.--Marshall & Ilsley Corporation, Milwaukee, WI; *U.S. Public*, pg. 1049
Stretrien, Tom, Exec. Dir.-Human Resources--Volkswagen of America, Inc., Auburn Hills, MI; *Int'l*, pg. 1474
Strickland, Judy, Dir.-Personnel, D.P. & Telecomm.--Eagle Lincoln Mercury Inc., Dallas, TX; *U.S. Private*, pg. 355
Strizak, Charles, Dir.-Personnel--Old Republic Life Insurance Co., Chicago, IL; *U.S. Public*, pg. 1218
Strohl, Dale S., Sr. V.P.-Opers.--Tiffany & Co., New York, NY; *U.S. Public*, pg. 1608
Strom, Leonard A., Sr. V.P.-H.R.--The Black & Decker Corporation, Towson, MD; *U.S. Public*, pg. 233
Stroman, Lori, Dir.-Human Resources--Drug Emporium, Inc., Powell, OH; *U.S. Public*, pg. 530
Strong, Bob, Dir.-H.R.--Lynden Incorporated, Seattle, WA; *U.S. Private*, pg. 683
Strother, Bob, V.P.-Human Resources--Noranda Forest Inc., Toronto, Canada; *Int'l*, pg. 434
Stroud, Gary B., Area Dir.-Human Resources--Paragon Health Network, Inc., Atlanta, GA; *U.S. Public*, pg. 1256
Stroud, Rae Beth, Dir.-H.R.--Mercury Air Group Inc., Los Angeles, CA; *U.S. Public*, pg. 1092
Strout, Mike, Exec. V.P.-Human Resources--Tops Markets, Inc., Amherst, NY; *Int'l*, pg. 750
Struck, K.A., Mgr.-H.R.--Northwestern Public Service, Huron, SD; *U.S. Public*, pg. 1200
Strupp, James J., Sr. V.P.-Human Resources--International Specialty Products, Inc., Wayne, NJ; *U.S. Public*, pg. 858
Stubblebine, Dorothy, V.P.-Human Resources & Security--Elkins-Sinn, Inc.-Lederle, Saint Davids, PA; *U.S. Public*, pg. 79
Stubbs, Wallace G., V.P.--Tecumseh Products Company, Tecumseh, MI; *U.S. Public*, pg. 1565
Stucky, Nick, V.P.-Human Resources--Printpack Inc., Atlanta, GA; *U.S. Private*, pg. 886
Studebaker, Dave, V.P.-Human Resources--Spectra-Physics Laserplane Inc., Dayton, OH; *U.S. Public*, pg. 1594
Studerus, Linda, Dir.-Human Resources--Sun Healthcare Group Inc., Albuquerque, NM; *U.S. Public*, pg. 1530
Stull, Brian, Mgr.-H.R.--Newell Co., Freeport, IL; *U.S. Public*, *pg. 1176*
Stump, David, Dir.-Human Resources--Associated Electric Co-op Inc., Springfield, MO; *U.S. Private*, pg. 89
Stuntz, Cathy, Mgr.-Personnel--Thermoplastics, Inc., Mishawaka, IN; *U.S. Public*, pg. 1590
Sturges, Ronald, Dir.-Human Resources--European Investment Bank, Luxembourg, Luxembourg; *Int'l*, pg. 465
Sturtz, Kenneth H., V.P.-Human Resources--Burnham, Lancaster, PA; *U.S. Public*, pg. 270
Sturzl, Edward, V.P.-Personnel--Sargento Foods Inc., Plymouth, WI; *U.S. Private*, pg. 966
Sturzl, Edward A., V.P.-H.R.--Sargento Foods Inc., Plymouth, WI; *U.S. Private*, pg. 966
Styles, Reid, V.P.-H.R.--The Franklin Institute, Philadelphia, PA; *U.S. Private*, pg. 424
Suchevitch, Thomas A., V.P.-Human Resources--Plantronics Inc., Santa Cruz, CA; *U.S. Public*, pg. 1308
Suerth, Chris, Mgr.-H.R.--ANGUS Chemical Company, Buffalo Grove, IL; *U.S. Private*, pg. 75
Sufi, A. Waseem, Mgr.-Personnel--Parke-Davis & Company, Limited, Karachi, Pakistan; *U.S. Public*, pg. 1739
Sugihara, Shigeyuki, Dir.-Human Resources--Nemic-Lambda KK, Tokyo, Japan; *Int'l*, pg. 1242
Sugiyama, Takeshi, Sr. Mng. Dir.-Auditing, Personnel, Education & Health--Yasuda Mutual Life Insurance Co., Tokyo, Japan; *Int'l*, pg. 1519
Suhrey, Fred, Dir.-Personnel--Cain's Coffee Co., Oklahoma City, OK; *U.S. Public*, pg. 351
Suing, Janine, Dir.-Human Resources--DSP Technology Inc., Fremont, CA; *U.S. Public*, pg. 475
Sujansky, Charles, V.P.-H.R.--Mellon Bank Corporation, Pittsburgh, PA; *U.S. Public*, pg. 1084
Sullens, William R., Dir.-Personnel--Atwood Oceanics, Inc., Houston, TX; *U.S. Public*, pg. 146
Sullivan, Brian R., Gen. Mgr.-Human Resources & Pub. Affairs--Elders Limited, Adelaide, Australia; *Int'l*, pg. 500
Sullivan, Carletta, Dir.-Employee Resources--CCAIR, Inc., Charlotte, NC; *U.S. Public*, pg. 276
Sullivan, Daniel L., Sr. V.P.-H.R.--QUALCOMM, San Diego, CA; *U.S. Public*, pg. 1348
Sullivan, Donald J., Dir.-Pur. & Personnel Trng. & Devel.--BR Associates, Inc., Jasper, IN; *U.S. Private*, pg. 107
Sullivan, John, V.P.-Customer Service--ABB Inc., Norwalk, CT; *Int'l*, pg. 3
Sullivan, John E., V.P.-Human Resources--Buttrey Food & Drug Company, Great Falls, MT; *U.S. Public*, pg. 271
Sullivan, Mary, V.P.-H.R.--Imax Corporation, Mississauga, Canada; *Int'l*, pg. 661
Sullivan, Rebecca, V.P. & Human Resources Dir.--Ingalls, Boston, MA; *U.S. Private*, pg. 562
Sullivan, Tom, V.P.-H.R.--Hunter Contracting Company, Gilbert, AZ; *U.S. Private*, pg. 549
Sullivan, William, Dir.-H.R.--Dietzgen Corporation, Palatine, IL; *U.S. Private*, pg. 332
Sulliven, Edward, V.P.-H.R.--Sullivan Paper Company, West Springfield, MA; *U.S. Private*, pg. 1050
Summerlin, Bruce, V.P.-Human Resources--Shorewood Packaging Corporation, New York, NY; *U.S. Public*, pg. 1468
Summers, Judy, Mgr.-Human Resources--Hurco Companies, Inc., Indianapolis, IN; *U.S. Public*, pg. 850
Summers, Judy, Mgr.-Human Resources--Hurco Manufacturing Company, Indianapolis, IN; *U.S. Public*, pg. 850
Summey, Sheila, Dir.-Human Resources--Atlanta Motor Speedway, Hampton, GA; *U.S. Public*, pg. 1498
Sunday, Harold R., V.P.-Human Resources--Collins & Aikman Corporation, Charlotte, NC; *U.S. Public*, pg. 399
Sunderland, Kent W., V.P. & Sec.--Ash Grove Cement Company, Shawnee Mission, KS; *U.S. Private*, pg. 87
Sundquist, Kathleen G., Dir.-Personnel--UFE Incorporated, Stillwater, MN; *U.S. Private*, pg. 1112
Sung, C.H., Dir.-Personnel Div.--Chinese Petroleum Corporation, Taipei, Taiwan; *Int'l*, pg. 286
Sunshine, Hope, Asst. V.P.--Maidenform Worldwide, New York, NY; *U.S. Private*, pg. 697
Suomela, Juhani, Exec. V.P.-Human Resources & Quality--FinnAir Oy, Helsinki, Finland; *Int'l*, pg. 485
Supinski, Margaret P., V.P.-Human Resources & Pension Admin.--The Ailing & Cory Company, Rochester, NY; *U.S. Public*, pg. 1666
Susco, Vincent F., Jr., V.P.-Admin. & Sec.--Connecticut Water Service, Inc., Clinton, CT; *U.S. Public*, pg. 431
Sussman, Shmuel, Dir.-Human Resources--Bank Leumi le-Israel B.M., Tel Aviv, Israel; *Int'l*, pg. 150
Sutherland, Fred, V.P.-H.R.--McCain Foods Limited, Florenceville, Canada; *Int'l*, pg. 850
Suzuki, Takehiko, Dir.-H.R.--Bridgestone Corporation, Tokyo, Japan; *Int'l*, pg. 213
Svana, Raymond E., Asst. V.P.-Personnel--Industrial Acoustics Company, Inc., Bronx, NY; *U.S. Public*, pg. 875
Sveinson, Pamela, V.P.-H.R.--Cowles Media Company, Minneapolis, MN; *U.S. Private*, pg. 280
Svensson, Herbert, Dir.-Personnel--SAFT Nife AB, Oskarshamn, Sweden; *Int'l*, pg. 54
Svoboda, Rick, Dir.-Human Resources--FMC Corp., Lithium Division, Gastonia, NC; *U.S. Public*, pg. 605
Swaine, Vicky, Dir.-Personnel--Aurora Pump, North Aurora, IL; *U.S. Public*, pg. 726
Swambar, Deborah, Dir.-H.R.--Squire-Cogswell Company, Gurnee, IL; *U.S. Private*, pg. 1027
Swan, A.W., Sec. & Dir.-Human Resources--Energizer Eveready Ltd., London, United Kingdom; *U.S. Public*, pg. 1360
Swanson, Anthia, Admin.-H.R.--Leupold & Stevens, Inc., Beaverton, OR; *U.S. Private*, pg. 662
Swanson, Dale, V.P.-H.R.--Mesirow Financial, Chicago, IL; *U.S. Private*, pg. 733
Swanson, David, Mgr.-Personnel--Arrow Industries, Inc., Carrollton, TX; *U.S. Public*, pg. 426
Swanson, David H., Dir.-Personnel--Fort Wayne National Corporation, Fort Wayne, IN; *U.S. Public*, pg. 673
Swanson, Neil W., Dir.-Risk Mngmt.--Unit Corporation, Tulsa, OK; *U.S. Public*, pg. 1672
Swanzey, Robert, Sr. V.P.-H.R. & Opers.--Century Business Credit Corporation, New York, NY; *U.S. Private*, pg. 225
Swartz, Dean, Mgr.-Opers.--RNL Facilities Corporation, Denver, CO; *U.S. Private*, pg. 905
Swartz, John, V.P.-Human Resources--PCS Health Systems, Inc., Scottsdale, AZ; *U.S. Public*, pg. 993
Swartz, Therese, Dir.-Personnel--Tetra Tech NUS, Inc., Gaithersburg, MD; *U.S. Public*, pg. 1582
Sweeney, Matthew T., Dir.-H.R.--Spartech Corporation, Clayton, MO; *U.S. Public*, pg. 1495
Sweeney, Paul, Dir.-Human Resources--Norcold, Sidney, OH; *U.S. Private*, pg. 352
Swerc, David, Mgr.-Personnel--Federal Screw Works, Detroit, MI; *U.S. Public*, pg. 616
Sweterlitsch, Veronica M., V.P.-Human Resources Div.--First National Bank in Massillon, Massillon, OH; *U.S. Public*, pg. 646
Swick, Carolyn, Dir.-Human Resources--General Housewares Corp., Terre Haute, IN; *U.S. Public*, pg. 715
Swick, Carolyn, Dir.-Human Res.--Chicago Cutlery, Inc., Terre Haute, IN; *U.S. Public*, pg. 716
Swiech, Alan M., V.P.-H.R.--Cambridge Industries Inc., Madison Heights, MI; *U.S. Private*, pg. 202
Swift, Margie, Mgr.-H.R.--Doane Products Co., Joplin, MO; *U.S. Private*, pg. 337
Swisher, Thane, V.P. & Sec.--CMI Corporation, Oklahoma City, OK; *U.S. Public*, pg. 278
Switzer, Meaghan, Mgr.-H.R.--Sonoma Valley Bank, Sonoma, CA; *U.S. Public*, pg. 1487
Swope, Samuel D., V.P.-Human Resources--JLG Industries, Inc., McConnellsburg, PA; *U.S. Public*, pg. 918
Sykes, Robert A., V.P.-Human Resources--Washington Gas Light Co., Springfield, VA; *U.S. Public*, pg. 1740
Sylvester, John, V.P.-H.R.--Linbeck Construction Corp, Houston, TX; *U.S. Private*, pg. 667
Symeon, Ted, Mgr.-Human Resources--FAG Bearings Corporation, Danbury, CT; *Int'l*, pg. 469
Synnett, Robert, V.P.-H.R. & Personnel Trng. & Devel.--M.B. Kahn Construction Co., Inc., Columbia, SC; *U.S. Private*, pg. 604
Syrett, Joanne, Dir.-Human Resources--Apple Computer (UK) Ltd., Uxbridge, United Kingdom; *U.S. Public*, pg. 121
Szakmary, Gary, Mgr.-H.R. Devel.--Moog Incorporated, East Aurora, NY; *U.S. Public*, pg. 1127
Szapiro, Nakhinr, V.P.-Human Resources & Corp. Communications--Banco Chase Manhattan, S.A., Santo Amaro, Brazil; *U.S. Public*, pg. 339
Szhebil, Stephanie, Mgr.-H.R.--Efficient Engineering Co., Troy, MI; *U.S. Private*, pg. 365
Szol, Edmund, V.P.-Human Resources--Royal Oak Mines Inc., Kirkland, WA; *U.S. Public*, pg. 1410
Szykowny, Paulette, Opers. Mgr.--Fahlgren, Toledo, OH; *U.S. Private*, pg. 391
Tackney, Jim, Dir.-H.R. (USA)--Synergistics Industries Limited, Mississauga, Canada; *U.S. Public*, pg. 734
Taddy, Paul, V.P.-Human Resources--Paragon Electric Co., Inc., Two Rivers, WI; *Int'l*, pg. 1243
Taegel, Harry, V.P.-Personnel--Canteen Corporation, Charlotte, NC; *Int'l*, pg. 324
Taets, Jim, Controller--Nord Resources Corporation, Albuquerque, NM; *U.S. Public*, pg. 1188
Taggart, Carol, Dir.-H.R.--KDI Precision Products, Inc., Cincinnati, OH; *U.S. Private*, pg. 603
Takahashi, Hiroyuki, Exec. Mng. Dir. & Gen. Mgr.-Personnel--Mitsui & Co., Ltd., Tokyo, Japan; *Int'l*, pg. 877
Takahashi, Tsuyoshi, Dir.-Budget, Personnel & Mngmt. Systems.--Asian Development Bank, Manila, Philippines; *Int'l*, pg. 88
Take, Kikuo, Gen. Mgr.-Human Resources--Terumo Corporation, Tokyo, Japan; *Int'l*, pg. 1375
Takebayashi, Mamoru, Exec. V.P.-Personnel, Admin. & Pub. Affairs--Mazda Motor Corporation, Hiroshima, Japan; *Int'l*, pg. 849
Taker, B., Mgr.-Human Resources--Ladbroke Group Plc, London, United Kingdom; *Int'l*, pg. 787
Taker, B.S., Sr. V.P.-Human Resources--Hilton International Co., Coral Gables, FL; *Int'l*, pg. 787
Tallent, Tom, Sr. V.P.-Fin. & H.R.--Gemtron Corporation, Sweetwater, TN; *Int'l*, pg. 1523
Talley, Richard, Dir.-H.R.--Concordia Publishing House, Saint Louis, MO; *U.S. Private*, pg. 261
Talton, James M., Sr. V.P.-Human Resources--Rite Aid Corporation, Camp Hill, PA; *U.S. Public*, pg. 1390
Talwar, Rana, Exec. Dir.-Corp. Banking (Africa, India, Pakistan & Middle East)--Standard Chartered Bank PLC, London, United Kingdom; *Int'l*, pg. 1294
Tamanini, Richard, Dir.-H.R.--Alumax Inc., Atlanta, GA; *U.S. Public*, pg. 59
Tamashasky, John, V.P.-H.R.--R.A. Jones & Co. Inc., Covington, KY; *U.S. Private*, pg. 597
Tanchico, Emiliano R., Asst. V.P.-Personnel Mgmnt. & Devel.--Philippine Long Distance Telephone Company, Manila, Philippines; *Int'l*, pg. 1051
Tani, Lili, Dir.-Human Resources--Turtle Bay Hilton Golf & Tennis Resort, Kahuku, HI; *U.S. Public*, pg. 829
Taniguchi, Sadao, Chief Fin Officer, Legal Officer & Dir.-Personnel & Inv. Rels.--Kosugi Sangyo Co., Ltd., Tokyo, Japan; *Int'l*, pg. 759
Tanks, Wallace T., Sr. V.P.-H.R.--Tennessee Valley Authority, Knoxville, TN; *U.S. Public*, pg. 1580
Tanner, Arthur, Dir.-Human Resources--IPC Magazines Limited, London, United Kingdom; *Int'l*, pg. 651
Tanner, Daken, V.P.-H.R.--Franklin Covey, Salt Lake City, UT; *U.S. Public*, pg. 679
Tanner, David, Mgr.-Personnel--CorryHiebert Corporation, Corry, PA; *U.S. Public*, pg. 772
Tapia, JoAnn, Dir.-H.R.--Shafer Commercial Seating Inc., Denver, CO; *U.S. Private*, pg. 988
Tarajano, Jose, Gen. Counsel & Mgr.-Personnel--Pala Group, Inc., Baton Rouge, LA; *U.S. Private*, pg. 834
Taravella, Sandra, Mgr.-Human Resources--Electronic Solutions, San Diego, CA; *U.S. Public*, pg. 1791
Tarwater, Dan, Exec. Dir.-H.R.--Sierra Health Services, Inc., Las Vegas, NV; *U.S. Public*, pg. 1469
Tate, Bailus, V.P.-Human Resources--Kansas City Power & Light Company, Kansas City, MO; *U.S. Public*, pg. 943
Tateriatou, Katsutosi, Dir.-Personnel--SmithKline Beecham Pharmaceuticals, Tokyo, Japan; *Int'l*, pg. 1266
Tatum, T.W., Sr. V.P.-Human Resources--Lafarge Canada Inc., Montreal, Canada; *Int'l*, pg. 789
Tatum, Thomas W., Sr. V.P.-Human Resources--Lafarge Corporation, Reston, VA; *Int'l*, pg. 788
Taunton, Christine, Dir.-Human Resources--InterDigital Communications Corp., King of Prussia, PA; *U.S. Public*, pg. 889
Tayama, Akira, Mng. Dir.-Personnel--Asahi Breweries Ltd., Tokyo, Japan; *Int'l*, pg. 83
Taylor, Barbara, V.P.-H.R./North America--Benckiser Consumer Products Inc., Greenwich, CT; *Int'l*, pg. 185
Taylor, Beth, Mgr.-H.R.--Zetec, Inc., Issaquah, WA; *U.S. Private*, pg. 1205
Taylor, Bob, V.P.-Human Resources--Telus Corporation, Edmonton, Canada; *Int'l*, pg. 1374
Taylor, Christine, V.P.-Human Resources--Xilinx, Inc., San Jose, CA; *U.S. Public*, pg. 1786
Taylor, Chuck, Mgr.-Human Resources--M/D Totco Instrumentation, Cedar Park, TX; *U.S. Public*, pg. 1709
Taylor, Darrach G., V.P.-Human Resources--Flowserve Corporation, Long Beach, CA; *U.S. Public*, pg. 658
Taylor, E., Dir.-Human Resources--Dowty Aerospace Yakima, Yakima, WA; *Int'l*, pg. 1337
Taylor, Elwyn, Dir.-Human Resources--Gaylord Entertainment/Opryland USA, Nashville, TN; *U.S. Public*, *pg. 704*
Taylor, Gwen, V.P.-Human Resources--Bellcore, Morristown, NJ; *U.S. Private*, pg. 976
Taylor, Kim, Mgr.-H.R.--Weiler & Company, Inc., Whitewater, WI; *U.S. Private*, pg. 1160

Taylor, Marilyn, V.P.-H.R.--New Century Energies, Inc., Denver, CO; *U.S. Public*, pg. 1170
Taylor, Michael, Dir.-Personnel--Homes of Merit Inc., Bartow, FL; *U.S. Private*, pg. 537
Taylor, Nancy, Dir.-Human Resources--Harden Furniture Company, McConnellsville, NY; *U.S. Private*, pg. 501
Taylor, Peter, Dir.-Mktg., Communications & Human Relations--Royal & Sun Alliance Insurance Group plc, London, United Kingdom; *Int'l*, pg. 1130
Teague, Becki, Mgr.-Personnel--Mallory, Inc., Carson City, NV; *U.S. Private*, pg. 698
Teague, Reva L., V.P.-H.R.--Texas Micro, Inc., Houston, TX; *U.S. Public*, pg. 1586
Teixeira, Marco A., Dir.-Personnel--Eli Lilly do Brasil Limitada, Sao Paulo, Brazil; *U.S. Public*, pg. 993
Telly, Theresa, Mgr.-Human Resources--Banner Pharmacaps Inc., High Point, NC; *Int'l*, pg. 1272
Ten Bruin, Linnea S., V.P.-H.R.--Intermatic Inc., Spring Grove, IL; *U.S. Private*, pg. 567
Tennant, James C., V.P.-H.R.--Placer Dome Inc., Vancouver, Canada; *Int'l*, pg. 1060
Tennant, R.A., Grp. Gen. Mgr.-H.R.--HSBC Holdings plc, London, United Kingdom; *Int'l*, pg. 579
Tennent, Wayne, V.P.-H.R.--AMF Bowling Worldwide, Richmond, VA; *U.S. Private*, pg. 6
TenRaa, Linda L., Exec. Asst. & Human Resources Specialist--Willis Corroon Corp. of Western Michigan, Grand Rapids, MI; *Int'l*, pg. 1507
Tepner, Ron, Dir.-Human Resources--Bridgestone/Firestone Inc. Retail Operations, Rolling Meadows, IL; *Int'l*, pg. 213
Tepper, Nan, V.P.-Human Resources-West Coast--CBS, New York, NY; *U.S. Public*, pg. 273
Terenzio, Peter, V.P.-H.R.--Petroleum Heat & Power Co., Stamford, CT; *U.S. Public*, pg. 1281
Terpenning, Linda M., V.P.-H.R.--L.B. Foster Company, Pittsburgh, PA; *U.S. Public*, pg. 675
Terryberry, Wesley S., V.P.-Human Resources--Spar Aerospace Limited, Toronto, Canada; *Int'l*, pg. 1287
Tessier, Robert, Dir.-H.R.--Uniboard Division Mont Laurier, Mont Laurier, Canada; *Int'l*, pg. 1431
Tessier, Robert, Dir.-H.R.--Uniboard Canada Inc.-LDI Division, Lac des Iles, Canada; *Int'l*, pg. 1431
Testa, Marta, Mgr.-Personnel--Bridgeport Fittings, Inc., Stratford, CT; *U.S. Private*, pg. 168
Tetreault, Thomas J., Mgr.-Personnel--Renold, Inc., Westfield, NY; *Int'l*, pg. 1104
Teutsch, Nancy, V.P.-Global H.R.--Haworth, Inc., Holland, MI; *U.S. Private*, pg. 511
Tew, Dwight, V.P.-Recruiting--American Rehability Services, Inc., Brentwood, TN; *U.S. Public*, pg. 1257
Thakarar, Gail, Mng. Dir.-Human Resources--Countrywide Funding Corporation, Pasadena, CA; *U.S. Public*, pg. 453
Thames, John E., V.P.-H.R.--Donaldson Company, Inc., Minneapolis, MN; *U.S. Public*, pg. 517
Tharp, Charles G., Sr. V.P.-Human Resources--Bristol-Myers Squibb Company, New York, NY; *U.S. Public*, pg. 253
Thayer, Vickey, V.P.-H.R.--Lozier Corporation, Omaha, NE; *U.S. Private*, pg. 679
Theisen, George, Mgr.-Personnel--Famous Restaurants Inc., Scottsdale, AZ; *U.S. Private*, pg. 393
Theisen, George, V.P.-Human Resources--Acapulco Restaurants, Long Beach, CA; *U.S. Private*, pg. 925
Theriault, Paul H., V.P.-Human Resources & Admin.--New Brunswick Power Corporation, Fredericton, Canada; *Int'l*, *pg. 923*
Therrien, Liz, Dir.-Human Resources--Cruise America, Inc., Mesa, AZ; *U.S. Private*, pg. 178
Theule, B.L., V.P.-Human Resources--Science Applications International Corp., San Diego, CA; *U.S. Private*, pg. 975
Theurer, Thomas N., Dir.-Personnel--Kunzler & Company, Inc., Lancaster, PA; *U.S. Private*, pg. 636
Thibeault, Jean-Claude, Gen. Mgr.-Personnel--Banque de France, Paris, France; *Int'l*, pg. 160
Thibeault, Maurice M., Dir.-H.R.--Algoma Steel Inc., Sault Sainte Marie, Canada; *Int'l*, pg. 56
Thibodeau, Michael A., Asst. V.P.-Admin.--Maine Public Service Company, Presque Isle, ME; *U.S. Public*, pg. 1038
Thibodeau, Pierre, Dir.-Human Resources--Imprimerie Quebecor Inc. Division Cheques, Saint Leonard, Canada; *Int'l*, pg. 1077
Thierfelder, Gottfried, Dir.-Personnel, Social Affairs & Environmental Protection--Eckes AG, Nieder-Olm, Germany; *Int'l*, pg. 432
Thill, Carlo, Gen. Mgr.-Personnel & Social Affairs--Banque Generale du Luxembourg SA, Luxembourg, Luxembourg; *Int'l*, pg. 161
Thill, Tom, Dir.-Personnel--Fort Dodge Animal Health, Overland Park, KS; *U.S. Public*, pg. 79
Thirlwell, John A., Mgr.-H.R.--Sheet & Coil Products Division, Port Kembla, Australia; *Int'l*, pg. 227
Thom, William O., V.P.-Human Resources--Patterson-Kelley Company, Tulsa, OK; *U.S. Public*, pg. 793
Thoma, Diane, Mgr.-Human Resources--Flexsteel Industries, Inc., Dubuque, IA; *U.S. Public*, pg. 653
Thoman, Terry, Dir.-H.R.--The Pfaltzgraff Co., York, PA; *U.S. Private*, pg. 860
Thomas, Anita, Mgr.-Human Resources--Wells/Bloomfield, Verdi, NV; *U.S. Public*, pg. 1497
Thomas, Gary, Exec. V.P.-Human Resources--JM Family Enterprises Inc., Deerfield Beach, FL; *U.S. Private*, pg. 577
Thomas, Gregory N., Dir.-H.R.--A. Levy & J. Zentner Co., Sacramento, CA; *U.S. Private*, pg. 663
Thomas, James, V.P.-Human Resources--Microsemi Corporation, Santa Ana, CA; *U.S. Public*, pg. 1107
Thomas, Jay, Mgr.-H.R.--Carroll's Foods, Inc., Warsaw, NC; *U.S. Private*, pg. 215
Thomas, John, V.P.-Personnel--Fruit of the Loom, Inc., Chicago, IL; *U.S. Public*, pg. 685
Thomas, Lee, Sec. & Mgr.-H.R.--California Cedar Products, Inc., Stockton, CA; *U.S. Private*, pg. 200
Thomas, M., Mgr.-Personnel--Meyer Forest Products Ltd, London, United Kingdom; *Int'l*, pg. 864
Thomas, Michael L., V.P. & Dir.-Human Resources--Granite Construction Incorporated, Watsonville, CA; *U.S. Public*, pg. 759
Thomas, Neil, Dir.-Personnel--NCH Corporation, Irving, TX; *U.S. Public*, pg. 1145
Thomas, Pauline G., V.P.-H.R.--Computer Products, Inc., Boca Raton, FL; *U.S. Public*, pg. 422
Thomas, Steven, Mgr.-Human Resources--Mox-Med, Inc., Portage, WI; *U.S. Public*, pg. 124
Thomas, Tom L., V.P.--Ferro Union, Inc., Torrance, CA; *U.S. Private*, pg. 402
Thompson, Don, Mgr.-Personnel--T.D. Williamson, Inc., Tulsa, OK; *U.S. Private*, pg. 1179
Thompson, Doug, Dir.-Human Resources--Galaxy Carpet Mills, Inc., Chatsworth, GA; *U.S. Public*, pg. 1121
Thompson, Gene, Dir.-H.R.--Stowe-Pharr Mills, Inc., Mc Adenville, NC; *U.S. Private*, pg. 1045
Thompson, Kathleen, V.P.-Human Resources--Tracor, Inc., Austin, TX; *U.S. Public*, pg. 1627
Thompson, Ken, Dir.-Human Resources--Chromcraft Corporation, Senatobia, MS; *U.S. Public*, pg. 352
Thompson, Lisa, Mgr.-H.R.--Laboratory Supply Company, Inc., Louisville, KY; *U.S. Private*, pg. 641
Thompson, Mark, Dir.-Personnel--Kesterson Food Company, Inc., Paris, TN; *U.S. Private*, pg. 616
Thompson, Michael, Sr. V.P. & Dir.-H.R.--CVB Financial Corp., Ontario, CA; *U.S. Public*, pg. 286
Thompson, Phil, Dir.-Human Resources--Grocers Supply Co. Inc., Houston, TX; *U.S. Private*, pg. 483
Thompson, Rosalind, Sr. V.P.-Human Resources--Fabri-Centers of America, Inc., Hudson, OH; *U.S. Public*, pg. 609
Thompson, Stan, Dir.-Human Resources--Zoological Society of San Diego, San Diego, CA; *U.S. Private*, pg. 1207
Thompson, Susan, Mgr.-Human Resources--Allegiant Physician Services, Atlanta, GA; *U.S. Public*, pg. 45
Thompson, Susan, Mgr.-Reg. Affairs--Pawling Corporation, Pawling, NY; *U.S. Private*, pg. 844
Thompson, Susan L., V.P.-H.R.--In Focus Systems, Inc., Wilsonville, OR; *U.S. Public*, pg. 873
Thompson, Tiona, Chief Human Resources Officer--The Progressive Corporation, Cleveland, OH; *U.S. Public*, pg. 1334
Thomson, Gregory M., Sr. V.P.-H.R.--Owens Corning, Toledo, OH; *U.S. Public*, pg. 1236
Thonney, Jean-Phillippe, Mgr.-Personnel--Banque Cantonale Vaudoise, Lausanne, Switzerland; *Int'l*, pg. 160
Thorne, James G., V.P.-Human Resources--Hillenbrand Industries, Inc., Batesville, IN; *U.S. Public*, pg. 828
Thornhill, Christine, V.P. & Asst. Sec.--Thornhill Oil Company, Inc., Fort Wayne, IN; *U.S. Private*, pg. 1084
Thornton, Carmen, Dir.-H.R.--Business Mens Insurance Corporation, Coral Gables, FL; *U.S. Private*, pg. 189
Thriffiley, Donald A., Jr., Dir.-H.R./Flowers Bakeries, Inc.--Flowers Industries, Inc., Thomasville, GA; *U.S. Public*, pg. 656
Tice, Debbie, Human Resources Rep.--Talley Industries, Inc., Phoenix, AZ; *U.S. Public*, pg. 307
Tiernay, Tim, Dir.-Human Resources--Imprimerie Quebecor Canada, Woodbridge, Canada; *Int'l*, pg. 1077
Tierno, Ross, Mgr.-Human Resources--Parsons Power Group, Inc., Reading, PA; *U.S. Private*, pg. 841
Tifft, D.C., V.P.-Personnel--Hardings, Inc., Elmira, NY; *U.S. Private*, pg. 502
Tighe, Steven, Sr. V.P.-Human Resources--Time Insurance, Milwaukee, WI; *Int'l*, pg. 499
Tijou, Philippe, Dir.-Human Resources--Sofamor Danek Group, Inc., Memphis, TN; *U.S. Public*, pg. 1482
Tilden, Cindy, Dir.-Human Resources--Michigan Milk Producers Association, Novi, MI; *U.S. Private*, pg. 741
Tilly, Duncan F., V.P.-Human Resources--Canada Trustco Mortgage Company, London, Canada; *Int'l*, pg. 112
Timberlake, Edgar F., V.P.-H.R.--Nash Finch Company, Edina, MN; *U.S. Public*, pg. 1151
Timberman, Terri, V.P.-Human Resources & Quality--Merix Corporation, Forest Grove, OR; *U.S. Public*, pg. 1096
Timko, Susan, Mgr.-H.R.--Edwards and Kelcey, Inc., Boston, MA; *U.S. Private*, pg. 364
Timm, Alean N., Mgr.-Corp. Office H.R.--Fortune Brands, Inc., Old Greenwich, CT; *U.S. Public*, pg. 674
Timmins, William, Dir.-Human Resources--AgrEvo USA Company, Wilmington, DE; *Int'l*, pg. 1203
Timmons, Michelle, Dir.-Personnel--ACS Industries, Inc., Woonsocket, RI; *U.S. Private*, pg. 3
Tinelli, Judith, V.P.-H.R.--American Management Systems, Inc., Fairfax, VA; *U.S. Public*, pg. 86
Tingle, Douglas R., V.P.-Human Resources-Bath Fashions--Home Furnishings Segment, Fort Mill, SC; *U.S. Public*, pg. 1500
Tinkler, Michael P., V.P.-H.R. & Organizational Devel.--Bombardier Inc., Montreal, Canada; *Int'l*, pg. 199
Tippens, Steve, V.P.-Human Resources & Pub. Rels.--Abingdon Press, Nashville, TN; *U.S. Private*, pg. 1123
Tisdale, Dianne, Mgr.-H.R.--Kingsbury Corporation, Keene, NH; *U.S. Private*, pg. 621
Titchenal, Kay, Dir.-Human Resources--Foodbrands America, Inc., Oklahoma City, OK; *U.S. Public*, pg. 852
Tjorstad, Eriu, Asst. V.P.-Personnel--A/S Ivaran Rederi, Lysaker, Norway; *Int'l*, pg. 696
Toburen, J.R., V.P. & Sec.--Flexfab Horizons International, Inc., Hastings, MI; *U.S. Private*, pg. 412
Tocash, Paul, V.P.-H.R.--Fairfield Communities, Inc., Little Rock, AR; *U.S. Public*, pg. 610
Todd, Maryann, Dir.-Human Resources--Powell Electronics Inc., Philadelphia, PA; *U.S. Private*, pg. 877
Toener, John, Dir.-Personnel & Mgr.-Plant--Hudepohl-Schoenling Brewing Company, Cincinnati, OH; *U.S. Private*, pg. 545
Tokar, Barbara, Mgr.-H.R.--Mill-Rose Company, Mentor, OH; *U.S. Private*, pg. 746
Tolbert, J. David, V.P.-H.R. & Corp. Risk--Alltrista Corporation, Muncie, IN; *U.S. Public*, pg. 56
Toliver, Larry, Dir.-Human Resources--Cincinnati Gear Company, Cincinnati, OH; *U.S. Private*, pg. 240
Tollefsen, Eric, Dir.-H.R.--Carr Gottstein Foods, Anchorage, AK; *U.S. Public*, pg. 308
Tolleson, Constance J., V.P.-Human Resources--HomeBase, Inc., Irvine, CA; *U.S. Public*, pg. 832
Tollison, Eugene, Mgr.-Personnel--Palmetto Spinning Corp., Laurens, SC; *U.S. Public*, pg. 1052
Tolson, Catherine, Human Resources Mgr.--Stackig Advertising and Public Relations, Mc Lean, VA; *U.S. Private*, pg. 1028
Tomas, Antonio Condal, Dir.-Legal, Pur. & Personnel--Agropecuaria de Guissona, S. Coop. Ltda., Guisona, Spain; *Int'l*, pg. 31
Tomasson, Gudjon, Dir.-Personnel--Landsvirkjun - The National Power Co., Reykjavik, Iceland; *Int'l*, pg. 801
Tombacher, Karen, V.P.-H.R.--Amerex USA, Inc., New York, NY; *U.S. Private*, pg. 49
Tomcyzk, Deb, V.P.-Employee Benefits & Human Resources--EFG Technologies Inc., Saint Paul, MN; *U.S. Public*, pg. 1679
Tomeo, Barbara, Mgr.-Personnel--E.J. Brooks Company, Newark, NJ; *U.S. Private*, pg. 172
Tomerlin, John L., V.P.-Human Resources--Enterprise Products Company, Houston, TX; *U.S. Private*, pg. 377
Tomko, Carole W., Sr. V.P.-Human Resources--Cardinal Health Inc., Dublin, OH; *U.S. Public*, pg. 304
Tomlinson, E.G., V.P.-Human Resources--The Torrington Co., Torrington, CT; *U.S. Public*, pg. 877
Tondato, M., Mgr.-H.R.--Benetton Group S.p.A., Ponzano Veneto, Italy; *Int'l*, pg. 186
Toner, Bruce, V.P.-Human Resources--Rentway Inc., Etobicoke, Canada; *Int'l*, pg. 1424
Toney, Glen O., Grp. V.P.-Global Human Resources--Applied Materials, Inc., Santa Clara, CA; *U.S. Public*, pg. 123
Tonkin, John B., Mgr.-Corp. Svcs.--Price Brothers Co., Dayton, OH; *U.S. Private*, pg. 883
Tonnellotto, G., Dir.-Personnel & Organization--Zanussi Metallurgica S.p.A., Maniago, Italy; *Int'l*, pg. 442
Toole, Lawrence J., Sr. V.P.-Human Resources--General Electric Capital Services, Inc., Stamford, CT; *U.S. Public*, *pg. 711*
Topp, Dave, Mgr.-Customer Service & Distr.--GSW Heating Products Company, Stoney Creek, Canada; *Int'l*, pg. 538
Torbett, Marcia, V.P.-H.R.--Cliffs Drilling Company, Houston, TX; *U.S. Public*, pg. 386
Torrance, Mary, Dir.-Personnel--Tidewater Inc., New Orleans, LA; *U.S. Public*, pg. 1608
Torre, John, V.P.-Personnel--Rhodes, Inc., Atlanta, GA; *U.S. Public*, pg. 805
Torrence, Joseph W., Asst. V.P. & Corp. H.R. Officer--Chemical Financial Corporation, Midland, MI; *U.S. Public*, *pg. 345*
Torreyson, J. Kenneth, Dir.-Personnel--Wachovia Corporation, Winston Salem, NC; *U.S. Public*, pg. 1730
Torsone, Johnna G., V.P.-Personnel--Pitney Bowes Inc., Stamford, CT; *U.S. Public*, pg. 1303
Tortelli, Ronald C., Sr. V.P.-Human Resources--SuperValu, Inc., Eden Prairie, MN; *U.S. Public*, pg. 1540
Toscano, Barbara, V.P.-Human Resources & Corp. Communications--Neuman Distributors, Inc., Ridgefield, NJ; *U.S. Public*, pg. 1169
Tosches, Camellia, Human Resources Mgr.--Goodby, Silverstein & Partners, San Francisco, CA; *U.S. Public*, pg. 1224
Tosh, Ed, Personnel--Media General, Inc., Richmond, VA; *U.S. Public*, pg. 1077
Tosh, Gay, Mgr.-Personnel--Pontiac-GMC Truck Division, Pontiac, MI; *U.S. Public*, pg. 720
Touretsky, Simeon, Mgr.-Personnel--Homasote Company, Trenton, NJ; *U.S. Public*, pg. 831
Town, Dave, Mgr.-Human Resources--Shoppers Drug Mart, Ltd., London, Canada; *Int'l*, pg. 112
Townes, Edward R., V.P.-Human Resources--Reliance Electric Company, Cleveland, OH; *U.S. Public*, pg. 1398
Townsend, David L., V.P.-Admin.--Walter Industries, Inc., Tampa, FL; *U.S. Public*, pg. 1736
Townsend, Margo, Dir.-Human Resources--Meridian Insurance Group, Inc., Indianapolis, IN; *U.S. Public*, pg. 1095
Townson, Brian, V.P.-H.R.--Rich Products Corp., Buffalo, NY; *U.S. Private*, pg. 928
Tozer, Gail, H.R. Mgr.--Long Haymes Carr, Inc., Winston Salem, NC; *U.S. Public*, pg. 909
Tracy, William B., Sr. V.P.--USAA (United Services Automobile Association), San Antonio, TX; *U.S. Private*, pg. 1114
Traina, Kathy, Dir.-Personnel--Tano Automation, Inc., Harahan, LA; *U.S. Public*, pg. 1763
Traina, Maria, Mgr.-Human Resources--The Western Group, Saint Louis, MO; *U.S. Private*, pg. 1165
Transtrum, Susan, Mgr.-H.R.--OEC Medical Systems, Inc., Salt Lake City, UT; *U.S. Public*, pg. 1207
Trapini, John, V.P.-Human Resources--Sybron Dental Specialties, Inc., Glendora, CA; *U.S. Public*, pg. 1545
Traub, Tom, V.P.-Human Resources--Grist Mill Company, Lakeville, MN; *U.S. Public*, pg. 766
Traver, Joyce, Dir.-Benefits--International Multifoods Corporation, Minneapolis, MN; *U.S. Public*, pg. 900
Travis, Peggy S., Exec. V.P.-Human Resources--Siecor Corporation, Hickory, NC; *U.S. Public*, pg. 449
Travis, Peggy S., Exec. V.P.-Human Resources--Siecor Corporation, Hickory, NC; *Int'l*, pg. 1245
Traylor, Linda G., V.P.-H.R. & Plng. & Devel.--Advantica Restaurant Group, Inc., Spartanburg, SC; *U.S. Public*, pg. 22
Treadway, J.E., V.P.-Human Resources--R.R. Donnelley & Sons Company, Chicago, IL; *U.S. Public*, pg. 517
Trebesh, Thomas R., V.P.-Personnel--Delchamps, Inc., Mobile, AL; *U.S. Private*, pg. 588
Tregenza, Arthur R., Dir.-Personnel & Pub. Rels.--Allison Transmission, Indianapolis, IN; *U.S. Public*, pg. 719
Trelut, James, V.P.-Human Resources--Nob Hill General Store, Inc., Gilroy, CA; *U.S. Private*, pg. 799

Treml, Bernard J., V.P.-H.R.--Wisconsin Public Service Corporation, Green Bay, WI; *U.S. Public*, pg. 1728

Treml, Bud, V.P.-H.R.--WPS Resources Corp., Green Bay, WI; *U.S. Public*, pg. 1728

Trent, David, Mgr.-Human Resouces--King & Prince Seafood Corporation, Brunswick, GA; *U.S. Private*, pg. 620

Tresarrieu, Didier, V.P.-Personnel Admin.--Lafarge S.A., Paris, France; *Int'l*, pg. 788

Tricamo, Frank, Dir.-H.R.--Associated Wholesale Grocers, Inc., Kansas City, KS; *U.S. Private*, pg. 93

Tricker, Graham, Mgr.-Grp. Personnel--Blue Circle Industries PLC, London, United Kingdom; *Int'l*, pg. 197

Trifelitti, Tony, Dir.-Human Resources--Johnson Matthey Inc., Wayne, PA; *Int'l*, pg. 713

Trinboli, Denise, Mgr.-Human Resources--Edwards High Vacuum, International, Grand Island, NY; *Int'l*, pg. 121

Trinkl, Hans, Mng. Dir.-Human Resources--Julius Meinl AG, Vienna, Austria; *Int'l*, pg. 856

Trip, Onno Laman, Corp. Dir.-Human Resources--Reed Elsevier plc, London, United Kingdom; *Int'l*, pg. 1093

Tripp, Daniel B., V.P.-H.R. & Pub. Rels.--Thomaston Mills, Inc., Thomaston, GA; *U.S. Public*, pg. 1599

Trivett, Tom, Dir.-Human Resources--Dillard, A ResourceNet International Company, Greensboro, NC; *U.S. Public*, pg. 901

Troccoli, Virginia, Mgr.-Personnel--National Baking, Chicago, IL; *U.S. Private*, pg. 1022

Trombley, Michael, Dir.-H.R.--Replogle Globes, Inc., Broadview, IL; *U.S. Private*, pg. 923

Tropitzsoh, Heiner, Dir.-H.R.--Daimler-Benz Aktiengesellschaft, Stuttgart, Germany; *Int'l*, pg. 366

Trosvig, Dale, Dir.-Personnel & Svcs.--Otter Tail Power Company, Fergus Falls, MN; *U.S. Public*, pg. 1234

Trotman, Sally, Mgr.-Human Resources & Office Mgr.--Land O'Lakes, Inc., Southampton, PA; *U.S. Private*, pg. 646

Troutman, Charles, Mgr.-Employee Devel.--Blue Ridge Electric Membership Corp., Lenoir, NC; *U.S. Private*, pg. 153

Troy, Michael A., V.P.-Human Resources--Siemens Energy & Automation Inc., Alpharetta, GA; *Int'l*, pg. 1245

Truelle, Nicolas, V.P.-Human Resources/Health--Elf Aquitane, Paris, France; *Int'l*, pg. 444

Truex, Paul, V.P.-Personnel--McNeil Consumer Products Company, Guelph, Canada; *U.S. Public*, pg. 931

Trumble, Betty, Mgr.-Personnel--Summit Plastic Solutions, Inc., Florence, MA; *U.S. Private*, pg. 1050

Trumbull, Lindsay, Dir.-Personnel--Golden West Broadcasters, Los Angeles, CA; *U.S. Private*, pg. 461

Tryens, Nancy, Dir.-H.R.--NAO, Inc., Philadelphia, PA; *U.S. Private*, pg. 771

Tsukimoto, Kazuyoshi, Mgr.-Human Resources--Maruzen Company Limited, Tokyo, Japan; *Int'l*, pg. 845

Tubito, Vincent, Sr. V.P.-HR--Jan Bell Marketing Inc., Sunrise, FL; *U.S. Public*, pg. 207

Tucci, Angela M., Dir.-Employee Rels. & Training--The Canada Life Assurance Company, Toronto, Canada; *Int'l*, *pg. 254*

Tucker, Cindy, Dir.-H.R.--PMC Capital Inc., Dallas, TX; *U.S. Public*, pg. 1242

Tucker, Clark, V.P.-Personnel--General Instrument Corporation, Horsham, PA; *U.S. Public*, pg. 716

Tucker, Marshall D., Chief Fin. Officer, V.P., Treas., Controller & Sec.--Dixon Paper Co., Denver, CO; *U.S. Public*, pg. 902

Tucker, Mike, Sr. V.P.-H.R.--Baxter International Inc., Deerfield, IL; *U.S. Public*, pg. 196

Tucker, Roberta, Human Resources Dir.--Waring & LaRosa, Inc., New York, NY; *U.S. Private*, pg. 1150

Tucker, W.A., Dir.-Human Resources--Vertex Communications Corporation, Kilgore, TX; *U.S. Public*, pg. 1717

Tull, Michael J., Dir.-Personnel & Employee Benefits--Louisiana Pacific Corporation, Portland, OR; *U.S. Public*, pg. 1015

Tullus, Nancy, V.P.-Human Resources--Micropolis Corporation, Chatsworth, CA; *U.S. Private*, pg. 742

Tully, Suzanne, V.P.-H.R.--The Leslie Fay Companies, Inc., New York, NY; *U.S. Public*, pg. 989

Turner, Becky, Dir.-Personnel--TRI-GLAS, Daleville, AL; *U.S. Private*, pg. 848

Turner, Jackie, Mgr.-Personnel--Houston Fearless 76 Inc., Compton, CA; *U.S. Private*, pg. 542

Turner, Kit, Dir.-Human Resources--Circus Circus - Las Vegas, Las Vegas, NV; *U.S. Public*, pg. 374

Turner, Kit, Dir.-Human Resources--Circus Circus Hotel Casinos, Inc., Las Vegas, NV; *U.S. Public*, pg. 374

Turner, Margaret, V.P.-Human Resources--California State Bank, West Covina, CA; *U.S. Public*, pg. 294

Turner, Mike, Dir.-H.R.--Mercury General Corporation, Los Angeles, CA; *U.S. Public*, pg. 1093

Turunen, Seppo, Sr. V.P.-H.R.--Outokumpu Oyj, Espoo, Finland; *Int'l*, pg. 1015

Twigt, A., Mgr.-Human Resources--Bakery Ingredients Division, Delft, Netherlands; *Int'l*, pg. 1142

Tyhacz, Virginia, Personnel Dir.--Universal Voltronics Corporation, Mount Kisco, NY; *U.S. Public*, pg. 1596

Tylinski, David, Dir.-Personnel--Marathon Cheese Corp., Marathon, WI; *U.S. Private*, pg. 701

Tyska, R., Mgr.-Personnel--Packard Instrument Co., Inc., Meriden, CT; *U.S. Private*, pg. 833

U'Ren, L.J., Assoc. Gen. Mgr.-Opers., Information & Human Services--Salt River Project Agricultural Improvement and Power District, Tempe, AZ; *U.S. Private*, pg. 962

Ubertaccio, Denise, V.P. & H.R. Dir.--Dugan Valva Contess Inc., Morristown, NJ; *U.S. Private*, pg. 345

Uebbing, Jorg Alexander, Mgr.-Recruitment--European Investment Bank, Luxembourg, Luxembourg; *Int'l*, pg. 465

Ugol, Marc, Sr. V.P.-H.R.--Platinum Technology, Inc., Oak Brook Terrace, IL; *U.S. Public*, pg. 1309

Uhlendorff, Sue, Dir.-Human Resources--Metal Masters Foodservice Equipment, Clayton, DE; *U.S. Private*, pg. 734

Uhler, Dorothy, Dir.-Human Resources--Letraset Nielsen & Bainbridge, Paramus, NJ; *Int'l*, pg. 460

Uhlich, George, Dir.-Personnel--National Bulk Carriers, Inc., New York, NY; *U.S. Private*, pg. 780

Uklist, Harvey, Dir.-Human Resources--New York Law Journal, New York, NY; *Int'l*, pg. 956

Ulbrandt, Laura, Sec.--Leucadia National Corporation, New York, NY; *U.S. Public*, pg. 989

Underhill, Stephen M., Chief Fin. Officer, Controller & Dir.-Personnel--R.O. Whitesell & Associates, Inc, Indianapolis, IN; *U.S. Private*, pg. 1173

Underwood, David, V.P.-Personnel--Universal Standard Healthcare, Inc., Southfield, MI; *U.S. Public*, pg. 1697

Underwood, John L., V.P.-Human Resources--Fine Paper Div., Chillicothe, OH; *U.S. Public*, pg. 1074

Underwood, Tammy, Mgr.-Personnel & Exec. Asst.--Antenna Products Corp., Mineral Wells, TX; *U.S. Public*, pg. 289

Underwood, W.W., Mgr.-Personnel--Alamco, Inc., Charleston, WV; *U.S. Public*, pg. 403

Unger, Carol, V.P.-Personnel--Parade Publications Inc., New York, NY; *U.S. Private*, pg. 20

Uppman, Jan-Eric, Dir.-Personnel--Ikea Svenska AB, Almhult, Sweden; *Int'l*, pg. 660

Urbas, James P., Dir.-Human Resources--MYR Group Inc., Rolling Meadows, IL; *U.S. Public*, pg. 1029

Urroz, Ricardo, Dir.-H.R.--Grupo Sidek, S.A. de C.V., Guadalajara, Mexico; *Int'l*, pg. 576

Usaj, Joseph S., V.P.-H.R. & Admin.--Consolidated Natural Gas Company, Pittsburgh, PA; *U.S. Public*, pg. 435

Usaj, Joseph S., V.P.-Human Resources Admin.--Consolidated Natural Gas Service Co., Inc., Pittsburgh, PA; *U.S. Public*, pg. 435

Utley, Carolyn, Dir.-Personnel--Alley-Cassetty Coal Co., Nashville, TN; *U.S. Private*, pg. 37

Utzinger, Tedd, Mgr.-Risk--LGC Management, Englewood, CO; *U.S. Private*, pg. 639

Uy, Conrad, Sec., Dir.-Personnel, & Pur. Agent--Atalanta Corporation, Elizabeth, NJ; *U.S. Private*, pg. 93

Vachey, Francois, V.P.-Human Resources--L'Oreal S.A., Clichy, France; *Int'l*, pg. 818

Vachon, Dianne, Dir.-Personnel--Simmons American Eagle Airlines, Dallas-Fort Worth Airport, TX; *U.S. Public*, pg. 10

Vachon, Mary, Dir.-Personnel--Raffi & Swanson, Inc., Wilmington, MA; *U.S. Private*, pg. 907

Vail, C.C., V.P.-H.R.--Benjamin Moore & Co., Montvale, NJ; *U.S. Private*, pg. 133

Vail, Gary, Dir.-Human Resources--Hvide Marine Incorporated, Fort Lauderdale, FL; *U.S. Public*, pg. 851

Valais, Jean-Pierre, V.P.-H.R. & Commun.--Pathe, Paris, France; *Int'l*, pg. 1024

Valdes, Fernando, V.P.-H.R.--Corporacion Industrial Sanluis, Mexico, Mexico; *Int'l*, pg. 332

Valdez, Lalo, Dir.-Human Resources--AMATI Communications Corp., San Jose, CA; *U.S. Public*, pg. 1585

Valent, Peter, Mng. Dir.--VOEST-ALPINE Austria Draht Ges.m.b.H., Bruck, Austria; *Int'l*, pg. 1470

Valenti, Michael J., Dir.-Human Resources--Los Angeles Times, Los Angeles, CA; *U.S. Public*, pg. 1616

Valentine, Bryan, Sr. V.P.-Human Resources--Structural Dynamics Research Corp., Milford, OH; *U.S. Public*, pg. 1525

Valentine, Linda J., V.P.-Compensation & Benefits--Hartmarx Corporation, Chicago, IL; *U.S. Public*, pg. 795

Valerio Trevino, Eloy, Dir.-Personnel--Copamex Industrias S.A. de C.V., Garza Garcia, Mexico; *Int'l*, pg. 330

Valli, Louis A., Sr. V.P.-Employee Rels.--USX Corporation, Pittsburgh, PA; *U.S. Public*, pg. 1661

Valtman, Ahuva, Mgr.-H.R.--IIS Intelligent Information Systems Ltd., Yokneam, Israel; *Int'l*, pg. 645

Van Aken, John, Sr. V.P.-H.R.--Visa U.S.A. Inc., San Francisco, CA; *U.S. Private*, pg. 1141

van Beers, Han, Sr. V.P.-Human Resources & Legal--Interface Europe B.V., Scherpenzeel, Netherlands; *U.S. Public*, pg. 889

Van Berkel, Jack, V.P.-H.R.--Western Digital Corporation, Irvine, CA; *U.S. Public*, pg. 1758

Van Berken, J. Thomas, Chief Human Resources Officer & Sr. V.P.--ADVO, Inc., Windsor, CT; *U.S. Public*, pg. 23

Van Bladel, Viveca, Dir.-Human Resources--Millicom International Cellular SA, Bertrange, Luxembourg; *Int'l*, pg. 867

Van Buren, Susan, V.P.-Human Resources & Employee Rels.--Restaura, Inc., Phoenix, AZ; *U.S. Public*, pg. 1718

Van Dale, Susan, Dir.-Personnel--Allen Telecom Inc., Solon, OH; *U.S. Public*, pg. 45

van de Weerd, J., Dir.-Human Resources--N.V. Koninklijke KNP BT, Amsterdam, Netherlands; *Int'l*, pg. 756

van der Geest, Edwin, Mgr.-Pub. Rels.--Bally Management AG, Schonenwerd, Switzerland; *Int'l*, pg. 996

van der Kloet, B.E., Mgr.-Personnel & Organisation--NORIT N.V., Amersfoort, Netherlands; *Int'l*, pg. 958

van der Laan, W., Dir.-Organizational Devel.--CSM N.V., Diemen, Netherlands; *Int'l*, pg. 243

van der Veen, A., Mgr.-Personnel--Bayer B.V., Mijdrecht, Netherlands; *Int'l*, pg. 175

van der Zwan, Arie Jacobs James, Exec. Dir. & Dir.-Legal, Mktg., Human Res., Tax Services & Plng.--The Southern Life Association Limited, Cape Town, South Africa; *Int'l*, pg. 77

van Dijk, A., Dir.-Personnel & Organization--Bestuurcentrum der Verenigde Bedrijven Nutricia B.V., Zoetermeer, Netherlands; *Int'l*, pg. 991

van Dijk, E., Mng. Dir.-Human Resources--Van Melle N.V., Breda, Netherlands; *Int'l*, pg. 1450

Van Dyke, Connie, Dir.-Human Resources--Bed Bath & Beyond Inc., Union, NJ; *U.S. Public*, pg. 200

Van Dyken, Nancy, Dir.-Human Resources--Chico's Fas Inc, Fort Myers, FL; *U.S. Public*, pg. 349

Van Fossan, Janet, Sr. Partner & Human Resources Dir.--Carmichael Lynch, Inc., Minneapolis, MN; *U.S. Private*, pg. 213

Van Gordon, Paul, V.P.-H.R.--Rosauers Supermarkets, Inc., Spokane, WA; *U.S. Private*, pg. 944

van Groenou, Leonard Broese, V.P.-Human Resources & Procurement--Air Products Europe, Inc., Allentown, PA; *U.S. Public*, pg. 30

Van Haitsma, John, Mgr.-H.R.--Gentex Corporation, Zeeland, MI; *U.S. Public*, pg. 731

van Haren, Jeannette, Dir.-H.R.--Det Norske Veritas, Rotterdam, Netherlands; *Int'l*, pg. 397

Van Hoeck, Mark, Dir.-H.R.--GIB Group, Brussels, Belgium; *Int'l*, pg. 532

Van Hoose, Michelle, V.P.-Human Resources--Gymboree Corporation, Burlingame, CA; *U.S. Public*, pg. 770

Van Horn, Charlie, Dir.-Human Resources--Thomas Steel Strip Corp., Warren, OH; *Int'l*, pg. 756

Van Keymeulen, R., Inspector Gen.-Personnel--Banque Nationale de Belgique, Brussels, Belgium; *Int'l*, pg. 162

van Lamsweerde, C.P.E.J.M., Dir.-Personnel--Royal Nedlloyd Group N.V., Rotterdam, Netherlands; *Int'l*, pg. 1143

Van Moer, Rose, Dir.-Personnel--Walman Optical Company, Minneapolis, MN; *U.S. Private*, pg. 1148

van Rooyen, J.J., Mgr.-Human Resources--Kloof Division, Kloof, South Africa; *Int'l*, pg. 738

van Rooyen, Johan, Mgr.-H.R.--Natref, Sasolburg, South Africa; *Int'l*, pg. 1197

Van Skyock, Jim, Dir.-Personnel--Union City Body Company, L.P., Union City, IN; *U.S. Private*, pg. 1118

van Stadem, C., Mgr.-Personnel--CIBA-GEIGY (Pty.) Ltd., Isando, South Africa; *Int'l*, pg. 978

Van Stedum, Edward J., Sr. V.P.-Human Resources--Genuine Parts Company, Atlanta, GA; *U.S. Public*, pg. 732

Van Vleet, Rick, Dir.-Telecommunications & Personnel--Diversco, Inc., Spartanburg, SC; *U.S. Private*, pg. 336

Van Vliet, Dawn, Mgr.-H.R.--Network Peripherals Inc., Milpitas, CA; *U.S. Public*, pg. 1169

van Vliet, S.T., Mgr.-H.R.--Delft Instruments N.V., Delft, Netherlands; *Int'l*, pg. 388

Van Wagoner, Jennifer, Mgr.-Employee Benefits--Graphic Technology, Inc., New Century, KS; *Int'l*, pg. 950

van Westerop, M.G., Mrs., Dir.-Personnel--Ballast Nedam NV, Amstelveen, Netherlands; *Int'l*, pg. 133

VandenBroeck, Pat, Mgr.-Human Resources--Fisher Broadcasting Inc., Seattle, WA; *U.S. Public*, pg. 648

Vander-Lann, Richard T., V.P.-H.R.--Vermeer Manufacturing Company, Pella, IA; *U.S. Private*, pg. 1137

Vanderbaan, Russ, Mgr.-Human Resources--Morgan Construction Co., Worcester, MA; *U.S. Private*, pg. 761

Vanderbroeck, Paul J., Dr., Dir.-H.R.--AGIE Charmilles Group, Zug, Switzerland; *Int'l*, pg. 488

Vanderford, Preston, Dir.-Personnel--St. Louis Post-Dispatch, Saint Louis, MO; *U.S. Public*, pg. 1343

VanderSluis, Kenneth C., V.P.-Human Resources--Huntington National Bank, Morgantown, WV; *U.S. Public*, *pg. 850*

Vandervalk, William, V.P.-H.R.--Nabi, Boca Raton, FL; *U.S. Public*, pg. 1148

VanDuzer, M. Keith, V.P.-Human Resources & Admin.--GTE Mobile Communications Incorporated, Atlanta, GA; *U.S. Public*, pg. 696

Vanek, Janet, Mgr.-H.R.--Security Mutual Life Insurance Co. of New York, Binghamton, NY; *U.S. Private*, pg. 981

Vangel, Tom, Mgr.-Personnel--Micro Networks Corp., Worcester, MA; *U.S. Private*, pg. 969

Vangroow, Kelli, Mgr.-H.R.--Sathers Inc., Round Lake, MN; *U.S. Private*, pg. 397

VanPelt, J.F., V.P.-H.R.--Graybar Electric Company, Inc., Clayton, MO; *U.S. Private*, pg. 472

Vanreqckavorsal, Joelle, Dir.-Human Resources--L'Oreal Belgilux SA, Brussels, Belgium; *Int'l*, pg. 819

Vanucci, Yvonne, Mgr.-H.R.--Cargill Detroit Corp., Clawson, MI; *U.S. Private*, pg. 210

Varasco, David, V.P.-H.R.--Smith Corona Corp., Cortland, NY; *U.S. Private*, pg. 1007

Vargas, Andres, Dir.-Personnel--Cash & Carry Grocer Inc., Chicago, IL; *U.S. Private*, pg. 218

Vargas, James F., V.P.-H.R.--The Copley Press, Inc., La Jolla, CA; *U.S. Private*, pg. 275

Vargas, Norma, Recruiter--GSD&M, Austin, TX; *U.S. Private*, *pg. 436*

Varitinos, Margaret, Mgr.-H.R. & Asst. to the Pres.--Deck House Inc., Acton, MA; *U.S. Private*, pg. 320

Varitinos, Margaret, Asst. to the Pres. & Mgr.-Human Resources--Acorn Structures, Acton, MA; *U.S. Private*, pg. 320

Varma, Bob, V.P.-Opers.--Nathan's Famous Inc., Westbury, NY; *U.S. Public*, pg. 1152

Vasara, Riitta, Mgr.-Human Resources--Cultor Ltd., Helsinki, Finland; *Int'l*, pg. 349

Vasilopoulos, Joan, V.P.-H.R.--Kronos Incorporated, Waltham, MA; *U.S. Public*, pg. 967

Vasquez, Henry S., V.P.-Human Resources--Bayou Steel Corporation, La Place, LA; *U.S. Public*, pg. 197

Vaugh, Curtis, Dir.-Personnel--Peterson Farms, Decatur, AR; *U.S. Private*, pg. 857

Vaughan, Alan, V.P.-H.R.--Minyard Food Stores, Inc., Coppell, TX; *U.S. Private*, pg. 752

Vaughn, Judy, Mgr.-Human Resources--The Murray Ohio Mfg. Co., Brentwood, TN; *Int'l*, pg. 1397

Vaughn, Ruby, Dir.-Personnel--C.B. Ragland Company, Nashville, TN; *U.S. Private*, pg. 907

Vaughn, William M., III, Exec. V.P.-Human Resources & Support Services--The Stop & Shop Companies, Inc., Quincy, MA; *Int'l*, pg. 750

Vaz, Gera M., V.P.-H.R.--The Good Guys, Inc., Brisbane, CA; *U.S. Public*, pg. 750

Vegter, Bill, Chief Fin. Officer & V.P.-Fin.--All-Phase Electric Supply Co., Benton Harbor, MI; *U.S. Private*, pg. 35

Veit, Dan, Mgr.-H.R.--The Habegger Corporation, Cincinnati, OH; *U.S. Private*, pg. 492

Veith, Hedwig M., Dir.-Human Resources--BayBanks, Inc., Boston, MA; *U.S. Public*, pg. 184

Velasco, Edward M., V.P.-Human Resources--Bentley Mills, Inc., City of Industry, CA; *U.S. Public*, pg. 889
Velmosky, Dave, V.P.-H.R.--Isolyser Company, Inc., Norcross, GA; *U.S. Public*, pg. 914
Velorde, Yolanda, Controller--Crispin Porter & Bogusky Advertising, Miami, FL; *U.S. Private*, pg. 290
Vencill, Gay, Dir.-H.R.--Dallas Semiconductor Corporation, Dallas, TX; *U.S. Public*, pg. 478
Vencill, Jeanne, Dir.-H.R.--Ciprico, Inc., Plymouth, MN; *U.S. Public*, pg. 370
Ventiera, Anthony, Dir.-H.R.--Graham-Field Health Products, Inc., Hauppauge, NY; *U.S. Public*, pg. 757
Venturas, Daphne, Mgr.-Personnel Policy--European Investment Bank, Luxembourg, Luxembourg; *Int'l*, pg. 465
Venzel, Jan, V.P.-H.R.--Danisco A/S, Copenhagen, Denmark; *Int'l*, pg. 378
Verdecia, Belia, V.P.-Human Resources & Bus. Admin. Dir.--The Bravo Group, New York, NY; *U.S. Private*, pg. 1197
Verdin, Juanita, Mgr.-H.R.--Pride International, Inc., Houston, TX; *U.S. Public*, pg. 1324
Vergne, Jean-Luc, Sr. V.P.-Human Resources/Elf--Elf Aquitane, Paris, France; *Int'l*, pg. 444
Verhagen, Timothy J., V.P.-H.R.--United Dominion Industries, Ltd., Charlotte, NC; *U.S. Public*, pg. 1675
Verhenne, Jan, Corp. V.P.-H.R. Mgmnt.--N.V. Bekaert S.A., Kortrijk, Belgium; *Int'l*, pg. 183
Verissimo, Edward, Mgr.-Human Resources--AFC Cable Systems, Inc., Providence, RI; *U.S. Public*, pg. 6
Vermeulen, Arie, Dir.-H.R.--Thorn Security Group, Ltd., Sunbury, United Kingdom; *Int'l*, pg. 1386
Vernon, Diane, Mgr.-Personnel--Elco Precision Stamping Div., Logansport, IN; *U.S. Public*, pg. 1590
Vernon, Gerald B., Sr. V.P.-Human Resources--ConAgra, Inc., Omaha, NE; *U.S. Public*, pg. 425
Vernon, Kenneth, V.P.-Fin.--Mid-West Automation Systems, Inc., Buffalo Grove, IL; *U.S. Public*, pg. 475
Verster, J.M., Gen. Mgr.-Grp. H.R.--Standard Bank Investment Corporation Limited, Johannesburg, South Africa; *Int'l*, pg. 1293
Verzaro, Gianfranco, Gen. Mgr. & Dir.-Human Resources & Organizing Devel.--Banca Nazionale del Lavoro Sj.A., Rome, Italy; *Int'l*, pg. 136
Vescuso, Michael A., Sr. V.P.-Human Resources--America West Airlines, Inc., Phoenix, AZ; *U.S. Public*, pg. 67
Vesper, T. Kent, V.P.-Human Resources--Hoffman Engineering Company, Anoka, MN; *U.S. Public*, pg. 1273
Vest, Carla K., Sr. V.P.-H.R.--Indianapolis Life Insurance Co., Indianapolis, IN; *U.S. Private*, pg. 560
Vestal, Charles, Mgr.-Human Resources--Jouan, Inc., Winchester, VA; *U.S. Private*, pg. 601
Vetta, Karen, Mgr.-Human Resources--Tekra Corporation, New Berlin, WI; *U.S. Private*, pg. 1073
Vetter, Jean, Dir.-Personnel--Times Printing Company, Inc., Random Lake, WI; *U.S. Private*, pg. 1087
Vezina, G. Robert, Exec. V.P.-Personnel--First Tennessee National Corporation, Memphis, TN; *U.S. Public*, pg. 638
Vezina, G. Robert, Exec. V.P.-Personnel--First Tennessee Bank National Association, Memphis, TN; *U.S. Public*, pg. 639
Viapiano, Janice, Mgr.-Personnel--Union Pen Company, Greenwich, CT; *U.S. Private*, pg. 1119
Vicente, Ana Maria, Chief Personnel Officer--Central de Cervejas, S.A., Lisbon, Portugal; *Int'l*, pg. 279
Vickars, Robert, Mgr.-Personnel--South Charleston Stamping & Manufacturing, South Charleston, WV; *U.S. Private*, pg. 1030
Vickers, Marcy, Dir.-Human Resources--Sonic Industries, Inc., Oklahoma City, OK; *U.S. Public*, pg. 1485
Vickery, Dave, Dir.-H.R. & Sr. Mgr.--Gordon Food Service Inc., Grand Rapids, MI; *U.S. Private*, pg. 465
Victor, Elyse, Mgr.-Personnel--Warren Gorham Lamont, New York, NY; *U.S. Public*, pg. 1602
Victor, Ron, Dir.-H.R. Medical Grp.--Coherent, Inc., Santa Clara, CA; *U.S. Public*, pg. 395
Victor, Ron, Dir.-Human Resources--Micronics Computers, Inc., Fremont, CA; *U.S. Public*, pg. 1106
Vidian, Sara, Dir.-Human Resources--Rainfair, Inc., Racine, WI; *U.S. Private*, pg. 907
Viesta, Lee, Mgr.-Personnel--Center Laboratories, Inc., Port Washington, NY; *U.S. Public*, pg. 813
Vieu, Pierre, Dir. Gen.-Human Resources--SNCF, Paris, France; *Int'l*, pg. 1163
Vieu, Pierre, Dir.-H.R.--SNCF, Paris, France; *Int'l*, pg. 1163
Vignali, Susan, Dir.-Human Resources--American Technical Ceramics Corp., Huntington Station, NY; *U.S. Public*, pg. 93
Vigneau, Jim, Sr. Mgr.-Human Resources--Alpine Electronics of America, Inc., Torrance, CA; *Int'l*, pg. 65
Villeneuve, Francois, V.P.-Mktg. & Human Resources-Eastern Canada Region--Costco Wholesale, Issaquah, WA; *U.S. Public*, pg. 451
Vinall, Britt, Rep.-H.R.--J.T. Slocomb Company, South Glastonbury, CT; *U.S. Private*, pg. 1006
Vincelette, Rene, Dir.-Human Resources--Peerless Carpet Corporation, Acton Vale, Canada; *Int'l*, pg. 1032
Vincent, Peter, Dir.-Human Resources--People, New York, NY; *U.S. Public*, pg. 1613
Vincent, Tami, Dir.-H.R.--East Jordan Iron Works, East Jordan, MI; *U.S. Private*, pg. 356
Vinson, Joe, V.P.-H.R.--Cameron, Houston, TX; *U.S. Public*, pg. 298
Vipperman, Joseph H., Exec. V.P.-Corp. Svcs.--American Electric Power Company, Inc., Columbus, OH; *U.S. Public*, pg. 71
Virtanen, Pekka, Sr. V.P.-Personnel--Metra Corporation, Helsinki, Finland; *Int'l*, pg. 862
Visone, William, Chief Fin. Officer--Pentech International, Inc., Edison, NJ; *U.S. Public*, pg. 1274
Voellinger, Korinn, Dir.-Commun.--BGW Systems, Inc., Hawthorne, CA; *U.S. Private*, pg. 107
Voge, Roger, V.P.-Interior Decoration--Star Lumber & Supply Company, Inc., Wichita, KS; *U.S. Private*, pg. 1034
Vogel, Gerhard, Dr., Chief Fin. Officer, V.P.-Fin. & Controller--Fuchs Petrolub AG Oel + Chemie, Mannheim, Germany; *Int'l*, pg. 517
Vogel, John, Mgr.-Human Resources & Corp. Benefits--Varlen Corporation, Naperville, IL; *U.S. Public*, pg. 1710
Vogel, P., Dir.-H.R.-Benelux--Dun & Bradstreet Eurinform SA-NV, Brussels, Belgium; *U.S. Public*, pg. 536
Vogel, Paul, Controller--Amcel Corp., Watertown, MA; *U.S. Private*, pg. 48
Vogt, Raymond, V.P.-Human Resources--The Lincoln Electric Company, Cleveland, OH; *U.S. Public*, pg. 996
Volden, Shelly, Mgr.-H.R.--Mattison Technologies, Inc., Rockford, IL; *U.S. Private*, pg. 714
Volk, Pam, Mgr.-Human Resources--Idaho Supreme Company, Firth, ID; *U.S. Private*, pg. 557
Vomero, Ronald, Dir.-Human Resources--Copes-Vulcan Inc., Lake City, PA; *U.S. Private*, pg. 274
Von Rueden, James, Controller & Sec.--Wausau Homes, Inc., Rothschild, WI; *U.S. Private*, pg. 1154
Von Solenjen, Delores, Mgr.-H.R.--McKinney & McKinney Advertising, Redondo Beach, CA; *U.S. Private*, pg. 723
von Waldthausen, Gottfried Wilhelm, Exec. V.P.-H.R.--Commerzbank AG, Frankfurt, Germany; *Int'l*, pg. 308
Voogt, C., Gen. Mgr.-Personnel--Rabobank Nederland, Utrecht, Netherlands; *Int'l*, pg. 1082
Vosburgh, Donald F., V.P.-Human Resources--IMO Industries Inc., Lawrenceville, NJ; *U.S. Public*, pg. 856
Voss, Steve, Exec. V.P. & H.R.--Golden West Financial Corporation, Oakland, CA; *U.S. Public*, pg. 750
Vuksinick, Brett, Mgr.-Human Resources--Radix Corporation, Salt Lake City, UT; *U.S. Private*, pg. 906
Vuolo, Gil, V.P.-Personnel--The Grand Union Company, Wayne, NJ; *U.S. Public*, pg. 758
Vuorio, Timo, Sr. V.P.-Grp. Admin.--Partek Corporation, Helsinki, Finland; *Int'l*, pg. 1024
Wachner, Barbara Jo, Exec. V.P.-Mktg., Personnel & Sec.--BGW Systems, Inc., Hawthorne, CA; *U.S. Private*, pg. 107
Wade, B., Dir.-Personnel--Red Wing Co. Inc., Fredonia, NY; *Int'l*, pg. 1398
Wade, Christeen, Dir.-Personnel--Tri-State Wholesale Associated Grocers, Inc., El Paso, TX; *U.S. Private*, pg. 1101
Wade, Janis M., Sr. V.P.-H.R. & Corp. Commun.--CCL Industries, Inc., Willowdale, Canada; *Int'l*, pg. 238
Wade, Jim, V.P.-Human Resources--Pacificare Health Systems, Santa Ana, CA; *U.S. Public*, pg. 1251
Wade, Suzanne, Mgr.-H.R.--ANGUS Chemical Company, Buffalo Grove, IL; *U.S. Private*, pg. 75
Wadler, Arnold L., Sr. V.P., Gen. Counsel & Sec.--Metromedia International Group, Inc., East Rutherford, NJ; *U.S. Public*, pg. 1102
Wagner, Becky, Mgr.-Human Resources--Objective Systems Integrators, Inc., Folsom, CA; *U.S. Public*, pg. 1209
Wagner, Cindy, Dir.-Human Resources--Hadron, Inc., Alexandria, VA; *U.S. Public*, pg. 773
Wagner, Donald, V.P.-H.R.--IVAX Corporation, Miami, FL; *U.S. Public*, pg. 914
Wagner, Gloria, Mgr.-H.R.--Berryman Products, Inc., Arlington, TX; *U.S. Private*, pg. 138
Wagner, Karen, Chief Fin. Officer, V.P. & Treas.--American Recreation Centers, Inc., Sacramento, CA; *U.S. Public*, pg. 90
Wagner, Larry A., Sr. V.P.-Human Resources--Fleming Companies, Inc., Oklahoma City, OK; *U.S. Public*, pg. 652
Wagner, Mary, Mgr.-H.R.--Donlee Technologies Inc., York, PA; *U.S. Private*, pg. 339
Wagner, Sylvia, Sr. V.P.-Human Resources--Fortis Benefits Insurance Company, Kansas City, MO; *Int'l*, pg. 499
Wagus, Donna, Dir.-H.R.--Bruning Paint Company, Baltimore, MD; *U.S. Private*, pg. 176
Waibel, James J., V.P.-Admin.--Elcor Corporation, Dallas, TX; *U.S. Public*, pg. 567
Waite, Brad A., Sr. V.P.-Human Resources--Consolidated Stores Corp., Columbus, OH; *U.S. Public*, pg. 437
Waite, Lavon, Mgr.-Human Resources--Cagle's Inc., Atlanta, GA; *U.S. Public*, pg. 291
Wakabayashi, Shigeyuki, Gen. Mgr.--Toyo Tire & Rubber Co., Ltd., Osaka, Japan; *Int'l*, pg. 1411
Wakamura, Shigekazu, Dir.-Human Resources--Murata Manufacturing Co., Ltd., Kyoto, Japan; *Int'l*, pg. 897
Wakefield, Christine, Dir.-Personnel--JSB Electrical PLC, Crewe, United Kingdom; *Int'l*, pg. 453
Wakefield, Mary Lou, Sr. V.P.-Human Resources--Ralphs Grocery Company, Compton, CA; *U.S. Private*, pg. 1202
Walberg, Kristin, Dir.-H.R.--American Enterprise Institute for Public Policy Research, Washington, DC; *U.S. Private*, pg. 53
Walck, David S., Sr. V.P.-Human Resources--Gibraltar Savings, Simi Valley, CA; *U.S. Public*, pg. 181
Walden, Cynthia, Mgr.-H.R.--Guard Publishing Company, Eugene, OR; *U.S. Private*, pg. 485
Walden, Joy, Personnel Mgr.--Grey Advertising Inc., Western Div., Los Angeles, CA; *U.S. Public*, pg. 764
Waldron, Chuck, V.P.-H.R.--Kelly Services, Inc., Troy, MI; *U.S. Public*, pg. 949
Wales, William, V.P.-Human Resources--DowBrands, L.P., Indianapolis, IN; *U.S. Public*, pg. 523
Walker, Aleta, Mgr.-Human Resources--Daihatsu America, Inc., Los Alamitos, CA; *Int'l*, pg. 365
Walker, Carl, V.P.-Human Resources--Sealright Company, Inc., De Soto, KS; *U.S. Public*, pg. 1451
Walker, David, Grp. Mgr.-Personnel & Info.--Avesta Sheffield AB, Stockholm, Sweden; *Int'l*, pg. 221
Walker, Dennis, Dir.-H.R. & Quality--PPP hc, Tunbridge Wells, United Kingdom; *Int'l*, pg. 1020
Walker, James A., V.P.-H.R.--Hunter Fan Company, Memphis, TN; *U.S. Private*, pg. 549
Walker, Joretta, Mgr.-Personnel--Sunnyland Refining Co., Inc., Birmingham, AL; *U.S. Private*, pg. 607
Walker, Kern, V.P.-H.R.--Kurt Manufacturing Co. Inc., Fridley, MN; *U.S. Private*, pg. 637
Walker, Mark, Dir.-Personnel--Klaussner Furniture Industry, Asheboro, NC; *U.S. Private*, pg. 625
Walker, Patricia, Mgr.-Personnel--Eurocamp Plc, Knutsford, United Kingdom; *Int'l*, pg. 464
Walker, Patsy, Dir.-Human Resources--Georgia/Durango Boot Company, Franklin, TN; *U.S. Public*, pg. 1684
Walker, Robert, Dir.-H.R.--Bell Industries, Inc., El Segundo, CA; *U.S. Public*, pg. 204
Walker, Sarah, Dir.-Human Resources--Interferon Sciences, Inc., New Brunswick, NJ; *U.S. Public*, pg. 694
Wall, Jim, Natl. Dir.-Human Resources--Deloitte & Touche LLP, Wilton, CT; *U.S. Private*, pg. 322
Wall, Karen, V.P. & Dir.-Human Resources--BTG, Inc., Fairfax, VA; *U.S. Public*, pg. 164
Wall, Kathleen, Dir.-Personnel--BMW (US) Holding Corporation, Woodcliff Lake, NJ; *Int'l*, pg. 177
Wall, Merrill, First V.P.-H.R.--H.F. Ahmanson & Co., Irwindale, CA; *U.S. Public*, pg. 29
Wall, Merrill, 1st V.P.-Human Resources--Home Savings of America, FSB, Irwindale, CA; *U.S. Public*, pg. 29
Wall, Steve F., Dir.-Human Resources--Broadcast Electronics, Inc., Quincy, IL; *U.S. Private*, pg. 531
Wallac, Judy, V.P.-Human Resources--VTEL Corporation, Austin, TX; *U.S. Public*, pg. 1703
Wallace, James A., Dir.-H.R.--Calavo Growers of California, Santa Ana, CA; *U.S. Private*, pg. 199
Wallace, Joan, V.P.-Opers.--The Mills Corporation, Arlington, VA; *U.S. Public*, pg. 1113
Wallace, Robert, Dir.-Personnel--Miami Mill, Dayton, OH; *Int'l*, pg. 434
Wallace, W.N., Mgr.-Human Resources--National Frozen Foods Corp., Seattle, WA; *U.S. Private*, pg. 783
Wallbridge, Lewis, V.P.-Human Resources--LSI Logic Corp., Milpitas, CA; *U.S. Public*, pg. 971
Waller, Diana D., Dir.-Human Resources--Yankee Energy System, Inc., Meriden, CT; *U.S. Public*, pg. 1787
Waller, John C., V.P.-Human Resources--Fair, Isaac and Company, Inc., San Rafael, CA; *U.S. Public*, pg. 609
Wallersheim, Lorrie, Dir.-H.R--H.C. Miller Company, Milwaukee, WI; *U.S. Private*, pg. 747
Walling, Naomi, V.P.-H.R.--Pacific Capital Bancorp, Salinas, CA; *U.S. Public*, pg. 1247
Walling, Naomi, V.P. & Mgr.-Human Resources--First National Bank of Central California, Salinas, CA; *U.S. Public*, pg. 1248
Wallskog, Klas, Dir.-Personnel--Preem Petroleum AB, Stockholm, Sweden; *Int'l*, pg. 1066
Walmsley, Linda, V.P.-Human Resources--Trinidad/Benham Corp., Denver, CO; *U.S. Private*, pg. 1103
Walraven, W.W., Personnel Mgr.--Van Melle Nederland B.V., Breda, Netherlands; *Int'l*, pg. 1451
Walser, Peter, Mgr.-Corp. Communications--Schindler Holding AG, Hergiswil, Switzerland; *Int'l*, pg. 1204
Walsh, Cathy, Dir.-Human Resources--Nova Scotia Power Inc., Halifax, Canada; *Int'l*, pg. 971
Walsh, Chris, Dir.-H.R.--David Jones Limited, Sydney, Australia; *Int'l*, pg. 714
Walsh, Edward F., V.P.-Human Resources--Campbell Soup Company, Camden, NJ; *U.S. Public*, pg. 298
Walsh, Jack, Mgr.-H.R.--Victor Corporation, West Warwick, RI; *U.S. Private*, pg. 1138
Walsh, Nancy, Mgr.-H.R.--Bertelsmann Inc., New York, NY; *Int'l*, pg. 191
Walsh, Patrick J., Sr. V.P.-Human Resources--Merrill Lynch & Co., Inc., New York, NY; *U.S. Public*, pg. 1097
Walsh, Patrick M., V.P.-Admin. & Human Res.--Reeves International, Spartanburg, SC; *U.S. Private*, pg. 507
Walsh, Richard F., Sr. V.P.-Human Resources--ABB Inc., Norwalk, CT; *Int'l*, pg. 3
Waltemath, Luanne, Partner-Human Resources--J.C. Bradford & Co., Nashville, TN; *U.S. Private*, pg. 163
Walter, Don, Mgr.-Human Resources--Hougen Manufacturing Inc., Swartz Creek, MI; *U.S. Private*, pg. 541
Walter, Patricia, Asst. V.P.-Human Resources--Atlas Van Lines, Inc., Evansville, IN; *U.S. Private*, pg. 97
Walters, Carolyn, Mgr.-H.R.--Hampton Print Works, Inc., Johnson City, TN; *U.S. Private*, pg. 498
Walters, Jack, V.P.-Human Resources--Alcon Laboratories, Inc., Fort Worth, TX; *Int'l*, pg. 916
Walters, Michael W., V.P.-H.R.--The Coca-Cola Company, Atlanta, GA; *U.S. Public*, pg. 392
Walthen, Sandra, Dir.-Personnel--Weichert Realty, Inc., Alexandria, VA; *U.S. Private*, pg. 1159
Walther, J., Mgr.-Human Resources--Kaufman Footwear, Kitchener, Canada; *Int'l*, pg. 725
Walvoord, Ellen M., Sr. V.P.-Human Resources--Abbott Laboratories, Abbott Park, IL; *U.S. Public*, pg. 12
Walz, Sharon, Mgr.-H.R.--Green Spot Packaging Inc., Claremont, CA; *U.S. Private*, pg. 477
Walztoni, Mark, V.P.-Human Resources--Computer Horizons Corp., Mountain Lakes, NJ; *U.S. Public*, pg. 421
Wandschneider, J.F., V.P.-H.R.--Bradley Corporation, Menomonee Falls, WI; *U.S. Private*, pg. 164
Wangbichler, R.J., V.P.-Employee Rels.--The Budd Company, Troy, MI; *Int'l*, pg. 1388
Wantman, Kay, Dir.-Personnel--UFP Technology, Georgetown, MA; *U.S. Private*, pg. 1112
Ward, Cornell, Dir.-Human Resources--Reynolds Metals Co.-Can Division Headquarters, Richmond, VA; *U.S. Public*, pg. 1386
Ward, J., Mgr.-Personnel--Cementation Piling & Foundations Limited, Rickmansworth, United Kingdom; *Int'l*, pg. 772
Ward, Wyman, V.P.-Human Resources--Coltec Industries Inc., Charlotte, NC; *U.S. Public*, pg. 401
Ward, Wyrot, 2nd V.P.-Trng. & Devel.--Phoenix Home Life Mutual Insurance Co., Hartford, CT; *U.S. Private*, pg. 863
Warfel, Lou, Mgr.-H.R.--Master Molded Products Corporation, Elgin, IL; *U.S. Private*, pg. 714
Wargo, Michael J., V.P. & Dir.-H.R.--Quality Dining Inc., Mishawaka, IN; *U.S. Public*, pg. 1349
Warlick-Jarvie, Lois, V.P.-Human Resources--Curtice Burns Foods, Rochester, NY; *U.S. Private*, pg. 887

Warman, Bruce, Mgr.-Personnel--Vauxhall Motors Limited, Luton, United Kingdom; *U.S. Public*, pg. 724
Warnock, J.S., Dir.-Personnel--John Menzies plc, Edinburgh, United Kingdom; *Int'l*, pg. 707
Warnstrom, Claes, Dir.-H.R., Sweden--Astra AB, Sodertalje, Sweden; *Int'l*, pg. 93
Warren, C., Mgr.-Personnel--Ransomes Plc, Ipswich, United Kingdom; *Int'l*, pg. 1087
Warren, David, Dir.-H.R.--Windmere-Durable Holdings, Hialeah, FL; *U.S. Public*, pg. 1771
Warren, Donna, V.P.-H.R. & Employee Benefits--Cooper Communities, Inc., Bella Vista, AR; *U.S. Private*, pg. 273
Warren, Jack, V.P.-Human Resources--Safelite AutoGlass, Columbus, OH; *U.S. Private*, pg. 960
Warren, John, Dir.-Human Resources--Hayward Industries, Inc., Elizabeth, NJ; *U.S. Private*, pg. 513
Warren, Robert, V.P.-Human Resources--Wilcox Electric, Inc., Kansas City, MO; *Int'l*, pg. 1384
Warwick, Donald, V.P.-Human Resources--Konica Business Machines USA, Inc., Windsor, CT; *Int'l*, pg. 748
Wascoe, Thomas M, V.P.-Human Resources--Abbott Diagnostic Products, North Chicago, IL; *U.S. Public*, pg. 13
Wasdin, Bonnie, Dir.-Personnel--Crown Crafts, Inc., Atlanta, GA; *U.S. Public*, pg. 465
Washburn, Pattie, Mgr.-H.R.--Allsop, Inc., Bellingham, WA; *U.S. Private*, pg. 44
Washburn, Richard V., Exec. V.P.-H.R. & Sec.--First of America Bank Corporation, Kalamazoo, MI; *U.S. Public*, pg. 636
Washington, Alvin, Sr. V.P.-Corp. Human Resources--The McGraw-Hill Companies, New York, NY; *U.S. Public*, pg. 1069
Washington, Lawrence J., Jr., V.P.-Environ., Health & Safety/Pub. Affairs--The Dow Chemical Company, Midland, MI; *U.S. Public*, pg. 522
Washington, Leslie, Buyer--International Cutlery, LTD, New York, NY; *U.S. Private*, pg. 569
Wasserman, Craig, V.P.-Human Resources & Employee Rels.--Browning-Ferris Industries, Inc., Houston, TX; *U.S. Public*, pg. 262
Watakeekul, Somkuan, Deputy Governor-Human Resources--Petroleum Authority of Thailand, Bangkok, Thailand; *Int'l*, pg. 1046
Waterman, Janice E., V.P.-H.R. & Opers.--Integrated Systems, Inc., Sunnyvale, CA; *U.S. Public*, pg. 885
Waters, Debbie, Mgr.-H.R.--Shakey's Incorporated, Irvine, CA; *U.S. Private*, pg. 989
Watford, Dennis M., Mgr.-H.R.--ChemFirst Inc., Jackson, MS; *U.S. Public*, pg. 344
Wathen, J. C., Gen. Mgr.-Human Resources--National Westminster Bank PLC, London, United Kingdom; *Int'l*, pg. 910
Watkin, Nancy, Gen. Counsel & Sec.--Tiger Direct, Inc., Miami, FL; *U.S. Public*, pg. 747
Watkins, Carole S., V.P.-Human Resources--Cardinal Distribution, Dublin, OH; *U.S. Public*, pg. 304
Watkins, Dean, Mgr.-H.R.--Taylor Machine Works, Inc., Louisville, MS; *U.S. Private*, pg. 1070
Watkins, Kathy, Dir.-H. R.--Seed Restaurant Group, Inc., Lexington, KY; *U.S. Private*, pg. 981
Watson, Barrie, Dir.-Human Resources--The Eurotunnel Group, London, United Kingdom; *Int'l*, pg. 466
Watson, I. Benjamin, Sr. V.P.-H.R.--Sprint Corporation, Westwood, KS; *U.S. Public*, pg. 1500
Watts, Denise, Mgr.-H.R.--Five Star Foods Incorporated, Dalton, GA; *U.S. Private*, pg. 409
Watts, Gail, Dir.-Field Services--Blue Cross of California, Woodland Hills, CA; *U.S. Private*, pg. 152
Watts, James B., Exec. V.P.-Human Resources--Associates Financial Services Corporation, Dallas, TX; *U.S. Public*, pg. 663
Watts, Peter, V.P.-Human Resources--Adams U.S.A., Morris Plains, NJ; *U.S. Public*, pg. 1739
Watts, W.J.C., Sec.--Watts Blake Bearne & Co. Plc, Newton Abbot, United Kingdom; *Int'l*, pg. 1487
Waxman, Irene, V.P.-Human Resources--Sanofi Beaute, Inc., New York, NY; *Int'l*, pg. 445
Weary, Robert, Dir.-Human Res.--Knouse Foods Inc., Peach Glen, PA; *U.S. Private*, pg. 627
Weatherholtz, Karen, V.P.-H.R.--McCormick & Company, Incorporated, Sparks, MD; *U.S. Public*, pg. 1066
Weatherly, E. Mitchell, Sr. V.P.-Human Resources--Pier 1 Imports, Inc., Fort Worth, TX; *U.S. Public*, pg. 1295
Weaver, Frank E., V.P.-H.R.--Pace Resources, Inc., York, PA; *U.S. Private*, pg. 829
Weaver, Pat, Mgr.-Human Resources--Mohawk Finishing Products, Inc., Amsterdam, NY; *U.S. Public*, pg. 1357
Weaver, Phillip W., V.P.-Human Resources--Triple S Plastics, Inc., Vicksburg, MI; *U.S. Public*, pg. 1639
Weaver, Sharon L., Sr. V.P.-Human Resources & Branch Admin.--National Penn Bank, Boyertown, PA; *U.S. Public*, *pg. 1159*
Webb, Elizabeth, Personnel Dir.--Devon Direct Marketing & Advertising, Inc., Berwyn, PA; *U.S. Private*, pg. 329
Webb, Linda, Dir.-H.R.--Wellco Enterprises, Inc., Waynesville, NC; *U.S. Public*, pg. 1752
Webb, Malcolm, Dir. Gen.-Human Resources--Petrofina S.A., Brussels, Belgium; *Int'l*, pg. 1043
Webb, Marci, Mng. Dir.-H.R.--BeautiControl Cosmetics, Inc., Carrollton, TX; *U.S. Public*, pg. 198
Webb, Susan M., V.P.-Human Resoures--Jervis B. Webb Company, Farmington Hills, MI; *U.S. Private*, pg. 1156
Webber, Susan, V.P.-Human Resources--Data I/O Corporation, Redmond, WA; *U.S. Public*, pg. 486
Weber, Gail E., Sr. V.P.-Human Resources & Corp. Serv.--The New England, Boston, MA; *U.S. Private*, pg. 737
Weber, Robert, V.P.-Employee Rels.--Preformed Line Products, Cleveland, OH; *U.S. Public*, pg. 1321
Weber, Robinn, V.P.-Human Resources--Russell Stover Candies, Inc., Kansas City, MO; *U.S. Private*, pg. 953
Weber, Susan, Dir.-H.R.--United Grocers Inc., Portland, OR; *U.S. Private*, pg. 1122
Weber, Warren G., V.P.-Admin. & Human Resources--Zurn Industries, Inc., Erie, PA; *U.S. Public*, pg. 1794
Webster, Chris, Mgr.-H.R.--The Buschman Co., Cincinnati, OH; *U.S. Private*, pg. 188
Webster, Connie, Dir.-Corp. Services--Howtek, Inc., Hudson, NH; *U.S. Public*, pg. 844
Wechsler, Allan B., Dir.-Human Resources--Brown Brothers Harriman & Co., New York, NY; *U.S. Private*, pg. 173
Wechsler, Barbara, Sec. & Dir.-Personnel & Employee Benefits--Continental Plastic Card Co., Coral Springs, FL; *U.S. Private*, pg. 269
Wechsler, F., V.P.-Human Resources--The Hartz Mountain Corp., Secaucus, NJ; *U.S. Private*, pg. 508
Wecker, Irwin, Sr. V.P.-H.R.--Morse Diesel International, Inc., New York, NY; *U.S. Private*, pg. 762
Weddle, Gloria Banks, V.P.-Corp. Services--Nevada Power Company, Las Vegas, NV; *U.S. Public*, pg. 1169
Weddleton, Ann, Mgr.-Human Resources--Loomis, Sayles & Co., Boston, MA; *U.S. Private*, pg. 737
Wedmalm, Alf, Grp. Mgr.-Personnel & Info.--Avesta Sheffield AB, Stockholm, Sweden; *Int'l*, pg. 221
Weed, Lindee, Mgr.-Human Resources--K-Tel International, Inc., Minneapolis, MN; *U.S. Public*, pg. 937
Weed, Mark, Mgr.-H. R.--Border States Industries, Inc., Fargo, ND; *U.S. Private*, pg. 160
Weekes, Bob, Exec. Gen. Mgr.-Human Resources--North Limited, Melbourne, Australia; *Int'l*, pg. 967
Weeks, Charles R., V.P.-H.R.--H.E. Sargent, Inc., Stillwater, ME; *U.S. Private*, pg. 966
Weeks, Edith J., Mgr.-Personnel--Bunker Hill Foods Inc., Bedford, VA; *U.S. Private*, pg. 219
Weeks, George E., Mgr.-Personnel--Maryland Plastics, Inc., Federalsburg, MD; *U.S. Private*, pg. 641
Wegner, D'Lane, Dir.-Human Resources--Uniden America Corporation, Fort Worth, TX; *Int'l*, pg. 1433
Wehking, Elisabeth, Mgr.-Personnel--Bols Strothmann Brennereien GmbH & Co. KG, Nordrhein-Westfalen, Germany; *Int'l*, pg. 751
Wehnes, Werner, Dir.-Personnel--Deutz AG, Cologne, Germany; *Int'l*, pg. 407
Weidemans, Mikelis, V.P.-Human Resources--Scancem AB, Malmo, Sweden; *Int'l*, pg. 1198
Weidman, Fred, V.P.-Human Resources--Walle Corporation, Harahan, LA; *U.S. Private*, pg. 1148
Weil, Joseph R., Mgr.-Human Resources--Flowserve Corporation, Rotating Equipment Grp., Dayton, OH; *U.S. Public*, pg. 658
Weiland, Barbara A., V.P. & Dir-H.R.--Robert F. Driver Co., Inc., San Diego, CA; *U.S. Private*, pg. 343
Weimer, Robert C., Dir.-Finance & Admin.--Union City Body Company, L.P., Union City, IN; *U.S. Private*, pg. 1118
Weinberg, Jo Ann, V.P.-H.R.--Hardin Construction Group, Inc., Atlanta, GA; *U.S. Private*, pg. 501
Weingarth, Glenn, V.P.-H.R.--Dentsply International Inc., York, PA; *U.S. Public*, pg. 498
Weininger, Harry, V.P.-Human Resources--Campbell Soup Company Ltd., Toronto, Canada; *U.S. Public*, pg. 299
Weinmann, Heinz, Dir.-Personnel & Social Policy--Hoechst Aktiengesellschaft, Frankfurt/Main, Germany; *Int'l*, pg. 624
Weinstein, Carl, Mgr.-Employee Benefits--DeVry Institutes, Oak Brook Terrace, IL; *U.S. Public*, pg. 503
Weinstein, Howard, V.P.-Employee Rels.--The Baltimore Sun Newspapers, Baltimore, MD; *U.S. Public*, pg. 1616
Weinstein, Janet, Dir.-Personnel--Iceland Group plc, Deeside, United Kingdom; *Int'l*, pg. 658
Weinstein, Jeri, Dir.-H.R.--Easy Day Manufacturing Company, Holliston, MA; *U.S. Private*, pg. 358
Weintraub, Jacqueline, Mgr.-H.R.--C.I. Hayes, Inc., Cranston, RI; *U.S. Private*, pg. 513
Weisbard, S., Mgr.-Human Resources--General Microwave Corporation, Amityville, NY; *U.S. Public*, pg. 717
Weisenberg, Michael, Dir.-Human Resources--Owens Corning/Foamular, Parsippany, NJ; *U.S. Public*, pg. 1237
Weiser, Ann, Sr. V.P.-Human Resources--R.R. Donnelley & Sons Company, Chicago, IL; *U.S. Public*, pg. 517
Weiser, David H., Sr. V.P.-Legal & Human Resources--Department 56 Inc., Eden Prairie, MN; *U.S. Public*, pg. 500
Weishaar, Henry A., V.P.-Human Resources--Abbott Hospital Products Division, North Chicago, IL; *U.S. Public*, pg. 13
Weiss, Hilary, Dir.-Personnel--Tenax Corporation, Danbury, CT; *Int'l*, pg. 193
Weiss, Lynn, Mgr.-Human Resources--G&K Services, Inc., Minnetonka, MN; *U.S. Public*, pg. 690
Weiss, Mary, Supervisor-Personnel--Baker & McKenzie, Attorneys At Law, Chicago, IL; *U.S. Private*, pg. 111
Welbrock, Lynne, Dir.-Human Resources--Blair Television, New York, NY; *U.S. Private*, pg. 148
Welch, Elayne, Dir.-Human Resources--SCS Engineers, Long Beach, CA; *U.S. Private*, pg. 955
Welch, Rick, Mgr.-Human Resources--McNaughton & Gunn, Inc., Saline, MI; *U.S. Private*, pg. 724
Welding, Maryann, V.P.-H.R.--Orbital Sciences Corporation, Dulles, VA; *U.S. Public*, pg. 1229
Welge, Rob, Dir.-Personnel--Gilster Mary Lee Corp., Chester, IL; *U.S. Private*, pg. 455
Welle, Bernie, Sr. V.P.-Human Resources--The Dial Corporation, Phoenix, AZ; *U.S. Public*, pg. 505
Wells Robert, Exec. V.P. & WW Human Resources Dir.--Young & Rubicam New York, New York, NY; *U.S. Private*, pg. 1198
Wells, Brian, Dir.-H.R.--National Utility Service, Inc., Park Ridge, NJ; *U.S. Private*, pg. 787
Wells, Dave, Mgr.-Personnel--Brooks Foods, Mount Summit, IN; *U.S. Private*, pg. 887
Wells, Henry, Sr. V.P.-H.R.--Brach & Brock Confections, Inc., Chicago, IL; *U.S. Private*, pg. 163
Wells, Henry M., III, V.P.-Human Resources--Banta Corporation, Menasha, WI; *U.S. Public*, pg. 187
Wells, Jeffrey, Sr. V.P.-Human Resources--Circuit City Stores, Inc., Richmond, VA; *U.S. Public*, pg. 374
Wells, Merla, Mgr.-Personnel & Risk Mngmt.--Devon Energy Corporation, Oklahoma City, OK; *U.S. Public*, pg. 503
Wells, Richard, Dir.-H.R., Europe--Caradon Plc, Weybridge, United Kingdom; *Int'l*, pg. 266
Wells, Sandra L., V.P.-H.R.--Central Reserve Life Corporation, Strongsville, OH; *U.S. Public*, pg. 326
Wells, Sandra L., Asst. V.P. & Dir.-Human Resources--Central Reserve Life of North America Insurance Co., Strongsville, OH; *U.S. Public*, pg. 326
Wellstein, Nanette, Dir.-Human Resources--American Appraisal Associates, Inc., Milwaukee, WI; *U.S. Private*, pg. 49
Welsh, Bethany, Mgr.-H.R.--Dot Printer, Inc., Irvine, CA; *U.S. Private*, pg. 341
Welsh, J.H., Dir.-Human Resources--OEA, Inc., Aurora, CO; *U.S. Public*, pg. 1206
Weltzin, Laurie, Mgr.-Personnel--Spectrum Industries, Inc., Chippewa Falls, WI; *U.S. Private*, pg. 1024
Wemlinger, Kathy, Dir.-H.R.--R.S. Owens, Chicago, IL; *U.S. Private*, pg. 824
Wendell, Barbara, Dir.-Human Resources--Amerimark Inc., Raleigh, NC; *U.S. Public*, pg. 1237
Wendell, Beth, Dir.-Personnel--The Great Lakes Cheese Co., Newbury, OH; *U.S. Private*, pg. 473
Wenhold, William R., V.P.-Human Resources--Oakite Products, Inc., Berkeley Heights, NJ; *Int'l*, pg. 861
Wenk, Steven, V.P.-Human Resources--Kurdziel Industries, Inc., Muskegon, MI; *U.S. Private*, pg. 637
Wenk, Steven, Dir.-Human Resources--Kurdziel Industries, Inc., Muskegon, MI; *U.S. Private*, pg. 637
Wenner, Linda, Dir.-H.R.--The Stellar Group Inc., Jacksonville, FL; *U.S. Private*, pg. 1040
Wenzel, Gilbert F., V.P.-H.R.--MSI Insurance Companies, Arden Hills, MN; *U.S. Private*, pg. 688
Werner, Goran, Dir.-Personnel--Gunnebo Industrier AB, Gunnebo, Sweden; *Int'l*, pg. 578
Werner, Olle, Sr. V.P.-H.R.--Akzo Nobel N.V., Arnhem, Netherlands; *Int'l*, pg. 42
Werschine, Jacques, Mgr.-Human Resources--Arianespace SA, Evry, France; *Int'l*, pg. 81
Werth, Christine, Mgr.-Welfare Benefits--Mark IV Industries Inc., Amherst, NY; *U.S. Public*, pg. 1044
Wessel, Kirk, V.P.-Human Resources--Associated Food Stores Inc., Salt Lake City, UT; *U.S. Private*, pg. 90
Wesson-Goffney, Carmen, Dir.-Human Resources--Golden West Baseball Club, Anaheim, CA; *U.S. Private*, pg. 461
West, Gloria, Dir.-Human Resources--Parker Drilling Company, Tulsa, OK; *U.S. Public*, pg. 1259
West, Ralph, Mgr.-Personnel--Idaho Supreme Company, Firth, ID; *U.S. Private*, pg. 557
West, Theresa, Dir.-Personnel--VV Publishing Corp., New York, NY; *U.S. Private*, pg. 1131
West, William, Dir.-H.R.--Bayer Clothing Group, New York, NY; *U.S. Private*, pg. 124
Westhoff, Jill, Mgr.-Employee Benefits--Maverick Tube Corporation, Chesterfield, MO; *U.S. Public*, pg. 1060
Westmark, David, Mgr.-H.R.--Tillamook County Creamery Assn., Tillamook, OR; *U.S. Private*, pg. 1086
Weston, Dan, V.P.-Human Resources--Greyhound Lines, Inc., Dallas, TX; *U.S. Public*, pg. 765
Westover, Kyle J., V.P.-Human Resources--Longs Drug Stores Corporation, Walnut Creek, CA; *U.S. Public*, pg. 1013
Westwater, Chris, Mgr.-Customer Srvc.--Dielectric Polymers, Inc., Holyoke, MA; *U.S. Public*, pg. 1258
Wetherell, Dawn, Dir.-Human Resources--Acceptance Insurance Co., Inc., Omaha, NE; *U.S. Public*, pg. 14
Wexler, Susan, V.P.-Human Resources--Macmillan Publishing USA, Indianapolis, IN; *U.S. Private*, pg. 777
Whalen, George, Dir.-Human Resources--Greer Steel Co., Dover, OH; *U.S. Private*, pg. 479
Whaley, Billy, Sr. V.P.-H.R.--Greenwood Mills, Inc., Greenwood, SC; *U.S. Private*, pg. 479
Whaley, Darlene K., V.P.-H.R.--Biomet, Inc., Warsaw, IN; *U.S. Public*, pg. 231
Whaling, Michael L., Dir.-Employee Rels.--The Newhall Land And Farming Company, Valencia, CA; *U.S. Public*, pg. 1178
Wharton, Graham, Mgr.-H.R.--Alliance UniChem PLC, Chessington, United Kingdom; *Int'l*, pg. 57
Whavers, Noella, Dir.-Human Resources--Pro-Line Corporation, Dallas, TX; *U.S. Private*, pg. 887
Wheeler, Camilla, Dir.-Human Resources--Rose's Stores, Inc., Henderson, NC; *U.S. Public*, pg. 1405
Wheeler, Roger, Mgr.-H.R.--Alamo Industrial Group, San Antonio, TX; *U.S. Private*, pg. 31
Whelan, Joseph, Dir.-Personnel--A-P-A Transport Corp., North Bergen, NJ; *U.S. Private*, pg. 2
Whisnant, John R., Chief Fin. Officer & V.P.-Fin.--Insignia Systems, Inc., Minnetonka, MN; *U.S. Public*, pg. 881
Whitacre, Naomi D., V.P.-H.R.--Mycogen Corporation, San Diego, CA; *U.S. Public*, pg. 1142
White, Ann R., V.P.-H.R.--Capstead Mortgage Corporation, Dallas, TX; *U.S. Public*, pg. 303
White, Anson, Mgr.-H.R.--United Dairymen of Arizona, Tempe, AZ; *U.S. Private*, pg. 1121
White, Barbara, Dir.-Human Resources--The Inland Group, Inc., Oak Brook, IL; *U.S. Private*, pg. 564
White, Barbara, Personnel Asst.--Netzsch Incorporated, Exton, PA; *U.S. Private*, pg. 792
White, Barry, Dir.-H.R.--Wallace Computer Services, Inc., Lisle, IL; *U.S. Public*, pg. 1735
White, Barry L., V.P.-H.R.--Wallace Computer Services, Inc., Lisle, IL; *U.S. Public*, pg. 1735
White, Corliss, Dir.-Human Resources--VASA Brougher, Inc., Indianapolis, IN; *Int'l*, pg. 464
White, Gary, Sr. V.P.--Commercial Federal Corporation, Omaha, NE; *U.S. Public*, pg. 411
White, Harold, Mgr.-Personnel--Aearo Company, Boston, MA; *U.S. Private*, pg. 23
White, J. Spratt, Sr. V.P.-Growth & Devel. & Human Resources--Springs Industries, Inc., Fort Mill, SC; *U.S. Public*, pg. 1499

White, John E., Asst. V.P.-Personnel--ChemDesign Corporation, Fitchburg, MA; *Int'l*, pg. 173
White, John F., V.P.-Human Resources--Montgomery KONE Inc., Moline, IL; *Int'l*, pg. 746
White, M.J., Dir.-Employee Rels.--Griffin Wheel Co., Chicago, IL; *U.S. Private*, pg. 68
White, Michael D., V.P.-H.R.--Gene B. Glick Company, Inc., Indianapolis, IN; *U.S. Private*, pg. 457
White, Mindy, Mgr.-H.R.--RK Mechanical, Inc., Denver, CO; *U.S. Private*, pg. 904
White, Robert, V.P.-Human Resources--Hobart Brothers Co., Troy, OH; *U.S. Public*, pg. 866
White, Robert G., V.P.-Human Resources--Bob Evans Farms, Inc., Columbus, OH; *U.S. Public*, pg. 596
White, Susan, V.P.-Human Resources--MTV Networks, New York, NY; *U.S. Private*, pg. 779
White, Terry, Dir.-H.R.--DMI, Inc., Goodfield, IL; *U.S. Private*, *pg. 305*
White, Tom R., V.P.-H.R. & Corp. Rels.--Hoechst Marion Roussel North America, Kansas City, MO; *Int'l*, pg. 625
Whiteman, Kirk, Dir.-Admin.--Bridgeport Fittings, Inc., Stratford, CT; *U.S. Private*, pg. 168
Whitesell, Frank, Mgr.-H.R.--Marketing Displays International, Farmington Hills, MI; *U.S. Private*, pg. 705
Whitfield, Doug, Dir.-Personnel--Maze Nails, Peru, IL; *U.S. Private*, pg. 718
Whiting, Dick, Mgr.-Personnel--Polar Ware Company, Sheboygan, WI; *U.S. Private*, pg. 873
Whitlock, Cleo, Admin.-Personnel--U.S. Filter/Davis Water & Waste Industries, Inc., Thomasville, GA; *U.S. Public*, pg. 1682
Whitlock, Laurita A., Mgr.-H.R.--Burlington Resources Inc., Houston, TX; *U.S. Public*, pg. 269
Whitney, Carol, Dir.-Human Resources--UDL Laboratories, Inc., Rockford, IL; *U.S. Public*, pg. 1143
Whitsitt, Zan, Dir.-H.R.--Devro-Teepak, Inc., Westchester, IL; *Int'l*, pg. 408
Wholley, Gina, V.P.-Mktg. & Human Resources--Lat Purser & Associates, Charlotte, NC; *U.S. Private*, pg. 896
Whyte, William R., V.P.-H.R.--Snap-On Tools Corporation, Kenosha, WI; *U.S. Public*, pg. 1480
Wickenberg, Ken, V.P.-Human Resources--The Edmonton Journal, Edmonton, Canada; *Int'l*, pg. 631
Wickham, Katherine C., V.P.-H.R.--The Dreyfus Corporation, New York, NY; *U.S. Public*, pg. 1085
Widler, Donald E., Sr. V.P.-Human Resources--Colorado National Bank, Denver, CO; *U.S. Public*, pg. 1680
Widmayer, Karen, V.P.-Commun.--CarrAmerica Realty, Washington, DC; *U.S. Public*, pg. 308
Widmer, Derrick, Dir.-Mngmt. Services--Holderbank Financiere Glaris Ltd., Glaris, Switzerland; *Int'l*, pg. 628
Wiest, Laurie, Corp. Mgr.-H.R.--ACC Corp., Rochester, NY; *U.S. Public*, pg. 2
Wiest, R., Mgr.-Personnel--Scott National, Calgary, Canada; *Int'l*, pg. 1012
Wiet, Shirley, Dir.-Personnel--Schumacher Electric Corporation, Mount Prospect, IL; *U.S. Private*, pg. 973
Wiggins, Michael, Asst. V.P.-H.R.--Southwire Company, Carrollton, GA; *U.S. Private*, pg. 1019
Wiggins, Spencer, V.P.-Human Resources--Godfather's Pizza, Inc., Omaha, NE; *U.S. Private*, pg. 458
Wiik, Billy, Personnel Mgr.--Bender Shipbuilding & Repair Company, Inc., Mobile, AL; *U.S. Private*, pg. 132
Wiklund, Jerry, Dir.- Personnel--Aftonbladet AB, Stockholm, Sweden; *Int'l*, pg. 29
Wiktorowicz, Karen, Dir.-Human Resources--Buena Vista Home Video, Burbank, CA; *U.S. Public*, pg. 513
Wilcox, Charles, Dir.-H.R.--Kirby Building Systems, Inc., Portland, TN; *Int'l*, pg. 699
Wilcox, Marna, Mgr.-Corp. Adv. & Communications--Utah Power & Light, Salt Lake City, UT; *U.S. Public*, pg. 1251
Wilcox, R., Gen. Mgr. & Mgr.-H.R.--Dawn Food Products, Inc., Jackson, MI; *U.S. Private*, pg. 316
Wilde, Bruce G., V.P.-Human Resources--Providence Energy Corporation, Providence, RI; *U.S. Public*, pg. 1337
Wilderman, Kathleen, Mgr.-Human Resources--First Financial Corporation, Stevens Point, WI; *U.S. Public*, pg. 140
Wilderman, Kathleen M., Sr. V.P.-Personnel/Human Resources--First Financial Bank, FSB, Stevens Point, WI; *U.S. Public*, pg. 140
Wildsmith, Rose, Dir.-H.R.--IKOS Systems, Inc., Cupertino, CA; *U.S. Public*, pg. 864
Wileczek, Ann, Mgr.-H.R.--Emons Transportation Group, Inc., York, PA; *U.S. Public*, pg. 578
Wiley, Mike, Dir.-Human Resources--Ensco International Incorporated (ENSCO), Dallas, TX; *U.S. Public*, pg. 585
Wilhelm, Julianne, V.P.-H.R.--Starter Corp., New Haven, CT; *U.S. Public*, pg. 1511
Wilhelmi, Rose, Supvr.-H.R.--Sioux Manufacturing Corp., Fort Totten, ND; *U.S. Private*, pg. 1003
Wiljanen, Dan, V.P.-H.R.--Steelcase Inc., Grand Rapids, MI; *U.S. Private*, pg. 1038
Wilk, James J., Sr. V.P.-Human Resources--Foundation Health Systems, Inc., Pueblo, CO; *U.S. Public*, pg. 678
Wilken, Bernhard, Mgr.-H.R.--Spar Handels AG, Schenefeld, Germany; *Int'l*, pg. 1288
Wilkenson, M., Grp. Dir.-H.R.--United Biscuits (Holdings) Plc, West Drayton, United Kingdom; *Int'l*, pg. 1442
Wilkes, J.C., V.P.-H.R.--Carus Corporation, Peru, IL; *U.S. Private*, pg. 217
Wilkes, S., Mgr.-Human Resources--Kilovac Corporation, Carpinteria, CA; *U.S. Private*, pg. 259
Wilkins, Barbara, Dir.-H.R.--InterBio Inc., Woodlands, TX; *U.S. Private*, pg. 566
Wilkins, Lee A., Dir.-H.R.--The Gorman-Rupp Company, Mansfield, OH; *U.S. Public*, pg. 754
Wilkins, Nancy, Mgr.-H.R.--Melbourne Port Corporation, Melbourne, Australia; *Int'l*, pg. 856
Wilkinson, John L., V.P.-Human Resources--Dynamics Research Corporation, Andover, MA; *U.S. Public*, pg. 539
Wilkinson, W. Floyd, Dir.-H.R.--Johnson Worldwide Associates, Inc., Sturtevant, WI; *U.S. Public*, pg. 932
Wilkinson, William J., Sr. V.P.-Human Resources--The Walt Disney Company, Burbank, CA; *U.S. Public*, pg. 511
Willey, William, V.P.-Human Resources--Primedia Informatin Group, New York, NY; *U.S. Public*, pg. 1328
Williams-Harvey, Denise, V.P. & Human Resources Dir.--Burrell Communications Group Inc., Chicago, IL; *U.S. Private*, pg. 188
Williams, B., Mgr.-Personnel--BTR plc, London, United Kingdom; *Int'l*, pg. 124
Williams, Barbara Coull, V.P.-H.R.--Pacific Gas & Electric Company, San Francisco, CA; *U.S. Public*, pg. 1241
Williams, Beverly J., V.P.-Personnel/Admin. & Sec.--Boss Manufacturing Company, Kewanee, IL; *U.S. Private*, pg. 1142
Williams, Dan, Dir.-Personnel & Pur.--M.A.B. Paints, Terre Haute, IN; *U.S. Private*, pg. 175
Williams, Darin, Mgr.-Human Resources--Heartland Express, Inc., Coralville, IA; *U.S. Public*, pg. 803
Williams, David, V.P.-H.R.--Pharmaceutical Product Development, Inc., Wilmington, NC; *U.S. Public*, pg. 1285
Williams, David R., Dir.-Human Resources--Pilling Weck, Research Triangle Park, NC; *U.S. Public*, pg. 1569
Williams, Debbie, Dir.-H.R.--Nashville Wire Product Co., Nashville, TN; *U.S. Private*, pg. 775
Williams, Diane, V.P.-Human Resources--Sequent Computer Systems, Inc., Beaverton, OR; *U.S. Public*, pg. 1459
Williams, Elaine, V.P. & Dir.-Human Resources--Essence Communications Inc., New York, NY; *U.S. Private*, pg. 383
Williams, Elaine A., Mgr.-H.R.--Hannay Reels, Westerlo, NY; *U.S. Private*, pg. 499
Williams, James, Sr. V.P.-Strategic Devel. & H.R.--Kaiser Permanente, Oakland, CA; *U.S. Private*, pg. 605
Williams, Janell, Dir.-H.R.--PMR Corporation, San Diego, CA; *U.S. Public*, pg. 1242
Williams, Jesse T., Sr., V.P.-Human Resources Policy, Employment Practices & Systems--The Goodyear Tire & Rubber Company, Akron, OH; *U.S. Public*, pg. 752
Williams, Joe, Mgr., Sls. & Personnel--T.K.G. International Corp., Macon, GA; *Int'l*, pg. 1349
Williams, L.M., V.P.-Human Resources--Indianapolis Water Company, Indianapolis, IN; *U.S. Public*, pg. 1185
Williams, Michael S., Dir.-H.R.--Herff Jones Inc., Indianapolis, IN; *U.S. Private*, pg. 523
Williams, Mike, V.P.-H.R.--Newbridge Networks Corporation, Kanata, Canada; *Int'l*, pg. 923
Williams, P.R., Dir.-Personnel--Vodafone Group PLC, Newbury, United Kingdom; *Int'l*, pg. 1469
Williams, Robert, V.P.-Human Resources--Symix Systems, Inc., Columbus, OH; *U.S. Public*, pg. 1546
Williams, Roberta, Mgr.-Personnel--Lockformer Company, Lisle, IL; *U.S. Public*, pg. 1100
Williams, Sandy, Mgr.-Personnel--Gertrude Hawk Chocolates, Inc., Dunmore, PA; *U.S. Private*, pg. 449
Williams, Susan Larson, V.P.-H.R.--VF Corporation, Wyomissing, PA; *U.S. Public*, pg. 1702
Williams, Valerie C., V.P.-Human Resources--GATX Capital Corporation, San Francisco, CA; *U.S. Public*, pg. 690
Williams, Wanda, V.P.-Human Resources--Tosco Corporation, Stamford, CT; *U.S. Public*, pg. 1624
Williamson, Luc, Mgr.-Human Resources--Cegelec, Levallois-Perret, France; *Int'l*, pg. 52
Williamson, Olivia, Personnel Admin.--Austron Inc., Austin, TX; *U.S. Public*, pg. 488
Willihnganz, Greg, Dir.-H.R.--Louisville Scrap Material Co., Inc., Louisville, KY; *U.S. Private*, pg. 677
Willis, Dudley, V.P.-Human Resources--Champion Laboratories, Inc., Albion, IL; *U.S. Private*, pg. 1113
Willis, S. E., V.P.-Indus. Rels.--AmerenUE, Saint Louis, MO; *U.S. Public*, pg. 66
Willoughby, John, Dir.-H.R.--North American Refractories Company, Cleveland, OH; *U.S. Private*, pg. 803
Willson, Roxanne, Sec. & Mgr.-Human Resources--Griffin Envelope, Inc., Seattle, WA; *U.S. Public*, pg. 1038
Wilmot, Patricia, Sr. V.P.-Human Resources--Alpo Pet Foods, Inc., Allentown, PA; *Int'l*, pg. 917
Wilseck, Joseph, Dir.-Human Resources--ISI Norgen, Inc., Fraser, MI; *Int'l*, pg. 646
Wilson, 'eter M., Mgr.-H.R.--Collieries Division, Wollongong, Australia; *Int'l*, pg. 226
Wilson, David E., Dir.-H.R.--Eagle-Picher Industries, Inc., Cincinnati, OH; *U.S. Private*, pg. 355
Wilson, Ellen Silva, V.P.-Human Resources--The Dallas Morning News, Inc., Dallas, TX; *U.S. Public*, pg. 209
Wilson, Jeff, Grp. Gen. Mgr.-Human Resources--Australian National Industries Limited, Pyrmont, Australia; *Int'l*, pg. 100
Wilson, Judy, Dir.-Personnel--Turner Holding LLC, Covington, TN; *U.S. Private*, pg. 1109
Wilson, Kalindi, Mgr.-Personnel--Jordache Enterprises, Inc., New York, NY; *U.S. Private*, pg. 597
Wilson, Larry, Dir.-Human Resources--Murphy-Phoenix Co., Solon, OH; *U.S. Public*, pg. 397
Wilson, Lyle, Mgr.-Human Resources & Exec. Asst.--Willis Corroon Corp. of Utah, Salt Lake City, UT; *Int'l*, pg. 1507
Wilson, Peter, Grp. Gen. Mgr.-Human Resources--Australia & New Zealand Banking Group Limited, Melbourne, Australia; *Int'l*, pg. 98
Wilson, Phil, Sr. V.P.-Human Resources--Oracle Corporation, Redwood City, CA; *U.S. Public*, pg. 1227
Wilson, Richard, Mgr.-Employee Rels.--Justiss Oil Co., Inc., Jena, LA; *U.S. Private*, pg. 602
Wilson, Roy, Sr. V.P.-H.R.--BMC Software, Inc., Houston, TX; *U.S. Public*, pg. 162
Wimberley, James R., V.P.-Human Resources--BancTec, Inc., Dallas, TX; *U.S. Public*, pg. 176
Wimberly, Riley J., V.P.-Human Resources--Defense & Launch Vehicles Division, Brigham City, UT; *U.S. Public*, pg. 1597
Wingate, Edwin H., Sr. V.P.-Personnel--Dayton Hudson Corporation, Minneapolis, MN; *U.S. Public*, pg. 489
Wingo, Bill, Dir.-Human Resources--Gilman, Janesville, WI; *Int'l*, pg. 1389
Winings, Michael, V.P.-Personnel--Small Parts, Inc., Logansport, IN; *U.S. Private*, pg. 1006
Winkle, Marshall, Mgr.-Human Resources--Ariel Corporation, Mount Vernon, OH; *U.S. Private*, pg. 81
Winkleman, Dennis R., V.P.-Human Resources--Zenith Electronics Corp., Glenview, IL; *U.S. Public*, pg. 1790
Winn, H.L., Dir.-H.R.--Smith Industries, Inc., Montgomery, AL; *U.S. Private*, pg. 1008
Winsauer, Paul, V.P.-Human Resources--A.M. Castle & Co., Franklin Park, IL; *U.S. Public*, pg. 312
Winschel, Richard, Mgr.-Personnel--Ridg-U-Rak, Inc., North East, PA; *U.S. Private*, pg. 930
Winston, Sandi, Human Resources Dir.--Asher/Gould Advertising, Inc., Los Angeles, CA; *U.S. Private*, pg. 88
Winston, Sharon, Sr. V.P.-Human Resources--Glendale Federal Bank, F.S.B., Glendale, CA; *U.S. Public*, pg. 747
Winton, Steve, Mgr.-Personnel--Grant-Lydick Beverage Co., San Antonio, TX; *U.S. Private*, pg. 470
Winvick, Stanley, Sr. V.P.-Human Resources--Advanced Micro Devices, Inc., Sunnyvale, CA; *U.S. Public*, pg. 21
Wirth, Matthew, Mgr.-Human Resources--Integrated Material Handling Company, Oshkosh, WI; *Int'l*, pg. 1397
Wirthmann-Rado, Julianna, Dir.-Pub. Rels. & H.R.--Budapest Marriott Hotel, Budapest, Hungary; *Int'l*, pg. 232
Wirtz, Joseph, Mgr.-Human Resources--Pitco Frialator Inc., Bow, NH; *U.S. Public*, pg. 1065
Wisdom, Jennifer, V.P.-H.R.--Triangle Pacific Corporation, Dallas, TX; *U.S. Public*, pg. 1634
Wisdom, Jennifer, Dir.-Human Resources--Bruce Hardwood Floors, Dallas, TX; *U.S. Public*, pg. 1634
Wise, Chris, Mgr.-H. R.--Southco Distributing Company, Goldsboro, NC; *U.S. Private*, pg. 1014
Wise, Dan, Dir.-Human Resources--Heery International, Inc., Atlanta, GA; *U.S. Private*, pg. 519
Wisecup, Reyne, Mgr.-Human Resources--Fastenal Company, Winona, MN; *U.S. Public*, pg. 614
Wishard, Linda, V.P.-H.R.--Taco Cabana, San Antonio, TX; *U.S. Public*, pg. 1559
Wisniewski, Jeanne, V.P.-H.R.--Oxford Health Plans Inc., Norwalk, CT; *U.S. Public*, pg. 1238
Wissman, Marian, Dir.-Personnel--U.M. Holding Limited, Haddonfield, NJ; *U.S. Private*, pg. 1113
Withes-Limmers, Lesley, Human Resource Specialist--The Flecto Co., Inc., Oakland, CA; *U.S. Private*, pg. 410
Witte, Jacqueline A., V.P.-Human Resources--United Missouri Bank of St. Louis, Saint Louis, MO; *U.S. Public*, *pg. 1655*
Witte, P. P., Sr. V.P.-Human Resources--Royal Pakhoed NV, Rotterdam, Netherlands; *Int'l*, pg. 1147
Wittenbach, Sheila, Mgr.-H.R.--Advance Packaging Corporation, Grand Rapids, MI; *U.S. Private*, pg. 18
Wittig, James R., V.P.-H.R.--American Seating Company, Grand Rapids, MI; *U.S. Private*, pg. 61
Wizeman, Ed, V.P.-Human Resources--The Earthgrains Company, Clayton, MO; *U.S. Public*, pg. 547
Woeppel, Robert, V.P.-Human Resources--Sorrento Cheese Company, Inc., Buffalo, NY; *Int'l*, pg. 323
Wohl, Barry, Dir.-Human Resources--Messier-Dowty Inc., Toronto, Ajax, Canada; *Int'l*, pg. 1340
Wojtowecz, Reita, Dir.-Personnel & Sec.--Espey Mfg. & Electronics Corp., Saratoga Springs, NY; *U.S. Public*, pg. 592
Wolf, H. William, V.P.-Human Resources--Boeing Defense & Space Group, Kent, WA; *U.S. Public*, pg. 240
Wolf, Rosemary C., Dir.-Human Resources--Brauns Fashions Corporation, Plymouth, MN; *U.S. Public*, pg. 251
Wolf, Susan J., V.P.-Admin.--Chicago Tube & Iron Co., Chicago, IL; *U.S. Private*, pg. 235
Wolfe, D.L., Dir.-Personnel--Cooper Tire & Rubber Company, Findlay, OH; *U.S. Public*, pg. 445
Wolfe, Ken, Dir.-H.R.--TRM Copy Centers Corporation, Portland, OR; *U.S. Public*, pg. 1558
Wolfe, Teri, Dir.-Personnel--Lost Arrow Corporation, Ventura, CA; *U.S. Private*, pg. 676
Wolff, Esther G., Dir.-Human Resources--Huls America Inc., Somerset, NJ; *Int'l*, pg. 1455
Wolski, Christine M., Asst. Corp. Sec.--Commerce Group Corp., Milwaukee, WI; *U.S. Public*, pg. 410
Wolter, Richard, Dir.-Personnel--Symons Corporation, Des Plaines, IL; *U.S. Private*, pg. 932
Wolverton, Michael G., Dir.-Personnel--Fleer-Skybox International Inc., Mount Laurel, NJ; *U.S. Public*, pg. 1052
Wood, Beverly, Mgr.-Personnel--Howden Fluid Systems, Santa Barbara, CA; *U.S. Public*, pg. 1045
Wood, Bruce, Dir.-Human Resources--Great Salt Lake Minerals Corp., Overland Park, KS; *U.S. Private*, pg. 505
Wood, Doug, Mgr.-Personnel--Trimfoot Company, Farmington, MO; *U.S. Public*, pg. 1684
Wood, Gerald, Dir.-Personnel--COMNET Corporation, Lanham, MD; *U.S. Public*, pg. 416
Wood, Jerry, Mgr.-Human Resources--Group 1 Software, Inc., Lanham, MD; *U.S. Public*, pg. 417
Wood, Kathryn C., V.P.-Human Resources--Plasti-Line, Inc., Knoxville, TN; *U.S. Public*, pg. 1308
Wood, Stephen W., Sr. V.P.-H.R. & Corp. Affairs--Advantica Restaurant Group, Inc., Spartanburg, SC; *U.S. Public*, pg. 22
Woodbury, David B., V.P.-H.R.--Asarco Incorporated, New York, NY; *U.S. Public*, pg. 137
Woodfield, Rich, Mgr.-H.R.--AGCO Corporation, Duluth, GA; *U.S. Public*, pg. 28
Woods, Cecilia, Dir.-Personnel--Sundt Corp., Tucson, AZ; *U.S. Private*, pg. 1051
Woods, Charles, V.P.-Human Resources--Picker International, Inc., Cleveland, OH; *Int'l*, pg. 545
Woods, Frederick P., V.P.-Personnel--Tredegar Industries Inc., Richmond, VA; *U.S. Public*, pg. 1633
Woods, Powell, V.P.-Human Resources & Corp. Rels.--Nestle Holdings, Inc., Stamford, CT; *Int'l*, pg. 916

Woodworth, George, V.P. & Dir.-Human Resources--Kyocera International, Inc., San Diego, CA; *Int'l,* pg. 775
Woodyard, Russ, V.P.-Human Resources--The Murray Ohio Mfg. Co., Brentwood, TN; *Int'l,* pg. 1397
Wooten, William D., Sr. V.P.-Human Resources--MCI Communications Corp., Atlanta, GA; *U.S. Public,* pg. 1023
Word, Tammy, Dir.-H.R. & Sec.--URS Logistics, Atlanta, GA; *U.S. Private,* pg. 1114
Workes, Mona, Mgr.-Personnel--Efco Corporation, Monett, MO; *U.S. Private,* pg. 353
Workman, Sandra, V.P.-H.R.--Computer Sales International Inc., Saint Louis, MO; *U.S. Private,* pg. 260
Worrell, James, Dir.-Human Resources--Georgia Gulf Corporation, Atlanta, GA; *U.S. Public,* pg. 734
Worthing, Marcia L., Sr. V.P.-Human Resources & Corp. Affairs--Avon Products, Inc., New York, NY; *U.S. Public,* pg. 155
Wowra, Erick, Mgr.-Personnel--House of Raeford Farms, Inc., Raeford, NC; *U.S. Private,* pg. 542
Wray, Richard W., V.P.-Human Resources--Bestop, Inc., Broomfield, CO; *Int'l,* pg. 830
Wrede, Nancy, Dir.-Personnel--Contadina Dalla Casa Buitoni, Glendale, CA; *Int'l,* pg. 916
Wremerslage, Paul, Mgr.-Human Resources--Andersen Corporation, Bayport, MN; *U.S. Private,* pg. 71
Wresinski, Sharon, Human Resources--ICI Explosives USA Inc., Dallas, TX; *Int'l,* pg. 663
Wright, Bruce T., V.P.-Human Resources--Nashua Corporation, Nashua, NH; *U.S. Public,* pg. 1152
Wright, Burt, Mgr.-Personnel--Hanel Lumber Co., Inc., Hood River, OR; *U.S. Private,* pg. 538
Wright, Diana, Coord.-Human Resources & Training & Devel.--Central and South West Services, Inc., Dallas, TX; *U.S. Public,* pg. 324
Wright, Elease, Sr. V.P.-Human Resources--Aetna Inc., Hartford, CT; *U.S. Public,* pg. 26
Wright, Frank, Dir.-H.R.--Thompson Tractor Company, Birmingham, AL; *U.S. Private,* pg. 1083
Wright, James T., V.P.-Human Resources--Georgia-Pacific Corporation, Atlanta, GA; *U.S. Public,* pg. 735
Wright, Kathy, Dir.-Admin. & Human Resources--ITC Learning Corp., Herndon, VA; *U.S. Public,* pg. 859
Wright, Laura, Mgr.-Human Resources--Hughes Supply, Inc., Orlando, FL; *U.S. Public,* pg. 846
Wright, Patricia, Human Resource Specialist--The News Tribune, Tacoma, WA; *U.S. Public,* pg. 1066
Wright, Randy, Mgr.-Personnel--Quik N Tasty Foods, Belton, MO; *U.S. Private,* pg. 901
Wright, Sheryl, Dir.-Human Resources--Isco Environmental Division, Lincoln, NE; *U.S. Public,* pg. 914
Wright, Sheryl L., Dir.-Human Resources--Isco, Inc., Lincoln, NE; *U.S. Public,* pg. 913
Wright, Stephen A., Dir.-H.R.--BJ Services Company, Houston, TX; *U.S. Public,* pg. 161
Wright, Tom, Dir.-Human Resources--Oildyne, Minneapolis, MN; *U.S. Public,* pg. 411
Wroblewski, Thomas, V.P.-Human Resources--Integrated Device Technology, Inc., Santa Clara, CA; *U.S. Public,* pg. 884
Wrona, Diane, Dir.-Human Resources--Motch Corporation, Cleveland, OH; *Int'l,* pg. 1128
Wryn, JoLene, Sr. V.P. & Dir.-H.R.--Downey Savings & Loan Association, F.A., Newport Beach, CA; *U.S. Public,* pg. 526
Wu, Herbert B.D., Sr. V.P. & Gen. Mgr.-Human Resources--The International Commercial Bank of China, Taipei, Taiwan; *Int'l,* pg. 683
Wullaert, Kathy, Mgr.-H.R.--American Precast Concrete, Inc., Indianapolis, IN; *U.S. Private,* pg. 60
Wuslich, Gary L., V.P.-Human Resources--AM General Corporation, South Bend, IN; *U.S. Private,* pg. 922
Wust, Pierre, Treas., Controller & Chief Fin. Officer--Sandoz Pharma Ltd., Eden Terrace, New Zealand; *Int'l,* pg. 985
Wyche, Chris, Dir.-Human Resources--Pizza Hut (UK) Ltd., Borehamwood, United Kingdom; *Int'l,* pg. 1499
Wyche, Chris, Dir.-Human Resources--Pizza Hut (UK) Ltd., Borehamwood, United Kingdom; *U.S. Public,* pg. 1637
Wyles, J.R., Mgr.-Personnel--Schenectady International, Inc., Schenectady, NY; *U.S. Private,* pg. 969
Wylie, W. Peter, V.P.-Human Resources & Admin.--General Dynamics Corporation, Falls Church, VA; *U.S. Public,* pg. 708
Wynns, Carolyn, V.P.-H.R. & Sec.--Tri-State Armature & Electric Works, Memphis, TN; *U.S. Private,* pg. 1100
Yager, K.E., Coord.-Pers. Rels.--Ohio Edison Co. Western Div., Sandusky, OH; *U.S. Public,* pg. 645
Yager, Pamela, Dir.-H.R.--People's Choice TV Corp., Shelton, CT; *U.S. Public,* pg. 1274
Yahner, Joe, V.P.-H.R. & Corp. Affairs--Guidant Corporation, Indianapolis, IN; *U.S. Public,* pg. 768
Yaing, Rox Anne, Dir.-Personnel--Peco Mfg. Co., Inc., Portland, OR; *U.S. Private,* pg. 846
Yake, Byron, Dir.-H.R.--The Associated Press, New York, NY; *U.S. Private,* pg. 92
Yamada, Corinne, Mgr.-H.R.--AC Martin Partners, Los Angeles, CA; *U.S. Private,* pg. 708
Yamada, Yoshinori, Gen. Mgr.-Personnel & Education--Yasuda Mutual Life Insurance Co., Tokyo, Japan; *Int'l,* pg. 1519
Yamaguchi, Noboru, Exec. Dir.--Advantest Corporation, Tokyo, Japan; *Int'l,* pg. 25
Yamamoto, Mitsuyo, Mgr.-Personnel--Yamaichi Securities Co., Ltd., Tokyo, Japan; *Int'l,* pg. 1516
Yamasaki, K., Mgr.-Personnel--Fotograbado Industrial Centro-Americano S.A., San Jose, Costa Rica; *Int'l,* pg. 1349
Yamazaki, Katsuo, Mgr.-Human Resources--Toto Ltd., Kitakyushu, Japan; *Int'l,* pg. 1410
Yamboonruang, Vichit, Dr., Asst. Governor-Human Resources--Petroleum Authority of Thailand, Bangkok, Thailand; *Int'l,* pg. 1046
Yanagi, Jeff, V.P.-Human Resources--Lotus Development Corporation, Cambridge, MA; *U.S. Public,* pg. 896
Yanagtani, Katsumi, Gen. Mgr.-Personnel Div.--The Nanto Bank, Ltd., Nara, Japan; *Int'l,* pg. 905
Yanca, Larry, Dir.-Personnel--C.W. Zumbiel Company, Norwood, OH; *U.S. Private,* pg. 1207
Yandell, Jerry P., V.P.-Opers.--TCA Cable TV, Inc., Tyler, TX; *U.S. Public,* pg. 1553
Yando, Jack, Mgr.-Personnel--Teknor Apex Company, Pawtucket, RI; *U.S. Private,* pg. 1073
Yanovitch, Bill, Dir.-H.R.--Dentsply International Inc., York, PA; *U.S. Public,* pg. 498
Yarborough, W. Glen, V.P.--Allied Research Corporation, Vienna, VA; *U.S. Public,* pg. 48
Yates, M., Mgr.-Human Resources--Mobil Oil Company, Ltd., Milton Keynes, United Kingdom; *U.S. Public,* pg. 1119
Yates, Veseth, V.P.-H.R.--Darigold, Inc., Seattle, WA; *U.S. Private,* pg. 311
Yates, Veseth, Dir.-H.R.--Darigold, Inc., Seattle, WA; *U.S. Private,* pg. 311
Yaverski, Anna, Mgr.-Personnel--Paul Inman Associates Inc., Farmington, MI; *U.S. Private,* pg. 564
Yeip, Robert L., Treas. & Corp. Sec.--Overhead Conveyor Co., Ferndale, MI; *U.S. Private,* pg. 822
Yeoland, Stuart A., Gen. Mgr.--Boral Limited, Sydney, Australia; *Int'l,* pg. 203
Yesulis, Norine, Mgr.-Personnel--Tang Industries Inc., Las Vegas, NV; *U.S. Private,* pg. 1068
Yezbick, Gary, V.P.-Human Resoures--Gelman Sciences, Inc., Ann Arbor, MI; *U.S. Public,* pg. 1253
Yoder, David, Mgr.-Employee Rels.--Houghton International Inc., Valley Forge, PA; *U.S. Private,* pg. 541
Yoder, Patti B., Sr. V.P. & Dir.-Human Resources--Riggs National Corporation, Washington, DC; *U.S. Public,* pg. 1389
Yonker, Charley, Dir.-H.R.--Giant Industries Inc., Scottsdale, AZ; *U.S. Public,* pg. 741
Yonker, Pat, Dir.-Mktg. Svcs.--GraphLine Inc., Tamarac, FL; *U.S. Private,* pg. 471
Yoon, Beyung H., Mgr.-Personnel--NURI Enterprise, Seoul, Korea; *Int'l,* pg. 348
York, Larry, V.P.-H.R.--Meadowcraft, Inc., Birmingham, AL; *U.S. Private,* pg. 725
York, Rich, V.P.-Human Resources--Orkin Exterminating Co., Inc., Atlanta, GA; *U.S. Public,* pg. 1404
York, Rob S., V.P.-H.R.--Weston Paper & Manufacturing Co., Terre Haute, IN; *U.S. Private,* pg. 1169
Yorke, Paul, Grp. V.P.-Human Resources--Hickson International Plc, Castleford, United Kingdom; *Int'l,* pg. 618
Yoshimura, Hisao, Exec. V.P.-Circulation & Advertising, Personnel--Nikkei Business Publications Inc., Tokyo, Japan; *Int'l,* pg. 929
Yoshisato, Sandy, Dir.-Human Resources--Puroflow Incorporated, Van Nuys, CA; *U.S. Public,* pg. 1345
Yost, Lois, Mgr.-Personnel--Doonan & Sons, Inc., Great Bend, KS; *U.S. Private,* pg. 340
Young, Cathy, Dir.-Personnel--Communications Instruments Inc., Fairview, NC; *U.S. Private,* pg. 259
Young, Chris, Dir.-H.R.--Chem-Trend Incorporated, Howell, MI; *Int'l,* pg. 235
Young, D.W., Dir.-Personnel Training & Devel.--Redland PLC, Reigate, United Kingdom; *Int'l,* pg. 1090
Young, Don, Mgr.-Employee Rels.--Nicholson File, Cullman, AL; *U.S. Public,* pg. 444
Young, E. Howard, V.P.--General Wholesale Company, Inc., Atlanta, GA; *U.S. Private,* pg. 445
Young, John, Sr. V.P.-Human Resources & Admin.--Four Seasons Hotels Inc., Don Mills, Canada; *Int'l,* pg. 502
Young, John F., V.P.-H.R.--Stratus Computer, Inc., Marlborough, MA; *U.S. Public,* pg. 1524
Young, Tim, V.P.-Human Resources--Hillshire Farm & Kahn's, Cincinnati, OH; *U.S. Public,* pg. 1433
Yount, Deborah E., Dir.-Personnel--UES, Inc., Dayton, OH; *U.S. Private,* pg. 1112
Yows, Tom, Mgr.-H.R.--Brazos Electric Power Cooperative, Inc., Waco, TX; *U.S. Private,* pg. 166
Yuill, Allison, Mgr.-Personnel--Nestle-Lyons Maid, Telford, United Kingdom; *Int'l,* pg. 922
Yusko, Gary J., Sr. V.P.-Fin.--Westwood One, Inc., New York, NY; *U.S. Public,* pg. 1763
Zabel, Ken, V.P.-Human Resources--Vertel, Woodland Hills, CA; *U.S. Public,* pg. 1717
Zabor, Thomas J., V.P.-Human Resources--Indiana Gas Company, Inc., Indianapolis, IN; *U.S. Public,* pg. 875
Zachariadis, Zacharias, Mgr.-Personnel Admin.--European Investment Bank, Luxembourg, Luxembourg; *Int'l,* pg. 465
Zadzora, Edward J., V.P.-Human Resources--Kronos, Inc., Houston, TX; *U.S. Private,* pg. 270
Zagel, Sandra, Dir.-H.R.--J.W. Messner, Inc., Grand Rapids, MI; *U.S. Private,* pg. 734
Zagrodny, Mike, Corp. Human Resources Dir.--Fahlgren, Dublin, OH; *U.S. Private,* pg. 391
Zainey, Michael Scott, Sr. V.P.-H.R.--Hibernia Corporation, New Orleans, LA; *U.S. Public,* pg. 825
Zak, D., Dir.-Personnel--The Toro Company Irrigation Products, Riverside, CA; *U.S. Public,* pg. 1624
Zak, Lawrence A., V.P.-Fin.--Armada Corporation, Detroit, MI; *U.S. Private,* pg. 82
Zakreski, James, Mgr.-H.R.--Keen Compressed Gas Co., Wilmington, DE; *U.S. Private,* pg. 611
Zaks, Ofer, V.P.-Human Resources--ECI Telecom Ltd., Petah Tiqwa, Israel; *Int'l,* pg. 643
Zaldivar, Polly, Mgr.-Human Resources--Peoples Telephone Company, Inc., Miami, FL; *U.S. Public,* pg. 1275
Zalka, Ivy, V.P.-Human Resources & Asst. Sec.--Sun City Industries, Inc., Fort Lauderdale, FL; *U.S. Public,* pg. 1529
Zambon, Nancy M., V.P.-Human Resources--First Health Group Corp., Downers Grove, IL; *U.S. Public,* pg. 635
Zamora, Nassry G., V.P.-H.R.--Phelps Dodge Intl. Corp., Coral Gables, FL; *U.S. Public,* pg. 1286
Zampini, Ralph, Dir.-H.R.--Krasdale Foods Inc., White Plains, NY; *U.S. Private,* pg. 635
Zandvoort, H., Dir.-Personnel & Organization--Nutricia BV, Zoetermeer, Netherlands; *Int'l,* pg. 991
Zaninovich, Paul, Mgr.-H.R.--Network Computing Devices, Inc., Mountain View, CA; *U.S. Public,* pg. 1168
Zanotti, Judith A., Sr. V.P.-Human Resources--Public Service Company of New Mexico, Albuquerque, NM; *U.S. Public,* pg. 1339
Zanton, Harold D., Dir.-Personnel--Zantop International Airlines, Inc., Ypsilanti, MI; *U.S. Private,* pg. 1204
Zapiola, Ernesto, Mgr.-H.R. & Devel.--Y.P.F., S.A., Buenos Aires, Argentina; *Int'l,* pg. 1515
Zarick, Robert S., Sr. V.P.-Human Resources--Central Reserve Life of North America Insurance Co., Strongsville, OH; *U.S. Public,* pg. 326
Zatina, Thomas, Chief Oper. Officer, Exec. V.P. & Asst. Sec.--Bozzuto's Inc., Cheshire, CT; *U.S. Public,* pg. 249
Zaupffel, C., Dir.-Human Resources--Groupe Strafor Facom, Morangis, France; *Int'l,* pg. 569
Zega, Robert, Dir.-Personnel--AEC, Inc., Wood Dale, IL; *U.S. Private,* pg. 500
Zeidman, Annette, Mgr.-Reg. Human Resources--Willis Corroon Corp. of Los Angeles, Glendale, CA; *Int'l,* pg. 1506
Zeigler, Kenneth B., V.P.-Human Resources--Brunswick Corporation, Lake Forest, IL; *U.S. Public,* pg. 265
Zeiher, Frank A., V.P.-Human Resources--Riser Foods, Inc., Bedford, OH; *U.S. Private,* pg. 450
Zeilmann, Judy, Principal-H.R.--Edward Jones, Saint Louis, MO; *U.S. Private,* pg. 597
Zeindler, Franz, Mgr.-Personnel & Purchasing--Oerlikon Buhrle Immobilien AG Zurich, Switzerland; *Int'l,* pg. 998
Zelenak, Joyce, Mgr.-Human Resources--Code-Alarm, Inc., Madison Heights, MI; *U.S. Public,* pg. 393
Zelenar, Joyce, Mgr.-Human Resources--Code Alarm Security Systems, Madison Heights, MI; *U.S. Public,* pg. 394
Zeller, Diane, Mgr.-Human Resources--Northland Aluminum Products, Inc., Minneapolis, MN; *U.S. Private,* pg. 805
Zeller, Dudley, Dir.-Personnel & Risk Mngmt.--Golden Gem Growers Inc., Umatilla, FL; *U.S. Private,* pg. 460
Zellers, Ledell, Asst. V.P. & Dir.-H.R.--National Guardian Life Insurance Company, Madison, WI; *U.S. Private,* pg. 784
Zemelman, David, Sr. V.P.-Human Resources--CBS Corporation, Pittsburgh, PA; *U.S. Public,* pg. 273
Zemmelman, David, Sr. V.P.-Human Resources--CBS, New York, NY; *U.S. Public,* pg. 273
Ziblut, John S., V.P.-Human Resources--Moore Business Forms & Systems Div., Lake Forest, IL; *Int'l,* pg. 890
Zidjunas, R.G., V.P.-Indus. Rels.--CWC Textron Company, Muskegon, MI; *U.S. Public,* pg. 1590
Ziegler, Debra, V.P.-Human Resources--The Dannon Co., Tarrytown, NY; *Int'l,* pg. 379
Ziegler, Ellero, V.P.-Personnel Devel. & Recruitment--Liechtenstein Global Trust Limited, Vaduz, Liechtenstein; *Int'l,* pg. 809
Ziegler, Gregory, Dir.-Personnel--Cincinnati Financial Corp., Fairfield, OH; *U.S. Public,* pg. 368
Ziegler, Marge, Mgr.-Human Resources--Axiom Inc., Moorestown, NJ; *U.S. Public,* pg. 157
Zierk, Robert, V.P.--Avnet, Inc., Great Neck, NY; *U.S. Public,* pg. 155
Zilinski, Joan, Mgr.-H.R.--C.J. Vitner Co., Chicago, IL; *U.S. Private,* pg. 1142
Zimmer, Herta, Mgr.-Human Resources--Superba, Inc., Los Angeles, CA; *U.S. Private,* pg. 1054
Zimmerman, Ronald, V.P.-H.R.--QuickLogic Corporation, Sunnyvale, CA; *U.S. Private,* pg. 901
Zimmerman, S. LaNette, Sr. V.P. & Dir.-Human Resources--Chicago Title & Trust Co., Chicago, IL; *U.S. Public,* pg. 42
Zimmerman, Wayne M., V.P.-Human Services Division--Caterpillar Inc., Peoria, IL; *U.S. Public,* pg. 315
Zimpel, Michael J., Mgr.-Personnel--Lampert Yards, Inc., Saint Paul, MN; *U.S. Private,* pg. 645
Zink, Al, Dir.-H.R.--NewsEdge Corporation, Burlington, MA; *U.S. Public,* pg. 1180
Zins, Mary, Mgr.-Personnel--Polaris Industries, Inc., Minneapolis, MN; *U.S. Public,* pg. 1313
Zipf, Betsy K., V.P.--BT Financial Corporation, Johnstown, PA; *U.S. Public,* pg. 163
Zito, Robert A., Jr., Sr. V.P.-Human Resources--Talegen Corporation, Seattle, WA; *U.S. Public,* pg. 1784
Zitzer, Gerald E., V.P.-Human Resources--Briggs & Stratton Corporation, Wauwatosa, WI; *U.S. Public,* pg. 252
Zix, Carolin, Dir.-Human Resources--Chyron Corp., Melville, NY; *Int'l,* pg. 1372
Zlinski, Janet, Dir.-H.R.--Victory Refrigeration Co. LC, Cherry Hill, NJ; *U.S. Private,* pg. 1139
Zmolek, Doug, V.P.--EMC Insurance Group, Inc., Des Moines, IA; *U.S. Public,* pg. 545
Zoss, Alan, Dir.-Human Resources--Sparton Corporation, Jackson, MI; *U.S. Public,* pg. 1496
Zoucha, Jan, Personnel--Woodmen Accident & Life Co., Lincoln, NE; *U.S. Private,* pg. 1187
Zub, Joseph, Dir.-Opers. & Mgr.-H.R.--H.O. Trerice Company, Oak Park, MI; *U.S. Private,* pg. 1099
Zug, Steve, Dir.-Human Resources--Wavetek Corporation, San Diego, CA; *U.S. Private,* pg. 1154
Zupon, Theresa, Dir.-H.R.--The Beverly Hills Hotel, Beverly Hills, CA; *U.S. Private,* pg. 142
Zurman, George D., V.P.-H.R.--Hubbell Incorporated, Orange, CT; *U.S. Public,* pg. 844
Zych, Frank, Dir.-Human Resources--Aerovox Inc., New Bedford, MA; *U.S. Public,* pg. 25

INVESTOR RELATIONS

Aaron, Mark L., V.P.-Investor Rels.--Tiffany & Co., New York, NY; *U.S. Public,* pg. 1608
Abel, James J., Chief Fin. Officer, Exec. V.P., Treas. & Sec.--The Lamson & Sessions Co., Cleveland, OH; *U.S. Public,* pg. 976

Abely, Joseph F., Pres. & Chief Oper. Officer--LoJack Corporation, Dedham, MA; *U.S. Public*, pg. 1012
Aberdeen, Jeffery, Controller--Commerce Bancshares, Inc., Kansas City, MO; *U.S. Public*, pg. 409
Abernathy, Jan, Dir.-Inv. Rels.--Dow Jones & Company, Inc., New York, NY; *U.S. Public*, pg. 524
Abrahamsen, R.J.N., Chief Fin. Officer & Mng. Dir.--KLM Royal Dutch Airlines, Amstelveen, Netherlands; *Int'l*, pg. 719
Abrams, Jerry, Chief Fin. Officer & Treas.--Hoogovens Aluminium Corp., Secaucus, NJ; *Int'l*, pg. 755
Abrams, Leigh J., Pres. & Chief Exec. Officer--Drew Industries Incorporated, White Plains, NY; *U.S. Public*, pg. 529
Abrego-Santucci, Patricia, Mgr.-Stockholder Rels.--Peoples Energy Corporation, Chicago, IL; *U.S. Public*, pg. 1274
Ackerman, Susan D., V.P. & Sec.--Phoenix American Incorporated, San Rafael, CA; *U.S. Private*, pg. 862
Ackermann, Juergen, Dir.-Investor Rels.--Commerzbank AG, Frankfurt, Germany; *Int'l*, pg. 308
Acosta, Jack, Chief Fin. Officer & Sr. V.P.--Sybase, Inc., Emeryville, CA; *U.S. Public*, pg. 1544
Adamou, Julie M., Ph.D., Assoc.-Investor & Media Rels.--MedImmune, Inc., Gaithersburg, MD; *U.S. Public*, pg. 1081
Adams, Raymond T., V.P.-Corp. Commun.--DSC Communications Corporation, Plano, TX; *U.S. Public*, pg. 475
Adams, Robert, Dir.-Investor Rels.--Puget Sound Energy, Inc., Bellevue, WA; *U.S. Public*, pg. 1342
Adams, Stephen P., Mgr.-Investor Rels.--Zurn Industries, Inc., Erie, PA; *U.S. Public*, pg. 1794
Adey, Amanda, Mgr.-Environment & Corp. Responsibility--EMI Group plc, London, United Kingdom; *Int'l*, pg. 426
Adler, Cindy F., Sec. & Dir.-Investor Rels.--Homasote Company, Trenton, NJ; *U.S. Public*, pg. 831
Aerni, Bernhard, Chief Fin. Officer & Sr. V.P.-Fin.--UMS Swiss Metalworks Holding Ltd, Dornach, Switzerland; *Int'l*, pg. 1427
Ahart, J.F., Chief Fin. Officer, V.P., Treas. & Sec.--Powell Industries, Inc., Houston, TX; *U.S. Public*, pg. 1319
Ahern, Shannon, Mgr.-Board & Shareholder Services--Alaska Airlines, Inc., Seattle, WA; *U.S. Public*, pg. 35
Ahlborn, Brian, V.P.-Strategic Plng.--A.G. Simpson Co. Limited, Scarborough, Canada; *Int'l*, pg. 1252
Aimone, Michael V., Chief Fin. Officer & V.P.--Mississippi Lime Co., Alton, IL; *U.S. Private*, pg. 753
Ainsworth, Phyllis B., Corp. Sec.--First Financial Holdings, Inc., Charleston, SC; *U.S. Public*, pg. 634
Aldrich, David J., V.P. & Treas.--Alpha Industries, Inc., Woburn, MA; *U.S. Public*, pg. 57
Aldrich, Deborah E., Mgr.-Admin--ESA, Inc., Chelmsford, MA; *U.S. Private*, pg. 354
Alexander, Glenn J., Controller--Blonder-Tongue Laboratories, Inc., Old Bridge, NJ; *U.S. Public*, pg. 237
Alexander, J.A.F., Investor Rels. Officer--Burmah Castrol plc, Swindon, United Kingdom; *Int'l*, pg. 234
Alguire, William M., Sec.--Electrohome Ltd., Kitchener, Canada; *Int'l*, pg. 438
Alivio, Bernie, Mgr.-Investor Rels.--Rexhall Industries, Inc., Lancaster, CA; *U.S. Public*, pg. 1384
Allek, John, Mgr.-Investor Rels.--ABB AB, Stockholm, Sweden; *Int'l*, pg. 7
Allen, Brad, Dir.-Investor Rels.--Imation Corporation, Oakdale, MN; *U.S. Public*, pg. 870
Allen, Brad, Dir.-Investor Rels.--Cray Research, Eagan, MN; *U.S. Public*, pg. 1473
Allen, Craig, Mgr.-Investor Rels.--CalEnergy Co., Omaha, NE; *U.S. Public*, pg. 292
Allen, David H., Treas.--Komag, Incorporated, San Jose, CA; *U.S. Public*, pg. 966
Allen, Ralph D., V.P. & Dir.-Investor Relations--ITT Industries, Inc., White Plains, NY; *U.S. Public*, pg. 859
Allencourt, Mary Ann, Mgr.-Investor Rels.--Scios Inc., Mountain View, CA; *U.S. Public*, pg. 1444
Allman, Anthony G., V.P.-Customer Service--Micros Systems Inc., Beltsville, MD; *U.S. Public*, pg. 1106
Allott, Anthony J., Chief Fin. Officer & V.P.--Applied Extrusion Technologies, Inc., Peabody, MA; *U.S. Public*, pg. 122
Almendros, Fernando Diaz, Mgr.-Investments--Banca March S.A., Palma de Mallorca, Spain; *Int'l*, pg. 136
Alonzi, Julie, Mgr.-Fin. Reporting--Hathaway Corporation, Littleton, CO; *U.S. Public*, pg. 798
Alonzo, Beth, Investor Rels.--Concurrent Computer Corporation, Fort Lauderdale, FL; *U.S. Public*, pg. 430
Altesi, Ann, Mgr.-Investor Rels.--Offshore Logistics, Inc., Lafayette, LA; *U.S. Public*, pg. 1212
Altick, Leslie L., Dir.-Investor Rels.--Wells Fargo & Company, San Francisco, CA; *U.S. Public*, pg. 1753
Altizer, Joseph W., II, Chief Fin. Officer--Jefferson Mills, Inc., Pulaski, VA; *U.S. Private*, pg. 584
Alvares, Antonio Carlos B., Mgr.-Indus. Rels.--Acos Villares Mechanical Engineering Unit, Sao Paulo, Brazil; *Int'l*, pg. 23
Amann, Scott, V.P.-Investor Rels.--Cameron, Houston, TX; *U.S. Public*, pg. 298
Amer, John C., Exec. V.P.-Fin. & Sec.--Reactive Metals & Alloys Corporation (REMACOR), West Pittsburg, PA; *U.S. Private*, pg. 913
Ames, Kimberly, Exec. Admin.--Checkers Drive-In Restaurants, Inc., Clearwater, FL; *U.S. Public*, pg. 342
Andersen, Nevin N., Chief Fin. Officer & V.P.--Shaklee Corporation, San Francisco, CA; *Int'l*, pg. 1518
Anderson, Adair, Sec.--John Menzies plc, Edinburgh, United Kingdom; *Int'l*, pg. 707
Anderson, Christine, Coord.-Investor Rels. & Asst. to the Pres.--MGM Grand, Inc., Las Vegas, NV; *U.S. Public*, pg. 1026
Anderson, David L., Dir.-Investor Rels.--GEICO Corporation, Washington, DC; *U.S. Public*, pg. 219
Anderson, David L., Dir.-Investor Rels.--Government Employees Insurance Co. (GEICO), Washington, DC; *U.S. Public*, pg. 220
Anderson, Don, Chief Fin. Officer & Sr. V.P.--Carr Gottstein Foods, Anchorage, AK; *U.S. Public*, pg. 308
Anderson, Erling J., Chief Fin. Officer & Dir.-Investor Rels.--Dotronix, Inc., New Brighton, MN; *U.S. Public*, pg. 520
Anderson, Hugh F., Mgr.-Investor Rels.--Cincinnati Bell Telephone, Cincinnati, OH; *U.S. Public*, pg. 367
Anderson, Margaret A., Chief Fin. Officer, Sr. V.P.-Admin. & Treas.--Aerospace Corporation, El Segundo, CA; *U.S. Private*, pg. 24
Anderson, Ronald A., Sec. & Asst. Treas.--St. Joe Corp., Jacksonville, FL; *U.S. Public*, pg. 1426
Anderson, Stuart, Mgr.-Grp. Investor Relations--Standard Chartered Bank PLC, London, United Kingdom; *Int'l*, pg. 1294
Anderson, Suzanne, Fund Asst.--Center Partners Management LLC, New York, NY; *U.S. Private*, pg. 222
Anderton, Dan, Investor Rels.--Caldor, Inc., Norwalk, CT; *U.S. Public*, pg. 292
Andrews, Donald L., Treas.--SRI International, Menlo Park, CA; *U.S. Private*, pg. 958
Andrews, William C., V.P. & Controller--Rohm and Haas Company, Philadelphia, PA; *U.S. Public*, pg. 1403
Angelich, Mark, Exec. V.P.--Amelco Corporation, Gardena, CA; *U.S. Public*, pg. 65
Anguilla, Rick, Dir.-Investor Rels.--Nike, Inc., Beaverton, OR; *U.S. Public*, pg. 1184
Antenberg, Bruce F., Sr. V.P. & Treas.--Great Western Financial Corporation, Chatsworth, CA; *U.S. Public*, pg. 1741
Antunes, Joao Gomes, Mgr.-Inv. Rels.--Acos Villares S.A., Sao Paulo, Brazil; *Int'l*, pg. 23
Apple, Steve, Mgr.-Investor Rels.--West Coast Entertainment Inc., Langhorne, PA; *U.S. Public*, pg. 1755
Arena, M. S., V.P. & Treas.--Alcon Laboratories, Inc., Fort Worth, TX; *Int'l*, pg. 916
Arfmann, Bruce L., Chief Fin. Officer, Treas. & Sec.--Colorado MEDtech, Inc., Boulder, CO; *U.S. Public*, pg. 401
Argent, John W., Chief Fin. Officer--Basic American Foods, Walnut Creek, CA; *U.S. Private*, pg. 121
Aris, Stanley J., Chief Fin. Officer & V.P.-Fin.--CTS Corporation, Elkhart, IN; *U.S. Public*, pg. 285
Arita, Hiromitsu, Gen. Mgr.-Investor Rels.--Tekken Corporation, Tokyo, Japan; *Int'l*, pg. 1362
Arlotta, Terry, Chief Fin. Officer--Peerless Importers, Inc., Brooklyn, NY; *U.S. Private*, pg. 847
Armato, Michael, Sec.--Knutson Construction Co., Minneapolis, MN; *U.S. Private*, pg. 627
Armell, Beverly L., Sec. & Mgr.-Investor Rels.--Helix Technology Corp., Mansfield, MA; *U.S. Public*, pg. 808
Armstrong, James C., First V.P.-Investor Rels.--SunTrust Banks, Inc., Atlanta, GA; *U.S. Public*, pg. 1537
Armstrong, P., Officer-Investor Rels.--Australian National Industries Limited, Pyrmont, Australia; *Int'l*, pg. 100
Armstrong, Theodore M., Chief Fin. Officer & Sr. V.P.-Fin. & Admin.--Angelica Corporation, Chesterfield, MO; *U.S. Public*, pg. 113
Arndt, Brennen M., Dir.-Investor Rels.--Air Products and Chemicals, Inc., Allentown, PA; *U.S. Public*, pg. 30
Arona, Giorgio, Dir.-Indus. Rels.--Olivetti SpA, Turin, Italy; *Int'l*, pg. 1002
Aronson, Sheree, Dir.-Investor Rels.--Apria Healthcare Group Inc., Costa Mesa, CA; *U.S. Public*, pg. 125
Arton, Gavin R., Sr. V.P.-Investor Rels. Officer--Exel Insurance Co. Ltd., Hamilton, Bermuda; *Int'l*, pg. 467
Asch, Michael A., Pres., Chief Oper. Officer, Chief Fin. Officer & Treas.--Rexx Environmental Corp., New York, NY; *U.S. Public*, pg. 1384
Asdia, George V., Dir.-Commun.--Environment/One Corporation, Niskayuna, NY; *U.S. Public*, pg. 586
Ash, H.K., Dir.-Investor Rels.--The Goodyear Tire & Rubber Company, Akron, OH; *U.S. Public*, pg. 752
Ashby, Michael, Chief Fin. Officer, V.P.-Fin./Admin. & Treas.--Bytex Corporation, Westborough, MA; *U.S. Public*, pg. 1522
Atenhan, Todd, Dir.-Inv. Rels.--Automobile Protection Corporation-APCO, Atlanta, GA; *U.S. Public*, pg. 150
Atherton, Dale R., Dir.-Fin. Mngmt. & Analysis--American Institute of C.P.A.'s Inc., New York, NY; *U.S. Private*, pg. 57
Atkins, Stanley B., V.P. & Sec.--Citation Corporation, Birmingham, AL; *U.S. Public*, pg. 376
Atkinson, Douglas B., Dir.-Investor Rels.--PPG Industries, Inc., Pittsburgh, PA; *U.S. Public*, pg. 1245
Attenhan, Todd, Dir.-Investor Rels.--Sonic Automotive, Inc., Charlotte, NC; *U.S. Public*, pg. 1485
Audet, Luc, V.P.-Inv. Rels.--Provigo Inc., Montreal, Canada; *Int'l*, pg. 1072
Austry, Kathleen, Dir.-Investor Rels.--Meridian Medical Technology, Inc., Columbia, MD; *U.S. Public*, pg. 1095
Avis, Robert G., Vice Chm., Exec. V.P. & Dir.-Investment Banking--A.G. Edwards, Inc., Saint Louis, MO; *U.S. Public*, pg. 565
Axelson, Michelle, Chief Fin. Officer & Mgr.-Investor Rels.--Scopus Technology, Inc., Emeryville, CA; *U.S. Public*, pg. 1444
Axten, Charles, Sr. Gen. Mgr.-Pub. Affairs & Communications--First National Bank Holdings Limited, Johannesburg, South Africa; *Int'l*, pg. 487
Ayers, Cheryl, V.P.-Shareholder Rels.--Centura Banks, Inc., Rocky Mount, NC; *U.S. Public*, pg. 328
Ayers, Dean, V.P.-Investor Rels.--NGC Corporation, Houston, TX; *U.S. Public*, pg. 1146
Baarman, Danielle, Mgr.-Investor Rels.--Manugistics Group, Inc., Rockville, MD; *U.S. Public*, pg. 1042
Babington, Catherine, V.P.-Investor Rels. & Pub. Affairs--Abbott Laboratories, Abbott Park, IL; *U.S. Public*, pg. 12
Bacciocco, James S., Treas.--The Kendall Company, Mansfield, MA; *U.S. Public*, pg. 1647
Bachman, Lee W., V.P.-Fin. & Treas.--Bachman's, Inc., Minneapolis, MN; *U.S. Private*, pg. 109
Baer, Ed, Mgr.-Investor Rels.--TVX Gold Inc., Toronto, Canada; *Int'l*, pg. 1345
Baeten, Ralph G., Treas.--WPS Resources Corp., Green Bay, WI; *U.S. Public*, pg. 1728
Baeten, Ralph G., V.P. & Treas.--Wisconsin Public Service Corporation, Green Bay, WI; *U.S. Public*, pg. 1728
Bagley, Patrick J., V.P.-Fin. & Treas.--Matlack Systems, Inc., Wilmington, DE; *U.S. Public*, pg. 1057
Bagley, Patrick J., Chief Fin. Officer, V.P.-Fin. & Treas.--Rollins Truck Leasing Corp., Wilmington, DE; *U.S. Public*, *pg. 1405*
Baiely, William, Chief Fin. Officer--Nobel Education Dynamics, Inc., Media, PA; *U.S. Public*, pg. 1185
Bailey, Don M., Pres. & Chief Exec. Officer--Comarco, Inc., Yorba Linda, CA; *U.S. Public*, pg. 406
Bailey, Robert, III, Pres.--Mid American Elevator Co., Inc., Chicago, IL; *U.S. Private*, pg. 743
Bain, Amy L., Exec. Asst.--J.B. Hunt Transport Services, Inc., Lowell, AR; *U.S. Public*, pg. 849
Baird, Anna M., Chief Fin. Officer & V.P.--Black Box Corporation of PA, Lawrence, PA; *U.S. Public*, pg. 235
Bajenski, Richard J., Dir.-Investor Rels.--Cooper Industries, Inc., Houston, TX; *U.S. Public*, pg. 442
Baker, Barbara, Dir.-Investor Rels.--Taubman Centers, Inc., Bloomfield Hills, MI; *U.S. Public*, pg. 1561
Baldwin, Ellen, Mgr.-Customer Commun.--Vanguard Cellular Systems, Inc., Greensboro, NC; *U.S. Public*, pg. 1707
Ball, Gary, Mgr.-Investor Rels.--Fluke Corporation, Everett, WA; *U.S. Public*, pg. 659
Ball, Stuart, Dir.-Investor Rels.--Entergy Corporation, New Orleans, LA; *U.S. Public*, pg. 585
Ballance, T.S., V.P.-Fin. & Treas.--Somerset Refinery Inc., Somerset, KY; *U.S. Private*, pg. 1013
Ballard, John W., III, Chief Fin. Officer & Sec.--TCI International Inc., Sunnyvale, CA; *U.S. Public*, pg. 1555
Bane, Pat, Asst. Sec.--Bindley Western Industries, Inc., Indianapolis, IN; *U.S. Public*, pg. 228
Banta, Ben, Dir.-Corp. Communications--Nextel Communications, Mc Lean, VA; *U.S. Public*, pg. 1180
Barber, Paul, Grp. Dir.-Corp.Affairs--Inchcape PLC, London, United Kingdom; *Int'l*, pg. 671
Barbieri, Joanne M., Mgr.-Investor Rels.--GPU, Inc., Morristown, NJ; *U.S. Public*, pg. 695
Barbieri, Joanne M., Mgr.-Investor Rels.--GPU Service Corp., Parsippany, NJ; *U.S. Public*, pg. 695
Barbour, Henry, Mgr.-Investor Rels.--Mobile Telecommunications Technologies Corp., Jackson, MS; *U.S. Public*, pg. 1120
Bardin, Beth, Asst. to the Pres.--Ark Restaurants Corp., New York, NY; *U.S. Public*, pg. 129
Bardwick, Catherine M., V.P.-Corp. Commun.--International Murex Technologies Corporation, Guelph, Canada; *Int'l*, pg. 684
Barker, Edwin F., Chief Fin. Officer & V.P.--Winnebago Industries, Inc., Forest City, IA; *U.S. Public*, pg. 1772
Barkley, Kenneth R., Chief Fin. Officer, Sr. V.P.-Fin. & Treas.--Cagle's Inc., Atlanta, GA; *U.S. Public*, pg. 291
Barna, Peter, Treas. & Principal Acctg. Officer--Crompton & Knowles Corporation, Stamford, CT; *U.S. Public*, pg. 459
Barnard, Aubrey D., Sec., Treas. & Controller--SouthTrust Corporation, Birmingham, AL; *U.S. Public*, pg. 1491
Barnes-Wallis, P., Controller & Mgr.-Inv. Rels.--Rolls-Royce plc, London, United Kingdom; *Int'l*, pg. 1126
Barnes, Donna E., Sec.--Pacific American Income Shares, Inc., Pasadena, CA; *U.S. Public*, pg. 1247
Barnes, Nancy, Investor Rels. Analyst--Comverse Network Systems, Wakefield, MA; *U.S. Public*, pg. 425
Barnes, Ralph S., V.P.-Investor Rels.--Semi-Tech Corporation, Markham, Canada; *Int'l*, pg. 1220
Barone, Rick, Dir.-Investor Rels.--Advanced Lighting Technologies, Inc., Twinsburg, OH; *U.S. Public*, pg. 20
Barr, Lauren L., V.P.-Investor Rels.--BRE Properties, Inc., San Francisco, CA; *U.S. Public*, pg. 163
Barraza, Richard D., V.P.-Investor Rels.--Calpine Corporation, San Jose, CA; *U.S. Public*, pg. 296
Barrett, William R., Dir.-Pub. Rels. & Adv.--Service Corporation International, Houston, TX; *U.S. Public*, pg. 1460
Barry, Jim, Dir.-Investor Rels.--American Vanguard Corporation, Newport Beach, CA; *U.S. Public*, pg. 94
Bartl, James F., Sec.--National Presto Industries, Inc., Eau Claire, WI; *U.S. Public*, pg. 1159
Bartlett, John B., Chief Fin. Officer & Sr. V.P.--UniFirst Corporation, Wilmington, MA; *U.S. Public*, pg. 1665
Bartlett, Paul D., Jr., Chm. Bd.--Bartlett and Company, Kansas City, MO; *U.S. Private*, pg. 118
Barwick, John O., Chief Fin. Officer, V.P.-Fin. & Treas.--Carmike Cinemas, Inc., Columbus, GA; *U.S. Public*, pg. 305
Barwick, T.G., Dir.-Corp. Affairs--Vodafone Group PLC, Newbury, United Kingdom; *Int'l*, pg. 1469
Basch, Jeff, Chief Acctg. Officer--The Progressive Corporation, Cleveland, OH; *U.S. Public*, pg. 1334
Basey, James L., Exec. V.P. & Chief Fin. Officer--Colorado National Bankshares, Inc., Denver, CO; *U.S. Public*, pg. 1680
Basham, J.D., Mgr.-Investor & Pub. Rels.--Dresser Industries, Inc., Dallas, TX; *U.S. Public*, pg. 528
Basham, Roxann R., Treas. & Corp. Sec.--Black Hills Corporation, Rapid City, SD; *U.S. Public*, pg. 235
Bassett, Amanda, Head-Corp. Rels.--The Burton Group PLC, London, United Kingdom; *Int'l*, pg. 237
Bassler, Elizabeth F., Mgr.-Investor Rels.--Inland Steel Industries, Inc., Chicago, IL; *U.S. Public*, pg. 879
Batkie, Ellen L., Sr. V.P.-Investor Rels.--Charter One Financial, Inc., Cleveland, OH; *U.S. Public*, pg. 336
Batson, S.D., Dir.-Fin.--Dan River Inc., Danville, VA; *U.S. Public*, pg. 478
Batten, Michael E., Chm. Bd. & Chief Exec. Officer--Twin Disc, Incorporated, Racine, WI; *U.S. Public*, pg. 1646
Battin, B. Norris, V.P.-Investor Rels.--The Cooper Companies, Inc., Irvine, CA; *U.S. Public*, pg. 442
Baumgartner, Beat, Dr., Chief Fin. Officer--Oerlikon-Buhrle Holding AG, Zurich, Switzerland; *Int'l*, pg. 996
Bauwens, Herwig, Mgr.-Investor Rels.--Kredietbank N.V., Brussels, Belgium; *Int'l*, pg. 760

Bawtree, Angela, Head-Investor Rels.--The Body Shop International, Littlehampton, United Kingdom; *Int'l*, pg. 199

Baxter, Randy P., Sec. & Treas.-Fin. Information Officer--Armada Corporation, Detroit, MI; *U.S. Private*, pg. 82

Beal, Leslie, Supvr.--El Paso Electric Company, El Paso, TX; *U.S. Public*, pg. 567

Beall, Pamela K.M., V.P., Treas., & Asst. Sec.--OHM Corporation, Findlay, OH; *U.S. Public*, pg. 1207

Beals, John, V.P.-Fin.--The First Years Inc., Avon, MA; *U.S. Public*, pg. 642

Bear, James W., Sr. V.P. & Treas.--Consolidated Products, Inc., Indianapolis, IN; *U.S. Public*, pg. 436

Beardwood, Bruce A., V.P.-Investor Rels.--Du Pont (E.I. Du Pont De Nemours & Co.), Wilmington, DE; *U.S. Public*, pg. 530

Beatty, Stephen E., Chief Fin. Officer & Treas.--The Dwyer Group, Inc., Waco, TX; *U.S. Public*, pg. 537

Beauchet, Jacques, Dir.-Investor Rels.--Promodes SA, Mondeville, France; *Int'l*, pg. 1071

Beavais, Robert, Chief Fin. Officer--Austin Group, Flint, MI; *U.S. Private*, pg. 99

Becker, Hugh E., Dir.-Corp. Communications--Robbins & Myers, Inc., Dayton, OH; *U.S. Public*, pg. 1393

Becker, William C., Chief Fin. Officer & V.P.-Fin.--Shopsmith, Inc., Dayton, OH; *U.S. Public*, pg. 1467

Bedard, Kipp A., V.P.-Corp. Affairs--Micron Technology Inc., Boise, ID; *U.S. Public*, pg. 1105

Bedewi, Elizabeth M., Sr. V.P, Sec. & Treas.--New Mexico & Arizona Land Co., Phoenix, AZ; *U.S. Public*, pg. 1172

Bedier, Roger H., Exec. Dir.-Investor Rels.--Viad Corp, Phoenix, AZ; *U.S. Public*, pg. 1718

Beggs, Susan L., Asst. V.P.-Shareholder Rels. & Asst. Sec.--Luby's Cafeterias, Inc., San Antonio, TX; *U.S. Public*, pg. 1017

Behymer, Jean M., Controller--Ghent Manufacturing, Inc., Lebanon, OH; *U.S. Private*, pg. 450

Beirise, John H., Grp. Pres.-Capital Markets--Mercantile Bancorporation Inc., Saint Louis, MO; *U.S. Public*, pg. 1087

Bell, Alisa, Mgr.-Investor Rels.--Mackie Designs, Inc., Woodinville, WA; *U.S. Public*, pg. 1030

Bell, Donald C., V.P. & Treas.--SENCORP, Newport, KY; *U.S. Private*, pg. 983

Bell, Mary, V.P.-Investor Rels.--Excel Communications, Inc., Dallas, TX; *U.S. Public*, pg. 598

Bell, Melissa, Mgr.-Pub. Rels.--Sky Network Television Limited, Auckland, New Zealand; *U.S. Public*, pg. 204

Bellande, Rolland, V.P.-Fin. & Investor Rels.--Chargeurs, Paris, France; *Int'l*, pg. 280

Belli, Susi, Mgr.-Mktg. & Investor Rels.--Luxottica Group S.p.A., Agordo, Italy; *Int'l*, pg. 822

Belliston, Marcus J., Dir.-Investor Rels.--Rouge Steel Company, Dearborn, MI; *U.S. Public*, pg. 1406

Belstock, Richard, Sr. V.P.--Sierra West Bancorp, Truckee, CA; *U.S. Public*, pg. 1470

Benaich, Pierre, Dir.-Investor Rels.--Danone Group, Paris, France; *Int'l*, pg. 379

Benedict, Robert, Chief Exec. Officer, Chief Fin. Officer & V.P.--Real World, Andover, MA; *U.S. Private*, pg. 913

Benger, Scott C., Sr. V.P.-Fin., Treas. & Sec.--Analytical Surveys, Inc., Colorado Springs, CO; *U.S. Public*, pg. 110

Benhase, Daniel B., Exec. V.P.-Trust Fin. Services & Private Banking--Starbanc Corporation, Cincinnati, OH; *U.S. Public*, pg. 1510

Bennett, Douglas M., Dir.-Mktg.--The Turner Corporation, New York, NY; *U.S. Public*, pg. 1645

Bennett, Emily P., Dir.-Corp. Services--Delta Natural Gas Company, Inc., Winchester, KY; *U.S. Public*, pg. 497

Bennett, Jan H., V.P.-Customer Service--APS, Phoenix, AZ; *U.S. Public*, pg. 1297

Bennett, Lynne M., Coord.-Paralegal & Investor Rels.--Gatefield Corporation, Fremont, CA; *U.S. Public*, pg. 703

Bennett, Ronald G., Pres.--Calavo Growers of California, Santa Ana, CA; *U.S. Private*, pg. 199

Benoit, David C., V.P.-Fin. & Treas.--Connecticut Water Service, Inc., Clinton, CT; *U.S. Public*, pg. 431

Benoit, Vincent, Dir.-Investor Rels.--Compagnie des Machines Bull, Louveciennes, France; *Int'l*, pg. 315

Bensen, Eric R., Chief Fin. Officer & V.P.--Cruise America, Inc., Mesa, AZ; *U.S. Private*, pg. 178

Benstock, Gerald M., Chm. Bd. & Chief Exec. Officer--Superior Surgical Mfg. Co., Inc., Seminole, FL; *U.S. Public*, pg. 1539

Bentley, Julia A., Sr. V.P.-Plng. & Inv. Rels. & Sec.--Proffitt's, Inc., Alcoa, TN; *U.S. Public*, pg. 1333

Berg, Steven L., V.P.-Investments & Human Resources--Millers Mutual Insurance Assn., Alton, IL; *U.S. Private*, pg. 748

Bergan, John W., V.P & Treas.--Morgan Construction Co., Worcester, MA; *U.S. Private*, pg. 761

Berger, Robert J., Chief Fin. Officer, Sr. V.P. & Treas.--ONBANCorp, Inc., Syracuse, NY; *U.S. Public*, pg. 631

Bergeson, Margo R., Corp. Sec.--Alta Gold Co., Henderson, NV; *U.S. Public*, pg. 58

Bergman, Janet E., V.P.-Investor Rels. & Corp. Affairs--Sara Lee Corporation, Chicago, IL; *U.S. Public*, pg. 1432

Berkeley, Frederick D., Chm. Bd. & Chief Exec. Officer--Graham Corporation, Batavia, NY; *U.S. Public*, pg. 757

Berliner, Debra, Dir.-Investor Rels.--Overseas Shipholding Group, Inc., New York, NY; *U.S. Public*, pg. 1236

Bernstein, David, Dir.-Investor Rels.--Royal Caribbean Cruises Ltd., Miami, FL; *U.S. Public*, pg. 1410

Berry, Glenn A., Chief Fin. Officer & Exec. V.P.--The Dixie Group, Inc., Chattanooga, TN; *U.S. Public*, pg. 514

Berry, Walter, Chief Fin. Officer & V.P.-Admin.--Bollinger Shipyards, Inc., Lockport, LA; *U.S. Private*, pg. 155

Bertoch, Ronald H., Exec. V.P.--BNI Coal, Ltd., Bismarck, ND; *U.S. Public*, pg. 1116

Bessant, Thomas A., Jr., Chief Fin. Officer, Sr. V.P. & Treas.--Cash America International, Inc., Fort Worth, TX; *U.S. Public*, pg. 312

Betuker, Kenneth S., Chief Fin. Officer, V.P. & Sec.--Noodle Kidoodle Inc., Syosset, NY; *U.S. Public*, pg. 1188

Beumer, Dale, V.P.-Treasury & Investor Rels.--Medtronic, Inc., Minneapolis, MN; *U.S. Public*, pg. 1082

Bhangali, Parag, Dir.-Investor Relations--Covance, Inc., Princeton, NJ; *U.S. Public*, pg. 453

Bhargava, Jitender, Dir.-Pub. Rels.--Air India, Mumbai, India; *Int'l*, pg. 37

Bibelnieks, Yanis, Dir.-Inv. Rels--C&D Charter Power Systems, Blue Bell, PA; *U.S. Public*, pg. 271

Bibi, Stacy, Mgr.-Investor Rels.--Saks Fifth Avenue, New York, NY; *U.S. Public*, pg. 1429

Bierman, Kerry, V.P.-Investor Rels.--The Scotts Company, Marysville, OH; *U.S. Public*, pg. 1446

Bihler, Theresa, Asst. Sec.--Rent-Way, Inc., Erie, PA; *U.S. Public*, pg. 1377

Bilek, George J., V.P.-Fin. & Treas.--Juno Lighting, Inc., Des Plaines, IL; *U.S. Public*, pg. 935

Biles, Kim, Mgr.-Investor Rels.--Killearn Properties, Inc., Stockbridge, GA; *U.S. Public*, pg. 956

Billy, Stacey L., Mgr.-Investor Rels.--Community First Bankshares, Inc., Fargo, ND; *U.S. Public*, pg. 416

Bilmes, Barry, V.P.-Fin. & Admin.--Brothers Gourmet Coffees, Inc., Boca Raton, FL; *U.S. Public*, pg. 259

Bimblick, Warren, V.P.-Investor Rels.--Primedia Inc., New York, NY; *U.S. Public*, pg. 1327

Bingaman, Larry L., V.P.-Corp. Rels. & Sec.--Aquarion Company, Bridgeport, CT; *U.S. Public*, pg. 126

Bingham, Paul M., Sr. V.P.-Fin.--Fleetwood Enterprises, Inc., Riverside, CA; *U.S. Public*, pg. 650

Binsle, John, Dir.-Investor Rels.--The B.F. Goodrich Company, Richfield, OH; *U.S. Public*, pg. 751

Birchfield, Ed, Mgr.-Corp. Rels.--Valmont Industries, Inc., Valley, NE; *U.S. Public*, pg. 1706

Bird, Patti, Controller--IEC Electronics Corp., Newark, NY; *U.S. Public*, pg. 854

Birney, Kathleen, Asst. Treas.--Arbor Drugs, Inc., Troy, MI; *U.S. Public*, pg. 126

Biro, Jon C., Sr. V.P. & Treas.--ICO, Inc., Houston, TX; *U.S. Public*, pg. 853

Bischoff, J. Michael, V.P.-Corp. Devel.--Marsh & McLennan Companies, Inc., New York, NY; *U.S. Public*, pg. 1048

Bishop, Carole, Mgr.-Investor Rels.--Tetra Technologies, Woodlands, TX; *U.S. Public*, pg. 1582

Bishop, Larry, V.P.-Commun. & Inv. Rels.--The Boeing Company, Seattle, WA; *U.S. Public*, pg. 239

Bishop, Laura M., Chief Fin. Officer & Sr. V.P.--Luby's Cafeterias, Inc., San Antonio, TX; *U.S. Public*, pg. 1017

Bisschops, Theo P.M., Sec. & Dir.-Investor Rels.--Gamma Holding N.V., Helmond, Netherlands; *Int'l*, pg. 539

Blackburn, Deirdre, Mgr.-Legal Sys.--Safeguard Scientifics, Inc., Wayne, PA; *U.S. Public*, pg. 1424

Blackburn, Gale, Dir.-Corp. Communications--Boca Research Inc., Boca Raton, FL; *U.S. Public*, pg. 239

Blackmon, Charles, Chief Fin. Officer & Exec. V.P.--American Buildings Co., Eufaula, AL; *U.S. Public*, pg. 69

Blair, Paul, Dir.-Investor Rels.--Illinois Power Company, Decatur, IL; *U.S. Public*, pg. 869

Blair, Robert J., Sr. V.P.-Corp. Investor Rels.--Western Digital Corporation, Irvine, CA; *U.S. Public*, pg. 1758

Blank, Julius, Sec.--Xicor, Inc., Milpitas, CA; *U.S. Public*, pg. 1785

Blaylock, Marcia, V.P. & Sec.--CLARCOR, Inc., Rockford, IL; *U.S. Public*, pg. 381

Bley, Janet, Dir.-Fin. Communications--McKesson Corporation, San Francisco, CA; *U.S. Public*, pg. 1072

Blizman, Wayne, V.P.-Corp. Plng. & Devel.--Durakon Industries, Inc., Lapeer, MI; *U.S. Public*, pg. 537

Blonder, Lloyd, Chief Fin. Officer, Sr. V.P. & Treas.--National Technical Systems, Inc., Calabasas, CA; *U.S. Public*, pg. 1161

Blum, Stephen D., Sr. V.P.-Corp. Commun.--Quaker State Corporation, Irving, TX; *U.S. Public*, pg. 1348

Blumenfeld, Peter, Pres. & Chief Oper. Officer--Sport Supply Group, Inc., Dallas, TX; *U.S. Public*, pg. 1499

Bobeff, Peter A., Sr. V.P.-Corp. Affairs--Foster's Brewing Group Limited, Southbank, Australia; *Int'l*, pg. 500

Bocarow, K., Mgr.-Investor Rels.--Software Spectrum, Inc., Garland, TX; *U.S. Public*, pg. 1483

Boe, Susan, V.P.-Investor Rels.--American Mutual Life Holding Co., Des Moines, IA; *U.S. Private*, pg. 59

Boehne, Rich, V.P.-Corp. Communications & Investor Rels.--The E.W. Scripps Company, Cincinnati, OH; *U.S. Public*, *pg. 1447*

Boenninghausen, Michael, Mgr.-Investor Rels.--Alza Corporation, Palo Alto, CA; *U.S. Public*, pg. 62

Boeve, Roger L., Chief Fin. Officer & Exec. V.P.--Performance Food Group Company, Richmond, VA; *U.S. Public*, pg. 1278

Bohn, David G., Pres.--Preferred Utilities Manufacturing Corp., Danbury, CT; *U.S. Private*, pg. 881

Bohs, G. Lee, Chief Fin. Officer & Exec. V.P.--Right Management Consultants, Inc., Philadelphia, PA; *U.S. Public*, pg. 1390

Boisseree, Brian, Treas. & Mgr.-Investor Rels.--Integrated Device Technology, Inc., Santa Clara, CA; *U.S. Public*, pg. 884

Boles, Christina L., Exec. V.P.-Loan Admin.--Compass Bank, Birmingham, AL; *U.S. Public*, pg. 418

Bolt, John, Treas.--Kellogg Company, Battle Creek, MI; *U.S. Public*, pg. 947

Bompard, Jean-Jacques, Corp. Sec.--Rossignol S.A., Voiron, France; *Int'l*, pg. 1127

Bondi, Cindy, Investor Rels. Coord.--Quantum Corporation, Milpitas, CA; *U.S. Public*, pg. 1350

Bondy, Timothy J., Chief Fin. Officer & V.P.--Northwestern Steel & Wire Co., Sterling, IL; *U.S. Public*, pg. 1201

Bonnet, Agnes, Dir.-Investor Rels.--The Eurotunnel Group, London, United Kingdom; *Int'l*, pg. 466

Bonsall, Mark B., Chief Fin. Officer & Assoc. Gen. Mgr.--Salt River Project Agricultural Improvement and Power District, Tempe, AZ; *U.S. Private*, pg. 962

Booraem, Jonathan W., Treas.--Central Vermont Public Service Corporation, Rutland, VT; *U.S. Public*, pg. 327

Booth, William B., V.P.-Investor & Pub. Affairs--Hecla Mining Company, Coeur D'Alene, ID; *U.S. Public*, pg. 803

Borg, M. Vincent, V.P.-Pub. Affairs & Communications--Barrick Gold Corporation, Toronto, Canada; *Int'l*, pg. 168

Borman, Mark, V.P.-Investor Rels.--ADC Telecommunications, Inc., Minnetonka, MN; *U.S. Public*, pg. 4

Borowy, David E., Investor Rels. Officer--Mercantile Bankshares Corporation, Baltimore, MD; *U.S. Public*, pg. 1088

Bothe, Brooke, Sec.--H.W. Kaufman Financial Group, Inc., Farmington, MI; *U.S. Private*, pg. 609

Bottini, Giancarlo, Chief Fin. Officer--Benetton Group S.p.A., Ponzano Veneto, Italy; *Int'l*, pg. 186

Boudreau, Kathy, Dir.-Investor Rels.--Sheldahl, Inc., Northfield, MN; *U.S. Public*, pg. 1465

Bourne, Katherine, Mgr.-Investor Rels.--Gulfmark Offshore Inc., Houston, TX; *U.S. Public*, pg. 769

Bowden, Andrew, Mgr.-Investor Rels.--National Australia Bank Limited, Melbourne, Australia; *Int'l*, pg. 906

Bowden, David G., V.P., Controller & Sec.--Griffin Group, Inc., New York, NY; *U.S. Private*, pg. 480

Bowen, Robert, Pres. & Chief Exec. Officer--COMNET Corporation, Lanham, MD; *U.S. Public*, pg. 416

Bownan, Charles, Dir.-Corp. Fin.--SPX Corporation, Muskegon, MI; *U.S. Public*, pg. 1420

Bowyer, Evelyn, Dir.-Investor Rels.--South Trust Bank of Georgia, Atlanta, GA; *U.S. Public*, pg. 1492

Boxer, Robert L., V.P., Gen. Counsel & Sec.--Moscom Corporation, Pittsford, NY; *U.S. Public*, pg. 1136

Boyd, Charles A., V.P.-Corp. Rel.--Sundt Corp., Tucson, AZ; *U.S. Private*, pg. 1051

Boyd, Jeffery, Exec. V.P. & Gen. Counsel--Oxford Health Plans Inc., Norwalk, CT; *U.S. Public*, pg. 1238

Boyd, Robert, Chief Fin. Officer & Exec. V.P.-Fin.--The Oshawa Group Limited, Etobicoke, Canada; *Int'l*, pg. 1012

Boyet, Charles, Controller & Treas.--Sigmund Cohn Corp., Mount Vernon, NY; *U.S. Private*, pg. 250

Boyle, Bruce, Dir.-Investor Rels.--National Media Corporation, Philadelphia, PA; *U.S. Public*, pg. 1158

Boyle, Celia, Investor Rels.--Argonaut Group, Inc., Los Angeles, CA; *U.S. Public*, pg. 129

Boynton, Mary, Sec., Librarian & Dir.-Investor Rels.--Newcor, Inc., Bloomfield Hills, MI; *U.S. Public*, pg. 1176

Bozarth, Glenn, Sr. V.P.-Corp. Commun.--Mattel, Inc., El Segundo, CA; *U.S. Public*, pg. 1057

Braddock, James L., Chm. Bd., Pres. & Treas.--Fastec Industrial, Elkhart, IN; *U.S. Private*, pg. 397

Bradley, Jessica, Mgr.-Investor Rels.--Pyramid Breweries, Inc.; *U.S. Public*, pg. 1345

Bradley, Todd, Mgr.-Investor Rels.--Hutchinson Technology Inc., Hutchinson, MN; *U.S. Public*, pg. 850

Bradtmiller, Phil, V.P.-Investor Rels.--American Standard Inc., Piscataway, NJ; *U.S. Public*, pg. 91

Brady, Jason, Assoc. Dir.-Investor Rels.--Synovus Financial Corp., Columbus, GA; *U.S. Public*, pg. 1548

Bramblett, Michael T., Exec. V.P.--Jones Medical Industries Inc., Saint Louis, MO; *U.S. Public*, pg. 933

Branca, Michael, Chief Fin. Officer--Reptron Electronics, Inc., Tampa, FL; *U.S. Public*, pg. 1377

Branch, John D., Chief Fin. Officer & Sr. V.P.-Fin.--Earl Scheib, Inc., Beverly Hills, CA; *U.S. Public*, pg. 1437

Brandt, Donald E., Sr. V.P.-Fin. & Corp. Services--AmerenUE, Saint Louis, MO; *U.S. Public*, pg. 66

Brandt, Gary G., V.P.-Investor Rels.--MFS WorldCom, Inc., Omaha, NE; *U.S. Public*, pg. 1779

Brandt, Lacey, Dir.-Investor Relations--Proteon, Inc., Westborough, MA; *U.S. Public*, pg. 1336

Bratton, Kevin J., V.P.--IGI, Inc., Buena, NJ; *U.S. Public*, pg. 855

Braun-Griep, Peggy, Mgr.-Investor Rels.--Unilever United States Inc., New York, NY; *Int'l*, pg. 1435

Braun, Kurt, Dir.-Investor Rels.--Lexmark International Group, Inc., Lexington, KY; *U.S. Public*, pg. 991

Braun, Kurt, Dir.-Investor Rels.--Lexmark International, Inc., Lexington, KY; *U.S. Public*, pg. 991

Brauns, Margaret, V.P. & Treas.--Informix Software, Menlo Park, CA; *U.S. Public*, pg. 876

Bravo, Lyssette, Mgr.-Investor Rels.--Consorcio G. Grupo Dina, S.A. de C.V., Mexico, Mexico; *Int'l*, pg. 326

Bray, David E., Treas.--Cone Mills Corporation, Greensboro, NC; *U.S. Public*, pg. 430

Brennan, Charles M., III, Chm. Bd. & Chief Exec. Officer--MYR Group Inc., Rolling Meadows, IL; *U.S. Public*, pg. 1029

Brennan, Ross A., V.P.-Investor Rels.--TrizecHahn Corporation, Toronto, Canada; *Int'l*, pg. 1424

Brennan, William J., Sr. V.P.-Admin.--Hosokawa Micron International Inc., New York, NY; *Int'l*, pg. 635

Brenner, Robin, Investor Rels. Liaison--Image Entertainment, Inc., Chatsworth, CA; *U.S. Public*, pg. 870

Bresky, Harry, Pres.--Seaboard Flour Corporation, Newton, MA; *U.S. Public*, pg. 1449

Brevard, Mary, Dir.-Investor Rels. & Commun.--Borg Warner Automotive, Inc., Chicago, IL; *U.S. Public*, pg. 245

Brewster, John E., Jr., V.P.-Corp. Devel. & Plng.--Howell Corporation, Houston, TX; *U.S. Public*, pg. 843

Brinberg, Simeon, Gen. Counsel--Gould Investors, L.P., Great Neck, NY; *U.S. Private*, pg. 466

Brissette, Johanne, Sr. Advisor-Investor Rels.--Gaz Metropolitain & Company, Montreal, Canada; *Int'l*, pg. 541

Britt, Anita, Dir.-Investor Rels.--Jones Apparel Group, Inc., Bristol, PA; *U.S. Public*, pg. 933

Brodsky, Bernard, V.P., Treas. & Sec.--Charming Shoppes, Inc., Bensalem, PA; *U.S. Public*, pg. 335

Brougham, John, Dir.-Investor Rels.--British Telecommunications plc, London, United Kingdom; *Int'l*, pg. 222

Brown, Benjamin A., V.P.-Fin. Rels. & Analysis--ENSERCH Corporation, Dallas, TX; *U.S. Public*, pg. 1587

Brown, Debbie, Mgr.-Pub. Rels.--Irwin Toy Ltd., Toronto, Canada; *Int'l*, pg. 688

Brown, Dennis, Chief Fin. Officer, V.P. & Treas.--Sybron International Corporation, Milwaukee, WI; *U.S. Public*, pg. 1544
Brown, Erica, Mgr.-Investor Rels.--Resource America, Inc., Philadelphia, PA; *U.S. Public*, pg. 1382
Brown, Frank C., V.P., Gen. Counsel & Corp. Sec.--Rexam Inc., Charlotte, NC; *Int'l*, pg. 1106
Brown, George, V.P.-Dir. Of H.R.--Paul Inman Associates Inc., Farmington, MI; *U.S. Private*, pg. 564
Brown, Jack R., Chief Fin. Officer, Treas. & Sec.--Florida Public Utilities Company, West Palm Beach, FL; *U.S. Public*, pg. 655
Brown, John E., Asst. Treas.-Shareholder Rels.--Sierra Pacific Resources, Reno, NV; *U.S. Public*, pg. 1470
Brown, Lorraine, Investor Rels.--T-NETIX, Inc., Englewood, CO; *U.S. Public*, pg. 1553
Brown, Monika, Dir.-Investor Rels.--HBOC, Atlanta, GA; *U.S. Public*, pg. 770
Brown, Paul M., Chief Fin. Officer & V.P.-Fin.--TRM Copy Centers Corporation, Portland, OR; *U.S. Public*, pg. 1558
Brown, Stuart, Dir.-Investor Rels.--Koninklijke Ahold NV, Zaandam, Netherlands; *Int'l*, pg. 749
Browning, Janet, Investor Rels.--Roberts Pharmaceutical Corporation, Eatontown, NJ; *U.S. Public*, pg. 1393
Brunka, Barbara A., Mgr.-Investor Rels.--ComEd, Chicago, IL; *U.S. Public*, pg. 1664
Brunko, C.E., Asst. Treas. & Asst. Sec.--Otter Tail Power Company, Fergus Falls, MN; *U.S. Public*, pg. 1234
Brunswick, Paul L., Chief Fin. Officer, V.P. & Treas.--GoodMark Foods, Inc., Raleigh, NC; *U.S. Public*, pg. 751
Buan, Catherine, Dir.-Investor Rels.--Oracle Corporation, Redwood City, CA; *U.S. Public*, pg. 1227
Bubin, Christopher J., V.P.-Pub. Rels. & Investor Rels.--First Citizens Banc Shares, Inc., Raleigh, NC; *U.S. Public*, pg. 628
Bubser, Jim, Broker Mgr.-Northeast--Pangburn Candy Company, Fort Worth, TX; *U.S. Private*, pg. 836
Buckley, Beverly A., Dir.-Investor Rels.--WorldCom, Inc., Jackson, MS; *U.S. Public*, pg. 1779
Buckley, G. Ian, Mng. Dir.-Investment Div.--Henderson Administration Group PLC, London, United Kingdom; *Int'l*, pg. 609
Buckley, Mark, Chief Fin. Officer & V.P.--Stern-Leach Company, Attleboro, MA; *Int'l*, pg. 329
Budd, Kevin, Dir.-Inv. Rels.--Methanex Corporation, Vancouver, Canada; *Int'l*, pg. 862
Budwick, Robert T., Exec. V.P. & Chief Investment Officer--MBL Life Assurance Corporation, Newark, NJ; *U.S. Private*, pg. 685
Buell, Nathan, Mgr.-Investor Rels.--Employee Solutions, Inc., Phoenix, AZ; *U.S. Public*, pg. 579
Bueno, Thomas, Chief Acctg. Officer & Controller--Apco Argentina Inc., Tulsa, OK; *U.S. Public*, pg. 119
Bugge, Anne Marie, V.P.-Corp. & Investor Rels.--ATL Ultrasound, Inc., Bothell, WA; *U.S. Public*, pg. 11
Buhrer, Gerhard, Mgr.-Treasury--Georg Fischer Ltd., Schaffhausen, Switzerland; *Int'l*, pg. 488
Bullock, Brian, Sec. & Mgr.-Commercial & Legal Affairs--Australian Oil & Gas Corporation Limited, Sydney, Australia; *Int'l*, pg. 101
Bunday, Dennis E., Treas.--Pope & Talbot, Inc., Portland, OR; *U.S. Public*, pg. 1316
Buns, Tom, V.P.-Fin. & Treas.--Corcom, Inc., Libertyville, IL; *U.S. Public*, pg. 446
Bunting, Davis M., Sr. V.P.--Riggs Bank N.A., Washington, DC; *U.S. Public*, pg. 1390
Burdett, Bonnie, V.P.-Corp. & Investor Rels.--Alza Corporation, Palo Alto, CA; *U.S. Public*, pg. 62
Burgess, Virginia Vance, Dir.-Inv. Rels. & Asst. Sec.--Northwest Natural Gas Company, Portland, OR; *U.S. Public*, pg. 1200
Burhop, Gary L., V.P.-Corp. Rels.--Harrah's Entertainment, Inc., Memphis, TN; *U.S. Public*, pg. 790
Burke, Larry W., Pres. & Chief Exec. Officer--Robinson Nugent, Inc., New Albany, IN; *U.S. Public*, pg. 1394
Burkett, Marvin D., Chief Fin. Officer, Sr. V.P. & Treas.--Advanced Micro Devices, Inc., Sunnyvale, CA; *U.S. Public*, pg. 21
Burkhalteo, Randy, Dir.-Investor Rels.--NorAm Energy Corp., Houston, TX; *U.S. Public*, pg. 843
Burkhalter, Randy, Dir.-Investor Rels.--Houston Industries Incorporated, Houston, TX; *U.S. Public*, pg. 842
Burmester, Wilhelm, Mgr.-Investor Rels.--BHF-BANK AG, Frankfurt, Germany; *Int'l*, pg. 119
Burnett, Penney, V.P.-Investor Rels.--Glaxo Wellcome plc, London, United Kingdom; *Int'l*, pg. 552
Burnham, Kate S., Dir-Corp. Communications--Reebok International Ltd., Stoughton, MA; *U.S. Public*, pg. 1369
Burns, Diane W., Sec.--CompuDyne Corporation, Willimantic, CT; *U.S. Public*, pg. 419
Burns, Hannah, Mng. Dir.-Corp. Communications--The Bear Stearns Companies Inc., New York, NY; *U.S. Public*, pg. 197
Burns, John E., Chief Fin. Officer & V.P.--First United Bancshares, Inc., El Dorado, AR; *U.S. Public*, pg. 641
Burns, Noreen E., Sec.--Brooktree Rockwell Semiconductor Systems Div., San Diego, CA; *U.S. Public*, pg. 1398
Burns, Ron, Chief Fin. Officer, V.P. & Sec.--Grede Foundries, Inc., Milwaukee, WI; *U.S. Private*, pg. 476
Burrell, Richard L., Sr. V.P.-Fin., Treas. & Sec.--R.G. Barry Corporation, Pickerington, OH; *U.S. Public*, pg. 192
Burton, Amanda J., Grp. Sec. & Legal Advisor--Meyer International PLC, London, United Kingdom; *Int'l*, pg. 864
Burton, Diana E., V.P.-Investor Rels.--U.S. Industries, Inc., Iselin, NJ; *U.S. Public*, pg. 1683
Burton, Robert, Dir.-Investor Rels.--Kmart Corporation, Troy, MI; *U.S. Public*, pg. 963
Bury, James, V.P.-Fin.--PremiumWear, Inc., Minneapolis, MN; *U.S. Public*, pg. 1323
Busby, Robert L., III, Chief Fin. & Admin. Officer, Sr. V.P. & Treas.--National Western Life Insurance Company, Austin, TX; *U.S. Public*, pg. 1161
Butcher, Jeff, V.P. & Mgr.-Fin. & Investor Rels.--Bay View Capital Corporation, San Mateo, CA; *U.S. Public*, pg. 197
Butenas, Carole F., V.P.-Investor Rels.--Lydall, Inc., Manchester, CT; *U.S. Public*, pg. 1020
Buterbaugh, Rick C., Dir.-Investor Rels.--Kerr-McGee Corporation, Oklahoma City, OK; *U.S. Public*, pg. 952
Byers, R.A., Chief Fin. Officer, V.P.-Fin. & Treas.--Pitt-Des Moines, Inc., Pittsburgh, PA; *U.S. Public*, pg. 1304
Byrnes, Christopher R., Dir.-Investor Rels.--PAR Technology Corporation, New Hartford, NY; *U.S. Public*, pg. 1256
Cady, Diane M., V.P.-Investor Rels.--Alpharma Inc., Fort Lee, NJ; *U.S. Public*, pg. 57
Calabrese, Joseph J., Jr., Chief Fin. Officer, Exec. V.P. & Sec.--Harvey Electronics, Inc., Lyndhurst, NJ; *U.S. Public*, pg. 796
Caldwell, James, Mgr.-Investor Rels.--Cabletron Systems, Inc., Rochester, NH; *U.S. Public*, pg. 288
Calhoon, J. Richard, V.P.-Investor Rels. & Asst. Treas.--Leggett & Platt, Incorporated, Carthage, MO; *U.S. Public*, pg. 985
Call, Lawrence M., Chief Fin. Officer & Sr. V.P.--Amway Corporation, Ada, MI; *U.S. Private*, pg. 69
Callicutt, Thomas L., Jr., Exec. V.P., Controller & Principal Acctg. Officer--First Commerce Corporation, New Orleans, LA; *U.S. Public*, pg. 629
Callihan, William, V.P.-Investor Rels.--PNC Bank Corp., Pittsburgh, PA; *U.S. Public*, pg. 1242
Calvillo, Jose, Mgr.-Fin.--Controladora Comercial Mexicana, S.A. de C.V., Mexico, Mexico; *Int'l*, pg. 328
Calvin, Amy, Dir.-Commun. & Corp. Librarian--Edison Brothers Stores, Inc., Saint Louis, MO; *U.S. Public*, pg. 563
Camacho, P. Bruce, Exec. V.P.-Investor Rels. & Dir.-Internal Devel.--American Bankers Life Assurance Co. of Florida, Miami, FL; *U.S. Public*, pg. 67
Cameron, Donald, Grp. Head-Pub. Rels.--Schroders PLC, London, United Kingdom; *Int'l*, pg. 1210
Cammarata, Betty, Dir.-Investor Rels.--RehabCare Group, Inc., Saint Louis, MO; *U.S. Public*, pg. 1373
Cammell, John R.O., Grp. Mgr.-Pub. Rels--Barlow Ltd., Sandton, South Africa; *Int'l*, pg. 167
Campali, Mary Beth, Dir.-Investor Rels.--The Reader's Digest Association, Inc., Pleasantville, NY; *U.S. Public*, pg. 1367
Campbell, Ann P., Sec.--The Flight International Group, Inc., Newport News, VA; *U.S. Public*, pg. 654
Campbell, LoAnn, Mgr.-Investor Rels.--Novellus Systems, Inc., San Jose, CA; *U.S. Public*, pg. 1204
Campbell, Mart, Mgr.-Investment--United Fire & Casualty Company, Cedar Rapids, IA; *U.S. Public*, pg. 1677
Campbell, Susan J., V.P.-Commun. & Investor Rels.--NovaCare Inc., King of Prussia, PA; *U.S. Public*, pg. 1203
Canary, Glenn, Dir.-Investor Rels.--Claire's Stores Inc., Pembroke Pines, FL; *U.S. Public*, pg. 381
Candelario, Ann, Mgr.-Investor Rels.--Network Equipment Technologies, Inc., Redwood City, CA; *U.S. Public*, pg. 1168
Cannada, Charles T., Sr. V.P.-Corp. Devel., Investor Rels. & Real Estate--LDDS WorldCom Inc., East Rutherford, NJ; *U.S. Public*, pg. 1779
Cannon, Dean G., Chm. Bd. & Pres.--Cannon Express Inc., Springdale, AR; *U.S. Public*, pg. 301
Cantie, J.S., Mgr.-Investor Rels.--LucasVarity plc, London, United Kingdom; *Int'l*, pg. 819
Capeancio, Darlene, Mgr.-Investor Rels.--Southwest Water Company, West Covina, CA; *U.S. Public*, pg. 1494
Capps, Vickie L., Chief Fin. Officer--Wavetek Corporation, San Diego, CA; *U.S. Private*, pg. 1154
Carchedi, Frank A., Chief Fin. Officer & Treas.--ITC Learning Corp., Herndon, VA; *U.S. Public*, pg. 859
Cardaro, Lynn, Dir.-Investor Rels. & Fin. Reporting--Syratech Corporation, East Boston, MA; *U.S. Private*, pg. 1060
Cargotch, Paul, Chief Fin. Officer & Exec. V.P.--Russ Berrie and Company, Inc., Oakland, NJ; *U.S. Public*, pg. 222
Carle-Poirier, Lynn, Head-Investor Rels.--Nova Scotia Power Inc., Halifax, Canada; *Int'l*, pg. 971
Carles, Robert S., Sec.--Lance, Inc., Charlotte, NC; *U.S. Public*, pg. 977
Carlevato, Jeff, Controller & Treas.--QST Industries, Inc., Chicago, IL; *U.S. Private*, pg. 897
Carlsen, Sigurd, Sr. V.P.-Investor Rels.--Christiania Bank og Kreditkasse ASA, Oslo, Norway; *Int'l*, pg. 289
Carlson, Ria, V.P.-Pub. & Investor Rels.--Sierra Health Services, Inc., Las Vegas, NV; *U.S. Public*, pg. 1469
Carlton, Ron, Ph.D., Dir.-Mktg.--AmeriPath, Inc., Riviera Beach, FL; *U.S. Public*, pg. 96
Carnahan, Karen L., Treas.--Cintas Corporation, Mason, OH; *U.S. Public*, pg. 370
Carnohan, Karel, V.P.-Investor Rels.--SunAmerica Inc., Los Angeles, CA; *U.S. Public*, pg. 1532
Carper, John T., Chief Fin. Officer--Sealright Company, Inc., De Soto, KS; *U.S. Public*, pg. 1451
Carr, Leonard L., Jr., V.P. & Dir.-Investor Rels.--Tidel Technologies, Inc., Houston, TX; *U.S. Public*, pg. 1608
Carr, Vivian J., V.P.-Investor Rels.--Liberty Media Corporation, Englewood, CO; *U.S. Public*, pg. 1555
Carr, William A., Treas.--Mercantile Stores Company, Inc., Fairfield, OH; *U.S. Public*, pg. 1089
Carradine, John M., V.P.-Fin. & Treas.--Intellicall, Inc., Carrollton, TX; *U.S. Public*, pg. 887
Carriere, D., Dir.-Indus. Rels.--La Brasserie Labatt Limitee, La Salle, Canada; *Int'l*, pg. 679
Carter, Cheryl C., Sec. & Dir.-Investor Rels.--Synalloy Corporation, Spartanburg, SC; *U.S. Public*, pg. 1547
Cartmell, Elizabeth B., Asst. Treas.--Aramark Corp., Philadelphia, PA; *U.S. Private*, pg. 78
Carton, Margaret, V.P.-Investor Rels. & Plng.--Coca-Cola Enterprises Inc., Atlanta, GA; *U.S. Public*, pg. 393
Cartwright, Jeffrey, Dir.-Investor Rels. & Communications--Borg-Warner Security Corporation, Chicago, IL; *U.S. Public*, pg. 245
Casey, Walter H., V.P.-Corp. Communications--ConAgra, Inc., Omaha, NE; *U.S. Public*, pg. 425
Cason, Marilynn, V.P., Gen. Counsel & Sec.--DeVry Institutes, Oak Brook Terrace, IL; *U.S. Public*, pg. 503
Cass, Susan M., V.P.-Invester Rels. & Fin. Plng.--The Ryland Group, Inc., Columbia, MD; *U.S. Public*, pg. 1414
Cassetty, Fred, Chm. Bd., Pres. & Chief Exec. Officer--Alley-Cassetty Coal Co., Nashville, TN; *U.S. Private*, pg. 37
Castain, Esther K., Corp. Sec. & Mgr.-Employee Rels.--Vacu-Dry Company, Sebastopol, CA; *U.S. Public*, pg. 1704
Castell, J. Ronald, Sr. V.P.-Investor Rels. & Communications--Florida Panthers Holdings, Inc., Fort Lauderdale, FL; *U.S. Public*, pg. 654
Castigliego, Nancy, Dir.-Investor Rels.--MacDermid Incorporated, Waterbury, CT; *U.S. Public*, pg. 1029
Catacosinos, William W., Dir.-Investor Rels.--Long Island Lighting Company, Hicksville, NY; *U.S. Public*, pg. 1013
Catlett, Pamela M., V.P.-Corp. & Investor Rels.--Kaiser Ventures, Inc., Ontario, CA; *U.S. Public*, pg. 941
Cattafesta, Joanne, Coord.-Pub. Rels.--B.M.J. Financial Corp., Bordentown, NJ; *U.S. Public*, pg. 1528
Caudill, Barbara, Dir.-Investor Rels.--North Carolina Natural Gas Corporation, Fayetteville, NC; *U.S. Public*, pg. 1194
Cavalier, Janet, Mgr.-Investor Commun.--Glenayre Technologies, Inc., Charlotte, NC; *U.S. Public*, pg. 746
Cavanagh, Patrick H., Dir.-Investor Rels.--Ferro Corporation, Cleveland, OH; *U.S. Public*, pg. 618
Cavanagh, Thomas G., V.P.-Investor Rels.--American Home Products Corporation, Madison, NJ; *U.S. Public*, pg. 79
Cavestany, J., Dir.-Investor Rels.--Corporacion MAPFRE, Compania Internacional de Reaseguros, S.A., Madrid, Spain; *Int'l*, pg. 332
Cecil, Allan V., V.P.-Investor Rels. & Corp. Commun.--Sonoco Products Company, Hartsville, SC; *U.S. Public*, pg. 1485
Chacko, Eapen, Dir.-Investor Rels.--Fingerhut Corp., Minnetonka, MN; *U.S. Public*, pg. 623
Chamberlain, E. Martin, V.P.-Regulatory Affairs & Sec.--Ballard Medical Products, Draper, UT; *U.S. Public*, pg. 171
Chambers, Janice, Admin. Asst.-Investor Rels.--Kent Electronics Corp., Houston, TX; *U.S. Public*, pg. 951
Chandarana, Pankaj, Dir.-Intl. Fin.--Clarins, Neuilly-sur-Seine, France; *Int'l*, pg. 295
Chandler, William E., Chief Fin. Officer, Sr. V.P.-Fin. & Sec.--Hunt Corporation, Philadelphia, PA; *U.S. Public*, pg. 848
Chang, K.H., Gen. Mgr.-Fin.--China Steel Corporation, Kaohsiung, Taiwan; *Int'l*, pg. 285
Chapko, Stephen J., Chief Fin. Officer, Exec. V.P., Treas. & Sec.--Kent Electronics Corp., Houston, TX; *U.S. Public*, pg. 951
Chapman, Donald R., Chief Fin. Officer & Exec. V.P.--Crawford & Company, Atlanta, GA; *U.S. Public*, pg. 458
Chapman, Margaret A., Asst. Sec.--Reliability Incorporated, Houston, TX; *U.S. Public*, pg. 1373
Charalambous, Katerina, Mgr.-Investor Rels.--Pharmaceutical Marketing Services Inc., Phoenix, AZ; *U.S. Public*, pg. 1284
Charles, Janet, Asst.-Investor Rels.--Oceaneering International, Inc., Houston, TX; *U.S. Public*, pg. 1211
Charlier, Marj, Dir.-Investor Rels.--Cyprus Amax Minerals Company, Englewood, CO; *U.S. Public*, pg. 470
Charlton, Ann E., Asst. to the Pres.--Aquila Biopharmaceuticals, Inc., Worcester, MA; *U.S. Public*, pg. 126
Charlton, Richard G., V.P.-Corp. Commun.--Parker Hannifin Corporation, Cleveland, OH; *U.S. Public*, pg. 1259
Chastin, Jil, Investor Rels.--Wall Street Deli, Inc., Birmingham, AL; *U.S. Public*, pg. 1734
Cheatham, Edward W., V.P.-Corp. Communications--The Racal Corporation, Sunrise, FL; *Int'l*, pg. 1082
Chen, Judy, Mgr.-Investor Rels.--The Clorox Company, Oakland, CA; *U.S. Public*, pg. 386
Cherry, Dean E., Exec. V.P.-Investor Rels. & Corp. Communications--World Color Press, Inc., Greenwich, CT; *U.S. Public*, pg. 1778
Chia Wee Chang, Joseph, Controller--Showpla Asia Limited, Singapore, Singapore; *Int'l*, pg. 1237
Chiafery, James, Dir.-Investor Rels.--Kulicke & Soffa Industries, Inc., Willow Grove, PA; *U.S. Public*, pg. 968
Chilcott, Katie, Mgr.-Investor Rels.--Merix Corporation, Forest Grove, OR; *U.S. Public*, pg. 1096
Chin, Henry W., Chief Fin. Officer, V.P.-Fin. & Sec.--Marshall Industries, El Monte, CA; *U.S. Public*, pg. 1051
Chipperfield, Lynn, V.P., Gen. Counsel & Sec.--Furniture Brands International Inc., Saint Louis, MO; *U.S. Public*, pg. 688
Chittka, Jorg, Dr., Mgr.-Inv. Rels.--IKB Deutsche Industriebank AG, Dusseldorf, Germany; *Int'l*, pg. 645
Choi, Myung-Ho, Dir.--Ssangyong Business Group, Seoul, Korea; *Int'l*, pg. 1291
Choo, Yoon H., Dr., Chm. Bd., Pres. & Chief Exec. Officer--National Micronetics, Inc., Kingston, NY; *Int'l*, pg. 1347
Chou, Sylvia, Mgr.-Investor & Employee Rels.--Solectron Corporation, Milpitas, CA; *U.S. Public*, pg. 1483
Christal, Nancy, V.P.-Investor Rels.--CVS Corp., Woonsocket, RI; *U.S. Public*, pg. 287
Christel, Henry E., V.P. & Treas.--William H. Sadlier, Inc., New York, NY; *U.S. Public*, pg. 1422
Christensen, Doug, Dir.-Shareholder & Govt. Rels.--Atomic Energy of Canada Ltd., Mississauga, Canada; *Int'l*, pg. 97
Christiana, Peter, Mgr.-Investor Rels.--Stratus Computer, Inc., Marlborough, MA; *U.S. Public*, pg. 1524
Christians, Sharon, Dir.-Corp. Affairs--EMI Group plc, London, United Kingdom; *Int'l*, pg. 426
Christie, Lorna, V.P.-Corp. Affairs & Communications--First USA Paymentech, Inc., Salem, NH; *U.S. Public*, pg. 174
Chua, Ler Ching, Chief Fin. Officer, Treas. & Sec.--GB Holdings, Jurong, Singapore; *Int'l*, pg. 531
Chung, William G., V.P.-Personnel & Indus. Rels.--Young Brothers, Ltd., Honolulu, HI; *U.S. Public*, pg. 800

Church, John F., Jr., Pres. & Chief Exec. Officer--The Cincinnati Cordage & Paper Company, Cincinnati, OH; *U.S. Private*, pg. 239
Churney, Lila J., V.P.-Investor Rels.--Fluor Corporation, Irvine, CA; *U.S. Public*, pg. 659
Ciangiulli, Helen Sands, Asst. Sec.--International Thoroughbred Breeders, Inc., Cherry Hill, NJ; *U.S. Public*, pg. 908
Ciocca, Kara, Mgr.-Investor Rels.--Ivex Packaging Corporation, Lincolnshire, IL; *U.S. Public*, pg. 915
Clark, Burt, V.P.-Fin.--Champion Ignition Products, Chesterfield, MO; *U.S. Public*, pg. 442
Clark, David, Pres. & Chief Oper. Officer--WSMP, Inc., Claremont, NC; *U.S. Public*, pg. 1729
Clark, Gerald, Chief Investment Officer & Sr. Exec. V.P.--Metropolitan Life Insurance Co., New York, NY; *U.S. Private*, pg. 737
Clark, Kevin, V.P. & Treas.--Fisher Scientific International, Hampton, NH; *U.S. Private*, pg. 658
Clark, Susanne G., Sr. V.P.-Investor Rels.--State Street Corporation, Boston, MA; *U.S. Public*, pg. 1513
Claus, Tim, Dir.-Inv. Rels.--SFX Broadcasting Incorporated, New York, NY; *U.S. Public*, pg. 1417
Clausen, Dick, Chm. Bd., Pres. & Chief Exec. Officer--Verbatim Tape Corporation, San Diego, CA; *Int'l*, pg. 872
Clauser, Fred, Sec.--Koh-I-Noor, Inc., Bloomsbury, NJ; *U.S. Private*, pg. 629
Clay, Wendy F., V.P.-Admin.--CPAC, Inc., Leicester, NY; *U.S. Public*, pg. 282
Clayborn, John C., Investor Rels. Officer--Old National Bancorp, Evansville, IN; *U.S. Public*, pg. 1217
Cleary, William F., V.P.- Investor & Corp. Rels.--AMETEK, Inc., Paoli, PA; *U.S. Public*, pg. 99
Clements, James E., Chief Fin. Officer & Sec.--Dorsey Trailers, Inc., Atlanta, GA; *U.S. Public*, pg. 520
Clements, Scott, Dir.-Investor Rels.--Honeywell Inc., Minneapolis, MN; *U.S. Public*, pg. 833
Cleveland, Joe, V.P. & Sec.--NCH Corporation, Irving, TX; *U.S. Public*, pg. 1145
Clinebell, Kenneth M., Chief Fin. Officer, Treas. & Sec.--Precision Systems, Inc., Saint Petersburg, FL; *U.S. Public*, pg. 1321
Coale, Joseph M., Dir.-Corp. Commun.--Crown Central Petroleum Corporation, Baltimore, MD; *U.S. Public*, pg. 462
Cobb, Alton H., Jr., Chief Fin. Officer & V.P.--Long MFG. NC, Inc., Tarboro, NC; *U.S. Private*, pg. 674
Coble, Ted C., V.P., Treas. & Asst. Sec.--Piedmont Natural Gas Co., Inc., Charlotte, NC; *U.S. Public*, pg. 1295
Cocco, Dennis A., Dir.-Corp. & Investor Affairs--The Geon Company, Avon Lake, OH; *U.S. Public*, pg. 733
Cochran, Connie, Coord-Investor Rels.--Mitel Corporation, Kanata, Canada; *Int'l*, pg. 870
Cockrell, D. Michael, Chief Fin. Officer & Treas.--Sanderson Farms, Inc., Laurel, MS; *U.S. Public*, pg. 1430
Cocoros, Lela, Sr. V.P.-Commun.--TCI Communications, Inc., Englewood, CO; *U.S. Public*, pg. 1554
Coenson, Rosemary, Investor Rels.--Pinkerton's Inc., Encino, CA; *U.S. Public*, pg. 1296
Coffey, Wendy, Dir.-Investor Rels.--Cerner Corporation, Kansas City, MO; *U.S. Public*, pg. 331
Coggins, Carol, Controller--Cattleman's, Inc., Detroit, MI; *U.S. Public*, pg. 318
Cogswell, Sherry, Dir.-Investor Rels.--Tecumseh Products Company, Tecumseh, MI; *U.S. Public*, pg. 1565
Cogswell, Susan P., Dir.-Investor Rels.--Genzyme Corporation, Cambridge, MA; *U.S. Public*, pg. 733
Cohen, Colin M., Chief Fin. Officer & Sr. V.P.--The Fairchild Corporation, Chantilly, VA; *U.S. Public*, pg. 610
Cohen, Donna, Mgr.-Investor Rels.--IIS Intelligent Information Systems Ltd., Yokneam, Israel; *Int'l*, pg. 645
Cohen, Lewis M., Pres. & Chief Exec. Officer--Acme Canvas Co., Inc., Malden, MA; *U.S. Private*, pg. 13
Cohen, Patti, Sr. V.P.-Pub. Rels.--Donna Karan, New York, NY; *U.S. Public*, pg. 517
Cohn, Richard, Pres.--Sigmund Cohn Corp., Mount Vernon, NY; *U.S. Private*, pg. 250
Cole, Joe C., V.P.-Corp. Commun.--Aztar Corporation, Phoenix, AZ; *U.S. Public*, pg. 158
Cole, John, Controller--Avnet, Inc., Great Neck, NY; *U.S. Public*, pg. 155
Coleman, Allan, Vice Chm.--King Wire Inc., North Chicago, IL; *U.S. Private*, pg. 621
Collado, Pablo, Dir. Gen.-Investor Rels.--Grupo Elektra S.A. de C.V., Mexico, Mexico; *Int'l*, pg. 573
Collins, Michael J., Dir., Pres. & Chief Exec. Officer--CEM Corporation, Matthews, NC; *U.S. Public*, pg. 277
Collis, Don, V.P.-Investor Rels.--Dell Computer Corporation, Round Rock, TX; *U.S. Public*, pg. 495
Columbus, Paul, V.P. & Dir.-Plng. & Investor Rels.--NVR, Inc., Mc Lean, VA; *U.S. Public*, pg. 1148
Comoreia, Tony, Mgr.-Investor Rels.--Syms Corporation, Secaucus, NJ; *U.S. Public*, pg. 1547
Conaton, Michael J., Vice Chm.--The Midland Company, Cincinnati, OH; *U.S. Public*, pg. 1110
Conder, Patrick, Treas.--Owensboro Grain Co., Inc., Owensboro, KY; *U.S. Private*, pg. 824
Condon, James E., V.P. & Treas.--Hartmarx Corporation, Chicago, IL; *U.S. Public*, pg. 795
Conforti, Daniel A., Dir.-Investor Rels.--Fortune Brands, Inc., Old Greenwich, CT; *U.S. Public*, pg. 674
Conley, John, Treas. & Dir.-Investor Rels.--Biogen, Inc., Cambridge, MA; *U.S. Public*, pg. 230
Conley, Olga L., Chief Fin. Officer--DM Management Company, Hingham, MA; *U.S. Public*, pg. 473
Conlin, Thomas R., V.P.-Pub. Affairs--Hubbell Incorporated, Orange, CT; *U.S. Public*, pg. 844
Conn, Richard, Treas. & Sec.--Ervin Industries, Inc., Ann Arbor, MI; *U.S. Private*, pg. 382
Connelly, Thomas J., Dir.-Investor Rels.--MCN Energy Group, Inc., Detroit, MI; *U.S. Public*, pg. 1024
Conner, Frank, Chief Fin. Officer & Exec. V.P.-Acctg.--American Freightways Corporation, Harrison, AR; *U.S. Public*, pg. 75
Connery, Bruce L., V.P.-Investor Rels.--Sonat Inc., Birmingham, AL; *U.S. Public*, pg. 1484
Conroy, James T., Sr. V.P.-Corp. Affairs--MacAndrews & Forbes Holdings Inc., New York, NY; *U.S. Private*, pg. 689
Conway, Christopher J., Chm. Bd. & Chief Exec. Officer--Mentor Corporation, Santa Barbara, CA; *U.S. Public*, pg. 1086
Conway, Michael A., Sr. V.P. & Sr. Investment Officer--AON Corporation, Chicago, IL; *U.S. Public*, pg. 117
Conway, Susan, Mgr.-Investor Rels.--Cognex Corporation, Natick, MA; *U.S. Public*, pg. 394
Cook, J.M., V.P. & Treas.--American Cast Iron Pipe Co., Birmingham, AL; *U.S. Private*, pg. 51
Cookson, John S., Chief Fin. Officer, V.P.-Fin., Treas. & Sec.--Kingsbury Corporation, Keene, NH; *U.S. Private*, pg. 621
Coomer, Lagena, Dir.-Investor Rels.--Proffitt's, Inc., Alcoa, TN; *U.S. Public*, pg. 1333
Coons, Robert C., Mgr.-Corp. Commun.--BJ Services Company, Houston, TX; *U.S. Public*, pg. 161
Cooper, Cathy, V.P.-Mktg. & Investor Rels.--Washington Federal Savings, Seattle, WA; *U.S. Public*, pg. 1740
Cooper, Doris, Asst. Sec. & Mgr.-Communications--General Employment Enterprises, Inc., Oak Brook Terrace, IL; *U.S. Public*, pg. 714
Cooper, Janis C., V.P.-Pub. Affairs--Maytag Corporation, Newton, IA; *U.S. Public*, pg. 1064
Cooper, Kimberly, Mgr.-Corp. Communications--Enzon, Inc., Piscataway, NJ; *U.S. Public*, pg. 587
Cooper, P. Harry, Chief Fin. Officer--Whatman plc, Maidstone, United Kingdom; *Int'l*, pg. 1498
Cooper, Steven D., Sr. V.P.-Plng., Gen. Counsel & Sec.--Electrolux Corporation, Atlanta, GA; *U.S. Private*, pg. 369
Coors, Holly, Dir.-Investor Rels.--ACX Technologies Inc., Golden, CO; *U.S. Public*, pg. 3
Copes, Rodney, Dir.-Investor Rels.--Harley-Davidson, Inc., Milwaukee, WI; *U.S. Public*, pg. 786
Copin, Charis, Dir.-Investor Rels.--PSC Inc., Webster, NY; *U.S. Public*, pg. 1245
Coppola, Sebastian, Sr. V.P. & Treas.--MCN Energy Group, Inc., Detroit, MI; *U.S. Public*, pg. 1024
Corbett, Michael, Chief Fin. Officer--Sholodge, Inc., Hendersonville, TN; *U.S. Public*, pg. 1467
Corby, Francis M. Jr., Exec. V.P.-Fin. & Admin.--Harnischfeger Industries, Inc., Saint Francis, WI; *U.S. Public*, pg. 788
Cornell, Rebecca, Mgr.-Inv. Rels--Encore Marketing International, Inc., Lanham, MD; *U.S. Public*, pg. 580
Corse, Elizabeth, Mgr.-Communications & Investor Rels.--State Street Corporation, Boston, MA; *U.S. Public*, pg. 1513
Corydon, G. Patrick, Mgr.-Investor Rels.--Baldwin & Lyons, Inc., Indianapolis, IN; *U.S. Public*, pg. 169
Cosaert, John P., Chief Fin. Officer, Exec. V.P.-Intl. Fin., Treas. & Controller--Heartland Express, Inc., Coralville, IA; *U.S. Public*, pg. 803
Cosgrove, Craig, Dir.-Investor Rels.--Terra Nitrogen Company, L.P., Tulsa, OK; *U.S. Public*, pg. 1581
Costello, Michael B., V.P.-Admin. & Corp. Commun.--Shared Medical Systems Corporation, Malvern, PA; *U.S. Public*, pg. 1463
Cottraux, Suzanne, V.P.-Corp. Commun. & Investor Rels.--Patriot American Hospitality, Inc., Dallas, TX; *U.S. Public*, *pg. 1265*
Couch, Stephen B., Chief Investment Officer & V.P.--The Acacia Group - Acacia Life Insurance Co., Bethesda, MD; *U.S. Private*, pg. 10
Coughlin, Deborah, V.P.-Investor Rels.--Computer Associates International, Inc., Islandia, NY; *U.S. Public*, pg. 420
Coursey, Diana, Coord.-Investor Rels.--American Business Products, Inc., Atlanta, GA; *U.S. Public*, pg. 70
Coventry, Mary, V.P.-Corp. Devel.--Sealed Air Corporation, Saddle Brook, NJ; *U.S. Public*, pg. 1450
Cowart, Jim C., Chm. Bd. & Chief Exec. Officer--Aurora Electronics, Inc., Irvine, CA; *U.S. Public*, pg. 147
Cox, John, Dir.-Tax & Investor Rels.--BMC Software, Inc., Houston, TX; *U.S. Public*, pg. 162
Cox, Judy, Mgr.-Investor Rels.--Xyvision, Inc., Wakefield, MA; *U.S. Public*, pg. 1787
Cox, Mark B., Treas.--Giant Industries Inc., Scottsdale, AZ; *U.S. Public*, pg. 741
Cox, Thomas L., Chief Fin. Officer--Field Container Company, L.P., Elk Grove Village, IL; *U.S. Private*, pg. 403
Crabtree, Todd A., Dir.-Investor Rels.--Berry Petroleum Company, Taft, CA; *U.S. Public*, pg. 223
Craig, David W., Chief Fin. Officer & V.P.--Convex Technology Center - Hewlett-Packard, Richardson, TX; *U.S. Public*, pg. 815
Craig, Paul, Chief Fin. Officer, Exec. V.P. & Treas.--Pac Rim Holding Corporation, Woodland Hills, CA; *U.S. Public*, pg. 1246
Craig, Suzanne, Dir.-Investor Rels.--Atmel Corporation, San Jose, CA; *U.S. Public*, pg. 145
Craigmile, Cindy, Chief Fin. Officer & V.P.--Downey Printing, Waukee, IA; *U.S. Private*, pg. 342
Crawford, Carol, Office Mgr.--ELXSI Corporation, Orlando, FL; *U.S. Public*, pg. 545
Crawford, Carolyn, Mgr.-Investor Rels.--U S West Inc., Englewood, CO; *U.S. Public*, pg. 1688
Crawford, Edward, Chm. Bd., Pres & Chief Exec. & Oper. Officer--Park-Ohio Industries, Inc., Cleveland, OH; *U.S. Public*, pg. 1258
Crawford, Karin, Dir.-Investor Rels.--NCC AB, Solna, Sweden; *Int'l*, pg. 898
Crawford, Peter D., Exec. Dir.-Investor Rels.--Bell Atlantic Corporation, New York, NY; *U.S. Public*, pg. 201
Creel, L. Anderson, Chief Fin. Officer, Sr. V.P., Treas. & Sec.--Prime Bancshares Inc., Houston, TX; *U.S. Public*, pg. 1326
Cribbin, Marge, Exec. Asst. to Chief Fin. Officer--Phoenix Technologies Ltd., San Jose, CA; *U.S. Public*, pg. 1292
Cribbs, Francis J., Exec. V.P., Chief Fin. Officer & Treas.--Lloyd Properties, Los Angeles, CA; *U.S. Private*, pg. 672
Crisanti, John, Treas.--The U.S. Baird Corporation, Stratford, CT; *U.S. Private*, pg. 1124
Criscillis, Paul A., Jr., Chief Fin. Officer & V.P.-Fin.--Crown Crafts, Inc., Atlanta, GA; *U.S. Public*, pg. 465
Crisera, Jim, Mgr.-Investor Rels.--Wall Data Incorporated, Kirkland, WA; *U.S. Public*, pg. 1734
Crockett, Charles, Dir.-Investor Rels. & Asst. Sec.--Hannaford Bros. Co., Scarborough, ME; *U.S. Public*, pg. 781
Cronin, Michael X., V.P. & Sec.--Central Steel & Wire Company, Chicago, IL; *U.S. Public*, pg. 327
Crookshank, George A., Chief Fin. Officer & V.P.-Fin.--Ocelot Energy Inc., Calgary, Canada; *Int'l*, pg. 996
Crosby, Sven, Mgr.-Investor Rels.--Elkem ASA, Oslo, Norway; *Int'l*, pg. 446
Crouch, C.H., Sr. V.P.-Investor Rels.--SouthTrust Corporation, Birmingham, AL; *U.S. Public*, pg. 1491
Cruise, Carrie, Mgr.-Investor Rels.--Centocor, Inc., Malvern, PA; *U.S. Public*, pg. 323
Csinicsek, Kenneth, Sr. V.P.-Mktg., Investor & Pub. Rels.--First Financial Bank, FSB, Stevens Point, WI; *U.S. Public*, pg. 140
Csiszar, Alex L., Sr. Dir.-Investor Rels.--Telxon Corporation, Akron, OH; *U.S. Public*, pg. 1573
Cuddiny, Kathy, Dir.-Corp. Affairs--Unigate PLC, London, United Kingdom; *Int'l*, pg. 1433
Cuellar, Carlos Tamez, Dir.-Indus. Rels.--Altos Hornos de Mexico, S.A., Monclova, Mexico; *Int'l*, pg. 66
Cuesta, Nancy, Asst. Dir.-Investor Rels.--Integrity Incorporated, Mobile, AL; *U.S. Public*, pg. 886
Cultrara, Dora, Coord.-Investor Relations--Geac Computer Corporation Limited, Markham, Canada; *Int'l*, pg. 532
Cummings, Tomi, Dir.-Inv. Rels.--Media Arts Group, Inc., San Jose, CA; *U.S. Public*, pg. 1077
Cummins, Mark R., Sr. V.P., Chief Investment Officer & Treas.--Harleysville Group, Harleysville, PA; *U.S. Public*, pg. 786
Cunnigham, Edward A., Dir.-Corp. Commun. & Investor Rels.--Tredegar Industries Inc., Richmond, VA; *U.S. Public*, pg. 1633
Cunningham, Peter J., V.P.-Investor Rels.--Astoria Financial Corporation, Lake Success, NY; *U.S. Public*, pg. 141
Curley, Sally J., Mgr.-Investor Rels.--EG & G, Inc., Wellesley, MA; *U.S. Public*, pg. 542
Curwin, Ronald, Chief Fin. Officer & Treas.--Bed Bath & Beyond Inc., Union, NJ; *U.S. Public*, pg. 200
Cutro, Dyan C., V.P.-Investor Rels.--Duty Free International, Inc., Ridgefield, CT; *Int'l*, pg. 103
Cypert, Skip, V.P.-Investor Rels.--Masco Corporation, Taylor, MI; *U.S. Public*, pg. 1052
Cytryn, Debra, Mgr.-Investor Rels.--National Beverage Corp., Plantation, FL; *U.S. Public*, pg. 1153
Czaja, Darlene E., Sec.--PC Quote, Inc., Chicago, IL; *U.S. Public*, pg. 1240
D'Andrea, Dennis, V.P.-Investor Rels.--Estee Lauder Companies Inc., New York, NY; *U.S. Public*, pg. 594
D'Arcy, Thomas P., Pres. & Chief Exec. Officer--Bradley Real Estate, Inc., Northbrook, IL; *U.S. Public*, pg. 250
D'Eliscu, Jeffrey B., V.P.-Corp. Communications--Allergan, Inc., Irvine, CA; *U.S. Public*, pg. 46
Dague, Arthur, Mgr.-Investor Rels.--Citizens Utilities Company, Stamford, CT; *U.S. Public*, pg. 379
Dailey, John E., Asst. V.P.-Fin. & Controller--NCC Industries, Inc., Cortland, NY; *U.S. Private*, pg. 697
Dalbeck, Richard W., Exec. V.P., Chief Fin. Officer & Sec.--The Guber Peters Entertainment Company, Los Angeles, CA; *Int'l*, pg. 1283
Dalesandro, Maria, Coord.-Investor Rels.--Platinum Technology, Inc., Oak Brook Terrace, IL; *U.S. Public*, pg. 1309
Dallacqua, John, Chief Fin. Officer, V.P.-Fin., Treas. & Sec.--Crowley, Milner & Company, Detroit, MI; *U.S. Public*, pg. 461
Dalongeville, Jean-Maurice, V.P.-Audit & Investor Rels.--Compagnie Generale de Geophysique, Massy, France; *Int'l*, pg. 241
Dalphon, Brian, Dir.-Investor Rels.--MBNA Corporation, Wilmington, DE; *U.S. Public*, pg. 1023
Damianakes, Amy, Dir.-Corp. Communications--AirTouch Communications, Inc., San Francisco, CA; *U.S. Public*, pg. 34
Damico, Tatiana, Investor Rels. Administrator--U.S. Bioscience, Inc., Conshohocken, PA; *U.S. Public*, pg. 1681
Damore, Donald, V.P.-Fin.--American List Corporation, Mineola, NY; *U.S. Public*, pg. 1481
Daneilson, Gilbert L., Chief Fin. Officer, V.P.-Fin. & Dir.-Investor Rels.--Aaron Rents, Inc., Atlanta, GA; *U.S. Public*, pg. 12
Danford, Philip C., V.P.-Investor Rels. & Treas.--The Dun & Bradstreet Corporation, Murray Hill, NJ; *U.S. Public*, pg. 535
Danian, Dick, Mgr.-Investor Rels.--ShopKo Stores, Inc., Green Bay, WI; *U.S. Public*, pg. 1467
Daniels, Christe, Dir.-Investor Rels.--Special Devices, Incorporated, Newhall, CA; *U.S. Public*, pg. 1496
Daniels, Ninanie, Mgr.-Corp. Communications--BICC plc, London, United Kingdom; *Int'l*, pg. 120
Danielson, John, V.P. & Treas.--Albertson's, Inc., Boise, ID; *U.S. Public*, pg. 38
Danielson, Kenneth L., Chief Fin. Officer & Treas.--Sound Advice, Inc., Dania, FL; *U.S. Public*, pg. 1488
Darbaz, Tufan, Dir.-Plng. & Investment--Sabanci Holding A.S., Istanbul, Turkey; *Int'l*, pg. 1167
Dardzinski, Jean, Dir.-Investor Rels.--Pennsylvania Real Estate Investment Trust, Fort Washington, PA; *U.S. Public*, pg. 1272
Dathe, Robert F., Chief Fin. Officer, Sr. V.P.-Fin., & Corp. Sec.--Marotta Scientific Controls, Inc., Montville, NJ; *U.S. Private*, pg. 706
Davenport, Anne G., V.P.-Treasury & Tax--HBOC, Atlanta, GA; *U.S. Public*, pg. 770

Davidson III, CFA, R. Andrew, V.P.-Investments--United Companies Life Insurance Co., Baton Rouge, LA; *U.S. Public*, pg. 1271
Davidson, Jan, Dir.-Investor Rels.--Arkansas Best Corporation, Fort Smith, AR; *U.S. Public*, pg. 130
Davies, Richard F., Treas. & Asst. Sec.--Penn Engineering & Manufacturing Corp., Danboro, PA; *U.S. Public*, pg. 1269
Davis, Geoffrey, Dir.-Investor Rels.--Hilton Hotels Corporation, Beverly Hills, CA; *U.S. Public*, pg. 828
Davis, Lloyd G., Chief Fin. Officer, Exec. V.P.-Fin., Treas. & Sec.--Baldor Electric Company, Fort Smith, AR; *U.S. Public*, pg. 168
Davis, Ray, V.P.-Investments--EMC Insurance Group, Inc., Des Moines, IA; *U.S. Public*, pg. 545
Davis, Raymond W., V.P.-Investments--EMC Insurance Companies, Des Moines, IA; *U.S. Public*, pg. 545
Davis, Ronald E., V.P.-Corp. Commun.--Franchise Finance Corp. of America, Scottsdale, AZ; *U.S. Public*, pg. 679
Davis, Sheila M., Mgr.-Pub. Rels.--Winnebago Industries, Inc., Forest City, IA; *U.S. Public*, pg. 1772
Davis, Spencer, Dir.-Investor Rels.--Computer Sciences Corporation, El Segundo, CA; *U.S. Public*, pg. 422
Davis, Tim J., Dir.-Communication & Admin.--Messier-Dowty, Abingdon, United Kingdom; *Int'l*, pg. 1340
Dawson, John C.F., Mgr.-Investor Rels.--TI Group plc, Abingdon, United Kingdom; *Int'l*, pg. 1337
de Jong, K.A., Dir.-Corp. Affairs--Nutricia BV, Zoetermeer, Netherlands; *Int'l*, pg. 991
de Laureal, Martin, V.P.-Investor Rels.--Stewart Enterprises, Inc., Metairie, LA; *U.S. Public*, pg. 1518
de Meel, R., Treas. & Dir.-Investor Rels.--VNU Verenigde Nederlandse Uitgeversbedrijven B.V., Haarlem, Netherlands; *Int'l*, pg. 1445
de Montille, Eric, Head-Inv. Rels.--Banque Nationale de Paris, Paris, France; *Int'l*, pg. 163
de Ridder, Adri, Dir.-Inv. Rels.--Avesta Sheffield AB, Stockholm, Sweden; *Int'l*, pg. 221
de Tastes, Renaud, Mgr.-Communications--Groupe Limagrain, Chappes, France; *Int'l*, pg. 566
De Vos, Patrick H., Dir.-Inv. Rels.--Electrabel S.A., Brussels, Belgium; *Int'l*, pg. 436
Dean, Jim, Mgr.-Investor Rels.--Key Energy Group Inc., East Brunswick, NJ; *U.S. Public*, pg. 953
Dean, Shannon C., Mgr.-Corp. Commun.--Dominguez Services Corporation, Long Beach, CA; *U.S. Public*, pg. 516
DeAngelo, Joseph A., Treas.--Moran Towing Corporation, Greenwich, CT; *U.S. Private*, pg. 760
DeChello, Kim, Dir.-H.R.--Essex Corporation, Columbia, MD; *U.S. Public*, pg. 593
Deering, Jeremy, Mgr.-Inv. Rels & Plng.--United Utilities plc, Warrington, United Kingdom; *Int'l*, pg. 1444
DeFelice, Patricia, Mgr.-Investor Rels.--Hanson North America, Woodbridge, NJ; *Int'l*, pg. 593
DeGrande, JoAnn, Asst. V.P. & Mgr.-Investor Rels.--Washington Mutual Inc., Seattle, WA; *U.S. Public*, pg. 1741
Del Carlo, Chris, Dir.-Investor Rels.--Infoseek Corporaton, Sunnyvale, CA; *U.S. Public*, pg. 876
Del Grande, Giacomo, Dir.-Investor Rels.--Fila Sport S.p.A., Biella, Italy; *Int'l*, pg. 484
Delaborde, Michel, V.P.-Corp. Communications--Total S.A., Paris, France; *Int'l*, pg. 1408
Delarue, Thierry, Mgr.-Investor Rels.--Compagnie Generale Maritime et Financiere, Suresnes, France; *Int'l*, pg. 322
DeLeon, Julio, V.P.-Fin.--Ocean Bio-Chem Inc., Fort Lauderdale, FL; *U.S. Public*, pg. 1211
Delmore, Timothy C., Chief Fin. Officer & Sec.--Arctic Cat Inc., Thief River Falls, MN; *U.S. Public*, pg. 128
DeLuca, August F., Chief Fin. Officer & V.P.-Fin.--Elco Textron, Rockford, IL; *U.S. Public*, pg. 1590
DeLuca, Patti, Investor Rels. Specialist--Designs, Inc., Needham, MA; *U.S. Public*, pg. 501
DeMarco, William, Chief Fin. Officer & V.P.--PrimeSource Corporation, Pennsauken, NJ; *U.S. Public*, pg. 1329
Demetter, Richard, Chief Fin. Officer & V.P.-Fin.--Sifco Industries, Inc., Cleveland, OH; *U.S. Public*, pg. 1470
DeMorrow, Melanie A., Asst. V.P.-Shareholder Rels.--Coachmen Industries, Inc., Elkhart, IN; *U.S. Public*, pg. 387
Denison, John B., V.P. & Sec.--National Gas & Oil Company, Newark, OH; *U.S. Public*, pg. 1156
Denny, Breck, R., Chief Fin. Officer, V.P.-Fin. & Treas.--Medusa Corporation, Cleveland, OH; *U.S. Public*, pg. 1084
DeNoewer, Michael, Chief Fin. Officer--Columbus Pipe & Equipment Company, Columbus, OH; *U.S. Private*, pg. 257
DeNovellis, Donato A., Chief Fin. Officer & Exec. V.P.--Ekco Group, Inc., Nashua, NH; *U.S. Public*, pg. 566
Derr, Robert A., II, V.P., Treas. & Dir.-Investor Rels.--IMO Industries Inc., Lawrenceville, NJ; *U.S. Public*, pg. 856
Derrico, Blaise E., Mgr.-Investor Rels.--Bethlehem Steel Corporation, Bethlehem, PA; *U.S. Public*, pg. 226
DeSantis, Donald A., Chief Fin. Officer, Sr. V.P. & Treas.--First Brands Corporation, Danbury, CT; *U.S. Public*, pg. 626
DeSantis, Lydia M., Sec.--GP Strategies Corporation, New York, NY; *U.S. Public*, pg. 694
DeStefano, Desiree, Mgr.-Investor Rels.--BEC Group, Inc., Rye, NY; *U.S. Public*, pg. 160
DeTata, Roberta, Dir.-Investor Rels.--Zitel Corporation, Fremont, CA; *U.S. Public*, pg. 1793
Devany, S., Mgr.-Pub. Affairs--Ladbroke Group Plc, London, United Kingdom; *Int'l*, pg. 787
Devlin, Gail E., Sr. V.P.-Fin. & Dir.-Investor Rels.--The Chubb Corporation, Warren, NJ; *U.S. Public*, pg. 354
Devos, Ron, Chief Fin. Officer, V.P.-Fin. & Sec.--Nathan's Famous Inc., Westbury, NY; *U.S. Public*, pg. 1152
DeWolf, Cathy, Mgr.-Investor Rels.--Aydin Displays (East), Horsham, PA; *U.S. Public*, pg. 158
Diaz, Isa, V.P.-Investor Rels.--Ramsay Health Care, Inc., Coral Gables, FL; *U.S. Public*, pg. 1360
Dickerson, Frank M., Chief Fin. Officer, V.P., Gen. Counsel & Sec.--Harza Engineering Co., Chicago, IL; *U.S. Private*, pg. 509
Dickerson, James H., Jr., Chief Fin. Officer--U.S. Healthcare, Inc., Blue Bell, PA; *U.S. Public*, pg. 26
Dickson, William D., Sr. V.P. & Treas.--Noble Affiliates, Inc., Ardmore, OK; *U.S. Public*, pg. 1186
DiCorti, Peter, Exec. V.P.-Fin. & Admin.--Novell Inc., San Jose, CA; *U.S. Public*, pg. 1203
Dietrich, Albert, Treas. & Dir.-Investor Rels.--Hilti AG, Schaan, Liechtenstein; *Int'l*, pg. 619
Dietzel, Alfred S., V.P.-Pub. Rels. & Investor Rels.--The Limited, Inc., Columbus, OH; *U.S. Public*, pg. 995
Dill, Linda, V.P.-Investor Rels.--TCI Communications, Inc., Englewood, CO; *U.S. Public*, pg. 1554
Diller, Charles H., Jr., Chief Fin. Officer & Exec. V.P.--JLG Industries, Inc., McConnellsburg, PA; *U.S. Public*, pg. 918
Dillon, R.I., Exec. V.P. & Treas.--Lafarge Construction Materials, Canfield, OH; *Int'l*, pg. 788
DiMaggio, Paige, Mgr.-Investor Rels.--Weatherford Enterra Incorporated, Houston, TX; *U.S. Public*, pg. 1749
Dinnick, Victoria, Dir.-Corp. Communications--Imax Corporation, Mississauga, Canada; *Int'l*, pg. 661
Diogenes, Jan, Mgr.-Investor Rels.--Ardent Software, Inc., Westborough, MA; *U.S. Public*, pg. 129
Dirs, Bruce L., Dir.-Investor Rels.--TRW Inc., Cleveland, OH; *U.S. Public*, pg. 1558
Dixon, Ashley, V.P.--Price Communications Corporation, New York, NY; *U.S. Public*, pg. 1324
Dixon, Gwen, Asst. Sec.--Iomega Corporation, Roy, UT; *U.S. Public*, pg. 912
Dixon, Mark, Chief Fin. Officer, V.P.-Fin. & Treas.--K-Tel International, Inc., Minneapolis, MN; *U.S. Public*, pg. 937
Doak, Margaret, Asst. Sec.--Bird Incorporated, Norwood, MA; *Int'l*, pg. 1170
Dodson, Bill D., V.P.-Fin. & Treas.--Marathon Electric Manufacturing Corp., Wausau, WI; *U.S. Public*, pg. 1371
Dodson, Linda S., Officer-Investment--United Missouri Bank of Carthage, Carthage, MO; *U.S. Public*, pg. 1654
Doerr, Hans-Henning, Mgr.-Investor Rels.--Heidelberger Zement A.G., Heidelberg, Germany; *Int'l*, pg. 605
Dolbeare, Gary, V.P.-Fin. & Sec.--Basler Electric Company, Highland, IL; *U.S. Private*, pg. 121
Dolphin, John A., V.P. & Dir.-Investor Rels.--Green Tree Financial Corporation, Saint Paul, MN; *U.S. Public*, pg. 761
Dominitz, Henry, Controller & Sec.--Jean Philippe Fragrances, Inc., New York, NY; *U.S. Public*, pg. 924
Dommershausen, Wolfgang, Mgr.-Press--Rheinmetall Group, Dusseldorf, Germany; *Int'l*, pg. 1108
Donadio, Mark C., Gen. Counsel & Sec.--Barrister Information Systems Corporation, Buffalo, NY; *U.S. Public*, pg. 192
Donahue, Dennis, Pres. & Chief Exec. Officer & Chief Oper. Officer--The Will-Burt Company, Orrville, OH; *U.S. Private*, pg. 1177
Donblaser, Thomas B., Mgr.-Investor Rels.--Buckeye Partners, L.P., Allentown, PA; *U.S. Public*, pg. 266
Doneda, Carlo, Mgr.-External Rels.--Banco Ambrosiano Veneto S.p.A., Milan, Italy; *Int'l*, pg. 138
Donofrio, Al, V.P.-Sls.--Eagle Button Co., Inc., Carlstadt, NJ; *U.S. Private*, pg. 354
Dooner, Marlene S., Dir.-Investor Rels.--Comcast Corporation, Philadelphia, PA; *U.S. Public*, pg. 406
Doran, Shelly, Dir.-Investor Rels.--Simon DeBartolo Group, Inc., Indianapolis, IN; *U.S. Public*, pg. 1474
Dorme, Patrick J., Chief Fin. Officer & V.P.-Fin.--Dynamics Corporation of America, Greenwich, CT; *U.S. Public*, pg. 286
Dorton, James H., V.P. & Treas.--Bowater Incorporated, Greenville, SC; *U.S. Public*, pg. 247
Dos Anjos, Marcio Fenelon, Coord-Inv. Rels.--Sao Paulo Alpargatas S.A., Sao Paulo, Brazil; *Int'l*, pg. 1193
Dotterer, Herbert T., Chief Fin. Officer, Sr. V.P.-Fin. & Admin. & Sec.--Eagle Food Centers, Inc., Milan, IL; *U.S. Public*, pg. 547
Dout, A. Jacqueline, Chief Fin. Officer & Exec. V.P.--Champion Enterprises, Inc., Auburn Hills, MI; *U.S. Public*, pg. 332
Douxchamps, Alain, Mgr.-Pub. Affairs--UCB, S.A., Brussels, Belgium; *Int'l*, pg. 1427
Downie, Nancy, Exec. Sec.--Versar Inc., Springfield, VA; *U.S. Public*, pg. 1717
Downs, Benjamin T., Chief Fin. Officer, V.P.-Fin. & Admin. & Treas.--Molten Metal Technology, Inc., Fall River, MA; *U.S. Public*, pg. 1123
Doyle, John A., Jr., Asst. Sec.--Foster Wheeler Corporation, Clinton, NJ; *U.S. Public*, pg. 676
Doyle, Mary, V.P.-Inv. Rels.--The Hallwood Group Incorporated, Dallas, TX; *U.S. Public*, pg. 777
Drablos, Kristi L., Mgr.-Investor Rels.--Humana Inc., Louisville, KY; *U.S. Public*, pg. 847
Drake, Chris, V.P.-Investor Rels.--Trigon Blue Cross & Blue Shield, Richmond, VA; *U.S. Public*, pg. 1637
Drantch, Doris, V.P.--Green Bus Lines, Inc., Jamaica, NY; *U.S. Private*, pg. 476
Drasner, Fred, Chief Exec. Officer--U.S. News & World Report, New York, NY; *U.S. Private*, pg. 1125
Dray, Kari, Exec. Sec.--Falcon Products, Inc., Saint Louis, MO; *U.S. Public*, pg. 611
Drennan, Bob, Mgr.-Fin. Plng. & Analysis--Carolina Power & Light Company, Raleigh, NC; *U.S. Public*, pg. 306
Drumheller, Terry L., Mgr.-Admin.--Scott & Stringfellow Financial, Inc., Richmond, VA; *U.S. Public*, pg. 1445
Drury, W.T., Jr., Asst. V.P.-Investor Rels.--BetzDearborn Inc., Trevose, PA; *U.S. Public*, pg. 226
Dryer, Carol, Mgr.-Investor Rels.--Rochester Gas And Electric Corporation, Rochester, NY; *U.S. Public*, pg. 1395
Dubbeldam, C., Mgr.-Internal & External Rels.--Grolsch N.V., Enschede, Netherlands; *Int'l*, pg. 559
Dubin, Stephen V., Sr. V.P., Gen. Counsel & Sec.--CSS Industries, Inc., Philadelphia, PA; *U.S. Public*, pg. 283
DuBois, Lois, Mgr.-Investor Rels.--Avanti, Fremont, CA; *U.S. Public*, pg. 151
Dubrule, Raphael, Gen. Counsel & Dir.-Investor Rels.--Sodexho S.A., Montigny-le-Bretonneux, France; *Int'l*, pg. 1274
Duckett, Stacy, V.P.-Corp. Commun.--TCBY Enterprises Inc., Little Rock, AR; *U.S. Public*, pg. 1553
Duello, J. Donald, Exec. V.P.-Fin.--Shelter Mutual Insurance Company, Columbia, MO; *U.S. Private*, pg. 992
Dufour, Paul V., Chief Fin. Officer & Exec. V.P.-Fin. & Admin.--IMCO Recycling Inc., Irving, TX; *U.S. Public*, pg. 870
Dugan, Thomas A., Pres., Chief Exec. Officer & Chief Fin. Officer--Dugan Production Corp., Farmington, NM; *U.S. Private*, pg. 345
Duncan, Bruce T., V.P.-Investor Rels.--The ServiceMaster Company, Downers Grove, IL; *U.S. Public*, pg. 1461
Duncan, Michael F., Mgr.-Pub. Rels.--Monaco Coach Corporation, Coburg, OR; *U.S. Public*, pg. 1123
Dunham, Michael D., Pres. & Chief Exec. Officer--Effective Management Systems, Milwaukee, WI; *U.S. Public*, pg. 565
Dunleavy, Marty, Shareholder Rels. Coord.--Cognos Inc., Ottawa, Canada; *Int'l*, pg. 305
Dunlevy, W. Greg, V.P.-Investor Rels.--Triton Energy Limited, Dallas, TX; *U.S. Public*, pg. 1640
Dunlop, Anna Marie, V.P.-Investor Rels.--Pacificare Health Systems, Santa Ana, CA; *U.S. Public*, pg. 1251
Dunlop, Earl, Mgr.-Investor Rels.--Placer Dome Inc., Vancouver, Canada; *Int'l*, pg. 1060
Dunn, Kathy, Mgr.-Investor Rels.--Sport Mart, Inc., Wheeling, IL; *U.S. Public*, pg. 1499
Dunn, Marianne, Sr. V.P.--Bradley Real Estate, Inc., Northbrook, IL; *U.S. Public*, pg. 250
Dunn, Norma F., V.P.-Investor & Pub. Rels.--El Paso Natural Gas Co., Houston, TX; *U.S. Public*, pg. 567
Dunn, Richard, Chief Fin. Officer & V.P.-Fin.--Supreme International Corp., Miami, FL; *U.S. Public*, pg. 1542
Dunnewald, David A., Mgr.-Fin. Rels.--Adolph Coors Company, Golden, CO; *U.S. Public*, pg. 445
Dunnigan, Jim, Dir.-Adv. & Pub. Rels.--City National Corporation, Beverly Hills, CA; *U.S. Public*, pg. 380
Durant, Eric, Sr. Mng. Dir.-Investor Rels.--Bankers Trust New York Corporation, New York, NY; *U.S. Public*, pg. 185
Durant, Eric R., Sr. V.P. & Dir.-Investor Rels.--BankAmerica Corporation, San Francisco, CA; *U.S. Public*, pg. 179
Durning, Peter F., Asst. Gen. Counsel & Asst. Sec.--Stone & Webster, Incorporated, Boston, MA; *U.S. Public*, pg. 1519
Dusossoit, Janine, V.P.-Investor Rels.--Teleflex Incorporated, Plymouth Meeting, PA; *U.S. Public*, pg. 1569
Dutrey, Eduardo, Mgr.-Investor Rels. (Intl.)--Y.P.F., S.A., Buenos Aires, Argentina; *Int'l*, pg. 1515
Dvorak, Kathleen S., V.P.-Investor Rels.--United Stationers Inc., Des Plaines, IL; *U.S. Public*, pg. 1689
Dvorchak, Thomas, Sr. V.P.--Bandag, Incorporated, Muscatine, IA; *U.S. Public*, pg. 177
Dwyer, Daniel P., Chief Fin. Officer, Exec. V.P.-Fin. & Treas.--CommNet Cellular Inc., Englewood, CO; *U.S. Public*, pg. 414
Dye, Robert M., V.P.-Corp. Commun.--Journal Communications Inc., Milwaukee, WI; *U.S. Private*, pg. 601
Dykema, Henry, Chief Fin. Officer & V.P.--Federal Signal Corporation, Oak Brook, IL; *U.S. Public*, pg. 616
Dykman, Susan, Exec. Asst.-Investor Rels.--Allegiant Physician Services, Atlanta, GA; *U.S. Public*, pg. 45
Eacott, J. Graham, V.P.-Investor Rels.--Royal Oak Mines Inc., Kirkland, WA; *U.S. Public*, pg. 1410
Eagon, Donald E., Jr., V.P.-Corp. Communications--Diebold, Incorporated, Canton, OH; *U.S. Public*, pg. 506
Earle, Malcolm, Mgr.-Investor Rels.--TSC Shannock Corporation, Burnaby, Canada; *Int'l*, pg. 1343
Eastman, Tracey, Mgr.-Corp. Commun.--Computer Task Group, Inc. (CTG), Buffalo, NY; *U.S. Public*, pg. 423
Ebeling, Gary A., Dir.-Investor Rels.--CILCORP Inc., Peoria, IL; *U.S. Public*, pg. 367
Eberhardt, M.C., V.P., Gen. Counsel & Sec.--Raytheon E-Systems, Greenville, TX; *U.S. Public*, pg. 1365
Eckert, Melody, V.P.-Investor Rels.--Technology Solutions Company (TSC), Chicago, IL; *U.S. Public*, pg. 1564
Eddy, David L., Sr. V.P. & Treas.--Northern Trust Corporation, Chicago, IL; *U.S. Public*, pg. 1195
Edelman, Susan D., Dir.-Stockholder Rels.--Stein Mart, Inc., Jacksonville, FL; *U.S. Public*, pg. 1514
Edmondson, Ralph, Mgr.-Investor Rels.--B.A.T Industries P.L.C., London, United Kingdom; *Int'l*, pg. 110
Edmundson, Jennifer, Investor Rels. Specialist--Open Market, Inc., Burlington, MA; *U.S. Public*, pg. 1226
Edris, James A., Dir.-Investor Rels.--Hershey Foods Corporation, Hershey, PA; *U.S. Public*, pg. 811
Edwards, Richard, Dir.-Investor Rels.--H.B. Fuller Company, Saint Paul, MN; *U.S. Public*, pg. 686
Edwards, Tracy, Chief Fin. Officer & V.P.--Bell Industries, Inc., El Segundo, CA; *U.S. Public*, pg. 204
Edwards, Warren, Sr. V.P.--Affiliated Computer Services, Inc., Dallas, TX; *U.S. Public*, pg. 27
Edwards, William F., Asst. V.P.-Investor Rels.--Questar Corporation, Salt Lake City, UT; *U.S. Public*, pg. 1352
Egert, Dana, Chm.--Jaclo Inc., Mountainside, NJ; *U.S. Private*, pg. 349
Eichenbaum, Samuel, Chief Fin. Officer & V.P.-Fin.--New Brunswick Scientific Co., Inc., Edison, NJ; *U.S. Public*, pg. 1169
Eichman, Margaret, V.P.-Investor Rels. & Corp. Affairs--The Quaker Oats Company, Chicago, IL; *U.S. Public*, pg. 1347
Eid, Caroline, Investor Rels. Officer--Authentic Fitness Corp., Los Angeles, CA; *U.S. Public*, pg. 147
Eidell, Ronald G., Sr. V.P. & Treas.--R.R. Donnelley & Sons Company, Chicago, IL; *U.S. Public*, pg. 517

Eisenhart, Mark, Investor Rels. Specialist--America Online Incorporated, Dulles, VA; *U.S. Public*, pg. 66
Ekstrom, Paul, Sec.--California Water Service Co., San Jose, CA; *U.S. Public*, pg. 294
Elbert, Stephen A., V.P.-Govt. Rels.--Amoco Corporation, Chicago, IL; *U.S. Public*, pg. 101
Elburn, Kathleen M., Sec.--The Arundel Corporation, Sparks, MD; *U.S. Public*, pg. 656
Eldredge, Charles, Dir.-Investor Rels.--Pacificare Health Systems, Santa Ana, CA; *U.S. Public*, pg. 1251
Eldridge, John W., Dir.-Investor Rels.--Sequent Computer Systems, Inc., Beaverton, OR; *U.S. Public*, pg. 1459
Elliott, Paula, Mgr.-Investor Rels.--Summit Technology, Inc., Waltham, MA; *U.S. Public*, pg. 1528
Elliott, Steve, Dir.-Investor Rels.--Portland General Electric Co., Portland, OR; *U.S. Public*, pg. 584
Ellis, C. Lee, Sr. V.P.-Investments--Alfa Investment Corp. & Builders Inc., Montgomery, AL; *U.S. Public*, pg. 40
Emery, Frank E., Mgr.-Plng. & Information--Watkins-Johnson Company, Palo Alto, CA; *U.S. Public*, pg. 1745
Emery, Lavinia Z., Sec. & Asst. Treas.--Driver-Harris Company, Harrison, NJ; *U.S. Public*, pg. 530
Emmanuelli, Milton, Controller & Treas.--Crown Andersen Inc., Peachtree City, GA; *U.S. Public*, pg. 462
Emmert, John C., Jr., Chief Fin. Officer, Sr. V.P. & Treas.--American Arbitration Association, New York, NY; *U.S. Private*, pg. 50
Emms, Nigel, Mgr.-Externa Rels.--Iveco-Ford Truck Ltd., Watford, United Kingdom; *Int'l*, pg. 484
England, Patricia A., V.P.-Corp. Communications & Sec.--Harding Lawson Associates Group, Inc., Novato, CA; *U.S. Public*, pg. 785
English, Paula, Asst. Investor Rels.--Electronic Data Systems Corporation, Plano, TX; *U.S. Public*, pg. 569
Ennis, John J., Dir.-Investor Rels.--Coltec Holdings Inc, Charlotte, NC; *U.S. Public*, pg. 401
Enriquez, Jackie, Controller, Treas., Dir.-Investor Rels. & Internal Auditor--Supertex, Inc., Sunnyvale, CA; *U.S. Public*, pg. 1539
Ensign, Gregory M., V.P., Gen. Counsel & Sec.--Kirkwood Industries, Inc., Cleveland, OH; *U.S. Private*, pg. 623
Entin, Bruce, V.P.-Investor Rels. & Corp. Communications--LSI Logic Corp., Milpitas, CA; *U.S. Public*, pg. 971
Epstein, Sidney, Chm. Bd.--A. Epstein and Sons, Intl., Inc., Chicago, IL; *U.S. Private*, pg. 379
Ericksson, Sixten, Investor Rels. Officer--Credit Suisse Group, Zurich, Switzerland; *Int'l*, pg. 345
Estela, Jorge, Mgr.-Investor Rels. (Natl.)--Y.P.F., S.A., Buenos Aires, Argentina; *Int'l*, pg. 1515
Esterman, Joseph, Div. V.P.-Investor Rels.--Nalco Chemical Company, Naperville, IL; *U.S. Public*, pg. 1150
Etzel, Linda, Dir.-Investor Rels.--OEC Medical Systems, Inc., Salt Lake City, UT; *U.S. Public*, pg. 1207
Eustes, Susan, Sec.--Amgen Boulder, Inc., Boulder, CO; *U.S. Public*, pg. 101
Evangelist, Frank E., Sr. V.P.-Fin. & Sec.--Regis Corporation, Minneapolis, MN; *U.S. Public*, pg. 1373
Evans, Beth, Mgr.-Investor Rels.--Regal Cinemas Inc., Knoxville, TN; *U.S. Public*, pg. 1371
Evans, Daniel, Dir.-Investor Rels.--Clearly Canadian Beverage Corp., Vancouver, Canada; *Int'l*, pg. 297
Evans, Eric W., Asst. V.P.-Investor Rels. & Sec.--Unicorp Canada Corporation, Toronto, Canada; *Int'l*, pg. 1433
Evazich, Dianne, Investor Rels.--Micro Component Technology Inc., Saint Paul, MN; *U.S. Public*, pg. 1104
Everhart, Sally, Sr. Fin. Analyst-Investor Rels.--Sprint Corporation, Westwood, KS; *U.S. Public*, pg. 1500
Eversull, Jack W., V.P.-Investor Rels.--Atmos Energy Corporation, Dallas, TX; *U.S. Public*, pg. 145
Ezerski, Ronald E., Chief Fin. Officer, Exec. V.P., Treas. & Sec.--Patterson Dental Company, Saint Paul, MN; *U.S. Public*, pg. 1265
Faber, Charles P., V.P.-Corp. Devel.--Belden & Blake Corporation, Canton, OH; *U.S. Private*, pg. 1078
Fairchild, Ellen, Dir.-Investor Rels.--UtiliCorp United Inc., Kansas City, MO; *U.S. Public*, pg. 1700
Falls, Nancy M., V.P.-Investor Rels.--MagneTek, Inc., Nashville, TN; *U.S. Public*, pg. 1037
Farmer, H. Randolph, Sr. V.P.-Corp. Commun. & Investor Rels.--Lawyers Title Insurance Corporation, Richmond, VA; *U.S. Public*, pg. 981
Farnesi, Michael, Mgr.-Corp. Commun. & Investor Rels.--Banyan Systems Inc., Westborough, MA; *U.S. Public*, pg. 189
Farrington, Tina M., Asst. V.P. & Dir.-Mktg.--Rurban Financial Corp., Defiance, OH; *U.S. Public*, pg. 1412
Fasel, William, Corp. Sec. & Dir.-Investor Rels.--AON Corporation, Chicago, IL; *U.S. Public*, pg. 117
Fauenstrom, Billie, Investor Rels.--Network Equipment Technologies, Inc., Redwood City, CA; *U.S. Public*, pg. 1168
Faulds, J.G., V.P.-Risk Mngmt. & Investor Rels.--Ranger Oil Limited, Calgary, Canada; *Int'l*, pg. 1086
Faur, Peter, Dir.-Corp. Communications--Mallinckrodt Inc., Saint Louis, MO; *U.S. Public*, pg. 1039
Favilla, Debbie, Mgr.-Investor Rels.--First Team Sports Inc., Anoka, MN; *U.S. Public*, pg. 638
Fawkes, Kurtis E., Asst. V.P.-Investor Rels.--Sprint Corporation, Westwood, KS; *U.S. Public*, pg. 1500
Fay, John T., Jr., V.P.-Corp. Affairs--Bergen Brunswig Corporation, Orange, CA; *U.S. Public*, pg. 213
Fayer, Elizabeth, Chm. Bd. & Chief Exec. Officer--Alfin, Inc., New York, NY; *U.S. Public*, pg. 40
Fears, Douglas, Chief Fin. Officer & V.P.-Fin.--Helmerich & Payne, Inc., Tulsa, OK; *U.S. Public*, pg. 808
Feder, Mary, V.P.-Investor Rels.--Long Island Bancorp, Inc., Melville, NY; *U.S. Public*, pg. 1013
Feehan, Daniel R., Pres. & Chief Oper. Officer--Cash America International, Inc., Fort Worth, TX; *U.S. Public*, pg. 312
Feld, David, Chm. Bd., Chief Exec. Officer & Founder--Today's Man, Inc., Moorestown, NJ; *U.S. Public*, pg. 1619
Felderman, Douglas, Chief Fin. Officer--Strouds, Inc., City of Industry, CA; *U.S. Public*, pg. 1525
Fellows, Linda, Treas. & Dir.-Investor Rels.--Intuit, Inc., Mountain View, CA; *U.S. Public*, pg. 911
Felts, Clarissa, Mgr.-Investor Rels.--Lowe's Companies, Inc., North Wilkesboro, NC; *U.S. Public*, pg. 1015
Felts, William H., Jr., V.P. & Dir-Personnel & Investor Rels.--American Indemnity Financial Corp., Galveston, TX; *U.S.* Public, pg. 83
Fenelon, Marcio, Investor Rels. Analyst--Iochpe-Maxion S.A., Sao Paulo, Brazil; *Int'l*, pg. 688
Fenendael, Lee F., Treas.--Condon Oil Company, Inc., Ripon, WI; *U.S. Private*, pg. 262
Ferguson, Felicia, Mgr.-Investor Rels.--Cinergy Corp., Cincinnati, OH; *U.S. Public*, pg. 368
Ferguson, Jack R., Chief Fin. Officer, V.P.-Fin. & Treas.--Ingles Markets, Incorporated, Black Mountain, NC; *U.S. Public*, pg. 878
Fernadez, Jean, Mgr.-Investor Rels.--Scherer Healthcare, Inc., Atlanta, GA; *U.S. Public*, pg. 1437
Fernandez, Suzanne, Mgr.-Corp. Commun.--Superior Telecommunications, Atlanta, GA; *U.S. Public*, pg. 58
Feye, Lyle J., Chief Fin. Officer, V.P.-Fin. & Treas.--AXIA Incorporated, Lombard, IL; *U.S. Private*, pg. 103
Fiedler, David L., Dir.-Investor Rels.--Eastman Kodak Company, Rochester, NY; *U.S. Public*, pg. 550
Figliozzi, Robert J., V.P.-Investor Rels.--International Recovery Corp., Miami Springs, FL; *U.S. Public*, pg. 906
Filstrip, Tom, Dir.-Investor Rels.--Whirlpool Corporation, Benton Harbor, MI; *U.S. Public*, pg. 1764
Fimbanit, Joe, Dir.-Investor Relations--Ingersoll-Rand Company, Woodcliff Lake, NJ; *U.S. Public*, pg. 876
Finger, Larry E., Chief Fin. Officer & Sr. V.P.--Washington Real Estate Investment Trust, Kensington, MD; *U.S. Public*, pg. 1743
Finkelman, David, Sr. V.P.-Corp. Commun.--BankAtlantic Bancorp, Inc., Fort Lauderdale, FL; *U.S. Public*, pg. 183
Finley, David, Chief Fin. Officer & Exec. V.P.--Broadway & Seymour, Inc., Charlotte, NC; *U.S. Public*, pg. 258
Finney, Deryl, Dir.-Corp. Commun.--General Automation, Inc., Irvine, CA; *U.S. Public*, pg. 706
Finnigan, G. Michael, Chief Fin. Officer, Exec. V.P., Treas. & Pres.-Gaming Div.--Hollywood Park, Inc., Inglewood, CA; *U.S. Public*, pg. 830
Fiordelisi, Rocco J., Officer-Investment Banking--United Missouri Bank of St. Louis, Saint Louis, MO; *U.S. Public, pg. 1655*
Fiore, Carl, Dir.-Investor Rels.--LeaRonal, Inc., Freeport, NY; *U.S. Public*, pg. 982
Fiorenza, David A., V.P. & Treas.--Ethyl Corporation, Richmond, VA; *U.S. Public*, pg. 595
Fishbeck, James, Dir.-Corp. Communications & Investor Rels.--Analog Devices, Inc., Norwood, MA; *U.S. Public*, pg. 107
Fisher, Jessica, V.P.-Investor Rels.--Allegiance Healthcare Corp., McGaw Park, IL; *U.S. Public*, pg. 44
Fisher, Margaret L., V.P.-Investor Relations--SunTrust Banks, Inc., Atlanta, GA; *U.S. Public*, pg. 1537
Fisher, Mark, Mgr.-Investor Rels. & Shareholder Services--Enova Corp, San Diego, CA; *U.S. Public*, pg. 583
Fisher, Mark, Mgr.-Investor Rels.--San Diego Gas & Electric Company, San Diego, CA; *U.S. Public*, pg. 584
Fisher, Susan, Dir.-Investor Rels.--Alternative Resources Corporation, Lincolnshire, IL; *U.S. Public*, pg. 59
Fitzgerald, Joseph M., V.P.-Investor Rels.--ABC, Inc, New York, NY; *U.S. Public*, pg. 511
Fitzgerald, Kathy, Sr. V.P.-Pub. Rels. & Investor Rels.--Lucent Technologies Inc., Murray Hill, NJ; *U.S. Public*, pg. 1017
Fitzgerald, Kevin G., Dir.-Investor Rels.--Murphy Oil Corporation, El Dorado, AR; *U.S. Public*, pg. 1141
Fitzgerald, Marie, Asst. Treas.--The Genlyte Group Incorporated, Union, NJ; *U.S. Public*, pg. 729
Fitzgerald, Traci, Mgr.-Investor Rels.--SkyWest Inc., Saint George, UT; *U.S. Public*, pg. 1476
Fitzsimmons, Robert J., Sr. V.P.-Treas.--The FINOVA Group Inc., Phoenix, AZ; *U.S. Public*, pg. 624
Flaherty, Walter J., Chief Fin. Officer & Sr. V.P.--Eastern Enterprises, Weston, MA; *U.S. Public*, pg. 548
Flanagan, Jim, Dir.-Investor Rels.--Primark Corporation, Waltham, MA; *U.S. Public*, pg. 1325
Flannery, Heidi A., Dir.-Investor Rels.--In Focus Systems, Inc., Wilsonville, OR; *U.S. Public*, pg. 873
Fleetwood, Ingrid, V.P.-Investor Rels.--Skandia Insurance Company Limited, Stockholm, Sweden; *Int'l*, pg. 1256
Fleischman, Marvin H., Pres.--Peerless Distributing Co., Southfield, MI; *U.S. Private*, pg. 847
Fleming, James, V.P.-Communications--Barrick Gold Corporation, Toronto, Canada; *Int'l*, pg. 168
Fleming, Kiley, Dir.-Investor Rels.--Dollar General Corporation, Nashville, TN; *U.S. Public*, pg. 515
Fleming, Mark A., Mgr.-Corp. Communications--Banta Corporation, Menasha, WI; *U.S. Public*, pg. 187
Flener, Michael, V.P. & Controller--J.E. Higgins Lumber Co., Concord, CA; *U.S. Private*, pg. 527
Fleshner, Barrie, Dir.-Investor Rels.--Holiday RV Superstores, Inc., Orlando, FL; *U.S. Public*, pg. 829
Flore, Klaus-Dieter, Dir.-Fin.--Deutz AG, Cologne, Germany; *Int'l*, pg. 407
Flores, Dana, Dir.-Communications--Philip Industrial Services Group, Houston, TX; *Int'l*, pg. 1050
Florio, Yolanda, Admin. Asst.-Fin.--Mylex Corporation, Fremont, CA; *U.S. Public*, pg. 1143
Floyd, Orilla, Sec.--CV Reit, Inc., West Palm Beach, FL; *U.S. Public*, pg. 286
Foerster, Molly, Dir.-Investor Rels.--QUALCOMM, San Diego, CA; *U.S. Public*, pg. 1348
Fokma, A. G., Dir.-Investor Rels.--Koninklijke Van Ommeren NV, Rotterdam, Netherlands; *Int'l*, pg. 758
Foley, Elizabeth A., Dir.-Investor Rels.--Bay State Gas Company, Westborough, MA; *U.S. Public*, pg. 196
Foltz, Jim, Dir.-Investor Rels.--National Semiconductor Corporation, Santa Clara, CA; *U.S. Public*, pg. 1159
Folwell, Ronald L., Sr., Chief Fin. Officer & V.P.-Fin., Leasing, Plng/Devel. & Real Est.--GSC Enterprises, Inc., Sulphur Springs, TX; *U.S. Private*, pg. 436
Fontoura Becker, Oscar Antonio, Chief Fin. Officer & Mng. Dir.-Investor Rels.--Iochpe-Maxion S.A., Saó Paulo, Brazil; *Int'l*, pg. 688
Foote, James M., V.P.-Investor Relations--Canadian National Railway Company, Montreal, Canada; *Int'l*, pg. 258
Forbes, Barbara B., Dir.-Investor Rels.--Nuevo Energy Company, Houston, TX; *U.S. Public*, pg. 1206
Ford, Bill, Chief Fin. Officer & Dir.-Investor Rels.--Ferrofluidics Corporation, Nashua, NH; *U.S. Public*, pg. 620
Ford, Debi, Dir.-Corp. Communications & Investor Rels.--Starwood Hotels & Resorts, Phoenix, AZ; *U.S. Public*, pg. 1512
Ford, Nancy, Dir.-Investor Rels.--The Coca-Cola Company, Atlanta, GA; *U.S. Public*, pg. 392
Foreman, Kathy, Mgr.-Investor Rels.--Comair Holdings, Inc., Erlanger, KY; *U.S. Public*, pg. 406
Forgione, Anthony, Chm. Bd. & Pres.--Boyer Candy Company Inc., Altoona, PA; *U.S. Private*, pg. 162
Forman, Willis M., Pres., Chief Exec. Officer & Treas.--Paper Calmenson & Co., Saint Paul, MN; *U.S. Private*, pg. 837
Forney, James L., Chief Fin. Officer & Treas.--Fone America, Inc., Portland, OR; *U.S. Public*, pg. 661
Forsythe, Patricia, Coord.-Investor Rels.--Provident Financial Group, Inc., Cincinnati, OH; *U.S. Public*, pg. 1338
Fort, Jean-Francois, Mgr.-Investor Rels.--Rhone-Poulenc Japan, Ltd., Tokyo, Japan; *Int'l*, pg. 1113
Foss, Adam, Corp. Commun. Officer--GN Great Nordic Ltd., Copenhagen, Denmark; *Int'l*, pg. 536
Fossenier, Patrick, Dir.-Investor Rels.--CNF Transportation Inc., Palo Alto, CA; *U.S. Public*, pg. 281
Foster, Diane, Dir.-Investor Communications--Pall Corporation, Greenvale, NY; *U.S. Public*, pg. 1253
Foster, Geraldine U., Sr. V.P.-Investor Rels. & Corp. Communications--Schering-Plough Corporation, Madison, NJ; *U.S. Public*, pg. 1438
Foster, James H., V.P.-Investor Rels.--Everest Reinsurance Holdings, Liberty Corner, NJ; *U.S. Public*, pg. 597
Foster, Lee B., II, Pres. & Chief Exec. Officer--L.B. Foster Company, Pittsburgh, PA; *U.S. Public*, pg. 675
Foster, Mickey, V.P.-Investor Rels.--Hanson North America, Woodbridge, NJ; *Int'l*, pg. 593
Foster, Robert J., V.P.-Fin.--National Machinery, Tiffin, OH; *U.S. Private*, pg. 785
Foudree, Charles M., Exec. V.P.-Fin., Treas. & Sec.--Harmon Industries, Inc., Blue Springs, MO; *U.S. Public*, pg. 788
Fowler, Frederick V., Jr., Chm. Bd., Pres. & Chief Exec. Officer--Fred V. Fowler Company, Inc., Newton, MA; *U.S.* Private, pg. 422
Fowler, Richard, V.P.-Investor Rels.--The Charles Schwab Corporation, San Francisco, CA; *U.S. Public*, pg. 1442
Fowlstone, G., Pres.-Corp. Affairs--Burns, Philp & Company Limited, Sydney, Australia; *Int'l*, pg. 236
Fox, Doug, Dir.-Investor Rels.--Universal Foods Corporation, Milwaukee, WI; *U.S. Public*, pg. 1695
Fox, Herbert C., Pres. & Chief Exec. Officer--Active Electrical Supply Company, Chicago, IL; *U.S. Private*, pg. 15
Fox, T. Sean, Mgr.-Investor Rels.--First Union Corporation, Charlotte, NC; *U.S. Public*, pg. 639
Frachon, Jacqueline, Mgr.-Image--Total S.A., Paris, France; *Int'l*, pg. 1408
Fraley, Claudia, Investor Rels.--Leasing Solutions, Inc., San Jose, CA; *U.S. Public*, pg. 982
Francis, Barry, Grp. Dir.-Pub. Rels.--Siebe plc, Windsor, United Kingdom; *Int'l*, pg. 1240
Francois, Mark, Dir.-Investor Rels.--Safeskin Corporation, San Diego, CA; *U.S. Public*, pg. 1425
Frankel, K., Dir.-Head of Investor Relations--NFC plc, London, United Kingdom; *Int'l*, pg. 901
Frankel, Ron A., V.P.-Corp. Commun. & Investor Rels.--New Plan Realty Trust, New York, NY; *U.S. Public*, pg. 1172
Frazzini, Maria, Dir.-Shareholders--Washington Gas Light Co., Springfield, VA; *U.S. Public*, pg. 1740
Freece, Robert A., Sr. V.P.--Vishay Intertechnology, Inc., Malvern, PA; *U.S. Public*, pg. 1721
Freedman, Charles M., V.P.-Corp. Excellence--Hawaiian Electric Company, Inc., Honolulu, HI; *U.S. Public*, pg. 800
Freeman, James I., Chief Fin. Officer & Sr. V.P.--Dillard's, Inc., Little Rock, AR; *U.S. Public*, pg. 509
Freeman, John P., Chief Fin. Officer & V.P.--Spectrum Control, Inc., Erie, PA; *U.S. Public*, pg. 1497
Freeman, Kevin, Coord.-Shareowner Rels.--OGE Energy Corp., Oklahoma City, OK; *U.S. Public*, pg. 1207
Freeman, Phyllis, Exec. V.P., Comptroller, Legal Officer & Dir.-Investor Rels.--Eagle Lincoln Mercury Inc., Dallas, TX; *U.S. Private*, pg. 355
Freeman, Steve, V.P. & Mgr.-Investments--FirstMerit Corporation, Akron, OH; *U.S. Public*, pg. 646
Freitas, Andre, Mgr.-Investor Rels.--Aracruz Celulose S.A., Rio de Janeiro, Brazil; *Int'l*, pg. 78
Freschi, Susan, Dir.-Investor Rels.--Nellcor Puritan Bennett Incorporated, Pleasanton, CA; *U.S. Public*, pg. 1039
Frew, Bill, Mgr.-Corp. Affairs--James Hardie Industries Ltd., Sydney, Australia; *Int'l*, pg. 596
Friedl, Robert R., Chief Fin. Officer & Sr. V.P.--The Manitowoc Company, Inc., Manitowoc, WI; *U.S. Public*, pg. 1040
Fries, Gregory L., Mgr.-Investor Rels.--Allegheny Power System, Inc., Hagerstown, MD; *U.S. Public*, pg. 42
Friesen, Eugene K., Chief Fin. Officer, Sr. V.P. & Treas.--Howard B. Wolf, Inc., Dallas, TX; *U.S. Public*, pg. 1774
Frith, Marlene, Dir.-Integrated Commun. & Investor Rels.--Brite Voice Systems, Inc., Heathrow, FL; *U.S. Public*, pg. 257

Froemming, Herb, Pres. & Chief Oper. Officer--Brauns Fashions Corporation, Plymouth, MN; *U.S. Public*, pg. 251
Fromstein, Mitchell S., Chm. Bd., Pres. & Chief Exec. Officer--Manpower Inc., Milwaukee, WI; *U.S. Public*, pg. 1042
Frost, William J., V.P.-Admin.--EDO Corporation, New York, NY; *U.S. Public*, pg. 541
Frouge, Tanina, Dir.-Investor Rels.--Nabi, Boca Raton, FL; *U.S. Public*, pg. 1148
Frye, Arlene Y., Dir.-Mktg. & Client Relations--General Electric Investment Corp., Stamford, CT; *U.S. Public*, pg. 712
Frye, John W., Chief Fin. Officer, Sr. V.P.-Fin. & Treas.--Old Dominion Freight Line, Inc., High Point, NC; *U.S. Public*, pg. 1216
Fuortes, Beverly, Dir.-Corp. Devel.--Amtech Corporation, Dallas, TX; *U.S. Public*, pg. 105
Furr, Virginia J., Mgr.-Shareholder Rels.--Walter Industries, Inc., Tampa, FL; *U.S. Public*, pg. 1736
Furrier, Julie, Mgr.-Investor Rels.--Town & Country Corporation, Chelsea, MA; *U.S. Public*, pg. 1625
Furth, Daniel R., Dir.-Corp. Rels.--MTL Inc., Plant City, FL; *U.S. Public*, pg. 1028
Gaedert, John R., Dir.-Investor Rels.--Spartan Motors, Inc., Charlotte, MI; *U.S. Public*, pg. 1495
Gailius, Gilbert K., Chief Fin. Officer & V.P.-Fin.--American Biltrite Inc., Wellesley Hills, MA; *U.S. Public*, pg. 68
Gallagher, Sheila E., V.P.-Corp. Communications--Centex Corporation, Dallas, TX; *U.S. Public*, pg. 322
Gallaher, J. Kirk, Chief Fin. Officer & Exec. V.P.--Uni-Marts, Inc., State College, PA; *U.S. Public*, pg. 1664
Gallaher, Jacqueline, Asst. Sec.--Phoenix Medical Technology, Inc., Andrews, SC; *U.S. Public*, pg. 1292
Gallant, Christine, Investor Rels. Coord.--The Molson Companies Limited, Toronto, Canada; *Int'l*, pg. 887
Galletly, Donald R., V.P.-Commun. & Investor Rels.--Dresser Industries, Inc., Dallas, TX; *U.S. Public*, pg. 528
Galow, Geoffrey G., Dir.-Investor Rels.--Quanex Corporation, Houston, TX; *U.S. Public*, pg. 1349
Galvin, John E., V.P. & Treas.--IMC Global, Bannockburn, IL; *U.S. Public*, pg. 856
Galvin, William W., III, Mgr.-Investor Rels.--Sea Containers Ltd., Hamilton, Bermuda; *Int'l*, pg. 1213
Ganje-Fischer, Joan, V.P.-Corp. Rels.--Super 8 Motels, Inc., Aberdeen, SD; *U.S. Public*, pg. 322
Garan, R.W., Dir.-Investor Rels.--Weirton Steel Corporation, Weirton, WV; *U.S. Public*, pg. 1751
Garcia-Tunon, Alvaro, V.P.-Investor Rels.--Westinghouse Air Brake Company, Wilmerding, PA; *U.S. Public*, pg. 1760
Garcia, Donna, Coord.-Investor Rels.--Sun Healthcare Group Inc., Albuquerque, NM; *U.S. Public*, pg. 1530
Garcia, Ileana, Treas. & Sec.--International Recovery Corp., Miami Springs, FL; *U.S. Public*, pg. 906
Gardiner, William J., Chief Fin. Officer, Sr. V.P. & Treas.--CRSS Inc., Houston, TX; *Int'l*, pg. 1415
Gardner, Ella D., Controller--Detection Systems, Inc., Fairport, NY; *U.S. Public*, pg. 501
Gardner, James R., Dr., V.P.-Investor Rels.--Pfizer Inc., New York, NY; *U.S. Public*, pg. 1281
Garnaat, G., Treas.--Koninklijke BolsWessanen nv, Amstelveen, Netherlands; *Int'l*, pg. 750
Garner, Robert E. Lee, Sec.--Builders Transport, Incorporated, Camden, SC; *U.S. Public*, pg. 267
Garofolo, Gary, Chief Fin. Officer & V.P.-Fin.--Harkins Builders, Inc., Silver Spring, MD; *U.S. Private*, pg. 502
Garrett, Andrea, Asst. V.P.-Investor Rels.--Resource Mortgage Capital, Inc., Glen Allen, VA; *U.S. Public*, pg. 1382
Garrett, James W., V.P.-Investor Rels.--Consolidated Natural Gas Company, Pittsburgh, PA; *U.S. Public*, pg. 435
Garrett, James W., V.P.-Investor Rels.--Consolidated Natural Gas Service Co., Inc., Pittsburgh, PA; *U.S. Public*, pg. 435
Garrett, Karen L., Corp. Sec.--TCA Cable TV, Inc., Tyler, TX; *U.S. Public*, pg. 1553
Garrison, Karen, Dir.-Commun.--Payless Cashways, Inc., Kansas City, MO; *U.S. Public*, pg. 1267
Garvey, Nancy A., V.P.-Investor Rels. & Treas.--AlliedSignal Inc., Morristown, NJ; *U.S. Public*, pg. 49
Gasper, Barbara, Dir.-Investor Rels.--Raytheon Company, Lexington, MA; *U.S. Public*, pg. 1364
Gasper, Carol, Dir.-Investor Rels.--Nordstrom, Inc., Seattle, WA; *U.S. Public*, pg. 1190
Gasper, Leslie, Sec.--Sturm, Ruger & Co., Inc., Southport, CT; *U.S. Public*, pg. 1526
Gates, Jordan, Chief Fin. Officer & Treas.--Expeditors International of Washington, Inc., Seattle, WA; *U.S. Public*, pg. 600
Gates, Richard D., Sr. V.P.-Investor Rels. & Bus. Devel.--Rubbermaid Incorporated, Wooster, OH; *U.S. Public*, pg. 1411
Gaydos, Paul, Mgr.-Investor Rels. & Dir.-Risk Mngmt.--Central Hudson Gas & Electric Corporation, Poughkeepsie, NY; *U.S. Public*, pg. 324
Gaylord, Edson I., Chm. Bd.--Ingersoll International Inc., Rockford, IL; *U.S. Private*, pg. 562
Gazmarian, Michael C., Chief Fin. Officer & Treas.--Insteel Industries, Inc., Mount Airy, NC; *U.S. Public*, pg. 882
Gazulis, Ted, Dir.-Investor Rels.--HS Resources, San Francisco, CA; *U.S. Public*, pg. 772
Gehl, William D., Chm. Bd., Pres. & Chief Exec. Officer--Gehl Company, West Bend, WI; *U.S. Public*, pg. 704
Geiger, Paul K., Chief Fin. Officer & Sr. V.P.--Kelly Services, Inc., Troy, MI; *U.S. Public*, pg. 949
Gelfman, Allison, Dir.-Treasury & Investor Rels.--Damark International, Inc., Minneapolis, MN; *U.S. Public*, pg. 478
Gell, M. E., Mgr.-Grp. Rels.--TNT Limited, Redfern, Australia; *Int'l*, pg. 1342
Gelman, Steven, Sr. V.P.--Wilshire Oil Co. of Texas, Jersey City, NJ; *U.S. Public*, pg. 1770
Gemkow, Stephan, Mgr.-Investor Rels.--Deutsche Lufthansa AG, Cologne, Germany; *Int'l*, pg. 407
Genicot, Jacques, V.P.-Foreign Investor Rels.--Amcor Capital Corporation, Coachella, CA; *U.S. Public*, pg. 64
Gentry, Boyd P., V.P.-Investor Rels. & Treas.--Paragon Health Network, Inc., Atlanta, GA; *U.S. Public*, pg. 1256
Gentry, Mary M., Sr. V.P. & Treas.--Carolina First Corporation, Greenville, SC; *U.S. Public*, pg. 306
George, B., Grp. Fin. Controller--Ransomes Plc, Ipswich, United Kingdom; *Int'l*, pg. 1087
George, Timothy, Dir.-Fin. & Corp. Strategy--The Vermont Teddy Bear Company, Inc., Shelburne, VT; *U.S. Public*, pg. 1716
Geraghty, Annette, Investor Rels. Admin.--PAXAR Corporation, White Plains, NY; *U.S. Public*, pg. 1266
Geraghty, Sharon, Mgr.-Investor Rels.--Bel Fuse Inc., Jersey City, NJ; *U.S. Public*, pg. 200
Gerber, Michel, Mgr.-Investor Rels.--Alusuisse-Lonza Holding Ltd., Zurich, Switzerland; *Int'l*, pg. 66
Geremski, Terrence E., Chief Fin. Officer, V.P. & Treas.--Guilford Mills, Inc., Greensboro, NC; *U.S. Public*, pg. 768
Gerhard, Gilbert C., Chief Fin. Officer, Sr. V.P.-Fin. & Admin. & Treas.--Arbor Drugs, Inc., Troy, MI; *U.S. Public*, pg. 126
Gering, Linda, Mgr.-Stockholder Svcs.--Brown-Forman Corporation, Louisville, KY; *U.S. Public*, pg. 261
Gerono, Gail A., Dir.-Investor Rels.--Calgon Carbon Corporation, Pittsburgh, PA; *U.S. Public*, pg. 292
Geuze, H.S., Mgr.-Inv. Rels--ING Groep N.V., Amsterdam, Netherlands; *Int'l*, pg. 647
Gianetti, Malinda, Project Asst.--Emerson Radio Corp., Parsippany, NJ; *U.S. Public*, pg. 578
Gibbons, Gregg M., V.P.-Corp. Affairs, Gen. Counsel & Sec.--Wynn's International, Inc., Orange, CA; *U.S. Public*, pg. 1782
Gibbs, James R., Pres. & Chief Exec. Officer--Wainoco Oil Corporation, Houston, TX; *U.S. Public*, pg. 1732
Gibson, Beverly A., Asst. Sec.--Pier 1 Imports, Inc., Fort Worth, TX; *U.S. Public*, pg. 1295
Gibson, Grant S., Dir.-Corp. Commun.--Protocol Systems, Inc., Beaverton, OR; *U.S. Public*, pg. 1336
Gibson, Jan, Mgr.-Investor Rels.--MacNeal-Schwendler Corp., Costa Mesa, CA; *U.S. Public*, pg. 1031
Gifford, S., Sec. & Dir.-Investor Rels.--Tate & Lyle PLC, London, United Kingdom; *Int'l*, pg. 1356
Gill, David, Chief Fin. Officer--Proudfoot USA Company, West Palm Beach, FL; *Int'l*, pg. 1072
Gill, Scott B., V.P.-Investor Rels.--Baker Hughes Incorporated, Houston, TX; *U.S. Public*, pg. 165
Gill, Zoreen B., Coord.-Investors/Pub. Rels.--St. Paul Bancorp, Inc., Chicago, IL; *U.S. Public*, pg. 1428
Gillen, Bunny, Mgr.-Personnel--Harbor Financial Mortgage Corp., Houston, TX; *U.S. Public*, pg. 644
Gillenwater, Debbie, Mgr.-Investor Rels.--Shared Medical Systems Corporation, Malvern, PA; *U.S. Public*, pg. 1463
Gillespie, Suzanne, Sec.--Bank of the Hudson, Poughkeepsie, NY; *U.S. Public*, pg. 1319
Gilman, Steven F., Chm. Bd., Pres, & Chief Exec. Officer--Gilrichco, Inc., Oxnard, CA; *U.S. Private*, pg. 454
Gilpin, John D., Sr. V.P. & Sec.--Lyman Lumber Company, Excelsior, MN; *U.S. Private*, pg. 683
Gilstrap, James J., Chief Fin. Officer, V.P. & Treas.--Florida Rock Industries, Inc., Jacksonville, FL; *U.S. Public*, pg. 655
Ginsberg, Sheldon, Chief Fin. Officer & Exec. V.P.--Lazare Kaplan Intl., Inc., New York, NY; *U.S. Public*, pg. 981
Ginther, Gary, V.P.-Fin.--Smart & Final, Vernon, CA; *Int'l*, pg. 563
Giussani, Stefano, Mgr.-Investor Rels.--Compart SpA, Milan, Italy; *Int'l*, pg. 324
Gladysz, Martin, V.P. & Treas.--Eckerd Corporation, Largo, FL; *U.S. Public*, pg. 917
Glass, John S., Dir.-Investor Rels.--Millipore Corporation, Bedford, MA; *U.S. Public*, pg. 1112
Glass, Laura, Mgr.-Investor Rels.--Micros Systems Inc., Beltsville, MD; *U.S. Public*, pg. 1106
Gleitz, Janet J., Corp. Sec. & Dir.-Investor Rels.--Ryan's Family Steak Houses, Inc., Greer, SC; *U.S. Public*, pg. 1413
Glenn, Robert C., DDS, Chm. Bd.--California State Bank-La Habra, La Habra, CA; *U.S. Public*, pg. 294
Glover, Jeff, Dir.-Investor Rels.--Century Telephone Enterprises, Inc., Monroe, LA; *U.S. Public*, pg. 329
Goldschein, Steven, Chief Exec. Officer, V.P.-Admin., Treas. & Sec.--Lambda Electronics Inc., Melville, NY; *Int'l*, pg. 1241
Goldstein, Barry J., Chief Fin. Officer, Exec. V.P.-Fin. & Sec.--Office Depot Inc., Delray Beach, FL; *U.S. Public*, pg. 1212
Gomez, Justo J., Dir.-Investor Rels.--Banco Espanol de Credito SA, Madrid, Spain; *Int'l*, pg. 143
Goncalves Caetano, Carlos Gilberto, Chief Fin. Officer & Dir.--Banco do Brasil, Brasilia, Brazil; *Int'l*, pg. 141
Goncalves, Antonio, Mgr.-Investor Rels.--Caixa Geral de Depositos, Lisbon, Portugal; *Int'l*, pg. 250
Gonzalez, Richard J., Chief Fin. Officer, V.P., Treas. & Sec.--Bayou Steel Corporation, La Place, LA; *U.S. Public*, pg. 197
Goodman, Bruce, Sr. V.P.-Global Media, Investor Rels. & Bus. Affairs--National Media Corporation, Philadelphia, PA; *U.S. Public*, pg. 1158
Goodman, Kenneth E., V.P.-Fin.--Forest Laboratories, Inc., New York, NY; *U.S. Public*, pg. 670
Goodman, Roy B., Sr. V.P.-Fin., Sec. & Treas.--Heilig-Meyers Company, Richmond, VA; *U.S. Public*, pg. 804
Gordan, Cynthia, V.P.-Human Resources & Legal Counsel--Quaker Fabric Corporation, Fall River, MA; *U.S. Public*, pg. 1347
Gordan, Ron E., Dir.-Investments--Cadim, Montreal, Canada; *Int'l*, pg. 249
Gordon, Annmarie, Exec. Asst.--Scan-Optics, Inc., Manchester, CT; *U.S. Public*, pg. 1436
Gordon, Christopher M., Dir.-Investor Rels.--National Fuel Gas Company, Buffalo, NY; *U.S. Public*, pg. 1156
Gordon, Ellen R., Pres. & Chief Oper. Officer--Tootsie Roll Industries, Inc., Chicago, IL; *U.S. Public*, pg. 1621
Gordon, S. Amber, Sec.--Hadron, Inc., Alexandria, VA; *U.S. Public*, pg. 773
Gordonsmith, John A., Exec. V.P.-Treasury, Legal & Corp. Sec.--FCA International Ltd., Westmount, Canada; *Int'l*, pg. 470
Gore, Nancy, Sr. Dir.-Investor Rels.--America West Airlines, Inc., Phoenix, AZ; *U.S. Public*, pg. 67
Gorin, Michael, Pres. & Chief Fin. Officer--Aeroflex Incorporated, Plainview, NY; *U.S. Public*, pg. 23
Gorin, Robert S., Sr. V.P., Gen. Counsel & Sec.--W.R. Berkley Corporation, Greenwich, CT; *U.S. Public*, pg. 215
Gorkuscha, Mischa, Chief Fin. Officer & Sr. V.P.--Liberty Bancorp, Inc., Oklahoma City, OK; *U.S. Public*, pg. 174
Gorman, Kirk E., Chief Fin. Officer & Sr. V.P.--Universal Health Services, Inc., King of Prussia, PA; *U.S. Public*, pg. 1696
Gosnell, Larry, Dir.-Investor Rels.--Advantica Restaurant Group, Inc., Spartanburg, SC; *U.S. Public*, pg. 22
Goto, Shinzo, Mng. Dir.-Investor Rels.--Matsushita Electric Works, Ltd., Osaka, Japan; *Int'l*, pg. 847
Goudis, Richard, V.P.-Investor Rels. & Corp. Plng.--Sunbeam Corporation, Delray Beach, FL; *U.S. Public*, pg. 1533
Gould, Barbara A., Dir.-Investor Rels. & Pub. Affairs--M.A. Hanna Company, Cleveland, OH; *U.S. Public*, pg. 780
Gould, Gerard J., Dir.-Investor Rels. & Communications--The Stanley Works, New Britain, CT; *U.S. Public*, pg. 1508
Gould, Jay S., Mgr.-Investor Rels.--Banc One Corporation, Columbus, OH; *U.S. Public*, pg. 172
Gowaty, Nina L., Sr. V.P.-Pub. Rels.--The Bank of Mid-Jersey, Bordentown, NJ; *U.S. Public*, pg. 1528
Grace, Julianne A., V.P.-Corp. Rels.--The Perkin-Elmer Corporation, Norwalk, CT; *U.S. Public*, pg. 1279
Grady, Patrick E., V.P.-Investor Rels. & Treas.--Western National Life Insurance Co., Houston, TX; *U.S. Public*, pg. 76
Grafer, William D., Chief Fin. Officer & V.P.-Fin.--National-Standard Co., Niles, MI; *U.S. Public*, pg. 1160
Graham, Howard L., V.P.-Corp. Svcs.--Kentucky Investors, Inc., Frankfort, KY; *U.S. Public*, pg. 951
Graham, John, V.P.-Corp. Affairs--BTG, Inc., Fairfax, VA; *U.S. Public*, pg. 164
Graham, Rob-Roy, Chief Fin. Officer , Sec. & Controller--InterVoice, Inc., Dallas, TX; *U.S. Public*, pg. 910
Grahn, Gary L., Pres. & Chief Exec. Officer--The Langer Biomechanics Group, Inc., Deer Park, NY; *U.S. Public*, pg. 978
Grant, Clark C., Exec. V.P.-Fin. & Treas.--Buffets, Inc., Eden Prairie, MN; *U.S. Public*, pg. 267
Grant, James, Mgr.-Investor Rels.--The Home Depot, Inc., Atlanta, GA; *U.S. Public*, pg. 831
Gray, Sherry, Analyst-Investor Rels.--Huntington Bancshares Inc., Columbus, OH; *U.S. Public*, pg. 849
Gray, Stanley, Dir.-Investor Rels.--WLR Foods, Inc., Timberville, VA; *U.S. Public*, pg. 1727
Graziano, Kristina, Mgr.-Investor Rels.--Ascend Communications, Inc., Alameda, CA; *U.S. Public*, pg. 138
Green, Anita, Mgr.-Shareholder Svcs.--Pax World Fund Family, Portsmouth, NH; *U.S. Public*, pg. 1266
Green, Dorrie, V.P.-Fin. & Admin.--Merry Land & Investment Company, Inc., Augusta, GA; *U.S. Public*, pg. 1098
Green, Jay M., V.P. & Dir.-Investor Rels.--Seitel, Inc., Houston, TX; *U.S. Public*, pg. 1454
Green, Mary Ann, V.P.-Pub. Rels.--MBL Life Assurance Corporation, Newark, NJ; *U.S. Private*, pg. 685
Green, Stanley D., Chief Fin. Officer & Exec. V.P.-Fin. & Corp. Devel.--Southwestern Energy Company, Fayetteville, AR; *U.S. Public*, pg. 1494
Greenberg, Daniel, Chm. Bd. & Chief Exec. Officer--Electro Rent Corporation, Van Nuys, CA; *U.S. Public*, pg. 568
Greer, Jana Waring, Pres.-SunAmerica Mktg. Inc. & Sr. V.P. SunAmerica, Inc. Affairs--SunAmerica Inc., Los Angeles, CA; *U.S. Public*, pg. 1532
Greer, Jon, Dir.-Investor Rels.--3M, Saint Paul, MN; *U.S. Public*, pg. 1604
Gregg, Dennis, V.P.-Fin.--Lindal Cedar Homes, Inc., Seattle, WA; *U.S. Public*, pg. 998
Gregory, Matthew, Investor Rels. Officer--Franklin Resources, Inc., San Mateo, CA; *U.S. Public*, pg. 679
Grein, Thomas W., Dir.-Investor Rels.--Eli Lilly and Company, Indianapolis, IN; *U.S. Public*, pg. 992
Greisman, Harvey W., V.P.-Pub. Affairs & Communications--GTE Corporation, Stamford, CT; *U.S. Public*, pg. 696
Grendel, Josef, Mgr.-Pub. Rels.--Deutsche Lufthansa AG, Cologne, Germany; *Int'l*, pg. 407
Grey, Deborah, Mgr.-Investor Rels.--American Power Conversion Corporation, West Kingston, RI; *U.S. Public*, pg. 89
Greyling, A.C., Gen. Mgr.-Legal & Admin. Services--Iscor, Pretoria, South Africa; *Int'l*, pg. 688
Griehs, L.F., Dir.-Inv. Rels.--Campbell Soup Company, Camden, NJ; *U.S. Public*, pg. 298
Griffith, James M., Sr. V.P.-Investor Rels. & Corp. Communication--Beverly Enterprises, Inc., Fort Smith, AR; *U.S. Public*, pg. 227
Griffith, Ronald L., Sr., Chief Fin. Officer, Sr. V.P.-Fin., Treas. & Sec.--Burnham, Lancaster, PA; *U.S. Public*, pg. 270
Grigsby, E.K., V.P.-Investor Rels.--Phillips Petroleum Company, Bartlesville, OK; *U.S. Public*, pg. 1290
Grimball, Edward B., Chief Fin. Officer & Exec. V.P.--Whitney Holding Corporation, New Orleans, LA; *U.S. Public*, pg. 1766
Grimone, Frank W., Chief Fin. Officer & Sr. Exec. V.P.--Central Reserve Life Corporation, Strongsville, OH; *U.S. Public*, pg. 326
Grimwade, F. S., Gen. Mgr.-Shareholder Rels.--Western Mining Corporation Holdings Limited, Southbank, Australia; *Int'l*, pg. 1494
Grimwade, Fred S., Sec. & Gen. Mgr.-Share Holder Rels.--Western Mining Corporation Holdings Limited, Southbank, Australia; *Int'l*, pg. 1494

Gross, Donald W., Sec.--Genovese Drug Stores, Inc., Melville, NY; *U.S. Public*, pg. 730

Grossman, Robert, Chm. Bd., Pres. & Chief Exec. Officer--Emons Transportation Group, Inc., York, PA; *U.S. Public, pg. 578*

Gruber, Robert S., V.P.-Corp. Rels.--Artra Group Incorporated, Northfield, IL; *U.S. Public*, pg. 136

Guffey, Scott D., V.P.-Fin., Acq. & Investor Rels.--ATC Communications Group, Inc., Dallas, TX; *U.S. Public*, pg. 11

Guidice, Eileen, Mgr.-Investor Rels.--Acclaim Entertainment, Inc., Glen Cove, NY; *U.S. Public*, pg. 15

Guidry, Leroy, Treas.--Pride International, Inc., Houston, TX; *U.S. Public*, pg. 1324

Guigou, Didier, Dir.-Investor Rels.--Rhone-Poulenc Chemicals Ltd., Watford, United Kingdom; *Int'l*, pg. 1112

Guimard, Anne, Mgr.-Investor Rels.--Alcatel Alsthom Compagnie Generale D'Electricite, Paris, France; *Int'l*, pg. 52

Guinness, B.L., Dir.-Investor Rels.--Pharmacia & Upjohn, Kalamazoo, MI; *Int'l*, pg. 1048

Gunnarsson, Helene, Mgr.-Investor Rels.--Sandvik AB, Sandviken, Sweden; *Int'l*, pg. 1185

Gunter, Celeste C., V.P.-Investor Rels.--Fort James Corporation, Richmond, VA; *U.S. Public*, pg. 670

Gurton, Lenora, Corp. Sec.--Benchmark Electronics Inc., Angleton, TX; *U.S. Public*, pg. 210

Gutmann, Leon J., Asst. Treas. & Asst. Sec.--The Topps Company, Inc., New York, NY; *U.S. Public*, pg. 1621

Haase, Michael, Dir.-Investor Rels.--QMS, Inc., Mobile, AL; *U.S. Public*, pg. 1346

Hadley, Debra, Dir.-Investor Rels.--Cardinal Health Inc., Dublin, OH; *U.S. Public*, pg. 304

Haertel, Valerie, Dir.-Inv. Rels.--Cable Michigan, Inc., Princeton, NJ; *U.S. Public*, pg. 287

Hager, Kathy E., V.P.-Pub. Affairs--Santa Fe Energy Resources, Inc., Houston, TX; *U.S. Public*, pg. 1431

Hager, Zack, Jr., Dir.-Investor Rels.--Forest Oil Corporation, Denver, CO; *U.S. Public*, pg. 670

Hagi, Kurt, Exec. V.P. & Sec.--Sulzer Ltd., Winterthur, Switzerland; *Int'l*, pg. 1305

Hagley, Thomas R., Dir.-Pub. Affairs--Alumax Inc., Atlanta, GA; *U.S. Public*, pg. 59

Hagstroem, Lennart, Sr. Exec. V.P.--Bergman & Beving AB, Stockholm, Sweden; *Int'l*, pg. 188

Haines, Stanley K., Asst. Treas.--Vanguard Cellular Systems, Inc., Greensboro, NC; *U.S. Public*, pg. 1707

Hale, J. Joseph, Jr., V.P.-Corp. Communications--Cinergy Corp., Cincinnati, OH; *U.S. Public*, pg. 368

Hale, Katherine L., Sec.--First American Federal Savings Bank, Bristol, VA; *U.S. Public*, pg. 624

Hall, Barbara, Mgr.-Investor Rels.--Trimble Navigation Limited, Sunnyvale, CA; *U.S. Public*, pg. 1638

Hall, Ed, Dir.-Inv. Rels. & Asst. Treas.--Northern States Power Company, Minneapolis, MN; *U.S. Public*, pg. 1195

Hall, Monica, Mgr.-Investor Rels.--AEGON USA, Inc., Louisville, KY; *Int'l*, pg. 26

Hall, William C. Jr., Asst. V.P.-Corp. Communications--Dominion Resources, Inc., Richmond, VA; *U.S. Public*, pg. 516

Halladay, Vanna, Investor Rels. Analyst--CMS Energy Corporation, Dearborn, MI; *U.S. Public*, pg. 279

Hallows, Michael, Sec. & Dir.-Internal Rels.--Joseph E. Seagram & Sons, Inc., New York, NY; *Int'l*, pg. 1215

Halperin, Scott, Dir.--Cucina Classica Italiana, Inc., Lakewood, NJ; *U.S. Public*, pg. 1435

Halvorson, Rebecca M., Mng. Dir.-Investor Rels.--FDX Corporation, Memphis, TN; *U.S. Public*, pg. 603

Hamblin, Connie, Sec. & Dir.-Corp. Commun.--Gentex Corporation, Zeeland, MI; *U.S. Public*, pg. 731

Hamilton, Dean C., Mgr.-Mktg. Communications--ATMI, Inc., Danbury, CT; *U.S. Public*, pg. 12

Hamilton, Scott, Dir.-Investor Rels.--Mobile Telecommunications Technologies Corp., Jackson, MS; *U.S. Public*, pg. 1120

Hammel, Philipp, Head-Investor Rels.--Clariant International Ltd., Muttenz, Switzerland; *Int'l*, pg. 624

Hamra, Charlene, Dir.-Investor Rels.--American International Group, Inc., New York, NY; *U.S. Public*, pg. 83

Hamrick, Grant L., Chief Fin. Officer, Sr. V.P. & Treas.--American City Business Journals, Inc., Charlotte, NC; *U.S. Private*, pg. 19

Hancock, John W., Sr. V.P. & Treas.--Atlantic American Corporation, Atlanta, GA; *U.S. Public*, pg. 143

Hanlon, Richard, V.P.-Investor Rels.--America Online Incorporated, Dulles, VA; *U.S. Public*, pg. 66

Hanneman, Christine, V.P.-Investor Rels.--Tupperware Corporation, Orlando, FL; *U.S. Public*, pg. 1644

Hanneman, Christine J., Mgr.-Investor Rels.--Premark International, Inc., Deerfield, IL; *U.S. Public*, pg. 1321

Hannity, Vincent, V.P.-Corp. Commun. & Investor Rels.--Boise Cascade Corporation, Boise, ID; *U.S. Public*, pg. 242

Hansen, Meryll, Mgr.-Corp. Communications & Pub. Rels.--Vishay Intertechnology, Inc., Malvern, PA; *U.S. Public*, pg. 1721

Hansen, Paul G., Chief Fin. Officer & V.P.-Fin.--Adaptec, Inc., Milpitas, CA; *U.S. Public*, pg. 19

Hansen, Richard A., Sr. V.P.--New York Life Insurance Company, New York, NY; *U.S. Private*, pg. 794

Harcourt, Patricia A., Dir.-Corp. Commun.--Belden & Blake Corporation, Canton, OH; *U.S. Private*, pg. 1078

Hardey, Matthew W., V.P.-Fin.--Newpark Resources, Inc., Metairie, LA; *U.S. Public*, pg. 1179

Hardy, Gene M., Treas. & Sec.--La-Z-Boy Incorporated, Monroe, MI; *U.S. Public*, pg. 972

Hardy, Susan E., V.P.-Investor Rels.--Houghton Mifflin Company, Boston, MA; *U.S. Public*, pg. 841

Harenberg, Ralf, Mgr.-Investor Rels.--Schering AG, Berlin, Germany; *Int'l*, pg. 1203

Harmon, Lowell D., Chm. Bd. & Pres.--Progressive Driver Services, Inc., Jacksonville, FL; *U.S. Private*, pg. 890

Harrington, Judy D., V.P.-Stockholder Rels. & Asst. Sec.--Bob Evans Farms, Inc., Columbus, OH; *U.S. Public*, pg. 596

Harris, Marie, Dir.-Investor Rels. & Pub. Rels.--Kronos Incorporated, Waltham, MA; *U.S. Public*, pg. 967

Harris, Mocllelland, III, Chief Fin. Officer & V.P.-Fin.--Southern California Water Company, San Dimas, CA; *U.S. Public*, pg. 1489

Harris, Robert G., Dir.-Investor Rels.--E.W. Blanch Holdings, Inc., Minneapolis, MN; *U.S. Public*, pg. 236

Harris, Titus H., III, Chief Fin. Officer & Sec.--The GNI Group, Inc., Deer Park, TX; *U.S. Public*, pg. 693

Harrison, Lynn, Dir.-Investor Rels.--CML Group, Inc., Acton, MA; *U.S. Public*, pg. 279

Hart, Robert M., Sr. V.P., Gen. Counsel & Sec.--Alleghany Corporation, New York, NY; *U.S. Public*, pg. 42

Hartl, William P., V.P.-Investor Rels.--Ashland, Inc., Russell, KY; *U.S. Public*, pg. 138

Harwood, Robert, V.P.-Investor Rels.--The Wackenhut Corporation, Palm Beach Gardens, FL; *U.S. Public*, pg. 1731

Haskell, Eric, Chief Fin. Officer, Sr. V.P.-Fin. & Admin., & Treas.--Systems & Computer Technology Corporation, Malvern, PA; *U.S. Public*, pg. 1552

Hastings, James H., V.P. & Treas.--Essex County Gas Company, Amesbury, MA; *U.S. Public*, pg. 593

Hastings, John J., Chief Fin. Officer, Exec. V.P., Treas. & Sec.--The Middleby Corporation, Rolling Meadows, IL; *U.S. Public*, pg. 1109

Hatcher, Kenneth, Chief Fin. Officer & V.P.-Fin.--Maynard Oil Co., Dallas, TX; *U.S. Public*, pg. 1064

Hatfield, James R., V.P. & Treas.--OGE Energy Corp., Oklahoma City, OK; *U.S. Public*, pg. 1207

Hathaway, Farrah, Mgr.-Investor Rels.--Ensco International Incorporated (ENSCO), Dallas, TX; *U.S. Public*, pg. 585

Hathaway, Peter S., Chief Acctg. Officer--Allied Waste Industries, Scottsdale, AZ; *U.S. Public*, pg. 49

Hattox, Patsy L., Chief Admin. Officer, V.P. & Sec.--Nichols Research Corporation, Huntsville, AL; *U.S. Public*, pg. 1182

Hauge, Marilyn I., Dir.-Corp. Compliance & Investor Rels.--Fremont General Corporation, Santa Monica, CA; *U.S. Public*, pg. 681

Hauk, Donald B., Chief Fin. Officer, Exec. V.P. & Sec.--Republic Automotive Parts, Inc., Brentwood, TN; *U.S. Public*, pg. 1377

Haven, Rachel, Investor Rels. Analyst--Adaptec, Inc., Milpitas, CA; *U.S. Public*, pg. 19

Hawkes, Cathy, Asst. Sec.--The Raymond Corporation, Greene, NY; *Int'l*, pg. 123

Hawkins, Julie, Coord.-Investor Rels.--Network Associates, Inc., Santa Clara, CA; *U.S. Public*, pg. 1168

Hawkins, Steve, V.P. & Dir.-Pub. Rels.--Great Western Financial Corporation, Chatsworth, CA; *U.S. Public*, pg. 1741

Hawkins, Steven B., Chief Fin. Officer, V.P.-Fin. & Admin., Treas. & Sec.--FFP Marketing Company, Inc., Fort Worth, TX; *U.S. Public*, pg. 604

Hawley, Edmund, Chief Exec. Officer & Sr. V.P.--Skyway Freight Systems, Inc., Watsonville, CA; *U.S. Private*, pg. 1005

Hawthorne, Joel, Dir.-Pub. & Investor Rels.--Acme Metals Incorporated, Riverdale, IL; *U.S. Public*, pg. 16

Hayden, Gerard M., Jr., Chief Fin. Officer, Sr. V.P. & Treas.--Allied Clinical Laboratories, Inc., Nashville, TN; *U.S. Public*, pg. 973

Hayden, P.L., Dir.-Investor Rels.(USA)--KLM Royal Dutch Airlines, Elmsford, NY; *Int'l*, pg. 719

Hayes, Jennifer, Dir.-Fin. & Mgr.-Investor Rels.--Kimmins Corp., Tampa, FL; *U.S. Public*, pg. 960

Hayes, Kevin J., Chief Fin. Officer, V.P., Treas. & Asst. Sec.--Methode Electronics Inc., Chicago, IL; *U.S. Public*, pg. 1101

Hayes, Linday, Investor Rels. Admin.--CarrAmerica Realty, Washington, DC; *U.S. Public*, pg. 308

Haynes, Jenny, V.P.-Investor Rels. & Pub. Rels.--Paging Network, Inc., Plano, TX; *U.S. Public*, pg. 1252

Hays, George G., Pres. & Chief Exec. Officer--Arizona Instrument Corporation, Phoenix, AZ; *U.S. Public*, pg. 129

Hazarian, Jeffrey R., Chief Fin. Officer & Exec. V.P.--Tenera, Inc., San Francisco, CA; *U.S. Public*, pg. 1576

Hazelbaker, Steven R., Chief Fin. Officer, V.P. & Treas.--Meridian Insurance Group, Inc., Indianapolis, IN; *U.S. Public*, pg. 1095

Heaberlin, David A., Chief Fin. Officer & Exec. V.P.--Bay View Capital Corporation, San Mateo, CA; *U.S. Public*, pg. 197

Headler, Robert, Grp. Mgr.-Corp. Affairs--Goodman Fielder Limited, Sydney, Australia; *Int'l*, pg. 555

Headrick, Jon C., Exec. V.P.-Investments--Ameritas Life Insurance Corp., Lincoln, NE; *U.S. Private*, pg. 65

Heard, Sandra E., Admin. Asst.--Valley Forge Corporation, San Rafael, CA; *U.S. Public*, pg. 1705

Hebert, Clifford J., Jr., V.P.-Fin., Treas. & Sec.--Eastern Utilities Associates, Boston, MA; *U.S. Public*, pg. 549

Hebert, William L., Chief Fin. Officer, Treas. & Dir.-Investor Rels.--Louisiana Pacific Corporation, Portland, OR; *U.S. Public*, pg. 1015

Heid, Michele C., V.P.-Investor Rels. & Corp. Controller--Raytheon Company, Lexington, MA; *U.S. Public*, pg. 1364

Heidbreder, Warren W., Chief Fin. Officer, V.P. & Sec.--Bandag, Incorporated, Muscatine, IA; *U.S. Public*, pg. 177

Heiligman, D.C., V.P.-Fin. & Corp. Sec.--Rochester Gas And Electric Corporation, Rochester, NY; *U.S. Public*, pg. 1395

Heit, Stephen A., Chief Fin. Officer & Treas.--AM Cosmetics Inc., Nyack, NY; *U.S. Private*, pg. 6

Hekeler, Manfred, Mgr.-Mktg. & Communications--Traub AG, Reichenbach, Germany; *Int'l*, pg. 1419

Helbring, Jean, Dir.-Investor Rels.--Staples, Inc., Westborough, MA; *U.S. Public*, pg. 1509

Helvey, J.L., Chief Fin. Officer, Exec. V.P. & Investor Rels. Officer--Golden West Financial Corporation, Oakland, CA; *U.S. Public*, pg. 750

Heming, Beth, Dir.-Investor Rels.--SuperValu, Inc., Eden Prairie, MN; *U.S. Public*, pg. 1540

Hemmer, Gary D., Exec. V.P.-Fin. Markets--Magna Group, Inc., Saint Louis, MO; *U.S. Public*, pg. 1037

Hemmingson, Charles, Mgr.-Employe Benefits--The Good Guys, Inc., Brisbane, CA; *U.S. Public*, pg. 750

Hemphill, J.B., Dir.-Corp. Fin./SCMB--Standard Bank Investment Corporation Limited, Johannesburg, South Africa; *Int'l*, pg. 1293

Hench, Ellen, Mgr.-Relations & Training--Tax Management, Inc., Washington, DC; *U.S. Private*, pg. 182

Hendrick, Howard, Asst. Treas. & Investor Rels.--BCE Inc., Montreal, Canada; *Int'l*, pg. 114

Hendrix, Daniel T., Chief Fin. Officer, Sr. V.P. & Treas.--Interface Inc., Atlanta, GA; *U.S. Public*, pg. 889

Hendrix, I.E., V.P. & Treas.--Parker Drilling Company, Tulsa, OK; *U.S. Public*, pg. 1259

Hennessey, Tim, Chief Fin. Officer--Peter Piper, Inc., Phoenix, AZ; *Int'l*, pg. 157

Henning, David, Chief Fin. Officer--Communications Instruments Inc., Fairview, NC; *U.S. Private*, pg. 259

Henry, Brian J., V.P.-Fin. & Treas.--Terex Corporation, Westport, CT; *U.S. Public*, pg. 1581

Henseler, Gerald A., Chief Fin. Officer & Exec. V.P.--Banta Corporation, Menasha, WI; *U.S. Public*, pg. 187

Hensley, Tom, Chief Fin. Officer & V.P.--Fieldale Corporation, Baldwin, GA; *U.S. Private*, pg. 403

Herald, Linda, Coord.-Investor Rels.--Respironics, Inc., Pittsburgh, PA; *U.S. Public*, pg. 1383

Herasimchuk, David A., V.P.-Mktg. Devel.--Global Marine Inc., Houston, TX; *U.S. Public*, pg. 748

Herlihy, Conor, Mgr.-Grp. Investor Rels.--Allied Irish Banks, p.l.c., Dublin, Ireland; *Int'l*, pg. 64

Hermanutz, G.E., Asst. Treas.--Pembina Pipeline Corporation, Calgary, Canada; *Int'l*, pg. 1032

Herron, Bonnie L., V.P. & Sec.--Intelligent Systems Corp., Norcross, GA; *U.S. Public*, pg. 888

Hersey, Liz, Dir.-Pub. Rels./Investor Rels.--Tricord Systems, Inc., Plymouth, MN; *U.S. Public*, pg. 1637

Hess, John S., V.P.-Investor Rels.--United Companies Financial Corporation, Baton Rouge, LA; *U.S. Public*, pg. 1675

Hew, Cliff, Staff Exec.-Investor Rels.--UAL Corporation, Elk Grove Village, IL; *U.S. Public*, pg. 1652

Hewitt, Robert C., Chief Fin. Officer, V.P.-Fin. & Sec.--Newport Corporation, Irvine, CA; *U.S. Public*, pg. 1179

Heyser, Jeffrey A., Exec. Dir.-Investor Rels.--Pacific Telesis Group, San Francisco, CA; *U.S. Public*, pg. 1415

Hibbs, Scott, Specialist-Investor Rels.--PacifiCorp, Portland, OR; *U.S. Public*, pg. 1251

Hickey, Michael, Sr. Fin. Analyst & Investor Rels.--Peak Technologies Group, Inc., New York, NY; *Int'l*, pg. 890

Hickman, Rebecca, Mgr.-Investor Rels.--Pinnacle West Capital Corporation, Phoenix, AZ; *U.S. Public*, pg. 1297

Hickman, Winston E., Chief Fin. Officer, Sr. V.P. & Sec.--Pacific Scientific Company, Newport Beach, CA; *U.S. Public*, pg. 1250

Hicks, Janet, Dir.-Investor Rels.--Flowserve Corporation, Dayton, OH; *U.S. Public*, pg. 658

Hicks, Kym, Investor Rels.--CMAC Investment Corporation, Philadelphia, PA; *U.S. Public*, pg. 278

Hicks, Michael, Treas.--GenCorp Inc., Fairlawn, OH; *U.S. Public*, pg. 705

Higgins, Michael R., Treas.--Amcast Industrial Corporation, Dayton, OH; *U.S. Public*, pg. 63

High, Lynne, Mgr.-Corp. Commun.--ADC Telecommunications, Inc., Minnetonka, MN; *U.S. Public*, pg. 4

Hignett, Kenneth L., Chief Fin. Officer, Sr. V.P. & Sec.--Morgan's Foods, Inc., Beachwood, OH; *U.S. Public*, pg. 1133

Hill, Joseph G., Chief Fin. Officer, V.P.-Fin., Treas. & Sec.--DMI Furniture Inc., Louisville, KY; *U.S. Public*, pg. 473

Hill, Linda K., V.P. & Treas.--Tyler Corporation, Dallas, TX; *U.S. Public*, pg. 1651

Hiller, Donald T., Dir.-Admin. Svcs.--Hahn Automotive Warehouse, Inc., Rochester, NY; *U.S. Public*, pg. 774

Hiller, Donald T., Mgr.-Investor Rels.--Professional Auto Warehouse, Rochester, NY; *U.S. Public*, pg. 774

Hilliers, Cynthia J., Mgr.-Corp. Commun.--Cannon, Grand Island, NY; *U.S. Private*, pg. 205

Hillin, Michael, V.P.-Investor Rels.--Bank of Ireland, Dublin, Ireland; *Int'l*, pg. 152

Himes, John W., V.P.-Investor Rels.--Du Pont (E.I. Du Pont De Nemours & Co.), Wilmington, DE; *U.S. Public*, pg. 530

Himes, Susan, Corp. Sec.--Standard Pacific Corp., Costa Mesa, CA; *U.S. Public*, pg. 1503

Hine, John, Mgr.-Corp. Affairs--Pacific Dunlop Limited, Melbourne, Australia; *Int'l*, pg. 1021

Hinrichs, Jim, Dir.-Investor Rels.--Merck & Co., Inc., Whitehouse Station, NJ; *U.S. Public*, pg. 1090

Hintz, Charles B., Treas.--Morgan Stanley Group Inc., New York, NY; *U.S. Public*, pg. 1132

Hinze, David H., V.P.-Corp. Commun.--Outsource International, Deerfield Beach, FL; *U.S. Public*, pg. 1236

Hladowicz, John, Dir.-Investor Relations--Corel Corporation, Ottawa, Canada; *Int'l*, pg. 331

Hobbs, Laura E., Mgr.-Investor Rels.--Southwest Gas Corporation, Las Vegas, NV; *U.S. Public*, pg. 1493

Hobor, Nancy A., V.P.-Commun. & Investor Rels.--Morton International Inc., Chicago, IL; *U.S. Public*, pg. 1134

Hobson, Holly, Dir.-Inv. Rels.--First Commerce Corporation, New Orleans, LA; *U.S. Public*, pg. 629

Hockenhull, Alexandra, Dir.-Corp. Communications--Medeva PLC, London, United Kingdom; *Int'l*, pg. 852

Hodges, Cheryl D., Sr. V.P., Sec. & Dir. Inv. Rels.--Omnicare, Inc., Covington, KY; *U.S. Public*, pg. 1223

Hoey, Peter E., Mng. Dir.-Investor Rels.--Financial Security Assurance Holdings Ltd., New York, NY; *U.S. Public*, pg. 622

Hoffman, Ronald S., Chief Fin. Officer & Sec.--Nantucket Industries, Inc., Melville, NY; *U.S. Public*, pg. 1151

Hohm, Dale J., V.P.-Fin. & Sec.--Numac Energy Inc., Calgary, Canada; *Int'l*, pg. 990

Holden, Michael J., Chief Fin. Officer--The Pep Boys-Manny, Moe & Jack, Philadelphia, PA; *U.S. Public*, pg. 1276

Holland, Jim D., Chief Fin. Officer, Sr. V.P. & Treas.--CMI Corporation, Oklahoma City, OK; *U.S. Public*, pg. 278

Holley, Norma B., Dir.-Investor Sls. & Opers.--Associates Financial Services Corporation, Dallas, TX; *U.S. Public*, pg. 663

Hollinger, William R., V.P. & Controller--Kaufman and Broad Home Corporation, Los Angeles, CA; *U.S. Public*, pg. 944

Hollister, Jeanne M., V.P.-Investor Rels.--Aetna Inc., Hartford, CT; *U.S. Public*, pg. 26

Holloway, Jim, Controller--Liqui-Box Corporation, Worthington, OH; *U.S. Public*, pg. 1000

Holmes, David, Dir.-Corp. Resources--British Airways PLC, London, United Kingdom; *Int'l*, pg. 218

Honzl, John J., Chief Fin. Officer & V.P.--Scicom Data Services, Ltd., Minnetonka, MN; *U.S. Private*, pg. 975

Hood, Elizabeth, Dir.-Investor Rels.--United Biscuits (Holdings) Plc, West Drayton, United Kingdom; *Int'l*, pg. 1442

Hoover, Rose, Sec. & Legal Asst.--Ampco-Pittsburgh Corporation, Pittsburgh, PA; *U.S. Public*, pg. 103

Hopkins, Tammy, Investor Rels.--The Sports Authority Inc., Fort Lauderdale, FL; *U.S. Public*, pg. 1499

Hopwood, Jim, Dir.-Fin.--Wickes Inc., Vernon Hills, IL; *U.S. Public*, pg. 1391

Horn, Randall, Dir.-Investor Rels. & Asst. Sec.--NICOR Inc., Naperville, IL; *U.S. Public*, pg. 1182

Horne, Jack, Mgr.-Investor Rels.--Edison International, Rosemead, CA; *U.S. Public*, pg. 564

Horswill, Douglas H., V.P.-Environ. & Corp. Affairs--Cominco, Ltd., Vancouver, Canada; *Int'l*, pg. 307

Horvat, Peter D., Chief Fin. Officer, V.P., Treas. & Sec.--Lenape Forge, Inc., West Chester, PA; *U.S. Private*, pg. 659

Hoskins, John M., V.P. & Treas.--Tennessee Valley Authority, Knoxville, TN; *U.S. Public*, pg. 1580

Hostler, William F., Sr. V.P.-Individual Mktg.--The Vanguard Group, Inc., Valley Forge, PA; *U.S. Private*, pg. 1133

Hotarek, Brian W., Chief Fin. Officer & Exec. V.P.--The Stop & Shop Companies, Inc., Quincy, MA; *Int'l*, pg. 750

Hough, Elizabeth A., Mgr.-Investor Rels.--The Smithfield Companies, Inc., Portsmouth, VA; *U.S. Public*, pg. 1479

Houle, David A., Chief Fin. Officer, Exec. V.P. & Treas.--Pacific Century Financial Corporation, Honolulu, HI; *U.S. Public*, pg. 1248

Houseknecht, Kenneth, Dir.-Investor Rels.--Gibraltar Steel Corp., Buffalo, NY; *U.S. Public*, pg. 742

Houseman, C., Mgr.-Investor Rels.--Loehmann's, Inc., Bronx, NY; *U.S. Public*, pg. 1010

Hovanec, Robert M., V.P. & Treas.--T.W. Phillips Gas and Oil Co., Butler, PA; *U.S. Private*, pg. 862

Howard, Rudy C., CPA, Chief Fin. Officer, V.P.-Fin., Treas. & Sec.--Pharmaceutical Product Development, Inc., Wilmington, NC; *U.S. Public*, pg. 1285

Howarth, Jack, Mgr.-Investor Rels.--Warner-Lambert Company, Morris Plains, NJ; *U.S. Public*, pg. 1738

Howe, Everett, V.P.-Investor Rels.--The Gillette Company, Boston, MA; *U.S. Public*, pg. 743

Hoy, Patrick, Chief Fin. Officer & V.P.--Pacesetter Corporation, Omaha, NE; *U.S. Private*, pg. 830

Hubbs, Thomas W., V.P. & Chief of Staff--VeriFone, Inc., Redwood City, CA; *U.S. Public*, pg. 815

Hubler, Sherry Winn, V.P.-Investor Rels.--NationsBank South, Atlanta, GA; *U.S. Public*, pg. 1163

Hudson, John, V.P.-Investor Rels.--Parametric Technology Corporation, Waltham, MA; *U.S. Public*, pg. 1257

Huffman, Charles P., Chief Fin. Officer, V.P. & Treas.--Mobile Gas Service Corp., Mobile, AL; *U.S. Public*, pg. 1120

Huffman, Kenneth J., V.P.-Investor Rels.--Occidental Petroleum Corporation, Los Angeles, CA; *U.S. Public*, pg. 1210

Hughes, Brian J., V.P.-Investments--Preferred Risk Mutual Insurance, West Des Moines, IA; *U.S. Private*, pg. 880

Hughes, Caroline, Dir.-Investor Rels.--Electronic Arts, San Mateo, CA; *U.S. Public*, pg. 569

Hughes, Shawn, Controller--Perryton Equity, Perryton, TX; *U.S. Private*, pg. 855

Hughes, Steve, Investor Rels.--FDX Corporation, Memphis, TN; *U.S. Public*, pg. 603

Hughes, Tom, Dir.-Investor Rels.--Columbia Energy Group, Reston, VA; *U.S. Public*, pg. 402

Hughes, W. Alan, Treas.--Fleischli Oil Company, Inc., Cheyenne, WY; *U.S. Private*, pg. 410

Humphries, Nancy C., Exec. Dir.-Investor Rels.--BellSouth Corporation, Atlanta, GA; *U.S. Public*, pg. 207

Hunley, Randy, Coord.-Investor Rels.--Central Parking Corp., Nashville, TN; *U.S. Public*, pg. 326

Hunnicutt, Donald P., Controller & Sec.--Graphic Industries, Inc., Atlanta, GA; *U.S. Public*, pg. 1735

Hunt, Bill, Sr. V.P.-Client Relations--Total System Services, Inc., Columbus, GA; *U.S. Public*, pg. 1550

Hunt, Marcus W., Dir.-Investor Rels.--Thiokol Corporation, Ogden, UT; *U.S. Public*, pg. 1596

Hunt, Mike, Intl. Controller--Griffin Corporation, Valdosta, GA; *U.S. Private*, pg. 480

Hurley, Sandra, V.P.-Indus. Rels.--Frequency Engineering Laboratories, Farmingdale, NJ; *U.S. Private*, pg. 427

Hurwitz, A. Richard, V.P.-Corp. Communications--Atlantis Plastic, Inc., Atlanta, GA; *U.S. Public*, pg. 145

Husband, Mark W., Staff V.P.-Investor Rels.--The Williams Companies, Inc., Tulsa, OK; *U.S. Public*, pg. 1769

Hutaserani, Krisda, Sr. V.P.--Siam City Bank Public Company Limited, Bangkok, Thailand; *Int'l*, pg. 1239

Hyde, Susan C., Mgr.-Investor Rels. & Asst. Sec.--W.P. Carey & Co., Inc., New York, NY; *U.S. Private*, pg. 209

Hyland, James J., V.P.-Investor Rels.--Comdisco, Inc., Rosemont, IL; *U.S. Public*, pg. 407

Hyre, John, Mgr.-Corp. Rels.--Roadway Express, Inc., Akron, OH; *U.S. Public*, pg. 1392

Iacovetti, Benedict J., Treas.--American Travellers Corporation, Bensalem, PA; *U.S. Public*, pg. 433

Igaki, Stan, Mgr.-Investor Rels.--Matsushita Electric Corporation of America, Secaucus, NJ; *Int'l*, pg. 847

Imamura, Kyozo, Dir.-Investor Rels.--Ishihara Sangyo Kaisha, Ltd., Osaka, Japan; *Int'l*, pg. 689

Imhoff, Herbert F., Chm. Bd. & Chief Exec. Officer--General Employment Enterprises, Inc., Oak Brook Terrace, IL; *U.S. Public*, pg. 714

Ingalls, Harold W., Chief Fin. Officer & V.P.--LaRoche Industries Inc., Atlanta, GA; *U.S. Private*, pg. 651

Ingish, Steve, Dir.-Pub. Rels.--MFS WorldCom, Inc., Omaha, NE; *U.S. Public*, pg. 1779

Ingman, Richard W., Chief Fin. Officer & Exec. V.P.--Pentair, Inc., Saint Paul, MN; *U.S. Public*, pg. 1273

Ingoldsby, John, Dir.-Investor Rels.--Palomar Medical Technologies, Lexington, MA; *U.S. Public*, pg. 1255

Inker, Emrys, Mgr.-Pub. Rels.--Weir Group PLC, Glasgow, United Kingdom; *Int'l*, pg. 1488

Itkin, Lawrence, Treas.--Furniture Consultants, New York, NY; *U.S. Public*, pg. 1686

Iverson, F. Kenneth, Chm. Bd.--Nucor Corporation, Charlotte, NC; *U.S. Public*, pg. 1205

Ivy, Conway G., V.P.-Corp. Plng. & Devel.--The Sherwin-Williams Company, Cleveland, OH; *U.S. Public*, pg. 1465

Jackson, Cindy, Mgr.-Investor Rels.--American Eco Corporation, Toronto, Canada; *Int'l*, pg. 73

Jackson, Janice, Mgr.-Investor Rels.--J. Alexanders Corporation, Nashville, TN; *U.S. Public*, pg. 40

Jackson, Peter, Grp. Mgr.-Communications--Royal & Sun Alliance Insurance Group plc, London, United Kingdom; *Int'l*, pg. 1130

Jackson, Ronald C., Asst. Comptroller & Dir.-Investor Rels.--Regions Financial Corporation, Birmingham, AL; *U.S. Public*, pg. 1371

Jackson, Wayne, Dir.-Corp. Communications & Investor Rels.--GRC International, Inc., Vienna, VA; *U.S. Public*, pg. 695

Jacob, Terry, Exec. Assst.--Inacom Corp., Omaha, NE; *U.S. Public*, pg. 873

Jacobson, Paul E., Dir.-Communications--Ascent Entertainment Group, Inc., Denver, CO; *U.S. Public*, pg. 138

Jaffe, Robert, Dir.-Corp. Commun.--IVAX Corporation, Miami, FL; *U.S. Public*, pg. 914

James, C.B., Dir.-Investors Rels.--Grand Metropolitan Plc, London, United Kingdom; *Int'l*, pg. 408

James, Catherine B., Chief Fin. Officer--Strategic Distribution Inc., Bensalem, PA; *U.S. Public*, pg. 1523

James, Donald W., V.P. & Sec.--B.M.J. Financial Corp., Bordentown, NJ; *U.S. Public*, pg. 1528

Jameson, Joyce, Sr. Investor Rels. Rep.--Allergan, Inc., Irvine, CA; *U.S. Public*, pg. 46

Jani, Rosana, Mgr.-Pub. Affairs--Liang Court Holdings Ltd., Singapore, Singapore; *Int'l*, pg. 807

Janikies, William N., Chief Oper. Officer--Jan-Co., Inc., Cranston, RI; *U.S. Private*, pg. 581

Janke, Kenneth S., Jr., Sr. V.P.-Investor Rels.--AFLAC Incorporated, Columbus, GA; *U.S. Public*, pg. 28

Japha, Daniel S., Gen. Counsel-Corp., Sec. & Dir.-Investor Rels.--M.D.C. Holdings, Inc., Denver, CO; *U.S. Public*, pg. 1025

Jarman, Mark W., Mgr.-Corp. Commun. & New Bus. Devel.--Dynamic Materials Corporation, Lafayette, CO; *U.S. Public*, pg. 539

Jarvis, Jean M., V.P.-Investor Rels.--The Times Mirror Company, Los Angeles, CA; *U.S. Public*, pg. 1615

Jarvis, Mark E., Chief Fin. Officer & Sr. V.P.--Tuesday Morning Corporation, Dallas, TX; *U.S. Public*, pg. 1644

Jasper, Ronald, Dir.-Investor Rels.--Becton Dickinson & Company, Franklin Lakes, NJ; *U.S. Public*, pg. 199

Javary, Manuel, V.P. & Treas.--CAP Gemini S.A., Paris, France; *Int'l*, pg. 263

Javier, Rey M., V.P.-Corp. Dev.--EEI Corporation, Manila, Philippines; *Int'l*, pg. 425

Jay, Dan, Pres., Chief Exec. Officer & Chief Fin. Officer--Campmor Inc., Upper Saddle River, NJ; *U.S. Private*, pg. 204

Jeanmougin, P., V.P.-Fin.--Mosler Inc., Hamilton, OH; *U.S. Private*, pg. 763

Jedicke, Victoria, Dir.-Investor Rels.--Tucson Electric Power Company, Tucson, AZ; *U.S. Public*, pg. 1670

Jeharajah, Neville, V.P.-Fin. Plng. & Investor Rels.--Baxter International Inc., Deerfield, IL; *U.S. Public*, pg. 196

Jenks, Kristen H., Dir.-Investor Rels.--Canandaigua Wine Company, Inc., Canandaigua, NY; *U.S. Public*, pg. 300

Jennings, Jeanne, Asst. V.P.-Investor & Govt. Rels.--Frontier Insurance Group, Inc., Rock Hill, NY; *U.S. Public*, pg. 684

Jensen, Kenneth L., Sr. V.P.-Corp. Devel. & Investor Rels.--Johns Manville Corporation, Denver, CO; *U.S. Public*, pg. 927

Jensen, Lynne, Mgr.-Investor Rels.--Newhawk Gold Mines LTD., Vancouver, Canada; *U.S. Public*, pg. 833

Jenter, Juergen, Mgr.-Press--Richard Hirschmann GmbH & Co., Neckartenzlingen, Germany; *Int'l*, pg. 1108

Jessick, David R., Chief Fin. Officer & Sr. V.P.-Fin.--Fred Meyer Stores, Portland, OR; *U.S. Public*, pg. 1103

Jessie, Janelle M., Asst. V.P. & Dir.-Adv. & Pub. Rels.--Chemed Corporation, Cincinnati, OH; *U.S. Public*, pg. 343

Jeub, Michael L., Chief Fin. Officer, Sr. V.P. & Treas.--Jenny Craig, Inc., La Jolla, CA; *U.S. Public*, pg. 926

Jewett, Robert William, Sr. V.P., Gen. Counsel & Sec.--Hooper Holmes Corporation, Basking Ridge, NJ; *U.S. Public*, pg. 835

Jewett, S., Chief Fin. Officer--Amplicon, Inc., Santa Ana, CA; *U.S. Public*, pg. 104

Jilbaum, Harvey, Mgr.-Opers.--Triumph Pet Industries, Inc., Warwick, NY; *U.S. Private*, pg. 1104

Johnasen, Renee, Dir.-Investor Rels.--Thomas & Betts Corporation, Memphis, TN; *U.S. Public*, pg. 1597

Johns, John D., Pres. & Chief Oper. Officer--Protective Life Corporation, Birmingham, AL; *U.S. Public*, pg. 1336

Johnsen, Scott, Mgr.-Investor Rels.--Mallinckrodt Inc., Saint Louis, MO; *U.S. Public*, pg. 1039

Johnson, Avis J., Dir.-Investor Rels.--Communications Systems, Inc., Hector, MN; *U.S. Public*, pg. 415

Johnson, Barbara, V.P.-Shareholder Rels.--Bacardi Limited, Pembroke, Bermuda; *Int'l*, pg. 131

Johnson, Brent E., V.P. & Controller--Mercantile Bank of Iowa, Des Moines, IA; *U.S. Public*, pg. 1087

Johnson, D. Lee, V.P.-Admin. & Investor Rels.--Dep Corporation, Rancho Dominguez, CA; *U.S. Public*, pg. 500

Johnson, Dale H., Chief Fin. Officer--Medical Graphics Corp., Saint Paul, MN; *U.S. Public*, pg. 1080

Johnson, Gerard G., Chief Fin. Officer & V.P.-Fin.--VF Corporation, Wyomissing, PA; *U.S. Public*, pg. 1702

Johnson, J. Fred, Chief Fin. Officer, Exec. V.P. & Treas.--Piccadilly Cafeterias, Inc., Baton Rouge, LA; *U.S. Public*, pg. 1294

Johnson, J. Keith, Mgr.-Investor Rels.--Mississippi Chemical Corporation, Yazoo City, MS; *U.S. Public*, pg. 1117

Johnson, Jennie, Mgr.-Investor Rels.--Tokheim Corporation, Fort Wayne, IN; *U.S. Public*, pg. 1620

Johnson, Monica, Mgr.-Investor Rels.--Linear Technology Corp., Milpitas, CA; *U.S. Public*, pg. 1000

Johnson, P.J., Dir-Pub. Rels. & Adv.--Nomura Securities International, Inc., New York, NY; *Int'l*, pg. 956

Johnson, Richard M., Dir.-Investor Rels.--Hoechst Marion Roussel North America, Kansas City, MO; *Int'l*, pg. 625

Johnson, Susan, Dir.-Investor Rels.--Moog Incorporated, East Aurora, NY; *U.S. Public*, pg. 1127

Johnson, Susan Glatthorn, V.P.-Legal Svcs. & Admin.--Echelon International Corporation, Saint Petersburg, FL; *U.S. Public*, pg. 560

Johnson, Terrie-Ann, Mgr.-Investor Rels.--Lend Lease Corporation Limited, Sydney, Australia; *Int'l*, pg. 806

Johnson, Thomas D., Dir.-Investor Rels.--Blount International, Inc., Montgomery, AL; *U.S. Public*, pg. 237

Johnson, Thomas D., Dir.-Investor Rels.--Blount, Inc., Montgomery, AL; *U.S. Public*, pg. 238

Johnston, Malcolm, Corp. Sec.--Cannon Rubber Ltd., London, United Kingdom; *Int'l*, pg. 261

Johnston, Mary Lu, Mgr.-Investor Rels.--Kansas City Southern Industries, Inc., Kansas City, MO; *U.S. Public*, pg. 943

Jolley, James D., Exec. V.P.-Correspondent Banking Dept.--Magna Group, Inc., Saint Louis, MO; *U.S. Public*, pg. 1037

Jones Kane, M'Liss, Sr. V.P., Gen. Counsel & Corp. Sec.--Fidelity National Financial, Inc., Irvine, CA; *U.S. Public*, pg. 620

Jones, Ann, Mgr.-Investor Rels.--Rainbow Technologies, Inc., Irvine, CA; *U.S. Public*, pg. 1359

Jones, Benjamin, III, W., Exec. V.P.-Legal & Acq.--IRT Property Company, Atlanta, GA; *U.S. Public*, pg. 858

Jones, Christine M., V.P.-Stockholder Rels. & Sec.--Haverty Furniture Companies, Inc., Atlanta, GA; *U.S. Public*, pg. 799

Jones, Diane S., Mgr.-Corp. Rels. & Bus. Devel.--Westmoreland Coal Co., Colorado Springs, CO; *U.S. Public*, pg. 1761

Jones, John P., Dir.-Indus. Rels.--YSD Industries, Youngstown, OH; *U.S. Private*, pg. 1194

Jones, Maribeth, Dir.-Investor Rels.--Fairfield Communities, Inc., Little Rock, AR; *U.S. Public*, pg. 610

Jones, Michael F., V.P.-Opers. & Plng.--Homeowners Group, Inc., Sunrise, FL; *U.S. Public*, pg. 832

Jones, Reginald, Chief Fin. Officer & Sr. V.P.-Fin.--Hycor Biomedical, Inc., Irvine, CA; *U.S. Public*, pg. 851

Jones, Richard, Investor Rels. Dir.--General Physics Corporation, Columbia, MD; *U.S. Public*, pg. 694

Jones, Roy, Mgr.-Corp. Commun.--MDIS Group plc, Hemel Hempstead, United Kingdom; *Int'l*, pg. 826

Jones, Ted C., Mgr.-Investor Rels.--Stewart Information Services Corporation, Houston, TX; *U.S. Public*, pg. 1518

Joseph, Randy M., Chief Fin. Officer, V.P. & Treas.--Advance Ross Corporation, Chicago, IL; *U.S. Public*, pg. 320

Josis, Nicole, Head-Investor Rels.--Bank Brussels Lambert, Brussels, Belgium; *Int'l*, pg. 146

Juanarena, Douglas B., Pres. & Chief Exec. Officer--Pressure Systems, Inc., Hampton, VA; *Int'l*, pg. 1130

Junkunc, Charles A., Chief Fin. Officer & V.P.--Brown & Sharpe Manufacturing Company, North Kingstown, RI; *U.S. Public*, pg. 260

Jurkoshek, Jack, Mgr.-Investor Rels.--Oceaneering International, Inc., Houston, TX; *U.S. Public*, pg. 1211

Jusco, Gerald M., V.P.-Corp. & Industry Rels.--ITT Automotive, Inc., Auburn Hills, MI; *U.S. Public*, pg. 859

Kacin, William L., Pres. & Chief Exec. Officer--Met-Pro Corporation, Harleysville, PA; *U.S. Public*, pg. 1100

Kahn, Susan, Dir.-Investor Rels.--Dayton Hudson Corporation, Minneapolis, MN; *U.S. Public*, pg. 489

Kaiser, Patrick, Head-Corp. Commun.--Danzas Holding Ltd., Basel, Switzerland; *Int'l*, pg. 382

Kakihara, Akira, Dir. & Gen. Mgr.--The Tokio Marine & Fire Insurance Company, Ltd., Tokyo, Japan; *Int'l*, pg. 1391

Kalanges, Nick, Chief Fin. Officer--Pacific Coast Building Products Inc., Sacramento, CA; *U.S. Private*, pg. 830

Kalish, Bernard, Chm. Bd. & Chief Exec. Officer--Lawson Products, Inc., Des Plaines, IL; *U.S. Public*, pg. 980

Kalmar, Janice, Dir.-Corp. Commun.--Grubb & Ellis Company, Northbrook, IL; *U.S. Public*, pg. 767

Kamaraskus, Tammy, Dir.-Investor Rels.--Andrew Corporation, Orland Park, IL; *U.S. Public*, pg. 112

Kamins, Aaron J., Chief Fin. Officer--Accurate Perforating Co., Chicago, IL; *U.S. Private*, pg. 12

Kane, Charles F., Chief Fin. Officer & V.P.-Fin.--Ardent Software, Inc., Westborough, MA; *U.S. Public*, pg. 129

Kane, Francis J., V.P.-Investor Rels. & Treas.--Cyprus Amax Minerals Company, Englewood, CO; *U.S. Public*, pg. 470

Kane, Frank T., Chief Fin. Officer & V.P.-Fin.--Chromcraft Revington, Inc., Delphi, IN; *U.S. Public*, pg. 352
Kangas, Martti E., Dir.-Investor Rels.--Rayrock Yellowknife Resources Inc., Toronto, Canada; *Int'l*, pg. 1089
Kankel, Keith V., V.P.-Fin., Treas. & Sec.--Patrick Industries Inc., Elkhart, IN; *U.S. Public*, pg. 1264
Kantz, Phil, Pres. & Chief Exec. Officer--Tab Products Co., Palo Alto, CA; *U.S. Public*, pg. 1559
Kaplan, Carol, Dir.-Investor Rels.--Sigma Designs, Inc., Fremont, CA; *U.S. Public*, pg. 1472
Kaplan, David E., Mgr.-Investor Rels.--PG&E Corporation, San Francisco, CA; *U.S. Public*, pg. 1240
Kaplan, Kenneth P., Chief Fin. Officer & V.P.--Regal-Beloit Corporation, Beloit, WI; *U.S. Public*, pg. 1370
Kaplan, Samuel, Pres., Chief Exec. Officer, Sec. & Dir.-Sls. & Pur.--Admiration Hosiery Mills, Inc., Charlotte, NC; *U.S. Private*, pg. 528
Kaprinski, Joan, Supvr.-Investor Rels.--Long Island Lighting Company, Hicksville, NY; *U.S. Public*, pg. 1013
Karida, Raija, V.P.-Investor Rels.--Cultor Ltd., Helsinki, Finland; *Int'l*, pg. 349
Karklins, George J., V.P.-Investor & Shareholder Rels.--CoreStates Financial Corp., Philadelphia, PA; *U.S. Public*, pg. 446
Karlsson, Stefan, Mgr.-Investor Rels.--AB Volvo, Goteborg, Sweden; *Int'l*, pg. 1476
Karsk, Bruce C., V.P.-Fin., Treas. & Sec.--Lindsay Manufacturing Company, Lindsay, NE; *U.S. Public*, pg. 999
Kasper, Albert, V.P.-Fin. & Controller--Savage Arms Inc., Westfield, MA; *U.S. Private*, pg. 968
Kasper, Kevin, V.P.-Corp. Communications--Fiserv, Inc., Brookfield, WI; *U.S. Public*, pg. 647
Kato, Norio, Gen. Mgr.-Investor Rels.--Cosmo Oil Co., Ltd., Tokyo, Japan; *Int'l*, pg. 335
Katz, Neil, Dir.-H.R. & Investor Rels.--Curtis Mathes Holding Corp., Dallas, TX; *U.S. Public*, pg. 1057
Kauffman, Emma Jo, Asst. Treas.--AutoZone, Inc., Memphis, TN; *U.S. Public*, pg. 150
Kaufman, Jack, Chief Fin. Officer--The Hain Food Group Inc., Uniondale, NY; *U.S. Public*, pg. 774
Kaufman, Jennifer, Dir.-Opers.--Catalina Lighting, Inc., Miami, FL; *U.S. Public*, pg. 314
Kaufmann, Mark, Assoc. Dir.-Strategic Plng. & Investor Rels.--MedImmune, Inc., Gaithersburg, MD; *U.S. Public*, pg. 1081
Kautz, Robert F., Pres. & Chief Fin. Officer--Koo Koo Roo, Inc., Los Angeles, CA; *U.S. Public*, pg. 966
Kawamoto, Edwina H., Dir.-Investor Rels.--Hawaiian Electric Industries, Inc., Honolulu, HI; *U.S. Public*, pg. 799
Kawamoto, Edwina H., Dir.-Investor Rels.--Hawaiian Electric Company, Inc., Honolulu, HI; *U.S. Public*, pg. 800
Kawamura, Kajiro, Mng. Dir.--Hosokawa Micron Corporation, Osaka, Japan; *Int'l*, pg. 635
Kay, Bruce A., V.P.-Investor Rels.--Markel Corporation, Glen Allen, VA; *U.S. Public*, pg. 1046
Kay, Lawrence Y., Dir.-Investor Rels.--Istituto Mobiliare Italiano, Rome, Italy; *Int'l*, pg. 692
Kay, Steven R., Chief Fin. Officer & Sr. V.P.--Amwest Insurance Group, Inc., Calabasas, CA; *U.S. Public*, pg. 106
Kaz, Noma, Dir.-Pub. Rels.--Pacific Crest Capital, Inc., Agoura Hills, CA; *U.S. Public*, pg. 1248
Keane, David L., V.P.-Fin./Admin. & Treas.--Penobscot Shoe Company, Old Town, ME; *U.S. Public*, pg. 1273
Kechejian, John, Dir.-Investor Rels.--ABB Asea Brown Boveri (Holding) Ltd., Zurich, Switzerland; *Int'l*, pg. 1
Keesee, April, Dir.-Investor Rels.--First Colony Life Insurance Co., Lynchburg, VA; *U.S. Public*, pg. 711
Kelley, John B., V.P.-Investor Rels.--Alexander & Baldwin, Inc., Honolulu, HI; *U.S. Public*, pg. 39
Kelley, Marian Herbst, Dir.-Pub. Rels.--Tracor, Inc., Austin, TX; *U.S. Public*, pg. 1627
Kelly, David A., V.P. & Treas.--Borden, Inc., Columbus, OH; *U.S. Private*, pg. 157
Kelly, Dennis P., Chief Fin. Officer & V.P.-Fin.--Oregon Metallurgical Corporation, Albany, OR; *U.S. Public*, pg. 43
Kelly, Kathy, Mgr.-Investor Rels.--The Kroger Co., Cincinnati, OH; *U.S. Public*, pg. 967
Kelly, Sharon, Dir.-Investor Rels.--Radius Inc., Sunnyvale, CA; *U.S. Public*, pg. 1358
Kennedy, J. Donald, Chief Fin. Officer & Exec. V.P.-Fin. & Admin.--King Kullen Grocery Co., Inc., Westbury, NY; *U.S. Private*, pg. 621
Kennedy, John, Chief Fin. Officer, Sr. V.P. & Treas.--Smith International, Inc., Houston, TX; *U.S. Public*, pg. 1478
Kennedy, Kara, Dir.-Investor Rels.--Ciber, Inc., Englewood, CO; *U.S. Public*, pg. 356
Kennedy, Quentin J., Exec. V.P. & Sec.--Imperial Bondware Corp., Montvale, NJ; *U.S. Public*, pg. 903
Kennedy, Russell M., Grp. Gen. Mgr.-Fin. & Inv. Rels.--Sasol Limited, Johannesburg, South Africa; *Int'l*, pg. 1196
Kenney, Bertha, Dir.-Investor Rels.--NextHealth Inc., Tucson, AZ; *U.S. Public*, pg. 1181
Kenny, Katharine, V.P.-Investor Rels.--Ruddick Corporation, Charlotte, NC; *U.S. Public*, pg. 1412
Kenny, Katharine W., Asst. V.P.-Investor Rels.--Pillowtex Corporation, Dallas, TX; *U.S. Public*, pg. 1296
Kent, Gaston, Dir.-Investor Rels.--Northrop Grumman Corporation, Los Angeles, CA; *U.S. Public*, pg. 1197
Ker, Alan S., Chief Fin. Officer, Treas. & Sec.--Universal Standard Healthcare, Inc., Southfield, MI; *U.S. Public*, pg. 1697
Kerr, Mary, Div. V.P.-Investor Rels.--The Bon Ton Stores, Inc., York, PA; *U.S. Public*, pg. 244
Kerr, R. A., Sr. V.P.-Underwriting--Potomac Insurance Co. of Illinois, Philadelphia, PA; *Int'l*, pg. 543
Kerrigan, Juanita I., V.P. & Sec.--Avatar Holdings Inc., Coral Gables, FL; *U.S. Public*, pg. 151
Kersey, Oonagh, Mgr.-Investor Rels.--DVI, Inc., Doylestown, PA; *U.S. Public*, pg. 476
Kessel, Silvia, Chief Fin. Officer, Exec. V.P. & Treas.--Metromedia International Group, Inc., East Rutherford, NJ; *U.S. Public*, pg. 1102
Kessler, Richard J., Chief Fin. Officer & V.P.-Fin. & Devel.--Oglebay Norton Company, Cleveland, OH; *U.S. Public*, pg. 1213
Keszler, Charles J., V.P.-Fin. & Corp. Rels. & Treas.--Lone Star Technologies, Inc., Dallas, TX; *U.S. Public*, pg. 1012
Key, Robert F., Treas.--The Seibels Bruce Group, Inc., Columbia, SC; *U.S. Public*, pg. 1453
Kiehnle, Robert C., Chief Fin. Officer, Exec. V.P. & Asst. Sec.--Fresh America Corp., Dallas, TX; *U.S. Public*, pg. 681
Kiernan, Mary, Acct. Asst.--Norstan, Inc., Plymouth, MN; *U.S. Public*, pg. 1192
Kilpatrick, Patricia, Mgr.-Indus. Rels.--Met-Coil Systems Corp., Cedar Rapids, IA; *U.S. Public*, pg. 1099
Kimball, Carroll E., Dir.-Investor Rels.--First American Corporation, Nashville, TN; *U.S. Public*, pg. 624
Kimiey, Karla J., Dir.-Investor Rels.--Vista Gold Corp., Denver, CO; *U.S. Public*, pg. 1723
Kindl, Nancy A., Chief Fin. Officer, Treas., Controller & Sec.--Portec, Inc., Lake Forest, IL; *U.S. Public*, pg. 1317
King, James C., Sr. V.P. & Sec.--BHA Group Holdings Inc., Kansas City, MO; *U.S. Public*, pg. 161
King, Jill, Investor Rels. Coord.--Alumax Inc., Atlanta, GA; *U.S. Public*, pg. 59
King, Thomas S., V.P.-Investments--American Family Mutual Insurance Co., Madison, WI; *U.S. Private*, pg. 53
Kinley, Donald D., V.P. & Treas.--First Commerce Bancshares, Inc., Lincoln, NE; *U.S. Public*, pg. 629
Kinoshita, Hajime, Mgr.-Inv. Rels., Legal & Admin. Div.--NEC Corporation, Tokyo, Japan; *Int'l*, pg. 899
Kinsey, Lisa, Mgr.-Investor Rels.--Egghead, Inc., Liberty Lake, WA; *U.S. Public*, pg. 566
Kinsey, Stephanie, Mgr.-Investor Rels.--Scientific-Atlanta, Inc., Norcross, GA; *U.S. Public*, pg. 1443
Kinzer, Donald M., V.P. & Chief Investments Officer--Shenandoah Life Insurance Company, Roanoke, VA; *U.S. Private*, pg. 992
Kinzler, Alexander C., V.P. & Sec.--Barnwell Industries, Inc., Honolulu, HI; *U.S. Public*, pg. 190
Kirbie, Ellis, V.P., Treas. & Asst. Sec.--Smith Environmental Technologies Corp., Plymouth Meeting, PA; *U.S. Public*, pg. 1477
Kirby, Kerry J., Chief Fin. Officer & Exec. V.P.-Fin.--TruServ Corporation, Chicago, IL; *U.S. Private*, pg. 1108
Kirhofer, Kimberly A., Sec.--Chicago Rivet & Machine Company, Naperville, IL; *U.S. Public*, pg. 348
Kirkendall, Robert E., Sec. & Asst. Treas.--The Gorman-Rupp Company, Mansfield, OH; *U.S. Public*, pg. 754
Kirkpatrick, James A., Dir. Investor Relations--Nationsbank/Tennessee, Nashville, TN; *U.S. Public*, pg. 1163
Kirshenbaum, William, V.P. & Treas.--New Plan Realty Trust, New York, NY; *U.S. Public*, pg. 1172
Kish, Cathy S., Dir.-Investor Rels.--Olympic Steel Inc., Cleveland, OH; *U.S. Public*, pg. 1221
Kisleiko, Irene M., Asst. Sec.--Quaker Chemical Corporation, Conshohocken, PA; *U.S. Public*, pg. 1346
Kitamuru, Mr., Mgr.-Corp. Commun.--Descente Ltd., Osaka, Japan; *Int'l*, pg. 395
Kitchen, Steven L., Chief Fin. Officer & Exec. V.P.--Western Resources, Inc., Topeka, KS; *U.S. Public*, pg. 1759
Kitterman, Alan, Mgr.-Investor Rels.--Cannon Express Inc., Springdale, AR; *U.S. Public*, pg. 301
Klajbor, Jerry, Chief Fin. Officer, V.P. & Sec.--Stanford Telecommunications, Sunnyvale, CA; *U.S. Public*, pg. 1508
Klatt, Roger J., Chief Fin. Officer, Sr. V.P., Treas. & Asst. Sec.--Gundle/SLT Environmental, Inc., Houston, TX; *U.S. Public*, pg. 769
Klaus, Robert, Pres. & Chief Exec. Officer--Klaus Radio Inc., Peoria, IL; *U.S. Private*, pg. 625
Kleemann, Stephen, Dir.-Investor Rels.--Cavco Industries, Inc., Phoenix, AZ; *U.S. Public*, pg. 323
Kleiber, Denis, Head-Investor Rels.--Credit Lyonnais S.A., Paris, France; *Int'l*, pg. 343
Kleiber, Robert, Dir.-Investor Rels.--Bemis Company, Inc., Minneapolis, MN; *U.S. Public*, pg. 210
Kleiber, Robert F., Dir.-Investor Rels.--National Computer Systems, Eden Prairie, MN; *U.S. Public*, pg. 1155
Klein, Douglas P., Chief Fin. Officer, V.P., Sec. & Treas.--Go-Video, Inc., Scottsdale, AZ; *U.S. Public*, pg. 748
Klein, Kathy, V.P.-Corp. Communications--Federal Realty Investment Trust, Rockville, MD; *U.S. Public*, pg. 616
Klein, Richard B., Sr. V.P.-Investor Rels.--Corning Incorporated, Corning, NY; *U.S. Public*, pg. 448
Klevecz, Lu Ann, Sec. & Dir.-Corp. Commun. & Investor Rels.--nVIEW Corporation, Newport News, VA; *U.S. Public*, pg. 1206
Kline, George I., Mgr.-Investor Services--PP&L Resources, Allentown, PA; *U.S. Public*, pg. 1244
Klinger, Ernest T., Chief Fin. Officer, V.P.-Fin. & Admin.--Arden Group, Inc., Los Angeles, CA; *U.S. Public*, pg. 128
Kloha, Pam, Asst. V.P.-Corp. Communications--Deposit Guaranty Corp., Jackson, MS; *U.S. Public*, pg. 500
Klosterman, Ronald, Chief Fin. Officer, V.P.-Fin. & Sec.--Flexsteel Industries, Inc., Dubuque, IA; *U.S. Public*, pg. 653
Knapp, Kristin N., Investor Rels. Admin.--Consumers Water Company, Portland, ME; *U.S. Public*, pg. 438
Knee, Peggy, Mgr.-Investor Rels.--British Telecommunications plc, London, United Kingdom; *Int'l*, pg. 222
Knees, Donna, Mgr.-Compensation & Benefits--Mitsubishi Silicon America, Salem, OR; *Int'l*, pg. 875
Kneisel, Frank, Sr. V.P.-Fin.--Champion International Corp., Stamford, CT; *U.S. Public*, pg. 333
Knicely, Howard V., Exec. V.P.-Human Resources & Communications--TRW Inc., Cleveland, OH; *U.S. Public*, pg. 1558
Knief, Wallace W., Mgr.-Corp. Commun. & Investor Rels.--Blockbuster Entertainment Group, Dallas, TX; *U.S. Private*, pg. 775
Kniffen, Jan R., Sr. V.P. & Treas.--The May Department Stores Company, Saint Louis, MO; *U.S. Public*, pg. 1063
Kniskern, Pauline A., Chief Fin. Officer & Exec. V.P.--CD Products, Inc., New Providence, NJ; *U.S. Public*, pg. 276
Knoebel, Cindy, Dir.-Investor Rels.--VF Corporation, Wyomissing, PA; *U.S. Public*, pg. 1702
Knowles, Douglas, Dir.-Investor Rels.--Serologicals Corporation, Clarkston, GA; *U.S. Public*, pg. 1460
Knowles, Robert E., Chief Fin. Officer & Exec. V.P.--S & K Famous Brands, Inc., Glen Allen, VA; *U.S. Public*, pg. 1414
Knox, Sioban M., Asst. to Chief Fin. Officer--Urban Outfitters, Inc., Philadelphia, PA; *U.S. Public*, pg. 1700
Knutts, Kim, Mgr.-Investor Rels.--Commonwealth Industries, Inc., Louisville, KY; *U.S. Public*, pg. 415
Kobele, Robert S., Chief Fin. Officer & V.P.-Fin.--Sbarro, Inc., Commack, NY; *U.S. Public*, pg. 1435
Koch, Richard E., V.P.-Investor Rels.--Olin Corporation, Norwalk, CT; *U.S. Public*, pg. 1218
Koebel, Wayne R., Chief Fin. Officer, Exec. V.P., Treas. & Sec.--Shoreline Financial Corp., Benton Harbor, MI; *U.S. Public*, pg. 1467
Koella, Carl, Mgr.-Investor Rels.--Clayton Homes, Inc., Knoxville, TN; *U.S. Public*, pg. 382
Koeneman, Bradford W., Exec. V.P.-Investor Rels. & Mktg.--Magna Group, Inc., Saint Louis, MO; *U.S. Public*, pg. 1037
Koenig, Jeffrey H., V.P.-Fin., Controller & Treas.--Executive Risk, Inc., Simsbury, CT; *U.S. Public*, pg. 599
Koenig, Mark E., V.P.-Investor Rels.--Enron Corp., Houston, TX; *U.S. Public*, pg. 584
Koepke, Allen C., V.P.-Bus. Devel. & Internal Audit--Regal Ware, Inc., Kewaskum, WI; *U.S. Private*, pg. 917
Koepke, Charles, V.P.-Investor Rels.--Amoco Corporation, Chicago, IL; *U.S. Public*, pg. 101
Koerber, Dirk, V.P.-Corp. Communications, Investor Rels. & Civic Affairs--Western Atlas Inc., Houston, TX; *U.S. Public*, pg. 1757
Koleszar, Connie L., Dir.-Investor Rels.--Wabash National Corp., Lafayette, IN; *U.S. Public*, pg. 1730
Komejan, Maryam, Sr. V.P.-Corp. Admin. & Corp. Sec.--Donnelly Corporation, Holland, MI; *U.S. Public*, pg. 519
Koopman, Deborah L., V.P.-Pub. Affairs & Investor Rels.--Spiegel, Inc., Downers Grove, IL; *U.S. Public*, pg. 1498
Korab, John J., Jr., V.P.-Corp. Devel.--Isco, Inc., Lincoln, NE; *U.S. Public*, pg. 913
Korman, Leonard I., Partner--Korman Services, L.P., Trevose, PA; *U.S. Private*, pg. 632
Kornberg, Fred, Chm. Bd., Pres. & Chief Exec. Officer--Comtech Telecommunications Corp., Melville, NY; *U.S. Public*, pg. 425
Korus, Paul, Dir.-Investor Rels.--Apache Corporation, Houston, TX; *U.S. Public*, pg. 119
Koss, Michael J., Pres., Chief Exec., Oper. & Fin. Officer--Koss Corporation, Milwaukee, WI; *U.S. Public*, pg. 966
Kotkin, Jeffrey R., Dir.-Investor Rels.--Northeast Utilities, Berlin, CT; *U.S. Public*, pg. 1194
Kovalik, Diane, Dir.-Investor Rels.--Vail Resorts, Inc., Vail, CO; *U.S. Public*, pg. 1704
Kowalsky, Roger J., Chief Fin. Officer & Exec. V.P.-Fin.--Galoob Toys, Inc., South San Francisco, CA; *U.S. Public*, *pg. 698*
Kramer, Phillip D., Chief Fin. Officer, Sr. V.P. & Treas.--Plains Resources Inc., Houston, TX; *U.S. Public*, pg. 1307
Krampt, Stacy, Mgr.-Investor Rels.--Miami Subs Corporation, Fort Lauderdale, FL; *U.S. Public*, pg. 1103
Kraus, Norma J., V.P.-Human Resources & Investor Rels.--Volt Information Sciences, Inc., New York, NY; *U.S. Public*, pg. 1724
Krause, Carolyn F., Admin.-Investor Rels.--Plains Resources Inc., Houston, TX; *U.S. Public*, pg. 1307
Kready, Richard D., Dir.-Investor Rels.--Western Resources, Inc., Topeka, KS; *U.S. Public*, pg. 1759
Krejca, Jack E., Chief Fin. Officer, Treas. & Controller--Curran Group, Inc., Crystal Lake, IL; *U.S. Private*, pg. 297
Krenek, Wilfred, Chief Fin. Officer, V.P., Treas. & Sec.--Bettis Corporation, Waller, TX; *U.S. Public*, pg. 482
Kresl, Miles L., Jr., V.P.-Admin., Treas. & Corp. Sec.--Badger Paper Mills, Inc., Peshtigo, WI; *U.S. Public*, pg. 165
Krieger, Walter L., V.P.-Fin. Opers.--Liz Claiborne, Inc., New York, NY; *U.S. Public*, pg. 1005
Krietzberg, David, Treas. & Dir.-Fin.--Executone Information Systems, Inc., Milford, CT; *U.S. Public*, pg. 599
Kristapovich, Mary Jo, Dir.-Investor Rels.--D & N Financial Corporation, Hancock, MI; *U.S. Public*, pg. 472
Krul, Joseph, Chief Fin. Officer & Sr. V.P.--Standard Federal Bank, Troy, MI; *Int'l*, pg. 10
Kuchinski, Thaddeus G., Chief Fin. Officer & Treas.--Holstein Association USA, Inc., Brattleboro, VT; *U.S. Private*, pg. 536
Kuk, Kenneth U., V.P.-Investments--Northwestern National Life Insurance Co., Minneapolis, MN; *U.S. Public*, pg. 1375
Kunkel, Otto, V.P.-Fin., Investor Rels.--Logitech International SA, Morges, Switzerland; *Int'l*, pg. 815
Kupp, Julie, V.P.-Investor Rels.--Sterling Software, Inc., Dallas, TX; *U.S. Public*, pg. 1516
Kurty, Diana R., Chief Fin. Officer & V.P.-Fin.--IEC Electronics Corp., Newark, NY; *U.S. Public*, pg. 854
Kurtz, Larry, Dir.-Corp. Communications--Chiron Corporation, Emeryville, CA; *U.S. Public*, pg. 349
Kusher, J.M., Admin.-Pub. & Investor Rels.--Stepan Company, Northfield, IL; *U.S. Public*, pg. 1514
Kusyk, Ola, Mgr.-Corp. & Investor Rels. Projects--Spiegel, Inc., Downers Grove, IL; *U.S. Public*, pg. 1498
Kutchin, Jill Pollack, V.P.-Corp. Affairs & Clerk--Parlex Corporation, Methuen, MA; *U.S. Public*, pg. 1264
Kyle, Nancy R., Dir.-Investor Rels.--The Pep Boys-Manny, Moe & Jack, Philadelphia, PA; *U.S. Public*, pg. 1276
Kyriakou, Linda G., V.P.-Commun.--Sequa Corporation, New York, NY; *U.S. Public*, pg. 1458

Lacativa, Roslyn, Corp. Sec.--Presidential Realty Corporation, White Plains, NY; *U.S. Public*, pg. 1323

LaComb, Charlotte, Mgr.-Investor Rels.--Lands' End, Inc., Dodgeville, WI; *U.S. Public*, pg. 977

Laehy, Timothy P., V.P.-Corp. Fin. & Treas.--Leasing Solutions, Inc., San Jose, CA; *U.S. Public*, pg. 982

Laffoon, Polk, IV, V.P.-Corp. Rels.--Knight-Ridder, Inc., Miami, FL; *U.S. Public*, pg. 963

LaFlame, Gregory F., Mgr.-Investor Rels.--FirstEnergy Corp., Akron, OH; *U.S. Public*, pg. 644

Lafontaine, M., V.P. & Treas.--Kruger Inc., Montreal, Canada; *Int'l*, pg. 761

LaForte, Mario J., Chief Fin. Officer--Minyard Food Stores, Inc., Coppell, TX; *U.S. Private*, pg. 752

LaMore, Terry, Dir.-Investor Rels.--BP America Inc., Cleveland, OH; *Int'l*, pg. 220

Lamps, Christopher, V.P.-Corp. Affairs & Investor Rels.--Ares-Serono S.A., Geneva, Switzerland; *Int'l*, pg. 80

Land, Thomas K., Chief Fin. Officer, Sr. V.P. & Asst. Sec.--Santa Fe Gaming Corporation, Las Vegas, NV; *U.S. Public*, pg. 1432

Landers, Melvin, Dir.-Investor Rels.--TJ International, Inc., Boise, ID; *U.S. Public*, pg. 1556

Landis, Edgar D., Exec. V.P.-Fin.--CDI Corp., Philadelphia, PA; *U.S. Public*, pg. 276

Lane, Chana, Investor Rels.--Dallas Semiconductor Corporation, Dallas, TX; *U.S. Public*, pg. 478

Lane, Lynn L., V.P.-Investor Rels. & Treas.--Burlington Industries, Inc., Greensboro, NC; *U.S. Public*, pg. 268

Laney, Steven H., V.P.-Investor Rels.--Micron Electronics, Inc., Nampa, ID; *U.S. Public*, pg. 1105

Lang, Sherry, Dir.-Investor Rels.--The TJX Companies, Inc., Framingham, MA; *U.S. Public*, pg. 1556

Lang, Stephen R., V.P., Gen. Counsel & Sec.--Carter-Wallace, Inc., New York, NY; *U.S. Public*, pg. 309

Langer, Carol B., Chief Fin. Officer, V.P.-Investor Rels. & Treas.--LTX Corporation, Westwood, MA; *U.S. Public*, pg. 972

Langford, Thomas L., Chief Fin. Officer & Exec. V.P.--Stone & Webster, Incorporated, Boston, MA; *U.S. Public*, pg. 1519

Lanier, Thomas, Exec. V.P., Chief Fin. Officer & Sec.--Salem Carpet Mills, Inc., Winston Salem, NC; *U.S. Public*, pg. 1464

Lanning, Jeffrey S., Asst. V.P.-Fin.--Sentry Technology Corp., Hauppauge, NY; *U.S. Public*, pg. 1458

Lanz, Gregor, Dir.-Investor Rels.--Erste Bank der oesterreichischen Sparkassen AG, Vienna, Austria; *Int'l*, pg. 459

Lap, Ben, V.P.-Investor Rels.--ICN Pharmaceuticals, Inc., Costa Mesa, CA; *U.S. Public*, pg. 853

LaPlante, Larry E., V.P.-Fin. & Treas.--Maine Public Service Company, Presque Isle, ME; *U.S. Public*, pg. 1038

LaPorte, Joseph J., V.P.-Corp. Rels.--General Binding Corporation, Northbrook, IL; *U.S. Public*, pg. 707

Larkin, A. C., Sr. V.P.-Fin. & Investor Rels.--Foster's Brewing Group Limited, Southbank, Australia; *Int'l*, pg. 500

Larsen, Jens Steen, Head-Inv. Rels--Danisco A/S, Copenhagen, Denmark; *Int'l*, pg. 378

Larson, Carolyn, Admin. Asst.--Waters Instruments, Inc., Rochester, MN; *U.S. Public*, pg. 1745

Larson, Eric J., Sr. V.P. & Dir.-Investor Rels.--General Mills, Inc., Minneapolis, MN; *U.S. Public*, pg. 717

LaRusso, David V., Chief Fin. Officer, Sr. V.P.-Fin. & Treas.--ROHN Industries, Inc., Peoria, IL; *U.S. Public*, pg. 1404

Lascar, Jack, V.P.-Investor Rels.--Tenneco Inc., Greenwich, CT; *U.S. Public*, pg. 1577

Lasche, Gary, Sr. V.P. & Asst. Treas.--UMB Financial Corporation, Kansas City, MO; *U.S. Public*, pg. 1653

Lattin, Marilyn, Dir.-Investor Rels.--Silicon Graphics, Inc., Mountain View, CA; *U.S. Public*, pg. 1473

Lauber, Debbie, Dir.-Investor Rels.--LSI Industries, Inc., Cincinnati, OH; *U.S. Public*, pg. 971

Lauffer, Marlee, V.P.-Corp. Commun.--The Newhall Land And Farming Company, Valencia, CA; *U.S. Public*, pg. 1178

Laurent, Jean Marie, Chief Fin. Officer & V.P.-Fin.--Poliet, Courbevoie, France; *Int'l*, pg. 1177

Laurent, Robert Jr., Chief Fin. Officer & Exec. V.P.-Fin. & Admin.--Fedders Corp., Liberty Corner, NJ; *U.S. Public*, pg. 614

Laures, Gerald M., V.P.-Fin., Sec. & Treas.--Cobra Electronics Corporation, Chicago, IL; *U.S. Public*, pg. 391

LaValliere, Robert, Mgr.-Investor Rels.--Cambior Inc., Montreal, Canada; *Int'l*, pg. 253

LaVigne, Gregory P., Treas.--The Reliable Life Insurance Company, Webster Groves, MO; *U.S. Public*, pg. 1374

Lawi, David S., Sec. & Treas.--Helm Resources Inc., Greenwich, CT; *U.S. Public*, pg. 808

Lawlor, John, V.P.-Corp. Commun.--Newbridge Networks Corporation, Kanata, Canada; *Int'l*, pg. 923

Lawrence, John E., Asst. V.P.-Fin.--Asahi/America, Inc., Malden, MA; *U.S. Public*, pg. 137

Lawson, Herbert S., V.P. & Treas.--COBE Laboratories, Inc., Lakewood, CO; *Int'l*, pg. 667

Lawson, Melanie, Fin. Analyst--Pre-Paid Legal Services, Inc., Ada, OK; *U.S. Public*, pg. 1320

Lawson, Mike, Dir.-Corp. Communications--Granite Construction Incorporated, Watsonville, CA; *U.S. Public*, pg. 759

Layden, A.J., Chm. Bd. & Chief Exec. Officer--Allright Corporation, Houston, TX; *U.S. Private*, pg. 42

Leach, Anthony, Chief Fin. Officer & Exec. V.P.--Occidental Petroleum Corporation, Los Angeles, CA; *U.S. Public*, pg. 1210

Leahy, Mark, Mgr.-Investor Rels.--Immunex Corporation, Seattle, WA; *U.S. Public*, pg. 871

Leany, Donna, Mgr.-Investor Rels.--Taco Cabana, San Antonio, TX; *U.S. Public*, pg. 1559

LeBeau, Teri S., Dir.-Investor Rels.--The Dow Chemical Company, Midland, MI; *U.S. Public*, pg. 522

LeBlanc, Kevin, Mgr.-Investor Rels.--Continental Mortgage and Equity Trust, Dallas, TX; *U.S. Public*, pg. 441

LeBlanc, Richard, Treas. & Dir.-Fin. & Investor Relations--Ensco International Incorporated (ENSCO), Dallas, TX; *U.S. Public*, pg. 585

Ledermann, Kurt, Dir.-Investor Rels.--Sika Finanz AG, Baar, Switzerland; *Int'l*, pg. 1248

Lee, C. William, Chief Fin. Officer & V.P.-Fin.--Matrix Service Company, Tulsa, OK; *U.S. Public*, pg. 1057

Lee, Jesse, Chief Fin. Officer, Sr. V.P. & Sec.--The IDI Group Companies, Arlington, VA; *U.S. Private*, pg. 554

Lee, Robbin A., Mgr.-Investor Rels.--Echo Bay Mines Ltd., Englewood, CO; *U.S. Public*, pg. 561

LeFort, G. Neil, V.P.-Investor Rels.--Molex Incorporated, Lisle, IL; *U.S. Public*, pg. 1121

Legner, Theresa M., Asst. Sec. & Mgr.-Pension Savings Plans--Wausau-Mosinee Paper Corporation, Mosinee, WI; *U.S. Public*, pg. 1747

Leheney, V., Mgr.-Investor Rels.--Imperial Chemical Industries PLC, London, United Kingdom; *Int'l*, pg. 662

Lehman, Sondra, Dir.-Investor Rels.--Bell Sports Corp., San Jose, CA; *U.S. Public*, pg. 207

Leibling, David, Mgr.-Investor Rels.--Lex Service PLC, Bourne, United Kingdom; *Int'l*, pg. 806

Leifert, John, Mgr.-Pension Admin. & Investor Rels.--Omaha Public Power District, Omaha, NE; *U.S. Private*, pg. 815

Leland, John M., Jr., Dir.-Investor & Banking Rels.--Lukens Inc., Coatesville, PA; *U.S. Public*, pg. 1019

Lenzmeier, Allen U., Chief Fin. Officer & Exec. V.P.--Best Buy Co., Inc., Eden Prairie, MN; *U.S. Public*, pg. 223

Leonard, Timothy M., Chief Fin. Officer, V.P.-Fin. & Treas.--DBT Online, Inc., Las Vegas, NV; *U.S. Public*, pg. 472

Lerch, Stephen E., Chief Fin. Officer & Exec. V.P.--Transmedia Network Inc., Miami, FL; *U.S. Public*, pg. 1631

Leshne, Jerry, Dir.-Investor Rels.--Sears, Roebuck and Co., Hoffman Estates, IL; *U.S. Public*, pg. 1452

Lester, Sue, Mgr.-Investor Rels.--Input/Output, Inc., Stafford, TX; *U.S. Public*, pg. 880

Letendre, Elizabeth R., Sec.--HEICO Corporation, Hollywood, FL; *U.S. Public*, pg. 804

Leunig, Mark W., V.P., Gen. Counsel & Sec.--Genesee Corporation, Rochester, NY; *U.S. Public*, pg. 728

Levin, Marc B., Exec. V.P.-Investor Rels. & Sec.--Integrated Health Services, Inc., Owings Mills, MD; *U.S. Public*, pg. 884

Levine, Stuart Z., Ph.D., Dir.-Investor Rels.--Roberts Pharmaceutical Corporation, Eatontown, NJ; *U.S. Public, pg. 1393*

Levinson, Anthony, Chief Fin. Officer, V.P. & Treas.--Automobile Protection Corporation-APCO, Atlanta, GA; *U.S. Public*, pg. 150

Levy, David, Exec. V.P.-Admin. & Counsel--National Service Industries, Inc., Atlanta, GA; *U.S. Public*, pg. 1160

Lewis, Cheryl, Mgr.-Investor Rels.--Digital Microwave Corporation, San Jose, CA; *U.S. Public*, pg. 508

Lewis, Janet, Asst. Controller--Hawkins Chemical, Inc., Minneapolis, MN; *U.S. Public*, pg. 800

Lewis, Jim, Chief Fin. Officer, V.P., Treas. & Sec.--Hale-Halsell Company, Tulsa, OK; *U.S. Private*, pg. 494

Lewis, Leora, Mgr.-Investor Rels.--Iwerks Entertainment, Burbank, CA; *U.S. Public*, pg. 915

Lewis, Leslie B., Chm. Bd., Pres. & Chief Exec. Officer--Asahi/America, Inc., Malden, MA; *U.S. Public*, pg. 137

Lewitzke, Gary, Dir.-Investor Rels.--Pearl Brewing Company, San Antonio, TX; *U.S. Private*, pg. 954

Liberty, Paul, V.P.-Investor Rels.--Metrocall, Inc., Alexandria, VA; *U.S. Public*, pg. 1102

Liddle, Lynn M., V.P.-Corp. Commun. & Investor Rels.--Valassis Communications, Inc., Livonia, MI; *U.S. Public*, pg. 1704

Lieb, George J., V.P.-Investor Rels.--GTE Corporation, Stamford, CT; *U.S. Public*, pg. 696

Lieb, Joan M., Dir.-Investor Rels.--Worthington Foods Inc., Worthington, OH; *U.S. Public*, pg. 1780

Lieberman, J.B. Richard, Dir.-Inv. Rels.--Swiss Reinsurance Company, Zurich, Switzerland; *Int'l*, pg. 1332

Lienhard, Thomas J., Mgr.-Investor Services--Consolidated Edison Company of New York, Inc., New York, NY; *U.S. Public*, pg. 434

Liepe, Arvid, Dir.-Inv. Rels.--AGA AB, Lidingo, Sweden; *Int'l, pg. 12*

Light, Kenneth B., Chief Fin. Officer, Chief Admin. Officer & Exec. V.P.--Allied Products Corporation, Chicago, IL; *U.S.* Public, pg. 48

Lightstone, Stephen, Chief Fin. Officer, Sr. V.P.-Fin. & Treas.--Payless Cashways, Inc., Kansas City, MO; *U.S. Public*, pg. 1267

Lilja, Lu Ann, Dir.-Corp. Communications--Dean Foods Company, Franklin Park, IL; *U.S. Public*, pg. 489

Liljebeck, Roy C., Chief Fin. Officer & Exec. V.P.--Airborne Freight Corporation, Seattle, WA; *U.S. Public*, pg. 32

Lindberg, Lisbeth, Dir.-Invetor Relations--Orkla A.S.A., Oslo, Norway; *Int'l*, pg. 1010

Lindeman, Martha, V.P.-Corp. Commun. & Investor Rels.--Playboy Enterprises, Inc., Chicago, IL; *U.S. Public*, pg. 1309

Lindquist, Melinda L., Dir.-Corp. Communications--Genetics Institute, Inc., Cambridge, MA; *U.S. Public*, pg. 79

Lindsay, Jack, Mgr.-Investor Rels.--Rollins, Inc., Atlanta, GA; *U.S. Public*, pg. 1404

Linek, Eleanor, Asst. Mgr.-Investor Rels.--OfficeMax, Shaker Heights, OH; *U.S. Public*, pg. 1212

Lingen, Charles, Chief Fin. Officer & Sr. V.P.--The Sportsman's Guide, Inc., Saint Paul, MN; *U.S. Public*, pg. 1499

Linne, R. Steven, Gen. Counsel & Sec.--Haynes International, Inc., Kokomo, IN; *U.S. Public*, pg. 801

Lintecum, Elaine, Dir.-Investor Rels.--McClatchy Newspapers Inc., Sacramento, CA; *U.S. Public*, pg. 1065

Lippincott, Adele, Investor Rels.--Today's Man, Inc., Moorestown, NJ; *U.S. Public*, pg. 1619

Liss, Victor, Vice Chm., Pres. & Chief Exec. Officer--Trans-Lux Corporation, Norwalk, CT; *U.S. Public*, pg. 1628

Littauer, Robert, V.P. & Chief Fin. Officer--NeoRx Corporation, Seattle, WA; *U.S. Private*, pg. 791

Little, Laurie, Mgr.-Investor Rels.--PacifiCare Health Systems, Inc., Cypress, CA; *U.S. Public*, pg. 1250

Littrell, Dee, Mgr.-Inv. Rels.--Transcontinental Realty Investors, Inc., Dallas, TX; *U.S. Public*, pg. 1630

Liu, Joseph, Chief Fin. Officer & V.P.-Opers.--Diodes Incorporated, Westlake Village, CA; *U.S. Public*, pg. 510

Lloyd, David G., Chief Fin. Officer & Sr. V.P.--Taco Cabana, San Antonio, TX; *U.S. Public*, pg. 1559

Lloyd, Gary, Dir.-Inv. Rels.--Transcanada Pipelines Limited, Calgary, Canada; *Int'l*, pg. 1416

Locher, Margret, Mgr.-Pub. Rels.--Coop Switzerland, Basel, Switzerland; *Int'l*, pg. 329

Loersch, Joan, Mgr.-Investor Rels.--Schultz Sav-O Stores, Inc., Sheboygan, WI; *U.S. Public*, pg. 1442

Loesby, Rex E., Dir.-Investor Rels.--Nord Resources Corporation, Albuquerque, NM; *U.S. Public*, pg. 1188

Lofbom, W. Sonny, Chief Fin. Officer & V.P.--Robert F. Driver Co., Inc., San Diego, CA; *U.S. Private*, pg. 343

Logan, Lacey, Sr. Dir.-Corp. Commun. & Pub. Rels.--The Stroh Brewery Company, Detroit, MI; *U.S. Private*, pg. 1047

Loh, R. Daniel, Mgr.-Investor Rels.--Alumax Inc., Atlanta, GA; *U.S. Public*, pg. 59

Loher, Brian H., Treas., Sec. & Dir.-Investor Rels.--Hall Contracting Corp., Louisville, KY; *U.S. Private*, pg. 495

Lohrmann, Barbara, Dir.-Investor Rels.--Polk Audio, Inc., Baltimore, MD; *U.S. Public*, pg. 1315

Lokmer-Brosko, Marion, Mgr.-Investor Rels.--The LTV Corporation, Cleveland, OH; *U.S. Public*, pg. 971

Lombard, Gilberte, Sr. V.P.-Investor Rels.--Credit Commercial de France, Paris, France; *Int'l*, pg. 341

Lonay, Nathalie, Mgr.-Investor Rels.--Cockerill Sambre, Brussels, Belgium; *Int'l*, pg. 301

Longley, John, Dir.-Investor Rels.--Fletcher Challenge Limited, Auckland, New Zealand; *Int'l*, pg. 494

Lonzono, Gloria, Investor Rels. Asst.--Sun City Industries, Inc., Fort Lauderdale, FL; *U.S. Public*, pg. 1529

Lorenz, Deborah S., V.P.-Investor Rels. & Corp. Commun.--EG & G, Inc., Wellesley, MA; *U.S. Public*, pg. 542

Lorenz, Donald N., Chief Fin. Officer & V.P.-Fin.--Price Brothers Co., Dayton, OH; *U.S. Private*, pg. 883

Lorigan, Julie, Dir.-Investor Rels.--Open Market, Inc., Burlington, MA; *U.S. Public*, pg. 1226

Loucks, Scott, Chief Fin. Officer & V.P.-Fin.--Technology Research Corporation, Clearwater, FL; *U.S. Public*, pg. 1564

Lougee, R.W., Jr., V.P.-Investor Rels. & Corp. Commun.--Arch Communications Group, Inc., Westborough, MA; *U.S. Public*, pg. 127

Loughnot, Katie, Dir.-Investor Rels.--Ross Stores, Inc., Newark, CA; *U.S. Public*, pg. 1405

Louis, Murray A., V.P.-Communications & Asst. Sec.--SEI Investments, Oaks, PA; *U.S. Public*, pg. 1417

Lovejoy, Robert M., Jr., V.P. & Treas.--General Host Corporation, Stamford, CT; *U.S. Public*, pg. 715

Loveless, Keith, Corp. Sec. & Assoc. Gen. Counsel--Alaska Air Group, Inc., Seattle, WA; *U.S. Public*, pg. 35

Loverine, Denis L., Treas.--Snap-On Tools Corporation, Kenosha, WI; *U.S. Public*, pg. 1480

Lowber, John M., Chief Fin. Officer, Sr. V.P., Treas. & Sec.--General Communication, Inc., Anchorage, AK; *U.S. Public*, pg. 708

Lowell, Doug, Dir.-Bus. Devel.--Trimark Holdings, Inc., Santa Monica, CA; *U.S. Public*, pg. 1638

Lowman, George S., Dir.-Communications--GATX Corporation, Chicago, IL; *U.S. Public*, pg. 690

Luddy, Robert, Pres. & Chief Exec. Officer--Captive-Aire Systems, Inc., Youngsville, NC; *U.S. Private*, pg. 207

Luengo, Justiniano, Dir.-Equity--Iberdrola, S.A., Bilbao, Spain; *Int'l*, pg. 657

Luke, James P., Chief Fin. Officer & Exec. V.P.--Blessings Corporation, Newport News, VA; *U.S. Private*, pg. 1179

Luker, Robert C., Chief Fin. Officer & V.P.--Kokomo Sanitary Pottery Corp., Kokomo, IN; *U.S. Private*, pg. 449

Lumidis, Anthony, Dir.-Investor Relations--Thermo Electron Corporation, Waltham, MA; *U.S. Public*, pg. 1591

Lundberg, Inga, Dir.-Investor Rels.--Trygg-Hansa, Stockholm, Sweden; *Int'l*, pg. 1425

Lunn, Linda, Investor Rels. Asst.--Alpharma Inc., Fort Lee, NJ; *U.S. Public*, pg. 57

Lupinski, Thomas M., Chief Fin. Officer & Sr. V.P.--Swiss Army Brands, Inc., Shelton, CT; *U.S. Public*, pg. 1544

Luskin, Meyer, Chm. Bd., Pres. & Chief Exec. Officer--Scope Industries, Santa Monica, CA; *U.S. Public*, pg. 1444

Mabry, James C., Mgr.-Investor Rels.--Wachovia Corporation, Winston Salem, NC; *U.S. Public*, pg. 1730

MacDonald, Bob, Chief Fin. Officer--Societe BIC S.A., Clichy, France; *Int'l*, pg. 1272

MacDonald, S. Kelley, V.P.-Corp. Communications--Unitrode Corporation, Merrimack, NH; *U.S. Public*, pg. 1694

Mackay, Don, V.P.-Indus. Rels.--Kwikset Corporation, Irvine, CA; *U.S. Public*, pg. 233

MacLeod, Donald J., Dir.-Investor Rels.--Mellon Bank Corporation, Pittsburgh, PA; *U.S. Public*, pg. 1084

Macnow, Joseph, Chief Fin. Officer & V.P.--Vornado Realty Trust, Saddle Brook, NJ; *U.S. Public*, pg. 1725

Madden, Sharon, Dir.-Investor Rels.--Daw Technologies, Inc., Salt Lake City, UT; *U.S. Public*, pg. 489

Madden, Thomas J., Chief Fin. & Acctg. Officer, V.P.-Fin. & Treas.--Daisytek International Corporation, Plano, TX; *U.S. Public*, pg. 477

Magary, Richard, Sr. V.P.-Admin. & Asst. Sec.--American Shared Hospital Services, San Francisco, CA; *U.S. Public*, pg. 91

Magee, Mary, Admin.-Investor Rels.--Calton, Inc., Manalapan, NJ; *U.S. Public*, pg. 296

Magruder, Logan, V.P.-Corp. Rels. & Bus. Devel.--Barrett Resources Corporation, Denver, CO; *U.S. Public*, pg. 191

Magyar, Mary K., V.P.-Corp. Communications--Associated Banc-Corp, Green Bay, WI; *U.S. Public*, pg. 140

Mahaffey, Robert L., V.P. & Treas.--Anderson Erickson Dairy Company, Des Moines, IA; *U.S. Private*, pg. 72

Mahoney, Frank G., Sr. V.P.-Annuity & Investment Products--Jefferson-Pilot Life Insurance Co., Greensboro, NC; *U.S. Public*, pg. 926

Mahoney, George R., Jr., Exec. V.P., Gen. Counsel & Sec.--Family Dollar Stores, Inc., Matthews, NC; *U.S. Public*, pg. 612

Mahoney, Stewart, Dir.-Treasury Svcs./Investor Rels.--Empire Company Limited, Stellarton, Canada; *Int'l*, pg. 453

Makonoff, Lon, Chief Fin. Officer--Sherwood Foods, Maple Heights, OH; *U.S. Private*, pg. 994

Makrakis, Kathleen B., Dir.-Investor Rels.--Tambrands Inc., Cincinnati, OH; *U.S. Public*, pg. 1331

Malkowicz, Edward, Chm. Bd.--Haskel International, Inc., Burbank, CA; *U.S. Public*, pg. 798

Mallory, Krista, Mgr.-Investor Rels.--Callaway Golf Company, Carlsbad, CA; *U.S. Public*, pg. 294

Malmer, Lars G., Dir.-Pub. Affairs & Investor Rels.--AB SKF, Goteborg, Sweden; *Int'l*, pg. 1156

Maloney, James V., Sec. & Dir.-Investor Rels.--Pulitzer Publishing Company, Saint Louis, MO; *U.S. Public*, pg. 1343

Maloney, Thomas K., V.P.-Opers. & Fin.--Voyager Emblems, Inc., Sanborn, NY; *U.S. Private*, pg. 1143

Mandeville, Leslie, Dir.-Investor Rels.--AMR Corporation, Fort Worth, TX; *U.S. Public*, pg. 9

Mandeville, Robert, Chief Fin. Officer, Treas. & Sec.--Cranston Print Works Company, Cranston, RI; *U.S. Private*, pg. 286

Maneki, Freya, Mgr.-Legal Admin.--Dole Food Company, Inc., Westlake Village, CA; *U.S. Public*, pg. 515

Manette, Lucy, Dir.-Investor Rels.--CD Products, Inc., New Providence, NJ; *U.S. Public*, pg. 276

Manis, Cheri, Mgr.-Commun. & Investor Rels.--Mycogen Corporation, San Diego, CA; *U.S. Public*, pg. 1142

Mann, David, Mgr.-Corp. Communications & Inv. Rels.--Talisman Energy Inc., Calgary, Canada; *Int'l*, pg. 1352

Mann, Norma, Dir.-Investor Rels.--Video Display Corporation, Tucker, GA; *U.S. Public*, pg. 1720

Manning, Jennifer B., Mgr.-Investor Rels.--Aaron Rents, Inc., Atlanta, GA; *U.S. Public*, pg. 12

Manning, William J., Asst. Treas.--Nashua Corporation, Nashua, NH; *U.S. Public*, pg. 1152

Manz, Steve, Mgr.-Investor Rels.--Noble Drilling Corporation, Houston, TX; *U.S. Public*, pg. 1186

Marchesi, Donna M., Corp. Sec.--CVB Financial Corp., Ontario, CA; *U.S. Public*, pg. 286

Marchuk, Raymond, V.P.-Fin. & Investor Rels.--Scholastic Corporation, New York, NY; *U.S. Public*, pg. 1440

Marcic, Irene S., Chief Fin. Officer, Exec. V.P., Treas. & Sec.--Astrex, Inc., Plainview, NY; *U.S. Public*, pg. 141

Marcus, Guy T., V.P.-Investor Rels.--Halliburton Company, Dallas, TX; *U.S. Public*, pg. 775

Marcus, Stephen, Chm. Bd., Pres. & Chief Exec. Officer--The Marcus Corporation, Milwaukee, WI; *U.S. Public*, pg. 1044

Marich, Ivo, Mgr.-Bus. Analysis--Gelman Sciences, Inc., Ann Arbor, MI; *U.S. Public*, pg. 1253

Marischen, Robert J., Vice Chm. & Chief Fin. Officer--Huntco Inc., Town and Country, MO; *U.S. Public*, pg. 849

Markel, Charles A., III, V.P.-Fin. & Treas.--LG & E Energy Corp., Louisville, KY; *U.S. Public*, pg. 970

Marque, Daniel, Dir.-Investor Rels.--Groupe Casino, Saint Etienne, France; *Int'l*, pg. 562

Marques, Emilio, Jr., Controller--Sao Paulo Alpargatas S.A., Sao Paulo, Brazil; *Int'l*, pg. 1193

Marram, Edward P., Dr., Chm. Bd., Pres., Chief Exec. Officer & Treas.--Geo-Centers, Inc., Newton, MA; *U.S. Private*, pg. 447

Marrin, Tom, V.P.-Fin.--Computer Power Incorporated, High Bridge, NJ; *U.S. Public*, pg. 421

Marsay, Christopher, Grp. Mgr.-Inv. Rels--The BOC Group plc, Windlesham, United Kingdom; *Int'l*, pg. 121

Marsden, Melissa, V.P.-Investor Rels.--Boston Chicken, Inc., Golden, CO; *U.S. Public*, pg. 247

Marshal, Eleanor, Mgr.-Investor Rels.--Bruncor, Inc., Saint John, Canada; *Int'l*, pg. 230

Marshall, Debbie, Mgr.-Investor Rels.--Autologic Information International, Inc., Thousand Oaks, CA; *U.S. Public*, pg. 1724

Marshall, John D., Treas.--Blount International, Inc., Montgomery, AL; *U.S. Public*, pg. 237

Marshall, Quintin G., Sr. V.P.-Corp. Devel.--Ogden Corporation, New York, NY; *U.S. Public*, pg. 1213

Marshall, Robert, Dir.-Investor Rels--Atlantic Electric Co., Pleasantville, NJ; *U.S. Public*, pg. 430

Marshall, Robin L., Pres. & Chief Exec. Officer--Great Lakes Technologies Corp., Kalamazoo, MI; *U.S. Private*, pg. 475

Marsteller, Helen S., Dir.-Investor Rels.--York International Corporation, York, PA; *U.S. Public*, pg. 1788

Martin, Cheryl A., Dir.-Investor Rels.--Canyon Resources Corporation, Golden, CO; *U.S. Public*, pg. 301

Martin, Paul F., Chief Fin. Officer--Rawlings Sporting Goods Company, Fenton, MO; *U.S. Public*, pg. 1361

Martin, Sandy, Mgr.-Investor Rels.--Pier 1 Imports, Inc., Fort Worth, TX; *U.S. Public*, pg. 1295

Martin, Steve, Dir.-Corp. Communications--M/A-COM Inc., Lowell, MA; *U.S. Public*, pg. 8

Martin, Tracy, Investor Rels.--Developers Diversified Realty Corporation, Moreland Hills, OH; *U.S. Public*, pg. 502

Martineau, P.R., V.P. & Treas.--GSW Inc., Guelph, Canada,; *Int'l*, pg. 538

Martinez, Alejandro Montano, Dir.-Corp. Communication--Telefonos de Mexico S.A. de C.V., Mexico, Mexico; *Int'l*, pg. 1373

Martinez, Walfrido A., Chief Fin. Officer, Sr. V.P. & Controller--E & B Marine Incorporated, Edison, NJ; *U.S. Public*, pg. 1756

Martore, Gracia, V.P.-Treasury Svcs. & Investor Rels.--Gannett Company, Inc., Arlington, VA; *U.S. Public*, pg. 698

Martz, Joanne F., Dir.-Investor Rels.--Objective Systems Integrators, Inc., Folsom, CA; *U.S. Public*, pg. 1209

Marusiak, Paul, Mgr.-Investor Relations--Worthington Industries, Inc., Columbus, OH; *U.S. Public*, pg. 1780

Marxer, Barbara, Dir.-Investor Rels.--Norrell Corporation, Atlanta, GA; *U.S. Public*, pg. 1192

Masefield, John, Chm. Bd., Pres. & Chief Exec. Officer--Isomedix Inc., Whippany, NJ; *U.S. Public*, pg. 1515

Maslick, Joseph R., Chief Fin. Officer, Exec. V.P. & Sec.--Griffith Laboratories Worldwide, Inc., Alsip, IL; *U.S. Private*, pg. 481

Mason, David A., Chief Fin. Officer, Exec. V.P. & Treas.--Moto Photo, Inc., Dayton, OH; *U.S. Public*, pg. 1136

Mason, Mike, Dir.-Investor Rels.--Cadbury Schweppes p.l.c., London, United Kingdom; *Int'l*, pg. 247

Mason, Tara, Mgr.-Investor Rels.--National Instruments Corp., Austin, TX; *U.S. Public*, pg. 1157

Masseth, Michael D., V.P.-Investor Rels.--Kimberly-Clark Corporation, Dallas, TX; *U.S. Public*, pg. 958

Masterson, James F., Dir.-Investor Rels.--Caterpillar Inc., Peoria, IL; *U.S. Public*, pg. 315

Mastrangelo, Laura A., V.P.-Corp. Commun.--VIMRx Pharmaceuticals, Inc., Wilmington, DE; *U.S. Public*, pg. 1702

Mastropolo, Michelle, Office Mgr.--Zing Technologies, Inc., Valhalla, NY; *U.S. Public*, pg. 1792

Mataya, Robert J., V.P.-Bus. Plng. & Devel.--Material Sciences Corporation, Elk Grove Village, IL; *U.S. Public*, pg. 1056

Matheny, Evelyne, Mktg. Analyst--Mystic Color Lab, Inc., Mystic, CT; *Int'l*, pg. 501

Matherne, Louis K., Jr., Treas.--Chesapeake Corporation, Richmond, VA; *U.S. Public*, pg. 346

Matherne, Todd A., V.P.-Investor Rels.--Service Corporation International, Houston, TX; *U.S. Public*, pg. 1460

Matheson, James A., V.P.-Fin.--Advanced Magnetics, Inc., Cambridge, MA; *U.S. Public*, pg. 20

Matteo, Rose, Mgr.-Investor Rels.--Oroamerica, Inc., Burbank, CA; *U.S. Public*, pg. 1232

Mattsson, Asa, Dir.-Investor Rels. & Fin. Information--Electrolux, AB, Stockholm, Sweden; *Int'l*, pg. 438

Matz, R. Kevin, Sr. V.P. & Treas.--EMCOR Group, Inc., Norwalk, CT; *U.S. Public*, pg. 571

Mauro, Judy, Dir.-Corp. Communications--Chyron Corp., Melville, NY; *Int'l*, pg. 1372

Mayer, Jeffrey P., Chief Fin. Officer--Bristol Hotels & Resorts, Dallas, TX; *U.S. Public*, pg. 253

Maynard, Roger, Dir.-Investments & Joint Ventures--British Airways PLC, London, United Kingdom; *Int'l*, pg. 218

Mayr, Charles, Dir.-Corp. Communications--Barr Laboratories Inc., Pomona, NY; *U.S. Public*, pg. 191

Mazer, Brian, V.P.-Investor Rels.--Waters Corporation, Milford, MA; *U.S. Public*, pg. 1745

Mazur, Leon T., Dir.-Investor Rels.--Niagara Mohawk Power Corporation, Syracuse, NY; *U.S. Public*, pg. 1181

McAlary, Sinead, Mgr.-Corp. Affairs--John Holland Group Pty. Ltd., Melbourne, Australia; *Int'l*, pg. 630

McAlpine, Lorraine, Dir.-Investor Rels.--Alias Wavefront, Toronto, Canada; *U.S. Public*, pg. 1474

McArdle, James F., V.P.-Investor Rels.--Transamerica Corporation, San Francisco, CA; *U.S. Public*, pg. 1629

McArthur, James L., Sec. & Mgr.-Investor Rels.--ChemFirst Inc., Jackson, MS; *U.S. Public*, pg. 344

McAulay, Jeffrey J., Chief Fin. Officer & V.P.--Moran Transporation Company, Greenwich, CT; *U.S. Private*, pg. 760

McBee, Serena, Coord.-Investor Rels.--American Freightways Corporation, Harrison, AR; *U.S. Public*, pg. 75

McBennett, Robert J., Treas.--Orange and Rockland Utilities, Inc., Pearl River, NY; *U.S. Public*, pg. 1229

McBride, Peter, V.P.-Communications & Investor Relations--Imasco Limited, Montreal, Canada; *Int'l*, pg. 112

McCabe, Joan, Dir.-Investor Rels.--The Dial Corporation, Phoenix, AZ; *U.S. Public*, pg. 505

McCahon, Jane W., V.P.-Corp. Rels.--Eastern Enterprises, Weston, MA; *U.S. Public*, pg. 548

McCallister, Jane, Dir.-Investor Rels.--SmithKline Beecham Corporation, Philadelphia, PA; *Int'l*, pg. 1264

McCallon, Anne D., Sr. V.P.-Corp. Fin. & Investor Rels.--Countrywide Funding Corporation, Pasadena, CA; *U.S. Public*, pg. 453

McCarthy, Michael W., Dir.-Investor Rels. & Corp. Commun.--Photronics, Inc., Brookfield, CT; *U.S. Public*, pg. 1293

McCauley, Anne Marie, Mgr.-Investor Rels.--Mercury Interactive Corp., Sunnyvale, CA; *U.S. Public*, pg. 1093

McConathy, J. Thompson, Chief Fin. Officer & V.P.-Fin.--OEA, Inc., Aurora, CO; *U.S. Public*, pg. 1206

McConnell, Thomas J., Chief Fin. Officer & V.P.-Fin.--Discount Drug Mart Inc., Medina, OH; *U.S. Private*, pg. 334

McConnell, William R., Chm. Bd. & Pres.--McConnell Cabinets, Inc., El Monte, CA; *U.S. Private*, pg. 720

McCorkell, Peter L., Sr. V.P., Gen. Counsel & Sec.--Fair, Isaac and Company, Inc., San Rafael, CA; *U.S. Public*, pg. 609

McCoy, Alan H., V.P.-Pub. Affairs--AK Steel Corporation, Middletown, OH; *U.S. Public*, pg. 7

McCoy, Jenny, Mgr.-Investor Communication--Meredith Corporation, Des Moines, IA; *U.S. Public*, pg. 1094

McCrady, Kenneth A., Chm. Bd.--Ennis Business Forms, Inc., Ennis, TX; *U.S. Public*, pg. 583

McCreary, Gordon A., V.P.-Inv. Rels.--Kinross Gold Corporation, Toronto, Canada; *Int'l*, pg. 734

McCusker, J., Sr. V.P.-Inv. Rels.--Heidemij Nederland BV, Arnhem, Netherlands; *Int'l*, pg. 607

McCusty, Paul R., Chief Fin. Officer & V.P.-Fin.--The Ohio Art Company, Inc., Bryan, OH; *U.S. Public*, pg. 1214

McDonagh, Bernard F., V.P.-Investor Rels. & Bus. Research--United HealthCare Corporation, Minnetonka, MN; *U.S. Public*, pg. 1677

McDonald, Jerry, Exec. V.P., Chief Fin. Officer & Treas.--Resistance Technology Inc., Arden Hills, MN; *U.S. Public*, pg. 1455

McEachern, Michael L., V.P.-Fixed Income Investment--American General Corporation, Houston, TX; *U.S. Public*, pg. 76

McFerren, Allison T., First V.P.-Investor Rels.--Comerica Incorporated, Detroit, MI; *U.S. Public*, pg. 408

McGarrigle, Maureen, Dir.-Investor Rels.--Digi International Inc., Minnetonka, MN; *U.S. Public*, pg. 506

McGee, F.D., Gen. Counsel & Sec.--National Sea Products Limited, Lunenburg, Canada; *Int'l*, pg. 909

McGovern, Helen, Mgr.-Inv. Rels--Tiger Direct, Inc., Miami, FL; *U.S. Public*, pg. 747

McGowan, Joseph C., Treas. & Sec.--Interstate Power Company, Dubuque, IA; *U.S. Public*, pg. 910

McGrail, Kelly, Mgr.-Corp. Commun.--Oil-Dri Corporation of America, Chicago, IL; *U.S. Public*, pg. 1214

McGrath, Lee U., V.P. & Treas.--Jostens, Minneapolis, MN; *U.S. Public*, pg. 934

McGuinness, Claire, Mgr.-Investor Rels.--CRH, plc, Dublin, Ireland; *Int'l*, pg. 242

McGuire, Bruce, Dir.-Investor Rels. & Pub. Rels.--Tyco Toys, Inc., Mount Laurel, NJ; *U.S. Public*, pg. 1058

McGyver, Bob, Dir.-Investor Rels.--International Game Technology, Reno, NV; *U.S. Public*, pg. 900

McHale, Jack F., V.P.-Investor & Corp. Communications--Unisys Corporation, Blue Bell, PA; *U.S. Public*, pg. 1671

McHugh, Wendy, Mgr.-Investor Rels.--Haemonetics Corporation, Braintree, MA; *U.S. Public*, pg. 773

McIlwaine, Charles B., V.P.-Communications--The Coleman Company, Inc., Golden, CO; *U.S. Private*, pg. 690

McIntosh, Sheila M., V.P.-Corp. Commun. & Investor Rels.--Canadian Pacific Limited, Calgary, Canada; *Int'l*, pg. 258

McIntyre, Tim, Gen. Mgr.-Investor Rels.--Joseph T. Ryerson & Son, Inc., Chicago, IL; *U.S. Public*, pg. 879

McIntyre, Tim, Gen. Mgr.-Investor Rels.--Ryerson Tull, Chicago, IL; *U.S. Public*, pg. 879

McKeever, Deborah, Dir.-Admin.--U.M. Holding Limited, Haddonfield, NJ; *U.S. Private*, pg. 1113

McKernan, Anton, Mgr.-Inv. Rels.--Pacific Dunlop Limited, Melbourne, Australia; *Int'l*, pg. 1021

McKnight, Andrew D., Chm. Bd., Pres. & Chief Exec. Officer--Tri-Chem, Inc., Harrison, NJ; *U.S. Private*, pg. 1100

McLachlin, Daniel, V.P. & Sec.--Nabors Industries, Inc., Houston, TX; *U.S. Public*, pg. 1148

McLain, Robert G., Asst. Investment Banking--United Missouri Bank of St. Louis, Saint Louis, MO; *U.S. Public*, pg. 1655

McLean, A. Alexander, III, Chief Fin. Officer & Exec. V.P.--World Acceptance Corporation, Greenville, SC; *U.S. Public*, pg. 1778

McLendon, Jim, Investor Rels.--Control Data Systems, Inc., Arden Hills, MN; *U.S. Public*, pg. 441

McLeod, Neil A., Jr., V.P.-H.R.--Glassmaster Company, Lexington, SC; *U.S. Public*, pg. 745

McMillan, Greg, Mgr.--Boral Limited, Sydney, Australia; *Int'l*, pg. 203

McNaughton, Tom, Dir.-Investor Rels.--Cabot Corporation, Boston, MA; *U.S. Public*, pg. 288

McNeal, Mary H., Dir.-Investor Rels.--Koger Equity Inc., Jacksonville, FL; *U.S. Public*, pg. 965

McNerey, Laura, Mgr.-Investor Rels.--Tenera, Inc., San Francisco, CA; *U.S. Public*, pg. 1576

McNulty, Tim, Mgr.-Investor Rels.--Canadian Airlines Corporation, Calgary, Canada; *Int'l*, pg. 255

McPhail, Douglas J., Pres., Chief Exec. & Fin. Officer & Treas.--Indiana Records Managers, Fishers, IN; *U.S. Private*, pg. 560

McRae, D. Gary, Chm. Bd., Pres. & Chief Exec. Officer--McRae Industries, Inc., Mount Gilead, NC; *U.S. Public*, pg. 1073

McWilliams, R.E., V.P.-Drilling & Dir.-Investor Rels.--Rowan Companies, Inc., Houston, TX; *U.S. Public*, pg. 1409

Mead, George W., Chm. Bd.--Consolidated Papers, Inc., Wisconsin Rapids, WI; *U.S. Public*, pg. 436

Meader, Peggy, Pres. & Chief Exec. Officer--Inland Associates, Olathe, KS; *U.S. Private*, pg. 563

Means, Michelle, Indus. Rels.--Buckman Laboratories Inc., Memphis, TN; *U.S. Private*, pg. 180

Medford, Dale L., Chief Fin. Officer & V.P.-Fin.--The Reynolds and Reynolds Company, Dayton, OH; *U.S. Public*, pg. 1384

Medly, Mary Beth, Mgr.-Investor & Shareholder Rels.--Intergraph Corporation, Huntsville, AL; *U.S. Public*, pg. 890

Meessen, Johanna, Mgr.-Communications--OBI Bau-und Heimwerkermaerkte GmbH & Co. KG, Wermelskirchen, Germany; *Int'l*, pg. 993

Meier, Tom, Dir.-Investor Rels. & Asst. Treas.--APL Limited, Oakland, CA; *Int'l*, pg. 912

Meijer, Freek, Mgr.-Investor Rels.--Oce-van der Grinten N.V., Venlo, Netherlands; *Int'l*, pg. 993

Meikle, Mark G., Chief Fin. Officer, V.P. & Treas.--Steel of West Virginia, Inc., Huntington, WV; *U.S. Public*, pg. 1513

Mekwunye, Deanna, Dir.-Investor Rels.--Wind River Systems, Inc., Alameda, CA; *U.S. Public*, pg. 1770

Melia, Elaine, Dir.-Investor Rels.--Bentley Pharmaceuticals, Inc., Tampa, FL; *U.S. Public*, pg. 212

Mella, Karen, Dir.-Investor Rels.--USLD Communications Corp., San Antonio, TX; *U.S. Public*, pg. 969

Melo, John, Dir.-Customer Service--Bradford & Bingley Building Society, Bingley, United Kingdom; *Int'l*, pg. 210

Merandi, Jane, Sec.--Alamco, Inc., Charleston, WV; *U.S. Public*, pg. 403

Mercer, Howard R., Dir.-Pub. Rels. & Adv.--Griffon Corp., Jericho, NY; *U.S. Public*, pg. 766

Merico, Judith A., Mgr.-Investor Rels. & Asst. Sec.--Huntington National Bank, Morgantown, WV; *U.S. Public*, pg. 850

Merriman, Susan, Mgr.-Investor Rels.--Exabyte Corporation, Boulder, CO; *U.S. Public*, pg. 597

Merritt, Robert S., Chief Fin. Officer, Sr. V.P.-Fin. & Treas.--Outback Steakhouse Inc., Tampa, FL; *U.S. Public*, pg. 1235

Merriwether, John, Dir.-Investor & Media Rels.--Health Management Associates, Inc., Naples, FL; *U.S. Public*, pg. 802

Merry, Carol, Dir.-Corp. & Shareholder Commun.--Lexford Residential Trust, Columbus, OH; *U.S. Public*, pg. 991

Messina, Angelo, Dir.-Investor Rels.--United Technologies Corporation, Hartford, CT; *U.S. Public*, pg. 1689

Messina, S.A., Dir.-Investor Rels.--Chrysler Corporation, Auburn Hills, MI; *U.S. Public*, pg. 352

Metzger, Tammy, Admin. Asst.--Exolon-Esk Company, Tonawanda, NY; *U.S. Public*, pg. 600

Meusborn, Mary, Mgr.-Cash Mngmt. & Investor Rels.--Syncor International Corporation, Woodland Hills, CA; *U.S. Public*, pg. 1548

Meyer, John, Mgr.-Investor Rels.--Mesaba Holdings, Inc., Minneapolis, MN; *U.S. Public*, pg. 1099

Meyer, Karen, Exec. Asst.--PolyMedica Industries, Inc., Woburn, MA; *U.S. Public*, pg. 1315

Meyer, Ronald A., V.P.-Fin. & Admin., Treas. & Sec.--Modern Controls, Inc., Minneapolis, MN; *U.S. Public*, pg. 1120

Meyers, Robert S., V.P.-Corp. Communications & Investor Rels.--Scientific-Atlanta, Inc., Norcross, GA; *U.S. Public*, pg. 1443

Meyers, Terry, V.P. & Treas.--U.S. Safety, Lenexa, KS; *U.S. Private*, pg. 1125

Micelli, Tony, V.P.-Fin., Treas. & Sec.--Metex Corporation, Edison, NJ; *U.S. Public*, pg. 1674

Michaels, C. Rand, Vice. Chm.--Lomak Petroleum Inc., Fort Worth, TX; *U.S. Public*, pg. 1012

Michelsen, Eric F., Gen. Mgr.-Fin.--The East Asiatic Company Ltd. A/S, Copenhagen, Denmark; *Int'l*, pg. 430

Michie, A.J., Sec.--Lloyds TSB Group PLC, London, United Kingdom; *Int'l*, pg. 812

Middleton, Peyton, Mgr.-Investor Rels.--Potomac Electric Power Company, Washington, DC; *U.S. Public*, pg. 1318

Midora, Kathleen, Dir.-Mktg. Svcs.--Angelo Brothers Co., Philadelphia, PA; *U.S. Private*, pg. 74

Miklich, Thomas R., Chief Fin. Officer, Treas., Gen. Counsel & Sec.--Invacare Corporation, Elyria, OH; *U.S. Public*, pg. 911

Milas, Joseph, Treas.--Plibrico Co., Chicago, IL; *U.S. Private*, pg. 872

Milet, Pierre, Chief Fin. Officer, V.P. & Sec.--Clarins, Neuilly-sur-Seine, France; *Int'l*, pg. 295

Millbranth, Janet, Coord.-Investor Rels.--Artisoft, Inc., Tucson, AZ; *U.S. Public*, pg. 136

Miller, Cory J., Chief Fin. Officer & V.P.-Fin.--Ciprico, Inc., Plymouth, MN; *U.S. Public*, pg. 370

Miller, Dawn, Dir.-Investor Rels.--Mylex Corporation, Fremont, CA; *U.S. Public*, pg. 1143

Miller, Kevin J., Dir.-Fin. Plng.--Baltimore Gas and Electric Company, Baltimore, MD; *U.S. Public*, pg. 172

Miller, Larry D., V.P.-Commun. & Investor Rels.--Alltrista Corporation, Muncie, IN; *U.S. Public*, pg. 56

Miller, Lylia, Investor Rels.--Snyder Oil Corporation, Fort Worth, TX; *U.S. Public*, pg. 1481

Miller, Sue, Head-Corp. Communications--T & N Plc, Manchester, United Kingdom; *Int'l*, pg. 1334

Miller, Teresa, Dir.-Investor Rels.--Genesco Inc., Nashville, TN; *U.S. Public*, pg. 728

Mills, Andrew, Dir.-Investor Rels.--Kingfisher plc, London, United Kingdom; *Int'l*, pg. 733

Milne, Cynthia J., Sec.--Andover Bancorp, Inc., Andover, MA; *U.S. Public*, pg. 111

Minihan, Steve, Asst. V.P.--The Hartford Financial Services Group Inc., Hartford, CT; *U.S. Public*, pg. 794

Minneman, Thomas J., Treas.--MTS Systems Corporation, Eden Prairie, MN; *U.S. Public*, pg. 1028

Misakian, Jeffrey D., Sr. V.P. & Dir.-Corp. Rels.--Glendale Federal Bank, F.S.B., Glendale, CA; *U.S. Public*, pg. 747

Mitchell, Jeanne, V.P.-Investor Rels. & Corp. Communications--Hanover Direct, Inc., Weehawken, NJ; *U.S. Public*, pg. 782

Mitchell, Michael, Dir.-Investor Rels.--Signet Group plc, London, United Kingdom; *Int'l*, pg. 1248

Mitchell, Michelle, Mgr.-Coord. Mktg.--Advanstar Communications, Cleveland, OH; *U.S. Private*, pg. 22

Mitchell, Richard C., Mgr.-Investor Rels.--Rigel Energy Corporation, Calgary, Canada; *Int'l*, pg. 1117

Mizuno, Toshiaki, Mgr.-Investor Relations--Mizuno Corporation, Osaka, Japan; *Int'l*, pg. 884

Moad, Martin, V.P.-Investor Rels.--Tandy Corporation, Fort Worth, TX; *U.S. Public*, pg. 1560

Moberley, Stuart Greville, Grp. Fin. Dir.--McKechnie PLC, Walsall, United Kingdom; *Int'l*, pg. 851

Modist, Scott J., Chief Fin. Officer, V.P.-Fin. & Treas.--Equitrac Corporation, Coral Gables, FL; *U.S. Public*, pg. 590

Moffett, David J., Chief Fin. Officer & Information Officer, Exec. V.P.--Starbanc Corporation, Cincinnati, OH; *U.S. Public*, pg. 1510

Moffitt, Judy, Coord.-Investor Rels.--St. Jude Medical, Inc., Saint Paul, MN; *U.S. Public*, pg. 1427

Mohlin, Katarina, Exec. V.P. & Corp. Commun. Officer--Skandia Insurance Company Limited, Stockholm, Sweden; *Int'l*, pg. 1256

Mohnkein, Kent W., V.P.-Inv. Rels.--UNUM Corporation, Portland, ME; *U.S. Public*, pg. 1699

Mohrman, Lou, Gen. Mgr.--Handling Systems Engineering, Jacksonville, FL; *U.S. Private*, pg. 499

Moine, Gerard, Exec. Dir.-Pub. Affairs--France Telecom, Paris, France; *Int'l*, pg. 503

Moller, Soren, Treas. & Mgr.-Communications--Sophus Berendsen A/S, Soeborg, Denmark; *Int'l*, pg. 1284

Molton, John, Controller--Ed Miniat, Inc., Chicago, IL; *U.S. Private*, pg. 750

Monaco, Susan, V.P.-Strategic Plng. & Corp. Affairs--Engelhard Corporation, Iselin, NJ; *U.S. Public*, pg. 582

Monaghan, Thomas S., Chm. Bd., Pres. & Chief Exec. Officer--Domino's Pizza Inc., Ann Arbor, MI; *U.S. Private*, pg. 339

Monahan, Michael, Dir.-Investor Rels.--Pitney Bowes Inc., Stamford, CT; *U.S. Public*, pg. 1303

Monahan, Michael J., V.P.-External Rels.--Ecolab Inc., Saint Paul, MN; *U.S. Public*, pg. 562

Monello, Joseph D., Chief Fin. Officer & V.P.--Kansas City Southern Industries, Inc., Kansas City, MO; *U.S. Public*, pg. 943

Monfor, Shelley, Dir.-Investor Rels.--Plum Creek Timber Co., L.P., Seattle, WA; *U.S. Public*, pg. 1311

Mongan, Michell E., Mkt. Res. Analyst--Paddock Publications, Inc., Arlington Heights, IL; *U.S. Private*, pg. 833

Monk, Robert D., Chief Fin. Officer--Triple S Plastics, Inc., Vicksburg, MI; *U.S. Public*, pg. 1639

Monsma, Calvin J., Chief Fin. Officer, V.P. & Sec.--Trion, Inc., Sanford, NC; *U.S. Public*, pg. 1639

Montgomery, R.L., Chief Fin. Officer, Exec. V.P. & Treas.--Columbus McKinnon Corp., Amherst, NY; *U.S. Public*, pg. 405

Moor, Samuel, Dir.-Inv. Rels.--Hesta Tex AG, Zug, Switzerland; *Int'l*, pg. 617

Moore, Dennis G., Chief Fin. Officer, Sr. V.P., Treas. & Sec.--J & J Snack Foods Corporation, Pennsauken, NJ; *U.S. Public*, pg. 916

Moore, Margaret D., V.P.-Investor Rels.--PepsiCo, Inc., Purchase, NY; *U.S. Public*, pg. 1276

Moore, Patricia K., Dir.-Investor Rels.--ESCO Electronics Corporation, Saint Louis, MO; *U.S. Public*, pg. 546

Mooty, Charles W., Chief Fin. Officer, V.P. & Treas.--International Dairy Queen, Inc., Minneapolis, MN; *U.S. Public*, pg. 220

Moran, Kathy, Mgr.-Investor Rels. & Admin. Asst.--Marine Drilling Companies, Inc., Sugar Land, TX; *U.S. Public*, pg. 1044

Moran, Patricia K., Corp. Sec. & Asst. Treas.--Zemex Corporation, Toronto, Canada; *Int'l*, pg. 1523

Morgan, Elizabeth K., Sec.--Hitox Corporation of America, Corpus Christi, TX; *U.S. Public*, pg. 829

Morgan, Laurie G., Exec. Dir.-Investor Rels.--Foster's Brewing Group Limited, Southbank, Australia; *Int'l*, pg. 500

Morgan, Marsha K., V.P.-Investor Relations & Sec.--Burlington Northern Santa Fe Corporation, Fort Worth, TX; *U.S. Public*, pg. 268

Morgensai, Lisa, Mgr.-Investor Rels.--Collagen Corporation, Palo Alto, CA; *U.S. Public*, pg. 399

Morin, Rudolph G., Chief Fin. Officer & Exec. V.P.-Opers. & Fin.--Network Computing Devices, Inc., Mountain View, CA; *U.S. Public*, pg. 1168

Morris, Donna R., Dir.-Investor Rels., Asst. Sec. & Treas.--Walk, Haydel & Associates, Inc., New Orleans, LA; *Int'l*, pg. 624

Morris, Jack H., V.P.-Corp. Rels.--Newmont Mining Corporation, Denver, CO; *U.S. Public*, pg. 1178

Morris, T.N., Jr., Chm., Pres. & Chief Exec. Officer--Calcasieu Lumber Company, Austin, TX; *U.S. Private*, pg. 200

Morrow, Kevin, Mgr.-Investor Rels.--Structural Dynamics Research Corp., Milford, OH; *U.S. Public*, pg. 1525

Morrow, Roy, Dir.-Corp. Communications--The Lincoln Electric Company, Cleveland, OH; *U.S. Public*, pg. 996

Morse, John B. Jr., Chief Fin. Officer & V.P.-Fin.--The Washington Post Company, Washington, DC; *U.S. Public*, pg. 1742

Morton, Billy, V.P.-Fin.--Plains Cotton Co-op Association, Lubbock, TX; *U.S. Private*, pg. 868

Mosby, Marty, Sr. V.P.-Strategic Plng. & Investor Rels.--First Tennessee National Corporation, Memphis, TN; *U.S. Public*, pg. 638

Moses, Linda, Dir.-Investor Rels.--Quest Medical, Inc., Allen, TX; *U.S. Public*, pg. 1352

Moskowitz, Melvin A., Gen. Mgr.-Investor Rels. & Information Coord.--Mobil Oil Corporation, Fairfax, VA; *U.S. Public*, pg. 1118

Mosley, Lyndell G., Chief Fin. Officer, Treas. & Asst. Sec.--Monarch Cement Co., Humboldt, KS; *U.S. Public*, pg. 1123

Moulding, Linton, Chief Fin. Officer--Instron Corporation, Canton, MA; *U.S. Public*, pg. 882

Mountcastle, Laura L., V.P.-Investor Rels.--CMS Energy Corporation, Dearborn, MI; *U.S. Public*, pg. 279

Mountcastle, Laura L., V.P.-Investor Rels.--Consumers Energy, Jackson, MI; *U.S. Public*, pg. 280

Moynahan, John F., V.P. & Treas.--Joy Mining Machinery, Warrendale, PA; *U.S. Public*, pg. 789

Mucciolo, Michael R., Chief Fin. Officer & Sr. V.P.--Beverage America, Inc., Holland, MI; *U.S. Private*, pg. 141

Mueller, Thomas W., Controller & Asst. Treas.--Kentucky Medical Insurance Company (KMIC), Louisville, KY; *U.S. Private*, pg. 741

Muhr, Alexandra, Dir.-Inv. Rels.--Heidelberger Druckmaschinen A.G., Heidelberg, Germany; *Int'l*, pg. 604

Muir, Bill, Gen. Dir.-New York--General Motors Corporation, Detroit, MI; *U.S. Public*, pg. 718

Muir, Douglas R., Sr. V.P., Treas. & Sec.--Oakwood Homes Corporation, Greensboro, NC; *U.S. Public*, pg. 1209

Mulligan, M. Isabelle, Sr. V.P.-Investor Rels.--Barrick Gold Corporation, Toronto, Canada; *Int'l*, pg. 168

Mulligan, Rosemary L., V.P.-Investor & Pub. Rels.--Centris Group Inc., Costa Mesa, CA; *U.S. Public*, pg. 328

Mullins, Roy L., Jr., Pres. & Chief Exec. Officer--Beacon Sales Corporation, Jacksonville, FL; *U.S. Private*, pg. 126

Mullis, Kristi, Dir.-Investor Rels.--Discount Auto Parts, Inc., Lakeland, FL; *U.S. Public*, pg. 510

Mundt, Thomas P., V.P.-Strategic Plng., Investor Rels. & Communications--Wolverine World Wide, Inc., Rockford, MI; *U.S. Public*, pg. 1775

Mura, H., V.P.-Joint Ventures & Plng.--Centeon, L.L.C., King of Prussia, PA; *Int'l*, pg. 626

Muracco, Louis J., Treas.--The Lehigh Press, Inc., Cherry Hill, NJ; *U.S. Private*, pg. 658

Murphy, Edwin J., Sr. V.P.-Equity & Investor Services--McGraw-Hill Financial Information Services Group, New York, NY; *U.S. Public*, pg. 1071

Murphy, William, Chief Fin. Officer, Exec. V.P. & Sec.--Computer Horizons Corp., Mountain Lakes, NJ; *U.S. Public*, pg. 421

Murray-Negron, Carol, V.P.-Investor Rels.--Avon Products, Inc., New York, NY; *U.S. Public*, pg. 155

Murray, Gregg A., V.P.-Client Services--Key Risk Management Services, Inc., Greensboro, NC; *U.S. Public*, pg. 216

Murray, John A., Chief Fin. Officer, V.P. & Treas.--Moore Medical Corp., New Britain, CT; *U.S. Public*, pg. 1128

Murray, John M., V.P.-Fin. & Treas.--American Precision Industries Inc., Buffalo, NY; *U.S. Public*, pg. 90

Murray, Marcia Y., Mgr.-Investor Rels.--Wolverine Tube Inc., Huntsville, AL; *U.S. Public*, pg. 1774

Musil, Ruthellyn, V.P.-Corp. Rels.--Tribune Company, Chicago, IL; *U.S. Public*, pg. 1635

Mycek, Patricia M., Sec.--Philadelphia Suburban Corporation, Bryn Mawr, PA; *U.S. Public*, pg. 1287

Myers, David, Mgr.-Investor Rels.--Kansas City Power & Light Company, Kansas City, MO; *U.S. Public*, pg. 943

Myers, Gary L., V.P., Gen. Counsel & Sec.--St. Joseph Light & Power Co., Saint Joseph, MO; *U.S. Public*, pg. 1427

Myers, Mark, Dir.-Fin. Analysis--Florida Progress Corporation, Saint Petersburg, FL; *U.S. Public*, pg. 655

Nabors, James D., Chief Fin. Officer & Exec. V.P.--Russell Corporation, Alexander City, AL; *U.S. Public*, pg. 1413

Nadal, Christian, Exec. V.P.-Corp. Communication & Pub. Affairs--Electricite de France, Paris, France; *Int'l*, pg. 437

Nagle, T.W., Exec. V.P.-Fin. & Admin.--Reading & Bates Corporation, Houston, TX; *U.S. Public*, pg. 1354

Nahirny, Michael, Chief Fin. Officer & Exec. V.P.-Fin. & Admin.--Cara Operations Limited, Toronto, Canada; *Int'l*, pg. 266

Nakamura, Hiroshi, Mgr.-Inv. Rels.--Futaba Corporation, Mobara, Japan; *Int'l*, pg. 531

Naman, Margie, V.P.-Investor Rels.--Ruby Tuesday, Inc., Mobile, AL; *U.S. Public*, pg. 1411

Namiot, Milton, Pres. & Chief Exec. Officer--Deering Ice Cream, Inc., Portland, ME; *U.S. Private*, pg. 403

Nance, Renne, V.P.-Member Rels.--Mid-America Dairymen, Inc., Springfield, MO; *U.S. Private*, pg. 743

Nardecchin, John, Mgr.-Finacial Reporting--Norstan, Inc., Plymouth, MN; *U.S. Public*, pg. 1192

Natathanapat, Chutima, Sr. V.P.-Policy & Plng.--The Industrial Finance Corporation of Thailand, Bangkok, Thailand; *Int'l*, pg. 677

Navarro, Agie, Asst. Corp. Sec.--Optical Coating Laboratory, Inc., Santa Rosa, CA; *U.S. Public*, pg. 1227

Navratil, Bonnie, Mgr.-Investor Rels. & Corp. Travel Planner--Innovex, Inc., Hopkins, MN; *U.S. Public*, pg. 880

Naylor, G.F., Dir.-Investor Rels. & Pub. Rels.--The RTZ Corporation PLC, London, United Kingdom; *Int'l*, pg. 1118

Neal, Donna, Dir.-Mkt. Res.--Miller Brewing Company, Milwaukee, WI; *U.S. Public*, pg. 1289

Neal, Mark, Sr. V.P.-Corp. Plng.--Coast Savings Financial, Inc., Los Angeles, CA; *U.S. Public*, pg. 388

Nehrkorn, William H., V.P., Gen. Counsel & Sec.--Heil Environmental Industries, Chattanooga, TN; *U.S. Public*, pg. 520

Neidus, Stuart D., Chief Fin. Officer & Exec. V.P.--Essef Corporation, Chardon, OH; *U.S. Public*, pg. 592

Neis, Douglas A., Chief Fin. Officer & Treas.--The Marcus Corporation, Milwaukee, WI; *U.S. Public*, pg. 1044

Nelson, Craig D., V.P.-Corp. Services--AmerenCIPS, Springfield, IL; *U.S. Public*, pg. 65

Nelson, Jane E., Gen. Counsel & Sec.--CPI Corp., Saint Louis, MO; *U.S. Public*, pg. 283

Nelson, L. Scott, Exec. V.P.-Investor Rels.--First Security Corporation, Salt Lake City, UT; *U.S. Public*, pg. 637

Nelson, Margaret, Dir.-Communications--Ponderosa Steakhouse, Dallas, TX; *U.S. Private*, pg. 736

Nelson, Rachel, Dir.-Investor Rels. & Copr. Communs.--Jumbo Sports Inc., Tampa, FL; *U.S. Public*, pg. 935

Nelson, Robert E., V.P.-Fin. Plng. & Investor Rels.--Costco Wholesale, Issaquah, WA; *U.S. Public*, pg. 451

Nelson, Wesley, V.P. & Sec.--H.E. Butt Grocery Co., San Antonio, TX; *U.S. Private*, pg. 190

Neonan, Michael D., Mgr.-Investor Rels.--Sterling Chemicals Holdings, Inc., Houston, TX; *U.S. Public*, pg. 1515

Nermyr, Jim, V.P. & Treas.--Musicland Group Inc., Minnetonka, MN; *U.S. Public*, pg. 1142

Nerone, Maureen, Chief Fin. Officer, V.P. & Controller--Colony Liquor Distributors, Inc., Kingston, NY; *U.S. Private*, pg. 254

Neskey, David A., Chief Fin. Officer & Exec. V.P.--Spaulding & Slye, Boston, MA; *U.S. Private*, pg. 1021

Netkovick, Michael J., Mgr.-Public Rels. & Investor Rels.--EnergyNorth, Inc., Manchester, NH; *U.S. Public*, pg. 581

Neville, James D., Chief Fin. Officer, Exec. V.P., Treas. & Sec.--The North American Manufacturing Co., Cleveland, OH; *U.S. Private*, pg. 803

Nevins, Lew, V.P.-Investor Rels.--USA Waste Services, Inc., Houston, TX; *U.S. Public*, pg. 1686

Newcomer, R.P., Chief Fin. Officer & Sr. V.P.--P.H. Glatfelter Company, Spring Grove, PA; *U.S. Public*, pg. 746

Newman, Betsy, Investor Rels.--Sterling Financial Corporation, Spokane, WA; *U.S. Public*, pg. 1516

Newman, Jeffrey C., Treas.--Madison Gas and Electric Company, Madison, WI; *U.S. Public*, pg. 1032

Newman, Ronald P., Chief Fin. Officer, V.P.-Fin., Treas. & Sec.--Watsco, Inc., Coconut Grove, FL; *U.S. Public*, pg. 1745

Newton, Clay, Chief Fin. Officer & Treas.--Equity Oil Company, Salt Lake City, UT; *U.S. Public*, pg. 590

Nichols, Donna C., V.P.-Corp. Communications--Agouron Pharmaceuticals, Inc., La Jolla, CA; *U.S. Public*, pg. 28
Nicholson, David C., Chief Fin. Officer & Sr. V.P.--Rock-Tenn Company, Norcross, GA; *U.S. Public*, pg. 1396
Nichter, Mark S., Controller, Sec. & Dir.-Investor Rels.--Continental Materials Corporation, Chicago, IL; *U.S. Public*, pg. 441
Nicks, John, Investor Rels.--I-Flow Corporation, Lake Forest, CA; *U.S. Public*, pg. 851
Nicoletti, Thomas, V.P.-Investor Rels. & Bus. Devel.--Altera Corporation, San Jose, CA; *U.S. Public*, pg. 59
Nida, Rick, Mgr.-Investor Rels.--Payless ShoeSource, Inc., Topeka, KS; *U.S. Public*, pg. 1268
Nielsen, Claude B., Pres. & Chief Exec. Officer--Coca-Cola Bottling Co. United, Inc., Birmingham, AL; *U.S. Private*, pg. 248
Niemann, Kimber, Mgr.-Investor Rels.--Sunstone Hotel Investors, Inc., San Clemente, CA; *U.S. Public*, pg. 1536
Nilsen, Barbara Y., Sec.--SJW Corp., San Jose, CA; *U.S. Public*, pg. 1418
Nilsson, David O., Mgr.-Plng. & Analysis--Pamida Holdings Corporation, Omaha, NE; *U.S. Public*, pg. 1255
Nix, Jerry W., Sr. V.P.-Fin.--Genuine Parts Company, Atlanta, GA; *U.S. Public*, pg. 732
Noble, Richard W., V.P. & Treas.--Hanovia Colight, Union, NJ; *Int'l*, pg. 17
Nobles, Dolores, Mgr.-Inv. Rels.--Southeastern Michigan Gas Enterprises, Inc., Port Huron, MI; *U.S. Public*, pg. 1489
Nobori, Tsuyoshi, Dir.-Pub. Rels.--Sankyo Company Limited, Tokyo, Japan; *Int'l*, pg. 1189
Nolan, Christopher W., Dir.-Investor Rels.--International Specialty Products, Inc., Wayne, NJ; *U.S. Public*, pg. 858
Nolan, Patrick J., Chief Fin. Officer & Sr. V.P.-Fin.--Levitz Furniture Incorporated, Boca Raton, FL; *U.S. Public*, pg. 990
Nolen, Kathleen F., Mgr.-Investor Rels.--Central Louisiana Electric Company, Inc., Pineville, LA; *U.S. Public*, pg. 325
Noorian, Robert E., Dir.-Investor Rels.--Southern Pacific Rail Corporation, San Francisco, CA; *U.S. Public*, pg. 1668
Norberg, Paul A., Chief Fin. Officer & Exec. V.P.--Western Staff Services, Walnut Creek, CA; *U.S. Public*, pg. 1760
Norelid, Jan A., Chief Fin. Officer, V.P.-Fin. & Treas.--Devcon International Corp., Deerfield Beach, FL; *U.S. Public*, pg. 502
Norman, E.J., V.P.-Admin., Gen. Counsel & Sec.--Trico Products Corporation, Buffalo, NY; *Int'l*, pg. 1397
Normansell, Susan, Officer-Investment--United Missouri Bank of St. Louis, Saint Louis, MO; *U.S. Public*, pg. 1655
Norris, Brian, Mgr.-Fin. & Shareholder Svcs.--Colonial Gas Company, Lowell, MA; *U.S. Public*, pg. 400
Norris, Kiley, Investor Rels.--Compuware Corporation, Farmington Hills, MI; *U.S. Public*, pg. 423
Norton, Mary, Dir.-Investor Rels.--GTECH Corporation, West Greenwich, RI; *U.S. Public*, pg. 767
Norton, Mike, Dir.-Investor Rels., Strategic Plng. & Budget--UCAR International Inc., Danbury, CT; *U.S. Public*, pg. 1662
Norton, Robert R., Chm. Bd., Pres. & Chief Exec. Officer--BeefAmerica Operating Co., Inc., Omaha, NE; *U.S. Private*, pg. 130
Nunemaker, Richard A., Chief Fin. Officer & V.P.-Fin.--Varlen Corporation, Naperville, IL; *U.S. Public*, pg. 1710
Nuzzo, Sal J., Chm. Bd. & Chief Exec. Officer--Datron Incorporated, Windsor, CT; *U.S. Private*, pg. 313
O'Brien, Stephen, Dir.-Corp. Affairs--Dixons Group plc, Hemel Hempstead, United Kingdom,; *Int'l*, pg. 413
O'Connell, Chris, Dir.-Investor Rels.--Medtronic, Inc., Minneapolis, MN; *U.S. Public*, pg. 1082
O'Connell, James M., Chief Fin. Officer, V.P., Treas. & Sec.--Landauer, Inc., Glenwood, IL; *U.S. Public*, pg. 977
O'Connor, Kevin, Sr. V.P. & Investment Officer--North Fork Bancorporation, Inc., Melville, NY; *U.S. Public*, pg. 1194
O'Connor, Kevin G., Dir.-Corp. Fin.--Arinc Inc. (Consolidated), Annapolis, MD; *U.S. Private*, pg. 81
O'Connor, Marie, Sec.--HMI Industries, Cleveland, OH; *U.S. Public*, pg. 771
O'Connor, Tim, V.P.-Investor Rels. & Treas.--ICF Kaiser International Inc., Fairfax, VA; *U.S. Public*, pg. 852
O'Donnell, Nancy, Dir.-Investor Rels.--Georgia Gulf Corporation, Atlanta, GA; *U.S. Public*, pg. 734
O'Donnell, Nancy R., Asst. V.P.-Investor Rels.--Equifax Inc., Atlanta, GA; *U.S. Public*, pg. 588
O'Hayre, David E., Sr. V.P.-Investments--Time Warner Cable, Stamford, CT; *U.S. Public*, pg. 1610
O'Keefe, John, Dir.-Investor Rels.--Oryx Energy, Dallas, TX; *U.S. Public*, pg. 1232
O'Leary, Bob, Chief Fin. Officer & Sr. V.P.--Cox Enterprises, Inc., Atlanta, GA; *U.S. Private*, pg. 281
O'Malia, David T., Exec. V.P. & Gen. Counsel--O'Malia Food Markets Inc., Carmel, IN; *U.S. Private*, pg. 816
O'Malley, Michael, Chief Oper. & Fin. Officer & V.P.-Fin.--TelCom Semiconductor, Inc., Mountain View, CA; *U.S. Public*, pg. 1569
O'Meara, Christopher G., V.P. & Treas.--Adaptec, Inc., Milpitas, CA; *U.S. Public*, pg. 19
O'Neil, Frank B., Sr. V.P.-Corp. Commun.--Medical Assurance, Inc., Birmingham, AL; *U.S. Public*, pg. 1079
O'Neill, John T., Chief Fin. Officer & Exec. V.P.--Hasbro, Inc., Pawtucket, RI; *U.S. Public*, pg. 797
O'Neill, Sean P., Mgr.-Investor Rels. & Plng.--Daniel Industries, Inc., Houston, TX; *U.S. Public*, pg. 482
O'Reilly, Dennis J., Asst. Treas.--Midwest Express Holdings, Inc., Oak Creek, WI; *U.S. Public*, pg. 1111
O'Rourke, Betsy Bromberg, V.P.-Corp. Rels.--Choice Hotels International, Inc., Silver Spring, MD; *U.S. Public*, pg. 351
O'Shea, Kevin, V.P.-Investor Rels. & Treas.--Bell & Howell Holdings, Skokie, IL; *U.S. Public*, pg. 201
Oak, Alan D., Chief Fin. Officer, Sr. V.P.-Fin. & Treas.--TECO Energy, Inc., Tampa, FL; *U.S. Public*, pg. 1565
Oakland, William, Dir.-Investor Rels.--AMP Incorporated, Harrisburg, PA; *U.S. Public*, pg. 7
Oatman, David C., V.P.-Investor Rels. & Corp. Devel.--Pool Energy Services Co., Houston, TX; *U.S. Public*, pg. 1316
Oberg, Leeny, Asst. V.P.-Investor Rels.--SLM Holding Corp., Washington, DC; *U.S. Public*, pg. 1419
Ocasek, Ronald W., Chief Fin. Officer, Sr. V.P. & Treas.--Riser Foods, Inc., Bedford, OH; *U.S. Private*, pg. 450
Ockrent, Isabelle, V.P.-Corp. Communications & External Rels.--SEITA, Societe Nationale D'Exploitation Industrielle des Tabacs et des Allumettes, Paris, France; *Int'l*, pg. 1219
Oftedal, Marianne, Mgr.-Inv. Rels.--Incentive AB, Stockholm, Sweden; *Int'l*, pg. 666
Oglesby, Donna, Dir.-Corp. Communications--Adams Resources & Energy, Inc., Houston, TX; *U.S. Public*, pg. 18
Ohmart, Misty, Mgr.-Investor Rels.--Autodesk, Inc., San Rafael, CA; *U.S. Public*, pg. 148
Ojert, Leno, V.P.-Communications & Pub. Affairs--Scancem AB, Malmo, Sweden; *Int'l*, pg. 1198
Okle, Debbie L., Dir.-Pub. Rels.--Commercial Metals Company, Dallas, TX; *U.S. Public*, pg. 411
Okun, Jane, Dir.-Investor Rels.--Northwest Airlines, Inc., Saint Paul, MN; *U.S. Public*, pg. 1200
Oliver, Darlene, Investor Rels. Specialist--Lam Research Corporation, Fremont, CA; *U.S. Public*, pg. 975
Oliveri, Elena R., V.P. & Treas.--Don Alleson, Inc., Rochester, NY; *U.S. Private*, pg. 339
Olson, David, V.P.-Investor Rels.--Foundation Health Systems, Inc., Pueblo, CO; *U.S. Public*, pg. 678
Olson, Joyce K., Admin. Asst.--Advantage Companies, Inc., Wichita, KS; *U.S. Private*, pg. 22
Olson, Karla, Dir.-Investor Rels.--Interpoint, Redmond, WA; *U.S. Public*, pg. 457
Olson, Nan R., Mgr.-Shareholder Svcs.--Minnesota Power, Duluth, MN; *U.S. Public*, pg. 1116
Olson, Rodney E., Chief Fin. Officer & Sr. V.P.-Fin. & Corp. Devel.--Sabreliner Corporation, Saint Louis, MO; *U.S. Private*, pg. 959
Omachinski, D.L., Chief Fin. Officer, V.P.-Fin. & Treas.--OshKosh B'Gosh, Inc., Oshkosh, WI; *U.S. Public*, pg. 1232
Ong, Bill, Dir.-Investor Rels.--Applied Materials, Inc., Santa Clara, CA; *U.S. Public*, pg. 123
Ong, John, Dir.-Corp. Rels.--Ladd Furniture, Inc., Greensboro, NC; *U.S. Public*, pg. 974
Onoda, John C., V.P.-Corp. Communications--General Motors Corporation, Detroit, MI; *U.S. Public*, pg. 718
Onodera, Yasuo, Gen. Mgr.-Corp. Commun.--Toyo Tire & Rubber Co., Ltd., Osaka, Japan; *Int'l*, pg. 1411
Oram, John, Pres.--ICC Industries, Inc., New York, NY; *U.S. Private*, pg. 553
Orlando, Anthony, V.P.-Investor Rels.--OppenheimerFunds Distributor, Inc., New York, NY; *U.S. Private*, pg. 818
Ornstein, R. Jeffrey, Chief Fin. Officer, V.P.-Fin. & Treas.--Superior Industries International, Inc., Van Nuys, CA; *U.S. Public*, pg. 1539
Orr, Graham, Exec. V.P.-Corp. Develop.--Magna International Inc., Markham, Canada; *Int'l*, pg. 829
Orza, Vincent F., Jr., Chm. Bd., Pres. & Chief Exec. Officer--Eateries, Inc., Oklahoma City, OK; *U.S. Public*, pg. 555
Osorio, Gus, Dir.-Pub. Rels.--The Toronto Dominion Bank, Toronto, Canada; *Int'l*, pg. 1401
Oster, Helen P., Sec.--Baldwin Technology Company, Inc., Norwalk, CT; *U.S. Public*, pg. 169
Oster, Richard, Chief Fin. Officer & Sr. V.P.-Fin.--Crowley Maritime Corporation, Oakland, CA; *U.S. Private*, pg. 292
Osterland, William, Dir.-Investor Rels.--The Clorox Company, Oakland, CA; *U.S. Public*, pg. 386
Osterman, John C., Pres., Chief Oper. Officer & Treas.--Chicago Rivet & Machine Company, Naperville, IL; *U.S. Public*, pg. 348
Otis, Clarence, Jr., Sr. V.P.-Investor Rels. & Treas.--Darden Restaurants, Inc., Orlando, FL; *U.S. Public*, pg. 483
Ott, James H., Chm. Bd.--Novar Electronics, Barberton, OH; *U.S. Private*, pg. 808
Ottem, Roger, Controller--Hawkins Chemical, Inc., Minneapolis, MN; *U.S. Public*, pg. 800
Otto, H., Mgr.-Inv. Rels.--Volkswagen AG, Wolfsburg, Germany; *Int'l*, pg. 1473
Ousback, Lars, Mgr.-Investor Rels.--Pharmacia & Upjohn, Inc., Windsor, United Kingdom; *Int'l*, pg. 1047
Outman, Janet, Mgr.-Investor Rels.--First of America Bank Corporation, Kalamazoo, MI; *U.S. Public*, pg. 636
Owada, Hitoshi, Dir.--Advantest Corporation, Tokyo, Japan; *Int'l*, pg. 25
Oxford, W. Cliff, Sr. V.P.-Corp. & Human Devel.--Lowe's Companies, Inc., North Wilkesboro, NC; *U.S. Public*, pg. 1015
Ozaslan, Linda, Admin.-Investor Rels.--Fresh Choice, Inc., Santa Clara, CA; *U.S. Public*, pg. 682
Ozoles, Nancy, Mgr.-Lnvestor Rels. & Office Svcs.--Applied Microsystems Corporation, Redmond, WA; *U.S. Public*, pg. 123
Pack, Sterling, Sr. V.P.-Investor Rels.--The Coastal Corporation, Houston, TX; *U.S. Public*, pg. 389
Page, Russell J., Dir.-Investor Rels.--NationsBank Corporation, Charlotte, NC; *U.S. Public*, pg. 1162
Pagrabs, Juris, V.P.-Investor Rels.--Woolworth Corporation, New York, NY; *U.S. Public*, pg. 1777
Pahidis, Gus P., Chm. Bd.--Cedar Farms Company, Inc., Philadelphia, PA; *U.S. Private*, pg. 221
Palea, Anna, Mgr.-Pub. Rels.--Cannon Rubber Ltd., London, United Kingdom; *Int'l*, pg. 261
Palizza, John M., Dir.-Investor Rels. & Asst. Treas.--Walgreen Co., Deerfield, IL; *U.S. Public*, pg. 1733
Palladino, Robert, Dir.-Investor Rels.--C.P. Clare Corporation, Beverly, MA; *U.S. Public*, pg. 382
Panagos, Gregory S., V.P.-Corp. Commun.--Pennzoil Company, Houston, TX; *U.S. Public*, pg. 1272
Paola, Carolyn, Coord.-Investor Rels.--Active Voice Corporation, Seattle, WA; *U.S. Public*, pg. 17
Paolercio, Michael Anthony, Sr. V.P. & Treas.--Michael Anthony Jewelers, Inc., Mount Vernon, NY; *U.S. Public*, pg. 1103
Papa, Vincent T., V.P. & Treas.--Orion Capital Corporation, New York, NY; *U.S. Public*, pg. 1231
Pape, Eldon C., Chief Fin. & Plng. Officer & Exec. V.P.--Omaha Public Power District, Omaha, NE; *U.S. Private*, pg. 815
Pappano, Robert D., V.P.-Fin. Reporting & Investor Rels.--W.W. Grainger, Inc., Lincolnshire, IL; *U.S. Public*, pg. 758
Paradis, Robert D., Chief Fin. Officer, V.P. & Sec.--Yale/Chase Materials Handling, Inc., City of Industry, CA; *U.S. Private*, pg. 1195
Paras, Philip G., V.P.-Fin. & Treas.--Seneca Foods Corporation, Pittsford, NY; *U.S. Public*, pg. 1456
Pardee, Diane Berry, V.P.-Corp. Commun.--Journal Register Company, Trenton, NJ; *U.S. Public*, pg. 934
Parke, Hervey, Dir.-Investor Rels.--International Business Machines Corporation, Armonk, NY; *U.S. Public*, pg. 895
Parker, Alan, Mgr.-Investor Rels.--Ben & Jerry's Homemade Inc., South Burlington, VT; *U.S. Public*, pg. 210
Parker, D. Michael, Chief Fin. Officer, V.P.-Fin., Sec. & Treas.--Kewaunee Scientific Corporation, Statesville, NC; *U.S. Public*, pg. 953
Parker, Earle L., V.P. & Treas.--C.R. Bard, Inc., Murray Hill, NJ; *U.S. Public*, pg. 189
Parker, Joanne, Dir.-Investor Rels.--Reebok International Ltd., Stoughton, MA; *U.S. Public*, pg. 1369
Parker, Keith L., Sr. V.P.--Mercury General Corporation, Los Angeles, CA; *U.S. Public*, pg. 1093
Parks, Walter J., Chief Fin. Officer & Sr. V.P.--AnnTaylor Stores Corporation, New York, NY; *U.S. Public*, pg. 116
Parsons, Craig A., Sr. V.P.-Corp. Commun. & Investor Rels.--Metro-Goldwyn-Mayer Inc., Santa Monica, CA; *U.S. Public*, pg. 1101
Pasinski, Janess, Mgr.-Investor Rels.--Apollo Group, Inc., Phoenix, AZ; *U.S. Public*, pg. 120
Pasley, George W., V.P.-Commun.--Global Industrial Technologies, Dallas, TX; *U.S. Public*, pg. 747
Paterson, David, V.P.-Corp. Affairs--Agra Inc., Calgary, Canada; *Int'l*, pg. 30
Patterson, Kate, Mgr.-Investor Rels.--3Com Corporation, Santa Clara, CA; *U.S. Public*, pg. 1603
Patton, Richard, V.P.-Investments--Ingram Industries Inc., Nashville, TN; *U.S. Private*, pg. 562
Paul, Gary S., Sr. V.P.--First Empire State Corporation, Buffalo, NY; *U.S. Public*, pg. 631
Payne, Dick, Grp. V.P.-Client Relations--Total System Services, Inc., Columbus, GA; *U.S. Public*, pg. 1550
Payne, Gayle S., Dir.-Shareholder Svcs.--WLR Foods, Inc., Timberville, VA; *U.S. Public*, pg. 1727
Payne, H. Alan, V.P.-Investor Rels.--Seagull Energy Corporation, Houston, TX; *U.S. Public*, pg. 1450
Payne, J., Gen. Mgr.-Investor Rels.--Qantas Airways Ltd., Mascot, Australia; *Int'l*, pg. 1074
Peapples, George A., V.P.-Indus. Govt. Rels.--General Motors Corporation, Detroit, MI; *U.S. Public*, pg. 718
Pearce, Randy L., V.P.-Fin. & Investor Rels.--Regis Corporation, Minneapolis, MN; *U.S. Public*, pg. 1373
Pearson, John W., Dir.-Investor Rels.--Pegasus Gold Corporation, Spokane, WA; *U.S. Public*, pg. 1269
Peck, David, Dir.-Fin. & Investor Rels.--Mitchell Energy & Development Corp., Spring, TX; *U.S. Public*, pg. 1117
Peck, Thomas K., V.P.-Investor Rels.--Duke Realty Investments, Inc., Indianapolis, IN; *U.S. Public*, pg. 535
Peddy, Courtland D., V.P. & Treas.--Republic Industries, Inc., Fort Lauderdale, FL; *U.S. Public*, pg. 1378
Peel, Walter W., Asst. Treas.--DIMON, Incorporated, Danville, VA; *U.S. Public*, pg. 509
Peier, Heino, Mgr.-Communication--Coop Switzerland, Basel, Switzerland; *Int'l*, pg. 329
Pekor, Allan J., V.P.-Fin.--Lennar Corporation, Miami, FL; *U.S. Public*, pg. 987
Pendergast, Robert W., V.P.-Corp. Communications--Media General, Inc., Richmond, VA; *U.S. Public*, pg. 1077
Penno, D. Bruce, Chief Fin. Officer & Treas.--Pridgeon & Clay, Inc., Grand Rapids, MI; *U.S. Private*, pg. 883
Pennza, Laura, Mgr.-Investor Rels.--Aydin Corporation, Horsham, PA; *U.S. Public*, pg. 158
Pentti, Petri, Treas.--FinnAir Oy, Helsinki, Finland; *Int'l*, pg. 485
Peoples, Dan, Dir.-Investor Rels.--Flowserve Corporation, Long Beach, CA; *U.S. Public*, pg. 658
Perkins, Mike, Mgr.-Investor Rels.--Methode Electronics Inc., Chicago, IL; *U.S. Public*, pg. 1101
Perkins, Robert, Dir.-Investor Rels.--QUALCOMM, San Diego, CA; *U.S. Public*, pg. 1348
Perkins, Roberta, Mgr.-Investor Rels.--Total Renal Care Holdings, Inc., Torrance, CA; *U.S. Public*, pg. 1625
Perlis, Morris, Pres.--Counsel Corporation, Toronto, Canada; *Int'l*, pg. 338
Pernorio, Maryann, Dir.-Investor Rels.--Providence Energy Corporation, Providence, RI; *U.S. Public*, pg. 1337
Perotina, Susan, Mgr.-Investor Rels.--Tesoro Petroleum Corporation, San Antonio, TX; *U.S. Public*, pg. 1581
Perruche, Christiane, Mng. Dir.-Investor Rels.--Groupe SEB, Ecueille, France; *Int'l*, pg. 568
Perry, Tracy, V.P.-Corp. Commun.--Maxwell Technologies, Inc., San Diego, CA; *U.S. Public*, pg. 1061
Pessin, Lisa, Investor Rels.--Apria Healthcare Group Inc., Costa Mesa, CA; *U.S. Public*, pg. 125
Peters, Jean, Mgr.-Investor Rels.--Allmerica Securities Trust, Worcester, MA; *U.S. Public*, pg. 54
Peters, Jean, V.P.-Investor Relations--Allmerica Financial Corporation, Worcester, MA; *U.S. Public*, pg. 54
Peters, Peggy, Mgr.-Investor Rels.--Tristar Corp., San Antonio, TX; *U.S. Public*, pg. 1640
Peterson, John D., V.P.-Investor Rels.--Grey Wolf, Inc., Houston, TX; *U.S. Public*, pg. 765
Peterson, Lisa, Coord.-Investor Rels.--ADFlex Solutions, Inc., Chandler, AZ; *U.S. Public*, pg. 20
Petersson, Roland, Dir.-Investor Rels.--Swedbank, Stockholm, Sweden; *Int'l*, pg. 1328
Petrie, Albert B., Dir.-Inv. Rels.--Burlington Resources Inc., Houston, TX; *U.S. Public*, pg. 269

Petrie, Albert B., Dir.-Investor Rels.--The Louisiana Land and Exploration Company, New Orleans, LA; *U.S. Public, pg. 269*

Pettine, John M., Chief Fin. Officer & V.P.--Tasty Baking Company, Philadelphia, PA; *U.S. Public,* pg. 1561

Pettipas, Gordon, Mgr.-Investor Rels.--Empire Company Limited, Stellarton, Canada; *Int'l,* pg. 453

Pfund, William H., V.P.-Investor Rels.--Rubbermaid Incorporated, Wooster, OH; *U.S. Public,* pg. 1411

Philips, Ronald, Controller--Key Food Stores Co-operative, Inc., Brooklyn, NY; *U.S. Private,* pg. 617

Philipsborn, Jan C., Dir.-Investor Communications--Pall Corporation, Greenvale, NY; *U.S. Public,* pg. 1253

Pickman, Steve, Dir.-Pub. & Investor Rels.--Midwest Grain Products, Inc., Atchison, KS; *U.S. Public,* pg. 1111

Pierce, Garrett E., Pres. & Chief Exec. Officer--Materials Research Corporation, Gilbert, AZ; *Int'l,* pg. 1283

Pierne, Jeffrey J., V.P.-Investor Rels. & Asst. Treas.--Sotheby's Holdings Inc., New York, NY; *U.S. Public,* pg. 1487

Pignone, Ed, Dir.-Investor Rels.--Wang Laboratories, Inc., Billerica, MA; *U.S. Public,* pg. 1737

Pihl, Larry D., Chief Fin. Officer, V.P.-Fin., Treas. & Controller--UTILX Corporation, Kent, WA; *U.S. Public,* pg. 1701

Pike, Lora L., Investor Rels. Specialist--Palomar Medical Technologies, Lexington, MA; *U.S. Public,* pg. 1255

Pike, William F., V.P.-Investor Rels.--Travelers Group, New York, NY; *U.S. Public,* pg. 1632

Pilliod, Barbara Kane, Mgr.- Investor Rels.--MapInfo Corp., Troy, NY; *U.S. Public,* pg. 1042

Pinsley, Barry, V.P.-Investor Rels.--Espey Mfg. & Electronics Corp., Saratoga Springs, NY; *U.S. Public,* pg. 592

Pinto, James J., Pres. & Chief Exec. Officer--Action Instruments, Inc., San Diego, CA; *U.S. Private,* pg. 15

Pinto, Susan, Dir.-Investor Rels.--Hyperion Software, Stamford, CT; *U.S. Public,* pg. 851

Piquee, Jean, Dir.-Investor Rels.--Elf Aquitane, Paris, France; *Int'l,* pg. 444

Pitcher, Sarah, V.P.-Corp. Commun.--Mesa Air Group, Las Vegas, NV; *U.S. Public,* pg. 1098

Pittman, David, Dir.-Mktg. Commun.--SPSS Inc., Chicago, IL; *U.S. Public,* pg. 1420

Pittman, Gary, Chm. Bd., Pres., Chief Exec., Chief Oper. & Chief Fin. Officer--PCI, Austin, TX; *U.S. Private,* pg. 826

Pittmen, Misty, Mgr.-Investor Rels.--Syntellect, Inc., Phoenix, AZ; *U.S. Public,* pg. 1550

Pitts, Kay, Coord.-Investor Rels.--UTILX Corporation, Kent, WA; *U.S. Public,* pg. 1701

Pleiman, Linda A., Mgr.-Investor Rels.--NS Group, Inc., Newport, KY; *U.S. Public,* pg. 1147

Plevyak, Laura, V.P.-Corp. Communications & Investor Rels.--CUC International, Inc., Stamford, CT; *U.S. Public, pg. 320*

Plott, Jackie, V.P.-Fin.--Associated Grocers of the South, Inc., Birmingham, AL; *U.S. Private,* pg. 91

Plunkett, William J., V.P.-Fin. & Investor Rels.--Waste Management, Inc., Oak Brook, IL; *U.S. Public,* pg. 1744

Polcyn, Steve, Sr. Dir.-Investor Rels.--Read-Rite Corporation, Milpitas, CA; *U.S. Public,* pg. 1366

Poling, Douglas E., Treas.--Ball Corporation, Muncie, IN; *U.S. Public,* pg. 170

Polishook, David, Chief Fin. Officer, Treas. & Sec.--The Strober Organization, Inc., Brooklyn, NY; *U.S. Private,* pg. 403

Pomerantz, Saul, Chief Fin. Officer, Sr. V.P. & Sec.--Movie Star, Inc., New York, NY; *U.S. Public,* pg. 1140

Pons, Miguel Angel, Dir.-Investor Rels.--El Puerto de Liverpool S.A., Mexico, Mexico; *Int'l,* pg. 435

Pope, Don L., V.P.-Investor Rels.--Burlington Resources Inc., Houston, TX; *U.S. Public,* pg. 269

Pope, J.M., Sec.--Cobham plc, Wimborne Minster, United Kingdom; *Int'l,* pg. 301

Pope, Maria M., Dir.-Inv. Rels. & Mgr.-Fin.--Pope & Talbot, Inc., Portland, OR; *U.S. Public,* pg. 1316

Porges, Dave, V.P.-Pub. Rels.--Coast Fed Services, Chatsworth, CA; *U.S. Public,* pg. 389

Porter, Ross, Mgr.-Investor Rels.--Newell Co., Freeport, IL; *U.S. Public,* pg. 1176

Posner, Barbara G., V.P.-Corp. Rels.--Tenneco Automotive, Deerfield, IL; *U.S. Public,* pg. 1577

Posner, Barbara L., V.P.-Fin. & Admin.--EA Engineering, Science & Technology, Inc., Hunt Valley, MD; *U.S. Public,* pg. 540

Possnecker, Falk, Mgr.-Investor Rels.--Durr AG, Stuttgart, Germany; *Int'l,* pg. 421

Post, Max H., Mgr.-Investor Rels.--Texas Instruments Incorporated, Dallas, TX; *U.S. Public,* pg. 1585

Potter, Michael J., Chief Fin. Officer & Sr. V.P.--Consolidated Stores Corp., Columbus, OH; *U.S. Public,* pg. 437

Powell, Jerry, Gen. Counsel & Sec.--Compass Bancshares, Inc., Birmingham, AL; *U.S. Public,* pg. 418

Powell, Joan, Mgr.-Investor Rels.--Consilium, Inc., Mountain View, CA; *U.S. Public,* pg. 434

Powell, Robert J., V.P.-Intl. Licensing, Sec. & Gen. Counsel--Signal Apparel Company, Inc., Chattanooga, TN; *U.S. Public,* pg. 1472

Prather, Robert S., Pres. & Chief Exec. Officer--Bull Run Corporation, Atlanta, GA; *U.S. Public,* pg. 267

Pressley, James Z., Jr., V.P.-Fin. & Admin. & Treas.--Transus Intermodal L.L.C., Atlanta, GA; *U.S. Private,* pg. 1097

Price, Barbara T., Supvr.-Investor Rels.--Nordson Corporation, Westlake, OH; *U.S. Public,* pg. 1188

Price, Bonnie J., V.P.-Investor Rels.--Federal-Mogul Corporation, Southfield, MI; *U.S. Public,* pg. 615

Price, Michael A., Treas.--RLI Corp., Peoria, IL; *U.S. Public,* pg. 1356

Price, Roy, Investor Rels.--CIS Technologies, Inc., Tulsa, OK; *U.S. Public,* pg. 1155

Prichard, David A., Mgr.-Investor Rels.--The Vigoro Corporation, Chicago, IL; *U.S. Public,* pg. 856

Prince, Michael, Investor Rels. Analyst--Devon Energy Corporation, Oklahoma City, OK; *U.S. Public,* pg. 503

Prince, Thomas E., Chief Fin. Officer & Exec. V.P.--Downey Savings & Loan Association, F.A., Newport Beach, CA; *U.S. Public,* pg. 526

Pritchard, Lisa, Dir.-Corp. Fin.--AGCO Corporation, Duluth, GA; *U.S. Public,* pg. 28

Pritchard, Mike, Mgr.-Fin. & Support Svcs.--New Century Energies, Inc., Denver, CO; *U.S. Public,* pg. 1170

Proctor, David C., Treas. & Asst. Clerk--Dynamics Research Corporation, Andover, MA; *U.S. Public,* pg. 539

Proell, Marge, Mgr.-Commun.--Piper Jaffray Companies, Inc., Minneapolis, MN; *U.S. Public,* pg. 1300

Proffer, Phylis, V.P.-Investor Rels.--ShopKo Stores, Inc., Green Bay, WI; *U.S. Public,* pg. 1467

Proost, Robert L., Corp. V.P. & Treas.--A.G. Edwards, Inc., Saint Louis, MO; *U.S. Public,* pg. 565

Prosser, John W., Jr., Sr. V.P.-Fin. & Admin. & Treas.--Jacobs Engineering Group Inc., Pasadena, CA; *U.S. Public,* pg. 921

Proveaux, Terry, Dir.-Investor Rels.--National Income Realty Trust, New York, NY; *U.S. Public,* pg. 1157

Provine, William, Dir.-Investor Rels.--Rowan Companies, Inc., Houston, TX; *U.S. Public,* pg. 1409

Przygoda, Martin, Asst. V.P.-Investor Rels.--The Allstate Corporation, Northbrook, IL; *U.S. Public,* pg. 55

Pulizzi, Louise E., Dir.-Corp. Communications--Clark Construction Group, Inc., Bethesda, MD; *U.S. Private,* pg. 242

Puliara, Gayle, Coord.-Inv. Rels.--Catalina Marketing Corporation, Saint Petersburg, FL; *U.S. Public,* pg. 314

Puma, Dennis, Investor Rels.--New Jersey Resources Corporation, Wall, NJ; *U.S. Public,* pg. 1172

Putnam, Eugene S., Jr., Sr. V.P.-Fin. & Investor Rels.--Crestar Financial Corporation, Richmond, VA; *U.S. Public,* pg. 458

Putnam, Richard, Dir.-Investor Rels.--Franklin Covey, Salt Lake City, UT; *U.S. Public,* pg. 679

Putrzebowski, Jeffrey, Dir.-Investor Rels.--Great Lakes Chemical Corporation, West Lafayette, IN; *U.S. Public,* pg. 760

Quadt, Gabriele, Dir.-Corp. Commun. & Investor Rels.--Dyckerhoff AG, Wiesbaden, Germany; *Int'l,* pg. 422

Quattrocchi, Cathy, Mgr.-Corp. Communications--Merisel, Inc., El Segundo, CA; *U.S. Public,* pg. 1095

Quemada, Jose MaMann, Dir.--Compania Espanola de Petroleos, S.A. (CEPSA), Madrid, Spain; *Int'l,* pg. 323

Quillard, Maria, Mgr.-Investor Rels.--Xilinx, Inc., San Jose, CA; *U.S. Public,* pg. 1786

Quillinan, Robert J., Chief Fin. Officer & Exec. V.P.--Coherent, Inc., Santa Clara, CA; *U.S. Public,* pg. 395

Quinlan, Elaine M., Mgr.-Investor Rels.--Meditrust Corporation, Needham, MA; *U.S. Public,* pg. 1081

Quinn, Tom, Chm. Bd.--American Safety Razor Company, Verona, VA; *U.S. Private,* pg. 597

Racine, Robert, Sr. V.P.-Pub. Affairs & Investor Rels.--SNC-Lavalin Group Inc., Montreal, Canada; *Int'l,* pg. 1161

Radisch, Judith C., Mgr.-Investor Rels.--MBIA Inc., Armonk, NY; *U.S. Public,* pg. 1023

Raffia, M.J., V.P.-Fin.--Kane-Miller Corp., Tarrytown, NY; *U.S. Private,* pg. 607

Ragland, David, Pres. & Chief Exec. Officer--Duncan Equipment Company, Oklahoma City, OK; *U.S. Private,* pg. 346

Rahmberg, Rolf, V.P.-Corp. Communications--Perstorp AB, Perstorp, Sweden; *Int'l,* pg. 1036

Railey, Susan B., V.P.-Shareholder Rels.--CRIIMI MAE, Rockville, MD; *U.S. Public,* pg. 459

Rajahalme, Aimo, Sr. V.P.-Fin. & Treas.--Kone Corporation, Helsinki, Finland; *Int'l,* pg. 746

Rajaji, Raj, Chief Fin. Officer & Sr. V.P.--BancTec, Inc., Dallas, TX; *U.S. Public,* pg. 176

Raleigh, John, Chief Fin. Officer & V.P.-Fin.--C.H. Heist Corp., Clearwater, FL; *U.S. Public,* pg. 807

Ralph, William L., Asst. Treas.--Number Nine Visual Technology, Lexington, MA; *U.S. Public,* pg. 1206

Ramat, Charles, Chm. Bd., Pres., Chief Exec. Officer & Asst. Sec.--Aris Industries, Inc., New York, NY; *U.S. Public,* pg. 129

Range, Cynthia A., Investor Rels. Specialist--Coca-Cola Enterprises Inc., Atlanta, GA; *U.S. Public,* pg. 393

Rangel, John J., Sr. V.P.-Fin.--K2 Inc., Los Angeles, CA; *U.S. Public,* pg. 940

Rant, Walter, V.P.-Investor Rels.--Essex Chemical Corporation, Clifton, NJ; *U.S. Public,* pg. 523

Rapp, James R., Dr., V.P.-Corp. Rels.--Hercules Incorporated, Wilmington, DE; *U.S. Public,* pg. 809

Rapp, Larry T., V.P. & Corp. Sec.--Electro Scientific Industries, Inc., Portland, OR; *U.S. Public,* pg. 568

Rasmussen, Dale L., Sr. V.P. & Sec.--AirSensors, Inc., Seattle, WA; *U.S. Public,* pg. 33

Rasmussen, Mogens Vang, Dir.-Investor Rels.-USA--Novo Nordisk A/S, Bagsvaerd, Denmark; *Int'l,* pg. 987

Ratkaj, Mira, Mgr.-Investor Rels.--Emco Limited, London, Canada; *Int'l,* pg. 452

Ravenel, Henry, Jr., V.P. & Dir.-Investor Rels.--Saul Centers Inc., Chevy Chase, MD; *U.S. Public,* pg. 1435

Ray, Daniel E., Sr. V.P.-Investment Banking--United Missouri Bank of St. Louis, Saint Louis, MO; *U.S. Public, pg. 1655*

Ray, Donna, Mgr.-Investor Publications--GPU, Inc., Morristown, NJ; *U.S. Public,* pg. 695

Ray, E. Wayne, Jr., Chief Fin. Officer, V.P. & Treas.--Riviana Foods Inc., Houston, TX; *U.S. Public,* pg. 1392

Rea, Jill M., Dir.-Investor Relations--Wellman, Inc., Shrewsbury, NJ; *U.S. Public,* pg. 1752

Read, Justin R., Mgr.-Investor Rels.--Hanson PLC, London, United Kingdom; *Int'l,* pg. 592

Reault, Cheryl, Dir.-Investor Rels.--Avid Technology, Inc., Tewksbury, MA; *U.S. Public,* pg. 154

Reece, Richard K., Chief Fin. Officer, V.P.-Fin. & Treas.--Belden Inc., Saint Louis, MO; *U.S. Public,* pg. 200

Reed, W. Earl, III, Chief Fin. Officer & Exec. V.P.--Vencor, Inc., Louisville, KY; *U.S. Public,* pg. 1711

Reed, Walter, Broker Mgr.-Southeast--Pangburn Candy Company, Fort Worth, TX; *U.S. Private,* pg. 836

Reeves, Katherine K., Mgr.--Krug International Corp., Houston, TX; *U.S. Public,* pg. 967

Regard, Gerard L., Asst. to Chm.--Holly Corporation, Dallas, TX; *U.S. Public,* pg. 830

Rehman, Mary Jane, Mgr.-Investor Rels.--Kimco Realty Corporation, New Hyde Park, NY; *U.S. Public,* pg. 960

Reichert, Jack, V.P.-Fin.--Interactive Technologies, Inc., Saint Paul, MN; *U.S. Public,* pg. 888

Reid, Timothy J., V.P.-Corp. Commun.--Brush Wellman Inc., Cleveland, OH; *U.S. Public,* pg. 266

Reiman, Beverly J., Dir.-Corp. Communication--The Standard Register Company, Dayton, OH; *U.S. Public,* pg. 1505

Reinhardt, J. Alec, Chief Fin. Officer & Exec. V.P.--Cooper Tire & Rubber Company, Findlay, OH; *U.S. Public,* pg. 445

Reiss, Nancy, Mgr.-Investor Communications--Southern New England Telecommunications Corporation, New Haven, CT; *U.S. Public,* pg. 1490

Reiter, William M., M.D., Chm. Bd., Pres. & Chief Exec. Officer--Health Professionals, Inc., Fort Lauderdale, FL; *U.S. Public,* pg. 802

Reitman, Alayne L., V.P.-Fin. & Treas.--The Tranzonic Companies, Pepper Pike, OH; *U.S. Public,* pg. 1632

Remedios, Robert T., Sr. V.P. & Cashier--SJNB Financial Corp., San Jose, CA; *U.S. Public,* pg. 1418

Renbarger, Larry D., Pres. & Chief Exec. Officer--Shelter Components Corporation, Elkhart, IN; *U.S. Public,* pg. 952

Rendano, Ronald E., Treas.--SEIKO Corporation of America, Mahwah, NJ; *Int'l,* pg. 1218

Renne, Paul F., Chief Fin. Officer & Exec. V.P.--H.J. Heinz Company, Pittsburgh, PA; *U.S. Public,* pg. 805

Renza, Karen, Mgr.-Investor Svcs.--Concord Assets Group, Boca Raton, FL; *U.S. Private,* pg. 261

Resweber, Lou, Sr. V.P.--Network Long Distance, Inc., Baton Rouge, LA; *U.S. Public,* pg. 1169

Retterath, William, Chief Fin. & Oper. Officer--Dakotah, Inc., Webster, SD; *U.S. Public,* pg. 477

Revak, Crystal L., Dir.-Investor Rels.--RMI Titanium Company, Niles, OH; *U.S. Public,* pg. 1662

Reville, David, Dir.-Corp. Commun.--Banknorth Group Inc., Burlington, VT; *U.S. Public,* pg. 186

Reyelts, Paul C., V.P.-Fin.--The Valspar Corporation, Minneapolis, MN; *U.S. Public,* pg. 1707

Reymann, Mary C., V.P.-Fin., Controller & Sec.--Flanigan's Enterprises, Inc., Fort Lauderdale, FL; *U.S. Public,* pg. 648

Reynolds, Debra, Mgr.-Investor Rels.--ShowBiz Pizza Time, Inc., Irving, TX; *U.S. Public,* pg. 1468

Reynolds, Marcia D., Coord.-Investor Rels.--Kuhlman Corporation, Savannah, GA; *U.S. Public,* pg. 968

Reynolds, Marion F., V.P., Treas. & Sec.--Middlesex Water Company, Iselin, NJ; *U.S. Public,* pg. 1110

Reynolds, Pat A., V.P. & Dir.-Investor Rels.--Synovus Financial Corp., Columbus, GA; *U.S. Public,* pg. 1548

Rhodes, Gary, Dir.-Investor Rels.--Gibson Greetings, Inc., Cincinnati, OH; *U.S. Public,* pg. 742

Rice, Fred B., Mgr.-Investor Rels.--Cleveland-Cliffs Inc, Cleveland, OH; *U.S. Public,* pg. 386

Rice, James, Sr V.P. & Controller--Essex International, Inc., Fort Wayne, IN; *U.S. Public,* pg. 593

Rice, Jerry, V.P.-Investor Rels.--Union Bank of California, San Francisco, CA; *Int'l,* pg. 157

Rice, Theresa, Exec. Admin. Asst.-Investor Rels.--ABC Rail Products Corp., Chicago, IL; *U.S. Public,* pg. 2

Rice, Thomas R., Dir.-Investor Rels.--Fleet Financial Group, Inc., Boston, MA; *U.S. Public,* pg. 648

Richardello, Michael, Co-owner--Butler Wholesale Products, Inc., Adams, MA; *U.S. Private,* pg. 190

Richardson, Charles, Dir.-Corp. Affairs--3i Group plc, London, United Kingdom; *Int'l,* pg. 1386

Richins, Paul O., Chief Admin. Officer, V.P. & Treas.--Utah Medical Products, Inc., Midvale, UT; *U.S. Public,* pg. 1700

Richter, Kirk A., Controller--Sigma-Aldrich Corporation, Saint Louis, MO; *U.S. Public,* pg. 1471

Riegel, Karen, Mgr.-Investor Rels.--Players International, Inc., Atlantic City, NJ; *U.S. Public,* pg. 1310

Riener, Tish, Mgr.-Investor Rels.--Physician Sales and Services Inc., Jacksonville, FL; *U.S. Public,* pg. 1293

Riess, Nancy, Mgr.-Investor Rels.--Airlease Ltd., San Francisco, CA; *U.S. Public,* pg. 33

Rietveld, Kim, Coord.-Investor Rels.--The Failure Group, Inc., Menlo Park, CA; *U.S. Public,* pg. 609

Rigoli, Thomas P., V.P.-Corp. Commun.--Cirrus Logic, Inc., Fremont, CA; *U.S. Public,* pg. 375

Riley, Joan R., Gen. Counsel, Sec. & Dir.-Investor Rels.--Quixote Corporation, Chicago, IL; *U.S. Public,* pg. 1353

Riley, Laura, Dir.-Investor Rels.--Montana Power Company, Butte, MT; *U.S. Public,* pg. 1126

Riley, Steve, Mgr.-Investor Rels.--Commercial Union plc, London, United Kingdom; *Int'l,* pg. 308

Ringel, Ellen, Mgr.-Pub. Rels.--Deloitte & Touche LLP, Wilton, CT; *U.S. Private,* pg. 322

Ringler, David, Dir.-Investor Rels.--Lam Research Corporation, Fremont, CA; *U.S. Public,* pg. 975

Riordan, Lisa, Dir.-Investor Rels. & Pub. Rels.--Bergen Brunswig Corporation, Orange, CA; *U.S. Public,* pg. 213

Ripley, John A., Pres. & Chief Exec. Officer--Precision Tune Autocare Inc., Leesburg, VA; *U.S. Public,* pg. 1321

Ritchie, Marianne, Coord.-Investor Rels.--Hologic, Inc., Waltham, MA; *U.S. Public,* pg. 831

Ritter, Becki, Exec. Asst.-Investor Rels.--President Casinos, Inc., Saint Louis, MO; *U.S. Public,* pg. 1323

Rivera, Angela, Mgr.-Corp. Communications--FPA Medical Management, Inc., San Diego, CA; *U.S. Public,* pg. 608

Roach, Beth, Investor Rels. Coord.--Blyth Industries, Greenwich, CT; *U.S. Public,* pg. 239

Roadman, Ross C., Grp. Dir.-Investor & Community Rels.--Ryder System, Inc., Miami, FL; *U.S. Public,* pg. 1413

Roath, Kenneth B., Chm. Bd., Pres. & Chief Exec. Officer--Health Care Property Investors, Inc., Newport Beach, CA; *U.S. Public*, pg. 801
Roberts, Bill, Dir.-Pub. Rels.--Bradlees Inc., Braintree, MA; *U.S. Public*, pg. 249
Roberts, Gary, Chief Fin. Officer, Sr. V.P.-Admin. & Sec.--Sierracin Corporation, Sylmar, CA; *U.S. Private*, pg. 999
Roberts, Linda, Exec. Sec.--Keystone Consolidated Industries, Inc., Dallas, TX; *U.S. Public*, pg. 955
Roberts, William E., Chief Fin. Officer, V.P., Controller & Treas.--Lone Star Industries, Inc., Stamford, CT; *U.S. Public*, pg. 1012
Robertson, Monroe W., Sr. V.P. & Sec.--Key Production Company, Inc., Denver, CO; *U.S. Public*, pg. 953
Robidoux, Roy, Sr. V.P.-Mktg. & Sls.--The Cerplex Group, Inc., Tustin, CA; *U.S. Public*, pg. 332
Robinson, David, Dir.-Investor Rels.--Rogers Communications, Inc., Toronto, Canada; *Int'l*, pg. 1122
Robinson, Douglas, Sr. V.P.-Investor Rels.--Computer Associates International, Inc., Islandia, NY; *U.S. Public*, pg. 420
Robinson, Joseph A., Chief Fin. Officer, Sr. V.P., Treas. & Sec.--Excel Industries, Inc., Elkhart, IN; *U.S. Public*, pg. 598
Robinson, Sandra, V.P.-Fin. Opers.--Harman International Industries, Inc., Woodbury, NY; *U.S. Public*, pg. 787
Robinson, Susan, V.P.-Operating--Federated Department Stores, Inc., Cincinnati, OH; *U.S. Public*, pg. 617
Robinson, Warren L., Chief Fin. Officer, V.P. & Treas.--MDU Resources Group, Inc., Bismarck, ND; *U.S. Public*, pg. 1025
Robson, Clark, Dir.-Investor Rels.--Xerox Corporation, Stamford, CT; *U.S. Public*, pg. 1783
Rockom, Joseph W., Chief Fin. Officer & V.P.-Fin. & Admin.--IKOS Systems, Inc., Cupertino, CA; *U.S. Public*, pg. 864
Rodgers, Doug, Grp. Mgr.-Corp. Affairs--CSR Limited, Sydney, Australia; *Int'l*, pg. 245
Rodriguez, Idalia, Mgr.-Investor Rels.--The Pep Boys-Manny, Moe & Jack, Philadelphia, PA; *U.S. Public*, pg. 1276
Rodriguez, Norma Y., Dir.-Investor Rels.--Brooklyn Union, Brooklyn, NY; *U.S. Public*, pg. 259
Rodriguez, Victoria, Dir.-Investor Rels.--Henry Schein, Inc., Melville, NY; *U.S. Public*, pg. 1437
Roesch, Rick, Dir.-Investor Rels.--Citicorp, New York, NY; *U.S. Public*, pg. 376
Rogalin, Peter, Chief Fin. Officer, V.P. & Treas.--Roberts Pharmaceutical Corporation, Eatontown, NJ; *U.S. Public*, pg. 1393
Rogers, Colleen, Mgr.-Investor Rels.--Palm Harbor Homes, Inc., Dallas, TX; *U.S. Public*, pg. 1254
Rogers, Gayle, Asst. Corp. Sec.--Niches, Inc., San Diego, CA; *U.S. Public*, pg. 1181
Rogers, John, Dir.-Inv. Rels.--Suncor Inc., Calgary, Canada; *Int'l*, pg. 1320
Rogers, John J., Jr., Chief Fin. Officer & V.P.-Fin. & Admin.--Cognex Corporation, Natick, MA; *U.S. Public*, pg. 394
Rogers, Kathie, Dir.-Investor Rels.--RPM, Inc., Medina, OH; *U.S. Public*, pg. 1356
Rogers, Walter B., V.P.-Investor Rels.--Duracell International Inc., Bethel, CT; *U.S. Public*, pg. 743
Romanok, David, Exec. V.P.--L&R Manufacturing Co., Kearny, NJ; *U.S. Private*, pg. 638
Romans, Suzanne, Dir.-Community Rels.--Churchill Downs, Inc., Louisville, KY; *U.S. Public*, pg. 356
Romig, William J., V.P. & Treas.--Norfolk Southern Corporation, Norfolk, VA; *U.S. Public*, pg. 1190
Ronchi, Bernard, Sr. Analyst-Investor Rels.--National Australia Bank Limited, Melbourne, Australia; *Int'l*, pg. 906
Roolf, James M., Sr. V.P. & Dir.-Corp. Communications--First Midwest Bancorp, Inc., Itasca, IL; *U.S. Public*, pg. 636
Rose, Harry, Asst. V.P.-Mktg. & Corp. Communications--Atlantic Gulf Communities Corporation, Miami, FL; *U.S. Public*, pg. 144
Rose, Stuart, Chm. Bd. & Chief Exec. Officer--Rex Stores Corp., Dayton, OH; *U.S. Public*, pg. 1384
Rosen, Andrew M., V.P. & Treas.--Brown Group, Inc., Saint Louis, MO; *U.S. Public*, pg. 262
Rosen, Jacqueline S., Asst. V.P.-Invesment Banking--United Missouri Bank of St. Louis, Saint Louis, MO; *U.S. Public*, pg. 1655
Rosenberg, Paul B., Treas.--Tech/Ops Sevcon, Inc., Boston, MA; *U.S. Public*, pg. 1563
Rosenfeld, Richard S., Chief Fin. Officer, V.P. & Treas.--Barringer Technologies Inc., New Providence, NJ; *U.S. Public*, pg. 191
Rosensteele, James W., V.P.--ADT Security Systems, Inc., Carmel, IN; *U.S. Public*, pg. 1649
Rosenthal, Addie, Dir.-Investor Rels.--Pomeroy Computer Resources, Hebron, KY; *U.S. Public*, pg. 1315
Rosinski, Michael J., Dir.-Investor Rels.--Tenneco Inc., Greenwich, CT; *U.S. Public*, pg. 1577
Ross, John H. III, Sr. V.P. & Gen. Counsel--Ash Grove Cement Company, Shawnee Mission, KS; *U.S. Private*, pg. 87
Ross, Richard A., Chief Fin. Officer & V.P.-Fin.--Inmet Mining Corporation, Toronto, Canada; *Int'l*, pg. 678
Ross, Robert W., Chief Fin. Officer, V.P., Treas. & Sec.--Selas Corporation of America, Dresher, PA; *U.S. Public*, pg. 1454
Ross, Wesley, Mgr.-Admin. & Investor Rels.--Easco Inc., Girard, OH; *U.S. Public*, pg. 548
Rosset, Claude, Dir.-Corp. Fin. & Investor Rels.--Holderbank Financiere Glaris Ltd., Glaris, Switzerland; *Int'l*, pg. 628
Rosso, Chiara, Dir.-Investor Rels./Benetton Group, Spa--Benetton U.S.A. Corporation, New York, NY; *Int'l*, pg. 186
Rothblum, David, Mgr.-Investor Rels.--Siemens AG, Munich, Germany; *Int'l*, pg. 1244
Rothenburg, Steve S., V.P.-Communications--Reliance Group Holdings, Inc., New York, NY; *U.S. Public*, pg. 1374
Rothrock, Judith, V.P.-Corp. Commun.--Lawson Software, Minneapolis, MN; *U.S. Private*, pg. 654
Rourke, Michael J., Sr. V.P.-Communications & Corp. Affairs--The Great Atlantic & Pacific Tea Company, Inc., Montvale, NJ; *Int'l*, pg. 1375
Rouse, James R., Chief Fin. Officer & Treas.--Reeds Jewelers, Inc., Wilmington, NC; *U.S. Public*, pg. 1370
Rowan, James C., Jr., V.P.- Investment Dept.--The Hartford Steam Boiler Inspection & Insurance Co., Hartford, CT; *U.S. Public*, pg. 795
Rowe, William N., V.P.-Investor Rels.--Nova Corporation, Calgary, Canada; *Int'l*, pg. 971
Rowland, Linda, Mgr.-Inv. Rels.--Carver Corporation, Lynnwood, WA; *U.S. Public*, pg. 310
Roycroft, D., Mgr.-Investor Rels.--Pilkington Plc, Saint Helens, United Kingdom; *Int'l*, pg. 1056
Rozelle, Mark A., V.P.-Investor Rels.--UST Inc., Greenwich, CT; *U.S. Public*, pg. 1660
Rubin, Donald S., Sr. V.P.-Inv. Rels.--The McGraw-Hill Companies, New York, NY; *U.S. Public*, pg. 1069
Rubin, Michael, Pres. & Chief Fin. Officer--Hudson General Corporation, Great Neck, NY; *U.S. Public*, pg. 845
Ruch, T.M., Investor Rels. Analyst--PECO Energy Company, Philadelphia, PA; *U.S. Public*, pg. 1268
Ruddick, Philip, Dir.-Investor Rels.--Polaroid Corporation, Cambridge, MA; *U.S. Public*, pg. 1313
Ruddock, Jennifer, Mgr.-Investor Rels.--Catellus Development Corporation, San Francisco, CA; *U.S. Public*, pg. 314
Rukeyser, Robert J., Sr. V.P.-Corp. Affairs--Fortune Brands, Inc., Old Greenwich, CT; *U.S. Public*, pg. 674
Rumeau, Philippe, Mgr.-Private Investor Relations--Rhone-Poulenc S.A., Courbevoie, France; *Int'l*, pg. 1108
Rusch, Jack C., Exec. V.P. & Treas.--First Federal Capital Corp., La Crosse, WI; *U.S. Public*, pg. 632
Rush, Carl V., Jr., Pres. & Chief Exec. Officer--The GNI Group, Inc., Deer Park, TX; *U.S. Public*, pg. 693
Rush, Mary, Sec. & Dir.-Investor Rels.--Tyson Foods, Inc., Springdale, AR; *U.S. Public*, pg. 1652
Russell, Paul J., V.P.-Investor Rels.--Tenet Healthcare Corporation, Santa Barbara, CA; *U.S. Public*, pg. 1576
Ruthig, M., Mgr.-Investor Rels.--Cott Corporation, Pointe-Claire, Canada; *Int'l*, pg. 337
Ruttenberg, Harold J., Chm. Bd., Principal Acctg. Officer, Chief Exec. Officer & Treas.--American Locker Group, Inc., Jamestown, NY; *U.S. Public*, pg. 85
Ruzza, Rick, Coord.-Investor Relations--Autodesk, Inc., San Rafael, CA; *U.S. Public*, pg. 148
Ryan, Allan, Mgr.-Investor Rels.--M.I.M. Holdings Ltd., Brisbane, Australia; *Int'l*, pg. 827
Ryan, Louis F., Exec. V.P., Gen. Counsel & Sec.--Landmark Communications, Inc., Norfolk, VA; *U.S. Private*, pg. 647
Ryder, Paul R., V.P.-Investor Rels.--Echlin Inc., Branford, CT; *U.S. Public*, pg. 560
Rydin, Wes, Chief Fin. Officer & V.P.--Malden Mills Industries, Inc., Lawrence, MA; *U.S. Private*, pg. 698
Rye, Walter L., Chm. Bd. & Chief Exec. Officer--Cincinnati Gear Company, Cincinnati, OH; *U.S. Private*, pg. 240
Ryland, Julie S., Dir.-Investor Rels.--Energen Corporation, Birmingham, AL; *U.S. Public*, pg. 581
Sabroff, Julie I., V.P.-Investor Rels.--National City Corporation, Cleveland, OH; *U.S. Public*, pg. 1154
Sachs, Harold, Treas.--Foodmaker, Inc., San Diego, CA; *U.S. Public*, pg. 661
Sadowski, Eileen, V.P.-Corp. Fin.--Crestar Financial Corporation, Richmond, VA; *U.S. Public*, pg. 458
Sadusky, Vincent L., Dir.-Fin. Reporting--Telemundo Group, Inc., Hialeah, FL; *U.S. Public*, pg. 1570
Sage, Ed, Dir.-Investor Rels.--Zeneca Group Plc, London, United Kingdom; *Int'l*, pg. 1524
Salky, Molly, Dir.-Inv. Rels. & Corp. Communications--The Earthgrains Company, Clayton, MO; *U.S. Public*, pg. 547
Saltzman, Nancy B., V.P. & Assoc. Counsel--Chartwell Re Corporation, Stamford, CT; *U.S. Public*, pg. 336
Salzmann, B., Chief Fin. Officer--Kuehne & Nagel International AG, Schindellegi, Switzerland; *Int'l*, pg. 763
Sammis, Elizabeth, Sr. Dir.-Communications--Mid Atlantic Medical Services, Inc., Rockville, MD; *U.S. Public*, pg. 1109
Sammons, Christopher D., V.P.-Investor Rels.--Freeport-McMoRan Inc., New Orleans, LA; *U.S. Public*, pg. 680
Samsal, Julia, Admin.-Investor & Shareholder Rels.--Network Systems Corporation, Minneapolis, MN; *U.S. Public*, pg. 1522
Samson, Brad, Dir.-Investor & Pub. Rels.--Wallace Computer Services, Inc., Lisle, IL; *U.S. Public*, pg. 1735
Sanchez-Flor, Arantxa, Mgr.-Investor Rels.--Sol Melia, Palma de Mallorca, Spain; *Int'l*, pg. 1277
Sanchez, Fernando, Mgr.-Inv. Rels.--Altos Hornos de Mexico, S.A., Monclova, Mexico; *Int'l*, pg. 66
Sanchez, Mauricio, Mgr.-Indus. Rels.--Duracell de Mexico S.A. de C.V., Naucalpan, Mexico; *U.S. Public*, pg. 743
Sandelin, Martin, Mgr.-Investor Rels.--Oy Nokia Ab/Nokia Group, Helsinki, Finland; *Int'l*, pg. 951
Sandelin, Martin, V.P.-Investor Rels.--NE-Products Oy, Oulu, Finland; *Int'l*, pg. 952
Sanders, Richard, Dir.-Corp. Communications--United News & Media plc, London, United Kingdom; *Int'l*, pg. 1443
Sanders, Stephanie, Mgr.-Investor Rels.--International Comfort Products, Franklin, TN; *U.S. Public*, pg. 898
Santana, Dario, V.P.-Investor Rels.--General Instrument Corporation, Horsham, PA; *U.S. Public*, pg. 716
Saporito, Craig E., V.P.-Investor Rels.--Freeport-McMoRan Inc., New Orleans, LA; *U.S. Public*, pg. 680
Sapp, Ronald V., Chief Fin. Officer, V.P.-Fin. & Treas.--Atlantic Southeast Airlines Inc., Atlanta, GA; *U.S. Public*, pg. 144
Sargent, Tina, Admin. Asst.--Inter-Tel, Incorporated, Phoenix, AZ; *U.S. Public*, pg. 888
Sauerlaender, J. Friedrich, Sr. V.P.-Corp. Communications & Investor Rels.--SGS Societe Generale de Surveillance Holding S.A., Geneva, Switzerland; *Int'l*, pg. 1153
Saunders, Keith C., Chief Fin. Officer, Exec. V.P. & Sec.--Zions Co-operative Mercantile Institution, Salt Lake City, UT; *U.S. Public*, pg. 1793
Saverhoff, Dave, Mgr.--Anheuser-Busch Companies, Inc., Saint Louis, MO; *U.S. Public*, pg. 113
Savitz, Richard J., V.P.-Fin., Treas. & Sec.--Justin Industries, Inc., Fort Worth, TX; *U.S. Public*, pg. 936
Saxon, Franklin N., Chief Fin. Officer, Sr. V.P., Treas. & Sec.--Culp, Inc., High Point, NC; *U.S. Public*, pg. 467
Sayatovic, Wayne P., Chief Fin. Officer & Sr. V.P.-Fin.--IDEX Corporation, Northbrook, IL; *U.S. Public*, pg. 862
Sayre, Larry, Chief Fin. Officer, V.P.-Fin., Controller & Treas.--Collins Industries, Inc., Hutchinson, KS; *U.S. Public*, pg. 399
Scarborough, Laurie G., Dir.-Investor Rels.--Humana Inc., Louisville, KY; *U.S. Public*, pg. 847
Scarpelli, Jemima G., Dir.-Investor Rels.--Itron Inc., Spokane, WA; *U.S. Public*, pg. 914
Scarpetta, Paul, Sr. V.P.-Shareholder Rels.--Federal Home Loan Mortgage Corporation, Mc Lean, VA; *U.S. Public*, pg. 615
Scartz, Don T., V.P.-Fin., Treas. & Sec.--Electromagnetic Sciences, Inc., Norcross, GA; *U.S. Public*, pg. 569
Scavullo, Ann, V.P.-Investor Rels.--Avon Products, Inc., New York, NY; *U.S. Public*, pg. 155
Schad, Diane, Staff V.P.-Fin.--Continental Airlines, Houston, TX; *U.S. Public*, pg. 439
Schaefer, John L., Chief Fin. Officer, V.P.-Fin. & Sec.--The Wm. Powell Company, Cincinnati, OH; *U.S. Private*, pg. 877
Schaeffer, Wayne G., Exec. V.P.--Citizens Banking Corporation, Flint, MI; *U.S. Public*, pg. 379
Schafer, Lee, V.P.-Corp. Plng.--Aetrium Inc., Saint Paul, MN; *U.S. Public*, pg. 27
Schall, Valeria, Exec. V.P.--All Star Gas Corporation, Lebanon, MO; *U.S. Private*, pg. 35
Schaus, Cynthia M., Mgr.-Corp. Commun.--Equitable of Iowa Companies, Des Moines, IA; *Int'l*, pg. 647
Schenkler, Sheldon M., V.P.-Fin. & Dir.-Investor Rels.--Cambex Corporation, Waltham, MA; *U.S. Public*, pg. 296
Scher, Barry F., V.P.-Pub. Affairs--Giant Food Inc., Landover, MD; *U.S. Public*, pg. 741
Scherer, Barbara, V.P. & Treas.--Micropolis Corporation, Chatsworth, CA; *U.S. Private*, pg. 742
Schiffel, Dennis, V.P.-Investor Rels.--Atlantic Richfield Company, Los Angeles, CA; *U.S. Public*, pg. 144
Schindler, David R., Treas.--Lykes Brothers Inc., Tampa, FL; *U.S. Private*, pg. 682
Schlomer, Aliston, Mgr.-Investor Rels.--Ultimate Electronics, Thornton, CO; *U.S. Public*, pg. 1662
Schmeider, Luke R., Pres., Treas. & Chief Exec. Officer--Mesa Laboratories, Inc., Wheat Ridge, CO; *U.S. Public*, pg. 1099
Schmidt, Gert, Dr., Dir.-Investor Rels. & Press Office--IKB Deutsche Industriebank AG, Dusseldorf, Germany; *Int'l*, pg. 645
Schmidt, Glenn W., Mgr.-Opers.--Market Facts, Inc., Arlington Heights, IL; *U.S. Public*, pg. 1046
Schmidt, Sherri, Coord.-Shareholder Rels.--The Colonial BancGroup, Inc., Montgomery, AL; *U.S. Public*, pg. 400
Schmitt, Henry A., V.P.-Corp. Rels.--CNF Transportation Inc., Palo Alto, CA; *U.S. Public*, pg. 281
Schmitz, Hans Richard, Head-Investor Rels.--RWE AG, Essen, Germany; *Int'l*, pg. 1081
Schmuck, Wolfran, Dir.-Pub. Rels.--Rewe-Handelsgruppe, Cologne, Germany; *Int'l*, pg. 1106
Schneider, Dawn, Mgr.-Investor Rels.--Kimco Realty Corporation, New Hyde Park, NY; *U.S. Public*, pg. 960
Schneider, Richard A., Chief Fin. Officer--NAI Technologies, Inc., Huntington, NY; *U.S. Public*, pg. 1144
Schoeffler, Michael H., Pres. & Chief Oper. Officer--Starcraft Corporation, Goshen, IN; *U.S. Public*, pg. 1510
Schoenberger, Diana L., V.P.-Mktg. Commun. & Investor Rels.--CitFed Bancorp, Inc., Dayton, OH; *U.S. Public*, pg. 376
Schofer, Werner, Mgr.-Investor Rels.--Zwick/Roell Group, Ulm, Germany; *Int'l*, pg. 1532
Schonau, Mark R., Chief Fin. Officer, Sec., Treas., & Investor Rels.--HBO & Company/Cycare Business Group, Scottsdale, AZ; *U.S. Public*, pg. 770
Schorr, Stephen I., V.P.-Fin., Treas. & Sec.--Westbrae Natural, Inc., Carson, CA; *U.S. Public*, pg. 774
Schreck, Richard H., Pres. & Chief Oper. Officer--Hofmann Industries, Inc., Sinking Spring, PA; *U.S. Private*, pg. 533
Schroeder, Scott C., Treas.--Cabot Oil & Gas Corporation, Houston, TX; *U.S. Public*, pg. 289
Schrum, Nancy, Dir.-H.R.--Carolina Mills, Inc., Maiden, NC; *U.S. Private*, pg. 214
Schubilske, Jim, Coord.-Investor Rels.--Wisconsin Energy Corporation, Milwaukee, WI; *U.S. Public*, pg. 1773
Schultz, Christopher F., Treas.--Asarco Incorporated, New York, NY; *U.S. Public*, pg. 137
Schultz, Nancy E., Dir.-Corp. Commun. & Investor Rels.--Merit Medical Systems, Inc., South Jordan, UT; *U.S. Public*, pg. 1096
Schwab, James E., Pres. & Chief Oper. Officer--Xtek, Inc., Cincinnati, OH; *U.S. Private*, pg. 1194
Schwach, Barry, Chief Fin. Officer & Exec. V.P.--Sunrise Leasing Corporation, Golden Valley, MN; *U.S. Public*, pg. 1535
Schwartz, Richard P., Mgr.-Investments--Unicom Corporation, Chicago, IL; *U.S. Public*, pg. 1664
Schwartz, Steve, Mgr.-Investor Rels.--Home Savings of America, FSB, Irwindale, CA; *U.S. Public*, pg. 29
Schweikher, Karen, Dir.-Corp. Communications & Investor Rels.--Ampex Corporation, Redwood City, CA; *U.S. Public*, pg. 104
Schwenk, Harold S., Jr., Dr., Chm. Bd., Pres., & Chief Exec. Officer--BGS Systems, Inc., Waltham, MA; *U.S. Public*, pg. 161

Scipione, Marianne, V.P.-Corp. Communications--U.S. Surgical Corp., Norwalk, CT; *U.S. Public*, pg. 1687
Scotinno, Tom, Mgr.-Investor Rels.--Tellabs Operations, Inc., Lisle, IL; *U.S. Public*, pg. 1572
Scott, Dianne, V.P.-Human Resources--The Titan Corporation, San Diego, CA; *U.S. Public*, pg. 1618
Scott, Dunlop, Dir.-Investor Rels.--Wang Laboratories, Inc., Billerica, MA; *U.S. Public*, pg. 1737
Scott, Geralyn, Coord.-Investor Rels.--UST Inc., Greenwich, CT; *U.S. Public*, pg. 1660
Scott, John W., V.P.-Investor Rels.--Bestfoods, Englewood Cliffs, NJ; *U.S. Public*, pg. 223
Scott, Mark R., Dir.-Investor Rels. & Fin. Analyst--Autocam Corporation, Grand Rapids, MI; *U.S. Public*, pg. 148
Scott, Mary, Dir.-Investor Rels.--Emulex Corporation, Costa Mesa, CA; *U.S. Public*, pg. 579
Scott, Steven, Controller--Sutherland Lumber Co., Kansas City, MO; *U.S. Private*, pg. 1057
Seaman, Janet W., Sec.--Seaman Timber Company, Inc., Montevallo, AL; *U.S. Private*, pg. 979
Seaver, Peter R., V.P.-Healthcare Policy & Professional Rels.--Pharmacia & Upjohn, Kalamazoo, MI; *Int'l*, pg. 1048
Sedwick, Lindsay M., Chief Fin. Officer & Sr. V.P.--Standex International Corporation, Salem, NH; *U.S. Public*, pg. 1505
Seega, Robert G., Dir.-Investor Rels.--New England Electric System, Westborough, MA; *U.S. Public*, pg. 1171
Seeliger, Michael, V.P.-Investor Rels. & Corp. Rels.--Horizon/CMS Healthcare Corporation, Albuquerque, NM; *U.S. Public*, pg. 836
Segrelles, Jorge, Dir.-External Rels., Mktg. & Sls. Network--Repsol S.A., Madrid, Spain; *Int'l*, pg. 1104
Seigfried, John P., V.P., Gen. Counsel, Sec. & Dir.-Investor Rels.--Medusa Corporation, Cleveland, OH; *U.S. Public*, pg. 1084
Seither, Mike, Dir.-Corp. Communications--Xilinx, Inc., San Jose, CA; *U.S. Public*, pg. 1786
Seitor, Susan, Dir.-Investor Rels.--BancTec, Inc., Dallas, TX; *U.S. Public*, pg. 176
Seligman, Scott J., Pres.--Seligman & Associates, Inc., Southfield, MI; *U.S. Private*, pg. 982
Selland, Clay E., Treas. & Asst. Sec.--Longs Drug Stores Corporation, Walnut Creek, CA; *U.S. Public*, pg. 1013
Seluka, Mary, Mgr.-Investor Rels.--Jack Henry & Associates, Inc., Monett, MO; *U.S. Public*, pg. 808
Sendelweck, Kenneth L., V.P. & Asst. Treas.--Kimball International, Inc., Jasper, IN; *U.S. Public*, pg. 956
Seo, S.C., Mgr.-Joint Ventures & Investments--Hyundai Electronics America, San Jose, CA; *Int'l*, pg. 641
Serell, Andrew, Dir.-Investor Rels.--Apertus Technologies Incorporated, Eden Prairie, MN; *U.S. Public*, pg. 119
Serrone, H. James, Gen. Mgr.--Torotel, Inc., Grandview, MO; *U.S. Public*, pg. 1624
Sevell, Kristin, Dir.-Commun.--Pete's Brewing Company, Palo Alto, CA; *U.S. Public*, pg. 1280
Severe, John, Pres. & Gen. Mgr.--Western Grain, Inc., Wichita, KS; *U.S. Private*, pg. 1165
Sevick, Daniel M., Chief Fin. Officer & Treas.--Environmental Resources Management, Exton, PA; *U.S. Private*, pg. 378
Sexton, Maripat, Dir.-Media Rels.--NGC Corporation, Houston, TX; *U.S. Public*, pg. 1146
Shah, Kumar, Dir.-Plng., Bus. Devel. & Investor Rels.--Cytec Industries Inc., West Paterson, NJ; *U.S. Public*, pg. 471
Shaked, Yonni, Chief Fin. Officer--Egged Israel Transport Cooperative Society Ltd., Tel Aviv, Israel; *Int'l*, pg. 435
Shakley, Allan D., Sec. & Asst. Treas.--United Water Management & Services, Harrington Park, NJ; *U.S. Public*, pg. 1692
Shamilzadeh, David, Chief Fin. Officer & Sr. V.P.-Fin.--Allou Health & Beauty Care, Inc., Brentwood, NY; *U.S. Public*, pg. 55
Shanahan, Kevin C., V.P.-Investor Rels.--LucasVarity Inc., Buffalo, NY; *Int'l*, pg. 820
Shapard, Bob, Mgr.-Investor Rels.--Texas Utilities Company, Dallas, TX; *U.S. Public*, pg. 1586
Shapell, Nathan, Chm. Bd., Pres. & Chief Exec. Officer--Shapell Industries, Inc., Beverly Hills, CA; *U.S. Private*, pg. 990
Shapiro, David, Chief Fin. Officer & V.P.-Fin.--Engle Homes, Inc., Boca Raton, FL; *U.S. Public*, pg. 583
Shapiro, Richard B., Chm. Bd., Pres. & Chief Exec. Officer--Charles River Data Systems, Inc., Framingham, MA; *U.S. Private*, pg. 230
Sharp, Liz, V.P.-Corp. Rels.--Three-Five Systems, Tempe, AZ; *U.S. Public*, pg. 1604
Shattuck, Suki, Dir.-Investor Rels.--HomeBase, Inc., Irvine, CA; *U.S. Public*, pg. 832
Shawe, Jan, Dir.-Corp. Rels.--Prudential Corporation PLC, London, United Kingdom; *Int'l*, pg. 1073
Shayne, Charleigh, Dir.-Investor Rels.--ODS Networks, Inc., Richardson, TX; *U.S. Public*, pg. 1206
Shea, Martin M., Sr. V.P.-Corp. Commun.--Triarc Companies, Inc., New York, NY; *U.S. Public*, pg. 1634
Shelby, Tony M., Chief Fin. Officer & Sr. V.P.--LSB Industries, Inc., Oklahoma City, OK; *U.S. Public*, pg. 970
Sheldon, Ted, Dir.-Investor Rels.--Echo Bay Mines Ltd., Englewood, CO; *U.S. Public*, pg. 561
Shelton, Suzanne, Dir.-Corp. Communications--Michaels Stores, Inc., Irving, TX; *U.S. Public*, pg. 1104
Shelton, Theresa, V.P.-Fin.--Rock Bottom Restaurants, Louisville, CO; *U.S. Public*, pg. 1396
Sherbin, Robert, Grp. V.P.-Corp. Commun.--First Pacific Company Limited, Hong Kong, Hong Kong; *Int'l*, pg. 487
Shewach, Shirle, Dir.-Investor Rels.--R.P. Scherer Corporation, Troy, MI; *U.S. Public*, pg. 1437
Shibley, Jenny, Dir.-Investor Rels.--Best Access Systems, Indianapolis, IN; *U.S. Public*, pg. 223
Shields, Bobby L., V.P.-Legal & Regulatory Affairs--Hospital Staffing Services, Inc., Fort Lauderdale, FL; *U.S. Public*, pg. 840
Shields, George, V.P.-Investor Rels.--Warner-Lambert Company, Morris Plains, NJ; *U.S. Public*, pg. 1738
Shillam, Paul L., Chief Fin. Officer--Diadora America, Inc., Kent, WA; *U.S. Private*, pg. 330
Shontell, Jayne J., Sr. V.P.-Investor Rels.--Federal National Mortgage Association (Fannie Mae), Washington, DC; *U.S. Public*, pg. 615
Shope, Michael A., Chief Fin. Officer & Treas.--Walbro Corporation, Cass City, MI; *U.S. Public*, pg. 1733
Shorter, Barbara, Grp. Dir.-Corp. Rels.--The BOC Group plc, Windlesham, United Kingdom; *Int'l*, pg. 121
Shreckengost, Kim, V.P.-Investor Rels.--The Home Depot, Inc., Atlanta, GA; *U.S. Public*, pg. 831
Shull, Douglas K., Chief Fin. Officer & Treas.--Casey's General Stores, Inc., Ankeny, IA; *U.S. Public*, pg. 312
Sickman, William J., V.P.-Corp. Rels.--Figgie International Inc., Cleveland, OH; *U.S. Public*, pg. 622
Sicree, Joseph, V.P. & Chief Acctg. Officer--Toll Brothers, Inc., Huntingdon Valley, PA; *U.S. Public*, pg. 1620
Sidman, Alan M., Chief Fin. Officer & Controller--Instrumentarium Imaging, Inc., Milwaukee, WI; *U.S. Private*, pg. 565
Siegal, Dean, Dir.-Corp. Communications & Pub. Rels.--Block Drug Company, Inc., Jersey City, NJ; *U.S. Public*, pg. 236
Siegel, Philip, Chief Fin. Officer & V.P.--Health Management Systems, Inc., New York, NY; *U.S. Public*, pg. 802
Sieja, Kathleen, Mgr.-Investor Rels.--WICOR, Inc., Milwaukee, WI; *U.S. Public*, pg. 1767
Sieracki, Eric P., Exec. V.P.-Corp. Fin. & Investor Rels.--Countrywide Funding Corporation, Pasadena, CA; *U.S. Public*, pg. 453
Sigman, Richard, Chief Fin. Officer--IWI Holding Limited, Westmont, IL; *U.S. Public*, pg. 861
Siles, Marc, Dir.-External Rels.--Club Mediterranee SA, Paris, France; *Int'l*, pg. 298
Silitch, Nicholas, V.P.--The Bank of New York Company, Inc., New York, NY; *U.S. Public*, pg. 178
Silles, Victor, Chief Fin. Officer & Treas.--Thetford Corporation, Ann Arbor, MI; *U.S. Private*, pg. 352
Silmon, Bob, V.P.-Fin.--CompUSA, Dallas, TX; *U.S. Public*, pg. 420
Silva, Karen A., Mgr.-Investor Rels.--SpeedFan International, Inc., Chandler, AZ; *U.S. Public*, pg. 1497
Silver, Joyce, Dir.-Investor Rels.--Health and Retirement Properties Trust, Newton, MA; *U.S. Public*, pg. 801
Silver, Lawrence A., Sr. V.P.-Investor Rels.--Raymond James Financial, Inc., Saint Petersburg, FL; *U.S. Public*, pg. 923
Silver, Richard L., Chm. Bd. & Chief Fin. Officer--Akrochem Corporation, Akron, OH; *U.S. Private*, pg. 30
Simolin, Botho, Dir.-Communications--Kemira Oy, Helsinki, Finland; *Int'l*, pg. 727
Simonett, Mark J., Sec.--Photo Control Corporation, Minneapolis, MN; *U.S. Public*, pg. 1292
Simonetti, Joseph F., Dir.-Investor Rels.--Torchmark Corporation, Birmingham, AL; *U.S. Public*, pg. 1622
Simons, Doyle R., Dir.-Investor Rels.--Temple-Inland Inc., Diboll, TX; *U.S. Public*, pg. 1574
Simpkins, Frank P., Mgr.-External Reporting--Kennametal Inc., Latrobe, PA; *U.S. Public*, pg. 950
Simpson, David J., Chief Fin. Officer, V.P. & Sec.--Stryker Corporation, Kalamazoo, MI; *U.S. Public*, pg. 1525
Simpson, Lynda, Corp. Sec.--Liuski International, Inc., Norcross, GA; *U.S. Public*, pg. 1005
Sinclair-Brown, Jacqueline, Mgr.-Corp. Communications--Blue Circle Industries PLC, London, United Kingdom; *Int'l*, pg. 197
Sinclair, Gloria J., Coord.-Investor Rels.--W.W. Grainger, Inc., Lincolnshire, IL; *U.S. Public*, pg. 758
Sinclair, Judy, Mgr.-Investor Rels.--Conseco Inc., Carmel, IN; *U.S. Public*, pg. 432
Singer, Howard S., Exec. V.P.-Corp. Fin. & Investor Rels.--Centris Group Inc., Costa Mesa, CA; *U.S. Public*, pg. 328
Sipila, Airi, Dir.-Investor Rels.--Rautaruukki Oy, Helsinki, Finland; *Int'l*, pg. 1088
Sivall, Sverker, Info. Coord.--AB Industrivarden, Stockholm, Sweden; *Int'l*, pg. 678
Skiera, Dorothy A., Corp. Sec.--S & C Electric Company, Chicago, IL; *U.S. Private*, pg. 954
Skule, John L., V.P.-Pub. Affairs--Bristol-Myers Squibb Company, New York, NY; *U.S. Public*, pg. 253
Slack, John L., Chm. Bd., Pres., Chief Exec. Officer & Acting Treas.--DBA Systems, Inc., Melbourne, FL; *U.S. Public*, pg. 472
Slaggie, Stephen M., Sec.--Fastenal Company, Winona, MN; *U.S. Public*, pg. 614
Slaughter, Mike, Dir.-Investor Rels.--Eagle USA Airfreight, Houston, TX; *U.S. Public*, pg. 547
Slifka, Alfred A., Pres. & Chief Exec. Officer--Global Petroleum Corp., Waltham, MA; *U.S. Private*, pg. 457
Sliva, Catherine L., Exec. V.P.--Domain Energy Corporation, Houston, TX; *U.S. Public*, pg. 515
Slongo, Sylvia, Coord.-Investor Rels.--Westinghouse Air Brake Company, Wilmerding, PA; *U.S. Public*, pg. 1760
Slooten, Joost, Dir.-Investor Rels.--Heidemij N.V., Arnhem, Netherlands; *Int'l*, pg. 606
Smalley, John G., V.P. & Dir.-Human Resources--The Canada Life Assurance Company, Toronto, Canada; *Int'l*, *pg. 254*
Smalley, Mark, V.P.-Investor Rels.--Glenayre Technologies, Inc., Charlotte, NC; *U.S. Public*, pg. 746
Smiley, Doug, Mgr.-Investor Rels.--Sundstrand Corporation, Rockford, IL; *U.S. Public*, pg. 1533
Smith, Alton, Exec. V.P. & Controller--Furr's/Bishops, Inc., Lubbock, TX; *U.S. Public*, pg. 689
Smith, Andrew, Mgr.-Investor Rels.--L. Luria & Son, Inc., Medley, FL; *U.S. Public*, pg. 1020
Smith, Bridgett, Investor Rels.--Danielson Holding Corporation, New York, NY; *U.S. Public*, pg. 483
Smith, Charles L., Mgr.-Investor Rels.--VTEL Corporation, Austin, TX; *U.S. Public*, pg. 1703
Smith, Christine, Coord.-Investor Rels.--Telco Systems, Inc., Norwood, MA; *U.S. Public*, pg. 1568
Smith, Colleen, Dir.-Commun. & Investor Rels.--Dominion Textile Inc., Montreal, Canada; *Int'l*, pg. 415
Smith, Craig, V.P. & Dir.-Mktg.--FirstFed Financial Corp., Santa Monica, CA; *U.S. Public*, pg. 645
Smith, David, Ph.D, Chief Exec. Officer--Whatman plc, Maidstone, United Kingdom; *Int'l*, pg. 1498
Smith, Douglas B., V.P. & Treas.--Primedia Inc., New York, NY; *U.S. Public*, pg. 1327
Smith, Elizabeth P., V.P.-Investor Rel. & Shareholder Grp.--Texaco Inc., White Plains, NY; *U.S. Public*, pg. 1582
Smith, Frank E., Chief Fin. Officer, Sr. V.P. & Sec.--West Coast Bancorp, Newport Beach, CA; *U.S. Public*, pg. 1755
Smith, Gary, V.P.-Fin. & Treas.--The Andersons Incorporated, Maumee, OH; *U.S. Public*, pg. 111
Smith, Jane A., V.P. & Sec.--O.I. Corporation, College Station, TX; *U.S. Public*, pg. 1208
Smith, Kathy, Corp. Sec.--Lund International Holdings, Inc., Anoka, MN; *U.S. Public*, pg. 1020
Smith, Kim, Mgr.-Investor Rels.--Emons Transportation Group, Inc., York, PA; *U.S. Public*, pg. 578
Smith, L.S., Dr., Chm. Bd., Chief Exec. Officer, Treas. & Sec.--Dallas Gold & Silver Exchange, Inc., Dallas, TX; *U.S. Public*, pg. 478
Smith, Laura, Dir.-Investor Rels.--US Airways Group, Inc., Arlington, VA; *U.S. Public*, pg. 1680
Smith, Marlan R., Chief Fin. Officer & Treas.--C.R.A. Holdings Inc., Kalamazoo, MI; *U.S. Private*, pg. 1029
Smith, Randall E., V.P. & Treas.--Horace Small Apparel Company, Nashville, TN; *Int'l*, pg. 635
Smith, Richard C., Treas.--The Stanley Consultants Group, Muscatine, IA; *U.S. Private*, pg. 1032
Smucker, Richard K., Pres.--J.M. Smucker Company, Orrville, OH; *U.S. Public*, pg. 1480
Smyre, Calvin, Exec. V.P.-Corp. Affairs--Synovus Financial Corp., Columbus, GA; *U.S. Public*, pg. 1548
Snood, Arvind K., Investor Relations Specialist & Contact--Rhone-Poulenc Inc., Princeton, NJ; *Int'l*, pg. 1112
Snyder, Kathy M., Dir.-Communications & Shareholder Rels.--The First American Financial Corporation, Santa Ana, CA; *U.S. Public*, pg. 624
Snyder, Paul H., Chief Fin. Officer & Sr. V.P.--Salient 3 Communications, Inc., Reading, PA; *U.S. Public*, pg. 1429
Snyder, Richard A., Chief Fin. Officer, V.P. & Treas.--Tennant Company, Minneapolis, MN; *U.S. Public*, pg. 1577
Sobo, William T., Jr., Chief Fin. Officer, Sr. V.P. & Treas.--PAREXEL International Corporation, Waltham, MA; *U.S. Public*, pg. 1257
Soefje, Shannon A., Sr. V.P.-Corp. Commun. & Sec.--HD Vest Financial Services, Irving, TX; *U.S. Public*, pg. 770
Soland, Norman R., V.P., Gen. Counsel & Sec.--Nash Finch Company, Edina, MN; *U.S. Public*, pg. 1151
Solano, Laura, Mgr.-Investor Rels.--Fomento Economico Mexicano, S.A. de CV, Monterrey, Mexico; *Int'l*, pg. 496
Soler, Vincent E., Jr., V.P., Treas. & Sec.--American National Insurance Company, Galveston, TX; *U.S. Public*, pg. 87
Solitro, Mark, Dir.-Investor Rels.--NewsEdge Corporation, Burlington, MA; *U.S. Public*, pg. 1180
Sollenberger, Mark L., Exec. V.P., Treas. & Asst. Sec.--BT Financial Corporation, Johnstown, PA; *U.S. Public*, pg. 163
Sommer, Ron W., V.P.-Investor Rels. & Communications--Dravo Corporation, Pittsburgh, PA; *U.S. Public*, pg. 527
Somoza, Kelly Fawcett, V.P.-Investor Rels.--U.S. Home Corporation, Houston, TX; *U.S. Public*, pg. 1682
Somrak, Wayne P., V.P. & Controller--Varian Associates, Inc., Palo Alto, CA; *U.S. Public*, pg. 1710
Sonksen, David R., Chief Fin Officer, V.P.-Fin., Treas. & Sec.--Microsemi Corporation, Santa Ana, CA; *U.S. Public*, pg. 1107
Sorenson, William G., V.P.-Investor Rels.--The News Corporation Limited, Sydney, Australia; *Int'l*, pg. 925
Sottile, John H., Pres. & Chief Exec. Officer--The Goldfield Corporation, Melbourne, FL; *U.S. Public*, pg. 750
Soyupak, Tamer, Mgr.-Fin.--Arcelik A.S., Istanbul, Turkey; *Int'l*, pg. 741
Spacht, David B., Chief Fin. Officer, V.P. & Treas.--Artesian Resources Corporation, Newark, DE; *U.S. Public*, pg. 135
Spaeth, Karl H., Sec.--Quaker Chemical Corporation, Conshohocken, PA; *U.S. Public*, pg. 1346
Spak, Jacqueline R., Asst. Dir.-Investor Rels.--Banc One Corporation, Columbus, OH; *U.S. Public*, pg. 172
Spatz, Ruth Carol, Corp. Sec.--Osmonics, Inc., Minnetonka, MN; *U.S. Public*, pg. 1233
Speer, L., Mgr.-Info. Resources & Librarian--Q.U.F. Industries Ltd., Brisbane, Australia; *Int'l*, pg. 1074
Spencer, Lawrence F., Dir.-Investor Rels.--Idaho Power Company, Boise, ID; *U.S. Public*, pg. 861
Spendley, Christopher, Chief Fin. Officer & Sr. V.P.--Washington Homes, Inc., Landover, MD; *U.S. Public*, pg. 1741
Spigelmyer, Toni R., Asst. V.P.-Investor & Media Rels.--Sysco Corporation, Houston, TX; *U.S. Public*, pg. 1550
Spinella, Pat, Dir.-Investor Rels.--Union Camp Corporation, Wayne, NJ; *U.S. Public*, pg. 1665
Spinelli, Linda M., Stock Transfer Supvr.--First Western Bancorp, Inc., New Castle, PA; *U.S. Public*, pg. 642
Spiro, Mark F., Chief Fin. Officer, V.P.-Fin., Treas. & Sec.--Calprop Corporation, Marina Del Rey, CA; *U.S. Public*, pg. 296
Spowart, Jay R., V.P.-Fin. & Corp. Sec.--Casio Phone-Mate, Inc., Torrance, CA; *Int'l*, pg. 274
Spratlen, Susan, Dir.-Investor Rels.--Pioneer Natural Resources Co., Irving, TX; *U.S. Public*, pg. 1299
Sprecher, Gregory A., Chief Fin. Officer & Sr. V.P.--Mauna Loa Macadamia Partners, L.P., Honolulu, HI; *U.S. Public*, *pg. 1060*
Spreng, C., Mgr.-Commun. & Media--General Accident Fire and Life Assurance Corporation p.l.c., Perth, United Kingdom; *Int'l*, pg. 542
Squier, Lori, Exec. Asst.--GTI Corporation, San Diego, CA; *U.S. Public*, pg. 767

Stagen, Marilyn, Coord.-Investor Rels.--Prime Hospitality Corp., Fairfield, NJ; *U.S. Public*, pg. 1326

Stallone, Ann, Dir.-Investor Rels.--Napco Security Systems, Inc., Amityville, NY; *U.S. Public*, pg. 1151

Standen, Robert A., V.P.-Indus. Rels.--American Greetings Corporation, Cleveland, OH; *U.S. Public*, pg. 77

Stanhope, Phillip, Dir.-Corp. Commun.--Titan International, Inc., Quincy, IL; *U.S. Public*, pg. 1618

Stanley, Brian C., V.P.-Investor Rels. & Controller--Valmont Industries, Inc., Valley, NE; *U.S. Public*, pg. 1706

Stavem, Ola, V.P.-Equity & Investor Rels.--Christiania Bank og Kreditkasse ASA, Oslo, Norway; *Int'l*, pg. 289

Steed, Tracey, Mgr.-Investor Rels.--Oshman's Sporting Goods, Inc., Houston, TX; *U.S. Public*, pg. 1233

Steele, John J., Chief Fin. Officer, V.P. & Treas.--Werner Enterprises, Inc., Omaha, NE; *U.S. Public*, pg. 1754

Steele, Lauren, V.P.-Corp. Affairs--Coca-Cola Bottling Co. Consolidated, Charlotte, NC; *U.S. Public*, pg. 391

Steeves, Michael A., Dir.-Investor Rels.--Homestake Mining Company, San Francisco, CA; *U.S. Public*, pg. 832

Steffenhagen, Jay, V.P.-Investor Rels.--Beckman Instruments, Inc., Fullerton, CA; *U.S. Public*, pg. 199

Steimel, Dirck H., Dir.-Investor Rels.--Pioneer Hi-Bred International, Inc., Des Moines, IA; *U.S. Public*, pg. 1298

Steinberg, Terry, V.P.-Admin.--Aceto Corporation, Lake Success, NY; *U.S. Public*, pg. 15

Steinkrauss, Mark A., V.P.-Investor Rels.--Fruit of the Loom, Inc., Chicago, IL; *U.S. Public*, pg. 685

Stephen, Robbie, Dir.-Investor Rels.--BHP Copper North America, Tucson, AZ; *Int'l*, pg. 224

Stephens, Elton B., Chm. Bd.--EBSCO Industries, Inc., Birmingham, AL; *U.S. Private*, pg. 358

Stephenson, Kirk, Dir.-Fin.--Coats Viyella plc, Manchester, United Kingdom; *Int'l*, pg. 299

Stephenson, Michael, Sr. Mgr.-Investor Rels.--HSBC Holdings plc, London, United Kingdom; *Int'l*, pg. 579

Stephenson, Mike, Mgr.-Inv. Rels.--Midland Bank PLC, London, United Kingdom; *Int'l*, pg. 580

Stetz, Gordon W., Jr., Asst. Treas.-Fin. Svcs.--McCormick & Company, Incorporated, Sparks, MD; *U.S. Public*, pg. 1066

Steul, William M., Chief Fin. Officer & Treas.--Eaton Vance Corp., Boston, MA; *U.S. Public*, pg. 559

Stevens, Gregory W., V.P. & Controller--Phelps Dodge Corporation, Phoenix, AZ; *U.S. Public*, pg. 1286

Stevens, Peter, Dir.-Corp. Communications--Willis Corroon Group PLC, London, United Kingdom; *Int'l*, pg. 1501

Stevens, R., Chief Fin. Officer & Exec. V.P.--Robertson-Ceco Corporation, San Ramon, CA; *U.S. Public*, pg. 1394

Stewart, A. William, Dir.-Fin. & Pub Rels.--Amdahl Corporation, Sunnyvale, CA; *Int'l*, pg. 527

Stewart, Allen J., Dir.-Investor Rels.--Duke Energy Corporation, Charlotte, NC; *U.S. Public*, pg. 534

Stewart, Graeme, Mgr.-Investor Rels.--Fritz Companies, Inc., San Francisco, CA; *U.S. Public*, pg. 683

Stewart, JoAn B., Sec.--Fair Grounds Corporation, New Orleans, LA; *U.S. Public*, pg. 609

Stewart, Karen M., V.P.-Investor Rels.--Telephone and Data Systems, Inc., Chicago, IL; *U.S. Public*, pg. 1570

Stewart, Karen M., V.P.-Investor Rels.--American Paging, Inc., Minneapolis, MN; *U.S. Public*, pg. 1570

Stillings, Susan T., Investor Rels.--Iomega Corporation, Roy, UT; *U.S. Public*, pg. 912

Stinson, Janice, Mgr.-Investor Rels.--Pre-Paid Legal Services, Inc., Ada, OK; *U.S. Public*, pg. 1320

Stitt, Kevin R., V.P.-Investor Rels.--NationsBank West, Saint Louis, MO; *U.S. Public*, pg. 1164

Stitt, Ron, Mgr.-Investor Rels.--ICO, Inc., Houston, TX; *U.S. Public*, pg. 853

Stoddart, George A., V.P.-Corp. Commun.--McDermott International, Inc., New Orleans, LA; *U.S. Public*, pg. 1067

Stoffere, Lisa, Sr. Mgr.-Commun. & Investor Rels.--NovaCare Inc., King of Prussia, PA; *U.S. Public*, pg. 1203

Stoltzfus, Dale, Mgr.-Investor Rels.--Oryx Energy, Dallas, TX; *U.S. Public*, pg. 1232

Stone, Daniel B., V.P.-Corp. Commun.--Alberto-Culver Company, Melrose Park, IL; *U.S. Public*, pg. 37

Stone, Sherrill, Chm. Bd.,Pres. & Chief Exec. Officer--Peerless Mfg. Co., Dallas, TX; *U.S. Public*, pg. 1268

Storat, Richard E., V.P.-Corp. Affairs--Gaylord Container Corporation, Deerfield, IL; *U.S. Public*, pg. 704

Story, Robert P., Jr., Chief Fin. Officer & Sr. V.P.--Courier Corporation, North Chelmsford, MA; *U.S. Public*, pg. 453

Stottlemyer, Todd A., V.P.-Corp. & Investor Rels.--BDM International, Inc., Mc Lean, VA; *U.S. Public*, pg. 1558

Stoudenmire, Stan, Chief Fin. Officer, V.P.-Fin. & Admin. & Sec.--Ross Systems, Inc., Atlanta, GA; *U.S. Public*, pg. 1406

Stout, Michael, Dir.-Pub. Rels.--Tidewater Marine Service, Inc., New Orleans, LA; *U.S. Public*, pg. 1608

Strauss, Jane, Investor Rels.--Cable Design Technologies Corporation, Pittsburgh, PA; *U.S. Public*, pg. 287

Streem, Craig A., V.P.-Investor Rels.--Household International, Inc., Prospect Heights, IL; *U.S. Public*, pg. 842

Strickland, Robert S., V.P.-Investor Rels.--Norwest Corporation, Minneapolis, MN; *U.S. Public*, pg. 1201

Strohl, Bruce E., Chief Exec. Officer & Sr. V.P.-Fin.--The Cosmetic Center Inc., Columbia, MD; *U.S. Private*, pg. 689

Strohm, Kimmerly, Dir.-Investor Relations--Ingram Micro Inc., Santa Ana, CA; *U.S. Public*, pg. 878

Stroik, Gregory J., Sr. V.P., Dir.-Investments, Taxes & Internal Audit & Asst. Treas.--Federated Mutual Insurance Company, Owatonna, MN; *U.S. Private*, pg. 399

Strong, Gary, Dir-Investor Rels.--Berg Electronics, Saint Louis, MO; *U.S. Public*, pg. 212

Stroud, Matthew, Dir.-Investor Rels.--Darden Restaurants, Inc., Orlando, FL; *U.S. Public*, pg. 483

Struckhoff, Charles O., Chief Fin. Officer, V.P.-Fin. & Admin., Treas. & Sec.--Maverick Tube Corporation, Chesterfield, MO; *U.S. Public*, pg. 1060

Strzelczyk, Frank A., V.P.-Shareholder Rels.--American Trading and Production Corporation, Baltimore, MD; *U.S. Private*, pg. 63

Suarez, Oscar, V.P. & Treas.--Bacardi Corporation, San Juan, PR; *Int'l*, pg. 131

Suedel, Kathleen L., Dir.-Investor Rels.--PETsMART, Inc., Phoenix, AZ; *U.S. Public*, pg. 1281

Suleman, Farid, Chief Fin. Officer & Sec.--Westwood One, Inc., New York, NY; *U.S. Public*, pg. 1763

Sullivan, John, Chief Fin. Officer , Sr. V.P.-Fin. & Treas.--Trans World Entertainment Corporation, Albany, NY; *U.S. Public*, pg. 1629

Sullivan, Robert W., V.P.-Investor Rels.--Cigna Corp., Philadelphia, PA; *U.S. Public*, pg. 356

Sullivan, Timothy J., Chief Fin. Officer, Chief Admin. Officer, Sr. V.P., Treas. & Sec.--Market Facts, Inc., Arlington Heights, IL; *U.S. Public*, pg. 1046

Sumner, Joan Nicolais, V.P.-Investor Rels.--Time Warner Inc., New York, NY; *U.S. Public*, pg. 1610

Sund, Mike, V.P.-Commun./Investor Rels. & Sec.--Mycogen Corporation, San Diego, CA; *U.S. Public*, pg. 1142

Sundvall, Boel, V.P.-Investor Rels. & Corp. Affairs--Swedish Match S.A., Stockholm, Sweden; *Int'l*, pg. 1328

Sung-Lee, Moo, Sr. V.P.-Fin.--Korean Airlines Co., Ltd., Seoul, Korea; *Int'l*, pg. 758

Sunseri, Patricia, V.P.-Investor & Pub. Rels.--Mylan Laboratories, Inc., Pittsburgh, PA; *U.S. Public*, pg. 1143

Superits, Steve, Dir.-Investor Rels.--Dana Corporation, Toledo, OH; *U.S. Public*, pg. 479

Surgala, David, Treas.--Keithley Instruments, Inc., Cleveland, OH; *U.S. Public*, pg. 946

Sussex, Thomas M., Jr., Dir.-Corp. Communications--Sparton Corporation, Jackson, MI; *U.S. Public*, pg. 1496

Sutter, Blanche M., Chief Fin. Officer, Exec. V.P. & Sec.--Caere Corporation, Los Gatos, CA; *U.S. Public*, pg. 291

Sutton, Dottie, Mgr.-Investor Rels.--Kemet Corporation, Simpsonville, SC; *U.S. Public*, pg. 949

Sutton, Susan, Mgr.-Shareholder Rels.--InterDigital Communications Corp., King of Prussia, PA; *U.S. Public*, pg. 889

Suuraho, Risto, V.P. & Treas.--Enso Oyj, Helsinki, Finland; *Int'l*, pg. 455

Swartwout, James R., Chm. Bd., Pres. & Chief Fin. Officer--Summa Industries, Torrance, CA; *U.S. Public*, pg. 1527

Swartz, Steve, Sr. V.P. & Dir.-Investor Rels.--H.F. Ahmanson & Co., Irwindale, CA; *U.S. Public*, pg. 29

Swearingen, Gregg, Dir.-Inv. Rels.--Promus Hotel Corporation, Memphis, TN; *U.S. Public*, pg. 1335

Sweda, G.J., Dir.-Pub. & Investor Rels.--Modine Manufacturing Company, Racine, WI; *U.S. Public*, pg. 1121

Sweeney, John, Jr., V.P.-Investor Rels.--USF&G Corporation, Baltimore, MD; *U.S. Public*, pg. 1659

Swift, John D., V.P.-Fin. & Chief Fin. Officer--Mohawk Industries, Inc., Calhoun, GA; *U.S. Public*, pg. 1121

Sydnor, E. Starke, Asst. Gen. Counsel & Dir.-Chemicals & Environmental--Vulcan Materials Company, Birmingham, AL; *U.S. Public*, pg. 1725

Szapor, Stephen J., V.P.-Strategic Plng.--Greate Bay Casino Corporation, Atlantic City, NJ; *U.S. Public*, pg. 760

Szymanski, Nancy, Mgr.-Shareholder Rels.--Silicon Valley Group, Inc., San Jose, CA; *U.S. Public*, pg. 1474

Taggert, Richard, V.P.-Investor Rels.--Weyerhaeuser Company, Federal Way, WA; *U.S. Public*, pg. 1764

Tagliafico, Vicki, Mgr.-Investor Rels.--Oregon Steel Mills Inc., Portland, OR; *U.S. Public*, pg. 1230

Takahashi, Hidemitsu, Chief Fin. Officer & Dir.-Investor Rels.--Pentel of America, Ltd., Torrance, CA; *Int'l*, pg. 1035

Takasawa, Hiroshi, Gen. Mgr.--Kayaba Industry Co., Ltd., Tokyo, Japan; *Int'l*, pg. 727

Takeda, Rebecca, Dir.-Investor Rels.--Smart Modular Technologies, Fremont, CA; *U.S. Public*, pg. 1476

Takeda, S., Mgr.-Corp. Communications--Fujisawa Pharmaceutical Co. Ltd., Osaka, Japan; *Int'l*, pg. 525

Taliaferro, Machele, Investor Rels. Asst.--Agouron Pharmaceuticals, Inc., La Jolla, CA; *U.S. Public*, pg. 28

Tan, Ricardo, Asst. V.P.-Investor Rels.--Philippine Long Distance Telephone Company, Manila, Philippines; *Int'l*, pg. 1051

Tang, Henry, Sr. V.P. & Dir.-Investment Services--Jefferies & Company, Inc., Los Angeles, CA; *U.S. Public*, pg. 925

Taniguchi, Sadao, Chief Fin Officer, Legal Officer & Dir.-Personnel & Inv. Rels.--Kosugi Sangyo Co., Ltd., Tokyo, Japan; *Int'l*, pg. 759

Tanner, Alison C., Dir.-Investor Rels.--Sensormatic Electronics Corporation, Boca Raton, FL; *U.S. Public*, pg. 1457

Tanner, Susan, Dir.-Investor Rels.--Isolyser Company, Inc., Norcross, GA; *U.S. Public*, pg. 914

Tanquary, Fred T., Controller--Mail Boxes Etc., San Diego, CA; *U.S. Public*, pg. 1687

Tapscott, Kim, Investor Rels.--Aloette Cosmetics, Inc., West Chester, PA; *U.S. Public*, pg. 57

Tarbell, Anne A., V.P.-Investor Rels.--ITT Corporation, New York, NY; *U.S. Public*, pg. 1512

Tarello, John A., Sr. V.P. & Treas.--Analogic Corporation, Peabody, MA; *U.S. Public*, pg. 109

Tarquine, Lauri, Mgr.-Investor Rels.--Hvide Marine Incorporated, Fort Lauderdale, FL; *U.S. Public*, pg. 851

Tarte, Bernard J., Jr., V.P. & Treas.--Bradner Central Company, Chicago, IL; *U.S. Private*, pg. 164

Taylor, Gregory D., Mgr.-Investor Rels.--The Lubrizol Corporation, Wickliffe, OH; *U.S. Public*, pg. 1016

Taylor, Jimmie, Mgr.-Cash Mngmt.--TCA Cable TV, Inc., Tyler, TX; *U.S. Public*, pg. 1553

Taylor, Julian H., V.P. & Treas.--Reynolds Metals Company, Richmond, VA; *U.S. Public*, pg. 1385

Taylor, Pamela C., V.P.-Corp. Commun.--Jacor Communications, Inc., Covington, KY; *U.S. Public*, pg. 922

Taylor, Susan, Dir.-Investor Rels.--Genentech, Inc., South San Francisco, CA; *Int'l*, pg. 1120

Taylor, Suzy, Dir.-Investor Rels.--FirstCity Financial Corporation, Waco, TX; *U.S. Public*, pg. 644

Teaks, Toni, Mgr.-Investor Rels.--Mac Frugal's Bargains Close-Outs Inc., Rancho Dominguez, CA; *U.S. Public*, pg. 437

Tebierio, Linda, Mgr.-Corp. Pub. Rels.--Emcee Broadcast Products, Inc., White Haven, PA; *U.S. Public*, pg. 570

Teeple, William W., Chief Fin. Officer, V.P. & Treas.--Stackpole Ltd., Newton, MA; *U.S. Private*, pg. 1028

Teeters, Bruce W., Sr. V.P.-Fin. & Treas.--Consolidated-Tomoka Land Co., Daytona Beach, FL; *U.S. Public*, pg. 437

Teibel, Darcy, Asst.-Investor Rels.--Canterbury Corporate Services, Inc., Medford, NJ; *U.S. Public*, pg. 301

Temmel, Karen, Mgr.-Corp. Commun. & Pub. Rels.--Correct Craft, Inc., Orlando, FL; *U.S. Private*, pg. 276

Temple, Michael, Dir.-Investor Rels.--Public Service Company of New Mexico, Albuquerque, NM; *U.S. Public*, pg. 1339

Teng, Clement, Dir.-Investor Rels.--Pacific Enterprises, Los Angeles, CA; *U.S. Public*, pg. 1249

Terry, Charles P., Sr. V.P.-Fin. & Treas.--Reed & Barton Corporation, Taunton, MA; *U.S. Private*, pg. 916

Terry, David, Sec. & Treas.--Fonar Corporation, Melville, NY; *U.S. Public*, pg. 661

Tervit, Margaret, Mgr.-Investor Rels.--Canadian Imperial Bank of Commerce, Toronto, Canada; *Int'l*, pg. 256

Tester, Becky, Mgr.-Investor Rels.--InterTAN Inc., Fort Worth, TX; *U.S. Public*, pg. 910

Thaden, Rogene A., V.P.-Communications--Northwestern Public Service, Huron, SD; *U.S. Public*, pg. 1200

Thalman, William M., Mgr.-Investor Rels.--The Carbide/Graphite Group, Inc., Pittsburgh, PA; *U.S. Public*, pg. 304

Thanepohn, Julie, Publicist--Circus Circus - Las Vegas, Las Vegas, NV; *U.S. Public*, pg. 374

Theil, Andreas, Dir.-Pub. Rels.--Solvay Osterreich AG, Ebensee, Austria; *Int'l*, pg. 1280

Thelin, Anders, Dir.-Investor Rels.--Proventus AB, Stockholm, Sweden; *Int'l*, pg. 1072

Thiel, Sally, Mgr.-Corp. Communications--C-COR Electronics, Inc., State College, PA; *U.S. Public*, pg. 272

Thiery, Linda, Mgr.-Shareholder Services--TCI Communications, Inc., Englewood, CO; *U.S. Public*, pg. 1554

Thold, D. Nicholas, Dir.-Investor Rels.--Union Carbide Corporation, Danbury, CT; *U.S. Public*, pg. 1666

Tholen, Steven W., Chief Fin. Officer, V.P. & Treas.--Penn Virginia Corporation, Radnor, PA; *U.S. Public*, pg. 1271

Thoma, Edward W., Sr. V.P.-Fin.--Oneida Ltd., Oneida, NY; *U.S. Public*, pg. 1225

Thomas, Carolyn, Coord.-Investor Rels.--Systems & Computer Technology Corporation, Malvern, PA; *U.S. Public*, pg. 1552

Thomas, David J., V.P. & Treas.--Frontier Communications Services, Bingham Farms, MI; *U.S. Public*, pg. 684

Thomas, Diana Lyn, Sec.--Cornerstone Natural Gas, Inc., Dallas, TX; *U.S. Public*, pg. 567

Thomas, Linda, Dir.-Investor Rels.--Unit Corporation, Tulsa, OK; *U.S. Public*, pg. 1672

Thomas, Maryann, Mgr.-Investor Rels.--EcoScience Corporation, East Brunswick, NJ; *U.S. Public*, pg. 563

Thompson, Bina, V.P.-Investor Rels.--Colgate-Palmolive Company, New York, NY; *U.S. Public*, pg. 397

Thompson, Clark, Dir.-Investor Rels.--SpaceLabs Medical, Inc., Redmond, WA; *U.S. Public*, pg. 1494

Thompson, Geoffrey P., Gen. Mgr.-Special Projects--Westpac Banking Corporation, Sydney, Australia; *Int'l*, pg. 1495

Thompson, John D., Sr. V.P.-Strategic & Bus. Devel.--The Dexter Corporation, Windsor Locks, CT; *U.S. Public*, pg. 504

Thompson, Linda, Asst. Sec. & Dir.-Investor Rels.--Interstate Bakeries Corporation, Kansas City, MO; *U.S. Public*, pg. 909

Thompson, Linda L., Dir.-Shareholder Rels. & Asst. Corp. Sec.--Interstate Brands Corporation, Kansas City, MO; *U.S. Public*, pg. 909

Thompson, Mark D., Chief Fin. Officer & Exec. V.P.--Lexford Residential Trust, Columbus, OH; *U.S. Public*, pg. 991

Thompson, R. Bruce, Chief Fin. Officer & Exec. V.P.--Circon Corporation, Santa Barbara, CA; *U.S. Public*, pg. 373

Thompson, Robert, V.P. & Treas.--Anchor Glass Container Corporation, Tampa, FL; *Int'l*, pg. 327

Thompson, Terry W., Chief Fin. Officer, V.P. & Treas.--Jack Henry & Associates, Inc., Monett, MO; *U.S. Public*, pg. 808

Thompson, W.H., Dir.-Investor Rels.--Shell Oil Company, Houston, TX; *Int'l*, pg. 1136

Thoren, Diane C., Mgr.-Investor Rels.--The Washington Water Power Company, Spokane, WA; *U.S. Public*, pg. 1744

Thornhill Jones, Lisa, Dir.-Mktg. Communications Trusted Div.--CyberGuard Corporation, Fort Lauderdale, FL; *U.S. Public*, pg. 470

Thornhill, Amie, Pres. & Asst. Treas.--Thornhill Oil Company, Inc., Fort Wayne, IN; *U.S. Private*, pg. 1084

Thornton, John, V.P.-Investor Rels.--Tecmar Technologies International, Inc., Concord, Canada; *Int'l*, pg. 1361

Thorp, Timothy J., Mgr.-Investor Rels.--Minnesota Power, Duluth, MN; *U.S. Public*, pg. 1116

Throop, Robert S., Chm. Bd. & Chief Exec. Officer--Anthem Electronics Inc., San Jose, CA; *U.S. Public*, pg. 134

Thurman, Doug, Dir.-Investor Rels.--Owens Corning, Toledo, OH; *U.S. Public*, pg. 1236

Tiegs, Sharon, Exec. Asst.--Grow Biz International, Inc., Minneapolis, MN; *U.S. Public*, pg. 767

Tighe, Gary, Chief Fin. Officer & Sr. V.P.--Staff Builders Inc., Lake Success, NY; *U.S. Public*, pg. 1501

Tirado, Patricia, Investor Rels. Analyst--Grupo Sidek, S.A. de C.V., Guadalajara, Mexico; *Int'l*, pg. 576

Tisdall, Mike, Gen. Mgr.-Inv. Rels.--Sasol Limited, Johannesburg, South Africa; *Int'l*, pg. 1196

Tobin, David S., Corp. Sec.--Peoples Telephone Company, Inc., Miami, FL; *U.S. Public*, pg. 1275

Tocci, Lynda, Asst. V.P. & Dir.-Pub. Rels.--UST Corporation, Boston, MA; *U.S. Public*, pg. 1660

Todd, Kevin, Mgr.-Investor Rels.--Noranda Inc., Toronto, Canada; *Int'l*, pg. 433

Ton, Gwaine, V.P.-Investor Rels.--Service Merchandise Company, Inc., Brentwood, TN; *U.S. Public*, pg. 1461

Toothman, Bob, Dir.-Communications--National Steel Corporation, Mishawaka, IN; *Int'l*, pg. 902

Torre, Maryann, Mgr.-Investor Rels.--The Sharper Image, San Francisco, CA; *U.S. Public*, pg. 1464

Torres, Jose O., V.P.-Fin., Treas. & Sec.--Puerto Rican Cement Co., Inc., Guaynabo, PR; *U.S. Public*, pg. 1341

Torres, Matt, Dir.-Investor Rels.--American Bankers Insurance Group, Inc., Miami, FL; *U.S. Public*, pg. 67

Townsend, T. Peter, V.P.-Investor Rels.--Exxon Corporation, Irving, TX; *U.S. Public*, pg. 601

Trationtin, Marlo, Mgr.-Investor Rels.--Arnoldo Mondadori Editore S.p.A., Segrate, Italy; *Int'l*, pg. 887

Traub, Burton D., Dir.-Investor Rels.--The Pittston Company, Glen Allen, VA; *U.S. Public*, pg. 1305

Treinen, David C., Sr. V.P.-Fin. & Sec.--International Aluminum Corporation, Monterey Park, CA; *U.S. Public*, pg. 894

Treschon, Lotta, Sr. V.P.-Investor Rels.--Skandinaviska Enskilda Banken, Stockholm, Sweden; *Int'l*, pg. 1258

Trigilio, Lisa, Dir.-Risk Mngmt.--Insight Health Services Corp., Newport Beach, CA; *U.S. Public*, pg. 880

Trinkman, Tammy, Mgr.-Investor Rels.--Wonderware Corporation, Irvine, CA; *U.S. Public*, pg. 1775

Triou, Florence, Mgr.-Institutional Investor Relations--Rhone-Poulenc S.A., Courbevoie, France; *Int'l*, pg. 1108

Triou, Florence, Mgr.-Investor Rels.--Saint-Gobain, Courbevoie, France; *Int'l*, pg. 1170

Tripp, David L., V.P. & Dir.-Investor Rels.--The Rouse Company, Columbia, MD; *U.S. Public*, pg. 1407

Troilo, Joseph C., Sr. V.P.-Fin. & Treas.--Foodarama Supermarkets, Inc., Freehold, NJ; *U.S. Public*, pg. 661

Troutman, Ellen, Dir.-Investor Rels.--Zoom Telephonics, Inc., Boston, MA; *U.S. Public*, pg. 1794

Trovillion, Raleigh A., Asst. V.P.-Investment Banking--United Missouri Bank of St. Louis, Saint Louis, MO; *U.S. Public, pg. 1655*

Trub, Aaron D., V.P., Treas. & Sec.--Smithfield Foods, Inc., Norfolk, VA; *U.S. Public*, pg. 1479

Trucksess, H.A., III, Chief Fin. Officer & Sr. V.P.-Fin.--Yellow Corporation, Overland Park, KS; *U.S. Public*, pg. 1788

Trudeau, Rosemary B., Contractor--Jan Bell Marketing Inc., Sunrise, FL; *U.S. Public*, pg. 207

Tsingos, Christine, V.P. & Treas.--Autodesk, Inc., San Rafael, CA; *U.S. Public*, pg. 148

Tucker, Bradford, Exec. V.P. & Gen. Counsel--Mustang Tractor & Equip. Co., Houston, TX; *U.S. Private*, pg. 768

Tucker, Deborah M., Dir.-Investor Rels.--CACI International Inc, Arlington, VA; *U.S. Public*, pg. 272

Tucker, W.A., Dir.-Human Resources--Vertex Communications Corporation, Kilgore, TX; *U.S. Public*, pg. 1717

Tully, Herbert B., V.P. & Treas.--Wilbur-Ellis Company & Connell Brothers Company, San Francisco, CA; *U.S. Private*, pg. 1175

Tunink, Paul C., Chief Fin. Officer, V.P.-Fin. & Treas.--Stuart Entertainment Inc., Council Bluffs, IA; *U.S. Public*, pg. 1526

Turk, Penny, Mgr.-Mktg. Commun.--Multigraphics Inc., Mount Prospect, IL; *U.S. Public*, pg. 1141

Turner, Janet M., V.P.-Investor Rels.--PLM International, Inc., San Francisco, CA; *U.S. Public*, pg. 1241

Tursi, Carl T., V.P. & Sec.--Amerada Hess Corporation, New York, NY; *U.S. Public*, pg. 65

Tutundgy, Carol S., V.P.-Investor Rels.--International Paper Company, Purchase, NY; *U.S. Public*, pg. 901

Tweedy, John, Dir.-Investor Rels.--Standard Microsystems Corp., Hauppauge, NY; *U.S. Public*, pg. 1502

Tyler, Cyrus L., V.P.-Corp. Communications--Konica Business Machines USA, Inc., Windsor, CT; *Int'l*, pg. 748

Tylka, Shawn, Corp. Communications Specialist--Scientific-Atlanta, Inc., Norcross, GA; *U.S. Public*, pg. 1443

Uhr, Stanley A., V.P.-Real Estate & Corp. Counsel--Deb Shops, Inc., Philadelphia, PA; *U.S. Public*, pg. 491

Ulbrandt, Laura, Sec.--Leucadia National Corporation, New York, NY; *U.S. Public*, pg. 989

Ulicsni, Eileen, Exec. Asst.--Reuter Manufacturing Inc., Hopkins, MN; *U.S. Public*, pg. 1383

Underwood, Tammy, Mgr.-Personnel & Exec. Asst.--Antenna Products Corp., Mineral Wells, TX; *U.S. Public*, pg. 289

Urbaniak, Susan, Dir.-Investor Rels.--Allied Research Corporation, Vienna, VA; *U.S. Public*, pg. 48

Urbantke, Ruth A., Dir.-Investor/Shareholder Rels.--Nevada Power Company, Las Vegas, NV; *U.S. Public*, pg. 1169

Vainonen, Valerie, V.P.-Investor Relations--Merita Bank Ltd., Helsinki, Finland; *Int'l*, pg. 858

Vale, Larry, Dir.-Mktg. Commun.--Keane, Inc., Boston, MA; *U.S. Public*, pg. 946

Vallaire, Jane, Mgr.-Investor Rels. & Admin.--Cheesecake Factory Incorporated, Calabasas Hills, CA; *U.S. Public*, pg. 343

Van Blarcum, Barbara H., V.P.-Investor Rels.--Fedders Corp., Liberty Corner, NJ; *U.S. Public*, pg. 614

van Bronkhorst, Jon, Dir.-Investor Rels.--Seagate Technology Inc., Scotts Valley, CA; *U.S. Public*, pg. 1449

Van Der Tuuk, Terry, Vice Chm.--Graphic Technology, Inc., New Century, KS; *Int'l*, pg. 950

Van Duzer, Charles B., Sec.--Reunion Industries, Inc., Stamford, CT; *U.S. Public*, pg. 1383

Van Dyke, Lester F., Dir.-Investor Rels. & Corp. Commun.--Battle Mountain Gold Company, Houston, TX; *U.S. Public*, pg. 193

van Haeringen, A.C., Dir.-Strategic Plng. & Investor Rels.--Ballast Nedam NV, Amstelveen, Netherlands; *Int'l*, pg. 133

van Rensburg, A.C. Janse, Mgr.-Investor Rels.--Standard Bank Investment Corporation Limited, Johannesburg, South Africa; *Int'l*, pg. 1293

Van Sant, Karen, Mkt. Res.--AirTouch Cellular - Western Region, Bellevue, WA; *U.S. Public*, pg. 34

Van Slyke, Tony, Mgr.-Investor Rels.--Pogo Producing Company, Houston, TX; *U.S. Public*, pg. 1312

Van Ufflin, Sue, Mgr.-Investor Rels.--Motorcar Parts & Accessories, Torrance, CA; *U.S. Public*, pg. 1136

van Westen, F., Dir.-Corp. Fin. & Investor Rels.--N.V. Koninklijke KNP BT, Amsterdam, Netherlands; *Int'l*, pg. 756

van Westrhenen, Peter, Mgr.-Corp. Communications--Heineken N.V., Amsterdam, Netherlands; *Int'l*, pg. 608

Vanaria, Robert, Chief Fin. Officer & Sr. V.P.-Admin.--Greenwich Air Services, Miami, FL; *U.S. Public*, pg. 710

Vance, Myrna, Dir.-Investor Rels.--Electronic Data Systems Corporation, Plano, TX; *U.S. Public*, pg. 569

Vancha, Colleen, Coord.-Inv. Rels.--CFP Foods, Saskatoon, Canada; *Int'l*, pg. 1195

vander Watt, Peet, Deputy Treas.--Transnet Ltd., Parkview, South Africa; *Int'l*, pg. 1417

Vandertuin, Bonnie, Mgr.-Corp. Affairs--Green Mountain Power Corporation, South Burlington, VT; *U.S. Public*, pg. 761

VanHouten, Ronald W., Sec.--Thomaston Mills, Inc., Thomaston, GA; *U.S. Public*, pg. 1599

VanTassel, Daniel R., Dir.-Corp. Communications--CF Industries, Inc., Long Grove, IL; *U.S. Private*, pg. 193

Vanzura, Cedric J., V.P.-Grp. Plng. & Resource Mngmt.--Borders Group, Inc., Ann Arbor, MI; *U.S. Public*, pg. 245

Vargas, Arnulfo, Pres., Chief Exec. Officer & Investor Rels. Dir.--Cash & Carry Grocer Inc., Chicago, IL; *U.S. Private, pg. 218*

Vass, Dennis B., Treas.--IES Industries Inc., Cedar Rapids, IA; *U.S. Public*, pg. 855

Vaughan, M.B., Mgr.-Investor Rels.--Chevron Corporation, San Francisco, CA; *U.S. Public*, pg. 347

Vaughan, Marcia P., Dir.-Corp. Commun.--Sunrise Medical, Inc., Carlsbad, CA; *U.S. Public*, pg. 1535

Vaughn, Shelly, Dir.-Investor Rels.--American Business Information, Inc., Omaha, NE; *U.S. Public*, pg. 69

Veatch, Jean K., Dir.-Investor Rels.--PCA International, Inc., Matthews, NC; *U.S. Public*, pg. 1240

Vegter, Bill, Chief Fin. Officer & V.P.-Fin.--All-Phase Electric Supply Co., Benton Harbor, MI; *U.S. Private*, pg. 35

Vidra, Carla, Dir.-Investor Rels.--Olivetti SpA, Turin, Italy; *Int'l*, pg. 1002

Vikkula, Kaisa, V.P.-Corp. Commun. & Investor Rels.--Partek Corporation, Helsinki, Finland; *Int'l*, pg. 1024

Vilandre, Charles A., Mgr.-Investor Rels.--Raytheon Company, Lexington, MA; *U.S. Public*, pg. 1364

Villanueva, Arturo, Dir.-Investor Rels.--Corporacion Internacional de Aviacion (CINTRA), Mexico, Mexico; *Int'l*, pg. 332

Villarreal, Jennifer, Mgr.-Press & Pub. Rels./N. America--Smiths Industries Aerospace & Defense Systems Inc.-Grand Rapids Operation, Grand Rapids, MI; *Int'l*, pg. 1268

Vinke, John T., Chief Fin. Officer & V.P.-Fin.--Special Devices, Incorporated, Newhall, CA; *U.S. Public*, pg. 1496

Virtue, Robert A., Chm. Bd., Pres. & Chief Exec. Officer--Virco Mfg. Corporation, Torrance, CA; *U.S. Public*, pg. 1721

Vivian, Robert, V.P.-Investor Rels.--Brinker International, Inc., Dallas, TX; *U.S. Public*, pg. 253

Vix, Carol A., Sr. Attorney & Asst. Sec.--Premark International, Inc., Deerfield, IL; *U.S. Public*, pg. 1321

Vogelzang, C.F., Mgr.-Investor Rels. & Pub. Rels.--Wolters Kluwer N.V., Amsterdam, Netherlands; *Int'l*, pg. 1512

Vogler, Sharlene, Dir.-Investor Rels.--Mark IV Industries Inc., Amherst, NY; *U.S. Public*, pg. 1044

Voltz, Trisha, V.P.-Investor Rels.--Hibernia Corporation, New Orleans, LA; *U.S. Public*, pg. 825

Von der Ruhr, Gerhard J., Chm. Bd., Pres. & Treas.--Criticare Systems, Inc., Waukesha, WI; *U.S. Public*, pg. 459

von Hofsten, Erik, Pub. Rels. Officer--Skanska AB, Danderyd, Sweden; *Int'l*, pg. 1260

Von Kennel, Timothy J., V.P.-State Rels.--ENSERCH Corporation, Dallas, TX; *U.S. Public*, pg. 1587

Von Kobylinski, K., Dir.-Investor Rels.--Continental AG, Hannover, Germany; *Int'l*, pg. 327

Vozick, David, Chm. Bd., Treas. & Sec.--AFP Imaging Corporation, Elmsford, NY; *U.S. Public*, pg. 6

Vu, Theresa, Mktg. Programs Specialist--Advanced Logic Research, Inc., Irvine, CA; *U.S. Public*, pg. 703

Wack, Patti, Dir.-Investor Rels.--Selective Insurance Group, Inc, Branchville, NJ; *U.S. Public*, pg. 1455

Wada, Akira, Mgr.-Investor Rels.--Rohto Pharmaceutical Co., Osaka, Japan; *Int'l*, pg. 1126

Wadsworth, Howard, V.P.-Fin. & Admin., Treas. & Sec.--Kaneb Services, Inc., Richardson, TX; *U.S. Public*, pg. 942

Wagner, Brooke, Dir.-Fin.--Software Publishing Corporation, Fairfield, NJ; *U.S. Public*, pg. 1483

Wagner, Michael J., Asst. Treas.--Consolidated Stores Corp., Columbus, OH; *U.S. Public*, pg. 437

Wailes, Kathleen M., V.P.-Corp. Commun. & Investor Rels.--Litton Industries, Inc., Woodland Hills, CA; *U.S. Public*, pg. 1002

Wait, Linda, Dir.-Investor Rels.--360 Degrees Communications Company, Chicago, IL; *U.S. Public*, pg. 1607

Waite, Robert E., V.P.-Corp. Rels. & Mktg.--CAE Inc., Toronto, Canada; *Int'l*, pg. 237

Walk, Paul W., Jr., Sr. V.P.--Virginia First Savings Bank, F.S.B., Petersburg, VA; *U.S. Public*, pg. 1721

Walker, Beth, Treas.--Spar Aerospace Limited, Toronto, Canada; *Int'l*, pg. 1287

Walker, Donald H., Chief Fin. Officer, V.P.-Fin.--Frisch's Restaurants, Inc., Cincinnati, OH; *U.S. Public*, pg. 682

Walker, James, V.P.-Mktg.--Koger Equity Inc., Jacksonville, FL; *U.S. Public*, pg. 965

Walker, Sandra, Corp. Asst.--Unitil Corporation, Hampton, NH; *U.S. Public*, pg. 1692

Walker, Thomas H., Jr., Sr. V.P.-Investor Rels.--American Re Corporation, Princeton, NJ; *Int'l*, pg. 897

Waller, Frank S., Chm. Bd.--Woodward-Clyde Group, Inc., Denver, CO; *U.S. Public*, pg. 1655

Walsh, Diane, Exec. Asst.--Old America Stores, Howe, TX; *U.S. Public*, pg. 1215

Walsh, Ellie, Dir.-Admin. Services--ABM Industries, San Francisco, CA; *U.S. Public*, pg. 2

Walsh, F. Michael, V.P.--First Marathon Inc., Toronto, Canada; *Int'l*, pg. 486

Walters, Beth, Dir.-Investor Rels.--Jabil Circuit, Inc., Saint Petersburg, FL; *U.S. Public*, pg. 919

Ward, David H., Gen. Mgr.-Investor Rels.--Australia & New Zealand Banking Group Limited, Melbourne, Australia; *Int'l*, pg. 98

Ward, R.D., Mgr.-Pub. Affairs--Laporte plc, Luton, United Kingdom; *Int'l*, pg. 801

Ward, Robert A., Exec. V.P.--Unifi Inc., Greensboro, NC; *U.S. Public*, pg. 1665

Ward, Simon, Mgr.-Investor Relations--Transamerican Natural Gas Corporation, Houston, TX; *U.S. Private*, pg. 1096

Ward, Thomas J., V.P.-Admin. & Sec.--Pennsylvania Enterprises Inc., Wilkes-Barre, PA; *U.S. Public*, pg. 1271

Warner, Jodi L., Mgr.-AMCOL Commun. & Investor Rels.--AMCOL International Corp., Arlington Heights, IL; *U.S. Public*, pg. 63

Warner, Susan B., Dir.-Communications--General Signal Corporation, Stamford, CT; *U.S. Public*, pg. 726

Warren, Harry, Dir.-Fin. Rels.--Washington Gas Light Co., Springfield, VA; *U.S. Public*, pg. 1740

Warren, Janice, Mgr.-Corp. Commun.--FiberMark Inc., Brattleboro, VT; *U.S. Public*, pg. 620

Warren, Joseph G., Chief Fin. Officer, V.P.-Fin., Treas. & Sec.--Bowmar Instrument Corporation, Phoenix, AZ; *U.S.* Public, pg. 248

Warren, Sheila A., Mgr.-Corp. Commun.--Biomet, Inc., Warsaw, IN; *U.S. Public*, pg. 231

Warrener, Richard C., Chief Fin. Officer & Sr. V.P.--Rurban Financial Corp., Defiance, OH; *U.S. Public*, pg. 1412

Wasser, Deb, Dir.-Investor Rels.--Veeco Instruments, Inc., Plainview, NY; *U.S. Public*, pg. 1711

Watkins, Heidi W., Investor Rels. Admin.--Chesapeake Utilities Corporation, Dover, DE; *U.S. Public*, pg. 347

Watkins, Wynfred C., V.P. & Dir.-Investor Rels.--JC Penney Company, Inc., Plano, TX; *U.S. Public*, pg. 916

Watson, Janet S., Treas. & Sec.--The Empire District Electric Company, Joplin, MO; *U.S. Public*, pg. 579

Watson, Joseph D., Dir.-Investor Rels.--Tosco Corporation, Stamford, CT; *U.S. Public*, pg. 1624

Watson, Ronald L., Sec.--Keystone Bank, Horsham, PA; *U.S. Public*, pg. 956

Watson, Susan V., V.P.-Investor Rels.--Cognizant Corporation, Westport, CT; *U.S. Public*, pg. 395

Watson, Weldon, Mgr.-Investor Rels.--ONEOK Inc., Tulsa, OK; *U.S. Public*, pg. 1226

Watt, William F., Exec. V.P. & Dir.-Mktg./Retail Banking--FirstFed Financial Corp., Santa Monica, CA; *U.S. Public*, pg. 645

Weaver, Donna B., Mgr.-Corp. Communications--Kellwood Company, Chesterfield, MO; *U.S. Public*, pg. 948

Webb, Stephen, Dir.-Investor Rels.--Safeway PLC, Hayes, United Kingdom; *Int'l*, pg. 1169

Webb, Wendy, V.P.-Investor Rels.--The Walt Disney Company, Burbank, CA; *U.S. Public*, pg. 511

Weber, Daniel W., Second V.P. & Dir.-Investor Rels.--Lincoln National Corporation, Fort Wayne, IN; *U.S. Public*, pg. 997

Weber, Dwight E., Dir.-Communications--Precision Castparts Corp., Portland, OR; *U.S. Public*, pg. 1320

Webster, Connie, Dir.-Corp. Services--Howtek, Inc., Hudson, NH; *U.S. Public*, pg. 844

Wee, Michelle, Div. Mgr.-Investor Rels. & Pub. Rels.--F.J. Benjamin Multimedia Pte Ltd., Singapore, Singapore; *Int'l*, pg. 187

Weiden, Jeff, Sr. V.P.-Fin. & Treas.--Firstar Corporation, Milwaukee, WI; *U.S. Public*, pg. 642

Weidner, Robert M., III, Gen. Mgr.-Communications & Shareholder Rels.--Inland Steel Industries, Inc., Chicago, IL; *U.S. Public*, pg. 879

Weiman, Lori, Dir.-Corp. Commun. & Investor Rels.--MGI PHARMA INC., Minneapolis, MN; *U.S. Public*, pg. 1026

Weinberg, David L., Chief Fin. Officer, V.P.-Fin. & Admin., Treas. & Sec.--Columbia Laboratories, Inc., Miami, FL; *U.S. Public*, pg. 405

Weinman, Thomas F., Treas.--Bar-S Foods Co., Phoenix, AZ; *U.S. Private*, pg. 114

Weisbarth, Mike, V.P.-Investor Rels.--OfficeMax, Shaker Heights, OH; *U.S. Public*, pg. 1212

Weisenborn, Jeanne A., Officer-Investment Banking--UMB First National Bank, Collinsville, IL; *U.S. Public*, pg. 1654

Weixel, Kenneth, Exec. V.P.-Health Care Fin. Bus. Strategy--PHP Healthcare Corporation, Reston, VA; *U.S. Public*, pg. 1241

Welborn, Richard L., Asst. V.P.-Fin. & Tax Admin.--Noland Company, Newport News, VA; *U.S. Public*, pg. 1187

Welch, Kim, Mgr.-Investor Rels.--AmeriCredit Corp., Fort Worth, TX; *U.S. Public*, pg. 96

Weldon, Dennis, Treas.--Mentor Graphics Corporation, Wilsonville, OR; *U.S. Public*, pg. 1086

Wellendorf, Donald R., V.P., Treas. & Investor Rels.--Mapco Inc., Tulsa, OK; *U.S. Public*, pg. 1042

Welshhans, Richard W., Chief Fin. Officer, V.P. & Treas.--Reflectone, Inc., Tampa, FL; *Int'l*, pg. 218

Weltscheff, Christina, V.P.-Investor Rels.--KV Pharmaceutical Company, Saint Louis, MO; *U.S. Public*, pg. 941

Wenhold, William R., V.P.-Human Resources--Oakite Products, Inc., Berkeley Heights, NJ; *Int'l*, pg. 861
Wenzler, Joseph P., Chief Fin. Officer, Sr. V.P. & Treas.--WICOR, Inc., Milwaukee, WI; *U.S. Public*, pg. 1767
Werneck, Mauricio, Mgr.-Corp Rels.--Aracruz Celulose S.A., Rio de Janeiro, Brazil; *Int'l*, pg. 78
Westberg, Bjorn, Sr. V.P.--Nordbanken AB, Stockholm, Sweden; *Int'l*, pg. 957
Westcott, Gayle, Communications Specialist--Southam Inc., Don Mills, Canada; *Int'l*, pg. 631
Westcott, Nancy V., V.P.-Investor Rels. & Communications--Caremark International Inc, Northbrook, IL; *U.S. Public*, pg. 1082
Wester, Mark, Chief Fin. Officer & V.P.-Fin.--Waxman Industries, Inc., Bedford, OH; *U.S. Public*, pg. 1748
Westerbeck, David F., Sr. V.P., Gen. Counsel & Sec.--The Union Central Life Insurance Co., Cincinnati, OH; *U.S. Private*, pg. 1118
Weston, Diane, Sr. Admin. Asst.--L.A. Gear, Inc., Santa Monica, CA; *U.S. Public*, pg. 969
Weyand, Victoria P., V.P. & Sec.--John H. Harland Company, Decatur, GA; *U.S. Public*, pg. 785
Weyer, Brian K., Treas.--AmeriSteel, Tampa, FL; *U.S. Private*, pg. 65
Whalen, Kathleen T., Mgr.-Investor Rels.--Culligan International Company, Northbrook, IL; *U.S. Public*, pg. 467
Whalen, Michael, V.P.-Acq. & Fin.--People's Choice TV Corp., Shelton, CT; *U.S. Public*, pg. 1274
Whalen, Mike, Dir.-Investor Rels.--Bangor Hydro-Electric Company, Bangor, ME; *U.S. Public*, pg. 178
Wharton, James R., Dir.-Investor Rels.--Gateway 2000, North Sioux City, SD; *U.S. Public*, pg. 703
Whatcott, Lee A., Chief Fin. Officer & Sr. V.P.--Westcorp, Irvine, CA; *U.S. Public*, pg. 1756
Wheatley, Bruce C., Sr. V.P.-Admin.--Commercial Intertech Corp., Youngstown, OH; *U.S. Public*, pg. 411
Wheeler, John, Asst. V.P.-Investor Rels.--Telus Corporation, Edmonton, Canada; *Int'l*, pg. 1374
Wheeler, Mike, Chief Fin. Officer, V.P. & Treas.--Hy-Vee Food Stores Incorporated, West Des Moines, IA; *U.S. Private*, pg. 550
Wheeless, Charlene, Dir.-Corp. Commun.--DynCorp, Reston, VA; *U.S. Private*, pg. 351
Whipps, Pamela, V.P. & Treas.--Huffy Corporation, Miamisburg, OH; *U.S. Public*, pg. 846
Whisnant, John R., Chief Fin. Officer & V.P.-Fin.--Insignia Systems, Inc., Minnetonka, MN; *U.S. Public*, pg. 881
Whitacre, Huntley R., Sr. V.P.-Investor Rels.--RJR Nabisco Holdings Corp., New York, NY; *U.S. Public*, pg. 1354
White, Bernard H., V.P.-Corp Affairs--Zapata Corporation, Houston, TX; *U.S. Public*, pg. 1789
White, Randall W., Chm. Bd., Pres. & Treas.--Educational Development Corporation, Tulsa, OK; *U.S. Public*, pg. 564
White, Stan, Chief Fin. Officer, V.P.-Fin., Sec. & Treas.--U.S. Filter/Davis Water & Waste Industries, Inc., Thomasville, GA; *U.S. Public*, pg. 1682
White, Vince, Dir.-Investor Rels.--Devon Energy Corporation, Oklahoma City, OK; *U.S. Public*, pg. 503
Whiteside, Jeffery W., Dir.-Investor Rels.--Indiana Energy, Inc., Indianapolis, IN; *U.S. Public*, pg. 874
Whitesides, K.R., Dir.-Investor Rels.--The Boots Company PLC, Nottingham, United Kingdom; *Int'l*, pg. 202
Whitlow, Michael D., V.P.-External Affairs--Albemarle Corporation, Richmond, VA; *U.S. Public*, pg. 37
Whitney, Kenneth C., Mng. Dir.--The Blackstone Group, New York, NY; *U.S. Private*, pg. 147
Whiton, A.E., V.P. & Controller--Ionics, Incorporated, Watertown, MA; *U.S. Public*, pg. 912
Whitten, John R., V.P.-Fin. & Treas.--Applied Industrial Technologies, Cleveland, OH; *U.S. Public*, pg. 122
Whynot, Geoff, Chief Fin. Officer & V.P.--Kerr Group, Inc., Lancaster, PA; *U.S. Public*, pg. 952
Wickham, D. M., Dir.-Corp. & Pub. Affairs--Carter Holt Harvey Limited, Auckland, New Zealand; *U.S. Public*, pg. 904
Widrig, Richard F., V.P.-Fin. & Investor Rels.--Western Waste Industries, Torrance, CA; *U.S. Public*, pg. 1686
Wieber, Michelle, Dir.-Investor Rels.--Network Associates, Inc., Santa Clara, CA; *U.S. Public*, pg. 1168
Wiedenhaupt, Kurt, Chm. Bd. & Pres.--American Precision Industries Inc., Buffalo, NY; *U.S. Public*, pg. 90
Wienroeder, Doris, Mgr.-Investors Rels.--FAG Group, Schweinfurt, Germany; *Int'l*, pg. 468
Wiese, Arienne, Dir.-Investor Relations--Ultrak Inc., Lewisville, TX; *U.S. Public*, pg. 1663
Wiethoff, Charlotte, V.P.-Admin. & Sec.--Viking Office Products, Torrance, CA; *U.S. Public*, pg. 1720
Wikander, Bengt, Sr. V.P.-Corp. Communications--Esselte AB, Solna, Sweden; *Int'l*, pg. 459
Wilcox, Beth, Investor Rels. Specialist--ADC Telecommunications, Inc., Minnetonka, MN; *U.S. Public*, pg. 4
Wilcox, Gregory G., Sr. V.P.-Investor Rels.--The Equitable Companies Incorporated, New York, NY; *U.S. Public*, pg. 588
Wiley, Michael, V.P.-Corp. Rels.--Quorum Health Group, Inc., Brentwood, TN; *U.S. Public*, pg. 1353
Wiley, Steve, Dir.-Investor Rels. & Plng.--Destec Energy, Inc., Houston, TX; *U.S. Public*, pg. 1146
Wilk, Steven J., Pres.--TransNet Corporation, Somerville, NJ; *U.S. Public*, pg. 1631
Wilks, Marylaurel E., V.P.-Commun., Gen. Counsel & Sec.--Speedway Motorsports, Inc., Concord, NC; *U.S. Public*, pg. 1498
Willard, Dean M., Chief Exec. Officer--Courtaulds Aerospace, Glendale, CA; *Int'l*, pg. 339
Willett, Charlie, V.P.--CBL & Associates Properties, Inc., Chattanooga, TN; *U.S. Public*, pg. 273
Williams, Andrew W., Chm. Bd. & Chief Exec. Officer--Florafax International, Inc., Vero Beach, FL; *U.S. Public*, pg. 654
Williams, Charles D., V.P.-Investor Rels.--USX Corporation, Pittsburgh, PA; *U.S. Public*, pg. 1661
Williams, Gloria, V.P., Controller, Treas. & Dir.-Investor Rels.--The Stop & Shop Companies, Inc., Quincy, MA; *Int'l*, pg. 750
Williams, H.E., Controller--Levlad, Inc., Chatsworth, CA; *U.S. Private*, pg. 663
Williams, Janice, Dir.-Investor Rels.--Chase Corporation, Braintree, MA; *U.S. Public*, pg. 337
Williams, Linda, Dir.-Investor Rels.--Illinois Tool Works Inc., Glenview, IL; *U.S. Public*, pg. 865
Williams, Lisa Y., Asst. Investor Rels.--Hyperion Software, Stamford, CT; *U.S. Public*, pg. 851
Williams, Nancy, Mgr.-Inv. Rels.--MicroAge, Inc., Tempe, AZ; *U.S. Public*, pg. 1104
Williams, Rayvon, Dir.-Investor Rels.--Tandem Computers Inc., Cupertino, CA; *U.S. Public*, pg. 417
Williams, Robert E., V.P. & Dir.-Investor/Pub. Rels.--St. Paul Bancorp, Inc., Chicago, IL; *U.S. Public*, pg. 1428
Williamson, Patricia, Asst. V.P.--DRS Technologies, Inc., Parsippany, NJ; *U.S. Public*, pg. 474
Wilson, David E., Exec. V.P.--Shipley Companies, York, PA; *U.S. Private*, pg. 994
Wilson, Des, Dir.-Corp. & Pub. Affairs.--BAA plc, London, United Kingdom; *Int'l*, pg. 103
Wilson, Gail S., Mgr.-Investor Rels.--Primex Technologies, Inc., Saint Petersburg, FL; *U.S. Public*, pg. 1329
Wilson, Katherine E., Dir.-Fin. Plng.--CSX Corporation, Richmond, VA; *U.S. Public*, pg. 284
Wilson, Robert M., Chief Fin. Officer, Exec. V.P., Gen. Counsel & Sec.--Roberds, Inc., Carrollton, OH; *U.S. Public*, pg. 1393
Wilson, Steven E., Mgr.-Investor Rels.--United Bankshares, Inc., Parkersburg, WV; *U.S. Public*, pg. 1674
Wimmer, Anita, Mgr.-Fin. Reporting--Stanley Furniture Co. Inc., Stanleytown, VA; *U.S. Public*, pg. 1508
Winbush, Rosemary, Exec. Asst.--Riverside Group, Inc., Jacksonville, FL; *U.S. Public*, pg. 1391
Winkler, Lawrence, Dir.-Investor Relations--The Mills Corporation, Arlington, VA; *U.S. Public*, pg. 1113
Winn, H.J., III, Mgr.-Investor Rels.--SCANA Corporation, Columbia, SC; *U.S. Public*, pg. 1436
Winroth, Jorgen L., V.P.-Investor Rels., U.S.A.--Pharmacia & Upjohn Biosystems AB, Uppsala, Sweden; *Int'l*, pg. 1047
Winslow, Sue, Mgr.-Investor Rels.--The Buckle, Inc., Kearney, NE; *U.S. Public*, pg. 267
Winter, Irwin W., Chief Fin. Officer & Exec. V.P.--Phillips-Van Heusen Corporation, New York, NY; *U.S. Public*, pg. 1291
Winters, Tracie, Mgr.-Investor Rels.--Gencor Industries, Inc., Orlando, FL; *U.S. Public*, pg. 705
Wirth, Peter, Dr., Pres. & Chief Exec. Officer--Mikron Holding AG, Biel, Switzerland; *Int'l*, pg. 866
Wirth, Ronald O., Dir.-Investor Rels.--Western Gas Resources, Inc., Denver, CO; *U.S. Public*, pg. 1758
Wischnia, Abe, Dir.-Corp. Commun.--Cubic Corporation, San Diego, CA; *U.S. Public*, pg. 466
Witherow, Brian C., Dir.-Investor Rels.--Cedar Fair, L.P., Sandusky, OH; *U.S. Public*, pg. 319
Witmer, Mark D., Asst. Treas.--Michael Foods, Inc., Minneapolis, MN; *U.S. Public*, pg. 1103
Woit, Erik P., V.P.-North America--Orient-Express Hotels Inc., New York, NY; *Int'l*, pg. 1213
Wojnowski, Leon A., Chief Oper. Officer, Chief Fin. Officer, Treas. & Sec.--Connelly Containers, Inc., Bala Cynwyd, PA; *U.S. Private*, pg. 264
Wolf, Christopher F., Chief Fin. Officer, Sr. V.P., Treas. & Sec.--Swank, Inc., Attleboro, MA; *U.S. Public*, pg. 1543
Wolf, Dale J., V.P.-Fin. & Sec.--UtiliCorp United Inc., Kansas City, MO; *U.S. Public*, pg. 1700
Wolf, Dennis, Chief Fin. Officer & Sr. V.P.-Opers. & Admin.--Centigram Communications Corporation, San Jose, CA; *U.S. Public*, pg. 323
Wolf, Joan, Dir.-Investor Rels.--Vicon Industries, Inc., Hauppauge, NY; *U.S. Public*, pg. 1719
Wolf, Roger J., Chief Fin. Officer, Sr. V.P., Sec. & Treas.--Hurco Companies, Inc., Indianapolis, IN; *U.S. Public*, pg. 850
Wolff, Kathy, Exec. Sec. & Mgr.-Shareholder Rels.--Simpson Industries, Inc., Plymouth, MI; *U.S. Public*, pg. 1474
Wolfson, Martin, Chief Fin. Officer & Sr. V.P.--Concord Fabrics Inc., New York, NY; *U.S. Public*, pg. 429
Wolke, Joseph, Dir.-IRM--Brunswick Corporation, Lake Forest, IL; *U.S. Public*, pg. 265
Wollen, A. Ross, Sr. V.P., Gen. Counsel & Sec.--General Cigar Holdings Inc, New York, NY; *U.S. Public*, pg. 707
Wolski, Christine M., Asst. Corp. Sec.--Commerce Group Corp., Milwaukee, WI; *U.S. Public*, pg. 410
Wolski, Lawrence G., Chief Exec. Officer--Joslyn Corporation, Chicago, IL; *U.S. Public*, pg. 481
Wong, Anita, Dir.-Investor Rels.--Applied Materials, Inc., Santa Clara, CA; *U.S. Public*, pg. 123
Wong, Michael, Exec. Dir.-Corp. Plng. & Investments--Sun Hung Kai Properties Ltd., Wan Chai, Hong Kong; *Int'l*, pg. 1318
Wood, C. Martin, III, Chief Fin. Officer & Sr. V.P.--Flowers Industries, Inc., Thomasville, GA; *U.S. Public*, pg. 656
Wood, Carol S., Chief Fin. Officer, Controller, Treas. & Sec.--Higginbotham-Bartlett Co., Lubbock, TX; *U.S. Private*, pg. 527
Wood, David R., Chief Fin. Officer, Exec. V.P.-Admin. & Treas.--The Sands Regent, Reno, NV; *U.S. Public*, pg. 1431
Wood, Fred, Asst. V.P.-Investor Rels.--Dominion Resources, Inc., Richmond, VA; *U.S. Public*, pg. 516
Wood, Lee, Dir.-Investor Rels.--Columbia/HCA Healthcare Corporation, Nashville, TN; *U.S. Public*, pg. 404
Woodhouse, Michael A., Chief Fin. Officer & Sr. V.P.--Cracker Barrel Old Country Store, Inc., Lebanon, TN; *U.S. Public*, pg. 455
Woodruff, Bea, Mgr.-Corp. Communications--Schneider Group, Mississauga, Canada; *Int'l*, pg. 1208
Woods, Randall J., Dir.-Investor Rels.--FMC Corporation, Chicago, IL; *U.S. Public*, pg. 604
Woodward, Patricia, Mgr.-Investor Rels.--Hawker Siddeley Canada Inc., Mississauga, Canada; *Int'l*, pg. 604
Worley, Phil, V.P.-Commun.--Taylor Capital Group, Wheeling, IL; *U.S. Private*, pg. 1070
Worries, Margo, Mgr.-Investor Rels.--System Software Associates, Inc., Chicago, IL; *U.S. Public*, pg. 1552
Woudstra, F. Robert, Exec. V.P. & Treas.--Foremost Corporation of America, Caledonia, MI; *U.S. Public*, pg. 667
Wrem, Jeffrey, Dir.-Fin.--New Cooperative Inc., Fort Dodge, IA; *U.S. Private*, pg. 792
Wright, B., Mgr.-Investor Rels.--Meyer International PLC, London, United Kingdom; *Int'l*, pg. 864
Wright, Franklin L., External Affairs Exec.--The Dime Savings Bank of New York, New York, NY; *U.S. Public*, pg. 509
Wright, James W., V.P.-Legal Affairs & Sec.--Lord Corporation, Cary, NC; *U.S. Private*, pg. 675
Wright, Robert E., V.P.-Investor Rels.--Unocal Corporation, El Segundo, CA; *U.S. Public*, pg. 1698
Wulf, N.L., Dir.-Investor Rels. & Asst. Treas.--Emerson Electric Co., Saint Louis, MO; *U.S. Public*, pg. 572
Wusslor, Debbie, Dir.-Investor Rels.--Microchip Technology, Inc., Chandler, AZ; *U.S. Public*, pg. 1105
Wust, Pierre, Treas., Controller & Chief Fin. Officer--Sandoz Pharma Ltd., Eden Terrace, New Zealand; *Int'l*, pg. 985
Wyant, Clyde, Chief Fin. Officer & Exec. V.P.--Lennox International Inc., Richardson, TX; *U.S. Private*, pg. 659
Wylie, Scott, Dir.-Corp. Communications--Raychem Corporation, Menlo Park, CA; *U.S. Public*, pg. 1362
Wyrwas, Margaret E., V.P.-Corp. Communications & Investor Relations--Ames Department Stores, Inc., Rocky Hill, CT; *U.S. Public*, pg. 99
Yamamura, Takehiko, Chief Fin. Officer, Exec. V.P. & Dir.-Inv. Rels.--Haseko Corporation, Tokyo, Japan; *Int'l*, pg. 599
Yamasaghi, Mr., Pres.--Leader Instruments Corporation, Hauppauge, NY; *U.S. Private*, pg. 655
Yancey, George F.T., Jr., Pres.--Perry's Ice Cream Co., Inc., Akron, NY; *U.S. Private*, pg. 855
Yankowski, George, Dir.-Investor Rels.--Southern Union Company, Austin, TX; *U.S. Public*, pg. 1491
Yates, Joanne, Mgr.-Investor Rels.--Sulcus Computer Corp., Greensburg, PA; *U.S. Public*, pg. 1527
Yawman, Philip H., Dir.-Investor Rels.--Frontier Corporation, Rochester, NY; *U.S. Public*, pg. 683
Yeager, Waldo E., Chief Fin. Officer & Treas.--Seaway Food Town, Inc., Maumee, OH; *U.S. Public*, pg. 1452
Yeager, William, Chief Fin. Officer--Menley & James Laboratories, Inc., Horsham, PA; *U.S. Public*, pg. 1086
Yearwood, Jonnie, Mgr.-Investor Rels.--Benton Oil & Gas Company, Carpinteria, CA; *U.S. Public*, pg. 212
Yeater, Ginny, Mgr.-Investor Rels.--Pacific Capital Bancorp, Salinas, CA; *U.S. Public*, pg. 1247
Yonker, George P., V.P.-Fin. & Dir.-Investor Rels.--SAFECO Corporation, Seattle, WA; *U.S. Public*, pg. 1423
Yoshino, Frank, Treas.--MTI Technology Corporation, Anaheim, CA; *U.S. Public*, pg. 1028
Youner, Lester W., Chief Fin. Officer, V.P. & Treas.--Trans Resources, Inc., New York, NY; *U.S. Private*, pg. 1096
Young, Tish, Investor Rels. Coord.--Drug Emporium, Inc., Powell, OH; *U.S. Public*, pg. 530
Yovanovich, J.R., Sec.--The Ziegler Companies, Inc., West Bend, WI; *U.S. Public*, pg. 1791
Yudzevich, Kathy, Mgr.-Investor Rels.--Intermagnetics General Corporation, Latham, NY; *U.S. Public*, pg. 893
Yurkovic, Leonard S., Pres. & Chief Exec. Officer--SI Handling Systems, Inc., Easton, PA; *U.S. Public*, pg. 1418
Yuska, John R., Chief Fin. Officer & Sr. V.P.--Avemco Corporation, Frederick, MD; *U.S. Public*, pg. 151
Zabaleta, Juan Romero, Dir.-Pub. Communications--Amper, S.A., Madrid, Spain; *Int'l*, pg. 1372
Zahrn, James F., Chief Fin. Officer & Sr. V.P.--Springs Industries, Inc., Fort Mill, SC; *U.S. Public*, pg. 1499
Zak, George R., V.P.-Investor Rels.--Analysts International Corporation, Minneapolis, MN; *U.S. Public*, pg. 110
Zak, Kenneth J., Dir.-Inv. Rels.--Masco Corporation, Taylor, MI; *U.S. Public*, pg. 1052
Zakas, Marietta Edmunds, V.P.-Investor Rels. & Corp. Sec.--Equifax Inc., Atlanta, GA; *U.S. Public*, pg. 588
Zamagna, Petra, Dr., Dir.-Inv. Rels.--Hoechst Aktiengesellschaft, Frankfurt/Main, Germany; *Int'l*, pg. 624
Zambelli, Thomas, Chief Fin. Officer & Sr. V.P.--Tops Appliance City, Edison, NJ; *U.S. Public*, pg. 1622
Zane, Tabitha, Dir.-Investor Rels.--Vanguard Cellular Systems, Inc., Greensboro, NC; *U.S. Public*, pg. 1707
Zanelli, Janine, Mgr.-Investor Rels.--Alliance Semiconductor Corp., San Jose, CA; *U.S. Public*, pg. 47
Zeinab, Valerie W., Coord.-Investor Rels.--Western Gas Resources, Inc., Denver, CO; *U.S. Public*, pg. 1758
Zeller, Tina, Corp. Admin.--Europa Cruises Corporation, Saint Petersburg, FL; *U.S. Public*, pg. 595
Zenger, Gerold, Chief Fin. Officer & Investor Rels.--Forbo Holding SA, Eglisau, Switzerland; *Int'l*, pg. 496
Zentz, Peter, Mgr.-Commun.--Benthos, Inc., North Falmouth, MA; *U.S. Public*, pg. 212
Zepf, Stephen J., Chief Fin. Officer & Treas.--Hughes Supply, Inc., Orlando, FL; *U.S. Public*, pg. 846
Ziegler, John K., Jr., Chief Fin. Officer & Controller--Willcox & Gibbs, Inc., Carteret, NJ; *U.S. Private*, pg. 1177
Ziegler, Kenneth, Mgr.-Communications & Govt. Rels.--Basin Electric Power Cooperative, Bismarck, ND; *U.S. Private*, pg. 121
Ziegler, Marie Z., Mgr.-Investor & Banking Rels. & Asst. Sec.--Deere & Company, Moline, IL; *U.S. Public*, pg. 491
Ziepfel, Terri, Chief Admin. Officer--First Financial Bancorp, Hamilton, OH; *U.S. Public*, pg. 632
Zimmer, Joan C., Mgr.-Investor Rels. & Asst. Sec.--Badger Meter, Inc., Milwaukee, WI; *U.S. Public*, pg. 164

Zimmerman, J.M., V.P.-Plng. & Investor Rels.--Union Texas Petroleum Holdings, Houston, TX; *U.S. Public*, pg. 1669
Zimmermann, Christine, Mgr.-Shareholder Rels.--Vertel, Woodland Hills, CA; *U.S. Public*, pg. 1717
Zock, George J., Sr. V.P.-Insurance Opers.--Horace Mann Educators Corporation, Springfield, IL; *U.S. Public*, pg. 835
Zordich, Steven A., Mgr.-Pub. Rels.--Consumers Ohio Water Company, Boardman, OH; *U.S. Public*, pg. 438
Zucco, Donato B., Ph.D, Chief Admin. Officer & Sr. V.P.--Crown American Realty Trust, Johnstown, PA; *U.S. Public*, pg. 461
Zulanas, George J., Jr., Chief Fin. Officer, V.P. & Treas.--Uniroyal Technology Corporation, Sarasota, FL; *U.S. Public*, pg. 1670
Zumwalt, LeAnne M., Chief Fin. Officer, Treas. & Sec.--Vivra Incorporated, San Mateo, CA; *U.S. Public*, pg. 1723
Zvonck, Dan, V.P.-Pub. & Investor Rels.--American Stores Company, Salt Lake City, UT; *U.S. Public*, pg. 92

MANAGING DIRECTOR

Aalders, G. Ch., Mng. Dir.--Interpharm bv, s Hertogenbosch, Netherlands; *Int'l*, pg. 681
Aanstoot, Hein, Mng. Dir.--ELVIA Levenverzekeringen N.V., Amsterdam, Netherlands; *Int'l*, pg. 60
Aanstoot, Hein, Mng. Dir.--ELVIA Schadeverzekeringen N.V., Amsterdam, Netherlands; *Int'l*, pg. 60
Aas, Svein Arne, Mng. Dir.--TiMar Seafood A/S, Trondheim, Norway; *Int'l*, pg. 1390
Abbott, Garry, Mng. Dir.--DMB&B Singapore, Singapore, Singapore; *U.S. Private*, pg. 304
Abbott, John, Mng. Dir.-U.S.A.--Schroff, Straubenhardt, Germany; *U.S. Public*, pg. 1274
Abe, Katsuhiko, Mng. Dir.--Yamaichi Advisory Services (Malaysia) Sdn. Bhd., Kuala Lumpur, Malaysia; *Int'l*, pg. 1517
Abecassis, Michel, Mng. Dir.--ISS France S.A., Arcueil, France; *Int'l*, pg. 656
Abeles, Peter, Mng. Dir.--ContiFinancial Services Corporation, New York, NY; *U.S. Public*, pg. 439
Abell, Keith W., Mng. Dir.--Greenwich Street Capital Partners, Inc., New York, NY; *U.S. Private*, pg. 479
Abend, Arie, Joint Mng. Dir. & Reg. Mgr.-Western Hemisphere--Bank Hapoalim B.M., New York, NY; *Int'l*, pg. 149
Abersek, Iztok, Mng. Dir.--Vision Factory Productions, Ljubljana, Slovenia; *U.S. Private*, pg. 305
Abrahamsen, R.J.N., Chief Fin. Officer & Mng. Dir.--KLM Royal Dutch Airlines, Amstelveen, Netherlands; *Int'l*, pg. 719
Abrahamson, R.J.N., Mng. Dir. & Chief Fin. Officer--KLM Royal Dutch Airlines, Elmsford, NY; *Int'l*, pg. 719
Abrams, Heni, Mng. Partner--Hanft Byrne Raboy Abrams & Partners, Inc., New York, NY; *U.S. Private*, pg. 499
Abu Bakar, Abdul Rahim bin, Chief Exec. Officer & Mng. Dir.--Petroliam Nasional Berhad (Petronas), Kuala Lumpur, Malaysia; *Int'l*, pg. 1046
Acey, David E., Mng. Dir.-Mktg.--Wheat First Butcher Singer, Inc., Richmond, VA; *U.S. Public*, pg. 640
Achi, Maher, Mng. Dir.--H&C, Leo Burnett, Beirut, Lebanon; *U.S. Private*, pg. 184
Acquaviva, Jean-Mark, Mng. Dir.--Autologic Information International, Inc., Ivry-sur-Seine, France; *U.S. Public*, pg. 1724
Adachi, Hiroshi, Mng. Dir.--Nanometrics Japan Ltd., Tokyo, Japan; *U.S. Public*, pg. 1151
Adair, Roy, Mng. Dir.--DDL Europe Ltd., Armagh, United Kingdom; *U.S. Public*, pg. 473
Adair, Roy, Mng. Dir.--DDL Electronics Ltd., Armagh, United Kingdom; *U.S. Public*, pg. 473
Adamopoulos, William, Mng. Dir.--Dow Jones Publishing Co. (Asia), Inc., Hong Kong, Hong Kong; *U.S. Public*, pg. 525
Adams, David, Mng. Dir.--Leo Burnett Denmark, Copenhagen, Denmark; *U.S. Private*, pg. 185
Adams, J., Mng. Dir.--Ascom Timeplex GmbH, Frankfurt, Germany; *Int'l*, pg. 87
Adams, Peter, Mng. Dir.--Costain Building Products Limited, Rickmansworth, United Kingdom; *Int'l*, pg. 336
Adams, Steve, Mng. Dir.--Outdoor Services, Dallas, TX; *U.S. Private*, pg. 1166
Adams, William, Mng. Dir.--Formica Limited, North Shields, United Kingdom; *Int'l*, pg. 129
Adant, Christian, Mng. Dir.--MECAR S.A., Petit-Roeulz-Lez-Nivelles, Belgium; *U.S. Public*, pg. 49
Adarraga, Luis, Mng. Dir.--Accesorios de Tuberia de Cobre S.A., Cordoba, Spain; *Int'l*, pg. 391
Adcock, Bob, Mng. Dir.--Nationwide Trust Ltd., Saint Albans, United Kingdom; *Int'l*, pg. 912
Adelmann, Fred, Mng. Dir.--Esselte Meto GmbH, Hirschhorn, Germany; *Int'l*, pg. 461
Admon, David, Mng. Dir.--Admon Advertising, Tel Aviv, Israel; *Int'l*, pg. 117
Admon, Eran, Mng. Dir.--Admon Advertising, Tel Aviv, Israel; *Int'l*, pg. 117
Affolter, Max, Mng. Dir.--Uto Albis AG, Zurich, Switzerland; *Int'l*, pg. 998
Agarwal, Rajiv, Mng. Dir.--Enterprise Nexus Communications, Mumbai, India; *U.S. Private*, pg. 678
Agnew, Mike, Mng. Dir.--Quebecor Printing Semline Inc., Westwood, MA; *Int'l*, pg. 1077
Aguiar, Geraldo de, Mng. Dir.--Alcan Finances B.V., Amsterdam, Netherlands; *Int'l*, pg. 51
Aguire, Hector, Mng. Dir.--Sensormatic S.A. de C.V., Mexico, Mexico; *U.S. Public*, pg. 1458
Ahlgren, Peter, Mng. Dir.--Gambro China Ltd, Hong Kong; *Int'l*, pg. 667
Ahlgren, Peter, Mng. Dir.--Gambro Jr. China Ltd., Tianjin, China; *Int'l*, pg. 667
Ahmad, Edward, Mng. Dir.-European N.V.H.--Simpson International (UK) Ltd., Huddersfield, United Kingdom; *U.S. Public*, pg. 1475
Ahmad, Edward, Mng. Dir.-European N.V.H.--Simpson International (UK) Ltd., West Yorkshire, United Kingdom; *U.S. Public*, pg. 1475
Ahopelto, Olli, Mng. Dir.--Schauman Iberica S.A., Las Rozas, Spain; *Int'l*, pg. 1429
Ahrela, Jouni, Mng. Dir.--Metsa-Serla Tissue Ltd., Cheam, United Kingdom; *Int'l*, pg. 864
Aihara, Hironori, Mng. Dir.-Informations Systems & Services--Mitsubishi Corporation, Tokyo, Japan; *Int'l*, pg. 871
Akahodani, S., Mng. Dir.--Sharp-Roxy Corporation (M) Sdn. Bhd., Sungai Petani, Malaysia; *Int'l*, pg. 1230
Akatsuka, Tamotsu, Mng. Dir.--Cosmo (Switzerland) Ltd., Zurich, Switzerland; *Int'l*, pg. 335
Akcakoca, Engin, Mng. Dir.--Kocbank A.S., Istanbul, Turkey; *Int'l*, pg. 741
Akermark, Henrik, Mng. Dir.--Neste Oxo AB, Stenungsund, Sweden; *Int'l*, pg. 915
Akita, Osamu, Mng. Dir.-Admin.--Mitsubishi Corporation, Tokyo, Japan; *Int'l*, pg. 871
Akiyama, Sumio, Sr. Mng. Dir.-Res. & Devel.--Tokuyama Corporation, Tokyo, Japan; *Int'l*, pg. 1393
Akkoyunlu, Salim, Mng. Dir.--Noksel A.S., Ankara, Turkey; *Int'l*, pg. 954
Ala-Jaaski, Eero, Mng. Dir.--Enso-Eurocan Far East Co. Ltd., Osaka, Japan; *Int'l*, pg. 457
Albrecht, G., Mng. Dir.--Nutricia Nahrungsmittel GmbH, Vienna, Austria; *Int'l*, pg. 992
Albrecht, Klaus-Dieter, Mng. Dir.--Knurr-Ercotec GmbH, Nettetal, Germany; *Int'l*, pg. 739
Albrecht, William, Mng. Dir.--Henry Jones Foods Pty. Ltd., Kyabram, Australia; *U.S. Public*, pg. 1480
Alday, Ray C., Mng. Dir.--IBP Ltd., Dunstable, United Kingdom; *Int'l*, pg. 391
Alden, M., Mng. Dir.--Bristol Street Motors Limited, Birmingham, United Kingdom; *Int'l*, pg. 216
Aldridge, Douglas R., Sr. Mng. Dir.-Private Client Grp.--Interstate/Johnson Lane Corporation, Charlotte, NC; *U.S. Public*, pg. 910
Aleixo, Fernando J., Mng. Dir.--D & B Zimbabwe (Pvt) Ltd., Harare, Zimbabwe; *U.S. Public*, pg. 536
Alexander, Charles, Dr., Mng. Dir.--Sasol Minchem, Johannesburg, South Africa; *Int'l*, pg. 1196
Alexander, Michael, Mng. Dir.--British Gas Trading Ltd., Staines, United Kingdom; *Int'l*, pg. 279
Alfieri, Margarida, Exec. Dir.--Young & Rubicam (Portugal), Lisbon, Portugal; *U.S. Private*, pg. 1199
Ali, Reza, Mng. Dir.--Bitopi Advertising Ltd., Dhaka, Bangladesh; *U.S. Private*, pg. 184
Allegretti, Cosimo, Mng. Dir.--Gestetner Italia SpA, Milan, Italy; *Int'l*, pg. 1115
Allegretti, Cosimo, Mng. Dir.--NRG Italia S.p.A., Milan, Italy; *Int'l*, pg. 1116
Allegue, J., Mng. Dir.--Saduc, Riyadh, Saudi Arabia; *Int'l*, pg. 823
Allein, Gilles, Mng. Dir.--Credit Lyonnais Japan, Tokyo, Japan; *Int'l*, pg. 344
Allen, David, Mng. Dir.--Bankgesellschaft Berlin (Ireland) plc, Dublin, Ireland; *Int'l*, pg. 160
Allen, David, Mng. Dir.--BGB Finance (Ireland) plc, IRL-I.F.S.C., Ireland; *Int'l*, pg. 160
Allen, G.J., Chief Exec. Officer & Mng. Dir.--IMI Plc, Witton, United Kingdom; *Int'l*, pg. 646
Allen, Kenneth D., V.P. & Mng. Dir.-Europe--Tenneco Inc., Greenwich, CT; *U.S. Public*, pg. 1577
Allford, Russel, Mng. Dir.--Leo Burnett/Connaghan & May (VIC.) Pty. Ltd., Melbourne, Australia; *U.S. Private*, pg. 185
Allona, Jose David, Deputy Mng. Dir. & Dir.-Information Tech. & Opers.--Caja de Madrid Group, Madrid, Spain; *Int'l*, pg. 251
Allsop, Graham, Mng. Dir.--Esselte Meto Pty. Ltd., Wantirna, Australia; *Int'l*, pg. 461
Allsopp, R.W., Mng. Dir.--GKN Technology Ltd., Wolverhampton, United Kingdom; *Int'l*, pg. 535
Almenara, Manuel, Mng. Dir.--Willis Faber North America, Inc.-Florida, Miami, FL; *Int'l*, pg. 1503
Alscher, Arnold, Dr., Mng. Dir.-Processing, Research & Devel.--Haltermann AG, Hamburg, Germany; *Int'l*, pg. 590
Althen, Wilhem, Mng. Dir.--Lufthansa Cargo AG, Frankfurt, Germany; *Int'l*, pg. 407
Altmann, Alain, Mng. Dir.--R.P. Scherer S.A., Beinheim, France; *U.S. Public*, pg. 1438
Alway, E.J., Mng. Dir.--Kiwi Brands Pty. Ltd., Clayton, Australia; *U.S. Public*, pg. 1434
Amano, Hideki, Mng. Dir.--NEC Electronics Hong Kong Limited, Hong Kong, Hong Kong; *Int'l*, pg. 901
Amase, Takao, Mng. Dir.--Bridgestone/Firestone Europe, S.A., Brussels, Belgium; *Int'l*, pg. 214
Ambwani, Narendra K., Pres. & Mng. Dir.--Johnson & Johnson Limited, Mumbai, India; *U.S. Public*, pg. 930
Amerin, Zeno J., Mng. Dir.--Audatex Holding AG, Zurich, Switzerland; *U.S. Public*, pg. 150
Amin, Shaheen, Mng. Dir.--Oman ORIX Leasing Saog, Muscat, Oman; *Int'l*, pg. 1009
Amit, Moshe, Joint Mng. Dir.-Corp. Fin.--Bank Hapoalim, Tel Aviv, Israel; *Int'l*, pg. 149
Amram, Isaac, Sr. Deputy Mng. Dir.-Info. Tech. & Opers.--Bank Hapoalim, Tel Aviv, Israel; *Int'l*, pg. 149
Amundsen, Svein Erik, Deputy Mng. Dir.-Fin. & Admin.--Bergesen d.y. A.S., Oslo, Norway; *Int'l*, pg. 188
Anasis, Emanuel, Mng. Dir.--Roehlen Industries Pty. Ltd. (Sidney Division), Kirrawee, Australia; *U.S. Public*, pg. 1507
Andenmatten, Fredy, Deputy Mng. Dir.-Information Systems--LGT Bank in Liechtenstein Aktiengesellschaft, Vaduz, Liechtenstein; *Int'l*, pg. 809
Andersen, Bjarne, Mng. Dir.--DanTransport Holding A/S, Glostrup, Denmark; *Int'l*, pg. 476
Anderson, Alistair, Mng. Dir.--Personal Performance Consultants UK Limited (PPC), London, United Kingdom; *Int'l*, pg. 1502
Anderson, Dick, Exec. V.P. & Co-Mng. Dir.--The Healthcare Connection, New York, NY; *U.S. Public*, pg. 1422
Anderson, R. John, Chief Exec. Officer, Ladbroke Group Properties--Ladbroke Group Plc, London, United Kingdom; *Int'l*, pg. 787
Anderson, Robert L., Mng. Dir.--ITT Flygt Limited, Silverwater, Australia; *U.S. Public*, pg. 860
Anderssen, Bjorn, Mng. Dir.--Berendsen Components A/S, Oslo, Norway; *Int'l*, pg. 1284
Andersson, Lennart, Mng. Dir.--Gisebo Vagnindustri AB, Jonkoping, Sweden; *Int'l*, pg. 436
Andersson, Sten, Mng. Dir.--Svenska Foder AB, Lidkoping, Sweden; *Int'l*, pg. 350
Andre, Pierre, Mng. Dir.--Beechmont Porsche Audi Inc., Cincinnati, OH; *U.S. Private*, pg. 129
Andres, Wernfried, Mng. Dir.--Sulzer-Escher Wyss AG, Zurich, Switzerland; *Int'l*, pg. 1305
Andresen, C., Mng. Dir.--Haden Drysys GmbH, Frankfurt, Germany; *Int'l*, pg. 586
Andrew, Robert H., Sr. Mng. Dir.--Rothschild Inc., New York, NY; *U.S. Private*, pg. 947
Andrews, Chrisopher, Dr., Mng. Dir.--Rhone-Poulenc Chemicals Ltd., Watford, United Kingdom; *Int'l*, pg. 1112
Andrews, Richard S., Mng. Dir.--Cutting Edges Pty. Ltd., Revesby, Australia; *Int'l*, pg. 391
Ankers, Neal, Chm. Bd. & Mng. Dir.--Hampton Trust Plc, London, United Kingdom; *Int'l*, pg. 591
Anspack, C.J., Mng. Dir.--Metalair-Filliat Limited, Spalding, United Kingdom; *Int'l*, pg. 1065
Antczack, Joachim, Mng. Dir.--LBB Betriebsservice GmbH, Berlin, Germany; *Int'l*, pg. 160
Anthony, A.J., Mng. Dir.--Lucas Aftermarket Operations, Solihull, United Kingdom; *Int'l*, pg. 819
Antila, Timo, Mng. Dir.--Tako Carton Plant Ltd., Tampere, Finland; *Int'l*, pg. 863
Antolinos, Michel, Mng. Dir.--McDonald's France SA, Guayancourt, France; *U.S. Public*, pg. 1069
Antoni, Manfred, Mng. Dir.--Wiley-VCH, Weinheim, Germany; *U.S. Public*, pg. 1768
Antoni, Manfred, Dr., Mng. Dir.--Schaffer-Poeschel Verlag, Stuttgart, Germany; *Int'l*, pg. 1478
Antsalo, Ari, Mng. Dir.--MD Papier GmbH, Dachau, Germany; *Int'l*, pg. 864
Antsalo, Ari, Mng. Dir.--MD Papier GmbH - Plattling Mill, Plattling, Germany; *Int'l*, pg. 864
Anwar, Khurshid, Deputy Mng. Dir.-Mktg.--Pakistan International Airlines Corporation, Karachi, Pakistan; *Int'l*, pg. 1021
Apicella, Alane, Grp. Mng. Dir.--TMP Worldwide/Recruitment Division, New York, NY; *U.S. Private*, pg. 1065
Appleton, Steven R., Dir.--Micron Semiconductor Asia Pacific Pte. Ltd., Singapore, Singapore; *U.S. Public*, pg. 1105
Appleton, Steven R., Dir.--Micron Semiconductor Asia Pacific Inc., Taipei, Taiwan; *U.S. Public*, pg. 1105
Aquila, George F., Mng. Dir.--OppenheimerFunds Distributor, Inc., New York, NY; *U.S. Private*, pg. 818
Arai, Junichi, Mng. Dir.-Publications, Pub. Rels. & Legal Affairs--Nihon Keizai Shimbun, Inc., Tokyo, Japan; *Int'l*, pg. 929
Arakawa, Kenichiro, Mng. Dir.--Nippon Express (Australia) Pty., Ltd., Mascot, Australia; *Int'l*, pg. 934
Arands, Peter, Mng. Dir.--Hamilton/Livingston, Veenendaal, Netherlands; *Int'l*, pg. 212
Aravind, Indira, Mng. Dir.--Daniel J. Edelman Sdn. Bhd., Kuala Lumpur, Malaysia; *U.S. Private*, pg. 363
Arble, James R., Dir.-Customer Service-Eastern Region--Mesaba Holdings, Inc., Minneapolis, MN; *U.S. Public*, pg. 1099
Arbuthnot, P.A., Mng. Dir.--Christie's Scotland Ltd., Glasgow, United Kingdom; *Int'l*, pg. 290
Archer, R. H., Mng. Dir.--WBB Pacific Clays Ltd., Singapore, Singapore; *Int'l*, pg. 1488
Archer, Ricardo A., Mng. Dir.--Publicidad Diaz, S.A. de C.V., San Salvador, El Salvador; *U.S. Private*, pg. 186
Archer, Tracy, Dir.--GGT Direct Manchester, Manchester, United Kingdom; *Int'l*, pg. 532
Argus, D.R., Chief Exec. Officer & Mng. Dir.--National Australia Bank Limited, Melbourne, Australia; *Int'l*, pg. 906
Armada, Jose Sainz, Dir. Gen.--Argentaria Corporacion Bancaria de Espana, S.A., Madrid, Spain; *Int'l*, pg. 80
Armiger, Jeff, Mng. Dir.--Eagle-Picher Fluid Systems Limited, Market Harborough, United Kingdom; *U.S. Private*, pg. 355
Armit, C., Mng. Dir.--Glaxo Wellcome Australia Ltd., Boronia, Australia; *Int'l*, pg. 553
Arnaldo, Jose A., Mng. Dir.--Heinz Iberica, S.A., Madrid, Spain; *U.S. Public*, pg. 806
Arnold, Edward, Mngng. Dir.--Arthur D. Little of Canada Ltd., Toronto, Canada; *U.S. Private*, pg. 671
Arnold, Peter, Asst. Dir.--Russ Reid Co., Washington, DC; *U.S. Private*, pg. 952
Aronen, Ilmo, Mng. Dir.--Raisio Feed Ltd., Raisio, Finland; *Int'l*, pg. 1085
Arppe, Martti, Mng. Dir.--Papierfabrik Albbruck GmbH, Albbruck, Germany; *Int'l*, pg. 864
Arreghini, Luciano, Mng. Dir.--Battenfeld Italia S.r.l., Saronno, Italy; *Int'l*, pg. 826
Arthur, Erik, Mng. Dir.--Dun & Bradstreet Sverige AB, Solna, Sweden; *U.S. Public*, pg. 537
Arthur, Erik, Mng. Dir.--Dun & Bradstreet Soliditet AB, Stockholm, Sweden; *U.S. Public*, pg. 537
Arunwattanakul, Somchai, Deputy Mng. Dir.--Bangkok Athletic Co., Ltd., Bangkok, Thailand; *Int'l*, pg. 146
Arzac, J. Pepe, Mng. Dir.--Simpson Industries S.A. de C.V. (Mexico), Mexico, Mexico; *U.S. Public*, pg. 1475
Arzac, J. Pepe, Mng. Dir.--Simpson Industries S.A. de C.V. (Mexico), San Luis Potosi, Mexico; *U.S. Public*, pg. 1475
Arzac, J. Pepe, Mng. Dir.--Simpson Industries, Ltda. (Brazil), Sao Paulo, Brazil; *U.S. Public*, pg. 1475
Asaba, Yoshiaki, Mng. Dir.--Citizen Watch Company, Ltd., Tokyo, Japan; *Int'l*, pg. 293

Asakura, Hideo, Mng. Dir.--Brother Industries (U.K.) Ltd.-Ruabon Factory, Wrexham, United Kingdom; *Int'l*, pg. 229
Asao, Takeshi, Mng. Dir.--Siam Asahi Technoglass Co., Ltd., Ban Si Racha, Thailand; *Int'l*, pg. 1238
Ashcroft, Dean, Mng. Dir. & V.P.-Greater Manchester--Guardian Media Group plc, Manchester, United Kingdom; *Int'l*, pg. 577
Ashcroft, Richard P., Mng. Dir.--Cambridge Vacuum Engineering Ltd., Waterbeach, United Kingdom; *Int'l*, pg. 1337
Ashford, Rodney, Mng. Dir.--Iggesund Board Sales Ltd. (Waltham Abbey), Milton Keynes, United Kingdom; *Int'l*, pg. 886
Ashiba, Yoshiro, Mng. Dir. & Sr. V.P.--Japan Airlines Company, Ltd., Tokyo, Japan; *Int'l*, pg. 699
Ashkar, Nabil, Mng. Dir.--Choice Hotels International, Inc., Silver Spring, MD; *U.S. Public*, pg. 351
Askerlund, F., Mng. Dir.--Haniel Reederei Holding GmbH, Duisburg, Germany; *Int'l*, pg. 592
Aspaas, Ulf A., Mng. Dir.--Jotun Cathodic Protection A/S, Langesund, Norway; *Int'l*, pg. 714
Aspden, Jane, Publr. & Mng. Dir.--Mitchell Beazley, London, United Kingdom; *Int'l*, pg. 1093
Assam, Peter, Mng. Dir.--Unicon Beton Holding A/S, Roskilde, Denmark; *Int'l*, pg. 475
Asscher, Jane, Mng. Dir.--Tequila UK Ltd., London, United Kingdom; *Int'l*, pg. 118
Asselineau, Michel, Mgr.--EURO RSCG Quartet, Dijon, France; *Int'l*, pg. 601
Assonitis, Andreas, Mng. Dir.--Geo-Young & Rubicam, Athens, Greece; *U.S. Private*, pg. 1199
Assuntajai, Prachak, Dep. Chm. & Mng. Dir.--International Cosmetics Co., Ltd., Bangkok, Thailand; *Int'l*, pg. 684
Astaris, Christos, Mng. Dir.--Ross Systems France S.A., Paris, France; *U.S. Public*, pg. 1406
Atallah, Edward, V.P. & Mng. Dir.-Intl. Opers.--Surgical Laser Technologies, Inc., Montgomeryville, PA; *U.S. Public*, pg. 1542
Atamian, Mitch, Mng. Dir.--A. Schulman, Inc., Schaumburg, IL; *U.S. Public*, pg. 1441
Atfield, R.J., Mng. Dir.--Mercantile Mutual Holdings Limited, Sydney, Australia; *Int'l*, pg. 650
Atkin, D.J., Mng. Dir.--Fortress Security Pty Limited, Mordialloc, Australia; *Int'l*, pg. 590
Atkin, Edward, Mng. Dir.--Cannon Rubber Ltd., London, United Kingdom; *Int'l*, pg. 261
Atkin, Edward, Mng. Dir.--Avent America Inc., Addison, IL; *Int'l*, pg. 261
Attolini, Gianfranco, Dr., Mng. Dir.--Ortho Clinical Diagnostic Systems S.p.A., Milan, Italy; *U.S. Public*, pg. 931
Aucoin, Charles, Mng. Dir.--SBC Warburg Dillon Read Inc., Boston, MA; *Int'l*, pg. 1329
Audouard, O., Mng. Dir.--Ascom SA, Antony, France; *Int'l*, pg. 87
Augustsson, Peter, Chief Exec. Officer & Mng. Dir.--AB SKF, Goteborg, Sweden; *Int'l*, pg. 1156
Aumont, Brigitte, Mgr.--EURO RSCG Est, Strasbourg, France; *Int'l*, pg. 600
Aurenche, Pascal, Mng. Dir.--International Marketing & Promotions, Asnieres-sur-Seine, France; *U.S. Private*, pg. 304
Austin, Bill, Mng. Dir.--Derby Cycle Corporation, Kent, WA; *Int'l*, pg. 394
Austin, M.J., Mng. Dir.--Crane Limited U.K., Ipswich, United Kingdom; *U.S. Public*, pg. 458
Austin, Richard S., V.P. & Mng. Dir.-Information Mngmt. Div./Europe--Bell & Howell Holdings, Skokie, IL; *U.S. Public*, pg. 201
Autio, J., Mng. Dir.--Ascom Energy Systems OY, Espoo, Finland; *Int'l*, pg. 87
Auyeung, Rex, V.P.-Reg. & Mng. Dir.--Principal International Asia Limited, Wan Chai, Hong Kong; *U.S. Private*, pg. 886
Auzenberga, Laila, Mng. Dir.--Norvista, Riga, Latvia; *Int'l*, pg. 486
Avnon, Shlomi, Mng. Dir.--Shalmor Avnon Amichay, Tel Aviv, Israel; *U.S. Private*, pg. 1063
Axberg, Peter, Mng. Dir.--Oy Getinge AB, Helsinki, Finland; *Int'l*, pg. 551
Aydiner, Selahattin, Mng. Dir.--Turk Maadin Sirketi A.S., Istanbul, Turkey; *U.S. Private*, pg. 735
Ayers, Robert L., Mng. Dir.--Sulzer Bingham Pumps Inc., Burnaby, Canada; *Int'l*, pg. 1305
Aykroyd, Nicholas C., Mng. Dir.--Crown Cork Company S.A. (Pty.) Ltd., Wadeville, South Africa; *U.S. Public*, pg. 464
Ayora, Martin, Mng. Dir.--Esselte S.A., Barcelona, Spain; *Int'l*, pg. 461
Baaijens, P.M.A., Mng. Dir.--Ballast Nedam IGB B.V., Amstelveen, Netherlands; *Int'l*, pg. 133
Baba, Eizo, Mng. Dir.--Chiyoda Mutual Life Insurance Company, Tokyo, Japan; *Int'l*, pg. 286
Babacan, Hasan, Mng. Dir.--Burgmann Endustriyel Sizdirmalik San Ve Tic Ltd Sti, Istanbul, Turkey; *Int'l*, pg. 233
Babel, Bernard, Mng. Dir.-Res. & Devel--AGIE AG (Fur Industrielle Elektronik), Lausanne, Switzerland; *Int'l*, pg. 488
Babits, Gerd, Mng. Dir., Creative Dir. & New Bus. Contact--Strobelgasse 2, Vienna, Austria; *Int'l*, pg. 1377
Bach, Jose Maria, Mng. Dir.--BASF Espanola S.A., Barcelona, Spain; *Int'l*, pg. 106
Bachey, John, V.P. & Mng. Dir.-United Glass Ltd.--Owens-Illinois, Inc., Toledo, OH; *U.S. Public*, pg. 1238
Bachle, Tony C., Mng. Dir.--Meto, Reinach, Switzerland; *Int'l*, pg. 462
Badran, Serge, Mng. Dir.--STECD, Tunis, Tunisia; *Int'l*, pg. 823
Baer, Stephen, Exec. V.P. & Mng. Partner-Creative--Wells BDDP, Inc., New York, NY; *Int'l*, pg. 117
Baert, Elmar, Mng. Dir.--Credit Europeen, Luxembourg, Luxembourg; *Int'l*, pg. 148
Baguley, P.J., Mng. Dir.--Boots Properties, Nottingham, United Kingdom; *Int'l*, pg. 203
Bahrami, Massoud, Mng. Dir.--Sulzer Iran, Tehran, Iran; *Int'l*, *pg. 1306*
Bailes, George, Mng. Dir.--C.G. Hibbert Ltd., Dover, United Kingdom; *Int'l*, pg. 63
Bailey, Geoffrey D., Mng. Dir.--SmithKline Beecham Research Limited, Pasig, Philippines; *Int'l*, pg. 1266
Bailey, Mike, Mgr.--BK&S Direct Marketing, New York, NY; *U.S. Private*, pg. 143
Bailey, P. L., Dr., Mng. Dir.--Memco Limited, Maidenhead, United Kingdom; *Int'l*, pg. 589
Bailey, Robert, Mng. Dir.--FlowMole Limited, Corby, United Kingdom; *U.S. Public*, pg. 1701
Bailey, Roger, Mng. Dir.--Banque Belge (Guernsey) Ltd., Saint Peter Port, United Kingdom; *Int'l*, pg. 547
Baillie, Brian, Mng. Dir.--Cascade (Africa) Pty. Ltd., Johannesburg, South Africa; *U.S. Public*, pg. 311
Bain, N.C., Mng. Dir.--J. & P. Coats Limited, Glasgow, United Kingdom; *Int'l*, pg. 299
Baixas, Javier, Mngng. Dir.--Arthur D. Little S.R.C., Madrid, Spain; *U.S. Private*, pg. 671
Baker, Lynne, Sr. V.P. & Mng. Dir.--Western International Media Corporation, Atlanta, GA; *U.S. Private*, pg. 1167
Baker, M.J., Mng. Dir.--Devlin Electronics Limited, Basingstoke, United Kingdom; *Int'l*, pg. 207
Baker, Peter R., Mng. Dir.-Properties--Marley PLC, Sevenoaks, United Kingdom; *Int'l*, pg. 843
Balakrishnan, Ajit, Mng. Dir.--Rediffusion-DY&R Pvt. Ltd., Mumbai, India; *U.S. Private*, pg. 326
Baldwin, Donald D., Dir.--Micron Europe Ltd., Bracknell, United Kingdom; *U.S. Public*, pg. 1105
Baldwin, Donald D., Dir.--Micron Semiconductor Asia Pacific Pte. Ltd., Singapore, Singapore; *U.S. Public*, pg. 1105
Baldwin, Donald D., Dir.--Micron Semiconductor Asia Pacific Inc., Taipei, Taiwan; *U.S. Public*, pg. 1105
Baldwin, Donald G., Dir.--Micron Semiconductor (Deutscland) GmbH, Aschheim, Germany; *U.S. Public*, pg. 1106
Ballard, Tony, Mng. Dir.--SSB Advertising Melbourne, Melbourne, Australia; *Int'l*, pg. 394
Balter, Wendy, Exec. V.P. & Mng. Dir.-Phase V--Grey Healthcare Group, New York, NY; *U.S. Public*, pg. 765
Balwa, Uman A.K., Mng. Dir.--Burgmann India Pvt. Ltd, Mumbai, India; *Int'l*, pg. 234
Bamford, Laura, Publr. & Mng. Dir.--Hamlyn/Octopus, London, United Kingdom; *Int'l*, pg. 1093
Bamford, Laura, Publr. & Mng. Dir.--Bounty Books, London, United Kingdom; *Int'l*, pg. 1093
Banchong-Silpa, Methei, Mng. Dir.--Siam Lemmerz Co., Ltd., Sara Buri, Thailand; *Int'l*, pg. 1238
Bandstigen, Bengt, Mng. Dir.--Sweden Table Tennis AB, Eskilstuna, Sweden; *U.S. Public*, pg. 591
Bandy, C.M., Mng. Dir.--Texaco Hong Kong Ltd., Hong Kong, Hong Kong; *U.S. Public*, pg. 1584
Bangert, Bruce A., Mng. Dir.--RHM Technology Ltd., High Wycombe, United Kingdom; *Int'l*, pg. 1396
Bankier, Alain, Exec. V.P. & Mng. Dir.--Banexi International Financial Services (North America) Corp., New York, NY; *Int'l*, pg. 163
Banks, Hamish, Mng. Partner--Noorderwliet & Winninghoff/Leo Burnett B.V., Amsterdam, Netherlands; *U.S. Private*, pg. 186
Banning, L., Mng. Dir.--Glaenzer-Seurre NV/SA, Drogenbos, Belgium; *Int'l*, pg. 536
Bannon, Robert, Mng. Dir.--Analytic TSA Global Asset Management Inc., Los Angeles, CA; *U.S. Public*, pg. 1672
Bantoft, Chris, Pres. & Mng. Dir.-ACC Europe--ACC Corp., Rochester, NY; *U.S. Public*, pg. 2
Banu, A. John, Mng. Dir.--ContiFinancial Services Corporation, New York, NY; *U.S. Public*, pg. 439
Baptista, Carlos J.F., Mng. Dir.--Crown Cork & Seal (Portugal) S.A., Lisbon, Portugal; *U.S. Public*, pg. 464
Barata, A., Mng. Dir.--Chaussures Bally Moulins SA, Moulins, France; *Int'l*, pg. 997
Barbara, Pedro, Mng. Dir.--R.J. Simpson International, SL (Spain), Barcelona, Spain; *U.S. Public*, pg. 1475
Barber, Rick, Mng. Dir.--Lake Placid Granite Co., Au Sable Forks, NY; *U.S. Private*, pg. 251
Barbero, Bruno, Mng. Dir.--Barbero S.p.A., Canale, Italy; *Int'l*, pg. 64
Barbi, Alessio, Mng. Dir.--SASIB Bakery Italia S.p.A., Verona, Italy; *Int'l*, pg. 1194
Barbieux, Yves, Pres. & Mng. Dir.--Nestle France, Courbevoie, France; *Int'l*, pg. 921
Barbovitch, Igor, Mng. Dir.--Costain Developments SA, Cadiz, Spain; *Int'l*, pg. 337
Barbovitch, Igor, Mng. Dir.--Alcaidesa Costain Developments S.A., Cadiz, Spain; *Int'l*, pg. 337
Barcroft, A. Paul, Mng. Dir.--The Langer Biomechanics Group (UK) Ltd., Stoke on Trent, United Kingdom; *U.S. Public*, pg. 978
Barden, Kevin, Mng. Dir.-Comalco Smelter Devel.--Comalco Limited, Brisbane, Australia; *Int'l*, pg. 307
Bardsley, Stephen, Mng. Dir.--Battenfeld Australia Pty. Ltd., Braeside, Australia; *Int'l*, pg. 825
Barenbuem, Carlos, Mng. Dir.--Sulzer Argentina S.A., Buenos Aires, Argentina; *Int'l*, pg. 1306
Barington, Rene, Mng. Dir.--B&K Ultrasound A/S, Gentofte, Denmark; *U.S. Public*, pg. 109
Barker, David, Mngng. Dir.--Arthur D. Little, Inc., San Francisco, CA; *U.S. Private*, pg. 670
Barker, Peter, Mng. Dir.--Rank Hovis Limited, High Wycombe, United Kingdom; *Int'l*, pg. 1396
Barnard, Edward K., Mng. Dir.--Commercial Intertech Corp., Hicksville, OH; *U.S. Public*, pg. 411
Barnes, C., Mng. Dir.--Lancer USA Inc., Longwood, FL; *Int'l*, *pg. 551*
Barnes, Christine, Mng. Dir.--Whybin/TBWA, Melbourne, Australia; *U.S. Private*, pg. 1063
Barnett, James, Mng. Dir.--Dun & Bradstreet (HK) Ltd., North Point, Hong Kong; *U.S. Public*, pg. 536
Barnett, Steve, Mng. Dir.--Check Point Software Technologies (UK) Ltd., Cambridge, United Kingdom; *U.S. Public*, pg. 342
Barney, Deborah D., Mng. Dir.--Coming Home Div.--Lands' End, Inc., Dodgeville, WI; *U.S. Public*, pg. 977
Barrett, Andrew, Mng. Dir.--Edelman Worldwide, Inc., Washington, DC; *U.S. Private*, pg. 362
Barrett, Roy, Mng. Dir.--Goodbody Stockbrokers, Dublin, Ireland; *Int'l*, pg. 64
Bartels, Peter, Chief Exec. Officer & Mng. Dir.--Coles Myer Ltd., Tooronga, Australia; *Int'l*, pg. 306
Barth, Hans J., Dr., Mng. Dir.--Prognos AG, Basel, Switzerland; *Int'l*, pg. 1480
Bartholomew, Martin F., Mng. Dir.--Periphonics Voice Processing Systems Ltd., Camberley, United Kingdom; *U.S. Public*, pg. 1279
Bartlett, Kevin W., Mng. Dir.-Secondary Mkts.--Countrywide Home Loans Inc., Pasadena, CA; *U.S. Public*, pg. 452
Bartlett, Kevin W., Mng. Dir.-Capital Markets--Countrywide Funding Corporation, Pasadena, CA; *U.S. Public*, pg. 453
Bartlett, Vivian Wade, Chief Exec. Officer & Mng. Dir.--First National Bank Holdings Limited, Johannesburg, South Africa; *Int'l*, pg. 487
Bartnik, Richard J., Dir.-Washington Opers.--Raytheon Company, Lexington, MA; *U.S. Public*, pg. 1364
Bartos, Jerzy, Mng. Dir.--Getinge Poland Sp.zo.o., Warsaw, Poland; *Int'l*, pg. 551
Basey, David, Mng. Dir.--Datarange Communications plc, High Wycombe, United Kingdom; *U.S. Private*, pg. 956
Basil, Steven E., Mng. Dir.--Brown Brothers Harriman (Luxembourg) S.A., Luxembourg, Luxembourg; *U.S. Private*, pg. 173
Bassil, Clive, Mng. Dir.--Costain Urban Enterprises Limited, Manchester, United Kingdom; *Int'l*, pg. 337
Bastam, Ina, Dr., Mng. Dir.--Wuestenrot Immobilien GmbH, Ludwigsburg, Germany; *Int'l*, pg. 1514
Bastien, Jean-Marie, Mng. Dir.--SMR (Societe Metallurgique de Revigny), Revigny, France; *Int'l*, pg. 571
Bate, David, Mng. Dir.--H.B. Fuller Coatings Ltd., Birmingham, United Kingdom; *U.S. Public*, pg. 686
Bateman, C.M., Mng. Dir.--Esso Malaysia Berhad, Kuala Lumpur, Malaysia; *U.S. Public*, pg. 602
Batet, Maisa, Mng. Dir.--Lowe MBAC, Barcelona, Spain; *U.S. Private*, pg. 678
Battin, Jim, Mng. Dir.--Partners & Shevack Direct, New York, NY; *U.S. Private*, pg. 842
Baumann, Jurgen, Mng. Dir.-Materials Tech. & Chemistry--Landis & Staefa AG, Zug, Switzerland; *Int'l*, pg. 800
Baumann, Theodor, Prof. Dr., Mng. Dir.-Structural Design--Dyckerhoff & Widmann AG, Munich, Germany; *Int'l*, pg. 423
Baumann, Thomas, Mng. Dir.--Schroedel Schulbuchverlag GmbH, Hannover, Germany; *Int'l*, pg. 1478
Baumann, Thomas, Mng. Dir.--Verlag Dr. Max Gehlen GmbH & Co. KG, Bad Homburg, Germany; *Int'l*, pg. 1479
Baume, Georges, Gen. Mgr.--Unicom, Rennes, France; *Int'l*, *pg. 601*
Baun, N.C., Mng. Dir.--Tootal Group plc, Manchester, United Kingdom; *Int'l*, pg. 300
Baxter, Travis, Mng. Dir.--Atlantic 252, Meath, Ireland; *Int'l*, pg. 561
Bayard, Roland, Mng. Dir.--Sulzer (Mexico) S.A. de C.V., Cuautitlan, Mexico; *Int'l*, pg. 1306
Bazie, Tracey A., Pres. & Mng. Dir.--Johnson & Johnson Hemisferica, Caguas, PR; *U.S. Public*, pg. 928
Bazie, Tracie A., Mng. Dir.--Johnson & Johnson (Jamaica) Limited, Kingston, Jamaica; *U.S. Public*, pg. 930
Bealmear, Michael W., V.P. & Mng. Dir.--Object Technology Group - Northeast Region, New York, NY; *Int'l*, pg. 1154
Beamish, Robert, Mng. Dir.--WBF Technologies, Mississauga, Canada; *Int'l*, pg. 193
Beardsell, K., Mng. Dir.--Hepworth Industrial Plastics Ltd., Burnley, United Kingdom; *Int'l*, pg. 615
Beauchet, Jacques, Dir.-Investor Rels.--Promodes SA, Mondeville, France; *Int'l*, pg. 1071
Bechivar, Stephen P., Mng. Dir.--Lands' End GmbH, Mettlach, Germany; *U.S. Public*, pg. 978
Becker, Heinz J., Mgr.-Fin.--Groschopp & Co. GmbH EMW Elektromotoren-Feinbauwerk, Viersen, Germany; *Int'l*, pg. 559
Becker, Lawrence K., Mng. Dir. & Controller--OppenheimerFunds Distributor, Inc., New York, NY; *U.S. Private*, pg. 818
Beckman, Jerry, Pres. & Mng. Dir.-Intl.--Simon Marketing, Inc., Los Angeles, CA; *U.S. Private*, pg. 1001
Beckman, Jerry, Pres. & Mng. Dir.-Intl.--Simon Marketing International GmbH - Munich, Unterhaching, Germany; *U.S. Private*, pg. 1001
Bednarzyk, Klaus, Mng. Dir.--LBB Kartenservice GmbH, Berlin, Germany; *Int'l*, pg. 160
Bedorf, Hans-Wolf, Mng. Dir.--Deutsche Hypothekenbank FrankfurtAG, Frankfurt/Main, Germany; *Int'l*, pg. 418
Beecroft, John, Mng. Dir.--SASIB Bakery UK Ltd., Newton-le-Willows, United Kingdom; *Int'l*, pg. 1194
Beer, Urs, Mng. Dir.--Advico Young & Rubicam AG, Zurich, Switzerland; *U.S. Private*, pg. 1198
Beesley, K., Mng. Dir.--Simon-Diasol, Hadnall, United Kingdom; *Int'l*, pg. 1251
Beg, Mohammad Yousuf, Mng. Dir.--National Refinery Limited, Karachi, Pakistan; *Int'l*, pg. 909
Begg, Alan, Dr., Mng. Dir.-T & N. Tech.--T & N Plc, Manchester, United Kingdom; *Int'l*, pg. 1334
Behar, Isaac M., Chief Fin. Officer & Sr. Deputy Mng. Dir.--Bank Hapoalim, Tel Aviv, Israel; *Int'l*, pg. 149
Behr, Soma Golden, Asst. Mng. Editor--The New York Times, New York, NY; *U.S. Public*, pg. 1174
Belche, Paul, Mng. Dir.-Sls. & Mktg.--STAHLwerke Bremen GmbH, Bremen, Germany; *Int'l*, pg. 79
Belec, Bob, Mng. Dir.--Kelly Services (Ltd.), Sydney, Australia; *U.S. Public*, pg. 949
Bell, Charlie, Mng. Dir.--McDonald's System of Australia Ltd., Thornleigh, Australia; *U.S. Public*, pg. 1069
Bell, Dan, Mng. Dir.--J.W. Messner, Inc., Cincinnati, OH; *U.S. Private*, pg. 734
Belloni, Giorgio, Mng. Dir.--Janssen-Cilag Farmaceutici S.p.A., Cologno Monzese, Italy; *U.S. Public*, pg. 929

Belloni, Giorgio, Dr., Mng. Dir.--Janssen-Cilag S.p.A., Milan, Italy; *U.S. Public*, pg. 929
Bellorin, E., Mng. Dir.--Gran Industria de Neumaticos Centroamericana, S.A., Guatemala, Guatemala; *U.S. Public*, pg. 753
Belmans, Eddy, Mng. Dir.--BBL Asset Management (Singapore) Pte. Ltd., Singapore, Singapore; *Int'l*, pg. 148
Belot, Eric, Mng. Dir.--Arthur D. Little International, Inc., Paris, France; *U.S. Private*, pg. 670
Ben-Asher, Ze'ev, Sr. Deputy Mng. Dir.-H.R.--Bank Hapoalim, Tel Aviv, Israel; *Int'l*, pg. 149
Bencomo, J., Mng. Dir.--Ayra Servicio SA, Barcelona, Spain; *Int'l*, pg. 535
Bender, T., Mng. Dir.--Timken de Mexico, S.A. de C.V., Tlalnepantla, Mexico; *U.S. Public*, pg. 1617
Bender, Theodore J., III, Mng. Dir. & Dir.--The Robinson-Humphrey Company, Inc., Atlanta, GA; *U.S. Public*, pg. 1633
Benetton, Gilberto, Vice Chm. & Mng. Dir.--Benetton Group S.p.A., Ponzano Veneto, Italy; *Int'l*, pg. 186
Beng, Choo Chiau, Chm. Bd. & Mng. Dir.--Keppel-Fels Ltd., Singapore, Singapore; *Int'l*, pg. 731
Bengelsdorff, Carl-Henrik, Mng. Dir.--Valmet Skandinavien AB, Karlstad, Sweden; *Int'l*, pg. 1448
Benko, Leo, Mng. Dir.--Addey Milner Limited, Salford, United Kingdom; *Int'l*, pg. 1462
Bennet, Carl, Mng. Dir.--Getinge AB, Getinge, Sweden; *Int'l, pg. 551*
Bennet, Melvynn, Mng. Dir.--Asia Computerworld, Quarry Bay, Hong Kong; *U.S. Private*, pg. 569
Bennett, Keith R., Mng. Dir.--Lapmaster International Ltd., Morton Grove, IL; *Int'l*, pg. 1338
Bennewitz, M., Mng. Dir.--Robert Bosch SpA, Milan, Italy; *Int'l*, pg. 206
Bensoussan-Torres, Robert, Mng. Dir.--Christian Lacroix U.K., London, United Kingdom; *Int'l*, pg. 782
Bentley, A., Dir. & Gen. Mgr.--Hamworthy Industramar Limited, Poole, United Kingdom; *Int'l*, pg. 1065
Berard, Jean-Jacques, Mng. Dir.--Ordo, Montaigu, France; *U.S. Private*, pg. 512
Berardi, Martin, Exec. V.P. & Mng. Dir.--Tubos de Acero de Mexico, S.A., Mexico, Mexico; *Int'l*, pg. 1426
Berenpas, E.J., Mng. Dir.--Verosol Fabrics B.V., Eibergen, Netherlands; *Int'l*, pg. 198
Berenpas, E.J., Mng. Dir.--De Haes Holland B.V., Eibergen, Netherlands; *Int'l*, pg. 198
Bergamini, Franco, Mng. Dir.--KONE Elevators, BU 1, Milan, Italy; *Int'l*, pg. 747
Berger, Hans, Mng. Dir.--Butler Building Systems Ltd., Kirkcaldy, United Kingdom; *U.S. Public*, pg. 271
Bergers, Diethard, Dr., Mng. Dir.--Krupp Entwicklungszentrum GmbH, Essen, Germany; *Int'l*, pg. 512
Bergman, Tor, Mng. Dir.--Raisio Chemicals Ltd., Raisio, Finland; *Int'l*, pg. 1085
Berkeley, Barry, Mng. Dir.--Chase Securities, Inc., Brooklyn, NY; *U.S. Public*, pg. 338
Berkeley, D.J., Chm. Bd. & Mng. Dir.--Standard Bank (Jersey) Limited, Saint Helier, United Kingdom; *Int'l*, pg. 1294
Berkenbosch, J., Mng. Dir.--Koninklijke De Ruyter BV, Baarn, Netherlands; *Int'l*, pg. 244
Bernatz, Gerald, Mng. Dir.--World Import Co., Saint Louis, MO; *U.S. Private*, pg. 1089
Bernhard, Urs, Mng. Dir.-Mngmt. Devel.--Landis & Staefa AG, Zug, Switzerland; *Int'l*, pg. 800
Bernois, Jean-Luc, Mng. Dir.--Johnson & Johnson Morocco S.A., Casablanca, Morocco; *U.S. Public*, pg. 931
Bernstein, Stephen, Sr. Mng. Dir. & Asst. Sec.--The Bear Stearns Companies Inc., New York, NY; *U.S. Public*, pg. 197
Berntssom, Leif, Mng. Dir.--Eldon Elmateriel AB, Nassjo, Sweden; *Int'l*, pg. 436
Berroll, Jean, Mng. Dir.--Beau Marais S.A. (France), Bethune, France; *Int'l*, pg. 850
Bertrand, Didier, Mng. Dir.--Esselte SA, Paris, France; *Int'l*, pg. 461
Best, Lauren, Mng. Dir.--Advisers Capital Management Inc., New York, NY; *U.S. Private*, pg. 23
Bester, Dave, Mng. Dir.--Hunt Lascaris/TBWA, Cape Town, South Africa; *U.S. Private*, pg. 1062
Besting, J., Mng. Dir.--GKN Service GmbH, Rosrath, Germany; *Int'l*, pg. 536
Beusse, Carlton G., Sr. V.P., Mng. Dir.-RMS, Exec. V.P. & Chief Oper. Officer-CRRUX--Willis Corroon Corp. of Wisconsin, Milwaukee, WI; *Int'l*, pg. 1507
Beutler, Eberhard, Mng. Dir.--TBWA Germany, Frankfurt/Main, Germany; *U.S. Private*, pg. 1063
Bezecny, Miroslav, Mng. Dir.--Lecotex, Tabor, Czech Republic; *Int'l*, pg. 193
Bhatti, Waheed, Mng. Dir.--P.T. Dentsu Young & Rubicam Indonesia (Jakarta), Jakarta, Indonesia; *U.S. Private*, pg. 325
Bianchi, Arduino, Mng. Dir.--McCormick de Centro America, S.A., San Salvador, El Salvador; *U.S. Public*, pg. 1067
Bianchi, Carisa, Mng. Dir.--The Leap Partnership, Santa Monica, CA; *U.S. Private*, pg. 655
Bichuetti, Jose Luiz, Mng. Dir.--Arthur D. Little de Argentina S.A., Buenos Aires, Argentina; *U.S. Private*, pg. 670
Bicque, Paul H., Mng. Dir.--Standard Wool, Inc., North Oxford, MA; *U.S. Public*, pg. 1502
Bide, R.W., Mng. Dir.-Human Resources--Tate & Lyle PLC, London, United Kingdom; *Int'l*, pg. 1356
Biel, Howard S., Sr. V.P. & Mng. Dir.-Devel.--Federal Realty Investment Trust, Rockville, MD; *U.S. Public*, pg. 616
Bielanski, Andrew, Mng. Dir.-Mktg.--Countrywide Home Loans Inc., Pasadena, CA; *U.S. Public*, pg. 452
Bienkowski, Detlef, Mng. Dir.--BB-Privat Finanz-Service GmbH, Berlin, Germany; *Int'l*, pg. 159
Bierschenck, Burkhard, Mng. Dir.--Werk-Verlag, Grafelfing, Germany; *Int'l*, pg. 1099
Biggins, K. W., Mng. Dir.--Rank Film Laboratories Limited, Uxbridge, United Kingdom; *Int'l*, pg. 1087
Biggs, Barton M., Mng. Dir.--Morgan Stanley Group Inc., New York, NY; *U.S. Public*, pg. 1132
Bignall, Kenneth Charles, Vice Chm. & Mng. Dir.--Barclays Financial Services Co. Ltd., London, United Kingdom; *Int'l*, pg. 164
Bignami, Franco, Chief Exec. Officer & Mng. Dir.--Foster Wheeler Italiana S.P.A. (Italy), Milan, Italy; *U.S. Public*, pg. 677
Bihler, Jurgen, Mng. Dir.--Iggesund Verkaufsgesellschaft G.m.b.H, Hamburg, Germany; *Int'l*, pg. 886
Binch, Stuart, Mng. Dir.--Syntron Europe Limited, Alfreton, United Kingdom; *U.S. Public*, pg. 1563
Binns, M., Mng. Dir.--The Fletcher Construction Company Limited, Penrose, New Zealand; *Int'l*, pg. 495
Bischoff, Carol, Mng. Editor--Human Sciences Press, Inc., New York, NY; *U.S. Public*, pg. 1311
Bishop, Dennis, Mgr.-Opers.--Woodward-Clyde International, North Point, Hong Kong; *U.S. Public*, pg. 1658
Bishop, Roger F., Mng. Dir.--John Crane Asia Pacific, Singapore, Singapore; *Int'l*, pg. 1339
Bissett, Keith, Mng. Dir.--Bourton Group, Rugby, United Kingdom; *U.S. Private*, pg. 162
Bitou, Mineo, Mng. Dir.--The Nikko Securities (Australia) Ltd., Sydney, Australia; *Int'l*, pg. 931
Biver, Jean-Claude, Mng. Dir.--Blancpain S.A., Le Brassus, Switzerland; *Int'l*, pg. 1160
Bjorklund, Elisabet Salander, Mng. Dir.--Stora Timber AB, Falun, Sweden; *Int'l*, pg. 1303
Bjorklund, Hakan, Mng. DIr.--Sodra Timber AB, Roskilde, Denmark; *Int'l*, pg. 1276
Bjorkman, P., Mng. Dir.--Balzers Sandvik Coating AB, Stockholm, Sweden; *Int'l*, pg. 997
Bjorn, Marjatta, Mng. Dir.--Seppala, Vantaa, Finland; *Int'l*, pg. 1301
Blackenhorn, Gunter, Dr., Mng. Dir.--R.P. Scherer GmbH, Baden Baden, Germany; *U.S. Public*, pg. 1438
Blackenhorn, Gunter, Dr., Mng. Dir.--R.P. Scherer GmbH-Werk Strehla, Strehla, Germany; *U.S. Public*, pg. 1438
Blackenhorn, Gunter, Dr., Mng. Dir.--Allcaps Weichgelatinekapseln GmbH, Backnang, Germany; *U.S. Public*, pg. 1438
Blair, Kelly, Mng. Dir.--Beechmont Hyundai, Cincinnati, OH; *U.S. Private*, pg. 129
Blake, Steven B., Chief Exec. Officer & Mng. Dir.--Geraghty & Miller, Inc., Denver, CO; *Int'l*, pg. 607
Blampied, Geoffrey, Mng. Dir.--Willis Corroon Limited, Wellington, New Zealand; *Int'l*, pg. 1509
Blanch, Stephen, Mng. Dir.--Texas Utilities Australia, Melbourne, Australia; *U.S. Public*, pg. 1588
Blashill, G.L., Dir.-Sls. & Mktg.--Imperial Tobacco Group, Ltd., Bristol, United Kingdom; *Int'l*, pg. 666
Blasso, Barbara, Exec. V.P. & Mng. Dir.-Phase V--Grey Healthcare Group, New York, NY; *U.S. Public*, pg. 765
Blazeby, James, Mng. Dir.--ICIS LOR-Europe, Sutton, United Kingdom; *Int'l*, pg. 1094
Bleackley, Frank, Mng. Dir.--Chubb Hong Kong Ltd., Kowloon, Hong Kong; *Int'l*, pg. 705
Blind, Francis, Mng. Dir.--Ethnor S.A., Neuilly-sur-Seine, France; *U.S. Public*, pg. 929
Blitz, Bonnie, Mng. Dir. & Media Dir.--Western International Media Corporation, Denver, CO; *U.S. Private*, pg. 1167
Block, John, Mng. Dir.--Market Growth Resources, Inc., Wilton, CT; *U.S. Public*, pg. 1641
Block, John, Mng. Dir.--MGR Performance Media, Wilton, CT; *U.S. Public*, pg. 1641
Blom, Inger Eriksson, Mng. Dir.--Berendsen PMC Oy AB, Vantaa, Finland; *Int'l*, pg. 1285
Bloxham, J.L., Chm. & Mng. Dir.--Cincinnati Milacron U.K. Limited, Birmingham, United Kingdom; *U.S. Public*, pg. 368
Bluestone, Robert J., Mng. Dir.--OppenheimerFunds Distributor, Inc., New York, NY; *U.S. Private*, pg. 818
Blum, Erich, Dr., Mng. Dir.--Berag GmbH, Dusseldorf, Germany; *Int'l*, pg. 1502
Blum, Reto, Mng. Dir.-Human Resources--Landis & Staefa AG, Zug, Switzerland; *Int'l*, pg. 800
Bluth, Michael, Mng. Dir.--International Sales, Oshkosh, WI; *U.S. Public*, pg. 1233
Blyth, Terry E., Mng. Dir.--John Heath & Co. Limited, Birmingham, United Kingdom; *U.S. Private*, pg. 64
Blythe, R.A., Reg. Mng. Dir.--Ballast Wiltshier Plc - South East Region, Canterbury, United Kingdom; *Int'l*, pg. 135
Boehme, Heiko, Mng. Dir.-Prod. & Tech.--Dr. Th. Boehme KG Chem. Fabrik GmbH & Co., Geretsried, Germany; *Int'l*, pg. 199
Boehme, Peter, Mng. Dir.-Res. & Devel.--Dr. Th. Boehme KG Chem. Fabrik GmbH & Co., Geretsried, Germany; *Int'l*, pg. 199
Boeskov, Jens, Mng. Dir. & Mgr.-Network--Willis Corroon A/S, Copenhagen, Denmark; *Int'l*, pg. 1509
Bogaerts, Eddie, Mng. Dir.--Arthur D. Little International, Inc., Brussels, Belgium; *U.S. Private*, pg. 671
Boglione, Enrico, Mng. Dir.--UTA, Turin, Italy; *Int'l*, pg. 1502
Bohart, John R., Mng. Dir.--Framatome Cogema Fuels, Lynchburg, VA; *Int'l*, pg. 503
Bohart, John R., Mng. Dir.--Framatome Technologies, Inc., Lynchburg, VA; *Int'l*, pg. 503
Bohlander, Frans A.C.M., Mng. Dir.--Sulzer Caliqua B.V., Tilburg, Netherlands; *Int'l*, pg. 1306
Bohle, Heinz, Mng. Dir.--Sulzer Triebwerke AG, Winterthur, Switzerland; *Int'l*, pg. 1307
Bohner, Gerhard, Mng. Dir.-Fin. & Controlling--Landis & Staefa AG, Zug, Switzerland; *Int'l*, pg. 800
Boidin, Michel, Mng. Dir.--ATEA, Carquefou, France; *Int'l*, pg. 503
Bol, G., Mng. Dir.--Crowcon Instruments B.V., Rotterdam, Netherlands; *Int'l*, pg. 590
Bole, Mark, Mng. Dir.--Nokia Telecommunications (H.K.) Ltd., Taikoo Shing, Hong Kong; *Int'l*, pg. 953
Bolleter, Ulrich, Mng. Dir.--Sulzer Innotec Ltd., Winterthur, Switzerland; *Int'l*, pg. 1306
Bolling, Klaus, Mng. Dir.--Krupp Bruninghaus GmbH, Werdohl, Germany; *Int'l*, pg. 508
Bolt, J.W., Mng. Dir.--Ballast Nedam Services B.V., Amstelveen, Netherlands; *Int'l*, pg. 134
Bommer, J., Mng. Dir.--Wolters Kluwer Business Publishing, Deventer, Netherlands; *Int'l*, pg. 1513
Bondi, Enrico, Chief Exec. Officer & Mng. Dir.--Compart SpA, Milan, Italy; *Int'l*, pg. 324
Bongrand, Laurent, Mng. Dir.--Watts Eurotherm, Fressenneville, France; *U.S. Public*, pg. 1747
Bonig, Klaus, Mng. Dir.--Bonig & Yamaoka International Public Relations, Hamburg, Germany; *Int'l*, pg. 1210
Bonnefin, Annie, Mgr.--Etoile Bleue, Tours, France; *Int'l*, pg. 600
Bonnevie, J.C., Mng. Dir.--Caterpillar France S.A., Grenoble, France; *U.S. Public*, pg. 317
Bonnington, Mark, Mgr.-Opers.--Woodward-Clyde International, Honiara, Solomon Islands,; *U.S. Public*, pg. 1658
Bonnotte, Franck, Mng. Dir.--Bertrand Faure Components Ltd. - Norfinch Plant, North York, Canada; *Int'l*, pg. 193
Bontemps, P.O., Mng. Dir.-France--Vodafone Group PLC, Newbury, United Kingdom; *Int'l*, pg. 1469
Bonyhady, Bruce, Mng. Dir.--NM Funds Management (Europe) Ltd. United Kingdom, Bournemouth, United Kingdom; *Int'l*, pg. 908
Bonzom, C., Mng. Dir.--Chaussures Bally Villeurbanne SA, Villeurbanne, France; *Int'l*, pg. 997
Boone, Thomas H., Chief Loan Admin. Officer & Mng. Dir.-Loan Admin.--Countrywide Home Loans Inc., Pasadena, CA; *U.S. Public*, pg. 452
Booth, Kent, Mng. Dir.--M.F. Bank & Company, Inc., Minneapolis, MN; *U.S. Private*, pg. 113
Booty, S., Mng. Dir.--Chep UK Limited, Addlestone, United Kingdom; *Int'l*, pg. 212
Bordelais, Jacques, Pres. & Chief Exec. Officer-BL/LB Group--Bordelais, Lemeunier-Leo Burnett Paris, Levallois-Perret, France; *U.S. Private*, pg. 184
Borden, Robert, Dir.--General Motors Overseas Corp., Dunstable, United Kingdom; *U.S. Public*, pg. 722
Borgersen, Bjarne, Chief Exec. Officer & Mng. Dir.--Fokus Bank A/S, Trondheim, Norway; *Int'l*, pg. 496
Borgschulte, Don, Mng. Dir.-Info. Tech. & Svcs.--New Century Energies, Inc., Denver, CO; *U.S. Public*, pg. 1170
Borjesson, Rolf, Chief Exec. Officer & Mng. Dir.--Rexam PLC, London, United Kingdom; *Int'l*, pg. 1106
Borne, Alan, Mng. Dir.-Publ.--American Automobile Association, Heathrow, FL; *U.S. Private*, pg. 50
Bos, Gerrit, Mng. Dir.--Krips Repro B.V., Meppel, Netherlands; *Int'l*, pg. 1100
Bosco, Lorenzo, Mng. Dir.--SI Sealing Parts SpA, Carpi, Italy; *Int'l*, pg. 1338
Bossard, Alexander, Mng. Dir.--De Pretto-Escher Wyss s.r.l., Schio, Italy; *Int'l*, pg. 1305
Bosse, Jon D., Mng. Dir.--NWQ Investment Managaement Company, Los Angeles, CA; *U.S. Public*, pg. 1673
Bostelmann, Henning, Dr. jur., Mng. Dir.--Dyckerhoff & Widmann AG, Munich, Germany; *Int'l*, pg. 423
Botha, Hannes, Mng. Dir.--Sasol Synthetic Fuels (Pty.) Ltd., Secunda, South Africa; *Int'l*, pg. 1197
Bouchet, Philippe, Dr., Mng. Dir.--Barringer Europe, SARL, Roissy, France; *U.S. Public*, pg. 192
Bouchier, Michael W., Chief Oper. Officer & Mng. Dir.--Sasol Fibres, Reunion, South Africa; *Int'l*, pg. 1196
Boulton, S., Mng. Dir.--Penny & Giles Aerospace Ltd., Christchurch, United Kingdom; *Int'l*, pg. 207
Bourez, Joel, Mng. Dir.-Business Devel./Intl. Projects--Landis & Staefa AG, Zug, Switzerland; *Int'l*, pg. 800
Bourgeaux, Eric, Mng. Dir.--Nokia Finance International B.V., Geneva Branch, Carouge, Switzerland; *Int'l*, pg. 954
Bourke, Paul, Mng. Dir.-Arnott's Ltd.--Bakery & Confectionary Division, Camden, NJ; *U.S. Public*, pg. 299
Bourne, N., Mng. Dir.--Staeng Limited, Cornwall, United Kingdom; *Int'l*, pg. 207
Bouteille, Francois, Deputy Mng. Dir.--NPI, Paris, France; *Int'l*, pg. 503
Bowman, John, Mng. Dir.--E-Z-EM Ltd., London, United Kingdom; *U.S. Public*, pg. 540
Box, Ray, Mng. Dir.-European--Autologic Information International Ltd., Saint Albans, United Kingdom; *U.S. Public*, pg. 1724
Boyce, Hugh, Mng. Dir.--Flexfab Horizons International, Inc., Hastings, MI; *U.S. Private*, pg. 412
Boyette, John V., Pres. & Mng. Dir.--Geraghty & Miller, Inc., Denver, CO; *Int'l*, pg. 607
Boylan, P. J., Mng. Dir.-Card Services--NatWest U.K., London, United Kingdom; *Int'l*, pg. 910
Boyle, G., Mng. Dir.--Isovel International Ltd., Andover, United Kingdom; *Int'l*, pg. 585
Boyle, Kevin, Mgr.-LDA Western Area--Team One Advertising, El Segundo, CA; *U.S. Public*, pg. 1422
Bracco, Diana, Dr., Chief Exec. Officer & Mng. Dir.--Bracco S.p.A., Milan, Italy; *Int'l*, pg. 209
Bradburn, Gareth G., Mng. Dir.--International Risk Management Group Ltd., Hamilton, Bermuda; *Int'l*, pg. 1333
Bradeen, Chet, Mng. Dir.--Sun Healthcare Group International Ltd., Windsor, United Kingdom; *U.S. Public*, pg. 1531
Brader, J.H.M., Mng. Dir.--Uitgeversmaatschappij De Stem bv, Breda, Netherlands; *Int'l*, pg. 1445
Bradford, Brian, Mng. Dir.--Reed Exhibition Companies (UK) Ltd., Richmond, United Kingdom; *Int'l*, pg. 1097
Bradford, Gregory R., Pres.-Mktg. Systems Grp. & Mng. Dir.-CACI Ltd.--CACI International Inc, Arlington, VA; *U.S.* Public, pg. 272
Bradley, J. Douglas, Mng. Dir.-Corp. Devel.--TrizecHahn Corporation, Toronto, Canada; *Int'l*, pg. 1424
Bradshaw, Tom, Mngng. Dir.--Arthur D. Little, Inc., Philadelphia, PA; *U.S. Private*, pg. 670
Brady, Gerald J.P., Mng. Dir.--Management International (Dublin) Limited, Dublin, Ireland; *Int'l*, pg. 151

Brady, Milton, Mng. Dir.--Skandinaviska Enskilda Banking, New York & Cayman Island Branch, New York, NY; *Int'l, pg. 1259*

Bramm, Soren, Mng. Dir.--Soren Berggreen & Co. A/S, Vejle, Denmark; *Int'l*, pg. 864

Brammertz, Dieter, Dr., Mng. Dir.--O&K Orenstein & Koppel Aktiengesellschaft, Dortmund, Germany; *Int'l*, pg. 516

Branchi, S., Mng. Dir.--Intochimica Marketing S.r.l., Milan, Italy; *Int'l*, pg. 682

Brantner, Richard, Mng. Dir.--Esselte Meto Ges mbH, Vienna, Austria; *Int'l*, pg. 461

Bratcher, S.V., Dir. & Gen. Mgr.--Hamworthy Heating Limited, Poole, United Kingdom; *Int'l*, pg. 1065

Braun, Bernhard, Dr., Mng. Dir.--Wuestenrot stavebni sporitelna a.s., Prague, Czech Republic; *Int'l*, pg. 1514

Braun, Ed, Exec. Dir.-Managed Care--Beltone Electronics Corporation, Chicago, IL; *U.S. Private*, pg. 132

Bray, Wes, Mng. Dir.--Market Growth Resources, Inc., Wilton, CT; *U.S. Public*, pg. 1641

Brear, S., Mng. Dir.-Bailey Telecom Ltd.-N.G. Bailey & Co. Ltd., Ilkley, United Kingdom; *Int'l*, pg. 132

Brear, S., Mng. Dir.--Bailey Telecom LTD, Leeds, United Kingdom; *Int'l*, pg. 133

Breen, Howard, Mng. Dir.--Young & Rubicam Ltd., Toronto, Canada; *U.S. Private*, pg. 1200

Breen, John J., Mng. Dir.-Admin.--Federal Farm Credit Banks Funding Corporation, Jersey City, NJ; *U.S. Private*, pg. 398

Breen, Oivind R., Mng. Dir.--BBDO Oslo, Oslo, Norway; *U.S. Public*, pg. 1224

Bregolato, J.L., Mng. Dir.--Quaker Chemical Industrial Comercio Ltda., Sao Paulo, Brazil; *U.S. Public*, pg. 1346

Brendecke, Hermann, Dr., Mng. Dir.--Heraeus Instruments GmbH, Hanau, Germany; *Int'l*, pg. 616

Brennan, Marty, V.P. & Reg. Dir.--Dugan Valva Contess-Chicago, Chicago, IL; *U.S. Private*, pg. 345

Brennan, Pat, Mng. Dir. & Gen. Mgr.-Opers.--Tygaflor Ltd., Littleborough, United Kingdom; *U.S. Public*, pg. 344

Brenner, Karen, Mng. Dir.--Noel Group, Inc., New York, NY; *U.S. Public*, pg. 1187

Brickwood, David J., Dr., Mng. Dir.--Janssen-Cilag Ltd., High Wycombe, United Kingdom; *U.S. Public*, pg. 929

Bricout, Michel, Vice Chm. & Sr. Exec. Mng. Dir.--Banque PSA Finance Holding, Paris, France; *Int'l*, pg. 1021

Brimble, A.J., Mng. Dir.--Babcock King - Wilkinson Limited, Crawley, United Kingdom; *Int'l*, pg. 131

Brito, Pedro, Mng. Dir.--Publinter/BDDP, Lisbon, Portugal; *Int'l*, pg. 118

Britton, Rob, Mng. Dir.-Corp. Communications--AMR Corporation, Fort Worth, TX; *U.S. Public*, pg. 9

Broc, Pierre, Mng. Dir.--Kenzo, Paris, France; *Int'l*, pg. 781

Broderick, Pat, Mng. Dir.--K-Tel Entertainment (U.K.) Ltd., London, United Kingdom; *U.S. Public*, pg. 938

Brodetsky, David, Mng. Dir.--Sourdillon SA, Esvres, France; *Int'l*, pg. 391

Brodie, Jerry, V.P.-Opers. & Mng. Dir.--The Campbell Group, Inc., Portland, OR; *U.S. Public*, pg. 1672

Brodkorb, Rudi, Mng. Dir.--IBP, West Bromwich, United Kingdom; *Int'l*, pg. 391

Broese van Groenou, Leonard, Mng. Dir.--Air Products S.A., Brussels, Belgium; *U.S. Public*, pg. 32

Bromberg, Sam, Partner-Creative Copy--Lewis Gace Bozell Healthcare Worldwide, Fort Lee, NJ; *U.S. Public*, pg. 1642

Brons, Jan, Mng. Dir.--SKF Condition Monitoring Inc., San Diego, CA; *Int'l*, pg. 1157

Brooks, Gary, Asst. Reg. Mng. Dir.-Bus. Devel.--Willis Corroon South Limited, Bristol, United Kingdom; *Int'l*, pg. 1503

Brooks, Tim, Mng. Dir.--EMAP Architecture Ltd., London, United Kingdom; *Int'l*, pg. 451

Brooks, Tim, Mng. Dir.--NCE Group, London, United Kingdom; *Int'l*, pg. 451

Brooks, Trevor G., Mng. Dir.--Smith Corona (U.K.) Ltd., Hertford, United Kingdom; *U.S. Private*, pg. 1007

Browell, Torbjorn, Mng. Dir.--SKF Services d.o.o., Zagreb, Croatia; *Int'l*, pg. 1159

Brown, John, Sr. V.P. & Mng. Dir.--State Street Australia Ltd., Sydney, Australia; *U.S. Public*, pg. 1513

Brown, K. N., Mng. Dir.--Portals (Bathford) Ltd., Bath, United Kingdom; *Int'l*, pg. 386

Brown, Robert, Mng. Dir.--Benford Limited, Warwick, United Kingdom; *Int'l*, pg. 1066

Brown, Steve, Midwest Region Dir.--Miller Advertising Agency Inc.-Chicago, Northfield, IL; *U.S. Private*, pg. 746

Brown, Suzanne, Mng. Partner & Gen. Mgr.--Gillespie, Lawrenceville, NJ; *U.S. Private*, pg. 453

Brown, Terence, Dir. Gen.-Risk--European Investment Bank, Luxembourg, Luxembourg; *Int'l*, pg. 465

Brown, Tim, Mng. Dir.--Fedders North America, Inc., Effingham, IL; *U.S. Public*, pg. 615

Browne, Nick, Mng. Dir.--Costain Oil, Gas & Process Limited Process Contracting Division, Manchester, United Kingdom; *Int'l*, pg. 336

Browning, Gary, Mng. Dir.--BDG/McColl, London, United Kingdom; *Int'l*, pg. 1482

Browning, J.M., Mng. Dir.--Reifenhauser Ltd., Tewkesbury, United Kingdom; *Int'l*, pg. 1101

Brownlee, Kevin, Mng. Dir.--Expamet Fencing, Hartlepool, United Kingdom; *Int'l*, pg. 467

Bruce, Bill, Mng. Dir.--Quorum Graphic Design Consultants Ltd., Glasgow, United Kingdom; *Int'l*, pg. 1226

Bruce, Douglas, Mng. Dir.--Bensons International Systems Pty. Ltd., Yagoona, Australia; *Int'l*, pg. 460

Bruce, P.J., Mng. Dir.--Glover Webb Ltd., Southampton, United Kingdom; *Int'l*, pg. 535

Bruder, Otto, Mng. Dir.--A. Schulman Plastics S.A., Givet, France; *U.S. Public*, pg. 1442

Bruins, Koert, Mng. Dir.--Iggesund Benelux B.V., Haren, Netherlands; *Int'l*, pg. 886

Brulot, Theodoor P.J.W., Mng. Dir.-Human Resources--Schmalbach-Lubeca AG, Braunschweig, Germany; *Int'l*, pg. 1206

Brummer, Barbara, Ph.D., Mng. Dir.--Johnson & Johnson Inc., Montreal, Canada; *U.S. Public*, pg. 930

Brun, Patrick, Mng. Dir.--Grace S.A, Epernon, France; *U.S. Public*, pg. 756

Brunet, Didier, Mng. Dir.--EURO RSCG Audience, Levallois-Perret, France; *Int'l*, pg. 600

Brunkel, Peter, Chief Exec. Officer & Mng. Dir.--DMB&B Reklamebureau A/S, Frederiksberg, Denmark; *U.S. Private*, pg. 304

Brunkel, Peter, Mng. Dir.--International Marketing & Promotions, Frederiksberg, Denmark; *U.S. Private*, pg. 304

Bruns, G., Mng. Dir.--Ascom Infrasys GmbH, Aachen, Germany; *Int'l*, pg. 87

Bryan, Marshall E., Mng. Dir.--Deutsche Goodyear GmbH, Cologne, Germany; *U.S. Public*, pg. 753

Bryans, Antony, Mng. Dir.--Banque Bruxelles Lambert Trust Company Ltd., Saint Helier, United Kingdom; *Int'l*, pg. 148

Bryant, Ken, Exec. Dir.--Principal Health Care of Georgia, Inc., Atlanta, GA; *U.S. Private*, pg. 885

Buchi, Rudolph, Mng. Dir.--Sulzer Bulachguss AG, Bulach, Switzerland; *Int'l*, pg. 1307

Buchloh, A., Mng. Dir.--Gesellschaft fur Elektrometallurgie m.b.H., Nuremberg, Germany; *U.S. Private*, pg. 735

Buckle, Peter, Mng. Dir.--R.A.R.E. (Pty) Ltd., Edenvale, South Africa; *Int'l*, pg. 1306

Buckle, T.J., Mng. Dir.--Edgcumbe Instruments Ltd., Glasgow, United Kingdom; *Int'l*, pg. 207

Buckley, D.C., Mng. Dir.--SEAC Limited, Leicester, United Kingdom; *Int'l*, pg. 590

Buckley, G. Ian, Mng. Dir.-Investment Div.--Henderson Administration Group PLC, London, United Kingdom; *Int'l*, pg. 609

Buckley, Michael D., Mng. Dir.--AIB Capital Markets plc, Dublin, Ireland; *Int'l*, pg. 64

Buckley, R., Dr., Mng. Dir.--Balzers Process Systems, Inc., Hudson, NH; *Int'l*, pg. 997

Budden, Richard G., Mng. Dir.--Wellman International Ltd., Kells, Ireland; *U.S. Public*, pg. 1753

Buenconsejo, V.B., Mng. Dir.--P.T. Ferro Mas Dinamika, Cibarusah-Bekosi, Indonesia; *U.S. Public*, pg. 619

Buerkle, John R., Exec. V.P. & Reg. Dir.-Consumer Products-Asia-Pacific--S.C. Johnson & Son, Inc., Racine, WI; *U.S. Private*, pg. 592

Buhring, Rolf, Mng. Dir.--Dyckerhoff & Widmann Berlin GmbH, Berlin, Germany; *Int'l*, pg. 423

Bullens, Han, Mng. Dir.-Real Estate--Landis & Staefa AG, Zug, Switzerland; *Int'l*, pg. 800

Bunnell, Keith, Exec. V.P. & Mng. Partner-Acct.--Wells BDDP, Inc., New York, NY; *Int'l*, pg. 117

Bunney, M., Mng. Dir.--Laporte Electronics, Riddings, United Kingdom; *Int'l*, pg. 802

Buono, Bernard, Gen. Mgr.--Unicom, Rennes, France; *Int'l*, pg. 601

Burgess, Steve, Mng. Dir.--Lake Region Medical, Inc., Pittsburgh, PA; *U.S. Private*, pg. 643

Burgis, Alan, Chief Exec. Officer & Mng. Dir.--EURO RSCG Partnership, Sydney, Australia; *Int'l*, pg. 602

Burke, John J., Chief Exec. Officer & Mng. Dir.--Bristol & West Building Society, Bristol, United Kingdom; *Int'l*, pg. 216

Burke, Michael K., Mng. Dir.--Syntron Asia Pte. Ltd., Singapore, Singapore; *U.S. Public*, pg. 1563

Burke, Patrick, Mng. Dir.--The Aegis Group, Inc., Atlanta, GA; *U.S. Public*, pg. 150

Burkle, Ronald, Mng. Partner--The Yucaipa Companies, Los Angeles, CA; *U.S. Private*, pg. 1202

Burlot, Sylvie, Mng. Dir.--Bertrand Faure Equipements SA, Nogent-sur-Seine, France; *Int'l*, pg. 192

Burns, C. Robert, Jr., Pres. & Mng. Dir.--Fencourt Reinsurance Co. Ltd., Hamilton, Bermuda; *U.S. Public*, pg. 795

Burns, Cathie, Mng. Dir.--Riley Advertising (Leeds) Ltd., Leeds, United Kingdom; *Int'l*, pg. 1117

Burns, Hannah, Mng. Dir.-Corp. Communications--The Bear Stearns Companies Inc., New York, NY; *U.S. Public*, pg. 197

Burns, Malcolm J., Mng. Dir.--BHP New Zealand Steel Ltd., Glenbrook, New Zealand; *Int'l*, pg. 226

Burns, William J.D., Mng. Dir.--Ortho Clinical Diagnostic N.V., Beersel, Belgium; *U.S. Public*, pg. 931

Burr, Christopher D., Pres. & Mng. Dir.--Johnson & Johnson Medical K.K., Tokyo, Japan; *U.S. Public*, pg. 931

Bursky, Andrew M., Mng. Dir.--Interlaken Capital, Inc., Greenwich, CT; *U.S. Private*, pg. 567

Burton, Ken, Mng. Dir.--Reed Business Information-East Grinstead, East Grinstead, United Kingdom; *Int'l*, pg. 1094

Buseyne, Valere, Mng. Dir.--ISS Food Hygiene S.A.-N.V., Brussels, Belgium; *Int'l*, pg. 657

Bussell, Scott R., Dir.-Maintenance Opers.--Mesaba Holdings, Inc., Minneapolis, MN; *U.S. Public*, pg. 1099

Busweiler, E., Mng. Dir.--VNU Business Publications bv, Amsterdam, Netherlands; *Int'l*, pg. 1445

Buthker, K., Deputy Mng. Dir.--Lowe & Jaegers GmbH, Duisburg, Germany; *Int'l*, pg. 1450

Butler, Shawn, Mng. Dir.--Lehman Brothers Holdings Inc., New York, NY; *U.S. Public*, pg. 987

Butterfield, Brian, Mng. Dir.--Bi-Tech Engineering, Dunleer, Ireland; *Int'l*, pg. 554

Butzlaff, Steve, V.P. & Mng. Dir.--The Northern Trust Company, Lake Forest, IL; *U.S. Public*, pg. 1197

Butzlaff, Steve, V.P. & Mng. Dir.--The Northern Trust Company, Lake Bluff, IL; *U.S. Public*, pg. 1197

Byers, Peter, Mng. Dir.--ORIX New Zealand (NZ) Limited, Auckland, New Zealand; *Int'l*, pg. 1010

Byrne, J. Dixon, Mng. Partner--Hanft Byrne Raboy Abrams & Partners, Inc., New York, NY; *U.S. Private*, pg. 499

Cabezon, Ignacio, Bus. Affairs & Fin. Dir.--Young & Rubicam, S.A., Madrid, Spain; *U.S. Private*, pg. 1199

Caboni, Giorgio M., Mng. Dir.--John Crane Iberica S.A., Madrid, Spain; *Int'l*, pg. 1339

Cabrera, Carlos, Mng. Dir.--Skandia Portugal Propriedades S.A., Lisbon, Portugal; *Int'l*, pg. 1258

Caddell, Lyn, Sr. Dir.-Information Systems--America West Airlines, Inc., Phoenix, AZ; *U.S. Public*, pg. 67

Cain, Keith, Mng. Dir.--Viking Direct Holding Co., Leicester, United Kingdom; *U.S. Public*, pg. 1721

Cakiroglu, Ender, Mng. Dir.--Turk Elektrik Endustrisi A.S., Istanbul, Turkey; *Int'l*, pg. 741

Caldentey, Juan M., Deputy Mng. Dir. & Sr. V.P.-Devel. City Div. Europe--Sol Melia, Palma de Mallorca, Spain; *Int'l*, pg. 1277

Calderon, Ramon, Mng. Dir.--Publispana/BDDP, Mexico, Mexico; *Int'l*, pg. 118

Calderon, Ramon, Chief Fin. Officer & V.P.--Young & Rubicam S.A. de C.V., Mexico, Mexico; *U.S. Private*, pg. 1200

Calladine, David G., Mng. Dir.--ITT Flygt Ltd., Colwich, United Kingdom; *U.S. Public*, pg. 860

Callaghan, Dennis J., Mng. Dir.-Resort Div.--Florida Panthers Holdings, Inc., Fort Lauderdale, FL; *U.S. Public, pg. 654*

Callaghan, Iain M., Mng. Dir.--John Menzies Wholesale, Edinburgh, United Kingdom; *Int'l*, pg. 707

Calleja, Tomas, Mng. Dir.-Corp. Devel. & Chief Information Officer--Iberdrola, S.A., Bilbao, Spain; *Int'l*, pg. 657

Callejo, Luis Miguel Jarillo, Mng. Dir.--Swiss Life (Espana), Madrid, Spain; *Int'l*, pg. 1332

Callens, Philippe, Mng. Dir.--FCB Brussels, Brussels, Belgium; *U.S. Private*, pg. 389

Callin, Bjoern M., Mng. Dir.--Grindex AB, Handen, Sweden; *U.S. Public*, pg. 860

Calliss, Brian L., Mng. Dir.--Pacific Scientific Ltd., Bourne, United Kingdom; *U.S. Public*, pg. 1250

Calton, Richard, Reg. Mng. Dir.--Willis Corroon South Limited, Reading, United Kingdom; *Int'l*, pg. 1503

Caluwaerts, Marc, Mng. Dir.--Bekaert-Stanwick N.V., Kortrijk, Belgium; *Int'l*, pg. 183

Calvert, Ian, Mng. Dir.--Bull Calvert Pace, Cape Town, South Africa; *U.S. Private*, pg. 678

Calvo, Jesus R., Mng. Dir.-Distribution & Customer--Iberdrola, S.A., Bilbao, Spain; *Int'l*, pg. 657

Camargo, A.N., Mng. Dir.--Morganite Isolantes Termicos Limitada, Rio de Janeiro, Brazil; *Int'l*, pg. 895

Campadese, Massimo, Mng. Dir.--Arthur D. Little International, Inc., Milan, Italy; *U.S. Private*, pg. 671

Campard, Gerard, Mng. Dir.--H.B. Fuller France, Le Trait, France; *U.S. Public*, pg. 687

Campbell, Jeffrey, Mng. Dir.-Corp. Fin.--AMR Corporation, Fort Worth, TX; *U.S. Public*, pg. 9

Campbell, P.L., Mng. Dir.--Metal Box South Africa Limited, Johannesburg, South Africa; *Int'l*, pg. 267

Campbell, Robyn, Sr. V.P. & Mng. Dir.--Western International Media Corporation, Minneapolis, MN; *U.S. Private*, pg. 1167

Campion, Julie, Exec. Dir.--Principal Health Care of the Mid-Atlantic, Inc., Rockville, MD; *U.S. Private*, pg. 886

Camus, Maria Isabel, Mng. Dir.--Codelco-France S.A.R.L., Paris, France; *Int'l*, pg. 303

Cannatelli, Vincenzo, Chief Exec. Officer & Mng. Dir.--ELSAG Bailey Process Automation N.V., Schiphol, Netherlands; *Int'l*, pg. 449

Capdevielle, Jean-Pierre, V.P. & Mng. Dir.-Intl.--Collagen Corporation, Palo Alto, CA; *U.S. Public*, pg. 399

Carbonnieres, Gerard, Co-Mgr.--Unicom, Nantes, France; *Int'l*, pg. 601

Carcelle, Yves, Mng. Dir.--Louis Vuitton Malletier, Paris, France; *Int'l*, pg. 781

Cardo, G., Mng. Dir.--NRG France S.A., Creteil, France; *Int'l*, pg. 1116

Cardo, Gerard, Mng. Dir.--Gestetner S.A., Creteil, France; *Int'l*, pg. 1115

Carell, Lars, Mng. Dir.--Janssen-Cilag AB, Sollentuna, Sweden; *U.S. Public*, pg. 929

Carey, H. Augustus, Sr. V.P. & Mng. Dir.--W.P. Carey & Co., Inc., New York, NY; *U.S. Private*, pg. 209

Carey, T.W., Mng. Dir.--Vivitar (Europe) Ltd. Hanimex-Vivitar, Swindon, United Kingdom; *Int'l*, pg. 1061

Carlin, Mark, Mng. Dir.--Smith Corona S.A., Waterloo, Belgium; *U.S. Private*, pg. 1007

Carloon, L., Mng. Dir. & Controller--Moore Paragon Svenska AB, Vastervik, Sweden; *Int'l*, pg. 890

Carlos, Simoes, Mng. Dir.--Nokia Telecomunicacones Portugal S.A., Lisbon, Portugal; *Int'l*, pg. 954

Carlson, Cynthia, Mng. Dir.--Electronic Tele-Communications, Inc., Pleasanton, CA; *U.S. Public*, pg. 570

Carlson, Jane, Exec. V.P. & Mng. Partner-Acct.--Wells BDDP, Inc., New York, NY; *Int'l*, pg. 117

Carlsson, Billy, Mng. Dir.--Norvista Travel AB, Stockholm, Sweden; *Int'l*, pg. 486

Carlsson, Milton, Mng. Dir.--Fraktarna AB, Helsingborg, Sweden; *Int'l*, pg. 476

Carrasquillo, Maruici, Mng. Dir.--The West Company de Colombia, S.A., Bogota, Colombia; *U.S. Public*, pg. 1756

Carree, Alain-Claude, Mng. Dir.-Pur.--Automobiles Citroen, Neuilly, France; *Int'l*, pg. 1020

Carrier, John, Mng. Dir.--NIG Skandia PLC, London, United Kingdom; *Int'l*, pg. 1258

Carroll, Mary Alice, Mng. Dir.--Grapheme Inc., Toronto, Canada; *Int'l*, pg. 336

Carter, Bruce, V.P.-Health Care Discovery & Devel.--Novo Nordisk A/S, Bagsvaerd, Denmark; *Int'l*, pg. 987

Carter, Derek, Mng. Dir.--EMAP Maclaren, Croydon, United Kingdom; *Int'l*, pg. 451

Carter, Rodney, Mng. Dir.-Mfg.--Whatman plc, Maidstone, United Kingdom; *Int'l*, pg. 1498

Carty, Brian, Mng. Dir.-Fin. Svcs. & Exec. V.P.-New Bus./Human Resources--Hill, Holliday, Connors, Cosmopulos, Inc., Boston, MA; *U.S. Private*, pg. 529

Case, Robert A., Mng. Dir.--Salomon Smith Barney Holdings, Inc., New York, NY; *U.S. Public*, pg. 1633

Casimir, Bill, Acting Mng. Dir.--ANZ Funds Management, Sydney, Australia; *Int'l*, pg. 98

Cassan, Jean-Pierre, Mng. Dir.--Laboratories Astra France, Nanterre, France; *Int'l*, pg. 94
Cassidy, Charles T., Sr. V.P. & Mng. Dir.--State Street Bank & Trust Co., London, London, United Kingdom; *U.S. Public*, pg. 1513
Cassis, Jorge, Mng. Dir.--Leo Burnett Chile, Santiago, Chile; *U.S. Private*, pg. 185
Caster, Douglas, Mng. Dir.--Ultra Electronics Sonar & Communications Systems, Greenford, United Kingdom; *Int'l*, pg. 1431
Catesby, Peter, Deputy Chm. & Joint Mng. Dir.--Vaux Group Plc, Sunderland, United Kingdom; *Int'l*, pg. 1453
Catt, Charles J., Mng. Dir.--NAC Reinsurance International Limited, London, United Kingdom; *U.S. Public*, pg. 1144
Cattell, Alan, Mng. Dir.-Corp. Tech. Tracking & Transfer--Landis & Staefa AG, Zug, Switzerland; *Int'l*, pg. 800
Catterall, F. A., Dr., Mng. Dir.--Glaxo Far East Pte. Ltd., Singapore, Singapore; *Int'l*, pg. 553
Cavalli-Bjorkman, Magnus, Mng. Dir.--Skandinaviska Enskilda Banken Hong Kong, Hong Kong, Hong Kong; *Int'l*, pg. 1259
Cawte, Dennis, Mng. Dir.--Keystone Valve (U.K.) Ltd., Glasgow, United Kingdom; *U.S. Public*, pg. 1650
Cayne, James E., Pres., Chief Exec. Officer & Sr. Mng. Dir.--The Bear Stearns Companies Inc., New York, NY; *U.S. Public*, pg. 197
Celentano, Daniel A., Sr. Mng. Dir.--The Bear Stearns Companies Inc., New York, NY; *U.S. Public*, pg. 197
Cenal, J., Mng. Dir.--GKN Ayra Cardan SA, Deba, Spain; *Int'l*, pg. 535
Centella, Larry, Mng. Dir.--Gambro Healthcare, Lakewood, CO; *Int'l*, pg. 667
Cerana, Nicoletta, Mng. Dir.--Ketchum Public Relations, SRL, Milan, Italy; *U.S. Private*, pg. 617
Cernak, Werner F., Mng. Dir.--Janssen Cilag GmbH, Neuss, Germany; *U.S. Public*, pg. 929
Chabannes, Jean-Antoine, Mng. Dir.--Societe suisse (France), Paris, France; *Int'l*, pg. 1332
Chachawal, Somboon, Mng. Dir.--Siam Cellulose Co., Ltd., Bangkok, Thailand; *Int'l*, pg. 1238
Chadronnier, J. M., Pres. & Dir. Gen.--Consortium Vinicole de Bordeaux et de la Gironde SA, Parempuyre, France; *Int'l*, pg. 752
Chadwick, Rodney L., Mng. Dir. & Chief Exec. Officer--Pacific Dunlop Limited, Melbourne, Australia; *Int'l*, pg. 1021
Chaffart, Ferdinand, Chm.-Exec. Committee & Mng. Dir.--Generale de Banque S.A., Brussels, Belgium; *Int'l*, pg. 546
Chaffe, George A., Mng. Dir.--Skandia International Risk Management (Vermont), Inc., Burlington, VT; *Int'l*, pg. 1257
Chai, C.F., Chief Oper. Officer & Mng. Dir.--Littelfuse Fareast, PTE Ltd., Singapore, Singapore; *U.S. Public*, pg. 1001
Chaldecott, Axel, Mng. Partner--Howell Henry Chaldecott Lury & Partners, London, United Kingdom; *Int'l*, pg. 637
Challender, Jerry, Gen. Mgr.--Ademco de Juarez, Chihuahua, Mexico; *U.S. Public*, pg. 1307
Chambraud, Eric, Mng. Dir.--Dumez Moscou, Moscow, Russia; *Int'l*, pg. 823
Chaminadour, Bernard, Mng. Dir.--Allo Pro France Sarl, Paris, France; *Int'l*, pg. 1307
Chamroendararussamee, Surachat, Mng. Dir.--The Siam Fiberglass Co., Ltd., Bangkok, Thailand; *Int'l*, pg. 1238
Chan, C., Mng. Dir.--Ascom Timeplex Far East Ltd., Hong Kong, Hong Kong; *Int'l*, pg. 87
Chan, Eric C.W., Mng. Dir.--Esselte Ltd., Wan Chai, Hong Kong; *Int'l*, pg. 461
Chan, Ky, V.P. & Mng. Dir.-Unitrode Electronics Asia--Unitrode Corporation, Merrimack, NH; *U.S. Public*, pg. 1694
Chan, Paul, Reg. Dir.-Opers.--DHL International (Hong Kong) Ltd., Wan Chai, Hong Kong; *U.S. Private*, pg. 302
Chan, Susan, Mng. Dir.--Stocker & Yale (HK) Ltd., North Point, Hong Kong; *U.S. Public*, pg. 1518
Chandler, Colin, Sir, Chief Exec. Officer--Vickers PLC, London, United Kingdom; *Int'l*, pg. 1466
Chandler, William F., Jr., Chm.-Management Committee, Principal & Mng. Dir.--National Asset Management Corporation, Louisville, KY; *U.S. Public*, pg. 1154
Chang, Ji-Soo, Chief Fin. Officer & Mng. Dir.--Jinbang Steel Co., Ltd., Pohang, Korea; *Int'l*, pg. 1291
Chapman, A.J., Mng. Dir.--Thames Side-Maywood Limited, Reading, United Kingdom; *Int'l*, pg. 590
Chapman, David, Exec. V.P. & Mng. Dir.--Thomas G. Ferguson Associates, Inc., Parsippany, NJ; *Int'l*, pg. 1483
Chapman, John S., Mng. Dir.--Baldwin (UK) Ltd., Dunstable, United Kingdom; *U.S. Public*, pg. 170
Charles, Ed, Mng. Dir.--Cold Spring Granite (Canada) Ltd., Cold Spring, MN; *U.S. Private*, pg. 251
Charles, Martyn, Mng. Dir.--Avery Flight International Limited, Isleworth, United Kingdom; *Int'l*, pg. 215
Charls, Ph.W., Mng. Dir.--RVS Verzekeringen NV, Brussels, Belgium; *Int'l*, pg. 651
Charlton, Edward, Mng. Dir.--Banque Internationale a Luxembourg S.A., London Branch, London, United Kingdom; *Int'l*, pg. 162
Charnkolrawee, Santi, Mng. Dir.--The Siam Iron and Steel Co., Ltd., Bangkok, Thailand; *Int'l*, pg. 1238
Charter, A.C., Mng. Dir.--Hong Kong Air Cargo Terminals Ltd., Kowloon, Hong Kong; *Int'l*, pg. 705
Chase, Andrew, Sr. V.P. & Mng. Dir.-Dir. Mail--Western International Media Corporation, Los Angeles, CA; *U.S. Private*, pg. 1165
Chemello, Roberto, Co-Chief Exec. Officer & Mng. Dir.--Luxottica Group S.p.A., Agordo, Italy; *Int'l*, pg. 822
Cheng, Chih-Wen, Mng. Dir.--Cathay Finance International (Holdings) Limited, Sydney, Australia; *Int'l*, pg. 684
Cheng, Robin, Mng. Dir.--AGRA (Hong Kong) Limited, Kowloon, Hong Kong; *Int'l*, pg. 31
Cheow, Michael, Mng. Dir.--Hoover Stainless Pte Ltd., Singapore, Singapore; *Int'l*, pg. 1322
Cher, Charles, Mng. Dir.--Reed International (Singapore) PTE Limited, Singapore, Singapore; *Int'l*, pg. 1095
Chernick, Vic, Mng. Dir.--Vivitar Corporation, Newbury Park, CA; *Int'l*, pg. 1060
Chernoyarov, V., Mng. Dir.--RECON, Moscow, Russia; *Int'l*, pg. 608
Cherry, A., Mng. Dir.--Ballast Wlitshier plc - Airport Services Div., Slough, United Kingdom; *Int'l*, pg. 135
Chesnoff, Gary, Mng. Dir.-Resort Div.--Florida Panthers Holdings, Inc., Fort Lauderdale, FL; *U.S. Public*, pg. 654
Chester, J. S., Mng. Dir.--NatWest Stockbrokers Limited, London, United Kingdom; *Int'l*, pg. 910
Cheung, B.C.S., Mng. Dir.--Wyeth (HK) Limited, Wan Chai, Hong Kong; *U.S. Public*, pg. 82
Cheung, B.C.S., Mng. Dir.--Wyeth-Ayerst (Asia) Ltd., Taipei, Taiwan; *U.S. Public*, pg. 82
Cheung, Randy, Mng. Dir.-Tyco International Asia, Inc.--Tyco International Ltd., Exeter, NH; *U.S. Public*, pg. 1647
Chevalier, Dominque, Mng. Dir.-Mktg.--Industrias Lever Portuguesa, Lda., Lisbon, Portugal; *Int'l*, pg. 1437
Chevrier, Christophe, Mng. Dir.--RTL9, Metz, France; *Int'l*, pg. 561
Chiba, N., Dir. & Office Chief-Tokyo--Man Nen Sha Inc., Osaka, Japan; *Int'l*, pg. 834
Chien, Mateo, Mng. Dir.--Lowe & Partners/Live, Causeway Bay, Hong Kong; *U.S. Private*, pg. 678
Chil-Lim, Park, Exec. Mng. Dir.-Construction Tech.--Daewoo Corporation, Seoul, Korea; *Int'l*, pg. 357
Child, R.E., Mng. Dir.--Systematic Drill Head Co. Ltd., Coventry, United Kingdom; *Int'l*, pg. 585
Childs, Mervyn, Mng. Dir.-Czech Republic--Bass International Brewers, Birmingham, United Kingdom; *Int'l*, *pg. 170*
Chiles, John G., Mng. Dir.--Jefferies & Company, Inc., Los Angeles, CA; *U.S. Public*, pg. 925
Chin, Wai W., Mng. Dir.-Asian Res.--Jacobs Asset Management, Fort Lauderdale, FL; *U.S. Public*, pg. 1673
Chiominto, Nicholas, Exec. Dir.-Host Computing--Countrywide Funding Corporation, Pasadena, CA; *U.S. Public*, pg. 453
Chiu, Bennett, V.P.-Asia Pacific--EURO RSCG Partnership, Quarry Bay, Hong Kong; *Int'l*, pg. 602
Chlapowski, Roland, Mng. Dir.--La Suisse - Assurances-vie (France), Lyon, France; *Int'l*, pg. 1332
Chlouverakis, Manolis, Mng. Dir.--Johnson & Johnson Hellas S.A., Athens, Greece; *U.S. Public*, pg. 930
Chobanova, Albena, Deputy Mng. Dir.--Champions, Sofia, Bulgaria; *U.S. Private*, pg. 1199
Choi, J.L., Mng. Dir.--Nanometrics Korea Ltd., Seoul, Korea; *U.S. Public*, pg. 1151
Choi, Sang-Jun, Chief Fin. Officer--Ssangyong Engineering Co., Ltd., Seoul, Korea; *Int'l*, pg. 1292
Chong, Angie, Deputy Mng. Dir.--F.J. Benjamin Fashions (M) Sdn. Bhd., Kuala Lumpur, Malaysia; *Int'l*, pg. 187
Choquette, Yvon, Dir.-Corp. Environmental Mngmnt.--Du Pont Canada Inc., Mississauga, Canada; *U.S. Public*, pg. 532
Choufoer, F. R., Mng. Dir.--DSM Energie B.V., Heerlen, Netherlands; *Int'l*, pg. 353
Chouhy-Oria, Santiago, Mng. Dir.--Johnson & Johnson de Argentina S.A., Buenos Aires, Argentina; *U.S. Public*, pg. 930
Chow, David H., Mng. Dir.--Castle-Harlan, Inc., New York, NY; *U.S. Private*, pg. 219
Christensen, Kaj, Mng. Dir.--Nitodan A/S, Haderslev, Denmark; *Int'l*, pg. 932
Christensen, Knut O., Mng. Dir.--Bang & Olufsen A/S, Drammen, Norway; *Int'l*, pg. 146
Christison, D., Mng. Dir.--Pacific Fire Hose Pty Ltd., Boronia, Australia; *Int'l*, pg. 1500
Christison, D., Mng. Dir.--Angus Fire Armour (Australia) Pty Ltd, Boronia, Australia; *Int'l*, pg. 1500
Chu, Paul, Mng. Dir.--PAXAR Far East Limited, Kowloon, Hong Kong; *U.S. Public*, pg. 1267
Chuamnsu, James, Mng. Dir.--McCormick-Philippines, Inc., Quezon City, Philippines; *U.S. Public*, pg. 1067
Chujo, Kunihiro, Chief Fin. Officer & Mng. Dir.--Honda Motor Co., Ltd., Tokyo, Japan; *Int'l*, pg. 634
Chutinaw, Alongkot, Mng. Dir.--The Siam Nawaloha Foundry Co., Ltd., Bangkok, Thailand; *Int'l*, pg. 1238
Ciccolella, Francesco, Mng. Dir.--Dodi S.p.A., Milan, Italy; *Int'l*, pg. 146
Cicurel, Michel, Deputy Chm. & Mng. Dir.--CERUS - Compagnies Europeennes Reunies, Paris, France; *Int'l*, pg. 240
Cieslak, Daniel, Mng. Dir.-H.R.--Dunham's Athleisure Corporation, Waterford, MI; *U.S. Private*, pg. 346
Cieza, Pedro, V.P. & Reg. Dir.-Consumer Prods.-Americas--S.C. Johnson & Son, Inc., Racine, WI; *U.S. Private*, pg. 592
Clack, Ian, Chief Exec. Officer & Mng. Dir.--Burns, Philp & Company Limited, Sydney, Australia; *Int'l*, pg. 236
Clancy, Michael, V.P. & Mng. Dir.-Topps Ireland Ltd.--The Topps Company, Inc., New York, NY; *U.S. Public*, pg. 1621
Clancy, Michael, Mng. Dir.--Topps Ireland Ltd., Ireland; *U.S. Public*, pg. 1622
Clancy, Michael J., Mng. Dir.--SSI Medical Systems, Inc., Solihull, United Kingdom; *U.S. Public*, pg. 828
Clare, B., Mng. Dir.--Boots Healthcare International, Nottingham, United Kingdom; *Int'l*, pg. 202
Claret, Philippe, Mgr.--EURO RSCG Quartet, Ecueille, France; *Int'l*, pg. 601
Clark, David, Mng. Dir.--Bankgesellschaft Berlin (UK) plc, London, United Kingdom; *Int'l*, pg. 160
Clark, Erin, Mng. Dir.--The Leap Partnership, Chicago, IL; *U.S. Private*, pg. 655
Clark, Harry, Mng. Partner--Clark & Weinstock, New York, NY; *U.S. Public*, pg. 1223
Clark, James, Mng. Dir.--AAR Allen Airmotive, Inc., Hoofddorp, Netherlands; *U.S. Public*, pg. 1
Clark, Kenneth, Mng. Dir.--3M Chile S.A., Santiago, Chile; *U.S. Public*, pg. 1606
Clark, Mark T., Mng. Dir.-Bus. Devel.--FirstEnergy Corp., Akron, OH; *U.S. Public*, pg. 644
Clark, Randall T., Mng. Dir.--Emery Global Logistics, Redwood City, CA; *U.S. Public*, pg. 281
Clarke, Bruce E., Pres. & Mng. Dir.--PanAgora Asset Managment, Inc., Boston, MA; *Int'l*, pg. 935
Clarke, Bruce E., Pres. & Mng. Dir.--PanAgora Asset Managment, Inc., Boston, MA; *U.S. Public*, pg. 987
Clarke, Rob, Mng. Dir.--Leo Burnett/Connaghan & May Pty. Ltd., Sydney, Australia; *U.S. Private*, pg. 185
Clarkson, Michael, Mng. Dir.--Kvaerner Boving, Doncaster, United Kingdom; *Int'l*, pg. 772
Clarkson, S.J., Reg. Mng. Dir.--Ballast Wiltshier Plc - Northern Region, Leeds, United Kingdom; *Int'l*, pg. 135
Clarkson, S.J., Reg. Mng. Dir.--Ballast Wiltshier Plc - East Midland Area, Nottingham, United Kingdom; *Int'l*, pg. 135
Clausen, Oluf, Mng. Dir.--SASIB Bakery Nordic A/S, Skovlunde, Denmark; *Int'l*, pg. 1194
Claver, Mariano Perez, Mng. Dir.-Fin.--Caja de Madrid Group, Madrid, Spain; *Int'l*, pg. 251
Clayman, D., Mng. Dir.--Esso Petroleum Company, Limited, London, United Kingdom; *U.S. Public*, pg. 602
Clayton, Richard, Mng. Dir.--Badger Meter de Mexico, S.A. de C.V., Nogales, Mexico; *U.S. Public*, pg. 165
Clement, Jean Michel, Mng. Dir.--Elsevier Thomas Fachverlag GmbH, Mainz, Germany; *Int'l*, pg. 1100
Clerc, Jacques, Mng. Dir.--Swiss Life (Luxembourg), Luxembourg, Luxembourg; *Int'l*, pg. 1332
Clifford, Justin T., Mng. Dir.--NWQ Investment Managaement Company, Los Angeles, CA; *U.S. Public*, pg. 1673
Clifton, David, Mng. Dir.-Asia Pacific--Resort Condominiums International, Indianapolis, IN; *U.S. Public*, pg. 322
Clinch, D. S., Mng. Dir.--De La Rue Services (Malaysia) Sdn Bhd, Petaling Jaya, Malaysia; *Int'l*, pg. 387
Clinton, John M., Mng. Dir.-McDermott Marine Construction Limited--McDermott International, Inc., New Orleans, LA; *U.S. Public*, pg. 1067
Cloes, Philippe, Mng. Dir.--Credit Lyonnais Belgium, Brussels, Belgium; *Int'l*, pg. 344
Close, Richard, Mng. Dir.-Fin.--The Post Office, London, United Kingdom; *Int'l*, pg. 1064
Cluchey, James, V.P. & Mng. Dir.-European Opers.--SQA, Inc., Burlington, MA; *U.S. Public*, pg. 1361
Coakley, David, Mng. Dir.--AEP/Borden Global Packaging (U.K.) Ltd., North Braddesley, United Kingdom; *U.S. Public*, pg. 5
Coates, David A., Dr., Gen. Mgr.--Johnson & Johnson Poland, Sp.z.o.o., Warsaw, Poland; *U.S. Public*, pg. 931
Cobo, Manuel, Deputy Mng. Dir. & Dir-Audit--Caja de Madrid Group, Madrid, Spain; *Int'l*, pg. 251
Coccia, C.M., Pres. & Mng. Dir.--Alcan Alluminio S.p.A., Pieve Emanuele, Italy; *Int'l*, pg. 50
Coenen, Erich, Dr., Mng. Dir.-Real Estate--Commerzbank AG, Frankfurt, Germany; *Int'l*, pg. 308
Coey, Ken, Mng. Dir.--Esselte Meto Ltd., Bracknell, United Kingdom; *Int'l*, pg. 461
Coine, Alain, Mng. Dir.--Rhone-Poulenc Japan, Ltd., Tokyo, Japan; *Int'l*, pg. 1113
Colaninno, Roberto, Chief Exec. Officer & Mng. Dir.--Olivetti SpA, Turin, Italy; *Int'l*, pg. 1002
Colas, Ady, Dr., Mng. Dir.--Wuestenrot International Management-Gesellschaft AG, Luxembourg, Luxembourg; *Int'l*, pg. 1514
Colas, Benjamin, Mng. Dir.--Darwin Digital, New York, NY; *U.S. Public*, pg. 1422
Colasanti, John, Mng. Partner & Acct. Mngmt. Dir.--Carmichael Lynch, Inc., Minneapolis, MN; *U.S. Private*, pg. 213
Cole, Scott, Mng. Dir.--Cole, Sherman & Associates Ltd., Thornhill, Canada; *U.S. Public*, pg. 1657
Collado, H., Mng. Dir.--Goodyear de Colombia S.A., Cali, Colombia; *U.S. Public*, pg. 753
Collart, J., Mng. Dir.--S.A. Chaussures Bally Schoenen N.V., Brussels, Belgium; *Int'l*, pg. 997
Colley, Blanaid, Mng. Dir.--Shandwick Public Relations Ltd., London, United Kingdom; *Int'l*, pg. 1226
Collier, Peter, Mng. Dir.--System Sensor Canada, Toronto, Canada; *U.S. Public*, pg. 1307
Colligan, Paul, Mng. Dir.--FCS Currency Management, Dublin, Ireland; *Int'l*, pg. 219
Collins, Brian P., Mng. Dir.--Bank of Ireland Securities Services Limited, Dublin, Ireland; *Int'l*, pg. 152
Collins, John M., Mng. Dir.--Arthur D. Little International, Inc., Sydney, Australia; *U.S. Private*, pg. 671
Collins, Roger, Mng. Dir.--Chalmette Medical Center, Chalmette, LA; *U.S. Public*, pg. 1697
Collins, Timothy C., Chief Exec. Officer & Sr. Mng. Dir.--Ripplewood Holdings L.L.C., New York, NY; *U.S. Private*, *pg. 931*
Colombo, Adolfo, Mng. Dir. & Gen. Mgr.--Metropolitana Milanese S.P.A., Milan, Italy; *Int'l*, pg. 863
Colonna, Bob, Mng. Dir.--Holiday RV Superstores, Inc.-Orlando, Orlando, FL; *U.S. Public*, pg. 830
Colonna, Peter, Pres., Chief Exec. Officer & Mng. Dir.--Colonna Bros., Inc., North Bergen, NJ; *U.S. Private*, pg. 254
Colquhoun, Proctor, Mng. Dir.--Intermarkets International, Richmond, United Kingdom; *U.S. Private*, pg. 1062
Commerro, Pietro, Mng. Dir.--Comtest Italy, Turin, Italy; *U.S. Public*, pg. 1596
Conde, Victor, Dir.--International Marketing & Promotions Madrid, Madrid, Spain; *U.S. Private*, pg. 304
Condon, Thomas J., Mng. Dir.--Provident Investment Counsel, Inc., Pasadena, CA; *U.S. Public*, pg. 1674
Conen, Ulrich, Mng. Dir.--N.V. Maxon International S.A., Vilvoorde, Belgium; *U.S. Private*, pg. 717
Conn, Alvin M., Jr., Mng. Dir.-Latin America--Ethyl Corporation, Richmond, VA; *U.S. Public*, pg. 595
Connolly, Amanda, Mng. Dir.--Coley Porter Bell, London, United Kingdom; *Int'l*, pg. 1482
Connolly, Sean, Mng. Dir.--Modem Media Hong Kong, Wan Chai, Hong Kong; *U.S. Public*, pg. 1641

Connor, Mark, Mng. Dir.--Ferrosan International A/S, Soeborg, Denmark; *Int'l*, pg. 987
Contess, Neil, Principal & Sr. Mng. Partner--Dugan Valva Contess Inc., Morristown, NJ; *U.S. Private*, pg. 345
Contreras, Fernando, Mng. Dir.--Johnson & Johnson de Mexico SA de CV, Mexico, Mexico; *U.S. Public*, pg. 930
Conway, Joe, Mng. Dir.--A. Schulman, Inc., Grand Rapids, MI; *U.S. Public*, pg. 1441
Cook, Barry, Mng. Dir.--DMB&B/London, London, United Kingdom; *U.S. Private*, pg. 304
Cook, Peter, Mng. Dir.--PPA Design Ltd., Central, Hong Kong; *Int'l*, pg. 118
Cook, Peter, Mng. Dir.--Intermotor, Nottingham, United Kingdom; *U.S. Public*, pg. 1503
Cooke, Mike, Mng. Dir.--DMG Business Media Ltd., Redhill, United Kingdom; *Int'l*, pg. 366
Cooney, Jack, Mgr.-LDA Southern Area--Team One Advertising, El Segundo, CA; *U.S. Public*, pg. 1422
Cooper, Betty Anne, Mng. Partner-Planning, Segmentation, Lists & Res.--Gillespie, Lawrenceville, NJ; *U.S. Private*, pg. 453
Cope, Mike D., Mng. Dir.--Neste Chemicals UK Ltd., Stockport, United Kingdom; *Int'l*, pg. 914
Cope, Roger, Mng. Dir.--Bestobell Service Co. Ltd., Maidenhead, United Kingdom; *Int'l*, pg. 853
Copijn, Lia M., Mng. Dir.--Copijn Utrecht Holding BV, Utrecht, Netherlands; *Int'l*, pg. 607
Copley, Michael, Mng. Dir.--Revertex-Americas, Saint Louis, MO; *U.S. Private*, pg. 324
Coppens, J., Mng. Dir.--Anco N.V., Turnhout, Belgium; *Int'l*, pg. 244
Corless, Tim, Mng. Dir.-Intl. Opers.--MET Solutions, LLC, Morris Plains, NJ; *U.S. Public*, pg. 1642
Cornale, P., Mng. Dir.--Nutricia S.p.A., Milan, Italy; *Int'l*, pg. 992
Cornelis, Francois, Vice Chm., Chief Exec. Officer & Mng. Dir.--Petrofina S.A., Brussels, Belgium; *Int'l*, pg. 1043
Cornelison, Mike, Mng. Dir.--Forest View Psychiatric Hospital, Grand Rapids, MI; *U.S. Public*, pg. 1697
Corneliussen, Arne, Mng. Dir.--Getinge Vaxjo A/S, Oslo, Norway; *Int'l*, pg. 552
Cornick, Robert, Mng. Dir.--RAECO, Scoresby, Australia; *Int'l*, pg. 462
Corrigan, E. Gerald, Mng. Dir.--Goldman, Sachs & Co., New York, NY; *U.S. Private*, pg. 462
Corsie, Ian, Mng. Dir.--Pitkin Guides, Andover, United Kingdom; *Int'l*, pg. 1094
Cortilier, G., Mng. Dir.--S.A. Cockerill Mechanical Industries C.M.I., Seraing, Belgium; *Int'l*, pg. 301
Corvino, Ron, Mng. Dir.--Media Incorporated, New York, NY; *U.S. Private*, pg. 726
Corvino, Ron, Mng. Dir.--Media Direct Partners, Incorporated, New York, NY; *U.S. Private*, pg. 726
Cosgrove, P., Mng. Dir.--Harvey Plant Limited, Bedworth, United Kingdom; *Int'l*, pg. 910
Costa, Massimo, Reg. Acct. Mng. Dir.--Young & Rubicam Italia, S.p.A., Milan, Italy; *U.S. Private*, pg. 1199
Costabella, Francesc, Gen. Mgr.--Caixa d'Estalvis de Catalunya, Barcelona, Spain; *Int'l*, pg. 249
Couchman, Richard, Mng. Dir.-VTEL Europe Ltd.--VTEL Corporation, Austin, TX; *U.S. Public*, pg. 1703
Couillard, Yves, Mng. Dir.--Packinox, Paris, France; *Int'l*, pg. 503
Courbon, Guy, Mng. Dir.--Bertrand Faure Sitztechnik GmbH & Co. KG, Stadthagen, Germany; *Int'l*, pg. 193
Courtier, Charles, Mng. Dir.-Media--Young & Rubicam Holdings Ltd., London, United Kingdom; *U.S. Private*, pg. 1199
Courtiere, Jean, Mng. Dir.--Givenchy S.A., Paris, France; *Int'l*, pg. 780
Cousins, John F., Mng. Dir.--Deep Sea Seals Ltd., Havant, United Kingdom; *Int'l*, pg. 1339
Cousins, John F., Mng. Dir.--John Cranes Marine International, Havant, United Kingdom; *Int'l*, pg. 1339
Covington, Howard, Mng. Dir.-London--Wasserstein Perella Group, Inc., New York, NY; *Int'l*, pg. 956
Cox, Barry, Mng. Dir.-U.K. Sls. & Mktg.--Waterford Wedgwood UK Plc, Stoke on Trent, United Kingdom; *Int'l*, pg. 1487
Cox, Pieter, Mng. Dir. & Chief Exec. Officer--Sasol Limited, Johannesburg, South Africa; *Int'l*, pg. 1196
Craig, William H., Asst. Mng. Dir.--Doctors Hospital of Shreveport, Shreveport, LA; *U.S. Public*, pg. 1697
Crail, Richard, Mng. Dir.--Aeroplex of Central Europe Ltd., Budapest, Hungary; *U.S. Public*, pg. 1006
Cramphorn, Alan, Mng. Dir.--TI Reynolds Rings Limited, Birmingham, United Kingdom; *Int'l*, pg. 1338
Crane, Anthony S., Mng. Dir.-Rapiscan UK--OSI Systems, Inc., Hawthorne, CA; *U.S. Public*, pg. 1208
Crassaris, Leonidas, Mng. Dir.--Rhone-Poulenc Hellas, Athens, Greece; *Int'l*, pg. 1113
Craven, Michael, Mng. Dir.--Market Access Limited, London, United Kingdom; *U.S. Public*, pg. 1225
Crawford, James E., V.P. & Mng. Dir.-Value Mngmt & Product R&D--Excel Industries, Inc., Elkhart, IN; *U.S. Public*, pg. 598
Crawford, Michael, Mng. Dir.-Mktg.--Ralston Purina Company, Saint Louis, MO; *U.S. Public*, pg. 1359
Crawford, Peter, Mng. Dir.--Willis Corroon North Limited, Sheffield, United Kingdom; *Int'l*, pg. 1503
Crean, Timothy, Mng. Dir.--Sifco Turbine Components, Ltd., Cork, Ireland; *U.S. Public*, pg. 1471
Creasman, Kenneth W., V.P. & Reg. Dir.-SC Johnson Comml. Markets North America--S.C. Johnson & Son, Inc., Racine, WI; *U.S. Private*, pg. 592
Crebs, C. Buck, Mng. Dir.-Europe--Brink's, Inc., Darien, CT; *U.S. Public*, pg. 1305
Creedy, Mark, Mng. Dir.-Chartwell Land--Kingfisher plc, London, United Kingdom; *Int'l*, pg. 733
Crehalet, Yves, Mng. Partner--Crehalet Pouget Poussielgues, Paris, France; *U.S. Private*, pg. 1152
Cresswell, J.C., Mng. Dir.--Sandiacre Screw Ltd., Nottingham, United Kingdom; *Int'l*, pg. 585
Crew, J. William, Mng. Dir.--Alcan Specialty Aerospace, Birmingham, United Kingdom; *Int'l*, pg. 51
Crewe, John, Mng. Dir.--American Express Europe Limited, London, United Kingdom; *U.S. Public*, pg. 74
Criadis, Michalis, Pres. & Mng. Dir.--Vitamin, Athens, Greece; *Int'l*, pg. 1377
Croasdale, Bill, V.P. & East Coast Mng. Dir.--Promotional Broadcast Services, New York, NY; *U.S. Private*, pg. 1166
Croasdale, Bill, Jr., V.P. & East Coast Mng. Dir.--Western Direct, New York, NY; *U.S. Private*, pg. 1166
Crocker, Nicholas, Mng. Dir.--Rhone-Poulenc Polska, Varsovie, Poland; *Int'l*, pg. 1113
Croe, Henri, Mng. Dir.--CINTA Compagnie Independante des Tabacs S.A., Brussels, Belgium; *Int'l*, pg. 1101
Croft, Edward S., III, Mng. Dir. & Dir.--The Robinson-Humphrey Company, Inc., Atlanta, GA; *U.S. Public*, pg. 1633
Crombez, Jean-Luc, Mng. Dir.--Kvaerner Pulping SA, Saint Germain-en-Laye, France; *Int'l*, pg. 768
Crompton, Bradley J., Mng. Dir.--Morgan Stanley Group Inc., New York, NY; *U.S. Public*, pg. 1132
Crook, David G., Mng. Dir.--Delta Circuit Protection & Controls Ltd., Birmingham, United Kingdom; *Int'l*, pg. 390
Crooks, Donald, Mng. Dir.--Lehman Brothers, New York, NY; *U.S. Public*, pg. 987
Crossland, James, Sr. V.P. & Dir.--GPC Government Policy Consultants (Federal), Ottawa, Canada; *U.S. Public*, pg. 1225
Croufer, Edouard, Dir. Gen.--UCB SA Pharma Sector, Braine-l'Alleud, Belgium; *Int'l*, pg. 1427
Crous, A., Chief Oper. Officer & Mng. Dir.--Hammerite Productos Especiales, Barcelona, Spain; *Int'l*, pg. 1501
Crowhurst, Geoff, Mng. Dir. & Dir.-Bldg. Services--Industrial Acoustics Company, Ltd., Staines, United Kingdom; *U.S. Public*, pg. 875
Crowley, Sean, Mng. Dir.-High Yield Fin.--Merrill Lynch & Co., Inc., New York, NY; *U.S. Public*, pg. 1097
Crozier, J., Mng. Dir.--Riley Advertising (London) Ltd., London, United Kingdom; *Int'l*, pg. 1117
Csomor, Laszlo, Mng. Dir.--EURO RSCG, Budapest, Hungary; *Int'l*, pg. 602
Cuadra, Gonzalo, Mng. Dir.--Chile Copper Ltd., London, United Kingdom; *Int'l*, pg. 303
Cubukcu, Aydin I., Mng. Dir.--Beko Elektronik A.S., Istanbul, Turkey; *Int'l*, pg. 741
Cuecos, Juan Antoinios, Mng. Dir.--Leo Burnett-Costa Rica, Barrio Francisco Peralta, Costa Rica; *U.S. Private*, pg. 185
Cuilhe, Michel, Deputy Mng. Dir.--Framatome Connectors International, Courbevoie, France; *Int'l*, pg. 503
Cuming, Pamela, Sr. Mng. Dir.-Corp. Mktg.--The Bear Stearns Companies Inc., New York, NY; *U.S. Public*, pg. 197
Cummings, P., Mng. Dir.--Hanimex Pty. Limited, Brookvale, Australia; *Int'l*, pg. 1115
Cunningham, S.M., Mng. Dir.--Interlaken Capital, Inc., Greenwich, CT; *U.S. Private*, pg. 567
Cunningham, Theodor R., Pres. & Mng. Dir.--Chrysler de Mexico S.A., Mexico, Mexico; *U.S. Public*, pg. 354
Curran, Josephine, Mng. Dir.--Lehman Brothers, New York, NY; *U.S. Public*, pg. 987
Curry, K.P., Mng. Dir.--R&H Australia Pty. Ltd., Melbourne, Australia; *Int'l*, pg. 681
Curtin, Paul C., Mng. Dir.--Stuart Entertainment, S.A. de C.V., Reynosa, Mexico; *U.S. Public*, pg. 1526
Cutts-Watson, Malcolm, Mng. Dir.--Willis Corroon Management Limited-Guernsey, Saint Peter Port, United Kingdom; *Int'l*, pg. 1503
Cyron, Alan J., Mng. Dir.--CBC-U.S.A Inc., Chicago, IL; *U.S. Public*, pg. 337
D'Epifanio, Luigi, Mng. Dir.--Johnson & Johnson Sihhi Malzeme Sanayi Ve Ticaret Ltd. Sti., Istanbul, Turkey; *U.S. Public*, pg. 931
d'Epinay, Thierry Lalive, Mng. Dir.-Corp. Tech. Innovation--Landis & Staefa AG, Zug, Switzerland; *Int'l*, pg. 800
Da Ronch, Mariano, Mng. Dir.--Gavino Sanna Associati, Milan, Italy; *U.S. Private*, pg. 304
da Silva, F.E., Mng. Dir.--Instituto Pasteur de Lisboa, Lisbon, Portugal; *U.S. Public*, pg. 81
Daboshi, Yoshikuni, Exec. Mng. Dir.--Kubota Corp., Osaka, Japan; *Int'l*, pg. 762
Daeppen, Hans-Ulrich, Mng. Dir.-Human Resources--Landis & Staefa AG, Zug, Switzerland; *Int'l*, pg. 800
Daffy, Paul, Mng. Dir.--Challenge Properties Limited, Auckland, New Zealand; *Int'l*, pg. 495
Dahl, Hans Ove, Mng. Dir.--Berendsen PMC A/S, Kokkedal, Denmark; *Int'l*, pg. 1284
Dahl, Lars Gorvell, Dir.--Kvaerner Fjellstrand (S) Pte Ltd., Hong Kong Representative Office, Happy Valley, Hong Kong; *Int'l*, pg. 767
Dahm, Jose, Mng. Dir.--Ares S.A., Rodange, Luxembourg; *Int'l*, pg. 79
Dahms, Christian, Chm. & Mng. Dir.--AON, Jauch & Huebener Gruppe, Hamburg, Germany; *U.S. Public*, pg. 118
Dahne, Helmut, Dr., Mng. Dir.--Rowohlt Verlag GmbH, Reinbek, Germany; *Int'l*, pg. 1478
Dalby, Glenn, Mng. Dir.--Gencor ACP Ltd., Leicester, United Kingdom; *U.S. Public*, pg. 705
Daliakopoulos, N.S., Mng. Dir.--Goodyear Hellas S.A.I.C., Athens, Greece; *U.S. Public*, pg. 753
Dalichook, Igar, Mng. Dir.--Reemtsma Cherkassy Tyutyunova Fabrika, Cherkassy, Ukraine; *Int'l*, pg. 1101
Dalle, Roger, Mng. Dir.--Bekaert Benelux N.V., Zwevegem, Belgium; *Int'l*, pg. 183
Dalrymple, Edwin A., Jr., Sr. Mng. Dir.-Private Client Grp.--Interstate/Johnson Lane Corporation, Charlotte, NC; *U.S. Public*, pg. 910
Dalzell, James, Mng. Dir.--Bridgeway Hospital, North Little Rock, AR; *U.S. Public*, pg. 1696
Danielsson, Ralf, Mgr. Dir.--Vitactiv AB, Askim, Sweden; *U.S. Public*, pg. 1536
Dantuma, Klaas, Mng. Dir.--Koninklijke Gazelle BV, Dieren, Netherlands; *Int'l*, pg. 394
Darouny, Roger, Mng. Dir.-Client Service--Targets-Leo Burnett Advertising, Jeddah, Saudi Arabia; *U.S. Private*, pg. 186
Darta, Andoko, Gen. Mgr.--Adwork! EURO RSCG Partnership, Jakarta, Indonesia; *Int'l*, pg. 602
Darwish, Mougahed, Mng. Dir.--ICB Ingenieurs Conseils, Marin, Switzerland; *Int'l*, pg. 1160
Darwish, Mougahed, Mng. Dir.--EM Microelectronic-Marin S.A., Marin, Switzerland; *Int'l*, pg. 1160
Darwish, Mougahed, Mng. Dir.--SMH Automobile AG, Bienne, Switzerland; *Int'l*, pg. 1161
Darwish, Raouf, Mng. Dir.--Darwish Consulting Engineers, Cairo, Egypt; *Int'l*, pg. 606
Dassing, Gunter, Mng. Dir.--AdPlus, Frankfurt/Main, Germany; *U.S. Private*, pg. 678
Daul, Pierre, Mng. Dir.--Jet Chandler International, Rungis, France; *Int'l*, pg. 560
Davaille, Jean-Pierre, Mng. Dir.--Janssen-Cilag S.A., Boulogne-Billancourt, France; *U.S. Public*, pg. 929
Davey, Graham, Reg. Mng. Dir.--DHL International (Singapore) Pte. Ltd., Singapore, Singapore; *U.S. Private*, pg. 302
David, Armel, Treas.--Promodes SA, Mondeville, France; *Int'l*, pg. 1071
Davidson, Ian, Mng. Dir.--OCLI Optical Coatings Ltd., Dunfermline, United Kingdom; *U.S. Public*, pg. 1227
Davidson, Neil, Mng. Dir.-Dairy--Northern Foods plc, Hull, United Kingdom; *Int'l*, pg. 967
Davidson, Patrick G., Mng. Partner--Black & Veatch, Kansas City, MO; *U.S. Private*, pg. 146
Davie, Anne, Mng. Dir.--Griffin Bacal Publicidad, Mexico, Mexico; *U.S. Private*, pg. 480
Davieau, Robert, Sr. V.P. & Mng. Dir.--The Corporate Communications Group, Whippany, NJ; *U.S. Private*, pg. 276
Davies, A.G., Mng. Dir.--Bonded Fibre Fabric Ltd., Bridgwater, United Kingdom; *Int'l*, pg. 798
Davies, Edward C., Mng. Dir.-Australia--Moore Corporation Limited, Toronto, Canada; *Int'l*, pg. 888
Davies, Peter, Mng. Dir.-Middle East & Central Europe--Tamra DMB&B, Dubai, United Arab Emirates; *U.S. Private*, pg. 305
Davies, Philip, Mng. Dir.--Allied Domecq Leisure, Bourne, United Kingdom; *Int'l*, pg. 63
Davis, Alan, Mng. Dir.-U.K.--MDIS Group plc, Hemel Hempstead, United Kingdom; *Int'l*, pg. 826
Davis, Geoff, Mng. Dir.--Bomford Turner Limited, Evesham, United Kingdom; *U.S. Public*, pg. 35
Davis, Homer, V.P. & Mng. Dir.--National Distributing Co., Inc., Albany, GA; *U.S. Private*, pg. 781
Davis, Leon A., Mng. Dir. & Chief Executive--CRA Limited, Melbourne, Australia; *Int'l*, pg. 1119
Davis, Nigel, Ph.D., Mng. Dir.--Innovir (UK) LTD, Cambridge, United Kingdom; *U.S. Public*, pg. 1703
Davis, Paula, Mng. Dir.--Triclinica Inc., New York, NY; *U.S. Private*, pg. 679
Davis, Philip C., V.P. & Mng. Dir.-China--Anheuser-Busch International, Inc., Saint Louis, MO; *U.S. Public*, pg. 114
Davis, Timothy, Principal Mng. Dir.--Allan Schneider Associates, Southampton, NY; *U.S. Private*, pg. 971
Davis, Timothy G., Mng. Parnter--Allan Schneider Associates, Southampton, NY; *U.S. Private*, pg. 971
Davison, Guy, Mng. Dir.--Ross Systems Europe N.V., Zaventem, Belgium; *U.S. Public*, pg. 1406
Dawes, Alan, Mng. Dir.--General Combustion Ltd., Billingshurst, United Kingdom; *U.S. Public*, pg. 705
Dawson, George, Mng. Dir. & Dir.-Aviation & Engrng.--Industrial Acoustics Company, Ltd., Staines, United Kingdom; *U.S. Public*, pg. 875
Day, Gordon, Exec. Dir.--First Brands Africa (Pty) Ltd., Johannesburg, South Africa; *U.S. Public*, pg. 627
Day, L. S., Mng. Dir.--Barlows Equipment Co., Sandton, South Africa; *Int'l*, pg. 167
Dayller, Jose, Mng. Dir.--Chilebras Metais Ltda., Sao Paulo, Brazil; *Int'l*, pg. 303
De Blieck, Benoit, Gen. Mgr.-Intl. Affairs--Bernheim-Comofi, Brussels, Belgium; *Int'l*, pg. 562
de Blieck, Pieter, Mng. Dir.--Kredietbank (Nederland) N.V., Rotterdam, Netherlands; *Int'l*, pg. 761
de Boissieu, Ghislain, Mng. Dir.--Chapelle Darblay Grand Couronne, Grand Couronne, France; *Int'l*, pg. 1428
de Bolmann, Yves, Sr. Mng. Dir.-Corp. Coverage U.K.--Bankers Trust New York Corporation, New York, NY; *U.S. Public*, pg. 185
De Bosschere, M., Mng. Dir.--NRG Belgium S.A., Brussels, Belgium; *Int'l*, pg. 1116
de Broglie, Frederic, Mng. Dir.--3i France, Neuilly, France; *Int'l*, pg. 1386
de Bruijn, Peter, Mng. Dir.-Sybron Chemie Nederland B.V.--Sybron Chemicals Inc., Birmingham, NJ; *U.S. Public*, pg. 1544
de Carvalho, Oswaldo, Mng. Dir.--Esselte Meto Ind. e. Com. Ltda., Sao Paulo, Brazil; *Int'l*, pg. 461
de Charette, J.R, Mng. Dir.--Gan Portugal Seguros, Lisbon, Portugal; *Int'l*, pg. 564
de Crook, Roger, Mng. Dir.-Oper. & Devel.--STAHLwerke Bremen GmbH, Bremen, Germany; *Int'l*, pg. 79
de David-Beauregard, Arnauld, Chief Oper. Officer & Mng. Dir.--Citroen Hispana S.A., Pontevedra, Spain; *Int'l*, pg. 1020
de Decker, D., Mng. Dir.--Getinge-D.S.E. NV, Antwerp, Belgium; *Int'l*, pg. 551
de Graaf, Cees, Mng. Dir.--Anacomp (Nederland) B.V., Almere-Haven, Netherlands; *U.S. Public*, pg. 107
de Groot, A., Mng. Dir.--Wolters Kluwer Trade Publishing, Utrecht, Netherlands; *Int'l*, pg. 1513
de Groot, C.A., Mng. Dir.--Big Balloon bv, Heemstede, Netherlands; *Int'l*, pg. 1445
de Jonge, M.W., Mng. Dir.--Fisher-Price Spielwaren GmbH, Bruhl, Germany; *U.S. Public*, pg. 1058
de Jons, C., Mng. Dir.--Industrial Pharmaceutical Products Division, Delft, Netherlands; *Int'l*, pg. 1142

de Keghel, Philippe, Mng. Dir.--Banque Internationale a Luxembourg BIL (Suisse) S.A., Lausanne, Switzerland; *Int'l*, pg. 162

De Keyser, Jean-Charles, Mng. Dir.--Bel RTL, Brussels, Belgium; *Int'l*, pg. 561

de Klerk, Bram, Mng. Dir.--Natref, Sasolburg, South Africa; *Int'l*, pg. 1197

De Knijf, Alfons, Mng. Dir.--Bekaert-Tinsley, Hemiksem, Belgium; *Int'l*, pg. 183

De Knoop, Michel, Mng. Dir.--Union de Banques Congolaises, Kinshasa, Congo; *Int'l*, pg. 149

de Kraker, Peter, Mng. Dir.--Ahold Finance Company (Nederlandse Antillen) NV, Curacao, Netherlands Antilles; *Int'l*, pg. 750

De Kroon, Peter, Mng. Dir.--Projecta B.V., Weert, Netherlands; *U.S. Private*, pg. 306

de la Vaissiere, Pierre Emmanuel, Bus. Mgr.--Devarrieux Villaret, Paris, France; *Int'l*, pg. 600

de Larminat, Pierre, Mng. Dir.--LM/Young & Rubicam, Nantes, France; *U.S. Private*, pg. 1199

de Looze, S., Mng. Dir.--Scott Western Ltd., Mansfield, United Kingdom; *Int'l*, pg. 552

de Murville, A. Couve, Mng. Dir.--Van Leeuwen Tubes SA, Chalette-sur-Loing, France; *Int'l*, pg. 1450

de Pinedo, Javier, Mng. Dir.-Generation--Iberdrola, S.A., Bilbao, Spain; *Int'l*, pg. 657

de Pou, Venancia, Mng. Dir.--Leo Burnett Inc., Santo Domingo, Dominican Republic; *U.S. Private*, pg. 185

de Pracomtal, Henri, Mng. Dir.--Hine U.K., London, United Kingdom; *Int'l*, pg. 782

de Ries, P.A.C., Mng. Dir.--Droste B.V., Vaassen, Netherlands; *Int'l*, pg. 243

De Risi, Frank, Mng. Dir.--Dun & Bradstreet Ltd., Dublin, Ireland; *U.S. Public*, pg. 505

de Ruijter, S.C.M., Mng. Dir.--Phenix Aluminium S.A., Ivoz-Ramet, Belgium; *Int'l*, pg. 755

de Ruiter, Leslie, Mng. Dir.--Sunrise Medical B.V., Nieuwegein, Netherlands; *U.S. Public*, pg. 1536

De Sauvage, Marc, Mng. Dir.--Bekaert Engineering, Zwevegem, Belgium; *Int'l*, pg. 183

de Schutter, W., Dr., Mng. Dir.--Wuestenrot Finance B.V., Amsterdam, Netherlands; *Int'l*, pg. 1514

de Silva, Harinda, Ph.D., Mng. Dir.--Analytic TSA Global Asset Management Inc., Los Angeles, CA; *U.S. Public*, pg. 1672

De Sutter, W., Mng. Dir.--S.A. Brother International (Belgium) N.V., Brussels, Belgium; *Int'l*, pg. 229

de Tinguy, Ch., Mng. Dir. & Gen. Mgr.--Gan Italia S.p.A., Rome, Italy; *Int'l*, pg. 564

De Vicq, Arnod, Mng. Dir.--154 Testa, Brussels, Belgium; *Int'l*, pg. 1377

de Villelongue, Thierry, Mng. Dir.--PT Sagita Dumez, Jakarta, Indonesia; *Int'l*, pg. 823

de Villelongue, Thierry, Mng. Dir.--Dumez-GTM Jakarta, Jakarta, Indonesia; *Int'l*, pg. 823

de Villiers, D.J.J., Chief Oper. Officer & Mng. Dir.--Sasol Oil (Pty) Ltd., Randburg, South Africa; *Int'l*, pg. 1197

de Vries, Max, Mng. Dir.--Mecatool AG, Flawil, Switzerland; *Int'l*, pg. 489

de Witt, W., Mng. Dir.--Uitgeverij Spaarnestad bv, Haarlem, Netherlands; *Int'l*, pg. 1445

De Witt, Marianne, Mng. Dir.--Arte Film, Turin, Italy; *Int'l*, pg. 1377

De-Hui, Yu, Mng. Dir.--Burgmann Shanghai Ltd., Shanghai, China; *Int'l*, pg. 234

DeBacker, D., Mng. Dir.--Mobrey SA-NV, Brussels, Belgium; *Int'l*, pg. 854

Dedehayir, Fevzi, Mng. Dir.--Valmet-Boustead Pty. Ltd., Braybrook, Australia; *Int'l*, pg. 1449

Deer, P. W., Reg. Mng. Dir.--National Westminster Bank Plc, Hong Kong, Hong Kong; *Int'l*, pg. 911

DeFay, C., Mng. Dir.--Ascom HPF SA, Bonneville, France; *Int'l*, pg. 87

Defline, Louis, Chief Exec. Officer & Mng. Dir.--ECIA-Equipments Et Composants Pour L'industrie Automobile, Audincourt, France; *Int'l*, pg. 1021

Degos, Philippe, Mng. Dir.--Constructora Dumez de Chile, Santiago, Chile; *Int'l*, pg. 823

Degos, Philippe, Mng. Dir.--Dumez-GTM, Buenos Aires, Argentina; *Int'l*, pg. 823

Deguchi, Toshihide, Mng. Dir.-Production Engrng.--Mazda Motor Corporation, Hiroshima, Japan; *Int'l*, pg. 849

DeGurian, Alex, Mgr.-LDA Central Area--Team One Advertising, El Segundo, CA; *U.S. Public*, pg. 1422

DeGuzman, Bobby, Mng. Dir.--Woodward-Clyde International, Manila, Philippines; *U.S. Public*, pg. 1658

Deignan, David, Dir.-Mktg.--Aaron's Rental Purchase, Atlanta, GA; *U.S. Public*, pg. 12

del Olmo Alonso, Carlos, Mng. Dir.--Igemisa, Madrid, Spain; *Int'l*, pg. 608

DeLagrange, Lawrence, Mng. Dir.--Society Francais Pour Le Development de la Porcelaine d'Art, Paris, France; *U.S. Public*, pg. 1609

Delanoe, Jacques, Co-Mgr.--Etoile Bleue, Nantes, France; *Int'l*, pg. 600

Delanoe, Jacques, Assoc. Gen. Mgr.--Etoile Bleue, Rennes, France; *Int'l*, pg. 600

Delanoe, Jacques, Mgr.--Etoile Bleue, Tours, France; *Int'l*, pg. 600

Delbard, Francois, Mng. Dir.--Georges Delbard S.A., Paris, France; *Int'l*, pg. 780

Delcour, Gerard, Mng. Dir.--Cosmeurop S.A., Strasbourg, France; *Int'l*, pg. 295

Deleau, Michel, Dir. Gen.-Lending Opers. Non-EEC Countries--European Investment Bank, Luxembourg, Luxembourg; *Int'l*, pg. 465

DeLeo, Richard, Mng. Dir.-Loan Admin.--Countrywide Home Loans Inc., Pasadena, CA; *U.S. Public*, pg. 452

Dell, Michael, Mng. Dir.--Beldray Limited, Bilston, United Kingdom; *U.S. Public*, pg. 968

Dellis, Fredy, Mng. Dir.-Europe--Resort Condominiums International, Indianapolis, IN; *U.S. Public*, pg. 322

Delorme, Jean-Louis, Mng. Dir.--Pochentong Airport Construction JV, Phnom Penh, Kampuchea; *Int'l*, pg. 823

Delvaux, S., Mng. Dir.--S.C. Corporations Efficiency Growth Through Information Systems CEGIS, Ougree, Belgium; *Int'l*, pg. 301

Demetrakakis, Demetris, Chief Fin. Officer--Geo-Young & Rubicam, Athens, Greece; *U.S. Private*, pg. 1199

Dempsey, William F., V.P. & Mng. Dir.-Valvoline Intl.--Valvoline Company, Lexington, KY; *U.S. Public*, pg. 139

den Toom, J.W.R., Mng. Dir.--Corporate New Business Development Div., Delft, Netherlands; *Int'l*, pg. 1142

Dench, Robert Graham, Chm. Bd. & Mng. Dir.--Barclays Insurance Brokers International Ltd., London, United Kingdom; *Int'l*, pg. 164

Dengler, Jean-Michel, Mng. Dir.--Stahlwerk Thuringen GmbH, Unterwellenborn, Germany; *Int'l*, pg. 79

Denholm, John, Mng. Dir.--The Leith Agency, Edinburgh, United Kingdom; *U.S. Private*, pg. 1152

Dening, A.R.J., Mng. Dir.--Jaguar Cars Finance Limited, Coventry, United Kingdom; *Int'l*, pg. 910

DeNiro, Mark J., Mng. Dir.--TL Ventures, Wayne, PA; *U.S. Public*, pg. 1424

Dennis, Andrew, Mng. Dir.--Willis Faber (Underwriting Management) Limited, Ipswich, United Kingdom; *Int'l*, pg. 1504

Dennis, Barry, Mng. Dir.--EMAP Pursuit Publishing, Peterborough, United Kingdom; *Int'l*, pg. 451

Dennis, Chris, Mng. Dir.--LifeScan Canada Ltd., Burnaby, Canada; *U.S. Public*, pg. 931

Denyer, Peter, Mng. Dir.--Vision Group plc, Edinburgh, United Kingdom; *U.S. Public*, pg. 519

Depiereux, D., Mng. Dir.--Stamco-Depiereux GMBH, Dueren, Germany; *U.S. Public*, pg. 1124

Depiereux, Gunter, Mng. Dir.--Busch Gmbh, Duren, Germany; *U.S. Public*, pg. 1124

Derby, Crispin, Mng. Dir.--LGC Communications Ltd., London, United Kingdom; *Int'l*, pg. 451

Derge, Klaus, V.P. & Mng. Dir.--OCLI Optical Coating Laboratory GmbH, Reinheim, Germany; *U.S. Public*, pg. 1227

Derham, Ken, Mng. Dir., Plenum Publishing Company Ltd.--Plenum Publishing Company, Ltd., London, United Kingdom; *U.S. Public*, pg. 1311

Derrick, K.G., Dir. & Gen. Mgr.--Hamworthy Pumps and Compressors Limited, Poole, United Kingdom; *Int'l*, pg. 1065

Derrick, K.G., Mng. Dir.--Hamworthy Marine Limited, Poole, United Kingdom; *Int'l*, pg. 1065

Desmarais, Pierre, V.P. & Mng. Dir.--WF Corroon-Ontario, Toronto, Canada; *Int'l*, pg. 1502

Desmazes, F., Mng. Dir. & Gen. Mgr.--Gan Espana Seguros Generales y Vida, Madrid, Spain; *Int'l*, pg. 564

Desmazes, F., Mng. Dir.--Uniseguros Vida y Pensiones (UNIVYP), Madrid, Spain; *Int'l*, pg. 565

Devaney, Steve, Mng. Dir.--Kintetsu Euro Transport Ltd., Slough, United Kingdom; *Int'l*, pg. 735

Devita, Robert J., Exec. Dir.--Marshfield Clinic, Marshfield, WI; *U.S. Private*, pg. 708

Devos, Doug, Sr. V.P. & Mng. Dir.-Amway N. America--Amway Corporation, Ada, MI; *U.S. Private*, pg. 69

Dew, Larry M., Jr., V.P. & Mng. Dir.--Mortgage Guaranty Insurance Corporation, Milwaukee, WI; *U.S. Public*, pg. 1026

Dewar-Durie, A. M., Mng. Dir.--Wm. Teacher & Sons Limited, Dumbarton, United Kingdom; *Int'l*, pg. 63

Dewar, Bob, Mng. Dir.--Activision UK, Reading, United Kingdom; *U.S. Public*, pg. 17

Dewey, R., Mng. Dir.--Penny & Giles Position Sensors Ltd., Christchurch, United Kingdom; *Int'l*, pg. 207

Dhaere, G., Mng. Dir.--Eurasem B.V., Nijmegen, Netherlands; *Int'l*, pg. 1133

Dhanvarjor, Opart, Mng. Dir.--Siam Furukawa Co., Ltd., Bangkok, Thailand; *Int'l*, pg. 1238

di Pace, Elio, Chief Exec. Officer & Mng. Dir.--Eurocom Concato di Pace Srl, Milan, Italy; *Int'l*, pg. 603

Diamond, Christopher S., Mng. Dir.--Mount Snow Resort, Mount Snow, VT; *U.S. Private*, pg. 61

Diaz-Gonzalez, Antonio, Mng. Dir.--Repsol Derivados, Madrid, Spain; *Int'l*, pg. 1104

Diaz, Alberto, Mng. Dir.--McCormick de Venezuela, C.A., Caracas, Venezuela; *U.S. Public*, pg. 1067

Diaz, Armando, Mng. Dir.--Talleres Uribarri, S.L., Bilbao, Spain; *U.S. Public*, pg. 1536

Dibie, Elaine, Mgr.-Mktg. & Special Events--Shurfine International, Inc., Northlake, IL; *U.S. Private*, pg. 997

Dickinson, S., Mng. Dir.--P.C. Henderson Limited, Romford, United Kingdom; *Int'l*, pg. 615

Diehl, R. U., Mng. Dir.--Glaxo Wellcome GmbH, Namburg, Germany; *Int'l*, pg. 553

Diekmann, Michael, Mng. Dir.--Allianz Asia Pacific, Singapore, Singapore; *Int'l*, pg. 59

Dieter, Polt, Mng. Dir.--Hermann Wangner, GmbH, Reutlingen, Germany; *Int'l*, pg. 1418

Dietlin, Francois, Mng. Dir.--Sulzer del Peru S.A., Lima, Peru; *Int'l*, pg. 1306

Dietrich, E., Mng. Dir.--Merck Balzers AG, Balzers, Liechtenstein; *Int'l*, pg. 997

Dietzsch, Dr. Michael, Mng. Dir.-Mktg.--Bitburger Brauerei Th. Simon GmbH, Bitburg, Germany; *Int'l*, pg. 197

DiGiovanni, Rico, Sr. V.P. & Mng. Dir.--IMPACT/FCB, Toronto, Canada; *U.S. Private*, pg. 389

Dilissen, Theo, Mng. Dir.--ISS Airport Services S.A.-N.V., Brussels, Belgium; *Int'l*, pg. 657

Dilissen, Theo, Mng. Dir.--ISS Healthcare S.A.-N.V., Brussels, Belgium; *Int'l*, pg. 657

Dilissen, Theo, Mng. Dir.--ISS Luxembourg S.A., Luxembourg, Luxembourg; *Int'l*, pg. 657

Dimou, Aphrodite, Mng. Dir.--Progress Advertising, Athens, Greece; *Int'l*, pg. 470

Dinaman, Saya, Mng. Dir.--Middle East Bank Kenya Ltd., Nairobi, Kenya; *Int'l*, pg. 548

Dingle, P.J., Mng. Dir.--Esso Exploration and Production UK Limited, London, United Kingdom; *U.S. Public*, pg. 602

DiNicolangelo, Nicholas, Mng. Dir.--Lakeside Enterprises, Inc., West Orange, NJ; *U.S. Private*, pg. 120

Diniz, Pedro, Fin. Dir.--Young & Rubicam (Portugal), Lisbon, Portugal; *U.S. Private*, pg. 1199

Dinmore, Fred, Mng. Dir.--Ark Life Assurance Company Limited, Dublin, Ireland; *Int'l*, pg. 64

DiNovi, Anthony J., Mng. Dir.--Thomas H. Lee Co., Boston, MA; *U.S. Private*, pg. 658

Dirkes, Christiane, Mng. Dir.--Shandwick Lutz Bohme Public Relations GmbH, Hamburg, Germany; *Int'l*, pg. 1227

Ditner, Anton, Acting Mng. Dir.--Becker, Karlsbad, Germany; *U.S. Public*, pg. 787

Dittrich, Reinhard, Gen. Counsel & Mng. Dir.-Insurance--Julius Meinl AG, Vienna, Austria; *Int'l*, pg. 856

Dixon, J.R., Mng. Dir.--Air UK (Leisure) Ltd., Stansted, United Kingdom; *Int'l*, pg. 39

Dixon, Peter, Mng. Dir.--CNT International, Uxbridge, United Kingdom; *U.S. Public*, pg. 421

Dixon, Peter, Mng. Dir.--Ultra GmbH, Hilden, Germany; *U.S. Public*, pg. 421

Djergian, John, Mng. Dir. & Chief Fin. Officer--Kovel Kresser & Partners, Santa Monica, CA; *U.S. Private*, pg. 634

Dobbin, Joe, Mng. Dir.--Javelin/Young & Rubicam, Dublin, Ireland; *U.S. Private*, pg. 1199

Doerflinger, Sue, Mng. Dir.--CPAC Equipment Division, Leicester, NY; *U.S. Public*, pg. 282

Doherty, Hugh, Chief Fin. Officer--Conquest Europe S.A.R.L., Neuilly-sur-Seine, France; *Int'l*, pg. 1484

Dohi, Masao, Mng. Dir.--ORIX Maritime Corporation, Tokyo, Japan; *Int'l*, pg. 1009

Doi, Hisato, Mng. Dir.--Sumitomo Life International (UK) Limited, London, United Kingdom; *Int'l*, pg. 1315

Doi, Hisato, Mng. Dir.--Sumitomo Life Realty (U.K.) Limited, London, United Kingdom; *Int'l*, pg. 1315

Doi, Tsuguo, Mng. Dir.--Nippon Express Hawaii Inc., Honolulu, HI; *Int'l*, pg. 934

Dokter, Ernst, Mng. Dir.--Caliqua AG, Basel, Switzerland; *Int'l*, pg. 1306

Dolan, Paul E., III, Exec. V.P. & Mng. Dir.-Fetzer Winery--Brown-Forman Beverages Worldwide, Louisville, KY; *U.S. Public*, pg. 261

Doman, Nico, Mng. Dir.-Engrng. Services Div.--Sasol Technology (Pty) Ltd., Sasolburg, South Africa; *Int'l*, pg. 1197

Doman, Nico, Mng. Dir.--Sasol Engineering Division, Secunda, South Africa; *Int'l*, pg. 1197

Domeyer, Debra, Exec. Dir.-Network Computing--Countrywide Funding Corporation, Pasadena, CA; *U.S. Public*, pg. 453

Don, Elliot, Dir.-Mdsg.--Duty Free International, Inc., Ridgefield, CT; *Int'l*, pg. 103

Donaghy, Jim, Mng. Dir.--Aston Martin Lagonda of North America, Inc., Mahwah, NJ; *U.S. Public*, pg. 664

Donnelly, Dennis J., Sr. Mng. Dir.--McDonald & Company Investments, Inc., Cleveland, OH; *U.S. Public*, pg. 1068

Donohue, Brendan, Mng. Dir.--BIAM Australia Pty Ltd., Melbourne, Australia; *Int'l*, pg. 153

Doolittle, Dennis, Mng. Dir.--Autologic Information International, Inc., Oakville, Canada; *U.S. Public*, pg. 1724

Dorau, Siegfried, Mng. Dir.--ISS Servisystem GmbH, Hamburg, Germany; *Int'l*, pg. 657

Dorey, Ray C., Mng. Dir.-Northern Territories--John Crane EAA, Slough, United Kingdom; *Int'l*, pg. 1338

Dorfs, Joachim, Mng. Dir.--VDI-Verlag GmbH, Dusseldorf, Germany; *Int'l*, pg. 1479

Doria, C., Mng. Dir.--Distribuidores Concesionarios S.A., Bilbao, Spain; *Int'l*, pg. 615

Dorkhom, G.H., Mng. Dir.--Contraves Inc., Pittsburgh, PA; *Int'l*, pg. 998

Dorman, B.J., Mng. Dir.--Nihon Timken K.K., Yokohama, Japan; *U.S. Public*, pg. 1617

Dornhaus, Ulrich, Mng. Dir.--Buckau-Walther AG, Essen, Germany; *Int'l*, pg. 516

Dornia, M., Dr., Mng. Dir.--Haniel Baustoff-Industrie GmbH, Duisburg, Germany; *Int'l*, pg. 592

Dorsey, Patrick B., Mng. Dir.--Tiffany & Co. Mexico, S.A. de C.V., Mexico, Mexico; *U.S. Public*, pg. 1609

Dorward, Colette, Mng. Dir.--Smythe Dorward Lambert, London, United Kingdom; *U.S. Public*, pg. 1225

Dorward, Don, Exec. V.P. & Mng. Dir.-San Francisco--Grey Advertising Inc., Western Div., Los Angeles, CA; *U.S. Public*, pg. 764

Dorward, Don, Exec. V.P. & Mng. Dir.--Grey Advertising Inc., San Francisco, CA; *U.S. Public*, pg. 764

Dory, Jerry, Mng. Dir.--Tejas Western Outlet, Fort Worth, TX; *U.S. Private*, pg. 681

Dotti, Pietro, Mng. Dir.-Torino--Armando Testa S.p.A, Rome, Italy; *Int'l*, pg. 1377

Doty, Jerry, Mng. Dir.--Luskeys Western Stores, Inc., Fort Worth, TX; *U.S. Private*, pg. 681

Dougherty, Peter, Mng. Dir.--PMI Motion Technologies Div., Commack, NY; *U.S. Public*, pg. 965

Dournel, Patrick, Mng. Dir.--Dumez-GTM, Hanoi, Vietnam; *Int'l*, pg. 823

Dovits, Ludwig, Mng. Dir.-Mktg.--Julius Meinl AG, Vienna, Austria; *Int'l*, pg. 856

Dow, Kevin D., Mng. Dir.--Health-Mor B.V., Rotterdam, Netherlands; *U.S. Public*, pg. 771

Dow, Stephen, Mng. Dir.--Cyclam SA, Amiens, France; *Int'l*, pg. 1339

Dowd, Peter, Mng. Dir.--Bank of Ireland, Frankfurt, Germany; *Int'l*, pg. 153

Dowling, Roderick A., Mng. Dir., Dir.-Corp. Fin. & Dir.--The Robinson-Humphrey Company, Inc., Atlanta, GA; *U.S. Public*, pg. 1633

Dowling, Steve, Mng. Dir.--Meggit Mobrey Ltd., Slough, United Kingdom; *Int'l*, pg. 853

Downie, Mike, Mng. Dir.--BICC Cables Limited, Chester, United Kingdom; *Int'l*, pg. 120

Doyle, P., Mng. Dir.--Coutts & Co (Guernsey) Limited, Saint Peter Port, United Kingdom; *Int'l*, pg. 910

Doyle, P., Mng. Dir.--NatWest International Trust Corporation (Guensey) Limited, Saint Peter Port, United Kingdom; *Int'l*, pg. 911

Doyle, Patrick, Mng. Dir.--Gunnebo Ireland Ltd., Dublin, Ireland; *Int'l*, pg. 578
Drake, Robin A., Mng. Dir.--Derby Industries (Pty.) Ltd., Sandton, South Africa; *Int'l*, pg. 394
Dreibelbis, Cindy, Mng. Dir.--R&R Advertising, Las Vegas, NV; *U.S. Private*, pg. 902
Driesens, Doeke, Mng. Dir.--Iggesund Paper & Board Service B.V., Maarssen, Netherlands; *Int'l*, pg. 886
Driver, Frank L., IV, Mng. Dir.--Irish Driver-Harris Co., Ltd., Walkinstown, Ireland; *U.S. Public*, pg. 530
Droessler, Carol, Mng. Dir.-Human Resources--American Automobile Association, Heathrow, FL; *U.S. Private*, pg. 50
Drolet, Gerry, Mng. Dir.--Barringer Asia-Pacific, Kuala Lumper, Malaysia; *U.S. Public*, pg. 192
Druitt, R.J., Mng. Dir.--Queensland Alumina Limited, Brisbane, Australia; *Int'l*, pg. 52
Druitt, R.J., Mng. Dir.--Queensland Alumina Limited, Brisbane, Australia; *U.S. Public*, pg. 1063
Dszynski, Waldemar, Mng. Dir.--Market Link, Warsaw, Poland; *U.S. Private*, pg. 1062
du Bois, G.B., Mng. Dir.--Spadel SA, Brussels, Belgium; *Int'l*, pg. 1287
Duailibi, Roberto, Mng. Partner--DPZ-Duailibi, Petit, Zaragoza, Propaganda S.A., Sao Paulo, Brazil; *Int'l*, pg. 352
Dubbeling, Ph., Mng. Dir.--P.T. Ballast Indonesia Construction, Jakarta, Indonesia; *Int'l*, pg. 134
Duchaussoy, Elisabeth, Gen. Mgr.--Unicom, Rennes, France; *Int'l*, pg. 601
Duckert, Jan, Mng. Dir.--Wibroe, Duckert & Partners, Copenhagen, Denmark; *U.S. Private*, pg. 678
Duclayan, Gina, Mng. Editor-Today's Science On File--Facts on File News Services, New York, NY; *U.S. Public*, *pg. 1327*
Ducos, Georges, Mng. Dir.--Siebret, Redon, France; *Int'l*, pg. 192
Dudack, Gail M., Mng. Dir. & Chief Equity Strategist--UBS Securities LLC, New York, NY; *Int'l*, pg. 1440
Duderstaedt, Hans, Mng. Dir.--Wuestenrot Lebensversicherungs-AG, Ludwigsburg, Germany; *Int'l*, pg. 1514
Dudley, Glenn, Mng. Dir.--Metal Manufactures Limited, Sydney, Australia; *Int'l*, pg. 120
Dueholm, John, Mng. Dir.--ISS Rengoringsservice, Copenhagen, Denmark; *Int'l*, pg. 656
Duff, Philip, Chief Fin. Officer & Mng. Dir.--Morgan Stanley Group Inc., New York, NY; *U.S. Public*, pg. 1132
Duffy, B.C., Mng. Dir.--Guinness Northern Ireland Limited, Belfast, United Kingdom; *Int'l*, pg. 412
Duffy, Gary, Mng. Dir.-Europe--Power Conversion, Boston, MA; *U.S. Public*, pg. 422
Duffy, Thomas J., Mng. Dir.--Fiduciary Trust International Asia Limited, Hong Kong, Hong Kong; *U.S. Public*, pg. 621
Dugan, Alan H., Mng. Dir.-Health & Welfare--Towers Perrin, New York, NY; *U.S. Private*, pg. 1093
Duhne, Jaap M., Mng. Dir.--Esselte Meto BV, Nieuwegein, Netherlands; *Int'l*, pg. 461
Duley, Francois, Mng. Dir.-Intl.--Groupe SEB, Ecueille, France; *Int'l*, pg. 568
Dumas, Michele, Deputy Mng. Dir.-Production--Hermes International, Paris, France; *Int'l*, pg. 617
DuMont-Corvino, Desiree, Mng. Dir.--Media Incorporated, New York, NY; *U.S. Private*, pg. 726
DuMont-Corvino, Desiree, Mng. Dir.--Media Direct Partners, Incorporated, New York, NY; *U.S. Private*, pg. 726
Duncan, Ian A., Deputy Chm. & Mng. Dir.-Fin.--Tomkins PLC, London, United Kingdom; *Int'l*, pg. 1395
Dundon, Peter, Oper. Group Leader--Woodward-Clyde, Milton, Australia; *U.S. Public*, pg. 1657
Dunn, Al, Chief Exec. Officer & Mng. Dir.--McDonald's System of New Zealand Ltd., Freeman's Bay, New Zealand; *U.S. Public*, pg. 1069
Dunn, Bill, Mng. Dir.--BMC Software (Australia) Pty. Ltd., Hawthorn, Australia; *U.S. Public*, pg. 162
Dunne, Harry, Mng. Dir.--TFM, Middlesbrough, United Kingdom; *Int'l*, pg. 452
Dupont, Bertrand, Mng. Dir.-Fin.--Groupe SEB, Ecueille, France; *Int'l*, pg. 568
Dupont, Francis, Mng. Dir.--McCain Espana S.A. (Spain), Burgos, Spain; *Int'l*, pg. 850
Duquemin, Philip, Mng. Dir.--Gestetner Asia Pacific Limited, Saint Sampson, United Kingdom; *Int'l*, pg. 1114
Durand-Reville, Blaise, Dir.-Intl. Affairs--Promodes SA, Mondeville, France; *Int'l*, pg. 1071
Durant, Eric, Sr. Mng. Dir.-Investor Rels.--Bankers Trust New York Corporation, New York, NY; *U.S. Public*, pg. 185
Durcan, Kelly, Mng. Dir.--Partners & Shevack Public Relations, New York, NY; *U.S. Private*, pg. 842
Dusenberry, Philip B., Vice Chm. & Dir.--BBDO Worldwide Inc., New York, NY; *U.S. Public*, pg. 1223
Duvall, Henry W., Jr., V.P. & Mng. Dir.--Mortgage Guaranty Insurance Corporation, Milwaukee, WI; *U.S. Public*, pg. 1026
Dworak, Peter, Mng. Dir.--Janssen/Cilag Pharmaceutica GmbH, Vienna, Austria; *U.S. Public*, pg. 929
Dworak, Peter, Dr., Mgr. Dir.--Janssen/Cilag G.m.b.H., Vienna, Austria; *U.S. Public*, pg. 929
Dyer, Chris, Chief Oper. Officer--Rhone-Poulenc Danmark A/S, Soeborg, Denmark; *Int'l*, pg. 1112
Dykstra, J.D., Mng. Dir.--LASMO Mineraria SpA, Rome, Italy; *Int'l*, pg. 804
Dyrnes, J.H., Mng. Dir.--Uni-Cardan Norge A/S, Vestby, Norway; *Int'l*, pg. 536
Dysche, David, Mngng. Dir.--Arthur D. Little, Inc., New York, NY; *U.S. Private*, pg. 670
Dytrich, W., Mng. Dir.--GKN Service-Austria GmbH, Vienna, Austria; *Int'l*, pg. 536
Eales, John C., Mng. Dir.--McCormick Glentham (Pty), Midrand, South Africa; *U.S. Public*, pg. 1067
Easton, M., Mng. Dir.-Facilities Mngmt.--Babcock International Group PLC, Amersham, United Kingdom; *Int'l*, pg. 130
Eatherley, P.C., Mng. Dir.--Tate & Lyle Specialty Sweeteners, Reading, United Kingdom; *Int'l*, pg. 1356
Ebel, Horst, Mng. Dir.--Media EMAP Verlag GmbH, Vienna, Austria; *Int'l*, pg. 451
Eberhardt, U., Mng. Dir.--Swiss Bank Corporation, London, United Kingdom; *Int'l*, pg. 1330
Ebert, R.L., Mng. Dir.--Texaco Limited, London, United Kingdom; *U.S. Public*, pg. 1584
Ebihara, Yushi, Mng. Partner & Chief Exec. Officer--Kovel Kresser & Partners, Santa Monica, CA; *U.S. Private*, pg. 634
Echevarria, Guido, Mng. Dir.--NRG Distribution Corporation, Guaynabo, PR; *Int'l*, pg. 1115
Echter, Michael, Mng. Partner-Pub. Rels.--Gillespie, Lawrenceville, NJ; *U.S. Private*, pg. 453
Eda, Shiro, Mng. Dir.-Sls.--Oji Paper Co., Ltd., Tokyo, Japan; *Int'l*, pg. 998
Edar, Itamar, Chief Oper. Officer & Mng. Dir.--IIS Intelligent Information Systems Ltd., Yokneam, Israel; *Int'l*, pg. 645
Edelsbacher, Willibald, Mng. Dir.-Export--Julius Meinl AG, Vienna, Austria; *Int'l*, pg. 856
Edgar, M., Mng. Dir.--Tasman Chile S.A., Santiago, Chile; *Int'l*, pg. 495
Edkins, P., Mng. Dir. & Tech. Opers.--CIBA-GEIGY (Pty.) Ltd., Isando, South Africa; *Int'l*, pg. 978
Edmonds, Frank, Gen. Mgr.--EDL Industries Ltd., Rugeley, United Kingdom; *Int'l*, pg. 821
Edstrom, Gustaf, Mng. Dir.--Esselte Chrono AB, Solna, Sweden; *Int'l*, pg. 459
Edwards, D.G., Mng. Dir.--British Alcan Rolled Products Limited, Newport, United Kingdom; *Int'l*, pg. 51
Edwards, Mark L., Mng. Dir.-Traffic Safety & Engrng.--American Automobile Association, Heathrow, FL; *U.S. Private*, pg. 50
Egan, J., Mng. Dir.--Bally Schoenhandel B.V., Hague, Netherlands; *Int'l*, pg. 997
Egan, J., Mng. Dir.--Bally Group (UK) Limited, London, United Kingdom; *Int'l*, pg. 997
Egan, J.G., Mng. Dir.--Bally UK Sales Ltd., London, United Kingdom; *Int'l*, pg. 997
Eggers, Claus, Mng. Dir.--Valley Hospital Medical Center, Las Vegas, NV; *U.S. Public*, pg. 1697
Ehrat, Rodolphe, Mng. Dir.--Sulzer Australia Pty. Limited, Hornsby, Australia; *Int'l*, pg. 1306
Ehrenkranz, Douglas, Mng. Dir.--Imperial Holly Corporation, Sugar Land, TX; *U.S. Public*, pg. 872
Eiche, James, Mng. Dir.--DMB&B Taiwan, Taipei, Taiwan; *U.S. Private*, pg. 304
Eide, R., Exec. V.P. & Mng. Dir.-Benelux--Dun & Bradstreet Eurinform SA-NV, Brussels, Belgium; *U.S. Public*, pg. 536
Eide, Rolv, Mng. Dir.--Dun & Bradstreet B.V., Rotterdam, Netherlands; *U.S. Public*, pg. 536
Eimbcke, Fernando, Mng. Dir.--Codelco-Kupferhandel GmbH, Dusseldorf, Germany; *Int'l*, pg. 303
Einhorn, Jessica, Mng. Dir.--The World Bank, Washington, DC; *U.S. Private*, pg. 1188
Eisenegger, Otto, Mng. Dir.--Media Daten AG, Zurich, Switzerland; *Int'l*, pg. 451
Eisenring, Teresa, Mng. Dir.--Cash Werbeagentur AG/DMB&B Zurich, Zurich, Switzerland; *U.S. Private*, pg. 303
El Nenaei, Maged, Mng. Dir.--Johnson & Johnson (Egypt) S.A.E., Cairo, Egypt; *U.S. Public*, pg. 930
Elbourne, John, Mng. Dir.--Prudential Assurance Co. Ltd., London, United Kingdom; *Int'l*, pg. 1073
Elgar, Clint, Mng. Dir.--Kvaerner Process Systems Asia Pacific Sdn Bhd., Raja Chulan, Malaysia; *Int'l*, pg. 768
Ellis, Barry, Mng. Dir.--Apartment Ventures, Inc., Bella Vista, AR; *U.S. Private*, pg. 274
Ellis, Barry, Pres. & Mng. Dir.--Essex House Limited Partnership, Bella Vista, AR; *U.S. Private*, pg. 274
Ellis, Barry, Pres. & Mngng. Dir.--Gardenwood Limited Partnership, Bella Vista, AR; *U.S. Private*, pg. 274
Ellis, Barry, Pres. & Mngng. Dir.--Highlands at Briarcliff Limited Partnership, Bella Vista, AR; *U.S. Private*, pg. 274
Ellis, Barry, Pres. of Gen. Partner & Mngng. Dir.--Blair Tower Limited Partnership, Bella Vista, AR; *U.S. Private*, pg. 274
Ellison, Francis, Mng. Dir.--Bank of Ireland Asset Management (UK) Limited, London, United Kingdom; *Int'l*, pg. 153
Ellmer, Klaus, Mng. Dir.-Nord Region--Dyckerhoff & Widmann AG, Munich, Germany; *Int'l*, pg. 423
Elnecave, Issac, Mng. Dir.--Principal Internacional, S.A. Compania de Seguros, Mexico, Mexico; *U.S. Private*, pg. 886
Elslander, M. Dick, Mng. Dir.--General Biscuits Belgie N.V., Herentals, Belgium; *Int'l*, pg. 380
Elsner, Bernd, Mng. Dir.--Haniel EnvirService GmbH, Duisburg, Germany; *Int'l*, pg. 592
Elstad, Tore, Mng. Dir.--Autologic Information International AB, Sollentuna, Sweden; *U.S. Public*, pg. 1724
Elten, Hartwig, Mng. Dir.--Neste Chemicals GmbH, Dusseldorf, Germany; *Int'l*, pg. 914
Elton, S., Mng. Dir.--Smythson of Bond Street, London, United Kingdom; *Int'l*, pg. 707
Emberton, Dave, Mng. Dir.--Gestetner Limited, Nairobi, Kenya; *Int'l*, pg. 1115
Emery, David, V.P. & Mng. Dir.-Asian/India Region--Dun & Bradstreet (Singapore) Pte. Ltd., Singapore, Singapore; *U.S. Public*, pg. 537
Emery, David J., Mng. Dir.--Dun & Bradstreet Schweiz AG, Urdorf, Switzerland; *U.S. Public*, pg. 537
Emondts, M.H.P.J., Dir. Gen.--Bols Benelux B.V., Zoetermeer, Netherlands; *Int'l*, pg. 751
Ena, Teruhiko, Pres.-Space Communications Corp.--Mitsubishi Corporation, Tokyo, Japan; *Int'l*, pg. 871
Ender, Christoph, Mng. Dir.--Sulzer Shanghai Eng. and Mach. Works Ltd., Shanghai, China; *Int'l*, pg. 1306
Enders, Bruce A., Mng. Dir.-General Domestic Appliances, Ltd.--G.E. Appliances, Louisville, KY; *U.S. Public*, pg. 710
Endrass, B., Mng. Dir.--Schwarz Extrusionswerkzeuge GmbH, Wolfratshausen, Germany; *Int'l*, pg. 825
Eng, M., Mng. Dir.--Quality Bakers (Asia) Pte Ltd., Singapore, Singapore; *Int'l*, pg. 555
English, Gerry, V.P. & Mng. Dir.--Option One, Minneapolis, MN; *U.S. Private*, pg. 710
Ennit, Tony, Mng. Dir.-Mgmt. Committee--FinansSkandic AB, Stockholm, Sweden; *Int'l*, pg. 1259
Enters, S., Mng. Dir.--Nihon Balzers K.K., Hiratsuka, Japan; *Int'l*, pg. 997
Epstein, Garcy C., Mng. Partner & Bus. Devel. Dir.--EURO RSCG Tatham, Chicago, IL; *Int'l*, pg. 601
Ercberger, Peter, Mng. Dir.-Mktg.--Scholz & Friends GmbH, Hamburg, Germany; *Int'l*, pg. 1210
Erdmann, Rainer, Mng. Dir.--Helaba Switzerland Ltd., Zurich, Switzerland; *Int'l*, pg. 799
Erener, Serdar, Chief Exec. Officer & Mng. Dir.--Young & Rubicam Turkey, Istanbul, Turkey; *U.S. Private*, pg. 1200
Erfort, George, Mng. Dir.--Concord Camera Corporation, Avenel, NJ; *U.S. Public*, pg. 429
Ericson, Hans F., Mng. Dir.--KONE Rulltrappor A.B., Kista, Sweden; *Int'l*, pg. 748
Eriksson, H.G., Mng. Dir.--Hellermann Scandinavia AB, Jarfalla, Sweden; *Int'l*, pg. 209
Eriksson, Jyrki, Mng. Dir.--Norvista, North York, Canada; *Int'l*, pg. 486
Eriksson, Rolf, Mng. Dir.--Hagglunds Drives Inc., Columbus, OH; *Int'l*, pg. 670
Eriksson, Ulf S., Mng. Dir.--RPM Belgium N.V., Tielt, Belgium; *U.S. Public*, pg. 1357
Erken, Tore, Mng. Dir.--MoDo Skog AB, Ornskoldsvik, Sweden; *Int'l*, pg. 887
Erlichman, Rob, Mng. Dir.--Modem media San Francisco, San Francisco, CA; *U.S. Public*, pg. 1641
Escosura, Luis, Mng. Dir.--Bertrand Faure Componentes SA, Madrid, Spain; *Int'l*, pg. 193
Esplen, Mike, Mng. Dir.--Heinemann English Language Teaching, Oxford, United Kingdom; *Int'l*, pg. 1479
Etheridge, P.W., Mng. Dir.--Edgars Stores Ltd., Crown Mines, South Africa; *Int'l*, pg. 1287
Etter, Christoph, Mng. Dir.--Sulzer International Ltd., Winterthur, Switzerland; *Int'l*, pg. 1306
Etter, H.J., Mng. Dir.--Contraves GmbH, Stockach, Germany; *Int'l*, pg. 998
Etzel, L.A., Sr. V.P.-Industrial--Sundt Corp., Tucson, AZ; *U.S. Private*, pg. 1051
Evans, Clive, Mng. Dir.--Zitel International Corp., Thatcham, United Kingdom; *U.S. Public*, pg. 1794
Evans, Cynthia, Mng. Dir.-Corp. Commun.--New Century Energies, Inc., Denver, CO; *U.S. Public*, pg. 1170
Evans, Ed, Mng. Dir.--Robinson Cone, Burlington, Canada; *Int'l*, pg. 417
Evans, Nicolas, Co-Mgr.--EURO RSCG Novation, Marseilles, France; *Int'l*, pg. 601
Evans, Phillip A., Mng. Dir.--TAB Products Pty. Ltd., Auburn, Australia; *U.S. Public*, pg. 1559
Everitt, David, Chm. Bd. & Mng. Dir.--John Deere (Pty.) Ltd., Nigel, South Africa; *U.S. Public*, pg. 493
Ewington, M. E., Mng. Dir.--Gestetner Malaysia Sdn Bhd, Petaling Jaya, Malaysia; *Int'l*, pg. 1115
Eyal, Joseph, V.P. & Mng. Dir.-Diamond & Jewelry Services--Brink's, Inc., Darien, CT; *U.S. Public*, pg. 1305
Eymery, Pierre, Mng. Dir.-Strategic Plng.--Groupe SEB, Ecueille, France; *Int'l*, pg. 568
Faasse, A., Mng. Dir.--Van Leeuwen Precision BV, Deventer, Netherlands; *Int'l*, pg. 1449
Fabiano, P., Chm. & Mng. Dir.--Enichem Finance (Overseas) Ltd., Grand Cayman, Cayman Islands; *Int'l*, pg. 429
Fabri, Franz, Mng. Dir.--Touraine & Jacobi GmbH, Dortmund, Germany; *Int'l*, pg. 597
Fabry, Georges, Mng. Dir.--Esselte NV Produktion, Saint-Niklaas, Belgium; *Int'l*, pg. 461
Fadel, Toufic, Mng. Dir.--Fouad & Toufic Fadel & Co., Beirut, Lebanon; *Int'l*, pg. 458
Fagan, Anthony F., Mng. Dir.-Europe--Ethyl Corporation, Richmond, VA; *U.S. Public*, pg. 595
Fagan, Anthony F., Mng. Dir.--Ethyl Petroleum Additives Ltd., Bracknell, United Kingdom; *U.S. Public*, pg. 595
Fahnenstich, Klaus, Mng. Dir.--Excellon Europa GmbH, Dietzenbach, Germany; *U.S. Public*, pg. 594
Fahnrich, Eberhard, Mng. Dir.--LBB Service Gesellschaft mbH, Berlin, Germany; *Int'l*, pg. 160
Faijean, Francois, Dir. Gen.--IMS, Neuilly-sur-Seine, France; *Int'l*, pg. 571
Fairbairn, Will, Mng. Dir.--Ashdown Press Ltd., London, United Kingdom; *Int'l*, pg. 1226
Fairs, John, Mng. Dir.-Watts Indust. Europe--Watts Industries, Inc., North Andover, MA; *U.S. Public*, pg. 1746
Fairs, John, Mng. Dir.--Watts Industries Europe B.V., Eerbeek, Netherlands; *U.S. Public*, pg. 1747
Falk, Patrice, Mgr.--Incognito, Clermont-Ferrand, France; *Int'l*, pg. 601
Falkland, Johan, Mng. Dir.--Avesta Prefab AB, Avesta, Sweden; *Int'l*, pg. 221
Fanfani, Marco, Chief Exec. Officer--Ata Tonic, Milan, Italy; *Int'l*, pg. 602
Faraci, J. V., Deputy Mng. Dir.--Carter Holt Harvey Limited, Auckland, New Zealand; *U.S. Public*, pg. 904
Farter, John, Mng. Dir.--Applied Magnetics (Malaysia) Sdn. Bhd., Penang, Malaysia; *U.S. Public*, pg. 123
Faruffini, G., Dr., Mng. Dir.--Balzers-Silmax S.p.A., Milan, Italy; *Int'l*, pg. 997
Fatum, Arthur L., Pres. & Mng. Dir.--AT&T Capital Europe--AT&T Capital Corporation, Morristown, NJ; *Int'l*, pg. 924
Fauquet-Lemaitre, Arnaud, Mgr.--EURO RSCG Media, Moscow, Russia; *Int'l*, pg. 603
Faure, Jean-Pierre, Chm. & Exec. Mng. Dir.--Faure Vadon Forest, Paris, France; *Int'l*, pg. 601
Fausti, Luigi, Vice Chm. & Mng. Dir.--Banca Commerciale Italiana, Milan, Italy; *Int'l*, pg. 135

Favre, Jacques, Mng. Dir.--Banque Bruxelles Lambert (Jersey) Ltd., Saint Helier, United Kingdom; *Int'l*, pg. 148

Fawbert, K.J.A., Deputy Mng. Dir. & Sec.--Birtley Engineering Ltd., Chesterfield, United Kingdom; *Int'l*, pg. 1139

Fearn, David, Mng. Dir.--Lambeth Commutators Ltd., Bath, United Kingdom; *Int'l*, pg. 390

Fee, Robert, Mng. Dir.--Turner South America, Sao Paulo, Brazil; *U.S. Public*, pg. 1646

Feierelsen, Andre, Mng. Dir.--Ewald Glebel Luxembourg G.m.b.H., Dudelange, Luxembourg; *Int'l*, pg. 79

Feinblum, R.M., Mng. Dir.--Conshu Holdings Ltd., Benmore, South Africa; *Int'l*, pg. 1287

Feinstein, Jack B., Mng. Dir.--Sulzer Pumps (PTE) Ltd., Singapore, Singapore; *Int'l*, pg. 1306

Feito, Marisa, Mng. Dir.--SKF Espanola S.A., Madrid, Spain; *Int'l*, pg. 1158

Felder, Mariano, Mng. Dir.--Banco Interfinanzas S.A., Buenos Aires, Argentina; *Int'l*, pg. 347

Feldman, Barbara, Mng. Dir.-Housing Fin. Grp.--Merrill Lynch & Co., Inc., New York, NY; *U.S. Public*, pg. 1097

Feldman, Klaus-Dieter, Mng. Dir.-Commercial--Baldwin-Grafotec GmbH, Augsburg, Germany; *U.S. Public*, pg. 170

Felix, Hans, Chm. Bd. & Mng. Dir.--Scholl AG, Reinach, Switzerland; *Int'l*, pg. 1209

Fenech, Derek, Mng. Dir.--Crown Advertising Ltd., Valetta, Malta; *U.S. Private*, pg. 303

Fennell, Jon, Mng. Dir.-European Opers.--Spirol International Corp., Danielson, CT; *U.S. Private*, pg. 1026

Fennell, Jon, Mng. Dir.--Spirol Ind. Ltd., Corby, United Kingdom; *U.S. Private*, pg. 1026

Fennings, Roger, Mng. Dir.--Intermarkets Public Relations (ME), Dubai, United Arab Emirates; *Int'l*, pg. 680

Fensgard, Oyund, Mng. Dir.--Corro-Coat (Thailand) Ltd., Bangkok, Thailand; *Int'l*, pg. 715

Fereira, Lucas, Grp. Mng. Dir.--Young & Rubicam South Africa, Johannesburg, South Africa; *U.S. Private*, pg. 1198

Ferguson, Ken, Mng. Dir.--MRNI, Bangor, United Kingdom; *Int'l*, pg. 554

Fernandez, Claude, Chief Fin. Officer, Exec. V.P., Sr. V.P. & Mng. Dir.--W.P. Carey & Co., Inc., New York, NY; *U.S. Private*, pg. 209

Fernandez, Guillermo, Mng. Dir.--Grace Portuguesa Lda., Savcavem, Portugal; *U.S. Public*, pg. 756

Fernandez, Guillermo, Mng. Dir.--Grace, S.A., Barcelona, Spain; *U.S. Public*, pg. 756

Fernandez, James N., Mng. Dir.--Tiffany & Co. Overseas Finance B.V., Amsterdam, Netherlands; *U.S. Public*, pg. 1609

Fernandez, Juan, Mng. Dir.--International Sales, Oshkosh, WI; *U.S. Public*, pg. 1233

Fernandez, Richard, M.D., Mng. Dir.--AmeriPath, Inc., Riviera Beach, FL; *U.S. Public*, pg. 96

Ferrara, Pier Luigi, Vice Chm. & Mng. Dir.--Nuovo Pignone S.p.a., Florence, Italy; *Int'l*, pg. 990

Ferrari, Gabriele, Mng. Dir.--CCP Positioning S.R.L., Milan, Italy; *Int'l*, pg. 394

Ferrarin, E., Chm. & Mng. Dir.--ECP - Enichem Polymers Netherlands B.V., Amsterdam, Netherlands; *Int'l*, pg. 429

Ferrazi, Tom, Mng. Dir.--Continental Airlines, Houston, TX; *U.S. Public*, pg. 439

Ferre, Serge F., Mng. Dir.--Nokia Mobile Phones France, Romainville, France; *Int'l*, pg. 952

Fetzer, Ed, Mng. Dir.--Menasha Foreign Sales Corporation, Neenah, WI; *U.S. Private*, pg. 731

Fetzer, Ed, Mng. Dir.--Menasha Transport Inc., Neenah, WI; *U.S. Private*, pg. 731

Fetzer, Gunther, Dr., Mng. Dir.--Droemersche Verlagsanstalt Th. Knaur Nachf. GmbH & Co., Munich, Germany; *Int'l*, pg. 1478

Fetzer, Gunther, Dr., Mng. Dir.--Scherz Verlag GmbH, Bern, Switzerland; *Int'l*, pg. 1480

Fewings, Don, Mng. Dir.--GN Rathdown, Ascot, United Kingdom; *Int'l*, pg. 537

Fiala, Gerd, Mng. Dir.-Training--Julius Meinl AG, Vienna, Austria; *Int'l*, pg. 856

Fiedler, Elfriede, Mng. Dir.-Produce Buying--Julius Meinl AG, Vienna, Austria; *Int'l*, pg. 856

Field, Martyn R., Mng. Dir.-UNUM Ltd.--UNUM Corporation, Portland, ME; *U.S. Public*, pg. 1699

Fielding, L.A., Grp. Mng. Dir.--HSS Hire Service Group PLC, Mitcham, United Kingdom; *Int'l*, pg. 385

Fielke, Neville, Mng. Dir.--H.J. Heinz Company Australia Ltd., Dandenong, Australia; *U.S. Public*, pg. 807

Fierens, Robert, Mng. Dir.--BBL Ireland, Dublin, Ireland; *Int'l*, pg. 148

Fierens, Robert L., Mng. Dir.--Bank Brussels Lambert - Dublin, Dublin, Ireland; *Int'l*, pg. 148

Figore, Daniel P., Mng. Dir.--Crown Cork & Seal (Thailand) Co., Ltd., Samutprakan, Thailand; *U.S. Public*, pg. 464

Fihri, Chakir Fassi, Mng. Dir.--SAGA Communications, Casablanca, Morocco; *U.S. Private*, pg. 305

Filmer, O.A., Gen. Mgr.--Comalco Aluminium (Bell Bay) Limited, Bell Bay, Australia; *Int'l*, pg. 307

Finas, Pierre, Mng. Dir.--Credit Lyonnais S.A., Seoul, Korea; *Int'l*, pg. 344

Finch, Fred, Mng. Dir.--Excellon U.K., Littlehampton, United Kingdom; *U.S. Public*, pg. 594

Finch, R.J., Mng. Dir.--Plant Construction Plc, Thamesmead, United Kingdom; *Int'l*, pg. 585

Findlay, Ian, Dir.-Strategic Mktg.--EMAP Business Communications Division, London, United Kingdom; *Int'l*, *pg. 451*

Finn, Billy, Mng. Dir.--AIB Finance & Leasing Ltd., Dublin, Ireland; *Int'l*, pg. 64

Finne, Harald, Mng. Dir.--Wisapak Oy Ab, Pietarsaari, Finland; *Int'l*, pg. 1429

Finnegan, Seamus, Mng. Dir.--Elsevier Reed Finance Ireland, Dublin, Ireland; *Int'l*, pg. 1093

Finney, Bill, Mng. Dir.--National Distributing Co., Inc., Orlando, FL; *U.S. Private*, pg. 781

Fiorani Piero, Jian, Mng. Dir.--Banca Mercantile S.p.A., Florence, Italy; *Int'l*, pg. 784

Firchow, Claus G., Mng. Dir.--Spektrum der Wissenschaft Verlagsgesellschaft mbH, Heidelberg, Germany; *Int'l*, pg. 1478

Fischer, Hans Erich, Mng. Dir.--WM Wirtschafts-Medien AG, Zurich, Switzerland; *Int'l*, pg. 1480

Fischer, Karl, Chief Fin. Officer--Young & Rubicam GmbH, Frankfurt/Main, Germany; *U.S. Private*, pg. 1199

Fischer, Peter, Mng. Dir.-Sls.--Inka Paletten GmbH, Hoehenkirchen, Germany; *Int'l*, pg. 678

Fisher, Kevin, Mng. Dir.--Dowty Woodville Polymer, Swadlincote, United Kingdom; *Int'l*, pg. 1338

Fishman, Martin, Mng. Dir.--Merisel Switzerland, Nyon, Switzerland; *U.S. Public*, pg. 1096

Fitz Gibbon, Herbert S., II, Mng. Dir.--OppenheimerFunds Distributor, Inc., New York, NY; *U.S. Private*, pg. 818

Fitzgerald, Kathleen, Mng. Dir.--Ilco Unican (SA) (PTY) Ltd., Benoni, South Africa; *Int'l*, pg. 1432

Fitzner, Wolf-Erhard, Mng. Dir.-Baden-Wurtemburg Region--Dyckerhoff & Widmann AG, Munich, Germany; *Int'l*, pg. 423

Fitzpatrick, Mark S., Mng. Dir.--AES Electric, Richmond, United Kingdom; *U.S. Public*, pg. 5

Flamein, Jean-Michel, Mng. Dir.--Battenfeld France S.A., Villepinte, France; *Int'l*, pg. 825

Flannery, Richard J., Mng. Dir.-Corp. & Tax Affairs--Delaware Management Holdings, Inc., Philadelphia, PA; *U.S. Public*, pg. 997

Flavel, P., Mng. Dir.--National Australia Financial Management Ltd., Melbourne, Australia; *Int'l*, pg. 906

Flecther, Arthur, Mng. Dir.--Kvaerner National Ltd., Aberdeen, United Kingdom; *Int'l*, pg. 768

Fleming, R.A., Mng. Dir.--Angus Fire Armour Limited, Thame, United Kingdom; *Int'l*, pg. 1500

Fletcher, Daniel G., Exec. V.P. & Mng. Dir.--J.W. Messner, Inc., Los Angeles, CA; *U.S. Private*, pg. 734

Fletcher, Geoffrey M., Mng. Dir.--Bankers Trust New York Corporation, New York, NY; *U.S. Public*, pg. 185

Flint, E.M., Pres. & Mng. Dir.--Esso Production Malaysia Inc., Kuala Lumpur, Malaysia; *U.S. Public*, pg. 602

Flint, R. D., Mng. Dir.--Lucas-TVS Ltd., Padi, India; *Int'l*, pg. 820

Flood, Teresa, Mng. Dir. & Brdcst. Dir.--Western International Media Corporation, Springfield, MO; *U.S. Private*, pg. 1167

Flood, Tom, Mgr.-LDA Eastern Area--Team One Advertising, El Segundo, CA; *U.S. Public*, pg. 1422

Florin, Gerd, Mng. Dir.--Sulzer Chemtech GmbH, Ravensburg, Germany; *Int'l*, pg. 1308

Flum, O., Mng. Dir.--Gestetner Buromaschinen-Verkaufsgesellschaft m.b.H., Vienna, Austria; *Int'l*, pg. 1115

Fok, Terry, Mng. Dir.--Kim Eng Securities (Hong Kong) Limited, Central, Hong Kong; *Int'l*, pg. 733

Fontana, Vincenzo, Mng. Dir.--Metalchimica srl, Turin, Italy; *U.S. Private*, pg. 735

Fontoura Becker, Oscar Antonio, Chief Fin. Officer & Mng. Dir.-Investor Rels.--Iochpe-Maxion S.A., Sao Paulo, Brazil; *Int'l*, pg. 688

Foo, K.K., Mng. Dir.--McCormick Ingredients Southeast Asia Pvt., Ltd., Jurong, Singapore; *U.S. Public*, pg. 1067

Foo, Vivian, Pres. & Mng. Dir.--Simon Marketing, Ltd., Wan Chai, Hong Kong; *U.S. Private*, pg. 1001

Forbes, A.D., Mng. Dir.--Ladybird Books Ltd., Loughborough, United Kingdom; *Int'l*, pg. 1025

Forcella, P., Mng. Dir.--Ascom Automation S.r.l., Milan, Italy; *Int'l*, pg. 86

Ford, Dee, Mng. Dir.--Viking Radio, Hull, United Kingdom; *Int'l*, pg. 452

Forde, John P., Managing Dir.--Times Fiber Communications, Inc., Wallingford, CT; *U.S. Private*, pg. 629

Fornasieri, Jean, Sr. V.P.-Mng. Dir.--Hachette Filipacchi Magazines Inc., New York, NY; *Int'l*, pg. 794

Forrest, Peter, Mng. Dir.--Pringle of Scotland Ltd, Hawick, United Kingdom; *Int'l*, pg. 385

Forster, Gordon, Gen. Mgr.--GPC Communications (Calgary), Calgary, Canada; *U.S. Public*, pg. 1225

Forster, Robert, Mng. Dir.--Biomet Ltd., Bridgend, United Kingdom; *U.S. Public*, pg. 232

Forsyth, Don, Mng. Dir.--Kvaerner Paladon Ltd., Hampton, United Kingdom; *Int'l*, pg. 768

Fortmann, G., Mng. Dir.--Kytta-Werk Sauter GmbH, Alpirsbach, Germany; *U.S. Public*, pg. 81

Foster, D., Mng. Dir.--Gestetner Limited, Blantyre, Malawi; *Int'l*, pg. 1115

Fothergill, Paul A., Mng. Dir. & Sec.--Analysis & Technology Australia Pty Limited, Kingston, Australia; *U.S. Public*, pg. 110

Fouks, Stephane, Gen. Mgr.--EURO RSCG Institutionnel, Levallois-Perret, France; *Int'l*, pg. 601

Foulas, Stephane, Mng. Dir.--EURO RSCG Institutionnel, Levallois-Perret, France; *Int'l*, pg. 600

Fouque, Alain, Mng. Dir.--Baldwin France Sarl, Verneuil en Halatte, France; *U.S. Public*, pg. 170

Fournier, Andre, Mng. Dir.--Quadrant International Pty. Ltd., Sydney, Australia; *Int'l*, pg. 528

Fournier, Marcel, Dir.--Castle-Harlan, Inc., New York, NY; *U.S. Private*, pg. 219

Fowler, Paul, Mng. Dir.--Tasman Forestry Limited, Rotorua, New Zealand; *Int'l*, pg. 495

Fowler, R., Mng. Dir.--Simon Petroleum Technology Ltd., Swanley, United Kingdom; *Int'l*, pg. 1251

Fowler, Theodore V., Mng. Dir.-Resort Div.--Florida Panthers Holdings, Inc., Fort Lauderdale, FL; *U.S. Public*, *pg. 654*

Fox, Alan, Mng. Dir.--Process Equipment, Manchester, United Kingdom; *Int'l*, pg. 1444

Foy, Bruce, Mng. Dir.--BBL Australia Limited, Sydney, Australia; *Int'l*, pg. 148

Fraback, Alan, Sr. V.P. & Mng. Dir.--Western International Media Corporation, Seattle, WA; *U.S. Private*, pg. 1167

Fragle, Brian, Mng. Dir.--Willis Corroon North Limited, Manchester, United Kingdom; *Int'l*, pg. 1503

Fragle, Brian, Mng. Dir.--Willis Corroon North Limited, Preston, United Kingdom; *Int'l*, pg. 1503

Frampton, Charles L., Mng. Dir.-Acctg. & Asst. Treas.--American Automobile Association, Heathrow, FL; *U.S. Private*, pg. 50

Franchi, Luigi, Mng. Dir.--SASIB Packaging Italia S.r.l., Pistoia, Italy; *Int'l*, pg. 1194

Francis, R.J., Mng. Dir.--T.H.E., Newcastle under Lyme, United Kingdom; *Int'l*, pg. 707

Francis, R.J., Mng. Dir.--The Games, Eastleigh, United Kingdom; *Int'l*, pg. 707

Francois, Jean, Mng. Dir.--Bertrand Faure Argentina SA, Cordoba, Argentina; *Int'l*, pg. 193

Francois, Jean, Mng. Dir.--PAB SA, Cordoba, Argentina; *Int'l*, pg. 193

Francq, W., Mng. Dir.--N.V. Galenco, Paal, Belgium; *Int'l*, pg. 991

Frandsen, Henning Korsbaek, Mng. Dir.--Kelly Vikarer, Copenhagen, Denmark; *U.S. Public*, pg. 949

Frankel, Stuart D., Mng. Dir.--Grotech Capital Group, Inc., Timonium, MD; *U.S. Private*, pg. 483

Franks, R.G., Mng. Dir.--Teamwork Corporation Sdn Bhd, Kuala Lumpur, Malaysia; *Int'l*, pg. 1360

Franssen, P.J.G., Mng. Dir.--Ballast Nedam & Industrie & Toelevering B.V., Soest, Netherlands; *Int'l*, pg. 133

Franz, Peter, Mng. Dir.--Battenfeld Chen Extrusion Systems Ltd., Guangdong, China; *Int'l*, pg. 825

Franzen, Peter, Mng. Dir.--MMI Insurance Group, Sydney, Australia; *Int'l*, pg. 60

Franzen, Pieter, Mng. Dir.--Anglo-Elementar Versicherungs-AG, Vienna, Austria; *Int'l*, pg. 60

Franzino, John, Mng. Dir.-Fin.--Labatt U.S.A., Darien, CT; *Int'l*, pg. 679

Fraser, A., Mng. Dir.--Riley Advertising (Edinburgh) Ltd., Edinburgh, United Kingdom; *Int'l*, pg. 1117

Fraser, A., Mng. Dir.--Riley Advertising (Scotland) Ltd., Glasgow, United Kingdom; *Int'l*, pg. 1117

Fraser, A., Mng. Dir.--Riley Advertising (Aberdeen) Ltd., Aberdeen, United Kingdom; *Int'l*, pg. 1117

Fraser, I., Mng. Dir.--TNT Australia Pty. Limited, Mascot, Australia; *Int'l*, pg. 1343

Frayle, Jose-Luis, Mng. Dir.--Asientos de Castilla Leon SA, Valladolid, Spain; *Int'l*, pg. 193

Frederiksen, Peter, Mng. Dir.--Ferrosan Danmark A/S, Soeborg, Denmark; *Int'l*, pg. 987

Freed, Amy, Mng. Editor-Software & CD ROM Reviews On File--Facts on File News Services, New York, NY; *U.S. Public*, pg. 1327

Frei, Philipp A., Mng. Dir.--Swiss Life International Services, Ridgewood, NJ; *Int'l*, pg. 1332

Frenner, Markus, Dr., Mng. Dir.--Wirtschaftswoche Zeitschriften-Verlagsgesellschaft m.b.H. & Co. KG, Vienna, Austria; *Int'l*, pg. 1479

Frere, Baron, Chm. Bd. & Mng. Dir.--Groupe Bruxelles Lambert S.A., Brussels, Belgium; *Int'l*, pg. 561

Frese, M., Mng. Dir.--Hoogovens Packaging Steel, Ijmuiden, Netherlands; *Int'l*, pg. 756

Frew, D., Mng. Dir.--Crowcon Detection Instruments Limited, Abingdon, United Kingdom; *Int'l*, pg. 589

Frey, Tom, Mng. Dir.--Howell Packaging, Burlington, Canada; *Int'l*, pg. 417

Frick, Per Erik, Mng. Dir.--Iggesund Timber AB, Hudiksvall, Sweden; *Int'l*, pg. 886

Frick, Urs, Mng. Dir.-Madrid, Creative & Pub. Rels. Dir.--Grupo Barro Testa, Madrid, Spain; *Int'l*, pg. 1377

Frid, Svante, Mng. Dir.--AGA Gas AB, Sundbyberg, Sweden; *Int'l*, pg. 12

Frie, Bernie, Mng. Dir.--Granit-Bronz, Inc., Cold Spring, MN; *U.S. Private*, pg. 251

Fried, Elliot M., Mng. Dir.--Vernitron Sensor Systems, Saint Petersburg, FL; *U.S. Public*, pg. 157

Friedel, Edward C., Mng. Dir.--NWQ Investment Managaement Company, Los Angeles, CA; *U.S. Public*, pg. 1673

Friedle, Jurgen, Dr., Mng. Dir.--TosoHaas GmbH, Stuttgart, Germany; *Int'l*, pg. 1408

Friedlich, James L., Mng. Dir.--Handelsblatt-Dow Jones GmbH, Frankfurt/Main, Germany; *Int'l*, pg. 1479

Frizzell, J.D., Vice Chm. & Mng. Dir.--NatWest International Trust Holdings Limited, Nassau, Bahamas; *Int'l*, pg. 911

Froelle, David, Mng. Dir.--ISS Energy Services, Inc., New York, NY; *Int'l*, pg. 656

Frohlich, Christoph, Mng. Dir.--Rex-Rotary AG, Bern, Switzerland; *Int'l*, pg. 1116

Frohlich, Herbert, Mng. Dir.-Frankfurt Region--Dyckerhoff & Widmann AG, Munich, Germany; *Int'l*, pg. 423

Froidevaux, Jean-Clause, Mng. Dir. & Auditor--Roche Holding Ltd., Basel, Switzerland; *Int'l*, pg. 1119

Froidevaux, Joseph, Mng. Dir.--Kammer Vannes, La Chaux de Fonds, Switzerland; *U.S. Public*, pg. 658

From, Mogens, Mng. Dir.--Thrige Electric, Odense, Denmark; *Int'l*, pg. 1387

From, Mogens, Mng. Dir.--Thrige Electric GmbH, Berching, Germany; *Int'l*, pg. 1387

Fronzoni, Alessio, Mng. Dir.--Leo Burnett Co., S.r.l., Milan, Italy; *U.S. Private*, pg. 185

Frost, D.M., Mng. Dir.--Schenectady Pratteln A.G., Pratteln, Switzerland; *U.S. Private*, pg. 970

Frost, Jack M., Mng. Dir.--Oxford Instruments-Medical Systems Div., Clearwater, FL; *Int'l*, pg. 1018

Frowein, Dietrich Kurt, Mng. Dir.-Asset & Relationship Mngmt.--Commerzbank AG, Frankfurt, Germany; *Int'l*, pg. 308

Frumento, Massimo, Mng. Dir.--DYWIT S.p.A., Milan, Italy; *Int'l*, pg. 425

Frye, M.J.E., Chief Exec. Officer & Mng. Dir.--B. Elliott plc., London, United Kingdom; *Int'l*, pg. 448

Fuchs, Ingrid, Mng. Dir.--AMC, Frankfurt/Main, Germany; *U.S. Private*, pg. 92

Fuentes, Ricardo, Mng. Dir.--Reemtsma Espana S.A., Madrid, Spain; *Int'l*, pg. 1101

Fuentes, Ricardo, Mng. Dir.--EMESTA Empressa Espanola de Tabacos S.L., Madrid, Spain; *Int'l*, pg. 1101
Fugalli, Gualberto, Country Mgr.--Ethicon S.p.A., Rome, Italy; *U.S. Public*, pg. 929
Fujii, Hirofumi, Mng. Dir.--IBJ-CA Consult Handels-und Investitionsberatungsgesellschaft m.b.H., Vienna, Austria; *Int'l*, pg. 347
Fujii, Juntaro, Chief Exec. Offier & Mng. Dir.--Tokyo-Mitsubishi International plc, London, United Kingdom; *Int'l*, pg. 158
Fujimoto, Mamoru, Mng. Dir.--Dai-ichi Life International (H.K.) Limited, Wan Chai, Hong Kong; *Int'l*, pg. 362
Fujimura, Takuya, Mng. Dir.--Tonen Corporation, Tokyo, Japan; *Int'l*, pg. 1398
Fujisawa, Osamu, Mng. Dir.--Kyocera Corporation, Kyoto, Japan; *Int'l*, pg. 775
Fujita, A., Mng. Dir.--Ebara Pumpen GmbH, Dietzenbach, Germany; *Int'l*, pg. 432
Fukada, Ryoji, Mng. Dir.--Elsevier Science Japan, Tokyo, Japan; *Int'l*, pg. 1100
Fukuda, Fumihiro, Mng. Dir.--Asahi Finance (Australia) Ltd., Sydney, Australia; *Int'l*, pg. 83
Fukuda, Hisao, Mng. Dir.--Hirayama Manufacturing Ltd., Kasukabe, Japan; *Int'l*, pg. 1306
Fukuhara, Kunio, Dir.-Quality Assurance--Tokuyama Corporation, Tokyo, Japan; *Int'l*, pg. 1393
Fukumoto, Takeo, Mng. Dir.--Nanto Credit Guarantee Co., Ltd., Nara, Japan; *Int'l*, pg. 905
Fukunishi, Masumi, Mng. Dir.--Nanto Computer Service Co., Ltd., Nara, Japan; *Int'l*, pg. 905
Fuller, Bonnie, Deputy Editor--Cosmopolitan, New York, NY; *U.S. Private*, pg. 517
Fuller, Brenton, Mng. Dir.--Dexion (Australia) Pty. Ltd., Blacktown, Australia; *U.S. Public*, pg. 893
Fuller, Edwin D., Exec. V.P & Mng. Dir.-Marriott Lodging Intl.--Marriott International, Inc., Washington, DC; *U.S. Public*, pg. 1047
Fuller, P.D., Mng. Dir.--Omnifit Ltd., Cambridge, United Kingdom; *Int'l*, pg. 589
Furst, John D., Mng. Dir.--Hicks, Muse, Tate & Furst Inc., Dallas, TX; *U.S. Private*, pg. 526
Furuhashi, Masao, Mng. Dir. & Sr. Gen. Mgr.-Devel.--West Japan Railway Company, Osaka, Japan; *Int'l*, pg. 1490
Furuhata, Shunichi, Mng. Dir.--Toyo Trust Asia Limited, Hong Kong, Hong Kong; *Int'l*, pg. 1411
Furuhjelm, Johan, Mng. Dir.--Kymi Paper Mills Ltd., Kuusankoski, Finland; *Int'l*, pg. 1428
Furukawa, Kiyoshi, Mng. Dir.-Corp. Plng. & Intl. Projects--Sumitomo Metal Industries, Ltd., Tokyo, Japan; *Int'l*, pg. 1315
Fyfe, Edward R., Mng. Dir.--Hexcel-Fyfe Company, Inc., Del Mar, CA; *U.S. Public*, pg. 824
Gabutina, Lorenz, Mng. Dir.--Marketforce Advertising Philippines Inc., Manila, Philippines; *U.S. Private*, pg. 325
Gaerttling, Sieghart, Mng. Dir.--Wuestenrot Staedtebau- und Entwicklungsgesellschaft mbH, Ludwigsburg, Germany; *Int'l*, pg. 1514
Gaffney, Michael D., Mng. Partner--Earle Palmer Brown, New York, NY; *U.S. Private*, pg. 173
Gaggin, Brian, Dir.-Sls.--Ultra Pac, Inc., Rogers, MN; *U.S. Public*, pg. 1662
Gagne, C., Chief Oper. Officer--Rawl S.A., Goussainville, France; *Int'l*, pg. 925
Gaillard, Pascal, Co-Mgr.--Unicom, Nantes, France; *Int'l*, pg. 601
Gailly, Pierre-Antoine, Mng. Dir.--Desfosses International, Paris, France; *Int'l*, pg. 780
Gainey, Mitch, Mng. Dir.--Machinery Manufacturing, Hartsville, SC; *U.S. Public*, pg. 1486
Gaisford, John, Publr. & Mng. Dir.--George Philip Limited, London, United Kingdom; *Int'l*, pg. 1093
Gaither, Charles L., Jr., Mng. Dir.--Milkco, Inc., Asheville, NC; *U.S. Public*, pg. 878
Gala, Nemesio Fernandez, Mng. Dir.-Opers.--Caja de Madrid Group, Madrid, Spain; *Int'l*, pg. 251
Galamba, A.J.M., Dr., Mng. Dir.--The Standard Bank of South Africa Limited Representative Office, Maputo, Mozambique; *Int'l*, pg. 1294
Galbreath, James H., Mng. Dir.--NWQ Investment Managaement Company, Los Angeles, CA; *U.S. Public*, pg. 1673
Galioni, M., Mng. Dir.--Wolters Kluwer Italy, Milan, Italy; *Int'l, pg. 1513*
Gall, Sheila, V.P. & Mng. Dir.--Sudler & Hennessey: Gall Inc., Montreal, Canada; *U.S. Private*, pg. 1200
Gallello, Claude, Mng. Dir. & Mgr.-U.S. Network Country--Willis Corroon International/Americas, New York, NY; *Int'l*, pg. 1507
Gallogly, Mark T., Sr. Mng. Dir.--The Blackstone Group, New York, NY; *U.S. Private*, pg. 147
Galme, Ralf, Mng. Dir.-Europe Tax-Free Shopping--Advance Ross Corporation, Chicago, IL; *U.S. Public*, pg. 320
Galovic, Robert D., Mng. Dir.-Info. Resources--American Automobile Association, Heathrow, FL; *U.S. Private*, pg. 50
Gamm, Ulrich, Mng. Dir.--Nokia Audio Electronics GmbH, Straubing, Germany; *Int'l*, pg. 954
Gan, K.S., Dr., Mng. Dir.--Methode Electronics FarEast PTE, Ltd., Jurong, Singapore; *U.S. Public*, pg. 1101
Gano, Michael B., Sr. V.P., Prod. Mgr. & Reg. Construction Mng. Dir.--Willis Corroon Corp. of Portland, Portland, OR; *Int'l*, pg. 1507
Gantchev, Galin Iordanov, Mng. Dir.--Jotun Bulgaria Ltd., Sofia, Bulgaria; *Int'l*, pg. 715
Garavaglia, M., Mng. Dir.--Ascom Safnat SpA, Milan, Italy; *Int'l*, pg. 87
Garcia, Carlos M., Mng. Dir.-Fin.--Countrywide Home Loans Inc., Pasadena, CA; *U.S. Public*, pg. 452
Garcia, Emilio Gasco, Mng. Dir.--MB Espana, S.A., Quart de Poblet, Spain; *U.S. Public*, pg. 798
Garcia, Jesus, Office Dir.--International Marketing & Promotions Barcelona, Barcelona, Spain; *U.S. Private*, pg. 304
Garcia, Jose, Mng. Dir.--Industrias Cousin Freres, Burlada, Spain; *Int'l*, pg. 193
Garcia, Lou, Exec. Dir.--Principal Health Care of Iowa, Inc., West Des Moines, IA; *U.S. Private*, pg. 885
Garcia, M. Perez, Mng. Dir.--Van Leeuwen Tubos Espana S.A.E., Madrid, Spain; *Int'l*, pg. 1450
Garcia, Mauricio, Mng. Dir.--Prolam/Young & Rubicam S.A., Santiago, Chile; *U.S. Private*, pg. 1200
Gardas, Peter, Mng. Dir.--Amway Hungaria Marketing KFT., Budapest, Hungary; *U.S. Private*, pg. 70
Garden, Greg, Mng. Dir.--Sonnenberg Murphy Leo Burnett, Sunninghill, South Africa; *U.S. Private*, pg. 186
Gardner, David A., Mng. Dir.--Fred's Inc., Memphis, TN; *U.S. Public*, pg. 680
Gardner, George D., Pres. & Mng. Dir.--Grocers Specialty Co., Los Angeles, CA; *U.S. Private*, pg. 227
Gardner, R.J.M., Mng. Dir.--De La Rue Payment Systems Division, Basingstoke, United Kingdom; *Int'l*, pg. 387
Garet, Bernard, Mng. Dir.--Limagrain Genetics Corp., Kirkland, IL; *Int'l*, pg. 566
Garland, Wallace, Mng. Dir.--Cadbury Kenya Limited, Nairobi, Kenya; *Int'l*, pg. 248
Garrick, Ronald, Sir, Chief Exec. Officer & Mng. Dir.--Weir Group PLC, Glasgow, United Kingdom; *Int'l*, pg. 1488
Garrido, Juan, Mng. Dir.--Battenfeld Iberica S.A., Montcada, Spain; *Int'l*, pg. 826
Garzone, Max, Mng. Dir.--MacDermid Italiana SRL, Cavaglia, Italy; *U.S. Public*, pg. 1030
Gasparkova, Jindrinska, Mng. Dir.--ISS Servisystem s.r.o., Prague, Czech Republic; *Int'l*, pg. 657
Gastiaux, G., Mng. Dir.--De Vaderlandsche Spaarbank N.V., Antwerp, Belgium; *Int'l*, pg. 648
Gastineau, Herve, Co-Mgr.--Etoile Bleue, Nantes, France; *Int'l*, pg. 600
Gates, Marshall M., Mng. Dir.-Devel. Mkts.--Countrywide Home Loans Inc., Pasadena, CA; *U.S. Public*, pg. 452
Gatfield, Steve, Reg. Mng. Dir.-Asia & Pacific--Leo Burnett Company, Inc., Chicago, IL; *U.S. Private*, pg. 183
Gauger, Hans Siegfried, Mng. Dir.--ITT Flygt GmbH, Langenhagen, Germany; *U.S. Public*, pg. 860
Gautier, Jean-Bernard, Chief Oper. Officer--Rhone-Poulenc Belgique S.A., Brussels, Belgium; *Int'l*, pg. 1112
Gavin, Sara, Mng. Dir.--Shandwick Minneapolis, Minneapolis, MN; *Int'l*, pg. 1227
Gavotto, Andrea, Exec. V.P. & Mng. Dir.--Testa International, Milan, Italy; *Int'l*, pg. 1376
Gay, P., Mng. Dir.--Glenco SA, Paris, France; *Int'l*, pg. 536
Gay, Tan Chen, Mng. Dir.--Ssangyong Cement (Singapore) Ltd., Singapore, Singapore; *Int'l*, pg. 1293
Gazpio, F., Mng. Dir.--Comercial Papelera Aldi S.A., Madrid, Spain; *Int'l*, pg. 886
Gedanke, Moyses, Mng. Dir.--Arthur D. Little Limitada, Sao Paulo, Brazil; *U.S. Private*, pg. 671
Geer, P. Nicholas, Vice Chm. & Mng. Dir.--Great Pacific Enterprises Inc., Vancouver, Canada; *Int'l*, pg. 557
Geertsema, Arie, Mng. Dir.-Res. & Devel. Div.--Sasol Technology (Pty) Ltd., Sasolburg, South Africa; *Int'l*, pg. 1197
Geiser, Edgar, Mng. Dir.--SMH (UK) Ltd., Eastleigh, United Kingdom; *Int'l*, pg. 1161
Gelain, Ronaldo, Mng. Dir.--The West Company Brasil Ltda., Sao Paulo, Brazil; *U.S. Public*, pg. 1755
Gelardi, Ronald N., Chief Oper. Officer, Mng. Dir. & Sec.--Barr Brothers & Co., Inc., New York, NY; *U.S. Private*, pg. 117
Gemmill, Jim, Dir.--Ademco MicroTech Limited, Glasgow, United Kingdom; *U.S. Public*, pg. 1307
Gendebien, Louis, Mng. Dir.--BDDP Belgique, Brussels, Belgium; *Int'l*, pg. 117
Genoud, Michel, Mgr.-Opers.--Woodward-Clyde International, Lyon, France; *U.S. Public*, pg. 1658
Gentles, R.G., Pres. & Mng. Dir.--Blue Circle America Inc., Marietta, GA; *Int'l*, pg. 197
George, Henry H., Mng. Dir.--Scott & Stringfellow Capital Management, Inc., Richmond, VA; *U.S. Public*, pg. 1445
Georgi, Peter, Mng. dir.--Georg Fischer, Inc., Lavalle, Argentina; *Int'l*, pg. 488
Georgscu, Calin, Mng. Dir.--Young & Rubicam Bucharest, Bucharest, Romania; *U.S. Private*, pg. 1199
Geraghty, Michael, Mng. Dir.--Bank of Ireland (Jersey) Limited, Saint Helier, United Kingdom; *Int'l*, pg. 153
Gerard, Jean-Pierre, Mng. Dir. & Gen. Mgr.--Royale Belge S.A., Brussels, Belgium; *Int'l*, pg. 562
Gering, Kurt, Mng. Dir.-Lark Div.--Ortho-Kinetics, Inc., Waukesha, WI; *U.S. Private*, pg. 820
Gerlach, Manfred, Mng. Dir.--Coron Verlag Monika Schoeller & Co., Lachen, Switzerland; *Int'l*, pg. 1479
Gerrard, Chris, Mng. Dir.--Cipirico Intertnational Ltd., Newbury, United Kingdom; *U.S. Public*, pg. 370
Gerrard, David, Mng. Dir.--Harman Audio, Borehamwood, United Kingdom; *U.S. Public*, pg. 787
Gerretsen, Wob, Chm. Bd. & Mng. Dir.--Costain Engineering & Construction Limited, London, United Kingdom; *Int'l*, pg. 336
Gershon, Norman B., Managing Dir.--Oil-Dri S.A., Zurich, Switzerland; *U.S. Public*, pg. 1215
Gestaut, Larry, Mng. Dir.--Heraeus De Nora Inc., Union, NJ; *Int'l*, pg. 616
Gestetner, G., Chief Oper. Officer & Mng. Dir.--Aqualisa Products Limited, Westerham, United Kingdom; *Int'l*, pg. 925
Geyer, Detlef, Mng. Dir.--Knurr-Taunus GmbH, Alfeld, Germany; *Int'l*, pg. 739
Ghorawat, Sunil, Mng. Dir.--Structural India Private, Limited, Goa, India; *U.S. Public*, pg. 593
Ghosh, S.K., Dir.-Tech.--Coal India Limited, Calcutta, India; *Int'l*, pg. 298
Giachetti, Edward J., Mng. Dir.--COBE Cardiovascular Inc., Arvada, CO; *Int'l*, pg. 667
Giacometti, William, Mng. Dir.--SASIB Bakery Holland N.V., Asperen, Netherlands; *Int'l*, pg. 1194
Gibbins, Roger N., Mng. Dir.--Signfix Ltd., Bristol, United Kingdom; *U.S. Public*, pg. 862
Gibson, Anthony, Mng. Dir.--Cineponto/Leo Burnett Publicidade Lda., Lisbon, Portugal; *U.S. Private*, pg. 184
Gibson, P., Mng. Dir.--Hanovia Limited, Slough, United Kingdom; *Int'l*, pg. 589
Gibson, Stephen E., Mng. Dir.--Putnam Investments, Inc., Boston, MA; *U.S. Public*, pg. 1049
Giegerich, Matthew, Exec. V.P. & Mng. Dir.--Thomas G. Ferguson Associates, Inc., Parsippany, NJ; *Int'l*, pg. 1483
Giesbrecht, Dieter, Mng. Dir.-Europe, Middle East & Africa--Symantec Corporation, Cupertino, CA; *U.S. Public*, pg. 1545
Gilardi, Carlo, Chief Exec. Officer & Mng. Dir.--Benetton Group S.p.A., Ponzano Veneto, Italy; *Int'l*, pg. 186
Gilbert, Anne, Mng. Dir.--Principal Investment Management Ltd., Sevenoaks, United Kingdom; *Int'l*, pg. 1020
Gilbert, David, Mng. Dir.--Currys Group plc, Hemel Hempstead, United Kingdom; *Int'l*, pg. 414
Gilbertson, David, Mng. Dir.--The Lancet Limited, London, United Kingdom; *Int'l*, pg. 1100
Gilchrist, Allan, Mng. Dir.--Nokia Products Ltd., Ajax, Canada; *Int'l*, pg. 952
Gill, David, Mng. Dir.--RHM Ingredient Supplies Limited, Ossett, United Kingdom; *Int'l*, pg. 1396
Gill, Robert, Mng. Dir.--Nokia Telecommunications NZ Limited, Parnell, New Zealand; *Int'l*, pg. 953
Gillette, Patricia, Mng. Dir.--Brimax Books Limited, Newmarket, United Kingdom; *Int'l*, pg. 1093
Gillingham, David, Mng. Dir.--New Zealand Milk Products (CIS) AO, Moscow, Russia; *Int'l*, pg. 923
Gillings, Ritson, Mng. Dir.--A. Schulman Inc. Limited, Newport, United Kingdom; *U.S. Public*, pg. 1441
Gilmore, Thomas K., Mng. Dir.--Notifier Middle East, Amman, Jordan; *U.S. Public*, pg. 1307
Gilroy, Rosalind, Co-Mng. Dir.--International Correspondence Schools (Australasia) Limited, Lane Cove, Australia; *U.S. Public*, pg. 784
Gingue, R., Mng. Dir.--Alphagary Corporation, Leominster, MA; *Int'l*, pg. 802
Giordano, Michael, Mng. Dir.--Fedders Asia Pte. Ltd., Singapore, Singapore; *U.S. Public*, pg. 615
Girardi, Michael N., Mng. Dir.--Jefferies & Company, Inc., Los Angeles, CA; *U.S. Public*, pg. 925
Gitz, E., Mng. Dir.--Ascom Teletron B.V., Nieuwegein, Netherlands; *Int'l*, pg. 87
Gitz, E., Mng. Dir.--Ascom Hasler BV, Arnhem, Netherlands; *Int'l*, pg. 87
Giuffre, Giuseppe, Mng. Dir.--Giuffre Editore SpA, Milan, Italy; *Int'l*, pg. 1095
Giuriceo, Raymond C., V.P. & Mng. Dir.-Intl. Licensing--Hartmarx Corporation, Chicago, IL; *U.S. Public*, pg. 795
Givens, Gordon, Mng. Dir.-EMEA--InterVoice, Inc., Dallas, TX; *U.S. Public*, pg. 910
Glasebrook, Richard J., II, Mng. Dir.--OppenheimerFunds Distributor, Inc., New York, NY; *U.S. Private*, pg. 818
Gleie, Axel, Mng. Dir.--Verlag Der Tagesspiegel, Berlin, Germany; *Int'l*, pg. 1479
Glen, Suzanne Tang, Mng. Dir.--The Asian Wall Street Journal Weekly, New York, NY; *U.S. Public*, pg. 524
Glenne, Tore, Mng. Dir.--Gorud, Oslo, Norway; *Int'l*, pg. 18
Glez del Peral, A., Mng. Dir.--SAB WABCO Dimetal Equipos Ferroviarrios, Madrid, Spain; *Int'l*, pg. 271
Glossop, Michael, Mng. Dir.--AP & T Ltd., Oxford, United Kingdom; *U.S. Public*, pg. 620
Gloystein, Peter, Dr., Mng. Dir.-Private Banking--Commerzbank AG, Frankfurt, Germany; *Int'l*, pg. 308
Glynn, Erin, Exec. Dir.--Principal Health Care of Louisiana, Inc., Metairie, LA; *U.S. Private*, pg. 885
Gnocchi, Gabrio, Mng. Dir.-Mktg. & Sls.--Opticos S.r.l., Brembate di Sopra, Italy; *Int'l*, pg. 1007
Godard, E., Mng. Dir.--S.A. Cockerill Forges and Ringmill C.F.R., Seraing, Belgium; *Int'l*, pg. 301
Godel, Jean-Claude, Mng. Dir.--Sulzer Canada Inc., Pointe-Claire, Canada; *Int'l*, pg. 1306
Godwin, I.D., Grp. Mgr.-Pub. Rels.--Johnson Matthey Public Limited Company, London, United Kingdom; *Int'l*, pg. 713
Goersch, Klaus, Dir.-Corp. Training & Standards--Mesaba Holdings, Inc., Minneapolis, MN; *U.S. Public*, pg. 1099
Goerth, Wolfgang J., Mng. Dir.--Heidelberg Graphic Equipment Ltd.-Heidelberg UK, Brentford, United Kingdom; *Int'l*, pg. 605
Goetschi, Pierre, Mng. Dir. & Adv.--Schweizerische Kaseunion AG, Bern, Switzerland; *Int'l*, pg. 1211
Goh, Han Hian, Mng. Dir.--Dowty Aerospace Aviation Services Pte Ltd, Singapore, Singapore; *Int'l*, pg. 1337
Golby, Paul, Mng. Dir.-Aylesbury Automation--Clayhithe P.L.C., Aylesbury, United Kingdom; *Int'l*, pg. 297
Gold, Mary, Mng. Dir.-Mktg.--Dreyer's Grand Ice Cream, Inc., Oakland, CA; *U.S. Public*, pg. 529
Goldberg, Henry, Mng. Dir.-Philip Morris/Australia--Philip Morris International Inc., Rye Brook, NY; *U.S. Public*, pg. 1289
Golden, J., Mng. Dir.--Ascom Timeplex SA, Montigny-le-Bretonneux, France; *Int'l*, pg. 87
Golden, Ray, Sr. Mng. Dir.--Bankers Trust New York Corporation, New York, NY; *U.S. Public*, pg. 185
Goldman, Glenn S., Mng. Dir.--ContiFinancial Services Corporation, New York, NY; *U.S. Public*, pg. 439
Goldman, Steve, Mng. Dir.--TBWA Chiat/Day Los Angeles, Venice, CA; *U.S. Private*, pg. 1062
Goldsack, Ross, Mng. Dir.--Goldsack Harris Thompson Advertising, Wellington, New Zealand; *U.S. Private*, pg. 184
Golightly, Roy, Mng. Dir.-Employee Commun.--FDX Corporation, Memphis, TN; *U.S. Public*, pg. 603
Gomendio, Pedro, Mng. Dir.--Lukcor, S.A., Larache, Morocco; *U.S. Public*, pg. 1067
Gomersall, J. E., Mng. Dir.--Pretoria Portland Cement Co. Ltd., Johannesburg, South Africa; *Int'l*, pg. 167
Gonzalez, Eddie, Grp. Mng. Dir.-Hong Kong & China--Dentsu Young & Rubicam Advertising Co., Ltd. (Beijing), Beijing, China; *U.S. Private*, pg. 325

Gonzalez, Eddie, Grp. Mng. Dir.-Hong Kong & China--Dentsu Young & Rubicam Limited (Hong Kong), Hong Kong, Hong Kong; *U.S. Private*, pg. 325

Gonzalez, Jose E., Mng. Dir.--Petroleos De Canarias, S.A. (PETROCAN), Las Palmas, Spain; *Int'l*, pg. 323

Goodall, Peter, Mng. Dir.--Tiffany & Co. (New York) Pty Limited, Sydney, Australia; *U.S. Public*, pg. 1609

Goodfellow, David, Mng. Dir.-Sls.--Hermann Pfauter GmbH & Co., Ludwigsburg, Germany; *Int'l*, pg. 617

Goodman, Mickey, Mng. Dir.--Market Growth Resources, Inc., Wilton, CT; *U.S. Public*, pg. 1641

Gordon, Beth, Pres. & Mng. Dir.--The Media Edge, New York, NY; *U.S. Private*, pg. 1079

Gordon, John M., Sr. V.P. & Mng. Dir.-Valvoline International--Valvoline Company, Lexington, KY; *U.S. Public*, pg. 139

Gordon, Mona, Mng. Dir.--Lexis Law Publishing, San Juan, PR; *Int'l*, pg. 1096

Goresh, Andrew, Mng.Dir.-H.R.--T. Rowe Price Associates, Inc., Baltimore, MD; *U.S. Public*, pg. 1324

Gorstoiago, Jose Antonio, Mng. Dir.--Asientos del Norte SA (ANSA), Pamplona, Spain; *Int'l*, pg. 193

Gosizk, Brian K., V.P. & Mngmt. Supvr.--Jordan Tamraz Caruso Advertising, Inc., Chicago, IL; *U.S. Private*, pg. 599

Goss, David T., Sr. Mng. Dir.-Asset Mng. Services--American International Group, Inc., New York, NY; *U.S. Public*, pg. 83

Goto, Shinzo, Mng. Dir.-Investor Rels.--Matsushita Electric Works, Ltd., Osaka, Japan; *Int'l*, pg. 847

Gotoh, H., Mng. Dir.--Esso Sekiyu Kabushiki Kaisha, Tokyo, Japan; *U.S. Public*, pg. 602

Gotthelf, Michael, Dr., Mng. Dir.--Metallbank GmbH, Frankfurt/Main, Germany; *Int'l*, pg. 861

Goudard, Jean-Michel, Pres.-Intl. & Dir.--BBDO Worldwide Inc., New York, NY; *U.S. Public*, pg. 1223

Gough, Malcolm, Mng. Dir.--EMAP Nationals, Peterborough, United Kingdom; *Int'l*, pg. 451

Grace, George, Co-Mng. Dir. & Fin. Dir.--AMA Leo Burnett, Giza, Egypt; *U.S. Private*, pg. 184

Gradman, Per, Mng. Dir.--Neopac A/S, Randers, Denmark; *Int'l*, pg. 864

Graham, Mike, Mng. Partner--RTCdirect, Washington, DC; *Int'l*, pg. 1483

Graham, Stuart, Mng. Dir.--ISS Servisystem Com. E. Ind. Ltda., Sao Paulo, Brazil; *Int'l*, pg. 657

Grajales, Eduardo, Mng. Dir.--Publispana/BDDP, Mexico, Mexico; *Int'l*, pg. 118

Grammatica, Robert, Sr. V.P. & Mng. Dir.--The Chapman Agency, New York, NY; *U.S. Private*, pg. 1197

Granger, Alain, Mng. Dir.--Hogamed S.A., Lyon, France; *Int'l*, pg. 668

Granger, Lee F., Mng. Dir.-Mktg.--American Automobile Association, Heathrow, FL; *U.S. Private*, pg. 50

Granrud, Ragnar, Mng. Dir.--Esselte Meto A/S, Oslo, Norway; *Int'l*, pg. 461

Grant, Cynthia, Mng. Dir.-Portland, SF Offices--CF2GS, Seattle, WA; *U.S. Private*, pg. 194

Grant, Cynthia, Mng. Dir.--CF2GS, Portland, OR; *U.S. Private*, pg. 194

Grant, Margaret, Mng. Dir.--Cascade Land Leasing Co., Seattle, WA; *U.S. Public*, pg. 311

Grant, R.S., Mng. Dir.--BOC Gases Australia Ltd., Chatswood, Australia; *Int'l*, pg. 121

Grasha, James D., Mng. Dir.--A.O. Smith-Water Products Co., Veldhoven, Netherlands; *U.S. Public*, pg. 1477

Grau, Juan, Mng. Dir.--TBWA Barcelona, Barcelona, Spain; *U.S. Private*, pg. 1063

Gray, David, Bus. Devel. Dir.-Europe--Young & Rubicam Holdings Ltd., London, United Kingdom; *U.S. Private*, pg. 1199

Gray, David, Mng. Dir.--Caledonian Paper Plc, Irvine, United Kingdom; *Int'l*, pg. 1430

Gray, G.A. David, Mng. Dir.-Fixed Income--Dewey Square Investors Corporation, Boston, MA; *U.S. Public*, pg. 1673

Gray, M.F., Dep. Mng. Dir.--Simon-Carves Ltd., Hulme, United Kingdom; *Int'l*, pg. 1251

Gray, Trevor, Mng. Dir.--VMark Asia-Pacific Pty. Ltd., Bondi Junction, Australia; *U.S. Public*, pg. 129

Green, A., Mng. Dir.-Res., Devel. & Info. Sys.--United Biscuits (Holdings) Plc, West Drayton, United Kingdom; *Int'l*, pg. 1442

Green, James, Mng. Editor--TimesFax, New York, NY; *U.S. Public*, pg. 1174

Green, Jim, Mng. Dir.--Ademco MicroTech Limited, Glasgow, United Kingdom; *U.S. Public*, pg. 1307

Green, Jim, Mng. Dir.--Ademco Microtech Security Ltd., East Kilbride, United Kingdom; *U.S. Public*, pg. 1307

Green, Lee, Exec. Dir.--Principal Health Care of Illinois, Inc., Oak Brook, IL; *U.S. Private*, pg. 885

Green, M.J., Mng. Dir.--Century Life, London, United Kingdom; *Int'l*, pg. 685

Green, Robert E., Mng. Dir.--W.R. Grace Ltd., London, United Kingdom; *U.S. Public*, pg. 756

Greenberg, Alan C., Chm. Bd. & Sr. Mng. Dir.--The Bear Stearns Companies Inc., New York, NY; *U.S. Public*, pg. 197

Greene, Jaime, Mng. Dir.--Leo Burnett Publicidade, Ltda., Sao Paulo, Brazil; *U.S. Private*, pg. 185

Greene, Mark T., Dr., Mng. Dir.--FGI Research, Washington, Fairfax, VA; *U.S. Private*, pg. 389

Greene, Marvin H., Mng. Dir.-Retirement--Towers Perrin, New York, NY; *U.S. Private*, pg. 1093

Greenhalgh, Nigel, Mng. Dir.--Dumez S.A. Emirates, Abu Dhabi, United Arab Emirates; *Int'l*, pg. 823

Greenshields, R., Mng. Dir.--AMP Asset Management Plc, London, United Kingdom; *Int'l*, pg. 100

Greenwood, Donald, Mng. Dir.--Nofsinger, Inc., Kansas City, MO; *U.S. Private*, pg. 187

Gregoire, Jean, Mng. Dir.--Carlton Cards France, Paris, France; *U.S. Public*, pg. 78

Gregoire, Sylvie, Dir.-Regulatory Affairs/Europe--Biogen, Inc., Cambridge, MA; *U.S. Public*, pg. 230

Gregori, S.R., Chm. & Mng. Dir.--Texaco Overseas (Nigeria) Petroleum Co., Lagos, Nigeria; *U.S. Public*, pg. 1584

Gregory, R.A., Mng. Dir.--Kyle Stewart Ltd., London, United Kingdom; *Int'l*, pg. 630

Greif, Karel, Mng. Dir.--Ceska Reklamni/TBWA, Prague, Czech Republic; *U.S. Private*, pg. 1062

Greisen, K. G., Mng. Dir.--Rex-Rotary S.A., Sarcelles, France; *Int'l*, pg. 1116

Greisen, Ken, Mng. Dir.--Lance International S.A., Sarcelles, France; *Int'l*, pg. 1116

Griffin, Ian, Mng. Dir.--EMAP Response Ltd., Peterborough, United Kingdom; *Int'l*, pg. 451

Griffin, Ian, Gen. Mng. Dir.--CAP Nationwide Motor Research, Skipton, United Kingdom; *Int'l*, pg. 451

Griffin, Ian, Gen. Mng. Dir.--Sewells International Ltd., Totnes, United Kingdom; *Int'l*, pg. 451

Griffiths, J., Mng. Dir.-Fin.--William Prym GmbH & Co. KG, Stolberg, Germany; *Int'l*, pg. 1499

Grigal, Dennis, Mng. Dir.--Donaldson Micro Pore S.A. de C.V., Aguascalientes, Mexico; *U.S. Public*, pg. 517

Griggs, M. Kim, Mng. Dir.--R & R Plastics, Swanton, OH; *U.S. Private*, pg. 431

Grill, Gerhard, Mng. Dir.--Pitney Bowes Ges.b.H., Vienna, Austria; *U.S. Public*, pg. 1304

Grillo, Anthony, Sr. Mng. Dir.--The Blackstone Group, New York, NY; *U.S. Private*, pg. 147

Grime, Sue, Mng. Dir.-T & N Properties--T & N Plc, Manchester, United Kingdom; *Int'l*, pg. 1334

Grimes, B.G., Reg. Mng. Dir.--Ballast Wiltshier Plc-South West Div., Reading, United Kingdom; *Int'l*, pg. 135

Grimes, B.G., Reg. Mng. Dir.--Ballast Wiltshier Plc - South West Region, Winchester, United Kingdom; *Int'l*, pg. 135

Grioli, J.C., Mng. Dir.-Malta--Vodafone Group PLC, Newbury, United Kingdom; *Int'l*, pg. 1469

Grippa, Vincent V., Sr. V.P. & Mng. Dir.--State Street Canada, Inc., Toronto, Canada; *U.S. Public*, pg. 1513

Groehl, Cornelia, Mng. Dir.--Johnson & Johnson G.m.b.H., Norderstedt, Germany; *U.S. Public*, pg. 930

Groenbaek, K., Mng. Dir.--Dansk Uni-Cardan A/S, Ballerup, Denmark; *Int'l*, pg. 535

Groll, David, Mng. Dir.--Respironics (HK), Ltd., Kowloon, Hong Kong; *U.S. Public*, pg. 1383

Grondelli, Ugo, Sr. Exec. V.P. & Deputy Mng. Dir.--Gambro AB, Lund, Sweden; *Int'l*, pg. 666

Groninger, Jim, Mng. Dir.--Beta Raven Inc., Bridgeton, MO; *U.S. Public*, pg. 1361

Gronmark, Bjarne, Mng. Dir.--Wisaforest (UK) Ltd., Uxbridge, United Kingdom; *Int'l*, pg. 1429

Gronow, Clive M., Mng. Dir.-ECC Intl. Europe--English China Clays Plc, Theale, United Kingdom; *Int'l*, pg. 455

Groos, Hubertus, Mng. Dir.--Creditanstalt Bankverein AG, Munich, Germany; *Int'l*, pg. 348

Gross, Jeremy V., Chief Tech. Officer & Mng. Dir.-Tech.--Countrywide Home Loans Inc., Pasadena, CA; *U.S. Public*, pg. 452

Grotloh, Karlheinz, Mng. Dir.--Sulzer-Burckhardt Engineering Works Ltd., Basel, Switzerland; *Int'l*, pg. 1305

Grout, Daniel, Chief Oper. Officer--Rhone-Poulenc Taiwan Ltd., Taipei, Taiwan; *Int'l*, pg. 1114

Grubb, John W., Mng. Dir.--Ok Tedi Mining Limited, Kiunga, Papua New Guinea; *Int'l*, pg. 228

Gruber, Reinhard, Mng. Dir.--Battenfeld Kunststoffmaschinen Ges. m.b.H., Kottingbrunn, Austria; *Int'l*, pg. 825

Grundy, Walter, Mng. Dir.--Johnson & Johnson de Venezuela, S.A., Caracas, Venezuela; *U.S. Public*, pg. 930

Gubanich, Kathleen, Mng. Dir.--The Vanguard Group, Inc., Valley Forge, PA; *U.S. Private*, pg. 1133

Gubert, Walter A., Mng. Dir. & Reg. Exec.-Europe, Middle East & Africa--J.P. Morgan Co. Incorporated, New York, NY; *U.S. Public*, pg. 1129

Guelke, Hans-Georg, Mng. Dir.--Wustenrot Hypothekenbank Aktiengesellschaft, Ludwigsburg, Germany; *Int'l*, pg. 1514

Guenthardt, Lukas, Mng. Dir.--K-Tron Switzerland-Soder Division, Niederlenz, Switzerland; *U.S. Public*, pg. 938

Guerini, Bernard, V.P. & Mng. Dir.-Carburos Metalicos--Air Products Europe, Inc., Allentown, PA; *U.S. Public*, pg. 30

Guerra, Fernando, Mng. Dir.--Anchor Foods Limited, Swindon, United Kingdom; *Int'l*, pg. 923

Guibout, Jean-Louis, Mgr.--EURO RSCG Nord, Roubaix, France; *Int'l*, pg. 601

Guibout, Jean-Louis, Gen. Mgr.--EURO RSCG Nord, Metz, France; *Int'l*, pg. 601

Guilbert, Dominique, Mng. Dir.--Bertrand Faure Equipements SA, Lure, France; *Int'l*, pg. 192

Guilbert, Dominique, Mng. Dir.--Bertrand Faure Equipements SA, Magny, France; *Int'l*, pg. 192

Guilemany, Xavier, Mng. Dir.--Commestsa, Barcelona, Spain; *Int'l*, pg. 193

Guilmil, J., Mng. Dir.--Claudius Peters (Iberica) S.A., Madrid, Spain; *Int'l*, pg. 131

Guimont-Hall, Ann, Sr. V.P. & Reg. Dir.--Outdoor Services, Seattle, WA; *U.S. Private*, pg. 1166

Guinddeau, Jean-Luc, Mng. Dir.--Gestetner Services S.A., Paris, France; *Int'l*, pg. 1115

Gullaksen, Bjorn, Chief Oper. Officer, Gen. Mgr. & Mng. Dir.--SAS Park Royal Hotel, Lysaker, Norway; *Int'l*, pg. 1202

Gulliford, Mike, Mng. Dir.--Burgmann Middle East, Dubai, United Arab Emirates; *Int'l*, pg. 234

Gunn, Robert, Mng. Dir.--VMark Software, Ltd., Bracknell, United Kingdom; *U.S. Public*, pg. 129

Gunter, H., Mng. Dir.--Ascom Hongkong Ltd., Hong Kong, Hong Kong; *Int'l*, pg. 87

Gunthel, Richard, Sr. Mng. Dir.-Real Estate--Bankers Trust New York Corporation, New York, NY; *U.S. Public*, pg. 185

Guoqing, Paul Liu, Mng. Dir.--Grand Generale Asia Ltd., Hong Kong, Hong Kong; *Int'l*, pg. 548

Gurrieri, John, Mng. Dir.-South Pacific Tires--Pacific Dunlop Limited, Melbourne, Australia; *Int'l*, pg. 1021

Gustafson, Tom-Henrik, Mng. Dir.--Pargas Plant, Pargas, Finland; *Int'l*, pg. 1198

Gustarsson, Jakob, Mng. Dir.--AGA RE, Lidingo, Sweden; *Int'l*, pg. 13

Gustavson, Hakan, Mng. Dir.--Hall & Cederquist/Young & Rubicam, Stockholm, Sweden; *U.S. Private*, pg. 1198

Guthrie, Catherine, Mng. Dir.--Leo Burnett Company, Ltd.-Taiwan Branch, Taipei, Taiwan; *U.S. Private*, pg. 185

Guthrie, Gus, Mng. Dir.-China--Bass International Brewers, Birmingham, United Kingdom; *Int'l*, pg. 170

Gutierrez, Gabriel, Mng. Dir.--3i Spain, Madrid, Spain; *Int'l*, pg. 1386

Gutknecht, Luther H., Mng. Dir.-Dwight Analytics--Dwight Asset Management Company, Burlington, VT; *U.S. Public*, pg. 1673

Gutteridge, J., Mng. Dir.-Westinghouse U.K.--Park Air Electronics Ltd., Peterborough, United Kingdom; *U.S. Public*, pg. 1198

Gutting, Bernd, Dr., Mng. Dir.--Allianz Asset Management (Hong Kong) Ltd., Hong Kong, Hong Kong; *Int'l*, pg. 59

Gyllenberg, Bengt-Ake, Mng. Dir.--Nokia Mobile Phones Italia S.r.l., Rome, Italy; *Int'l*, pg. 952

Gyssels, Raoul, Mng. Dir.--Radiant Color NV, Houthalen, Belgium; *U.S. Public*, pg. 1357

Haack, Hans-Christel, Mng. Dir.-Material Supply Mngmt.--Dyckerhoff & Widmann AG, Munich, Germany; *Int'l*, pg. 423

Haag, Joachim, Mng. Dir.--Bohlin Instruments Vetriebs GmbH, Muhlacker, Germany; *Int'l*, pg. 208

Haase, Daniel, Sr. V.P. & Mng. Dir.--BankAmerica Trust & Banking Corp. (Cayman) Ltd., Georgetown, Cayman Islands; *U.S. Public*, pg. 183

Habaieb, Taofik, Mng. Dir.--TH Com, Tunis, Tunisia; *U.S. Private*, pg. 305

Habegger, Christian, Mng. Dir.--Sulzer Hydro AG, Kriens, Switzerland; *Int'l*, pg. 1307

Habib, Laurent, Mng. Dir.--EURO RSCG Institutionnel, Levallois-Perret, France; *Int'l*, pg. 600

Hackett, Kenneth, Exec. Dir.--Catholic Relief Services, Baltimore, MD; *U.S. Private*, pg. 220

Hackwell, David J., Mng. Dir.--Esselte UK Ltd., Feltham, United Kingdom; *Int'l*, pg. 461

Hadaway, R.H., Mng. Dir.--Alcan Consumer Products, Amersham, United Kingdom; *Int'l*, pg. 51

Hadden, Abel, Mng. Dir.--Daniel J. Edelman Ltd., London, United Kingdom; *U.S. Private*, pg. 363

Haderlein, Mary, Mng. Partner & Mngmt. Dir.--Grant/Jacoby, Inc., Chicago, IL; *U.S. Private*, pg. 470

Haenig, G., Dr., Mng. Dir.--Grillo-Werke AG, Duisburg, Germany; *Int'l*, pg. 861

Haertel, Rainer M., Mng. Dir.--Loctite Europa Gesellschaft mbH, Vienna, Austria; *Int'l*, pg. 611

Haeusler, Gerd, Mng. Dir.-Investment Opers.--Dresdner Bank AG, Frankfurt/Main, Germany; *Int'l*, pg. 417

Haffey, Kevin, Mng. Dir.--SKF New Zealand Ltd., Auckland, New Zealand; *Int'l*, pg. 1159

Hagel, Rauno, Mng. Dir.--Valmet Dura Oy, Jarvenpaa, Finland; *Int'l*, pg. 1448

Hageman, Romanus, Mng. Dir.--Dominion Vertriebs, G.m.b.H., Karben, Germany; *U.S. Public*, pg. 938

Hagens, Jack, Mng. Dir.--Tukkers Milieu-onderzoek BV, Woerden, Netherlands; *Int'l*, pg. 607

Hahn-Petersen, Vilhelm, Mng. Dir.--FLS Aerospace Engineering Ltd., Stansted, United Kingdom; *Int'l*, pg. 475

Hakata, Kazuyasu, Mng. Dir.--Fuji International Finance (HK) Limited, Central, Hong Kong; *Int'l*, pg. 521

Hale, W. R., Mng. Dir.--Anglesey Aluminium Limited, Holyhead, United Kingdom; *U.S. Public*, pg. 1063

Hale, W. R., Mng. Dir.--Anglesey Aluminium Limited, Holyhead, United Kingdom; *Int'l*, pg. 1119

Halkema, A.R.T., Mng. Dir.--Nutricia S.A., Madrid, Spain; *Int'l*, pg. 992

Hall, B., Mng. Dir.--Timken Argentina S.R.L., Buenos Aires, Argentina; *U.S. Public*, pg. 1617

Hall, J.E., Mng. Dir.--NatWest International Trust Corporation (Cayman) Limited, Georgetown, Cayman Islands; *Int'l*, pg. 911

Hall, Ken, V.P. & Mng. Dir.--ABC-Ademco Security Products, Saint-Laurent, Canada; *U.S. Public*, pg. 1306

Hall, Larry, Mng. Dir.--Ferro Enamel do Brasil I.C.L., Sao Paulo, Brazil; *U.S. Public*, pg. 619

Hall, Nigel, Mng. Dir.--Ginn & Co. Limited, Aylesbury, United Kingdom; *Int'l*, pg. 1094

Hall, R. Wayne, Mng. Dir. & Controller--Provident Bank of Maryland, Baltimore, MD; *U.S. Public*, pg. 1337

Hall, Wayne F., Chief Fin. Officer--Black & Veatch, Kansas City, MO; *U.S. Private*, pg. 146

Hallard, Jose, Mng. Dir.--DMR Group (Belgium) S.A.-N.V., Brussels, Belgium; *Int'l*, pg. 528

Hallowell, Chris, Sr. V.P. & Mng. Dir.--The Program Exchange, New York, NY; *U.S. Public*, pg. 1422

Hallstrom, Ulf, Chief Exec. Officer & Mng. Dir.--D'Arcy Masius Benton & Bowles AB, Stockholm, Sweden; *U.S. Private*, pg. 304

Halpin, Charles, Mng. Dir.--Bowker-Saur Ltd., East Grinstead, United Kingdom; *Int'l*, pg. 1094

Halston, Mike, Mgr.-Natl. Sls.--Carfel, Inc., Miami, FL; *U.S. Private*, pg. 210

Halvorson, Rebecca M., Mng. Dir.-Investor Rels.--FDX Corporation, Memphis, TN; *U.S. Public*, pg. 603

Hamada, Mamoru, Mng. Dir. & Dir.-Gen. Affairs, Personnel & Legal--Showa Denko K.K., Tokyo, Japan; *Int'l*, pg. 1236

Hamazaki, Yasuhiro, Mng. Dir.--NEC Home Electronics (Malaysia) Sdn. Bhd., Sungai Petani, Malaysia; *Int'l*, pg. 900

Hambleton, J., Mng. Dir.--Eagle Aviation Ltd., Hamilton, New Zealand; *Int'l*, pg. 38

Hambly, Bill, Mng. Dir.--Sudler & Hennessey/Gall Inc., Toronto, Canada; *U.S. Private*, pg. 1200

Hamilton, Murray, Mng. Dir.--Butterworths Australia, Sydney, Australia; *Int'l*, pg. 1095

Hamilton, Thomas, Mng. Dir.--Tin Plate Containers, Ltd., Twyford, United Kingdom; *Int'l*, pg. 1126

Hamilton, William K., V.P. & Reg. Construction Mng. Dir.--Willis Corroon Corp. of Knoxville, Knoxville, TN; *Int'l*, pg. 1506

Hammar, Orjan, Mng. Dir.--Gunnebo Baltic Sp z o o, Gdynia, Poland; *Int'l*, pg. 578

Hammer, C., Mng. Dir.--Lancer S.A., Tournefeuille, France; *Int'l*, pg. 552

Hammersley, Paul, Mng. Dir.--Lowe Howard-Spink, London, United Kingdom; *U.S. Private*, pg. 678

Hammond, John P., Mng. Dir. & Publisher--National Retail Hardware Assn., Indianapolis, IN; *U.S. Private*, pg. 786

Hammond, Peter W., Chief Exec. Officer & Mng. Dir.--Spicers Paper Limited, Preston, Australia; *Int'l*, pg. 72

Hampson, M., Mng. Dir.--Air Movement Group Ltd., Dudley, United Kingdom; *Int'l*, pg. 1267

Han, Moo-Wang, Mng. Dir.--Cho Hung Finance Limited, Central, Hong Kong; *Int'l*, pg. 288

Hanado, Kenji, Mng. Dir.--Kayaba Industry Co., Ltd., Tokyo, Japan; *Int'l*, pg. 727

Hanaoka, Sakato, Sr. Mng. Dir.-Corp. Opers. Grp., Admin. Grp.--Dentsu Inc., Tokyo, Japan; *Int'l*, pg. 392

Hanazaki, Yoshio, Mng. Dir.-Mktg., Railway Opers. & Credit Cards--East Japan Railway Company, Tokyo, Japan; *Int'l*, pg. 431

Hancke, Marek, Gen. Mgr.--EURO RSCG Poland, Warsaw, Poland; *Int'l*, pg. 603

Handtmann, George E., III, Mng. Dir.--Provident Investment Counsel, Inc., Pasadena, CA; *U.S. Public*, pg. 1674

Hanft, Adam, Mng. Partner & Pres.--Hanft Byrne Raboy Abrams & Partners, Inc., New York, NY; *U.S. Private*, pg. 499

Hanna, J.M., Mng. Dir. & Chief Exec. Officer--Email Limited, Waterloo, Australia; *Int'l*, pg. 450

Hannaway, Terence, Mng. Dir.--Bank of Ireland (IOM) Limited, Douglas, United Kingdom; *Int'l*, pg. 153

Hanoka, Maurice, Mng. Dir.--Lumiere, Paris, France; *U.S. Private*, pg. 1199

Hanrahan, Paul T., Mng. Dir.--AES China Generating, Beijing, China; *U.S. Public*, pg. 5

Hansen, John C., Mng. Dir.--Industrial Galvanizers Corporation Pty. Ltd., Brisbane, Australia; *Int'l*, pg. 391

Hanson, Graham, Mng. Dir.--Comtext International, London, United Kingdom; *Int'l*, pg. 537

Hanssel, Roland, Mng. Dir.--Manus Presse GmbH, Stuttgart, Germany; *Int'l*, pg. 1478

Hanssens, M. Ignace, Mng. Dir.--General Biscuits Espana (GBE), Barcelona, Spain; *Int'l*, pg. 381

Hara, Kimimochi, Exec. Mng. Dir.--Sumitomo Heavy Industries, Ltd., Tokyo, Japan; *Int'l*, pg. 1314

Harbing, L.P., Mng. Dir.--Getinge International Inc., Lakewood, NJ; *Int'l*, pg. 551

Hardind, Nick, Mng. Dir.--H.J. Heinz Foodservice, Hayes, United Kingdom; *U.S. Public*, pg. 806

Harding, Andrew B., Mng. Dir.--Methode Mikon Limited, Haverhill, United Kingdom; *U.S. Public*, pg. 1101

Hardy, Don C.A.M., Mng. Dir.--ENVIRAS, Deurne, Belgium; *Int'l*, pg. 608

Harg, Morten, Chief Exec. Officer--D'Arcy Masius Benton & Bowles, Oslo, Norway; *U.S. Private*, pg. 304

Hari, Shunichi, Mng. Dir.--Yamaichi Bank Nederland N.V., Strawinskylaan, Netherlands; *Int'l*, pg. 1517

Hari, Shunichi, Mng. Dir.--Yamaichi Bank Nederland Custody N.V., Amsterdam, Netherlands; *Int'l*, pg. 1517

Harithaitavorw, Surapong, Mng. Dir.--The CPAC Concrete Products Co., Ltd., Nonthaburi, Thailand; *Int'l*, pg. 1237

Harrelson, Harvey D., Sr. Mng. Dir.-Fixed Income Capital Markets Grp.--Interstate/Johnson Lane Corporation, Charlotte, NC; *U.S. Public*, pg. 910

Harrington, Jim, Mng. Dir.--Kinney Shoe Corporation, New York, NY; *U.S. Public*, pg. 1777

Harris, John, Mng. Dir.--The Aluminum Powder Company, Sutton Coldfield, United Kingdom; *U.S. Private*, pg. 735

Harris, Lloyd, Mng. Dir.--Bondware, Toronto, Canada; *Int'l*, pg. 417

Harris, Tony, Mng. Dir.--EMAP Computing Ltd., London, United Kingdom; *Int'l*, pg. 451

Harrison, Brian, Mng. Dir.--Dentsu Young & Rubicam/Singapore, Singapore, Singapore; *U.S. Private*, pg. 325

Harrison, Chris, Mng. Dir.--Ayton Young & Rubicam Ltd., Nairobi, Kenya; *U.S. Private*, pg. 1198

Harrison, Fiona, Mng. Dir.--Jaeger Holdings Limited, London, United Kingdom; *Int'l*, pg. 300

Harrison, Ian, V.P. & Mng. Dir.--Leasing Solutions, Inc., San Jose, CA; *U.S. Public*, pg. 982

Harrison, Julia, Mng. Dir.--GPC Market Access Europe, Brussels, Belgium; *U.S. Public*, pg. 1225

Harrison, Ritchie J., Mng. Dir.--Reemtsma Japan Ltd., Tokyo, Japan; *Int'l*, pg. 1101

Harrison, Ritchie J., Mng. Dir.--Reemtsma International Far East Pte. Ltd., Singapore, Singapore; *Int'l*, pg. 1101

Harrison, Wayne, Mng. Dir.--Kollmorgen Tandon India, Mumbai, India; *U.S. Public*, pg. 966

Harrison, William E., PE, Mng. Dir.--Giffels Associates Inc., Phoenix, AZ; *U.S. Private*, pg. 452

Hart, Jeff R., Mng. Dir.--Swiss Re Life Company America, New York, NY; *Int'l*, pg. 1333

Hart, John W., Mng. Dir.--Bermuda Trust (Cook Islands) Limited, Rarotonga, Cook Islands; *Int'l*, pg. 151

Hart, Jonathan, Mng. Dir.--Dixons Stores Group Ltd., Hemel Hempstead, United Kingdom; *Int'l*, pg. 414

Harte, Maurice, Mng. Dir.-Investment Managers--Allied Irish Banks, p.l.c., Dublin, Ireland; *Int'l*, pg. 64

Harte, Maurice, Mng. Dir.--AIB Investment Managers Ltd., Dublin, Ireland; *Int'l*, pg. 64

Hartley, J.M., Mng. Dir.--Bally Shoe Co. Ltd., London, United Kingdom; *Int'l*, pg. 997

Hartmann, Hans Ulrich, Mng. Dir.-Fin. & Controller--AGIE AG (Fur Industrielle Elektronik), Lausanne, Switzerland; *Int'l*, pg. 488

Hartmann, Udo B., Mng. Dir.--BB-Kapitalbeteiligungs gesellschaft GmbH, Berlin, Germany; *Int'l*, pg. 159

Hartnett, Brian, Dr., Mng. Dir.--Tasmanian Alkaloids Pty. Ltd., Westbury, Australia; *U.S. Public*, pg. 932

Harvey, Dan, Mng. Dir.-AIB Grp. (UK) Plc, Gen. Mgr.-Retail Banking--Allied Irish Banks, p.l.c., Dublin, Ireland; *Int'l*, pg. 64

Harvey, David C., Mng. Dir.--System Sensor Ltd., Horsham, United Kingdom; *U.S. Public*, pg. 1307

Hash, Bert J., Jr., Mng. Dir.-Community Rels.--Provident Bank of Maryland, Baltimore, MD; *U.S. Public*, pg. 1337

Hashimi, F.A., Mng. Dir.--Gestetner (Private) Limited, Karachi, Pakistan; *Int'l*, pg. 1115

Hashimoto, Takashi, Mng. Dir.--Yamaichi Australia Ltd., Sydney, Australia; *Int'l*, pg. 1517

Hassell, June, Exec. V.P. & Mng. Dir.--Outdoor Services, New York, NY; *U.S. Private*, pg. 1166

Haste, John, Mng. Dir.-Stores Implementation--PRO Group, Inc., Englewood, CO; *U.S. Private*, pg. 887

Hatcher, Peter, Asst. Reg. Mng. Dir.-Client Servicing--Willis Corroon South Limited, Bristol, United Kingdom; *Int'l*, pg. 1503

Hatclisse, Mike, Mng. Dir.--Scope Ketchum Communications Ltd., London, United Kingdom; *U.S. Private*, pg. 617

Hattori, Masami, Mng. Dir.--Wako International (Europe) Limited, London, United Kingdom; *Int'l*, pg. 1485

Hauck, Steve, Mng. Dir.--A. Schulman, Inc., Piscataway, NJ; *U.S. Public*, pg. 1441

Hauff, A., Mng. Dir.--Ebara Germany GmbH, Hanau, Germany; *Int'l*, pg. 432

Hauser, Helmut, Mng. Dir.--Sudkurier GmbH, Konstanz, Germany; *Int'l*, pg. 1478

Havander, Goran, Mng. Dir. & Grp. Chief Exec.--Cederroth International AB, Upplands Vasby, Sweden; *U.S. Public*, pg. 38

Havenstein, Ralph, Mng. Dir.--Sasol Chemical Industries Ltd., Sasolburg, South Africa; *Int'l*, pg. 1196

Haverbeke, Peter, Mng. Dir.--Keystone Valve (Europa) B.V., Breda, Netherlands; *U.S. Public*, pg. 1650

Haverstick, M., Mng. Dir.--Yale Industrial Products, Forrest City, AR; *U.S. Public*, pg. 406

Haveus, Peter, Mng. Dir.--AB Tvattman Textil Service, Malmo, Sweden; *Int'l*, pg. 1286

Hawken, Sue, Mng. Dir.--EMAP Elan, London, United Kingdom; *Int'l*, pg. 451

Hawkins, Phillip, Mng. Dir.--CarrAmerica Realty, Washington, DC; *U.S. Public*, pg. 308

Hayashi, Yoshiro, Sr. Mng. Dir.--Ebara Corporation, Tokyo, Japan; *Int'l*, pg. 431

Hayashi, Yutaka, Mng. Dir.-Res. & Devel.--Sumitomo Metal Industries, Ltd., Tokyo, Japan; *Int'l*, pg. 1315

Hayek, G. Nicolas, Jr., Mng. Dir.--SMH Italia S.P.A., Rozzano, Italy; *Int'l*, pg. 1161

Hayes, Stephen, Mng. Dir.-Pub. Rels.--American Automobile Association, Heathrow, FL; *U.S. Private*, pg. 50

Haynes, Thomas, Mng. Partner & Exec. Creative Dir.--Lewis Gace Bozell Healthcare Worldwide, Fort Lee, NJ; *U.S. Public*, pg. 1642

Haynie, John H., Sr. Mng. Dir.-Opers.--Interstate/Johnson Lane Corporation, Charlotte, NC; *U.S. Public*, pg. 910

Hayward, Les, Mng. Dir.--ISS Contract Clean Midlands Ltd., Milton Keynes, United Kingdom; *Int'l*, pg. 657

Hazenberg, P.R., Mng. Dir.--Schering Nederland B.V., Weesp, Netherlands; *Int'l*, pg. 1204

Head, Gerry, Mng. Dir.-Mfg., Logistics & Quality--Thorn Security Group, Ltd., Sunbury, United Kingdom; *Int'l*, pg. 1386

Head, Mike, Mng. Dir.--Johnson & Johnson Limited, Maidenhead, United Kingdom; *U.S. Public*, pg. 930

Healy, David, Mng. Dir.--ISS Contract Cleaners Ltd., Dublin, Ireland; *Int'l*, pg. 657

Hean, Scott B., Mng. Dir.--Corporate & Institutional Financial Services - Vancouver, Vancouver, Canada; *Int'l*, pg. 153

Hearn, D., Mng. Dir.--Bowthorpe (NZ) Limited, Christchurch, New Zealand; *Int'l*, pg. 208

Hearn, Michael D., Sr. Mng. Dir., Gen. Counsel & Sec.--Interstate/Johnson Lane Corporation, Charlotte, NC; *U.S. Public*, pg. 910

Heavisides, Henry, Mng. Dir.--Lands' End Direct Merchants UK Limited, Rutland, United Kingdom; *U.S. Public*, pg. 978

Heckel, Vincent, Mng. Dir.--Bureau Rhone-Poulenc SA, Budapest, Hungary; *Int'l*, pg. 1112

Hecker, Peter, Dr., Mng. Dir.-Personnel--Dyckerhoff & Widmann AG, Munich, Germany; *Int'l*, pg. 423

Heddema, Ton, Mng. Dir.--Euroconsult BV, Arnhem, Netherlands; *Int'l*, pg. 606

Heddema, Ton, Mng. Dir.--ILIS International Land Information Services CV, Arnhem, Netherlands; *Int'l*, pg. 606

Hedenstrom, Anders, Mng. Dir.--S-E-Banken Fonder AB, Stockholm, Sweden; *Int'l*, pg. 1259

Hedley, R.J.G., Mng. Dir.--Alcan Chemicals Europe, Gerrards Cross, United Kingdom; *Int'l*, pg. 51

Hedquist, Jan, Vice Chm.-Europe--Young & Rubicam Holdings Ltd., London, United Kingdom; *U.S. Private*, pg. 1199

Hedvold, Ralf, Mng. Dir.--Berendsen Components AB, Stockholm, Sweden; *Int'l*, pg. 1284

Hefti, Hans, Mng. Dir.--Harrington International Insurance Ltd., Hamilton, Bermuda; *Int'l*, pg. 1333

Hegbrant, Jorgen, Mng. Dir.--Park Dialys AB, Lund, Sweden; *Int'l*, pg. 667

Heggenes, Per, Mng. Dir.-Human Resources Worldwide (New York)--Burson-Marsteller, New York, NY; *U.S. Private*, pg. 1197

Heiliger, Klaus A., Mng. Dir.--Bankgesellschaft Berlin International S.A., Luxembourg, Luxembourg; *Int'l*, pg. 159

Heimes, Peter T., Mng. Dir.--Super RTL, Cologne, Germany; *Int'l*, pg. 562

Hein, Michael L., Mng. Dir.-U.S./Japan Bus. Devel.--Capital Markets Assurance Corporation, New York, NY; *U.S. Public*, pg. 1023

Heinrichs, Arlene, Mng. Dir.--BHP Steel SE Asia Pte Ltd., Singapore, Singapore; *Int'l*, pg. 227

Heischmann, Wilhelm, Mng. Dir.--Dresdnerbank Asset Management S.A., Senningerberg, Luxembourg; *Int'l*, pg. 420

Heiskanen, Risto, Mng. Dir.--Raisio Polska Foods Sp. z.o.o., Warsaw, Poland; *Int'l*, pg. 1085

Heiskanen, Risto T., Mng. Dir.--Oy McCormick Ab, Helsinki, Finland; *U.S. Public*, pg. 1067

Hellberg, C.E., Chief Oper. Officer--Creative Productions, Pittsburgh, PA; *U.S. Private*, pg. 288

Heller, Wayne C., Dir.-Dispatch & Crew Scheduling--Mesaba Holdings, Inc., Minneapolis, MN; *U.S. Public*, pg. 1099

Hellwig, Peter, Mng. Dir.--BRC Weldmesh (SEA) Pte Ltd., Jurong, Singapore; *Int'l*, pg. 227

Helmer, Svend, Mng. Dir.--Danisco Distillers, Copenhagen, Denmark; *Int'l*, pg. 378

Helmy, Hassan A., Dr., Mng. Dir.--R.P. Scherer Egypt, Alexandria, Egypt; *U.S. Public*, pg. 1438

Helomaa, Jouku, Mng. Dir.--Merita Capital Ltd., Helsinki, Finland; *Int'l*, pg. 859

Heming, Bob, Mng. Dir.--Musicland Group Inc., Minnetonka, MN; *U.S. Public*, pg. 1142

Henderson, Barbara, Sr. V.P. & Mng. Dir.-Pub. Rels.--Ingalls, Boston, MA; *U.S. Private*, pg. 562

Henderson, Frederick A., Pres. & Mng. Dir.--General Motors do Brasil Ltda., Sao Caetano do Sul, Brazil; *U.S. Public*, pg. 722

Henderson, Keith, Mng. Dir.--Seal Sands Chemicals Ltd., Middlesbrough, United Kingdom; *U.S. Public*, pg. 297

Henderson, Kirk, Chief Oper. Officer & Mng. Dir.--Great Pacific Enterprises Inc., Vancouver, Canada; *Int'l*, pg. 557

Hendrickson, John J., Mng. Dir.--Securitas Capital Partners I, L.P., Hamilton, Bermuda; *Int'l*, pg. 1333

Henley, Barry S., Mng. Dir.--Chubb Singapore Private Limited, Singapore, Singapore; *Int'l*, pg. 1250

Hennessey, B.J., Mng. Dir.--Decoflex Limited, Hartlepool, United Kingdom; *Int'l*, pg. 889

Hennessey, J., Mng. Dir.--Ascom Timeplex Ltd. (New Zealand), Wellington, New Zealand; *Int'l*, pg. 87

Henninger, Christian, Mng. Dir.--Sulzer International (Deutschland) GmbH, Ravensburg, Germany; *Int'l*, pg. 1308

Henocq, Jacques, Co-Mng. Dir.--TBWA Paris, Paris, France; *U.S. Private*, pg. 1063

Henrion, Romain, Mng. Dir.--ProfilARBED, Esch-sur-Alzette, Luxembourg; *Int'l*, pg. 79

Henrot, Jacques, Mng. Dir.--ETCD, Casablanca, Morocco; *Int'l*, pg. 823

Henson, A.J., Mng. Dir.--Richard Simon and Sons Limited, Nottingham, United Kingdom; *U.S. Public*, pg. 789

Henstra, R., Mng. Dir.--Hoogovens Steel Primary Products, Ijmuiden, Netherlands; *Int'l*, pg. 756

Heppener, Jan, Mng. Dir.-Stena Line BV--Stena Line AB, Goteborg, Sweden; *Int'l*, pg. 1300

Hepple, John, Mng. Dir.--Lightcraft, Jeannette, PA; *U.S. Private*, pg. 749

Herbert, Lawrence, Mng. Dir.--International Correspondence Schools (Overseas) Limited, Glasgow, United Kingdom; *U.S. Public*, pg. 784

Herenstein, Ira, Mng. Dir.--Datastream International Ltd., London, United Kingdom; *U.S. Public*, pg. 1325

Hermoni, Avner, V.P. & Mng. Dir.--K&S (Israel) Ltd.--Kulicke & Soffa Industries, Inc., Willow Grove, PA; *U.S. Public*, pg. 968

Hermoni, Avner, V.P. & Mng. Dir.--Kulicke & Soffa (Israel) Ltd., Haifa, Israel; *U.S. Public*, pg. 969

Herrero, Javier, Mng. Dir.--Iberdrola, S.A., Bilbao, Spain; *Int'l*, pg. 657

Herrill, Doug, Mng. Dir.--Trimble Navigation Europe Ltd., Hook, United Kingdom; *U.S. Public*, pg. 1638

Herrloff, Tommy, Mng. Dir.--Skanska London, London, United Kingdom; *Int'l*, pg. 1261

Herrmann, Joachim, Mng. Dir.--DYWIT S.p.A., Milan, Italy; *Int'l*, pg. 425

Herskovitz, Stephen, Mng. Dir.--MC2 Adams, New York, NY; *U.S. Private*, pg. 679

Herter, Walter, Mng. Dir.--Sulzer (Thailand) Ltd., Bangkok, Thailand; *Int'l*, pg. 1307

Hervert, Jean, Mng. Dir.--J.V. Laing-GTM Europe, Bristol, United Kingdom; *Int'l*, pg. 823

Hess, Jean Pierre, Gen. Mgr.--PromoPub/DMB&B Kuwait, Kuwait, Kuwait; *U.S. Private*, pg. 305

Hessel, Peter, Mng. Dir.--TBWA Dusseldorf GmbH, Dusseldorf, Germany; *U.S. Private*, pg. 1063

Hettich, James, Sr. V.P. & Grp. Dir.--Wolf Mansfield Bolling Advertising Inc., Buffalo, NY; *U.S. Private*, pg. 1186

Heuser, Eberhard, Mng. Dir.--Eldon GmbH, Neuss, Germany; *Int'l*, pg. 436

Heutink, R., Mng. Dir.--Nutricia Cujik B.V., Cuyk, Netherlands; *Int'l*, pg. 991

Hew, C.T., Mng. Partner--Scotchbrook Communications Ltd., Wan Chai, Hong Kong; *U.S. Private*, pg. 411

Hey, Dr., Mng. Dir.--Robert Bosch Produktie NV, Brussels, Belgium; *Int'l*, pg. 206

Hick, Paul, Mng. Dir.-Intl. Opers.--Waterford Wedgwood UK Plc, Stoke on Trent, United Kingdom; *Int'l*, pg. 1487

Hickman, Thomas K., Mng. Dir.-OSI Singapore & OSI Malaysia--OSI Systems, Inc., Hawthorne, CA; *U.S. Public*, pg. 1208

Hicks, Chris, Mng. Dir.--Phase Components Ltd., Horsham, United Kingdom; *U.S. Public*, pg. 93

Hicks, Thomas O., Chm. Bd., Chief Exec. Officer & Mng. Dir.--Hicks, Muse, Tate & Furst Inc., Dallas, TX; *U.S. Private*, pg. 526

Hierselmann, Reinhold, Mng. Dir.--3M Deutschland GmbH, Neuss, Germany; *U.S. Public*, pg. 1606

Hiester, Thomas R., Mng. Dir.--Zurn Thailand, Bangkok, Thailand; *U.S. Public*, pg. 1795

Higaki, Taiji, Mng. Dir.-Res. & Devel.--Oji Paper Co., Ltd., Tokyo, Japan; *Int'l*, pg. 998

Higbee, Ann G., Mng. Partner-EMA Pub. Rels. Services--Eric Mower and Associates, Inc., Syracuse, NY; *U.S. Private*, pg. 765
Higgins, J.S., Chief Fin. Officer & Mng. Dir.--The Fremont Group, San Francisco, CA; *U.S. Private*, pg. 427
Higuchi, Masanori, Mng. Dir.--Chuo Trust Asia Limited, Hong Kong, Hong Kong; *Int'l*, pg. 291
Hijmans, K., Mng. Dir.--Kaagro B.V., Zoetermeer, Netherlands; *Int'l*, pg. 991
Hildrew, P. D., Mng. Dir.--Garny AG, Morfelden, Germany; *Int'l*, pg. 387
Hildyard, N., Mng. Dir.--Smith & Nephew Medical Ltd., Kingston-upon-Hull, United Kingdom; *Int'l*, pg. 1263
Hilfiker, Andre, Dr., Mng. Dir.--CIBA-GEIGY Colombiana S.A., Bogota, Colombia; *Int'l*, pg. 976
Hill, J. Tomilson, Sr. Mng. Dir.--The Blackstone Group, New York, NY; *U.S. Private*, pg. 147
Hill, Melanie, Exec. V.P. & Mng. Dir.--Ackerman McQueen, Inc., Tulsa, OK; *U.S. Private*, pg. 13
Hill, Roger W., Mng. Dir.--Imperial Holly Corporation, Sugar Land, TX; *U.S. Public*, pg. 872
Hillebrand, G., Mng. Dir.--Fuchs' Sche Tongruben GmbH & Co. Ltd., Ransbach-Baumbach, Germany; *Int'l*, pg. 1488
Hiller, David B., Principal & Mng. Dir.--National Asset Management Corporation, Louisville, KY; *U.S. Public*, pg. 1154
Hillert, Jurgen, Mng. Dir.--MHI Partners Werbeagentur GMBH, Starnberg, Germany; *U.S. Public*, pg. 1422
Hillgath, Tristan, Mng. Dir.--Invesco Europe Ltd., London, United Kingdom; *Int'l*, pg. 685
Hilliard, M., Exec. V.P. & Mng. Dir.--BBDO Canada, Toronto, Canada; *U.S. Private*, pg. 104
Hillion, Herve, Mng. Dir.-Res. & Devel.--Landis & Staefa AG, Zug, Switzerland; *Int'l*, pg. 800
Hilton, John R., Mng. Dir.--Delta Fasteners Pty. Ltd., Welshpool, Australia; *Int'l*, pg. 391
Himebauch, Steven F., V.P. & Mng. Dir.--Mortgage Guaranty Insurance Corporation, Milwaukee, WI; *U.S. Public*, pg. 1026
Hinchcliff, Richard H., Mng. Dir.--General Re Europe Limited, London, United Kingdom; *U.S. Public*, pg. 726
Hind, A.J., Mng. Dir.--Horstman Timers & Controls Limited, Bath, United Kingdom; *Int'l*, pg. 297
Hind, David, Mng. Dir.--Ortho Clinical Diagnostic Systems Limited, Amersham, United Kingdom; *U.S. Public*, pg. 931
Hinge, M.G., Chm. Bd. & Joint Mng. Dir.--Taylor Woodrow Management Ltd., Southall, United Kingdom; *Int'l*, pg. 1359
Hinojosa, Santiago, Chm. & Mng. Dir.--DMB&B S.A. de C.V., Mexico, Mexico; *U.S. Private*, pg. 304
Hinrup, Peter, Mng. Dir.--Dancall Telecom A/S, Pandrup, Denmark; *Int'l*, pg. 206
Hintz, David, Dir.-Mktg.--Cousins Submarines, Menomonee Falls, WI; *U.S. Private*, pg. 280
Hirai, Keitaro, Mng. Dir.--Sumitomo Finance International plc, London, United Kingdom; *Int'l*, pg. 1310
Hirai, Norio, Sr. Mng. Dir.-Human Resources--Omron Corporation, Kyoto, Japan; *Int'l*, pg. 1005
Hirano, Satoshi, Mng. Dir. & Sr. V.P.--Japan Airlines Company, Ltd., Tokyo, Japan; *Int'l*, pg. 699
Hirata, Yukihiro, Exec. Mng. Dir., Sr. Gen. Mgr.-Plant Engrng.--Kawasaki Heavy Industries, Ltd., Kobe, Japan; *Int'l*, pg. 725
Hirata, Yukio, Mng. Dir.--Chuo Trust International Limited, London, United Kingdom; *Int'l*, pg. 291
Hirayama, Yoshio, Sr. Mng. Dir.--Ebara Corporation, Tokyo, Japan; *Int'l*, pg. 431
Hirono, Masakazu, Mng. Dir. & Gen. Mgr.-Gen. Affairs--Hokuriku Electric Industry Co., Ltd., Toyama, Japan; *Int'l*, *pg. 627*
Hirshkowitz, Brian, Exec. Dir.-Business Partner Intergration--Countrywide Funding Corporation, Pasadena, CA; *U.S. Public*, pg. 453
Hisamoto, Shoji, Mng. Dir. & Gen. Mgr.-Dentsu Inc. Chubu--Dentsu Inc., Tokyo, Japan; *Int'l*, pg. 392
Hjertstedt, Gouran, Mng. Dir.--SKF Mekan AB, Katrineholm, Sweden; *Int'l*, pg. 1157
Hjorth, Lars, Deputy Mng. Dir.-Retail Bus. & Support Units--KF/Konsum Coop Group, Stockholm, Sweden; *Int'l*, pg. 718
Hlavac, Jozef, Mng. Dir.--Istropolitana/DMB&B Bratislava, Bratislava, Slovakia; *U.S. Private*, pg. 304
Ho, S., Mng. Dir.--Hanimex Vivitar (H.K.) Ltd., Kowloon, Hong Kong; *Int'l*, pg. 1061
Hochheuser, Kurt, Mng. Dir.-Corp. Banking--Commerzbank AG, Frankfurt, Germany; *Int'l*, pg. 308
Hochstrasser, Bruno, Mng. Dir.--Studer, Regensdorf, Switzerland; *U.S. Public*, pg. 788
Hodt, Rolf, Mng. Dir.--TBWA Oslo, Oslo, Norway; *U.S. Private*, pg. 1063
Hofer, Jurg, Mng. Dir.--Nokia Telecommunications AG, Dubendorf, Switzerland; *Int'l*, pg. 953
Hoffman-Petersen, Erik, Mng. Dir.--FLS Miljo A/S, Valby, Denmark; *Int'l*, pg. 475
Hoffman, Dieter, Mng. Dir.--Allgemeine Privatkundenbank AG, Hannover, Germany; *Int'l*, pg. 159
Hoffman, Michel B., Sr. Mng. Dir.--The Blackstone Group, New York, NY; *U.S. Private*, pg. 147
Hoffman, Patty, V.P. & Mng. Dir.--Western International Media Corporation, Sacramento, CA; *U.S. Private*, pg. 1167
Hogg, Peter, Mng. Dir.--Willis Faber (Far East) Limited, Wan Chai, Hong Kong; *Int'l*, pg. 1510
Hohling, Heinrich, Mng. Dir.--ISS Food Hygiene Service GmbH, Flensburg, Germany; *Int'l*, pg. 657
Hohling, Heinrich, Mng. Dir.--ISS Holzl GmbH Servisystem, Munich, Germany; *Int'l*, pg. 657
Hoiden, John, Mng. Dir.--Getinge Vaxjo A/S, Lyngby, Denmark; *Int'l*, pg. 552
Hoketsu, Hiroshi, Pres. & Mng. Dir.--Ortho Clinical Diagnostic Systems K.K., Tokyo, Japan; *U.S. Public*, pg. 931
Holckner, David, Gen. Mgr.--Smorgon Fencing, Melbourne, Australia; *Int'l*, pg. 1269
Holderness-Roddam, T., Mng. Dir.--United Molasses Company, London, United Kingdom; *Int'l*, pg. 1356
Holding, J., Mng. Dir.--Texaco Exploration Norway A/S, Oslo, Norway; *U.S. Public*, pg. 1584
Holfeld, Bernd, Mng. Dir.-Nordrhein-Westfalen Region--Dyckerhoff & Widmann AG, Munich, Germany; *Int'l*, pg. 423
Holland, John, Mng. Dir.--Edelman Public Relations Worldwide Pte. Ltd., Singapore, Singapore; *U.S. Private*, pg. 363
Hollest, Roger H., Mng. Dir.--Phillips Fine Art Auctioneers, New York, NY; *U.S. Private*, pg. 861
Holm, Egon, Mng. Dir.--Metsa-Serla Tissue A/S, Tastrup, Denmark; *Int'l*, pg. 864
Holmes, Beverly, Dir.-Pub. Rels--Lands' End, Inc., Dodgeville, WI; *U.S. Public*, pg. 977
Holmes, Earl E., V.P. & Mng. Dir.--Mortgage Guaranty Insurance Corporation, Milwaukee, WI; *U.S. Public*, pg. 1026
Holmes, Roger, Mng. Dir.--McLean Europe, Smethwick, United Kingdom; *U.S. Public*, pg. 1791
Holmstrom, Veikko, Mng. Dir.--ZAO KONE Lifts St. Petersburg, Saint Petersburg, Russia; *Int'l*, pg. 748
Holter-Sorensen, Erik, Chm. Bd. & Mng. Dir.--A/S Ivaran Rederi, Lysaker, Norway; *Int'l*, pg. 696
Holwerda, R., Mng. Dir.--Baars Kaas B.V., Schoonrewoerd, Netherlands; *Int'l*, pg. 752
Hong, Dong-Peu, Mng. Dir.--Ssangyong Oil Refining Co. Ltd., Seoul, Korea; *Int'l*, pg. 1292
Hong, Sa-Seung, Chief Fin. Officer--Ssangyong Cement Industrial Co., Ltd., Seoul, Korea; *Int'l*, pg. 1291
Hood, Christy, Mng. Dir.-Pub. Rels.--Donna Karan, New York, NY; *U.S. Public*, pg. 517
Hoogendijk, E., Mng. Dir.--Hartwell Corporation, Placentia, CA; *U.S. Private*, pg. 1168
Hoogendoorn, Jaap, Mng. Dir.--Horticom BV, De Lier, Netherlands; *Int'l*, pg. 1099
Hoogenraat, P. W., Mng. Dir.--City Com B.V., Rotterdam, Netherlands; *Int'l*, pg. 681
Hoong, Leong Mun, Mng. Dir.--Strombecker (HK) Ltd., Kowloon, Hong Kong; *U.S. Private*, pg. 1047
Hoover, J.E., Mng. Dir.--Australian Timken Proprietary Ltd., Ballarat, Australia; *U.S. Public*, pg. 1617
Hoover, Jeff, Mng. Editor-Issues & Controversies On File--Facts on File News Services, New York, NY; *U.S. Public*, *pg. 1327*
Hope, Frank, Dr., Mng. Dir.--Ultra Electrics, Cheltenham, United Kingdom; *Int'l*, pg. 1431
Hopkins, Bob, Mng. Dir.-Pur. & Admin.--American Automobile Association, Heathrow, FL; *U.S. Private*, pg. 50
Hopkins, Grahme, Mng. Dir.-The Strategic Grp.--EvansGroup, Dallas, TX; *U.S. Private*, pg. 385
Hore, G., Mng. Dir.--S.A. Societe Caroloregienne de Cokefaction CARCOKE, Terte, Belgium; *Int'l*, pg. 301
Hori, Hiroaki, Mng. Dir.--Daiko Communications Asia Co., Ltd., Hong Kong, Hong Kong; *Int'l*, pg. 366
Horlacher, Rainer, Mng. Dir.-Acctg. & Taxes--Dyckerhoff & Widmann AG, Munich, Germany; *Int'l*, pg. 423
Horn, Karen, Mng. Dir. & Head-Intl. Private Banking--Bankers Trust New York Corporation, New York, NY; *U.S. Public*, pg. 185
Horner, Russ, Mng. Dir.--Australian Newsprint Mills, Hobart, Australia; *Int'l*, pg. 495
Horowitz, Peter M., Sr. Mng. Dir.-Firmwide Communications--Price Waterhouse L.L.P. - U.S., New York, NY; *U.S. Private*, pg. 883
Horstman, M., Mng. Dir.--Hepworth Minerals and Chemicals S.A., Bourron, France; *Int'l*, pg. 615
Horton, Gary J., Deputy Mng. Dir. & Chief Creative Officer--DMB&B Detroit, Troy, MI; *U.S. Private*, pg. 302
Hosoda, Yuji, Mng. Dir.--Toyo Tire & Rubber Co., Ltd., Osaka, Japan; *Int'l*, pg. 1411
Hosokawa, J., Sr. Mng. Dir.-Mktg.--The Kyoei Life Insurance Co., Ltd., Tokyo, Japan; *Int'l*, pg. 776
Hosokawa, Toyohiro, Mng. Dir.-Res. & Devel.--Tonen Corporation, Tokyo, Japan; *Int'l*, pg. 1398
Hosoya, Eiji, Mng. Dir.-Fin. & Health & Welfare--East Japan Railway Company, Tokyo, Japan; *Int'l*, pg. 431
Hossack, G.M., Chm. & Mng. Dir.--GKN Chep SA (Pty) Ltd., Wandsbeck, South Africa; *Int'l*, pg. 536
Hotan, Ernst, Mng. Dir.--Crown Obrist AG, Reinach, Switzerland; *U.S. Public*, pg. 465
Hotsinpiller, Terry, Mng. Dir.--HAWG Hauling & Disposal, Inc., Buckhannon, WV; *U.S. Public*, pg. 403
Houche, Bernard, Mng. Dir.--O.K. Personnel, Neuchatel, Switzerland; *U.S. Public*, pg. 949
Houdmont, B.W.C., Mng. Dir.--Wolters Kluwer Spain, Madrid, Spain; *Int'l*, pg. 1514
Hough, Nick, Mng. Dir.--Lowe Kuiper & Schouten, Amsterdam, Netherlands; *U.S. Private*, pg. 678
House, Frank, Jr., Chm. Bd. & Reg. Construction Mng. Dir.--Willis Corroon Corp. of Birmingham, Birmingham, AL; *Int'l*, pg. 1505
Howard-Jonese, Peter, Mng. Dir.--Rayovac/Vidor Limited, Maidstone, United Kingdom; *U.S. Private*, pg. 912
Howard, K.A., Mng. Dir.--Concrete Industries Sector, Auckland, New Zealand; *Int'l*, pg. 495
Howard, Stefan, Mng. Dir.--MHI Partners Werbeagentur GMBH, Starnberg, Germany; *U.S. Public*, pg. 1422
Howard, Will, Sr. V.P. & Mng. Dir.--Western International Media Corporation, Chicago, IL; *U.S. Private*, pg. 1167
Howe, R.W., Mng. Dir.--Goodyear Malaysia Berhad, Kuala Lumpur, Malaysia; *U.S. Public*, pg. 753
Howe, Travis L., Mng. Dir.--Meto, USA, Morris Plains, NJ; *Int'l*, pg. 460
Howell, David, Mng. Dir.--EURO RSCG Partnership, Bangkok, Thailand; *Int'l*, pg. 602
Howell, Rupert, Mng. Partner--Howell Henry Chaldecott Lury & Partners, London, United Kingdom; *Int'l*, pg. 637
Howells, K., Mng. Dir.--Certech International Ltd., Corby, United Kingdom; *U.S. Public*, pg. 308
Howes, Mike, Mng. Dir.--John Crane (Pty) Ltd., Transvaal, South Africa; *Int'l*, pg. 1339
Hoysentruyt, Paul, Mng. Dir.--Bekintex N.V., Wetteren, Belgium; *Int'l*, pg. 183
Hrushetska, Layna, Mng. Dir.--Leo Burnett Kyiv, Ukraine; *U.S. Private*, pg. 185
Hsiung, Richard, Mng. Dir.--Dentsu Young & Rubicam/Taipei, Taipei, Taiwan; *U.S. Private*, pg. 325
Huang, C.S. Warren, V.P. & Mng. Dir.-Mktg./Far East--Ethyl Corporation, Richmond, VA; *U.S. Public*, pg. 595
Hubbel, Robert C., Mng. Dir.-Commun.--Andersen Worldwide, New York, NY; *U.S. Private*, pg. 72
Huber, Franz, Mng. Dir.--Cerner Solutions Center -SNI Health Solutions Div., Pfeffenhausen, Germany; *U.S. Public*, pg. 331
Huber, Martin, Chief Exec. Officer & Pres.-Exec. Committee--Georg Fischer Ltd., Schaffhausen, Switzerland; *Int'l*, pg. 488
Hudson-Smith, Eric, Mgr.-Office--Woodward-Clyde, Perth, Australia; *U.S. Public*, pg. 1657
Hudson, Eric, Mng. Dir.--Angelica International Ltd., Warrington, United Kingdom; *U.S. Public*, pg. 113
Hudson, P.M.G., Mng. Dir.--De La Rue Holographics Limited, Basingstoke, United Kingdom; *Int'l*, pg. 387
Hufnagel, Joachim, Mng. Dir.-Baden-Wurtemburg Region--Dyckerhoff & Widmann AG, Munich, Germany; *Int'l*, pg. 423
Hughes, Donal, Mng. Dir.--Chilton Electric, Dunleer, Ireland; *Int'l*, pg. 554
Hughes, W. Thomas, V.P. & Mng. Dir.--Mortgage Guaranty Insurance Corporation, Milwaukee, WI; *U.S. Public*, pg. 1026
Hui, Hong Chong, Mng. Dir.--Inoue-Nissei Engineering Pte Ltd., Singapore, Singapore; *Int'l*, pg. 1322
Hull, Hardwood Campbell, Mng. Dir.--Leo Burnett Co. Inc., Buenos Aires, Argentina; *U.S. Private*, pg. 185
Humphrey, D.A., Mng. Dir.--Nutricia (Asia-Pacific) Ltd., Wan Chai, Hong Kong; *Int'l*, pg. 992
Humphreys, Ed, Mng. Dir.--Nestle Lyons Maid, York, United Kingdom; *Int'l*, pg. 918
Hunkvale, Steve, Mng. Dir. & V.P.--Moog Controls Ltd., Gloucester, United Kingdom; *U.S. Public*, pg. 1128
Hunn, Michael, Mng. Dir.--Del Amo Hospital, Torrance, CA; *U.S. Public*, pg. 1697
Hunner, Brad, Dir.--Studio 70, Eden Prairie, MN; *U.S. Public*, *pg. 1541*
Hunt, Edward, Mng. Dir.--Sulzer Papertec Manchester Ltd., Manchester, United Kingdom; *Int'l*, pg. 1306
Hunt, Peter, Chm. Bd. & Mng. Dir.--Land Securities Plc, London, United Kingdom; *Int'l*, pg. 798
Hunziker, Fredy W., Mng. Dir.--LeaRonal AG, Littau, Switzerland; *U.S. Public*, pg. 982
Huotelin, Martti, Mng. Dir.--Helsingen Pantti-Osakeyhtio, Helsinki, Finland; *Int'l*, pg. 859
Huppertz, John, Ph.D., Mng. Partner-Mktg. & Res. Services--Eric Mower and Associates, Inc., Syracuse, NY; *U.S. Private*, pg. 765
Hur, Jong Wook, Deputy Pres. & Dir.--Cho Hung Bank, Seoul, Korea; *Int'l*, pg. 287
Hurksman, Jacques, Mng. Dir.--Arthur D. Little International, Inc., Rotterdam, Netherlands; *U.S. Private*, pg. 670
Husseini, Tony, Mng. Dir.-Dubai--Tamra DMB&B, Dubai, United Arab Emirates; *U.S. Private*, pg. 305
Hussey, Jay, Mng. Dir.--Resource Marketing, Inc., San Francisco, CA; *U.S. Private*, pg. 924
Hutchins, Glenn H., Sr. Mng. Dir.--The Blackstone Group, New York, NY; *U.S. Private*, pg. 147
Hutchison, James, Mgr.-Office--Woodward-Clyde, Jakarta, Indonesia; *U.S. Public*, pg. 1657
Hutter, Heidi, Mng. Dir.--Swiss Re America Corporation, New York, NY; *Int'l*, pg. 1333
Hutton, Andrew J., Mng. Dir.--Wolseley Centers Ltd., Ripon, United Kingdom; *Int'l*, pg. 1511
Huttonen, Jussi, Mng. Dir.--Enso Marketing Co. Ltd., Orpington, United Kingdom; *Int'l*, pg. 457
Huurman, B.N.J., Mng. Dir.--Hak B.V., Giessen, Netherlands; *Int'l*, pg. 244
Huysentruyt, Paul, Mng. Dir.--N.V. Bekaert S.A., Zwevegem, Belgium; *Int'l*, pg. 183
Huysman, Marc, Mng. Dir.--S.M.P., Prague, Czech Republic; *Int'l*, pg. 823
Hwee, Koh Boon, Chief Exec. Officer & Mng. Dir.--Liang Court Holdings Ltd., Singapore, Singapore; *Int'l*, pg. 807
Hyatt, Harry J., Chief Oper. Officer & Mng. Dir.--Sasol Alpha Olefins, Rosebank, South Africa; *Int'l*, pg. 1196
Hyde, D.W., Mng. Dir.--Alcan Metal Centres, Tipton, United Kingdom; *Int'l*, pg. 51
Hypponen, Heikki, Mng. Dir.--Merita Real Estate Ltd., Helsinki, Finland; *Int'l*, pg. 859
Hyvonen, Tuula, Mng. Dir.--ZAO Norvista - St. Petersburg, Saint Petersburg, Russia; *Int'l*, pg. 486
Hyytiainen, Matti, Mng. Dir.--PT KSB Indonesia, Java, Indonesia; *Int'l*, pg. 721
Ibison, J., Mng. Dir.--Riley Advertising (Manchester) Ltd., Manchester, United Kingdom; *Int'l*, pg. 1117
Icart, Jose Maria, Mng. Dir.--Icart S.A., Barcelona, Spain; *U.S. Public*, pg. 310
Ichikawa, Katsuhiko, Mng. Dir.--Central Japan Railway Company-Sydney Office, Sydney, Australia; *Int'l*, pg. 279
Ichimura, Hiroshi, Sr. Mng. Dir.-Oper. Systems--Nippon Shinpan Co., Ltd., Tokyo, Japan; *Int'l*, pg. 939
Ichiyanagi, Yoshiki, Mng. Dir.--Dai Nippon Printing Co. (Australia) Pty. Ltd., Sydney, Australia; *Int'l*, pg. 363
Ide, Christopher G., Mng. Dir.--Swiss Life (UK) Group, Sevenoaks, United Kingdom; *Int'l*, pg. 1332
Ide, Magane, Mng. Dir.--Fuji Investment Management Company (Europe) Limited, London, United Kingdom; *Int'l*, pg. 521
Idres, Abdul Jalil, Mng. Dir.--Johnson & Johnson Medical Mfg., Sdn. Bhd., Shah Alam, Malaysia; *U.S. Public*, pg. 931
Idris, Abdul Jalil, Mng. Dir.--Johnson & Johnson Sdn. Bhd., Petaling Jaya, Malaysia; *U.S. Public*, pg. 931

Igarashi, Osamu, Sr. V.P. -Corp. Plng. & Sr. Mng. Dir.--Japan Airlines Company, Ltd., Tokyo, Japan; *Int'l*, pg. 699
Igarashi, Tadayoshi, Mng. Dir.--Nippon Express (Belgium) N.V./S.A., Zaventem, Belgium; *Int'l*, pg. 934
Igd, Werner, Mng. Dir.--UPM-Kymmene Deutschland GmbH, Dorpen, Germany; *Int'l*, pg. 1430
Ikeda, Kazuo, Sr. Mng. Dir.-Affiliates & Admin.--Nippon Shinpan Co., Ltd., Tokyo, Japan; *Int'l*, pg. 939
Ikeda, Yasuo, Chief Officer-Environment, Safety & Gas--Japan Energy Corporation, Tokyo, Japan; *Int'l*, pg. 702
Ikeda, Yukio, Mng. Dir.--Ebara Corporation, Tokyo, Japan; *Int'l*, pg. 431
Ikegami, Fumio, Mng. Dir. & Gen. Mgr.-Admin.--Hokuriku Electric Industry Co., Ltd., Toyama, Japan; *Int'l*, pg. 627
Ikegami, Kunio, Mng. Dir.--Daiwa Europe (Spain) Sociedad de Valores S.A., Madrid, Spain; *Int'l*, pg. 375
Ikematsu, Masayoshi, Exec. Dir. & Pres. of Dentsu Actis Inc.--Dentsu Inc., Tokyo, Japan; *Int'l*, pg. 392
Ikuta, Shigemi, Mng. Dir.--The Meiji Life Insurance Company Frankfurt Office, Frankfurt, Germany; *Int'l*, pg. 854
Ilda, Michio, Chief Fin. Officer & Sr. Mng. Dir.--Fujisawa Pharmaceutical Co. Ltd., Osaka, Japan; *Int'l*, pg. 525
Ilvessalo, Seppo, Mng. Dir.--Merita Life Assurance Ltd., Espoo, Finland; *Int'l*, pg. 859
Ilzarbe, Miguel Angel, Mng. Dir.--Heinemann Iberia SA, Madrid, Spain; *Int'l*, pg. 1094
Imai, Kazuhiko, Mng. Dir.--Thai Fuji Finance and Securities Company Ltd., Bangkok, Thailand; *Int'l*, pg. 521
Imazumi, Michiaki, Mng. Dir.-Sls. & Mktg. Div.--Fujisawa Pharmaceutical Co. Ltd., Osaka, Japan; *Int'l*, pg. 525
Imbault, Dominique, Mng. Dir.--Alice, Paris, France; *U.S. Private*, pg. 678
Imeson, Jo, Mng. Dir.--CineBooks, Inc., New York, NY; *Int'l*, *pg. 925*
Impellizeri, Marisa, Mng. Dir.--Norvista S.R.L., Milan, Italy; *Int'l*, pg. 486
Imperial, Phil, Mng. Dir.-Strategic Communications & Industry Affairs--MET Solutions, LLC, Morris Plains, NJ; *U.S. Public*, pg. 1642
Ingall, Geoff, Mng. Dir.--Young & Rubicam Mattingly, Richmond, Australia; *U.S. Private*, pg. 1198
Ingall, Geoffrey, Mng. Dir.--Y&R Mattingly, Richmond, Australia; *U.S. Private*, pg. 325
Ingham, Clive, Mng. Dir.--Moore Europe, Lausanne, Switzerland; *Int'l*, pg. 889
Ingold, Urs, Mng. Dir.--Reed Exhibition Companies-Switzerland, Fallanden, Switzerland; *Int'l*, pg. 1097
Ingolfsson, Eirikur, Mng. Dir.--ISS pjonustan hf., Reykjavik, Iceland; *Int'l*, pg. 657
Ingram, Mark, Mng. Dir.-Operational Services--Pacific Coast Building Products Inc., Sacramento, CA; *U.S. Private*, pg. 830
Ingram, Robert A., Mng. Dir.--Media Incorporated, New York, NY; *U.S. Private*, pg. 726
Ingram, Robert A., Mng. Dir.--Media Direct Partners, Incorporated, New York, NY; *U.S. Private*, pg. 726
Inokuchi, Takuya, Mng. Dir.-Fin. & Acctg. & Information Sys.--Sumitomo Chemical Company, Ltd., Tokyo, Japan; *Int'l*, pg. 1310
Inoue, Masanori, Mng. Dir.--Nittsu Shoji Co., Ltd., Tokyo, Japan; *Int'l*, pg. 934
Inove, Shigeo, Mng. Dir.--Japan Universal Securities (Hong Kong) Limited, Hong Kong, Hong Kong; *Int'l*, pg. 1444
Interno, Antonio, Mng. Dir.--Meridian Diagnostics Europe s.r.l., Milan, Italy; *U.S. Public*, pg. 1095
Iordache, Ioana, Mng. Dir.--Leo Burnett & Target, Bucharest, Romania; *U.S. Private*, pg. 184
Ipsen, Sven, Mng. Dir.--ISS Specialservice, Copenhagen, Denmark; *Int'l*, pg. 656
Irion, Guido, Mng. Dir.--Sulzer Infra (Schweiz) AG, Winterthur, Switzerland; *Int'l*, pg. 1306
Irisawa, Koji, Mng. Dir.--The Sakura Bank (Luxembourg) S.A., Luxembourg, Luxembourg; *Int'l*, pg. 1180
Isaka, Sakae, Mng. Dir.-Store Opers.--Ito-Yokado Co., Ltd., Tokyo, Japan; *Int'l*, pg. 693
Isejima, Isao, Mng. Dir.--Shiseido (Australia) Pty. Limited, Pyrmont, Australia; *Int'l*, pg. 1235
Ishibashi, Yasuji, Chief Fin. Officer & Sr. Mng. Dir.--Ishihara Sangyo Kaisha, Ltd., Osaka, Japan; *Int'l*, pg. 689
Ishida, Nobuyuki, Mng. Dir.--Shizuoka Bank (Europe) S.A., Brussels, Belgium; *Int'l*, pg. 1236
Ishida, Tateaki, Mng. Dir.--Tokai Capital Markets Limited, London, United Kingdom; *Int'l*, pg. 1391
Ishida, Yoshiaki, Sr. Mng. Dir.-Intl. Headquarters--Orix Corporation, Tokyo, Japan; *Int'l*, pg. 1008
Ishihara, Toru, Mng. Dir.--The Fuji Futures (Singapore) Pte., Limited, Singapore, Singapore; *Int'l*, pg. 521
Ishikawa, Kozo, Mng. Dir.--The Nikko Merchant Bank (Singapore) Ltd., Singapore, Singapore; *Int'l*, pg. 931
Israel, Michael, Partner--Goldner Hawn Johnsons & Morrison Incorporated, Minneapolis, MN; *U.S. Private*, pg. 462
Issakainen, Markku, Chief Exec. Officer--VPV EURO RSCG, Helsinki, Finland; *Int'l*, pg. 603
Ito, Hisashi, Exec. Mng. Dir.--Sankyo Company Limited, Tokyo, Japan; *Int'l*, pg. 1189
Ito, Junji, Sr. Mng. Dir.-Client Service--Dentsu, Sudler & Hennessey Inc., Tokyo, Japan; *U.S. Private*, pg. 325
Ito, Takeshi, Mng. Dir.--The Meijiseimei Investment Singapore Pte. Ltd., Singapore, Singapore; *Int'l*, pg. 854
Ito, Tetsuya, Mng. Dir.--Nippon Express (Nederland) B.V., Schiphol, Netherlands; *Int'l*, pg. 934
Ito, Toshio, Sr. Mng. Dir. & Gen. Mgr.-Engnrg., Mfg. & Informations Systems--Mitsubishi Electric Corporation, Tokyo, Japan; *Int'l*, pg. 872
Itoh, Koichi, Mng. Dir.--Handy & Harman International, Ltd., Tokyo, Japan; *U.S. Public*, pg. 780
Itoh, Yuji, Chief Fin. Officer & Mng. Dir.--Kyocera Corporation, Kyoto, Japan; *Int'l*, pg. 775
Itty, Benjamin, Strategic Plng. Dir.--Young & Rubicam Hungary, Budapest, Hungary; *U.S. Private*, pg. 1199
Itzaina, Francisco A., Mng. Dir.-Brazil--Moore Corporation Limited, Toronto, Canada; *Int'l*, pg. 888
Ives, Christopher L., Ph.D., Mng. Dir.--PolyMedica Industries UK, Ltd., Tarvin, United Kingdom; *U.S. Public*, pg. 1315
Iwanaga, Mitsuo, Mng. Dir.--Kubota Corp., Osaka, Japan; *Int'l*, pg. 762
Iwao, Yoshio, Sr. Mng. Dir. & Sr. V.P.-Flight Opers. Div.--Japan Airlines Company, Ltd., Tokyo, Japan; *Int'l*, pg. 699
Iwasa, Yoshito, Sr. Mng. Dir--Sakata Seed Corporation, Yokohama, Japan; *Int'l*, pg. 1178
Iwatake, Katsuji, Mng. Dir.--Brother International (Singapore) Pte. Ltd., Singapore, Singapore; *Int'l*, pg. 230
Jackman, P., Mng. Dir.--Swish Products Ltd., Tamworth, United Kingdom; *Int'l*, pg. 925
Jackson, Geoff K., Mng. Dir.-HEAL--Halifax plc, Halifax, United Kingdom; *Int'l*, pg. 589
Jackson, P., Mng. Dir.--De La Rue Cash Handling Product Group, Havant, United Kingdom; *Int'l*, pg. 387
Jacobs, Dick, Partner & Creative Dir.--Potentia Healthcare Communications Partners, Chicago, IL; *U.S. Public*, pg. 1224
Jacobsen, Finn, Mng. Dir.--KE-Burgmann A/S, Vejen, Denmark; *Int'l*, pg. 234
Jacobsen, Per K., Mng. Dir.-Engrng.--Landis & Staefa AG, Zug, Switzerland; *Int'l*, pg. 800
Jacobson, Susie, Sr. V.P. & Mngmt. Dir.--Grant/Jacoby, Inc., Chicago, IL; *U.S. Private*, pg. 470
Jaggard, Ian, Mng. Dir.--Check Technology Limited, Crawley, United Kingdom; *U.S. Public*, pg. 342
Jaine, Olivier, Co-Mgr.--EURO RSCG Novation, Villeneuve-Loubet, France; *Int'l*, pg. 601
Jakobsen, Jesper H., Mng. Dir.--DanTransport A/S, Glostrup, Denmark; *Int'l*, pg. 476
James, Denis, Deputy Reg. Mng. Dir.--Willis Corroon North Limited, Newcastle upon Tyne, United Kingdom; *Int'l*, pg. 1503
James, Peter Richard, Mng. Dir.-Asia Pacific Services--Computer Power Group Limited, Melbourne, Australia; *Int'l*, pg. 325
James, S., Mng. Dir.--Rossing Uranium Ltd., Windhoek, Namibia; *Int'l*, pg. 1119
Jameson, Teena, Mng. Dir.--AIS Media Brisbane, Brisbane, Australia; *Int'l*, pg. 15
Jamieson, Diarmid, Mgr.-Opers.--Woodward-Clyde International, Windsor, United Kingdom; *U.S. Public*, pg. 1658
Jamme, Norbert, Mng. Dir.--Rhone-Poulenc Philippines Inc., Manila, Philippines; *Int'l*, pg. 1113
Janczyk, W., Mng. Dir.--Business Management & Finance International Ltd., Warsaw, Poland; *Int'l*, pg. 1332
Janneryd, L.B., Deputy Mng. Dir.-Comml. Opers.--Crosfield Electronics Limited, Hemel Hempstead, United Kingdom; *U.S. Public*, pg. 532
Jaquet, Andre, Mng. Dir.--Sulzer Belgium S.A., Brussels, Belgium; *Int'l*, pg. 1306
Jarding, J.L., Mng. Dir.--Phillips Petroleum Singapore Chemicals Pte. Ltd., Singapore, Singapore; *U.S. Public*, pg. 1291
Jardon, Mickey, Mng. Dir.--Market Growth Resources, Inc., Wilton, CT; *U.S. Public*, pg. 1641
Jarvis, J. Paul, Mng. Dir.--Anacomp (Canada) Ltd., Markham, Canada; *U.S. Public*, pg. 107
Jarvis, John, Sr. V.P.-Europe & Mng. Dir.-Wiley Europe Ltd.--Wiley Europe Limited, Chichester, United Kingdom; *U.S.* Public, pg. 1768
Jarvis, Paul, Mng. Dir.--Desoutter Brothers (Holdings) plc, London, United Kingdom; *Int'l*, pg. 96
Je, Man-Ho, Chief Fin. Officer--Ssangyong Information & Communication Corporation, Seoul, Korea; *Int'l*, pg. 1292
Jean, Christian, Mng. Dir.--Bundy SNC, Amboise, France; *Int'l*, pg. 1342
Jean, Raymond, Mng. Dir.--Walter Herzog G.m.b.H., Lauda, Germany; *U.S. Public*, pg. 1711
Jebsen, Finn, Exec. V.P. & Mng. Dir. Denofa-Lilleborg--Orkla A.S.A., Oslo, Norway; *Int'l*, pg. 1010
Jeffers, Nigel, Mng. Dir.--Nashua Photo Limited, Newton Abbot, United Kingdom; *U.S. Public*, pg. 1152
Jeffrey, Robert, Exec. V.P. & Mng. Dir.-San Francisco--Lowe & Partners/SMS, New York, NY; *U.S. Private*, pg. 678
Jeffries, Mary, Mng. Dir.--Shandwick Minneapolis, Minneapolis, MN; *Int'l*, pg. 1227
Jeger, Bernard, Assoc. Gen. Mgr.--EURO RSCG Communicance, Reims, France; *Int'l*, pg. 600
Jenkins, M.J.W., Mng. Dir.--Mills Manufacturing Technology, Norwich, United Kingdom; *Int'l*, pg. 585
Jenkins, Roy, Mng. Dir.--D. Anderson & Son Ltd., Stretford, United Kingdom; *Int'l*, pg. 659
Jennett, Francois, Mng. Dir.--Arthur D. Little, A.G., Thalwil, Switzerland; *U.S. Private*, pg. 670
Jennings, Donald, Mng. Dir.--American Ingredients Company, Dolton, IL; *Int'l*, pg. 244
Jennings, W. H., Mng. Dir.--Coutts & Co (Bahamas) Limited, Nassau, Bahamas; *Int'l*, pg. 911
Jensen, Benny Balle, Mng. Dir.--Pedershaab A/S, Bronderslev, Denmark; *Int'l*, pg. 475
Jenssen, Per Sture, Mng. Dir.--Madshus A/S, Biri, Norway; *U.S. Public*, pg. 940
Jett, Ernest C., V.P., Mng. Dir.-Legal Dept. & Sec.--Leggett & Platt, Incorporated, Carthage, MO; *U.S. Public*, pg. 985
Jiumtipanat, Somlak, Mng. Dir.--Siam Compressor Industry Co., Ltd., Ban Si Racha, Thailand; *Int'l*, pg. 1238
Job, P., Chief Exec. Officer--Reuters Holdings PLC, London, United Kingdom; *Int'l*, pg. 1105
Jobard, George, Mng. Dir.--Clextral, Firminy, France; *Int'l*, pg. 503
Jockenhofer, Gisbert, Mng. Dir.--BNP-Dresdner Bank (CR) a.s., Prague, Czech Republic; *Int'l*, pg. 418
Johansen, Bjarne, Mng. Dir.--SKF Japan Ltd., Tokyo, Japan; *Int'l*, pg. 1159
Johansen, Roger, Mng. Dir.--Getinge Disinfection Inc., Toms River, NJ; *Int'l*, pg. 551
Johanson-Hedberg, B., Mng. Dir.--Wolters Kluwer Sweden, Stockholm, Sweden; *Int'l*, pg. 1514
Johansson, Kurt J., Mng. Dir.--Dayco Europe AB, Solvesborg, Sweden; *U.S. Public*, pg. 1045
Johansson, Roger, Mng. Dir.--Baldwin Europe Consolidated, Inc., Geldrop, Netherlands; *U.S. Public*, pg. 170
Johansson, S., Mng. Dir.--Nordiska Balzers AB, Kungsbacka, Sweden; *Int'l*, pg. 998
John, Christopher, Mng. Dir.--Krafft, S.A., Andoain, Spain; *Int'l*, pg. 323
Johns, R.W., Jr., Mng. Dir.--Electronic Tele-Communications, Inc., Atlanta, GA; *U.S. Public*, pg. 570
Johnson, Arve K., Mng. Dir.--Carl Jonsson Papir A/S, Oslo, Norway; *Int'l*, pg. 864
Johnson, Carl, Grp. Mng. Dir.--Simons Palmer Denton Clemmow & Johnson Ltd., London, United Kingdom; *Int'l*, pg. 1252
Johnson, Dave, Mng. Dir.--Aero Engine Equipment Group, Birmingham, United Kingdom; *Int'l*, pg. 127
Johnson, Graham, Mng. Dir.--Paper Agencies (Aust.) Pty. Ltd., Hawthorn, Australia; *Int'l*, pg. 458
Johnson, Nigel, Mng. Dir.--Excerpta Medica Medical Communications BV, Amsterdam, Netherlands; *Int'l*, pg. 1099
Johnson, Peter T., Mng. Dir.-Fin. & Secretariat Div.--Henderson Administration Group PLC, London, United Kingdom; *Int'l*, pg. 609
Johnson, Randall, Mng. Dir.--Corporate & Institutional Financial Services - Calgary, Calgary, Canada; *Int'l*, pg. 153
Johnson, Sandy, Mng. Dir.--Black & Edgington Ltd., London, United Kingdom; *Int'l*, pg. 197
Johnson, T. Radey, Sr. Mng. Dir.--Rothschild Inc., New York, NY; *U.S. Private*, pg. 947
Johnson, Verdia, Mng. Dir.--Graham Gregory Bozell, Inc., New York, NY; *U.S. Public*, pg. 1642
Johnston, A., Mng. Dir.--Heatric Ltd., Poole, United Kingdom; *Int'l*, pg. 853
Johnston, Craig, Mng. Dir.-Intl. Div.--Columbus McKinnon Corp., Amherst, NY; *U.S. Public*, pg. 405
Johnston, Ian D., Mng. Dir.--Cadbury International Limited, Birmingham, United Kingdom; *Int'l*, pg. 248
Johnston, Max, Mng. Dir.--Johnson & Johnson Pacific Pty. (New Zealand) Ltd., East Tamaki, New Zealand; *U.S. Public*, pg. 931
Johnston, Norm, Mng. Dir.--Modem Media U.K., London, United Kingdom; *U.S. Public*, pg. 1641
Jolkkonen, Pentti, Mng. Dir.--Metsa-Serla AG, Zurich, Switzerland; *Int'l*, pg. 864
Jolstedt, Anders, Mng. Dir.--Grafiskt Paper & Norden AB, Vallingby, Sweden; *Int'l*, pg. 864
Jonas, M., Mng. Dir.--Getinge GmbH, Langenfeld, Germany; *Int'l*, pg. 551
Jones, Gary, Mng. Dir.-Prods. Devel.--BeautiControl Cosmetics, Inc., Carrollton, TX; *U.S. Public*, pg. 198
Jones, Gordon, Sr. V.P. & Mng. Dir.--Allergan Limited, High Wycombe, United Kingdom; *U.S. Public*, pg. 46
Jones, Jeffrey B., Dir.-Market Plng.--Mesaba Holdings, Inc., Minneapolis, MN; *U.S. Public*, pg. 1099
Jones, Landon Y., Mng. Editor--People, New York, NY; *U.S.* Public, pg. 1613
Jones, Merv, Mgr.-Office--Woodward-Clyde, Auckland, New Zealand; *U.S. Public*, pg. 1657
Jones, Russell, Chm. & Mng. Dir.--Batey Couldrey Jones Advertising, Wan Chai, Hong Kong; *Int'l*, pg. 117
Jonge, K., Dr., Mng. Dir.--AE Goetze GmbH, Burscheid, Germany; *Int'l*, pg. 1334
Jonkhans, G. A., Mng. Dir.--Purac Far East, Singapore, Singapore; *Int'l*, pg. 245
Jonsson, Anders, Mng. Dir.--Cementa AB (Skovde), Skovde, Sweden; *Int'l*, pg. 1199
Jonsson, Per, Mng. Dir.--Stora Dalum A/S, Odense, Denmark; *Int'l*, pg. 1303
Joo-Young, Jung, Mng. Dir.--Korea Heavy Industries & Construction Co., Ltd., Seoul, Korea; *Int'l*, pg. 758
Joosten, Mark, Mng. Dir.--DMB&B Prague, Prague, Czech Republic; *U.S. Private*, pg. 304
Joseph, F., Mng. Dir.--GKN Walterscheid Presswerk GmbH, Trier, Germany; *Int'l*, pg. 536
Joseph, Rishya, Mng. Dir. & V.P.-Reg. Mgr.--Dentsu Young & Rubicam Sdn. Bhd. (Kuala Lumpur), Kuala Lumpur, Malaysia; *U.S. Private*, pg. 325
Joshi, Shriniwas K., Mng. Dir.--Sulzer India Ltd., Mumbai, India; *Int'l*, pg. 1306
Joss, Robert, Chief Exec. Officer & Mng. Dir.--Westpac Banking Corporation, Sydney, Australia; *Int'l*, pg. 1495
Joyce, Julie, Mng. Dir.-Human Resources--Wheat First Butcher Singer, Inc., Richmond, VA; *U.S. Public*, pg. 640
Juch, D.R., Mng. Dir.--Kulk & Kramer Kantoorsystemen B.V., Zoetermeer, Netherlands; *Int'l*, pg. 1116
Jung-Kyu, Kyun, Mng. Dir.-Quality Assurance & Technical Services--Korea Heavy Industries & Construction Co., Ltd., Seoul, Korea; *Int'l*, pg. 758
Jung, Peter, Mng. Dir.--Bertrand Faure Sitztechnik GmbH & Co. kg, Stadthagen, Germany; *Int'l*, pg. 193
Jung, Taesoo, Mng. Dir.--Arthur D. Little Korea, Inc., Seoul, Korea; *U.S. Private*, pg. 671
Jungwirth, Dieter, Prof. Dr., Mng. Dir.-Res. & Devel.--Dyckerhoff & Widmann AG, Munich, Germany; *Int'l*, pg. 423
Jurgens, Robert J., Mng. Dir.-European Res.--Jacobs Asset Management, Fort Lauderdale, FL; *U.S. Public*, pg. 1673
Justino, Jose A., Mng. Dir.--Johnson & Johnson de Colombia S.A., Cali, Colombia; *U.S. Public*, pg. 930
Juul, Arne, Mng. Dir.--Bates Emballage A/S, Noerresundby, Denmark; *Int'l*, pg. 476
Kaartinen, Kalevi, Mng. Dir.--Nokia Mobile Phones GmbH, Dusseldorf, Germany; *Int'l*, pg. 952
Kadlec, Lubomir, Mng. Dir.--Obalex, A.S., Znojmo, Czech Republic; *U.S. Public*, pg. 440
Kadoyama, Tetsuo, Mng. Dir.-Personnel & Pur.--UBE Industries Ltd., Tokyo, Japan; *Int'l*, pg. 1426
Kaesbeck, Norbert, Dr., Mng. Dir.-Org. & Construction Mngmt.--Commerzbank AG, Frankfurt, Germany; *Int'l*, pg. 308

Kageyama, Kenji, Mng. Dir.--Ilco Unican Mexico S.A. de C.V., Tlalnepantla, Mexico; *Int'l*, pg. 1432
Kahmeyer, Heinrich, Co-Mng. Dir.--Krupp Hoesch Dienstleistigungen GmbH, Essen, Germany; *Int'l*, pg. 512
Kahn, Mansoor Ali, Sr. Mng. Dir.-Engrng.--National Refinery Limited, Karachi, Pakistan; *Int'l*, pg. 909
Kaija, Matti, Mng. Dir.--A. Jalander Oy, Muurla, Finland; *Int'l, pg. 727*
Kairakbayev, Bakhyt, Mng. Dir.--EurAsia Consult, Almaty, Kazakhstan; *Int'l*, pg. 606
Kaji, Gautam, Mng. Dir.--The World Bank, Washington, DC; *U.S. Private*, pg. 1188
Kajita, Susumu, Mng. Dir.-Osaka Head Office--Nihon Keizai Shimbun, Inc., Tokyo, Japan; *Int'l*, pg. 929
Kale, Keith, Mng. Dir.-Mktg.--Piper Jaffray Companies, Inc., Minneapolis, MN; *U.S. Public*, pg. 1300
Kalliala, Kari, Mng. Dir.--Papeteries de Docelles, Docelles, France; *Int'l*, pg. 1430
Kallman, Andrew, Mng. Dir.--Outdoor Services, Southfield, MI; *U.S. Private*, pg. 1166
Kalloren, H., Mng. Dir.--Finnish Chemicals Oy, Aetsa, Finland; *Int'l*, pg. 954
Kallstrom, Willy, Mng. Dir.--ITT Flygt Werk GmbH, Pforzheim, Germany; *U.S. Public*, pg. 860
Kalvik, Jan-Tore, Mng. Dir.--Hagglunds Drives A/S, Sandvika, Norway; *Int'l*, pg. 670
Kambli, R., Mng. Dir.--Bally Hong Kong Ltd., Kowloon, Hong Kong; *Int'l*, pg. 997
Kamegai, Kiyoshi, Mng. Dir.-Food Res.--Ajinomoto Company Inc., Tokyo, Japan; *Int'l*, pg. 40
Kameyama, Ken, Mng. Dir.--Dentsply Japan, Tokyo, Japan; *U.S. Public*, pg. 499
Kamigori, Katsuhiko, Joint Mng. Dir.--Dentsu Europe Ltd.-London, London, United Kingdom; *Int'l*, pg. 393
Kamijo, Kiyofumi, Sr. Mng. Dir. & Mgr.-Fin.--Tokyu Corporation, Tokyo, Japan; *Int'l*, pg. 1394
Kanai, Akira, Mng. Dir. & Sr. Gen. Mgr.-Tokyo Headquarters--West Japan Railway Company, Osaka, Japan; *Int'l*, pg. 1490
Kandus, Marhan, Mng. Dir.--Banka Creditanstalt d.d., Ljubljana, Slovenia; *Int'l*, pg. 347
Kaneko, Isao, Mng. Dir. & Sr. V.P.-Industrial Rels. & Medical Svcs.--Japan Airlines Company, Ltd., Tokyo, Japan; *Int'l*, pg. 699
Kang, H.J., Mng. Dir.--Van Leeuwen Pipe and Tube Korea Ltd., Seoul, Korea; *Int'l*, pg. 1450
Kappes, Hans-Peter, Chief Fin. Officer & Mng. Dir.--Bausparkasse Gemeinschaft der Freunde Wuestenrot gem.GmbH, Ludwigsburg, Germany; *Int'l*, pg. 1514
Karcher, Xavier, Vice Chm. & Mng. Dir.--Automobiles Citroen, Neuilly, France; *Int'l*, pg. 1020
Karches, Peter F., Mng. Dir.--Morgan Stanley Group Inc., New York, NY; *U.S. Public*, pg. 1132
Karisson, Carl-Ake, Mng. Dir.--Jotun Sverige A.B., Vastra Frolunda, Sweden; *Int'l*, pg. 715
Karjalainen, Markku, Mng. Dir.--Kalso-Teollisuus Oy, Vuohijarvi, Finland; *Int'l*, pg. 1428
Karjaluoto, Johan, Mng. Dir.--Wisaforest Oy Ab, Pietarsaari, Finland; *Int'l*, pg. 1429
Karkhanis, P.S., Mng. Dir.--Simpson Industries, Inc., Pune, India; *U.S. Public*, pg. 1475
Karl, Klaus, Mng. Dir.--Pitney Bowes Deutschland G.m.b.H., Heppenheim, Germany; *U.S. Public*, pg. 1304
Karppinen, Lassi, Mng. Dir.--Perimistoimisto Contant Oy, Turku, Finland; *Int'l*, pg. 859
Karsenti, Rene, Dir. Gen.-Fin.--European Investment Bank, Luxembourg, Luxembourg; *Int'l*, pg. 465
Kartau, Madis, Mng. Dir.--AS Neopac-Elkson, Maakond, Estonia; *Int'l*, pg. 863
Karutz, P., Mng. Dir.--Ascom GmbH, Frankfurt, Germany; *Int'l*, pg. 87
Karwoski, Glenn, V.P. & Mng. Dir.--Karwoski & Courage, Minneapolis, MN; *U.S. Private*, pg. 710
Kasko, Heikki, Mng. Dir.--Nokia Telecommunications (Thailand) Ltd., Bangkok, Thailand; *Int'l*, pg. 954
Kasper, Herbert, Mng. Dir.-Buying--Julius Meinl AG, Vienna, Austria; *Int'l*, pg. 856
Kass, Warren, Mng. Dir.--Partners & Shevack Design, New York, NY; *U.S. Private*, pg. 842
Kastner, George, Mngng. Dir.--Arthur D. Little de Venezuela, C.A., Caracas, Venezuela; *U.S. Private*, pg. 670
Katawczik, Dennis, Co-Mng. Dir.--Fort Pitt Acquisitions, Inc., Coraopolis, PA; *U.S. Private*, pg. 419
Kate, Nancy Ten, Mng. Editor--American Demographics, Inc., Ithaca, NY; *U.S. Private*, pg. 281
Kato, Isaoio, Mng. Dir. & Gen. Mgr.--Fashion Business Group, Nagoya, Japan; *Int'l*, pg. 229
Katsushima, I., Mng. Dir.--NatWest Investment Management Japan Limited, Tokyo, Japan; *Int'l*, pg. 911
Katsuya, Yoshiro, Mng. Dir.--The Nikko Securities Co., (Asia) Limited, Central, Hong Kong; *Int'l*, pg. 931
Kauffman, Beat, Grp. Mng. Dir.--Schiesser Eminence Holding AG, Stein, Switzerland; *Int'l*, pg. 618
Kaufmann, O.A., Mng. Dir.--GKN Birfield SpA, Bruneck, Italy; *Int'l*, pg. 535
Kaupas, Jan P., Mng. Dir.--ISS Building Maintenance, Inc., New York, NY; *Int'l*, pg. 656
Kauranen, Timo, Chief Exec. Officer & Mng. Dir.--Foster Wheeler Energia Oy, Helsinki, Finland; *U.S. Public*, pg. 677
Kavourakis, Sam, Mng. Dir.--National Mutual Funds Management (Global) Ltd., Melbourne, Australia; *Int'l*, pg. 908
Kawabarayashi, Seji, Chm. & Mng. Dir.--Mitsui & Co. (Australia), Brisbane, Australia; *Int'l*, pg. 880
Kawaguchi, Toshiro, Sr. Mng. Dir.-Machinery & Engrng.--UBE Industries Ltd., Tokyo, Japan; *Int'l*, pg. 1426
Kawaji, Kazuhisa, Sr. Mng. Dir. International--Settsu Corporation, Amagasaki, Japan; *Int'l*, pg. 1225
Kawamura, Kajiro, Mng. Dir.--Hosokawa Micron Corporation, Osaka, Japan; *Int'l*, pg. 635
Kawamura, Yasushi, Sr. Mng. Dir.--The Daishi Bank, Ltd., Niigata, Japan; *Int'l*, pg. 372
Kawamura, Yuko, Mng. Dir. & Gen. Mgr.-Mktg. Devel. Headquarters--Nihon Keizai Shimbun, Inc., Tokyo, Japan; *Int'l*, pg. 929
Kawanaka, Katsuo, Mng. Dir.-Tokyo Sls.--Orix Corporation, Tokyo, Japan; *Int'l*, pg. 1008
Kawano, Hiroshi, Mng. Dir.--Fuji Bank (Deutschland) AG, Frankfurt/Main, Germany; *Int'l*, pg. 521
Kaye, Debra, Mng. Dir.--BDDP Mancebo Kaye, Madrid, Spain; *Int'l*, pg. 117
Kearley, Gary, Mng. Dir.--Young & Rubicam Sydney Pty. Ltd., Sydney, Australia; *U.S. Private*, pg. 1200
Keel, Lenz, Mng. Dir.--Swiss Re Southern Africa Ltd., Johannesburg, South Africa; *Int'l*, pg. 1333
Keeling, Ian, Mng. Dir.--Fine Organics Limited, Middlesbrough, United Kingdom; *Int'l*, pg. 802
Keenan, Michael E., Mng. Dir.--Western International Media Corporation, New York, NY; *U.S. Private*, pg. 1166
Keenan, Paul, Mng. Dir.--EMAP Fashion Ltd., London, United Kingdom; *Int'l*, pg. 451
Keep, D.J., Mng. Dir.--Yale Security Products, Ltd., Wolverhampton, United Kingdom; *Int'l*, pg. 1499
Keigel, Ch., Mng. Dir.--Bally Gesellschaft mbH, Vienna, Austria; *Int'l*, pg. 997
Keir, G, Mng. Dir.--De La Rue Fortronic Limited, Dunfermline, United Kingdom; *Int'l*, pg. 387
Keisling, Gary M., Mng. Dir.--Intertext Group, Ltd., Glasgow, United Kingdom; *U.S. Public*, pg. 784
Keisling, Gary M., Mng. Dir.--International Correspondence Schools (New Zealand) Limited, Wellington, New Zealand; *U.S. Public*, pg. 784
Kelberg, George, Mng. Dir.--Styx & Leo Burnett, Almaty, Kazakhstan; *U.S. Private*, pg. 186
Keller, Isaac Rodrigo, Mng. Dir.--Arte y Cemento SA, Bilbao, Spain; *Int'l*, pg. 1099
Kells, Geoffrey, Pres. & Mng. Dir.--CSR Limited, Sydney, Australia; *Int'l*, pg. 245
Kelly, Christopher H., Mng. Dir.--Johnson & Johnson Korea, Ltd., Seoul, Korea; *U.S. Public*, pg. 930
Kelly, Kevin J., Mng. Dir.-AIB Bank--Allied Irish Banks, p.l.c., Dublin, Ireland; *Int'l*, pg. 64
Kelly, William T., Mng. Dir.--Bensons International Systems, Mississauga, Canada; *Int'l*, pg. 460
Kemp, Michael, Mng. Dir.-Franklin Europe--Franklin Electronic Publishers, Inc., Burlington, NJ; *U.S. Public*, pg. 679
Kemp, Tony M., Mng. Dir.-Blue Circle Properties--Blue Circle Industries PLC, London, United Kingdom; *Int'l*, pg. 197
Kempel, M., Mng. Dir.--Robert Bosch A/S, Ballerup, Denmark; *Int'l*, pg. 205
Kemper, Martin, Mng. Dir.--The West Company France, S.A., Le Nouvion-en-Thierache, France; *U.S. Public*, pg. 1756
Kemsley, M.A., Chief Oper. Officer & Mng. Dir.--Yale Security Products (Hong Kong) Ltd., Causeway Bay, Hong Kong; *Int'l*, pg. 1499
Kendrick, Graham, Mng. Dir.--Scottish Courage Limited, Staines, United Kingdom; *Int'l*, pg. 1212
Kenjo, Nobuyuki, Mng. Dir.--Kintetsu World Express (Australia) Pty. Ltd., Matraville, Australia; *Int'l*, pg. 735
Kennedy, Iain, Mng. Dir.--Solectron Scotland Limited, Dunfermline, United Kingdom; *U.S. Public*, pg. 1483
Kennedy, Rod, Mng. Dir.--Beazer Homes (Yately) Limited, Camberley, United Kingdom; *Int'l*, pg. 182
Kenole, Nick, Mng. Dir.--LNG Energy, Inc., Phoenix, AZ; *U.S. Public*, pg. 1493
Kent, Jack, Mng. Partner-Publishing--Gillespie, Lawrenceville, NJ; *U.S. Private*, pg. 453
Kepecs, G., Mng. Dir.--AB-AEGON Altalanos Biztosito Rt, Budapest, Hungary; *Int'l*, pg. 28
Keranen, Ulla-Maija, Mng. Dir.--Fidenta Oy, Espoo, Finland; *Int'l*, pg. 859
Kerr, Ian, Mng. Dir.--Hepworth Minerals and Chemicals Limited, Sandbach, United Kingdom; *Int'l*, pg. 615
Kerr, John, Reg. Mng. Dir.--DHL International (Hong Kong) Ltd., Wan Chai, Hong Kong; *U.S. Private*, pg. 302
Keskasemsook, Anant, Mng. Dir.--Siam Guardian Glass Co., Ltd., Nong Khae, Thailand; *Int'l*, pg. 1238
Kespohl, Horst, Mng. Dir.--Bertrand Faure Sitztechnik GmbH & Co. KG, Geiselhoring, Germany; *Int'l*, pg. 193
Kessaratos, Frank, Mng. Dir.-Intl. Sls.--Landis & Staefa AG, Zug, Switzerland; *Int'l*, pg. 800
Kessissoglou, J., Mng. Dir.--Forest Products S.A., Maroussi, Greece; *Int'l*, pg. 458
Ketchum, Thomas B., Mng. Dir. & Reg. Exec.-Americas--J.P. Morgan Co. Incorporated, New York, NY; *U.S. Public*, pg. 1129
Kettemann, Tim, Mng. Dir.--Bankgesellschaft Berlin Investment GmbH, Berlin, Germany; *Int'l*, pg. 159
Kettemann, Tim, Mng. Dir.--BB-Asset Management Vermogensverwaltung GmbH, Berlin, Germany; *Int'l*, pg. 159
Key, John L., Mng. Dir.--Red Dog, Kotzebue, AK; *Int'l*, pg. 308
Keys, Wesley, Mng. Dir.--Heil Europe, Dunfermline, United Kingdom; *U.S. Public*, pg. 521
Khan, A., Mng. Dir.--Wyeth Laboratories (Pakistan) Ltd., Karachi, Pakistan; *U.S. Public*, pg. 82
Khan, Anis A., Mng. Dir.--Manhattan Pakistan (Private) Limited, Karachi, Pakistan; *U.S. Private*, pg. 186
Khan, Nazir, Mng. Dir.--PCS Nitrogen-Trinidad, Couva, Trinidad & Tobago; *Int'l*, pg. 1064
Khasitsakul, Decha, Mng. Dir.--Asset Development Co., Ltd., Bangkok, Thailand; *Int'l*, pg. 619
Khilnari, Dipi, Mng. Dir.--Donaldson Filter Systems Pvt. Ltd., New Delhi, India; *U.S. Public*, pg. 517
Khor, Charles, Mng. Dir.--Sime Diamond Leasing (Malaysia) Sdn. Bhd., Kuala Lumpur, Malaysia; *Int'l*, pg. 158
Kibe, Yoshito, Mng. Dir. & Gen. Mgr.-TIS Headquarters--West Japan Railway Company, Osaka, Japan; *Int'l*, pg. 1490
Kida, Haruo, Sr. Mng. Dir.-Sls., Mktg. & Prod. Devel.--Nisshin Steel Co., Ltd., Tokyo, Japan; *Int'l*, pg. 946
Kidd, Douglas, Sr. Mng. Dir.-Corp. Affairs--Bankers Trust New York Corporation, New York, NY; *U.S. Public*, pg. 185
Kiely, Leonard, Mng. Dir.--SPS International Ltd., Shannon, Ireland; *U.S. Public*, pg. 1420
Kilpelainen, Jukka, Mng. Dir.--Tervakoski Oy, Tervakoski, Finland; *Int'l*, pg. 456
Kilpinen, Esko, Mng. Dir.--KONE Elevators Poland Sp.zo.o., Warsaw, Poland; *Int'l*, pg. 747
Kim, Chul-Woong, Mng. Dir.--Awabed - Ssangyong Contracting Co., Dhahran, Saudi Arabia; *Int'l*, pg. 1292
Kim, Hong-Sik, Chief Fin. Officer--Ssangyong Precision Industry Co., Ltd., Inchon, Korea; *Int'l*, pg. 1292
Kim, Jae Sung, Mng. Dir.--Daltrading Limited, Seoul, Korea; *U.S. Public*, pg. 414
Kim, Young C., Exec. V.P. & Mng. Dir.--Sunkyong America, Inc., New York, NY; *Int'l*, pg. 1320
Kim, Young-Ik, Mng. Dir.--Ssangyong Motor Company, Seoul, Korea; *Int'l*, pg. 1292
Kimes, David, V.P. & Mng. Dir.-U.K. Production Opers.--Kerr-McGee Oil (U.K.) PLC, London, United Kingdom; *U.S. Public*, pg. 952
Kimmett, Robert, Mng. Dir.-Washington Corp. Fin. Office--Lehman Brothers, New York, NY; *U.S. Public*, pg. 987
Kimmo, Osmo, Mng. Dir.--Tietokesko Oy, Helsinki, Finland; *Int'l*, pg. 732
Kimura, Kanji, Mng. Dir.--All Nippon Airways Co. Ltd., Tokyo, Japan; *Int'l*, pg. 57
Kimura, Makoto, Mng. Dir.--Dai-ichi Life International (Australia) Limited, Sydney, Australia; *Int'l*, pg. 362
Kimura, Mikihiko, Mng. Dir.-Corp. Plng.--Diamond Lease Co., Ltd., Tokyo, Japan; *Int'l*, pg. 413
Kindinger, Wolfgang, Mng. Dir.--Burgmann Seals Australia Pty. Ltd., Sydney, Australia; *Int'l*, pg. 234
Kindland, Anne Kirsten, Consultant--Holiday RV Superstores, Inc., Orlando, FL; *U.S. Public*, pg. 829
Kindlund, Newton C., Managing Dir.--Holiday RV Superstores of South Atlanta, Inc., Forest Park, GA; *U.S.* Public, pg. 830
Kindlund, Newton C., Mng. Dir.--Holiday RV Superstores, Inc.-Tampa, Tampa, FL; *U.S. Public*, pg. 830
King, A. Philip, Mng. Dir.--Delta Fluid Products Ltd., Saint Helens, United Kingdom; *Int'l*, pg. 391
King, Ray C., Mng. Dir.--Mildara Blass Wines, Albert Park, Australia; *Int'l*, pg. 501
King, Tim, Mng. Dir.--Sensormatic Australia Pty Limited, Sydney, Australia; *U.S. Public*, pg. 1457
Kingdon, B.J., Sr. Mng. Dir.-Global Institutional Services Grp.--Bankers Trust New York Corporation, New York, NY; *U.S. Public*, pg. 185
Kinkead-Weekes, Rod, Mng. Dir.-Comalco Minerals & Alumina--Comalco Limited, Brisbane, Australia; *Int'l*, pg. 307
Kinnear, Anthony, Mng. Dir.--Butterworths Asia, Singapore, Singapore; *Int'l*, pg. 1095
Kinnunen, Matti, Mng. Dir.--D. Carnegie AB, Stockholm, Sweden; *Int'l*, pg. 272
Kinoshita, Kunio, Mng. Dir.--Sakura Bank (Deutschland) GmbH, Frankfurt/Main, Germany; *Int'l*, pg. 1180
Kinoshita, Masahiro, Mng. Dir.--All Nippon Airways Co. Ltd., Tokyo, Japan; *Int'l*, pg. 57
Kinsella, P.J., Mng. Dir.--Cow & Gate Nutricia (Ireland) Ltd., Dublin, Ireland; *Int'l*, pg. 991
Kirac, Suna, Vice Chm. & Mng. Dir.--Koc Holding A.S., Istanbul, Turkey; *Int'l*, pg. 741
Kirano, Akira, Mng. Dir.--Nikko Bank (Luxembourg) S.A., Luxembourg, Luxembourg; *Int'l*, pg. 930
Kirberg, Ralf, Mng. Dir.--LHI Leasing fur Handel und Industrie GmbH, Munich, Germany; *Int'l*, pg. 160
Kircheis, F., Mng. Dir.--Ascom Hasler SpA, Milan, Italy; *Int'l, pg. 87*
Kirk, Philip, Mng. Dir.--Butterworths New Zealand, Wellington, New Zealand; *Int'l*, pg. 1095
Kirk, Simon, Mng. Dir.--British Gas Energy Centres Ltd., Nottingham, United Kingdom; *Int'l*, pg. 279
Kirkland, George, Mng. Dir.-Chevron Nigeria Ltd.--Chevron Corporation, San Francisco, CA; *U.S. Public*, pg. 347
Kirkpatrick, Brad, Mng. Dir.--Express Scripts Vision, Earth City, MO; *U.S. Public*, pg. 601
Kirsch, Adam, Mng. Dir.--Bain Capital, Boston, MA; *U.S. Private*, pg. 110
Kirsch, Dieter, Mng. Dir.--BB-Leasing GmbH, Frankfurt/Main, Germany; *Int'l*, pg. 159
Kishida, Seiji, Sr. Mng. Dir.-Corp. Plng.--Settsu Corporation, Amagasaki, Japan; *Int'l*, pg. 1225
Kitahara, Mamoru, Mng. Dir.--Wako International (Hong Kong) Limited, Hong Kong, Hong Kong; *Int'l*, pg. 1485
Kitahara, Tsuyoshi, Mng. Dir.--Neste Chemicals (Japan) Co., Ltd., Tokyo, Japan; *Int'l*, pg. 914
Kitajima, Hiroyuki, Mng. Dir.--Nippon Express do Brasil Transportes Internacionais Ltda., Sao Paulo, Brazil; *Int'l*, pg. 934
Kitamine, M., Mng. Dir.--Sharp Manufacturing Corporation (M) Sdn. Bhd., Batu Pahat, Malaysia; *Int'l*, pg. 1230
Kitamura, Akihisa, Mng. Dir.--Dentsu Young & Rubicam Inc. (Tokyo), Tokyo, Japan; *U.S. Private*, pg. 325
Kitching, Peter, Mng. Dir.--Colin Stewart Minchem Limited, Winsford, United Kingdom; *Int'l*, pg. 858
Kiyono, Naoshi, Mng. Dir., Gen. Mgr.-Intl. Investments & Sec.--Yasuda Mutual Life Insurance Co., Tokyo, Japan; *Int'l*, pg. 1519
Klasen, Joachim, Mng. Dir.--Volksfreund-Druckerei Nikolaus Koch GmbH & Co. KG, Trier, Germany; *Int'l*, pg. 1479
Klassen, R., Far East Area Mng. Dir.--Ferro Far East Ltd., Kowloon, Hong Kong; *U.S. Public*, pg. 619
Klassen, R.L., Far East Area Mng. Dir.--Ferro Industrial Products Ltd., Tao-yuan, Taiwan; *U.S. Public*, pg. 619
Kleiberg, A.B.M., Mng. Dir.--Van Leeuwen Pipe and Tube Eastern Australia Pty. Ltd., Girraween, Australia; *Int'l*, pg. 1450
Klein, Jacques, Deputy Mng. Dir.--Young & Rubicam France, Paris, France; *U.S. Private*, pg. 1199
Klein, Ludwig, Mng. Dir.--Hartek Beverage Handling GmbH, Radevormwald, Germany; *U.S. Public*, pg. 1445

Klein, Manfred, Dr., Dir.-Fin.--Joh. A. Benckiser GmbH, Ludwigshafen, Germany; *Int'l*, pg. 185
Klein, Patrick, Mng. Dir.--Visea THORN, Tassin-la-Demi-Lune, France; *Int'l*, pg. 1386
Klemp, P., Mng. Dir.--Ascom Nordic A/S, Brondby, Denmark; *Int'l*, pg. 87
Kleyn, Hendrik J.C., Mng. Dir.--Heraeus Electro-Nite International N.V., Houthalen, Belgium; *Int'l*, pg. 616
Kliem, M., Mng. Dir.--Pfrimmer Nutricia GmbH & Co. KG, Erlangen, Germany; *Int'l*, pg. 992
Klifa, Pierre, Mgr.--EURO RSCG Est, Mulhouse, France; *Int'l*, pg. 601
Klovstad, Oystein, Pres. & Mng. Dir.--Toyota Norge A/S, Drammen, Norway; *Int'l*, pg. 1414
Kluge, Alexander, Mng. Dir.--Development Company for TV-Program GmbH, Dusseldorf, Germany; *Int'l*, pg. 394
Klumb, Uwe, Dr., Mng. Dir.--Grillo-Werke AG, Duisburg, Germany; *Int'l*, pg. 861
Knapper, W., Mng. Dir.--GKN Gelenkwellenbau GmbH, Essen, Germany; *Int'l*, pg. 536
Knetsch, Werner, Mngng. Dir.--Arthur D. Little International, Inc., Berlin, Germany; *U.S. Private*, pg. 670
Knight, Andrew, Mng. Dir.--Information Trust Corporation (Pty.) Ltd., Johannesburg, South Africa; *U.S. Public*, pg. 537
Knight, Thomas, Mng. Dir.--Cathodic Protection Services Company, Houston, TX; *U.S. Private*, pg. 297
Knight, Thomas, Mng. Dir.--Cathodic Protection Services Company, Houston, TX; *U.S. Public*, pg. 1213
Knocz, I., Mng. Dir.--Consulting and Engineering Agrober Company, Budapest, Hungary; *Int'l*, pg. 607
Knop, U., Mng. Dir.--TPS, Krefeld, Germany; *Int'l*, pg. 1145
Knott, Roland, Mng. Dir.--Berendsen Fluid Power Ltd., Tamworth, United Kingdom; *Int'l*, pg. 1284
Knowles, Jonathan, Mng. Dir.-Global Pharmaceutical Res.--Roche Holding Ltd., Basel, Switzerland; *Int'l*, pg. 1119
Knudsen, Lars Secher, Mng. Dir.--Radiometer GmbH, Willich, Germany; *Int'l*, pg. 1084
Knuutinen, Reijo, Mng. Dir.--Merita Securities Ltd., Helsinki, Finland; *Int'l*, pg. 859
Koba, Yukio, Mng. Dir.--LTCB Merchant Bank (Singapore) Limited, Singapore, Singapore; *Int'l*, pg. 816
Kobayashi, Hiromi, Mng. Dir.--ORIX Investment and Management Private Limited, Singapore, Singapore; *Int'l*, pg. 1009
Kobayashi, Isao, Sr. Mng. Dir.-Gen. Store Devel.--Ito-Yokado Co., Ltd., Tokyo, Japan; *Int'l*, pg. 693
Kobayashi, Katsunobu, Mng. Dir.--Ebara Corporation, Tokyo, Japan; *Int'l*, pg. 431
Kobayashi, Sadaya, Mng. Dir.--Central Japan Railway Company-London Office, London, United Kingdom; *Int'l*, pg. 279
Kobayashi, Yoshiaki, Mng. Dir.--Turk Sakura Bank A.S., Istanbul, Turkey; *Int'l*, pg. 1180
Kobenter, W., Mng. Dir.--Getinge GmbH, Murzzuschlag, Austria; *Int'l*, pg. 551
Kobori, Teruo, Mng. Dir. & Gen. Mgr.-Personnel--Mitsubishi Chemical Corporation, Tokyo, Japan; *Int'l*, pg. 870
Kocass, W., Grp. Mng. Dir.--Gammon Construction Ltd., Quarry Bay, Hong Kong; *Int'l*, pg. 775
Koch-Weser, Caio, Mng. Dir.--The World Bank, Washington, DC; *U.S. Private*, pg. 1188
Koch, Jean-Claude, V.P. & Mng. Dir.--State Street Bank (Luxembourg) S.A., Luxembourg, Luxembourg; *U.S. Public*, pg. 1513
Kochi, Susumu, Mng. Dir.-Mktg. Div.--Dentsu Inc., Tokyo, Japan; *Int'l*, pg. 392
Kocsis, D., Dr., Mng. Dir.--Reemtsma Debreceni Dohanygyar Kft, Debrecen, Hungary; *Int'l*, pg. 1101
Koeberl, M., Mng. Dir.--O&K Antriebstechnik GmbH, Hattingen Works, Hattingen, Germany; *Int'l*, pg. 516
Koether, Albert, Mng. Dir.--Kalso S.A., Hortes, France; *Int'l*, pg. 1428
Koetzier, C., Mng. Dir.--Hoogovens Ijmuiden Verkoopkantoor B.V., Ijmuiden, Netherlands; *Int'l*, pg. 754
Koffenberger, Linda A., Mng. Dir.-Housepaint Chemicals, N. America--Union Carbide Corporation, Danbury, CT; *U.S. Public*, pg. 1666
Koffenberger, Linda A., Mng. Dir.--Amerchol Corporation, Edison, NJ; *U.S. Public*, pg. 1667
Kohara, Hidetsugu, Mng. Dir.--Pioneer Electronics Manufacturing NV, Erpe, Belgium; *Int'l*, pg. 1058
Kohata, Florencio, Mng. Dir.--Dun & Bradstreet SA, Lima, Peru; *U.S. Public*, pg. 537
Kohlhaupt, Fritz, Mng. Dir.--Gebruder Sulzer-Escher Wyss-Kaltetechnik GmbH, Lauterach, Austria; *Int'l*, pg. 1306
Kohlrusch, Dietmar, Mng. Dir.--KKW, Kulmbach, Germany; *Int'l*, pg. 554
Kohn, Mathias, Mng. Dir.--ISS Hospital Service AG, Oberentfelden, Switzerland; *Int'l*, pg. 657
Koike, Hiroshi, Mng. Dir.-Res. & Devel.--Matsushita Electric Works, Ltd., Osaka, Japan; *Int'l*, pg. 847
Koizumi, Takashi, Mng. Dir.-Intl Hdq.--Orix Corporation, Tokyo, Japan; *Int'l*, pg. 1008
Kojima, Akira, Mng. Dir.--Brother Finance (Netherlands) B.V., Amsterdam, Netherlands; *Int'l*, pg. 229
Kojima, Iwao, Mng. Dir. & Gen. Mgr.-Res. & Tech.--Showa Denko K.K., Tokyo, Japan; *Int'l*, pg. 1236
Kojima, Kikuo, Mng. Dir.-Inquiry & Audit Depts., Admin. & Pub. Rels.--East Japan Railway Company, Tokyo, Japan; *Int'l*, pg. 431
Kojima, T., Mng. Dir.--Tyton Hellermann Asia Pacific Ltd., Singapore, Singapore; *Int'l*, pg. 209
Kojima, Takao, Mng. Dir.--Cosmo Oil Co., Ltd., Tokyo, Japan; *Int'l*, pg. 335
Kojima, Tsugumasa, Mng. Dir. & Chief Exec. Officer--Sakura Finance International Limited, London, United Kingdom; *Int'l*, pg. 1180
Kojima, Tsugumasa, Chief Exec. & Mng. Dir.--Sakura Trust Internaional Limited, London, United Kingdom; *Int'l*, pg. 1180
Kojima, Yoshiharu, Sr. Mng. Dir.-Admin. & Treas.--Sogei Inc., Tokyo, Japan; *Int'l*, pg. 1277
Kokubo, Masaaki, Mng. Dir.--Fuji International Finance (Australia) Limited, Sydney, Australia; *Int'l*, pg. 521
Kollisch, Herbert, Mng. Dir.--Intercord Tongesellschaft mbH, Stuttgart, Germany; *Int'l*, pg. 428
Komiya, Kazuhiko, Sr. Mng. Dir.--All Nippon Airways Co. Ltd., Tokyo, Japan; *Int'l*, pg. 57
Komiya, Yozo, Mng. Dir.--Nippon Express (Malaysia) Sdn. Bhd., Petaling Jaya, Malaysia; *Int'l*, pg. 934
Komiyama, Tetsuji, Mng. Dir.--ORIX Rentec (Singapore) Pte. Limited, Singapore, Singapore; *Int'l*, pg. 1010
Kondoh, Y., Mng. Dir.--Sharp Thebnakorn Co., Ltd. (Bangkok), Bangkok, Thailand; *Int'l*, pg. 1230
Konrad, Robert, Mng. Dir.--Sulzer Betriebsliegenschaften AG, Winterthur, Switzerland; *Int'l*, pg. 1307
Konynendyk, Adrian, Mng. Dir.--Willis Corroon Scheuer, Amsterdam, Netherlands; *Int'l*, pg. 1509
Koob, Hans Konrad, Mng. Dir.--Koob & Partner/The Corporate Company, Mulheim an der Ruhr, Germany; *Int'l*, pg. 117
Koper, M.A., Mng. Dir.--Ebara Pumps United Kingdom Limited, Hounslow, United Kingdom; *Int'l*, pg. 432
Koponen, Matti, Mng. Dir.--SAMAB Cia. Industria e Comercio de Papel, Sao Paulo, Brazil; *Int'l*, pg. 458
Kopp, Larry S., Mng. Dir.-Global Mktg.--Frank Russell Company, Tacoma, WA; *U.S. Private*, pg. 952
Koppensteiner, Walter, Pres. & Mng. Dir.--AGA Ges.m.b.H., Vienna, Austria; *Int'l*, pg. 13
Koptev, Sergey, Chief Exec. Officer, Mng. Dir.--DMB&B Moscow, Moscow, Russia; *U.S. Private*, pg. 304
Korbel, Rene, Mng. Dir.--Halten GmbH & Co. KG, Dusseldorf, Germany; *Int'l*, pg. 592
Koreman, Jan, Mng. Dir.--TBWA Campaign Company, Amsterdam, Netherlands; *U.S. Private*, pg. 1063
Korkmaz, Fares F., Mng. Dir.--Interstate Resources, Inc., Rosslyn, VA; *U.S. Private*, pg. 573
Korn, Gerhard, Mng. Dir.-Frankfurt Region--Dyckerhoff & Widmann AG, Munich, Germany; *Int'l*, pg. 423
Kornemann, Rolf, Dr., Mng. Dir.-Economics & Information Systems--Bausparkasse Gemeinschaft der Freunde Wuestenrot gem.GmbH, Ludwigsburg, Germany; *Int'l*, pg. 1514
Kortelainen, Tito, Mng. Dir.--Kesped Ltd., Vantaa, Finland; *Int'l*, pg. 732
Kosonen, Jorma, Mng. Dir.--K-Tel International Finland O.Y., Helsinki, Finland; *U.S. Public*, pg. 938
Kotani, Yukihito, Mng. Dir.--NLI International Singapore Pte. Ltd., Singapore, Singapore; *Int'l*, pg. 936
Kotecha, Mahesh K., Mng. Dir.-Asia Bus. Devel.--Capital Markets Assurance Corporation, New York, NY; *U.S. Public*, pg. 1023
Kotterman, Gary L., Dir.--Micron Europe Ltd., Bracknell, United Kingdom; *U.S. Public*, pg. 1105
Kotterman, Gary L., Dir.--Micron Semiconductor (Deutscland) GmbH, Aschheim, Germany; *U.S. Public*, pg. 1106
Kovensky, Sheldon, Mng. Dir.--Allergan Inc., Markham, Canada; *U.S. Public*, pg. 46
Kow, G.C.M., Mng. Dir.--Glaxo Wellcome China Ltd., Wan Chai, Hong Kong; *Int'l*, pg. 553
Kraehe, G.J., Chief Exec. Officer & Mng. Dir.--Southcorp Holdings Ltd., Adelaide, Australia; *Int'l*, pg. 1287
Kranendoch, J., Mng. Dir.--Jamin, Oosterhout, Netherlands; *Int'l*, pg. 749
Kreigenfeld, Friedrich, Mng. Dir.--O&K Mining GmbH, Dortmund Works, Dortmund, Germany; *Int'l*, pg. 516
Krieg, Mark, Mng. Dir.--Sulzer South Africa Ltd., Elandsfontein, South Africa; *Int'l*, pg. 1306
Kriegel, Ralf, Mng. Dir.--Schabmuller GmbH, Berching, Germany; *Int'l*, pg. 1387
Kroeger, Kevin, Mng. Dir.--Heinemann Publishers (Pty) Ltd., Johannesburg, South Africa; *Int'l*, pg. 1094
Kroes, P., Mng. Dir.--P.T. Nutricia Indonesia Sejaharta, Jakarta, Indonesia; *Int'l*, pg. 992
Kroesbergen, A.P., Mng. Dir.--BW Industrial Products B.V., Winterswijk, Netherlands; *Int'l*, pg. 198
Kronborg, Jens, Mng. Dir.--Nyborg Plast International A/S, Nyborg, Denmark; *Int'l*, pg. 476
Krouse, Diane, Mng. Dir.--DMB&B Los Angeles, Los Angeles, CA; *U.S. Private*, pg. 303
Kruger-Herbert, Peter, New Bus. Dir.--Lowe & Partners GmbH, Hamburg, Germany; *U.S. Private*, pg. 678
Kruger, Mark, Exec. V.P. & Gen. Mgr.--Pragmaton, Chicago, IL; *U.S. Public*, pg. 1224
Kruger, Udo, Mng. Dir.--Allianz Insurance (Singapore) Pte. Ltd., Singapore, Singapore; *Int'l*, pg. 59
Kruse, Ernst Michel, Chm. Bd. & Mng. Dir.--BHF-BANK AG, Frankfurt, Germany; *Int'l*, pg. 119
Kruzic, Tim, Mngng. Dir.--Arthur D. Little, Inc., Arlington, VA; *U.S. Private*, pg. 670
Ku, Richard, Mng. Dir.--GP Battery Marketing (HK) Ltd., Kwai Chung, Hong Kong; *Int'l*, pg. 537
Kubin, Michael, Mng. Dir.--Media Incorporated, New York, NY; *U.S. Private*, pg. 726
Kubin, Michael, Mng. Dir.--Media Direct Partners, Incorporated, New York, NY; *U.S. Private*, pg. 726
Kubo, Tetsuya, Mng. Dir.--All Nippon Airways Co. Ltd., Tokyo, Japan; *Int'l*, pg. 57
Kubota, Teruhisa, Mng. Dir.--Nippon Truck Co., Ltd., Tokyo, Japan; *Int'l*, pg. 934
Kuchenbrandt, Ingo, Mng. Dir.--Danisco Sugar GmbH, Anklam, Germany; *Int'l*, pg. 378
Kudo, Hironaka, Sr. Mng. Dir.-Gen. Affairs--Ito-Yokado Co., Ltd., Tokyo, Japan; *Int'l*, pg. 693
Kugelman, Stephanie, Vice Chm., Mng. Dir.-Y&R NY & Insights Grp. Dir.--Young & Rubicam New York, New York, NY; *U.S. Private*, pg. 1198
Kuhl, Richard G., Dir. Gen.--Velcromex S.A. de C.V., Agua Prieta, Mexico; *Int'l*, pg. 1462
Kuhne, Peter, Mng. Dir.--Nokia Telecommunications Ltd., Huntingdon, United Kingdom; *Int'l*, pg. 953
Kuhnert, Walter R., Mng. Dir.--Triumph International, Sacavem, Portugal; *Int'l*, pg. 1424
Kuijpers, J.F.C., Mng. Dir.--Van Leeuwen Tubes Ltd., Barnsley, United Kingdom; *Int'l*, pg. 1450
Kuijvenhoven, Pieter, Mng. Dir.--Navar BDDP, Rotterdam, Netherlands; *Int'l*, pg. 117
Kukral, John Z., Sr. Mng. Dir.--The Blackstone Group, New York, NY; *U.S. Private*, pg. 147
Kulman, Miguel, Fin. Dir. & Human Resources Mgr.--Bilbao/Y&R, Asuncion, Paraguay; *U.S. Private*, pg. 1200
Kult, Gottfried, Mng. Dir.-Food Processing & Tech. Service--Julius Meinl AG, Vienna, Austria; *Int'l*, pg. 856
Kumada, Fukuhisa, Mng. Dir.--Sumitomo Life Investment Singapore Limited, Singapore, Singapore; *Int'l*, pg. 1315
Kumar, U., Chm. Bd. & Mng. Dir.--South Eastern Coalfields Limited, Bilaspur, India; *Int'l*, pg. 299
Kumpulainen, Kari, Mng. Dir.--Enso Trading AB, Uppsala, Sweden; *Int'l*, pg. 457
Kunitzsch, Eberhard, Mng. Dir.--Knurr-Lommatec GmbH & Co. KG, Lommatzsch, Germany; *Int'l*, pg. 739
Kunsch, Matthias, Mng. Dir.--Creditanstalt Rt., Budapest, Hungary; *Int'l*, pg. 348
Kunze, Manfred, Mng. Dir.--Arthur D. Little International GmbH, Vienna, Austria; *U.S. Private*, pg. 670
Kunzel, H., Mng. Dir.--Nedlloyd Districenters International, Amsterdam, Netherlands; *Int'l*, pg. 1144
Kupien, Dieter, Mng. Dir.--ISS Holding GmbH, Munich, Germany; *Int'l*, pg. 657
Kupper, Bruce D., Mng. Partner--Kupper Parker Communications Inc., Saint Louis, MO; *U.S. Private*, pg. 637
Kuranz, John, V.P. & Mng. Dir.-Pub. Prods. Div.--Find/SVP, Inc., New York, NY; *U.S. Public*, pg. 623
Kurebayashi, Shunichi, Exec. Mng. Dir.--Sankyo Company Limited, Tokyo, Japan; *Int'l*, pg. 1189
Kuribayashi, Hiroshi, Mng. Dir.--Pioneer Electronics Asia Centre Pte. Ltd., Singapore, Singapore; *Int'l*, pg. 1058
Kurihara, Tsutomu, Exec. Mng. Dir.--Sumitomo Heavy Industries, Ltd., Tokyo, Japan; *Int'l*, pg. 1314
Kuroda, Keiji, Mng. Dir.--The Meiji Life Insurance Company Sydney Office, Sydney, Australia; *Int'l*, pg. 854
Kuroda, Keiji, Mng. Dir.--The Meijiseimei Property Australia Ltd., Sydney, Australia; *Int'l*, pg. 854
Kurose, Yuichiro, Mng. Dir.-Sls.--Japan Tobacco Inc., Tokyo, Japan; *Int'l*, pg. 703
Kurth, Hans, Mng. Dir.--SMH Australia Ltd., Windsor, Australia; *Int'l*, pg. 1161
Kushiyama, Hisao, Mng. Dir.--NEC Electronics Singapore Pte. Ltd., Singapore, Singapore; *Int'l*, pg. 901
Kutsuma, Shiro, Mng. Dir.--Daiwa Middle East E.C., Manama, Bahrain; *Int'l*, pg. 375
Kuwano, Fumio, Mng. Dir. & Sr. V.P.-Information Sys.--Japan Airlines Company, Ltd., Tokyo, Japan; *Int'l*, pg. 699
Kuwao, Kentaro, Mng. Dir.--Kwe-Kintetsu World Express(S)Pte Ltd., Singapore, Singapore; *Int'l*, pg. 735
Kwak, A.C., Mng. Dir.--Delicia B.V., Tilburg, Netherlands; *Int'l*, pg. 752
Kwee Chong, John Moo, Grp. Mng. Dir.--CSA Holdings Ltd., Singapore, Singapore; *Int'l*, pg. 242
Kwok, Raymond, Vice Chm. & Mng. Dir.--Sun Hung Kai Properties Ltd., Wan Chai, Hong Kong; *Int'l*, pg. 1318
Kwok, Thomas, Vice Chm. & Mng. Dir.--Sun Hung Kai Properties Ltd., Wan Chai, Hong Kong; *Int'l*, pg. 1318
Kwon, Hugh, Pres. & Mng. Dir.--Leo Burnett Sonyon Inc., Seoul, Korea; *U.S. Private*, pg. 185
Kyriacou, K., Mng. Dir.--Bally Australia Pty. Ltd., Camperdown, Australia; *Int'l*, pg. 997
L'Heureux, Willard J., Mng. Dir.-Intl.--TrizecHahn Corporation, Toronto, Canada; *Int'l*, pg. 1424
Laan, S P., Mng. Dir.--California B.V., Harderwijk, Netherlands; *Int'l*, pg. 243
Laas, Madis, Chief Exec. Officer & Mng. Dir.--Kontuur-Leo Burnett/Estonia, Tallinn, Estonia; *U.S. Private*, pg. 184
Laband, P.A.K., Mng. Dir.--National Australia Asset Management, Melbourne, Australia; *Int'l*, pg. 906
Labathari, M., Mng. Dir.--Nutricia Hellas S.A., Athens, Greece; *Int'l*, pg. 992
Lack, Steve, Mng. Dir.--Ross Systems (UK) Limited, Northampton, United Kingdom; *U.S. Public*, pg. 1406
Lacy, R., Mng. Dir.-Switchgear & Instrumentation Ltd.--N.G. Bailey & Co. Ltd., Ilkley, United Kingdom; *Int'l*, pg. 132
Ladinig, V., Mng. Dir.--Commenda Baustoff A.G., Vienna, Austria; *Int'l*, pg. 1501
Laento, Kari, Mng. Dir.--Neste Alfa Oy, Espoo, Finland; *Int'l*, pg. 914
LaFlotte, Roberta, Partner-Creative--Lewis Gace Bozell Healthcare Worldwide, Fort Lee, NJ; *U.S. Public*, pg. 1642
Lagerstrom, Nils, Mng. Dir.--Nokia Telecommunications AB, Kista, Sweden; *Int'l*, pg. 953
Lahe, C.R., Mng. Dir.--Wyman-Gordon Limited, Livingston, United Kingdom; *U.S. Public*, pg. 1782
Lahteenmaki, Risto, Mng. Dir.--Schauman Wood AB, Stockholm, Sweden; *Int'l*, pg. 1429
Lahtinen, Antero, Deputy Mng. Dir.--Norvista, London, United Kingdom; *Int'l*, pg. 486
Laiho, Jarmo, Mng. Dir.--Merita Finance Ltd., Helsinki, Finland; *Int'l*, pg. 859
Laird, Thomas J., Mng. Dir.--NWQ Investment Managaement Company, Los Angeles, CA; *U.S. Public*, pg. 1673
LaLanne, M.R., Mng. Dir.--Texaco Cote d'Ivorie, Abidjan, Cote d'Ivoire; *U.S. Public*, pg. 1584
Lam, Mike, Mng. Dir.--Notifier Far East, Kowloon, Hong Kong; *U.S. Public*, pg. 1306
Lam, Perry, Reg. Dir.-Sls.--DHL International (Hong Kong) Ltd., Wan Chai, Hong Kong; *U.S. Private*, pg. 302
Lambert, Peter, Mng. Dir.--Nordson Australia Pty., Ltd., Seven Hills, Australia; *U.S. Public*, pg. 1189
Lambert, Peter, Mng. Dir.--Nordson Australia Pty. Limited., Melbourne, Australia; *U.S. Public*, pg. 1189
Lambert, W., Mng. Dir.--Kerry Ultrasonics Limited, Hitchin, United Kingdom; *Int'l*, pg. 589
Lambourne, R. E., Mng. Dir.--Hepworth Refractories Ltd., Alfreton, United Kingdom; *Int'l*, pg. 615
Lamm, Henri, Mng. Dir.-Adv.--Julius Meinl AG, Vienna, Austria; *Int'l*, pg. 856

Lamminpaa, Osmo, Mng. Dir.--Valmet-Gorizia S.p.A., Gorizia, Italy; *Int'l*, pg. 1448
Lampinen, Paavo, Mng. Dir.--SO Oviteollisuus OY, Kuopio, Finland; *Int'l*, pg. 1302
Lanary, R.S., Mng. Dir.--Hamworthy Combustion Equipment Limited, Poole, United Kingdom; *Int'l*, pg. 1065
Lancaster, Jeremy, Chm. Bd. & Mng. Dir.--Wolseley Plc., Droitwich, United Kingdom; *Int'l*, pg. 1511
Lancelot, Jean Luc, Mng. Dir.--Acieries De Ploermel, Ploermel, France; *U.S. Public*, pg. 1711
Lang, G.F.J., Mng. Dir.--Liberty of London Prints Limited, London, United Kingdom; *Int'l*, pg. 807
Langagne, Jean Paul, Mng. Dir.--Sulzer Metco (France) S.A., Vaulx, France; *Int'l*, pg. 1308
Lange, Hans H., Mng. Dir.--Jeppesen and Co. GmbH, Frankfurt/Main, Germany; *U.S. Public*, pg. 1617
Lange, Wolfgang, Mng. Dir.--Emil Schlemper G.m.b.H., Solingen, Germany; *U.S. Public*, pg. 17
Langhorn, Brian L., Dir.--Flouro-Precision Coatings, Cranleigh, United Kingdom; *Int'l*, pg. 1338
Lanning, E. Smith, Mng. Dir.--Arthur D. Little (Japan), Inc., Tokyo, Japan; *U.S. Private*, pg. 671
Lanscombe, M., Mng. Dir.--Beazer Homes (Doncaster) Limited, Doncaster, United Kingdom; *Int'l*, pg. 182
Lanuza, Luis, Grp. Dir.--de la Cruz & Associates, San Juan, PR; *U.S. Private*, pg. 318
Lanz, Ruedi, Mng. Dir.--K-Tron France, Boissy-Saint-Leger, France; *U.S. Public*, pg. 938
Lanzi Gillespie, Donna, Mng. Partner-Media & Human Resources--Gillespie, Lawrenceville, NJ; *U.S. Private*, pg. 453
LaPointe, Bill, Mng. Dir.--Andover Controls Corp., Andover, MA; *Int'l*, pg. 120
Lapointe, Jacques, Mng. Dir.-UK Comml. Opers.--Glaxo Wellcome plc, London, United Kingdom; *Int'l*, pg. 552
Laponder, Charles, Mng. Dir.--Berendsen PMC B.V., Rijswijk, Netherlands; *Int'l*, pg. 1285
Larder, E., Mng. Dir.--Riley Advertising (Birmingham) Ltd., Birmingham, United Kingdom; *Int'l*, pg. 1117
Larracoechea, Ignacio, Mng. Dir.--Johnson & Johnson S.A. Consumer, Madrid, Spain; *U.S. Public*, pg. 931
Larsen, Kris, Sr. V.P. & Mng. Dir.--Interbrand Schechter, Chicago, IL; *U.S. Public*, pg. 1224
Larsson, Ake, Mng. Dir.--Gambro K.K., Shiga, Japan; *Int'l*, pg. 668
Larsson, Ake, Mng. Dir.--Gambro K.K., Tokyo, Japan; *Int'l*, pg. 668
Larsson, Bjorn, Mng. Dir.--Lowe Brindfors, Stockholm, Sweden; *U.S. Private*, pg. 678
Larsson, Goran, Mng. Dir.--Young & Rubicam Business Communications S.A., Geneva, Switzerland; *U.S. Private*, *pg. 1199*
Larsson, Uno, Mng. Dir.--Iggesund Paperboard Inc., Southport, CT; *Int'l*, pg. 886
Lassahn, Sonnich, Mng. Dir. & Spokesman--Wuestenrot Bank AG, Ludwigsburg, Germany; *Int'l*, pg. 1514
Lassen, T., Mng. Dir.--Gestetner A/S, Vaerlose, Denmark; *Int'l*, pg. 1115
Last, Billy, Mng. Dir.--Butterworths South Africa, Durban, South Africa; *Int'l*, pg. 1095
Latham, George, Mng. Dir.--R.P. Scherer Limited, Swindon, United Kingdom; *U.S. Public*, pg. 1438
Latz, Gert, Mng. Dir.--Kommunalconsult Gesellschaft fur die Beratung de Offentlichen Hand mbH, Berlin, Germany; *Int'l*, pg. 160
Lauren, Ollie, Mng. Dir.--Patons & Baldwins Limited, Darlington, United Kingdom; *Int'l*, pg. 300
Laurent-Mazerolle, Louis, Mng. Dir.--Bang & Olufsen France S.A., Saint Denis, France; *Int'l*, pg. 146
Laurent, D.H., Mng. Dir.--Texaco Italiana SpA, Rome, Italy; *U.S. Public*, pg. 1584
Laurent, Jean-Louis, Mng. Dir.--Brambles Europe S.A., Brussels, Belgium; *Int'l*, pg. 212
Laux, Andre, Mng. Dir.--Laminoir de Dudelange S.A., Dudelange, Luxembourg; *Int'l*, pg. 79
LaVallee, Charles, Exec. Dir.--Western Pennslyvania Caring Foundation, Inc., Pittsburgh, PA; *U.S. Private*, pg. 529
Laveroni, Sherrie, Reg. V.P. & Mng. Dir.--Regency Hotel, New York, NY; *U.S. Public*, pg. 1011
Lavoie, C., Mng. Dir.--Monserco Limited, Brampton, Canada; *Int'l*, pg. 993
Law, A.J., Mng. Dir.--Standard Cressall Limited, Leicester, United Kingdom; *Int'l*, pg. 590
Law, C.W., Mng. Dir.--Dexter Asia Pacific Limited, Kowloon, Hong Kong; *U.S. Public*, pg. 505
Law, T.R., Mng. Dir.--Alumina Company Limited, Widnes, United Kingdom; *Int'l*, pg. 51
Lawner, Ron, Mng. Partner & Chief Creative Officer--Arnold Communications, Inc., Boston, MA; *U.S. Private*, pg. 83
Lawrence, D.M., Mng. Dir.--Firstcorp Merchant Bank LImited, Johannesburg, South Africa; *Int'l*, pg. 487
Lawrence, State, Exec. V.P. & Mng. Partner-Acct.--Wells BDDP, Inc., New York, NY; *Int'l*, pg. 117
Lawrence, W., Mng. Dir.--PT IPCindo SISKOMDATA, Jakarta, Indonesia; *Int'l*, pg. 651
Lawson, Thomas E., Mng. Partner & Chief Oper. Officer--Arnold Communications, Inc., Boston, MA; *U.S. Private*, pg. 83
Le Lay, Patrick, Grp. Dir.-Commun.--Bouygues, Saint Quentin-en-Yvelines, France; *Int'l*, pg. 206
Le Morvan, Jacques, Mng. Dir.--Bertrand Faure Components Ltd., Mississauga, Canada; *Int'l*, pg. 193
Le Nir, Max, Mng. Dir.--CFG SA, Orleans, France; *Int'l*, pg. 608
Le Poidevin, Keith R., Mng. Dir.--Banque Belge Trust Company Ltd., Saint Peter Port, United Kingdom; *Int'l*, pg. 547
le Proux de la Riviere, Bruno, Mng. Dir.--Dun & Bradstreet France SA, Nanterre, France; *U.S. Public*, pg. 536
Leach, P.S., Mng. Dir.--Haden Drysys International Ltd., Birmingham, United Kingdom; *Int'l*, pg. 585
Leach, P.S., Mng. Dir.--Haden Drysys Ltd., Birmingham, United Kingdom; *Int'l*, pg. 585
Leather, Cathy, Mng. Dir.-MIS--Labatt U.S.A., Darien, CT; *Int'l*, pg. 679
Lebeer, Chris, Mng. Dir.--Delaware Industrial Services N.V., Zwijnaarde, Belgium; *Int'l*, pg. 183
LeBlanc, David M., Mng. Dir.--Lincoln Electric Mexicana S.A. de C.V., Mexico, Mexico; *U.S. Public*, pg. 997
Lebreiro, P., Mng. Dir.--Nutricia Portugal L.D.A., Parede, Portugal; *Int'l*, pg. 992
Lecercle, Patrick, Deputy Mng. Dir.--Young & Rubicam France, Paris, France; *U.S. Private*, pg. 1199
Lechner, F., Mng. Dir.--GKN Distribution GmbH, Rosrath, Germany; *Int'l*, pg. 536
Lechner, Hartmut, Mng. Dir.-Admin. & Human Resources--Bausparkasse Gemeinschaft der Freunde Wuestenrot gem.GmbH, Ludwigsburg, Germany; *Int'l*, pg. 1514
Lecoq, Franck, Mng. Dir.--Bertrand Faure Componentes SA, Barcelona, Spain; *Int'l*, pg. 193
Lecouvey, Alain, Mng. Dir.--Rhone-Poulenc Argentina S.A., Buenos Aires, Argentina; *Int'l*, pg. 1112
Lecumberri, Alfredo, Mng. Dir.--Tecnoconfort SA, Pamplona, Spain; *Int'l*, pg. 193
Ledieu, G., Mng. Dir.--GKN Florange SARL, Florange, France; *Int'l*, pg. 536
Ledieu, G., Mng. Dir.--GKN Glaenzer Spicer SA, Poissy, France; *Int'l*, pg. 536
Lee-Emery, Adrian, Mng. Dir.--HBA Insurance Ltd., Hamilton, Bermuda; *U.S. Public*, pg. 342
Lee, Alfred, Mng. Dir.--IPC Systems (M) Sdn Bhd, Petaling Jaya, Malaysia; *Int'l*, pg. 651
Lee, David, Mng. Dir.--The Anvil Consultancy, Marlow, United Kingdom; *U.S. Public*, pg. 1224
Lee, Dong Myun, Mng. Dir.--Cho Hung Bank (Deutschland) GmbH, Frankfurt/Main, Germany; *Int'l*, pg. 288
Lee, Doo-Hwan, Pres.--Ssangyong Uni-Charm Co., Ltd., Kumi, Korea; *Int'l*, pg. 1291
Lee, James, Mng. Dir.--Burgmann Korea Ltd., Seoul, Korea; *Int'l*, pg. 233
Lee, Jong Keun, Exec. V.P. & Dir.--Cho Hung Bank, Seoul, Korea; *Int'l*, pg. 287
Lee, Lawrence, Mng. Dir.--Regent Motors Limited, Singapore, Singapore; *Int'l*, pg. 1251
Lee, Martin, Mng. Dir.--Weyburn-Bartel Ltd., Godalming, United Kingdom; *Int'l*, pg. 1334
Lee, Phillip, Mng. Dir.--CMC International (S.E. Asia) Pte. Limited, Singapore, Singapore; *U.S. Public*, pg. 413
Lee, Sang-Jun, Mng. Dir.--Ssangyong Paper Co., Ltd., Seoul, Korea; *Int'l*, pg. 1292
Lee, Simon, Mng. Dir.--Circle Airfreight International Korea, Seoul, Korea; *U.S. Public*, pg. 372
Lee, Simon, Mng. Dir.--MRI UK, London, United Kingdom; *U.S. Private*, pg. 727
Lee, Yoon Hee, Chm. & Mng. Dir.--Cho Hung Bank Luxembourg S.A., Luxembourg, Luxembourg; *Int'l*, pg. 288
Lee, Yoon-Jung, Chief Fin. Officer & Mng. Dir.--EMTEC Magnetics GmbH, Ludwigshafen, Germany; *Int'l*, pg. 743
Leeds, Paul T., Mng. Dir.--AIS Media South, Melbourne, Australia; *Int'l*, pg. 15
Leeflang, Karel, Mng. Dir.--Elsevier Science Ireland Limited, Shannon, Ireland; *Int'l*, pg. 1100
Lefevre, Jean-Marie, Mng. Dir.--Champagne Pommery S.A., Reims, France; *Int'l*, pg. 780
Lefevre, Marc, Assoc. Mgr.--EURO RSCG Communicance, Reims, France; *Int'l*, pg. 600
Lefkariti, Despo, Mng. Dir.--De La Ma/TBWA, Nicosia, Cyprus; *U.S. Private*, pg. 1062
Legallet, Georges, Mng. Dir.--Simpson Industries E.U.R.L. (France), Lyon, France; *U.S. Public*, pg. 1475
Legallet, Georges, Mng. Dir.--Simpson Techniparts E.U.R.L. (France), Lyon, France; *U.S. Public*, pg. 1475
Leggetter, Barry, Pres., Sr. Partner, Mng. Dir. & Exec. V.P.--Fleishman-Hillard U.K. Limited, London, United Kingdom; *U.S. Private*, pg. 411
LeGrande, E. David, Mng. Dir.-Export Division & Treas.--Gudebrod, Inc., Pottstown, PA; *U.S. Private*, pg. 486
Lehman, Mark E., Exec. V.P. & Sr. Mng. Dir.--The Bear Stearns Companies Inc., New York, NY; *U.S. Public*, pg. 197
Lehmusto-Eranen, Kirsti, Mng. Dir.-Mktg.--Academic Bookstore, Helsinki, Finland; *Int'l*, pg. 1301
Lehni, Markus, Dr., Mng. Dir.-Corp. Environment--Landis & Staefa AG, Zug, Switzerland; *Int'l*, pg. 800
Lehtinen, Lasse, Mng. Dir.--Sesto, Helsinki, Finland; *Int'l*, pg. 1301
Lehtinen, Olavi, Mng. Dir.-Mktg. & Buying--Sesto, Helsinki, Finland; *Int'l*, pg. 1301
Lehtovaara, Ari, Mng. Dir.--Nokia Telecommunications Italia S.r.l., Gessate, Italy; *Int'l*, pg. 953
Leicht, Ronald J., Sr. Mng. Dir.-Mktg.--Mazda Motor Corporation, Hiroshima, Japan; *Int'l*, pg. 849
Leimer, Hans Jorg, Mng. Dir.--Neef Elektrotechnik GmbH & Co., Karlsruhe, Germany; *Int'l*, pg. 1306
Lekander, Monika, Mng. Dir.--Nordic Synthesis AB, Karlskoga, Sweden; *U.S. Public*, pg. 297
Lekkerkerk, J., Mng. Dir.--Trencon Vuurvast BV, Oude Tonge, Netherlands; *Int'l*, pg. 894
Lemaire, Luc, Fin. Mgr.--Devarrieux Villaret, Paris, France; *Int'l*, pg. 600
Lemener, George, Mng. Dir.--IBL S.A., Paris, France; *Int'l*, pg. 21
Lemieux, J.F., Mng. Dir.--Oerlikon Aerospace, Inc., Saint Jean-sur-Richelieu, Canada; *Int'l*, pg. 998
Lemmer, Juergen, Mng. Dir.-Treas.--Commerzbank AG, Frankfurt, Germany; *Int'l*, pg. 308
Lemon, David, Mng. Dir.--Hepworth Building Products Limited, Stocksbridge, United Kingdom; *Int'l*, pg. 615
Lenarduzzi, John, Mng. Dir.--Esselte S.P.A., Cusago, Italy; *Int'l*, pg. 461
Lennartsson, Lars, Mng. Dir.--John Crane Sverige AB, Goteborg, Sweden; *Int'l*, pg. 1339
Lens, J.W., Mng. Dir.--N.V. Nutricia, Zoetermeer, Netherlands; *Int'l*, pg. 991
Lenz, Sidney, Mng. Dir.--Countrywide Home Loans Inc., Pasadena, CA; *U.S. Public*, pg. 452
Leon, Jesus Gaban, Mng. Dir.--Petroleos Del Sur, S.A. (PETROSUR), Spain; *Int'l*, pg. 323
Leonetti, Bernard, Mng. Dir.--John Crane France, Courbevoie, France; *Int'l*, pg. 1339
Leongnarktongdee, Boonlieng, Mng. Dir.--Thai Containers Ltd., Bangkok, Thailand; *Int'l*, pg. 1238
Leongnarktongdee, Boonlieng, Mng. Dir.--Thai Containers Industry Co., Ltd., Bangkok, Thailand; *Int'l*, pg. 1238
Leongnarktongdee, Boonlieng, Mng. Dir.--Thai Containers Ratchaburi (1989) Co., Ltd., Bangkok, Thailand; *Int'l*, pg. 1238
Leonhardt, Clark M., Plant Mgr.-Eastern Div.--Allied Diagnostic Imaging Resources, Inc., Norcross, GA; *U.S. Public*, pg. 282
Lepage, Alphonse, Mng. Dir.--Swiss Re Life Canada, Toronto, Canada; *Int'l*, pg. 1333
Lercari, Franco, Mng. Dir.--KONE Elevators Overseas S.r.l., Bologna, Italy; *Int'l*, pg. 748
Lerouge, Michel, Mng. Dir.--Dumez-GTM Portugal, Lisbon, Portugal; *Int'l*, pg. 823
Lester, C. Jackson, Mng. Dir.-Europe Bus. Devel.--Capital Markets Assurance Corporation, New York, NY; *U.S. Public*, pg. 1023
Letzelter, Pierre, Mng. Dir.--Champagne Moet & Chandon, Epernay, France; *Int'l*, pg. 779
Leung Ting-Mow, Kenneth, Sr. Mng. Dir.--Kwong On Bank, Limited, Central, Hong Kong; *Int'l*, pg. 521
Leung, Tony, Mng. Dir.--Associated Merchandising-Singapore, Singapore, Singapore; *U.S. Private*, pg. 92
Levendusky, Greg, Mng. Dir.-Europe--The Weber Group, London, United Kingdom; *U.S. Private*, pg. 1157
Lever, A.J., Mng. Dir.--Palintest Limited, Gateshead, United Kingdom; *Int'l*, pg. 589
Levett, B., Mng. Dir.--Bohlin Instruments Ltd., Gloucester, United Kingdom; *Int'l*, pg. 207
Levi, D., Mng. Dir.--M&A Societa di Mergers & Acquisitions S.p.A., Milan, Italy; *Int'l*, pg. 1330
Levine, Richard J., Mng. Editor & V.P.-Dow Jones New Services--AP-Dow Jones News Service, New York, NY; *U.S. Public*, pg. 524
Levitt, Steve, Mng. Dir.--Standard Products Limited, Huntingdon, United Kingdom; *U.S. Public*, pg. 1505
Levy, Jacques, Co-Mng. Dir.--TBWA Paris, Paris, France; *U.S. Private*, pg. 1063
Levy, Rich, Sr. V.P. & Mng. Dir.--Western International Media Corporation, Hollywood, FL; *U.S. Private*, pg. 1167
Lewis, Bill, Mng. Dir.--Volclay Standard Pty. Ltd., Geelong, Australia; *U.S. Public*, pg. 64
Lewis, David, Mng. Dir.--Pasta Foods Limited, Saint Albans, United Kingdom; *Int'l*, pg. 1396
Lewis, E.J., Mng. Dir.--Bestobeli Aviation, Slough, United Kingdom; *Int'l*, pg. 853
Lewis, Eric, Mng. Dir.--Avica, Hemel Hempstead, United Kingdom; *Int'l*, pg. 853
Lewis, Eric, Mng. Dir.--Meggitt Composites, Dudley, United Kingdom; *Int'l*, pg. 853
Lewis, Eric, Mng. Dir.--Silicone Engineering, Blackburn, United Kingdom; *Int'l*, pg. 853
Lewis, Richard S., Chief Admin. Officer & Mng. Dir.-Admin.--Countrywide Home Loans Inc., Pasadena, CA; *U.S. Public*, pg. 452
Lewis, T.C., Mng. Dir.--Strategic Systems International Limited, Basingstoke, United Kingdom; *Int'l*, pg. 1065
Lexa, M., Chm. & Mng. Dir.--ANTEA SA, Orleans, France; *Int'l*, pg. 607
Lichtenauer, P.A., Mng. Dir.--bv Televizier, Amsterdam, Netherlands; *Int'l*, pg. 1445
Liddell, W.K., Mng. Dir.--SPACECON, Inc., New Castle, DE; *U.S. Public*, pg. 913
Liddle, Lori A., V.P. & Mng. Dir.-Lands' End Catalog--Lands' End, Inc., Dodgeville, WI; *U.S. Public*, pg. 977
Liedtke, M., Mng. Dir.--Robert Bosch Ltd., Uxbridge, United Kingdom; *Int'l*, pg. 205
Lievens, Hugo, Mng. Dir.--Innovative Sputtering Technology IST, Zulte, Belgium; *Int'l*, pg. 183
Ligeti, Jack, Mng. Dir.--Sabiem Elevators (Pty.) Ltd., Johannesburg, South Africa; *Int'l*, pg. 748
Lim, Barry, Mng. Dir.--Esselte Meto SDN BHD, Kuala Lumpur, Malaysia; *Int'l*, pg. 461
Lim, Hang Sun, Mng. Dir.--Dentsu Young & Rubicam/Seoul, Seoul, Korea; *U.S. Private*, pg. 325
Lim, Javis, Mng. Dir.--ESPAN Corporation, Singapore, Singapore; *U.S. Public*, pg. 1358
Lim, Jong Moon, Mng. Dir.--Kum Yang Otsuka Chemical Co., Ltd., Ulsan, Korea; *Int'l*, pg. 1014
Lim, Lionel, Dir.--Micron Semiconductor Asia Pacific Pte. Ltd., Singapore, Singapore; *U.S. Public*, pg. 1105
Limay, Luis A., Mng. Dir.--San Cristobal Mill & Plant, San Salvador, El Salvador; *U.S. Public*, pg. 410
Limwattanakul, Suebpong, Asst. Mng. Dir.--Siam City-Showa Leasing Co., Ltd., Bangkok, Thailand; *Int'l*, pg. 1239
Lin, Anthony, Mng. Dir.--Christie's Hong Kong Ltd., Hong Kong, Hong Kong; *Int'l*, pg. 290
Lin, Anthony, Mng. Dir.--Christie's Taiwan, Taipei, Taiwan; *Int'l*, pg. 290
Lincoln, Dave, Mng. Dir.--Piccadilly Radio, Manchester, United Kingdom; *Int'l*, pg. 452
Lincoln, Dave, Mng. Dir.--Red Rose Radio, Preston, United Kingdom; *Int'l*, pg. 452
Lincoln, David F., Mng. Dir.--EnerTech Capital Partners, Wayne, PA; *U.S. Public*, pg. 1424
Lindberg, William P., Mgr.--System One Control, Saint Paul, MN; *U.S. Private*, pg. 851
Lindblad, Anders, Chief Oper. Officer & Mng. Dir.--Hagglunds Drives AB, Mellansel, Sweden; *Int'l*, pg. 670
Lindelof, Ulf, Mng. Dir.--Iggesund Paperboard Norden, Goteborg, Sweden; *Int'l*, pg. 886
Lindenthal, John G., Mng. Dir.--OppenheimerFunds Distributor, Inc., New York, NY; *U.S. Private*, pg. 818
Lindh, Lars, Deputy Mng. Dir.-Europe Tax Free Shopping--Advance Ross Corporation, Chicago, IL; *U.S. Public*, pg. 320

Lindh, Lars, Deputy Mng. Dir.--Europe Tax-Free Shopping Ltd., Chicago, IL; *U.S. Public*, pg. 320

Lindhardt, Ivan, Mng. Dir.--Neproma Textiel Service B.V., Arnhem, Netherlands; *Int'l*, pg. 1285

Lindhoff, Bjoern F., Mng. Dir.--ITT Flygt S.p.A., Milan, Italy; *U.S. Public*, pg. 860

Lindquist, Lennart, Mng. Dir.--Esselte Meto AB, Solna, Sweden; *Int'l*, pg. 459

Lindroos, Satu, Mng. Dir.--Lowe Brindfors, Helsinki, Finland; *U.S. Private*, pg. 678

Lindsay, JoLynnn, Partner & Acct. Supvr.--Lewis Gace Bozell Healthcare Worldwide, Fort Lee, NJ; *U.S. Public*, pg. 1642

Ling, Michael, Mng. Dir.--DMB&B/Warsaw, Warsaw, Poland; *U.S. Private*, pg. 304

Linsell, Liz, Mng. Dir.--Linsell Advertising Associates, Harare, Zimbabwe; *U.S. Public*, pg. 1422

Linski, Taisto, Mng. Dir.--Lappeenranti Plant, Villmanstrand, Finland; *Int'l*, pg. 1198

Linton, John, V.P. & Mng. Dir.-Methanex New Zealand Ltd. & Asia Pacific--Methanex Corporation, Vancouver, Canada; *Int'l*, pg. 862

Lipson, Howard A., Sr. Mng. Dir.--The Blackstone Group, New York, NY; *U.S. Private*, pg. 147

Little, C.A., Chief Exec. Officer & Mng. Dir.--British Mohair Spinners Limited, Bradford, United Kingdom; *Int'l*. pg. 219

Little, H.L., Mng. Dir.--Powell Duffryn Tools Limited, Poole, United Kingdom; *Int'l*, pg. 1066

Little, John, Grp. Mng. Dir.--Sonnenberg Murphy Leo Burnett, Sunninghill, South Africa; *U.S. Private*, pg. 186

Little, M.J., Mng. Dir.-UK--United Biscuits (Holdings) Plc, West Drayton, United Kingdom; *Int'l*, pg. 1442

Little, Paul, Mng. Dir.--Turner Construction Company, Atlanta, GA; *U.S. Public*, pg. 1645

Littleboy, P.A.E., Mng. Dir.--Coutts & Co (Jersey) Limited, Saint Helier, United Kingdom; *Int'l*, pg. 910

Livanovics, Andrejs, Mng. Dir.--KONE Lifti Latvija Oy, Riga, Latvia; *Int'l*, pg. 747

Livet, R.G., Mng. Dir.--Monenco Nigeria Limited, Lagos, Nigeria; *Int'l*, pg. 31

Livingston, Mark, Mng. Dir.--Tall Wall Media, Los Angeles, CA; *U.S. Private*, pg. 1166

Livingston, Robert W., Chm. Bd., Pres. & Chief Exec. Officer--GB Holdings, Jurong, Singapore; *Int'l*, pg. 531

Livingston, Robert W., Pres. & Mng. Dir.--American Marine Pte. Ltd., Jurong, Singapore; *Int'l*, pg. 531

Livingston, Robert W., Mng. Dir.--Grand Banks Yachts, Ltd., Southport, CT; *Int'l*, pg. 531

Ljung, Ake, Mng. Dir.--Nokia Satellite Systems AB, Motala, Sweden; *Int'l*, pg. 954

Llewellyn, Chris, Mng. Dir.-Intl.--EMAP France, Paris, France; *Int'l*, pg. 451

Lloyd, Charles, Mng. Dir.--CPC/AJI (Hong Kong) Ltd., Tai No, Hong Kong; *U.S. Public*, pg. 225

Lloyd, J.R.C., Mng. Dir.--Powell Duffryn Storage Limited, Felixstowe, United Kingdom; *Int'l*, pg. 1065

Lloyd, Stuart, Mng. Dir.--FCB Singapore, Singapore, Singapore; *U.S. Private*, pg. 389

Loc, Truong, Mng. Dir.--Vietnam Marketing Center, Ho Chi Minh City, Vietnam; *U.S. Private*, pg. 305

Lockwood, Stephen, Mng. Dir.--Dawson Fur Fabrics Ltd, Huddersfield, United Kingdom; *Int'l*, pg. 385

Loeb, David J., Mng. Dir.-Consulting & Trng.--Intellicorp Inc., Mountain View, CA; *U.S. Public*, pg. 887

Loewenguth, Alfred, Mng. Dir.--Schachenmann & Co. AG, Basel, Switzerland; *Int'l*, pg. 1306

Loffler, Gerd, Dr., Mng. Dir.--Krupp Hoesch Berufsbildung GmbH, Essen, Germany; *Int'l*, pg. 512

Lohia, Sri Prakash, V.P. & Mng. Dir.--Indo Rama Synthetics P.T., Jakarta, Indonesia; *Int'l*, pg. 673

Loibl, Dipl.-Ing., Chief of Telecom Grp. & Deputy Gen. Dir.--Austrian Postal & Telegraph Administration, Vienna, Austria; *Int'l*, pg. 101

Lom, Tom, Exec. V.P. & Co-Mng. Dir.--The Healthcare Connection, New York, NY; *U.S. Public*, pg. 1422

Lombardi, Marco, Strategic Plng. Dir.--Young & Rubicam Italia, S.p.A., Milan, Italy; *U.S. Private*, pg. 1199

Lommer, Mel, Mng. Dir.--Royal Melrose Granites, Cold Spring, MN; *U.S. Private*, pg. 251

London, J.P., Dr., Mng. Dir.--CACI N.V., London, United Kingdom; *U.S. Public*, pg. 272

Long, David M., Mng. Dir.--Scott & Stringfellow Capital Management, Inc., Richmond, VA; *U.S. Public*, pg. 1445

Lonyay, Alexander, Mng. Dir.--GGK Occidental Holding AG, Vienna, Austria; *Int'l*, pg. 1335

Lopatka, Lubos, Mng. Dir.--KONE Lifts s.r.o., Bratislava, Slovakia; *Int'l*, pg. 747

Lopez, Carmen, V.P. & Mng. Dir.-Sls.--The New Yorker Magazine, New York, NY; *U.S. Private*, pg. 795

Lopez, Fernando, Mng. Dir.--Tissu Canarias S.A., Telde, Spain; *Int'l*, pg. 864

Lorain, G., Mng. Dir.--Vilmorin Inc., Empire, CA; *Int'l*, pg. 566

Lorenz, Juan, Mng. Dir.--Ortho Diagnostic Systems G.m.b.H., Neckargemund, Germany; *U.S. Public*, pg. 932

Louca, Danny, Mng. Dir.--Farouk Advertising, Jeddah, Saudi Arabia; *U.S. Private*, pg. 304

Lough, K.G., Mng. Dir.--LASMO North Sea PLC, London, United Kingdom; *Int'l*, pg. 804

Louie, John Y., Mng. Dir.--Schindler Lifts (Hong Kong) Ltd., Quarry Bay, Hong Kong; *Int'l*, pg. 1205

Loulan, John, Mng. Dir.--Goodyear-Luxembourg, Colmar, Luxembourg; *U.S. Public*, pg. 753

Lowenberg, John D., Mng. Dir. & Dir.--The Robinson-Humphrey Company, Inc., Atlanta, GA; *U.S. Public*, pg. 1633

Lozano, Maria L., Mng. Dir.--Electronica Pantera, S.A. de C.V., Zapopan, Mexico; *U.S. Public*, pg. 919

Lozano, Maria Luisa, Gen. Dir.-Pantera--The JPM Company, Lewisburg, PA; *U.S. Public*, pg. 919

Lubert, Ira M., Mng. Dir.--TL Ventures, Wayne, PA; *U.S. Public*, pg. 1424

Lucas, Glenn R., Mng. Dir.--Aluminum Co. of Malaysia Berhad, Petaling Jaya, Malaysia; *Int'l*, pg. 51

Lucas, Peter, Mng. Dir.--Tegel Foods Limited, Newmarket, New Zealand; *U.S. Public*, pg. 807

Lucas, Rolf, Mng. Dir.--ZK Hospital Bedarfs GmbH, Oer-Erkenschwick, Germany; *Int'l*, pg. 552

Lucas, W., Mng. Dir.--Firma E. Lucas Med. Technik GmbH, Munster, Germany; *Int'l*, pg. 551

Luchai, Shane, Mng. Dir.--Siam Tyre Industry Co., Ltd., Nong Khae, Thailand; *Int'l*, pg. 1238

Lucius, T. Wayne, V.P. & Mng. Dir.--Mortgage Guaranty Insurance Corporation, Milwaukee, WI; *U.S. Public*, pg. 1026

Ludeckel, Frank, Mng. Dir.--AVE Gesellschaft fur Fernsehproduktion mbH, Unterfoehring, Germany; *Int'l*, pg. 1478

Lueneberg, Olaf, Mng. Dir.--Ethicon G.m.b.H. & Co. KG, Norderstedt, Germany; *U.S. Public*, pg. 929

Luff, R., Mng. Dir.--Aluminum Corporation, Dolgarrog, United Kingdom; *Int'l*, pg. 51

Lukes, Edward F., Pres. & Mng. Dir.--SHL Systemhouse Europe Ltd., London, United Kingdom; *Int'l*, pg. 1154

Lumsden, Gregory A., Mng. Dir.-Loan Origination--Countrywide Home Loans Inc., Pasadena, CA; *U.S. Public*, pg. 452

Lund-Hansen, Per, Mng. Dir.--Scan Globe A/S, Havdrup, Denmark; *U.S. Private*, pg. 923

Lund, Mark J., Mng. Dir.-Institutional/Intl., Pension & Offshore Funds--Henderson Administration Group PLC, London, United Kingdom; *Int'l*, pg. 609

Lundberg, Leif, Mng. Dir.--Nokia Audio & Electronics AB, Motala, Sweden; *Int'l*, pg. 954

Lundell, Claes, Mng. Dir.--Icopal ab, Malmo, Sweden; *Int'l*, pg. 659

Lundin, Goran, Mng. Dir.--Holmen Paper AB, Norrkoping, Sweden; *Int'l*, pg. 885

Lundqvist, Stefan, Mng. Dir.--Gunnebo do Brasil Ltda, Sao Paulo, Brazil; *Int'l*, pg. 578

Lurati, M., Mng. Dir.--Robert Bosch AG, Otelfingen, Switzerland; *Int'l*, pg. 205

Lury, Adam, Mng. Partner--Howell Henry Chaldecott Lury & Partners, London, United Kingdom; *Int'l*, pg. 637

Lusetti, Gianni, Mng. Dir.--Bundy SpA, Busalla, Italy; *Int'l*, pg. 1341

Lutz, Bernd, Dr., Mng. Dir.--J.B. Metzler Verlag, Stuttgart, Germany; *Int'l*, pg. 1478

Lynch, Leland T., Chm., Chief Exec. Officer & Mng. Partner--Carmichael Lynch, Inc., Minneapolis, MN; *U.S. Private*, pg. 213

Lyon, Douglas Lawson, Mng. Dir.--Pearsalls Sutures, Taunton, United Kingdom; *Int'l*, pg. 215

Lyons, Steve, Mng. Dir.--Ford Espana S.A., Madrid, Spain; *U.S. Public*, pg. 665

Ma, D., Mng. Dir.--Wuxi Quaker Chemical Co. Ltd., Wuxi, China; *U.S. Public*, pg. 1347

Ma, Victor, Mng. Dir.--Kemet Electronics Asia Ltd., Kowloon Bay, Hong Kong; *U.S. Public*, pg. 949

Maas, Onno, Mng. Dir. & Chief Exec. Officer--DMB&B/Worldwide Communications Amsterdam, Amsterdam, Netherlands; *U.S. Private*, pg. 304

MacDonald, Mary, Chief Exec. Officer & Mng. Dir.--DMB&B/Yellow Pages, Northbrook, IL; *U.S. Private*, pg. 303

Macfarlane, Don B., Mng. Dir.--Amcor Limited, Melbourne, Australia; *Int'l*, pg. 71

MacFarlane, Ian, Mng. Dir.--Young & Rubicam Tholet, Cape Town, South Africa; *U.S. Private*, pg. 1198

MacFarlane, Ray, Mng. Dir.-Scottish Enterprise Oper.--Scottish Enterprise, Glasgow, United Kingdom; *Int'l*, pg. 1212

Machtinger, Steve, Mng. Dir.--Hambrecht & Quist LLC., San Francisco, CA; *U.S. Public*, pg. 778

Maciver, W.K., Mng. Dir.--Lucas Aerospace, Solihull, United Kingdom; *Int'l*, pg. 819

Mackay, Ian M., Mng. Dir.--Adams Rite (Europe) Ltd., Swanley, United Kingdom; *U.S. Private*, pg. 17

Mackay, Terry D., Mng. Dir.--KWB Controls Ltd., Tromode, United Kingdom; *Int'l*, pg. 391

MacKenzie, Larry L., V.P.-Revenue Opers., Dorney Park & Wildwater Kingdom--Cedar Fair, L.P., Sandusky, OH; *U.S. Public*, pg. 319

Mackie, T.M., Mng. Dir.--Ross & Catherall Limited, Sheffield, United Kingdom; *Int'l*, pg. 1467

MacNamara, John, V.P. & Mng. Dir.-Western Direct--Western Direct, New York, NY; *U.S. Private*, pg. 1166

MacNamee, Gordon, Mng. Dir.--Red Dragon Radio, Cardiff, United Kingdom; *Int'l*, pg. 452

Macozoma, Saki, Mng. Dir.--Transnet Ltd., Parkview, South Africa; *Int'l*, pg. 1417

MacPherson, R., Mng. Dir.--Ascom Timeplex Inc., Richmond Hill, Canada; *Int'l*, pg. 87

MacRae, G.D., Mng. Dir.--Abru Aluminium Limited, Launceston, United Kingdom; *Int'l*, pg. 615

Macrez, Roland, Mng. Dir.--Davum-Armatures, Puteaux, France; *Int'l*, pg. 571

Madarasz, Laszlo, Mng. Dir.--BNP-Dresdner Bank (Hungaria) Rt., Budapest, Hungary; *Int'l*, pg. 418

Maddocks, Christopher, V.P. & Mng. Dir.-Check Technology Ltd.--Check Technology Corporation, Minnetonka, MN; *U.S. Public*, pg. 342

Madeling, Christian H., Mng. Dir.-PLP Europe--P.L. Porter Co., Woodland Hills, CA; *U.S. Private*, pg. 876

Maeda, Hiromi, Mng. Dir.--Tonen Corporation, Tokyo, Japan; *Int'l*, pg. 1398

Maffei, Italo, Mng. Dir.--Swiss Life (Italia), Milan, Italy; *Int'l*, pg. 1332

Maffei, Italo, Mng. Dir.--Swiss Life (Italia) Infortuni e Malattie, Milan, Italy; *Int'l*, pg. 1332

Magarity, Russell L., Mng. Dir.--BankBoston Corporation, Boston, MA; *U.S. Public*, pg. 183

Magiera, Horst R., Mng. Dir.--Banque Europeenne pour l'Amerique Latine (BEAL) S.A., Brussels, Belgium; *Int'l*, pg. 1493

Magnan, Jean-Francois, Dir. Gen.--Imphy S.A., Puteaux, France; *Int'l*, pg. 571

Magrady, Jane, Mng. Dir.-Tech. Planning, R&D, GIS & N.O. Systems--American Automobile Association, Heathrow, FL; *U.S. Private*, pg. 50

Mahapun, Somgiat, Gen. Mgr.--Janssen Pharmaceutical Ltd., Bangkok, Thailand; *U.S. Public*, pg. 930

Mahmud, Arshad, Deputy Mng. Dir.-Fin.--Pakistan International Airlines Corporation, Karachi, Pakistan; *Int'l, pg. 1021*

Mahony, Ken, Mng. Dir.--Willis Corroon Ireland Limited, Dublin, Ireland; *Int'l*, pg. 1504

Maier-Rothe, Christoph, Mngng. Dir.--Arthur D. Little International, Inc., Munich, Germany; *U.S. Private*, pg. 670

Maier, Scott C., Mng. Dir.--Quality Hotel Central, Cincinnati, OH; *U.S. Public*, pg. 682

Maier, Scott C , Mng. Dir.--Quality Hotel Riverview, Covington, KY; *U.S. Public*, pg. 682

Maile, Wolfgang, Dr., Mng. Dir.--Wuestenrot International Management-Gesellschaft AG, Luxembourg, Luxembourg; *Int'l*, pg. 1514

Maingst, Rex, Mng. Dir.--Bermudez-Binswanger, Philadelphia, PA; *U.S. Private*, pg. 144

Maini, Roshan, Mng. Dir.--Vascutek Limited, Glasgow, United Kingdom; *Int'l*, pg. 1307

Maitland, William T., Exec. Mng. Dir. & Chief Legal Officer--Nomura Securities International, Inc., New York, NY; *Int'l*, pg. 956

Majorin, Erkki, Mng. Dir.--S.A. Comptoir Finlandais N.V., Brussels, Belgium; *Int'l*, pg. 457

Majorin, Erkki, Mng. Dir.--S.A. Enso N.V., Brussels, Belgium; *Int'l*, pg. 457

Mak, Caroline, Mng. Dir.--Dantas Holdings Ltd., Sha Tin, Hong Kong; *Int'l*, pg. 704

Makela, Erkki, Mng. Dir.--KONE Elevators, Kiev, Ukraine; *Int'l*, pg. 747

Maki, Hisashi, Mng. Dir.-Personnel & Gen. Mgr.-Gen. Affairs Bureau, Tokyo--Nihon Keizai Shimbun, Inc., Tokyo, Japan; *Int'l*, pg. 929

Maki, Pekka Santeri, Mng. Dir.--Fokusz Marketing Kommunikacio Kft., Budapest, Hungary; *U.S. Private*, pg. 1062

Makinen, Heikki, Mng. Dir.--Schauman Panels Ltd., Mersey, United Kingdom; *Int'l*, pg. 1429

Makinen, Risto, Mng. Dir.--Nokia Mobile Phones Produktions GmbH, Bochum, Germany; *Int'l*, pg. 952

Male, S.F., Mng. Dir.--Presstech Controls Limited, Hemel Hempstead, United Kingdom; *U.S. Public*, pg. 789

Malfait, Louis, Mng. Dir.-Italy & European Sales--Chargeurs Wool, Paris, France; *Int'l*, pg. 280

Malhotra, I.S., Chm. Bd. & Mng. Dir.--Keystone Valve (India) PVT. Ltd., Baroda, India; *U.S. Public*, pg. 1650

Maliekel, George, V.P. & Mng. Dir.-Latin America--Rexam Medical Packaging, Inc., Mundelein, IL; *Int'l*, pg. 1107

Malik, Shahid A., Sr. V.P. & Mng. Dir.--Ferrellgas Houston, Houston, TX; *U.S. Public*, pg. 618

Malizia, R., Mng. Dir.--Ballast Nedam Grond en Wegen Projecten B.V., Amstelveen, Netherlands; *Int'l*, pg. 133

Malka, Martti, Mng. Dir.--Nokia Mobile Phones Australia Pty. Ltd., Bondi Junction, Australia; *Int'l*, pg. 952

Mallo de la Calzada, Jose R., Mng. Dir.--Sulzer Sistemas e Instalaciones S.A., Madrid, Spain; *Int'l*, pg. 1306

Mallon, Bill, Mng. Dir.--Brian Pulfrey Ltd., Bingham, United Kingdom; *U.S. Public*, pg. 1267

Malosse, Alain, Mng. Dir.--Smith Corona (France) S.A.R.L., Carrieres-sur-Seine, France; *U.S. Private*, pg. 1007

Manabe, Nobukatsu, Mng. Dir.--NEC Semiconductors Singapore Pte. Ltd., Singapore, Singapore; *Int'l*, pg. 900

Mancini, Sergio, Exec. Mng. Dir.--Best S.p.A., Fabriano, Italy; *U.S. Public*, pg. 1194

Mander, Christopher, Mng. Dir.--Inter-Continental Hotels Corporation, London, United Kingdom; *Int'l*, pg. 1178

Mann, Lindsay, Mng. Dir.--National Mutual Funds Management NZ Limited, Wellington, New Zealand; *Int'l, pg. 909*

Mann, Rick, Dir.-MIS--Arctic Cat Inc., Thief River Falls, MN; *U.S. Public*, pg. 128

Mannekens, R.D., Mng. Dir.--N.V. Nutricia Belgie, Bornem, Belgium; *Int'l*, pg. 992

Mannes, Scott M., Mng. Dir.--ContiFinancial Services Corporation, New York, NY; *U.S. Public*, pg. 439

Manning, Lynne, Mng. Dir.--Kelly Services Canada, Ltd., Toronto, Canada; *U.S. Public*, pg. 949

Mannix, John E., Mng. Dir.-Travel Related Services--American Automobile Association, Heathrow, FL; *U.S. Private*, pg. 50

Mansbach, Claude E., Mng. Dir.--S.A. John Crane Belgium N.V., Brussels, Belgium; *Int'l*, pg. 1339

Mansfield, Mark, Mng. Dir.--Raymond Granite Co., Raymond, CA; *U.S. Private*, pg. 251

Mansfield, William G., Sr. V.P. & Mng. Dir.--National Distributing Co., Inc., Jacksonville, FL; *U.S. Private*, pg. 781

Manson, D.S., Mng. Dir.--MB Toyo Glass Nigeria Limited, Lagos, Nigeria; *Int'l*, pg. 267

Mantini, Franco, Mng. Dir.--Best S.p.A., Fabriano, Italy; *U.S.* Public, pg. 1194

Manzagol, Jeff, Mng. Dir.--SKF South Africa (Pty.) Ltd., Boksburg, South Africa; *Int'l*, pg. 1159

Manzi, Anthony, Mng. Dir.--ESCO Pest Control Services, New York, NY; *Int'l*, pg. 656

Manzon, Ugo, Mng. Dir.-Milan--Armando Testa S.p.A, Rome, Italy; *Int'l*, pg. 1377

Mapp, D., Mng. Dir.--Tom Cobleigh plc, Mansfield, United Kingdom; *Int'l*, pg. 1087

Marais, Georges, Vice Chm. & Deputy Mng. Dir.--Compagnie Generale Maritime et Financiere, Suresnes, France; *Int'l*, pg. 322

Marano, Antonio, Mng. Dir.--Creditanstalt Finanziaria S.p.A., Milan, Italy; *Int'l*, pg. 348

Marconi, V., Mng. Dir.--NMB Italia S.r.l., Milan, Italy; *Int'l*, pg. 868

Marguez, Jose-Antonio, Mng. Dir.--Nokia Mobile Phones, Madrid, Spain; *Int'l*, pg. 952
Mariatta, Miguel, Mng. Dir.--Johnson & Johnson de Uruguay, S.A., Montevideo, Uruguay; *U.S. Public*, pg. 930
Marinelli, Davide, Mng. Dir.--Anacomp Italia, Milan, Italy; *U.S. Public*, pg. 107
Marischka, Gerhard, Mng. Dir.--ISS Central Europe GesmbH, Vienna, Austria; *Int'l*, pg. 656
Marius, Steen, Mng. Dir.--Elkem Materials, Kristiansand, Norway; *Int'l*, pg. 447
Mark, Lothar, Mng. Dir.--Metallbank GmbH, Frankfurt/Main, Germany; *Int'l*, pg. 861
Marks, Horst, Mng. Dir.--O&K Rolltreppen GmbH, Hattingen Works, Hattingen, Germany; *Int'l*, pg. 516
Maroun, Mary, Mng. Dir.--TBWA Chiat/Day New York, New York, NY; *U.S. Private*, pg. 1062
Marques, Albano Pires, Mng. Dir.--Esselte Meto Portugal LDA, Oeiras, Portugal; *Int'l*, pg. 461
Marrakchi, Saad, Mng. Dir.--Sherazade Conseil, Casablanca, Morocco; *Int'l*, pg. 118
Marsh, H. John, Jr., Mng. Dir.-Fin. Mngmt. Div.--Federal Farm Credit Banks Funding Corporation, Jersey City, NJ; *U.S. Private*, pg. 398
Marsh, R., Reg. Mng. Dir.--Ballast Wiltshier Plc - London Region, Barking, United Kingdom; *Int'l*, pg. 135
Marshall, A., Mng. Dir.--LASMO Nederland B.V., Beverwijk, Netherlands; *Int'l*, pg. 804
Marshall, David, Mng. Dir.--Willis Corroon South Limited, Bristol, United Kingdom; *Int'l*, pg. 1503
Marshall, Elmore, Mng. Dir.--SCI Operations Division, Sasolburg, South Africa; *Int'l*, pg. 1196
Marshall, Jim, Mng. Dir.--The Media Centre, London, United Kingdom; *Int'l*, pg. 852
Marshall, S., Dr., Mng. Dir.--Potterton Myson, Warwick, United Kingdom; *Int'l*, pg. 197
Marshall, Tony, Mng. Dir.--Butlin's Limited, Hemel Hempstead, United Kingdom; *Int'l*, pg. 1086
Martell, Michel, Mng. Dir.--Arthur D. Little de Columbia, Ltda., Bogota, Colombia; *U.S. Private*, pg. 670
Martin, Bernard, V.P. & Grp. Mng. Dir.-Atlantic Cluster--S.C. Johnson & Son, Inc., Racine, WI; *U.S. Private*, pg. 592
Martin, Bob, Mng. Dir.--Willis Corroon Asia Pacific Limited, Singapore, Singapore; *Int'l*, pg. 1509
Martin, Gregorio, Mng. Dir.-Wholesale Banking--Caja de Madrid Group, Madrid, Spain; *Int'l*, pg. 251
Martin, I., Mng. Dir.--GKN Ayra Durex SA, Zumaya, Spain; *Int'l*, pg. 535
Martin, Ian, Sr. Mng. Dir.-Investment Mngmt. Grp.--Bankers Trust New York Corporation, New York, NY; *U.S. Public*, pg. 185
Martin, Jerry, Mng. Dir.--Lincoln Steel, Lincoln, NE; *U.S. Private*, pg. 824
Martin, R.J., Mng. Dir.--Seaforth Maritime Limited, Aberdeen, United Kingdom; *U.S. Public*, pg. 776
Martinez, Carlos M., Mng. Dir.-Corp. Banking--Caja de Madrid Group, Madrid, Spain; *Int'l*, pg. 251
Martinez, Enrique de la Torre, Deputy Mng. Dir. & Sec.--Caja de Madrid Group, Madrid, Spain; *Int'l*, pg. 251
Martinez, Jose M., Mng. Dir.-Diversification--Iberdrola, S.A., Bilbao, Spain; *Int'l*, pg. 657
Martinez, Jose Manuel Martinez, Mng. Dir. & Chief Exec. Officer--Corporacion MAPFRE, Compania Internacional de Reaseguros, S.A., Madrid, Spain; *Int'l*, pg. 332
Martyres, Raul J., Mng. Dir.--Access Advertising Limited, Nairobi, Kenya; *U.S. Private*, pg. 303
Maruyama, Takashi, Mng. Dir.--Tosoh Corporation, Tokyo, Japan; *Int'l*, pg. 1407
Mas, Frederico, Mng. Dir.--Turbinas y Equipos Industriales, S.A. de C.V., Morelia, Mexico; *Int'l*, pg. 1306
Masago, Yukio, Sr. Mng. Dir.--Shoko Chukin Bank, Tokyo, Japan; *Int'l*, pg. 1236
Mashimo, Tsugio, Mng. Dir. & Gen. Mgr.-Plng.--Gunze Sangyo, Inc., Tokyo, Japan; *Int'l*, pg. 578
Mason, Henry, Mng. Dir.--Haskel Energy Systems Ltd., Sunderland, United Kingdom; *U.S. Public*, pg. 798
Mastej, Mike, Mng. Dir.--Victoria Regional Medical Center, Victoria, TX; *U.S. Public*, pg. 1697
Masters, C.R., Mng. Dir.--NatWest International Trust Corporation (Bahamas) Limited, Nassau, Bahamas; *Int'l*, pg. 911
Masters, Geoff, Gen. Mgr.-Prod.--Spirol International Corp., Cuyahoga Falls, OH; *U.S. Private*, pg. 1026
Masuda, Hideki, Sr. Mng. Dir.-Intl.--Omron Corporation, Kyoto, Japan; *Int'l*, pg. 1005
Masumoto, Yuzuru, Mng. Dir.--All Nippon Airways Co. Ltd., Tokyo, Japan; *Int'l*, pg. 57
Maten, Gerrit J., Mng. Dir.--KLM Aerocarto BV, Arnhem, Netherlands; *Int'l*, pg. 607
Mathiesen, Lars, Mng. Dir.--NY*BO*E, Copenhagen, Denmark; *Int'l*, pg. 993
Mathieson, Michael C., Mng. Dir.-GSE Lining Tech. GmbH--Gundle/SLT Environmental, Inc., Houston, TX; *U.S. Public*, pg. 769
Mathieu, Francis, Dir.-Human Resources & Training--Promodes SA, Mondeville, France; *Int'l*, pg. 1071
Mathisen, Arne, Mng. Dir.--Norsk Rehab AS, Nesoddtangen, Norway; *U.S. Public*, pg. 1536
Mathisen, Avild, Mng. Dir.--Pripps Ringnes a.s., Oslo, Norway; *Int'l*, pg. 1011
Mathison, Neil, Mng. Dir.--Sun Microsystems of California Ltd., Wan Chai, Hong Kong; *U.S. Public*, pg. 1532
Mathoret, Jean-Francois, Mng. Dir.--CRMA, Elancourt, France; *Int'l*, pg. 560
Mathot, Jos, Mng. Dir.--Security House, Purmerend, Netherlands; *U.S. Public*, pg. 1307
Mathot, Jos, Mng. Dir.--Security House, Pumerend, Netherlands; *U.S. Public*, pg. 1307
Mathrani, Arjun, Sr. Mng. Dir.-Global Asset Mnmgt. & Private Banking--The Chase Manhattan Bank, New York, NY; *U.S. Public*, pg. 338
Mathur, R.B., Chm. Bd. & Mng. Dir.--Central Mine Planning & Design Institute Limited, Ranchi, India; *Int'l*, pg. 298
Matovcik, Victor, Mng. Dir.--Slovak International Tabak, a.s. (S.I.T.), Bratislava, Slovakia; *Int'l*, pg. 1101
Matsuda, Sadao, Mng. Dir. & Gen. Mgr.-Pub. Use & Bldg. Systems--Mitsubishi Electric Corporation, Tokyo, Japan; *Int'l*, pg. 872
Matsuda, Yoshifumi, Dir.-Gen. Affairs & Personnel--Tokuyama Corporation, Tokyo, Japan; *Int'l*, pg. 1393
Matsui, Isamu, Sr. Mng. Dir.-Mfg., Tech. & Engrng.--Murata Machinery, Ltd., Kyoto, Japan; *Int'l*, pg. 897
Matsumoto, Teruomi, Mng. Dir.--Daiko Advertising, Inc., Osaka, Japan; *Int'l*, pg. 366
Matsumura, Akio, Mng. Dir.-Plng. & Admin.--UBE Industries Ltd., Tokyo, Japan; *Int'l*, pg. 1426
Matsuo, Yoshio, Mng. Dir.--NEC Technologies (UK) Ltd., Telford, United Kingdom; *Int'l*, pg. 900
Matsuoka, Michiya, Area Dir.-Asia & Oceania--Dentsu East Japan Inc., Tokyo, Japan; *Int'l*, pg. 393
Matsuoka, Michiya, Area Dir.--Area Headquarters-ASIA & OCEANIA, Tokyo, Japan; *Int'l*, pg. 393
Matsushima, Kunihiro, Deputy Reg. Dir.-East Asia--Dentsu Young & Rubicam Limited (Hong Kong), Hong Kong, Hong Kong; *U.S. Private*, pg. 325
Matsuura, Koichi, Mng. Dir.--Ebara Corporation, Tokyo, Japan; *Int'l*, pg. 431
Matsuyama, Norio, Chief Oper. Officer--P.T. Standard Toyo Polymer, Jakarta, Indonesia; *Int'l*, pg. 1408
Matter, Daniel, Mng. Dir., Creative Dir. & New Bus. Contact--Matter Leo Burnett, Zurich, Switzerland; *U.S. Private*, pg. 186
Matter, Heidi, Mng. Dir.--Janssen-Cilag Pharmaceutica AG, Baar, Switzerland; *U.S. Public*, pg. 929
Matthew, John, Mng. Dir.--Reckitt & Colman Products Pty. Ltd., Ermington, Australia; *Int'l*, pg. 1090
Matthews, William E., Mng. Dir.-U.K. & Ireland--The F.A. Bartlett Tree Expert Co., Stamford, CT; *U.S. Private*, pg. 119
Matthews, William E., Mng. Dir.--Southern Tree Surgeons, Ltd., Crawley, United Kingdom; *U.S. Private*, pg. 119
Matthys, Paul, Vice Chm., Pres. & Mng. Dir.--Sidmar N.V., Gent, Belgium; *Int'l*, pg. 79
Mattinson, Graham, Mng. Dir.--PPP Beaumont PLC, High Wycombe, United Kingdom; *Int'l*, pg. 1020
Mattot, E., Mng. Dir.--Inbar Computer Training Ltd., Tel Aviv, Israel; *Int'l*, pg. 1007
Matza, Robert, Mng. Dir.--Lehman Brothers Holdings Inc., New York, NY; *U.S. Public*, pg. 987
Maughan, H.B., Chief Oper. Officer & Mng. Dir.--Kidde Thorn Fire Protection Limited, Oldham, United Kingdom; *Int'l*, pg. 1500
Maule, Helmut, Mng. Dir.--Hausbau Wuestenrot GmbH, Ludwigsburg, Germany; *Int'l*, pg. 1514
Mauri, D., Mng. Dir.--NRG Comunicaciones S.A., Barcelona, Spain; *Int'l*, pg. 1116
Maury, Mireille, Deputy Mng. Dir.-Fin.--Hermes International, Paris, France; *Int'l*, pg. 617
Max, M., Mng. Dir.--Reckitt & Colman Industrial Ltda., Sao Paulo, Brazil; *Int'l*, pg. 1090
May, David, V.P. & Mng. Dir.-Sls.--The New Yorker Magazine, New York, NY; *U.S. Private*, pg. 795
May, David L., V.P. & Mng. Dir.-Corp. New Prods. & Tech.--S.C. Johnson & Son, Inc., Racine, WI; *U.S. Private*, pg. 592
May, George, Mng. Dir.-Civil Engrng. Div.--Costain Building & Civil Engineering Limited, Maidenhead, United Kingdom; *Int'l*, pg. 336
Mayer, Paul, Mng. Dir.-Store Opers.--PAMPAM Warenhandel Ges.m.b.H., Vienna, Austria; *Int'l*, pg. 856
Mayne, W.F.S., Mng. Dir.--BOCM PAULS Limited, Ipswich, United Kingdom; *Int'l*, pg. 598
Mazzo, James, Mng. Dir.--Allergan S.p.A., Pomezia, Italy; *U.S. Public*, pg. 46
McAleenan, Patrick, Chief Fin. Officer & Dir.-Fin.--EMAP Business Communications Division, London, United Kingdom; *Int'l*, pg. 451
McAleer, Ian, Mng. Dir.--Evode Group Ltd., Stafford, United Kingdom; *Int'l*, pg. 802
McAnally, J., Mng. Dir.--Bally South Africa Ltd., Parklands, South Africa; *Int'l*, pg. 997
McCabe, Kenneth T., Mng. Dir.--Acme United Ltd.-Surmanco Division, Sheffield, United Kingdom; *U.S. Public*, pg. 17
McCain, Allison, Chief Exec. Officer & Mng. Dir.--McCain Foods (GB) Limited, Scarborough, United Kingdom; *Int'l*, pg. 850
McCann, Bob, Exec. V.P. & Mng. Dir., KGF--A.C. Nielsen Company, Schaumburg, IL; *U.S. Public*, pg. 1183
McCarthy, Des, Mng. Dir.--Willis Corroon Management Limited-Dublin, Dublin, Ireland; *Int'l*, pg. 1509
McCarthy, Sean, Mng. Dir.-PK Ltd. UK--Plasti-Kote Company Inc., Medina, OH; *U.S. Private*, pg. 870
McCarthy, Terry, Mng. Dir.--Product Plus International, London, United Kingdom; *U.S. Public*, pg. 1225
McCarty, Kevin, Mng. Dir.--Kasser/Laird Distilling Co., Horsham, PA; *U.S. Private*, pg. 643
McCauley, D., Mng. Dir.--Coutts & Co (Isle of Man) Limited, Onchan, United Kingdom; *Int'l*, pg. 910
McClean, Murray R., Mng. Dir.--CMC (Australia) Pty. Limited, Sydney, Australia; *U.S. Public*, pg. 413
McClure, B., Mng. Dir.--Ascom Nexion Inc., Acton, MA; *Int'l*, pg. 86
McClure, Charles G., V.P. & Mng. Dir.-European Opers.--Johnson Controls, Inc., Plymouth, MI; *U.S. Public*, pg. 932
McConnell, Douglass, Mng. Dir.-Corp. Fin. Div.--Duff & Phelps Utilities Income Inc., Chicago, IL; *U.S. Public*, pg. 534
McCormick, P.C., Mng. Dir.--Swiss Bank Corporation, New York, NY; *Int'l*, pg. 1329
McCrea, James, Chief Exec. Officer & Mng. Dir.--Air New Zealand Ltd., Auckland, New Zealand; *Int'l*, pg. 38
McCrea, N.G., Mng. Dir.-Edward Baker Limited--BOCM PAULS Limited, Ipswich, United Kingdom; *Int'l*, pg. 598
McCready, P.R., Mng. Dir.--Johnson's Wax Espanola, S.A., Madrid, Spain; *U.S. Private*, pg. 593
McCullough, Ronald L., Mng. Dir.-Equities--Dewey Square Investors Corporation, Boston, MA; *U.S. Public*, pg. 1673
McCutcheon, R. L.O., Mng. Dir.--Delta EMS Ltd., Walsall, United Kingdom; *Int'l*, pg. 391
McDaniel, William P., Mng. Dir.--OppenheimerFunds Distributor, Inc., New York, NY; *U.S. Private*, pg. 818
McDermott, Kelly, V.P. & Mng. Dir.--Western Interactive Media, Los Angeles, CA; *U.S. Private*, pg. 1166
McDonald, Francis X., Sr. V.P. & Mng. Dir.-Construction--Willis Corroon Corp. of Penn., Radnor, PA; *Int'l*, pg. 1507
McDonald, James S., Exec. V.P. & Mng. Dir.--Pell, Rudman & Company, Boston, MA; *U.S. Public*, pg. 1673
McDonald, Kerry, Mng. Dir.-Comalco New Zealand--Comalco Limited, Brisbane, Australia; *Int'l*, pg. 307
McDonald, Michael, Mng. Dir.--Talisman Energy (U.K.) Limited, Aberdeen, United Kingdom; *Int'l*, pg. 1352
McDonald, T.K., Mng. Dir.--Comalco New Zealand, Wellington, New Zealand; *Int'l*, pg. 307
McDonnell, Charlie, Joint Mng. Dir.--Quinn McDonnell Pattison DMB&B Dublin, Dublin, Ireland; *U.S. Private*, pg. 305
McDonnell, Christopher, Mng. Dir.--E Wood Limited, Northallerton, United Kingdom; *Int'l*, pg. 858
McFarlane, Larry, V.P.-Corp. Commun.--Nu Skin International, Provo, UT; *U.S. Private*, pg. 808
McFarlane, Ron, Mng. Dir.--SSB Advertising Brisbane, Brisbane, Australia; *Int'l*, pg. 394
McGahan, Glenn, Mgr.--TN Media Inc., Auckland, New Zealand; *U.S. Public*, pg. 1642
McGarry, Jack, Mng. Dir.--Willis Corroon Harris Marrian Limited, Belfast, United Kingdom; *Int'l*, pg. 1502
McGaughey, Michael J., Mngng. Dir.--Arthur D. Little Asia Pacific Inc., Hong Kong, Hong Kong; *U.S. Private*, pg. 670
McGee, Gerald, Exec. V.P. & Mng. Dir.-O & M L.A.--Ogilvy & Mather Worldwide, Inc., New York, NY; *Int'l*, pg. 1483
McGhee, Douglas, Mng. Dir.--Newage Industries Inc., Testing Instruments Group, Willow Grove, PA; *U.S. Private*, pg. 796
McGovern, Ted, Mng. Dir.--ICS Building Society, Dublin, Ireland; *Int'l*, pg. 152
McGowan, Kelly, Chief Info. Officer & Mng. Dir.--Cowen & Company, New York, NY; *U.S. Private*, pg. 280
McIlheney, Barry, Mng. Dir.--EMAP Metro, London, United Kingdom; *Int'l*, pg. 451
McIlroy, R., Mng. Dir.--Christie's Australia Pty. Ltd., Yarram, Australia; *Int'l*, pg. 290
McIlwrath, John, Mng. Dir.--Ferro Chemicals S.A., Port-de-Bouc, France; *U.S. Public*, pg. 619
McIsaac, Larry W., Mng. Dir.--Black & Decker (Australasia) Pty. Limited, Croydon, Australia; *U.S. Public*, pg. 234
McKechnie, B., Mng. Dir.--Babcock Construction Limited, Renfrew, United Kingdom; *Int'l*, pg. 130
McKenna, Francis B., Mng. Dir.-Pub. Fin.--Merrill Lynch & Co., Inc., New York, NY; *U.S. Public*, pg. 1097
McKenzie, Douglas C., Mng. Dir.--Methode Electronics Europe Limited, Dumbarton, United Kingdom; *U.S. Public*, pg. 1101
McKinnon, Malcolm, Mng. Dir.--Hawkeye Construction, Inc., Troutdale, OR; *U.S. Public*, pg. 1029
Mclatchie, Colin, Mng. Dir. & Chief Info. Officer--PanAgora Asset Management Limited, London, United Kingdom; *Int'l*, pg. 936
McLaughlin, David, V.P. & Mng. Dir.-Ingalls Recruitment Adv.--Ingalls, Boston, MA; *U.S. Private*, pg. 562
McLaughlin, P., Mng. Dir.--Getinge Australia Pty. Ltd., Bulimba, Australia; *Int'l*, pg. 551
McLaughlin, Thomas K., Chief Fin. Officer & Mng. Dir.--Countrywide Home Loans Inc., Pasadena, CA; *U.S. Public*, pg. 452
McLean, A., Mng. Dir.--Ballast Wiltshier Plc - Scotland, Berwick-upon-Tweed, United Kingdom; *Int'l*, pg. 135
McLornan, Brian, Mng. Dir.--Glen Electric, Newry, United Kingdom; *Int'l*, pg. 554
McMahon, Kevin W., Vice Chm.-Prod. & W. Div. & Reg. Construction Mng. Dir.--Willis Corroon Corp. of California, San Francisco, CA; *Int'l*, pg. 1505
McMurray, Charley, Mng. Dir.--Advanced Filtration Systems, Inc., Champaign, IL; *U.S. Public*, pg. 316
McMurty, Peter, Mng. Dir.--Renishaw (Ireland) Limited, Dublin, Ireland; *Int'l*, pg. 1103
McNamee, Gordon, Mng. Dir.--Kiss FM, London, United Kingdom; *Int'l*, pg. 452
McNeely, Larry, Mng. Dir.--Corro-Coat (Malaysia) Sdn. Bhd., Shah Alam, Malaysia; *Int'l*, pg. 715
McNeill, R.J.B., Mng. Dir.--Northern Ireland Carpets Ltd., Newtownards, United Kingdom; *Int'l*, pg. 797
McNeill, R.J.B., Mng. Dir.--B.H. McCleery & Co. Ltd., Newtownards, United Kingdom; *Int'l*, pg. 797
McNeill, R.J.B., Mng. Dir.--Hollybank Bleach & Dye Works Ltd., Ballyclare, United Kingdom; *Int'l*, pg. 798
McPartland, Peter, Mng. Dir.--Radio Aire, Leeds, United Kingdom; *Int'l*, pg. 452
McVay, Larry D., Mng. Dir. & Gen. Mgr.-Amoco--Amoco Corporation, Chicago, IL; *U.S. Public*, pg. 101
McWalters, James G., Mng. Dir.--PM Realty Advisors Inc., Newport Beach, CA; *U.S. Private*, pg. 831
Mead, D., Mng. Dir.--National Australia Trustees Ltd., Melbourne, Australia; *Int'l*, pg. 906
Mealling, Bobbie, V.P. & Mng. Dir.--Standard Distributing Co. Inc., Brunswick, GA; *U.S. Private*, pg. 781
Medart, Ch., Mng. Dir.--Ascom Hasler SA, Brussels, Belgium; *Int'l*, pg. 87
Meenan, Hubert V., Sr. V.P. & Mng. Dir.--Price/McNabb, Inc., Charlotte, NC; *U.S. Private*, pg. 883
Meert, Jacques, Mng. Dir.--H.J. Heinz Central Europe S.A., Brussels, Belgium; *U.S. Public*, pg. 806
Meert, Jacques, Mng. Dir.--H.J. Heinz Northern Europe, Brussels, Belgium; *U.S. Public*, pg. 806
Meeusen, Dan I., Mng. Dir.--Sulzer Pompen Benelux B.V., Hengelo, Netherlands; *Int'l*, pg. 1306
Meffre, Jean-Marie, Mng. Dir.--Renishaw S.A., Marne la Vallee, France; *Int'l*, pg. 1103

Mehling, E., Mng. Dir.--VEM Erz und Stahl GmbH, Essen, Germany; *Int'l*, pg. 682
Mehrotra, Sunit, Mng. Dir.--TBWA Stockholm, Stockholm, Sweden; *U.S. Private*, pg. 1063
Meier Nolte, J. D., Mng. Dir.--Konatec Nassbaggertechnik GmbH, Monchengladbach, Germany; *Int'l*, pg. 608
Meier, H., Mng. Dir.--Oerlikon-Contraves Pyrotec AG, Zurich, Switzerland; *Int'l*, pg. 998
Meister, Peter, Mng. Dir.--Burgmann Seals South Africa (Pty) Ltd., Evendale, South Africa; *Int'l*, pg. 234
Mekarporn, Phairuch, Mng. Dir.--Siam Kraft Industry Co., Ltd., Bangkok, Thailand; *Int'l*, pg. 1238
Mekarporw, Phairuch, Mng. Dir.--Thai Kraft Paper Industry Co., Ltd., Bangkok, Thailand; *Int'l*, pg. 1238
Melgaard, J., Mng. Dir.--Livsforsikrings-Aktieselskabet Utrecht, Copenhagen, Denmark; *Int'l*, pg. 499
Melham, Elie, Mng. Dir.--Nanjing Goulds Pumps Limited, Nanjing, China; *U.S. Public*, pg. 861
Melkus, Thomas D., Mng. Dir.--CCL Security Products, New Britain, CT; *U.S. Public*, pg. 548
Melle, Jean-Louis, V.P. & Mng. Dir.--Groupe DMR S.A., Paris, France; *Int'l*, pg. 528
Melliger, Rene H., Mng. Dir.-Controlling & Accounting--LGT Bank in Liechtenstein Aktiengesellschaft, Vaduz, Liechtenstein; *Int'l*, pg. 809
Mello, Robert L., Mng. Dir.--Bank of Montreal - New York, New York, NY; *Int'l*, pg. 154
Melville, Jo, Mng. Dir.--TML Reed Exhibitions (Pty.) Ltd.-Africa, Randburg, South Africa; *Int'l*, pg. 1097
Menard, Antoine, Mng. Dir.-Europe--Insituform Technologies, Inc., Chesterfield, MO; *U.S. Public*, pg. 881
Mencacci, Dante, Mng. Dir.--EMAP Business International Ltd., London, United Kingdom; *Int'l*, pg. 451
Mence, Ian, Mng. Dir.--Ultra Electronics Magnetics, Cannock, United Kingdom; *Int'l*, pg. 1431
Mendez, Michael C., Mng. Dir.--NWQ Investment Managaement Company, Los Angeles, CA; *U.S. Public*, pg. 1673
Mendoza, R., Mng. Dir.--Ascom Hasler SA, Madrid, Spain; *Int'l*, pg. 87
Mendrinos, Sotirios, Mng. Dir.--Grace Hellas Industrial & Commercial L.L.C., Athens, Greece; *U.S. Public*, pg. 756
Meng Wah, Alex Chan, Chief Exec. Officer & Mng. Dir--Yeo Hiap Seng Limited, Singapore, Singapore; *Int'l*, pg. 1008
Mengelt, Jurg, Mng. Dir.-Plng. & Control--Landis & Staefa AG, Zug, Switzerland; *Int'l*, pg. 800
Mercer, Laura, Sr. V.P. & Mng. Dir.--Price/McNabb, Inc., Charlotte, NC; *U.S. Private*, pg. 883
Merchant, Ali, Mng. Dir.--Triton Communications, Mumbai, India; *Int'l*, pg. 118
Merchant, Shabbir, V.P. & Mng. Dir.-Simulation Div.--ETC Simulation Group, Orlando, FL; *U.S. Public*, pg. 587
Merchant, Shabbir H., V.P.-Simulation Div. & Mng. Dir.--Environmental Tectonics Corporation (ETC), Southampton, PA; *U.S. Public*, pg. 587
Mermilliod, M., Mng. Dir.--Robert Bosch (France) SA, Saint Ouen, France; *Int'l*, pg. 205
Meroni, Filippo, V.P. & Grp. Mng. Dir.-Europe--S.C. Johnson & Son, Inc., Racine, WI; *U.S. Private*, pg. 592
Meroni, Filippo, V.P., Grp. Mng. Dir. & Gen. Mgr.--Johnson Wax S.p.A., Milan, Italy; *U.S. Private*, pg. 593
Merrick, P.R., Mng. Dir.--Charterhouse Group International, Inc., New York, NY; *U.S. Private*, pg. 230
Merrifield, Peter, Mng. Dir.-Europe, Middle East & Africa--Gandalf Technologies Inc., Nepean, Canada; *Int'l*, pg. 540
Merten, Jost, Mng. Dir.--Merit-Malta Methode Ltd., Mriehel, Malta; *U.S. Public*, pg. 1101
Meschkat, Reihard, Dr., Mng. Dir.--Bertrand Faure Sitztechnik GmbH & Co. KG, Neuburg an dew Donau, Germany; *Int'l*, pg. 193
Metcalfe, David, Mng. Dir.--Trade Promotion Services Ltd., London, United Kingdom; *Int'l*, pg. 451
Meyer, Lutz, Mng. Dir.--Shandwick Deutschland GmbH, Bonn, Germany; *Int'l*, pg. 1227
Meyer, Wolfgang, Mng. Dir.--Battenfeld Canada Ltd., Mississauga, Canada; *Int'l*, pg. 825
Meyers, C. Thomas, Mng. Dir.-Credit Enhancement--Capital Markets Assurance Corporation, New York, NY; *U.S. Public*, pg. 1023
Michael, Wolf, Mng. Dir.--Solectron GmbH, Herrenburg, Germany; *U.S. Public*, pg. 1483
Michaels, Janet, Exec. Dir.--American Health Assistance Foundation, Rockville, MD; *U.S. Private*, pg. 56
Michelin, Edouard, Mng. Dir. & Dir.-Mktg.--Compagnie Generale des Etablissements Michelin, Clermont, France; *Int'l*, pg. 322
Micyk, Rysard, Mng. Dir.--Willis Corroon Polska Spolka Akeyjna, Warsaw, Poland; *Int'l*, pg. 1509
Middleditch, M.R., Mng. Dir. & Sec.--Spar (UK) Ltd., Harrow, United Kingdom; *Int'l*, pg. 1288
Middlemiss, J.M., Reg. Mng. Dir.--Ballast Wiltshier Plc - Scotland, Glasgow, United Kingdom; *Int'l*, pg. 135
Middleton, David, Mng. Dir.--Tonermex S.A. de C.V., Toluca, Mexico; *Int'l*, pg. 1116
Middleton, P.E., Mng. Dir.--Wayfarer Transit Systems Ltd., Poole, United Kingdom; *Int'l*, pg. 853
Middleton, Ron, Mng. Dir.--Sulzer New Zealand Limited, Auckland, New Zealand; *Int'l*, pg. 1306
Mieszczak, Boguslaw, Mng. Dir.--TI Poland sp zo.o., Bielsko-Biala, Poland; *Int'l*, pg. 1341
Migliazza, M., Mng. Dir.--Witco Italiana, Milan, Italy; *U.S. Public*, pg. 1774
Mijangos, Victor, Mng. Dir.--Burgmann Mexico S.A. De C.V., Mexico, Mexico; *Int'l*, pg. 233
Milano, Gilbert, Mng. Dir.--SLE S.a.r.l., Nice, France; *U.S. Public*, pg. 1045
Milano, Marco, Mng. Dir.--Merloni Domestic Appliances Ltd, Uxbridge, United Kingdom; *Int'l*, pg. 860
Milenekiotov, Georgia Garinois, Mng. Dir.--Neutrogena Corporation SARL, Paris, France; *U.S. Public*, pg. 928
Miler, Russ, Mng. Dir.--Asuransi Jiwa Principal Egalita Indonesia, Jakarta, Indonesia; *U.S. Private*, pg. 886
Miles, Stephen A., Mng. Dir.-Europe--Lands' End, Inc., Dodgeville, WI; *U.S. Public*, pg. 977
Miliou, Elana, Chief Exec. Officer, Mng. Dir.--International Marketing & Promotions, Athens, Greece; *U.S. Private*, pg. 304
Miliou, Elena, Chief Exec. Officer & Mng. Dir.--DMB&B Athens, Athens, Greece; *U.S. Private*, pg. 303
Miller, Caroline, Editor-In-Chief--New York Magazine, New York, NY; *U.S. Public*, pg. 1328
Miller, Christy, Mng. Dir.--Supreme Corporation of Texas, Cleburne, TX; *U.S. Public*, pg. 1542
Miller, Christy, Mng. Dir.--Supreme MidAtlantic Corporation, Jonestown, PA; *U.S. Public*, pg. 1542
Miller, Christy, Mng. Dir.--Supreme Murphy Corp., Wilson, NC; *U.S. Public*, pg. 1542
Miller, H.C.W., Mng. Dir.--De La Rue Identity Systems Limited, Basingstoke, United Kingdom; *Int'l*, pg. 387
Miller, Jeffrey J., Mng. Dir.--Provident Investment Counsel, Inc., Pasadena, CA; *U.S. Public*, pg. 1674
Miller, John, U.K. Mng. Dir.--Alberto-Culver Company (U.K.) Limited, Basingstoke, United Kingdom; *U.S. Public*, pg. 38
Miller, Michael S., Mng. Dir.--The Vanguard Group, Inc., Valley Forge, PA; *U.S. Private*, pg. 1133
Miller, Richard, Sr. V.P. & Mng. Dir.-Pub. Rels.--Northlich Stolley LaWarre Public Relations, Cincinnati, OH; *U.S. Private*, pg. 806
Mills, Colin, Mng. Dir.--TBWA Moscow, Moscow, Russia; *U.S. Private*, pg. 1063
Mills, Ernest, Mng. Dir.--Holiday RV Superstores of New Mexico Inc., Las Cruces, NM; *U.S. Public*, pg. 830
Millweard, Tom, Exec. V.P. & Mng. Dir.--Ackerman McQueen, Inc., Irving, TX; *U.S. Private*, pg. 13
Milner, D.A., Mng. Dir.--Castell Safety International Limited, London, United Kingdom; *Int'l*, pg. 589
Min, Woo-Ki, Mng. Dir.--Bum-A Petroleum Co., Ltd., Seoul, Korea; *Int'l*, pg. 1292
Minagawa, Takashi, Mng. Dir.--NLI Properties UK Limited, London, United Kingdom; *Int'l*, pg. 936
Minassian, Michael, Mng. Dir.--Costain Middle East, Dubai, United Arab Emirates; *Int'l*, pg. 337
Minato, Shungo, Chm. & Mng. Dir.--Pioneer Electronic (Europe) NV, Melsele, Belgium; *Int'l*, pg. 1058
Minkin, Gustav, Mng. Dir.--Nearby Eggs, Inc., Spring Grove, PA; *U.S. Public*, pg. 1529
Minner, Tom, Mng. Dir.--GNB Technologies, Atlanta, GA; *Int'l*, pg. 1021
Minor, David J., Mng. Dir.--Black Warrior Transmission Corp., Brookwood, AL; *U.S. Public*, pg. 1485
Minott, L.O., Mng. Dir.--MB Jamaica Limited, Kingston, Jamaica; *Int'l*, pg. 267
Mirabaud, Bertrand, Mng. Dir.--Lagon, Puteaux, France; *Int'l*, pg. 601
Miron, Steven, Mng. Dir.--John Wiley & Sons (Asia) Pte. Ltd., Singapore; *U.S. Public*, pg. 1768
Mirsky, P.J., Mng. Dir.-North American & Australian Sugar Div.--Tate & Lyle PLC, London, United Kingdom; *Int'l*, pg. 1356
Mishima, Shiro, Mng. Dir.--OYO Corporation, Tokyo, Japan; *Int'l*, pg. 1019
Mishra, R.N., Chm. Bd. & Mng. Dir.--Northern Coalfields Limited, Sidhi, India; *Int'l*, pg. 299
Mita, Keiji, Mng. Dir. & Standing Auditor--The Yokohama Rubber Co., Ltd., Tokyo, Japan; *Int'l*, pg. 1521
Mitchell, G.E., Mng. Dir.--Bundaberg Sugar Company, Brisbane, Australia; *Int'l*, pg. 1357
Mitchell, James R., Mng. Dir.--Janssen-Cilag Pty. Ltd., Lane Cove, Australia; *U.S. Public*, pg. 929
Mitchell, John, Mng. Dir.--Avana Bakeries Ltd., Cardiff, United Kingdom; *Int'l*, pg. 1396
Mitchelson, C. S., Mng. Dir.--Cascade (U.K.) Ltd., Cramlington, United Kingdom; *U.S. Public*, pg. 311
Mitra, Tapan, Mng. Dir.--Indian Aluminium Co. Ltd., Calcutta, India; *Int'l*, pg. 51
Mitsuhashi, Takashi, Mng. Dir. & Gen. Mgr.-Corp. Engrng.--Mitsubishi Electric Corporation, Tokyo, Japan; *Int'l*, pg. 872
Mitsuoka, Teruo, Sr. Mng. Dir.-Domestic Mktg. & Sls.--Mazda Motor Corporation, Hiroshima, Japan; *Int'l*, pg. 849
Mitta, Raj, Mng. Dir.--Arthur D. Little Far East, Inc., Singapore, Singapore; *U.S. Private*, pg. 670
Mitta, Raj, Mng. Dir.--Arthur D. Little (Malaysia) Sdn Bhd, Kuala Lumpur, Malaysia; *U.S. Private*, pg. 671
Miu, Bernard, Mng. Dir.--Union Carbide Asia Ltd., Kowloon, Hong Kong; *U.S. Public*, pg. 1667
Miura, Mamoru, Chm. & Rep. Dir.--Tokyu Agency Inc., Tokyo, Japan; *Int'l*, pg. 1394
Miura, Yuichi, Mng. Dir.-Corp. Plng.--Tokuyama Corporation, Tokyo, Japan; *Int'l*, pg. 1393
Miyakawa, Kazuo, Area Dir.--Area Headquarters-EUROPE & MIDDLE EAST, London, United Kingdom; *Int'l*, pg. 393
Miyanaga, Kazuhori, Mng. Dir. & Gen. Mgr.--Takugin International (Asia) Ltd., Hong Kong, Hong Kong; *Int'l*, pg. 627
Miyoshi, Koichiro, Mng. Dir.--Hosokawa Micron Corporation, Osaka, Japan; *Int'l*, pg. 635
Mizera, Sue, Strategic Plng. & Devel. Dir.--Young & Rubicam Business Communications S.A., Geneva, Switzerland; *U.S. Private*, pg. 1199
Mizobuchi, Yasuo, Mng. Dir.--Sumitomo International Finance Australia Limited, Sydney, Australia; *Int'l*, pg. 1310
Mizuno, Kosuke, Mng. Dir.--Hakuhodo Inc., Hiroshima, Japan; *Int'l*, pg. 587
Mizuno, Takashi, Mng. Dir.--NEC Deutschland GmbH, Ismaning, Germany; *Int'l*, pg. 901
Moberg, Per, Mng. Dir.--Emil Moestue as, Oslo, Norway; *Int'l*, pg. 460
Mobsby, Timothy P., Mng. Dir.--Kellogg Company of Great Britain Ltd., Manchester, United Kingdom; *U.S. Public*, pg. 947
Mockel, Alfred, Mng. Dir. & Div. Head.-Fin. Mkts.--BHF-BANK AG, Frankfurt, Germany; *Int'l*, pg. 119
Moden, John, Mng. Dir.--Margetts Foods Limited, Tenbury, United Kingdom; *Int'l*, pg. 732
Moekersoms, Jacques, Gen. Mgr.--L'Oreal Technique Professional Div., Brussels, Belgium; *Int'l*, pg. 819
Moens, Marcel, Mng. Dir.--Leo Burnett Brussels, Brussels, Belgium; *U.S. Private*, pg. 185
Moere, B.W.V., Mng. Dir.--Taylor Woodrow Services Ltd., Southall, United Kingdom; *Int'l*, pg. 1359
Mohally, Bryan, Mng. Dir.--Janssen Pharmaceutical Limited, Little Island, Ireland; *U.S. Public*, pg. 930
Mohri, K., Mng. Dir.--Bally Japan Ltd., Osaka, Japan; *Int'l*, pg. 997
Molan, John C., Mng. Dir.--McCormick (UK) Plc., Haddenham, United Kingdom; *U.S. Public*, pg. 1067
Molenar, Nico, V.P. & Mng. Dir.-CTG Europe--Computer Task Group, Inc. (CTG), Buffalo, NY; *U.S. Public*, pg. 423
Molenar, Nico, Mng. Dir.--Computer Task Group Europe B.V., Amsterdam, Netherlands; *U.S. Public*, pg. 423
Molinaro, Samuel L., Jr., Chief Fin. Officer & Sr. Mng. Dir.--The Bear Stearns Companies Inc., New York, NY; *U.S. Public*, pg. 197
Mollenhauer, Michael, Mng. Dir.--Arthur D. Little International, Inc., Wiesbaden, Germany; *U.S. Private*, pg. 671
Moller-Christensen, Hans, Mng. Dir.--Nykredit Bank A/S, Copenhagen, Denmark; *Int'l*, pg. 993
Moller, Christopher, Ph.D., Mng. Dir.--TL Ventures, Wayne, PA; *U.S. Public*, pg. 1424
Moller, Gerhard, Mng. Dir.--David, Munich, Germany; *U.S. Public*, pg. 787
Moloney, David, Mng. Dir.--Gelman Ireland Ltd., Dublin, Ireland; *U.S. Public*, pg. 1253
Molyneux, John, Mng. Dir.--Apple Computer (UK) Ltd., Uxbridge, United Kingdom; *U.S. Public*, pg. 121
Momose, Nabuo, Area Dir.--Area Headquarters-THE AMERICAS, New York, NY; *Int'l*, pg. 393
Monbaron, Maurice, Mng. Dir.--Credit Lyonnais Suisse SA, Geneva, Switzerland; *Int'l*, pg. 344
Mondavi, Timothy J., Mng. Dir. & Winegrower--Robert Mondavi Winery, Inc., Oakville, CA; *U.S. Public*, pg. 1393
Monerris, Francisco, Res. Dir.--Vinizius/Young & Rubicam S.A., Barcelona, Spain; *U.S. Private*, pg. 1199
Monica, R., Mng. Dir.-Beverages--Kraft Jacobs Suchard, Velizy-Villacoublay, France; *U.S. Public*, pg. 1290
Monnier, Nicolas, Pres. & Mng. Dir.--Alice, Paris, France; *U.S. Private*, pg. 678
Monsivais, Alfonso, Mng. Dir.--Preformados De Mexico SA, Mexico, Mexico; *U.S. Public*, pg. 1321
Montenegro, Cesar, Mng. Dir.--Sulzer de Venezuala S.A., Caracas, Venezuela; *Int'l*, pg. 1306
Montgomery, B.K., Mng. Dir.--GKN Wheels, Telford, United Kingdom; *Int'l*, pg. 535
Montgomery, B.K., Mng. Dir.--GKN Wheels Nagbol A/S, Lunderskov, Denmark; *Int'l*, pg. 535
Montgoris, William J., Chief Oper. Officer & Sr. Mng. Dir.--The Bear Stearns Companies Inc., New York, NY; *U.S. Public*, pg. 197
Monthan, Erkki, Mng. Dir.--Merita Bank Ltd.-Tallinn Branch, Tallinn, Estonia; *Int'l*, pg. 859
Montuori, Mario, Mng. Dir.--Johnson & Johnson Taiwan Ltd., Taipei, Taiwan; *U.S. Public*, pg. 931
Moolhuijsen, Fred, Mng. Dir.--PMSVW/Young & Rubicam B.V., Amsterdam, Netherlands; *U.S. Private*, pg. 1199
Moon, Scott, Mng. Dir.--Service Motor Co., Stevens Point, WI; *U.S. Private*, pg. 986
Moore, Brian S., Mng. Dir.-External Rels.--AMBAC Financial Group, Inc., New York, NY; *U.S. Public*, pg. 62
Moore, James, Mng. Dir.--Morphy Richards Appliances, Mexborough, United Kingdom; *Int'l*, pg. 554
Moore, James E., Pres. & Mng. Dir.--ContiFinancial Services Corporation, New York, NY; *U.S. Public*, pg. 439
Moore, Jim, Mng. Dir.-Consumer Mktg.-STP--First Brands Corporation, Danbury, CT; *U.S. Public*, pg. 626
Moore, Jim, Mng. Dir.-Consumer Mktg. & Automotive Prods.--STP Corporation, Danbury, CT; *U.S. Public*, pg. 627
Moore, John O., Mng. Dir.--Duncan Equipment Company, Oklahoma City, OK; *U.S. Private*, pg. 346
Mora, Jose, Mng. Dir.--Janssen Farmaceutica, S.A. de C.V., Mexico, Mexico; *U.S. Public*, pg. 929
Moradpour, Edouard, Mng. Dir.--Leo Burnett & Moradpour/Moscow, Moscow, Russia; *U.S. Private*, pg. 184
Morales, Vicky, Country Mgr.--Grace Central America, Guatemala, Guatemala; *U.S. Public*, pg. 755
Morbilli, Alessandro, Dir. Gen.-Legal--European Investment Bank, Luxembourg, Luxembourg; *Int'l*, pg. 465
Moreno, Frutos, Mng. Dir.-Madrid--TBWA Madrid, S.A., Madrid, Spain; *U.S. Private*, pg. 1063
Morent, Hubert, Fin. Dir.--Young & Rubicam Belgium S.A., Brussels, Belgium; *U.S. Private*, pg. 1199
Moreton, Paul, Mng. Dir.--Coopers Payen Ltd., Slough, United Kingdom; *Int'l*, pg. 1334
Morgan, Harvey, Exec. Mng. Dir.-Genesis Merchant Grp. Securities LLC--Burlington Coat Factory Warehouse Corporation, Burlington, NJ; *U.S. Public*, pg. 268
Morgan, J.H., Mng. Dir.--Coral Racing Ltd., Barking, United Kingdom; *Int'l*, pg. 170
Morgan, Peter, Mng. Dir.-Specialty Group--Coles Myer Ltd., Tooronga, Australia; *Int'l*, pg. 306
Morgan, Rick, Mng. Dir.--Spectral Technology Group Ltd., Slough, United Kingdom; *U.S. Public*, pg. 1189
Morimoto, N., Mng. Dir.--ITT Flygt Ltd., Tokyo, Japan; *U.S. Public*, pg. 860
Morishige, Toru, Vice Chm. & Mng. Dir.--PanAgora Asset Managment, Inc., Boston, MA; *Int'l*, pg. 935
Morishige, Toru, Vice Chm. & Mng. Dir.--PanAgora Asset Managment, Inc., Boston, MA; *U.S. Public*, pg. 987
Moritz, Francis, Mng. Dir.--Ilco Unican (U.K.) Ltd., London, United Kingdom; *Int'l*, pg. 1432
Moritz, Francis, Mng. Dir.--Ilco Unican France S.A., Courbevoie, France; *Int'l*, pg. 1432

Moriya, Kazuhiko, Sr. Mng. Dir.--Dentsu Young & Rubicam Inc. (Tokyo), Tokyo, Japan; *U.S. Private*, pg. 325
Morley, S., Mng. Dir.--Getinge AB Japan, Tokyo, Japan; *Int'l*, pg. 551
Morns, R.R., Mng. Dir.--Chemoxy International plc, Middlesbrough, United Kingdom; *Int'l*, pg. 88
Moroishi, Mitsuhiro, Mng. Dir.-Legal & Personnel--Sumitomo Chemical Company, Ltd., Tokyo, Japan; *Int'l*, pg. 1310
Morribot, Joel, Gen. Dir.-Kaufman & Broad Housing--Kaufman and Broad Home Corporation, Los Angeles, CA; *U.S. Public*, pg. 944
Morris, Faith, V.P. & Mng. Dir.-Burrell Pub. Rels.--Burrell Communications Group Inc., Chicago, IL; *U.S. Private*, pg. 188
Morris, Gill, Mng. Dir.--GPC Connect (London), London, United Kingdom; *U.S. Public*, pg. 1225
Morris, R.H, Mng. Dir.--Beazer Homes (Bridgwater) Limited, Bridgwater, United Kingdom; *Int'l*, pg. 182
Morris, R.R., Mng. Dir.--Dawmec Limited, Southampton, United Kingdom; *Int'l*, pg. 88
Morris, Tom, Mng. Dir.-Adv.--AMR Corporation, Fort Worth, TX; *U.S. Public*, pg. 9
Morrison, J.A., Mng. Dir.--Minebea Electronics (UK) Ltd., Glasgow, United Kingdom; *Int'l*, pg. 868
Morrissey, Mark, Exec. V.P. & Mng. Dir.--Mezzina/Brown Inc., New York, NY; *U.S. Private*, pg. 739
Morschel, John, Chief Exec. Officer & Mng. Dir.--Lend Lease Corporation Limited, Sydney, Australia; *Int'l*, pg. 806
Mortenson, Ken, Mng. Dir.--OppenheimerFunds Distributor, Inc., New York, NY; *U.S. Private*, pg. 818
Morton, C. Cammack, Sr. Mng. Dir.--Rothschild Inc., New York, NY; *U.S. Private*, pg. 947
Mortusewicz, Romuald, Mng. Dir.--Schmitt & Weitz Baustoffwerke GmbH & Co. KG, Kleinostheim, Germany; *Int'l*, pg. 606
Moscon, Antonio, Mng. Dir.--Fundinox Ltda., Sao Paulo, Brazil; *Int'l*, pg. 1305
Moseley, David, Mng. Dir.--Ferro Corporation (Australia) Pty. Ltd., Melbourne, Australia; *U.S. Public*, pg. 619
Moseley, T., Mng. Dir.--Ascom Timeplex Australia Pty. Ltd., Sydney, Australia; *Int'l*, pg. 87
Moser, Hans-Peter, Mng. Dir.-Corp. Information Tech.--Landis & Staefa AG, Zug, Switzerland; *Int'l*, pg. 800
Moser, Peter, Mng. Dir.--Sulzer Friotherm Ltd., Winterthur, Switzerland; *Int'l*, pg. 1306
Mosimann, Philip, Mng. Dir.--Sulzer Thermatec Ltd., Winterthur, Switzerland; *Int'l*, pg. 1307
Mossberg, Anders, Mng. Dir.--S-E-Banken Forsakring, Stockholm, Sweden; *Int'l*, pg. 1259
Mossman, James J., Sr. Mng. Dir.--The Blackstone Group, New York, NY; *U.S. Private*, pg. 147
Mostonen, Jussi, Mng. Dir.--Merita Fund Management Ltd., Helsinki, Finland; *Int'l*, pg. 859
Mottershead, Derek, Mng. Dir.--Bang & Olufsen United Kingdom Ltd., Wokingham, United Kingdom; *Int'l*, pg. 146
Moudarri, Soubhi, Mng. Dir.--Farouk Advertising, Jeddah, Saudi Arabia; *U.S. Private*, pg. 304
Moxley, Bruce, Partner-Production--Lewis Gace Bozell Healthcare Worldwide, Fort Lee, NJ; *U.S. Public*, pg. 1642
Moya Ferrera, Fernando, Mng. Dir.--Comunica Leo Burnett Panama, S.A., Panama, Panama; *U.S. Private*, pg. 184
Moynihan, Brian T., Mng. Dir.-Corp. Strategy & Devel.--Fleet Financial Group, Inc., Boston, MA; *U.S. Public*, pg. 648
Mrig, G.C., Chm. Bd. & Mng. Dir.--Bharat Coking Coal Limited, Dhanbad, India; *Int'l*, pg. 298
Muck, Henry, Mng. Dir.--ComAlloy International Company, Nashville, TN; *U.S. Public*, pg. 1441
Mudge, Daniel, Sr. Mng. Dir.-Risk Mngmt.--Bankers Trust New York Corporation, New York, NY; *U.S. Public*, pg. 185
Mueller-Gebel, Klaus, Mng. Dir.-H.R. & Legal Svcs.--Commerzbank AG, Frankfurt, Germany; *Int'l*, pg. 308
Mueller, Klaus-Peter, Mng. Dir.-Intl. Bank Rels.--Commerzbank AG, Frankfurt, Germany; *Int'l*, pg. 308
Muessel, Maryam H., Mng. Dir.-Fin. Engrng.--Capital Markets Assurance Corporation, New York, NY; *U.S. Public*, pg. 1023
Mujagic, Christophe, Mng. Dir.--Chargeurs Wool, Paris, France; *Int'l*, pg. 280
Mulder, N., Mng. Dir.--Dynadro bv, s Hertogenbosch, Netherlands; *Int'l*, pg. 681
Mulford, David C., Vice Chm. & Mng. Dir.--Credit Suisse First Boston, Inc., New York, NY; *Int'l*, pg. 345
Muller-Bunz, Manfred, Mng. Dir.--Wuestenrot Grundstuecksverwertungs-GmbH, Ludwigsburg, Germany; *Int'l*, pg. 1514
Muller, Eduard, Mng. Dir.--Salzgitter Oberflachentechnik GmbH, Salzgitter, Germany; *Int'l*, pg. 1308
Muller, Hans, Mng. Dir.--Sulzer Papertec GmbH, Krefeld, Germany; *Int'l*, pg. 1305
Muller, Hermann, Mng. Dir.--Sulzer Korea Ltd., Seoul, Korea; *Int'l*, pg. 1306
Muller, Karl, Mng. Dir.--Dun & Bradstreet Norge AS, Oslo, Norway; *U.S. Public*, pg. 536
Muller, L., Mng. Dir.--GKN Remanufacturing GmbH, Offenbach/Main, Germany; *Int'l*, pg. 536
Mullis, Karen L., Mng. Dir.--Review Publishing Company Ltd., Hong Kong, Hong Kong; *U.S. Public*, pg. 525
Mulvey, S., Mng. Dir.--Kvaerner Process Systems Inc., Calgary, Canada; *Int'l*, pg. 768
Mundy, Ray, Mng. Dir.-John Sands Grp.--American Greetings Corporation, Cleveland, OH; *U.S. Public*, pg. 77
Munro, Richard, Mng. Dir.--Hanimex (NZ) Limited, Albany, New Zealand; *Int'l*, pg. 1116
Munsell, John G., Dir.--Provident Bank of Florida, Sarasota, FL; *U.S. Public*, pg. 1338
Muntjewerf, A.K., Mng. Dir.--Analytisch Biochemisch Laboratorium B.V., Assen, Netherlands; *Int'l*, pg. 991
Murad, Humayun, Mng. Dir.--ORIX Leasing Pakistan Limited, Karachi, Pakistan; *Int'l*, pg. 1010
Murakami, Kimiharu, Mng. Dir.-Fin.--Settsu Corporation, Amagasaki, Japan; *Int'l*, pg. 1225
Murakami, Kunio, Mng. Dir.--Yamaichi International (Middle East) E.C., Manama, Bahrain; *Int'l*, pg. 1518
Murakami, Toshihiko, Mng. Dir.--Kayaba Industry Co., Ltd., Tokyo, Japan; *Int'l*, pg. 727
Muraoka, Noboru, Mng. Dir.--Hanimex Vivitar Japan K.K., Tokyo, Japan; *Int'l*, pg. 1061
Murase, Makoto, Mng. Dir.-Human Resources--Oji Paper Co., Ltd., Tokyo, Japan; *Int'l*, pg. 998
Murata, Yoshihiko, Mng. Dir. & Sr. V.P.-Engrng., Res. & Devel.--Japan Airlines Company, Ltd., Tokyo, Japan; *Int'l*, pg. 699
Murayama, Kyoji, Mng. Dir.-Legal Affairs Div.--Fujisawa Pharmaceutical Co. Ltd., Osaka, Japan; *Int'l*, pg. 525
Murphy, Chris, Mgr. Dir.--Kiewit Mining Group, Inc., Omaha, NE; *U.S. Private*, pg. 619
Murphy, James, Pres. & Mng. Dir.--Provident Securities & Investment Company, Cincinnati, OH; *U.S. Public*, pg. 1338
Murphy, Ronan M., Mng. Dir.--Bank of Ireland International Finance Limited, Dublin, Ireland; *Int'l*, pg. 152
Murray, S.P., Mng. Dir.--Boots Opticians, Nottingham, United Kingdom; *Int'l*, pg. 202
Murray, Simon, Mng. Dir.-Tech. Svcs.--BAA plc, London, United Kingdom; *Int'l*, pg. 103
Murray, Tony, Mng. Dir.--Willcox & Gibbs, Ltd., Braintree, United Kingdom; *U.S. Private*, pg. 1177
Musesengwa, S.H., Reg. Dir.-Africa--ZSR Corporation Ltd., Harare, Zimbabwe; *Int'l*, pg. 1357
Mustoe, William T., Grp. Mng. Dir.-Campbell U.K.--Campbell Soup Company, Camden, NJ; *U.S. Public*, pg. 298
Muttupulle, E.C.S.R., Mng. Dir.--Lanka ORIX Leasing Company Limited, Rajagirya, Sri Lanka; *Int'l*, pg. 1009
Myers, Jim, Mng. Dir.--Information & Engineering Technology, Fairfax, VA; *U.S. Private*, pg. 351
Myers, Joe, Mng. Dir.--Beach Patrol Inc., Carson, CA; *U.S. Private*, pg. 125
Myers, Stuart, Pres. & Mng. Dir.--Otsuka Pharmaceutical Australia Pty. Ltd., Pymble, Australia; *Int'l*, pg. 1014
Myrup, Niels Chr., Mng. Dir.--FLS Data A/S, Valby, Denmark; *Int'l*, pg. 476
Nabielsky, Gabriel, Mng. Dir.--American Textil, S.A. de C.V., Santa Clara, Mexico; *U.S. Public*, pg. 769
Nadal, Domingo, Mng. Dir.--Velcro Europe S.A., Argentona, Spain; *Int'l*, pg. 1462
Nadal, Domingo, Mng. Dir.--Velcro Italia S.R.L., Milan, Italy; *Int'l*, pg. 1462
Naegeli, John P., Mng. Dir.--Sulzer Pumps Ltd., Winterthur, Switzerland; *Int'l*, pg. 1306
Nagahata, Osamu, Mng. Dir.--All Nippon Airways Co. Ltd., Tokyo, Japan; *Int'l*, pg. 57
Nagano, Shinobu, Gen. Mgr.--Nippo Corporation, Europe Branch, Amsterdam, Netherlands; *Int'l*, pg. 932
Nagasawa, Toshio, Mng. Dir.-Res. & Devel.--UBE Industries Ltd., Tokyo, Japan; *Int'l*, pg. 1426
Nagata, Teruyuki, Mng. Dir.--Kintetsu World Express (Taiwan), Inc., Taipei, Taiwan; *Int'l*, pg. 735
Nagelstad, Bjorn, Mng. Dir.--Jotun Thailand Ltd., Bangkok, Thailand; *Int'l*, pg. 715
Naito, Tsuneo, Mng. Dir.-Mngmt. Strategy--Sega Enterprises Ltd., Tokyo, Japan; *Int'l*, pg. 1218
Nakada, Fumio, Exec. Mng. Dir.--Kubota Corp., Osaka, Japan; *Int'l*, pg. 762
Nakagawa, Kenzo, Chm. Bd. & Mng. Dir.--Showpla Asia Limited, Singapore, Singapore; *Int'l*, pg. 1237
Nakagawa, Teruyuki, Mng. Dir.--Showpla International Pte. Ltd., Singapore, Singapore; *Int'l*, pg. 1237
Nakai, Nobukazu, Mng. Dir.--Kintetsu World Express (U.K.) Ltd., Slough, United Kingdom; *Int'l*, pg. 735
Nakajima, Kenkichi, Mng. Dir. & Chief Exec.--Yamaichi International (Europe) Ltd., London, United Kingdom; *Int'l*, pg. 1518
Nakajima, Shinji, Sr. Mng. Dir.--All Nippon Airways Co. Ltd., Tokyo, Japan; *Int'l*, pg. 57
Nakamura, Minoru, Mng. Dir. & Gen. Mgr.-Gen. Plng. Div.--The Nanto Bank, Ltd., Nara, Japan; *Int'l*, pg. 905
Nakamura, Yoshiharu, Mng. Dir.--Sakura Finanz (Deutschland) GmbH, Dusseldorf, Germany; *Int'l*, pg. 1180
Nakasnishi, T., Mng. Dir.--Nippon Kaiji Kyokai, Fort Lee, NJ; *Int'l*, pg. 934
Nakayama, Tsunehiro, Mng. Dir. & Chief Exec.--IBJ International plc, London, United Kingdom; *Int'l*, pg. 676
Nam, Hyon Min, Mng. Dir.--Korea Orix Lease and Finance Limited, Hong Kong, Hong Kong; *Int'l*, pg. 1009
Nam, Kee-Il, Chief Fin. Officer--Ssangyong Heavy Industries Co., Ltd., Seoul, Korea; *Int'l*, pg. 1292
Nambiar, P.G., Mng. Dir.--Bowthorpe Thermometrics (India) Pvt. Ltd., Bangalore, India; *Int'l*, pg. 208
Namekawa, Nobutada, Mng. Dir. & Chief Exec.-Mktg.--Meiji Life Insurance Company, Tokyo, Japan; *Int'l*, pg. 854
Namokel, S., Mng. Dir.--Gebr. Becker Sportanlagenbau GmbH, Taunusstein, Germany; *Int'l*, pg. 608
Nanda, Arun, Chm. Bd. & Mng. Dir.--Rediffusion-DY&R Pvt. Ltd., Mumbai, India; *U.S. Private*, pg. 326
Nanri, M., Mng. Dir.--Sharp-Roxy Electronics Corporation (M) Sdn. Bhd., Batu Pahat, Malaysia; *Int'l*, pg. 1230
Nardone, John, Mng. Dir., Media Dir. & Res. Dir.--Modem Media New York, New York, NY; *U.S. Public*, pg. 1641
Narita, Akihiko, Mng. Dir. & Pres.-Japan--Symantec Corporation, Cupertino, CA; *U.S. Public*, pg. 1545
Narita, Shigeyuki, Mng. Dir.-Corp. Communications--Omron Corporation, Kyoto, Japan; *Int'l*, pg. 1005
Narsey, Chittu B., Mng. Dir.--Khimline Pumps Limited, Thane, India; *Int'l*, pg. 1305
Nassauer, G., Mng. Dir.--Elektrowerk Weisweiler GmbH, Eschweiler, Germany; *U.S. Private*, pg. 735
Nathikanchanalab, Thirasakdi, Mng. Dir.--SCT Co., Ltd., Bangkok, Thailand; *Int'l*, pg. 1238
Navarro, Luis, Fin. Dir.--EURO RSCG-Venezuela, Caracas, Venezuela; *Int'l*, pg. 603
Navi, Menashe, Mng. Dir.--Autologic Information International Ltd., Ramat Gan, Israel; *U.S. Public*, pg. 1724
Nawratil, Franz, V.P. & Mng. Dir.-Europe, Africa & Middle East Opers.--Hewlett-Packard Company, Palo Alto, CA; *U.S. Public*, pg. 813
Neame, John, Mng. Dir.--EMAP Enterprise Events, Purley, United Kingdom; *Int'l*, pg. 451
Neblett, Mortimer S., Jr., Mng. Dir. & Dir.--The Robinson-Humphrey Company, Inc., Atlanta, GA; *U.S. Public*, pg. 1633
Neervoort, A.F., Mng. Dir.--Hoogovens Buizen B.V., Oosterhout, Netherlands; *Int'l*, pg. 754
Negoro, Takashi, Sr. Mng. Dir.-Personnel, Gen. Affairs & Paperboard--Settsu Corporation, Amagasaki, Japan; *Int'l*, pg. 1225
Neill, Michael R., Mng. Dir.--PM Realty Advisors Inc., Newport Beach, CA; *U.S. Private*, pg. 831
Neiva, Edmilson, Mng. Dir.--Rhone-Poulenc de Mexico S.A. de C.V., Mexico, Mexico; *Int'l*, pg. 1113
Nelissen, Willy, Mng. Dir.--Delaware Computing Zwevegem, Zwevegem, Belgium; *Int'l*, pg. 183
Nello, Hugues, Mng.Dir.--Mitchell Sports SA, Marignier, France; *U.S. Public*, pg. 933
Nellul, Frederic, Mng. Dir.--Credit Lyonnais Capital Markets plc, London, United Kingdom; *Int'l*, pg. 344
Nelson, Greg, Dir.-MIS--Ultra Pac, Inc., Rogers, MN; *U.S. Public*, pg. 1662
Nelson, Scott, V.P.-Acct. Services & Mng. Dir.--Western International Media Corporation, Salt Lake City, UT; *U.S. Private*, pg. 1167
Nerlet, N., Mng. Dir.--Credit Lyonnais Espana SA, Madrid, Spain; *Int'l*, pg. 344
Neu, Christian, Dr., Gen. Dir.--ELVIA Leben, Geneva, Switzerland; *Int'l*, pg. 60
Neubauer, Friedrich, Mng. Dir.--ISS Marischka spol.s.r.o., Bratislava, Slovakia; *Int'l*, pg. 657
Neumann, Gunter, Mng. Dir.--Waggonbau Bruninghaus GmbH, Schwerte, Germany; *Int'l*, pg. 509
Neumann, Hans Joergen, Reg. Mng. Dir.--Berendsen PMC A/S, Ski, Norway; *Int'l*, pg. 1285
Neuss, Wolfgang, Mng. Dir.--Bertrand Faure Sitztechnik GmbH & Co. KG, Bad Abbach, Germany; *Int'l*, pg. 193
New, Michael J., Mng. Dir-H.R.--Banknorth Group Inc., Burlington, VT; *U.S. Public*, pg. 186
Newman, Arthur B., Sr. Mng. Dir.--The Blackstone Group, New York, NY; *U.S. Private*, pg. 147
Newton, Schaloj, V.P. & Mng. Dir.--Allergan K.K., Tokyo, Japan; *U.S. Public*, pg. 46
Ng, Tony, Mng. Dir.--Woodhead Asia Pte. Ltd., Singapore, Singapore; *U.S. Public*, pg. 1776
Ngiam, David, Mng. Dir.--Corex Technology (S) Pte Ltd., Singapore, Singapore; *Int'l*, pg. 651
Niccolls, Philip, Dr., Mng. Dir.--Battenfeld Gloenco Extrusion Systems Ltd., Droitwich, United Kingdom; *Int'l*, pg. 825
Nichols, Francis T., Mng. Partner-EMA Mngmt. Services Group, Inc.--Eric Mower and Associates, Inc., Syracuse, NY; *U.S. Private*, pg. 765
Nickerson, Melody, Strategic Plng. Dir.--Heil-Brice Retail Advertising, Newport Beach, CA; *U.S. Private*, pg. 519
Nicklous, Michael, Mng. Dir.--MAINCO Elevator Services Co., Long Island City, NY; *Int'l*, pg. 656
Niclasson, Bjorn, Mng. Dir.--Stroms Bruk, Stromsnabruk, Sweden; *Int'l*, pg. 886
Nicolai, Julius A., Mng. Dir.--OppenheimerFunds Distributor, Inc., New York, NY; *U.S. Private*, pg. 818
Nicolai, Willi, Mng. Dir.--Battenfeld Schweiz AG, Volketswil, Sweden; *Int'l*, pg. 826
Nicoliasen, B.N., Mng. Dir.-European & African Opers.--Osmonics, Inc., Minnetonka, MN; *U.S. Public*, pg. 1233
Nicolosi, V., Mng. Dir.--Silvani Antincendi SpA, Milan, Italy; *Int'l*, pg. 1500
Niebel, Volker, Mng. Dir.--SECON GmbH, Dransfeld, Germany; *Int'l*, pg. 669
Niemeyer, Frank, Mng. Dir. & Chief Fin. Officer--Frese & Wolff Werbeagentur, Oldenburg, Germany; *U.S. Private*, pg. 304
Nienstedt, Heinz-Werner, Dr., Mng. Dir.--Verlagsgruppe Handelsblatt GmbH, Dusseldorf, Germany; *Int'l*, pg. 1479
Niki, Yasuhiko, Mng. Dir.--Kayaba Industry Co., Ltd., Tokyo, Japan; *Int'l*, pg. 727
Niklasson, Sten, Mng. Dir.--Neste Sverige AB, Stockholm, Sweden; *Int'l*, pg. 915
Nikopoulos, George, Mng. Dir.--Producta-TBWA, Athens, Greece; *U.S. Private*, pg. 1062
Nikulski, Heinz, Mng. Dir.--Harman Deutschland GmbH, Heilbronn, Germany; *U.S. Public*, pg. 787
Nilson, Marianne, Pres. & Mng. Dir.--Atlet AB, Molnlycke, Sweden; *Int'l*, pg. 97
Nilsson, N.O., Mng. Dir.--GKN Nordiska Kardan AB, Amal, Sweden; *Int'l*, pg. 536
Nisbet, Sue, Deputy Mng. Dir.--DMB&B Frankfurt, Frankfurt/Main, Germany; *U.S. Private*, pg. 303
Nishiguchi, Yasuo, Sr. Mng. Dir.--Kyocera Corporation, Kyoto, Japan; *Int'l*, pg. 775
Nishii, M., Sr. Mng. Dir.--Esso Sekiyu Kabushiki Kaisha, Tokyo, Japan; *U.S. Public*, pg. 602
Nishikiori, Shinichi, Mng. Dir.--Sumitomo Finance (Dublin) Limited, Dublin, Ireland; *Int'l*, pg. 1310
Nishimoto, Kohzo, Sr. Mng. Dir. & Chief Exec.-Corp. Mktg.--Meiji Life Insurance Company, Tokyo, Japan; *Int'l*, pg. 854
Nishimura, Hiroshi, Mng. Dir.-New Business Admin., Res. Labs, New Matls. & Biomed.--Sumitomo Metal Industries, Ltd., Tokyo, Japan; *Int'l*, pg. 1315
Nishimura, Katsuhiko, Sr. Mng. Dir.-Admin.--Sega Enterprises Ltd., Tokyo, Japan; *Int'l*, pg. 1218
Nishimura, Kazuhiko, Mng. Dir.-Corp. Admin. Div.--Tokuyama Corporation, Tokyo, Japan; *Int'l*, pg. 1393
Nissen-Sollie, Jan, Mng. Dir.--Beaumont-Bennett A/S, Sandefjord, Norway; *Int'l*, pg. 714
Nissen, E. Jagd, Mng. Dir.--ITT Flygt A/S, Glostrup, Denmark; *U.S. Public*, pg. 860

Nissen, Ejvind Jagd, Mng. Dir.--ITT Flygt A/S, Oslo, Norway; *U.S. Public*, pg. 860
Nixon, B., Mng. Dir.--Fletcher Homes Limited, Auckland, New Zealand; *Int'l*, pg. 495
Nixon, J. L., Mng. Dir. & Chief Exec. Officer--Rio Tinto Zimbabwe Limited, Harare, Zimbabwe; *Int'l*, pg. 1119
Noakes, Brian, Mng. Dir.--Oneida Silversmiths, U.K., Ruislip, United Kingdom; *U.S. Public*, pg. 1226
Noar, Stephen, Chm. & Mng. Dir.--Denplan Limited, Winchester, United Kingdom; *Int'l*, pg. 1020
Noble, Michael C., Mng. Dir.--Fleet Investment Services, Providence, RI; *U.S. Public*, pg. 650
Nobuta, Kazuhiro, Joint Mng. Dir.--Dentsu Europe-Dusseldorf, Dusseldorf, Germany; *Int'l*, pg. 393
Noens, Benny, V.P.-Europe & Mngng. Dir.-Metrologic GmbH--Metrologic Instruments, Inc., Blackwood, NJ; *U.S. Public*, pg. 1102
Noens, Benny, V.P.-European Sls. & Mng. Dir.-Metrologic GmbH--Metrologic Instruments GmbH, Munich, Germany; *U.S. Public*, pg. 1102
Nojima, Takeshi, Mng. Dir.-Admin., Risk Mngmt. & Credit Res.--Daiwa Securities Co. Ltd., Tokyo, Japan; *Int'l*, pg. 374
Nolan, Peter, Mng. Dir.--Incentive International Finance, Dublin, Ireland; *Int'l*, pg. 669
Nomura, Kaoru, Mng. Dir.--Brother Industries (Ireland) Ltd., Drogheda, Ireland; *Int'l*, pg. 229
Nomura, Shinya, Mng. Dir.--Kayaba Industry Co., Ltd., Tokyo, Japan; *Int'l*, pg. 727
Nora, George, Mng. Dir.--Scanpoint Technology A/S, Brondby, Denmark; *U.S. Public*, pg. 466
Nordblad, Tony, Mng. Dir.--SINSER (Luxembourg) Sarl, Luxembourg, Luxembourg; *Int'l*, pg. 1258
Norman, B., Mng. Dir.--British Chrome & Chemicals Ltd., Stockton on Tees, United Kingdom; *Int'l*, pg. 598
Norrey, Ronald W., Mng. Dir.--AKAPP Electro Industries B.V., Barneveld, Netherlands; *U.S. Public*, pg. 1776
Norris, Graham, Mng. Dir.--Allianz Cornhill Insurance (Far East) Ltd., Hong Kong, Hong Kong; *Int'l*, pg. 59
Norton, Peter R.E., Chief Oper. Officer & Mng. Dir.--Sasol Chemicals Europe Limited, Solihull, United Kingdom; *Int'l*, pg. 1196
Nosworthy, John R., Mng. Dir.--MEM Ltd. 500V, Birmingham, United Kingdom; *Int'l*, pg. 390
Nothard, P., Mng. Dir.--Xerox South Africa, Isando, South Africa; *U.S. Public*, pg. 1785
Noto, Pete, Mng. Partner-Creative Art--Lewis Gace Bozell Healthcare Worldwide, Fort Lee, NJ; *U.S. Public*, pg. 1642
Noto, Toshiyuki, Sr. Mng. Dir.--Toyo Tire & Rubber Co., Ltd., Osaka, Japan; *Int'l*, pg. 1411
Novak, John F., Mng. Dir.-Consumer Lending--Provident Bank of Maryland, Baltimore, MD; *U.S. Public*, pg. 1337
Novik, Jay A., Mng. Dir.--Swiss Re Atrium Corporation, New York, NY; *Int'l*, pg. 1333
Novosselsky, Vladimir, Deputy Mng. Dir.--Leo Burnett & Moradpour/Moscow, Moscow, Russia; *U.S. Private*, pg. 184
Nuckles, Craig, Mng. Dir.--Two Rivers Psychiatric Hospital, Kansas City, MO; *U.S. Public*, pg. 1697
Nuckols, Jim, Mng. Dir.--Hill-Rom/Le Couviour S.A., Pluvigner, France; *U.S. Public*, pg. 828
Numaguchi, Motohiko, Pres. & Mng. Dir.-Mitsubishi Intl. Corp.--Mitsubishi Corporation, Tokyo, Japan; *Int'l*, pg. 871
Numrich, Dieter, Mng. Dir.--BFR GmbH, Berlin, Germany; *Int'l*, pg. 657
Nunlist, Hans, Mng. Dir.-Corp. Intellectual Property Rights--Landis & Staefa AG, Zug, Switzerland; *Int'l*, pg. 800
Nunn, R., Mng. Dir.--Air UK Engineering Ltd., Stansted, United Kingdom; *Int'l*, pg. 39
Nyberg, Olavi, Mng. Dir.--Neopac Oy, Tampere, Finland; *Int'l*, pg. 863
Nybondas, Mats, Mng. Dir.--Dun & Bradstreet Finland Oy., Espoo, Finland; *U.S. Public*, pg. 536
Nyman, Lars-Erik, Mng. Dir.--Mactec AB, Kristianstad, Sweden; *U.S. Public*, pg. 860
Nzeribe, May, Mng. Dir.--Sunrise Marketing Communications Ltd., Lagos, Nigeria; *U.S. Private*, pg. 305
O'Brien, Vincent, Chm. Bd. & Mng. Dir.--Texaco (Ireland) Ltd., Dublin, Ireland; *U.S. Public*, pg. 1584
O'Callaghan, Tim, Mng. Dir.--Standex (Ireland) Ltd., Mountmellick, Ireland; *U.S. Public*, pg. 1508
O'Connell, Dan, Mng. Dir.--Shandwick USA, New York, NY; *Int'l*, pg. 1227
O'Connell, Thomas C., Mng. Dir.--Johnson & Johnson (Ireland) Ltd., Dublin, Ireland; *U.S. Public*, pg. 930
O'Donnell, J., Mng. Dir.--AIB International Financial Services Ltd, Dublin, Ireland; *Int'l*, pg. 64
O'Donnell, J., Mng. Dir.--AIB Corporate Finance Ltd., Dublin, Ireland; *Int'l*, pg. 64
O'Flaherty, Tom, Mng. Dir.--Luxo Lamp Corporation, Port Chester, NY; *Int'l*, pg. 821
O'Floinn, Ruairi, Mng. Dir.--Lifetime Assurance Co. Limited, Dublin, Ireland; *Int'l*, pg. 152
O'Hearn, Andrew M., Mng. Editor--Atlantic Mutual Companies, New York, NY; *U.S. Private*, pg. 95
O'Keefe, Robert T., Jr., Mng. Dir.-Strategy & Planning--American Automobile Association, Heathrow, FL; *U.S. Private*, pg. 50
O'Keeffe, Patrick, Mng. Dir.-Mkt. Research--AMR Corporation, Fort Worth, TX; *U.S. Public*, pg. 9
O'Leary, David C., Mng. Dir.-Human Resources--Credit Suisse First Boston, Inc., New York, NY; *Int'l*, pg. 345
O'Mholt, A., Mng. Dir.--Dresser-Rand Sales, Houston, TX; *U.S. Public*, pg. 529
O'Neill, Thomas M., Mng. Dir. & Chief Investment Officer--Fleet Investment Advisors, Inc., Boston, MA; *U.S. Public*, pg. 650
O'Regan, Frank, Mng. Dir.--Lake Region Manufacturing Co., Ltd., New Ross, Ireland; *U.S. Private*, pg. 643
Oakley, Thomas G., V.P. & Mng. Dir.-Asia--Tenneco Inc., Greenwich, CT; *U.S. Public*, pg. 1577
Oates, Keith, Dep. Chm. & Joint Mng. Dir.--Marks & Spencer PLC, London, United Kingdom; *Int'l*, pg. 842
Oberauer, Heinrich, Mng. Dir.-Store Devel. & Construction--Julius Meinl AG, Vienna, Austria; *Int'l*, pg. 856
Ocampo, Juan M., Mng. Dir.--Securitas Capital Partners I, L.P., Hamilton, Bermuda; *Int'l*, pg. 1333
Occhipinti, Umberto, Chm. Bd. & Mng. Dir.--Assiprogetti S.p.A., Milan, Italy; *Int'l*, pg. 138
Ochoa, Joaquin, Mng. Dir.-Human Resources--Iberdrola, S.A., Bilbao, Spain; *Int'l*, pg. 657
Oda, Hiroshi, Mng. Dir. & Gen. Mgr.-Chita Oil--Japan Energy Corporation, Tokyo, Japan; *Int'l*, pg. 702
Odden, Eddy, Mng. Dir.--Leo Burnett/Connaghan & May (QLD.) Pty. Ltd., Milton, Australia; *U.S. Private*, pg. 185
Odeishi, Tsunehiro, Mng. Dir.--Cascade (Japan) Ltd., Osaka, Japan; *U.S. Public*, pg. 311
Odgers, E.T., Mng. Dir.--Amalgamated Beverage Industries, Wendywood, South Africa; *Int'l*, pg. 1286
Odienne, Eric, Mng. Dir.--Societe Anonyme Mediterraneene de Salaisons, Biot, France; *U.S. Public*, pg. 429
Oeter, Heinz, Mng. Dir.--Krupp Stahlbau Berlin GmbH & Co. KG, Berlin, Germany; *Int'l*, pg. 508
Ogawa, Harunobu, Mng. Dir.--NEC Hong Kong Limited, Kowloon, Hong Kong; *Int'l*, pg. 900
Ogborne, Peter M., Grp. Mng. Dir.-Opers.--Photo-Me International plc, Bookham, United Kingdom; *Int'l*, pg. 1055
Ogilvie, Gael, Mgr.-Opers.--Woodward-Clyde International, North Point, Hong Kong; *U.S. Public*, pg. 1658
Ogura, Yasuhiko, Mng. Dir.--Tonen Corporation, Tokyo, Japan; *Int'l*, pg. 1398
Oh, Dong-Hwee, Pres.--Ssangyong Research Institute, Seoul, Korea; *Int'l*, pg. 1292
Ohayon, Elie, Deputy Mng. Dir.--Young & Rubicam France, Paris, France; *U.S. Private*, pg. 1199
Ohgawara, T., Mng. Dir.--Sharp Electronics (Thailand) Ltd., Kaohsiong, Thailand; *Int'l*, pg. 1230
Ohling, Jannes C., Mng. Dir. & V.P.--GATX Financial Services GmbH, Frankfurt/Main, Germany; *U.S. Public*, pg. 691
Ohlson, Johnny, Mng. Dir.--Griffin Bacal Ltd., London, United Kingdom; *U.S. Private*, pg. 480
Ohlsson, Kenth, Mng. Dir.--Sodra Skogagarna, Vaxjo, Sweden; *Int'l*, pg. 1275
Ohlsson, Magnus, Mng. Dir.--Handelsbanken Liv, Stockholm, Sweden; *Int'l*, pg. 1327
Ohmori, Keizo, Exec. Mng. Dir.--Kubota Corp., Osaka, Japan; *Int'l*, pg. 762
Ohnuki, Yoshiaki, Exec. Mng. Dir. & Gen. Mgr.-Corp. Plng.--Mitsui & Co., Ltd., Tokyo, Japan; *Int'l*, pg. 877
Ohtani, Yukio, Chief Exec. Officer & Mng. Dir.--Japan Airlines American Region, New York, NY; *Int'l*, pg. 700
Ohuchi, H., Mng. Dir.--Sharp Electronics (Singapore) Pte. Ltd., Singapore, Singapore; *Int'l*, pg. 1230
Oka, Tomoshige, Sr. Mng. Dir.--Citizen Watch Company, Ltd., Tokyo, Japan; *Int'l*, pg. 293
Okano, Jun, Chief Exec. Officer & Mng. Dir.--Nikko Europe Plc, London, United Kingdom; *Int'l*, pg. 930
Okawa, Terumitsu, Mng. Dir.--Dentsu Young & Rubicam Ltd. (Bangkok), Bangkok, Thailand; *U.S. Private*, pg. 325
Oksanen, Jouni, Mng. Dir.--K-Maatalousyhtiot Oy, Vantaa, Finland; *Int'l*, pg. 732
Okubo, T., Sr. Mng. Dir.-Gen. Affairs--The Kyoei Life Insurance Co., Ltd., Tokyo, Japan; *Int'l*, pg. 776
Okuno, Kazuo, Mng. Dir.--NEC Semiconductors (Malaysia) Sdn. Berhad, Kuala Langat, Malaysia; *Int'l*, pg. 900
Olankun, Sitthichai, Mng. Dir.--Astra (Thai) Ltd., Bangkok, Thailand; *Int'l*, pg. 94
Oldham, Frank, Mng. Dir.--CD Products (UK) Ltd., London, United Kingdom; *U.S. Public*, pg. 276
Olholm, Svend, Mng. Dir.--GN Great Nordic Ltd., Copenhagen, Denmark; *Int'l*, pg. 536
Olholm, Svend, Mng. Dir.--GN Ejendomme, Copenhagen, Denmark; *Int'l*, pg. 537
Olieman, F.J., Mng. Dir.--CSM Suiker BV, Diemen, Netherlands; *Int'l*, pg. 243
Oliver, Robert, Mng. Dir.--Datascope SARL, Creteil, France; *U.S. Public*, pg. 488
Olle, Antonio, Gen. Mgr.--BBL Sucursal de Barcelona, Barcelona, Spain; *Int'l*, pg. 148
Ollivier-Lamarque, Florence, Mng. Dir.--Flik Flak, Itingen, Switzerland; *Int'l*, pg. 1160
Ollivier-Lamarque, Florence, Mng. Dir.--SMH Belgium SA, Brussels, Belgium; *Int'l*, pg. 1161
Olsen, Terje, Mng. Dir.--Multiass Assicurazioni S.p.A., Milan, Italy; *Int'l*, pg. 1256
Olsen, Terje, Mng. Dir.--Uniass Assicurazioni S.p.A., Rome, Italy; *Int'l*, pg. 1256
Omiya, Tadashu, Mng. Dir.--Fuji Bank (Luxembourg) S.A., Luxembourg, Luxembourg; *Int'l*, pg. 521
Onestinghel, Diego, Mng. Dir.--ESI Stampa Medica Srl, Milan, Italy; *Int'l*, pg. 1099
Oni, Bunmi, Chief Exec. & Mng. Dir.--Cadbury Nigeria PLC, Ikeja, Nigeria; *Int'l*, pg. 248
Ono, Kozo, Chief Exec. & Mng. Dir.--Yamaichi Bank (U.K.) Plc, London, United Kingdom; *Int'l*, pg. 1517
Ono, Nobuyoshi, Mng. Dir.-Acctg. & MIS--Settsu Corporation, Amagasaki, Japan; *Int'l*, pg. 1225
Ono, Takashi, Mng. Dir.--Nippon Express (U.K.), Ltd., Hounslow, United Kingdom; *Int'l*, pg. 934
Ono, Yoshio, Mng. Dir.--ORIX Europe Limited, London, United Kingdom; *Int'l*, pg. 1009
Onstad, Ken, Mng. Dir.-United Kingdom--Musicland Group Inc., Minnetonka, MN; *U.S. Public*, pg. 1142
Oomens, W.H., Mng. Dir.--Nutricia Export B.V., Zoetermeer, Netherlands; *Int'l*, pg. 991
Oord, W.R., Mng. Dir.--Damco Maritime International B.V., Rotterdam, Netherlands; *Int'l*, pg. 1144
Ootani, Yukio, Mng. Dir. & Sr. V.P.-The Americas--Japan Airlines Company, Ltd., Tokyo, Japan; *Int'l*, pg. 699
Opdahl, Torgeir, Mng. Dir.--Saga Petroleum ASA - Libya, Tripoli, Libya; *Int'l*, pg. 1169
Openshaw, David, Mng. Dir.--ISS Servisystem Ltd., London, United Kingdom; *Int'l*, pg. 657
Openshaw, David, Mng. Dir.--ISS Airport Services Ltd., Hounslow, United Kingdom; *Int'l*, pg. 657
Orban, Peter, Mng. Dir.--Young & Rubicam Hungary, Budapest, Hungary; *U.S. Private*, pg. 1199
Orbeck, Ulf, Mng. Dir.--Bold, Oslo, Norway; *U.S. Private*, pg. 678
Ord, Kent, Sr. V.P. & Mng. Dir.--FUTUREWORKS, Seattle, WA; *U.S. Private*, pg. 385
Oren, Daniel L., Mng. Dir.--Dart Transit Company, Eagan, MN; *U.S. Private*, pg. 311
Orito, Hisanao, Sr. Mng. Dir.-Res. & Devel.--Makita Corporation, Anjo, Japan; *Int'l*, pg. 831
Oropeza, Gabriel, Mng. Dir.-Latin America--Resort Condominiums International, Indianapolis, IN; *U.S. Public*, pg. 322
Orr, James, Mng. Dir.--HLA Envirosciences Pty. Ltd., Pymble, Australia; *U.S. Public*, pg. 785
Osborne, Bob, Mng. Dir.--Heinemann Educational Publishing, Oxford, United Kingdom; *Int'l*, pg. 1094
Osborne, Peter, Mng. Dir.--Haymarket Exhibitions Ltd., London, United Kingdom; *Int'l*, pg. 114
Oskin, D. W., Chief Exec. Officer & Mng. Dir.--Carter Holt Harvey Limited, Auckland, New Zealand; *U.S. Public*, pg. 904
Osman, Borhanuddin, Mng. Partner & Mng. Dir.--Paragon Communications Sdn. Bhd. (Kuala Lumpur), Kuala Lumpur, Malaysia; *U.S. Private*, pg. 325
Osman, Peter M., Mng. Dir.--Gibson Greetings International Limited, Telford, United Kingdom; *U.S. Public*, pg. 742
Osman, Wayne, Mng. Dir.--Dexion Ltd.-Storage Div., Hemel Hempstead, United Kingdom; *U.S. Public*, pg. 893
Ostendorf, Danny, Mng. Dir.--Norvista B.V., Amsterdam, Netherlands; *Int'l*, pg. 486
Ostlund, Bert, Mng. Dir.--Celbi SA, Figueira da Foz, Portugal; *Int'l*, pg. 1303
Ostlund, Torbjorn, Mng. Dir.--Reemtsma International Praha spol. s.r.o., Prague, Czech Republic; *Int'l*, pg. 1101
Ostmeier, Konrad, Mng. Dir.--Solvitol Limited, Birtley, United Kingdom; *Int'l*, pg. 858
Ostrom, Bjorn, Mng. Dir.--Christiania Bank Luxembourg S.A., Luxembourg, Luxembourg; *Int'l*, pg. 289
Osugi, Masami, Mng. Dir.--Asahi Investment Australia Ltd., Sydney, Australia; *Int'l*, pg. 85
Osugi, Masami, Mng. Dir.--Asahi Property Australia Pty. Ltd., Sydney, Australia; *Int'l*, pg. 85
Otegui, I., Mng. Dir.--GKN Forjas de Precision de Legazpia SA, Legazpia, Spain; *Int'l*, pg. 536
Ottl, Josef, Mng. Dir.-Tech.--Baldwin-Grafotec GmbH, Augsburg, Germany; *U.S. Public*, pg. 170
Otto, D., Mng. Dir.--Bally Moda SA, Madrid, Spain; *Int'l*, pg. 997
Oudshoorn, R.H., Pres. & Mng. Dir.--Fredestein Banden, Enschede, Netherlands; *Int'l*, pg. 504
Ouwehand, Hans, Chief Oper. Officer & Mng. Dir.--Littelfuse B.V., Utrecht, Netherlands; *U.S. Public*, pg. 1001
Owada, Nobuyuki, Mng. Dir.--Cosmo Securities (Europe) Limited, London, United Kingdom; *Int'l*, pg. 335
Owen, David, Mng. Dir.--The Gates Rubber Company Ltd., Dumfries, United Kingdom; *Int'l*, pg. 1397
Owen, David H., Mng. Dir.--Morse Controls Ltd., Basildon, United Kingdom; *U.S. Public*, pg. 857
Owen, James P., Mng. Dir.--NWQ Investment Managaement Company, Los Angeles, CA; *U.S. Public*, pg. 1673
Owen, Robert E., Pres. & Mng. Dir.--Paxton & Vierling, Omaha, NE; *U.S. Private*, pg. 824
Oyola, Victor, Grp. Dir.--de la Cruz & Associates, San Juan, PR; *U.S. Private*, pg. 318
Ozaki, Kazumasa, Mng. Dir.--McCormick-Lion Ltd., Tokyo, Japan; *U.S. Public*, pg. 1067
Paasikivi, Henry, Mng. Dir.--Sako Oy, Riihimaki, Finland; *Int'l*, pg. 954
Pabbruwe, H.A., Mng. Dir.--Wolters Kluwer Law and Taxation, Deventer, Netherlands; *Int'l*, pg. 1513
Pacinda, Mark G., Mng. Dir.--Arby's Canada Inc., Mississauga, Canada; *U.S. Public*, pg. 1635
Pack, Troy, Mng. Dir.--Ultrak Inc., Lewisville, TX; *U.S. Public*, pg. 1663
Packalen, Kristian, Chief Oper. Officer & Mng. Dir.--Copap, Paris, France; *Int'l*, pg. 457
Packer, John, Mng. Dir.--Texas Granite Corp., Marble Falls, TX; *U.S. Private*, pg. 251
Pagano, Phillip, Exec. Dir.--Metra, Commuter Rail Service Board, Chicago, IL; *U.S. Private*, pg. 919
Pagneaux, Bernard, Mng. Dir.--Viking Direct S.A.R.L., Paris, France; *U.S. Public*, pg. 1721
Paillaud, Guy, Dir.-Mngmt. Control--Promodes SA, Mondeville, France; *Int'l*, pg. 1071
Painter, Adrian, Mng. Dir.--Kvaerner EnviroPower Ltd., London, United Kingdom; *Int'l*, pg. 767
Pakebusch, Joachim, Mng. Dir.--Emsland-Raisio Chemie GmbH, Hamburg, Germany; *Int'l*, pg. 1086
Palacek, Peter V., Mng. Dir.--Arthur D. Little International, Inc., Prague, Czech Republic; *U.S. Private*, pg. 671
Palframan, Stephen, Mng. Dir.-Bristow Helicopters Ltd.--Offshore Logistics, Inc., Lafayette, LA; *U.S. Public*, pg. 1212
Palijchook, Sergej O., Mng. Dir.--Reemtsma Ukraine, Kiev, Ukraine; *Int'l*, pg. 1101
Palladino, Marco, Chm. & Mng. Dir.--Hydrocarbons International Holding Co., Zurich, Switzerland; *Int'l*, pg. 429
Palm, Stanley D., Mng. Dir.--Crisson Securities NV, Willemstad, Netherlands Antilles; *Int'l*, pg. 1115
Palmer, N., Mng. Dir.--NRG Group Limited, Northampton, United Kingdom; *Int'l*, pg. 1114
Palmer, N. J., Mng. Dir.--Gestetner (Ireland) Limited, Dublin, Ireland; *Int'l*, pg. 1115
Palmer, Paul V., Chief Fin. Officer & Mng. Dir.--Capital Markets Assurance Corporation, New York, NY; *U.S. Public*, pg. 1023
Palusci, P., Mng. Dir.--Goodyear Italiana S.p.A., Rome, Italy; *U.S. Public*, pg. 753

Pander, Vince, Mng. Dir.--Johnson & Johnson Limitada, Queluz, Portugal; *U.S. Public*, pg. 930
Pankakoski, Isto, Mng. Dir.--Nokia Mobile Phones UK Sales Ltd., Godmanchester, United Kingdom; *Int'l*, pg. 952
Panoff, Oleg, Mgr.--EURO RSCG Media, Moscow, Russia; *Int'l*, pg. 603
Paplowski, Gunter, Mng. Dir.--LBS Immobilien GmbH Berlin, Berlin, Germany; *Int'l*, pg. 160
Parise, Joseph R., Sr. V.P. & Mng. Dir.--Imperial Credit Commercial Mortgage Investment Corp., Los Angeles, CA; *U.S. Public*, pg. 872
Parish, Robert C., Dr., Exec. V.P. & Mng. Dir.-London--Scientific Software-Intercomp, Inc., Denver, CO; *U.S. Public*, pg. 1443
Park, Byung-Keun, Mng. Dir.--Ssangyong Shipping Co. Ltd., Seoul, Korea; *Int'l*, pg. 1292
Parke, Raymond, Mng. Dir.--Thrige-Scott Ltd., Belfast, United Kingdom; *Int'l*, pg. 1387
Parker, Guy, Mng. Dir.--K-Tron Great Britain, Ltd., Oldham, United Kingdom; *U.S. Public*, pg. 938
Parker, Jonathan, Mng. Dir.--Osprey, London, United Kingdom; *Int'l*, pg. 1093
Parker, Timothy, Chief Exec. Officer--Clarks International, Street, United Kingdom; *Int'l*, pg. 296
Parkinson, Ron, V.P. & Mng. Dir.-East--J.W. Messner, Inc., Grand Rapids, MI; *U.S. Private*, pg. 734
Parkinson, Ron, V.P. & Mng. Dir.--J.W. Messner, Inc., Pittsburgh, PA; *U.S. Private*, pg. 734
Parks, Gordon, Mng. Dir.--Roteq Services Sdn. Bhd., Terengganu, Malaysia; *Int'l*, pg. 1305
Parmigiano, John M., Gen. Mgr. & Mng. Dir.--Unocal Netherlands, Hague, Netherlands; *U.S. Public*, pg. 1698
Parrish, S., Mng. Dir.--British Sterilizer Ltd., Mansfield, United Kingdom; *Int'l*, pg. 551
Parrish, S., Mng. Dir.--The Sterilizing Equipment Co. Ltd., Mansfield, United Kingdom; *Int'l*, pg. 552
Parsons, Peter, Mng. Dir.--Park Lane Tobacco Company Ltd., Maidenhead, United Kingdom; *Int'l*, pg. 1101
Partridge, Keith J., Chief Exec. Officer & Mng. Dir.--Carlton Paper Corp. Ltd., Johannesburg, South Africa; *U.S. Public*, pg. 959
Pasquinelli, Nino, Mng. Dir.--Pibiviesse SpA (PBVS), Nerviano, Italy; *U.S. Public*, pg. 1747
Passera, Corrado, Chief Exec. Officer, Mng. Dir. & Gen. Mgr.--Banco Ambrosiano Veneto S.p.A., Milan, Italy; *Int'l*, pg. 138
Patai, Mihaly, Dr., Mng. Dir.--Hungaria Biztosito Rt., Budapest, Hungary; *Int'l*, pg. 60
Patig, Klaus M., Mng. Dir.-Corp. Fin., Global Bonds & Equities--Commerzbank AG, Frankfurt, Germany; *Int'l*, pg. 308
Patradhilok, Prasert, Mng. Dir.--IFCT Finance & Securities Co., Ltd., Bangkok, Thailand; *Int'l*, pg. 677
Pattinson, John, Mng. Dir.--Dresdner Australia Ltd., Sydney, Australia; *Int'l*, pg. 419
Pattison, James A., Chm. Bd., Pres., Chief Exec. Officer & Mng. Dir.--Great Pacific Enterprises Inc., Vancouver, Canada; *Int'l*, pg. 557
Patton, Gary, Dir.-ILS Services--Aydin Corporation, Horsham, PA; *U.S. Public*, pg. 158
Paull, Mitchell S., Mng. Dir.--MacTavish Furniture Industries, Atlanta, GA; *U.S. Public*, pg. 12
Paulson, Larry M., Mng. Dir.--Nokia Products Corporation, Melbourne, FL; *Int'l*, pg. 952
Pavlowski, Sylvain, Mng. Dir.--VMark Software, Ltd., Bologna, Italy; *U.S. Public*, pg. 129
Payne, D., Mng. Dir.--Kemet Electronics SA, Geneva, Switzerland; *U.S. Public*, pg. 949
Payne, David, Mng. Dir.--Payne Stracey Ltd. (direct marketing), London, United Kingdom; *U.S. Private*, pg. 1152
Peak, J., Mng. Dir.--Westminster Contractors Ltd., Wirral, United Kingdom; *Int'l*, pg. 135
Peake, A., Dr., Mng. Dir.--Linatex Limited, Surrey, United Kingdom; *Int'l*, pg. 598
Pearce, Dave, Mng. Dir.-BVSGL--Brite Voice Systems, Inc., Heathrow, FL; *U.S. Public*, pg. 257
Pearson, Fiona, Mng. Dir.--The Flight Data Company Ltd., West Drayton, United Kingdom; *Int'l*, pg. 207
Pearson, James, Dr., Joint Mng. Dir.--London & Scandinavian Metallurgical Co. Limited, London, United Kingdom; *U.S. Private*, pg. 735
Peckham, Neil, Mng. Dir.--Skycell Communications Private Limited, Madras, India; *U.S. Public*, pg. 209
Pedersen, Kjeld Lercke, Mng. Dir.--HyperVision A/S, Skovlunde, Denmark; *Int'l*, pg. 146
Pederson, Karen, Exec. Dir.--Principal Health Care of Nebraska, Inc., Omaha, NE; *U.S. Private*, pg. 886
Peek, Henk, Mng. Dir. & Mgr.-Human Resources--Kelly Uitzendburo, Hague, Netherlands; *U.S. Public*, pg. 949
Peek, Phil, Mng. Dir.--Timloc Building Products Ltd., Goole, United Kingdom; *Int'l*, pg. 467
Peerbhoy, Bunty, Chm. Bd., Chief Exec. Officer & Mng. Dir.--MAA Communications Bozell, Bangalore, India; *U.S. Public*, pg. 1642
Peitzmeier, N., Mng. Dir.--Kidde-Deugra GmbH, Ratingen, Germany; *Int'l*, pg. 1500
Pelkonen, Paavo, Mng. Dir.--KONE Middle East GIBCA Ltd., Dubai, United Arab Emirates; *Int'l*, pg. 747
Pena, Manuel, V.P.--Young & Rubicam Damaris, C. por A., Santo Domingo, Dominican Republic; *U.S. Private*, pg. 1200
Penny, M.W., Mng. Dir.--Redland Roof Tiles Ltd., Reigate, United Kingdom; *Int'l*, pg. 1091
Pepper, Ken, Mng. Dir.--ISS Food Hygiene Ltd., Birmingham, United Kingdom; *Int'l*, pg. 657
Pepper, Ken, Mng. Dir.--ISS Cleaning Services Ltd., Aylesbury, United Kingdom; *Int'l*, pg. 657
Percy, James R., V.P. & Mng. Dir.--SHL Systemhouse - Atlantic Region, Halifax, Canada; *Int'l*, pg. 1154
Perelson, Jerome M., Chief Credit Officer & Mng. Dir.--ContiFinancial Services Corporation, New York, NY; *U.S. Public*, pg. 439
Perlman, Peter, Mng. Dir.--Haworth Thailand Company Ltd., Bangkok, Thailand; *U.S. Private*, pg. 512
Pero, Dan, V.P.-Communications & Dir.-Pub. Rels.--Eckerd Corporation, Largo, FL; *U.S. Public*, pg. 917
Perrazzo, M., Mng. Dir.--SBS SIM S.p.A., Milan, Italy; *Int'l*, pg. 1331
Perric, D.W., Mng. Dir.--Beazer Homes (Glaston) Limited, Cumbernauld, United Kingdom; *Int'l*, pg. 182
Perrin, Robert, Mng. Dir.--Kollmorgan Artus, Avrille, France; *U.S. Public*, pg. 966
Pessl, Harald, Mng. Dir.--Battenfeld Automatisierungstechnik Ges.m.b.H., Kottingbrunn, Austria; *Int'l*, pg. 825
Peters, John, Mng. Dir.--Young & Rubicam Adelaide Pty. Ltd., Dulwich, Australia; *U.S. Private*, pg. 1198
Peters, Tom, Mng. Dir.--Kewaunee Engineering Corp., Kewaunee, WI; *U.S. Private*, pg. 703
Petersen, Peter, Mng. Dir.--Swatch Telecom AG, Bienne, Switzerland; *Int'l*, pg. 1161
Petersen, Peter, Mng. Dir.--Swatch S.A., Bienne, Switzerland; *Int'l*, pg. 1161
Petersen, Peter, Mng. Dir.--SMH Japan KK, Tokyo, Japan; *Int'l*, pg. 1161
Petersen, Peter, Mng. Dir.--SMH (Korea) Ltd., Seoul, Korea; *Int'l*, pg. 1161
Petit, Francesc, Mng. Partner--DPZ-Duailibi, Petit, Zaragoza, Propaganda S.A., Sao Paulo, Brazil; *Int'l*, pg. 352
Petit, L.J.J.M., Mng. Dir.--Van Swaay Toegangstechniek bv, Capelle aan den Ijssel, Netherlands; *Int'l*, pg. 680
Petrie, William, Mng. Dir.--Brush Electrical Machines Ltd., Loughborough, United Kingdom; *Int'l*, pg. 124
Petroungarung, Songsri, Asst. Mng. Dir.--Bangkok Athletic Co., Ltd., Bangkok, Thailand; *Int'l*, pg. 146
Petry, Ulrich, Mng. Dir.--Ketchum Advertising GmbH, Frankfurt, Germany; *U.S. Private*, pg. 617
Pettersson, Folke, Mng. Dir.--Kvaerner Pulping Oy, Helsinki, Finland; *Int'l*, pg. 768
Pettersson, Hans, Mng. Dir.--MoDo Paper AB, Ornskoldsvik, Sweden; *Int'l*, pg. 886
Pettine, Antonio Luis, Mng. Dir.--KONE Ascensores S.A., Buenos Aires, Argentina; *Int'l*, pg. 747
Pettit, T. Christopher, Mng. Partner--Lehman Brothers, New York, NY; *U.S. Public*, pg. 987
Peuiere, Y., Mng. Dir.--Ascom Elsydel SA, Paris, France; *Int'l*, pg. 87
Pfeffer, Joseph, Mng. Dir.--RAFI GmbH & Co. Elektrotechnische Spezialfabrik, Berge, Germany; *Int'l*, pg. 516
Pfeifle, D., Dr., Mng. Dir.--Robert Bosch GmbH, Hildesheim, Germany; *Int'l*, pg. 204
Pfeifle, Dr., Mng. Dir.--Blaupunkt-Werke GmbH, Hildesheim, Germany; *Int'l*, pg. 203
Pfitzer, W., Dr., Mng. Dir.--Ascom GCT GmbH & Co., Kerpen, Germany; *Int'l*, pg. 87
Phifer, Jack, Mng. Dir.--Leo Burnett S.A. de C.V., Mexico, Mexico; *U.S. Private*, pg. 185
Philippen, L., Mng. Dir.--Ballast Nedam Bouwmaterieel B.V., Almere, Netherlands; *Int'l*, pg. 133
Philpot, T.A., Mng. Dir.--Cementation Piling & Foundations Limited, Rickmansworth, United Kingdom; *Int'l*, pg. 772
Phippen, Peter, Mng. Dir.--BBC Magazines, London, United Kingdom; *Int'l*, pg. 114
Piancastelli, Paolo, Mng. Dir.--Allo Pro Italia s.r.l., Milan, Italy; *Int'l*, pg. 1307
Piattoli, Roberto, Chm. & Mng. Dir.--Snamprogetti International S.A., Geneva, Switzerland; *Int'l*, pg. 429
Picchi, Giordano, Mng. Dir.--Ademco-Italia S.p.A., Milan, Italy; *U.S. Public*, pg. 1307
Pickersgill, J.B., Mng. Dir.--Top Rank Limited, Maidenhead, United Kingdom; *Int'l*, pg. 1087
Pickles, R., Mng. Dir.--Verosol Australia Pty.Ltd., Kingsgrove, Australia; *Int'l*, pg. 198
Picks, Rolf, Mng. Dir.--ISS Servisystem GmbH, Frankfurt, Germany; *Int'l*, pg. 657
Pieraccioni, Gianni, Mng. Dir.--Johnson & Johnson S.p.A., Rome, Italy; *U.S. Public*, pg. 931
Pierburg, B., Mng. Dir.--GKN Gelenkwellenwerk Mosel GmbH, Mosel, Germany; *Int'l*, pg. 535
Pierburg, B., Mng. Dir.--Lohr & Bromkamp GmbH, Offenbach/Main, Germany; *Int'l*, pg. 536
Pierburg, B., Mng. Dir.--GKN Gelenkwellenwerk Kiel GmbH, Kiel, Germany; *Int'l*, pg. 536
Pierce, P.P., Mng. Dir.--Esso Sekiyu Kabushiki Kaisha, Tokyo, Japan; *U.S. Public*, pg. 602
Pieroni, Peter, Mng. Dir.--SPS Technologies Ltd., Coventry, United Kingdom; *U.S. Public*, pg. 1420
Pietzsch, L., Mng. Dir.--Ascom Hasler GmbH, Olching, Germany; *Int'l*, pg. 87
Piggot, K.J., Mng. Dir.--Do It All, Dudley, United Kingdom; *Int'l*, pg. 203
Pike, J. Steven, Mng. Dir.-Business Markets Division--American Automobile Association, Heathrow, FL; *U.S. Private*, pg. 50
Pikering, John, II, Chief Oper. Officer & Mng. Dir.--Brown Brothers Harriman Trustee Services (Ireland) Limited, Dublin, Ireland; *U.S. Private*, pg. 173
Pikrallidas, Susan, Mng. Dir.-Govt. Rels.--American Automobile Association, Heathrow, FL; *U.S. Private*, pg. 50
Pillard, L.G., Chief Oper. Officer & Mng. Dir.-Sugar & Starch Opers.--Tate & Lyle PLC, London, United Kingdom; *Int'l*, pg. 1356
Pilot, Lynne, Mng. Dir.--Western International Media Corporation, Toronto, Canada; *U.S. Private*, pg. 1168
Pilus, Azizan M., Mng. Dir.--Sapura-Nokia Telecommunications Sdn. Bhd., Kuala Lumpur, Malaysia; *Int'l*, pg. 954
Pingeon, Jean, Dir.-Strategy & Devel.--Promodes SA, Mondeville, France; *Int'l*, pg. 1071
Pink, Krut, Mng. Dir.--Lincoln Smitweld GmbH, Erkrath, Germany; *U.S. Public*, pg. 997
Pinney, R.E., Mng. Dir.--National Australia Group (UK) Limited, Glasgow, United Kingdom; *Int'l*, pg. 906
Pinomaa, Juha, Mng. Dir.--Nokia Mobile Phones, S.E.A. Pte. Ltd., Singapore, Singapore; *Int'l*, pg. 952
Pirchl, Helmut, Mng. Dir.--Sulzer Ruti Limited, Ruthi, Switzerland; *Int'l*, pg. 1307
Pirella, Emanuele, Pres. & Mng. Dir.--Pirella Gottsche Lowe, Milan, Italy; *U.S. Private*, pg. 678
Pirkner, Gabor, Mng. Dir.--Gebruder Sulzer Gesellschqaft mbH, Anlagen- und Gebaudetechnik, Vienna, Austria; *Int'l*, pg. 1306
Pitkowsky, Murray, Mng. Dir.--Datascope SARL, Creteil, France; *U.S. Public*, pg. 488
Pitman, M.D., Mng. Dir.--Analytical Development Company Limited, Hoddesdon, United Kingdom; *Int'l*, pg. 589
Pitt, David, Mng. Dir.--Kvaerner Engineering (UK) Ltd., Slough, United Kingdom; *Int'l*, pg. 772
Pittaway, David B., Mng. Dir.--Castle-Harlan, Inc., New York, NY; *U.S. Private*, pg. 219
Pittenger, Bruce R., Mng. Dir.-Gen. Mngmt.--Towers Perrin, New York, NY; *U.S. Private*, pg. 1093
Plank, F., Mng. Dir.--Ascom Austria Ges.mbH, Vienna, Austria; *Int'l*, pg. 86
Plant, J.C., Mng. Dir.--Lucas Electrical and Electronic Systems, Shirley, United Kingdom; *Int'l*, pg. 819
Platt, George, Mng. Dir.-Asia Pacific--InterVoice, Inc., Dallas, TX; *U.S. Public*, pg. 910
Platzer, W., Mng. Dir.--Quaker Chemical B.V., Uithoorn, Netherlands; *U.S. Public*, pg. 1346
Ploszaj, Ed, Mng. Dir.-Printpack Europe--Printpack Inc., Atlanta, GA; *U.S. Private*, pg. 886
Plugge, Nico, Mng. Dir.--Simco (Nederland) B.V., Lochem, Netherlands; *U.S. Public*, pg. 869
Plumbe, Colin, Mng. Dir.--Todd & Duncan Ltd., Kinross, United Kingdom; *Int'l*, pg. 385
Plumeri, Joseph, II, Mng. Partner--Lehman Brothers, Inc., New York, NY; *U.S. Public*, pg. 987
Poddar, Saroj, Mng. Dir.--Caristrap India, Calcutta, India; *Int'l*, pg. 272
Poeschko, Kurt, Mng. Dir.--Det Norske Veritas, Zurich, Switzerland; *Int'l*, pg. 397
Poeschko, Kurt, Mng. Dir.--Det Norske Veritas, Vienna, Austria; *Int'l*, pg. 397
Pohl, Bruno, Mng. Dir.--Anacomp, GmbH, Wiesbaden, Germany; *U.S. Public*, pg. 107
Polak, David A., Mng. Dir.--NWQ Investment Managaement Company, Los Angeles, CA; *U.S. Public*, pg. 1673
Polan, Josh, Mng. Dir.--Interlaken Capital, Inc., Greenwich, CT; *U.S. Private*, pg. 567
Pollari, Kristiina, Mng. Dir.--Johnson & Johnson KFT, Budapest, Hungary; *U.S. Public*, pg. 930
Polmar, Morten, Mng. Dir.--Leo Burnett A/S, Oslo, Norway; *U.S. Private*, pg. 184
Pong, Cheong Kim, Chm. Bd., Chief Exec. & Oper. Officer--Hong Fok Corporation Ltd., Singapore, Singapore; *Int'l*, pg. 635
Ponroy, Thibault, Mng. Dir.--Johnson & Johnson AG, Spreitenbach, Switzerland; *U.S. Public*, pg. 930
Ponte, Ramon, Mng. Dir.--E-Z-EM Caribe, Inc., San Lorenzo, PR; *U.S. Public*, pg. 540
Pontiakas, George, V.P. & Gen. Mgr.--Wavetek Corporation, San Diego, CA; *U.S. Private*, pg. 1154
Pontin, Paul, Mng. Dir.--Universal Calibration Laboratories Ltd., Romsey, United Kingdom; *Int'l*, pg. 390
Poole, Richard, Mng. Dir.--K-Tron Germany, Soder Division, Gelnhausen, Germany; *U.S. Public*, pg. 938
Popenko, Oleg, Mng. Dir.--DMB&B LLC/Kiev, Kiev, Ukraine; *U.S. Private*, pg. 304
Poppell, Larry, Mng. Dir.--National Distributing Co., Inc., Augusta, GA; *U.S. Private*, pg. 781
Porrati, Guillermo, Mng. Dir.--Toys "R" Us Deutschland GmbH, Berlin, Germany; *U.S. Public*, pg. 1626
Porrone, Roberto, Mng. Dir.-Torino--Armando Testa S.p.A, Rome, Italy; *Int'l*, pg. 1377
Porter, James, Mng. Dir.--Hunt Lascaris/TBWA Durban, Westville, South Africa; *U.S. Private*, pg. 1062
Portera, Juan Astorqui, Mng. Dir.-Corp. Communications--Caja de Madrid Group, Madrid, Spain; *Int'l*, pg. 251
Poulakos, George, Mng. Dir.-The Resource Grp.--Klemtner Advertising Inc., New York, NY; *U.S. Public*, pg. 1422
Poulin, Claude, Mng. Dir.--Tarif Media S.A., Paris, France; *Int'l*, pg. 451
Poulson, S., Mng. Dir.--G.W. Sprinkler A/S, Glamsbjerg, Denmark; *Int'l*, pg. 1500
Poulter, Mike, Mng. Dir.--ISS Contract Cleaning Services (South), Bracknell, United Kingdom; *Int'l*, pg. 657
Powell, Brian, Mng. Dir.--Hepworth Home Products Limited, Belper, United Kingdom; *Int'l*, pg. 615
Powell, D.T., Mng. Dir.--Barlow Information Systems (Pty) Ltd., Rivonia, South Africa; *Int'l*, pg. 167
Powell, Michael, Mng. Dir.--MacGREGOR (HKG), Ltd., Kowloon, Hong Kong; *Int'l*, pg. 671
Powers, Roy, V.P. & Mng. Dir.--Western International Media Corporation, Reno, NV; *U.S. Private*, pg. 1167
Pralehunhangsit, Adisorn, Mng. Dir.--The Nawaloha Industry Co., Ltd., Sara Buri, Thailand; *Int'l*, pg. 1238
Prasad, A.S., Chm. Bd. & Mng. Dir.--Mahanadi Coalfields Limited, Sambalpur, India; *Int'l*, pg. 298
Pratoomsuvarw, Arthit, Mng. Dir.--The Siam Pipe Products Co., Ltd., Bangkok, Thailand; *Int'l*, pg. 1238
Pratoomsuvaw, Arthit, Mng. Dir.--The Siam Fibre-Cement Co., Ltd., Bangkok, Thailand; *Int'l*, pg. 1238
Premuroso, Ron, Acting Mng. Dir.--Sensormatic Australia Pty Limited, Sydney, Australia; *U.S. Public*, pg. 1457
Presley, Ottis A., Mgr.-Opers.--Laboratory Supply Company, Inc., Louisville, KY; *U.S. Private*, pg. 641
Press, Phil, Exec. Dir.--Media Incorporated, New York, NY; *U.S. Private*, pg. 726
Preston, Jeremy, Mng. Dir.--Cereal Partners Worldwide, Morges, Switzerland; *U.S. Public*, pg. 718
Pretzsch, Timothy E., Sr. V.P. & Acct. Mng. Dir.--Young & Rubicam Chicago, Chicago, IL; *U.S. Private*, pg. 1198
Preuss, Armin, Mng. Dir.--H.B. Fuller GmbH, Luneburg, Germany; *U.S. Public*, pg. 687
Price, John, Mng. Dir.--Willenhall Steel Stockholders Ltd., Rowley Regis, United Kingdom; *Int'l*, pg. 79
Price, John, Mng. Dir.--Howard E. Perry & Co. Ltd., Willenhall, United Kingdom; *Int'l*, pg. 79

Price, John, Mng. Dir.--Hughes & Spencer Steel Ltd., Stourbridge, United Kingdom; *Int'l*, pg. 79
Price, Martin, Mng. Dir.--InterVoice, Inc., Singapore, Singapore; *U.S. Public*, pg. 910
Price, Robin, Mng. Partner & Fin.--Howell Henry Chaldecott Lury & Partners, London, United Kingdom; *Int'l*, pg. 637
Pringels, Philippe, Mng. Dir.--Equator, Brussels, Belgium; *Int'l*, pg. 602
Pringle, Ken, Mng. Dir.--The Tetley Group Limited, Greenford, United Kingdom; *Int'l*, pg. 1377
Pritchard, Mark, Mng. Dir.-Custom Fixture Devel.--Dann Dee Display Fixtures, Niles, IL; *U.S. Private*, pg. 310
Probst, Urs, Mng. Dir.--Metawa-Tray B.V., Tiel, Netherlands; *Int'l*, pg. 1307
Prohorenko, Nikolaj, Mng. Dir.--Reemtsma Kiew Tyutyunova Fabrika, Kiev, Ukraine; *Int'l*, pg. 1101
Provencher, Dave, Mng. Dir.--Comtech Antenna Systems, Inc., Saint Cloud, FL; *U.S. Public*, pg. 425
Pucci, Giovanni, Mng. Dir.--Pucci Sulzer, Zurich, Switzerland; *Int'l*, pg. 1377
Puech, Bertrand, Deputy Mng. Dir.-Human Resources--Hermes International, Paris, France; *Int'l*, pg. 617
Puel, Henri Paul, Dir.--AIR Training Center, Toulouse, France; *Int'l*, pg. 29
Pugh, Gordon, Reg. Mng. Dir.--Willis Corroon South Limited, Maidstone, United Kingdom; *Int'l*, pg. 1503
Pugh, Graham, Chm. & Mng. Dir.--Datel Technologies Ltd., Preston, United Kingdom; *Int'l*, pg. 384
Pugh, Graham, Mng. Dir.--Ferranti Air Systems Ltd., Manchester, United Kingdom; *Int'l*, pg. 384
Puignero, Josep Ricart i, Mng. Dir.--Elsevier Prensa SA, Barcelona, Spain; *Int'l*, pg. 1100
Punoose, Salil, Chm. Bd. & Mng. Dir.--Corn Products Co. (India) Ltd., Mumbai, India; *U.S. Public*, pg. 224
Purainen, H., Mng. Dir.--Guilin-Nokia Telecom Ltd., Guilin, China; *Int'l*, pg. 954
Purcell, Eileen, Sr. V.P. & Mng. Dir.--The Chapman Agency, New York, NY; *U.S. Private*, pg. 1197
Purtinen, Olli, Mng. Dir.--Ifi OY, Kerava, Finland; *Int'l*, pg. 501
Pyle, Robyn, Mng. Dir.--NWW Properties Limited, Risley, United Kingdom; *Int'l*, pg. 1444
Pytel, W., Mng. Dir.--Nokia Telecommunications Sp.z.o.o., Warsaw, Poland; *Int'l*, pg. 954
Questa, Koldo Ruiloba, Mng. Dir.--Lubriner (Lubricantes Del Nervion, S.A.), Bilbao, Spain; *Int'l*, pg. 323
Quilty, Jay, Exec. V.P. & Mng. Dir.--The Sawtooth Group, Woodbridge, NJ; *U.S. Private*, pg. 969
Quin, David, Mng. Dir.--Emery Expedite!, Overland Park, KS; *U.S. Public*, pg. 281
Quinlan, Robert, Mng. Dir.--Provident Bankshares Corporation, Baltimore, MD; *U.S. Public*, pg. 1337
Quinn, Conor, Joint Mng. Dir.--Quinn McDonnell Pattison DMB&B Dublin, Dublin, Ireland; *U.S. Private*, pg. 305
Quinn, Jay, Mng. Partner--Eric Mower and Associates, Rochester, NY; *U.S. Private*, pg. 765
Quinn, N., Mng. Dir.--Apollo Fire Detectors Limited, Havant, United Kingdom; *Int'l*, pg. 589
Quintanal, J., Mng. Dir.--AEGON-Union Aseguradora, S.A. de Seguros y Reaseguros, Madrid, Spain; *Int'l*, pg. 28
Quirke, Mike, Mng. Dir.--Costain Construction Limited, Maidenhead, United Kingdom; *Int'l*, pg. 336
Quirke, Mike, Mng. Dir.-Construction & Management Div.--Costain Building & Civil Engineering Limited, Maidenhead, United Kingdom; *Int'l*, pg. 336
Raad, Ramzi, Mng. Dir.--Intermarkets UAE, Dubai, United Arab Emirates; *U.S. Private*, pg. 1062
Raasch, Jochen, Mng. Dir.--OPTIMALGRUND Bautragergesellschaft mbH, Munich, Germany; *Int'l*, pg. 423
Raboy, Doug, Mng. Partner--Hanft Byrne Raboy Abrams & Partners, Inc., New York, NY; *U.S. Private*, pg. 499
Rackley, Thomas E., Mng. Dir.--OppenheimerFunds Distributor, Inc., New York, NY; *U.S. Private*, pg. 818
Rademaker, Richard J., Mng. Dir.--Trinc Company, Bryan, OH; *U.S. Public*, pg. 1214
Radis, Steve, Mngng. Dir.--Arthur D. Little, Inc., Santa Barbara, CA; *U.S. Private*, pg. 670
Radmer, Joachim, Mng. Dir.--Spektrum Fachverlage GmbH, Stuttgart, Germany; *Int'l*, pg. 1478
Radmer, Joachim, Mng. Dir.--Gustav Fischer Verlag GmbH & Co. KG, Stuttgart, Germany; *Int'l*, pg. 1478
Ragland, David, Pres. & Chief Exec. Officer--Duncan Equipment Company, Oklahoma City, OK; *U.S. Private*, pg. 346
Ragosta, Guy, Mng. Dir.-N. America Captive Mngmt. Opers.--Willis Corroon Management (Vermont) Ltd., Burlington, VT; *Int'l*, pg. 1505
Raikkonen, Antti, Mng. Dir.--Nokia Telecommunications (Singapore) Pte. Ltd., Singapore, Singapore; *Int'l*, pg. 954
Raina, Ishan, Mgr.--EURO RSCG-Bombay, Mumbai, India; *Int'l*, pg. 602
Raithel, Rainer, Mng. Dir.-Munich Region--Dyckerhoff & Widmann AG, Munich, Germany; *Int'l*, pg. 423
Ramaer, John W., Mng. Dir.--Boise Cascade Sales Ltd., Amersham, United Kingdom; *U.S. Public*, pg. 243
Ramirez, Jorge, Mng. Dir.--Bank of Boston, Montevideo, Uruguay; *U.S. Public*, pg. 184
Rammelt, Anthony W.E., Sr. V.P. & Intl. Mng. Dir.-Europe--Regis Corporation, Minneapolis, MN; *U.S. Public*, pg. 1373
Rancke, Hans-Herbert, Mng. Dir.--Det Norske Veritas, Hamburg, Germany; *Int'l*, pg. 397
Randal, J.D., Mng. Dir. & Chief Exec. Officer--MFI Furniture Center PLC, London, United Kingdom; *Int'l*, pg. 827
Rangonir, Franscesco, Mng. Dir.--Lear Corporation Italia S.p.A., Orbassano, Italy; *U.S. Public*, pg. 982
Ranki, Kari, Mng. Dir.--Partita Ltd., Helsinki, Finland; *Int'l*, pg. 859
Rantala, Esko, Mng. Dir.--LK Products Oy, Kempele, Finland; *Int'l*, pg. 952
Rapp, Mel W., Mng. Dir.--Quality Chekd Dairies, Inc., Naperville, IL; *U.S. Private*, pg. 898
Rasheed, Aslam, Mng. Dir.--Euroconsult Pakistan, Lahore, Pakistan; *Int'l*, pg. 606
Rasmussen, Hans-Henrik, Mng. Dir.--Young & Rubicam Copenhagen, Copenhagen, Denmark; *U.S. Private*, pg. 1199
Ratanawichiew, Pakdee, Mng. Dir.--Thai CRT Co., Ltd., Ban Si Racha, Thailand; *Int'l*, pg. 1238
Rathbone, Jim, Mng. Dir.--Sensormatic CamEra Ltd., Warwick, United Kingdom; *U.S. Public*, pg. 1457
Raty, Anssi, Mng. Dir.--Nokia Mobile Phones Manufacturing (USA) Ltd., Fort Worth, TX; *Int'l*, pg. 952
Ratz, William, Vice Chm. & Mng. Dir.-Willis Corroon Construction Div.--Willis Corroon Marine & Energy, Houston, TX; *Int'l*, pg. 1508
Ratz, William H., Reg. Construction Mng. Dir.--Willis Corroon Corp. of Texas, Houston, TX; *Int'l*, pg. 1507
Raukko, Raimo, Mng. Dir.--Mykora Oy, Kiukainen, Finland; *Int'l*, pg. 728
Raupeter, Gerd, Mng. Dir.--McDonald's Deutschland GmbH, Munich, Germany; *U.S. Public*, pg. 1069
Ravera, Philippe, Mng. Dir.--Neste Chimie France S.N.C., Silic, France; *Int'l*, pg. 914
Ravid, Shimon, Dr., Joint Mng. Dir.-Fin. & Intl. Activity--Bank Hapoalim, Tel Aviv, Israel; *Int'l*, pg. 149
Raymond, Paul, Mng. Dir.--Sulzer (UK) Ltd., Farnborough, United Kingdom; *Int'l*, pg. 1307
Rayner, Adrian G., V.P. & Mng. Dir.-Europe--Intellicorp Inc., Mountain View, CA; *U.S. Public*, pg. 887
Razouki, Seham Abdul Razzak, Mng. Dir.-Fin., Admin. & External Relations--Kuwait Petroleum Corporation, Safat, Kuwait; *Int'l*, pg. 764
Read, Michael J., Chief Fin. Officer, Treas. & Mng. Dir.--Barr Brothers & Co., Inc., New York, NY; *U.S. Private*, pg. 117
Rebne, Bjorn, Mng. Dir.--Vel-Vask Tekstil Service A/S, Oslo, Norway; *Int'l*, pg. 1286
Reckert, J., Mng. Dir.--Bally-Biver S.a.r.l., Luxembourg, Luxembourg; *Int'l*, pg. 997
Reddin, Don, Exec. V.P. & Mng. Dir.-West Coast--Alcone Marketing Group, Irvine, CA; *U.S. Public*, pg. 1223
Redman, Franz, Mng. Dir.--Julius Meinl Grosshandels-Ges.m.b.H., Vienna, Austria; *Int'l*, pg. 856
Redman, Ray, Dir.-Sls. & Distr.--Logan Corporation, Huntington, WV; *U.S. Private*, pg. 672
Redo, D.L., Sr. V.P. & Mng. Dir.--The Fremont Group, San Francisco, CA; *U.S. Private*, pg. 427
Redondi, Attilio, Mng. Dir.--Dega S.r.l., Mori, Italy; *U.S. Public*, pg. 807
Reed, Brian D., Mng. Dir.--The Illinois Lock Co. Div., Wheeling, IL; *U.S. Public*, pg. 548
Reed, John, Mng. Dir.--H.R. Williams Inc., Kansas City, MO; *U.S. Private*, pg. 1078
Reed, Michael, Mng. Dir.-Opers. Improvement--FDX Corporation, Memphis, TN; *U.S. Public*, pg. 603
Rees, Arwel, Mng. Dir.--Aero Motive (U.K.) Ltd., Ebbw Vale, United Kingdom; *U.S. Public*, pg. 1776
Reeve, Robert, Mng. Dir.--Inverness UK LTD., Slough, United Kingdom; *U.S. Private*, pg. 574
Reeves, Jenner, Mng. Dir.--Costain Oil, Gas & Process Limited Pipeline & Offshore Division, Wirral, United Kingdom; *Int'l*, pg. 336
Reeves, Thomas P., Sr. V.P. & Mng. Dir.-Merisel Europe, Inc.--Merisel, Inc., El Segundo, CA; *U.S. Public*, pg. 1095
Reeves, Thomas P., Mng. Dir.--Merisel Europe, Brentford, United Kingdom; *U.S. Public*, pg. 1096
Regnier, Francois, Mng. Dir.--The Brand Company, Boulogne, France; *Int'l*, pg. 116
Rehn, Jan-Peter, Mng. Dir.--Merita Bank Luxembourg S.A., Luxembourg, Luxembourg; *Int'l*, pg. 859
Rehn, Peter F., Mng. Dir.--CSC Australia, Saint Leonards, Australia; *U.S. Public*, pg. 423
Reichel, Michael M., Mng. Dir.--Commerzbank AG-Beijing Representative Office, Beijing, China; *Int'l*, pg. 311
Reichert, H., Mng. Dir.--Shure Brothers Incorporated, Evanston, IL; *U.S. Private*, pg. 997
Reid, Charles, Mng. Dir.--Baker Div., Hartselle, AL; *U.S. Public*, pg. 1486
Reid, Mike, Mng. Partner-Creative Copy--Lewis Gace Bozell Healthcare Worldwide, Fort Lee, NJ; *U.S. Public*, pg. 1642
Reijonen, Petri, Mng. Dir.--Nokia Telecommunications Kft, Budapest, Hungary; *Int'l*, pg. 953
Reilly, David N., Mng. Dir.--Vauxhall Motors Limited, Luton, United Kingdom; *U.S. Public*, pg. 724
Reilly, James P., Dir.--Carsen Group Inc., Markham, Canada; *U.S. Public*, pg. 301
Reilly, N.A., Mng. Dir.--De La Rue Smurfit Limited, Bray, Ireland; *Int'l*, pg. 386
Reilly, Nick, Chm. Bd. & Mng. Dir.--Vauxhall, Luton, United Kingdom; *U.S. Public*, pg. 724
Reinecke, Ebbe, Mng. Dir.--Esselte A/S, Frederiksberg, Denmark; *Int'l*, pg. 460
Reinskou, Svein, Mng. Dir.--Neste Kjemi A/S, Larvik, Norway; *Int'l*, pg. 915
Reischl, Rudolf-Markus, Mng. Dir.--RTL 2, Grunwald, Germany; *Int'l*, pg. 562
Reisner, Franz, Mng. Dir.-Store Devel. & Construction--Julius Meinl AG, Vienna, Austria; *Int'l*, pg. 856
Reisner, Rudolf, Mng. Dir.--Leo Burnett & Wirz, Vienna, Austria; *U.S. Private*, pg. 184
Reitsema, Keith, Mng. Dir.--DMR Gruppe GmbH, Eschborn, Germany; *Int'l*, pg. 528
Relen, Daniel, Mng. Dir.--Construtora Dumez-GTM Ltda, Santo Amaro, Brazil; *Int'l*, pg. 823
Remes, P., Mng. Dir.--Nutricia France S.A., Paris, France; *Int'l*, pg. 992
Renerd, L., Mng. Dir.--S.C. Recherche et Developpement du Groupe Cockerill Sambre R.D.C.S., Ougree, Belgium; *Int'l*, pg. 301
Rensmann, Ruper, Mng. Dir.--Ketchum Advertising France, Paris, France; *U.S. Private*, pg. 617
Rensmann, Rupert, Mgr.--EURO RSCG Est, Strasbourg, France; *Int'l*, pg. 600
Reny, David, V.P. & Mng. Dir.-Standard Fin. Systems--Standard Duplicating Machines Corp., Andover, MA; *U.S. Private*, pg. 1031
Renzi, R., Chief Oper. Officer & Mng. Dir.--Yale Security Products S.p.A. (Italy), Aprilia, Italy; *Int'l*, pg. 1499
Requien, Francois, Co-Mgr.--Euro RSCG Ensemble, Lyon, France; *Int'l*, pg. 600
Rey, Yves, Mng. Dir.--McCain Sunnyland Belgium, Turnhout, Belgium; *Int'l*, pg. 850
Reynolds, Mike, Mng. Dir.--BellSouth New Zealand, Auckland, New Zealand; *U.S. Public*, pg. 208
Reynoldson, Peter, Mng. Dir.-Australia--Cooper Tools Pty. Ltd., Albury, Australia; *U.S. Public*, pg. 445
Rhodes, J.S., Mng. Dir.--Superform Metals, Blackpool, United Kingdom; *Int'l*, pg. 52
Rhodes, Peter, Mng. Dir.--Reed MIDEM Organisation-UK, London, United Kingdom; *Int'l*, pg. 1096
Ribes, Jean-Martial, Mng. Dir.--Ketchum Public Relations/Paris, Levallois-Perret, France; *U.S. Private*, pg. 617
Ricarte, Ramon Ferraz, Mng. Dir.-Strategic Mktg., Studies & Organization--Caja de Madrid Group, Madrid, Spain; *Int'l*, *pg. 251*
Richard, Laurence E., Mng. Dir.-European Bus. Grp.--Chemfab Corporation, Merrimack, NH; *U.S. Public*, pg. 344
Richards, Andrew, Mng. Dir.--3i Germany, Frankfurt/Main, Germany; *Int'l*, pg. 1386
Richards, Bruce, Mng. Dir.--Benton Plastics, Inc., Clinton, TN; *U.S. Public*, pg. 537
Richards, David L., Chief Exec. Officer & Mng. Dir.--Warwick International Ltd., Flintshire, United Kingdom; *U.S. Public*, pg. 1459
Richards, Jim, Mng. Dir.--Quebecor Integrated Media, Fife, WA; *Int'l*, pg. 1076
Richards, Michael, Mng. Dir.--Durkopp Adler (UK) Ltd., Rugby, United Kingdom; *Int'l*, pg. 469
Richardson, David J., Mng. Dir.--Engineered Seals, Tewkesbury, United Kingdom; *Int'l*, pg. 1338
Richardson, David W., Mng. Dir.-Portfolio Mgr.--Dwight Asset Management Company, Burlington, VT; *U.S. Public*, pg. 1673
Richardson, John, Exec. Dir.-End User Computing--Countrywide Funding Corporation, Pasadena, CA; *U.S. Public*, pg. 453
Richardson, Joy S., Mng. Dir.-Latin America Bus. Devel.--Capital Markets Assurance Corporation, New York, NY; *U.S. Public*, pg. 1023
Richardson, Les, Mng. Dir.--Flexitallic Ltd, Cleckheaton, United Kingdom; *U.S. Private*, pg. 413
Richardson, Peter, Mng. Dir.--Battenfeld UK Ltd., High Wycombe, United Kingdom; *Int'l*, pg. 826
Richmond, John A., Mng. Dir.--Imperial Holly Corporation, Sugar Land, TX; *U.S. Public*, pg. 872
Richon, Jean-Louis, Gen. Dir.-Kaufman, Broad Apts. & Comml.--Kaufman and Broad Home Corporation, Los Angeles, CA; *U.S. Public*, pg. 944
Richter, Helmut, Mng. Dir.--Autologic Information International Inc., Eschborn, Germany; *U.S. Public*, pg. 1724
Richter, Michael, Mng. Dir.--Young & Rubicam GmbH, Frankfurt/Main, Germany; *U.S. Private*, pg. 1199
Richvalsky, George M., Sr. Mng. Dir.--Rothschild Inc., New York, NY; *U.S. Private*, pg. 947
Riddell, Peter, Mgr.-Office--Woodward-Clyde, Auckland, New Zealand; *U.S. Public*, pg. 1657
Riepe, James S., Vice Chm. & Mng. Dir.--T. Rowe Price Associates, Inc., Baltimore, MD; *U.S. Public*, pg. 1324
Rietberg, P.L., Mng. Dir.--P. Van Leeuwen Jr's Buizenhandel B.V., Zwijndrecht, Netherlands; *Int'l*, pg. 1449
Rietveld, K., Mng. Dir.--Lancer Holland BV, Wamel, Netherlands; *Int'l*, pg. 552
Riggs, Charles, Mng. Dir.--Maxim Integrated Products, Inc., Sunnyvale, CA; *U.S. Public*, pg. 1061
Riihinen, Kalevi, Mng. Dir.--Savon Sellu Oy, Kuopio, Finland; *Int'l*, pg. 863
Rikli, Eduard, Mng. Dir.--Sulzer Turbo Ltd., Zurich, Switzerland; *Int'l*, pg. 1305
Riley, Peter, Mng. Dir.--Beazer Homes (Redditch) Limited, Sudley, United Kingdom; *Int'l*, pg. 182
Riley, Stephen J., Mng. Dir.--Swiss Reinsurance Company UK Ltd., London, United Kingdom; *Int'l*, pg. 1333
Rintala, J., Mng. Dir.--Ascom Fintel OY, Vantaa, Finland; *Int'l*, pg. 87
Rinus, U., Mng. Dir.--Ascom Tateco GmbH, Frankfurt, Germany; *Int'l*, pg. 87
Ritchie, Malcom, Chief Exec. Officer & Mng. Dir.--H.J. Heinz Company, Limited, Hayes, United Kingdom; *U.S. Public*, pg. 806
Rivarola, Cristina, Mng. Dir.--BNP (Uruguay) SA, Montevideo, Uruguay; *Int'l*, pg. 164
Rivella, Dr. Ezio, Mng. Dir.--Castello Banfi Srl., Siena, Italy; *U.S. Private*, pg. 113
Rivella, Ezio, Dr., Mng. Dir.-Montalcino--Banfi Vintners, Old Brookville, NY; *U.S. Private*, pg. 113
Riviello, John, Mng. Dir.--Kruger Recycling Inc., Albany, NY; *Int'l*, pg. 762
Rivier, Paul, Gen. Mgr.--Groupe SEB, Ecueille, France; *Int'l*, *pg. 568*
Roberge, Bernard, Mng. Dir.--Fibro Friction, Anjou, Canada; *U.S. Public*, pg. 1503
Roberts, Christopher W., Mng. Dir. & Chief Risk Officer--Credit Suisse First Boston, Inc., New York, NY; *Int'l*, pg. 345
Roberts, Paul, Mng. Dir.--Kammer Vannes S.A.R.L., Cergy-Pontoise, France; *U.S. Public*, pg. 659
Robertson, Andrew, Mng. Dir.--Robertson Leo Burnett Pty. Ltd., Adelaide, Australia; *U.S. Private*, pg. 186
Robertson, Clive A.M., Mng. Dir.--MEM Ltd. 250 V, Oldham, United Kingdom; *Int'l*, pg. 390
Robertson, Jim, Area V.P.-WAII-Asia/Pacific--Wyeth Australia Pty. Ltd., Baulkham Hills, Australia; *U.S. Public*, *pg. 82*

Robertson, Peter, Mng. Dir.--Iggesund Converters Ltd., Milton Keynes, United Kingdom; *Int'l*, pg. 886

Robinet, Bernard, Mng. Dir.--BNP-Dresdner Bank (Polska) S.A., Warsaw, Poland; *Int'l*, pg. 418

Robinson, Brian D., Mng. Dir.--Quality Bakers Australia Ltd., Eastwood, Australia; *Int'l*, pg. 555

Robinson, Chris J., Mng. Dir.--Russ Berrie (U.K.) Limited, Chandlers Ford, United Kingdom; *U.S. Public*, pg. 223

Robinson, Greg, Mng. Dir.--Holiday RV Superstores, Inc., Greer, SC; *U.S. Public*, pg. 829

Robinson, J.F., Mng. Dir.--Byron Mediplastics Limited, Nottingham, United Kingdom; *U.S. Public*, pg. 789

Robinson, J.H., Jr., Mng. Partner--Black & Veatch, Kansas City, MO; *U.S. Private*, pg. 146

Robinson, Michael H., Mng. Dir.-Personnel--Henderson Administration Group PLC, London, United Kingdom; *Int'l*, pg. 609

Robinson, Philip, V.P. & Mng. Dir.-Europe--Armor All Products Group, Oakland, CA; *U.S. Public*, pg. 387

Robinson, S. J., Mng. Dir.--John Menzies Retail, Edinburgh, United Kingdom; *Int'l*, pg. 707

Robson, I.D., Mng. Dir.--De La Rue Card Technology Limited, Tewkesbury, United Kingdom; *Int'l*, pg. 387

Robson, Richard E., Mng. Dir.--Fermec Holdings, Ltd., Manchester, United Kingdom; *U.S. Public*, pg. 312

Robuste V., Fidias, Pres. & Mng. Dir.-MONACA--International Multifoods Corporation, Minneapolis, MN; *U.S. Public*, pg. 900

Robuste, Fidias, Exec. V.P. & Mng. Dir.--Molinos Nacionales, C.A. (Venezuela), Caracas, Venezuela; *U.S. Public*, pg. 901

Roche, B., Mng. Dir.--Boyers & Co. Limited, Dublin, Ireland; *Int'l*, pg. 81

Roche, George A., Chm. Bd., Pres. & Mng. Dir.--T. Rowe Price Associates, Inc., Baltimore, MD; *U.S. Public*, pg. 1324

Roche, P., Mng. Dir.--AG Stanley Limited, Holmes Chapel, United Kingdom; *Int'l*, pg. 202

Rodelli, Richard, Mng. Dir.--The Bank of New York Company, Inc., New York, NY; *U.S. Public*, pg. 178

Rodelli, Richard, Mng. Dir.--The Bank of New York, New York, NY; *U.S. Public*, pg. 178

Rodilossa, Philip T., Mng. Dir.--OppenheimerFunds Distributor, Inc., New York, NY; *U.S. Private*, pg. 818

Rodman, Leonard C., Mng. Partner--Black & Veatch, Kansas City, MO; *U.S. Private*, pg. 146

Rodriguez, Cecilia, Grp. Dir.--de la Cruz & Associates, San Juan, PR; *U.S. Private*, pg. 318

Rodriguez, Godofredo R., Pres. & Mng. Dir.--Johnson & Johnson Medical (Philippines), Inc., Manila, Philippines; *U.S. Public*, pg. 931

Rodriguez, Godofredo R., Pres. & Gen. Mgr.--Johnson & Johnson (Philippines) Inc., Manila, Philippines; *U.S. Public*, pg. 931

Rodriquez, Richard, V.P. & Mng. Dir.-Intl. Div.--Warrantech Corporation, Stamford, CT; *U.S. Public*, pg. 1740

Rodruquez-Coluvi, Ellena, Mng. Dir.--TBWA Madrid, S.A., Madrid, Spain; *U.S. Private*, pg. 1063

Roebuck, P.T., Mng. Dir.--Cow & Gate Nutricia Ltd., Trowbridge, United Kingdom; *Int'l*, pg. 991

Roeder, Marc, Mng. Dir.--Protek Synthes S.A., Etupes, France; *Int'l*, pg. 1307

Roedy, William, Mng. Dir.--MTV Europe, London, United Kingdom; *U.S. Private*, pg. 779

Roesler, Gerd, Mng. Dir.--Gambro Medizintechnik GmbH, Planegg, Germany; *Int'l*, pg. 668

Roether, Kim, Mng. Dir.--Derby Cycle Werke GmbH, Cloppenburg, Germany; *Int'l*, pg. 394

Rogan, David, Mng. Dir.--Alliance Paper Group PLC, Manchester, United Kingdom; *Int'l*, pg. 863

Roger, Maurice, Mng. Dir.--Parfums Christian Dior, Paris, France; *Int'l*, pg. 781

Rogy, Bernard, Mng. Dir.--Creusot-Loire Industrie, Puteaux, France; *Int'l*, pg. 571

Rohle, Michael, Mng. Dir. & Chief Exec. Officer-Frankfurt--DMB&B Hamburg, Hamburg, Germany; *U.S. Private*, pg. 303

Rohm, Keith, Mng. Dir.--Service Motor Co., Seymour, WI; *U.S. Private*, pg. 986

Rojmeta, Pornsiri, Mng. Dir.-Thailand & Indochina--Leo Burnett Ltd. Thailand, Bangkok, Thailand; *U.S. Private*, pg. 185

Rolland, Jan, Mng. Dir., Chief Exec. Officer--Clarion I.M.P. A/S, Oslo, Norway; *U.S. Private*, pg. 303

Roller, Norbert, Mng. Dir.--H.F. Vogel Gmbh Elektrotechnische Fabrik, Nottingen, Germany; *U.S. Public*, pg. 1776

Romano, Rene, Mng. Dir.--Cerca, Paris, France; *Int'l*, pg. 503

Rominger, Eileen P., Mng. Dir.--OppenheimerFunds Distributor, Inc., New York, NY; *U.S. Private*, pg. 818

Romney, W. Mitt, Mng. Dir.--Bain Capital, Boston, MA; *U.S. Private*, pg. 110

Ronbinson, Charles, Mng. Dir.--Progress International Limited, Plainview, NY; *U.S. Public*, pg. 141

Ronsberg, Kare Bergsvein, Mng. Dir.--Det Norske Veritas, Aberdeen, United Kingdom; *Int'l*, pg. 397

Ronzio, Lucio, Mng. Dir.--Ethicon S.p.A., Rome, Italy; *U.S. Public*, pg. 929

Rook, Lennart, Mng. Dir.--Willis Faber Gothia AB, Goteborg, Sweden; *Int'l*, pg. 1510

Roquelpo, Bruno, Chm. Bd. & Mng. Dir.--Campbell Distillers Limited, Brentford, United Kingdom; *Int'l*, pg. 567

Rosales, Manuel Gutierrez, Deputy Mng. Dir.-Human Resources--Caja de Madrid Group, Madrid, Spain; *Int'l*, pg. 251

Rosch, Klaus W., Chief Oper. Officer & Mng. Dir.--Bausparkasse Gemeinschaft der Freunde Wuestenrot gem.GmbH, Ludwigsburg, Germany; *Int'l*, pg. 1514

Rose, Bill, Mng. Dir.--Noble Drilling (West Africa) Ltd., Lagos, Nigeria; *U.S. Public*, pg. 1187

Rosen, Michael S., Mng. Dir.--Rochester Fund Municipals, Rochester, NY; *U.S. Private*, pg. 937

Rosenberg, Channa, Deputy Mng. Dir. & Chief Legal Adviser--Bank Hapoalim, Tel Aviv, Israel; *Int'l*, pg. 149

Rosenwald, E. John, Jr., Vice Chm. & Sr. Mng. Dir.--The Bear Stearns Companies Inc., New York, NY; *U.S. Public*, pg. 197

Ross, Chris, Mngng. Dir.--Arthur D. Little, Inc., Houston, TX; *U.S. Private*, pg. 670

Ross, Colin, Dr., Mng. Dir.--Noise & Vibration Systems, Cambridge, United Kingdom; *Int'l*, pg. 1431

Ross, Gordon, Mng. Dir.--Merisel U.K., Brentford, United Kingdom; *U.S. Public*, pg. 1096

Ross, Mike, Grp. Chief Exec.--Scottish Widows' Fund & Life Assurance Society, Edinburgh, United Kingdom; *Int'l*, pg. 1212

Ross, Wilbur L., Jr., Sr. Mng. Dir.--Rothschild Inc., New York, NY; *U.S. Private*, pg. 947

Rossetti, Angela, Mng. Dir.--Alpha Wave Healthcare Communications, New York, NY; *U.S. Private*, pg. 617

Rossiter, Gregory M., Mng. Dir.-Pub. Rels.--FDX Corporation, Memphis, TN; *U.S. Public*, pg. 603

Rossiter, Paul, Mng. Dir.--Lynwood Scientific Developments Limited, Farnham, United Kingdom; *U.S. Public*, pg. 1144

Rosskelly, Noel, Mng. Dir.--Keystone Pacific Pty. Ltd., Nowra, Australia; *U.S. Public*, pg. 1650

Roswall, Lars, Mng. Dir.--UPM-Kymmene Deutschland GmbH, Hamburg, Germany; *Int'l*, pg. 1430

Rothmuller, Claudio, Mng. Dir.--Editora Campus Ltda., Rio de Janeiro, Brazil; *Int'l*, pg. 1100

Rottier, A.H.M., Mng. Dir.--Gist-Brocades France S.A., Seclin, France; *Int'l*, pg. 1142

Rottland, Javier, Mng. Dir.--Arthur D. Little International, Inc., Lisbon, Portugal; *U.S. Private*, pg. 671

Rottman, Robert, Mng. Dir. & Controller--Nomura Securities International, Inc., New York, NY; *Int'l*, pg. 956

Rough, Greg, Deputy Mng. Dir.--Wyeth Australia Pty. Ltd., Baulkham Hills, Australia; *U.S. Public*, pg. 82

Rouix, Roy, Mng. Dir.--Amite Foundry and Machine, Inc., Amite, LA; *U.S. Public*, pg. 142

Rouse, John William, Dep. Mng. Dir. & Sec.--Fuji International Finance PLC, London, United Kingdom; *Int'l*, pg. 521

Rousso, Raul Yafe, Mng. Dir. & Client Service--Nucleo Publicidad, Montevideo, Uruguay; *U.S. Private*, pg. 186

Rouxel, Jean, Mng. Dir.--Compagnie de Construction Mecanique Sulzer, Mantes-la-Jolie, France; *Int'l*, pg. 1305

Rowland, Wally, Mng. Dir.-Quality Assurance--U.S. Can Company, Oak Brook, IL; *U.S. Public*, pg. 1681

Royston, Samantha, Mng. Dir.--Lynne Franks Ltd., London, United Kingdom; *Int'l*, pg. 117

Rozenbroek, Lex, Mng. Dir.--International Equipment News Europe NV, Brussels, Belgium; *Int'l*, pg. 1099

Rubiani Yanho, Pascual, Mng. Dir.--Mass Publicidad S.R.L., Asuncion, Paraguay; *U.S. Private*, pg. 186

Rubin, Robert Stephen, Chm. Bd. & Mng. Dir.--Pentland Group PLC, London, United Kingdom; *Int'l*, pg. 1035

Ruck, M.J.D., Deputy Mng. Dir.-SCMB--Standard Bank Investment Corporation Limited, Johannesburg, South Africa; *Int'l*, pg. 1293

Ruddy, John H., Mng. Dir.--Bermuda Trust Executors (Jersey) Limited, Saint Helier, United Kingdom; *Int'l*, pg. 151

Rudge, Donald, Mng. Dir.--ServiceMaster Ltd., Leicester, United Kingdom; *U.S. Public*, pg. 1462

Ruff, Edward C., Chief Fin. Officer & Sr. Mng. Dir.--Interstate/Johnson Lane Corporation, Charlotte, NC; *U.S. Public*, pg. 910

Ruikka, Seppo, Mng. Dir.--Finnsugar Bioproducts, Helsinki, Finland; *Int'l*, pg. 349

Runciman, A. James, Mng. Dir.--Donhad Armco Pty. Ltd., Bassendean, Australia; *Int'l*, pg. 391

Runk, John, Mng. Dir.-Mktg. & Sls.--Directory Distributing Associates, Inc., Scarborough, Canada; *U.S. Private*, pg. 334

Ruotsalainen, Pirjo, Mng. Dir.--Unitas Congres Center Ltd., Helsinki, Finland; *Int'l*, pg. 859

Ruprecht, William, Mng. Dir.--Sotheby's Inc., New York, NY; *U.S. Public*, pg. 1487

Rus, Jan, Mng. Dir.--ZwitserLeven, Amsterdam, Netherlands; *Int'l*, pg. 1332

Rusbarsky, Joseph M., Mng. Dir.-Mktg.--OppenheimerFunds Distributor, Inc., New York, NY; *U.S. Private*, pg. 818

Russell, S.G., Mng. Dir.--Boots The Chemists, Nottingham, United Kingdom; *Int'l*, pg. 203

Russo, Thomas, Mng. Dir.--Lehman Brothers, New York, NY; *U.S. Public*, pg. 987

Russolo, Paolo, Mng. Dir.--Profarmaco Nobel S.r.l., Milan, Italy; *U.S. Public*, pg. 297

Rutan, Burt, Mng. Dir.--Scaled Composites, Inc., Mojave, CA; *U.S. Public*, pg. 1782

Rutter, Lee, Mng. Dir.--Torin Limited, Swindon, United Kingdom; *Int'l*, pg. 1267

Ryan, Babs, Mng. Dir.--Waring & LaRosa Direct, New York, NY; *U.S. Private*, pg. 1150

Ryan, Irene, Mng. Dir.--SINSER (Ireland) Ltd., Dublin, Ireland; *Int'l*, pg. 1258

Ryan, J. Stuart, Mng. Dir.--AES Transpower, Singapore, Singapore; *U.S. Public*, pg. 5

Rydin, Claes, Mng. Dir.--Jac Jacobsen AB, Molndal, Sweden; *Int'l*, pg. 821

Rygh, Tom Vidar, Exec. V.P. & Mng. Dir. Fin. Investments--Orkla A.S.A., Oslo, Norway; *Int'l*, pg. 1010

Saari, Timo, Mng. Dir.--OFA Oy Ab, Jokioinen, Finland; *Int'l*, pg. 578

Saarikoski, Erkki, Mng. Dir.--Nokia Telecommunications S.A., La Moraleja-Alcogendas, Spain; *Int'l*, pg. 954

Saastamoinen, Ahti, Mng. Dir.--Puhos-Board Oy, Puhos, Finland; *Int'l*, pg. 1428

Sabbatini, Fabrizio, Chm. & Mng. Dir.--TBWA Italia S.p.A., Milan, Italy; *U.S. Private*, pg. 1063

Saby, Nadine, Sr. V.P.--GPC Communications (Ontario), Toronto, Canada; *U.S. Public*, pg. 1225

Sac, Jean-Claude, Country Mgr.--Nokia France S.A., Romainville, France; *Int'l*, pg. 954

Sachdev, G.K., Mng. Dir.--Quaker Chemical India Ltd., Calcutta, India; *U.S. Public*, pg. 1346

Saeki, Y., Mng. Dir.--Sharp-Roxy Sales & Service Company (M) sdn. Bhd., Petaling Jaya, Malaysia; *Int'l*, pg. 1230

Saeki, Y., Mng. Dir.--Sharp-Roxy Appliances Corp. (M) Sdn. Bhd., Petaling Jaya, Malaysia; *Int'l*, pg. 1230

Saeng-Xuto, Chaisak, Mng. Dir.--The Siam Pulp and Paper Co., Ltd., Bangkok, Thailand; *Int'l*, pg. 1238

Sagara, Jiro, Mng. Dir. & Sr. V.P.-Acctg.--Japan Airlines Company, Ltd., Tokyo, Japan; *Int'l*, pg. 699

Sager, Esther, Mng. Dir.--Pendia Pension Fund Services, Zurich, Switzerland; *Int'l*, pg. 1332

Saha, Saibal K., Mng. Dir.--P.T. Johnson & Johnson Indonesia, Jakarta, Indonesia; *U.S. Public*, pg. 930

Said, Mohammed Haji, Dato, Mng. Dir.--Sime UEP Properties Berhad, Petaling Jaya, Malaysia; *Int'l*, pg. 1250

Said, Perves, Mng. Dir.--Johnson & Johnson Pakistan (Private) Ltd., Karachi, Pakistan; *U.S. Public*, pg. 931

Saigo, Shujio, Mng. Dir.--NSK Ltd., Tokyo, Japan; *Int'l*, pg. 903

Saint Ouen, Marc, Mng. Dir.--EURO RSCG Institutionnel, Levallois-Perret, France; *Int'l*, pg. 600

Sainz de la Pena, Rolando, Mng. Dir.--Vitruvio-Leo Burnett, Madrid, Spain; *U.S. Private*, pg. 186

Sajjavudh, Niphon, Mng. Dir--Batey Ads Thailand, Bangkok, Thailand; *Int'l*, pg. 117

Sakabe, Hiroshi, Mng. Dir.--All Nippon Airways Co. Ltd., Tokyo, Japan; *Int'l*, pg. 57

Sakai, Takeo, Sr. Mng. Dir.--Nisshin Steel Co., Ltd., Tokyo, Japan; *Int'l*, pg. 946

Sakai, Tsutomu, Dir.--Asahi Advertising Inc., Sapporo, Japan; *Int'l*, pg. 81

Sakai, Yukio, Mng. Dir.--Tokai Australia Finance Corporation Limited, Sydney, Australia; *Int'l*, pg. 1391

Sakamoto, Takahiko, Mng. Dir. & Gen. Mgr.-Tokyo Branch & Tokyo Liason Office--The Nanto Bank, Ltd., Nara, Japan; *Int'l*, pg. 905

Sakamoto, Teiji, Mng. Dir.--Kawasho Corporation, Tokyo, Japan; *Int'l*, pg. 726

Sakano, Yoshikazu, Mng. Dir.-Sls.--Asatsu Inc., Tokyo, Japan; *Int'l*, pg. 85

Sakata, Sueo, Mng. Dir. & Gen. Mgr.-Osaka Branch Office--Japan Energy Corporation, Tokyo, Japan; *Int'l*, pg. 702

Sakellaridis, Fotis, Mng. Dir.--Janssen/Cilag S.A.C.I., Athens, Greece; *U.S. Public*, pg. 929

Sakko, Jorma, Mng. Dir.--Zeofinn Oy, Hamina, Finland; *U.S. Private*, pg. 545

Sakurai, Daizaburo, Mng. Dir.-Mngmt. Strategy--Sega Enterprises Ltd., Tokyo, Japan; *Int'l*, pg. 1218

Sakurai, Koichi, Mng. Dir. & Gen. Mgr.-Tech. Devel.--West Japan Railway Company, Osaka, Japan; *Int'l*, pg. 1490

Sakurai, T., Mng. Dir.--Metallurg (Far East) Limited, Tokyo, Japan; *U.S. Private*, pg. 735

Salathe, Willy, Mng. Dir.--Asulab S.A., Biel, Switzerland; *Int'l*, pg. 1160

Salathe, Willy, Mng. Dir.--Comadur S.A., Le Locle, Switzerland; *Int'l*, pg. 1161

Salathe, Willy, Mng. Dir.--Lasag AG, Thun, Switzerland; *Int'l*, pg. 1161

Salathe, Willy, Mng. Dir.--Omega Electronics SA, Bienne, Switzerland; *Int'l*, pg. 1161

Salathe, Willy, Mng. Dir.--Oscilloquartz SA, Neuchatel, Switzerland; *Int'l*, pg. 1161

Salmon, J.D., Mng. Dir.--Crosfield Electronics Limited, Hemel Hempstead, United Kingdom; *U.S. Public*, pg. 532

Salsbury, Peter, Joint Mng. Dir.-Grp. Estates, Personnel, Store Opers. & Devel.--Marks & Spencer PLC, London, United Kingdom; *Int'l*, pg. 842

Salter, Graham, Mng. Dir.--West Footscray Engineering Works Pty. Ltd., Footscray, Australia; *Int'l*, pg. 392

Salvador, Aldo, Mng. Dir.--Rhone-Poulenc Chine, Beijing, China; *Int'l*, pg. 1112

Salvador, Diosdado C., Jr., Mng. Dir.--Johnson & Johnson (Thailand) Ltd., Bangkok, Thailand; *U.S. Public*, pg. 931

Sambol, David, Mng. Dir.-Capital Mkts.--Countrywide Home Loans Inc., Pasadena, CA; *U.S. Public*, pg. 452

Sambonet, Sergio, Mng. Dir.--3i Italy, Milan, Italy; *Int'l*, pg. 1386

Samet, Marcy, Mng. Dir. & Direct Mktg.--Gillespie, Lawrenceville, NJ; *U.S. Private*, pg. 453

Samman, Salim, Mng. Dir., Chief Oper. Officer, Europe & Dir.--BBDO Worldwide Inc., New York, NY; *U.S. Public*, pg. 1223

Sampedro, A., Mng. Dir.--GKN Indugasa SA, Vigo, Spain; *Int'l*, pg. 536

Sampogna, Frank, Mng. Partner-Adv. Services--Gillespie, Lawrenceville, NJ; *U.S. Private*, pg. 453

Sampson, Brian, Mng. Dir.-Retail Div.--Sensormatic Australia Pty Limited, Sydney, Australia; *U.S. Public*, pg. 1457

Samuels, Sandor E., Mng. Dir.-Legal, Gen. Counsel & Sec.--Countrywide Home Loans Inc., Pasadena, CA; *U.S. Public*, pg. 452

Samuelsson, Tore, Mng. Dir.--S-E-Banken Luxembourg S.A., Luxembourg, Luxembourg; *Int'l*, pg. 1259

San Pedro, Jose Luis, Controller, Treas. & Mng. Dir.-Economy & Fin.--Iberdrola, S.A., Bilbao, Spain; *Int'l*, pg. 657

Sancerres, Guy, Mng. Dir.--BNP Bank N.V., Amsterdam, Netherlands; *Int'l*, pg. 163

Sanchez-Incera, Bernardo, Mng. Dir.--Banca Jover, Barcelona, Spain; *Int'l*, pg. 344

Sanchez, Evagio, Chief Oper. Officer--Sol Melia America, Miami, FL; *Int'l*, pg. 1277

Sanchez, Rene, Mng. Dir.--COBE Renal Care, Inc., Tijuana, Mexico; *Int'l*, pg. 667

Sanders, John J., Dir.-Opers./Serck Controls Ltd.--Clayhithe P.L.C., Aylesbury, United Kingdom; *Int'l*, pg. 297

Sanderson, James E., Reg. Dir.-Organizational Services--Cyprus Foote Mineral Co., Kings Mountain, NC; *U.S. Public*, pg. 471

Sandoz, David, Mng. Dir.--Newport Instruments Canada Corp., Mississauga, Canada; *U.S. Public*, pg. 1179

Sands, Dick, Mng. Dir.--CMC (UK) Limited, Egham, United Kingdom; *U.S. Public*, pg. 414
Sands, Graeme, Mng. Dir.--Barrie Knitwear, Hawick, United Kingdom; *Int'l*, pg. 385
Sandsten, Ragnar, Mng. Dir.--RM Industrial Group A/S, Ballerup, Denmark; *Int'l*, pg. 476
Sandstrom, Sven, Mng. Dir.--The World Bank, Washington, DC; *U.S. Private*, pg. 1188
Sanford, Robert A., Mng. Dir.--Brown Brothers Harriman Trust Co. (Cayman) Ltd., Georgetown, Cayman Islands,; *U.S. Private*, pg. 173
Sann, Ted, Co-Chief Oper. Officer-New York & Dir.--BBDO Worldwide Inc., New York, NY; *U.S. Public*, pg. 1223
Sanner, G. Bradley, Mng. Dir.-Comml. Banking--Provident Bank of Maryland, Baltimore, MD; *U.S. Public*, pg. 1337
Sano, Yoshihide, Sr. Mng. Dir.-Sls.--Asatsu Inc., Tokyo, Japan; *Int'l*, pg. 85
Sansome, Frank, Mng. Dir.--Barringer Instruments-U.K., Ltd., Crawley, United Kingdom; *U.S. Public*, pg. 192
Saper, Lawrence, Mng. Dir.--Datascope SARL, Creteil, France; *U.S. Public*, pg. 488
Sar, N., Chm. Bd. & Mng. Dir.--Eastern Coalfields Limited, Burdwan, India; *Int'l*, pg. 298
Sara-aho, Sirpa, Mng. Dir.--Merita Bank Ltd. - Moscow Representative Office, Moscow, Russia; *Int'l*, pg. 859
Sardi, Gino, Mng. Dir.--Bundy Mexico SA, Tultitlan, Mexico; *Int'l*, pg. 1342
Saren, Jane, Mng. Dir.--GPC Market Access Scotland, Edinburgh, United Kingdom; *U.S. Public*, pg. 1225
Sarns, David, Chief Admin. Officer & Mng. Dir.--Cowen & Company, New York, NY; *U.S. Private*, pg. 280
Sasaki, K., Mng. Dir.--Sharp-Roxy (Hong Kong) Ltd., Hong Kong, Hong Kong; *Int'l*, pg. 1230
Sasaki, Mikio, Mng. Dir.-Admin.--Mitsubishi Corporation, Tokyo, Japan; *Int'l*, pg. 871
Sasaki, Shunji, Sr. Mng. Dir.-District Sls. Hdq.--Orix Corporation, Tokyo, Japan; *Int'l*, pg. 1008
Sasao, Mitsuhiko, Deputy Mng. Dir. & Chief Creative Officer--Leo Burnett Kyodo Co. Ltd., Tokyo, Japan; *U.S. Private*, pg. 185
Sasso, Christian, Mng. Dir.--Etablissement d'Istres, Istres, France; *Int'l*, pg. 383
Sato, Hideki, Mng. Dir.-Res. & Devel.--Sega Enterprises Ltd., Tokyo, Japan; *Int'l*, pg. 1218
Sato, Hiroshi, Mng. Dir.-Tech.--Narumi China Corporation, Nagoya, Japan; *Int'l*, pg. 906
Sato, Kazuyoshi, Mng Dir.--Brewster Transport Co. Ltd., Banff, Canada; *U.S. Public*, pg. 1719
Sato, Norimasa, Mng. Dir.--Japan Cosmo Securities (Hong Kong) Limited, Hong Kong, Hong Kong; *Int'l*, pg. 335
Satoh, Osamu, Mng. Dir.-Tokyo Area Sls.--Japan Tobacco Inc., Tokyo, Japan; *Int'l*, pg. 703
Satoh, Yoshio, Mng. Dir.--Dentsu Young & Rubicam Inc. (Tokyo), Tokyo, Japan; *U.S. Private*, pg. 325
Sattelberger, S., Dr., Mng. Dir.--Gesellschaft fur Elektrometallurgie m.b.H., Nuremberg, Germany; *U.S. Private*, pg. 735
Satterthwaite, Chris, Mng. Partner--Howell Henry Chaldecott Lury & Partners, London, United Kingdom; *Int'l*, pg. 637
Saukko, Pirjo, Mng. Dir.--Oy Helsingen Huuttokauppakamari, Helsinki, Finland; *Int'l*, pg. 859
Saunders, John, Deputy Mng. Dir.--Willis Corroon North Limited, Newcastle upon Tyne, United Kingdom; *Int'l*, pg. 1503
Saunders, John F., Mng. Dir.--Fleishman-Hillard Saunders Limited, Dublin, Ireland; *U.S. Private*, pg. 411
Saur, Klaus, Dr., Mng. Dir.--K.G. Saur, Munich, Germany; *Int'l*, pg. 1099
Sauter, George, Mng. Dir.--The Vanguard Group, Inc., Valley Forge, PA; *U.S. Private*, pg. 1133
Sauvage, Alex, Mng. Dir.--Banque Bruxelles Lambert France Succursale de Lille, Lille, France; *Int'l*, pg. 148
Savage, Nigel, Mng. Dir.--Chattem (U.K.) Ltd., Basingstoke, United Kingdom; *U.S. Public*, pg. 342
Saville, Erik L., Mng. Dir.--Signal Investment & Management Co., Wilmington, DE; *U.S. Public*, pg. 342
Sawamura, Fumio, Sr. Mng. Dir.--Hosokawa Micron Corporation, Osaka, Japan; *Int'l*, pg. 635
Sayag, A., Mng. Dir.--Stirn Industries S.A., Joigny, France; *Int'l*, pg. 552
Sayag, Alain, Mng. Dir.--Lequeux S.A., Dourdan, France; *Int'l*, pg. 552
Saylak, Thomas J., Sr. Mng. Dir.--The Blackstone Group, New York, NY; *U.S. Private*, pg. 147
Scales, Robert, Mng. Dir.--Dynamec, Walton, KY; *Int'l*, pg. 193
Scandellari, Pier Luigi, Mng. Dir.--Sirmac Officine Meccaniche SpA, Bologna, Italy; *U.S. Public*, pg. 1619
Scarfo, Henry J., Mng. Dir.-Corp. Affairs & Asst. Sec.--American Automobile Association, Heathrow, FL; *U.S. Private*, pg. 50
Scarlini, Giovanni, Mng. Dir.--Speedline S.p.A., Viano, Italy; *U.S. Public*, pg. 63
Scavone, Sergio, Dir.--PLP Produtos Para Linhas Proformados Ltda., Sao Paulo, Brazil; *U.S. Public*, pg. 1321
Schaaf, Peter, Mng. Dir.-Endine GMBH Germany--Enidine Incorporated, Orchard Park, NY; *U.S. Private*, pg. 377
Schaberl, Bob, Admin. Services--Target Stamped Products Corp., Kinsman, OH; *U.S. Private*, pg. 1069
Schacht, Andy, Partner & Gen. Mgr.--Earle Palmer Brown/ Bethesda, Bethesda, MD; *U.S. Private*, pg. 174
Scharff, Roland, Mng. Dir. & Div. Head-Fin. Mkts.--BHF-BANK AG, Frankfurt, Germany; *Int'l*, pg. 119
Scharin, Ulf, Mng. Dir.--MoDo Merchants AB, Stockholm, Sweden; *Int'l*, pg. 886
Schaub, Rodolfo, Mng. Dir.--Fabrimetal S.A., Santiago, Chile; *Int'l*, pg. 748
Schearer, Chris, Mng. Dir.--Honda East, Cincinnati, OH; *U.S. Private*, pg. 129
Scheerlinck, Rik, Mng. Dir.--Kredietbank-Bankverein AG, Bremen, Germany; *Int'l*, pg. 761
Scheetz, Steve, Mng. Dir.-Personnel Trng. & Devel.--Bank of America Illinois, Chicago, IL; *U.S. Public*, pg. 180
Schehr, Robert, V.P. & Mng. Dir.--National Distributing Co., Inc., Pensacola, FL; *U.S. Private*, pg. 781
Scheidel, Irmgard, Mng. Dir.--Johnson & Johnson G.m.b.H., Hallein, Austria; *U.S. Public*, pg. 930
Scheinkman, Steven W., Pres., Chief Fin. Officer & Mng. Dir.--Samsteel, Inc., Torrance, CA; *U.S. Private*, pg. 402
Schellenberg, David, Mng. Dir.-Acctg. & Admin.--Great Pacific Enterprises Inc., Vancouver, Canada; *Int'l*, pg. 557
Scherini, Robert, Mng. Dir.--Johnson & Johnson Medical Pty. Ltd., Sydney, Australia; *U.S. Public*, pg. 931
Scherr, Patrick, Mng. Dir.--ARIOS SA, Orleans, France; *Int'l*, pg. 607
Scherrer, Urs, Mng. Dir.--Sulzer Wintec Ltd., Winterthur, Switzerland; *Int'l*, pg. 1307
Scheurer, John M., Mng. Dir.--Allied Capital Corporation, Washington, DC; *U.S. Public*, pg. 47
Schicker, P., Mng. Dir.--Schaffner-Behrend AG, Unterengstringen, Switzerland; *Int'l*, pg. 536
Schildt, Hannu, Mng. Dir.--Kaukas Oy, Lappeenranta, Finland; *Int'l*, pg. 1428
Schimmelpenninck, Rutger J., Mng. Dir.--British Land Investments N.V., Amsterdam, Netherlands; *Int'l*, pg. 219
Schipper, A.J., Mng. Dir.--Van Leeuwen Pipe and Tube (Far East) Pte. Ltd., Singapore, Singapore; *Int'l*, pg. 1450
Schirmer, Andreas, Mng. Dir.--Bauverlag GmbH, Walluf, Germany; *Int'l*, pg. 451
Schlichting, Hatmut, Mng. Dir.--Melitta Pacific Ltd., Hong Kong, Hong Kong; *Int'l*, pg. 857
Schlue, Carl-Hans, Mng. Dir.--BNP-Dresdner Bank (Rossija), Saint Petersburg, Russia; *Int'l*, pg. 418
Schlumpf, G., Mng. Dir.--Contraves Advanced Devices, Sdn. Bhd., Melaka, Malaysia; *Int'l*, pg. 998
Schmid, Dietmar, Mng. Dir. & Div. Head-Personnel & Admin.--BHF-BANK AG, Frankfurt, Germany; *Int'l*, pg. 119
Schmidt, Hans, Mng. Dir.--GGK Vienna, Vienna, Austria; *Int'l*, pg. 1336
Schmidt, Steven M., Mng. Dir.-U.S.--A.C. Nielsen, Stamford, CT; *U.S. Public*, pg. 1183
Schmidt, Ted, Pres. & Mng. Dir.-Ball Asia Pacific Ltd., Hong Kong--Ball Corporation, Muncie, IN; *U.S. Public*, pg. 170
Schmidt, Uwe, Mng. Dir.-Social Affairs--STAHLwerke Bremen GmbH, Bremen, Germany; *Int'l*, pg. 79
Schmitt, Helmut, Mng. Dir.--Merisel Germany, Munich, Germany; *U.S. Public*, pg. 1096
Schmitt, Helmut, Mng. Dir.--Merisel Austria, Vienna, Austria; *U.S. Public*, pg. 1096
Schmoyer, Ron, Mng. Dir.--ISS Landscape Management Services, Inc., Tampa, FL; *Int'l*, pg. 656
Schneider, Achim, Mng. Dir.--Georg Fischer Pty Ltd., Oakleigh, Australia; *Int'l*, pg. 488
Schneider, Andreas, Mgr.-Office--Woodward-Clyde, Wuppertal, Germany; *U.S. Public*, pg. 1658
Schneider, Dieter, Chief Fin. Officer & Mng. Dir.--O&K Orenstein & Koppel Aktiengesellschaft, Dortmund, Germany; *Int'l*, pg. 516
Schneider, Norbert J., Mng. Dir.--The Fuller Brush Company, Great Bend, KS; *U.S. Public*, pg. 282
Schober, Alois, Mng. Dir.--Young & Rubicam GmbH, Vienna, Austria; *U.S. Private*, pg. 1199
Schoen, Mel, Mng. Dir.--TBWA Hamburg GmbH, Hamburg, Germany; *U.S. Private*, pg. 1063
Schofield, G. Anthony, Exec. Dir., Mng. Dir.-Branch Banking Div.--The Royal Bank of Scotland plc, Edinburgh, United Kingdom; *Int'l*, pg. 1132
Schollhammer, Stefan, Mng. Dir.--Klafs Saunabau GmbH & Co. KG Medizinische Technik, Schwabisch Hall, Germany; *Int'l*, pg. 736
Schonenberger, Herr, Mng. Dir.--Burgmann do Brasil, Campinas, Brazil; *Int'l*, pg. 233
Schoon, Sven-Erik, Mng. Dir.--Hagglunds Lidan AB, Lidkoping, Sweden; *Int'l*, pg. 670
Schoonmaker, Tim, Mng. Dir.--EMAP Radio, London, United Kingdom; *Int'l*, pg. 451
Schops, Gerhard, Chm. & Mng. Dir.--EURO RSCG, Dusseldorf, Germany; *Int'l*, pg. 602
Schossleitner, Dieter, Gen. Mng. Dir.--Maschinenfabrik Andritz AG, Graz, Austria; *Int'l*, pg. 14
Schou, Nico, Bus. Dir.--Young & Rubicam Copenhagen, Copenhagen, Denmark; *U.S. Private*, pg. 1199
Schreiber, Hans, Mng. Dir.--Metallgesellschaft AG, Frankfurt, Germany; *Int'l*, pg. 860
Schrems, Rainer, Mng. Dir.-Strategic Devel.--Julius Meinl AG, Vienna, Austria; *Int'l*, pg. 856
Schreuder, P.R.L., Mng. Dir.--Traditional Beer Investments, Sloane Park, South Africa; *Int'l*, pg. 1287
Schubert, Alexander, Deputy Mng. Dir.--DMB&B Frankfurt, Frankfurt/Main, Germany; *U.S. Private*, pg. 303
Schubert, John, Chief Exec. Officer & Mng. Dir.--Pioneer International Ltd., Sydney, Australia; *Int'l*, pg. 1058
Schuerch, Hans Rudolph, Mng. Dir.--Sulzermedica Japan K.K., Tokyo, Japan; *Int'l*, pg. 1307
Schulz, Hans, Mng. Dir.--Balzers Verschleissschutz GmbH, Bingen, Germany; *Int'l*, pg. 997
Schulz, Jurgen W., Mng. Dir.--Sulzer Weise GmbH, Bruchsal, Germany; *Int'l*, pg. 1306
Schulzezur Wiersch, Ulrich, Sr. V.P. & Mng. Dir.--Pharm-Allergan GmbH, Ettlingen, Germany; *U.S. Public*, pg. 46
Schuster, Carol, Exec. V.P. & Mng. Dir.--DMB&B New York, New York, NY; *U.S. Private*, pg. 302
Schutz, Gerhard, Mng. Dir.--Sulzer Chemtech AG, Winterthur, Switzerland; *Int'l*, pg. 1307
Schwaebe, Hans H., Exec. Dir.--Dixie Union Verpackungen GmbH, Kempten, Germany; *U.S. Public*, pg. 440
Schwarczer, Etienne, Mng. Dir.--Hidepito, Budapest, Hungary; *Int'l*, pg. 823
Schwartz, Alan D., Exec. V.P. & Sr. Mng. Dir.--The Bear Stearns Companies Inc., New York, NY; *U.S. Public*, pg. 197
Schwartz, Joseph B., Sr. Mng. Dir.--Rothschild Inc., New York, NY; *U.S. Private*, pg. 947
Schweitzer, Mike, Exec. V.P. & Mng. Dir.--Western International Media Corporation, Orlando, FL; *U.S. Private*, pg. 1167
Schwendimann, Carlo, Mng. Dir.--Del Bosco & C.S.R.L., Milan, Italy; *Int'l*, pg. 303
Schwenk, Oscar J., Mng. Dir.--Pilatus Flugzeugwerke AG, Stans, Switzerland; *Int'l*, pg. 998
Schwizer, Arthur, Mng. Dir.--Sulzer Medical Technology Ltd., Winterthur, Switzerland; *Int'l*, pg. 1307
Scott, David Maxwell, Mng. Dir.--Matthew Gloag & Son Limited, Perth, United Kingdom; *Int'l*, pg. 619
Scott, Patrick, Mng. Dir.-Europe--The Weather Channel, Atlanta, GA; *U.S. Private*, pg. 647
Scrimshaw, J. Eric, Mng. Dir.--United Kingdom Plant, Loughborough, United Kingdom; *U.S. Public*, pg. 443
Scully, Tim, Mng. Dir.-Treasury--Musicland Group Inc., Minnetonka, MN; *U.S. Public*, pg. 1142
Searle, Graham, Dep. Chm. & Mng. Dir.-Opers.--Laura Ashley Holdings Plc, Maidenhead, United Kingdom; *Int'l*, pg. 804
Seay, Austin, Mng. Dir.--Tidex (Malaysia) Sdn. Bhd., New Orleans, LA; *U.S. Public*, pg. 1608
Secades, Jose Bourkaib, Mng. Dir.--CC Banque Belgique, Brussels, Belgium; *Int'l*, pg. 144
See, Johnson, Mng. Dir.--KONE Elevator Pte. Ltd., Singapore, Singapore; *Int'l*, pg. 747
Seetti, Franco, Mng. Dir.--Sperlari, S.R.L., Milan, Italy; *U.S. Public*, pg. 812
Seguin, J-M, Mng. Dir.--Ascom Monetel SA, Guilherand-Granges, France; *Int'l*, pg. 87
Segura, Judith Garrett, Pres. & Exec. Dir.-A.H. Belo Corporation Foundation--A.H. Belo Corporation, Dallas, TX; *U.S. Public*, pg. 209
Seki, Yoshinao, Sr. Mng. Dir. & Chief Investment Officer-Loans/Real Estate--Yasuda Mutual Life Insurance Co., Tokyo, Japan; *Int'l*, pg. 1519
Sekido, Yoshio, Exec. Mng. Dir.--Sanyo Electric Co., Ltd., Osaka, Japan; *Int'l*, pg. 1190
Sekiguchi, Masumi, Mng. Dir.--Wako Merchant Bank (Singapore) Limited, Singapore, Singapore; *Int'l*, pg. 1485
Sekine, Tatsuhiro, Sr. Mng. Dir.-Fin.--Ito-Yokado Co., Ltd., Tokyo, Japan; *Int'l*, pg. 693
Seksaf, Nadia, Intl. Dir.--Crehalet Pouget Poussielgues, Paris, France; *U.S. Private*, pg. 1152
Sellers, Basil, Vice Chm. & Mng. Dir.--Chiltem Group SAM, Monaco, Monaco; *Int'l*, pg. 65
Selmer, B., Mng. Dir.--GKN Glaenzer Cardan SA, Poissy, France; *Int'l*, pg. 536
Semones, Lewis F., Jr., Sr. Mng. Dir.-Strategic Plng. & Bus. Devel.--Interstate/Johnson Lane Corporation, Charlotte, NC; *U.S. Public*, pg. 910
Sendler, Israel, Mng. Dir.--Orbotech Pacific Ltd., Wan Chai, Hong Kong; *Int'l*, pg. 1007
Seng, Chew Choon, Dep. Mng. Dir. & Dir.-Fin.--Singapore Airlines Ltd., Singapore, Singapore; *Int'l*, pg. 1374
Seng, Soon Boon, Mng. Dir.--Baymont Malaysia SDN BHD, Kuala Lumpur, Malaysia; *Int'l*, pg. 31
Seng, Soon Boon, Mng. Dir.--Baymont Technologies (PTE) Ltd., Singapore, Singapore; *Int'l*, pg. 31
Sengupta, P.K., Dir.-Fin.--Coal India Limited, Calcutta, India; *Int'l*, pg. 298
Sentuna, C., Mng. Dir.--Bilar Bilgi Araclari Ticaret A.S., Istanbul, Turkey; *Int'l*, pg. 1115
Serafini, Claudio, Chief Exec. Officer & Mng. Dir.--Heinz Food Service S.r.l., Commessaggio, Italy; *U.S. Public*, pg. 806
Serafini, Claudio, Chief Exec. Officer & Mng. Dir.--Heinz Plasmon Dietetci Alimentari S.p.A., Milan, Italy; *U.S. Public*, pg. 806
Serafini, Claudio, Chief Exec. Officer & Mng. Dir.--PLADA S.p.A., Milan, Italy; *U.S. Public*, pg. 807
Serafini, Claudio, Mng. Dir.--AIAL (Arimpex S.r.l. Industrie Alimentari), Commessaggio, Italy; *U.S. Public*, pg. 807
Sergeant, K., Mng. Dir.--Vent-Axia Ltd., Crawley, United Kingdom; *Int'l*, pg. 1267
Serirak, Tavisale, Mng. Dir.--The Siam Construction Steel Co., Ltd., Bangkok, Thailand; *Int'l*, pg. 1238
Serrano, Isidoro, Pres. & Regional Dir.--Leo Burnett Comunica S.A., Guatemala, Guatemala; *U.S. Private*, pg. 185
Setterberg, Per, Deputy Mng. Dir.-Europe Tax Free Shopping--Advance Ross Corporation, Chicago, IL; *U.S. Public*, pg. 320
Setterberg, Per, Deputy Mng. Dir.--Europe Tax-Free Shopping Ltd., Chicago, IL; *U.S. Public*, pg. 320
Setzer, Robert L., Mng. Dir., Dir.-Pub. Fin. & Dir.--The Robinson-Humphrey Company, Inc., Atlanta, GA; *U.S. Public*, pg. 1633
Seuss, James C., V.P. & Mng. Dir.--Tiffany & Co., New York, NY; *U.S. Public*, pg. 1608
Seutin, Guy, Chief Exec. Officer & Mng. Dir.--SAIT-RadioHolland Group S.A., Brussels, Belgium; *Int'l*, pg. 1151
Sevensson, Roland, Chief Exec. Officer & Mng. Dir.--KF/ Konsum Coop Group, Stockholm, Sweden; *Int'l*, pg. 718
Severson, Allan W., Sr. V.P.-California Admin.--Zions Bancorporation, Salt Lake City, UT; *U.S. Public*, pg. 1792
Seward, Ben, Mng. Dir.-Risk Mngmt. & Pension Admin.--FDX Corporation, Memphis, TN; *U.S. Public*, pg. 603
Seyama, Hirotada, Mng. Dir. & Gen. Mgr.--The Tokio Marine & Fire Insurance Company, Ltd., Tokyo, Japan; *Int'l*, pg. 1391
Shah, S. Mir Muhammad, Dr., Deputy Mng. Dir.--Pakistan International Airlines Corporation, Karachi, Pakistan; *Int'l*, pg. 1021
Shaheen, G.L., Mng. Dir.--Caterpillar Overseas S.A., Geneva, Switzerland; *U.S. Public*, pg. 316
Shaheen, Gabriel, Mng. Dir.--Lincoln Assurance Limited, Uxbridge, United Kingdom; *U.S. Public*, pg. 998
Shaheen, Gabriel, Mng. Dir.--Lincoln National (UK) plc, Oxbridge, United Kingdom; *U.S. Public*, pg. 998
Shanahan, Pat, Mng. Dir.--Tellabs Ltd., Shannon, Ireland; *U.S. Public*, pg. 1573

Shani, Shaul, Mng. Dir.-Sls. Devel.--Sapiens International Corporation N.V., Curacao, Netherlands Antilles; *Int'l*, pg. 1193
Shanken, Ross, V.P. & Mng. Dir.--Western Interactive Media, Los Angeles, CA; *U.S. Private*, pg. 1166
Sharma, Arvind, Mng. Dir.--Chaitra Leo Burnett Private Ltd., Mumbai, India; *U.S. Private*, pg. 184
Sharp, F., Mng. Dir.--Endevco UK Ltd., Royston, United Kingdom; *Int'l*, pg. 853
Sharp, Keith, Mng. Dir.-Affiliate Rels. (London)--Burson-Marsteller, New York, NY; *U.S. Private*, pg. 1197
Sharpe, Anthony, Mng Dir.-Wackenhut U.K.--Wackenhut Intl., Inc., Coral Gables, FL; *U.S. Public*, pg. 1731
Sharpe, Anthony, Mng. Dir.-Wackenhut U.K.--Wackenhut U.K., Ltd., London, United Kingdom; *U.S. Public*, pg. 1732
Sharpe, Peter J., Deputy Mng. Dir.--Cherry Electrical Products, Ltd., Harpenden, United Kingdom; *U.S. Public*, pg. 346
Shaughnessy, Dennis J., Mng. Dir.--Grotech Capital Group, Inc., Timonium, MD; *U.S. Private*, pg. 483
Shaw, D. R., Mng. Dir.--NatWest Ventures Limited, London, United Kingdom; *Int'l*, pg. 910
Shaw, H., Mng. Dir.--Ascom Timeplex SA, Brussels, Belgium; *Int'l*, pg. 87
Shaw, John, Mng. Dir.--OIP, Paris, France; *Int'l*, pg. 1097
Shaw, Philip, Mng. Dir.--Butterworth-Heinemann Limited, Oxford, United Kingdom; *Int'l*, pg. 1094
Shea, Tom, Exec. V.P. & Mng. Dir.--Shorewood Packaging Corporation of Canada, Ltd., Scarborough, Canada; *U.S. Public*, pg. 1468
Shei, Johnson, Mng. Dir.--Seika Electric Co., Euclid, OH; *Int'l*, pg. 1218
Sheith, Nipun, Mng. Dir.--Battenfeld India Ltd., Gujarat, India; *Int'l*, pg. 825
Shek, Clara, Mng. Dir.--Edelman Worldwide (Hong Kong) Limited, Causeway Bay, Hong Kong; *U.S. Private*, pg. 363
Sheldon, Alan J., Vice Chm. & Mng. Dir.-Y&R Inc.--Young & Rubicam Inc., New York, NY; *U.S. Private*, pg. 1196
Shelton, Charles B., III, Mng. Dir. & Dir.--The Robinson-Humphrey Company, Inc., Atlanta, GA; *U.S. Public*, pg. 1633
Shen, Frank H.L., Mng. Dir.--Raw Materials Ltd., Taipei, Taiwan; *Int'l*, pg. 303
Shenton, Graham, Mng. Dir.-European Opers.--Wind River Systems, Inc., Alameda, CA; *U.S. Public*, pg. 1770
Shepherd, N., Mng. Dir.--Gestetner Australasia Limited, Brookvale, Australia; *Int'l*, pg. 1115
Shepherd, Peter, Dr., Mng. Dir.--Elsevier Science SA, Lausanne, Switzerland; *Int'l*, pg. 1100
Shepherd, William, Chief Exec.--Reed Educational and Professional Publishing, Oxford, United Kingdom; *Int'l*, pg. 1094
Sheridan, Philip R., Mng. Dir.-West Instruments, Ltd.--Danaher Corporation, Washington, DC; *U.S. Public*, pg. 480
Sheridan, Susan, Mng. Dir.--SCT, Rochester, NY; *U.S. Public*, pg. 1552
Sherriff, Anthony G., Mng. Dir.--Perfect Pizza Ltd., Chertsey, United Kingdom; *Int'l*, pg. 1213
Sherwood, Patrick, Mng. Dir.--DMB&B Detroit, Troy, MI; *U.S. Private*, pg. 302
Sheth, Nipun, Mng. Dir.--Battenfeld India Ltd., Mumbai, India; *Int'l*, pg. 825
Shibata, Naoshige, Mng. Dir.--Nippon Life (Deutschland) GmbH, Frankfurt/Main, Germany; *Int'l*, pg. 936
Shibuya, Isao, Mng. Dir.-Osaka--Daiwa Securities Co. Ltd., Tokyo, Japan; *Int'l*, pg. 374
Shimamura, Kimizo, Mng. Dir. & Gen. Mgr.--The Industrial Bank of Japan, Limited (London Branch), London, United Kingdom; *Int'l*, pg. 675
Shimamura, Takeshi, Sr. Mng. Dir.-Kinki & Shikoku Area Sls.--Daiwa Securities Co. Ltd., Tokyo, Japan; *Int'l*, pg. 374
Shimaoka, Tadafumi, Mng. Dir.--Haseko Corporation, Tokyo, Japan; *Int'l*, pg. 599
Shimaya, Noriaki, Mng. Dir. & Gen. Mgr.--Yokohama Asia Limited, Central, Hong Kong; *Int'l*, pg. 159
Shimazaki, Kaname, Sr. Mng. Dir. & Gen. Mgr.-Osaka Branch--Mitsubishi Corporation, Tokyo, Japan; *Int'l*, pg. 871
Shimizu, Tsuyoshi, Mng. Dir.-Pub. Rels & Adv.--Ajinomoto Company Inc., Tokyo, Japan; *Int'l*, pg. 40
Shimmin, Maxine, Mng. Dir.-Dixons Insurance Services--Dixons Group plc, Hemel Hempstead, United Kingdom,; *Int'l*, pg. 413
Shimmin, Maxine, Mng. Dir.--Dixons Finance Plc, London, United Kingdom; *Int'l*, pg. 414
Shimomura, Ryoichi, Mng. Dir.--Kyowa Hakko Industry (Singapore) Pte. Ltd., Singapore, Singapore; *Int'l*, pg. 778
Shimpi, Prakash A., Mng. Dir.--Swiss Re Financial Products, New York, NY; *Int'l*, pg. 1333
Shine, Cheri, Exec. Dir.-Training & Information Support--Countrywide Funding Corporation, Pasadena, CA; *U.S. Public*, pg. 453
Shinmachi, Koji, Mng. Dir. & Sr. V.P.-Airport Opers.--Japan Airlines Company, Ltd., Tokyo, Japan; *Int'l*, pg. 699
Shinmura, Takuji, Mng. Dir. & Gen. Mgr.-Pur.--Mitsubishi Electric Corporation, Tokyo, Japan; *Int'l*, pg. 872
Shinomiya, Norio, Mng. Dir. & Gen. Mgr.-Construction Dept.--West Japan Railway Company, Osaka, Japan; *Int'l*, pg. 1490
Shitoto, Hideo, Mng. Dir.--Intermedics Japan K.K., Tokyo, Japan; *Int'l*, pg. 1307
Shmuely, M., Mng. Dir.--Elta Electronics Industries, Ltd., Ashdod, Israel; *Int'l*, pg. 690
Shockley, Jim, Mng. Dir.--Bluefield Gas Company, Bluefield, WV; *U.S. Public*, pg. 1393
Shonov, Georgi, Mng. Dir.--KONE Representative Office, Moscow, Russia; *Int'l*, pg. 747
Shuttleworth, R., Mng. Dir.--WBB Devon Clays Ltd., Newton Abbot, United Kingdom; *Int'l*, pg. 1487
Sibois, Jean Bernard, Mng. Dir.--Bureau Rhone-Poulenc, Cairo, Egypt; *Int'l*, pg. 1112
Sidwell, David H., Mng. Dir. & Controller--J.P. Morgan Co. Incorporated, New York, NY; *U.S. Public*, pg. 1129
Sieben, Tony, Mng. Dir.--ISS Contract Cleaning Services (North), Middleton, United Kingdom; *Int'l*, pg. 657
Siegal, Jeffrey M., Mng. Dir.--Castle-Harlan, Inc., New York, NY; *U.S. Private*, pg. 219
Siegel, Stuart N., Pres. & Mng. Dir.--Sotheby's International Realty, New York, NY; *U.S. Public*, pg. 1487
Siegers, R., Mng. Dir.--Faxion B.V., Amsterdam, Netherlands; *Int'l*, pg. 1144
Siegrist, Fred, Mng. Dir.--Swiss Life Portfolio Management, Zurich, Switzerland; *Int'l*, pg. 1332
Sieracki, Eric P., Mng. Dir.-Corp. Fin. & Commun.--Countrywide Home Loans Inc., Pasadena, CA; *U.S. Public*, pg. 452
Sijbesma, F., Mng. Dir.--Food Specialties Division, Delft, Netherlands; *Int'l*, pg. 1142
Silander, Harald, Mng. Dir.--BTL Sweden AB, Goteborg, Sweden; *Int'l*, pg. 123
Silberfeld, Jacques, Mng. Dir.--ISS Net Inter S.A., Pantin, France; *Int'l*, pg. 657
Silberman, Rick, Exec. Dir.--Douglas Elliman, New York, NY; *U.S. Private*, pg. 341
Silberman, Simon, Mng. Dir.--Zircotube, Paris, France; *Int'l*, pg. 503
Silk, Robert, Mng. Dir.--E-Z Lok, Gardena, CA; *U.S. Private*, pg. 1063
Sillantaka, Erkki, Mng. Dir.--VV-Auto Oy, Helsinki, Finland; *Int'l*, pg. 732
Silva, Cesar, Chief Oper. Officer--Gambro Lda., Parede, Portugal; *Int'l*, pg. 668
Silver, Michael, Exec. V.P. & Mng. Partner-Acct.--Wells BDDP, Inc., New York, NY; *Int'l*, pg. 117
Simal, Joao, Mng. Dir.-Sls.--Sensormatic Lda., Lisbon, Portugal; *U.S. Public*, pg. 1458
Simcic, Christian A., V.P. & Mng. Dir.-Asia Pacific--Avery Dennison Corporation, Pasadena, CA; *U.S. Public*, pg. 152
Simmoms, Jed, Mng. Dir.-Excite Intl.--Excite, Inc., Redwood City, CA; *U.S. Public*, pg. 599
Simone, Ginny, Sr. V.P. & Mng. Dir.--The Mercury Group, Alexandria, VA; *U.S. Private*, pg. 13
Simonis, Jerry, Mng. Dir.--Pierre Balmain, Saint Imier, Switzerland; *Int'l*, pg. 1160
Simonis, Jerry, Mng. Dir.--Columna S.A., Lausanne, Switzerland; *Int'l*, pg. 1160
Simpson, S., Sr. V.P. & Mng. Dir.--BBDO Canada, Toronto, Canada; *U.S. Private*, pg. 104
Sinders, John W., Jr., Mng. Dir.--Jefferies & Company, Inc., Los Angeles, CA; *U.S. Public*, pg. 925
Singer, Gary, Mng. Dir. & Chief Oper. Officer--DMB&B St. Louis, Saint Louis, MO; *U.S. Private*, pg. 303
Singh, R.A.P., Dir.-Personnel & Indus. Rels.--Coal India Limited, Calcutta, India; *Int'l*, pg. 298
Sinke, Huib W., Mng. Dir.--Heidemij Realisatie BV, Arnhem, Netherlands; *Int'l*, pg. 607
Sinke, Huib W., Mng. Dir.--Heidemij Realisatie Lelystad BV, Arnhem, Netherlands; *Int'l*, pg. 607
Sipahi, Galip, Mng. Dir.--Ardem Pisiriciler Ve Isitici San. A.S., Istanbul, Turkey; *Int'l*, pg. 741
Siquiera, Valdir, Mng. Dir.--V&S Comunicacoes, Rio de Janeiro, Brazil; *U.S. Private*, pg. 1200
Sire, Philippe, Mng. Dir.--Dumez-GTM Cambodge, Phnom Penh, Kampuchea; *Int'l*, pg. 823
Siridhara, Dhanit, Mng. Dir.--Siam Cement Industrial Land Co., Ltd., Nong Khae, Thailand; *Int'l*, pg. 1238
Sirisantana, Vanich, Mng. Dir.--The Thai Wanaphan Co., Ltd., Samutprakan, Thailand; *Int'l*, pg. 1239
Sivey, Paul, Mng. Dir.-Intl. Div.--Costain Building & Civil Engineering Limited, Maidenhead, United Kingdom; *Int'l*, pg. 336
Sivey, Paul, Mng. Dir.--Costain Marine International Limited, Maidenhead, United Kingdom; *Int'l*, pg. 336
Sjoblom, S., Mng. Dir.--Ascom Energy Systems AB, Vaxjo, Sweden; *Int'l*, pg. 87
Sjoegren, Stig, Mng. Dir.--Bicapa-Bjoernklaeder AB, Hisings Backa, Sweden; *Int'l*, pg. 1285
Sjolund, Erik, Mng. Dir.--Iggesund Paperboard AB, Iggesund, Sweden; *Int'l*, pg. 886
Skeppner, Ake, Chief Exec. Officer & Mng. Dir.--Eldon AB, Nassjo, Sweden; *Int'l*, pg. 436
Skierczynska-Rocca, Katarzyna, Mng. Dir.--R.F.R./ARIP, Warsaw, Poland; *Int'l*, pg. 1377
Skinner, P.D., Pres. & Mng. Dir.-Shell Intl. Trading & Shipping Co. Ltd.--Royal Dutch/Shell Group of Companies, Hague, Netherlands; *Int'l*, pg. 1135
Skirka, Kenneth John, Pres., Chief Exec. & Oper. Officer, Mng. Dir.--Australian Oil & Gas Corporation Limited, Sydney, Australia; *Int'l*, pg. 101
Skoglund, Bjorn, Mng. Dir. & Chief Fin. Officer--W.R. Grace AB, Helsingborg, Sweden; *U.S. Public*, pg. 755
Skoglund, Bjorn, Mng. Dir.--W.R. Grace A/S, Herlev, Denmark; *U.S. Public*, pg. 755
Skoglund, Bjorn, Mng. Dir.--Grace (Sweden) AB, Helsingborg, Sweden; *U.S. Public*, pg. 756
Skott, Preben, Mng. Dir.--Novo Nordisk Pharmaceuticals Pty. Ltd., North Rocks, Australia; *Int'l*, pg. 988
Skov, Kurt, Mng. Dir.--Howard Maschinenfabrik GmbH, Michelstadt, Germany; *Int'l*, pg. 1387
Skrbensky-Meinl, Jeanette, Mng. Dir.-Buying--Julius Meinl AG, Vienna, Austria; *Int'l*, pg. 856
Slaats, Louis, Mng. Dir.--Ross Systems Nederland B.V., Utrecht, Netherlands; *U.S. Public*, pg. 1406
Slater, Martin, Mng. Dir.--Noesis/The Corporate Company, Milan, Italy; *Int'l*, pg. 117
Slater, P.J.H., Mng. Dir.--Piher International Ltd., Swindon, United Kingdom; *Int'l*, pg. 853
Slaven, Mary-Gene, Mng. Dir.--NWQ Investment Management Company, Los Angeles, CA; *U.S. Public*, pg. 1673
Sletsjoe, Kjell, Mng. Dir.--Jotun (Malaysia) Sdn. Bhd., Shah Alam, Malaysia; *Int'l*, pg. 715
Sloan, J. David, V.P. & Mng. Dir.--Toronto Dominion-Hong Kong Branch, Hong Kong, Hong Kong; *Int'l*, pg. 1401
Slotte, Karsten, Mng. Dir.--Vaasamills Ltd., Helsinki, Finland; *Int'l*, pg. 349
Slusser, Sarah, Mng. Dir.--AES Aurora, Arlington, VA; *U.S. Public*, pg. 5
Smale, Leo, Mng. Dir.--Comtest Limited, Wokingham, United Kingdom; *U.S. Public*, pg. 1596
Small, Phillip, Mng. Dir.--CSC Financial Services Group, Austin, TX; *U.S. Public*, pg. 422
Smans, Ludo, Mng. Dir.--GEDAS NV, Deurne, Belgium; *Int'l*, pg. 608
Smart, John, Sr. V.P. & Mng. Dir.--Interbrand Schechter, San Francisco, CA; *U.S. Public*, pg. 1224
Smeulders, A.A.F.H., Mng. Dir.--Sugro B.V., Zaltbommel, Netherlands; *Int'l*, pg. 991
Smith, Alan, Mng. Dir.--Reed Publishing (NZ) Ltd., Birkenhead, New Zealand; *Int'l*, pg. 1094
Smith, Andrew, Mng. Dir.--Autologic Information International Ltd., Saint Albans, United Kingdom; *U.S. Public*, pg. 1724
Smith, D.C., Chief Oper. Officer & Mng. Dir.--Hammerite Products Limited, Prudhoe, United Kingdom; *Int'l*, pg. 1501
Smith, David, Mng. Dir.--Chartham Papers, Canterbury, United Kingdom; *Int'l*, pg. 1107
Smith, Dennis, Mng. Dir.-Adv.-Motors--Toyota Motor Distributors (Ireland) Ltd., Dublin, Ireland; *Int'l*, pg. 1413
Smith, Derek, Mng. Dir.--Hong Kong Air Terminal Services Ltd., Kowloon, Hong Kong; *Int'l*, pg. 705
Smith, F., Mng. Dir.-Asia & Market Devel.--United Biscuits (Holdings) Plc, West Drayton, United Kingdom; *Int'l*, pg. 1442
Smith, F., Mng. Dir.--United Biscuits Asia Pacific, West Drayton, United Kingdom; *Int'l*, pg. 1442
Smith, Geoffrey F., Mng. Dir.-UK & N. America--Messier-Dowty Ltd., Gloucester, United Kingdom; *Int'l*, pg. 1340
Smith, Geoffrey F., Mng. Dir.-UK & N. America--Messier-Dowty Inc., Toronto, Ajax, Canada; *Int'l*, pg. 1340
Smith, Geoffrey F., Mng. Dir.-UK & N. America--Messier-Dowty Electronics, Peterborough, Canada; *Int'l*, pg. 1340
Smith, Geoffrey F., Mng. Dir.-UK & N. America--Messier-Dowty Inc., Montreal, Saint-Janvier, Canada; *Int'l*, pg. 1340
Smith, J.K., Mng. Dir.--Wolters Kluwer Academic Publishers, Dordrecht, Netherlands; *Int'l*, pg. 1512
Smith, James Craven, Mng. Dir.--Hugh Baird & Sons Limited, Witham, United Kingdom; *U.S. Public*, pg. 428
Smith, Jeffrey, Mng. Dir.--Woodward-Clyde, Richmond, Australia; *U.S. Public*, pg. 1657
Smith, Lance C.R., Reg. Mng. Dir.-DMB&B Europe & Dir.-The Way--DMB&B Communications, New York, NY; *U.S. Private*, pg. 302
Smith, Lane, Mng. Dir.-Client Services Grp.--MET Solutions, LLC, Raleigh, NC; *U.S. Public*, pg. 1642
Smith, Leon C., Mng. Dir.-S.A. Greetings Corp. (PTY) Ltd.--American Greetings Corporation, Cleveland, OH; *U.S. Public*, pg. 77
Smith, Liz, Exec. V.P. & Mng. Dir.-Peer Med--Lally, McFarland & Pantello Inc., New York, NY; *Int'l*, pg. 601
Smith, M., Mng. Dir.--CSP Pacific, Auckland, New Zealand; *Int'l*, pg. 495
Smith, Neil C., Mng. Dir.--Bell-IRH Industries Pty. Ltd., Lidcombe, Australia; *Int'l*, pg. 391
Smith, Norm, Mng. Dir.- Managed Care Initiatives--Klemtner Advertising Inc., New York, NY; *U.S. Public*, pg. 1422
Smith, Norman, Mng. Dir.--Instron International Ltd., Offenbach/Main, Germany; *U.S. Public*, pg. 883
Smith, Norman, Mng. Dir.--Amsler Otto Wolpert Werke GmbH, Ludwigshafen, Germany; *U.S. Public*, pg. 883
Smith, Norman L., V.P. & Mng. Dir.-Instron Ltd.--Instron Corporation, Canton, MA; *U.S. Public*, pg. 882
Smith, Paul, Mng. Dir.--Beazer Homes (Colchester) Limited, Witham, United Kingdom; *Int'l*, pg. 182
Smith, R.J., Dir.-Lights, North America--Eveready Battery Co., Saint Louis, MO; *U.S. Public*, pg. 1360
Smith, Robert R., Mng. Dir.--SpeedFam GmbH, Ingelfingen, Germany; *U.S. Public*, pg. 1498
Smith, Rosemary, Mng. Dir.--Mardev, London, United Kingdom; *Int'l*, pg. 1094
Smith, Tim, Mng. Dir.--Kitchens of Sara Lee-United Kingdom, Bridlington, United Kingdom; *U.S. Public*, pg. 1434
Smith, William, V.P. & Mng. Dir.--Crown Cork Coordination Center N.V., Deurne, Belgium; *U.S. Public*, pg. 464
Smits, Bert, Member-Bd. of Mngmt.--Wella Group, Darmstadt, Germany; *Int'l*, pg. 1489
Smits, J. C., Mng. Dir.--Baukje Beheer bv, Rijssen, Netherlands; *Int'l*, pg. 243
Snape, David W., Mng. Dir.--Home Automation Group Ltd., Chippenham, United Kingdom; *Int'l*, pg. 390
Snow, Mark, Mng. Dir.--River Crest Hospital, San Angelo, TX; *U.S. Public*, pg. 1697
Sobottka, Evelin, Mng. Dir.--Lausitzer Rundschau Verlag und Druckerei GmbH, Cottbus, Germany; *Int'l*, pg. 1478
Soderbom, Berndt, Mng. Dir.--Kreasindo Advertising & Marketing Consultants, Jakarta, Indonesia; *U.S. Private*, pg. 184
Soderstrom, Bjorn, Mng. Dir.--Enso (Holland) B.V., Amsterdam, Netherlands; *Int'l*, pg. 457
Soderstrom, Bjorn, Mng. Dir.--Fins Verkoopkantoor, Amsterdam, Netherlands; *Int'l*, pg. 458
Soegiharto, Soebagio, Mng. Dir.--P.T. Burgmann Indonesia, Bekasi, Indonesia; *Int'l*, pg. 233
Soennichsen, Torbin, Dir.-Sls. & Mktg.--Vestjyske Slagterier, Struer, Denmark; *Int'l*, pg. 1464
Soerjoesing, Georg D., Mng. Dir.--Ilaco Suriname NV, Paramaribo, Suriname; *Int'l*, pg. 606
Soga, Yoshiki, Mng. Dir. & Chief Exec. Officer-Intl. Banking Grp., the Americas--The Long-Term Credit Bank of Japan, Limited, Tokyo, Japan; *Int'l*, pg. 815
Sohm, Woo-Heon, Pres.--Ssangyong Investment Management Co., Ltd., Seoul, Korea; *Int'l*, pg. 1292

Sohm, Woo-Heun, Chief Fin. Officer--Ssangyong Investment & Securities Co., Ltd., Seoul, Korea; *Int'l*, pg. 1292
Solberg, Robert A., Mng. Dir.--Getty Petroleum Ireland, Ltd., White Plains, NY; *U.S. Public*, pg. 1583
Soltermann, Bernhard, Mng. Dir.--Comteco S.A., Bogota, Colombia; *Int'l*, pg. 1306
Solway, Anthony C.J., Mng. Dir.-Admin.--Henderson Administration Group PLC, London, United Kingdom; *Int'l*, pg. 609
Soma, Ramesh, Mng. Dir.-Australia--W.R. Grace Australia Ltd., Fawkner, Australia; *U.S. Public*, pg. 755
Somers, Nicholas, Mng. Dir.--Greenwich Street Capital Partners, Inc., New York, NY; *U.S. Private*, pg. 479
Somerville, Brent, Mng. Dir.--Datastream International (Hong Kong) Limited, Central, Hong Kong; *U.S. Public*, pg. 1326
Sommer, Sue, Mng. Dir.--IVTx, Maryland Heights, MO; *U.S. Public*, pg. 601
Soong, Ronnie, Mng. Dir.--Galco International Toys, N.V., Kowloon, Hong Kong; *U.S. Public*, pg. 698
Soous, C., Mng. Dir.--VCST Industrial Products N.V., Saint Truiden, Belgium; *Int'l*, pg. 1134
Soranson, Robyn, Deputy Mng. Dir.--Aetna International (Australia) Pty. Ltd., Chatswood, Australia; *U.S. Public*, pg. 27
Sorel, Bernard, Mng. Dir.--Bombardier Eurorail, Brussels, Belgium; *Int'l*, pg. 200
Sorensen, Marina Hother, Mng. Dir.--ISS University Hotel, Holte, Denmark; *Int'l*, pg. 656
Sorenson, S., Mng. Dir.--Nutricia Danmark A/S, Copenhagen, Denmark; *Int'l*, pg. 992
Soto, J., Mng. Dir.--Goodyear de Chile S.A.I.C., Santiago, Chile; *U.S. Public*, pg. 753
Sotoca, Jose Luis, Mng. Dir.--Janssen-Cilag, Madrid, Spain; *U.S. Public*, pg. 929
Soules, A.A., Mng. Dir.--Kohler de Mexico, S.A. de C.V., Mexico, Mexico; *U.S. Private*, pg. 631
Soussan, Andre, Mng. Dir.--Rhone-Poulenc Afrique Centrale, Douala, Cameroon; *Int'l*, pg. 1112
Southcott, Andrea, Mng. Dir.--Bryant, Fulton & Shee, Vancouver, Canada; *U.S. Private*, pg. 678
Southwood, Kevin, Mng. Dir.-Personnel & Fin. Services--Alliance & Leicester Building Society, London, United Kingdom; *Int'l*, pg. 57
Southworth, Roger, Mng. Dir.-Consumer--Johnson & Johnson Poland, Sp.z.o.o., Warsaw, Poland; *U.S. Public*, pg. 931
Spadaro, Romano, Mng. Dir.--ISS Hasco Management AG, Oberentfelden, Switzerland; *Int'l*, pg. 657
Spanholtz, Charlotte, Gen. Mgr.--DMB&B Beijing, Beijing, China; *U.S. Private*, pg. 303
Speakes, Jeffrey K., Mng. Dir.-Strategic Plng. & Risk Mngmt.--Countrywide Home Loans Inc., Pasadena, CA; *U.S. Public*, pg. 452
Spear, C.W., Jr., Mng. Dir.--Mediquip SDN. BHD., Kangar, Malaysia; *U.S. Public*, pg. 1648
Spector, Arthur R., Mng. Dir.--TL Ventures, Wayne, PA; *U.S. Public*, pg. 1424
Spector, Warren J., Exec. V.P. & Sr. Mng. Dir.--The Bear Stearns Companies Inc., New York, NY; *U.S. Public*, pg. 197
Speights, Debra, V.P. & Mng. Dir.-Burrell Pub. Rels.--Burrell Communications Group, Inc., Atlanta, GA; *U.S. Private*, pg. 188
Spence, Robin, Chief Exec. Officer--Oakley Young/4th Dimension, Whetstone, United Kingdom; *Int'l*, pg. 1482
Sperling, Scott M., Mng. Dir.--Thomas H. Lee Co., Boston, MA; *U.S. Private*, pg. 658
Sperry, Bill, Mng. Dir.--Costain South East Asia, Wan Chai, Hong Kong; *Int'l*, pg. 337
Sperry, Robert, Mng. Dir.--International Home Foods Inc., Parsippany, NJ; *U.S. Private*, pg. 526
Spicer, Roger, Mng. Dir.--Puritan Maid Ltd., Aylesbury, United Kingdom; *Int'l*, pg. 210
Spickschen, Thorlef, Mng. Dir.--Knoll AG, Ludwigshafen, Germany; *Int'l*, pg. 104
Spiegel, Franz, Mng. Dir.--Franz Spiegel Buch GmbH, Ulm, Germany; *Int'l*, pg. 1478
Spiers, David, Dr., Mng. Dir.--Dynacast International Limited, Alcester, United Kingdom; *Int'l*, pg. 299
Spinetti, Alberto, Mng. Dir.--Valmet-Rotomec S.p.A., San Giorgio, Italy; *Int'l*, pg. 1449
Spirig, Otto, Fin. Dir.--Advico Young & Rubicam AG, Zurich, Switzerland; *U.S. Private*, pg. 1198
Spong, Doug, Mng. Partner-Carmichael Lynch Spong Public Relations--Carmichael Lynch, Inc., Minneapolis, MN; *U.S. Private*, pg. 213
Spratt, Q., Mng. Dir.--Hepworth Building Products International, Stocksbridge, United Kingdom; *Int'l*, pg. 615
Springer, Joe, Mng. Dir.--Buckbee-Mears Europe GmbH, Mullheim-Baden, Germany; *U.S. Public*, pg. 162
Springer, Pat, Mng. Dir. & Acct. Supvr.--Western International Media Corporation, Pittsburgh, PA; *U.S. Private*, pg. 1167
Staaf, Ove, Mng. Dir.--Skandia Marine Insurance Company (UK) Ltd., London, United Kingdom; *Int'l*, pg. 1257
Stack, Ronald A., Mng. Dir.--Lehman Brothers, Inc., New York, NY; *U.S. Public*, pg. 987
Stahr, E., Mng. Dir.--NTO, Hannover, Germany; *Int'l*, pg. 1145
Stallmeyer, Jan, Exec. Dir.--Principal Health Care of Kansas City, Inc., Kansas City, MO; *U.S. Private*, pg. 885
Stalmans, F. R., Mng. Dir.--N.V. Red Band S.A., Turnhout, Belgium; *Int'l*, pg. 245
Stanbrook, Steven P., Exec. V.P. & Reg. Dir.-Consumer Products, Europe--S.C. Johnson & Son, Inc., Racine, WI; *U.S. Private*, pg. 592
Stancliffe, P.W., Mng. Dir. & Chief Exec. Officer--Australian National Industries Limited, Pyrmont, Australia; *Int'l*, pg. 100
Stansbury, Douglas A., V.P.-Retail Opers.--Byerly's Inc., Edina, MN; *U.S. Private*, pg. 680
Stansfeld, A., Mng. Dir.--Pilatus Britten-Norman Ltd., Bembridge, United Kingdom; *Int'l*, pg. 998
Stanway, W., Chm. & Grp. Mng. Dir.--London & Edinburgh Insurance Group Limited, Worthing, United Kingdom; *U.S. Public*, pg. 795
Stapor, Edward, Mng. Dir. & V.P.--Lally, McFarland & Pantello Advertising Canada Ltd., Montreal, Canada; *Int'l*, pg. 603
Starliper, Dennis A., Mng. Dir. & Treas.--Provident Bank of Maryland, Baltimore, MD; *U.S. Public*, pg. 1337
Stas, J., Mng. Dir.--Morgan Thermal Ceramics GmbH, Wiesbaden, Germany; *Int'l*, pg. 894
Stasiak, Ernestd, Mng. Dir.--Gestetner Colombia S.A., Bogota, Colombia; *Int'l*, pg. 1115
Stauffer, Heinrich, Mng. Dir.--Sulzer Sistemas e Instalaciones (Chile) S.A., Santiago, Chile; *Int'l*, pg. 1306
Staveley, Rick, Dir.-Strategic Plng.--Equitrac Corporation, Coral Gables, FL; *U.S. Public*, pg. 590
Steck, Joachim, Dr., Mng. Dir.--Metallbank GmbH, Frankfurt/Main, Germany; *Int'l*, pg. 861
Steckel, Peter, Div. Mgr.--Mitsui Foods, Inc., Western Div., Burlingame, CA; *Int'l*, pg. 879
Steed, J., Mng. Dir.--Riley Advertising (Bristol) Ltd., Bristol, United Kingdom; *Int'l*, pg. 1117
Steele, Graham, Mng. Dir.--Superdrug Stores PLC, Croydon, United Kingdom; *Int'l*, pg. 734
Steele, J.H., Mng. Dir.--Esso UK plc, London, United Kingdom; *U.S. Public*, pg. 602
Steele, Randall, Mng. Dir.--ISS Southern Management Company, Chattanooga, TN; *Int'l*, pg. 656
Steeskov, Poul, Mng. Dir.--Danisco Foods, Copenhagen, Denmark; *Int'l*, pg. 378
Steffan, Rob, Mng. Dir.--State Advertising Agency, Inc., Chicago, IL; *U.S. Public*, pg. 597
Steffensen, Mads, Mng. Dir.--Scan Care A/S, Copenhagen, Denmark; *Int'l*, pg. 656
Stein, Stan, Sr. V.P. & Mng. Dir.--DMB&B Public Relations, Troy, MI; *U.S. Private*, pg. 303
Steinbach, Minoslov, Exec. Dir.--Young & Rubicam Prague, Prague, Czech Republic; *U.S. Private*, pg. 1199
Steinbach, R., Mng. Dir.--Wm. H. Muller & Co. Bremen/Hamburg, Hamburg, Germany; *Int'l*, pg. 682
Steinherr, Alfred, Dir. Gen.-Economics--European Investment Bank, Luxembourg, Luxembourg; *Int'l*, pg. 465
Stephens, Lindsay, Mng. Dir.--Howard Pacific Ltd., Palmerston North, New Zealand; *Int'l*, pg. 1387
Stephens, Lindsay, Mng. Dir.--Howard Australia Pty. Ltd., Seven Hills, Australia; *Int'l*, pg. 1387
Stephens, Lindsay, Mng. Dir.--Howard Engineering Ltd., Palmerston North, New Zealand; *Int'l*, pg. 1387
Stephens, Lindsay, Mng. Dir.--Howard Rotavator Co., Palmerston North, New Zealand; *Int'l*, pg. 1387
Stephens, Lindsay, Mng. Dir.--Howard Machinery (Pty.) Ltd., Howick, South Africa; *Int'l*, pg. 1387
Stevenson, J. Alan, Mng. Dir.--Multi-Arc (U.K.) Ltd., Durham, United Kingdom; *Int'l*, pg. 1198
Stever, Bob, Mng. Dir.--ENV Services, Inc., King of Prussia, PA; *U.S. Public*, pg. 517
Steves, Susan S., Sr. V.P. & Mgr.-Securities Grp.--ABN-AMRO North America Inc., Chicago, Chicago, IL; *Int'l*, pg. 10
Stewart, Eric, Mng. Dir.--Kvaerner Computing & Consultancy Ltd., Gateshead, United Kingdom; *Int'l*, pg. 771
Stewart, Karl, Mng. Dir.-Comalco Smelting--Comalco Limited, Brisbane, Australia; *Int'l*, pg. 307
Steyn, C.G., Mng. Dir.--RMP Properties Ltd., Crown Mines, South Africa; *Int'l*, pg. 1081
Steyn, C.G., Chm. & Mng. Dir.--Barprop Ltd., Crown Mines, South Africa; *Int'l*, pg. 1081
Steyn, Peet, Mng. Dir.--Sasol Petroleum International (Pty) Ltd., Rosebank, South Africa; *Int'l*, pg. 1197
Stiller, Bernd, Mng. Dir.--Dexion GmbH, Laubach, Germany; *U.S. Public*, pg. 893
Stillings, Robert, V.P.-Opers., Sls., Mktg. & Dir.-Personnel--Presto Food Stores, Inc., Plant City, FL; *U.S. Private*, pg. 882
Stinson, Paul, Mng. Dir.--AES Silk Road, Richmond, United Kingdom; *U.S. Public*, pg. 5
Stirnimann, Kurt, Mng. Dir.--Charmilles Technologies SA, Meyrin, Switzerland; *Int'l*, pg. 489
Stjernvall, Henrik, Mng. Dir.--S.A. Enso N.V. Enso West, Antwerp, Belgium; *Int'l*, pg. 457
Stockdale, William, Chief Exec. Officer & Mng. Dir.--HSB Engineering Insurance Limited, London, United Kingdom; *U.S. Public*, pg. 795
Stockley, P., Mng. Dir.--Balzers Ltd., Milton Keynes, United Kingdom; *Int'l*, pg. 997
Stockman, David, Sr. Mng. Dir.--The Blackstone Group, New York, NY; *U.S. Private*, pg. 147
Stockmann, Doris, Mng. Dir.--Academic Bookstore, Helsinki, Finland; *Int'l*, pg. 1301
Stokol, John E., Mng. Dir.--Union Carbide Austria GmbH, Vienna, Austria; *U.S. Public*, pg. 1667
Stokol, John E., Mng. Dir.--Union Carbide Benelux NV, Antwerp, Belgium; *U.S. Public*, pg. 1667
Stokol, John E., Pres. & Mng. Dir.--Union Carbide (Europe) S.A., Meyrin, Switzerland; *U.S. Public*, pg. 1667
Stolker, G. H., Mng. Dir.--Konijn Baggertechniek BV, Hoorn, Netherlands; *Int'l*, pg. 607
Stoll, Kurt, Dr. I, Pres. & Mng. Dir.--Festo AG & Co., Esslingen am Neckar, Germany; *Int'l*, pg. 480
Stone, Andrew, Mng. Dir.--Credit Suisse First Boston, Inc., New York, NY; *Int'l*, pg. 345
Stone, Maryanne R., Mng. Dir.-SAP Consulting & Trng.--Intellicorp Inc., Mountain View, CA; *U.S. Public*, pg. 887
Storch, Wendy, Exec. V.P. & Mng. Dir.--Promotion House, San Francisco, CA; *U.S. Private*, pg. 1166
Storkaas, Frode, Mng. Dir.--ISS Darenas a.s., Oslo, Norway; *Int'l*, pg. 656
Storm, Colin, Mng. Dir.--Guinness Ireland (Holdings) Ltd., Dublin, Ireland; *Int'l*, pg. 412
Stoutjesdijk, P. G., Mng. Dir.--PURAC Group, Gorcum, Netherlands; *Int'l*, pg. 244
Stover, W.G., Jr., Dir.--Micron Europe Ltd., Bracknell, United Kingdom; *U.S. Public*, pg. 1105
Stover, W.G., Jr., Dir.--Micron Semiconductor Asia Pacific Pte. Ltd., Singapore, Singapore; *U.S. Public*, pg. 1105
Stoychev, Kancho, Mng. Dir.--Champions, Sofia, Bulgaria; *U.S. Private*, pg. 1199
Stoyell, Richard, V.P.--Rivas & Herrera C./Young & Rubicam, Quito, Ecuador; *U.S. Private*, pg. 1200
Stradling, Pap G., Pres. & Mng. Dir.--Coutts & Co Trust Holdings Limited, Nassau, Bahamas; *Int'l*, pg. 911
Strahm, Peter, Mng. Dir.--Novelair-Sifrag AG, Zurich, Switzerland; *Int'l*, pg. 1306
Strath, A., Mng. Dir.--Compugraphics International Limited, Glenrothes, United Kingdom; *Int'l*, pg. 802
Strathdee, S., Mng. Dir.-Intl. Div.--Tate & Lyle PLC, London, United Kingdom; *Int'l*, pg. 1356
Stratton, Doug, Exec. Dir.--Principal Health Care of Indiana, Inc., Indianapolis, IN; *U.S. Private*, pg. 885
Stratton, Tony, Chief Exec. Officer--CPM International, Thame, United Kingdom; *U.S. Public*, pg. 1225
Straub, Helmut, Mng. Dir.-Human Resources--Landis & Staefa AG, Zug, Switzerland; *Int'l*, pg. 800
Strauss, Jurgen, Mng. Dir.--Schweizerische Rentenanstalt, Munich, Germany; *Int'l*, pg. 1332
Street, Peter C.R., Mng. Dir.--Roe Lee Paper Chemicals Co. Ltd., Blackburn, United Kingdom; *Int'l*, pg. 1086
Streule, Roland, Mng. Dir.--Rado Uhren AG, Lengnau, Switzerland; *Int'l*, pg. 1160
Streule, Roland, Mng. Dir.--SMH (U.S.) Inc., Weehawken, NJ; *Int'l*, pg. 1161
Strey, Kurt, Mng. Dir.--Fishery Foods GmbH, Cuxhaven, Germany; *Int'l*, pg. 492
Stringfellow, R.J., Mng. Dir.--Southern Sun Hotel Holdings Limited, Sandton, South Africa; *Int'l*, pg. 1287
Stringfellow, R.S., Mng. Dir.--OK Bazaars (1929) Ltd., Germiston, South Africa; *Int'l*, pg. 1287
Strnad, Bostjan, Mng. Dir.--Votan Leo Burnett, Ljubljana, Slovenia; *U.S. Private*, pg. 186
Stroebel, Piet, Mng. Dir.--Sasol Two Div., Secunda, South Africa; *Int'l*, pg. 1197
Strom, Vesa Svart, Mng. Dir.--Berendsen Components OY, Vantaa, Finland; *Int'l*, pg. 1284
Stromberg, J.C., Mng. Dir.-Fin.--Bechtel Enterprises, Inc., San Francisco, CA; *U.S. Private*, pg. 128
Stuart, Douglas, Mng. Dir.--Spar Aerospace (U.K.) Limited, Hayes, United Kingdom; *Int'l*, pg. 1288
Stuben, Hans-Hinrich, Mng. Dir.-Nord Region--Dyckerhoff & Widmann AG, Munich, Germany; *Int'l*, pg. 423
Stuckalov, V. D., Mng. Dir.--AMT, Moscow, Russia; *Int'l*, pg. 954
Stuckey, Robert, Mng. Dir.--CarrAmerica Realty, Washington, DC; *U.S. Public*, pg. 308
Studener, Wolfgang, Mng. Dir.--Battenfeld Extrusionstechnik GmbH, Bad Oeynhausen, Germany; *Int'l*, pg. 825
Stump, Nick W., Mng. Dir. & Chief Exec.--M.I.M. Holdings Ltd., Brisbane, Australia; *Int'l*, pg. 827
Sturrock, Ian, Mng. Dir.--Willis Corroon Scotland Limited, Dundee, United Kingdom; *Int'l*, pg. 1503
Sturt, Trevor H., Mng. Dir.--Thermal Processing Group Ltd., Exhall, United Kingdom; *Int'l*, pg. 1338
Subphon, Siri, Mng. Dir.--Anju Jewelry Limited, Kowloon, Hong Kong; *U.S. Public*, pg. 1625
Suda, Nokio, Mng. Dir.--Nikko Bank (Deutschland) GmbH, Frankfurt/Main, Germany; *Int'l*, pg. 930
Suda, Shunichiro, Mng. Dir.--Sakata Seed Corporation, Yokohama, Japan; *Int'l*, pg. 1178
Sudiran, Lahuree bin, Mng. Dir.--W.R. Grace (Malaysia) Sdn. Bhd., Pahang, Malaysia; *U.S. Public*, pg. 756
Sueki, Otaro, Sr. Mng. Dir.-Information Systems--Japan Energy Corporation, Tokyo, Japan; *Int'l*, pg. 702
Sugimoto, Masaho, Exec. Mng. Dir.--Sanyo Electric Co., Ltd., Osaka, Japan; *Int'l*, pg. 1190
Sugiura, Toshiro, Mng. Dir.--Asahi Finance (U.K.) Ltd., London, United Kingdom; *Int'l*, pg. 83
Sugiyama, Takeshi, Sr. Mng. Dir.-Auditing, Personnel, Education & Health--Yasuda Mutual Life Insurance Co., Tokyo, Japan; *Int'l*, pg. 1519
Suhonen, Olli, Mng. Dir.--Nokia Switching Systems, Saint Petersburg, Russia; *Int'l*, pg. 954
Suijkerbuijik, D.P., Mng. Dir.--Nedlloyd Road Cargo Division, Dusseldorf, Germany; *Int'l*, pg. 1145
Suijkerbuijk, D.P., Mng. Dir.--Nedlloyd Road Cargo FTL, Moerdijk, Netherlands; *Int'l*, pg. 1145
Sullivan, Larry K., Mng. Dir.--PM Realty Advisors Inc., Newport Beach, CA; *U.S. Private*, pg. 831
Sullivan, Thomas C., Jr., Deputy Mng. Dir.--ESPAN Corporation, Singapore, Singapore; *U.S. Public*, pg. 1358
Sultan, Nader Hamad, Dep. Chm. & Mng. Dir.-Plng.--Kuwait Petroleum Corporation, Safat, Kuwait; *Int'l*, pg. 764
Sum, Y.C., Mng. Dir.--Amersham Far East Trading Limited, Sha Tin, Hong Kong; *Int'l*, pg. 993
Sumitomo, Yasuji, Mng. Dir.--Sumitomo Financial Futures (Singapore) pte. Ltd., Singapore, Singapore; *Int'l*, pg. 1310
Sundaran, S. K., Mng. Dir.--Glaxo Wellcome Singapore Pte. Ltd., Singapore, Singapore; *Int'l*, pg. 553
Sundararajan, U., Chm. Bd. & Mng. Dir.--Bharat Petroleum Corporation Ltd., Mumbai, India; *Int'l*, pg. 194
Sunderland, Trevor, V.P. & Mng. Dir.--BankAmerica Trust & Banking Corp. (Bahamas) Ltd., Nassau, Bahamas; *U.S. Public*, pg. 183
Sundstrom, Rolf, Mng. Dir.--Motala Hissar A.B., Motala, Sweden; *Int'l*, pg. 748
Sundvik, Carl, Mng. Dir.--S-E-Banken BoLan AB, Stockholm, Sweden; *Int'l*, pg. 1259
Sung, T.Y., Dr., Mng. Dir.--SangAm Communications Co., Ltd., Seoul, Korea; *U.S. Public*, pg. 765
Suplick, Michael, Mng. Dir.--Total Research Corporation, Minneapolis, MN; *U.S. Public*, pg. 1625
Surface, R. C., Mng. Dir.--Pearl Group Plc, Peterborough, United Kingdom; *Int'l*, pg. 100
Surin, Arthur A., Sr. V.P. & Mng. Dir.-NY Hilton--Hilton Hotels Div., Beverly Hills, CA; *U.S. Public*, pg. 829

Sutherland, Joe, Mng. Dir.--GN Nettest, Datacom Division, Markham, Canada; *Int'l*, pg. 537
Sutherland, T.F., Mng. Dir.--Trico Pty. Ltd., Springvale, Australia; *Int'l*, pg. 1397
Suto, Shinzo, Sr. Mng. Dir. & Sr. V.P.-Intl. Passenger Mktg. Div.--Japan Airlines Company, Ltd., Tokyo, Japan; *Int'l*, pg. 699
Suzuki, Gen, Mng. Dir.--NLI International Hong Kong Limited, Central, Hong Kong; *Int'l*, pg. 936
Suzuki, Hisashi, Mng. Dir.-Res. & Devel.--Sega Enterprises Ltd., Tokyo, Japan; *Int'l*, pg. 1218
Suzuki, K., Sr. Mng. Dir.--Esso Sekiyu Kabushiki Kaisha, Tokyo, Japan; *U.S. Public*, pg. 602
Suzuki, Tadahiro, Mng. Dir.-Internal Audit--Daiwa Securities Co. Ltd., Tokyo, Japan; *Int'l*, pg. 374
Suzuki, Tatsuro, Mng. Dir.--Tokai Financial Futures (Singapore) Pte. Ltd., Singapore, Singapore; *Int'l*, pg. 1391
Suzuki, Yoichiro, Mng. Dir.--National Mutual Funds Management (Japan) Limited, Tokyo, Japan; *Int'l*, pg. 909
Suzuki, Yukuo, Mng. Dir.-Plng. & Pur., Logistics & Pur., Fertilizer--UBE Industries Ltd., Tokyo, Japan; *Int'l*, pg. 1426
Suzumura, Koichi, Sr. Mng. Dir.--Nippon Yusen K.K., Tokyo, Japan; *Int'l*, pg. 941
Svantesson, Lennart, Mng. Dir.--Arthur D. Little, A.B., Goteborg, Sweden; *U.S. Private*, pg. 670
Svantesson, Lennart, Mng. Dir.--Arthur D. Little International, Inc., Copenhagen, Denmark; *U.S. Private*, pg. 671
Svantesson, Per, Mng. Dir.-Europe--Esab AB, Goteborg, Sweden; *Int'l*, pg. 281
Svendsen-Tune, Rene, Mng. Dir.--Nokia Telecommunications A/S, Tastrup, Denmark; *Int'l*, pg. 953
Svendsson, Sven, Mng. Dir.--Kvaerner Gotfab AB, Goteborg, Sweden; *Int'l*, pg. 767
Svensson, Ragnar, Mng. Dir.--Johnson & Johnson AB, Sollentuna, Sweden; *U.S. Public*, pg. 930
Swann, Phillip, Publr.--Commtek Communications, Corp., Vienna, VA; *U.S. Private*, pg. 258
Swartz, Ted, Sr. V.P. & Mng. Dir.-Bus.-to-Bus. Grp.--Grant/Jacoby, Inc., Chicago, IL; *U.S. Private*, pg. 470
Sweeney, Kevin, Mng. Dir.--Professional Auto Warehouse, Rochester, NY; *U.S. Public*, pg. 774
Swobe, Caryn, Mng. Dir.--R&R Advertising, Reno, NV; *U.S. Private*, pg. 902
Sy, Victor, Mng. Dir.--Shanghai McCormick Seasoning & Foodstuffs Company, Limited, Shanghai, China; *U.S. Public*, pg. 1067
Sychta, P., Mng. Dir.--Ascom Timeplex Ltd., Slough, United Kingdom; *Int'l*, pg. 87
Sydow, Hans, Mng. Dir.--Anderson & Lembke Inc., New York, NY; *U.S. Private*, pg. 72
Sylvan, Ulf, Mng. Dir. & Grp. Chief Exec. UK--Svenska Handelsbanken London, London, United Kingdom; *Int'l*, pg. 1327
Symes, Peter, Mng. Dir.--Yorkshire Guernsey, Saint Peter Port, United Kingdom; *Int'l*, pg. 1522
Syvanen, Veikko, Mng. Dir.--Hobby Hall, Helsinki, Finland; *Int'l*, pg. 1301
Szuchman, Mark, Mng. Dir.--MGR Sports, Wilton, CT; *U.S. Public*, pg. 1641
T'Joens, Frans, Mng. Dir.--Bekaert International Trade, Zwevegem, Belgium; *Int'l*, pg. 183
Tabak, Mark J., V.P.-Admin.--QVC, Inc., West Chester, PA; *U.S. Private*, pg. 897
Tabrett, Ian, Mng. Dir.--Reed Business Information Pty. Limited, Chatswood, Australia; *Int'l*, pg. 1094
Tachikawa, Naoki, Exec. Mng. Dir.--Ajinomoto Company Inc., Tokyo, Japan; *Int'l*, pg. 40
Tack, Johan, Mng. Dir.-Mktg.--Generale de Banque S.A., Brussels, Belgium; *Int'l*, pg. 546
Taglauer, H.J., Mgr.-Sls.--Groschopp & Co. GmbH EMW Elektromotoren-Feinbauwerk, Viersen, Germany; *Int'l*, pg. 559
Taguchi, Fumio, Mng. Dir.--Brother Office Equipment S.p.A., Milan, Italy; *Int'l*, pg. 230
Tahvanainen, Olli-Matti, Mng. Dir.--Metsa-Serla Tissue GmbH, Dusseldorf, Germany; *Int'l*, pg. 864
Tai, Hidenori, Mng. Dir. & Gen. Mgr.--Takugin Finance International Ltd., London, United Kingdom; *Int'l*, pg. 627
Taiana, Erich, Mng. Dir.--Sulzer Energy Consulting Inc., Winterthur, Switzerland; *Int'l*, pg. 1306
Taida, H., Mng. Dir.--Marubeni U.K. Plc., London, United Kingdom; *Int'l*, pg. 845
Tajiri, Akira, Area Dir.-China--Dentsu East Japan Inc., Tokyo, Japan; *Int'l*, pg. 393
Tajiri, Akira, Area Dir.--Area Headquarters-CHINA, Tokyo, Japan; *Int'l*, pg. 393
Takacs, L., Mng. Dir.--EGIS-Nutricia Kft, Budapest, Hungary; *Int'l*, pg. 991
Takagi, Kunio, Sr. Mng. Dir.-Credit, Loans & Fin.--Nippon Shinpan Co., Ltd., Tokyo, Japan; *Int'l*, pg. 939
Takahashi, Hiroyuki, Exec. Mng. Dir. & Gen. Mgr.-Personnel--Mitsui & Co., Ltd., Tokyo, Japan; *Int'l*, pg. 877
Takahashi, Kumiko, Sr. Mng. Dir.-Mktg. Svcs.--Asatsu Inc., Tokyo, Japan; *Int'l*, pg. 85
Takahashi, Kunio, Sr. Mng. Dir.--Mitsui Fudosan Co., Ltd., Tokyo, Japan; *Int'l*, pg. 882
Takahashi, N., Mng. Dir.--Ebara Engineering (Malaysia) Sdn. Bhd., Kuala Lumpur, Malaysia; *Int'l*, pg. 432
Takahashi, Tetsuro, Exec. Mng. Dir., Sr. Gen. Mgr.-Consumer Prods.--Kawasaki Heavy Industries, Ltd., Kobe, Japan; *Int'l*, pg. 725
Takahashi, Tsutomu, Sr. Mng. Dir.--Ebara Corporation, Tokyo, Japan; *Int'l*, pg. 431
Takakura, Hisashi, Pres. & Chief Oper. Officer--Clarins KK, Tokyo, Japan; *Int'l*, pg. 295
Takano, Morihisa, Mng. Dir. & Mgr.-Acctg.--Mitsubishi Chemical Corporation, Tokyo, Japan; *Int'l*, pg. 870
Takayama, Naoki, Mng. Dir.--Korea-Japan Finance Company Limted (KJF), Central, Hong Kong; *Int'l*, pg. 816
Takens, R.J., Mng. Dir.--Audisio Industrie Alumentari SRL, Fossano, Italy; *Int'l*, pg. 244
Takeuchi, Kiichiro, Exec. Mng. Dir.--Fujikura Ltd., Tokyo, Japan; *Int'l*, pg. 525
Takeuchi, M., Mng. Dir. & Gen. Mgr.--CM Human Services Co. Ltd., Kanagawa, Japan; *U.S. Public*, pg. 317
Takeyama, Hajime, Mng. Dir.--Nippon Express (Deutschland) GmbH, Monchengladbach, Germany; *Int'l*, pg. 934
Taki, Masatoshi, Mng. Dir.--Nippon Express Tours (Europe) Ltd., London, United Kingdom; *Int'l*, pg. 934
Takiguchi, Tadahiko, Mng. Dir.-Prod. Planning, Res. & Devel.--Mazda Motor Corporation, Hiroshima, Japan; *Int'l*, pg. 849
Takis, Avio, Mng. Dir.--Estravel, Tallinn, Estonia; *Int'l*, pg. 486
Tal-Shir, Amos, Chief Exec. Officer--Ariely Advertising, Tel Aviv, Israel; *U.S. Private*, pg. 678
Talagrand, Noel, Pres.-Facom & Mng. Dir.-Strafor facom--Groupe Strafor Facom, Morangis, France; *Int'l*, pg. 569
Talwar, Rana, Exec. Dir.-Corp. Banking (Africa, India, Pakistan & Middle East)--Standard Chartered Bank PLC, London, United Kingdom; *Int'l*, pg. 1294
Tamayo, Jesus, Mng. Dir.--Productos Asfalticos, S.A. (PROAS), Madrid, Spain; *Int'l*, pg. 323
Tan, Cheng T., Mng. Dir.--Sulzer Metco (Singapore) PTE Ltd., Singapore, Singapore; *Int'l*, pg. 1308
Tan, Jonathan, Mng. Dir.--Keystone Southeast Asia Pty. Ltd., Jurong, Singapore; *U.S. Public*, pg. 1650
Tan, K.B., Mng. Dir.--Bally Singapore (Pte) Ltd., Singapore, Singapore; *Int'l*, pg. 997
Tanabe, Makoto, Sr. Mng. Dir.-Corp. Planning--Nippon Shinpan Co., Ltd., Tokyo, Japan; *Int'l*, pg. 939
Tanaka, Akira, Sr. Mng. Dir.-Fin.--UBE Industries Ltd., Tokyo, Japan; *Int'l*, pg. 1426
Tanaka, Gen, Dir. & Gen. Mgr.-Seibu (Fukuoka) Main Office--Nihon Keizai Shimbun, Inc., Tokyo, Japan; *Int'l*, pg. 929
Tanaka, Yasuo, Sr. Mng. Dir.-Acct. Service & Promo.--Sogei Inc., Tokyo, Japan; *Int'l*, pg. 1277
Tanaka, Yoichi, Mng. Dir.--Kintetsu World Express (H.K.) Ltd., Kowloon, Hong Kong; *Int'l*, pg. 735
Tang, C.C., Mng. Dir.--Smith Corona (PTE) Ltd., Singapore, Singapore; *U.S. Private*, pg. 1007
Tang, Joe, Mng. Dir.--Solectron Technology Sdn. Bhd, Penang, Malaysia; *U.S. Public*, pg. 1483
Tani, Michio, Mng. Dir.--Fuji Capital Markets (HK) Limited, Central, Hong Kong; *Int'l*, pg. 521
Tani, Takao, Mng. Dir.-Prod. & Engrng.--Ajinomoto Company Inc., Tokyo, Japan; *Int'l*, pg. 40
Tanigawa, H., Mng. Dir.--Sharp-Roxy Sales (Singapore) Pte. Ltd., Singapore, Singapore; *Int'l*, pg. 1230
Taniguchi, Ichiro, Mng. Dir. & Gen. Mgr.-Electronics--Mitsubishi Electric Corporation, Tokyo, Japan; *Int'l*, pg. 872
Tanji, Tadao, Mng. Dir. & Gen. Mgr.-Audio-Visual--Mitsubishi Electric Corporation, Tokyo, Japan; *Int'l*, pg. 872
Tannion, K., Mng. Dir.--John Wyeth & Brother (N.Z.) Ltd., Auckland, New Zealand; *U.S. Public*, pg. 82
Tanoue, Katsuyasu, Mng. Dir.--Home Electronics Co., Ltd., Bangkok, Thailand; *Int'l*, pg. 1239
Tapernoux, Guy, Mng. Dir.--Bacardi-Martini Belgium, Brussels, Belgium; *U.S. Private*, pg. 109
Tarng, Karen, Mng. Dir./Partner--EURO RSCG Partnership, Taipei, Taiwan; *Int'l*, pg. 602
Tarnopol, Michael L., Vice Chm. & Sr. Mng. Dir.--The Bear Stearns Companies Inc., New York, NY; *U.S. Public*, pg. 197
Tashjian, Larry D., Mng. Dir.--Provident Investment Counsel, Inc., Pasadena, CA; *U.S. Public*, pg. 1674
Tatsula, Richard A., Mng. Dir.--Homestake Gold of Australia Limited, Perth, Australia; *U.S. Public*, pg. 833
Tatsutomi, Yasuo, Mng. Dir.-Quality , Cost Plng. & Domestic Mktg. & Sls.--Mazda Motor Corporation, Hiroshima, Japan; *Int'l*, pg. 849
Tavel, Mark K., Sr. Mng. Dir.--Rothschild Inc., New York, NY; *U.S. Private*, pg. 947
Tawarada, Tadashi, Mng. Dir.--Kemira-Ube Ltd., Tokyo, Japan; *Int'l*, pg. 728
Taylor, Albert G., Mng. Dir.-Mexico--Moore Corporation Limited, Toronto, Canada; *Int'l*, pg. 888
Taylor, Albert G., Mng. Dir.--Moore Business Forms de Mexico S.A. de C.V., Tlalnepantla, Mexico; *Int'l*, pg. 889
Taylor, Frances, Exec. V.P. & Mng. Dir.--BA Asia Ltd., Hong Kong, Hong Kong; *U.S. Public*, pg. 182
Taylor, Frank, Exec. Dir.-Production Control--GM Powertrain Group, Pontiac, MI; *U.S. Public*, pg. 719
Taylor, Graham, Exec. Pub. Dir.--EMAP Images, London, United Kingdom; *Int'l*, pg. 451
Taylor, John, Mng. Dir.--Trebor Bassett Ltd., Maple Cross, United Kingdom; *Int'l*, pg. 248
Taylor, John, Mng. Dir.--Ultra Electronics Command & Control Systems, High Wycombe, United Kingdom; *Int'l*, pg. 1431
Taylor, John, Reg. Mng. Dir.--Willis Corroon South Limited, Cheltenham, United Kingdom; *Int'l*, pg. 1503
Taylor, John L., Mng. Dir.--Manganese Metal Co. Pty. Ltd., Johannesburg, South Africa; *Int'l*, pg. 392
Taylor, Louis R., Mng. Dir.-Community Banking--Provident Bank of Maryland, Baltimore, MD; *U.S. Public*, pg. 1337
Taylor, Michael F., Mng. Dir.-MIS--Dunham's Athleisure Corporation, Waterford, MI; *U.S. Private*, pg. 346
Taylor, P.N., Mng. Dir.--Ascom Telecommunications Ltd., Cardiff, United Kingdom; *Int'l*, pg. 87
Taylor, Peter J., Mng. Dir.--Opella Ltd., Hereford, United Kingdom; *Int'l*, pg. 391
Taylor, R., Mng. Dir.--St. Katharine by the Tower Limited, London, United Kingdom; *Int'l*, pg. 1358
Tazaki, Kaziaki, Chm. & Mng. Dir.--Brother U.K., Ltd., Manchester, United Kingdom; *Int'l*, pg. 230
Tazaki, Masamitsu, Mng. Dir.--Sakata Seed do Brasil Ltda., Sao Paulo, Brazil; *Int'l*, pg. 1178
Tchida, Diana, Exec. Dir.--Principal Health Care of Texas, Inc., Corpus Christi, TX; *U.S. Private*, pg. 886
Tearprasert, Tada, Mng. Dir.--The CPAC Roof Tile Co., Ltd., Bangkok, Thailand; *Int'l*, pg. 1237
Techasupatkul, Pramote, Mng. Dir.--Siam Yamato Steel Co., Ltd., Bangkok, Thailand; *Int'l*, pg. 1238
Teck, Kwek Chye, Mng. Dir.--ORIX Leasing Singapore Limited, Singapore, Singapore; *Int'l*, pg. 1010
Tedbury, Steve, Mng. Dir.-Strategic Plng.--Tate & Lyle PLC, London, United Kingdom; *Int'l*, pg. 1356
Tegeder, Volker, Mng. Dir.--Livingston Services GmbH, Darmstadt, Germany; *Int'l*, pg. 212
Temme, Wilmar, Co-Mng. Dir.--Blefa GmbH, Kreuztal, Germany; *Int'l*, pg. 508
Templar, B.S., Mng. Dir.--Transfleet Services Limited, Coventry, United Kingdom; *Int'l*, pg. 911
Templeman, Miles, Mng. Dir.-Beer Co.--Whitbread PLC, London, United Kingdom; *Int'l*, pg. 1498
Templeton, Ken, Mng. Dir.--ERI Laboratories, Fair Lawn, NJ; *U.S. Private*, pg. 574
Teng, Michael, Mng. Dir.--The West Company Singapore Pty. Ltd., Singapore, Singapore; *U.S. Public*, pg. 1756
Teran, Jose Alberto, Mng. Dir.--Teran TBWA Publicidad, Mexico, Mexico; *U.S. Private*, pg. 1063
Terashima, Toru, Mng. Dir.--The Industrial Bank of Japan (Luxembourg) S.A., Luxembourg, Luxembourg; *Int'l*, pg. 676
Terrazone, Claude, Dir.--Avions Div., Paris, France; *Int'l*, pg. 29
Tessier, Jacques, Dir.-Acctg.--Promodes SA, Mondeville, France; *Int'l*, pg. 1071
Tesstore, Roberto, Mng. Dir.--Fiat Auto SpA, Turin, Italy; *Int'l*, pg. 480
Testa, M. David, Vice Chm. & Mng. Dir.--T. Rowe Price Associates, Inc., Baltimore, MD; *U.S. Public*, pg. 1324
Testa, Roberto, Mng. Dir.--The West Company Argentina S.A., Buenos Aires, Argentina; *U.S. Public*, pg. 1755
Tetlow, Mary, Mng. Dir.--TBWA Chiat/Day St. Louis, Saint Louis, MO; *U.S. Private*, pg. 1062
Tezuka, Hiroyuki, Mng. Dir.--Siam Toyota Manufacturing Co., Ltd., Bangkok, Thailand; *Int'l*, pg. 1239
Thakarar, Gail, Mng. Dir.-Human Resources--Countrywide Funding Corporation, Pasadena, CA; *U.S. Public*, pg. 453
Thalmaier, Gerald, Mng. Dir.--ISS Servisystem GesmbH, Graz, Austria; *Int'l*, pg. 657
Thamarak, Chavalit, Mng. Dir.--Aggregate Supply Co., Ltd., Bangkok, Thailand; *Int'l*, pg. 1237
Thanh, Dinh Ba, Mgr.--Vietnam Advertising Co., Ho Chi Minh City, Vietnam; *Int'l*, pg. 602
Thater, John, Mng. Dir.--EMAP Media, London, United Kingdom; *Int'l*, pg. 451
Thater, John, Mng. Dir.--EMAP Media Ltd., London, United Kingdom; *Int'l*, pg. 451
Thean Seng, Douglas Russell Ooi, Mng. Dir.--Kim Eng Securities (Private) Limited, Singapore, Singapore; *Int'l*, pg. 733
Theobald, Thomas B., V.P. & Mng. Dir.--Mortgage Guaranty Insurance Corporation, Milwaukee, WI; *U.S. Public*, pg. 1026
Thierfelder, Gottfried, Dir.-Personnel, Social Affairs & Environmental Protection--Eckes AG, Nieder-Olm, Germany; *Int'l*, pg. 432
Tholet, Clem, Exec. Dir.--Young & Rubicam Tholet, Cape Town, South Africa; *U.S. Private*, pg. 1198
Thoma, Helmut, Dr., Mng. Dir.--RTL Television, Cologne, Germany; *Int'l*, pg. 561
Thomas, David, Mng. Dir.--ISS U.K. Ltd., Hounslow, United Kingdom; *Int'l*, pg. 657
Thomas, E.G., Mng. Dir.--Trico Ltd., Pontypool, United Kingdom; *Int'l*, pg. 1397
Thomas, Geryk, Mng. Dir.--Weatherford Norge, A/S, Stavanger, Norway; *U.S. Public*, pg. 1750
Thomas, Jeffrey S., Chief Investment Officer, Exec. V.P., Mng. Dir.--Pell, Rudman & Company, Boston, MA; *U.S. Public*, pg. 1673
Thomas, Peter G., Pres. & Mng. Dir.--Holden's Engine Products Overseas Corporation, Melbourne, Australia; *U.S. Public*, pg. 723
Thomas, Phyllis G., Mng. Dir.--NWQ Investment Managaement Company, Los Angeles, CA; *U.S. Public*, pg. 1673
Thompson, Alan, Mng. Dir.-Hong Kong & China--DMB&B/Hong Kong, Quarry Bay, Hong Kong; *U.S. Private*, pg. 303
Thompson, David A., Joint Grp. Mng. Dir. & Dir.-Fin.--The Boots Company PLC, Nottingham, United Kingdom; *Int'l*, pg. 202
Thompson, Fred, Mng. Partner--Kerry Kelly Thompson, Greenwich, CT; *U.S. Private*, pg. 174
Thompson, Harry, Mng. Dir.--Swiss Army Brands, Inc., Shelton, CT; *U.S. Public*, pg. 1544
Thompson, John F., Mng. Dir.--Merisel Latin America, Miami, FL; *U.S. Public*, pg. 1096
Thompson, Rob, Mng. Dir.--Valtek/Australia, Scoresby, Australia; *U.S. Public*, pg. 659
Thonus, Bernard, Mng. Dir.--Creep, Boulogne, France; *U.S. Private*, pg. 1199
Thornborough, Wayne D., Mng. Dir.--UBS Asset Management (New York) Inc., New York, NY; *Int'l*, pg. 1440
Thorogood, L.C, Mng. Dir.--MB Kenya Limited, Nairobi, Kenya; *Int'l*, pg. 267
Thorpe, John, Mng. Dir.--Ademco MicroTech Limited, Glasgow, United Kingdom; *U.S. Public*, pg. 1307
Thorpe, Peter, Mng. Dir.--Volclay Limited, Wallasey, United Kingdom; *U.S. Public*, pg. 64
Thousand, Gary, Dir.-Telecommunications--Aaron Rents, Inc., Atlanta, GA; *U.S. Public*, pg. 12
Thue, Ernst, Mng. Dir.--Esselte A/S, Oslo, Norway; *Int'l*, pg. 460
Thunborg, Bo, Mng. Dir.--AB Ferrolegeringar, Stockholm, Sweden; *U.S. Private*, pg. 735

Tiensuu, Lief, Mng. Dir.--KOPO AB, Haparanda, Sweden; *Int'l*, pg. 1353
Tiget, M., Mng. Dir.--Balzers S.A., Meudon, France; *Int'l*, pg. 997
Tigler, Bjorn, Mng. Dir.--S-E-Banken Fastigheter AB, Stockholm, Sweden; *Int'l*, pg. 1259
Tilby, Peter, Reg. Dir.-Mktg.--DHL International (Hong Kong) Ltd., Wan Chai, Hong Kong; *U.S. Private*, pg. 302
Tillmanns, Hanns Joachim, Co-Mng. Dir.--Krupp Hoesch Dienstleistigungen GmbH, Essen, Germany; *Int'l*, pg. 512
Timm, Simon, Mng. Dir.--EMAP Finance & Freight Ltd., London, United Kingdom; *Int'l*, pg. 451
Timms, T., Mng. Dir.--Target Technology Ltd., Ashford, United Kingdom; *Int'l*, pg. 853
Ting, Agnes, Deputy Mng. Dir.--Review Publishing Company Ltd., Hong Kong, Hong Kong; *U.S. Public*, pg. 525
Ting, Lee S., V.P. & Mng. Dir.-Geographic Opers.--Hewlett-Packard Company, Palo Alto, CA; *U.S. Public*, pg. 813
Tiong, Choo Boon, Mng. Dir.--International Factors Leasing Pte Ltd., Singapore, Singapore; *Int'l*, pg. 684
Tipping, Keith, Mng. Dir.--Komatsu UK, Ltd., Chester, United Kingdom; *Int'l*, pg. 744
Tisdall, Mike, Chief Oper. Officer & Mng. Dir.--Sasol Chemicals Pacific Limited, Wan Chai, Hong Kong; *Int'l*, pg. 1196
Tiusanen, Bertil, Deputy Mng. Dir.-Fin. Mngmt. & Control--KF/Konsum Coop Group, Stockholm, Sweden; *Int'l*, pg. 718
Tjornemark, Bent, Mng. Dir.--Danisco A/S, Copenhagen, Denmark; *Int'l*, pg. 378
Tjornemark, Bent, Mng. Dir.--Danisco Finance Plc, Dublin, Ireland; *Int'l*, pg. 378
Tkachuk, Bordan, Mng. Dir.--Viglen Limited, Alperton, United Kingdom; *Int'l*, pg. 1468
Todd, Mark, Chief Oper. Officer & Mng. Dir.--Raleigh Industries Ltd., Nottingham, United Kingdom; *Int'l*, pg. 394
Toengi, Ferdi, Mng. Dir.-Mktg. & European Sls.--AGIE AG (Fur Industrielle Elektronik), Lausanne, Switzerland; *Int'l*, pg. 488
Tohyama, Tsutomu, Mng. Dir.--Brother Industries Technology (M) Sdn. Bhd., Johor Baharu, Malaysia; *Int'l*, *pg. 229*
Tokiwa, Toshiji, Mng. Dir. & Gen. Mgr.--Dai-Ichi Kangyo Bank, Ltd.-New York, New York, NY; *Int'l*, pg. 359
Tolensky, Steven M., Pres.-Men's & Intl. Divisions--Jockey International, Inc., Kenosha, WI; *U.S. Private*, pg. 588
Toma, Yoshiyuki, Sr. Mng. Dir.-Overseas Sls.--Makita Corporation, Anjo, Japan; *Int'l*, pg. 831
Tomio, Hideharu, Mng. Dir.-Sls.--Kawasho Corporation, Tokyo, Japan; *Int'l*, pg. 726
Tomiyama, N., Sr. Mng. Dir. & Sec.--General Sekiyu K.K., Tokyo, Japan; *U.S. Public*, pg. 602
Tomiyama, Shoichi, Mng. Dir.--Marubeni Corporation, Osaka, Japan; *Int'l*, pg. 844
Tomkinson, P., Mng. Dir.--Durham Chemicals Ltd., Chester le Street, United Kingdom; *Int'l*, pg. 598
Tommasini, Bernard, Mng. Dir. & V.P.--Kelly Services, Paris, France; *U.S. Public*, pg. 949
Tomomori, Hiroshi, Mng. Dir. & Chief Oper. Officer--Nissho Iwai Deutschland GmbH, Hamburg, Germany; *Int'l*, pg. 948
Tomotake, Michisada, Chief Exec. & Sr. Mng. Dir-Intl. Div.--Wako Securities Co., Ltd., Tokyo, Japan; *Int'l*, pg. 1485
Tomsett, John, V.P. & Mng. Dir.--Shakespeare Company United Kingdom, Redditch, United Kingdom; *U.S. Public*, pg. 940
Toner, Mark, Mng. Dir.--Williams Worldwide, New York, NY; *U.S. Private*, pg. 1179
Tordoir, P.P., Mng. Dir.--VNU Business Information Europe, Haarlem, Netherlands; *Int'l*, pg. 1445
Torneus, Jan-Erik, Mng. Dir.--Svenska Blount AB, Varberg, Sweden; *U.S. Public*, pg. 239
Torok, R., Mng. Dir.--NRG Latin America S.A., Montevideo, Uruguay; *Int'l*, pg. 1116
Torok, R., Mng. Dir.--NRG South America S.A., Montevideo, Uruguay; *Int'l*, pg. 1116
Torok, Robert, Mng. Dir.--Gestetner Regional Services Inc. (USA), Coral Gables, FL; *Int'l*, pg. 1115
Torres, Agnel, Mng. Dir.--Esselte S.A., Terrassa, Spain; *Int'l*, *pg. 461*
Torres, Manuel, Mng. Dir.-Latin America--Bujias Champion de Mexico, S.A. de C.V., Mexico, Mexico; *U.S. Public*, pg. 444
Tosa, Masanobu, Mng. Dir. & Gen. Mgr.-Automotive--Mitsubishi Electric Corporation, Tokyo, Japan; *Int'l*, pg. 872
Touhill, Tom, Exec. V.P. & Mng. Dir.--CheckMark Communications, Saint Louis, MO; *U.S. Private*, pg. 231
Towers, J., Mng. Dir.--Riley Advertising (Norwich) Ltd., Norwich, United Kingdom; *Int'l*, pg. 1117
Towers, J., Mng. Dir.--Riley Advertising (Nottingham) Ltd., Nottingham, United Kingdom; *Int'l*, pg. 1117
Townsend, Michael, Chief Fin. Officer & Dir.-Fin.--Rolls-Royce plc, London, United Kingdom; *Int'l*, pg. 1126
Toyooka, Hirotaka, Mng. Dir.--Bingo Express Co., Ltd., Hiroshima, Japan; *Int'l*, pg. 934
Toyooka, Isao, Mng. Dir.--Ebara Corporation, Tokyo, Japan; *Int'l*, pg. 431
Traboulsi, Jean, Mng. Dir. & Pub. Rels. Coord.--AMA Leo Burnett, Giza, Egypt; *U.S. Private*, pg. 184
Tracey, Doug, Sr. V.P., Mng. Dir.-On Cue & Natl. Distr.--On Cue, Inc., Minnetonka, MN; *U.S. Public*, pg. 1142
Tracy, Laurie, Dir.-Wholesale Admin. Sls. & Mktg.--DFI/Inflight, Inc., Ridgefield, CT; *Int'l*, pg. 103
Trad, Raja, Reg. Mng. Dir.--Radius Leo Burnett, Dubai, United Arab Emirates; *U.S. Private*, pg. 186
Trager, Oliver, Mng. Editor-Editorials On File--Facts on File News Services, New York, NY; *U.S. Public*, pg. 1327
Traill, Lindsay, Mng. Dir.--H.B. Fuller Co. (N.Z.) Ltd., Auckland, New Zealand; *U.S. Public*, pg. 687
Trankjaer, Ove, Mng. Dir.--Nilfisk-Gerni A/S, Randers, Denmark; *Int'l*, pg. 932
Travis, Brian T., Mng. Dir.--Donald Brown (Brownall) Ltd., Manchester, United Kingdom; *Int'l*, pg. 390
Treutler, Kurt, Mng. Dir.--Sulzer Chemtech GmbH, Butzbach, Germany; *Int'l*, pg. 1308
Triaire, Didier, Mng. Dir.--Check Technology France S.A., Lisses, France; *U.S. Public*, pg. 342
Tribe, G.B. H., Mng. Dir.--NatWest International Trust Corporation (Jersey) Limited, Saint Helier, United Kingdom; *Int'l*, pg. 911
Tribouillier, Jean-Pierre, Co-Mgr.--EURO RSCG Novation, Marseilles, France; *Int'l*, pg. 601
Tribouillier, Jean-Pierre, Co-Mgr.--EURO RSCG Novation, Villeneuve-Loubet, France; *Int'l*, pg. 601
Trigg, Greg, Chief Fin. Officer & Co-Mng. Dir.--International Correspondence Schools (Australasia) Limited, Lane Cove, Australia; *U.S. Public*, pg. 784
Trillo, Jesus, Mng. Dir.-Legal--Iberdrola, S.A., Bilbao, Spain; *Int'l*, pg. 657
Trilsus, N., Dr., Mng. Dir.--GKN Componenti Firenze SpA, Campi Bisenzio, Italy; *Int'l*, pg. 536
Trinchitella, Chuck, Exec. Dir.--Principal Health Care of the Carolinas, Inc., Charlotte, NC; *U.S. Private*, pg. 885
Trinkl, Hans, Mng. Dir.-Human Resources--Julius Meinl AG, Vienna, Austria; *Int'l*, pg. 856
Trippacher, Kurt, Mng. Dir.-Global Procurement--Landis & Staefa AG, Zug, Switzerland; *Int'l*, pg. 800
Tromp, J. T., Mng. Dir.--R. & H. Systems B.V., Rotterdam, Netherlands; *Int'l*, pg. 680
Troussel, Jean-Pierre, Mng. Dir.--Swiss Life (Belgium), Brussels, Belgium; *Int'l*, pg. 1332
Troutaud, Michel, Mng. Dir.--Allied Domecq Spirits & Wine (UK) Ltd., Horsham, United Kingdom; *Int'l*, pg. 63
Trumbull, George r., Chief Exec. Officer & Mng. Dir.--Australian Mutual Provident, Sydney, Australia; *Int'l*, pg. 100
Truscott, John, Mng. Dir.--TBWA Chiat/Day Los Angeles, Venice, CA; *U.S. Private*, pg. 1062
Trusler, Colin, Mng. Dir.-United Kingdom--Shandwick International Plc, London, United Kingdom; *Int'l*, pg. 1226
Tsuboi, Takayori, Mng. Dir. & Gen. Mgr.-Petrochemical--Mitsubishi Chemical Corporation, Tokyo, Japan; *Int'l*, pg. 870
Tsuchiya, Takashi, Mng. Dir.--Tosoh Corporation, Tokyo, Japan; *Int'l*, pg. 1407
Tsuchiya, Yoshihiro, Mng. Dir.-Admin. Div., Corp. Plng. & Acctg.--Nippo Corporation, Tokyo, Japan; *Int'l*, pg. 932
Tsuda, Akitake, Mng. Dir.--NEC Electronics (Europe) GmbH, Dusseldorf, Germany; *Int'l*, pg. 901
Tsuji, Keiichi, Mng. Dir. & Chief Exec.--IBJ Australia Bank Limited, Sydney, Australia; *Int'l*, pg. 676
Tsuji, Masatsugu, Sr. Mng. Dir.-Admin.--Asatsu Inc., Tokyo, Japan; *Int'l*, pg. 85
Tsukada, Yoshihiro, Mng. Dir.--Nippon Express (H.K.) Co., Ltd., Kowloon, Hong Kong; *Int'l*, pg. 934
Tsutsumi, Seiji, Mng. Dir.--Sakura Finance Asia Ltd., Hong Kong, Hong Kong; *Int'l*, pg. 1180
Tsutsumi, Seiji, Mng. Dir.--Sakura Bank Hong Kong Trustee Limited, Hong Kong, Hong Kong; *Int'l*, pg. 1180
Tsuura, Takashi, Sr. Mng. Dir.-Iron & Steel Grp.--Sumitomo Corporation, Tokyo, Japan; *Int'l*, pg. 1312
Tudball, Mike, Exec. Dir.--Reed Elsevier (Singapore) PTE Limited, Singapore, Singapore; *Int'l*, pg. 1095
Tunon, Ricardo Diaz, Mng. Dir.--Rhone-Poulenc Colombia Ltda., Bogota, Colombia; *Int'l*, pg. 1112
Turett, Nancy, Mng. Dir.-Edelman Healthcare Communications--Edelman Worldwide, Inc., New York, NY; *U.S. Private*, pg. 362
Turner, Cliff, Mng. Dir.--Kontite, U.K., Ltd., Bolton, United Kingdom; *U.S. Public*, pg. 780
Turner, David, Mng. Dir.--Barclays Property Holdings, London, United Kingdom; *Int'l*, pg. 165
Turner, Linda S., Dir.--Micron Semiconductor Asia Pacific Pte. Ltd., Singapore, Singapore; *U.S. Public*, pg. 1105
Turner, Linda S., Dir.--Micron Semiconductor Asia Pacific Inc., Taipei, Taiwan; *U.S. Public*, pg. 1105
Turner, M.W., Mng. Dir.--Lombard NatWest Commercial Services Limited, Feltham, United Kingdom; *Int'l*, pg. 910
Turner, Roger G., Mng. Dir.--United Gas Co. Ltd., London, United Kingdom; *U.S. Public*, pg. 1701
Tweitmann, Bruce, Dir.-Fin.--Fenton Hill American Limited, Valley Stream, NY; *Int'l*, pg. 103
Twomley, D.E., Mng. Dir.--Specialty Foods Investment Inl., Worthington, OH; *U.S. Public*, pg. 1780
Tychsen, Ulf, Mng. Dir.--The West Company Holding, G.m.b.H, Eschweiler, Germany; *U.S. Public*, pg. 1756
Tynell, Markku, Mng. Dir.--Amerpap Oy, Helsinki, Finland; *Int'l*, pg. 863
U'Pritchard, David C., Mng. Dir.-Res. & Devel.--SmithKline Beecham plc, Brentford, United Kingdom; *Int'l*, pg. 1264
Ubaid, M.A., Chm. Bd. & Mng. Dir.--Central Coalfields Limited, Ranchi, India; *Int'l*, pg. 298
Uchiyama, Akio, Mng. Dir.-Creative & Mktg.--Nippo Corporation, Tokyo, Japan; *Int'l*, pg. 932
Uchiyama, Kensuke, Mng. Dir.-Res. & Devel.--Japan Tobacco Inc., Tokyo, Japan; *Int'l*, pg. 703
Ueda, Koichi, Mng. Dir.-Customer Service, Office Systems Plng. & Admn.--Yasuda Mutual Life Insurance Co., Tokyo, Japan; *Int'l*, pg. 1519
Uehara, Naoyoshi, Sr. Mng. Dir. & Gen. Mgr.-Kansai Branch--Mitsubishi Corporation, Tokyo, Japan; *Int'l*, pg. 871
Uehlinger, Hans-Martin, Mng. Dir.-Corp. Communications--Landis & Staefa AG, Zug, Switzerland; *Int'l*, pg. 800
Uhrich, Marie, Mng. Dir.-Corp. Commun.--Piper Jaffray Companies, Inc., Minneapolis, MN; *U.S. Public*, pg. 1300
Ulrich, Jake, Mng. Dir.--Accord Energy Ltd., Slough, United Kingdom; *Int'l*, pg. 279
Umeda, Masatoshi, Mng. Dir. & Gen. Mgr.-Corp. Acctg. Dept.--Mitsubishi Electric Corporation, Tokyo, Japan; *Int'l*, pg. 872
Umemoto, Kaoru, Mng. Dir.--Central Japan Railway Company-Tokyo Head Office, Tokyo, Japan; *Int'l*, pg. 279
Underwood, Elaine, Mng. Dir.--J.A. Sharwood & Company Limited, Egham, United Kingdom; *Int'l*, pg. 1396
Underwood, Elaine, Mng. Dir.--RHM Grocery Ltd., Egham, United Kingdom; *Int'l*, pg. 1396
Ungerer, Scott B., Mng. Dir.--EnerTech Capital Partners, Wayne, PA; *U.S. Public*, pg. 1424
Upson, Dick, Exec. V.P. & Acct. Mng. Dir.--Young & Rubicam New York, New York, NY; *U.S. Private*, pg. 1198
Upson, I.W., Mng. Dir.--Esso UK plc, London, United Kingdom; *U.S. Public*, pg. 602
Urbank, Ernst, Mng. Dir.-Internal Auditing--Julius Meinl AG, Vienna, Austria; *Int'l*, pg. 856
Uresch, Andreas, Mng. Dir.--Leo Burnett Budapest KFT, Budapest, Hungary; *U.S. Private*, pg. 185
Urita, Ken, Mng. Dir.-Endine Co Ltd Japan--Enidine Incorporated, Orchard Park, NY; *U.S. Private*, pg. 377
Urquidi, J.C., Mng. Dir.--Laboratorios Wyeth-Whitehall Ltd., Sao Paulo, Brazil; *U.S. Public*, pg. 81
Ursin-Smith, Kjell, Mng. Dir.--Kvaerner a.s London Office, London, United Kingdom; *Int'l*, pg. 771
Uurala-Corbion, Leena, Mng. Dir.--Norvista, Paris, France; *Int'l*, pg. 486
Uusimae, Pekka, Mng. Dir.--Nokia (Malaysia) Sdn. Bhd., Kuala Lumpur, Malaysia; *Int'l*, pg. 953
Vahlmann, Wilfried, Mng. Dir.--BASF S.A., Sao Bernardo do Campo, Brazil; *Int'l*, pg. 107
Vaidya, Rajiv, Mng. Dir.--Triton Communications, New Delhi, India; *Int'l*, pg. 118
Valencia, Fernando, Mng. Dir.--Valencia y Asociados Publicidad, Quito, Ecuador; *U.S. Private*, pg. 186
Valenzuela, Pablo, Mng. Dir.--Frederick & Valenzuela/TBWA, Santiago, Chile; *U.S. Private*, pg. 1062
Valerie, Sylvain, Mng. Dir.--Goodyear, Rueil-Malmaison, France; *U.S. Public*, pg. 753
Valkonen, Harri, Mng. Dir.--Merita Bank Ltd., Beijing Representative Office, Beijing, China; *Int'l*, pg. 859
Valla, Francois, Mng. Dir.--Credit Lyonnais, Chicago, IL; *Int'l*, pg. 344
Valles, Renee, Exec. Dir.-Conferences--Barnett International/PAREXEL, Media, PA; *U.S. Public*, pg. 1258
Vallinkoski, Ilkka, Mng. Dir.--Enso Trading Handelsgesellschaft mbH, Vienna, Austria; *Int'l*, pg. 457
Van Agtmaal, J.G., Mng. Dir.--Balzers Process Systems Eurpoe N.V., Maarssen, Netherlands; *Int'l*, pg. 997
Van Agtmaal, J.G., Mng. Dir.--S.A. Balzers N.V., Zaventem, Belgium; *Int'l*, pg. 998
Van Allen, Barbara, Mng. Dir.-Corp. Communications--Cushman & Wakefield, Inc., New York, NY; *Int'l*, pg. 873
Van Brusselt, Roger, Mng. Dir.--Bundy Belgium SA, Wandre, Belgium; *Int'l*, pg. 1341
van Cann, J.H., Mng. Dir.--bv Aldipress, De Meern, Netherlands; *Int'l*, pg. 1445
van Dalen, M.J., Mng. Dir.--Wolters Kluwer Educational Activities, Groningen, Netherlands; *Int'l*, pg. 1513
van Dam, B., Mng. Dir.--Van Leeuwen Buizen Europa BV, Zwijndrecht, Netherlands; *Int'l*, pg. 1449
van Damme, Frank, Mng. Dir.--MoDo Papier Belgium, Kallo, Belgium; *Int'l*, pg. 886
Van den Bergh, Hugo, Mng. Dir.--Monti NV, Lier, Belgium; *Int'l*, pg. 462
van den Bosch, Jos, Mng. Dir.--Multicom TBWA Advertising B.V., Eindhoven, Netherlands; *U.S. Private*, pg. 1062
van den Brink, J., Mng. Dir.--Ballast Nedam Grondstoffen B.V., Zaandam, Netherlands; *Int'l*, pg. 133
Van den Eynde, Alain, Mng. Dir. & Legal Dir.--Garbarski EURO RSCG, Brussels, Belgium; *Int'l*, pg. 603
van der Hee, H.C., Mng. Dir.--Ascom Zarli BV, Zoeterwoude-Rijndijk, Netherlands; *Int'l*, pg. 87
van der Helm, Frits C., Mng. Dir.--Schilperoort Beheer, B.V., Rotterdam, Netherlands; *Int'l*, pg. 1306
van der Hoek, J., Mng. Dir.--Nedlloyd Road Cargo International, Dusseldorf, Germany; *Int'l*, pg. 1145
van der Lande, M.R.B., Mng. Dir.--Lakatex B.V., Goor, Netherlands; *Int'l*, pg. 198
Van der Motten, Michael, Mng. Dir.--Battenfeld Belgium N.V., Aarschot, Belgium; *Int'l*, pg. 825
Van der Poll, Frank, Mng. Dir.-N. Europe--Gandalf Technologies Inc., Nepean, Canada; *Int'l*, pg. 540
van der Talen, A., Mng. Dir.--ABI Imtech NV, Tielrode, Belgium; *Int'l*, pg. 681
van der Walle, L., Mng. Dir.-Continental Europe--United Biscuits (Holdings) Plc, West Drayton, United Kingdom; *Int'l*, pg. 1442
van der Weijden, Job J.J., Mng. Dir.--Sulzer Keuls B.V., Heerlen, Netherlands; *Int'l*, pg. 1306
van der Westhuizen, Jannie, Mng. Dir.--Sasol Mining (Pty.) Ltd., Secunda, South Africa; *Int'l*, pg. 1197
van der Wyck, H.C., Vice Chm. & Mng. Dir.--SBC Warburg Group plc, London, United Kingdom; *Int'l*, pg. 1330
van Dijk, H., Mng. Dir.--Getinge-D.S.E. BV, Antwerp, Belgium; *Int'l*, pg. 551
van Dijk, H., Mng. Dir.--Getinge-D.S.E. BV, Rosmalen, Netherlands; *Int'l*, pg. 551
van Dord, Hans, Mng. Dir.--Heidemij Advies BV, Arnhem, Netherlands; *Int'l*, pg. 607
van Eynde, Paul, Mng. Dir.--Brooktree Central Europe, Munich, Germany; *U.S. Public*, pg. 1398
Van Ginckel, Leo, Mng. Dir.--Janssen/Cilag B.V., Tilburg, Netherlands; *U.S. Public*, pg. 929
Van Ginkel, Leo, Mng. Dir.--Taxandria Pharmaceutica B.V., Tilburg, Netherlands; *U.S. Public*, pg. 932
Van Gogh, Ger W.P., Mng. Dir.--Amersham Nederland BV, Das' Hertogenbosch, Netherlands; *Int'l*, pg. 993
van Hedel, T.J.M., Mng. Dir.--Nutricia Nederland B.V., Zoetermeer, Netherlands; *Int'l*, pg. 991
Van Herk, A., Mng. Dir.--Tiffany & Co. Overseas Finance B.V., Amsterdam, Netherlands; *U.S. Public*, pg. 1609
Van Holle, Paul, Gen. Mgr.--Sikel N.V., Genk, Belgium; *Int'l*, *pg. 79*
van Humalda Eysinga, F.W.B., Mng. Dir.--Wolters Kluwer Professional Training, Nyon, Switzerland; *Int'l*, pg. 1514

van Kempen, C.H., Mng. Dir.--Wolters Kluwer Australia, Sydney, Australia; *Int'l*, pg. 1513
van Leeuwen, Marianne, Mng. Dir.--Toeristiek BV, Pufmerend, Netherlands; *Int'l*, pg. 1099
van Lieshout, J.J.M., Mng. Dir.--Comfort Financieringen Nederland BV, Houten, Netherlands; *Int'l*, pg. 911
van Loon, G.A., Mng. Dir.--N.V. Antradex Nutricia Americas, Willemstad, Netherlands Antilles; *Int'l*, pg. 991
van Melsen, Henk, Mng. Dir.--Robinson Nugent (Europe) B.V., Eindhoven, Netherlands; *U.S. Public*, pg. 1395
Van Mierln, Jan, Mng. Dir.--McCain Foods Belgium N.V. (Belgium), Turnhout, Belgium; *Int'l*, pg. 850
Van Nes, Irving, Mng. Dir.--Mead Holdings B.V., Rotterdam, Netherlands; *U.S. Public*, pg. 1076
Van Ness, Irvin, Mng. Dir.--Mead Packboard B.V., Rotterdam, Netherlands; *U.S. Public*, pg. 1076
van Prooijen, W., Mng. Dir.--Honig Foods-B.V., Koog aan de Zaan, Netherlands; *Int'l*, pg. 244
Van Raamt, Helbert, Mng. Dir.-Europe--Nellcor Puritan Bennett Incorporated, Pleasanton, CA; *U.S. Public*, pg. 1039
van Riet, F.W., Mng. Dir.--Neddrill Nederland B.V., Rotterdam, Netherlands; *Int'l*, pg. 1144
Van Schooten, Antoine, Mng. Dir.--Bregal, Bremer Galvanislerungs GmbH, Bremen, Germany; *Int'l*, pg. 79
Van Steen Kiste, P., Mng. Dir.--N.V. Acotech S.A., Zwevegem, Belgium; *Int'l*, pg. 183
van Stek, Hans, Mng. Dir.--BMC Software B.V., Nieuwegein, Netherlands; *U.S. Public*, pg. 162
van Stuijvenberg, Pieter A., Mng. Dir.--BMB Management Consulting for Development BV, Arnhem, Netherlands; *Int'l*, pg. 606
van Tongeren, H., Mng. Dir.--Ballast Nedam Engineering B.V., Amstelveen, Netherlands; *Int'l*, pg. 133
van Tuil, Ton, Mng. Dir.--Kimball Systems BV, Terborg, Netherlands; *Int'l*, pg. 461
van Uitert, H.G., Mng. Dir.--Ballast Nedam Grond en Wegen Specialiteiten B.V., Leerdam, Netherlands; *Int'l*, pg. 133
van Uitert, H.G., Mng. Dir.--Ballast Nedam Petrol Stations, Rosmalen, Netherlands; *Int'l*, pg. 133
van Wel, P.W., Mng. Dir.--Wolters Kluwer U.K., Kingston upon Thames, United Kingdom; *Int'l*, pg. 1514
van Zutphen, Rik S.F., Mng. Dir.--Shandwick Van de Meeberg PR, Hague, Netherlands; *Int'l*, pg. 1227
Van Zyl, E.W., Deputy Chief Exec.--Delta S.A. (Pty.) Ltd., Sandown, South Africa; *Int'l*, pg. 392
van't Hoff, R., Mng. Dir.--Amici, Houten, Netherlands; *Int'l*, pg. 750
van't Zelfde, W.C., Mng. Dir.--Van Leeuwen Stainless, Beesd, Netherlands; *Int'l*, pg. 1449
Vandaele, Herman, Mng. Dir.--Bekaert Coordinatiecentrum, Kortrijk, Belgium; *Int'l*, pg. 183
Vander Wertt, Jim, Dir.-Ag Equip.--Vermeer Manufacturing Company, Pella, IA; *U.S. Private*, pg. 1137
VanderPoll, Frank, Mng. Dir.--Gandalf Nederland B.V., Hoofddorp, Netherlands; *Int'l*, pg. 540
Vanghelder, Marc, Gen. Mgr.--EURO RSCG Est, Strasbourg, France; *Int'l*, pg. 600
Vanghelder, Marc, Gen. Mgr.--EURO RSCG Opinions, Issy-les-Moulineaux, France; *Int'l*, pg. 601
Vanghelder, Marc, Gen. Mgr.--EURO RSCG Est, Mulhouse, France; *Int'l*, pg. 601
vanGorp, H.A., Mng. Dir.--Logistic Services Division, Rotterdam, Netherlands; *Int'l*, pg. 1144
Varis, Erkki, Mng. Dir.--Oy Metsa-Botnia AB, Espoo, Finland; *Int'l*, pg. 863
Varlet, Jean-Francois, Mng. Dir.--BNP Public Limited Co. (London), London, United Kingdom; *Int'l*, pg. 164
Varma, S.P., Chm. Bd. & Mng. Dir.--Western Coalfields Limited, Nagpur, India; *Int'l*, pg. 299
Vatanen, Leo, Mng. Dir.--Prospectus Ltd., Helsinki, Finland; *Int'l*, pg. 859
Vatanen, Matti, Mng. Dir.--Kesko Export Ltd., Helsinki, Finland; *Int'l*, pg. 732
Vaughan, D.M., Mng. Dir.--Moygashel Ltd., Dungannon, United Kingdom; *Int'l*, pg. 798
Vdcoff, George J., Mng. Dir.--Ferrolegeringar AG, Dubendorf, Switzerland; *U.S. Private*, pg. 735
Vedo, Rene, Mng. Dir.--ISS Data A/S, Copenhagen, Denmark; *Int'l*, pg. 656
Vedo, Rene, Mng. Dir.--ISS Tele Response, Copenhagen, Denmark; *Int'l*, pg. 656
Vehara, Norio, Mng. Dir.--MIM Industries, Inc., Miamisburg, OH; *Int'l*, pg. 229
Vehmas, Jaakko-Pekka, Mng. Dir.--Finnish Rich Coffee Ltd., Vantaa, Finland; *Int'l*, pg. 732
Veilledent, Louis, Mng. Dir.--Eurafrican Bank (Tanzania) Ltd., Dar es Salaam, Tanzania; *Int'l*, pg. 548
Venier, Gianmarco, Chm. Bd. & Mng. Dir.--Caboto International S.A., Lugano, Switzerland; *Int'l*, pg. 138
Ventosa, Antonio S., Deputy Mng. Dir.--Hemisphere-Leo Burnett, Inc., Manila, Philippines; *U.S. Private*, pg. 184
Verberg, G.H.B., Mng. Dir.--N.V. Nederlandse Gasunie, Groningen, Netherlands; *U.S. Public*, pg. 602
Verbosh, Robert R., Gen. Dir.-Pantera--The JPM Company, Lewisburg, PA; *U.S. Public*, pg. 919
Verbosh, Robert R., Mng. Dir.--Electronica Pantera, S.A. de C.V., Zapopan, Mexico; *U.S. Public*, pg. 919
Verbrugghe, Willy L., V.P. & Mng. Dir.-Europe--Brink's, Inc., Darien, CT; *U.S. Public*, pg. 1305
Verdecia, Belia, V.P.-Human Resources & Bus. Admin. Dir.--The Bravo Group, New York, NY; *U.S. Private*, pg. 1197
Vere, Stuart, Mng. Dir.--Priory Hospitals Group, London, United Kingdom; *U.S. Public*, pg. 1716
Verga, Nicoletta, Mng. Dir. & Media Dir.--Gariboldi Parisi Verga/Interad, Milan, Italy; *U.S. Private*, pg. 678
Verheul, Peet W.B., Mng. Dir.--IMd Micon BV, Barneveld, Netherlands; *Int'l*, pg. 607
Verhey, J., Mng. Dir.--Ascom EBS Elektronische Bank Systeme GmbH, Frickenhausen, Germany; *Int'l*, pg. 86
Verklin, David, Exec. V.P. & Mng. Dir.--Hal Riney & Partners, Inc., San Francisco, CA; *U.S. Private*, pg. 931
Verkroost, Fredrik C., Dr., Mng. Dir.-Corp. Devel.--Landis & Staefa AG, Zug, Switzerland; *Int'l*, pg. 800
Vermille, Marc, Mng. Dir.--Banque Indosuez-South Africa, Johannesburg, South Africa; *Int'l*, pg. 314
Vernizzi, Alberto, Mng. Dir.--Bipiemme-Gestione Polizze di Assicurazione S.p.A., Milan, Italy; *Int'l*, pg. 137
Verver, R.W., Mng. Dir.--Verosol Nederland B.V., Enschede, Netherlands; *Int'l*, pg. 198
Vesala, H., Mng. Dir.--Hellermann Finland, Vantaa, Finland; *Int'l*, pg. 209
Vesterinen, Eero, Mng. Dir.--K-linkki Oy, Helsinki, Finland; *Int'l*, pg. 732
Vick, G. Etheridge, Mng. Dir.--CCA International, Inc., Nashville, TN; *U.S. Public*, pg. 451
Vick, G. Ethridge, III, V.P. & Mng. Dir.-Intl. Opers.--Corrections Corporation of America, Nashville, TN; *U.S. Public*, pg. 450
Vidal, Christian, Mng. Dir.--Dumez Guyane, Kourou, French Guiana; *Int'l*, pg. 823
Vidal, M., Mng. Dir.--Alcantara, Lisbon, Portugal; *Int'l*, pg. 1357
Vidalenche, Gerard, Mng. Dir.--Investir Publications, Paris, France; *Int'l*, pg. 780
Videler, Fre, Mng. Dir.--Bovil, Maastricht, Netherlands; *Int'l*, pg. 117
Vigild, Peter, Mng. Dir.--Hydap S.A., Herblay, France; *Int'l*, pg. 1285
Vijayan, Uday, Exec. V.P.-Bangalore Branch--MAA Communications Bozell, Bangalore, India; *U.S. Public*, pg. 1642
Villa, A., Vice Chm. & Mng. Dir.--AGIP (Suisse) S.A., Lausanne, Switzerland; *Int'l*, pg. 428
Villa, E., Mng. Dir.--Saunier Duval Italia Srl, Milan, Italy; *Int'l*, pg. 615
Vilsmeier, Gerhart, Mng. Dir.--Heraeus Quarzglas GmbH, Hanau, Germany; *Int'l*, pg. 616
Virley, Peter, Mng. Dir.--Scherer DDS Ltd., Swindon, United Kingdom; *U.S. Public*, pg. 1438
Viseu, Guy, Mng. Dir.--Bertrand Faure Equipamentos para Automoveis SA, San Joao da Madeira, Portugal; *Int'l*, pg. 193
Visscher, Frans, Mng. Dir.--Elsevier Science (The Netherlands), Amsterdam, Netherlands; *Int'l*, pg. 1099
Visscher, Frans, Mng. Dir.--Elsevier Science Limited, Kidlington, United Kingdom; *Int'l*, pg. 1100
Visser, A.G., Mng. Dir.--De Geillustreerde Pers/MC, Amsterdam, Netherlands; *Int'l*, pg. 1445
Visser, A.G., Mng. Dir.--De Geillustreerde Pers bv, Amsterdam, Netherlands; *Int'l*, pg. 1445
Visser, Y., Mng. Dir.--Aannemingsbedrijf Van Oudbroekhuizen B.V., Nieuwegin, Nieuwegein, Netherlands; *Int'l*, pg. 681
Viviani, Massimo, Mng. Dir.--EMAP Publishing srl, Milan, Italy; *Int'l*, pg. 451
Vizcaino, Carlos, Pres. & Mng. Dir.--Young & Rubicam, S.A. de C.V., Mexico, Mexico; *U.S. Private*, pg. 1200
Vogel, Manfred, Mng. Dir.--SKF Gleitlager GmbH, Puttlingen, Germany; *Int'l*, pg. 1158
Vogel, R.B., Mng. Dir.--Hoogovens Steel Strip Mill Products, Ijmuiden, Netherlands; *Int'l*, pg. 754
Vogelezang, Eef, Mng. Dir.--Northprint B.V., Meppel, Netherlands; *Int'l*, pg. 1100
Vogels, Paul, Mng. Dir.--Gesellschaft fuer Markt- und Absatzforschung mbH, Ludwigsburg, Germany; *Int'l*, pg. 1514
Vogt, Gunter, Mng. Dir.--Kammer Ventile GmbH, Essen, Germany; *U.S. Public*, pg. 659
Volland, Hansjorg, Mng. Dir.--Volland Telemetry GmbH, Shaftlach, Germany; *Int'l*, pg. 209
Volpi, V., Mng. Dir.--Swiss Bank Corporation, Tokyo, Japan; *Int'l*, pg. 1330
von Broembsen, Tim, Mng. Dir.--Von Broembsen Marson Leo Burnett/Harare, Harare, Zimbabwe; *U.S. Private*, pg. 186
von Fieandt, Henrik, Mng. Dir.--Industrial Bank of Finland Ltd., Helsinki, Finland; *Int'l*, pg. 859
von Hymmen, Dirk, Mng. Dir.--Reemtsma International GmbH - Russia, Moscow, Russia; *Int'l*, pg. 1101
von Koskull, Karin, Mng. Dir.-Institutional Sls.--Academic Bookstore, Helsinki, Finland; *Int'l*, pg. 1301
von Pentz, H.D., Dr., Chief Exec. Officer & Mng. Dir.--Hoechst Australia Ltd., Melbourne, Australia; *Int'l*, pg. 626
von Poser, Hilmar, Dr., Mng. Dir.--AVE Gesellschaft fur Horfunkbeteiligungen mbH, Hannover, Germany; *Int'l*, pg. 1478
von Sivers, Peter, Mng. Dir.--Skandia Investment Management Ltd., London, United Kingdom; *Int'l*, pg. 1258
von Troil, Eric, Mng. Dir.--OY Willis Faber AB, Helsinki, Finland; *Int'l*, pg. 1510
von Zech, Louis Graf, Mng. Dir.-Private Banking--BHF-BANK AG, Frankfurt, Germany; *Int'l*, pg. 119
von zur Muhlen, Bernt, Mng. Dir.--104.6 RTL, Berlin, Germany; *Int'l*, pg. 561
Voss, Dr. Gerd, Chief Exec. Officer & Mng. Dir.--Pfleiderer Industrie GmbH Wirus-Werke Guetersloh, Gutersloh, Germany; *Int'l*, pg. 1047
Voss, Gary, Chm. Bd. & Mng. Dir.--Lever Brothers West Indies Ltd., Champs Fleurs, Trinidad & Tobago; *Int'l*, pg. 1437
Vrba, John, Sr. V.P. & Mng. Dir.--Western International Media Corporation, Newport Beach, CA; *U.S. Private*, pg. 1167
Vreezen, William Jan, Mng. Dir.--Etos bv, Zaandam, Netherlands; *Int'l*, pg. 749
Vriens, J.A., Mng. Dir.--Exploitatiemaatschappij Transportbeton B.V., Diemen, Netherlands; *Int'l*, pg. 134
Vuoria, H., Mng. Dir.--Nutricia Fennica Oy, Turku, Finland; *Int'l*, pg. 992
Vyner, R.T., Deputy Chm. & Joint Mng. Dir.--J. Sainsbury plc, London, United Kingdom; *Int'l*, pg. 1169
Waddington, Martyn, Mng. Dir.--Moog Norden AB, Askim, Sweden; *U.S. Public*, pg. 1128
Wade, Rod, Mng. Dir.--Talisman (Asia) Ltd., Jakarta, Indonesia; *Int'l*, pg. 1352
Wagemans, A.T.J., Mng. Dir.--Montair Andersen B.V., Sevenum, Netherlands; *U.S. Public*, pg. 462
Wagner, Dieter, Mng. Dir.--MMG Division, Goslar, Germany; *U.S. Public*, pg. 1227
Wagner, Dieter, Dr., Mng. Dir.--BASF Argentina S.A., Buenos Aires, Argentina; *Int'l*, pg. 105
Wahlin, Olof, Pres. & Mng. Dir.--Foga System International AB, Vastra Frolunda, Sweden; *Int'l*, pg. 496
Wahrn, Mikael, Mng. Dir. & Gen. Mgr.--Merita Merchant Bank Singapore Ltd., Singapore, Singapore; *Int'l*, pg. 859
Wain, K.S., Mng. Dir.--Herr Voss Ltd., Derby, United Kingdom; *U.S. Private*, pg. 962
Waitz, Richard, Mng. Dir.--Ford Motor Norge A/S, Kolbotn, Norway; *U.S. Public*, pg. 666
Wakelin, A., Mng. Dir.--Valor Ltd., Birmingham, United Kingdom; *Int'l*, pg. 925
Wakeman, Martyn, Mng. Dir.--Sermatech (U.K.) Limited, Ripley, United Kingdom; *U.S. Public*, pg. 1570
Waldhof, Jens, Mng. Dir.--Rhone-Poulenc Rorer GmbH, Cologne, Germany; *Int'l*, pg. 1113
Walker, Doug, Mng. Dir.--Beazer Homes (Stockport) Limited, Stockport, United Kingdom; *Int'l*, pg. 182
Walker, Geoff, Mng. Dir.--Milk Products Holdings (Middle East) EC, Manama, Bahrain; *Int'l*, pg. 923
Walker, J.H.W., Mng. Dir.-European Sugar Div.--Tate & Lyle PLC, London, United Kingdom; *Int'l*, pg. 1356
Walker, J.H.W., Mng. Dir.--Tate & Lyle Sugars, London, United Kingdom; *Int'l*, pg. 1356
Wall, Chris, Chief Fin. Officer & Mng. Dir.--Vicon Industries (U.K.) Ltd., Fareham, United Kingdom; *U.S. Public*, pg. 1719
Wallace, John, Mng. Dir.--Conran Octopus Limited, London, United Kingdom; *Int'l*, pg. 1093
Waller, Dennis A., V.P. & Mng. Dir.--Mortgage Guaranty Insurance Corporation, Milwaukee, WI; *U.S. Public*, pg. 1026
Walley, W. John, V.P. & Mng. Dir.-Global Retail--S.C. Johnson & Son, Inc., Racine, WI; *U.S. Private*, pg. 592
Wallot, George, Mng. Dir.--Electronica Condor De Mexico, S.A., Cuauhtemoc, Mexico; *U.S. Public*, pg. 1419
Walsh, Matt, Deputy Grp. Mng. Dir. & Mgr.-Mktg.--Avonmore Waterford Group plc, Killkenny, Ireland; *Int'l*, pg. 102
Wanner, Paul, Mng. Dir.--SLM Immobilien AG, Winterthur, Switzerland; *Int'l*, pg. 1305
Wanner, Paul, Mng. Dir.--Sulzer Immobilien AG, Winterthur, Switzerland; *Int'l*, pg. 1306
Waraich, Riaz, Mng. Dir.--Old World Industries, Inc., Northbrook, IL; *U.S. Private*, pg. 814
Ward, Andrew, Acting Mng. Dir.--ANZ Banking Group (New Zealand) Ltd., Wellington, New Zealand; *Int'l*, pg. 98
Wareham, Peter, Mng. Dir.--Frontel Communications Services, London, United Kingdom; *U.S. Public*, pg. 684
Warland, P.G., Mng. Dir.--British European Associated Publishers Ltd., London, United Kingdom; *Int'l*, pg. 1445
Warmington, Richard C., Mng. Dir.-Asia Pacific--Hewlett-Packard Company, Palo Alto, CA; *U.S. Public*, pg. 813
Warner, Greg, Mng. Dir.--A. Schulman, Inc., Hockessin, DE; *U.S. Public*, pg. 1441
Warnick, Miles, Mng. DIr.--Chesswood Produce Ltd., Thakeham, United Kingdom; *Int'l*, pg. 1396
Warrelmann, Veiko, Mgr.-Opers.--Woodward-Clyde International, Chemnitz, Germany; *U.S. Public*, pg. 1658
Warren, Delfin L., Mng. Dir.--P.T. Darya-Varia Laboratoria, Jakarta, Indonesia; *Int'l*, pg. 487
Wascher, Uwe S., Sr. Mng. Dir.-G.E. Plastics/Europe--G.E. Plastics, Pittsfield, MA; *U.S. Public*, pg. 710
Wasem, Robert, Mng. Dir.--F. Heusser AG, Zurich, Switzerland; *Int'l*, pg. 1306
Wastell, Ernie, Mng. Dir.--Coats Cucirini S.p.A., Milan, Italy; *Int'l*, pg. 300
Watanabe, Akira, Mng. Dir.-Yokohama Area Sls.--Japan Tobacco Inc., Tokyo, Japan; *Int'l*, pg. 703
Watanabe, Hideo, Mng. Dir. & Mgr.-Corp. Plng.--Mitsubishi Chemical Corporation, Tokyo, Japan; *Int'l*, pg. 870
Watanabe, Kuino, Mng. Dir.--Nippon Express (Singapore) Pte., Ltd., Singapore, Singapore; *Int'l*, pg. 934
Watanabe, Satoru, Sr. Mng. Dir.-Overseas Sls.--Makita Corporation, Anjo, Japan; *Int'l*, pg. 831
Waterhouse, Rod, Mng. Dir.--Ilco Unican Australia (Pty.) Ltd., Willoughby, Australia; *Int'l*, pg. 1432
Waterlow, A.J., Asst. Mng. Dir.--Kodak Limited, Hemel Hempstead, United Kingdom; *U.S. Public*, pg. 553
Watson, Bob, Mng. Dir.--Iggesund Paperboard (Workington) Ltd., Workington, United Kingdom; *Int'l*, pg. 886
Watson, D., Reg. Mng. Dir.--Ballast Wiltshier Plc - North East Region, Stockton on Tees, United Kingdom; *Int'l*, pg. 135
Watson, D.J., Reg. Mng. Dir.--Ballast Wiltshier Plc - North East Region, Gateshead, United Kingdom; *Int'l*, pg. 135
Watson, David, Mng. Dir.--Donnelly Mirrors, Limited, Naas, Ireland; *U.S. Public*, pg. 519
Watson, John, Mng. Dir.--Daniel Industries Ltd., Falkirk, United Kingdom; *U.S. Public*, pg. 483
Watson, John C., Dir.-European Investments--Wolseley Plc., Droitwich, United Kingdom; *Int'l*, pg. 1511
Watts, Robert G., Mng. Dir.--Swiss Re Australia Ltd., Melbourne, Australia; *Int'l*, pg. 1333
Wayman, Reva, Sr. V.P. & Mng. Dir.-Pub. Rels.--Harrison & Star, Inc., New York, NY; *U.S. Private*, pg. 506
Weaver, C. Giles H., Mng. Dir.--Murray Johnstone Limited, Glasgow, United Kingdom; *U.S. Public*, pg. 1674
Webb, Cheryl L., V.P. & Mng. Dir.--Mortgage Guaranty Insurance Corporation, Milwaukee, WI; *U.S. Public*, pg. 1026
Webb, Jon, Mng. Dir.--NEXIS UK, London, United Kingdom; *Int'l*, pg. 1096
Webb, Marci, Mng. Dir.-H.R.--BeautiControl Cosmetics, Inc., Carrollton, TX; *U.S. Public*, pg. 198
Webb, Mike, Mng. Dir.--DMR Group Limited, West Drayton, United Kingdom; *Int'l*, pg. 528
Webb, R. Brian, Mng. Dir.-Res.--Aetna Inc., Hartford, CT; *U.S. Public*, pg. 26

Webels, H., Mng. Dir.--GKN Informatik GmbH, Rosrath, Germany; *Int'l*, pg. 536
Weber-Krebs, Fridolin, Dir. Gen.-Lending Opers.--European Investment Bank, Luxembourg, Luxembourg; *Int'l*, pg. 465
Weber, Helene, Mng. Dir.--Bally (Schweiz) S.A., Zurich, Switzerland; *Int'l*, pg. 996
Weber, Vin, Mng. Partner--Clark & Weinstock, Washington, DC; *U.S. Public*, pg. 1223
Webster, Michael, Mng. Dir.--D.W. Thorpe-Australia, Melbourne, Australia; *Int'l*, pg. 1095
Weck, M.J.F., Mng. Dir.--Ballast Nedam Telecom Infrastructures, Amstelveen, Netherlands; *Int'l*, pg. 133
Weibler, Klaus P., Mng. Dir.-Gentex GmbH--Gentex Corporation, Zeeland, MI; *U.S. Public*, pg. 731
Weibler, Klaus P., Mng. Dir.--Gentex GmbH, Neckarsulm, Germany; *U.S. Public*, pg. 732
Weiglein, Franz W., Mng. Dir.-Tailored--Lands' End, Inc., Dodgeville, WI; *U.S. Public*, pg. 977
Weinberger, Gerald, Mng. Dir.--A. Schulman GmbH, Kerpen, Germany; *U.S. Public*, pg. 1441
Weinberger, Gerald M., Mng. Dir.-Germany--A. Schulman, Inc., Akron, OH; *U.S. Public*, pg. 1441
Weinryb, Gideon, Mng. Dir.--Aladdin Industries, Palaiseau, France; *U.S. Private*, pg. 31
Weinstein, Jeffrey A., Pres. & Mng. Dir.--Ekco Group, Inc., Nashua, NH; *U.S. Public*, pg. 566
Weinstein, Jeffrey A., Pres. & Mng. Dir.--Ekco International, Inc., Nashua, NH; *U.S. Public*, pg. 566
Weinstock, Davis, Mng. Partner--Clark & Weinstock, New York, NY; *U.S. Public*, pg. 1223
Weir, Donald, Dr., Mng. Dir.-Corp. Tech. Strategy--Landis & Staefa AG, Zug, Switzerland; *Int'l*, pg. 800
Weir, Kevin, Co-Mng. Dir. & Exec. V.P.--Fort Pitt Acquisitions, Inc., Coraopolis, PA; *U.S. Private*, pg. 419
Weisfeld, Brian, Mng. Dir.-Imax Theatres & Commun.--Imax Corporation, Mississauga, Canada; *Int'l*, pg. 661
Weisser, Freddy, Mng. Dir.--TBWA/GGK, Zurich, Switzerland; *U.S. Private*, pg. 1063
Weitzel, John, Exec. V.P. & Mng. Dir.--J.W. Messner, Inc., Seattle, WA; *U.S. Private*, pg. 734
Wen, Danny, Mng. Dir.--Merita Bank Ltd., Beijing Representative Office, Beijing, China; *Int'l*, pg. 859
Wermter, Volkmar, Mng. Dir.--TBWA Munich, Munich, Germany; *U.S. Private*, pg. 1063
West, L., Mng. Dir.--Britax Wingard Limited, Chichester, United Kingdom; *Int'l*, pg. 216
Westbury, A.J., Mng. Dir.--S & P Coil Products Limited, Leicester, United Kingdom; *Int'l*, pg. 590
Westermann, Rainer, Mng. Dir.--Fleishman-Hillard Germany, Frankfurt/Main, Germany; *U.S. Private*, pg. 411
Westland, Jan, Mng. Dir.--Blount GmbH, Gartringen, Germany; *U.S. Public*, pg. 239
Wetzel, D., Mng. Dir.--Societe de Banque Suisse (Luxembourg) S.A., Luxembourg, Luxembourg; *Int'l*, pg. 1331
Wheatley, Joe, Mng. Dir.--AIB Securities Services Ltd., Dublin, Ireland; *Int'l*, pg. 64
Wheeler, Rob, Mng. Dir.--Gunnebo Mayor Ltd., Uckfield, United Kingdom; *Int'l*, pg. 578
Wheen, Ivan, Mng. Dir.-Strategic Plng.--Bankers Trust International (Asia) Ltd., Singapore, Singapore; *U.S. Public*, pg. 186
Whelan, J.D., Mng. Dir.--Wyman-Gordon Forgings, Inc., Houston, TX; *U.S. Public*, pg. 1782
Whitaker, C.J., Mng. Dir.--Sonnex Investments (Pty) Ltd, Windhoek, Namibia; *Int'l*, pg. 167
Whitbread, I., Mng. Dir.--Bally's Shoe Factories (Norwich) Ltd., Norwich, United Kingdom; *Int'l*, pg. 997
Whitcraft, Steve, Mng. Dir.--Turner Construction Company, Dallas, TX; *U.S. Public*, pg. 1646
White, Richard, Mng. Dir.--Goulds Pumps Singapore PTE, Ltd., Jurong, Singapore; *U.S. Public*, pg. 861
White, Robert, Exec. Dir.--Principal Health Care of Delaware, Inc., Wilmington, DE; *U.S. Private*, pg. 885
White, Warren, V.P. & Reg. Dir.--Dugan Valva Contess-Dallas, Dallas, TX; *U.S. Private*, pg. 345
Whitehead, Alan, Mng. Dir.--Raisio Chemicals Canada Inc., Vancouver, Canada; *Int'l*, pg. 1086
Whitfield, Steven, Mng. Dir.--Eurocamp Independent Limited, Knutsford, United Kingdom; *Int'l*, pg. 465
Whitham, J., Exec. V.P. & Mng. Dir.--BBDO Canada, Toronto, Canada; *U.S. Private*, pg. 104
Whitney, Kenneth C., Mng. Dir.--The Blackstone Group, New York, NY; *U.S. Private*, pg. 147
Whitton, Barry, Mng. Dir.--Ademco-Sontrix (Australia) Pty. Ltd., Mortdale, Australia; *U.S. Public*, pg. 1307
Wichmann, Egon, Reg. Mng. Dir.--Berendsen PMC GmbH, Dusseldorf, Germany; *Int'l*, pg. 1285
Widmer, Hans, Mng. Dir.--Vernicolor A.G., Gruningen, Switzerland; *U.S. Public*, pg. 505
Wieland, Werner, Mng. Dir.--Reed Exhibition Companies-Austria, Salzburg, Austria; *Int'l*, pg. 1097
Wiener, Jude B., Corp. Counsel--Lone Star Equities Inc., Lynbrook, NY; *U.S. Private*, pg. 674
Wierzbicki, Jan, Mng. Dir.--WWT (Wytwornia Wyrobow Tytoniowych) S.A., Warsaw, Poland; *Int'l*, pg. 1101
Wigmans, T., Mng. Dir.-Tech.--NORIT N.V., Amersfoort, Netherlands; *Int'l*, pg. 958
Wijnen, Willem, Mng. Dir.--Hydrowa B.V., Eindhoven, Netherlands; *Int'l*, pg. 1285
Wild, Keith, Mng. Dir.--Hedsorboard Ltd., Surbiton, United Kingdom; *Int'l*, pg. 864
Wilfinger, Horst, Mng. Dir.--Austria III, Vienna, Austria; *U.S. Private*, pg. 1062
Wilk, Stuart, Mng. Editor--The Dallas Morning News, Inc., Dallas, TX; *U.S. Public*, pg. 209
Wilke, Manfred, Mng. Dir.--Novoferm GmbH, Rees, Germany; *Int'l*, pg. 509
Wilken, Dick, Mng. Dir.--Norta Timber B.V., Amsterdam, Netherlands; *Int'l*, pg. 458
Wilkes, D.R., Mng. Dir.-Paul's Malt Limited--BOCM PAULS Limited, Ipswich, United Kingdom; *Int'l*, pg. 598
Wilkins, Robert, Mng. Dir.--Beazer Homes (Bedford) Limited, Bedford, United Kingdom; *Int'l*, pg. 182
Willamo, Matti, Mng. Dir.--Merita Customer Finance Ltd., Helsinki, Finland; *Int'l*, pg. 859
Willemsen, A.J., Mng. Dir.--Ennia Caribe N.V., Willemstad, Netherlands Antilles; *Int'l*, pg. 28
Williams, Dane, Mgr.-Credit Card Center--Diamond Shamrock Credit Card Center, Amarillo, TX; *U.S. Public*, pg. 1663
Williams, David, Mng. Dir.--Bunzl PLC, London, United Kingdom; *Int'l*, pg. 232
Williams, Derek, Mng. Dir.--K-Tron Asia Pacific Pte, Singapore, Singapore; *U.S. Public*, pg. 938
Williams, Douglas A., Mng. Dir.-Fin.--Federal Farm Credit Banks Funding Corporation, Jersey City, NJ; *U.S. Private*, pg. 398
Williams, G., Mng. Dir.--Coutts & Co (Cayman) Limited, Grand Cayman, Cayman Islands; *Int'l*, pg. 911
Williams, G. Cabell, III, Mng. Dir.--Allied Capital Corporation, Washington, DC; *U.S. Public*, pg. 47
Williams, Graham, Mng. Dir.-Nelson/Word Ltd. (U.K.)--Word, Incorporated, Dallas, TX; *U.S. Public*, pg. 704
Williams, John, Mng. Dir.--Luxfer, Nottingham, United Kingdom; *Int'l*, pg. 51
Williams, R., Mng. Dir.--Gestetner SA, Caracas, Venezuela; *Int'l*, pg. 1115
Williamson, Dave, Mng. Dir.--NVR Building Products, Gaithersburg, MD; *U.S. Public*, pg. 1148
Williamson, George T., Mng. Dir.--Port of Houston Authority, Houston, TX; *U.S. Private*, pg. 876
Wilson, Alan A., Mng. Dir.--Royal Skandia Life Assurance Ltd., Douglas, United Kingdom; *Int'l*, pg. 1257
Wilson, Alan A., Mng. Dir.--Professional Life Assurance Co. Ltd., Southampton, United Kingdom; *Int'l*, pg. 1257
Wilson, Allen, Mng. Dir.--Killington Limited, Killington, VT; *U.S. Private*, pg. 61
Wilson, Anthony J., Chief Exec. Officer & Mng. Dir.--Guilford Europe, Ltd., Derby, United Kingdom; *U.S. Public*, pg. 769
Wilson, C. Kenneth, Sr. V.P. & Mng. Dir.-B.F. Wine Brands--Brown-Forman Beverages Worldwide, Louisville, KY; *U.S. Public*, pg. 261
Wilson, David, Mng. Dir.--K-Tron Institute, Pitman, NJ; *U.S. Public*, pg. 938
Wilson, J., Pres. & Dir.--Hilton International (Switzerland) AG, Basel, Switzerland; *Int'l*, pg. 788
Wilson, James, Mng. Dir.--Callaway Golf (U.K.) Limited, Chessington, United Kingdom; *U.S. Public*, pg. 295
Winblad, Mads, Mng. Dir.--Nokia Mobile Phones AB, Kista, Sweden; *Int'l*, pg. 952
Winblad, Mats, Mng. Dir.--Nokia Mobile Phones, Copenhagen, Denmark; *Int'l*, pg. 952
Windsor, Mike, Mng. Dir.--Anderson & Lembke Inc., San Francisco, CA; *U.S. Private*, pg. 72
Wing, Rodney, Mng. Dir.--Cirrus Logic International Ltd., Bridgetown, Barbados; *U.S. Public*, pg. 375
Wingate, D.C.M., Mng. Dir.-Green's Flour Mills--BOCM PAULS Limited, Ipswich, United Kingdom; *Int'l*, pg. 598
Winkelhaus, Kathy, Mng. Dir.--Walden Book Company, Ann Arbor, MI; *U.S. Public*, pg. 245
Winning, Don, Mng. Dir.--Reed Technology and Information Services (Europe), London, United Kingdom; *Int'l*, pg. 1096
Winter, Terry M., Div. Mgr.-Power Opers.--San Diego Gas & Electric Company, San Diego, CA; *U.S. Public*, pg. 584
Wipperman, Klaus Peter, Mng. Dir.--EOC Normalien GmbH & Co. KG, Ludenscheid, Germany; *Int'l*, pg. 75
Wippermann, Klaus Peter, Mng. Dir.--EOC Formsystem GmbH, Mahlberg, Germany; *Int'l*, pg. 75
Wirth, Tracy, Mng. Dir.-GB! Griffin Bacal Promotions--Griffin Bacal Inc., New York, NY; *U.S. Private*, pg. 480
Wise, G. J., Mng. Dir.-Mortgage Services--NatWest U.K., London, United Kingdom; *Int'l*, pg. 910
Wise, W., Mng. Dir.--Brother International Corporation do Brazil, Sao Paulo, Brazil; *Int'l*, pg. 229
Wiseman, John S., V.P. & Mng. Dir.--Mortgage Guaranty Insurance Corporation, Milwaukee, WI; *U.S. Public*, pg. 1026
Wiskel, Dave, Mng. Dir.--Betrand Faure Components Ltd. - Vipond Plant, Mississauga, Canada; *Int'l*, pg. 193
Wissing, Lars, Mng. Dir.--Flavoring AB, Norrkoping, Sweden; *Int'l*, pg. 349
Witcher, Bryce J., Mng. Dir.--Tasman Pulp & Paper Company Limited, Auckland, New Zealand; *Int'l*, pg. 495
Witschonke, Ross P., Mng. Dir.-Prod. Planning, Res. & Devel.--Mazda Motor Corporation, Hiroshima, Japan; *Int'l*, pg. 849
Witt, Ricardo, Mng. Dir.--Battenfeld-Pugliese Equipamentos Ltda., Osasco, Brazil; *Int'l*, pg. 825
Wittering, Peter E., Chief Oper. Officer & Mng. Dir.--Sturmey-Archer Limited, Nottingham, United Kingdom; *Int'l*, pg. 394
Wittkotter, Gerd, Mng. Dir.-Baden-Wurttemburg Region--Dyckerhoff & Widmann AG, Munich, Germany; *Int'l*, pg. 423
Wittmann, Jens-Peter, Mng. Dir.--K-Tron Germany-Hasler Division, Lengerich, Germany; *U.S. Public*, pg. 938
Wittstock, Ullrich, Mng. Dir.--Sachsen-Schwertransport GmbH, Dresden, Germany; *Int'l*, pg. 423
Woffard, J., Mng. Dir.--Gates Hydraulics Ltd., Huntingdon, United Kingdom; *Int'l*, pg. 1397
Wogensen, Bertil, Mng. Dir.--Merita Bank Ltd., Warsaw Representative Office, Warsaw, Poland; *Int'l*, pg. 859
Woicke, Peter L., Mng. Dir. & Reg. Exec.-Asia/Pacific--J.P. Morgan Co. Incorporated, New York, NY; *U.S. Public*, pg. 1129
Wolfensberger, Gunter, Mng. Dir.--Rohm Electronics GmbH, Willich, Germany; *Int'l*, pg. 1125
Wolff, Christine, Mng. Dir.--WCI Umwelttechnik GmbH Frankfurt, Dreieich, Germany; *U.S. Public*, pg. 1657
Wolff, Hans, Mng. Dir. & Chief Exec. Officer--Frese & Wolff Werbeagentur, Oldenburg, Germany; *U.S. Private*, pg. 304
Wolfs-Kokkeler, L.M., Mng. Dir.--Ballast Nedam Projectontwikkeling B.V., Rotterdam, Netherlands; *Int'l*, pg. 134
Woltzen, Hugh A., Mng. Dir.--Grotech Capital Group, Inc., Timonium, MD; *U.S. Private*, pg. 483
Wong, Dennis, Mng. Dir.-Leo Burnett/Greater China--Leo Burnett Worldwide Asia/Pacific Hdqtrs., Hong Kong, Hong Kong; *U.S. Private*, pg. 186
Wong, Harry, Mng. Dir.--Enso-Eurocan Hong Kong Ltd., Causeway Bay, Hong Kong; *Int'l*, pg. 457
Wong, Luther, Mng. Dir.--LeaRonal S.E. Asia Ltd., Kowloon, Hong Kong; *U.S. Public*, pg. 982
Wongcharoew, Termsak, Mng. Dir.--Thai Engineering Products Co., Ltd., Bangkok, Thailand; *Int'l*, pg. 1238
Wood, Brian, Mng. Dir.--PPP Lifetime plc, Stratford-on-Avon, United Kingdom; *Int'l*, pg. 1020
Wood, Lynne, Mng. Dir.--Radio City, Liverpool, United Kingdom; *Int'l*, pg. 452
Wood, M.S., Mng. Dir.--Metal Box Nigeria Limited, Apapa, Nigeria; *Int'l*, pg. 267
Wood, Mark, Editor-in-Chief & Exec. Dir.--Reuters Holdings PLC, London, United Kingdom; *Int'l*, pg. 1105
Wood, Michael, Mng. Dir.--Leo Burnett Advertising, Representative Office, Ho Chi Minh City, Vietnam; *U.S. Private*, pg. 184
Wood, Roger, Mng. Dir.--British Gas Services Ltd., Staines, United Kingdom; *Int'l*, pg. 279
Woodall, James, Mgr.-Opers.--Beechmont Investments Inc., Cincinnati, OH; *U.S. Private*, pg. 129
Woodlock, Maren, Sr. V.P. & Mng. Dir.--Quantum Media International, Inc., Chicago, IL; *U.S. Private*, pg. 899
Woodruff, Jack D., Mng. Dir.--International Pin, Park Forest, IL; *U.S. Private*, pg. 269
Woodruff, Jack D., Mng. Dir.--PATCO L.P., Park Forest, IL; *U.S. Private*, pg. 269
Woods, Bill, Mng. Dir.--Interfab, El Paso, TX; *U.S. Private*, pg. 786
World, Tore, Mng. Dir.--Kelley Bemanningslosninger, Oslo, Norway; *U.S. Public*, pg. 949
Woxne, A.K., Mng. Dir.--Nutricia Nordica AB, Stockholm, Sweden; *Int'l*, pg. 992
Wrederbrand, Torbjorn, Mng. Dir.--Ikea Svenska Forsaljnings AB, Almhult, Sweden; *Int'l*, pg. 660
Wright, David, Mng. Dir.--Camera House Limited, Auckland, New Zealand; *Int'l*, pg. 1115
Wright, Norman, Mng. Dir.--Choice Publications Ltd, Peterborough, United Kingdom; *Int'l*, pg. 451
Wright, Robin, Deputy Mng. Dir.-Edelman Medical Comms. Worldwide--Daniel J. Edelman Ltd., London, United Kingdom; *U.S. Private*, pg. 363
Wuhrer, Wolfgang, Mngng. Dir.--Sulzer-Escher Wyss GmbH, Ravensburg, Germany; *Int'l*, pg. 1305
Wuhrer, Wolfgang, Mng. Dir.--Sulzer Hydro GmbH, Ravensburg, Germany; *Int'l*, pg. 1308
Wullschleger, B., Mng. Dir.--Ascom Installationen AG, Bern, Switzerland; *Int'l*, pg. 86
Wurmli, Hanspeter, Mng. Dir.--Junior Discount Service AG,, Dallenwil, Switzerland; *Int'l*, pg. 501
Wycherley, R., Mng. Dir.--Bally, Inc., New Rochelle, NY; *Int'l*, pg. 997
Wygard, Andrew, Mng. Dir.--Arthur D. Little Mexicana, S.A. de C.V., Monterrey, Mexico; *U.S. Private*, pg. 671
Wylie, Duncan, Exec. Mng. Dir.--Banque Indosuez New Zealand Limited, Wellington, New Zealand; *Int'l*, pg. 315
Yabu, Kazuya, Sr. Mng. Dir. & Gen. Mgr.-Mktg.--Mitsubishi Electric Corporation, Tokyo, Japan; *Int'l*, pg. 872
Yagaki, Norihiko, Mng. Dir. & Gen. Mgr.--Sumitomo Finance (Middle East) E.C., Manama, Bahrain; *Int'l*, pg. 1310
Yagihashi, Tadashi, Dir. & Gen. Mgr.-Capital Markets--The Haokkaido Takushoku Securities Co. (Sapporo), Sapporo, Japan; *Int'l*, pg. 626
Yahas, Dan, Mng. Dir.-Poalim Capital Markets & Investments--Bank Hapoalim, Tel Aviv, Israel; *Int'l*, pg. 149
Yamada, Hiroshi, Sr. Mng. Dir. & Chief Exec.-Investment--Meiji Life Insurance Company, Tokyo, Japan; *Int'l*, pg. 854
Yamada, Kazutoshi, Exec. Mng. Dir.--Ajinomoto Company Inc., Tokyo, Japan; *Int'l*, pg. 40
Yamada, Minoru, Mng. Dir.--Yamaichi Futures Pte. Ltd., Singapore, Singapore; *Int'l*, pg. 1517
Yamada, Satoshi, Sr. Mng. Dir.-Intl. Bus. Devel. & Overseas Mktg. & Sls.--Mazda Motor Corporation, Hiroshima, Japan; *Int'l*, pg. 849
Yamada, Tsuneo, Mng. Dir. & Gen. Mgr.-Power & Indus. Systems Grp.--Mitsubishi Electric Corporation, Tokyo, Japan; *Int'l*, pg. 872
Yamaguchi, Kunihiko, Mng. Dir.--Hakuhodo Inc., Kobe, Japan; *Int'l*, pg. 587
Yamaguchi, Yoshito, Mng. Dir. & Gen. Mgr.-Overseas Mktg. Grp.--Mitsubishi Electric Corporation, Tokyo, Japan; *Int'l*, pg. 872
Yamamoto, Katsuaki, Mng. Dir.-Pur. & Domestic Mktg. & Sls.--Mazda Motor Corporation, Hiroshima, Japan; *Int'l*, pg. 849
Yamamoto, Kazuyoshi, Mng. Dir.-Admin.--Mitsubishi Corporation, Tokyo, Japan; *Int'l*, pg. 871
Yamamoto, Michihisa, Sr. Mng. Dir.--Kyocera Corporation, Kyoto, Japan; *Int'l*, pg. 775
Yamamoto, Noriyuki, Mng. Dir.--Shougang NEC Electronics Co., Ltd., Beijing, China; *Int'l*, pg. 901
Yamamoto, Sadao, Sr. Mng. Dir.--Kyocera Corporation, Kyoto, Japan; *Int'l*, pg. 775
Yamamoto, Shoji, Mng. Dir.--Dai-ichi Life Insurance Agency Europe Limited, London, United Kingdom; *Int'l*, pg. 362
Yamamoto, Shuji, Mng. Dir.--NEC Electronics Taiwan Ltd., Taipei, Taiwan; *Int'l*, pg. 901
Yamamura, Yuzo, Sr. Mng. Dir.--Kyocera Corporation, Kyoto, Japan; *Int'l*, pg. 775
Yamana, Keiji, Sr. Mng. Dir.-Creative--Dentsu, Sudler & Hennessey Inc., Tokyo, Japan; *U.S. Private*, pg. 325
Yamanami, Masanori, Mng. Dir. & Gen. Mgr.--Nikko Investment Banking (Middle East) E.C., Manama, Bahrain; *Int'l*, pg. 931

Yamane, Hisao, Sr. Mng. Dir.-Petroleum Retail Mktg.--Japan Energy Corporation, Tokyo, Japan; *Int'l*, pg. 702
Yamane, Hisao, Mng. Dir.-Petroleum Retail Mktg.--Japan Energy Corporation, Tokyo, Japan; *Int'l*, pg. 702
Yamanoi, Akio, Exec. Mng. Dir.--Ajinomoto Company Inc., Tokyo, Japan; *Int'l*, pg. 40
Yamanokuchi, Yoshizo, Mng. Dir.--Hosokawa Micron Corporation, Osaka, Japan; *Int'l*, pg. 635
Yamaoka, Thomas, Mng. Dir.--Bonig & Yamaoka International Public Relations, Hamburg, Germany; *Int'l*, pg. 1210
Yamashiro, Kenji, Mng. Dir.--NEC Electronics (UK) Limited, Milton Keynes, United Kingdom; *Int'l*, pg. 901
Yamashita, Koji, Mng. Dir.--All Nippon Airways Co. Ltd., Tokyo, Japan; *Int'l*, pg. 57
Yamashita, Sumio, Mng. Dir.--Kintetsu World Express (Thailand) Co., Ltd., Bangkok, Thailand; *Int'l*, pg. 735
Yamazaki, Hisao, Mng. Dir.--Nippon Express France, S.A., Roissy Charles de Gaulle, France; *Int'l*, pg. 934
Yamazaki, Takeaki, Sr. Mng. Dir.--Dentsu Young & Rubicam Inc. (Tokyo), Tokyo, Japan; *U.S. Private*, pg. 325
Yanaranop, Chollanat, Mng. Dir.--Thai Polyethylene Co., Ltd., Bangkok, Thailand; *Int'l*, pg. 1239
Yap, Cyril M.F., Mng. Dir.--Jefferies Pacific Limited, Central, Hong Kong; *U.S. Public*, pg. 925
Yarom, Yosef, Chief Internal Auditor & Deputy Mng. Dir.--Bank Hapoalim, Tel Aviv, Israel; *Int'l*, pg. 149
Yasunaga, Yoshihiro, Mng. Dir.--Cosmo Oil Co., Ltd., Tokyo, Japan; *Int'l*, pg. 335
Yatabe, Makoto, Mng. Dir.--The Meijiseimei International Hong Kong, Ltd., Hong Kong, Hong Kong; *Int'l*, pg. 854
Yates, Graham, Mng. Dir.--BHC Aerovox Ltd., Weymouth, United Kingdom; *U.S. Public*, pg. 26
Yau-Lai, Winston, Exec. Chm. & Mng. Dir.--Vitasoy International Holdings Ltd., Tuen Mun, Hong Kong; *Int'l*, pg. 1468
Yau, Joseph, Chief Exec. Officer & Mng. Dir.--Metropolitan Life Insurance Company of Hong Kong, Ltd., Hong Kong, Hong Kong; *U.S. Private*, pg. 738
Yeo, Harold, Mng. Dir.--DBS-Capital Trust Securities India Pvt. Ltd., New Delhi, India; *Int'l*, pg. 351
Yeung, Lillienne, Dr., Mng. Dir.--Shanghai Johnson & Johnson Ltd., Shanghai, China; *U.S. Public*, pg. 932
Yoda, Masatoshi, Mng. Dir.--Ebara Corporation, Tokyo, Japan; *Int'l*, pg. 431
Yokotsuka, Masaaki, Sr. Mng. Dir.-Corp. Plng. & Coordination--Sumitomo Chemical Company, Ltd., Tokyo, Japan; *Int'l*, pg. 1310
Yolalan, Ahmed, Chief Fin. Officer--Young & Rubicam Turkey, Istanbul, Turkey; *U.S. Private*, pg. 1200
Yoneda, T., Dir. & Office Chief-Osaka--Man Nen Sha Inc., Osaka, Japan; *Int'l*, pg. 834
Yonekura, Hidekazu, Sr. Mng. Dir.-Corp. Communication & Domestic Mktg. & Sls.--Mazda Motor Corporation, Hiroshima, Japan; *Int'l*, pg. 849
Yonekura, Hiromasa, Mng. Dir.-Plng. & Coordination--Sumitomo Chemical Company, Ltd., Tokyo, Japan; *Int'l*, pg. 1310
Yoneyama, Koji, Sr. Mng. Dir.-Intl.--Daiwa Securities Co. Ltd., Tokyo, Japan; *Int'l*, pg. 374
York, D., Mng. Dir.--Ballast Phoenix Ltd., Bourne, United Kingdom; *Int'l*, pg. 133
Yorke, D., Mng. Dir.--Alexander Drew & Sons Ltd., Rochdale, United Kingdom; *Int'l*, pg. 798
Yoshida, Hitoshi, Mng. Dir.--The Meijiseimei International, London Ltd., London, United Kingdom; *Int'l*, pg. 854
Yoshida, Hitoshi, Mng. Dir.--The Meijiseimei Property U.K. Ltd., London, United Kingdom; *Int'l*, pg. 855
Yoshie, Hiroshi, Exec. Mng. Dir.--Sanyo Electric Co., Ltd., Osaka, Japan; *Int'l*, pg. 1190
Yoshimura, Masayoshi, Mng. Dir.--Nanto Business Service Co., Ltd., Nara, Japan; *Int'l*, pg. 905
Yoshitome, Yasuo, Pres., Mng. Dir.--Dentsu (Thailand) Ltd., Bangkok, Thailand; *Int'l*, pg. 394
Younger, Alvin M., Jr., Chief Fin. Officer, Mng. Dir., Treas. & Sec.--T. Rowe Price Associates, Inc., Baltimore, MD; *U.S. Public*, pg. 1324
Youngman, Frank W., Mng. Dir.--Delta Precision Ltd., Enfield, United Kingdom; *Int'l*, pg. 391
Yu, Kenneth K., V.P. & Mng. Dir.-Lattice, Asia--Lattice Semiconductor Corporation, Hillsboro, OR; *U.S. Public*, pg. 979
Yuen, John A., Mng. Dir.--Johnson & Johnson Medical Hong Kong, Kowloon, Hong Kong; *U.S. Public*, pg. 931
Yuen, Norman K.T., Mng. Dir.-Corp. Devel. & Opers.--Hong Kong Telecommunications Limited, Quarry Bay, Hong Kong; *Int'l*, pg. 247
Yuen, Richard, Mng. Dir.-Celebrity Hong Kong--Celebrity Incorporated, Tyler, TX; *U.S. Public*, pg. 319
Yuen, Tim, Pres. & Mng. Dir.--GrandeTel Technologies Inc., Richmond, Canada; *Int'l*, pg. 556
Yuhjtman, Alexander, Sr. Deputy Mng. Dir.-Asset Mgmnt. & Logistics--Bank Hapoalim, Tel Aviv, Israel; *Int'l*, pg. 149
Yuill, Jeremy, Mng. Dir.--Arthur Hart Webbing, Somerset, United Kingdom; *Int'l*, pg. 215
Yule, Robert J., Mng. Dir.--EnergyNorth Propane, Inc., Concord, NH; *U.S. Public*, pg. 582
Yurko, Allen, Chief Exec. Officer & Mng. Dir.--Siebe plc, Windsor, United Kingdom; *Int'l*, pg. 1240
Zajak, Robert, Mng. Dir.--Mountaingate Engineering, Inc., Campbell, CA; *U.S. Public*, pg. 1188
Zak, Arieh, Mng. Dir.--Datascope GmbH, Bensheim, Germany; *U.S. Public*, pg. 488
Zak, M., Mng. Dir.--Datascope B.V., Hoevelaken, Netherlands; *U.S. Public*, pg. 488
Zalduondo, Carlos, V.P. & Mng. Dir.--Allergan-Lok Produtos, Farmaceuticos, Ltda., Sao Paulo, Brazil; *U.S. Public*, pg. 46
Zaman, Shafi-uz, Deputy Mng. Dir.-Engrng.--Pakistan International Airlines Corporation, Karachi, Pakistan; *Int'l*, pg. 1021
Zandee, D.W., Mng. Dir.--Placer Pacific Limited, Sydney, Australia; *Int'l*, pg. 1060
Zangerle, E., Mng. Dir.--Bally Trading AG, Schonenwerd, Switzerland; *Int'l*, pg. 996
Zangerle, E., Mng. Dir.--Bally Schuhfabriken S.A., Schonenwerd, Switzerland; *Int'l*, pg. 996
Zaragoza, Jose, Mng. Partner--DPZ-Duailibi, Petit, Zaragoza, Propaganda S.A., Sao Paulo, Brazil; *Int'l*, pg. 352
Zarza, Jean-Michel, Mng. Dir.--Thrige Electric S.A., Nogent-sur-Seine, France; *Int'l*, pg. 1387
Zarza, Jean-Michel, Mng. Dir.--Electro Navale Moteurs SAS, Saint-Herblain, France; *Int'l*, pg. 1387
Zavasky, Michael S., V.P. & Mng. Dir.-Reinsurance--Erie Family Life Insurance Company, Erie, PA; *U.S. Public*, pg. 590
Zech, Winfried, Mng. Dir.-Nordrhein-Westfalen Region--Dyckerhoff & Widmann AG, Munich, Germany; *Int'l*, pg. 423
Zechnall, Dr., Mng. Dir.--MotoMeter AG, Leonberg, Germany; *Int'l*, pg. 204
Zee, Jesse, Mng. Dir.--Smart Shirts Ltd., Kowloon, Hong Kong; *U.S. Public*, pg. 948
Zeeck, David A., Editor--The News Tribune, Tacoma, WA; *U.S. Public*, pg. 1066
Zeigon, James, Sr. Mng. Dir.-Global Svcs.--The Chase Manhattan Bank, New York, NY; *U.S. Public*, pg. 338
Zeitoun, Raymond, Mng. Dir.--SMH do Brazil, Sao Paulo, Brazil; *Int'l*, pg. 1161
Zeitoun, Raymond, Mng. Dir.--SMH Sweden AB, Stockholm, Sweden; *Int'l*, pg. 1161
Zeitoun, Raymond, Mng. Dir.--SMH Espana S.A., Madrid, Spain; *Int'l*, pg. 1161
Zibung, Andre, Mng. Dir.--Editor AG Multimedia und Design, Kusnacht, Switzerland; *Int'l*, pg. 666
Zider, Kim, Mng. Dir.--Finebrand Division, Los Angeles, CA; *U.S. Private*, pg. 781
Ziebinski, Jarek, Mng. Dir.--Leo Burnett Warsaw SP.Z.O.O., Warsaw, Poland; *U.S. Private*, pg. 186
Ziegler, F., Mng. Dir.--Christie's (International) S.A., Rome, Italy; *Int'l*, pg. 290
Ziegler, H., Mng. Dir.--Alfred Ziegler Molkerei Schluctern GmbH & Co. KG, Schluctern, Germany; *Int'l*, pg. 992
Ziffzer, Stefan, Dr., Mng. Dir.--AV Euromedia Gesellschaft fur Audiovision mbH, Stuttgart, Germany; *Int'l*, pg. 1478
Zinkann, Karl-Heinz, Co-Mng. Dir.--Blefa GmbH, Kreuztal, Germany; *Int'l*, pg. 508
Zipperer, M.L., Mng. Dir.--Transtates Properties, Inc., Savannah, GA; *U.S. Public*, pg. 1666
Zollner, Hanns, Mng. Dir.--Commercial Metals (International) AG, Zug, Switzerland; *U.S. Public*, pg. 414
Zollner, Hanns, Mng. Dir.--CMC Trading AG, Zug, Switzerland; *U.S. Public*, pg. 414
Zschokke, A., Mng. Dir.--Bally (Italia) S.r.l., Florence, Italy; *Int'l*, pg. 997
Zultowsky, Dennis, Mng. Partner-Creative Art--Lewis Gace Bozell Healthcare Worldwide, Fort Lee, NJ; *U.S. Public*, pg. 1642
Zwicky, Elisabeth, Deputy Mng. Dir.-Legal & Projects--LGT Bank in Liechtenstein Aktiengesellschaft, Vaduz, Liechtenstein; *Int'l*, pg. 809
Zyke, J.C., Mng. Dir.--GKN Ribemont SARL, Ribemont, France; *Int'l*, pg. 536

MANUFACTURING

Abernethy, Fred, Dir.-Mfg.--Carolina Glove Co., Newton, NC; *U.S. Private*, pg. 214
Abetz, John, Dir.-Tech.--Fansteel VR/Wesson-Plantsville, Plantsville, CT; *U.S. Public*, pg. 612
Abouhamad, Emilio, Mgr.-Trading & Supply--Petroleos de Venezuela S.A., Caracas, Venezuela; *Int'l*, pg. 1045
Abrams, Edward, V.P.-Mfg. & Safety Environment--Hardman Division of Harcros Chemicals, Inc., Belleville, NJ; *Int'l*, pg. 598
Adams, Alton W., V.P.-Mfg.--UST Inc., Greenwich, CT; *U.S. Public*, pg. 1660
Adams, Billy J., V.P.-Mfg. & Support Svcs.--The Cessna Aircraft Co., Wichita, KS; *U.S. Public*, pg. 1589
Adams, Bob, V.P. & Dir.-Production--Automotive News, Detroit, MI; *U.S. Private*, pg. 284
Adams, Dave, V.P.-Engrng.--Euclid Hitachi, Cleveland, OH; *Int'l*, pg. 622
Adams, Robert C., V.P.-Production--Crain Communications, Inc., Chicago, IL; *U.S. Private*, pg. 284
Adamsen, David A., V.P.-Mfg.--The Penn Traffic Company, Syracuse, NY; *U.S. Public*, pg. 1270
Adamson, Oliver, Prod. Mgr.--Mallinckrodt Medical, Athlone, Ireland; *U.S. Public*, pg. 1040
Adcock, W.E., V.P.-Engrng.--Alabama Tennessee Natural Gas Company, Muscle Shoals, AL; *U.S. Public*, pg. 1109
Adreas, John, V.P.-Mfg.--Continental Can Co., Norwalk, CT; *U.S. Public*, pg. 439
Agner, Bud, V.P.-Mfg.--Mercury Marine, Fond Du Lac, WI; *U.S. Public*, pg. 265
Aguilera, Luis, Sr. V.P.-Mfg.--Checkpoint Systems Inc., Thorofare, NJ; *U.S. Public*, pg. 343
Aguilera, Luis A., V.P.-Mfg.--Checkpoint Systems Inc., Thorofare, NJ; *U.S. Public*, pg. 343
Aides, Charles, V.P.-Apparel Mfg. & Sourcing--Woolrich, Inc., Woolrich, PA; *U.S. Private*, pg. 1188
Ainsley, C., Mgr.-Mfg.--Philip Morris Limited, Moorabbin, Australia; *U.S. Public*, pg. 1290
Akers, H. James, Jr., V.P.-Melt Opers.--Roanoke Electric Steel Corporation, Roanoke, VA; *U.S. Public*, pg. 1392
Al-Othman, A.S., Dir.-Mfr.--Al-Jubail Petrochemical Company, Tareet, Saudi Arabia; *U.S. Public*, pg. 601
Alameddine, Hisham, Dir.-Engrng.--Burke Industries, Inc., San Jose, CA; *U.S. Private*, pg. 183
Albright, Roger, Chief Engr.--Hempt Brothers, Inc., Camp Hill, PA; *U.S. Private*, pg. 521
Alcantara, Bartolo, V.P. & Gen. Mgr.--TII Industries, Inc., Copiague, NY; *U.S. Public*, pg. 1556
Alden, Derek, V.P.-Commercial & Entertainment Prods.--Reflectone, Inc., Tampa, FL; *Int'l*, pg. 218
Alegre, Ignasi, Asst. Mgr.--Caixa d'Estalvis de Catalunya, Barcelona, Spain; *Int'l*, pg. 249
Alexander, Doug, Plant Mgr.--United Air Specialists, Inc., Cincinnati, OH; *U.S. Public*, pg. 382
Alifonso, Jorge, Dir.-Opers.--Alcon (Puerto Rico) Inc., Humacao, PR; *Int'l*, pg. 916
Allemang, Arnold, V.P.-Mfg. & Engrng.--The Dow Chemical Company, Midland, MI; *U.S. Public*, pg. 522
Allison, John, Mgr.-Mfg.--Solitec Wafer Processing, Inc., San Jose, CA; *U.S. Private*, pg. 1013
Allison, Thomas L., V.P.-Mdsg.--Bergen Brunswig Drug Company, Orange, CA; *U.S. Public*, pg. 213
Alonso, Jose Carlos, Dir.-Mfg.--SmithKline Beecham Laboratorios Ltda., Rio de Janeiro, Brazil; *Int'l*, pg. 1266
Alonzo, Roy, V.P.-Mfg.--S.C. Johnson & Son, Limited, Brantford, Canada; *U.S. Private*, pg. 593
Alquist, Gil, Gen. Mgr.-Mfg.--Lund International Holdings, Inc., Anoka, MN; *U.S. Public*, pg. 1020
Alscher, Arnold, Dr., Mng. Dir.-Processing, Research & Devel.--Haltermann AG, Hamburg, Germany; *Int'l*, pg. 590
Althouse, John, Dir.-Engrng.--Narrow Fabric Industries, Inc., Reading, PA; *U.S. Private*, pg. 774
Alworth, R.L., V.P.-Metal-Enclosed Gear Prods. Div.--S & C Electric Company, Chicago, IL; *U.S. Private*, pg. 954
Amels, L., Mfg. Engr.--Stamco Industries Inc., Euclid, OH; *U.S. Private*, pg. 1029
Ammerman, Lynn, Mgr.-Plant--Beer Nuts, Inc., Bloomington, IL; *U.S. Private*, pg. 130
Amurgis, A.W., V.P.-Engrng.--Columbia Gas Distribution Companies, Columbus, OH; *U.S. Public*, pg. 402
Anderko, Frank, V.P.-Mfg. & Sec.--Worzalla Publishing Co., Inc., Stevens Point, WI; *U.S. Private*, pg. 1191
Anderson, Charles, V.P.-Mfg.--Hinckley & Schmitt, Inc., Chicago, IL; *Int'l*, pg. 1322
Anderson, Dave, Exec. V.P.-Opers.--Regal Ware, Inc., Kewaskum, WI; *U.S. Private*, pg. 917
Anderson, David, V.P.-Mfg.--I. Spiewak & Sons, Inc., New York, NY; *U.S. Private*, pg. 1025
Anderson, Don, V.P.-Engrng.--Fire Lite Alarms, Inc./Notifier Co., Northford, CT; *U.S. Public*, pg. 1306
Anderson, Frederick W., V.P.-Mfg. Machine Div.--The Lincoln Electric Company, Cleveland, OH; *U.S. Public*, pg. 996
Anderson, Ian, Sr. Dir.-Mfg.--Ball Metal Food Container Corp., Westminster, CO; *U.S. Public*, pg. 171
Anderson, Jack, Sr. V.P.-Mfg.--American Color Graphics, Brentwood, TN; *U.S. Public*, pg. 1132
Anderson, James G., Dir.-Mfg.--Selas Corporation of America, Dresher, PA; *U.S. Public*, pg. 1454
Anderson, Jon, V.P.-Mfg.--Printco Group, Greenville, MI; *U.S. Public*, pg. 228
Anderson, Kenneth F., V.P.-Mfg.--Waterloo Industries, Inc., Waterloo, IA; *U.S. Public*, pg. 675
Anderson, Richard, Exec. V.P.-Mfg.--Valassis Communications, Inc., Livonia, MI; *U.S. Public*, pg. 1704
Anderson, Robert, Exec. V.P.--C.J. Vitner Co., Chicago, IL; *U.S. Private*, pg. 1142
Anderson, Ted, V.P. & Gen. Mgr.--Communications Instruments Inc., Fairview, NC; *U.S. Private*, pg. 259
Andolina, Vince, Mgr.-Opers.--Sealing Devices Inc., Lancaster, NY; *U.S. Private*, pg. 978
Andreatta, A.P., Dir.-Cable & Component BU--Delphi Packard Electric Systems, Beachwood, OH; *U.S. Public*, pg. 719
Andres, Thomas, V.P.-Mfg.--Thermal Industries, Inc., Pittsburgh, PA; *U.S. Private*, pg. 490
Andrews, S. J., V.P.-Mfg.--Westco Products, Inc., Pico Rivera, CA; *Int'l*, pg. 244
Andrews, T. Michael, V.P.-Mfg.--Stewart & Stevenson Services, Inc., Houston, TX; *U.S. Public*, pg. 1517
Andrus, Scott, V.P.-Opers.--Premier Coatings, Inc., Elk Grove Village, IL; *Int'l*, pg. 1488
Angel, Marvin, Dir.-Engrng.--Cowden Metal Specialties, Inc., Chino, CA; *U.S. Private*, pg. 280
Angelini, Andrea, Mgr.-Mfg.--Dateo Import S.P.A., Milan, Italy; *Int'l*, pg. 385
Angell, Tom, Mgr.-Mfg.--Framesi USA, Inc./Roffler Industries, Inc./Casa di Colore, Inc., Coraopolis, PA; *U.S. Private*, pg. 419
Angerer, Richard E., Dir.-Mfg.--Ithaco Inc., Ithaca, NY; *U.S. Private*, pg. 576
Anker, Bradford C., V.P.-Mfg.--Acuson Corporation, Mountain View, CA; *U.S. Public*, pg. 18
Anson, Virginia, Dir.-Production--The Putnam & Grosset Group, New York, NY; *Int'l*, pg. 1027
Anthony, Aubra, Sr., V.P.-Mfg.--Anthony Forest Products Co., Inc., El Dorado, AR; *U.S. Private*, pg. 76
Anthony, Dale, V.P.-Mfg.--Pacesetter Corporation, Omaha, NE; *U.S. Private*, pg. 830
Antic, Rick, Mgr.-Mfg.--Champlain Cable Corp., Colchester, VT; *Int'l*, pg. 637
Antonissen, Henk, V.P.-Prod.--Lips United B.V., Drunen, Netherlands; *Int'l*, pg. 812
Antos, John M., V.P.-Engrng.--Thetford Corporation, Ann Arbor, MI; *U.S. Private*, pg. 352
Appel, Jack, V.P.-Engrng.--Efco Corporation, Monett, MO; *U.S. Private*, pg. 353
Applebaum, David, V.P.-Mfg. & Treas.--Triangle Marketing Corp., New York, NY; *U.S. Private*, pg. 1102
Archibald, Thomas L., V.P.-Mfg.--Rohm and Haas Company, Philadelphia, PA; *U.S. Public*, pg. 1403
Areias, Armando M. Ferreira M., Mgr.-Prod.--Sao Paulo Alpargatas S.A., Sao Paulo, Brazil; *Int'l*, pg. 1193
Argens, Robert, Dir.-Opers.--Altec Lansing Technologies, Inc., Milford, PA; *U.S. Private*, pg. 479
Argyris, Thomas A., Div. V.P.--Toll Brothers, Inc., Huntingdon Valley, PA; *U.S. Public*, pg. 1620
Arignon, Jean-Jacques, Plant Superintendent--Muskin Leisure Products, Inc., Wilkes-Barre, PA; *U.S. Private*, pg. 768
Armiento, Mike, V.P.-Mfg.--S. Schwab Company, Cumberland, MD; *U.S. Private*, pg. 974

Armistead, Frank, V.P.-Mfg.--Horace Small Apparel Company, Nashville, TN; *Int'l*, pg. 635
Armstrong, Hugh III, Mfg. Mgr.--Danaher Tool Group, Chicago, IL; *U.S. Public*, pg. 481
Armstrong, Michael J., V.P.-Mfg.--U.S. News & World Report, New York, NY; *U.S. Private*, pg. 1125
Arndorfer, Frank M., V.P.-Finishing Opers.--Quad/Graphics, Inc., Pewaukee, WI; *U.S. Private*, pg. 897
Arndt, David, V.P.-Engrg.--A.G. Simpson Co. Limited, Scarborough, Canada; *Int'l*, pg. 1252
Arnold, Brad, Mgr.-Opers.--The Brulin Corporation, Indianapolis, IN; *U.S. Private*, pg. 176
Aronson, Carl, Mgr.-Mfr. Private Brands--Osborn Manufacturing, Cleveland, OH; *U.S. Public*, pg. 924
Arora, Govind K., V.P.-Mfg.--General Binding Corporation, Northbrook, IL; *U.S. Public*, pg. 707
Arrowsmith, G. Jay, V.P.-Mfg.--Unitog Company, Kansas City, MO; *U.S. Public*, pg. 1693
Arthur, R.B., Mgr.-Mfg. & Sls.--North State Pyrophyllite, Greensboro, NC; *U.S. Private*, pg. 924
Artus, J.P., Industrial Mgr.--Rossignol S.A., Voiron, France; *Int'l*, pg. 1127
Asen, Shel F., Sr. V.P.-Mfg. & Pur.--The McGraw-Hill Companies, New York, NY; *U.S. Public*, pg. 1069
Ash, Paul, V.P.-Domestic Mfg.--Stockham Valves & Fittings, Inc., Birmingham, AL; *U.S. Private*, pg. 1043
Ashby, P., V.P.-Fabric Mfg.--Champion Products, Winston Salem, NC; *U.S. Public*, pg. 1433
Asher, Rafael Ben, V.P.-Mfg.--ECI Telecom Ltd., Petah Tiqwa, Israel; *Int'l*, pg. 643
Ashmore, Doug, V.P. & Dir.-Mfg.--AMVAC Chemical Corporation, Los Angeles, CA; *U.S. Public*, pg. 94
Ashton, L.J., V.P.-Engrng.--Raypak, Inc., Westlake Village, CA; *Int'l*, pg. 1022
Assicurato, C.P., Sr. V.P.-Opers.--Beiersdorf, Inc., Norwalk, CT; *Int'l*, pg. 182
Astbury, Arthur A., V.P.-Mfg.--Altron Incorporated, Wilmington, MA; *U.S. Public*, pg. 59
Atkinson, David M., Dir.-Mfg.--Wausau Papers of New Hampshire, Inc., Groveton, NH; *U.S. Public*, pg. 1748
Aucutt, Larry, Mgr.-Plant--Noel Canning Corporation, Yakima, WA; *U.S. Private*, pg. 800
August, Stanley, V.P.-Fabric Opers.--Fab Industries, Inc., New York, NY; *U.S. Public*, pg. 603
Augustine, Corinne Z., V.P.-Sequoia Mfg. Opers.--Acuson Corporation, Mountain View, CA; *U.S. Public*, pg. 18
Augustine, Joseph L., V.P. & Opers. Controller--Gould Electronics Inc., Eastlake, OH; *U.S. Public*, pg. 1591
Austin, Wade, Mgr.-Plant--Kroehler Furniture Manufacturing Company, Inc., Hickory, NC; *U.S. Private*, pg. 972
Autrey, Ronald, V.P.-Estimating & Engrng.--Miller Electric Company, Jacksonville, FL; *U.S. Private*, pg. 747
Aversano, Robert J., V.P.-Mfg.--B.H. Aircraft Co., Inc., Farmingdale, NY; *U.S. Private*, pg. 107
Avery, Larry, V.P.-Engrng. & Opers.--Alabama Electric Cooperative, Inc., Andalusia, AL; *U.S. Private*, pg. 30
Avery, R., Mgr.-Factory--Thomas De La Rue Ltd., Gateshead, United Kingdom; *Int'l*, pg. 386
Ax, Wayne, Mgr.-Mfg.-Automotive--Elco Textron, Rockford, IL; *U.S. Public*, pg. 1590
Aycock, Robert M., V.P.-Mfg.--United States Pipe & Foundry Company, Inc., Birmingham, AL; *U.S. Public*, pg. 1736
Baars, Paul, Mgr.-Mfg.--J.T. Slocomb Company, South Glastonbury, CT; *U.S. Private*, pg. 1006
Babcock, Gary, Dir.-Engrng.--Suspa, Inc., Grand Rapids, MI; *Int'l*, pg. 1322
Babuder, Kirt M., Dir.-Engrng.--The Machine Tool Group, Cleveland, OH; *U.S. Public*, pg. 503
Bach, William, V.P.-Mfg.--Battenfeld Gloucester Engineering Co. Inc., Gloucester, MA; *U.S. Private*, pg. 123
Backiel, Dana, Chief Engineer--Seattle City Light, Seattle, WA; *U.S. Private*, pg. 979
Backus, James, Exec. V.P.-Engrng. & Construction--Wilmorite, Inc., Rochester, NY; *U.S. Private*, pg. 1180
Bader, Fredric G., Sr. V.P.-Mfg. & Pharmaceutical Devel.--Genetics Institute, Inc., Cambridge, MA; *U.S. Public*, pg. 79
Baert, Ray, Dir.-Mfg.--Eagle Packaging Group, Oakland, CA; *U.S. Private*, pg. 832
Bagwell, Charles F., V.P. & Dir.-Mfg. & Pur.--The Kent Manufacturing Co., Pickens, SC; *U.S. Private*, pg. 615
Bailey, Frank, Plant Mgr.--Zoeller Co., Louisville, KY; *U.S. Private*, pg. 1207
Bailey, Neil, V.P.-Opers. & Engrng.--Holsum Bakery, Inc., Phoenix, AZ; *U.S. Private*, pg. 536
Bailey, Robert J., Sr. V.P.-Quality Assurance & Admin.--The Hertz Corporation, Park Ridge, NJ; *U.S. Public*, pg. 664
Bailey, Russ, V.P.-Mfg.--Duck Head Apparel, Winder, GA; *U.S. Public*, pg. 498
Baird, Richard, V.P.-Technical Services & Opers.--The Stop & Shop Companies, Inc., Quincy, MA; *Int'l*, pg. 750
Baker, Brian V., V.P.-Mfg.--Alamo Industrial Group, San Antonio, TX; *U.S. Private*, pg. 31
Baker, Mark, V.P.-Mdsg./Midwest Div.--The Home Depot, Inc., Atlanta, GA; *U.S. Public*, pg. 831
Baker, Randy D., V.P.-Mfg.--Lattice Semiconductor Corporation, Hillsboro, OR; *U.S. Public*, pg. 979
Baker, Ray, Mgr.-Mfg.--Atlas Electric Devices Co., Chicago, IL; *U.S. Private*, pg. 96
Baker, Ray, V.P.-Mfg.--Uvex Safety, Inc., Smithfield, RI; *Int'l*, pg. 132
Baker, Sherri, Mdsg. Controller--Lamonts Apparel, Inc., Kirkland, WA; *U.S. Public*, pg. 975
Baldini, Carl L., V.P.-Systems Hardware Devel.--ICL, Inc., Irvine, CA; *Int'l*, pg. 529
Ball, David, V.P.-Mfg.--Mason Shoe Mfg. Co., Chippewa Falls, WI; *U.S. Private*, pg. 712
Balsters, Scott, Plant Mgr.--Elixir Industries, Meridian, ID; *U.S. Private*, pg. 371
Baltz, William, Grp. V.P.-Engrng., Pur. & Construction--Monfort, Inc., Greeley, CO; *U.S. Public*, pg. 427
Bank, Richard P., V.P.-Engrng. Services--ICL, Inc., Irvine, CA; *Int'l*, pg. 529
Banks, Bob, Dir.-Quality & Prod. Performance--SGS-Thomson Microelectronics, Inc., Carrollton, TX; *Int'l*, pg. 1153
Banks, Kevin, V.P. & Bus. Mgr.-Compound Mfg.--Synergistics Industries Limited, Mississauga, Canada; *U.S. Public*, pg. 734
Banks, Lee, Dir.-Mfg.--Continental Web Press Of Kentucky, Walton, KY; *U.S. Private*, pg. 269
Baptista, Carlos M., Chief Exec. Officer, Dir.-Mfg. & Fin.--Apolo Produtos de Aco S.A., Rio de Janeiro, Brazil; *Int'l*, pg. 78
Baraglia, Bill, V.P.-Mfg.--Chicago White Metal Casting, Inc., Bensenville, IL; *U.S. Private*, pg. 236
Barancin, J., Dir.-Mfg.--Wacker Silicones Corporation, Adrian, MI; *Int'l*, pg. 625
Barbarosa, Gilberto R., Mgr.-Plng. & Prod. Control--Acos Villares Mechanical Engineering Unit, Sao Paulo, Brazil; *Int'l*, pg. 23
Barber, Joe, Mgr.-Mfg.--Airguard Industries Inc., Louisville, KY; *U.S. Public*, pg. 382
Barber, John C., Dir.-Mfg.--Luton Plant--Vauxhall Motors Limited, Luton, United Kingdom; *U.S. Public*, pg. 724
Bardash, N. Larry, Sr. V.P.-Supermarket Opers.--Big Bear Stores Company, Columbus, OH; *U.S. Public*, pg. 1270
Barenberg, J., Mgr.-Production--Kloof Division, Kloof, South Africa; *Int'l*, pg. 738
Barham, Beth, Mgr.-Production--Business Journal Publications, Inc., San Antonio, TX; *U.S. Private*, pg. 19
Barker, John, V.P.-Engrng.--Media 100, Inc., Marlborough, MA; *U.S. Public*, pg. 1079
Barnard, Dale, V.P.-Mfg.--Pneumatic Scale Corporation, Cuyahoga Falls, OH; *U.S. Private*, pg. 118
Barnes, Ken, Product Mgr.--Pfaff-Pegasus of U.S.A., Suwanee, GA; *Int'l*, pg. 1046
Barnes, Robert, Supvr.-Mfg.--Southern Ohio Fabricators, Inc., Batavia, OH; *U.S. Private*, pg. 1017
Barnes, Robert, V.P.-Mfg.--CMC Kalamazoo Inc., Kalamazoo, MI; *U.S. Private*, pg. 1030
Barnhart, Joel, V.P.-Mfg.--Fruit of the Loom, Inc., Chicago, IL; *U.S. Public*, pg. 685
Barnhart, Ralph, Gen. Foreman--E.H. Titchener & Company, Binghamton, NY; *U.S. Private*, pg. 1089
Barnot, Donald, Chief Engr.--Rokop Corporation, Bridgeville, PA; *U.S. Private*, pg. 941
Barr, Jeff, Mgr.-Mfg.--Lancaster Malleable Castings Company, Lancaster, PA; *U.S. Private*, pg. 645
Barr, Wendy, Controller-Mfg. Div.--Reptron Electronics, Inc., Tampa, FL; *U.S. Public*, pg. 1377
Barrett, Barrie, Dir.-Mfg. Div.--Brunel Holdings Plc, Chippenham, United Kingdom; *Int'l*, pg. 230
Barrett, Robert L., Prod. Engineer--Marquette Coppersmithing Co., Inc., Philadelphia, PA; *U.S. Private*, pg. 706
Barrett, Thomas E., Dir.-Mfg.--GenRad, Inc., Westford, MA; *U.S. Public*, pg. 731
Barrick, Alan L., V.P.-Engrng. & Mfg.--Weis Markets, Inc., Sunbury, PA; *U.S. Public*, pg. 1751
Barrocas, Jacob, V.P.-Mfg.--Injection Footwear Corp., Miami, FL; *U.S. Private*, pg. 563
Barros, Gil Leite, Mgr.-Mfg.--Henkel S/A. Industrias Quimicas, Sao Paulo, Brazil; *Int'l*, pg. 613
Barrows, Raymond H., V.P.-Mfg.--Finch, Pruyn & Co., Inc., Glens Falls, NY; *U.S. Private*, pg. 405
Bartholomew, Gary, V.P.-Mfg.--L.R. Nelson Corporation, Peoria, IL; *U.S. Private*, pg. 790
Bartlett, Ken, Mgr.-Plant--Streamlight Inc., Norristown, PA; *U.S. Private*, pg. 1047
Bartosh, Kenneth R., Mgr.-Prod.--Hanover Foods Corporation, Hanover, PA; *U.S. Private*, pg. 499
Bartsch, Art, V.P.-Bakery / R&D--The Swiss Colony, Inc, Monroe, WI; *U.S. Private*, pg. 1059
Bason, Jim, Mgr.-Production--Snyder Berlin, Berlin, PA; *U.S. Private*, pg. 887
Bass, Mike, V.P.-Mfg.--Imax Corporation, Mississauga, Canada; *Int'l*, pg. 661
Bassett, David J., Mgr.-Mfg. & Engrng--The W.E. Bassett Company, Shelton, CT; *U.S. Private*, pg. 122
Bassett, Jeb E., III, V.P. & Dir.-Wood Mfg.--Bassett Furniture Industries, Incorporated, Bassett, VA; *U.S. Public*, pg. 193
Bassi, Vic, V.P.-Mfg. & Mktg.--NTC/Contemporary Publishing Group, Lincolnwood, IL; *U.S. Public*, pg. 1635
Bastow, Kenneth W., Asst. V.P.-Mdse. Handling--Blair Corporation, Warren, PA; *U.S. Public*, pg. 236
Batista, Robert, Mfg. Engr.--Overton Gear & Tool Corp., Addison, IL; *U.S. Private*, pg. 823
Batliner, Doug, Dir.-Production & Pur.--Beach Mold & Tool Inc., New Albany, IN; *U.S. Private*, pg. 125
Batt, David, Mgr.-Mfg.--Muro Pharmaceutical, Inc., Tewksbury, MA; *U.S. Private*, pg. 767
Batton, Phil D., V.P.-Engrng.--General Cinema Theatres, Inc., Chestnut Hill, MA; *U.S. Public*, pg. 693
Baugh, Gene, V.P.-Mfg.--The Frymaster Corporation, Shreveport, LA; *Int'l*, pg. 188
Baugstat, Harald, Dir.-Pur. & Engrng.--Baumann Springs USA, Inc., Pineville, NC; *Int'l*, pg. 171
Baum, Eric, V.P.-Mfg.--Squire-Cogswell Company, Gurnee, IL; *U.S. Private*, pg. 1027
Bauman, David J., V.P.-Mfg.--John Crane North America, Morton Grove, IL; *Int'l*, pg. 1339
Baumgartner, John, Chief Engineer--T. Bruce Sales, Inc., West Middlesex, PA; *U.S. Private*, pg. 175
Bautzmann, John, Dir.-Opers.--Norwalk Co., Inc., Norwalk, CT; *U.S. Private*, pg. 807
Baxter, Charles, V.P.-Engrng.--Polaris Industries, Inc., Minneapolis, MN; *U.S. Public*, pg. 1313
Baxter, Steve, Dir.-Mfg.--Hitox Corporation of America, Corpus Christi, TX; *U.S. Public*, pg. 829
Bayer, Chris, V.P.-Mfg., Engrng. & Devel.--Precision Valve Corporation, Yonkers, NY; *U.S. Private*, pg. 880
Bayne, Jay S., V.P.-Engrng., Res. & Devel.--Bailey Controls Company, Wickliffe, OH; *Int'l*, pg. 654
Bayne, William, Jr., V.P.-Mfg.--Cablewave Systems, North Haven, CT; *U.S. Private*, pg. 197
Beale, Nathan, V.P.-Mfg.--Lee Company, Westbrook, CT; *U.S. Private*, pg. 657
Beam, Bryan H., Sr. V.P.-Distr. & Transportation--Heilig-Meyers Company, Richmond, VA; *U.S. Public*, pg. 804
Bean, William E., V.P.-Mfg.--D.D. Bean & Sons Co., Jaffrey, NH; *U.S. Private*, pg. 126
Beary, John, V.P.-Mfg.--HPM Corporation, Mount Gilead, OH; *U.S. Private*, pg. 492
Beatty, J. Keith, V.P.-Mfg./Office Furniture Casegoods--Kimball International, Inc., Jasper, IN; *U.S. Public*, pg. 956
Becker, William H., V.P.-Mfg.--The Wooster Brush Company, Wooster, OH; *U.S. Private*, pg. 1188
Beckman, Mike, Chief Engr.--Jarke Corporation, Niles, IL; *U.S. Private*, pg. 583
Beckwith, Scott, V.P.-Mfg.--Efco Corporation, Monett, MO; *U.S. Private*, pg. 353
Beery, Earl, Sr. V.P.-Prod.--Bob Evans Farms, Inc. Restaurant Division, Columbus, OH; *U.S. Public*, pg. 596
Beery, L. Merl, Sr. V.P.-Pur. & Tech. Services--Bob Evans Farms, Inc., Columbus, OH; *U.S. Public*, pg. 596
Beeson, Thomas, V.P.-Mfg.--Bose Corporation, Framingham, MA; *U.S. Private*, pg. 160
Befort, Glenn, V.P.-Desktop Prods., Mfg.--Siemens Business Communication Systems, Inc., Santa Clara, CA; *Int'l*, pg. 1245
Behencourt, Daniel, Dir.-Mfg. & Logistics--Proteon, Inc., Westborough, MA; *U.S. Public*, pg. 1336
Beill, David, Dir.-Mfg.--Hayward Industrial Products-Strainer Div., Elizabeth, NJ; *U.S. Private*, pg. 513
Bekes, Michael J., Chief Oper. Officer & V.P.--Badger Paper Mills, Inc., Peshtigo, WI; *U.S. Public*, pg. 165
Bell, Charles E., V.P.-Engrng.--Pharmacia & Upjohn, Kalamazoo, MI; *Int'l*, pg. 1048
Bellavita, Steve, Dir.-Mfg.--Atotech U.S.A. Inc., Rock Hill, SC; *U.S. Private*, pg. 97
Belle, Raymond, V.P. & Dir.-Mfg.--Societe d'Applications Generales d'Electricite et de Mechanique, Paris, France; *Int'l*, pg. 1273
Beltrand, Thomas L., Exec. V.P.-Opers.--Reuter Manufacturing Inc., Hopkins, MN; *U.S. Public*, pg. 1383
Bence, Frederick J., Mgr.-Distr.--Delta International Machinery Corp., Pittsburgh, PA; *U.S. Public*, pg. 1273
Benda, Brian, Dir.-Mfg.--Control Systems Inc., Saint Paul, MN; *U.S. Private*, pg. 271
Benedetti, Tom, Dir.-Printing--American Mathematical Society, Inc., Providence, RI; *U.S. Private*, pg. 59
Benguerel, Mark, V.P.-Mfg.--Prescolite Moldcast Lighting Company, San Leandro, CA; *U.S. Public*, pg. 1684
Bennert, Ken, Acting V.P.-Mfg.--Nellcor Puritan Bennett Incorporated, Pleasanton, CA; *U.S. Public*, pg. 1039
Bennett, James A., V.P.-Mfg.--K2 Corporation, Vashon, WA; *U.S. Public*, pg. 940
Bennett, Lester, Mgr.-Production--The Paty Company, Piney Flats, TN; *U.S. Private*, pg. 844
Bens, Andre, Ph.D., V.P.-Corp. Mfg. & Engrng.--Alcon Laboratories, Inc., Fort Worth, TX; *Int'l*, pg. 916
Bensch, Leonard, Dr., V.P. & Dir.-Scientific & Engrng. Services--Pall Corporation, Greenvale, NY; *U.S. Public*, pg. 1253
Bentley, Gene, V.P.-Production--Hygeia Dairy Co., Inc., Harlingen, TX; *U.S. Private*, pg. 552
Bentley, Gordon W., V.P.-Mfg. Instruments--Astro-Med, Inc., West Warwick, RI; *U.S. Public*, pg. 141
Bentley, Jon D., V.P. & Gen. Superintendent--The Homer Laughlin China Company, Newell, WV; *U.S. Private*, pg. 653
Benton, Robert L., Dir.-Mfg.--Flowers Industries, Inc., Thomasville, GA; *U.S. Public*, pg. 656
Berger, Don, V.P.- Mfg. & Sys.--Domore Corporation, Elkhart, IN; *U.S. Private*, pg. 339
Bergers, T.J.M.A., Mgr.-Production--Clyde Petroleum - Netherlands, Hague, Netherlands; *Int'l*, pg. 578
Berghahn, Walter G., V.P.-Mfg. Systems--Bristol-Myers Products, New York, NY; *U.S. Public*, pg. 254
Bergstrom, Len, V.P.-Mfg.--Beverage America, Inc., Holland, MI; *U.S. Private*, pg. 141
Beringer, Phil, Mgr.-Production--ACBJ Business Journals, Inc., Miami, FL; *U.S. Private*, pg. 19
Berkeley, Herbert, Mgr.-Prod.--Willis Corroon Corp. of Los Angeles, Glendale, CA; *Int'l*, pg. 1506
Berkey, Richard, V.P.-Mfg.--Universal Folding Box Company, Inc., Hoboken, NJ; *U.S. Private*, pg. 1127
Berkshire, M., Dir.-Quality Assurance & Technical Srvcs.--Brooks Foods, Mount Summit, IN; *U.S. Private*, pg. 887
Berman, Jody, Plant Mgr.--Benchmark Electronics Inc., Angleton, TX; *U.S. Public*, pg. 210
Bernard, John, Dir.-Mfg.--O.S. Walker Co. Inc., Worcester, MA; *U.S. Private*, pg. 1147
Bernel, Mark, V.P.-Mfg.--Mother's Cake & Cookie Co., Oakland, CA; *U.S. Private*, pg. 1022
Berntson, B., V.P.-Mktg. & Engrng.--Emerson Motor Company, Sturgeon Bay, WI; *U.S. Public*, pg. 573
Berrey, Howard J., Grp. V.P.-Real Estate & Construction--Bob Evans Farms, Inc., Columbus, OH; *U.S. Public*, pg. 596
Berry, Bill, Mgr.-Production--Latrobe Brewing Co., Latrobe, PA; *Int'l*, pg. 680
Berteau, Clement J., V.P.-Exploration--HCO Energy Ltd., Calgary, Canada; *U.S. Public*, pg. 782
Bertran, David R., Sr. V.P.-Mfg. & Logistics--Nalco Chemical Company, Naperville, IL; *U.S. Public*, pg. 1150
Best, Alex B., Sr. V.P.-Engrng.--Cox Communications, Inc., Atlanta, GA; *U.S. Public*, pg. 454
Bettle, Chip, Sr. V.P.-Technical Srvcs.--Joseph E. Seagram & Sons, Inc., New York, NY; *Int'l*, pg. 1215
Bezemer, A. D., Dir.-Mfg. & Logistics--Oce-van der Grinten N.V., Venlo, Netherlands; *Int'l*, pg. 993
Bezousek, Richard, V.P.-Production--Omaha Steaks, Omaha, NE; *U.S. Private*, pg. 815
Bhachaiyud, Chusak, V.P.-Tech.--Thai Airways International Ltd., Bangkok, Thailand; *Int'l*, pg. 1381
Bhandari, Harry, V.P.-Mfg.--Replogle Globes, Inc., Broadview, IL; *U.S. Private*, pg. 923

Bichai, Joseph, Sr. V.P.-Mfr.--Genfoot Inc., Montreal, Canada; *Int'l*, pg. 549
Bidart, Martin, V.P.-Mfg.--Penn Engineering & Manufacturing Corp., Danboro, PA; *U.S. Public*, pg. 1269
Bidenweg, Baron, V.P.-Mfg.--Harris-Kayot, Inc., Fort Wayne, IN; *U.S. Private*, pg. 506
Biller, Kenneth V., V.P.-Mfg.--RAYOVAC Corporation, Madison, WI; *U.S. Private*, pg. 912
Billingsly, Bob, Dir.-Processing & Devel.--Sanderson Farms, Inc., Laurel, MS; *U.S. Public*, pg. 1430
Billington, Timothy B., V.P.-Mfg. Opers.--Microchip Technology, Inc., Chandler, AZ; *U.S. Public*, pg. 1105
Bingham, Michael, V.P.-Mfg.--Rich Products Corp., Buffalo, NY; *U.S. Private*, pg. 928
Binkley, Bruce, Dir.-WH Opers.--T.D. Williamson, Inc., Tulsa, OK; *U.S. Private*, pg. 1179
Bird, Alan R., V.P.-Engrng.--Sunshine Biscuits, Inc., Woodbridge, NJ; *U.S. Private*, pg. 434
Bird, Alan R., V.P.-Engrng.--Sunshine Biscuits, Inc., Woodbridge, NJ; *U.S. Public*, pg. 657
Birnstiel, Edward G., V.P.-Global Mfg.--BetzDearborn Inc., Trevose, PA; *U.S. Public*, pg. 226
Bischoff, John, Plant Mgr.--Ardmore Farms, De Land, FL; *U.S. Public*, pg. 1348
Bishop, Ray, Plant Superintendent--Palm Beach Beauty Products Co., Minneapolis, MN; *U.S. Private*, pg. 834
Bizios, Harry, V.P.-Mfg.--Lennox International Inc., Richardson, TX; *U.S. Private*, pg. 659
Bjorkman, Jeffrey, V.P.-Mfg.--Polaris Industries, Inc., Minneapolis, MN; *U.S. Public*, pg. 1313
Bjurstrom, Edward E., V.P.-Mfg.--Amgen Inc., Thousand Oaks, CA; *U.S. Public*, pg. 100
Black, Dave, V.P.-Mfg. Opers.--Cavco Industries, Inc., Phoenix, AZ; *U.S. Public*, pg. 323
Black, Don, Chief Engr.--King & Prince Seafood Corporation, Brunswick, GA; *U.S. Private*, pg. 620
Black, Duane, Chief Oper. Officer & V.P.-Construction/Devel.--Suncor Development Company, Phoenix, AZ; *U.S. Public*, pg. 1298
Black, Herbert, Plant Engr.--Gertrude Hawk Chocolates, Inc., Dunmore, PA; *U.S. Private*, pg. 449
Blair, Jeff, V.P.-Mfg., Georgia--Crown Crafts, Inc., Atlanta, GA; *U.S. Public*, pg. 465
Blakely, J.M., Mgr.-Scheduling, Shipper Rels.--Colonial Pipeline Company, Atlanta, GA; *U.S. Private*, pg. 254
Blakeman, Douglas, Mgr.-Engrng.--Dreis & Krump Manufacturing Company, Chicago, IL; *U.S. Private*, pg. 342
Blalock, Alvin C., V.P., Sec. & Dir.-Mfg.--GoodMark Foods, Inc., Raleigh, NC; *U.S. Public*, pg. 751
Blanc, Gerard, V.P.-Prod.--SEITA, Societe Nationale D'Exploitation Industrielle des Tabacs et des Allumettes, Paris, France; *Int'l*, pg. 1219
Blasko, John, Dir.-Mfg.--Capital Controls Company Inc., Colmar, PA; *Int'l*, pg. 1226
Blennis, Dennis R., Mgr.-Mfg.--Hannay Reels, Westerlo, NY; *U.S. Private*, pg. 499
Blevins, David, Mgr.-Prod.--Universal Dynamics, Inc., Woodbridge, VA; *Int'l*, pg. 484
Blevins, James L., V.P.-Wire & Cable Mfr.--Southwire Company, Carrollton, GA; *U.S. Private*, pg. 1019
Block, Daryl, Mgr.-Mfg.--Eagle Food Centers, Inc., Milan, IL; *U.S. Public*, pg. 547
Blok, J., Works Dir.--Breda Sugar Factory, Breda, Netherlands; *Int'l*, pg. 244
Blount, David L., V.P.-Mfg.--American Woodmark Corporation, Winchester, VA; *U.S. Public*, pg. 96
Blum, David B., Dr., V.P.-Engrng.--Electrocatalytic, Inc., Union, NJ; *U.S. Private*, pg. 369
Blum, L.J., V.P.-Production--The Kirk & Blum Mfg. Co., Cincinnati, OH; *U.S. Private*, pg. 623
Blum, Stan, Head Engr.--L&R Manufacturing Co., Kearny, NJ; *U.S. Private*, pg. 638
Blumin, Laura, Mgr.-Production--Architectural Record, New York, NY; *U.S. Public*, pg. 1070
Blumling, Frank, Mgr.-Mfg.--Procter & Gamble Venezuela, C.A., Caracas, Venezuela; *U.S. Public*, pg. 1332
Bobita, Dennis, V.P.-Tech. Services--Alpo Pet Foods, Inc., Allentown, PA; *Int'l*, pg. 917
Bock, M., V.P.-Mfg., U.S. Opers.--Fleck Manufacturing Inc., Tillsonburg, Canada; *Int'l*, pg. 955
Bock, Frank, Dir.-Production & Engrng.--Cardinal Aluminum Co., Louisville, KY; *U.S. Private*, pg. 208
Boddy, Brian, Mgr.-Grp. Mfg.--The National Magazine Company Ltd., London, United Kingdom; *U.S. Private*, pg. 518
Boehme, Heiko, Mng. Dir.-Prod. & Tech.--Dr. Th. Boehme KG Chem. Fabrik GmbH & Co., Geretsried, Germany; *Int'l*, pg. 199
Boeve, Wayne, V.P.-Mfg.--Castex Incorporated, Holland, MI; *U.S. Public*, pg. 1577
Bohannon, Ralph, V.P.-Mfg.--Atmel Corporation, San Jose, CA; *U.S. Public*, pg. 145
Bohman, R., V.P.-Mfg. & Engrng.--Lehigh Portland Cement Company, Allentown, PA; *Int'l*, pg. 605
Bohn, Gabriela E., V.P.-Corp. Pur.--The May Department Stores Company, Saint Louis, MO; *U.S. Public*, pg. 1063
Bokor, James, Jr., Mgr.-Production--Robert James Sales Inc., Buffalo, NY; *U.S. Private*, pg. 935
Boling, Michael, V.P.-Engineered Piping Systems--Bristol Metals, L.P., Bristol, TN; *U.S. Public*, pg. 1548
Bollimpalli, Rao G., Sr. V.P.-Engrng.--JLG Industries, Inc., McConnellsburg, PA; *U.S. Public*, pg. 918
Bolls, Jim, V.P.-Mfg.--Carl Zeiss Optical, Inc., Petersburg, VA; *Int'l*, pg. 1523
Bolson, Tom, V.P.-Mfg. Design--Amtech Corporation, Dallas, TX; *U.S. Public*, pg. 105
Bolte, John, V.P.-Mfg.--National Machinery, Tiffin, OH; *U.S. Private*, pg. 785
Bolton, John, Mgr.-Mfg.--Ohio Gear/Richmond Gear - Liberty Div., Liberty, SC; *U.S. Public*, pg. 1370
Bolton, Ronald, Ph.D., Sr. Dir.-Mfg.--Nabi, Boca Raton, FL; *U.S. Public*, pg. 1148
Bonanno, Salvatore J., Exec. V.P.-Mfr.--Foamex International Inc., Linwood, PA; *U.S. Private*, pg. 1094
Bonczar, Lawrence J., V.P.-Engrng.--Casket Shells, Inc., Eynon, PA; *U.S. Private*, pg. 218
Bonina, Tony, Dir.-Tech. Mktg.--Eaton IDT, Westerville, OH; *U.S. Public*, pg. 558
Bonner, John J., V.P.-Mfg.--Bailey, Fischer & Porter Company, Warminster, PA; *Int'l*, pg. 449
Bonnett, A.H., V.P.-Engrng.--U.S. Electrical Motor Division, Saint Louis, MO; *U.S. Public*, pg. 573
Bonneville, Pamela M., V.P.-Admin.--Spirol International Corp., Danielson, CT; *U.S. Private*, pg. 1026
Booth, M., Dir.-Prod.--British Mohair Spinners Limited, Bradford, United Kingdom; *Int'l*, pg. 219
Boqusevic, Thomas, Dir.-Mfg. & Engrng.--Breuer/Tornado, Chicago, IL; *U.S. Private*, pg. 167
Boratko,E., Dir.-Mfg.--Detex Corporation, New Braunfels, TX; *U.S. Private*, pg. 327
Borchardt, Roger, V.P.-Mfg.--Jones Dairy Farm, Fort Atkinson, WI; *U.S. Private*, pg. 596
Bordewyk, Wayne, V.P.-Opers.--Brink Electric Construction Company, Rapid City, SD; *U.S. Private*, pg. 169
Borel, Robert J., V.P.-Engrng.--Worthington Industries, Inc., Columbus, OH; *U.S. Public*, pg. 1780
Borges, Jerry, Mgr.-Production--East Kentucky Power Co-op, Winchester, KY; *U.S. Private*, pg. 356
Borozan, Dan Duke, V.P.-Opers.--Caere Corporation, Los Gatos, CA; *U.S. Public*, pg. 291
Borror, Richard J., Jr., V.P.-Mfg.--Biomet, Inc., Warsaw, IN; *U.S. Public*, pg. 231
Borsellino, David S., V.P.-Mfr.--DoFasco, Inc., Hamilton, Canada; *Int'l*, pg. 414
Boruff, Robert E., V.P.-Mfg. Opers.--The Saturn Corporation, Troy, MI; *U.S. Public*, pg. 721
Botterbush, Fred, V.P.-Mfg.--The Pfaltzgraff Co., York, PA; *U.S. Private*, pg. 860
Boucher, Richard, V.P.-Mfg./Quebec Refinery--Ultramar Diamond Shamrock Corporation, San Antonio, TX; *U.S. Public*, pg. 1663
Bourg, Robert A., V.P.-Mfg.--Interform Corporation, Bridgeville, PA; *U.S. Public*, pg. 333
Bournias, William, Sr. V.P. & Grp. Exec.-Mfg. Systems--Western Atlas Inc., Houston, TX; *U.S. Public*, pg. 1757
Boutin, Christian, Sr. V.P.-Mfg.--Cosmair, Inc., New York, NY; *Int'l*, pg. 818
Bowen, Derrick, V.P.-Mfg.--ChemDesign Corporation, Fitchburg, MA; *Int'l*, pg. 173
Bowen, Leon O., Jr., V.P.-Engrng.--Rangaire Inc., Cleburne, TX; *U.S. Public*, pg. 1193
Bowers, James R., Mgr.-Production Control--Scott Mills, Gastonia, NC; *U.S. Private*, pg. 625
Bowers, William S., Chief Engineer--European Technical Center, Bascharage, Luxembourg; *U.S. Public*, pg. 721
Bowman, Bruce, Sr. Dir.-Opers.--Ben & Jerry's Homemade Inc., South Burlington, VT; *U.S. Public*, pg. 210
Bowman, Kent, Mgr.-Mfg.--Foga Systems, Oxnard, CA; *Int'l, pg. 496*
Box, George, Dir.-Engrng.--Capital Industries, Inc., Seattle, WA; *U.S. Private*, pg. 206
Boyd, Dale, V.P.-Greige Mfg.--Greenwood Mills, Inc., Greenwood, SC; *U.S. Private*, pg. 479
Boyen, Richard, V.P.--Eastco Industrial Safety Corp., Huntington Station, NY; *U.S. Public*, pg. 548
Boyer, Dale, Superintendent-Plant--John Copes Food Products, Inc., Rheems, PA; *U.S. Private*, pg. 274
Boyette, Rich, V.P.-Resinite Mfg.--AEP Industries, Inc., South Hackensack, NJ; *U.S. Public*, pg. 4
Boykin, William S., Jr., V.P.-Mfg.--The Ward Machinery Company, Hunt Valley, MD; *U.S. Private*, pg. 1149
Boyles, Chuck, Plant Mgr.--Svedala Industries-Universal Engineering, Cedar Rapids, IA; *Int'l*, pg. 1326
Brace, Raymond, V.P.-Mfg.--Hershey Chocolate U.S.A., Hershey, PA; *U.S. Public*, pg. 812
Bracken, J.F., V.P.-Engrng.--Simplicity Manufacturing, Inc., Port Washington, WI; *U.S. Private*, pg. 1002
Braden, William I., V.P.-Engrng./Facilities & Validation--MedImmune, Inc., Gaithersburg, MD; *U.S. Public*, pg. 1081
Bradley, Peter, Mgr.-Mfg.--C. Cakebread, London, United Kingdom; *Int'l*, pg. 460
Brahmstadt, Clifford A., V.P.-Mfg.--Bachman Company, Reading, PA; *U.S. Private*, pg. 109
Brakebill, James H., V.P.-Mfg.--Tuscarora Incorporated, New Brighton, PA; *U.S. Public*, pg. 1646
Brand, Larry, V.P.-Oper.--IBT, Inc., Merriam, KS; *U.S. Private*, pg. 553
Brant, Dennis, Dir.-Mfg.--Airtex Products, Fairfield, IL; *U.S. Private*, pg. 1113
Brasser, Ronald, V.P.-Engrng.--Howden Fluid Systems, Santa Barbara, CA; *U.S. Public*, pg. 1045
Brauks, Craig, Mgr.-Mfg.--Guth Lighting Company, Saint Louis, MO; *Int'l*, pg. 821
Brazeal, Chuck, V.P.-Mfg.--Hutchens Industries Inc., Springfield, MO; *U.S. Private*, pg. 550
Brazeal, Russ, V.P.-Engrng.--Hutchens Industries Inc., Springfield, MO; *U.S. Private*, pg. 550
Brdlik, Bruce, Mgr.-Mfg.--Foote-Jones/Illinois Gear, Chicago, IL; *U.S. Public*, pg. 1370
Brennan, E.J., V.P.-Engrng.--B/E Aerospace Seating Products Group, Litchfield, CT; *U.S. Public*, pg. 159
Brennan, Joseph, Dir.-Engrng.--Courier Corporation, North Chelmsford, MA; *U.S. Public*, pg. 453
Bressanelli, Jerome P., Pres.--Canton Drop Forge, Canton, OH; *U.S. Private*, pg. 205
Brettner, Donald M., V.P.-Mfg. Services--Advanced Micro Devices, Inc., Sunnyvale, CA; *U.S. Public*, pg. 21
Brewer, Danny, Dir.-Engrng.--Kilgore Operations, Toone, TN; *U.S. Public*, pg. 47
Brewer, Kevin, Dir.-Engrng.--New Standard Corporation, Mount Joy, PA; *U.S. Private*, pg. 794
Brewster, John, V.P.-Production--Cajun Electric Power Co-op, Baton Rouge, LA; *U.S. Private*, pg. 199
Brezezinski, John, Prod. Mgr.-Dari-Kool-Bou-Matic, Madison, WI; *U.S. Private*, pg. 301
Brickner, Louis C., V.P.-Engrng. & Prod. Devel.--Delta International Machinery Corp., Pittsburgh, PA; *U.S. Public*, pg. 1273
Bridwell, Joe, V.P.-Opers.--NWS Inc., Chicago, IL; *U.S. Private*, pg. 772
Briegel, Jack, V.P.-Mfg.--McNaughton & Gunn, Inc., Saline, MI; *U.S. Private*, pg. 724
Briggs, Terry, Dir. Mfg. & Res.--Weetabix Limited, Kettering, United Kingdom; *Int'l*, pg. 1488
Briick, Gerald, Dir.-Mfg. & Customer Services-Midwest--W. Braun Company, Chicago, IL; *U.S. Private*, pg. 166
Brill, Virgil E., V.P.-Energy Supply--The Empire District Electric Company, Joplin, MO; *U.S. Public*, pg. 579
Brink, K., Dir.-Mfg.--Castrol A/S, Copenhagen, Denmark; *Int'l*, pg. 235
Brisbois, Mike, Dir.-Mfg.--Spalding Sports Worldwide, Chicopee, MA; *U.S. Private*, pg. 630
Britt, Ron, Sr. V.P.-Mfg.--Belvedere Company, Belvidere, IL; *U.S. Private*, pg. 1008
Britten, Roy, V.P.-Mfg.--Sullivan Paper Company, West Springfield, MA; *U.S. Private*, pg. 1050
Brock, Paul, Jr., V.P.-Mfg.--Brach & Brock Confections Inc., Chattanooga, TN; *U.S. Private*, pg. 163
Brohas, Robert, V.P.-Engrng.--Plastic Moldings Corp., Cincinnati, OH; *U.S. Private*, pg. 871
Broman, Donald E., Sr. V.P.-Mfg. & Tech.--Snap-On Tools Corporation, Kenosha, WI; *U.S. Public*, pg. 1480
Brong, P.T., V.P.-Mfg.--Moore Business Forms & Systems Ltd., Mississauga, Canada; *Int'l*, pg. 889
Bronson, Joseph R., Grp. V.P.-Worldwide Mfg. Opers.--Applied Materials, Inc., Santa Clara, CA; *U.S. Public*, pg. 123
Brooks, George R., V.P.-Mfg.--Cox Wood Preserving Co., Orangeburg, SC; *U.S. Private*, pg. 283
Brooks, Patrick J., Dir.-Mfg. Svcs.--United McGill Corp., Groveport, OH; *U.S. Private*, pg. 1122
Brooks, Wayne I., V.P.-Distr. & Engrng.--Essex County Gas Company, Amesbury, MA; *U.S. Public*, pg. 593
Brorup, Carl, Mgr.-Engrng.--Horton Homes, Inc., Eatonton, GA; *U.S. Private*, pg. 540
Broslat, Bill, Mgr.-Pkgng. Devel.--Empire Berol U.S.A., Brentwood, TN; *U.S. Public*, pg. 1178
Brotsis, Gus, V.P.-Engrng.--Keymark Corporation, Fonda, NY; *U.S. Private*, pg. 618
Browder, Hugh E., V.P.-Mfg.--ABT Building Products Corporation, Neenah, WI; *Int'l*, pg. 20
Brown, Birchel, V.P.-Sterling Steel Opers.--Northwestern Steel & Wire Co., Sterling, IL; *U.S. Public*, pg. 1201
Brown, Calvin, V.P.-Mdsg.--Cliftex, New Bedford, MA; *U.S. Public*, pg. 1777
Brown, Dennis, Mgr.-Mfg.--Victaulic Company of America, Easton, PA; *U.S. Private*, pg. 1138
Brown, Gene, V.P.-Mfg.--Kysor/Warren, Conyers, GA; *U.S. Public*, pg. 1445
Brown, James, V.P.-Mfg., Roseland--B&G Foods, Inc., Roseland, NJ; *U.S. Private*, pg. 105
Brown, Jean, Mgr.-Pur.--George Lithograph, Brisbane, CA; *U.S. Private*, pg. 448
Brown, M. Ross, V.P.-Opers.--Analogic Corporation, Peabody, MA; *U.S. Public*, pg. 109
Brown, Marion L., V.P.-Mfg.--Kysor Panel Systems, Fort Worth, TX; *U.S. Public*, pg. 1445
Brown, Neil L., Dir.-Mfg.--National Presto Industries, Inc., Eau Claire, WI; *U.S. Public*, pg. 1159
Brown, Todd, V.P. & Mill Mgr.--Republic Paperboard Co.-Commerce City Mill, Commerce City, CO; *U.S. Public*, pg. 1378
Browning, John S., Jr., V.P.-Mfg.--Nalleys Fine Foods, Tacoma, WA; *U.S. Private*, pg. 887
Browning, Toni E., Pres.-Mdsg. & Sls.--Proffitt's, Inc., Alcoa, TN; *U.S. Public*, pg. 1333
Brownstein, Larry, V.P.-Mfg.--Rokeach Food Distributing Inc., Newark, NJ; *U.S. Private*, pg. 940
Bruce, Douglas M., V.P.-Aspen & XP Mfg.--Acuson Corporation, Mountain View, CA; *U.S. Public*, pg. 18
Brucker, Steven, V.P.-Office Systems Devel.--ICL, Inc., Irvine, CA; *Int'l*, pg. 529
Brumfield, Donald L., V.P.-Pur. & Engrng.--Treasure Chest Advertising Co., Inc., Glendora, CA; *U.S. Public*, pg. 228
Brummitt, S.W., V.P.-Mfg.--Harriet & Henderson Yarns, Inc., Henderson, NC; *U.S. Private*, pg. 504
Bruno, Amedo, Plant Mgr.--Batten Graphics, Toronto, Canada; *U.S. Public*, pg. 1437
Bruyere, Paul, Dir.-Mfg.--Cockerill Sambre, Brussels, Belgium; *Int'l*, pg. 301
Bryan, Phillip T., Dir.-Mfg.--Computational Systems Inc., Knoxville, TN; *U.S. Public*, pg. 572
Bryant, Richard, V.P.-Mfg.--Sullivan Paper Company, West Springfield, MA; *U.S. Private*, pg. 1050
Bryant, Ron, V.P.-Central Engrng. Services--APV Crepaco, Inc., Rosemont, IL; *Int'l*, pg. 1240
Bucaro, Benjamin, Mgr.-Prod.--Mark Lighting Fixture Co., Inc., Edison, NJ; *U.S. Private*, pg. 704
Bucheit, Larry M., V.P.-Mfg.--Heatilator Inc., Mount Pleasant, IA; *U.S. Public*, pg. 772
Buchinski, Brian, Dir.-Mfg.--Environment/One Corporation, Niskayuna, NY; *U.S. Public*, pg. 586
Buck, Thomas A., V.P.-Mfg.--Titanium Metals Corporation, Denver, CO; *U.S. Private*, pg. 270
Buckley, William N., V.P.-Strategic Plng.--Micros Systems Inc., Beltsville, MD; *U.S. Public*, pg. 1106
Buckson, Dave, V.P.-Mfg.--Office Electronics, Inc., Itasca, IL; *U.S. Private*, pg. 812
Buclheit, Richard, Mgr.-Mfg.--Keystone Powdered Metal Company, Saint Marys, PA; *U.S. Private*, pg. 619
Budd, Richard L., Chief Engr.--Pittsburgh Tube Co., Moon Township, PA; *U.S. Private*, pg. 867
Buehler, Robert G., Plant Mgr.--Stainless Incorporated, Deerfield Beach, FL; *U.S. Private*, pg. 1029
Bugby, David S., V.P.-Mfg.--Victaulic Company of America, Easton, PA; *U.S. Private*, pg. 1138
Bullock, Robert H., Dir.-Construction--Famous Restaurants Inc., Scottsdale, AZ; *U.S. Private*, pg. 393

Bultmann, Alfons, Tech. Mgr.-Plywood & Concrete Components--Westag & Getalit AG, Rheda-Wiedenbruck, Germany; *Int'l*, pg. 1491
Bumgarner, J. Steven, V.P.-Opers.--Shuford Mills, Inc., Hickory, NC; *U.S. Private*, pg. 996
Bunch, Drexel R., V.P.-Mfg.--Nordson Corporation, Westlake, OH; *U.S. Public*, pg. 1188
Bunke, Herbert, V.P.-Mfg.--The Metal Ware Corp., Two Rivers, WI; *U.S. Private*, pg. 734
Burad, Rug, V.P.-Mfg.--Tyco Toys, Inc., Mount Laurel, NJ; *U.S. Public*, pg. 1058
Burbulys, G., Dir.-Tech. Affairs & Mfr.--Alva/Amco Pharmacal Companies, Inc., Chicago, IL; *U.S. Private*, pg. 47
Burd, Larry W., Sr. V.P.-Mfg.--Kreonite, Inc., Wichita, KS; *U.S. Private*, pg. 635
Burden, Dave, Mgr.-Mfg.--Cognos Inc., Ottawa, Canada; *Int'l*, pg. 305
Burger, Danie W., Jr., V.P.-Manufacturing (Europe)--Du Pont (E.I. Du Pont De Nemours & Co.), Wilmington, DE; *U.S. Public*, pg. 530
Burger, Thomas T., Jr., V.P.-F/A-18 & Military Subcontracts Enterprise--Aircraft Division, Hawthorne, CA; *U.S. Public*, pg. 1198
Burgett, W. Barth, V.P.-Equipment & Maintenance--Kokosing Construction Company, Inc., Fredericktown, OH; *U.S. Private*, pg. 631
Burggraaf, J.D., V.P.-Mfg.--Bissell Inc., Grand Rapids, MI; *U.S. Private*, pg. 145
Burghard, Fernand, Mfg.--Millipore S.A., Molsheim, France; *U.S. Public*, pg. 1113
Burk, Craig A., V.P.-Mfg.--E-Z-Em, Inc., Westbury, NY; *U.S. Public*, pg. 540
Burkart, John B., Exec. V.P.-Sr. Mfg. Advisor--Diamond Star Motors, Normal, IL; *Int'l*, pg. 875
Burke, James, Mgr.-Extrusion--KCL Corporation, Shelbyville, IN; *U.S. Private*, pg. 603
Burkhammer, Mary, Dir.-Manuf. Engrng.--Sofamor Danek Group, Inc., Memphis, TN; *U.S. Public*, pg. 1482
Burkhammer, Stephen, V.P.-Mfg.--Lake Shore, Inc., Kingsford, MI; *U.S. Private*, pg. 814
Burns, Doug, V.P.-Mfg.--Circle Plastics Products, Inc., Circleville, OH; *U.S. Private*, pg. 240
Burns, Ralph, Sr. V.P.-Mfg. & Res./Devel.--Peerless Carpet Corporation, Acton Vale, Canada; *Int'l*, pg. 1032
Burris, Richard L., V.P.-Mfg.--Rainbow Technologies, Inc., Irvine, CA; *U.S. Public*, pg. 1359
Burrows, John, Dir.-Mfg.--Astec Europe Limited, Stourbridge, United Kingdom; *Int'l*, pg. 93
Busch, Joseph F., Exec. V.P.--Ederer Inc., Seattle, WA; *U.S. Private*, pg. 363
Buschette, Mic, Mgr.-Opers.--Dynamic Homes, Inc., Detroit Lakes, MN; *U.S. Public*, pg. 538
Bussell, Lloyd B., V.P.-Mfg.--Kronos Incorporated, Waltham, MA; *U.S. Public*, pg. 967
Bustard, Frederick C., V.P.-Power Supply & Environ.--Maine Public Service Company, Presque Isle, ME; *U.S. Public*, pg. 1038
Butcher, James, V.P.-Mfg.--Reed & Barton Corporation, Taunton, MA; *U.S. Private*, pg. 916
Butkus, Dan, V.P.-Engrng.--Gallagher-Kaiser Corp., Detroit, MI; *U.S. Private*, pg. 438
Butler, Jerry, Exec. V.P.-WW Opers. & Mfg.--Brite Voice Systems, Inc., Heathrow, FL; *U.S. Public*, pg. 257
Butler, Robert D., Exec. V.P.-Opers.--Baldor Electric Company, Fort Smith, AR; *U.S. Public*, pg. 168
Buzzi, P., Mgr.-Mfg.--Zanussi Componenti Plastica S.p.A., Oderzo, Italy; *Int'l*, pg. 442
Bye, Scott J., V.P.-Mfg.--Kysor/Michigan Fleet, Grand Rapids, MI; *U.S. Public*, pg. 968
Byrd, Bill, V.P.-Mfg.--Thermalloy, Inc., Farmers Branch, TX; *Int'l*, pg. 208
Byrne, J. David, V.P.-Mfg. & Engrng.--Galileo Corp., Sturbridge, MA; *U.S. Public*, pg. 698
Byrne, John J., V.P.-Mfg.--General Felt Industries, Inc., Linwood, PA; *U.S. Private*, pg. 1094
Byrnes, Richard, Jr., Sr. V.P.-Opers.--Swank, Inc., Attleboro, MA; *U.S. Public*, pg. 1543
Byrnes, Robert L., V.P.-Mfg.--Cerberus Pyrotronics Inc., Cedar Knolls, NJ; *Int'l*, pg. 1246
Byron, Cliff, Mgr.-Opers.--Berryman Products, Inc., Arlington, TX; *U.S. Private*, pg. 138
Cable, Gary L., Dir.-Intl. Mfg. Devel.--Foster Wheeler Corporation, Clinton, NJ; *U.S. Public*, pg. 676
Cadmus, Robert B., V.P.-Mfg.--Accu-Sort Systems, Inc., Telford, PA; *U.S. Private*, pg. 11
Cahill, J., Dir.-Commercial--CRH, plc, Dublin, Ireland; *Int'l*, pg. 242
Cahn, Richard, Dir.-Mfg.--Movie Star, Inc., New York, NY; *U.S. Public*, pg. 1140
Cairns, J.A., Dir.-Production--Redland Tile & Brick, Crumlin, United Kingdom; *Int'l*, pg. 1091
Cakus, Al, Dir.-Plant Opers.--Beutler Heating & Air Conditioning Inc., Sacramento, CA; *U.S. Private*, pg. 141
Caldwell, Greg, Dir.-Facility Engrng.--Lowe's Food Stores, Inc., Winston Salem, NC; *U.S. Private*, pg. 657
Call, Charlie, Pres.-Trim Company--JPE, Inc., Ann Arbor, MI; *U.S. Public*, pg. 919
Call, Ralph, Pres. & Chief Exec. Officer--WINCO, Le Center, MN; *U.S. Private*, pg. 350
Call, Scott, V.P.-Mfg.--Sentinel Consumer Products, Inc., Mentor, OH; *U.S. Private*, pg. 984
Call, W. Lowell, V.P.-Production--Bob Evans Farms, Inc., Columbus, OH; *U.S. Public*, pg. 596
Calvo, Luis, Dir.-Tech.--Polymer Plastics Corporation, Hauppauge, NY; *U.S. Private*, pg. 875
Cameron, Gordon, V.P.-Mfg.--Ce De Candy, Inc., Union, NJ; *U.S. Private*, pg. 220
Camiolo, Shirley, Mgr.-Mdsg.--Duty Free International, Inc., Ridgefield, CT; *Int'l*, pg. 103
Campbell, Alma, Mgr.-Production Scheduling--Retail Bag Division - Yulee Plant, Yulee, FL; *U.S. Public*, pg. 1521
Campbell, David D., V.P. & Gen. Mgr.-Rear Wheel Drive Product Team--General Motors Corporation, Detroit, MI; *U.S. Public*, pg. 718
Campbell, Jack, V.P.-Mfg.--Medical Laboratory Automation, Inc., Pleasantville, NY; *U.S. Private*, pg. 727
Campbell, Terry, Mgr.-Mfg.--Wire Rope Corporation of America, Inc., Saint Joseph, MO; *U.S. Private*, pg. 1184
Campbell, Tom, Mgr.-Prod.--Kit Manufacturing Company, Long Beach, CA; *U.S. Public*, pg. 962
Cannady, Cynthia, V.P.-Law, Devel. & Mfg.--Apple Computer, Inc., Cupertino, CA; *U.S. Public*, pg. 121
Cannizzaro, Ben, Dir.-Production--Macromedia Incorporated, Hackensack, NJ; *U.S. Private*, pg. 693
Canterino, Joseph, Dir.-Mfg.--Espey Mfg. & Electronics Corp., Saratoga Springs, NY; *U.S. Public*, pg. 592
Canty, Wayne, V.P.-Mfg.--Rockbestos-Suprenant Cable Corp., Clinton, MA; *U.S. Private*, pg. 938
Capitano, Jim, Sr. V.P.-Mfg.--Duron, Inc., Beltsville, MD; *U.S. Private*, pg. 349
Caplan, Jay, V.P.-Mfg.--Candela Corporation, Wayland, MA; *U.S. Public*, pg. 300
Caple, George, Mgr.-Prod.--American Electronics, Inc., Fullerton, CA; *U.S. Private*, pg. 5
Caplenor, Jeff, V.P.-Mfg.--Fruit of the Loom, Inc., Chicago, IL; *U.S. Public*, pg. 685
Capone, Donald W., V.P.-Engrng. & Construction--AmerenUE, Saint Louis, MO; *U.S. Public*, pg. 66
Caponigro, Leonard, V.P.-Opers.--Tork, Inc., Mount Vernon, NY; *U.S. Private*, pg. 1092
Cappadona, Tom, Mgr.-Mfg.--Kaz, Inc., New York, NY; *U.S. Private*, pg. 610
Carango, Keith, V.P.-Bakery Opers.--Cheesecake Factory Incorporated, Calabasas Hills, CA; *U.S. Public*, pg. 343
Carder, Dane L., Sr., Dir.-Mfg.--YSD Industries, Youngstown, OH; *U.S. Private*, pg. 1194
Cardinal, R.W., V.P.-Mfg.--Zinc Products Company, Greeneville, TN; *U.S. Public*, pg. 57
Cardner, Bill, Dir.-Mfg. Opers.--Aurora Metals Division L.P.C., Montgomery, IL; *U.S. Private*, pg. 529
Cardoso, Jose L., Dir.-Production--Eli Lilly do Brasil Limitada, Sao Paulo, Brazil; *U.S. Public*, pg. 993
Carey, Dermot, Dir.-Plant Opers.--United Dairymen of Arizona, Tempe, AZ; *U.S. Private*, pg. 1121
Carey, John, V.P.-Mfg.--Liebert Corporation, Columbus, OH; *U.S. Public*, pg. 573
Carlin, Al, V.P.-Mfg.--International Specialty Products, Inc., Wayne, NJ; *U.S. Public*, pg. 858
Carlson, David, Dir.-Mfg.--Criticare Systems, Inc., Waukesha, WI; *U.S. Public*, pg. 459
Carlson, Richard E., V.P.-Mfg.--Computer Network Technology Corporation, Minneapolis, MN; *U.S. Public*, pg. 421
Carmean, William M., V.P.-Opers.--Allied Mineral Products, Inc., Columbus, OH; *U.S. Private*, pg. 39
Carney, Keith, V.P.-Engrng.--Welsbach Electric Corp., College Point, NY; *U.S. Public*, pg. 572
Carr, David B.C., V.P.-Mfg. & Material--Williams International, Walled Lake, MI; *U.S. Private*, pg. 1178
Carrieri, Warren, Dir.-Engrng.--Johnson & Towers, Inc., Mount Laurel, NJ; *U.S. Private*, pg. 590
Carrol, Bill, Dir.-Production--Jack Schwartz Shoes, Inc., New York, NY; *U.S. Private*, pg. 974
Carroll, Gary, V.P.-Engrng.--Aerofin Corp., Lynchburg, VA; *U.S. Public*, pg. 103
Carroll, Gerard P., Sr. V.P.-Mfg. & Engrng.--National Gypsum Company, Charlotte, NC; *Int'l*, pg. 790
Carroll, Seamus, V.P.-Opers.--AFP Imaging Corporation, Elmsford, NY; *U.S. Public*, pg. 6
Carroll, William J., Plant Mgr.-Chicago--Hickman, Williams & Company of Kentucky, Chicago, IL; *U.S. Private*, pg. 525
Carron, Don, Mgr.-Production--Marketing Displays International, Farmington Hills, MI; *U.S. Private*, pg. 705
Carrozzo, Guilherme T.M., Mgr.-Mfg.--Acos Villares Steel Unit, Sao Paulo, Brazil; *Int'l*, pg. 23
Carter, Jack, V.P.-Mfg.--KMW Systems Corporation, Austin, TX; *U.S. Public*, pg. 112
Carter, Rodney, Mng. Dir.-Mfg.--Whatman plc, Maidstone, United Kingdom; *Int'l*, pg. 1498
Carter, Scott, Dir.-Mfg.--The Will-Burt Company, Orrville, OH; *U.S. Private*, pg. 1177
Caruso, Carl, V.P.-Mfg.--Aeroflex Incorporated, Plainview, NY; *U.S. Public*, pg. 23
Carver, William N., V.P.-Engrng.--ScanTron Corporation, Tustin, CA; *U.S. Public*, pg. 786
Casa, Robert, Mgr.-Mfg.--FTP Software Inc., Andover, MA; *U.S. Public*, pg. 609
Case, Don, V.P.-Mfg.--Standun, Inc., Inglewood, CA; *U.S. Private*, pg. 1032
Case, Don, V.P.-Mfg.--Zephyr Mfg. Co., Inglewood, CA; *U.S. Private*, pg. 1032
Case, Gerard, V.P.-Design & Mfg.--Oxford University Press, Inc., New York, NY; *Int'l*, pg. 1019
Casey, J., Dir.-Mfg.--Hepworth Refractories Ltd., Alfreton, United Kingdom; *Int'l*, pg. 615
Casper, Richard, V.P.-Engrng.--Aeroflex Laboratories Inc., Plainview, NY; *U.S. Public*, pg. 24
Cassar, Charles J., V.P.-Jewelry Mfg. & Prod. Devel.--QVC, Inc., West Chester, PA; *U.S. Private*, pg. 897
Casteline, John R., Mgr.-Prod.--Aquamine, LLC, Bristol, TN; *U.S. Private*, pg. 1138
Castle, David R., V.P. & Bus. Grp. Mgr.--Weigh-Tronix, Inc., Fairmont, MN; *Int'l*, pg. 1299
Catani, Albert J., II, V.P.-Mfg.--The Lamson & Sessions Co., Cleveland, OH; *U.S. Public*, pg. 976
Catellier, Al, V.P.-Mfg.--Lynx Golf, Inc., City of Industry, CA; *U.S. Private*, pg. 684
Cathey, Terry H., V.P.-Matl. Handling Opers.--Cascade Corporation, Troutdale, OR; *U.S. Public*, pg. 310
Cauwells, Chuck, V.P.-Mfg.--The Middleby Corporation, Rolling Meadows, IL; *U.S. Public*, pg. 1109
Caverly, Chuck, V.P.-Mfg.--Justin Boot Company, Fort Worth, TX; *U.S. Public*, pg. 937
Cayouette, D., V.P.-Mfg./Corner Brook & Manistique Papers, Inc.--Kruger Inc., Montreal, Canada; *Int'l*, pg. 761
Cayouette, Donald, V.P.-Mfg.--Kruger Urban Forest Products, Inc., Bromptonville, Canada; *Int'l*, pg. 761
Cayouette, Donald J., V.P.-Mfg.--Corner Brook Pulp & Paper Limited, Corner Brook, Canada; *Int'l*, pg. 761
Cebulski, Joseph, Gen. Mgr.-Mfg.--Mitchell Corporation of Owosso, Owosso, MI; *U.S. Private*, pg. 753
Cecil, Roy, V.P.-Mfg.--Monroe City Division, Monroe City, MO; *U.S. Public*, pg. 986
Cehun, T., Gen. Mgr.-Mfg. & Tech.--Hoechst Australia Ltd., Melbourne, Australia; *Int'l*, pg. 626
Cercone, Ronald J., V.P. & Gen. Mgr.-Merocel Mfg.--Xomed Surgical Products, Jacksonville, FL; *U.S. Public*, pg. 253
Cerini, Martin, Dir.-Mfg.--American Technical Ceramics Corp., Huntington Station, NY; *U.S. Public*, pg. 93
Cerquiera, Luiz, V.P.-Mfg.--Carrington Laboratories, Inc., Irving, TX; *U.S. Public*, pg. 309
Chadwell, Charles L., V.P.-Prod.--G.E. Aircraft Engines, Cincinnati, OH; *U.S. Public*, pg. 710
Chafe, Gary, Mgr.-Mfg.--Electra-Gear Div., Anaheim, CA; *U.S. Public*, pg. 1370
Chamblee, Paul, V.P.-Mfg.--D.P. Fitness, Opelika, AL; *U.S. Public*, pg. 1354
Chandler, Doug, Dir.-Mfg.--Carolina Builders Corporation, Marietta, GA; *Int'l*, pg. 1512
Chang-Yong, Jang, Gen. Mgr.--Korea Heavy Industries & Construction Co., Ltd., Seoul, Korea; *Int'l*, pg. 758
Channell, Bob, V.P.-Mfg.--Keymark Corporation, Fonda, NY; *U.S. Private*, pg. 618
Chantiam, Clement F., Exec. V.P.-Mfg.--Stuart Entertainment Inc., Council Bluffs, IA; *U.S. Public*, pg. 1526
Chao-Jung, Kuo, Mgr.-Mfg.--Singapore Petroleum Company Ltd., Singapore, Singapore; *U.S. Public*, pg. 102
Chaplin, James, V.P.-Engrng. & Mfg.--Racine Federated, Inc., Racine, WI; *U.S. Private*, pg. 906
Chapman, Carl, Dir.-Steel Plant--Artco-Bell Corporation, Temple, TX; *U.S. Private*, pg. 86
Chapman, H. George, V.P.-Mfg.--Vermont American Tool Corp., Louisville, KY; *U.S. Public*, pg. 575
Charles, Mike, Dir.-Mfg.--Daktronics, Inc., Brookings, SD; *U.S. Public*, pg. 478
Charlson, G., V.P.-Mfg.--Simmons Juvenile Products Co., Inc., New London, WI; *U.S. Private*, pg. 1001
Charlton, Scott, V.P.-Mfg.--Publix Supermarkets Inc., Lakeland, FL; *U.S. Private*, pg. 893
Chase, Rich, V.P.-Mfg.--Aquion, Elk Grove Village, IL; *U.S. Private*, pg. 78
Chastain, J. Dee, Div. V.P.-Mfg.--Baldwin Piano & Organ Company, Loveland, OH; *U.S. Public*, pg. 169
Chelton, John, Corp. Mfg.--Estee Lauder, Melville, NY; *U.S. Public*, pg. 594
Chenault, John, V.P.-Metals--Novellus Systems, Inc., San Jose, CA; *U.S. Public*, pg. 1204
Cheney, Tom, V.P.-Prod. & Mfg.--The Orr Felt Company, Piqua, OH; *U.S. Private*, pg. 820
Cheng, T.T., V.P.-Production Div.--China Steel Corporation, Kao-hsiung, Taiwan; *Int'l*, pg. 285
Cheremeteff, Nikita, V.P.-Mfg.--Loctite Corporation, Rocky Hill, CT; *Int'l*, pg. 611
Cherenson, Edward, V.P.-Engrng.--King Industries, Inc., Norwalk, CT; *U.S. Private*, pg. 620
Cherry, Wayne K., V.P.-Design Staff--General Motors Corporation, Detroit, MI; *U.S. Public*, pg. 718
Chesnut, Powe, Dir.-Mfg.--Sanderson Plumbing Products Inc., Columbus, MS; *U.S. Private*, pg. 964
Chetaud, Lou, V.P.-Mfg. Opers.--Analog Devices, Santa Clara, CA; *U.S. Public*, pg. 108
Chiado, James, V.P.-Mfg. & Mktg.--Kauffman Products, Inc., Carmel, IN; *U.S. Private*, pg. 609
Chicoine, Thomas A., V.P.-Mfg. & Distr.--Dairy Mart Convenience Stores, Inc., Cuyahoga Falls, OH; *U.S. Public*, pg. 476
Chiddix, James, Sr. V.P.-Engrng.--Time Warner Cable, Stamford, CT; *U.S. Public*, pg. 1610
Chinchilla, Ernest, V.P.-Mfg.--Automatic Signal/Eagle Signal, Austin, TX; *Int'l*, pg. 1245
Chionchio, M.A., V.P.-Mfg.--Senior Engineering Company-USA, City of Commerce, CA; *Int'l*, pg. 1222
Chipman, Tim, Gen. Mgr.--B & P Manufacturing, Cadillac, MI; *U.S. Private*, pg. 105
Chisholm, John, Plant Mgr.--M K Diamond Products, Inc., Torrance, CA; *U.S. Private*, pg. 684
Chmielowiec, Ronald, Mgr.-Production--Hinkley Lighting Inc., Cleveland, OH; *U.S. Private*, pg. 530
Chokshi, Matt, V.P.-Mfg.--JTS Corporation, San Jose, CA; *U.S. Public*, pg. 919
Christian, David, Sr. V.P.-Opers.--Courtaulds Fibers Inc., Axis, AL; *Int'l*, pg. 339
Christiansen, T., Gen. Mgr.-Mfg. & Opers.--Peters & Brownes Foods Ltd., Balcatta, Australia; *Int'l*, pg. 1040
Christianson, Rod, Mgr.-Mfg.--Cargill Salt, Newark, CA; *U.S. Private*, pg. 210
Christophersen, Robert L., Exec. V.P.-Mfg.--American Banknote Corp., New York, NY; *U.S. Public*, pg. 68
Christopherson, J.E., Mgr.-Service-Factory--Badger Equipment Co., Winona, MN; *U.S. Private*, pg. 102
Chronley, Kevin, Mgr.-Mfg.--Hammond Group Inc., Hammond, IN; *U.S. Private*, pg. 498
Chumney, Jim C., Sr. V.P.-Engrng.--Inter-Tel, Incorporated, Phoenix, AZ; *U.S. Public*, pg. 888
Church, Richard, V.P.-Opers.--Markem Corporation, Keene, NH; *U.S. Private*, pg. 704
Churchill, Robert, V.P.-Engrng.--Menasco Aerosystems Division, Euless, TX; *U.S. Public*, pg. 402
Churchman, J., Dir.-Mfg.--Addison Tube Forming Limited, Preston, United Kingdom; *Int'l*, pg. 448
Ciaccia, Nicholas, Dir.-Mfg.--Rapid Power Technologies, Inc., Brookfield, CT; *U.S. Private*, pg. 910
Cidlik, W., Mgr.-Mfg.--Arrow Gear Company, Downers Grove, IL; *U.S. Private*, pg. 85
Ciemnieski, John, V.P.-Mfg.--Superior Steel Acquisition Corporation, Cheshire, CT; *Int'l*, pg. 75
Cieplak, John, Mgr.-Mfg.--Tricon Electromechanical Div., Downers Grove, IL; *U.S. Private*, pg. 1103

Cimaroli, Richard, Mgr.-Engrng.--Vacudyne Inc., Chicago Heights, IL; *U.S. Private*, pg. 46

Cipau, Gabriel R., Sr. V.P.-Production & Engrng.--Glaxo Wellcome PLC, Research Triangle Park, NC; *Int'l*, pg. 553

Cipresso, Guy, Dir.-Mfg.--Mutoh America Inc., Phoenix, AZ; *Int'l*, pg. 897

Cipriano, Joseph A., Mgr.-Production--Descente America Inc., Englewood, CO; *Int'l*, pg. 395

Cirillo, Anthony, Dir.-Mfg.--John Dusenbery Co., Inc., Randolph, NJ; *U.S. Private*, pg. 349

Cirone, Bill, V.P.-Mfg.--Rapid Mounting & Finishing Co., Chicago, IL; *U.S. Private*, pg. 910

Cisneros, Dave, V.P.-Mfg.--Tomco Auto Products, Inc., Los Angeles, CA; *U.S. Private*, pg. 1090

Cisneros, Radishel, Mgr.-Production--Theochem Labs., Inc., Tampa, FL; *U.S. Private*, pg. 1079

Claassen, James G., Sr. V.P.-Sls. & Sls. Services--Montgomery KONE Inc., Moline, IL; *Int'l*, pg. 746

Claibourn, Bill, Mgr.-Mfg.--Davis Paint Company, Kansas City, MO; *U.S. Private*, pg. 315

Clapp, Robert W., V.P.-Mfg.--EMPI, Inc., Saint Paul, MN; *U.S. Public*, pg. 545

Clark, Brad, V.P.-Mfg.--Fruit of the Loom, Inc., Chicago, IL; *U.S. Public*, pg. 685

Clark, Glenn, Mgr.-Mfg.--Plastic Products Division, Tillsonburg, Canada; *U.S. Private*, pg. 428

Clark, Mark, Sr. V.P.-Mfg.--Rotterdam Ventures Inc., Guilderland Center, NY; *U.S. Private*, pg. 437

Clarke, Eugene, V.P.-Corp. Mfg. Services--HarperCollins Publishers, New York, NY; *Int'l*, pg. 926

Clemens, Fritz, Mgr.-Mfr.--Namco Controls Corporation, Highland Heights, OH; *U.S. Public*, pg. 482

Clifford, R.L., Exec. Dir.-Mining--The RTZ Corporation PLC, London, United Kingdom; *Int'l*, pg. 1118

Clink, Donald, Mgr.-Mfg. & Human Resources--Amot Controls Corporation, Richmond, CA; *U.S. Public*, pg. 1405

Clyburn, Bill, Mgr.-Mfg.--Schilling Plant, Salinas, CA; *U.S. Public*, pg. 1066

Cobian, Francis J., Dir.-Production--Land O'Lakes, Inc., Kiel, WI; *U.S. Private*, pg. 646

Cocce, John, Sr. V.P.-Mfg.--American Media, Inc., Lake Worth, FL; *U.S. Public*, pg. 87

Cockrell, Charles F., V.P.-Mfg.--Glen-Gery Corporation, Wyomissing, PA; *Int'l*, pg. 658

Coco, David, V.P.-Tech. Svcs.--National Fruit Product Company, Winchester, VA; *U.S. Private*, pg. 783

Coda, Andrea, Mgr.-Production--Self, New York, NY; *U.S. Private*, pg. 20

Coffman, Fred, Mgr.-Mfg.--Zetec, Inc., Issaquah, WA; *U.S. Private*, pg. 1205

Cohen, Jerry I., V.P.-Mdse. Control--Noodle Kidoodle Inc., Syosset, NY; *U.S. Public*, pg. 1188

Cohen, Sanford, Sr. V.P.-Technology--Sipex Corporation, Billerica, MA; *Int'l*, pg. 1415

Cohrs, Mark, Mgr.-Mfg.--Code-Alarm, Inc., Madison Heights, MI; *U.S. Public*, pg. 393

Colado, Joe, Mgr.-Plant--Symons Corporation, Des Plaines, IL; *U.S. Private*, pg. 932

Colby, G.R., Dir.-Matls. Mngmt.--ABB Air Preheater Inc., Wellsville, NY; *Int'l*, pg. 3

Colby, Peter, Dir.-Mfg.--Alloy Technology International Inc., West Nyack, NY; *U.S. Private*, pg. 42

Colehamer, Glen, Dir.-Mfg.--Label-Aire Inc., Fullerton, CA; *U.S. Private*, pg. 641

Coleman, Cherb, Dir.-Opers.--Coleman Dairy LLC, Little Rock, AR; *U.S. Private*, pg. 251

Coleman, Robert C., V.P.-Mfg.--American Packaging Corporation, Philadelphia, PA; *U.S. Private*, pg. 60

Collins, Bill, Gen. Mgr.-Indus.--Titeflex Corporation, Springfield, MA; *Int'l*, pg. 1340

Collins, Greg, Dir.-Mfg.--C P Converters, Inc., York, PA; *U.S.* Private, pg. 192

Collins, J., V.P.-Mfg.--Aluminum Shapes, LLC, Delair, NJ; *U.S. Private*, pg. 47

Collins, Robert, Jr., V.P.-Mfg.--Wheeled Coach Industries, Inc., Winter Park, FL; *U.S. Public*, pg. 400

Colnitis, Steven J., Sr. Assoc. Mgr.-Adv.--Clarion Cosmetics, Hunt Valley, MD; *U.S. Public*, pg. 1330

Colombatta, J., V.P.-Mfg.--Moore Response Graphics, Green Bay, WI; *Int'l*, pg. 890

Coltart, Mike, Sr. V.P.-Mfg.--Brach & Brock Confections, Inc., Chicago, IL; *U.S. Private*, pg. 163

Colvin, Joe, V.P.-Mfg.--Hardings, Inc., Elmira, NY; *U.S. Private*, pg. 502

Combs, Jack, Mgr.-Mfg.--Kimray, Inc., Oklahoma City, OK; *U.S. Private*, pg. 620

Compain, Oscar, V.P.-Mfg.--Diamedix Corporation, Miami, FL; *U.S. Public*, pg. 914

Componovo, William, V.P.-Production Svcs.--QVC, Inc., West Chester, PA; *U.S. Private*, pg. 897

Cone, Stanley, V.P.-Mfg.--Stern & Stern Industries Inc., New York, NY; *U.S. Private*, pg. 1041

Conish, Mark, V.P.-Mfg. & Distr.--Church & Dwight Co., Inc., Princeton, NJ; *U.S. Public*, pg. 355

Conklin, David L., Sr. V.P. & Pres.-Chemical Mfg.--Merck Manufacturing Div., Rahway, NJ; *U.S. Public*, pg. 1091

Conkovich, John, Gen. Mgr.-Hodges--Falcon Products, Inc., Saint Louis, MO; *U.S. Public*, pg. 611

Conley, Bruce, Dir.-Indus. Rels.--Sun-Maid Growers of California, Kingsburg, CA; *U.S. Private*, pg. 1051

Conley, Eldon, Dir.-Production & Inventory Control--Precision Twist Drill Co., Crystal Lake, IL; *Int'l*, pg. 1185

Conners, Carl, Paper Production Mgr.--Industrial Bag Division - Jacksonville Plant, Jacksonville, AR; *U.S. Public*, pg. 1521

Consolo, Joseph J., V.P.-Visual Mdsg.--The May Department Stores Company, Saint Louis, MO; *U.S. Public*, pg. 1063

Conte, Gary, V.P.-Pharmaceutical Intermediates & Custom Mfg.--Aceto Corporation, Lake Success, NY; *U.S. Public, pg. 15*

Cook, D., Mgr.-Specialty Mfg.--Comdial Corporation, Charlottesville, VA; *U.S. Public*, pg. 407

Cook, Ray, Mgr.-Mfg.--Eriez Magnetics, Erie, PA; *U.S. Private*, pg. 381

Cook, Richard, V.P.-Opers.--Acorn Engineering Company, City of Industry, CA; *U.S. Private*, pg. 14

Cooley, William H., V.P.-Mfg.--Mack Molding Company Inc., Arlington, VT; *U.S. Private*, pg. 691

Coombes, Richard, V.P.-Engrng.--Joan Fabrics Corp., Tyngsboro, MA; *U.S. Private*, pg. 588

Coombs, David, Mfg./Oper.--Aydin Displays (East), Horsham, PA; *U.S. Public*, pg. 158

Cooper, C. Martin, Sr. V.P. & Dir.-Mfg.--ITT Fluid Technology Corporation, Midland Park, NJ; *U.S. Public*, pg. 860

Cooper, Gary, Exec. V.P.-Mfg.--Trelleborg YSH, Inc., South Haven, MI; *Int'l*, pg. 1422

Cooper, J.B., V.P.-Production--General Shale Products Corp., Johnson City, TN; *Int'l*, pg. 843

Cooper, J.B., V.P.-Prod.--General Shale Products Corp., Elizabethton, TN; *Int'l*, pg. 843

Cooper, J.L., V.P. & Dir.-Mfg.--Winn-Dixie Stores, Inc., Jacksonville, FL; *U.S. Public*, pg. 1771

Cooper, James A., V.P.-Opers.--Cox Newspapers, Inc., Atlanta, GA; *U.S. Private*, pg. 281

Cooper, Richard, Mgr.-Engrng.--Allomatic Products Company, Sullivan, IN; *U.S. Public*, pg. 1363

Copeland, Randall, V.P.-Mfg.--Alpo Pet Foods, Inc., Allentown, PA; *Int'l*, pg. 917

Copen, Gene, Dir.-Mfg.--Adams Rite Manufacturing Co., City of Industry, CA; *U.S. Private*, pg. 17

Coppola, Silvia, Dir.-Production--Woman's Day, New York, NY; *Int'l*, pg. 795

Corbett, Dr. John, V.P.-Technology--Clairol, Inc., Stamford, CT; *U.S. Public*, pg. 254

Corbin, Larry, Dir.-Mfg.--Nestle Confectionery, Toronto, Canada; *Int'l*, pg. 922

Cordeau, Fracois, V.P.-Semiconductor Mfg. Oper.--Mitel Semiconductor, Bromont, Canada; *Int'l*, pg. 870

Cordeau, Francis, V.P.-Semiconductor Mfg. Opers.--Mitel Semiconductor AB, Jarfalla, Sweden; *Int'l*, pg. 870

Cordeau, Francois, V.P.-Semiconmducor Mfg. & Opers.--Mitel Corporation, Kanata, Canada; *Int'l*, pg. 870

Cordes, Dan, V.P. & Dir.-Pharmacy--Express Scripts, Inc., Maryland Heights, MO; *U.S. Public*, pg. 600

Cordy, David, V.P.-Production--Singleton Seafood Co., Tampa, FL; *U.S. Public*, pg. 427

Core, Jeffrey R., Sr. Designer--The Ohio Art Company, Inc., Bryan, OH; *U.S. Public*, pg. 1214

Corlett, B., Mgr.-Mfg.--British Steel Seamless Tubes-Wednesfield Works, Wolverhampton, United Kingdom; *Int'l*, pg. 220

Corlett, Joseph J., V.P.-Mfg.--Grolier Inc., Danbury, CT; *Int'l, pg. 794*

Cornett, E.W., V.P.-Mfg.--SmithKline Beecham Laboratories, Bristol, TN; *Int'l*, pg. 1264

Cornish, Noel H., Mgr.-Mills & Distribution--Rod & Bar Products Division, Port Waratah, Australia; *Int'l*, pg. 227

Cornu, Joseph, Exec. V.P.-Technical & Opers.--Alcatel N.V., Amsterdam, Netherlands; *Int'l*, pg. 55

Corona, Francisco, Dir.-Mfg.--BYK Gulden, S.A. de C.V., Mexico, Mexico; *Int'l*, pg. 66

Corray, Bill, V.P.-Production--B-Line Systems, Inc., Highland, IL; *U.S. Public*, pg. 1471

Corriveau, Paul, V.P.-Mfg.--Cortland Line Co., Inc., Cortland, NY; *U.S. Private*, pg. 277

Corvin, Joe E., Pres. & Chief Oper. Officer--Oregon Steel Mills Inc., Portland, OR; *U.S. Public*, pg. 1230

Costello, Craig T., Chief Oper. Officer & Exec. V.P.-Opers.--Weirton Steel Corporation, Weirton, WV; *U.S. Public*, pg. 1751

Cota, Ray, Plant Mgr.--Good Companies, Carson, CA; *U.S. Private*, pg. 463

Coulter, David, Sr. Dir.-Mfg.--Ball Metal Food Container Corp., Westminster, CO; *U.S. Public*, pg. 171

Counterman, W.S., Dir.-Tech.--ABB Air Preheater Inc., Wellsville, NY; *Int'l*, pg. 3

Couper, David N., V.P.-Mfg.--Weyco Group, Inc., Milwaukee, WI; *U.S. Public*, pg. 1763

Coupland, Gary, Dir.-Engrng.--American Welding & Manufacturing Co., Warren, OH; *U.S. Private*, pg. 425

Coutinho, Artur A.V., Sr. V.P.-Prod.--Embraer-Empresa Brasileira de Aeronautica S.A., Sao Jose dos Campos, Brazil; *Int'l*, pg. 452

Coutts, Robert, Gen Mgr.-Foundry--Electron Corp., Littleton, CO; *U.S. Private*, pg. 370

Covert, G. Chris, V.P.-Mfg.--Simplicity Manufacturing, Inc., Port Washington, WI; *U.S. Private*, pg. 1002

Cowburn, L.H., V.P.-Mfg.--ABB Air Preheater Inc., Wellsville, NY; *Int'l*, pg. 3

Cowell, Gary, V.P.-Production--Broughton Foods Company, Marietta, OH; *U.S. Public*, pg. 259

Cowie, Donald J., Grp. V.P.-Original Equip. Mfg.--Recoton Auto Corporation, Lincolnshire, IL; *U.S. Public*, pg. 1369

Cozad, John D., V.P.-Mfg.--Xtek, Inc., Cincinnati, OH; *U.S. Private*, pg. 1194

Cozad, Wayne, Mgr.-Molding--Ultra Tool & Plastics, Inc., Amherst, NY; *U.S. Private*, pg. 1116

Crane, Christopher, V.P.-Mfg.--Crane & Co., Inc., Dalton, MA; *U.S. Private*, pg. 286

Crane, Michelle A., V.P.-Mfg.--Artistic Greetings, Inc., Elmira, NY; *U.S. Public*, pg. 136

Crasnianski, Serge, Grp. Mng. Dir.-Mfg., Res. & Devel. & Sls.--Photo-Me International plc, Bookham, United Kingdom; *Int'l*, pg. 1055

Cravey, Sally, V.P.-Mfg.--Primedia Inc., Mahwah, NJ; *U.S. Public*, pg. 1328

Crawford, Dick, Dir.-Mfg. & Opers.--Kinetic Concepts, Inc., San Antonio, TX; *U.S. Private*, pg. 620

Crawford, Donald, V.P.-Private Labels--Tanner Co., Rutherfordton, NC; *U.S. Private*, pg. 1068

Crawford, Jeff, Dir.-Opers.--Ohmite Manufacturing Company, Skokie, IL; *U.S. Private*, pg. 813

Crawford, Michael A., V.P.-Engrng.--L3 Communications Telemetry & Instrumentation Div., San Diego, CA; *U.S. Private*, pg. 639

Creen, Nathan, Mgr.-Paper Production--Industrial Bag Division - Des Moines Plant, Des Moines, IA; *U.S. Public, pg. 1521*

Cripe, Brad, Mgr.-Production--St. Louis Business Journal Corp., Saint Louis, MO; *U.S. Private*, pg. 20

Cron, David, Exec. V.P.-Mfg.--AEP Industries, Inc., South Hackensack, NJ; *U.S. Public*, pg. 4

Cronin, Frederick R., V.P.-Technology--General DataComm, Inc., Middlebury, CT; *U.S. Public*, pg. 708

Cross, L.W., V.P.-Mfg.--RFL Electronics, Inc., Boonton, NJ; *U.S. Private*, pg. 903

Crouch, Bob, Mgr.-Prod. Sls.--KCL Corporation, Shelbyville, IN; *U.S. Private*, pg. 603

Crowley, Christopher, V.P.-Mfg.--Polar Beverages, Worcester, MA; *U.S. Private*, pg. 873

Crownover, Daniel, Chief Engr.--Apache Plastics, L.P., Lodi, CA; *U.S. Private*, pg. 77

Croxford, S., Dir.-Mfg.--Robertson Tooling Ltd., Kempston, United Kingdom; *Int'l*, pg. 449

Crump, Ivey, Mgr.-Production--Retail Bag Division - Yulee Plant, Yulee, FL; *U.S. Public*, pg. 1521

Crunkleton, Charles H., V.P.-Mfg.--Mylan Pharmaceuticals Inc., Morgantown, WV; *U.S. Public*, pg. 1143

Cuddy, James A., Dir.-Mfg.--Troy Mills, Inc., Troy, NH; *U.S. Private*, pg. 1106

Cuenin, James E., Jr., Exec. V.P.--Edwin B. Stimpson Company, Inc., Bayport, NY; *U.S. Private*, pg. 1043

Culbertson, Bob, V.P.-Mfg.--Schlosser Forge Company, Rancho Cucamonga, CA; *U.S. Private*, pg. 970

Culich, Nick, Chief Oper. Officer--Union City Body Company, L.P., Union City, IN; *U.S. Private*, pg. 1118

Cummings, Mark, V.P.-Mfg.--Osicom Technologies Inc., Annapolis Junction, MD; *U.S. Public*, pg. 1233

Cummings, Thomas J., V.P.-Opers. & Chief Engr.--Noteworthy Industries Inc., Amsterdam, NY; *U.S. Private, pg. 808*

Cunningham, Jim, Project Mgr.-Wire Mill Devel.--Building & Industrial Products Division, Sydney, Australia; *Int'l*, pg. 225

Cunningham, William J., Sr. V.P.-Mfg. & Prod. Devl.--Data General Corporation, Westborough, MA; *U.S. Public*, pg. 485

Cupp, Carl, Mgr.-Mfg. & Eng.--Pachmayr LTD, Monrovia, CA; *U.S. Private*, pg. 683

Curlee, Bill, Dir.-Mfg.--American Furniture Company, Incorporated, Martinsville, VA; *U.S. Public*, pg. 974

Curran, Edward, V.P.-Mfg.--Gould Instrument Systems, Inc., Valley View, OH; *U.S. Public*, pg. 1592

Curtis, James T., V.P.-Equipment & Maintenance--ABF Freight System, Inc., Fort Smith, AR; *U.S. Public*, pg. 130

Curtney, Donald, V.P.-Mfr. & Distr.--Finish Line, Inc., Indianapolis, IN; *U.S. Public*, pg. 623

Cushman, Floyd E., V.P.-Steel & Wire Processing--MNP Corp., Utica, MI; *U.S. Private*, pg. 687

Custer, Janice, Mgr.-Plant--Laird & Company, Eatontown, NJ; *U.S. Private*, pg. 642

Cuthbertson, Don, Dir.-Mfg.--Excel Industries, Inc., Hesston, KS; *U.S. Private*, pg. 387

Cutler, Jim, V.P.-Mfg.--Jacobsen Textron, Racine, WI; *U.S. Public*, pg. 1589

Cwiertny, Anthony J., Dir.-Technical Applications--Northrop Grumman Corporation, Los Angeles, CA; *U.S. Public*, pg. 1197

Cybulski, Zach, V.P.-Dev. & Mfg./Tachyarrhythmia Mngmt. Bus.--Medtronic, Inc., Minneapolis, MN; *U.S. Public*, pg. 1082

D'Amelio, Frank D., V.P., Gen. Mgr.-Video Div. & Chief Mfg. Officer--Circon Corporation, Santa Barbara, CA; *U.S. Public*, pg. 373

D'Angelo, John, Mgr.-Mfg.--Woodstream Corporation, Lititz, PA; *U.S. Public*, pg. 566

d'Auguste, John, V.P.-Mfg./Americas Group--Gateway 2000, North Sioux City, SD; *U.S. Public*, pg. 703

Dagley, Robert C., Grp. V.P.-Mfg.--American & Efird, Inc., Mount Holly, NC; *U.S. Public*, pg. 1412

Daguin, Andre, Dir.-Indus.--Sciaky S.A., Vitry-sur-Seine, France; *Int'l*, pg. 1211

Daignault, Gary, Mgr.-Cylinder Opers.--AGA Gas, Inc., Independence, OH; *Int'l*, pg. 13

Dalessandro, Nick, V.P.-Mfg.--JII/Sales Promotion Associates, Inc., Coshocton, OH; *U.S. Private*, pg. 598

Dalland, Don, V.P.-Mfg.--Waters Instruments, Inc., Rochester, MN; *U.S. Public*, pg. 1745

Dalton, Larry H., V.P.-Opers. Mfg.--Lilly Industries, Inc., Indianapolis, IN; *U.S. Public*, pg. 994

Danberry, Michael, Mgr.-Plant--Mico Inc., North Mankato, MN; *U.S. Private*, pg. 741

Dandorf, Warren, Mgr.-Mfg.--Dacon Electronics Plc., Hemel Hempstead, United Kingdom; *U.S. Public*, pg. 395

Danheiser, Scott, Mgr.-Mfg. Service-Eastern Reg.--W. Braun Co., Lyndhurst, NJ; *U.S. Private*, pg. 166

Dano, Margaret S., V.P.-Mfg. & Engrng.--Avery Dennison Corporation, Pasadena, CA; *U.S. Public*, pg. 152

Danyluk, Paul T., V.P.-Engrng.--Fairbanks Morse Engine Division, Beloit, WI; *U.S. Public*, pg. 401

Darby, Jerome S., V.P.-Mfg. Opers.--Combe Incorporated, White Plains, NY; *U.S. Private*, pg. 257

Darby, Jonathan, Sr. V.P.-Production--Tri-Star Pictures, Inc., Culver City, CA; *Int'l*, pg. 1282

Darchis, Mathieu, Dir.-Mfg. & Engrng.--Bundy Belgium SA, Wandre, Belgium; *Int'l*, pg. 1341

Darmos, Frank E., Chief Oper. Officer & Dir.-Opers.--Cramer Company, Old Saybrook, CT; *U.S. Public*, pg. 1238

Dattomo, Lou, V.P.-Mfg.--The Segerdahl Corp., Wheeling, IL; *U.S. Private*, pg. 981

Daule, C.R., Dir.-Prod.--Bridport Aviation Products, Dorset, United Kingdom; *Int'l*, pg. 215

Daut, John F., V.P.-Mfg.--Sensormatic Electronics Corporation, Boca Raton, FL; *U.S. Public*, pg. 1457

Davenport, Bob, Mgr.-Production--Welco Lumber Company, Marysville, WA; *U.S. Private*, pg. 1161
David, Robert, Exec. V.P.-Mfg.--Clairson International Corp., Ocala, FL; *U.S. Public*, pg. 575
Davidson, Issac J., V.P.-Production--Reed Minerals, Highland, IN; *U.S. Public*, pg. 793
Davidson, Jim, Mgr.-Editing & Production--McGraw-Hill Book Co. Australia Pty. Ltd., Roseville, Australia; *U.S. Public*, pg. 1072
Davidson, Robert R., Mgr.-Mfg. & Pur. Agent--Oildyne, Minneapolis, MN; *U.S. Public*, pg. 411
Davies, Harry, V.P.-Mfg.--Industrial Acoustics Company S.C. Inc., Moncks Corner, SC; *U.S. Public*, pg. 875
Davies, Joel, Mgr.-Production--American City Business Journals, Inc., Jacksonville, FL; *U.S. Private*, pg. 19
Davies, R.A., V.P.-Mfg.--The Kelly-Springfield Tire Company, Cumberland, MD; *U.S. Public*, pg. 753
Davis, Charles, V.P.-Opers.--FieldBrook Farms, Inc., Dunkirk, NY; *U.S. Private*, pg. 403
Davis, H.F., V.P.-Mfg.--Dixon Industries, Inc., Coffeyville, KS; *U.S. Public*, pg. 238
Davis, Harold, V.P.-Mfg. & Dist.--Weider Publications, Inc., Woodland Hills, CA; *U.S. Private*, pg. 1159
Davis, James, V.P.-Mfg.--Lindberg, A General Signal Company, Watertown, WI; *U.S. Public*, pg. 727
Davis, Linda, Publr.--Dorling Kindersley Ltd., London, United Kingdom; *Int'l*, pg. 417
Davis, Lynn, V.P.-Sls., Mktg., Pur. & Mfg.--Lithotype Company, Inc., South San Francisco, CA; *U.S. Private*, pg. 670
Davis, Lynn J., Sr. V.P. & Pres.-Broadband Connectivity Grp.--ADC Telecommunications, Inc., Minnetonka, MN; *U.S. Public*, pg. 4
Davis, Thomas O., V.P.-Mfg.--American Greetings Corporation, Cleveland, OH; *U.S. Public*, pg. 77
Dawson, Craig, Dir.-Engrng.--Sensall, Div. of Rosemount, Inc., Hauppauge, NY; *U.S. Public*, pg. 574
Dawson, G., Dir.-Engrng.--Hypertronics Corporation, Hudson, MA; *Int'l*, pg. 1268
Day, Randy, V.P.-QA & Prod. Devel.--Perdue Farms Incorporated, Salisbury, MD; *U.S. Private*, pg. 852
Dayley, Gil, Dir.-Quality Control & Prod. Mgr.--Idaho Supreme Company, Firth, ID; *U.S. Private*, pg. 557
de Benetti, Lionel, V.P.-Oper. & mfg.--Clarins, Neuilly-sur-Seine, France; *Int'l*, pg. 295
de Broves, Louis, Dir.-Prod.--Sciaky S.A., Vitry-sur-Seine, France; *Int'l*, pg. 1211
De Mattos, Joao G., Mgr.-Footwear Prod.--Sao Paulo Alpargatas S.A., Sao Paulo, Brazil; *Int'l*, pg. 1193
De Mautort, Laurent, Mgr.-Industry--European Investment Bank, Luxembourg, Luxembourg; *Int'l*, pg. 465
de Pinedo, Javier, Mng. Dir.-Generation--Iberdrola, S.A., Bilbao, Spain; *Int'l*, pg. 657
De Vore, Russel J., V.P-Mfg.--Kysor Panel Systems, Portland, OR; *U.S. Public*, pg. 1445
Dean, David I., Dir.-Mfg. Opers.--The Ohio Art Company, Inc., Bryan, OH; *U.S. Public*, pg. 1214
Dean, Tim, Mgr.-Production--R.C.A. Rubber Company, Akron, OH; *U.S. Private*, pg. 902
Deandred, Charles, V.P.-Mfg.--Accra Pac Group, Elkhart, IN; *U.S. Private*, pg. 11
Deary, Donald R., Co.-Chm. & V.P.-Mfg.--Nor-Cal Beverage Co., Inc., West Sacramento, CA; *U.S. Private*, pg. 801
Decaix, Christian, Dir.-Production--Etablissement de Velizy, Velizy-Villacoublay, France; *Int'l*, pg. 383
Deckman, J.T., Gen. Mgr.-H.S. Peterson--Master Builders Inc., Cleveland, OH; *Int'l*, pg. 1465
Dedman, Paul, V.P.-Mfg.--Universal Fasteners Inc., Lawrenceburg, KY; *Int'l*, pg. 1515
Dedow, D.R., Dir.-Pasds BU--Delphi Packard Electric Systems, Beachwood, OH; *U.S. Public*, pg. 719
DeFontaine, Yves, Dir.-Manuf.--Sofamor Danek Group, Inc., Memphis, TN; *U.S. Public*, pg. 1482
DeGraan, Edward, V.P.-Mfg. & Technical Opers.--The Gillette Company, Gillette Grooming Products, USA, Boston, MA; *U.S. Public*, pg. 744
DeGroff, Charles, Dir.-Mfg.--Hamilton Co., Inc., Reno, NV; *U.S. Private*, pg. 497
Deka, John, Mgr.-Traffic--Eastern Color Printing Company, Avon, CT; *U.S. Private*, pg. 357
del Campo, Ralph, V.P.-Mfg. Opers.--The Liposome Company, Inc., Princeton, NJ; *U.S. Public*, pg. 1000
del Campo, Ralph, V.P.-Mfg.--The Liposome Manufacturing Company, Inc., Indianapolis, IN; *U.S. Public*, pg. 1000
DeLegge, D.J., Dir.-Mfg.--Lawter International, Inc., Kenosha, WI; *U.S. Public*, pg. 980
Dellamano, Joseph, Mgr.-Production--Patson's Press, Sunnyvale, CA; *U.S. Private*, pg. 843
Dellamaria, Tom, Sr. V.P.-Production & Mfg.--Reed Elsevier Business Information, Newton, MA; *Int'l*, pg. 1095
Dellinger, Kenneth S., Grp. V.P.-Mfg.--American & Efird, Inc., Mount Holly, NC; *U.S. Public*, pg. 1412
DeLong, Al, V.P.-Mfg.--Spartanburg Steel Products, Spartanburg, SC; *U.S. Private*, pg. 300
DeLuca, Paul, V.P.-Mfg.--Candela Corporation, Wayland, MA; *U.S. Public*, pg. 300
Delzell, Gary, V.P.-Mfg.--Ato-Findley, Inc., Wauwatosa, WI; *Int'l*, pg. 445
Demars, Patrick, Sr. V.P.-Corp. Technical Services--Lafarge Corporation, Reston, VA; *Int'l*, pg. 788
Deml, Ken, V.P.-Mfg.--Winona Knitting Mills, Inc., Winona, MN; *U.S. Public*, pg. 779
DeMott, Thomas, V.P.-Meat & Food Mdsg.--Safeway Inc., Pleasanton, CA; *U.S. Public*, pg. 1426
Denham, W.A., V.P.-Mfg.--Speakman Company, Wilmington, DE; *U.S. Private*, pg. 1021
Denning, Robert W., V.P.-Pur. & Distr.--Motion Industries, Inc., Irondale, AL; *U.S. Public*, pg. 732
Denzel, John E., V.P.-Mfg.--Ultratech Stepper, Inc., San Jose, CA; *U.S. Public*, pg. 1663
DePhillips, James V., V.P.-Mfg.--Tommy Armour Golf, Morton Grove, IL; *U.S. Public*, pg. 1683
DePierro, Alfred, V.P.-Engrng. Micro Computer Applications--Napco Security Systems, Inc., Amityville, NY; *U.S. Public*, pg. 1151
Deram, Thomas, Mgr.-Quality Control--Buehler, Limited, Lake Bluff, IL; *U.S. Public*, pg. 574
Derrick, Frank, Gen. Mgr.--Reading Anthracite Co., Pottsville, PA; *U.S. Private*, pg. 913
Dertz, Robert, V.P.-Mfg.--Louis Allis Company, Milwaukee, WI; *U.S. Private*, pg. 677
DeRusso, Thomas, Dir.-Mkg.--Scanforms, Inc., Bristol, PA; *U.S. Public*, pg. 228
Deschene, C.D., Mgr.-Mktg.--Maine Public Service Company, Presque Isle, ME; *U.S. Public*, pg. 1038
Desiere, Phil, Dir.-Mfg.--Concord Litho Co., Inc., Concord, NH; *U.S. Private*, pg. 261
Despain, James E., V.P.-Track-type Tractors--Caterpillar Inc., Peoria, IL; *U.S. Public*, pg. 315
Detourbet, Gerard, Sr. V.P.-Mechanical Engrng. & Mfg.--Renault, Boulogne-Billancourt, France; *Int'l*, pg. 1102
Dev, Ranthi, V.P.-Biotechnology Production--Glaxo Wellcome PLC, Research Triangle Park, NC; *Int'l*, pg. 553
Devaney, John A., V.P.-Mfg.--Mentholatum Company, Buffalo, NY; *Int'l*, pg. 1126
Dewey, Jeff, Dir.-Production--Kemps Foods, Inc., Lancaster, PA; *Int'l*, pg. 752
Dewey, Robert G., Sr. V.P.-Mfg. Services--Mestek, Inc., Westfield, MA; *U.S. Public*, pg. 1099
Dewitt, Donald E., V.P.-Engrng.--Dwyer Instruments Inc., Michigan City, IN; *U.S. Private*, pg. 350
DeWitt, Ted, V.P.-Mfg.--Wolfer Printing Company, City of Commerce, CA; *U.S. Private*, pg. 1186
Diamond, Robert, V.P.-Production--Diamond Chemical Co., Inc., East Rutherford, NJ; *U.S. Private*, pg. 330
Dice, George C., Chief Engineer--Weldon Machine Tool, Inc., York, PA; *U.S. Private*, pg. 1161
DiCecco, John A., Sr. V.P.-Logistics & Mfg.--General Nutrition, Inc., Pittsburgh, PA; *U.S. Public*, pg. 725
Dicken, Arthur, Head-Mfg. Tech.--Imperial Chemical Industries PLC, London, United Kingdom; *Int'l*, pg. 662
Dicken, Donald R., V.P.-Tech. & Mfg.--Corning Japan K.K., Shizuoka, Japan; *U.S. Public*, pg. 449
Dickler, Steve, Mgr.-Mfg.--Parisi Inc./Royal Store Fixture, Philadelphia, PA; *U.S. Private*, pg. 839
Dickson, Jim, Mgr.-Bus. Unit--Revcor, Inc., Carpentersville, IL; *U.S. Private*, pg. 925
Dickson, M.V., Jr., V.P.-Exploration & Production--Esso Norge a.s., Oslo, Norway; *U.S. Public*, pg. 602
Dieme, David, Dir.-Mfg.--National Label Company, Lafayette Hill, PA; *U.S. Private*, pg. 785
Dietrich, William K., Sr. V.P.-Exploration & Production--Du Pont (E.I. Du Pont De Nemours & Co.), Wilmington, DE; *U.S. Public*, pg. 530
Diggs, W.E., V.P.-Exploration & Production--ONEOK Resources Co., Tulsa, OK; *U.S. Public*, pg. 1226
Dihigo, Mario, Plant Mgr.--Nashville Machine Co. Inc., Nashville, TN; *U.S. Private*, pg. 774
Dill, Peter, Exec. V.P.-Sulzer Escher Wyss Group--Sulzer Ltd., Winterthur, Switzerland; *Int'l*, pg. 1305
Dillon, Jack, Dir.-Intl. Mfg. & Tech.--Continental General Tire, Inc., Charlotte, NC; *Int'l*, pg. 327
DiMatteo, Carmen, Sr. V.P.-Services & Sls.--Semco Industries Inc., Stoughton, MA; *U.S. Private*, pg. 983
DiMinno, Frank D., Pres.-Industrial Div.--Edmund Scientific Company, Barrington, NJ; *U.S. Private*, pg. 364
DiOrio, Joseph J., Dir.-Prod. Res. & Devel.--Computer Systems Research, Inc., Avon, CT; *U.S. Public*, pg. 1070
DiPietro, John J., Gen. Mgr.-Mfg.--Steelox Systems Inc., Mason, OH; *U.S. Private*, pg. 1038
Dircks, J.H., Mgr.-Mfg.--Svedala Industries Inc., Appleton, WI; *Int'l*, pg. 1325
Dishaw, Rick, V.P.-Engrng.--McCord Payen Inc., Wyandotte, MI; *Int'l*, pg. 1334
Dixon, David, Mgr.-Engrng.--D.C.I., Inc., Saint Cloud, MN; *U.S. Private*, pg. 301
Dlesk, David, Sr. Dir.-Mfg. & Engrng.--Biogen, Inc., Cambridge, MA; *U.S. Public*, pg. 230
Dodd, Leon J., V.P.-Mfg./Furniture; OEM & BIC--Ameriwood Industries International Inc., Grand Rapids, MI; *U.S. Public*, pg. 98
Dolye, Steven, Plant Mgr.--Seymour Manufacturing Company, Seymour, IN; *U.S. Private*, pg. 988
Dominguez, Anthony, V.P.-Engrng.--O.S. Walker Co. Inc., Worcester, MA; *U.S. Private*, pg. 1147
Dominguez, Armando Ferriz, Dir.-Tech.--Altos Hornos de Mexico, S.A., Monclova, Mexico; *Int'l*, pg. 66
Dominik, Jurgen G., V.P.-Production--The NutraSweet Kelco Company, San Diego, CA; *U.S. Public*, pg. 1125
Don, Elliot, Dir.-Mdsg.--Duty Free International, Inc., Ridgefield, CT; *Int'l*, pg. 103
Donald, Earl, V.P.-Plant Oper.--American Metal Products, Olive Branch, MS; *U.S. Public*, pg. 1053
Donnellan, Kevin G., V.P.-Mfg. Opers.--Grant-Lydick Beverage Co., San Antonio, TX; *U.S. Private*, pg. 470
Donnelly, Frank L., V.P.-Engrng.--Miller Brewing Company, Milwaukee, WI; *U.S. Public*, pg. 1289
Donofrio, Nicholas M., Sr. V.P. & Grp. Exec.-Res., Mfg. & Procurement--International Business Machines Corporation, Armonk, NY; *U.S. Public*, pg. 895
Dordi, Kersi, V.P.-Mfg.--Exolon-Esk Company, Tonawanda, NY; *U.S. Public*, pg. 600
Dornau, Peter G., Chm. Bd. & Pres.--Ocean Bio-Chem Inc., Fort Lauderdale, FL; *U.S. Public*, pg. 1211
Dorsey, Ken, V.P.-Prod.--David Michael & Co. Inc., Philadelphia, PA; *U.S. Private*, pg. 740
Dotsey, John, V.P.-Mfg.--Roessing Bronze Co., Mars, PA; *U.S. Private*, pg. 939
Dougherty, James, V.P.-Mfg.--Milwaukee Cylinder Division, Cudahy, WI; *U.S. Public*, pg. 124
Dow, Kirk, Plant Mgr.--Kurdziel Industries, Inc., Muskegon, MI; *U.S. Private*, pg. 637
Dow, Philip L., V.P.-Mfg. & Engrng.--Philips Elmet Corporation, Lewiston, ME; *Int'l*, pg. 1055
Dowling, Peter, Pres.-Worldwide Mfg.--Loctite Corporation, Rocky Hill, CT; *Int'l*, pg. 611
Dowling, Peter, V.P.-Mfg./Europe--Loctite (Ireland) Ltd., Dublin, Ireland; *Int'l*, pg. 611
Downes, Wayne, V.P.-Mfg., B&G--B&G Foods, Inc., Roseland, NJ; *U.S. Private*, pg. 105
Downing, Kenneth G., V.P.-Opers. & Production--Thermon Manufacturing Company, San Marcos, TX; *U.S. Private*, pg. 1080
Doyle, Dennis, V.P.-Mfg.--Synergis Technologies Group, Grand Rapids, MI; *U.S. Private*, pg. 1060
Doyle, James M., Sr. V.P.-Mfg.--King Milling Company, Lowell, MI; *U.S. Private*, pg. 621
Doyle, Stephen R., V.P.--King Milling Company, Lowell, MI; *U.S. Private*, pg. 621
Drake, Tom, Plant Mgr.--Central Illinois Steel Company, Carlinville, IL; *U.S. Private*, pg. 223
Dray, Peter, V.P.-Mfg.--GFA Brands, Inc., Cresskill, NJ; *U.S. Private*, pg. 435
Drewes, Robert W., V.P.-Procurement & Mfg.--Raytheon Company, Lexington, MA; *U.S. Public*, pg. 1364
Drewniak, Michael J., V.P.-Mfg.--The Topps Company, Inc., New York, NY; *U.S. Public*, pg. 1621
Drubel, Jim, V.P.-Engrng.--International Paint Co., Inc., Union, NJ; *Int'l*, pg. 338
Dryburgh, Paul E., V.P.-Engrng.--Rexair, Inc., Troy, MI; *U.S. Public*, pg. 1684
Dubbert, Hans-Gerd, Mgr.-Mfg.--Wurzner Dauerbackwaren GmbH, Wurzen, Germany; *Int'l*, pg. 1514
Dube, Al, Mgr.-Mfg.--CorryHiebert Corporation, Corry, PA; *U.S. Public*, pg. 772
Ducharme, Edward, Mgr.-Mfg.--Cadillac Motor Car Division, Warren, MI; *U.S. Public*, pg. 720
Dudek, Joseph, Mgr.-Opers. & Mfg.--Hoogovens Aluminium Corp., Secaucus, NJ; *Int'l*, pg. 755
Duff, Chris, Plant Mgr.--Manville Canada Inc. (Innisfail), Innisfail, Canada; *U.S. Public*, pg. 927
Duffy, John, Sr. Exec. V.P. & Chief of Mfg.--Callaway Golf Company, Carlsbad, CA; *U.S. Public*, pg. 294
Duke, Willie L., Grp. V.P.-Softwood Lumber--Georgia-Pacific Corporation, Atlanta, GA; *U.S. Public*, pg. 735
Dulton, Richard, Dir.-Mfg.--Guideposts Associates, Inc., Carmel, NY; *U.S. Private*, pg. 487
Dulude, Jim, V.P.-Pur. & Mfg.--Quaker Fabric Corporation, Fall River, MA; *U.S. Public*, pg. 1347
Dumas, Brad, Mfg. Mgr.--Cohart De Mexico, S.A. DE C.V., Tijuana, Mexico; *U.S. Public*, pg. 1749
Dumas, Jean-Louis, Exec. V.P.-Mfg.--N. Schlumberger & Cie, Guebwiller, France; *Int'l*, pg. 1206
Duncan, Jeffrey, V.P.-Engrng. & Mfg.--Dataram Corporation, Princeton, NJ; *U.S. Public*, pg. 487
Dunham, Robert, Plant Mgr.--Medico Industries, Inc., Wilkes-Barre, PA; *U.S. Private*, pg. 728
Dunlap, Bob, V.P.-Mfg.--Merle Norman Cosmetics, Inc., Los Angeles, CA; *U.S. Private*, pg. 733
Dunlap, D.D., V.P.-Mfg.--Warren Petroleum Company, Houston, TX; *U.S. Public*, pg. 1146
Dunlap, Robert E., Sr. V.P.-Mfg.--Broan Mfg. Co., Inc., Hartford, WI; *U.S. Public*, pg. 1193
Dunstan, Ericson M., Sr. V.P.-Corp. Engrng. & Sec.--Micropolis Corporation, Chatsworth, CA; *U.S. Private*, pg. 742
Duquette, Richard H., V.P.-Aeroquip Mfg. Performance & Chief Mfg. Officer--Aeroquip-Vickers, Inc., Maumee, OH; *U.S. Public*, pg. 24
Durr, Jim, Mgr.-Mfg.--Bayley/Fan Group, Lebanon, IN; *Int'l*, pg. 1398
Dusel, Martin C., V.P.-Mfg.--Citizens Gas & Coke Utility, Indianapolis, IN; *U.S. Private*, pg. 241
Duvall, William R., Sr. V.P.-Opers.--LoJack Corporation, Dedham, MA; *U.S. Public*, pg. 1012
Dvoretsky, William, V.P.-Mfg.--Royle Systems Group, Pompton Lakes, NJ; *U.S. Private*, pg. 949
Dykhuizen, George, V.P.-Mfg.--Metals Div. Extruded Metals, Belding, MI; *Int'l*, pg. 1335
Eade, Phil, Mgr.-Mining & Geo-Technology--Collieries Division, Wollongong, Australia; *Int'l*, pg. 226
Eagan, Lawrence F., V.P.-Mfg.--Collins Electric Company, Inc., Chicopee, MA; *U.S. Private*, pg. 253
Eagle, Michael L., V.P.-Mfg.--Eli Lilly and Company, Indianapolis, IN; *U.S. Public*, pg. 992
Eagles, Charles W., Mgr.-Mfg.--Industra Service Corporation, New Westminster, Canada; *Int'l*, pg. 74
Eagles, Charles W., Mgr.-Mfr.--Canadian Energy Services, New Westminster, Canada; *Int'l*, pg. 74
Earley, Dave C., Mgr.-Mfg.--The Spencer Turbine Co., Windsor, CT; *U.S. Private*, pg. 1025
East, Thomas S., V.P.-Engrng.--Southeastern Michigan Gas Company, Port Huron, MI; *U.S. Public*, pg. 1489
Easton, Marie, Mgr.-Mfg.--Power Conversion, Inc., Elmwood Park, NJ; *Int'l*, pg. 127
Eby, James C., V.P.-Quality Assurance & Mfg.--Digital Sound Corporation, Carpinteria, CA; *U.S. Public*, pg. 508
Eccleston, Wayne, Gen. Mgr.--Velvet Drive Transmissions, New Bedford, MA; *U.S. Public*, pg. 1370
Ecke, Karl, Systems Devel. Engineer--AirTronics Co., Elgin, IL; *U.S. Public*, pg. 944
Eckloff, Donald E., Plant Engineer--Pabst Brewing Co./Tumwater, Tumwater, WA; *U.S. Private*, pg. 954
Eckman, Warner, V.P.-Mfg.--The Dannon Co., Tarrytown, NY; *Int'l*, pg. 379
Economos, James J., V.P.-Opers.--Imperial Schrade Corp., Ellenville, NY; *U.S. Private*, pg. 559
Eddy, Carson, Dir.-Engrng.--Aetna Bearing Company, Chicago, IL; *U.S. Private*, pg. 25
Edelman, Paul, Mgr.-Conversion & Printing--KCL Corporation, Shelbyville, IN; *U.S. Private*, pg. 603
Edwards, Carol, Mgr.-Pur.--All-Luminum Products, Inc., Philadelphia, PA; *U.S. Private*, pg. 34
Edwards, Robert, Div. Gen. Mgr.-BHP Lifting & Indus. Prods.--Building & Industrial Products Division, Sydney, Australia; *Int'l*, pg. 225
Eeles, Stan W., Dir.-Mfg.--IGT-(Australia), Pty. Limited, Rosebery, Australia; *U.S. Public*, pg. 900

Egan, Edward, V.P.-Mfg.--K-III Media Group, New York, NY; *U.S. Public*, pg. 1328

Eggert, Jeff, Mgr.-Plant--Sokol & Company, Countryside, IL; *U.S. Private*, pg. 1012

Egmont, Steven, Dir.-Engrng.--Connecticut Container Corporation, North Haven, CT; *U.S. Private*, pg. 263

Ehlinger, Jack, V.P.-Opers.--Zeller Corp., Defiance, OH; *U.S. Private*, pg. 1204

Ehrlich, Charles R., V.P.-Mfg.--Wabash National Corp., Lafayette, IN; *U.S. Public*, pg. 1730

Eichelberger, Charles F., V.P.-Mfg. Opers.--Thomaston Mills, Inc., Thomaston, GA; *U.S. Public*, pg. 1599

Eichenberger, Robert, Dir.-Opers.--Cubix Corporation, Carson City, NV; *U.S. Private*, pg. 294

Eicherberger, Norman, V.P.-Mfg.--Shasta Beverages, Inc., Hayward, CA; *U.S. Public*, pg. 1153

Einarson, Gudmundur, Sr. V.P.-Silicon Div.--Elkem ASA, Oslo, Norway; *Int'l*, pg. 446

Eitel, Robert C., V.P.-Oper. & Corp. Sec.--The C.P. Hall Company, Chicago, IL; *U.S. Private*, pg. 495

Ekstrom, John, Grp. V.P.-Fluid Systems--Norton Performance Plastics, Wayne, NJ; *Int'l*, pg. 1174

Eldridge, R.W., Dir.-Plant Opers.--Sunkist Growers, Inc., Sherman Oaks, CA; *U.S. Private*, pg. 1052

Ellers, Steven A., V.P.-Opers.--The West Company, Incorporated, Lionville, PA; *U.S. Public*, pg. 1755

Elliot, Paul, Mgr.-Production--Long MFG. NC, Inc., Tarboro, NC; *U.S. Private*, pg. 674

Elliott, Harold, V.P.-Mfg.--Howard Miller, Zeeland, MI; *U.S. Private*, pg. 747

Elliott, Rob, Mgr.-Bulk Handling--Barney Point Coal Terminal, Gladstone, Australia; *Int'l*, pg. 223

Ellis, Robert, V.P.-Mfg. & Distr.-Lawn, Farm & Garden Chemicals--Universal Cooperatives, Inc., Minneapolis, MN; *U.S. Private*, pg. 1127

Elmy, R.L., V.P.-Design Engrng.--The Murray Ohio Mfg. Co., Brentwood, TN; *Int'l*, pg. 1397

Elrod, Mike, V.P.-Prod.--Correct Craft, Inc., Orlando, FL; *U.S. Private*, pg. 276

Emery, Ron, V.P.-Mfg.--Croscill, Inc., New York, NY; *U.S. Private*, pg. 290

Emge, Leonard E., V.P.-Mfg.--A. Schulman, Inc., Akron, OH; *U.S. Public*, pg. 1441

Enger, Thorleif, Dir.-Exploration & Prod.--Norsk Hydro a.s, Oslo, Norway; *Int'l*, pg. 959

Engle, Charles J., Dir.-Mfg.--Nixdorff Krein Industries Inc., Saint Louis, MO; *U.S. Private*, pg. 799

Engle, Robert, V.P.-Mfg.--Burke Industries, Inc., San Jose, CA; *U.S. Private*, pg. 183

Englert, John, V.P.-Engrng.--Relm Communications, Inc., Indianapolis, IN; *U.S. Public*, pg. 1376

English, Curt, Mgr.-Mfg.--Buck Knives, Inc., El Cajon, CA; *U.S. Private*, pg. 177

Enholm, Sten, Plant Mgr.--Berner Ltd., Helsinki, Finland; *Int'l*, pg. 189

Enquist, Thomas, V.P.-Prod.-Power Train--Saab Automobile AB, Nykoping, Sweden; *Int'l*, pg. 687

Enquist, Thomas, V.P.-Prod.-Power Train--Saab Automobile AB, Nykoping, Sweden; *U.S. Public*, pg. 725

Enright, Peter, Plant Mgr.--FAG Bearings Corporation, Danbury, CT; *Int'l*, pg. 469

Ensley, Ronnie L., Sr. V.P.-Mfg.--American & Efird, Inc., Mount Holly, NC; *U.S. Public*, pg. 1412

Epstein, Cliff, Chief Mdsg. Officer--Jumbo Sports Inc., Tampa, FL; *U.S. Public*, pg. 935

Erdei, Martin J., V.P.-H.R. & Mfg.--Ruslander & Sons, Inc., Buffalo, NY; *U.S. Private*, pg. 952

Erdman, Rick, Gen. Mgr.-Mfg.--Tylan General, Inc.-Flow Division, Compton, CA; *U.S. Public*, pg. 1112

Erickson, Bill, V.P.-Opers. & Mgr.-Production--Demco Inc., Madison, WI; *U.S. Private*, pg. 323

Erickson, Gerald, Mgr.-Plant--Perfection Bakeries Inc., Fort Wayne, IN; *U.S. Private*, pg. 852

Erikstrup, Dan, Dir.-Mfg.--Ultra Pac, Inc., Rogers, MN; *U.S. Public*, pg. 1662

Erlen, Hubertus, Dr., Exec. Dir.-Personnel, Production & Environmental Protection--Schering AG, Berlin, Germany; *Int'l*, pg. 1203

Ertel, Rick, V.P.-Mfg.--M&W, Gibson City, IL; *U.S. Public*, pg. 35

Esche, Alan C., V.P.-Mfg. & Engrng.--Chroma Corporation, McHenry, IL; *U.S. Private*, pg. 238

Eschenbacher, Robert, Dir.-Opers.--F.N. Burt Company, Inc., Buffalo, NY; *U.S. Private*, pg. 188

Esson, Robert L., Sr. V.P.-Mfg. & Distr.--BeautiControl Cosmetics, Inc., Carrollton, TX; *U.S. Public*, pg. 198

Ester, Steve, V.P.-Mfg.--Cummings Inc., Nashville, TN; *U.S. Private*, pg. 295

Estes, Jerry B., V.P.-Mfg.--Tennsco Corporation, Dickson, TN; *U.S. Private*, pg. 1077

Estival, Juan, Sr. V.P.-Opers. Div.--Grupo Synkro, S.A. de C.V., Mexico, Mexico; *Int'l*, pg. 576

Etzel, L.A., Sr. V.P.-Industrial--Sundt Corp., Tucson, AZ; *U.S. Private*, pg. 1051

Evans, Carl, V.P.-Mfg.--Eva-Tone Inc., Clearwater, FL; *U.S. Private*, pg. 384

Evans, John, Sr. V.P. & Production Dir.--Omni Publications International Ltd., New York, NY; *U.S. Private*, pg. 444

Evans, Larry, V.P.-Mfg.--Lamina Inc., Oak Park, MI; *Int'l*, pg. 75

Evans, Larry, V.P.-Mfg.--Lamina Inc., Bellaire Plant, Bellaire, MI; *Int'l*, pg. 75

Evans, R.E., V.P.-Refining & Engrng.--Amoco Oil Company, Chicago, IL; *U.S. Public*, pg. 102

Everett, Dwight E., V.P.-Mfg. Opers.--PerSeptive Biosystems, Inc., Framingham, MA; *U.S. Public*, pg. 1279

Everhart, Robert, V.P.-Mfg.--Frank Ix & Sons, Inc., New York, NY; *U.S. Private*, pg. 423

Eversmann, Craig, Dir.-Mfg.--Marsh Company, Belleville, IL; *U.S. Private*, pg. 707

Eves, B.K., Mgr.-Mfg.--Hussmann Store Equipment Limited, Brantford, Canada; *U.S. Public*, pg. 1766

Ewing, Joe, Dir.-Distr. & Pur.--Mississippi Chemical Corporation, Yazoo City, MS; *U.S. Public*, pg. 1117

Ezoye, Yasuto, Gen. Mgr.-Pur.--Toto Ltd., Kitakyushu, Japan; *Int'l*, pg. 1410

Fabbri, Stephen L., V.P.-Mfg.--CiMatrix L.L.C., Canton, MA; *U.S. Public*, pg. 1395

Facco, G., V.P.-Engrng.-Furnaces--Italimpianti of America, Incorporated, Coraopolis, PA; *Int'l*, pg. 655

Faivre, James, Mgr.-Mfg.--Ventre Packing Company, Inc., Syracuse, NY; *U.S. Private*, pg. 1135

Falino, Andrew, Mgr.-Mfg.--Andrea Electronics Corporation, Long Island City, NY; *U.S. Public*, pg. 112

Falk, Jeff, Mgr.-Mfg.--Banta Information Services Group, Spanish Fork, UT; *U.S. Public*, pg. 188

Fallarino, John, Pres.--Metpar Corp., Westbury, NY; *U.S. Private*, pg. 735

Farach, Joe, Mgr.-Bulk Prod. Opers.--AGA Gas, Inc., Independence, OH; *Int'l*, pg. 13

Faris, Mervyn L., V.P.-Engrng.--Sun Coast Closures of Florida, Inc., Sarasota, FL; *U.S. Public*, pg. 1530

Farley, Joseph J., V.P.-Mktg. & Engrng.--Helm Resources Inc., Greenwich, CT; *U.S. Public*, pg. 808

Farley, L., V.P.-Mfg.--Broderick & Bascom Rope Co., Sedalia, MO; *U.S. Private*, pg. 68

Farr, R.E., V.P.-Mfg.--Oliver Rubber Co., Athens, GA; *U.S. Public*, pg. 1504

Fask, Richard, V.P.-Mfg.--Elkay Products, Inc., Shrewsbury, MA; *U.S. Private*, pg. 372

Fatinski, John, Mgr.-Mfg.--Hope's Architectural Products Inc., Jamestown, NY; *U.S. Private*, pg. 538

Faulkner, Ian, Div. Gen. Mgr.-BHP Bldg. & Construction--Building & Industrial Products Division, Sydney, Australia; *Int'l*, pg. 225

Feehly, Michael, V.P.-Prod.--Massachusetts Container Corporation, Marlborough, MA; *U.S. Private*, pg. 263

Feely, Charles, V.P.-Mfg.--CASI-RUSCO Inc., Boca Raton, FL; *U.S. Private*, pg. 218

Feeney, James E., Sr. V.P.-Mfg.--Wheatland Tube Company, Collingswood, NJ; *U.S. Private*, pg. 1170

Feenstra, Mark, Dir.-Mfg. & Engrng.--Bradford Company, Holland, MI; *U.S. Private*, pg. 163

Felicetti, Dominick, V.P.-Worldwide Sourcing/Mfg. & Production--The Leslie Fay Companies, Inc., New York, NY; *U.S. Public*, pg. 989

Fenster, Jonathan G., V.P.-Opers.--Parlux Fragrances Inc., Fort Lauderdale, FL; *U.S. Public*, pg. 1264

Fenstermaker, Dennis, V.P.-Mfg.--Vital Signs, Inc., Totowa, NJ; *U.S. Public*, pg. 1723

Fenstermaker, John, V.P.-Opers.--Staodyn Inc., Longmont, CO; *U.S. Public*, pg. 1509

Fenton, D.R., Dir.-Engrng.--Dexter Company, Fairfield, IA; *U.S. Private*, pg. 329

Ferguson, Robert, V.P.-Technical Services--Bristol-Myers Products, New York, NY; *U.S. Public*, pg. 254

Fernald, Steven, V.P.-Engrng.--Frontier Communications Services, Bingham Farms, MI; *U.S. Public*, pg. 684

Fernandes, Edward, Mgr.-Mfg.--Tube Fittings Div., Eaton, OH; *U.S. Public*, pg. 1261

Ferrari, Jose, Mgr.-Mfg.--La Nacion S.A., Buenos Aires, Argentina; *Int'l*, pg. 785

Ferreira, John, Plant Mgr.--Bridgeport Fittings, Inc., Stratford, CT; *U.S. Private*, pg. 168

Ferreira, Wayne, V.P.-Mfg.--Deck House Inc., Acton, MA; *U.S. Private*, pg. 320

Ferreira, Wayne, V.P.-Mfg.--Acorn Structures, Acton, MA; *U.S. Private*, pg. 320

Fetty, Waid, Mgr.-Mfg.--Hanna-Sherman International, Inc., Portland, OR; *U.S. Private*, pg. 499

Fey, Mike, Plant Mgr.--Hanel Lumber Co., Inc., Hood River, OR; *U.S. Private*, pg. 538

Fichter, Mark, V.P.-Mfg.--Pioneer Plastics Corporation, Auburn, ME; *U.S. Private*, pg. 867

Field, William D., V.P. & Gen. Mgr.-St. Joseph Mfg.--Altec Industries, Inc., Birmingham, AL; *U.S. Private*, pg. 47

Fielding, David, V.P.-Mdse. Controller--Kmart Corporation, Troy, MI; *U.S. Public*, pg. 963

Filson, Dave R., V.P.-Pork Opers.--Farmland Industries, Inc., Kansas City, MO; *U.S. Private*, pg. 395

Finch, Bill, Sr. V.P.-Mfg. & Distr.--Thomas Nelson Inc., Nashville, TN; *U.S. Public*, pg. 1167

Finch, W.D., III, V.P.-Mfg.--C.R. Gibson Co., Norwalk, CT; *U.S. Public*, pg. 1168

Finley, C. Sue, V.P.-Opers. & Dir.-Sls.--Spartech Plastics, Portage, WI; *U.S. Public*, pg. 1496

Finnegan, Bob, V.P.-Mfg.--The Shelburne Corporation, Shelburne, VT; *U.S. Private*, pg. 991

Finnerty, Jack, V.P.-Mfg.--Northern Telecom Inc., Rochester, NY; *Int'l*, pg. 970

Finney, Richard, V.P.-Mfg. Opers.--Celeritek, Inc., Santa Clara, CA; *U.S. Public*, pg. 319

Finnigan, Jerry, Gen. Mgr.-Mfr.--Cruise America, Inc., Mesa, AZ; *U.S. Private*, pg. 178

Fiorini, P., Mgr.-Human Resources--Marcegaglia SpA, Mantova, Italy; *Int'l*, pg. 841

Fischer, H. Clifton, V.P.-Commissary--Frisch's Restaurants, Inc., Cincinnati, OH; *U.S. Public*, pg. 682

Fischer, Helmut G., V.P. & Gen. Mgr.-Corp. Opers.-Germany--Procter & Gamble GmbH, Schwalbach, Germany; *U.S. Public*, pg. 1332

Fischer, Mike, V.P.-Mfg.--Dorner Manufacturing Corp., Hartland, WI; *U.S. Private*, pg. 340

Fischer, Robert, V.P. & Chief Engineer--American Plastic Toys Inc., Walled Lake, MI; *U.S. Private*, pg. 60

Fisher, John, V.P.-Engrng.--Alamo Group, Inc., Seguin, TX; *U.S. Public*, pg. 34

Fisher, John, V.P.-Technical Svcs. & Mfg.--Rubatex Corporation, Roanoke, VA; *U.S. Private*, pg. 56

Fisher, Norman, Mgr.-Distr.--Triumph Pet Industries, Inc., Warwick, NY; *U.S. Private*, pg. 1104

Fisher, Robert J., V.P.-Mfg.--Graniteville Company, Graniteville, SC; *U.S. Private*, pg. 103

Fitch, Mark, V.P.-Mfg.--Knoll Pharmaceutical Company, Whippany, NJ; *Int'l*, pg. 105

Fitzgerald, Neil, V.P.-Mfg.--Ames Safety Envelope Company, Inc., Somerville, MA; *U.S. Private*, pg. 66

Fitzgerald, Tim, Dir.-Opers.--Sun Process Converting Company, Elk Grove Village, IL; *U.S. Private*, pg. 1051

Fitzpatrick, Jim M., Mgr.-Integrated Steel--Rod & Bar Products Division, Port Waratah, Australia; *Int'l*, pg. 227

Fitzsimmons, C. Victor, Sr. V.P.-Worldwide Mfg.--Printronix, Inc., Irvine, CA; *U.S. Public*, pg. 1329

Fitzsimmons, Steve, V.P.- Mfg. & Opers.--Capitol Industries-EMI Inc., Hollywood, CA; *Int'l*, pg. 427

Flak, Ricky, V.P.-Mfg.-Smith Tool--Smith International, Inc., Houston, TX; *U.S. Public*, pg. 1478

Flanagan, William, V.P.-Compatible Processor Products--Amdahl Corporation, Sunnyvale, CA; *Int'l*, pg. 527

Flanders, Byron, V.P.-Mfg.--Giga-Tronics Incorporated, San Ramon, CA; *U.S. Public*, pg. 742

Flannery, Wesely, Mgr.-Production--Western States Machine Company, Hamilton, OH; *U.S. Private*, pg. 1168

Flannigan, J. Steven, V.P.-Systems Engrng.--COMPAQ Computer Corporation, Houston, TX; *U.S. Public*, pg. 417

Flavel, Blair, Supvr.-Production--Hylar Metal Products, Regina, Canada; *Int'l*, pg. 388

Fleck, Philip B., V.P.-Res. & Mfg.--Arrow International, Inc., Reading, PA; *U.S. Public*, pg. 135

Fleming, A.D., V.P.-Prod.--CNG Producing Co., New Orleans, LA; *U.S. Public*, pg. 435

Flexsenhar, Michael A., V.P.-Mining & Construction Equipment Div.--Caterpillar Inc., Peoria, IL; *U.S. Public*, pg. 315

Florek, Phil, V.P.-Mfg.--Integrated Material Handling Company, Oshkosh, WI; *Int'l*, pg. 1397

Florey, Donald L., V.P.-Mfg.--I-Flow Corporation, Lake Forest, CA; *U.S. Public*, pg. 851

Flournoy, Kenoth H., Mgr.-Prod. Engrng.--Maguire Oil Co., Dallas, TX; *U.S. Private*, pg. 696

Floyd, C., Dir.-Plastic Opers.--Abbott Laboratories/Ashland, Ashland, OH; *U.S. Public*, pg. 13

Floyd, Robert, V.P.-Mfg.--Garland Commercial Industries, Inc., Freeland, PA; *Int'l*, pg. 188

Floyd, Scott, Dir.-Opers.--Chattanooga Group, Inc., Hixson, TN; *U.S. Private*, pg. 231

Flynn, Vincent, Mgr.-Mfg.--Certified Alloy Products, Inc., Long Beach, CA; *Int'l*, pg. 1467

Foley, Tim, V.P.-Mfg.--Aetrium Inc., Saint Paul, MN; *U.S. Public*, pg. 27

Foote, Emerson L., Sr. V.P.-Mfg. & Tech. Support/Agricultural Div.--Bayer Corporation, Pittsburgh, PA; *Int'l*, pg. 172

Forberich, Helmut, Mgr.-Prod. & Sls.--Durkopp Adler AG, Bielefeld, Germany; *Int'l*, pg. 468

Forbes, Darren, Dir.-Mdsg.--Erickson Oil Products, Inc., Hudson, WI; *U.S. Private*, pg. 381

Ford, Tim, V.P.-Mfr.--Rose Art Industries, Livingston, NJ; *U.S. Private*, pg. 945

Forester, William C., Sr. V.P.-Mfg./Polymers Div.--Bayer Corporation, Pittsburgh, PA; *Int'l*, pg. 172

Forgiano, Joseph P., V.P.-Mfg.--The At-A-Glance Group, Sidney, NY; *U.S. Private*, pg. 295

Forrester, M., Mgr.-Mfr.--Akers Packaging Service Inc., Middletown, OH; *U.S. Private*, pg. 29

Forsberg, Ken, Mgr.-Production Opers.--Elgin Dairy Foods, Inc., Chicago, IL; *U.S. Private*, pg. 370

Foster, George, V.P.-Mfg.--Blitz USA, Inc., Miami, OK; *U.S. Private*, pg. 149

Foster, Jim, V.P.-Mfg.--Revell-Monogram Inc., Morton Grove, IL; *U.S. Private*, pg. 926

Fowler, Greg, V.P.-Mfg. Opers.--Fire Control Instruments, Inc., Waltham, MA; *U.S. Private*, pg. 406

Fox, Herbert A., Jr., V.P.--Murphy Oil Corporation, El Dorado, AR; *U.S. Public*, pg. 1141

Fox, Michael R., Mgr.-Mfg. Services--American Mail-Well Envelope, Englewood, CO; *U.S. Public*, pg. 1038

Foy, J. Franklin, V.P.-Dyeing & Finishing--Russell Corporation, Alexander City, AL; *U.S. Public*, pg. 1413

Francis, A.L., Mgr.-Mfg.--National Electrical Carbon Canada, Mississauga, Canada; *Int'l*, pg. 892

Francisco, John, V.P.-Mfg.--Norwalk Furniture Corporation, Norwalk, OH; *U.S. Private*, pg. 807

Frank, Earl, V.P.-Mfg.--Kasper Machine Company, Madison Heights, MI; *U.S. Private*, pg. 608

Frank, Kenneth, V.P.-Engrng.--Coleman Powermate, Inc., Omaha, NE; *U.S. Private*, pg. 691

Frank, Ronald, V.P.-Mfg.--Frank Industries, Inc., Brown City, MI; *U.S. Private*, pg. 423

Frankenbach, Linda, V.P.-Programming--The Time Warner Cable Group, Stamford, CT; *U.S. Public*, pg. 1610

Frankie, Dave, V.P.-Opers.--Tekelec, Calabasas, CA; *U.S. Public*, pg. 1566

Franks, Darrel, Mgr.-Mfg.--Arrow Tank & Engineering Co., Minneapolis, MN; *U.S. Private*, pg. 85

Fraser, Andrew, Plant Mgr.--Pioneer/Eclipse Corp., Sparta, NC; *Int'l*, pg. 71

Fraser, Malcolm J., V.P.-Mfg. & Technology--Copperweld Fayetteville Division, Fayetteville, TN; *Int'l*, pg. 662

Frasheffki, Larry, Dir.-Mfg.--Bassick by Kaspar, Shiner, TX; *U.S. Private*, pg. 122

Frasier, Dan, Mgr.-Production--Pac Paper Inc., Vancouver, WA; *U.S. Private*, pg. 828

Fratantanio, Domenic, V.P.-Mfg.--David Clark Company Incorporated, Worcester, MA; *U.S. Private*, pg. 242

Free, David, Mgr.-Production--Crossroads Press, Inc., Honolulu, HI; *U.S. Private*, pg. 19

Freeman, Burton, V.P.-Mfg.--Hershey Pasta and Grocery Group, Hershey, PA; *U.S. Public*, pg. 812

Freeman, Kevin, Mgr.-Production--Bibler Brothers, Inc., Russellville, AR; *U.S. Private*, pg. 142

Frey, W. Steve, V.P.-Mfg.--Reily Foods Company, New Orleans, LA; *U.S. Private*, pg. 919

Fridlington, G.E., Dir.-Mfg.--Kenwood Appliances Plc, Havant, United Kingdom; *Int'l*, pg. 730

Frigo, Jack, Mgr.-Plant--Hirsh Company, Skokie, IL; *U.S. Public*, pg. 963

Fritts, A.W., Dir.-Bus. Mfg.--Harwick Standard Distribution Corporation, Akron, OH; *U.S. Private*, pg. 509

Fritz, Charles, Gen. Mgr.-Mfg.--South Pacific Tyres, Somerton, Australia; *Int'l*, pg. 1021

Frock, J. Daniel, V.P.-Mfg.--Hanover Wire Cloth, Hanover, PA; *U.S. Private*, pg. 193
Fruth, Marc, Mgr.-Production--Sauder Manufacturing Corporation, Archbold, OH; *U.S. Private*, pg. 967
Fry, John, V.P.-Mfg. Opers.--Red Devil Inc., Union, NJ; *U.S. Private*, pg. 915
Fry, R.W., V.P.-Mfg.--Landis, Waynesboro, PA; *U.S. Public*, pg. 1699
Fryberg, George, V.P.-Mfg.--Stocker & Yale, Inc., Salem, NH; *U.S. Public*, pg. 1518
Frye, Jeff, V.P.-Mfg.--Schneller, Inc., Kent, OH; *U.S. Private*, pg. 971
Fryml, Martin, V.P.-Mfg.--American Fast Print, Limited, Spartanburg, SC; *U.S. Private*, pg. 53
Fuchs, Renato, Ph.D., Sr. V.P.-Mfg. & Devel. Opers.--Chiron Corporation, Emeryville, CA; *U.S. Public*, pg. 349
Fujiwara, Hana, Mgr.-Mfg.--Nissin Foods (U.S.A.) Co. Ltd., Gardena, CA; *Int'l*, pg. 949
Fulgham, Brandt, Plant Mgr.--Protective Closures Co., Inc., Buffalo, NY; *U.S. Public*, pg. 1045
Fuller, Michael E., V.P.-Mfg.--Electrolux Corporation, Atlanta, GA; *U.S. Private*, pg. 369
Fuller, Robert E., V.P.-Mfg.--E & A Industries, Inc., Indianapolis, IN; *U.S. Private*, pg. 352
Fulmer, L.C., V.P.-Engrng.--Lockheed Martin Tactical Defense Systems (Akron), Akron, OH; *U.S. Public*, pg. 1009
Fulp, William, V.P.-Mfg.--Kingsdown, Inc., Mebane, NC; *U.S. Private*, pg. 622
Fulton, Dick, V.P.-Mfg., U.S. Plastics Group--Dearborn Division, Dearborn, MI; *U.S. Public*, pg. 1504
Furman, Sam, V.P.-Mfg.--Mogas Industries, Inc., Houston, TX; *U.S. Private*, pg. 755
Fyffe, Roy, V.P.-Mfg.--Raytheon Systems Co., Kirkwood, NY; *U.S. Public*, pg. 1364
Gabbay, Moses A., V.P.-Engrng.--Boston Acoustics, Inc., Peabody, MA; *U.S. Public*, pg. 246
Gabbe, Fred, Exec V.P.-Worldwide Opers.--Mr. Christmas Inc., New York, NY; *U.S. Private*, pg. 765
Gabrielli, Mark, V.P.-Winemaking & Production--Canandaigua Wine Company Div., Canandaigua, NY; *U.S. Public*, pg. 300
Gabrielli, Milton Luiz, Dir.-Prod.--Petrobras - Petroleo Brasileiro S.A., Rio de Janeiro, Brazil; *Int'l*, pg. 1041
Gaffney, Shawn, V.P.-Mfg.--Clestra Hauserman, Inc., Solon, OH; *Int'l*, pg. 569
Gagnon, R., Mgr.-Distribution--La Brasserie Labatt Limitee, La Salle, Canada; *Int'l*, pg. 679
Gaiteri, Frank T., V.P.-Engrng.--New York Wire Co., Mount Wolf, PA; *U.S. Private*, pg. 795
Galland,Henri, Dir.-Indus. Opers.--Alcatel Business Systems (France), Colombes, France; *Int'l*, pg. 55
Galloway, Jack, V.P.-Mfg.--Suttle Press, Inc, Waunakee, WI; *U.S. Public*, pg. 1570
Gamache, Brian, V.P.-Plant Opers.--Alvey Systems, Inc, Saint Louis, MO; *U.S. Private*, pg. 47
Gambrell, Jerry, V.P.-Mfg.--Reeves Southeastern Corporation, Tampa, FL; *U.S. Private*, pg. 916
Gamel, W., V.P.-Mfg.--Bush Hog Division, Selma, AL; *U.S. Public*, pg. 48
Gamundi, Bartolome, V.P.-Mfg.--Electro-Biology, Inc., Guaynabo, PR; *U.S. Public*, pg. 231
Gantt, Larry O., Div. V.P.-Mfg.--Consumer Products Div., Hartsville, SC; *U.S. Public*, pg. 1486
Garabedian, Robert, V.P.-Engrng.--Printed Circuit Corporation, Woburn, MA; *U.S. Private*, pg. 886
Garbuio, Franco, V.P.-Mfg.-Quebec--Bauer Sports Inc., Montreal, Canada; *U.S. Public*, pg. 1184
Gardenhour, Eugene C., Sr. V.P.-Engrng.--Grove WorldWide, Shady Grove, PA; *Int'l*, pg. 593
Gardner, David W., V.P.-Mfg.--Heatilator Inc., Mount Pleasant, IA; *U.S. Public*, pg. 772
Gardner, Jim, Mgr.-Plant--Radix Wire Company, Cleveland, OH; *U.S. Private*, pg. 907
Gardner, Larry, V.P.-Mfg.--Alumacraft Boat Co., Arkadelphia, AR; *U.S. Private*, pg. 1088
Garnaat, G., Treas.--Koninklijke BolsWessanen nv, Amstelveen, Netherlands; *Int'l*, pg. 750
Garner, Ron, Mgr.-Production--Mansion Homes, Robbins, NC; *U.S. Public*, pg. 318
Garrett, Brad, V.P.-Opers.--Advanced Input Devices, Inc., Coeur D'Alene, ID; *U.S. Private*, pg. 21
Garrett, Thomas S., V.P.-Opers.--Optek Technology, Inc., Carrollton, TX; *U.S. Public*, pg. 1227
Garrett, Victor, V.P.-Mfg.--Gilman Building Products Co., Saint Marys, GA; *U.S. Private*, pg. 454
Garriott, Marty, Mgr.-Mfg.--Monaco Coach Corporation, Coburg, OR; *U.S. Public*, pg. 1123
Garrison, D., V.P.-Mfg.-Steel Div.--Russell-Stanley Corporation, Red Bank, NJ; *U.S. Private*, pg. 953
Garvey, John, Sr. V.P.--Parade Publications Inc., New York, NY; *U.S. Private*, pg. 20
Gatesman, Jake, Mgr.-Prodn.--Astro Homes, Shippenville, PA; *U.S. Public*, pg. 318
Gatti, Robert, Exec. V.P.-Mfg.--Rieter Automotive North America Inc, Farmington Hills, MI; *Int'l*, pg. 1117
Gaudio, Raymond, V.P.-Engrng. Software Applications--Napco Security Systems, Inc., Amityville, NY; *U.S. Public*, pg. 1151
Gavin, Robert, Dir.-Mfg.--Harper Audio, New York, NY; *Int'l*, pg. 926
Gay, Charles W., V.P.-Opers. & Mfg.--Cincinnati Gear Company, Cincinnati, OH; *U.S. Private*, pg. 240
Gaykan, Steven, Dir.-Mfg.--UniFirst Corporation, Wilmington, MA; *U.S. Public*, pg. 1665
Gdovka, Karl, Dir.-Mfg.--Alcan Aluminum Corporation, Cleveland, OH; *Int'l*, pg. 50
Gebhardt, Lawrence J., Plant Mgr.-Fontana--Hickman, Williams & Company of Kentucky, Chicago, IL; *U.S. Private*, pg. 525
Geisen, Dick, Mgr.-Mfg. & Opers.--Heat Controller, Inc., Jackson, MI; *U.S. Private*, pg. 518
Geiser, Hal, V.P.-Tech. Service--NT Dor-omatic, Harwood Heights, IL; *U.S. Private*, pg. 771
Gelderloos, Mark I., Sr. Dir.-Engrng. Construction--White Castle System, Inc., Columbus, OH; *U.S. Private*, pg. 1171
Genday, Richard E., Sr. V.P.-Engrng. Grp.--L. Robert Kimball & Associates, Ebensburg, PA; *U.S. Private*, pg. 619
Gentry, Jon, Dir.-Engrng.-Dry Mix Plant--Continental Mills, Inc., Tukwila, WA; *U.S. Private*, pg. 269
George, Julius, Mgr.-Construction--Omega Environmental Services, Lorton, VA; *U.S. Public*, pg. 1222
Georges, John, Mgr.-Mfg.--All-Luminum Products, Inc., Philadelphia, PA; *U.S. Private*, pg. 34
Georgi, Craig C., V.P.-Mfg.--Polk Audio, Inc., Baltimore, MD; *U.S. Public*, pg. 1315
Gephardt, Norm, Mgr.-Plant--Turner Holding LLC, Covington, TN; *U.S. Private*, pg. 1109
Gerads, Lyle, V.P.-Mfg.--Zero-Max, Inc., Minneapolis, MN; *Int'l*, pg. 866
Geraghty, Gerry, V.P.-Mfg.--Gandalf Technologies Inc., Nepean, Canada; *Int'l*, pg. 540
Geraghty, Martin J., Sr. V.P.-Mfg.--Wm. Wrigley Jr. Company, Chicago, IL; *U.S. Public*, pg. 1781
Gerhart, Lynn, Dir.-Mfg.--Allen Telecom Inc., Solon, OH; *U.S. Public*, pg. 45
Gerrior, Richard, V.P.-Mfg.--Intertape Polymer Group Inc., Saint-Laurent, Canada; *Int'l*, pg. 684
Gerver, Tim, V.P.-Mfg.--The Airolite Company, Marietta, OH; *U.S. Private*, pg. 29
Getzloff, W.C., V.P.-Mfg.--ESAB Consumables, Hanover, PA; *Int'l*, pg. 281
Gewin, T. Ronald, V.P.-Opers./TPG--Kewaunee Scientific Corporation, Statesville, NC; *U.S. Public*, pg. 953
Ghary, Raj, Mgr.-Mfg.--Snap-Tite, Inc., Erie, PA; *U.S. Private*, pg. 1010
Gherardi, Mark, Sr. V.P.-Mfg.--Rock of Ages Canada, Inc., Beebe, Canada; *U.S. Public*, pg. 1396
Ghobrial, H., Mgr.-Production--Voyager Emblems, Inc., Sanborn, NY; *U.S. Private*, pg. 1143
Giagtzis, Theodora, Mgr.-Proposals--Jacobs Engineering Group Inc., Houston, TX; *U.S. Public*, pg. 921
Giampaolo, Nick, Plant Mgr.--Chicago Lock Company, Pleasant Prairie, WI; *U.S. Private*, pg. 235
Giannuzzi, Louis, V.P.-Engrng.--Powers Fastening, Inc., New Rochelle, NY; *U.S. Private*, pg. 878
Giard, Ronald G., V.P.-Mfg.--Geiger Brothers, Lewiston, ME; *U.S. Private*, pg. 442
Giauque, Steve, Mgr.-Mfg.--The Gerstenslager Company, Wooster, OH; *U.S. Public*, pg. 1780
Gibbon, Michael A., Sr. V.P.-Tech.--Imax Corporation, Mississauga, Canada; *Int'l*, pg. 661
Gibbons, Bob, V.P.-Mfg.--North American Publishing Company, Philadelphia, PA; *U.S. Private*, pg. 803
Gibbs, David E., Jr., Exec. V.P.-Fin.--Pannier Corporation, Pittsburgh, PA; *U.S. Private*, pg. 837
Gibson, Craig, Mgr.-Mfg.--Oneida Rostone Corporation, Oneida, NY; *U.S. Public*, pg. 1383
Gibson, Scott, V.P.-Mfg. & Engrng.--Automotive, Wayne, NJ; *Int'l*, pg. 234
Gihlstorf, John, Mgr.-Mfg.--Samuel Cabot, Inc., Newburyport, MA; *U.S. Private*, pg. 198
Gilbert, Arthur, V.P.-Mfg.--Sandoz Agro, Inc., Des Plaines, IL; *Int'l*, pg. 974
Gilbert, Donald, V.P.-Mfg.--ICL, Inc., Irvine, CA; *Int'l*, pg. 529
Gilbert, John, Mgr.-Mfr.--Wolf Range Co., Compton, CA; *U.S. Public*, pg. 1322
Gilbert, Russell D., V.P.-Mfg.--Medeva Pharmaceuticals, Rochester, NY; *Int'l*, pg. 852
Gilbertson, James, Dir.-Mfg.--McNaughton & Gunn, Inc., Saline, MI; *U.S. Private*, pg. 724
Gill, Joseph P., Mgr.-Engrng. & Consultant--Cosmos Broadcasting Corp., Greenville, SC; *U.S. Public*, pg. 992
Gillespey, C. Wayne, Sr. V.P.-Mfg.--Crane Pumps & Systems Inc., Piqua, OH; *U.S. Public*, pg. 457
Gillespey, Wayne, V.P.-Mfg.--Sellers Cleaning Systems, Piqua, OH; *U.S. Public*, pg. 457
Gillette, Andy, Mgr.-Mfg.--Dunn-Edwards Corporation, Los Angeles, CA; *U.S. Private*, pg. 347
Gillette, Thomas, Mgr.-Paint & Ass.--Acme Design Technology, Co., Crozet, VA; *U.S. Private*, pg. 13
Ginko, Sigmund, V.P.-Corp. Mfg.--Macrotech Plyseal, Inc., Salt Lake City, UT; *U.S. Private*, pg. 693
Ginsiorsky, M., Mgr.-U.S. Plant Opers.--PQ Corporation, Berwyn, PA; *U.S. Private*, pg. 827
Girdin, Jean-Claude, Dir.-Mfg.--Krups GmbH & Co. KG, Solingen, Germany; *Int'l*, pg. 896
Givens, Dan, V.P.-Prod.--Pacific Trail Inc., Seattle, WA; *U.S. Private*, pg. 673
Givens, Michael, Plant Supvr.--Microflect Company, Inc., Salem, OR; *U.S. Public*, pg. 1707
Glade, John F., V.P.-Engrng. & Mfg. & Sec.--Alpha Microsystems, Santa Ana, CA; *U.S. Public*, pg. 57
Glader, Douglas J., Sr. V.P.-Mfg. Opers.--Digi International Inc., Minnetonka, MN; *U.S. Public*, pg. 506
Glass, Donald L., Exec. V.P.-Bldg. Prods., Mfg. & Sls.--Georgia-Pacific Corporation, Atlanta, GA; *U.S. Public*, pg. 735
Gleckler, Tom, Plant Mgr.--Fulton Industries Inc., Wauseon, OH; *U.S. Private*, pg. 431
Gledhill, John, Dir.-Mfg.--United Dominion Industries, Ltd., Charlotte, NC; *U.S. Public*, pg. 1675
Glenister, Bryan, V.P.-Mfg. & Engrng.--KRC (Hewitt) Inc., Neenah, WI; *Int'l*, pg. 1202
Glennon, G., V.P.-Mfg.--Abbott Ball Company, West Hartford, CT; *U.S. Private*, pg. 9
Glickstein, Robert, V.P.-Mfg.--Inwood Laboratories, Inc., Inwood, NY; *U.S. Public*, pg. 670
Glogovsky, E., Dir.-Mfg. & Engrng.--CPC Latin American Consumer Foods Division, Englewood Cliffs, NJ; *U.S. Public*, pg. 447
Glover, R. John, Mgr.-Mining Opers.--Mineral Deposits Pty. Ltd., Bundall, Australia; *Int'l*, pg. 224
Glover, Tom, V.P.-Mfg.--GSW Water Heating Company, Fergus, Canada; *Int'l*, pg. 538
Glowe, Gary, V.P.-Mfg.--OEC Medical Systems, Inc., Salt Lake City, UT; *U.S. Public*, pg. 1207
Godfrey, John, V.P. & Gen. Mgr.-Access/Intimate/Cosmetics--Crowley, Milner & Company, Detroit, MI; *U.S. Public*, pg. 461
Goelz, Werner, V.P.-Facilities--Heller Seasonings & Ingredients, Inc., Bedford Park, IL; *U.S. Private*, pg. 520
Goenner, Gary, V.P.-Prod.--Lifetouch, Portrait Studios, Eden Prairie, MN; *U.S. Private*, pg. 667
Goff, Charles N., V.P.-Mfg.--Emulex Corporation, Costa Mesa, CA; *U.S. Public*, pg. 579
Goff, R., Mgr.-Mfg.--O-Z/Gedney, Nelson Firestop Products, Tulsa, OK; *U.S. Public*, pg. 726
Goggiano, Stephen, Sr. V.P.-Mfg.--Silicon Graphics, Inc., Mountain View, CA; *U.S. Public*, pg. 1473
Goik, Mark, V.P.-Mfg.--GSE, Inc., Farmington, MI; *U.S. Public*, pg. 1676
Goldsby, T.K., V.P.-Mfg.--Harwick Standard Distribution Corporation, Akron, OH; *U.S. Private*, pg. 509
Goldschmidt, Nick, Winemaker--Simi Winery, Healdsburg, CA; *Int'l*, pg. 781
Golumbeski, John M., V.P.-Mfg.--Andersen 2000 Inc., Peachtree City, GA; *U.S. Public*, pg. 462
Gombotz, John L., Dir.-System Technical Services--Yankee Energy System, Inc., Meriden, CT; *U.S. Public*, pg. 1787
Gomez, Enidio, Exec. V.P.-Opers.--Security Plastics, Inc., Hialeah, FL; *U.S. Private*, pg. 981
Gonnerman, Todd A., Mgr.--Galamba Metals, Inc., Kansas City, KS; *U.S. Private*, pg. 437
Gonsalves, Dennis, V.P.-Mfg.--SGS-Thomson Microelectronics, Inc., Carrollton, TX; *Int'l*, pg. 1153
Gonyo, Joseph, V.P.-Mfg.--Berlin Glove Company Ltd., Berlin, WI; *U.S. Private*, pg. 136
Good, Barry L., V.P.-Mfg.--Wolverine Gasket & Manufacturing Co., Inkster, MI; *U.S. Private*, pg. 355
Good, Don, Mgr.-Plant--Turner Holding LLC, Memphis, TN; *U.S. Private*, pg. 1109
Goodacre, Daniel, V.P.-Mfg.--Pandrol Jackson, Inc., Ludington, MI; *Int'l*, pg. 280
Goodale, David, V.P.-Mfg.--Pullman Industries, Inc., Pullman, MI; *U.S. Private*, pg. 894
Goode, Wallace H., V.P.-Mfg. Opers--Mead Publishing Paper, Escanaba, MI; *U.S. Public*, pg. 1074
Goodger, William, Plant Mgr.--Stanbee Company, Inc., Carlstadt, NJ; *U.S. Private*, pg. 1030
Goodwait, Vernon G., V.P.-Mfg.--Ney Dental International, Bloomfield, CT; *Int'l*, pg. 388
Goodwin, G. William, V.P.-Mfg.--Independent Can Company, Belcamp, MD; *U.S. Private*, pg. 559
Goodwin, Ian M., Mgr.-Supply--BHP Manganese, Melbourne, Australia; *Int'l*, pg. 224
Goodwin, J.D., V.P.-Mfg.--Hallmark Cards, Inc., Kansas City, MO; *U.S. Private*, pg. 495
Gorcyca, Ray, V.P.-Mfg.--Orbit Valve Co., Little Rock, AR; *U.S. Private*, pg. 819
Gordon, Robert, Dir.-Opers.--ESA, Inc., Chelmsford, MA; *U.S. Private*, pg. 354
Gorenc, D., Dir.-Mfg. Opers.--Plastic Packaging Company, Muncie, IN; *U.S. Public*, pg. 57
Gornet, Michel, Sr. V.P.-Mfg.--Renault, Boulogne-Billancourt, France; *Int'l*, pg. 1102
Gorski, Paul, V.P.-Mfg. & Mgr.-Quality Control--Leblanc Communications, Inc., Richardson, TX; *U.S. Private*, pg. 656
Gossett, Chuck, Mill Mgr.--Bearden Lumber Company, Inc., Bearden, AR; *U.S. Private*, pg. 127
Gossnel, Mark, V.P.-Uphol. Mfg.--Bassett Furniture Industries, Incorporated, Bassett, VA; *U.S. Public*, pg. 193
Gottschall, Herb, Mgr.-Mfg.--Jamison Plastic Corporation, Allentown, PA; *U.S. Private*, pg. 581
Goughneour, Richard, Mgr.-Mfg. Svcs.--T & S Brass & Bronze Works, Inc., Travelers Rest, SC; *U.S. Private*, pg. 1061
Graham, E.W., V.P.-Mfg.--Medrad, Inc., Indianola, PA; *Int'l*, pg. 1204
Graham, William, Mgr.-Production--Modern Plastics, New York, NY; *U.S. Public*, pg. 1071
Grande, Steve, V.P.-Mfg.--CMP Media, Inc., Manhasset, NY; *U.S. Public*, pg. 279
Granito, Maria, V.P.-Mfg. Opers.--Mentor Opthalmics, Inc., Santa Barbara, CA; *U.S. Public*, pg. 1086
Granthan, James, V.P.-Mfg. & Engrng.--Blue Bird Corporation, Macon, GA; *U.S. Private*, pg. 151
Grassman, Jeff, Chief Engr.--Microflect Company, Inc., Salem, OR; *U.S. Public*, pg. 1707
Graves, John, V.P.-Mfg.--TST/Impreso, Inc., Coppell, TX; *U.S. Private*, pg. 1066
Gray, J.H., Sr. V.P.-Mfg. & Engrng.--Dunlop Tire Corporation, Buffalo, NY; *Int'l*, pg. 1317
Gray, William R., V.P.-Engrng.--Telsmith, Inc., Mequon, WI; *U.S. Public*, pg. 141
Graziani, R. Doug, Sr. Process Engr.--Newport Steel Corporation, Newport, KY; *U.S. Public*, pg. 1147
Greany, Dennis, Exec. V.P.-Mfg. Grp.--Mary Kay, Inc., Dallas, TX; *U.S. Private*, pg. 711
Greco, Barbara, Mgr.-Production--Parents Magazine, New York, NY; *Int'l*, pg. 191
Green, Ken, Gen. Mgr.-Milwaukee Opers. & Mgr.-Loose Leaf Bindery--H.C. Miller Company, Milwaukee, WI; *U.S. Private*, pg. 747
Green, Reynold K., V.P.-Sls.--Merrimac Industries, Inc., West Caldwell, NJ; *U.S. Public*, pg. 1098
Green, Stuart C., V.P.-Mfg.--Bandag, Incorporated, Muscatine, IA; *U.S. Public*, pg. 177
Green, Thomas, V.P.-Opers.--AMI Industries, Inc., Colorado Springs, CO; *U.S. Public*, pg. 401
Gregory, Tom, Mgr.-Mfg.--Hunt Corporation, Philadelphia, PA; *U.S. Public*, pg. 848
Grengs, Mike, Dir.-Mfg.--Ciprico, Inc., Plymouth, MN; *U.S. Public*, pg. 370
Grenzel, Moshe, V.P.-Mfg.--Elscint Ltd., Haifa, Israel; *Int'l*, pg. 450

Grieser, J.R., V.P.-Mfg.--Sauder Woodworking Co., Archbold, OH; *U.S. Private*, pg. 967
Grieve, D.V., V.P.-Engrng.--The Grieve Corporation, Round Lake, IL; *U.S. Private*, pg. 480
Griffey, Lee, V.P.-Intl. Mfg.--The Clorox Company, Oakland, CA; *U.S. Public*, pg. 386
Griffin, Jack, Mgr.-Mfg.--Adams Wine Co., Atlanta, GA; *U.S. Private*, pg. 17
Griffith, Mike, Dir.-Mfg.--Bostrom Seating, Inc., Piedmont, AL; *U.S. Public*, pg. 933
Grissom, James, V.P.-Mfg.--Pennzoil Products Co., Houston, TX; *U.S. Public*, pg. 1272
Grobowski, Frank, V.P.-Book Mfg.--Scholastic Inc., New York, NY; *U.S. Public*, pg. 1440
Groce, A. Ben, Sr. V.P.-Mfg., Paper Div.--Boise Cascade Corporation, Boise, ID; *U.S. Public*, pg. 242
Groce, A. Ben, Sr. V.P.-Mfg.--Boise Cascade Paper Div., Boise, ID; *U.S. Public*, pg. 243
Grondin, James, V.P.-Mfg. Services--Kleinert's, Inc., of Alabama, Elba, AL; *U.S. Private*, pg. 625
Groppe, Marc, Plant Mgr.--Central States Diversified, Inc., Saint Louis, MO; *U.S. Private*, pg. 224
Grossinger, Robert, V.P.-Mfg.--Elgin Watch Company, Long Island City, NY; *U.S. Private*, pg. 371
Grossman, Sharon, Mgr.-Prod. Devel.--School Annual Publishing Co., Coshocton, OH; *U.S. Private*, pg. 598
Grozman, Desiderio M., Sr. V.P.-Mfg.--La Tondena Distillers, Inc., Manila, Philippines; *Int'l*, pg. 785
Gruse, Werner, V.P.-Mfg.--Diebel Manufacturing Co., Morton Grove, IL; *U.S. Private*, pg. 331
Grzenia, Richard, Exec. V.P.-Mfg.--Tekra Corporation, New Berlin, WI; *U.S. Private*, pg. 1073
Guariglia, Carol, Mgr.-Mfg.--New York Law Journal, New York, NY; *Int'l*, pg. 956
Guay, Serge, Corp. V.P.-Mfg.--Scott Paper Limited, Mississauga, Canada; *Int'l*, pg. 762
Gubau, Josep, Dir.-Production--Mattel Espana, S.A., Barcelona, Spain; *U.S. Public*, pg. 1059
Guidi, Peter, V.P.-Mfg.--Ward Manufacturing, Inc., Blossburg, PA; *U.S. Private*, pg. 1149
Guiles, Ron, V.P.-Mfg., Res. & Devel.--Columbia Paint & Coatings, Spokane, WA; *U.S. Private*, pg. 256
Guiley, Base, V.P.-Pub. Support Oper.--John Wiley & Sons, Inc., New York, NY; *U.S. Public*, pg. 1768
Guion, James F., Sr. V.P.-Prod. & Opers.--Kerr-McGee Corporation, Oklahoma City, OK; *U.S. Public*, pg. 952
Guittonneau, Francis, Sr. V.P.-Engrng.--Systra-Sofretu-Sofrerail, Paris, France; *Int'l*, pg. 1165
Gulluni, Joseph, Sr. V.P.-Opers.--Milton Bradley Company, East Longmeadow, MA; *U.S. Public*, pg. 797
Gulluscio, J., Mgr.-Mfg.--Yardney Technical Products, Inc., Pawcatuck, CT; *U.S. Private*, pg. 376
Gunnard, Russell J., V.P.-Mfg.--Roberts Systems, Inc., Charlotte, NC; *Int'l*, pg. 395
Guralnick, Robert, Exec. V.P.-Prod.--Warner Bros. Studios, Inc., Burbank, CA; *U.S. Public*, pg. 1611
Gurch, James M., Sr. V.P.-Opers.--Marlette Homes, Inc., Middlebury, IN; *U.S. Public*, pg. 1442
Gurley, Dennis, V.P.-Mfg.--Shelby Williams Industries, Inc., Morristown, TN; *U.S. Public*, pg. 1464
Gustafson, Wallace H., V.P.-Engrng.--United Stationers Inc., Des Plaines, IL; *U.S. Public*, pg. 1689
Gustilo, Rudolfo B., V.P.-Mfg.--Certified Alloy Products, Inc., Long Beach, CA; *Int'l*, pg. 1467
Gustin, Wayne, Mgr.-Plant--Lee Pharmaceuticals, South El Monte, CA; *U.S. Public*, pg. 984
Gutkneckt, John, V.P.-Mfg.--Rauland-Borg Corporation, Skokie, IL; *U.S. Private*, pg. 911
Guy, Thomas D., Sr. V.P.-Opers.--U.S. Surgical Corp., Norwalk, CT; *U.S. Public*, pg. 1687
Guyer, Steve, V.P.-Mfg.--Red Calliope & Associates, Inc., Los Angeles, CA; *U.S. Public*, pg. 465
Haahr, Robert L., Dir.-Mfg.--Isco Environmental Division, Lincoln, NE; *U.S. Public*, pg. 914
Hackworth, Brett, V.P.- Mfg.--King Louie International, Grandview, MO; *U.S. Private*, pg. 621
Hackworth, Donald E., V.P. & Gen. Mgr.-Cadillac/Luxury Car Engrng. & Mfg. Div.--Cadillac Motor Car Division, Warren, MI; *U.S. Public*, pg. 720
Hadnes, Steve, Dir.-Mfg.--Center Laboratories, Inc., Port Washington, NY; *U.S. Public*, pg. 813
Hafenbreidel, Louis B., Sr. V.P.-Mfg.--Pepsi-Cola General Bottlers, Inc., Rolling Meadows, IL; *U.S. Public*, pg. 1277
Hafner, Volker W., Sr. V.P.-Engrng.--Acorn Engineering Company, City of Industry, CA; *U.S. Private*, pg. 14
Hageman, Larissa, Mgr.-Production--Wichita Business Journal, Inc., Wichita, KS; *U.S. Private*, pg. 20
Hagen, Ty, Chief Engr.--Brown-Minneapolis Tank & Fabricating Co., Eagan, MN; *U.S. Public*, pg. 914
Hahne, William N., V.P.-Houston Div. Prod.--The Louisiana Land and Exploration Company, New Orleans, LA; *U.S. Public*, pg. 269
Hak, H.C., Dir.-Prod. & Tech.--Hak B.V., Giessen, Netherlands; *Int'l*, pg. 244
Hale, John, Dir.-Southern Mfg.--Frito-Lay Inc., Charlotte, NC; *U.S. Public*, pg. 1277
Hall, Don, Sr. V.P.-Mfg.--Helen of Troy Corporation, El Paso, TX; *U.S. Public*, pg. 807
Hall, E.A., V.P.-Mfg.--Sandusky International Inc., Sandusky, OH; *U.S. Private*, pg. 964
Hall, Eric K., V.P.-Mfg.--Trimtex Co. Inc., Williamsport, PA; *U.S. Private*, pg. 1103
Hall, Gary, V.P.-Greige Mfg.--Greenwood Mills, Inc., Greenwood, SC; *U.S. Private*, pg. 479
Hall, Jerry L., V.P.-Tech. Services--Charmilles Technologies Corp., Lincolnshire, IL; *Int'l*, pg. 489
Hall, Robert, Mgr.-Mfr.--The Grandoe Corp., Gloversville, NY; *U.S. Private*, pg. 469
Halterman, Dave, V.P.-Mfg.--Toastmaster, Inc., Columbia, MO; *U.S. Public*, pg. 1619
Hamamoto, Arlene, Dir.-Mfg.--Rice Growers Association of California, West Sacramento, CA; *U.S. Private*, pg. 927
Hamel, Brian, Dir.-Mfg.--Sam Dick Industries, Inc., Seattle, WA; *U.S. Private*, pg. 360
Hamill, Randy A., Sr. V.P.-Mfg. & Resources--Square Two Golf Incorporated, Fairfield, NJ; *U.S. Public*, pg. 1501
Hamilton, Keith, Mgr.-Plant--Datasouth Computer Corporation, Charlotte, NC; *U.S. Public*, pg. 267
Hamilton, Kyle, Mgr.-Plant--Our Sunday Visitor, Inc., Huntington, IN; *U.S. Private*, pg. 821
Hammel, Wally, V.P.-Mfg.--Collins & Aikman Floorcoverings, Inc., Dalton, GA; *U.S. Private*, pg. 192
Hammett, Roy, V.P.-Mfg. & Res.--International Container Systems, Tampa, FL; *Int'l*, pg. 685
Hand, B.J., V.P.-Engrng.--American Cast Iron Pipe Co., Birmingham, AL; *U.S. Private*, pg. 51
Handerhan, Joseph P., Gen. Mgr.-Mfg.--Diamond Power Specialty Co., Lancaster, OH; *U.S. Public*, pg. 1068
Hankins, Thomas R., V.P.-Mfg.--Sunnen Products Company, Saint Louis, MO; *U.S. Private*, pg. 1053
Hanline, James, Mgr.-Mfg.--Hull/Finmac, Inc., Warminster, PA; *U.S. Private*, pg. 547
Hannan, Pam, Mgr.-Production--The Business Journal of Portland, Inc., Portland, OR; *U.S. Private*, pg. 19
Hannemann, Timothy W., Exec. V.P. & Gen. Mgr.-TRW Space & Electronics Grp.--TRW Inc., Cleveland, OH; *U.S. Public*, pg. 1558
Hanner, Cliff, V.P.-Engrng.--Brubaker Tool Corp., Millersburg, PA; *U.S. Public*, pg. 368
Hans, Harry L., Grp. V.P.-Engines & Power Train Components--Tecumseh Products Company, Tecumseh, MI; *U.S. Public*, pg. 1565
Hansberger, W.L., V.P.-Mfg.--RAM Golf Corporation, Melrose Park, IL; *U.S. Private*, pg. 908
Hansen, Eric R., V.P.-Technical Dir.--Ash Grove Cement Company, Shawnee Mission, KS; *U.S. Private*, pg. 87
Hansen, Jim, Mgr.-Mfg.--Tricon Brazing Alloys & Chemical Products Div., Downers Grove, IL; *U.S. Private*, pg. 1103
Hansen, Kenneth R., V.P.-Mfg.--Intermec Technologies Corporation, Everett, WA; *U.S. Public*, pg. 1699
Hansen, Morris, Mgr.-Plant--Smith Frozen Foods, Inc., Weston, OR; *U.S. Private*, pg. 1008
Hanson, R. Edward, V.P.-Production--Central Maine Power Company, Augusta, ME; *U.S. Public*, pg. 325
Hapgood, Paul, V.P.-Mfg.--Dennison Stationery Products Company, Holyoke, MA; *U.S. Public*, pg. 153
Hardegger, Alfred, Mgr.-Mfg.--Coop Switzerland, Basel, Switzerland; *Int'l*, pg. 329
Harding, Thomas, Mgr.-Mfg. Tech.--PTA Corporation, Oxford, CT; *U.S. Private*, pg. 828
Hardison, Douglas, Mgr.-Production--Hyspan Precision Products, Inc., Chula Vista, CA; *U.S. Private*, pg. 552
Harlan, Timothy J., Asst. V.P.-Mdse. Handling--Blair Corporation, Warren, PA; *U.S. Public*, pg. 236
Harley, James T., V.P.-Mfg.--Bentley Mills, Inc., City of Industry, CA; *U.S. Public*, pg. 889
Harney, William J., V.P.-Mfg.--Raytheon Optical Systems, Lexington, MA; *U.S. Public*, pg. 1364
Harper, Charles, Dir.-Matl. Procurement--Duo-Fast Corporation, Huntley, IL; *U.S. Private*, pg. 347
Harper, George, V.P.-Yarn Mfg.--Columbus Mills, Inc., Columbus, GA; *U.S. Private*, pg. 256
Harpin, C., V.P.-Mfg.--Nantucket Industries, Inc., Melville, NY; *U.S. Public*, pg. 1151
Harrah, C. Dana, Dir.-Mfg.--Wausau-Mosinee Paper Corporation, Mosinee, WI; *U.S. Public*, pg. 1747
Harrah, C. Danah, Dir.-Mfg.--Pulp & Paper Div., Mosinee, WI; *U.S. Public*, pg. 1747
Harris, Frank, Mgr.-Plant--Relief Printing, Baldwin Park, CA; *U.S. Private*, pg. 921
Harris, John K., V.P.-Mfg.--Ambrake Corporation, Elizabethtown, KY; *U.S. Public*, pg. 721
Harris, Tom, V.P.-Engrng.--Hillerich & Bradsby Co., Louisville, KY; *U.S. Private*, pg. 530
Harrison, Doug, V.P.-Mfg.--Thomas Built Buses, Inc., High Point, NC; *U.S. Private*, pg. 1082
Harrison, Ron, V.P.-Production--Jones Apparel Group, Inc., Bristol, PA; *U.S. Public*, pg. 933
Harrison, William R., Jr., V.P.-Mfr. (Asia/Pacific)--Du Pont (E.I. Du Pont De Nemours & Co.), Wilmington, DE; *U.S. Public*, pg. 530
Harrits, Susan M., V.P.-Mfg. & Opers.--Patrick Cudahy Inc., Cudahy, WI; *U.S. Public*, pg. 1479
Harrod, Allen, V.P.-Mfg.--Printing House, Inc., Quincy, FL; *U.S. Private*, pg. 886
Hart, Arthur S., V.P.-Mfg.--Shurflo Pump Manufacturing Co., Santa Ana, CA; *U.S. Public*, pg. 1767
Hart, Steve, Dir.-Prod.--American Textil, S.A. de C.V., Santa Clara, Mexico; *U.S. Public*, pg. 769
Harter, Wade, V.P.-Engrng.--Greenwood Mills, Inc., Greenwood, SC; *U.S. Private*, pg. 479
Hartman, Stephen, V.P.-Opers.--The Cornelius Company, Anoka, MN; *Int'l*, pg. 646
Hartmann, Siegfried, Mgr.-Mfg.--NL Industries, Inc., Houston, TX; *U.S. Private*, pg. 270
Haselwander, Jack, Exec. V.P.-Mfg.--Salem Carpet Mills, Inc., Winston Salem, NC; *U.S. Public*, pg. 1464
Hashimoto, Hashi, Mgr.-Mfg.--Medtronic Japan Co., Ltd., Hokkaido, Japan; *U.S. Public*, pg. 1084
Haskamp, William, Chief Oper. Officer--Faribault Woolen Mill Co., Faribault, MN; *U.S. Private*, pg. 394
Haskelson, Pierre A., V.P.-Mfg.--Porta Systems Corp., Syosset, NY; *U.S. Public*, pg. 1317
Haslanger, Paul A., V.P.-Mfg.--Foamex, L.P., Linwood, PA; *U.S. Private*, pg. 1094
Hassan, Emil E., V.P.-Opers.--Nissan Motor Mfg. Corp., U.S.A., Smyrna, TN; *Int'l*, pg. 945
Hassler, Don, V.P.-Mfg.--Midway Games, Inc., Chicago, IL; *U.S. Public*, pg. 1727
Hasting, John, V.P.-Mfg.--Binney & Smith Inc., Easton, PA; *U.S. Private*, pg. 496
Hatfield, Terry, V.P.-Mfr.--Mattison Technologies, Inc., Rockford, IL; *U.S. Private*, pg. 714
Haun, S. Wesley, V.P.-Mktg. & Gas Supply--K N Energy, Inc., Lakewood, CO; *U.S. Public*, pg. 937
Hauner, J., Mgr.-Mfg.--Hitachi Instruments, Inc., San Jose, CA; *Int'l*, pg. 622
Hauser, Gene W., V.P.-Engrng.--Aircraft Division, Hawthorne, CA; *U.S. Public*, pg. 1198
Hawes, Dave, Chief Engineer--API Harowe, West Chester, PA; *U.S. Public*, pg. 90
Hawkings, W.E., V.P.-Engrng.--MacMillan Bloedel Limited, Vancouver, Canada; *Int'l*, pg. 828
Hawkins, Gary, V.P.-Mfg.--Sinclair Printing & Litho, Inc., Los Angeles, CA; *U.S. Private*, pg. 1003
Hawkins, Jay L., V.P.-Opers.--Micron Technology Inc., Boise, ID; *U.S. Public*, pg. 1105
Hayden, William J., V.P.-Mfg.--Ford of Europe, Incorporated, Dearborn, MI; *U.S. Public*, pg. 664
Hayes, Ed, V.P.-Mfg.--Pressman Toy Corp., New York, NY; *U.S. Private*, pg. 882
Hayes, J., Dir.-Mfg. & Quality--ICI Paints, Cleveland, OH; *Int'l*, pg. 664
Haynie, Tony, V.P.-Mfg.--Williamson-Dickie Mfg. Co., Fort Worth, TX; *U.S. Private*, pg. 1179
Head, Gerry, Mng. Dir.-Mfg., Logistics & Quality--Thorn Security Group, Ltd., Sunbury, United Kingdom; *Int'l*, pg. 1386
Headley, Rex, Mgr.-Mfg.--Franklin Baking Co., Inc., Goldsboro, NC; *U.S. Private*, pg. 424
Healey, Jim, V.P.-Mfg.--Mosler Inc., Hamilton, OH; *U.S. Private*, pg. 763
Healy, Francis J., Mgr.-Plant--Gudebrod, Inc., Pottstown, PA; *U.S. Private*, pg. 486
Healy, Robert, V.P.-Mfg.--The American Group, Ferndale, WA; *U.S. Private*, pg. 56
Hearn, Tom, Mgr.-Opers.--River Ranch Northeast, Inc., Buffalo, NY; *U.S. Private*, pg. 934
Hearp, Wyatt, V.P.-Mfg.--Tom's Foods, Inc., Columbus, GA; *U.S. Private*, pg. 1090
Heath, Alan L., V.P.-Opers. & Engrng.--Delta Natural Gas Company, Inc., Winchester, KY; *U.S. Public*, pg. 497
Hechler, Mark, V.P.-Mfg.--Frequency Electronics, Inc., Uniondale, NY; *U.S. Public*, pg. 681
Hedquist, Jack, V.P.-Mfg.--Precision Carbide Tool Company, Inc., Niles, IL; *U.S. Private*, pg. 879
Heilman, D.R., Dir.-Engrng.-Packard International SBU--Delphi Packard Electric Systems, Beachwood, OH; *U.S. Public*, pg. 719
Heimbach, Paul A., Sr. V.P.-Engrng./Network Opers. Ctr.--MTV Networks, New York, NY; *U.S. Private*, pg. 779
Hellinger, David, Mgr.-Production--Nocona Boot Co., Nocona, TX; *U.S. Public*, pg. 937
Hellman, Laurence M., V.P.-Mdse. & Consumer Res.--The May Department Stores Company, Saint Louis, MO; *U.S. Public*, pg. 1063
Helms, Jack R., Dir.-Production--The Free Lance-Star Publishing Co., Fredericksburg, VA; *U.S. Private*, pg. 424
Helms, Roger, V.P.-Web Mfg.--The Hennegan Company, Florence, KY; *U.S. Private*, pg. 522
Hemby, J. Ray, V.P.-Mfg.--Mar-Mac Manufacturing Company, Inc., McBee, SC; *U.S. Private*, pg. 701
Hemp, Peter W., V.P.-Copper Div. & Broadband Connectivity Grp.--ADC Telecommunications, Inc., Minnetonka, MN; *U.S. Public*, pg. 4
Hemrich, Kurt J., Sr. Exec. V.P.--Fender Musical Instruments, Scottsdale, AZ; *U.S. Private*, pg. 400
Henderson, Dan, V.P.-Mfg.--H. R. Kaminsky & Sons, Inc., Fitzgerald, GA; *U.S. Private*, pg. 606
Henderson, W. Harold, V.P.-Mfg.--Arrow Automotive Industries, Inc., Framingham, MA; *U.S. Public*, pg. 133
Hendery, William J., V.P.-Project Mngmt.--Bennington Iron Works, Inc., Bennington, VT; *U.S. Private*, pg. 133
Hendrickson, Bruce I., V.P.-Engrng. Services--Browning-Ferris Industries, Inc., Houston, TX; *U.S. Public*, pg. 262
Hennessey, T., V.P.-Mfg.--Emerson Motor Company, Sturgeon Bay, WI; *U.S. Public*, pg. 573
Henry, Paul J., Exec. V.P.-Tech. Services--IMI Cornelius Inc. (MN), Anoka, MN; *Int'l*, pg. 646
Henson, Lisa, V.P.-Production--Warner Bros. Studios, Inc., Burbank, CA; *U.S. Public*, pg. 1611
Herbst, George, Sr. V.P.-Mfg.--Ball Metal Beverage Container Corp., Westminster, CO; *U.S. Public*, pg. 171
Herdman, William R., V.P.-Mfg. & Gen. Mgr.--Kennedy Tank & Manufacturing Co., Inc., Indianapolis, IN; *U.S. Private*, pg. 614
Hermann, Walter, V.P.-Production--Holz-Her U.S. Inc., Charlotte, NC; *Int'l*, pg. 1101
Hernke, Keith G., V.P.-Prod.--Quad/Graphics, Inc., Pewaukee, WI; *U.S. Private*, pg. 897
Herrell, R.E., Sr. V.P.-Mfg.--Celotex Corporation, Tampa, FL; *U.S. Private*, pg. 221
Herrera, Frank, V.P. & Dir.-Distr.--Hearst Magazines Division, New York, NY; *U.S. Private*, pg. 516
Herschbein, Irving, V.P.-Mfg. & Distr.--The Conde Nast Publications Inc., New York, NY; *U.S. Private*, pg. 20
Hersey, Lester, Mgr.-Mfg.--Maine Potato Growers, Inc., Presque Isle, ME; *U.S. Private*, pg. 697
Hertz, Kevin, V.P.-Opers.--Poco Petroleums Ltd., Calgary, Canada; *Int'l*, pg. 1061
Herzinger, Mike, Mgr.-Plant--Graphic Systems, Saint Louis, MO; *U.S. Public*, pg. 1060
Hess, George W., V.P.-Opers.--Midway Products Corporation, Monroe, MI; *U.S. Private*, pg. 744
Hevert, C.H., V.P.-Opers. Mfg.--Kearfott Guidance & Navigation Corp., Wayne, NJ; *U.S. Private*, pg. 93
Hickey, David M., Exec. V.P.-Mfg. & Intl. Opers.--Corrpro Companies, Inc., Medina, OH; *U.S. Public*, pg. 451
Hickey, Kevin G., V.P.-Mfg. & Dist.--Self, New York, NY; *U.S. Private*, pg. 20
Hickman, Gerald A., V.P.-Mfg.--Ameriwood Industries International Inc., Grand Rapids, MI; *U.S. Public*, pg. 98
Hicks, Bob, Mgr.-Engrng.--Dotronix, Inc., New Brighton, MN; *U.S. Public*, pg. 520
Hicks, Ken, Dir.-Mfg.--H.J. Baker & Bro., Inc., Stamford, CT; *U.S. Private*, pg. 112
Higginson, William J., V.P.-Production--Journal Register Company, Trenton, NJ; *U.S. Public*, pg. 934
Highhouse, Milton D., Dir.-Mfg.--Chemtech Products Inc., Saint Louis, MO; *U.S. Private*, pg. 39

Hilgers, Wayne, V.P.-Mfg., Olefins & Vinyl Div.--Condea Vista Company, Houston, TX; *Int'l*, pg. 325
Hill, David, V.P.-Supply Chain--NIBCO, Inc., Elkhart, IN; *U.S. Private*, pg. 798
Hill, Joan, Chief Oper. Officer & V.P.-H.R.--Jami, Inc., Shawnee Mission, KS; *U.S. Private*, pg. 581
Hill, Linda, Dir.-Pur. & Mfg.--Blue Coral Systems, Tucson, AZ; *U.S. Public*, pg. 1348
Hillpot, William, V.P.-Materials Mngmt. & Wire Opers.--Northwestern Steel & Wire Co., Sterling, IL; *U.S. Public*, pg. 1201
Hingley, Noel G., V.P.-Mfg.--Blount, Inc. Oregon Cutting Systems Division, Portland, OR; *U.S. Public*, pg. 238
Hinkson, George, V.P.-Mfg.--Roussel Corporation, Montvale, NJ; *Int'l*, pg. 625
Hinton, Bobby, Mgr.-Production--Industrial Bag Division - Wellsburg Plant, Wellsburg, WV; *U.S. Public*, pg. 1521
Hirsch, Jamie, V.P.-Mfg. & Pur.--Structural Industries, Inc., Hicksville, NY; *U.S. Private*, pg. 1048
Hirst, Ian, Dr., Dir.-Mfg.--Biogen, Inc., Cambridge, MA; *U.S. Public*, pg. 230
Hlavacek, James C., V.P.--Minerallac Co., Addison, IL; *U.S. Private*, pg. 750
Hoback, John, V.P.-Mfg.--The Keller Manufacturing Co., Inc., Corydon, IN; *U.S. Private*, pg. 612
Hobbs, Royce, Mgr.-Production--Homestead Homes, Cordele, GA; *U.S. Public*, pg. 318
Hobby, Kenneth L., V.P.-Maintenance & Engrng.--Horizon Air Industries, Seattle, WA; *U.S. Public*, pg. 35
Hodapp, Norbert, V.P.-Mfg.--Action Technology Company, Rockaway, NJ; *U.S. Private*, pg. 15
Hodge, J.E., V.P.-Opers.--The Lubrizol Corporation, Wickliffe, OH; *U.S. Public*, pg. 1016
Hodges, Bobby, Sr. V.P.-Mfg.--Stanley Furniture Co. Inc., Stanleytown, VA; *U.S. Public*, pg. 1508
Hodges, Wayne, V.P.-Opers.--North American Capacitor Co., Indianapolis, IN; *U.S. Private*, pg. 803
Hodgins, Keith, Mgr.-Brewing--Pabst Brewing Co., San Antonio, TX; *U.S. Private*, pg. 954
Hoefer, Robert, V.P.-Mfg.--Acacia Networks, Inc., Lowell, MA; *U.S. Private*, pg. 11
Hoerres, Bob, Plant Mgr.--Enzopac, Inc., Sheboygan, WI; *U.S. Private*, pg. 379
Hoerscher, Don, V.P.-Mfg.--Mark Andy, Inc., Chesterfield, MO; *U.S. Public*, pg. 521
Hof, August J., V.P.-Mfg. Opers.--General Datacomm Industries, Inc., Middlebury, CT; *U.S. Public*, pg. 708
Hoffecker, Joe, Mgr.-Production--ACBJ Business Publications, Inc., Cincinnati, OH; *U.S. Private*, pg. 19
Hoffman, John, Plant Mgr.--Pac Paper Inc., Vancouver, WA; *U.S. Private*, pg. 828
Hoffman, John, V.P.-Pkgng.--Leslie Paper, Minneapolis, MN; *U.S. Public*, pg. 903
Hoffman, Michael J., V.P.-Mfg.--Constar International, Inc., Atlanta, GA; *U.S. Public*, pg. 463
Hoffman, Robert, Dir.-Mfg.--Interplastic Corp., Saint Paul, MN; *U.S. Private*, pg. 572
Hoffnagle, B.M., Mgr.-Matls. Services--Salt River Project Agricultural Improvement and Power District, Tempe, AZ; *U.S. Private*, pg. 962
Hofher, Lynn, Asst. Managing Editor--Self, New York, NY; *U.S. Private*, pg. 20
Hofmann, Martin J., V.P.-Mfg.--Hofmann Industries, Inc., Sinking Spring, PA; *U.S. Private*, pg. 533
Hofner, Kevin E., V.P.-Refinery Opers.--BHP Hawaii, Inc., Honolulu, HI; *Int'l*, pg. 225
Hofner, Kevin E., V.P.-Refining Opers.--Gasco, Inc., Honolulu, HI; *Int'l*, pg. 225
Hogan, Bill, V.P.-Mdsg./Western Reg.--The Home Depot, Inc., Atlanta, GA; *U.S. Public*, pg. 831
Hohenschuh, Paul F., V.P.-Mfg.--Genentech, Inc., South San Francisco, CA; *Int'l*, pg. 1120
Hohl, Andreas, Dir.-Works--Baumann Federn AG, Ruti, Switzerland; *Int'l*, pg. 171
Hohmeier, John C., Dir.-Mfg.--MTD Products Limited, Kitchener, Canada; *U.S. Private*, pg. 688
Holden, Gary, Mgr.-Production--FMC FoodTech/Fran Rica, Stockton, CA; *U.S. Public*, pg. 605
Holdredge, Ernest C., V.P.-Mfg.--Structural Foam Plastics, Inc., Winchester, KY; *U.S. Private*, pg. 1048
Hollis, Patrick, V.P.-Opers.--Asahi/America, Inc., Malden, MA; *U.S. Public*, pg. 137
Hollstein, Carl P., Jr., V.P.-Mfg.--Protocol Systems, Inc., Beaverton, OR; *U.S. Public*, pg. 1336
Holmberg, Carl, Chief Engr.--Peerless Confection Company, Chicago, IL; *U.S. Private*, pg. 847
Holshouser, Kermit, Dir.-Mfg.--Hickory Hill Furniture Corporation, Valdese, NC; *U.S. Private*, pg. 808
Holzhaeusser, Heinz, Mgr.-Mfg.--Mill-Rose Company, Mentor, OH; *U.S. Private*, pg. 746
Holzhauser, Ronald, V.P.-Engrng.--Thomas Built Buses, Inc., High Point, NC; *U.S. Private*, pg. 1082
Holzwasser, Robert A., V.P.-Engrng. Opers.--Arrow Automotive Industries, Inc., Framingham, MA; *U.S. Public*, pg. 133
Homa, Michael, V.P.-Mfg.--Tamaqua Cable Products Corp., Schuylkill Haven, PA; *Int'l*, pg. 417
Homburger, Jim, Mgr.-Prod.--Kit Manufacturing Company, Long Beach, CA; *U.S. Public*, pg. 962
Hood, J.D., Dir.-Mfg.--Franklin Baking Co., Inc., Goldsboro, NC; *U.S. Private*, pg. 424
Hood, Jay, Dir.-Mfg.--Regal Marine Industries Inc., Orlando, FL; *U.S. Private*, pg. 917
Hookway, Warren, Exec. V.P.-Mfg.--Labelon Corporation, Canandaigua, NY; *U.S. Private*, pg. 641
Hoover, Jim C., V.P.-Mfg. Opers.--Aircraft Division, Hawthorne, CA; *U.S. Public*, pg. 1198
Hope, Stan, Mgr.-Opers.--Progress Paint Mfg. Co., Louisville, KY; *U.S. Private*, pg. 890
Hopkins, Jesse, Dir.-Mfg.--BJ Services Company, Houston, TX; *U.S. Public*, pg. 161
Hopkins, Jesse E., Dir.-Mfg.--Jefferson Mills, Inc., Pulaski, VA; *U.S. Private*, pg. 584
Hopkins, Quahn, Dir.-Mfg.--FMC Corp., Lithium Division, Gastonia, NC; *U.S. Public*, pg. 605
Hopkins, Tim, Dir.-Pur.--Walden Book Company, Ann Arbor, MI; *U.S. Public*, pg. 245
Hopp, Robert G., V.P.-Opers.--Na-Churs Plant Food Company, Marion, OH; *U.S. Private*, pg. 1096
Hopp, Tony, Plant Mgr.--Rodman Industries, Marinette, WI; *U.S. Private*, pg. 402
Hopps, Peter D., V.P.-Plant Opers.--Baskin-Robbins Canada, Etobicoke, Canada; *Int'l*, pg. 63
Horan, David, V.P.-Engrng.--Control Module, Inc., Enfield, CT; *U.S. Private*, pg. 271
Horner, J.F., V.P.-Refining--Amoco Oil Company, Chicago, IL; *U.S. Public*, pg. 102
Horning, John I., V.P.-Exploration & Production--Du Pont (E.I. Du Pont De Nemours & Co.), Wilmington, DE; *U.S. Public*, pg. 530
Horton, R., Mgr.-Plant Opers.--Fairmont Snack Group, Inc., Independence, OH; *U.S. Private*, pg. 392
Hotman, Les H., V.P.-Supply, Rates & Plng.--The Berkshire Gas Company, Pittsfield, MA; *U.S. Public*, pg. 216
Houghtalen, Joseph, V.P.-Mfg.--Automotive Safety Products, Ogden, UT; *U.S. Public*, pg. 1134
Houlton, Alan J., V.P.-Mfg.--Millennium Petrochemicals, Inc., Cincinnati, OH; *Int'l*, pg. 594
Houseworth, Paul, Mgr.-Plant--Delta Consolidated Industries, Inc. (Co. Headquarters), Jonesboro, AR; *U.S. Public*, pg. 481
Housman, Mark, V.P.-Mfg.--Armatron International, Inc., Melrose, MA; *U.S. Public*, pg. 131
Houston, B., Mgr.-Distribution--Metro Brewery, Etobicoke, Canada; *Int'l*, pg. 679
Howard, Bob, V.P.-Mfg.--Magee Co., Pocahontas, AR; *U.S. Public*, pg. 1561
Howard, Donald, V.P.-Mfg.--HMI Industries, Cleveland, OH; *U.S. Public*, pg. 771
Howard, John, V.P.-Power Prod.--Alabama Electric Cooperative, Inc., Andalusia, AL; *U.S. Private*, pg. 30
Howarth, J., Dir.-Mfg.--BBA Friction LTD., Cleckheaton, United Kingdom; *Int'l*, pg. 112
Howe, Joanne, Mgr.-Production--Business First of New York, Inc., Albany, NY; *U.S. Private*, pg. 19
Howell, Linda, Mgr.-Producton--ACBJ Business Journals, Inc., Kansas City, MO; *U.S. Private*, pg. 19
Howell, Robert, V.P.-Mfg.--Carhartt, Inc., Dearborn, MI; *U.S. Private*, pg. 210
Howes, Paul, V.P.-Engrng. Svcs.--Flint Ink Corp., Detroit, MI; *U.S. Private*, pg. 413
Howse, Geoff, Assoc. Dir.-Engrng.--Industrial Acoustics Company, Ltd., Staines, United Kingdom; *U.S. Public*, pg. 875
Hren, Vincent, V.P.-Opers.--Three-Five Systems, Tempe, AZ; *U.S. Public*, pg. 1604
Hu, Jennifer, V.P.-Opers. & Mfg.--Liuski International, Inc., Norcross, GA; *U.S. Public*, pg. 1005
Huber, Jan, Plant Mgr.--Shopsmith, Inc., Dayton, OH; *U.S. Public*, pg. 1467
Hudson, Art, Dir.-Mfg.--Elastomeric Technologies, Inc., Hatboro, PA; *U.S. Public*, pg. 1598
Huffman, Dave, V.P.-Engrng.--Lockheed Martin Information Display Systems, Atlanta, GA; *U.S. Public*, pg. 1008
Huffman, Tom, V.P.-Mfg., Surfactants & Specialities Div.--Condea Vista Company, Houston, TX; *Int'l*, pg. 325
Hufnail, Mark, Sr. V.P.-Production--The Guber Peters Entertainment Company, Los Angeles, CA; *Int'l*, pg. 1283
Hug, James A., V.P.-Transmission/Chassis--Simpson Industries, Inc., Plymouth, MI; *U.S. Public*, pg. 1474
Hughes, Fred, Dir.-Prod.--Heckethorn Mfg. Company, Inc., Dyersburg, TN; *U.S. Private*, pg. 519
Hughes, John, Mgr.-Mfg.--Merriam-Webster, Inc., Springfield, MA; *U.S. Private*, pg. 375
Hughes, Roger, Mgr.-Production--Phoenix Medical Technology, Inc., Andrews, SC; *U.S. Public*, pg. 1292
Hughes, Sonja, Mgr.-Mfg.--View-Master, Inc., Mount Laurel, NJ; *U.S. Public*, pg. 1058
Hughes, Tavy A., V.P.-Mfg.--Pinnacle Systems, Inc., Mountain View, CA; *U.S. Public*, pg. 1297
Hull, C.E., Dir.-Works--James Walker & Co. Limited, Woking, United Kingdom; *Int'l*, pg. 1485
Humason, Steve, V.P.-Engrng.--Airco Mechanical Inc., Sacramento, CA; *U.S. Private*, pg. 29
Hummel, Joe, Mgr.-Mfg.--Jomac, Inc., Warrington, PA; *U.S. Private*, pg. 595
Humphrey, David, V.P.-Opers.--Hoover Group, Inc., Alpharetta, GA; *U.S. Private*, pg. 538
Humphrey, Jim, V.P.-Mfg.--American Wyott Corporation, Cheyenne, WY; *U.S. Private*, pg. 1193
Hundsdoerfer, W., Mgr.-Mfg.--Jagenberg, Inc., Enfield, CT; *Int'l*, pg. 1108
Hunt, Bob, Dir.-Mfg.--Genova Products, Inc., Davison, MI; *U.S. Private*, pg. 447
Hunt, Peter, V.P.-Mfg.--Greenfield Industries, Cleveland, OH; *U.S. Public*, pg. 950
Hunter, James M., V.P.-Mfg.--Harris Teeter, Inc., Charlotte, NC; *U.S. Public*, pg. 1412
Hunter, John, Sr. V.P.-Mfg. & Engrng. Plastic Div.--Russell-Stanley Corporation, Red Bank, NJ; *U.S. Private*, pg. 953
Hunter, Mark, Mgr.-Production--Beacon Container of PA, Montoursville, PA; *U.S. Private*, pg. 125
Hunter, Mike S., V.P.-California Silicon Mfg.--Integrated Device Technology, Inc., Santa Clara, CA; *U.S. Public*, pg. 884
Hunter, Robin, Dir.-Mfg.--Eagle-Picher Fluid Systems Limited, Market Harborough, United Kingdom; *U.S. Private*, pg. 355
Huntley, Max, Sr. V.P.-Mfg.--Parkdale Mills, Gastonia, NC; *U.S. Private*, pg. 840
Huot, Serge, V.P.-Global Sourcing & Mfg.--G.E. Medical Systems, Milwaukee, WI; *U.S. Public*, pg. 710
Huot, Serge, V.P.-Technology & Production--Camco Inc., Mississauga, Canada; *U.S. Public*, pg. 713
Hurlbut, Randy, Mgr.-Mfg.--Magnetrol International, Downers Grove, IL; *U.S. Private*, pg. 696
Hurless, Mark, Mgr.-Opers.--Kennedy Manufacturing Company, Van Wert, OH; *U.S. Private*, pg. 614
Husky, Gary W., Dir.-Electric Trans. & Distr.--SIGCORP, Inc., Evansville, IN; *U.S. Public*, pg. 1471
Hussar, Nick, Dir.-Production & Tech.--Miracle Feeds Inc., London, Canada; *U.S. Private*, pg. 432
Hutzler, Larry, V.P.-Mfg.--David White, L.L.C., Germantown, WI; *U.S. Public*, pg. 1765
Hutzler, Larry, V.P.-Mfg.--David White, L.L.C., Germantown, WI; *U.S. Private*, pg. 1765
Hyde, James, V.P.-Mfg.--Plasti-Kote Company Inc., Medina, OH; *U.S. Private*, pg. 870
Ibrahim, Samy H., V.P.-Gas Supply--Commonwealth Energy System, Gas Division, Cambridge, MA; *U.S. Public*, pg. 414
Iceman, T.L., V.P.-Mfg.--The Gerstenslager Company, Wooster, OH; *U.S. Public*, pg. 1780
Ide, Takashi, Dir. & Gen. Mgr.--Cosmo Oil Co., Ltd., Tokyo, Japan; *Int'l*, pg. 335
Ikeda, Yukio, Mng. Dir.--Ebara Corporation, Tokyo, Japan; *Int'l*, pg. 431
Ilardi, A., Dir.-Mfg.--Eli Lilly Italia, S.p.A., Sesto Fiorentino, Italy; *U.S. Public*, pg. 994
Inagaki, Katsuya, Gen. Mgr.-Prod.--Makita Corporation, Anjo, Japan; *Int'l*, pg. 831
Inazumi, Teiji, Exec. Dir.-Mfg.--Japan Tobacco Inc., Tokyo, Japan; *Int'l*, pg. 703
Ingebretsen, Bud, V.P.-Opers.--Patterson Frozen Foods, Inc., Patterson, CA; *U.S. Private*, pg. 843
Ingelhuber, James E., Grp. V.P.-Mfg. Opers. & Human Resources--Metal Container Corporation, Saint Louis, MO; *U.S. Public*, pg. 114
Ingram, Bill, Dir.-Wafer Mfg.--Supertex, Inc., Sunnyvale, CA; *U.S. Public*, pg. 1539
Inners, R.L., II, Mgr.-Spring Grove Mill--P.H. Glatfelter Company, Spring Grove, PA; *U.S. Public*, pg. 746
Ioan, Claudia, Chief Engineer--Master Products Mfg. Co., Los Angeles, CA; *Int'l*, pg. 340
Irimajiri, Shoichiro, Exec. V.P.-Res., Devel. & Mfg.--Sega Enterprises Ltd., Tokyo, Japan; *Int'l*, pg. 1218
Irish, Bruce J., Dir.-Mfg.--McGraw-Hill Information Systems Co. of Canada Ltd., North York, Canada; *U.S. Public*, pg. 1072
Isaac, Cruz, Mgr.-Production--Signtech USA, Ltd., San Antonio, TX; *U.S. Private*, pg. 999
Isaacks, John, V.P.-Production--Analytical Surveys, Inc., Colorado Springs, CO; *U.S. Public*, pg. 110
Itahara, Seiji, V.P.-Mfg.--RHC/Spacemaster Corporation, Melrose Park, IL; *U.S. Private*, pg. 904
Ito, Toshio, Sr. Mng. Dir. & Gen. Mgr.-Engnrg., Mfg. & Informations Systems--Mitsubishi Electric Corporation, Tokyo, Japan; *Int'l*, pg. 872
Iverson, Dennis, Mgr.-Prod.--Barrel O'Fun Snack Foods Co., Perham, MN; *U.S. Private*, pg. 118
Iverson, Grant D., V.P.-Mfg.--Union Pump Company, Battle Creek, MI; *U.S. Private*, pg. 1119
Ives, Ralph R., V.P.-Mfg.--Peregrine Incorporated, Southfield, MI; *U.S. Private*, pg. 852
Jackson, Bob, Mgr.-Mfg. Opers.--Aerco International Inc., Northvale, NJ; *U.S. Private*, pg. 23
Jackson, Dennis, V.P.-Mfg., North Carolina--Crown Crafts, Inc., Atlanta, GA; *U.S. Public*, pg. 465
Jackson, Geoffrey G., Sr. V.P.-Central Mfg.--Quebecor Printing (USA) Corp., Greenwich, CT; *Int'l*, pg. 1078
Jacobson, Rolf, Dir.-Mfg. & Devel.--AB SKF, Goteborg, Sweden; *Int'l*, pg. 1156
Jacot, William, V.P.-Mfg. & Opers.--California Offset Printers, Inc., Glendale, CA; *U.S. Private*, pg. 196
Jakosz, William, V.P.-Mfg.--Harrington & King, Chicago, IL; *U.S. Private*, pg. 504
James, Lee, V.P.-Mfg.--The Biltrite Corporation, Waltham, MA; *U.S. Private*, pg. 144
Janda, Robert L., V.P.-Mfg.--International Paper Company, Purchase, NY; *U.S. Public*, pg. 901
Jankowski, Dave, Mgr.-Mfg.--Ingrid Division of Lawnware, Morton Grove, IL; *U.S. Private*, pg. 654
Jannausch, William A., V.P.-Mfg. Maintenance & Services--Inland Steel Products Company, East Chicago, IN; *U.S. Public*, pg. 879
Jansen, Robert, V.P.-Opers.--A.E. Staley Manufacturing Co., Decatur, IL; *Int'l*, pg. 1356
Jansen, Rolf R., Exec. V.P.--Stora Feldmuhle AG, Dusseldorf, Germany; *Int'l*, pg. 1303
Jaros, Robert J., Dir.-Mfg.--FMC Corp., Agricultural Products Group, Philadelphia, PA; *U.S. Public*, pg. 605
Jarvis, Chris, Mgr.-Engrng.--H.B. Smith Co., Inc., Westfield, MA; *U.S. Private*, pg. 1008
Jayne, Ronald C., Dir.-Technical Services--The Edward J. DeBartolo Corporation, Youngstown, OH; *U.S. Private*, pg. 319
Jean, Raymond A., Pres. & Chief Oper. Officer--Varlen Corporation, Naperville, IL; *U.S. Public*, pg. 1710
Jeannot, Louis D., Dir.-Industrial Contracts & Opers.--Arianespace SA, Evry, France; *Int'l*, pg. 81
Jeanquart, Norb, V.P.-Oper.--Packerland Packing Co., Green Bay, WI; *U.S. Private*, pg. 833
Jefferson, Rolla R., V.P.-Mfg. & Engrng.--Fruit of the Loom, Inc., Chicago, IL; *U.S. Public*, pg. 685
Jeffery, T., V.P.-Mfg.--Tuthill Pump, Alsip, IL; *U.S. Private*, pg. 1111
Jeffords, John, V.P.-Production--Jennie-O Foods, Inc., Willmar, MN; *U.S. Public*, pg. 840
Jellinek, Gabor, V.P.-Production--The Seagram Company Ltd., Montreal, Canada; *Int'l*, pg. 1214
Jeltrup, Eric H., Chief Tech. Officer & Exec. V.P.--PCA International, Inc., Matthews, NC; *U.S. Public*, pg. 1240
Jenkins, Dennis E., V.P.-Mfg.--Sta-Rite Industries, Inc., Delavan, WI; *U.S. Public*, pg. 1767
Jenkins, E, Mgr.-Mfg. & Shipping/Warehouse--SA-SO Company, Dallas, TX; *U.S. Private*, pg. 955
Jenkins, Gene M., Mgr.-Steel Fabrication--J.S. Alberici Construction Co., Inc., Saint Louis, MO; *U.S. Private*, pg. 32

Jenkins, Len, Dir.-Weirton Tech. Ctr.--Weirton Steel Corporation, Weirton, WV; *U.S. Public*, pg. 1751
Jensen, Dieter, Exec. V.P.-Prod.--Koenig & Bauer-Albert AG, Wurzburg, Germany; *Int'l*, pg. 742
Jensen, Donald, Plant Mgr.--Dimensional Merchandising, Inc., Wharton, NJ; *U.S. Private*, pg. 333
Jent, Ron, Mgr.-Mfg.--Wavetek Communications Div., Indianapolis, IN; *U.S. Private*, pg. 1155
Jermsted, Gordon, V.P.-Mill Service--Philip Metals Inc., Cleveland, OH; *Int'l*, pg. 1050
Jestice, Marvin R., V.P.-Mfg.--Detector Electronics Corporation, Minneapolis, MN; *Int'l*, pg. 1500
Jetland, Mary M., V.P.-Mfg. & Corp. Services--Ag-Chem Equipment Co., Inc., Minnetonka, MN; *U.S. Public*, pg. 6
Johannessen, Eric, V.P.-Mfg.--Megapulse, Inc., Bedford, MA; *U.S. Private*, pg. 729
Johanssen, J., V.P.-Mfg.--Van Leer Containers, Inc., Alsip, IL; *Int'l*, pg. 1146
Johansson, Halvar, V.P.-Grp. Mfg., Tech., WEBV--Whirlpool Corporation, Benton Harbor, MI; *U.S. Public*, pg. 1764
Johns, Barry D., V.P.-Mfg.--Shakespeare Monofilament, Columbia, SC; *U.S. Public*, pg. 940
Johns, Robert M., V.P.-Mfg.--White Castle System, Inc., Columbus, OH; *U.S. Private*, pg. 1171
Johnson, A.P., Dir.-Mfg.--Mobil Oil Company, Ltd., Milton Keynes, United Kingdom; *U.S. Public*, pg. 1119
Johnson, Aldie, V.P.-Mfg.--Calmar Inc., City of Industry, CA; *U.S. Private*, pg. 201
Johnson, Arnold, V.P.-Mfg.--Swift-Cor Tool Engineering, Gardena, CA; *U.S. Private*, pg. 1058
Johnson, B., Dir.-Mfg. & Opers.--Presstek, Inc., Hudson, NH; *U.S. Public*, pg. 1324
Johnson, Bill, Mgr.-Prod.--Mautz Paint Co., Madison, WI; *U.S. Private*, pg. 715
Johnson, Dana, Mgr.-Mfg.--Fastenal Company, Winona, MN; *U.S. Public*, pg. 614
Johnson, David, V.P.-Mfg.--Marlite, Dover, OH; *U.S. Private*, *pg. 705*
Johnson, Doyle, Mgr.-Mfg. Services--Griffin Envelope, Inc., Seattle, WA; *U.S. Public*, pg. 1038
Johnson, Edward F., V.P.-Mfg. Resource Devel.--Fruit of the Loom, Inc., Chicago, IL; *U.S. Public*, pg. 685
Johnson, John, V.P.-Mfg.--Best Manufacturing, Inc., New York, NY; *U.S. Private*, pg. 139
Johnson, John, V.P.-Mfg. & Pur.--Reliable Knitting Works, Milwaukee, WI; *U.S. Private*, pg. 920
Johnson, Ken, Mgr.-Mfg.--Fiberesin Industries Inc., Oconomowoc, WI; *U.S. Private*, pg. 402
Johnson, Kent R., V.P.-Mfg.--Mutoh America Inc., Phoenix, AZ; *Int'l*, pg. 897
Johnson, Mark, Dir.-Mfg.--Rama Group of Companies, Cheektowaga, NY; *U.S. Private*, pg. 908
Johnson, Mark, V.P.-Mdsg. & Procurement--Performance Food Group Company, Richmond, VA; *U.S. Public*, pg. 1278
Johnson, Richard W., V.P.-Engrng.--Acustar, Inc., Troy, MI; *U.S. Public*, pg. 353
Johnson, Robert M., V.P.-Pharmaceutical Oper.--MGI PHARMA INC., Minneapolis, MN; *U.S. Public*, pg. 1026
Johnson, Ronald D., V.P.-Process Dev. & Manufacturing--Chiron Corporation, Emeryville, CA; *U.S. Public*, pg. 349
Johnson, Scott, Plant Mgr.--AE Farms, Inc., Des Moines, IA; *U.S. Private*, pg. 72
Johnson, Skip, V.P.-Mfr.--Don Miguel Mexican Foods, Inc., Anaheim, CA; *U.S. Private*, pg. 339
Johnson, Stephen L., V.P.-Mfg.--Washburn Graphics, Inc., Charlotte, NC; *U.S. Public*, pg. 291
Johnson, Steve, V.P.-Mfg.--Guidant Corporation-Vascular Intervention Group, Santa Clara, CA; *U.S. Public*, pg. 768
Johnson, Thomas R., Jr., Exec. V.P.-Mfg.--Russell Corporation, Alexander City, AL; *U.S. Public*, pg. 1413
Johnson, Tim, Mgr.-Mfg.--East Moline Metal Products Company, East Moline, IL; *U.S. Private*, pg. 357
Johnsonbaugh, Richard D., Mgr.-Mfg./Eastern Reg.--Oil-Dri Corporation of America, Chicago, IL; *U.S. Public*, pg. 1214
Johnston, David, Mng. Dir.--BHA Group, Newport News, VA; *U.S. Public*, pg. 161
Joly, D.C., Dir.-Production--Charmilles Technologies SA, Meyrin, Switzerland; *Int'l*, pg. 489
Jonas, Nelson J., Sr. V.P.-Construction Opers.--Bartlett Cocke, Inc., San Antonio, TX; *U.S. Private*, pg. 249
Jones, Allen, V.P. & Bus. Mgr.-Pkgng. & Medical Prods.--Synergistics Industries Limited, Mississauga, Canada; *U.S. Public*, pg. 734
Jones, Bob, Mgr.-Molding--Ultra Tool & Plastics, Inc., Amherst, NY; *U.S. Private*, pg. 1116
Jones, Bob, V.P.-Engrng.--American Cablevision of Indianapolis, Inc., Indianapolis, IN; *U.S. Public*, pg. 1610
Jones, Charlie J., V.P.-Electrical Engrng.--Abbey Etna Machine Company, Perrysburg, OH; *U.S. Private*, pg. 9
Jones, D., Mgr.-Mfg.--BEAU Interconnect Systems, Gilford, NH; *U.S. Public*, pg. 157
Jones, J.G., Mgr.-Opers.--The Mount Cook Group Limited, Christchurch, New Zealand; *Int'l*, pg. 38
Jones, John F., V.P.-Mfg.--Rauch Industries, Inc., Gastonia, NC; *U.S. Private*, pg. 1061
Jones, Keith A., Dir.-Corp. Mktg.--Fermec Holdings, Ltd., Manchester, United Kingdom; *U.S. Public*, pg. 312
Jones, Kelly, V.P.-Mfg.--Linfinity Microelectronics Inc., Garden Grove, CA; *U.S. Public*, pg. 1547
Jones, M. Bruce, Sr. V.P.-Mfg.--Mannington Resilient Floors, Salem, NJ; *U.S. Private*, pg. 700
Jones, M.H., Dir.-Fuse Prods Div.--S & C Electric Company, Chicago, IL; *U.S. Private*, pg. 954
Jones, P., Dir.-Mfg.--TP Manipulations, Oldbury, United Kingdom; *Int'l*, pg. 1222
Jones, Peter, Dir.-Mfg. Svcs.--Specialty Textile Products, Talladega, AL; *U.S. Private*, pg. 1023
Jones, Rex, Pres.--Schilling Motors, Inc., Germantown, TN; *U.S. Private*, pg. 970
Jones, William, Mgr.-Mfg.--Virginia Metal Industries, Inc., Orange, VA; *U.S. Private*, pg. 1141
Jordan, Joseph F., V.P. & Mgr.-Plant--Jordan's Meats, Portland, ME; *U.S. Private*, pg. 599
Jordan, Ken, Mgr.-Mfg.--Benthos, Inc., North Falmouth, MA; *U.S. Public*, pg. 212
Jordan, Laurence, V.P.-Opers.--Alliance Semiconductor Corp., San Jose, CA; *U.S. Public*, pg. 47
Joseph, Ed, Prod. Mgr.-Sanitation--Bou-Matic, Madison, WI; *U.S. Private*, pg. 301
Jost, Douglas, V.P.-Mfg.--Glines & Rhodes, Inc., Attleboro, MA; *U.S. Private*, pg. 457
Joyner, Al, Pres.-Mfg.--Tanner Co., Rutherfordton, NC; *U.S. Private*, pg. 1068
Juang, P.H., Dir.-Mfg. Div.--Chinese Petroleum Corporation, Taipei, Taiwan; *Int'l*, pg. 286
Juneau, J. Bradley, Exec. V.P.-Exploration--Sonat Exploration GOM Inc., Houston, TX; *U.S. Public*, pg. 1485
Junyont, Frances, Dir.-Mfg.--Kalifarma S.A., Barcelona, Spain; *Int'l*, pg. 1279
Jyawook, Sam, V.P.-Engrng.--Kingston-Warren Corporation, Newfields, NH; *U.S. Public*, pg. 796
Kabler, J.F., Mgr.-Mfg.--The Kingsford Products Company, Oakland, CA; *U.S. Public*, pg. 387
Kaczynski, Roy, Mgr.-Mfr.--Nuttall Gear Corporation, Niagara Falls, NY; *U.S. Private*, pg. 809
Kaelin, Toni, Mgr.-Production--Baumann Springs USA, Inc., Pineville, NC; *Int'l*, pg. 171
Kagel, William W., Sr. V.P.-Prod.--Payco American Corporation, Brookfield, WI; *U.S. Public*, pg. 1267
Kageyama, Paul, Dir.-Mfg.--EXAR Corporation, Fremont, CA; *U.S. Public*, pg. 597
Kain, Richard A., V.P.-Mfg.--Symbol Technologies, Portable Systems Division, Costa Mesa, CA; *U.S. Public*, pg. 1546
Kaiser, Mark P., Sr. V.P.-Sls., Mktg. & Procurement--JP Foodservice, Inc., Columbia, MD; *U.S. Public*, pg. 918
Kaldi, Lajos, V.P.-Mfg.--Daedal Division, Harrison City, PA; *U.S. Public*, pg. 1259
Kalinowski, Gerhard, Tech. Mgr.-Doors & Frames--Westag & Getalit AG, Rheda-Wiedenbruck, Germany; *Int'l*, pg. 1491
Kallweit, Frank, Dir.-Prod.--Martin Merkel-I.M.S., Petaling Jaya, Malaysia; *Int'l*, pg. 860
Kalm, Richard, Dir.-Process Instrumentation--Associated Process Controls, Pleasanton, CA; *U.S. Private*, pg. 92
Kaminski, David M., Dir.-Opers.--Continental/Midland, Inc., Park Forest, IL; *U.S. Private*, pg. 268
Kanaly, Timothy, V.P.-Pur., Prod. & Distrib.--Vicorp Restaurants, Inc., Denver, CO; *U.S. Public*, pg. 1719
Kane, Gary, V.P.-Mfg.--Richardson Bros. Co. Div., Sheboygan Falls, WI; *U.S. Private*, pg. 929
Kanemoto, Timothy, V.P.-Prod. Opers.--Xicor, Inc., Milpitas, CA; *U.S. Public*, pg. 1785
Kanthamneni, Sudhakar, V.P.-Mfg. & Tech.--Maverick Tube Corporation, Chesterfield, MO; *U.S. Public*, pg. 1060
Kappler, George P., Jr., Chief Exec. Officer--Kappler Safety Group, Inc., Guntersville, AL; *U.S. Private*, pg. 607
Karlson, Gene, V.P.-Opers.--Northland Aluminum Products, Inc., Minneapolis, MN; *U.S. Private*, pg. 805
Karr, Bob, Mgr.-Mfg.--Netzsch Incorporated, Exton, PA; *U.S.* Private, pg. 792
Kastavek, Joseph, V.P.-Mfg.--Michael Anthony Jewelers, Inc., Mount Vernon, NY; *U.S. Public*, pg. 1103
Kathman, J. C., V.P.-Mfg.--Post Glover Resistors Inc., Erlanger, KY; *Int'l*, pg. 590
Katkaveck, Frank, Dir.-Mfg.--Abbott Laboratories/Ashland, Ashland, OH; *U.S. Public*, pg. 13
Katterhagen, Joel, Mgr.-Opers.--Pickering Inc., Tacoma, WA; *U.S. Private*, pg. 864
Kauffman, Donald E., V.P.-Mfg.--Hercon Laboratories Corp., New York, NY; *U.S. Public*, pg. 802
Kaufman, Stanley, V.P.-Mfg.--Lebhar-Friedman, Inc., New York, NY; *U.S. Private*, pg. 656
Kaye, Gilbert D., V.P.-Mfg.--The Hartz Mountain Corp., Secaucus, NJ; *U.S. Private*, pg. 508
Kayne, Jack, V.P.-Engrng.--Slant/Fin Corporation, Greenvale, NY; *U.S. Private*, pg. 1005
Kearns, Pat, Mgr.-Res. & Devel.--Team, Inc., Alvin, TX; *U.S.* Public, pg. 1562
Keating, Joseph W., Sr.V.P. & Pres.-Pharmaceutical Mfg.--Merck Manufacturing Div., Rahway, NJ; *U.S. Public*, pg. 1091
Keeling, William S., Sr. V.P.-Opers.--Gateway Press, Inc., Louisville, KY; *U.S. Private*, pg. 441
Keener, Marian M., V.P.-Mfg.--The Chardon Rubber Co., Chardon, OH; *U.S. Private*, pg. 229
Keep, Randy, Dir.-Sls.--Magna Lomason Corp., Farmington Hills, MI; *Int'l*, pg. 830
Kegg, Richard L., V.P.-Tech. & Mfg. Devel.--Cincinnati Milacron Inc., Cincinnati, OH; *U.S. Public*, pg. 368
Keim, Michael D., V.P.-Mfg. Sys.--Wallace Computer Services, Inc., Lisle, IL; *U.S. Public*, pg. 1735
Keller, Dennis, Mgr.-Mfr.--Dearborn Gage Company, Garden City, MI; *U.S. Private*, pg. 319
Keller, Harold, Dir.-Engrng. Opers.--Mader Construction Corp, Elma, NY; *U.S. Private*, pg. 693
Keller, Ralph, V.P.-Mfg.--Videojet Systems International, Inc., Wood Dale, IL; *Int'l*, pg. 545
Kelley, Don, Mgr.-Production--Buccaneer Homes, Inc., Hamilton, AL; *U.S. Public*, pg. 318
Kelley, Robert, Dir.-Mfg.--Slim-Fast Foods Company, West Palm Beach, FL; *U.S. Private*, pg. 1006
Kellman, Cheri, V.P.-Architectural Glass Div.--Globe-Amerada Glass Company, Elk Grove Village, IL; *U.S. Private*, pg. 458
Kellogg, Tom, Mgr.-Mfg.--Royal Paper Box of California, Montebello, CA; *U.S. Private*, pg. 949
Kelly-Green, Edith, V.P.-Pur.--FDX Corporation, Memphis, TN; *U.S. Public*, pg. 603
Kelly, Donald F., Sr. V.P.-Production, Engrng. & Power Supply--Central Maine Power Company, Augusta, ME; *U.S. Public*, pg. 325
Kelly, James J., V.P.-Mfg. & Research--M.A. Bruder & Sons, Incorporated, Broomall, PA; *U.S. Private*, pg. 175
Kelly, Kenneth, Dir.-Mfr.--Barr Laboratories Inc., Pomona, NY; *U.S. Public*, pg. 191
Kelly, Michael N., Sr. V.P.-Opers.--Baxter Research Medical, Inc., Midvale, UT; *U.S. Public*, pg. 196
Kelly, William M., Exec. V.P.-Oper.--Blue Tee Corporation, New York, NY; *U.S. Private*, pg. 153
Keltz, Martin J., V.P.-Scholastic Production--Scholastic Inc., New York, NY; *U.S. Public*, pg. 1440
Kennedy, John C., Chm. Bd., Pres. & Chief Exec. Officer--Autocam Corporation, Grand Rapids, MI; *U.S. Public*, pg. 148
Kennon, George, Dir.-Opers.--Stanback Company, Salisbury, NC; *U.S. Private*, pg. 1030
Kent, Dennis E., V.P.-Mfg.-Ontario--Bauer Sports Inc., Montreal, Canada; *U.S. Public*, pg. 1184
Kent, S.W., Mgr.-Mfg.--Ormandy & Stollery Electronic Components Limited, Brightlingsea, United Kingdom; *Int'l*, pg. 892
Kenworthy, A., Mgr.-Engrng.--The Mount Cook Group Limited, Christchurch, New Zealand; *Int'l*, pg. 38
Keohane, Lawrence J., V.P.-Mfg.--Anderson Bakery Co., Inc., Lancaster, PA; *U.S. Private*, pg. 65
Kernan, J., V.P.-Mfg.--Harris Corp., RF Communications Group Marketing Division, Rochester, NY; *U.S. Public*, pg. 792
Kero, Paul, Mgr.-Mfg.--Beltone Electronics Corporation, Chicago, IL; *U.S. Private*, pg. 132
Kerr, Nelson, Dir.-Mfg.--Wynn's-Precision, Inc., Lebanon, TN; *U.S. Public*, pg. 1783
Kerr, Robert, V.P.-Mfg.--Broan Limited, Mississauga, Canada; *U.S. Public*, pg. 1194
Kerrick, Jon P., V.P.-Engrng.--Advance Circuits, Inc., Minnetonka, MN; *Int'l*, pg. 713
Kessler, R.L., Plant Mgr.--Oliver Rubber Co., Athens, GA; *U.S. Public*, pg. 1504
Kestler, Hans G., Dir.-Brewing--Joseph Huber Brewing Co., Inc., Monroe, WI; *U.S. Private*, pg. 545
Ketner, Mike, V.P.-Mfg.--Natalie Knitting Mills, Chilhowie, VA; *U.S. Public*, pg. 779
Kidd, Robert W., Dir.-Mfg./Cake Grp.--Mrs. Smith's Bakeries, Inc., Thomasville, GA; *U.S. Public*, pg. 657
Kieras, Francis, Mgr.-Mfg.--DCG Precision Manufacturing Corporation, Bethel, CT; *U.S. Private*, pg. 301
Kiernan, Allan F., V.P.-Production--AEC Oil & Gas, Calgary, Canada; *Int'l*, pg. 48
Kiester, Charles E., Sr. V.P.-Engrng., Quality & Mfg. Svcs.--3M, Saint Paul, MN; *U.S. Public*, pg. 1604
Kietzke, Howard, V.P.-Opers. & Mfg. Mgr.--Nordco, Inc., Milwaukee, WI; *U.S. Public*, pg. 1209
Kim, Im H., Dir.-Pur.--Crown Confectionery Co., Ltd., Seoul, Korea; *Int'l*, pg. 348
Kim, Moo N., Chief Exec. Officer, Exec. V.P. & Mgr.-Mfg.--Crown Confectionery Co., Ltd., Seoul, Korea; *Int'l*, pg. 348
Kimk, Mike, Plant Superintendent--Snap-Tite, Inc., Erie, PA; *U.S. Private*, pg. 1010
Kincaid, Jerry L., V.P.-Mfg. & Communication Papers--Georgia-Pacific Corporation, Atlanta, GA; *U.S. Public*, pg. 735
Kindlund, Newton C., Chm. Bd., Pres., Chief Exec. & Chief Oper. Officer--Holiday RV Superstores, Inc., Orlando, FL; *U.S. Public*, pg. 829
King, Brian, Dir.-Mfg.--Yorktown Tool & Die Corporation, Yorktown, IN; *U.S. Private*, pg. 1196
King, D.L., Mgr.-Mfg. Admin.--Hughes Christensen, Houston, TX; *U.S. Public*, pg. 166
King, Dennis, V.P.-Mfg.--Transkrit Corporation, Roanoke, VA; *U.S. Private*, pg. 782
King, Watson B., V.P.-Mill Opers.--Roanoke Electric Steel Corporation, Roanoke, VA; *U.S. Public*, pg. 1392
Kingsley, Robert F., Mgr.-Mfg.--H.B. Smith Co., Inc., Westfield, MA; *U.S. Private*, pg. 1008
Kink, J.S., Mgr.-Mfg.--Thrall Car Mfg. Co., Chicago Heights, IL; *U.S. Private*, pg. 344
Kinkel, Paul H., V.P.-Engrng.--Consolidated Edison Company of New York, Inc., New York, NY; *U.S. Public*, pg. 434
Kinsey, D., Dir.-Mfg.--Menley & James Laboratories, Inc., Horsham, PA; *U.S. Public*, pg. 1086
Kirk, Arlene, Plant Mgr.--S.A.S.I. Corporation, Collinsville, IL; *U.S. Private*, pg. 955
Kirkpatrick, William, V.P.-Mfg.--Reliable Automatic Sprinkler Co., Inc., Mount Vernon, NY; *U.S. Private*, pg. 920
Kirkus, Chris, Dir.-Opers.--Sencore, Inc., Sioux Falls, SD; *U.S. Private*, pg. 983
Kirschner, Richard, V.P.-Mfg.--Belden Inc., Saint Louis, MO; *U.S. Public*, pg. 200
Kissel, Horst, Dir.-Engrng.--Surftran Division, Madison Heights, MI; *Int'l*, pg. 204
Klancnik, Al, V.P.-Mfg. & Opers.--Serta, Inc., Itasca, IL; *U.S.* Private, pg. 985
Klein, Arnold, V.P.-Mfg.--Slant/Fin Corporation, Greenvale, NY; *U.S. Private*, pg. 1005
Klein, Tom, Exec. V.P.-Mfg.--MNP Corp., Utica, MI; *U.S. Private*, pg. 687
Kleinman, Abe, V.P.-Mfg.--Nature's Bounty Inc., Bohemia, NY; *U.S. Public*, pg. 1166
Kleinsmith, Mark, V.P.-Mfg. & IS--Lozier Corporation, Omaha, NE; *U.S. Private*, pg. 679
Klemer, Thomas, V.P.-Mfg.--Faribault Woolen Mill Co., Faribault, MN; *U.S. Private*, pg. 394
Kleps, Keith, V.P.-Mfg.--Emson, Inc., Bridgeport, CT; *U.S. Private*, pg. 375
Kline, Cullen, Mgr.-Materials--Tricon Brazing Alloys & Chemical Products Div., Downers Grove, IL; *U.S. Private*, *pg. 1103*
Klocke, H. Gene, V.P.-Engrng.--Champion Pneumatic Machinery Co., Inc., Princeton, IL; *U.S. Private*, pg. 228
Kluge, Armin, V.P.-Mfg.--Small Parts, Inc., Logansport, IN; *U.S. Private*, pg. 1006
Klus, Steve, V.P.-Mfg.--Northland Cranberries, Inc., Wisconsin Rapids, WI; *U.S. Public*, pg. 1197
Kniebel, Chuck, V.P.-Engrng.--Coleman Powermate Compressors, Springfield, MN; *U.S. Private*, pg. 691

Knight, Gordon R., V.P.-Engrng. & Tech.--Maxoptix Corp., Fremont, CA; *Int'l*, pg. 762
Knight, Paul D., Mgr.-Brewing--Pabst Brewing Co./ Tumwater, Tumwater, WA; *U.S. Private*, pg. 954
Knirk, Gary, Dir.-Opers.--H & H Tube & Manufacturing Co., Vanderbilt, MI; *U.S. Private*, pg. 489
Knupfer, Helmut, Mgr.-Mfg.--Hermal Kurt Herrmann & Co., Reinbek, Germany; *Int'l*, pg. 616
Knupp, Richard, V.P.-Mfg.--Cornell Iron Works, Inc., Mountain Top, PA; *U.S. Private*, pg. 276
Knuth, Stephen B., V.P.-Opers. & Engrng.--Casio Phone-Mate, Inc., Torrance, CA; *Int'l*, pg. 274
Knutson, Dale A., V.P.-Technology--Applied Power Inc., Butler, WI; *U.S. Public*, pg. 124
Koch, John, V.P.-Prod.--Acme Brick Co., Fort Worth, TX; *U.S Public*, pg. 936
Koenitzer, Jeff D., Pres.--Helwig Carbon Products, Inc., Milwaukee, WI; *U.S. Private*, pg. 521
Koepchen, Hans-Martin, Exec. V.P.-Exploration & Production--Deminex-Deutsche GmbH, Essen, Germany; *Int'l*, pg. 1460
Koerbitz, Gary, V.P.-Production--Honeymead Products Co., Mankato, MN; *U.S. Private*, pg. 537
Kohl, Dave, Mgr.-Production, Mineral Wells--Town & Country Homes, Fort Worth, TX; *U.S. Public*, pg. 319
Kohler, John C., V.P.-Mfg.--Tellabs Operations, Inc., Lisle, IL; *U.S. Public*, pg. 1572
Kohn, Rich, Mgr.-Prod.--Kit Manufacturing Company, Long Beach, CA; *U.S. Public*, pg. 962
Kohner, Peter, V.P.-Mfg.--Industrial Acoustics Company, Inc., Bronx, NY; *U.S. Public*, pg. 875
Kojima, Shinji, Mgr.-Mfg.--Takagi Chokoku Co., Ltd., Wakayama, Japan; *Int'l*, pg. 1349
Kolk, Art, V.P.-Production--Select Canfield, Chicago, IL; *U.S. Private*, pg. 982
Kondro, Greg M., V.P.-Production--Ocelot Energy Inc., Calgary, Canada; *Int'l*, pg. 996
Kong, E., Mgr.-Mfg. Dy.--Mobil Oil Singapore Pte. Ltd., Singapore, Singapore; *U.S. Public*, pg. 1119
Konomi, Toshio, Exec. Dir.-Mfg. Div.--Fujisawa Pharmaceutical Co. Ltd., Osaka, Japan; *Int'l*, pg. 525
Koops, Thomas H., V.P.-Tech. & Logistics--BJ Services Company, Houston, TX; *U.S. Public*, pg. 161
Kopec, Michael J., V.P.-Mfg.--Carter-Wallace, Inc., New York, NY; *U.S. Public*, pg. 309
Kopjo, Jerry, Dir.-Engrng.--Brencal Contractors Inc., Detroit, MI; *U.S. Private*, pg. 106
Kornhauser, Mark L., V.P.-Mfg. & Opers.--Hunter Fan Company, Memphis, TN; *U.S. Private*, pg. 549
Kos, Peter, V.P.-Mfg.--Universal Industrial Products Co., Pioneer, OH; *U.S. Public*, pg. 1677
Koskloski, George, Dir.-Mfg.--Mercury Computer Systems, Inc., Chelmsford, MA; *U.S. Private*, pg. 732
Kotula, Ron, V.P.-Mfg.--Pangburn Candy Company, Fort Worth, TX; *U.S. Private*, pg. 836
Kowal, Steven K., V.P.-Engrng. Mfg.--Integral Systems, Inc., Lanham, MD; *U.S. Public*, pg. 883
Koyama, Keiji, Dir.-Watch Production--Seiko Corporation, Tokyo, Japan; *Int'l*, pg. 1218
Kozloski, Gary L., Dir.-Coating Opers.--Sierra Coating Technologies, De Pere, WI; *U.S. Private*, pg. 998
Kramer, Henry, Plant Mgr.--Durable Specialties Division, Quakertown, PA; *U.S. Public*, pg. 620
Kramer, Nelson, Dir.-Engrng.--Riddell Sports, Inc., Chicago, IL; *U.S. Public*, pg. 1389
Kranz, Richard, V.P.-Production--Tension Envelope Corp., Kansas City, MO; *U.S. Private*, pg. 1077
Krasavage, Kenneth W., V.P.-Technical Opers.--Mead Johnson Nutritional Group, Evansville, IN; *U.S. Public*, pg. 254
Kraus, Alvin S., Mgr.-Mfg.--Buehler, Limited, Lake Bluff, IL; *U.S. Public*, pg. 574
Krause, Desmond, Mgr.-Mfg.--Flowserve Duriron Canada, Woodbridge, Canada; *U.S. Public*, pg. 659
Krchnavy, Jon A., V.P.-Mfg.--The Producto Machine Co., Bridgeport, CT; *U.S. Private*, pg. 889
Kreidler, William J., V.P.-Opers.--FileNet Corporation, Costa Mesa, CA; *U.S. Public*, pg. 622
Kreishman, John, V.P.-Architecture & Engrng.--First Financial Building Corporation, Manchester, MO; *U.S. Private*, pg. 407
Kress, Glenn, Mgr.-Mfg. & Engrng.--Wells/Bloomfield, Verdi, NV; *U.S. Public*, pg. 1497
Kreussling, Charles, Exec. V.P.-Mfg.--Shorewood Packaging Corporation, New York, NY; *U.S. Public*, pg. 1468
Krist, R., Technical Dir.--Red Band Venco, Breda, Netherlands; *Int'l*, pg. 244
Krogh, Marty, V.P.-Mfg.--WEN Products, Inc., Bensenville, IL; *U.S. Private*, pg. 1144
Krumm, Joyce, V.P. & Dir.-Mfg. Tech. Services--Hoffmann-La Roche Inc., Nutley, NJ; *Int'l*, pg. 1120
Kruse, Duff, Dir.-Opers.--Cramer Inc., Kansas City, KS; *U.S. Private*, pg. 285
Kruszynski, Richard J., Dir.-Mfg.--American Science & Engineering, Inc., Billerica, MA; *U.S. Public*, pg. 90
Krutz, David, Plant Mgr.--Enger-Kress Company, West Bend, WI; *U.S. Private*, pg. 376
Kuecker, Belinda, Mgr.-Mfg.--Dakotah, Inc., Webster, SD; *U.S. Public*, pg. 477
Kugo, Takahiro, Gen. Mgr.-Ashitaka Factory--Terumo Corporation, Tokyo, Japan; *Int'l*, pg. 1375
Kulesza, Kris, V.P.-Mdsg.--Peoples Jewellers Corporation, Don Mills, Canada; *Int'l*, pg. 1036
Kullgren, Don, Dir.-Mfg.--Advanced Logic Research, Inc., Irvine, CA; *U.S. Public*, pg. 703
Kunda, Ken, V.P.-Pur. & Mfg.--Inductotherm Corp., Rancocas, NJ; *U.S. Private*, pg. 560
Kunkel, David, Sr. V.P.-Mfg.--Ford Meter Box Company, Wabash, IN; *U.S. Private*, pg. 418
Kuno, Yasuhiro, Exec. Dir.-Tobacco, Mfg. & Gen. Affairs--Japan Tobacco Inc., Tokyo, Japan; *Int'l*, pg. 703
Kuper, Gregory W., Exec. V.P.-Mfg./Office Furniture--Kimball International, Inc., Jasper, IN; *U.S. Public*, pg. 956
Kuphal, Paul, V.P.-Mfg. & Engr.--Formation, Inc., Moorestown, NJ; *U.S. Private*, pg. 419
Kuramoto, Roy, Dr., V.P.-Pharmaceutical Mfg. Opers. & Tech.--Syntex, Palo Alto, CA; *Int'l*, pg. 1120
Kuramoto, Toyohisa, Mng. Dir.-Prod., Procurement, Quality Control & Prod. Liability--Nikon Corporation, Tokyo, Japan; *Int'l*, pg. 931
Kurtti, C.M., V.P.-Mfg. & Engrng.--Neenah Foundry Company, Neenah, WI; *U.S. Private*, pg. 790
Kustra, John P., Dir.-Engrng.--Thermal Transfer Corp., Monroeville, PA; *U.S. Public*, pg. 29
Kwasniewicz, John, V.P.-Mfg.--Spotnails, Rolling Meadows, IL; *U.S. Private*, pg. 845
Kwiatkowshi, Gery, Dir.-Mfr. Services--Hirsh Company, Skokie, IL; *U.S. Public*, pg. 963
Kwiatkowski, Ed, V.P.-Mfg. & Engrng.--Vital Signs, Inc., Totowa, NJ; *U.S. Public*, pg. 1723
La Rosa, Thomas, Dir.-Mfg., Spice Opers.--M. Kamenstein, Inc., Elmsford, NY; *U.S. Private*, pg. 606
LaCamp, Jerry, Mgr.-Prod.--Guard Publishing Company, Eugene, OR; *U.S. Private*, pg. 485
Lacy, R., Mng. Dir.-Switchgear & Instrumentation Ltd.--N.G. Bailey & Co. Ltd., Ilkley, United Kingdom; *Int'l*, pg. 132
Laederich, Tom, Dir.-Mfg.--Embedded Performance, Inc., Milpitas, CA; *U.S. Private*, pg. 373
Lagarhus, Otto, Sr. V.P.-Prod. Div.--Scandinavian Airlines System (SAS), Solna, Sweden; *Int'l*, pg. 1201
Lain, Brent R., V.P.-Mfg.--Deposition Technologies, Inc., San Diego, CA; *U.S. Public*, pg. 1056
Lakes, Hearld, Mgr.-Mfg./Power Tools--Cooper Power Tools Division, Lexington, SC; *U.S. Public*, pg. 444
Lamb, Dwight, Jr., V.P., Treas. & Production Mgr.-Post--Benjamin Franklin Literary & Medical Society, Inc., Indianapolis, IN; *U.S. Private*, pg. 133
Lamb, W. Doyle, V.P.-Engrng.--IMI Cash Valve, Inc., Cullman, AL; *Int'l*, pg. 646
Lambert, William M., V.P. & Gen. Mgr.-Safety Prods.--Mine Safety Appliances Co., Pittsburgh, PA; *U.S. Public*, pg. 1114
Lambrecht, Richard W., Jr., V.P.--Hickman, Williams & Co. Inc., Cincinnati, OH; *U.S. Private*, pg. 525
Lampi, Joseph, Mgr.-Plant--Precision Roll Grinders, Inc., Allentown, PA; *U.S. Private*, pg. 880
Landi, John, V.P.-Mfg.--Smith-Edwards-Dunlap Company, Philadelphia, PA; *U.S. Private*, pg. 1007
Landy, Bernie M., Mgr.-Hot Rolled Prod.--Slab & Plate Products Division, Wollongong, Australia; *Int'l*, pg. 227
Lang, Edward J., Sr. V.P.-Mfg. Opers.--R.J. Reynolds Tobacco Intl., Inc., Geneva, Switzerland; *U.S. Public*, pg. 1355
Lange, James, V.P.-Mfg.--Ocean Spray Cranberries, Inc., Middleboro, MA; *U.S. Private*, pg. 811
Lange, Klaus, Dir.-Mfg.--Lincoln Industrial, Saint Louis, MO; *U.S. Public*, pg. 1273
Langenbrunner, Tom, Mgr.-Value Added Dept.--Hughes-Peters, Inc., Cincinnati, OH; *U.S. Private*, pg. 546
Languay, Ken, Reg. V.P.-Mfg.--Quebecor Printing Aurora, Aurora, Canada; *Int'l*, pg. 1076
Lanrani, C., Dir.-Mfg.--Laboratoires Polymedic, S.A., Casablanca, Morocco; *U.S. Public*, pg. 1092
Lansing, Harry B., Dir.-Mfg. Opers.--LiphaTech, Inc., Milwaukee, WI; *Int'l*, pg. 812
LaPrade, Steve, Mgr.-Prod.--Bontex, Buena Vista, VA; *U.S. Public*, pg. 734
Lapraik, Scott, Mgr.-Engrng.--Thomas & Betts Electronics Division, Memphis, TN; *U.S. Public*, pg. 1597
Lapriore, W., Mgr.-Mfg.--Abbott Ball Company, West Hartford, CT; *U.S. Private*, pg. 9
Larrimore, M., Mgr.-Mfg.--Dale Industries Inc., Dearborn, MI; *U.S. Private*, pg. 308
Larsen, James W., V.P.-Mfg.--Moore Business Forms & Systems Div., Lake Forest, IL; *Int'l*, pg. 890
Larsen, W. Bruce, V.P.-Plastic Container Mfg.--Owens-Illinois, Inc., Toledo, OH; *U.S. Public*, pg. 1238
Larson, David A., V.P.-Mfg.--Giant Food Inc., Landover, MD; *U.S. Public*, pg. 741
Larson, Paul, Dir.-Mfg.--Wenger Corporation, Owatonna, MN; *U.S. Private*, pg. 1162
Larter, Craig, V.P.-Mfg.--Nalge Company, Rochester, NY; *U.S. Public*, pg. 1545
Lasky, Jack S., V.P.-Res. & Engrng.--The Okonite Company, Ramsey, NJ; *U.S. Private*, pg. 813
Laufgraben, Allan, Sr. V.P.-Mdsg.--Deb Shops, Inc., Philadelphia, PA; *U.S. Public*, pg. 491
Laumann, D., V.P.-Mfg.--Sub-Zero Freezer Co., Inc., Madison, WI; *U.S. Private*, pg. 1048
Lauzon, G., Mgr.-Distribution--La Brasserie Labatt Limitee, La Salle, Canada; *Int'l*, pg. 679
Lavigne, Randy, Mgr.-Prod.--The Turning Systems Div., Keene, NH; *U.S. Private*, pg. 622
Laviolette, Rene, Sr. V.P.-Prod. Devel.--Manufacturers Technologies, Inc., West Springfield, MA; *U.S. Private*, pg. 701
Lawler, James P., V.P.-Mfg.--Varco BJ Oil Tools, Orange, CA; *U.S. Public*, pg. 1709
Lawler, Jim, V.P.-Mfg. & Logistics--Varco BJ Oil Tools B.V., Etten-Leur, Netherlands; *U.S. Public*, pg. 1709
Lawniczak, Joseph H., Dir.-Mfg.--Molex Incorporated, Lisle, IL; *U.S. Public*, pg. 1121
Lawrence, Bill, V.P.-Engrng.--MAC America Communications, Inc., Phoenix, AZ; *U.S. Private*, pg. 685
Lawson, G. Richard, Sr. V.P.-Opers.--Harlequin Enterprises Ltd., Don Mills, Canada; *Int'l*, pg. 1402
Lawson, John W., V.P.-Mfg.--Lear Corporation, Rochester Hills, MI; *U.S. Public*, pg. 982
Lawton, Henry H., V.P.-Mfg./CCI Div.--Communication Cable, Inc., Sanford, NC; *U.S. Public*, pg. 968
Layman, Bruce, Plant Mgr.--Southwest Recreational Industries Inc., Leander, TX; *U.S. Private*, pg. 1018
Layman, David A., V.P.-Mfg.--La-Z-Boy Incorporated, Monroe, MI; *U.S. Public*, pg. 972
Laymon, John L., V.P.-Mfg.--Rexair, Inc., Troy, MI; *U.S. Public*, pg. 1684
Leach, Donald R., Dir.-Mfg.--Art's-Way Manufacturing Co., Inc., Armstrong, IA; *U.S. Public*, pg. 136
Leach, Robert, V.P.-Mfg.--Osmose Wood Preserving, Inc., Buffalo, NY; *U.S. Private*, pg. 821
LeBrun, Maurice, V.P.-Engrng.--JA/MONT N.V. - Technology Office, Muntzenheim, France; *U.S. Public*, pg. 673
Leddy, Ronald G., V.P.-Mfg.--F.E. Myers, Ashland, OH; *U.S. Public*, pg. 1273
Lee, David R., Mgr.-Neenah Mill--P.H. Glatfelter Company, Spring Grove, PA; *U.S. Public*, pg. 746
Lee, Doug, Mgr.-Processing--Sanderson Farms, Inc., Laurel, MS; *U.S. Public*, pg. 1430
Lee, Paul, Chief Engineer--American Electronics, Inc., Fullerton, CA; *U.S. Private*, pg. 5
Lehman, Donald, V.P.-Mfg.--Micro Component Technology Inc., Saint Paul, MN; *U.S. Public*, pg. 1104
Lehmann, D.M., V.P.-Mfg.--Solar Turbines Incorporated, San Diego, CA; *U.S. Public*, pg. 316
Leichsenring, Detlef, Div. Mgr.--Durkopp Adler AG, Bielefeld, Germany; *Int'l*, pg. 468
Leicht, Jeffrey, V.P.-Mfg.--Eclipse Manufacturing Company, Sheboygan, WI; *U.S. Private*, pg. 361
Leising, Paul, V.P.-Opers. & Mfg.--Giorgio Beverly Hills, Santa Monica, CA; *U.S. Public*, pg. 1331
Leith, A. L., Exec. V.P.-Brewing--Foster's Brewing Group, Toronto, Canada; *Int'l*, pg. 501
Leiva, Fernando, Mgr.-Mfg.--Nuevo Federal S.A., Buenos Aires, Argentina; *Int'l*, pg. 990
Lelik, Andrew, V.P.-Opers.--Braeburn Alloy Steel, Lower Burrell, PA; *U.S. Private*, pg. 193
Lemba, Lou, Plant Mgr.--Aldine Technologies Industries Inc., Carlstadt, NJ; *U.S. Private*, pg. 33
Lemen, Richard, Mgr.-Materials--Harford Systems, Inc., Aberdeen, MD; *U.S. Private*, pg. 641
Lempp, Gerhart H., V.P.-Mfg.--Werner & Pfleiderer Corporation, Ramsey, NJ; *Int'l*, pg. 511
Lendner, Oded, V.P.-Opers.--Kulicke & Soffa Industries, Inc., Willow Grove, PA; *U.S. Public*, pg. 968
Lenk, Edward, V.P.--Unisystems, Inc., New York, NY; *U.S. Private*, pg. 1120
Lennox, William, V.P.-Engrng.--Microdyne Corporation, Alexandria, VA; *U.S. Public*, pg. 1105
Lent, Kevin, V.P.-Engrng.--Tyler Industries, Benson, MN; *U.S. Private*, pg. 1112
Leonard, Paul, V.P.-Mfg.--Horn Packaging Corporation, Ayer, MA; *U.S. Private*, pg. 539
Leonard, Randall, Dir.-Mfg.--A-Dec, Inc., Newberg, OR; *U.S. Private*, pg. 2
Leonhart, Charles, V.P.-Engrng.--Nuarc Company, Inc., Niles, IL; *U.S. Private*, pg. 808
Lerner, Michael W., Mgr.-Service Opers.--Delta International Machinery Corp., Pittsburgh, PA; *U.S. Public*, pg. 1273
Lervick, Mark, V.P.-Opers.--Twin City Foods, Inc., Stanwood, WA; *U.S. Private*, pg. 1111
Lesha, Frank, Dir.-Plant--S. Bent & Brothers, Inc., Gardner, MA; *U.S. Private*, pg. 134
Lessard, Donald, V.P.-Mfg.--Inverness Corp., Fair Lawn, NJ; *U.S. Private*, pg. 574
Lestage, Jean-Pierre, V.P.-Mfg.--Quebecor Printing Hazleton Inc., Hazleton, PA; *Int'l*, pg. 1076
Letendre, Norman, V.P.-Engrng.--Dynamic Metal Products Company, Manchester, CT; *U.S. Private*, pg. 350
Lettenbauer, Gustav, Dr., Dir.-Mfg.--Boehringer Mannheim GmbH, Mannheim, Germany; *Int'l*, pg. 331
Leuchs, Hans-Jurgen, Dr., Dir.-Corp. Bd.-Tech. & Pharmaceutical Div.--Boehringer Ingelheim GmbH, Ingelheim, Germany; *Int'l*, pg. 199
Levy, Jonathan, Dir.-Information Systems--The Mills Corporation, Arlington, VA; *U.S. Public*, pg. 1113
Lewallen, William J., V.P.-Engrng.--Sivalls, Inc., Odessa, TX; *U.S. Private*, pg. 1004
Lewandowski, Roger, V.P.-Mfg.--Carrier Corp., Indianapolis, IN; *U.S. Public*, pg. 1690
Lewis, B.W., V.P.-Pur.--Trico Products Corporation, Buffalo, NY; *Int'l*, pg. 1397
Lewis, Cecil H., Dir.-Engrng.--Midway Products Corporation, Monroe, MI; *U.S. Private*, pg. 744
Lewis, Everett D., V.P.-Mfg.--Hawaiian Independent Refinery, Inc., Honolulu, HI; *Int'l*, pg. 225
Lewis, George E., V.P.-Prod.--Hoffman Laces, Ltd., Cobleskill, NY; *U.S. Public*, pg. 769
Lewis, Larry, Dir.-U.S. Safety Opers.--Aearo Company, Boston, MA; *U.S. Private*, pg. 23
Ley, June, V.P. & Gen. Mgr.-RTW--Crowley, Milner & Company, Detroit, MI; *U.S. Public*, pg. 461
Liberman, Isaac, V.P.-Mfg.--Teleglobe, Inc., Montreal, Canada; *Int'l*, pg. 1373
Liddic, Steve, V.P.-Mfg.--Gertrude Hawk Chocolates, Inc., Dunmore, PA; *U.S. Private*, pg. 449
Liebeno, B., Mgr.-Mfg. Engrng.--Plastic Packaging Company, Muncie, IN; *U.S. Public*, pg. 57
Liebregts, F., Dir.-Mfg.--Steelweld Division Zweigniederlassung Bonn der Ambac B.V., Saint Augustin, Germany; *Int'l*, pg. 71
Light, Gene, V.P.-Mfg.--Chorus Line Corporation, Vernon, CA; *U.S. Private*, pg. 238
Liguori, Ralph, Grp. V.P.-Mfg.--Del Laboratories, Inc., Farmingdale, NY; *U.S. Public*, pg. 494
Lillie, Lenore, Dir.-Opers.--Koss Corporation, Milwaukee, WI; *U.S. Public*, pg. 966
Lim, Chin Min, V.P-Mfg.--Salz Leathers, Inc., Santa Cruz, CA; *U.S. Private*, pg. 963
Limanni, David E., V.P.-Tamor Mfg.--Home Products International, Inc., Chicago, IL; *U.S. Public*, pg. 832
Lin, M.Y., Gen. Mgr.--Acer Incorporated, Taipei, Taiwan; *Int'l*, pg. 22
Lincoln, Nate, Mgr.-Mfg.--Weir Floway Inc., Fresno, CA; *Int'l*, pg. 1489
Lindell, C., V.P.-Quality Assurance & Mfg. Services--KDI Precision Products, Inc., Cincinnati, OH; *U.S. Private*, pg. 603
Linden, Herbert H., V.P. & Mfg. Dir.--Sunset Publishing Corporation, Menlo Park, CA; *U.S. Public*, pg. 1613

Lindfors, Bo, Exec. V.P.-Exploration & Prod.--Neste Oy, Espoo, Finland; *Int'l*, pg. 912

Lindmeier, Joel, V.P.-Mfg.--Stearns Manufacturing Company, Sauk Rapids, MN; *U.S. Public*, pg. 940

Lindsey, Darryl, V.P.-Opers.--Plains Cotton Co-op Association, Lubbock, TX; *U.S. Private*, pg. 868

Lines, K.K., Mgr.-Prod.--Corporate New Business Development Div., Delft, Netherlands; *Int'l*, pg. 1142

Lingenfelter, Ron, Dir.-Mfg.--The Thermos Company, Schaumburg, IL; *Int'l*, pg. 938

Link, August L., V.P.-Engrng. & Mfg.--Lancaster Glass Corporation, Lancaster, OH; *U.S. Public*, pg. 977

Link, Herbert, Chief Oper. Officer-Corp. Mfg.--Clariant International Ltd., Muttenz, Switzerland; *Int'l*, pg. 624

Linville, Roger, Mgr.-Production--Retail Bag Division - Richmond Plant, Richmond, VA; *U.S. Public*, pg. 1521

Lipsky, Barry J., Exec. V.P.--Franklin Electronic Publishers, Inc., Burlington, NJ; *U.S. Public*, pg. 679

Littleton, Darryl A., V.P.-Mfg.--General Signal Corporation, Stamford, CT; *U.S. Public*, pg. 726

Litty, Greg, Dir.-Mfg.--American Marketing Industries, Inc., Kansas City, MO; *U.S. Private*, pg. 58

Ljungstrom, Bo, Dir.-Garment Mfg. Div.--Helly-Hansen A/S, Moss, Norway; *Int'l*, pg. 1010

Lloyd, Paul, V.P.-Men's Mfg.--Wolverine World Wide, Inc., Rockford, MI; *U.S. Public*, pg. 1775

Lobo, Carlos, V.P.-Power Train Mfg.--Chrysler Corporation, Auburn Hills, MI; *U.S. Public*, pg. 352

Locke, John, V.P.-Mdsg.--Sysco Corporation, Houston, TX; *U.S. Public*, pg. 1550

Lockwood, R., Dir.-Mfg.--Senior Green Economiser Division, Wakefield, United Kingdom; *Int'l*, pg. 1221

Loewen, Wally, Chief Engr.--Salwasser Manufacturing Company, Inc., Reedley, CA; *U.S. Private*, pg. 963

Loftin, Wayne, Chief Engineer--Affiliated Foods Southwest, Little Rock, AR; *U.S. Private*, pg. 26

Logan, John, V.P.-Mfg.--Melard Manufacturing Corporation, Passaic, NJ; *U.S. Private*, pg. 729

Loge, David B., Exec. V.P.-Mfg. & Ancillary Bus.--Costco Wholesale, Issaquah, WA; *U.S. Public*, pg. 451

Loghry, Richard M., Pres. & Chief Exec. Officer--Mason & Hanger Corporation, Inc., Lexington, KY; *U.S. Private*, pg. 711

Lombardi, Paul, V.P.-Mfg.--McNally Industries, Inc., Grantsburg, WI; *U.S. Private*, pg. 724

Lonergan, Keith, V.P.-Mfg.--Morgan Trailer Manufacturing Co., Morgantown, PA; *U.S. Private*, pg. 761

Long, Philip A., V.P.-Mfg.--Metalloy Corporation, Hudson, MI; *U.S. Private*, pg. 735

Lonnebotn, Trygve, Sr. V.P.-Opers.--RAYOVAC Corporation, Madison, WI; *U.S. Private*, pg. 912

Loomer, Marc A., V.P.-Bus. Forms Mfg. & Div. Mgr.--Wallace Computer Services, Inc., Lisle, IL; *U.S. Public*, pg. 1735

Loos, Uwe, Mgr.-Prod. & Logistics--Porsche AG, Stuttgart, Germany; *Int'l*, pg. 1063

Lopez, Juan, V.P.-Engrng. & Mfg.--Diagraph Corporation, Earth City, MO; *U.S. Private*, pg. 330

Loprest, Jay, Asst. V.P.-Mfg. & Purchasing--Naz-Dar Company, Chicago, IL; *U.S. Private*, pg. 1084

Lorimer, Lawrence, V.P. & Editorial Dir.--Grolier Inc., Danbury, CT; *Int'l*, pg. 794

Loring, John R., Design Dir.--Tiffany & Co., New York, NY; *U.S. Public*, pg. 1608

Loschmann, C.W., V.P.-Opers.--CPC Baking Business, Bay Shore, NY; *U.S. Public*, pg. 224

Loseke, Clifford P., V.P.-Mfg.--Lindsay Manufacturing Company, Lindsay, NE; *U.S. Public*, pg. 999

Losito, N.A., Dir.-Res. & Devel.--Tech-Tran Corporation, Rancocas, NJ; *U.S. Private*, pg. 560

Loughran, James, Chief Engineer--Arrow Fluid Power, Broadview, IL; *U.S. Private*, pg. 85

Loveless, Donald, Mgr.-Production--Buccaneer Homes, Inc., Hamilton, AL; *U.S. Public*, pg. 318

Lovell, Dale, V.P.-Mfg.--Proto Systems of Atlanta, Alpharetta, GA; *U.S. Private*, pg. 891

Low, Duncan, V.P.-BioProcess Technology--Pharmacia & Upjohn Biotech Inc., Piscataway, NJ; *Int'l*, pg. 1047

Low, Philip F., V.P.-Mfg./Singapore--Printronix, Inc., Irvine, CA; *U.S. Public*, pg. 1329

Lowe, Dan, Mgr.-Mfg. Engrng.--Titan International, Inc., Quincy, IL; *U.S. Public*, pg. 1618

Lower, Edgar, Plant Mgr.--Preferred Utilities Manufacturing Corp., Danbury, CT; *U.S. Private*, pg. 881

Lowry, William D., Dir.-Mfg. Dir.--Sampler Publications Inc., Saint Charles, IL; *U.S. Private*, pg. 963

Lucas, Charles, V.P.-Engrng. & Chief Engineer--McKissick Products Co., Tulsa, OK; *Int'l*, pg. 473

Lucas, Dan, Dir.-Mfg.--Bud Industries, Inc., Willoughby, OH; *U.S. Private*, pg. 178

Luhm, Ralph, V.P.-Engrng.--Allfast Fastening Systems, Inc., City of Industry, CA; *U.S. Private*, pg. 37

Luken, Phyllis, Mgr.-Mdsg.--Dillard's, Inc., Little Rock, AR; *U.S. Public*, pg. 509

Lundy, Frank, II, V.P. & Chief Engr.--Lundy Construction Co., Inc., Williamsport, PA; *U.S. Private*, pg. 681

Lupkas, John, V.P.-Mfr.--Truelove & Maclean Inc., Waterbury, CT; *U.S. Private*, pg. 1107

Lutz, L.H., Sr. V.P.-Tech.--Bliss-Salem, Inc., Salem, OH; *U.S. Private*, pg. 149

Lye, Derik, Sr. Mgr.-Production--GB Holdings, Jurong, Singapore; *Int'l*, pg. 531

Lyle, David A., V.P.-Mix Mfg.--Dairy Queen of Georgia, Inc., Decatur, GA; *U.S. Public*, pg. 220

Lyons, David J., Dir.-Mfg./Dessert Grp.--Mrs. Smith's Bakeries, Inc., Thomasville, GA; *U.S. Public*, pg. 657

Lyons, L.D., Mgr.-Engrng. & Plng.--Oldsmobile Div. General Motors Corp., Lansing, MI; *U.S. Public*, pg. 720

Ma, Di, V.P.-Mfg.--Standard Microsystems Corp., Hauppauge, NY; *U.S. Public*, pg. 1502

MacAskill, Philip R., Sr. V.P.-Eastern Mfg.--Quebecor Printing (USA) Corp., Greenwich, CT; *Int'l*, pg. 1078

MacDonald, Norm, V.P.-Mfg.--Anderson-Barrows Metals Corp., Palmdale, CA; *U.S. Public*, pg. 1746

MacDonald, Rod, V.P.-Production/McCain Foods (Canada)--McCain Foods Limited, Florenceville, Canada; *Int'l*, pg. 850

MacDonald, Wallace, Dir.-Engrng.--Pneumatic Scale Corporation, Cuyahoga Falls, OH; *U.S. Private*, pg. 118

MacGirr, Dell, Plant Mgr.--Mid-Continent Screw Products Co., Lincolnwood, IL; *U.S. Private*, pg. 743

Machala, Edward W., V.P.-Opers., Mfg. & Treas.--American Power Conversion Corporation, West Kingston, RI; *U.S. Public*, pg. 89

Machin, Bruce, V.P.-Mfg.--Standard Products (Canada) Ltd., Stratford, Canada; *U.S. Public*, pg. 1505

Macholt, Fred, V.P.-Mfg.--Key Handling Systems, Inc., Moonachie, NJ; *U.S. Private*, pg. 618

Macklin, John, Plant Mgr.--Magnus Metals, Fremont, NE; *U.S. Private*, pg. 394

MacLaughun, Andy, V.P.--Atlas Roofing Corp., Meridian, MS; *U.S. Private*, pg. 96

Madison, Dick, Jr., V.P. & Gen. Mgr.-DCI of Utah--D.C.I., Inc., Saint Cloud, MN; *U.S. Private*, pg. 301

Maehl, Doug, Sr. V.P.-Mfg., Pur. & Distr.--Safelite AutoGlass, Columbus, OH; *U.S. Private*, pg. 960

Magallanes, Paolo, Mgr.-Production Oper.--C.A. Cigarrera Bigott, Sucs., Caracas, Venezuela; *Int'l*, pg. 111

Maggioni, Domenico, Mgr.-Mfg.--Opticos S.r.l., Brembate di Sopra, Italy; *Int'l*, pg. 1007

Mahaney, David, V.P.-Mfg.--Studley Products Co., Inwood, NY; *U.S. Public*, pg. 1193

Maheras, Jim, Dir.-Mfg. & Opers.--Moore Business Equipment Div., Dover, NH; *Int'l*, pg. 890

Mai, Chao C., Dr., Sr. V.P.-Wafer Fabrication & Tech. Devel.--Dallas Semiconductor Corporation, Dallas, TX; *U.S. Public*, pg. 478

Maier, Lothar, V.P.-Mfg.--Cypress Semiconductor Corporation, San Jose, CA; *U.S. Public*, pg. 470

Maillefer, Rene, Dir.-Prod.--Nouvelle Lemania S.A., Lorient, Switzerland; *Int'l*, pg. 971

Mair, Scott, V.P.-Mfg.--Forstmann & Company, Inc., New York, NY; *U.S. Public*, pg. 670

Major, David P., V.P.-Greige Mfg.--Russell Corporation, Alexander City, AL; *U.S. Public*, pg. 1413

Makowski, Stephen R., V.P.-Engrng.--Michigan Gas Company, Three Rivers, MI; *U.S. Public*, pg. 1489

Maldini, Henry C., V.P.-Engrng.--Superior Industries International, Inc., Van Nuys, CA; *U.S. Public*, pg. 1539

Malere, Ernesto Pedro, Mgr.-Mfg., Rolling Mill Rolls--Acos Villares Steel Unit, Sao Paulo, Brazil; *Int'l*, pg. 23

Malfeo, Gerrardo, Sr. V.P-Mfg.--Intercontinental Branded Apparel, Buffalo, NY; *U.S. Public*, pg. 796

Malinowski, Emil, Dir.-Mfg.--Lands' End, Inc., Dodgeville, WI; *U.S. Public*, pg. 977

Maliszewski, Raymond M., Sr. V.P.-System Plng.--American Electric Power Service Corp., Columbus, OH; *U.S. Public*, pg. 72

Mallery, John L., V.P. & Plant Mgr.--Mallery Lumber Corp., Emporium, PA; *U.S. Private*, pg. 698

Malliris, Richard E., V.P.-Mfg.--KB Alloys, Inc., Sinking Spring, PA; *U.S. Private*, pg. 249

Maloney, Frank, Mgr.-Mfg.--Peerless Tube Company, Bloomfield, NJ; *U.S. Public*, pg. 1269

Malvaso, Jim, V.P.-Mfg.--Pfaudler, Inc., Rochester, NY; *U.S.* Public, pg. 1393

Mancini, Paul, V.P.-Mfg.--Dylex Limited, Toronto, Canada; *Int'l*, pg. 425

Manco, Carl, Dir.-Mfg.--Thermometrics, Inc., Edison, NJ; *Int'l*, pg. 208

Manesh, Shaun, V.P.-Mfg.--ACT Networks, Inc., Camarillo, CA; *U.S. Public*, pg. 3

Manetta, Jon L., V.P.-Transportation & Mechanical--Norfolk Southern Corporation, Norfolk, VA; *U.S. Public*, pg. 1190

Manford, F.A., Exec. Dir.-Transport & Indus. Services, Western Div.--Brambles Holdings Limited, Sydney, Australia; *Int'l*, pg. 211

Manley, Paul R., V.P.-Mfg.--The Ohio Art Company, Inc., Bryan, OH; *U.S. Public*, pg. 1214

Manning, Bill, V.P.-Mfg.--Boss Manufacturing Company, Kewanee, IL; *U.S. Private*, pg. 1142

Mantz, Rick L., V.P.-Engrng.--General Datacomm Industries, Inc., Middlebury, CT; *U.S. Public*, pg. 708

Mantz, Rick L., V.P.-Engrng.--General DataComm, Inc., Middlebury, CT; *U.S. Public*, pg. 708

Marbert, Larry, V.P.-Tech.--Knight-Ridder, Inc., Miami, FL; *U.S. Public*, pg. 963

Marble, C.E., Chief Exec. Officer-Mfg.--NIPA Hardwicke, Inc., Wilmington, DE; *U.S. Private*, pg. 771

March, Owen, Exec. Dir.--Burgess & Niple, Limited, Columbus, OH; *U.S. Private*, pg. 182

Marchand, Dennis, Mgr.-Mfg.--Ausco Products, Inc., Benton Harbor, MI; *U.S. Private*, pg. 299

Marchant, Albert, Chief Engr.--Alimak Elevator Company, Bridgeport, CT; *U.S. Private*, pg. 34

Marhoefer, Kurt E., V.P.-Fin.--Dresher, Inc., Carthage, MO; *U.S. Public*, pg. 986

Marion, Robert, V.P.-Prod.--Weldon, Williams & Lick, Inc., Fort Smith, AR; *U.S. Private*, pg. 1161

Marsh, Carl P., Sr. V.P.-Mfg. & Mdsg.--Maui Divers of Hawaii, Honolulu, HI; *U.S. Private*, pg. 715

Marsh, Peter, V.P.-Prod.--Metroland Printing & Distributing, Mississauga, Canada; *Int'l*, pg. 1402

Marshall, Ken, Sr. V.P.-Mfg., Res., Design & Devel.--The Rockport Company, Marlborough, MA; *U.S. Public*, pg. 1370

Marshall, Kenneth W., V.P.-Flight Opers.--Comair, Inc., Erlanger, KY; *U.S. Public*, pg. 406

Marshall, Rob, V.P.-Worldwide Mfg.--Analog Devices, Inc., Norwood, MA; *U.S. Public*, pg. 107

Marta, Francis, V.P.-Engrng.--Circle A.W. Products, Co., Portland, OR; *U.S. Public*, pg. 1471

Martin, Donald, V.P.-Engrng.--Tyco Toys, Inc., Mount Laurel, NJ; *U.S. Public*, pg. 1058

Martin, Jose L., V.P.-Production Opers.--Equitrac Corporation, Coral Gables, FL; *U.S. Public*, pg. 590

Martin, Reginald, V.P.-Mktg. & Prod. Devel.--Bufkor, Inc., Clearwater, FL; *U.S. Private*, pg. 179

Martin, Robert W., Mgr.-Mfg.--Great Northern Paper, Inc., Millinocket, ME; *U.S. Public*, pg. 248

Martinet, Gilbert, V.P.-Mfr. & Environment--Quebecor Printing, Inc., Montreal, Canada; *Int'l*, pg. 1076

Martinet, Gilbert, V.P.-Mfg. & Environment--Imprimerie Quebecor Inc., Montreal, Canada; *Int'l*, pg. 1077

Martinez, Daniel A., Sr. V.P.-Pulp & Paper Mfg.--Georgia-Pacific Pulp & Paper Division, Atlanta, GA; *U.S. Public*, pg. 735

Martinez, J., Mgr.-Production--McGraw Hill Interamericana de Espana S.A., Madrid, Spain; *U.S. Public*, pg. 1072

Martinez, Tom, Dir.-Quality Control & Mfg.--Treibacher Schleifmittel Corp., Niagara Falls, NY; *U.S. Private*, pg. 1099

Marvin, George G., III, V.P.-Mfg.--Marvin Lumber & Cedar Company, Warroad, MN; *U.S. Private*, pg. 710

Marx, Gilda, Dir.-Mdsg.--Gilda Marx Inc., Los Angeles, CA; *U.S. Private*, pg. 710

Massey, W. Mark, Sr. V.P.-Mfg.--Forest Products & Recycled Paperboard Div., Montvale, NJ; *U.S. Public*, pg. 903

Massey, W. Mark Jr., Sr. V.P.-Mfg.--Imperial Bondware Corp., Montvale, NJ; *U.S. Public*, pg. 903

Massingill, Glynn, V.P.-PAC Mfg. & Distr.--Precision Tune Autocare Inc., Leesburg, VA; *U.S. Public*, pg. 1321

Mastalski, Leo, V.P.-Mfg.--Freeway Corporation, Cleveland, OH; *U.S. Private*, pg. 426

Masters, Kenneth H., V.P.-Mfg.--OshKosh B'Gosh, Inc., Oshkosh, WI; *U.S. Public*, pg. 1232

Masters, William, Dir.-Engrng.--Homes of Merit Inc., Bartow, FL; *U.S. Private*, pg. 537

Mastrodicasa, B., Exec. V.P.-Mfg. & Distribution--Great Lakes Confectionery, Cleveland, OH; *Int'l*, pg. 865

Mastrull, John, Mgr.--New Brunswick Scientific Co., Inc., Edison, NJ; *U.S. Public*, pg. 1169

Mathes, Ted L., Plant Mgr.--The Ohio Art Company, Inc., Bryan, OH; *U.S. Public*, pg. 1214

Mathews, Garry, V.P.-Pur. & Mfg.--All-Luminum Products, Inc., Philadelphia, PA; *U.S. Private*, pg. 34

Matsui, Isamu, Sr. Mng. Dir.-Mfg., Tech. & Engrng.--Murata Machinery, Ltd., Kyoto, Japan; *Int'l*, pg. 897

Mattern, Gene, Dir.-Mfg.--Dowty Aerospace Yakima, Yakima, WA; *Int'l*, pg. 1337

Matthews, B., Dir.-Mfg.--DuPont Merck Pharm, Garden City, NY; *U.S. Public*, pg. 1091

Matthys, Paul, Sr. V.P.-Trading, Stainless Steel/Brazil--Arbed S.A., Luxembourg, Luxembourg; *Int'l*, pg. 78

Matz, Robert, V.P.-Mfg.--Industrial Coatings Group, Inc., Chicago, IL; *U.S. Private*, pg. 434

Maudlin, Judy, V.P.-Opers.--Sunbeam Corporation, Delray Beach, FL; *U.S. Public*, pg. 1533

Mauk, William, V.P.-Plant Opers.--Dudek & Bock Spring Manufacturing Company, Chicago, IL; *U.S. Private*, pg. 344

Mauney, Eddie, Gen. Mgr. & Mgr.-Production--Mauney Hosiery Mills, Inc., Kings Mountain, NC; *U.S. Private*, pg. 715

Maurer, Roger, Chief Engr.--A.J. Gerrard and Company, Des Plaines, IL; *U.S. Private*, pg. 449

Mauro, George T., V.P.-Mfg.--Delta Consolidated Industries, Inc. (Co. Headquarters), Jonesboro, AR; *U.S. Public*, pg. 481

Maxwell, Paul G., V.P.-Opers.--Southeastern Michigan Gas Company, Port Huron, MI; *U.S. Public*, pg. 1489

May, F., Dir.-Environmental & Mfg. Services--USG Corporation, Chicago, IL; *U.S. Public*, pg. 1660

May, R. G., Mgr.-Supply--Slab & Plate Products Division, Wollongong, Australia; *Int'l*, pg. 227

May, Robert, V.P.-Mfg.--Mackie Designs, Inc., Woodinville, WA; *U.S. Public*, pg. 1030

Maybaum, Richard, V.P. & Dir.-Engrng.--Accurate Bushing Co., Inc., Garwood, NJ; *U.S. Private*, pg. 11

Mayer, C., V.P.-Mfg.--Haskel International, Inc., Burbank, CA; *U.S. Public*, pg. 798

Mayer, Joe, V.P.-Mfg.--Trumpf Inc., Farmington, CT; *U.S. Private*, pg. 1108

Mayer, Steven D., V.P.--Cole Hersee Company, Boston, MA; *U.S. Private*, pg. 251

Mays, Dale, V.P.-Mfg.--Copes-Vulcan Inc., Lake City, PA; *U.S. Private*, pg. 274

Mazurek, Ken, V.P.-Mfg.--W.H. Salisbury & Company, Skokie, IL; *Int'l*, pg. 1244

Mazzola, Joseph, Mgr.-Mfg. & Engrng.--STAR Anchors & Fasteners, Mountainville, NY; *U.S. Private*, pg. 1033

McBee, C. William, V.P.-Mfg.--Liqui-Box Corporation, Worthington, OH; *U.S. Public*, pg. 1000

McBride, David, Chief Information Officer--McBride and Associates, Inc., Albuquerque, NM; *U.S. Private*, pg. 719

McCaffrey, William P., V.P.-Mfg.--Kysor/Westran, Byron, IL; *U.S. Public*, pg. 968

McCallion, Robert J., V.P.-Mfg.--Micros Systems Inc., Beltsville, MD; *U.S. Public*, pg. 1106

McCart, Ken, V.P.-Mfg.--Studley Products Co., Inwood, NY; *U.S. Public*, pg. 1193

McCartin, Jim, Dir.-Construction--Ark Restaurants Corp., New York, NY; *U.S. Public*, pg. 129

McCartney, Phillip D., V.P.-Technical Operations & Engrng.--Guilford Mills, Inc., Greensboro, NC; *U.S. Public*, pg. 768

McCarty, Dennis, V.P.-Mfg.--D.C.I., Inc., Saint Cloud, MN; *U.S. Private*, pg. 301

McCaughey, Mark, V.P.-Mfg.--Bird Machine Company, South Walpole, MA; *U.S. Public*, pg. 166

McClanahan, Ivan, Mgr.-Production--M.C. Gill Corporation, El Monte, CA; *U.S. Private*, pg. 453

McClelland, D., Mgr.-Mfg.-Clean Room--Laminaire Corporation, Rahway, NJ; *U.S. Public*, pg. 1596

McCormick, Jerry, V.P.-Mfg.--Milwaukee Electric Tool Corp., Brookfield, WI; *Int'l*, pg. 96

McCullough, Kevin, V.P.-Mfg.--Dennis Chemical Co., Inc., Saint Louis, MO; *U.S. Private*, pg. 324

McCullough, Morley, V.P. & Gen. Mgr.-Casting Opers.--Fisher Gauge Limited, Peterborough, Canada; *Int'l*, pg. 491

McCullough, Morley, V.P. & Gen. Mgr.-Mfg.--Fishercast, Peterborough, Canada; *Int'l*, pg. 491
McCullough, R.J., V.P.-Opers.--IDenticard Systems, Inc., Lancaster, PA; *U.S. Private*, pg. 557
McCullough, Robert, Mgr.-Production--Industrial Bag Division - Cantonment Plant, Cantonment, FL; *U.S. Public*, pg. 1521
McCurley, Jim, V.P.-Mfg. Services--Parmalat Canada Ltd., Etobicoke, Canada; *Int'l*, pg. 1023
McCutcheon, Mark, V.P.-Mfg.--Golden Flake Snack Foods, Inc., Birmingham, AL; *U.S. Public*, pg. 750
McDaniel, Jack, Mgr.-EPS Mfg. Plant--Speedling Incorporated, Sun City, FL; *U.S. Private*, pg. 1024
McDonald, Timothy R., Dir.-Tech.--Hazen Paper Company, Holyoke, MA; *U.S. Private*, pg. 514
McDowell, Jerry T., Chief Oper. Officer & Sr. V.P.--Alltrista Corporation, Muncie, IN; *U.S. Public*, pg. 56
McGary, Francis H., V.P.-Mfg.--Star Bronze Company, Alliance, OH; *U.S. Private*, pg. 1034
McGehee, Bill, Mgr.-Mfg.--FWD/Seagrave Fire Apparatus, Inc., Clintonville, WI; *U.S. Private*, pg. 390
McGehee, Charles, V.P. & Dir.-Mfg.--Croft Metals, Inc., McComb, MS; *U.S. Private*, pg. 290
McGettigan, David J., V.P.-Distribution--Quality Stores Inc., Muskegon, MI; *U.S. Private*, pg. 899
McGoveren, Jim, V.P.-Mfg.--Peerless Confection Company, Chicago, IL; *U.S. Private*, pg. 847
McGovern, Frank, Mgr.-Prod.--Nokia Mobile Phones, Espoo, Finland; *Int'l*, pg. 951
McGovern, Joseph P., Chief Tech. Advisor--White Rock Distilleries Inc., Lewiston, ME; *U.S. Private*, pg. 1173
McGovern, Terry, Mgr.-Plant--Frost Inc., Grand Rapids, MI; *U.S. Private*, pg. 430
McGowen, Oliver W., V.P.-Mfg.--Interface Flooring Systems Inc., La Grange, GA; *U.S. Public*, pg. 889
McGrady, Edward J., V.P.-Mfg.--Davis Standard Corporation, Pawcatuck, CT; *U.S. Public*, pg. 459
McGuire, Gary, Mgr.-Mfg.--Admiral Heintz, Inc., Wadsworth, OH; *U.S. Public*, pg. 1143
McHugh, Marion E., V.P.-Mfg.--Northrop Grumman Corporation, Los Angeles, CA; *U.S. Public*, pg. 1197
McIlwain, Don C., V.P.-Opers.--Apertus Technologies Incorporated, Eden Prairie, MN; *U.S. Public*, pg. 119
McIntyre, William S., Chief Design Engr.--J.H. Fletcher & Co., Huntington, WV; *U.S. Private*, pg. 412
McJunkin, H. P., V.P.-Mfg.--McJunkin Corporation, Charleston, WV; *U.S. Private*, pg. 722
McKee, Robert E., III, V.P.-Exploration & Production--Du Pont (E.I. Du Pont De Nemours & Co.), Wilmington, DE; *U.S. Public*, pg. 530
McKeithan, James R., V.P.-Mfg.--Easco Inc., Girard, OH; *U.S. Public*, pg. 548
McKeller, Charles, V.P.-Mfg. Services--Glen Raven Mills, Inc., Glen Raven, NC; *U.S. Private*, pg. 456
McKenzie, John, Sr. V.P. & Chief Engr.--Key Handling Systems, Inc., Moonachie, NJ; *U.S. Private*, pg. 618
McKincey, Dave, Mgr.-Mfg.--Carver, Inc., Savannah, GA; *U.S. Private*, pg. 217
McKinney, Allen, Dir.-Mfg. Services--Holt Hosiery Mills, Inc., Burlington, NC; *U.S. Private*, pg. 536
McKinney, Louis, Mgr.-Prod.--Redco Corporation, Red Lion, PA; *U.S. Private*, pg. 915
McKnatt, Gene, Supvr.-Telecommunications Engrng.--Memphis Light, Gas & Water, Memphis, TN; *U.S. Private*, pg. 731
Mclaine, Tim, Mgr.-Mfr.--DBA Systems, Inc., Melbourne, FL; *U.S. Public*, pg. 472
McLaughlin, David A., Chief Oper. Officer & Sr. V.P.-Opers./Nutritionals--Jones Medical Industries Inc., Saint Louis, MO; *U.S. Public*, pg. 933
McLaughlin, Stephen M., V.P.-Mfg.--IKOS Systems, Inc., Cupertino, CA; *U.S. Public*, pg. 864
McLaughlin, W.P., Mfg. Dir.--Bomford Turner Limited, Evesham, United Kingdom; *U.S. Public*, pg. 35
McLeod, Peter D., V.P.-Mfg., Engrng. & Tech.--Colgate-Palmolive Company, New York, NY; *U.S. Public*, pg. 397
McMahon, George, Mgr.-Engrng.--Pitco Frialator Inc., Bow, NH; *U.S. Public*, pg. 1065
McManus, H.S., V.P.-Mfg.--Morrison Textile Machinery Co., Fort Lawn, SC; *U.S. Private*, pg. 762
McMaster, John, Mgr.-Mfg./Western Reg.--Oil-Dri Corporation of America, Chicago, IL; *U.S. Public*, pg. 1214
McMillan, Roy, V.P.-Sourcing & Mfg.--Victoria's Secret Stores, Reynoldsburg, OH; *U.S. Public*, pg. 995
McNair, Danny, V.P.-Mfg.--Harriss & Covington Hosiery Mills, High Point, NC; *U.S. Private*, pg. 500
McNally, Thomas M., Sr. V.P.-Ross Products--Abbott Laboratories, Abbott Park, IL; *U.S. Public*, pg. 12
McNeill, Rob, V.P.-Mfg.--Stuart Entertainment Inc., Council Bluffs, IA; *U.S. Public*, pg. 1526
McNeilly, Ellen, V.P.-Production--Alfred A. Knopf, Inc., New York, NY; *U.S. Private*, pg. 21
McNulty, Steve, V.P.-Mfg.--Playtex Products Inc., Westport, CT; *U.S. Public*, pg. 1310
McNurlin, Thomas, V.P.-Opers.--Red Wing Shoe Co., Inc., Red Wing, MN; *U.S. Private*, pg. 915
McPhedrain, Larry L., Exec. V.P.-Opers.--Mary Maxim, Inc., Port Huron, MI; *U.S. Private*, pg. 716
McQuillen, Denis, Sr. V.P. Mfg.--Consolidated Cigar Corporation, Fort Lauderdale, FL; *U.S. Private*, pg. 690
Meador, K., V.P.-Mfg. & Devel.--Van Melle USA, Inc., Erlanger, KY; *Int'l*, pg. 1451
Meccariello, Joe, V.P.-Mfg./Hong Kong--Bel Fuse Inc., Jersey City, NJ; *U.S. Public*, pg. 200
Mecredy, Robert C., V.P.-Ginna Nuclear Production--Rochester Gas And Electric Corporation, Rochester, NY; *U.S. Public*, pg. 1395
Meddendorf, Gary, Mgr.-Mfg.--Projects Unlimited, Inc., Dayton, OH; *U.S. Private*, pg. 890
Meers, Randy, Plant Mgr.--Ohio Valley Aluminum Company, Shelbyville, KY; *U.S. Private*, pg. 567
Meiland, Nico J., Sr. V.P.-Worldwide Mfg. & Procurement--S.C. Johnson & Son, Inc., Racine, WI; *U.S. Private*, pg. 592
Melchior, Barry R., Dir.-Corp. Engrng. & Mfg. Services--Imation Corporation, Oakdale, MN; *U.S. Public*, pg. 870
Meldahl, M.J., V.P.-Technology Div.--Entech, Inc., Butte, MT; *U.S. Public*, pg. 1127
Melnick, David, Chief Oper. Officer--Pentech International, Inc., Edison, NJ; *U.S. Public*, pg. 1274
Meloche, Ronald, V.P.-Mfg.--Anchor Lamina Inc., Windsor, Canada; *Int'l*, pg. 75
Melton, James P., Pres.-Chemical Res. & Tech. & V.P.-Press Opers.--Quad/Graphics, Inc., Pewaukee, WI; *U.S. Private*, pg. 897
Melvin, Ralph, Mgr.-Mfg.--Stanley Steemer International, Inc., Dublin, OH; *U.S. Private*, pg. 1033
Mendelow, Robert, V.P.-Mfg.--Irwin Toy Ltd., Toronto, Canada; *Int'l*, pg. 688
Mendez, Abundio Juarez, Asst. Dir.-Primary Prod.--Petroleos Mexicanos, Mexico, Mexico; *Int'l*, pg. 1046
Mendez, Raymond, Dir.-Mfg.--Sentry Technology Corp., Hauppauge, NY; *U.S. Public*, pg. 1458
Menegoni, Tony, Dir.-Mfg. Plant--S. Bent & Brothers, Inc., Gardner, MA; *U.S. Private*, pg. 134
Menke, Andrew G., V.P.-Opers.--Ardco, Inc., Alsip, IL; *U.S. Private*, pg. 80
Mentzel, Klaus, Dr., Mgr.-Prod.--Reemtsma Cigarettenfabriken GmbH, Hamburg, Hamburg, Germany; *Int'l*, pg. 1100
Mercer, James T., V.P.-Mfg.--Plant City Steel Co., Plant City, FL; *U.S. Public*, pg. 793
Mercer, Joe, V.P.-Mfg.--Plastic Packaging, Inc., Hickory, NC; *U.S. Private*, pg. 871
Mericle, Steve, Mgr.-Mfg.--Hagie Manufacturing Co., Clarion, IA; *U.S. Private*, pg. 493
Merk, Richard, V.P.-Mfg. Special Projects--Callaway Golf Company, Carlsbad, CA; *U.S. Public*, pg. 294
Merl, Murray, V.P.-Mfg.--Robby Len Fashions, New York, NY; *U.S. Public*, pg. 121
Merrill, Douglas W., V.P.-Mfg. Opers.--Kelly-Moore Paint Company, Inc., San Carlos, CA; *U.S. Private*, pg. 613
Mertens, Heinz, Mgr.-Plant--Warrens Waller Press, Inc., South San Francisco, CA; *U.S. Private*, pg. 1151
Messer, F.E., Mgr.-Mfg.--Wellco Enterprises, Inc., Waynesville, NC; *U.S. Public*, pg. 1752
Meyer, T.R., V.P.-Engrng.--Meret Communications, San Diego, CA; *U.S. Public*, pg. 1233
Meyerhoffer, Donn, Dir.-Opers.--ComSonics, Inc., Harrisonburg, VA; *U.S. Private*, pg. 260
Michaud, Gary L., Dir.-Mfg.--Dey Laboratories Inc., Napa, CA; *Int'l*, pg. 812
Michaud, Leo P., Dir.-Opers. & Mfg.--Operations & Maintenance Division, Cleveland, OH; *U.S. Public*, pg. 1134
Michels, Josef, Tech. Mgr.-Furniture Components--Westag & Getalit AG, Rheda-Wiedenbruck, Germany; *Int'l*, pg. 1491
Michie, Fred, V.P.-Mfg.--Cliftex, New Bedford, MA; *U.S. Public*, pg. 1777
Migeott, Andree, Dir.-Mfg. & Engrng.--Automobiles Citroen, Neuilly, France; *Int'l*, pg. 1020
Mikiten, Brian, V.P.-Mfg.--Adtec Detention Systems, San Antonio, TX; *U.S. Private*, pg. 18
Miller, Ben, V.P.-Engrng.--Remcor Products Co., Glendale Heights, IL; *Int'l*, pg. 646
Miller, Bob, Mgr.-Prod.--York Barbell Co., Inc., York, PA; *U.S. Private*, pg. 1196
Miller, Charles, V.P.-Mfg.--Narrow Fabric Industries, Inc., Reading, PA; *U.S. Private*, pg. 774
Miller, Christy, V.P.-Mfg.--Supreme Industries, Inc., Goshen, IN; *U.S. Public*, pg. 1541
Miller, Don, V.P.-Opers.--Reliance Elevator Company, Chicago, IL; *U.S. Private*, pg. 921
Miller, Donald, Mgr.-Mfg.--Sybron Chemicals Inc., Salem, VA; *U.S. Public*, pg. 1544
Miller, Donald F., V.P.-Opers. & Mfg.--C-COR Electronics, Inc., State College, PA; *U.S. Public*, pg. 272
Miller, Edward, V.P.-Engrng.--Edwards Systems Tech, Cheshire, CT; *U.S. Public*, pg. 726
Miller, Gary S., Sr. V.P.-Design & Devel.--Herman Miller, Inc., Zeeland, MI; *U.S. Public*, pg. 1111
Miller, Howard, V.P.-Engrng.--InteCom, Dallas, TX; *Int'l*, pg. 794
Miller, Jack, Mgr.-Mfg.--Systems Bio Industries, Langhorne, PA; *Int'l*, pg. 445
Miller, Jerry W., V.P.-Mfg.--Dyersburg Corporation, Dyersburg, TN; *U.S. Public*, pg. 538
Miller, John J., V.P.--Danisco Ingredients USA, Inc., New Century, KS; *Int'l*, pg. 370
Miller, Marvin, V.P.-Engrng. & Sec.--The Keller Manufacturing Co., Inc., Corydon, IN; *U.S. Private*, pg. 612
Miller, Michael, Chief Oper. Officer--Cragar Industries, Inc., Phoenix, AZ; *U.S. Public*, pg. 456
Miller, Michael G., Dir.-Engrng.--Duff-Norton, Charlotte, NC; *U.S. Public*, pg. 406
Miller, Robert, V.P.-Engrng.--Holley Replacement Parts Division, Bowling Green, KY; *U.S. Public*, pg. 402
Miller, Robert F., V.P.-Engrng.--Indianapolis Water Company, Indianapolis, IN; *U.S. Public*, pg. 1185
Miller, Susan, V.P.-Corp. Licensing--Warner Bros. Consumer Products, Burbank, CA; *U.S. Public*, pg. 1610
Miller, William, Dir.-Opers.--Better Baked Foods, Inc., North East, PA; *U.S. Private*, pg. 141
Milliken, William, V.P. & Corp. Dir.-Mfg.--Instron Corporation, Canton, MA; *U.S. Public*, pg. 882
Milo, Bob, Exec. V.P.-Mfg.--Coastcast Corporation, Gardena, CA; *U.S. Public*, pg. 391
Milzcik, Greg, V.P.-Mfg.--Precision Standard, Inc., Denver, CO; *U.S. Public*, pg. 1321
Mimerd, Regis, V.P.-Mfg.--Teledyne Fluid Systems, Brecksville, OH; *U.S. Public*, pg. 43
Miner, James J., Sr. V.P.-Farm Production--Pilgrim's Pride Corporation, Pittsburg, TX; *U.S. Public*, pg. 1296
Minor, Travis, V.P.-Mfg.--P.W. Minor & Son, Inc., Batavia, NY; *U.S. Private*, pg. 751
Mintline, Larry, Dir.-Warehousing, Distr. & Transportation--The Cosmetic Center Inc., Columbia, MD; *U.S. Private*, pg. 689
Minton, Keith G., V.P.-Mfg.--Hoover Company, Canton, OH; *U.S. Public*, pg. 1065
Mirghanbari, M., V.P.-Mfg. & Engrng.--Stepan Company, Northfield, IL; *U.S. Public*, pg. 1514
Misaka, Shigeo, Sr. Exec. Dir.-Electronic Components & Devices--Sharp Corporation, Osaka, Japan; *Int'l*, pg. 1228
Miskew, John, Asst. V.P.-Field Engrng.--Monroe Systems For Business, Inc., Morris Plains, NJ; *U.S. Private*, pg. 757
Mitchel, David, V.P.-Mfg.--Mitchel & Scott Machine Co., Inc., Indianapolis, IN; *U.S. Private*, pg. 753
Mitchell, Charles, V.P.-Opers. & Mfg.--World Carpets, Inc., Dalton, GA; *U.S. Private*, pg. 1190
Mitchell, Gerald, V.P.-Mfg.--BGF Industries Inc., Greensboro, NC; *U.S. Private*, pg. 106
Mitchell, Mike, V.P.-Engrng.--Breeze Eastern, Union, NJ; *U.S. Public*, pg. 1632
Mitchell, Pete M., V.P.-Opers.--IMC Agribusiness, Collinsville, IL; *U.S. Public*, pg. 856
Mitchell, Steve, V.P.-Mfg.--Southern Mills, Inc., Union City, GA; *U.S. Private*, pg. 1016
Mitchell, Terry, Mgr.-Opers.--Marilyn Miglin, L.P., Chicago, IL; *U.S. Private*, pg. 745
Mitsuhashi, Takashi, Mng. Dir. & Gen. Mgr.-Corp. Engrng.--Mitsubishi Electric Corporation, Tokyo, Japan; *Int'l*, pg. 872
Mitter, Lawrence, V.P.-Engrng.--Young & Franklin, Inc., Liverpool, NY; *U.S. Private*, pg. 1196
Miura, Steve, V.P.-Quality & Test--Komag, Incorporated, San Jose, CA; *U.S. Public*, pg. 966
Mixer, Charles, Sr. V.P.-Mktg. & Engrng.--Telephonics Corp., Farmington, NY; *U.S. Public*, pg. 766
Miyamoto, Kazuyuki, Gen. Mgr.-Pur.--Makita Corporation, Anjo, Japan; *Int'l*, pg. 831
Mizer, M.A., V.P.-Engrng.--Carver, Inc., Savannah, GA; *U.S. Private*, pg. 217
Moberg, Guy, Plant Engineer--Pabst Brewing Co., San Antonio, TX; *U.S. Private*, pg. 954
Mobley, Ossie, V.P.-Mfg.--Mark III Industries, Ocala, FL; *U.S. Private*, pg. 704
Mocny, R.C., V.P.-Mfg. & Engrng.--Patent Construction Systems, Paramus, NJ; *U.S. Public*, pg. 793
Moeckel, Alfred J., Sr. V.P.-Mfg.--American Trouser, Inc., Columbus, MS; *U.S. Private*, pg. 64
Moffa, Roy, V.P.-Mfg.--3Com Corporation, Southborough, MA; *U.S. Public*, pg. 1604
Mohney, Steven, Mgr.-Mfg. Engrng.--Humphrey Products Company, Kalamazoo, MI; *U.S. Private*, pg. 547
Mohr, David, Dir.-Mfg.--Agouron Pharmaceuticals, Inc., La Jolla, CA; *U.S. Public*, pg. 28
Molinaro, Elvi, V.P.-Mfg.--Fort James Canada, Inc., Toronto, Canada; *U.S. Public*, pg. 672
Moll, Sheldon H., Dr., Sr. V.P.-Tech.--Amray, Inc., Bedford, MA; *U.S. Private*, pg. 67
Molnar, Thomas, V.P.-Mktg. & Mfg.--Gibbs Wire & Steel Company, Inc., Southington, CT; *U.S. Private*, pg. 451
Monahan, Alan R., V.P.-Mfg. Support--Xerox Corporation, Stamford, CT; *U.S. Public*, pg. 1783
Monzon, Medardo, Mgr.-Sls. & Mktg.--Arizona Chemical Div., Panama City, FL; *U.S. Public*, pg. 901
Moody, Dale, Dir.-Electrical Opers.--Wisconsin Power & Light Company, Madison, WI; *U.S. Public*, pg. 1728
Mooney, Joseph M., Sr. V.P.-Opers.--EAC Corporation, Saint Louis, MO; *U.S. Private*, pg. 353
Moore, Alice C., Mgr.-Prod. Plng.--Ocean Spray Cranberries-Bordentown Plant, Bordentown, NJ; *U.S. Private*, pg. 811
Moore, Bob, Div. Gen. Mgr.-BHP Wire Prods.--Building & Industrial Products Division, Sydney, Australia; *Int'l*, pg. 225
Moore, Charles E., V.P.-Mfg.--Day-Glo Color Corp., Cleveland, OH; *U.S. Public*, pg. 1357
Moore, Kenneth, Mgr.-Promotions & Mdsg.--Bruncor, Inc., Saint John, Canada; *Int'l*, pg. 230
Moore, R., Mgr.-Mfg.--Castrol Canada Inc., Toronto, Canada; *Int'l*, pg. 235
Moore, R.L., Sr. Exec. V.P.-Tech. Opers--Konica Business Machines USA, Inc., Windsor, CT; *Int'l*, pg. 748
Moorer, McE., Mgr.-Production--Industrial Bag Division - Los Angeles Plant, Los Angeles, CA; *U.S. Public*, pg. 1521
Moraes, Leo, Dir.-Mfg.--AMD Industries Inc., Cicero, IL; *U.S. Private*, pg. 6
Moran, John, Dir.-Technical Services--Industrial Bag Division - Cantonment Plant, Cantonment, FL; *U.S. Public*, pg. 1521
Moran, Robert A., V.P.-Mfg. Svcs.--Bowater Incorporated, Greenville, SC; *U.S. Public*, pg. 247
Morath, Paul, V.P.-Mfg.--Ring Screw Works, Madison Heights, MI; *U.S. Private*, pg. 931
Morecroft, Michael J., V.P.-Engrng. & Prod. Devel.--Hamilton Beach/Proctor-Silex, Inc., Glen Allen, VA; *U.S. Public*, pg. 1149
Morelli, Roger H., V.P.-Mfg.--Magna Lomason Corp., Farmington Hills, MI; *Int'l*, pg. 830
Morello, Tim, Mgr.-Engrng.--Control Module, Inc., Enfield, CT; *U.S. Private*, pg. 271
Morgan, D.L., V.P.-Mfg.--Morton International Inc., Chicago, IL; *U.S. Public*, pg. 1135
Morgan, Dave, Mgr.-Production--Larson Manufacturing Company, Brookings, SD; *U.S. Private*, pg. 652
Morgan, Ersel, V.P.-Production--Petroleum Development Corporation, Bridgeport, WV; *U.S. Public*, pg. 1280
Morgan, George B., III, V.P.-Prod. Engrng.--Texas Metal Works, Inc., Beaumont, TX; *U.S. Private*, pg. 1078
Morgan, Ronald F., V.P.-Mfg.--Brown Wooten Mills, Inc., Burlington, NC; *U.S. Private*, pg. 174
Moroz, Eugene, V.P.-Production--Allen Organ Company, Macungie, PA; *U.S. Public*, pg. 45

Morris, Brent, Plant Mgr.--Greer Steel Co., Dover, OH; *U.S. Private*, pg. 479
Morris, Mark, Dir.-Mfg.--Tone Commander Systems, Mukilteo, WA; *U.S. Private*, pg. 1090
Morrison, Angus, V.P.-Mfg.--LePage's Limited, Brampton, Canada; *Int'l*, pg. 613
Morrison, Larry, V.P.-Mfg.--Columbus Mills, Inc., Columbus, GA; *U.S. Private*, pg. 256
Morrison, Paul K., V.P.-Engrng.--WHX Corporation, New York, NY; *U.S. Public*, pg. 1726
Morse, Mike, V.P.-Mfg.--Fruit of the Loom, Inc., Chicago, IL; *U.S. Public*, pg. 685
Morton, Gerald, Dir.-Mfg.--Miss Elaine Inc., Saint Louis, MO; *U.S. Private*, pg. 752
Morton, Thomas C., Jr., V.P.-Mfg.--United Distillers USA, Inc., Stamford, CT; *Int'l*, pg. 412
Moschini, Andrea, Exec. Dir.-Prod.--Bulgari SPA, Rome, Italy; *Int'l*, pg. 232
Moseby, Debbie, Mgr.-Production--Griffin Manufacturing Co., Muskogee, OK; *U.S. Private*, pg. 481
Mosher, Kirk, Mgr.-Mfg.--Ruska Instrument Corporation, Houston, TX; *U.S. Private*, pg. 952
Mosher, William, Sr. Pres.-Sls.--Circle Plastics Products, Inc., Circleville, OH; *U.S. Private*, pg. 240
Mossholder, Steve, V.P.-Mfg.--Baldwin Filters, Kearney, NE; *U.S. Public*, pg. 381
Mostellor, Don, Mgr.-Mfg.--Tighe Industries, Inc., York, PA; *U.S. Private*, pg. 1086
Moulton, Chet, Plant Mgr.--Capital City Press, Inc., Berlin, VT; *U.S. Private*, pg. 205
Moulton, John, Exec. V.P.-Mfg.--Robert Bosch Corporation, Broadview, IL; *Int'l*, pg. 204
Moyer, Carter, V.P.-Mfg.--Gold Lance, Inc., Houston, TX; *U.S. Public*, pg. 1625
Moyer, Roger, Plant Mgr.--Harter, Middlebury, IN; *U.S. Private*, pg. 581
Mozade, Stanley, Dir.-Engrng.--Tekni-Plex, Inc., Somerville, NJ; *U.S. Private*, pg. 1073
Mucklin, Jerry, Mgr.-Mfg.--Alling-Lander, Union Grove, WI; *U.S. Public*, pg. 1370
Mueller, Everett, V.P.-Mfg.--Winona Knitting Mills, Inc., Winona, MN; *U.S. Public*, pg. 779
Mueller, Peter, Exec. V.P.-Mfg.--Stihl Inc., Virginia Beach, VA; *Int'l*, pg. 1301
Mueller, Richard, V.P.-Engrng.--Vienna Sausage Mfg. Co., Chicago, IL; *U.S. Private*, pg. 1139
Muggridge, S. Clayton, Dir.-Mfg./Bread Grp.--Mrs. Smith's Bakeries, Inc., Thomasville, GA; *U.S. Public*, pg. 657
Muir, Earl, Sr. V.P.-Engrng. & Research--Copeland Corporation, Sidney, OH; *U.S. Public*, pg. 573
Mulcahy, M., Mgr.-Engrng.--Tuthill Pump, Alsip, IL; *U.S. Private*, pg. 1111
Muldoon, W. Niall, V.P.-Fabric Prod.--Hoffman Laces, Ltd., Cobleskill, NY; *U.S. Public*, pg. 769
Muldowney, Michael R., V.P.-Production & Mfg.--King & Prince Seafood Corporation, Brunswick, GA; *U.S. Private*, pg. 620
Mulhall, R., Indus. Mgr.-Conductive & Impact Prods.--Potters Industries, Inc., Valley Forge, PA; *U.S. Private*, pg. 827
Muller, Wolfgang, Mgr.-Engrng.--Hermann Pfauter GmbH & Co., Ludwigsburg, Germany; *Int'l*, pg. 617
Mullins, H.G., Controller & Mgr.-Mfg.--Flowserve Corporation, Foundry Div., Dayton, OH; *U.S. Public*, pg. 658
Mullman, O. Michael, V.P.-Mfg.--Gear Products Inc., Tulsa, OK; *U.S. Public*, pg. 238
Mumford, Michael, V.P.--Immunex Corporation, Seattle, WA; *U.S. Public*, pg. 871
Mumford, Michael, V.P.-Mfg.--Immunex Manufacturing Corporation, Seattle, WA; *U.S. Public*, pg. 871
Munson, George, Sr. Dir.-Mfg.--Periphonics Corp., Bohemia, NY; *U.S. Public*, pg. 1278
Murad, Francis A., Ph.D., PE, V.P.--Giffels Associates, Inc., Southfield, MI; *U.S. Private*, pg. 452
Murakami, Toshihiko, Mng. Dir.--Kayaba Industry Co., Ltd., Tokyo, Japan; *Int'l*, pg. 727
Murcia, Sr. Carlos, Dir.-Commercial (Soldering Products)--Praxair Espania S.A., Madrid, Spain; *U.S. Public*, pg. 1320
Murphy, Brian, V.P.-Mfg.--Murphy-Phoenix Co., Solon, OH; *U.S. Public*, pg. 397
Murphy, Ken, V.P.-Prod. & Admin.--The Discovery Channel, Willowdale, Canada; *Int'l*, pg. 1343
Murray, Wayne P., V.P.-Mfg.--Edelbrock Corp., Torrance, CA; *U.S. Public*, pg. 563
Murschel, William H., Pres. & Chief Oper. Officer--Skyline Corporation, Elkhart, IN; *U.S. Public*, pg. 1476
Muselman, Thomas, Exec. V.P.-Mfg.--E.P. Graphics, Inc., Berne, IN; *U.S. Private*, pg. 354
Musgrave, J., Mgr.-Prod.--Industrial Pharmaceutical Products Division, Delft, Netherlands; *Int'l*, pg. 1142
Mussgnug, Hans, V.P.-Mfg. Plng.--Freightliner Corp., Portland, OR; *Int'l*, pg. 368
Myhand, J.R., V.P.-Mfg.--Brown & Williamson Tobacco Corp., Louisville, KY; *Int'l*, pg. 111
Nackley, John, V.P.-Mfg.--Cognex Corporation, Natick, MA; *U.S. Public*, pg. 394
Nagasako, Kizo, Dir.-Mfg. Tech. Div.--Tokuyama Corporation, Tokyo, Japan; *Int'l*, pg. 1393
Nagel, Kenneth, Dir.-Engrng.--The Wiegmann Company, Freeburg, IL; *U.S. Public*, pg. 845
Naidus, Joel D., Sr. V.P.-Engineering & Mfg.--Lockheed Martin Microwave-FSI, Chelmsford, MA; *U.S. Public*, pg. 1008
Nakagawa, Brian, V.P.-Info. Sys.--Glacier Water Services Inc., Carlsbad, CA; *U.S. Public*, pg. 745
Nam, S.H., Mgr.-Production--Bundy Systems Korea, Ansan, Korea; *Int'l*, pg. 1341
Napeorkowski, George, V.P.-Opers.--Pavey Envelope & Tag Corp., Jersey City, NJ; *U.S. Public*, pg. 1038
Nardecchia, Vince, Sr. V.P.-Mfg.--Quebecor Printing Clarksville, Clarksville, TN; *Int'l*, pg. 1076
Narducci, Lawrence, Mgr.-Mfg.--Molded Fiber Glass Companies, Ashtabula, OH; *U.S. Private*, pg. 755
Nauert, Andy, Mgr.-Production, Ft. Worth--Town & Country Homes, Fort Worth, TX; *U.S. Public*, pg. 319
Neal, Carlos, Mgr.-Prod.--MD Pneumatics, Springfield, MO; *U.S. Private*, pg. 1111
Necker, Joseph H., Jr., V.P. & Dir.-Engrng.--Rouse Office & Community Development Div., Columbia, MD; *U.S. Public*, pg. 1407
Neeley, David, V.P.-Mfg.--Yogen Fruz Worldwide Inc., Markham, Canada; *Int'l*, pg. 1520
Neely, Jay, V.P.-Mfg.--Kendale Industries, Inc., Valley View, OH; *U.S. Private*, pg. 614
Nehrt, J., Chief Engineer--Willert Home Products, Inc., Saint Louis, MO; *U.S. Private*, pg. 1177
Neiberger, Claude, V.P.-Mfg.--Bayer Clothing Group, New York, NY; *U.S. Private*, pg. 124
Neidhart, John F., V.P.-Mfg.--Oakite Products, Inc., Berkeley Heights, NJ; *Int'l*, pg. 861
Neill, W., V.P.-Mfg.--Weldon, Inc., Columbus, OH; *Int'l*, pg. 449
Nelson, Bob, V.P.-Engrng.--System Sensor Division, Saint Charles, IL; *U.S. Public*, pg. 1306
Nelson, Carl S., Jr., V.P.-Engrng.--Magnasync Moviola Corporation, Hollywood, CA; *U.S. Private*, pg. 576
Nelson, Donald, V.P.-Mfg.--The Okonite Company, Ramsey, NJ; *U.S. Private*, pg. 813
Nelson, Keith, Dir.-Technical Svcs.--Pentax Precision Instrument Corp., Orangeburg, NY; *Int'l*, pg. 85
Nelson, Larry W., Mgr.-Ecusta Mill--P.H. Glatfelter Company, Spring Grove, PA; *U.S. Public*, pg. 746
Nelson, Todd, Mgr.-D.P.--Trend Offset Printing Services, Los Alamitos, CA; *U.S. Private*, pg. 1099
Nelstead, J.T., Mgr.-Production Plng.--Industrial Bag Division - Louisville Plant, Louisville, KY; *U.S. Public*, pg. 1521
Neshat, Mike, Mgr.-Engrng--Douglas/Quikut, Walnut Ridge, AR; *U.S. Public*, pg. 217
Neugeboren, Mark, V.P.-Production--Concord Fabrics Inc., New York, NY; *U.S. Public*, pg. 429
Neuman, Fred, V.P.-Mfg.--Andiamo, Inc., Fountain Valley, CA; *U.S. Private*, pg. 73
Nevers, Leon, V.P.-Mfg.--Roll Forming Corporation, Shelbyville, KY; *U.S. Private*, pg. 941
Newbill, George A., V.P.-Mfg.--Albemarle Corporation, Richmond, VA; *U.S. Public*, pg. 37
Newcomb, Ronald, V.P. Mfg.--AlliedSignal Aerospace, Stratford, CT; *U.S. Public*, pg. 50
Newitt, A., Dir.-Prod.--Garryson-Insley Ltd., Ibstock, United Kingdom; *Int'l*, pg. 448
Newlin, John W., Jr., V.P.-Mfg.--Tootsie Roll Industries, Inc., Chicago, IL; *U.S. Public*, pg. 1621
Newlin, T., V.P.-Mfg.--Cella's Confections, Inc., New York, NY; *U.S. Public*, pg. 1621
Newman, P.V., V.P. & Mgr.-Exploration--Anadarko Algeria Corporation, Houston, TX; *U.S. Public*, pg. 107
Newsome, John L., Jr., Div. V.P.-Mfg., Paper--Sonoco Products Company, Hartsville, SC; *U.S. Public*, pg. 1485
Newton, William, V.P.-Mfg.--R.M. Palmer Company, Reading, PA; *U.S. Private*, pg. 835
Nichols, Nick, Dir.-Mfg.-Smith Diamond Tech.--Smith International, Inc., Houston, TX; *U.S. Public*, pg. 1478
Nicholson, Ronald P., V.P.-Environment & Technical Services--Cape Breton Development Corporation, Glace Bay, Canada; *Int'l*, pg. 265
Nickerson, J.T., V.P.-Mfg.--Southern Ohio Fabricators, Inc., Batavia, OH; *U.S. Private*, pg. 1017
Nickerson, J.T., V.P.-Mfg.--Spfco Erectors, Inc., Cincinnati, OH; *U.S. Private*, pg. 1017
Nicketta, Chuck, Dir.-Mfg.--John B. Sanfilippo & Son, Inc., Elk Grove Village, IL; *U.S. Public*, pg. 1431
Nickless, Donald, V.P.-Mfg.--The House of Seagram, New York, NY; *Int'l*, pg. 1217
Niehaus, Mike, Mgr.-Plant--Whitfield Foods, Inc., Montgomery, AL; *U.S. Private*, pg. 1173
Niemi, Matti, Mgr.-Mfg.--ADI Data Furniture, Halikko, Finland; *Int'l*, pg. 460
Nilsen, Douglas N., Exec. V.P.-Mdsg.--Big Dog Holdings Inc., Santa Barbara, CA; *U.S. Public*, pg. 227
Nishimura, Osamu, Dir.-Mfg.--Settsu Corporation, Amagasaki, Japan; *Int'l*, pg. 1225
Nogueira, Jose Carlos A., Gen. Mgr.-Mfg.--Acos Villares Sao Caetano Plant, Sao Caetano do Sul, Brazil; *Int'l*, pg. 23
Nogueira, Marcos Stuart, Mgr.-Mfg., Rolling Mill Rolls--Acos Villares Steel Unit, Sao Paulo, Brazil; *Int'l*, pg. 23
Nolden, K., Dir.-Mfg.--Champion Pneumatic Machinery Co., Inc., Princeton, IL; *U.S. Private*, pg. 228
Noll, John L., V.P.-Opers.--A.H. Hoffman, Inc., Landisville, PA; *U.S. Private*, pg. 532
Norman, Earl P., Jr., V.P.-Tech.--Sonoco Products Company, Hartsville, SC; *U.S. Public*, pg. 1485
Noroovi, Hal, V.P.-Mfg. & Engrng.--Evans Tempcon Inc., Grand Rapids, MI; *U.S. Private*, pg. 7
Norris, Bradley, Mgr.-Opers.--Hydrolectric Lift Trucks Inc., Wilmington, OH; *U.S. Public*, pg. 61
Norton, John Phelps, V.P.-Prod.--J.R. Norton Company, Phoenix, AZ; *U.S. Private*, pg. 807
Nothnagel, Dr. Karlheinz, Mng. Dir. Production--Rohm GmbH, Darmstadt, Germany; *Int'l*, pg. 1454
Novak, Edward K., V.P.-Mfg.--PMC Industries Inc., Wickliffe, OH; *U.S. Private*, pg. 827
Novitsky, D., Dir.-Engrng.--Laubeck Corporation/Cross, Carbondale, PA; *U.S. Private*, pg. 652
Nowak, Edward, Mgr.-Mfg.--Marotta Scientific Controls, Inc., Montville, NJ; *U.S. Private*, pg. 706
Nunes, F.M., Mgr.-Indus.--Souza Cruz, S.A., Rio de Janeiro, Brazil; *Int'l*, pg. 112
Nunez, Tony, Sr. V.P.-Mfg.--The Spring Air Company, Des Plaines, IL; *U.S. Private*, pg. 1027
Nyman, Lee, V.P.-Mfg. Brass Mngmt. Engrng.--Mueller Industries, Inc., Memphis, TN; *U.S. Public*, pg. 1141
O'Brien, Stephen, V.P.-Plant Opers.--Amcel Corp., Watertown, MA; *U.S. Private*, pg. 48
O'Coin, Peter, V.P.-Mfg.--Kwikset Corporation, Irvine, CA; *U.S. Public*, pg. 233
O'Connell, Bradley D., Dir.-Mfg.--Crenlo, Inc., Rochester, MN; *U.S. Private*, pg. 288
O'Connell, Tim, Mgr.-Engrng.--Superior Linkage Division, New Haven, IN; *U.S. Private*, pg. 1111
O'Connor, Frank, Mgr.-Matls. Procurement & Pur.--Vance Industries, Inc., Chicago, IL; *U.S. Private*, pg. 1133
O'Connor, Sydney P., V.P.-Mfg.--Tensolite Company, Saint Augustine, FL; *U.S. Public*, pg. 305
O'Larey, Maureen L., V.P.-Mfg.--Data I/O Corporation, Redmond, WA; *U.S. Public*, pg. 486
O'Neil, Frank, V.P.-Mfg.--Electroid Co., Springfield, NJ; *U.S. Private*, pg. 369
O'Neill, William, V.P.-Mfg.--Cambridge Products Corporation, Bloomfield, CT; *U.S. Private*, pg. 598
O'Shaughnessy, Kathy, Dir.-Mfg.--Money, New York, NY; *U.S. Public*, pg. 1613
O'Shea, G., V.P.-Mfg.--TGM Detectors Inc., Waltham, MA; *Int'l*, pg. 892
Oakley, Charles, V.P.-Opers.--Inter-Tel, Incorporated, Phoenix, AZ; *U.S. Public*, pg. 888
Oberegger, Peter, Mgr.-Dist.--Nokia Monitors, Munich, Germany; *Int'l*, pg. 951
Oda, Kanji, Exec. V.P.--Toshiba America Consumer Products Manufacturing Div., Lebanon, TN; *Int'l*, pg. 1405
Odle, John H., Exec. V.P.-Commercial, Mfg. & Pur.--RMI Titanium Company, Niles, OH; *U.S. Public*, pg. 1662
Oesterreicher, Hugh A., V.P. & Dir.-Construction--Rouse Office & Community Development Div., Columbia, MD; *U.S. Public*, pg. 1407
Oglesby, Edward J., V.P.-Mfg.--Fujisawa U.S.A. Inc., Deerfield, IL; *Int'l*, pg. 525
Ognjanov, John, V.P.-Engrng.--Restaura, Inc., Phoenix, AZ; *U.S. Public*, pg. 1718
Ogura, Yasuhiko, Mng. Dir.--Tonen Corporation, Tokyo, Japan; *Int'l*, pg. 1398
Oka, Tomoshige, Sr. Mng. Dir.--Citizen Watch Company, Ltd., Tokyo, Japan; *Int'l*, pg. 293
Olanyk, Eugene, Plant Mgr.-Deerfield Opers.--Cains Foods, L.P., Ayer, MA; *U.S. Private*, pg. 199
Oligny, Vance, Dir.-Mfg.--Caddock Electronics, Inc., Riverside, CA; *U.S. Private*, pg. 198
Olsby, Richard W., Dir.-Mfg.--John Roberts Company, Minneapolis, MN; *U.S. Private*, pg. 935
Olsen, Gary, V.P.-Soy Opers. & Corn Opers.--Ag Processing Inc., A Cooperative, Omaha, NE; *U.S. Private*, pg. 26
Olsen, Ib, Sr. V.P.-Mfg.--Sudamtex de Uruguay, S.A., Montevideo, Uruguay; *Int'l*, pg. 1304
Olsen, Rick, V.P.-Mfg.--Graphics Arts Center, Pasadena, CA; *U.S. Public*, pg. 1038
Olson, Alan, V.P.-Mfg.--Rockford Acromatic Product Co., Rockford, IL; *U.S. Private*, pg. 938
Olson, Robert J., V.P.-Mfg.--Winnebago Industries, Inc., Forest City, IA; *U.S. Public*, pg. 1772
Ong, Thye Hey, Dir.-Mfg.--Malaysian Tobacco Co./B.A.T. Indust., Kuala Lumpur, Malaysia; *Int'l*, pg. 111
Onken, C., Dir.-Engrng.--Norcold, Sidney, OH; *U.S. Private*, pg. 352
Ooi, Boon Chye, V.P.-Intel Prods. Grp. & Dir.-Mfg.--Intel Corporation, Santa Clara, CA; *U.S. Public*, pg. 886
Oosterkamp, J., Mgr.-Prod. & Tech.--CSM Food Division, Diemen, Netherlands; *Int'l*, pg. 243
Opatik, Frank, V.P. & Dir.-Engrng.--Wausau Homes, Inc., Rothschild, WI; *U.S. Private*, pg. 1154
Ophey, Lothar, Dr. Ing., Exec. V.P.-Prod.--Traub AG, Reichenbach, Germany; *Int'l*, pg. 1419
Oppeneer, Steve, V.P.-Mfg.--Nemschoff Chairs, Inc., Sheboygan, WI; *U.S. Private*, pg. 791
Opperman, Carl, V.P.-Indus. Div.--AEP Industries, Inc., South Hackensack, NJ; *U.S. Public*, pg. 4
Oppermann, Joachim, Dir.-Pharmaceutical Prod.--Schering AG, Berlin, Germany; *Int'l*, pg. 1203
Oravits, T., V.P.-Engrng.--Sterling Davis Standard, South Plainfield, NJ; *Int'l*, pg. 1240
Orlin, David, Dir.-Mfr.--Gruner + Jahr USA Publishing, Inc., New York, NY; *Int'l*, pg. 190
Orr, N., Sr. V.P.-Production--Chieftain Development Co. Ltd., Edmonton, Canada; *Int'l*, pg. 49
Orthaber, John, V.P.-Mfg. & Mgr.-Plant--Michigan Wheel Corporation, Grand Rapids, MI; *U.S. Private*, pg. 741
Osborne, B.P., V.P.-Research, Technology & Engrng.--Lockheed Aeronautical Systems Company, Marietta, GA; *U.S. Public*, pg. 1007
Owen, William T., V.P.-Mfg.--Leupold & Stevens, Inc., Beaverton, OR; *U.S. Private*, pg. 662
Oxford, M.O., Mgr.-Factory--Crane Australia Pty. Ltd., Saint Marys, Australia; *U.S. Public*, pg. 457
Pacifico, Vince, V.P.-Opers.--Blue Bird Coach Lines Inc., Olean, NY; *U.S. Private*, pg. 150
Packard, James L., Jr., Mgr.-Mfg.--Mastergear Division, Roscoe, IL; *U.S. Public*, pg. 1370
Padilla, James, Exec. Dir.-Engrng. & Mfg.--Jaguar Cars Limited, Coventry, United Kingdom; *U.S. Public*, pg. 666
Pagan, Ralph, Mgr.-Product--The House of Seagram, New York, NY; *Int'l*, pg. 1217
Paine, Charlie, Plant Foreman--Brudi, Inc., Ridgefield, WA; *U.S. Private*, pg. 675
Palafax, Luis Miguel, Mgr.-Production--McGraw-Hill/Interamericana de Mexico, S.A. de CV, Mexico, Mexico; *U.S. Public*, pg. 1072
Palmer, James A., Sr. V.P.-Opers.--VeriFone, Inc., Redwood City, CA; *U.S. Public*, pg. 815
Palmer, Thomas D., V.P.-Mfg.--E.D. Bullard Company, Cynthiana, KY; *U.S. Private*, pg. 180
Paloch, Dave, Dir.-Mfg.--Perry's Ice Cream Co., Inc., Akron, NY; *U.S. Private*, pg. 855
Pane, Philip, V.P.-Mfg. & Pur.--White Pine Software, Nashua, NH; *U.S. Private*, pg. 1173
Papera, Joseph F., V.P.-Mfg.--Allstate Can Corporation, Parsippany, NJ; *U.S. Private*, pg. 44
Parent, Lucien N., V.P.-Mfg. Svcs.--Donohue Inc., Quebec, Canada; *Int'l*, pg. 1075

Parent, Mick, V.P.-Opers.--Grist Mill Company, Lakeville, MN; *U.S. Public*, pg. 766

Paris, Richard R., V.P.-Production--Chiron Corporation, Saint Louis, MO; *U.S. Public*, pg. 350

Paris, Robert, V.P.-Opers.--J. Crew Group, Inc., New York, NY; *U.S. Private*, pg. 1078

Parish, Richard L., III, V.P.-Mfg.--American Flange & Manufacturing Co. Inc., Carol Stream, IL; *Int'l*, pg. 1146

Park, Dave, V.P. & Dir.-Technology--Bird Machine Company, South Walpole, MA; *U.S. Public*, pg. 166

Parke, John O., V.P.-Mfg.--Freedom Forge Corporation, Burnham, PA; *U.S. Private*, pg. 425

Parker, Gerhard H., Sr. V.P. & Gen. Mgr.-Tech. & Mfg. Group--Intel Corporation, Santa Clara, CA; *U.S. Public*, pg. 886

Parker, Patricia M., Dir.-Mfg.--Advanced Magnetics, Inc., Cambridge, MA; *U.S. Public*, pg. 20

Parnell, William, V.P.-Mfg.--PSC Inc., Webster, NY; *U.S. Public*, pg. 1245

Parr, Craig, V.P.-Mfg.--Durakon Industries, Inc., Lapeer, MI; *U.S. Public*, pg. 537

Parrish, Robert, Mgr.-Mfg.--Perry Products, Hainesport, NJ; *U.S. Private*, pg. 855

Parrott, R., Grp. Mgr.-Mfg. Services--Laporte plc, Luton, United Kingdom; *Int'l*, pg. 801

Parrott, Rex, V.P.-Customer Satisfaction--Wyandot Inc., Marion, OH; *U.S. Private*, pg. 1193

Parsons, Earl B., Jr., V.P.-Power Generation & Transmission--Gulf Power Company, Pensacola, FL; *U.S.* Public, pg. 1490

Pasley, Tony, Dir.-Mfg.--Danskin, York, PA; *U.S. Public*, pg. 483

Passariello, Eugene, V.P.-Mfg.--General Bearing Corp., West Nyack, NY; *U.S. Public*, pg. 706

Passaro, Louis C., V.P.-Mfg.--Telecommunications Group, Gaithersburg, MD; *U.S. Public*, pg. 1745

Pateet, George, V.P.-Mfg.--National Safety Associates, Memphis, TN; *U.S. Private*, pg. 786

Patel, Arvind A., Exec. V.P.-Mfg. & Engrng.--Intermatic Inc., Spring Grove, IL; *U.S. Private*, pg. 567

Patel, Girish A., Mgr.-Plant--Superior Dairy, Inc., Canton, OH; *U.S. Private*, pg. 1054

Patel, Mahendra, Pres., Chief Exec. Officer & Gen. Mgr.--Philway Products, Inc., Ashland, OH; *U.S. Private*, pg. 862

Patel, Mayor, Plant Mgr.--Capsonic Group, Inc., Elgin, IL; *U.S. Private*, pg. 207

Patel, Roy, Mgr.-Mfg.--Weiser Lock, Tucson, AZ; *U.S. Public*, pg. 1053

Patkay, Jean-Pierre, V.P.-Mfg./Enterprise Sys.--3Com Corporation, Santa Clara, CA; *U.S. Public*, pg. 1603

Patrick, Michael, Dir.-Opers.--Interstate Electronics Corp., Anaheim, CA; *U.S. Public*, pg. 622

Pattarino, Eduardo, Mgr.-Mfg.--Baccardi-Martini Uruguay S.A., Montevideo, Uruguay; *U.S. Private*, pg. 109

Patterson, Deb, Dir.-Mfg.--The Vermont Teddy Bear Company, Inc., Shelburne, VT; *U.S. Public*, pg. 1716

Patton, Bruce, V.P.-Bus. Devel.--Northern Telecom Inc., Rochester, NY; *Int'l*, pg. 970

Patton, Robert, Mgr.-Mfg.--McDowell Mfg. Co. Inc., Du Bois, PA; *U.S. Private*, pg. 300

Paulik, Michael, V.P.-Mfg. Opers.--Alza Corporation, Palo Alto, CA; *U.S. Public*, pg. 62

Paull, Mitchell S., V.P. & Treas.--Aaron Rents, Inc., Atlanta, GA; *U.S. Public*, pg. 12

Pauls, Charles W., Chief Engr.--National Cooperative Refinery Association, Mc Pherson, KS; *U.S. Private*, pg. 781

Paulson, Bob, V.P.-Mfg.--Maytag Company, Newton, IA; *U.S. Public*, pg. 1064

Pavao, Manuel, Engr.--Whaling Industries, Inc., Fall River, MA; *U.S. Private*, pg. 1170

Pawelski, Mark, V.P. & Gen. Mgr.-Mfg.--Daubert Chemical Company, Inc., Chicago, IL; *U.S. Private*, pg. 313

Pawley, Dennis K., Exec. V.P.-Mfg.--Chrysler Corporation, Auburn Hills, MI; *U.S. Public*, pg. 352

Pawlowsky, Hal, Mgr.-Engrng.--Fill-Rite Division, Fort Wayne, IN; *U.S. Private*, pg. 1110

Paxton, Gary C., V.P.-Mfg.--Hormel Foods Corp., Austin, MN; *U.S. Public*, pg. 840

Payne, Mike, Mgr.-Mfg.--Cucina Classica Italiana, Inc., Lakewood, NJ; *U.S. Public*, pg. 1435

Payne, Steve B., V.P.-Mfg./Intercomp Div.--Communication Cable, Inc., Sanford, NC; *U.S. Public*, pg. 968

Pearlman, Dan, V.P.-Mfg.--Reading Body Works, Inc., Reading, PA; *U.S. Private*, pg. 913

Pearse, J., Grp. V.P.-Engrng.--Leviton Mfg. Co., Inc., Little Neck, NY; *U.S. Private*, pg. 663

Pearson, David, Dir.-Mfg. & Intl. Best Practice--Guilford Europe, Ltd., Derby, United Kingdom; *U.S. Public*, pg. 769

Pearson, Terry, Mgr.-Mfg.--Durst Div., Beloit, WI; *U.S. Public*, pg. 1370

Pease, David H., III, V.P.-Engrng., Mfg. & Sec.--Pease Industries, Inc., Fairfield, OH; *U.S. Private*, pg. 845

Peck, Thomas A., Sr. V.P.-Mfg.--Starcraft Automotive Group, Inc., Goshen, IN; *U.S. Public*, pg. 1511

Pedersen, Arnie, V.P.-Mfg.--Handgards Inc., Northbrook, IL; *U.S. Private*, pg. 499

Pellerin, Richard, V.P.-Mfg.--Morrison Berkshire Inc., North Adams, MA; *U.S. Private*, pg. 762

Pello, Joanne, Sr. V.P.-Mfg. & Inventory--Book of the Month Club, New York, NY; *U.S. Public*, pg. 1612

Pemberton, Alan, Mgr.-New Prods.--Austral Bronze Crane Copper Limited, Wetherill Park, Australia; *Int'l*, pg. 340

Pendleton, Roger, Mgr.-Mfg., U.K.--Pneumatic Div., Cannock, United Kingdom; *U.S. Public*, pg. 1264

Pennington, David W., Mgr.-Mfg.--Detection Systems, Inc., Fairport, NY; *U.S. Public*, pg. 501

Pennington, Linda, V.P.-Opers.--Brothers Gourmet Coffees, Inc., Boca Raton, FL; *U.S. Public*, pg. 259

Pepper, C.J., Dir.-Mfg.--Cyanamid of Great Britain Ltd., Gosport, United Kingdom; *U.S. Public*, pg. 81

Pereira, Robert, V.P.-Opers.--AFC Cable Systems, Inc., Providence, RI; *U.S. Public*, pg. 6

Perez Ramirez, Pedro, Plant Mgr.--Eagle-Picher Espana, S.A., Soria, Spain; *U.S. Private*, pg. 355

Perillo, John, V.P.-Opers.--The Topps Company, Inc., New York, NY; *U.S. Public*, pg. 1621

Peroni, Peter, V.P.-Engrng.--La France Corporation, Philadelphia, PA; *U.S. Private*, pg. 640

Perrin, Jean Marc, Dir.-Prod--Jade S.A., Saint Mesmin, France; *Int'l*, pg. 859

Perry, G.B., Dir.-Production--Stafford-Miller Limited, Welwyn Garden City, United Kingdom; *U.S. Public*, pg. 237

Perry, Robert, V.P.-Mfg. Opers.--Mercury Computer Systems, Inc., Chelmsford, MA; *U.S. Private*, pg. 732

Peters, Anne-Francoise, Mgr.-Mfg. & Site Devel.-Pumps--S.A. Durco Europe N.V., Petit-Rechain, Belgium; *U.S. Public*, pg. 659

Peters, Greg, V.P.-Mfg.--Rohr, Inc., Chula Vista, CA; *U.S. Public*, pg. 751

Petersen, Gary L., V.P.-Mfg.--Powerine Oil Company, Santa Fe Springs, CA; *U.S. Public*, pg. 314

Peterson, Lowell, Dir.-Mfg.--Dayco PTI, Inc., Red Wing, MN; *U.S. Public*, pg. 1045

Peterson, Marland, Plant Mgr.--Western States Envelope Co., Milwaukee, WI; *U.S. Private*, pg. 1168

Peterson, Ron, Mgr.-Mfg.--Hull Corporation, Hatboro, PA; *U.S. Private*, pg. 547

Petit, Henri D., Chief Oper. Officer-Tech., Mfg. & Prod. Devel.--Eastman Kodak Company, Rochester, NY; *U.S. Public*, pg. 550

Petko, Daniel, Mgr.-Mfg. & Procurement--R.P. Adams Company, Inc., Tonawanda, NY; *U.S. Public*, pg. 19

Petoin, Jean-Claude, Dir.-Programming--Arianespace SA, Evry, France; *Int'l*, pg. 81

Petote, Tom, Mgr.-Engrng.--Genesee Metal Stampings, Inc., West Henrietta, NY; *U.S. Private*, pg. 446

Petrei, Massino, Chief Engr.--Dunmore Corporation, Newtown, PA; *U.S. Private*, pg. 346

Petrie, Dale, Dir.-Engrng. & Mgr.-Prod.--Sommer Metalcraft Corporation, Crawfordsville, IN; *U.S. Private*, pg. 1013

Petroungarung, Songsri, Asst. Mng. Dir.--Bangkok Athletic Co., Ltd., Bangkok, Thailand; *Int'l*, pg. 146

Petrovs, Valdis, V.P.-Mfg., U.S. Automotive Rubber Group--Dearborn Division, Dearborn, MI; *U.S. Public*, pg. 1504

Petschke, Robert L, V.P.-Mfg.--Brown & Bigelow, Inc., Saint Paul, MN; *U.S. Private*, pg. 172

Pettinger, Ron, Mgr.-Production--Industrial Bag Division - Louisville Plant, Louisville, KY; *U.S. Public*, pg. 1521

Pezo, M.S., Dir.-Mfg.--Preformed Line Products, Cleveland, OH; *U.S. Public*, pg. 1321

Pfander, Wilhelm, V.P.-Mfg. & Prod. Devel.--Penobscot Shoe Company, Old Town, ME; *U.S. Public*, pg. 1273

Pfeiffer, Hal, V.P.-Mfg.--Unex Conveying Systems, Inc., Jackson, NJ; *U.S. Private*, pg. 1117

Philip, Harold, V.P.-Cement Mfg.--Lone Star Industries, Inc., Stamford, CT; *U.S. Public*, pg. 1012

Philipp, Gerald A., V.P.-Mfg.--SBE, Inc., San Ramon, CA; *U.S. Public*, pg. 1416

Philips, Donald, V.P.-Prod. Devel.--Dayco Swan Corporation, Worthington, OH; *U.S. Public*, pg. 1045

Phillip, Jim, V.P.-Mfg. & Opers.--Desa International, Bowling Green, KY; *U.S. Private*, pg. 326

Phillipi, J., V.P.-Mfg.--R.A. Industries, Inc., Lansdale, PA; *U.S. Private*, pg. 902

Phillips, David, V.P.-Opers.--Kamax-G.B. DuPont L.P., Troy, MI; *U.S. Private*, pg. 606

Phillips, Gregory, V.P.-Mfg.--Hougen Manufacturing Inc., Swartz Creek, MI; *U.S. Private*, pg. 541

Phillips, I.R., V.P.-Mfg.--Ames Company, Parkersburg, WV; *U.S. Public*, pg. 1683

Phillips, Jimmy R., V.P.-Mfg.--Great Dane Trailers, Inc., Savannah, GA; *U.S. Private*, pg. 1030

Phillips, Les, V.P.-Mfg.--Keystone Steel & Wire Co., Peoria, IL; *U.S. Public*, pg. 955

Phillips, William F., Sr. V.P.-Film Production--Columbia TriStar Television, Culver City, CA; *Int'l*, pg. 1282

Philpott, D.K., Prod. Mgr.--MB-Clarke Ltd., Peterborough, United Kingdom; *Int'l*, pg. 386

Philpott, Joseph, Exec. V.P.-Mfg.--Bassett Furniture Industries, Incorporated, Bassett, VA; *U.S. Public*, pg. 193

Phogat, M.S., Mgr-Production--Tata McGraw-Hill Publishing Co., Private Limited, New Delhi, India; *U.S. Public*, pg. 1072

Piatz, Julius, Mgr.-Mfg.--Steiner Co., Inc., Chicago, IL; *U.S. Private*, pg. 1039

Picata, Charles, Mgr.-Production--Pace Press, Inc., Moonachie, NJ; *U.S. Private*, pg. 829

Pick, Richard, V.P.-Engrng., Exploration & Devel.--ARCO Coal Company, Denver, CO; *U.S. Public*, pg. 144

Piec, C.J., V.P.-Mfg.--Duraco Products, Inc., Streamwood, IL; *U.S. Private*, pg. 348

Piecuch, Andrew J., Mgr.-Prod.--Hazen Paper Company, Holyoke, MA; *U.S. Private*, pg. 514

Pierantoni, Joe, V.P.-Mfg.--Medstone International, Inc., Aliso Viejo, CA; *U.S. Public*, pg. 1082

Pierce, Ed, V.P.-Production--Ash Grove Cement Company, Shawnee Mission, KS; *U.S. Private*, pg. 87

Pierce, Patrick, V.P.-Mfg.--Austin Productions, Inc., Holbrook, NY; *U.S. Private*, pg. 100

Pilliter, Charles, Mgr.-Mfg.--Certified Grocers of California, Los Angeles, CA; *U.S. Private*, pg. 226

Pilsy, Chuck, Dir.-Opers. & Supvr.-Graphics--Continental Plastic Card Co., Coral Springs, FL; *U.S. Private*, pg. 269

Pim, Robert, V.P.-Mfg.--Gundle/SLT Environmental, Inc., Houston, TX; *U.S. Public*, pg. 769

Pine, Wong Yung, Chief Oper. Officer--GB Holdings, Jurong, Singapore; *Int'l*, pg. 531

Pipkin, Luther N., Jr., V.P.-Appliance & Electronics--W.S. Badcock Corporation, Mulberry, FL; *U.S. Private*, pg. 109

Pipkin, Wayne M., Mgr.-Matls.--Superior Machine Company Of South Carolina, Inc., Florence, SC; *U.S. Private*, pg. 1055

Pipkorn, David, Gen. Mgr.-Mfg.--Hanover Direct, Inc., Weehawken, NJ; *U.S. Public*, pg. 782

Pipkorn, David, Gen. Mgr.-Mfg.--American Down & Textile Company, La Crosse, WI; *U.S. Public*, pg. 782

Pirchl, Helmut, Exec. V.P.-Sulzer Ruti Group--Sulzer Ltd., Winterthur, Switzerland; *Int'l*, pg. 1305

Pitcher, Max G., Exec. V.P.-Exploration & Production--Conoco Inc., Houston, TX; *U.S. Public*, pg. 531

Pittenger, Wayne A., V.P.-Opers.--Sequent Computer Systems, Inc., Beaverton, OR; *U.S. Public*, pg. 1459

Pitts, Derrill, V.P.-Mfg. Opers.--Chattem, Inc., Chattanooga, TN; *U.S. Public*, pg. 341

Plagens, Siegfried G., Brewmaster & Plant Mgr.--Minnesota Brewing Company, Saint Paul, MN; *U.S. Public*, pg. 1115

Plank, Robert, V.P.-Opers.--ACCO Canada Inc., Willowdale, Canada; *U.S. Public*, pg. 674

Plasse, E., V.P.-Mfg.--Sterling Davis Standard, South Plainfield, NJ; *Int'l*, pg. 1240

Plattner, Robert F., V.P.-Engrng.--Lincoln Foodservice Products, Inc., Fort Wayne, IN; *Int'l*, pg. 188

Plewinski, Frank A., Plant Mgr.--Saint-Gobain Advanced Materials Corporation, Louisville, KY; *Int'l*, pg. 1173

Pliner, Tom, Gen. Mgr.-Mfg.--Good Companies, Carson, CA; *U.S. Private*, pg. 463

Plomske, T.I., Mgr.-Brand & Mdsg.--Shell Canada Ltd., Calgary, Canada; *Int'l*, pg. 1138

Plymale, Corbin, Dir.-Mfg.--Galileo Corp., Sturbridge, MA; *U.S. Public*, pg. 698

Poccurel, R., Mgr.-Eng. & Mfg.--APLI Combustion, S.A., Barcelona, Spain; *U.S. Private*, pg. 361

Podeschi, David, Mgr.-Merchandise--Ito-Yokado Capitol Division, Alexandria, VA; *Int'l*, pg. 694

Poe, Lynn, Sr. V.P.-Mfg.--Whitin Roberts Co., Sanford, NC; *U.S. Private*, pg. 309

Pofelski, Daniel V., V.P.-Mfg.--Herbert Malarkey Roofing Company, Portland, OR; *U.S. Private*, pg. 698

Pohl, Hermann H., Exec. V.P.-Logistics & Manufacturing--Kraft Jacobs Suchard AG, Zurich, Switzerland; *U.S. Public*, pg. 1288

Polhmann, Edgar, Dir.-Mfg.--Ceras Johnson Ltda., Rio de Janeiro, Brazil; *U.S. Private*, pg. 593

Polizzi, Frank, V.P.-Opers.--Farmland Dairies, Wallington, NJ; *U.S. Private*, pg. 395

Pollansky, Emil, Dir.-Mfg. & Engrng.--Cortland Line Co., Inc., Cortland, NY; *U.S. Private*, pg. 277

Polzin, James J., V.P.-Mfg.--Monarch Ware, Inc., Algoma, WI; *U.S. Private*, pg. 735

Pombo, Eliseo, V.P.-Mfg.--Prime Tanning Co., Inc., Rochester, NH; *U.S. Private*, pg. 884

Pond, Randall E., V.P.-Mfg. Order Fulfillment--Cisco Systems, Inc., San Jose, CA; *U.S. Public*, pg. 375

Ponzi, Larry, Mgr.-Production--Buffalo Law Journal, Buffalo, NY; *U.S. Private*, pg. 19

Pope, Gary, V.P.-Mfg.--George Fischer Sloane, Inc., Little Rock, AR; *Int'l*, pg. 430

Popiel, Ronald D., V.P.-Mfg.--Kewaunee Scientific Corporation, Statesville, NC; *U.S. Public*, pg. 953

Poradek, Frank, Mgr.-Mfg. & Plant Mgr.--R.S. Owens, Chicago, IL; *U.S. Private*, pg. 824

Porter, Abel, Sr. V.P.-Intermountain Reg.--Smith's Food & Drug Centers, Inc., Salt Lake City, UT; *U.S. Public*, pg. 1103

Porter, Chris, Dir.-Prod. Devel.--Go-Video, Inc., Scottsdale, AZ; *U.S. Public*, pg. 748

Post, Jerry, Mgr.-Mfg.--Hubbard Hall Inc., Waterbury, CT; *U.S. Private*, pg. 544

Post, Sarah, V.P.-Admin. Services--C. B. Fleet Co., Inc., Lynchburg, VA; *U.S. Private*, pg. 410

Postlewait, Timothy R., V.P.-Plant Opers.--Bayou Steel Corporation, La Place, LA; *U.S. Public*, pg. 197

Poteete, Carl, V.P.-Mfg.--Applied Microsystems Corporation, Redmond, WA; *U.S. Public*, pg. 123

Potts, John, Dir.-Pur. & Mgr.-Mfg.--World Dryer Corp., Berkeley, IL; *U.S. Public*, pg. 1497

Pougher, D., Dir.-Production--British Gypsum Ltd., Loughborough, United Kingdom; *Int'l*, pg. 122

Powell, David, Grp. V.P.-Mfg.--Solvay Pharmaceuticals, Inc., Marietta, GA; *Int'l*, pg. 1278

Powell, Joe, V.P.-Feed Mfg.--MFA Incorporated, Columbia, MO; *U.S. Private*, pg. 686

Powers, Jerry W., V.P.-Mfr.--Kingsbury, Inc., Philadelphia, PA; *U.S. Private*, pg. 622

Powers, John M., V.P.-Energy Supply--Commonwealth Energy System, Electric Division, Cambridge, MA; *U.S. Public*, pg. 414

Powers, Joseph W., V.P.-Mfg.--Keystone Valvtron, Inc., Houston, TX; *U.S. Public*, pg. 1650

Powers, Mike T., V.P.-Mfg.--RELA, Inc., Boulder, CO; *U.S. Public*, pg. 401

Powers, Ralph F., V.P.-Mfg.--Geneva Steel, Vineyard, UT; *U.S. Public*, pg. 729

Powers, Tom, V.P.-Fleet--United States Bakery, Portland, OR; *U.S. Private*, pg. 1124

Prah, Joel, Dir.-Quality Control--Electronic Tele-Communications, Inc., Waukesha, WI; *U.S. Public*, pg. 570

Preisel, Thomas G., V.P.-Opers., Sls. & Mktg.--Baltek Corporation, Northvale, NJ; *U.S. Public*, pg. 171

Prest, Charles, Mgr.-Opers.--Victor Corporation, West Warwick, RI; *U.S. Private*, pg. 1138

Price, Gerald F., Exec. V.P.-Mfg. & Engrng.--Barr Laboratories Inc., Pomona, NY; *U.S. Public*, pg. 191

Price, James E., V.P.-Mfg. Flooring--Triangle Pacific Corporation, Dallas, TX; *U.S. Public*, pg. 1634

Price, Joseph, V.P.-Mfg. & Sec.--Dettra Flag Company, Oaks, PA; *U.S. Private*, pg. 328

Price, R.K., Sr. Exec. V.P.-Mining & Mfg.--R.T. Vanderbilt Company, Inc., Norwalk, CT; *U.S. Private*, pg. 1133

Price, W. Ralph, Exec. V.P.--Doron Precision Systems, Inc., Binghamton, NY; *U.S. Private*, pg. 341

Pride, Harvey, Jr., V.P.-Mfg.--Lakeland Industries, Inc., Ronkonkoma, NY; *U.S. Public*, pg. 975

Pridgen, Arthur, Mgr.-Production--Brigadier Homes of North Carolina, Nashville, NC; *U.S. Public*, pg. 318

Priester, Rick, Supvr.-Mfg.--The Felters Company, Roebuck, SC; *U.S. Private*, pg. 400
Prinsloo, L., Mgr.-Metallurgical--Libanon Division, Libanon, South Africa; *Int'l*, pg. 738
Prior, Kenneth, V.P.-Mfg.--Ervin Industries, Inc., Ann Arbor, MI; *U.S. Private*, pg. 382
Prischak, Dennis J., V.P.-Engrng.--Plastek Group, Erie, PA; *U.S. Private*, pg. 870
Pritchard, Robert, Technical Dir.-Consumer Brands--SmithKline Beecham Corporation, Philadelphia, PA; *Int'l*, pg. 1264
Profeta, J.F., Mgr.-Mfg.--ITT Jabsco, Costa Mesa, CA; *U.S. Public*, pg. 860
Props, Kent, V.P.-Mfr.--Warren Industries, Inc., Lafayette, IN; *U.S. Private*, pg. 945
Protheroe, Alwyn, Chief Engineer--Cowin & Company, Inc., Birmingham, AL; *U.S. Private*, pg. 280
Prow, Thomas, V.P.-Mfg.--Fruit of the Loom, Inc., Chicago, IL; *U.S. Public*, pg. 685
Pruitt, William, V.P.-Mfg.--International Envelope Company, Exton, PA; *U.S. Public*, pg. 70
Pryde, Rick, V.P.-Production/McCain Foods (Canada)--McCain Foods Limited, Florenceville, Canada; *Int'l*, pg. 850
Przebylski, Dave, Mgr.-Mfg.--Times Printing Company, Inc., Random Lake, WI; *U.S. Private*, pg. 1087
Pugliese, Joseph, V.P.-Mfg.--Brodart Company, Williamsport, PA; *U.S. Private*, pg. 170
Pulizzano, Joel, Mgr.-Plant--Joseph Huber Brewing Co., Inc., Monroe, WI; *U.S. Private*, pg. 545
Pultz, Arthur, Mgr.-Production & Quality Control Coord.--Strahman Valves, Inc., Florham Park, NJ; *U.S. Private*, pg. 1046
Puwalski, Richard, V.P.-Mfg.--Surgical Specialties, Reading, PA; *U.S. Private*, pg. 1056
Pye, E. Kendall, Dr., V.P.-Science & Tech.--Repap New Brunswick Inc., Montreal, Canada; *Int'l*, pg. 1104
Pyle, Jay, V.P.-Mfg.--General Automation, Inc., Irvine, CA; *U.S. Public*, pg. 706
Pyle, Jim, V.P.-Mfg.--Landa, Inc., Portland, OR; *U.S. Private, pg. 646*
Pyron, A.T., Dir.-Engrng.--Delta Air Lines, Inc., Atlanta, GA; *U.S. Public*, pg. 497
Pyryemybida, Stephen J., Dir.-Process Optimization--Northrop Grumman Corporation, Los Angeles, CA; *U.S. Public*, pg. 1197
Quadracci, Thomas A., Pres.-Quad/Tech. & V.P.-Mfg. & Tech.--Quad/Graphics, Inc., Pewaukee, WI; *U.S. Private, pg. 897*
Qualigari, Fred, Mgr.-Production--Nexus Plastics, Inc., Hawthorne, NJ; *U.S. Private*, pg. 797
Quam, Roger D., V.P.-Composite Matls.--Sheldahl, Inc., Northfield, MN; *U.S. Public*, pg. 1465
Quance, C. Murray, V.P.-Mfg.--Bestop, Inc., Broomfield, CO; *Int'l*, pg. 830
Quasey, James, Plant Mgr.-Mfg.--Respironics, Inc., Pittsburgh, PA; *U.S. Public*, pg. 1383
Queen, Bill, V.P.-Engrng.--Baldwin Hardware Corporation, Reading, PA; *U.S. Public*, pg. 1053
Query, William, V.P.-Opers.--Gaston County Dyeing Machine Co., Mount Holly, NC; *U.S. Private*, pg. 441
Quievre, Claude, Adjoint Dir. Gen. & Dir.-Tech. & Indus.--Arianespace SA, Evry, France; *Int'l*, pg. 81
Quigley, Richard M., V.P.-Mfg.--Cogsdill Tool Products, Inc., Lugoff, SC; *U.S. Private*, pg. 250
Quinn, Stephen E., V.P.-Nuclear Power--Consolidated Edison Company of New York, Inc., New York, NY; *U.S. Public*, pg. 434
Rabion, Dawn, V.P.-Mfg.--Season-All Industries, Inc., Indiana, PA; *Int'l*, pg. 267
Rabold, David C., V.P.-Mfg. Div.--Fuller Company, Bethlehem, PA; *Int'l*, pg. 475
Race, Kevin S., V.P.-Mfg.--Crowe Rope Industries L.L.C., Waterville, ME; *U.S. Private*, pg. 291
Rackard, T., Dir.-Prod. Planning & Devel.--Binning's Building Products, Inc., Lexington, NC; *U.S. Public*, pg. 67
Rackow, Martin, Maintenance Engr.--Andes Candies Inc., Delavan, WI; *U.S. Private*, pg. 163
Radcliffe, Kenneth, V.P.-Aerosol Mfg.--Precision Valve Corporation, Yonkers, NY; *U.S. Private*, pg. 880
Rade, Henry, V.P.-Mfg.--American Louver Co., Skokie, IL; *U.S. Private*, pg. 58
Radford, Enoch, V.P. & Sec.--Plant Maintenance Service Corporation, Memphis, TN; *U.S. Private*, pg. 869
Raezler, Don, V.P.-Opers.--McCain Citrus Inc., Oak Brook, IL; *Int'l*, pg. 850
Ragogna, Don, V.P.-Mfg.--General Time Corp., Norcross, GA; *U.S. Private*, pg. 445
Rahmede, Rainer, Mgr.-Mfg.--EOC Formsystem GmbH, Mahlberg, Germany; *Int'l*, pg. 75
Rahmede, Raner, Mgr.-Mfg.--EOC Normalien GmbH & Co. KG, Ludenscheid, Germany; *Int'l*, pg. 75
Rahn, Bill, V.P.-Engrng.--Reading Body Works, Inc., Reading, PA; *U.S. Private*, pg. 913
Raines, Larry R., V.P.-Mfg. Prod.--Manitowoc Debanking Technology, Memphis, TN; *U.S. Private*, pg. 518
Raman, Georges, Dir.-Mdsg.--Laboratoire LaChartre S.A., Blois, France; *U.S. Public*, pg. 1331
Ramano, Anthony, V.P.-Mfg. & Distr.--Hachette Filipacchi Magazines Inc., New York, NY; *Int'l*, pg. 794
Ramirez, Gloria, Producer-Audio Video--Quest Medical, Inc., Allen, TX; *U.S. Public*, pg. 1352
Ramsay, Charles, V.P.-Engrng.--Plasti-Line, Inc., Knoxville, TN; *U.S. Public*, pg. 1308
Ramsey, Matthewson, V.P.-Mfg.--LEGO Systems, Inc., Enfield, CT; *Int'l*, pg. 805
Ramsey, William M., V.P.-Mfg.-PCB Operations--COMPAQ Computer Corporation, Houston, TX; *U.S. Public*, pg. 417
Randall, Richard C., V.P.-Engrng. Svcs.--Saunders Brothers, Westbrook, ME; *U.S. Private*, pg. 968
Randles, Darrell, Plant Mgr.--Fleischer Manufacturing, Inc., Columbus, NE; *U.S. Private*, pg. 410
Rankin, Diana, Mgr.-Production--American City Business Journals, Inc., Houston, TX; *U.S. Private*, pg. 19
Ranson, Dan L., V.P.-Mfg.--Clayton Corporation, Fenton, MO; *U.S. Private*, pg. 244
Rapage, Louis, Dir.-Program., Promo., & Prod.--KERO-TV, Bakersfield, CA; *U.S. Public*, pg. 1070
Rapelje, Nate, Mgr.-Warehouse--Ebeling & Reuss Company, Allentown, PA; *U.S. Private*, pg. 358
Rapisarda, Oscar, Mgr.-Mfg.--Fate S.A., San Fernando, Argentina; *Int'l*, pg. 478
Rappange, L., Dir.-Tech. & Prod.--Honig Foods-B.V., Koog aan de Zaan, Netherlands; *Int'l*, pg. 244
Rasmussen, Neil E., V.P.-Engrng.--American Power Conversion Corporation, West Kingston, RI; *U.S. Public*, pg. 89
Rasor, John F., Sr. V.P.-Forest Resources--Georgia-Pacific Corporation, Atlanta, GA; *U.S. Public*, pg. 735
Ratchford, Bob, Pres.-Mfg.--Shurfine International, Inc., Northlake, IL; *U.S. Private*, pg. 997
Rathkamp, Hermann, Dir.-Mfg. & Matls.--Baker Hughes INTEQ, Houston, TX; *U.S. Public*, pg. 166
Ratliff, Gary, V.P.-Mfg.--International Women's Apparel Group, Easton, PA; *U.S. Public*, pg. 796
Rauscher, Tom, V.P.-Mfg. & Distr.--Tab Products Co., Palo Alto, CA; *U.S. Public*, pg. 1559
Rawlinson, Donald M., V.P.-Production, Bristol Bay Opers.--Peter Pan Seafoods, Inc., Seattle, WA; *Int'l*, pg. 928
Rawls, Brian, Sr. V.P.-S. Zone Domestic Mfg.--Haggar Corporation, Dallas, TX; *U.S. Public*, pg. 774
Ray, Russell A., V.P.-Engrng.--LDDS WorldCom, Tulsa, OK; *U.S. Public*, pg. 1779
Razavi, Fred, V.P.-Mfg.--Glastic Corporation, Cleveland, OH; *Int'l*, pg. 740
Razavi, Fred, Dir.-Mfg.--Glastic Corporation, Cleveland, OH; *Int'l*, pg. 740
Reale, Michael A., Sr. V.P.-Mfg.--Boca Research Inc., Boca Raton, FL; *U.S. Public*, pg. 239
Reardon, Hugh, V.P.-Quality Assurance--Marathon Electric Manufacturing Corp., Wausau, WI; *U.S. Public*, pg. 1371
Rebelo, Jose G., Dir. Gen.-Exploration & Production--Petrofina S.A., Brussels, Belgium; *Int'l*, pg. 1043
Reber, R.E., Jr., Gen. Mgr.-Melting & Large Bar Mfg.--Carpenter Specialty Alloys Operations, Reading, PA; *U.S. Public*, pg. 307
Rebilas, J., Plant Superintendent--American Inks & Coatings Corp., Phoenixville, PA; *U.S. Private*, pg. 56
Rebmann, Manfred, V.P.-Engrng., Mfg. & Service--Bosch Packaging Machinery Division, South Plainfield, NJ; *Int'l*, pg. 204
Reddick, T., Dir.-Mfg.--Hepworth Building Products Limited, Stocksbridge, United Kingdom; *Int'l*, pg. 615
Redeker, Alan E., V.P.-Mfg.--Medusa Corporation, Cleveland, OH; *U.S. Public*, pg. 1084
Redfield, Carl, V.P.-Mfg. & Logistics--Cisco Systems, Inc., San Jose, CA; *U.S. Public*, pg. 375
Reed, Cindi, Mgr.-Mfg.--Aaron Brothers, Inc., City of Commerce, CA; *U.S. Public*, pg. 1104
Reed, Kevin, V.P.-Mfg.--Wisconsin Pharmacal Co., Inc., Jackson, WI; *U.S. Private*, pg. 1185
Reeher, Dan, Mgr.-Mfg.--Target Stamped Products Corp., Kinsman, OH; *U.S. Private*, pg. 1069
Reese, Donald E., Sr. V.P.-Mfg.--ACF Industries, Inc., Saint Charles, MO; *U.S. Private*, pg. 556
Regula, Keith, Dir.-Mfg.--Emcee Broadcast Products, Inc., White Haven, PA; *U.S. Public*, pg. 570
Reichelt, Dieter, Dr., Mng. Dir.-Admin. & Mfg.--Hermann Pfauter GmbH & Co., Ludwigsburg, Germany; *Int'l*, pg. 617
Reichert, Thomas A., M.D., V.P.-Medical Affairs--Becton Dickinson & Company, Franklin Lakes, NJ; *U.S. Public*, pg. 199
Reid, Jack R., Exec. V.P.-Refining--Holly Corporation, Dallas, TX; *U.S. Public*, pg. 830
Reilly, Trip, V.P.-Mfg.--Sherman & Reilly, Inc., Chattanooga, TN; *U.S. Private*, pg. 993
Reinhardt, Dave, Mgr.-Mfg.--Nematron Corp., Ann Arbor, MI; *U.S. Private*, pg. 791
Reister, Mike, V.P.-Mfg.--Alloy Products Corp, Waukesha, WI; *U.S. Private*, pg. 42
Reiszel, John, Mgr.-Mfg.--Champion Aluminum Window Corporation, Syosset, NY; *U.S. Private*, pg. 227
Remish, Joe, Mgr.-Mfg.--Pittsburgh Tube Monaca Div., Monaca, PA; *U.S. Private*, pg. 868
Renaud, Paul F., Jr., V.P.-Engrng.--Kysor/Warren, Conyers, GA; *U.S. Public*, pg. 1445
Renfro, James Gregory, V.P.-Mfg.--Varco BJ Drilling Systems, Orange, CA; *U.S. Public*, pg. 1709
Rensi, E. Samuel, Exec. V.P.-Mfg.--Remington Arms Company, Inc., Madison, NC; *U.S. Private*, pg. 921
Renwick, Vaughn, V.P.-Mfg.--Wangner Systems Corporation, Greenville, SC; *Int'l*, pg. 1418
Resnick, Al, Dir.-Assembly & Mfg.--TelCom Semiconductor, Inc., Mountain View, CA; *U.S. Public*, pg. 1569
Revell, Ronald F., Dir.-Mdsg.--White Hen Pantry, Inc., Elmhurst, IL; *U.S. Private*, pg. 1172
Revels, Ray V., Jr., V.P.-Distr. & Mfg.--Harris Teeter, Inc., Charlotte, NC; *U.S. Public*, pg. 1412
Reynen, John, Mgr.-Mfg.--AirTronics Co., Elgin, IL; *U.S. Public*, pg. 944
Reynolds, Robert L., V.P.-Mfg.--Standard-Knapp, Inc., Portland, CT; *U.S. Private*, pg. 1031
Reynolds, William D., Sr. V.P.-Mfg.--Varco-Pruden Buildings, Memphis, TN; *U.S. Public*, pg. 1677
Reznick, Jerry W., Mgr.-Production--Industrial Bag Division - Salt Lake City Plant, Salt Lake City, UT; *U.S. Public*, pg. 1521
Rheaume, Jean-Yves, V.P.-Opers.--Davie Industries Inc., Levis, Canada; *Int'l*, pg. 385
Rhein, Ralph, V.P.-Mfg.--Color Arts, Inc., Racine, WI; *U.S. Private*, pg. 254
Rheingrover, Robert, V.P.-Mfg.--George Lithograph, Brisbane, CA; *U.S. Private*, pg. 448
Rhodes, R.B., Dir.-Heat Recovery Systems--ABB Air Preheater Inc., Wellsville, NY; *Int'l*, pg. 3
Rhor, Jorge, Mgr.-Mfg.--Duro-Test Corporation, Fairfield, NJ; *U.S. Private*, pg. 349
Rice, Richard W., V.P.-Engrng.--Phelps Dodge Corporation, Phoenix, AZ; *U.S. Public*, pg. 1286
Rich, David M., Gen. Mgr.-Mfg.--Culligan International Company, Northbrook, IL; *U.S. Public*, pg. 467
Richard, Kevin P., V.P.-Mfg., Engrng. & Maint.--Mohawk Paper Mills, Inc., Cohoes, NY; *U.S. Private*, pg. 755
Richards, D.A., V.P.-Mfg.--Research Products Corporation, Madison, WI; *U.S. Private*, pg. 924
Richards, Evan, V.P.-Opers. & Engrng.--Ameritech Cellular and Paging Services, Hoffman Estates, IL; *U.S. Public*, pg. 98
Richards, Ken, V.P.-Mfg./Perception Div.--Brite Voice Systems, Inc., Heathrow, FL; *U.S. Public*, pg. 257
Richardson, Al, Dir.-Mfg.--Dwyer Instruments Inc., Michigan City, IN; *U.S. Private*, pg. 350
Richardson, L.J., V.P.-Mdse.--Heilig-Meyers Company, Richmond, VA; *U.S. Public*, pg. 804
Richie, Kevis F., V.P.-Engrng.--Vulcan Iron Works, Inc., Detroit, MI; *U.S. Private*, pg. 1144
Richmond, G., V.P.-Mfg.--Cresline Plastic Pipe Co. Inc., Evansville, IN; *U.S. Private*, pg. 289
Richter, W., Mgr.-Mfg.--Wallace Computer Services, Inc., Lisle, IL; *U.S. Public*, pg. 1735
Rico, Patsy, Mgr.-Production--Business Journal Publications, Inc., San Francisco, CA; *U.S. Private*, pg. 19
Riddle, Ivin, V.P.-Mfr.--Maxitrol Co., Southfield, MI; *U.S. Private*, pg. 716
Rieck, Robert E., V.P.-Opers.--Conap Inc., Olean, NY; *U.S. Private*, pg. 261
Riedel, Richard, Dir.-Mfg.--Baker Hughes INTEQ, Houston, TX; *U.S. Public*, pg. 166
Riegel, Tyrone E., Exec. V.P.-Mfg.--O'Sullivan Industries Holdings, Lamar, MO; *U.S. Public*, pg. 1234
Rinauro, Paul, V.P.-Retreading--The Hercules Tire & Rubber Company, Findlay, OH; *U.S. Private*, pg. 523
Rinehart, William, V.P.-Mfg.--Data Documents, Inc., Omaha, NE; *U.S. Public*, pg. 449
Ring, Randy, V.P.-Mfg.--Network Computing Devices, Inc., Mountain View, CA; *U.S. Public*, pg. 1168
Ringlet, Vincent, Mgr.-Mfg. & Site Devel.-Valves--S.A. Durco Europe N.V., Petit-Rechain, Belgium; *U.S. Public*, pg. 659
Rippe, Herb, V.P.-O.E.M.--Copeland Corporation, Sidney, OH; *U.S. Public*, pg. 573
Rippy, James B., Sr. V.P.-Mfg. Opers.--Continental General Tire, Inc., Charlotte, NC; *Int'l*, pg. 327
Risher, Ronald R., V.P.-Opers.--Cassens Transport Company, Edwardsville, IL; *U.S. Private*, pg. 219
Risimini, Ralph, V.P.-Mfg.--United Farm Tools, Inc., Glasgow, KY; *U.S. Private*, pg. 1122
Ritter, K.E., Dir.-Tech. Service Support, Heat Recovery Services--ABB Air Preheater Inc., Wellsville, NY; *Int'l*, pg. 3
Rivas, Guillermo, Sprvr.-Construction & Pur.--Windsor Fashions, Los Angeles, CA; *U.S. Private*, pg. 1182
Rivella, Ezio, Dr., Mng. Dir.-Montalcino--Banfi Vintners, Old Brookville, NY; *U.S. Private*, pg. 113
Rizner, Ken, V.P.-Mfg.--Hyde Manufacturing Co., Southbridge, MA; *U.S. Private*, pg. 551
Rizzi, Paul, Dr., Dir.-Technic--VP-Schickedanz AG, Nuremberg, Germany; *U.S. Public*, pg. 1333
Robb, William M., Grp. V.P.-Prods. Mfg.--Pennzoil Company, Houston, TX; *U.S. Public*, pg. 1272
Roberts, P., V.P.-Mfg.--Gemtron Corporation, Sweetwater, TN; *Int'l*, pg. 1523
Roberts, Vince, V.P.-Engrng. & Opers.--The Disney Channel, Burbank, CA; *U.S. Public*, pg. 513
Robertson, Andrew, Plant Mgr.--Amos-Hill Associates, Inc., Edinburgh, IN; *U.S. Private*, pg. 67
Robinson, Bruce, Div. Gen. Mgr.-BHP Reinforcing Prods.--Building & Industrial Products Division, Sydney, Australia; *Int'l*, pg. 225
Robinson, Gary, Mgr.-Production--Idaho Supreme Company, Firth, ID; *U.S. Private*, pg. 557
Robinson, J., Mgr.-Mfg.--Quality Bakers of America Cooperative, Inc., Greenwich, CT; *U.S. Private*, pg. 898
Robinson, Terry, V.P.-Engrng.--FATA Production Machinery, Cleveland, OH; *Int'l*, pg. 474
Robson, John, Dir.-Production--Blackwell Science, Oxford, United Kingdom; *Int'l*, pg. 197
Robson, M.K., V.P.-Mfg.--Schlumberger Oilfield Services, Houston, TX; *U.S. Public*, pg. 1439
Roca, J., Mgr.-Factory--De La Rue Lerchundi Personalizacion SA, Badalona, Spain; *Int'l*, pg. 386
Roddy, Keith, Mgr.-Production--Business Journals of North Carolina, LLC, Charlotte, NC; *U.S. Private*, pg. 19
Rodgers, Joyn, Mgr.-Engrng.--Nodak Electric Co-op, Grand Forks, ND; *U.S. Private*, pg. 800
Rodrigues de Souza, Djalma, Dir.-Drilling--Petrobras - Petroleo Brasileiro S.A., Rio de Janeiro, Brazil; *Int'l*, pg. 1041
Rodriguez L., Miguel, Mgr.-Mfg.--Grace Quimica Cia. Ltda., Santiago, Chile; *U.S. Public*, pg. 756
Rogers, Lee, Plant Mgr.--Owen Industries, Inc., Carter Lake, IA; *U.S. Private*, pg. 824
Rohr, Wayne, Mgr.-Mfg.--Cashco, Inc., Ellsworth, KS; *U.S. Private*, pg. 218
Rokowski, Al, Chief Engr.--Eagle Button Co., Inc., Carlstadt, NJ; *U.S. Private*, pg. 354
Rolf, Dave, Plant Mgr.--Penreco, Karns City, PA; *U.S. Public*, pg. 1273
Rolland, Bruno, Dir.-Indus.--Posso S.A., Paris, France; *Int'l*, pg. 1064
Rollins, Glaze, Mgr.-Mfg.--Embers Charcoal Company, Inc., Conway, SC; *U.S. Private*, pg. 373
Romero, Alvaro, V.P.-Mfg.--Conway Import Co. Inc., Elmsford, NY; *U.S. Private*, pg. 272
Ronquillo, Andy, Production Mgr.--Expo Partes S.a. de C.V., Mexicali, Mexico; *U.S. Public*, pg. 1709
Rosa, Bob, Dir.-Production--Sanderson Farms, Inc., Laurel, MS; *U.S. Public*, pg. 1430
Rosa, Bruno, V.P.-Engrng. & Pur.--AP North American Aftermarket Division, Goldsboro, NC; *U.S. Private*, pg. 230

Rosbottom, Richard, V.P.-Opers.--DMI Furniture Inc., Louisville, KY; *U.S. Public*, pg. 473

Rose, Michael C., Sr. V.P.--Marketing Communications, Lenexa, KS; *U.S. Public*, pg. 794

Rose, Stuart, Dr., V.P.-Worldwide Mfg. & Logistics--ICN Pharmaceuticals, Inc., Costa Mesa, CA; *U.S. Public*, pg. 853

Rose, William D., V.P.-Integrated Bus. Sys. Bldg. Prods. Mfg. & Sls.--Georgia-Pacific Corporation, Atlanta, GA; *U.S. Public*, pg. 735

Rosen, Lars, V.P. & Dir.-Mfg.--ITT Flygt AB, Solna, Sweden; *U.S. Public*, pg. 860

Rosewall, Raymond A., V.P.-Mfg.--Harmon Industries, Inc., Blue Springs, MO; *U.S. Public*, pg. 788

Rosimo, Veijo, Dir.-Production--AMER TOBACCO Ltd., Tuusula, Finland; *Int'l*, pg. 72

Ross, Edward C., Pres.-Tech. & Mfg. Grp.--Cirrus Logic, Inc., Fremont, CA; *U.S. Public*, pg. 375

Ross, J.A., V.P.-Mfg.--MacMillan Bathurst Inc., Mississauga, Canada; *Int'l*, pg. 20

Ross, Michael, Mgr.-Plant Production--Retail Bag Division - Savage Plant, Savage, MD; *U.S. Public*, pg. 1521

Rossman, Dan, Plant Mgr.--Independent Metals, Germantown, WI; *U.S. Private*, pg. 559

Rostan, Dan, V.P.-Mfg.--Hampshire Hosiery, Inc., Spruce Pine, NC; *U.S. Public*, pg. 778

Roth, Jim, Dir.-Mfg.--Rawlings Sporting Goods Company, Fenton, MO; *U.S. Public*, pg. 1361

Roth, John, V.P.-Opers.--Action Instruments, Inc., San Diego, CA; *U.S. Private*, pg. 15

Rottenberg, J., V.P.-Mfg.--Isfel Company, Inc., Rahway, NJ; *U.S. Private*, pg. 576

Rotundo, Carlos, Mgr.-Mfg.--Gillette Argentina S.A., Buenos Aires, Argentina; *U.S. Public*, pg. 744

Roubaud, Luis Alberto, Mgr.-Mfg.--Acos Villares S.A., Sao Paulo, Brazil; *Int'l*, pg. 23

Routhier, B., Grp. V.P.-Paper & Pkgng.--Kruger Inc., Montreal, Canada; *Int'l*, pg. 761

Routhier, Bernard, V.P.-Mfg.--Trois-Rivieres Mill, Trois-Rivieres, Canada; *Int'l*, pg. 761

Rowan, Larry, V.P.-Mfg.--Moore Document Solutions, Lake Forest, IL; *Int'l*, pg. 890

Roy, Fred, Jr., Dir.-Design--Dansk International Designs Ltd., White Plains, NY; *U.S. Public*, pg. 261

Rozzini, Paul J., V.P.-Mfg.--Chyron Corp., Melville, NY; *Int'l*, pg. 1372

Rudolph, M., V.P.-Mfg.--The Entwistle Company, Hudson, MA; *U.S. Private*, pg. 378

Rudolph, Wolfdieter, Dir.-Mfg.--Kleber Reifen und Technische Gummiwaren AG, Saint Ingbert, Germany; *Int'l*, pg. 322

Rudy, Ronald, Sr. V.P.-Opers.--International Aluminum Corporation, Monterey Park, CA; *U.S. Public*, pg. 894

Ruffley, Douglas, Chief Engineer--De-Sta-Co, A Dover Resources Co., Troy, MI; *U.S. Public*, pg. 521

Rufino, Robert, V.P.-Visual Mdsg.--Tiffany & Co., New York, NY; *U.S. Public*, pg. 1608

Rugotzke, Tom, Sr. V.P.-Opers.--Bush Brothers & Company, Knoxville, TN; *U.S. Private*, pg. 189

Ruiz, G., Dir.-Mfr.--Gator Industries Inc., Hialeah, FL; *U.S. Private*, pg. 441

Rujak, J., V.P.-Mfg.-Edmonton Div.--Barber Industries Inc., Calgary, Canada; *Int'l*, pg. 164

Rujak, John, V.P.-Mfg.--Barber Industries, Inc., Edmonton, Canada; *Int'l*, pg. 164

Rundall, Leland, Sr. V.P.-Mfg.--SGI Integrated Graphic Systems, Houston, TX; *U.S. Public*, pg. 971

Runser, John, Mgr.-Production--Erie Plastics, Corry, PA; *U.S. Private*, pg. 381

Runyan, Doward, V.P.-Mfg.--The Oilgear Company, Milwaukee, WI; *U.S. Public*, pg. 1215

Rusch, Edward A., V.P.-Engrng.--Altec Lansing Corp., Buchanan, MI; *U.S. Private*, pg. 479

Rushing, Ray, V.P.--ElectroCom Automation L.P., Arlington, TX; *Int'l*, pg. 1244

Rushwin, Shamel T., V.P.-Intl. Mfg. & Minivan Assembly Opers.--Chrysler Corporation, Auburn Hills, MI; *U.S. Public*, pg. 352

Russell, Bill, Dir.-Pur. Admin.--George W. Park Seed Co., Inc., Greenwood, SC; *U.S. Private*, pg. 839

Russell, W. Horton, V.P.-Mfg., Safety, Health & Environment--Grow Group, Inc., Cleveland, OH; *Int'l*, pg. 663

Russo, Domenic, V.P.-Opers.--F.H. Chase, Inc., Mansfield, MA; *U.S. Private*, pg. 230

Russo, Fred, V.P.-Production--Bel-Art Products, Pequannock, NJ; *U.S. Private*, pg. 130

Russo, John, V.P.-Mfg.--Ideal Forging Corporation, Southington, CT; *U.S. Private*, pg. 557

Rust, Don, Dir.-Opers. & Mfg.--Broadcast Electronics, Inc., Quincy, IL; *U.S. Private*, pg. 531

Rusugno, Jamie, V.P.-Mfg.--V-Band Corporation, Elmsford, NY; *U.S. Public*, pg. 1701

Ruth, Gary R., Dir.-Prod.--American Bible Society, New York, NY; *U.S. Private*, pg. 51

Ruud, Morten, Dir.-Exploration & Production, Intl.--Norsk Hydro a.s, Oslo, Norway; *Int'l*, pg. 959

Ryan, Don, Dir.-Pur.--Western States Machine Company, Hamilton, OH; *U.S. Private*, pg. 1168

Ryan, Nancy E., Dir.-Communications & Media--Klockner Pentaplast of America, Inc., Gordonsville, VA; *Int'l*, pg. 737

Rychlinski, Victor Z., Dir.-Engrng.--Brad Foote Gear Works, Inc., Cicero, IL; *U.S. Private*, pg. 417

Saboia, J.L., Dir.-Industrial--Souza Cruz, S.A., Rio de Janeiro, Brazil; *Int'l*, pg. 112

Sack, Marcus, Chief Engineer--Burgess Pigment Co., Sandersville, GA; *U.S. Private*, pg. 182

Sackes, Robert, Dir.-Mfg.--Bill Communications, Inc., New York, NY; *Int'l*, pg. 1446

Saco, Bruno, Dir.-Design--Mercedes-Benz AG, Stuttgart, Germany; *Int'l*, pg. 368

Sadler, Dick, V.P.-Engrng.--IGT North America, Reno, NV; *U.S. Public*, pg. 900

Safran, F.S., V.P.-Engrg.--Intool Rotor Company, Cleveland, OH; *U.S. Private*, pg. 547

Sagastegui, Javier, Mgr.-Engrng.--Eagle Packaging Group, Oakland, CA; *U.S. Private*, pg. 832

Sager, Harry C., Exec. V.P.-Exploration & Production--Conoco Inc., Houston, TX; *U.S. Public*, pg. 531

Saiia, Tony J., V.P.-Engrng.--Jacobsen Textron, Racine, WI; *U.S. Public*, pg. 1589

Saito, Yutaka, Dir.-Mfg.--Matsushita Electric Works, Ltd., Osaka, Japan; *Int'l*, pg. 847

Sakulich, Richard, Dir.-Mfg.--DSM Engineering Plastic Products, Reading, PA; *Int'l*, pg. 354

Salahi, Memmet, V.P.-Mfg. & Engrng.--Diasonics Ultra Sound, Inc., Santa Clara, CA; *Int'l*, pg. 644

Salehi, Ali, V.P.-Engrng. & Mfg.--Columbia Manufacturing Inc., Westfield, MA; *U.S. Private*, pg. 255

Salgueiro, Louis G., V.P.-Mfg.--C.R. Bard, Inc., Murray Hill, NJ; *U.S. Public*, pg. 189

Salisbury, Mark, V.P.-Mfg.--R & B Machine Tool Co., Saline, MI; *U.S. Private*, pg. 901

Salvagni, Carlos A., Sr. V.P.-Worldwide Mfg. & Engrng.--Pharmacia & Upjohn, Kalamazoo, MI; *Int'l*, pg. 1048

Samant, Suresh, V.P.-Mfg.--American Saw & Mfg. Company, East Longmeadow, MA; *U.S. Private*, pg. 61

Sample, Bill, Grp. V.P.-Case Goods--The HON Co., Williamsport Plant, Williamsport, PA; *U.S. Public*, pg. 772

Samples, O. Mark, V.P.-Mfg.--Quest Medical, Inc., Allen, TX; *U.S. Public*, pg. 1352

Samson, Joseph, Plant Mgr.-Ayer Opers.--Cains Foods, L.P., Ayer, MA; *U.S. Private*, pg. 199

Sanchez, Mario, Mgr.-Mfg.--Nissan Forklift Corporation, North America, Marengo, IL; *Int'l*, pg. 944

Sander, Don, V.P.-Mfg.--Hastings Manufacturing Company, Hastings, MI; *U.S. Public*, pg. 798

Sandercock, Gary L., V.P.-Mfg.--Hexcel Corporation, Pleasanton, CA; *U.S. Public*, pg. 824

Sanders, Mark, V.P.-Mfg.--Bates Container, Inc., North Richland Hills, TX; *U.S. Private*, pg. 122

Sandorf, Michael J., Dir.-Mfg.--Thermal Transfer Corp., Monroeville, PA; *U.S. Public*, pg. 29

Sandroni, John, Mgr.-Prod.--Identification Systems, Seneca Falls, NY; *U.S. Public*, pg. 1059

Sandru, Nicholas L., V.P.-Mfg.--Bondo/Mar-Hyde Corporation, Cleveland, OH; *U.S. Public*, pg. 1357

Sandru, Nicholas L., V.P.-Mfg.--Paramount Technical Products, Inc., Spearfish, SD; *U.S. Public*, pg. 1357

Sanford, Michael L., V.P.-Mfg.--Sterling Plumbing Group, Inc., Rolling Meadows, IL; *U.S. Private*, pg. 630

Santos, Francisco, Dir.-Mfg.--Sein Mendez Laboratories, Inc., Rio Piedras, PR; *U.S. Public*, pg. 670

Sanz, Robert, V.P.-Supply & Distr.--Wickland Corporation, Sacramento, CA; *U.S. Private*, pg. 1174

Sarrail, H.B., V.P.-Production--McConnell Cabinets, Inc., El Monte, CA; *U.S. Private*, pg. 720

Sarver, Terry, Sr. V.P.-Mfg.--Bawden Printing, Inc., Eldridge, IA; *U.S. Private*, pg. 124

Sassenfeld, Helmut, Ph.D., V.P.-Process Devel.--Immunex Manufacturing Corporation, Seattle, WA; *U.S. Public*, pg. 871

Sasser, Bob L., Sr. V.P.-Mdsg. & Mktg.--Rose's Stores, Inc., Henderson, NC; *U.S. Public*, pg. 1405

Sasser, Duffy, V.P.-TV Stations Opers. & Engrng.--National Broadcasting Co., Inc., New York, NY; *U.S. Public*, pg. 712

Sasson, Pete, Mgr.-Mfg.--Photo Control Corporation, Minneapolis, MN; *U.S. Public*, pg. 1292

Sato, Kikumi, Dir.-Mfg.--Rohto Pharmaceutical Co., Osaka, Japan; *Int'l*, pg. 1126

Sato, Yosh, V.P.-Mfg.--Proxim, Inc., Mountain View, CA; *U.S. Public*, pg. 1338

Saul, John, V.P.-Domestic Systems Engrng.--Emcee Broadcast Products, Inc., White Haven, PA; *U.S. Public*, pg. 570

Saunders, Paul, Dir.-Mfg.--Sterling Chemicals, Inc., Houston, TX; *U.S. Public*, pg. 1515

Saurez, Louis, V.P.-Opers.--Kenyon Industries, Inc., Kenyon, RI; *U.S. Public*, pg. 778

Sauvageau, Michael, Mfg. Mgr.--St. Jude Medical Ltd., Saint-Hyacinthe, Canada; *U.S. Public*, pg. 1428

Savage, Steven A., Sr. V.P.-Mfg.--Terra Nitrogen Company, L.P., Tulsa, OK; *U.S. Public*, pg. 1581

Savanyu, J., V.P.-Mfg.--Dukane Corporation, Saint Charles, IL; *U.S. Private*, pg. 345

Saving, Frank, Chief Engineer--Airguard Industries Inc., Louisville, KY; *U.S. Public*, pg. 382

Savini, Robert D., V.P.-Opers.--Metal Trades, Inc., Hollywood, SC; *U.S. Private*, pg. 734

Sawaya, William J., Ph.D., Sr. V.P.-Mfg.--Daw Technologies, Inc., Salt Lake City, UT; *U.S. Public*, pg. 489

Sawicki, Gary, Dir.-Opers.--Cooper Instrument Corp., Middlefield, CT; *U.S. Private*, pg. 274

Sayer, Brian, V.P.-Mfg.--Nacan Products Ltd., Brampton, Canada; *Int'l*, pg. 1436

Sayers, T., V.P.-Mfg. Opers.--B/E Aerospace Seating Products Group, Litchfield, CT; *U.S. Public*, pg. 159

Sayre, John B., Jr., V.P.-Mfg.--Scan-Optics, Inc., Manchester, CT; *U.S. Public*, pg. 1436

Scaffede, Russell B., V.P.-N. America Mfg.--Donnelly Corporation, Holland, MI; *U.S. Public*, pg. 519

Scalise, Randall A., V.P.-Mdse. Handling--Blair Corporation, Warren, PA; *U.S. Public*, pg. 236

Scarborough, Richard, V.P.-Mfg.--IPAC, Inc., Niagara Falls, NY; *U.S. Private*, pg. 555

Scarola, Joe, Mgr.-Systems--Hy-Tek Material Handling, Inc., Columbus, OH; *U.S. Private*, pg. 550

Scarpace, James, V.P.-Prod.--Pacific Coast Producers, Lodi, CA; *U.S. Private*, pg. 830

Scatoloni, Mark, Mgr.-Engrng.--Faber Enterprises, Inc., Canoga Park, CA; *U.S. Private*, pg. 390

Schaefer, Hans D., V.P.-Production--Buehler, Limited, Lake Bluff, IL; *U.S. Public*, pg. 574

Schanback, Warren, Sr. V.P.-Mfg.--Friendship Dairies, Inc., Jericho, NY; *U.S. Private*, pg. 429

Schaub, Sherry J., V.P.-Pur.--The Quaker Oats Company, Chicago, IL; *U.S. Public*, pg. 1347

Schaumann, U., Dr., Mgr.-Mfg.--H.A. Schlatter AG, Schlieren, Switzerland; *Int'l*, pg. 1205

Scheifele, Carl, Mgr.-Plant--Colonial Beef Co., Philadelphia, PA; *U.S. Private*, pg. 253

Schelich, A.J., V.P.-Mfg.--Sporlan Valve Company, Washington, MO; *U.S. Private*, pg. 1026

Schelin, Ray, Mgr.-Mfg.--DSP Technology Inc., Fremont, CA; *U.S. Public*, pg. 475

Schenzel, John, Mgr.-Mdse.--Weinbrenner Shoe Company, Inc., Merrill, WI; *U.S. Private*, pg. 1160

Scherrer, Anton, Dr., Dir.-Mfg.--Migros, Zurich, Switzerland; *Int'l*, pg. 865

Scherrer, Urs, Exec. V.P.-Sulzer Winterthur Group--Sulzer Ltd., Winterthur, Switzerland; *Int'l*, pg. 1305

Schibline, Pat, V.P.-Engrng.--Marathon Electric Manufacturing Corp., Wausau, WI; *U.S. Public*, pg. 1371

Schielo, E. Frederick, V.P.-Mfg.--Electro Scientific Industries, Inc., Portland, OR; *U.S. Public*, pg. 568

Schilling, Glen, Dir.-Mfg.--Wausau Homes, Inc., Rothschild, WI; *U.S. Private*, pg. 1154

Schindehette, Art, Mgr.-Production--Brigadier Homes of North Carolina, Nashville, NC; *U.S. Public*, pg. 318

Schippert, Manfred A., Sr. V.P.-Engrng.--Amray, Inc., Bedford, MA; *U.S. Private*, pg. 67

Schlerf, Steven G., V.P.-Mfg. & Tech. Opers.--New England Business Service, Inc., Groton, MA; *U.S. Public*, pg. 1170

Schlick, John, Mgr.-Plant--Intertractor America Corporation, Elkhorn, WI; *Int'l*, pg. 1511

Schlosser, Steven M., V.P.--BTG, Inc., Fairfax, VA; *U.S. Public*, pg. 164

Schmale, Jurgen, Mgr.-Logistics--Groschopp & Co. GmbH EMW Elektromotoren-Feinbauwerk, Viersen, Germany; *Int'l*, pg. 559

Schmid, Dr. Jung Edgar, V.P.-Sealing & Filtration Prods./Europe--Reinz-Dichtungs-GmbH, Neu-Ulm, Germany; *U.S. Public*, pg. 480

Schmidt, Harvey W., V.P.-Mfg.--MI-Jack Products, Inc., Hazel Crest, IL; *U.S. Private*, pg. 740

Schmidt, Richard, V.P.-Mfg.--Spontex, Inc., Columbia, TN; *Int'l*, pg. 1409

Schmidt, Robert, V.P.-Engrng.--Rogers Group Inc., Nashville, TN; *U.S. Private*, pg. 939

Schmidt, Steve, Dir.-Mfg.--Marlite, Dover, OH; *U.S. Private*, pg. 705

Schmitt, Jack, Chief Engineer--C.W. Zumbiel Company, Norwood, OH; *U.S. Private*, pg. 1207

Schmitt, James P., V.P.-Intl. Mfg.--Avery International Converting Group, Azusa, CA; *U.S. Public*, pg. 152

Schmittbetz, Klaus, Sr. V.P.-Prod.--Deutz AG, Cologne, Germany; *Int'l*, pg. 407

Schmitz, Barbara, Dir.-Mfg.--F & W Publications, Inc., Cincinnati, OH; *U.S. Private*, pg. 388

Schmoller, Stanley, V.P.-Mfg.--Andover Togs, Inc., New York, NY; *U.S. Public*, pg. 112

Schneider, Joseph, V.P.-Engrng., Mfg. & Service--Access Corporation, Cincinnati, OH; *Int'l*, pg. 994

Schneuwly, Peter, Pres. & Chief Exec. Officer--UMS Swiss Metalworks Holding Ltd, Dornach, Switzerland; *Int'l*, pg. 1427

Schockemoel, Gene, Mgr.-Mfg.--Braden Manufacturing Co., Tulsa, OK; *U.S. Public*, pg. 924

Schodowski, Mark, Mgr.-Plant--Voss Industries, Inc., Cleveland, OH; *U.S. Private*, pg. 1143

Schoenberger, Albert H., Jr., V.P.-Mfg.--Central Sprinkler Company, Lansdale, PA; *U.S. Public*, pg. 327

Schomburger, Rick, Dir.-Southbridge Opers.--Aearo Company, Boston, MA; *U.S. Private*, pg. 23

Schomer, Gary W., V.P.-Mfg. Tech.--Weston Paper & Manufacturing Co., Terre Haute, IN; *U.S. Private*, pg. 1169

Schonke, David W., Asst. V.P.-Electric Distr. Engrng.--Wisconsin Public Service Corporation, Green Bay, WI; *U.S. Public*, pg. 1728

Schoof, Milton, Mgr.-Import Mfg. Sls.--ADT Automotive, Inc., Nashville, TN; *U.S. Public*, pg. 1648

Schoones, E.J.J., Plant Mgr.--Bakery Ingredients Division, Delft, Netherlands; *Int'l*, pg. 1142

Schott, Greg, Mgr.-Production--Perry & Derrick Co., Cincinnati, OH; *U.S. Private*, pg. 854

Schottelkotte, W.F., V.P.-Engrng.--Dupps Company, Germantown, OH; *U.S. Private*, pg. 348

Schreiber, Sallo, Dir.-Mfg.--Poly Pak America, Inc., Los Angeles, CA; *U.S. Private*, pg. 875

Schrock, David, Plant Engr.--Sauder Manufacturing Corporation, Archbold, OH; *U.S. Private*, pg. 967

Schroeder, Edward, Mgr.-Opers.--Southland Oil Company, Jackson, MS; *U.S. Private*, pg. 1018

Schroeder, Ray, V.P.-Mfg. Opers.--Keithley Instruments, Inc., Cleveland, OH; *U.S. Public*, pg. 946

Schroeder, Richard P., V.P.-Mfg.--AlliedSignal Inc., Morristown, NJ; *U.S. Public*, pg. 49

Schueller, John F., V.P.-Mfg. & Corp. Quality--Armor All Products Group, Oakland, CA; *U.S. Public*, pg. 387

Schuetze, Larry W., V.P.-Mfg. Opers.-North American Consumer Prods.--S.C. Johnson & Son, Inc., Racine, WI; *U.S. Private*, pg. 592

Schummer, Arthur, Dir.-Iron & Steelmaking/Long Prods.--Arbed S.A., Luxembourg, Luxembourg; *Int'l*, pg. 78

Schuster, Tom, V.P.-Mfg.--Yokogawa Corporation of America, Newnan, GA; *Int'l*, pg. 1521

Schutz, Garrett, Dir.-Mfg.--Qualheim, Inc., New Hartford, CT; *U.S. Public*, pg. 286

Schwager, Jeff, V.P.-Mfg.--Rite-Hite Corporation (WI), Milwaukee, WI; *U.S. Private*, pg. 933

Schwarting, Bob, Mgr.-Mfg.--Coleman Powermate, Inc., Omaha, NE; *U.S. Private*, pg. 691

Schwartz, Donna, Mgr.-Production--Business First of Columbus, Inc., Columbus, OH; *U.S. Private*, pg. 19

Schwartz, T.M., Dir.-Tech. Services--Schering-Plough Animal Health, Union, NJ; *U.S. Public*, pg. 1438

Schwarz, Gene, V.P.-Mfg.--Selfix, Inc., Chicago, IL; *U.S. Public*, pg. 832
Schwarz, Steven, V.P.-Mfg. & New Products--Don Alleson, Inc., Rochester, NY; *U.S. Private*, pg. 339
Schweibinz, Joanne, Mgr.-Mfg.--Peerless Lighting Corp., Berkeley, CA; *U.S. Private*, pg. 847
Schweizer, Leslie, Exec. V.P.-Engrng.--Schweizer Aircraft Corporation, Big Flats, NY; *U.S. Private*, pg. 975
Schwelm, Frederick, V.P.-Mfg.--BIW Cable Systems, Inc., Franklin, MA; *Int'l*, pg. 417
Schwer, Walter, Dir.-Engrng.--Ortronics, Inc., Pawcatuck, CT; *Int'l*, pg. 806
Scott, Gary L., Mgr.-Prod. Scheduling--Rundel Products, Inc., Portland, OR; *U.S. Private*, pg. 951
Scott, L.S., Mgr.-Mfg.--Flexible Technologies Inc., Abbeville, SC; *Int'l*, pg. 1267
Scott, W.N., V.P.-Engrng.--The Murray Ohio Mfg. Co., Brentwood, TN; *Int'l*, pg. 1397
Scown, Gordon H., Mgr.-Production--Bundy Tubing Co. (Australia) Pty. Ltd., Adelaide, Australia; *Int'l*, pg. 1341
Scrmizzi, Alberto, Dir.-Mfg.--Vitromex, S.A., Saltillo, Mexico; *Int'l*, pg. 1469
Scullin, Joseph P., Mgr.-Matls.--Moore Products Co., Spring House, PA; *U.S. Public*, pg. 1128
Seabeck, Scott, Mgr.-Production--Ken-Mac Metals, Inc., Cleveland, OH; *Int'l*, pg. 1388
Seabrook, William E., V.P.-Engrng.--Seabrook Brothers & Sons, Inc., Seabrook, NJ; *U.S. Private*, pg. 978
Seagrave, Richard A., V.P.-Mfg.--Construction Equipment Div., Racine, WI; *U.S. Public*, pg. 311
Seaman, Mike, Plant Mgr.--Modern Concrete Septic Tank Company, Ottsville, PA; *U.S. Private*, pg. 754
Searles, Bud, Dir.-Distr.--Swiss Army Brands, Inc., Shelton, CT; *U.S. Public*, pg. 1544
Sears, Robert W., V.P.-Prod.--BHP Petroleum (Americas) Inc., Houston, TX; *Int'l*, pg. 225
Securcher, F. John, V.P.-Mfg./Imperial Bondware Corp.--Imperial Bondware Corp., Montvale, NJ; *U.S. Public*, pg. 903
Sedlastschek, Robert L., Dir.-Engrng.--Glastic Corporation, Cleveland, OH; *Int'l*, pg. 740
Seib, G., V.P.-Opers.--Propak Systems Ltd., Airdrie, Canada; *Int'l*, pg. 1071
Seifert, Harry A., Jr., V.P.-Forms Mfg.--The Standard Register Company, Dayton, OH; *U.S. Public*, pg. 1505
Sellers, Danny C., V.P.-Mfg. Support--Bender Shipbuilding & Repair Company, Inc., Mobile, AL; *U.S. Private*, pg. 132
Selvala, Richard L., Gen. Dir.-Mfg.--GM Powertrain Group, Pontiac, MI; *U.S. Public*, pg. 719
Semke, L. Kirk, V.P.-Mfg. Technology--Forest Products & Recycled Paperboard Div., Montvale, NJ; *U.S. Public*, pg. 903
Semon, William, V.P.-Mfg.--Casket Shells, Inc., Eynon, PA; *U.S. Private*, pg. 218
Senay, William, Plant Mgr.--Sorrento Cheese Company, Inc., Buffalo, NY; *Int'l*, pg. 323
Sengupta, Sunil B., Dir.-Mfg.--Ethyl Corporation, Richmond, VA; *U.S. Public*, pg. 595
Sennefelder, Klaus, Production--Richardson G.m.b.H., Schwalbach, Germany; *U.S. Public*, pg. 1333
Seo, C.H., V.P.-Mfg./West--Zenith Electronics Corp., Glenview, IL; *U.S. Public*, pg. 1790
Seraiva, Fernando, V.P.-Mfg.--Merco/Savory Inc., Lakewood, NJ; *Int'l*, pg. 189
Sernik, Kleber Antonio, Gen. Mgr.-Mfg.--Acos Villares Sao Caetano Plant, Sao Caetano do Sul, Brazil; *Int'l*, pg. 23
Sestrick, Robert, V.P.-Mfg.--PSC Inc., Webster, NY; *U.S. Public*, pg. 1245
Setter, Claude, Dir.-Mfg.--Kodak Pathe S.A., Paris, France; *U.S. Public*, pg. 554
Setterholm, David, V.P.-Mfg.--Scoville Press, Inc., Minneapolis, MN; *U.S. Private*, pg. 977
Severin, Emery S., Mgr.-BHP Packaging Prod.--Slab & Plate Products Division, Wollongong, Australia; *Int'l*, pg. 227
Sevier, John, V.P.-Mfg.--Moeller Products Co., Inc., Greenville, MS; *U.S. Private*, pg. 755
Sevilla, F. Manzanilla, Asst. Dir.-Projects & Constr.--Petroleos Mexicanos, Mexico, Mexico; *Int'l*, pg. 1046
Seward, Brian, Dir.-Production--Pauls Malt Limited, Newmarket, United Kingdom; *Int'l*, pg. 598
Seybold, L., Mgr.-Mfg.--G.E. Canada Power Systems, Lachine, Canada; *U.S. Public*, pg. 713
Seyfert, Steve, Mgr.-Production--Beacon Container Corporation, Birdsboro, PA; *U.S. Private*, pg. 125
Sferra, James P., Exec. V.P.-Mfg.--LSI Industries, Inc., Cincinnati, OH; *U.S. Public*, pg. 971
Shabla, George, Supvr.-Mfg.--Morris Coupling Co., Erie, PA; *U.S. Private*, pg. 762
Shaffer, Dale, V.P.-Mfg.--The Kay Company, Inc., Frankfort, IN; *U.S. Private*, pg. 610
Shaffer, Dane, V.P.-Mfg.--Pace International L.P., Kirkland, WA; *U.S. Private*, pg. 829
Shaffer, M. Todd, Dir.-Pur. & Mfg. Svcs.--Tru-Weld Grating, Inc., Wexford, PA; *U.S. Private*, pg. 1107
Shaharun, Mohamed Zohari Mohamed, V.P.-Exploration & Prod.--Petroliam Nasional Berhad (Petronas), Kuala Lumpur, Malaysia; *Int'l*, pg. 1046
Shamas, Tom, Dir.-Mfg.--Springfield Precision Instruments, Inc., Wood Ridge, NJ; *U.S. Private*, pg. 1027
Shane, Ken, Dir.-Hospitality--Brutger Equities, Inc., Saint Cloud, MN; *U.S. Private*, pg. 176
Sharp, Bob, V.P.-Textiles--The Coleman Company, Inc., Golden, CO; *U.S. Private*, pg. 690
Sharp, Roger L., Exec. V.P. & Chief-Global Opers.--Witco Corporation, Greenwich, CT; *U.S. Public*, pg. 1773
Shauf, Jack E., V.P.-Mfg.--Intool Rotor Company, Cleveland, OH; *U.S. Private*, pg. 574
Shaw, Al, V.P.-Opers.--United Stationers Inc., Des Plaines, IL; *U.S. Public*, pg. 1689
Shaw, James C., V.P.-Mfg.--Encore Computer Corporation, Fort Lauderdale, FL; *U.S. Public*, pg. 580
Shaw, Jeff, V.P.-Mfg.--Microtouch Systems, Inc., Methuen, MA; *U.S. Public*, pg. 1108
Shaw, M. Bane, Jr., Grp. V.P.-Mfg.--American & Efird, Inc., Mount Holly, NC; *U.S. Public*, pg. 1412
Shaw, Steve, V.P.-Prod.--Helmerich & Payne, Inc., Tulsa, OK; *U.S. Public*, pg. 808
Shea, Daniel C., Mgr.-Prod.--New England Coffee Company, Malden, MA; *U.S. Private*, pg. 792
Shearer, Gerald, V.P.-Engrng.--The Fusco Corporation, New Haven, CT; *U.S. Private*, pg. 432
Sheets, Allen, V.P.-Mfg.--Rocky Shoes & Boots, Inc., Nelsonville, OH; *U.S. Public*, pg. 1402
Shei, Kurt, Dir.-Mfg.--Essex Specialty Products, Auburn Hills, MI; *U.S. Public*, pg. 523
Shei, W.G., Dir.--Taiwan Power Company, Taipei, Taiwan; *Int'l*, pg. 1348
Shenber, James A., V.P.-Procurement & Mfg. Services--Materials Group North America, Painesville, OH; *U.S. Public*, pg. 153
Shepard, J.M., V.P.-Engrng.--Nacan Products Ltd., Brampton, Canada; *Int'l*, pg. 1436
Shephard, John E., Jr., V.P.-Mfg. & Process Innovation--Newport News Shipbuilding, Inc., Newport News, VA; *U.S. Public*, pg. 1179
Shepherd, D., V.P.-Mfg.--Global Steel Products Corporation, Deer Park, NY; *U.S. Private*, pg. 457
Sheppard, Charles R., V.P.-Mfg.--North American Salt Company, Overland Park, KS; *U.S. Private*, pg. 505
Sherlock, Michael J., Pres.-New Technology--National Broadcasting Co., Inc., New York, NY; *U.S. Public*, pg. 712
Sherman, Cynthia, Mgr.-Production--The Denver Business Journal, LLC, Denver, CO; *U.S. Private*, pg. 19
Shibata, Mamoru, Gen. Mgr.--Okuma Corporation, Niwa, Japan; *Int'l*, pg. 1000
Shibata, Roberto, Chief Mgr.-Engrng.--Yamaha Motor do Brasil Ltda., Convica, Brazil; *Int'l*, pg. 1516
Shields, S.N., V.P.-Engrng.--Atwood & Morrill Co., Inc., Salem, MA; *Int'l*, pg. 1489
Shiels, Walter, V.P.-Mfg.--Arkay Packaging Corporation, Hauppauge, NY; *U.S. Private*, pg. 82
Shillinger, Michael J., V.P.-Advanced Mfg. Tech.--Applied Magnetics Corporation, Goleta, CA; *U.S. Public*, pg. 123
Shinomiya, Norio, Mng. Dir. & Gen. Mgr.-Construction Dept.--West Japan Railway Company, Osaka, Japan; *Int'l*, pg. 1490
Shoff, Randy, V.P.-Mfg.--Anderson, Greenwood & Co., Stafford, TX; *U.S. Public*, pg. 1650
Shook, Michael D., V.P.-Mfg. & Engrng.--Riceland Foods, Inc., Stuttgart, AR; *U.S. Private*, pg. 928
Shor, M.L., V.P.-Mfg. Opers.--Carpenter Specialty Alloys Operations, Reading, PA; *U.S. Public*, pg. 307
Shor, M.L., V.P.-Mfg. Opers.--Carpenter Steel Div., Orangeburg, SC; *U.S. Public*, pg. 307
Shor, Michael L., V.P.-Mfg. Opers.--Carpenter Technology Corporation, Reading, PA; *U.S. Public*, pg. 307
Show, M.L., V.P.-Mfg. Opers.--Carpenter Steel Div., Fryeburg, ME; *U.S. Public*, pg. 307
Shue, James, Mgr.-Mfg.--Donlee Technologies Inc., York, PA; *U.S. Private*, pg. 339
Shuld, Cliff, V.P.-Mfg.--Miniature Precision Components, Walworth, WI; *U.S. Private*, pg. 750
Shumejda, John M., Exec. V.P.-Mfg. & Tech.--AGCO Corporation, Duluth, GA; *U.S. Public*, pg. 28
Siddiqi, Sadiq, Dir.-Engrng. & Maintenance--Pakistan International Airlines Corporation, Karachi, Pakistan; *Int'l*, *pg. 1021*
Siddiqui, I.H., Plant Mgr.--Parke-Davis & Company, Limited, Karachi, Pakistan; *U.S. Public*, pg. 1739
Sidell, Hans, V.P.-Mfg.--Industrial Wire Products Corporation, Pomona, CA; *U.S. Private*, pg. 561
Siegel, Aaron, Treas. & Consultant--Butler Ventamatic Corp., Mineral Wells, TX; *U.S. Private*, pg. 190
Siegel, Alvan, Sr. V.P.-Production--Murry's, Inc., Upper Marlboro, MD; *U.S. Private*, pg. 768
Siegler, Steve, Mgr.-Mfg.--Lawrence Metal Products, Inc., Bay Shore, NY; *U.S. Private*, pg. 654
Siehoff, Don, Mgr.-Mfg.--Robert Bosch Fluid Power Corporation, Racine, WI; *Int'l*, pg. 204
Sigmund, Ron, V.P.-Engrng.--Bird Machine Company, South Walpole, MA; *U.S. Public*, pg. 166
Sikes, William, V.P.-Production--Baker Commodities, Inc., Los Angeles, CA; *U.S. Private*, pg. 111
Silberstein, Jonathan A., V.P.--Columbus Pipe & Equipment Company, Columbus, OH; *U.S. Private*, pg. 257
Sills, Milton D., V.P.-Engrng.--The Cessna Aircraft Co., Wichita, KS; *U.S. Public*, pg. 1589
Silva, Joel Affonso M., Mgr.-Mfg.--Acos Villares Plant - Pindamonhangaba, Pindamonhangaba, Brazil; *Int'l*, pg. 23
Silver, Jack, V.P.-Mfg.--Braden Manufacturing Co., Tulsa, OK; *U.S. Public*, pg. 924
Silverman, Barry, V.P.-Mdsg./Northeast Div.--The Home Depot, Inc., Atlanta, GA; *U.S. Public*, pg. 831
Simitoski, Paul, Dir.-Mfg.--Penn Champ, East Butler, PA; *U.S. Private*, pg. 145
Simmons, Ron, V.P.-Mfg.--Via Tech Publishing Solutions, Bay Shore, NY; *U.S. Private*, pg. 1138
Sims, John, Dir.-Mfg.--Nalle Plastics Inc., Austin, TX; *U.S. Private*, pg. 773
Sines, R.K., V.P.-Mfg.--Bailey Controls Company, Wickliffe, OH; *Int'l*, pg. 654
Sinister, Jim, Mgr.-Mfg.--McCauley Propeller Systems, Vandalia, OH; *U.S. Public*, pg. 1589
Sinka, George, V.P.-Mfg.--Sleepeck Printing Company, Bellwood, IL; *U.S. Private*, pg. 1005
Sipe, George, Jr., V.P.-Mfg.--Weldon Machine Tool, Inc., York, PA; *U.S. Private*, pg. 1161
Siripocanont, Chusak, V.P.-Mfg.--Centigram Communications Corporation, San Jose, CA; *U.S. Public*, *pg. 323*
Sirvoy, Loel J., Sr. V.P.-Opers. & Outboard Mktg.--Hach Company, Loveland, CO; *U.S. Public*, pg. 773
Sisterman, Roger L., Corp. V.P.-Mfg.--Allegiance Healthcare Corp., McGaw Park, IL; *U.S. Public*, pg. 44
Sites, Stephen, Mfg. Svc. Mgr.-South Eastern Reg.--W. Braun Co., Opa Locka, FL; *U.S. Private*, pg. 166
Skarupa, Emery E., Sr. V.P.-Mfg. & Matls.--Anacomp, Inc., Indianapolis, IN; *U.S. Public*, pg. 106
Skinner, Grant, Dir.-Mfg.--Messier-Dowty Ltd., Gloucester, United Kingdom; *Int'l*, pg. 1340
Skipinski, Skip, V.P.-Engrng.--Symbol Technologies, Portable Systems Division, Costa Mesa, CA; *U.S. Public*, *pg. 1546*
Skowronski, Robert, Mgr.-Opers. Prod. Control--Eastman Worldwide, Buffalo, NY; *U.S. Private*, pg. 358
Skretta, Fabian, V.P.-Mfg.--Fire Lite Alarms, Inc./Notifier Co., Northford, CT; *U.S. Public*, pg. 1306
Skryness, Jack, Dir.-Contract Admin.--Advanced Circuit Technology, Nashua, NH; *U.S. Private*, pg. 21
Slagel, Steve, V.P.-Engrng.--Carpenter Industries, Inc., Richmond, IN; *U.S. Private*, pg. 215
Slat, William, V.P.-Opers. & Mfg. Dir.--Plastipak Packaging Inc., Plymouth, MI; *U.S. Private*, pg. 872
Slate, Burton, V.P.-Mfg.--Spencer's Inc., Mount Airy, NC; *U.S. Private*, pg. 1025
Slate, Tracy, V.P.-Mfg.--United Design Corporation, Noble, OK; *U.S. Private*, pg. 1121
Slater, Jerry, V.P.-Mfg.--Carter Day International, Inc., Minneapolis, MN; *U.S. Private*, pg. 217
Sloan, Dave, Dir.-Engrng.-Frozen Mix Plants--Continental Mills, Inc., Tukwila, WA; *U.S. Private*, pg. 269
Sloop, John E., V.P.-Mfg. & Contract--La-Z-Boy Incorporated, Monroe, MI; *U.S. Public*, pg. 972
Small, Douglas, V.P.-Opers.--Unitrode Corporation, Merrimack, NH; *U.S. Public*, pg. 1694
Smeader, William, V.P.-Mfg.--Metrologic Instruments, Inc., Blackwood, NJ; *U.S. Public*, pg. 1102
Smelewski, Bob, Mgr.-Mfr.--Dearborn Gage Company, Garden City, MI; *U.S. Private*, pg. 319
Smith, A.R., V.P.-Mfg.--The Canadian Coleman Co., Ltd., Toronto, Canada; *U.S. Private*, pg. 691
Smith, Billy, V.P.-Mfg.--PremiumWear, Inc., Minneapolis, MN; *U.S. Public*, pg. 1323
Smith, C. Thomas, V.P.-Opers.--Lesco, Inc., Rocky River, OH; *U.S. Public*, pg. 989
Smith, Dave, Dir.-S. Electric Svcs.--Seattle City Light, Seattle, WA; *U.S. Private*, pg. 979
Smith, Dick, V.P.-Mfg.--Raynor Garage Doors, Dixon, IL; *U.S. Private*, pg. 912
Smith, Douglas, Sr. V.P.-Mfg.--Konica Imaging USA, Inc., Glen Cove, NY; *Int'l*, pg. 749
Smith, Douglas F., Dir.-Opers.--Moscom Corporation, Pittsford, NY; *U.S. Public*, pg. 1136
Smith, Douglas M., V.P.-Mfg.--McWhorter Technologies, Inc., Carpentersville, IL; *U.S. Public*, pg. 1074
Smith, Frank, V.P.-Mfg.--Wheeled Coach Industries, Inc., Hutchinson, KS; *U.S. Public*, pg. 400
Smith, J., Dir.-Engrng.--Carbone of America, Commutation Components Div., Farmville, VA; *Int'l*, pg. 1028
Smith, J. S., V.P.-Mfg.--Carlisle Tire & Wheel Company, Aiken, SC; *U.S. Public*, pg. 305
Smith, J. Stewart, V.P.-Production Opers.--Wyman-Gordon, North Grafton, MA; *U.S. Public*, pg. 1782
Smith, Jack S., Sr. V.P.-Domestic Mfg.--Haggar Corporation, Dallas, TX; *U.S. Public*, pg. 774
Smith, Jerry, V.P.-Mfg.--Cosco, Inc., Columbus, IN; *U.S. Private*, pg. 277
Smith, Jimmie, V.P.-Mfg.--Klipsch, Inc., Hope, AR; *U.S. Private*, pg. 626
Smith, Jimmie H., V.P.-Mfg.--Baldwin Piano & Organ Company, Loveland, OH; *U.S. Public*, pg. 169
Smith, John, V.P.-Mfg. Devel.--Fellowes Manufacturing Co., Itasca, IL; *U.S. Private*, pg. 400
Smith, Juan A., V.P.-Mfg. & Quality Control--Fruit of the Loom, Inc., Chicago, IL; *U.S. Public*, pg. 685
Smith, Ken J., Dir.-Engrng.--Metalloy Corporation, Hudson, MI; *U.S. Private*, pg. 735
Smith, Kenneth, Sr. V.P.-Opers.--Marotta Scientific Controls, Inc., Montville, NJ; *U.S. Private*, pg. 706
Smith, L.L., V.P.-Prod.--Shell Oil Company, Houston, TX; *Int'l*, pg. 1136
Smith, Patrick, V.P.-Mfg. Opers.--Trus Joist MacMillan, Boise, ID; *Int'l*, pg. 829
Smith, Patrick, V.P.-Mfg. Opers.--Trus Joist MacMillan, Boise, ID; *U.S. Public*, pg. 1556
Smith, Patrick D., Sr. V.P.-Mfg. Opers.--TJ International, Inc., Boise, ID; *U.S. Public*, pg. 1556
Smith, Paul A., Chief Oper. Officer & V.P.-Mfg.--Eversharp Pen Co., Franklin Park, IL; *U.S. Private*, pg. 386
Smith, Richard, V.P.-Engrng. & Mfg.--Litecontrol Corporation, Hanson, MA; *U.S. Private*, pg. 669
Smith, Sean, Mgr.-Plant--Karnak Corporation, Clark, NJ; *U.S. Private*, pg. 607
Smith, Tom, Chief Engineer--Franklin Baking Co., Inc., Goldsboro, NC; *U.S. Private*, pg. 424
Smith, William F., V.P.-Petroleum & Mining--Raytheon Engineers & Constructors, Inc., Englewood, CO; *U.S. Public*, pg. 1366
Smithey, Cary, Mgr.-Plant--Stoneville Furniture Co. Inc., Stoneville, NC; *U.S. Private*, pg. 1045
Snow, R., V.P.-Mfg.--Ideal Industries, Inc., Sycamore, IL; *U.S. Private*, pg. 557
Snyder, Dale E., V.P.-Truck Mfg.--Navistar International Corporation, Chicago, IL; *U.S. Public*, pg. 1167
Snyder, Robert, Exec. V.P.-Opers.--American Manufacturing Company, Chattanooga, TN; *U.S. Private*, pg. 58
Sodul, John, Asst. Plant Mgr.--Bachmann Industries, Inc., Philadelphia, PA; *U.S. Private*, pg. 109
Soler, Jaime, Dir.-Engrng.--Alcon (Puerto Rico) Inc., Humacao, PR; *Int'l*, pg. 916
Solly, Geoffrey M. O., V.P.-Engrng.--BC Gas Inc., Vancouver, Canada; *Int'l*, pg. 114
Solter, Lance E., V.P.-Color/Mfg.--Universal Foods Corporation, Milwaukee, WI; *U.S. Public*, pg. 1695
Somerville, Charles H., V.P.-Prod.--Mooney Aircraft Corporation, Kerrville, TX; *U.S. Private*, pg. 759
Sommerland, Gary D., V.P.-Mfg.--Aero Systems Engineering Inc., Saint Paul, MN; *Int'l*, pg. 276

Sondak, Steve, Mgr.-Pin Opers.--Spirol International Corp., Danielson, CT; *U.S. Private*, pg. 1026

Sonderegger, Hans, Mgr.-Mfg.--Brauerei AG, Zurich, Switzerland; *Int'l*, pg. 479

Sonne, Philip, Dir.-Production--Time/System International A/S, Allerod, Denmark; *Int'l*, pg. 73

Soo-Kang, Lee, Exec. V.P.-Production & Indus. Machinery--Korea Heavy Industries & Construction Co., Ltd., Seoul, Korea; *Int'l*, pg. 758

Soong, Ronnie, Mng. Dir.--Galco International Toys, N.V., Kowloon, Hong Kong; *U.S. Public*, pg. 698

Sorensen, Jamey, V.P.-Pur.--RK Mechanical, Inc., Denver, CO; *U.S. Private*, pg. 904

Sorenson, Mary, Mgr.-Production--Master Appliance Corp., Racine, WI; *U.S. Private*, pg. 713

Sorenson, Max E., Sr. V.P-Engrng., Mfg. & Tech.--Geneva Steel, Vineyard, UT; *U.S. Public*, pg. 729

Sosankin, Robert S., Sr. V.P.-Mdsg.--The Cato Corporation, Charlotte, NC; *U.S. Public*, pg. 318

Sotherden, Ronald, Plant Mgr.--Worthington Foods Inc., Worthington, OH; *U.S. Public*, pg. 1780

Sotok, Fred, V.P.-Mfg.--Prince Corporation, Holland, MI; *U.S. Private*, pg. 932

Sougarret, Luis, Asst. Mgr.-Prod.--Salvador Division, El Salvador, Chile; *Int'l*, pg. 302

Southwell, M.T., Dir.-Prod.--Bass Brewers Ltd., Burton on Trent, United Kingdom; *Int'l*, pg. 170

Spadafora, Loretta, Dir.-Mfg.--Electro-Science Laboratories, Inc., King of Prussia, PA; *U.S. Private*, pg. 369

Speice, B.D., V.P.-Opers.--Baltimore Aircoil Company, Jessup, MD; *U.S. Private*, pg. 68

Speich, David, V.P.-Engrng.--Clearing-Niagara, Buffalo, NY; *U.S. Private*, pg. 196

Spencer, Pete, Dir.-Mfg.--Crosman Airguns, East Bloomfield, NY; *U.S. Private*, pg. 291

Spickler, Gary W., Sr. V.P.-Mfg. Opers.--Grove WorldWide, Shady Grove, PA; *Int'l*, pg. 593

Spinoso, Jose, Mgr.-Prod.--Cora Texas Manufacturing Co., Inc., White Castle, LA; *U.S. Private*, pg. 275

Splinter, Michael R., V.P.-Microcomputer Components Group Mfg.--Intel Microcomputer Group, Santa Clara, CA; *U.S. Public*, pg. 887

Spooner, Worthington, V.P.-Intl. Sls. & Systems--Emcee Broadcast Products, Inc., White Haven, PA; *U.S. Public*, pg. 570

Sporer, Norbert, Dir.-Mfg.--Cherry Mikroschalter GmbH, Auerbach, Germany; *U.S. Public*, pg. 346

Spragg, Gregory, Exec. V.P.-Sls. & Mdsg.--FINAST, Maple Heights, OH; *Int'l*, pg. 750

Sprague, R.M., Coordinator-Exploration & Prod.--Royal Dutch/Shell Group of Companies, Hague, Netherlands; *Int'l*, pg. 1135

Springer, Carl M., V.P.-Mfg. & Engrng.--Binks Sames Corporation, Franklin Park, IL; *U.S. Public*, pg. 229

St. John, Kevin, Dir.-Mfg.--Skinner Valve Division, New Britain, CT; *U.S. Public*, pg. 1260

Stacho, Robert, Pres. & Chief Oper. Officer--Midco International Inc., Chicago, IL; *U.S. Private*, pg. 744

Stachura, Robert D., V.P. & Exec. Mgr.-Mfg.--Magna Lomason Corp., Farmington Hills, MI; *Int'l*, pg. 830

Stadtmiller, Martin B., Chief Mfg. Officer, V.P.-Opers. & Sec.--Edwards Brothers, Inc., Ann Arbor, MI; *U.S. Private*, pg. 365

Stafford, Robert, Dir.-Mfg.--ACR Industries Inc., Macomb Township, MI; *U.S. Private*, pg. 3

Stafford, Thomas, Exec. V. P. & Gen. Mgr.-Mfg.--Gilman Paper Co., Saint Marys, GA; *U.S. Private*, pg. 454

Stagni, Paolo, V.P.-Mfg. & Services--G.D. Packaging Machinery Inc., Richmond, VA; *Int'l*, pg. 531

Stagno, Anthony, V.P.-Mfg. & Opers.--Ascend Communications, Inc., Alameda, CA; *U.S. Public*, pg. 138

Stalker, Altan, V.P.-Opers. & Engrng. Grp.--Group W Satellite Communications, Stamford, CT; *U.S. Public*, pg. 275

Stancliffe, Walter D., V.P.-Engrng. & Production--Wilshire Oil Co. of Texas, Jersey City, NJ; *U.S. Public*, pg. 1770

Stanford, J.E., V.P.-Mfg.--The Murray Ohio Mfg. Co., Brentwood, TN; *Int'l*, pg. 1397

Staniec, Ted, V.P.-Mfg.--Synchro-Start Products, Inc., Niles, IL; *U.S. Private*, pg. 627

Starita, Michael S., V.P.-Mfg.--Rheometric Scientific, Piscataway, NJ; *U.S. Public*, pg. 1387

Starky, Michael, V.P.-Mfg.--Goldenberg Group, Inc., Lynwood, CA; *U.S. Public*, pg. 1193

Stastny, John, Mgr.-Warehouse & Distr.--Hickory Farms Catalogues of America, Inc., Maumee, OH; *U.S. Private*, pg. 525

Staudt, Daniel E., Pres.-Mfg. & Distribution--Shoney's, Inc., Nashville, TN; *U.S. Public*, pg. 1467

Steadman, Geoff, V.P.-Mfg.--Aerofin Corp., Lynchburg, VA; *U.S. Public*, pg. 103

Stefaniak, Istvan, Tech. Mgr.-Plywood--Westag & Getalit AG, Rheda-Wiedenbruck, Germany; *Int'l*, pg. 1491

Stein, David, V.P.-Mfg.--Federal APD, Inc., Farmington, MI; *U.S. Public*, pg. 616

Steinhauer, Tom, V.P.-Opers.--Global Van Lines, Inc., Orange, CA; *U.S. Private*, pg. 458

Steininger, Peter C., V.P. & Dir.-Construction--Bob Evans Farms, Inc., Columbus, OH; *U.S. Public*, pg. 596

Steinke, Sue, Dir.-Production & Mfg.--Coleman Powermate Compressors, Springfield, MN; *U.S. Private*, pg. 691

Steinmann, Russ, V.P.-Mfg.--Minor Rubber Co., Inc., Bloomfield, NJ; *U.S. Private*, pg. 751

Stelmack, Stan, V.P.-Mfg.--Hercules Chemical Co., Inc., Passaic, NJ; *U.S. Private*, pg. 523

Stempnewicz, Dieter, Dir.-Mfg.--Heidelberger Druckmaschinen A.G., Heidelberg, Germany; *Int'l*, pg. 604

Stenbit, John P., Acting Exec. V.P. & Gen. Mgr.-TRW Systems Integration Grp.--TRW Inc., Cleveland, OH; *U.S.* Public, pg. 1558

Stenzel, Gary, Mgr.-Pur.--Peerless Chain Company, Winona, MN; *U.S. Public*, pg. 1268

Stephens, Roy G., Dir.-Mfg.--Trion, Inc., Sanford, NC; *U.S. Public*, pg. 1639

Stewart, Dennis, Chief Engr.--Phototype Color Graphics, Inc., Pennsauken, NJ; *U.S. Private*, pg. 864

Stewart, Jack, V.P.-Mfg.--Guardian Products, Inc., Simi Valley, CA; *U.S. Public*, pg. 1535

Stewart, William, V.P.-Mfg.--Conso Products Company, Union, SC; *U.S. Public*, pg. 434

Stickelmaier, Chuck, Sr. V.P.-Mfg.--Prince Golf International, Bordentown, NJ; *U.S. Private*, pg. 884

Stiles, Robert N., V.P.-Opers.--Houston Fearless 76 Inc., Compton, CA; *U.S. Private*, pg. 542

Stockham, George, Mgr.-Mfg.--Bruning Paint Company, Baltimore, MD; *U.S. Private*, pg. 176

Stocks, J.M., V.P.-Mfg.--Peco Mfg. Co., Inc., Portland, OR; *U.S. Private*, pg. 846

Stoecker, Gary, Sr. V.P.-Mfg.--Sea Ray, Knoxville, TN; *U.S. Public*, pg. 266

Stoker, Lindell G., Grp. V.P.-Mfg.--American & Efird, Inc., Mount Holly, NC; *U.S. Public*, pg. 1412

Stoltz, Don H., Dir.-Quality--Fenn Manufacturing Co., Newington, CT; *U.S. Public*, pg. 1676

Stolzer, E., V.P.-Mfg.--Quality Bakers of America Cooperative, Inc., Greenwich, CT; *U.S. Private*, pg. 898

Stone, Bruce, Dir.-Power Production--Associated Electric Co-op Inc., Springfield, MO; *U.S. Private*, pg. 89

Stone, Michael, Mgr.-Engrng.--MD Pneumatics, Springfield, MO; *U.S. Private*, pg. 1111

Stos, Charles J., V.P.-Non-Retail Procurement--The Vons Companies, Inc., Arcadia, CA; *U.S. Public*, pg. 1426

Stotts, James, V.P.-Mktg.--Arctic Slope Regional Corporation, Barrow, AK; *U.S. Private*, pg. 80

Stoude, Mark, V.P.-Mfg.--Renaissance Publishing Co., Inc., Auburn, IN; *Int'l*, pg. 185

Stouffer, Peter, V.P.-Engrng. & Mfg.--Code-Alarm, Inc., Madison Heights, MI; *U.S. Public*, pg. 393

Stoutenberg, Bob, V.P.-Mfg.--Progressive Tool & Industries Co., Southfield, MI; *U.S. Private*, pg. 890

Stovall, Bill, Grp. V.P.--Koh-I-Noor, Inc., Bloomsbury, NJ; *U.S. Private*, pg. 629

Stover, Larry, V.P.-Mfg. Accessories Div.--Bradley Corporation, Menomonee Falls, WI; *U.S. Private*, pg. 164

Stowers, Dennis A., Dir.-Mfg.--Daig Corporation, Minnetonka, MN; *U.S. Public*, pg. 1428

Strachan, Rick, V.P. & Pres.-Mfg.--Clayton Homes, Inc., Knoxville, TN; *U.S. Public*, pg. 382

Strak, Matt, Mgr.-Mfg.--Selfix, Inc., Chicago, IL; *U.S. Public*, pg. 832

Straka, Michael, Sr. V.P.-Mfg.--Tropical Sportswear International, Tampa, FL; *U.S. Private*, pg. 1105

Strang, Richard M., Chief Tech. Officer, VLSI Sys.--SBE, Inc., San Ramon, CA; *U.S. Public*, pg. 1416

Stratter, William, Sr. V.P.-Mfg.--Electronic Data Magnetics, Inc., High Point, NC; *U.S. Private*, pg. 370

Straub, Riener, Mgr.-Mfr.--Wandel & Goltermann GmbH & Co., Elektronische Messtechnik, Eningen, Germany; *Int'l, pg. 1485*

Strauss, Lean, Gen. Mgr.-Mfg. & Supply--Sasol Oil (Pty) Ltd., Randburg, South Africa; *Int'l*, pg. 1197

Street, Elmer H., Plant Supvr.--AC Corporation, Greensboro, NC; *U.S. Private*, pg. 3

Street, Joe, Mgr.-Mfg.--The Vernon Company, Newton, IA; *U.S. Private*, pg. 1137

Strelzoff, Alan, Mgr.-Advanced Engrng.--Schneider Automation, Inc., North Andover, MA; *Int'l*, pg. 1208

Strode, Jim, V.P.-Mfg.--Williams Scotsman Group, Inc., Santa Fe Springs, CA; *U.S. Private*, pg. 977

Stroh, A.J., Sr. V.P.-Mfg.--Trico Products Corporation, Buffalo, NY; *Int'l*, pg. 1397

Strohl, Dale S., Sr. V.P.-Opers.--Tiffany & Co., New York, NY; *U.S. Public*, pg. 1608

Stropki, John M., Exec. V.P.-Sls. & Mfg.--The Lincoln Electric Company, Cleveland, OH; *U.S. Public*, pg. 996

Stuart, K. Michael, Sr. V.P.-Aircraft Opers.--Comair, Inc., Erlanger, KY; *U.S. Public*, pg. 406

Stuckert, J., V.P.-Mfg.--NT Dor-omatic, Harwood Heights, IL; *U.S. Private*, pg. 771

Stull, John, V.P.-Mfg.--Malt-O-Meal Company, Minneapolis, MN; *U.S. Private*, pg. 699

Stump, Jeffery J., V.P.-Mfg.--Cowden Metal Specialties, Inc., Chino, CA; *U.S. Private*, pg. 280

Sugg, Rolin, V.P.-Mfg.--Baldwin Hardware Corporation, Reading, PA; *U.S. Public*, pg. 1053

Sullivan, Gary, V.P.-Mfg.--H.L. Bouton Company Inc., Buzzards Bay, MA; *U.S. Private*, pg. 162

Sullivan, Gary, V.P.-Mfg.--Lensclean, Inc., Buzzards Bay, MA; *U.S. Private*, pg. 162

Sullivan, Marc, Dir.-Energy Mngmt. Svcs.--Seattle City Light, Seattle, WA; *U.S. Private*, pg. 979

Sullivan, Rose, V.P.-Mfg. & Distr.--Financial World Partners, New York, NY; *U.S. Private*, pg. 404

Sullivant, Jim, Dir.-Mfg.--Gish Biomedical, Inc., Irvine, CA; *U.S. Public*, pg. 745

Summers, Roy, Mng. Dir.-Prod.--Scottish & Courage Beer Div., Edinburgh, United Kingdom; *Int'l*, pg. 1212

Suson, Irwin, Mgr.-Plant--Shafer Commercial Seating Inc., Denver, CO; *U.S. Private*, pg. 988

Sussman, Ph.D., Joseph L., Sr. V.P.-Mfg./Diagnostics Div.--Bayer Corporation, Pittsburgh, PA; *Int'l*, pg. 172

Sutherland, Allan R., Pres. & Chief Oper. Officer-Industrial Technologies--Derlan Industries Limited, Toronto, Canada; *Int'l*, pg. 395

Sutliff, David R., V.P.-Engrng.--ACF Industries, Inc., Saint Charles, MO; *U.S. Private*, pg. 556

Sutton, Michael E., V.P.-Mfg.--North American Products Corp., Jasper, IN; *U.S. Private*, pg. 803

Suzuki, Shoichiro, Dir.-Mfg., Tech. & Engrng.--Oji Paper Co., Ltd., Tokyo, Japan; *Int'l*, pg. 998

Svet, Frank, V.P.-Engrng.--Harris Corp. Broadcast Div., Quincy, IL; *U.S. Public*, pg. 791

Swanson, Brian, V.P.-Technology & Quality Control--Glastic Corporation, Cleveland, OH; *Int'l*, pg. 740

Swanson, John F., V.P.-Engrng.--Cox Broadcasting Inc., Atlanta, GA; *U.S. Private*, pg. 281

Swanson, Joseph, V.P. & Gen. Mgr.-Mfg.--Regal Ware, Inc., Kewaskum, WI; *U.S. Private*, pg. 917

Swanson, R.E., Sr. V.P.-Mfg.--Consolidated Papers, Inc., Wisconsin Rapids, WI; *U.S. Public*, pg. 436

Swanson, Robert, Supvr.-Production--Ocean Spray Cranberries-Bordentown Plant, Bordentown, NJ; *U.S. Private*, pg. 811

Swart, D., Tech. Dir.--Neddrill Nederland B.V., Rotterdam, Netherlands; *Int'l*, pg. 1144

Sweeney, Paddy, Mgr.-Mfg.--Lancashire Dairies Ltd., Manchester, United Kingdom; *Int'l*, pg. 798

Swem, Robert, V.P.-Mfg.--VTEL Corporation, Austin, TX; *U.S. Public*, pg. 1703

Swenson, Russell, V.P.-Engrng. & Prod.--Alumacraft Boat Co., Saint Peter, MN; *U.S. Private*, pg. 1088

Swilik, Robert C., V.P.-Mfg. & Seasonal Divison--American Greetings Corporation, Cleveland, OH; *U.S. Public*, pg. 77

Switalski, David, V.P.-Mfg.--Quipp Systems, Inc., Hialeah, FL; *U.S. Public*, pg. 1353

Sydlowski, F., V.P.-Mfg.--Owens Corning/Foamular, Parsippany, NJ; *U.S. Public*, pg. 1237

Sydorenko, Paul, Mgr.-Plant--Blue Coral/Slick 50, Cleveland, OH; *U.S. Public*, pg. 1348

Sylvester, John E., Sr. V.P.-Opers.--Nutri/System Inc., Horsham, PA; *U.S. Private*, pg. 859

Sylvestor, Michael P., Mgr.-Plant--Advance Packaging Corporation, Grand Rapids, MI; *U.S. Private*, pg. 18

Szorc, Steve, Mgr.-Bus. Unit--Revcor, Inc., Carpentersville, IL; *U.S. Private*, pg. 925

Szotkowski, David, Sr. Mgr.-Mfg.--TCI International Inc., Sunnyvale, CA; *U.S. Public*, pg. 1555

Szucs, J.S., Mgr.-Factory--Tocco, Inc., Boaz, AL; *U.S. Public*, pg. 1259

Szymanski, C., V.P.-Res. & Engrng.--Lever Brothers Co., New York, NY; *Int'l*, pg. 1435

Tabatabai, Michael, V.P.-Worldwide Opers.--Autodesk, Inc., San Rafael, CA; *U.S. Public*, pg. 148

Tacheny, James, V.P.-Combustion & Hydro Operations--Northern States Power Company, Minneapolis, MN; *U.S.* Public, pg. 1195

Tachikawa, A., Dir.-Mfg.--Avon Products Co., Ltd., Tokyo, Japan; *U.S. Public*, pg. 156

Tacik, Wolfram, Mgr.-Mfg.--Eagle-Picher Wolverine GmbH, Ohringen, Germany; *U.S. Private*, pg. 355

Tack, W., Mgr.-Mfg.--Agfa-Gevaert N.V., Antwerp, Belgium; *Int'l*, pg. 174

Tait, C. Robert, Jr., V.P.-Mfg.--Tinius Olsen Testing Machine Co., Inc., Willow Grove, PA; *U.S. Private*, pg. 1088

Tait, R.J., Mgr.-Mfg. Group--AGR International, Inc., Butler, PA; *U.S. Private*, pg. 5

Takahashi, Tsutomu, Sr. Mng. Dir.--Ebara Corporation, Tokyo, Japan; *Int'l*, pg. 431

Takamura, Eimei, V.P.-Production--Q & B Foods, Inc., Irwindale, CA; *Int'l*, pg. 1074

Talbert, J.E., V.P.-Engrng.--Morrison Textile Machinery Co., Fort Lawn, SC; *U.S. Private*, pg. 762

Talluto, Mario J., Dir.-Production--Business Week, New York, NY; *U.S. Public*, pg. 1069

Talpas, John B., V.P.-Mfg.--Great Lakes Chemical Corporation, West Lafayette, IN; *U.S. Public*, pg. 760

Tamkin, Michael S., V.P.-Mfg.--Proxima Corporation, San Diego, CA; *U.S. Public*, pg. 1339

Tan, P.C., Gen. Mgr.-Mfg.--Mobil Oil Singapore Pte. Ltd., Singapore, Singapore; *U.S. Public*, pg. 1119

Tan, Thian H., V.P. & Mng. Dir-Mfg./Plng.--Komag, Incorporated, San Jose, CA; *U.S. Public*, pg. 966

Tanhuanpaa, Matti, Mgr.-Mfg.--Bronto Skylift Oy AB, Tampere, Finland; *U.S. Public*, pg. 617

Tani, Takao, Mng. Dir.-Prod. & Engrng.--Ajinomoto Company Inc., Tokyo, Japan; *Int'l*, pg. 40

Tani, Tatsuro, Gen. Mgr.-Production--Terumo Corporation, Tokyo, Japan; *Int'l*, pg. 1375

Tanner, Jack, V.P.-Mfg.--Advance Business Graphics, Mira Loma, CA; *U.S. Private*, pg. 18

Tapada, J., Mgr.-Mfg.--Industrias Lever Portuguesa, Lda., Lisbon, Portugal; *Int'l*, pg. 1437

Tarpley, Blake, V.P.-Mfg.--Fruit of the Loom, Inc., Chicago, IL; *U.S. Public*, pg. 685

Tarpley, Richard, Exec.V.P.-Mfg.--CPI Corp., Saint Louis, MO; *U.S. Public*, pg. 283

Tarrh, Vern J., V.P.-Mfg.--Alumax Mill Products, Inc., Morris, IL; *U.S. Public*, pg. 59

Tattersfield, Rick, Gen. Mgr.-Mfg. & Opers./Germany--Instron Schenck Testing Systems Limited, High Wycombe, United Kingdom; *U.S. Public*, pg. 883

Tatum, Don, V.P.-Engrng. & Environmental--Riverwood International Corporation, Atlanta, GA; *U.S. Public*, pg. 1391

Taylor, Brent, V.P.-Opers.--Rudolph Foods Company, Lima, OH; *U.S. Private*, pg. 950

Taylor, Bruce, V.P.-Mfg.--Flambeau Corporation, Baraboo, WI; *U.S. Private*, pg. 409

Taylor, Cecil, Plant Production Mgr.--Industrial Bag Division - New Philadelphia Plant, New Philadelphia, OH; *U.S. Public*, pg. 1521

Taylor, D.R., V.P.-Production--Texas Refinery Corp., Fort Worth, TX; *U.S. Private*, pg. 1078

Taylor, J.L., V.P.-Mfg.--Daubert Coated Products, Inc., Westchester, IL; *U.S. Private*, pg. 313

Taylor, Jerry, V.P.-Mfg. & Memory Prods.--Integrated Device Technology, Inc., Santa Clara, CA; *U.S. Public*, pg. 884

Taylor, Kit, V.P.-Mfg.--Times Mirror Magazines, Inc., New York, NY; *U.S. Public*, pg. 1616

Taylor, Larry, V.P.-Engrng.--Taylor Corporation, Mankato, MN; *U.S. Private*, pg. 1070

Taylor, R.H., Div. Mgr.-Mfg.--Meadow Lea Foods Ltd., Mascot, Australia; *Int'l*, pg. 555

Taylor, Ron, Sr. Leader-Audio Div. Mfg.--Crown International, Inc., Elkhart, IN; *U.S. Private*, pg. 293

Taylor, Stephen R., V.P.-Fabric Filter Mfg.--BHA Company, Inc., Kansas City, MO; *U.S. Public*, pg. 161

Taylor, Ty, V.P.-Opers.--Carmun International, San Antonio, TX; *Int'l*, pg. 646

Taylor, Will, Mgr.-Production--Washington Business Journal, Inc., Arlington, VA; *U.S. Private*, pg. 20
Teasdale, Jean, Mgr.-Mfg.--Utah Medical Products, Inc., Midvale, UT; *U.S. Public*, pg. 1700
Tegeler, Vernon, V.P.-Prod.--Siemer Milling Company, Teutopolis, IL; *U.S. Private*, pg. 998
Tehranian, Yalda, V.P.-Prod. & Acq.--LIVE Film & Mediaworks, Van Nuys, CA; *U.S. Private*, pg. 671
Tejeda, Gerard, V.P.-Mfg.--Integrated Metal Technologies, Inc., Spring Lake, MI; *U.S. Public*, pg. 1112
Tener, James R., V.P.-Opers.--Pier 1 Imports, Inc., Fort Worth, TX; *U.S. Public*, pg. 1295
Teodosic, Momcilo, V.P.-Mfg.--Acustar, Inc., Troy, MI; *U.S. Public*, pg. 353
Termaat, Bob, V.P.-Mfg.--Ajay Leisure Products, Inc., Delavan, WI; *U.S. Public*, pg. 34
Tesch, William, V.P.-Red Star BioProducts/Mfg. Opers.--Universal Foods Corporation, Milwaukee, WI; *U.S. Public*, pg. 1695
Thaler, Arnold, Exec. V.P.-Prod. Dev., Engineering & Manufacturing--Windmere-Durable Holdings, Hialeah, FL; *U.S. Public*, pg. 1771
Tharaldson, Jim, Chief Engineer--United Farm Tools, Inc., Glasgow, KY; *U.S. Private*, pg. 1122
Thatcher, James L., V.P.-Opers.--SI Handling Systems, Inc., Easton, PA; *U.S. Public*, pg. 1418
Theodore, Michael, V.P.-Mfg. Opers--SouthCo. Inc., Concordville, PA; *U.S. Private*, pg. 1014
Theriot, Scott, V.P.-Production--Bollinger Shipyards, Inc., Lockport, LA; *U.S. Private*, pg. 155
Thiessen, Robert, Mgr.-Plant--Ice Cream Specialties, Inc., Lafayette, IN; *U.S. Private*, pg. 879
Thiessen, Wayne, Dir.-Mfg.--Wrigley Canada Inc., Don Mills, Canada; *U.S. Public*, pg. 1781
Thomas, David, V.P.-Mfg.--Williams, White & Co., Moline, IL; *U.S. Private*, pg. 1179
Thomas, Geoffrey R.M., V.P. & Gen. Mgr.-ADSC--Analog Devices, Inc., Norwood, MA; *U.S. Public*, pg. 107
Thomas, J.C., V.P.-Mfg.--Steel Technologies Inc., Louisville, KY; *U.S. Public*, pg. 1513
Thomas, James E., V.P.-Mfr.--Altron Systems Corporation, Fremont, CA; *U.S. Public*, pg. 59
Thomas, R.A., V.P.-Engrng. & Res.--Talley Defense Systems, Inc., Mesa, AZ; *U.S. Public*, pg. 308
Thomas, Robert M., V.P.-Mfg. Services--COMSAT RSI, Inc., Sterling, VA; *U.S. Public*, pg. 424
Thomas, Roger, V.P.-Mfg.--Empire Berol U.S.A., Brentwood, TN; *U.S. Public*, pg. 1178
Thomas, Roy, V.P.-Opers.--Ensoniq, Malvern, PA; *U.S. Private*, pg. 377
Thomason, Jim, V.P.-Mfg.--Selkirk Metalbestos, Dallas, TX; *U.S. Public*, pg. 1794
Thome, Joe, Mgr.-Mfg.--Miller-St. Nazianz, Inc., Saint Nazianz, WI; *U.S. Private*, pg. 748
Thompson, A., Dir.-Production Services--British Gypsum Ltd., Loughborough, United Kingdom; *Int'l*, pg. 122
Thompson, Bill, V.P.-Mfg.--Oil-Dri Corporation of America, Chicago, IL; *U.S. Public*, pg. 1214
Thompson, Charles L., V.P.-Engrng.--Union Electric Steel Corp., Carnegie, PA; *U.S. Public*, pg. 103
Thompson, Duncan, Chief Engr.--Arrow Pneumatics Co. Inc., Lake Zurich, IL; *U.S. Private*, pg. 85
Thompson, Ed, Dir.-Mfg.--Paradyne, Largo, FL; *U.S. Private*, pg. 838
Thompson, Jerry E., V.P.-Corp. Plng. & Economics--Citgo Petroleum Corporation, Tulsa, OK; *Int'l*, pg. 1045
Thompson, Jimmy, V.P.-Greenwood Mills--Greenwood Mills, Inc., Greenwood, SC; *U.S. Private*, pg. 479
Thompson, John G., V.P.-Corp. Mfg.--Iomega Corporation, Roy, UT; *U.S. Public*, pg. 912
Thompson, K., Mgr.-Production--Becton Dickinson Canada Inc., Mississauga, Canada; *U.S. Public*, pg. 200
Thompson, Ken, V.P. & Gen. Mgr.-Mfg. Tech.--Intel Components Technology & Manufacturing Group, Santa Clara, CA; *U.S. Public*, pg. 886
Thomson, Donald, V.P.-Tech.--LeaRonal, Inc., Freeport, NY; *U.S. Public*, pg. 982
Thorn, Ken, Mgr.-Consumer Products Mfg.--MTD Products Limited, Kitchener, Canada; *U.S. Private*, pg. 688
Thornton, Michael A., V.P.-Prod.--Progress Printing Company, Lynchburg, VA; *U.S. Private*, pg. 890
Thorpe, Brian, Dir.-Mfg.--Austin Productions, Inc., Holbrook, NY; *U.S. Private*, pg. 100
Threde, Roger, V.P.-Mfg.--Carus Chemical Company, Chemical Div., Peru, IL; *U.S. Private*, pg. 217
Thurber, Robert C., V.P.-Mdsg.-Perishable Prods.--Sysco Corporation, Houston, TX; *U.S. Public*, pg. 1550
Tidwell, Richard, Asst. Exec. Dir.-Opers.--Metra, Commuter Rail Service Board, Chicago, IL; *U.S. Private*, pg. 919
Tiffany, John E., V.P.-Mfg.--Banta Corporation, Menasha, WI; *U.S. Public*, pg. 187
Tighe, William, V.P.-Mfg.--West Mill Clothes, Inc., Woodside, NY; *U.S. Private*, pg. 1163
Tiistola, Pentti, Mgr.-Matls. Mngmt.--Hobby Hall, Helsinki, Finland; *Int'l*, pg. 1301
Tilley, Julius, V.P.-Mfg.--Metal Masters Foodservice Equipment, Clayton, DE; *U.S. Private*, pg. 734
Tindal, Evans, Mgr.-Mfg. Resources--Cheraw Yarn Mills, Inc., Cheraw, SC; *U.S. Private*, pg. 233
Tingle, Dan, Mgr.-Corp. Opers.--Samtec Inc., New Albany, IN; *U.S. Private*, pg. 963
Tinkel, Gary, V.P.-Mfg.--Spangler Candy Company, Bryan, OH; *U.S. Private*, pg. 1020
Tjian, Hans T.Y., Sr. V.P.-Opers. & Systems--Westamerica Bank, San Rafael, CA; *U.S. Public*, pg. 1756
Todd, George, V.P.-Mfg.--Kalamazoo Holdings, Inc., Kalamazoo, MI; *U.S. Private*, pg. 606
Todd, Jim, V.P.-Mfg.--Preservative Paint Company, Seattle, WA; *U.S. Private*, pg. 613
Todd, Russ, V.P.-Mfg.--Martin Industries, Inc. (AL), Florence, AL; *U.S. Private*, pg. 709
Toellner, Ken, Mgr.-Mfg.--Mayville Engineering Co., Inc., Mayville, WI; *U.S. Private*, pg. 718
Tolford, George K., V.P.-Mfg.--Webster Industries Inc., Tiffin, OH; *U.S. Private*, pg. 1157
Toner, Jeffrey M., V.P.-Mfg.--Kingsbury Corporation, Keene, NH; *U.S. Private*, pg. 621
Toomey, Kenton C., Chief Oper. Officer & V.P.-Oper.--Osmonics, Inc., Minnetonka, MN; *U.S. Public*, pg. 1233
Torvund, Tore, Dir.-Exploration & Production, Norway--Norsk Hydro a.s, Oslo, Norway; *Int'l*, pg. 959
Toussaint, John-Charles, Chief Oper. Officer & V.P.--Propper Manufacturing Co., Inc., Long Island City, NY; *U.S. Private*, pg. 891
Townsend, Larry, V.P.-Mfg.--The National Super Service Co., Toledo, OH; *U.S. Private*, pg. 787
Tramel, Charles, Dir.-Opers. & Memphis Mfg.--Insituform Technologies, Inc., Chesterfield, MO; *U.S. Public*, pg. 881
Tranberg, G.L., V.P.-Mfg.--Intertape Polymer Group, Green Bay, WI; *Int'l*, pg. 685
Trangsrud, Lowell, V.P.-Worldwide Mfg.--Tandem Computers Inc., Cupertino, CA; *U.S. Public*, pg. 417
Transou, Robert H., Grp. V.P.-Mfg.--Ford Motor Company, Dearborn, MI; *U.S. Public*, pg. 661
Trauth, Andrew, V.P.-Engrng.--Trauth Dairy Inc., Newport, KY; *U.S. Private*, pg. 1098
Trauth, Steven A., V.P.-Prod. & Sec.--Trauth Dairy Inc., Newport, KY; *U.S. Private*, pg. 1098
Traver, William, Sr. V.P.-Mfg.--World Color-Chicago Div., Elk Grove Village, IL; *U.S. Public*, pg. 1778
Traviss, D.P., V.P.-Refining & Petrochemical--UOP, Des Plaines, IL; *U.S. Public*, pg. 52
Tremblay, Jacquelin, Mgr.-Prod.--Security Chimneys International Ltd., Laval, Canada; *Int'l*, pg. 1217
Treml, Raymond F., Sr. V.P.-Mfg.--JLG Industries, Inc., McConnellsburg, PA; *U.S. Public*, pg. 918
Tribie, Charles, V.P.-Mfg.--U.S. Surgical Corp., Norwalk, CT; *U.S. Public*, pg. 1687
Trickey, Gregory M., Chief Oper. Officer--Wolverine Tube Inc., Huntsville, AL; *U.S. Public*, pg. 1774
Trimarco, Gregorio, Dir.-Mfg.--Colgate-Palmolive S.A.I.C., Lavalle, Argentina; *U.S. Public*, pg. 399
Truax, J.E., Dir.-Mfg.--Master Builders Inc., Cleveland, OH; *Int'l*, pg. 1465
Trushel, John, V.P.-Mfr.--Circon Corporation, Santa Barbara, CA; *U.S. Public*, pg. 373
Tsakiridis, Christos, V.P.-Mfg.--Sellstrom Manufacturing Co., Palatine, IL; *U.S. Private*, pg. 983
Tsuda, Shinji, Dir.-Production--Hokuriku Electric Industry Co., Ltd., Toyama, Japan; *Int'l*, pg. 627
Tuchman, Walter, Sr. V.P.-Engrng.--Amperif Corporation, Chatsworth, CA; *U.S. Public*, pg. 1523
Tuchner, Marcel, Exec. V.P.-Mfg. & Engrng.--Cinram Ltd., Scarborough, Canada; *Int'l*, pg. 293
Tucker, Crystal, Mgr.-Production--The Seattle Business Journal, Inc., Seattle, WA; *U.S. Private*, pg. 20
Tucker, Richard G., V.P.-Mfg.--Lance, Inc., Charlotte, NC; *U.S. Public*, pg. 977
Tucker, Robert L., Dir.-Production--The Dispatch Printing Company, Columbus, OH; *U.S. Private*, pg. 334
Tuit, Charles, Plant Mgr.--Pacific Handy Cutter, Inc., Costa Mesa, CA; *U.S. Private*, pg. 831
Turnage, John A., V.P.-Mfg. & Sourcing--Kellwood Company, Chesterfield, MO; *U.S. Public*, pg. 948
Turner, Bert, V.P.-Mfg.--Morgan Foods, Inc., Austin, IN; *U.S. Private*, pg. 761
Turner, Lloyd, V.P.-Opers.--Littelfuse, Inc., Des Plaines, IL; *U.S. Public*, pg. 1001
Turner, M., Dir.-Mfg.--Russell Castings Ltd., Leicester, United Kingdom; *Int'l*, pg. 449
Turpin, Richard, Dir.-Engrng.--The Greenbrier, White Sulphur Springs, WV; *U.S. Public*, pg. 284
Tuthill, Dewayne, Exec. V.P.-Mfg.--WHX Corporation, New York, NY; *U.S. Public*, pg. 1726
Tweed, Edward, Mgr.-Mfg.--Plastic Suppliers, Inc., Columbus, OH; *U.S. Private*, pg. 871
Tymczak, Romuald W., V.P. & Mgr.-Reg. Production--Glen-Gery Corporation, Wyomissing, PA; *Int'l*, pg. 658
Tymkiw, Andrew, V.P.-Mfg.--Vital Signs, Englewood, CO; *U.S. Public*, pg. 1723
Uhlig, Richard, V.P. & Gen. Mgr.-Custom Molding Div. & Caltube--Acorn Engineering Company, City of Industry, CA; *U.S. Private*, pg. 14
Uhrinek, John, Mgr.-Mfg.--T.L. Smith Machine, Springville, NY; *U.S. Private*, pg. 1009
Ulabari, Tony, Supvr.-Mfg. & Matls.--Software Publishing Corporation, Fairfield, NJ; *U.S. Public*, pg. 1483
Ulfig, Mark, V.P.-OEM Sls.--Sanden International (U.S.A.), Inc., Wylie, TX; *Int'l*, pg. 1184
Ulibee, Steve, Plant Mgr.--General Housewares Corp., Terre Haute, IN; *U.S. Public*, pg. 715
Underwood, John, V.P.-Mfg. Prod. & Tech. Svcs.--Darigold, Inc., Seattle, WA; *U.S. Private*, pg. 311
Ungar, Manny, Exec. V.P.-Mfg.--Queens Group, Inc., Long Island City, NY; *U.S. Private*, pg. 900
Unis, Jim, Dir.-Facilities--Active Tool & Manufacturing Co., Inc., Roseville, MI; *U.S. Private*, pg. 16
Uritz, Carmen, Electrical Engr.--Medico Industries, Inc., Wilkes-Barre, PA; *U.S. Private*, pg. 728
Urizzo, John, Mgr.-Prod.--Plascal Corporation, Farmingdale, NY; *U.S. Private*, pg. 870
Urmson, Tom, Mgr.-Engrng.--Portec Inc., Railway Maintenance Products Div., Pittsburgh, PA; *U.S. Public*, pg. 1318
Urquhart, Clive, Assoc. Dir.-Mfg.--Industrial Acoustics Company, Ltd., Staines, United Kingdom; *U.S. Public*, pg. 875
Ussery, Ron, V.P.-Mfg.--Viking Range Corp., Greenwood, MS; *U.S. Private*, pg. 1140
Ustian, Daniel C., Gen. Mgr.-Engine & Foundry--Navistar International Transportation Corp., Chicago, IL; *U.S. Public*, pg. 1167
Vail, John, Plant Mgr.--Bock Industries Inc., Elkhart, IN; *Int'l*, pg. 265
Valencia de Freitas, Luciano, Dir.-Mfg.--Sao Paulo Alpargatas S.A., Sao Paulo, Brazil; *Int'l*, pg. 1193
Valters, Tim, Dir.-Mfg. & Engrng.--GSW Heating Products Company, Stoney Creek, Canada; *Int'l*, pg. 538
Valvanis, John, Mgr.-Plant--Staflex Products, Carteret, NJ; *U.S. Private*, pg. 495
Van Andel, Dave, V.P.-Mfg. Opers.--Amway Corporation, Ada, MI; *U.S. Private*, pg. 69
van Appeldoorn, H., Sr. Dir.-Steel Processing--Koninklijke Hoogovens N.V., Ijmuiden, Netherlands; *Int'l*, pg. 753
Van Bruaene, Dave, Mgr.-Scholastic Div. Opers.--Herff Jones Inc., Indianapolis, IN; *U.S. Private*, pg. 523
Van Buren, David M., V.P.-Production--B-2 Division, Pico Rivera, CA; *U.S. Public*, pg. 1198
van de Pas, J. J., Dir.-Prod. & Tech.--Koninklijke De Ruyter BV, Baarn, Netherlands; *Int'l*, pg. 244
Van Drouff, Harold, Dir.-Mfg.--Televideo, Inc., San Jose, CA; *U.S. Public*, pg. 1572
Van Dyke, Garritt, Mgr.-Engrng.--Bridgeport Fittings, Inc., Stratford, CT; *U.S. Private*, pg. 168
van Loenhout, J., Dir.-Production--Holmatro Industrial & Rescue Equipment, Raamsdonksveer, Netherlands; *Int'l*, pg. 632
van Luijk, G.L., Coordinator-Mfg.--Royal Dutch/Shell Group of Companies, Hague, Netherlands; *Int'l*, pg. 1135
van Melle, H.P., Sr. V.P.-Production & Logistics & Planning--Van Melle N.V., Breda, Netherlands; *Int'l*, pg. 1450
Van Rooy, Michael G., V.P.-Mfg.--Knape & Vogt Mfg. Co., Grand Rapids, MI; *U.S. Public*, pg. 963
Van Rosmalen, Walter, Dir.-Petrochemicals--Repsol Quimica, Madrid, Spain; *Int'l*, pg. 1104
Van Tatenhove, Craig, V.P.-Mfg.--Myron Manufacturing Corporation, Maywood, NJ; *U.S. Private*, pg. 771
Van Winkle, Kenneth J., V.P.-Mfg. Systems--Kimball International, Inc., Jasper, IN; *U.S. Public*, pg. 956
Vancant, Mike, Mgr.-Mfg.--South Bend Plastics, Inc., Mishawaka, IN; *U.S. Private*, pg. 1014
Vance, Linda, Mgr.-Production--ACBJ Business Publications, Inc., Louisville, KY; *U.S. Private*, pg. 19
Vandegrift, Rich R., Gen. Mgr.-Opers.--RMI Titanium Company, Niles, OH; *U.S. Public*, pg. 1662
Vandensande, Jean-Guy, Mgr.-Mdse.--Digital Equipment N.V./S.A., Brussels, Belgium; *U.S. Public*, pg. 508
Vanderbergh, Bram, Dir.-Mfg.--Future Foam, Inc., Council Bluffs, IA; *U.S. Private*, pg. 433
Vanderminden, R., Jr., V.P. & Mgr.-Prod.--Telescope Casual Furniture, Inc., Granville, NY; *U.S. Private*, pg. 1074
Varga, John, Mgr.-Mfg.--The U.S. Baird Corporation, Stratford, CT; *U.S. Private*, pg. 1124
Varian, Donna, Mgr.-Prod.--Imperial Bondware Corp., Montvale, NJ; *U.S. Public*, pg. 903
Vastag, Harold, V.P.-Mfg.--Good Humor/Breyers Ice Cream, Green Bay, WI; *Int'l*, pg. 1435
Vaughan, Tom, Chief Engineer--Baker Commodities, Inc., Los Angeles, CA; *U.S. Private*, pg. 111
Verba, Andrew F., Plant Mgr.--Ludowici Roof Tile, Inc., New Lexington, OH; *Int'l*, pg. 1171
Verdoorn, Ronald D., Exec. V.P.-Mfg.--Seagate Technology Inc., Scotts Valley, CA; *U.S. Public*, pg. 1449
Verhassel, Jean-Pierre, Sr.Exec. V.P.-Mfg. & Opers.--Ares-Serono S.A., Geneva, Switzerland; *Int'l*, pg. 80
Verkamp, Andrew, Mgr.-Mfg.--Decora', Jasper, IN; *U.S. Public*, pg. 675
Vermeulen, M.M.A.I., Mgr.-Prod.--Industrial Pharmaceutical Products Division, Delft, Netherlands; *Int'l*, pg. 1142
Verstijen, C., Mgr.-Mfg.--Campina Melkunie BV, Zaltbommel, Netherlands; *Int'l*, pg. 254
Vesotsky, Barry, V.P.-Mdsg.--Deb Shops, Inc., Philadelphia, PA; *U.S. Public*, pg. 491
Vest, Archie, Dir.-Mfg.--Velsicol Chemical Corporation, Rosemont, IL; *U.S. Private*, pg. 1135
Vickery, Eric L., Mgr.-Steel Prods.--Long Products Division, Whyalla, Australia; *Int'l*, pg. 227
Vidal, Humberto, Mgr.-Mfg.--Petroleos de Venezuela S.A., Caracas, Venezuela; *Int'l*, pg. 1045
Vidyarthi, A.D., V.P.-Mfg.--Miller Chemical & Fertilizer Corp., Hanover, PA; *U.S. Private*, pg. 33
Villadsen, Ove, V.P.-Engrng.--Comdial Corporation, Charlottesville, VA; *U.S. Public*, pg. 407
Vincent, M., Mgr.-Production--FMC Food Machinery France, S.A., Aulnay-sous-Bois, France; *U.S. Public*, pg. 606
Vink, J., Mgr.-Mfg.--Bac Color Franseweg, Steenbergen, Netherlands; *Int'l*, pg. 131
Vinson, Stan, Exec. V.P.-Mfg.--Union Underwear Co., Inc., Bowling Green, KY; *U.S. Public*, pg. 686
Viola, Joseph, V.P.-Mfg.--Uniflex, Inc., Hicksville, NY; *U.S. Public*, pg. 1665
Visconti, John E., Exec. V.P.-Mfg.--Pannier Corporation, Pittsburgh, PA; *U.S. Private*, pg. 837
Vispi, Donald R., V.P.-Mfg. & Distr.--Haddon Craftsmen, Inc., Scranton, PA; *U.S. Public*, pg. 518
Vitzthum, Anton F., Sr. V.P.-Mfg.--Material Sciences Corporation, Elk Grove Village, IL; *U.S. Public*, pg. 1056
Vogesong, Tom, Dir.-Engrng.--Criticare Systems, Inc., Waukesha, WI; *U.S. Public*, pg. 459
Vogler, Eric V., Mgr.-Mfg.--Airflex Div. Eaton Corp., Cleveland, OH; *U.S. Public*, pg. 556
Voglimacci, J.P., Exec. V.P.-Opers.--Compagnie Generale de Geophysique, Massy, France; *Int'l*, pg. 241
Vogt, Joachim, Member-Mngmt. Bd.--Hugo Boss AG, Metzingen, Germany; *Int'l*, pg. 637
Voith, Bruno, Dir.-Mfg.--Pittler Maschinenfabrik AG, Langen, Germany; *Int'l*, pg. 1128
Voll, Frank, Mgr.-Works--Eastman Worldwide, Buffalo, NY; *U.S. Private*, pg. 358
Vollmer, Brent, Mgr.-Prod.--National R.V., Inc., Perris, CA; *U.S. Public*, pg. 1159
Vollmer, Carl, Chief Engineer--Hopple Plastics, Inc., Florence, KY; *U.S. Private*, pg. 538
Von Deylen, Larry, Sr. V.P.-Mfg.--Oregon Freeze Dry, Inc., Albany, OR; *U.S. Private*, pg. 819
Vonderheide, Dean M., V.P.-Mfg./Kimball Upholstered Prods.--Kimball International, Inc., Jasper, IN; *U.S. Public*, pg. 956
Voos, Jared, V.P.-Mfg.--Ultimate Technology Corporation, Victor, NY; *U.S. Public*, pg. 1637

Votaw, Dennis, Dir.-Mdsg.--Bergen Brunswig Corporation, Orange, CA; *U.S. Public*, pg. 213
Vruggink, Jay, Mgr.-Production--Trendway Corporation, Holland, MI; *U.S. Private*, pg. 1099
Wacaser, James R., Mgr.-Mfg.--Hollymatic Corporation, Countryside, IL; *U.S. Private*, pg. 535
Wada, Norio, Exec. V.P.-Mfg.--Bridgestone/Firestone Tire Manufacturing Operations, Nashville, TN; *Int'l*, pg. 213
Waddell, Rex, V.P.-Electronic Combat--Lockheed Martin Electro-Optical Systems, Pasadena, CA; *U.S. Public*, pg. 1008
Wade, Edward, V.P.-Mfg. Opers.--VideoServer, Inc., Burlington, MA; *U.S. Public*, pg. 1720
Wadell, Jerry, Dir.-Mfg. Opers.--Karsten Manufacturing Corporation, Phoenix, AZ; *U.S. Private*, pg. 608
Wadeson, Timothy C.A., Dir.-Technical--Minorco, Luxembourg, Luxembourg; *Int'l*, pg. 77
Wagner, Hugh, V.P.-Engrng.--Barnstead/Thermolyne Corporation, Dubuque, IA; *U.S. Public*, pg. 1545
Wagner, T., V.P.-Mfg.--Kester Solder, Des Plaines, IL; *U.S. Public*, pg. 1003
Wagner, Thomas, Sr. V.P.-Mfg.--Ocean Spray Cranberries, Inc., Middleboro, MA; *U.S. Private*, pg. 811
Wahlgren, George, Chief Engr. & Mgr.-Factory--National Tool & Manufacturing Company, Kenilworth, NJ; *U.S. Private*, pg. 787
Wald, Gary, Chief Fin. Officer--Health Products Corporation, Yonkers, NY; *U.S. Private*, pg. 514
Walden, P. Wayne, V.P.-Mfg.--Robinson Helicopter Company, Torrance, CA; *U.S. Private*, pg. 936
Walden, Phillip, V.P.-Mfg.--InterVoice, Inc., Dallas, TX; *U.S. Public*, pg. 910
Waldrop, John C., V.P.-Mfg.--Fruit of the Loom, Inc., Chicago, IL; *U.S. Public*, pg. 685
Walker, Johnny, Plant Mgr.--Pro-Line Boats, Crystal River, FL; *U.S. Private*, pg. 58
Walker, Larry K., Plant Mgr.--TCI Aluminum, Gardena, CA; *U.S. Private*, pg. 1063
Walker, Larry M., Exec. V.P.-Mfg.--Oakwood Homes Corporation, Greensboro, NC; *U.S. Public*, pg. 1209
Walker, Marvin, V.P.-Mfg.--Fishman & Tobin, Inc., Conshohocken, PA; *U.S. Private*, pg. 408
Walker, Mauro J., Sr. V.P. & Dir.-Mfg.--Motorola, Inc., Schaumburg, IL; *U.S. Public*, pg. 1136
Walker, Steve, Dir.-Mfg.--Bollinger Shipyards, Inc., Lockport, LA; *U.S. Private*, pg. 155
Walker, Terry, Dir.-Mfg.--Sloan Technology, Santa Barbara, CA; *U.S. Public*, pg. 1711
Walkley, R., V.P.-Mfg.--BIF, North Wales, PA; *U.S. Public*, pg. 726
Wallend, Paul, Mgr.-Distr. Center--Chorus Line Corporation, Vernon, CA; *U.S. Private*, pg. 238
Walley, Carol, V.P.-Mfg.--Key Industries, Inc., Fort Scott, KS; *U.S. Private*, pg. 618
Wallin, Kjell, Dir.-Mfg.--Perstorp Pharma AB, Lund, Sweden; *Int'l*, pg. 1036
Wallitsch, Frank, Jr., V.P.-Mfg.--Pennsylvania Crusher Corp., Broomall, PA; *U.S. Private*, pg. 850
Walsh, J., V.P.-Engrng.--Cornell Iron Works, Inc., Mountain Top, PA; *U.S. Private*, pg. 276
Walsh, Kevin, V.P.-Mfg.--Overton Gear & Tool Corp., Addison, IL; *U.S. Private*, pg. 823
Walsh, Mike, Mgr.-Mfg.--Griffin Envelope, Inc., Seattle, WA; *U.S. Public*, pg. 1038
Walsh, William J., V.P.-Opers.--Amurol Confections Co., Yorkville, IL; *U.S. Public*, pg. 1781
Walsworth, Edgar, Exec. V.P.-Mfg. & Comml. Sls.--Walsworth Publishing Company, Inc., Marceline, MO; *U.S. Private*, pg. 1148
Walters, Ron, Mgr.-Plant--Nobles Mfg. Inc., Saint Croix Falls, WI; *U.S. Private*, pg. 800
Walters, Ronald J., V.P.-Mfg. & Sr. Mgr.--Erie Plastics, Corry, PA; *U.S. Private*, pg. 381
Walton, D.M., Dir.-Mfg.--Senior Phoenix RFS Limited, Bridgnorth, United Kingdom; *Int'l*, pg. 1221
Walton, Joseph, Mgr.-Mfg.--FMC-Crosby Valve, Inc., Wrentham, MA; *U.S. Public*, pg. 605
Walton, T. Campbell, V.P.-Mfg.--Marathon Electric Manufacturing Corp., Wausau, WI; *U.S. Public*, pg. 1371
Wamhoff, Fredrick, V.P., Gn. Counsel & Sec.--Rawson-Koenig, Inc., Houston, TX; *U.S. Public*, pg. 1362
Wandersee, Roger A., V.P.-Mfg.--E.R. Moore Co., Chicago, IL; *U.S. Private*, pg. 759
Wandzilak, Mark J., Plant Mgr.--Ludlow Textiles Co., Inc., Ludlow, MA; *U.S. Private*, pg. 680
Wangen, R.L., V.P.-Mfg.--Consolidated Papers, Inc., Wisconsin Rapids, WI; *U.S. Public*, pg. 436
Ward, Doug, V.P.-Mfg.--Anchor Continental Incorporated, Columbia, SC; *U.S. Private*, pg. 70
Ward, Lawrence, V.P.-Mfr. & Mtls.--Exabyte Corporation, Boulder, CO; *U.S. Public*, pg. 597
Ward, Ralph, V.P.-Mfg.--Stinson Seafood Company, Prospect Harbor, ME; *U.S. Private*, pg. 1043
Ward, Randy, Mgr.-Mfg. Opers.--MTS Systems Corporation, Eden Prairie, MN; *U.S. Public*, pg. 1028
Wargo, Chris A., V.P.-Engrng.--Aeronautical Radio, Inc., Annapolis, MD; *U.S. Private*, pg. 81
Warner, Charles, Mgr.-Mfg.--Magnetic Metals Corp., Camden, NJ; *U.S. Private*, pg. 560
Wasylko, Steve, V.P.-Mfg.--Par Industries, Inc., Medina, OH; *U.S. Private*, pg. 838
Waszak, E.F., V.P.-Engrng.--Morton International Inc., Chicago, IL; *U.S. Public*, pg. 1135
Watkins, Wendell, V.P.-Mfg.--The Harwood Companies, Inc., Fort Lauderdale, FL; *U.S. Public*, pg. 1433
Watson, Al, V.P.-Engrng.--Electro-Voice, Inc., Buchanan, MI; *U.S. Private*, pg. 479
Watson, David C., V.P.-Mfg.--Precision Industries Division, Malvern, AR; *U.S. Public*, pg. 986
Watson, George, V.P.-Prod. Mfg.--The New Piper Aircraft, Inc., Vero Beach, FL; *U.S. Private*, pg. 794
Wattjes, Harold, V.P.-Mfg.--Russell Stover Candies, Inc., Kansas City, MO; *U.S. Private*, pg. 953
Wawrzyniak, Steve, V.P.-Tech. Svcs.--Doane Products Co., Joplin, MO; *U.S. Private*, pg. 337
Way, Richard D., Pres. & Chief Oper. Officer--Northwestern Steel & Wire Co., Sterling, IL; *U.S. Public*, pg. 1201
Weaver, Gary D., Sr. V.P.-Worldwide Mfg. Opers.--AST Research Inc., Irvine, CA; *Int'l*, pg. 1181
Weaver, Mike, V.P.-Mfr.--Hess Engineering Inc., Niles, MI; *U.S. Private*, pg. 524
Webb, Robert M., V.P.-Mfg. & Logistics--Hyponex Corporation, Marysville, OH; *U.S. Public*, pg. 1447
Weber, Andrew, Exec. V.P.-Mfg. & New Prod. Info.--Reed Elsevier Business Information, Newton, MA; *Int'l*, pg. 1095
Weber, B.I., V.P.-Mfg.--Kaufman Footwear, Kitchener, Canada; *Int'l*, pg. 725
Weber, Paul, Mgr.-Mfg.--Simpson Electric Co., Elgin, IL; *U.S. Private*, pg. 1002
Wehr, Danny W., V.P.-Mfg./Contract & Furniture Grps.--Kimball International, Inc., Jasper, IN; *U.S. Public*, pg. 956
Weinerman, Lee S., Chief Engineer--Eberhard Manufacturing, Strongsville, OH; *U.S. Public*, pg. 548
Weinert, Carl J., V.P.-Mfg.--Wausau Papers - Printing & Writing Div., Brokaw, WI; *U.S. Public*, pg. 1747
Weingarth, Roger E., V.P.-Mfg.--Network Systems Corporation, Minneapolis, MN; *U.S. Public*, pg. 1522
Weintraub, Leigh, Chief Oper. Officer--Merit Medical Systems, Inc., South Jordan, UT; *U.S. Public*, pg. 1096
Weir, Joe, Sr. Engr.-Mfg.--Standard Locknut, Inc., Westfield, IN; *U.S. Private*, pg. 1031
Weis, Eric, V.P.-Indus. Prods.--Capintec Inc., Ramsey, NJ; *U.S. Private*, pg. 205
Weisberg, Ira, V.P.-Mfg.--Interferon Sciences, Inc., New Brunswick, NJ; *U.S. Public*, pg. 694
Weise, Stephen, V.P.-Mfg.--Chock Full O' Nuts Corporation, New York, NY; *U.S. Public*, pg. 351
Weiserseel, Charles, V.P.-Mfg.--Monarch Tile, Inc., Florence, AL; *U.S. Private*, pg. 287
Weiss, Richard, Chief Oper. Officer--United Receptical, Inc., Pottsville, PA; *U.S. Private*, pg. 1123
Weiss, Steve, Mgr.-Production--Data Communications, New York, NY; *U.S. Public*, pg. 1070
Weisser, Al, V.P.-Mfg. & Supvr.-Plant--Stanley Knight Corporation, New Troy, MI; *U.S. Private*, pg. 1033
Weisser, Helmut, V.P.-Mfg.--S-B Power Tool Company, Chicago, IL; *Int'l*, pg. 205
Welch, Dean, V.P.-Prod. & Res.--Solvay Animal Health, Inc., Mendota Heights, MN; *Int'l*, pg. 1277
Welch, Dean, V.P.-Prod. & Res.--Salsbury Laboratories, Inc., Charles City, IA; *Int'l*, pg. 1277
Welch, William E., V.P.-Mfg.--Lane Limited, Tucker, GA; *Int'l*, pg. 1129
Weliczko, Edward, Mgr. Mfg.--Dreis & Krump Manufacturing Company, Chicago, IL; *U.S. Private*, pg. 342
Weller, Ralph, Mgr.-Mfg.--Wavetek Corporation, San Diego, CA; *U.S. Private*, pg. 1154
Wells, Clarence B., V.P.-Mfg.--CCX Fiberglass Products, Walterboro, SC; *U.S. Private*, pg. 193
Wells, H. Rickey, V.P.-Opers.--K N Energy, Inc., Lakewood, CO; *U.S. Public*, pg. 937
Wells, James, V.P.-Chemical Mfg.--Radiator Specialty Company, Charlotte, NC; *U.S. Private*, pg. 906
Welton, Dan, V.P.-Mfg.--Electroglas, Inc., Santa Clara, CA; *U.S. Public*, pg. 727
Wempe, Roman, V.P.-Industrial Mfg.--Gates Canada Inc., Brantford, Canada; *Int'l*, pg. 1396
Wenger, Ron, V.P.-Mfg.--Bard Mfg. Co., Bryan, OH; *U.S. Private*, pg. 116
Wenisch, Lou, V.P.-Mfg.--Hampshire Designers Inc., Anderson, SC; *U.S. Public*, pg. 778
Wenisch, Lou, V.P.-Mfg.--Glamourette Fashion Mills, Quebradillas, PR; *U.S. Public*, pg. 779
Wenner, Hal, V.P.-Opers.--Sunroc Corporation, Dover, DE; *U.S. Private*, pg. 1053
Wentworth, Jerry, Plant Mgr.--Holcomb & Hoke Mfg. Company, Inc., Indianapolis, IN; *U.S. Private*, pg. 533
Wentz, Roy, V.P.-Opers.--Sorrento Cheese Company, Inc., Buffalo, NY; *Int'l*, pg. 323
Werner, Thomas, V.P.-Mfg./Carrier Sys.--3Com Corporation, Santa Clara, CA; *U.S. Public*, pg. 1603
West, Harry, Jr., Plant Superintendent--Snap-Tite, Inc., Erie, PA; *U.S. Private*, pg. 1010
Westner, Bill, Mgr.-Prod.--Ultra Tool & Plastics, Inc., Amherst, NY; *U.S. Private*, pg. 1116
Weston, Roger L., Chm. Bd., Pres. & Chief Exec. Officer--GreatBanc, Inc., Aurora, IL; *U.S. Public*, pg. 760
Wey, Sonny S., V.P.-Prod. Devel.--Komag, Incorporated, San Jose, CA; *U.S. Public*, pg. 966
Wheeler, Jeff, Production Dir.--Vishay Components (U.K.) Ltd., Sunderland, United Kingdom; *U.S. Public*, pg. 1722
Wheeler, Norma, Dir.-Mfg.--Gamma Biologicals Inc., Houston, TX; *U.S. Public*, pg. 698
Whetzel, Charlie, Exec. V.P.-Opers.--The William Carter Company, Morrow, GA; *U.S. Private*, pg. 217
Whitler, Margaret, Mgr.-Mfg.--Gatefield Corporation, Fremont, CA; *U.S. Public*, pg. 703
White, Charles A., V.P.-Mfg. & Engrng.--Preferred Instruments, Danbury, CT; *U.S. Private*, pg. 881
White, Charles A., III, V.P.-Mfg. & Engrng.--Preferred Utilities Manufacturing Corp., Danbury, CT; *U.S. Private*, pg. 881
White, James D., Sr. V.P.-Worldwide Indus. Equip.--Deere & Company, Moline, IL; *U.S. Public*, pg. 491
White, James D., Sr. V.P.-Mfg.--John Deere Industrial Equipment Company, Moline, IL; *U.S. Public*, pg. 492
White, Noel W., V.P.-Fresh Meats Mfg.--IBP, Inc., Dakota City, NE; *U.S. Public*, pg. 852
White, Thomas A., V.P.-Mfg.--The Valspar Corporation, Minneapolis, MN; *U.S. Public*, pg. 1707
Whitley, Carl, V.P.-Mfg.--Cutler Manufacturing Corporation, Lakeland, FL; *U.S. Private*, pg. 298
Whitley, Carl, V.P.-Mfg.--Leslie - Locke, Inc., Atlanta, GA; *U.S. Public*, pg. 989
Whitlock, T.L., Mgr.-Plant--Mount Vernon Mills, Inc., Riegel Consumer Products Div., Johnston, SC; *U.S. Private*, pg. 835
Whitmore, Laurel G., V.P.-Sls.--Rauch Industries, Inc., Gastonia, NC; *U.S. Private*, pg. 1061
Whittemore, Dennis, V.P.-Mfg.--Data Industrial Corporation, Pocasset, MA; *U.S. Public*, pg. 487
Wicks, John, V.P.-Mdsg./Southern Div.--The Home Depot, Inc., Atlanta, GA; *U.S. Public*, pg. 831
Wiechers, Lothar, Dir.-Distrib.--Warsteiner Brauerei Haus Cramer GmbH & Co., Warstein, Germany; *Int'l*, pg. 1486
Wiedenhoft, Charles, Sr. V.P.-Mfg.--Ash Grove Cement Company, Shawnee Mission, KS; *U.S. Private*, pg. 87
Wiedmann, W. J., V.P.-Mfg.--Wisconsin Machine and Tool Corporation, Milwaukee, WI; *U.S. Private*, pg. 1185
Wiencek, Donald, Dir.-Mfg. & Pur.--Continental Web Press, Inc., Itasca, IL; *U.S. Private*, pg. 269
Wiertsema, Gerry, Dir.-Engrng.--Midwest Industries, Inc., Ida Grove, IA; *U.S. Private*, pg. 744
Wiese, Paul, V.P.-Mfg.--Boyer Candy Company Inc., Altoona, PA; *U.S. Private*, pg. 162
Wiggins, Jim, Dir.-Mfg.--Stowe-Pharr Mills, Inc., Mc Adenville, NC; *U.S. Private*, pg. 1045
Wilcheck, Michael, Dir.-Mfg. & Engrng.--Varity Dayton Walther, Dayton, OH; *Int'l*, pg. 820
Wilcox, Robert K., Sr. V.P.-Mfg.--American Banknote Corp., New York, NY; *U.S. Public*, pg. 68
Wild, Bernhard, Dir.-Tech. Opers.--Braun AG, Kronberg, Germany; *U.S. Public*, pg. 744
Wildeboer, Scott L., V.P.-Mfg.--Top Air Manufacturing, Inc., Cedar Falls, IA; *U.S. Public*, pg. 1621
Wilk, Joe, V.P.-Mfg.--Boston Whaler, Inc., Edgewater, FL; *U.S. Private*, pg. 689
Wilkinson, James A., V.P.-Mfg.--General Chemical Corporation, Parsippany, NJ; *U.S. Public*, pg. 707
Williams, David, Plant Mgr.--Engelhard Corp.-Quincy Operations, Quincy, FL; *U.S. Public*, pg. 582
Williams, Doug, Sr. V.P.-Mfg.--Hooker Furniture Corporation, Martinsville, VA; *U.S. Private*, pg. 538
Williams, Doug, V.P.-Mfg.--Sanden International (U.S.A.), Inc., Wylie, TX; *Int'l*, pg. 1184
Williams, Gary, V.P.-Mfg., Alcoa Bldg. Products--Alcoa Building Products, Inc., Sidney, OH; *U.S. Public*, pg. 61
Williams, Kerry, V.P.-Mfg.--Corel Corporation, Ottawa, Canada; *Int'l*, pg. 331
Williams, Michael P., II, Chief Tech. Officer--Cadillac Products, Inc., Troy, MI; *U.S. Private*, pg. 198
Williams, Paul, V.P.-Mfg.-SD&C--Smith International, Inc., Houston, TX; *U.S. Public*, pg. 1478
Williams, Ron, Dir.-Bakery--O'Malia Food Markets Inc., Carmel, IN; *U.S. Private*, pg. 816
Williamson, John, Dir.-Opers.--Acme Design Technology, Co., Crozet, VA; *U.S. Private*, pg. 13
Willie, Gerry, V.P.-Field Opers.--Edward Hines Lumber Co., Itasca, IL; *U.S. Private*, pg. 530
Willmes, John, V.P.-Mfg.--Barnstead/Thermolyne Corporation, Dubuque, IA; *U.S. Public*, pg. 1545
Willoughby, Bonnie, Mgr.-Pur.--Heartland Express, Inc., Coralville, IA; *U.S. Public*, pg. 803
Willson, Rick, Oper. Mgr.-Weiss--Fred B. Johnston Company, Inc., Chapin, SC; *U.S. Private*, pg. 595
Wilson, Charles, V.P.-Mfg.--McKee Foods Corporation, Collegedale, TN; *U.S. Private*, pg. 723
Wilson, Don, V.P.-Mfg. Mgr.--Gem-Dandy, Inc., Madison, NC; *U.S. Private*, pg. 442
Wilson, Howard, Plant Mgr.-Detroit--Quaker Chemical Corporation, Conshohocken, PA; *U.S. Public*, pg. 1346
Wilson, J., V.P.-Mfg.--New Balance Athletic Shoe, Inc., Boston, MA; *U.S. Private*, pg. 792
Wilson, Joe, Mgr.-Mfg.--Interbath, Inc., City of Industry, CA; *U.S. Private*, pg. 566
Wilson, Steve, V.P.-Engrng.--Duo-Fast Corporation, Huntley, IL; *U.S. Private*, pg. 347
Wine, Raymond L., V.P.-Mfg.--Acheson Industries, Inc., Port Huron, MI; *U.S. Private*, pg. 12
Wingrove, George H., Dir.-Mfg.--Isco, Inc., Lincoln, NE; *U.S. Public*, pg. 913
Wingrove, George H., Dir.-Mfg.--Isco Separation Instruments Division, Lincoln, NE; *U.S. Public*, pg. 914
Winkler, Hermann, V.P.--Seton Company, Norristown, PA; *U.S. Private*, pg. 987
Winter, Roy E., V.P.-Mfg. Services & Information Services--NRI Schools, Washington, DC; *U.S. Public*, pg. 1071
Winters, Bobby M., V.P.-Mfg.--Pace Industries of Mexico, L.L.C., Saltillo, Mexico; *U.S. Public*, pg. 578
Winters, Ken, Dir.-Mfg.--Chromcraft Corporation, Senatobia, MS; *U.S. Public*, pg. 352
Wipff, Dan R., Pres.-Telxon Prods.--Telxon Corporation, Akron, OH; *U.S. Public*, pg. 1573
Wireman, Jerry, Mgr.-Mfg.--Thetford Corporation, Ann Arbor, MI; *U.S. Private*, pg. 352
Wirth, Don, Gen. Mgr.-Mfg.--Du Pont (Australia) Ltd., Sydney, Australia; *U.S. Public*, pg. 532
Wisler, Dean, Mgr.-Mfg.--Hollingsworth Saco Lowell Corporation, Inc., Easley, SC; *U.S. Private*, pg. 535
Witkewics, Joe, Dir.-Mfg.--Softsoap Enterprises, Inc., Chaska, MN; *U.S. Public*, pg. 397
Woehler, Sam, Mgr.-Production--George Koch Sons, Inc., Evansville, IN; *U.S. Private*, pg. 628
Wolcott, Harold R., Exec. V.P. & Gen. Mgr.--Ballard Medical Products, Draper, UT; *U.S. Public*, pg. 171
Wolf, Lee, V.P.-Mfg.--Polar Ware Company, Sheboygan, WI; *U.S. Private*, pg. 873
Wolfe, James, V.P.-Opers.--Buffalo Rock Company, Birmingham, AL; *U.S. Private*, pg. 179
Wolfe, Roger, V.P. & Dir.-Mfg.--ITT Cannon, Santa Ana, CA; *U.S. Public*, pg. 859
Wolfe, Ronald C., V.P.-Mfg.--Avon Products, Inc., New York, NY; *U.S. Public*, pg. 155
Wolfe, T. Robert, V.P.-Production--Alfred Nickles Bakery, Inc., Navarre, OH; *U.S. Private*, pg. 799
Wolfer, Ernest, Sr. V.P.-Mfg.--Marcal Paper Mills, Inc., Elmwood Park, NJ; *U.S. Private*, pg. 701

Wolff, Jean, Dir.-Mfg.--Automobiles Citroen, Neuilly, France; *Int'l*, pg. 1020
Wollman, Don, V.P.-Production--Dick Clark Productions, Inc., Burbank, CA; *U.S. Public*, pg. 382
Wolo, Mike, Mgr.-Mfg.--Trimfoot Company, Farmington, MO; *U.S. Public*, pg. 1684
Wolski, Frank, Mgr.-Matls.--Ektelon, Bordentown, NJ; *U.S. Private*, pg. 884
Wolsky, William J., V.P.-Opers.--Norgren Co., Littleton, CO; *Int'l*, pg. 647
Wolthuis, Jon A., V.P.-Refinery Opers.--California & Hawaiian Sugar Company Inc., Crockett, CA; *U.S. Public*, *pg. 39*
Wong, Tak, Dir.-Fin. & Mfg.--Epson Canada Limited, Willowdale, Canada; *Int'l*, pg. 1219
Wood, Ann, Mgr.-Mfg. Engrng.--IEC Electronics Corp., Newark, NY; *U.S. Public*, pg. 854
Wood, Barbara, V.P.-Production/Opers.--The General Publishing Group, Reading, MA; *Int'l*, pg. 1026
Wood, C.F., Sr. V.P.-Mfg., Engrng. & Devel.--Aluma Systems Corp., Toronto, Canada; *Int'l*, pg. 1423
Wood, D.M., Sr. V.P.-Engrng.--Trico Products Corporation, Buffalo, NY; *Int'l*, pg. 1397
Wood, Gary, V.P.-Mfg.--Fruit of the Loom, Inc., Chicago, IL; *U.S. Public*, pg. 685
Wood, Tony, V.P.-Mfg. Opers.--Messier-Dowty Inc., Toronto, Ajax, Canada; *Int'l*, pg. 1340
Woodley, Michael, Sr. V.P.-Architecture--Kaufman and Broad Home Corporation, Los Angeles, CA; *U.S. Public*, pg. 944
Woods, Walter, Dir.-Mfg.--Plymouth Rubber Company, Inc., Canton, MA; *U.S. Public*, pg. 1311
Woodward, William, Chief Oper. Officer--Maxcor Manufacturing, Inc., Colorado Springs, CO; *U.S. Private*, pg. 716
Wratney, Donald, Chief Engr.--Cornell Forge Company, Chicago, IL; *U.S. Private*, pg. 276
Wredberg, Conrad, Sr. V.P.--Scientific-Atlanta, Inc., Norcross, GA; *U.S. Public*, pg. 1443
Wright, Bruce, V.P.-Mfg.--Apollo Colors Inc., Northbrook, IL; *U.S. Private*, pg. 77
Wright, Michael D., V.P.-Mfg.--Abolite Lighting Inc., Cincinnati, OH; *U.S. Public*, pg. 971
Wright, Tom, V.P.-Mfg.--Turkey Hill Dairy, Inc., Conestoga, PA; *U.S. Private*, pg. 1109
Wright, Warren E., Chm Bd. & Chief Oper. Officer--Renosol Corp., Saline, MI; *U.S. Private*, pg. 922
Wrona, Jim, Mgr.-Engrng. & Mfg.--McCain Bindery Systems, Inc., Chicago, IL; *U.S. Private*, pg. 719
Wu, David, V.P.-Mfg.--Oroamerica, Inc., Burbank, CA; *U.S. Public*, pg. 1232
Yamaoka, Hugo, Mgr.-Mfg.--Acos Villares Plant - Mogi das Cruz, Sao Paulo, Brazil; *Int'l*, pg. 23
Yamashita, Bruce, V.P.-Engrng.--Menasco Aerospace Ltd., Oakville, Canada; *U.S. Public*, pg. 402
Yankey, Lowell, V.P.-Mfg.--Fruit of the Loom, Inc., Chicago, IL; *U.S. Public*, pg. 685
Yarberry, Lee, V.P.-Mfg.--The Buschman Co., Cincinnati, OH; *U.S. Private*, pg. 188
Yarborough, V.A., Dir.-Engrng.--Colonial Pipeline Company, Atlanta, GA; *U.S. Private*, pg. 254
Yashiro, Hiroyuki, Mgr.-Hub-Mfg.--Nemic-Lambda KK, Tokyo, Japan; *Int'l*, pg. 1242
Yates, Larry G., V.P.-Materials Mngmt.--Peabody Holding Company, Inc., Saint Louis, MO; *Int'l*, pg. 594
Yeager, Don, Mgr.-Production--Larson Manufacturing Company, Brookings, SD; *U.S. Private*, pg. 652
Yeh, T.S., Dir.-Exploration & Prod. Div.--Chinese Petroleum Corporation, Taipei, Taiwan; *Int'l*, pg. 286
Yeomans, Mike, Mgr.-Construction & Engrng.--Benderson Development Co., Inc., Buffalo, NY; *U.S. Private*, pg. 132
Yock, Joseph, Mgr.-Mfg.--C.W. Zumbiel Company, Norwood, OH; *U.S. Private*, pg. 1207
Yorgenson, Jim, V.P.-Mining & Processing--J.R. Simplot Company, Minerals & Chemicals Group, Pocatello, ID; *U.S. Private*, pg. 1002
Yoshimura, Kouichi, Mgr.-Mfg.--Nippon Oil Company, Limited (NiSSEKI), Tokyo, Japan; *Int'l*, pg. 936
Youell, Gerald W., Sr. V.P.-Production & Exploration--Chieftain International, Inc., Edmonton, Canada; *Int'l*, pg. 284
Young, Bob, V.P.-Mfg. & Engrng.--OMC Marine Power Products Group, Waukegan, IL; *U.S. Private*, pg. 478
Young, James H., Chief Oper. Officer & Exec. V.P.--Reactive Metals & Alloys Corporation (REMACOR), West Pittsburg, PA; *U.S. Private*, pg. 913
Young, Mark D., V.P.-Mfg. & Process Devel.--Amgen Boulder, Inc., Boulder, CO; *U.S. Public*, pg. 101
Young, Matt, V.P.-Corp. Mfg.--Melitta U.S.A., Inc., Clearwater, FL; *Int'l*, pg. 857
Young, Steven O., V.P.-Mfg., Eastern Reg.--Magneco/Metrel, Inc., Addison, IL; *U.S. Private*, pg. 695
Young, Warner, Mgr.-Matls.--Kauffman Products, Inc., Carmel, IN; *U.S. Private*, pg. 609
Yungkans, Ken, V.P.-Mfg.--Dansk International Designs Ltd., White Plains, NY; *U.S. Public*, pg. 261
Yunk, Jim, Mgr.-Mfr.--Marine Travelift, Inc., Sturgeon Bay, WI; *U.S. Private*, pg. 703
Yurksaitis, Vin, V.P.-Mfg.--Bridgeport Machines, Inc., Bridgeport, CT; *U.S. Public*, pg. 251
Yven, Richard, V.P.-Finished Mfg. Tech.--American & Efird, Inc., Mount Holly, NC; *U.S. Public*, pg. 1412
Zaagman, Michael E., V.P.-Opers.--Triple S Plastics, Inc., Vicksburg, MI; *U.S. Public*, pg. 1639
Zabron, F.S., V.P.-Engrng.--Habisat Globe Inc., Buffalo, NY; *Int'l*, pg. 585
Zaffino, Frank D., V.P. & Gen. Mgr.-Equipment Mfg.--Eastman Kodak Company, Rochester, NY; *U.S. Public*, pg. 550
Zaheeruddin, M., Gen. Mgr.-ComTech--National Refinery Limited, Karachi, Pakistan; *Int'l*, pg. 909
Zakaria, Adel A., Sr. V.P.-Worldwide Engrng. & Mfg.--Deere & Company, Moline, IL; *U.S. Public*, pg. 491
Zamarbide, Guillermo, Sr. V.P.-Mfg.--Sudamtex de Uruguay, S.A., Montevideo, Uruguay; *Int'l*, pg. 1304
Zane, Robert J., Sr. V.P.-Mfg. & Sourcing--Liz Claiborne, Inc., New York, NY; *U.S. Public*, pg. 1005
Zanfino, Martin, V.P.-Engrng.--Harman Consumer Group, Woodbury, NY; *U.S. Public*, pg. 787
Zarlenga, Louis A., V.P.-Engrng.--The Edward J. DeBartolo Corporation, Youngstown, OH; *U.S. Private*, pg. 319
Zatcoff, Roy, Pres.-SCT Mfg. & Distr. Sys., Inc.--Systems & Computer Technology Corporation, Malvern, PA; *U.S. Public*, pg. 1552
Zawada, Richard, V.P.-Mfg.--Sommer & Maca Industries, Inc., Cicero, IL; *U.S. Private*, pg. 1013
Zdrojkowski, Floyd J., V.P.-Constuction & Engrng. Pur. Divs.--The Edward J. DeBartolo Corporation, Youngstown, OH; *U.S. Private*, pg. 319
Zelinski, John, V.P.-Mfg.--Bristol Metals, L.P., Bristol, TN; *U.S. Public*, pg. 1548
Zemke, Hermann, V.P.-Mfg.--Tesa Tuck Inc., Sparta, MI; *Int'l*, pg. 182
Ziebart, Judy, Mgr.-Matls.--Heath Consultants Incorporated, Houston, TX; *U.S. Private*, pg. 518
Ziegler, Bernard, Sr. V.P.-Engrng.--Airbus Industrie, Blagnac, France; *Int'l*, pg. 39
Ziegler, Greg, V.P.-Production--Quiksilver, Inc., Costa Mesa, CA; *U.S. Public*, pg. 1353
Zielinski, David, V.P.-Mfg.--Circon ACMI, Stamford, CT; *U.S.* Public, pg. 373
Zimmerman, Gary, V.P.-Mfg. & Gen. Mgr.--McCormick Flavor Division-U.S.A., Hunt Valley, MD; *U.S. Public*, pg. 1066
Zimmers, Robert A., Dir.-Mfg. & Engrng.--John Crane North America, Morton Grove, IL; *Int'l*, pg. 1339
Zitting, Ron, V.P.-Mfg.--Macrotech Plyseal, Inc., Salt Lake City, UT; *U.S. Private*, pg. 693
Zizzo, John, Plant Mgr.--Fred Usinger, Inc., Milwaukee, WI; *U.S. Private*, pg. 1129
Zoetemeyer, R. J., Dir.-Tech. & Prod.--PURAC Group, Gorcum, Netherlands; *Int'l*, pg. 244
Zoga, Chris, Exec. V.P.-Mfg.--Premier Mill Corp., Reading, PA; *U.S. Private*, pg. 881
Zoga, Chris, Exec. V.P.-Mfg.--Integrated Press Systems, Reading, PA; *U.S. Private*, pg. 881
Zowinsky, J., Dir.-Opers.--Marsh Bellofram Corp., Newell, WV; *U.S. Private*, pg. 707
Zub, Joseph, Dir.-Opers. & Mgr.-H.R.--H.O. Trerice Company, Oak Park, MI; *U.S. Private*, pg. 1099
Zulaski, J.A., Dir.-Electronic Prods. Div.--S & C Electric Company, Chicago, IL; *U.S. Private*, pg. 954
Zuza, Joaquin J., Dir.-Truck Components Opers., Europe--Eaton Limited, Hounslow, United Kingdom; *U.S. Public*, pg. 558
Zvoncheck, Ken, Mgr.-Production--Quinlan Pretzel Co., Inc., Denver, PA; *U.S. Private*, pg. 158

MARKETING

Aaberg, Erick, Grp. V.P.-Mktg.--Jotun A/S, Sandefjord, Norway; *Int'l*, pg. 714
Aalto, Eero, V.P.-Mktg.--MTV Finland, Helsinki, Finland; *Int'l*, *pg. 827*
Aarons, Michael S., Sr. V.P.-Mktg.--Great Western Bank, Chatsworth, CA; *U.S. Public*, pg. 1741
Aaronson, Morton C., Chief Mktg. Officer & V.P.--K N Energy, Inc., Lakewood, CO; *U.S. Public*, pg. 937
Abate, Mario, Dr., Dir.-Mkt. Res.--Adams U.S.A., Morris Plains, NJ; *U.S. Public*, pg. 1739
Abbate, Eileen, V.P.-Adv. & Mktg.--PharmHouse, Inc., New York, NY; *U.S. Public*, pg. 1286
Abbate, Ryan, V.P.-Mktg. Communications--Allergan, Inc., Irvine, CA; *U.S. Public*, pg. 46
Abboud, Dennis, V.P.-Sls. & Mktg.--The Chas. Levy Company, Chicago, IL; *U.S. Private*, pg. 664
Abdallah, Davina, Mgr.-Adv. & Mktg.--Henry Birks & Sons (1993) Inc., Montreal, Canada; *Int'l*, pg. 196
Abe, Noburu, Dir.-Mktg.--Matsushita Electric Works, Ltd., Osaka, Japan; *Int'l*, pg. 847
Abel, Curtis, V.P.-Sls.--Mitek Systems, Inc., San Diego, CA; *U.S. Public*, pg. 1117
Abel, Sam, V.P.-Mktg./T. Nelson Inc.--C.R. Gibson Co., Norwalk, CT; *U.S. Public*, pg. 1168
Abell, Sam, V.P.-Mktg. Gift Products--Thomas Nelson Inc., Nashville, TN; *U.S. Public*, pg. 1167
Abels, Terry, Sr. V.P.-Sls. & Mktg.--CFA Holding Company, Charlotte, MI; *U.S. Private*, pg. 194
Abend, David, Mgr.-Mktg. & Sls. Promo.--Leach International, Buena Park, CA; *U.S. Private*, pg. 655
Abernathy, Susan, Adm. Asst.--Seth Thomas, Norcross, GA; *U.S. Private*, pg. 445
Abernathy, Tod, Dir.-Market Res.--Security Pacific Financial Services Inc., San Diego, CA; *U.S. Public*, pg. 181
Abraham, Frances, V.P.-Mktg.--Bulova Corporation, Woodside, NY; *U.S. Public*, pg. 1010
Abraham, Jay, V.P.-Mktg.--Food Lion, Inc., Salisbury, NC; *Int'l*, pg. 463
Abraham, Rob, Mgr.-Mktg.--Olivetti Africa Pty. Ltd., Johannesburg, South Africa; *Int'l*, pg. 1003
Abram, Nancy, Sr. V.P.-Mktg.--Hardee's Food Systems, Inc., Rocky Mount, NC; *U.S. Public*, pg. 278
Abramowitz, Mike, V.P.-Mktg.--Sun Microsystems Federal Inc., Mc Lean, VA; *U.S. Public*, pg. 1531
Abrams, Bruce R., Sr. V.P.-Mktg.--Western National Corporation, Houston, TX; *U.S. Public*, pg. 76
Abrams, Bruce R., Sr. V.P.-Mktg.--Western National Life Insurance Co., Houston, TX; *U.S. Public*, pg. 76
Abramson, Mark, Dir.-Mktg.--Cadaco, Chicago, IL; *U.S. Private*, pg. 910
Abrink, Kenneth, Dir.-Mktg.--Saab AB, Linkoping, Sweden; *Int'l*, pg. 686
Accola, Richard M., V.P.-Sls. & Mktg.--Gravymaster Inc., Branford, CT; *U.S. Private*, pg. 471
Acerra, Peter, V.P.-Mktg.--Naturistics--Del Laboratories, Inc., Farmingdale, NY; *U.S. Public*, pg. 494
Acey, David E., Mng. Dir.-Mktg.--Wheat First Butcher Singer, Inc., Richmond, VA; *U.S. Public*, pg. 640
Achenbaum, John, V.P.-Mktg.--Helene Curtis Industries, Inc., Chicago, IL; *Int'l*, pg. 1434
Ackad, Marie, Marketing Planner--ITT Barton Instruments, City of Industry, CA; *U.S. Public*, pg. 860
Ackerberg, Jeff, Dir.-Mktg.--Sterling Plumbing Group, Inc., Rolling Meadows, IL; *U.S. Private*, pg. 630
Ackles, Paul, V.P.-Mktg.--Cuisinart Inc., Stamford, CT; *U.S. Private*, pg. 261
Ackley, Robert, V.P.-Mktg.--Span-America Medical Systems Inc., Greenville, SC; *U.S. Public*, pg. 1495
Acosta, F., Mgr.-Mktg.--Grupo Sitra, S.A. DE C.V., Piso, Mexico; *Int'l*, pg. 775
Acuff, Keith, Exec. V.P. & Chief Mktg. Officer--Noble & Associates, Springfield, MO; *U.S. Private*, pg. 800
Acuff, Keith, Sr. V.P., Chief Mktg. Officer-Consumer Brands & Dir.--Noble & Associates Promotion Group, Springfield, MO; *U.S. Private*, pg. 800
Acusti, Pere, Dir.-Mktg. & Adv.--Mattel Espana, S.A., Barcelona, Spain; *U.S. Public*, pg. 1059
Adair, Browning, Mgr.-Direct Mktg.--Benson's, Inc., Bogart, GA; *U.S. Private*, pg. 134
Adair, Jim, Dir.-Mktg.--Suncor Development Company, Phoenix, AZ; *U.S. Public*, pg. 1298
Adam, Alain C., V.P.-Automotive Mktg.--A. Schulman, Inc., Akron, OH; *U.S. Public*, pg. 1441
Adam, J. Marc, V.P.-Mktg.--3M, Saint Paul, MN; *U.S. Public*, *pg. 1604*
Adam, Shawn, V.P.-Sls. & Mktg.--Columbia Paint & Coatings, Spokane, WA; *U.S. Private*, pg. 256
Adams, Annette, Mgr.-Mktg.--Vactor Mfg. Inc., Streator, IL; *U.S. Public*, pg. 617
Adams, Christopher S., Jr., V.P.-Bus. Devel.--Scientific Communications, Inc., Garland, TX; *U.S. Public*, pg. 112
Adams, D. Scott, Sr. Mgr.-Sls. & Mktg.--Deck House Inc., Acton, MA; *U.S. Private*, pg. 320
Adams, Darlene, Dir.-Sls. & Mktg.--The Beverly Hills Hotel, Beverly Hills, CA; *U.S. Private*, pg. 142
Adams, Fred, Dir.-Mktg.--International Aluminum Corporation, Monterey Park, CA; *U.S. Public*, pg. 894
Adams, John, Mgr.-Mktg.-Protein--Central Soya Company, Inc., Fort Wayne, IN; *Int'l*, pg. 324
Adams, Lee, Sr. V.P.-Intl. Mktg.--American Rice Inc., Houston, TX; *U.S. Public*, pg. 591
Adams, Lynn, Dir.-Mktg.--R.W. Beck, Inc., Seattle, WA; *U.S.* Private, pg. 128
Adams, Piar, Mgr.-Mktg.--Carefree of Colorado, Broomfield, CO; *U.S. Public*, pg. 217
Adams, Ricardo, Dir.-Mktg.--Philips do Brasil-Walita Div., Sao Paulo, Brazil; *Int'l*, pg. 1055
Adams, Robert J., Jr., V.P.-Mktg. & Inside Sls.--Pervasive Software Inc., Austin, TX; *U.S. Public*, pg. 1280
Adams, Stephen M., V.P.-Mktg.--BIW Cable Systems, Inc., Franklin, MA; *Int'l*, pg. 417
Adams, Stephen P., Mgr.-Investor Rels.--Zurn Industries, Inc., Erie, PA; *U.S. Public*, pg. 1794
Adams, Tim, Dir.-Sls. & Mktg.--Ipsen International, Inc., Cherry Valley, IL; *Int'l*, pg. 1149
Adamsen, Julia, Sr. V.P. & Dir.-Corp. Mktg.--Keycorp, Cleveland, OH; *U.S. Public*, pg. 954
Adamson, Julie, Sr. V.P.-Corp. Mktg. Communications--Society National Bank, Cleveland, OH; *U.S. Public*, pg. 954
Adans, J.P., Mgr.-Mktg.--S.A. Olivetti Belgium N.V., Brussels, Belgium; *Int'l*, pg. 1003
Addis, Roland T., V.P.-New Prods. Mktg.--Comcast Cable Communications, Inc., Philadelphia, PA; *U.S. Public*, pg. 407
Addy, Michele, Mktg. Coord.--W. Atlee Burpee Co., Warminster, PA; *U.S. Private*, pg. 187
Adelman, Michael, V.P.-Mktg.--Polychrome Corp. Div., Fort Lee, NJ; *Int'l*, pg. 370
Adilerri, John, Sr. V.P.-Mktg.--CSE Insurance Group, San Francisco, CA; *U.S. Private*, pg. 197
Adkins, Brooke, V.P.-Catalogue, Mktg. & Pub. Rels.--F.A.O. Schwarz, New York, NY; *Int'l*, pg. 750
Adkins, Tony, V.P.-Mktg.--Friden Alcatel, Hayward, CA; *Int'l*, *pg. 55*
Adler, Asa, V.P.-Mktg.--Chase Bank of Florida, N.A., Tampa, FL; *U.S. Public*, pg. 338
Adler, James, V.P.-Mktg.--Myron Manufacturing Corporation, Maywood, NJ; *U.S. Private*, pg. 771
Adler, Stephanie, Mktg. Communications Specialist--Axiom Inc., Moorestown, NJ; *U.S. Public*, pg. 157
Admans, Jim, V.P.-Mktg.--CPC Foodservice Group, Franklin Park, IL; *U.S. Public*, pg. 224
Adolf, Mary M., V.P.-US Mktg.--National Cattlemen's Beef Association, Chicago, IL; *U.S. Private*, pg. 780
Adrian, R.E., Mgr.-Mktg.--MidCon Gas Services Corp., Houston, TX; *U.S. Public*, pg. 1210
Adrien, Dan, Exec. V.P.-Mktg.--Burgess Pigment Co., Sandersville, GA; *U.S. Private*, pg. 182
Aebersold, Kristin L., V.P.-Mktg.--South Carolina Electric & Gas Co. (SCE&G), Columbia, SC; *U.S. Public*, pg. 1436
Agan, Dan, V.P.-Mktg.--Excalibur Technologies Corporation, Vienna, VA; *U.S. Public*, pg. 598
Aggers, Jane, Exec. V.P.-Mdsg. & Mktg.--Fabri-Centers of America, Inc., Hudson, OH; *U.S. Public*, pg. 609
Agis-Wahl, Emily, Dir.-Mktg. Opers.--BMC Software, Inc., Houston, TX; *U.S. Public*, pg. 162
Agnese, Carlos E., Exec. V.P.-Bus. Devel., Mktg., Estimating & Contract Admin.--Norfolk Shipbuilding & Drydock Corporation, Norfolk, VA; *U.S. Private*, pg. 802
Agnew, Val, Coord.-Mktg.--Tucson Electric Power Company, Tucson, AZ; *U.S. Public*, pg. 1670
Agosti, Jennifer, Dir.-Mktg. Commun.--The National Super Service Co., Toledo, OH; *U.S. Private*, pg. 787
Agresta, Tony, Product Mgr.-Database Mktg.--Group 1 Software, Inc., Lanham, MD; *U.S. Public*, pg. 417
Aguilar, Maggie, Mgr.-Mktg. Communications--Elgar Corporation, San Diego, CA; *U.S. Public*, pg. 789
Aguillard, John, Dir.-Mktg. & Adv.--Superior Auctioneers & Marketing, Inc., San Antonio, TX; *U.S. Private*, pg. 1054

Ahart, Cynthia, Dir.-Mktg.--Computerworld, Inc., Framingham, MA; *U.S. Private*, pg. 569
Ahearn, Jeffrey, Dir.-Mktg.--Imperial Schrade Corp., Ellenville, NY; *U.S. Private*, pg. 559
Ahern, Bill, V.P.-Sls. & Mktg.--Lehman Brothers, New York, NY; *U.S. Public*, pg. 987
Ahern, Dan, V.P.-Mktg. & Sls.--Eatelcorp Inc., Gonzales, LA; *U.S. Private*, pg. 358
Ahern, Dan, V.P.-Mktg. & Sls.--East Ascension Telephone Company, Inc., Gonzales, LA; *U.S. Private*, pg. 358
Ahlrichs, Gary, V.P.-Sls. & Mktg.--Home Juice Co., Melrose Park, IL; *U.S. Private*, pg. 537
Ahlstrom, Craig, Dir.-Adv., Mktg., Opers. & Sls.--Farnsworth Development Co., Mesa, AZ; *U.S. Private*, pg. 397
Ahmad, Egaz, Mgr.-Mktg.--Pakistan International Airlines Corporation, New York, NY; *Int'l*, pg. 1022
Ahmer, Al, V.P.-Sls. & Mktg.--Calavo Growers of California, Santa Ana, CA; *U.S. Private*, pg. 199
Ahnger, Ane, V.P.-Mktg.--Valmet Corporation, Helsinki, Finland; *Int'l*, pg. 1447
Ahrensdorf, Rob, V.P.-Sls. & Mktg.--Coleman Spas, Inc., Chandler, AZ; *U.S. Private*, pg. 691
Aikawa, Hiroshi, Dir.-Mktg.--Haseko Urbest Inc., Tokyo, Japan; *Int'l*, pg. 600
Aikawa, Syuji, Sr. V.P. & Gen. Mgr.-Overseas Mktg. Div.--Anritsu Corporation, Tokyo, Japan; *Int'l*, pg. 77
Aikens, C., V.P.-Sls.--Donohue Paper Sales Corporation, Jericho, NY; *Int'l*, pg. 1075
Aimar, Cherie, Exec. Sec.--Ruscon Corp., Charleston, SC; *U.S. Private*, pg. 952
Ain, Aron J., V.P.-Mktg. & Worldwide Field Opers.--Kronos Incorporated, Waltham, MA; *U.S. Public*, pg. 967
Airey, Andrew, Dir.-Mktg.--Magnet Ltd., Keighley, United Kingdom; *Int'l*, pg. 188
Aitken, Mark A., Dir.-Mktg.--Comark Communications, Inc., Chalfont, PA; *Int'l*, pg. 1383
Aizawa, T., Dir.-Gen. Mktg., Sls. & Adv.--Otto Sumisho Inc., Tokyo, Japan; *Int'l*, pg. 1015
Aizawa, Takashi, Grp. Head-Market Trading--The Long-Term Credit Bank of Japan, Limited, Tokyo, Japan; *Int'l*, pg. 815
Aizenstros, D., Mktg. Dir.--Moore Business Systems Australia Ltd., Richmond, Australia; *Int'l*, pg. 889
Akerman, S., V.P.-Mktg.--Gates Europe, Erembodegem, Belgium; *Int'l*, pg. 1396
Akers, Ann, Dir.-Mktg.--Empire Diamond Corporation, New York, NY; *U.S. Private*, pg. 374
Akerson, Dean W., V.P.-Mktg.--Diemakers, Inc., Monroe City, MO; *U.S. Private*, pg. 332
Akimoto, Toshio, Gen. Mgr.-Special Corp. Mktg.--Meiji Life Insurance Company, Tokyo, Japan; *Int'l*, pg. 854
Akins, Kathleen, Dir-Mktg. & Grp. Sls.--Murdoch Magazines, New York, NY; *Int'l*, pg. 925
Akre, Ron, Mgr.-Mktg. Services--Farnam Companies, Inc., Phoenix, AZ; *U.S. Private*, pg. 396
Alamiloo Mendoza, Jose Luis, Dir.-Mktg.--Grupo SYR, S.A. de C.V., Mexico, Mexico; *Int'l*, pg. 576
Alamin, Steve, Dir.-Mktg.--Allsop, Inc., Bellingham, WA; *U.S. Private*, pg. 44
Albanese, John, V.P. & Gen. Mgr.--Friendship Dairies, Inc., Jericho, NY; *U.S. Private*, pg. 429
Albanese, John, V.P.-Sls. & Mktg.--Friendship Dairies, Inc., Friendship, NY; *U.S. Private*, pg. 429
Albanese, John F., V.P.-Retail Devel.--Bassett Furniture Industries, Incorporated, Bassett, VA; *U.S. Public*, pg. 193
Albaugh, Robert, Mgr.-Mktg.--Hurco Companies, Inc., Indianapolis, IN; *U.S. Public*, pg. 850
Alberding, Bob, Sr. Mgr.-Mktg.--SPS Payment Systems, Inc., Riverwoods, IL; *U.S. Public*, pg. 1132
Albert, Christian E., Mgr.-Brand-Pimm's Cup, Appleton Rum & Crawford--Shieffelin Somerset Co., New York, NY; *Int'l*, pg. 412
Albert, Paul J., Mgr.-Mktg. Communications--Krautkramer-Branson, Inc., Lewistown, PA; *U.S. Public*, pg. 574
Albertson, Bob, Sr. V.P.-Direct Mktg.--Fairfield Communities, Inc., Little Rock, AR; *U.S. Public*, pg. 610
Albertson, Jan, V.P.-Mktg. Services--Sioux Tools, Inc., Sioux City, IA; *U.S. Public*, pg. 1480
Albonetti, Joseph G., Exec. V.P. & Hispanic/Intl. Mktg. Dir.--Tinsley Advertising, Miami, FL; *U.S. Private*, pg. 1088
Albrecht, John, Sr. V.P.-Sls. & Mktg.--Mexicana Airlines, Los Angeles, CA; *Int'l*, pg. 332
Albright, Steve, V.P.-Product Mktg.--John H. Harland Company, Decatur, GA; *U.S. Public*, pg. 785
Albright, Steve, V.P. Prod. Mktg.--The Check Store, Lakewood, CO; *U.S. Public*, pg. 785
Alcott, V., Mgr.-Industrial Design & Mktg. Communications--G.E. Appliances, Louisville, KY; *U.S. Public*, pg. 710
Alderson, David, Mgr.-Marketing--IGC Advanced Superconductors, Inc., Waterbury, CT; *U.S. Public*, pg. 893
Alderson, Kristian, Mgr.-Sls. & Mktg. Svcs.--Rexnord Corporation, Milwaukee, WI; *Int'l*, pg. 127
Aldren, C., Mgr.-Mkt. Support--Moore Paragon Svenska AB, Vastervik, Sweden; *Int'l*, pg. 890
Aldrich, Martin, Mgr.-Mktg.--Motch Corporation, Cleveland, OH; *Int'l*, pg. 1128
Alesi, Pierre, Dir.-Mktg.--SNECMA - Societe Nationale d'Etude et de Construction de Moteurs d'Aviation, Paris, France; *Int'l*, pg. 1165
Alexakos, Lee, Dir.-Corp. Mktg. Svcs.--Cedar Fair, L.P., Sandusky, OH; *U.S. Public*, pg. 319
Alexander-Hargraves, Gundula, Mgr.-Mktg.--Windmoeller & Hoelscher Corp., Lincoln, RI; *Int'l*, pg. 1511
Alexander, Anthony T., Jr., V.P.-Intl. Mktg.--Rexair, Inc., Troy, MI; *U.S. Public*, pg. 1684
Alexander, Bill, Mgr.-Mktg. & Prod. Devel.--Mine Safety Appliances Co., Pittsburgh, PA; *U.S. Public*, pg. 1114
Alexander, Brad, V.P.-Mktg./Flowers Bakeries, Inc.--Flowers Industries, Inc., Thomasville, GA; *U.S. Public*, pg. 656
Alexander, Charles, Dr., Mgr.-Sls. & Mktg.--Sasol Alpha Olefins, Rosebank, South Africa; *Int'l*, pg. 1196
Alexander, Karen, Mgr.-Mktg.--British Film Institute, London, United Kingdom; *Int'l*, pg. 219
Alexander, Leigh, Sr. V.P.-Mktg. & Bus. Devel.--Paging Network, Inc., Plano, TX; *U.S. Public*, pg. 1252
Alexander, Mark, V.P.-Mktg.--Environment/One Corporation, Niskayuna, NY; *U.S. Public*, pg. 586
Alexander, Phillip, V.P.-Mktg. & Adv.--Pearle Vision, Inc., Dallas, TX; *U.S. Public*, pg. 397
Alexander, Randy, V.P.-Sls. & Mktg.--Chiron Vision, Irvine, CA; *U.S. Public*, pg. 350
Alexandre, Jacques, Gen. Mgr.-Intl. & Mktg. Strategy--Groupe SEB, Ecueille, France; *Int'l*, pg. 568
Alexy, George N., Chief Mktg. & Prods. Officer--Cirrus Logic, Inc., Fremont, CA; *U.S. Public*, pg. 375
Alfano, Dino, Dir.-Mktg. & Product Mgr.--Bard Diagnostic Sciences, Redmond, WA; *U.S. Public*, pg. 189
Alfieri, John, V.P.-Sls. & Mktg.--Lista International Corporation, Holliston, MA; *Int'l*, pg. 812
Aliabadi, Manoocher Mansouri, V.P.-Corp. Mktg./UDT Sensors--OSI Systems, Inc., Hawthorne, CA; *U.S. Public*, *pg. 1208*
Alias, Patrick, Exec. V.P.-Sls. & Mktg.--Cognex Corporation, Natick, MA; *U.S. Public*, pg. 394
Alibau, Maite, Sls. & Mktg. Mgr.--Whitehall Spain, Barcelona, Spain; *U.S. Public*, pg. 82
Alioto, Mario, V.P.-Mktg. & Sls.--San Francisco Giants Baseball Club, San Francisco, CA; *U.S. Private*, pg. 964
Allan, Sian, Dir.-Mktg. & Corp. Devel.--Hanson PLC, London, United Kingdom; *Int'l*, pg. 592
Allard, Ronald, V.P.-Corp. Mktg.--Granite State Manufacturing Co., Manchester, NH; *U.S. Private*, pg. 36
Allebrand, John, V.P. & Dir.-Adv. & Mktg.--Glendale Federal Bank, F.S.B., Glendale, CA; *U.S. Public*, pg. 747
Alleman, Ray, V.P.-Specialty Trades & Shoe Care Products--Kiwi Brands, Douglassville, PA; *U.S. Public*, pg. 1433
Allen, Bob, V.P.-Mktg.--Vigortone AG Products, Inc., Cedar Rapids, IA; *Int'l*, pg. 1357
Allen, Clark R., V.P.-New Product Devel.--Combe Incorporated, White Plains, NY; *U.S. Private*, pg. 257
Allen, David, Chm. Bd., Pres., Chief Exec. Officer & Chief Fin. Officer--AMD Industries Inc., Cicero, IL; *U.S. Private*, *pg. 6*
Allen, Frank, V.P.-Sls. & Mktg.--The Arnold Engineering Company, Marengo, IL; *U.S. Public*, pg. 1420
Allen, George Stephen, Sr. V.P. & Dir.-Branch Devel.--H.W. Kaufman Financial Group, Inc., Farmington, MI; *U.S. Private*, pg. 609
Allen, Hugh L., Sr. Exec. V.P.-Sls. & Mktg.--Lawson Products, Inc., Des Plaines, IL; *U.S. Public*, pg. 980
Allen, Judith, Sr. V.P.-Mktg. & Programming--Cable Television Division, New Canaan, CT; *U.S. Public*, pg. 329
Allen, Liz, Dir.-Mktg.--Boston Chicken, Inc., Golden, CO; *U.S. Public*, pg. 247
Allen, Mark, Mgr.-Mktg. Services--PACCAR Australia Pty. Ltd., Bayswater, Australia; *U.S. Public*, pg. 1247
Allen, Meredith, V.P.-Mktg.--Staple Cotton Cooperative Association, Greenwood, MS; *U.S. Private*, pg. 1033
Allen, Merlin, Dir.-Mktg.--The Barden Corporation (U.K.) Ltd., Bracknell, United Kingdom; *Int'l*, pg. 468
Allen, Mike, V.P.-Sls. & Mktg.-C Stores, Airlines & New Business--Aladdin Synergetics, Inc., Nashville, TN; *U.S. Private*, pg. 31
Allen, Mike, Mgr.-Mktg.--IDP Vertical Turbine Pump Division, Hastings, NE; *U.S. Public*, pg. 877
Allen, Peter R., Dir.-Mktg. & Sls.--Muro Pharmaceutical, Inc., Tewksbury, MA; *U.S. Private*, pg. 767
Allen, Stephen L., Exec. V.P.--MCRB Service Bureau, Inc., Chatsworth, CA; *U.S. Private*, pg. 686
Allen, Thomas G., V.P.-Sls. & Mktg.--Effective Management Systems, Milwaukee, WI; *U.S. Public*, pg. 565
Allen, Thomas L., Corp. V.P.-Mktg.--Skyline Chili, Inc., Fairfield, OH; *U.S. Public*, pg. 1475
Allen, Wayne E., Dir.-Sls. & Mktg. & Corp. Sec.--Idaho Supreme Company, Firth, ID; *U.S. Private*, pg. 557
Allenbaugh, Bruce, V.P.-Mktg. Svcs.--Nextlink Communications Inc., Bellevue, WA; *U.S. Public*, pg. 1181
Allery, Jesse, Dir.-New Business--Sioux Manufacturing Corp., Fort Totten, ND; *U.S. Private*, pg. 1003
Alles, Don, Mgr.-Mktg. Communications--Eaton Corporation, Truck Components Operations-North America, Galesburg, MI; *U.S. Public*, pg. 557
Allessio, Robert M., V.P.-Mktg. & Distribution--The Berkshire Gas Company, Pittsfield, MA; *U.S. Public*, pg. 216
Alley, B. James, Exec. V.P.-Mktg.--Tyco Toys, Inc., Mount Laurel, NJ; *U.S. Public*, pg. 1058
Alley, Keith, Mgr.-Mktg.--Stamler Corporation, Millersburg, KY; *U.S. Private*, pg. 814
Alley, Shirley, Mgr.-Mktg. Communications--DSP Technology Inc., Fremont, CA; *U.S. Public*, pg. 475
Allford, Suzanne, Sr. V.P.-Mktg. & Admin.--Sam's Clubs Div., Bentonville, AR; *U.S. Public*, pg. 1733
Alligood, James C., V.P.-Retail Mktg.--Mapco Petroleum Inc., Tulsa, OK; *U.S. Public*, pg. 1042
Allison, John, Mgr.-Mktg. & Sls.--Ardell Industries Inc., Union, NJ; *U.S. Private*, pg. 597
Allman, James, Mgr.-Sls. & Mktg.--The Computer Patch of Joplin, Joplin, MO; *U.S. Private*, pg. 995
Allona, Cesar, Dir.-Sls. & Mktg.--Fate S.A., San Fernando, Argentina; *Int'l*, pg. 478
Allsopp, Craig, V.P.-Sls & Mktg.--Dow Jones Telerate Holdings, Inc., Jersey City, NJ; *U.S. Public*, pg. 525
Allsopp, Fleur, Mktg. Officer--Smorgon Fencing, Melbourne, Australia; *Int'l*, pg. 1269
Allsopp, J.E., III, V.P.-Sls. & Mktg.--Florida Crushed Stone Company, Leesburg, FL; *U.S. Private*, pg. 414
Allyn, Laurie, Dir.-Mktg.--Catalina, Los Angeles, CA; *U.S. Public*, pg. 148
Allyn, Laurie, Dir.-Mktg.--Cole of California, Los Angeles, CA; *U.S. Public*, pg. 148
Almandinger, Keith, Dir.-Mktg.--Nissan Forklift Corporation, North America, Marengo, IL; *Int'l*, pg. 944
Almeida, Manny, V.P.-Mktg.-Consumer Mktg. Div.--Fuji Photo Film U.S.A., Inc., Elmsford, NY; *Int'l*, pg. 524
Almeida, Rodrigo de, Mgr.-Corp. Communications--Monsanto do Brasil Ltda. (Mobra S.A.), Sao Paulo, Brazil; *U.S. Public*, pg. 1125
Almond, Jeff, Dir.-Mktg.--Heatcraft, Inc.-Refrigeration Products Division, Stone Mountain, GA; *U.S. Private*, pg. 659
Almond, Kitty, Mgr.-Mktg.--Mason Shoe Mfg. Co., Chippewa Falls, WI; *U.S. Private*, pg. 712
Alperson, Steven, Exec. V.P.--Rolled Steel Products Corporation, Los Angeles, CA; *U.S. Private*, pg. 941
Alpert, Don, V.P.-Mktg.--Super Sagless Corp., Tupelo, MS; *U.S. Public*, pg. 986
Alpert, Ellin G., Mktg. Mgr.--Jack Levy Associates, Chicago, IL; *U.S. Private*, pg. 664
Alpin, Jerome P., Sr. V.P. & Gen. Mgr.-Intl. Sls. & Mktg.--Dep Corporation, Rancho Dominguez, CA; *U.S. Public*, pg. 500
Alpsteg, Hans, V.P.-Mktg.--Baldwin Filters, Kearney, NE; *U.S. Public*, pg. 381
Alspach, G., Coord.-Corp. Mktg.--Fostoria Industries, Inc., Fostoria, OH; *U.S. Private*, pg. 421
Altavilla, Pat, V.P.-Mktg.--Mentor H/S, Inc., Santa Barbara, CA; *U.S. Public*, pg. 1086
Alter, Susan, V.P.-Creative Mktg. & Promo.--Hachette Filipacchi Magazines Inc., New York, NY; *Int'l*, pg. 794
Althaus, Rob, V.P.-Circulation--Detroit Newspapers, Detroit, MI; *U.S. Public*, pg. 965
Althoff, Todd, V.P.-Mktg.--Royal Consumer Business Products, Bridgewater, NJ; *Int'l*, pg. 1002
Altizer, Lance, Dir.-Sls. & Mktg.--Gomar Manufacturing Co., Inc., Linden, NJ; *U.S. Public*, pg. 51
Altmix, John, Mgr.-Mktg.--Sweco, Florence, KY; *U.S. Public*, *pg. 574*
Alton, Vickie J., V.P.-Mktg. Trng.--The Franklin Life Insurance Company, Springfield, IL; *U.S. Public*, pg. 76
Alvarez Villafane, Primo, Dir.-Sls., Mktg. & Pur.--Grupo Comercial Chedraui S.A. de C.V., Veracruz, Mexico; *Int'l*, *pg. 573*
Alvarez Villafane, Primo, Dir.-Sls., Mktg. & Pur.--Tiendas Chedraui S.A. de C.V., Veracruz, Mexico; *Int'l*, pg. 573
Alves, Charles, V.P.-Sls. & Mktg.--So-Lo-Food, Inc., Baltimore, MD; *U.S. Private*, pg. 1011
Alvin, Bjorn, Dir.-Mktg.--Tretorn AB, Helsingborg, Sweden; *Int'l*, pg. 1072
Alvord, George H., Mgr.-Mktg. & Sls.--Dobbs International Services, Inc., Memphis, TN; *U.S. Public*, pg. 1718
Amaral, Francisco, Dr., Dir.-Mktg.--Nestle Portugal, S.A., Carnaxide, Portugal; *Int'l*, pg. 921
Amatriain, Belen, Dir.-Mktg.--Telefonica Publicidad e Informac., Madrid, Spain; *Int'l*, pg. 1372
Amberger, Tom, Dir.-Mktg.--Galardi Group, Inc., Newport Beach, CA; *U.S. Private*, pg. 437
Ambrosi, Sharon, Mktg. Coord.-Midwest Region--ResourceNet International, Shawnee Mission, KS; *U.S. Public*, pg. 903
Amell, Hans B., Sr. V.P.-Mktg.--Cognizant Corporation, Westport, CT; *U.S. Public*, pg. 395
Ameluxen, Jim, Mgr.-Div. Mktg., East--Taco John's International, Inc., Cheyenne, WY; *U.S. Private*, pg. 1066
Amico, Dan, Dir.-Mktg.--Sound Advice, Inc., Dania, FL; *U.S. Public*, pg. 1488
Amistabi, Richard, V.P.-Sls. & Mktg.--The Doe Run Company, Saint Louis, MO; *U.S. Private*, pg. 922
Ammerman, Silvia, Dir.-Mktg.--Attachmate, Bellevue, WA; *U.S. Private*, pg. 98
Ammons, Dennis, V.P.-Mktg.--American Drew, Greensboro, NC; *U.S. Public*, pg. 974
Amonette, Jan, V.P.-Media, Mktg. Res. & Database Mktg.--Caldwell VanRiper, Inc., Indianapolis, IN; *U.S. Private*, pg. 200
Amos, Holly, Mgr.-Mktg.--Kettle Restaurants, Houston, TX; *U.S. Private*, pg. 617
Amos, M. Edward, III, V.P. & Dir.-Mktg.--Willis Corroon Corp. of Maryland, Hunt Valley, MD; *Int'l*, pg. 1506
AmRhein, Dick, Mgr.- Mktg. Communications & Training--Miller Fluid Power Corp., Bensenville, IL; *U.S. Private*, pg. 747
Amsden, Deborah C., Mgr.-Bus. Devel.--Alliance Construction Solutions, Inc., Fort Collins, CO; *U.S. Private*, pg. 38
Amsley, Joel, V.P.-Sls. & Mktg.--Jerr-Dan Corporation, Greencastle, PA; *U.S. Public*, pg. 537
Amster, B.R., Sr. V.P.-Mktg. & Sls.--Canadian Airlines International Ltd., Calgary, Canada; *Int'l*, pg. 256
Amundson, Roger D., Mgr.-Mktg.--Communications Systems, Inc., Hector, MN; *U.S. Public*, pg. 415
Anacona, Barbara, Mgr.-Mktg.--Industrial Equipment News, New York, NY; *U.S. Private*, pg. 1082
Anandan, Tanya, Mgr.-Mktg.--Wall Colmonoy Corp., Madison Heights, MI; *U.S. Private*, pg. 1148
Anatt, Tracy, Dir.-Mktg.--Charter Clinic Nightingale, London, United Kingdom; *U.S. Public*, pg. 1036
Anctil, Paula, Dir.-Mktg. & Adv.--United Grocers Inc., Portland, OR; *U.S. Private*, pg. 1122
Anderholm, Jeff, V.P.-Mktg.--Art Technology Group, Boston, MA; *U.S. Private*, pg. 86
Anderon, Joe, V.P.-Sls. & Mktg.--Stusser Electric Company, Seattle, WA; *U.S. Private*, pg. 265
Anders, Mary, Dir.-Sls. & Mktg.--Levlad, Inc., Chatsworth, CA; *U.S. Private*, pg. 663
Andersch, Jennifer, Mktg. Communicaitons Specialist--Metrologic Instruments, Inc., Blackwood, NJ; *U.S. Public*, *pg. 1102*
Andersen, Linda, V.P.-Music Club Adv.--Columbia House Music Club, New York, NY; *Int'l*, pg. 1281
Andersen, Mariette, V.P.-Mktg. & Sec.--Coolidge Glass Co., Inc., Waukesha, WI; *U.S. Private*, pg. 273
Andersen, R., Consultant-Mktg. Vehicles--Toyota Norge A/S, Drammen, Norway; *Int'l*, pg. 1414
Andersen, Scott, Mgr.-Prod. & Market--SK Hand Tool Corp., Chicago, IL; *Int'l*, pg. 570

Anderson-Shew, Pat, Mgr- Mktg. Services--Raytheon Appliances, Ripon, WI; *U.S. Public*, pg. 1366

Anderson, Alice, Mgr.-Media/Mktg. Services--Radisson Hotel Corporation, Minneapolis, MN; *U.S. Private*, pg. 212

Anderson, Angi, Dir.-Mktg.--Affiliated Computer Services, Inc., Dallas, TX; *U.S. Public*, pg. 27

Anderson, Arden, V.P.-Mktg.--Mitsubishi Silicon America, Palo Alto, CA; *Int'l*, pg. 875

Anderson, Barbara, Dir.-Mktg. Communications--Applied Biosystems, Foster City, CA; *U.S. Public*, pg. 1279

Anderson, Caroline, Mgr.-Mktg., Promo. & Pub. Rels.--The News Tribune, Tacoma, WA; *U.S. Public*, pg. 1066

Anderson, Caroline, Bus. Devel. Mgr.--Roose & Partners, London, United Kingdom; *Int'l*, pg. 1377

Anderson, Catherine, Mgr.-Mktg. & Communications--O.I. Corporation, College Station, TX; *U.S. Public*, pg. 1208

Anderson, Craig L., Dir.-Mktg.--Polyflex Business Unit, Houston, TX; *U.S. Public*, pg. 1260

Anderson, David, Mgr.-Media Relations--ENSERCH Corporation, Dallas, TX; *U.S. Public*, pg. 1587

Anderson, Derek, V.P.-Mktg. & Prod. Devel.--Merisel Canada, Concord, Canada; *U.S. Public*, pg. 1096

Anderson, Dick, Mgr.-Global Mktg.--Tipper Tie, Inc., Apex, NC; *U.S. Public*, pg. 520

Anderson, Dick, Mgr.-Mktg.--Alpine Lace Brands, Inc., Maplewood, NJ; *U.S. Private*, pg. 646

Anderson, Donald, V.P.-Sls. & Mktg.--Minnesota Valley Engineering/Cryogenic Association, Bloomington, MN; *U.S. Private*, pg. 751

Anderson, Doug, V.P.-Sls. & Mktg.--Active Voice Corporation, Seattle, WA; *U.S. Public*, pg. 17

Anderson, Ed, Mgr.-Mktg. & Brand Devel.--PYA/Monarch, Inc., Greenville, SC; *U.S. Public*, pg. 1433

Anderson, Gary, V.P.-Sls. & Mktg. Automotive--American Suzuki Motor Corporation, Brea, CA; *Int'l*, pg. 1323

Anderson, Ian, Mgr.-Mktg.--James Walker & Co. Limited, Woking, United Kingdom; *Int'l*, pg. 1485

Anderson, Jack, Sr. V.P.-Sls. & Mktg.--Holland America Line Westours, Seattle, WA; *U.S. Public*, pg. 306

Anderson, Jayne, Mgr.-Communications & Mktg.--Evans & Sutherland Computer Corporation, Salt Lake City, UT; *U.S. Public*, pg. 595

Anderson, Joe D., Exec. V.P.-Consumer Mkts. Div.--Countrywide Home Loans Inc., Pasadena, CA; *U.S. Public*, pg. 452

Anderson, John A., V.P.-Mktg./Fibers Grp.--Wellman, Inc., Shrewsbury, NJ; *U.S. Public*, pg. 1752

Anderson, John T., Dir.-Mktg.--Delphi Harrison Thermal Systems, Lockport, NY; *U.S. Public*, pg. 719

Anderson, Jon, V.P.-Mktg.-Europe--Columbia Tri-Star Films (UK), London, United Kingdom; *Int'l*, pg. 1281

Anderson, Kimberly, Mgr.-Mktg.--International Typeface Corporation (ITC), New York, NY; *Int'l*, pg. 460

Anderson, Kyle, V.P.-Mktg.--Quill Corp., Lincolnshire, IL; *U.S. Private*, pg. 901

Anderson, Larry C., Dir.-Marine Mktg.--Datamarine International, Inc., Mountlake Terrace, WA; *U.S. Public*, pg. 486

Anderson, Lisa A., Mgr.-Mktg. Communications--Dexter Nonwovens Division, Windsor Locks, CT; *U.S. Public*, pg. 504

Anderson, Liz, V.P. & Gen. Mgr.-Mktg. & Sls., Vaccines & Pediatrics--Wyeth-Ayerst Laboratories, Inc., Philadelphia, PA; *U.S. Public*, pg. 80

Anderson, Malcolm, Dir.-Field Opers.--Carlson Retail Marketing, Minneapolis, MN; *U.S. Private*, pg. 212

Anderson, Mark, Dir.-Mktg.--Quebecor Printing (USA) Corp., Boston, MA; *Int'l*, pg. 1076

Anderson, Neil, Dir.-Sls. & Mktg.--Simmons American Eagle Airlines, Dallas-Fort Worth Airport, TX; *U.S. Public*, pg. 10

Anderson, Neil, Sr. V.P.-Sls. & Mktg.--Ball Corporation, Muncie, IN; *U.S. Public*, pg. 170

Anderson, Neil M., Sr. V.P.-Mktg. & Sls.--Ball Metal Beverage Container Corp., Westminster, CO; *U.S. Public*, pg. 171

Anderson, Peter S., Mgr.-Mktg.--Marinette Marine Corporation, Marinette, WI; *U.S. Private*, pg. 703

Anderson, Phil, Mgr.-Mktg.--Thorntons PLC, Darbyshire, United Kingdom; *Int'l*, pg. 1386

Anderson, R. Jeff, Sr. V.P.-Mktg. & Bus. Devel.--Syroco Inc., Peabody, MA; *Int'l*, pg. 844

Anderson, Rex, Dir.-Mktg. Communications--Carrier Corporation, Indianapolis, IN; *U.S. Public*, pg. 1689

Anderson, Rich, Dir.-Mktg.--Orthofix Inc., Richardson, TX; *Int'l*, pg. 1011

Anderson, Richard S., V.P.-Matl. Handling Prod. Grp.--Cascade Corporation, Troutdale, OR; *U.S. Public*, pg. 310

Anderson, Robin, V.P.-Sls. & Mktg.--The Metal Ware Corp., Two Rivers, WI; *U.S. Private*, pg. 734

Anderson, Scott, Exec. V.P.-Mktg.--HFS, Incorporated, Parsippany, NJ; *U.S. Public*, pg. 321

Anderson, Scott, V.P.-Mktg.--McGill Manufacturing Company, Inc., Valparaiso, IN; *U.S. Public*, pg. 573

Anderson, Shannon L., Coord.-Mktg.--Dugan & Meyers Interests, Inc., Cincinnati, OH; *U.S. Private*, pg. 345

Anderson, Sue Ellen, Dir.-Mktg.--NCH Corporation, Irving, TX; *U.S. Public*, pg. 1145

Anderson, Thor, V.P.-Mktg.--Express Scripts, Inc., Maryland Heights, MO; *U.S. Public*, pg. 600

Anderson, W. Kent, V.P.-Americas--Binks Sames Corporation, Franklin Park, IL; *U.S. Public*, pg. 229

Anderson, Wayne E., V.P.-Mktg. Opers.--Phillips Petroleum Company, Bartlesville, OK; *U.S. Public*, pg. 1290

Andersson, Ingvar, Mgr.-Mktg.--JM Byggnads och Fastighets AB, Stockholm, Sweden; *Int'l*, pg. 1260

Andersson, Malte, Dir.-Paper Mktg.--MoDo Paper AB, Ornskoldsvik, Sweden; *Int'l*, pg. 886

Andert, Gene, Gen. Mgr.-Mktg.--Rea Magnet Wire Company, Inc., Fort Wayne, IN; *U.S. Private*, pg. 913

Andler, Gary, Dir.-Mktg.--IXL Cabinets, Dallas, TX; *U.S. Public*, pg. 1634

Andler, Steve, V.P.-Mktg.--Phoenix Technologies Ltd., San Jose, CA; *U.S. Public*, pg. 1292

Andre, Stan, Sr. V.P.-Mktg.--Nulaid Foods, Ripon, CA; *U.S. Private*, pg. 809

Andreas, Martin L., Sr. V.P.-Sls. & Mktg.--Archer Daniels Midland Company (ADM), Decatur, IL; *U.S. Public*, pg. 127

Andresen, Eva A., V.P.-Mktg. Info. Svcs.--Hilton Hotels Div., Beverly Hills, CA; *U.S. Public*, pg. 829

Andress, Brad, V.P.-Mktg.--Lund International Holdings, Inc., Anoka, MN; *U.S. Public*, pg. 1020

Andress, Brad, V.P.-Mktg.--Lund Industries Inc., Anoka, MN; *U.S. Public*, pg. 1020

Andrew, Bob, Mgr.-Mktg. Commun.--Best Power, Necedah, WI; *U.S. Private*, pg. 140

Andrew, Joan Mariani, V.P.-Sls. & Mktg.--X-Rite, Incorporated, Grandville, MI; *U.S. Public*, pg. 1783

Andrews, Allison, Dir.-Mktg.--Royal Oak Enterprises, Inc., Atlanta, GA; *U.S. Private*, pg. 948

Andrews, Beth, Dir.-Mktg. Communications--Cincinnati Bell Telephone Company, Cincinnati, OH; *U.S. Public*, pg. 367

Andrews, Dennis, Mktg. Rep.--Cargill, Wayzata, MN; *U.S. Private*, pg. 210

Andrews, Jay, V.P.-Mktg.--Kleinert's, Inc., Plymouth Meeting, PA; *U.S. Public*, pg. 625

Andrews, Scott, Dir.-Mktg.--Animal Nutrition Div., Chicago, IL; *U.S. Private*, pg. 268

Andrews, William H., Jr., Sr. V.P.-Mktg.--Union Planters Corporation, Cordova, TN; *U.S. Public*, pg. 1668

Andrich, Kristen, Mgr.-Mktg. Research--Samsung Electronics America, Inc., Ridgefield Park, NJ; *Int'l*, pg. 1183

Andries, Linda, Dir.-CD ROM Mktg.--Encyclopaedia Britannica, Inc., Chicago, IL; *U.S. Private*, pg. 375

Anello, Patrick, Dir.-Mktg.--Wahl Clipper Corp., Sterling, IL; *U.S. Private*, pg. 1146

Anes, Luis, Dir.-Mktg.--John Crane Venezuela, Barquisimeto, Venezuela; *Int'l*, pg. 1340

Angelilli, Frank G., Mgr.-Mktg. & Sls.--McGraw-Hill Securities Trading, Inc., New York, NY; *U.S. Public*, pg. 1071

Angelo, Keith, V.P.-Mktg.--Chips and Technologies, Inc., San Jose, CA; *U.S. Public*, pg. 349

Angus, Jan, Dir.-Mktg. Communications--AlliedSignal Aerospace, Torrance, CA; *U.S. Public*, pg. 50

Ankiewicz, Kurt E., V.P.-Sls. & Mktg.--Arnold Transportation Services, Camp Hill, PA; *U.S. Public*, pg. 132

Anneberg, Karen, Mgr.-Mktg.--NTH Consultants, Ltd., Farmington, MI; *U.S. Private*, pg. 772

Annis, Jerry, Dir.-Mktg.--Schlegel Corporation, Rochester, NY; *Int'l*, pg. 128

Anti, Bill, Dir.-Prod. Mktg.-KitchenAid Brand--Whirlpool Corporation, Benton Harbor, MI; *U.S. Public*, pg. 1764

Antil, Jerome, Dir.-Mktg.--Lawn Doctor Inc., Holmdel, NJ; *U.S. Private*, pg. 653

Anton, Denise, Sr. V.P.-Mktg.--Taubman Centers, Inc., Bloomfield Hills, MI; *U.S. Public*, pg. 1561

Anton, Jewel, Supvr.-Mktg. Communications--3M Unitek Corporation, Monrovia, CA; *U.S. Public*, pg. 1606

Anton, William L., V.P.-Intl. Mktg.--Vertex Communications Corporation, Kilgore, TX; *U.S. Public*, pg. 1717

Antonowich, Robert J., V.P.-Mktg.--National Western Life Insurance Company, Austin, TX; *U.S. Public*, pg. 1161

Anwandter, Carlos, Mgr.-Mktg.--General Motors Chile S.A., Industria Automotriz, Santiago, Chile; *U.S. Public*, pg. 721

Anwar, Khurshid, Deputy Mng. Dir.-Mktg.--Pakistan International Airlines Corporation, Karachi, Pakistan; *Int'l*, pg. 1021

Apatov, Craig, Sr. V.P.-Strategic Mktg.--The Weather Channel, Atlanta, GA; *U.S. Private*, pg. 647

Apicella, Alane, Grp. Mktg. Dir.--TMP Worldwide Recruitment Division, New York, NY; *U.S. Private*, pg. 1065

Apollo, Denise, Mgr.--Merry Land & Investment Company, Inc., Augusta, GA; *U.S. Public*, pg. 1098

Appel, Kristen, Dir.-Mktg.--Hovnanian Enterprises, Inc., Red Bank, NJ; *U.S. Public*, pg. 843

Appell, Rick, Dir.-Field Mktg.--Krystal Company, Chattanooga, TN; *U.S. Private*, pg. 636

Appiotti, Gino, Dir.-Mktg.--Pepsico de Mexico, S.A. de C.V., Mexico, Mexico; *U.S. Public*, pg. 1277

Applewhite, Laurie, Dir.-Mktg.--Florida Residential Treatment Centers, Inc., West Palm Beach, FL; *U.S. Public*, pg. 1035

Apthorpe, Bob, Dir.-Sls. & Mktg.--Gast Mfg. Corp., Benton Harbor, MI; *U.S. Private*, pg. 440

Aragon, Jose, V.P.-Mktg.-Wines--Bacardi-Martini, USA, Inc., Miami, FL; *U.S. Private*, pg. 109

Arakelian, David, Dir.-Sls. & Mktg.--Standard Manufacturing Co., Inc., Troy, NY; *U.S. Private*, pg. 1031

Arasi, Tom, V.P.-Mktg., Crown Plaza--Holiday Inn Worldwide, Atlanta, GA; *Int'l*, pg. 170

Arbour, Daniel C., V.P.-Serials Mktg.--UMI, Ann Arbor, MI; *U.S. Public*, pg. 201

Arcadipane, Diana, Mktg. Communs. Mgr.--CPS Direct, Inc., Woburn, MA; *U.S. Private*, pg. 196

Arcangeli, Jeancardo, Dir.-Mktg.--Fiat Auto Belgio SA, Brussels, Belgium; *Int'l*, pg. 481

Archer, David, V.P.-Bus. Devel.-Viacom World Wide--Viacom Enterprises, New York, NY; *U.S. Private*, pg. 779

Archer, Michael, V.P.-Mktg.--Roundy's, Milwaukee Division, Milwaukee, WI; *U.S. Private*, pg. 948

Archibald, David R., Sr. V.P.-Corp. Mktg.--Huntington National Bank, Columbus, OH; *U.S. Public*, pg. 850

Arcure, Lee, Mgr.-Sls. & Mktg.--Venturi Inc., Traverse City, MI; *U.S. Private*, pg. 1136

Ardigliano, Salvatore A., V.P.-Mktg. & Gas Supply Services--The Southern Connecticut Gas Company, Bridgeport, CT; *U.S. Public*, pg. 431

Ardizzone, Siobhan, Mgr.-Mktg. Communications--The Morning Call, Allentown, PA; *U.S. Public*, pg. 1616

Arendale, Scott E., Asst. V.P.-Intl. Sls. Dept.--National Western Life Insurance Company, Austin, TX; *U.S. Public*, pg. 1161

Arends, Al, V.P.-Mktg.--Smead Manufacturing Company, Hastings, MN; *U.S. Private*, pg. 1006

Arends, L., Mgr.-Mktg. Svcs.--G & W Electric Co., Blue Island, IL; *U.S. Private*, pg. 433

Aretakis, Tony, Mgr.-Mktg. & Sls.-Silver--Yardney Technical Products, Inc., Pawcatuck, CT; *U.S. Private*, pg. 376

Argentin, Sil, Mgr.-Mktg. Commun.--S-B Power Tool Company, Chicago, IL; *Int'l*, pg. 205

Argeroudis, Nick, V.P.-Sls., Mktg. & Branch Opers.-Film & Advanced Products Div.--Tekra Corporation, New Berlin, WI; *U.S. Private*, pg. 1073

Argyropoulos, Andrew, Mgr.-Mktg.--Dow Hellas, Nea Smirni, Greece; *U.S. Public*, pg. 524

Ariotti, S., Mgr.-Mktg.--Olivetti Nederland B.V., Leiden, Netherlands; *Int'l*, pg. 1003

Arledge, Sol, V.P.-Sls. & Mktg.--Discount Labels, Inc., New Albany, IN; *U.S. Public*, pg. 70

Arling, Steve, V.P.-Mktg.--G.E. Harris Energy Control Systems, LLC, Melbourne, FL; *U.S. Public*, pg. 712

Armbrust, Rick, Dir.-Mktg.--Square D Automation Products, Milwaukee, WI; *Int'l*, pg. 1208

Armer, Michael S., Dir.-Mktg.--Frozfruit Corporation, Gardena, CA; *U.S. Private*, pg. 430

Armstrong, Anthony, Mgr.-Mktg. & Sls. Opers.--Semtech Corporation, Newbury Park, CA; *U.S. Public*, pg. 1456

Armstrong, B.J., Mgr.-Mktg. Svcs.--Navistar International Corporation, Chicago, IL; *U.S. Public*, pg. 1167

Armstrong, Betty, Mgr.-Mktg.--Navistar International Transportation Corp., Chicago, IL; *U.S. Public*, pg. 1167

Armstrong, Darril, V.P.-Sls. & Mktg.--Jac Pac Foods, Ltd., Manchester, NH; *U.S. Private*, pg. 579

Armstrong, H.S., Controller-Mktg.--General Motors of Canada Ltd., Oshawa, Canada; *U.S. Public*, pg. 722

Armstrong, Karine, V.P.-Mktg., Resorts--Hyatt Hotels Corporation, Chicago, IL; *U.S. Private*, pg. 551

Armstrong, Karine, V.P.-Mktg.--Princess Cruise Lines, Los Angeles, CA; *Int'l*, pg. 1035

Armstrong, Kevin, Dir.-Mktg.--Subway Franchise Advertising Fund Trust, Milford, CT; *U.S. Private*, pg. 1048

Armstrong, Nicole, Mgr.-Mktg.--Interface Inc., Atlanta, GA; *U.S. Public*, pg. 889

Armstrong, Scott, V.P.-Mktg.--The Keller Manufacturing Co., Inc., Corydon, IN; *U.S. Private*, pg. 612

Arnaud, Tawny, Mgr.-Gen. Sls.--Galpin Motors, North Hills, CA; *U.S. Private*, pg. 438

Arndt, Betty, Dir.-Mktg. & Pub. Rels.--Johnson Controls, Inc., Controls Group, Milwaukee, WI; *U.S. Public*, pg. 932

Arndt, Betty, Mgr.-Mktg. Communications--Square D Automation Products, Milwaukee, WI; *Int'l*, pg. 1208

Arnhold, John P., Co-Pres.--Arnhold and S. Bleichroeder, Inc., New York, NY; *U.S. Private*, pg. 83

Arnholt, Christine, Dir.-Mktg. Svcs.--Carnival Corporation, Miami, FL; *U.S. Public*, pg. 306

Arnold, Bill, V.P., Sls. & Intl. Mktg.--Garvey International, Inc., Saint Charles, IL; *U.S. Private*, pg. 440

Arnold, David, Dir.-Corp. Mktg. & Pres.-Tulsa Div.--Nabholz Construction Corp., Conway, AR; *U.S. Private*, pg. 772

Arnold, Gary L., V.P.-Mktg.--Best Buy Co., Inc., Eden Prairie, MN; *U.S. Public*, pg. 223

Arnold, Jennifer, Mktg. Asst.--IAC Industries, Brea, CA; *U.S. Private*, pg. 553

Arnold, Kim M., Dir.-Sls. & Mktg.--The Gorman-Rupp Company, Mansfield, OH; *U.S. Public*, pg. 754

Arnold, Mary, Asst. Dir.-Mktg.--Christian Children's Fund, Inc., Richmond, VA; *U.S. Private*, pg. 238

Arnold, Ron, V.P.-Sls. & Mktg.--Philipp Brothers Chemicals, Inc., Fort Lee, NJ; *U.S. Private*, pg. 861

Arnold, William, V.P.-Frozen Div.--J.W. Allen & Company, Wheeling, IL; *U.S. Private*, pg. 37

Aro, Richie, V.P.-Mktg.--Worldwide Food Products Inc., Jamaica, NY; *U.S. Private*, pg. 1191

Arrasgate, Dawn, Dir.-Mktg.--North Fork Bancorporation, Inc., Melville, NY; *U.S. Public*, pg. 1194

Arriola, David, Dir.-Mktg.--Globe Furniture Rentals, Cincinnati, OH; *U.S. Private*, pg. 458

Arriola, Eddy, V.P.-Sls. & Mktg.--Inktel Marketing, Miami, FL; *U.S. Private*, pg. 101

Arsano, Stephan, Mgr.-Mktg.--BOMAG, Boppard, Germany; *U.S. Public*, pg. 1677

Arthur, David R., V.P.-Sls. & Mkyg.--Sunnen Products Company, Saint Louis, MO; *U.S. Private*, pg. 1053

Artis, Jeffrey, V.P.-Mktg.--Vanstar Corporation, Pleasanton, CA; *U.S. Public*, pg. 1708

Artman, Pam, Mgr.-Mktg. Svcs.--Leggett & Platt, Incorporated, Carthage, MO; *U.S. Public*, pg. 985

Arts, Ad, Intl. Mktg. Mgr.--Inamed B.V., Breda, Netherlands; *U.S. Public*, pg. 874

Artz, Brenda, Dir.-Mktg.--Johnston & Murphy Co., Nashville, TN; *U.S. Public*, pg. 728

Arum, Herbert R., Mgr.-Mktg.--Designatronics, Inc., New Hyde Park, NY; *U.S. Private*, pg. 327

Asalone, Mike, V.P.-Sls.--M. Kamenstein, Inc., Elmsford, NY; *U.S. Private*, pg. 606

Asboth, Kara, Mgr.-Adv.--Fournier Furniture, Saint Paul, VA; *U.S. Private*, pg. 422

Ascani, Gary, V.P.-Mktg.--Diamedix Corporation, Miami, FL; *U.S. Public*, pg. 914

Ash, Jeff, Sr. Mktg. Mgr.--Fuji Computer Media Div., Elmsford, NY; *Int'l*, pg. 524

Ashbaugh, H.S., Sr. V.P.-Sls. & Mktg.--Allvac, Monroe, NC; *U.S. Public*, pg. 43

Ashe, Deborah, Mktg. Coord.--Rockett, Burkhead, Lewis & Winslow, Raleigh, NC; *U.S. Private*, pg. 938

Ashenfelter, Jayne E., Sr. V.P.-Mktg. District Mgr. (PA)--U.S. Healthcare, Inc., Blue Bell, PA; *U.S. Public*, pg. 26

Ashetty, Bob, Mgr.-Mktg. Commun. & Res.--BMW of North America, Inc.-Eastern Region, Ramsey, NJ; *Int'l*, pg. 177

Ashing, Derek, Mgr.-Mktg.--Ocelot Energy Inc., Calgary, Canada; *Int'l*, pg. 996

Ashley, Ken, Dir.-Mktg. Svcs.--WGGB-TV, Springfield, MA; *U.S. Private*, pg. 439

Ashley, Louis, V.P.-Mktg.--Six Flags Over Georgia, Austell, GA; *U.S. Public*, pg. 1612
Ashton, Ric, V.P.-Mktg.--Baker Hughes INTEQ, Houston, TX; *U.S. Public*, pg. 166
Ashworth, Catherine, Dir.-Mktg. & Sls.--British Printing Company Ltd., London, United Kingdom; *Int'l*, pg. 220
Ashworth, Jen, Mgr.-Mktg.--Circle International Group, Inc., San Francisco, CA; *U.S. Public*, pg. 370
Askaw, Christine, Mgr.-Natl. Mktg. & Pub. Rels.--Shiseido (Australia) Pty. Limited, Pyrmont, Australia; *Int'l*, pg. 1235
Askew, L. Rudolph, V.P.-Sls. & Mktg.--Jouan, Inc., Winchester, VA; *U.S. Private*, pg. 601
Askew, William E., Exec. V.P.- Retail Banking--Regions Financial Corporation, Birmingham, AL; *U.S. Public*, pg. 1371
Aspery, Peter, Mgr.-Mktg.--G.E. Canada, Peterborough, Peterborough, Canada; *U.S. Public*, pg. 713
Assad, Dennis, V.P.-Sls. & Mktg.--UniFirst Corporation, Wilmington, MA; *U.S. Public*, pg. 1665
Assel, Kris, Mgr.-Worldwide Mktg. Communications--Xerox Engineering Systems Division, Rochester, NY; *U.S. Public*, pg. 1784
Assimon, Bill, V.P.-Mktg.--Sentry Group, Rochester, NY; *U.S. Private*, pg. 984
Assvm, Zen Dan, Dir.-Mktg.--DAF Trucks N.V., Eindhoven, Netherlands; *U.S. Public*, pg. 1247
Astorino, Michael, V.P.-Mktg. & Sls.--Kex Products, Inc., La Vergne, TN; *U.S. Private*, pg. 138
Atha, Allen, III, V.P. & Chief Mktg. Officer--Amvestors Financial Corporation, Topeka, KS; *U.S. Private*, pg. 59
Atha, Allen, III, V.P.-Mktg.--American Investors Life Insurance Company, Topeka, KS; *U.S. Private*, pg. 59
Atherley, Darrell, V.P.-Sls. & Mktg.--The Family Channel Inc., Toronto, Canada; *Int'l*, pg. 1482
Athern, Frank, V.P.-Sls. & Mktg./Turbines--Coppus Murray Group, Tuthill Corporation, Millbury, MA; *U.S. Private*, pg. 1110
Atkin, Michael, V.P.-Mktg.--Lands' End, Inc., Dodgeville, WI; *U.S. Public*, pg. 977
Atkinson, Doug, V.P. & Dir.-Mktg.--Stock Yards Packing Co., Inc., Chicago, IL; *U.S. Private*, pg. 1043
Atkinson, Gregg, Dir.-Mktg.--North Coast Electric Company, Bellevue, WA; *U.S. Private*, pg. 804
Atkinson, Lloyd W., V.P.-Mktg.--General Datacomm Industries, Inc., Middlebury, CT; *U.S. Public*, pg. 708
Atkinson, Scott, Dir.-Mktg.--Augat, Inc., Automotive Division, Mount Clemens, MI; *U.S. Public*, pg. 1598
Attardo, Chris, Mgr.-Mktg. Services--Burnham, Atlanta, GA; *Int'l*, pg. 686
Atwood, Howard, Mgr.-Mktg.--Teledyne Continental Motors, Mobile, AL; *U.S. Public*, pg. 43
Aubuchon, William E., III, Chief Exec. Officer & V.P.-Mktg. & Adv.--W.E. Aubuchon Co., Inc., Westminster, MA; *U.S. Private*, pg. 98
Auch, Donald G., V.P.-Mktg.--Donnelly Corporation, Holland, MI; *U.S. Public*, pg. 519
Auchinleck, R.H., Sr. V.P.-Intl. & Mktg.--Gulf Canada Resources Ltd., Calgary, Canada; *Int'l*, pg. 577
Aufmuth, George, Mgr.-Mktg. Commun./Uniroyal Brand--Michelin Americas Small Tires (MAST), Greenville, SC; *Int'l*, pg. 322
Augurt, Dr. Tom, V.P.-Product Plng. & Devel.--Propper Manufacturing Co., Inc., Long Island City, NY; *U.S. Private*, pg. 891
Augustine, Patrick, V.P.-Sls. & Mktg.--Eva-Tone Inc., Clearwater, FL; *U.S. Private*, pg. 384
Augustyn, Richard, V.P.-Mktg. & Sls.--King Group, Inc., Ann Arbor, MI; *U.S. Private*, pg. 620
Auker, John, Mktg.-Sls.--Wilsey Foods, Inc., Atlanta, GA; *Int'l*, pg. 879
Aukigan, Regina, Dir.-Mktg. Vascalen--Meadox Medicals, Inc., Oakland, NJ; *U.S. Public*, pg. 247
Auletta, Sally, Mktg. Mgr.--Western International Media Corporation, New York, NY; *U.S. Private*, pg. 1166
Aumiller, Gerald E., Sr. V.P. & Dir.-Human Resources--Keystone Financial Inc., Harrisburg, PA; *U.S. Public*, pg. 956
Austin, Bill, Mgr.-Mktg.--Industra Inc., Seattle, WA; *Int'l*, pg. 74
Austin, Diane, V.P.-Mktg. Devel. Grp.--Rich Products Corp., Buffalo, NY; *U.S. Private*, pg. 928
Austin, Doug, Dir.-Mktg.--Crystal Cabinet Works, Inc., Princeton, MN; *U.S. Private*, pg. 293
Austin, George V., Sr. V.P.-Mktg.--ChemDesign Corporation, Fitchburg, MA; *Int'l*, pg. 173
Austin, John T., Jr., V.P.-Regional Sls.--James Austin Co., Mars, PA; *U.S. Private*, pg. 99
Austin, Maureen, V.P.-Mktg.--Danaher Tool Group, Lancaster, PA; *U.S. Public*, pg. 480
Austin, Terry, Dir.-Mktg.-London Region--Shoppers Drug Mart, Ltd., London, Canada; *Int'l*, pg. 112
Austvold, Christine, Mgr.-Mktg. Programs--Dun & Bradstreet Software Services, Atlanta, GA; *Int'l*, pg. 532
Auth, Greg, V.P.-Mktg. & Sls.--Tenneco Specialty Products, Deerfield, IL; *U.S. Public*, pg. 1579
Autio, Markku, Mgr.-Mktg.--Lielahti CTMP Mill, Tampere, Finland; *Int'l*, pg. 863
Averell, Donna J., Coord.-Sls. & Mktg.-Environmental Systems--Environmental Tectonics Corporation (ETC), Southampton, PA; *U.S. Public*, pg. 587
Aversenti, Candida C., Pres., Chief Oper. Officer & V.P.-Mktg.--General Magnaplate Corporation, Linden, NJ; *U.S. Public*, pg. 717
Avery, Dan, Mgr.-Mktg. & Plng.--Eaton Corporation Automotive Controls Division, Carol Stream, IL; *U.S. Public*, pg. 557
Avery, Kate, Dir.-Mktg.--Legal & General Group PLC, London, United Kingdom; *Int'l*, pg. 805
Avery, Kelley, Sr. V.P.-Retail Mktg.--Buena Vista Home Video, Burbank, CA; *U.S. Public*, pg. 513
Avitable, Michael L., V.P. & Dir.-Mktg.--Marie Brizard Wines & Spirits USA, North Miami, FL; *U.S. Private*, pg. 702
Awsumb, Judi, V.P.-Mktg. & Pub. Rels.--Ikon Office Solutions, Orlando, FL; *U.S. Public*, pg. 863
Axelsson, Per, Mgr.-Mktg.--Robur, Stockholm, Sweden; *Int'l, pg. 1328*
Ayer, William S., V.P.-Mktg. & Plng.--Alaska Air Group, Inc., Seattle, WA; *U.S. Public*, pg. 35
Ayers, Les, Exec. V.P.-Sls. & Mktg.--Simmons Company, Atlanta, GA; *Int'l*, pg. 686
Ayers, Scott, Dir.-Sls. & Mktg.--Mohawk Finishing Products, Inc., Amsterdam, NY; *U.S. Public*, pg. 1357
Ayers, T.W., Dir.-Mktg.--Hunter Douglas Architectural Products Inc., Duluth, GA; *Int'l*, pg. 639
Aylward, A., V.P.-Sls. & Mktg.--Neenah Foundry Company, Neenah, WI; *U.S. Private*, pg. 790
Aylward, Cindy, V.P.-Mktg.--Imax Corporation, Mississauga, Canada; *Int'l*, pg. 661
Ayre, Michael G., V.P.-Mktg. & Sls.--Davie Industries Inc., Levis, Canada; *Int'l*, pg. 385
Aziz, Doug, V.P.-Mktg./Specialty Papers--Wausau-Mosinee Paper Corporation, Mosinee, WI; *U.S. Public*, pg. 1747
Aziz, Douglas, V.P.-Sls. & Mktg.--The Sorg Paper Co., Middletown, OH; *U.S. Public*, pg. 1747
Baach, Michael K., Exec. V.P.-Sls. & Mktg.--Corrpro Companies, Inc., Medina, OH; *U.S. Public*, pg. 451
Baasch, Don, Sr. V.P. & Dir.-Mktg. & Franchise Sls.--AVC/Nu-Vision, Inc., Flint, MI; *U.S. Private*, pg. 9
Babcock, Glenn A., Mgr.-Mktg. Services--Baltimore Aircoil Company, Jessup, MD; *U.S. Private*, pg. 68
Babcock, Kevin, Mgr.-Sls. & Mktg./Tools--Apex Operation, Dayton, OH; *U.S. Public*, pg. 444
Babiarz, Bruce, Dir.-Mktg.--Ghafari Associates, Inc., Dearborn, MI; *U.S. Private*, pg. 450
Babics, David, Mgr.-Mktg.--Plews/Edelmann, Buffalo Grove, IL; *Int'l*, pg. 1396
Babilino, Danielle, V.P.-Sls. & Mktg.--Bally's Grand Inc. (Las Vegas), Las Vegas, NV; *U.S. Public*, pg. 829
Babinski, John, V.P.-Mktg.--Belle Tire Distributor Inc., Allen Park, MI; *U.S. Private*, pg. 132
Babrowski, Mike, V.P.-Mktg. & Sls.--Zoeller Co., Louisville, KY; *U.S. Private*, pg. 1207
Baca, Mal, Exec. V.P.--TACTech, Inc., Yorba Linda, CA; *U.S. Public*, pg. 1792
Bacallao, Josie, V.P.-Mktg. Services--The Miami Herald, Miami, FL; *U.S. Public*, pg. 964
Bach, Caroline, V.P.-Pub. Rels. & Mktg.--Bravo Network, Woodbury, NY; *U.S. Public*, pg. 288
Bach, Tim, Mgr.-Mktg.--Curtis 1000, Inc., Atlanta, GA; *U.S. Public*, pg. 70
Bach, W. Douglas, V.P.-Mktg. & Bus. Devel.--Herberts-O'Brien Inc., Houston, TX; *Int'l*, pg. 626
Bache, Bob, Mgr.-Mktg.--Spectronics Corporation, Westbury, NY; *U.S. Private*, pg. 1024
Bache, Bob, Mgr.-Mktg.--Tracer Products, Westbury, NY; *U.S. Private*, pg. 1024
Bachelder, Cheryl, V.P.-Mktg.--Domino's Pizza Inc., Ann Arbor, MI; *U.S. Private*, pg. 339
Bachman, C. Russ, Jr., V.P.-Mktg. Services--Inland Container-Container Division, Indianapolis, IN; *U.S. Public*, pg. 1575
Bachofner, Gabriela, Dir.-Mktg.--Ascom Holding AG, Bern, Switzerland; *Int'l*, pg. 86
Bachus, Richard, V.P.--Southern Missouri Containers Inc., Springfield, MO; *U.S. Private*, pg. 1017
Bacile, Nick, V.P.-Mktg.--California Micro Devices, Milpitas, CA; *U.S. Public*, pg. 293
Backman, Wayne, Asst. Gen. Mgr.-Mktg.--Basin Electric Power Cooperative, Bismarck, ND; *U.S. Private*, pg. 121
Bacon, Cole, Mgr.-Mktg. Promo.--Alban Tractor Co. Inc., Baltimore, MD; *U.S. Private*, pg. 32
Baden, Marvin, V.P.-Mktg. & Sls., Treas. & Sec.--Producers Rice Mill Inc., Stuttgart, AR; *U.S. Private*, pg. 888
Badenhorst, Chris, Mgr.-Mktg./Alpha Olefins--Sasol Chemicals Europe Limited, Solihull, United Kingdom; *Int'l*, pg. 1196
Badger, Cary, V.P.-Mktg. Svcs.--Kaiser Permanente, Oakland, CA; *U.S. Private*, pg. 605
Badger, Timothy C., V.P.-Mktg.--Arrow Financial Corporation, Glens Falls, NY; *U.S. Public*, pg. 135
Badrick, John, Pres.--Turnkey Technologies, Inc., Edison, NJ; *U.S. Private*, pg. 1110
Baedeker, Rick, V.P.-Mktg. & Pub. Rels.--Hollywood Park, Inc., Inglewood, CA; *U.S. Public*, pg. 830
Bagger, Guy, Mgr.-Mktg. & Adv.--Raynor Garage Doors, Dixon, IL; *U.S. Private*, pg. 912
Baggett, Louise, Mgr.-Adv.--Sport Supply Group, Inc., Dallas, TX; *U.S. Public*, pg. 1499
Baglien, James, Mgr.-Mkt. Devel.--Oregon Freeze Dry, Inc., Albany, OR; *U.S. Private*, pg. 819
Bagnall, Ted J., Mgr.-Mktg & Coal Bus.--Collieries Division, Wollongong, Australia; *Int'l*, pg. 226
Bagni, Greg, V.P.-Mktg.--Schwinn Holdings, Boulder, CO; *U.S. Private*, pg. 975
Bagni, Greg, V.P.-Mktg.--Schwinn Cycling & Fitness Inc., Boulder, CO; *U.S. Private*, pg. 975
Baiden, Jan, V.P.-Mktg.--Successories, Inc., Aurora, IL; *U.S.* Private, pg. 1049
Bailey, Arlene, V.P. & Mkt. Analysis Dir.--Western International Media Corporation, Los Angeles, CA; *U.S. Private*, pg. 1165
Bailey, James, Dir.-Mktg.--Coca-Cola Consolidated, Charlotte, NC; *U.S. Public*, pg. 392
Bailey, Janet, Dir.-Global Mktg.--Elsevier Science (International), Amsterdam, Netherlands; *Int'l*, pg. 1099
Bailey, Joe, Dir.-Mktg.--Gwaltney of Smithfield, Ltd., Smithfield, VA; *U.S. Public*, pg. 1479
Bailey, Linda, Dir.-Mktg.--Bickford's Family Restaurants, Brighton, MA; *U.S. Public*, pg. 545
Bailey, Lisa, Dir.-Mktg. & Customer Service--Midwest Express Airlines, Inc., Oak Creek, WI; *U.S. Public*, pg. 1111
Bailey, Robert J., V.P.-Mktg.--Pioneer-Standard Electronics, Inc., Cleveland, OH; *U.S. Public*, pg. 1300
Bailey, Robert, III, Pres.--Mid American Elevator Co., Inc., Chicago, IL; *U.S. Private*, pg. 743
Bailey, Ron, Dir.-Sls. & Mktg.--GSW Jackes-Evans Manufacturing Co., Saint Louis, MO; *Int'l*, pg. 538
Bailey, Ron, V.P.-Sls. & Mktg.--Tempo Products Company, Solon, OH; *U.S. Private*, pg. 870
Bailey, Ronald G., Dir.-Mktg.--Smith Wholesale Drug Div., Spartanburg, SC; *U.S. Private*, pg. 1008
Bailey, Tom, Mgr.-Mktg.--Copperweld Metallon Div., Pawtucket, RI; *Int'l*, pg. 662
Bailleux, Didier, Dir.-Mktg. & Comminications--Voyage, Issy-les-Moulineaux, France; *U.S. Private*, pg. 647
Baillie, Doug, Dir.-Mktg. Communications--MagneTek Lighting Products Group, Nashville, TN; *U.S. Public*, pg. 1037
Baily, Jim, Dir.-Mktg.-Consumer Prods. Div.--Rich SeaPak Corp., Saint Simons Island, GA; *U.S. Private*, pg. 928
Bain, Thom, Dir.-Sls. & Mktg.--Thermometrics, Inc., Edison, NJ; *Int'l*, pg. 208
Bair, Brock, Mktg. Supvr.--Ingalls, Boston, MA; *U.S. Private, pg. 562*
Baird, Barbara, V.P.-Mktg.--Allaire Corporation, Cambridge, MA; *U.S. Private*, pg. 36
Baird, Michael, V.P.-Mktg.--Skyland Scientific Services, Inc., Bozeman, MT; *U.S. Public*, pg. 1515
Baird, Richard S., Dir.-Mktg.--AFCO Credit Corp., New York, NY; *U.S. Public*, pg. 1085
Bairrington, P.D., V.P.-Mktg. & Transportation--Phillips Petroleum Company, Bartlesville, OK; *U.S. Public*, pg. 1290
Baisley, Bill, V.P.-Mktg.--Peterson Farms, Decatur, AR; *U.S. Private*, pg. 857
Baker, Beth, Mgr.-Mktg.--Bata Shoe Co., Inc., Belcamp, MD; *U.S. Private*, pg. 195
Baker, Bridget, Mgr.-Mktg. Communications--Mitek Systems, Inc., San Diego, CA; *U.S. Public*, pg. 1117
Baker, Clyde H., Dir.-Sls. & Mktg.--Research Industries Corp., Midvale, UT; *U.S. Public*, pg. 196
Baker, Donald, Dir.-Medical Mktg.--Radiometer America Inc., Westlake, OH; *Int'l*, pg. 1083
Baker, Dwight, V.P.-Sls. & Mktg.--Le Tourneau, Inc., Longview, TX; *U.S. Public*, pg. 1410
Baker, Frank, Dir.-Mktg.--Landstar Development Company, Orlando, FL; *U.S. Private*, pg. 649
Baker, Gary, Mgr.-Mktg.--Dialight Corporation, Manasquan, NJ; *Int'l*, pg. 1130
Baker, Gary, V.P.-Mktg.--SunGard Trust Systems Inc., Charlotte, NC; *U.S. Public*, pg. 1535
Baker, H. Forrest, V.P. & Oper. Mgr.-Filtration Div.--Perry Equipment Corporation, Mineral Wells, TX; *U.S. Private*, pg. 855
Baker, Hamzah bin, Dir.-Refining & Mktg.--Petroliam Nasional Berhad (Petronas), Kuala Lumpur, Malaysia; *Int'l*, pg. 1046
Baker, J.C., V.P.-Power Mktg. & Trading--American Electric Power Service Corp., Columbus, OH; *U.S. Public*, pg. 72
Baker, Janice, Mktg.--Regions Bank/Blount County, Oneonta, AL; *U.S. Public*, pg. 1372
Baker, Jeff, Dir.-Mktg.--GNI Chemical Corporation, Deer Park, TX; *U.S. Public*, pg. 694
Baker, John, V.P.-Mktg./U.S.--ACC Corp., Rochester, NY; *U.S. Public*, pg. 2
Baker, John, Mgr.-Mktg.--ACC TeleCom, Rochester, NY; *U.S. Public*, pg. 3
Baker, Kelli, Mgr.-Mktg. & Adv.--Park Distributors, Inc., Bridgeport, CT; *U.S. Private*, pg. 839
Baker, Kelli, Mgr.-Mktg. & Adv.--Universal Relay, Bridgeport, CT; *U.S. Private*, pg. 839
Baker, Linda, Mktg. Services--Hasbro, Cincinnati, OH; *U.S. Public*, pg. 797
Baker, Liz, Mgr.-Mktg.--Gatorade Worldwide Division, Chicago, IL; *U.S. Public*, pg. 1347
Baker, Matt, Dir.-Mktg. Services--Nextel Communications, Mc Lean, VA; *U.S. Public*, pg. 1180
Baker, Melody, Mktg. Communications Assoc.--GIW Industries, Inc., Grovetown, GA; *Int'l*, pg. 721
Baker, Micki, Mgr.-Mktg. Communications--Bird Machine Company, South Walpole, MA; *U.S. Public*, pg. 166
Baker, Paul D., V.P.-Mktg. Commun.--Comverse Technology, Inc., Woodbury, NY; *U.S. Public*, pg. 425
Baker, Rick, V.P.-Mktg. & Sls.--Silver Dollar City, Inc., Branson, MO; *U.S. Private*, pg. 1000
Baker, Rick, V.P.-Mktg. & Sls.--Spectra-Physics Scanning Systems Inc., Eugene, OR; *U.S. Public*, pg. 1594
Baker, Robert, Dir.-Mktg.--Wagner Lighting Products, Chesterfield, MO; *U.S. Public*, pg. 442
Baker, Robert L., Pres.--Plant Maintenance Service Corporation, Memphis, TN; *U.S. Private*, pg. 869
Baker, T.R., Gen. Mgr.-Mktg., Communication & IT Policy--MLC Limited, Sydney, Australia; *Int'l*, pg. 806
Baker, Timothy J., V.P.-Plng.--Blair Corporation, Warren, PA; *U.S. Public*, pg. 236
Baker, Vandy, V.P.-Mktg.--Bench Craft, Inc., Blue Mountain, MS; *U.S. Private*, pg. 432
Baker, William, V.P. & Gen. Mgr.--Hearst Business Publishing, Inc./UTP Division, Garden City, NY; *U.S. Private*, pg. 515
Bakhuis, Donald, Dir.-Mktg.--Xerox - Antillana N.V., Curacao, Netherlands Antilles; *U.S. Public*, pg. 1785
Bakken, J.T., Dir.-Mktg.--Military Avionics Division, Minneapolis, MN; *U.S. Public*, pg. 834
Bakker, Karen, Mgr.-Grp. Mktg.--Marcal Paper Mills, Inc., Elmwood Park, NJ; *U.S. Private*, pg. 701
Balaz, Beverly, Mktg. & Sls.--Grolier Educational Corporation, Danbury, CT; *Int'l*, pg. 794
Balbach, Cheryl, Mktg. Services--Casio, Inc., Dover, NJ; *Int'l*, pg. 274
Balch, Kenna, Dir.-Mktg.--Sholodge, Inc., Hendersonville, TN; *U.S. Public*, pg. 1467
Baldovin, Christopher S., V.P.-Sls. & Mktg.--Lava World International/Haggerty Enterprises, Inc., Chicago, IL; *U.S. Private*, pg. 653
Baldridge, Doris, Coord.-Sls. & Adv.--Trinity Difco, Findlay, OH; *U.S. Public*, pg. 1639
Baldridge, Jennifer, Mktg. Dir.--Barkley Evergreen & Partners Public Relations, Kansas City, MO; *U.S. Private, pg. 116*

Baldwin, Bruce, Mgr.-Sls. & Mktg.--The Entwistle Company, Hudson, MA; *U.S. Private*, pg. 378
Baldwin, David, V.P.-Wire Grp.--National-Standard Co., Niles, MI; *U.S. Public*, pg. 1160
Baldwin, Donald D., V.P.-Sls. & Mktg.--Micron Technology Inc., Boise, ID; *U.S. Public*, pg. 1105
Baldwin, Mike, Mgr.-Sls.--Justrite Manufacturing Company, Des Plaines, IL; *U.S. Public*, pg. 617
Baldwin, Robert D., Sr. V.P.-Sls. & Mktg.--Forest Products & Recycled Paperboard Div., Montvale, NJ; *U.S. Public*, pg. 903
Baldwin, Roger M., Dir.-Mktg. & Bus. Devel.--Dugan & Meyers Interests, Inc., Cincinnati, OH; *U.S. Private*, pg. 345
Baldwin, Susan, V.P.-Natl. Accts.--Kaiser Permanente, Oakland, CA; *U.S. Private*, pg. 605
Bales, John T., V.P.-Mktg.--Beloit Corporation, Beloit, WI; *U.S. Public*, pg. 789
Bali, Vinita, Dir.-Mktg.-Latin America Grp.--The Coca-Cola Company, Atlanta, GA; *U.S. Public*, pg. 392
Balint, Peter, V.P.-Mktg.--Morgan Products Ltd., Williamsburg, VA; *U.S. Public*, pg. 1132
Ball, Brad A., Sr. V.P.-U.S. Mktg.--McDonald's Corporation, Oak Brook, IL; *U.S. Public*, pg. 1068
Ball, Don H., Sr. Exec. V.P.-Mktg.--Willis Corroon Corp. of Illinois, Chicago, IL; *Int'l*, pg. 1506
Ball, Gary, Mgr.-Mktg.--Casablanca Fan Company, Pomona, CA; *U.S. Private*, pg. 549
Ball, Gary, Mgr.-Mktg. Svcs.--Casablanca Fan Co., Inc., Memphis, TN; *U.S. Private*, pg. 549
Ball, Graham, Dir.-Mktg./Columbia--Sony Music Entertainment (UK) Limited, London, United Kingdom; *Int'l*, pg. 1284
Ball, Roger, V.P. & Mgr.-Mktg.--Land Rover North America, Lanham, MD; *Int'l*, pg. 177
Ball, Susann C., Dir.-Travel & Mktg. Svcs.--The Quaker Oats Company, Chicago, IL; *U.S. Public*, pg. 1347
Ballard, Al, V.P.-Mktg.--Polk Audio, Inc., Baltimore, MD; *U.S. Public*, pg. 1315
Ballard, Chuck, Dir.-sls.& Mktg.--President Baking-Louisville, Louisville, KY; *Int'l*, pg. 1069
Ballard, Karen, Mgr.-Mktg.-Media--Budget Rent A Car Corporation, Lisle, IL; *U.S. Private*, pg. 178
Ballard, Karen, Coord.-Mktg.--Rock Bottom Restaurants, Louisville, CO; *U.S. Public*, pg. 1396
Ballard, Peggy, Dir.-Mktg. Communications--Scientific-Atlanta, Inc., Norcross, GA; *U.S. Public*, pg. 1443
Ballinger, Sean, Mgr.-Mktg.--Enerfab Inc., Cincinnati, OH; *U.S. Private*, pg. 376
Balsiger, Rick, Dir.-Mktg.--Mazda Motor of America, Inc. Western Region, Irvine, CA; *Int'l*, pg. 849
Balson, John, Dir.-Corp. Mktg. & Prod. Devel.--Data Broadcasting Corporation, Jackson, WY; *U.S. Public*, pg. 484
Balton, Sheri, Admin. Asst.--Cookie Tree Inc., Salt Lake City, UT; *U.S. Private*, pg. 273
Baltronis, Joe, Dir.-Mktg.--Spalding & Evenflo Companies, Inc., Chicopee, MA; *U.S. Private*, pg. 629
Baltronis, Joe, Dir.-Mktg.--Spalding Sports Worldwide, Chicopee, MA; *U.S. Private*, pg. 630
Baltus, Jerry, V.P.-Mktg. & Sls.--Polar Ware Company, Sheboygan, WI; *U.S. Private*, pg. 873
Balty, Jack, Mgr.-Sls. & Mktg./Groceries--Metro Foods, Inc., Olive Branch, MS; *U.S. Private*, pg. 736
Balza, Guy, Dir.-Intl. Mktg.--Interbrew S.A., Leuven, Belgium; *Int'l*, pg. 679
Balzano, Vincent, Dir.-Media & Planning--Carter-Wallace, Inc., New York, NY; *U.S. Public*, pg. 309
Balzer, Glen, V.P.-Sls. & Mktg., N. America--Philips Semiconductors, Sunnyvale, CA; *Int'l*, pg. 1054
Bamford, Carol, V.P.-Mktg.--UMI, Ann Arbor, MI; *U.S. Public*, pg. 201
Banas, Phil, Dir.-Mktg.--Invincible Office Furniture, Manitowoc, WI; *U.S. Private*, pg. 575
Bandeira Vieira, Henrique, Exec. Dir.-Mktg.--Petrofina S.A., Brussels, Belgium; *Int'l*, pg. 1043
Bandoli, Joanne, Mgr.-Promo.--Crain's Detroit Business, Detroit, MI; *U.S. Private*, pg. 285
Bandou, Vaso, Mgr.-Mktg.--Dr. D.A. Delis AG, Athens, Greece; *Int'l*, pg. 108
Bane, Marc, Dir.-Mktg. Commun.--Information Builders, New York, NY; *U.S. Private*, pg. 561
Baner, Mike, V.P.-Mktg.--Ragu Foods, Inc., Trumbull, CT; *Int'l*, pg. 1436
Banerjee, Nic, Sr. V.P.-Mktg.--Union Bank of California, San Francisco, CA; *Int'l*, pg. 157
Bang, Sherrie, V.P.-Mktg.--Six Flags Magic Mountain & Six Flags Hurricane Harbor, Valencia, CA; *U.S. Public*, pg. 1611
Bank, Bob, Mgr.-Natl. Mktg.--Cleaning Solutions Group/Cello, Havre De Grace, MD; *U.S. Public*, pg. 1466
Bankers, Eugene E., Sr. V.P.-Mktg.--Ames Department Stores, Inc., Rocky Hill, CT; *U.S. Public*, pg. 99
Banks, Mark, V.P.-Mktg.--Bearing Service Company, Pittsburgh, PA; *U.S. Private*, pg. 127
Banks, Tom L., Sr. V.P.-Mktg.--Countrywide Funding Corporation, Pasadena, CA; *U.S. Public*, pg. 453
Bannell, Scott, V.P.-Mktg. & Adv.--The Stanley Works, New Britain, CT; *U.S. Public*, pg. 1508
Bannerman, Carolyn, Admin.-Mktg.--Chatsworth Data Corporation, Chatsworth, CA; *U.S. Private*, pg. 231
Bannon, Bruce, V.P.-Mktg. & Sls.--Whittaker Controls, Inc., North Hollywood, CA; *U.S. Public*, pg. 1767
Bannon, Theresa, Sr. Dir.-Mktg.--Spirit Cruises, Inc., Norfolk, VA; *Int'l*, pg. 1274
Banta, F., Mgr.-Inst. Sls. Center--Johnson Yokogawa Corporation, Newnan, GA; *Int'l*, pg. 1521
Baracz, Robert, Mgr.-Mktg.--Zoological Society of San Diego, San Diego, CA; *U.S. Private*, pg. 1207
Baradari, Fotus, Mgr.-Mktg.--Microlog Corporation, Germantown, MD; *U.S. Public*, pg. 1105
Baratoff, Michael, Dir.-Mktg. & Sls.--Metropolitan Sunday Newspapers, Inc., New York, NY; *U.S. Private*, pg. 739
Baratta, Tricia, Mgr.-Mktg.--Systems Bio Industries, Langhorne, PA; *Int'l*, pg. 445
Barba, Chris, V.P.-Sls. & Mktg.--Warner Books, Inc., New York, NY; *U.S. Public*, pg. 1614
Barbaria, Rick, Mktg. Dir.--APL Limited, Oakland, CA; *Int'l*, pg. 912
Barbeau, Thierry, Sls. Engr.--Lee Company S.A., Voisins-le-Bretonneaux, France; *U.S. Private*, pg. 657
Barber, C. Lewis, Mgr.-Project--National Welders Supply Co. Inc., Charlotte, NC; *U.S. Private*, pg. 788
Barber, James P., Mgr.-Mktg.--Algoma Steel Inc., Sault Sainte Marie, Canada; *Int'l*, pg. 56
Barber, Timothy C., V.P.-Sls. & Mktg.--Expeditors International of Washington, Inc., Seattle, WA; *U.S. Public*, pg. 600
Barber, Tom, Mgr.-Mktg.--Aeroglide Corporation, Cary, NC; *U.S. Private*, pg. 24
Barbera, William, Mgr.-Mktg.--Wire-Pro Inc., Salem, NJ; *U.S. Private*, pg. 1184
Barbosa, Nelson Brum, Mgr.-Mktg.--Esselte Meto Ind. e. Com. Ltda., Sao Paulo, Brazil; *Int'l*, pg. 461
Barbour, Scott, V.P.-Mktg.--Copeland Corporation, Sidney, OH; *U.S. Public*, pg. 573
Barclay, Chris, Mgr.-OEM Sls. & Customer Support--Cascade Corporation, Troutdale, OR; *U.S. Public*, pg. 310
Barclay, Susan, V.P.-Mktg.-Health Care--Versa Services Ltd., Etobicoke, Canada; *U.S. Private*, pg. 79
Barden, Ed, Dir.-Mktg.-Beer Portfolio--Seagram Beverage Co., New York, NY; *Int'l*, pg. 1215
Barden, Mark, V.P.-Mktg.--Barden & Robeson Corporation, Middleport, NY; *U.S. Private*, pg. 116
Barden, Rob, Mgr.-Mktg.--Sencore, Inc., Sioux Falls, SD; *U.S. Private*, pg. 983
Bardon, Larry, Dir.-Mktg. & Sls.--The New Piper Aircraft, Inc., Vero Beach, FL; *U.S. Private*, pg. 794
Bardsley, Bill, Dir.-Mktg.--LogEtronics Corporation, Springfield, VA; *U.S. Public*, pg. 6
Barefoot, Philip S., V.P.-Mktg.--Chesapeake Utilities Corporation, Dover, DE; *U.S. Public*, pg. 347
Baretto, James, Mgr.-Mktg. Svcs.--ATS Automation Tooling Systems, Inc., Cambridge, Canada; *Int'l*, pg. 18
Barfod, Lars, V.P.-Mktg.--Genentech, Inc., South San Francisco, CA; *Int'l*, pg. 1120
Barger, Maurice W., Jr., Exec. V.P. & Chief Mktg. Officer--NACOLAH Holding Corp. Inc., Chicago, IL; *U.S. Private*, pg. 963
Barhite, James T., V.P.-Sls. & Mktg.--Interface Electronics Corporation, Hopkinton, MA; *U.S. Private*, pg. 567
Bari, Anthony R., V.P.-Mktg.--Bay View Capital Corporation, San Mateo, CA; *U.S. Public*, pg. 197
Barker, Bruce J., Gen. Mgr.-Mkt. Devel.--Oglebay Norton Refractories & Minerals, Inc., Cleveland, OH; *U.S. Public, pg. 1214*
Barker, Graham, V.P.-Mktg. & Sls.--Norwalk Co., Inc., Norwalk, CT; *U.S. Private*, pg. 807
Barker, Jerry, Sr. V.P.-Mktg.--Tom's Foods, Inc., Columbus, GA; *U.S. Private*, pg. 1090
Barker, Steve, V.P.-Mktg. & Communications--Rexel, Inc., Coral Gables, FL; *Int'l*, pg. 1107
Barker, Steven, V.P.-Sls. & Mktg.--Ris Paper Company, Long Island City, NY; *U.S. Private*, pg. 932
Barkman, Floyd, V.P.-Sls. & Mktg.--Collins Bus Corp., South Hutchinson, KS; *U.S. Public*, pg. 400
Barley, Gilbert R., Dir.-Communication--Thiokol Corporation, Ogden, UT; *U.S. Public*, pg. 1596
Barnardo, Alan T., Exec. V.P.-Gen. Mgr.-Opers.--Santa Fe Drilling Co., Alhambra, CA; *Int'l*, pg. 765
Barnes, Chester, Dir.-Sls. & Mktg.--Watts Automatic Control Valves, Inc., Houston, TX; *U.S. Public*, pg. 1747
Barnes, Don, Sr. V.P.-Sls. & Mktg.--Presidential Life Corporation, Nyack, NY; *U.S. Public*, pg. 1323
Barnes, Judith, Dir.-Mktg.--Cohoes Fashions, Inc., Cohoes, NY; *U.S. Public*, pg. 268
Barnes, Lee, Sr. V.P.-Sls. & Mktg.--Spectrulite Consortium, Inc., Madison, IL; *U.S. Private*, pg. 1024
Barnes, Wally, Mgr.-Mktg.--Orange-Co., Inc., Bartow, FL; *U.S. Public*, pg. 1229
Barnett, April, Mgr.-Mktg.--Southwest Chemical/Services, Houston, TX; *U.S. Public*, pg. 781
Barnett, Dale, Mgr.-Retail Sls.--The Amalgamated Sugar Company LLC, Ogden, UT; *U.S. Private*, pg. 48
Barnett, Dennis, V.P.-Sls. & Mktg.--Republic Beverage Company, Houston, TX; *U.S. Private*, pg. 149
Barnett, Dennis, V.P.-Sls. & Mktg.--Republic Beverage Co., Dallas, TX; *U.S. Private*, pg. 150
Barnett, Harold, Mgr.-Mktg.--Galderma Laboratories, Inc., Fort Worth, TX; *Int'l*, pg. 819
Barnett, Joanne, Mktg.-Coord.--Ridg-U-Rak, Inc., North East, PA; *U.S. Private*, pg. 930
Barnett, Kelley, Mgr.-Mktg.--Pollo Tropical, Inc., Miami, FL; *U.S. Public*, pg. 1315
Barnett, Mike, Dir.-Plng. & Residential Mktg.--Energen Corporation, Birmingham, AL; *U.S. Public*, pg. 581
Barney, Barb, Dir.-Mktg.--Castex Incorporated, Holland, MI; *U.S. Public*, pg. 1577
Barnhardt, Boyd, Dir.-Mktg.--Broyhill Furniture Industries, Inc., Saint Louis, MO; *U.S. Public*, pg. 688
Barnhart, Dale A., Sr. V.P.-Mktg. & Sls.--Wolverine Tube Inc., Huntsville, AL; *U.S. Public*, pg. 1774
Barnhart, Mike, V.P.-Mktg. & Mdsg.--Quality Food Centers, Inc., Bellevue, WA; *U.S. Public*, pg. 1349
Barnholt, Brandon, Exec. V.P.-Mktg. (St. Louis)--Clark Refining & Marketing Inc., Saint Louis, MO; *U.S. Private*, pg. 243
Barns, D. Mitchell, Mgr.-Mktg.--BASES Worldwide, Covington, KY; *U.S. Private*, pg. 120
Barnthouse, Donald, Mgr.-Mktg.--Plymouth Industries, Inc., Plymouth, OH; *U.S. Private*, pg. 873
Baron, Steven R., Sr. V.P.-Mktg. & Leasing/CBD Office--Prime Group Realty Trust, Chicago, IL; *U.S. Public*, pg. 1326
Barone, Jodi, Dir.-Mktg.--The Children's Place Retail Stores, Inc., West Caldwell, NJ; *U.S. Private*, pg. 237
Barr, Kathryn, Mgr.-Mktg. Trust--BOK Financial Corp., Tulsa, OK; *U.S. Public*, pg. 163
Barr, Michael, V.P.-Mktg. & Adv.--American Century Investments, Kansas City, MO; *U.S. Private*, pg. 52
Barr, R.G., Dir.-Sls. & Mktg.--Bespak plc, Norfolk, United Kingdom; *Int'l*, pg. 193
Barr, Thomas, Mgr.-Mktg. & Commun.--Sellstrom Manufacturing Co., Palatine, IL; *U.S. Private*, pg. 983
Barrera, Joaquin, Mgr.-Mktg. Devel.--Milk Products Holdings (Latin America) Ltd., Fort Lauderdale, FL; *Int'l*, pg. 923
Barreto, Francisco, Mgr.-Mktg.--Souza Cruz, S.A., Rio de Janeiro, Brazil; *Int'l*, pg. 112
Barrett, Edward L., Sr. V.P. & Dir.-Sls.--Marquette Coppersmithing Co., Inc., Philadelphia, PA; *U.S. Private*, pg. 706
Barrett, James E., Jr., V.P.-Mktg.--Hunter Fan Company, Memphis, TN; *U.S. Private*, pg. 549
Barrett, Michael P., V.P.-Sls. & Mktg.--Casella Waste Systems, Inc., Rutland, VT; *U.S. Public*, pg. 312
Barrett, Pete, Sr. V.P.-Affil. Mktg. & Stragic Plng.--ABC Television Network Group, New York, NY; *U.S. Public*, pg. 511
Barrett, Richard, V.P.-Mktg. & Sls.--Hubbell Lighting Inc., Christiansburg, VA; *U.S. Public*, pg. 844
Barrette, Lance, Dir.-Mktg. & Mgr.-Sls.--Dresser Canada, Inc., Mississauga, Canada; *U.S. Public*, pg. 529
Barringer, Thomas, Sr. V.P.-Mass Mktg.--Fieldcrest Cannon, Inc., Kannapolis, NC; *U.S. Public*, pg. 1296
Barrios-LeVeille, Shelly, V.P.-Sls. & Secular Accts.--Bridgestone Multi-Media Group, Chandler, AZ; *U.S. Private*, pg. 168
Barrocas, Jose E., V.P.-Mktg.--Injection Footwear Corp., Miami, FL; *U.S. Private*, pg. 563
Barroll, Patricia, V.P.-Mktg. Communications--Carillon Importers, Ltd., Fort Lee, NJ; *Int'l*, pg. 409
Barron-Binder, Diane, Asst. V.P.-Mktg.--United Bankshares, Inc., Parkersburg, WV; *U.S. Public*, pg. 1674
Barron, Pamela, Dir.-Direct Mktg.--Diebold, Incorporated, Canton, OH; *U.S. Public*, pg. 506
Barron, William, V.P.-Sls. & Mktg.--Littelfuse, Inc., Des Plaines, IL; *U.S. Public*, pg. 1001
Barrow, Judy, Mktg. Analyst--U.S. Filter/Davis Water & Waste Industries, Inc., Thomasville, GA; *U.S. Public*, pg. 1682
Barrows, James E., Dir.-Mktg.--GF Office Furniture Ltd., Gallatin, TN; *U.S. Private*, pg. 434
Barry, James P., V.P.-Sls. & Mktg.--Remcor Products Co., Glendale Heights, IL; *Int'l*, pg. 646
Barry, Jerry, Dir.-Sls. & Mktg.--Dwyer Instruments Inc., Michigan City, IN; *U.S. Private*, pg. 350
Barry, S.H., Dir.-Mktg.--LePage's Limited, Brampton, Canada; *Int'l*, pg. 613
Barsky, Jeanette, V.P.-Mktg.--Merisel, Inc., El Segundo, CA; *U.S. Public*, pg. 1095
Barsky, Richard, V.P.-Mktg. & Adv.--Field Packing Company, Owensboro, KY; *U.S. Private*, pg. 403
Bartek, Bernard M., V.P.-Mktg. & Sls.--Corson Lime Company, Plymouth Meeting, PA; *U.S. Public*, pg. 1685
Barth, Ronald W., Commercial Dir.-Indus. Nitrogen Prods.--LaRoche Industries Inc., Atlanta, GA; *U.S. Private*, pg. 651
Barth, Wendy, V.P.-Mktg. & Sls.--The Southland Corporation, Dallas, TX; *Int'l*, pg. 693
Barth, Wendy, V.P.-Mktg.--7-Eleven Stores, Dallas, TX; *Int'l, pg. 693*
Bartlebaugh, Bob, Mgr.-Mktg.--Vari Tronics Company, Inc., Duarte, CA; *U.S. Private*, pg. 1134
Bartlett, Brad, Dir.-Mktg. & Adv.--North American Recreation Products Company, Wichita, KS; *U.S. Private, pg. 691*
Bartlett, David, Dir.-Sls. & Mktg.--Park Air Electronics Ltd., Peterborough, United Kingdom; *U.S. Public*, pg. 1198
Bartlett, Phil, Sr. V.P.-Sls. & Mktg.--Russell-Stanley Corporation, Red Bank, NJ; *U.S. Private*, pg. 953
Bartley, Amy, Mgr.-Mktg.--Rocky Rococo Corporation, Oconomowoc, WI; *U.S. Private*, pg. 938
Bartok, Pat, Mgr.-Mkt. Devel. & Asst. to Grp. V.P.--Bowman Distribution, Cleveland, OH; *U.S. Public*, pg. 190
Barton, Bill, Dir.-Mktg.--Alcon Laboratories, Inc., Fort Worth, TX; *Int'l*, pg. 916
Barton, Clive, Mgr.-Mktg. Services--RMC Group p.l.c., Egham, United Kingdom; *Int'l*, pg. 1078
Barton, Dave, V.P.-Mktg.--Akorn, Inc., Lincolnshire, IL; *U.S. Public*, pg. 34
Barton, J. Michael, V.P.-Mktg.--Ardco, Inc., Alsip, IL; *U.S. Private*, pg. 80
Barton, Marshal, V.P.-Mktg.--Exabyte Corporation, Boulder, CO; *U.S. Public*, pg. 597
Bartos, Ron, V.P.-Sls. & Mktg.--Savage Arms Inc., Westfield, MA; *U.S. Private*, pg. 968
Bartosh, Becki, Mgr.-Circulation--Business Journal Publications, Inc., San Antonio, TX; *U.S. Private*, pg. 19
Basanez, Marc, Mgr.-Mktg. & Sls.--Conrac Display Products, Monrovia, CA; *U.S. Private*, pg. 264
Basciani, Cynthia, Sr. V.P.-Intl. Mktg.--Columbia Tri-Star Home Video, Burbank, CA; *Int'l*, pg. 1282
Bascom, Sari, Asst.-Mktg.--Golden Grain Company, Pleasanton, CA; *U.S. Public*, pg. 1348
Bascomb, Stuart, Exec. V.P.-Sls. & Mktg.--Express Scripts, Inc., Maryland Heights, MO; *U.S. Public*, pg. 600
Baseler, Theodore, Exec. V.P.-Sls., Mktg. & Corp. Affairs--Stimson Lane Ltd., Woodinville, WA; *U.S. Public*, pg. 1661
Basford, Gregory, Mgr.-Mktg.--All Size Corrugated, Lancaster, PA; *U.S. Private*, pg. 177
Basham, Nicola, Mgr.-Mktg. UK--Hasbro Europe UK Limited, Uxbridge, United Kingdom; *U.S. Public*, pg. 797
Bashaw, David, Dir.-Mktg.--Gillette UK Ltd., Isleworth, United Kingdom; *U.S. Public*, pg. 745
Basile, Steve, V.P.-Sls. & Mktg.--Schein Pharmaceutical, Inc., Florham Park, NJ; *U.S. Private*, pg. 969
Bason, Kevin, Asst. V.P.-Mktg.--FirstMerit Corporation, Akron, OH; *U.S. Public*, pg. 646

Basquin, Paul, Dir.-Intl. Mktg.--Miller Brewing Company, Milwaukee, WI; *U.S. Public*, pg. 1289

Bass, Andrea, V.P.-Mktg.--Chock Full O' Nuts Corporation, New York, NY; *U.S. Public*, pg. 351

Bass, Curt, Mgr.-Mktg. Communications--Lindberg, A General Signal Company, Watertown, WI; *U.S. Public*, pg. 727

Bass, George, V.P.-Cloth Prod.--Amicale Industries, Inc., New York, NY; *U.S. Private*, pg. 66

Bassi, Lisa Lynn, V.P.-Individual Service--Phoenix Home Life Mutual Insurance Company, Hartford, CT; *U.S. Private*, pg. 863

Bassi, Vic, V.P.-Mfg. & Mktg.--NTC/Contemporary Publishing Group, Lincolnwood, IL; *U.S. Public*, pg. 1635

Bastian, Robert R., Dir.-Mktg.--Powell Electronics Inc., Philadelphia, PA; *U.S. Private*, pg. 877

Bastin, David J., Exec. Dir.-Mktg.--Delco Electronics Corporation, Kokomo, IN; *U.S. Public*, pg. 720

Bastyr, Mike, Dir.-Mktg.--Starkey Laboratories, Inc., Eden Prairie, MN; *U.S. Private*, pg. 1035

Batchelar, Peter, V.P.-Sls.--Jason Industrial, Inc., Fairfield, NJ; *U.S. Private*, pg. 583

Batcheler, G.H., Gen. Mgr.-Intl. Mktg. & Bus. Devel.--Global Businesses, Houston, TX; *U.S. Public*, pg. 1583

Batchelor, Greg, Prod. Mgr.-Mktg.--Optimaxx International, Rockleigh, NJ; *U.S. Private*, pg. 818

Bate, Michael, Mng. Dir.--Totes U.K. Limited, Billericay, United Kingdom; *U.S. Private*, pg. 111

Bateman, Gordon, V.P.-Mktg. & Sls.--AP North American Aftermarket Division, Goldsboro, NC; *U.S. Private*, pg. 230

Bateman, Lesley, Dir.-Mktg. Commun. & Pub. Rels.--Paradyne, Largo, FL; *U.S. Private*, pg. 838

Batenic, Mark K., Sr. V.P.-Retail Sls. & Mktg.--Fleming Companies, Inc., Oklahoma City, OK; *U.S. Public*, pg. 652

Bates, Christa, Bus. Devel. & Mktg. Coord.--Lafarge Construction Materials, Canfield, OH; *Int'l*, pg. 788

Bates, David, V.P.-Fine Paper & Pulp Mktg.--Willamette Industries, Inc., Portland, OR; *U.S. Public*, pg. 1768

Bates, Jody, Dir.-Mktg.--Summit Family Restaurants, Inc., Salt Lake City, UT; *U.S. Public*, pg. 278

Bates, Kari, V.P.-Mktg.--Stanley Steemer International, Inc., Dublin, OH; *U.S. Private*, pg. 1033

Batezel, Doug, Dir.-Natl. Prods.--Bergen Brunswig Corporation, Orange, CA; *U.S. Public*, pg. 213

Bathke, Michael K., V.P.-Mktg.--American West Insurance Company, Grand Forks, ND; *U.S. Public*, pg. 216

Batra, Naresh, V.P.-Strategic Mktg.--TelCom Semiconductor, Inc., Mountain View, CA; *U.S. Public*, pg. 1569

Batson, Andrew, Dir.-Prod. Mktg.-Whirlpool Brand--Whirlpool Corporation, Benton Harbor, MI; *U.S. Public*, pg. 1764

Battaglia, Carol, Mgr.-Mktg. & Commun.--Dataram Corporation, Princeton, NJ; *U.S. Public*, pg. 487

Battaglia, Mark, V.P.-Mktg.--SPSS Inc., Chicago, IL; *U.S. Public*, pg. 1420

Battani, Larry, Sr. V.P.-Mktg.--American Republic Insurance Co., Des Moines, IA; *U.S. Private*, pg. 61

Batten, John, V.P.-Mktg.--Malcolm Pirnie, Inc., White Plains, NY; *U.S. Private*, pg. 867

Battin, Jim, Sr. V.P.-Interactive & Mktg. Dir.--Partners & Shevack, Inc., New York, NY; *U.S. Private*, pg. 842

Battison, William J., Exec. V.P.-Mktg. & Sls.--Iwerks Entertainment, Burbank, CA; *U.S. Public*, pg. 915

Battista, Bernie, Sr. V.P.-Mktg.-Americas Group--Dow Jones Telerate Holdings, Inc., Jersey City, NJ; *U.S. Public*, pg. 525

Baty, Curtis, Dir.-Mktg.--Affiliated Foods, Inc., Amarillo, TX; *U.S. Private*, pg. 25

Bauer, Bruce, Mgr.-Intl. Sls. & Mktg.--Modern Controls, Inc., Minneapolis, MN; *U.S. Public*, pg. 1120

Bauer, Harold, Mgr.-Mktg. Services--UnionTools, Inc., Columbus, OH; *U.S. Public*, pg. 17

Bauer, Liz, V.P.-Mktg.--Cable Services Group, Omaha, NE; *U.S. Public*, pg. 283

Bauer, Mike, Exec. V.P.-Sls. & Mktg.--Empire of Carolina, Inc., Delray Beach, FL; *U.S. Public*, pg. 579

Bauer, Richard, Dir.-Mktg.--Lambda Electronics Inc., Melville, NY; *Int'l*, pg. 1241

Bauer, Vineeta, Mgr.-Sls. & Retail Mktg.--Firstar Corporation, Milwaukee, WI; *U.S. Public*, pg. 642

Bauert, Hermann, Dir.-Corp. Mktg. Services--Holderbank Financiere Glaris Ltd., Glaris, Switzerland; *Int'l*, pg. 628

Baughan, Mike, V.P.-Sls. & Mktg.--B/E Aerospace Seating Products Group, Litchfield, CT; *U.S. Public*, pg. 159

Bauler, Beth, V.P.-Sls. & Mktg.--Bridgestone Multi-Media Group, Chandler, AZ; *U.S. Private*, pg. 168

Baum, Christopher, V.P.-Sls. & Mktg. Communications--Sonesta International Hotels Corporation, Boston, MA; *U.S. Public*, pg. 1485

Baumann, David, Dir.-Adv. & Promo.--KSTP-TV, Saint Paul, MN; *U.S. Private*, pg. 544

Baumann, Henrik, Dir.-Mktg.--Toyota Norge A/S, Drammen, Norway; *Int'l*, pg. 1414

Baumann, John, Pres.--The Swiss Colony, Inc, Monroe, WI; *U.S. Private*, pg. 1059

Bauoudin, Jaques, Mgr.-Individual & Prof. Mkts. Div.--Credit Lyonnais S.A., Paris, France; *Int'l*, pg. 343

Bausch, C. Dennis, Exec. V.P.-Mktg. & Planning--Magna International Inc., Markham, Canada; *Int'l*, pg. 829

Bause, Jay, V.P.-Mktg. & Sls.--Elco Textron, Rockford, IL; *U.S. Public*, pg. 1590

Bausewine, George, Gen. Mgr.-Sls. & Mktg.--Central Louisiana Electric Company, Inc., Pineville, LA; *U.S. Public*, pg. 325

Baxter, B.C., V.P. & Dir.-Mktg.--Winn-Dixie Stores, Inc., Jacksonville, FL; *U.S. Public*, pg. 1771

Baxter, Brian, Dir.-Mktg. & Sls.--EECO, Switch, Cambridge, United Kingdom; *U.S. Public*, pg. 1631

Baxter, Harry, Vice Chm.--Bancorp South Inc., Tupelo, MS; *U.S. Public*, pg. 176

Baxter, James G., Chief Fin. Officer & Pres.-Consumer Prods. Grp.--CSS Industries, Inc., Philadelphia, PA; *U.S. Public*, pg. 283

Baxter, Jim, V.P.-Mktg.--Coachmen Industries, Inc., Elkhart, IN; *U.S. Public*, pg. 387

Baxter, John T., V.P.-Sls. & Mktg.--Alpha Associates, Inc., Woodbridge, NJ; *U.S. Private*, pg. 44

Baxter, Kurt, Mgr.-Mktg.--Albert Fisher North America, Dallas, TX; *Int'l*, pg. 491

Baxter, Leslie, Mgr.-Mktg Communication Accts.--Sun Data Inc., Norcross, GA; *U.S. Private*, pg. 1050

Bayer, Charles, V.P.-Sls. & Mktg.--Crescent Manufacturing Company, Fremont, OH; *U.S. Private*, pg. 289

Bayley, John, V.P.-Mktg.--SNE Enterprises, Inc., Mosinee, WI; *U.S. Public*, pg. 1193

Bayley, Peter, V.P.-Product Mktg.--Wall Data Incorporated, Kirkland, WA; *U.S. Public*, pg. 1734

Bazlamit, Tanya, New Bus. Devel. Dir.--Ingalls, Boston, MA; *U.S. Private*, pg. 562

Beach, David, V.P.- Mktg. & Sls.--International Correspondence Schools, Inc., Scranton, PA; *U.S. Public*, pg. 783

Beach, David A., Dir.-Mktg. & Sls.--ICS Learning Systems, Inc., Scranton, PA; *U.S. Public*, pg. 783

Beach, Mary Anne, Sr. V.P.-Customer Information & Mktg.--First American Corporation, Nashville, TN; *U.S. Public*, pg. 624

Beacham, Wayne, V.P.-Sls. & Mktg.--Corporate Express, Inc., Broomfield, CO; *U.S. Public*, pg. 449

Beachum, John, Dir.-Promotion & Publicity--Carson Pirie Scott & Co., Milwaukee, WI; *U.S. Public*, pg. 309

Beadleson, Brett, Mgr.-Intl. Sls./Paper Div.--Boise Cascade Corporation, Boise, ID; *U.S. Public*, pg. 242

Beahm, Clyde W., Grp. V.P.-Prods. & Mktg.--Pennzoil Company, Houston, TX; *U.S. Public*, pg. 1272

Beahm, Clyde W., Exec. V.P.-Mktg.--Pennzoil Products Co., Houston, TX; *U.S. Public*, pg. 1272

Beal, Steve, V.P.-Mktg. & Sls.--Applied Magnetics Corporation, Goleta, CA; *U.S. Public*, pg. 123

Beam, Michael W., V.P.-Mktg. & Sls.--Dynamic Materials Corporation, Lafayette, CO; *U.S. Public*, pg. 539

Beam, Olan, V.P.-Mktg.--Hanes Hosiery, Inc., Winston Salem, NC; *U.S. Public*, pg. 1434

Beam, Pam, Coord.-Sls. & Mktg.--John Boos & Company, Effingham, IL; *U.S. Private*, pg. 156

Bean, Russell, Mgr.-Mktg.--Groen, A Dover Industries Co., Elk Grove Village, IL; *U.S. Public*, pg. 521

Beard, Jim, V.P.-Mktg.--Diversey Water Technologies, Inc., Chagrin Falls, OH; *U.S. Public*, pg. 1150

Beardsley, Sarah, V.P.-Local Services--MCI Systemhouse, Atlanta, GA; *U.S. Public*, pg. 1024

Beasley, B.F., V.P.-Sls. & Mktg.--Parkdale Mills, Gastonia, NC; *U.S. Private*, pg. 840

Beasley, Thomas, V.P.-Mktg.--Kinro, Inc., Arlington, TX; *U.S.* Public, pg. 529

Beason, John, Sr. V.P.-Sls. & Mktg.--Guilford of Maine, Inc., Guilford, ME; *U.S. Public*, pg. 889

Beattie, David, Sr. V.P.-Sls. & Mktg.--McNaughton-McKay Electric Co., Madison Heights, MI; *U.S. Private*, pg. 724

Beattie, Douglas, Sr. V.P.-Sls. & Mktg.--Liquid Controls LLC, Lake Bluff, IL; *U.S. Private*, pg. 669

Beattie, Jim, V.P.-Sls. & Mktg.--GSW Heating Products Company, Stoney Creek, Canada; *Int'l*, pg. 538

Beatty, Bill, Dir.-Mktg.--True Temper Sports Division, Memphis, TN; *U.S. Public*, pg. 233

Beaty, Bryan, Sr. V.P.-Mktg.--Western Interactive Media, Los Angeles, CA; *U.S. Private*, pg. 1166

Beaver, Bryan, V.P.-Mktg.--Carter Companies, Kansas City, MO; *U.S. Private*, pg. 216

Beaver, John, Dir.-Mktg. Commun.--Thor Industries, Inc., Jackson Center, OH; *U.S. Public*, pg. 1602

Beavers, Bob, Dir.-Mktg.--Cleveland Group, Inc., Atlanta, GA; *U.S. Private*, pg. 246

Beavers, Bob, Dir.-Mktg.--Cleveland Electric Co., Atlanta, GA; *U.S. Private*, pg. 246

Beavis, Cameron, Mgr.-Mktg. Systems--James Hardie Industries Ltd., Sydney, Australia; *Int'l*, pg. 596

Bebb, Wayne A., Dir.-Mktg. Svcs.--Mother's Cake & Cookie Co., Oakland, CA; *U.S. Private*, pg. 1022

Bebee, Gary, V.P.-Customer Mktg.--Wm. Wrigley Jr. Company, Chicago, IL; *U.S. Public*, pg. 1781

Bebee, Steve, Gen. Mgr.-Mailing Efficiency & Database Mktg.--Group 1 Software, Inc., Lanham, MD; *U.S. Public*, *pg. 417*

Bechler, Shirley, Mgr.-Mktg. Services--Enger-Kress Company, West Bend, WI; *U.S. Private*, pg. 376

Becht, Julie A., Mgr.-Mktg.--F.N. Burt Company, Inc., Buffalo, NY; *U.S. Private*, pg. 188

Bechta, Matthew, V.P.-Mktg.--Essex Corporation, Columbia, MD; *U.S. Public*, pg. 593

Beck, Alexander, Mgr.-Mktg.--Standard Motor Products Inc., Long Island City, NY; *U.S. Public*, pg. 1503

Beck, Bob, V.P.-Mktg.--Great Salt Lake Minerals Corp., Overland Park, KS; *U.S. Private*, pg. 505

Beck, Charles A., Jr., Dir.-Mktg. Programs--Atlas Van Lines, Inc., Evansville, IN; *U.S. Private*, pg. 97

Beck, Dan, Sr. V.P.-Mktg./Artist Devel.--Sony Music Entertainment, Inc., New York, NY; *Int'l*, pg. 1281

Beck, Diane, Mktg. Asst.--In-Sink-Erator, Racine, WI; *U.S. Public*, pg. 573

Beck, Douglas A., V.P.-Sls. & Mktg.--Clark Grave Vault Co., Columbus, OH; *U.S. Private*, pg. 243

Beck, Douglas J., Sr. V.P.-Bus. Devel.--ICF Kaiser International Inc., Fairfax, VA; *U.S. Public*, pg. 852

Beck, Rick, V.P. & Dir.-Mktg.--Burns & McDonnell Waste Consultants, Inc., Kansas City, MO; *U.S. Private*, pg. 187

Beck, Robert, V.P.-Prod. & Devel.--Vecta, Grand Prairie, TX; *U.S. Private*, pg. 1038

Becker, Don, V.P.-Systems Bus. Unit--Xerox Engineering Systems Division, Rochester, NY; *U.S. Public*, pg. 1784

Becker, Eugene E., Chief Mktg. Officer--American Bankers Insurance Group, Inc., Miami, FL; *U.S. Public*, pg. 67

Becker, Gary, V.P.-Mktg.--The Ertl Company, Inc, Dyersville, IA; *U.S. Public*, pg. 1684

Becker, Hugh E., Dir.-Corp. Communications--Robbins & Myers, Inc., Dayton, OH; *U.S. Public*, pg. 1393

Becker, Jamie, Coord.-Mktg. Commun. Projects--Trendway Corporation, Holland, MI; *U.S. Private*, pg. 1099

Becker, Leon, V.P.-Mktg.--L3 Communications Narda-Microwave West Div., Folsom, CA; *U.S. Private*, pg. 638

Becker, Patricia, Dir.-Mktg. Commun.--Gelco Information Network, Inc., Eden Prairie, MN; *U.S. Private*, pg. 442

Becker, Patrick J., Sr. V.P.-Sls. & Mktg.--NxTrend Technology, Inc., Colorado Springs, CO; *U.S. Private*, pg. 809

Becker, Scott, Dir.-Foods Mktg.--Thomas J. Lipton Company, Englewood Cliffs, NJ; *Int'l*, pg. 1435

Becker, Shelley, V.P.-Mktg.--Helly-Hansen (US), Inc., Redmond, WA; *Int'l*, pg. 1010

Becker, Susan, Mgr.-Promo. & Special Events.--Nextel Communications, Mc Lean, VA; *U.S. Public*, pg. 1180

Becker, Tom, V.P.--Grocers Supply Co. Inc., Houston, TX; *U.S. Private*, pg. 483

Beckley, Karyn, V.P.-Corp. Admin. Svcs.--SpaceLabs Medical, Inc., Redmond, WA; *U.S. Public*, pg. 1494

Beckley, Ron, Mgr.-Mktg.--Subaru Western Region, Irvine, CA; *Int'l*, pg. 523

Becks, Peter, Mgr.-Sls. & Mktg.--Kimball Systems BV, Terborg, Netherlands; *Int'l*, pg. 461

Beckwith, David, Gen. Mgr.-Mktg.--Commercial Intertech Distribution Services, La Porte, IN; *U.S. Public*, pg. 411

Bedard, Lisa, Mktg. Analyst--Breed Technologies, Sterling Heights, MI; *U.S. Public*, pg. 251

Bedbury, Scott, Sr. V.P.-Mktg.--Starbucks Coffee Company, Seattle, WA; *U.S. Public*, pg. 1510

Bede, Jessica I., Sr. V.P.-Medical Products--Capintec Inc., Ramsey, NJ; *U.S. Private*, pg. 205

Bednarz, Judith A., V.P.-Mktg.--Candela Corporation, Wayland, MA; *U.S. Public*, pg. 300

Bedrosian, Peter, V.P.-Mktg.--National Utility Service, Inc., Park Ridge, NJ; *U.S. Private*, pg. 787

Beebe, Whit, Dir.-Adv.--Snapple Beverage Company, White Plains, NY; *U.S. Public*, pg. 1635

Beehler, Barry, V.P.-Mktg.-Watercraft Marine Prods.--Kawasaki Motors Corp., U.S.A., Irvine, CA; *Int'l*, pg. 725

Beekman, Catherine, Mgr.-Mktg.--Media Networks Inc., Stamford, CT; *U.S. Public*, pg. 1612

Beemer, Liz, Dir.-Mktg.--Playtex Apparel Canada, Ltd., Malton, Canada; *U.S. Public*, pg. 1433

Beer, Susan, Dir.-Mktg.--Dansk International Designs Ltd., White Plains, NY; *U.S. Public*, pg. 261

Beerck, Douglas, Mgr.-Mktg.--M & M Precision Systems Corporation, Carrollton, OH; *U.S. Public*, pg. 482

Beers, Bob, Sr. V.P.-Mktg. & Bus. Devel.--KTI, Orange, CA; *U.S. Public*, pg. 939

Beeson, Laurie, V.P.-Mktg.--Boise Cascade Office Products Corporation, Itasca, IL; *U.S. Public*, pg. 243

Beffa, Carlene, V.P.-Mktg.--Physicians Mutual Insurance Co., Omaha, NE; *U.S. Private*, pg. 864

Begis, Laurie, Mgr.-Mktg.--ColorTyme, Inc., Irving, TX; *U.S. Private*, pg. 255

Begley, Amy, Coordinator-Mktg.--Acurex Environmental Corp., Mountain View, CA; *Int'l*, pg. 607

Begley, John, Dir.-Mktg.--Simco, Hatfield, PA; *U.S. Public*, pg. 865

Behnke, William, Sr. V.P.-Sls. & Mktg.--General Communication, Inc., Anchorage, AK; *U.S. Public*, pg. 708

Beigie, Christopher, V.P.-Sls. & Mktg.--Brown-Bridge, Troy, OH; *U.S. Public*, pg. 1022

Beilner, Otto, Dir.-Sls. & Mktg.--AGA Ges.m.b.H., Vienna, Austria; *Int'l*, pg. 13

Beindorff, Michael, Exec. V.P.-Mktg. & Product Mngmt.--Visa U.S.A. Inc., San Francisco, CA; *U.S. Private*, pg. 1141

Belaga, David, V.P.-Mktg.--Pharmaceutical Formulations, Inc., Edison, NJ; *U.S. Public*, pg. 1284

Belanger, Marc J., Mktg. Specialist--Merriam-Webster, Inc., Springfield, MA; *U.S. Private*, pg. 375

Belche, Paul, Mng. Dir.-Sls. & Mktg.--STAHLwerke Bremen GmbH, Bremen, Germany; *Int'l*, pg. 79

Belik, D., Mgr.-Mktg.--Hunter Douglas do Brazil Ltda., Sao Paulo, Brazil; *Int'l*, pg. 640

Belikove, Paula, Dir.-Global Mktg. Communications--VeriFone, Inc., Redwood City, CA; *U.S. Public*, pg. 815

Belin, Murielle, Dir.-Mktg.--Thierry Mugler Parfums, Neuilly-sur-Seine, France; *Int'l*, pg. 295

Belk, Mark S., V.P.-Info. Tech. & Dir.-Mktg.--Kimball International, Inc., Jasper, IN; *U.S. Public*, pg. 956

Belkowitz, Mike, Dir.-Sls. & Mktg.--Hochiki America Corporation, Huntington Beach, CA; *Int'l*, pg. 623

Bell, Adrian, Mgr.-Mktg. Communications--Metromail Corporation, Lombard, IL; *U.S. Public*, pg. 1102

Bell, Bradford D., V.P.-Mktg. & Intl.--Ballard Medical Products, Draper, UT; *U.S. Public*, pg. 171

Bell, Charles C., Dir.-Mktg. & Adv.--Baker Knapp & Tubbs Inc., Grand Rapids, MI; *U.S. Private*, pg. 630

Bell, Lawrence M., V.P.-Mktg. (Cement-U.S. Div.)--St. Lawrence Cement Inc., Montreal, Canada; *Int'l*, pg. 628

Bell, Marsha, Mgr.-Mktg.--Wichita Raytheon Learning Center, Wichita, KS; *U.S. Public*, pg. 219

Bell, Robert, Dir.-Mktg.--Lyon Metal Products, Inc., Montgomery, IL; *U.S. Private*, pg. 638

Bell, Rosalind, Dir.-Mktg.--Six Flags Fiesta Texas, San Antonio, TX; *U.S. Public*, pg. 1611

Bell, Rosalind, Dir.-Mktg.--Six Flags Hurricane Harbor, Arlington, TX; *U.S. Public*, pg. 1611

Bell, Rosalind, V.P.-Mktg.--Six Flags Over Texas, Arlington, TX; *U.S. Public*, pg. 1612

Bell, T., Dir.-Mktg.--Scholl Plc, Newton, United Kingdom; *Int'l*, pg. 1209

Bell, Vance D., V.P.-Mktg.--Shaw Industries, Inc., Dalton, GA; *U.S. Public*, pg. 1464

Bella, Michelle, Dir.-Mktg.--Galavision, New York, NY; *U.S. Private*, pg. 230

Bellamy, Debbie, C.B.C., Dir.-Mktg. Services--American Software, Inc., Atlanta, GA; *U.S. Public*, pg. 91

Bellej, Michelle, V.P.-Shopping Ctr. Mktg. (Ohio)--The Edward J. DeBartolo Corporation, Youngstown, OH; *U.S. Private*, pg. 319

Bellessa, David, V.P.-Mktg.--Romacorp, Inc., Dallas, TX; *U.S. Public*, pg. 1147

Belli, Susi, Mgr.-Mktg. & Investor Rels.--Luxottica Group S.p.A., Agordo, Italy; *Int'l*, pg. 822

Bellin, Jay, Dir.-Corp. Mktg.--Fritz Companies, Inc., San Francisco, CA; *U.S. Public*, pg. 683

Bellman, Debra, Admin.-Mktg. & Sls.--F. Korbel Bros. Inc., Guerneville, CA; *U.S. Private*, pg. 632

Bellnap, J.K., V.P.-Mktg.--J.M. Huber, Clay Div., Macon, GA; *U.S. Private*, pg. 545

Bello, David, V.P.-Mktg. & Bus. Devel.--Citizens Telecommunications, Stamford, CT; *U.S. Public*, pg. 380

Bello, Omar, Mktg. & Res. Dir.--Gowland Publicidad S.A., Buenos Aires, Argentina; *U.S. Public*, pg. 1642

Bellocq, Remi, Dir.-Mktg.--Turf Paradise, Inc., Phoenix, AZ; *U.S. Public*, pg. 831

Belmont, Dennis, Mgr.-Mktg.--A.L. Hansen Manufacturing Co., Waukegan, IL; *U.S. Private*, pg. 500

Belt, Don, Sr. V.P.-Mktg. & Strategic Devel.--TruServ Corporation, Chicago, IL; *U.S. Private*, pg. 1108

Belyea, Jeff, Dir.-Mktg.--Pollack Corporation, Scarborough, ME; *U.S. Private*, pg. 874

Belzer, John D., Pres. & Chief Oper. Officer--TCI Aluminum, Gardena, CA; *U.S. Private*, pg. 1063

Ben Dov, S., Mgr.-Mktg.--Olivetti Sanay Ve Ticaret A.S., Istanbul, Turkey; *Int'l*, pg. 1003

Bender, R.W., Mgr.-Mktg. Communications--Carborundum Abrasives North America, High Point, NC; *Int'l*, pg. 1174

Bendheim, Thomas, Dir.-Mktg.--Dansk International Designs Ltd., White Plains, NY; *U.S. Public*, pg. 261

Bendix, Richard C., V.P.-Mktg.--Lindal Cedar Homes, Inc., Seattle, WA; *U.S. Public*, pg. 998

Bendixen, Knut, Sr. V.P.-Automotive Sls., Mktg. & Service--Bosch Sales Group, Broadview, IL; *Int'l*, pg. 205

Benetton, Mauro, Mgr.-Mktg.--Benetton Group S.p.A., Ponzano Veneto, Italy; *Int'l*, pg. 186

Benfield, James, Exec. Dir.-Childrenswear & Home Furnishings--Marks & Spencer PLC, London, United Kingdom; *Int'l*, pg. 842

Bengen, Bob, Dir.-Dir. Mktg. & Res.--Lark Luggage Company, Inc., Denver, CO; *U.S. Public*, pg. 1430

Benham, Bret L., V.P.-Agency Mktg.--Kansas City Life Insurance Co., Kansas City, MO; *U.S. Public*, pg. 942

Benham, Chris, Dir.-Strategic Mktg.--Symantec Corporation, Cupertino, CA; *U.S. Public*, pg. 1545

Bening, G. J., Dir.-Mktg. & Sls.--PURAC Group, Gorcum, Netherlands; *Int'l*, pg. 244

Benjamin, Martin, V.P.-Sls. & Mktg.--Pueblo International, Inc.-P.R. Div., Carolina, PR; *U.S. Private*, pg. 894

Benkovich, Jeanine, Coord.-Mktg. & Sls.--LINC Capital Group, Chicago, IL; *U.S. Public*, pg. 996

Benn, David J., Mgr.-Mktg.--Muro Pharmaceutical, Inc., Tewksbury, MA; *U.S. Private*, pg. 767

Benner, Brian, Mgr.-Mktg. Communications--Mutoh America Inc., Phoenix, AZ; *Int'l*, pg. 897

Bennett, Brenda, Mktg.--Regions Bank/Athens/Lauderdale County/Florence, Athens, AL; *U.S. Public*, pg. 1371

Bennett, Craig, Sr. V.P.-Sls. & Mktg.--Utility Trailer Manufacturing Co., City of Industry, CA; *U.S. Private*, pg. 1130

Bennett, Dave, Mgr.-Sls.--G.E. Superabrasives, Worthington, OH; *U.S. Public*, pg. 711

Bennett, Elizabeth, Dir.-Sls. & Mktg.--Kodansha America, Inc., New York, NY; *Int'l*, pg. 742

Bennett, Farren E., Dir.-Mktg. Communications--Hilti Inc., Tulsa, OK; *Int'l*, pg. 620

Bennett, George, V.P.-Bus. Devel.--Medical Assurance, Inc., Birmingham, AL; *U.S. Public*, pg. 1079

Bennett, James, V.P.-Mktg.--McBee Systems, Inc., Parsippany, NJ; *U.S. Private*, pg. 718

Bennett, Jessica Ann, Dir.-Adv. & Mktg.--Carfel, Inc., Miami, FL; *U.S. Private*, pg. 210

Bennett, Pat, Asst. V.P.-Sls.--Moran Towing of Maryland, Baltimore, MD; *U.S. Private*, pg. 761

Bennett, Philip, V.P.-Communication & Mktg.--Lafarge PlatresInternational, Sorges, France; *Int'l*, pg. 789

Bennett, R.L., Sr. V.P.-Mktg. & Sls.--Danek Medical Inc., Memphis, TN; *U.S. Public*, pg. 1482

Bennett, R.M., V.P.-Sls. & Mktg.--Smith & Sons Foods, Inc., Macon, GA; *U.S. Private*, pg. 1006

Bennett, Stephen, V.P.-European Sls. & Mktg.--Utility Trailer Manufacturing Co., City of Industry, CA; *U.S. Private*, pg. 1130

Bennett, Tony, Dir.-Mktg. & Sls.--Sketchley Plc, Hinckley, United Kingdom; *Int'l*, pg. 1261

Bennett, Wallace, Dir.-Sls. & Mktg.--Kansas City Chiefs Football Club, Inc., Kansas City, MO; *U.S. Private*, pg. 607

Bennier, J.M., V.P.-Sls. & Mktg.--A.Y. McDonald Mfg. Co., Dubuque, IA; *U.S. Private*, pg. 721

Benning, Juergen, Dir.-Mktg.--Champion Pneumatic Machinery Co., Inc., Princeton, IL; *U.S. Private*, pg. 228

Benninger, Ben, Sr. V.P.-Mktg.--U.S. Borax Inc., Valencia, CA; *Int'l*, pg. 1119

Benoit, Dean, Mgr.-Mktg.--TSC Shannock Corporation, Burnaby, Canada; *Int'l*, pg. 1343

Benoit, Tom, Mgr.-Corp. Mktg.--Phoenix Technologies Ltd., San Jose, CA; *U.S. Public*, pg. 1292

Benson, Ben, Dir.-Adv.--SAFECO Corporation, Seattle, WA; *U.S. Public*, pg. 1423

Benson, Frank, V.P.-Sls. & Mktg.--Hill Phoenix, Colonial Heights, VA; *U.S. Public*, pg. 521

Benson, Jo-Dee, Mgr.-Mktg. Communications--Crystal Semiconductor Corporation, Austin, TX; *U.S. Public*, pg. 375

Benson, Sara, Mktg.--Regions Bank/Chilton County, Thorsby, AL; *U.S. Public*, pg. 1372

Benson, Stan M., Sr. V.P.-Sls. & Mktg.--Amgen Inc., Thousand Oaks, CA; *U.S. Public*, pg. 100

Bent, A. Lopez, Mgr.-Sls. & Mktg.--Moore Portuguesa Limitada, Mem Martins, Portugal; *Int'l*, pg. 890

Bent, Catherine, Mgr.-Mktg.--Masterfoods Ltd., Dublin, Ireland; *U.S. Private*, pg. 707

Bentley, John, Asst. Sls. Mgr.--O'Sullivan Corporation, Winchester, VA; *U.S. Public*, pg. 1234

Bentley, Steve, Mgr.-Mktg.--MacNeal-Schwendler Corp., Costa Mesa, CA; *U.S. Public*, pg. 1031

Bentley, Todd, Dir.-Mktg.--The Sportsman's Guide, Inc., Saint Paul, MN; *U.S. Public*, pg. 1499

Bentley, Yvonne, Dir.-Mktg.--Bentley & Bentley, Fremont, CA; *U.S. Private*, pg. 1186

Bento, Mario, Dir.-Mktg.--Transbrasil S.A. Linhas Aereas, Sao Paulo, Brazil; *Int'l*, pg. 1416

Benton, Michael K., Exec. Dir.--Irving Convention & Visitors Bureau, Irving, TX; *U.S. Private*, pg. 575

Benza, Jorge, Dir.-Mktg.--Mathieu Peru, Lima, Peru; *Int'l*, pg. 846

Beran, Patty, Asst. Mgr.-Adv.--J-Star Industries, Inc., Fort Atkinson, WI; *U.S. Private*, pg. 576

Beranek, P.F., V.P.-Mktg.--American Beverage Corp. Inc., Akron, OH; *Int'l*, pg. 752

Beranek, P.F., V.P.-Mktg.--American Beverage Corporation, Verona, PA; *Int'l*, pg. 752

Beranek, Sue, V.P.-Mktg.--Taco John's International, Inc., Cheyenne, WY; *U.S. Private*, pg. 1066

Berard, Joseph, Sr. V.P.-Mktg.--Empire Blue Cross & Blue Shield, New York, NY; *U.S. Private*, pg. 374

Beraud, Jill, Dir.-Mktg.--Victoria's Secret Stores, Reynoldsburg, OH; *U.S. Public*, pg. 995

Berci, Winton L., V.P.-Mktg. & Sls.--Circon Corporation, Santa Barbara, CA; *U.S. Public*, pg. 373

Berci, Winton L., V.P.-Mktg. & Sls.--Circon ACMI, Stamford, CT; *U.S. Public*, pg. 373

Berdine, Jamie, Mgr.-Mktg. Commun.--CENTRIA, Moon Township, PA; *U.S. Private*, pg. 225

Berdusco, Roger, Sr. V.P.-Mktg.--Frito-Lay Company, Plano, TX; *U.S. Public*, pg. 1277

Berentson, Lynne, Mgr.-Mktg.--Seventeen Magazine, New York, NY; *U.S. Public*, pg. 1328

Berezinski, Roman, V.P.-Mktg.--Lake States Insurance Co., Traverse City, MI; *U.S. Public*, pg. 787

Berg, Bill, V.P.-Market Devel.--Plastics, Inc., Saint Paul, MN; *U.S. Public*, pg. 1177

Berg, Don, V.P.-Sls. & Mktg.--Channel Master, Smithfield, NC; *U.S. Private*, pg. 228

Berg, George H., V.P.-Mktg. & Sls.--Na-Churs Plant Food Company, Marion, OH; *U.S. Private*, pg. 1096

Berg, Robin, Dir.-Mktg.--Academy Corporation, Katy, TX; *U.S. Private*, pg. 11

Berg, Terri, V.P.-Mktg.--Invesco Funds Group, Denver, CO; *Int'l*, pg. 685

Bergamin, Mario, V.P.-Mktg. & Sls.--Security Chimneys International Ltd., Laval, Canada; *Int'l*, pg. 1217

Bergant, Paul R., Exec. V.P.-Mktg.--J.B. Hunt Transport Services, Inc., Lowell, AR; *U.S. Public*, pg. 849

Bergen, Douglas, Sr. V.P.-Mktg. & Sales--Forma Scientific Inc., Marietta, OH; *U.S. Public*, pg. 1595

Berger, Bruce, Dir.-Property Mktg.--Willis Corroon Corp. of Los Angeles, Glendale, CA; *Int'l*, pg. 1506

Berger, David A., Exec. V.P.-Mktg. & Adv.--The Coast Distribution System, San Jose, CA; *U.S. Public*, pg. 388

Berger, Jan, V.P.-Mktg.--Datapoint Corporation, Paris, France; *Int'l*, pg. 384

Berggren, A., Mgr.-Mktg.--Olivetti A/B, Upplands Vasby, Sweden; *Int'l*, pg. 1003

Berghley, Kristine, Mgr.-Mktg. Communications--Datapro Information Services Grp., Delran, NJ; *U.S. Public*, pg. 1070

Berghoef, Julie, Mgr.-Mktg. Commun.--Trendway Corporation, Holland, MI; *U.S. Private*, pg. 1099

Bergland, Nancy, V.P.-Mktg.--Healthsource North Carolina, Inc., Morrisville, NC; *U.S. Public*, pg. 360

Bergland, Nancy, V.P.-Mktg.--Healthsource South Carolina, Inc., Charleston, SC; *U.S. Public*, pg. 360

Berglass, David, V.P.-Domestic Sls. & Mktg.--Dep Corporation, Rancho Dominguez, CA; *U.S. Public*, pg. 500

Bergman, David C., V.P.-Prod. Devel.--Processed Plastic Company, Montgomery, IL; *U.S. Private*, pg. 888

Bergman, Dick, V.P. & Dir.-Opers. & Mktg.--Rice Food Markets Inc., Houston, TX; *U.S. Private*, pg. 927

Bergman, Kevin, Dir.-Sls. & Mktg.--The Holiday Inn Lancaster Host Hotel & Conference Center, Lancaster, PA; *U.S. Private*, pg. 534

Bergquist, Al, V.P.-Mktg.--Howmet Corporation, Greenwich, CT; *U.S. Private*, pg. 213

Bergquist, Al, V.P.-Mktg.--Howmet Corporation, Greenwich, CT; *U.S. Public*, pg. 1597

Bergsman, Jim, Dir.-Mktg. Indus. Bus. Unit--Chicago Rawhide, Elgin, IL; *Int'l*, pg. 1157

Bergstein, Barry L., Natl. Sls. & Mktg. Mgr.--BKI, Simpsonville, SC; *U.S. Public*, pg. 1506

Bergstrom, John, Sr. V.P. & Chief Mktg. Officer--Berkshire Life Insurance Company, Pittsfield, MA; *U.S. Private*, pg. 136

Berical, Timothy, Mgr.-Mktg.--NBBJ, Columbus, OH; *U.S. Private*, pg. 771

Berionc, Roberto M., Dir.-Mktg.--Merloni Elettrodomestici S.P.A., Fabriano, Italy; *Int'l*, pg. 860

Berish, Brian, V.P.-Mktg.--Whitman's Candies, Inc., Kansas City, MO; *U.S. Private*, pg. 953

Berkenbile, Terry, Sr. V.P.-Sls. & Mktg.--Pilgrim's Pride Corporation, Pittsburg, TX; *U.S. Public*, pg. 1296

Berkey, Donald L., Dir.-Sls. & Mktg.--Hollymatic Corporation, Countryside, IL; *U.S. Private*, pg. 535

Berkus, David, Mgr.-Corp. Mktg. Communications--Sanyo Fisher Company, Chatsworth, CA; *Int'l*, pg. 1191

Berkwitt, Glenn, Mgr.-Mktg. Commun.--Applied Microsystems Corporation, Redmond, WA; *U.S. Public*, pg. 123

Berliant, Jennie, Dir.-Mktg.--F & W Publications, Inc., Cincinnati, OH; *U.S. Private*, pg. 388

Berling, Henry, Exec. V.P.-Partnership Devel.--Owens & Minor Inc., Glen Allen, VA; *U.S. Public*, pg. 1236

Berling, Julie, Mgr.-Mktg. Communications--Gold'n Plump Poultry, Saint Cloud, MN; *U.S. Private*, pg. 577

Berman, Bernard, Gen. Mgr.--Butler Ventamatic Corp., Mineral Wells, TX; *U.S. Private*, pg. 190

Berman, David, Sr. V.P.-Mktg. & Bus. Devel.--PHP Healthcare Corporation, Reston, VA; *U.S. Public*, pg. 1241

Berman, James, Dir.-Sls.--Stackhouse Inc., Riverside, CA; *U.S. Public*, pg. 1591

Berman, Leonard J., Mgr.-Healthcare Mktg.--Superior Surgical Mfg. Co., Inc., Seminole, FL; *U.S. Public*, pg. 1539

Bernard, Edward C., Dir.-Individual Mktg.--T. Rowe Price Associates, Inc., Baltimore, MD; *U.S. Public*, pg. 1324

Bernard, Nicole, Dir.-Mktg.--Cape Cod Potato Chip Company, Hyannis, MA; *U.S. Private*, pg. 205

Bernardini, Joseph, Mgr.-Corp. Commun.--Edwards and Kelcey, Inc., Boston, MA; *U.S. Private*, pg. 364

Berney, Paul, V.P.-Mktg.--Cosco, Inc., Columbus, IN; *U.S. Private*, pg. 277

Bernhard, Eggli, Dir.-Mktg.--Swiss Bank Corporation, Basel, Switzerland; *Int'l*, pg. 1329

Bernhard, Lisa A, Mgr.-Mktg.--The Flecto Co., Inc., Oakland, CA; *U.S. Private*, pg. 410

Bernier, Kristi, Coord.-Mktg. Services--J.R. Simplot Company, Minerals & Chemicals Group, Pocatello, ID; *U.S. Private*, pg. 1002

Bernlohr, Timothy J., V.P.-Sls. & Mktg.--RBX Corporation, Roanoke, VA; *U.S. Private*, pg. 56

Bernlohr, Timothy J., V.P.-Sls. & Mktg.--Rubatex Corporation, Roanoke, VA; *U.S. Private*, pg. 56

Bernstein, Richard, Dir.-Mktg. Services--Triple A Specialty Company, Chicago, IL; *U.S. Private*, pg. 1103

Berntson, B., V.P.-Mktg. & Engrng.--Emerson Motor Company, Sturgeon Bay, WI; *U.S. Public*, pg. 573

Berolzheimer, Charles, II, V.P.--California Cedar Products, Inc., Stockton, CA; *U.S. Private*, pg. 200

Berridge, Linda, Dir.-Mktg.--Two Rivers Psychiatric Hospital, Kansas City, MO; *U.S. Public*, pg. 1697

Berris, Brian, Partner-Private Client--Brown Brothers Harriman & Co., New York, NY; *U.S. Private*, pg. 173

Berry, Benjamin, V.P.-Mktg.--AMATI Communications Corp., San Jose, CA; *U.S. Public*, pg. 1585

Berry, Daniel H., Sr. V.P.-Sls., Service & Mktg.--Ultratech Stepper, Inc., San Jose, CA; *U.S. Public*, pg. 1663

Berry, Nicki, Mgr.-Mktg.--Scientific Imaging Systems, New Haven, CT; *U.S. Public*, pg. 550

Berry, Phyllis, V.P.-Corp. Communications--Sun Healthcare Group Inc., Albuquerque, NM; *U.S. Public*, pg. 1530

Berry, Tony, Sls./Mktg. Dir.--CiMatrix Ltd., Stourbridge, United Kingdom; *U.S. Public*, pg. 1395

Berson, Howard, Dir.-Mktg.--Flexi-Van Leasing, Inc., Kenilworth, NJ; *U.S. Private*, pg. 413

Berstin, Sean, Asst. Mgr.-Mktg./Steak & Ale--Bennigan's, Dallas, TX; *U.S. Private*, pg. 736

Bert, Paul A., Sr. V.P.-Mktg. Consumer Svcs.--The ServiceMaster Company, Downers Grove, IL; *U.S. Public*, pg. 1461

Bert, Paul A., Sr. V.P.-Mktg.--ServiceMaster Consumer Services Company, Memphis, TN; *U.S. Public*, pg. 1461

Bertelli, Rich, V.P.-Mktg. & Sls.--Crosman Corp., East Bloomfield, NY; *U.S. Private*, pg. 291

Bertelli, Rich, V.P.-Sls. & Mktg.--Benjamin Sheridan Co., East Bloomfield, NY; *U.S. Private*, pg. 291

Bertelli, Rich, V.P.-Mktg. & Sls.--Crosman Airguns, East Bloomfield, NY; *U.S. Private*, pg. 291

Berthiaume, Guy, Dir.-Mktg.- Vachon Div.--Culinar Inc., Montreal, Canada; *Int'l*, pg. 348

Berthold, Harold, Dir.-Grocery--The Food Emporium, Bronx, NY; *Int'l*, pg. 1375

Berthold, R., Mgr.-Mktg.--Crane Defense Systems, Conroe, TX; *U.S. Public*, pg. 456

Berthoud, John D., V.P.-Mktg. & Quality Mngmt.--Nalco Chemical Company, Naperville, IL; *U.S. Public*, pg. 1150

Bertoch, Ronald H., Exec. V.P.--BNI Coal, Ltd., Bismarck, ND; *U.S. Public*, pg. 1116

Bertolucci, Ken, Dir.-Mktg.--Quartet Manufacturing Co., Skokie, IL; *U.S. Public*, pg. 707

Bertram, Jim, V.P.-Sls. & Mktg.Dir.--Primedia Information Inc., Hightstown, NJ; *U.S. Public*, pg. 1328

Bertrand, J. C., Asst.-Mktg. & Adv.--Ferraz Corporation, Parsippany, NJ; *Int'l*, pg. 1028

Bertti, Eriksson, Dir.-Mktg.--Leiras Oy, Turku, Finland; *Int'l*, pg. 639

Bertz, Holly, Mktg.--Wavetek Corp., San Diego, GA; *U.S. Private*, pg. 1155

Berube, Victoria, Mgr.-Mktg. Admin.--Velcro USA Inc., Manchester, NH; *Int'l*, pg. 1462

Besch, Andrew, Sr. V.P.-Mktg.--USA Networks, New York, NY; *U.S. Public*, pg. 1686

Besecke, Edmund E., Pres.--Wurzner Dauerbackwaren GmbH, Wurzen, Germany; *Int'l*, pg. 1514

Beseler, Chris, Sr. V.P.-Mktg. & Sls.--Waccamaw Corporation, Myrtle Beach, SC; *U.S. Private*, pg. 1145

Beshara, Dawn, Dir.-Regional Mktg.--The Cafaro Co., Youngstown, OH; *U.S. Private*, pg. 198

Beshel, Joseph, V.P.-Mktg. & Sls., EDI Lederle--Wyeth-Ayerst Laboratories, Inc., Philadelphia, PA; *U.S. Public*, pg. 80

Bess, Gordon, Dir.-Mktg. Communications--General American Life Insurance Co., Saint Louis, MO; *U.S. Private*, pg. 443

Bessler, Paul, Dir.-Mktg. Res.--Del Webb Corporation, Phoenix, AZ; *U.S. Public*, pg. 494

Besso, Michael, Dir.-Mktg.--Bertolli USA, Inc., Secaucus, NJ; *Int'l*, pg. 655

Best-Devereux, Igor, Dir.-Asia Pacific Opers.--3Com Personal Communications Div., Skokie, IL; *U.S. Public*, pg. 1604

Best, Wayne, Sr. V.P.-Mktg. & Sls.--The Frymaster Corp., Shreveport, LA; *Int'l*, pg. 188

Besten, C. Henry, Jr., V.P.-Strategic Mktg.--Arch Coal, Inc., Saint Louis, MO; *U.S. Public*, pg. 139

Besthoff, Ginnie, Dir.-Mktg. Services--Nu Horizons Electronics Corp., Melville, NY; *U.S. Public*, pg. 1205

Betteridge, Jim Carlton, Dir.-Mktg.--Royal Mail, London, United Kingdom; *Int'l*, pg. 1064

Betts, Greg, Dir.-Mktg.--Merix Corporation, Forest Grove, OR; *U.S. Public*, pg. 1096

Betts, Thomas, Dir.-Mktg. Info. Svcs.--Battenfeld of America, West Warwick, RI; *Int'l*, pg. 825

Beu, Robert, Chief Strategic Officer & Exec. V.P.--Hutchins/Young & Rubicam, Rochester, NY; *U.S. Private*, pg. 1197

Beutel, Nina, V.P.-Catalog Mktg.--Smith & Hawken, Mill Valley, CA; *U.S. Public*, pg. 279

Beutgen, J.J., Exec. V.P.-Mktg.--Olive Garden Italian Restaurants, Orlando, FL; *U.S. Public*, pg. 484

Bevilaqua, Victor H., V.P.-Mktg.--The B. Manischewitz Company, Jersey City, NJ; *U.S. Private*, pg. 699

Bevins, Donald E., V.P.-Mktg. & Sls.--Farmers Mutual Hail Insurance Co. of Iowa, Des Moines, IA; *U.S. Private*, pg. 395

Bevis, Harold, Sr. V.P.-Product Mngmt.--General Cable Corporation, Highland Heights, KY; *Int'l*, pg. 1486

Bewit, Marlene, Dir.-Mass Market Devel.--Carolina Power & Light Company, Raleigh, NC; *U.S. Public*, pg. 306

Bexon, R., Sr. V.P.-Mktg. Sls.--Brown & Williamson Tobacco Corp., Louisville, KY; *Int'l*, pg. 111

Beyeler, Dana, Dir.-Mktg.--National Forge Company, Irvine, PA; *U.S. Private*, pg. 783

Beyeler, Les, V.P.-Sls. & Mktg.--Graphic Enterprises of Ohio, Inc., Canton, OH; *U.S. Private*, pg. 471

Beyer, Paul K., Mgr.--USAA Federal Savings Bank, San Antonio, TX; *U.S. Private*, pg. 1114

Beynon, Don, Coord.-Motorcycles Mktg. & Adv.--Honda Canada Inc., Scarborough, Canada; *Int'l*, pg. 635

Beyrer, Cindy, Mktg. Specialist--Videojet Systems International, Inc., Wood Dale, IL; *Int'l*, pg. 545

Bezak, Sharon, Pres. & V.P.-Sls. & Mktg.--Sharon Concepts, Millburn, NJ; *U.S. Private*, pg. 990

Bhanoo, Milind, Prod. Mgr.--Cyberex, Inc., Mentor, OH; *U.S. Public*, pg. 481

Bhat, Jayaram, V.P.-Mktg.--Mercury Interactive Corp., Sunnyvale, CA; *U.S. Public*, pg. 1093

Bhatia, Samir, Dir.-Mktg.--Photomatrix Corporation, San Diego, CA; *U.S. Public*, pg. 1292

Bhatt, Andrea, V.P.-Sls. & Mktg.--General Alum & Chemical, Holland, OH; *U.S. Private*, pg. 443

Bhide, A., Mgr.-Mktg./Wintriss Prods.--Data Instruments, Inc., Acton, MA; *U.S. Private*, pg. 312

Bianco, James W., Jr., Dir.-Mktg. & Sls.--Control Module, Inc., Enfield, CT; *U.S. Private*, pg. 271

Bicho, Adrian, Mktg. Officer--The San Francisco Co., San Francisco, CA; *U.S. Public*, pg. 1430

Bichsel, Dean, V.P.- Mktg.--Osborn Manufacturing, Cleveland, OH; *U.S. Public*, pg. 924

Bickford, Michael, Sr. V.P.-Derivative Securities Mktg.--The American Stock Exchange, New York, NY; *U.S. Private*, pg. 62

Bicknell, Bob, Sr. V.P.-Mktg. & Sls.--Campbell Hausfeld Division of Scott Fetzer, Harrison, OH; *U.S. Public*, pg. 217

Biddison, Margaret A., V.P.-Global Mktg.--QAD Inc, Carpinteria, CA; *U.S. Public*, pg. 1345

Biddlecom, Charles H., V.P.-Mktg.--Astronics Corporation, Buffalo, NY; *U.S. Public*, pg. 142

Biddlecom, Charles H., V.P.-Mktg.--MOD-PAC CORP, Buffalo, NY; *U.S. Public*, pg. 142

Bidwell, Donald, Jr., Dir.-Mktg. & Pub. Relations--Bidwell Industrial Group, Inc., Middletown, CT; *U.S. Private*, pg. 142

Bidwell, Donald, Jr., V.P.-Mktg.--Magnagrip, Middletown, CT; *U.S. Private*, pg. 142

Bidwell, Donald, Sr., Dir.-Mktg. & Pub. Rels.--Blu-Ray, Middletown, CT; *U.S. Private*, pg. 142

Bidwell, Michael M., Dir.-Sls.--Blu-Ray, Middletown, CT; *U.S. Private*, pg. 142

Bidwill, Nicole, Mgr.-Mktg.--Arizona Cardinals, Phoenix, AZ; *U.S. Private*, pg. 81

Bieker, Don, V.P.-Sls. & Mktg. & Adv.--Columbia Manufacturing Inc., Westfield, MA; *U.S. Private*, pg. 255

Bielanski, Andrew, Mng. Dir.-Mktg.--Countrywide Home Loans Inc., Pasadena, CA; *U.S. Public*, pg. 452

Bierleier, William G., V.P.-Transmission, Storage & Commodity--BC Gas Inc., Vancouver, Canada; *Int'l*, pg. 114

Bierman, Norman F., Exec. V.P.-Corp. Mktg. & Sls.--Intellisource, Fairfield, CT; *U.S. Public*, pg. 1425

Biery, David, Dir.-Mktg.--Food Lion, Inc., Salisbury, NC; *Int'l*, *pg. 463*

Biesiada, Michael, V.P.-Mktg.--Apcoa, Inc., Cleveland, OH; *U.S. Private*, pg. 533

Biesman, Jeff, Mgr.-Adult's Mktg.--L.A. Gear, Inc., Santa Monica, CA; *U.S. Public*, pg. 969

Bievenour, Raymond, V.P.-Sls. & Mktg.--Penn Engineering & Manufacturing Corp., Danboro, PA; *U.S. Public*, pg. 1269

Bigelow, Elizabeth, Mgr.-Adv.--Edward Hines Lumber Co., Itasca, IL; *U.S. Private*, pg. 530

Biggs, Craig, V.P.-Mktg. & Sls.--Electrovert, Grand Prairie, TX; *Int'l*, pg. 328

Biggs, Mickey, Sr. V.P.-Sls. & Mktg.--Henry Lee Company, Miami, FL; *U.S. Private*, pg. 657

Bigley, M., Dir.-Electronic Mktg.--Pathmark Stores Incorporated, Woodbridge, NJ; *U.S. Private*, pg. 843

Bigos, Irene, V.P.-Mktg.--Ogden Corporation, New York, NY; *U.S. Public*, pg. 1213

Biles, Homer, Dir.-Grocery Sls. & Mktg.--J.L. Lester & Son, Inc., Rockmart, GA; *U.S. Private*, pg. 660

Bilger, Brent R., V.P.-Mktg.--MMC Networks, Inc., Sunnyvale, CA; *U.S. Public*, pg. 1027

Biljan, John, V.P.-Sls. & Mktg.--Relm Communications, Inc., Indianapolis, IN; *U.S. Public*, pg. 1376

Billante, Samuel J., V.P.-Mktg.--American General Life & Accident Insurance Co., Nashville, TN; *U.S. Public*, pg. 76

Billetdeaux, Joe, Dir.-Mdsg.--Pittsburgh Pirates, Pittsburgh, PA; *U.S. Private*, pg. 867

Billingsley, Kay, V.P.-Adv., Mktg. Commun. & Special Projects--Trigon Blue Cross & Blue Shield, Richmond, VA; *U.S. Public*, pg. 1637

Billock, John K., Pres.-Sls. & Mktg.--Home Box Office, Inc., New York, NY; *U.S. Public*, pg. 1612

Bilney, Jody, V.P.-Mktg.--GTE Information Services Incorporated, Dallas-Fort Worth Airport, TX; *U.S. Public*, pg. 696

Binard, Laurent, Dir.-Mktg.--Lotus Development, SA, Saint Quentin-en-Yvelines, France; *U.S. Public*, pg. 896

Binder, Edward, V.P.-Integrated Mktg.--Dunkin' Donuts Incorporated, Randolph, MA; *Int'l*, pg. 63

Binder, Sheila, Dir.-Mktg. Communications--Platinum Solutions, Inglewood, CA; *U.S. Public*, pg. 1309

Binet, Carole, V.P.-Sls. & Mktg.--Logo of the Americas, Fort Lauderdale, FL; *Int'l*, pg. 462

Bingaman, Larry L., V.P.-Corp. Rels. & Sec.--Aquarion Company, Bridgeport, CT; *U.S. Public*, pg. 126

Bingham, Gordon J., Sr. V.P.-Mktg.--Olsten Corporation, Melville, NY; *U.S. Public*, pg. 1220

Bingham, Kevin J., Dir.-Mktg.--Lifetime Products Inc., Clearfield, UT; *U.S. Private*, pg. 667

Binkert, Chris, V.P. & Dir.-Mktg.--The Fifth Third Bank, Cincinnati, OH; *U.S. Public*, pg. 621

Binkert, Christopher C., V.P. & Dir.-Mktg.--Fifth Third Bancorp, Cincinnati, OH; *U.S. Public*, pg. 621

Binks, Sid, V.P.-Mktg.--Cook Moving Systems, Inc., Buffalo, NY; *U.S. Private*, pg. 272

Binzer, Corrina, Mgr.-Pub. Rels.--Knurr AG, Munich, Germany; *Int'l*, pg. 739

Birch, Del, Mgr.-Mktg.--CorryHiebert Corporation, Corry, PA; *U.S. Public*, pg. 772

Bird, David A., Chief Mktg. Officer & Exec. V.P.--American Heritage Life Investment Corp., Jacksonville, FL; *U.S. Public*, pg. 78

Bird, David A., Chief Mktg. Officer & Exec. V.P.--American Heritage Life Insurance Co., Jacksonville, FL; *U.S. Public*, pg. 79

Bird, Ken, Dir.-Mktg.--Cintas Corporation, Mason, OH; *U.S. Public*, pg. 370

Bird, Mike, Mgr.-Design & Mktg. Services--Sea Containers Ltd., Hamilton, Bermuda; *Int'l*, pg. 1213

Birdsall, Douglas, V.P.-Mktg. Affiliates & Strategic Plng.--Northwest Airlines, Inc., Saint Paul, MN; *U.S. Public*, pg. 1200

Birk, James A., V.P.-Mktg. & Sls./Kimball Lodging Group--Kimball International, Inc., Jasper, IN; *U.S. Public*, pg. 956

Birkhauser, Dave, Sr. V.P.-Sls.-Grove Crane--Grove WorldWide, Shady Grove, PA; *Int'l*, pg. 593

Birkhead, Rob, V.P.-Mktg.--Thomas Nelson Inc., Nashville, TN; *U.S. Public*, pg. 1167

Birnbaum, Richard, Exec. V.P.-Mktg. & Opers.--Circuit City Stores, Inc., Richmond, VA; *U.S. Public*, pg. 374

Birnie, Bob, V.P.-Mktg. & Sls.--International Tubular Products, Inc., Claremore, OK; *U.S. Private*, pg. 14

Bischmann, Joanne, V.P.-Mktg.--Harley-Davidson Motor Company, Milwaukee, WI; *U.S. Public*, pg. 786

Bischoff, E.A., Export Mgr.--Coe Manufacturing Co, Painesville, OH; *U.S. Private*, pg. 249

Bisek, J.D., V.P.-Sls. & Mktg.--WRR Environmental Services Co., Inc., Eau Claire, WI; *U.S. Public*, pg. 1792

Bisgard, Julie, Dir.-Mktg.--American Water Works Association, Denver, CO; *U.S. Public*, pg. 94

Bish-Jones, Trevor, Dir.-Mktg./Dixons--Dixons Group plc, Hemel Hempstead, United Kingdom,; *Int'l*, pg. 413

Bishop, Don, Grp. V.P.-Sls. & Mktg.--Gulf States Toyota, Inc., Houston, TX; *U.S. Private*, pg. 488

Bishop, Eileen, Dir.-Retail Mktg.--Levitz Furniture Incorporated, Boca Raton, FL; *U.S. Public*, pg. 990

Bishop, Eileen, V.P.-Retail Mktg.--Levitz Furniture Corporation, Boca Raton, FL; *U.S. Public*, pg. 990

Bishop, Robert E., V.P.-Sls. & Mktg.--The Gunlocke Company, Wayland, NY; *U.S. Public*, pg. 772

Biterman, Joel, V.P.-Mktg.--LG Group Inc., Englewood Cliffs, NJ; *Int'l*, pg. 779

Bitz, Ginger, Mktg. Asst.--Schlumberger Malco Inc., Owings Mills, MD; *Int'l*, pg. 1206

Biulco, Frank, V.P.-Mktg.--Coca-Cola USA, Atlanta, GA; *U.S. Public*, pg. 392

Biver, Jean-Claude, Mgr.-Mktg. & Distr.--Omega SA, Bienne, Switzerland; *Int'l*, pg. 1160

Bixby, B.C., Chm. Bd.--Bixby International Corp., Newburyport, MA; *U.S. Private*, pg. 146

Bixler, Colleen, Coord.-Mktg. Communications--Shimadzu Scientific Instruments, Inc., Columbia, MD; *Int'l*, pg. 1232

Bixler, Joe, V.P.-Mktg.--Solvay Animal Health, Inc., Mendota Heights, MN; *Int'l*, pg. 1277

Bizego, Melody, Mgr.-Mktg.--Mustang Tractor & Equip. Co., Houston, TX; *U.S. Private*, pg. 768

Bjork, David, V.P.-Mktg. & Prod. Mngmt.--Physician Computer Network, Inc., Morris Plains, NJ; *U.S. Public*, pg. 1293

Bjork, John, Reg. Mktg. Mgr.--Blockbuster Music, Dallas, TX; *U.S. Private*, pg. 776

Bjorneboe, Jan, Dir.-Mktg. & Adv. & Sls. Mgr.--ISS Norge a.s., Oslo, Norway; *Int'l*, pg. 656

Bjornsson, Steinn Logi, Sr. V.P.--Icelandair, Reykjavik, Iceland; *Int'l*, pg. 658

Blabes, Gene, Dir.-Mktg.--Fiat Auto S.p.A., Milan, Italy; *Int'l*, pg. 481

Black-Fusco, Nancy, Mgr.-Mktg.-Food Service--WLR Foods, Inc., Timberville, VA; *U.S. Public*, pg. 1727

Black, Chris, Dir.-Mktg./Jazz & Classical--Sony Music Entertainment (UK) Limited, London, United Kingdom; *Int'l*, pg. 1284

Black, David, Pres.-MacIntosh Div.--Clarion Corporation of America, Gardena, CA; *Int'l*, pg. 296

Black, David, Sr. V.P.-Sls.--Camco International Inc., Houston, TX; *U.S. Public*, pg. 297

Black, Donald V., Sr. V.P.-Mktg. & Airline Fin.--McDonnell Aircraft & Missile Systems Div., Berkeley, MO; *U.S. Public*, pg. 241

Black, John, Dir.-Mktg. Services--White-Rodgers Div., Emerson Electric Co., Saint Louis, MO; *U.S. Public*, pg. 573

Black, Michael, V.P.-U.S. Sales & Mktg.--Datapoint Corporation, San Antonio, TX; *Int'l*, pg. 384

Black, Mitch, V.P.-Mktg.--Wells Fargo Alarm Services, Inc., King of Prussia, PA; *U.S. Public*, pg. 246

Black, Peter D., Sr. V.P.-Mktg.--BPA International, New York, NY; *U.S. Private*, pg. 107

Black, Polly, V.P.-Mktg.--Sara Lee Knit Products, Winston Salem, NC; *U.S. Public*, pg. 1434

Black, Randy D., V.P.-Mktg.--Rawlings Sporting Goods Company, Fenton, MO; *U.S. Public*, pg. 1361

Black, Rita A., Mgr.-Mktg. & Adv.--Deloitte & Touche LLP, Wilton, CT; *U.S. Private*, pg. 322

Black, Robert W., V.P.-Mktg.--Steelcase Inc., Grand Rapids, MI; *U.S. Private*, pg. 1038

Black, William J., Dir.-Adv. & Mktg.--Sun TV & Appliances, Inc., Groveport, OH; *U.S. Public*, pg. 1532

Blackburn, Jack, Sr. V.P.-Mktg.--Country Life Insurance Company, Bloomington, IL; *U.S. Private*, pg. 278

Blackburn, John, Sr. V.P.-Mktg.--CC Services, Bloomington, IL; *U.S. Private*, pg. 279

Blackford, Scott, Dir.-Mktg.--Todco, Marion, OH; *U.S. Private*, pg. 823

Blackledge, Teresa W., V.P.-Mktg.--Emulex Corporation, Costa Mesa, CA; *U.S. Public*, pg. 579

Blackman, Mark, V.P.-Sls. & Mktg.--International Division, Chicago, IL; *U.S. Private*, pg. 459

Blackstone, James, V.P.-Mktg.--Strippit, Inc., Akron, NY; *U.S. Public*, pg. 862

Blackstone, Mark J., V.P.-Mktg.--Oasis Corp., Columbus, OH; *U.S. Private*, pg. 810

Blackwell, Dick, V.P.-Mktg.--Amtech Corporation, Dallas, TX; *U.S. Public*, pg. 105

Blackwell, Dick, V.P.-Mktg.--Amtech Systems Corporation, Dallas, TX; *U.S. Public*, pg. 105

Blackwell, John, Exec V.P.-Sls. & Mktg.--Moulinex Appliances, Inc., Closter, NJ; *Int'l*, pg. 896

Blackwell, John C., V.P.-Mktg. & Sls.--General Housewares Corp., Terre Haute, IN; *U.S. Public*, pg. 715

Blackwell, Robert J., V.P.-Mktg. & Strategic Plng.--OHM Corporation, Findlay, OH; *U.S. Public*, pg. 1207

Blackwell, Robert J., Sr. V.P.-Mktg.--OHM Remediation Services Corp., Findlay, OH; *U.S. Public*, pg. 1208

Blackwell, Susan C., Mktg. Asst.--Coyne Beahm Inc., Colfax, NC; *U.S. Private*, pg. 283

Blade, Jeffrey, Dir.-Fin. Mktg. Services--Kraft Foods, Inc., Northfield, IL; *U.S. Public*, pg. 1287

Blades, J., Dir.-Mktg.--Fiat Auto SpA, Turin, Italy; *Int'l*, pg. 480

Blagaich, Alvin, V.P.-Sls. & Mktg.--Fenton Press, Inc., Addison, IL; *U.S. Private*, pg. 400

Blain, Michelle, Mgr.-Intl. Sls. & Communications Div.--Titeflex Corporation, Springfield, MA; *Int'l*, pg. 1340

Blair, David G., V.P.-Mktg. Asphalt & LPG--Holly Corporation, Dallas, TX; *U.S. Public*, pg. 830

Blair, Jeb, Mgr.-Mktg.--Newage Industries Inc., Testing Instruments Group, Willow Grove, PA; *U.S. Private*, pg. 796

Blair, Kelly, Mng. Dir.--Beechmont Hyundai, Cincinnati, OH; *U.S. Private*, pg. 129

Blair, Rebecca, Dir.-Mktg.--Valley Hospital Medical Center, Las Vegas, NV; *U.S. Public*, pg. 1697

Blair, Rick, Exec. V.P.-Sls. & Mktg.--Weider Nutrition Intl., Salt Lake City, UT; *U.S. Private*, pg. 1159

Blais, Dave, Dir.-Mktg.--Quad/Graphics, Inc., Pewaukee, WI; *U.S. Private*, pg. 897

Blais, Jean-Paul, V.P.-Mktg.--Imperial Tobacco Limited, Montreal, Canada; *Int'l*, pg. 112

Blais, Russell A., V.P.-Mktg.--Naylor Pipe Company, Chicago, IL; *U.S. Private*, pg. 789

Blaisdell-Snowdon, Deborah, Exec. V.P. & Corp. Sec.--The U.S. Baird Corporation, Stratford, CT; *U.S. Private*, pg. 1124

Blake, Gary E., V.P.-Retail Mktg.--Kentucky Utilities Company, Lexington, KY; *U.S. Public*, pg. 941

Blake, Lyn, V.P.-Trade Sls. & Mktg.--Macmillan Publishing USA, Indianapolis, IN; *U.S. Private*, pg. 777

Blakemore, Bob, Mgr.-Sls. & Mktg.--Ultra Electronics Magnetics, Cannock, United Kingdom; *Int'l*, pg. 1431

Blakeslee, H. Ed, V.P.-Customer Services & Mktg.--Mississippi Power Co., Gulfport, MS; *U.S. Public*, pg. 1490

Blalock, Adam, V.P.-Sls. & Mktg.--Daisy Manufacturing Company, Inc., Rogers, AR; *U.S. Private*, pg. 308

Blanchat, Nancy, Dir.-Mktg. Communications--The Coleman Company, Inc., Golden, CO; *U.S. Private*, pg. 690

Blanco, Maria Jose, Mgr.-Mktg. & Communications--A.C. Nielsen Company S.A., Madrid, Spain; *U.S. Public*, pg. 1183

Blank, Monique, Dir.-Mktg. & Mdsg.--Alpha Shirt Co., Inc., Philadelphia, PA; *U.S. Private*, pg. 45

Blank, Robert E., V.P.- Mktg. & Sls.--Littleford Day Inc., Florence, KY; *U.S. Private*, pg. 671

Blankenship, Maurice, Exec. V.P.--Berryman Products, Inc., Arlington, TX; *U.S. Private*, pg. 138

Blanks, Tracy, V.P.-Mktg.--Premier Parks Inc., Oklahoma City, OK; *U.S. Public*, pg. 1323

Blanton, Graham P., V.P.-Sls. & Mktg.--Asbury Carbons, Inc., Asbury, NJ; *U.S. Private*, pg. 87

Blaser, Marlies E., Mgr.-Mktg.--Singapore Tourist Promotion Board - Zurich, Zurich, Switzerland; *Int'l*, pg. 1254

Blashill, G.L., Dir.-Sls. & Mktg.--Imperial Tobacco Group, Ltd., Bristol, United Kingdom; *Int'l*, pg. 666

Blasic, Linda, Dir.-Regional Mktg.--The Cafaro Co., Youngstown, OH; *U.S. Private*, pg. 198

Blasig, Ron, Mgr.-Mktg.--Genzyme Diagnostics, Medix Biotech, San Carlos, CA; *U.S. Public*, pg. 733

Blatherwick, Jeff W., V.P.--New York Casualty Insurance Co., Watertown, NY; *U.S. Public*, pg. 787

Blatto, Norma Saulino, Dir.-Mktg.--Time Inc. Health, San Francisco, CA; *U.S. Public*, pg. 1613

Bleacher, Carol, Mktg. Asst.--Turkey Hill Dairy, Inc., Conestoga, PA; *U.S. Private*, pg. 1109

Bleibler, Alex, Mgr.-Mktg. Construction Chemicals--Sika Finanz AG, Baar, Switzerland; *Int'l*, pg. 1248

Blethen, Robert, Mgr.-Corp. Mktg.--Seattle Times Company, Seattle, WA; *U.S. Private*, pg. 980

Bletzacker, Karl R., Mgr.-Gas Acquisition & Mktg.--National Gas & Oil Company, Newark, OH; *U.S. Public*, pg. 1156

Blicha, John, Mgr.-Mktg. Svcs.--Joy Mining Machinery, Warrendale, PA; *U.S. Public*, pg. 789

Blicha, John, Mgr.-Mktg. Services--Joy Mining Machinery, Warrendale, PA; *U.S. Public*, pg. 790

Bliesath, Nick, Market Anayst--Plastic Suppliers, Inc., Columbus, OH; *U.S. Private*, pg. 871

Block, Paul, V.P. & Mgr.-Bus. Unit-Dannon Water--Great Brands of Europe, Stamford, CT; *Int'l*, pg. 381

Block, Randolf E., V.P.-Sls. & Promo.--Screw Conveyor Corp., Hammond, IN; *U.S. Private*, pg. 977

Block, Terry, Exec. V.P.-Pet Prods.--Ralston Purina Company, Saint Louis, MO; *U.S. Public*, pg. 1359

Blocksom, Douglas, Dir.-Mktg.--Pneumatic Products Corp., Ocala, FL; *U.S. Public*, pg. 1676

Blohm, Chris, Sec.-Sls. & Mktg.--Red Wings Inc., Fredonia, NY; *Int'l*, pg. 1398

Blomberg, Bengt, Dir.-Pulp Mktg.--MoDo Paper AB, Ornskoldsvik, Sweden; *Int'l*, pg. 886

Bloom, Allen J., Exec. V.P.-Mktg & Sls.--Ringling Bros., Barnum & Bailey Combined Shows, Inc., Vienna, VA; *U.S. Private*, pg. 400

Bloom, Richard A., Gen. Mgr.-Sls. & Mktg.--Bloom Electric Services, Inc., Oklahoma City, OK; *U.S. Private*, pg. 150

Bloom, Rob, Dir.-Mktg. Comm.--PSDI, Bedford, MA; *U.S. Private*, pg. 828

Bloss, Douglas V., V.P.-Mktg. & Sls.--Armstrong International, Inc., Three Rivers, MI; *U.S. Private*, pg. 83

Blossom, Charles C., Jr., Sr. V.P.-Mktg.--Action Performance Companies, Inc., Phoenix, AZ; *U.S. Public*, pg. 17

Blot, Edward J., V.P.-Sls. & Mktg., Stainless & Specialty Steels--Republic Engineered Steels, Inc., Massillon, OH; *U.S. Public*, pg. 1378

Blue, Jeff, V.P.-Sls. & Mktg.--Goldsmiths, Inc., Wichita, KS; *U.S. Private*, pg. 462

Blum, Bill, Mgr.-Mktg. Communications--Chevron Chemical Co., San Ramon, CA; *U.S. Public*, pg. 348

Blum, Bill, Dir.-Mktg.--Sonoma Mission Inn & Spa, Sonoma, CA; *U.S. Private*, pg. 1014

Blum, Pam, V.P.-Mktg. Svcs.-Universal Pictures--Universal Pictures, Universal City, CA; *Int'l*, pg. 1216

Blum, Randy, V.P.-Mktg.--Preferred Risk Mutual Insurance, West Des Moines, IA; *U.S. Private*, pg. 880

Blumenstock, Mike, V.P.-Mktg. & Sls.--EGA, Seymour, CT; *Int'l*, pg. 436

Blumenthal, R. Dean, V.P.--Lion Brand Yarn Co., New York, NY; *U.S. Private*, pg. 669

Blumenthal, Richard, V.P.-Mktg.--Steck-Vaughn Distribution Company, Austin, TX; *U.S. Public*, pg. 784

Blumenthal, Richard Y., V.P.-Mktg.--Steck-Vaughn Company, Austin, TX; *U.S. Public*, pg. 784

Blumenthal, Richard Y., V.P.-Mktg.--Steck-Vaughn Publishing Corporation, Austin, TX; *U.S. Public*, pg. 784

Blundell-Pound, George, Commercial Dir.--Caledonian Airways Ltd, Gatwick, United Kingdom; *Int'l*, pg. 219

Blythe, Mac, Dir.-Mktg.--Manufacturers' Services Ltd., Concord, MA; *U.S. Private*, pg. 701

Blythe, Ron, Dir.-Mktg.--Stanley Fastening Systems, East Greenwich, RI; *U.S. Public*, pg. 1509

Boatwalla, Cyrus, Gen. Mgr.--H.H. Brown Shoe Company, Inc., Greenwich, CT; *U.S. Public*, pg. 217

Boatwright, P.J., Dir.-Mktg. & Communications--Fortune, New York, NY; *U.S. Public*, pg. 1613

Bobich, Tom, Dir.-Adv. & Mktg.--AirTouch Communications, Inc., San Francisco, CA; *U.S. Public*, pg. 34

Bobrowich, John, Mgr.-Mktg.--Siemens Power Corp., Milwaukee, WI; *Int'l*, pg. 1246

Bock, Arthur, V.P.-Sls. & Mktg.--Philip Fritze & Sons, Inc., Whippany, NJ; *U.S. Private*, pg. 429

Bock, Gayle, V.P.-Adv. & Consumer Mktg.--Delta Air Lines, Inc., Atlanta, GA; *U.S. Public*, pg. 497

Bockenfeld, Jim, Dir.-Sls. & Mktg.--The Knapheide Mfg. Co., Quincy, IL; *U.S. Private*, pg. 626

Bodart, Francois, Mgr.-Mktg.--Olivetti Malaysia Sdn Bhd, Kuala Lumpur, Malaysia; *Int'l*, pg. 1003

Bodecoat, S.C., Mgr.-Mktg.--Quest International, Naarden, Netherlands; *Int'l*, pg. 1438

Boden, Sune, Dir.-Mktg.--Avesta Sandvik Tube AB, Fagersta, Sweden; *Int'l*, pg. 221

Bodenheimer, George W., Exec. V.P.-Mktg. & Sls.--ESPN, Inc., Bristol, CT; *U.S. Public*, pg. 512

Bodkin, Lawrence, V.P.-Mktg. & Sls.--White Rock Products Corp., Whitestone, NY; *U.S. Private*, pg. 1173

Bodvig, Colleen, Mgr.-Mktg.--Bourton Group, Rockford, IL; *U.S. Private*, pg. 162

Boender, Brian H., V.P.-Sls., Mktg. & Engr. Prods.--Trion, Inc., Sanford, NC; *U.S. Public*, pg. 1639

Boesing, Danny, Mgr.-Mktg.--Samtec Inc., New Albany, IN; *U.S. Private*, pg. 963

Bogard, Stacy, Coord.-Mktg. Communications--Cold Spring Granite Company, Cold Spring, MN; *U.S. Private*, pg. 250

Bogart, Tom, V.P.-Mktg.--Utell International-Oak Brook, Oak Brook, IL; *Int'l*, pg. 1098

Bogden, Rick, Dir.-Mktg.--Wisconsin Label Corporation, Algoma, WI; *U.S. Private*, pg. 1184

Boggess, W.T., V.P.-Strategic Plng.--Emerson Power Transmission Corporation, Ithaca, NY; *U.S. Public*, pg. 573

Boggs, Roger, Mgr.-Mktg. Communications--DePuy, Inc., Warsaw, IN; *Int'l*, pg. 331

Boghigian, Harry, V.P. & Dir.-Mkt. Plng.--Hoffmann-La Roche Inc., Nutley, NJ; *Int'l*, pg. 1120

Boguais, Christian, Dir.-Mktg.--Merinos, Saint Quentin-en-Yvelines, France; *Int'l*, pg. 858

Bohacek, Peter, V.P.-Mktg.--Tandem Telecommunications Systems, Inc., Plano, TX; *U.S. Public*, pg. 417

Bohach, John P., V.P.-Mktg. Services & Adv.--Tyco Toys, Inc., Mount Laurel, NJ; *U.S. Public*, pg. 1058

Bohan, Peter, V.P.-Mktg. & Sls.--Bird Machine Company, South Walpole, MA; *U.S. Public*, pg. 166

Bohling, Lavon O., V.P.-Mktg.--Reinke Manufacturing Co., Inc., Deshler, NE; *U.S. Private*, pg. 920

Bohlman, Victor, Dir.-Mktg.--RHC/Spacemaster Corporation, Melrose Park, IL; *U.S. Private*, pg. 904

Bohnet, Mike, V.P.-Sls. & Mktg.--Robertshaw Tennessee, Knoxville, TN; *Int'l*, pg. 1243

Boissinot, Timothy, Mgr.-Mktg.--Imprimeries Quebecor Canada, Richmond Hill, Canada; *Int'l*, pg. 1077

Bojanowski, Ted, V.P.-Global Mktg.--Garlock Sealing Technologies, Palmyra, NY; *U.S. Public*, pg. 402

Bokermann, Mark, Mgr.-Mktg.--The Arnold Engineering Company, Marengo, IL; *U.S. Public*, pg. 1420

Bolan, Michael, V.P.-Mktg. & Prod. Devel.--Dallas Semiconductor Corporation, Dallas, TX; *U.S. Public*, pg. 478

Bolanowski, Patii, Mgr.-Mktg.--Jimlar Corporation, Great Neck, NY; *U.S. Private*, pg. 587

Boldig, Kathleen, Mgr.-Adv. & Mktg.--Ajay Leisure Products, Inc., Delavan, WI; *U.S. Public*, pg. 34

Boldrini, Ezo, Mgr.-Corp. Mktg.--3M Chile S.A., Santiago, Chile; *U.S. Public*, pg. 1606

Bolduc, Pierre, Exec. V.P.-New Business Devel. & Intl. Affairs--Hydro-Quebec, Montreal, Canada; *Int'l*, pg. 640

Bolen, Mike, Dir.-Sls. & Mktg.--The Zippertubing Co., Los Angeles, CA; *U.S. Private*, pg. 1207

Bolger, Declan, V.P.-Mktg.--Florida Panthers Holdings, Inc., Fort Lauderdale, FL; *U.S. Public*, pg. 654

Bolger, Donal, Dir.-Mktg.--CPC Foods (Ireland) Ltd., Dublin, Ireland; *U.S. Public*, pg. 225

Bolhuis, Rolf, V.P.-Mktg.--Lipton, Toronto, Canada; *Int'l*, pg. 1438

Bolin, Paul, V.P.-Mktg.--Kennedy Tank & Manufacturing Co., Inc., Indianapolis, IN; *U.S. Private*, pg. 614

Boling, Bart, V.P.-Opers. Support--Cash America International, Inc., Fort Worth, TX; *U.S. Public*, pg. 312

Bolit, Jim, V.P.-Mktg. & Engrng.--Astec America Inc., Carlsbad, CA; *Int'l*, pg. 93

Bollinger, Eric, Dir.- Mktg. & Sls.--Bollinger Shipyards, Inc., Lockport, LA; *U.S. Private*, pg. 155

Bollinger, Eric, Dir.-Sls. & Mktg.--Bollinger Algiers Inc., New Orleans, LA; *U.S. Private*, pg. 155

Bologna, Karen, Mgr.-Mktg. Communications--Hexcel Corporation, Pleasanton, CA; *U.S. Public*, pg. 824

Bolte, R.H., V.P.-Corp. Mktg. Svcs.--The Clorox Company, Oakland, CA; *U.S. Public*, pg. 386

Boltin, George, V.P.-Sls. & Mktg.--Kurz-Kasch, Inc., Wilmington, OH; *U.S. Private*, pg. 637

Bolton, James R., Sr. V.P.-Mktg.-Networking/Data Commun.--Wyle Electronics, Irvine, CA; *Int'l*, pg. 1457

Bolton, Robin, V.P.-Mktg.--The Manufacturers Life Insurance Company of America, Toronto, Canada; *Int'l*, pg. 840

Boltri, Mario, V.P.-Mktg.--Hughes-Treitler Manufacturing Corporation, Garden City, NY; *U.S. Private*, pg. 547

Bombal, Catherine, Mgr.-Mktg. & Res.--Clarins, Neuilly-sur-Seine, France; *Int'l*, pg. 295

Bombet, Jean-Pierre, Dir.-Mktg.--A.T. Cross Ltd., Ballina, Ireland; *U.S. Public*, pg. 461

Bonaccorsi, Christi, Mgr.-Media & Trade Shows--Diagraph Corporation, Earth City, MO; *U.S. Private*, pg. 330

Bond, David, Dir.-Mktg.--Major Pharmaceuticals Corp., Auburn Hills, MI; *U.S. Private*, pg. 475

Bond, Jane, Supvr.-Mktg. Communications--Quincy Compressor Division Coltec Industries, Quincy, IL; *U.S. Public*, pg. 402

Bond, Marian, Dir.-Mktg. Services--Sylvan Learning Systems Inc., Baltimore, MD; *U.S. Public*, pg. 1545

Bondioli, Carlo, Mgr.-Prod. & Mktg.--Bondioli & Pavesi S.p.A., Suzzara, Italy; *Int'l*, pg. 201

Bonekat, Harold, Exec. V.P.-Mktg.--Golden Valley Microwave Foods, Inc., Edina, MN; *U.S. Public*, pg. 427

Bones, Martin, V.P.-Mktg. Communications--Everex Systems Inc., Fremont, CA; *Int'l*, pg. 498

Bonetti, Tina, Mgr.-Mktg. Communi.--MTS Systems Corporation, Eden Prairie, MN; *U.S. Public*, pg. 1028

Bonham, Mike, Sr. V.P.-Sls. & Mktg.--Cerprobe Corporation, Gilbert, AZ; *U.S. Public*, pg. 332

Bonifield, John, V.P.-Mktg.--Days Inns of America, Inc., Parsippany, NJ; *U.S. Public*, pg. 321

Bonilla, Pedro P., Pres.--Allied Diagnostic Imaging Resources, Inc., Norcross, GA; *U.S. Public*, pg. 282

Bonistalli, James, Dir.-Mktg.--Metra, Commuter Rail Service Board, Chicago, IL; *U.S. Private*, pg. 919

Bonnell, Pat, V.P.-Mktg.--Emery Waterhouse Company, Portland, ME; *U.S. Private*, pg. 373

Bonnet, Michel, Sr. V.P.-Mktg. & Public Affairs--Elf Aquitane, Paris, France; *Int'l*, pg. 444

Bonnett, Madelyn C., Supvr.-Mktg. Commun.--EBSCO Industries, Inc., Birmingham, AL; *U.S. Private*, pg. 358

Bonnette, Joan, V.P.-Mktg., Existing Card Members--Citibank N.A., Long Island City, NY; *U.S. Public*, pg. 377

Bonora, Christine, Admin.-MKtg.--Gish Biomedical, Inc., Irvine, CA; *U.S. Public*, pg. 745

Bonucelli, Bernie, Dir.-Mktg.-Dorney Park & Wildwater Kingdom--Cedar Fair, L.P., Sandusky, OH; *U.S. Public*, pg. 319

Bonwill, Mary Ellen, Dir.-Adv.--Cerdec Corporation, Washington, PA; *Int'l*, pg. 292

Bonyun, David, Coord.-Adv. & Mktg.--McGuffey's Restaurants, Inc., Asheville, NC; *U.S. Private*, pg. 721

Boodjeh, David, V.P.-Mktg.--Discount Drug Mart Inc., Medina, OH; *U.S. Private*, pg. 334

Bookstaver, Chuck, V.P.-Mktg.--Flexible Flyer Toys, West Point, MS; *U.S. Private*, pg. 412

Boone-Isaacs, Cheryl, Pres.-Theatrical Mktg.--New Line Cinema Corporation, New York, NY; *U.S. Public*, pg. 1614

Boone, David, V.P.-Prod. Devel. & Mktg.--Lynx Golf, Inc., City of Industry, CA; *U.S. Private*, pg. 684

Boone, Sharon, V.P.-Sls. & Mktg.--Johnson Products Co., Inc., Chicago, IL; *U.S. Public*, pg. 915

Boos, Pat, V.P.-Sls. & Mktg.--Lenox Collections, Langhorne, PA; *U.S. Public*, pg. 261

Boot, John, Mgr.-Mktg. Communications--Attwood Corporation, Lowell, MI; *U.S. Private*, pg. 1038

Booth, Bill, Mgr.-Mktg.--Adidas America, Los Angeles, CA; *Int'l*, pg. 24

Booth, John, V.P.-Mktg. & Mdsg.--Associated Grocers, Inc., Seattle, WA; *U.S. Private*, pg. 90

Booth, Mark, Dir.-Grp. Mktg.--Royal & Sun Alliance Insurance Group plc, London, United Kingdom; *Int'l*, pg. 1130

Booth, Neil, V.P.-Sls. & Mktg.--Brown & Haley, Tacoma, WA; *U.S. Private*, pg. 173

Booth, Peter, V.P.-Mktg.--Superior Graphite Co., Chicago, IL; *U.S. Private*, pg. 1054

Boozer, Larry, V.P.-Sls.--Lancaster Malleable Castings Company, Lancaster, PA; *U.S. Private*, pg. 645

Borda, Bryan, V.P.-Mailing Efficiency & Database Mktg.--Group 1 Software, Inc., Lanham, MD; *U.S. Public*, pg. 417

Bordeaux, Phillip, Sr. V.P.-Mktg. & Customer Service--Intermountain Gas Co., Boise, ID; *U.S. Private*, pg. 568

Bordegon, Bill, V.P.-Mktg.--Fleer-Skybox International Inc., Mount Laurel, NJ; *U.S. Public*, pg. 1052

Borden, Robert C., Jr., V.P.-Mktg.--Shipley Companies, York, PA; *U.S. Private*, pg. 994

Boren, Jeff, V.P.-Mktg.--TST/Impreso, Inc., Coppell, TX; *U.S. Private*, pg. 1066

Borgan, J., V.P.-Sls. & Mktg.--Crane Valves/North American, Joliet, IL; *U.S. Public*, pg. 457

Borgensen, Ray, Mgr.-Mktg.--Tecknit Incorporated, Cranford, NJ; *U.S. Private*, pg. 1072

Borger, Karen, Mgr.-Mktg. Communications--AlliedSignal, Automotive Aftermarket, Rumford, RI; *U.S. Public*, pg. 51

Borger, William, Dir.-Partnership Mktg.--Busch Entertainment Corp., Clayton, MO; *U.S. Public*, pg. 114

Borgmann, Carolyn, Exec. Asst.--Beacon Container Corporation, Birdsboro, PA; *U.S. Private*, pg. 125

Borja, Susan, Dir.-Mktg. & Adv.--I. Spiewak & Sons, Inc., New York, NY; *U.S. Private*, pg. 1025

Borja, Susan, Dir.-Mktg. & Adv.--Golden Fleece Outerwear Co., New York, NY; *U.S. Private*, pg. 1025

Bormann, John H., V.P.-Sls. & Mktg.--Rymer Meat Inc., Chicago, IL; *U.S. Public*, pg. 1414

Borne, Cheryl Ann, Mgr.-Mktg. Comm.--Computer Power Incorporated, High Bridge, NJ; *U.S. Public*, pg. 421

Bornhuetter, Doug, V.P.-Sls. & Mktg.--Gunite Corporation, Rockford, IL; *U.S. Public*, pg. 933

Borow, Leonard, Chief Oper. Officer & Exec. V.P.--Aeroflex Incorporated, Plainview, NY; *U.S. Public*, pg. 23

Borseth, John D., Sr. V.P.-Sls. & Mktg.--Newcor, Inc., Bloomfield Hills, MI; *U.S. Public*, pg. 1176

Borshell, David, Sr. V.P.-Sls. & Mktg.--Image Entertainment, Inc., Chatsworth, CA; *U.S. Public*, pg. 870

Borton, Todd K., CFA, Dir.-Mktg.--Jacobs Asset Management, Fort Lauderdale, FL; *U.S. Public*, pg. 1673

Bortone, Lou, V.P.-Mktg.--Saban Entertainment, Los Angeles, CA; *U.S. Private*, pg. 959

Bosart, Julie, Coord.-Mktg.--The W.E. Bassett Company, Shelton, CT; *U.S. Private*, pg. 122

Bosch, Karen, Dir.-Mktg.--Dyckerhoff & Widmann AG, Munich, Germany; *Int'l*, pg. 423

Boschen, Chris, V.P.-Mktg., Sls. & Business Devel.--L3 Communications Telemetry & Instrumentation Div., San Diego, CA; *U.S. Private*, pg. 639

Boschski, Joe, Dir.-Mktg.--Zenger-Miller, San Jose, CA; *U.S. Public*, pg. 1617

Bosher, Robert, Mgr.--Congress Life Insurance Company, Minnetonka, MN; *U.S. Private*, pg. 980

Bosken-Diebels, Paul, Dr., Pres.--Diebels Private Brewery, Issum, Germany; *Int'l*, pg. 413

Boskey, William, Dir.-Intl. Sls., Mktg. & Joint Ventures--GM Powertrain Group, Pontiac, MI; *U.S. Public*, pg. 719

Bosmans, Willy, Gen. Mgr.-Mktg., Admin. & Fin.--Electrabel S.A., Brussels, Belgium; *Int'l*, pg. 436

Boss, Lynn, Asst.-Mktg.--Ted Cook Tours Islands in the Sun, Costa Mesa, CA; *Int'l*, pg. 21

Boster, Kari, Dir.-Mktg.--Bluewater, Mora, MN; *U.S. Private*, pg. 153

Bostick, Robert L., Mgr.-Mktg.--Baltimore Gas and Electric Company, Baltimore, MD; *U.S. Public*, pg. 172

Bostrom, Andrew, V.P.-Sls. & Mktg.--Ace Tank & Equipment Co., Seattle, WA; *U.S. Private*, pg. 12

Botd, Martin, Mgr.-Mktg.--Dayton Parts, Inc., Harrisburg, PA; *U.S. Public*, pg. 919

Boter, Marina, Product Mgr.-Mktg. & Adv.--Telefonica de Espana, S.A., Madrid, Spain; *Int'l*, pg. 1371

Bother, David, Mgr.-Adv.--CNF Transportation Inc., Palo Alto, CA; *U.S. Public*, pg. 281

Bottcher, Jan, V.P.-Mktg.--Lender's Bagel Bakery, White Plains, NY; *U.S. Public*, pg. 1288

Botticher, Pam, Mgr.-Mktg. Coord.--Manatron, Inc., Kalamazoo, MI; *U.S. Public*, pg. 1040

Bottino, Ron, V.P.-Sls. & Mktg.--Connecticut Spring & Stamping Corporation, Farmington, CT; *U.S. Private*, pg. 263

Bottomley, Winn, Mgr.-Mktg.--Philadelphia Reserve Supply Company, Croydon, PA; *U.S. Private*, pg. 861

Bottorff, JoAnne, Dir.-Mktg.--Jasper Seating Co., Inc., Jasper, IN; *U.S. Private*, pg. 583

Bottorff, Joanne, Dir.-Mktg.--JSI, French Lick, IN; *U.S. Private*, pg. 583

Boudour, Abdu, V.P.-Sls. & Mktg.--QC Optics, Inc., Wilmington, MA; *U.S. Public*, pg. 1345

Boudrau, Andre, Mgr.-Mktg.--Thomas & Betts Ltd., Iberville, Canada; *U.S. Public*, pg. 1598

Boudreaux, Frank, V.P.-Sls. & Mktg.--SOLOCO, Inc., Lafayette, LA; *U.S. Public*, pg. 1179
Boudreaux, O'Neil, V.P.-Sls. & Mktg.--General American Life Insurance Co., Saint Louis, MO; *U.S. Private*, pg. 443
Bouffard, Gary, V.P.-Sls. & Mktg.--Ideal Forging Corporation, Southington, CT; *U.S. Private*, pg. 557
Bouffard, Gaston, Sr. V.P./Sls. & Mktg./Paper & Bus. Devel.--Donohue Inc., Quebec, Canada; *Int'l*, pg. 1075
Boulay, David, V.P.-Mktg. Custom Packaging--Ventura Foods, City of Industry, CA; *U.S. Private*, pg. 508
Boulton, Ian, Mgr.-Mktg.--SmithKline Beecham Pharmaceuticals, Tokyo, Japan; *Int'l*, pg. 1266
Bounds, Martin, Dir.-Assoc. Mktg.--Time, New York, NY; *U.S. Public*, pg. 1613
Boundy, Edward, V.P.-Sls. & Mktg.--The Weetabix Company, Inc., Clinton, MA; *Int'l*, pg. 1488
Bourdin, Pascal, Dir.-Mktg.-Coffee--Kraft Jacobs Suchard, Velizy-Villacoublay, France; *U.S. Public*, pg. 1290
Bourguet, Bruno, Dir.-Sls. & Mktg.--Amtech International, Nanterre, France; *U.S. Public*, pg. 106
Bourque, Marilyn, Supvr.-Mktg. Communications--FMC-Crosby Valve, Inc., Wrentham, MA; *U.S. Public*, pg. 605
Bousquelte, Jarine, V.P.-Brand Mktg.--Pepsi-Cola Company, Somers, NY; *U.S. Public*, pg. 1277
Bousquette, Matt, Exec. V.P.-Mktg.-Boys Line--Mattel, Inc., El Segundo, CA; *U.S. Public*, pg. 1057
Boutcher, Ann, V.P.-Mktg. Svcs.--Audiovox Corporation, Hauppauge, NY; *U.S. Public*, pg. 147
Boutros, Nadia, Mktg. Admin.--Medstone International, Inc., Aliso Viejo, CA; *U.S. Public*, pg. 1082
Boutwell, Julie, Mgr.-Mktg. Communications--Genicom Corporation, Chantilly, VA; *U.S. Public*, pg. 729
Bovalino, Michael J., Sr. V.P.-Mktg.--Rochester Gas And Electric Corporation, Rochester, NY; *U.S. Public*, pg. 1395
Bovard, Pierre, V.P. & Gen. Mgr.-Radio--The Arbitron Company, New York, NY; *U.S. Public*, pg. 331
Bove, James V., Jr., Mgr.-Mktg./Consumer Prods.--Everpure Inc., Westmont, IL; *U.S. Public*, pg. 467
Boville, Ramon Sanjuan, Dir.-Mktg., Pub. Rels., Sls. & Adv.--Cabinas Telefonicas, S.A. (Cabitel), Madrid, Spain; *Int'l*, pg. 1371
Bovis, George S., Sr. V.P.-Devel. & Growth Plng.--White Hen Pantry, Inc., Elmhurst, IL; *U.S. Private*, pg. 1172
Bowe, Julia, Dir.-Mktg.--Liberty PLC, London, United Kingdom; *Int'l*, pg. 807
Bowen, Marcus D., Dir.-Mktg.--American General Life Insurance Company, Houston, TX; *U.S. Public*, pg. 76
Bowen, Mary, Dir.-Mktg.--Power & Telephone Supply Company, Memphis, TN; *U.S. Private*, pg. 877
Bowen, Maurice, Dir.-Mktg.--Hyundai Motor America, Fountain Valley, CA; *Int'l*, pg. 641
Bowen, Steve K., Dir.-Residential Mktg.--Public Service Company of North Carolina, Inc., Gastonia, NC; *U.S. Public*, pg. 1340
Bower, Barbara, Sr. V.P.-Mktg. Services--Trammell Crow Company, Dallas, TX; *U.S. Public*, pg. 1628
Bower, Scott, Sr. V.P.-Sls. & Mktg.--AST Research Inc., Irvine, CA; *Int'l*, pg. 1181
Bowers, Kip, Mgr.-Prod. Devel.--Benjamin Anseht Company, Saint Louis, MO; *U.S. Private*, pg. 75
Bowers, W.P., Sr. V.P.-Mktg.--Georgia Power Co., Atlanta, GA; *U.S. Public*, pg. 1490
Bowes, Bob, V.P.-Sls. & Mktg.--National Truck Leasing System, Oak Brook Terrace, IL; *U.S. Private*, pg. 787
Bowes, John, Dir.-Intl. Mktg. & Sls.--Behlen Mfg. Co., Columbus, NE; *U.S. Private*, pg. 130
Bowes, Karen, Mgr.-Mktg.--Shakey's Incorporated, Irvine, CA; *U.S. Private*, pg. 989
Bowlby, Ann, Mgr.-Mktg.--Taylor Hobson Pneumo, Rolling Meadows, IL; *Int'l*, pg. 1087
Bowles, Bill, Grp. V.P.-Mktg. & Devel.--Olympus America Inc., Melville, NY; *Int'l*, pg. 1005
Bowman, Mary, Mgr.-Mktg.--Builders Square, Inc., San Antonio, TX; *U.S. Private*, pg. 477
Bowman, Sandra, V.P.-Remarketing--Leasing Solutions, Inc., San Jose, CA; *U.S. Public*, pg. 982
Bowman, Steve E., V.P. & Dir.-Sls. & Mktg.--Shuford Mills, Inc., Hickory, NC; *U.S. Private*, pg. 996
Bowman, Ted, Mgr.-North American Sls. & Mktg.--International Lottery & Totalizator Systems, Inc., Carlsbad, CA; *U.S. Public*, pg. 900
Bowser, James F., V.P.-New Prod. Devel.--Three-Five Systems, Tempe, AZ; *U.S. Public*, pg. 1604
Bowser, Scott, Mgr.-Mktg.--The Pierce Co., Inc., Upland, IN; *U.S. Private*, pg. 102
Bowshler, Robert R., V.P.-Individual Mktg.--Security American Financial Enterprises, Inc., Minnetonka, MN; *U.S. Private*, pg. 980
Bowsher, Robert R., Mgr.--Security Life Insurance Company of America, Minnetonka, MN; *U.S. Private*, pg. 980
Bowsher, Steven J., V.P.-Sls. & Mktg.--Inland Steel Industries, Inc., Chicago, IL; *U.S. Public*, pg. 879
Bowsher, Steven J., V.P.-Sls. & Mktg./ISFPC--Inland Steel Products Company, East Chicago, IN; *U.S. Public*, pg. 879
Boyajian, Ed, V.P.-Mktg.--The Butcher Company, Marlborough, MA; *U.S. Private*, pg. 189
Boyajian, Karen, Mktg. Asst.--Deck House Inc., Acton, MA; *U.S. Private*, pg. 320
Boyce, Hugh, Mng. Dir.--Flexfab Horizons International, Inc., Hastings, MI; *U.S. Private*, pg. 412
Boyd, Margaret, Sr. V.P.-Sls. & Mktg.--First Tennessee National Corporation, Memphis, TN; *U.S. Public*, pg. 638
Boyd, R.B., Exec. V.P.--Puget Western, Inc., Bellevue, WA; *U.S. Public*, pg. 1342
Boyd, Stan, Sr. V.P.-Sls. & Mktg.--The Fairmont Hotels, San Francisco, CA; *U.S. Private*, pg. 391
Boyer, Alan, Mgr.-New Customer Mktg.--Foster & Gallagher, Inc., Peoria, IL; *U.S. Private*, pg. 420
Boyer, Alan, Mgr.-New Customer Mktg.--Spring Hill Nurseries Co., Peoria, IL; *U.S. Private*, pg. 420
Boyer, Parke, V.P.-Mktg.--Master Builders Inc., Cleveland, OH; *Int'l*, pg. 1465
Boyers, Bruce, Dir.-Mktg.--Executive Software, Glendale, CA; *U.S. Private*, pg. 388
Boyette, Mary, V.P.-Mktg.--Stendhal, New York, NY; *Int'l*, pg. 445
Boyke, Dale C., V.P.-Mktg. & Sls.--The Oilgear Company, Milwaukee, WI; *U.S. Public*, pg. 1215
Boylan, Gerald W., V.P.-Bus. Devel.--Masco Corporation, Taylor, MI; *U.S. Public*, pg. 1052
Boylan, John, V.P.-Sls. & Mktg.--Harriss & Covington Hosiery Mills, High Point, NC; *U.S. Private*, pg. 506
Boyle, David, Sr. Dir.-Mktg.--McCain Foods (Australia) Pty, Ltd., Ballarat, Australia; *Int'l*, pg. 850
Boyle, Frank J., V.P.-Sls. & Engrng.--Selas Corporation of America, Dresher, PA; *U.S. Public*, pg. 1454
Boyle, John C., V.P. & Gen. Mgr.--Heluva Good Cheese Inc., Sodus, NY; *Int'l*, pg. 752
Boyle, Tom, Dir.-Mktg. Worldwide Communications--PerSeptive Biosystems, Inc., Framingham, MA; *U.S. Public*, pg. 1279
Boylen, Lisa, V.P.-Mktg.--First Charter Corporation, Concord, NC; *U.S. Public*, pg. 627
Boyles, Brad, Mgr.-Adv., Sls. & Mktg.--Gunver Manufacturing Co., Manchester, CT; *U.S. Private*, pg. 488
Boynton, Laura-Jo, Mktg. & Adv.--Swiss Prestige, Inc., Winchester, VA; *Int'l*, pg. 697
Boyo, Mel, Dir.-Mktg.--Beutler Heating & Air Conditioning Inc., Sacramento, CA; *U.S. Private*, pg. 141
Boytos, Geoff, V.P.-Database Mktg.--Micro Warehouse, Inc., Norwalk, CT; *U.S. Public*, pg. 1104
Boyum, Ronald L., V.P.-Sls. & Sports Mktg.--The Topps Company, Inc., New York, NY; *U.S. Public*, pg. 1621
Braatz, Nancy, Mktg. Communications Coord.--Waukesha Engine Division, Waukesha, WI; *U.S. Public*, pg. 528
Bracci, George T., V.P.-Sls. & Mktg.--EAO Switch Corporation, Milford, CT; *Int'l*, pg. 444
Brachocki, Edward, V.P.-Corp. Devel.--Go-Video, Inc., Scottsdale, AZ; *U.S. Public*, pg. 748
Brackett, Regina P., V.P.-Mktg.--Home Federal Bank, Hamilton, OH; *U.S. Public*, pg. 633
Bradbury, Dick, Prod. Mgr.-CNC Products--Bridgeport Machines, Inc., Bridgeport, CT; *U.S. Public*, pg. 251
Bradely, Mildred, V.P.-Mktg. Svcs.--Centimark Corporation, Canonsburg, PA; *U.S. Private*, pg. 222
Bradford, Michael, V.P.-Sls. & Mktg.--West Penetone Corporation, Tenafly, NJ; *U.S. Private*, pg. 1158
Bradie, Stacey, Dir.-Mktg.--Clarins USA Inc., New York, NY; *Int'l*, pg. 295
Bradley, Andrew, Exec. V.P.-Mktg., Nestle Ice Cream Co.--Nestle Frozen, Refrigerated, and Ice Cream Companies, Solon, OH; *Int'l*, pg. 918
Bradley, Daniel J., Div. V.P.-Sls. & Mktg./N. America--Ethyl Corporation, Richmond, VA; *U.S. Public*, pg. 595
Bradley, David, V.P.-Mktg.--Qualex Inc., Durham, NC; *U.S. Public*, pg. 551
Bradshaw, Morris, Dir.-Mktg.--Oakland Raiders, Alameda, CA; *U.S. Private*, pg. 809
Bradshaw, Steven M., Exec. V.P.-Mktg.--Dixie Carriers, Inc., Houston, TX; *U.S. Public*, pg. 962
Brady, Don, Sr. V.P.-Sls. & Mktg.--Bruning Paint Company, Baltimore, MD; *U.S. Private*, pg. 176
Brady, Julie, V.P.-Mktg.--Croscill, Inc., New York, NY; *U.S. Private*, pg. 290
Brady, Michelle, Mgr.-Mktg. & Sls. Promo.--Kettle Restaurants, Houston, TX; *U.S. Private*, pg. 617
Brady, Richard, V.P.-Mktg.--HomeTown Communications Network, Inc., Livonia, MI; *U.S. Private*, pg. 537
Brady, Stephen J., V.P.-Strategy & Mktg.--Sodexho USA, Waltham, MA; *Int'l*, pg. 1274
Brady, William J., V.P.-Plng., Resources & Fin.--Mobil Mining & Minerals Company, Ashland, VA; *U.S. Public*, pg. 1118
Bragg, Donald, Dir.-Mktg.--Teleflex Fluid Systems Inc., Suffield, CT; *U.S. Public*, pg. 1569
Brahl, Doug, V.P.-Sls. & Mktg.--U.S. Safety, Lenexa, KS; *U.S. Private*, pg. 1125
Brahm, Cliff, Dir.-Sls. & Mktg.--Huffy Service First, Inc., Miamisburg, OH; *U.S. Public*, pg. 846
Brain, Roger A., V.P.-Mktg. & Sls.--Cominco, Ltd., Vancouver, Canada; *Int'l*, pg. 307
Brainard, Douglas M., V.P.-Sls. & Mktg.--Sales Technologies, Atlanta, GA; *U.S. Public*, pg. 395
Brainerd, Michael R., Mgr.-Mktg. Services--Dremel, Racine, WI; *U.S. Public*, pg. 574
Brainin, Ricky, Mgr.-Mktg.--Vacudyne Inc., Chicago Heights, IL; *U.S. Private*, pg. 46
Brakefield, Jan, Mktg.--Regions Bank/Tuscaloosa, Tuscaloosa, AL; *U.S. Public*, pg. 1373
Braley, Peter, V.P.-Sls. & Mktg.--WMF/USA, Farmingdale, NY; *U.S. Private*, pg. 1144
Bralower, Steve, Sr. V.P.-Leasing--Carr Real Estate Services, Washington, DC; *U.S. Public*, pg. 309
Bramen, Bruce, V.P.-Mktg.--William B. Reily & Co., Inc., New Orleans, LA; *U.S. Private*, pg. 919
Bramer, Joan, Mgr.-Mktg.--PAREXEL International Corporation, Waltham, MA; *U.S. Public*, pg. 1257
Bramlett, Michael, Dir.-Sls.--Mrs. Smith's Bakeries, Inc., Thomasville, GA; *U.S. Public*, pg. 657
Bramwell, Steven, V.P.-Sls.--Bay State Milling Co., Quincy, MA; *U.S. Private*, pg. 124
Brancato, Tom, Mgr.-Electronic Pre-Press--GraphLine Inc., Tamarac, FL; *U.S. Private*, pg. 471
Brand, Shiela, Mgr.-Mktg.--Beckman Instruments, Inc., Fullerton, CA; *U.S. Public*, pg. 199
Brandimarti, Elizabeth A., V.P. & Dir.-Corp. Mktg.--Mellon Bank Corporation, Pittsburgh, PA; *U.S. Public*, pg. 1084
Brands, Robert F., V.P.-Fixtures Mktg.-Plumbing No. America--Kohler Company, Kohler, WI; *U.S. Private*, pg. 630
Brandt, James E., Mgr.-Mktg. Services--Simpson Door Company, McCleary, WA; *U.S. Private*, pg. 1003
Brandt, Jan, Pres.-Mktg.--America Online Incorporated, Dulles, VA; *U.S. Public*, pg. 66
Brandt, Michael, Dir.-Mktg. Commun.--Veryfine Products, Inc., Westford, MA; *U.S. Private*, pg. 1137
Brandt, Richard, Dir.-New Product Mktg.--Dahlberg, Inc., Golden Valley, MN; *U.S. Public*, pg. 194
Brandt, Roden A., Sr. V.P.-Plng. & Mktg.--Trans World Airlines, Inc., Saint Louis, MO; *U.S. Public*, pg. 1629
Brandt, Ronald D., V.P.-Mktg. & Sls.--United Life Insurance Company, Cedar Rapids, IA; *U.S. Public*, pg. 1677
Branger, Kathy, Mktg. Communications & Media Specialist--Applied Power Inc., Butler, WI; *U.S. Public*, pg. 124
Brannen, Charles A., V.P.--Overton Gear & Tool Corp., Addison, IL; *U.S. Private*, pg. 823
Brannigan, Bonnie, V.P.-Strategic Plng. & Mktg.--Max & Erma's Restaurants, Columbus, OH; *U.S. Public*, pg. 1060
Brannon, Timothy H., V.P.-Pulp Mktg.--Rayonier Inc., Stamford, CT; *U.S. Public*, pg. 1363
Brantingham, Julie, Mgr.-Mktg & Communications--Dionex Corporation, Sunnyvale, CA; *U.S. Public*, pg. 510
Branton, Gene, Mgr.-Product & Mktg.--Funk Manufacturing Co., Coffeyville, KS; *U.S. Public*, pg. 492
Branton, Robert, V.P.-Sls. & Mktg.--United Hardware Distributing Co., Plymouth, MN; *U.S. Private*, pg. 335
Branum, A. Don, Sr. V.P.-Mktg.--Vertex Communications Corporation, Kilgore, TX; *U.S. Public*, pg. 1717
Brasser, Bob, Sr. V.P.-Consumer Prods.--Riddell Sports, Inc., New York, NY; *U.S. Public*, pg. 1389
Braswell, Karen, Sr. Dir.-MKtg.--Bojangles' Restaraunts, Inc., Charlotte, NC; *U.S. Private*, pg. 154
Bratz, Keith, Dir.-Communications--Provident Mutual Life Insurance Co., Berwyn, PA; *U.S. Private*, pg. 891
Braumann, Horst, Mgr.-Intl. Mktg.--Automatic Switch Co., Florham Park, NJ; *U.S. Public*, pg. 573
Braun, Dave, Dir.-Mktg.--Nationwide Mutual Insurance Co., Columbus, OH; *U.S. Private*, pg. 789
Braun, Doug, V.P.-Mktg.--Herbalife International of America, Inc., Century City, CA; *U.S. Public*, pg. 809
Braun, James, V.P.-Mktg. & Sls.--Recoton Auto Corporation, Lincolnshire, IL; *U.S. Public*, pg. 1369
Braun, Jerry, Dir.-Mktg.--Newly Weds Foods Inc., Chicago, IL; *U.S. Private*, pg. 796
Braun, Kim, Mktg. Specialist--Unify Corporation, San Jose, CA; *U.S. Public*, pg. 1665
Braun, Morris, V.P. & Sec.--W. Braun Company, Chicago, IL; *U.S. Private*, pg. 166
Brauss, K.A., V.P.-Sls. & Mktg.--Marley Electric Heating Company, Bennettsville, SC; *U.S. Public*, pg. 1676
Bravieri, Richard, Mgr.-Mktg. Svcs.--Safety-Kleen Corp., Elgin, IL; *U.S. Public*, pg. 1425
Bravo, Massimo, Exec. V.P.-Mktg.--Istituto Bancario San Paolo Di Torino S.p.A., Turin, Italy; *Int'l*, pg. 691
Brawley, Keith, Dir.-Mktg. Svcs.--Fender Musical Instruments, Scottsdale, AZ; *U.S. Private*, pg. 400
Brawley, Tom, V.P.-Automotive/Lubricants--Universal Cooperatives, Inc., Minneapolis, MN; *U.S. Private*, pg. 1127
Bray, Jim, Mgr.-Mktg.--Milk Products Holdings (North America) Inc., Santa Rosa, CA; *Int'l*, pg. 923
Bray, Maggie, Mgr.-Mktg.--Tippins Incorporated, Pittsburgh, PA; *U.S. Private*, pg. 1088
Brazell, Amelia, Dir.-Mktg.--Zoological Society of San Diego, San Diego, CA; *U.S. Private*, pg. 1207
Breard, Jack H., V.P. & Dir.-Mktg.--EBSCO Industries, Inc., Birmingham, AL; *U.S. Private*, pg. 358
Breck, Daniel H., V.P.-Mktg. & Prod. Devel.-Fibreco Pulp Inc.--Slocan Forest Products Ltd., Richmond, Canada; *Int'l*, pg. 1263
Breed, Carl, Dir.-Mktg.--Blue Bell Creameries, L.P., Brenham, TX; *U.S. Private*, pg. 150
Breejen, Daniel, Mgr.-Mktg.--H & H Tube & Manufacturing Co., Vanderbilt, MI; *U.S. Private*, pg. 489
Breen, Donald, Jr., Sr. V.P.-Sls. & Mktg.--John Morrell & Co., Cincinnati, OH; *U.S. Public*, pg. 1479
Breen, Edward, Pres.--Broadband Networks Group, Hatboro, PA; *U.S. Public*, pg. 716
Breen, Ginger, Dir.-Mktg.--Ramada Express, Laughlin, NV; *U.S. Public*, pg. 158
Brehob, Tina, Coord.-Mktg.--Bickford's Family Restaurants, Brighton, MA; *U.S. Public*, pg. 545
Breickner, John, Product Mgr.--Electronic Measurements, Inc., Neptune, NJ; *U.S. Private*, pg. 138
Breitbarth, Meredith, V.P.-Mktg. & Sls. Promo.--Showtime Networks Inc., New York, NY; *U.S. Private*, pg. 779
Bremmer, Jackie, Admin. & Telephone Mktg.--Western Direct, Phoenix, AZ; *U.S. Private*, pg. 1166
Brener, Arthur H., Dir.-Mktg.--Good Food Magazine, New York, NY; *Int'l*, pg. 925
Brennan, Jim, V.P.-Mktg. & Sls./Motors--Marathon Electric Manufacturing Corp., Wausau, WI; *U.S. Public*, pg. 1371
Brennan, Molly, V.P.-Showrooms & Mktg.--Jack Lenor Larsen, Inc., New York, NY; *U.S. Private*, pg. 652
Brennan, Vin, V.P.-Community Mkts.Sls.--The Check Store, Lakewood, CO; *U.S. Public*, pg. 785
Brenneman, James H., V.P.-Opers. & Plng.--Bell Atlantic Enterprises Corporation, Philadelphia, PA; *U.S. Public*, pg. 202
Brennen, Fran, Mgr.-Mktg. & Commun.--Veeco Instruments, Inc., Plainview, NY; *U.S. Public*, pg. 1711
Brennen, Fran, Mgr.-Mktg. Communications/Veeco-NY--Sloan Technology, Santa Barbara, CA; *U.S. Public*, pg. 1711
Brenner, David H., Sr. V.P.-Mktg. Devel.--Amway Corporation, Ada, MI; *U.S. Private*, pg. 69
Brently, Dennis, V.P.-Sls.--Coleman Powermate, Inc., Omaha, NE; *U.S. Private*, pg. 691
Brenton, Keith, V.P.-Sls. & Mktg.--Autoswage Products, Inc., Shelton, CT; *U.S. Private*, pg. 101
Breseman, Rick, Sr. V.P.-Mktg.--Sealaska Timber Corporation, Ketchikan, AK; *U.S. Private*, pg. 978
Bresler, Andrew R., V.P. & Dir.-Mktg.--Ralcorp Holdings Inc., Saint Louis, MO; *U.S. Public*, pg. 1359
Bressler, Andrew, V.P.-Mktg.--Ralston Foods, Inc., Saint Louis, MO; *U.S. Public*, pg. 1359

Breth, Robin, Dir.-Mktg. & Adv.--Gold Medal Products Co., Cincinnati, OH; *U.S. Private*, pg. 459
Breton, John, V.P.-Sls. & Mktg.--Nalle Plastics Inc., Austin, TX; *U.S. Private*, pg. 773
Brett, Paul, V.P.-Mktg. & Sls.--R.F. Technology, Inc., Norwalk, CT; *Int'l*, pg. 1289
Bretz, Charles B., Sr. V.P.-Mktg. Div.--Compass Bank, Birmingham, AL; *U.S. Public*, pg. 418
Brevik, John, Exec. V.P.-Sls., Adv. & Mktg.--Exotic Rubber & Plastics Corp., Farmington Hills, MI; *U.S. Private*, pg. 388
Brewer, Brian, Sr. V.P.-Bus. Mktg.--MCI Communications Corp., Atlanta, GA; *U.S. Public*, pg. 1023
Brewer, Nadine, Sr. Dir.-Mktg. Res.--Kentucky Fried Chicken Corporation (KFC), Louisville, KY; *U.S. Public*, pg. 1636
Brewer, O.G., V.P.-Mktg.--Mead Containerboard, Atlanta, GA; *U.S. Public*, pg. 1074
Brewer, Reagan, V.P.-Mktg.--Grolsch Importers Inc., Atlanta, GA; *Int'l*, pg. 559
Brewer, Yvonne, Dir.-Adv.--Big Valley Marketing Corp., Fremont, CA; *U.S. Private*, pg. 1186
Bricco, Bruce, Mgr.-Mktg.--BJ Services Company, Houston, TX; *U.S. Public*, pg. 161
Brice, Carolyn, Dir.-Mktg UK/Europe--McGraw-Hill Book Co. (U.K.) Ltd., Maidenhead, United Kingdom; *U.S. Public*, pg. 1072
Brickell, Rob, Mgr.-Mktg. Commun.--Trion, Inc., Sanford, NC; *U.S. Public*, pg. 1639
Bridge, Jude, Dir.-Mktg./Snacks Div.--United Biscuits (UK) Limited, West Drayton, United Kingdom; *Int'l*, pg. 1442
Bridgewater, Carol, Mgr.-Mktg.--Danka Business Systems, La Grange, IL; *Int'l*, pg. 379
Briedenbach, Rainer, Sr. V.P.-Sls. & Mktg.--Deutz AG, Cologne, Germany; *Int'l*, pg. 407
Briggs, David, Dir.-Mktg. & Sls.--Frequency and Time Systems, Inc., Beverly, MA; *U.S. Public*, pg. 488
Briggs, Kirsten, Mktg. Asst.--Stonco Genlyte, Union, NJ; *U.S. Public*, pg. 730
Briggs, Matt, Res. Analyst-Mktg.--Reilly Industries, Inc., Indianapolis, IN; *U.S. Private*, pg. 919
Brigham, Debbie, Supvr.-Mktg. Svcs.--Sanderson Plumbing Products Inc., Columbus, MS; *U.S. Private*, pg. 964
Bright, James, Dir.-Mktg. & Mgr.-Natl. Sls.--Sprayway, Inc., Addison, IL; *U.S. Private*, pg. 462
Bright, Stacey, Coord.-Mktg.--Popeye's Chicken & Biscuits, Atlanta, GA; *U.S. Private*, pg. 5
Brill, Roberta, Exec. V.P.-Mktg.--Patient Care, Inc., West Orange, NJ; *U.S. Public*, pg. 344
Brill, Steven, Mgr.-Mktg.--Medical Professional Liability Agency, Ltd., Bedford Hills, NY; *U.S. Public*, pg. 685
Brim, W.F., V.P. & Dir.-Seafood--Winn-Dixie Stores, Inc., Jacksonville, FL; *U.S. Public*, pg. 1771
Bringgold, Terese, Mgr.-Mktg. Communications--Food & Beverage, Saint Paul, MN; *U.S. Public*, pg. 562
Brink, Lyle, V.P.-Mktg.--Brink Electric Construction Company, Rapid City, SD; *U.S. Private*, pg. 169
Brinks, Jim, Mgr.-Sls. & Mktg.--Reedspectrum, Holden, MA; *Int'l*, pg. 624
Bristow, A., Dir.-Sls. & Mktg.--Andres Wines (Atlantic) Ltd., Dartmouth, Canada; *Int'l*, pg. 76
Bristow, Julie, Dir.-Mktg.--Jeff Wyler Dealer Group, Inc., Cincinnati, OH; *U.S. Private*, pg. 1193
Britt, Arie C., V.P.-Oil & Gas Mktg.--Hunt Oil Company, Dallas, TX; *U.S. Private*, pg. 548
Brittain, L.H., Jr., V.P.-Mktg.--Citgo Petroleum Corporation, Tulsa, OK; *Int'l*, pg. 1045
Broad, Donald, Dir.-Mktg.--McGraw-Hill Ryerson, Ltd., Whitby, Canada; *U.S. Public*, pg. 1072
Broadhead, Dean, V.P.-Mktg.--Sony Music Entertainment, Inc., New York, NY; *Int'l*, pg. 1281
Broadhead, R., V.P.-Mktg.--The UCS Group, Toronto, Canada; *Int'l*, pg. 792
Broca, Renee, Dir.-Mktg.--Tom Thumb Food & Pharmacy, Dallas, TX; *U.S. Private*, pg. 909
Brocco, Frank A., Dir.-Sls. & Mktg.--First American Title Insurance Co. of N.Y., New York, NY; *U.S. Public*, pg. 626
Broce, Alan, Sr. V.P.-Mktg.--MTV: Music Television, New York, NY; *U.S. Private*, pg. 779
Brock, Jim, V.P.-Mktg.--Pacific Hide & Fur Depot, Great Falls, MT; *U.S. Private*, pg. 831
Brock, Stephen P., Sr. V.P.-Sls. & Mktg.--Baldwin Piano & Organ Company, Loveland, OH; *U.S. Public*, pg. 169
Brock, Tom, Mgr.-Mktg.--Stationery Products Division, Boston, MA; *U.S. Public*, pg. 744
Brockett, Patrick J., Exec. V.P.-World Wide Mktg. & Sls.--National Semiconductor Corporation, Santa Clara, CA; *U.S. Public*, pg. 1159
Brockmann, Sue, V.P.-Mktg.--Recreational Equipment, Inc., Kent, WA; *U.S. Private*, pg. 914
Brockschmidt, John W., Mgr.-Casualty Mktg.--Willis Corroon Corp. of Michigan, Livonia, MI; *Int'l*, pg. 1506
Broder, M., V.P.-Mktg.--Israel Aircraft Industries Ltd., Israel; *Int'l*, pg. 689
Broderick, Kathleen, Dir.-Mktg.-Bennigan's--Bennigan's, Dallas, TX; *U.S. Private*, pg. 736
Broderick, Matthew, Grp. V.P.-Mktg.--Turtle Wax, Inc., Chicago, IL; *U.S. Private*, pg. 1110
Broderick, Peter, Mgr.-Mktg. Communications--AGFA EPS Division, Wilmington, MA; *Int'l*, pg. 172
Broderick, William H., III, Principal-On-Line Mktg.--Edward Jones, Saint Louis, MO; *U.S. Private*, pg. 597
Brodey, Larry, Pres.-Jaclo Inc., Mountainside, NJ; *U.S. Private*, pg. 349
Brody, Carolyn, Dir.-Pub. Rels.--Harry Winston, Inc., New York, NY; *U.S. Private*, pg. 1183
Brody, Michael, V.P.-Sls. & Mktg.--M.S. Walker, Inc., Somerville, MA; *U.S. Private*, pg. 1147
Brogan, Mike, V.P.-Sls. & Mktg./Generator Set--Detroit Diesel Corp., Detroit, MI; *U.S. Private*, pg. 850
Brogan, Pat, V.P.-Mktg. & Sls.--Elo TouchSystems, Inc., Fremont, CA; *U.S. Public*, pg. 1362
Broghammer, Mike, Mgr.-Mktg.--United Fire & Casualty Company, Cedar Rapids, IA; *U.S. Public*, pg. 1677
Brommeland, Olav, Mgr.-Mktg. & Sls.--SAS Park Royal Hotel, Lysaker, Norway; *Int'l*, pg. 1202
Brondi, Dennis, Dir.-Mktg.--Power-One, Inc., Camarillo, CA; *U.S. Private*, pg. 878
Broniman, Carol, Product Mgr.-Mktg.--Allen Telecom Inc., Solon, OH; *U.S. Public*, pg. 45
Bronner, Beth L., V.P.-Mktg.--Citicorp, New York, NY; *U.S. Public*, pg. 376
Brook, J.A., V.P.- Mktg. & Commun.--Alabama Electric Cooperative, Inc., Andalusia, AL; *U.S. Private*, pg. 30
Brook, Robert P., Sr. V.P.-Sls. & Mktg.--EBP Life Insurance Co., Minneapolis, MN; *U.S. Public*, pg. 635
Brookes, A. Stafford, Mktg. Mgr.--AlliedSignal Aerospace Service Corporation, Munich, Germany; *U.S. Public*, pg. 52
Brooklier, John, Dir.-Mktg.--Heller International, Chicago, IL; *U.S. Private*, pg. 520
Brookman, Marc J., V.P.--UAM Retirement Plan Services, Inc., New York, NY; *U.S. Public*, pg. 1674
Brooks, Craig L., V.P.-Prod. Mktg.--Amgen Inc., Thousand Oaks, CA; *U.S. Public*, pg. 100
Brooks, Gary, V.P.-Sls. & Mktg. & Mgr.-Graphics Prods.--Dunmore Corporation, Newtown, PA; *U.S. Private*, pg. 346
Brooks, George, V.P.-Mktg.--Trader Publishing Company, Norfolk, VA; *U.S. Private*, pg. 649
Brooks, Henry A., Dir.-Sls.--Lawter International, Inc., Kenosha, WI; *U.S. Public*, pg. 980
Brooks, Jeffrey, V.P.-Global Brand Mktg. & Communications--Digital Equipment Corporation, Maynard, MA; *U.S. Public*, pg. 507
Brooks, Joe, V.P.-Mktg.--Swingster Company, Kansas City, MO; *U.S. Private*, pg. 58
Brooks, Joeseph, V.P.-Mktg.--American Marketing Industries, Inc., Kansas City, MO; *U.S. Private*, pg. 58
Brooks, Kenneth, Mgr.-Mktg.--Preferred Utilities Manufacturing Corp., Danbury, CT; *U.S. Private*, pg. 881
Brooks, Kenneth, Dir.-Mktg.--Preferred Instruments, Danbury, CT; *U.S. Private*, pg. 881
Brooks, Lindsay H., Mgr.-Mktg.--Chattem (Canada) Inc., Mississauga, Canada; *U.S. Public*, pg. 342
Brooks, Steve, V.P.-Mktg.--Roy Anderson Corp., Gulfport, MS; *U.S. Private*, pg. 72
Brooks, TaJuana, Mgr.-Mktg. Svcs.--Carlisle Food Service Products, Oklahoma City, OK; *U.S. Public*, pg. 305
Brophy, Frank, Dir.-Mktg.--Gillette Canada Inc., Kirkland, Canada; *U.S. Public*, pg. 744
Brossard, Gerry, V.P.-Sls. & Mktg.--Laidlaw Environmental Services, Inc., Columbia, SC; *U.S. Public*, pg. 975
Broth, Tim, Dir.-Mktg. & Sls.--National Lamination Co., Des Plaines, IL; *U.S. Private*, pg. 1068
Brothers, Carl W., Sr. V.P.-Intl. Rice & Partnership--Riceland Foods, Inc., Stuttgart, AR; *U.S. Private*, pg. 928
Brothers, Jeff, Sr. V.P.-Mktg.--Raytheon Appliances, Ripon, WI; *U.S. Public*, pg. 1366
Broughton, George W., Exec. V.P.-Sls. & Mktg.--Broughton Foods Company, Marietta, OH; *U.S. Public*, pg. 259
Broughton, Reginald C., V.P.-Mktg.--ICL, Inc., Irvine, CA; *Int'l*, pg. 529
Brous, David, V.P.-Mktg.--JM Company, Hasbrouck Heights, NJ; *U.S. Private*, pg. 577
Brovo, Berto, Dir.-Mktg.--3M Do Brasil Ltda., Sao Paulo, Brazil; *U.S. Public*, pg. 1606
Brower, Mardyne, Mgr.-Pub. Rels.--Farmers State Bank, Liberty, IN; *U.S. Public*, pg. 633
Brower, Paul, V.P.-Mktg. & Bus. Devel.--West Texas Utilities Co., Abilene, TX; *U.S. Public*, pg. 324
Brown, Ada, Mktg. Mgr.--Clarion Cosmetics, Hunt Valley, MD; *U.S. Public*, pg. 1330
Brown, Anneliese, Mgr.-Intl. Mktg.--Armor All Products Group, Oakland, CA; *U.S. Public*, pg. 387
Brown, Arthur A., Dir.-Mktg., Plumbling, Heating & Air Conditioning--Noland Company, Newport News, VA; *U.S. Public*, pg. 1187
Brown, Barbara, V.P.-Mktg.--Sam's Clubs Div., Bentonville, AR; *U.S. Public*, pg. 1733
Brown, Barry L., V.P.-Sls. & Mktg.--Michigan Sugar Company, Saginaw, MI; *U.S. Public*, pg. 873
Brown, Beth, Sr. Mgr.-Mktg. Svcs.--Enterprises Media Group, Hawthorne, NY; *U.S. Public*, pg. 393
Brown, Bob, Exec. V.P.-Consumer Mkts. Prod./Midwest & Northeast Div.--Countrywide Home Loans Inc., Pasadena, CA; *U.S. Public*, pg. 452
Brown, Bob, V.P.-Sls. & Mktg.--Robertshaw Controls Company, Richmond, VA; *Int'l*, pg. 1243
Brown, C. Douglas, V.P.-Sls. & Mktg.--Intermet Corporation, Troy, MI; *U.S. Public*, pg. 894
Brown, Chris, Mgr.-Mktg.--Teleflex Marine, Limerick, PA; *U.S. Public*, pg. 1569
Brown, D.L., Mgr.-Sls.--HBD Industries, Inc., Bellefontaine, OH; *U.S. Private*, pg. 489
Brown, Danael J., V.P.-Mktg.--Rice Lake Weighing Systems, Rice Lake, WI; *U.S. Private*, pg. 927
Brown, Daniel, Sr. V.P.-Sls. & Mktg.--J.H. Heafner Co. Inc., Lincolnton, NC; *U.S. Private*, pg. 514
Brown, David, V.P.-Sls. & Mktg.--Cargill Detroit Corp., Clawson, MI; *U.S. Private*, pg. 210
Brown, Don, V.P.-Sls. & Mktg., Surgical Products--Mentor Urology, Inc., Santa Barbara, CA; *U.S. Public*, pg. 1086
Brown, Earl, Mgr.-Branch--GAI Consultants, Inc., Charleston, WV; *U.S. Private*, pg. 434
Brown, G. Robert, Sr. V.P.-Mktg. & Sls.--Deltak Inc., Plymouth, MN; *U.S. Public*, pg. 924
Brown, Gary, V.P.-Mktg. & Engrng.--Gould Instrument Systems, Inc., Valley View, OH; *U.S. Public*, pg. 1592
Brown, Gene, Exec. V.P.-Sls. & Mktg.--Groendyke Transports, Inc., Enid, OK; *U.S. Private*, pg. 483
Brown, Greg, V.P.-Mktg.--Automotive Moulding Company, Warren, MI; *U.S. Private*, pg. 485
Brown, Howard, Dir.-Sls. & Mktg.--Crown Prince, Inc. (CA), City of Industry, CA; *U.S. Private*, pg. 293
Brown, J.J., V.P.-OE Sls.--Abex Friction Products, Winchester, VA; *U.S. Public*, pg. 443
Brown, Jack, V.P.-Sls. & Mktg.--The Wm. Powell Company, Cincinnati, OH; *U.S. Private*, pg. 877
Brown, Jack V., Chief Mktg. Officer--Liberty National Life Insurance Co., Birmingham, AL; *U.S. Public*, pg. 1622
Brown, James, Dir.-Mktg.--Microsoft Press, Bellevue, WA; *U.S. Public*, pg. 1107
Brown, Jeffrey N., Exec. V.P.-Mktg.--Webster Financial Corporation, Waterbury, CT; *U.S. Public*, pg. 1751
Brown, Jody A., Dir.-Bus. Commun.--CACI International Inc, Arlington, VA; *U.S. Public*, pg. 272
Brown, John, Dir.-Mktg.--Campbell Hausfeld Division of Scott Fetzer, Harrison, OH; *U.S. Public*, pg. 217
Brown, John W., V.P.-Pub. Rels.--Arvin Industries, Inc., Columbus, IN; *U.S. Public*, pg. 136
Brown, Judy Simms, Mgr.-Mktg. Communications--Watlow Winona, Inc., Winona, MN; *U.S. Private*, pg. 1153
Brown, Karen, Dir.-Global Marketing--AAF-International, Louisville, KY; *U.S. Private*, pg. 3
Brown, Kathy, Dir.-Adv. & Mktg.--Williams Controls, Inc., Portland, OR; *U.S. Public*, pg. 1769
Brown, Laurie, V.P. & Dir.-Mktg. & Sls.--Farrar, Straus & Giroux, Inc., New York, NY; *Int'l*, pg. 1479
Brown, Le Rue, Dir.-Mktg.--York Wallcoverings Inc., York, PA; *U.S. Private*, pg. 1196
Brown, Loretta, Coord.-Mktg.--Boyer Candy Company Inc., Altoona, PA; *U.S. Private*, pg. 162
Brown, Lorne M., Dir.-Mktg.--Financial Life Assurance Co. of Canada, Etobicoke, Canada; *U.S. Public*, pg. 77
Brown, Lynn, V.P.-Sls. & Mktg.--Wells Aluminum Corp., Baltimore, MD; *U.S. Private*, pg. 1161
Brown, Lynn J., Dir.-Mktg.--Wachovia Bank of North Carolina, N.A., Winston Salem, NC; *U.S. Public*, pg. 1730
Brown, Maria, Mktg. Asst.--AT&T Wireless Services, Kirkland, WA; *U.S. Public*, pg. 11
Brown, Martin S., Exec. V.P.-Sls. & Mktg.--Foster Wheeler Environmental Corporation, Livingston, NJ; *U.S. Public*, pg. 677
Brown, Mike, Sr. V.P. & Asst. Oper.-Sls. & Mktg.--Alvey Systems, Inc, Saint Louis, MO; *U.S. Private*, pg. 47
Brown, Mimi, V.P.-Mktg. & Sls.--Denver Nuggets Limited Partnership, Denver, CO; *U.S. Public*, pg. 138
Brown, Morry, Mgr.-Sls., Mktg. & Customer Service--Northern Cable Holdings Ltd., Montreal, Canada; *Int'l*, pg. 241
Brown, Phillip L., V.P.-Sls. & Mktg.--Pandrol Jackson, Inc., Ludington, MI; *Int'l*, pg. 280
Brown, Renee C., Sr. V.P.-Adv., Sls. & Mktg.--Pro-Line Corporation, Dallas, TX; *U.S. Private*, pg. 887
Brown, Richard A., V.P.-Sls. & Mktg.--DMI, Inc., Goodfield, IL; *U.S. Private*, pg. 305
Brown, Ron, Dir.-Mktg.--Draper Texmaco, Inc., Spartanburg, SC; *U.S. Private*, pg. 342
Brown, Ruben, Mktg. Specialist--Crane Carrier Company, Tulsa, OK; *U.S. Private*, pg. 286
Brown, T.J., V.P.-Mktg. & Sls.--Alberox Corporation, New Bedford, MA; *Int'l*, pg. 893
Brown, Terry, V.P.-Sls. & Mktg.--Lindberg Corporation, Rosemont, IL; *U.S. Public*, pg. 999
Brown, Tom, Mgr.-Mktg.--Frick Company, Waynesboro, PA; *U.S. Public*, pg. 1788
Brown, William M., Jr., Dir.-Sls. & Mktg.--Bayou Steel Corporation, La Place, LA; *U.S. Public*, pg. 197
Browning, Lewis, Dir.-Mktg.--Ambac International Corp., Columbia, SC; *U.S. Private*, pg. 48
Brownrigg, Steve, Mgr.-Mktg.--SA-SO Company, Dallas, TX; *U.S. Private*, pg. 955
Brownstein, Hy, V.P.-Mktg.--Uniflex, Inc., Hicksville, NY; *U.S. Public*, pg. 1665
Broxterman, Bruce, Exec. V.P.--Richards Industries, Inc., Cincinnati, OH; *U.S. Private*, pg. 929
Broyles, Susan, Dir.-Brand Devel.--Price Pfister, Inc., Pacoima, CA; *U.S. Public*, pg. 234
Brua, Rick, V.P.-Sls. & Mktg.--Mile High Equipment Co., Denver, CO; *Int'l*, pg. 189
Bruce, Jim, V.P.-Sls. & Mktg.--Amrion Inc., Boulder, CO; *U.S. Public*, pg. 1767
Bruce, Mary C., Mgr.-Mktg. Services--Radiometer America Inc., Westlake, OH; *Int'l*, pg. 1083
Bruce, Rick, Mktg. Devel.--Puritan/Churchill Chemical Company, Atlanta, GA; *U.S. Private*, pg. 895
Bruchert, Bill, Dir.-Sls. & Mktg.--DeSoto Inc., Joliet, IL; *U.S. Public*, pg. 956
Bruck, M., Dir.-Mktg. & Pub. Rels.--ALZ N.V., Genk, Belgium; *Int'l*, pg. 79
Bruck, Rodney, V.P.-Individual Sls. & Mktg.--Standard Insurance Co., Portland, OR; *U.S. Private*, pg. 1031
Brugler, Stephanie, Dir.-Mktg.--McKesson Health Systems, San Francisco, CA; *U.S. Public*, pg. 1073
Bruha, Tammy, Coord.-Mktg.--CAIRE, Inc., Burnsville, MN; *U.S. Private*, pg. 751
Brum, Jeff, Dir.-Mktg.--Electrohome Ltd., Kitchener, Canada; *Int'l*, pg. 438
Brumm, Dan, Mktg. Mgr.--Triad Retail Hardlines & Lumber Div., Livermore, CA; *U.S. Private*, pg. 193
Bruneheim, Jan, Dir.-Mktg.--Trygg-Hansa, Stockholm, Sweden; *Int'l*, pg. 1425
Brunicardi, Pat, Mgr.-Mktg.--Cracker Barrel Old Country Store, Inc., Lebanon, TN; *U.S. Public*, pg. 455
Brunner, Vernon A., Exec. V.P.-Mktg.--Walgreen Co., Deerfield, IL; *U.S. Public*, pg. 1733
Bruno, John, Sr. V.P.-Sls. & Mktg.--Cagle's Inc., Atlanta, GA; *U.S. Public*, pg. 291
Brush, James, Exec. V.P.-Sls. & Mktg.--Sentry Group, Rochester, NY; *U.S. Private*, pg. 984
Brusher, Nancy C., Dir.-Mktg. Communications & Adv.--Stiles Corporation, Fort Lauderdale, FL; *U.S. Private*, pg. 1043
Bruskotter, Thomas, V.P.-Supply, Distribution & Mktg.--Gary-Williams Energy Corporation, Denver, CO; *U.S. Private*, pg. 440
Bryan, Gary G., V.P.-Sls. & Mktg.--Chroma Corporation, McHenry, IL; *U.S. Private*, pg. 238

Bryant, Bill, Mgr.-Mktg.--Sasol Solvents, Rosebank, South Africa; *Int'l*, pg. 1196
Bryant, Carleton F., III, Chief Oper. Officer, Exec. V.P., Treas. & Sec.--Westerbeke Corporation, Avon, MA; *U.S. Public*, pg. 1757
Bryant, Carlton, V.P.-Bus. Devel.--Aerolyte Passage Media Corporation, Seattle, WA; *U.S. Private*, pg. 60
Bryant, Frank, V.P.-Mktg.--In-Sink-Erator, Racine, WI; *U.S. Public*, pg. 573
Bryant, John, V.P.-Mktg./Memory Prods.--Atmel Corporation, San Jose, CA; *U.S. Public*, pg. 145
Bryant, Nancy, Mgr.-Mktg. Commun.--Aerolyte Systems, Washington, MO; *U.S. Private*, pg. 24
Bryant, Roy, Exec. V.P.-Sls. & Mktg.--Castleberry/Snow's Brands Inc., Augusta, GA; *U.S. Private*, pg. 219
Bryant, Stephen H., V.P.-Mktg. Svcs.--Connecticut Natural Gas Corporation, Hartford, CT; *U.S. Public*, pg. 285
Bryant, Stephen H., V.P.-Mktg. & Customer Rels.--Commonwealth Gas Co., Cambridge, MA; *U.S. Public*, pg. 415
Bryson, Garff, Sr. V.P.-Sls. & Mktg.--Tropical Sportswear International, Tampa, FL; *U.S. Private*, pg. 1105
Bryson, Polly, Sr. V.P.-Mktg.--Spaulding & Slye, Boston, MA; *U.S. Private*, pg. 1021
Buan, Tee May, Sr. Mgr.-Corp. Mktg.--Standard Chartered Bank Malaysia Berhad, Kuala Lumpur, Malaysia; *Int'l*, pg. 1295
Bucaco, Gina, Mgr.-Mktg.--Bostonian Shoe Co., Newton, MA; *Int'l*, pg. 297
Bucaille, Aliu, Mktg, Innovation & Technology--Lafarge Materiaux de Specialites, Montrouge, France; *Int'l*, pg. 789
Bucchi, Richard A., Sr. V.P.-Sls. & Mktg.--Moore Medical Corp., New Britain, CT; *U.S. Public*, pg. 1128
Bucci, David, Dir.-Mktg.--InterBold, Canton, OH; *U.S. Public*, *pg. 506*
Buccola, Tony, V.P.-Sls. & Mktg.--Cumberland Packing Corp., Brooklyn, NY; *U.S. Private*, pg. 295
Buch, R.H., V.P.-Mktg.--Barden Precision Bearings, Danbury, CT; *Int'l*, pg. 468
Buchelhofer, Robert, Dr., Dir.-Mktg. & Sls.--Volkswagen AG, Wolfsburg, Germany; *Int'l*, pg. 1473
Buchler, Bill, V.P.-MKtg.-Improvements & Safety Zone--Hanover Direct, Inc., Weehawken, NJ; *U.S. Public*, pg. 782
Buchna, John, Mgr.-Mktg.-Mech. Div.--Lord Corporation, Cary, NC; *U.S. Private*, pg. 675
Buchna, John J., Mgr.-Mktg. Comm.--Lord Corporation, Mechanical Products Division, Erie, PA; *U.S. Private*, pg. 676
Buck, David, Dir.-Adv. Sls.--The Phillies-A Limited Partnership, Philadelphia, PA; *U.S. Private*, pg. 861
Buck, G.A., Mgr.-Mktg.--ZF Great Britain Ltd., Nottingham, United Kingdom; *Int'l*, pg. 1522
Buckalter, Amy, V.P.-Sls. & Mktg., In-line Skates--K2 Corporation, Vashon, WA; *U.S. Public*, pg. 940
Buckingham, James, Dir.-Mktg.--Hydro-Mill Co., Chatsworth, CA; *U.S. Public*, pg. 1640
Buckland, Ross, Chief Exec. Officer--Unigate PLC, London, United Kingdom; *Int'l*, pg. 1433
Buckler, James M., Mgr.-Mktg.--Research Products Corporation, Madison, WI; *U.S. Private*, pg. 924
Buckler, Kit, Dir.-Mktg.-Concept--Sony Music Entertainment (UK) Limited, London, United Kingdom; *Int'l*, pg. 1284
Bucklew, Phyllis, Exec. V.P.-Consumer Mkts. Prod./ Southeast Div.--Countrywide Home Loans Inc., Pasadena, CA; *U.S. Public*, pg. 452
Buckley, Andrew, Mgr.-Mktg.--Yamaha Motor Corp., U.S.A., Cypress, CA; *Int'l*, pg. 1516
Buckley, James W., Dir.-Mktg.--A&W Restaurants, Inc., Livonia, MI; *U.S. Private*, pg. 1
Buckley, Mike, Sr. V.P.-Mktg.--American General Life & Accident Insurance Co., Nashville, TN; *U.S. Public*, pg. 76
Buckley, Mike, V.P.-Mktg.--Beverage America, Inc., Holland, MI; *U.S. Private*, pg. 141
Buckley, Mike, V.P.-Mktg.--Brooks Beverage Management, Inc., Columbus, OH; *U.S. Private*, pg. 142
Buckley, Paula, Coord.-Mktg.--Electron Corp., Littleton, CO; *U.S. Private*, pg. 370
Buckman, Phillip, Grp. Mgr.-Mktg. Services--Nestle U.K. Ltd., Croydon, United Kingdom; *Int'l*, pg. 922
Buczik, Christopher, Dir.-Mktg. Services--Bon Appetit Magazine, New York, NY; *U.S. Private*, pg. 20
Buczynski, Julie M., Mgr.-Mktg.--National Auto Credit Inc., Solon, OH; *U.S. Public*, pg. 1152
Budd, Karl, Dir.-Mktg.--National Tool & Manufacturing Company, Kenilworth, NJ; *U.S. Private*, pg. 787
Budd, Patti, Coord.-Mktg. Communications--Philips Automotive Electronics, Cheshire, CT; *Int'l*, pg. 1054
Buddig, Thomas R., V.P.-Sls. & Mktg.--Carl Buddig & Company, Homewood, IL; *U.S. Private*, pg. 178
Budgen, Donald, V.P.-Mktg.--Magnetic Analysis Corp., Mount Vernon, NY; *U.S. Private*, pg. 695
Buente, Robert, V.P.-Sls. & Mktg.--The Okonite Company, Ramsey, NJ; *U.S. Private*, pg. 813
Buente, Robert W., Mktg. & Sls.--The Okonite Company, Ramsey, NJ; *U.S. Private*, pg. 813
Buetow, Kathleen M., V.P.-Sls. & Mktg.--F.E. Myers, Ashland, OH; *U.S. Public*, pg. 1273
Buff, Alan, Dir.-Mktg. & Sls.--Reed & Barton Corporation, Taunton, MA; *U.S. Private*, pg. 916
Bugbee, David, Dir.-Automotive Prods.--Ark-Les Corporation, Stoughton, MA; *U.S. Private*, pg. 82
Buhl, Ralph, Mktg. Systems Analyst--Mason Shoe Mfg. Co., Chippewa Falls, WI; *U.S. Private*, pg. 712
Buhrdorf, Anne, Mgr.-Mktg.--Comare Products, Hialeah, FL; *U.S. Public*, pg. 1771
Bukovinsky, Edward F., Sr. V.P.-Mktg. & Tech. Services--Willis Corroon Corp. of Seattle, Seattle, WA; *Int'l*, pg. 1507
Bukowski, Gary, V.P.-Sls. & Mktg.--Key Industries, Inc., Fort Scott, KS; *U.S. Private*, pg. 618
Buler, David, Sr. V.P.-Mktg.--The Israel Electric Corporation Ltd., Haifa, Israel; *Int'l*, pg. 690
Bulger, Jill, Mgr.-Mktg. Services--Blimpie International, Inc., Atlanta, GA; *U.S. Public*, pg. 236
Bull, C. Marshall, V.P.-Mktg. Information Services Division--Integrated Marketing Services, Omaha, NE; *U.S. Public*, pg. 631
Bullard, Barbara, Mgr.-Mktg. Communications--Perfecseal Company, Philadelphia, PA; *U.S. Public*, pg. 210
Bullard, David, V.P.-Mktg.--Amerock Corporation, Rockford, IL; *U.S. Public*, pg. 1177
Buller, S.R., Mgr.-Intl. Mktg.--Dynacast International Limited, Alcester, United Kingdom; *Int'l*, pg. 299
Bullinger, Roy D., Sr. V.P.-Bus. Mngmnt. & Mktg.--Safety-Kleen Corp., Elgin, IL; *U.S. Public*, pg. 1425
Bullock, Gene, Mgr.-Mktg. Communications--Data Instruments, Inc., Acton, MA; *U.S. Private*, pg. 312
Bullock, Ron, V.P.-Mktg.--Fill-Rite Division, Fort Wayne, IN; *U.S. Private*, pg. 1110
Bunch, Nancy, Dir.-Sls.--Cavalier Corporation, Chattanooga, TN; *U.S. Private*, pg. 220
Bundy, Merlin, V.P.-Newsprint Sls. & Mktg.--Donohue Inc., Quebec, Canada; *Int'l*, pg. 1075
Bune, Ole, Mgr.-Mktg.--Esselte A/S, Frederiksberg, Denmark; *Int'l*, pg. 460
Bunn, Cindy, Sr. Mgr.-Mktg. & Pub. Rels.--Catalina Marketing Corporation, Saint Petersburg, FL; *U.S. Public*, *pg. 314*
Bunner, Hency, V.P.-Mktg. & Sls.--Louis Allis Company, Milwaukee, WI; *U.S. Private*, pg. 677
Bunworth, David, Dir.-Sls. & Mktg.--Aer Lingus, Dublin, Ireland; *Int'l*, pg. 28
Burbach, Lyle, Dir.-Intl. Mktg. & Sls.--Behlen Mfg. Co., Columbus, NE; *U.S. Private*, pg. 130
Burbage, C.T., V.P.-Bus. Devel. & Product Support--Lockheed Aeronautical Systems Company, Marietta, GA; *U.S. Public*, pg. 1007
Burbick, Ron L., V.P.-Mktg.--Schneller, Inc., Kent, OH; *U.S. Private*, pg. 971
Burchette, Emmy Lou, V.P.-Mktg.--Duke Energy Corporation, Charlotte, NC; *U.S. Public*, pg. 534
Burchman, Suzanne, Asst. V.P.-Adv. & Mktg. Support--Sanwa Bank California, Los Angeles, CA; *Int'l*, pg. 1189
Burckardt, Richard, Mgr.-Mktg. Svcs.--Gehl Company, West Bend, WI; *U.S. Public*, pg. 704
Burd, Carolyn, Mgr.-Mktg.--Experience In Software, Inc., Berkeley, CA; *U.S. Private*, pg. 388
Burfield, Bill, V.P.-Natl. Sls. & Mktg.--TTC Illinois Inc., Kankakee, IL; *U.S. Private*, pg. 1066
Burford, Helen, V.P.-Mktg. Communications--Celebrity Cruises, Inc., Miami, FL; *U.S. Public*, pg. 1410
Burger, John F., V.P.-Mktg., Personal Storage Grp.--Western Digital Corporation, Irvine, CA; *U.S. Public*, pg. 1758
Burgette, Dennis, Exec. V.P.-Sls. & Mktg.--Action Industries, Inc., Tupelo, MS; *U.S. Public*, pg. 688
Burgher, Rex, V.P.-Mktg.--Benderson Development Co., Inc., Buffalo, NY; *U.S. Private*, pg. 132
Burgman, William, V.P.-Mktg.--Standard Manifold Company, Inc., Chicago, IL; *U.S. Private*, pg. 1031
Burgoyne, Paul F., V.P.-Mktg.--Edward Don & Company, North Riverside, IL; *U.S. Private*, pg. 339
Burin, Ralph R., Mgr.-New Product Devel.--Amurol Confections Co., Yorkville, IL; *U.S. Public*, pg. 1781
Burke, David, Exec. V.P.-Sls. & Mktg.--B&G Foods, Inc., Roseland, NJ; *U.S. Private*, pg. 105
Burke, Donald B., Exec. V.P.-Mktg. & Sls.--Worthington Foods Inc., Worthington, OH; *U.S. Public*, pg. 1780
Burke, Donald R., V.P.-Mktg.--LePage's, Inc., Pittsburgh, PA; *U.S. Private*, pg. 598
Burke, Donna, Dir.-Mktg. Communications--Computer Network Technology Corporation, Minneapolis, MN; *U.S.* Public, pg. 421
Burke, George, Sr. V.P.-Mktg.--Globe Life And Accident Insurance Co., Oklahoma City, OK; *U.S. Public*, pg. 1622
Burke, Jim, Exec. V.P.- Sls. & Mktg.--Fox Television Stations Inc., Los Angeles, CA; *Int'l*, pg. 926
Burke, John, V.P.-Sls. & Mktg.--Trek Bicycle Corporation, Waterloo, WI; *U.S. Private*, pg. 1099
Burke, John D., Chief Mktg. Officer & Exec. V.P.--Plasti-Line, Inc., Knoxville, TN; *U.S. Public*, pg. 1308
Burke, Lisa, Dir.-Mktg.--Elida Faberge (Ireland) Ltd., Dublin, Ireland; *Int'l*, pg. 1437
Burke, Marie, Admin. Asst.-Mktg.--Shoney's, Inc., Nashville, TN; *U.S. Public*, pg. 1467
Burke, Michael, Mktg. Coord.--Flambeau Products Corp., Middlefield, OH; *U.S. Private*, pg. 409
Burke, Mike, V.P.-Mktg.--Sea Ray, Knoxville, TN; *U.S. Public*, pg. 266
Burke, Nancy, Mgr.-Mktg. & Communications--Hubbell Lighting Inc., Christiansburg, VA; *U.S. Public*, pg. 844
Burke, Robert P., Sr. V.P.-Mktg.--Luby's Cafeterias, Inc., San Antonio, TX; *U.S. Public*, pg. 1017
Burke, Sharon L., Pub. Rels. & Mktg. Officer--United Missouri Bank of Monett, Monett, MO; *U.S. Public*, pg. 1655
Burke, Skip, V.P.-Special Mkts.--Aladdin Synergetics, Inc., Nashville, TN; *U.S. Private*, pg. 31
Burke, Therese, Sr. V.P.-Sls. & Mktg. Devel.--HarperCollins Publishers, New York, NY; *Int'l*, pg. 926
Burke, Thomas, Dir.-Commercial Sls. & Mktg.--Waring Products, New Hartford, CT; *U.S. Public*, pg. 286
Burke, Tom, V.P.-Mktg.--Discovery Networks, Inc., Bethesda, MD; *U.S. Private*, pg. 334
Burkehart, Byron C., Sr. V.P.-Grp. Mktg.--Jefferson-Pilot Life Insurance Co., Greensboro, NC; *U.S. Public*, pg. 926
Burkett, Cynthia, Mktg. Strategist--GS Electric, Carlisle, PA; *U.S. Public*, pg. 726
Burkett, Walter, V.P.-Mktg.--The PBS&J Corporation, Miami, FL; *U.S. Private*, pg. 825
Burkhalter, Charles, Dir.-Mktg.--Salant Corporation, New York, NY; *U.S. Public*, pg. 1429
Burkhardt, Steve, V.P.-Mktg.--Eveready Battery Co., Saint Louis, MO; *U.S. Public*, pg. 1360
Burkhart, Jay, V.P.-Mktg.--Monroe Auto Equipment Co., Monroe, MI; *U.S. Public*, pg. 1577
Burkhart, Jay, V.P.-Mktg.--Walker Manufacturing Co., Deerfield, IL; *U.S. Public*, pg. 1578
Burkill, Terry, Asst. Dir.-Mktg.--Rogers, Lunt & Bowlen Co., Greenfield, MA; *U.S. Private*, pg. 939
Burks, Alan, Sr. V.P.-Mktg.--Haggar Corporation, Dallas, TX; *U.S. Public*, pg. 774
Burlingame, Keith, Mgr.-Sls. Admin. & Mktg.--Easco Inc., Girard, OH; *U.S. Public*, pg. 548
Burmeister, Hans, Dir.-Mktg.--Sodra Cell AB, Vaxjo, Sweden; *Int'l*, pg. 1275
Burmester, Klaus, Mgr.-Sls. & Mktg.--Hermal Kurt Herrmann & Co., Reinbek, Germany; *Int'l*, pg. 616
Burnett, Bruce, Dir.-Mktg.--Trebor Bassett Ltd., Maple Cross, United Kingdom; *Int'l*, pg. 248
Burnett, Jeff, Mgr.-Mktg. Services--The Vernon Company, Newton, IA; *U.S. Private*, pg. 1137
Burnett, W.G., V.P.-Mktg. Svcs.--Kansas City Life Insurance Co., Kansas City, MO; *U.S. Public*, pg. 942
Burnett, William, Mgr.-Mktg.--Wichita Cessna Learning Center, Wichita, KS; *U.S. Public*, pg. 219
Burnette, H.L., Dir.-Prod. Support--Lockheed Aeronautical Systems Company, Marietta, GA; *U.S. Public*, pg. 1007
Burnham, Chip, V.P.-Mktg.--Flow International Corporation, Kent, WA; *U.S. Public*, pg. 656
Burns, Charles, Sr. V.P.-Adv.--Minyard Food Stores, Inc., Coppell, TX; *U.S. Private*, pg. 752
Burns, Jennifer, Dir.-Domestic Mktg.--Hanna-Barbera Productions, Inc., Hollywood, CA; *U.S. Public*, pg. 1614
Burns, Larry, V.P.-Sales & Mktg.--Vitamilk Dairy, Inc., Seattle, WA; *U.S. Private*, pg. 1142
Burns, Pat, V.P.-Mktg. & Domestic Sls.--Pinnacle Systems, Inc., Mountain View, CA; *U.S. Public*, pg. 1297
Burns, Ralph, Mgr.-Mktg.--Victaulic Company of America, Easton, PA; *U.S. Private*, pg. 1138
Burns, Robert D., V.P.-Sls. & Mktg.--Conway Import Co. Inc., Elmsford, NY; *U.S. Private*, pg. 272
Burns, William, V.P.-Sls. & Mktg.--Coronet/MTI, Saint Louis, MO; *U.S. Private*, pg. 863
Burns, William, V.P.-Sls. & Mktg.--BFA Educational Media, Saint Louis, MO; *U.S. Private*, pg. 863
Burns, William, V.P.-Sls. & Mktg.--Phoenix Films & Video, Saint Louis, MO; *U.S. Private*, pg. 863
Burns, William, Dir.-Mktg.--F. Hoffmann-La Roche Ltd., Basel, Switzerland; *Int'l*, pg. 1119
Burr, David T., Mgr.-Mktg.--Interlake Material Handling Div., Naperville, IL; *U.S. Public*, pg. 893
Burridge, Jeffrey, V.P.-Sls. & Mktg.--Surgical Specialties, Reading, PA; *U.S. Private*, pg. 1056
Burrington, Harry, Dir.-Mktg.--Southwestern Energy Company, Fayetteville, AR; *U.S. Public*, pg. 1494
Burroughs, Michael, Exec. V.P.-Mktg.--Cragar Industries, Inc., Phoenix, AZ; *U.S. Public*, pg. 456
Burrows, Stephen J., V.P.-Intl. Mktg.--Anheuser-Busch Companies, Inc., Saint Louis, MO; *U.S. Public*, pg. 113
Burrows, Thomas, V.P.-Mktg. & Sls.--Griffith Laboratories Worldwide, Inc., Alsip, IL; *U.S. Private*, pg. 481
Bursh, Thomas, Mgr.-Sls. & Mktg.--Acme Design Technology, Co., Crozet, VA; *U.S. Private*, pg. 13
Burstein, Arnold, V.P.-Intl. Sls. & Mktg.--Inverness Corp., Fair Lawn, NJ; *U.S. Private*, pg. 574
Burstein, Arnold, V.P.-Sls. & Mktg--ERI Laboratories, Fair Lawn, NJ; *U.S. Private*, pg. 574
Burstein, Baruch, Deputy Gen. Mgr.-Mktg.--El Al Israel Airlines, Ltd., New York, NY; *Int'l*, pg. 435
Burt, A.J., Mgr.-Mktg. Communications--ABB Kent-Taylor Ltd., Huntingdon, United Kingdom; *Int'l*, pg. 7
Burtch, George, Dir.-Mktg. Svcs.--Milton Bradley Company, East Longmeadow, MA; *U.S. Public*, pg. 797
Burth, Willy, Div. Mgr.-Food Mktg.--Migros, Zurich, Switzerland; *Int'l*, pg. 865
Burton, Chuck, Dir.-Adv. & Mktg.--Tandy Corporation, Fort Worth, TX; *U.S. Public*, pg. 1560
Burton, A. Tracy, V.P.-Mktg.--Advantage Companies, Inc., Wichita, KS; *U.S. Private*, pg. 22
Burton, Bonnie, V.P.-Mktg. & Adv.--Kay-Bee Toy & Hobby Shops, Inc., Pittsfield, MA; *U.S. Public*, pg. 437
Burton, Doug, Sr. V.P.-Mktg.--Westlake Hardware, Inc., Lenexa, KS; *U.S. Private*, pg. 1169
Burton, R., Mgr.-Mktg.--Servo Corporation of America, Westbury, NY; *U.S. Private*, pg. 987
Burton, Warren, V.P.-Mktg. & Pur.--Multifoods Specialty Distribution Inc., Denver, CO; *U.S. Public*, pg. 901
Burzynski, Mike, Dir.-Pur.--The Scotts Company, Marysville, OH; *U.S. Public*, pg. 1446
Busch, August A., III, Chm. Bd. & Pres. & V.P.-Mktg.--Anheuser-Busch Companies, Inc., Saint Louis, MO; *U.S. Public*, pg. 113
Busch, Guy, V.P.-Sls. & Mktg.--Chem-Trend Incorporated, Howell, MI; *Int'l*, pg. 235
Busch, Madeline S., Dir.-Mktg.--Trustco Bank, N.A., Schenectady, NY; *U.S. Public*, pg. 1643
Buschinelli, Flavio, Mgr.-Mktg.--TI Brazil Industria E Comerico Ltda., Sao Jose dos Campos, Brazil; *Int'l*, pg. 1342
Buschmann, Martin, Dir.-Mktg. & Sls.--GESTRA GmbH, Bremen, Germany; *Int'l*, pg. 549
Bush, Al, Dir.-Mktg.--H.B. Fuller Company, Saint Paul, MN; *U.S. Public*, pg. 686
Bush, David L., V.P.-Mktg.--Ambar, Inc., Lafayette, LA; *U.S. Private*, pg. 126
Bush, Douglas, V.P.-Mdsg.--Bush Industries Inc., Jamestown, NY; *U.S. Public*, pg. 270
Bush, Howard J., V.P.-Mktg. & Sls.--Brenco, Inc., Petersburg, VA; *U.S. Public*, pg. 1710
Bush, James, V.P.-Sls. & Mktg.--The Holland Hitch Company, Holland, MI; *U.S. Private*, pg. 534
Bush, Ken, Dir.-Mktg.--Industrial Towel & Uniform, New Berlin, WI; *U.S. Private*, pg. 561
Bush, Roger, Mktg. Dir.--Commercial Union Life Assurance Company of Canada, Scarborough, Canada; *Int'l*, pg. 308

Bushey, A. Scott, Exec. V.P.-Strategic Plng.--USLIFE Corporation, New York, NY; *U.S. Public*, pg. 77
Bushor, Ed, Dir.-Mktg.--McConnell Cabinets, Inc., El Monte, CA; *U.S. Private*, pg. 720
Bushor, Ed, Dir.-Mktg.--Coastal Wood Products, Inc., City of Industry, CA; *U.S. Private*, pg. 720
Busse, Robert L., V.P.-Sls.--Heatilator Inc., Mount Pleasant, IA; *U.S. Public*, pg. 772
Bussone, Frank, V.P.-Mktg.--Trend-Lines Inc., Revere, MA; *U.S. Private*, pg. 1099
Butch, Melissa, Mgr.-Pub. Rels.--Arizona Instrument Corporation, Phoenix, AZ; *U.S. Public*, pg. 129
Butcher, Charles, Mgr.-Market Res.--Scottish Widows' Fund & Life Assurance Society, Edinburgh, United Kingdom; *Int'l*, pg. 1212
Butcher, Mike, Dir.-Mktg. Commun.--The Dow Chemical Company, Midland, MI; *U.S. Public*, pg. 522
Butensky, Martin, Dir.-Mktg.--Vernitron Sensor Systems, Saint Petersburg, FL; *U.S. Public*, pg. 157
Butler, J., Mgr.-Mktg.--Weyburn Bartel, Inc., Grand Haven, MI; *Int'l*, pg. 1334
Butler, James R., V.P. Mktg.--Alza Corporation, Palo Alto, CA; *U.S. Public*, pg. 62
Butler, Jane, V.P.-Mktg.--Panel Publishers, Inc., New York, NY; *Int'l*, pg. 1513
Butler, Jane, V.P.-Mktg.--Aspen Publishers, Inc., Gaithersburg, MD; *Int'l*, pg. 1513
Butler, Jean, V.P.-Mktg.--Yorktowne, Inc., Red Lion, PA; *U.S. Private*, pg. 1196
Butler, K.H., Dir.-Mktg. Communications--Columbus McKinnon Corp., Amherst, NY; *U.S. Public*, pg. 405
Butler, LuAnn, V.P.-Sls. & Mktg.--Kaufman and Broad Home Corporation, Los Angeles, CA; *U.S. Public*, pg. 944
Butler, LuAnn, V.P.-Sls. & Mktg.--Kaufman and Broad of Texas, Ltd., San Antonio, TX; *U.S. Public*, pg. 945
Butler, Mark R., V.P.-Special Projects-Mktg.--The Franklin Life Insurance Company, Springfield, IL; *U.S. Public*, pg. 76
Butler, Marty, V.P.-Mktg.--Partridge Meats, Inc., Cincinnati, OH; *U.S. Public*, pg. 75
Butler, Marty W., V.P.-Mktg.--John Morrell & Co., Cincinnati, OH; *U.S. Public*, pg. 1479
Butler, Norman D., V.P.-Sls. & Mktg., Service Parts Div.--Foley-PLP Company, Rochester, NY; *U.S. Private*, pg. 416
Butler, Oliver, V.P.-Mktg. & Sls.,Pharmaceutical--Wyeth-Ayerst Laboratories, Inc., Philadelphia, PA; *U.S. Public*, pg. 80
Butler, Patricia, Mgr.-Trade Shows--Bell Helicopter Textron, Hurst, TX; *U.S. Public*, pg. 1588
Butler, Ronald H., Exec. V.P.-Mktg.--PETsMART, Inc., Phoenix, AZ; *U.S. Public*, pg. 1281
Butler, Tom, Mgr.-Mktg.--National Cabinet Lock, Inc., Mauldin, SC; *U.S. Private*, pg. 270
Butler, Van H., Sr. V.P.-Mktg. & Div. Mdse. Mgr.--Toys "R" Us United States, Paramus, NJ; *U.S. Public*, pg. 1626
Buto, T.J., V.P.-Mktg.--Carbon Products Operation Inc., East Stroudsburg, PA; *Int'l*, pg. 891
Butt, Jan, Mgr.-Mktg. Communications--Dow Corning Corporation, Midland, MI; *U.S. Public*, pg. 523
Butta, Philip, V.P.-Devel. Prod.--Ariel Corporation, Mount Vernon, OH; *U.S. Private*, pg. 81
Butterfield, Mindi, V.P.-Mktg.--Sybase, Inc., Emeryville, CA; *U.S. Public*, pg. 1544
Butters, Norm, Sr. V.P.-Sls. & Mktg.--Norpac Foods, Inc., Stayton, OR; *U.S. Private*, pg. 802
Button, Brian T., V.P.-Mktg. & Sls.--Proxim, Inc., Mountain View, CA; *U.S. Public*, pg. 1338
Buxton, Max, Mgr.-Intl. Mktg.-Timber & Wood Prods.--Boise Cascade Corporation, Boise, ID; *U.S. Public*, pg. 242
Buyko, John, V.P.-Sls. & Mktg.--Aeroflex Incorporated, Plainview, NY; *U.S. Public*, pg. 23
Buyko, John, V.P.-Mktg.-Microelectronics--Aeroflex Laboratories Inc., Plainview, NY; *U.S. Public*, pg. 24
Buzolin, L. F., Mgr.-Mktg.--Freios Varga S/A, Limeira, Brazil; *Int'l*, pg. 820
Buzzard, James A., V.P.-Fine Paper Sls. & Mktg.--Westvaco Corporation, New York, NY; *U.S. Public*, pg. 1762
Buzzard, James A., V.P. & Mgr.-Div. Sls. & Mktg.--Westvaco Corporation-Fine Papers Div., Richmond, VA; *U.S. Public*, pg. 1762
Bye, Conrad, Dir.-Fin.--Dynamic Homes, Inc., Detroit Lakes, MN; *U.S. Public*, pg. 538
Bye, Laro Erik, Mgr.-Mktg.--Helly-Hansen Distributie B.V., Sittard, Netherlands; *Int'l*, pg. 1010
Bye, Salley, Dir.-Fuel Mktg.--Mobil Oil Company, Ltd., Milton Keynes, United Kingdom; *U.S. Public*, pg. 1119
Byerlein, Julie, Sr. V.P.-Mktg.--Mrs. Fields' Original Cookies, Inc., Salt Lake City, UT; *U.S. Private*, pg. 688
Byerly, Ron, V.P.-Training, Mktg. & Adv.--O'Reilly Automotive Inc., Springfield, MO; *U.S. Public*, pg. 1230
Byers, Joseph M., V.P.-Sls. & Mktg.--Easco Inc., Girard, OH; *U.S. Public*, pg. 548
Byers, Ronald L., V.P.-Land Mktg.--Pope Resources, Poulsbo, WA; *U.S. Public*, pg. 1317
Byington, Steven C., V.P. & Dir.-Mktg./Mktg. Res.--Community Bank N.A., De Witt, NY; *U.S. Public*, pg. 416
Bykerk, Larry, V.P.-Sls.--Apollo Colors Inc., Northbrook, IL; *U.S. Private*, pg. 77
Byrd, Andy, European Bus. Devel. Dir.--DMB&B/London, London, United Kingdom; *U.S. Private*, pg. 304
Byrd, Vincent C., V.P. & Gen. Mgr.-Consumer Mkt.--J.M. Smucker Company, Orrville, OH; *U.S. Public*, pg. 1480
Byrne, Chris, V.P. & Gen. Mgr.--NHT, Benicia, CA; *U.S. Public*, pg. 1369
Byrne, Joseph J., V.P.-Sls. & Mktg.--Mead Specialty Paper, South Lee, MA; *U.S. Public*, pg. 1074
Byrne, Paul, V.P.-Sls. & Mktg.--Precor, Inc., Bothell, WA; *U.S. Public*, pg. 1322
Byrnes, Ralph R., Sr. V.P.-Automotive Resource Dir.--Consumers Financial Corporation, Camp Hill, PA; *U.S. Public*, pg. 437
Byrnes, Terrence J., V.P.-Sls. & Mktg.--Enerfab Inc., Cincinnati, OH; *U.S. Private*, pg. 376
Byrom, Gary, Mgr.-Sls. & Mktg./U.K. & Ireland--Dexter Specialty Materials, Ltd., Twickenham, United Kingdom; *U.S. Public*, pg. 505
Byron, Jill C., Principal Area Leader-Corp. Branding & Customer--DTE Energy Company, Detroit, MI; *U.S. Public*, pg. 475
Caballero, Theresa, Exec. V.P.-Mktg. & Promo.--Puerto Rico Tourism Company, San Juan, PR; *U.S. Private*, pg. 894
Cable, Susan B., Dir.-Mktg.--Inter-Tel, Incorporated, Phoenix, AZ; *U.S. Public*, pg. 888
Cables, Robert A., Dir.-Mktg.--Yankee Energy System, Inc., Meriden, CT; *U.S. Public*, pg. 1787
Cadbury, Nick, Dir.-Mktg./PC World--Dixons Group plc, Hemel Hempstead, United Kingdom,; *Int'l*, pg. 413
Caddock, Richard E. Jr., V.P.-Engrng. & Mktg.--Caddock Electronics, Inc., Riverside, CA; *U.S. Private*, pg. 198
Caddoo, Gary, V.P.-Mktg.--NationsCredit Commercial Corporation, Cleveland, OH; *U.S. Public*, pg. 1165
Cadena, Jeanette, Mgr.-Mktg.--Earl Construction Company, West Sacramento, CA; *U.S. Private*, pg. 1051
Caffiero, Nancy, V.P.-Mktg.--Aesculap, Inc., South San Francisco, CA; *Int'l*, pg. 29
Caffrey, C. J., Gen. Mgr.-Mktg.--BHP Petroleum, Melbourne, Australia; *Int'l*, pg. 224
Cager, Steven, Mgr.-Mktg.--Goodyear Jamaica Limited, Kingston, Jamaica; *U.S. Public*, pg. 753
Caglioti, Rosemarie, Mgr.-Mktg. & Promo.--Geyer-McAllister Publications, Inc., New York, NY; *U.S. Private*, pg. 450
Cagney, Marilyn, Dir.-Mktg.--Del Amo Hospital, Torrance, CA; *U.S. Public*, pg. 1697
Cain, Kenneth, V.P.-Mktg.--Branch Group Inc., Upper Marlboro, MD; *U.S. Private*, pg. 165
Cainas, Elana, Dir.-Mktg.--Memphis Publishing Co., Memphis, TN; *U.S. Public*, pg. 1448
Caine, Linda, Dir.-Sls. & Mktg.--Walden Book Company, Ann Arbor, MI; *U.S. Public*, pg. 245
Calabria, A., V.P.-Commercial--Sulzer Bingham Pumps Inc., Portland, OR; *Int'l*, pg. 1305
Calabro, Brian, V.P.-Forms Sls. & Mktg.--The Standard Register Company, Dayton, OH; *U.S. Public*, pg. 1505
Calaguire, Frank, V.P.-Mktg. Mngmt.--Renaissance International Hotels, Cleveland, OH; *U.S. Public*, pg. 1048
Calahan, Katie, Dir.-Mktg.--Country Home Bakery, Inc., Bridgeport, CT; *U.S. Private*, pg. 278
Calarco, Michelle, Mgr.-Category-Special Mkts.--Comstock Michigan Fruit, Rochester, NY; *U.S. Private*, pg. 887
Calautti, Barbara, Mktg. Dir.--Town & Country Corporation, Chelsea, MA; *U.S. Public*, pg. 1625
Caldarone, Bob, Dir.-Mktg.--Cruise America, Inc., Mesa, AZ; *U.S. Private*, pg. 178
Calderin, Roberto, Sr. V.P. & Field Mktg. Dir.--DMB&B New York, New York, NY; *U.S. Private*, pg. 302
Caldwell, Peggy K., Sr. V.P.-Mktg.--Tech Data Corporation, Clearwater, FL; *U.S. Public*, pg. 1562
Caldwell, Tom, Mgr.-Mktg.--Setco, Cincinnati, OH; *U.S. Private*, pg. 987
Calhoon, Donald, Sr. V.P.-Corp. Mktg.--Wendy's International Inc., Dublin, OH; *U.S. Public*, pg. 1754
Calhoun, Leann, Coord.-Media & Mktg. Services--Radisson Hotel Corporation, Minneapolis, MN; *U.S. Private*, pg. 212
Cali, Karen, Mgr.-Mktg.--Ranir Corporation/DCP, Grand Rapids, MI; *U.S. Private*, pg. 909
Caliri, Rich, Sr. V.P.-Mktg.--Envoy Corporation, Nashville, TN; *U.S. Public*, pg. 587
Calise, Paula, Dir.-Mktg.--InteCom, Dallas, TX; *Int'l*, pg. 794
Calkins, Brad, V.P. & Dir.-Mktg.--Rochester Midland Corporation, Rochester, NY; *U.S. Private*, pg. 937
Calkins, Paul, Dir.-Mktg.--Cracker Barrel Old Country Store, Inc., Lebanon, TN; *U.S. Public*, pg. 455
Call, James L., II, Sr. V.P.-Mktg.--Financial Protection Marketing Inc., Indianapolis, IN; *U.S. Public*, pg. 1336
Callahan, Bob, Sr. V.P.-Sls., Mktg. & Oper.--U.S. Tsubaki, Inc., Wheeling, IL; *Int'l*, pg. 1425
Callahan, K.J., Dir.-Mktg. Programs--WESCO Distribution, Inc., Pittsburgh, PA; *U.S. Private*, pg. 244
Callahan, Mike, Dir.-Product Mktg.--Attachmate, Bellevue, WA; *U.S. Private*, pg. 98
Callahan, Neil, Dir.-Mktg. & Flavor Sls.--Robertet Flavors, South Plainfield, NJ; *Int'l*, pg. 1119
Callahan, Richard D., Sr. Exec. V.P.-Opers. & Mktg. Svcs.--HSBC Americas, Buffalo, NY; *Int'l*, pg. 580
Callahan, Sheila, Mgr.-Mktg.--Instinet Corporation, New York, NY; *Int'l*, pg. 1106
Callahan, Stacey, Mgr.-Contract Mktg.--H.B. Ives, Wallingford, CT; *U.S. Private*, pg. 506
Calleja, Carmen Lopez, Dir.-Mktg.--Iberia Air Lines of Spain, Miami, FL; *Int'l*, pg. 575
Callejon, Donna M., Sr. V.P.-Mktg.--Federal National Mortgage Association (Fannie Mae), Washington, DC; *U.S. Public*, pg. 615
Calmeyer, John, V.P.-Mktg. & Pub. Rels.--Callaway Vineyard & Winery, Temecula, CA; *Int'l*, pg. 63
Caltabiano, Joe, Dir.-Sls. & Mktg.--Camillus Cutlery Co., Camillus, NY; *U.S. Private*, pg. 203
Calthorpe, William A., V.P.-Sls., Adv. & Mktg.--Weeks Dairy Foods, Inc., Concord, NH; *Int'l*, pg. 752
Calton, John, Dir.-Mktg. Communications--Owens Corning/Foamular, Parsippany, NJ; *U.S. Public*, pg. 1237
Caltron, Steve, V.P.-Mktg. & Sls.--Kansas City Power & Light Company, Kansas City, MO; *U.S. Public*, pg. 943
Caluori, Peter, V.P.-Mktg. & Advertising--Liechtenstein Global Trust Limited, Vaduz, Liechtenstein; *Int'l*, pg. 809
Calvert, Mona, Mgr.-Mktg.--CIS Technologies, Inc., Tulsa, OK; *U.S. Public*, pg. 1155
Calvert, Nancy, Dir.-Mktg. Communications--Shure Brothers Incorporated, Evanston, IL; *U.S. Private*, pg. 997
Calvo, Jesus R., Mng. Dir.-Distribution & Customer--Iberdrola, S.A., Bilbao, Spain; *Int'l*, pg. 657
Camacho, Tony, Dir.-Mktg.--Air UK Ltd., Stansted, United Kingdom; *Int'l*, pg. 38
Camara, Paul, Exec. V.P.-Creative, Sls. & Mktg.--TMP Worldwide, Inc., New York, NY; *U.S. Private*, pg. 1064
Camas, Walter, Dir.-Mktg.--Precision Valve Corporation, Yonkers, NY; *U.S. Private*, pg. 880
Cambournac, Gilles, V.P.-Sls. & Mktg.--SEITA, Societe Nationale D'Exploitation Industrielle des Tabacs et des Allumettes, Paris, France; *Int'l*, pg. 1219
Camden, Carl, Exec. V.P.-Mktg., Sls. & Pub. Rels.--Kelly Services, Inc., Troy, MI; *U.S. Public*, pg. 949
Camerata, Joe, V.P.-Sls. & Mktg.--Atlas Copco Wagner Inc., Portland, OR; *Int'l*, pg. 96
Cameron, Russell, Dir.-Mktg.--Malaysian Tobacco Co./B.A.T. Indust., Kuala Lumpur, Malaysia; *Int'l*, pg. 111
Camille, Gerard, Dir.-Devel. & Mktg.--Credit Mutuel, Paris, France; *Int'l*, pg. 344
Camp, Andrew, Mgr.-Grp. MKtg.--Calor Group plc, Warwick, United Kingdom; *Int'l*, pg. 1155
Camp, Chuck, Dir.-Mktg.--Lake Region Manufacturing, Inc., Chaska, MN; *U.S. Private*, pg. 643
Campagna, Curt, Dir.-Mktg.--Lawson Products, Inc., Des Plaines, IL; *U.S. Public*, pg. 980
Campagna, Fred, V.P.-Intl. Sls. & Mktg.--Aerco International Inc., Northvale, NJ; *U.S. Private*, pg. 23
Campbell, A.A., Sr. V.P.-Sls. & Mktg.--Celotex Corporation, Tampa, FL; *U.S. Private*, pg. 221
Campbell, Bill, Sr. V.P.-Mktg.--United Farm Family Life Insurance Co., Indianapolis, IN; *U.S. Private*, pg. 1122
Campbell, Chris, V.P.-Mktg.--Tyco Toys, Inc., Mount Laurel, NJ; *U.S. Public*, pg. 1058
Campbell, Donald, V.P.-Mktg.--Ross Systems, Inc., Atlanta, GA; *U.S. Public*, pg. 1406
Campbell, Earl, Mgr.-Market Rep.--American Honda Motor Co., Inc. Automobile Sales Division, Torrance, CA; *Int'l*, pg. 634
Campbell, Joe, Mgr.-Mktg.--Sunny Fresh Foods, Monticello, MN; *U.S. Private*, pg. 210
Campbell, Linda, Sr. Mktg. Specialist-Western Div.--Southwestern Life Insurance Company, Dallas, TX; *U.S. Private*, pg. 1018
Campbell, Melba, V.P.-Bus. Devel. & Dir.-Mktg.--Washington Gas Light Co., Springfield, VA; *U.S. Public*, pg. 1740
Campbell, Nick, Sr. V.P.-Mktg.--The Penn Traffic Company, Syracuse, NY; *U.S. Public*, pg. 1270
Campbell, Reg, Dir.-Mktg. & Sls.--Kasle Steel Corporation, Dearborn, MI; *U.S. Private*, pg. 608
Campbell, Richard, Exec. V.P. & Mktg.--Lally, McFarland & Pantello Inc., New York, NY; *Int'l*, pg. 601
Campbell, Robin W., Mgr.-Mktg. Svcs. & Adv.--Stanley Furniture Co. Inc., Stanleytown, VA; *U.S. Public*, pg. 1508
Campbell, Scott, V.P.-Sls. & Mktg.--Microdot/Recoil, Placentia, CA; *U.S. Public*, pg. 940
Campbell, William H., Mgr.-Mktg.--A & B Development Co. (California), Honolulu, HI; *U.S. Public*, pg. 39
Campeau, Cliff, Sr. V.P.-Mktg.--Venture Stores, Inc., O Fallon, MO; *U.S. Public*, pg. 1716
Canac, Claude, Mktg. & Adv.--C.M.C. SA, Saint Quentin-en-Yvelines, France; *Int'l*, pg. 792
Candito, Peter, Sr. Dir.-Mktg. & Mgr.-DMS--CMP Media, Inc., Manhasset, NY; *U.S. Public*, pg. 279
Candray, Jean, Coord.-Mktg.--SGS U.S. Testing Company, Inc., Fairfield, NJ; *Int'l*, pg. 1153
Canegraei, Eino, Mgr.-Mktg.--Hewlett-Packard Italiana S.p.A., Milan, Italy; *U.S. Public*, pg. 820
Canepa, Christine, Mgr.-Mktg.--Scripto-Tokai Corp., Fontana, CA; *U.S. Private*, pg. 977
Cangas, Luis, Mgr.-Mkgt--McDonald's Sistemas de Espana, Madrid, Spain; *U.S. Public*, pg. 1069
Canning, Lynn, Dir.-Media--Buena Vista Home Video, Burbank, CA; *U.S. Public*, pg. 513
Canning, Marilyn, Sr. Dir.-Mktg.--Martindale-Hubbell, New Providence, NJ; *Int'l*, pg. 1096
Canning, Tim, V.P.-Mktg. & Adv.--Premier, Inc., Greenwich, CT; *U.S. Private*, pg. 647
Cannon, Marv, Dir.-Mktg., Bus. Plng. & Sls.--Delphi Packard Electric Systems, Beachwood, OH; *U.S. Public*, pg. 719
Cannon, Paul, V.P.-Buffalo Mktg.--Cannon, Grand Island, NY; *U.S. Private*, pg. 205
Cannon, Roger F., Exec. V.P.-Sls. & Mktg.--Lawson Products, Inc., Des Plaines, IL; *U.S. Public*, pg. 980
Cannon, Woodrow B., V.P.-Mktg.--BellSouth Communication Systems, Inc., Roanoke, VA; *U.S. Public*, pg. 209
Canny, Yolanda, Sr. V.P.-Global Mktg.--Pilkington Barnes Hind (PBH), San Diego, CA; *U.S. Private*, pg. 111
Canonaco, Laura, Dir.-Mktg.--Hinckley & Schmitt, Inc., Chicago, IL; *Int'l*, pg. 1322
Cantafio, Anne, Supvr.-Mktg. Svcs.--Drew Industrial, Boonton, NJ; *U.S. Public*, pg. 139
Cantamessa, J.F., Mktg. Rep.-France--Carpenter Technology (France) SARL, Bellerive-sur-Allier, France; *U.S. Public*, pg. 308
Canto, Glynis, Mgr.-Mktg.--Long Beach Learning Center, Long Beach, CA; *U.S. Public*, pg. 218
Canton, Alan, V.P.-Intl. Mkt.--Sun-Maid Growers of California, Kingsburg, CA; *U.S. Private*, pg. 1051
Cantone, Marie, Dir.-Mktg.--Winstar Global Products, Inc., Fairfield, NJ; *U.S. Public*, pg. 1772
Cantor, Allyson, Coord.-Mktg.--Lifetime Television/ABC, New York, NY; *U.S. Public*, pg. 512
Cantor, Allyson, Coord.-Mktg.--Lifetime Television/ABC, New York, NY; *U.S. Private*, pg. 516
Cantrell, Kevin, Mgr.-Mktg.--American Tank & Fabricating Co., Cleveland, OH; *U.S. Private*, pg. 63
Capdevila, Joaquen, Mgr.-Mktg.--Banco Espanol de Credito SA, Madrid, Spain; *Int'l*, pg. 143
Caperan, L., Dr., Dir.-Commercial--Fiat Auto SpA, Turin, Italy; *Int'l*, pg. 480
Capes, Tom, Mgr.-Mkt. Devel.--AAF-International, Louisville, KY; *U.S. Private*, pg. 3
Caplan, John, Mktg. Dir.--Berenter Greenhouse & Webster, Inc., New York, NY; *U.S. Private*, pg. 135
Capone, Andrew, Sr. V.P.-Mktg.--National Broadcasting Co., Inc., New York, NY; *U.S. Public*, pg. 712
Caponi, Colleen, Dir.-Mktg. & Adv.--Apple Vacations West Inc., Elk Grove Village, IL; *U.S. Private*, pg. 78

Cappa, Sylvia, Asst. V.P.-Mktg. & Publications--The Wheatley Group, Inc., Stamford, CT; U.S. Public, pg. 152
Cappellino, Mary H., Mgr.-Prod. Training--Garlock Sealing Technologies, Palmyra, NY; U.S. Public, pg. 402
Cappello, John, V.P.-Mktg. & Sls.--MidAmerican Energy Holdings, Des Moines, IA; U.S. Public, pg. 1109
Capria, Ernest, Sr. V.P. & Dir.-Mktg.--Carillon Importers, Ltd., Fort Lee, NJ; Int'l, pg. 409
Caputo, Art, Sr. V.P.-Sls. & Mktg.--Waters Corporation, Milford, MA; U.S. Public, pg. 1745
Caradonna, Robin, Mgr.-Mktg. Communications--Breed Technologies, Sterling Heights, MI; U.S. Public, pg. 251
Caramela, Laurence M., Dir.-Mktg., Bottle/Can--Central Coca-Cola Bottling Company, Inc., Richmond, VA; U.S. Private, pg. 222
Caranski, Denise, Asst. V.P.-Mktg.--Fleer-Skybox International Inc., Mount Laurel, NJ; U.S. Public, pg. 1052
Carazo, Dan, Mgr.-Mktg. Communications--Sulzer Metco (Westbury) Inc., Westbury, NY; Int'l, pg. 1307
Carballo, Bernard A., Exec. V.P.-Sls., Mktg. & Product Line Mngmt.--Seagate Technology Inc., Scotts Valley, CA; U.S. Public, pg. 1449
Carbee, Patty, 2nd V.P.-Mktg.--National Life Insurance Company, Montpelier, VT; U.S. Private, pg. 785
Carbonari, James J., V.P.-Sls. & Mktg.--Osmonics, Inc., Minnetonka, MN; U.S. Public, pg. 1233
Carbone, Steve, V.P. & Gen. Mgr.-Resolution Graphics & Mktg.--Grey Direct, New York, NY; U.S. Public, pg. 764
Carchedi, Steven A., V.P.-Commercial Systems--Integral Systems, Inc., Lanham, MD; U.S. Public, pg. 883
Carcone, Joseph A., V.P.-Mktg. & Sls.--Sanyo Energy (U.S.A.) Corporation, San Diego, CA; Int'l, pg. 1191
Card, Keith, Dir.-Mktg. & Pub. Rels.--Benihana, Inc., Miami, FL; U.S. Public, pg. 211
Card, Keith, Dir.-Mktg. & Pub. Rels.--Benihana International, Inc., Miami, FL; U.S. Public, pg. 212
Card, Kerry, Sls. & Mktg. Admin.--LFE Industrial Systems Corporation, Clinton, MA; U.S. Public, pg. 1045
Cardella, Thomas, V.P.-Mktg.--Labatt U.S.A., Darien, CT; Int'l, pg. 679
Cardillo, Robert, V.P.-Worldwide Mktg.--Avis Car Leasing, Garden City, NY; U.S. Public, pg. 321
Cardillo, Robert, V.P.-Worldwide Mktg.--Avis Rent A Car System, Inc., Garden City, NY; U.S. Public, pg. 321
Cardwell, Colleen, Mgr.-Mktg.--GF Office Furniture Ltd., Gallatin, TN; U.S. Private, pg. 434
Carey, Carolyn, V.P.-Mktg.--Knott's Berry Farm, Buena Park, CA; U.S. Private, pg. 627
Carey, Christopher J., Dir.-Mktg.--OSV Partners, Greenwich, CT; U.S. Public, pg. 1673
Carey, J. Paul, Exec. V.P.-Mktg & Servicing--SLM Holding Corp., Washington, DC; U.S. Public, pg. 1419
Carey, Michael, Dir.-Mktg.--Irish Biscuits Ltd., Dublin, Ireland; Int'l, pg. 688
Carey, Peter, Dir.-Mktg.--Diamond Brands, Inc., Cloquet, MN; U.S. Private, pg. 330
Carey, Tom, V.P.-Mktg.--Builders Square, Inc., San Antonio, TX; U.S. Private, pg. 477
Carey, Verian, V.P.-Sls.--Kelly-Moore Paint Company, Inc., San Carlos, CA; U.S. Private, pg. 613
Carhart, E.J., V.P.-Mktg. & Sls.--Automotive, Wayne, NJ; Int'l, pg. 234
Carhart, Lisa, Dir.-Mktg.- Sperry--The Stride Rite Corporation, Lexington, MA; U.S. Public, pg. 1524
Carillino, George, Dir.-Mktg.--Trophy Holdings Inc., Elmwood Park, NJ; U.S. Private, pg. 1105
Carini, Franco, V.P.-Mktg.--Pirelli Armstrong Tire Corporation, New Haven, CT; Int'l, pg. 1058
Cariolo, Cosimo, Dir.-Sls. & Mktg.--Warren E. Collins, Inc., Braintree, MA; U.S. Private, pg. 253
Carl, David L., V.P.-Mktg. & Bus. Plng.--Cross Pointe Paper Corporation, Saint Paul, MN; Int'l, pg. 434
Carlberg, Thomas, Mgr.-Mktg. Servies--Sandvik, Inc., Fair Lawn, NJ; Int'l, pg. 1185
Carle, Ed, Prod. Mgr.-Consumer Products--Riceland Foods, Inc., Stuttgart, AR; U.S. Private, pg. 928
Carley, Tom, Dir.-Database Mktg.--The New York Times Company, New York, NY; U.S. Public, pg. 1173
Carlin, Lisa, Dir.-Mktg. Communications--General Signal Networks, Shelton, CT; U.S. Public, pg. 727
Carlisle, Jim, V.P. & Dir.-Mktg. & Opers.--Morton Automotive Coatings, Lansing, IL; U.S. Public, pg. 1135
Carlisle, Kevin, V.P.-Mktg.--Springs Industries, Bedding Division, Charlotte, NC; U.S. Public, pg. 1500
Carlo, Judith, V.P.-Mktg. & Creative--Zotos International, Darien, CT; Int'l, pg. 1236
Carlsen, Dennis, Sls./Mktg.--Cowden Metal-San Jose, San Jose, CA; U.S. Private, pg. 280
Carlson, Art, V.P.-Devel.--Dick Clark Restaurants, Inc., Burbank, CA; U.S. Public, pg. 382
Carlson, Craig, Asst. V.P.-Mktg.-Wheeling--ACCO World Corporation, Lincolnshire, IL; U.S. Public, pg. 674
Carlson, D.A., Mgr.-Mktg.--The Uncle Toby's Company Ltd., Richmond, Australia; Int'l, pg. 555
Carlson, David, Dir.-Acctg.--Sofamor Danek Group, Inc., Memphis, TN; U.S. Public, pg. 1482
Carlson, Doug, V.P.-Mktg.--Delaware Ribbon Manufacturers, Inc., Philadelphia, PA; U.S. Private, pg. 322
Carlson, Jack, V.P.-Mktg.--Square D Company, Palatine, IL; Int'l, pg. 1208
Carlson, John S., V.P.-Mktg.--Sysco Corporation, Houston, TX; U.S. Public, pg. 1550
Carlson, Julie, Mgr.-Mktg. Communications--Harris Corp., Digital Telephone Systems Div., Novato, CA; U.S. Public, pg. 791
Carlson, Kathleen, V.P.-Mktg. & Commun.--Grubb & Ellis Company, Northbrook, IL; U.S. Public, pg. 767
Carlson, Kimberly, Mktg. Officer & Product/Sls. Promo. Mgr.--North Fork Bancorporation, Inc., Melville, NY; U.S. Public, pg. 1194
Carlson, Kjell, Mgr.-Mktg.--ESAB Sverige AB, Goteborg, Sweden; Int'l, pg. 281
Carlson, Margaret, V.P.-Spec. Prods. Mktg.--Ore-Ida Foods, Inc., Boise, ID; U.S. Public, pg. 805
Carlson, Nancy, Global Brand Mgr.--Mobil Oil Corporation, Fairfax, VA; U.S. Public, pg. 1118
Carlson, Peggy, Specialist-Mktg.--Menasha Corp., Printed Systems Div., Neenah, WI; U.S. Private, pg. 731
Carlson, Ray, Mgr.-Mktg.--Hedwin Corporation, Baltimore, MD; Int'l, pg. 1278
Carlson, Robert E., Exec. V.P.--Northwestern Mutual Life Insurance Co., Milwaukee, WI; U.S. Private, pg. 807
Carlson, Roger C., V.P.-Mktg.--Delavan Gas Turbine Products Division, West Des Moines, IA; U.S. Public, pg. 401
Carlson, Ruth, V.P.-Mktg.--Scholl U.S.A., Memphis, TN; U.S. Public, pg. 1438
Carlson, Terry, Sr. V.P.-Mktg.--Vermont American Tool Corp., Louisville, KY; U.S. Public, pg. 575
Carlston, Kira, Sls. & Mktg. Coord.--The Zippertubing Co., Los Angeles, CA; U.S. Private, pg. 1207
Carlton, Randall, Mgr.-Mktg.--Basler Electric Company, Highland, IL; U.S. Private, pg. 121
Carlton, Robert Bruce, V.P.-Mktg.--National Western Life Insurance Company, Austin, TX; U.S. Public, pg. 1161
Carlton, Ron, Ph.D., Dir.-Mktg.--AmeriPath, Inc., Riviera Beach, FL; U.S. Public, pg. 96
Carlton, Thomas J., V.P.-Sls. & Mktg.--Corrugated Metals, Inc., Bedford Park, IL; U.S. Private, pg. 277
Carman, Thomas W., Exec. V.P.-Corp. Devel.--Healthsouth Corporation, Birmingham, AL; U.S. Public, pg. 803
Carmody, Dan, Dir.-Mktg.--Channing L. Bete Co., Inc., South Deerfield, MA; U.S. Private, pg. 140
Carmon, William C., V.P.-Bus. Devel.--United Cities Gas Company, Brentwood, TN; U.S. Public, pg. 146
Carnes, Crais, V.P.-Sls. & Mktg.-Flooring--Burke Industries, Inc., San Jose, CA; U.S. Private, pg. 183
Carnes, Rodney, V.P.-Mktg.--Prestone Products Corporation, Danbury, CT; U.S. Public, pg. 51
Carney, Mike, Dir.-Mktg. Commun.--Lowrance Electronics, Inc., Tulsa, OK; U.S. Public, pg. 1015
Carnwath, Richard K., V.P.-Plng. & Devel.--Vulcan Materials Company, Birmingham, AL; U.S. Public, pg. 1725
Carocci, Bruce, Dir.-Mktg.--Flir Systems, Inc., Portland, OR; U.S. Public, pg. 654
Caron, Chris, V.P.-Mktg.--Duraflame, Inc., Stockton, CA; U.S. Private, pg. 348
Caropino, Stephen, Exec. V.P.--Pacifica Services, Inc., Pasadena, CA; U.S. Private, pg. 832
Carosi, Al, V.P.-Sls. & Mktg.--Hedstrom Corporation, Mount Prospect, IL; U.S. Private, pg. 526
Carothers, George E., Gen. Mgr.-Sls.--WHX Corporation, New York, NY; U.S. Public, pg. 1726
Carpenter, E.W., V.P.-Mktg. & Sls.--Durametallic Corp., Kalamazoo, MI; U.S. Public, pg. 658
Carpenter, Jeanne, V.P.-Mktg.--Shandwick Minneapolis, Minneapolis, MN; Int'l, pg. 1227
Carpenter, John H., V.P.-Mktg.--Prima Energy Corporation, Denver, CO; U.S. Public, pg. 1325
Carpenter, Marian J., Dir.-Corp. Communications--Republic Engineered Steels, Inc., Massillon, OH; U.S. Public, pg. 1378
Carpenter, Michael A., Vice Chm. & Exec. V.P.-Strategic Plng.--Travelers Group, New York, NY; U.S. Public, pg. 1632
Carpenter, Mike, V.P.-Sls. & Mktg.--The Vollrath Company, L.L.C., Sheboygan, WI; U.S. Private, pg. 1143
Carpenter, Patrick, Mgr.-Pub. Rels.--Alcan Aluminum Corporation, Cleveland, OH; Int'l, pg. 50
Carpenter, Rodney S., Dir.-Sls. & Mktg.--Durco GmbH Atomac Division, Ahaus, Germany; U.S. Public, pg. 659
Carpenter, Virginia, Coord.-Mktg. Communications--Uvex Safety, Inc., Smithfield, RI; Int'l, pg. 132
Carr, John, Mgr.-MKtg.--Sorrento Cheese Company, Inc., Buffalo, NY; Int'l, pg. 323
Carr, Robert F., IV, Asst. V.P.-Mktg.--Fiduciary Management Associates, Inc., Chicago, IL; U.S. Public, pg. 1673
Carr, Robin, Sr. V.P. & Brand Mktg. Partner--DMB&B Detroit, Troy, MI; U.S. Private, pg. 302
Carr, W. Brad, V.P.-Sls. & Mktg.--Luwa Bahnson, Inc., Winston Salem, NC; U.S. Private, pg. 682
Carrasco, Courtney, Mgr.-Mktg.--Blimpie International, Inc., Atlanta, GA; U.S. Public, pg. 236
Carrasco, Patricia A., Mgr.-Pub. Rels., Adv. & Mktg.--Casio, Inc., Dover, NJ; Int'l, pg. 274
Carraway, Kris, Dir.-Mktg.--Westlake Medical Center, Westlake Village, CA; U.S. Public, pg. 1697
Carrejo, Gene, V.P.-Sls. & Mktg.--Price's Creameries, El Paso, TX; U.S. Public, pg. 491
Carrelli, Bill, V.P.-Mktg.--Structural Dynamics Research Corp., Milford, OH; U.S. Public, pg. 1525
Carrier, Tracie, Mktg. Admin.--Microdyne Corporation, Alexandria, VA; U.S. Public, pg. 1105
Carrington, Eartha, Mktg. Coord.--Houston Fearless 76 Inc., Compton, CA; U.S. Private, pg. 542
Carrithers, Pat, Exec. V.P.-Mktg.--Bollinger Industries Inc., Grand Prairie, TX; U.S. Public, pg. 243
Carroll, Amy, Mgr.-Mktg. Services--GoodMark Foods, Inc., Raleigh, NC; U.S. Public, pg. 751
Carroll, Crawford, V.P. & Dir.-Mktg. Services--The Times-Picayune Publishing Corp., New Orleans, LA; U.S. Private, pg. 1087
Carroll, Ed, Sr. V.P.-Mktg.--Rainbow Programming Holdings, Inc., Woodbury, NY; U.S. Public, pg. 288
Carroll, Edward, Jr., Exec. V.P.-Sls. Promo. & Mktg.--Carson Pirie Scott & Co., Milwaukee, WI; U.S. Public, pg. 309
Carroll, John, V.P.-Mktg.--Weight Watchers Gourmet Food Company, Pittsburgh, PA; U.S. Public, pg. 806
Carroll, Mike, Dir.-Prod. Mktg.--Sandoz Pharmaceuticals Corp., East Hanover, NJ; Int'l, pg. 974
Carroll, Ronald, V.P.-Sls. & Mktg.--Hoffman Laces, Ltd., Cobleskill, NY; U.S. Public, pg. 769
Carroll, Thomas M., V.P.-Mktg.--Kay Home Products, Inc., Cleveland, OH; U.S. Public, pg. 1258
Carroll, Thomas S., Exec. V.P.-Mktg.--Viking Yacht Co., New Gretna, NJ; U.S. Private, pg. 1140
Carroll, William J., V.P. & Dir.-Mktg.--American Vanguard Corporation, Newport Beach, CA; U.S. Public, pg. 94
Carsalade, Joao Felipe, Chief Mktg. Officer--Aracruz Celulose S.A., Rio de Janeiro, Brazil; Int'l, pg. 78
Carson, Charles, Sr. V.P.-Mktg. & Sls.--Genesee Corporation, Rochester, NY; U.S. Public, pg. 728
Carson, David, Mgr.-Adv.--Panduit Corp., Tinley Park, IL; U.S. Private, pg. 836
Carson, Pati, Mgr.-Mktg.--Franklin Electronic Publishers, Inc., Burlington, NJ; U.S. Public, pg. 679
Cartaya, Luis, Dir.-Int'l. Mktg.--Standard Motor Products Inc., Long Island City, NY; U.S. Public, pg. 1503
Carter, Bill, V.P.-Sls.--Aladdin Industries, Incorporated, Nashville, TN; U.S. Private, pg. 30
Carter, Dennis, V.P. -Corp. Mktg. Grp.--Intel Corporation, Santa Clara, CA; U.S. Public, pg. 886
Carter, Greg, Mktg.--Jackson & Perkins, Medford, OR; Int'l, pg. 1518
Carter, Jeanette, V.P.-Mktg. & Plng.--La Petite Academy Inc., Overland Park, KS; U.S. Private, pg. 640
Carter, Joel, V.P.-Mktg. & Adv.--Computer City, Fort Worth, TX; U.S. Public, pg. 1560
Carter, John, V.P.-Mktg.--Henschel Corp., Newburyport, MA; U.S. Private, pg. 957
Carter, John M., Chm. Bd. & Chief Exec. Officer--Carco Electronics, Menlo Park, CA; U.S. Private, pg. 208
Carter, Kirk T., Mgr.-Bus. Devel.--Potter-Shackelford Construction Co., Greenville, SC; U.S. Private, pg. 877
Carter, Marilyn, Mgr.-Mktg.--Mediatex Communications Corporation, Austin, TX; U.S. Private, pg. 727
Carter, Mark, Sr. V.P.-Mktg.--American Express Financial Advisor, Minneapolis, MN; U.S. Public, pg. 73
Carter, S.D., V.P.-Mktg.--Confederation Trust Company, Toronto, Canada; Int'l, pg. 326
Carter, Tricia, Mktg. Asst.--Intertek Testing Services, Andover, MA; Int'l, pg. 672
Cartolano, P., Dir.-Mktg. & Sls. Services--Shieffelin Somerset Co., New York, NY; Int'l, pg. 412
Cartwright, Lynn, V.P.-Mktg.--Kent & Spiegel Direct, Culver City, CA; U.S. Private, pg. 615
Caruba, Walter J., V.P.-Sls. & Mktg.--Tultex Corporation, Martinsville, VA; U.S. Public, pg. 1644
Carus, Inga, V.P.-Sls. & Mktg.--Carus Corporation, Peru, IL; U.S. Private, pg. 217
Carus, Inga, V.P.-Mktg.--Carus Chemical Company, Chemical Div., Peru, IL; U.S. Private, pg. 217
Carvajal, Joseph, Mgr.-Mktg.--Roy Rogers Restaurants, Linthicum Heights, MD; U.S. Public, pg. 1069
Carvalho, Flavio, V.P.-Mktg. & Sls.--Transbrasil Airlines, Inc., Miami, FL; Int'l, pg. 1416
Carver, Linda, Mgr.-Mktg. Commun.--HBOC, Atlanta, GA; U.S. Public, pg. 770
Cary, John P., Dir.-Mktg.--ITT Jabsco, Costa Mesa, CA; U.S. Public, pg. 860
Casagrande, Ron, Mgr.-Mktg.--Aerospace Products, Inc., Wilmington, MA; U.S. Public, pg. 100
Casale, Michael J., Sr. V.P.-Direct Mktg.--American Bankers Life Assurance Co. of Florida, Miami, FL; U.S. Public, pg. 67
Casale, Ralph, Exec. V.P. & Chief Mktg. Officer--New York Life Worldwide Holding, Inc., New York, NY; U.S. Private, pg. 795
Cascio, Bill, Exec. V.P.-Natl. Sls. & Mktg.--Fetzer Vineyards California Wines, Hopland, CA; U.S. Public, pg. 261
Case, John J., V.P.-Mktg./Residential--La-Z-Boy Incorporated, Monroe, MI; U.S. Public, pg. 972
Case, Rod, V.P.-Mktg. Svcs.--Nestle Beverage Company, Glendale, CA; Int'l, pg. 917
Casellari, Mario R., Dir.-Sls. & Mktg.--IGT-(Australia), Pty. Limited, Rosebery, Australia; U.S. Public, pg. 900
Casey, Christine, Dir.-Mktg. Services--Baccarat, Inc., Edison, NJ; Int'l, pg. 132
Casey, Faye, Mktg. Communications Mgr.--Getinge/Castle, Inc., Rochester, NY; U.S. Private, pg. 449
Casey, James, V.P.-Sls. & Mktg.--IBJ Schroder Bank & Trust Company, New York, NY; Int'l, pg. 674
Casey, Jerry, V.P.-Diagnostic Prods.--Genzyme Corporation, Cambridge, MA; U.S. Public, pg. 733
Casey, Karen, V.P. & Mktg. Dir.-Humanities & Social Sciences--Oxford University Press, Inc., New York, NY; Int'l, pg. 1019
Casey, Kevin, Dir.-Sls. & Mktg.--Educational Insights, Inc., Carson, CA; U.S. Public, pg. 565
Casey, Peter R., V.P.-Opers.--Block Drug Company, Inc., Jersey City, NJ; U.S. Public, pg. 236
Casey, Sean, Dir.-Mktg.--Riverdale Chemical Co., Glenwood, IL; U.S. Private, pg. 934
Cash, Jim, Dir.-Mktg.--Precision Imaged Products Group, Tully, NY; U.S. Public, pg. 162
Cashin, Brian, Dir.-Mktg.--Air Canada, Hounslow, United Kingdom; Int'l, pg. 37
Cashin, John R., Exec. V.P. & Dir.-Mktg.--Willis Faber North America, Inc.-New York, New York, NY; Int'l, pg. 1503
Casillas, Jose Antonio, Dir.-Mktg.--Cigarrera la Moderna, SA de CV, Monterrey, Mexico; Int'l, pg. 112
Casner, John, V.P.-Sls. & Mktg.--Hayward Industrial Products-Strainer Div., Elizabeth, NJ; U.S. Private, pg. 513
Caso, Joseph, V.P.-Mktg.--Schering Laboratories, Kenilworth, NJ; U.S. Public, pg. 1438
Casoni, Vito, Mgr.-Mktg.--Barbero S.p.A., Canale, Italy; Int'l, pg. 64
Casoni, Vito, Dir.-Mktg.--Barbero 1891 SpA, Canale, Italy; Int'l, pg. 164
Caspall, Ken, V.P.-Sls.--MFA Oil Company, Columbia, MO; U.S. Private, pg. 687
Caspar, Dietmar, Dir.-Sls. & Mktg.--EMS Kurierpost GmbH, Bonn, Germany; Int'l, pg. 407
Casper, Bert, V.P.-Mktg.--Remmele Engineering, Inc., New Brighton, MN; U.S. Private, pg. 921
Casper, Michael, V.P.-Sls. & Mktg.--KYB Corporation of America, Lombard, IL; Int'l, pg. 727
Casper, Wayne, Exec. V.P.-Mktg.--Sargento Foods Inc., Plymouth, WI; U.S. Private, pg. 966

Casperson, Curt, Dir.-Mktg.--The First American Financial Corporation, Santa Ana, CA; *U.S. Public*, pg. 624
Casperson, Curt, V.P.-Mktg.--First American Title Insurance Co., Santa Ana, CA; *U.S. Public*, pg. 625
Cassel, Carlis, Dir.-Mktg.--National-Standard Co., Niles, MI; *U.S. Public*, pg. 1160
Cassidy, Charles T., Sr. V.P.-Mktg. & Prod. Devel.--State Street Bank & Trust Co., Boston, MA; *U.S. Public*, pg. 1513
Cassidy, Joseph, V.P.-Mktg.--The Orvis Company, Inc., Manchester, VT; *U.S. Private*, pg. 820
Cassidy, Madelaine, Admin.-Mktg. Communications--Pentax Corporation, Englewood, CO; *Int'l*, pg. 85
Cassidy, Maureen, V.P.-Mktg.--WWF Paper Corporation - Mid Atlantic, Annapolis, MD; *U.S. Private*, pg. 1145
Cassin, Thomas C., V.P.-Mktg.--Pitco Frialator Inc., Bow, NH; *U.S. Public*, pg. 1065
Cassner, Brian, Mgr.-Mktg.--Rotary Forms Press, Inc., Hillsboro, OH; *U.S. Private*, pg. 947
Castaldi, Tony, V.P.-Mktg.--Cutco Industries, Inc., Syosset, NY; *U.S. Public*, pg. 470
Castanzo, W. Kenneth, V.P.-Global Mktg.--Grace Packaging, Duncan, SC; *U.S. Public*, pg. 755
Castelli, Joe, Dir.-Mktg--Roberts Pharmaceutical Corporation, Eatontown, NJ; *U.S. Public*, pg. 1393
Casterina, Mayra, Coord.-Mktg.--Heath Consultants Incorporated, Houston, TX; *U.S. Private*, pg. 518
Castilho da Silva, Marcelo, Dir.-Supply & Mktg.--Petrobras - Petroleo Brasileiro S.A., Rio de Janeiro, Brazil; *Int'l*, pg. 1041
Castillo, Nancy M., Sr. Mgr.-Adv. & Sls.--Quintus Corporation, Fremont, CA; *U.S. Private*, pg. 901
Castor, Joe, Dir.-Mktg.--Arizona Cardinals, Phoenix, AZ; *U.S. Private*, pg. 81
Castro Yllanes, Miguel, Mgr.-Commercial--Quimica S.A. de C.V., Mexico, Mexico; *Int'l*, pg. 1075
Catalano, James A., Mgr.-Mktg.--Ludwig Industries, Monroe, NC; *U.S. Public*, pg. 1514
Catalano, Rosalie, V.P.-Mktg.--YSI Incorporated, Yellow Springs, OH; *U.S. Private*, pg. 1195
Catanio, Mike, Dir.-Natl. Prods.--Bergen Brunswig Corporation, Orange, CA; *U.S. Public*, pg. 213
Catanzaro, Paula, Dir.-Mktg.--Taylor-Morley, Inc., Saint Louis, MO; *U.S. Private*, pg. 1071
Cates, Max, Dir.-Mtkg. Communications--Associated Electric Co-op Inc., Springfield, MO; *U.S. Private*, pg. 89
Catlett, Timothy P., V.P.-Sls. & Mktg.--Barr Laboratories Inc., Pomona, NY; *U.S. Public*, pg. 191
Cato, Joan, Dir.-Mktg.--Aladdin Industries, Incorporated, Nashville, TN; *U.S. Private*, pg. 30
Cator, Mike, Dir.-Mktg.--Dresser-Rand Sales, Houston, TX; *U.S. Public*, pg. 529
Catsicas, Costas, Sls. & Mktg. Mgr.--Whitehall Greece, Athens, Greece; *U.S. Public*, pg. 82
Catt, John, Mktg. Div.--Totes Incorporated, Loveland, OH; *U.S. Private*, pg. 111
Cattermole, G.R., Dir.-Mktg.--Du Pont (E.I. Du Pont De Nemours & Co.), Wilmington, DE; *U.S. Public*, pg. 530
Cattini, Mark, V.P.- Sls. & Mktg.--MapInfo Corp., Troy, NY; *U.S. Public*, pg. 1042
Cattlin, Sara, Coord.-Mktg. & Adv.--Chico's Fas Inc, Fort Myers, FL; *U.S. Public*, pg. 349
Caudell, Brad, Dir.-Mktg.--Wallace Computer Services, Inc., Lisle, IL; *U.S. Public*, pg. 1735
Caudell, Karen, V.P.-Adv.--Peoples National Bank, Lawrenceville, IL; *U.S. Public*, pg. 1217
Caulfield, Richard J., V.P.-Mktg. & Sls.--Roberts Pharmaceutical Corporation, Eatontown, NJ; *U.S. Public*, *pg. 1393*
Caulkins, William, V.P.-Adv. & Prod. Devel.--Sherman & Reilly, Inc., Chattanooga, TN; *U.S. Private*, pg. 993
Causey, Mary, Coord.-Mktg.--BGF Industries Inc., Greensboro, NC; *U.S. Private*, pg. 106
Cavalier, Clark, V.P.-Mktg.--Southern Farm Bureau Casualty Insurance Company, Ridgeland, MS; *U.S. Private*, pg. 1016
Cavallero, Mike, V.P.-Mktg. & Sls./Fresh Fruit--Dole Food Company, Inc., Westlake Village, CA; *U.S. Public*, pg. 515
Cavanagh, John, Mgr.-Mktg. Masking Prods.--Ivex Packaging Corporation-Industrial Products Division, Newton, MA; *U.S. Public*, pg. 915
Cavanagh, Leo, V.P. & Gen. Mgr.-Trade Rels. & Special Mkts.--Fuji Photographic Products Div., Elmsford, NY; *Int'l*, pg. 524
Cavanaugh, Bill, Mgr.-Mktg.--Enterprise Management, Reston, VA; *U.S. Private*, pg. 351
Cavanaugh, David, V.P.-Sls. & Mktg.--Airtex Products, Fairfield, IL; *U.S. Private*, pg. 1113
Cavegn, Rico, Mktg. Mgr.--Texas Instruments (Switzerland) AG, Dietikon, Switzerland; *U.S. Public*, pg. 1586
Cavello, Butch, Mgr.-Mktg.--American Louver Co., Skokie, IL; *U.S. Private*, pg. 58
Cayne, Janis, Mgr.-Mktg. Svcs.--The Spencer Turbine Co., Windsor, CT; *U.S. Private*, pg. 1025
Cazaly, Phillip, Dir.-Mktg.--Jaguar Cars Limited, Coventry, United Kingdom; *U.S. Public*, pg. 666
Cecil, William E., V.P.-Worldwide Mktg. & Tech.--Mead Packaging, Atlanta, GA; *U.S. Public*, pg. 1074
Cedarleaf, Calvin, Dir.-Mktg.--Dexter Aerospace Materials Division, Pittsburg, CA; *U.S. Public*, pg. 504
Cedillo, Serigo, Dir.-Mktg.--Laboratorios Pharmacia & Upjohn, C.A., Caracas, Venezuela; *Int'l*, pg. 1049
Ceglia, Rose, Sr. Dir.-Relationship Mktg.--America West Airlines, Inc., Phoenix, AZ; *U.S. Public*, pg. 67
Celani, Kristen, Mgr.-Mktg.--Enidine Incorporated, Orchard Park, NY; *U.S. Private*, pg. 377
Celentano, Domenick A., Jr., V.P.-Mktg. & Adv.--Celentano Bros. Inc., Verona, NJ; *U.S. Private*, pg. 221
Cellier, Cecile, Mgr.-Mktg. & Export--BG SAS, Le Tholy, France; *Int'l*, pg. 201
Celmer, Theresa, Mgr.-Mktg. Commuinications-Computer Accessories Div.--Fellowes Manufacturing Co., Itasca, IL; *U.S. Private*, pg. 400
Celsi, Rob, Mgr.-Mktg.--Sutter Home Winery, Inc., Saint Helena, CA; *U.S. Private*, pg. 1057
Cephus, Will, Sr. V.P.-Sls. & Mktg.--The Arnold Palmer Golf Company, Ooltewah, TN; *U.S. Public*, pg. 132
Cerminara, Robert J., Mgr.-Mktg.--Erving Paper Products, Inc., Green Bay, WI; *U.S. Private*, pg. 382
Cerullo, Pat, V.P.-Sls. & Mktg.--Tesma International Inc., Concord, Canada; *Int'l*, pg. 830
Cervantes, Joseph P., V.P.-Sls. & Mktg.--Crowley Foods, Inc., Binghamton, NY; *Int'l*, pg. 752
Cerza, Bob, V.P.-Mktg.--Timesavers Inc., Crystal, MN; *U.S. Private*, pg. 1088
Cerza, Robert, V.P.-Sls. & Mktg.--Pharmacia & Upjohn Deltec, Inc., Arden Hills, MN; *Int'l*, pg. 1049
Ceyrac, Regis, Gen. Mgr.-Mktg.--Compagnie Laitiere BESNIER, Laval, France; *Int'l*, pg. 322
Cezauru, Nat, Sr. V.P.-Sls. & Mktg.--4C Foods Corporation, Brooklyn, NY; *U.S. Private*, pg. 421
Cha, In-Sue, Mng. Dir.-Sls. & Beverage Mktg.--Dong-Suh Foods Corporation, Inchon, Korea; *Int'l*, pg. 416
Chabot, Elizabeth, V.P.-Mktg.--Saks Fifth Avenue, New York, NY; *U.S. Public*, pg. 1429
Chabot, Tina, Coord.-Mktg.--Glaxo Wellcome Inc., Mississauga, Canada; *Int'l*, pg. 553
Chadwick, Peter, Dir.-Mktg.--Ford Motor Norge A/S, Kolbotn, Norway; *U.S. Public*, pg. 666
Chaffetz, Jason, Dir.-Mktg. & Personal Care--Nu Skin International, Provo, UT; *U.S. Private*, pg. 808
Chagares Urso, Diane, Mgr.-Mktg.--Survey Sampling, Inc., Fairfield, CT; *U.S. Private*, pg. 1056
Chahil, Satjiv S., Sr. V.P.-Worldwide Corp. Mktg.--Apple Computer, Inc., Cupertino, CA; *U.S. Public*, pg. 121
Chaiken, Lynn, V.P.-Mktg.--Woman's Day, New York, NY; *Int'l*, pg. 795
Chaille, Susan, Mktg. Specialist--Universal Flavors-U.S.A., Indianapolis, IN; *U.S. Public*, pg. 1696
Chainey, David E., Mgr.-Sls. & Mktg.--Amicon Canada Ltd., Oakville, Canada; *U.S. Public*, pg. 1113
Chainey, Hughette, Dir.-Promo.--Domtar Inc., Montreal, Canada; *Int'l*, pg. 416
Chalgren, William, Mgr.-Mktg.--Holmatro, Inc., Glen Burnie, MD; *Int'l*, pg. 632
Chamberlain, Mary, Mgr.-Promo.--Modern Healthcare, Chicago, IL; *U.S. Private*, pg. 285
Chambers, J.W., Sr. V.P.-Sls. & Mktg.--Hartwell Corporation, Placentia, CA; *U.S. Private*, pg. 1168
Chambers, Jack, Dir.-Mktg.--Discount Tire, Scottsdale, AZ; *U.S. Private*, pg. 334
Chambers, Mark, Gen. Mgr.-Mktg.--White Consolidated Industries, Inc., Cleveland, OH; *Int'l*, pg. 439
Chambers, Mark, Gen. Mgr.-Mktg.--Gibson Appliances, Dublin, OH; *Int'l*, pg. 439
Chambers, Mark, Gen. Mgr.-Mktg.--Kelvinator Appliances, Dublin, OH; *Int'l*, pg. 440
Chambers, Paul, Dir.-Mktg.--American Mathematical Society, Inc., Providence, RI; *U.S. Private*, pg. 59
Champlin, Charles, V.P.-Sls. & Mktg.--Faribault Woolen Mill Co., Faribault, MN; *U.S. Private*, pg. 394
Champlin, H.A., Exec. V.P.-Mktg. & Comml. Devel.--Akzo Nobel Coatings Inc. (KY), Louisville, KY; *Int'l*, pg. 47
Chan, Allan, V.P. & Gen. Mgr.-Precision Products Div.--Innovex, Inc., Hopkins, MN; *U.S. Public*, pg. 880
Chan, Felicia, Dir.-Mktg.--Revo, Inc., Sunnyvale, CA; *U.S. Public*, pg. 195
Chan, Frances, Mgr.-Retail Mktg.--DBS Asset Management Ltd., Singapore, Singapore; *Int'l*, pg. 350
Chan, Pamela, Mgr.-Mktg.--DBS Trading Pte. Ltd., Singapore, Singapore; *Int'l*, pg. 351
Chan, Philip, Mgr.-Mktg.-Logs & Wood Prods.--Weyerhaeuser (Far East) Ltd., Wan Chai, Hong Kong; *U.S. Public*, pg. 1764
Chan, William, Mgr.-Sls. & Mktg.--Asama Pte. Ltd., Asia, Singapore, Singapore; *U.S. Private*, pg. 1046
Chance, Guy P., First V.P.--Scott & Stringfellow Financial, Inc., Richmond, VA; *U.S. Public*, pg. 1445
Chance, Larry, Mgr.-Distr.--E.C. Barton & Company, Jonesboro, AR; *U.S. Private*, pg. 119
Chandler, J. Harold, Sr. Exec. V.P.-Mktg.--NationsBank South, Atlanta, GA; *U.S. Public*, pg. 1163
Chandler, John, V.P.-Mktg., Holiday Inn Hotels--Holiday Inn Worldwide, Atlanta, GA; *Int'l*, pg. 170
Chandler, John F., Sr. V.P.-Mktg. & Pipelines--Western Gas Resources, Inc., Denver, CO; *U.S. Public*, pg. 1758
Chandler, Patrick, Mgr.-Direct Mktg.--Comerica Incorporated, Detroit, MI; *U.S. Public*, pg. 408
Chang, Gareth C.C., Sr. V.P.-Mktg.--Hughes Electronics Corporation, Westchester, CA; *U.S. Public*, pg. 720
Channer, Wayne, Sr. V.P.-Sls. & Mktg.--Interactive Data Corporation, Lexington, MA; *Int'l*, pg. 1025
Chantrenne, A., Mgr.-Mktg.--Esselte SA, Paris, France; *Int'l*, *pg. 461*
Chapel, John, V.P.-Mktg.--Kern's Bakeries, Incorporated, Knoxville, TN; *U.S. Public*, pg. 547
Chapin, Kent, Mgr.-Mktg.--The Athlete's Foot Group, Inc., Kennesaw, GA; *U.S. Private*, pg. 94
Chapman, Anthony D., V.P. & Chief Mktg. Officer-Agency Div.--Atlantic American Life Insurance Company, Atlanta, GA; *U.S. Public*, pg. 143
Chapman, Anthony D., V.P. & Chief Mktg. Officer-Agency Div.--Bankers Fidelity Life Insurance Company, Atlanta, GA; *U.S. Public*, pg. 143
Chapman, Burt, V.P.-Mktg. & Adv.--Today's Man, Inc., Moorestown, NJ; *U.S. Public*, pg. 1619
Chapman, Donna, Mgr.-Mktg.--Reed Business Information Pty. Limited, Chatswood, Australia; *Int'l*, pg. 1094
Chapman, Fred, V.P.-Bus. Devel.--Betac International Corporation, Alexandria, VA; *U.S. Private*, pg. 140
Chapman, John, Dir.-Mktg.--Caradon Plc, Weybridge, United Kingdom; *Int'l*, pg. 266
Chapman, Katherine, Mktg. Dir.--FUTUREWORKS, Seattle, WA; *U.S. Private*, pg. 385
Chapman, Peter K., V.P.-Mktg. & Bus. Devel.--AAR Corp., Wood Dale, IL; *U.S. Public*, pg. 1
Chappell, John, V.P.-Brand Devel.--Boston Beer Company, Boston, MA; *U.S. Public*, pg. 246
Charbonneau, Elizabeth, Dir.-Retail Mktg. & Sls. Promotion--Congoleum Corporation, Mercerville, NJ; *U.S. Public*, pg. 69
Charbonneau, K.X., Dir.-Color Mktg.--Benjamin Moore & Co., Montvale, NJ; *U.S. Private*, pg. 133
Charland, Thomas, V.P.-Mktg. & Communications--Control Data Systems, Inc., Arden Hills, MN; *U.S. Public*, pg. 441
Charles, Nick, Mgr.-Prod. Mktg.--Microtel International Inc., Ontario, CA; *U.S. Public*, pg. 1108
Charlton, Bob, Dir.-Mktg.--The Walworth Company USA, Houston, TX; *U.S. Private*, pg. 1149
Charlton, David, V.P.-Mktg.-Central--British Airways, Flushing, NY; *Int'l*, pg. 219
Charlton, Paul, Dir.-Mktg.--Littleton Coin Co., Inc., Littleton, NH; *U.S. Private*, pg. 671
Charmelo, Dominic, Supvr.-Mktg. Communications--Dukane Corporation, Saint Charles, IL; *U.S. Private*, pg. 345
Charney, M. Jeffrey, V.P.-Mktg. & Commun.--Kaufman and Broad Home Corporation, Los Angeles, CA; *U.S. Public*, pg. 944
Charters, George, Dir.-Mktg. & Trading--Safeway PLC, Hayes, United Kingdom; *Int'l*, pg. 1169
Chartier, Keith A., Dir.-Adv.--Ogden Publishing, Topeka, KS; *U.S. Private*, pg. 812
Chase, Brad, V.P.-Developer Rels. & Mktg./Internet Client & Collaboration--Microsoft Corporation, Redmond, WA; *U.S. Public*, pg. 1107
Chase, Ronald J., Dir.-Human Relations & Pub. Communications--Green Bay Packaging Inc., Green Bay, WI; *U.S. Private*, pg. 476
Chase, William, Exec. V.P.-Sls. & Mktg.--American Business Information, Inc., Omaha, NE; *U.S. Public*, pg. 69
Chasen, Sherwin, V.P.-Indus. Production--Cook Composites & Polymers Inc., Kansas City, MO; *Int'l*, pg. 1409
Chasm, James G., V.P.-Sls. & Mktg.--SK Hand Tool Corp., Chicago, IL; *Int'l*, pg. 570
Chastain, Jim D., Pres.-Commodity Mktg. Division--The Scoular Company, Omaha, NE; *U.S. Private*, pg. 977
Chastain, Marilyn, Mgr.-Mktg.--Wang's International, Inc., Memphis, TN; *U.S. Private*, pg. 1149
Chastain, Roger W., Pres. & Chief Oper. Officer--Mount Vernon Mills, Inc., Greenville, SC; *U.S. Private*, pg. 835
Chastain, Stephanie, Dir.-Mktg.--California Strawberry Commission, Watsonville, CA; *U.S. Private*, pg. 201
Chastanet, Allen, V.P.-Mktg & Sls.--Air Jamaica Ltd., Miami, FL; *U.S. Private*, pg. 28
Chatel, Marc, V.P.-Mktg. & Retail Sls.--Logitech International SA, Morges, Switzerland; *Int'l*, pg. 815
Chatting, Keith G., V.P.- Mktg.--Jerome Foods Inc., Barron, WI; *U.S. Private*, pg. 586
Chavez Sitters, Sylvia, Mgr.-Mktg.--San Antonio Express News, San Antonio, TX; *U.S. Private*, pg. 517
Chavez, Cassandra, Art Dir.--Heald Colleges, San Francisco, CA; *U.S. Private*, pg. 514
Chavous, Joyce A., Admin.-Sls. & Mktg.--Magnetic Metals Corp., Camden, NJ; *U.S. Private*, pg. 560
Chay, Ken, Mgr.-Mktg. Communications--APL Limited, Oakland, CA; *Int'l*, pg. 912
Cheeseman, Peter, Dir.-Sls. & Mktg.--Wayfarer Transit Systems Ltd., Poole, United Kingdom; *Int'l*, pg. 853
Chegwidden, J.A., Gen. Mgr.-Mktg.--Highveld Steel & Vanadium Corporation, Witbank, South Africa; *Int'l*, pg. 76
Chella, Karen, Coord.-Reg. Mktg. & Promos.--Baskin-Robbins Incorporated, Glendale, CA; *Int'l*, pg. 63
Chemer, Jenny, Mgr.-Mktg. Svcs.--Wisconsin Pharmacal Co., Inc., Jackson, WI; *U.S. Private*, pg. 1185
Chen, Edward, V.P.-Mktg.--Tatung Company of America, Long Beach, CA; *Int'l*, pg. 1357
Chen, Monique, Mgr.-Mktg.--Haking Enterprises, Quarry Bay, Hong Kong; *Int'l*, pg. 586
Chen, T.T., Gen. Mgr.-Mktg.--China Steel Corporation, Kaohsiung, Taiwan; *Int'l*, pg. 285
Chen, Ted, Exec. V.P.-Mktg. & Corp. Devel.--Storage Dimensions, Inc., Milpitas, CA; *U.S. Public*, pg. 1522
Chenes, Barry, Dir.-Mktg.--Qualidyne Systems Inc., San Diego, CA; *Int'l*, pg. 1241
Cheng, Robert J., V.P.-Mktg./Americas Group--Gateway 2000, North Sioux City, SD; *U.S. Public*, pg. 703
Cheramie, Dean, Dir.-Mktg.--Veeder-Root Company, Simsbury, CT; *U.S. Public*, pg. 482
Cherney-Roca, Natalia, Dir.-Mktg.--The CIT Group/Capital Finance Inc., New York, NY; *Int'l*, pg. 360
Cheron, Jennifer, Brands Mgr.--Chateau St. Jean Winery, Kenwood, CA; *Int'l*, pg. 1321
Cherriaud, Olivier, Dir.-Mktg.--Remy Cointreau, Paris, France; *Int'l*, pg. 1102
Cherry, Kim, Mgr.-Mktg.--Star-Telegram Newspaper, Inc., Fort Worth, TX; *U.S. Public*, pg. 964
Chester, G. Scott, Mgr.-Sls. & Mktg.--Nashua Imaging Supplies Div., Nashua, NH; *U.S. Public*, pg. 1152
Chetelat, John, V.P.-Mktg.--Fire Lite Alarms, Inc./Notifier Co., Northford, CT; *U.S. Public*, pg. 1306
Cheung, K.W., Mgr.-Mktg.--Olivetti Hong Kong Ltd., Causeway Bay, Hong Kong; *Int'l*, pg. 1003
Cheung, Raymong, Dir.-Mktg.--Bel Fuse Ltd., Kowloon, Hong Kong; *U.S. Public*, pg. 200
Chevalier, Dominque, Mng. Dir.-Mktg.--Industrias Lever Portuguesa, Lda., Lisbon, Portugal; *Int'l*, pg. 1437
Chevallier, Raymond, V.P.-Corp. Mktg.--F. Schumacher & Co., New York, NY; *U.S. Private*, pg. 973
Cheyrou, Francois, Mgr.-Mktg.--CSR Pampryl, La Courneuve, France; *Int'l*, pg. 566
Chiado, James, V.P.-Mfg. & Mktg.--Kauffman Products, Inc., Carmel, IN; *U.S. Private*, pg. 609
Chidester, Craig, Mgr.-Mktg. & Sls.--Eaton Corporation, Electric Drives Division, Kenosha, WI; *U.S. Public*, pg. 556
Chiera, Louis J., Dir.-Mktg. Services--Sensormatic Electronics Corporation, Boca Raton, FL; *U.S. Public*, pg. 1457

Chiericozzi, Pete, V.P.-Mktg. & Sls.--Wisconsin Tissue Mills, Inc., Menasha, WI; *U.S. Public*, pg. 347
Chihocky, Janet, Mgr.-Corp. Commun.--Orbital Sciences Corporation, Dulles, VA; *U.S. Public*, pg. 1229
Childers, April, Mgr.-Mktg.--Cracker Barrel Old Country Store, Inc., Lebanon, TN; *U.S. Public*, pg. 455
Childers, Bruce S., Exec. V.P.-Mktg. Info. Services--Meldrum & Fewsmith Communications Inc., Cleveland, OH; *U.S. Private*, pg. 730
Childers, Jackie, Sr. V.P.-Mktg.--Prime Option Services, Sandy, UT; *U.S. Public*, pg. 1132
Childs, Carl, V.P.-Sls. & Mktg.--Raytheon Aircraft Company, Wichita, KS; *U.S. Public*, pg. 1365
Chin, George, V.P.-Sls., Mktg. & Bus. Devel.--Pharmaceutical Formulations, Inc., Edison, NJ; *U.S. Public*, pg. 1284
Chin, James, Mgr.-Mktg.--Springer-Verlag New York Inc., New York, NY; *Int'l*, pg. 1291
Chinnery, R.J., Mktg. Communications Asst.--Thermal Ceramics Inc., Augusta, GA; *Int'l*, pg. 894
Chinnici, J.A., Jr., V.P.-Major Accounts--Great Lakes Lithograph Co., Cleveland, OH; *U.S. Private*, pg. 474
Chiostergi, Bob, V.P.-Mktg. & Sls.--Southern Mills, Inc., Union City, GA; *U.S. Private*, pg. 1016
Chisholm, Bridget, Dir.-Mktg.--Apple South, Inc., Madison, GA; *U.S. Public*, pg. 121
Chisom, Sherman, V.P.-Mktg. & Sls. Promo.--American Eurocopter Corp., Grand Prairie, TX; *Int'l*, pg. 29
Chittick, S. Woodworth, V.P.-Plng. & Bus. Devel.--Ocean Spray Cranberries, Inc., Middleboro, MA; *U.S. Private*, pg. 811
Chittum, Dru, Mktg. Coord.--The Flight International Group, Inc., Newport News, VA; *U.S. Public*, pg. 654
Chiu, Frieda, Mktg. Asst.--Vance Industries, Inc., Chicago, IL; *U.S. Private*, pg. 1133
Chizek, Joye, Mgr.-Mktg.--Kewanee Boiler Manufacturing Company, Inc., Kewanee, IL; *U.S. Public*, pg. 270
Cho, Soo Ho, Exec. V.P.-Sls., Mktg. & Traffic--Korean Airlines Co., Ltd., Seoul, Korea; *Int'l*, pg. 758
Choate, Eugene, Pres.--Bankers Fidelity Life Insurance Company, Atlanta, GA; *U.S. Public*, pg. 143
Choi, Chong-Hee, Mgr.--Ssangyong Precision Industry Co., Ltd., Inchon, Korea; *Int'l*, pg. 1292
Choi, Jae-Ho, Mgr.--Ssangyong Finance Inc., Seoul, Korea; *Int'l*, pg. 1292
Chole, Raquel, Mktg. Specialist--Dudek & Bock Spring Manufacturing Company, Chicago, IL; *U.S. Private*, pg. 344
Chomakos, James, Sr. V.P. & Mgr.-Mktg. Admin.--First Federal of Michigan, Detroit, MI; *U.S. Public*, pg. 336
Chong, Ivan, Mgr.-Mktg.--United Pulp & Paper Company Limited, Jurong, Singapore; *Int'l*, pg. 1444
Chong, Kaye, Mgr.-Admin, Mktg. & Sls.--Air Jamaica Ltd., Miami, FL; *U.S. Private*, pg. 28
Choo, Thomas, Dir.-Sls. & Mktg./RMS Opers.--Dun & Bradstreet Information Services (M) Sdn. Bhd., Kuala Lumpur, Malaysia; *U.S. Public*, pg. 536
Choppa, Robert, V.P.-Upholstery Mdsg.--Century Furniture Industries, Hickory, NC; *U.S. Private*, pg. 226
Chorney, Alvan F., Sr. V.P.-Sls. & Mktg.--Ferrofluidics Corporation, Nashua, NH; *U.S. Public*, pg. 620
Chou, Robert B.D., V.P.-Mktg.--Formosa Plastics Corp., U.S.A., Livingston, NJ; *Int'l*, pg. 498
Chowins, Chuck, Dir.-Media Logistics--Payless Cashways, Inc., Kansas City, MO; *U.S. Public*, pg. 1267
Chrietzberg, Gloria, Dir.-Mktg.--One Price Clothing Stores, Inc., Duncan, SC; *U.S. Public*, pg. 1225
Chriqui, Florence, Dir.-Intl. Mktg.--Berriel Vittel France, Paris, France; *Int'l*, pg. 918
Christa, Judy, V.P.-Mktg.--Adventure Tours USA, Inc., Dallas, TX; *U.S. Private*, pg. 22
Christenberry, Boyd E., Exec. V.P.-Mktg.--Alfa Life Insurance Corp., Montgomery, AL; *U.S. Public*, pg. 40
Christensen, Greg, Dir.-Mktg.--AJD, Richmond, VA; *U.S. Private*, pg. 510
Christensen, James, Dir.-Natl. Sls. & Mktg.--Decora', Jasper, IN; *U.S. Public*, pg. 675
Christensen, Palle, Mgr.-Mktg.--Aydin Telecom Division, Horsham, PA; *U.S. Public*, pg. 158
Christensen, Pam, Sr. Mgr.-Mktg.--Lifetouch, Portrait Studios, Eden Prairie, MN; *U.S. Private*, pg. 667
Christenson, Beth, Mgr.-Mktg.--Northland Aluminum Products, Inc., Minneapolis, MN; *U.S. Private*, pg. 805
Christenson, Rich, V.P.-Mktg.--Winona Knitting Mills, Inc., Winona, MN; *U.S. Public*, pg. 779
Christiansen, Kelly, Mgr.-Sls. & Mktg.--Ling Electronics Inc., Anaheim, CA; *U.S. Public*, pg. 1077
Christiansen, P., Mgr.-Mktg.--Toyota Norge A/S, Drammen, Norway; *Int'l*, pg. 1414
Christiansen, Poul Erik, Exec. V.P.-Mktg.--Royal Copenhagen A/S, Frederiksberg, Denmark; *Int'l*, pg. 1134
Christianson, Beth, Mgr.-Mktg.--Nordic Ware, Minneapolis, MN; *U.S. Private*, pg. 806
Christianson, C.H., Dir.-Mktg.--Iveco-Ford Truck Ltd., Watford, United Kingdom; *Int'l*, pg. 484
Christie, David, V.P.-Mktg.--Spicers Paper, Santa Fe Springs, CA; *Int'l*, pg. 72
Christie, Paul, Gen. Mgr.-Life Customer Services--Life Division, Rondebosch, South Africa; *Int'l*, pg. 77
Christie, Shelly Graziano, Mgr.-Mktg. Svcs.--Wausau Papers - Printing & Writing Div., Brokaw, WI; *U.S. Public*, pg. 1747
Christoff, Greg, V.P.-Mktg.--Paterno Imports Limited, Lake Bluff, IL; *U.S. Private*, pg. 843
Christy, Tom, Mgr.-Mktg. & Sls.--Comtech Antenna Systems, Inc., Saint Cloud, FL; *U.S. Public*, pg. 425
Chrysskopoulos, Dimitrios, Dir.-North & South America--Olympic Airways, New York, NY; *Int'l*, pg. 1004
Chu, Albert, V.P.-Mktg. Alliances & Rels.--Apple Computer, Inc., Cupertino, CA; *U.S. Public*, pg. 121
Chuchola, Tom, V.P.-Mktg--Jack Nadel, Inc., Culver City, CA; *U.S. Private*, pg. 773
Chudyte, Kevin, V.P.-Sls. & Mktg.--Nelmor Co., Inc., North Uxbridge, MA; *U.S. Private*, pg. 1041
Chudyte, Kevin, V.P.-Mktg. & Sls.--AEC/Whitlock, Inc., Wood Dale, IL; *U.S. Private*, pg. 1041
Chun, Tai Vee, V.P.-Prod.--Mutual Welding Co., Ltd, Honolulu, HI; *U.S. Private*, pg. 770
Chung, D.K., Dir.-ISD Mktg.--Samsung Electronics America, Inc., Ridgefield Park, NJ; *Int'l*, pg. 1183
Chung, Jong-Moo, Chief Fin. Officer--Ssangyong Resources Development Co., Ltd., Tonghae, Korea; *Int'l*, pg. 1291
Church, Jack, V.P.-Mktg. & Sls.--Hitchcock Industries, Inc., Bloomington, MN; *U.S. Private*, pg. 531
Churgen, Andy, Dir.-Mktg.--Gerry Baby Products Company, Thornton, CO; *U.S. Private*, pg. 629
Chwalek, Joe, V.P.-Sls. & Mktg.--IKG Industries, Clark, NJ; *U.S. Public*, pg. 793
Chye, Tan Peng, Sr. Mgr.-Mktg.--The Great Eastern Life Assurance Company Limited, Singapore, Singapore; *Int'l, pg. 557*
Cianciaruso, C. J., Mgr.-Sls.--Dunn Industries Inc., Kansas City, MO; *U.S. Private*, pg. 347
Cianciaruso, C.J., Sr. V.P.-Mktg.-Special Projects--J.E. Dunn Construction Co., Kansas City, MO; *U.S. Private*, pg. 347
Ciappi, A., Dir.-Mktg.--Eli Lilly Italia, S.p.A., Sesto Fiorentino, Italy; *U.S. Public*, pg. 994
Ciesmier, S.M., Mgr.-Mktg.--Dussek Campbell, Inc., Skokie, IL; *Int'l*, pg. 234
Cimalore, Patti, Mgr.-Sls. & Mktg.--Jan-Co., Inc., Cranston, RI; *U.S. Private*, pg. 581
Cini, Chrishiun, Dir.-Mktg.- Alfa Romeo--Fiat Auto Suisse SA, Geneva, Switzerland; *Int'l*, pg. 481
Cionetti, Doug, Mgr.-Mktg.-PCSD--Aromat Corporation, New Providence, NJ; *Int'l*, pg. 847
Cira, Laura, Mgr.-Adv.--Holiday Rambler, Wakarusa, IN; *U.S.* Public, pg. 1123
Cirilli, Dante, Pres. & Dir.-Mktg. Div.--Grolier Inc., Danbury, CT; *Int'l*, pg. 794
Cisek, R., Dir.-Mktg.--Tubed Products, Inc., Easthampton, MA; *U.S. Public*, pg. 1066
Cisler, Michael, V.P.-Mktg.--JanSport, Appleton, WI; *U.S. Public*, pg. 1702
Civanbay, Osman, Mgr.-Domestic Mktg.--Arcelik A.S., Istanbul, Turkey; *Int'l*, pg. 741
Claassen, James G., Sr. V.P.-Sls. & Sls. Services--Montgomery KONE Inc., Moline, IL; *Int'l*, pg. 746
Claes, Marry Anne, Mgr.-Mktg.--Lee Europe N.V., Brussels, Belgium; *U.S. Public*, pg. 1702
Claesson, Beugt, Mgr.-Sls. & Mktg.--Ledu International AB, Bohus, Sweden; *Int'l*, pg. 821
Claflin, Bruce L., Sr. V.P.-Sls. & Mktg.--Digital Equipment Corporation, Maynard, MA; *U.S. Public*, pg. 507
Claire, Franklin, V.P.-Distr.--The B. Manischewitz Company, Jersey City, NJ; *U.S. Private*, pg. 699
Clancy, Joe, Gen. Mgr.-Customer Mktg.--Star-Kist Foods Inc., Newport, KY; *U.S. Public*, pg. 805
Clapes, Jorge, Chief Fin. Officer--Johnson & Johnson de Argentina, S.A., Buenos Aires, Argentina; *U.S. Public*, pg. 930
Clapp, Amy, Mgr.-Mktg. Commun.--TelCom Semiconductor, Inc., Mountain View, CA; *U.S. Public*, pg. 1569
Clapper, Sarah, Mgr.-Mktg. Communications--Nalge Company, Rochester, NY; *U.S. Public*, pg. 1545
Clare, Bob, Dir.-Mktg.--Federal Farm Credit Banks Funding Corporation, Jersey City, NJ; *U.S. Private*, pg. 398
Clark, Alvin W., V.P.-Transmission Mktg.--El Paso Natural Gas Co., Houston, TX; *U.S. Public*, pg. 567
Clark, Celeste, Dir.-Mktg.--Medieval Times Dinner & Tournament, Inc., Buena Park, CA; *U.S. Private*, pg. 728
Clark, Celeste A., V.P.-Worldwide Nutrition Mktg.--Kellogg Company, Battle Creek, MI; *U.S. Public*, pg. 947
Clark, Courtney, Dir.-Mktg.--Kenneth Cole Productions, New York, NY; *U.S. Public*, pg. 951
Clark, Debra, V.P.-Mktg.--First Union National Bank of Florida, Jacksonville, FL; *U.S. Public*, pg. 640
Clark, Duane D., V.P.-Gas Mktg.--Belden & Blake Corporation, Canton, OH; *U.S. Private*, pg. 1078
Clark, Duncan, Pres.-Columbia TriStar Film Distr.--Columbia Pictures, Culver City, CA; *Int'l*, pg. 1281
Clark, J., Dir.-Sls. & Mktg.--Oland Breweries Limited, Halifax, Canada; *Int'l*, pg. 679
Clark, Kenneth J., V.P.-Mktg.--Baldwin Piano & Organ Company, Loveland, OH; *U.S. Public*, pg. 169
Clark, Lamar, V.P.-Adv., Mktg. & Sls.--Binning's Building Products, Inc., Lexington, NC; *U.S. Public*, pg. 67
Clark, Larry, Mgr.-Mkt. Devel.--Subaru Mid-America, Inc., Addison, IL; *Int'l*, pg. 523
Clark, Lewis, V.P.-Sls. & Mktg.-Controls--Kidde-Fenwal, Inc., Ashland, MA; *Int'l*, pg. 1500
Clark, MacDonald, Chief Mktg. Officer--Alamo Rent-A-Car Inc., Fort Lauderdale, FL; *U.S. Public*, pg. 1379
Clark, Paul, V.P.-Mktg.--The Sports Network (TSN), Willowdale, Canada; *Int'l*, pg. 1343
Clark, Peter, V.P.-Sls. & Mktg.-Protection--Kidde-Fenwal, Inc., Ashland, MA; *Int'l*, pg. 1500
Clark, Richard A., Mgr.-Sls. & Mktg.--Target Oilfield Pipe & Supply Company (TOPS), Canton, OH; *U.S. Private*, pg. 1078
Clark, Robert, V.P.-Mktg. Strategy & Sls. Plng.--John B. Sanfilippo & Son, Inc., Elk Grove Village, IL; *U.S. Public*, pg. 1431
Clark, Robert J., V.P.-Sls. & Mktg.--Alden Shoe Co., Inc., Middleboro, MA; *U.S. Private*, pg. 33
Clark, Sarah F., Asst. Dir.-Mktg.--Yale University Press, New Haven, CT; *U.S. Private*, pg. 1195
Clark, Sharon R., V.P.-Corp. Mktg.--Marcam Solutions, Inc., Newton, MA; *U.S. Public*, pg. 1042
Clark, Steve, Mgr.-Mktg.--Varian X-Ray Tube Products, Salt Lake City, UT; *U.S. Public*, pg. 1710
Clark, Tim, Dir.-Mktg.--Medic Computer Systems, Inc., Raleigh, NC; *Int'l*, pg. 870
Clark, Tony, Dir.-Mktg.-Commercial--Sony Music Entertainment (UK) Limited, London, United Kingdom; *Int'l*, pg. 1284
Clark, Traci, Mktg. Coord.--Utah Medical Products, Inc., Midvale, UT; *U.S. Public*, pg. 1700
Clark, Veda, V.P.-Mktg. & Sls.--Litecontrol Corporation, Hanson, MA; *U.S. Private*, pg. 669
Clarke, Graeme, Sr. V.P.-AAA Products & Services--American Automobile Association, Heathrow, FL; *U.S. Private*, pg. 50
Clarke, John, Dir.-Mktg.--Tempo Products Company, Solon, OH; *U.S. Private*, pg. 870
Clarke, John G., Sr. V.P.-Mktg.--Dr. Pepper Co., Dallas, TX; *Int'l*, pg. 248
Clarke, Tim, Mgr.-Mktg.-West--Intermountain Gas Co., Boise, ID; *U.S. Private*, pg. 568
Claus, Catherine, Mktg. Communications Specialist--Carborundum Abrasives North America, High Point, NC; *Int'l*, pg. 1174
Clause, Pascal, Dir.-Mktg., Salomon--Salomon S.A., Annecy, France; *Int'l*, pg. 1181
Clawson, Lynne, Mgr.-Mktg. Services--Dillard, A ResourceNet International Company, Greensboro, NC; *U.S. Public*, pg. 901
Clayton, Richard M., V.P.-Mktg.--Mining Services International, Inc., Sandy, UT; *U.S. Public*, pg. 1115
Cleage, Erik, V.P.-Mktg.--Altera Corporation, San Jose, CA; *U.S. Public*, pg. 59
Cleary, Aileen, Mgr.-Mktg. Instrument Grp.--Barnes Engineering, Shelton, CT; *U.S. Public*, pg. 542
Cleary, Jeff, V.P.-Mktg.--Galoob Toys, Inc., South San Francisco, CA; *U.S. Public*, pg. 698
Cledeland, Kathleen Donegan, Dir.-Mktg.--Acme Boot Co., Inc., El Paso, TX; *U.S. Private*, pg. 394
Cleeremans, Catherine, Sr. Mgr.-Mktg.--J. Hungerford Smith Company, Fullerton, CA; *U.S. Public*, pg. 428
Clegg, Tom, Sr. V.P.-Brand Mktg.--Sargento Foods Inc., Plymouth, WI; *U.S. Private*, pg. 966
Clegg, Tom, V.P.-Mktg.--Sargento Foods Inc., Plymouth, WI; *U.S. Private*, pg. 966
Clelland, Jim, V.P.-Sls. & Mktg.--Alcoa Forged Products, Cleveland, OH; *U.S. Public*, pg. 60
Clem, Patricia, Mgr.-Mktg. Communications--UTILX Corporation, Kent, WA; *U.S. Public*, pg. 1701
Clement, Mark, Mgr.-Mktg.--Rod & Bar Products Division, Port Waratah, Australia; *Int'l*, pg. 227
Clement, Susan, Principal Area Leader-Mktg. Promos.--DTE Energy Company, Detroit, MI; *U.S. Public*, pg. 475
Clement, Teri, Asst. V.P. & Mgr.-Mktg.--Robert F. Driver Co., Inc., San Diego, CA; *U.S. Private*, pg. 343
Clements, M., Dir.-Bus. Devel.--Quadrastat Corp., City of Industry, CA; *U.S. Private*, pg. 17
Clements, Rob, Exec. V.P.-Sls. & Mktg.--Clairson International Corp., Ocala, FL; *U.S. Public*, pg. 575
Clemmons, Neil, V.P.-Mktg./Personal Commun. Div.--3Com Corporation, Santa Clara, CA; *U.S. Public*, pg. 1603
Clemmons, Neil, V.P.-Mktg.--3Com Personal Communications Div., Skokie, IL; *U.S. Public*, pg. 1604
Clemons, Maurine, Mktg.--Regions Bank/Albertville/Guntersville/Arab, Albertville, AL; *U.S. Public*, pg. 1371
Cleveland, Arthur E., Dir.-Prod. Devel. & Mktg.--Spartech Plastics, Portage, WI; *U.S. Public*, pg. 1496
Cleveland, Colleen, V.P.-Mktg.--Snack America, Los Angeles, CA; *U.S. Private*, pg. 1010
Cleveland, Colleen, V.P.-Mktg.--Internut, Secaucus, NJ; *U.S.* Private, pg. 1010
Cleveland, Jeff, Market Devel. Specialist--Aerolyte Systems, Washington, MO; *U.S. Private*, pg. 24
Cleveland, Rich, Dir.-Mktg.--Parker Brothers, Beverly, MA; *U.S. Public*, pg. 797
Clevenger, Mark, Mgr.-Mktg. Communications--Inland Container Corporation, Indianapolis, IN; *U.S. Public*, pg. 1575
Clifford, John, Dir.-Containerboard Sls. & Mktg.--Gaylord Container Corporation, Deerfield, IL; *U.S. Public*, pg. 704
Clifford, John W., V.P. -Mktg.--Killington Limited, Killington, VT; *U.S. Private*, pg. 61
Clifton, Dianne, Mgr.-Mktg. & Communications--Centex Corporation, Dallas, TX; *U.S. Public*, pg. 322
Clifton, Paul H., Jr., Sr. V.P.-Sls. & Mktg.--Colonial Companies, Inc., Columbia, SC; *U.S. Public*, pg. 1699
Cline, Amy, Dir.-Mktg.--ATCOM, Inc., Research Triangle Park, NC; *U.S. Private*, pg. 94
Cline, Randy, Sr. V.P.-Mktg.--Regence BlueCross BlueShield of Oregon, Portland, OR; *U.S. Private*, pg. 917
Cline, Robbie, Supvr.-Mktg. Communications--Siecor Corporation, Hickory, NC; *U.S. Public*, pg. 449
Cline, Robbie, Supvr.-Mktg. Communications--Siecor Corporation, Hickory, NC; *Int'l*, pg. 1245
Clinton, Stephen P., Chief Oper. Officer & Sr. V.P.--Hayes, Seay, Mattern & Mattern, Inc., Roanoke, VA; *U.S. Private*, pg. 513
Clinton, Tom, Dir.-Reg. Sls.--Nissan Forklift Corporation, North America, Marengo, IL; *Int'l*, pg. 944
Close, Allyn D., Pres., Chief Exec. Officer & Mgr.-Sls. & Mktg.--Interpacific Investors Services, Seattle, WA; *U.S. Private*, pg. 572
Close, Ross, V.P.-Sls. & Mktg.--Astra Pharma Inc., Mississauga, Canada; *Int'l*, pg. 94
Clouatre, Francis, Mgr.-Mktg.--Jordan's Foods-Westbrook Division, Westbrook, ME; *U.S. Private*, pg. 599
Cloud, Eugene H., V.P.-Mktg.--Micron Technology Inc., Boise, ID; *U.S. Public*, pg. 1105
Clough, Andy, Dir.-Mktg.--Fifth Quarter, Nashville, TN; *U.S. Public*, pg. 1467
Clough, Barry, Dir.-Mktg. Support Services--Caterpillar Inc., Peoria, IL; *U.S. Public*, pg. 315
Cloyd, Wade W., Dir.-Media & Mktg.--Ethika Corporation, Hilton Head Island, SC; *U.S. Public*, pg. 595
Clunk, James, Mgr.-Sls.--The Hall China Company, East Liverpool, OH; *U.S. Private*, pg. 494
Clyde, Jim, V.P.-Mktg.--Atlas Copco Wagner Inc., Portland, OR; *Int'l*, pg. 96
Clyde, Robert W., Exec. V.P.-Mktg. & Sls.--The Acacia Group - Acacia Life Insurance Co., Bethesda, MD; *U.S. Private*, pg. 10

Coalter, Rick, Dir.-Mktg.--J.A. Sexauer, Inc., Scarsdale, NY; *U.S. Private*, pg. 352

Coatesman, Hillary, Dir.-Mktg.--Gestetner Holdings PLC, London, United Kingdom; *Int'l*, pg. 1114

Cobb, Alice, Second V.P.-Mktg. Admin.--Columbian Mutual Life Insurance Co., Binghamton, NY; *U.S. Private*, pg. 256

Cobb, John W., Sr. V.P.-Mktg.--McGraw-Hill Continuing Education Center, Washington, DC; *U.S. Public*, pg. 1070

Cobb, John W., Jr., Sr. V.P.-Mktg.--NRI Schools, Washington, DC; *U.S. Public*, pg. 1071

Cobb, Maria, Mgr.-Apparel--Coats North America, Charlotte, NC; *Int'l*, pg. 300

Cobb, Michael, Dir.-Mktg.--Stratton Corporation, Stratton Mountain, VT; *Int'l*, pg. 685

Cobbledick, Paul C., Dir.-Sls. & Mktg.--Reynolds Metals Co.-Can Division Headquarters, Richmond, VA; *U.S. Public*, pg. 1386

Cobelo, H.R., Dr., Dir.-Mktg. & Sls.-USA--Leiner-Davis International Limited, Gladesville, Australia; *Int'l*, pg. 555

Coben, John B., Exec. V.P.-Mktg.--Nashville Machine Co. Inc., Nashville, TN; *U.S. Private*, pg. 774

Cobuzzi, Peter, V.P.-Mktg.--Tourneau Inc., New York, NY; *U.S. Private*, pg. 1093

Cocco, Dennis A., Dir.-Corp. & Investor Affairs--The Geon Company, Avon Lake, OH; *U.S. Public*, pg. 733

Cochran, Charles T., V.P.-Sls. & Mktg., Cold Finished Bar Div.--Republic Engineered Steels, Inc., Massillon, OH; *U.S. Public*, pg. 1378

Cochran, John R., III, Sr. Vice Chm. & Chief Mktg. Officer--MBNA Corporation, Wilmington, DE; *U.S. Public*, pg. 1023

Cochran, John R., III, Sr. Vice Chm. & Chief Mktg. Officer--MBNA America Bank N.A., Wilmington, DE; *U.S. Public*, pg. 1023

Cochran, Julie M., Dir.-Mktg. & Client Service--Rogge Global Plc, London, United Kingdom; *U.S. Public*, pg. 1674

Cochran, Ron, Mgr.-Mktg.--American Marking Systems, Clifton, NJ; *U.S. Private*, pg. 58

Cochran, Ron, Dir.-Mktg.--Kokosing Construction Company, Inc., Fredericktown, OH; *U.S. Private*, pg. 631

Cockrell, Glenn, V.P.-Sls. & Mktg.--Shealy Electrical Wholesalers, Greenville, SC; *U.S. Private*, pg. 991

Cockrill, Al, V.P.-Sls. & Mktg.--York Barbell Co., Inc., York, PA; *U.S. Private*, pg. 1196

Cockuyt, Alec, Dir.-Sls. & Mktg.--The Yorkville Printing Group Limited, Mississauga, Canada; *Int'l*, pg. 538

Coddington, Arthur, Brand Mgr.--Wham-O, Inc., San Francisco, CA; *U.S. Private*, pg. 1170

Coe, Roger, V.P.-Sls. & Mktg.--Andiamo, Inc., Fountain Valley, CA; *U.S. Private*, pg. 73

Coen, Terrence F., V.P. & Dir.-Sls. & Mktg.--Survey Sampling, Inc., Fairfield, CT; *U.S. Private*, pg. 1056

Coerver, Todd, Mgr.-Mktg.--Whataburger, Inc., Corpus Christi, TX; *U.S. Private*, pg. 1170

Cof, Daniel S., New Prod. Mktg. Mgr.--Reynolds Metals Co.-Can Division Headquarters, Richmond, VA; *U.S. Public*, pg. 1386

Coffeen, W.G., III, V.P.-Mktg.--Mobile Gas Service Corp., Mobile, AL; *U.S. Public*, pg. 1120

Coffey, Patrick, V.P.-Mktg.--Citizens Insurance Company of America, Howell, MI; *U.S. Public*, pg. 54

Coffman, Debbie, Dir.-Mktg.--Overseas Service Corporation, West Palm Beach, FL; *U.S. Private*, pg. 823

Coffman, H. Frank, V.P.-Customer Service & Communications--The Standard Register Company, Dayton, OH; *U.S. Public*, pg. 1505

Cogen, Jeff, V.P.-Mktg. & Adv.--Dallas Stars, Irving, TX; *U.S. Private*, pg. 309

Cogger, Nancy, Dir.-Mktg.--Arby's Canada Inc., Mississauga, Canada; *U.S. Public*, pg. 1635

Coggin, Michael L., V.P.-Mktg. Services--Russell Corporation, Alexander City, AL; *U.S. Public*, pg. 1413

Coggin, Robert W., Exec. V.P.-Mktg.--Delta Air Lines, Inc., Atlanta, GA; *U.S. Public*, pg. 497

Cohen-Tanugi, Florence, Dir.-Mktg.-Chocolate--Kraft Jacobs Suchard, Velizy-Villacoublay, France; *U.S. Public*, pg. 1290

Cohen, Alan, Exec. V.P.-Mktg.-ABC Television Network--ABC, Inc, New York, NY; *U.S. Public*, pg. 511

Cohen, Alan, V.P.-Brand Mngmt.--JBB Worldwide, Inc., Deerfield, IL; *U.S. Public*, pg. 675

Cohen, Bernard G., Dir.-Business Devel.--SRA International Inc., Arlington, VA; *U.S. Private*, pg. 957

Cohen, Joel H., V.P.-Sls. & Mktg.--Queen Carpet Corporation, Dalton, GA; *U.S. Private*, pg. 900

Cohen, Leslie, V.P.-Consumer Mktg.--Harrison & Star, Inc., New York, NY; *U.S. Private*, pg. 506

Cohen, Louis D., V.P.-Mktg.--Allen Foods, Inc., Saint Louis, MO; *U.S. Private*, pg. 37

Cohen, Mark J., Exec. V.P.-Sls. & Mktg.--All-Luminum Products, Inc., Philadelphia, PA; *U.S. Private*, pg. 34

Cohen, Meryl, Pres.-Mktg.--Paramount Pictures Corporation, Los Angeles, CA; *U.S. Private*, pg. 776

Cohen, Nina, V.P.-Mktg.--Norwegian Cruise Line, Miami, FL; *U.S. Private*, pg. 808

Cohen, Stuart, V.P.-Worldwide Mktg.--In Focus Systems, Inc., Wilsonville, OR; *U.S. Public*, pg. 873

Cohlst, C.G., Pres.-Mktg. & Sls.--UBO Verzekeringen, Utrecht, Netherlands; *Int'l*, pg. 26

Cohn, Derek, Sr. V.P.-Mktg. & Sls.--International Plastics Company, New York, NY; *U.S. Private*, pg. 571

Cohn, Julie Ann, Exec. V.P. & Database Mktg. Dir.--Western International Media Corporation, Los Angeles, CA; *U.S. Private*, pg. 1165

Cohn, Martin, Dir.-Industrial, Office & Real Estate--Vornado Realty Trust, Saddle Brook, NJ; *U.S. Public*, pg. 1725

Cohn, Thomas, V.P. & Dir.-Mktg.--Sigmund Cohn Corp., Mount Vernon, NY; *U.S. Private*, pg. 250

Cohodes, Mary D., Admin.--Independent Metals, Germantown, WI; *U.S. Private*, pg. 559

Coker, Murray, V.P.-Mktg.--Camping World, Inc., Bowling Green, KY; *U.S. Private*, pg. 204

Coker, Terry C., Dir.-Mktg.--Old Fashion Foods, Inc., Austell, GA; *U.S. Private*, pg. 814

Coladarci, Paul, V.P.-Mktg.--Broad National Bank, Newark, NJ; *U.S. Public*, pg. 257

Coladarci, Paul H., V.P.-Mktg.--Broad National Bancorporation, Newark, NJ; *U.S. Public*, pg. 257

Colamussi, Karen, Sr. V.P.-Mktg.--Atlantic Recording Corporation, New York, NY; *U.S. Public*, pg. 1611

Colando, Greg, Sr. V.P.-Sls. & Mktg.--Interface Flooring Systems Inc., La Grange, GA; *U.S. Public*, pg. 889

Colavita, Tracy, Mgr.-Mktg.--Woodward-Clyde, Raleigh, NC; *U.S. Public*, pg. 1656

Colaw, Lisa, Field Mktg. Specialist--La Petite Academy Inc., Overland Park, KS; *U.S. Private*, pg. 640

Colburn, Robert B., V.P.-Sls. & Mktg.--Bauer Sports Inc., Montreal, Canada; *U.S. Public*, pg. 1184

Colby, Albert A., Jr., V.P.-Domestic Phosphate, Treas. & Sec.--International Chemical Company, Tulsa, OK; *U.S. Private*, pg. 568

Colcord, Diana, Coord.-Mktg.--Eneco Tech Group, Denver, CO; *U.S. Private*, pg. 376

Cole, Barry D., Mgr.-Mktg. Com.--Norton Company, Worcester, MA; *Int'l*, pg. 1173

Cole, Charles, Dir.-Sls. & Mktg.--Protective Closures Co., Inc., Buffalo, NY; *U.S. Public*, pg. 1045

Cole, Chuck, Dir.-Mktg.--Utility Trailer Manufacturing Co., City of Industry, CA; *U.S. Private*, pg. 1130

Cole, Jack, V.P.-Healthcare Mktg.--Pall Corporation, Greenvale, NY; *U.S. Public*, pg. 1253

Cole, Jodi, Coord.-Mktg. Services--Tesa Tuck Inc., Sparta, MI; *Int'l*, pg. 182

Cole, Julie, Mgr.-Mktg.--Barnhardt Manufacturing Co., Charlotte, NC; *U.S. Private*, pg. 116

Cole, Ray, Dir.-Mktg.--Allied Tire Sales, Orlando, FL; *U.S. Private*, pg. 41

Cole, Robert M., V.P.-Mktg. & Sls.--Arkwright, Inc, Fiskeville, RI; *Int'l*, pg. 994

Cole, Sebastian, Dir.-Sls. & Mktg.--Colex International, Ltd., Leicester, United Kingdom; *U.S. Private*, pg. 796

Cole, Steven, V.P.-Sls. & Mktg.--Park Foods L.P., Barrington, IL; *U.S. Private*, pg. 839

Coleburns, Will, V.P.-Mktg. & Sls.--Koh-I-Noor, Inc., Bloomsbury, NJ; *U.S. Private*, pg. 629

Coleman, Bob, V.P.-& Mktg.--BWAY Corp., Atlanta, GA; *U.S. Public*, pg. 164

Coleman, Bob, V.P.-Mktg.--Brockway Standard Ohio, Inc., Solon, OH; *U.S. Public*, pg. 164

Coleman, Don, Dir.-Mktg.--Coca-Cola Consolidated, Charlotte, NC; *U.S. Public*, pg. 392

Coleman, Mary, V.P.-Mktg.--M. Kamenstein, Inc., Elmsford, NY; *U.S. Private*, pg. 606

Coleman, Paul, V.P.- Adv. & Mktg.--Farmer Jack Supermarkets, Detroit, MI; *Int'l*, pg. 1375

Coleman, R. Glen, V.P.-Mktg.--Xomed Surgical Products, Jacksonville, FL; *U.S. Public*, pg. 253

Coleman, Robert, V.P. & Gen. Mgr.--Fasson Films, Painesville, OH; *U.S. Public*, pg. 153

Coleman, Roxanne, Supvr.-Mktg., Adv. & Sls.--Shakespeare Fishing Tackle, Columbia, SC; *U.S. Public*, pg. 940

Coleman, W. Stephen, V.P.-Mktg.--Moore Business Forms & Systems Div., Lake Forest, IL; *Int'l*, pg. 890

Colen, Mary Leach, Sr. V.P.-Mktg.--L.F. Driscoll Co., Bala Cynwyd, PA; *U.S. Private*, pg. 343

Coles, Carl R., Mgr.-Mktg.--MD Pneumatics, Springfield, MO; *U.S. Private*, pg. 1111

Coletti, Alexandre, Mgr.-Clothing Mktg.--Sao Paulo Alpargatas S.A., Sao Paulo, Brazil; *Int'l*, pg. 1193

Coley, Connie, Mktg.--Regions Bank/Cherokee County, Centre, AL; *U.S. Public*, pg. 1372

Colford, Matt, Mgr.-Mktg.--Old Dutch Foods, Inc., Roseville, MN; *U.S. Private*, pg. 814

Coll, Edward M., Gen. Mgr.-Systems Div.--Moore Products Co., Spring House, PA; *U.S. Public*, pg. 1128

Coll, Esteban, Dir.-Mktg.--Refinerias de Maiz S.A.I.C.F., Buenos Aires, Argentina; *U.S. Public*, pg. 448

Collard, Lori A., Dir.-Mktg.--Minnesota Power, Duluth, MN; *U.S. Public*, pg. 1116

Colletti, Deborah, V.P.-Mktg.--NOVUS Financial Corporation, Riverwoods, IL; *U.S. Public*, pg. 1132

Colletti, Gaspare, Dir.-Sls. & Mktg.--Reynolds Extrusion Company, Richmond Hill, Canada; *U.S. Public*, pg. 1387

Colliander, Dan, Dir.-Mktg.--Braun, North America, Woburn, MA; *U.S. Public*, pg. 743

Collier, Deanie, V.P.-Adv.--Stein Mart, Inc., Jacksonville, FL; *U.S. Public*, pg. 1514

Collins, Carol A., Leader-Services Delivery--Bay State Gas Company, Westborough, MA; *U.S. Public*, pg. 196

Collins, Carroll, Mgr.-Consumer Promotion--Futuro Inc., Milford, OH; *Int'l*, pg. 182

Collins, Dan, Dir.-Mktg.--The Ritz-Carlton Hotel Company LLC, Atlanta, GA; *U.S. Private*, pg. 594

Collins, Gerry, V.P.-Sls. & Mktg.--M K Diamond Products, Inc., Torrance, CA; *U.S. Private*, pg. 684

Collins, Jane, Mgr.-Retail Mktg.--Little, Brown & Co., New York, NY; *U.S. Public*, pg. 1612

Collins, Janet, Dir.-Communications--Philips Medical Systems North America Company, Shelton, CT; *Int'l*, pg. 1055

Collins, Karen, V.P.-Mktg.--First Bank N.A., Milwaukee, WI; *U.S. Public*, pg. 1680

Collins, Marie M., V.P.-Mktg.--Columbia Tri-Star Film Distributors International, Culver City, CA; *Int'l*, pg. 1281

Collins, Maureen, Specialist-Mktg.--Textron Systems, Wilmington, MA; *U.S. Public*, pg. 1589

Collins, Michael, V.P.-Mktg.--Monticello Drug Co., Jacksonville, FL; *U.S. Private*, pg. 759

Collins, Michael, Sr. Dir.-Mktg.--Software AG Americas, Inc., Reston, VA; *U.S. Public*, pg. 1482

Collins, Randy, V.P.-Sls. & Mktg.--Gorges/Quik-To-Fix Foods, Dallas, TX; *U.S. Private*, pg. 465

Collins, Richard, Sr. V.P.-Sls. & Mktg.--Golden Books Family Entertainment Inc., New York, NY; *U.S. Public*, pg. 749

Collins, Stephen, Dir.-Intl. Mktg.--IGI, Inc., Buena, NJ; *U.S. Public*, pg. 855

Collins, Susan, V.P.-Consumer Mktg.--DirecTV Inc., El Segundo, CA; *U.S. Public*, pg. 720

Collins, Tom, V.P.-Mktg.--Hancock Fabrics, Inc., Tupelo, MS; *U.S. Public*, pg. 779

Collison, Buffy, V.P.-Worldwide Mktg.--J.D. Edwards & Company, Denver, CO; *U.S. Private*, pg. 365

Colman, John, III, V.P.-Mktg.--Adams Extract Co., Inc., Austin, TX; *U.S. Private*, pg. 16

Colombatto, Jay, Dir.-Mktg.--Core-Mark International, South San Francisco, CA; *U.S. Private*, pg. 275

Colon, Conrad O., V.P.-Mktg.--Goya Foods, Inc., Secaucus, NJ; *U.S. Private*, pg. 468

Colonna, Mark, Chief Oper. Officer-Mktg & Exec. V.P.--Colonna Bros., Inc., North Bergen, NJ; *U.S. Private*, pg. 254

Colpo, Terri, V.P.-Mktg.--20th Century Industries, Woodland Hills, CA; *U.S. Public*, pg. 1646

Colson, Jim, V.P.-Sls. & Customer Service--AT&T Alascom, Anchorage, AK; *U.S. Public*, pg. 10

Coltin, Rachel D., Mgr.-Mktg. Communications--Tuscarora Incorporated, New Brighton, PA; *U.S. Public*, pg. 1646

Coltman, David A., Sr. V.P.-Mktg.--UAL Corporation, Elk Grove Village, IL; *U.S. Public*, pg. 1652

Colucci, James, Sr. V.P. Sls., Mktg. & Dir.-Creative & Mgr.-Sls. Promo.--Consolidated Cigar Corporation, Fort Lauderdale, FL; *U.S. Private*, pg. 690

Coluccio, Shelly, Dir.-Mktg.--Tanning Research Labs., Inc., Ormond Beach, FL; *U.S. Private*, pg. 1068

Colwell, Mike, Dir.-Mktg.--Norand Mobile Systems Div., Cedar Rapids, IA; *U.S. Public*, pg. 1699

Combe, Christopher B., Pres.--Combe Incorporated, White Plains, NY; *U.S. Private*, pg. 257

Combs, T.H., Sr. Mgr.-Prod./Tobacco--Conwood Company L.P., Memphis, TN; *U.S. Private*, pg. 272

Comer, Carol L., Rep.-Mktg. Services--BF Goodrich Avionic Systems, Inc., Grand Rapids, MI; *U.S. Public*, pg. 751

Comer, John, Gen. Mgr.-Consumer Pkgng.--Flexible Packaging Division, Chicago, IL; *U.S. Public*, pg. 1521

Comerford, Mark, Mgr.-Mktg. Commun.--Alpha Industries, Inc., Woburn, MA; *U.S. Public*, pg. 57

Comiskey, Paul, V.P.-Mktg.--World Carpets, Inc., Dalton, GA; *U.S. Private*, pg. 1190

Commander, Dave, V.P.-Mktg.--Russell Corp., Athletic Div., Alexander City, AL; *U.S. Public*, pg. 1413

Commette, Liz, Dir.-Mktg.--Kathabar Incorporated, Somerset, NJ; *U.S. Private*, pg. 609

Compton, Sherre, Mgr.-Mktg. & Adv.--Wells/Bloomfield, Verdi, NV; *U.S. Public*, pg. 1497

Compton, Tim, Dir.-Mktg.--Foley-Belsaw Company, Minneapolis, MN; *U.S. Private*, pg. 416

Comyn, Barbara, Mgr.-Film Mktg.--Agfa-Gevaert S.A., Rueil-Malmaison, France; *Int'l*, pg. 174

Conabee, Earl, V.P.-Mktg.--Thermo Materials, Scottdale, GA; *U.S. Public*, pg. 330

Conarroe, Richard, V.P.-Mktg. & Sls.--The Thermos Company, Schaumburg, IL; *Int'l*, pg. 938

Conaway, Ken, Dir.-Mktg. & Sls.--Future Foam, Inc., Council Bluffs, IA; *U.S. Private*, pg. 433

Concepcion, Antonio V., Sr. V.P. & Chief Mktg. Officer--La Tondena Distillers, Inc., Manila, Philippines; *Int'l*, pg. 785

Conciatu, Chris, Mgr.-Mktg. Analyst--Bundy North America, Warren, MI; *Int'l*, pg. 1340

Conda, Joseph V., V.P.-Glass Container Sls. & Mktg.--Owens-Illinois, Inc., Toledo, OH; *U.S. Public*, pg. 1238

Conda, Joseph V., V.P.-Sls. & Mktg.--Owens-Brockway Glass Containers, Toledo, OH; *U.S. Public*, pg. 1238

Conde, Clemente, Dir.-Mktg.--Easy Gardener Inc., Waco, TX; *U.S. Public*, pg. 1682

Conde, Clemente, Dir.-Mktg.--Weatherly Consumer Products, Paris, KY; *U.S. Public*, pg. 1682

Condiles, Gus, V.P.-Mktg.-Bed & Bath--CHF Industries, Inc., New York, NY; *U.S. Private*, pg. 1094

Condom, Mark, V.P.-Publications/Mktg.--CUNA Service Group, Inc., Madison, WI; *U.S. Private*, pg. 288

Condon, Richard, V.P.-Mktg.--Banfi Vintners, Old Brookville, NY; *U.S. Private*, pg. 113

Condon, Stephen, Dir.-Mktg.--DirecTV Inc., El Segundo, CA; *U.S. Public*, pg. 720

Cone, Angela, Mgr.-Mktg.--Numetrix Ltd., Manchester, United Kingdom; *Int'l*, pg. 990

Cone, Tim, Dir.-Sls. & Mktg.--Hahn Automotive Warehouse, Inc., Rochester, NY; *U.S. Public*, pg. 774

Confusione, Jack, V.P. & Dir.-Mktg. & Cash Mngmt.--Credit Lyonnais Americas, New York, NY; *Int'l*, pg. 344

Congleton, George L., V.P.-Mktg.--Baker Commodities, Inc., Los Angeles, CA; *U.S. Private*, pg. 111

Conibear, Jon, Dir.-Mktg.--Blackwell Science, Oxford, United Kingdom; *Int'l*, pg. 197

Conklin, Kevin, V.P.-Mktg.--Concord Communications, Inc., Marlborough, MA; *U.S. Public*, pg. 429

Conklin, Margaret N., Mgr.-Mktg. Communications--Strathmore Paper, Granby, CT; *U.S. Public*, pg. 903

Conley, George M., V.P.-Mktg.--American City Business Journals, Inc., Charlotte, NC; *U.S. Private*, pg. 19

Conlin, R.F., V.P.-Mktg.--General Motors of Canada Ltd., Oshawa, Canada; *U.S. Public*, pg. 722

Conlon, Caryn, Mgr.-Mktg.--Turner Steiner International, New York, NY; *U.S. Public*, pg. 1646

Connell, Susan L., V.P.-Mktg.--Deltec, San Diego, CA; *Int'l*, pg. 126

Connelly, Marcie, Dir.-Mktg.--Burdick, Inc., Milton, WI; *U.S. Private*, pg. 181

Conner, Betty, Direct Mktg./Direct Response--McGraw-Hill Financial Information Services Group, New York, NY; *U.S. Public*, pg. 1071

Conner, Gail, Dir.-Mktg.--Sara Lee Hosiery, Winston Salem, NC; *U.S. Public*, pg. 1434

Conner, Gail, Dir.-Mktg.--L'eggs Products, Inc., Winston Salem, NC; *U.S. Public*, pg. 1434

Connolly, Brian, V.P.-Sls. & Mktg.--Emson, Inc., Bridgeport, CT; *U.S. Private*, pg. 375
Connor, Brad, V.P.-Mktg.--Harker's Distribution, Inc., Le Mars, IA; *U.S. Private*, pg. 502
Connor, Brandt D., Sr. V.P. & Relationship Mktg. Dir.--Long Haymes Carr, Inc., Winston Salem, NC; *U.S. Public*, pg. 909
Connor, Denis, V.P.-Mktg.--Maritime Telegraph & Telephone Company, Ltd., Halifax, Canada; *Int'l*, pg. 116
Connor, Eric, Mgr.-Mktg. & Sls.--Industra Inc., Greenville, SC; *Int'l*, pg. 74
Connor, Vernon J., Sr. V.P.-Mktg.--Voyager Group, Inc., Jacksonville, FL; *U.S. Public*, pg. 68
Connor, Vernon J., Sr. V.P.-Mktg.--Voyager Indemnity Insurance Company, Fort Worth, TX; *U.S. Public*, pg. 68
Connors, Lynne, Dir.-Mktg. Communications--Encore Computer Corporation, Fort Lauderdale, FL; *U.S. Public*, pg. 580
Connors, Richard, Sr. V.P.-Mktg.--The Mutual Life Insurance Company of New York, New York, NY; *U.S. Private*, pg. 769
Conolly, Mike, Dir.-Operational Mktg.--J. Sainsbury plc, London, United Kingdom; *Int'l*, pg. 1169
Conrad, Jim, V.P.-Mktg.--Industrial Ceramics, Inc., Lima, NY; *U.S. Private*, pg. 560
Conrad, Melinda, Sr. Mktg. Communications Specialist--Diebold, Incorporated, Canton, OH; *U.S. Public*, pg. 506
Conrey, Robert, Sr. V.P.-Mktg.--American Eagle Group, Inc., Dallas, TX; *U.S. Public*, pg. 71
Conroy, Thomas J., Dir.-Sls. & Mktg.--ChemPump, Warrington, PA; *U.S. Public*, pg. 456
Constantine, Toby, Dir.-Mktg.--News International plc, London, United Kingdom; *Int'l*, pg. 927
Contardi, James, V.P.-Sls. & Mktg.--Aurora Electronics, Inc., Irvine, CA; *U.S. Public*, pg. 147
Conte, Leo, Pres. & Chief Exec. Officer--Montebello Brands Inc., Baltimore, MD; *U.S. Private*, pg. 758
Contreras, Tony, V.P.-Mktg.--Sugar Cane Growers Cooperative of Florida, Belle Glade, FL; *U.S. Private*, pg. 1049
Contu, Xavier, Mgr.-Mktg.--Vitromex, S.A., Saltillo, Mexico; *Int'l*, pg. 1469
Converse, Gary, V.P.-Mktg. & Bus. Devel.--Osmose Wood Preserving, Inc., Buffalo, NY; *U.S. Private*, pg. 821
Converse, Gary, V.P. & Dir.-Mktg.--Osmose Wood Preserving, Inc., Griffin, GA; *U.S. Private*, pg. 821
Converse, Stephen, Dir.-Mktg.--Keller Construction Company Ltd., El Monte, CA; *U.S. Private*, pg. 612
Conway, Barry, Exec. V.P.-Sls. & Mktg.--Adams Business Forms, Topeka, KS; *U.S. Private*, pg. 16
Conway, Joan I., Treas.--Rayrock Yellowknife Resources Inc., Toronto, Canada; *Int'l*, pg. 1089
Conway, Kelly, V.P.-Mktg. & Adv.--The Sports Authority Inc., Fort Lauderdale, FL; *U.S. Public*, pg. 1499
Conway, Michael, Dir.-Mktg. & Sls.--Sermatech (U.K.) Limited, Ripley, United Kingdom; *U.S. Public*, pg. 1570
Conway, Peter, Dir.-Mktg.--British Telecommunications plc, London, United Kingdom; *Int'l*, pg. 222
Conway, William S., Exec. V.P.-Mktg.--Mutual of America Life Insurance Company, New York, NY; *U.S. Private*, pg. 769
Conway, William S., Exec. V.P.-Mktg.--American Life Insurance Company of New York, New York, NY; *U.S. Private*, pg. 769
Cook, Bob, Sr. V.P.-Mktg. & Adv.--The Guber Peters Entertainment Company, Los Angeles, CA; *Int'l*, pg. 1283
Cook, Jack H., V.P.-Devel.--Aramark Educational Resources Inc. Inc., Golden, CO; *U.S. Private*, pg. 79
Cook, Jim, Dir.-Mktg.--Fluidtec Engineer Products, Greensboro, NC; *U.S. Public*, pg. 401
Cook, Larry, Mgr.-Sls.--Executive Car Leasing, Inc., Los Angeles, CA; *U.S. Private*, pg. 388
Cook, Martin, Mktg. Controller--Lancashire Dairies Ltd., Manchester, United Kingdom; *Int'l*, pg. 798
Cook, Mike, Sports Mktg. Dir.--The Arnold Agency, Richmond, VA; *U.S. Private*, pg. 84
Cook, Norman, Sr. V.P.-Mktg.--Universal Life Insurance Company, Memphis, TN; *U.S. Private*, pg. 1127
Cook, Paul, Dir.-Mktg. & Sls.--Labatt Brewing Company Limited, Toronto, Canada; *Int'l*, pg. 679
Cook, Sandra, Mgmt. Asst.-Mktg.--First Tennessee National Corporation, Memphis, TN; *U.S. Public*, pg. 638
Cook, Sid, Sr. V.P. & Dir.-Mktg.--Bank One, Indiana, N.A., Indianapolis, IN; *U.S. Public*, pg. 173
Cook, Stephen, V.P.-Sls. & Mktg.--Kaufman and Broad Home Corporation, Los Angeles, CA; *U.S. Public*, pg. 944
Cook, Stephen, Mgr.-Mktg. & Sls.--Kaufman and Broad Colorado Division, Denver, CO; *U.S. Public*, pg. 945
Cook, T.R., Mgr.-Mktg.--J.M. Huber, Solem Div., Norcross, GA; *U.S. Private*, pg. 545
Cook, Tony, Mgr.-Mktg.--Schumann Sasol GmbH & Co KG, Hamburg, Germany; *Int'l*, pg. 1197
Cook, William S., Jr., V.P.-Strategic Plng. & Acq.--L.B. Foster Company, Pittsburgh, PA; *U.S. Public*, pg. 675
Cooke, J.G., V.P.-Mktg. Opers.--A&W Food Services of Canada Inc., North Vancouver, Canada; *Int'l*, pg. 1
Cookson, Linda, Coord.-Mktg. Support--Winchester Electronics, Watertown, CT; *U.S. Public*, pg. 1003
Coomber, Ian M., Exec. Dir.-Sls. & Mktg.--Vauxhall Motors Limited, Luton, United Kingdom; *U.S. Public*, pg. 724
Coombs, John, Dir.-Mktg.--Van den Bergh Foods Ltd., Crawley, United Kingdom; *Int'l*, pg. 1434
Coombs, Whitney, V.P.-Mktg.--Hanover Foods Corporation, Hanover, PA; *U.S. Private*, pg. 499
Coon, Andy, V.P.-Comml. Mktg.--General Communication, Inc., Anchorage, AK; *U.S. Public*, pg. 708
Coon, John, Dir.-Mktg.--Data General Limited, Brentford, United Kingdom; *U.S. Public*, pg. 486
Coons, Robert L., V.P.-Mktg. & Sls.--Burnham, Lancaster, PA; *U.S. Public*, pg. 270
Cooper-Taylor, Kris, V.P.-Mktg.--Maui Divers of Hawaii, Honolulu, HI; *U.S. Private*, pg. 715
Cooper, B. Ray, V.P.-Sls. & Mktg.--Gaston County Dyeing Machine Co., Mount Holly, NC; *U.S. Private*, pg. 441
Cooper, Bob, Dir.-Mktg.--Tomco Auto Products, Inc., Los Angeles, CA; *U.S. Private*, pg. 1090
Cooper, Bobbie, Dir.-Mktg. Services--Bourns, Inc., Riverside, CA; *U.S. Private*, pg. 161
Cooper, Brace, V.P.-Sls. & Mktg.--Mark Andy, Inc., Chesterfield, MO; *U.S. Public*, pg. 521
Cooper, Brian, V.P.-Adv. & Mktg.--First American Corporation, Nashville, TN; *U.S. Public*, pg. 624
Cooper, Cathy, V.P.-Mktg. & Investor Rels.--Washington Federal Savings, Seattle, WA; *U.S. Public*, pg. 1740
Cooper, Deborah, V.P.-Mac Mktg.--Micro Warehouse, Inc., Norwalk, CT; *U.S. Public*, pg. 1104
Cooper, Debra, Dir.-Corp. & Mktg. Commun.--Steelcase Inc., Grand Rapids, MI; *U.S. Private*, pg. 1038
Cooper, Edward B., V.P.-Mktg.--Legato Systems, Inc., Palo Alto, CA; *U.S. Public*, pg. 984
Cooper, Frank, Dir.-Sls. & Mktg.--Electronic Solutions, San Diego, CA; *U.S. Public*, pg. 1791
Cooper, Glynis, Dir.-Ladies/Mens Fashions & Accessories Mktg.--Bentalls plc, Kingston upon Thames, United Kingdom; *Int'l*, pg. 187
Cooper, Gordon, Dir.-Mktg. & Communications--Stone Container Corporation, Chicago, IL; *U.S. Public*, pg. 1520
Cooper, Jay, Mgr.-Mktg.--Robbins, Inc., Cincinnati, OH; *U.S. Private*, pg. 934
Cooper, Karen, Dir.-Mktg.--Electrospace Systems, Inc., Richardson, TX; *U.S. Public*, pg. 1365
Cooper, Mark A., Dir.-Sls. & Mktg.--Gorman-Rupp Industries Div., Bellville, OH; *U.S. Public*, pg. 754
Cooper, Phil, V.P.-Sls. & Mdsg.--BarcaLounger Company, Rocky Mount, NC; *U.S. Private*, pg. 265
Cooper, Polly, Coord.-Mktg.--Barnhill Contracting Company, Tarboro, NC; *U.S. Private*, pg. 117
Cooper, Steven D., Sr. V.P.-Plng., Gen. Counsel & Sec.--Electrolux Corporation, Atlanta, GA; *U.S. Private*, pg. 369
Cooper, Tina, Corporate Travel Planner-Mktg. Dept.--Antenna Products Corp., Mineral Wells, TX; *U.S. Public*, pg. 289
Coover, Edward J., V.P.-Mktg.--National Travelers Life Co., West Des Moines, IA; *U.S. Private*, pg. 787
Copeland, R. Bruce Jr., V.P.-Mktg. & Pub. Rels.--First Financial Holdings, Inc., Charleston, SC; *U.S. Public*, pg. 634
Copelin, Bill, Mktg.--Fike Corporation, Blue Springs, MO; *U.S. Private*, pg. 404
Copley, Ralph T., Asst. V.P.-Mktg.--Agronaut Great Central Insurance Co., Peoria, IL; *U.S. Public*, pg. 129
Coppel Luken, Agustin, Dir.-Mktg.--Coppel S.A. de C.V., Culiacan, Mexico; *Int'l*, pg. 330
Coppersmith, Syd, Mgr.-Mktg. Commun.--Dallas Semiconductor Corporation, Dallas, TX; *U.S. Public*, pg. 478
Coppinger, Donna, V.P.-Mktg. Services--Duke Realty Investments, Inc., Indianapolis, IN; *U.S. Public*, pg. 535
Coppola, Karen, V.P.-Mktg.--T.J. Maxx, Framingham, MA; *U.S. Public*, pg. 1557
Copps, Stephen L., Sr. V.P.-Corp. Mktg.-Govt.--Intermetrics, Inc., Burlington, MA; *U.S. Private*, pg. 567
Corbett, Dave, V.P.-Sls. & Mktg.--Crane Manufacturing, Cudahy, WI; *U.S. Private*, pg. 286
Corbett, Jeff, Sr. V.P.-Sls. & Mktg.--DHL Worldwide Express, Redwood City, CA; *U.S. Private*, pg. 301
Corbett, Jeff, Sr. V.P.-Mktg. & Sls.--DHL Airways, Inc., Redwood City, CA; *U.S. Private*, pg. 302
Corbett, Lee, Dir.-Mktg.--Michaels Stores, Inc., Irving, TX; *U.S. Public*, pg. 1104
Corbin, Dave, Dir.-Component Mktg.--MIPS Technologies, Inc., Mountain View, CA; *U.S. Public*, pg. 1473
Corbitt, James, Mgr.-Mktg.--Bike Athletic Co., Knoxville, TN; *U.S. Private*, pg. 143
Corcoran, Mike, Dir.-Mktg.--Information Builders, New York, NY; *U.S. Private*, pg. 561
Cordeau, Jacques, Dir.-Mktg. & Sls./Food Sevice--Aliments Flamingo, Iberville, Canada; *Int'l*, pg. 57
Corden, Paul, Dir.-Mktg.--Beverage-Air Co., Spartanburg, SC; *U.S. Public*, pg. 1496
Cordery, Alan, Dir.-Global Mktg. & Strategy Devel.--Grand Metropolitan Plc, London, United Kingdom; *Int'l*, pg. 408
Cordes, Charles, Dir.-Mktg. & Communications--American Annuity Group, Cincinnati, OH; *U.S. Public*, pg. 74
Cordier, Tom, V.P.-Sls. & Mktg.--Wah Chang, Albany, OR; *U.S. Public*, pg. 44
Cordray, Kevin, Dir.-List Mktg.--Meredith Corporation, Des Moines, IA; *U.S. Public*, pg. 1094
Corigliano, Valerie, Asst. V.P. & Mktg. Coord.--General Magnaplate Corporation, Linden, NJ; *U.S. Public*, pg. 717
Corinaldi, Viv, Mgr.-Mktg.--Sasol Oil (Pty) Ltd., Randburg, South Africa; *Int'l*, pg. 1197
Corlett, Sandy, V.P.-Mktg.--Lexmark Canada Inc., Markham, Canada; *U.S. Public*, pg. 991
Cornelison, Dave, V.P.-Sls. & Mktg.--M & C Specialties Company, Southampton, PA; *U.S. Private*, pg. 684
Cornelius, Bob, V.P.-Mktg. & Sls.--Saztec International, Inc., Billerica, MA; *U.S. Public*, pg. 1435
Cornelius, Connie, Dir.-Mktg. & Sls.--American Educational Products, Boulder, CO; *U.S. Public*, pg. 71
Cornelson, Dennis W., V.P.-Mktg.--AEC Oil & Gas, Calgary, Canada; *Int'l*, pg. 48
Cornett, Bruce H., V.P.-Customer Services--Cummings Inc., Nashville, TN; *U.S. Private*, pg. 295
Cornick, Robert, Dir.-Mktg.--Videojet Systems International, Inc., Wood Dale, IL; *Int'l*, pg. 545
Cornwall, Dave, Dir.-Adv.--Press Enterprise Company, Riverside, CA; *U.S. Public*, pg. 209
Cornwell, John, Mgr.-Corp. Mktg. & Pub. Affairs--3M, Saint Paul, MN; *U.S. Public*, pg. 1604
Corona, Ben, V.P.-Sls. & Mktg.-Americas--Kerr-McGee Chemical Corp., Oklahoma City, OK; *U.S. Public*, pg. 952
Corpora, Placido, Pres.-Book Div.--Rodale Press, Inc., Emmaus, PA; *U.S. Private*, pg. 939
Corr, Thomas E., V.P.-Mktg. & Sls.--Tootsie Roll Industries, Inc., Chicago, IL; *U.S. Public*, pg. 1621
Corrao, Manny, V.P.-Mktg.--Players International, Inc., Atlantic City, NJ; *U.S. Public*, pg. 1310
Correia, Brian, Dir.-Mktg.--CRC Industries, Inc., Warminster, PA; *U.S. Private*, pg. 138
Correia, Neal, Dir.-Mktg.--Sporto Corp., Boston, MA; *U.S. Private*, pg. 1026
Correll, Debra, Dir.-Mktg.--Gold'n Plump Poultry, Saint Cloud, MN; *U.S. Private*, pg. 577
Corrigan-Davis, Mary Ann, V.P.-Prod. Devel.--American Greetings U.S. Greeting Card Division, Cleveland, OH; *U.S. Public*, pg. 78
Corsiglia, Jennifer, Mgr.-Mktg.--Vitasoy (U.S.A.) Inc., South San Francisco, CA; *Int'l*, pg. 1469
Corso, Joy, Mgr.-Mktg.--GZA GeoEnvironmental Technologies, Inc., Newton, MA; *U.S. Public*, pg. 697
Corson, Tom, Sr. V.P.-Mktg.--Sony Music Entertainment, Inc., New York, NY; *Int'l*, pg. 1281
Corsten, Josefine, Dir.-Corp. Commun.--KSB Aktiengesellschaft, Frankenthal, Germany; *Int'l*, pg. 721
Cortes Moreno, Luis G., Exec. V.P.-Mktg.--Grupo Casa Autrey, Mexico, Mexico; *Int'l*, pg. 573
Cortes, Alberto, Dir.-Mktg. NA--LanChile Airlines, Miami, FL; *U.S. Private*, pg. 645
Corvalan, Fernando, Head-Mktg.-PH--CIBA-GEIGY Colombiana S.A., Bogota, Colombia; *Int'l*, pg. 976
Corwin, Ronald D., Exec. V.P.-Mktg.--The American Stock Exchange, New York, NY; *U.S. Private*, pg. 62
Coseno, Phil, Mgr.-Mktg.--Lawrence Pumps, Inc., Lawrence, MA; *U.S. Private*, pg. 654
Cosette, Barry, Mgr.-Mktg. Professional Prods.--Wynn Oil Company, Azusa, CA; *U.S. Public*, pg. 1782
Cosgrove, Jeff, Exec. V.P.-Mktg.--The Rockport Company, Marlborough, MA; *U.S. Public*, pg. 1370
Cosgrove, Joseph, Dir.-Pur. & Mktg.--Neuman Distributors, Inc., Ridgefield, NJ; *U.S. Public*, pg. 1169
Cosker, Phillip, V.P.-Mktg.--Great American Insurance Company, Cincinnati, OH; *U.S. Public*, pg. 74
Cosmides, Shelli, Mgr.-Mktg. Svcs.--Kvaerner Davy, Pittsburgh, PA; *Int'l*, pg. 774
Cosner, David, Dir.-Sls. & Mktg.--Universal Dynamics, Inc., Woodbridge, VA; *Int'l*, pg. 484
Costamagna, Bob, V.P.-Mktg.--Gilroy Foods, Inc., Gilroy, CA; *U.S. Public*, pg. 428
Costanzo, Donald J., Dir.-Mktg. & Product Devel.--The Vernon Company, Newton, IA; *U.S. Private*, pg. 1137
Costello, J., V.P.-Mktg.--Unbrako Div., Jenkintown, PA; *U.S. Public*, pg. 1420
Costello, John H., Sr. Exec. V.P. & Gen. Mgr.-Mktg.--Sears, Roebuck and Co., Hoffman Estates, IL; *U.S. Public*, pg. 1452
Costello, Laura, Mgr.-Mktg.--International Comfort Products Corp., Lewisburg, TN; *U.S. Public*, pg. 898
Costello, Wade, Mgr.-Mktg.--Bodine Assembly and Test Systems, Bridgeport, CT; *U.S. Private*, pg. 154
Coston, Larry B., Sr. V.P.-Mktg.--Precision Drilling Corporation, Calgary, Canada; *Int'l*, pg. 1066
Cote, Al, Gen. Mgr.--Dean Industries, Inc., Gardena, CA; *Int'l*, pg. 188
Cote, David, V.P.-Corp. Mktg.--Integrated Device Technology, Inc., Santa Clara, CA; *U.S. Public*, pg. 884
Cote, James R., V.P.-Sls. & Mktg.--ROHN Industries, Inc., Peoria, IL; *U.S. Public*, pg. 1404
Cote, James R., Mgr.-Mktg. & Sls.--UNR-Rohn Div., Peoria, IL; *U.S. Public*, pg. 1404
Cothren, J.W., V.P.-Mktg.--Conwood Company L.P., Memphis, TN; *U.S. Private*, pg. 272
Cothrum, Missy, Mgr.-Mktg.--Celebrity Incorporated, Tyler, TX; *U.S. Public*, pg. 319
Cotner, Margaret, Dir.-Mktg.--Security Bank & Trust Co., Mount Carmel, IL; *U.S. Public*, pg. 1217
Cotney, Anita M., V.P.-Sls. & Mktg.--Russell Corporation, Alexander City, AL; *U.S. Public*, pg. 1413
Cotrim Ribas, Sergio Wiz, Mgr.-Mktg.--Banco do Brasil, Brasilia, Brazil; *Int'l*, pg. 141
Cotter, Richard, Sr. V.P.-Mktg.--Bentley Mills, Inc., City of Industry, CA; *U.S. Public*, pg. 889
Cottle, Michael, V.P.-Worldwide Sls. & Mktg.--Multigen Inc., San Jose, CA; *U.S. Public*, pg. 1425
Cotton, John T., V.P.-Mktg.--ProEquities, Inc., Birmingham, AL; *U.S. Public*, pg. 1336
Cotton, Lisa, Mgr.-Mktg.--Braun Canada Ltd., Mississauga, Canada; *U.S. Public*, pg. 744
Cotton, Robert W., V.P.-Sls. & Mgr.-Mktg.--Hohner/HSS Inc., Ashland, VA; *U.S. Private*, pg. 533
Cotton, Susan, Sr. V.P. & Dir.-Mktg. Info. & Analysis--BankAmerica Corporation, San Francisco, CA; *U.S. Public*, pg. 179
Cottrell, Louise, Dir.-Affiliate Sls. & Mktg.--Travel U.K., London, United Kingdom,; *U.S. Private*, pg. 647
Cottrell, Matthew, Dir.-Intl. Mktg.--Grindmaster Corporation, Louisville, KY; *U.S. Private*, pg. 482
Coucerio, Joseph, Dir.-Mktg. Team, Sls., Promo. & Partnerships--Busch Entertainment Corp., Clayton, MO; *U.S. Public*, pg. 114
Couch, Jennifer, Dir.-Mktg.--GPD/Embraco North America, Inc., Norcross, GA; *U.S. Public*, pg. 1765
Couchman, Miles, Dir.-Grp. Mktg. Devel.--Sutcliffe Catering Group Ltd., London, United Kingdom; *Int'l*, pg. 1035
Coughlin, Jim, V.P.-Sls. & Mktg.--Seyfert Foods, Inc., Fort Wayne, IN; *U.S. Private*, pg. 988
Coughlin, Neil P., V.P.-Sls. & Mktg.--Kingsbury Corporation, Keene, NH; *U.S. Private*, pg. 621
Coughlin, P., Dir.-Mktg.-Paint Stores--ICI Paints, Cleveland, OH; *Int'l*, pg. 664
Coulombe, Paul, V.P.-Mktg.--Maine Bottlers, Lewiston, ME; *U.S. Private*, pg. 1173
Coulter, Ken, V.P.-Sls. & Mktg.--Mark IV Automotive Canada Inc., Weston, Canada; *U.S. Public*, pg. 1045
Courant, Jean-Paul, Dir.-Mktg.--The Eurotunnel Group, London, United Kingdom; *Int'l*, pg. 466
Courtade, Judy, Dir.-Sls. & Mktg./Knopt Grp.--Random House, Inc., New York, NY; *U.S. Private*, pg. 20

Courtade, Judy, Dir.-Sls. & Mktg.--Alfred A. Knopf, Inc., New York, NY; *U.S. Private*, pg. 21
Cousineau, Charles, Sr. V.P.-Mktg.--Environetx, Itasca, IL; *U.S. Private*, pg. 378
Cousineau, Renee, Mgr.-Mktg.--Hermes Electronics, Inc., Dartmouth, Canada; *Int'l*, pg. 1431
Cousins, Steve, Exec. V.P.-Sls. & Mktg.--Delicato Vineyards, Manteca, CA; *U.S. Private*, pg. 322
Couteaux, Philippe, Dir.-Strategy & Mktg.--Messier-Dowty, Abingdon, United Kingdom; *Int'l*, pg. 1340
Couture, Francois, Dir.-Mktg.--Charcuterie la Tour Eiffel Inc., Ville Vanier, Canada; *Int'l*, pg. 850
Couvert, F., Dir.-Mktg. & Sls.--Steelweld Division Zweigniederlassung Bonn der Ambac B.V., Saint Augustin, Germany; *Int'l*, pg. 71
Covenko, Howard L., V.P.-Sls. & Mktg.--Major Smith Inc., New Holland, PA; *Int'l*, pg. 201
Cover, Ken, Product Mgr.--Joern's Sunrise Medical, Stevens Point, WI; *U.S. Public*, pg. 1536
Covette, Daniel, Country Sls. Mgr.--Trinova S.A.-Aeroquip Div., Chambery, France; *U.S. Public*, pg. 25
Covey, Stephen M.R., Exec. V.P.-Mktg. & Innovation--Franklin Covey, Salt Lake City, UT; *U.S. Public*, pg. 679
Coville, James K., V.P.-Field Opers.--Citizens Insurance Company of America, Howell, MI; *U.S. Public*, pg. 54
Covington, Charles, Dir.-Mktg.--Durrett-Sheppard Steel Co., Inc., Baltimore, MD; *U.S. Private*, pg. 349
Cowan, Peter, Grp. Gen. Mgr.-Mktg.--New Zealand Dairy Board, Wellington, New Zealand; *Int'l*, pg. 923
Cowan, Richard, V.P.-Mktg.--Little America Refining, Inc., Evansville, WY; *U.S. Private*, pg. 1003
Coward, Mike, Chief Mktg. Officer & V.P.--Nichols Research Corporation, Huntsville, AL; *U.S. Public*, pg. 1182
Cowden, Jarrett, V.P.-Mktg.--Vermeer Manufacturing Company, Pella, IA; *U.S. Private*, pg. 1137
Cowell, Jeff, Dir.-Commercial Mktg. & Sls.--Quaker Oats Limited, Southall, United Kingdom; *U.S. Public*, pg. 1348
Cowell, Mary K., V.P.-Mktg.--Lippincott-Raven Publishing, New York, NY; *Int'l*, pg. 1513
Cowen, Nancy, Dir.-Mktg. Svcs.--Borden Foods Corporation, Columbus, OH; *U.S. Private*, pg. 157
Cower, John, V.P.-Sls. & Mktg.--Crouse-Hinds, Syracuse, NY; *U.S. Public*, pg. 444
Cowling, J.C., Mgr.-Mktg.--Casio Electronics Co., Ltd., London, United Kingdom; *Int'l*, pg. 274
Cowman, Chad, Dir.-Adv. & Mktg.--Drug Emporium, Inc., Powell, OH; *U.S. Public*, pg. 530
Cox-Castaldi, Nancy, Dir.-Mktg. & Communications--Care Matrix Corp., Needham, MA; *U.S. Public*, pg. 305
Cox, Amalia, Dir.- Sls. & Mktg.--Kitchen Fair, Jacksonville, AR; *U.S. Private*, pg. 917
Cox, Barry, Mng. Dir.-U.K. Sls. & Mktg.--Waterford Wedgwood UK Plc, Stoke on Trent, United Kingdom; *Int'l*, pg. 1487
Cox, Dennis, V.P.-Mktg.--Casio Phone-Mate, Inc., Torrance, CA; *Int'l*, pg. 274
Cox, Douglas B., V.P. & Dir.-Mktg. Services & Corp. Communications--SmithKline Beecham Consumer Healthcare, U.S., Pittsburgh, PA; *Int'l*, pg. 1264
Cox, Faye, Dir.-Mktg. Admin--International Family Entertainment, Inc., Virginia Beach, VA; *Int'l*, pg. 927
Cox, Gary L., Mgr.-Mktg. & Sls.--Mitchel & Scott Machine Co., Inc., Indianapolis, IN; *U.S. Private*, pg. 753
Cox, Jerry, V.P.-Sls. & Mktg.--Union City Body Company, L.P., Union City, IN; *U.S. Private*, pg. 1118
Cox, Kathleen, V.P.-Mktg.--ATAPCO Office Products Group, Saint Louis, MO; *U.S. Private*, pg. 64
Cox, Martha, V.P.-Mktg.--Healthsource Tennessee, Inc., Brentwood, TN; *U.S. Public*, pg. 360
Cox, Patti, V.P.-Adv.--Pergament Home Centers, Inc., Melville, NY; *U.S. Private*, pg. 853
Cox, Tony, Mktg.--Regions Bank/Birmingham, Birmingham, AL; *U.S. Public*, pg. 1371
Coy, Craig, V.P.-Mktg.--UNC Aviation Services, Inc., Annapolis, MD; *U.S. Public*, pg. 710
Coyle, Larry, V.P.-Mktg.--Smith Fiberglass Products Inc., Little Rock, AR; *U.S. Public*, pg. 1477
Coyle, Thomas, V.P.-Mktg.-N. American Grain Div.--Continental Grain Company, New York, NY; *U.S. Private*, *pg. 268*
Coyne, Katie, Dir.-Mktg.--Heluva Good Cheese Inc., Sodus, NY; *Int'l*, pg. 752
Coyner, Teresa A., V.P.-Mktg.--Arrhythmia Research Technology, Inc., Austin, TX; *U.S. Public*, pg. 133
Crago, Shirley, Mgr.-Mktg. Svcs.--Furnishings International, Inc., Thomasville, NC; *U.S. Private*, pg. 431
Craig, Harriet A., Mgr.-Mktg. Commu.--Battelle Memorial Institute, Columbus, OH; *U.S. Private*, pg. 123
Craig, Helen, Mgr.-Mktg.--Lancashire Dairies Ltd., Manchester, United Kingdom; *Int'l*, pg. 798
Craig, Ian, Dir.-Mktg.--Digital Switching Div., Research Triangle Park, NC; *Int'l*, pg. 969
Craig, James, V.P.-Mktg.--Getty Petroleum Marketing Inc., Jericho, NY; *U.S. Public*, pg. 740
Craig, John, Dir.-Sls. & Mktg.--Heil Environmental Industries, Chattanooga, TN; *U.S. Public*, pg. 520
Craig, Ron, Mgr.-Mktg.--Speedy Muffler King, Inc., Toronto, Canada; *U.S. Public*, pg. 1578
Craig, Tom, Sr. V.P.-Sls. & Mktg.--Golden Flake Snack Foods, Inc., Birmingham, AL; *U.S. Public*, pg. 750
Craigs, Anne F., Sr. V.P.--Androscoggin Savings Bank, Lewiston, ME; *U.S. Private*, pg. 74
Crail, Bonnie, V.P.-Global Mktg.--K2 Inc., Los Angeles, CA; *U.S. Public*, pg. 940
Cramer, Barbara, Dir.-Mktg. & Sls. Support--GTE Supply, Irving, TX; *U.S. Public*, pg. 697
Cramer, W.H., Sr. V.P.-Mktg.--Central Vermont Railway, Inc., Saint Albans, VT; *Int'l*, pg. 258
Crandall, Jill, V.P.-Sls. & Mktg.--Crystal Cabinet Works, Inc., Princeton, MN; *U.S. Private*, pg. 293
Crandell, Mark T., Prod. Mgr.-Lifeline Prods.--Detex Corporation, New Braunfels, TX; *U.S. Private*, pg. 327
Crane, D., V.P.-System Sls. & Mktg.--Bran & Luebbe Inc., Buffalo Grove, IL; *Int'l*, pg. 1378
Crane, Lisa, V.P.-Mktg.-Universal New Media Grp.--Universal Studios, Inc., Universal City, CA; *Int'l*, pg. 1215
Crary, Ken, Mgr.-Mktg.--Spafas, Inc., Preston, CT; *U.S. Public*, pg. 195
Craske, A.G., V.P.-Mktg. & Sls.--Isco, Inc., Lincoln, NE; *U.S. Public*, pg. 913
Crateau, Neil, Dir.-Mktg., Automotive/Bellows--Robertshaw Tennessee, Knoxville, TN; *Int'l*, pg. 1243
Crater, Ann-Margaret, Mgr.-Mktg.--The CIT Group/ Commercial Services, New York, NY; *Int'l*, pg. 360
Crave, Bridget, Dir.-Mktg.--Dremel, Racine, WI; *U.S. Public*, pg. 574
Craves, Robert E., Sr. V.P.-Membership & Mktg.--Costco Wholesale, Issaquah, WA; *U.S. Public*, pg. 451
Crawford, Andrew, Dir.-Commercial Mktg.--CPC (United Kingdom) Ltd., Esher, United Kingdom; *U.S. Public*, pg. 225
Crawford, Ed, V.P.-Strategic Mktg.--Philips Lighting, Somerset, NJ; *Int'l*, pg. 1055
Crawford, Michael, Mng. Dir.-Mktg.--Ralston Purina Company, Saint Louis, MO; *U.S. Public*, pg. 1359
Crawford, Tom, Exec. V.P.-Sls. & Mktg.--Lozier Corporation, Omaha, NE; *U.S. Private*, pg. 679
Creary, Brian, V.P.-Sls. & Mktg.--Global Beverage Co., Rochester, NY; *U.S. Private*, pg. 457
Creech, Freda, Coord.-Sls. & Mktg.--National Retail Hardware Assn., Indianapolis, IN; *U.S. Private*, pg. 786
Creed, Christine, Dir.-Mktg.--Great Clips, Inc., Minneapolis, MN; *U.S. Private*, pg. 473
Creel, Brady W., Sr. V.P. & Chief Mktg. Officer--The Franklin Life Insurance Company, Springfield, IL; *U.S. Public*, pg. 76
Creel, John A., Sr. V.P.-U.S. Marketing--Goody Products, Inc., Peachtree City, GA; *U.S. Public*, pg. 1177
Cregar, Holly, Mgr.-Mktg.--TNT Vacations, Boston, MA; *U.S. Private*, pg. 1065
Crego, Al, V.P.-Mktg.--Mark Antenna Products, Inc., Des Plaines, IL; *U.S. Public*, pg. 424
Creiger, Frank, Dir.-Bus. Devel. Male Underwear--Sara Lee Knit Products, Winston Salem, NC; *U.S. Public*, pg. 1434
Crenshaw, Helene, Dir.-Intl. Sls. & Mktg.--Farnam Companies, Inc., Phoenix, AZ; *U.S. Private*, pg. 396
Cress, Dave, Dir.-Sales & Mktg.--CTS Corp. Frequency Controls, Sandwich, IL; *U.S. Public*, pg. 285
Crete, Rejean, V.P.-Mktg.--Quebecor Multimedia Inc., Montreal, Canada; *Int'l*, pg. 1076
Cribbin, Dan, Dir.-Sls. & Mktg.--Vile-Goller, Fine Art Printing & Lithography, Kansas City, KS; *U.S. Private*, pg. 1140
Cribbin, Tom, Mgr.-Mktg. Svcs.--Vision One, Norwich, CT; *U.S. Private*, pg. 1141
Crichton, Ian, Mgr.-Mktg.- Shavers & Clocks--Braun, North America, Woburn, MA; *U.S. Public*, pg. 743
Crick, Robert, Mgr.-Mktg.--Benmar Marine Electronics, Inc., Santa Ana, CA; *U.S. Private*, pg. 133
Crider, John, V.P.-Mktg.--The Crystal Tissue Co., Middletown, OH; *U.S. Private*, pg. 294
Crim, Mike, V.P.-Sls.--Mogas Industries, Inc., Houston, TX; *U.S. Private*, pg. 755
Crimmons, Steve, Dir.-Mktg.--Ralston Purina Company, Saint Louis, MO; *U.S. Public*, pg. 1359
Crisp, David, Gen.-Mgr.--Bison Foods Company, Buffalo, NY; *U.S. Private*, pg. 1129
Cristo, Gus, Exec. V.P. & Dir.-Sls. & Mktg.--Ferguson International, Inc., Dallas, TX; *U.S. Private*, pg. 401
Cristofoli, Nino M., Sr. V.P.-Sls. & Mktg., Nestle Refigerated Food Co.--Nestle Frozen/Refrigerated Food Co., Solon, OH; *Int'l*, pg. 918
Critchlow, Paul, Sr. V.P.-Mktg. & Communications--Merrill Lynch & Co., Inc., New York, NY; *U.S. Public*, pg. 1097
Crivelli, Mark, Sr. V.P.-Secondary Mktg.--Kaufman and Broad Mortgage Co., Woodland Hills, CA; *U.S. Public*, pg. 945
Crivelli, Robert, V.P.-Sls. & Mktg.--Santo Tours & Travel, Inc., Buffalo, NY; *U.S. Private*, pg. 23
Crocetta, Mike, Dir.-Mktg.--Mentor Opthalmics, Inc., Santa Barbara, CA; *U.S. Public*, pg. 1086
Crocker, Melinda, Mktg. Coord.--The American Group, Ferndale, WA; *U.S. Private*, pg. 56
Crockett, Ed, V.P.-Mktg.--Lepage Bakery, Inc., Auburn, ME; *U.S. Private*, pg. 660
Croft, Robert, Dir.-Mktg.--Associated Testing Laboratories, Inc., Burlington, MA; *U.S. Public*, pg. 1341
Cromelin, Margaret, V.P.-Mktg.--Mellon Bank (MD), Rockville, MD; *U.S. Public*, pg. 1085
Cromwell, Josias J. II, Dir.-Mktg.--Mercantile Bankshares Corporation, Baltimore, MD; *U.S. Public*, pg. 1088
Cron, Robert W., V.P.-Indus. Prods. Div.--AEP Industries, Inc., South Hackensack, NJ; *U.S. Public*, pg. 4
Cronin, Larry, Mgr.-Mktg. Communications--Meadox Medicals, Inc., Oakland, NJ; *U.S. Public*, pg. 247
Cronin, William, V.P.-Grp. Mktg.--Canon U.S.A., Inc., Lake Success, NY; *Int'l*, pg. 262
Cronin, William F., Exec. V.P.-Mktg.--CPI Corp., Saint Louis, MO; *U.S. Public*, pg. 283
Cronkite, George F., V.P.-Sls. & Mktg.--Windsor Door, Little Rock, AR; *U.S. Public*, pg. 69
Crook, David, Mgr.-Agricultural/Industrial Mktg.--Aetna Bearing Company, Chicago, IL; *U.S. Private*, pg. 25
Crorey, David, Exec. V.P.-Sls. & Mktg.--ISI Norgen, Inc., Fraser, MI; *Int'l*, pg. 646
Cross, Andy, Exec. V.P.-Sls. & Mktg.--MobileComm, Ridgefield Park, NJ; *U.S. Public*, pg. 1120
Cross, Ian, Dir.-Mktg. Commun.--Wang Laboratories, Inc., Billerica, MA; *U.S. Public*, pg. 1737
Cross, Ian, Dir.-Mktg. & Communications--Wang (UK) Limited, Isleworth, United Kingdom; *U.S. Public*, pg. 1738
Cross, Jay, Dir.-Mktg.--Omega Performance Group, Sausalito, CA; *U.S. Private*, pg. 816
Cross, Maria, V.P.-Sls. & Mktg.--Optimaxx International, Rockleigh, NJ; *U.S. Private*, pg. 818
Crossen, Mike, Mgr.-Adv.--Essex Industries, New Haven, CT; *Int'l*, pg. 18
Crossin, Hugh, V.P.-Mktg.--Genesee Corporation, Rochester, NY; *U.S. Public*, pg. 728
Crossman, Paul, Asst. V.P.-Mktg. & Sls.--National Fire Protection Association, Quincy, MA; *U.S. Private*, pg. 782
Crosson, William M., V.P.-Mktg., Specialty Brands--ConAgra Frozen Food Company, Omaha, NE; *U.S. Public*, pg. 427
Crother, David, Dir.-Mktg.-Secondary Bks.--Reed Educational and Professional Publishing, Oxford, United Kingdom; *Int'l*, pg. 1094
Crotty, Robert S., V.P. & Dir.-Mktg.--Van Dyne-Crotty, Inc., Dayton, OH; *U.S. Private*, pg. 1132
Crouch, Andrea, V.P.-Mktg.-Toiletries--Chattem, Inc., Chattanooga, TN; *U.S. Public*, pg. 341
Crouch, Andrea, V.P.-Mktg.-Toiletries--Chattem, Inc., Consumer Products Division, Chattanooga, TN; *U.S. Public*, pg. 341
Crouch, Robert D., Sr. V.P.-Sls. & Mktg.--Respironics, Inc., Pittsburgh, PA; *U.S. Public*, pg. 1383
Crouch, Taylor J., Sr. V.P.-Worldwide Client Rels. & Mktg.--PAREXEL International Corporation, Waltham, MA; *U.S. Public*, pg. 1257
Crow, Phillip W., V.P.-Sls. & Mktg.--Dawn Food Products, Inc., Jackson, MI; *U.S. Private*, pg. 316
Crowe, G. Donald, Dir.-Mktg.-Cold Drink--Central Coca-Cola Bottling Company, Inc., Richmond, VA; *U.S. Private*, pg. 222
Crowe, Jan, Mgr.-Mktg. & Communications--Mobil Oil Corporation, Fairfax, VA; *U.S. Public*, pg. 1118
Crowell, Steve, Mgr.-Mktg.--Cincinnati Gear Company, Cincinnati, OH; *U.S. Private*, pg. 240
Crowley, Bernadette, Mgr.-Mktg.--Sea Containers British Isles Ltd., London, United Kingdom; *Int'l*, pg. 1214
Crowley, John, Mgr.-Mktg.--Champ/Pik-A-Nut Service Line, Edwardsville, KS; *U.S. Public*, pg. 1503
Crowley, Stephen, V.P.-Mktg. & Sls.--Rome Cable Corporation, Rome, NY; *U.S. Private*, pg. 942
Cruce, Tom, Mgr.-Sls. & Mktg.--Westvaco Corporation-Envelope Div., Springfield, MA; *U.S. Public*, pg. 1762
Cruickshank, Burt, Dir.-Commun. & Mktg.-Reg. Aircraft--Bombardier Aerospace, Dorval, Canada; *Int'l*, pg. 200
Cruikshank, Kirk, Sr. V.P.-Mktg.--Arbor Software Corporation, Sunnyvale, CA; *U.S. Public*, pg. 127
Cruke, Gaetan, Dir.-Sls. & Mktg.--Wyeth Australia Pty. Ltd., Baulkham Hills, Australia; *U.S. Public*, pg. 82
Crum, Ben, V.P.-Sls. & Mktg.--Sargent-Welch Scientific Company, Buffalo Grove, IL; *U.S. Public*, pg. 1704
Crumbaugh, Susan, Mgr.-Agency Devel.--State Farm Mutual Automobile Insurance Company, Bloomington, IL; *U.S. Private*, pg. 1036
Crump, Terry, V.P.-Mktg.--Beaulieu United, Dalton, GA; *U.S. Private*, pg. 128
Cruse, C.L., Contract Mgr.--Sulzer Bingham Pumps Inc., Portland, OR; *Int'l*, pg. 1305
Cruz, John, V.P.-Mktg.--American Bible Society, New York, NY; *U.S. Private*, pg. 51
Csehill, John, Dir.-Mktg.--Admiral Maintenance Service L.P., Lincolnwood, IL; *U.S. Private*, pg. 17
Csinicsek, Kenneth, Sr. V.P.-Mktg., Investor & Pub. Rels.--First Financial Bank, FSB, Stevens Point, WI; *U.S. Public*, pg. 140
Cubbage, William, V.P.-Animal Health & Nutrition--Universal Cooperatives, Inc., Minneapolis, MN; *U.S. Private*, pg. 1127
Cubell, Lee, Dir.-Mktg., Adv. & Pub. Rels.--Kingsdown, Inc., Mebane, NC; *U.S. Private*, pg. 622
Cuddihy, Rita M., V.P.-Mktg. & Distrib. Plng.--US Airways Group, Inc., Arlington, VA; *U.S. Public*, pg. 1680
Cullen, Rachel, Dir.-Mktg.--Pollio Dairy Products Company, Mineola, NY; *U.S. Public*, pg. 1288
Cullen, Rachel, Dir.-Mktg.--Pollio Dairy Products, Mineola, NY; *U.S. Public*, pg. 1288
Cullen, William P., V.P.-Sls. & Mktg.--Communication Cable, Inc., Sanford, NC; *U.S. Public*, pg. 968
Cullers-Delp, Carolyn, Dir.-Field Mktg., Promo. & Adv.--Max & Erma's Restaurants, Columbus, OH; *U.S. Public*, pg. 1060
Culleton, Julie, Coord.-Mktg.--D.A. Stuart Company, Warrenville, IL; *U.S. Private*, pg. 1048
Culleton, Kathleen, V.P.-Mktg. Opers.--CBS Television Network, New York, NY; *U.S. Public*, pg. 274
Culley, P.L., Mgr.-Mktg. Communications--ABB Kent Plc, Luton, United Kingdom; *Int'l*, pg. 2
Culligan, Elizabeth, Sr. V.P.-Biscuit Mktg.--Nabisco Inc., Parsippany, NJ; *U.S. Public*, pg. 1355
Cullison, Theresa, Mgr.-Mktg.--Mark III Industries, Ocala, FL; *U.S. Private*, pg. 704
Culpepper, Lewis, Mgr.-Sls. & Mktg.--Southern Pilot Insurance Company, Greensboro, NC; *Int'l*, pg. 346
Culver, Daniel, Mgr.-Mktg.--Fonar Corporation, Melville, NY; *U.S. Public*, pg. 661
Culver, John A., Dir.-Sls. & Mktg.--Giumarra Vineyards, Edison, CA; *U.S. Private*, pg. 455
Cuming, Lou, V.P.-Mktg.--Allied Digital Technologies, Elk Grove Village, IL; *U.S. Public*, pg. 48
Cuming, Pamela, Sr. Mng. Dir.-Corp. Mktg.--The Bear Stearns Companies Inc., New York, NY; *U.S. Public*, pg. 197
Cumming, Louise, V.P.-Mktg.--Weston Bakeries Limited, Etobicoke, Canada; *Int'l*, pg. 1495
Cummings, Bruce E., Exec. V.P.-Mktg.--Lotus Word Processing Division, Atlanta, GA; *U.S. Public*, pg. 896
Cummings, Steve, Dir.-Mktg.--A.J. Gerrard and Company, Des Plaines, IL; *U.S. Private*, pg. 449
Cummins, Don, Dir.-Mktg./Fax--Brother International Corporation, Somerset, NJ; *Int'l*, pg. 229
Cummins, Harold, Mgr.-Prod.--Hesco, Inc., Teterboro, NJ; *U.S. Private*, pg. 524
Cummins, Marianne, Mgr.-Mktg. Svcs.--SPSS Inc., Chicago, IL; *U.S. Public*, pg. 1420
Cummins, Sandy, Mktg. Admin.--Winchell's Donut Houses, L.P., Santa Ana, CA; *Int'l*, pg. 1230
Cundari, Linda, Mktg. Coord.--Superior Coffee and Foods, Bensenville, IL; *U.S. Public*, pg. 1434
Cunningham, Bob, Sr. V.P.-Sls. & Mktg.--Pico Products, Inc., Lake View Terrace, CA; *U.S. Public*, pg. 1294

Cunningham, J.G., Dir.-Mktg. Services--Procter & Gamble Ltd., Newcastle upon Tyne, United Kingdom; *U.S. Public, pg. 1332*
Cunningham, Michael, Dir.-Mktg. & Sls.--Pawling Corporation, Pawling, NY; *U.S. Private*, pg. 844
Cunningham, Philip F., Exec. V.P.-Mktg. & Pres.-Mackenzie Financial Services Inc.--Mackenzie Financial Corporation, Toronto, Canada; *Int'l*, pg. 828
Curcio, Alida, V.P.-Mktg.--Scott's Miracle-Gro Products, Inc., Port Washington, NY; *U.S. Public*, pg. 1447
Curi, Maurico, Superintendent-Mktg.--Fiat Automisveis S.A., Sao Paulo, Brazil; *Int'l*, pg. 483
Curley, Dave, V.P.-Mktg.--Mitel Corporation, Kanata, Canada; *Int'l*, pg. 870
Curran, Charles, Sr. V.P.-Mktg.-COMAIR, INC.--Comair Holdings, Inc., Erlanger, KY; *U.S. Public*, pg. 406
Curran, D.J., Dir.-Mktg.--Fishery Products International USA, Danvers, MA; *Int'l*, pg. 492
Curran, J. Michael, V.P.-Franchise Mktg.--Hilton Hotels Div., Beverly Hills, CA; *U.S. Public*, pg. 829
Curran, Kitty, Admin. Asst.-Adv. & Mktg.--Dahlberg, Inc., Golden Valley, MN; *U.S. Public*, pg. 194
Curran, Martha, Mgr.-Consumer Mktg.--H.B. Ives, Wallingford, CT; *U.S. Private*, pg. 506
Curran, Martha, Mktg. Communications Coord.--Chomerics Inc., Woburn, MA; *U.S. Public*, pg. 1262
Current, Gloster, V.P.-Mktg. & Pub. Rels.--Lincoln National Corporation, Fort Wayne, IN; *U.S. Public*, pg. 997
Currey, Russell M., Sr. V.P.-Mktg. & Plng.--Rock-Tenn Company, Norcross, GA; *U.S. Public*, pg. 1396
Currie, Bill, Dir.-Mktg. & Sls.--Canadian Kenworth Co., Mississauga, Canada; *U.S. Public*, pg. 1247
Currier, W. Brent, V.P.-Sls. & Mktg.--General Cigar Company, Inc., Bloomfield, CT; *U.S. Public*, pg. 708
Currin, Celia, Dir.-Mktg. Svcs.--Dow Jones & Company, Inc., New York, NY; *U.S. Public*, pg. 524
Curry, S., Mgr.-Mktg.--Rothmans (UK) Ltd., Aylesbury, United Kingdom; *Int'l*, pg. 1130
Curry, Terry, Dir.-Mktg.--Godfather's Pizza, Inc., Omaha, NE; *U.S. Private*, pg. 458
Curtin, Nick, V.P.-Sls. & Mktg.--Precision Dynamics Corporation, San Fernando, CA; *U.S. Private*, pg. 879
Curtis, Alvin L., V.P.-Mktg.--Serigraph, Inc., West Bend, WI; *U.S. Private*, pg. 985
Curtis, Christopher L., V.P.-Sls. & Mktg.--Peabody COALSALES Company, Saint Louis, MO; *Int'l*, pg. 594
Curtis, H.L., V.P.-Mktg.--J.M. Huber, Oil & Gas Div., Houston, TX; *U.S. Private*, pg. 545
Curtis, Michael, Dir.-Sls. & Mktg.--Penn Racquet Sports, Phoenix, AZ; *U.S. Public*, pg. 706
Curtis, Trumbull, Dir.-Adv. & Mktg. Services--BankBoston Corporation, Boston, MA; *U.S. Public*, pg. 183
Curtis, William M., Dir.-Mktg.--L.N. Curtis & Sons, Oakland, CA; *U.S. Private*, pg. 297
Curtiss, JoAnn, Coord.-Mktg.--A.L. Hansen Manufacturing Co., Waukegan, IL; *U.S. Private*, pg. 500
Curto, D., Coord.-Mktg.--Echelon International Corporation, Saint Petersburg, FL; *U.S. Public*, pg. 560
Cury, Oscar, Dir.-Mktg. & Corp. Communications--Travel Channel-Latin America, Miami, FL; *U.S. Private*, pg. 647
Cusack, Richard J., Jr., V.P.-Sls. & Mktg.--Berkley Risk Managers, Somerset, NJ; *U.S. Public*, pg. 215
Cusano, Donna, Dir.-Intl. Mktg. & Adv.--Avis Rent A Car System, Inc., Garden City, NY; *U.S. Public*, pg. 321
Cushing, Frank, Dir.-Mktg.--Imperial Bondware Corp., Montvale, NJ; *U.S. Public*, pg. 903
Cusick, Walt, Corp. Mgr.-Sls. & Mktg.--McInnes Steel Company, Corry, PA; *U.S. Private*, pg. 722
Cuss, Martin, Dir.-Sls. & Mktg.-Education--Oxford University Press, Oxford, United Kingdom; *Int'l*, pg. 1018
Cusson, Audrey, Dir.-Mktg.--The Putnam & Grosset Group, New York, NY; *Int'l*, pg. 1027
Cusson, Real M., V.P.-Mktg.--Canadian Natural Resources Limited, Calgary, Canada; *Int'l*, pg. 258
Custer, Colleen, Mktg. Coord.--Senior Flexonics Inc., Bartlett, IL; *Int'l*, pg. 1222
Custer, John, Mgr.-Mktg. & Communications--Sigma Chemical Co., Saint Louis, MO; *U.S. Public*, pg. 1472
Custer, Phyllis, Mgr.-Mktg. Communications--Schleicher & Schuell, Inc., Keene, NH; *Int'l*, pg. 1206
Cuthbertson, Jim, Dir.-Mktg. Svcs.--Florida Tile Industries, Inc., Lakeland, FL; *U.S. Public*, pg. 1322
Cutler, Linda B., V.P.-Corp. Commun. & Investor Rels.--USCS International, Inc., Rancho Cordova, CA; *U.S. Public*, pg. 1659
Cutler, Timothy, Dir.-Sls.& Mktg.--Miracle Adhesives, Buffalo, NY; *U.S. Public*, pg. 1466
Cutlip, Kathy, Mktg. Specialist--Anacomp Magnetics, Inc., Atlanta, GA; *U.S. Public*, pg. 107
Cutting, Gary, Supvr.-Mktg. Svcs.--Keeney Manufacturing Co., Newington, CT; *U.S. Private*, pg. 611
Cuttle, Jim, Dir.-Mktg.-Local Prods.--Astra Pharma Inc., Mississauga, Canada; *Int'l*, pg. 94
Cyr, F., V.P.-Sls. & Mktg.--National Rivet & Manufacturing Company, Waupun, WI; *U.S. Private*, pg. 786
Czaja, Michael, V.P.-Sls. & Mktg.--Sentinel Consumer Products, Inc., Mentor, OH; *U.S. Private*, pg. 984
Czerwionka, Debby, Mgr.-Mktg.--Mid Res Service Div., Niles, IL; *U.S. Public*, pg. 1026
Czikowsky, Dennis, Mgr.-Mktg.--Vision One, Norwich, CT; *U.S. Private*, pg. 1141
Czyzewski, Ken, Sls. Mgr.--A&A Manufacturing Co., New Berlin, WI; *U.S. Private*, pg. 1
D'Alessandro, Rich, V.P.-Mktg. & Sls.--Spectra-Physics Laserplane Inc., Dayton, OH; *U.S. Public*, pg. 1594
D'Alessandro, Richard, Dir.-Strategic Plng. & Projects--National Forge Company, Irvine, PA; *U.S. Private*, pg. 783
D'Amico, Tom, Dir.-Mktg.--Preservative Paint Company, Seattle, WA; *U.S. Private*, pg. 613
D'Amora, Edith, Mgr.-Mktg.--Stroehmann Bakeries, L.C., Horsham, PA; *Int'l*, pg. 1495
D'Andrea-Herns, Cynthia, V.P.-Mktg.-Feminine Hygiene & Skin Care--Combe Incorporated, White Plains, NY; *U.S. Private*, pg. 257
D'Antonio, Frank, Dir.-Sls. & Mktg.--Healthsource Kentucky, Louisville, KY; *U.S. Public*, pg. 360
D'Arcy, Paul, Sr. V.P.-Sls. & Mktg.--Sanyo Office Automation, Chatsworth, CA; *Int'l*, pg. 1191
D'Arezzo, James, V.P.-Corp. Mktg.--Autodesk, Inc., San Rafael, CA; *U.S. Public*, pg. 148
D'Armond, Jackson, Mgr.-Mktg. Communications--Stihl Inc., Virginia Beach, VA; *Int'l*, pg. 1301
D'audiffret, Bruno, Dir.-Mktg.--Groupe Strafor Facom, Morangis, France; *Int'l*, pg. 569
d'Enfert, Jerome, V.P.-Intl. Mktg.--Hoechst Marion Roussel, Inc., Bridgewater, NJ; *Int'l*, pg. 624
D'Jaen, Richard, Dir.-Sls. & Mktg.--Sam Dick Industries, Inc., Seattle, WA; *U.S. Private*, pg. 360
D'Onofrio, Joseph, Chief Fin. Officer & V.P.-Sls.--My Own Meals, Inc., Deerfield, IL; *U.S. Private*, pg. 770
D'Orazio, John S., Dir.-Mktg. & New Construction--Roanoke Gas Company, Roanoke, VA; *U.S. Public*, pg. 1392
D'Uva, Nick, Dir.-Sls. & Mktg.--Alfa Romeo Distributors of North America, Orlando, FL; *Int'l*, pg. 481
Dabrowski, Mary, Exec. V.P.-Mktg., Fashion--Hampshire Hosiery, Inc., Spruce Pine, NC; *U.S. Public*, pg. 778
Dacey, Michael, Mgr.-Mktg. Communications--Hayward Industries, Inc., Elizabeth, NJ; *U.S. Private*, pg. 513
Dack, Helen, Dir.-Mktg.--D. Anderson & Son Ltd., Stretford, United Kingdom; *Int'l*, pg. 659
Dacuycuy, Tony, V.P.-Mktg.--J.C. Carter Company, Inc., Costa Mesa, CA; *U.S. Private*, pg. 81
Dadaro, Dan, Mgr.-Sls. & Promo.--Pannier Corporation, Pittsburgh, PA; *U.S. Private*, pg. 837
Dadiego, Sharon, Admin.-Sls. & Mktg.--Connors Brunswick, Inc., South Portland, ME; *U.S. Private*, pg. 264
Dadoun, Joy, Mgr.-Corp. Communications--Fox Valley Corporation, Appleton, WI; *U.S. Private*, pg. 422
Daggett, John, Dir.-Mktg. Svcs. & Corp. Communication--RAYOVAC Corporation, Madison, WI; *U.S. Private*, pg. 912
Dahl, Cheri, Dir.-Devel.--Christian Children's Fund, Inc., Richmond, VA; *U.S. Private*, pg. 238
Dahlager, Ken, V.P.-Sls. & Mkgt.--Smith System Manufacturing Company, Plano, TX; *U.S. Private*, pg. 1009
Dahle, James, Dir.-Mktg.--Crain Associated Enterprises, Chicago, IL; *U.S. Private*, pg. 285
Dahlen, Tom, Sr. V.P.-Mktg.--Ralphs Grocery Company, Compton, CA; *U.S. Private*, pg. 1202
Dahlquist, John E., V.P.-Mktg.--Harmonic Lightwaves, Sunnyvale, CA; *U.S. Public*, pg. 788
Dailey, Ann R., V.P.-Media & Database Mktg.--Russ Reid Company, Inc., Pasadena, CA; *U.S. Private*, pg. 952
Dailey, Bruce C., V.P.-Consumer Mktg. & Opers.--Agway Retail Services, Syracuse, NY; *U.S. Private*, pg. 27
Dailey, Kenneth E., Gen. Mgr.--Seaman Timber Company, Inc., Montevallo, AL; *U.S. Private*, pg. 979
Daily, H. Pete, V.P.-Crude Supply and Prods. Mktg.--Mapco Petroleum Inc., Tulsa, OK; *U.S. Public*, pg. 1042
Dajani, Bassem, V.P.-Intl. Bus. Devel.--Intermarkets Advertising, Beirut, Lebanon; *Int'l*, pg. 680
Dale, Anthony, V.P.-Mktg.--Lion Brothers Company, Inc., Owings Mills, MD; *U.S. Private*, pg. 669
Dale, Peter, Mktg. Dir.--Young & Rubicam Bogota, Bogota, Colombia; *U.S. Private*, pg. 1200
Daley, Alex, V.P.-Sls. & Mktg.--C-Cube Microsystems, Milpitas, CA; *U.S. Public*, pg. 272
Daley, Ed, Dir.-Mktg.--Carter Products Canada, Mississauga, Canada; *U.S. Public*, pg. 310
Dalfonso, Flip, Dir.-Mktg.--Pentax Corporation, Englewood, CO; *Int'l*, pg. 85
Dallaire, Lucien, Mgr.-Sls. & Mktg.--NAPCO, Inc., Terryville, CT; *U.S. Public*, pg. 1592
Dalland, Don, V.P.-Mfg.--Waters Instruments, Inc., Rochester, MN; *U.S. Public*, pg. 1745
Dallmeyer, Kathy, Supvr.-Mktg. Admin.--Lark Luggage Company, Inc., Denver, CO; *U.S. Public*, pg. 1430
Dallow, K. S., Mgr.-Mktg. Communications--Sensall, Div. of Rosemount, Inc., Hauppauge, NY; *U.S. Public*, pg. 574
Dally, Karen, V.P.-Mktg.--Nalge Company, Rochester, NY; *U.S. Public*, pg. 1545
Dalrymple, Ted L., V.P.-Global Mktg.--AMP Incorporated, Harrisburg, PA; *U.S. Public*, pg. 7
Dalton, Kasay, Mktg. Asst.--Burns & McDonnell Engineers-Architects-Consultants, Kansas City, MO; *U.S. Private*, pg. 187
Dalton, Mike, Mktg. Assoc.--Gulf States Manufacturers, Inc., Starkville, MS; *Int'l*, pg. 699
Dalvi, Ajit M., Sr. V.P.-Mktg. & Programming--Cox Communications, Inc., Atlanta, GA; *U.S. Public*, pg. 454
Daly, J., Sr. V.P.-Mktg.--Metal Improvement Co., Paramus, NJ; *U.S. Public*, pg. 469
Daly, Martin B., V.P. & Dir.-Sls. & Mktg.--CBS Television Network, New York, NY; *U.S. Public*, pg. 274
Daly, Tom, Dir.-Mktg.--Godiva Chocolatier, Inc., New York, NY; *U.S. Public*, pg. 299
Daman, Tim, Dir.-Adv. & Mktg.--Spartan International Inc., Holt, MI; *U.S. Private*, pg. 1020
DAmare, Dennis, V.P.-Sls. & Mktg.--LASCO Bathware, Anaheim, CA; *Int'l*, pg. 1398
Damask, Donald, Sr. V.P.-Mktg.--Brown Group, Inc., Saint Louis, MO; *U.S. Public*, pg. 262
Damato, Bob, Dir.-Deli & Bakery--The Food Emporium, Bronx, NY; *Int'l*, pg. 1375
Dambold, John, V.P.-Mktg. & Sls.--Fleming Foods of Alabama, Inc., Geneva, AL; *U.S. Public*, pg. 653
Dame, Polly, Mgr.-Mktg.--Vindicator Technologies, Austin, TX; *U.S. Private*, pg. 1141
Damiano, Paul, V.P.-Mktg.--Kaman Music Corp., Bloomfield, CT; *U.S. Public*, pg. 942
Dams, Ed, Mgr.-Mktg.--Waterloo Industries, Inc., Waterloo, IA; *U.S. Public*, pg. 675
Damveld, Gary, Exec. V.P. & Dir.-Mktg.--S & P Company, Mill Valley, CA; *U.S. Private*, pg. 954
Dancer, Jeanie, Mktg. Coord.--Dollar Rent A Car, Tulsa, OK; *U.S. Public*, pg. 354
Dandrea, Michael A., V.P.-Mktg.--Allegheny Power System, Inc., Hagerstown, MD; *U.S. Public*, pg. 42
Dandurand, Curran, Exec. V.P.-Mktg.--Mary Kay, Inc., Dallas, TX; *U.S. Private*, pg. 711
Dandy, Bill, Sr. V.P.-Mktg.--Famous Footwear, Madison, WI; *U.S. Public*, pg. 262
Danenberg, Alan M., Mgr.-Mdsg. & Mktg. Commun.--Elkay Manufacturing Company, Oak Brook, IL; *U.S. Private*, pg. 372
Daniel, Jeanne B., Exec. V.P.-Mdsg. & Mktg.--Tiffany & Co., New York, NY; *U.S. Public*, pg. 1608
Daniell, James, Dir.-Mktg.--Russell Corp., Jerzees Div., Alexander City, AL; *U.S. Public*, pg. 1413
Daniels, Andrew R., V.P.-Mktg. Dir., Bus. Plng. & Devel.--Risk Sciences Group, Inc., Atlanta, GA; *U.S. Public*, pg. 458
Daniels, Kristin, Pub. Rels. & Mktg. Communications--Williams Worldwide, Santa Monica, CA; *U.S. Private*, pg. 1179
Daniels, Penny, Mgr.-Mktg.--Reed Elsevier Legal Division, London, United Kingdom; *Int'l*, pg. 1095
Daniels, Steven L., V.P.-Mktg.--Marketing & Project Development, Erie, PA; *U.S. Public*, pg. 1794
Danielsen, Pete, V.P.-Mktg. & Communications--MTV Networks, New York, NY; *U.S. Private*, pg. 779
Danielsen, Peter, V.P.-Mktg.--CNBC, Fort Lee, NJ; *U.S. Public*, pg. 712
Danko, Dan, Mgr.-Mkt. Adv. & Special Projects--Mack Trucks, Inc., Allentown, PA; *Int'l*, pg. 1102
Danti, Joe, Mktg.--Banco Chase Manhattan S.A., Rio de Janeiro, Brazil; *U.S. Public*, pg. 339
Danuser, Steve, V.P.-Mktg.--Rollins, Inc., Atlanta, GA; *U.S. Public*, pg. 1404
Danysh, Natalie, V.P.-Mktg.-Skin Care--Chesebrough-Pond's USA Co., Greenwich, CT; *Int'l*, pg. 1435
Danza, Thomas, V.P.-Mktg.--Templeton, Kenly & Co., Inc., Broadview, IL; *U.S. Private*, pg. 1075
Dardade, Gustavo, Dir.-Mktg.--Sancor Cooperativas Unidas Limitadas, Buenos Aires, Argentina; *Int'l*, pg. 1183
Dardinski, Joy, Mgr.-Mktg. Communications--Ardent Software, Inc., Westborough, MA; *U.S. Public*, pg. 129
Dargan, Orla, Head-Corp. Devel.--Hepworth Plc, London, United Kingdom; *Int'l*, pg. 614
Dargery, Joan, V.P.-Mktg. & New Bus. Devel.--CPC Baking Business, Bay Shore, NY; *U.S. Public*, pg. 224
Darnton, Phillip, Grp. Dir.-Global Mktg.--Reckitt & Colman plc, London, United Kingdom; *Int'l*, pg. 1089
Darosa, Mario, V.P.-Mktg.--Sandvik/Milford Corporation, Branford, CT; *Int'l*, pg. 1185
Darr, Lauren, Mgr.-Mktg.--Harris Broadcast Division, Richmond, IN; *U.S. Public*, pg. 791
Darragh, Robert J., Sr. V.P.-Mktg. & Sls.--Copes-Vulcan Inc., Lake City, PA; *U.S. Private*, pg. 274
Darville, Monsell, Mgr.-Mktg.--Bacardi-Martini, USA, Inc., Miami, FL; *U.S. Private*, pg. 109
Darwin, Gary R., Exec. V.P.--Cardinal Inc., Rahway, NJ; *U.S. Private*, pg. 208
Dasal, Jason, Retail Mktg. Mgr.--Johnston & Murphy Co., Nashville, TN; *U.S. Public*, pg. 728
DaSilva, Suzanne, Mgr.-Mktg. & Communications--Clicquot, Inc., New York, NY; *Int'l*, pg. 781
Datar, G., Head-Mktg. Commun.--Nationwide Building Society, Swindon, United Kingdom; *Int'l*, pg. 912
Datoo, Bashir, Dr., Sr. V.P.-Strategic Mktg. Services--Total Research Corporation, Princeton, NJ; *U.S. Public*, pg. 1625
Dau, Diane, Mgr.-Mktg.--Lackman Food Service, Woodbury, NY; *U.S. Private*, pg. 642
Daugherty, Ed, Dir.-Sls. & Mktg.--Alcan Rolled Products Division, Cleveland, OH; *Int'l*, pg. 50
Daugherty, J.R., Sr. V.P.-Sls. & Mktg.--The Chas. H. Lilly Co., Portland, OR; *U.S. Private*, pg. 667
Daugherty, Paul J., Mgr.-Adv. & Mkt. Analyst--Sandusky International Inc., Sandusky, OH; *U.S. Private*, pg. 964
Dave, Bharat, Sr. V.P.-Mktg. & Field Support--Siemens Business Communication Systems, Inc., Santa Clara, CA; *Int'l*, pg. 1245
Davenport, Gordon L., Jr., V.P.-Mktg.--Krystal Company, Chattanooga, TN; *U.S. Private*, pg. 636
Davenport, Marilyn, Mgr.-Mktg.--Kaufman and Broad New Mexico Division, Albuquerque, NM; *U.S. Public*, pg. 945
Davenport, Scott, Mgr.-Mktg.--Subaru Central Region, Inc., Aurora, CO; *Int'l*, pg. 523
Daves, Howard, Dir.-Intl. Mktg.--Bain Hogg Group plc, London, United Kingdom; *Int'l*, pg. 671
David Guthrie, V.P.-Sls. & Mktg.--Monarch Tile, Inc., Florence, AL; *U.S. Private*, pg. 287
David, Dawn, Mgr.-Mktg.--Bernard Matthews PLC, Norwich, United Kingdom; *Int'l*, pg. 189
Davidson, Alberta, V.P.-Corp. Mktg.--TrizecHahn Centers Inc., San Diego, CA; *Int'l*, pg. 1425
Davidson, Brian, Mgr.-Mktg.--Engineer Control Intl., Elon College, NC; *U.S. Private*, pg. 376
Davidson, Charles T., Chm. Bd., Pres. & Chief Exec. Officer--J.A. Jones, Inc., Charlotte, NC; *Int'l*, pg. 633
Davidson, Cheryl, Admin. Asst.-Mktg.--IMC Agribusiness, Collinsville, IL; *U.S. Public*, pg. 856
Davidson, Christopher, Dir.-Pub. Rel. & Corp. Communications--Guinness Plc, London, United Kingdom; *Int'l*, pg. 412
Davidson, Daniel E., Database Dir. & Targeted Mktg. Dir.--CheckMark Communications, Saint Louis, MO; *U.S. Private*, pg. 231
Davidson, John, Dir.-Mktg.--Henkel Surface Technologies, Madison Heights, MI; *Int'l*, pg. 610
Davidson, Leslye, Mgr.-Mktg.--Awrey Bakeries, Inc., Livonia, MI; *U.S. Private*, pg. 103
Davidson, Robert, V.P.-European Sls. & Opers.--Vicorp, N.V., Utrecht, Netherlands; *U.S. Public*, pg. 1321
Davidson, Todd, Dir.-Mktg.--Gorges/Quik-To-Fix Foods, Dallas, TX; *U.S. Private*, pg. 465

Davies, Barry, V.P. & Gen. Mgr.-Sls. & Mktg.--Fisher Gauge Limited, Peterborough, Canada; *Int'l*, pg. 491
Davies, Bob, V.P.-Mktg.--Warrens Waller Press, Inc., South San Francisco, CA; *U.S. Private*, pg. 1151
Davies, Catherine, Dir.-Mktg.-Epic--Sony Music Entertainment (UK) Limited, London, United Kingdom; *Int'l*, pg. 1284
Davies, G., Sr. V.P.-Mktg.--Canadian National Railway Company, Montreal, Canada; *Int'l*, pg. 258
Davies, G. Basil, Sr. V.P.-Sls. & Mktg.--Copperweld Fayetteville Division, Fayetteville, TN; *Int'l*, pg. 662
Davies, G. Basil, Dir.-Sls. & Mktg.--Copperweld Fayetteville Division, Fayetteville, TN; *Int'l*, pg. 662
Davies, G. Basil, Sr. V.P.-Sls. & Mktg.--Copperweld Chicago Division, Chicago, IL; *Int'l*, pg. 662
Davies, Hugh, Mktg. Svcs. Dir.--Leo Burnett Ltd. Thailand, Bangkok, Thailand; *U.S. Private*, pg. 185
Davies, Robert, V.P.-Intl. Mktg.--Target Technology Ltd., Ashford, United Kingdom; *Int'l*, pg. 853
Davies, Russ, Mgr.-Mktg. Communications--Aro Fluid Products Division, Bryan, OH; *U.S. Public*, pg. 877
Davies, William, V.P.-Mktg.--Salsbury Laboratories, Inc., Charles City, IA; *Int'l*, pg. 1277
Davis-Fritsch, Doris, Mgr.-Mktg. Communications--Danka Office Imaging, Rochester, NY; *U.S. Public*, pg. 551
Davis, Aaron L., V.P.-Mktg.--American Power Conversion Corporation, West Kingston, RI; *U.S. Public*, pg. 89
Davis, Alan, Mng. Dir.-U.K.--MDIS Group plc, Hemel Hempstead, United Kingdom; *Int'l*, pg. 826
Davis, Allen S., Sr. V.P.-Mktg. & Mdsg. Services--White Hen Pantry, Inc., Elmhurst, IL; *U.S. Private*, pg. 1172
Davis, Bruce, Dir.-Mktg.--PG Energy, Inc., Wilkes-Barre, PA; *U.S. Public*, pg. 1271
Davis, C., V.P.-Mktg. & Sls.--The Budd Company, Troy, MI; *Int'l*, pg. 1388
Davis, David, V.P.-Mktg.--Duro Bag Manufacturing Co., Ludlow, KY; *U.S. Private*, pg. 348
Davis, Dennis, V.P.-Adv., Sls. & Mktg.--Davis Wood Products, Inc., Hudson, NC; *U.S. Private*, pg. 315
Davis, Dewayn, V.P.-Sls. & Mktg.--Auto-trol Technology Corporation, Denver, CO; *U.S. Public*, pg. 148
Davis, Doug, V.P.-Mktg.--B&B Corporate Holdings, Inc., Tampa, FL; *U.S. Private*, pg. 104
Davis, Earl E., Exec. V.P.-Commercial--Weirton Steel Corporation, Weirton, WV; *U.S. Public*, pg. 1751
Davis, Errol, Telephone Marketing Dir.--Western Direct, Phoenix, AZ; *U.S. Private*, pg. 1166
Davis, Erroll, Telephone Mktg. Dir.--Western International Media Corporation, Atlanta, GA; *U.S. Private*, pg. 1167
Davis, Fred, Dir.-Mktg.--Email Limited-Major Appliance Group, Riverwood, Australia; *Int'l*, pg. 450
Davis, Gene A., V.P.-Sls. & Mktg.--Environmental Tectonics Corporation (ETC), Southampton, PA; *U.S. Public*, pg. 587
Davis, Grady, V.P.-Sls. & Mktg.--Tolleson Lumber Company, Inc., Perry, GA; *U.S. Private*, pg. 1090
Davis, J. Brad, Sr. V.P.-Mktg. & Corp. Rels.--Washington Mutual Inc., Seattle, WA; *U.S. Public*, pg. 1741
Davis, J. Dan, V.P.-Sls. & Mktg.--Prym-Dritz Corporation, Spartanburg, SC; *Int'l*, pg. 1499
Davis, J.R., V.P.-Sls. & Mktg.--Atlas Roofing Corp., Meridian, MS; *U.S. Private*, pg. 96
Davis, James M., Sr. V.P.-Mktg. & Adv.--Quality Stores Inc., Muskegon, MI; *U.S. Private*, pg. 899
Davis, Jeffrey, Dir.-Mktg. & Adv.--Tuffy Associates Corp., Toledo, OH; *U.S. Private*, pg. 1109
Davis, Jeffrey L., V.P.-Mktg. & Customer Service--SIGCORP, Inc., Evansville, IN; *U.S. Public*, pg. 1471
Davis, Jeffrey L., V.P.-Mktg. & Customer Service--Southern Indiana Gas & Electric Co., Evansville, IN; *U.S. Public*, pg. 1471
Davis, John, Dir.-Sls. & Mktg.--Simpson Dura-Vent Co., Inc., Vacaville, CA; *U.S. Public*, pg. 1474
Davis, Kaylee, V.P.-Mktg., Children's Div.--Golden Books Family Entertainment Inc., New York, NY; *U.S. Public*, pg. 749
Davis, Kaylee, V.P.-Mktg., Children's Div.--Golden Books Publishing, New York, NY; *U.S. Public*, pg. 749
Davis, Linda G., Coord.-Mktg.--Jacobs Applied Technology, Inc., Orangeburg, SC; *U.S. Public*, pg. 921
Davis, Lloyd, V.P.-Sls. & Mktg.--North American Salt Company, Overland Park, KS; *U.S. Private*, pg. 505
Davis, Lynn, V.P.-Sls., Mktg., Pur. & Mfg.--Lithotype Company, Inc., South San Francisco, CA; *U.S. Private*, pg. 670
Davis, Marci, V.P.-Mktg. & Communications--Cineplex Odeon Corporation, Toronto, Canada; *Int'l*, pg. 292
Davis, Mariko, Mgr.-Mktg. Commun.--Rollerblade, Inc., Minnetonka, MN; *U.S. Private*, pg. 941
Davis, Michael G., V.P.-Mktg. & Customer Svcs.--OGE Energy Corp., Oklahoma City, OK; *U.S. Public*, pg. 1207
Davis, Michelle, Mktg. & Adv.--Howell Instruments Inc., Fort Worth, TX; *U.S. Private*, pg. 543
Davis, Mickey, Sr. V.P.-Mktg.--Plasti-Line, Inc., Knoxville, TN; *U.S. Public*, pg. 1308
Davis, Mickey, Sr. V.P.-Mktg. & Sls.--American Sign & Marketing Services, Inc., Florence, KY; *U.S. Public*, pg. 1309
Davis, Mike, Exec. V.P.-Mktg./Locum Tenens, Inc.--Allegiant Physician Services, Atlanta, GA; *U.S. Public*, pg. 45
Davis, Mike, Dir.-Mktg.--W.M. Barr & Co., Inc., Memphis, TN; *U.S. Private*, pg. 117
Davis, Mike, Mgr.-Mktg. & Adv.--Flavor House Products, Inc., Dothan, AL; *U.S. Private*, pg. 410
Davis, Nissen, Dir.-Customer Services--Hughes Electronics Corporation, Westchester, CA; *U.S. Public*, pg. 720
Davis, P. Michael, V.P.-Dedicated Fleet--Builders Transport, Incorporated, Camden, SC; *U.S. Public*, pg. 267
Davis, Randal R., V.P.-Sls. & Mktg.--Dexter Nonwovens Division, Windsor Locks, CT; *U.S. Public*, pg. 504
Davis, Rick A., V.P.-Sls. & Mktg.-Displays--American Manufacturing Company, Chattanooga, TN; *U.S. Private*, pg. 58
Davis, Robert, V.P.-Mktg. & Sales--Ryobi Motor Products, Anderson, SC; *Int'l*, pg. 1151
Davis, Robert W., Sr. V.P.-Sls. & Mktg.--Andres Wines Ltd., Winona, Canada; *Int'l*, pg. 75
Davis, Ronald W., V.P.-Mktg. (Air Systems)--Engineered Support Systems Inc., Saint Louis, MO; *U.S. Public*, pg. 583
Davis, Stephen, V.P.-Mktg.--Heineken USA Inc., White Plains, NY; *Int'l*, pg. 608
Davis, Stuart, Mgr.-Mktg.--Teledyne Brown Engineering, Huntsville, AL; *U.S. Public*, pg. 43
Davis, T., Dir.-Mktg.--Whittaker Electronic Systems, Simi Valley, CA; *U.S. Public*, pg. 1767
Davis, Tim, Dir.-Mktg.-Toppings, Peanut Butter & Specialties--J.M. Smucker Company, Orrville, OH; *U.S. Public*, pg. 1480
Davis, Tom, Pres.-Inpatient Svcs.--RehabCare Group, Inc., Saint Louis, MO; *U.S. Public*, pg. 1373
Davis, Tracy, Exec. V.P.-Mktg. & Operations--AppleTree Markets, Houston, TX; *U.S. Private*, pg. 78
Davison, Ken, V.P.-Prod. Mngmt. & Mktg.--Gelco Information Network, Inc., Eden Prairie, MN; *U.S. Private*, pg. 442
Davison, Ken, V.P.-Global Mktg.--Newbridge Networks Corporation, Kanata, Canada; *Int'l*, pg. 923
Dawahare, A.F., Pres. & Dir.-Sls. & Mktg.--Dawahares, Inc., Lexington, KY; *U.S. Private*, pg. 316
Dawson, Patricia, Dir.-Mktg.--SpecTran Corporation, Sturbridge, MA; *U.S. Public*, pg. 1497
Dawson, Vicki, Mgr.-Mktg.--Fidelity National Financial, Inc., Irvine, CA; *U.S. Public*, pg. 620
Day, Jack, Dir.-Direct Response Mktg. & Sls./Prof., Ref. & Trade Grp.--John Wiley & Sons, Inc., New York, NY; *U.S. Public*, pg. 1768
Day, Laura, Dir.-Corp. Mktg.--Minnesota Twins Baseball Club, Minneapolis, MN; *U.S. Private*, pg. 750
Day, Leslie, Dir.-Mktg.--Bar-S Foods Co., Phoenix, AZ; *U.S. Private*, pg. 114
Day, Mark, Mgr.-Pub. Rels. & Mktg. Communications--Teledyne Ryan Aeronautical, San Diego, CA; *U.S. Public*, pg. 43
Daza, Joyce P., Mgr.-Regional Mktg.--ALLTEL Answering Service, Inc., Export, PA; *U.S. Public*, pg. 55
Daza, Joyce P., Mgr.-Regional Mktg.--ALLTEL Pennsylvania, Inc., Kittanning, PA; *U.S. Public*, pg. 56
de Almeida, Alexandre Vieira, Mgr.-Mktg.--Central de Cervejas, S.A., Lisbon, Portugal; *Int'l*, pg. 279
De Armas, John A., V.P.-Intl. Mktg.--Phelps Dodge Intl. Corp., Coral Gables, FL; *U.S. Public*, pg. 1286
de Barbe, Mr., Supvr.-Mktg. & Communications--N.V. Kodak S.A., Vilvoorde, Belgium; *U.S. Public*, pg. 554
de Bodinat, Henri, Sr. Exec. V.P.-Mktg., Sls. & Prods.--Club Mediterranee SA, Paris, France; *Int'l*, pg. 298
De Boisseson, Dominque, Dir.-Mktg.--Alcatel Alsthom Compagnie Generale D'Electricite, Paris, France; *Int'l*, pg. 52
De Broqueville, Olivier, Chief Mgr.-Mktg.--Bank Brussels Lambert, Brussels, Belgium; *Int'l*, pg. 146
de Combret, Bernard, Exec V.P.-Refinig, Mktg. & Trading--Elf Aquitane, Paris, France; *Int'l*, pg. 444
de Fougeroux, Guy, Dir.-Plng. & Devel.--Au Bon Marche, Paris, France; *Int'l*, pg. 97
De Freitas Leite, Luiz Flavio, Mgr.-Mktg.--Novo Nordisk Bioindustrial do Brasil Ltda., Parana, Brazil; *Int'l*, pg. 988
de Heer, William, Dir.-Mktg. & Sls.--OPEL Nederland B.V., Sliedrecht, Netherlands; *U.S. Public*, pg. 723
De Herder, Richard G., Sr. V.P. & Gen. Mgr.-Sls. & Mktg. Support--Mattel, Inc., El Segundo, CA; *U.S. Public*, pg. 1057
de Kesel, Jan, Dir.-Mktg.--Digital Equipment N.V./S.A., Brussels, Belgium; *U.S. Public*, pg. 508
de Koiste, A., Mgr.-Mktg.--Campina Melkunie BV, Zaltbommel, Netherlands; *Int'l*, pg. 254
de les Voin, Jean, Dir.-Mktg.--Elida Faberge, Paris, France; *Int'l*, pg. 1437
de Lopez, Arlene, Mgr.-Mktg.--McDonald's Panama, Panama, Panama; *U.S. Public*, pg. 1069
de los Angeles Alvarez, Maria, Rep.-Marketing--Singapore Tourist Promotion Board - Buenos Aires, Buenos Aires, Argentina; *Int'l*, pg. 1254
De Mange, Lorraine Petit, Mgr.-Mktg. Devel.--Transnet Group, London, United Kingdom; *Int'l*, pg. 1418
de Marzi, Fedora, Dir.-Mktg.--Industrias Pacocha S.A. (Unilever), Lima, Peru; *Int'l*, pg. 1437
De Palma, Mark, V.P.-Mktg.--First Empire State Corporation, Buffalo, NY; *U.S. Public*, pg. 631
De Paolis, L. Andrew, V.P.-Adv. & Mktg.--The Grand Union Company, Wayne, NJ; *U.S. Public*, pg. 758
de Place, Guy, Mgr.-Mktg.--Schneider S.A., Boulogne-Billancourt, France; *Int'l*, pg. 1207
de Preux, Philippe, Sr. V.P.-Sls. & Mktg.--Bobst S.A., Lausanne, Switzerland; *Int'l*, pg. 198
De Queiroz, Juarez, Dir.-Mktg.--Souza Cruz, S.A., Rio de Janeiro, Brazil; *Int'l*, pg. 112
De Rocco, Beatrice, V.P.-Mktg. & Sls.--Computer Task Group, Inc. (CTG), Buffalo, NY; *U.S. Public*, pg. 423
De Rosa, Cathy, V.P.-Mktg.--Symix Systems, Inc., Columbus, OH; *U.S. Public*, pg. 1546
De Roy Vanzunewijn, Rudolph F., Mgr.-Adv.--OPEL Nederland B.V., Sliedrecht, Netherlands; *U.S. Public*, pg. 723
de Saint Albin, Stanilas, Dir.-Mktg.--Bull S.A., Louveciennes, France; *Int'l*, pg. 315
de Saint Perier, Fredericka, Dir.-U.S. Mktg.--Tambrands Inc., Cincinnati, OH; *U.S. Public*, pg. 1331
De Thomas, Frank, Dir.-Mktg.--Perstorp Analytical Inc. Division NIRSystems, Silver Spring, MD; *Int'l*, pg. 1039
De Vos, Jim, V.P.-Mktg.--Morrison Health Care Inc., Smyrna, GA; *U.S. Public*, pg. 1133
De Zao, Tom, Dir.-Mktg--Chiron Corporation, Emeryville, CA; *U.S. Public*, pg. 349
Deahr, Ronald, V.P.-Sls. & Mktg.--Isomedix Operations Inc., Whippany, NJ; *U.S. Public*, pg. 1515
Deahr, Ronald, V.P.-Sls. & Mktg.--Isomedix Management Inc., Whippany, NJ; *U.S. Public*, pg. 1515
Deal, Mary Jo, V.P.-Mktg.--Hycor Biomedical, Inc., Irvine, CA; *U.S. Public*, pg. 851
Deal, Pat, Supvr.-Mktg. Communications--Kelley Dock Systems, Milwaukee, WI; *U.S. Private*, pg. 612
Dean, Len A., Dir.-Mktg.--BHP Iron Ore, Perth, Australia; *Int'l*, pg. 224
Dean, Sharon, Mgr.-Mktg. Support--Southwestern/Great American Inc., Nashville, TN; *U.S. Private*, pg. 1018
Dear, Derek, Gen. Mgr.-Mktg. Communications--British Airways PLC, London, United Kingdom; *Int'l*, pg. 218
Dearborn, Bonny, Coord.-Mktg.--Manufacturers Technologies, Inc., West Springfield, MA; *U.S. Private*, pg. 701
DeArmas, Celeste, Sr. V.P.-Mktg., Nestle Refrigerated Foods--Nestle Frozen, Refrigerated, and Ice Cream Companies, Solon, OH; *Int'l*, pg. 918
Deaton, Scott, Sr. V.P.-Mktg.--Follett College Stores Corp., Elmhurst, IL; *U.S. Private*, pg. 417
DeBell, Daniel H., Dir.-Mktg.--Ithaco Inc., Ithaca, NY; *U.S. Private*, pg. 576
DeBeradinis, Robert L., Dir.-Mktg./Military Products--Microphase Corporation, Norwalk, CT; *U.S. Private*, pg. 742
Debiase, Mark, Mgr.-Adv. & Mktg. Svcs.--Grinnell Corporation, Exeter, NH; *U.S. Public*, pg. 1651
Debord, Connie Snapp, Sr. V.P. & Strategic Mktg. Dir.--Russ Reid Company, Inc., Pasadena, CA; *U.S. Private*, pg. 952
Debrodt, Donna, Dir.-Mktg.--Compuware Corporation, Farmington Hills, MI; *U.S. Public*, pg. 423
DeBroux, Jim, V.P.-Mktg.-Vans--Anderson Trucking Service Inc., Saint Cloud, MN; *U.S. Private*, pg. 72
Dec, Richard, V.P.-Mktg.--Merrimac Industries, Inc., West Caldwell, NJ; *U.S. Public*, pg. 1098
Decaluwe, Lieve, Mgr.-Mktg.--Innovative Sputtering Technology IST, Zulte, Belgium; *Int'l*, pg. 183
DeCardlis, Anthony, V.P.-Sls. & Mktg.--Fischer Imaging Corporation, Denver, CO; *U.S. Public*, pg. 647
DeCesare, Nella, Coord.-Mktg.--Famous Restaurants Inc., Scottsdale, AZ; *U.S. Private*, pg. 393
Dechamps, Guy, Dir.-Mktg. & Sls.--Amicon, Inc., Beverly, MA; *U.S. Public*, pg. 1113
Decio, Terrence M., Sr. Exec. V.P.-Sls. & Mktg.--Skyline Corporation, Elkhart, IN; *U.S. Public*, pg. 1476
Deck, Bernard, Dir.-Mktg.--First Recovery, Lexington, KY; *U.S. Public*, pg. 139
Deck, Christi, V.P.-Global Mktg.--Genzyme Corporation, Cambridge, MA; *U.S. Public*, pg. 733
Decker Ward, James, Exec. V.P.-Mktg.--Encyclopaedia Britannica Educational Corporation, Chicago, IL; *U.S. Private*, pg. 375
Decker, Dave, Coord.-Mktg.--Dwyer Instruments Inc., Michigan City, IN; *U.S. Private*, pg. 350
Decker, James, V.P.-Mktg.--Progress Lighting, Spartanburg, SC; *U.S. Public*, pg. 1684
Decker, Karen, Dir.-Mktg.--WorldCom, Inc., Jackson, MS; *U.S. Public*, pg. 1779
Decker, Leonard, Dir.-Mktg.--Blaw-Knox Construction Equipment Corporation, Mattoon, IL; *U.S. Public*, pg. 877
Decker, Paul H., Mgr.-Mktg. Admin.--Preformed Line Products, Cleveland, OH; *U.S. Public*, pg. 1321
Declementi, Bruno, Dir. Mktg./Dir. Response--Editions du Juris-Classeur, Paris, France; *Int'l*, pg. 1095
Dederding, H., Sr. V.P.-Mktg.--Princess Hotels International Inc., New York, NY; *Int'l*, pg. 818
Dedio, Barbara, Mgr.-Special Mkt.--Replogle Globes, Inc., Broadview, IL; *U.S. Private*, pg. 923
Dedmond, Dennis, Dir.-Mktg.--Nakano Foods, Burlingame, CA; *Int'l*, pg. 883
Dedmond, Dennis, Dir.-Mktg.--Nakano Foods Inc., Arlington Heights, IL; *Int'l*, pg. 883
Dedrick, Greg, Sr. V.P.-Human Resources--Kentucky Fried Chicken Corporation (KFC), Louisville, KY; *U.S. Public*, pg. 1636
Deeg, Rudy, Mgr.-Mktg.--Beloit Lenox, Div., Lenox, MA; *U.S. Public*, pg. 789
Deem, Peter, Sr. V.P.-Mktg.--Holnam Inc. (West Division), Lakewood, CO; *Int'l*, pg. 628
Deering, Christopher, Exec. V.P.-Mktg. & Sls.--Columbia Tri-Star Home Video, Burbank, CA; *Int'l*, pg. 1282
Dees, Alvin H., Jr., Exec. V.P.-Mktg.--Alfa Corporation, Montgomery, AL; *U.S. Public*, pg. 40
DeFreitas, Mark, Mgr.-Key Acct.--Lever Brothers West Indies Ltd., Champs Fleurs, Trinidad & Tobago; *Int'l*, pg. 1437
Degelman, Jack, Mgr.-Mktg.--Degelman Industries Ltd., Regina, Canada; *Int'l*, pg. 388
DeGeorge, Patricia, Dir.-Ladies Mktg.--Swank, Inc., Attleboro, MA; *U.S. Public*, pg. 1543
DeGeorge, Sal, Sr. V.P.-Sls. & Mktg.--Bridgford Foods Corporation, Anaheim, CA; *U.S. Public*, pg. 252
DeGood, Paul W., Mgr.-Mktg. Services--M.C. Gill Corporation, El Monte, CA; *U.S. Private*, pg. 453
Degraff, John, Mgr.-Mktg.--Jones Dairy Farm, Fort Atkinson, WI; *U.S. Private*, pg. 596
DeGray, J.H., V.P.-Mktg.--The Kerite Company, Seymour, CT; *U.S. Public*, pg. 844
DeGreef, Anne, V.P.-Mktg.--Ultrak Inc., Lewisville, TX; *U.S. Public*, pg. 1663
Degroot, Rob, Dir.-Mktg.--Joh. A. Benckiser GmbH, Ludwigshafen, Germany; *Int'l*, pg. 185
DeHart, Pete, Sr. V.P.-Sls. & Mktg.--Alpha Therapeutic Corp., Los Angeles, CA; *Int'l*, pg. 558
DeHart, W.E., V.P.-Sls. & Mktg.--Powell Electrical Mfg. Co., Houston, TX; *U.S. Public*, pg. 1319
Dehenain, Mr., Dir.-Mktg.--Laboratory Div., Brussels, Belgium; *Int'l*, pg. 819
Dehne, Don, V.P.-Mktg.--The Ohio Casualty Insurance Group, Hamilton, OH; *U.S. Public*, pg. 1214
Deignan, David, Dir.-Mktg.--Aaron's Rental Purchase, Atlanta, GA; *U.S. Public*, pg. 12

Deitel, Alan, Gen. Mgr.-Component Div.--Philips Components, Jupiter, FL; *Int'l*, pg. 1054
Dejardin, Emily, Mktg. Asst.--Papa John's International Inc., Louisville, KY; *U.S. Public*, pg. 1255
Dek, P., Mgr.-Mktg.--CSM Suiker BV, Diemen, Netherlands; *Int'l*, pg. 243
Dekel, Elie, Exec. V.P.-Mktg. & Adv.--Saban Entertainment, Los Angeles, CA; *U.S. Private*, pg. 959
Del Belso, Richard, Sr. V.P.-Worldwide Adv. & Mktg. Res.--Warner Bros. Studios, Inc., Burbank, CA; *U.S. Public*, pg. 1611
Del Castillo, Maria Victoria, Mgr.-Mktg.-NutraSweet--Monsanto Argentina S.A.I.C., Buenos Aires, Argentina; *U.S. Public*, pg. 1125
del la Haba, Larry, V.P.-Mktg.--Lumex Medical Products, Bay Shore, NY; *U.S. Public*, pg. 758
Del Mercado, Andres Vazquez, Dir.-Mktg.--Telefonos de Mexico S.A. de C.V., Mexico, Mexico; *Int'l*, pg. 1373
Del Neri, Edoardo, Exec. V.P.-Sls. & Mktg.--Merloni Elettrodomestici S.P.A., Fabriano, Italy; *Int'l*, pg. 860
Del Rua, Guido, V.P.-Sls. & Mktg.--Furness North America Inc., Houston, TX; *Int'l*, pg. 530
Del Valle, Egnacio, Mgr.-Mktg. & Adv.--Bacardi Centroamerica, S.A., Panama, Panama; *Int'l*, pg. 132
del Valle, Fernando, Dir.-Mktg.--Aerolineas Argentinas, Buenos Aires, Argentina; *Int'l*, pg. 575
Del Valle, Jose, Mgr.-House Mktg.--Plan International USA, Inc., Warwick, RI; *U.S. Private*, pg. 869
Delacolette, Yves, Mgr.-Mktg.--Credit Lyonnais Belgium, Brussels, Belgium; *Int'l*, pg. 344
Delacroix, Chuck, V.P.-Mktg.--Gulf States Toyota, Inc., Houston, TX; *U.S. Private*, pg. 488
Delafield, C.H., Dir.-Intl. Mktg.--Stafford-Miller Limited, Welwyn Garden City, United Kingdom; *U.S. Public*, pg. 237
Delagrave, Yves, V.P.-Mktg. (Cement-Quebec & the Maritimes Div.)--St. Lawrence Cement Inc., Montreal, Canada; *Int'l*, pg. 628
Delahoussaye, M. Kathy, V.P.-Mktg. Commun.--Excel Communications, Inc., Dallas, TX; *U.S. Public*, pg. 598
Delahunt, G., Dir.-Sls. & Mktg.--Colgate-Palmolive, Dublin, Ireland; *U.S. Public*, pg. 398
DeLaMata, Luis, Dir.-Mktg.--Bustelo Coffee Roasting Co., Bronx, NY; *Int'l*, pg. 1377
Delaney, Marnie, Sr. V.P. & Dir.-Adv. & Mktg. Communcaitons--BankAmerica Corporation, San Francisco, CA; *U.S. Public*, pg. 179
Delaney, R. Edward, Mgr.-Mktg.--Eaton Corporation-Heinemann Products, Commercial Controls Division, Salisbury, MD; *U.S. Public*, pg. 557
Delaney, Richard M., Sr. V.P. & Dir.-Mktg.--UMB Financial Corporation, Kansas City, MO; *U.S. Public*, pg. 1653
Delaney, Steven C., Exec. V.P. & Dir.-Capital Mkts.--Scott & Stringfellow Financial, Inc., Richmond, VA; *U.S. Public*, pg. 1445
Delany, George, Pres.--Powermatic, McMinnville, TN; *U.S. Public*, pg. 502
Delatte, Joe, Dir.-Mktg.--The Virginian-Pilot, Norfolk, VA; *U.S. Private*, pg. 649
Delbalzo, G., Mgr.-Mktg.--Pirelli U.K. Tyres Limited, Burton on Trent, United Kingdom; *Int'l*, pg. 1059
Deleenheer, Ronald V., V.P.-Mktg.--Ash Grove Cement Company, Shawnee Mission, KS; *U.S. Private*, pg. 87
Delehanty, Daniel L., Dir.-Mktg.--Marlite, Dover, OH; *U.S. Private*, pg. 705
DeLeo, William J., V.P.-Mktg. & Corp. Performance--Duquesne Light Company, Pittsburgh, PA; *U.S. Public*, pg. 474
DeLeonard, Dennis, Dir.-Mktg./Passenger & Light Truck Div.--Continental General Tire, Inc., Charlotte, NC; *Int'l*, pg. 327
Delevich, Walt, Dir.-Mktg. VSM/HDOE Bus. Unit--Chicago Rawhide, Elgin, IL; *Int'l*, pg. 1157
Delevich, Walt, Dir.-Mktg. Services--CR Services, Elgin, IL; *Int'l*, pg. 1157
Delfino, Donatella, Mgr.-Mktg.--Procter & Gamble Health & Beauty Care So. Europe, Rome, Italy; *U.S. Public*, pg. 1332
DelGaudio, Alan, Dir.-Mktg.--Excel Technology, Inc., New York, NY; *U.S. Public*, pg. 599
Deliberato, Carmine J., Dir.-Mktg. & Sls.--Lavelle Company, Philadelphia, PA; *U.S. Private*, pg. 653
DeLime, Bridie, Dir.-Mktg.--Maddak Inc., Pequannock, NJ; *U.S. Private*, pg. 130
Delizio, Dale, Sr. Mgr.-Mktg.--Goshen Rubber Co., Inc., Goshen, IN; *U.S. Private*, pg. 465
Della Bernarda, Rick, V.P. & Dir.-Mktg.--J. Baker, Inc., Canton, MA; *U.S. Public*, pg. 167
Dellert, Susan, Dir.-Mktg.--Crested Butte Mountain Resort, Inc., Crested Butte, CO; *U.S. Private*, pg. 289
Dellinger, Bob, Pres.-Sls. & Mktg./Bed Div.--Fieldcrest Cannon, Inc., Kannapolis, NC; *U.S. Public*, pg. 1296
DeLonghi, Charles S., Mgr.-Bus. Unit--ITW Woodworth, Ferndale, MI; *U.S. Public*, pg. 867
Delorenzo, Dick, V.P.-Sls. & Mktg.--Datapro Information Services Grp., Delran, NJ; *U.S. Public*, pg. 1070
Delp, Mark, Sr. V.P.-Sls. & Mktg.--Gemtron Corporation, Sweetwater, TN; *Int'l*, pg. 1523
DelRossi, Laura, V.P.-Mktg. Services--CoreStates Financial Corp., Philadelphia, PA; *U.S. Public*, pg. 446
Deltour, Etienne, Mgr.-Mktg.--Bekaert-Tinsley, Hemiksem, Belgium; *Int'l*, pg. 183
DeLuca, Sirio, Dir.-Mktg.--Dominion Industrial Fabrics Company, Montreal, Canada; *Int'l*, pg. 415
Delzio, Jerry, V.P.-Sls. & Mktg.--Bolliger, Inc., Stamford, CT; *U.S. Private*, pg. 155
DeMaille, Leon, Mgr.-Mktg.--Erisco, Inc., New York, NY; *U.S. Public*, pg. 395
DeMain, Dominic P., Sr. V.P. -Mktg.--Combe Incorporated, White Plains, NY; *U.S. Private*, pg. 257
DeMarco, Rick, V.P.-Mktg.--Carrier Corporation, Indianapolis, IN; *U.S. Public*, pg. 1689
DeMarino, Louis T., Sr. V.P.-Sls. & Mktg.--The Jaydor Corporation, Millburn, NJ; *U.S. Private*, pg. 584
DeMars, Charles, V.P.-Mktg.--ELCO Corporation, Huntingdon, PA; *Int'l*, pg. 775
DeMars, Tim, Mgr.-Mktg. Communications--Miller Electric Manufacturing Co., Appleton, WI; *U.S. Public*, pg. 867
Demarse, Elisabeth, Dir.-Mktg.--Bloomberg L.P., New York, NY; *U.S. Private*, pg. 150
DeMartino, Jerry A., Sr. V.P.-Global Strategy--MCI Communications Corp., Atlanta, GA; *U.S. Public*, pg. 1023
Demeo, Joe, Dir.-Sls. & Mktg., Western Reg.--BGW Systems, Inc., Hawthorne, CA; *U.S. Private*, pg. 107
DeMeo, Ronald C., Sr. V.P.-Mktg. & Sls. & Sec.--Marietta Corporation, Cortland, NY; *U.S. Private*, pg. 702
Demers, Richard P., V.P.-Mktg., Sls. & Adv.--EnergyNorth, Inc., Manchester, NH; *U.S. Public*, pg. 581
Deming, Derrell, Dir.-Mktg.--Polka Dot Dairy/Tom Thumb, Inc., Hastings, MN; *U.S. Private*, pg. 874
Deming, Derrell, Dir.-Sls. & Mktg.--Polka Dot Dairy/Tom Thumb Food Markets, Hastings, MN; *U.S. Private*, pg. 874
Demintruk, Ann, Mgr.-Mktg.--Kenworth Truck Company, Kirkland, WA; *U.S. Public*, pg. 1246
Demko, Michael P., Jr., Dir.-Mktg.--Mellon Bank, N.A.-Northeastern Region, Wilkes-Barre, PA; *U.S. Public*, pg. 1085
Demmel, William, Mgr.-Mktg.--TB Wood's Corporation, Chambersburg, PA; *U.S. Public*, pg. 1562
Demmer, Kurt, Dr., Dir.-Economics & Mktg.--IKB Deutsche Industriebank AG, Dusseldorf, Germany; *Int'l*, pg. 645
Dempsey, Paul, Sr. V.P.-Mktg.--Pioneer New Media Technologies, Long Beach, CA; *U.S. Private*, pg. 866
Den Adel, Verlan, Mgr.-Mkt. Devel.--Pella Corporation, Pella, IA; *U.S. Private*, pg. 848
DeNardin, Tom, V.P.-Mktg. & Adv.--Thrifty Rent-a-Car System, Inc., Tulsa, OK; *U.S. Public*, pg. 354
Denby, D.J., V.P.-Mktg.--Sterling Pulp Chemicals, Ltd., Etobicoke, Canada; *U.S. Public*, pg. 1580
Denby, William C., V.P.-Sls. & Mktg.--Agouron Pharmaceuticals, Inc., La Jolla, CA; *U.S. Public*, pg. 28
Denges, James, V.P.-Mktg. & Pur.--Central Grocers Co-op, Franklin Park, IL; *U.S. Private*, pg. 223
Denig, Kaaryn, V.P. & Dir.-Mktg. & Adv.--Jordache Enterprises, Inc., New York, NY; *U.S. Private*, pg. 597
Denison, Ray L., Dir.-Mktg.--Mead School & Office Products, Dayton, OH; *U.S. Public*, pg. 1074
Denman, Mimi, V.P.-Mktg.--Adecco S.A., Lausanne, Switzerland; *Int'l*, pg. 23
Denman, Mimi Garrity, V.P.-Mktg.--Adecco Employment Services, Redwood City, CA; *Int'l*, pg. 24
Denmman, Harry, V.P.-Mktg.--Medicalodges, Inc., Coffeyville, KS; *U.S. Private*, pg. 728
Denney, Gary, V.P.-Sls.--Multi Metals Div., Louisville, KY; *U.S. Public*, pg. 575
Dennis, Bruce C., V.P.-Mktg.--Boeing Commercial Airplane Group, Renton, WA; *U.S. Public*, pg. 240
Dennis, Kenneth D., Sr. V.P.-Mktg.--Brinker International, Inc., Dallas, TX; *U.S. Public*, pg. 253
Denoble, Kristen, Mgr.-Graphic Arts Mktg.--Graymills Corp., Chicago, IL; *U.S. Private*, pg. 473
Densen, Larry E., V.P.--Eastco Industrial Safety Corp., Huntington Station, NY; *U.S. Public*, pg. 548
Densmore, Tom, Dir.-Sls. & Mktg.--Whitfield Foods, Inc., Montgomery, AL; *U.S. Private*, pg. 1173
Denson, Ann, Mgr.-Mktg. Promotions--Allied Clinical Laboratories, Inc., Nashville, TN; *U.S. Public*, pg. 973
Dent, Doug, Dir.-Bus. Devel.--Weaver Popcorn Company, Inc., Van Buren, IN; *U.S. Private*, pg. 1156
Denton, Hal, V.P.-Product Mktg.--InteCom, Dallas, TX; *Int'l*, pg. 794
Denton, Norman, Sr. V.P.-Sls. & Mktg.--Rainbow Technologies, Inc., Irvine, CA; *U.S. Public*, pg. 1359
DePaolo, Joseph, Sr. V.P. & Dir.-Mktg.--Republic New York Corporation, New York, NY; *U.S. Public*, pg. 1380
DePeau, Norman, Dir.-Sls. & Mktg.--Lewis Engineering Company, Naugatuck, CT; *U.S. Public*, pg. 402
Depillo, Tracy, Mgr.-Mktg. Prod.--North American Van Lines, Inc., Fort Wayne, IN; *U.S. Public*, pg. 1191
Depp, Herbert D., V.P.-Mktg. & Sls.--G.E. Aircraft Engines, Cincinnati, OH; *U.S. Public*, pg. 710
DePrater, Johan, V.P.-Mktg.--Coats North America, Charlotte, NC; *Int'l*, pg. 300
Deputato, John, Grp. Mktg. Dir.-Fragrance--Coty Inc., New York, NY; *Int'l*, pg. 185
Depuy, John, Dir.-Mktg.--Kao Infosystems Company (MA), Plymouth, MA; *Int'l*, pg. 717
Depuy, Shelley, Dir.-Mktg.--Tokheim Corporation, Fort Wayne, IN; *U.S. Public*, pg. 1620
Derasmo, Jack, V.P.-Mktg. & Sls. Mgr.--Glen Raven Marketing Corporation, Pearl River, NY; *U.S. Private*, pg. 456
Derber, Scott, Mgr.-Mktg. Svcs.--Adams Extract Co., Inc., Austin, TX; *U.S. Private*, pg. 16
Derby, Jon, Mktg. Services--Southwestern Industries, Inc., Rancho Dominguez, CA; *U.S. Private*, pg. 1019
Derby, Michael, Dir.-Mktg. & Adv.--Seed Corporation of America, Baltimore, MD; *U.S. Private*, pg. 981
Derby, Michael P., Dir.-Adv.--Green Seed Co., Baltimore, MD; *U.S. Private*, pg. 477
Derderian, John, V.P.-Sls. & Mktg.--Pathmark Stores Incorporated, Woodbridge, NJ; *U.S. Private*, pg. 843
Derham Cato, John P., Vice Chm., Pres. & Chief Oper. Officer--The Cato Corporation, Charlotte, NC; *U.S. Public*, pg. 318
Derkach, John, Dir.-Mktg.--PepsiCo. Holdings Ltd. (UK), London, United Kingdom; *U.S. Public*, pg. 1277
Derleth, April, V.P.-Sls. & Mktg.--Mueller Sports Medicine, Inc., Prairie Du Sac, WI; *U.S. Private*, pg. 766
Derobert, Eric, Dir.-Mktg.--Asea Brown Boveri AG, Baden, Switzerland; *Int'l*, pg. 1
DeRoche, Mark J., Mgr.-Mktg.--Mil Systems Engineering, Ottawa, Canada; *Int'l*, pg. 385
DeRosa, Tom, Reg. Mgr.--Cargill Salt, Newark, CA; *U.S. Private*, pg. 210
DeRose, Camille, Dir.-Mktg.--The Gibson-Homans Company, Twinsburg, OH; *U.S. Private*, pg. 451
DeRouchey, Susan, Product Mgr.--Joern's Sunrise Medical, Stevens Point, WI; *U.S. Public*, pg. 1536
Derrenbacher, Richard, Mgr.-Mktg.--Channel Master, Smithfield, NC; *U.S. Private*, pg. 228
Deryes, Phil, Exec. Dir.-Sls. & Mktg. Promo.--Atlanta Motor Speedway, Hampton, GA; *U.S. Public*, pg. 1498
Desantis, Patricia, V.P.-Sls. Promo.--Wm. E. Wright Limited Partnership, West Warren, MA; *U.S. Private*, pg. 1192
DeSarle, Andrew, V.P.-Ancillary Prod. Mktg.--Penton Publishing, Inc., Cleveland, OH; *U.S. Public*, pg. 1306
Desbiens, Michel, Sr. V.P.-Sls. & Corp. Devel.--Donohue Matane, Inc., Quebec, Canada; *Int'l*, pg. 1075
Deschamps, Ruben, Dir.-Mktg.--Copamex Industrias S.A. de C.V., Garza Garcia, Mexico; *Int'l*, pg. 330
Deschene, C.D., Mgr.-Mktg.--Maine Public Service Company, Presque Isle, ME; *U.S. Public*, pg. 1038
Descubes, Henri, Mgr.-Commercial Network--Iveco France S.A., Trappes, France; *Int'l*, pg. 696
DeShano, Don, V.P.-Mktg. & Adv.--LaSalle Bristol Corp., Elkhart, IN; *Int'l*, pg. 618
Desiderio, William R., V.P.-Mktg./Eastern U.S.--Dassault Falcon Jet Corp., South Hackensack, NJ; *Int'l*, pg. 383
Desjardin, Chris, Dir.-Mktg.--Yogen Fruz Worldwide Inc., Markham, Canada; *Int'l*, pg. 1520
Desmedt, Christel, Dir.-Mktg.--Barry Callebaut N.V., Lebbeke, Belgium; *Int'l*, pg. 252
Desocio, Tony A., Mgr.-Mktg.--Trayer Products, Inc., Elmira, NY; *U.S. Private*, pg. 1098
Despain, Christie, Mktg. Rep.--Christensen Products, Salt Lake City, UT; *U.S. Public*, pg. 981
Despins, Meredith A., Dir.-Client Mktg.--The L & B Group, Dallas, TX; *U.S. Public*, pg. 1673
Despres, Germain L., Exec. V.P.--Danisco Ingredients USA, Inc., New Century, KS; *Int'l*, pg. 378
DesRoches, Christopher M., V.P.-Sls. & Mktg.--Casella Waste Systems, Inc., Rutland, VT; *U.S. Public*, pg. 312
Desronier, Jim, Sr. V.P.-Mktg.--Excite, Inc., Redwood City, CA; *U.S. Public*, pg. 599
Desrosier, Jim, Exec. V.P.-Corp. Mktg.--Excite, Inc., Redwood City, CA; *U.S. Public*, pg. 599
Desrosiers, Michael, Dir.-Mktg.--Alimentation Couche Tard Inc., Vimont, Canada; *Int'l*, pg. 57
DeStefano, Michael, V.P.-Mktg./Adv.--Mercantile Stores Company, Inc., Fairfield, OH; *U.S. Public*, pg. 1089
Detch, Charles C., Dir.-Mktg.--Holstein-Friesian Services, Inc., Brattleboro, VT; *U.S. Private*, pg. 536
Detjen, Dale, V.P.-Mktg.--Dakota Electric Association, Farmington, MN; *U.S. Private*, pg. 308
Detmers, Dave, Mgr.-Mktg. Communications--LifeScan, Inc., Milpitas, CA; *U.S. Public*, pg. 928
DeTour, Walter, V.P.-Mktg. & Sls.--Universal Photonics, Inc., Hicksville, NY; *U.S. Private*, pg. 1127
Dettmann, Robert J., V.P.-Sls. & Mktg.--Action Technology Company, Rockaway, NJ; *U.S. Private*, pg. 15
Deutch, Liz, V.P., Acct. Supvr., Mktg. Dir.--Ammirati, Puris & Lintas, Inc., New York, NY; *U.S. Private*, pg. 66
Deutsch, Ellen, V.P.-Mktg.--The Hain Food Group Inc., Uniondale, NY; *U.S. Public*, pg. 774
Deutsch, Jon, Dir.-Prod. Mktg.--Information Builders, New York, NY; *U.S. Private*, pg. 561
Devaleria, Robert, V.P.-Mktg.--Ampacet Corporation, Tarrytown, NY; *U.S. Private*, pg. 67
Devine, Beth, Dir.-Mktg.--Plasticrete Block & Supply Corp., North Haven, CT; *U.S. Private*, pg. 871
Devine, John, Dir.-Sls. & Mktg.--Metex Corporation, Edison, NJ; *U.S. Public*, pg. 1674
Devine, Mary, Mktg. Associate--Watson Wyatt Worldwide, Bethesda, MD; *U.S. Private*, pg. 1154
Devine, Richard, V.P.-Intl. Sls.--Circon Corporation, Santa Barbara, CA; *U.S. Public*, pg. 373
Devinney, Debbie, Dir.-Graphics--Continental Plastic Card Co., Coral Springs, FL; *U.S. Private*, pg. 269
Devitt, George, V.P.-Americas Mktg.--VeriFone, Inc., Redwood City, CA; *U.S. Public*, pg. 815
Devlin, Heidi, Dir.-Database Mktg.--CVS Corp., Woonsocket, RI; *U.S. Public*, pg. 287
Devlin, Joe, Dir.-Corp. Communications--Mitsubishi Fuso Truck of America, Inc., Bridgeport, NJ; *Int'l*, pg. 875
Devor, Cory, V.P.-Sls. & Mktg.--Tricord Systems, Inc., Plymouth, MN; *U.S. Public*, pg. 1637
DeVos, Peter, Function Leader-Plgn. & Database Mktg.--TELUS Marketing Communications, Edmonton, Canada; *Int'l*, pg. 1374
DeWald, Lloyd, V.P.-Mktg. & Sls.--Pierce Manufacturing, Inc., Appleton, WI; *U.S. Public*, pg. 1233
Dewar, Susan, V.P.-Mktg. & Adv.--Markel Corporation, Glen Allen, VA; *U.S. Public*, pg. 1046
Dewey, Brian G., Dir.-Mktg.--Lane Limited, Tucker, GA; *Int'l*, pg. 1129
Dewey, James F., Sr. V.P.-Mktg. & Branch Admin.--The Norwich Savings Society, Norwich, CT; *U.S. Public*, pg. 1203
Dewitt, Jim, Sr. V.P.-Sls.--Robson Communities, Sun Lakes, AZ; *U.S. Private*, pg. 937
DeWitt, Stephen W., V.P.-Mktg. Cisco IOS & Network Mngmt.--Cisco Systems, Inc., San Jose, CA; *U.S. Public*, pg. 375
DeWitt, Stephen W., V.P.-Mktg.--Symantec Corporation, Cupertino, CA; *U.S. Public*, pg. 1545
DeYoung, Carla, Mgr-Mktg.--Armour Food Company, Downers Grove, IL; *U.S. Public*, pg. 427
Dezek, R.J., V.P.-Sls. & Mktg.--Young Radiator Company, Racine, WI; *U.S. Private*, pg. 1201
Dhurana, Anand, Mgr.-Mktg.--Sachs Boge of America, Westlake, OH; *Int'l*, pg. 835
Di Marco, M., Gen. Mgr.-Corp. Mktg. & Sls.--Nuovo Pignone S.p.a., Florence, Italy; *Int'l*, pg. 990
Di Zazzo, James G., Pres.--Oomphies, Inc., Lawrence, MA; *U.S. Private*, pg. 817
Diaddezzio, Fred, Grp. V.P.-Mktg.--First Citizens Banc Shares, Inc., Raleigh, NC; *U.S. Public*, pg. 628

Diamond, David, Exec. V.P.-Mktg. & New Applications--Catalina Marketing Corporation, Saint Petersburg, FL; *U.S. Public*, pg. 314
Diamond, Harry A., AIA, Exec. V.P. & Treas.--Giffels Hoyem Basso, Inc., Troy, MI; *U.S. Private*, pg. 452
Diamond, Randy, Dir.-Mktg.--Accu-Sort Systems, Inc., Telford, PA; *U.S. Private*, pg. 11
Dianda, Jean Luc., Mgr.-Mktg.--The Kendall Co., Antony, France; *U.S. Public*, pg. 1647
Dias, Georgio, Mgr.-Sls.--Overholtzer Church Furniture, Inc., Modesto, CA; *U.S. Private*, pg. 823
Diaz, Adolfo, V.P.-Mktg.-Latin America--Greenwich Air Services, Miami, FL; *U.S. Public*, pg. 710
Diaz, Cass F., Sr. V.P.-Worldwide Sls. & Mktg.--ATL Ultrasound, Inc., Bothell, WA; *U.S. Public*, pg. 11
Diaz, Jorge, Mgr.-Mktg. & Special Programs--Wang Fed Inc., Mc Lean, VA; *U.S. Public*, pg. 1737
Diaz, Manuel F., V.P. & Gen. Mgr.-Solutions Sls. & Delivery Grp./Computer Sys. Org--Hewlett-Packard Company, Palo Alto, CA; *U.S. Public*, pg. 813
Diaz, Nicolas, Mktg. Dir.--Graffiti/DMB&B, Buenos Aires, Argentina; *U.S. Private*, pg. 304
Diaz, Ricardo A., V.P. & Gen. Mgr.--Farinon Div. Harris Corp., Redwood City, CA; *U.S. Public*, pg. 791
Dibden, Susan, Dir.-Mktg.--Ascom Canada Limited, Markham, Canada; *Int'l*, pg. 86
DiBenedetto, Joe, Dir.-Meat & Seafood--The Food Emporium, Bronx, NY; *Int'l*, pg. 1375
Dibie, Elaine, Mgr.-Mktg. & Special Events--Shurfine International, Inc., Northlake, IL; *U.S. Private*, pg. 997
DiCanio, Theresa, Mktg. Communications Specialist--Videojet Systems International, Inc., Wood Dale, IL; *Int'l*, *pg. 545*
Dichiara, Barbara, Dir.-Mktg.--Town & Country Fine Jewelry Group, Inc., Chelsea, MA; *U.S. Public*, pg. 1625
Dichter, Elizabeth, Exec. V.P.-Strategic Mktg.--PCS Health Systems, Inc., Scottsdale, AZ; *U.S. Public*, pg. 993
DiCicco, Robert, V.P.-Mktg.--Comtech Systems, Inc., Saint Cloud, FL; *U.S. Public*, pg. 425
Dick, Alan, Mgr. of Opers. Analysis--Culinary Foods Group, Glendale, CA; *Int'l*, pg. 917
Dick, Charlie, Mgr.-Mktg.--Environmental Air Systems, Inc., Greensboro, NC; *U.S. Private*, pg. 378
Dick, Elie M., Asst. Gen. Mgr. & Dir.-Mktg.--Isco Environmental Division, Lincoln, NE; *U.S. Public*, pg. 914
Dicker, Carole S., Mgr.-Business Devel. & Civil Programs--SRA International Inc., Arlington, VA; *U.S. Private*, pg. 957
Dickhoff, Bill, Dir.-Sls., Mktg. & Adv.--Roofing Wholesale Co., Inc., Phoenix, AZ; *U.S. Private*, pg. 943
Dickie, Angie, Mgr.-Mktg.--World Carpets, Inc., Dalton, GA; *U.S. Private*, pg. 1190
Dickie, D. Kent, Dir.-Mktg.--McGean-Rohco, Inc., Cleveland, OH; *U.S. Private*, pg. 721
Dicks, Tom, Dir.-Sls. & Mktg.--American Fluorescent Corporation, Waukegan, IL; *U.S. Private*, pg. 54
Dickson, David, V.P.-Mktg. Activewear--Fruit of the Loom, Inc., Chicago, IL; *U.S. Public*, pg. 685
Dickson, James G., Jr., Sr. V.P.--Prime Bancshares Inc., Houston, TX; *U.S. Public*, pg. 1326
Dickson, John R., V.P.-Corp. Mktg. & MIS--Andrew Corporation, Orland Park, IL; *U.S. Public*, pg. 112
Dickson, Wayne, V.P.-Mktg.--Helen of Troy Corporation, El Paso, TX; *U.S. Public*, pg. 807
DiCola, Anthony, V.P.-Sls. & Mktg.--Wrought Washer Mfg., Inc., Milwaukee, WI; *U.S. Private*, pg. 1192
Didion, Jean-Francois, V.P.-Mktg. & Intl.--Lyonnaise des Eaux S.A., Nanterre, France; *Int'l*, pg. 822
Diebert, Beth, Mgr.-Mktg. & Customer Services--Decora', Jasper, IN; *U.S. Public*, pg. 675
Diecidue, Maria, Dir.-Global Mktg.--System Software Associates, Inc., Chicago, IL; *U.S. Public*, pg. 1552
Dieckman, Christine, Dir.-Mktg.--New Plan Realty Trust, New York, NY; *U.S. Public*, pg. 1172
Diehl, Robert, Exec. V.P.-Mktg. Services--Alcone Marketing Group, Irvine, CA; *U.S. Public*, pg. 1223
Diehr, Jeff S., V.P.-Sls. & Mktg.--The Fremont Co., Fremont, OH; *U.S. Private*, pg. 426
Diem, Darrin, Mgr.-Mktg.--Southern Agricultural Insecticides, Inc., Palmetto, FL; *U.S. Private*, pg. 1015
Diemer, Susan, Mgr.-Product Devel.--Candle-Lite, A Lancaster Colony Co., Cincinnati, OH; *U.S. Public*, pg. 976
Diener, P.R., Gen. Mgr.-Mktg.--Australian Timken Proprietary Ltd., Ballarat, Australia; *U.S. Public*, pg. 1617
Diependaal, D., Dir.-Mktg. Services--MultiCopy International B.V., Amsterdam, Netherlands; *Int'l*, pg. 890
Dietel, George, V.P.-Mktg. - Men's--The Rockport Company, Marlborough, MA; *U.S. Public*, pg. 1370
Dietel, Ken, Strategic Mktg. Dir.--Thomas G. Ferguson Associates, Inc., Parsippany, NJ; *Int'l*, pg. 1483
Dieterich, Laurent, Dir. Sls. & Mktg.--Berlitz Schools of Languages AG, Geneva, Switzerland; *U.S. Public*, pg. 222
Dietrich, Alan D., Sr. V.P. & Mktg. Oper. Officer--Cerner Corporation, Kansas City, MO; *U.S. Public*, pg. 331
Dietrich, Edward, Dir.-Sls. & Mktg.--American Banknote Holographics, Elmsford, NY; *U.S. Public*, pg. 68
Dietrich, George, V.P.-Mktg. & Prod. Svcs.--SofTechnics Inc., Garland, TX; *U.S. Private*, pg. 1012
Dietrich, Lovonne, V.P.-Sls. & Mktg.--Stella Foods, Inc., Green Bay, WI; *U.S. Private*, pg. 1040
Dietz, Gerardo, Coord.-Mktg.--Bayer Argentina S.A., Munro, Argentina; *Int'l*, pg. 175
Dietzsch, Dr. Michael, Mng. Dir.-Mktg.--Bitburger Brauerei Th. Simon GmbH, Bitburg, Germany; *Int'l*, pg. 197
Diez, Valentin, Mgr.-Sls. & Mktg.--Grupo Modelo S.A., Mexico, Mexico; *U.S. Public*, pg. 115
Digby, Kent S., Exec. V.P.-Mngmt. & Mktg.--The Mills Corporation, Arlington, VA; *U.S. Public*, pg. 1113
Diggs, Charles M., Sr. V.P.-Mktg.--SouthTrust Corporation, Birmingham, AL; *U.S. Public*, pg. 1491
DiGiacomo, Mike, V.P.-Sls. & Mktg.--Compas Electronics, Inc., Kanata, Canada; *Int'l*, pg. 36
Digman, Garrett, V.P.-Mktg.--Brite Voice Systems, Inc., Heathrow, FL; *U.S. Public*, pg. 257
DiGrazia, Mike, V.P.-Mktg. & Fin. Mngmt.--Comdisco, Inc., Rosemont, IL; *U.S. Public*, pg. 407
Dilday, Ted, Mgr.-Sls. & Mktg.--Nelsen Steel & Wire Co., Franklin Park, IL; *U.S. Private*, pg. 790
DiLiddo, John, Dir.-Mktg. Cardiac Assist--Datascope Corp., Montvale, NJ; *U.S. Public*, pg. 487
Dill, Elaina, Mge.-Automotive Mktg.--Sackner-Automotive Sales Office, Rochester, MI; *U.S. Public*, pg. 924
Dillenback, Scott, V.P.-Res. & Devel.--Conmed Corporation, Utica, NY; *U.S. Public*, pg. 431
Diller, Robert, V.P.-Mktg.--Brinkmann Instruments (Canada) Ltd., Mississauga, Canada; *U.S. Private*, pg. 169
Dilling, Carlsten, Dir.-Mktg.--IBM Danmark A/S, Danish Div., Lyngby, Denmark; *U.S. Public*, pg. 897
Dillon, Edmond, V.P.-Mktg.--Thomas Publishing Company, New York, NY; *U.S. Private*, pg. 1082
Dillon, J.W., Gen. Mgr.-Tech.--Latrobe Steel Company, Latrobe, PA; *U.S. Public*, pg. 1617
Dillon, James, Mgr.--E Z Loader Boat Trailers, Inc., Spokane, WA; *U.S. Private*, pg. 353
Dillon, Richard, Dir.-Lighting Prods.--Dual-Lite, Cheshire, CT; *U.S. Public*, pg. 726
DiLullo, Richard, Mgr.-Mktg. & Promo.--Southeastern Pennsylvania Transportation Authority, Philadelphia, PA; *U.S. Private*, pg. 1015
DiLuvo, Michael, V.P.-Mktg.--Hitachi Data Systems Inc., Montreal, Canada; *Int'l*, pg. 622
Dilworth, Donald, Mgr.-Mktg.--Spectrum Control, Connecting Devices Div., Erie, PA; *U.S. Public*, pg. 1497
Dilworth, Mary, Mgr.-Mktg. Communications--G&K Services, Inc., Minnetonka, MN; *U.S. Public*, pg. 690
DiMatteo, Carmen, Sr. V.P.-Services & Sls.--Semco Industries Inc., Stoughton, MA; *U.S. Private*, pg. 983
DiMattio, Shelly, Dir.-Mktg. Svcs.--Century Products Co., Macedonia, OH; *U.S. Private*, pg. 226
DiMeglio, Nicholas, V.P.-Mktg.--Guest Services, Inc., Fairfax, VA; *U.S. Private*, pg. 486
Dimitroff, Mike, Mgr.-Sls. & Mktg.--Chicago White Metal Casting, Inc., Bensenville, IL; *U.S. Private*, pg. 236
Dimmick, Bob, Corp. V.P.-Mktg.--National Car Rental System, Inc., Minneapolis, MN; *U.S. Public*, pg. 1379
Dimmick, Rhonda, Dir.-Mktg.--Security Lawn & Garden Co., Phoenix, AZ; *U.S. Private*, pg. 397
Dimond, Michael J., Sr. V.P.-Mktg.--Gaylord Entertainment Co., Nashville, TN; *U.S. Public*, pg. 704
Dimuzio, Mark, Dir.-Mktg.--Cottman Transmission Systems, Inc., Fort Washington, PA; *U.S. Private*, pg. 278
DiNardo, Lou, V.P.-Mktg.--Linear Technology Corp., Milpitas, CA; *U.S. Public*, pg. 1000
Ding, Ian, Mgr.-Intl. Mktg.--Master Foods, Kings Lynn, United Kingdom; *U.S. Private*, pg. 707
Dinkel, Linda, V.P.--Andover Bancorp, Inc., Andover, MA; *U.S. Public*, pg. 111
Dinkel, Linda, Dir.-Mktg.--Andover Bank, Andover, MA; *U.S. Public*, pg. 112
Dinnocenzo, Debra, Sr. V.P.-Mktg.--Learning International, Stamford, CT; *U.S. Public*, pg. 1617
Dinter, Henry, Mgr.-Industrial Mktg.--BC Gas Inc., Vancouver, Canada; *Int'l*, pg. 114
Dionisio, Jim, V.P.-Mktg.--CF & I Steel, L.P., Pueblo, CO; *U.S. Public*, pg. 1230
Dionne, Chuck, Mgr.-Credit--Colonial Beef Co., Philadelphia, PA; *U.S. Private*, pg. 253
DiPalma, Goffredo, Mgr.-Strategic Mktg.--Autogerma S.p.A., Verona, Italy; *Int'l*, pg. 1474
DiPaolo, Elizabeth, V.P.-Mktg.--Princess House, Inc., North Dighton, MA; *U.S. Public*, pg. 399
Dirat, Henri, Mgr.-Communications--Compaq Computer S.A.R.L., Les Ulis, France; *U.S. Public*, pg. 418
Dirckx, Chris, Service & Mktg. Rep.--PACCAR Winch Division, Broken Arrow, OK; *U.S. Public*, pg. 1246
Dirkes, Mark, Sr. V.P.-Mktg.--Interstate Bakeries Corporation, Kansas City, MO; *U.S. Public*, pg. 909
Dirks, Robert E., Sr. V.P.-Mktg.--Hilton Hotels Corporation, Beverly Hills, CA; *U.S. Public*, pg. 828
Dirks, Robert E., Sr. V.P.-Mktg.--Hilton Hotels Div., Beverly Hills, CA; *U.S. Public*, pg. 829
DiRocco, Joe, V.P.-Mktg.--Orchard Supply Hardware, San Jose, CA; *U.S. Public*, pg. 1452
DiSalvo, Joseph, Dir.-Mktg.--GE Hydro, Lachine, Canada; *U.S. Public*, pg. 713
DiSante, Cathy, Dir.-Mktg.--Art Van Furniture Inc., Warren, MI; *U.S. Private*, pg. 86
Disbury, Brian E., V.P.-Mktg. & Sls.--Magma Metals Company, Tucson, AZ; *Int'l*, pg. 224
DiSilvestro, John, Mgr.- Mktg.--EG & G Rotron, Woodstock, NY; *U.S. Public*, pg. 543
Disque, Don R., Sr. V.P.-Sls. & Mktg.--Phelps Dodge Magnet Wire Co., Fort Wayne, IN; *U.S. Public*, pg. 1286
Ditch, Randy, V.P.-Sls. & Mktg.--Weldon Machine Tool, Inc., York, PA; *U.S. Private*, pg. 1161
Dittmer, Gonde, Dr., Exec. Mgr.-Tech. & Mktg.--AE Goetze GmbH, Burscheid, Germany; *Int'l*, pg. 1334
Ditto, Laura, Mgr.-Adv. & Mktg.--Central Mutual Insurance Co., Van Wert, OH; *U.S. Private*, pg. 223
Dittrich, Alan, Dir.-Mktg.--Intertek Testing Services, Andover, MA; *Int'l*, pg. 672
Diveley, L.R., V.P., Mktg. Dir. & Acct. Services--Simmons, Durham & Associates, Saint Louis, MO; *U.S. Private*, pg. 1000
Dix, Ian, V.P.-XL Connect--Intelligent Electronics, Inc., Exton, PA; *U.S. Public*, pg. 887
Dix, Ron, Sr. V.P.-Mktg. & Sls.--Bush Brothers & Company, Knoxville, TN; *U.S. Private*, pg. 189
Dixon, Jeff, Grp. Exec. Gen. Mgr.-Commercial--Qantas Airways Ltd., Mascot, Australia; *Int'l*, pg. 1074
Dixon, Kim, V.P.-Mktg.--Corel Corporation, Ottawa, Canada; *Int'l*, pg. 331
Dixon, Maureen, Supvr.-Mktg. Commun.--Teledyne Laars/Jandy Products, Novato, CA; *U.S. Public*, pg. 43
Dixon, Tom, V.P.-Mktg.--Coastcast Corporation, Gardena, CA; *U.S. Public*, pg. 391
Djurle, Gunilla, Sls. & Mktg. Mgr.--Whitehall Sweden, Stockholm, Sweden; *U.S. Public*, pg. 82
Doak, Robin, Sr. Mgr.-Mktg.--Permark International (Pty.) Ltd., Johannesburg, South Africa; *Int'l*, pg. 1036
Dobbs, Mark, V.P.-Retail & Commercial Markets--Dri Mark Products, Inc., Port Washington, NY; *U.S. Private*, pg. 342
Dobbs, Meredith, Prod. & Event Mktg.--Home Shopping Network, Inc., Saint Petersburg, FL; *U.S. Public*, pg. 1685
Dobner, Bernd, Dir.-Mktg.--Sun Electric Deutschland, Mettmann, Germany; *U.S. Public*, pg. 1481
Dobson, Jay, Mgr.-Mktg.--Autocon Technologies, Inc., Farmington, MI; *U.S. Public*, pg. 850
Dobson, John R., Mgr.-Sls. & Mktg.--Paxton & Vierling, Omaha, NE; *U.S. Private*, pg. 824
Dobson, Reuben, Mgr.-Natl. Sls. & Mktg.--NUS International Pty. Ltd., Sydney, Australia; *U.S. Private*, pg. 787
Dobson, Rich, Sr. V.P.-Adv.--Milwaukee Journal Sentinel, Milwaukee, WI; *U.S. Private*, pg. 601
Docteur, Sue, Sec. Mktg.--Canandaigua Wine Company, Inc., Canandaigua, NY; *U.S. Public*, pg. 300
Dodez, Gary, V.P.-Sls. & Mktg.--Malta Div.-Tomkins Industries, Inc., Malta, OH; *Int'l*, pg. 1398
Dodge, Cathy, Dir.-Mktg.--Colorado National Bank, Denver, CO; *U.S. Public*, pg. 1680
Dodge, Gill, Mgr.-Medical Mktg.--Stafford-Miller Limited, Welwyn Garden City, United Kingdom; *U.S. Public*, pg. 237
Dodge, Larry, Dir.-Sls. & Mktg.--Booth Newspapers, Inc., Grand Rapids, MI; *U.S. Private*, pg. 157
Dodge, Laura F., Dir.-Mktg. & Adv.--Dodge Regupol, Inc., Lancaster, PA; *U.S. Private*, pg. 337
Dodson, Jan W., Dir.-Corp. Commun.--American Management Systems, Inc., Fairfax, VA; *U.S. Public*, pg. 86
Dodson, Julie, Dir.-Mktg.--Chattanooga Choo-Choo Holiday Inn, Chattanooga, TN; *U.S. Private*, pg. 231
Dodson, Larry, Mgr.-Sls.--North American Royalties, Inc., Chattanooga, TN; *U.S. Private*, pg. 803
Doeckel, Bill, V.P.-Mktg.--Pan-American Seed Co., West Chicago, IL; *U.S. Private*, pg. 112
Doenik, Ulihe, Mgr.-Adv. & Mktg.--Bayerische Vereinsbank Group, Munich, Germany; *Int'l*, pg. 178
Doering, Roy, V.P.-Sls. & Mktg.--Hurd Millwork Company, Inc., Medford, WI; *U.S. Private*, pg. 1113
Doering, Tim, V.P. & Dir.-Mktg.--PNC Bank Corp., Pittsburgh, PA; *U.S. Public*, pg. 1242
Doerner, Joe, Sr., V.P.-Mktg.--Northfield Metal Products Ltd., Waterloo, Canada; *U.S. Public*, pg. 987
Doerner, Melanie, Asst. Dir.-Mktg.--Banfi Vintners, Old Brookville, NY; *U.S. Private*, pg. 113
Doerr, Dave, V.P.-Sls. & Mktg.--The Falk Corporation, Milwaukee, WI; *U.S. Public*, pg. 1534
Doherty, John F., Mgr.-Mktg.--Sequentia Inc., Strongsville, OH; *U.S. Private*, pg. 985
Dokach, John, Dir.-Mktg.--Pepsi-Co. International, Surrey, United Kingdom; *U.S. Public*, pg. 1277
Dokes, John, Mgr.-Mktg.--Marvel Entertainment Group, New York, NY; *U.S. Public*, pg. 1052
Dokken, Wade, Chief Mktg. Officer--American Skandia Marketing, Inc., Shelton, CT; *Int'l*, pg. 1257
Dolan, Bob, V.P.-Franchise Sls.--International Center for Entrepreneurial Development, Inc., Cypress, TX; *U.S. Private*, pg. 568
Dolan, Jeff, Sr. V.P.-Sls. & Mktg.--Selfix, Inc., Chicago, IL; *U.S. Public*, pg. 832
Dolan, Jeffrey R., Sr. V.P.-Sls. & Mktg.-Selfix--Home Products International, Inc., Chicago, IL; *U.S. Public*, pg. 832
Dolan, Peter R., Sr. V.P.-Mktg.--Bristol-Myers Products, New York, NY; *U.S. Public*, pg. 254
Dolgin, Tracy, Exec. V.P.-Mktg./Fox Sports--Fox Broadcasting Company (FBC), Beverly Hills, CA; *Int'l*, pg. 926
Dolin, Penny Ann, Mgr.-Corp. Mktg.--American Color, Phoenix, AZ; *U.S. Public*, pg. 1133
Dolinar, Paul F., V.P.-Mktg.--Synchro-Start Products, Inc., Niles, IL; *U.S. Private*, pg. 627
Doll, Ron, Mgr.-Mktg.--The Falk Corporation, Milwaukee, WI; *U.S. Public*, pg. 1534
Dollahon, Gary, Dir.-Mktg. Communications--Brunswick Outdoor Recreation Group, Tulsa, OK; *U.S. Public*, pg. 265
Dolle, Guy, Exec. V.P.--Groupe Usinor, Paris, France; *Int'l*, pg. 570
Doller, Florence, Asst. V.P.-Mktg.--NBT Bancorp Inc., Norwich, NY; *U.S. Public*, pg. 1144
Dolnack, Christopher C., Dir.-Mktg. & Services--Smith & Wesson Corp., Springfield, MA; *Int'l*, pg. 1397
Domalewski, Chris, Sr. Dir.-Mktg. & Sls.--NJ Transit, Newark, NJ; *U.S. Private*, pg. 794
Domaschofsky, Matt, Dir.-Mktg.--Crestar Food Products, Inc., Brentwood, TN; *U.S. Public*, pg. 805
Domaschossky, Matt, Gen. Mgr.-Sls. & Mktg.--Crestar Food Products, Inc., Brentwood, TN; *U.S. Public*, pg. 805
Dombreval, Thierry, V.P.-Mktg.--Renault, Boulogne-Billancourt, France; *Int'l*, pg. 1102
Dombrowski, Maryrose, V.P.-Mktg.--Refco Group Ltd., Chicago, IL; *U.S. Private*, pg. 917
Domine, Douglas E., Dir.-Grocery Mktg.--Nash Finch Company, Edina, MN; *U.S. Public*, pg. 1151
Dominguez, Jose Morueco, Mgr.-Indus. Mkts.--Loctite Espana, S.A., Madrid, Spain; *Int'l*, pg. 611
Dominioni, Valerie A., Mgr.-Mktg.--Cucina Classica Italiana Inc., Lakewood, NJ; *U.S. Public*, pg. 1435
Domm, Virginia, V.P.-Retail Mktg.--Jimmy Dean Foods, Cordova, TN; *U.S. Public*, pg. 1433
Donabauer, Michael, V.P.-Mktg.-Wolverine Footwear Grp.--Wolverine World Wide, Inc., Rockford, MI; *U.S. Public*, pg. 1775
Donahue-Dalton, Ellen I., Sr. V.P.-Mktg. & Pres.-GameScape, Inc.--GTECH Corporation, West Greenwich, RI; *U.S. Public*, pg. 767

Donahue, Bob, V.P.-Mktg.--Bank of Boston Connecticut, Hartford, CT; *U.S. Public*, pg. 184
Donahue, Robert, V.P. & Adv. Mgr.--Bank of Boston Connecticut, Hartford, CT; *U.S. Public*, pg. 184
Donahue, Sue, Dir.-Mktg.--Walpole Woodworkers, Inc., Walpole, MA; *U.S. Private*, pg. 1148
Donaire, Enrique, Dir.-Sls.--Viva, Madrid, Spain; *Int'l*, pg. 575
Donald, Glen, V.P.-Mktg.--AgrEvo USA Company, Wilmington, DE; *Int'l*, pg. 1203
Donaldson, P. Kit, V.P.-Mktg. & Adv.--Man-Gill Chemical Company, Cleveland, OH; *U.S. Private*, pg. 699
Donars, Rene J., V.P.-Sls. & Mktg.--Porter-Cable Corporation, Jackson, TN; *U.S. Public*, pg. 1274
Donegan, K.F., Mgr.-Mktg.--Cementation Piling & Foundations Limited, Rickmansworth, United Kingdom; *Int'l*, pg. 772
Dong-Wook, Choi, Exec. Mng. Dir.-Overseas Construction Mktg.--Daewoo Corporation, Seoul, Korea; *Int'l*, pg. 357
Doninger, Jeff, Mgr.-Mktg.--Norton Performance Plastics, Wayne, NJ; *Int'l*, pg. 1174
Donly, Stephen M., Sr. V.P.-Mktg./Ryder Transportation Svcs.--Ryder System, Inc., Miami, FL; *U.S. Public*, pg. 1413
Donnantuono, Michael J., V.P.-Mktg.--Blistex, Inc., Oak Brook, IL; *U.S. Private*, pg. 149
Donnelly, Michael E., V.P.-Sls. & Mktg.--Starcrest Products of California, Perris, CA; *U.S. Private*, pg. 1035
Donnelly, Richard, V.P.-Sls. & Mktg.--Amtrak-National Railroad Passenger Corp., Washington, DC; *U.S. Private, pg. 68*
Donnelly, Robert, Exec. V.P.-Sls. & Mktg.--Glastic Corporation, Cleveland, OH; *Int'l*, pg. 740
Donnelly, Roisin, Dir.-Mktg.--Giorgio Beverly Hills, Santa Monica, CA; *U.S. Public*, pg. 1331
Donnelly, W.T., Dir.-Sls. & Mktg.--Aston Martin Lagonda of North America, Inc., Mahwah, NJ; *U.S. Public*, pg. 664
Donofrio, Richard M., Sr. V.P.-Mktg. & Sls.--The Southern New England Telephone Company, New Haven, CT; *U.S. Public*, pg. 1491
Donoghue, John, Sr. V.P.-Consumer Mktg.--MCI Communications Corp., Atlanta, GA; *U.S. Public*, pg. 1023
Donoghue, John, Sr. V.P.-Consumer Mktg.--MCI Telecommunications Corp., Washington, DC; *U.S. Public, pg. 1024*
Donoghue, R.J., Dir.-Mktg.--Wyman-Gordon Forgings, Inc., Houston, TX; *U.S. Public*, pg. 1782
Donoghue, Thomas F., Mgr.-Mktg. & Sls., Kraft Plng.--Kraft Paper Div., Memphis, TN; *U.S. Public*, pg. 903
Donohoe, Michael P., Sr. V.P.-Sls. & Mktg.--JBB Worldwide, Inc., Deerfield, IL; *U.S. Public*, pg. 675
Donovan, James M., Exec. Dir.-Mktg. & Sls.--Wyeth-Ayerst Laboratories, Inc., Philadelphia, PA; *U.S. Public*, pg. 80
Donovan, John, Sr. V.P.-Leasing--Carr Real Estate Services, Washington, DC; *U.S. Public*, pg. 309
Donovan, Rodrick S., V.P.-Gas Mktg.--Westar Energy, Topeka, KS; *U.S. Public*, pg. 1759
Donovan, Stephen, Jr., Dir.-Mktg.--The Folger Coffee Company, Cincinnati, OH; *U.S. Public*, pg. 1331
Donovan, Thomas, Dir.-Mktg.--The Richman Brothers Co., Fall River, MA; *U.S. Public*, pg. 1777
Donovan, Vincent L., Dir.-Sls. & Mktg.--Manchester Plastics, Troy, MI; *U.S. Public*, pg. 399
Donza, John, Product Mgr.-Mktg.--Jaco Electronics, Inc., Hauppauge, NY; *U.S. Public*, pg. 920
Doodson, K., Mgr.-Sls. & Mktg./Meat--Metro Foods, Inc., Olive Branch, MS; *U.S. Private*, pg. 736
Dooey, H.P., Dir.-Sls. & Mktg.--Powerscreen International Plc, Dungannon, United Kingdom; *Int'l*, pg. 1066
Dooley, Kristen, Coord.-Mktg.--Fox Valley Corporation, Appleton, WI; *U.S. Private*, pg. 422
Dooley, Kristen, Coord.-Mktg.--Fox River Paper Company, Appleton, WI; *U.S. Private*, pg. 422
Dooley, Robert, Sr. V.P.-Worldwide Computer Sls. & Mktg.--Global Direct Mail Corp, Port Washington, NY; *U.S. Public*, pg. 747
Dooley, Susan, Dir.-Mktg.-Clarks--Clarks Cos. N.A., Newton, MA; *Int'l*, pg. 297
Doorbar, Mark, Dir.-Consumer Mktg.--H.P. Bulmer Holdings Plc, Hereford, United Kingdom; *Int'l*, pg. 232
Doray, David, Dir.-Mktg.--U.S. Tsubaki, Inc., Wheeling, IL; *Int'l*, pg. 1425
Dorfman, Robert, Pres.--King Wire Inc., North Chicago, IL; *U.S. Private*, pg. 621
Dorfman, Robert M., Sr. V.P.-Mktg. & Bus. Devel.--Marriott Distribution Services (MDS), Washington, DC; *U.S. Public*, pg. 1048
Doris-Smith, Mary, Sr. V.P.-Customer Relationship Mktg.--Ross Roy Communications, Inc., Bloomfield Hills, MI; *U.S. Private*, pg. 946
Dorney, M., Dir.-Mktg.--Budd Plastics Design Center, Troy, MI; *Int'l*, pg. 1388
Dorris, Don T., Mgr.-Mktg. & Plng.--Delphi Harrison Thermal Systems, Lockport, NY; *U.S. Public*, pg. 719
Dorris, William C., V.P.-Corp. Devel. & Tech.--Lilly Industries, Inc., Indianapolis, IN; *U.S. Public*, pg. 994
Dosier, Robin, Coord.-Mktg.--Flambeau Corporation, Baraboo, WI; *U.S. Private*, pg. 409
Doster, Gary A., V.P.-Sls. & Mktg.--F.N. Burt Company, Inc., Buffalo, NY; *U.S. Private*, pg. 188
Dotson, Mary, Mgr.-Mktg.--Curtis Mathes Corporation, Dallas, TX; *U.S. Public*, pg. 1057
Doty, Tom D., V.P.-Mktg.--Pace Industries, Inc., Fayetteville, AR; *U.S. Public*, pg. 986
Dotzauer, Virginia, V.P.-Mktg./Personal Care--The Mennen Company, New York, NY; *U.S. Public*, pg. 397
Dougherty, Carolyn, Dir.-Mktg.--Blackwell Publishers Ltd., Oxford, United Kingdom; *Int'l*, pg. 197
Dougherty, Dave, Mgr.-North American Mktg.--Blount, Inc. Oregon Cutting Systems Division, Portland, OR; *U.S. Public*, pg. 238
Dougherty, Kevin P., V.P.-Grp. Mktg. & Sls.--Sun Life of Canada, Toronto, Canada; *Int'l*, pg. 1319
Doughty, Kerry, V.P.-Sls. & Mktg.--Fast Food Merchandisers Inc., Rocky Mount, NC; *U.S. Public*, pg. 278
Douglas, Jim, V.P.-Sls. & Mktg.--AAF-International, Louisville, KY; *U.S. Private*, pg. 3
Douglas, Stephanie W., Dir.-Mktg. Svcs. & Corp. Communications--Harza Engineering Co., Chicago, IL; *U.S. Private*, pg. 509
Douglas, Wayne, Dir.-Mktg.--VR/Wesson Hydro Carbide, Latrobe, PA; *U.S. Public*, pg. 612
Douglass, Tom, V.P.-Marine Sls. & Mktg.--Teleflex Marine, Limerick, PA; *U.S. Public*, pg. 1569
Doukakis, Harry W., Mgr.-Mktg.--Elkton DLV Operations, Elkton, MD; *U.S. Public*, pg. 1597
Douma, J., Mgr.-Mktg. & Prod. Devel.--National Electrical Carbon Canada, Mississauga, Canada; *Int'l*, pg. 892
Dovits, Ludwig, Mng. Dir.-Mktg.--Julius Meinl AG, Vienna, Austria; *Int'l*, pg. 856
Dow, Jerry, Mgr.-Mktg. Commun.--Pella Corporation, Pella, IA; *U.S. Private*, pg. 848
Dow, Rick, V.P.-Mktg. Programs & Worldwide Adv.--Northwest Airlines, Inc., Saint Paul, MN; *U.S. Public*, pg. 1200
Dow, Sarah, Mgr.-Mktg. Commun.--Vermeer Manufacturing Company, Pella, IA; *U.S. Private*, pg. 1137
Dowd, Gerard, Sr. V.P.-Foodservice Sls. & Mktg.--Tyson Foods, Inc., Springdale, AR; *U.S. Public*, pg. 1652
Dowd, Tom, Mgr.-Mktg.--Grossman's, Inc., Stoughton, MA; *U.S. Private*, pg. 585
Dowding, William, Dir.- Mktg.-Tool Div.--American Saw & Mfg. Company, East Longmeadow, MA; *U.S. Private*, pg. 61
Dowdle, Anne W., V.P.-Mktg. & Employee Benefits Div.--Northwestern National Life Insurance Co., Minneapolis, MN; *U.S. Public*, pg. 1375
Dowers, John D., V.P.-Mktg., Nestle Ice Cream Co.--Nestle Frozen/Refrigerated Food Co., Solon, OH; *Int'l*, pg. 918
Dowis, Randy, Dir.-Mktg.--NHT, Benicia, CA; *U.S. Public*, pg. 1369
Dowling, Ellen, Dir.-Promo. Mktg.--Toys "R" Us, Inc., Paramus, NJ; *U.S. Public*, pg. 1626
Dowling, Stephen E., Sr. V.P.-Sls. & Mktg.--Lincoln Foodservice Products, Inc., Fort Wayne, IN; *Int'l*, pg. 188
Downes, John F., V.P.-Mktg. & Branch Admin.--Prime Bancorp, Inc., Fort Washington, PA; *U.S. Public*, pg. 1326
Downing, John, V.P.-Mktg.--Guideposts Associates, Inc., Carmel, NY; *U.S. Private*, pg. 487
Downing, Mike, Dir.-Mktg.--Metz Baking Company, Deerfield, IL; *U.S. Private*, pg. 1022
Downs, Stephen, V.P.-Mktg., Mergers & Acquisitions--Rhone-Poulenc Rorer - U.S., Collegeville, PA; *Int'l*, pg. 1110
Doyer, Lee F., V.P.-Mktg.--Pennsylvania Crusher Corp., Broomall, PA; *U.S. Private*, pg. 850
Doyle, Bob, Mgr.-Mktg.--BIC Corporation, Milford, CT; *Int'l*, pg. 1273
Doyle, C.E., Mgr.-Sls. & Mktg.--TGM Detectors Inc., Waltham, MA; *Int'l*, pg. 892
Doyle, David, First V.P.-Consumer Mktg.--Countrywide Home Loans Inc., Pasadena, CA; *U.S. Public*, pg. 452
Doyle, Elizabeth M., V.P.-Admin. & Production & Sec.--My Own Meals, Inc., Deerfield, IL; *U.S. Private*, pg. 770
Doyle, Francis X., V.P.--The Worcester Insurance Co., Worcester, MA; *U.S. Public*, pg. 787
Doyle, Jim, V.P.-Mktg. & Sls.--A. Finkl & Sons Co., Chicago, IL; *U.S. Private*, pg. 405
Doyle, John F., Sr. V.P.-Mktg.--The Camden Fire Insurance Assn., Philadelphia, PA; *Int'l*, pg. 543
Doyle, Katie, V.P.-Adv. & Mktg.--McKesson Corporation, San Francisco, CA; *U.S. Public*, pg. 1072
Doyle, Katie, V.P.-Strategic Mktg.--McKesson U.S. Health Care, San Francisco, CA; *U.S. Public*, pg. 1073
Doyle, Patricia, Mgr.-Mktg.--Malco Products, Inc., Barberton, OH; *U.S. Private*, pg. 698
Doyle, Paul, V.P.-Mktg.--A.O. Smith Electrical Products Company, Tipp City, OH; *U.S. Public*, pg. 1477
Doyle, Robert W., Dir.-Mktg. Logistics--Parke-Davis Group, Morris Plains, NJ; *U.S. Public*, pg. 1739
Doylen, Jan, Channel Mktg.--Media 100, Inc., Marlborough, MA; *U.S. Public*, pg. 1079
Dozier, Bruce, Coord.-Mktg.--Mooney Aircraft Corporation, Kerrville, TX; *U.S. Private*, pg. 759
Drachman, Ronnie, Dir.-Promo.--Business Insurance, Chicago, IL; *U.S. Private*, pg. 285
Drajer, Rob, Intl. Mktg. Mgr.--Inamed B.V., Breda, Netherlands; *U.S. Public*, pg. 874
Drapeau, Norman, Exec. V.P.-Worldwide Sls. & Mktg.--PSDI, Bedford, MA; *U.S. Private*, pg. 828
Draper, Mary D., V.P.-Mktg.--Williams Field Services, Tulsa, OK; *U.S. Public*, pg. 1769
Drasher, Glenn D., Exec. V.P.-Mktg.--Buffets, Inc., Eden Prairie, MN; *U.S. Public*, pg. 267
Drassler, Carolyn, V.P.-Mktg. & Sls.--MTI Vacations, Inc., Downers Grove, IL; *U.S. Private*, pg. 688
Drayton, James, V.P.-Mktg., Airport Services--Cara Operations Limited, Toronto, Canada; *Int'l*, pg. 266
Drebes, Karen Ann, Mgr.-Mktg.--Gaylord Printing, Inc., Detroit, MI; *U.S. Private*, pg. 441
Dredla, Dan, Dir.-Mktg.--Inland Valley Regional Medical Center, Wildomar, CA; *U.S. Public*, pg. 1697
Dreher, Michael, V.P.-Mktg.--ELX Group, Wichita Falls, TX; *Int'l*, pg. 439
Dreier, Kyla, Dir.-Mktg.--Friedman, Eisenstein, Raemer and Schwartz, LLP, Chicago, IL; *U.S. Private*, pg. 428
Dreistadt, Edward, V.P.-Mktg.--Busch Gardens Williamsburg, Williamsburg, VA; *U.S. Public*, pg. 114
Drenth, Reinoud, V.P.-Worldwide Mktg.--Diebold, Incorporated, Canton, OH; *U.S. Public*, pg. 506
Dresser, W. Donald, Exec. V.P., Dir.-Devel. & Asst. Sec.--United Foods, Inc., Bells, TN; *U.S. Public*, pg. 1677
Drever, K., Mgr.-Pub. Affairs--ATCO Group Co., Calgary, Canada; *Int'l*, pg. 95
Drexel, Carolyn, Dir.-Mktg.--North Fork Bancorporation, Inc., Melville, NY; *U.S. Public*, pg. 1194
Drexinger, Jim, V.P.-Mktg. & Sls.--NIBCO, Inc., Elkhart, IN; *U.S. Private*, pg. 798
Driansky, Harvey, Sr. V.P.-Mktg.--Movado Group, Inc., Lyndhurst, NJ; *U.S. Public*, pg. 1140
Drimer, David, Dir.-Mktg.--Traffic World, New York, NY; *Int'l, pg. 1026*
Driscoll, Amy, Dir.-MKtg.--Jillian's Entertainment Corporation, Boston, MA; *U.S. Private*, pg. 587
Driscoll, Dan, Specialist-Mktg.--Goodwill Industries International, Bethesda, MD; *U.S. Private*, pg. 464
Driscoll, Dennis, V.P.-Mktg.--Envoy Corporation, Nashville, TN; *U.S. Public*, pg. 587
Driscoll, Donald J., Mgr.-Sls. & Mktg.--Sheet & Coil Products Division, Port Kembla, Australia; *Int'l*, pg. 227
Driscoll, John P., Exec. V.P.--Murata Electronics North America, Inc., Smyrna, GA; *Int'l*, pg. 897
Driscoll, Patrick, Dir.-Sls. & Mktg.--Artistic Carton Company, Elgin, IL; *U.S. Private*, pg. 87
Drohan, Matthew, V.P.-Brand Mktg.--Amoco Corporation, Chicago, IL; *U.S. Public*, pg. 101
Drohan, Matthew, V.P.-Brand Mktg.--Amoco Oil Company, Chicago, IL; *U.S. Public*, pg. 102
Drolen, Randy, Mgr.-Mktg. Communications--Landis & Staefa, Inc., Buffalo Grove, IL; *Int'l*, pg. 800
Drons, Amiee, Dir.-Mktg.--Outlook Eyewear Company, Denver, CO; *U.S. Public*, pg. 195
Drotch, Amy, Coord.-Mktg. & Public Rels.--Thermal Industries, Inc., Pittsburgh, PA; *U.S. Private*, pg. 490
Drouillard, Tom, V.P.-Mktg.--SRDS, Des Plaines, IL; *U.S. Private*, pg. 958
Drumey, J., Dir.-Mktg.--Trebor Bassett Ltd., Sheffield, United Kingdom; *Int'l*, pg. 248
Drumgool, James E., V.P.-Intl. Mktg.--Raytheon Company, Lexington, MA; *U.S. Public*, pg. 1364
Drumgoole, Michael J., Sr. V.P.-Sls. & Mktg.--Medical Resources Inc., Hackensack, NJ; *U.S. Public*, pg. 1080
Drummond, Jim, Dir.-Mktg.--Hitachi Home Electronics (America) Inc., Norcross, GA; *Int'l*, pg. 622
Drummond, Tom, V.P.-Mktg.--Andes Candies Inc., Delavan, WI; *U.S. Private*, pg. 163
Drummond, Tom, V.P.-Sls. & Mktg.--Standard Candy Co., Inc., Nashville, TN; *U.S. Private*, pg. 1030
Drury, David, V.P.-Corp. Mktg.--FORE Systems, Inc., Warrendale, PA; *U.S. Public*, pg. 667
Drury, Kathryn A., V.P.-Mktg.--Moto Photo, Inc., Dayton, OH; *U.S. Public*, pg. 1136
Drury, Tom, Mgr.-Mktg. & Sls.--American White Cross, Dayville, CT; *U.S. Public*, pg. 694
Druzba, Tami Thomas, Mgr.-Mktg. Services--Macklanburg-Duncan Co., Oklahoma City, OK; *U.S. Private*, pg. 692
Dry, Andrea, Mgr.-Mktg.--Zoltek Companies, Inc., Saint Louis, MO; *U.S. Public*, pg. 1794
Dry, Chris, Gen. Mgr.-Direct Mktg. Div.--Intermarkets U.A.E., Dubai, United Arab Emirates; *Int'l*, pg. 680
Dryburgh, Douglas T., Sr. V.P.-Sls. & Mktg.--Starter Corp., New Haven, CT; *U.S. Public*, pg. 1511
Du Bois, Robert, Dir.-Mktg.--World Financial Properties, Inc., New York, NY; *Int'l*, pg. 1004
du Toit, J.S., Mgr.-Mktg.--Sasol Phenolics, Rosebank, South Africa; *Int'l*, pg. 1196
Duane, Paul, Dir.-Mktg. & New Prods.--Litecontrol Corporation, Hanson, MA; *U.S. Private*, pg. 669
Dubas, Leonard, V.P.-Mktg. & Adv.--Angelo Brothers Co., Philadelphia, PA; *U.S. Private*, pg. 74
Dube, Cindy, Coord.-Mktg.--NESLAB Instruments, Inc., Newington, NH; *U.S. Public*, pg. 1595
Dubin, Thomas G., Pres.--Manufacturers' News, Inc., Evanston, IL; *U.S. Private*, pg. 700
Dubois, Colette, Gen. Mgr.-Sls. & Mktg./France, Switzerland, Benelux & Africa--Utell International-France, Paris, France; *Int'l*, pg. 1098
DuBose, Adrian, V.P.-Mktg.--Louisiana Gas Service Co., Harvey, LA; *U.S. Public*, pg. 380
Dubreuil, Mark, Dir.-Mktg. & Oper. Mgr.--PTA Corporation, Oxford, CT; *U.S. Private*, pg. 828
DuBroe, Carmen, Exec. V.P.-Mktg.--Weight Watchers International, Inc., Woodbury, NY; *U.S. Public*, pg. 806
Duckering, Russill, V.P.-Advanced Mktg.--West Coast Life Insurance Co., San Francisco, CA; *U.S. Public*, pg. 1336
Duckworth, Amanda, Dir.-Corp. Commun.--NationsBank Montgomery Securities LLC, San Francisco, CA; *U.S. Public*, pg. 1162
Duda, Dan, Dir.-Natl. Mktg.--A. Duda & Sons Inc., Oviedo, FL; *U.S. Private*, pg. 344
Duell, Joyce, Dir.-Mktg. & Plng.--AE Goetze-North America, Plymouth, MI; *Int'l*, pg. 1334
Duerst, Mark A., V.P.-Sls. & Mktg.--Hologic, Inc., Waltham, MA; *U.S. Public*, pg. 831
Duff-Bloom, Gale, Pres.-Mktg. & Co. Communications--JC Penney Company, Inc., Plano, TX; *U.S. Public*, pg. 916
Duffner, Robert, Mktg. Dir.--Hawthorne Adv., Inc., Philadelphia, PA; *U.S. Private*, pg. 512
Dufford, Eric, V.P.-Sls. & Mktg.--Quest Medical, Inc., Allen, TX; *U.S. Public*, pg. 1352
Dufft, Peter, Dir.-Mktg.--Deutsche Unilever Gmbh, Hamburg, Germany; *Int'l*, pg. 1436
Duffus, Cheryl, Asst. V.P. & Mgr.-Mktg.--Pacific Capital Bancorp, Salinas, CA; *U.S. Public*, pg. 1247
Duffy, Maureen, Dir.-Children's Mktg.--Pagoda, Saint Louis, MO; *U.S. Public*, pg. 262
Duffy, Peter A., V.P.-Sls. & Mktg.--Haskel International, Inc., Burbank, CA; *U.S. Public*, pg. 798
Duffy, Richard, V.P.-Mktg.--Goulds Pumps, Incorporated, Fairport, NY; *U.S. Public*, pg. 860
Duffy, Tom, Mgr.-Adv.--Wajax Limited, Delta, Canada; *Int'l*, pg. 1484
Duffy, William, V.P.-Worldwide Supplies Mktg.--Lexmark International Group, Inc., Lexington, KY; *U.S. Public*, pg. 991
Duffy, William, V.P.-Worldwide Supplies Mktg.--Lexmark International, Inc., Lexington, KY; *U.S. Public*, pg. 991
Dufour, Gerard, Sr. Dir.-Mktg.--Philips Electronics N.V., Eindhoven, Netherlands; *Int'l*, pg. 1051

Dufrene, Otis, V.P.-Sls. & Mktg.--The Crosby Group Inc., Tulsa, OK; *Int'l*, pg. 473
Dugan, Daniel R., Sr. V.P.-Worldwide Sls., Service & Mktg.--Acuson Corporation, Mountain View, CA; *U.S. Public*, pg. 18
Dugan, Dennis, Sr. V.P.-Sls. & Mktg.--Burns & Roe Enterprises, Inc., Oradell, NJ; *U.S. Private*, pg. 187
Duggan, Melissa, Mktg. Communications Coord.--Galileo Corp., Sturbridge, MA; *U.S. Public*, pg. 698
Duggan, Michael, Pres.--Melard Manufacturing Corporation, Passaic, NJ; *U.S. Private*, pg. 729
Duggan, Peter, Sr. V.P.-Sls. & Mktg.--Lance, Inc., Charlotte, NC; *U.S. Public*, pg. 977
Duggins, P., Mgr.-Mktg.--Alumax Mill Products, Inc., Morris, IL; *U.S. Public*, pg. 59
Dugo, Barbara, Mgr.-Adv.--Butera Finer Foods Inc., Elgin, IL; *U.S. Private*, pg. 189
Duguid, Mike, Dir.-Adv., Pub. Rels. & Mktg.--York International Corporation, York, PA; *U.S. Public*, pg. 1789
Duke, Ellen B., Dir.-Sls. & Mktg--Inamed Development Company, Carpinteria, CA; *U.S. Public*, pg. 873
Duke, Tom, V.P.-Mktg.--Macrotech Plyseal, Inc., Salt Lake City, UT; *U.S. Private*, pg. 693
Duley, Francois, Mng. Dir.-Intl.--Groupe SEB, Ecueille, France; *Int'l*, pg. 568
Dull, William B., Dir.-Sls. & Mktg.--Tamura Corporation of America, Temecula, CA; *U.S. Private*, pg. 1067
Dullnig, Kurt, V.P.-Mktg.--Living Centers of America, Houston, TX; *U.S. Public*, pg. 1257
Dumas, Chantal, Mktg. Sec.--Culinar Inc., Montreal, Canada; *Int'l*, pg. 348
Dumas, Kathleen, Coord.-Mktg. Commun.--Magnetrol International, Downers Grove, IL; *U.S. Private*, pg. 696
Dunagin, Terry, Dir.-Mktg.--Boston Whaler, Inc., Edgewater, FL; *U.S. Private*, pg. 689
Duncan, G., V.P.-New Prods. & Mktg.--Econolite Control Products, Inc., Anaheim, CA; *U.S. Private*, pg. 361
Duncan, Gordon, V.P.-Sls. & Mktg.--LFE Industrial Systems Corporation, Clinton, MA; *U.S. Public*, pg. 1045
Duncan, Helena, Mgr.--The Colonial BancGroup, Inc., Montgomery, AL; *U.S. Public*, pg. 400
Duncan, Helena, Mgr.-Mktg.--Colonial Bank, Montgomery, AL; *U.S. Public*, pg. 400
Duncan, James A., Dir.-Mktg.--Charlotte Motor Speedway, Concord, NC; *U.S. Public*, pg. 1498
Duncan, Katherine, Dir.-Mktg.--Refrigiwear, Inc., Dahlonega, GA; *U.S. Private*, pg. 917
Duncan, Mark, Mktg. & Adv.--Ferguson Limited, Enfield, United Kingdom; *Int'l*, pg. 1384
Duncan, Michael, Dir.-Mktg. & Sls.--Electro-Motive Division, La Grange, IL; *U.S. Public*, pg. 719
Duncan, Michael, Mgr.-Mktg.--Monaco Coach Corporation, Coburg, OR; *U.S. Public*, pg. 1123
Duncan, Michael F., Mgr.-Pub. Rels.--Monaco Coach Corporation, Coburg, OR; *U.S. Public*, pg. 1123
Duncan, N.P., Mgr.-Mktg. Communications--Curtis 1000, Inc., Atlanta, GA; *U.S. Public*, pg. 70
Duncan, Robert A., V.P.-Mktg.--Kearney Company, Tucker, GA; *U.S. Public*, pg. 444
Duncan, Susan, Mgr.-Mktg.--Courier Corporation, North Chelmsford, MA; *U.S. Public*, pg. 453
Duncan, Suzanne, Dir.-Adv.--Riggs National Corporation, Washington, DC; *U.S. Public*, pg. 1389
Duncan, William J., Mgr.-Mktg.--Rohrer Corporation, Wadsworth, OH; *U.S. Private*, pg. 940
Duncheon, Charles S., Sr. V.P.-Mktg. & Sls.--Adept Technology, Inc., San Jose, CA; *U.S. Public*, pg. 19
Dunkerson, Dennis L., Sr. V.P.-Mktg. Support--USLIFE Corporation, New York, NY; *U.S. Public*, pg. 77
Dunkin, Eugene, V.P.-Sls. & Mktg.--Godiva Chocolatier, Inc., New York, NY; *U.S. Public*, pg. 299
Dunlap, Chris, Mgr.-Mktg. Communications--Murata Electronics North America, Inc., Smyrna, GA; *Int'l*, pg. 897
Dunlap, Michael, Dir.-Mktg.--Suspa, Inc., Grand Rapids, MI; *Int'l*, pg. 1322
Dunlea, Linda, Mgr.-Mktg.--Philips Speech Processing, Atlanta, GA; *Int'l*, pg. 1055
Dunlop, David D., V.P.-Pur. & Mktg.--Bindley Western Industries, Inc., Indianapolis, IN; *U.S. Public*, pg. 228
Dunn, Bryan C., Chief Mktg. Officer & Sr. V.P.--The Western and Southern Life Insurance Company, Cincinnati, OH; *U.S. Private*, pg. 1164
Dunn, Chris, V.P.-Mktg.--Suntory Water Group, Inc., Marietta, GA; *Int'l*, pg. 1321
Dunn, Gordon, Mgr.-Mktg.--Electric Furnace Co., Salem, OH; *U.S. Private*, pg. 367
Dunn, Michael, Sr. V.P.-Mktg.--20th Century Fox Home Entertainment, Los Angeles, CA; *U.S. Public*, pg. 275
Dunn, Michael, Sr. V.P.-Mktg.--20th Century Fox Home Entertainment, Los Angeles, CA; *Int'l*, pg. 926
Dunn, Michelle, Mgr.-Adv.--Aviva Sport, Inc., El Segundo, CA; *U.S. Public*, pg. 1058
Dunn, Michelle, Mgr.-Adv.--Mattel Games/Puzzles, El Segundo, CA; *U.S. Public*, pg. 1058
Dunn, Mike, V.P.-Natl. Sls. & Mktg--Watkins Manufacturing Corp./Hot Spring Portable Spas, Vista, CA; *U.S. Public*, pg. 1054
Dunn, Phillip, V.P.-Retail Mktg.--Mass Market Division, Greensboro, NC; *U.S. Public*, pg. 1702
Dunn, William, V.P.-Sls. & Mktg.--Durable Specialties Division, Quakertown, PA; *U.S. Public*, pg. 620
Dunne, Matt, Dir.-Mktg.--Logic Associates, Inc., White River Junction, VT; *U.S. Private*, pg. 673
Dunne, Patrick, Dir.-Mktg.--3i Group plc, London, United Kingdom; *Int'l*, pg. 1386
Dunne, William, Dir.-Mktg. & Sls.--New Brunswick Scientific Co., Inc., Edison, NJ; *U.S. Public*, pg. 1169
Dupuis, Robert E., V.P.-Mktg. & Business Plng.--COMSAT World Systems, Bethesda, MD; *U.S. Public*, pg. 424
Dupuy, William L., V.P.-Corp. Communications--Charter One Financial, Inc., Cleveland, OH; *U.S. Public*, pg. 336
Durden, Liston, Exec. V.P.-Mktg. & Prod. Devel.--Viking Range Corp., Greenwood, MS; *U.S. Private*, pg. 1140
Durgin, Harold, Dir.-Sls. & Mktg.--George T. Schmidt, Niles, IL; *U.S. Private*, pg. 970
Durham, B.W., Jr., Exec. V.P.-Mktg.--Simmons, Durham & Associates, Saint Louis, MO; *U.S. Private*, pg. 1000
Durham, Darrell, Dir.-Mktg.--The Dispatch Printing Company, Columbus, OH; *U.S. Private*, pg. 334
Durkee, Steve, Dir.-Mktg.--Hypro Corporation, New Brighton, MN; *U.S. Public*, pg. 1767
Durlam, Joyce, Dir.-Mktg.--Anderson Erickson Dairy Company, Des Moines, IA; *U.S. Private*, pg. 72
Durning, Ken, V.P.-Sls. & Mktg.--Galaxy Carpet Mills, Inc., Chatsworth, GA; *U.S. Public*, pg. 1121
Durso, Edwin M., Exec. V.P.-Admin.--ESPN, Inc., Bristol, CT; *U.S. Public*, pg. 512
Dusek, Glen, Dir.-Mktg. & Adv.--Contractors Steel Company, Livonia, MI; *U.S. Private*, pg. 270
Dutka, June, V.P.-Mktg. & Sls.--Bright Star Industries, Inc., Wilkes-Barre, PA; *U.S. Public*, pg. 1341
Dutton, John, Mgr.-Mktg.--O-Ring Div., Lexington, KY; *U.S. Public*, pg. 1262
Dutton, Kate, Coord.-Mktg.--Bojangles' Restaraunts, Inc., Charlotte, NC; *U.S. Private*, pg. 154
Duval, Andre, Coord.-Mktg. Services-Bath Mat--Peerless Carpet Corporation, Acton Vale, Canada; *Int'l*, pg. 1032
Duval, Nicole, Dir.-Mktg.--Lilly France S.A., Saint Cloud, France; *U.S. Public*, pg. 994
Duzan, Lisa, Coord.-Mktg.--Immunex Corporation, Seattle, WA; *U.S. Public*, pg. 871
Dvorak, Nick, Dir.-Mktg. & Sls.--Weather Tec Corporation, Fresno, CA; *U.S. Private*, pg. 1155
Dwelley, David S., V.P.-Strategic Bus. Devel.--Raytheon Company, Lexington, MA; *U.S. Public*, pg. 1364
Dwinell, Rich, Mgr.-Opers.--Granny Goose Foods, Inc., Oakland, CA; *U.S. Private*, pg. 469
Dworznik, Art, Mgr.-Mktg. & Adv.--Freeway Corporation, Cleveland, OH; *U.S. Private*, pg. 426
Dwyer, C., Mgr.-Mktg.--GF Food Services, Alexandria, Australia; *Int'l*, pg. 555
Dwyer, Herb, V.P.-Sls. & Mktg.--Varity Zecal, Churchville, NY; *Int'l*, pg. 820
Dwyer, James E., Jr., Sr. V.P.-Mktg.--Tropicana Dole Beverages North America, Bradenton, FL; *Int'l*, pg. 1217
Dwyer, Walter, Dir.-Adv. & Mktg.--Airtron, Morris Plains, NJ; *U.S. Public*, pg. 1003
Dybvad, Larry E., Sr. V.P.-PPGA Mktg.--American Mutual Life Holding Co., Des Moines, IA; *U.S. Private*, pg. 59
Dybwad, Nils, Mgr.-Mktg.--Elkem ASA Ferrosilicon Division, Oslo, Norway; *Int'l*, pg. 448
Dyckman, David, V.P.-Mktg. & Intl. Sls.--Veeder-Root Company, Simsbury, CT; *U.S. Public*, pg. 482
Dyer, Raymond W., V.P.-Mktg.--Respironics, Inc., Pittsburgh, PA; *U.S. Public*, pg. 1383
Dyke, Mark, Dir.-Mktg.--Micron Separations, Inc., Westborough, MA; *U.S. Private*, pg. 742
Dykema, Bill, V.P.-Mktg.--MEG, Cambridge City, IN; *U.S. Private*, pg. 686
Dziedzuila, Ronald E., V.P.-Mktg./KCI Therapeutic Svcs.--Kinetic Concepts, Inc., San Antonio, TX; *U.S. Private*, pg. 620
Dziewiatkowski, John, Dir.-Project Devel.--Sampler Publications Inc., Saint Charles, IL; *U.S. Private*, pg. 963
Eaccarino, Lou, Exec. V.P.-Sls. & Mktg.--A.J. Brandon, Vernon, CA; *U.S. Public*, pg. 948
Eades, Vincent, Sr. V.P.-Specialty Sls. & Mktg.--Starbucks Coffee Company, Seattle, WA; *U.S. Public*, pg. 1510
Eady, Brian, V.P.-Mktg.--Wedgwood U.S.A., Wall, NJ; *Int'l*, pg. 1487
Eagan, Edward, Sr. V.P.-Mktg.--Universal Pictures, Universal City, CA; *Int'l*, pg. 1216
Eagan, Lynne, Dir.-Mktg.--United Air Specialists, Inc., Cincinnati, OH; *U.S. Public*, pg. 382
Eakin, Joe, Consultant-Sls. & Mktg.--Bassick by Kaspar, Shiner, TX; *U.S. Private*, pg. 122
Eargle, David H., Exec. V.P.--Eastex Energy Inc., Houston, TX; *U.S. Public*, pg. 567
Earl, Bryan R., Dir.-Mktg. Communications & Adv.--American Woodmark Corporation, Winchester, VA; *U.S. Public*, pg. 96
Earl, Eric, Mgr.-Sls. & Mkt. Res.--Haviland Enterprises, Grand Rapids, MI; *U.S. Private*, pg. 511
Easley, Matthew, V.P.-Mktg.-Life Company--Nationwide Insurance Enterprise, Columbus, OH; *U.S. Private*, pg. 788
East, Bob, V.P.-Sls. & Mktg.--GSW Thermoplastics Company, Barrie, Canada; *Int'l*, pg. 538
East, Rick, V.P.-Sls. & Mktg.--Gerry Baby Products Company, Thornton, CO; *U.S. Private*, pg. 629
Easthope, Paul, V.P.-Mktg. & Sls.--ACCO Canada Inc., Willowdale, Canada; *U.S. Public*, pg. 674
Eastman, Polly, Sr. Dir.-Mktg.-Woman Wear--Polo/Ralph Lauren Corporation, New York, NY; *U.S. Private*, pg. 874
Eaton, Ken K., V.P.-Mktg.--Ultramar Diamond Shamrock Corporation, San Antonio, TX; *U.S. Public*, pg. 1663
Eavenson, Donald, V.P.-Mktg. OTC--Schering-Plough Healthcare Products Inc., Liberty Corner, NJ; *U.S. Public*, pg. 1438
Eaves, John W., V.P.-Mktg.--Arch Coal, Inc., Saint Louis, MO; *U.S. Public*, pg. 139
Ebeck, Bill, Mgr.-Reg. Sls. & Mktg.--Ivex Packaging Corporation-Grove City, Grove City, PA; *U.S. Public*, pg. 915
Eberhardt, Alice, Mgr.-Adv.--Ortho-Kinetics, Inc., Waukesha, WI; *U.S. Private*, pg. 820
Eberhardt, John, V.P.-Mktg. & Sls.--Delta Faucet Corporation, Indianapolis, IN; *U.S. Public*, pg. 1053
Eberhardt, Josehp W., Jr., V.P.-Sls. & Mktg.--Sanford Beroc Corp., Brentwood, TN; *U.S. Public*, pg. 1178
Eberly, Rick, V.P.-Sls. & Mktg.--Meridian Diagnostics, Inc., Cincinnati, OH; *U.S. Public*, pg. 1094
Ebnet, Paul, V.P.-Sls. & Mktg.--Stearns Manufacturing Company, Sauk Rapids, MN; *U.S. Public*, pg. 940
Ebsen, Greg, Sr. V.P.-Sls. & Mktg.--J.R. Simplot Company Food Group, Boise, ID; *U.S. Private*, pg. 1002
Eck, Bob, V.P.-Mktg.--Chesapeake Bagel Bakery, Atlanta, GA; *U.S. Private*, pg. 5
Eckard, Dalthard, Sr. V.P.-Sls. & Mktg.--The Berkline Corporation, Morristown, TN; *U.S. Private*, pg. 432
Eckel, Elizabeth B., V.P.-Mktg.--The Washington Trust Company, Westerly, RI; *U.S. Public*, pg. 1744
Ecker, Jackie, Coord.-Mktg. & Adv.--Interstate Van Lines, Inc., Springfield, VA; *U.S. Private*, pg. 573
Eckert, Craig D., V.P.-Mktg. & Sls.--Century Telephone Enterprises, Inc., Monroe, LA; *U.S. Public*, pg. 329
Eckhardt, Klaus, Dir.-Mktg.--FAG Group, Schweinfurt, Germany; *Int'l*, pg. 468
Eckstein, Helene, V.P.-Sls. & Mktg.--Prep - STAT/Spectrum, Franklin, KY; *U.S. Private*, pg. 882
Ecleberry, Ronald, V.P.-Sls. & Mktg.--Modern Welding Co., Inc., Owensboro, KY; *U.S. Private*, pg. 755
Economos, George, Sr. V.P. & Dir.-Mktg.--The Dartnell Corporation, Chicago, IL; *U.S. Private*, pg. 312
Edberg, Sue, Dir.-WorldPerks Program--Northwest Airlines, Inc., Saint Paul, MN; *U.S. Public*, pg. 1200
Edel, Anne, Corp Mktg.--Kinko's Corporation, Ventura, CA; *U.S. Private*, pg. 622
Edgar, Jon, Dir.-Intl. Mktg.--Puma North America, Brockton, MA; *Int'l*, pg. 1072
Edgel, Bill R., V.P.-Mktg.--Barry's Jewelers, Inc., Monrovia, CA; *U.S. Public*, pg. 192
Edgington, D., Dir.-Mktg.--Kelco International Ltd., London, United Kingdom; *U.S. Public*, pg. 1091
Edgington, Kenen, Exec. V.P.-Sls. & Mktg.--The Wurlitzer Company, Loveland, OH; *U.S. Public*, pg. 169
Edgington, Robert, Dir.-Mktg.--Woven Products Div., Corbin, KY; *U.S. Public*, pg. 1161
Edington, B.D., V.P.-Sls. & Mktg.--Logo 7, Inc., Indianapolis, IN; *U.S. Public*, pg. 1644
Edison, Mary Alice, Mgr.-Commun.--T & S Brass & Bronze Works, Inc., Travelers Rest, SC; *U.S. Private*, pg. 1061
Edlund, John, Dir.-Mktg.--Molin Auto Parts Inc., Buffalo, NY; *U.S. Private*, pg. 756
Edmiston, Jim, V.P.-Mktg.--Bushnell Corporation, Overland Park, KS; *U.S. Private*, pg. 1191
Edmondson, Dave, Sr. V.P.-Adv. & Mktg.--RadioShack, Fort Worth, TX; *U.S. Public*, pg. 1560
Edmondson, James R., V.P.-Loan Servicing & Secondary Mktg.--First American Federal Savings Bank, Bristol, VA; *U.S. Public*, pg. 624
Edmundson, John, Dir.-Mktg./Comml. Print--Wallace Computer Services, Inc., Lisle, IL; *U.S. Public*, pg. 1735
Edmundson, Neil, Dir.-Corp. Mktg.--Universal Instruments Corporation, Binghamton, NY; *U.S. Public*, pg. 522
Edward, Linda, V.P.-Sls. & Mktg.--Kaufman and Broad Home Corporation, Los Angeles, CA; *U.S. Public*, pg. 944
Edwards, Allan L., V.P.-Sls. & Mktg.--Simpson Industries, Inc., Plymouth, MI; *U.S. Public*, pg. 1474
Edwards, Benjamin F., IV, Exec. V.P. & Dir.-Sls. & Mktg.--A.G. Edwards, Inc., Saint Louis, MO; *U.S. Public*, pg. 565
Edwards, Brian, Dir.-Mktg.--New York Islanders Hockey Club, Uniondale, NY; *U.S. Private*, pg. 794
Edwards, Carrie, Dir.-Telemarketing--Security Pacific Financial Services Inc., San Diego, CA; *U.S. Public*, pg. 181
Edwards, Chris, Mgr.-Mktg. Opers.--Attachmate, Bellevue, WA; *U.S. Private*, pg. 98
Edwards, John, Mgr.-Mktg. & Pub. Rels.--Porsche Cars Great Britain Ltd., Reading, United Kingdom; *Int'l*, pg. 1063
Edwards, John J., Chief Oper. Officer & V.P.--Edwards Brothers, Inc., Ann Arbor, MI; *U.S. Private*, pg. 365
Edwards, Karen, Dir.-Mktg.-Brand Mngmt.--Yahoo!, Inc., Santa Clara, CA; *U.S. Public*, pg. 1787
Edwards, Linda, V.P.-Sls. & Mktg.--Kaufman and Broad Coastal, Newport Beach, CA; *U.S. Public*, pg. 945
Edwards, Linda, V.P.-Sls. & Mktg.--Kaufman and Broad of San Diego, Inc., San Diego, CA; *U.S. Public*, pg. 945
Edwards, Malcolm, Mgr.-Mktg.--GN Rathdown, Ascot, United Kingdom; *Int'l*, pg. 537
Edwards, Meg, Mktg. Coord.--EMCON, San Mateo, CA; *U.S. Public*, pg. 571
Edwards, Neville, Dir.-Mktg.--Fisons Consumer Health Plc, Witham, United Kingdom; *Int'l*, pg. 1110
Edwards, Richard M., Sr. V.P.-Intl. Mktg.--National Western Life Insurance Company, Austin, TX; *U.S. Public*, pg. 1161
Edwards, Robert W., Mgr.-Mktg.--American Norit Co. Inc., Jacksonville, FL; *Int'l*, pg. 958
Edwards, T.J., Mgr.-Mktg.--National Vendors, Bridgeton, MO; *U.S. Public*, pg. 457
Eelman, Art, V.P.-Mktg.--Mead Johnson Nutritional Group, Evansville, IN; *U.S. Public*, pg. 254
Egan, Edward, Sr. V.P.-Mktg.--TriStar Pictures, Culver City, CA; *Int'l*, pg. 1283
Egan, Greg, Dir.-Mktg.--EMC Corporation, Hopkinton, MA; *U.S. Public*, pg. 545
Egan, James J., III, Dir.-Sys. Mktg. & Pub. Rels.--Fallon Community Health Plan, Worcester, MA; *U.S. Private*, pg. 392
Egan, Neil, Sr. Dir.-Mktg. & Adv.--Snapper Power Equipment, Mc Donough, GA; *U.S. Public*, pg. 1103
Egan, Thomas F., V.P.-Mktg. & Sls.--Suprema Specialties, Inc., Paterson, NJ; *U.S. Public*, pg. 1541
Egeland, Arnold, Dir.-Sls. & Mktg.--Royal Olympic Cruises, New York, NY; *U.S. Public*, pg. 1411
Egeler, D., Mgr.-Mktg.-Holland--Grolsch N.V., Enschede, Netherlands; *Int'l*, pg. 559
Egen, Bob, Exec. V.P. & Gen. Mgr.--Sherwood-Davis & Geck, Saint Louis, MO; *U.S. Public*, pg. 80
Eger, Jack, V.P.-Mktg.--Craftex Mills Inc. of Pennsylvania, Blue Bell, PA; *U.S. Private*, pg. 284
Eggebrecht, Jim, Mgr.-Reg. Mktg.--Global Beverage Co., Rochester, NY; *U.S. Private*, pg. 457
Egger, Gregory, Chief Mktg. Officer--Legacy Marketing Group, Petaluma, CA; *U.S. Private*, pg. 658

Eggert, Charles, Pres.--Pacific Foods, Inc., Kent, WA; *U.S. Private*, pg. 831
Eglinton, Dave, V.P.-Sls. & Mktg.--L.R. Nelson Corporation, Peoria, IL; *U.S. Private*, pg. 790
Ehren, Patrick, Mgr.-Mktg.--Huffy Sports Company, Sussex, WI; *U.S. Public*, pg. 846
Ehrlich, Jay, V.P.-Sls. & Mktg.-Printing Equip.--Wisconsin Automated Machinery Corp., Oshkosh, WI; *U.S. Private*, pg. 1184
Ehrlich, R., Dir.-Mktg. & Sls.- Confectionery--Warner-Lambert K.K., Tokyo, Japan; *U.S. Public*, pg. 1739
Ehrlund, Ronald A., V.P.-Sls. & Mktg./Medical Equipment--Carsen Group Inc., Markham, Canada; *U.S. Public*, pg. 301
Ehrman, Geoff, Mgr.-Mktg.--Benjamin Obdyke, Inc., Warminster, PA; *U.S. Private*, pg. 810
Eichler, Larry, V.P.-Sls. & Mktg.--Prentiss Incorporated, Floral Park, NY; *U.S. Private*, pg. 882
Eichorn, Mike, Mgr.-Reg. Mktg.--Precision Tune Autocare Inc., Leesburg, VA; *U.S. Public*, pg. 1321
Eichstaedt, Vickie, Dir.-Mktg.--Triple S Plastics, Inc., Vicksburg, MI; *U.S. Public*, pg. 1639
Eicksteadt, Shirley, Mktg. Specialist--The Arnold Engineering Company, Marengo, IL; *U.S. Public*, pg. 1420
Eiler, R., Sr. V.P.-Mktg. & Sls.--GAB Robins North America, Inc., Parsippany, NJ; *Int'l*, pg. 1153
Einhauser, James G., Exec. V.P.-Sls. & Mktg.--Wigwam Mills, Inc., Sheboygan, WI; *U.S. Private*, pg. 1175
Einhorn, Margaret, Mgr.-Mktg. Svcs.--Peerless Lighting Corp., Berkeley, CA; *U.S. Private*, pg. 847
Eiriksson, Petur, Sr. V.P.-Mktg.--IceLandAir, Columbia, MD; *Int'l*, pg. 658
Eisenberg, Alan I., V.P.-Sls. & Mktg.--Plymouth Rubber Company, Inc., Canton, MA; *U.S. Public*, pg. 1311
Eisenberg, David M., V.P.-Law, Mktg. & Sls.--Sprint Corporation, Westwood, KS; *U.S. Public*, pg. 1500
Eisenmenger, Paul, Dir.-Mktg.--Precision Twist Drill Co., Crystal Lake, IL; *Int'l*, pg. 1185
Eisenthal, Julia, V.P.-Mktg.--Sony Music Entertainment, Inc., New York, NY; *Int'l*, pg. 1281
Eiserman, Jeri, Mgr.-Mktg.--Hudson, RCI, Temecula, CA; *U.S. Private*, pg. 546
Eitmant, Paul, V.P.-Intl. Mktg.--Ideal Industries, Inc., Sycamore, IL; *U.S. Private*, pg. 557
Eitreim, Jeffrey D., V.P.-Sls. & Mktg.--MediVators, Inc., Eagan, MN; *U.S. Public*, pg. 301
Ek, Carl, Dir.-Sls. & Mktg.--Jonkopings Lantman Ek. For., Jonkoping, Sweden; *Int'l*, pg. 714
Elba, Clyde, V.P.-Fleet & Remarketing Opers.--Mitsubishi Motor Sales of America, Inc., Cypress, CA; *Int'l*, pg. 875
Elberg, Dale, Sr. V.P.-Sls. & Mktg.--Royal Oak Enterprises, Inc., Atlanta, GA; *U.S. Private*, pg. 948
Elefson, Matt, Mgr.-Sls.--L.G. Everist Inc., Sioux Falls, SD; *U.S. Private*, pg. 386
Elek, Edward E., Exec. V.P.-Mktg.--Cosco Fire Protection Inc., Gardena, CA; *U.S. Public*, pg. 1795
Elfenbein, Reed, V.P.-Sls. & Mktg./Scientific, Tech. & Medical Grp.--John Wiley & Sons, Inc., New York, NY; *U.S. Public*, pg. 1768
Elias, William, Dir.-Mktg. & Sls.--Gehl Company, West Bend, WI; *U.S. Public*, pg. 704
Elisiario, Joao M., Sr. V.P.-Mktg.--Banco Espirito Santo e Comercial de Lisboa SA, Lisbon, Portugal; *Int'l*, pg. 142
Ellenberger, David J., V.P.-Mktg./Corp.--Data General Corporation, Westborough, MA; *U.S. Public*, pg. 485
Eller, Betty Lynn, Dir.-Adv. & Consumer Mktg.--Drexel Heritage Furnishings Inc., Drexel, NC; *U.S. Private*, pg. 432
Eller, Jay E., Mgr.-Mktg.--Twin City Die Castings Co., Minneapolis, MN; *U.S. Private*, pg. 1111
Eller, S. Heidi, Dir.-Mktg.--The Great Lakes Cheese Co., Newbury, OH; *U.S. Private*, pg. 473
Ellett, B.R., Dir. Mktg.--Livingston UK Ltd., Teddington, United Kingdom; *Int'l*, pg. 212
Ellickson, Nancy, V.P.-Bus. Mktg.--Genus Inc., Sunnyvale, CA; *U.S. Public*, pg. 732
Ellifritz, Maryann, Mgr.-Mktg. Commun.--Consolidated Natural Gas Company, Pittsburgh, PA; *U.S. Public*, pg. 435
Elliot, Walter, V.P.-Mktg.--Pilot Software, Cambridge, MA; *U.S. Private*, pg. 872
Elliott, A. Wright, Exec. V.P.-Corp. Mktg. & Communications--The Chase Manhattan Corporation, New York, NY; *U.S. Public*, pg. 337
Elliott, D.E., V.P.-Intl. Business--Oliver Rubber Co., Athens, GA; *U.S. Public*, pg. 1504
Elliott, Dean, Dir.-Mktg.--Staodyn Inc., Longmont, CO; *U.S. Public*, pg. 1509
Elliott, Dee, Mktg. Asst.--Trumbull Corporation/P.J. Dick, Inc., West Mifflin, PA; *U.S. Private*, pg. 1107
Elliott, E., V.P.-Mktg., Plumbing & Heating--Watts Regulator Co., Andover, MA; *U.S. Public*, pg. 1747
Elliott, Gary L., V.P.-Mktg. & Sls.-Commodity Chemicals Grp.--Georgia Gulf Corporation, Atlanta, GA; *U.S. Public*, *pg. 734*
Elliott, Marc G., V.P.-Mktg.--Gencor Industries, Inc., Orlando, FL; *U.S. Public*, pg. 705
Elliott, Mark W., Gen. Mgr.-Worldwide Software Sls. & Mktg.--International Business Machines Corporation, Armonk, NY; *U.S. Public*, pg. 895
Elliott, Michael R., V.P.-Sls. & Mktg.--Strattec Securities Corporation, Milwaukee, WI; *U.S. Public*, pg. 1523
Elliott, Thomas, Mgr.-Mktg.--J&H Marsh & McLennan, Inc., New York, NY; *U.S. Public*, pg. 1049
Ellis, Alexander, III, Dir.-Mktg.--Kenetech Corp., San Francisco, CA; *U.S. Public*, pg. 950
Ellis, Bernie, V.P.-Mktg.--Acme Markets, Malvern, PA; *U.S. Public*, pg. 93
Ellis, G.H.G., Chm. Bd. & Dir.-Lube Mktg.--Mobil Oil Company, Ltd., Milton Keynes, United Kingdom; *U.S. Public*, pg. 1119
Ellis, Gary P., V.P.-Sls. & Mktg.--Crenlo, Inc., Rochester, MN; *U.S. Private*, pg. 288
Ellis, Jim, Mgr.-Mktg.--Canadian Kawasaki Motors Inc., Don Mills, Canada; *Int'l*, pg. 726
Ellis, Lynda, Mrg.-Mktg.--Spirol International Corp., Cuyahoga Falls, OH; *U.S. Private*, pg. 1026
Ellis, Rob, Dir.-Comm Mktg.-Adv.--Eaton IDT, Westerville, OH; *U.S. Public*, pg. 558
Ellis, Robert, V.P.-Brand Mktg.--LEGO Systems, Inc., Enfield, CT; *Int'l*, pg. 805
Ellis, Robert, V.P.-Mktg.--Watson Wyatt Worldwide, Bethesda, MD; *U.S. Private*, pg. 1154
Ellis, Sally, Mgr.-Mktg.--Meggitt plc, Wimborne Minster, United Kingdom; *Int'l*, pg. 853
Ellis, Walter, Dir.-Mktg. & Sls.--SASIB Packaging North America, Skokie, IL; *Int'l*, pg. 1194
Ellison, Kevin, Dir.-Mktg./Electric--LG & E Energy Corp., Louisville, KY; *U.S. Public*, pg. 970
Ellison, William, Dir.-Energy Mngmt.--Superior Water, Light & Power Company, Superior, WI; *U.S. Public*, pg. 1116
Ellixson, Marita, Mktg. Editor--Game Time, Inc., Fort Payne, AL; *U.S. Public*, pg. 1543
Ellwood, Suzanne, V.P.-Mkt. Devel.--Detroit Newspapers, Detroit, MI; *U.S. Public*, pg. 965
Elman, Robert H., Mktg. Partner--PATCO L.P., Park Forest, IL; *U.S. Private*, pg. 269
Elmore, Don, Dir.-Mktg.--Central Data Corporation, Champaign, IL; *U.S. Private*, pg. 223
Elorza Diaz, Roberto, V.P.-Mktg.--Grupo Continental S.A., Tampico, Mexico; *Int'l*, pg. 573
Elosa, Ms., Dir.-Mktg.--Gemey Div., Brussels, Belgium; *Int'l*, pg. 819
Elowitz, David, V.P.--Honey Fashions Ltd., New York, NY; *U.S. Private*, pg. 537
Elrod, Thomas R., Pres.-Mktg. & Entertainment--Walt Disney Attractions Division, Anaheim, CA; *U.S. Public*, pg. 511
Elsasser, J.T., V.P.-Bearings-Europe, Africa, West Asia--The Timken Company, Canton, OH; *U.S. Public*, pg. 1617
Elsner, Louis J., V.P.-New Bus. Devel.--Brunswick Indoor Recreation Group, Lake Forest, IL; *U.S. Public*, pg. 265
Elving, Stefan, Dir.-Mktg.--ICA Handlarnas AB, Solna, Sweden; *Int'l*, pg. 642
Ely, Edward A., V.P. & Dir.-Land Sls. & Mktg.--Rouse Office & Community Development Div., Columbia, MD; *U.S. Public*, pg. 1407
Embertson, David E., Mgr.-Mktg.--Dresser Industries Wayne Division, Austin, TX; *U.S. Public*, pg. 528
Emerson, Howard, V.P.-Mktg.--Acer America Corporation, San Jose, CA; *Int'l*, pg. 22
Emerson, Mary Ann, Coord.-Mktg. & Adv.--C.I. Hayes, Inc., Cranston, RI; *U.S. Private*, pg. 513
Emerson, Mike, Mgr.-Worldwide Mktg. & Corp. Communication--Rainbow Technologies, Inc., Irvine, CA; *U.S. Public*, pg. 1359
Emmerling, Paul E., V.P.-Sls., Mktg. & Gen. Mgr.--American Welding & Manufacturing Co., Warren, OH; *U.S. Private*, pg. 425
Emmons, Gary F., V.P.-Sls. & Mktg./Semiconductor Group--SpeedFan International, Inc., Chandler, AZ; *U.S. Public*, pg. 1497
Endean, James, Dir.-Sls. & Mktg.--Uniflow Manufacturing Co., Erie, PA; *U.S. Private*, pg. 1117
Endean, James, Mgr.-Sls. & Mktg.--Kold Draft, Erie, PA; *U.S. Private*, pg. 1117
Endelson, Jennifer, Mgr.-Mktg. Svcs.--Graham-Field Health Products, Inc., Hauppauge, NY; *U.S. Public*, pg. 757
Endieveri, Tony, V.P.-Mktg.--ICO, Inc., Houston, TX; *U.S. Public*, pg. 853
Endieveri, Tony, V.P.-Mktg.--Wedco Technology, Bloomsbury, NJ; *U.S. Public*, pg. 854
Endres, William S., Sr. V.P.-Mktg.--The Rival Company, Kansas City, MO; *U.S. Public*, pg. 1391
Engan, Mike, V.P.-Sls. & Mktg.- Domestic--Miracle Recreation Equipment Company, Monett, MO; *U.S. Private*, pg. 752
Engel, Gail, Mgr.-Production--Goldbergs Marine Distributors, Edison, NJ; *U.S. Public*, pg. 1756
Engel, Lawrence, Acting Mgr.-Mktg.--Dorr-Oliver Incorporated, Milford, CT; *Int'l*, pg. 839
Engel, Phil, V.P.-Sls. & Mktg.--Harcros Chemicals Inc., Kansas City, KS; *Int'l*, pg. 598
Engen, James, Dir.-Sls. & Mktg.--Acrometal Companies, Inc., Plymouth, MN; *U.S. Private*, pg. 14
Enger, Trond, V.P.-Sls. & Mktg.--Aquatic Animal Health, Oslo, Norway; *U.S. Public*, pg. 58
England, Donald, V.P.-Sls. & Mktg.--PAR Microsystems Corporation, New Hartford, NY; *U.S. Public*, pg. 1256
Englande, Arnold, V.P.-Mktg.--VideoServer, Inc., Burlington, MA; *U.S. Public*, pg. 1720
Englander, Ken, Sr. V.P.-Mktg.--Central Lewmar, Newark, NJ; *U.S. Private*, pg. 223
Engle, E.E., V.P.-Mktg. Svcs.--Thrall Car Mfg. Co., Chicago Heights, IL; *U.S. Private*, pg. 344
English, Lew, V.P.-Mktg.--Hickory Hill Furniture Corporation, Valdese, NC; *U.S. Private*, pg. 808
English, Robin L., Dir.-Mktg.--Reed Grain & Bean Company, Buhl, ID; *U.S. Private*, pg. 916
Englund, Dennis, V.P. & Dir.-Mktg.--Bytex Corporation, Westborough, MA; *U.S. Public*, pg. 1522
Ennals, Ford, Dir.-Mktg.--Lloyds TSB Group PLC, London, United Kingdom; *Int'l*, pg. 812
Ennamorato, Robert J., V.P.-Mktg. & Sls.--The Fibre-Metal Products Company, Concordville, PA; *U.S. Private*, pg. 402
Eno, Julius Ralph, Pres.--Hamamatsu Corp., Bridgewater, NJ; *U.S. Private*, pg. 497
Eorgoff, Monica, Dir.-Adv. & Mktg. Svcs.--National Cattlemen's Beef Association, Chicago, IL; *U.S. Private*, pg. 780
Ephron, Michael, Dir.-Mktg.--Vanity Fair, New York, NY; *U.S. Private*, pg. 20
Epkoran, Diane, V.P.-Mktg.--The Jel Sert Co., West Chicago, IL; *U.S. Private*, pg. 585
Epron, Luc, Dir.-Plng. & Mktg.--Automobiles Citroen, Neuilly, France; *Int'l*, pg. 1020
Epstein, Ronald M., Mgr.-Sls. & Mktg.--Halocarbon Products Corp., River Edge, NJ; *U.S. Private*, pg. 496
Erb, Denise, Mktg. Coord.--Wallace Laboratories, Cranbury, NJ; *U.S. Public*, pg. 310
Erbin, Mike, V.P.-Sls. & Mktg.--Gunnebo Fastening Corp., Lonoke, AR; *U.S. Private*, pg. 488
Ercberger, Peter, Mng. Dir.-Mktg.--Scholz & Friends GmbH, Hamburg, Germany; *Int'l*, pg. 1210
Erdner, Thomas E., Mgr.-Mktg. Communications--Calgon Corporation, Pittsburgh, PA; *Int'l*, pg. 455
Erickson, Don, V.P.-Mktg.--McNally Industries, Inc., Grantsburg, WI; *U.S. Private*, pg. 724
Erickson, Harry, Dir.-Mktg.--Middleby Marshall/CTX, Elgin, IL; *U.S. Public*, pg. 1110
Erickson, James, Mgr.-Sls. & Cargo Mktg.--Kuwait Airways, Northeast Region, Jamaica, NY; *Int'l*, pg. 764
Eriksson, Ake, Dir.-Mktg.--ISS Sverige AB, Stockholm, Sweden; *Int'l*, pg. 656
Eriusen, Frode, Mgr.-Mktg.--A/S Ivaran Rederi, Lysaker, Norway; *Int'l*, pg. 696
Erjavec, Tim, Dir.-Mktg.--Chips and Technologies, Inc., San Jose, CA; *U.S. Public*, pg. 349
Erker, Charles F., Mgr.-Mktg. & Sls.--Commerce Bank, N.A., Clayton, MO; *U.S. Public*, pg. 409
Erlacher, Gunther, Mgr.-Mktg.--KONE Sowitsch AG, Vienna, Austria; *Int'l*, pg. 748
Erlander, Clare S., V.P.-Mktg. Svcs.--Security Pacific Financial Services Inc., San Diego, CA; *U.S. Public*, pg. 181
Erler, Richard, V.P.-NAPA Sls. & Mktg.--Tenneco Automotive, Deerfield, IL; *U.S. Public*, pg. 1577
Erlich, David, Dir.-Mktg.--Perstorp Pharma AB, Lund, Sweden; *Int'l*, pg. 1036
Ernest, Bob, V.P.-Customer Support--Integrated Metal Technologies, Inc., Spring Lake, MI; *U.S. Public*, pg. 1112
Ernie, Ann M., Mgr.-Mktg. Communicatons--Thoro, Jacksonville, FL; *U.S. Private*, pg. 505
Ernst, Jurgen, Dir.-Mktg.--Bols Strothmann Brennereien GmbH & Co. KG, Nordrhein-Westfalen, Germany; *Int'l*, pg. 751
Ernst, Matthew, Mktg. Specialist--Carter Day International, Minneapolis, MN; *U.S. Private*, pg. 216
Ernsting, Kenneth W., Sr. V.P.-Sls. & Mktg.--Physician Computer Network, Inc., Morris Plains, NJ; *U.S. Public*, pg. 1293
Erol, Robert R., V.P.-Sls. & Mktg.-Commercial Prods. Div.--Reading Tube Corp., Reading, PA; *U.S. Private*, pg. 202
Eronimous, Randy, Mgr.-Mktg.--Crowley Foods, Inc., Binghamton, NY; *Int'l*, pg. 752
Erridge, Ian, V.P.-Sls. & Mktg.--Blue Diamond Growers, Sacramento, CA; *U.S. Private*, pg. 152
Erskine, Ken J., Mgr.-Natl. Sls. & Mktg.--Precision Roll Grinders, Inc., Allentown, PA; *U.S. Private*, pg. 880
Ervin, J. Patrick, V.P.-Sls. & Mktg.--Hardings, Inc., Elmira, NY; *U.S. Private*, pg. 502
Escher, William, V.P. & Dir.-Mktg. Svcs.--Brown-Forman Corporation, Louisville, KY; *U.S. Public*, pg. 261
Eshleman, Dennis N., V.P.-Mktg.--Hershey Pasta and Grocery Group, Hershey, PA; *U.S. Public*, pg. 812
Eshow, Joanne, Mgr.-Pub. Rels.--Trus Joist MacMillan, Boise, ID; *Int'l*, pg. 829
Eshow, Joanne, Mgr.-Pub. Rels.--Trus Joist MacMillan, Boise, ID; *U.S. Public*, pg. 1556
Espenschied, David, 1st V.P.-Portfolio Mktg.--Countrywide Funding Corporation, Pasadena, CA; *U.S. Public*, pg. 453
Esper, Michael, V.P.-Mktg. Svcs.--SunTrust Banks of Georgia, Inc., Atlanta, GA; *U.S. Public*, pg. 1538
Espinoza, Matt, Dir.-Adv.--Clayton Industries Co., El Monte, CA; *U.S. Private*, pg. 245
Esplin, Brian, Mgr.-Natl. Sls. & Mktg.--Goodman Fielder Mills Ltd., Eastwood, Australia; *Int'l*, pg. 555
Essam, Alan, Dir.-Mktg.--Anacomp Magnetics, Inc., Atlanta, GA; *U.S. Public*, pg. 107
Essen, Arthur, Mgr.-Mktg. & Adv.--American Express Service Europe Ltd., Amsterdam, Netherlands; *U.S. Public*, pg. 74
Esterling, Gary, Mgr.-Automotive Mktg.--Aetna Bearing Company, Chicago, IL; *U.S. Private*, pg. 25
Esto, Dave, V.P.-Mktg.--Anthem Electronics Inc., San Jose, CA; *U.S. Public*, pg. 134
Estreicher, Saul, Mgr.-Mktg. Support & Admin.--Bridgeport Machines, Inc., Bridgeport, CT; *U.S. Public*, pg. 251
Etheredge, Charles E., Sr. V.P.-Sls. & Mktg.--Lockwood Greene Engineers, Inc., Spartanburg, SC; *Int'l*, pg. 633
Etherington-Smith, Meredith, Dir.-Mktg.--Christies International plc, London, United Kingdom; *Int'l*, pg. 289
Etiel, Yoav, Sr. V.P.-Mktg.--Bentley Systems, Inc., Exton, PA; *U.S. Private*, pg. 134
Etka, Jack L., V.P.-Mktg.--Ardco, Inc., Alsip, IL; *U.S. Private*, *pg. 80*
Etling, Jon, Dir.-Mktg.--Reyco Industries, Inc., Springfield, MO; *U.S. Private*, pg. 926
Ettelson, Stephen, V.P., Sec. & Mgr.-Natl. Sls.--Electro Brand, Inc., Chicago, IL; *U.S. Private*, pg. 368
Eubank, Teresa, Mktg. Coordinator--Willis Corroon Corp. of Utah, Salt Lake City, UT; *Int'l*, pg. 1507
Eukovich, Robert, V.P.-Sls. & Mktg.--Pullman/Holt Corp., Tampa, FL; *U.S. Private*, pg. 1173
Eusanio, Rita, Dir.-Mktg.--Greyhound Lines, Inc., Dallas, TX; *U.S. Public*, pg. 765
Euson, Gregory S., V.P. & Dir.-Sls. & Mktg.--Houghton Mifflin Trade & Reference Div., Boston, MA; *U.S. Public*, pg. 841
Evans Hardy, Sandra T., Mktg. Svcs. Specialist--Harwick Standard Distribution Corporation, Akron, OH; *U.S. Private*, pg. 509
Evans, A. H., Dir.-Mktg.--Laser Systems, Apopka, FL; *U.S. Public*, pg. 1002
Evans, Bill, Dir.-Sls. & Mktg./Foodservice--Beatrice Cheese Co., Waukesha, WI; *U.S. Public*, pg. 426
Evans, Bryan D., V.P.-Mktg.--Terra Nitrogen Company, L.P., Tulsa, OK; *U.S. Public*, pg. 1581

Evans, Carolyn, Exec. Dir.-Mktg. & Customer Rels.--Saladmaster, Arlington, TX; *U.S. Private*, pg. 961
Evans, D., Mgr.-Mktg.--Spectra Diode Laboratories, San Jose, CA; *U.S. Public*, pg. 1785
Evans, Doug, Mgr.-Sls. & Mktg.--Perstorp Analytical Inc., Silver Spring, MD; *Int'l*, pg. 1039
Evans, G., V.P.-Sls. & Mktg.--Waukesha Foundry Inc., Waukesha, WI; *U.S. Private*, pg. 1154
Evans, Hank, V.P.-Mktg.--Ground Round Inc., Braintree, MA; *U.S. Public*, pg. 766
Evans, Kenneth M., V.P.-Sls. & Mktg.--Waste Management, Inc., Oak Brook, IL; *U.S. Public*, pg. 1744
Evans, Michael, V.P.-Sls. & Mktg.--Kikkoman International, Inc., San Francisco, CA; *Int'l*, pg. 733
Evans, Philip, Mgr.-Mktg. & Bus. Devel.--Pipetronix Ltd., Concord, Canada; *Int'l*, pg. 1071
Evans, Stephanie, Mktg. Mgr.--Ingalls, Boston, MA; *U.S. Private*, pg. 562
Evans, Steve, V.P.-Sls.--Perdue Farms Incorporated, Salisbury, MD; *U.S. Private*, pg. 852
Evans, Tom, Mktg. Mgr.-Great Plains, Mkt. Res. & Promo.--Great Plains Manufacturing, Inc., Salina, KS; *U.S. Private*, pg. 475
Evdoe, Brian, Dir.-Mktg. & Sls.--ACF Industries, Inc., Saint Charles, MO; *U.S. Private*, pg. 556
Evensrud, S.R., Mgr.-Mktg.--Opel Norge AS, Skedsmokorset, Norway; *U.S. Public*, pg. 723
Everett, D., Mgr.-Sls. & Mktg.--Ensign-Bickford, Bromhof, South Africa; *Int'l*, pg. 1196
Everett, Leigh Ann, Asst. Sec.--Lincoln Property Company, Dallas, TX; *U.S. Private*, pg. 668
Everett, Samuel, Dir.-Corp. Communications--JPS Elastomerics Corp., Holyoke, MA; *U.S. Private*, pg. 578
Everett, Scott, V.P.-New Prods., Mktg. & Strategic Plng.--Bayer Corporation/Consumer Care Division, Morristown, NJ; *Int'l*, pg. 173
Everette, Tony, V.P.-Mktg.--Coleman Powermate Compressors, Springfield, MN; *U.S. Private*, pg. 691
Everhart, D.R., V.P.-Mktg.--ITT Fluid Handling, Morton Grove, IL; *U.S. Public*, pg. 860
Everingham, Roy, Dir.-Mktg. & Sls.--Perfection-Schwank Inc., Waynesboro, GA; *U.S. Private*, pg. 853
Everling, Lawrence J., V.P.-Mktg. & Adv.--The CIT Group/Equipment Financing, Livingston, NJ; *Int'l*, pg. 360
Everlove, Ron, Dir.-Mktg.--Telair International, Oxnard, CA; *U.S. Public*, pg. 1570
Eversgerd, Eric, Coord.-Mktg.--MiTek, Inc., Chesterfield, MO; *Int'l*, pg. 1106
Eves, Brian, Gen. Mgr.--Hussmann Store Equipment Limited, Brantford, Canada; *U.S. Public*, pg. 1766
Evjy, Richard, Mgr.-Mktg.--Robertson Factories, Inc., Taunton, MA; *U.S. Private*, pg. 936
Ewald, Jessica, Mgr.-Mktg.--Plastag Corporation, Elk Grove Village, IL; *U.S. Private*, pg. 870
Ewanick, Joel, Gen. Mgr.-Mktg.--Porsche Cars North America, Inc., Reno, NV; *Int'l*, pg. 1063
Ewing, Kevin, Sr. Mgr.-Mktg.--Thermotron Industries, Holland, MI; *U.S. Private*, pg. 1136
Eynon, Stuart F., Mgr.-Mktg.--Heath Consultants Incorporated, Houston, TX; *U.S. Private*, pg. 518
Eynon, Ted, Mgr.-Mktg.--Heath Consultants Incorporated, Houston, TX; *U.S. Private*, pg. 518
Eyre, Alvin, Mgr.-Sales & Mktg.--Carbone of America, Ultra Carbon Div., Bay City, MI; *Int'l*, pg. 1028
Eyre, John, Dir.-Communications--Kingfisher plc, London, United Kingdom; *Int'l*, pg. 733
Ezekiel, Sam, Sr. V.P.-Mktg.--Network Equipment Technologies, Inc., Redwood City, CA; *U.S. Public*, pg. 1168
Ezell, Mark, Sr. V.P.-Sls. & Mktg.--Purity Dairies Inc., Nashville, TN; *U.S. Private*, pg. 895
Fabbri, M., Dir.-Grp. Intl. Opers. & Mktg. Devel.--SASIB SpA, Bologna, Italy; *Int'l*, pg. 1194
Fabel, Gary, Dir.-Mktg.--Bongards Creameries Inc., Norwood, MN; *U.S. Private*, pg. 156
Faber, Charles P., V.P.-Corp. Devel.--Belden & Blake Corporation, Canton, OH; *U.S. Private*, pg. 1078
Fabian, Bud, V.P.-Sls. & Mktg.--Everett Charles Technologies, Pomona, CA; *U.S. Private*, pg. 386
Fabiano, Maureen, Grp. Mgr.-Mktg.--Thorntons PLC, Darbyshire, United Kingdom; *Int'l*, pg. 1386
Fabriele, John B., V.P.-Mktg.--SpecialtyChem Products Corporation, Marinette, WI; *Int'l*, pg. 173
Fabrizio, Joe, Dir.-Stores--Boscov's Department Store, Inc., Reading, PA; *U.S. Private*, pg. 160
Fabry, Alain, V.P.-Mktg.--Lyonnaise des Eaux S.A., Nanterre, France; *Int'l*, pg. 822
Fachet, Greg, V.P.-Sls. & Mktg.--Steiner Co., Inc., Chicago, IL; *U.S. Private*, pg. 1039
Facius, Tim, Dir.-Mktg.--Baltimore Aircoil Company, Jessup, MD; *U.S. Private*, pg. 68
Factor, Sari, V.P.-Mktg.--McDougal/Littell, Evanston, IL; *U.S. Public*, pg. 841
Fadders, Carol, Acting V.P.-Mktg.--Soft Sheen Products, Inc., Chicago, IL; *U.S. Private*, pg. 1012
Fagan, Kenneth, V.P.-Mktg. & Sls.--Fone America, Inc., Portland, OR; *U.S. Public*, pg. 661
Fahey, Jack, V.P.-Sls. & Mktg.--Temco Fireplace Products, Inc., Nashville, TN; *U.S. Public*, pg. 1576
Fahey, John, Asst. V.P.-Mktg.--Huntington National Bank, Morgantown, WV; *U.S. Public*, pg. 850
Faigen, Steve, Dir.-Mktg.--Booz, Allen & Hamilton Inc., New York, NY; *U.S. Private*, pg. 157
Fain, John W., Sr. V.P.-Mktg. & Sls.--Overnite Transportation Co., Richmond, VA; *U.S. Public*, pg. 1668
Fairfax, Barry, V.P.-Sls. & Mktg.--Red Ball Corporation, Seattle, WA; *U.S. Private*, pg. 97
Fairhurst, Thomas, V.P.-Mktg.--Marietta Corporation, Cortland, NY; *U.S. Private*, pg. 702
Fairlie, Graeme, V.P.-Sls. & Mktg.--Deposition Technologies, Inc., San Diego, CA; *U.S. Public*, pg. 1056
Fairweather, Bob, V.P.-Mktg.--National Computer Print, Inc., Birmingham, AL; *U.S. Private*, pg. 780
Falcone, John C., V.P.-Sls. & Mktg.--Sennheiser Electronic Corp., Old Lyme, CT; *U.S. Private*, pg. 984
Falconer, Liz, Dir.-Mktg., Oscar de la Renta--Sanofi Beaute, Inc., New York, NY; *Int'l*, pg. 445
Falduto, James M., Exec. V.P.-Sls. & Mktg.--Wilton Corporation, Palatine, IL; *U.S. Private*, pg. 1181
Fales, Marsha, Dir.-Media & Mktg.--Norman Levy Associates, Inc., Southfield, MI; *U.S. Private*, pg. 664
Falk, Jurgen, Mktg. Res. Dir.--Westag Werbeagentur, Cologne, Germany; *Int'l*, pg. 1491
Fallon, James N., Dir.-Mktg. Communications & Adv.--ITW Signode, Glenview, IL; *U.S. Public*, pg. 867
Fallon, John, Dir.-Mktg. & Sls.--Westronics, Inc., Kingwood, TX; *U.S. Public*, pg. 1593
Fallot, John, V.P.-Mktg. & Sls.--Mercer Transportation Co., Louisville, KY; *U.S. Private*, pg. 732
Fallow, Rod, V.P.-Sls. & Mktg.--Swagelok Company, Solon, OH; *U.S. Private*, pg. 1057
Falls, James K., V.P.-Sls. & Mktg.--Sealing Equipment Products Co., Inc., Pelham, AL; *U.S. Private*, pg. 978
Falzer, L., V.P.-Mktg. & Adv.--Raypak, Inc., Westlake Village, CA; *Int'l*, pg. 1022
Fancher, David, V.P.-Mktg. & Sls.--The Cooper Companies, Inc., Irvine, CA; *U.S. Public*, pg. 442
Fanning, Michael R., Exec. V.P. & Chief Mktg. Officer--Washington Square Securities, Minneapolis, MN; *U.S. Public*, pg. 1376
Fantine, Jose, Dir.-Planning--Petrobras - Petroleo Brasileiro S.A., Rio de Janeiro, Brazil; *Int'l*, pg. 1041
Farabelli, Michael, V.P.-Mktg.--Bellcore, Morristown, NJ; *U.S. Private*, pg. 976
Farache, Michel, V.P.-Mktg., Japan & Asia Pacific--Imax Corporation, Mississauga, Canada; *Int'l*, pg. 661
Faraci, Vic, Exec. V.P. & Dir.-Mktg--Elektra Entertainment, New York, NY; *U.S. Public*, pg. 1612
Faranda, Joseph A., V.P.-Mktg. Res.--Avon Products, Inc., New York, NY; *U.S. Public*, pg. 155
Farber, Bernard, Sr. V.P.-Sls. & Mdsg.--West Mill Clothes, Inc., Woodside, NY; *U.S. Private*, pg. 1163
Faria, Donald F., V.P.-Mktg.--QuickLogic Corporation, Sunnyvale, CA; *U.S. Private*, pg. 901
Farias, Brandt G., Sr. V.P.-Mktg. Communications Div.--First Hawaiian Bank, Honolulu, HI; *U.S. Public*, pg. 634
Farisei, U., Gen. Mgr.-Mktg. & Bus. Devel.--Nuovo Pignone S.p.a., Florence, Italy; *Int'l*, pg. 990
Farkas, Steve, V.P.-Strategic Devel.--3Com Personal Communications Div., Skokie, IL; *U.S. Public*, pg. 1604
Farland, Jim, V.P.-Sls. & Mktg.--UnionTools, Inc., Columbus, OH; *U.S. Public*, pg. 17
Farley, Jim, Mgr.-Natl. Sls.-Ice Cream--Solon Manufacturing Company, Solon, ME; *U.S. Private*, pg. 1013
Farley, Joseph J., V.P.-Mktg. & Engrng.--Helm Resources Inc., Greenwich, CT; *U.S. Public*, pg. 808
Farley, Michael G., V.P.-Mktg.--Thorn Apple Valley, Inc., Southfield, MI; *U.S. Public*, pg. 1602
Farley, Steve, Sr. V.P.-Mktg.--Payless ShoeSource, Inc., Topeka, KS; *U.S. Public*, pg. 1268
Farlsei, U., Mgr.-Mktg. & Bus. Devel.--Nuovo Pignone S.p.a., Florence, Italy; *Int'l*, pg. 990
Farmer, David, Dir.-Corp. Communications--Sierra Pacific Resources, Reno, NV; *U.S. Public*, pg. 1470
Farmer, Glenda, Mgr.-Mktg.--Senior Engineering, Lyman, SC; *Int'l*, pg. 1222
Farmer, Mike, Mgr.-Contract Sls.--The Paty Company, Piney Flats, TN; *U.S. Private*, pg. 844
Farmer, Robert, V.P.--Farmers Copper & Industrial Supply, Galveston, TX; *U.S. Private*, pg. 422
Farmer, Tony, Mgr.-Sls. & Mktg./UK & Ireland--Transnet Group, London, United Kingdom; *Int'l*, pg. 1418
Farnam, Deborah B., Dir.-Mktg.--The Atlantic Monthly Magazine, Boston, MA; *U.S. Private*, pg. 95
Farnham, Craig, Dir.-Mktg.--Teledyne Portland Forge, Portland, IN; *U.S. Public*, pg. 43
Farnham, Deborah, V.P. & Dir.-Mktg.--U.S. News & World Report, New York, NY; *U.S. Private*, pg. 1125
Farnsworth, Robert, Exec. V.P.-Mktg. & Mdsg.--The Pfaltzgraff Co., York, PA; *U.S. Private*, pg. 860
Farnsworth, Robert, Exec. V.P.-Mktg.--The Pfaltzgraff Co., York, PA; *U.S. Private*, pg. 860
Faro Wood, Linda, Mgr.-Corp. Commun.--Edwards and Kelcey, Inc., Boston, MA; *U.S. Private*, pg. 364
Farooqi, S.A., Mgr.-Mktg. Services--Organon Pakistan (Private) Limited, Karachi, Pakistan; *Int'l*, pg. 45
Farr, Greg, Dir.-Mktg.-Custom Horizonal Prod.--Hunter Douglas, Inc., Upper Saddle River, NJ; *Int'l*, pg. 639
Farrell, Dee, Sr. Mktg. Coord.--Geraghty & Miller, Inc., Denver, CO; *Int'l*, pg. 607
Farrell, Joann, Mgr.-Promo.--Journal of Commerce, Inc., New York, NY; *Int'l*, pg. 1026
Farrell, John E., V.P.-Mktg.--Continental Plastic Containers, Inc., Norwalk, CT; *U.S. Public*, pg. 440
Farrell, Kathleen, V.P.-Mktg.--Empire National Bank, Traverse City, MI; *U.S. Private*, pg. 374
Farrell, Mary, Mgr.-Mktg. Services--Aquion, Elk Grove Village, IL; *U.S. Private*, pg. 78
Farrell, Mary, Mgr.-Mktg. Svcs.--RainSoft Water Treatment Systems, Elk Grove Village, IL; *U.S. Private*, pg. 78
Farrell, Moira, Sr. V.P.-Corp. Res. & Sls. Mktg.--King World Productions, Inc., New York, NY; *U.S. Public*, pg. 961
Farrell, Moira, Sr. V.P.-Corp. Res. & Sls. Mktg.--King World Productions, Los Angeles, CA; *U.S. Public*, pg. 961
Farrington, Tina M., Asst. V.P. & Dir.-Mktg.--Rurban Financial Corp., Defiance, OH; *U.S. Public*, pg. 1412
Farris, John, V.P.-New Mkt. Devel.--Pall Corporation, Greenvale, NY; *U.S. Public*, pg. 1253
Farris, Michael G., V.P.-Sls. & Mktg.--MW Manufacturers Inc., Rocky Mount, VA; *Int'l*, pg. 593
Fartsing, Joseph D., V.P.-Mktg.--Minerals Div., Reno, NV; *U.S. Private*, pg. 355
Faruolo, Edward, Asst. V.P.-Corp. Mktg.--Cigna Corp., Philadelphia, PA; *U.S. Public*, pg. 356
Fasanelli, Richard, Dir.-Bus. Devel.--UST Inc., Greenwich, CT; *U.S. Public*, pg. 1660
Fasano, Lorraine, Dir.-Mktg.--High Point Financial Corp., Branchville, NJ; *U.S. Public*, pg. 826
Fasano, William, Sr. V.P.-Mktg. & Opers.--News America Marketing, Norwalk, CT; *Int'l*, pg. 925
Fassnacht, Debra Kerr, Sr. V.P.-Mktg. & Pub. Affairs--John G. Shedd Aquarium, Chicago, IL; *U.S. Private*, pg. 991
Faulk, Rick, V.P.-Mktg.--PictureTel, Andover, MA; *U.S. Public*, pg. 1294
Faulkner, David, Dir.-Strategic Planning--McCormick Flavor Division-U.S.A., Hunt Valley, MD; *U.S. Public*, pg. 1066
Faulkner, Dick, V.P.-Mktg.--Security Bank & Trust Co., Vincennes, IN; *U.S. Public*, pg. 1217
Faunce, David B., Jr., V.P.-Adv., Sls. & Mktg.--Mauney Hosiery Mills, Inc., Kings Mountain, NC; *U.S. Private*, pg. 715
Faura, Joaquin, Mgr.-Sls. & Mktg.--Tabacalera, S.A., Madrid, Spain; *Int'l*, pg. 1345
Fawcett, I.E., Mgr.-Mktg. Communications--Vauxhall, Luton, United Kingdom; *U.S. Public*, pg. 724
Fawcett, Laura C., Mgr.-Mktg. Communications--Garlock Sealing Technologies, Palmyra, NY; *U.S. Public*, pg. 402
Fawcett, Scott, Sr. V.P.-Sls. & Mktg.--Springs Window Fashions Division, Middleton, WI; *U.S. Public*, pg. 1500
Fazzari, Anthony, Sr. V.P.-Retail Mktg. & Sls.--Chock Full O' Nuts Corporation, New York, NY; *U.S. Public*, pg. 351
Fazzini, Christopher A., V.P.-Sls. & Mktg.--Reliance Standard Life Insurance Company, Philadelphia, PA; *U.S. Public*, pg. 496
Fearing, Judy, Sr. V.P.-Mktg.--ESPN, Inc., Bristol, CT; *U.S. Public*, pg. 512
Fecteau, Louise, Sr. Dir.-Mktg.--Eskimo Pie Corporation, Richmond, VA; *U.S. Public*, pg. 592
Federico, Ronda, Dir.-Mktg.--Turtle Wax, Inc., Chicago, IL; *U.S. Private*, pg. 1110
Fedor, David S., V.P.-Mktg.--Ithaco Inc., Ithaca, NY; *U.S. Private*, pg. 576
Fee, James P., Jr., V.P.-Sls. & Mktg.--Protocol Systems, Inc., Beaverton, OR; *U.S. Public*, pg. 1336
Fee, Michael R., V.P.-Mktg.--Reliable Automatic Sprinkler Co., Inc., Mount Vernon, NY; *U.S. Private*, pg. 920
Feely, Tom, V.P.-Mktg., N.A.--Dana Corporation, Toledo, OH; *U.S. Public*, pg. 479
Feenstra, Jim, V.P.-Mktg.--Penske Logistics, Reading, PA; *U.S. Private*, pg. 851
Fehlig, Kenneth L., V.P.-Sls. & Mktg.--Lincoln Automotive, Saint Louis, MO; *U.S. Public*, pg. 1273
Feichtner, Jack P., V.P.-Adv. & Mktg.--Central Tractor Farm & Country, Inc., Des Moines, IA; *U.S. Private*, pg. 237
Feigin, Barbara S., Exec. V.P. & Strategic Svcs. Dir.--Grey Advertising Inc., New York, NY; *U.S. Public*, pg. 764
Feil, Kim, Sr. V.P.-Mktg--Cadbury Beverages, Stamford, CT; *Int'l*, pg. 248
Feiler, Mike, Dir.-Mktg.--Minnesota Power, Duluth, MN; *U.S. Public*, pg. 1116
Feinberg, Marcee, Mgr.-Mktg.--Lazare Kaplan Intl., Inc., New York, NY; *U.S. Public*, pg. 981
Feinstein, Bob, V.P.-Mktg.--Health Products Corporation, Yonkers, NY; *U.S. Private*, pg. 514
Feipel, Larry, Sr. V.P.-Telemarketing & Incentives--Ross Roy Communications, Inc., Bloomfield Hills, MI; *U.S. Private*, pg. 946
Feist, Peter, V.P.-Mktg.--Gatefield Corporation, Fremont, CA; *U.S. Public*, pg. 703
Fela, Leonard J., Mgr.-Mktg.--Lightnin Mixers, Rochester, NY; *U.S. Public*, pg. 726
Felberdaum, Peter, Exec. V.P.-Mktg.--SDI Technologies Inc., Rahway, NJ; *U.S. Private*, pg. 956
Feldman, Clark, Exec. V.P. & Dir.-Mktg.--Vita Food Products, Inc., Chicago, IL; *U.S. Private*, pg. 1142
Feldman, Max, V.P.-Customer Service & Mktg.--Transcanada Pipelines Limited, Calgary, Canada; *Int'l*, pg. 1416
Feldman, Peter, Sr. Mktg. Specialist--Computer Language Research, Inc., Carrollton, TX; *U.S. Public*, pg. 421
Feldman, Scott, Dir.-Mktg.--Pollo Tropical, Inc., Miami, FL; *U.S. Public*, pg. 1315
Feldman, Steve, V.P.-Mktg.--Michael Anthony Jewelers, Inc., Mount Vernon, NY; *U.S. Public*, pg. 1103
Feldmann, Thomas, Mgr.-Mktg.--West Central Cooperative, Ralston, IA; *U.S. Private*, pg. 1163
Fell, W., Mgr.-Mktg.--G.E. Canada Power Systems, Lachine, Canada; *U.S. Public*, pg. 713
Feller, Bob, V.P.-Mktg.--Shelter Mutual Insurance Company, Columbia, MO; *U.S. Private*, pg. 992
Feller, Tom, Dir.-Special Event Mktg.--Justin Boot Company, Fort Worth, TX; *U.S. Public*, pg. 937
Fellona, Joseph, V.P.-LV Mktg.--American Isuzu Motors Inc., Whittier, CA; *Int'l*, pg. 692
Fellows, Bill, Dir.-Mktg. & Adv.--Kepner-Tregoe, Inc., Skillman, NJ; *U.S. Public*, pg. 1659
Feltenstein, George, Sr. V.P.-Worldwide Mktg., Classics--MGM/UA Home Entertainment, Inc., Santa Monica, CA; *U.S. Public*, pg. 1102
Fenerin, Michael N., Grp. V.P.-Mktg.--Bergen Brunswig Drug Company, Orange, CA; *U.S. Public*, pg. 213
Fenn, Wade R., Exec. V.P.-Mktg.--Best Buy Co., Inc., Eden Prairie, MN; *U.S. Public*, pg. 223
Fennell, Frank, Gen. Mgr.-Mktg./Underwater Prods.--Nikon Inc., Melville, NY; *Int'l*, pg. 931
Fenrich, Jean Ann, Mgr.-Mktg. Communications--Weigh-Tronix, Inc., Fairmont, MN; *Int'l*, pg. 1299
Fenwick, Robert, Sr. V.P.-Sls. & Mktg.--Vital Signs, Englewood, CO; *U.S. Public*, pg. 1723
Fenwick, Vivienne, Dir.-Mktg.--Perrier UK Ltd., London, United Kingdom; *Int'l*, pg. 919
Ference, R. Keith, Mgr.-Mktg. Services--Svedala Bulk Materials Handling Engineered Products, Pittsburgh, PA; *Int'l*, pg. 1326
Fergerson, Joe, V.P.-Mktg.--Atlas Supply Company, Atlanta, GA; *U.S. Private*, pg. 96
Fergus, Holly, V.P.-Mktg. & Communications--ATC Communications Group, Inc., Dallas, TX; *U.S. Public*, pg. 11

Ferguson, Bob, V.P.-Sls. & Mktg.--Setco, Cincinnati, OH; *U.S. Private,* pg. 987

Ferguson, Bob, Sr. V.P.-Mktg. & Sls. Promo.--Younkers, Inc., Des Moines, IA; *U.S. Public,* pg. 1334

Ferguson, Donald J., Exec. V.P.-Sls. & Mktg.--Intermatic Inc., Spring Grove, IL; *U.S. Private,* pg. 567

Ferguson, Hugh C., Exec. V.P.-Sls. & Mktg.--Fayette Tubular Products, Troy, MI; *U.S. Public,* pg. 481

Ferguson, J., Asst. V.P. & Dir.-Mktg. Svcs.--American National Insurance Company, Galveston, TX; *U.S. Public,* pg. 87

Ferguson, Jack, Dir.-Mktg.--Delta Mills Marketing Company, New York, NY; *U.S. Public,* pg. 498

Ferguson, James M., V.P.-OEM Mktg. Grp.--Superior Industries International, Inc., Van Nuys, CA; *U.S. Public,* pg. 1539

Ferguson, Joellyn, V.P.-Mktg.--The Mills Corporation, Arlington, VA; *U.S. Public,* pg. 1113

Ferguson, Larry J., V.P.-Sls. & Mktg.--Master Molded Products Corporation, Elgin, IL; *U.S. Private,* pg. 714

Ferguson, N., V.P.-Sls. & Mktg.-Furnaces--Italimpianti of America, Incorporated, Coraopolis, PA; *Int'l,* pg. 655

Fermino, Alex, Mktg. & Adv. Coord.--DX Communications, Inc., Deerfield Beach, FL; *Int'l,* pg. 694

Fernandez, Benigno Gomez, Dir.-Tech. & Mktg.--Loctite Espana, S.A., Madrid, Spain; *Int'l,* pg. 611

Fernandez, Donald, Mktg. Exec.--Utell International-Saudi Arabia, Jeddah, Saudi Arabia; *Int'l,* pg. 1099

Fernandez, Juan, Dir.-Mktg. Analysis--Mission Industries, Las Vegas, NV; *U.S. Private,* pg. 752

Fernandez, Manuel, Mgr.-Mktg.--Esselte S.A., Barcelona, Spain; *Int'l,* pg. 461

Fernet, Michel, Dir.-Mktg.-Mercure--Societe Internationale des Hotels Novotel, Evry, France; *Int'l,* pg. 21

Fernstrom, Jim, Mgr.-Mktg.--Thermal Ceramics Inc., Augusta, GA; *Int'l,* pg. 894

Ferrans, Frank, Prod. Mgr.-Mkt. Healthcare Systems--Executone Information Systems, Inc., Milford, CT; *U.S. Public,* pg. 599

Ferrans, Kristine, Mgr.-Mktg. & Sls.--Copperweld Fayetteville Division, Fayetteville, TN; *Int'l,* pg. 662

Ferrans, Kristine, Mgr.-Sls. & Mktg.--Copperweld Chicago Division, Chicago, IL; *Int'l,* pg. 662

Ferrans, Kristine, Mgr.-Sls. & Mktg.--Copperweld Miami Division, Piqua, OH; *Int'l,* pg. 662

Ferranti, Richard, V.P.-Intl. Mktg.--Rich Products Corp., Buffalo, NY; *U.S. Private,* pg. 928

Ferrari, Nicholas J., Dir.-Mktg. Communications--Advertising Age, Chicago, IL; *U.S. Private,* pg. 284

Ferraris, Frank, V.P.-Mktg.--Sun Diamond Growers of California, Pleasanton, CA; *U.S. Private,* pg. 1051

Ferraro, Karen L., Dir.-Mktg.--Periphonics Corp., Bohemia, NY; *U.S. Public,* pg. 1278

Ferraton, Olivia, Dir.-Mktg.--Xerox South Africa, Isando, South Africa; *U.S. Public,* pg. 1785

Ferreira, David, Dir.-Mktg.--Syratech Corporation, East Boston, MA; *U.S. Private,* pg. 1060

Ferrell, Ernest E., Jr., V.P.-Mktg. & Asst. Treas.--Salem Carpet Mills, Inc., Winston Salem, NC; *U.S. Public,* pg. 1464

Ferrer, Dionisio, Dir.-Mktg.--Kalifarma S.A., Barcelona, Spain; *Int'l,* pg. 1279

Ferrino, David, Dir.-Natl. Sls. & Mktg.--Joseph Huber Brewing Co., Inc., Monroe, WI; *U.S. Private,* pg. 545

Ferris, Andrew T., Mgr.-Mktg.--Technic Incorporated, Cranston, RI; *U.S. Private,* pg. 1071

Ferris, Deborah A., Mgr.-Mktg.--Albert Kahn Associates, Inc., Detroit, MI; *U.S. Private,* pg. 604

Ferris, Gerald P., Mgr.-Gen. Sls. & Mktg.--Boston Gear, Quincy, MA; *U.S. Public,* pg. 857

Ferrise, Sam, II, V.P.-Sls. & Mktg.--Bandag, Incorporated, Muscatine, IA; *U.S. Public,* pg. 177

Ferrucci, Anne, Asst. V.P.-Mktg.--The F.A. Bartlett Tree Expert Co., Stamford, CT; *U.S. Private,* pg. 119

Ferry, Dan, Sr. Dir.-Mktg.--Meridian Medical Technology, Inc., Columbia, MD; *U.S. Public,* pg. 1095

Feserman, Doug, V.P.-Mktg.--TCI Communications, Inc., Englewood, CO; *U.S. Public,* pg. 1554

Fess, John, Sr. V.P.-Database Mktg.--Cohn & Wells, San Francisco, CA; *Int'l,* pg. 601

Fetner, Bay, Sr. V.P. & Mgr.-Mktg.--Congress Financial Corp., New York, NY; *U.S. Public,* pg. 447

Fette, Jim, Sr. Mgr.-Mktg. Commun. & Adv.--LCI International, Inc., Dublin, OH; *U.S. Public,* pg. 969

Feuer, Stephanie, Dir.-Mktg. & Promotion--WQXR/FM, WQEW/AM, New York, NY; *U.S. Public,* pg. 1174

Fiala, Theres, Dir.-Mktg.--Procter & Gamble Austria GmbH, Vienna, Austria; *U.S. Public,* pg. 1332

Ficek, Kenneth J., Dir.-Bus. Devel.--Carus Corporation, Peru, IL; *U.S. Private,* pg. 217

Fichuk, Ted, V.P.-Mktg. Dir., Measurement Services--A.C. Nielsen Company, Schaumburg, IL; *U.S. Public,* pg. 1183

Fick, Russell, V.P.-Mktg.-Valve Prods.--Automatic Switch Co., Florham Park, NJ; *U.S. Public,* pg. 573

Ficken, Bill, Sr. V.P.-Sls. & Mktg.--Gerber Plumbing Fixtures Corporation, Chicago, IL; *U.S. Private,* pg. 449

Ficocelli, Peter, V.P.-Europe--Teleglobe, Inc., Montreal, Canada; *Int'l,* pg. 1373

Fidler, Karen L., V.P.-Mktg.--Bachman Company, Reading, PA; *U.S. Private,* pg. 109

Fiebiger, Ray, V.P.-Mktg. & Sls.--Laserscope Surgical Systems, San Jose, CA; *U.S. Public,* pg. 979

Fiedler, Barry, Mgr.-Mktg.--Anritsu Wiltron, Morgan Hill, CA; *Int'l,* pg. 77

Fiedler, Eric W., V.P.-Sls. & Mktg.--Crown Fence Co., Long Beach, CA; *U.S. Private,* pg. 292

Fiegel, Kirby, V.P.-Equip. Mktg.--Phoenix American Incorporated, San Rafael, CA; *U.S. Private,* pg. 862

Field, Cher, Dir.-Mktg.--Conroy's Flowers, Long Beach, CA; *U.S. Private,* pg. 366

Field, David, V.P.-Sls. & Mktg.--Trendway Corporation, Holland, MI; *U.S. Private,* pg. 1099

Field, Jack, Dir.-Mktg.--Tru-Form, Wilkes-Barre, PA; *Int'l,* pg. 1338

Field, James L., Mgr.-Vision Products Mktg.--Electro Scientific Industries, Inc., Portland, OR; *U.S. Public,* pg. 568

Fields, Larkin W., Mgr.--USAA Life Insurance Co., San Antonio, TX; *U.S. Private,* pg. 1115

Fieler, Tony, V.P.-Sls. & Mktg.--Lucas Body Systems - North America, Winona, MN; *Int'l,* pg. 820

Fifield, D., Mgr.-Mktg.--Castrol Canada Inc., Toronto, Canada; *Int'l,* pg. 235

Figg, Marjorie, Mgr.-Mktg.--Georg Fischer Disa, Inc., Holly, MI; *Int'l,* pg. 490

Figueras, Armand, Sr. V.P.-Sls. & Mktg.--M. Kamenstein, Inc., Elmsford, NY; *U.S. Private,* pg. 606

Files, Glenn, V.P.-Mktg. & Bus. Devel.--Central Power and Light Company, Corpus Christi, TX; *U.S. Public,* pg. 324

Filipelli, Tony, Sr. V.P.-Mktg. Svcs.--Rhea & Kaiser Marketing Communications, Naperville, IL; *U.S. Private,* pg. 927

Fillpot, Mike, V.P.-Mktg. Grp.--Siemens Nixdorf Information Systems Inc., Burlington, MA; *Int'l,* pg. 1245

Finacana, Ann, Sr. V.P.-Corp. Mktg.--Fleet National Bank, Providence, RI; *U.S. Public,* pg. 649

Finacana, Ann, Sr. V.P.-Corp. Mktg., Fleet Fin. Grp.--Fleet Bank-NH, Nashua, NH; *U.S. Public,* pg. 649

Finazzo, P. P., V.P.-Sls.--American Excelsior Company, Arlington, TX; *U.S. Private,* pg. 53

Finch, Jeff, V.P.-Sls. & Mktg., Aeroquip--Aeroquip-Vickers, Inc., Maumee, OH; *U.S. Public,* pg. 24

Fincham, M., Mgr.-Mktg.--AE Goetze Automotive, Bradford, United Kingdom; *Int'l,* pg. 1334

Findlay, Ian, Dir.-Strategic Mktg.--EMAP Business Communications Division, London, United Kingdom; *Int'l, pg. 451*

Findlay, Robert J., V.P. & Mgr.-Sls.--National Utility Service (Canada) Ltd., North York, Canada; *U.S. Private,* pg. 787

Findley, Norman P., Sr. V.P.-Intl. Mktg. & Pres.-European Grp.--Coca-Cola Enterprises Inc., Atlanta, GA; *U.S. Public,* pg. 393

Findley, Scott, V.P.-Mktg. & Distribution--Silcorp Limited, Scarborough, Canada; *Int'l,* pg. 1249

Fine, Christopher, Mgr.-Mktg. Commun.--Alvey Systems, Inc, Saint Louis, MO; *U.S. Private,* pg. 47

Fine, D., V.P.-Mktg.--Fedmet International Inc., Mississauga, Canada; *Int'l,* pg. 1150

Fine, David, V.P.-Mktg.--Prism Integrated Sanitation Management, Inc., Miami, FL; *U.S. Private,* pg. 592

Fine, Jay, Chief Oper. Officer & Exec. V.P.--Fort Lock Corporation, River Grove, IL; *U.S. Private,* pg. 419

Finelli, Henri, V.P. & Bus. Mgr.-Wire & Cable--Synergistics Industries Limited, Mississauga, Canada; *U.S. Public,* pg. 734

Fingerhut, Pete, Dir.-Mktg.--Premier Parks Inc., Oklahoma City, OK; *U.S. Public,* pg. 1323

Finigan, Nancy, Dir.-Mktg.--TimeMed Labeling Systems, Inc., Burr Ridge, IL; *U.S. Private,* pg. 1087

Fink, Bill, Mgr.-Mktg.--Polyloom Corp. of America, Dayton, TN; *U.S. Private,* pg. 875

Fink, Eileen, Dir.-Mktg.--Delair Group, L.L.C., Delair, NJ; *U.S. Private,* pg. 47

Fink, Jim, Mgr.-Mktg.--J.H. Larson Electrical Company, Golden Valley, MN; *U.S. Private,* pg. 652

Finkbiner, Thomas L., V.P.-Intermodal Mktg.--Norfolk Southern Corporation, Norfolk, VA; *U.S. Public,* pg. 1190

Finke, Douglas, V.P.-Mktg.--Standard Microsystems Corp., Hauppauge, NY; *U.S. Public,* pg. 1502

Finkelstein, Gayle, Coord.-Mktg. & Pub. Rels.--Billboard Magazine, New York, NY; *Int'l,* pg. 1446

Finley, Gene, Mgr.-Natl. Mktg.--A.M. Castle & Co., Franklin Park, IL; *U.S. Public,* pg. 312

Finley, Jon, Dir.-Sls. & Mktg.--Rundel Products, Inc., Portland, OR; *U.S. Private,* pg. 951

Finley, Richard L., Sr. V.P.-Sls. & Mktg.--Allied Security, Inc., Pittsburgh, PA; *U.S. Private,* pg. 40

Finn, N., Dir.-Mktg.--Chloride Industrial Batteries Ltd., Manchester, United Kingdom; *Int'l,* pg. 125

Finn, Patrick, Dir.-Mktg.--Cannon, Grand Island, NY; *U.S. Private,* pg. 205

Finnen, Paula, Mgr.-Category--United Dairy Farmers, Inc., Cincinnati, OH; *U.S. Private,* pg. 1121

Finneran, Ben, Dir.-Mktg.--Dairy Mart Southeast, Louisville, KY; *U.S. Public,* pg. 476

Finneran, Tom, Sr. V.P.-Mktg.--Quaker Fabric Corporation, Fall River, MA; *U.S. Public,* pg. 1347

Finnerty, Patrick, Dir.-Sls. & Mktg.--Kaufman and Broad Inland Empire, Anaheim, CA; *U.S. Public,* pg. 945

Finnerty, Patrick, Mgr.-Mktg.--Kaufman and Broad-Antelope Valley Regional Office, Palmdale, CA; *U.S. Public,* pg. 945

Finney, Deborah, Mgr.-Sls. & Mktg.--ISS London Ltd., London, United Kingdom; *Int'l,* pg. 657

Finney, Kate, Mgr.-Mktg. Communications--Duquesne Light Company, Pittsburgh, PA; *U.S. Public,* pg. 474

Finnie, Darren, Dir.-Consumer Mktg.--CNBC, Fort Lee, NJ; *U.S. Public,* pg. 712

Finucane, Michael F., V.P.-Sls., Mktg. & Devel.--Nichols-Homeshield, Davenport, IA; *U.S. Public,* pg. 1350

Fiore, Catherine E., Admin. Asst.-Mktg.--Calumet Construction Corporation, Hammond, IN; *U.S. Private,* pg. 201

Fiore, Pete, V.P.-Mktg.--Ardent Software, Inc., Westborough, MA; *U.S. Public,* pg. 129

Fiorentino, Patrick, V.P.-Sls.--Tiger Direct, Inc., Miami, FL; *U.S. Public,* pg. 747

Fiorini, Peter, V.P.-Sls. & Mktg./Industrial--Rainfair, Inc., Racine, WI; *U.S. Private,* pg. 907

Fiorito, Nicole, Admin. Asst.-Mktg.--Doak Dermatologics, Westbury, NY; *U.S. Public,* pg. 250

Firestone, Tmmy, Dir.-Mktg.--Morton's of Chicago, Inc., Chicago, IL; *U.S. Public,* pg. 1136

First, Doug, Mgr.-Mktg. Res.--Lands' End, Inc., Dodgeville, WI; *U.S. Public,* pg. 977

Firth, J. Roy, Mgr.-Mktg.--Laurentian Bank of Canada, Montreal, Canada; *Int'l,* pg. 396

Fischer, John, Dir.-Field Mktg.--Bonanza Restaurants, Dallas, TX; *U.S. Private,* pg. 736

Fischer, Meredith B., V.P.-Communications, Mktg. & Strategy--Pitney Bowes Inc., Stamford, CT; *U.S. Public,* pg. 1303

Fischer, Mike, Mgr.-Creative Services--CNBC, Fort Lee, NJ; *U.S. Public,* pg. 712

Fischerbacher, Robert, Dir.-Pub. Rels.--Knurr AG, Munich, Germany; *Int'l,* pg. 739

Fischioni, Phillip, Exec. V.P. & Corp. Dir.-Mktg.--Paul Inman Associates Inc., Farmington, MI; *U.S. Private,* pg. 564

Fishback, Denise, Sr. Dir.-Mktg.--Westwood-Squibb Pharmaceuticals Inc., Buffalo, NY; *U.S. Public,* pg. 255

Fisher, Alan, Dir.-Mktg.--Ultra Electronics Controls, Greenford, United Kingdom; *Int'l,* pg. 1431

Fisher, Bill, Dir.-Mktg.--Adventure Lands of America, Inc., Des Moines, IA; *U.S. Private,* pg. 22

Fisher, Bruce, V.P.-Mktg. & Gen. Mgr.--Hayward Industries, Inc., Elizabeth, NJ; *U.S. Private,* pg. 513

Fisher, Craig, Mgr.-Mktg.--Peterbilt Motors Co., Denton, TX; *U.S. Public,* pg. 1247

Fisher, David, V.P.-Mktg.--Sanofi Pharmaceuticals, Inc., New York, NY; *Int'l,* pg. 445

Fisher, David McClure, Dir. & Mng. Dir.-Hogg Marketing Services--Bain Hogg Group plc, London, United Kingdom; *Int'l,* pg. 671

Fisher, Edwin, Exec. V.P. & Chief Mktg. Officer--The Medical Protective Company, Fort Wayne, IN; *U.S. Private,* pg. 728

Fisher, Frank, Jr., Mgr.-Mktg.--Magneco/Metrel, Inc., Addison, IL; *U.S. Private,* pg. 695

Fisher, Frank, Sr., Mktg. Consultant--Magneco/Metrel, Inc., Addison, IL; *U.S. Private,* pg. 695

Fisher, James A., Dir.-Mktg.--Ball Metal Beverage Container Corp., Westminster, CO; *U.S. Public,* pg. 171

Fisher, James D., V.P.-Mktg.--Cracker Barrel Old Country Store, Inc., Lebanon, TN; *U.S. Public,* pg. 455

Fisher, Marshall, Dir.-Mktg.--Carolina Glove Co., Newton, NC; *U.S. Private,* pg. 214

Fisher, Michael D., Mgr.-Sls., Services & Mktg.--Arrow Oilfield Service Company, Canton, OH; *U.S. Private,* pg. 1078

Fisher, Millicent, Coord.-Mktg.--Unistrut Corporation, Wayne, MI; *U.S. Public,* pg. 1651

Fisher, Phelps, Exec. V.P.-Mktg. Dir.--Fisher Broadcasting Inc., Seattle, WA; *U.S. Public,* pg. 648

Fisher, Robert B., Mktg. Specialist--Metra Commuter Rail, Chicago, IL; *U.S. Private,* pg. 919

Fisher, Sara B., Sr. V.P. & Dir.-Mktg.--NBSC Corporation, Columbia, SC; *U.S. Public,* pg. 1549

Fisher, Warren F., V.P.-Sls. & Mktg.--Moeller Products Co., Inc., Greenville, MS; *U.S. Private,* pg. 755

Fishlin, J., V.P.-Mktg.--U.S. Bioscience, Inc., Conshohocken, PA; *U.S. Public,* pg. 1681

Fisk, G.W., Mgr.-Mktg. & Sls.--British Steel Seamless Tubes-Wednesfield Works, Wolverhampton, United Kingdom; *Int'l,* pg. 220

Fissel, Craig, Sls. Mgr.-Mktg.--Peyton Meats, El Paso, TX; *U.S. Public,* pg. 75

Fito, Armengol Balaguero, Mgr.-Mktg.--Agropecuaria de Guissona, S. Coop. Ltda., Guisona, Spain; *Int'l,* pg. 31

Fitts, Michael, Dir.-Mktg.--Instron Corporation, Canton, MA; *U.S. Public,* pg. 882

Fitz, Bruce, V.P.-Commerical Lines Mktg.--American Manufacturers Mutual Insurance Company, Long Grove, IL; *U.S. Private,* pg. 614

Fitzenhagen, Alexander R., Dir.-Client Mktg.--The L & B Group, Dallas, TX; *U.S. Public,* pg. 1673

Fitzgerald, Brian, Dir.-Adv. & External Rels.--Ameritech Corporation, Chicago, IL; *U.S. Public,* pg. 97

Fitzgerald, Brian J., V.P.-Leasing--Washington Real Estate Investment Trust, Kensington, MD; *U.S. Public,* pg. 1743

Fitzgerald, Catherine, Mktg. Supvr.--Ingalls, Boston, MA; *U.S. Private,* pg. 562

Fitzgerald, Douglas, V.P.-Mktg.--Wallace Computer Services, Inc., Lisle, IL; *U.S. Public,* pg. 1735

Fitzgerald, Jean, Dir.-Corp. Mktg. & Brandnames--Ameritech, Milwaukee, WI; *U.S. Public,* pg. 97

Fitzgerald, Jean, Dir.-Corp. Mktg. & Brandnames--Ameritech Phone Company, Cleveland, OH; *U.S. Public,* pg. 98

Fitzgerald, Katie, Mgr.-Mktg.--Vienna Sausage Mfg. Co., Chicago, IL; *U.S. Private,* pg. 1139

Fitzgerald, Michael W., V.P.-Sls. & Mktg.--Nice-Pak Products, Inc., Orangeburg, NY; *U.S. Private,* pg. 798

Fitzgibbons, Debbie, Mgr.-Mktg. Communications & Adv.--Thermo Jarrell Ash Corporation, Franklin, MA; *U.S. Public,* pg. 1594

Fitzmaurice, Robert, Sr. V.P.-Mktg.--UST Inc., Greenwich, CT; *U.S. Public,* pg. 1660

Fitzpatrick, Michael, Mgr.-Mktg.--Orbit Valve International, Inc., Little Rock, AR; *U.S. Private,* pg. 819

Fitzpatrick, Phil, V.P.-Mktg. & Sls./Packaged Foods--Dole Food Company, Inc., Westlake Village, CA; *U.S. Public,* pg. 515

Fitzpatrick, Shawn, Mgr.-Mktg.--Crystal Geyser, Calistoga, CA; *U.S. Private,* pg. 294

Fitzpatrick, Tom, V.P.-Mktg. & Sls.--Thermal Ceramics Inc., Augusta, GA; *Int'l,* pg. 894

Fixa, Charles W., Dir.-Sls. & Mktg. & Mgr.-Adv. & Pub. Rels.--Spectrol Electronics Corporation, Ontario, CA; *U.S. Private,* pg. 351

Fjellhed, Arne, Mgr.-Mktg.--Skanska International Civil Engineering AB, Danderyd, Sweden; *Int'l,* pg. 1260

Flaemig, Horst, Dir.-Mktg.--Girmes GmbH, Grefrath, Germany; *Int'l,* pg. 552

Flaherty, James P., V.P.-Adv. & Mktg.--Nature's Bounty Inc., Bohemia, NY; *U.S. Public,* pg. 1166

Flaherty, Pat, V.P.-Mktg.--Warner Publisher Services, Inc., New York, NY; *U.S. Public,* pg. 1614

Flaherty, Sharon, V.P.-Sls., Mktg. & Client Svcs.--National Research Corporation, Lincoln, NE; *U.S. Public,* pg. 1159

Flaherty, W., Dir.-Sls.-Rubber--Farrel Corporation, Ansonia, CT; *U.S. Public,* pg. 614

Flament, Alain, Dir.-Mktg.--Giesecke & Devrient Engineering, Inc., Bedford, MA; *U.S. Private*, pg. 452
Flanagan, James, Dir.-Sls. & Mktg.--PCC Specialty Products, Inc., Worcester, MA; *U.S. Public*, pg. 1321
Flanagan, Mike, Sr. Dir.-Mktg.--Lifetouch, Portrait Studios, Eden Prairie, MN; *U.S. Private*, pg. 667
Flanagan, Steve, Mgr.-Mktg.--Chicago Title & Trust Co., Chicago, IL; *U.S. Public*, pg. 42
Flannery, John J., Sr. Mgr.-Prod. Mktg.--Ames Company, Parkersburg, WV; *U.S. Public*, pg. 1683
Flannery, Patrick, Mgr.-Mktg.--Oakhurst Dairy, Portland, ME; *U.S. Private*, pg. 809
Flathau, Robert, Dir.-New Prod. Devel.--Symons Corporation, Des Plaines, IL; *U.S. Private*, pg. 932
Flaugher, Teresa A., Dir.-Mktg. Svcs.--Weaver Popcorn Company, Inc., Van Buren, IN; *U.S. Private*, pg. 1156
Flaxer, Mark E., V.P.-Mktg./SED--Southern Electronics Corporation, Tucker, GA; *U.S. Public*, pg. 1490
Flechtner, Gretchen, Adv. & Mktg. Asst.--Webster Industries Inc., Tiffin, OH; *U.S. Private*, pg. 1157
Fleetwood, Scott, Dir.-Mktg.--FMC Corp., Agricultural Products Group, Philadelphia, PA; *U.S. Public*, pg. 605
Fleischer, Joyce S., Sr. V.P.-Mktg.--Citizens Savings Bank, Providence, RI; *Int'l*, pg. 1132
Fleischer, Joyce S., Sr. V.P.-Mktg.--Citizens Trust Company, Providence, RI; *Int'l*, pg. 1132
Fleit, Caren, V.P.-Mktg.--Guerlain, Inc., New York, NY; *Int'l*, pg. 780
Fleitz, James, Dir.-Mktg.--Speakman Company, Wilmington, DE; *U.S. Private*, pg. 1021
Fleming, Gary, Dir.-Mktg.--Baskin-Robbins Canada, Etobicoke, Canada; *Int'l*, pg. 63
Fleming, Gary, Exec.-Mktg.--NationsBank Virginia, Richmond, VA; *U.S. Public*, pg. 1163
Fleming, Jack, Bentree Real Estate Grp.--Calprop Corporation, Marina Del Rey, CA; *U.S. Public*, pg. 296
Fleming, Thomas E., V.P.-Mktg.--Mooney Chemicals, Cleveland, OH; *U.S. Public*, pg. 1208
Fleming, Tom, Dir.-Mktg.--Cape Breton Development Corporation, Glace Bay, Canada; *Int'l*, pg. 265
Flemming, Deborah, Dir.-Mktg.--Eastman Worldwide, Buffalo, NY; *U.S. Private*, pg. 358
Flemming, Melanie, Sr. Mgr.-Mktg. Communications--Xerox Imaging Systems, Inc., Peabody, MA; *U.S. Public*, pg. 1785
Fleshman, James, V.P.-Mktg. & Sls.--Consumer Products Div., San Francisco, CA; *U.S. Public*, pg. 1318
Fletcher, Peter, V.P.-Mktg., West Coast--Sony Music Entertainment, Inc., New York, NY; *Int'l*, pg. 1281
Fletcher, Roger, V.P.-Mktg.--Diamond Comic Distributors, Inc., Timonium, MD; *U.S. Private*, pg. 330
Fliegler, Ritchie, V.P.-Mktg. Amplifiers & Pro Sound--Fender Musical Instruments, Scottsdale, AZ; *U.S. Private*, pg. 400
Flik, Beer, Mktg. Dir. & Acct. Dir.--HLPB, Amsterdam, Netherlands; *Int'l*, pg. 1377
Flinn, Jeff, V.P.-Sls. & Mktg.--Spartan Tool, Mendota, IL; *U.S. Private*, pg. 860
Flint, Bill, Jr., V.P.-Mktg.--Flambeau Corporation, Baraboo, WI; *U.S. Private*, pg. 409
Flint, Richard, Mgr.-Adv. & Mktg.--Mautz Paint Co., Madison, WI; *U.S. Private*, pg. 715
Flora, Michael J., V.P.-Sls.--GuestInformant, Inc., Woodland Hills, CA; *U.S. Public*, pg. 11
Flores, Roehl, Mgr.-Mktg.--California & Hawaiian Sugar Company Inc., Crockett, CA; *U.S. Public*, pg. 39
Florian, Susana, V.P.-Sls. & Mktg.--Baker Mellon Stuart Construction, Inc., Pittsburgh, PA; *U.S. Public*, pg. 168
FlorJancic, Ronald J., Exec. V.P.-Mktg.--Consol, Pittsburgh, PA; *U.S. Public*, pg. 531
FlorJancic, Ronald J., Exec. V.P.-Mktg.--Consol, Pittsburgh, PA; *Int'l*, pg. 1081
Florsheim, John W., V.P.--Weyco Group, Inc., Milwaukee, WI; *U.S. Public*, pg. 1763
Flory, Don, Mgr.-Mktg. Services--R.A. Jones & Co. Inc., Covington, KY; *U.S. Private*, pg. 597
Flosdorff, Gerhard, Dir.-Mktg.--Hugo Boss AG, Metzingen, Germany; *Int'l*, pg. 637
Flower, Sally, Controller-Mktg. Services--Scottish & Newcastle plc, Edinburgh, United Kingdom; *Int'l*, pg. 1211
Flowers, David M., Exec. V.P.-Mktg.--AmeriSource Health Corp., Malvern, PA; *U.S. Public*, pg. 96
Floyd, Tom, Chief Mktg. Officer--Pennzoil Company, Houston, TX; *U.S. Public*, pg. 1272
Fluharty, James R., V.P.-Corp. Mktg.--IDEX Corporation, Northbrook, IL; *U.S. Public*, pg. 862
Fluri, D., Dir.-Mktg. & Sls.--Mikron AG Nidau, Nidau, Switzerland; *Int'l*, pg. 866
Flynn, James, Dir.-Sls. & Mktg.--Precision Resource Inc., Shelton, CT; *U.S. Private*, pg. 880
Flynn, Kevin, Dir.-Mktg.--Finish Line, Inc., Indianapolis, IN; *U.S. Public*, pg. 623
Flynn, Lucy A., Sr. V.P.-Corp. Mktg. & Commun.--Wang Laboratories, Inc., Billerica, MA; *U.S. Public*, pg. 1737
Flynn, Nancy, Dir.-Mktg.--Design Concepts Integration, Inc., Bloomington, MN; *U.S. Private*, pg. 572
Flynn, Steven, Exec. V.P.-Mktg.--Gramercy Pictures, Beverly Hills, CA; *U.S. Private*, pg. 468
Fobare, Pete, Grp. V.P.-Sls. & Mktg.--Oneida Ltd., Oneida, NY; *U.S. Public*, pg. 1225
Foden, Jennifer, Mgr.-Mktg.--Advanced Circuit Technology, Nashua, NH; *U.S. Private*, pg. 21
Fogarty, Paula, V.P.-Mktg.--Kindel Furniture Company, Grand Rapids, MI; *U.S. Private*, pg. 620
Fogge, Len, Exec. V.P.-Creative/Mktg. Services--Showtime Networks Inc., New York, NY; *U.S. Private*, pg. 779
Fogwell, Douglas, Sr. V.P.-Mktg.--Diners Club Inc., Chicago, IL; *U.S. Public*, pg. 377
Foley, Adrian M., V.P.-Mktg.--CalEnergy Co., Omaha, NE; *U.S. Public*, pg. 292
Foley, Daniel P., Second V.P.-Mktg. Tech.--Security Mutual Life Insurance Co. of New York, Binghamton, NY; *U.S. Private*, pg. 981
Foley, Dave, Mgr.-Mktg.-U.S. Industrial--Spraying Systems Co., Wheaton, IL; *U.S. Private*, pg. 1026
Foley, Lisa, V.P.-Mktg. & Sls.--National City Bank, Cleveland, OH; *U.S. Public*, pg. 1154
Foley, Mike, Mgr.-Mktg.--San Francisco Newspaper Agency, San Francisco, CA; *U.S. Private*, pg. 239
Foley, Ron, Mgr.-Mktg. Communications--LSI Industries, Inc., Cincinnati, OH; *U.S. Public*, pg. 971
Foley, Thomas P., V.P.-Sls. & Mktg.--DynaVac, Hingham, MA; *U.S. Private*, pg. 1076
Foley, William H., V.P.-Market Support--Grove WorldWide, Shady Grove, PA; *Int'l*, pg. 593
Folkes, Sally, Dir.-Mktg. Communications--General Binding Corporation, Northbrook, IL; *U.S. Public*, pg. 707
Folts, Jacque, Mgr.-Mktg. & Pub. Rels.--Atalanta Corporation, Elizabeth, NJ; *U.S. Private*, pg. 93
Fong, Kim, Mgr.-Mktg.--Prime Matrix Wireless Communications, Calabasas, CA; *U.S. Private*, pg. 884
Fong, Wong Ai, Gen. Mgr.-Multimedia--F. J. Benjamin Holdings Ltd., Singapore, Singapore; *Int'l*, pg. 187
Fonkalsrud, David, Mgr.-Mktg. Communications--DHL Worldwide Express, Redwood City, CA; *U.S. Private*, pg. 301
Fontana d'Avila, Eduardo, Dir.-Mktg.--Sadia Group, Barueri, Brazil; *Int'l*, pg. 1168
Fontanne, Nancy, Mgr.-Mktg. Communications--Lumonics Inc., Kanata, Canada; *Int'l*, pg. 1314
Foore, Carry, Mgr.-Catalogue Mktg.--R.R. Donnelley & Sons Company, Chicago, IL; *U.S. Public*, pg. 517
Footer, Eli, V.P.-Sls. & Mktg.--Schwartz & Benjamin, Inc., New York, NY; *U.S. Private*, pg. 974
Foran, Louis, V.P.-Als. & Mktg.--Legg Mason, Inc., Baltimore, MD; *U.S. Public*, pg. 984
Forassippi, Lee, Exec. V.P.--Chicago Fire Brick Co., Chicago, IL; *U.S. Private*, pg. 194
Forbes, Greg F., Mgr.-Mktg.--BHP Manganese, Melbourne, Australia; *Int'l*, pg. 224
Forbes, Jack, Dir.-Sls. & Mktg.--Universal Coach Parts, Inc., Des Plaines, IL; *Int'l*, pg. 326
Forbush, James S., Sr. V.P.-Catalog Sls. & Mktg.--Staples, Inc., Westborough, MA; *U.S. Public*, pg. 1509
Forcelle, Joyce, Mgr.-Intl. Sls.--WINCO, Le Center, MN; *U.S. Private*, pg. 350
Ford, Bernard R., V.P.-Intl. Mktg. & Corp. Bus. Devel.--The Scotts Company, Marysville, OH; *U.S. Public*, pg. 1446
Ford, Dennis, Dir.-Mktg. Communications--USG Corporation, Chicago, IL; *U.S. Public*, pg. 1660
Ford, Dennis, Dir.-Mktg. & Communications--USG Interiors, Inc., Chicago, IL; *U.S. Public*, pg. 1660
Ford, Don, V.P.-Sls. & Mktg.--Union Special Corp., Huntley, IL; *Int'l*, pg. 716
Ford, H. Dallas, Jr., V.P.-Residential & Commercial Mktg. & Communications--NorAm Energy Corp., Houston, TX; *U.S. Public*, pg. 843
Ford, H. Dallas, Jr., V.P.-Residential & Commercial Mktg. & Communications--Entex, Houston, TX; *U.S. Public*, pg. 843
Ford, John, Mgr.-Mktg. Svcs.--Daisy Manufacturing Company, Inc., Rogers, AR; *U.S. Private*, pg. 308
Ford, John, Sr. V.P.-Mktg. & Sls.--UDL Laboratories, Inc., Rockford, IL; *U.S. Public*, pg. 1143
Ford, Michael, Dir.-Mktg.--Swinerton Inc., San Francisco, CA; *U.S. Private*, pg. 1059
Ford, Orell, Mktg.--Regions Bank/Choctaw County, Butler, AL; *U.S. Public*, pg. 1372
Ford, V. Kevin, V.P.-Sls. & Mktg.--Kalmbach Publishing Co., Waukesha, WI; *U.S. Private*, pg. 606
Forgay, Dave, Bus. Unit Head-Coffee Mktg.--Kraft Canada Inc., Don Mills, Canada; *U.S. Public*, pg. 1288
Forget, Gerard, V.P.-Sls. & Mktg.--Gaz Metropolitain & Company, Montreal, Canada; *Int'l*, pg. 541
Forhan, Phillip, Dir.-Bus. Devel.--Active Tool & Manufacturing Co., Inc., Roseville, MI; *U.S. Private*, pg. 16
Fornal, Bob, V.P.-Sls. & Mktg.--S.P. Richards Co., Smyrna, GA; *U.S. Public*, pg. 732
Fornasier, Diane, V.P.-Mktg. & Bus. Admin.-Universal New Media Software--Universal Studios, Inc., Universal City, CA; *Int'l*, pg. 1215
Fornataro, Mark, Mgr.-Mktg. Communications--Overnite Transportation Co., Richmond, VA; *U.S. Public*, pg. 1668
Forni, Jim, V.P.-Sls. & Mktg.--Bradley Printing Company, Des Plaines, IL; *U.S. Public*, pg. 1778
Forrest, Jennifer, Mktg. Asst.--Coscient-Astral Distribution, Toronto, Canada; *Int'l*, pg. 335
Forsans, Susan, Mgr.-Mktg.--Phoenix Learning Resources, New York, NY; *U.S. Private*, pg. 863
Forster, Jilly, Dir.-Strategic Mktg.--The Body Shop International, Littlehampton, United Kingdom; *Int'l*, pg. 199
Forster, Tim, Dir.-Mktg.--Modo Merchants Ltd., Byfleet, United Kingdom; *Int'l*, pg. 886
Forsyth, Curtis, V.P.-Mktg.--Healthsource New York, De Witt, NY; *U.S. Public*, pg. 360
Forsyth, Dana, Dir.-Mktg.--Catalina Marketing Corporation, Saint Petersburg, FL; *U.S. Public*, pg. 314
Fortgang, Adam, Dir.-Mktg.--Princeton University Press, Princeton, NJ; *U.S. Private*, pg. 885
Forti, Patty, V.P.-Adv. & Mktg.--Huffman Koos, River Edge, NJ; *U.S. Private*, pg. 546
Fortier, Bud, Mgr.-Mktg.--Hano Document Printers, Inc., Conyers, GA; *U.S. Public*, pg. 1686
Fortier, James E., V.P.-Mktg.-Lancaster Colony Automotive Group--Lancaster Colony Automotive Group, Dublin, OH; *U.S. Public*, pg. 977
Fortier, L., V.P.-Sls. & Mktg.--La Brasserie Labatt Limitee, La Salle, Canada; *Int'l*, pg. 679
Fortin, Mark, Mgr.-Sls.--Accurate Forging Corp., Bristol, CT; *Int'l*, pg. 391
Fortis, Jerry, Sr. V.P. & Dir.-Mktg.--RAM Golf Corporation, Melrose Park, IL; *U.S. Private*, pg. 908
Fortney, Cynthia M., V.P.--Fidelity Federal Savings Bank, Marion, IN; *U.S. Public*, pg. 632
Fortune, Connie, Dir.-Mktg.--SAIC Canada, Ottawa, Canada; *U.S. Private*, pg. 976
Foss, Adam, Corp. Commun. Officer--GN Great Nordic Ltd., Copenhagen, Denmark; *Int'l*, pg. 536
Foss, Lisa, V.P.-Mktg. & Computer Sys. Grp.--NCR Corporation, Dayton, OH; *U.S. Public*, pg. 1146
Fost, Dennis L., V.P.-Mktg. & Comml. Devel.--Mona Industries, Inc., Paterson, NJ; *U.S. Private*, pg. 756
Foster, Allan, V.P.-Sls. & Mktg.--J.W. Allen & Company, Wheeling, IL; *U.S. Private*, pg. 37
Foster, Cassandra, Mgr.-Land--Maynard Oil Co., Dallas, TX; *U.S. Public*, pg. 1064
Foster, Craig, V.P.-Sls. & Mktg.--Capital Pacific Holdings, Newport Beach, CA; *U.S. Public*, pg. 302
Foster, Douglas J., V.P.-Sls. & Mktg.--Emery Worldwide, Redwood City, CA; *U.S. Public*, pg. 281
Foster, F.S., Mgr.-Mktg. & Adv.--Electroid Co., Springfield, NJ; *U.S. Private*, pg. 369
Foster, Gary, V.P.-Mktg.--The Foxboro Company, Foxboro, MA; *Int'l*, pg. 1243
Foster, George, Dir.-Mktg.--Pacific Coast Building Products Inc., Sacramento, CA; *U.S. Private*, pg. 830
Foster, Gordon, Mgr.-Sls. & Mktg.--Royale Coach, Elkhart, IN; *U.S. Public*, pg. 1123
Foster, Jim, V.P.-Sls. & Mktg.--Tweddle Litho Company, Clinton Township, MI; *U.S. Private*, pg. 1111
Foster, John R., V.P.-Sls. & Mktg.--Caraustar Industries, Inc., Austell, GA; *U.S. Public*, pg. 303
Foster, Lawrence, V.P.-Sls. & Mktg.--Lawnware Products, Inc., Morton Grove, IL; *U.S. Private*, pg. 653
Foster, Lawrence, V.P.-Sls. & Mktg.--Ingrid Division of Lawnware, Morton Grove, IL; *U.S. Private*, pg. 654
Foster, Michael, Dir.-Mktg.--Wells Fargo Alarm Services, Inc., King of Prussia, PA; *U.S. Public*, pg. 246
Foster, Michael S., V.P.-Worldwide Sls. & Mktg., PC/SF--Shipley Co., LLC, Marlborough, MA; *U.S. Public*, pg. 1403
Foster, Sheila, V.P.-Mktg. Communications--Database America Companies, Montvale, NJ; *U.S. Private*, pg. 312
Fouche, J.A.L., Dir.-Mktg.--Distillers Corporation S.A., Stellenbosch, South Africa; *Int'l*, pg. 1129
Foulkes-Jones, Robert, Chief Exec. Officer--Brammer plc, Altrincham, United Kingdom; *Int'l*, pg. 212
Foundeur, Paula, Mgr.-Information Mktg.--People, New York, NY; *U.S. Public*, pg. 1613
Fountain, Brad, Controller-Sls. & Mktg.--Jami, Inc., Shawnee Mission, KS; *U.S. Private*, pg. 581
Fourmann, Jeanne, Dir.-Mktg.--Banque Internationale a Luxembourg S.A., Luxembourg, Luxembourg; *Int'l*, pg. 162
Foust, Carolyn, Dir.-Mktg.--Indianapolis Newspapers, Inc., Indianapolis, IN; *U.S. Public*, pg. 326
Foust, George, Dir.-Sls.--Delta Foremost Chemical Corp., Memphis, TN; *U.S. Private*, pg. 322
Fowler, Alan L., V.P.-Mktg.--James N. Gray Construction Co., Inc., Lexington, KY; *U.S. Private*, pg. 472
Fowler, C. Thomas, Sr. V.P.-Mktg.--Motion Industries, Inc., Irondale, AL; *U.S. Public*, pg. 732
Fowler, Fred V., III, V.P.-Adv. & Sls.--Fred V. Fowler Company, Inc., Newton, MA; *U.S. Private*, pg. 422
Fox, Charles, V.P.-Hard Wire--Xilinx, Inc., San Jose, CA; *U.S. Public*, pg. 1786
Fox, David, Mktg. Coord.--LiphaTech, Inc., Milwaukee, WI; *Int'l*, pg. 812
Fox, Douglas, V.P.-Mktg.--International Paper Company, Purchase, NY; *U.S. Public*, pg. 901
Fox, Eva-Marie, V.P.-Mktg.--T & S Brass & Bronze Works, Inc., Travelers Rest, SC; *U.S. Private*, pg. 1061
Fox, Herbert A., Jr., V.P.--Murphy Oil Corporation, El Dorado, AR; *U.S. Public*, pg. 1141
Fox, John W., Jr., V.P.-Coal Mktg.--Norfolk Southern Corporation, Norfolk, VA; *U.S. Public*, pg. 1190
Fox, John W., Jr., V.P.-Coal Mktg.--Norfolk Southern Railway Company, Norfolk, VA; *U.S. Public*, pg. 1191
Fox, Keith, V.P.-Corp. Mktg.--Cisco Systems, Inc., San Jose, CA; *U.S. Public*, pg. 375
Fox, Kerri, Dir.-Corp. Mktg.--Gruner + Jahr USA Publishing, Inc., New York, NY; *Int'l*, pg. 190
Fox, Laura, V.P.-Electrical Retailing & Catalog Mktg.--Kent & Spiegel Direct, Culver City, CA; *U.S. Private*, pg. 615
Fox, Mary Lou, Sr. V.P.-Mktg.--Omnicare, Inc., Covington, KY; *U.S. Public*, pg. 1223
Fox, Sandra, Dir.-Mktg.--Thomson & Thomson, Quincy, MA; *U.S. Public*, pg. 1601
Fox, Susan S., V.P.-Consumer Mktg.--Wm. Wrigley Jr. Company, Chicago, IL; *U.S. Public*, pg. 1781
Fox, Will, Mgr.-Mktg.--Walter Lorenz Surgical, Inc., Jacksonville, FL; *U.S. Public*, pg. 231
Foy, Donna, Dir.-Mktg.--House of Raeford Farms, Inc., Raeford, NC; *U.S. Private*, pg. 542
Foy, Ron, Dir.-Mktg.--Baldwin Hardware Corporation, Reading, PA; *U.S. Public*, pg. 1053
Fraga, Cheryl, Mgr.-Mktg.--Thomas Lighting-C&I Outdoor Division, San Leandro, CA; *U.S. Public*, pg. 1599
Fraioli, Dennis, V.P.-Sls. & Mktg.--Jeneric/Pentron Corp., Wallingford, CT; *U.S. Private*, pg. 298
Fraker, Karen, V.P.-Mktg.--The Fifth Third Bank of Northwestern Ohio, National Association, Toledo, OH; *U.S. Public*, pg. 622
Frame, Mark, Product/Brand Mgr.--Russell Stover Candies, Inc., Kansas City, MO; *U.S. Private*, pg. 953
Framke, Donna, V.P.-Adv. & Mktg.--Beverly Bancorporation Inc., Chicago, IL; *U.S. Public*, pg. 227
Franceschi, Connie, Dir.-Mktg.--Harmony Foods Corporation, Santa Cruz, CA; *U.S. Private*, pg. 503
Francis, David, Mgr.-Mktg.--Fred V. Fowler Company, Inc., Newton, MA; *U.S. Private*, pg. 422
Francis, Karen, V.P.-Mktg.--Empire Berol U.S.A., Brentwood, TN; *U.S. Public*, pg. 1178
Francis, Scott, Dir.-Mktg.--Dean Pickle & Specialty Products Co., Green Bay, WI; *U.S. Public*, pg. 490
Francis, T. Sanford, V.P. & Mgr.-Mktg.--Windsor Industries, Inc., Englewood, CO; *U.S. Private*, pg. 1182

Francken, Rene, Dir.-Sls. & Mktg.--Montair Andersen B.V., Sevenum, Netherlands; *U.S. Public*, pg. 462
Francoeur, Lucie, Dir.-Mktg.--Air Alliance, Sainte-Foy, Canada; *Int'l*, pg. 36
Francolini, Angie, Dir.-Mktg.--McCormick Canada, Ltd., London, Canada; *U.S. Public*, pg. 1067
Frangipane, Joe, Exec. V.P.-Sls. & Mktg. (U.S. & Canada)--Alcan Cable Division, Atlanta, GA; *Int'l*, pg. 50
Frank, J. Louis, Exec. V.P.-Marathon Oil Co.--USX Corporation, Pittsburgh, PA; *U.S. Public*, pg. 1661
Frank, J. Louis, Exec. V.P.-Refining, Mktg. & Transportation--Marathon Oil Company, Houston, TX; *U.S. Public*, pg. 1661
Frank, Jeff, V.P.-Sls. & Mktg.--POLESTAR Labs, Inc., Escondido, CA; *U.S. Private*, pg. 874
Frank, Jim, V.P.-Mdsg.--Wickes Inc., Vernon Hills, IL; *U.S. Public*, pg. 1391
Frank, Joan, Mgr.-Mktg.--Medline Industries, Inc., Mundelein, IL; *U.S. Private*, pg. 728
Frank, Tom, Mgr.-Mktg.--Procter & Gamble Pharmaceuticals, Inc., Cincinnati, OH; *U.S. Public*, pg. 1331
Franke, Donna, Dir.-Mktg.--Beverly National Bank, Wilmington, IL; *U.S. Public*, pg. 227
Franke, Steve R., V.P.-Mktg.--Nautilus Insurance Company, Scottsdale, AZ; *U.S. Public*, pg. 216
Frankel, Eileen, Dir.-Mktg.--Cole Vision Corporation, Cleveland, OH; *U.S. Public*, pg. 396
Frankel, Norman, V.P.-Sls. & Mktg.--Standard Textile Co., Inc., Cincinnati, OH; *U.S. Private*, pg. 1032
Frankel, Richard, V.P.-Sls. & Mktg.--Universal Industrial Products Co., Pioneer, OH; *U.S. Public*, pg. 1677
Frankhouser, Paul L., V.P.-Mktg.--Arrow International, Inc., Reading, PA; *U.S. Public*, pg. 135
Frankiewicz, Anita, Dir.-Mktg.--Restonic Mattress Corporation, Rosemont, IL; *U.S. Private*, pg. 925
Franklin, David, Dir.-Mktg., Sls. & Automation--Brodart Company, Williamsport, PA; *U.S. Private*, pg. 170
Franklin, Ellen, V.P.-Sls. & Mktg.--Wizards of the Coast, Renton, WA; *U.S. Private*, pg. 1185
Franklin, Ellen, V.P.-Sls. & Mktg.--TSR, Inc., Renton, WA; *U.S. Private*, pg. 1185
Franklin, James R., V.P.-Sls. & Mktg.--Sellstrom Manufacturing Co., Palatine, IL; *U.S. Private*, pg. 983
Franklin, John R., Mgr.-Mktg. & Adv.--Baltimore Stationery Co./Total Office, Baltimore, MD; *U.S. Private*, pg. 113
Franklin, Richard, V.P.-Sls. & Mktg.--Garden State Paper Co., Inc., Elmwood Park, NJ; *U.S. Public*, pg. 1078
Franklin, Ronald, Exec. V.P. & Mktg. Services Dir.--Don Coleman Advertising, Inc., Southfield, MI; *U.S. Private*, pg. 251
Franks, Debra, Coord.-Mktg.--Barco of California, Gardena, CA; *U.S. Private*, pg. 115
Franks, J.E., Mgr.-Mktg. Communications--WESCO Distribution, Inc., Pittsburgh, PA; *U.S. Private*, pg. 244
Franks, John, Dir.-Mktg.--Astec Europe Limited, Stourbridge, United Kingdom; *Int'l*, pg. 93
Fransen, F., Dir.-Mktg. & Mgr.-Sls. Promo & Mdsg.--Sidmar N.V., Gent, Belgium; *Int'l*, pg. 79
Franz, Earl, Dir.-Mktg./Honeycomb Bus. Unit--Hunter Douglas, Inc., Upper Saddle River, NJ; *Int'l*, pg. 639
Franz, Pam, Dir.-Mktg.--Modern Controls, Inc., Minneapolis, MN; *U.S. Public*, pg. 1120
Franzese, Stephen, V.P.-Interactive Mktg.--Apple Computer, Inc., Cupertino, CA; *U.S. Public*, pg. 121
Frasch, Richard, Mgr.-Mktg.--Cargill Animal Nutrition Div., Minneapolis, MN; *U.S. Private*, pg. 210
Frasco, Dave, Dir.-Mktg.--Chyron Corp., Melville, NY; *Int'l*, pg. 1372
Fraser, Alex, Mgr.-Mktg.--Kaman Music Corp., Bloomfield, CT; *U.S. Public*, pg. 942
Fraser, Heidi, Admin.-Mktg.--Au Bon Pain Co., Inc., Boston, MA; *U.S. Public*, pg. 146
Fraser, James D., Dir.-Mktg.--Brewster Transport Co. Ltd., Banff, Canada; *U.S. Public*, pg. 1719
Fraser, John, Dir.-Mktg.--Vanguard Plastics, Inc., Mc Pherson, KS; *U.S. Private*, pg. 1134
Frash, Bill, V.P.-Bus. Devel.--Carat ICG, Los Angeles, CA; *U.S. Private*, pg. 207
Frazier, Walter, V.P.-Sls. & Mktg.--Roller Derby Skate Corp., Litchfield, IL; *U.S. Private*, pg. 941
Frederick, Glen, V.P.-Mktg.--Harvey Industries, Inc., Waltham, MA; *U.S. Private*, pg. 508
Frederick, Marty, Dir.-Mktg. Opers.--Lawson Software, Minneapolis, MN; *U.S. Private*, pg. 654
Frederick, Robert A., V.P. & Dir.-Mktg.--Omega Financial Corporation, State College, PA; *U.S. Public*, pg. 1222
Frederick, Robert A., V.P. & Dir.-Mktg. & Pub. Rels.--Peoples National Bank of Central Pennsylvania, State College, PA; *U.S. Public*, pg. 1222
Frederick, William A., Pres.-Special Markets Div.--Thomas & Betts Corporation, Memphis, TN; *U.S. Public*, pg. 1597
Fredrick, William A., Pres.-Special Mkts. Div.--Thomas & Betts Reznor Division, Memphis, TN; *U.S. Public*, pg. 1598
Fredrickson, Gary, Dir.-Sls. & Mktg.--Diehl Machines, Wabash, IN; *U.S. Public*, pg. 944
Fredriksen, Fleming, Mktg. Mgr.--Intralox A/S, Hjorring, Denmark; *U.S. Private*, pg. 643
Freeborn, Bill, V.P.-Sls. & Mktg.--CSC United States, Wilmington, DE; *U.S. Private*, pg. 197
Freed, Gene, V.P.-Special Mkts.--Durex Consumer Products, Norcross, GA; *Int'l*, pg. 815
Freed, Vicki, Sr. V.P.-Sls. & Mktg.--Carnival Corporation, Miami, FL; *U.S. Public*, pg. 306
Freedlander, Terry, Dir.-Mktg.--Pacificare Health Systems, Santa Ana, CA; *U.S. Public*, pg. 1251
Freeland, Bethany, Mgr.-Mktg.--Renosol Corp., Saline, MI; *U.S. Private*, pg. 922
Freeman-Cardone, Marian, Mgr.-Mktg. Communications--Anorad Corporation, Hauppauge, NY; *U.S. Private*, pg. 75
Freeman, Donald W., Sr. V.P.-Bus. Devel.--Rentenbach Engineering Company, Knoxville, TN; *U.S. Private*, pg. 923
Freeman, Jill, V.P.-Mktg.--Freeman Cosmetic Corp., Los Angeles, CA; *U.S. Private*, pg. 426
Freeman, John, Chief Oper. Officer, V.P.-Sls. & Mktg.--Johnson & Quin, Inc., Niles, IL; *U.S. Private*, pg. 590
Freeman, Lawrence, Dir.-Circulation--Forbes, Inc., New York, NY; *U.S. Private*, pg. 417
Freeman, Randy, V.P.-Global Mktg.--Rockwell Automation, Milwaukee, WI; *U.S. Public*, pg. 1397
Freeman, Ronald L., V.P. & Mgr.-Mktg.--Willis Corroon Corp. of Chattanooga, Chattanooga, TN; *Int'l*, pg. 1505
Freeman, Stephen, V.P.-Alloy Prods.--Brush Wellman Inc., Cleveland, OH; *U.S. Public*, pg. 266
Freeman, Steve, V.P.-Mktg.--Knoll Pharmaceutical Company, Whippany, NJ; *Int'l*, pg. 105
Freeman, Tina, Dir.-Mktg.--Prince Foods Div., Lowell, MA; *U.S. Private*, pg. 158
Freeman, Wayne, Mgr.-Mktg.--Otari Corporation, Foster City, CA; *Int'l*, pg. 1013
Freeze, Cynthia J., Mgr.-Mktg. Services--Kewaunee Scientific Corporation, Statesville, NC; *U.S. Public*, pg. 953
Freitas, Ken, V.P.-Mktg. & Adv.--The Timberland Company, Stratham, NH; *U.S. Public*, pg. 1609
Freitas, Stephen, V.P.-Mktg.--Eller Media Company, Phoenix, AZ; *U.S. Public*, pg. 383
Freiwald, Ray, Mgr.-Adv. Support--Warner Electric Industrial Products Division, South Beloit, IL; *U.S. Public*, pg. 480
French, James, V.P.-Mktg.--Airguard Industries Inc., Louisville, KY; *U.S. Public*, pg. 382
French, Nick, Mgr.-Reg. Mktg.--Sasol Chemicals Pacific Limited, Wan Chai, Hong Kong; *Int'l*, pg. 1196
French, Tom, Dir.-Mktg.--Famous Footwear, Madison, WI; *U.S. Public*, pg. 262
Frericks, Peter, Chief Exec. Officer & Gen. Mgr.--Sandoz Pharma Ltd., Eden Terrace, New Zealand; *Int'l*, pg. 985
Freschi, John, V.P.-Sls. & Mktg.--Country Home Bakery, Inc., Bridgeport, CT; *U.S. Private*, pg. 278
Freshwater, Georgia, Asst. V.P.-Mktg.--First Interstate Bank of Oregon, N.A., Portland, OR; *U.S. Public*, pg. 1753
Freudenberger, Kent W., Exec. V.P.-Mktg. Div.--Airborne Freight Corporation, Seattle, WA; *U.S. Public*, pg. 32
Freuler, Susan, Mgr.-Mktg. Services--The Vendo Company, Fresno, CA; *Int'l*, pg. 1184
Freund, Irv, Dir.-Mktg.--M.C. Gill Corporation, El Monte, CA; *U.S. Private*, pg. 453
Freundlich, David, V.P.-Mktg.--Elscint Ltd., Haifa, Israel; *Int'l, pg. 450*
Frey, James E., V.P.-Bus. Devel.--J.S. Alberici Construction Co., Inc., Saint Louis, MO; *U.S. Private*, pg. 32
Frey, Lawrence D., Sr. V.P.-Sls. & Mktg.--The Buschman Co., Cincinnati, OH; *U.S. Private*, pg. 188
Friberg, Peter A., Sr. V.P.-Memorial Sls. & Dir.-Sls. & Mktg.--Rock of Ages Corporation, Graniteville, VT; *U.S. Public*, pg. 1396
Frick, Charles, Dir.-Mktg.--Quintana Petroleum Corp., Houston, TX; *U.S. Private*, pg. 901
Friday, Sally, Dir.-Mktg.--Amurcon Corporation, Southfield, MI; *U.S. Private*, pg. 69
Fried, Betty, Dir.-Mktg. Commun.--SAS Institute Inc., Cary, NC; *U.S. Private*, pg. 966
Fried, Robert, Sr. V.P.-Mktg.--Signature Eyewear, Inc., Inglewood, CA; *U.S. Public*, pg. 1473
Frieden, David, V.P.-Sls. & Mktg.--Iowa Precision Industries, Cedar Rapids, IA; *U.S. Public*, pg. 1100
Friedle, Jurgen, Dr., Mng. Dir.--TosoHaas GmbH, Stuttgart, Germany; *Int'l*, pg. 1408
Friedman, David M., V.P.-Mktg.--United States Cellular Corporation, Chicago, IL; *U.S. Public*, pg. 1572
Friedman, Ira S., V.P.-Mktg.--Boston Acoustics, Inc., Peabody, MA; *U.S. Public*, pg. 246
Friedman, Mark, V.P.-Mktg.--Compnay Store--Hanover Direct, Inc., Weehawken, NJ; *U.S. Public*, pg. 782
Friedmann, Andrea, Mktg. Comm. Specialist--Yuasa-Exide, Inc., Reading, PA; *Int'l*, pg. 1522
Friedson-Garrett, Barbara, Pres.-Windmere U.S. Sls. & Mktg.--Windmere-Durable Holdings, Hialeah, FL; *U.S. Public*, pg. 1771
Friel, Eunan, Dir.-Mktg.--Johnson & Johnson (Ireland) Ltd., Dublin, Ireland; *U.S. Public*, pg. 930
Friel, John P., Sr. V.P. & Gen. Mgr.--Medrad, Inc., Indianola, PA; *Int'l*, pg. 1204
Friend, Howard, Pres.--On-Cor Frozen Foods Inc., Northbrook, IL; *U.S. Private*, pg. 817
Friend, Kent, Sr. V.P.-Sls. & Mktg.--Kraco Enterprises, Inc., Compton, CA; *U.S. Private*, pg. 634
Friend, N., Dir.-Mktg.--Swish Products Ltd., Tamworth, United Kingdom; *Int'l*, pg. 925
Friend, Ross D., Sr. V.P., Gen. Counsel & Sec.--The Franklin Life Insurance Company, Springfield, IL; *U.S. Public*, pg. 76
Friese, Marianne, Partner & Global Brand Mktg. Dir.--Ketchum Public Relations, GmbH, Munich, Germany; *U.S. Private*, pg. 617
Friesen, Kevin, Dir.-Mktg.--A&W Food Services of Canada Inc., North Vancouver, Canada; *Int'l*, pg. 1
Frinier, Richard, Exec. V.P.-Design & Mktg.--Brown Jordan Company, El Monte, CA; *U.S. Private*, pg. 174
Frisk, Lars, Dir.-Sls. & Mktg.--AGA Ges.m.b.H., Vienna, Austria; *Int'l*, pg. 13
Fritts, W. Allen, Sr. V.P.-Sls. & Mktg.--Fire Lite Alarms, Inc./Notifier Co., Northford, CT; *U.S. Public*, pg. 1306
Fritz, Bruce, V.P.-Comml. Mktg.--Kemper Insurance Companies, Long Grove, IL; *U.S. Private*, pg. 614
Fritz, Bruce, V.P. Commercial Lines Mktg.--Lumbermen's Mutual Casualty Company, Long Grove, IL; *U.S. Private*, pg. 614
Fritz, Bruce, V.P.-Commercial Lines Mktg.--American Motorists Insurance Co., Long Grove, IL; *U.S. Private*, pg. 614
Fritz, Bruce, V.P.-Commercial Lines Mktg.--American Protection Insurance Co., Long Grove, IL; *U.S. Private*, pg. 614
Fritz, Norbert, Dr., Sr. Gen. Mgr.--Heidelberger Zement A.G., Heidelberg, Germany; *Int'l*, pg. 605
Fritzson, Paul, Sr. V.P.-Mktg., Mdsg. & Distrib.--Hannaford Bros. Co., Scarborough, ME; *U.S. Public*, pg. 781
Froehlich, Randy W., Dir.-Mktg.-Commercial Prods.--Pre Finish Metals Incorporated, Elk Grove Village, IL; *U.S. Public*, pg. 1056
Fromm, Julie, Mgr.-Mktg. Svcs.--Pacific Trail Inc., Seattle, WA; *U.S. Private*, pg. 673
Froreich, Keith, V.P.-Mktg.--Sizzler International, Inc., Los Angeles, CA; *U.S. Public*, pg. 1475
Fross, Vern, Sr. V.P.-Sls. & Mktg.--Ingram Entertainment Inc., La Vergne, TN; *U.S. Private*, pg. 563
Frost, Richard, Dir.-Mktg.--Cadbury Limited, Birmingham, United Kingdom; *Int'l*, pg. 248
Frost, Woody, V.P.-Mktg.--DataCard Equipment, Minnetonka, MN; *U.S. Private*, pg. 312
Fruth, Steve, Dir.-Mktg.--Fostoria Industries, Inc., Fostoria, OH; *U.S. Private*, pg. 421
Fry, G. Rogan, Dir.-Sls. & Mktg.--Conley Frog/Switch & Forge Co., Memphis, TN; *U.S. Private*, pg. 263
Frye, Arlene Y., Dir.-Mktg. & Client Relations--General Electric Investment Corp., Stamford, CT; *U.S. Public*, pg. 712
Frye, Bob, V.P.-Mktg.--FieldBrook Farms, Inc., Dunkirk, NY; *U.S. Private*, pg. 403
Frye, Christine, V.P.-Mktg.--ALLTEL Corporation, Little Rock, AR; *U.S. Public*, pg. 55
Frye, Harvey J., V.P.-Sls. & Mktg.--Trikon Technologies Inc., Chatsworth, CA; *U.S. Public*, pg. 1638
Fryman, Margaret R., V.P.-Mktg.--Stonhard, Inc., Maple Shade, NJ; *U.S. Public*, pg. 1358
Fuchs, Robert, Dir.-Mktg.--Schweizer Verband der Raiffeisenbanken, Saint Gallen, Switzerland; *Int'l*, pg. 1211
Fuchs, Wilhelm, Exec. V.P.--Stora Feldmuhle AG, Dusseldorf, Germany; *Int'l*, pg. 1303
Fudun, Neil, V.P. & Creative Dir.--Macy's East, New York, NY; *U.S. Public*, pg. 618
Fuenzalida, Sergio F., V.P.-Mktg.--Minera Escondida Limitada, Santiago, Chile; *Int'l*, pg. 227
Fuerst, Chuck, Coord.-Mktg.--Computer Network Technology Corporation, Minneapolis, MN; *U.S. Public*, pg. 421
Fuggetta, Vincent, Asst. Gen. Mgr.-Mktg.-A.C.--Aromat Corporation, New Providence, NJ; *Int'l*, pg. 847
Fujahara, Mary, V.P.-Mktg.--Atari Games Corporation, Milpitas, CA; *U.S. Public*, pg. 1727
Fujimoto, Shiro, V.P.-Mktg.--Mutoh America Inc., Phoenix, AZ; *Int'l*, pg. 897
Fujiwara, Setsuraku, Dir.-Mkt. Devel.--Sankyo Company Limited, Tokyo, Japan; *Int'l*, pg. 1189
Fukuchi, Hiroshi, Mgr.-Mktg.--O.S. Engines Mfg. Co., Ltd., Osaka, Japan; *Int'l*, pg. 531
Fukumuro, K., V.P.-Mktg./Clocks--SEIKO Corporation of America, Mahwah, NJ; *Int'l*, pg. 1218
Fuldner, John E., Mgr.-Mktg. & Adv.--Efco Corporation, Monett, MO; *U.S. Private*, pg. 353
Fulford, John H., III, Sr. V.P.-Mktg.--Federal National Mortgage Association (Fannie Mae), Washington, DC; *U.S. Public*, pg. 615
Fulks, Robert, Dir.-Mktg.--Weatherford Enterra Incorporated, Houston, TX; *U.S. Public*, pg. 1749
Fuller, Devra, Mgr.-Mktg. Communications--Decibel Products, Inc., Dallas, TX; *U.S. Public*, pg. 46
Fuller, Leslie, Mgr.-Mktg.--Research, Incorporated, Eden Prairie, MN; *U.S. Public*, pg. 1382
Fullerton, D. Rush, V.P.-Sls. & Mktg., Gen. Mgr.--Sandvik Sorting Systems, Louisville, KY; *Int'l*, pg. 1186
Fullerton, Danny, Sr. V.P.-Strategy-P/C Company--Nationwide Insurance Enterprise, Columbus, OH; *U.S. Private*, pg. 788
Fullington, William, Dir.-Mktg. Svcs.--The Richard E. Jacobs Group, Westlake, OH; *U.S. Private*, pg. 580
Fullmer, John H., Chief Mktg. Officer & Sr. V.P.--CUC International, Inc., Stamford, CT; *U.S. Public*, pg. 320
Fumagalli, Aldo, Dir.-Commercial & Product Mgr.-Gasfire & Kelvinator--Candy S.p.A., Brugherio, Italy; *Int'l*, pg. 259
Fumagalli, Beppe, Dir.-Mktg. & Product Mgr.-Candy--Candy S.p.A., Brugherio, Italy; *Int'l*, pg. 259
Funck, G.P., V.P.-Mktg.--IDenticard Systems, Inc., Lancaster, PA; *U.S. Private*, pg. 557
Funk, Edmund, Dr., Dir.-Mktg.--Sun Chemical General Printing Inc., Northlake, IL; *Int'l*, pg. 370
Fuqua, Gary, V.P.-Mktg.--UNR Home Products Div., Ruston, LA; *U.S. Public*, pg. 1404
Fuqua, Mark, Dir.-Mktg.--Midcoast Energy Resources, Inc., Houston, TX; *U.S. Public*, pg. 1109
Furlong, Mark, V.P.-Mktg.--American Machine & Tool Company, Inc., Royersford, PA; *U.S. Private*, pg. 58
Furman, Diana, Mgr.-Dir. Mktg.--Caswell-Massey Co. Ltd., Edison, NJ; *U.S. Private*, pg. 219
Furnandez, Donna, V.P.-Sls. & Mktg. Admin.--Johnson & Johnson Medical, Inc., Arlington, TX; *U.S. Public*, pg. 928
Furr, Caroline, Mgr.-Mktg. Programs--Spirit Cruises, Inc., Norfolk, VA; *Int'l*, pg. 1274
Furst, Ditlef, Sr. V.P.-Mktg.--BT Industries AB, Mjolby, Sweden; *Int'l*, pg. 123
Fusco, Lynn R., V.P.-Mktg.--The Fusco Corporation, New Haven, CT; *U.S. Private*, pg. 432
Fusco, Tim, V.P.-Sls., Mktg. & Res. Information--UMI, Ann Arbor, MI; *U.S. Public*, pg. 201
Gabe, Jon, V.P.-Sls. & Mktg.--Fred Usinger, Inc., Milwaukee, WI; *U.S. Private*, pg. 1129
Gabelier, Philippe, V.P.-Pub. Affairs--Caisse de depot et placement du Quebec, Montreal, Canada; *Int'l*, pg. 249
Gable, James, V.P.-AppleSoft Mktg.--Apple Computer, Inc., Cupertino, CA; *U.S. Public*, pg. 121
Gable, Lydia, Grp. Dir.-Mktg.--Sega of America Inc., Redwood City, CA; *Int'l*, pg. 1218

Gable, William H., V.P.-Sls. & Mktg.--Alabama Metal Industries Corporation, Birmingham, AL; *U.S. Private*, pg. 30

Gabriel, Ralph, Mgr.-Mktg.--R.S. Owens, Chicago, IL; *U.S. Private*, pg. 824

Gabuzda, George, V.P.-Sls. & Mktg.--Electronics Division-Materials, Bear, DE; *U.S. Public*, pg. 165

Gadbois, Ray, V.P.-Corp. Mktg.--PeopleSoft, Inc., Pleasanton, CA; *U.S. Public*, pg. 1276

Gade, Bill, Dir.-Mktg.--Hubbard Feeds Inc., Mankato, MN; *Int'l*, pg. 1116

Gaffin, Mark, Mgr.-Corp. Mktg.--American Packaging Corporation, Philadelphia, PA; *U.S. Private*, pg. 60

Gaffney, Matthew, V.P.-Worldwide Mktg. & Sls.--Virginia Tourism Corp., Richmond, VA; *U.S. Private*, pg. 1141

Gaffney, Tina, Mgr.-Mktg. Svcs.--Thomas Publishing Company, New York, NY; *U.S. Private*, pg. 1082

Gaffney, Tony T., V.P.-Mktg.--Strategic Technology Services, Cerritos, CA; *Int'l*, pg. 1154

Gagliano, Charles, Exec. V.P.-Mktg.--Pepsi-Cola General Bottlers, Inc., Rolling Meadows, IL; *U.S. Public*, pg. 1277

Gagliardi, Ed, V.P.-Mktg.--Colgate-Palmolive Co., Institutional Products Div., Tenafly, NJ; *U.S. Public*, pg. 397

Gagliardi, Joseph, V.P.-Mktg.--Hertz Equipment Rental Corp., Park Ridge, NJ; *U.S. Public*, pg. 664

Gagliardi, T., Mgr.-Mktg. Svcs.--RFL Electronics, Inc., Boonton, NJ; *U.S. Private*, pg. 903

Gagnon, Luc, Dir.-Mktg. & Sls./Retail--Aliments Flamingo, Iberville, Canada; *Int'l*, pg. 57

Gagnon, Norbert, Dir.-Mktg.--Aliments Flamingo, Iberville, Canada; *Int'l*, pg. 57

Gagnon, Pierre, Sr. Grp. V.P.-Sls. & Mktg.--Mitsubishi Motor Sales of America, Inc., Cypress, CA; *Int'l*, pg. 875

Gaige, Chris, Dir.-Mktg. & Sls.--MascoTech Tubular Products, Inc., Canton, MI; *U.S. Public*, pg. 1055

Gaines, Robert, Dir.-Mktg.--Remington Products Company, L.L.C., Bridgeport, CT; *U.S. Private*, pg. 921

Gaines, Tami C., Mgr.-Mktg.--American Safety Razor Company, Verona, VA; *U.S. Private*, pg. 597

Gaiss, Michael, V.P.-Mktg.--IQ Software Corporation, Norcross, GA; *U.S. Public*, pg. 858

Gaither, Tom, V.P.-Mktg.--Epsilon/West, San Francisco, CA; *U.S. Public*, pg. 74

Galamba, Marienne J., Coord.-Mktg.--Galamba Metals, Inc., Kansas City, KS; *U.S. Private*, pg. 437

Galbraith, Ted, V.P.-Mktg.--Foxworth-Galbraith Lumber Co., Dallas, TX; *U.S. Private*, pg. 423

Gale, Nelson, V.P.-Mtkg. & Sls.--AmeriServe of Norcross, Norcross, GA; *U.S. Private*, pg. 533

Galhi, C., Mgr.-Mktg.--Elektro-Apparatebau Olten AG, Olten, Switzerland; *Int'l*, pg. 444

Gallacher, Lynne, Assoc. Mgr.-Mktg.--Kimberly-Clark Inc., Mississauga, Canada; *U.S. Public*, pg. 959

Gallagher, J., Dir.-Sls. & Mktg. Services--Menley & James Laboratories, Inc., Horsham, PA; *U.S. Public*, pg. 1086

Gallagher, Karen, Mgr.-Mktg.- Household Prods.--Braun, North America, Woburn, MA; *U.S. Public*, pg. 743

Gallagher, Margaret L., V.P.-Mktg.--The Raymond Corporation, Greene, NY; *Int'l*, pg. 123

Gallagher, Shay, Sr. V.P. & Gen. Mgr.-Mktg.--Bradford Exchange Ltd., Niles, IL; *U.S. Private*, pg. 163

Gallaher, Edward W., Sr., Pres., Chief Exec. Officer & Treas.--Phoenix Medical Technology, Inc., Andrews, SC; *U.S. Public*, pg. 1292

Gallaher, Stephanie, Mgr.-Mktg.--Squire-Cogswell Company, Gurnee, IL; *U.S. Private*, pg. 1027

Gallengo, Michael, V.P.-Mktg.--XRE Corporation, Littleton, MA; *U.S. Public*, pg. 1595

Gallian, Robert, Exec. V.P. & V.P.-Sls. & Mktg.--Pet Life Foods, Inc., Willowbrook, IL; *U.S. Private*, pg. 856

Galligan, Marty, Dir.-Integrated Mktg.--Xerox Canada Ltd., North York, Canada; *U.S. Public*, pg. 1785

Gallivan, Quentin, V.P.-Sls. & Mktg.--LASCO Fluid Distribution Products, Brownsville, TN; *Int'l*, pg. 1398

Gallo, Giorgio, V.P.-Mktg.--Sofamor, S.N.C., Rang-du-Fliers, France; *U.S. Public*, pg. 1482

Galloway, James C., V.P.-Mktg.--Alfa Corporation, Montgomery, AL; *U.S. Public*, pg. 40

Galmes Marti, Simon, Dir.-Mktg.--Banca March S.A., Palma de Mallorca, Spain; *Int'l*, pg. 136

Galovan, James W., V.P. & Dir.-H.R. & Mktg.--General Mills, Inc., Minneapolis, MN; *U.S. Public*, pg. 717

Galpin, Donna, Dir.-Mktg.--Charming Shoppes, Inc., Bensalem, PA; *U.S. Public*, pg. 335

Galser, Robert J., V.P.-Mktg. & Sls.--Merck Vaccine Division, Rahway, NJ; *U.S. Public*, pg. 1091

Galvin, J., Dir.-Grp. Sls. & Mktg.--Beazer Group Plc, Bath, United Kingdom; *Int'l*, pg. 181

Galvin, James, Dir.-Adv. & Mktg. & Mgr.-Sls.--MAC America Communications, Inc., Phoenix, AZ; *U.S. Private*, pg. 685

Galvin, Kathleen, Dir.-Mktg.--Parlux Fragrances Inc., Fort Lauderdale, FL; *U.S. Public*, pg. 1264

Galvin, Kathleen, Dir.-Mktg.--Parlux, Ltd., Fort Lauderdale, FL; *U.S. Public*, pg. 1264

Gamache, Brian, Dir.-Resort Div. Sls. & Mktg.--Hyatt Hotels Corporation, Chicago, IL; *U.S. Private*, pg. 551

Gambill, Anita, Mktg. Communications Specialist--Seradyn, Inc., Indianapolis, IN; *Int'l*, pg. 871

Gamble, Charles D., V.P.-Mktg.--Mesa Environmental, Fort Worth, TX; *U.S. Public*, pg. 1300

Gamble, Pat, Mktg.--Regions Bank/Phenix City, Phenix City, AL; *U.S. Public*, pg. 1372

Ganal, Michael, Dr., Dir.-Mktg.--Daimler-Benz Aerospace AG, Munich, Germany; *Int'l*, pg. 367

Gandy, Hary, V.P.-Sls. & Mktg.--Signtech USA, Ltd., San Antonio, TX; *U.S. Private*, pg. 999

Ganek, Carol, Dir.-Mktg.--Rowe International, Inc., Grand Rapids, MI; *U.S. Private*, pg. 904

Ganga, Dr., Dir.-Mktg.--Boehringer Ingelheim Italia S.p.A., Reggello, Italy; *Int'l*, pg. 199

Gange, George, V.P. & Dir.-Mktg.--Hammond Group Inc., Hammond, IN; *U.S. Private*, pg. 498

Gangstee, Gary, V.P.-Mktg. & Sls./Medical--Reuter Manufacturing Inc., Hopkins, MN; *U.S. Public*, pg. 1383

Ganis, Sid, Pres.-Mktg. & Distr.--Sony Pictures Studios, Culver City, CA; *Int'l*, pg. 1283

Gannon, Lori, Coord.-Mktg. Communications--Worcester Controls Corp., Marlborough, MA; *Int'l*, pg. 128

Gans, Mary Anne, Dir.-Mktg.--Globelle Corporation, Mississauga, Canada; *Int'l*, pg. 554

Ganskopp, C. Robert, V.P.-Sls. & Mktg.--SouthCo. Inc., Concordville, PA; *U.S. Private*, pg. 1014

Gantner, Robert, Sr. V.P.-Mktg.--Magna Group, Inc., Saint Louis, MO; *U.S. Public*, pg. 1037

Ganus, C.A., V.P.-Mktg.--Murphy Oil USA, Inc., El Dorado, AR; *U.S. Public*, pg. 1142

Ganzell, Larry, V.P.-Strategic Partners & Pub. Rels.--ScanTron Corporation, Tustin, CA; *U.S. Public*, pg. 786

Ganzenmuller, Fritz, Dir.-Mktg.--Stadtsparkasse Munchen, Munich, Germany; *Int'l*, pg. 1293

Garavaglia, Antonio, Dir.-Mktg.--Recordati Industria Chimica e Farmaceutica S.p.A., Milan, Italy; *Int'l*, pg. 1090

Garavaglia, Antonio, Dir.-Mktg.--Recordati Pharmaceutical Chemicals Division:, Milan, Italy; *Int'l*, pg. 1090

Garber, David, Exec. V.P.-T.V. & New Media--LIVE Film & Mediaworks, Van Nuys, CA; *U.S. Private*, pg. 671

Garber, David, Dir.-Mktg.--Kemps Foods, Inc., Lancaster, PA; *Int'l*, pg. 752

Garber, Josie, Sr. V.P. & Database Mktg. Dir.--Wunderman Cato Johnson, New York, NY; *U.S. Private*, pg. 1197

Garber, Van L., V.P.-Mktg.--Norandex Vinyl Products Co., Macedonia, OH; *U.S. Public*, pg. 1237

Garbuzinski, Kathy, Coord. & Mgr.-Corp. Communications--Morgan Keegan, Inc., Memphis, TN; *U.S. Public*, pg. 1131

Garcia de la Inglesia, Jose H., Mgr.-Mktg.--Porsche Espana S.A., Madrid, Spain; *Int'l*, pg. 1063

Garcia, Fran, V.P.-Mktg.--Specialty Brands, San Francisco, CA; *Int'l*, pg. 237

Garcia, Frank, Jr., Dir.-Commercial Mktg.--Sargent-Fletcher Inc., El Monte, CA; *Int'l*, pg. 301

Garcia, Joe, Sr. Dir.-Field Mktg.--IHOP Corp., Glendale, CA; *U.S. Public*, pg. 862

Garcia, Kathleen, Mgr.-Mktg.--Monrovia Nursery Co., Azusa, CA; *U.S. Private*, pg. 757

Garcia, Raquel, Mgr.-Mktg. Communications--BAX Global, Irvine, CA; *U.S. Public*, pg. 1305

Gard, Jim, Dir.-Mktg. Information--La Quinta Inns, Inc., San Antonio, TX; *U.S. Public*, pg. 972

Gardner, Christopher, Dir.-Mktg.--Vitesse Semiconductor Corporation, Camarillo, CA; *U.S. Public*, pg. 1723

Gardner, Julie, V.P.-Adv. & Mktg.--Eckerd Corporation, Largo, FL; *U.S. Public*, pg. 917

Gardner, Julie, V.P.-Adv. & Mktg.--Eckerd Drug Co., Clearwater, FL; *U.S. Public*, pg. 917

Gardner, Philip, V.P.-Mktg.--Alfred Nickles Bakery, Inc., Navarre, OH; *U.S. Private*, pg. 799

Gardner, Philip, V.P.-Mktg.--Nickles Bakery of Indiana Inc., Elkhart, IN; *U.S. Private*, pg. 799

Gardner, Philip, V.P.-Mktg.--Nickles Bakery of Ohio Inc., Lima, OH; *U.S. Private*, pg. 799

Gardner, Richard P., Sr. V.P.-Worldwide Sls. & Mktg.--BMC Software, Inc., Houston, TX; *U.S. Public*, pg. 162

Gardner, Thomas D., V.P.-Mktg./Reader's Digest USA--The Reader's Digest Association, Inc., Pleasantville, NY; *U.S. Public*, pg. 1367

Garel, John R., Sr. V.P.-Mktg. & Sls.--America West Airlines, Inc., Phoenix, AZ; *U.S. Public*, pg. 67

Gargas, David E., V.P.-Sls. & Mktg.--Alphabet Division, Warren, OH; *U.S. Private*, pg. 1044

Gargel, Elaine, Mktg. Dept.--McNeil Consumer Products Company, Fort Washington, PA; *U.S. Public*, pg. 928

Garicano, Jose, Dir.-Pub. Rels.--Opel Espana, Zaragoza, Spain; *U.S. Public*, pg. 724

Garlock, E. Ted, Dir.-Mktg.--Mail-Well Inc., Englewood, CO; *U.S. Public*, pg. 1037

Garlock, Garth, V.P.-Mktg. & Sls.--Midland Life Insurance Co., Columbus, OH; *U.S. Private*, pg. 744

Garman, Kenny, V.P.-Mktg.--Kruse International, Auburn, IN; *U.S. Private*, pg. 636

Garner, James, Mgr.-Mktg. Communications--Camco International Inc., Houston, TX; *U.S. Public*, pg. 297

Garrabrant, Lori, Dir.-Sls. & Mktg.--Golden Books Family Entertainment Inc., New York, NY; *U.S. Public*, pg. 749

Garrabrant, Lori, Dir.-Sls. & Mktg.--Golden Books Publishing, New York, NY; *U.S. Public*, pg. 749

Garrett, Fay, Dir.-Mktg.--Alumax Inc., Atlanta, GA; *U.S. Public*, pg. 59

Garrett, Suzanne, V.P.-Prod. Mngmt. & Mktg.--Daisytek International Corporation, Plano, TX; *U.S. Public*, pg. 477

Garrett, Suzanne, V.P.-Prod. Mngmt. & Mktg.--Daisytek Incorporated, Plano, TX; *U.S. Public*, pg. 477

Garrett, Suzanne, V.P.-Prod. Mngmt. & Mktg.--Daisytek (Canada) Inc., Toronto, Canada; *U.S. Public*, pg. 477

Garrett, Suzanne, V.P.-Prod. Mngmt. & Mktg.--Daisytek Latin America, Miami, FL; *U.S. Public*, pg. 477

Garrett, Suzanne, V.P.-Prod. Mngmt. & Mktg.--Daisytek De Mexico S.A. de C.V., Mexico, Mexico; *U.S. Public*, pg. 477

Garrett, Suzanne, V.P.-Prod. Mngmt. & Mktg.--Priority Fulfillment Services, Inc., Plano, TX; *U.S. Public*, pg. 477

Garrett, Suzanne, V.P.-Prod. Mngmt. & Mktg.--Daisytek Australia Pty. Ltd., Alexandria, Australia; *U.S. Public*, pg. 477

Garrimger, Colleen, Dir.-Mktg.--Mystic Color Lab, Inc., Mystic, CT; *Int'l*, pg. 501

Garrison, John, Sr. V.P.-Sls. & Mktg./Consumer Electronics--Samsung Electronics America, Inc., Ridgefield Park, NJ; *Int'l*, pg. 1183

Garrison, Lynda, V.P.-Mktg.--Falcon Products, Inc., Saint Louis, MO; *U.S. Public*, pg. 611

Garrity, Jim, Sr. V.P. & Dir.-Adv. & Mktg.--First Union Corporation, Charlotte, NC; *U.S. Public*, pg. 639

Garro, Robert, Dir.-Mktg.--Reynolds Machine Tool Corp., Melrose Park, IL; *U.S. Private*, pg. 926

Garro, Robert, Dir.-Mktg.--RMT Technology, Bellwood, IL; *U.S. Private*, pg. 927

Garry, Jeff, Mgr.-Adv., Sls. & Mktg.-Sportswear--Raven Industries, Inc., Sioux Falls, SD; *U.S. Public*, pg. 1361

Garry, Jeffrey R., Dir.-Sls. & Mktg.--Raven Industries Sportswear Div., Sioux Falls, SD; *U.S. Public*, pg. 1361

Garthwaite, Robert L., Jr., V.P.-Prod. Devel.--Franklin Electronic Publishers, Inc., Burlington, NJ; *U.S. Public*, pg. 679

Gartman, Sally, Dir.-Sls. & Mktg.-Sterling--Wausau Homes, Inc., Rothschild, WI; *U.S. Private*, pg. 1154

Garvey, James R., V.P.-Mktg. & Sls. Services--Bristol-Myers Squibb U.S. Pharmaceutical Group, Evansville, IN; *U.S. Public*, pg. 254

Garvey, Tom J., Mgr.-Mktg.--Sioux Tools, Inc., Sioux City, IA; *U.S. Public*, pg. 1480

Garvick, Debra, Mgr.-Mktg.--Buck Knives, Inc., El Cajon, CA; *U.S. Private*, pg. 177

Gasca Neri, Enrique, Sr. V.P.-Mktg. & Quality--Grupo Acerero del Norte S.A. de C.V. (GAN), Mexico, Mexico; *Int'l*, pg. 572

Gaspar, Fernando, Dir.-Mktg.--Vercoope-Uniao Das Adegas Cooperativas da Regiao Dos Vinhoa Verdes, U.C.R.L., Santo Tirso, Portugal; *Int'l*, pg. 1463

Gaspard, Ronnie L., V.P.-Mktg.--Sundowner Offshore Services, Inc., Houston, TX; *U.S. Public*, pg. 1149

Gates, Carole O'Connor, Exec. V.P.-Mktg.--Star Markets Company, Inc., Cambridge, MA; *U.S. Private*, pg. 1035

Gates, Ellen, Mgr.-Mktg.--Delta Woodside Industries, Inc., Greenville, SC; *U.S. Public*, pg. 497

Gates, Greg, V.P.-Direct Mktg. & Adv.--Nationwide Insurance Enterprise, Columbus, OH; *U.S. Private*, pg. 788

Gates, Marshall M., Mng. Dir.-Devel. Mkts.--Countrywide Home Loans Inc., Pasadena, CA; *U.S. Public*, pg. 452

Gatman, James A., V.P.-Mktg.--Thomson Consumer Electronics Inc., Indianapolis, IN; *Int'l*, pg. 1383

Gatti, Brent, Sr. V.P.-Pricing & Mktg.--Manufacturers Consolidation Service, Inc., Memphis, TN; *U.S. Private*, pg. 700

Gattinella, Wayne, Sr. V.P.-Mktg.--MEDCO Containment Services, Inc., Montvale, NJ; *U.S. Public*, pg. 1091

Gatto, Andrew K., Exec. V.P.-Mktg.--Toy Biz, Inc., New York, NY; *U.S. Public*, pg. 1625

Gaudet, Phil, Dir.-Sls. & Mktg.--The Dee Howard Company, San Antonio, TX; *U.S. Private*, pg. 542

Gaughan, Kevin, Dir.-Mktg.--Kyocera America, Inc., San Diego, CA; *Int'l*, pg. 775

Gaul, David, V.P.--Denver Wholesale Florists Company, Denver, CO; *U.S. Private*, pg. 326

Gauld, Frank, V.P.-Mktg.--Wellington Industries Inc., Madison, GA; *U.S. Private*, pg. 1161

Gault, David, V.P.-Mktg.--Hoover Company, Canton, OH; *U.S. Public*, pg. 1065

Gault, Matt, Sls. & Mktg.--Paradigm National Yellow Pages Group, Tampa, FL; *U.S. Private*, pg. 838

Gaunt, Bobbie, Gen. Mgr.-Mktg.--Ford Division, Detroit, MI; *U.S. Public*, pg. 662

Gaunt, Richard J., Mgr.-Mktg. Corp. Affairs--British Alcan Aluminium plc, Gerrards Cross, United Kingdom; *Int'l*, pg. 51

Gause, Erich, Mgr.-Adv.--Public Service Company of Oklahoma, Tulsa, OK; *U.S. Public*, pg. 324

Gavelek, Mike, Dir.-Mktg. Svcs.--Budget Rent A Car Corporation, Lisle, IL; *U.S. Private*, pg. 178

Gaver, Charles C., Jr., Mgr.-Sls. & Mktg.--Belmont Metals, Inc., Brooklyn, NY; *U.S. Private*, pg. 132

Gavin, John, Exec. V.P.--Right Management Consultants, Inc., Philadelphia, PA; *U.S. Public*, pg. 1390

Gawthorpe, Lynn, Mgr.-Mktg.--Bostik Ltd., Leicester, United Kingdom; *Int'l*, pg. 1409

Gay, W. Ross, Mktg. Mgr.--Bleached Board Folding Carton Div., Newark, DE; *U.S. Public*, pg. 1762

Gaylor, Albert L., Asst. V.P.-Mktg. Svcs.--Sysco Corporation, Houston, TX; *U.S. Public*, pg. 1550

Gearlings, Caroline, V.P.-Mktg.--Christian Dior Perfumes Inc., New York, NY; *Int'l*, pg. 781

Geary, James, V.P.-Mktg.--Security Dynamics Technologies, Bedford, MA; *U.S. Public*, pg. 1453

Geddes, Bob, V.P.-Mktg. & Sls.--Giga-Tronics Incorporated, San Ramon, CA; *U.S. Public*, pg. 742

Geddes, Kristine M., Mgr.-Mktg. Communications--Woods Equipment Company, Oregon, IL; *U.S. Private*, pg. 249

Gedge, Patrick, Dir.-Mktg.--Transalta Corporation, Calgary, Canada; *Int'l*, pg. 1416

Geedey, Harry, V.P.-Sls. & Mktg.--Empire Kosher Poultry, Inc., Mifflintown, PA; *U.S. Private*, pg. 374

Geib, Bob, Mgr.-Mktg. Communications--Aeroflex Laboratories Inc., Plainview, NY; *U.S. Public*, pg. 24

Geiger, Peter E., V.P.-Sls.--Geiger Brothers, Lewiston, ME; *U.S. Private*, pg. 442

Geiger, Sylvie, Mktg. Dir.--EURO RSCG Babinet, Erra, Tong Cuong, Levallois-Perret, France; *Int'l*, pg. 600

Geis, Carol, V.P.-Mktg.--The Levy Organization, Chicago, IL; *U.S. Private*, pg. 664

Geis, Kit, Dir.-Mktg.--The Sporting News Publishing Company, Saint Louis, MO; *U.S. Public*, pg. 1616

Geiselman, R.D., Mgr.-Mktg. Communications--Houghton International Inc., Valley Forge, PA; *U.S. Private*, pg. 541

Geisenberg, Bob, Mgr.-Mktg.--Rogers Foods, Turlock, CA; *U.S. Public*, pg. 1696

Geishecker, Edward P., V.P.-U.S. & Canada Sls. & Mktg.--Ionics, Incorporated, Watertown, MA; *U.S. Public*, pg. 912

Geisler, Jim, Mgr.-Mktg. Communications--Killark Electric Manufacturing Co., Saint Louis, MO; *U.S. Public*, pg. 844

Geissberger, Heinz, Mgr.-Sls. & Mktg.--K-Tron Switzerland-Soder Division, Niederlenz, Switzerland; *U.S. Public*, pg. 938

Gekas, Irene M., Mgr.-Mktg. Programs--New York Wire Co., Mount Wolf, PA; *U.S. Private*, pg. 795

Gekler, Brooks, Sr. V.P.-Mktg.--General Mills Canada Inc., Etobicoke, Canada; *U.S. Public*, pg. 718

Gelernter, Melissa, Mgr.-Mktg.--Marcel Dekker, Inc., New York, NY; *U.S. Private*, pg. 321
Geli, Giovanni, Dir.-Mktg.--Ideal Form Team S.r.L., Monsano, Italy; *Int'l*, pg. 659
Gelinas, Keith, Dir.-Mktg.--Boler Company, Itasca, IL; *U.S. Private*, pg. 155
Gelise, Paul, Mgr.-Mktg.--Cockerill Sambre, Brussels, Belgium; *Int'l*, pg. 301
Geller, Avrum, V.P.-Mktg. Services--Block Drug Company, Inc., Jersey City, NJ; *U.S. Public*, pg. 236
Gelose, James, Dir.-Mktg.-Systems--GN Nettest Fiber Optic Division, Utica, NY; *Int'l*, pg. 536
Gelpi, Al, Mktg. Research Analyst--American Nucleonics Corp., Westlake Village, CA; *U.S. Public*, pg. 556
Gelvin, Tim, V.P.-Corp. Mktg. Svcs. & Product Devel.--UtiliCorp United Inc., Kansas City, MO; *U.S. Public*, pg. 1700
Gemignani, Gino, Sr. V.P.-Mktg. Bus. Devel.--The Whiting-Turner Contracting Co., Baltimore, MD; *U.S. Private*, pg. 1174
Gemko, Bob, Dir.-Mktg.--L&J Technologies, Hillside, IL; *U.S. Private*, pg. 638
Gemmell, Alison, Dir.-Mktg.--SkyWest Inc., Saint George, UT; *U.S. Public*, pg. 1476
Gencarelli, Frank, Exec. V.P.-Mktg.--First Colony Life Insurance Co., Lynchburg, VA; *U.S. Public*, pg. 711
Gendron, Tom, Mgr.-Customer Support & Bus. Devel.--Woodward Governor Company, Rockford, IL; *U.S. Public*, pg. 1776
Genest, David, Dir.-Mktg. & Corp. Communications--Brown & Sharpe Manufacturing Company, North Kingstown, RI; *U.S. Public*, pg. 260
Genest, David, Mgr.-Mktg.--Measuring Systems Division, North Kingstown, RI; *U.S. Public*, pg. 260
Gengozian, Gary, Mktg. Communications--Heil Environmental Industries, Chattanooga, TN; *U.S. Public*, pg. 520
Genovese, Jan, Sr. Dir.-Mktg.--Casual Corner Group Inc., Enfield, CT; *U.S. Private*, pg. 219
Genoways, Jeffrey, Coord.-Mktg.--National Twist Drill Div., South Beloit, IL; *U.S. Public*, pg. 1370
Gentilcore, James, V.P.-Sls. & Mktg.--Advanced Energy Industry, Fort Collins, CO; *U.S. Public*, pg. 20
Gentili, Gene, V.P.-Sls. & Mktg./Consumer Pkgng. Div.--Ivex Packaging Corporation, Lincolnshire, IL; *U.S. Public*, pg. 915
Gentry, Gary, Dir.-Mktg.--Seagate Control Data, Oklahoma City, OK; *U.S. Public*, pg. 1450
Gentz, Jim, Sr. V.P.-Sls. & Mktg.--Yamaha Motor Corp., U.S.A., Cypress, CA; *Int'l*, pg. 1516
Genzano, Emilio, Dir.-Mktg.--Turner Construction Company, Albany, NY; *U.S. Public*, pg. 1645
Geocaris, Dan, V.P.-Sls. & Mktg.--Little Lady Foods, Inc., Elk Grove Village, IL; *U.S. Private*, pg. 671
George, Dan, Dir.-Mktg.--Melnor Inc., Winchester, VA; *U.S. Public*, pg. 1234
George, Debbie, Mgr.-Mktg.--Titeflex Corporation, Springfield, MA; *Int'l*, pg. 1340
George, G., Dir.-Buying & Mktg.--Lillywhites Ltd., London, United Kingdom; *Int'l*, pg. 706
George, John W., Pres.--Autocon Technologies, Inc., Farmington, MI; *U.S. Public*, pg. 850
George, Kim, Sls. & Mktg. Asst.--Jamison Bedding, Inc., Franklin, TN; *U.S. Private*, pg. 581
George, Marcella, Mgr.-Mktg.--Swiss Army Brands, Inc., Shelton, CT; *U.S. Public*, pg. 1544
George, Margaret, Capital Mktg. Dir.--Dewe Rogerson Limited, London, United Kingdom; *Int'l*, pg. 408
George, Martin, Dir.-Mktg.--British Airways PLC, London, United Kingdom; *Int'l*, pg. 218
George, R. D., Dir.-Mktg.--Duke Manufacturing Co., Inc., Saint Louis, MO; *U.S. Private*, pg. 346
George, Stephen M., V.P.-Mktg.--Melody Foods, Inc., Farmington Hills, MI; *U.S. Private*, pg. 730
George, Thindusa, Mgr.-Economics & Mktg.--National Bank of Malawi, Blantyre, Malawi; *Int'l*, pg. 1296
Georgiadis, Gus P., Exec. V.P.-Sls. & Mktg.--Highmark Inc., Pittsburgh, PA; *U.S. Private*, pg. 528
Georgian, Paul, Dir.-Mkt. Research--Avis Rent A Car System, Inc., Garden City, NY; *U.S. Public*, pg. 321
Georgieff, Gregory, Sr. V.P.-Mktg.--Chubb & Son, Inc., Warren, NJ; *U.S. Public*, pg. 355
Geotis, Charles, Dir.-Mktg.--La Amistad Residential Treatment Center, Maitland, FL; *U.S. Public*, pg. 1697
Geraghty, Dennis, Dir.-Mktg.--Wechsler Coffee Corp., Moonachie, NJ; *U.S. Private*, pg. 1158
Gerard, Gary L., Natl. Dir.-Mktg. & Communications--Deloitte & Touche LLP, Wilton, CT; *U.S. Private*, pg. 322
Gerard, Jackie, Mgr.-Promo.--Dahlberg, Inc., Golden Valley, MN; *U.S. Public*, pg. 194
Gerber, Dylan, Sr. V.P.-Adv. & Mktg.--UPN-United Paramount Network, Los Angeles, CA; *U.S. Public*, pg. 352
Gerber, Dylan, Sr. V.P.-Adv. & Mktg.--UPN-United Paramount Network, Los Angeles, CA; *U.S. Private*, pg. 777
Gerdin, Carole, Dir.-Mktg.--Noville, South Hackensack, NJ; *U.S. Private*, pg. 808
Geresy, William, Mgr.-Mktg.--CIBA Specialty Chemicals, East Lansing, MI; *Int'l*, pg. 291
Gerichter, Peggy, Mgr.-Mktg.--Colgate-Palmolive (Central America) S.A., Guatemala, Guatemala; *U.S. Public*, pg. 398
Gerigery, Kelly, Dir.-Corp. Mktg.--Donnelly Corporation, Holland, MI; *U.S. Public*, pg. 519
German, Gary H., V.P.-Sls. & Mktg.--Ultimate Technology Corporation, Victor, NY; *U.S. Public*, pg. 1637
Gerrardi, Mark, Dir.-Mktg.--Genzyme Genetics Div., Santa Fe, NM; *U.S. Public*, pg. 733
Gerrity, Thomas E., V.P.-Sls. & Mktg.--E-Z Serve Corp., Houston, TX; *U.S. Public*, pg. 540
Gerrity, Thomas E., Mgr.-Sls. & Mktg.--E-Z Serve Convenience Stores, Inc., Houston, TX; *U.S. Public*, pg. 540
Gershaw, Gerald, Pres.-Intl. Div.--Therapedic Associates, Inc., Middlesex, NJ; *U.S. Private*, pg. 1079
Gershberg, Jay, Sr. V.P. & Pres.-Travel Nurse Grp.--Hospital Staffing Services, Inc., Fort Lauderdale, FL; *U.S. Public*, pg. 840
Gerstein, Mel, Treas. & Dir.-Mktg., Adv. & Pub. Rels.--Thermwell Products Co., Inc., Paterson, NJ; *U.S. Private*, pg. 1081
Gertz, William, Sr. V.P.-Mktg.--American Institute for Foreign Study, Greenwich, CT; *U.S. Private*, pg. 56
Gervin, Kelly, Mktg. Coord.--Moulinex Canada Ltd., Richmond Hill, Canada; *Int'l*, pg. 896
Getchis, Randy E., Sr. V.P.-Sls. & Mktg.--Automotive Rentals, Inc. (ARI), Mount Laurel, NJ; *U.S. Private*, pg. 535
Getson, Lisa M., Sr. V.P-Mktg.--Apria Healthcare Group Inc., Costa Mesa, CA; *U.S. Public*, pg. 125
Getsy, Jean, Mktg. Communications Assoc.--Crouse-Hinds, Syracuse, NY; *U.S. Public*, pg. 444
Geulafargue, James, Mgr.-Mktg.--Merchant Bank of Central Africa Limited, Harare, Zimbabwe; *Int'l*, pg. 149
Gewart, Larry, Dir.-Mktg.--Honeywell, Inc., Fort Washington, PA; *U.S. Public*, pg. 834
Geysen, R., Mgr.-Mktg.--Nourypharma Nederland B.V., Oss, Netherlands; *Int'l*, pg. 44
Gezon, Bruce, V.P.-Mktg.--Helmick Corporation, Fairmont, WV; *U.S. Private*, pg. 520
Gezundhajt, B., Sr. V.P.-Mktg. & Sls.--Zim-American Israeli Shipping Co., New York, NY; *U.S. Private*, pg. 1206
Ghest, Clive, V.P.-Bus. Devel.--Advanced Micro Devices, Inc., Sunnyvale, CA; *U.S. Public*, pg. 21
Ghiloni, Peter, Sr. V.P.-Mktg.--Swisher International Group, Inc., Darien, CT; *U.S. Public*, pg. 1543
Giacchetti, Richard, V.P.-Mktg.--Fox River Paper Company, Appleton, WI; *U.S. Private*, pg. 422
Giacoio, Dianne, V.P.-Mktg.--Capezio Ballet Makers Inc., Totowa, NJ; *U.S. Private*, pg. 205
Giacolone, Bob, V.P.-Mktg.--Duracell International Inc., Bethel, CT; *U.S. Public*, pg. 743
Giacomodonato, Silvio, V.P.-In-Store Mktg.--The Bay, Toronto, Canada; *Int'l*, pg. 637
Giacona, Carolyn, Mgr.-Mktg.--Mele Manufacturing Co., Inc., Utica, NY; *U.S. Private*, pg. 730
Giambra, Ernie, V.P.-Mktg. & Sls.--Pioneer Life Insurance Co. of Illinois, Rockford, IL; *U.S. Public*, pg. 434
Giammarco, Ralph, V.P.-Sls. & Mktg.-Advanced Technologies Grp.--Tekra Corporation, New Berlin, WI; *U.S. Private*, pg. 1073
Giamo, Kathy, Dir.-Sls. & Mktg.--Reckson Associates Realty Corp., Melville, NY; *U.S. Public*, pg. 1368
Giandinoto, John, Asst. to V.P.-Mktg.--National Indemnity Co., Omaha, NE; *U.S. Public*, pg. 221
Gianferante, Richard, V.P.-Mktg. & Sls.--Northwestern Golf Company, Elmhurst, IL; *U.S. Private*, pg. 806
Giangiulio, Mary Ellen, Mgr.-Mktg.--Streamlight Inc., Norristown, PA; *U.S. Private*, pg. 1047
Giani, Nading, Dir.-New Member Mktg./LGA--Doubleday Direct, Garden City, NY; *U.S. Private*, pg. 191
Giannola, Ralph, Sr. V.P.-Consumer Mktg.--Marriott Hotels, Resorts, and Suites, Washington, DC; *U.S. Public*, pg. 1048
Giannoni, Kay, Dir.-Mktg.--J.F. Ahern Co., Fond Du Lac, WI; *U.S. Private*, pg. 27
Giansante, Dan, Mgr.-Mktg.--Rubbermaid Canada Inc. Consumer Products, Mississauga, Canada; *U.S. Public*, pg. 1411
Giardina, Jay, Mgr.-Mktg.--Tubular Steel Inc., Saint Louis, MO; *U.S. Private*, pg. 1108
Giattino, Chris, Mgr.-Sls.--Fownes Brothers & Co., Inc., New York, NY; *U.S. Private*, pg. 422
Giazzon, Al, Dir.-Mktg.--Gateway 2000, North Sioux City, SD; *U.S. Public*, pg. 703
Gibbey, Brewnan, V.P.-Sls. & Mktg.--Allison-Erwin Co. Inc., Charlotte, NC; *U.S. Private*, pg. 41
Gibbons, Duane, Dir.-Adv. & Mktg.--Photo Control Corporation, Minneapolis, MN; *U.S. Public*, pg. 1292
Gibbons, Jeffrey, V.P.-Mktg.--Printronix, Inc., Irvine, CA; *U.S. Public*, pg. 1329
Gibbons, Paul, V.P.-Mktg.--ColorTyme, Inc., Irving, TX; *U.S. Private*, pg. 255
Gibbons, Tom, Dir.-Mktg.--Norwest Financial, Inc., Des Moines, IA; *U.S. Public*, pg. 1202
Gibbs, Dave, Gen. Mgr.-Mktg. & Business Devel.--Diamond Power Specialty Co., Lancaster, OH; *U.S. Public*, pg. 1068
Gibbs, David G., Mgr.-Bus. Devel.--Electro Kinetics Div., Santa Barbara, CA; *U.S. Public*, pg. 1250
Gibbs, John A., Dir.-Mktg.--Gerald H. Phipps, Inc., Denver, CO; *U.S. Private*, pg. 862
Gibney, Robert, Dir.-Pigment Sls. & Mktg./Americas--Kerr-McGee Chemical Corp., Oklahoma City, OK; *U.S. Public*, pg. 952
Gibson, Brian, Dir.-Mktg. Communications--Tech Data Corporation, Clearwater, FL; *U.S. Public*, pg. 1562
Gibson, Cindy, Mgr.-Mktg.--Truevision, Inc., Santa Clara, CA; *U.S. Public*, pg. 1642
Gibson, D., Mgr.-Mktg.--Air UK Engineering, Norfolk, United Kingdom; *Int'l*, pg. 39
Gibson, D., Mgr.-Sls. & Mktg.--Air UK Engineering Ltd., Stansted, United Kingdom; *Int'l*, pg. 39
Gibson, James, V.P.-Mktg.--Royal Life Insurance Company of Canada, Oakville, Canada; *Int'l*, pg. 1130
Gibson, Jane, Dir.-Mktg.--Plantation Foods Inc., Waco, TX; *U.S. Private*, pg. 869
Gibson, Jeff, Mgr.-Mktg. Svcs.--Pan-American Seed Co., West Chicago, IL; *U.S. Private*, pg. 112
Gibson, John A., Chief Mktg. Officer--CUNA Mutual Insurance Society, Madison, WI; *U.S. Private*, pg. 296
Gibson, Pam, Mgr.-Category--United Dairy Farmers, Inc., Cincinnati, OH; *U.S. Private*, pg. 1121
Gibson, Peter, V.P.-Mktg. & Sls.--U.S. Turbine Corporation, Maineville, OH; *Int'l*, pg. 1127
Gibson, Tom, V.P.-Mktg.--Sony Music Entertainment, Inc., New York, NY; *Int'l*, pg. 1281
Gibson, Wayne C., Mgr.-Wholesale Mktg.--Murphy Oil USA, Inc., El Dorado, AR; *U.S. Public*, pg. 1142
Gieyer, Janet, Mgr.-Tactical Mktg.--Shimadzu Scientific Instruments, Inc., Columbia, MD; *Int'l*, pg. 1232
Giffault, Katy, Dir.-Mktg. Services--AT&T Wireless Services, Paramus, NJ; *U.S. Public*, pg. 11
Gifford, Alexa, Mgr.-Elec. Mktg.--New York State Electric & Gas Corporation, Binghamton, NY; *U.S. Public*, pg. 1173
Gignac, Jim, Dir.-Sls. & Mktg.--Elgin Dairy Foods, Inc., Chicago, IL; *U.S. Private*, pg. 370
Gilbert, Ken W., Sr. V.P.-Mktg. (Mistic & Snapple)--Triarc Companies, Inc., New York, NY; *U.S. Public*, pg. 1634
Gilbert, Ken W., Sr. V.P.-Mktg./Mistic & Snapple--Triarc Beverage Group, White Plains, NY; *U.S. Public*, pg. 1635
Gilbert, Ken W., Sr. V.P.-Mktg.--Snapple Beverage Company, White Plains, NY; *U.S. Public*, pg. 1635
Gilbert, R.W., Exec. V.P.-Sls. & Mktg. & Treas.--Shure Brothers Incorporated, Evanston, IL; *U.S. Private*, pg. 997
Gilbert, Robert, V.P.-Sls.--Benchmark Electronics Inc., Angleton, TX; *U.S. Public*, pg. 210
Gilbert, Susanne, Dir.-Mktg.--Specialty Coated Products, Merrimack, NH; *U.S. Public*, pg. 1152
Gilbert, Timothy, Mgr.-Mktg. Communications--The Raymond Corporation, Greene, NY; *Int'l*, pg. 123
Gilbertson, Cydney, Mgr.-Mktg. Communications--Chemical Leaman Corporation, Exton, PA; *U.S. Private*, pg. 233
Gilchrist, Neil, Mgr.-Mktg.--Dettra Flag Company, Oaks, PA; *U.S. Private*, pg. 328
Gildea, Mark, V.P.-Alternate Site Svcs.--Manor Healthcare Corp., Gaithersburg, MD; *U.S. Public*, pg. 1041
Gilker, Phyllis, Dir.-Mktg.--Florida Health Facilities, Inc., Lutz, FL; *U.S. Public*, pg. 1035
Gill, Andrew, Comml. Dir.--International Thomson Business Publishing, London, United Kingdom; *U.S. Public*, pg. 1601
Gill, Carl, Dir.-Mktg.--Fawcett Memorial Hospital, Inc., Port Charlotte, FL; *U.S. Public*, pg. 404
Gill, James P., Chief Oper. Officer, Exec. V.P., Gen. Mgr. & Dir.-Mktg.--Jackson Hole Ski Resort, Teton Village, WY; *U.S. Private*, pg. 579
Gill, Mark, Pres.-Mktg.--Miramax Films, Inc., New York, NY; *U.S. Public*, pg. 514
Gilla, Werner, Dir.-Mktg.--G.M. Pfaff Aktiengesellschaft, Kaiserslautern, Germany; *Int'l*, pg. 1046
Gillespie, D., Mktg. Dir.--Rodenstock Precision Optics, Inc., Rockford, IL; *Int'l*, pg. 1007
Gillespie, Dennis G., Pres.-Worldwide Mktg. & Domestic Sls.--Viacom Enterprises, New York, NY; *U.S. Private*, pg. 779
Gillette, Patty, Dir.-Mktg.--Colonial Gas Company, Lowell, MA; *U.S. Public*, pg. 400
Gillies, Andrew G., V.P.-Mktg.--DMI Furniture Inc., Louisville, KY; *U.S. Public*, pg. 473
Gillies, James, Sr. V.P.-Canadian Mkt. Devel.--Newell Industries Canada, Inc., Scarborough, Canada; *U.S. Public*, pg. 1178
Gillies, James E., Sr. V.P.-Canadian Mkt. Devel.--Newell Co., Freeport, IL; *U.S. Public*, pg. 1176
Gilligan, Fred, Dir.-Bus. Devel.--Raytheon Optical Systems, Lexington, MA; *U.S. Public*, pg. 1364
Gilligan, Peter, Mgr.-Mktg.--New Zealand Lamb Co., Inc., White Plains, NY; *U.S. Private*, pg. 796
Gilliland, Daniel, Dir.-Mktg.--Cab-o-Sil Div. Cabot Corp., Tuscola, IL; *U.S. Public*, pg. 289
Gilliland, Robert, Dir.-Sls. & Mktg.--Texon Materials Inc., Russell, MA; *U.S. Private*, pg. 1079
Gillis, E.J., V.P.-Mktg.--P.H. Glatfelter Company, Spring Grove, PA; *U.S. Public*, pg. 746
Gillooly, Edward F., Sr. V.P.-Mktg.--BJ's Wholesale Club, Inc., Natick, MA; *U.S. Public*, pg. 162
Gillott, Terry, V.P.-Sls. & Mktg.--Jacuzzi Bros., Jacuzzi, Inc., Little Rock, AR; *U.S. Public*, pg. 1684
Gilman, Patti, Asst. Dir.-Mktg.--McLaughlin Manufacturing Company, Greenville, SC; *U.S. Private*, pg. 724
Gilman, Robin, Dir.-Mktg.--Kayem Foods, Inc., Chelsea, MA; *U.S. Private*, pg. 610
Gilmer, William, V.P.-Sls. & Mktg.--The Homestead L.C., Hot Springs, VA; *U.S. Private*, pg. 247
Gilmore, Bill, V.P.-Sls. & Mktg.--Beloit Lenox, Div., Lenox, MA; *U.S. Public*, pg. 789
Gilmore, Ronald J., Exec. V.P.-Adv. & Mktg.--CompUSA, Dallas, TX; *U.S. Public*, pg. 420
Gilroy, Kathleen, Mgr.-Mktg. Communications--The Forum Corporation, Boston, MA; *U.S. Private*, pg. 420
Gilroy, Rosalind, Co-Mng. Dir.--International Correspondence Schools (Australasia) Limited, Lane Cove, Australia; *U.S. Public*, pg. 784
Giniat, Gary V., Dir.-Mktg.-Franchise Opers.--Gingiss International, Addison, IL; *U.S. Private*, pg. 455
Ginkel, Bob, Gen. Mgr.-Retail Mktg.--Ore-Ida Foods, Inc., Boise, ID; *U.S. Public*, pg. 805
Ginter, Steven J., V.P.-Mktg.--New Penn Motor Express, Inc., Lebanon, PA; *U.S. Public*, pg. 132
Gioia, Philip, Mgr.-Mktg.--Barr Laboratories Inc., Pomona, NY; *U.S. Public*, pg. 191
Giordano, Alexander, Exec. V.P. & Chief Mktg. Officer--Standard Security Life Insurance Company of New York, New York, NY; *U.S. Private*, pg. 446
Giordano, Bill, Mgr.-Mktg.--Nikon Inc., Melville, NY; *Int'l*, pg. 931
Giordano, Gary, V.P.-Mktg.--Jaco Electronics, Inc., Hauppauge, NY; *U.S. Public*, pg. 920
Giorgianni, George, Exec. V.P.-Sls. & Mktg.--Allegiant Physician Services, Atlanta, GA; *U.S. Public*, pg. 45
Giovanni, Bianchini, Dir.-Public Relations--Banca Popolare di Milano, Milan, Italy; *Int'l*, pg. 137
GiPietro, Frank, Mktg. Coord.--B.A. Ballou & Co. Inc., East Providence, RI; *U.S. Private*, pg. 112
Gipson, William, V.P.-Commercial Opers.--The Empire District Electric Company, Joplin, MO; *U.S. Public*, pg. 579
Girard, Robert, Exec. Dir.--United Dairymen of Arizona, Tempe, AZ; *U.S. Private*, pg. 1121

Girardot, Richard, Dir.-French Mktg.--Berriel Vittel France, Paris, France; *Int'l*, pg. 918
Girouard, Michael, Dir.-Mktg./Wound Care--Kinetic Concepts, Inc., San Antonio, TX; *U.S. Private*, pg. 620
Gish, Rollin, V.P., Strategist & Designer-Mktg. Communications--Ross Roy Communications, Inc., Bloomfield Hills, MI; *U.S. Private*, pg. 946
Gitelman, Shelly, V.P.-Sls.--Gilster Mary Lee Corp., Chester, IL; *U.S. Private*, pg. 455
Gitter, Blossom, Mktg. Commun. & Res. Coord.--BMW of North America, Inc.-Eastern Region, Ramsey, NJ; *Int'l*, pg. 177
Giuffrida, Caroline, Mgr.-Mktg.-Retail--Cains Foods, L.P., Ayer, MA; *U.S. Private*, pg. 199
Giugni, Mark, Sr. Product Planner--Harris Corp., Digital Telephone Systems Div., Novato, CA; *U.S. Public*, pg. 791
Giuseppetti, Susan, Mgr.-Mktg. Communications--Harris Corp., RF Communications Group Marketing Division, Rochester, NY; *U.S. Public*, pg. 792
Given, Cecil, V.P.-Sls. & Mktg.--The Flood Company, Hudson, OH; *U.S. Private*, pg. 414
Given, Richard, Exec. Dir.-Mktg. & Pub. Rels.--Mann Theatres, Encino, CA; *U.S. Private*, pg. 239
Givens, J.M., Mktg. & Sls.--Autolease Fleets Limited, Birmingham, United Kingdom; *Int'l*, pg. 216
Givoni, Zvi, Mgr.-Mktg.--Harrison Div., Burbank, CA; *U.S. Private*, pg. 999
Gladfelter, Carl F., V.P.-Mktg.--The Pep Boys-Manny, Moe & Jack, Philadelphia, PA; *U.S. Public*, pg. 1276
Gladfelter, Carl F., V.P.-Mktg.--The Pep Boys-Manny, Moe & Jack of California, Los Angeles, CA; *U.S. Public*, pg. 1276
Gladfelter, Thomas R., V.P.-Sls.,Mktg. & Adv.--Spontex, Inc., Columbia, TN; *Int'l*, pg. 1409
Gladson, James F., Mgr.--USAA Buying Service, San Antonio, TX; *U.S. Private*, pg. 1114
Glasgow, Gerry, V.P.-Mktg.--E. & J. Gallo Winery, Modesto, CA; *U.S. Private*, pg. 438
Glasheen, Shana, Sr. Mktg. Specialist--Proxima Corporation, San Diego, CA; *U.S. Public*, pg. 1339
Glasmann, Susan, V.P.-Mktg.--Mountain Fuel Supply Company, Salt Lake City, UT; *U.S. Public*, pg. 1352
Glatzau, Sandy, Sr. V.P.-Mktg. & Sls.--Browning-Ferris Industries, Inc., Houston, TX; *U.S. Public*, pg. 262
Glauberman, Jay D., V.P.-Mktg.--Malco Products, Inc., Barberton, OH; *U.S. Private*, pg. 698
Glazire, Bill, Dir.-Natl. Mktg.--MIPS Technologies, Inc., Mountain View, CA; *U.S. Public*, pg. 1473
Gleason, John S., V.P.-European Opers.--Construction Equipment Div., Racine, WI; *U.S. Public*, pg. 311
Gleason, Tom, V.P.-Mktg.--Ward Manufacturing, Inc., Blossburg, PA; *U.S. Private*, pg. 1149
Gleaves, Leon R., V.P.-Mktg. & Sls.--Wilkins-Rogers Incorporated, Ellicott City, MD; *U.S. Private*, pg. 1176
Gleeson, David, Dir.-Sls. & Mktg.--Reilly Industries, Inc., Indianapolis, IN; *U.S. Private*, pg. 919
Gleeson, Mary-Pat, V.P.-Mktg.--Alliance Communications Corporation, Toronto, Canada; *Int'l*, pg. 57
Gleichenhaus, Lionel, Dir.-Mktg.--Alaron Inc., Auburn Hills, MI; *U.S. Private*, pg. 31
Glendinning, Iain, V.P.-Mktg.--SabreTech, Inc., Phoenix, AZ; *U.S. Private*, pg. 959
Glenn, Alison, V.P.-Mktg.--Taco Cabana, San Antonio, TX; *U.S. Public*, pg. 1559
Glenn, Gary, Mgr.-Mktg.--Tasco Sales Inc., Miramar, FL; *U.S. Private*, pg. 928
Glenn, T. Michael, Sr. V.P.-Worldwide Mktg., Customer Service & Corp. Communications--FDX Corporation, Memphis, TN; *U.S. Public*, pg. 603
Glick, Pam, Mgr.-Adver. & Mktg.--Snorkel, Saint Joseph, MO; *U.S. Private*, pg. 500
Glick, Peter H., V.P.-Mktg. & Bus. Devel.--Genzyme Transgenics, Framingham, MA; *U.S. Public*, pg. 733
Glickman, Steve, V.P.-Mktg.--Sears Portrait Studios, Saint Louis, MO; *U.S. Public*, pg. 283
Glickman, Steve, V.P.-Mktg.--CPI Corp., Brampton, Canada; *U.S. Public*, pg. 283
Glinert, Floyd S., Exec. V.P.-Mktg.--Shorewood Packaging Corporation, New York, NY; *U.S. Public*, pg. 1468
Glisson, F.W., Sr. V.P.-Devel.--Hunt-Wesson, Inc., Fullerton, CA; *U.S. Public*, pg. 428
Glover, Del, V.P. & Gen. Mgr.-General Products & Mktg.--Du Pont Canada Inc., Mississauga, Canada; *U.S. Public*, pg. 532
Glover, M., Dir.-Mktg. & Sls.--Labatt Breweries of Canada - Prairie Region, Edmonton, Canada; *Int'l*, pg. 679
Glover, P., V.P.-Business Devel.--Chandler Evans Control Systems Division, West Hartford, CT; *U.S. Public*, pg. 401
Glowiak, Matthew, Mgr.-Sls. & Mktg.--H. Wilson Company, South Holland, IL; *U.S. Private*, pg. 359
Gluckin, Neil, V.P.-Mktg.--Morgan Guaranty Trust Company of New York, New York, NY; *U.S. Public*, pg. 1129
Glusko, John, Mgr.-Mktg.--Central Hudson Gas & Electric Corporation, Poughkeepsie, NY; *U.S. Public*, pg. 324
Glynn, Tom, V.P.-Mktg.--Sciaky, Inc., Chicago, IL; *U.S. Private*, pg. 862
Gmiter, Patrick J., V.P.-Mktg.--Cox Broadcasting Inc., Atlanta, GA; *U.S. Private*, pg. 281
Gnesda, Thomas A., V.P.-Sls. & Mktg.--EcoScience Produce Systems Corp., Orlando, FL; *U.S. Public*, pg. 563
Gnocchi, Gabrio, Mng. Dir.-Mktg. & Sls.--Opticos S.r.l., Brembate di Sopra, Italy; *Int'l*, pg. 1007
Gobble, Harry, Mgr.-Mktg.--Glen Raven Mills, Inc., Glen Raven, NC; *U.S. Private*, pg. 456
Gobern, June C., Asst. Dir.-Sls. & Tech. Mktg. Opers.--Cytogen Corporation, Princeton, NJ; *U.S. Public*, pg. 471
Gobin, Raymond, Dir.-Mktg.--Dietzgen Corporation, Palatine, IL; *U.S. Private*, pg. 332
Goddard, Melanie L., Mgr.-Sls. & Mktg.--Koehler Manufacturing Company, Marlborough, MA; *U.S. Private*, pg. 706
Godecker, Bill, Dir.-Mktg.--Howden Fluid Systems, Santa Barbara, CA; *U.S. Public*, pg. 1045
Goderis, Willy, Dir.-Mktg.--Sabena, Zaventem, Belgium; *Int'l*, pg. 1168
Godfrey, Alan, Dir.-Mktg.--Sandvik, Inc., Fair Lawn, NJ; *Int'l*, pg. 1185
Godfrey, James, Pres. & Mgr.-Mktg.--Marti Electronics, Cleburne, TX; *U.S. Private*, pg. 531
Godfrey, Tony, V.P.-Sls. & Mktg.--Columbus Mills, Inc., Columbus, GA; *U.S. Private*, pg. 256
Godhwani, Neeta, Sr. Mgr.-Mktg. Services--Genzyme Diagnostics, Medix Biotech, San Carlos, CA; *U.S. Public*, pg. 733
Godin, Julio C., Dir.-Mktg.--CIBA-GEIGY Uruguaya S.A., Montevideo, Uruguay; *Int'l*, pg. 980
Godshall, Ken, Dir.-Consumer Mktg.--Time, New York, NY; *U.S. Public*, pg. 1613
Godwin, Marsha, Mgr.-Mktg.--J. Hungerford Smith Company, Fullerton, CA; *U.S. Public*, pg. 428
Goeb, Carl, Mgr.-Mktg.--Neway Anchorlok International Inc., Muskegon, MI; *U.S. Private*, pg. 796
Goedhart, E., Dir.-Mktg. & Sls.--Fokker Aircraft Services B.V., Hoogerheyde, Netherlands; *Int'l*, pg. 1304
Goergen, J.P., V.P.-Intl. Mktg.--Gould Electronics Inc., Foil Division, Eastlake, OH; *U.S. Public*, pg. 1592
Goetz, Bill, V.P.-Mktg. & Mdsg.--Cintas Corporation, Mason, OH; *U.S. Public*, pg. 370
Goetz, Tim, Chief Fin. Officer, Treas. & Dir.-Mktg.--Robinson Helicopter Company, Torrance, CA; *U.S. Private*, pg. 936
Goez, Paula, Mgr.-Institutional Mktg.--Geneva Pharmaceuticals, Inc., Broomfield, CO; *Int'l*, pg. 973
Goff, Ken, V.P.- Mktg.--American Safety Razor Company, Verona, VA; *U.S. Private*, pg. 597
Goff, Larry, Dir.-Mktg.--Transnational Motors Inc., Grand Rapids, MI; *U.S. Private*, pg. 1097
Goff, Roger, Sr. V.P.-Mktg. & Customer Service--The Cornelius Company, Anoka, MN; *Int'l*, pg. 646
Goff, Steven E., Dir.-Mktg. & Adv.--Mrs. Giles Country Kitchens, Inc., Lynchburg, VA; *U.S. Public*, pg. 596
Goffi, Ernest, V.P.-Mktg. & Sls.--Fosbel, Inc., Berea, OH; *Int'l*, pg. 234
Goffman, Richard, V.P.-Mktg.--Star Video Entertainment, L.P., Jersey City, NJ; *U.S. Private*, pg. 1132
Goffredo, David B., V.P.-Pharmaceutical Prods. Mktg. & Sls.--Abbott Laboratories, Abbott Park, IL; *U.S. Public*, pg. 12
Goforth, David E., V.P.-Connective Mktg.--Sterling Electronics Corporation, Houston, TX; *U.S. Public*, pg. 1051
Goggin, Jim, Mktg.-Sls.--Wilsey Foods, Inc., Salem, OR; *Int'l*, pg. 879
Goh, Clara, Mgr.-Mktg. Svcs.--F.J. Benjamin Fashions (M) Sdn. Bhd., Kuala Lumpur, Malaysia; *Int'l*, pg. 187
Gohata, Ed, Mgr.-Adv.--Ancra International LLC, Hawthorne, CA; *U.S. Private*, pg. 71
Gohsman, Robin, V.P.-Mktg.--Wisconsin Pharmacal Co., Inc., Jackson, WI; *U.S. Private*, pg. 1185
Goit, Whitney, Exec. V.P.-Mktg. & Sls.--A&E Television Networks, New York, NY; *U.S. Private*, pg. 515
Goit, Whitney, II, Exec. V.P.-Sls. & Mktg.--Arts & Entertainment Network/ABC/NBC, New York, NY; *U.S. Public*, pg. 512
Goit, Whitney, II, Exec. V.P.-Sls. & Mktg.--Arts & Entertainment Network/ABC/NBC, New York, NY; *U.S. Private*, pg. 516
Gola, Oswaldo, Dir.-Commercial Sls. & Mktg.--SmithKline Beecham Laboratorios Ltda., Rio de Janeiro, Brazil; *Int'l*, pg. 1266
Golby, S.A., Mgr.-Corp. Devel.--Powell Duffryn PLC, Bracknell, United Kingdom; *Int'l*, pg. 1065
Gold, Harriet, Dir.-Brand Mgmt.-Mktg. Communications--Northern Illinois Gas Company, Naperville, IL; *U.S. Public*, pg. 1183
Gold, Mary, Mng. Dir.-Mktg.--Dreyer's Grand Ice Cream, Inc., Oakland, CA; *U.S. Public*, pg. 529
Gold, Rick, Dir.-Mktg. & Sls.--The Eureka Company, Bloomington, IL; *Int'l*, pg. 440
Gold, Trish, Dir.-Mktg.--Van Melle USA, Inc., Erlanger, KY; *Int'l*, pg. 1451
Goldberg, Andy, Sr. V.P.--Publishers Clearing House, Port Washington, NY; *U.S. Private*, pg. 893
Goldberg, Bruce, Sr. V.P.-Mktg.--Brink's Home Security, Inc., Irving, TX; *U.S. Public*, pg. 1305
Goldberg, David, V.P.--Hooper Holmes Corporation, Basking Ridge, NJ; *U.S. Public*, pg. 835
Goldberg, Eugene, V.P.-Mktg.--Case Paper Co., Inc., Long Island City, NY; *U.S. Private*, pg. 218
Goldberg, Marshall, Mgr.-Mktg. Prod.--Sigma Designs, Inc., Fremont, CA; *U.S. Public*, pg. 1472
Goldberg, Rick, Dir.-Mktg.-Face & Color Prods.-Revitalizing Line--Maybelline, Inc., New York, NY; *Int'l*, pg. 819
Golden, Paul, V.P.-Mktg.--Dranetz-BMI, Edison, NJ; *U.S. Private*, pg. 1144
Goldenberg, Sandy, Coord.-Mktg. Communications--Datasouth Computer Corporation, Charlotte, NC; *U.S. Public*, pg. 267
Goldfarb, David, Dir.-Mktg.--Consolidated Cigar Corporation, Fort Lauderdale, FL; *U.S. Private*, pg. 690
Goldfarb, David, Dir.-Mktg.--Consolidated Cigar Corp., Fort Lauderdale, FL; *U.S. Private*, pg. 690
Goldklank, Mitchell, Sr. V.P.-Sls. & Mktg.--LCS Industries, Inc., Clifton, NJ; *U.S. Public*, pg. 970
Goldman, Alfred E., Sr. V.P.-Tech. Market Analysis--A.G. Edwards & Sons, Inc., Saint Louis, MO; *U.S. Public*, pg. 565
Goldman, Allan, Sr. V.P.-Mktg.--The Cosmetic Center Inc., Columbia, MD; *U.S. Private*, pg. 689
Goldman, Budd, V.P.-Mktg.--Russ Berrie and Company, Inc., Oakland, NJ; *U.S. Public*, pg. 222
Goldman, David, V.P.-Mktg.--Ross Stores, Inc., Newark, CA; *U.S. Public*, pg. 1405
Goldman, Ed, Mktg. & Adv.--Avia, Irvine, CA; *U.S. Private*, pg. 62
Goldman, Marc, Pres. & Chief Exec. Officer--Farmland Dairies, Wallington, NJ; *U.S. Private*, pg. 395
Goldman, Rich, V.P.-Mktg.--Men's Wearhouse, Fremont, CA; *U.S. Public*, pg. 1086
Goldschmidt, Mark, V.P. & Dir.-Corp. Mktg. & Sls.--Hearst Magazines Division, New York, NY; *U.S. Private*, pg. 516
Goldschmidt, Mark E., Sr. V.P.-Adv. & Mktg.--Hearst Magazines Division, New York, NY; *U.S. Private*, pg. 516
Goldsmith, Marvin, Pres.-Sls. & Mktg.-TV Network--ABC, Inc, New York, NY; *U.S. Public*, pg. 511
Goldsmith, Marvin, Pres.-Sls. & Mktg.--ABC Television Network Group, New York, NY; *U.S. Public*, pg. 511
Goldstein, Adam, Dir.-Mktg.--National Institute of Business Management, Inc., Mc Lean, VA; *U.S. Private*, pg. 785
Goldstein, Adam, Sr. V.P.-Mktg.--Royal Caribbean Cruises Ltd., Miami, FL; *U.S. Public*, pg. 1410
Goldstein, Arnold, V.P.-Sls. & Mktg.--Danzas Corporation, Bellevue, WA; *Int'l*, pg. 382
Goldstein, Mark E., V.P.-Sls. & Mktg.--Stanley Door Systems, Troy, MI; *U.S. Public*, pg. 1509
Goldstein, Richard J., V.P.-Sls. & Mktg.--Industrial Electronics Division, Collinsville, CT; *Int'l*, pg. 204
Goldstein, Steve, Mgr.-Mktg.--Ross Technology, Inc., Austin, TX; *Int'l*, pg. 526
Goldstein, Wendy, Mgr.-Mktg. Communications--ITT Sheraton Corporation, Boston, MA; *U.S. Public*, pg. 1512
Goldstrom, Mark E., Mgr.-Mktg.--American Stone-Mix, Inc., Towson, MD; *U.S. Private*, pg. 62
Goliger, Nancy, Exec. V.P.-Mktg. & Creative Affairs--Paramount Pictures Corporation, Los Angeles, CA; *U.S. Private*, pg. 776
Golledge, Angela, Dir.-Mktg.--Circle International Group, Inc., San Francisco, CA; *U.S. Public*, pg. 370
Goltz, Paul, Dir.-Intl. Mktg.--Hach Company, Loveland, CO; *U.S. Public*, pg. 773
Golz, Dave, Dir.-Mktg.--Furst-McNess Company, Freeport, IL; *U.S. Private*, pg. 432
Gomar, R. Ian, V.P.-Mktg.--Starter Corp., New Haven, CT; *U.S. Public*, pg. 1511
Gomatos, John, Dir.-Mktg.--Kirin USA, Inc., Los Angeles, CA; *Int'l*, pg. 736
Gomeau, Mary Ellen, V.P.-Sls. & Mktg.--Phonetics, Inc., Aston, PA; *U.S. Private*, pg. 863
Gomes, Carlos S., Mgr.-Mktg.--Esselte Meto Portugal LDA, Oeiras, Portugal; *Int'l*, pg. 461
Gomez, John, Sr. Mgr.-Mktg.--Bacardi-Martini, USA, Inc., Miami, FL; *U.S. Private*, pg. 109
Gomez, Jose, Dir.-Sls. & Mktg.--La Reina, Inc., Los Angeles, CA; *U.S. Private*, pg. 640
Goncalves, Heitor Laso, Mgr.-Mktg. Services--Brastemp S.A., Sao Bernardo do Campo, Brazil; *U.S. Public*, pg. 1765
Gonczy, Gary, Dir.-Mktg.--Kwik Trip Inc., La Crosse, WI; *U.S. Private*, pg. 637
Gonedes, Jim, V.P.-Mktg.--Golden Books Publishing, New York, NY; *U.S. Public*, pg. 749
Gonos, G., Dir.-Mktg.--Leader Instruments Corporation, Hauppauge, NY; *U.S. Private*, pg. 655
Gonzales, Leopoldo, V.P.-Business Devel.--U.S. Operations Div., Hato Rey, PR; *U.S. Public*, pg. 176
Gonzalez-Adalid, Fernando Galbis, Dir.-Polyolefins--Repsol Quimica, Madrid, Spain; *Int'l*, pg. 1104
Gonzalez, Kay, Mgr.-Mktg. Support--CIE America, Inc., Irvine, CA; *Int'l*, pg. 694
Gonzalez, Peter, Mgr.-Mktg. Svcs.--Caltrol, Inc., Glendora, CA; *U.S. Private*, pg. 201
Gonzalez, Rita, Dir.-Mktg.--Lennar Corporation, Miami, FL; *U.S. Public*, pg. 987
Gonzalez, Rita, Dir.-Mktg.--Lennar Homes Inc., Miami, FL; *U.S. Public*, pg. 988
Good, David S., V.P.-Sls. & Mktg.--Engineered Systems Group, Jackson, MI; *U.S. Public*, pg. 24
Good, Gerald, Exec. V.P.-Mktg. & Mdsg.--The Great Atlantic & Pacific Tea Company, Inc., Montvale, NJ; *Int'l*, pg. 1375
Good, James L., V.P.-Corp. Commun. & Mktg.--California Water Service Co., San Jose, CA; *U.S. Public*, pg. 294
Good, James W., V.P.-Mktg.--Baldwin & Lyons, Inc., Indianapolis, IN; *U.S. Public*, pg. 169
Good, Jim, V.P.-Domestic Sls.--Liebert Corporation, Columbus, OH; *U.S. Public*, pg. 573
Goodell, Brenda, V.P.-Mktg. Communications--Reebok International Ltd., Stoughton, MA; *U.S. Public*, pg. 1369
Goodman, John, V.P.-Mktg.--Helzberg's Diamond Shops, Inc., Kansas City, MO; *U.S. Public*, pg. 220
Goodman, Kaye, Sr. Sec.-Mktg. Communications--Freightliner Corp., Portland, OR; *Int'l*, pg. 368
Goodman, Larry, Pres.-CNN Sls. & Mktg.--CNN (Cable News Network), Atlanta, GA; *U.S. Public*, pg. 1614
Goodman, Patti, Dir.-Mktg.--Franklin Electronic Publishers, Inc., Burlington, NJ; *U.S. Public*, pg. 679
Goodman, Stanley, Dir.-Mktg.--Ace Comb Company Inc., Booneville, AR; *U.S. Public*, pg. 1177
Goodpaster, Rob L., V.P.-Natl. Mktg.--Capital Senior Living, Inc., Dallas, TX; *U.S. Public*, pg. 302
Goodson, Buddy, Dir.-Mktg.--Pepper-Lawson, Katy, TX; *U.S. Private*, pg. 851
Goodwin, Brad, Dir.-Mktg.--S.C. Johnson & Son, Limited, Brantford, Canada; *U.S. Private*, pg. 593
Goodwin, Kathleen, Grp. Mktg. Dir.--PC Magazine, New York, NY; *Int'l*, pg. 1276
Goodwyn, William H., Jr., Exec. V.P.-Sls. & Mktg.--Lawyers Title Insurance Corporation, Richmond, VA; *U.S. Public*, pg. 981
Goon, Julie, Dir.-Adv.--Columbian Mutual Life Insurance Co., Binghamton, NY; *U.S. Private*, pg. 256
Goosen, P.A., Mgr.-Mktg.--Sasol Oil, Rosebank, South Africa; *Int'l*, pg. 1197
Gorbett, Richard, V.P.-Mktg., Special Tran. Grp.--Atlas Specialized Transportation, Evansville, IN; *U.S. Private*, pg. 97
Gorby, Jane, V.P.-Mktg. Dir.--Downey Savings & Loan Association, F.A., Newport Beach, CA; *U.S. Public*, pg. 526

Gorchow, Jonathan R., V.P.-Mktg. & Sls.--Comcast Cable Communications, Inc., Philadelphia, PA; *U.S. Public*, pg. 407
Gordon, Cheryl, Dir.-Mktg. & Sls.--Rothschild North America Inc., New York, NY; *U.S. Private*, pg. 947
Gordon, Cheryl, Dir.-Sls. & Mktg.--Rothschild Inc., New York, NY; *U.S. Private*, pg. 947
Gordon, Dave, Dir.-Mktg.-Swine & Poultry Prods.--Elanco Animal Health, Indianapolis, IN; *U.S. Public*, pg. 993
Gordon, Ian, Mgr.-Mktg. & Personal Wash--Lever Pond's Limited, Toronto, Canada; *Int'l*, pg. 1438
Gordon, Kenneth, Dir.-Adv. & Card Brand Strategy--Citibank Credit Card Marketing, Long Island City, NY; *U.S. Public*, *pg. 377*
Gordon, Lorraine, Mgr.-Mktg.--Crown Central Petroleum Corporation, Baltimore, MD; *U.S. Public*, pg. 462
Gordon, Lynn, Dir.-Mktg.--Fairmont Snack Group, Inc., Independence, OH; *U.S. Private*, pg. 392
Gordon, Lynn, Exec. V.P.-Mktg.--Reading Body Works, Inc., Reading, PA; *U.S. Private*, pg. 913
Gordon, Melvin S., Pres. & Chief Exec. Officer--Paradise, Inc., Plant City, FL; *U.S. Public*, pg. 1256
Gordon, Russell L., Dir.-Corp. Devel.--RPM, Inc., Medina, OH; *U.S. Public*, pg. 1356
Gordon, Sam, Dir.-Prod. Devel.--A-Dec, Inc., Newberg, OR; *U.S. Private*, pg. 2
Gordon, Steve, Exec. V.P. & Dir.-Sls. & Mktg.--Columbia Paint & Coatings, Spokane, WA; *U.S. Private*, pg. 256
Gordon, William, Exec. V.P.-Mktg.--Electronic Arts, San Mateo, CA; *U.S. Public*, pg. 569
Gore, Gary, Mgr.-Mktg.--SJL of Kansas Corp., Wichita, KS; *U.S. Public*, pg. 984
Gormally, Pat, Mgr.-Prod. Mkt.--Vitramon, Incorporated, Monroe, CT; *U.S. Public*, pg. 1722
Gorman, Jon, Dir.-Sls. & Mktg.--Power Contracting & Engineering Corp., Schaumburg, IL; *U.S. Private*, pg. 877
Gorman, Richard, V.P.-Mktg.--Interim Services Inc., Fort Lauderdale, FL; *U.S. Public*, pg. 892
Gorska, Barbara, Dir.-Mktg.--LOT Polish Airlines SA, New York, NY; *Int'l*, pg. 1062
Gorzalski, Edward, Sr. V.P.-Plng., Market Res. & Media Services--Thomas G. Ferguson Associates, Inc., Parsippany, NJ; *Int'l*, pg. 1483
Goshien, Gerald, Controller & Treas.-Sls. For Meats & Produce--The Mad Butcher, Inc., Pine Bluff, AR; *U.S. Private*, pg. 693
Gosling, Denise, Mgr.-Mktg. Communications--Electrohome Ltd., Kitchener, Canada; *Int'l*, pg. 438
Goss, J.H., Dir.-Mktg.--Solar Turbines Incorporated, San Diego, CA; *U.S. Public*, pg. 316
Goss, Mary, Mgr.-Mktg. Services--Danaher Tool Group, Lancaster, PA; *U.S. Public*, pg. 480
Goss, Mary, Mgr.-Mktg. Services--Danaher Tool Group, Chicago, IL; *U.S. Public*, pg. 481
Gosselin, Keith, Dir.-Mktg.--Standard Communications Corp., Torrance, CA; *Int'l*, pg. 841
Goto, Milton K., Dir.-Mktg. Svcs. & Adv.--Aloha Airgroup, Inc., Honolulu, HI; *U.S. Private*, pg. 44
Gott, Leigh, Dir.-Mktg.--Wisconsin Machine and Tool Corporation, Milwaukee, WI; *U.S. Private*, pg. 1185
Gottschalk, Heinz Dieter, Mgr.-Corp. Mktg. & Eurobond Trading--Bankgesellschaft Berlin, Berlin, Germany; *Int'l*, pg. 159
Goudge, Dave, V.P.-Prod. Mktg./Office Prods.--Boise Cascade Corporation, Boise, ID; *U.S. Public*, pg. 242
Goudge, Dave, V.P.-Prod. Mktg.--Boise Cascade Office Products Corporation, Itasca, IL; *U.S. Public*, pg. 243
Goudie, Peter G., Exec. V.P.-Primary Metals Mktg.--Inco Limited, Toronto, Canada; *Int'l*, pg. 672
Goudriaan, Jan, Mgr.-Mktg.--Bekaert Benelux N.V., Zwevegem, Belgium; *Int'l*, pg. 183
Gould, Doyle, V.P. & Gen. Mgr.-Flow Measure Div.--Perry Equipment Corporation, Mineral Wells, TX; *U.S. Private*, pg. 855
Gould, Jay D., Sr. V.P. & Chief Mktg. Officer--The Minute Maid Company, Houston, TX; *U.S. Public*, pg. 392
Gould, Jean R., Mktg. Asst.--Magnetic Analysis Corp., Mount Vernon, NY; *U.S. Private*, pg. 695
Gould, William, Mgr.-Sls. & Mktg.--Brady Enterprises, Inc., East Weymouth, MA; *U.S. Private*, pg. 165
Gould, William, Mgr.-Sls. & Mktg.--The William G. Bell Company, East Weymouth, MA; *U.S. Private*, pg. 165
Goulding, Barry W., V.P.-Mktg. & Lender Prods.--SLM Holding Corp., Washington, DC; *U.S. Public*, pg. 1419
Goulding, Thomas, V.P.-Sls. & Mktg., Interconnect Produdts Div.--Altron Incorporated, Wilmington, MA; *U.S. Public*, pg. 59
Gouze, Stephen P., V.P.-Sls. & Mktg.--INCSTAR Corporation, Stillwater, MN; *Int'l*, pg. 483
Gowaty, Nina L., Sr. V.P.-Human Resources--B.M.J. Financial Corp., Bordentown, NJ; *U.S. Public*, pg. 1528
Goyette, Richard C., V.P.-Sls. & Mktg.--Scan-Optics, Inc., Manchester, CT; *U.S. Public*, pg. 1436
Goyette, Susan, Dir.-Corp. Mktg.--The Mills Corporation, Arlington, VA; *U.S. Public*, pg. 1113
Graafland, R. Hooft, Dir.-Mktg.--Heineken N.V., Amsterdam, Netherlands; *Int'l*, pg. 608
Grabber, Michele, Dir.-Mktg.--Inland Associates, Olathe, KS; *U.S. Private*, pg. 563
Graber, Christine, V.P.-Mktg.-Retail--Hanover Stores, Newton, MA; *Int'l*, pg. 297
Grabowski, Dave, V.P.-Sls. & Mktg.--Allied Healthcare Products, Inc., Saint Louis, MO; *U.S. Public*, pg. 48
Grabski, Dennis, V.P.-Sls.--Outlook Packaging, Inc., Oak Creek, WI; *U.S. Public*, pg. 1236
Grace, John, V.P.-Program Mktg.--WTTW (Channel 11), Chicago, IL; *U.S. Private*, pg. 1145
Grace, Karyn, Dir.-Mktg. Communications--Elf Atochem North America, Inc., Philadelphia, PA; *Int'l*, pg. 445
Graciotti, Sr., Mgr.-Mktg.--Advanced Micro Devices S.p.a., Milan, Italy; *U.S. Public*, pg. 21
Grady, Dennis, V.P.-Health Care Programs--Sandoz Pharmaceuticals Corp., East Hanover, NJ; *Int'l*, pg. 974
Grady, R. Paul, V.P.-Sls. & Opers.--AmeriGas, Inc., Valley Forge, PA; *U.S. Public*, pg. 1653
Grady, Rob, Mgr.-Partnership Mktg.--Delta Air Lines, Inc., Atlanta, GA; *U.S. Public*, pg. 497
Graf, David, Mgr.-Mktg.--Berkel Incorporated, La Porte, IN; *Int'l*, pg. 545
Graf, Walter, Mgr.-Mktg. Plng.--Coop Switzerland, Basel, Switzerland; *Int'l*, pg. 329
Graff, Michael, V.P.-Strategic Mktg.--Harris Semiconductor, Melbourne, FL; *U.S. Public*, pg. 792
Graham, David, Head-Mktg.--Scottish Widows' Fund & Life Assurance Society, Edinburgh, United Kingdom; *Int'l*, pg. 1212
Graham, Doug, V.P.-Sls., Mktg. & Customer Service--Utilimaster Corp., Wakarusa, IN; *U.S. Private*, pg. 1130
Graham, Fiona, Mgr.-Dental Mktg.--Stafford-Miller Limited, Welwyn Garden City, United Kingdom; *U.S. Public*, pg. 237
Graham, Garry, Dir.-Mktg.--Burlington Coat Factory Warehouse Corporation, Burlington, NJ; *U.S. Public*, pg. 268
Graham, Heather, Dir.-Mktg.--Campbell Distillers Limited, Brentford, United Kingdom; *Int'l*, pg. 567
Graham, Jeff, Mgr.-Mktg.--N Base Comunications, Chatsworth, CA; *U.S. Public*, pg. 1027
Graham, Jim, Sr. V.P.-Corp. Sls. & Mktg.--Time Inc., New York, NY; *U.S. Public*, pg. 1612
Graham, John, Mgr.-Mktg. & Sls.--The Citadel Assurance Companies, Toronto, Canada; *Int'l*, pg. 346
Graham, John, Mgr.-Direct Mktg./Direct Response & Mktg.--Paddock Publications, Inc., Arlington Heights, IL; *U.S. Private*, pg. 833
Graham, Marc, Exec. V.P. & Gen. Mgr.--PACCAR Automotive Inc., Renton, WA; *U.S. Public*, pg. 1247
Graham, Michael, Mgr.-Mktg./Safety & Security Papers--Boise Cascade Corporation, Boise, ID; *U.S. Public*, pg. 242
Graham, Roy, Sr. V.P.-Sls. & Mktg.--Wyse Technology Inc., San Jose, CA; *U.S. Private*, pg. 1194
Graham, Susan, Dir.-Mktg.--The CIT Group/Sales Financing, Inc., Livingston, NJ; *Int'l*, pg. 360
Graham, Tom, Dir.-Natl. Mktg.--Yamaha Electronics Corp. USA, Buena Park, CA; *Int'l*, pg. 1516
Graham, William A., Jr., V.P.-Mktg.--Peoples Federal Savings & Loan Association, Conway, SC; *U.S. Public*, pg. 634
Gralen, Kevin, V.P.-Mktg.--Centigram Communications Corporation, San Jose, CA; *U.S. Public*, pg. 323
Granacki, Evelyn, Sr. Mgr.-Mktg. Communications--Computer Sciences Corporation, El Segundo, CA; *U.S. Public*, pg. 422
Granahan, Mark, V.P.-Mktg.--Linfinity Microelectronics Inc., Garden Grove, CA; *U.S. Public*, pg. 1547
Granas, M., Mgr.-Mktg.--Olivetti Hellas S.A., Athens, Greece; *Int'l*, pg. 1003
Grandinetti, Michael A., V.P.-Mktg.--Millipore Tylan Products, San Diego, CA; *U.S. Public*, pg. 1112
Grandle, Pat, Sec. & Mgr.-Mktg. & Adv.--Tricon Industries, Inc., Lisle, IL; *U.S. Private*, pg. 1102
Granger, Lee F., Mng. Dir.-Mktg.--American Automobile Association, Heathrow, FL; *U.S. Private*, pg. 50
Granont, Claire, Dir.-Mktg.--Editions Scientifiques et Medicales Elsevier, Paris, France; *Int'l*, pg. 1099
Grant, Bruce, V.P.-Sls. & Mktg.--Engineered Polymers Corporation, Mora, MN; *Int'l*, pg. 328
Grant, Chris, Sr. V.P.-Mngmt. Svcs.--The ServiceMaster Company, Downers Grove, IL; *U.S. Public*, pg. 1461
Grant, D.E., V.P.-Consumer Mktg.--Wrigley Canada Inc., Don Mills, Canada; *U.S. Public*, pg. 1781
Grant, Garth, Mgr.-Mktg.--H.E. Sargent, Inc., Stillwater, ME; *U.S. Private*, pg. 966
Grant, Lawrence Hunter, V.P.-Sls. & Mktg.--Matthew Bender & Company, Incorporated, New York, NY; *U.S. Public*, pg. 1616
Granucci, Leo, Sr. V.P.-Mktg. & Sls.--Core-Mark International, South San Francisco, CA; *U.S. Private*, pg. 275
Grass, Harry, Dir.-Sls. & Mktg.--CGF Sign, Inc., Denver, CO; *U.S. Private*, pg. 194
Grassl, Georg, Dir.-Mktg.--Henkel Austria Group, Vienna, Austria; *Int'l*, pg. 611
Grasso, Amanda, Mgr.-Adv. & Mktg.--Giles & Ransome, Inc., Bensalem, PA; *U.S. Private*, pg. 453
Graubart, Barry, V.P.-Database Devel. & Mktg.--Nelson Publications, Port Chester, NY; *U.S. Public*, pg. 1328
Gravely, Gates, Dir.-Indus. Mktg.--Dillard, A ResourceNet International Company, Greensboro, NC; *U.S. Public*, pg. 901
Gravener, I., Dir.-Mktg.--Canon (U.K.) Ltd., Wallington, United Kingdom; *Int'l*, pg. 263
Graves, David, V.P.-Mktg.--Sylvan Learning Systems Inc., Baltimore, MD; *U.S. Public*, pg. 1545
Graves, James, Dir.-Mktg.--Masco Corporation, Taylor, MI; *U.S. Public*, pg. 1052
Graves, Matthew, Pres.--Medusa Minerals Co, Thomasville, PA; *U.S. Public*, pg. 1084
Graves, Michael, V.P.-Pur. & Mktg.--D & K Healthcare Resources, Inc., Saint Louis, MO; *U.S. Public*, pg. 471
Graves, Peter, V.P.-Prod. Mktg.--Selfix, Inc., Chicago, IL; *U.S. Public*, pg. 832
Graves, Peter L., V.P.-Selfix Prod. Mktg.--Home Products International, Inc., Chicago, IL; *U.S. Public*, pg. 832
Graves, Richard, Sr. V.P.-Mktg.--Lexington Furniture Industries, Lexington, NC; *U.S. Private*, pg. 432
Gravlin, Edward N., V.P.-Mktg.--Sames Electrostatic, Inc., Livonia, MI; *U.S. Public*, pg. 229
Gray-Goodman, Tracey, Mgr.-Mktg.--Pennaco Hosiery, New York, NY; *U.S. Public*, pg. 483
Gray, Andrew, Supvr.-Mktg.--Yamaha Motor Canada Ltd., North York, Canada; *Int'l*, pg. 1516
Gray, Andy, V.P.-Mktg.--Rexall Sundown Inc., Boca Raton, FL; *U.S. Public*, pg. 1384
Gray, Andy, V.P.-Mktg.--Thompson Nutritional Products, Boca Raton, FL; *U.S. Public*, pg. 1384
Gray, Barry, V.P.-Sls. & Mktg.--Weiler & Company, Inc., Whitewater, WI; *U.S. Private*, pg. 1160
Gray, Cynthia J., Sr. V.P.-Mktg.--Norwest Corporation, Minneapolis, MN; *U.S. Public*, pg. 1201
Gray, David, Mgr.-Mktg.--CamEra, Inc., Saint Petersburg, FL; *U.S. Public*, pg. 1457
Gray, Donald, Dir.-Circulation & Mktg.--Express Newspapers plc, London, United Kingdom; *Int'l*, pg. 1443
Gray, Jim, Dir.-Mktg. Svcs.--Aearo Company, Boston, MA; *U.S. Private*, pg. 23
Gray, Judy, Dir.-Mktg.--Florasynth Inc., Teterboro, NJ; *Int'l*, pg. 173
Gray, Larry, V.P.-Consumer Sls. & Mktg.--The Fuller Brush Company, Great Bend, KS; *U.S. Public*, pg. 282
Gray, Larry H., V.P.-Consumer Sls. & Mktg.--The Fuller Brush Company, Great Bend, KS; *U.S. Public*, pg. 282
Gray, Lisa, Gen. Mgr.-Mktg.--The National Mutual Life Association of Australia Limited, Melbourne, Australia; *Int'l*, pg. 909
Gray, Richard, V.P.-Sls. & Mktg.--Rochester-Midland ICL, Omaha, NE; *U.S. Private*, pg. 937
Gray, Roland, V.P.-Mktg.--Blue Bird Corporation, Macon, GA; *U.S. Private*, pg. 151
Gray, Scott A., V.P.-Sls. & Mktg.--Gray Printing Co., Fostoria, OH; *U.S. Private*, pg. 472
Gray, Stephan, Dir.-Mktg.--Cabletron Systems, Inc., Rochester, NH; *U.S. Public*, pg. 288
Gray, William J., Sr. V.P.-Mktg. & Supply--Holly Corporation, Dallas, TX; *U.S. Public*, pg. 830
Grayston, Eric, Mgr.-Mktg.--Parker & Amchem, Etobicoke, Canada; *Int'l*, pg. 612
Graziano, F.J., Mgr.-Mktg.--Sterno, Inc., New York, NY; *U.S. Public*, pg. 397
Grba, Joanne P., V.P.-Mktg.--Tab Products Co., Palo Alto, CA; *U.S. Public*, pg. 1559
Greathouse, Keith, Dir.-Worldwide Mktg.--Dermik Laboratories, Inc., Collegeville, PA; *Int'l*, pg. 1110
Greaves, Andy Wilson, Dir.-Mktg.--IBM United Kingdom Holdings Limited, Portsmouth, United Kingdom; *U.S. Public*, pg. 897
Grebey, Nancy V., Sr. V.P.-Mktg. & Adv.--Crestar Financial Corporation, Richmond, VA; *U.S. Public*, pg. 458
Greco, David A., V.P.-Mktg.--Mortgage Guaranty Insurance Corporation, Milwaukee, WI; *U.S. Public*, pg. 1026
Greeff, Neil, Mgr.-Mktg./Phenolics--Sasol Chemicals Europe Limited, Solihull, United Kingdom; *Int'l*, pg. 1196
Green, Barry, Sr. V.P.-Sls. & Mktg.--Active International, Pearl River, NY; *U.S. Private*, pg. 15
Green, Clifford, V.P.-Sls., Mktg. & Adv.--Highfield Manufacturing Co., Bridgeport, CT; *Int'l*, pg. 127
Green, David B., Sr. V.P.-Mktg.--McDonald's Corporation, Oak Brook, IL; *U.S. Public*, pg. 1068
Green, J., Mgr.-Contracts--Australian Oil & Gas Corporation Limited, Sydney, Australia; *Int'l*, pg. 101
Green, Jan, Mgr.-Pub. Rels.--Union Trust Bank, Union City, IN; *U.S. Public*, pg. 633
Green, Jim, V.P.-Bakery & Deli--Rich Products Corp., Buffalo, NY; *U.S. Private*, pg. 928
Green, John, V.P.-Mktg.--Quipp, Inc., Hialeah, FL; *U.S. Public*, pg. 1353
Green, John, V.P.-Mktg. Contracts--Quipp Systems, Inc., Hialeah, FL; *U.S. Public*, pg. 1353
Green, Kevin, V.P.-Mktg.--Lillian Vernon Corporation, New Rochelle, NY; *U.S. Public*, pg. 1716
Green, Lanny R., Sr. V.P.-Mktg.--VASA Brougher, Inc., Indianapolis, IN; *Int'l*, pg. 464
Green, Mark E., Mgr.-Natl. Mktg. Communications--Permabond International, Englewood, NJ; *Int'l*, pg. 1435
Green, Michael, Sr. V.P.-Mktg.--Parisian, Inc., Birmingham, AL; *U.S. Public*, pg. 1333
Green, Paul, Mgr.-Mktg.--Barra, Inc., Berkeley, CA; *U.S. Public*, pg. 191
Green, Rick, V.P.-Sls. & Mktg.--Sensall, Div. of Rosemount, Inc., Hauppauge, NY; *U.S. Public*, pg. 574
Green, Sam, Dir.-Mktg.--Philip Laser Magnetic Storage, Colorado Springs, CO; *Int'l*, pg. 1054
Green, Tom, V.P.-Sls. & Mktg.--North American Capacitor Co., Indianapolis, IN; *U.S. Private*, pg. 803
Green, Tom, V.P.-Mktg.--Senco Products, Inc., Cincinnati, OH; *U.S. Private*, pg. 984
Greenberg, Catherine, Dir.-Mktg. & Stategic Devel.--The Roanoke Times, Roanoke, VA; *U.S. Private*, pg. 649
Greenberg, George, Exec. V.P.-Mktg.--Fox Broadcasting Company (FBC), Beverly Hills, CA; *Int'l*, pg. 926
Greenberg, Mark, Exec. V.P.-Mktg. & Communications--Showtime Networks Inc., New York, NY; *U.S. Private*, pg. 779
Greendale, Christopher H., Exec. V.P.-Mktg.--Cambridge Technology Partners, Cambridge, MA; *U.S. Public*, pg. 1424
Greene, Gilbert K., Mgr.-Mktg. Svcs.--Victaulic Company of America, Easton, PA; *U.S. Private*, pg. 1138
Greene, Wendy, Mgr.-Pub. Rels.--Hughes Communications, Inc., Long Beach, CA; *U.S. Public*, pg. 721
Greenfield, Rick, Sr. V.P. & Mktg. Res. Dir.--Colle & McVoy, Inc., Minneapolis, MN; *U.S. Private*, pg. 252
Greenisen, G., Dir.-Mktg.--Wilkinson Company, Inc., Stow, OH; *U.S. Private*, pg. 368
Greenisen, Phil, Mktg.--Turner Machine Company, Salem, OH; *U.S. Private*, pg. 368
Greenwald, Mark, Dir.-Mktg. & Adv.--D&H Distributing Company, Harrisburg, PA; *U.S. Private*, pg. 300
Greenwood, Mary, V.P.-Mktg.--Goldwell Cosmetics (USA) Inc., Linthicum Heights, MD; *Int'l*, pg. 718
Greenwood, Scott, V.P.-Mktg.--Dole Food Company, Inc., Westlake Village, CA; *U.S. Public*, pg. 515
Greer, Jana Waring, Pres.-SunAmerica Mktg. Inc. & Sr. V.P. SunAmerica, Inc. Affairs--SunAmerica Inc., Los Angeles, CA; *U.S. Public*, pg. 1532
Greer, Lou, V.P.-Partners Mktg.--Network Computing Devices, Inc., Mountain View, CA; *U.S. Public*, pg. 1168
Greer, Rita, V.P.-Design--Halper Bros., Milwaukee, WI; *U.S. Private*, pg. 920

Greer, W. Miles, V.P.-Mktg. & Customer Services--Savannah Electric & Power Co., Savannah, GA; *U.S. Public*, pg. 1490

Greg, Barry, Supvr.--Erico International, Solon, OH; *U.S. Private*, pg. 381

Gregersen, Klaus, Mgr.-Mktg.--Hewlett-Packard A/S, Birkerod, Denmark; *U.S. Public*, pg. 818

Gregg, Ann M., V.P.-Mktg.--San Jose Mercury News, San Jose, CA; *U.S. Public*, pg. 964

Gregg, David E., V.P. & Dir.-Mktg.--Noland Company, Newport News, VA; *U.S. Public*, pg. 1187

Gregg, Edward G., V.P.-Sls. & Mktg.--Roppe Corp., Fostoria, OH; *U.S. Private*, pg. 944

Gregg, Jay, Mgr.-Mktg. Communications--Owens-Corning Canada, North York, Canada; *U.S. Public*, pg. 1237

Gregg, Rob, V.P.-Mktg.--Jacob Leinenkugel Brewing Co., Chippewa Falls, WI; *U.S. Public*, pg. 1289

Gregoire, Sarah, Mgr.-Mktg./Rapid Test System--Genzyme Diagnostics, Medix Biotech, San Carlos, CA; *U.S. Public*, pg. 733

Gregory, Cary, Dir.-Mktg.--Ames Company, Parkersburg, WV; *U.S. Public*, pg. 1683

Gregory, Dave, Dir.-Mktg. & Mdsg.--Star Lumber & Supply Company, Inc., Wichita, KS; *U.S. Private*, pg. 1034

Gregory, Gail, V.P.-Mktg.--Henry Schein, Inc., Melville, NY; *U.S. Public*, pg. 1437

Gregory, Michael, Dir.-Sls. & Mktg.--The North American Coal Corporation, Dallas, TX; *U.S. Public*, pg. 1149

Gregory, Scott S., Dir.-Mktg.--The Machine Tool Group, Cleveland, OH; *U.S. Public*, pg. 503

Gregory, Vince, Mgr.-Mkt. Intelligence, Plng. & Systems Support--The Goodyear Tire & Rubber Company, Akron, OH; *U.S. Public*, pg. 752

Gregovits, Vic, V.P.-Mktg. & Broadcasting--Pittsburgh Associates, Pittsburgh, PA; *U.S. Private*, pg. 867

Greinke, Donald, Dir.-Mktg.--AmeriGas, Inc., Valley Forge, PA; *U.S. Public*, pg. 1653

Greinor, Robert, Sr. V.P.-CATV Sls.--Pico Products, Inc., Lake View Terrace, CA; *U.S. Public*, pg. 1294

Greisl, Kevin P., V.P.-Sls.--Mid-America Capital Resources, Inc., Indianapolis, IN; *U.S. Public*, pg. 913

Grelis, Wink, V.P.-Mktg.--Adobe Systems Incorporated, San Jose, CA; *U.S. Public*, pg. 20

Gremaud, Laurent, Chief Information Officer & Sr. V.P.-Mktg.--UMS Swiss Metalworks Holding Ltd, Dornach, Switzerland; *Int'l*, pg. 1427

Greminger, Dick, Dir.-Sls. & Mktg.--Biltbest Windows, Saint Genevieve, MO; *U.S. Public*, pg. 1683

Grenko, Craig, Dir.-Mktg.--Valvoline Instant Oil Change, Inc., Lexington, KY; *U.S. Public*, pg. 139

Grennan, Don, Dir.-Mktg.--Gordon Publications, Inc., Morris Plains, NJ; *Int'l*, pg. 1096

Grepp, Dave W., V.P.-Sls. & Mktg.--The Chardon Rubber Co., Chardon, OH; *U.S. Private*, pg. 229

Gress, Robert, Mgr.-Mktg.--Technology for Communications International, Sunnyvale, CA; *U.S. Public*, pg. 1555

Greubel, Richard, Mgr.-Mktg.-Crop Protection--Monsanto Argentina S.A.I.C., Buenos Aires, Argentina; *U.S. Public*, pg. 1125

Grey, Thomas, V.P.-Sls. & Mktg.--Lawson Mardon Flexible Packaging, Inc., Bellwood, IL; *Int'l*, pg. 67

Grieco, John L., Dir.-Mktg.--Stratton Growth Fund, Inc., Plymouth Meeting, PA; *U.S. Private*, pg. 1046

Griesdorn, Monica, Natl. Mgr.-Mktg.--Crane & Co., Inc., Dalton, MA; *U.S. Private*, pg. 286

Griesenauer, Quentin, Corp. Dir.-Mktg.--Diagraph Corporation, Earth City, MO; *U.S. Private*, pg. 330

Griessel, Richard, Dir.-Mktg. & Sls.--Semikron International, GmbH & Co. KG, Nuremberg, Germany; *Int'l*, pg. 1220

Griffin, Charles, Sr. Dir.-Sls. & Mktg.--Sequus Pharmaceuticals, Inc., Menlo Park, CA; *U.S. Public*, pg. 1460

Griffin, Don, Dir.-Mktg.--Dayco Swan Corporation, Worthington, OH; *U.S. Public*, pg. 1045

Griffin, John, Pres.-Magazine Div.--Rodale Press, Inc., Emmaus, PA; *U.S. Private*, pg. 939

Griffin, Reva, Mktg. Services Admin.--American Wyott Corporation, Cheyenne, WY; *U.S. Private*, pg. 1193

Griffith, Anne E., V.P.-Mktg.--Sheaffer Inc., Fort Madison, IA; *Int'l*, pg. 542

Griffith, David, V.P.-Sls. & Mktg.--Earle Industries, Inc., Earle, AR; *U.S. Private*, pg. 356

Griffith, Greg, V.P.-Sls. & Mktg.--Delta Pride Catfish, Inc., Indianola, MS; *U.S. Private*, pg. 322

Griffith, Greg, Dir.-Pub. Affairs & Admin.--Great Lakes Chemical Corporation, West Lafayette, IN; *U.S. Public*, pg. 760

Griffith, J.W., V.P.-North American Automotive, Rail, Asia Pac. & Latin America--The Timken Company, Canton, OH; *U.S. Public*, pg. 1617

Griffith, Mary H., Sr. V.P.-Mktg. Commun.--National City Corporation, Cleveland, OH; *U.S. Public*, pg. 1154

Griffith, T.R., V.P.-Mktg.--Cooper Tire & Rubber Company, Findlay, OH; *U.S. Public*, pg. 445

Griffith, T.R., V.P.-Mktg.--The Cooper Tire Company, Findlay, OH; *U.S. Public*, pg. 445

Griggs, Jack, V.P. & Dir.-Mktg.--Firstbank of Illinois Co., Springfield, IL; *U.S. Public*, pg. 643

Griggs, Steven, Dir.-Mktg.--Fruit of the Loom Limited, London, United Kingdom; *U.S. Public*, pg. 686

Grignon, Michel, Exec. V.P.-Mktg.--Hydro-Quebec, Montreal, Canada; *Int'l*, pg. 640

Grilhault, Jean-Luc Des F., V.P.-Comml. Affairs, USA--Air France, New York, NY; *Int'l*, pg. 560

Grillo, Frank, Sr. V.P.-Mktg.--WorldCom, Inc., Jackson, MS; *U.S. Public*, pg. 1779

Grimes, Gary, V.P.-Sls. & Mktg.--Directory Distributing Associates, Inc., Saint Louis, MO; *U.S. Private*, pg. 334

Grimes, Michele M., Mgr.-Mktg./Midwest--Checkers Drive-In Restaurants, Inc., Clearwater, FL; *U.S. Public*, pg. 342

Grimes, Rick, V.P.-Mktg.--Rockford Acromatic Product Co., Rockford, IL; *U.S. Private*, pg. 938

Grimm, Clyde L., Sr. V.P.-U.S. Sls., Mktg. & Service & Gen. Mgr.--Bayer Corporation, Pittsburgh, PA; *Int'l*, pg. 172

Grimm, Dan, Dir.-Mktg. & Communications--Becton Dickinson & Company, Franklin Lakes, NJ; *U.S. Public*, pg. 199

Grimm, F. Jerome, Dir.-Mktg.--Hagler, Mastrovita & Hewitt, Inc., Boston, MA; *U.S. Public*, pg. 1673

Grimm, Michael, Exec. V.P.-Sls. & Mktg.--MTL Inc., Plant City, FL; *U.S. Public*, pg. 1028

Grimm, Michael, Exec. V.P.-Sls. & Mktg.--Montgomery Tank Lines, Inc., Plant City, FL; *U.S. Public*, pg. 1028

Grindley, Mitchell P., V.P.-Mktg.--Plaskolite Inc., Columbus, OH; *U.S. Private*, pg. 870

Grindstaff, Evelyn S., V.P.-Sls.--Chi Systems Division, Ann Arbor, MI; *U.S. Public*, pg. 1539

Griner, Lyn, Pres.-Mktg. & Co. Communications--JC Penney Company, Inc., Plano, TX; *U.S. Public*, pg. 916

Grinnell, Jane, Mgr.-Mktg. Communications--Magna International Inc., Markham, Canada; *Int'l*, pg. 829

Grinnell, Suzanne, Mktg. Specialist--Frank Consolidated Enterprises Inc., Des Plaines, IL; *U.S. Private*, pg. 423

Gris, J., Dir.-Mktg.--Revlon, S.A., Madrid, Spain; *U.S. Private*, pg. 690

Grisso, Ed, V.P.-Sls. & Mktg.--Harcrest International, Ltd., Clark, NJ; *U.S. Private*, pg. 500

Grissom, Chip, V.P.-Mktg.--Norrell Corporation, Atlanta, GA; *U.S. Public*, pg. 1192

Grissom, Chip, V.P.-Mktg.--Norrell Services Inc., Atlanta, GA; *U.S. Public*, pg. 1192

Grissom, Victoria West, Dir.-Client Mktg.--The L & B Group, Dallas, TX; *U.S. Public*, pg. 1673

Grivas, Rose, Coord.-Mktg.--Ryder System, Inc., Miami, FL; *U.S. Public*, pg. 1413

Grizzle, Annie, Mgr.-Mktg. Asst.--Wheatland Tube Company, Collingswood, NJ; *U.S. Private*, pg. 1170

Grob, J. Murray, Pres.--Caravan Brokay, Totowa, NJ; *U.S. Private*, pg. 208

Groen, Ron, V.P.-Sls. & Mktg.--Texas Micro, Inc., Houston, TX; *U.S. Public*, pg. 1586

Groff, Kerlayn, Mgr.-Mktg. Commun.--Ecolab Inc., Saint Paul, MN; *U.S. Public*, pg. 562

Groff, Randall, Mgr.-Corp. Mktg.--IMC Global, Bannockburn, IL; *U.S. Public*, pg. 856

Grogan, Shelly, Asst. V.P. & Mgr.-Mktg.--Willis Corroon Corp. of Minnesota, Minneapolis, MN; *Int'l*, pg. 1506

Grogman, Roger, V.P.-Mktg.--McLane Company, Inc., Temple, TX; *U.S. Public*, pg. 1733

Gronfors, Antti, Mgr.-Export--Meijeriosuuskunta/Mejeriandelslaget Milka, Helsinki, Finland; *Int'l*, pg. 854

Gronite, Al, Mgr.-Mktg--Astre Corporate Group, Alexandria, VA; *U.S. Private*, pg. 93

Gronlund, Jan-Erik, Dir.-Mktg.--AMER TOBACCO Ltd., Tuusula, Finland; *Int'l*, pg. 72

Gronroos, Henri, Dir.-Mktg.--Wisapak Oy Ab, Pietarsaari Factory, Pietarsaari, Finland; *Int'l*, pg. 1429

Groom, Karen, Dir.-Pub. Rels. & Hosptiality Mktg.--Gaylord Entertainment/Opryland USA, Nashville, TN; *U.S. Public*, pg. 704

Groschopp, Rudolfo, Dir.-Mktg.--AGCO Argentina S.A., Haedo, Argentina; *Int'l*, pg. 30

Gross, Annette, Mgr.-Mktg. & Distrb.--Ingersoll Equipment Co., Inc., Winneconne, WI; *Int'l*, pg. 1129

Gross, Gary, Dir.-Mktg.--McKesson Water Products Company, Pasadena, CA; *U.S. Public*, pg. 1073

Gross, Perry, Mgr.--Parsons Brinckerhoff Construction Services, Inc., Herndon, VA; *U.S. Private*, pg. 841

Gross, Steve, Sr. V.P.-Mktg.--MobileComm, Ridgefield Park, NJ; *U.S. Public*, pg. 1120

Grosse, George, V.P.-Comml. Mktg.--Wilkins-Rogers Incorporated, Ellicott City, MD; *U.S. Private*, pg. 1176

Grossman, Bernard, V.P.-Sls., Mktg. & Fin.--M. Grossman & Son, Inc., Passaic, NJ; *U.S. Private*, pg. 483

Grossman, Fredric, V.P.--International Components Corporation, Melville, NY; *U.S. Private*, pg. 569

Grossman, Janice, Exec. V.P.-Mktg. & Adv.--New York Magazine, New York, NY; *U.S. Public*, pg. 1328

Grosso, Anthony J., Sr. V.P.-Mktg.--PMA Reinsurance Corporation, Philadelphia, PA; *U.S. Public*, pg. 1272

Grot, Cindy, Coord.-Mktg.--Pascoe Building Systems, Inc., Columbus, GA; *U.S. Private*, pg. 842

Grota, Rodrigo, Mgr.-Mktg.--Henkel S/A. Industrias Quimicas, Sao Paulo, Brazil; *Int'l*, pg. 613

Grotberg, Jean, Specialist-Mktg.--Power House Technologies, Inc., Bozeman, MT; *U.S. Public*, pg. 1319

Grote, Dominic, Mgr.-Mktg.--Grote Industries, Madison, IN; *U.S. Private*, pg. 483

Grovenstein, Marsha, V.P.-Mktg.--Gulfstream Aerospace Corporation, Savannah, GA; *U.S. Private*, pg. 419

Grover, Charles W., Exec. V.P.--The Union Central Life Insurance Co., Cincinnati, OH; *U.S. Private*, pg. 1118

Grover, William G., Sr. V.P.-Sls. & Mktg.--Comdial Corporation, Charlottesville, VA; *U.S. Public*, pg. 407

Groves, Donald C., Dir.-Mktg.--Sulphite Pulp, Temiscaming, Canada; *Int'l*, pg. 1375

Grow, Robert B., Dir.-Adv.--Raytheon Systems Co., Kirkwood, NY; *U.S. Public*, pg. 1364

Gruber, Richard L., V.P.-Mktg.--NUI Corporation, Bedminster, NJ; *U.S. Public*, pg. 1147

Gruen, Judy, Dir.-Mktg. & Ad Sls.--Discovery Communications, Inc., Bethesda, MD; *U.S. Private*, pg. 334

Grueneberg, Jeffrey, Mgr.-Mktg.--Rockford Products Corp., Rockford, IL; *U.S. Private*, pg. 938

Grulke, Ted, V.P.-Sls. & Mktg./Govt.--Detroit Diesel Corp., Detroit, MI; *U.S. Private*, pg. 850

Gruner, Lester, Asst. V.P.-Mktg.--G.E. Capital Assurance, Seattle, WA; *U.S. Public*, pg. 712

Grupp, Andreas, Dir.-Adv. & Mktg.--Spindelfabrik Suessen, Suessen, Germany; *Int'l*, pg. 1290

Grymes, John, Pres.-Williamhouse Div.--American Pad and Paper Company, Dallas, TX; *U.S. Public*, pg. 88

Grzelecki, Art, Dir.-Mktg.--Klosterman Baking Company, Inc., Cincinnati, OH; *U.S. Private*, pg. 626

Gualtieri, Ed, V.P.-Mktg.--Barton Brands, Ltd., Chicago, IL; *U.S. Public*, pg. 300

Gualtieri, Pat, Sr. Dir.-Mktg. & Adv.--Medicine Shoppe International, Inc., Saint Louis, MO; *U.S. Public*, pg. 304

Guan, Cheng Keng, Mgr.-Mktg.--Champion Motors (1975) Pte. Ltd., Singapore, Singapore; *Int'l*, pg. 672

Guarascio, Philip, V.P. & Gen. Mgr-Mktg. & Adv.-NAO--General Motors Corporation, Detroit, MI; *U.S. Public*, pg. 718

Guariglia, Michael, V.P. & Dir.-Sls. & Mktg.--CBS Television Network, New York, NY; *U.S. Public*, pg. 274

Guarnaccia, Richard T., V.P. & Dir.-Sls. & Mktg.--Reeves International, Spartanburg, SC; *U.S. Private*, pg. 507

Guazzo, Al, Dir.-Mktg.--Power Control Div., Bowling Green, KY; *U.S. Public*, pg. 556

Gudors, Sandra, Dir.-Mktg.--McAlpin's, Cincinnati, OH; *U.S. Public*, pg. 1090

Guenther, Jeffrey P., Dir.-Mktg.--Hastings Manufacturing Company, Hastings, MI; *U.S. Public*, pg. 798

Guenther, John, V.P.-Mktg.--The Wickman Corp., Oak Park, MI; *U.S. Private*, pg. 1175

Guerico, Vincent M., Sr. V.P.-Worldwide Sls. & Mktg.--General Semiconductor, Inc., Melville, NY; *U.S. Public*, pg. 726

Guerraoui, May, Dir.-Mktg.--Fiat Auto Suisse SA, Geneva, Switzerland; *Int'l*, pg. 481

Guerreau, Bernard, Dir.-Sls. & Mktg. (France)--Automobiles Citroen, Neuilly, France; *Int'l*, pg. 1020

Guerriugue, Jon, Mgr.-Mktg.--Linotype-Hell Company, Hauppauge, NY; *Int'l*, pg. 604

Guertin, Joseph A., Dir.-Mktg. Commun.--TRW Inc., Cleveland, OH; *U.S. Public*, pg. 1558

Guertin, Marci, V.P. & Mgr.-Intl. Mktg.--The International Publishing Group, Reading, MA; *Int'l*, pg. 1027

Gugliotti, Carmine, Mgr.-Mktg.-Airpax Instruments--Philips Automotive Electronics, Cheshire, CT; *Int'l*, pg. 1054

Guha, Richard, Sr. V.P.-Mktg.--MediaOne, Boston, MA; *U.S. Public*, pg. 1688

Guiardo, Paul, Exec. V.P.-Mktg.--America's Store, Saint Petersburg, FL; *U.S. Public*, pg. 1685

Guillet, Laurence, Mktg. Team Asst.--Gillette France, S.A., Levallois-Perret, France; *U.S. Public*, pg. 744

Guillory, Grace, Dir.-Food Pur.--IHOP Corp., Glendale, CA; *U.S. Public*, pg. 862

Guillory, Winston, Sr. V.P.-Sls., Mktg. & Field Opers.--Amtech Systems Corporation, Dallas, TX; *U.S. Public*, pg. 105

Guillotte, Choppy, Dir.-Affiliate Mktg. & Promo--UPN-United Paramount Network, Los Angeles, CA; *U.S. Public*, pg. 352

Guillotte, Choppy, Dir.-Affiliate Mktg. & Promo--UPN-United Paramount Network, Los Angeles, CA; *U.S. Private*, pg. 777

Guise, Tom, Dir.-Adv. & Mktg.--PRO Group, Inc., Englewood, CO; *U.S. Private*, pg. 887

Guldalian, Ken, Dir.-Mktg. & Sls.--Guth Lighting Company, Saint Louis, MO; *Int'l*, pg. 821

Gulden, Gary W., V.P.-Mktg. & Sls.--JJI Lighting Group Inc., Greenwich, CT; *Int'l*, pg. 821

Gulien, Richard, Dir.-Mktg. Corp. Communications--Sextant Avionique, Meudon, France; *Int'l*, pg. 29

Gulley, James L., Mgr.-Mktg. Promo.--Moscom Corporation, Pittsford, NY; *U.S. Public*, pg. 1136

Gulliksen, J.E., Dir.-Mktg.--Koehler Manufacturing Company, Marlborough, MA; *U.S. Private*, pg. 706

Gullo, Gaye, V.P.-Field Mktg. Opers.--Harrah's Entertainment, Inc., Memphis, TN; *U.S. Public*, pg. 790

Gulpen, Ir. N., Dir.-Mktg.--DSM Resins B.V., Zwolle, Netherlands; *Int'l*, pg. 353

Gund, E., Dir.-Mktg.--Lockheed Information Management Services Co., Teaneck, NJ; *U.S. Public*, pg. 1009

Gunderson, Gary G., V.P.-Mktg.--C.F. Haglin & Sons, Edina, MN; *U.S. Private*, pg. 493

Gunderson, Priscilla, Mgr.-Mktg.--EMPI, Inc., Saint Paul, MN; *U.S. Public*, pg. 545

Gunn, Charlene, Dir.-Mktg. & Industry Sls.--Payless Car Rental System, Inc., Saint Petersburg, FL; *U.S. Private*, pg. 844

Gunn, Michael W., Sr. V.P.-Mktg.--AMR Corporation, Fort Worth, TX; *U.S. Public*, pg. 9

Gunn, Norman L., Dir.-Mktg.--Interstate/Johnson Lane, Inc., Charlotte, NC; *U.S. Public*, pg. 909

Gunnarsson, Goran, Dir.-Savings Bank Zone Central- Mktg. & Savings Prods.--Swedbank, Stockholm, Sweden; *Int'l*, pg. 1328

Gupta, Pravin, Gen. Mgr.-Mktg.--Precision Fasteners Ltd., Thane, India; *U.S. Public*, pg. 1420

Gupta, Satish K., V.P.-Corp. Mktg. & Bus. Devel.--Cirrus Logic, Inc., Fremont, CA; *U.S. Public*, pg. 375

Gura, Jerry, Dir.-Pub. Affairs--Amsted Industries Incorporated, Chicago, IL; *U.S. Private*, pg. 68

Gurkin, Martin, Asst. Gen. Mgr. & Dir.-Sls. & Mktg.--Isco Separation Instruments Division, Lincoln, NE; *U.S. Public*, pg. 914

Gusinde, Susan, V.P.-Mktg.--AMCORE Bank N.A., Northwest, Woodstock, IL; *U.S. Public*, pg. 64

Gust, Pam, Dir.-Mktg.--Warner Press, Inc., Anderson, IN; *U.S. Private*, pg. 1150

Gustapane, Alessandro, Dir.-Mktg. & Intl. Affairs--Agusta S.P.A., Varese, Italy; *Int'l*, pg. 32

Gustavson, Susann, Mgr.-Mktg.--Laura Ashley (USA) Inc., Boston, MA; *Int'l*, pg. 804

Gustin, Carl E., Jr., Sr. V.P. & Chief Mktg. Officer--Eastman Kodak Company, Rochester, NY; *U.S. Public*, pg. 550

Gustin, L. Carl, Sr. V.P.-Corp. Rels.--Boston Edison Company, Boston, MA; *U.S. Public*, pg. 247

Gustitus, Cheryl, Dir.-Mktg.--Primark Corporation, Waltham, MA; *U.S. Public*, pg. 1325

Gustitus, Cheryl, Dir.-Mktg.--Disclosure Incorporated, Bethesda, MD; *U.S. Public*, pg. 1325

Guthrie, A. D., Dir.-Adv. & Mgr.- Sls. & Mktg.--Sterling Davis Standard, South Plainfield, NJ; *Int'l*, pg. 1240

Guthrie, Frances, Exec. V.P.-Mktg. & Sls.--Fortis Benefits Insurance Company, Kansas City, MO; *Int'l*, pg. 499

Guthrie, James, Sr. V.P.-Sls. & Mktg.--Petersen Publishing Company, L.L.C., Los Angeles, CA; *U.S. Private*, pg. 856

Gutierrez, Eileen, V.P.-Mktg. Svcs.--United Laboratories, Inc., Saint Charles, IL; *U.S. Private*, pg. 1122
Gutierrez, Manuel D., Mgr.-Mkt. Research--Kohler Company, Kohler, WI; *U.S. Private*, pg. 630
Gutleber, Sam, Dir.-Mktg.--Guardian Alarm Co., Southfield, MI; *U.S. Private*, pg. 485
Gutman, Irving, V.P.-Lambda N. American Opers.--Lambda Electronics Inc., Melville, NY; *Int'l*, pg. 1241
Gutterman, Alison, V.P.-Mktg.--Jelmar Company, Lincolnwood, IL; *U.S. Private*, pg. 585
Gutterman, Allen, Sr. V.P.-Mktg.--New York City Off-Track Betting Corp., New York, NY; *U.S. Private*, pg. 794
Guttroff, George, Dir.-Mktg.--Dentsply New Image, Carlsbad, CA; *U.S. Public*, pg. 499
Guy, Kenneth, V.P.-Member Devel. & Creative Svcs.--Topco Associates, Inc., Skokie, IL; *U.S. Private*, pg. 1091
Guyardo, Paul, Exec. V.P.-Mktg.--Home Shopping Network, Inc., Saint Petersburg, FL; *U.S. Public*, pg. 1685
Guze, Jack, Chief Mktg. Officer--Reebok International Ltd., Stoughton, MA; *U.S. Public*, pg. 1369
Guzek, Tom, V.P.-Prod. & Mktg. Devel.--Bussmann Division, Ellisville, MO; *U.S. Public*, pg. 443
Gvwinner, Pierre, Dir.-Mktg. & Pub. Rels.--Brauerei Eichhof, Lucerne, Switzerland; *Int'l*, pg. 213
Gwinner, Pierre, Dir.-Mktg.--Societe Hoteliere Paris Vanves, Evry, France; *Int'l*, pg. 20
Gwozdz, Pamela, Mgr.-Mktg.--Laser Diode Products, New Brunswick, NJ; *Int'l*, pg. 892
Haanpaa, Jouni, Mgr.-Office Supplies--Academic Bookstore, Helsinki, Finland; *Int'l*, pg. 1301
Haapakoski, Pauli, Mgr.-Mktg.--Finnsementti Oy Ab, Pargas, Finland; *Int'l*, pg. 1198
Haar, Steve, Reg. Mktg. Mgr.--TMP Worldwide/Recruitment Division, Chicago, IL; *U.S. Private*, pg. 1065
Haas, B.K., Pres.--Bud Industries, Inc., Willoughby, OH; *U.S. Private*, pg. 178
Haas, Jean, Dir.-Mktg.--MSC Industrial Supply Co., Plainview, NY; *U.S. Private*, pg. 998
Haas, Mike, V.P.-Sls. & Mktg.--Columbia Paint & Coatings, Spokane, WA; *U.S. Private*, pg. 256
Haas, Sandra J., Dir.-Mktg.--Mellon Bank, N.A.-Northern Region, Erie, PA; *U.S. Public*, pg. 1085
Haas, Thomas, Mgr.-Mktg. Communications--Siemens Corporation, New York, NY; *Int'l*, pg. 1245
Habenicht, Nelson A., V.P.-Mktg.--Unigard Insurance Co., Bellevue, WA; *Int'l*, pg. 345
Habenicht, Nelson A., V.P.-Mktg.--Unigard Indemnity Co., Bellevue, WA; *Int'l*, pg. 345
Haber, Barry, Sr. V.P.-Consumer Electronics & Cuisinart--Conair Corporation, Stamford, CT; *U.S. Private*, pg. 261
Haberland, B.W., Mgr.-Mktg. Services--Schering Nederland B.V., Weesp, Netherlands; *Int'l*, pg. 1204
Habetler, Chuck, Mgr.-Sls. & Mktg.--Atlas Cylinder, Eugene, OR; *U.S. Public*, pg. 1261
Hacking, Grant, Mgr.-Mktg.--Victaulic International, Easton, PA; *U.S. Private*, pg. 1138
Hackman, Dodd, Sr. V.P.-Sls. & Mktg.--TABS Direct (Operating Div.), Stafford, TX; *U.S. Private*, pg. 482
Hackman, Roger D., V.P.-Mktg. & Sls.--Seymour Manufacturing Company, Seymour, IN; *U.S. Private*, pg. 988
Hadfield, Mike, Pres.--Robert Bosch Fluid Power Corporation, Racine, WI; *Int'l*, pg. 204
Hadley, Bret R, Sr. V.P.-Mktg.-Boys Line--Aviva Sport, Inc., El Segundo, CA; *U.S. Public*, pg. 1058
Hadley, Bret R., Sr. V.P.-Mktg.-Boys Line--Mattel, Inc., El Segundo, CA; *U.S. Public*, pg. 1057
Haffner, John, Dir.-Sls. & Mktg.--Integrated Health Concepts, Walnut Creek, CA; *U.S. Public*, pg. 1013
Hagan, Henry J., Chief Mktg. Officer & Sr. V.P.--Monumental Life Insurance Company, Baltimore, MD; *Int'l*, pg. 27
Hagan, James J., Dir.-Mktg.--Harza Environmental Services, Inc., Chicago, IL; *U.S. Private*, pg. 509
Hage, Dave, V.P.-Sls. & Mktg.--Power-One, Inc., Camarillo, CA; *U.S. Private*, pg. 878
Hageman, Mark, Mgr.-Mktg. Communications--Weyerhaeuser Forest Products Company, Federal Way, WA; *U.S. Public*, pg. 1764
Hageman, Ted, V.P.-Mktg. Services--Lowe's Companies, Inc., North Wilkesboro, NC; *U.S. Public*, pg. 1015
Hagen, Lisa, Mktg. & Pur. Rep.--Raleigh Enterprises, Inc., Santa Monica, CA; *U.S. Private*, pg. 907
Hagerman, John, Sr. V.P.-Mktg.--Maxtor Corporation, Milpitas, CA; *Int'l*, pg. 641
Hagerty, Kevin, Dir.-Mktg./Ryder Integrated Logistics--Ryder System, Inc., Miami, FL; *U.S. Public*, pg. 1413
Hagerty, Patrick, V.P.-Mktg. & Pur.--VSA, Inc., Denver, CO; *U.S. Public*, pg. 901
Hagler, Chris, Dir.-Mktg.--Sonoco Engraph, Inc., Atlanta, GA; *U.S. Public*, pg. 1486
Hagman, Larry, Mgr.-Mktg.--Manitowoc Ice, Inc., Manitowoc, WI; *U.S. Public*, pg. 1041
Hagorty, Carl, V.P.-Sls. & Mktg.--Fire Control Instruments, Inc., Waltham, MA; *U.S. Private*, pg. 406
Hahn, Alan C., Sr. V.P.-Deal Direct Mktg.--Jackson National Life Insurance Company, Lansing, MI; *Int'l*, pg. 1073
Hahn, David, Mgr.-Mktg. Communications--Davol Inc., Cranston, RI; *U.S. Public*, pg. 189
Hahn, David, V.P.-Mktg.--John Brown Plastics Machinery, Attleboro, MA; *Int'l*, pg. 773
Hahn, John, Dir.-Sls. & Mktg.--Fiatallis North America, Inc., Carol Stream, IL; *Int'l*, pg. 483
Hahn, Licia, V.P.-Mktg.--KPIX-TV, San Francisco, CA; *U.S. Public*, pg. 275
Hahn, Susan, Mktg.--EAO Switch Corporation, Milford, CT; *Int'l*, pg. 444
Hahnenstein, Geri, V.P.-Mktg. Commun.--Allegiance Healthcare Corp., McGaw Park, IL; *U.S. Public*, pg. 44
Haidis, John, Dir.-Mktg.--Energizer Eveready Ltd., London, United Kingdom; *U.S. Public*, pg. 1360
Haifleigh, David, Exec. V.P.-Mktg.--EvansGroup, Denver, CO; *U.S. Private*, pg. 385
Haik, Sam, Dir.-Mktg. & Prod. Warranties--Wynn Oil Company, Azusa, CA; *U.S. Public*, pg. 1782
Haines, Christopher L., V.P.-Mktg.--Riviana Foods Inc., Houston, TX; *U.S. Public*, pg. 1392
Hairston, Jim, Dir.-Sls. & Mktg.--Hooker Industries, Ontario, CA; *U.S. Private*, pg. 538
Hajek, Joy, Mgr.-Mktg.--American Appraisal Associates, Inc., Milwaukee, WI; *U.S. Private*, pg. 49
Hake, William D., Sr. V.P.-Coal--Kerr-McGee Coal Corp., Oklahoma City, OK; *U.S. Public*, pg. 952
Hakewill, Hank, V.P.-Mktg. & Corp. Institutional Services--Northern Trust Corporation, Chicago, IL; *U.S. Public*, pg. 1195
Hakoda, Mary M., V.P.-Sls. & Mktg.--Malama Pacific Corp., Honolulu, HI; *U.S. Public*, pg. 800
Hakulinen, Terhi, Mgr.-Mktg.-Tour Production, Grp. Travel & Etumatkat Tours--Finland Travel Bureau Ltd., Helsinki, Finland; *Int'l*, pg. 485
Halahal, Ted, Mgr.-Mktg.--Serfilco, Ltd., Northbrook, IL; *U.S. Private*, pg. 985
Halbach, Hans, Exec. V.P.-Sls. & Mktg.--Saab Automobile AB, Nykoping, Sweden; *Int'l*, pg. 687
Halbach, Hans, Exec. V.P.-Sls. & Mktg.--Saab Automobile AB, Nykoping, Sweden; *U.S. Public*, pg. 725
Hale, Joseph E., Sr. V.P.-Mktg.--Aloha Airgroup, Inc., Honolulu, HI; *U.S. Private*, pg. 44
Hale, Joseph E., Sr. V.P.-Mktg.--Aloha Airlines, Inc., Honolulu, HI; *U.S. Private*, pg. 44
Hale, Thomas, V.P.-Sls. & Mktg.--Ball Metal Food Container Corp., Westminster, CO; *U.S. Public*, pg. 171
Haley, Brad, V.P.-Mktg. Communications--Foodmaker, Inc., San Diego, CA; *U.S. Public*, pg. 661
Haley, Mark O., Dir.-Mktg.--KLLM Transport Services, Inc., Jackson, MS; *U.S. Public*, pg. 939
Haliburda, Dan, Dir.-Sls. & Mktg.--Go-Video, Inc., Scottsdale, AZ; *U.S. Public*, pg. 748
Hall, Anne, Dir.-Mktg.--MFG Tray Co., Linesville, PA; *U.S. Private*, pg. 756
Hall, B. D., Sr. V.P. & Mktg. Analysis Dir.--Howard, Merrell & Partners, Inc., Raleigh, NC; *U.S. Private*, pg. 542
Hall, Cindy, V.P.-Mktg.--AMCORE Bank N.A., Rock River Valley, Sterling, IL; *U.S. Public*, pg. 64
Hall, David L., Mgr.-Res. & Mktg.--Faraday, Inc., Tecumseh, MI; *Int'l*, pg. 1246
Hall, Diane, Mgr.-Mkt. Devel.--Plastic Suppliers, Inc., Columbus, OH; *U.S. Private*, pg. 871
Hall, Dulany, Dir.-Mktg.--The Cloister, Sea Island, GA; *U.S. Private*, pg. 978
Hall, James D., V.P.-Product Mngmt. & Mktg.--Aearo Company, Boston, MA; *U.S. Private*, pg. 23
Hall, John, V.P.-Mktg. & Sls.--Dan River, Inc., New York, NY; *U.S. Public*, pg. 479
Hall, John, V.P.-Sls. & Mktg.--The Milnot Company, Saint Louis, MO; *U.S. Private*, pg. 749
Hall, Kevin, Dir.-Mktg.--Vidal Sassoon, Cincinnati, OH; *U.S. Public*, pg. 1330
Hall, Laura, Mgr.-Mktg. Res.--Southern Progress Corporation, Birmingham, AL; *U.S. Public*, pg. 1612
Hall, Marshall, Mgr.-Prod.--Vari Tronics Company, Inc., Duarte, CA; *U.S. Private*, pg. 1134
Hall, Peter, Dir.-Export Sls. & Mktg.--Gaylord Container Corporation, Deerfield, IL; *U.S. Public*, pg. 704
Hall, R., Dir.-Mktg.-Photo Div.--Canon (U.K.) Ltd., Wallington, United Kingdom; *Int'l*, pg. 263
Hall, Robin, V.P.-Mktg. & Sls. Promo.--Loehmann's, Inc., Bronx, NY; *U.S. Public*, pg. 1010
Hall, Sarah, Mgr.-Mktg.--Brauns Fashions Corporation, Plymouth, MN; *U.S. Public*, pg. 251
Hall, Stephen T., Dir.-Mktg. Svcs.--Eastern Utilities Associates, Boston, MA; *U.S. Public*, pg. 549
Hall, Trey, V.P.-Mktg.--Boston Chicken, Inc., Golden, CO; *U.S. Public*, pg. 247
Hallam, Barry, Mgr.-Mktg. Communications--SNE Enterprises, Inc., Mosinee, WI; *U.S. Public*, pg. 1193
Hallberg, John, Sr. V.P.-Worldwide Mktg.--Encyclopaedia Britannica, Inc., Chicago, IL; *U.S. Private*, pg. 375
Hallenbeck, Jack, Sr. V.P.-Sls. & Mktg.--Beatrice Cheese Co., Waukesha, WI; *U.S. Public*, pg. 426
Halley, Tom, Exec. V.P.-Consumer Mkts. Div./Central Div.--Countrywide Home Loans Inc., Pasadena, CA; *U.S. Public*, pg. 452
Halligan, Cathy, V.P.-Mktg.--Williams-Sonoma, Inc., San Francisco, CA; *U.S. Public*, pg. 1770
Hallman, Russel, Sr. V.P.-Mktg. & Sls.--Electronic Data Magnetics, Inc., High Point, NC; *U.S. Private*, pg. 370
Hallom, William, Dir.-Sls. & Mktg.--DeMert & Dougherty, Inc., Coal City, IL; *U.S. Private*, pg. 323
Halloran, Don, Mgr.-Natl. Sls. & Mktg.--Anemostat Products, Scranton, PA; *U.S. Public*, pg. 286
Hallquist, Harlan, V.P.--Adolfson & Peterson, Inc., Minneapolis, MN; *U.S. Private*, pg. 17
Hallstedt, Fred, V.P-Sls. & Mktg.--AmeriServe of Grand Rapids, Grand Rapids, MI; *U.S. Private*, pg. 533
Hallstrom, Per, Mgr.-Mktg.--Atlas Copco Berema AB, Nacka, Sweden; *Int'l*, pg. 96
Halpern, Cheryl, V.P.-Global Prod. Mktg.--Mary Kay, Inc., Dallas, TX; *U.S. Private*, pg. 711
Halpin, John, V.P.-Mktg.--Foster & Gallagher, Inc., Peoria, IL; *U.S. Private*, pg. 420
Halpin, John, Sr. V.P.-Direct Mktg.--Successories, Inc., Aurora, IL; *U.S. Private*, pg. 1049
Halpin, Kevin, Gen. Mgr.-Mktg.--South Pacific Tyres, Somerton, Australia; *Int'l*, pg. 1021
Halstead, Russ, Mgr.-Sls. & Mktg.--Victor Products, Lisle, IL; *U.S. Public*, pg. 480
Haluska, Scott, Mgr.-Mktg.--Williams Advanced Materials, Inc., Buffalo, NY; *U.S. Public*, pg. 266
Halverson, Kenneth A., Sr. V.P.-Mktg.--Comdisco, Inc., Rosemont, IL; *U.S. Public*, pg. 407
Halverson, Mike, Dir.-Mktg.--Sathers Inc., Round Lake, MN; *U.S. Private*, pg. 397
Hamann, Per, Dir.-Sls. & Mktg.--Time/System International A/S, Allerod, Denmark; *Int'l*, pg. 73
Hamburger, Steve, Sr. V.P.-Mktg.--Gibraltar Savings, Simi Valley, CA; *U.S. Private*, pg. 181
Hamill, D., V.P.-Sls. & Mktg.--Alumax Mill Products, Inc., Morris, IL; *U.S. Public*, pg. 59
Hamilton, Carl, Mgr.-Mktg.--B & R Industrial Automation, Roswell, GA; *U.S. Private*, pg. 105
Hamilton, David L., Pres. & Chief Oper. Officer--George W. Auch Co., Pontiac, MI; *U.S. Private*, pg. 98
Hamilton, Dean C., Mgr.-Mktg. Communications--ATMI, Inc., Danbury, CT; *U.S. Public*, pg. 12
Hamilton, Fred, Dir.-Mktg. & Communications--The Franklin Institute, Philadelphia, PA; *U.S. Private*, pg. 424
Hamilton, George, Mgr.-Mktg.--Jamison Door Company, Hagerstown, MD; *U.S. Private*, pg. 581
Hamilton, James E., V.P.-Mktg.--Martin Electronics, Inc., Perry, FL; *U.S. Private*, pg. 709
Hamilton, Marilyn, Sr. V.P.-Mktg.--Sunrise Medical Mobility Products, Fresno, CA; *U.S. Public*, pg. 1536
Hamilton, Mark, Dir.-Mktg.--Lazard Freres & Co., New York, NY; *Int'l*, pg. 1027
Hamilton, Richard, Dir.-Mktg.--Crest Fruit Co., Alamo, TX; *U.S. Public*, pg. 1506
Hamilton, Rick, Dir.-Mktg. Commun.--Windsor Industries, Inc., Englewood, CO; *U.S. Private*, pg. 1182
Hamilton, Tim, V.P.-Sls. & Mktg.--J.M. Peters Co., Newport Beach, CA; *U.S. Public*, pg. 302
Hamilton, Ward, V.P.-Mktg.--Zoll Medical Corporation, Burlington, MA; *U.S. Private*, pg. 1207
Hamlin, Janice, V.P.-Mktg.--Bassett Furniture Industries, Incorporated, Bassett, VA; *U.S. Public*, pg. 193
Hamlin, Paul, V.P.-Mktg.--Searle & Co., Skokie, IL; *U.S. Public*, pg. 1125
Hamm, Jerry T., Pres.--Jerry Hamm Chevrolet Inc., Jacksonville, FL; *U.S. Private*, pg. 497
Hammalrath, Mark, V.P.-Mktg. & Adv.--Riverwood International Corporation, Atlanta, GA; *U.S. Public*, pg. 1391
Hammant, Sarah, Dir.-Mktg. & Communications--Dell Computer Corporation Ltd., Bracknell, United Kingdom; *U.S. Public*, pg. 496
Hammill, Dick, Sr. V.P.-Adv. & Mktg.--The Home Depot, Inc., Atlanta, GA; *U.S. Public*, pg. 831
Hammons, Lora Cassano, Coord.-Pub. Rels. Mktg.--Cassano's Int'l Inc., Dayton, OH; *U.S. Private*, pg. 218
Hamnett, Mark, Mgr.-Mktg.--Tuchenhagen GmbH, Buchen, Germany; *Int'l*, pg. 1426
Hampson, Jim, Sr. V.P.-Mktg.--Great Western Consumer Finance Group, Tampa, FL; *U.S. Public*, pg. 1741
Hampton, Craig, V.P.-Sls. & Mktg.--DSM Sheffield Plastics, Sheffield, MA; *Int'l*, pg. 354
Hampton, Kay, Dir.-Adv. & Mktg./Corp.--Computer Language Research, Inc., Carrollton, TX; *U.S. Public*, pg. 421
Hampton, Mark, V.P.-Mktg.--United Stationers Inc., Des Plaines, IL; *U.S. Public*, pg. 1689
Hampton, Randy, V.P.-Mktg.--Willis Corroon Corp. of Georgia, Atlanta, GA; *Int'l*, pg. 1506
Hampton, Wade, V.P.-Mktg.--Koger Equity Inc., Jacksonville, FL; *U.S. Public*, pg. 965
Hamrick, John, Mgr.-Mktg.--Advance Seed Co., Fulton, KY; *Int'l*, pg. 566
Hamwey, Larry, Dir.-Mktg.--Carnation Products Div., Glendale, CA; *Int'l*, pg. 916
Hanazaki, Yoshio, Mng. Dir.-Mktg., Railway Opers. & Credit Cards--East Japan Railway Company, Tokyo, Japan; *Int'l*, pg. 431
Hanby, Deborah, Dir.-Forms Mktg.--The Standard Register Company, Dayton, OH; *U.S. Public*, pg. 1505
Hancock, Edward R., Mktg. Dir.--Farnam Sealing Systems Division, Troy, MI; *U.S. Public*, pg. 401
Hancock, Jayne, V.P.-Sports Mktg.--DirecTV Inc., El Segundo, CA; *U.S. Public*, pg. 720
Hancock, John, V.P.-Sls. & Mktg.--Coburn Optical Industries Inc., Tulsa, OK; *U.S. Private*, pg. 248
Hancock, Kevin, Dir.-Media--Giant Food Inc., Landover, MD; *U.S. Public*, pg. 741
Hancock, Larry, Dir.-Mktg.--Hayes Microcomputer Products, Inc., Norcross, GA; *U.S. Public*, pg. 801
Hancock, Richard, Dir.-Mktg.--Computational Systems Inc., Knoxville, TN; *U.S. Public*, pg. 572
Hancock, Scott, Sr. V.P.-Mktg. & Sls.--Unapix Entertainment Inc., New York, NY; *U.S. Public*, pg. 1664
Hancocks, Ian, Dir.-Mktg.--Phildas Ltd., Pontefract, United Kingdom; *Int'l*, pg. 585
Hand, Gerry, V.P.-Mktg.--Superior Graphite Co., Chicago, IL; *U.S. Private*, pg. 1054
Hand, Judi, V.P.-Business Mktg.--U S West Inc., Englewood, CO; *U.S. Public*, pg. 1688
Handler, Howard, V.P.-Mktg.--National Football League Properties, Inc., New York, NY; *U.S. Private*, pg. 783
Handler, Jeff, V.P.-Intl. Mktg.--Toys "R" Us, Inc., Paramus, NJ; *U.S. Public*, pg. 1626
Handler, Mitch, Gen. Mgr.--Tru-Form, Wilkes-Barre, PA; *Int'l*, pg. 1338
Handley, John M., Sr. V.P.-Mktg. & Sls.--Industrial Acoustics Company, Inc., Bronx, NY; *U.S. Public*, pg. 875
Handley, Lynn, Mgr.-Mktg. & Communications--GTE Supply, Irving, TX; *U.S. Public*, pg. 697
Handy, Steve, Store Mktg.--Service Merchandise Company, Inc., Brentwood, TN; *U.S. Public*, pg. 1461
Hankin, Lewis, V.P.-Field Mktg.--Showtime Networks Inc., New York, NY; *U.S. Private*, pg. 779
Hankins, Bill, Team Leader-Managed Care--Boehringer Ingelheim Pharmaceuticals, Inc., Ridgefield, CT; *Int'l*, pg. 199
Hankins, Cathy, V.P.-Sls. & Mktg.--Memphis Group, Inc., Memphis, TN; *U.S. Private*, pg. 730
Hanks, Douglas R., Sr. V.P.-Mktg.--CNB Bancshares, Inc., Evansville, IN; *U.S. Public*, pg. 280
Hanks, Tom, Dir.-Mktg.--Lebanon Valley Farmers Bank, Lebanon, PA; *U.S. Public*, pg. 688
Hanlon, D.E., Jr., V.P.-Mktg. & Sls.--Unimark Plastics Company, Greer, SC; *U.S. Public*, pg. 57

Hanna, David E., Mgr.-Sls. & Mktg.--Owatonna Canning Company, Owatonna, MN; *U.S. Public*, pg. 349
Hannagan, Kathie, V.P.--Publishing Div., Tulsa, OK; *U.S. Public*, pg. 565
Hannagen, Niall W., Asst. V.P.-Tech. Mktg.--BetzDearborn Metals Process Group, Horsham, PA; *U.S. Public*, pg. 226
Hannah, J., Dir.-Sls. & Mktg.--British Gypsum Ltd., Loughborough, United Kingdom; *Int'l*, pg. 122
Hannah, Marcia, V.P.-Mktg., Roofing Prods. Grp.--Ludowici Roof Tile, Inc., New Lexington, OH; *Int'l*, pg. 1171
Hannah, Steve, V.P.-Mktg.--Peebles, Inc., South Hill, VA; *U.S. Private*, pg. 846
Hannaher, Thomas J., V.P.-Mktg.--Cambridge Soundworks, Inc., Newton, MA; *U.S. Private*, pg. 202
Hanneck, E.V., Mng. Dir. & Dir.-Mktg.--Neff (UK) Limited, Milton Keynes, United Kingdom; *Int'l*, pg. 912
Hanneke, Tim L., Promo. Production Services Dir. & Promo. Admin. Dir.--CheckMark Communications, Saint Louis, MO; *U.S. Private*, pg. 231
Hannes, Peter J., Pres.-Special Mkts.--Jockey International, Inc., Kenosha, WI; *U.S. Private*, pg. 588
Hannezo, Hubert, V.P.-Mktg. & Sls./MAST & Flag Brands--Michelin Americas Small Tires (MAST), Greenville, SC; *Int'l*, pg. 322
Hannikainen, Anna, Mgr.-Mktg.--Masterfoods Oy, Helsinki, Finland; *U.S. Private*, pg. 707
Hannon, Ann Marie, Dir.-Mktg.--New Haven Mfg. Corp., New Haven, CT; *U.S. Public*, pg. 793
Hannum, Bill, Mgr.-Mktg.--Great Lakes Dredge & Dock Co., Oak Brook, IL; *U.S. Private*, pg. 474
Hanock, Lisa, Mgr.-Commun.--Dakotah, Inc., Webster, SD; *U.S. Public*, pg. 477
Hanover, Frederick, Dir.-Mktg.--SecurityLink from Ameritech, Columbus, OH; *U.S. Public*, pg. 98
Hanrahan, Timothy J., Sr. V.P.--Meridian Insurance Group, Inc., Indianapolis, IN; *U.S. Public*, pg. 1095
Hanrahan, Timothy J., Dir.-Mktg.--Meridian Security Insurance Company, Indianapolis, IN; *U.S. Public*, pg. 1095
Hans, Judy, Mgr.-Mktg Publications Dept.--United American Insurance Co., Dallas, TX; *U.S. Public*, pg. 1623
Hansberger, Tom, V.P.-Special Markets--Hansberger Precision Golf Inc., Pontotoc, MS; *U.S. Private*, pg. 499
Hansberry, Joe, Mgr.-Mktg.--TapTone Container Inspection Systems, North Falmouth, MA; *U.S. Public*, pg. 212
Hansbury, Ben, Dir.-Sls. & Mktg.--Nordberg-Read, Inc., Middleboro, MA; *Int'l*, pg. 1428
Hansen, Chris, V.P.-Mktg.--Lane Bryant, Reynoldsburg, OH; *U.S. Public*, pg. 995
Hansen, Flo, Dir.-Mktg.--The Pilot Pen Corp. of America, Trumbull, CT; *Int'l*, pg. 1057
Hansen, Jerry, Mgr.-Prod. Mktg.--Proxima Corporation, San Diego, CA; *U.S. Public*, pg. 1339
Hansen, John, V.P.-Mktg.--Mueller Industries, Inc., Memphis, TN; *U.S. Public*, pg. 1141
Hansen, Kent, V.P.-Mktg. Sales & Adv.--Nobel Insurance Limited, Hamilton, Bermuda; *Int'l*, pg. 951
Hansen, Mogens, Dir.-Mktg.--Castrol A/S, Copenhagen, Denmark; *Int'l*, pg. 235
Hansen, R., Mgr.-Mktg.--Crane Resistoflex/Defense, Jacksonville, FL; *U.S. Public*, pg. 457
Hansen, R., Mgr.-Mktg.--Engineered Fasteners Div., Massillon, OH; *U.S. Public*, pg. 557
Hansen, R.M., V.P.-Mktg. & Sls.--Pyle Inc., Elmhurst, IL; *U.S. Private*, pg. 629
Hansen, Stephan, Mgr.-Mktg.--Scan Globe A/S, Havdrup, Denmark; *U.S. Private*, pg. 923
Hanson, Barbara, Dir.-Mktg.--Thomas Publishing Company, New York, NY; *U.S. Private*, pg. 1082
Hanson, Brenda, Mgr.-Sls. & Mktg.--West Virginia Cellular Telephone Corp., Charleston, WV; *U.S. Public*, pg. 1708
Hanson, Gary W., Dir.-Mktg. Communications--Electronic Data Systems Corporation, Plano, TX; *U.S. Public*, pg. 569
Hanson, Gregory, V.P.-Mktg.--Cole Papers Inc., Fargo, ND; *U.S. Private*, pg. 251
Hanson, Jean, V.P.-Mktg.--Communications Equipment Co., New Providence, NJ; *U.S. Public*, pg. 276
Hanson, Juliet, Mgr.-Adv. & Promo.--Xerox South Africa, Isando, South Africa; *U.S. Public*, pg. 1785
Hanson, Larry, V.P.-Mktg. & Sls.--Twin City Foods, Inc., Stanwood, WA; *U.S. Private*, pg. 1111
Hanson, Maureen, Mgr.-Mktg. & Communications--GN Nettest Fiber Optic Division, Utica, NY; *Int'l*, pg. 536
Hanson, Peter, Mgr.-Sls. & Mktg. Chicago--Banta Publications Group, Long Prairie, MN; *U.S. Public*, pg. 188
Hanson, Richard, Sr. V.P.-Sls. & Mktg.--Nordic Ware, Minneapolis, MN; *U.S. Private*, pg. 806
Hanson, Sherry, Mgr.-Mktg.--Bridon Cordage Inc., Albert Lea, MN; *Int'l*, pg. 215
Hanson, William, V.P.-Sls. & Mktg.--Hamlin, Inc., Lake Mills, WI; *U.S. Public*, pg. 251
Harada, Eikoh, V.P.-Consumer Mktg.--Apple Computer, Inc., Cupertino, CA; *U.S. Public*, pg. 121
Haraguchi, M., Dir.-Mktg.--The Tokyo Electric Power Co., Inc., Tokyo, Japan; *Int'l*, pg. 1394
Harakal, Joe, Mgr.-Mktg. & Commun.--Digital Link Corporation, Sunnyvale, CA; *U.S. Public*, pg. 508
Haraldson, William, Chief Oper. Officer & Exec. V.P.-Mktg.--Rosauers Supermarkets, Inc., Spokane, WA; *U.S. Private*, pg. 944
Harbaugh, Jim, Prod. Mgr.--Welding Products Group, Niles, MI; *U.S. Public*, pg. 1161
Harbaugh, John C., Mgr.-Mktg. & Adv.--Landis, Waynesboro, PA; *U.S. Public*, pg. 1699
Harbaugh, Katie, Mgr.-Residential Mktg.--Schlage Lock Company, Colorado Springs, CO; *U.S. Public*, pg. 876
Harbeck, Tom, Sr. V.P.-Nickelodean Mktg. & On-Air Promo. & Creative Dir.--Nickelodeon/Nick At Nite, New York, NY; *U.S. Private*, pg. 779
Harbold, Lin, Mgr.-Sls. & Mktg.--Iceland Seafood Corporation, Newport, VA; *U.S. Private*, pg. 556
Harbula, Gene, V.P.-Govt. Mktg. & Corp. Communications--Sabreliner Corporation, Saint Louis, MO; *U.S. Private*, pg. 959
Harcourt, Patricia A., Dir.-Corp. Commun.--Belden & Blake Corporation, Canton, OH; *U.S. Private*, pg. 1078
Hardek, Margaret A., Mgr.-Mktg.--The CIT Group/Equipment Financing, Livingston, NJ; *Int'l*, pg. 360
Hardie, Norman D.A., V.P.-Mktg.--Metall Mining Corporation, Toronto, Canada; *Int'l*, pg. 862
Hardies, Albert C., V.P.-Mktg. & Sls.--Zinc Corporation of America, Monaca, PA; *U.S. Private*, pg. 540
Harding, Bryan L., Dir.-Mktg. Commun.--Entergy Corporation, New Orleans, LA; *U.S. Public*, pg. 585
Harding, Bryan L., Dir.-Mktg. Communications--Entergy Louisiana, Inc., New Orleans, LA; *U.S. Public*, pg. 586
Harding, Bryan L., Dir.-Mktg. Communications--Entergy New Orleans, Inc., New Orleans, LA; *U.S. Public*, pg. 586
Harding, John, Dir.-Mktg.--Surgical Information Systems, Atlanta, GA; *U.S. Public*, pg. 45
Hardison, Jack, Dir,-Sls. & Mktg.--Pool Energy Services Co., Houston, TX; *U.S. Public*, pg. 1316
Hardman, R., Dir.-Mktg.--Seven Seas Limited, Hull, United Kingdom; *Int'l*, pg. 593
Hardy, Joseph, Mktg. Mgr.--BTR Precision Die Casting, Inc., Russellville, KY; *Int'l*, pg. 127
Hardy, Thomas, Mgr.-Mktg.--Hyde Manufacturing Co., Southbridge, MA; *U.S. Private*, pg. 551
Hare, Ed, Mgr.-Intl. Mktg.--Noble Drilling International, Inc., Houston, TX; *U.S. Public*, pg. 1186
Harford, Woody, V.P.-Bus. Travel. Mktg.--British Airways, Flushing, NY; *Int'l*, pg. 219
Hargrove, George, V.P.-Sls. & Mktg.--Barnhardt Manufacturing Co., Charlotte, NC; *U.S. Private*, pg. 116
Hargrove, George, V.P.-Sls. & Mktg.--Carolina Absorbent Cotton Co., Charlotte, NC; *U.S. Private*, pg. 117
Hargrove, Joseph, V.P.-Mktg.--Key Risk Management Services, Inc., Greensboro, NC; *U.S. Public*, pg. 216
Harkless, Brad, Exec. V.P.-Sls. & Mktg.--L & S Bearing Co., Oklahoma City, OK; *U.S. Public*, pg. 970
Harlan, David M., V.P.-Natl. Sls. & Mktg.--United States Cold Storage, Inc., Cherry Hill, NJ; *U.S. Private*, pg. 1124
Harlan, Richard K., V.P.-Sls. & Mktg.--E.W. Knauss & Son, Inc., Quakertown, PA; *U.S. Private*, pg. 626
Harless, I., Dir.-Mktg. & Sls.--Tri Tech Laboratories, Inc., Lynchburg, VA; *U.S. Private*, pg. 1101
Harley, Susan, Mgr.-Mktg.--Bruncor, Inc., Saint John, Canada; *Int'l*, pg. 230
Harlow, Rick, V.P.-Engrng. & Dir.-Mktg. & Sls.--Universal Fasteners Inc., Lawrenceburg, KY; *Int'l*, pg. 1515
Harman, Gina, V.P.-Mktg.-Consumer Group--Harman International Industries, Inc., Woodbury, NY; *U.S. Public*, pg. 787
Harmon, Roy, V.P.-Mktg.--Healthsource North Texas, Inc., Fort Worth, TX; *U.S. Public*, pg. 360
Harms, Sarah, Dir.-Mktg./Oral Health Products--Teledyne Water Pik, Fort Collins, CO; *U.S. Public*, pg. 44
Harnes, Jay, V.P.-Sls. & Mktg.--A.O. Smith Water Products Company, Irving, TX; *U.S. Public*, pg. 1477
Harness, Larry, Sr., Consultant-Sls. & Mktg.--Bassick by Kaspar, Shiner, TX; *U.S. Private*, pg. 122
Harold, Ann, Exec. V.P.-Mktg. & Sls.--Weber-Stephen Products Co., Palatine, IL; *U.S. Private*, pg. 1157
Harp, Paul L., V.P.-Sls. & Mktg./Processed Meats--Gwaltney of Smithfield, Ltd., Smithfield, VA; *U.S. Public*, pg. 1479
Harp, Sidney, II, Exec. V.P. & Agency Dir.--Security Industrial Insurance Co., Inc., Donaldsonville, LA; *Int'l*, pg. 814
Harper, Elizabeth, Mktg.--Regions Bank/Shelby County, Pelham, AL; *U.S. Public*, pg. 1373
Harper, Greg, V.P.-Mktg.--Johnny Appleseed's, Inc., Beverly, MA; *U.S. Private*, pg. 590
Harper, Linda, V.P.-Mktg. & Creative, Eve St. Laurent--Sanofi Beaute, Inc., New York, NY; *Int'l*, pg. 445
Harper, Phil, Mgr.-Mktg. & Product Devel.--Tucson Electric Power Company, Tucson, AZ; *U.S. Public*, pg. 1670
Harper, Richard, Dir.-Mktg.--Westpac Banking Corporation, Sydney, Australia; *Int'l*, pg. 1495
Harper, Robert, Pres.-Mktg.--Twentieth Century Fox Film Corp., Los Angeles, CA; *Int'l*, pg. 926
Harper, Ron, Dir.-Mktg.--Material Sciences Corporation, Elk Grove Village, IL; *U.S. Public*, pg. 1056
Harper, Ron, Dir.-Mktg.--Pre Finish Metals Incorporated, Elk Grove Village, IL; *U.S. Public*, pg. 1056
Harradine, Robert P., Mgr.-Sls.--Genesee Metal Stampings, Inc., West Henrietta, NY; *U.S. Private*, pg. 446
Harrawood, Larry, V.P.-Mktg. & Bus. Devel.--OEC Medical Systems, Inc., Salt Lake City, UT; *U.S. Public*, pg. 1207
Harrelo, Donato, Dir.-Mktg.--Cavexsa, Basauri, Spain; *U.S. Private*, pg. 694
Harrick, G. Thomas, Sr. V.P.-Polyurethanes Polymers Division--Bayer Corporation, Pittsburgh, PA; *Int'l*, pg. 172
Harrington, Bob, V.P.-Fin. & Plng.--Wisconsin Tissue Mills, Inc., Menasha, WI; *U.S. Public*, pg. 347
Harrington, David, V.P.-Mktg.--Human Affairs International Inc., Sandy, UT; *U.S. Public*, pg. 1036
Harrington, Elleen, Mgr.-Mktg.--The CIT Group/Capital Finance Inc., New York, NY; *Int'l*, pg. 360
Harrington, John, Dir.-Mktg.--First Data Corporation, Englewood, CO; *U.S. Public*, pg. 631
Harris, Alan F., Exec. V.P.-Cereal Div.-Mktg. & Sls.--Kellogg USA Inc., Battle Creek, MI; *U.S. Public*, pg. 947
Harris, Albert, V.P.-Mktg. & Sls.--Johnson & Towers, Inc., Mount Laurel, NJ; *U.S. Private*, pg. 590
Harris, Barbara, Dir.-Product Mktg.--DHL Worldwide Express, Redwood City, CA; *U.S. Private*, pg. 301
Harris, Bob, V.P.-Sls. & Mktg.-Durango Boot--Georgia/Durango Boot Company, Franklin, TN; *U.S. Public*, pg. 1684
Harris, E., Dir.-Mktg. & Application Engrng.--S & C Electric Canada Ltd., Toronto, Canada; *U.S. Private*, pg. 954
Harris, Gregory L., V.P.-Sls. & Mktg.--Ault Incorporated, Minneapolis, MN; *U.S. Public*, pg. 147
Harris, Jeff, Sr. V.P.-Marketing--Brookwood Companies Inc., New York, NY; *U.S. Public*, pg. 777
Harris, Jennifer S., Mgr.-Mktg.--Scott & Stringfellow Financial, Inc., Richmond, VA; *U.S. Public*, pg. 1445
Harris, K., Mgr.-Natl. Sls. & Mktg.--Goodman Fielder Mills (NZ) Ltd., Auckland, New Zealand; *Int'l*, pg. 556
Harris, King, Pres. & Chief Exec. Officer--Pittway Corporation, Chicago, IL; *U.S. Public*, pg. 1305
Harris, Marilee, V.P.-Mktg.--Chapters Inc., Etobicoke, Canada; *Int'l*, pg. 280
Harris, Peter, V.P.-Sls. & Mktg.--American Science & Engineering, Inc., Billerica, MA; *U.S. Public*, pg. 90
Harris, Tim C., V.P.-Mktg.--Coyne Beahm Inc., Colfax, NC; *U.S. Private*, pg. 283
Harrison-Dees, Geoffrey, Gen. Mgr.-Sls. & Mktg.--Sun Life and Provincial Holdings plc, London, United Kingdom; *Int'l*, pg. 1318
Harrison, Diane, Dir.-Mail Mktg.--The Tog Shop, Americus, GA; *U.S. Private*, pg. 1090
Harrison, George, V.P.-Corp. Mktg. & Corp. Communications--Nintendo of America, Redmond, WA; *Int'l*, pg. 932
Harrison, James F., Sr. V.P.-Sls. & Mktg.--Muzak Limited Partnership, Seattle, WA; *U.S. Private*, pg. 222
Harrison, Jim, Mgr.-Sls.--SouthTrust Corporation, Birmingham, AL; *U.S. Public*, pg. 1491
Harrison, Keith, Dir.-Mktg.--Hong Kong Telecommunications Limited, Quarry Bay, Hong Kong; *Int'l*, pg. 247
Harrison, Tom, Dir.-Mktg. Services--Samsonite Corporation, Denver, CO; *U.S. Public*, pg. 1430
Harrison, Tom, Dir.-Mktg. Services--American Tourister, Inc., Warren, RI; *U.S. Public*, pg. 1430
Harrison, Walter, Mgr.-Mktg.--Delta Pride Catfish, Inc., Indianola, MS; *U.S. Private*, pg. 322
Harriton, Lorraine, Sr. V.P.-Mktg. & Bus. Devel.--Network Computing Devices, Inc., Mountain View, CA; *U.S. Public*, pg. 1168
Harsh, John, Exec. V.P.--Pratt-Read Corporation, Bridgeport, CT; *U.S. Private*, pg. 879
Hart, David, V.P.-Sls. & Mktg.--American Granby, Inc., Liverpool, NY; *U.S. Private*, pg. 55
Hart, Donald M., Dir.-AccuRay Mktg.--ABB Industrial Systems, Inc., Columbus, OH; *Int'l*, pg. 4
Hart, Gill, Mgr.-Mktg. Continental Europe--The Financial Times Ltd., London, United Kingdom; *Int'l*, pg. 1025
Hart, Kay, V.P.-Mktg.--Informix Software, Menlo Park, CA; *U.S. Public*, pg. 876
Hart, Kris, Dir.-Mktg.--Arch Communications Group, Inc., Westborough, MA; *U.S. Public*, pg. 127
Hart, Linda, V.P.-Mktg.--The Cook Bates Division, Venice, FL; *Int'l*, pg. 815
Hart, Mike, Dir.-Mktg.--Miller Brewing Company, Milwaukee, WI; *U.S. Public*, pg. 1289
Hart, Richard W., Dir.-Mktg.--Pharmax Ltd., Bexley, United Kingdom; *U.S. Public*, pg. 670
Hart, Tracey, V.P.-Mktg.--Tarlton Corporation, Saint Louis, MO; *U.S. Private*, pg. 1069
Hart, Tracy E., Dir.-Client Svcs. & Quality--Tarlton Corporation, Saint Louis, MO; *U.S. Private*, pg. 1069
Harter, Laura, Mktg. Asst.--Everest & Jennings, Inc., Earth City, MO; *U.S. Public*, pg. 758
Hartfield, Marianne, Mgr.-Mkt. Communication--Thermo Separation Products, San Jose, CA; *U.S. Public*, pg. 1594
Harthun, Ken, V.P.-Sls. & Mktg.--Dormeyer Industries, Chicago, IL; *U.S. Private*, pg. 340
Harting, Tom, V.P.-Sls. & Mktg.--Mrs. Alison's Cookie Company, Saint Louis, MO; *U.S. Private*, pg. 765
Hartley, Richard, V.P.-Sls. & Mktg.--Mattison Technologies, Inc., Rockford, IL; *U.S. Private*, pg. 714
Hartley, Sharon, Dir.-Mktg.--Hasbro, Inc., Pawtucket, RI; *U.S. Public*, pg. 797
Hartman, Jeff, Mgr.-Mktg.--G&K Services, Inc., Minnetonka, MN; *U.S. Public*, pg. 690
Hartman, Karen S., V.P.-Mktg. & Sls.--E.R. Moore Co., Chicago, IL; *U.S. Private*, pg. 759
Hartman, Rich, Mgr.-Mktg.--Juno Lighting, Inc., Des Plaines, IL; *U.S. Public*, pg. 935
Hartmann, Joe, Mgr.-Market Analyst--Williams Electronics Games, Inc., Chicago, IL; *U.S. Public*, pg. 1727
Hartmann, Patty, Mgr.-Mktg.--Hanna-Sherman International, Inc., Portland, OR; *U.S. Private*, pg. 499
Hartquist, John, Dir.-Mktg.--Paccar Inc., Bellevue, WA; *U.S. Public*, pg. 1246
Hartranft, Debbie, Mgr.-Mktg.--Reading Body Works, Inc., Reading, PA; *U.S. Private*, pg. 913
Hartsook, Pieter, V.P.-Mktg. Analysis & Res.--Apple Computer, Inc., Cupertino, CA; *U.S. Public*, pg. 121
Hartung, Mathew, V.P.Mktg.--Jenkins & Associates, Shawnee Mission, KS; *U.S. Private*, pg. 585
Hartwell, Woody, Mgr.-Mktg.--Kathryn Beich, Inc., Bloomington, IL; *Int'l*, pg. 917
Hartz, Karen, Dir.-Mktg. & Communications--Brooktree Rockwell Semiconductor Systems Div., San Diego, CA; *U.S. Public*, pg. 1398
Harvey, Mary, Asst. Mgr.-Sls. & Mktg.--Cres-Cor, Cleveland, OH; *U.S. Private*, pg. 288
Harvey, Sue, Mgr.-European Mktg.--DRI Europe (U.K.) Ltd., London, United Kingdom; *U.S. Public*, pg. 1072
Harvey, Thomas A., V.P.-Sls. & Mktg.--Faroudja, Inc., Sunnyvale, CA; *U.S. Public*, pg. 613
Harvie, Ed, Mgr.-Sls. & Mktg.--KSB Inc., Richmond, VA; *Int'l*, pg. 721
Harvie, Jeff, Mgr.-Sls. & Mktg.--Kombi, Ltd., Essex Junction, VT; *U.S. Private*, pg. 631
Harvin, Pam, Mktg.--Regions Bank/Enterprise, Enterprise, AL; *U.S. Public*, pg. 1372
Harwick, Warren, Dir.-Mktg.--IMO Industries Inc., Lawrenceville, NJ; *U.S. Public*, pg. 856
Harwood, Carol, Team Leader-Adv. & Mktg.--CFX Bank, Keene, NH; *U.S. Public*, pg. 277
Harwood, Mary, V.P.-Mktg.--Attachmate, Bellevue, WA; *U.S.* Private, pg. 98

Hasbach, Gary, V.P.-Sls. & Mktg.--Florida Tile Industries, Inc., Lakeland, FL; *U.S. Public*, pg. 1322
Hasegawa, Akira, Sr. Exec. V.P.--All Nippon Airways Co. Ltd., Tokyo, Japan; *Int'l*, pg. 57
Hasek, Ronald W., Mgr.-Mktg. Services & Pub. Rels.--Ampco-Pittsburgh Corporation, Pittsburgh, PA; *U.S. Public*, pg. 103
Haselton, Susan, Customer Service Coord.--Venturi Inc., Traverse City, MI; *U.S. Private*, pg. 1136
Haskell, Kim, New Bus. Devel.--TBWA Chiat/Day Los Angeles, Venice, CA; *U.S. Private*, pg. 1062
Haskell, Rich, V.P.-Mktg. Services--Champion International Corp., Stamford, CT; *U.S. Public*, pg. 333
Haskins, Bob, V.P.-Mktg. System Tech.--Edwards Systems Tech, Cheshire, CT; *U.S. Public*, pg. 726
Haslen, Dick, Dir.-Mktg.--Purity Wholesale Grocers, Boca Raton, FL; *U.S. Private*, pg. 896
Hasselbalch, Anja, Mgr.-Mktg.--Kraft Jacobs Suchard AG, Zurich, Switzerland; *U.S. Public*, pg. 1288
Hassler, Bryan G., V.P.-Mktg.--Barrett Resources Corporation, Denver, CO; *U.S. Public*, pg. 191
Hassler, Helen, Sr. Mktg. Specialist--First Financial Bancorp, Hamilton, OH; *U.S. Public*, pg. 632
Hasson, J.A., Mgr.-Mktg. Svcs.--Houghton International Inc., Valley Forge, PA; *U.S. Private*, pg. 541
Hastings, Lyndell, Dir.-Mktg. Commun.--Atomic Energy of Canada Ltd., Mississauga, Canada; *Int'l*, pg. 97
Hatch, Dave, V.P.-Mktg.--Restaura, Inc., Phoenix, AZ; *U.S. Public*, pg. 1718
Hatch, J.E., Jr., Sr. V.P.-Mktg.--The Hite Company, Altoona, PA; *U.S. Private*, pg. 531
Hatch, Mark, V.P.-Sls. & Mktg.--Data Instruments, Inc., Acton, MA; *U.S. Private*, pg. 312
Hatcher, David, V.P.-Mktg.--Maitland-Smith U.S., Inc., High Point, NC; *U.S. Private*, pg. 432
Hatcher, Jerry, Dir.-Mktg.--Marley Electric Heating Company, Bennettsville, SC; *U.S. Public*, pg. 1676
Hatfield, Michele, Mgr.-Mktg. Communications-Paper Prods.--ABB Industrial Systems, Inc., Columbus, OH; *Int'l*, pg. 4
Hauca, Gregory J., V.P.-Mktg.--Distribution America, Des Plaines, IL; *U.S. Private*, pg. 335
Hauer, Dale, V.P.-Sls. & Mktg.--Ajax Paving Industries Inc., Madison Heights, MI; *U.S. Private*, pg. 29
Haug, Nancy, Dir.-Mktg.--Airborne Freight Corporation, Seattle, WA; *U.S. Public*, pg. 32
Hauger, Gary, V.P.-Mktg.--Gander Mountain Retail, Bloomington, MN; *U.S. Private*, pg. 534
Haun, S. Wesley, V.P.-Mktg. & Gas Supply--K N Energy, Inc., Lakewood, CO; *U.S. Public*, pg. 937
Hausladen, Valerie, Dir.-Integrated Mktg.--Storage Technology Corporation, Louisville, CO; *U.S. Public*, pg. 1522
Hausler, Robert J., V.P.-Sls. & Mktg.--Mark Lighting Fixture Co., Inc., Edison, NJ; *U.S. Private*, pg. 704
Havener, Mike, Mgr.-Mktg.--Hydro Group, Inc., Bridgewater, NJ; *U.S. Private*, pg. 552
Havens, Christopher, Sr. V.P.-Retail Mktg.--Ultramar Diamond Shamrock Corporation, San Antonio, TX; *U.S. Public*, pg. 1663
Haver, Giovanni, Gen. Mgr. & Dir.-Mktg.--Banca Nazionale del Lavoro Sj.A., Rome, Italy; *Int'l*, pg. 136
Hawes, Aubrey, Sr. V.P.-Corp. Mktg. Resources--The Chase Manhattan Bank, New York, NY; *U.S. Public*, pg. 338
Hawes, Jim, Mgr.-Corp. Mktg.--The Orioles, Inc., Baltimore, MD; *U.S. Private*, pg. 819
Hawk, J.T., Dir.-Mktg.--J.M. Huber, Calcium Carbonate Division, Quincy, IL; *U.S. Private*, pg. 545
Hawk, Nelson, V.P. & Group Exec.-Mktg.--Oglethorpe Power Corp., Tucker, GA; *U.S. Private*, pg. 812
Hawkes, John, Sr. V.P. & Chief Mktg. Officer--McDonald's Hamburgers Limited, London, United Kingdom; *U.S. Public*, pg. 1069
Hawkes, Phil, Sr. V.P.-Sls. & Mktg.--Abco Markets, Inc., Phoenix, AZ; *U.S. Private*, pg. 10
Hawkins-Santini, Merri C., Mgr.-Mktg.--The Converse Professional Group, Inc., Monrovia, CA; *U.S. Private*, pg. 271
Hawkins, Augela, Dir.-Mktg.--Hanes Hosiery, Inc., Winston Salem, NC; *U.S. Public*, pg. 1434
Hawkins, John, Dir.-Mktg.--Tax Management, Inc., Washington, DC; *U.S. Private*, pg. 182
Hawkins, Kim, Dir.-Mktg.--Cherokee Inc., Van Nuys, CA; *U.S. Public*, pg. 345
Hawkins, Natasha, Mktg. Asst.--Shiseido (Australia) Pty. Limited, Pyrmont, Australia; *Int'l*, pg. 1235
Hawks, Eric B., Mgr.-Mkt. Communications--Steelcraft Manufacturing Company, Cincinnati, OH; *U.S. Public*, pg. 877
Hawley, Henry, V.P.-Mktg.--Seagram Beverage Co., New York, NY; *Int'l*, pg. 1215
Haworth, Missy, V.P.-Sls. & Mktg.--Broder Bros. Co., Plymouth, MI; *U.S. Private*, pg. 170
Hawrysz, Joe, Mgr.-Mktg. Services--Evans Tempcon Inc., Grand Rapids, MI; *U.S. Private*, pg. 7
Haws, C. Randall, V.P.-Paragon Gas Mktg.--Eastex Hydrocarbons, Inc., Houston, TX; *U.S. Public*, pg. 567
Hawthorne, Bill, Mgr.-Mktg.--BICC Pyrotenax, Trenton, Canada; *Int'l*, pg. 120
Hay, Bill, V.P.-Sls. & Mktg.--Larson Manufacturing Company, Brookings, SD; *U.S. Private*, pg. 652
Hayano, Stephanie, V.P.-Mktg.-Sally Hansen--Del Laboratories, Inc., Farmingdale, NY; *U.S. Public*, pg. 494
Hayano, Stephanie, V.P.-Mktg./Sally Hansen Nails--Sally Hansen, Farmingdale, NY; *U.S. Public*, pg. 494
Hayden, John, Dir.-Mktg. & Sls. Support--The West Company, Incorporated, Lionville, PA; *U.S. Public*, pg. 1755
Hayden, Julian G., Jr., V.P.-Mktg.--Owensboro Grain Co., Inc., Owensboro, KY; *U.S. Private*, pg. 824
Haydon, Ted, Sr. V.P.-Sls. & Mktg.--Rock of Ages Canada, Inc., Beebe, Canada; *U.S. Public*, pg. 1396
Hayek, G. Nicolas, Jr., Mgr.-Mktg.--Swatch S.A., Bienne, Switzerland; *Int'l*, pg. 1161
Hayek, John, V.P.-Mktg.--The At-A-Glance Group, Sidney, NY; *U.S. Private*, pg. 295
Hayes, C.A., Dir.-Pur., Adv. & Mktg.--Blevins Inc., Nashville, TN; *U.S. Private*, pg. 149
Hayes, Charles, Dir.-Mktg.--Inland Motor Div., Radford, VA; *U.S. Public*, pg. 965
Hayes, Chuck, Mgr.-Corp. Commun.--Merchants Group, Inc., Buffalo, NY; *U.S. Public*, pg. 1090
Hayes, Douglas, V.P.-Mktg.--Adidas (Canada) Ltd., Downsview, Canada; *Int'l*, pg. 24
Hayes, Jack D., Sr. V.P.-Mktg.--Kansas City Life Insurance Co., Kansas City, MO; *U.S. Public*, pg. 942
Hayes, John J., Exec. V.P.-Mktg.--DM Management Company, Hingham, MA; *U.S. Public*, pg. 473
Hayes, Kelsey, Dir.-Mktg.--Lincoln Property Company, Dallas, TX; *U.S. Private*, pg. 668
Hayes, Linda, V.P.-Mktg. Communications--Zenith Data Systems, Deerfield, IL; *Int'l*, pg. 317
Hayes, Peter, V.P.-Interactive Mktg.--SicolaMartin Inc., Austin, TX; *U.S. Private*, pg. 998
Hayes, Roxanne, Mktg. Svcs. Specialist--CFA Holding Company, Charlotte, MI; *U.S. Private*, pg. 194
Hayes, Terri, Mgr.-Mktg.--Persoft, Inc., Madison, WI; *U.S. Private*, pg. 856
Hayhirst, Sandi, Mktg. Dir.--Poulter Communications PLC, Leeds, United Kingdom; *Int'l*, pg. 1065
Hayman, Derick, Mgr.-Mktg. Services--The Valspar Corp. Protective Coatings Div., Baltimore, MD; *U.S. Public*, pg. 1707
Hayne, Mary, Dir.-Mktg.--Industrial Indemnity Company, San Francisco, CA; *U.S. Public*, pg. 681
Haynes, John, Dir.-Mktg.--Simplex Time Recorder Co., Gardner, MA; *U.S. Private*, pg. 1002
Haynes, Leonard J., V.P.-Mktg.--Georgia Power Co., Atlanta, GA; *U.S. Public*, pg. 1490
Hayward, Craig, Dir.-Mktg. & Sls.--Acco Chain & Lifting Products, York, PA; *Int'l*, pg. 473
Hazard, Richard, V.P.-Mktg.--ADCS, Inc., Austin, TX; *U.S. Public*, pg. 12
Hazard, William, Grp. Mgr.-Mktg.--Goodman Fielder Limited, Sydney, Australia; *Int'l*, pg. 555
Hazelet, David, Dir.-Mktg.--Sheetz, Inc., Altoona, PA; *U.S. Private*, pg. 991
Hazell, Tim, Dir.-Sls.--Matthew Clark Taunton, Ltd., Bristol, United Kingdom; *Int'l*, pg. 848
Hazelrigg, Robert C., V.P.-Mktg. & Pub. Rels.--Delta Natural Gas Company, Inc., Winchester, KY; *U.S. Public*, pg. 497
Hazen, Herman A., V.P.-Sls. & Mktg.--Ferag Inc., Bristol, PA; *Int'l*, pg. 1484
Head, George V., V.P.-Sls.--Southland Mower Corp., Selma, AL; *U.S. Private*, pg. 1144
Headrick, V. Roger, V.P.-Sls. & Mktg.--Dr. T.C. Smith Co. Inc., Asheville, NC; *U.S. Public*, pg. 214
Healey, Marsha, Mgr.-Corp. Communications--Plantronics Inc., Santa Cruz, CA; *U.S. Public*, pg. 1308
Healy, Alan, Dir.-Mktg.--Apple Computer (UK) Ltd., Uxbridge, United Kingdom; *U.S. Public*, pg. 121
Healy, Dennis, Mgr.-Mktg. & Sls.--Barko Hydraulics, Superior, WI; *U.S. Private*, pg. 859
Hearn, William J., Jr., Sr. V.P.-Trust Mktg.--SunTrust Banks, Inc., Atlanta, GA; *U.S. Public*, pg. 1537
Heath, Patricia, Mgr.-Mktg.--Apple Canada Ltd., Markham, Canada; *U.S. Public*, pg. 121
Heazlitt, Michael, V.P.-Sls. & Mktg.--Paoli, Inc., Orleans, IN; *U.S. Private*, pg. 837
Hebel, Michael, Dir.-Mktg.--Birds Eye Walls Ltd., Walton-on-Thames, United Kingdom; *Int'l*, pg. 1434
Heber, Yosi, V.P.-Mktg.--Lea & Perrins, Inc., Fair Lawn, NJ; *Int'l*, pg. 380
Hebert, Wally, Dir.-Adv. & Sls. & Mktg.--JRN, Inc., Columbia, TN; *U.S. Private*, pg. 578
Hech, Rainer, Dir.-Mktg.--Albert Roller GmbH & Co. KG, Waiblingen, Germany; *Int'l*, pg. 1126
Hecht, Donald W., Dir.-Mktg.-Cattle Prods.--Elanco Animal Health, Indianapolis, IN; *U.S. Public*, pg. 993
Hecht, Stephen, Sr. V.P.-Sls & Mktg.--Centimark Corporation, Canonsburg, PA; *U.S. Private*, pg. 222
Hecks, Trudy, Exec. Admin.-Mktg.--Crabar Business Systems, Dayton, OH; *U.S. Private*, pg. 283
Hedgcoth, Virgle L., Mgr.-Mktg.--Tosoh USA, Inc.-San Francisco Office, San Francisco, CA; *Int'l*, pg. 1407
Hedges, Helen, Dir.-Mktg.--Jack Schwartz Shoes, Inc., New York, NY; *U.S. Private*, pg. 974
Hedges, John D., Dir.-Hoffco Power Equip. Div.--Hoffco/Comet Industries, Inc., Richmond, IN; *U.S. Private*, pg. 532
Hedges, Pat, Mgr.-Field Mktg.--Pinkerton's Inc., Encino, CA; *U.S. Public*, pg. 1296
Hedley, Janette, Mktg. Assoc.--The Canadian Coleman Co., Ltd., Toronto, Canada; *U.S. Private*, pg. 691
Heer, A., Gen Mgr-Export--Wander AG, Bern, Switzerland; *Int'l*, pg. 972
Heer, Eric, Dir.-Mktg.- Hospitals--Zoll Medical Corporation, Burlington, MA; *U.S. Private*, pg. 1207
Heffke, Jodi, Mktg. Communications Asst.--Pioneer-Standard Electronics, Inc., Cleveland, OH; *U.S. Public*, pg. 1300
Heffron, Tom, V.P.- Mktg.--Fishery Products International USA, Danvers, MA; *Int'l*, pg. 492
Hefner, Hilary, Mgr.-Mktg.--Fox Broadcasting Company (FBC), Beverly Hills, CA; *Int'l*, pg. 926
Hegeman, John, Sr. V.P.-Mktg. & Distr.--MGM/UA Distribution Co., Santa Monica, CA; *U.S. Public*, pg. 1102
Heggie, Theresa, V.P.-Mktg.--Ohmeda, Inc., Liberty Corner, NJ; *Int'l*, pg. 121
Heggie, Theresa, V.P.-Mktg. Svcs.--Ohmeda, Liberty Corner, NJ; *Int'l*, pg. 121
Heiden, Gudrun, Dir.-Mktg. & Mgr.-Sls.--ISS Servisystem GesmbH, Vienna, Austria; *Int'l*, pg. 657
Heider, Ed, Mgr.-Natl. Sls.--Akzo Nobel Coatings Inc., Columbus, OH; *Int'l*, pg. 48
Heider, Robert, V.P.-Regulatory Affairs & Mktg.--TQM Pipeline Partnership, Montreal, Canada; *Int'l*, pg. 541
Heidl, Deb, Admin. Asst.--Integrated Material Handling Company, Oshkosh, WI; *Int'l*, pg. 1397
Heidt, Kimberly, Mgr.-Mktg.--The Albany Herald Publishing Co., Inc., Albany, GA; *U.S. Public*, pg. 759
Heil, John, V.P.-Nutrition & Specialty Product--Star-Kist Foods Inc., Newport, KY; *U.S. Public*, pg. 805
Heil, Louis, Sls. & Mktg.--Steel Ceilings Inc., Coshocton, OH; *U.S. Private*, pg. 29
Heilman, Don, Mgr.-Mktg. & Special Events--Shurfine International, Inc., Northlake, IL; *U.S. Private*, pg. 997
Heilmann, Bernd, V.P.-Sls. & Mktg.--Hako-Werke GmbH & Co., Bad Oldesloe, Germany; *Int'l*, pg. 587
Heilstedt, John, V.P.-Sls. & Mktg.--Elkay Manufacturing Company, Oak Brook, IL; *U.S. Private*, pg. 372
Heimbecker, David A., Mgr.-Mktg.--Binney & Smith Ltd., Lindsay, Canada; *U.S. Private*, pg. 496
Heine, Charles, V.P.-Sls.--Bayer Clothing Group, New York, NY; *U.S. Private*, pg. 124
Heine, Michael J., V.P.-Mktg.--Keystone Bank, Horsham, PA; *U.S. Public*, pg. 956
Heiner, Clyde M., Sr. V.P.--Questar Corporation, Salt Lake City, UT; *U.S. Public*, pg. 1352
Heinkel, F.G., V.P.-Sls. & Mktg.--PrimeSource Corporation, Pennsauken, NJ; *U.S. Public*, pg. 1329
Heintz, D.A., Dir.-Mktg. & Creative--Reynolds Metals Co.-Flexible Packaging Products Division, Richmond, VA; *U.S. Public*, pg. 1386
Heintz, Julie, Mktg. Coord.--Chi Systems Division, Ann Arbor, MI; *U.S. Public*, pg. 1539
Heinz, Christian, Dir.-Mktg., Adv. & Pub. Rels.--Credit Suisse, Zurich, Switzerland; *Int'l*, pg. 345
Heinze, Harold, Dir.-Mktg.--Mrs. Baird's Bakeries, Inc., Fort Worth, TX; *U.S. Private*, pg. 765
Heithau, Hank, Mgr.-Mktg. Retail--Murphy Oil Corporation, El Dorado, AR; *U.S. Public*, pg. 1141
Heithaus, Henry J., Mgr.-Retail Mktg.--Murphy Oil USA, Inc., El Dorado, AR; *U.S. Public*, pg. 1142
Heitsch, Gary, Mgr.-Mktg.--Rollex Corporation, Elk Grove Village, IL; *U.S. Private*, pg. 941
Helbling, Helska, Dir.-Mktg.--Charter Medical of England Ltd., London, United Kingdom; *U.S. Public*, pg. 1036
Helier, Bernard B., V.P.-Mktg. & Sls.--Zero Corporation, Los Angeles, CA; *U.S. Public*, pg. 1791
Helland, Sue, Mkt. Res.--Johnson Worldwide Associates, Inc., Sturtevant, WI; *U.S. Public*, pg. 932
Hellberg, S.W., Sr. V.P.-Mktg. & Sls.--Creative Productions, Pittsburgh, PA; *U.S. Private*, pg. 288
Hellriegel, Rob, Mgr.-Mktg.--Sky Network Television Limited, Auckland, New Zealand; *U.S. Public*, pg. 204
Helm, Michelle, V.P.-Mktg./Membership--Sam's Clubs Div., Bentonville, AR; *U.S. Public*, pg. 1733
Helmlinger, Terri, Dir.-Comml./Indus. Market Devel.--Carolina Power & Light Company, Raleigh, NC; *U.S. Public*, pg. 306
Helms, Terry, Dir.-Mktg.--Hughes Supply, Inc., Orlando, FL; *U.S. Public*, pg. 846
Helstein, Richard, V.P.-Adv. & Mktg. Services/Kraft--Kraft Foods Inc., Rye Brook, NY; *U.S. Public*, pg. 1288
Hemberger, Hubert, Dr., Dir.-Mktg.--Deutsche Spezialglas AG, Glunanplan, Germany; *Int'l*, pg. 1523
Hembree, Mark, Dir.-Mktg.--Waxman Industries, Inc., Bedford, OH; *U.S. Public*, pg. 1748
Hemjum, Scott, Dir.-Mktg. Communication Services--Tower Group International, New York, NY; *U.S. Public*, pg. 1071
Hemmelgarn, Richard A., V.P.-Sls. & Mktg.--Blount, Inc. Forestry & Industrial Equipment Division, Zebulon, NC; *U.S. Public*, pg. 238
Hemmens, P., Grp. Gen. Mgr.--LASMO plc, London, United Kingdom; *Int'l*, pg. 803
Hemmer, Gary D., Exec. V.P.-Fin. Markets--Magna Group, Inc., Saint Louis, MO; *U.S. Public*, pg. 1037
Hemrick, Christine, V.P.-Mktg. Internet Bus. Unit--Cisco Systems, Inc., San Jose, CA; *U.S. Public*, pg. 375
Henaire, Patrice, V.P.-Sls. & Mktg.--Venmar Ventilation, Inc., Drummondville, Canada; *U.S. Public*, pg. 1194
Henceroth, David, Mgr.- Sls. & Mktg.--Testronics, Freeport, TX; *U.S. Private*, pg. 487
Henderson-Hernandez, Susan, V.P.-Mktg.--IHOP Corp., Glendale, CA; *U.S. Public*, pg. 862
Henderson, David, V.P. & Gen. Mgr.--American Locker Group, Inc., Jamestown, NY; *U.S. Public*, pg. 85
Henderson, Jim, Exec. V.P.-Sls. & Mktg.--BGF Industries Inc., Greensboro, NC; *U.S. Private*, pg. 106
Henderson, Michael, V.P.-Sls. & Mktg.--Northern Telecom Inc., Rochester, NY; *Int'l*, pg. 970
Hendin, Marty, V.P.-Community Rels.--St. Louis National Baseball Club L.P., Saint Louis, MO; *U.S. Private*, pg. 961
Hendricks, Adele, Pres. & Retail Dir.--Dean's Photo Service, San Diego, CA; *U.S. Private*, pg. 319
Hendricks, Andrew J., Sr. V.P.-Mktg.--Mission American Insurance Company, Rancho Dominguez, CA; *U.S. Public*, pg. 483
Hendricks, John, Sr. V.P.--Moyer Packing Company, Souderton, PA; *U.S. Private*, pg. 765
Hendricks, Teresa, Mgr.-Mktg. Commun.--Pioneer Hi-Bred International, Inc., Des Moines, IA; *U.S. Public*, pg. 1298
Hendrickson, Julie, Pres.-Mktg.--Equity Services, Inc., Montpelier, VT; *U.S. Private*, pg. 785
Hendrie, Richard, Sr. V.P.-Mktg.--Unique Casual Restaurants, inc., Danvers, MA; *Int'l*, pg. 324
Hendrix, Greg, Mgr.-Book Mktg.--R.R. Donnelley & Sons Company, Chicago, IL; *U.S. Public*, pg. 517
Hendrix, Kay, Pur.--Regions Bank/Gadsden, Gadsden, AL; *U.S. Public*, pg. 1372
Hendy, John, Mgr.-Mktg.-Desserts--UB Frozen & Chilled Limited, Grimsby, United Kingdom; *Int'l*, pg. 1442
Heneberry, David, V.P.-Mktg.--The Ryland Group, Inc., Columbia, MD; *U.S. Public*, pg. 1414
Heneghan, Frank M., V.P.-Sls. & Mktg.--McArdle Printing Co., Inc., Upper Marlboro, MD; *U.S. Private*, pg. 182
Henke, Jurgen, Mgr.-Mktg. Comm.--Tuchenhagen GmbH, Buchen, Germany; *Int'l*, pg. 1426

Henkel, Arnold D., Sr. V.P. & Chief Mktg. Officer--Ministers Life Resources, Saint Paul, MN; *U.S. Private*, pg. 750
Henkin, Raphael, Ph.D., V.P.-Mktg. & Engrng.--Del Mar Avionics, Irvine, CA; *U.S. Private*, pg. 321
Hennen, Jerry, Mgr.-Sls. & Mktg.--Arrow Tru-Line, Inc., Archbold, OH; *U.S. Private*, pg. 85
Hennessy, Leslie, V.P.-Mktg.--Lovejoy Inc., Downers Grove, IL; *U.S. Private*, pg. 677
Hennesey, Larry, Dir.-Mktg. Communications--The Gates Rubber Company, Denver, CO; *Int'l*, pg. 1396
Hennington, Rolf, V.P.-Sls. & Mktg.--Industrial Coatings Group, Inc., Chicago, IL; *U.S. Private*, pg. 434
Henry, Charles, V.P.-Sls. & Mktg.--Xentek, Inc., San Marcos, CA; *Int'l*, pg. 1349
Henry, Ed, Mgr.-Sls. & Mktg.--Viking Electronics, Inc., Chatsworth, CA; *U.S. Private*, pg. 1184
Henry, Michael, Dir.-Mktg., Eve St. Laurent--Sanofi Beaute, Inc., New York, NY; *Int'l*, pg. 445
Henry, Neil, Dir.-Mktg.--Spar (UK) Ltd., Harrow, United Kingdom; *Int'l*, pg. 1288
Henry, R.D., Mgr.-Prod. Control--Hilliard Corporation, Elmira, NY; *U.S. Private*, pg. 530
Henry, Terry, Dir.-Mktg.--Harris Corp., Digital Telephone Systems Div., Novato, CA; *U.S. Public*, pg. 791
Henry, Thomas J., Dir.-Mktg.--Armstrong International, Inc., Three Rivers, MI; *U.S. Private*, pg. 83
Hensel, Nancy, V.P.-Mktg. & Mdsg.--The Popcorn Factory, Lake Forest, IL; *U.S. Private*, pg. 421
Henshaw, Brett, Dir.-Mktg.--Colgate-Palmolive Ltd., Guildford, United Kingdom; *U.S. Public*, pg. 398
Henson, Jim L., Sr. V.P. & Chief Mktg. Officer--Shenandoah Life Insurance Company, Roanoke, VA; *U.S. Private*, pg. 992
Henthorne, Hazel, Mktg. Asst.--Victoria's Secret Stores, Reynoldsburg, OH; *U.S. Public*, pg. 995
Henwood, Bill, Sr. V.P.-Sls. & Mktg.--Nicklaus Golf Company, L.C., West Palm Beach, FL; *U.S. Private*, pg. 799
Hepburn, carman D., V.P.-Sls. & Mktg.--Knape & Vogt Canada Inc., Etobicoke, Canada; *U.S. Public*, pg. 963
Hepler, Katherine, V.P.-Mktg.--Realty One, Cleveland, OH; *U.S. Private*, pg. 914
Heppner, John, V.P.-Mktg. & New Bus.--Master Lock Company, Milwaukee, WI; *U.S. Public*, pg. 675
Herasimchuk, David A., V.P.-Mktg. Devel.--Global Marine Inc., Houston, TX; *U.S. Public*, pg. 748
Herb, B., Mgr.-Mktg.--AGRA Earth & Environmental, Inc., Anaheim, CA; *Int'l*, pg. 31
Herb, Robert, V.P.-Strategic Mktg./Computation Prods. Grp.--Advanced Micro Devices, Inc., Sunnyvale, CA; *U.S. Public*, pg. 21
Herberg, Richard, Chief Oper. Officer & V.P.-Mktg.--Bachman's, Inc., Minneapolis, MN; *U.S. Private*, pg. 109
Herbert, Betsy, V.P.-Mktg. & Sls.--Danco Products, Concordville, PA; *U.S. Public*, pg. 1145
Herbert, C.G., Dir.-Mktg.--VG Analytical Ltd., Manchester, United Kingdom; *Int'l*, pg. 1110
Herbert, R. Pat, V.P.-Mktg. Devel. & Tech.--Baker Hughes Incorporated, Houston, TX; *U.S. Public*, pg. 165
Herbits, Stephen E., Exec. V.P.-Corp. & External Affairs--Joseph E. Seagram & Sons, Inc., New York, NY; *Int'l*, pg. 1215
Herbst, Rosanne, Coord.-Mktg. Commun.--Littelfuse, Inc., Des Plaines, IL; *U.S. Public*, pg. 1001
Herbster, William M., V.P.-Mktg.--RemedyTemp, Inc., San Juan Capistrano, CA; *U.S. Public*, pg. 1376
Herchenroder, Frank, Dir.-Procurement & Mdsg.--Bozzuto's Inc., Cheshire, CT; *U.S. Public*, pg. 249
Herera, Joe, V.P.-Mktg.--El Pollo Loco, Irvine, CA; *U.S. Public*, pg. 23
Herkamp, W.J., V.P.-Sls. & Mktg.--Sweco, Florence, KY; *U.S. Public*, pg. 574
Herker, Larry, V.P.& Mktg.--General American Door Company, Montgomery, IL; *U.S. Private*, pg. 732
Herling, Robert, V.P.-Sls. & Mktg.--Atlas Electric Devices Co., Chicago, IL; *U.S. Private*, pg. 96
Herlitz, Klaus, V.P.-Mktg.--Herlitz PBS Aktiengesellschaft, Berlin, Germany; *Int'l*, pg. 616
Herman, Daniel, V.P. & Dir.-Mktg.--Jabel, Inc., Irvington, NJ; *U.S. Private*, pg. 579
Herman, Edwin, Dir.-Mktg.--Manhattan Industries Intl. Div., New York, NY; *U.S. Public*, pg. 1429
Herman, Howard, V.P.-Mktg.--Bermil Industries Corp., Inwood, NY; *U.S. Private*, pg. 136
Herman, Kim, V.P.-Strategic Mktg. & Sls. Support--Olsten Health Services, Melville, NY; *U.S. Public*, pg. 1221
Herman, Laurie, Dir.-External Affairs--AT&T Alascom, Anchorage, AK; *U.S. Public*, pg. 10
Hermann, David T., V.P.-Mktg.--Potters Industries, Inc., Valley Forge, PA; *U.S. Private*, pg. 827
Hermansson, Tomas, Mktg. Mgr.--ESAB Tech AB, Vastra Frolunda, Sweden; *Int'l*, pg. 281
Hermosillo, Alberto Cabal, V.P.-Mktg. & Plng.--Grupo Synkro, S.A. de C.V., Mexico, Mexico; *Int'l*, pg. 576
Hermoso, Juan, Mgr.-Mktg. & Promo.--El Corte Ingles SA, Madrid, Spain; *Int'l*, pg. 435
Hermsen, Louise, V.P.-Plng. & Support Svcs.--Harnischfeger Industries, Inc., Saint Francis, WI; *U.S. Public*, pg. 788
Hern, Roy D., Dir.-Sls. & Mktg.--Hardings, Inc., Elmira, NY; *U.S. Private*, pg. 502
Hernandez-Carstens, Eduardo, V.P.-Mktg.--BITOR America Corp., Boca Raton, FL; *Int'l*, pg. 1045
Hernandez, Carlos, V.P.-Mktg.--CalMat Co., Los Angeles, CA; *U.S. Public*, pg. 295
Hernandez, Cynthia, V.P.-Sls. & Mktg.--Chip Supply Inc., Orlando, FL; *U.S. Private*, pg. 237
Hernandez, Jacqueline, Dir.-Mktg.--VV Publishing Corp., New York, NY; *U.S. Private*, pg. 1131
Hernandez, Rafael, Dir.-Mktg.--Fiesta Mart Inc., Houston, TX; *U.S. Private*, pg. 403
Hernandez, Rodolfo, Dir.-Mktg.--Renault Argentina, Buenos Aires, Argentina; *Int'l*, pg. 1103
Herndon, Lin, Dir.-Global Mktg.--Elsevier Science (International), Amsterdam, Netherlands; *Int'l*, pg. 1099
Herndon, Vince, Pres. & Chief Oper. Officer--Holcomb & Hoke Mfg. Company, Inc., Indianapolis, IN; *U.S. Private*, pg. 533
Heron, Elaine J., Ph.D., V.P.-Worldwide Sls. & Mktg.--The Perkin-Elmer Corporation, Norwalk, CT; *U.S. Public*, pg. 1279
Herot, Frederick, V.P.-Mktg.--Weichert Company, Morris Plains, NJ; *U.S. Private*, pg. 1159
Herren, William, Div. Dir.-Mktg. Strategy--Delphi Energy & Engine Management Systems, Flint, MI; *U.S. Public*, pg. 719
Herrera, Juan E., V.P.-Mktg.--CODELCO Chile (Corporacion Nacional Del Cobre De Chile), Santiago, Chile; *Int'l*, pg. 302
Herrick, Mary Ann, Mgr.-Mktg.--Plasti-Line, Inc., Knoxville, TN; *U.S. Public*, pg. 1308
Herrick, William, Mgr.-Intl. Mktg. Svcs.--Michigan Wheel Corporation, Grand Rapids, MI; *U.S. Private*, pg. 741
Herrin, Elaine, V.P.-Worldwide Sls. & Mktg.--Applied Biosystems, Foster City, CA; *U.S. Public*, pg. 1279
Herring, Terry, Customer Mktg.--Solvay Pharmaceuticals, Inc., Marietta, GA; *Int'l*, pg. 1278
Herrington, Bill, V.P.-Mktg. Natl. & Intl. Accts.--Manna Pro Corporation, Saint Louis, MO; *U.S. Private*, pg. 700
Herron, Michael, Dir.-Communications--Environmental Resources Management, Exton, PA; *U.S. Private*, pg. 378
Hershbell, D.A., Mgr.-Mktg. & Tech. Svcs.--Lenape Forge, Inc., West Chester, PA; *U.S. Private*, pg. 659
Hershey, Leon, V.P.-Sls. & Mktg.--Sunline Coach Co., Inc., Denver, PA; *U.S. Private*, pg. 1053
Herskowitz, Sam, Dir.- Mktg. & Adv.--Sterling Vision, Inc., East Meadow, NY; *U.S. Public*, pg. 1516
Hertel, G. T., V.P.-Mktg.--Krupp Robins, Inc., Englewood, CO; *Int'l*, pg. 511
Hervey, Frank Jr., Mgr.-Mktg.--Hyspan Precision Products, Inc., Chula Vista, CA; *U.S. Private*, pg. 552
Herzfeld, R., Mktg.--Knorr-Bremse AG, Munich, Germany; *Int'l*, pg. 738
Herzka, Daniel, V.P. & Gen. Mgr.-Desktop Solutions--Linotype-Hell Company, Hauppauge, NY; *Int'l*, pg. 604
Herzog, Jim, Mgr.-Corp. Communications, Sls., Mktg. & Adv.--Armco Inc., Pittsburgh, PA; *U.S. Public*, pg. 131
Hesler, Mark, V.P.-Bus. Devel.--Webcraft Technologies, Inc., North Brunswick, NJ; *U.S. Public*, pg. 228
Hess, Ron, Dir.-Mktg./North America--AGCO Corporation, Duluth, GA; *U.S. Public*, pg. 28
Hess, William R., Exec. V.P.-Mktg. & Sls.--Farmers and Traders Life Insurance Co., Syracuse, NY; *U.S. Private*, pg. 394
Hessenthaller, Lee, Dir.-Mktg.--Northland Cranberries, Inc., Wisconsin Rapids, WI; *U.S. Public*, pg. 1197
Hester, Randy, V.P.-Mktg.--Cinemark USA, Inc., Dallas, TX; *U.S. Private*, pg. 240
Hester, S.R., V.P.-Mktg. & Sls.--Rocky Rococo Corporation, Oconomowoc, WI; *U.S. Private*, pg. 938
Hetherwick, Gilbert, Sr. V.P.-Intl. Mktg., Sony Classical--Sony Music Entertainment, Inc., New York, NY; *Int'l*, pg. 1281
Hetterich, Paul, V.P.-Mktg.--Canandaigua Wine Company, Inc., Canandaigua, NY; *U.S. Public*, pg. 300
Hetterich, Paul, V.P.-Mktg.--Canandaigua Wine Co., Canandaigua, NY; *U.S. Public*, pg. 300
Hettrick, Craig, V.P.-Sls. & Mktg.--Frionor U.S.A. Inc., New Bedford, MA; *Int'l*, pg. 516
Heubner, Warren, V.P.-Petroleum Mktg.--Cenex/Land O'Lakes, Inc., Inver Grove Heights, MN; *U.S. Private*, pg. 222
Heule, Michael D., V.P.-Special Projects--Ocelot Energy Inc., Calgary, Canada; *Int'l*, pg. 996
Heuley, Joseph F., V.P.-Mktg.--Cummins Mid-South, Inc., Memphis, TN; *U.S. Private*, pg. 295
Heysler, Thomas, Mgr.-Mktg.--Falcon Products, Inc., Saint Louis, MO; *U.S. Public*, pg. 611
Hewett, Robert M., Sr. V.P.-Customer Opers. & Mktg.--Kentucky Utilities Company, Lexington, KY; *U.S. Public*, pg. 941
Hewett, Sheila, V.P.-Mktg.--Calvin Klein Cosmetics Company, New York, NY; *Int'l*, pg. 1435
Hewey, Stacey, Mgr.-Direct Mktg.--Success Development International, Jacksonville, FL; *U.S. Private*, pg. 1048
Hewgley, William M., Jr., Exec. V.P.-Sls. & Mktg.--American Manufacturing Company, Chattanooga, TN; *U.S. Private*, pg. 58
Hewitt, Bill, V.P.-Mktg.--Hyperion Software, Stamford, CT; *U.S. Public*, pg. 851
Hewitt, Dave, V.P. & Gen. Mgr.-Mktg.--Binney & Smith Inc., Easton, PA; *U.S. Private*, pg. 496
Heyamoto, Dave, Mgr.-Mktg.--The Washington Water Power Company, Spokane, WA; *U.S. Public*, pg. 1744
Heyen, Sean, Mgr.-Mktg. Communications--Transcrypt International, Lincoln, NE; *U.S. Public*, pg. 1630
Heyer, Steven J., Pres.-Worldwide Sls., Mktg., Distr. & Intl. Networks Group--Turner Broadcasting System Inc., Atlanta, GA; *U.S. Public*, pg. 1614
Heyman, Richard, V.P.-Information Technology & Measured Mktg.--Baker's Supermarkets, Inc., Omaha, NE; *U.S. Public*, pg. 652
Hiatt, Bob, Mgr.-Mktg.--Willis Corroon Corp. of Florida, Tampa, FL; *Int'l*, pg. 1505
Hibray, Blake, V.P.-Mktg. & Sls., Natl. Accts.--Sigma Chemical Co., Saint Louis, MO; *U.S. Public*, pg. 1472
Hickerson, Jennifer, Prod. Mgr.--Sathers Inc., Round Lake, MN; *U.S. Private*, pg. 397
Hickey, Jerry D., Dir.-Mktg. Communications--IMO Industries Inc., Lawrenceville, NJ; *U.S. Public*, pg. 856
Hickey, Stephen, Sr. V.P.-Mktg.--La Quinta Inns, Inc., San Antonio, TX; *U.S. Public*, pg. 972
Hicklen, William, Mgr.-Mktg.--Nooter Corporation, Saint Louis, MO; *U.S. Private*, pg. 801
Hickling, Donna, Mgr.-Mktg. Communications--Schlegel Corporation, Rochester, NY; *Int'l*, pg. 128
Hickman, Barrett, V.P.-Sls. & Mktg.--Imax Corporation, Mississauga, Canada; *Int'l*, pg. 661
Hickman, Michael, V.P.-Mfg. & Engrng.--GSW Pump Company, Fergus, Canada; *Int'l*, pg. 538
Hickock, Ned, V.P.-Natl. Mktg.--The Disney Channel, Burbank, CA; *U.S. Public*, pg. 513
Hickox, Jennifer, Sls. & Mktg. Asst.--Sunroc Corporation, Dover, DE; *U.S. Private*, pg. 1053
Hickox, Jennifer, Sls. & Mktg. Asst.--Telkee, Dover, DE; *U.S. Private*, pg. 1053
Hicks, Ken, V.P.-Sls. & Mktg.--Argo-Tech Corporation, Cleveland, OH; *U.S. Private*, pg. 81
Hicks, Terry, Mgr.-Prod. Mktg.--Proxima Corporation, San Diego, CA; *U.S. Public*, pg. 1339
Hicks, Thomas, V.P.--American Laubscher Corp., Farmingdale, NY; *U.S. Private*, pg. 58
Hiebsch, Steve F., Mgr.-Mktg. Svcs.--OGE Energy Corp., Oklahoma City, OK; *U.S. Public*, pg. 1207
Hienrich, Andreas J., Prod. Mgr.--Inka Paletten GmbH, Hoehenkirchen, Germany; *Int'l*, pg. 678
Hietanen, S., Dir.-Mktg. Svcs.--Enso Oyj, Helsinki, Finland; *Int'l*, pg. 455
Higginbotham, Colleen, Coord.-Media--Distillers Corporation S.A., Stellenbosch, South Africa; *Int'l*, pg. 1129
Higgins, Becky, Dir.-Mktg.--Zale Corporation, Irving, TX; *U.S. Public*, pg. 1789
Higgins, Mary, Mgr.-Mktg. Communications--Switchcraft, Inc., Chicago, IL; *U.S. Public*, pg. 1366
Higgins, Robert, Dir.-Sls. & Mktg.--DHL International Express Ltd., Mississauga, Canada; *U.S. Private*, pg. 302
Higgins, T.J., V.P.-Mktg.--Durex Consumer Products, Norcross, GA; *Int'l*, pg. 815
Higgs, Philip, Dir.-Mktg.--Glynwed Metal Services Ltd., Kingston, United Kingdom; *Int'l*, pg. 554
Higham, Jay, V.P.-Mktg. & Devel.--IntegraMed America, Purchase, NY; *U.S. Public*, pg. 883
Higham, Paul H., Sr. V.P.-Mktg. & Sls. Promo.--Wal-Mart Stores, Inc., Bentonville, AR; *U.S. Public*, pg. 1732
Highmark, D.M., V.P.-Mktg. & Res.--Purina Mills, Inc., Saint Louis, MO; *U.S. Private*, pg. 895
Hightower, Dana E., Dir.-New Bus. Devel.--Avanti Press Inc., Miami, FL; *U.S. Private*, pg. 101
Hightower, Sharon, V.P. & Dir.-Mktg.--South Trust Bank of Georgia, Atlanta, GA; *U.S. Public*, pg. 1492
Hilbrands, W.J., Mgr.-Mktg. & Sls.--Corporate New Business Development Div., Delft, Netherlands; *Int'l*, pg. 1142
Hild, Julie L., Mktg. Support/Trade Show Coord.--White Pine Software, Nashua, NH; *U.S. Private*, pg. 1173
Hildebrand, James, V.P.-Sls. & Mktg.--GF Office Furniture Ltd., Gallatin, TN; *U.S. Private*, pg. 434
Hildebrand, Phillip, Exec. V.P.-Sls. & Mktg.--New York Life Insurance Company, New York, NY; *U.S. Private*, pg. 794
Hildebrandt, H. John, V.P.-Mktg., Cedar Fair--Cedar Fair, L.P., Sandusky, OH; *U.S. Public*, pg. 319
Hildebrandt, John, V.P.-Mktg. & Sls.--Cedar Point, Sandusky, OH; *U.S. Public*, pg. 319
Hildner, Jack, Exec. V.P.-Sls. & Mktg.--American Color Graphics, Brentwood, TN; *U.S. Public*, pg. 1132
Hilgert, Jeffrey R., Dir.-Mktg.--Branson Ultrasonics Corp. - Precision Cleaning Div., Danbury, CT; *U.S. Public*, pg. 574
Hill, B.P., V.P.-Mktg.--Wesgo Inc., Belmont, CA; *Int'l*, pg. 893
Hill, Cindy, Dir.-MKtg.--El Chico Restaurants, Inc., Dallas, TX; *U.S. Private*, pg. 283
Hill, Dan J., Sr. V.P.-Terminaling & Mktg.--The Coastal Corporation, Houston, TX; *U.S. Public*, pg. 389
Hill, Dave, Dir.-Mktg. Communications--Symantec Corporation - Beaverton Site, Beaverton, OR; *U.S. Public*, pg. 1545
Hill, David, V.P.-Mktg.--Willis Corroon Melling Ltd., Edmonton, Canada; *Int'l*, pg. 1509
Hill, David, Dir.-Mktg. Communications--Symantec Corporation, Cupertino, CA; *U.S. Public*, pg. 1545
Hill, David F., Sr. V.P.-Strategic Mktg.--Northwestern National Life Insurance Co., Minneapolis, MN; *U.S. Public*, pg. 1375
Hill, Denise, Mgr.-Mktg. & Sls.--Carme' Cosmeceutical Sciences, Inc., Napa, CA; *U.S. Private*, pg. 213
Hill, Douglas E., Principal-Mktg.--Edward Jones, Saint Louis, MO; *U.S. Private*, pg. 597
Hill, Gene, Mgr.-Natl. Sls.--Yamaha Motor Corp., U.S.A., Cypress, CA; *Int'l*, pg. 1516
Hill, Graeme, Gen. Mgr.-Mktg. Devel.--The Southern Life Association Limited, Cape Town, South Africa; *Int'l*, pg. 77
Hill, Jane, Dir.-Mktg.--Reed Business Information, Sutton, United Kingdom; *Int'l*, pg. 1094
Hill, Jonathan, Dir.-Sls.--Pauls Malt Limited, Newmarket, United Kingdom; *Int'l*, pg. 598
Hill, Louis, Dir.-Mktg.--PSB Co., Columbus, OH; *U.S. Private*, pg. 1172
Hill, Spencer, V.P.-Sls. & Mktg.--Clover Club Foods, Inc., Kaysville, UT; *U.S. Private*, pg. 469
Hill, Tim, V.P.-Mktg.--Software AG Americas, Inc., Reston, VA; *U.S. Public*, pg. 1482
Hill, Vada, Sr. V.P.-Mktg.--Taco Bell Corp., Irvine, CA; *U.S. Public*, pg. 1637
Hiller, Cary, Mgr.-Mktg. Communications--Rockwell Automation, Milwaukee, WI; *U.S. Public*, pg. 1397
Hiller, Yvonne, Dir.-Mktg. & Adv.--Elsinore Corporation, Las Vegas, NV; *U.S. Public*, pg. 570
Hilliard, Al, V.P.--IBM Canada Limited, Markham, Canada; *U.S. Public*, pg. 896
Hillis, Michael, Mgr.-Sls. & Mktg.--Tober Industries, Inc., Saint Louis, MO; *U.S. Private*, pg. 1089
Hilmarsson, Hannes, Mgr.-Sls.-U.S.A. & Canada--IceLandAir, Columbia, MD; *Int'l*, pg. 658
Hilsenbeck, Susan, V.P.-Mktg., Sls. & Promo.--General Host Corporation, Stamford, CT; *U.S. Public*, pg. 715
Hilsenbeck, Susan M., V.P.-Mktg.--Frank's Nursery & Crafts, Inc., Detroit, MI; *U.S. Public*, pg. 715
Hilty, Gerald A., Mgr.-Mktg.--Material Handling Systems Div., Chalfont, PA; *U.S. Public*, pg. 605

Hilty, Heather, Mgr.-Mktg.--Zoll Medical Corporation, Burlington, MA; *U.S. Private*, pg. 1207
Hilty, John, Mgr.-Direct Mktg.--Traveling Software Inc., Bothell, WA; *U.S. Private*, pg. 1098
Hilty, Tom, Mgr.-Mktg.--Reliance Electric Company, Cleveland, OH; *U.S. Public*, pg. 1398
Himburg, Chris, V.P.-Mktg.--Long's Electronics, Inc., Birmingham, AL; *U.S. Private*, pg. 675
Himei, Makato, Mgr.-Mktg. Devel.--Toto Ltd., Kitakyushu, Japan; *Int'l*, pg. 1410
Himmel, Anne-Marie, Mgr.-Mktg.--Kaepa Inc., Greenville, SC; *U.S. Private*, pg. 604
Himoff, Jon, Dir.-Mktg.--Circle Freight International (U.S.A.), San Francisco, CA; *U.S. Public*, pg. 370
Hinchcliff, Catherine, Mgr.-Mktg. Svcs.--Energizer Eveready Ltd., London, United Kingdom; *U.S. Public*, pg. 1360
Hindle, John, V.P.-Mktg. Communications--Northern Telecom, Nashville, TN; *Int'l*, pg. 969
Hindle, Kurt, Dir.-Mktg.--Smith & Wesson Corp., Springfield, MA; *Int'l*, pg. 1397
Hindle, Roy, Mgr.-Mktg. Support--Bohler-Uddeholm Corp., Rolling Meadows, IL; *Int'l*, pg. 1471
Hindman, Donald D., V.P.-Sls. & Mktg.--Clark Foodservice, Inc., Elk Grove Village, IL; *U.S. Private*, pg. 242
Hines, Art, Dir.-Mktg.--Prepress Solutions, Inc., Billerica, MA; *U.S. Private*, pg. 882
Hines, Denise, Mgr.-Mktg.--Crown Prince, Inc. (CA), City of Industry, CA; *U.S. Private*, pg. 293
Hines, James, Sr. Dir.-Mktg.--Sara Lee Sock Company, High Point, NC; *U.S. Public*, pg. 1434
Hines, Perry G., V.P.-Mktg.--American States Insurance Companies, Indianapolis, IN; *U.S. Public*, pg. 442
Hines, Steve, Mgr.-Gen. Sls. & Mktg.--Belliss & Morcom, Birmingham, United Kingdom; *Int'l*, pg. 1065
Hines, Steve J., Dir.-Mktg. & Indus. Sweeteners--United Sugars Corp., Bloomington, MN; *U.S. Private*, pg. 52
Hinge, Claus, V.P.-European Sls. & Mktg.--Printronix, Inc., Irvine, CA; *U.S. Public*, pg. 1329
Hingiss, Mark H., Sr. V.P.-Mktg.--Honeymead Products Co., Mankato, MN; *U.S. Private*, pg. 537
Hinkle, Jane K., V.P.-Sls. & Mktg.--Octagon Process Inc., Edgewater, NJ; *U.S. Private*, pg. 811
Hintchman, Jennifer, Mgr.-Mktg.--Barra, Inc., Berkeley, CA; *U.S. Public*, pg. 191
Hinton, Howard W., V.P.-Fuel Alcohol Mktg.--Midwest Grain Products, Inc., Atchison, KS; *U.S. Public*, pg. 1111
Hintsa, Mark, Dir.-Mktg. Franchise Devel.--Time Inc., New York, NY; *U.S. Public*, pg. 1612
Hintz, David, Dir.-Mktg.--Cousins Submarines, Menomonee Falls, WI; *U.S. Private*, pg. 280
Hinze, Lisa, Mktg. Asst.--Andes Candies Inc., Delavan, WI; *U.S. Private*, pg. 163
Hippensteel, Bill, Sr. V.P.-Mktg.--AMCORE Mortgage, Inc., Rockford, IL; *U.S. Public*, pg. 64
Hippensteel, William R., Sr. V.P. & Mgr.-Corp. Mktg.--AMCORE Bank N.A., Rockford, Rockford, IL; *U.S. Public*, pg. 64
Hippensteel, William T., Sr. V.P. & Mgr.-Corp. Mktg.--Amcore Financial, Inc., Rockford, IL; *U.S. Public*, pg. 64
Hipple, Therese, Coord.-Mktg. Services--CiMatrix L.L.C., Canton, MA; *U.S. Public*, pg. 1395
Hipps, Jeff, Sr. V.P.-Mktg.--Inkel USA Corporation, La Mirada, CA; *U.S. Private*, pg. 563
Hipsley, Andrew, Dir.-Mktg.--McDonald's System of Australia Ltd., Thornleigh, Australia; *U.S. Public*, pg. 1069
Hipwell, Roger, Sr. V.P.-Sls. & Mktg.--Bay State Milling Co., Quincy, MA; *U.S. Private*, pg. 124
Hire, Steve, Dir.-Mktg.--Delta Consolidated Industries, Inc., Raleigh, NC; *U.S. Public*, pg. 481
Hire, Steve, Dir.-Mktg. Programs--Delta Consolidated Industries, Inc. (Co. Headquarters), Jonesboro, AR; *U.S. Public*, pg. 481
Hirooka, Sueyuki, Exec. Dir. & Grp. Gen. Mgr.-Intl. Mktg.--Sharp Corporation, Osaka, Japan; *Int'l*, pg. 1228
Hirsch, Erin, Mgr.-Product Devel.--Goddess Bra Company, East Boston, MA; *U.S. Private*, pg. 458
Hirschfeld, Ron, Exec. V.P.-Intl. Sls. & Mktg.--Galoob Toys, Inc., South San Francisco, CA; *U.S. Public*, pg. 698
Hirst, Andrew, V.P. & Gen. Mgr.--Nurses Inc., Houston, TX; *Int'l*, pg. 1285
Hirst, C., Dir.-Mktg.--Alcan Metal Centres, Tipton, United Kingdom; *Int'l*, pg. 51
Hisbrook, David, V.P.-Mktg. & Adv.--Barnes & Noble Inc., New York, NY; *U.S. Public*, pg. 189
Hiser, Dennis, Sr. V.P.-Sls. & Mktg.--World Color-Chicago Div., Elk Grove Village, IL; *U.S. Public*, pg. 1778
Hitch, John L., Mgr.-Mktg. Communications--Belden Wire & Cable Company, Richmond, IN; *U.S. Public*, pg. 201
Hitchen, P.J., Mgr.-Communications--Raytheon Electronics Systems, Portsmouth, RI; *U.S. Public*, pg. 1364
Hite, Aubrey, Mgr.-Mktg.--Frederick Trading Company, Frederick, MD; *U.S. Private*, pg. 335
Hittman, Tammy S., Supvr.-Mkt. Devel.--Polar Ware Company, Sheboygan, WI; *U.S. Private*, pg. 873
Hitz, Rochelle, Mktg. Service Rep.--American Tool Companies, Inc., Lincoln, NE; *U.S. Private*, pg. 63
Ho, Bob, Mgr.-Sls. & Mktg.--Aydin Corporation West, San Jose, CA; *U.S. Public*, pg. 158
Hoadley, James, Gen. Mgr.-Sls. & Mktg.--ITW Screen Process Specialist, Ltd., Plymouth, WI; *U.S. Public*, pg. 867
Hoag, Kim, Dr., Sr. V.P.-Mktg.--Tetra Tech, Inc., Pasadena, CA; *U.S. Public*, pg. 1582
Hoagland, James, Dir.-Mktg.--Shady Brook Farms, Dayton, VA; *U.S. Private*, pg. 937
Hoagland, James P., Corp. Dir.-Mktg. & Product Devel.--Rocco Inc., Harrisonburg, VA; *U.S. Private*, pg. 937
Hoban, Joe, Mgr.-Mktg. & Sls.--Kaufman and Broad-Monterey Bay, Inc., Salinas, CA; *U.S. Public*, pg. 945
Hobbie, Lynn K., V.P.-Mktg.--Madison Gas and Electric Company, Madison, WI; *U.S. Public*, pg. 1032
Hobbie, S. Reeve, Mgr.-Mktg. Commun.--Electrical Products Division, Austin, TX; *U.S. Public*, pg. 1605
Hobbs, Richard, Mgr.-Mktg. Prod.--North American Van Lines, Inc., Fort Wayne, IN; *U.S. Public*, pg. 1191
Hobson, Tony, Pres.-AG Mktg. & Commun.--Adair Greene Advertising, Atlanta, GA; *U.S. Private*, pg. 16
Hocevar, Greg, V.P.-Sls. & Mktg.--Bata Shoe Co., Inc., Belcamp, MD; *U.S. Private*, pg. 195
Hoch, Steve, V.P.-Mktg.--IGI, Inc., Buena, NJ; *U.S. Public*, pg. 855
Hockett, Wendy, Dir.-Mktg.--Auburn General Hospital, Auburn, WA; *U.S. Public*, pg. 1696
Hockin, Jeff, V.P.-Sls. & Mktg.--Crum Electric Supply Co., Inc., Casper, WY; *U.S. Private*, pg. 293
Hodapp, John, Sr. V.P.-Mktg.--Florists' Mutual Insurance Co., Edwardsville, IL; *U.S. Private*, pg. 415
Hodder, Linda, Mgr.-Contract Sls. & Mktg.--Marietta Canada, Inc., Toronto, Canada; *U.S. Private*, pg. 703
Hodge, F. Galen, V.P.-Mktg.--Haynes International, Inc., Kokomo, IN; *U.S. Public*, pg. 801
Hodge, Maggie, Coord.-Mktg.--People's Choice TV of Tucson, Inc., Tucson, AZ; *U.S. Public*, pg. 1274
Hodges, J.A., Mng. Dir.-Lingerie Div.--Charnos plc, Ilkeston, United Kingdom; *Int'l*, pg. 280
Hodges, Wayne, V.P.-Sls. & Mktg.--The Standard Products Company, Dearborn, MI; *U.S. Public*, pg. 1504
Hodges, Wendell, Exec. V.P.-Sls. & Mktg.--Towne Square Furniture, Inc., Hillsboro, TX; *U.S. Private*, pg. 1093
Hodgkinson, W.M., Chief Gen. Mgr.-Sls. & Mktg.--Pearl Group Plc, Peterborough, United Kingdom; *Int'l*, pg. 100
Hodson, Thomas, Sr. V.P.-Mktg. Sls.--Ford Meter Box Company, Wabash, IN; *U.S. Private*, pg. 418
Hoeferlia, Michelle, Dir.-Mktg.--Molded Fiber Glass Co., Ashtabula, OH; *U.S. Private*, pg. 756
Hoel, W. P., Mgr.-Sls. & Mktg.-Specialty Prods.--Masonite Corporation, Chicago, IL; *U.S. Public*, pg. 904
Hoelscher, S.H., Dir.-Mktg.--Reading & Bates Drilling Co., Houston, TX; *U.S. Public*, pg. 1354
Hoelscher, Scott H., Dir.-Mktg.--Reading & Bates Corporation, Houston, TX; *U.S. Public*, pg. 1354
Hoelsher, Pete, Dir.-Mktg.--Acxiom Corporation, Conway, AR; *U.S. Public*, pg. 18
Hoenich, Ben, Mgr.-Mktg. Svcs.--Glen-Gery Corporation, Wyomissing, PA; *Int'l*, pg. 658
Hoerner, John Lee, Grp. Chief Exec.--The Burton Group PLC, London, United Kingdom; *Int'l*, pg. 237
Hoes, R., Dir.-Mktg.--Rothmans (UK) Ltd., Aylesbury, United Kingdom; *Int'l*, pg. 1130
Hof, Michael, V.P.-Sls. & Mktg.--Bostrom Seating, Inc., Piedmont, AL; *U.S. Public*, pg. 933
Hoffman, Al, V.P.-Sls. & Mktg.--Pryon Corporation, Menomonee Falls, WI; *U.S. Public*, pg. 1336
Hoffman, Al, V.P.-Domestic Sls.--Bird Products Corporation, Palm Springs, CA; *U.S. Public*, pg. 1591
Hoffman, Allan, Mktg. Coord.--Dairyland Power Cooperative, La Crosse, WI; *U.S. Private*, pg. 307
Hoffman, Amy, V.P.-Product Mktg.--Ingram Micro Inc., Santa Ana, CA; *U.S. Public*, pg. 878
Hoffman, David, Mgr.-Mktg.--HomeGoods, Framingham, MA; *U.S. Public*, pg. 1557
Hoffman, F., V.P.-Fin. & Mktg.--American Aggregates Corp., Dayton, OH; *Int'l*, pg. 245
Hoffman, Frank, Gen. Mgr.-Mktg. & Sls.--Duquesne Light Company, Pittsburgh, PA; *U.S. Public*, pg. 474
Hoffman, Gordon, V.P.-Mktg.--Plews/Edelmann, Buffalo Grove, IL; *Int'l*, pg. 1396
Hoffman, James, V.P.-Catalog Mktg.--Damark International, Inc., Minneapolis, MN; *U.S. Public*, pg. 478
Hoffman, Jeffrey, V.P.-Product & Design--Deckers Outdoor Corporation, Goleta, CA; *U.S. Public*, pg. 491
Hoffman, John, V.P.-Sls. & Mktg.--Outlook Group Corporation, Neenah, WI; *U.S. Public*, pg. 1235
Hoffman, John, Mgr.-Sls.--Waters Instruments, Inc., Rochester, MN; *U.S. Public*, pg. 1745
Hoffman, Judy, Sr. V.P.-Sls. & Mktg.--Lionel LLC, Chesterfield, MI; *U.S. Private*, pg. 669
Hoffman, Marv, V.P.-Mktg. Communications & Franchise Sls.--National Real Estate Services, Inc., Vancouver, Canada; *Int'l*, pg. 909
Hoffman, Nancye, Mgr.-Mktg. & Adv. Coord.--Nationwide Homes, Inc., Martinsville, VA; *U.S. Private*, pg. 788
Hoffman, Susan, Mgr.-Mktg. Svcs.--Hein-Werner Corporation, Waukesha, WI; *U.S. Public*, pg. 805
Hoffman, Todd, V.P.-Sls. & Mktg.--Lykes Meat Group, Plant City, FL; *U.S. Public*, pg. 1479
Hofmann, Rob, Sr. V.P.-Adv. & Mktg.--Chittenden Corporation, Burlington, VT; *U.S. Public*, pg. 350
Hofstetter, Gerhardt, Sales, Mktg., Fin.--Diehl & Eagle-Picher GmbH, Nuremberg, Germany; *U.S. Private*, pg. 355
Hofverberg, U.J., V.P.-Sls. & Mktg.--Mead Pulp Sales, Inc., Dayton, OH; *U.S. Public*, pg. 1074
Hog, Jorgen, V.P.-Strategic Mktg.--Olicom A/S, Lyngby, Denmark; *Int'l*, pg. 1001
Hogan, Bob, V.P.-Mktg.--Blackeyed Pea Restaurants Inc., Scottsdale, AZ; *U.S. Public*, pg. 498
Hogan, Bob, Dir.-Sls. & Mktg.--Minigrip Zip-Pak, Orangeburg, NY; *U.S. Public*, pg. 867
Hogan, James J., Sr. V.P.-Corp. Mktg. & Commun.--Wang Laboratories, Inc., Billerica, MA; *U.S. Public*, pg. 1737
Hogan, Miller, V.P. & Mktg. Svcs. Dir.--Bader Rutter & Assoc., Inc., Brookfield, WI; *U.S. Private*, pg. 110
Hogan, Paul B., V.P.-Sls. & Mktg.--Sealed Air Corporation, Saddle Brook, NJ; *U.S. Public*, pg. 1450
Hogan, Peter J., Dir.-Mktg.--Lym-Tech Scientific, Chicopee, MA; *U.S. Private*, pg. 683
Hogan, Robert L., V.P.-Mktg.--DenAmerica Corp., Scottsdale, AZ; *U.S. Public*, pg. 498
Hogan, Robert N.D., Exec. V.P.-Credit, Fin. & Mktg. Svcs.--Hudson's Bay Company, Toronto, Canada; *Int'l*, pg. 637
Hogan, William, Exec. V.P.-Sls. & Mktg.--Clestra Hauserman, Inc., Solon, OH; *Int'l*, pg. 569
Hoganson, R.B., V.P.-Mktg.--Broderick & Bascom Rope Co., Sedalia, MO; *U.S. Private*, pg. 68
Hoglund, Kathleen, Mgr.-Mktg. Communications--AmClyde Engineered Products Co., Inc., Saint Paul, MN; *U.S. Public*, pg. 778
Hogrese, Larry, Dir.-Mktg.--ConAgra Poultry Co., Duluth, GA; *U.S. Public*, pg. 427
Hohenstein, Bob, Dir.-Mktg.--Six Flags Over Texas, Arlington, TX; *U.S. Public*, pg. 1612
Hohle, Bill, Dir.-Mktg.--Smart Cards & Systems, Minnetonka, MN; *U.S. Private*, pg. 312
Hojas, Ignacio, Mgr.-Mktg.--Bagley S.A., Buenos Aires, Argentina; *Int'l*, pg. 379
Holben, Barry, V.P.-Sls.--Allen Organ Company, Macungie, PA; *U.S. Public*, pg. 45
Holbrook, Ken, V.P.-OEM & Intl. Sls.--Bestop, Inc., Broomfield, CO; *Int'l*, pg. 830
Holbrook, Michele, Sr. Mgr.-Corp. Commun.--National Fuel Gas Distribution Corp., Buffalo, NY; *U.S. Public*, pg. 1156
Holcman, Linda, Mgr.-Mktg.--Supreme International Corp., Miami, FL; *U.S. Public*, pg. 1542
Holcomb, Jim, V.P.-Mktg. & Strategic Plng.--Royal Appliance Mfg. Co., Cleveland, OH; *U.S. Public*, pg. 1410
Holcomb, Mike, Dir.-Mktg.--CCAIR, Inc., Charlotte, NC; *U.S. Public*, pg. 276
Holden, Fred, V.P.-Mktg.--World Finer Foods, Inc., Bloomfield, NJ; *U.S. Private*, pg. 1190
Holden, James P., Exec. V.P.-Sls. & Mktg.--Chrysler Corporation, Auburn Hills, MI; *U.S. Public*, pg. 352
Holden, Jeffrey, V.P.-Sls. & Mktg.--J.L. Hammett Company, Braintree, MA; *U.S. Private*, pg. 498
Holder, John, Mgr.-Corp. Mktg.--Gaymar Industries, Inc., Orchard Park, NY; *U.S. Private*, pg. 442
Holder, Robert, V.P.-Mktg.--A.P.S., Inc., Houston, TX; *U.S. Public*, pg. 10
Holdmeyer, Kurt, Prod. Mgr.-Pork--AJC International, Inc., Atlanta, GA; *U.S. Private*, pg. 6
Holdren, Mark, V.P.-Mktg. Svcs.--Genesee Corporation, Rochester, NY; *U.S. Public*, pg. 728
Holdsworth, Carolyn, Mgr.-U.S. Mktg.--Mary Kay, Inc., Dallas, TX; *U.S. Private*, pg. 711
Holford, Bill, Dir.-Mktg.--The Mighty Ducks of Anaheim, Anaheim, CA; *U.S. Public*, pg. 513
Holford, Liz, Dir.-Mktg.--Carlton Film Distributors, London, United Kingdom; *Int'l*, pg. 272
Holifield, Steve, Dir.-Engrng. & Pur.--Peavey Electronics Corp., Meridian, MS; *U.S. Private*, pg. 845
Holiway, Jeff, Mgr.-Mktg.--Lamb-Weston, Inc., Kennewick, WA; *U.S. Public*, pg. 427
Hollabaugh, Michael D., V.P.-Worldwide Sls. & Mktg.--GTI Corporation, San Diego, CA; *U.S. Public*, pg. 767
Holland, Jed, V.P.-Mktg., Sheer Hosiery--Kayser-Roth Corporation, Inc., Greensboro, NC; *Int'l*, pg. 576
Hollander, Kristen, Mktg. Svcs. Admin.--Allsop, Inc., Bellingham, WA; *U.S. Private*, pg. 44
Hollander, Marty N., V.P.-Mktg. & Bus. Devel.--Intellicorp Inc., Mountain View, CA; *U.S. Public*, pg. 887
Hollandsworth, Ed, Mgr.-Mktg.-Airel Prods.--Hendrix Wire & Cable, Milford, NH; *U.S. Public*, pg. 1598
Holley, Chuck, Mgr.-Mktg. Svcs.--Delta Consolidated Industries, Inc., Raleigh, NC; *U.S. Public*, pg. 481
Hollick, Clive, Lord, Chief Exec. Officer--United News & Media plc, London, United Kingdom; *Int'l*, pg. 1443
Hollignsworth, David, Dir.-Sls. & Mktg.--Millennium Technology Services, Inc., White City, OR; *U.S. Private*, pg. 746
Holliman, Skip, V.P.-Mktg.--Action Industries, Inc., Tupelo, MS; *U.S. Public*, pg. 688
Hollinger, Carl, Dir.-Sls. & Mktg.--John Copes Food Products, Inc., Rheems, PA; *U.S. Private*, pg. 274
Hollis, David, Dir.-Mktg.--Holstein Association USA, Inc., Brattleboro, VT; *U.S. Private*, pg. 536
Hollis, Mark, Sr. V.P.-Sls. & Mktg.--Inverness Corp., Fair Lawn, NJ; *U.S. Private*, pg. 574
Hollister, G.D., V.P.-Mktg.--Ideal Industries, Inc., Sycamore, IL; *U.S. Private*, pg. 557
Holloway, Altom, V.P.-Real Estate & Devel.--J.H. Harvey Company, Nashville, GA; *U.S. Private*, pg. 508
Holloway, Bill, Dir.-Sls. & Mktg.--Gulf States Manufacturers, Inc., Starkville, MS; *Int'l*, pg. 699
Holloway, J. David, V.P.-Mktg.--American Technical Publishers, Inc., Homewood, IL; *U.S. Private*, pg. 63
Holly, Chuck, Mgr.-Mktg. Svcs.--Delta Consolidated Industries, Inc. (Co. Headquarters), Jonesboro, AR; *U.S. Public*, pg. 481
Holm, Kim R., Exec. V.P.-Mktg. & Sls.--Salem Carpet Mills, Inc., Winston Salem, NC; *U.S. Public*, pg. 1464
Holmes, David, Dir.-Mktg.--Dorling Kindersley Ltd., London, United Kingdom; *Int'l*, pg. 417
Holmes, Denise, Mktg.--Regions Bank/Cullman/Walker County, Cullman, AL; *U.S. Public*, pg. 1372
Holmes, Glenn, V.P.-Mktg.--Quidel Corporation, San Diego, CA; *U.S. Public*, pg. 1352
Holmes, Irvin R., Jr., V.P.-Mktg.--Del Monte Foods, San Francisco, CA; *U.S. Private*, pg. 321
Holmes, John, Exec. V.P., Mktg. Dir. & Sec.--Paradigm Communications, Tampa, FL; *U.S. Private*, pg. 838
Holmes, Mike, V.P. & Gen. Mgr.--Hershey Foods Corporation, Hershey, PA; *U.S. Public*, pg. 811
Holmes, Roy, V.P.-Sls.- Branded Prods.--Chicopee Inc., Dayton, NJ; *Int'l*, pg. 113
Holmes, Terry, Admin. Asst.-Tech Mktg.--Dade Behring Inc., Westwood, MA; *U.S. Private*, pg. 110
Holmgren, Steven, Dir.-Mktg.--J.H. Findorff & Son, Inc., Madison, WI; *U.S. Private*, pg. 405
Holmquist, Richard, Mgr.-Sls. & Mktg.--Bryan Steam Corporation, Peru, IN; *U.S. Private*, pg. 176
Holopainen, Kaisu, Dir.-Mktg.--Tapiola-Yhtiot, Espoo, Finland; *Int'l*, pg. 1354
Holowell, Brent, Dir.-Mktg. Services--Adidas International, Portland, OR; *Int'l*, pg. 24
Holroyd, Charles, Exec. V.P.-Mktg.--Countrywide Home Loans Inc., Pasadena, CA; *U.S. Public*, pg. 452
Holstad, Kathleen, Admin. Mgr.-Mktg.--Tillamook County Creamery Assn., Tillamook, OR; *U.S. Private*, pg. 1086

Holstein, Michael P., V.P.-Corp. Strategy & Mktg.--Ipalco Enterprises, Inc., Indianapolis, IN; *U.S. Public*, pg. 912
Holstrom, Jeff, V.P.-Mktg. & Sls.--TFP Data Systems, Oxnard, CA; *U.S. Private*, pg. 1070
Holt, Jeremy W., V.P.-Product Engrng. & Mktg.--AE Goetze-North America, Plymouth, MI; *Int'l*, pg. 1334
Holt, Jim, Sr. V.P.-Global Mktg.--Telxon Corporation, Akron, OH; *U.S. Public*, pg. 1573
Holt, Ralph M., III, V.P.-Sls. & Mktg.--Holt Hosiery Mills, Inc., Burlington, NC; *U.S. Private*, pg. 536
Holt, Ron, Mgr.-Mktg.--John Fabick Tractor Company, Fenton, MO; *U.S. Private*, pg. 390
Holt, Wayne, Dir.-Mktg.--Hornady Manufacturing Company, Grand Island, NE; *U.S. Private*, pg. 539
Holtman, Bryan, Dir.-Mktg.--Elco Textron, Rockford, IL; *U.S. Public*, pg. 1590
Holtzman, Andy, V.P.-Events Mktg.--Discovery Communications, Inc., Bethesda, MD; *U.S. Private*, pg. 334
Holub, Michael, Mgr.-Mktg.--Castrol Austria GmbH, Wiener Neustadt, Austria; *Int'l*, pg. 235
Holzapfel, Tony, Exec. V.P.-Sls. & Mktg.--First Data Resources, Omaha, NE; *U.S. Public*, pg. 631
Holzman, Larry, Dir.-Mktg.--Culligan International Company, Northbrook, IL; *U.S. Public*, pg. 467
Homler, Robert, Mgr.-Mktg.--John M. Smyth Co., Downers Grove, IL; *U.S. Public*, pg. 990
Honckler, Roger, Mgr.-Sls.--Holiday RV Superstores, Inc., Greer, SC; *U.S. Public*, pg. 829
Hone, W.K.L., Gen. Mgr.-Mktg. Strategy--Iscor, Pretoria, South Africa; *Int'l*, pg. 688
Honsman, Mark, V.P.-Mktg.--Paradyne, Largo, FL; *U.S. Private*, pg. 838
Hood, Robert, V.P.-Mktg.--Casey's General Stores, Inc., Ankeny, IA; *U.S. Public*, pg. 312
Hoogewind, William H., Sec. & Dir.-Mktg.--Clipper Belt Lacer Company, Grand Rapids, MI; *U.S. Private*, pg. 413
Hoogstraten, Robert, Dir.-Mktg.--Siemens-Nixdorf Informationssysteme AG, Paderborn, Germany; *Int'l*, pg. 1245
Hook, Jim, V.P.-Mktg.--Wright Medical Technology, Arlington, TN; *U.S. Private*, pg. 1192
Hooker, Jeff, Dir.-Prod. Mktg. Devel.--British Steel Plc, London, United Kingdom; *Int'l*, pg. 220
Hookway, Scott, V.P.-Mktg.--Unitog Company, Kansas City, MO; *U.S. Public*, pg. 1693
Hooper, Ken, V.P.-Mktg. & Sls.--Gould Electronics Inc., Shawmut Circuit Protection Division, Newburyport, MA; *U.S. Public*, pg. 1592
Hoorweg, R.P.A., V.P.-Mktg. & Sls.--Europe Combined Terminals B.V., Rotterdam, Netherlands; *Int'l*, pg. 682
Hoover, Arthur, Sec. & Prod. Mgr.--T. Bruce Sales, Inc., West Middlesex, PA; *U.S. Private*, pg. 175
Hoover, Brian, Dir.-Commun.--Triple F, Inc., Des Moines, IA; *U.S. Private*, pg. 1104
Hope, J., Dir.-Mktg.--ITT Fluid Handling, Morton Grove, IL; *U.S. Public*, pg. 860
Hope, John, V.P.-Mktg., Sls. & Product Dev.--Imprimerie Quebecor Canada, Woodbridge, Canada; *Int'l*, pg. 1077
Hope, Mike, Mgr.-Mktg.--McGraw-Hill Book Co. Australia Pty. Ltd., Roseville, Australia; *U.S. Public*, pg. 1072
Hope, Rick, Mgr.-Mktg. Services--Pioneer Electronics (USA) Inc., Long Beach, CA; *Int'l*, pg. 1058
Hopersberger, Paul, Dir.-Mktg.--Jervis B. Webb Company, Farmington Hills, MI; *U.S. Private*, pg. 1156
Hopkins, Dom, Dir.-Mktg. Communications--Lafarge Canada Inc., Montreal, Canada; *Int'l*, pg. 789
Hopkins, James L., Chief Fin. Officer & V.P.-Strategic Mktg.--STB Systems, Inc., Richardson, TX; *U.S. Public*, pg. 1421
Hopkins, Jim, V.P.-Sls. & Mktg.--BIW Cable Systems, Inc., Franklin, MA; *Int'l*, pg. 417
Hopkins, Robert, V.P.-Sls., Mktg. & Tech. Services--Fleischli Oil Company, Inc., Cheyenne, WY; *U.S. Private*, pg. 410
Hopkins, Roger, V.P.-Sls. & Mktg.--San Diego Division, San Diego, CA; *U.S. Public*, pg. 27
Hopkins, Sheila, V.P.-U.S. Mktg.--Tambrands Inc., Cincinnati, OH; *U.S. Public*, pg. 1331
Hopper, Pat, Dir.-Mktg.--Ocean Mist Farms Corp., Castroville, CA; *U.S. Private*, pg. 811
Horack, James F., Mgr.-Natl. Sls.--Linde Hydraulics Corporation, Canfield, OH; *Int'l*, pg. 810
Horel, Tom, V.P.-Mktg., Sls. & Pub. Rels.--American Metal Products, Olive Branch, MS; *U.S. Public*, pg. 1053
Horisawa, Yasuo, Mgr.-Mktg.--Matsuya Company Ltd., Tokyo, Japan; *Int'l*, pg. 848
Horler, J.E., V.P.-Mktg.--Talisman Energy Inc., Calgary, Canada; *Int'l*, pg. 1352
Horn, Gregory T., Sr. V.P.-Retail Sls. & Mktg.--General Nutrition, Inc., Pittsburgh, PA; *U.S. Public*, pg. 725
Horn, Rick, V.P.-Sls. & Mktg.--Supreme Industries, Inc., Goshen, IN; *U.S. Public*, pg. 1541
Horn, Rick, V.P.-Mktg & Sls.--Supreme Corporation, Goshen, IN; *U.S. Public*, pg. 1542
Horn, Rick, V.P.-Sls. & Mktg.--Supreme Corporation of Texas, Cleburne, TX; *U.S. Public*, pg. 1542
Horn, Rick, V.P.-Sls. & Mktg.--Supreme MidAtlantic Corporation, Jonestown, PA; *U.S. Public*, pg. 1542
Horn, Rick, V.P.-Sls. & Mktg.--Supreme Murphy Corp., Wilson, NC; *U.S. Public*, pg. 1542
Horn, Scott, V.P.-Mktg.--M.A. Hanna Resin Distribution, Kent, WA; *U.S. Public*, pg. 781
Horn, Wendy, V.P.-Bus. Devel.--Hospital Affiliates Development Corporation, Nashville, TN; *U.S. Private*, pg. 540
Hornaday, David T., Mgr.-Mktg.--Wire Rope Corporation of America, Inc., Saint Joseph, MO; *U.S. Private*, pg. 1184
Horne, Ander, Sr. V.P.-Sls. & Mktg.--Ridgeview, Inc., Newton, NC; *U.S. Private*, pg. 930
Horne, Denise, Mgr.-Mktg.--Cracker Barrel Old Country Store, Inc., Lebanon, TN; *U.S. Public*, pg. 455
Horne, F.L., Jr., V.P. & Gen. Mgr.--Gas-Fired Products, Inc., Charlotte, NC; *U.S. Private*, pg. 440
Horner, Kathleen, V.P.-Mktg.--Hillshire Farm & Kahn's, Cincinnati, OH; *U.S. Public*, pg. 1433
Horton, Colin, Mgr.-Mktg.-Distribution Prods.--C-COR Electronics, Inc., State College, PA; *U.S. Public*, pg. 272
Horton, E. Mackie, Dir.-Sls. & Mktg.--Union Camp Container Div., Wayne, NJ; *U.S. Public*, pg. 1666
Horton, John D., Div. V.P.- Sls. & Mktg.--High Density Film Prods. Div., Hartsville, SC; *U.S. Public*, pg. 1486
Horton, Loree, Dir.-Mktg.--The Thompson's Company, Memphis, TN; *U.S. Public*, pg. 1466
Horton, Roger, Dir.-Sls. & Mktg.--Taylor & Francis Group Ltd., London, United Kingdom; *Int'l*, pg. 1357
Horton, Ronald C., V.P.-Mktg.--John Hancock Variable Life Insurance Co., Boston, MA; *U.S. Private*, pg. 590
Horuath, John J., V.P.-Sls. & Mktg.--Bondo/Mar-Hyde Corporation, Cleveland, OH; *U.S. Public*, pg. 1357
Horvath, J., Mgr.-Mktg. Commun.--Bodine Electric Company, Chicago, IL; *U.S. Private*, pg. 154
Horvath, Joseph C., Dir.-Mktg. Services--Postgraduate Medicine, Minneapolis, MN; *U.S. Public*, pg. 1071
Hoskin, Daniel W., Sr. V.P.-Sls. & Mktg.--Kenney Manufacturing Company, Warwick, RI; *U.S. Private*, pg. 615
Hoskins, Alan, Dir.-Mktg.--Eveready Battery Co., Saint Louis, MO; *U.S. Public*, pg. 1360
Hosokawa, J., Sr. Mng. Dir.-Mktg.--The Kyoei Life Insurance Co., Ltd., Tokyo, Japan; *Int'l*, pg. 776
Hossord, Adrian, Dir.-Mktg./Talk 21st Century Program--British Telecommunications plc, London, United Kingdom; *Int'l*, pg. 222
Hostak, Mark, Mgr.-Mktg.--Sunrise Medical Mobility Products, Fresno, CA; *U.S. Public*, pg. 1536
Hostetter, Sharon S., V.P.-Mktg. & Sls.--Baltimore Gas and Electric Company, Baltimore, MD; *U.S. Public*, pg. 172
Hostler, William F., Sr. V.P.-Individual Mktg.--The Vanguard Group, Inc., Valley Forge, PA; *U.S. Private*, pg. 1133
Hotchkin, W.F., Dir.-Mktg. & Sls.--Stamco Industries Inc., Euclid, OH; *U.S. Private*, pg. 1029
Hotchkiss, M., Dir.-Sls.-Plastics--Farrel Corporation, Ansonia, CT; *U.S. Public*, pg. 614
Hotchkiss, Stephen H., V.P.-Sls. & Mktg.--IEC Electronics Corp., Newark, NY; *U.S. Public*, pg. 854
Hotham, Stephen, Mgr.-Mktg.--DMG Business Media Ltd., Redhill, United Kingdom; *Int'l*, pg. 366
Hotman, Les H., V.P.-Supply, Rates & Plng.--The Berkshire Gas Company, Pittsfield, MA; *U.S. Public*, pg. 216
Hotson, P., Dir.-Mktg.--Kenwood Appliances Plc, Havant, United Kingdom; *Int'l*, pg. 730
Hotz, Larry, Dir.-Mktg.--Hugo Boss Fashions Inc., New York, NY; *Int'l*, pg. 637
Hougaard, Henrik, Sr. V.P.-Communications--Nykredit, Copenhagen, Denmark; *Int'l*, pg. 993
Hough, W.R., V.P. & Dir.-Mktg.--CHEMCENTRAL Corporation, Bedford Park, IL; *U.S. Private*, pg. 231
Houlihan, Anne, Dir.-Mktg.--Jagenberg, Inc., Enfield, CT; *Int'l*, pg. 1108
Houlihan, Bob, Dir.-Sls. & Mktg.--Ashworth Bros., Inc., Fall River, MA; *U.S. Private*, pg. 89
House, Joel, Staff V.P.-Mktg. Svcs.--Michigan Cat, Novi, MI; *U.S. Private*, pg. 740
Houser, Michael R., Exec. V.P. & Dir.-Mktg. & Mdsg.--Schultz Sav-O Stores, Inc., Sheboygan, WI; *U.S. Public*, pg. 1442
Houseworth, Lucile, Sr. V.P. & Dir.-Mktg.--SunTrust Banks of Tennessee, Inc., Nashville, TN; *U.S. Public*, pg. 1538
Houston, Allan, Mgr.-Mktg.--Sonoco Engraph, Inc., Atlanta, GA; *U.S. Public*, pg. 1486
Houston, Donald, Dir.-Mktg.--Champion Laboratories, Inc., Albion, IL; *U.S. Private*, pg. 1113
Houston, Tom, Mgr.-Sls. Promo.--Tension Envelope Corp., Kansas City, MO; *U.S. Private*, pg. 1077
Hovorka, Jeffrey, Mgr.-ID Solutions, Div.--Intelligent Controls Inc., Lynnwood, WA; *U.S. Private*, pg. 566
Howard, Bill, V.P.-Product Devel.--JanSport, Appleton, WI; *U.S. Public*, pg. 1702
Howard, Chanta, Sec.-Mktg. & Communications Dept.--Shell Chemical Co., Houston, TX; *Int'l*, pg. 1136
Howard, Chris, Dir.-Mktg.--Clear Springs Foods, Inc., Buhl, ID; *U.S. Private*, pg. 245
Howard, Richard M., Dir.-Mktg.--Shafer Commercial Seating Inc., Denver, CO; *U.S. Private*, pg. 988
Howard, Sharon, Dir.-Mktg.--Kirby Building Systems, Inc., Portland, TN; *Int'l*, pg. 699
Howard, Stephen, Dir.-Mktg. Services--Columbus Mills, Inc., Columbus, GA; *U.S. Private*, pg. 256
Howard, Steve, V.P.-Sls. & Mktg.--American Television Time, Inc., Austin, TX; *U.S. Private*, pg. 63
Howard, Timothy, V.P.-Mktg.--Fisher Scientific International, Hampton, NH; *U.S. Private*, pg. 658
Howarth, Duncan, Controller & Dir.-Mktg.--Miller Freeman PLC, London, United Kingdom; *Int'l*, pg. 1443
Howarth, Ken, Sr. V.P.-Sls. & Mktg.--Imax Corporation, Mississauga, Canada; *Int'l*, pg. 661
Howe, Larry M., JD, CLU, V.P.-Mktg. Svcs.--Farmers and Traders Life Insurance Co., Syracuse, NY; *U.S. Private*, pg. 394
Howe, Michael, Dir.-Mktg. Communications--UAL Corporation, Elk Grove Village, IL; *U.S. Public*, pg. 1652
Howe, Robert, Dir.-Adv. & Field Mktg.--Miami Subs Corporation, Fort Lauderdale, FL; *U.S. Public*, pg. 1103
Howe, Stephen, Mgr.-Mktg.--Cerner Corporation Pty Ltd., Milsons Point, Australia; *U.S. Public*, pg. 331
Howell, Josh, Sr. V.P.-Corp. Mktg.--MFS WorldCom, Inc., Omaha, NE; *U.S. Public*, pg. 1779
Howell, Marvin, V.P.-Mktg. Resources--Anacomp Magnetics, Inc., Atlanta, GA; *U.S. Public*, pg. 107
Howie, Cleveland M., Dir.-Mktg.--Precision Standard, Inc., Denver, CO; *U.S. Public*, pg. 1321
Howland, Cynthia, V.P.-Mktg.--Premier Cruises, Miami, FL; *U.S. Private*, pg. 293
Howlett, John, Dir.-Mktg. Communication US--Merial Ltd., Iselin, NJ; *U.S. Public*, pg. 1092
Howlett, John, Dir.-Mktg. Communication US--Merial Ltd., Iselin, NJ; *Int'l*, pg. 1109
Howski, Roman, Mgr.-Mktg.--Aircraft Products Company, Delray Beach, FL; *U.S. Public*, pg. 159
Hoxton, Jerome, Sr. V.P.-Sls. & Mktg.--Renaissance Publishing Co., Inc., Auburn, IN; *Int'l*, pg. 185
Hoyt, Gunther, V.P.-Mktg. & Sls.--Xaloy, Inc., Pulaski, VA; *U.S. Private*, pg. 1194
Hoyt, Linda, Mgr.-Mktg.--Maguire Partners, Los Angeles, CA; *U.S. Private*, pg. 696
Hoyt, Norman G., V.P.-Sls. & Mktg.--Lancaster Glass Corporation, Lancaster, OH; *U.S. Public*, pg. 977
Hoyt, Walter A., III, Dir.-Mktg.--Wolverine Vinyl Siding, Valley Forge, PA; *Int'l*, pg. 1171
Hroblak, Gerald, Pres. & Chief Exec. Officer--United Broadcasting L.P., Bethesda, MD; *U.S. Private*, pg. 1121
Hsiu, D.M., Dir.-Mktg. & Transportation Div.--Chinese Petroleum Corporation, Taipei, Taiwan; *Int'l*, pg. 286
Huang, C.H., Mgr.-Mktg.--China Steel Structure Co., Ltd., Kao-hsiung, Taiwan; *Int'l*, pg. 286
Huang, C.S. Warren, V.P. & Mng. Dir.-Mktg./Far East--Ethyl Corporation, Richmond, VA; *U.S. Public*, pg. 595
Huang, Claire, V.P.-Bus. Devel. & Mktg.--Wise Foods, Inc., Parsippany, NJ; *U.S. Private*, pg. 157
Hubbard, Cynthia, Mgr.-Pub. Rels.--Interbath, Inc., City of Industry, CA; *U.S. Private*, pg. 566
Hubbard, Jan V., Asst. V.P.-Commercial Mktg.--Texas Commerce Bank, Houston, TX; *U.S. Public*, pg. 339
Hubbard, Peter E., Sr. V.P.-Sls. & Mktg.--Midland Enterprises Inc., Cincinnati, OH; *U.S. Public*, pg. 549
Hubble, Chris M., V.P.-Sls. & Mktg.--Elastomer Seals - North America, Morton Grove, IL; *Int'l*, pg. 1338
Hubel, William, V.P.-Mktg.--National Propane Corp., Cedar Rapids, IA; *U.S. Public*, pg. 1635
Huber, L., Gen. Mgr. & Dir.-Mkt. Devel.-Eastern Europe--Moore Ges.m.b.H., Vienna, Austria; *Int'l*, pg. 889
Hubner, Henrik, Mgr.-Mktg.--Berendsen PMC A/S, Kokkedal, Denmark; *Int'l*, pg. 1284
Hubscher, Albin, V.P.-Sls. & Mktg.--CIBA Seeds, Greensboro, NC; *Int'l*, pg. 973
Hudak, Thomas, V.P.- Sls. & Mktg.--O-Z/Gedney Co., Farmington, CT; *U.S. Public*, pg. 727
Huddleston, C., Mgr.-Mktg Communications--Square D Company, Smyrna, TN; *Int'l*, pg. 1208
Hudec, Michele, Dir.-Mktg.--The Chicago Faucet Co., Des Plaines, IL; *U.S. Private*, pg. 234
Hudes, Jack, Mgr.-Sls. & Mktg.--Kaiser Permanente, California Division, Oakland, CA; *U.S. Private*, pg. 605
Hudgins, A. Mark, Dir.-New Prod. Devel.--Automatic Signal/ Eagle Signal, Austin, TX; *Int'l*, pg. 1245
Hudish, D. R., Dir.-Mktg.-Laboratory Prods.--Mallinckrodt Baker Inc., Phillipsburg, NJ; *U.S. Public*, pg. 1039
Hudson, Derick, Grp. Product Mgr.--Batchelors (Ireland) Ltd., Dublin, Ireland; *Int'l*, pg. 968
Hudson, Hershall, Mgr.-Pur.--Hydraulics Div., Shawnee, OK; *U.S. Public*, pg. 557
Hudson, Jerry, Mgr.-Mktg.--Seabrook Wallcoverings, Inc., Memphis, TN; *U.S. Private*, pg. 978
Hudson, Linda, Sr. Sec.--Del Webb's Coventry Homes, Phoenix, AZ; *U.S. Public*, pg. 495
Hudson, Mary Swatek, V.P.-Mktg. & Plng.--AMBI Inc., Tarrytown, NY; *U.S. Public*, pg. 7
Hudson, Michael, Sr. V.P.-Mktg.--Tidel Engineering, Inc., Carrollton, TX; *U.S. Public*, pg. 1608
Hudson, P.E., Dr., Sr. Exec. V.P.--Radian International LLC, Austin, TX; *U.S. Public*, pg. 522
Hudson, Phillip F., Exec. V.P.-Retail Banking & Mktg. Grp.--First Security Service Company, Salt Lake City, UT; *U.S. Public*, pg. 638
Huebner, Wayne, Mgr.-Mktg.--Capital Controls Company Inc., Colmar, PA; *Int'l*, pg. 1226
Huegelmann, Karsten, Dir.-Mktg.--Axel Springer Verlag AG, Berlin, Germany; *Int'l*, pg. 102
Huegin, Gene, Dir.-Channel Mktg.--Cooper Hand Tools, Raleigh, NC; *U.S. Public*, pg. 444
Huerta, Manuel, Mgr.-Mktg.--Gemisa S.A. de C.V., Tlalnepantla, Mexico; *Int'l*, pg. 614
Huether, Richard D., Pres. & Chief Exec. Officer--Independent Can Company, Belcamp, MD; *U.S. Private*, pg. 559
Huett, Greg, V.P.-Wholesale Club Sls. & Mktg.--Tyson Foods, Inc., Springdale, AR; *U.S. Public*, pg. 1652
Huey, Steve, Dir.-Mktg.--Omni Hotels, Irving, TX; *U.S. Private*, pg. 1065
Huff, Sarah, V.P.-Mktg. & Computer Prods. Grp.--Wyle Electronics, Irvine, CA; *Int'l*, pg. 1457
Huffman, Jim, Mgr.-Mktg.--Funk Manufacturing Co., Coffeyville, KS; *U.S. Public*, pg. 492
Hugh, D.C., Dir.-Sls. & Mktg.--Senior Foster Wheeler Power Division, Wembley, United Kingdom; *Int'l*, pg. 1221
Hughes, Bill, V.P.-Mktg. & Sls.--Arkansas Lime Co., Batesville, AR; *U.S. Public*, pg. 1685
Hughes, Bill R., V.P.-Sls. & Mktg.--Texas Lime Co., Cleburne, TX; *U.S. Public*, pg. 1685
Hughes, David, Mgr.-Consumer Mktg.--Stafford-Miller Limited, Welwyn Garden City, United Kingdom; *U.S. Public*, pg. 237
Hughes, Elaine K., Dir.-Mktg.--Sturgeon Electric Company, Henderson, CO; *U.S. Public*, pg. 1029
Hughes, Jack, V.P.-Consumer Mktg.--General Communication, Inc., Anchorage, AK; *U.S. Public*, pg. 708
Hughes, James, V.P.-Mktg.-Licensed--J. Baker, Inc., Canton, MA; *U.S. Public*, pg. 167
Hughes, James, V.P.-Mktg.-Licensed--Morse Shoe, Inc., Canton, MA; *U.S. Public*, pg. 168
Hughes, Kim, Mgr.-Mktg. & Adv.--Clothestime Stores, Inc., Anaheim, CA; *U.S. Public*, pg. 387
Hughes, Mickele, Mktg. Mgr.--Media That Works, Cincinnati, OH; *U.S. Private*, pg. 727
Hughes, Patrick, Sr. V.P.-Mktg. & Sls.--Blue Cross and Blue Shield of Massachusetts, Boston, MA; *U.S. Private*, pg. 151
Hughes, Sandra, V.P.-Liscencee Integration--Budget Rent A Car Corporation, Lisle, IL; *U.S. Private*, pg. 178

Hughes, Sharon, Dir.-Mktg.--American Consumer Products, Solon, OH; *U.S. Private*, pg. 1142
Hughes, Tom, Dir.-Mktg.--Clemens Markets Inc., Kulpsville, PA; *U.S. Private*, pg. 245
Hui, Clive, Mgr.-Mktg.--Esselte Ltd., Wan Chai, Hong Kong; *Int'l*, pg. 461
Huisken, Duane, Mgr.-Natl. Mktg.--Monier Inc., Irvine, CA; *Int'l*, pg. 1091
Huizinga, Bruce G., V.P.-Sls. & Mktg.--Magic Valley Foods, Inc., Rupert, ID; *U.S. Private*, pg. 695
Huldeen, William M., V.P.-New Markets--Fingerhut Corp., Minnetonka, MN; *U.S. Public*, pg. 623
Hulden, Rich, Dir.-Mktg.--Balkamp, Inc., Indianapolis, IN; *U.S. Public*, pg. 732
Huldt, Patrik, Mgr.-Mktg. & Sls.--Esselte Chrono AB, Solna, Sweden; *Int'l*, pg. 459
Hull, Dennis, Dir.-Mktg.--Butterball Turkey Company, Downers Grove, IL; *U.S. Public*, pg. 426
Hull, Erin, V.P.-Mktg.--Sun Diamond Growers of California, Pleasanton, CA; *U.S. Private*, pg. 1051
Hull, Jim, V.P.-Sls. & Mktg.--Wide-Lite, San Marcos, TX; *U.S. Public*, pg. 730
Hull, John L., Vice Chm. & Sec.--Hull Corporation, Hatboro, PA; *U.S. Private*, pg. 547
Hull, Randolph, Dir.-Mktg. & Sls., Caribbean & Central America--Block Drug Company, International Division, Jersey City, NJ; *U.S. Public*, pg. 237
Hullman, Klaus, Dir.-Mktg. Commun.--Dresdner Bank AG, Frankfurt/Main, Germany; *Int'l*, pg. 417
Hulse, Doug, Dir.-Intl. Mktg.--Taylor Machine Works, Inc., Louisville, MS; *U.S. Private*, pg. 1070
Hulsebosch, Betsey, V.P. & Dir.-Creative Mktg./Bantam--Bantam Doubleday Dell Publishing Group, Inc., New York, NY; *Int'l*, pg. 191
Hulsey, Slona, Dir.-Mktg. & Pub. Rels.--Pancho's Mexican Buffet, Inc., Fort Worth, TX; *U.S. Public*, pg. 1255
Hulsing, Dennis I., Dir.-Sls. & Corp. Mktg.--Omni Hotels, Irving, TX; *U.S. Private*, pg. 1065
Hultberg, Peter, Mgr.-Sls. & Mktg.--Jimek, Arlov, Sweden; *U.S. Public*, pg. 170
Hultquist, Kent, Mgr.-Mktg.--Myresjo AB, Vetlanda, Sweden; *Int'l*, pg. 1260
Hulvat, Scott, Sr. V.P.-Sls. & Mktg.--F&F Foods, Chicago, IL; *U.S. Private*, pg. 388
Humbert, Philippe, V.P.-Intl. Devel.--SNECMA - Societe Nationale d'Etude et de Construction de Moteurs d'Aviation, Paris, France; *Int'l*, pg. 1165
Humes, Robert, V.P.-Mktg.--Ameritech, Detroit, MI; *U.S. Public*, pg. 97
Humphrey, James, V.P.-Vet. Mktg.--Hill's Pet Nutrition, Topeka, KS; *U.S. Public*, pg. 397
Humphreys, Sharon, Dir.-Mktg. Resources--Mead Containerboard, Atlanta, GA; *U.S. Public*, pg. 1074
Humphries, French P., Exec. V.P.--B.B. Walker Company, Asheboro, NC; *U.S. Public*, pg. 1734
Huneycutt, Al, V.P.-Mktg.--Halsey Taylor, Oak Brook, IL; *U.S. Private*, pg. 372
Hung, Philip, Pres. & V.P.-Mktg.--Braun, North America, Woburn, MA; *U.S. Public*, pg. 743
Hunke, David, Exec. V.P.-Mktg.--The Cincinnati Enquirer, Inc., Cincinnati, OH; *U.S. Public*, pg. 700
Hunsaker, Jeff, Dir.-Mktg.--Corel Corporation, Orem, UT; *Int'l*, pg. 331
Hunsinger, Tina, Dir.-Mktg.--Avatar Holdings Inc., Coral Gables, FL; *U.S. Public*, pg. 151
Hunsinger, Tina, Dir.-Mktg.--Avatar Properties Inc., Miami, FL; *U.S. Public*, pg. 151
Hunt, Dan, V.P.-Mktg. & Devel.--Mason Shoe Mfg. Co., Chippewa Falls, WI; *U.S. Private*, pg. 712
Hunt, Dave, Mgr.-Mktg. Svcs.--The HON Co., Muscatine, IA; *U.S. Public*, pg. 772
Hunt, Glen, V.P.-Mktg.--Netrix, Corp., Herndon, VA; *U.S. Private*, pg. 791
Hunt, Ivor J., Dir.-Mktg.--J. Sainsbury plc, London, United Kingdom; *Int'l*, pg. 1169
Hunt, Jeffrey S., V.P.--BT Financial Corporation, Johnstown, PA; *U.S. Public*, pg. 163
Hunt, Patty, Mktg. Asst.--The Murray Ohio Mfg. Co., Brentwood, TN; *Int'l*, pg. 1397
Hunt, Roger, V.P. & Regional Mgr.-London--Santa Fe Drilling Co., Alhambra, CA; *Int'l*, pg. 765
Hunt, Tony, Dir.-Mktg./Richmond--William Grant & Sons Distillers Ltd., Bellshill, United Kingdom; *Int'l*, pg. 557
Hunter, Bruce, V.P.-Mktg.--Kraft Canada Inc., Don Mills, Canada; *U.S. Public*, pg. 1288
Hunter, Carla, Dir.-Mktg.--Nissin Foods (U.S.A.) Co. Ltd., Gardena, CA; *Int'l*, pg. 949
Hunter, Diane, Grp. Mktg. & Customer Service--Bayer Corporation/Diagnostics Division, Tarrytown, NY; *Int'l*, pg. 173
Hunter, Flo, Mgr.-Mktg.--BR Associates, Inc., Jasper, IN; *U.S. Private*, pg. 107
Hunter, George, Dir.-Mktg.--Grosvenor Marketing Ltd., Paramus, NJ; *Int'l*, pg. 92
Hunter, George J., Exec. V.P.--Bonanza Bus Lines, Inc., Providence, RI; *U.S. Private*, pg. 156
Hunter, Kate, Dir.-Mktg.--Kal Grafx, Kentwood, MI; *U.S. Private*, pg. 387
Hunter, Robin, Mktg.--Regions Bank/Huntsville, Huntsville, AL; *U.S. Public*, pg. 1372
Hunter, Stanley, V.P.-Mktg.--Hansen Coupling Division, Berea, OH; *U.S. Private*, pg. 1110
Hunter, Warren, Exec. V.P. & Chief Mktg. Officer--The McClure Group, Wayne, PA; *U.S. Private*, pg. 719
Hunter, Warren, Chief Mktg. Officer--The McClure Group, Annapolis, MD; *U.S. Private*, pg. 720
Huntington, Mike, Gen. Mgr. & Dir.-Mktg. & Public Affairs--Intermountain Gas Co., Boise, ID; *U.S. Private*, pg. 568
Huppertz, John, Ph.D., Mng. Partner-Mktg. & Res. Services--Eric Mower and Associates, Inc., Syracuse, NY; *U.S. Private*, pg. 765
Huppertz, John, Ph.D., Mng. Partner-Mktg. & Res. Services--Eric Mower and Associates/Buffalo, Inc., Buffalo, NY; *U.S. Private*, pg. 765
Huppertz, John, Ph.D., Mng. Partner-Mktg. & Res. Services--Eric Mower & Associates, Albany, NY; *U.S. Private*, pg. 765
Huppertz, John, Ph.D., Mng. Partner-Mkgt. & Res. Services--Eric Mower & Associates, Atlanta, GA; *U.S. Private*, pg. 765
Hurcomb, Thomas J., V.P.-Mktg. & Public Affairs--Central Vermont Public Service Corporation, Rutland, VT; *U.S. Public*, pg. 327
Hurlbert, J.P., Gen. Mgr.-Mktg.--Chevrolet Motor Div. General Motors Corp., Warren, MI; *U.S. Public*, pg. 720
Hurley, J.T., Sr. V.P.-Mktg.--Consolidated Papers, Inc., Wisconsin Rapids, WI; *U.S. Public*, pg. 436
Hurley, John, Mgr.-Secondary Mktg.--Virginia First Mortgage, Woodbridge, VA; *U.S. Public*, pg. 1721
Hurley, Ramona, Dir.-Mktg.--Golf Host Resorts, Inc., Tarpon Springs, FL; *U.S. Private*, pg. 1036
Hurst, Charles, V.P.-Sls. & Mktg.--Fischer Packing Co., Louisville, KY; *Int'l*, pg. 201
Hurst, M.J., Dir.-Sls. & Mktg.--Tube Products, Oldbury, United Kingdom; *Int'l*, pg. 1222
Hurst, Peter, Mgr.-Mktg.--Lynwood Scientific Developments Limited, Farnham, United Kingdom; *U.S. Public*, pg. 1144
Hurst, Timm M., V.P.-Sls. & Mktg.--Serologicals Corporation, Clarkston, GA; *U.S. Public*, pg. 1460
Hurston, Jim, Dir.-Food Svcs. Sls. & Mktg.--Victory Refrigeration Co. LC, Cherry Hill, NJ; *U.S. Private*, pg. 1139
Hurt, Tom, Dir.-Mktg.--Plano Molding Co., Plano, IL; *U.S. Private*, pg. 869
Hurtubise, Ken, Sr. V.P.-Sls. & Mktg.--ECRM, Tewksbury, MA; *U.S. Private*, pg. 353
Hurwitz, Steven L., Sr. V.P.-Mktg.--Rhodes, Inc., Atlanta, GA; *U.S. Public*, pg. 805
Huso, Nathan, Mgr.-Comm. & Mktg.--Dakota Electric Association, Farmington, MN; *U.S. Private*, pg. 308
Hussain, S. Khalid, Dir.-Mktg.--Parke-Davis & Company, Limited, Karachi, Pakistan; *U.S. Public*, pg. 1739
Huston, Dennis, Mgr.-Sls. & Mktg./LVL--Boise Cascade Corporation, Boise, ID; *U.S. Public*, pg. 242
Huston, John, Exec. V.P.-Mktg.--National Cattlemen's Beef Association, Chicago, IL; *U.S. Private*, pg. 780
Huston, Richard T., Exec. V.P.-Mktg.--ShowBiz Pizza Time, Inc., Irving, TX; *U.S. Public*, pg. 1468
Hutchens, Doug, Dir.-Mktg.--Fiskars-Gerber, Portland, OR; *Int'l*, pg. 492
Hutchin, James W., Dir.-Natl. Mktg.--Willis Corroon International/Americas, Radnor, PA; *Int'l*, pg. 1507
Hutchings, Doug, Mgr.-Mktg.--ODL Incorporated, Zeeland, MI; *U.S. Private*, pg. 809
Hutchinson, David, Dir.-Sls. & Mktg.-Hosiery--Charnos plc, Ilkeston, United Kingdom; *Int'l*, pg. 280
Hutchinson, Eileen, Dir.-Mktg. Commun.--Humana Inc., Louisville, KY; *U.S. Public*, pg. 847
Hutchinson, Lisa, Mgr.-Mktg.--Turkey Hill Dairy, Inc., Conestoga, PA; *U.S. Private*, pg. 1109
Hutchinson, Steve, Dir.-Mktg.--Dryden Oil of New England, Worcester, MA; *Int'l*, pg. 235
Hutchison, M.N., Sr. V.P.-S.F. Opers. & Dir.-Sls. & Mktg.-Nonferrous Sector--Davy International, San Francisco, San Ramon, CA; *Int'l*, pg. 774
Hutchison, Patricia, V.P.-Mktg.--The Edmonton Journal, Edmonton, Canada; *Int'l*, pg. 631
Huthoefer, Andy, V.P.-Mktg.--Carl Zeiss Optical, Inc., Petersburg, VA; *Int'l*, pg. 1523
Hutton, Jeff, V.P.-Mktg.--Cabot Oil & Gas Corporation, Houston, TX; *U.S. Public*, pg. 289
Huxley, David, Mgr.-Mktg. & New Prods.--Merisel Australia, Lane Cove, Australia; *U.S. Public*, pg. 1096
Huxley, Robin F., V.P.-Mktg.-Cub & Intl.--Carlton & United Breweries Ltd., Southbank, Australia; *Int'l*, pg. 500
Hwa, Roy Tsou Chen, Sr. V.P.-Mktg.--Singapore Petroleum Company Ltd., Singapore, Singapore; *U.S. Public*, pg. 102
Hwang, Tae-In, Mgr.--Ssangyong Information & Communication Corporation, Seoul, Korea; *Int'l*, pg. 1292
Hyams, Fair, Dir.-Client Communications--First National Bank of Commerce, New Orleans, LA; *U.S. Public*, pg. 629
Hyatt, Les, Mgr.-Mktg.--Andersen Group, Inc., Bloomfield, CT; *U.S. Public*, pg. 111
Hyatt, Leslie A., Mgr.-Mktg.--The J.M. Ney Company, Bloomfield, CT; *U.S. Public*, pg. 111
Hyde, Howard, V.P.-Sls. & Mktg.--Baccarat, Inc., Edison, NJ; *Int'l*, pg. 132
Hyde, Leslie, Mgr.-Mktg.--Westbrae Natural, Inc., Carson, CA; *U.S. Public*, pg. 774
Hydell, Martin H., V.P.-Mktg. (Commercial Coated Papers)--Fine Paper Div., Chillicothe, OH; *U.S. Public*, pg. 1074
Hylands, John, Gen. Mgr.-Mktg.--Standard Life Assurance, Edinburgh, United Kingdom; *Int'l*, pg. 1297
Hyman, Susan, V.P.-Mktg.--Susie's Deals, City of Industry, CA; *U.S. Private*, pg. 1056
Hyslop, Jim, Dir.-Mktg. Sls.--Armco Inc.-Coshocton Operations, Coshocton, OH; *U.S. Public*, pg. 131
Iannaccone, Emil, Exec. V.P. & Mktg. Dir.--Western International Media Corporation, Los Angeles, CA; *U.S. Private*, pg. 1165
Iannucci, Patricia J., V.P.-Mktg. Services--Pall Corporation, Greenvale, NY; *U.S. Public*, pg. 1253
Iannuzzi, Vincent, Mgr.-Sls.--Manning & Lewis Engineering Co., Union, NJ; *U.S. Private*, pg. 700
Ibberson, Vicky, Mgr.-Mktg.--Austin Reed Limited, London, United Kingdom; *U.S. Public*, pg. 796
Ibenhard, Eileen, V.P.-Corp. Mktg.--Seer Technologies, Inc., Cary, NC; *U.S. Public*, pg. 1453
Ice, David R., Mgr.-Sls. & Mktg.--U.S. Axle, Inc., Pottstown, PA; *U.S. Private*, pg. 1124
Idei, Akitaka, Dir.-Mktg. Div.--Rohm Co., Ltd., Kyoto, Japan; *Int'l*, pg. 1124
Idell, J.B., Sr. V.P.-Corp. Devel.--Science Applications International Corp., San Diego, CA; *U.S. Private*, pg. 975
Iezzi, Bob, V.P.-Mktg.--Thornton Oil Corp., Louisville, KY; *U.S. Private*, pg. 1084
Iglesias-Enriquez, Avelina, Gen. Mgr.-Sls. & Mktg./Mediterranean & Middle East--Utell International-Spain, Madrid, Spain; *Int'l*, pg. 1099
Ignatius, Howard, Mgr.-Product Mktg.--Electroglas, Inc., Santa Clara, CA; *U.S. Public*, pg. 727
Ikeda, Roger A., Dir.-Mktg.--REAL Applications, Ltd., Woodland Hills, CA; *U.S. Private*, pg. 366
Ikuta, Kohei, Exec. V.P.-Fin., Plng., Admin. & Mktg.--Diamond Star Motors, Normal, IL; *Int'l*, pg. 875
Ilaria, Peter E., Dir.-Mktg. & Sls.--Tropar Mfg. Co., Inc., Florham Park, NJ; *U.S. Private*, pg. 1105
Iles, T. Randall, Sr. V.P.-Mktg. & Sls.--Pella Corporation, Pella, IA; *U.S. Private*, pg. 848
Ilko, Ray, Mgr.-Mktg.--Cres-Cor, Cleveland, OH; *U.S. Private*, pg. 288
Illig, Lynn, Mgr.-Mktg. Commun.--Matthews International Corp., Pittsburgh, PA; *U.S. Public*, pg. 1059
Imanishi, Akio, V.P.-Mktg.--Aiwa America, Inc., Mahwah, NJ; *Int'l*, pg. 1280
Imazumi, Michiaki, Mng. Dir.-Sls. & Mktg. Div.--Fujisawa Pharmaceutical Co. Ltd., Osaka, Japan; *Int'l*, pg. 525
Imazumi, Michiaki, Exec. Dir.-Ethical Pharmaceuticals Mktg. Div.--Fujisawa Pharmaceutical Co. Ltd., Osaka, Japan; *Int'l*, pg. 525
Imbrogna, Michelle, Mgr.-Event Mktg.--American Express Publishing Corporation, New York, NY; *U.S. Public*, pg. 74
Imler, Dan, Dir.-Adv. & Communications--Tension Envelope Corp., Kansas City, MO; *U.S. Private*, pg. 1077
Imman, Page, V.P.-Mktg--Inman Construction Corporation, Memphis, TN; *U.S. Private*, pg. 564
Immel, Chuck, V.P.-Global Mktg.--Baxter-Hyland, Glendale, CA; *U.S. Public*, pg. 196
Immerman, Darcy, Mgr.-Mktg.--EUA Cogenex Corporation, Lowell, MA; *U.S. Public*, pg. 549
Immerman, Darcy, Mgr.-Mktg.--EUA Cogenex West, Boulder, CO; *U.S. Public*, pg. 549
Impey, Bill, Sr. V.P.-Mktg. & Prod. Devel.--Oregon Freeze Dry, Inc., Albany, OR; *U.S. Private*, pg. 819
Inamura, Toshimichi, Gen. Mgr.-Sls. & Mktg.--Kintetsu World Express (H.K.) Ltd., Kowloon, Hong Kong; *Int'l*, pg. 735
Incontri, Joe, Mgr.-Mktg.--ITT Barton Instruments, City of Industry, CA; *U.S. Public*, pg. 860
Indyk, William, V.P.-Mktg. & Sls.--White Rock Products Corp., Whitestone, NY; *U.S. Private*, pg. 1173
Infanti, Daniel, V.P.-Corp. Communications & Mktg.--Sharp Electronics Corporation, Mahwah, NJ; *Int'l*, pg. 1228
Ingelbrink, Mark, Dir.-Mktg.--BHP Copper North America, Tucson, AZ; *Int'l*, pg. 224
Ingraham, Stan, V.P.-Sls. & Mktg.--VWS, Inc., Cleveland, OH; *Int'l*, pg. 440
Ingram, Karen, Dir.-Corp. Commun.--USLD Communications Corp., San Antonio, TX; *U.S. Public*, pg. 969
Ingram, Robert, V.P.-Sls.--Covington Industries, Atlanta, GA; *U.S. Private*, pg. 280
Ingram, Robert E., V.P.-Mktg.--Firemen's Insurance Company of Washington, D.C., Bethesda, MD; *U.S. Public*, pg. 215
Inlow, Brand, Real Estate Analyst-DE, MD & VA--United Dominion Realty Trust, Inc., Richmond, VA; *U.S. Public*, pg. 1677
Inman, Leslie, V.P.-Mktg. & Plng.--Ameritas Life Insurance Corp., Lincoln, NE; *U.S. Private*, pg. 65
Innocent, Jean, Mgr.-Mktg. Communications--TRC Companies, Inc., Windsor, CT; *U.S. Public*, pg. 1557
Inomata, Ichiro, Dir.-Watch Mktg.--Seiko Corporation, Tokyo, Japan; *Int'l*, pg. 1218
Inoue, Tadashi, Dir. & Deputy Grp. Gen. Mgr.-Intl. Mktg.--Sharp Corporation, Osaka, Japan; *Int'l*, pg. 1228
Inouye, Wayne R., Sr. V.P.-Mktg./Computers & Home Office--Best Buy Co., Inc., Eden Prairie, MN; *U.S. Public*, *pg. 223*
Insalaco, J., Sr. V.P.-Mktg.--California Products Corp., Cambridge, MA; *U.S. Private*, pg. 201
Insco, Jeff, Mktg., Res. & Pub. Rels. Dir.--AGA Catalog Marketing & Design, New York, NY; *U.S. Private*, pg. 5
Insel, Jackie, Dir.-Mktg., Pub. Rels. & Adv.--Phillips Fine Art Auctioneers, New York, NY; *U.S. Private*, pg. 861
Insognia, Dennis J., V.P.-Sls. & Mktg.--Imperial Nurseries Inc., Granby, CT; *U.S. Public*, pg. 707
Interlandi, Daniel G., Sr. V.P. & Gen. Mgr.--Leisure & Entertainment Prods.--Micros Systems Inc., Beltsville, MD; *U.S. Public*, pg. 1106
Intrator, David, V.P.-Mktg. & Programming--Marcus Cable Company, L.P., Dallas, TX; *U.S. Private*, pg. 702
Iorio, Vince, Mgr.-Mktg.-ATV, Utility, Power Prod.--Kawasaki Motors Corp., U.S.A., Irvine, CA; *Int'l*, pg. 725
Ippolito, Karlyn, Asst. V.P.-Mktg.--Atlantic Mutual Companies, New York, NY; *U.S. Private*, pg. 95
Iramola, Enrique, V.P.-Mktg. & Sls.--Kaufman y Broad de Mexico SA de CV, Mexico, Mexico; *U.S. Public*, pg. 945
Irby, Mark, V.P.-Mktg. & Adv.--Publix Supermarkets Inc., Lakeland, FL; *U.S. Private*, pg. 893
Irelan, E. Glenn, Exec. V.P.-Mktg., Stores & Real Estate--Catherines Stores Corporation, Memphis, TN; *U.S. Public*, pg. 317
Irion, Randy, V.P.-Mktg. Services--Armour Swift Eckrich, Downers Grove, IL; *U.S. Public*, pg. 426
Irion, Randy, V.P.-Mktg. Services--Armour Food Company, Downers Grove, IL; *U.S. Public*, pg. 427
Irner, Klaus, Mgr.-Mktg.--Comtext International, London, United Kingdom; *Int'l*, pg. 537
Ironside, Mike, Dir.-Adv.--Associated Newspaper Holdings Ltd., London, United Kingdom; *Int'l*, pg. 366
Irvin, John W., Pres.-Catalog Div.--Spiegel, Inc., Downers Grove, IL; *U.S. Public*, pg. 1498
Irwin, A. Scott, Sr. V.P.-Mktg.--Irwin Toy Ltd., Toronto, Canada; *Int'l*, pg. 688
Irwin, Marie, Dir.-Mktg.--Carrols Corporation, Syracuse, NY; *U.S. Private*, pg. 216
Irwin, Mike, Dir.-Mktg.--WD-40 Company, San Diego, CA; *U.S. Public*, pg. 1726

Isaac, Steven R., Grp. V.P.-Cadmus Mktg. Commun. Grp., Inc.--Cadmus Communications Corporation, Richmond, VA; *U.S. Public*, pg. 290

Isaacson, Bob, Dir.-Mktg.--UniFirst Corporation, Wilmington, MA; *U.S. Public*, pg. 1665

Isabell, M., V.P.-Mktg.--Simplicity Engineering, Inc., Durand, MI; *Int'l*, pg. 1066

Isacsson, Curt, Mgr.-Mktg.--Skanska Maskin AB, Danderyd, Sweden; *Int'l*, pg. 1261

Isenberg, Debra, Sr. V.P.-Mktg.--Dow Jones Markets, Jersey City, NJ; *U.S. Public*, pg. 525

Isentol, Bruce, V.P.-Mktg.--Hilti Inc., Tulsa, OK; *Int'l*, pg. 620

Isham, Carol A., Dir.-Adv.--SLJ Retail LLC, Smyrna, GA; *U.S. Private*, pg. 957

Isherwood, Madeleine, Dir.-Mktg. Sls. Admin.--Winthrop-Atkins Co., Inc., Middleboro, MA; *U.S. Private*, pg. 1183

Isherwood, Yvonne, Mgr.-Mktg.--Fortnum & Mason PLC, London, United Kingdom; *Int'l*, pg. 500

Ishibashi, Shu, Dir.-Mktg.--Bridgestone/Firestone, Inc., Nashville, TN; *Int'l*, pg. 213

Ishibashi, Shu, Dir.-Mktg.--Bridgestone/Firestone Inc. Retail Operations, Rolling Meadows, IL; *Int'l*, pg. 213

Ishihara, Ken, V.P.-Adv.--Toshiba America Inc., New York, NY; *Int'l*, pg. 1405

Ishrak, Omar, V.P.-Mktg.--Diasonics Ultra Sound, Inc., Santa Clara, CA; *Int'l*, pg. 644

Ising, E. James, 2nd V.P.-Field Incentives & Communications--Providian Agency Group, Louisville, KY; *Int'l*, pg. 27

Isles, Mike, Dir.-Mktg.--Rhone-Poulenc Rorer Ltd., West Malling, United Kingdom; *Int'l*, pg. 1110

Islinger, Bob, Sr. V.P.-Mktg.--Payless Cashways, Inc., Kansas City, MO; *U.S. Public*, pg. 1267

Isman, Barbara, Asst. V.P. & Mgr.-Corp. Affairs--Cargill Ltd., Winnipeg, Canada; *U.S. Private*, pg. 210

Isola, George, Mgr.-Direct Mktg.--D & N Financial Corporation, Hancock, MI; *U.S. Public*, pg. 472

Isola, Thomas, V.P.-Mktg. & Pub. Rels.--Silver State Disposal Service, Inc., Las Vegas, NV; *U.S. Public*, pg. 1380

Israel, Karen, Coord.-Mktg. Communications--Worcester Controls Corp., Marlborough, MA; *Int'l*, pg. 128

Israel, Rich, Dir.-Mktg.--San Diego Chargers, San Diego, CA; *U.S. Private*, pg. 964

Itkin, Stuart M., V.P.-Worldwide Mktg.--PSC Inc., Webster, NY; *U.S. Public*, pg. 1245

Ito, Tsugio, V.P.-Corp. Plng. & Mktg.--Mitsubishi Motor Sales of America, Inc., Cypress, CA; *Int'l*, pg. 875

Iunghuhn, Kathy, Dir.-Corp. Mktg.--Simon DeBartolo Group, Inc., Indianapolis, IN; *U.S. Public*, pg. 1474

Ivey, John, Dir.-Mktg.--Flomaster Div., Canon City, CO; *U.S. Public*, pg. 1318

Ivey, John, Dir.-Mktg.--Pathfinder Div., Canon City, CO; *U.S. Public*, pg. 1318

Ivic, Bart, V.P.-Mktg. Communications--Blue Coral/Slick 50, Cleveland, OH; *U.S. Public*, pg. 1348

Ivon, Susan, Admin. Asst.-Sls. & Mktg.--Dexol, Torrance, CA; *U.S. Public*, pg. 1390

Izquierdo, Alfredo, Sr. V.P.-Opers.--PonceBank, F.S.B., Ponce, PR; *U.S. Public*, pg. 1316

Izzard, David, Dir.-Mktg.-Spec Indus.--The NutraSweet Kelco Company, San Diego, CA; *U.S. Public*, pg. 1125

Izzo, Joan, Mktg. Comm.--Alfa Laval Thermal Inc., Richmond, VA; *Int'l*, pg. 1378

Jablansky, John, V.P.-Prod. Mktg.--All American Semiconductor, Inc., Miami, FL; *U.S. Public*, pg. 41

Jablonski, Brian J., Exec. V.P.-Sls. & Mktg.--Lason, Inc., Troy, MI; *U.S. Public*, pg. 979

Jablonski, Scott, Analyst-Sls. & Mktg.--The Davey Tree Expert Company, Kent, OH; *U.S. Private*, pg. 314

Jacino, John, 1st V.P.-Sls. & Mktg.--Wetsel-Oviatt Lumber Company, El Dorado Hills, CA; *U.S. Private*, pg. 1170

Jackere, Gary, Mgr.-New Prod. Devel.--Triboro Electric Co., Doylestown, PA; *U.S. Private*, pg. 1102

Jackling, Michael, V.P.-Sls. & Mktg.--Ferrari North America, Inc., Englewood Cliffs, NJ; *Int'l*, pg. 483

Jackson, A., Dir.-Sls. & Mktg.--Oxford University Press, Oxford, United Kingdom; *Int'l*, pg. 1018

Jackson, Brett, Exec. V.P.-Sls. & Mktg.--Axent Technologies, Rockville, MD; *U.S. Public*, pg. 157

Jackson, Cynthia A., Mktg. Coordinator--Baxter Hodell Donnelly Preston Inc., Cincinnati, OH; *U.S. Private*, pg. 124

Jackson, Dave, Mgr.-Direct Mktg. & Pub. Rels.--Hechinger Company Investors II, L.P., Largo, MD; *U.S. Private*, pg. 477

Jackson, Ira A., Sr. V.P.-External Affairs--BankBoston Corporation, Boston, MA; *U.S. Public*, pg. 183

Jackson, Jake, V.P.-Sls. & Mktg.--Dillard, A ResourceNet International Company, Greensboro, NC; *U.S. Public*, pg. 901

Jackson, Marshall, Sr. V.P.-Mktg.--AVX Corporation, Myrtle Beach, SC; *Int'l*, pg. 775

Jackson, Mike, Dir.-Mktg.--WSMP, Inc., Claremont, NC; *U.S. Public*, pg. 1729

Jackson, Mike, Dir.-Mktg.--First Interstate Bank of Montana, N.A., Kalispell, MT; *U.S. Public*, pg. 1753

Jackson, Owen R., V.P.-Sls. & Mktg.--Technology Research Corporation, Clearwater, FL; *U.S. Public*, pg. 1564

Jackson, Phil, V.P.-Mktg. Brands Global--Parker Brothers, Beverly, MA; *U.S. Public*, pg. 797

Jackson, Riley, V.P.-Mktg., Pur. & Adv.--Federal Savings Bank, Fort Smith, AR; *U.S. Private*, pg. 614

Jackson, Robert E., V.P.-Corp. Mktg.--Greenhorne & O'Mara, Inc., Greenbelt, MD; *U.S. Private*, pg. 477

Jackson, Sharon Palaisa, Mgr.-Mktg.--Dettra Flag Company, Oaks, PA; *U.S. Private*, pg. 328

Jackson, Stephen K., V.P.-Distr. Div., Mktg. & Adv.--Georgia-Pacific Distribution Div., Atlanta, GA; *U.S. Public*, *pg. 735*

Jacob, William, V.P.-Mktg. & Sls.--Transicoil, Inc., Valley Forge, PA; *U.S. Private*, pg. 538

Jacobs, Daniel F., Dir.-Mktg.--RNL Facilities Corporation, Denver, CO; *U.S. Private*, pg. 905

Jacobs, Don, Brand Mgr.--Avia, Irvine, CA; *U.S. Private*, pg. 62

Jacobs, Donald W., V.P.-Mktg. & Engrng.--R&B, Inc., Colmar, PA; *U.S. Public*, pg. 1354

Jacobs, G., Asst. Dir.-Bus. Unit Printing Systems--Oce-van der Grinten N.V., Venlo, Netherlands; *Int'l*, pg. 993

Jacobs, James, Coord.-Adv.--Jersey Central Power & Light Co., Morristown, NJ; *U.S. Public*, pg. 695

Jacobs, Jim, Bus. Devel. Mgr.--Advanced Marine Enterprises, Inc., Arlington, VA; *U.S. Public*, pg. 1182

Jacobs, John H., Exec. V.P.--The Union Central Life Insurance Co., Cincinnati, OH; *U.S. Private*, pg. 1118

Jacobsen, Tom, Dir.-Mktg.--Schwan's Sales Enterprises, Marshall, MN; *U.S. Private*, pg. 974

Jacobson, Brian, Dir.-Mktg.--Hess Engineering Inc., Niles, MI; *U.S. Private*, pg. 524

Jacobson, Chris, V.P.-Mktg.--Waffle House, Incorporated, Norcross, GA; *U.S. Private*, pg. 1146

Jacobson, Howard, V.P.-Sls. & Mktg.--Canandaigua Wine Company Div., Canandaigua, NY; *U.S. Public*, pg. 300

Jacobson, Pat, Mgr.-Mktg.--MSI Insurance Companies, Arden Hills, MN; *U.S. Private*, pg. 688

Jacobson, Sue, Asst. Mgr.-Catalogue Mktg.--Pleasant Company, Middleton, WI; *U.S. Private*, pg. 872

Jacobus, Steven, V.P.-Sls. & Mktg.--Subaru Distributor Corp., Orangeburg, NY; *Int'l*, pg. 523

Jacoby, Donald, V.P.-Sls. & Mktg.--Northrup King Co., Golden Valley, MN; *Int'l*, pg. 974

Jacoby, Richard E., Dir.-Mkt. Analysis--Zinc Corporation of America, Monaca, PA; *U.S. Private*, pg. 540

Jacoby, Rodger, Mgr.-Mktg.--Viking Pump, Inc., Cedar Falls, IA; *U.S. Public*, pg. 862

Jacques, Barbara, Mgr.-Mktg.--Tyco International Ltd., Exeter, NH; *U.S. Public*, pg. 1647

Jacques, Maurice E., V.P.-Mktg. & Sls.--Varco BJ Drilling Systems, Orange, CA; *U.S. Public*, pg. 1709

Jaeckin, Philippe, Exec. V.P.--Danone Group, Paris, France; *Int'l*, pg. 379

Jaeger, Michael, Sr. V.P.-Mktg.--Sutter Home Winery, Inc., Saint Helena, CA; *U.S. Private*, pg. 1057

Jaffa, Paul, Dir.-Mktg.--Weatherall Green & Smith, London, United Kingdom; *Int'l*, pg. 1488

Jaffe, Jeremy, Asst. V.P.-Mktg.--Keyport Life Insurance Company, Boston, MA; *U.S. Private*, pg. 666

Jaffe, Stewart, Mgr.-Mktg.--Surgical Laser Technologies, Inc., Montgomeryville, PA; *U.S. Public*, pg. 1542

Jago, Richard, Exec. V.P.-Mktg.--Old World Industries, Inc., Northbrook, IL; *U.S. Private*, pg. 814

Jago, Rick, Dir.-Mktg.--Old World Automotive Products, Northbrook, IL; *U.S. Private*, pg. 814

Jain, Susan, Dir.-Strategic Mktg.--Dun & Bradstreet Software Services, Atlanta, GA; *Int'l*, pg. 532

Jakab, Joseph J., Gen. Mgr.-Sls.--Moore Tool Company, Inc., Bridgeport, CT; *U.S. Private*, pg. 889

Jakes, Tina, Concept Devel.--Pargo's Restaurants, Nashville, TN; *U.S. Public*, pg. 1467

Jalma, Louise, V.P.-Mktg.--Check Technology Corporation, Minnetonka, MN; *U.S. Public*, pg. 342

Jalvsted, Bjorn, Dir.-Mktg.--Procordia Food AB, Malmo, Sweden; *Int'l*, pg. 1011

Jameison, Katherine, Mktg. Asst.--The Promotion in Motion Companies, Closter, NJ; *U.S. Private*, pg. 890

James-Gilboe, Lynda, V.P.-Mktg.--Gale Research Inc., Detroit, MI; *U.S. Public*, pg. 1600

James, Betty M., Pres. & Dir.-Mktg. & Pub. Rels.--James Industries Inc., Hollidaysburg, PA; *U.S. Private*, pg. 580

James, Bob, Mktg. Analyst--Lilly Industries, Inc., Indianapolis, IN; *U.S. Public*, pg. 994

James, Gordon L., V.P.-Mktg.--The Quaker Oats Co. of Canada Ltd., Peterborough, Canada; *U.S. Public*, pg. 1348

James, Ira, V.P.-Mktg.--Acapulco Restaurants, Long Beach, CA; *U.S. Private*, pg. 925

James, Jim, Mgr.-Mktg.--ITW Fluid Products Group, Norcross, GA; *U.S. Public*, pg. 866

James, M.C., Mgr.-Mktg.--WBB Devon Clays Ltd., Newton Abbot, United Kingdom; *Int'l*, pg. 1487

James, Michael A., V.P.-Brady Mktg.--Medtronic, Inc., Minneapolis, MN; *U.S. Public*, pg. 1082

James, Michele A., Mgr.-Mktg.--Snyder Berlin, Berlin, PA; *U.S. Private*, pg. 887

James, Mike, Dir.-Mktg. & Sls.--Carefree of Colorado, Broomfield, CO; *U.S. Public*, pg. 217

James, Randy, Mgr.-Adv.-Chicago--Scientific American, Inc., New York, NY; *Int'l*, pg. 1479

James, Thomas, Controller--Elder Manufacturing Company, Creve Coeur, MO; *U.S. Private*, pg. 367

Jameson, Jonathan, V.P.-Mktg.--Denny's, Inc., Spartanburg, SC; *U.S. Public*, pg. 23

Jamison-Lenz, Pam, Mgr.-Mktg. (ARMD)--I.C. System, Inc., Vadnais Heights, MN; *U.S. Private*, pg. 553

Jamison, Martin, Dir.-Mktg. & Adv.--Dale Farm Dairies Ltd., Ballymena, United Kingdom; *Int'l*, pg. 968

Janelli, Mary Jane, Mgr.-Mktg. & Sls.--DeVault Foods, Devault, PA; *U.S. Private*, pg. 329

Janiga, Ken, V.P.-Consumer Mktg. & Sls.--The White Lily Foods Co., Knoxville, TN; *U.S. Private*, pg. 866

Janisch, Patrick, Dir.-Mktg. & Pub. Rels.--Bridgeman's Restaurants Inc., Minnetonka, MN; *U.S. Private*, pg. 167

Janke, Scott L., Commercial Dir.-Fluorocarbons--LaRoche Industries Inc., Atlanta, GA; *U.S. Private*, pg. 651

Jankovic, Paul, V.P.-Sls. & Mktg.--Gessner/Miller Corporation, Worcester, MA; *U.S. Private*, pg. 435

Jankowski, Jeff, Mgr.-Mktg.-Commercial Div.--Continental General Tire, Inc., Charlotte, NC; *Int'l*, pg. 327

Jans, Karin, Mgr.-Adv. & Mktg. Services--C.P. Clare Corporation, Beverly, MA; *U.S. Public*, pg. 382

Jansen, Bill, Mgr.-Mktg.--Carson Pirie Scott & Co., Milwaukee, WI; *U.S. Public*, pg. 309

Jansen, Jim, Dir.-Mktg.--Farm Fresh, Inc., Norfolk, VA; *U.S. Public*, pg. 1388

Jansen, Kristen, Dir.-Mktg.--Aaron Rents, Inc., Atlanta, GA; *U.S. Public*, pg. 12

Jansen, Tom, Mgr.-Mktg.--Olivetti (Schweiz) AG, Wallisellen, Switzerland; *Int'l*, pg. 1003

Janson, Danielle, Mgr.-Mktg.--Uniboard Canada Inc., Laval, Canada; *Int'l*, pg. 1431

Janssen, Martin, Gen. Mgr.-Magnetic Component Div.--Philips Components, Jupiter, FL; *Int'l*, pg. 1054

Jansson, Ingrid, Sr. V.P.-Mktg.--Trygg-Hansa, Stockholm, Sweden; *Int'l*, pg. 1425

Jantzi, Gerald P., V.P.-Mktg.--Sunshine Biscuits, Inc., Woodbridge, NJ; *U.S. Private*, pg. 434

Jantzi, Gerald P., V.P.-Mktg.--Sunshine Biscuits, Inc., Woodbridge, NJ; *U.S. Public*, pg. 657

Janz, Rainer, Dir.-Mktg.--Otis GmbH, Berlin, Germany; *U.S. Public*, pg. 1690

Jaouen, Sandy, Mgr.-Mktg.--Alpha Wire Company, Elizabeth, NJ; *U.S. Public*, pg. 201

Jardine, Ian, Dir.-Mktg.--Finnigan Corporation, San Jose, CA; *U.S. Public*, pg. 1591

Jarnot, John, Dir.-Mktg. Services & Sls. Promo.--AON Corporation, Chicago, IL; *U.S. Public*, pg. 117

Jarosinski, Richard, Mgr.-Mktg., Sls. & Services--Portec Inc., Railway Maintenance Products Div., Pittsburgh, PA; *U.S. Public*, pg. 1318

Jarosz, Dennis, V.P.-Mktg.--Congoleum Corporation, Mercerville, NJ; *U.S. Public*, pg. 69

Jarrett, Ian, Mgr.-Mktg.--Anderson, Clayton S.A., Sao Paulo, Brazil; *Int'l*, pg. 1436

Jarrold, Tom, Mgr.-Mktg. Communications--Cincinnati Milacron Plastics Machinery Group, Batavia, OH; *U.S. Public*, pg. 368

Jarry, Philippe, V.P.-Mktg.--Airbus Industrie, Blagnac, France; *Int'l*, pg. 39

Jarvis, Ann, V.P.-Advanced Prods.--Steelcase Inc., Grand Rapids, MI; *U.S. Private*, pg. 1038

Jarvis, T.J., Mgr.-Strategic Mktg. Plng.--Oldsmobile Div. General Motors Corp., Lansing, MI; *U.S. Public*, pg. 720

Jaskiewicz, S.A., Mgr.-Mktg.--ChemPump, Warrington, PA; *U.S. Public*, pg. 456

Jaskoviak, James, V.P.-Sls. & Mktg.--Winnebago Industries, Inc., Forest City, IA; *U.S. Public*, pg. 1772

Jaso, Robert J., V.P.-Mktg. & Bus. Devel.--Harleysville Group, Harleysville, PA; *U.S. Public*, pg. 786

Jaster, Eugene N., V.P.-Sls. & Mktg.--Detector Electronics Corporation, Minneapolis, MN; *Int'l*, pg. 1500

Jaworski, Rick, Mgr.-Mktg.--Wavetek Communications Div., Indianapolis, IN; *U.S. Private*, pg. 1155

Jaxtimer, Joanne, V.P.-Corp. Affairs & Mtkg.--The Boston Company, Inc., Boston, MA; *U.S. Public*, pg. 1085

Jaxtimer, Joanne, V.P.-Corp. Affairs & Corp. Mktg.--Boston Safe Deposit & Trust Co., Boston, MA; *U.S. Public*, pg. 1085

Jay, John, Assoc. Publisher/Dir.-Mktg.--Sports Illustrated, New York, NY; *U.S. Public*, pg. 1613

Jay, John E., Dir.-Mktg., Sports Illustrated-Assoc. Publisher-Time Inc., New York, NY; *U.S. Public*, pg. 1612

Jayme, John E., III, V.P.-Mktg.--American Waste Services, Inc., Warren, OH; *U.S. Public*, pg. 94

Jayson, Judith P., Dir.-Mktg.--J.M. Jayson & Co., Inc., Getzville, NY; *U.S. Private*, pg. 584

Jean, James, V.P.-Mktg.--United Service Equipment Company, Murfreesboro, TN; *U.S. Public*, pg. 1507

Jeannot, Richard, Dir.-Mktg.--UNC Johnson Technology, Muskegon, MI; *U.S. Public*, pg. 710

Jeanquenin, Adrian, Mgr.-Sls.--Tempil Inc., South Plainfield, NJ; *U.S. Private*, pg. 90

Jech, Jean, Mgr.-Sls. & Mktg.--CIBA Seeds, Greensboro, NC; *Int'l*, pg. 973

Jefferies, Brian, V.P.-Gas Mktg.--Western Gas Resources, Inc., Denver, CO; *U.S. Public*, pg. 1758

Jefferies, Jim T., V.P.-Mktg. Components--Pioneer-Standard Electronics, Inc., Cleveland, OH; *U.S. Public*, pg. 1300

Jefferson, Robert F., V.P.-Mktg.--Arinc Inc. (Consolidated), Annapolis, MD; *U.S. Private*, pg. 81

Jefferson, Robert F., Mgr.-Mktg.--Aeronautical Radio, Inc., Annapolis, MD; *U.S. Private*, pg. 81

Jeffery, Thomas, Dir.-Mktg.--L.M. Scofield Company, Los Angeles, CA; *U.S. Private*, pg. 976

Jeffrey, Simon, V.P.-Mktg.--Virgin Interactive Entertainment Inc., Irvine, CA; *U.S. Private*, pg. 776

Jeffries, April, V.P.-Bakery Bus. Mktg.--Pepperidge Farm, Incorporated, Norwalk, CT; *U.S. Public*, pg. 299

Jeffries, Jim, V.P.-Industrial Sls., Mktg. & Tech.--Favorite Brands International, Inc., Lincolnshire, IL; *U.S. Private*, pg. 397

Jeiger, Steve, Mgr.-Mktg. Commun. & Consumer Printers--Lexmark International Group, Inc., Lexington, KY; *U.S. Public*, pg. 991

Jeiger, Steve, Mgr.-Mktg. Commun. & Consumer Printers--Lexmark International, Inc., Lexington, KY; *U.S. Public*, pg. 991

Jelkin, Jerry, Dir.-Sls. & Mktg.--Optrex Glass, Plymouth, MI; *Int'l*, pg. 84

Jellett, Hugo, Mgr.-Mktg.--Harper Audio, New York, NY; *Int'l*, pg. 926

Jembelis, Thomas, Sr. V.P.--Nozaki America, Inc., New York, NY; *Int'l*, pg. 990

Jendzejec, Mark, Dir.-Mktg.--Logicon Eagle Technology, Inc., Winter Park, FL; *U.S. Public*, pg. 1199

Jeney, Steve, Dir.-Mktg.--National Electric Coil, Columbus, OH; *U.S. Private*, pg. 782

Jenkins, Colin, Dir.-Mktg. & Sls.--Chattem (U.K.) Ltd., Basingstoke, United Kingdom; *U.S. Public*, pg. 342

Jenkins, David, V.P.-Sls. & Mktg.--Chemical Leaman Tank Lines, Inc., Exton, PA; *U.S. Private*, pg. 233

Jenkins, Dennis, V.P.-Sls. & Mktg.--American Security Distribution, Anaheim, CA; *U.S. Private*, pg. 61

Jenkins, Don, V.P.-Mktg.--Nocona Boot Co., Nocona, TX; *U.S. Public*, pg. 937

Jenkins, Janice, Exec. V.P.-Mktg.--Fox Photo, Inc., Saint Louis, MO; *U.S. Public*, pg. 283

Jenkins, Jerry, Mktg. Services Coord.--Edwards Systems Tech, Cheshire, CT; *U.S. Public*, pg. 726

Jenkins, Karen, Sr. Dir.-Mktg. Communications--Magellan Health Services, Inc., Atlanta, GA; *U.S. Public*, pg. 1033

Jenkins, Peter, Sr. V.P.-Mktg. & Sls.--Hawaiian Airlines, Inc., Honolulu, HI; *U.S. Public*, pg. 799
Jenkins, Peter W., Sr. V.P.-Mktg. & Sls.--Hawaiian Airlines, Inc., Honolulu, HI; *U.S. Public*, pg. 799
Jenkins, Rob, Mgr.-Mktg. Svcs.--Rev-A-Shelf, Louisville, KY; *U.S. Private*, pg. 925
Jenks, Cliff, Exec. V.P.-North American Sls. & Mktg.--Zenith Data Systems, Deerfield, IL; *Int'l*, pg. 317
Jenner, B., Gen. Mgr.-Mktg.--Gallaher Limited, Weybridge, United Kingdom; *Int'l*, pg. 539
Jennings, Dale, Mgr.-Sls. & Mktg.--Pacific Handy Cutter, Inc., Costa Mesa, CA; *U.S. Private*, pg. 831
Jennings, Dinah, Coord.-Mktg. Projects--Cross Creek Apparel, Inc., Mount Airy, NC; *U.S. Public*, pg. 1413
Jennings, Karen P., Sr. V.P.-Mktg.--George W. Park Seed Co., Inc., Greenwood, SC; *U.S. Private*, pg. 839
Jenquin, Philip, V.P.-Intl. Mktg.--OmniTRACS Division, San Diego, CA; *U.S. Public*, pg. 1349
Jensen, Dick, V.P. & Gen. Mgr.-Assembly & Advanced Products--Dexter Electronic Materials Division, City of Industry, CA; *U.S. Public*, pg. 504
Jensen, Gary, V.P.-Mktg.--The Earthgrains Company, Clayton, MO; *U.S. Public*, pg. 547
Jensen, Marcia, Mgr.-Mktg. Communications--U.S. Bancorp, Minneapolis, MN; *U.S. Public*, pg. 1680
Jensen, Robin, V.P.-Food Service Mktg.--Tyson Foods, Inc., Springdale, AR; *U.S. Public*, pg. 1652
Jensen, Steve, Asst. V.P.-Mktg.--Pacesetter Corporation, Omaha, NE; *U.S. Private*, pg. 830
Jensen, Terry, Mgr.-Mktg. Services--Xerxes Corporation, Minneapolis, MN; *U.S. Private*, pg. 1194
Jeon, Keon-Ho, Mgr.--Ssangyong Information & Communication Corporation, Seoul, Korea; *Int'l*, pg. 1292
Jeppsson, Bert, Sr. V.P-Mktg.--Ericsson Components AB, Stockholm, Sweden; *Int'l*, pg. 1363
Jerkovich, Carolyn, Mktg. Asst.--ELE International, Inc./ Soiltest, Lake Bluff, IL; *Int'l*, pg. 1287
Jernigan, Paul, V.P.-Sls. & Mktg.--Gibson Musical Instruments, Inc., Nashville, TN; *U.S. Private*, pg. 451
Jespersen, Jim, Prod. Mgr.--Rubber Group, Niles, MI; *U.S. Public*, pg. 1160
Jestin, P., Dir.-Mktg.--Consortium Vinicole de Bordeaux et de la Gironde SA, Parempuyre, France; *Int'l*, pg. 752
Jeter, Jeff, Sr. Dir.-Mktg. Devel. & New Bus. & Acting Dir.-Mktg.--Iomega Corporation, Roy, UT; *U.S. Public*, pg. 912
Jett, Sandy, Coord.-Mktg. Svcs.--Price Pfister, Inc., Pacoima, CA; *U.S. Public*, pg. 234
Jimenez, Joseph, Exec. V.P.-Mktg.--Atlantic City Hilton, Atlantic City, NJ; *U.S. Public*, pg. 829
Jipp, Peter, Dir.-Mktg.--Motoren-Werke Mannheim AG, Mannheim, Germany; *Int'l*, pg. 408
Joachim, Walt, V.P.-Sls.--Furnival/State Machinery Co., Hatfield, PA; *Int'l*, pg. 744
Joanis, Robert W., V.P.-Mktg.--Coors Brewing Company, Golden, CO; *U.S. Public*, pg. 445
Jobe, Michael, Mgr.-Sls. & Mktg.--Rotary Lift, Madison, IN; *U.S. Public*, pg. 521
Jobes, Steven D., V.P.-Mktg., Mdsg, Sls. & Natl. Accts.--CORT Business Services Corporation, Fairfax, VA; *U.S. Public*, pg. 451
Joch, Susan, V.P.-Mktg.--First Team Sports Inc., Anoka, MN; *U.S. Public*, pg. 638
Jodar, Joey, Dir.-Mktg.--Wadsworth Publishing co., Belmont, CA; *U.S. Public*, pg. 1600
Jodzio, Greg, Dir.-Mktg. Communications--Advance Machine Company, Plymouth, MN; *Int'l*, pg. 932
Joerres, Jeffrey A., Sr. V.P.-Mktg. & Major Accts.--Manpower Inc., Milwaukee, WI; *U.S. Public*, pg. 1042
Joest, Rita, Mktg. Officer--CNB Bancshares, Inc., Evansville, IN; *U.S. Public*, pg. 280
Joflin, Minda, Asst. Mgr.-Mktg.--Summit Family Restaurants, Inc., Salt Lake City, UT; *U.S. Public*, pg. 278
Johannes, Nick, Dir.-Mktg.--Harris Waste Mgmt. Group, Inc., Peachtree City, GA; *Int'l*, pg. 473
Johannsen, Linda, Sr. Mgr.-Mktg. Services--Sensormatic Electronics Corporation, Boca Raton, FL; *U.S. Public*, pg. 1457
Johansen, Benjamin C., V.P.-Mdsg.--EZ Paintr Corp., Saint Francis, WI; *U.S. Public*, pg. 1177
John, David, Exec. Dir.-Mktg.--Inchcape PLC, London, United Kingdom; *Int'l*, pg. 671
Johns, Elaine, Mgr.-Pricing & Rates--Oglethorpe Power Corp., Tucker, GA; *U.S. Private*, pg. 812
Johns, Patrick, Dir.-Mktg.--Prudential Portfolio Managers Limited, London, United Kingdom; *Int'l*, pg. 1073
Johns, Rolland L., V.P.-Mktg.--Southdown, Inc., Houston, TX; *U.S. Public*, pg. 1488
Johnson, Abbey, Dir.-Mktg.--Bridgeway Hospital, North Little Rock, AR; *U.S. Public*, pg. 1696
Johnson, Allen, Mgr.-Mktg. & Sls.--Rubatex Corporation, Roanoke, VA; *U.S. Private*, pg. 56
Johnson, Allison, Mktg. Analyst--Fred B. Johnston Company, Inc., Chapin, SC; *U.S. Private*, pg. 595
Johnson, Amy, V.P.-Sls. & Mktg.--Rosemount Measurement Division, Eden Prairie, MN; *U.S. Public*, pg. 574
Johnson, Andrew V., Sr. V.P.-Mktg.--Fingerhut Corp., Minnetonka, MN; *U.S. Public*, pg. 623
Johnson, Andy, Dir.-Mktg.--Jefferson Smurfit Corporation, Saint Louis, MO; *Int'l*, pg. 1269
Johnson, B.B., V.P.-Mktg.--RPS Inc., Coraopolis, PA; *U.S. Public*, pg. 604
Johnson, Barry, Sr. Dir.-Portrait Mktg.--Moto Photo, Inc., Dayton, OH; *U.S. Public*, pg. 1136
Johnson, Craig, V.P.-Mktg.--National Auto Credit Inc., Solon, OH; *U.S. Public*, pg. 1152
Johnson, D., Mgr.-Mktg.-Household & Polish--Kiwi Brands Pty. Ltd., Clayton, Australia; *U.S. Public*, pg. 1434
Johnson, D.A., Dir.-Vehicle Brand Mktg.--General Motors of Canada Ltd., Oshawa, Canada; *U.S. Public*, pg. 722
Johnson, Dale D., Sr. V.P.--The Union Central Life Insurance Co., Cincinnati, OH; *U.S. Private*, pg. 1118
Johnson, Dan, Mgr.-Sls. & Mktg.--Hunter/Krey Foods, Hazelwood, MO; *U.S. Public*, pg. 75
Johnson, Darrell, V.P. & Mgr.-Mktg.--Felton Brush Inc., Manchester, NH; *U.S. Private*, pg. 400
Johnson, Daryl, V.P.-Mktg. & Sls.--Pharmaceutical Basics, Inc., Chicago, IL; *Int'l*, pg. 48
Johnson, David, V.P.-Sls. & Mktg.--National Sea Products Incorporated, Portsmouth, NH; *Int'l*, pg. 909
Johnson, David H., Mgr.-Mktg. Communications--Twin Disc, Incorporated, Racine, WI; *U.S. Public*, pg. 1646
Johnson, Debby, Exec. V.P. & Mktg Dir.--Ackerman McQueen, Inc., Oklahoma City, OK; *U.S. Private*, pg. 12
Johnson, Dennis, V.P.-Mktg. & Sls.--Harper-Wyman Co., Aurora, IL; *U.S. Public*, pg. 1209
Johnson, Don, Dir.-Adv. & Mktg.--Detecto Scale Company, Webb City, MO; *U.S. Private*, pg. 209
Johnson, Donald E., Dir.-Mktg.--Radix Corporation, Salt Lake City, UT; *U.S. Private*, pg. 906
Johnson, Dwayne, Mgr.-Mktg. Communications & Adv.--Republic Automotive-AEA Division, Charlotte, NC; *U.S. Public*, pg. 1377
Johnson, Ed, Exec. V.P.-Sls. & Mktg.--Star-Kist Foods Inc., Newport, KY; *U.S. Public*, pg. 805
Johnson, Edward, Dir.-Bus. Devl.--Dowty Woodville Polymer, Swadlincote, United Kingdom; *Int'l*, pg. 1338
Johnson, Edward C., V.P.-Mktg.--Dynamics Research Corporation, Andover, MA; *U.S. Public*, pg. 539
Johnson, Eric, V.P.-Mktg.--Activision, Santa Monica, CA; *U.S. Public*, pg. 17
Johnson, Eric, V.P.-Sls. & Mktg.--John Boos & Company, Effingham, IL; *U.S. Private*, pg. 156
Johnson, Evelyn, Mgr.-Corp. Commun.--Access Industries, Grandview, MO; *U.S. Private*, pg. 11
Johnson, Geralyn, Dir.-Adv.--Yankee Gas Services Company, Meriden, CT; *U.S. Public*, pg. 1788
Johnson, H. Gene, Mgr.-Mktg. Commun.--Telsco Industries, Garland, TX; *U.S. Private*, pg. 1074
Johnson, Howard, Asst.-Mktg.--Shogyo International Corporation, Plainview, NY; *U.S. Private*, pg. 996
Johnson, J. Dennis, V.P.-Mktg.--Kentucky Medical Insurance Company (KMIC), Louisville, KY; *U.S. Private*, pg. 741
Johnson, J.B., Jr., Sr. V.P.--Birdsong Corporation, Suffolk, VA; *U.S. Private*, pg. 145
Johnson, James R., Exec. V.P. & Sec.--Johnson Storage Moving Co, Denver, CO; *U.S. Private*, pg. 594
Johnson, James R., Exec. V.P.--Security Van Lines, Kenner, LA; *U.S. Private*, pg. 594
Johnson, Jeff, Gen. Mgr.-Indus. Pkgng.--Flexible Packaging Division, Chicago, IL; *U.S. Public*, pg. 1521
Johnson, Jeffrey R., Chief Mktg. Officer--Equifax Inc., Atlanta, GA; *U.S. Public*, pg. 588
Johnson, Jim, V.P.-Sls. & Mktg.--Midwest Mutual Insurance Co., West Des Moines, IA; *U.S. Private*, pg. 881
Johnson, Kenneth, V.P.-Sls. & Mktg.--FieldBrook Farms, Inc., Dunkirk, NY; *U.S. Private*, pg. 403
Johnson, Kevin, Dir.-Mktg. Commun.--ADC Telecommunications, Inc., Minnetonka, MN; *U.S. Public*, pg. 4
Johnson, L.E., V.P.-Mktg.--Ziegler Leasing Corp., West Bend, WI; *U.S. Public*, pg. 1792
Johnson, L.E., V.P.-Mktg.--Ziegler Medical Equipment Group, Inc., Omaha, NE; *U.S. Public*, pg. 1792
Johnson, Lee Ann, Dir.-Mktg.--Revell-Monogram Inc., Morton Grove, IL; *U.S. Private*, pg. 926
Johnson, Lou, Mgr.-Mktg.--Military Products Div., Sunnyvale, CA; *Int'l*, pg. 1054
Johnson, Mark, Gen. Mgr.--W. Heath & Co., Los Angeles, CA; *U.S. Public*, pg. 84
Johnson, Mark, Dir.-Mktg.--Malt-O-Meal Company, Minneapolis, MN; *U.S. Private*, pg. 699
Johnson, Mark, Mgr.-Mktg.--Union Pump Company, Battle Creek, MI; *U.S. Private*, pg. 1119
Johnson, Mark, V.P.-Mdsg. & Procurement--Performance Food Group Company, Richmond, VA; *U.S. Public*, pg. 1278
Johnson, Mark R.S., Co-Chief Exec. Officer & Pres.-Mktg.--Hastings Manufacturing Company, Hastings, MI; *U.S. Public*, pg. 798
Johnson, Martin C., Sr. V.P.-Mktg.--Robert Mondavi Winery, Inc., Oakville, CA; *U.S. Public*, pg. 1393
Johnson, Michael A., Exec. V.P.-Admin. & Mktg.--Western Financial Bank, Irvine, CA; *U.S. Public*, pg. 1757
Johnson, Michelle, Coord.-Mktg. & Adv.--Heraeus Amersil Inc., Duluth, GA; *Int'l*, pg. 616
Johnson, Mike, Dir.-Gen. Mdse. Opers. & Mktg.--Marks & Spencer PLC, London, United Kingdom; *Int'l*, pg. 842
Johnson, Mike, Dir.-Mktg.--Westcorp, Irvine, CA; *U.S. Public, pg. 1756*
Johnson, P.J., Dir-Pub. Rels. & Adv.--Nomura Securities International, Inc., New York, NY; *Int'l*, pg. 956
Johnson, Patty, Sr. Mgr.-Mktg. Svcs.--Converse Inc., North Reading, MA; *U.S. Public*, pg. 441
Johnson, Paul, V.P.-Mktg.--Duo-Fast Corporation, Huntley, IL; *U.S. Private*, pg. 347
Johnson, R.E., V.P.-Reg. Baltimore--Tristate Electrical Supply Co., Inc., Hagerstown, MD; *U.S. Private*, pg. 1104
Johnson, Randy, Dir.-Mktg. & Adv.--Barrel O'Fun Snack Foods Co., Perham, MN; *U.S. Private*, pg. 118
Johnson, Rick, Exec. V.P.-Automotive Sls.--Radiator Specialty Company, Charlotte, NC; *U.S. Private*, pg. 906
Johnson, Rick, Plant Mgr.-Mktg.--Warner Candy Company, Inc., Schiller Park, IL; *U.S. Private*, pg. 1150
Johnson, Robert, V.P.-Mktg. & Sls.-Midwest Region--ResourceNet International, Shawnee Mission, KS; *U.S. Public*, pg. 903
Johnson, Ron, V.P.-Sls. & Mktg.--AmTran Corporation, Conway, AR; *U.S. Public*, pg. 1167
Johnson, Ronald A., V.P.-Mktg.--Berkley Administrators, Minneapolis, MN; *U.S. Public*, pg. 216
Johnson, Ronald A., V.P.-Sls. & Mktg.--Key Risk Management Services, Inc., Greensboro, NC; *U.S. Public*, pg. 216
Johnson, Scott, Mgr.-Fin. Mktg.--Jacobson Stores Inc., Jackson, MI; *U.S. Public*, pg. 922
Johnson, Shelly, Mgr.-Mktg. & Pub. Rels.--MCO Properties Inc., Fountain Hills, AZ; *U.S. Public*, pg. 1062
Johnson, Sidney, Dir.-Mktg.--Jayco Inc., Middlebury, IN; *U.S. Private*, pg. 583
Johnson, Stan, Dir.-Mktg. Devel.--Growmark, Inc., Bloomington, IL; *U.S. Private*, pg. 484
Johnson, Stephen B., V.P.-Mktg. & Customer Services--Minnegasco, Minneapolis, MN; *U.S. Public*, pg. 843
Johnson, Suzanne, Mgr.-Mktg. Svcs.--Riverwood International Corporation, Atlanta, GA; *U.S. Public*, pg. 1391
Johnson, Timothy L., Sr. V.P. & Dir.-Mktg.--MetLife Capital Holdings, Inc., Bellevue, WA; *U.S. Private*, pg. 737
Johnson, Tom, V.P.-Mktg. & Sls.--Atlas/Soundolier, Fenton, MO; *U.S. Private*, pg. 64
Johnson, Tom, V.P.-Intl. Mktg. Devel.--Corporate Express, Inc., Broomfield, CO; *U.S. Public*, pg. 449
Johnston, Bill, V.P.-Mktg.--Smart Modular Technologies, Fremont, CA; *U.S. Public*, pg. 1476
Johnston, Geoffrey B., Dir.-Mktg.--First Gibraltar Bank, Irving, TX; *U.S. Public*, pg. 181
Johnston, J. Tyler, V.P.-Mktg.--Dreyer's Grand Ice Cream, Inc., Oakland, CA; *U.S. Public*, pg. 529
Johnston, Jeffrey D., V.P.-Intl. Sls. & Mktg.--Ruslander & Sons, Inc., Buffalo, NY; *U.S. Private*, pg. 952
Johnston, Jeffrey D., V.P.-Sls. & Mktg.--Jewett International Corp., Buffalo, NY; *U.S. Private*, pg. 952
Johnston, Jerome B., V.P.-Corp. Mktg.--3Com Corporation, Santa Clara, CA; *U.S. Public*, pg. 1603
Johnston, Ken, Dir.-Mktg.--Butlin's Limited, Hemel Hempstead, United Kingdom; *Int'l*, pg. 1086
Johnston, Les, Dir.-Sls. & Mktg.--Fasco Controls Corporation, Shelby, NC; *Int'l*, pg. 125
Johnston, Martha, V.P.-Southern Living Shows--Southern Progress Corporation, Birmingham, AL; *U.S. Public*, pg. 1612
Johnston, Ron, V.P.-Mktg.--Racet Computes Limited, Brea, CA; *Int'l*, pg. 740
Jokerst, Raymond W., V.P.-Mktg. & Sls.--Magnetek Motors & Generators, Saint Louis, MO; *U.S. Public*, pg. 1037
Jokinen, Kari, Dir.--Raisio Group plc-Margarine, Raisio, Finland; *Int'l*, pg. 1085
Jolivette, John, Mgr.-Mktg.--Crystal Flash Petroleum Corp., Indianapolis, IN; *U.S. Private*, pg. 294
Jolivette, Jordan, Mgr.-Sls. & Mktg.--E & A Industries, Inc., Indianapolis, IN; *U.S. Private*, pg. 352
Jolley, Don, Mgr.-Adv. & Mktg. Communications--Thermal Ceramics Inc., Augusta, GA; *Int'l*, pg. 894
Jollymore, Peter, V.P.-Plng. & Mktg.--The New Brunswick Telephone Company, Limited (NBTel), Saint John, Canada; *Int'l*, pg. 230
Jollymore, Peter G., V.P.-Plng. & Mktg.--Bruncor, Inc., Saint John, Canada; *Int'l*, pg. 230
Jonap, Scott T., V.P.-Sls. & Mktg., Consumer Prods. Div.--Foley-PLP Company, Rochester, NY; *U.S. Private*, pg. 416
Jonas, Donald L., Vice Chm., Chief Exec. Officer & Dir.-Mktg.--Lechters, Inc., Harrison, NJ; *U.S. Public*, pg. 983
Jondahl, Kenneth E., V.P.-Intl. Sls. & Mktg.--Osmonics, Inc., Minnetonka, MN; *U.S. Public*, pg. 1233
Jones, A.E., Gen. Mgr.-Sls.--National Utility Service Ltd., Croydon, United Kingdom; *U.S. Private*, pg. 787
Jones, Alan D., Mgr.-Mktg. Services--Mallinckrodt Baker Inc., Phillipsburg, NJ; *U.S. Public*, pg. 1039
Jones, Andy, Dir.-Mktg. Opers.--Vauxhall, Luton, United Kingdom; *U.S. Public*, pg. 724
Jones, Diane S., Mgr.-Corp. Rels. & Bus. Devel.--Westmoreland Coal Co., Colorado Springs, CO; *U.S. Public*, pg. 1761
Jones, Elliott M., Exec. V.P.-Mktg. & Tech. Services--Willis Corroon Corp. of Illinois, Chicago, IL; *Int'l*, pg. 1506
Jones, Gail, Mgr.-Mktg. Svcs.--Van Dyne-Crotty, Inc., Dayton, OH; *U.S. Private*, pg. 1132
Jones, Garteh Vaughan, Dir.-Mktg.--Eurocamp Travel Limited, Knutsford, United Kingdom; *Int'l*, pg. 465
Jones, J.B., V.P.-Sls. & Mktg.--Coldwater Seafood Corporation, Rowayton, CT; *U.S. Private*, pg. 251
Jones, Jack, Mgr.-Dir. Mktg./Dir. Response--Burlington Motor Holdings Inc., Daleville, IN; *U.S. Private*, pg. 183
Jones, James L., Sr., Chm. Bd. & Chief Exec. Officer--Jones & Jones, Inc., McAllen, TX; *U.S. Private*, pg. 596
Jones, Jeff, V.P.-Mktg. & Prod. Devel.--Sony Music Entertainment, Inc., New York, NY; *Int'l*, pg. 1281
Jones, Judy, Dir.-Mktg. Commun.--Napco Security Systems, Inc., Amityville, NY; *U.S. Public*, pg. 1151
Jones, Keith A., Dir.-Corp. Mktg.--Fermec Holdings, Ltd., Manchester, United Kingdom; *U.S. Public*, pg. 312
Jones, Larry, V.P.-Mktg./Nick at Nite/T.V. Land--Nickelodeon/Nick At Nite, New York, NY; *U.S. Private*, pg. 779
Jones, Lloyd, Exec. V.P.--A.G. Simpson Co. Limited, Scarborough, Canada; *Int'l*, pg. 1252
Jones, Louise, Mgr.-Adv. & Mktg. Specialist--Schneider Group, Mississauga, Canada; *Int'l*, pg. 1208
Jones, Mary, Dir.-Mktg.--Rainbow Technologies, Ltd., Chertsey, United Kingdom; *U.S. Public*, pg. 1359
Jones, Melissa, Mktg. Asst.--Instinet Corporation, New York, NY; *Int'l*, pg. 1106
Jones, Mickey, V.P.-Mktg.--Mason & Hanger Engineering Inc., Lexington, KY; *U.S. Private*, pg. 711
Jones, Patrick, V.P.-Mktg.--Jones Company, Inc., Waycross, GA; *U.S. Private*, pg. 596
Jones, Paul, Dir.-Intl. Mktg.--Armor All Products Group, Oakland, CA; *U.S. Public*, pg. 387
Jones, R.F., V.P.-Sls.--Ziegler Leasing Corp., West Bend, WI; *U.S. Public*, pg. 1792
Jones, Richard, Mktg. Coord.--Corken, Inc., Oklahoma City, OK; *U.S. Public*, pg. 862
Jones, Robert D., V.P.-Mktg.--Celeritek, Inc., Santa Clara, CA; *U.S. Public*, pg. 319
Jones, Rodney A., V.P.-Mktg.--Sinclair/Ameritone Paint Corp., Los Angeles, CA; *Int'l*, pg. 663
Jones, Roy, Mgr.-Mktg. Svcs.--Sullair Corporation, Michigan City, IN; *U.S. Public*, pg. 1534
Jones, Shane, Dir.-Mktg.--Bioproducts, Inc., Fairlawn, OH; *U.S. Private*, pg. 145

Jones, Stephanie, Mgr.-Mktg. & Communications--Instrument Specialties Company, Delaware Water Gap, PA; *U.S. Private*, pg. 565

Jones, Steve, Mgr.-Mktg--Rowenta (USA), Inc., Medford, MA; *Int'l*, pg. 569

Jones, Stu, Mgr.-Communication Coord.--Svedala Industries Inc., York, PA; *Int'l*, pg. 1325

Jones, Susan S., Mgr.-Mktg. Communications--BNA Software, Washington, DC; *U.S. Private*, pg. 182

Jones, Thomas, Exec. V.P.-Sales, Mktg. & Cust. Serv.--MDL Information Systems, Inc., San Leandro, CA; *Int'l*, pg. 1100

Jones, Wiley, V.P. & Mgr.-Mktg & Adv.--Green Spot Packaging Inc., Claremont, CA; *U.S. Private*, pg. 477

Jones, Yvonne, Mgr.-Mktg. Communications--Standard Register-Barrington, Barrington, IL; *U.S. Public*, pg. 1505

Jonica, Kathleen, Dir.-Mktg.--IMO Pump, Monroe, NC; *U.S. Public*, pg. 857

Jordan, Candis, V.P.-Mktg.--Roman Meal Company, Tacoma, WA; *U.S. Private*, pg. 942

Jordan, James, Dir.-Mktg. & Adv.--Multiple Allied Services, Inc., Hayward, CA; *U.S. Private*, pg. 767

Jordan, James P., V.P.-Mktg.--Jewelers Mutual Insurance Company, Neenah, WI; *U.S. Private*, pg. 587

Jordan, Jim, Dir.-Mktg.--Meadox Medicals, Inc., Oakland, NJ; *U.S. Public*, pg. 247

Jordan, Lynn, Mktg. Communications Specialist--Curtis 1000, Inc., Atlanta, GA; *U.S. Public*, pg. 70

Jordan, Nicholas, Exec. V.P.-Sls. & Mktg.--CPS Corporation, Franklin, TN; *U.S. Private*, pg. 422

Jordan, Yvonne, Dir.-Mktg. Communications-Broadband--Scientific-Atlanta, Inc., Norcross, GA; *U.S. Public*, pg. 1443

Jorgenien, Rick, Mktg.--Mid Continent Bottlers, Inc, West Des Moines, IA; *U.S. Private*, pg. 142

Jorgensen, Lauri, Dir.-Mktg. Services--BPA International, New York, NY; *U.S. Private*, pg. 107

Jorgensen, Leif, Dir.-Mktg.--Skandinavisk Henkel A/S, Copenhagen, Denmark; *Int'l*, pg. 614

Jorgensen, Marty, V.P.-Mktg.--Ingram Entertainment Inc., La Vergne, TN; *U.S. Private*, pg. 563

Jorgenson, Bruce, V.P.-Sls. & Mktg.--Rexam Medical Packaging, Inc., Mundelein, IL; *Int'l*, pg. 1107

Jory, Jim, Dir.-Mktg. & Sls. Integration--Clarke American Corp., San Antonio, TX; *Int'l*, pg. 267

Jose, Fran U., Sr. V.P.-Mktg. & Visual--Proffitt's, Inc., Alcoa, TN; *U.S. Public*, pg. 1333

Joseph, Debbie, Mgr.-Adv.- Cuprinol & Thompsons' Water Seal--Sherwin-Williams Consumer Brands Division, Cleveland, OH; *U.S. Public*, pg. 1466

Joseph, Justin, Dir.-Mktg.--A.O. Smith/Uppco, Inc., Monticello, IL; *U.S. Public*, pg. 1477

Joseph, Mark M., Mgr.-Mktg. Communications--Fel-Pro Incorporated, Skokie, IL; *U.S. Private*, pg. 399

Joseph, Meril, Sr. V.P.-Mktg. & Communications--Fortis, Inc., New York, NY; *Int'l*, pg. 499

Joseph, Moses, V.P.-Mktg.--Integrated Systems, Inc., Sunnyvale, CA; *U.S. Public*, pg. 885

Joseph, Randi, V.P.-Sls.--The Penn Companies, Philadelphia, PA; *U.S. Private*, pg. 849

Joss, Steve, V.P.-Mktg. Services--Farm Progress Publications, Carol Stream, IL; *U.S. Public*, pg. 513

Joulin, Nathalie, Dir.-Mktg./Boyle France--Reckitt & Colman S.A., Massy, France; *Int'l*, pg. 1090

Jovanovski, Jovan, V.P.-Stroh Intl.--The Stroh Brewery Company, Detroit, MI; *U.S. Private*, pg. 1047

Joyce, Brenda, Dir.-Mktg.--Scott Specialty Gases, Plumsteadville, PA; *U.S. Private*, pg. 977

Joyce, William, Dir.-Mktg.--Buehler, Limited, Lake Bluff, IL; *U.S. Public*, pg. 574

Joyner, Barrett, V.P.-North American Mktg. & Sls.--SAS Institute Inc., Cary, NC; *U.S. Private*, pg. 966

Joyner, Henry, V.P.-Mktg. Plng.--American Airlines, Inc., Fort Worth, TX; *U.S. Public*, pg. 9

Jroejer, Rudolf, Dir.-Mktg.--Karl M. Reich Maschinenfabrik GmbH, Nurtingen, Germany; *Int'l*, pg. 1101

Ju, Chester, V.P.-Encoder Div. & Metrigraphics Div.--Dynamics Research Corporation, Andover, MA; *U.S. Public*, pg. 539

Juarez, F., Mktg./Sls.--Candy Iberica S.A., Barcelona, Spain; *Int'l*, pg. 260

Juda, Chuck, Mgr.-Mktg.--Namco Controls Corporation, Highland Heights, OH; *U.S. Public*, pg. 482

Juday, Floyd, Mgr.-Mktg.--Trus Joist MacMillan Limited, Surrey, Canada; *Int'l*, pg. 829

Juday, Floyd, V.P.-Mktg. Svcs.--Trus Joist MacMillan, Boise, ID; *Int'l*, pg. 829

Juday, Floyd, V.P.-Mktg. Services--TJ International, Inc., Boise, ID; *U.S. Public*, pg. 1556

Juday, Floyd, Mgr.-Mktg.--Trus Joist MacMillan Limited, Surrey, Canada; *U.S. Public*, pg. 1556

Juday, Floyd, Mgr.-Mktg.--Trus Joist (Western) Ltd., Surrey, Canada; *U.S. Public*, pg. 1556

Juday, Floyd, Mgr.-Mktg.--Norco Windows, Inc., Boise, ID; *U.S. Public*, pg. 1556

Juday, Floyd, V.P.-Mktg. Svcs.--Trus Joist MacMillan, Boise, ID; *U.S. Public*, pg. 1556

Juday, Floyd J., V.P.-Mktg.--MacMillan Bloedel Inc., Alpharetta, GA; *Int'l*, pg. 829

Judson, Ted, Dir.-Retail Mktg.--Electronic Arts, San Mateo, CA; *U.S. Public*, pg. 569

Juenger, Steven, Dir.-Mktg. & Sls.--Reliance Medical Products, Inc., Mason, OH; *U.S. Private*, pg. 921

Juenger, Teresa, Dir.-Mktg.--ICI Explosives USA Inc., Dallas, TX; *Int'l*, pg. 663

Juengling, Bob, V.P.-Bus. Devel.--Betac International Corporation, Alexandria, VA; *U.S. Private*, pg. 140

Julian, John, Sr. V.P.-Worldwide Mktg.--ICN Pharmaceuticals, Inc., Costa Mesa, CA; *U.S. Public*, pg. 853

Julian, Ken, Dir.-Corp. Communications--Harsco Corporation, Camp Hill, PA; *U.S. Public*, pg. 792

Julian, Malcolm, Exec. V.P.-Sls. & Mktg.--Winstar Global Products, Inc., Fairfield, NJ; *U.S. Public*, pg. 1772

Jullien, Alexis, Dir.-Mktg. Devel.--C.M.C. SA, Saint Quentin-en-Yvelines, France; *Int'l*, pg. 792

Julow, James, Exec. Dir.-Corp. Mktg.--Chrysler Corporation, Auburn Hills, MI; *U.S. Public*, pg. 352

Jump, Tom, V.P.-Mktg. Svcs.--Long John Silver's, Inc., Lexington, KY; *U.S. Private*, pg. 674

Jung, Andrea, Exec. V.P. & Pres.-Global Mktg. & New Bus.--Avon Products, Inc., New York, NY; *U.S. Public*, pg. 155

Jung, Peter, Dir.-Mktg., Plus--Tengelmann Warenhandelsgesellschaft, Mulheim, Germany; *Int'l*, pg. 1375

Jurczyk, Ann, Dir.-Mktg.--Group 1 Software, Inc., Lanham, MD; *U.S. Public*, pg. 417

Juredine, David, V.P.-Sls. & Mktg.--Ohio Indemnity Company, Columbus, OH; *U.S. Public*, pg. 175

Jurek, Noreen, Sr. Mgr.-Mktg. Commun.--Tekelec, Calabasas, CA; *U.S. Public*, pg. 1566

Just, Mark, V.P.-Sls. & Mktg.--Bradley Printing Company, Des Plaines, IL; *U.S. Public*, pg. 1778

Justesen, Agner, Mgr.-Mktg., Trailers--Eldon AB, Nassjo, Sweden; *Int'l*, pg. 436

Justice, Hal, Exec. V.P.-Sls. & Mktg.--URS Logistics, Atlanta, GA; *U.S. Private*, pg. 1114

Justice, Michael, Dir.-Sls. & Mktg.--RB&W Corporation, Cleveland, OH; *U.S. Public*, pg. 1259

Jutzi, Robert, Asst. Mgr.-Sls.--Bommer Industries, Inc., Landrum, SC; *U.S. Private*, pg. 156

Kabella, Albert B., V.P.-Sls. & Mktg.--Calumet Construction Corporation, Hammond, IN; *U.S. Private*, pg. 201

Kack, Steve, Mktg. Coord.--Davie Industries Inc., Levis, Canada; *Int'l*, pg. 385

Kacvinsky, Ray C., V.P.-Mktg. & Sls.-Generators--Marathon Electric Manufacturing Corp., Wausau, WI; *U.S. Public*, pg. 1371

Kaczynski, Steve, Exec. V.P.-Sls. & Mktg.--Giant Food Stores Inc., Carlisle, PA; *Int'l*, pg. 750

Kaeck, Lisa, V.P.-Mktg.--Quest Staffing, Atlanta, GA; *U.S. Public*, pg. 45

Kafarakis, Phil, V.P.-Sls. & Mktg.--Jones Dairy Farm, Fort Atkinson, WI; *U.S. Private*, pg. 596

Kaffer, William J., V.P.-Mktg.--Theodore Barry & Associates, Los Angeles, CA; *U.S. Private*, pg. 118

Kafka, Rick, Pres. & Dir.-Mktg.--Gosnell Builders, Phoenix, AZ; *U.S. Private*, pg. 873

Kafkarkou, George, V.P.-Sls. & Mktg.--Infresco Corporation, Sarasota, FL; *U.S. Public*, pg. 420

Kagen, Jancy, Mgr.-Retail Mktg.--Geneva Pharmaceuticals, Inc., Broomfield, CO; *Int'l*, pg. 973

Kahill, Brian, Mgr.-Corp. Mktg. Svcs.--Lawyers Cooperative Publishing Co., Rochester, NY; *U.S. Public*, pg. 1602

Kahmann, Mike, Sr. V.P.-Mktg.--The CIT Group/Capital Finance Inc., New York, NY; *Int'l*, pg. 360

Kahn, Caryn, Dir.-Mktg.--World's Finest Chocolate, Inc., Chicago, IL; *U.S. Private*, pg. 1191

Kahn, Jan, Pres., Sls. & Mktg.--Caron International, De Kalb, IL; *U.S. Private*, pg. 786

Kahn, Judith, Mgr.-Pub. Rels.--Ark Restaurants Corp., New York, NY; *U.S. Public*, pg. 129

Kahn, Lawrence, V.P.-Mktg./Automotive Div.--Armor All Products Group, Oakland, CA; *U.S. Public*, pg. 387

Kahn, Michael, V.P. & Dir.-Franchise Sls. & Consumer Mktg.--The Great Frame Up Systems, Inc., Franklin Park, IL; *U.S. Private*, pg. 473

Kahover, Stacie, Mktg. Specialist--Inter-Tel, Incorporated, Phoenix, AZ; *U.S. Public*, pg. 888

Kaiser, Mark P., Sr. V.P.-Sls., Mktg. & Procurement--JP Foodservice, Inc., Columbia, MD; *U.S. Public*, pg. 918

Kaiser, Mark P., Sr. V.P.-Sls., Mktg. & Procurement--JP Foodservice Distributors, Inc., Columbia, MD; *U.S. Public*, pg. 918

Kalasky, Mike, Sr. V.P. & Dir.-Mktg./Intl. RMS--Willis Corroon Corp. of Nashville, Nashville, TN; *Int'l*, pg. 1506

Kalberer, Dave, Dir.-Mktg.-Consumer Prods.--Hunt Corporation, Philadelphia, PA; *U.S. Public*, pg. 848

Kalbfell, Karl-Heinz, Dir.-Mktg.--Bayerische Motoren Werke Aktiengesellschaft, Munich, Germany; *Int'l*, pg. 177

Kale, Keith, Mng. Dir.-Mktg.--Piper Jaffray Companies, Inc., Minneapolis, MN; *U.S. Public*, pg. 1300

Kalell, Susan, Mgr.-Pub. Rels.--SPSS Inc., Chicago, IL; *U.S. Public*, pg. 1420

Kalick, Irving B., Exec. V.P.-Affiliate Sls. & Mktg.--QVC, Inc., West Chester, PA; *U.S. Private*, pg. 897

Kalil, A.J., V.P.-Sls. & Mktg.--PHB Die Casting, Fairview, PA; *U.S. Private*, pg. 826

Kalinowski, Roger, V.P.-Mktg.--Keebler Company, Elmhurst, IL; *U.S. Public*, pg. 657

Kalishman, John F., Dir.-Mktg.--Insituform Technologies, Inc., Chesterfield, MO; *U.S. Public*, pg. 881

Kalister, D. Scott, V.P.-Mktg.--Raytheon Aircraft Company, Wichita, KS; *U.S. Public*, pg. 1365

Kalka, Terrence, Mgr.-Mktg.-Metal Working Fluids--Troy Corporation, Florham Park, NJ; *U.S. Private*, pg. 1105

Kallaway, Mike, Dir.-Mktg.--John Cranes Marine International, Havant, United Kingdom; *Int'l*, pg. 1339

Kallio, Tuula, Mktg. Dir.--Oy Dagmar Ab, Helsinki, Finland; *Int'l*, pg. 359

Kalmuck, John, V.P.-Sls. & Mktg.--La Marche Mfg. Co., Des Plaines, IL; *U.S. Private*, pg. 640

Kalous, Dave, V.P.-Mktg.--Duo-Fast Corporation, Huntley, IL; *U.S. Private*, pg. 347

Kalt, Robert, V.P.-Mktg.--H.B. Zachry, San Antonio, TX; *U.S. Private*, pg. 1203

Kalter, Marjorie, Exec. V.P. & Mktg. Dir.--Wunderman Cato Johnson, New York, NY; *U.S. Private*, pg. 1197

Kaluza, Johannes, Dir.-Mktg. & Adv.--Eckes AG, Nieder-Olm, Germany; *Int'l*, pg. 432

Kalviatis, Ramunas, V.P.-Mktg.--SierraCom, Hopkinton, MA; *U.S. Private*, pg. 999

Kambe, Nobuyoshi, Dir.-Non-Watch Bus. Mktg.--Seiko Corporation, Tokyo, Japan; *Int'l*, pg. 1218

Kamena, Karl, Mgr.-Sls. & Mktg.--Nanocor, Inc., Arlington Heights, IL; *U.S. Public*, pg. 64

Kamins, Aaron J., Chief Fin. Officer--Accurate Perforating Co., Chicago, IL; *U.S. Private*, pg. 12

Kaminski, Robert M., Dir.-Sls. & Mktg.--Continental/Midland, Inc., Park Forest, IL; *U.S. Private*, pg. 268

Kaminsky, H. Penson, V.P.--H. R. Kaminsky & Sons, Inc., Fitzgerald, GA; *U.S. Private*, pg. 606

Kamis, Don, V.P.-Opers.--Aero Systems Engineering Inc., Saint Paul, MN; *Int'l*, pg. 276

Kammer, Greg, Mgr.-Mktg.--Magline, Inc., Pinconning, MI; *U.S. Private*, pg. 695

Kammerer, Mark, Dir.-Mktg. Services--Royal Caribbean Cruises Ltd., Miami, FL; *U.S. Public*, pg. 1410

Kammerhuber, Ernst, Mgr.-Mktg.--Scanvest Olivetti A/S, Oslo, Norway; *Int'l*, pg. 1004

Kammersgard, Dana W., V.P.-Sls. & Mktg.--Artecon, Inc., Carlsbad, CA; *U.S. Private*, pg. 409

Kamo, Yasushi, Exec. Mgr.-Mktg.--Sony Corporation of Panama, Panama, Panama; *Int'l*, pg. 1284

Kamps, P., Dir.-Sls. & Mktg.--Howard Maschinenfabrik GmbH, Michelstadt, Germany; *Int'l*, pg. 1387

Kanas, Marilyn T., V.P.-Software Mktg.--Zitel Corporation, Fremont, CA; *U.S. Public*, pg. 1793

Kanatzar, Dave, Dir.-Mktg.--Wynn's-Precision, Inc., Lebanon, TN; *U.S. Public*, pg. 1783

Kandel, Dave, V.P.-Mktg.--Herff Jones Inc., Indianapolis, IN; *U.S. Private*, pg. 523

Kane, Cheryl, Dir.-Trade Mktg.--CRN International, Inc., Hamden, CT; *U.S. Private*, pg. 197

Kane, Heather, Mktg. Analyst--Maytag International, Inc., Chicago, IL; *U.S. Public*, pg. 1065

Kane, Jack, V.P.-Mktg.--The Wooster Brush Company, Wooster, OH; *U.S. Private*, pg. 1188

Kane, Kelley, Mgr.-Prod./Mktg.--Azon Corporation, Johnson City, NY; *U.S. Private*, pg. 104

Kane, Patrick, Sr. V.P., Corp. Devel. & New Bus. Contact--CRN International, Inc., Hamden, CT; *U.S. Private*, pg. 197

Kangas, Mel, V.P.-Sls. & Mktg.--Capacity of Texas, Inc., Longview, TX; *U.S. Public*, pg. 400

Kangisser, Stephen, V.P.-Mktg.--Eskimo Pie Corporation, Richmond, VA; *U.S. Public*, pg. 592

Kania, Gene, Mgr.-Bus. Unit--Senior Flexonics Inc., Bartlett, IL; *Int'l*, pg. 1222

Kanka, Richard, Dir.-Mktg.--Cosmetique, Inc., Vernon Hills, IL; *U.S. Private*, pg. 277

Kano, Shigehiko, Gen. Mgr.-Mktg. Dept.--Maruha Corporation, Tokyo, Japan; *Int'l*, pg. 845

Kanokwatanawan, Samran, Exec. V.P.-Mktg.--Finance One Public Company Limited, Bangkok, Thailand; *Int'l*, pg. 484

Kantarian, Arlen, Chief Oper. Officer-Entertainment & Mktg.--Radio City Productions, New York, NY; *Int'l*, pg. 873

Kanter, Don, Dir.-Sls. & Mktg.--F. D. Kees Power Equipment, Beatrice, NE; *U.S. Private*, pg. 1195

Kantra, Andrew, Dir.-Mktg.-Outdoor--Trans-Lux Corporation, Norwalk, CT; *U.S. Public*, pg. 1628

Kantzler, A., Dir.-Sls. & Mktg.--Moore Business Equipment Div., Dover, NH; *Int'l*, pg. 890

Kapellen, Daniel R., Dir.-Mktg.--Synchro-Start Products, Inc., Niles, IL; *U.S. Private*, pg. 627

Kaplan, Barbara, Mgr.-Mktg. Communications--Air Techniques, Inc., Hicksville, NY; *U.S. Private*, pg. 28

Kaplan, Barbara, Sr. V.P.-Mktg. & Sls. Promo.--Fortunoff, Uniondale, NY; *U.S. Private*, pg. 420

Kaplan, Beth, Mgr.-Mktg. Communications--Collagen Corporation, Palo Alto, CA; *U.S. Public*, pg. 399

Kaplan, Beth, Exec. V.P.-Mktg.--Rite Aid Corporation, Camp Hill, PA; *U.S. Public*, pg. 1390

Kaplan, George, Mgr.-Sls. & Mktg.--The Entwistle Company, Hudson, MA; *U.S. Private*, pg. 378

Kaplan, Howard, Assoc. Publr.--The Goldhirsh Group, Boston, MA; *U.S. Private*, pg. 461

Kaplan, Marcie, Mktg. Communications--Stone Container Corporation, Chicago, IL; *U.S. Public*, pg. 1520

Kaplan, Martin, Sr. V.P.-Mktg.--New York Life Insurance Company, New York, NY; *U.S. Private*, pg. 794

Kaplan, Michael M., V.P.-Sls. & Mktg.--Life Sciences International, Philadelphia, PA; *U.S. Private*, pg. 317

Kaplan, Robert E., V.P.-Opers. & Mktg. Services--Greenwood Mills, Inc., New York, NY; *U.S. Private*, pg. 479

Kapp, Steve, Mktg. Dir.--Berry Network, Inc., Dayton, OH; *U.S. Private*, pg. 137

Kappen, Don, Mgr.-Mktg. & Sls.--Bodolay/Pratt Div., Lakeland, FL; *U.S. Private*, pg. 832

Kapsen, Terrance J., V.P.-Mktg.--Medical Graphics Corp., Saint Paul, MN; *U.S. Public*, pg. 1080

Kaptur, Casey, Dir.-Mktg.--ARCO Coal Company, Denver, CO; *U.S. Public*, pg. 144

Kapur, Dilip, Dir.-Mktg.--Supertex, Inc., Sunnyvale, CA; *U.S. Public*, pg. 1539

Karaban, Michael, V.P.-Mktg.--J & J Snack Foods Corporation, Pennsauken, NJ; *U.S. Public*, pg. 916

Karaga, Steve, V.P.-Sls. & Mktg.--Hitachi Koki U.S.A. Ltd., Norcross, GA; *Int'l*, pg. 620

Karam, F. Abi, V.P.-Mktg.--King Industries, Inc., Norwalk, CT; *U.S. Private*, pg. 620

Karass, Audrey, V.P.-Mktg. & Dir.-Corp. Video Systems & Telecommunications--Caristrap International Inc., Laval, Canada; *Int'l*, pg. 271

Karban, Laura, Asst. Prod. Mgr.--Wilhold Inc., Cleveland, OH; *U.S. Public*, pg. 78

Kardon, Brian, Sr. V.P.-Corp. Mktg.--Reed Elsevier Business Information, Newton, MA; *Int'l*, pg. 1095

Karig, Mitch, Asst. V.P.-Mktg.--Capital Markets Assurance Corporation, New York, NY; *U.S. Public*, pg. 1023

Karlin, Steve, Mgr.-Mktg.--M-B Companies Inc. of Wisconsin, Chilton, WI; *U.S. Private*, pg. 684

Karlsson, Hans-Olof, Sr. V.P.-Corp. Communications--NCC AB, Solna, Sweden; *Int'l*, pg. 898

Karlsson, Kennet, Mgr.-Mktg.--Sparbanken Finans, Stockholm, Sweden; *Int'l*, pg. 1328

Karp, M., Dir.-Mktg.--Elbit Computers Ltd., Haifa, Israel; *Int'l*, *pg. 644*

Karr, Don, Mgr.-Mktg. Svcs.--Barber Industries Inc., Calgary, Canada; *Int'l*, pg. 164

Karrasch, Steven, Mgr.-Mktg. Svcs.--The Vollrath Company, L.L.C., Sheboygan, WI; *U.S. Private*, pg. 1143

Karrels, Jane, Mgr.-Corp. Communications--Effective Management Systems, Milwaukee, WI; *U.S. Public*, pg. 565

Karrels, Jane, Mgr.-Mktg.--EMS Central Regional Office (Corporate), Milwaukee, WI; *U.S. Public*, pg. 565

Karter, Norma, V.P.-Mktg.--Eateries, Inc., Oklahoma City, OK; *U.S. Public*, pg. 555

Karter, Norma, V.P.-Mktg.--Pepperoni Grill, Oklahoma City, OK; *U.S. Public*, pg. 555

Karve, M. D., Strategic Alliances--Buckman Laboratories Inc., Memphis, TN; *U.S. Private*, pg. 180

Kase, Dale L., Dir.-Mktg.--Schult Homes Corporation, Middlebury, IN; *U.S. Public*, pg. 1442

Kaselar, Richard A., V.P.-Mktg.--Eastman Worldwide, Buffalo, NY; *U.S. Private*, pg. 358

Kasemsuvan, Pongsak, Mktg. Dir.--Avon Cosmetics (Thailand) Ltd., Bangkok, Thailand; *U.S. Public*, pg. 156

Kaspar, Dan A., Mgr.-Prods.--Kaspar Wire Works, Inc., Shiner, TX; *U.S. Private*, pg. 608

Kasper, Ted, Dir.-Adv. & Mktg.--Hutchenson Seal Corporation, Downey, CA; *U.S. Private*, pg. 550

Kass, Warren, V.P. & Integrated Mktg. Dir.--Partners & Shevack, Inc., New York, NY; *U.S. Private*, pg. 842

Kasten, Robert, V.P.-Sls. & Mktg.--Hoffer's Inc., Schofield, WI; *U.S. Private*, pg. 239

Katatski, Laurie, Sr. V.P.-Mktg.--Chi-Chi's Inc., Louisville, KY; *U.S. Private*, pg. 393

Katayama, Michnori, Dir.-Mktg.--TDK Corporation, Tokyo, Japan; *Int'l*, pg. 1336

Kately, Richard, Exec. V.P.-Mktg.--Heitman Financial Ltd., Chicago, IL; *U.S. Public*, pg. 1673

Katopis, Christopher, V.P.-Sls. & Mktg.--Cains Foods, L.P., Ayer, MA; *U.S. Private*, pg. 199

Katsafanas, Parry, V.P.-Mktg. & Sls.--UNR-Leavitt Div., Chicago, IL; *U.S. Public*, pg. 1404

Katz, B. Jeffrey, V.P.-Mktg.--Atmel Corporation, San Jose, CA; *U.S. Public*, pg. 145

Katz, Barry, V.P.-Sls.--Unitel Video, Inc., New York, NY; *U.S. Public*, pg. 1692

Katz, Bita, Mgr.-Mktg.--Diodes Incorporated, Westlake Village, CA; *U.S. Public*, pg. 510

Katz, Charles, Sr. V.P.-Mktg.-Universal Studios Home Video--Universal Pictures, Universal City, CA; *Int'l*, pg. 1216

Katz, Martin, Sr. V.P.-Bus. Plng. & Mktg.--WSFS Financial Corporation, Wilmington, DE; *U.S. Public*, pg. 1728

Kaufman, Joe, V.P.-Customer Mkts. Resources--Multi-Ad Services, Incorporated, Peoria, IL; *U.S. Private*, pg. 766

Kaufman, William, Dir.-Tech. & Mktg.--Oryx Energy, Dallas, TX; *U.S. Public*, pg. 1232

Kaufmann, Debbie, Mgr.-Mktg.--Disclosure Incorporated, Bethesda, MD; *U.S. Public*, pg. 1325

Kaunonen, Antti, Dir.-Mktg.--Valmet Automation Inc., Helsinki, Finland; *Int'l*, pg. 1449

Kausmeyer, Edward E., V.P.-North American Mktg.--Kolmar Laboratories, Inc., Port Jervis, NY; *Int'l*, pg. 239

Kavassilis, Daphne, Mgr.-Natl. Mktg.--W.A. Flick & Co. Pty. Limited, Lane Cove, Australia; *Int'l*, pg. 495

Kawa, C.J., Mgr.-Commercial Devel.--Alco Chemical, Chattanooga, TN; *Int'l*, pg. 1435

Kawada, Y., V.P.-Mktg.--SEIKO Corporation of America, Mahwah, NJ; *Int'l*, pg. 1218

Kawamura, Y., Exec. Dir.-Mktg.--Tsudakoma Corp., Kanazawa, Japan; *Int'l*, pg. 1425

Kawamura, Yuko, Mng. Dir. & Gen. Mgr.-Mktg. Devel. Headquarters--Nihon Keizai Shimbun, Inc., Tokyo, Japan; *Int'l*, pg. 929

Kawano, Hidemichi, Dir.-Mktg. & Mgr.-Sls.--Fotograbado Industrial Centro-Americano S.A., San Jose, Costa Rica; *Int'l*, pg. 1349

Kawashima, William, Grp. V.P.-Mktg. & Adv.--Servco Pacific Inc., Honolulu, HI; *U.S. Private*, pg. 986

Kawczynski, Randy, V.P.-Mktg. & Sls.--Sawhill Tubular Div., Sharon, PA; *U.S. Public*, pg. 131

Kawol, Jane, Coord.-Mktg.--AE Goetze-North America, Plymouth, MI; *Int'l*, pg. 1334

Kaye, Tim, Consumer & Trade Mktg. Dir.--Daniel J. Edelman Ltd., London, United Kingdom; *U.S. Private*, pg. 363

keane, Michael, V.P.-Sls. & Mktg.--Arburg, Inc., Newington, CT; *U.S. Private*, pg. 79

Kearney, Richard P., Mgr.-Mktg. & Sls.--W.R. Case & Sons Cutlery Company, Bradford, PA; *U.S. Private*, pg. 1207

Kearney, T. Scott, V.P.-Sls. & Mktg./Furniture--Ameriwood Industries International Inc., Grand Rapids, MI; *U.S. Public*, pg. 98

Kearns, Paul, Dir.-Sls. & Mktg.--Lancashire Dairies Ltd., Manchester, United Kingdom; *Int'l*, pg. 798

Keaveney, Vincent J., Asst. V.P.-Mktg.--Commercial Travelers Mutual Insurance Company, Utica, NY; *U.S. Private*, pg. 258

Keble-White, Kim, Dir.-Mktg.--Utell International, Brentford, United Kingdom; *Int'l*, pg. 1098

Kebrdle, Dave, Pres.-Sls. & Mktg.--Domore Corporation, Elkhart, IN; *U.S. Private*, pg. 339

Kedzierski, Suzy, Mgr.-Mktg. Commun.--New Brunswick Scientific Co., Inc., Edison, NJ; *U.S. Public*, pg. 1169

Keefer, Tom B., V.P.-Sls. & Mktg.--AC Corporation, Greensboro, NC; *U.S. Private*, pg. 3

Keegan, Beth, Dir.-Adv.--Ames Department Stores, Inc., Rocky Hill, CT; *U.S. Public*, pg. 99

Keegan, Bill, Dir.-Sls. & Mktg.--Central States Can Co., Massillon, OH; *U.S. Public*, pg. 463

Keegan, Hugh, Adv. & Mkt. Res.--Ventre Packing Company, Inc., Syracuse, NY; *U.S. Private*, pg. 1135

Keeler, Barbara, Mgr.-Worldwide Mktg. Support--Beckman Instruments, Inc., Fullerton, CA; *U.S. Public*, pg. 199

Keeler, Robert, Exec. V.P.-Mktg--WWF Paper Corporation, Bala Cynwyd, PA; *U.S. Private*, pg. 1145

Keeley, Alvin W., Sr. V.P.-Mktg.--Payco American Corporation, Brookfield, WI; *U.S. Public*, pg. 1267

Keen, Willard, V.P.-Sls. & Mktg.--Keen Compressed Gas Co., Wilmington, DE; *U.S. Private*, pg. 611

Keenan, Dine, Mgr.-Mktg.--Framesi USA, Inc./Roffler Industries, Inc./Casa di Colore, Inc., Coraopolis, PA; *U.S. Private*, pg. 419

Keenan, Heather, Mktg. Commun. Specialist--IEC Electronics Corp., Newark, NY; *U.S. Public*, pg. 854

Keenan, Joe, Mgr.-Sls. & Mktg.--Hughes-Peters, Inc., Cincinnati, OH; *U.S. Private*, pg. 546

Keenan, Keith J., Dir.-Mktg. Devel.--Tower Group International, New York, NY; *U.S. Public*, pg. 1071

Keener, Barney, Dir.-Mktg.--Greenlee Textron, Rockford, IL; *U.S. Public*, pg. 1589

Keever, Paul, Mgr.-Mktg.--Arden International Kitchens, Inc., Lakeville, MN; *U.S. Private*, pg. 972

Kehoe, Burton, Dir.-Mktg. & Bus. Devel. for Substrates--Hunt Corporation, Philadelphia, PA; *U.S. Public*, pg. 848

Kehoe, Carol, Dir.-Mktg.--The London Free Press, London, Canada; *Int'l*, pg. 1320

Keith, Camille T., V.P.-Special Mktg.--Southwest Airlines Co., Dallas, TX; *U.S. Public*, pg. 1493

Keith, Judi, V.P.-Mktg.--J.T. Davenport & Sons, Inc., Sanford, NC; *U.S. Private*, pg. 314

Keld, Sharon, Mgr.-Mktg.--Barton Brands, Ltd., Chicago, IL; *U.S. Public*, pg. 300

Keleshian, Alyssa, Dir.-Mktg.--MacDonald Communications, New York, NY; *U.S. Private*, pg. 691

Kell, Tom, Dir.-Mktg.--Plymouth Rubber Company, Inc., Canton, MA; *U.S. Public*, pg. 1311

Kellagher, Bob, V.P.-Mktg.--The Times Leader, Wilkes-Barre, PA; *U.S. Public*, pg. 964

Kellam, Douglas, V.P.-Mktg.--First Alert, Inc., Aurora, IL; *U.S. Private*, pg. 406

Kelleher, Jerome, Dir.-Mktg.--The Borden Co. A/S, Esbjerg, Denmark; *U.S. Private*, pg. 159

Kelleher, K.B., Exec. V.P.-Mktg. & Sls.--CNB International, Inc., Charleston, SC; *U.S. Private*, pg. 196

Kelleher, K.B., Exec. V.P.-Mktg. & Sls.--Clearing-Niagara, Buffalo, NY; *U.S. Private*, pg. 196

Keller, Candace, Dir.-Mktg. Commun.--Jami, Inc., Shawnee Mission, KS; *U.S. Private*, pg. 581

Keller, Conni, Mktg. Communications Coord.--Ohmeda, Inc., Liberty Corner, NJ; *Int'l*, pg. 121

Keller, Jim, V.P.-Mktg.--Houck Industries, Inc., Visalia, CA; *U.S. Private*, pg. 541

Keller, Kurt, V.P.-Mktg. & Sls.--Seal Group, Irvine, CA; *U.S. Public*, pg. 1262

Keller, Michael, Exec. V.P.-Mktg.--Koo Koo Roo, Inc., Los Angeles, CA; *U.S. Public*, pg. 966

Kellersman, John, V.P.-Sls. & Mktg.--Cooper Instrument Corp., Middlefield, CT; *U.S. Private*, pg. 274

Kellett, Clive, Mgr.-Mktg.--The Glacier Metal Co. Ltd., Northwood, United Kingdom; *Int'l*, pg. 1334

Kelley, Alice, Dir.-Mktg. Communications & Services--Andersen Corporation, Bayport, MN; *U.S. Private*, pg. 71

Kelley, Jack, Exec. V.P.-Mktg.--Liberty National Life Insurance Co., Birmingham, AL; *U.S. Public*, pg. 1622

Kelley, Mary Lou, Sr. Dir.-Bus. Devel. & Mktg. Res.--Ben & Jerry's Homemade Inc., South Burlington, VT; *U.S. Public*, pg. 210

Kelley, William E., Sr. V.P.-Sls., Adv. & Mktg.--Mohawk Paper Mills, Inc., Cohoes, NY; *U.S. Private*, pg. 755

Kellogg, Jeanette, V.P.-Sls. & Mktg.--Genova Products, Inc., Davison, MI; *U.S. Private*, pg. 447

Kelly-Bartley, Kim, Dir.-Mktg. & Pub. Rels.--White Castle System, Inc., Columbus, OH; *U.S. Private*, pg. 1171

Kelly-Ennis, Debra, Sr. V.P.-Mktg.--Gerber Products Company, Fremont, MI; *Int'l*, pg. 973

Kelly-Ennis, Debra J., V.P.-Mktg.--Alpo Pet Foods, Inc., Allentown, PA; *Int'l*, pg. 917

Kelly, Barbara, V.P.-Sls., Mktg. & Customer Service--Time Warner Cable of New York City, New York, NY; *U.S. Public*, pg. 1611

Kelly, Brian T., Sr. V.P.-Global Mktg. & Sls.--Occidental Chemical Corporation, Dallas, TX; *U.S. Public*, pg. 1210

Kelly, Craig J., Exec. V.P.-Strategic mktg.--Crestar Financial Corporation, Richmond, VA; *U.S. Public*, pg. 458

Kelly, Craig T., Grp. Exec. V.P.-Strategic Mktg.--Crestar Bank, Richmond, VA; *U.S. Public*, pg. 458

Kelly, Cris, Coord.-Mktg.--Spalding Canada, Concord, Canada; *U.S. Private*, pg. 630

Kelly, Ed, Exec. V.P.-Mdsg. & Mktg.--Eckerd Corporation, Largo, FL; *U.S. Public*, pg. 917

Kelly, Elaine, V.P.-Mktg.--Best Software, Inc., Reston, VA; *U.S. Public*, pg. 223

Kelly, Francis J., III, Mng. Partner & Chief Mktg. Officer--Arnold Communications, Inc., Boston, MA; *U.S. Private*, pg. 83

Kelly, James E., Dir.-Mktg.-Hair Care--Combe Incorporated, White Plains, NY; *U.S. Private*, pg. 257

Kelly, John, V.P.-Mktg.--Hoechst Marion Roussel, Inc., Bridgewater, NJ; *Int'l*, pg. 624

Kelly, John, V.P.-Mktg.--Hoechst Marion Roussel North America, Kansas City, MO; *Int'l*, pg. 625

Kelly, John M., Exec. V.P.-Mktg. & Sls.--Desa International, Bowling Green, KY; *U.S. Private*, pg. 326

Kelly, Judith, Mktg. & Promo. Svcs.--Rums of Puerto Rico, New York, NY; *U.S. Private*, pg. 951

Kelly, Julia, Dir.-Adv. & Pub. Rels.--Suncor Development Company, Phoenix, AZ; *U.S. Public*, pg. 1298

Kelly, Karen, Mgr.-Bus. Devel.--Alex J. Etkin, Inc., Farmington, MI; *U.S. Private*, pg. 384

Kelly, Keith, V.P.-Intl. Sls. & Mktg.--Mile High Equipment Co., Denver, CO; *Int'l*, pg. 189

Kelly, Larry, Mgr.- Mktg.Svcs.--EG & G Rotron, Woodstock, NY; *U.S. Public*, pg. 543

Kelly, Mark, Dir.-Mktg. & Prod. Mgmt.-ATV, Utility, Power Prod.--Kawasaki Motors Corp., U.S.A., Irvine, CA; *Int'l*, pg. 725

Kelly, Mark F., Mgr.-Mktg.--King Fifth Wheel Co., Mountain Top, PA; *Int'l*, pg. 1337

Kelly, Michael D., Exec. V.P.-Mktg.--Perkins Family Restaurants, Memphis, TN; *U.S. Private*, pg. 925

Kelly, Patrick T., V.P.-Sls. & Mktg.--Haws Drinking Faucet Co., Berkeley, CA; *U.S. Private*, pg. 512

Kelly, Robin, V.P.-Sls. & Mktg.--ENPAC, Eastlake, OH; *U.S. Public*, pg. 592

Kelly, Timothy, V.P.-Mktg.--Nielsen Dillingham Builders, Inc., San Diego, CA; *U.S. Private*, pg. 333

Kelly, Tom, Chief Mktg. Officer & V.P.--Nextel Communications, Mc Lean, VA; *U.S. Public*, pg. 1180

Kelsay, Kris, V.P.-Mktg. Commun.--Wall Data Incorporated, Kirkland, WA; *U.S. Public*, pg. 1734

Kelsey, John L., V.P.-Mktg.--A.P. Green Industries, Inc., Mexico, MO; *U.S. Public*, pg. 761

Kelso, William J., V.P.-Mktg.--Zenith Products Corp., New Castle, DE; *U.S. Public*, pg. 1054

Kemmer, Chris, Mgr.-Mktg.--Varity Dayton Walther, Dayton, OH; *Int'l*, pg. 820

Kemmere, A.J., Mgr.-Mktg.--Philips International B.V., Eindhoven, Netherlands; *Int'l*, pg. 1051

Kemp, M., Dir.-Sls. & Mktg.--Decoflex Limited, Hartlepool, United Kingdom; *Int'l*, pg. 889

Kemp, Patrick, Exec. Dir.-Mktg. NAO--General Motors Corporation, Detroit, MI; *U.S. Public*, pg. 718

Kemper, Thomas, Dir.-Mktg.--Harpen AG, Dortmund, Germany; *Int'l*, pg. 597

Kemph, Chris, V.P.-Mktg.--Site Oil Company of Missouri, Clayton, MO; *U.S. Private*, pg. 1004

Kemple, Art, Mgr.-Industry Mktg.--Drying Division, Minneapolis, MN; *U.S. Public*, pg. 1382

Kendall, Jerry D., V.P.-Mktg.--Acme Steel Co., Riverdale, IL; *U.S. Public*, pg. 16

Kendall, Jerry T., Pres.-North American Retail Opers.--Sensormatic Electronics Corporation, Boca Raton, FL; *U.S. Public*, pg. 1457

Kendall, Vic, V.P.-Multiwall Sls.--Industrial & Retail Bag Division, Chicago, IL; *U.S. Public*, pg. 1521

Kendis, Randall J., Dir.-Mktg. & Bus. Devel.--Washington Inventory Service, San Diego, CA; *U.S. Public*, pg. 846

Kendra, Joe, V.P.-Brand Mktg.--Long John Silver's, Inc., Lexington, KY; *U.S. Private*, pg. 674

Kennard, John V.O., Sr. V.P. Mktg.-Louisville--Brown-Forman Corporation, Louisville, KY; *U.S. Public*, pg. 261

Kennedy, B.J., Mktg. Asst.--Speakman Company, Wilmington, DE; *U.S. Private*, pg. 1021

Kennedy, Brian, V.P.-Mktg. & Sls.--Hertz Corporation, Newark, NJ; *U.S. Public*, pg. 664

Kennedy, Brian, V.P.-Mktg. & Sls.--Hertz Corporation, Trenton, NJ; *U.S. Public*, pg. 664

Kennedy, Brian J., Exec. V.P.-Sls. & Mktg.--The Hertz Corporation, Park Ridge, NJ; *U.S. Public*, pg. 664

Kennedy, Charles E., V.P.-Mktg.--Tangram Enterprise Solutions, Inc., Cary, NC; *U.S. Public*, pg. 1424

Kennedy, David, Sr. V.P.-Mktg.--SunGard Employee Benefits Systems, Birmingham, AL; *U.S. Public*, pg. 1534

Kennedy, Edward, Exec. V.P.-sls. & Mktg.--LePage's, Inc., Pittsburgh, PA; *U.S. Private*, pg. 598

Kennedy, J. Michael, V.P. & Reg. Bus. Devel. Mgr.-New England--Gilbane Building Company, Providence, RI; *U.S. Private*, pg. 452

Kennedy, Jim, Mgr.-Mktg.--Northwestern Public Service, Huron, SD; *U.S. Public*, pg. 1200

Kennedy, Joseph J., V.P.-Sls., Service & Mktg.--The Saturn Corporation, Troy, MI; *U.S. Public*, pg. 721

Kennedy, Mark, V.P.-Mktg.--Medeco Security Locks, Inc., Salem, VA; *U.S. Public*, pg. 828

Kennedy, Maureen, V.P.& Dir.-Mktg., Illinois--Citibank, Federal Savings Bank (Illinois), Chicago, IL; *U.S. Public*, pg. 378

Kennedy, P. R., V.P.-Natl. Mktg.--Carlton & United Breweries Ltd., Southbank, Australia; *Int'l*, pg. 500

Kennedy, P.J., Mgr.-Trade Mktg.--Rothmans (UK) Ltd., Aylesbury, United Kingdom; *Int'l*, pg. 1130

Kennedy, Richard, V.P.-Mktg.-Abrasives--Norton Company, Worcester, MA; *Int'l*, pg. 1173

Kennedy, Susan, Dir.-Mktg.--Nob Hill General Store, Inc., Gilroy, CA; *U.S. Private*, pg. 799

Kennedy, Susan, Mgr.-Mktg.--Sloan Valve Company, Franklin Park, IL; *U.S. Private*, pg. 1006

Kenney, Danielle, Mgr.-Mktg. Communications--Alnor Instrument Company, Skokie, IL; *U.S. Public*, pg. 1559

Kenney, Susan M., Dir.-Mktg.--The Seibels Bruce Group, Inc., Columbia, SC; *U.S. Public*, pg. 1453

Kenney, Susan M., V.P.-Mktg.--Consolidated American Insurance Co., Columbia, SC; *U.S. Public*, pg. 1454

Kenney, Susan M., Dir.-Mktg.--Catawba Insurance Co., Columbia, SC; *U.S. Public*, pg. 1454

Kenney, Susan M., Dir.-Mktg.--Investors National Life Insurance Co., Columbia, SC; *U.S. Public*, pg. 1454

Kenney, Susan M., Dir.-Mktg.--Kentucky Insurance Co., Louisville, KY; *U.S. Public*, pg. 1454

Kenney, Susan M., Dir.-Mktg.--Seibels, Bruce & Co., Columbia, SC; *U.S. Public*, pg. 1454

Kenney, Susan M., Dir.-Mktg.--Agency Specialty Inc., Columbia, SC; *U.S. Public*, pg. 1454

Kenney, Susan M., Dir.-Mktg.--Forest Lake Travel Service, Inc., Columbia, SC; *U.S. Public*, pg. 1454

Kenney, William, Dir.-Sls. & Mktg.--The Kent Manufacturing Co., Pickens, SC; *U.S. Private*, pg. 615

Kenny, Paul, Dir.-Mktg.-Intl. & Coconut--Kraft Food Ingredients Corp., Memphis, TN; *U.S. Public*, pg. 1288

Kenshol, David R., Sr. V.P.-Mktg. & Adv.--HomeBase, Inc., Irvine, CA; *U.S. Public*, pg. 832

Kent, Becky, Mgr.-Mktg.--Mountain Valley Spring Company, Hot Springs National Park, AR; *U.S. Private*, pg. 963

Kent, David, Mgr.-Mktg. Communications--Medrad, Inc., Indianola, PA; *Int'l*, pg. 1204

Kenworthy, Dave, Dir.-Promo., Mktg. & Community Affairs--KMGH-TV, Denver, CO; *U.S. Public*, pg. 1070

Kenyon, Art, V.P.-Sls. & Mktg.--Red Wing Shoe Co., Inc., Red Wing, MN; *U.S. Private*, pg. 915

Kenyon, Jeff, Mgr.-Mktg. Communications--Keithley Test Instrumentation Group, Cleveland, OH; *U.S. Public*, pg. 946

Keowen, Matt, Dir.-Mktg. & Public Rels.--Fujitsu Computer Products of America, Inc., San Jose, CA; *Int'l*, pg. 526

Kepler, Gary, Dir.- Mktg. Svcs.--Sargent & Greenleaf, Inc., Nicholasville, KY; *U.S. Private*, pg. 965
Kerans, Douglas E., V.P.-Mktg.--Radix Wire Company, Cleveland, OH; *U.S. Private*, pg. 907
Kercher, Heidi, Dir.-Mktg.--Vail Associates, Inc., Vail, CO; *U.S. Public*, pg. 1704
Kerezman, Jeffrey, Dir.-Mktg.--Gish Biomedical, Inc., Irvine, CA; *U.S. Public*, pg. 745
Kerezman, Jeffrey, Dir.-Mktg.--Gish International, Inc., Irvine, CA; *U.S. Public*, pg. 745
Kerlee, Martha, Admin. Asst.-Mktg.--Romacorp, Inc., Dallas, TX; *U.S. Public*, pg. 1147
Kerlin, Ken, Mgr.-Mktg.--Kysor/Warren, Conyers, GA; *U.S. Public*, pg. 1445
Kerman, Richard, Exec. V.P.-Mktg.--Steiner Electric Company, Chicago, IL; *U.S. Private*, pg. 1039
Kermode, Larry, Dir.-Mktg.--Little Giant Pump Company, Oklahoma City, OK; *U.S. Public*, pg. 1566
Kern, Kevin, Dir.-Digital Systems Solutions & New Product Devel.--Konica Business Machines USA, Inc., Windsor, CT; *Int'l*, pg. 748
Kern, Michael, Sr. V.P.-Mktg.--Long John Silver's, Inc., Lexington, KY; *U.S. Private*, pg. 674
Kern, Richard C., Mgr.-Sls. & Mktg.--Kern Industries, City of Industry, CA; *U.S. Private*, pg. 616
Kerns, Ed, V.P.-Sls. & Mktg.-Plumbing Prods. Div.--Reading Tube Corp., Reading, PA; *U.S. Private*, pg. 202
Kerr, Carolyn, Mgr.-Mktg. Communications--Philips Lighting, Somerset, NJ; *Int'l*, pg. 1055
Kerr, Elsa, Dir.-Mktg.--Stow Davis Furniture Co., Kentwood, MI; *U.S. Private*, pg. 1038
Kerr, Mary Ann, Dir.-Mktg.--US SerVis, West Orange, NJ; *U.S. Public*, pg. 1687
Kerr, Virginia, Asst.-Mktg.--CNBC, Fort Lee, NJ; *U.S. Public*, pg. 712
Kershaw, Doug, Mgr.-Mktg. Services--Dayco Products Inc., Miamisburg, OH; *U.S. Public*, pg. 1045
Kershaw, Peter, V.P.-Sls. & Mktg.--Tenax Corporation, Danbury, CT; *Int'l*, pg. 193
Kerstein, David, Exec. V.P.-Retail & Mktg.--Old Kent Bank, Grand Rapids, MI; *U.S. Public*, pg. 1216
Kersting, Hermann, Mgr.-Mktg.--KM-Europa Metal Aktiengesellschaft, Osnabruck, Germany; *Int'l*, pg. 719
Kersting, Kurt, V.P.-Sls. & Mktg.--Duro-Test Corporation, Fairfield, NJ; *U.S. Private*, pg. 349
Kersting, Kurt, V.P.-Sls. & Mktg.--Duro-Test Intl. Corp., Fairfield, NJ; *U.S. Private*, pg. 349
Kessler, Eric, Sr. V.P.-Mktg.--HBO Video, Inc., New York, NY; *U.S. Public*, pg. 1612
Kessler, Lance E., Sr. V.P.-Mktg.--Keystone Financial Inc., Harrisburg, PA; *U.S. Public*, pg. 956
Kessler, Thomas, Dir.-Mktg.--Hilton International (Switzerland) AG, Basel, Switzerland; *Int'l*, pg. 788
Kesterson, Danny, Exec. V.P.-Sls. & Mktg.--Kesterson Food Company, Inc., Paris, TN; *U.S. Private*, pg. 616
Ketter, Phillip, Dir.-Mktg. Services--Regal Ware, Inc., Kewaskum, WI; *U.S. Private*, pg. 917
Kettwig, Kay A., Mgr.-Corp. Commun.--Osmonics, Inc., Minnetonka, MN; *U.S. Public*, pg. 1233
Key, James A., V.P.-Mktg. Services--Continental Conveyor & Equipment Company, Winfield, AL; *U.S. Private*, pg. 791
Keyes, Cathleen J., Sr. V.P.-Mktg.--National Bank of Alaska, Anchorage, AK; *U.S. Public*, pg. 1153
Keyes, Greg, V.P.-Mktg.-Southern Living--Southern Progress Corporation, Birmingham, AL; *U.S. Public*, pg. 1612
Keyes, Joe, Dir.-Retail Sls.--Parks LLC, Baltimore, MD; *U.S. Private*, pg. 840
Keyes, L. Shawn, Dir.-Mktg. & Adv.--Mohawk Commercial Carpet, Atlanta, GA; *U.S. Public*, pg. 1121
Keysor, David, V.P.-Sls. & Mktg.--Prime Matrix Wireless Communications, Calabasas, CA; *U.S. Private*, pg. 884
Khawaja, Shahid Waheed, Sr. Mgr.-Supply--National Refinery Limited, Karachi, Pakistan; *Int'l*, pg. 909
Khoury, Patrick, Gen. Mgr.-Mktg. & Sls.-The Americas--Asiana Airlines, Los Angeles, CA; *U.S. Private*, pg. 89
Khwaja, I.H., Dir.-Mktg.--Coats Pakistan Limited, Karachi, Pakistan; *Int'l*, pg. 300
Kiarashi, Sonia, Dir.-Mktg. & Sls.--Newcom, Inc., Westlake Village, CA; *U.S. Public*, pg. 147
Kicklighter, Frank, Mgr.-Mkt.-Wood--Troy Corporation, Florham Park, NJ; *U.S. Private*, pg. 1105
Kida, Haruo, Sr. Mng. Dir.-Sls., Mktg. & Prod. Devel.--Nisshin Steel Co., Ltd., Tokyo, Japan; *Int'l*, pg. 946
Kidder, Brian, Dir.-Pub. Rels.--Allright Corporation, Houston, TX; *U.S. Private*, pg. 42
Kiebler, Ed, Mgr.-Automotive Mktg.--Sunnen Products Company, Saint Louis, MO; *U.S. Private*, pg. 1053
Kiefer, Cindy, Dir.-Mktg.--Idea Man, Inc., Los Angeles, CA; *U.S. Private*, pg. 557
Kiehl, J. L., V.P.-Mktg. & Sls.--Carlisle Tire & Wheel Company, Aiken, SC; *U.S. Public*, pg. 305
Kiel, Bob, Dir.-Mktg.-Bostonian--Clarks Cos. N.A., Newton, MA; *Int'l*, pg. 297
Kiel, Bob, Dir.-Mktg.--Bostonian Shoe Co., Newton, MA; *Int'l*, pg. 297
Kiernan, Paul E., Dir.-Corp. Mktg.--Thermo Fibertek, Inc., Waltham, MA; *U.S. Public*, pg. 1593
Kierszenbaum, Martin, Sr. Dir.-Intl. Mktg.--A&M Records, Hollywood, CA; *Int'l*, pg. 1052
Kieves, Ronald S., V.P.-Mktg.--Transmedia Network Inc., Miami, FL; *U.S. Public*, pg. 1631
Kiey, Maura, V.P.-Strategic Plng. & Devel.--Warren Gorham Lamont, New York, NY; *U.S. Public*, pg. 1602
Kiezits, Hermann, Mgr.-Mktg. Communications--Shell Nederland Verkoop MIJ B.V., Rotterdam, Netherlands; *Int'l*, pg. 1135
Kihlblom, Gunnar, Mgr.-Mktg.--Ahlens AB, Stockholm, Sweden; *Int'l*, pg. 708
Kiker, Vickie, Dir.-Mktg. Communications--CEM Corporation, Matthews, NC; *U.S. Public*, pg. 277
Kilbane, Paul, V.P.-Mktg.--E.T. Browne Drug Co., Inc., Englewood Cliffs, NJ; *U.S. Private*, pg. 175
Kilcollins, Raymond, Mgr.-Mktg.--Maine Potato Growers, Inc., Presque Isle, ME; *U.S. Private*, pg. 697
Kilcoyne, Raymond, V.P.-Foodservice Sls. & Mktg.--Cains Foods, L.P., Ayer, MA; *U.S. Private*, pg. 199
Kiley, Thomas M., V.P.-Mktg. & Bus. Devel.--Victaulic Company of America, Easton, PA; *U.S. Private*, pg. 1138
Kilfoyle, Shawn, Mgr.-Mktg.--Baldwin Graphic Systems, Inc., Shelton, CT; *U.S. Public*, pg. 170
Kilgannon, Susan B., V.P.-Mktg. & Commun.--URS Corporation, San Francisco, CA; *U.S. Public*, pg. 1655
Kilgannon, Susan B., V.P.-Mktg. & Commun.--URS Greiner, New York, NY; *U.S. Public*, pg. 1659
Kilgore, J. Thomas, Jr., Gen. Mgr.-Mktg.--Gulf Power Company, Pensacola, FL; *U.S. Public*, pg. 1490
Killarney, Rebecca, Dir.-Mktg.--Blimpie International, Inc., Atlanta, GA; *U.S. Public*, pg. 236
Killarney, Rebecca D., V.P.-Mktg.--Blimpie International, Inc., Atlanta, GA; *U.S. Public*, pg. 236
Killiam, Greg, Gas Supply Rep.--Enogex Inc., Oklahoma City, OK; *U.S. Public*, pg. 1207
Killian, James, Dir.-Mktg.--S L C Graphics, LP, Pittston, PA; *U.S. Private*, pg. 955
Killian, Jim, V.P.-Intl. Opers.--Telex Communications, Inc., Minneapolis, MN; *U.S. Private*, pg. 1074
Killingsworth, Deborah, V.P.-Sls. & Mktg.--Total System Services, Inc., Columbus, GA; *U.S. Public*, pg. 1550
Killion, Larry D., V.P.-Mktg. & Bus. Devel.--BHP Petroleum Ltd., London, United Kingdom; *Int'l*, pg. 225
Killoren, Jack K., Sr. V.P.-Mktg.--Sterling Electronics Corporation, Houston, TX; *U.S. Public*, pg. 1051
Killoy, Christopher J., Dir.-Comml. Sls.--Smith & Wesson Corp., Springfield, MA; *Int'l*, pg. 1397
Killus, Linell, V.P.-Mktg. Services--Jenny Craig, Inc., La Jolla, CA; *U.S. Public*, pg. 926
Kilpatrick, Allen, V.P.-Mktg. & Sls.--Atomic Energy of Canada Ltd., Mississauga, Canada; *Int'l*, pg. 97
Kim, Alexis S., Mgr.-Project--UHP Healthcare, Inglewood, CA; *U.S. Private*, pg. 1113
Kim, Bong-Young, Dir.-Mktg. Communication--Grand Hyatt Seoul, Seoul, Korea; *U.S. Private*, pg. 551
Kim, Heung-Sik, Mgr.--Ssangyong Heavy Industries Co., Ltd., Seoul, Korea; *Int'l*, pg. 1292
Kim, Hyun S., Dir.-Mktg.--Crown Confectionery Co., Ltd., Seoul, Korea; *Int'l*, pg. 348
Kim, Jae-Hong, Mgr.--Ssangyong Investment & Securities Co., Ltd., Seoul, Korea; *Int'l*, pg. 1292
Kim, Jeong-Yoon, Mgr.--Dongseong Express Tourists Co., Ltd., Busan, Korea; *Int'l*, pg. 1292
Kim, Joong-Soo, Mgr.--Ssangyong Engineering Co., Ltd., Seoul, Korea; *Int'l*, pg. 1292
Kim, Jung Yoon, Mktg. & Research Dir.--SangAm Communications Co., Ltd., Seoul, Korea; *U.S. Public*, pg. 765
Kim, Mary, Dir.-Mktg.--Parents Magazine, New York, NY; *Int'l*, pg. 191
Kim, Myung-Roung, Mgr.--Ssangyong Heavy Industries Co., Ltd., Seoul, Korea; *Int'l*, pg. 1292
Kim, N.H., Dir.-Mktg.--Daewoo International America Corp. - New York, New York, NY; *Int'l*, pg. 357
Kim, Sang-Kyo, Mgr.--Ssangyong Oil Refining Co. Ltd., Seoul, Korea; *Int'l*, pg. 1292
Kim, Yong T., Dir.-Mktg.--NURI Enterprise, Seoul, Korea; *Int'l*, pg. 348
Kim, Young-Bok, Mgr.--Ssangyong Cement Industrial Co., Ltd., Seoul, Korea; *Int'l*, pg. 1291
Kim, Young-Soo, Mgr.-Mktg.--Ssangyong Engineering & Construction (America), Inc., Garden Grove, CA; *Int'l*, pg. 1292
Kimball, Debbie, Mgr.-Mktg--Columbia Paint & Coatings, Spokane, WA; *U.S. Private*, pg. 256
Kimball, Deborah, Dir.-Database Mktg.--Toys "R" Us, Inc., Paramus, NJ; *U.S. Public*, pg. 1626
Kimball, Douglas, V.P.-Oil Equip. & Related Services--Eaton Metal Products Company, Denver, CO; *U.S. Private*, pg. 358
Kimball, Jack, V.P.-Mktg.--Advance Circuits, Inc., Minnetonka, MN; *Int'l*, pg. 713
Kimball, John R., Sr. V.P.-Mktg.--L. Robert Kimball & Associates, Ebensburg, PA; *U.S. Private*, pg. 619
Kimbell, Alan R., V.P.-Mktg.--IWC Resources Corporation, Indianapolis, IN; *U.S. Public*, pg. 1185
Kimmet, Gary, V.P.-Opers./Americas--The Gleason Works, Rochester, NY; *U.S. Public*, pg. 746
Kimpton, Greg, Mgr.-Intl.--Projects Unlimited, Inc., Dayton, OH; *U.S. Private*, pg. 890
Kimura, Shinji, Mktg. Dir.--Meitsu Inc., Tokyo, Japan; *Int'l*, pg. 856
Kimura, Yaichi, Dir. & Gen. Mgr.--Cosmo Oil Co., Ltd., Tokyo, Japan; *Int'l*, pg. 335
Kincade, John, Dir.-Mktg.--Circus Circus - Las Vegas, Las Vegas, NV; *U.S. Public*, pg. 374
Kincaid, David, V.P.-Mktg.-LBOC--Labatt Breweries of Canada, Toronto, Canada; *Int'l*, pg. 679
Kincl, James A., V.P.-Salary Savings--National Western Life Insurance Company, Austin, TX; *U.S. Public*, pg. 1161
Kinder, Glen, Dir.-Gas Mktg.--Transamerican Natural Gas Corporation, Houston, TX; *U.S. Private*, pg. 1096
Kinderdick, Don, V.P.-Mktg. & Prod. Devel.--Sterner Lighting Systems Incorporated, Eden Prairie, MN; *U.S. Private*, pg. 1042
Kindlund, Newton C., Chm. Bd., Pres., Chief Exec. & Chief Oper. Officer--Holiday RV Superstores, Inc., Orlando, FL; *U.S. Public*, pg. 829
King, Ann, Dir.-Mktg.--Weichert Realty, Inc., Alexandria, VA; *U.S. Private*, pg. 1159
King, Becky, Sr. Mktg. Communications Specialist--Aurora Pump, North Aurora, IL; *U.S. Public*, pg. 726
King, David, Mgr.-Mktg.--British Steel Tubes & Pipes, Corby, United Kingdom; *Int'l*, pg. 221
King, George, Mgr.-Sls. & Mktg.--Automatic Machine Products Company, Attleboro, MA; *U.S. Private*, pg. 101
King, H. Alan, V.P.-Sls. & Mktg.--Rogers Tool Works, Inc., Rogers, AR; *U.S. Public*, pg. 950
King, James D., V.P.-Sls. & Mktg.--Consumer Products Company, Muncie, IN; *U.S. Public*, pg. 56
King, Jim, Mgr.-Mktg.--Networks and Peripherals Ltd., Huntingdon, United Kingdom; *Int'l*, pg. 645
King, Joe, V.P.-Sls. & Mktg.--American Sightseeing International, San Francisco, CA; *U.S. Private*, pg. 61
King, Joe, V.P.-Sls. & Mktg.--Carmun International, San Antonio, TX; *Int'l*, pg. 646
King, Joe, V.P.-Mktg.--PTS Electronics Corporation, Bloomington, IN; *U.S. Private*, pg. 828
King, John, Dir.-Mktg.--Perkins Family Restaurants, Memphis, TN; *U.S. Private*, pg. 925
King, Kathleen, Mgr.-Mktg.--Southern Union Company, Austin, TX; *U.S. Public*, pg. 1491
King, Larry, V.P.-Sls. & Mktg.--Ryan Herco Products Corp., Burbank, CA; *U.S. Private*, pg. 953
King, Marc, Dir.-Mktg., Taylor Made--Salomon S.A., Annecy, France; *Int'l*, pg. 1181
King, Mark A., V.P.-Sls. & Mktg.--Voyager Emblems, Inc., Sanborn, NY; *U.S. Private*, pg. 1143
King, Maureen, Dir.-Mktg.--Bruce Hardwood Floors, Dallas, TX; *U.S. Public*, pg. 1634
King, Neal, V.P.-Grp. Sls. & Mktg.--Standard Insurance Co., Portland, OR; *U.S. Private*, pg. 1031
King, Ralph, Mgr.-Mktg.--Eaton Corporation Commercial Controls Division, Selma, NC; *U.S. Public*, pg. 556
King, Regina, Mgr.-Mktg. Communications--Ohmeda, Inc., Liberty Corner, NJ; *Int'l*, pg. 121
King, Roger, V.P.-Sls. & Mktg.--Software Spectrum, Inc., Garland, TX; *U.S. Public*, pg. 1483
Kingeter, Cathy, Dir.-Mktg.--InterVoice, Inc., Dallas, TX; *U.S. Public*, pg. 910
Kingham, E.E., Dir.-Mktg.--Convenience Plus Partners Ltd., Denver, CO; *U.S. Private*, pg. 271
Kingrey, Connie, Mgr.-Special Mktg.--Catholic Digest, Saint Paul, MN; *U.S. Private*, pg. 220
Kingsbry, Liz, Grp. Mgr.- Commun.--AMEC Plc, Northwich, United Kingdom; *Int'l*, pg. 16
Kingsbury, Bean, Mgr.-Mktg.--Riddell Sports, Inc., New York, NY; *U.S. Public*, pg. 1389
Kingsmill, I.P., Mgr.-Mktg.--MidCon Texas Pipeline Operator, Inc., Houston, TX; *U.S. Public*, pg. 1210
Kingston, Eric, Dir.-Mktg.--Standard Industries, Inc., Salt Lake City, UT; *U.S. Private*, pg. 1031
Kinkler, Linda, V.P.-Adv. & Mktg. Services--WestPoint Stevens Inc., West Point, GA; *U.S. Public*, pg. 1762
Kinnaird, Don, V.P. & Mgr.-Mktg.--Union Bank of California, San Francisco, CA; *Int'l*, pg. 157
Kinnamon, B., Dir.-Mktg.-Consumer Tires-North America--The Goodyear Tire & Rubber Company, Akron, OH; *U.S. Public*, pg. 752
Kinnemann, Mark, Mgr.-Mktg.--Ingersoll Cutting Tool Co., Rockford, IL; *U.S. Private*, pg. 562
Kinney, Edward, V.P.-Mktg.--Klaussner Furniture Industry, Asheboro, NC; *U.S. Private*, pg. 625
Kinney, Richard, Exec. V.P.--All-Phase Electric Supply Co., Benton Harbor, MI; *U.S. Private*, pg. 35
Kinning, Rick L., Pres. & Treas.--RK Mechanical, Inc., Denver, CO; *U.S. Private*, pg. 904
Kinning, Ronald L., Chm. Bd. & Chief Exec. Officer--RK Mechanical, Inc., Denver, CO; *U.S. Private*, pg. 904
Kinnison, Jerome W., V.P.-Color/Mktg.--Universal Foods Corporation, Milwaukee, WI; *U.S. Public*, pg. 1695
Kinsey, Jo, V.P.-Sls.--First Commerce Bancshares, Inc., Lincoln, NE; *U.S. Public*, pg. 629
Kinsman, Mike, Dir.-Sls. & Mktg.--Cal-Air Inc., Whittier, CA; *U.S. Private*, pg. 199
Kintz, Steve, Dir.-Coffee Mktg.--Melitta U.S.A., Inc., Clearwater, FL; *Int'l*, pg. 857
Kinzelberg, Chad, V.P.-Mktg.--Caere Corporation, Los Gatos, CA; *U.S. Public*, pg. 291
Kipisz, Pat, Dir.-Mktg.--ASICS Tiger Corporation, Fountain Valley, CA; *U.S. Private*, pg. 89
Kippen, John, Sr. V.P.-Mktg.& Sls.--Plano Molding Co., Plano, IL; *U.S. Private*, pg. 869
Kirby, Alice, Dir.-Mktg.--Chi-Chi's Inc., Louisville, KY; *U.S. Private*, pg. 393
Kirby, Carol, Exec. V.P.-Mktg.--Motel 6 Operating L.P., Dallas, TX; *Int'l*, pg. 21
Kirby, Jim, Dir.-Adv. & Mktg.--NHD Hardware, Stoughton, MA; *U.S. Private*, pg. 3
Kirby, Mike, V.P.-Mktg.--Magline, Inc., Pinconning, MI; *U.S. Private*, pg. 695
Kirby, Paul, V.P.-Sls.& Mktg.--Hodgson Mill, Inc., Gainesville, MO; *U.S. Private*, pg. 998
Kirchhoff, Lars, Reg. Mgr.-Mktg.--Precision Standard, Inc., Denver, CO; *U.S. Public*, pg. 1321
Kirchner, Steven A., V.P.-Mktg.--Valvoline Company, Lexington, KY; *U.S. Public*, pg. 139
Kirk, Brad, Sr. V.P.-Mktg.--20th Century Fox Home Entertainment, Los Angeles, CA; *U.S. Public*, pg. 275
Kirk, Brad, Sr. V.P.-Mktg.--20th Century Fox Home Entertainment, Los Angeles, CA; *Int'l*, pg. 926
Kirk, C. Scott, V.P.-Natural Gas Mktg.--The Louisiana Land and Exploration Company, New Orleans, LA; *U.S. Public*, pg. 269
Kirk, Doug, Dir.-Business Devel.-North America--Rogerson Aircraft Corporation, Irvine, CA; *U.S. Private*, pg. 940
Kirk, S.D., Dir.-Comml.--Inco Alloys International, Inc., Huntington, WV; *Int'l*, pg. 672
Kirkelie, Susan, Dir.-Mktg. Programs--Southwest Airlines Co., Dallas, TX; *U.S. Public*, pg. 1493
Kirkland, Bob, Dir.-Mktg.--Bergen Brunswig Corporation, Orange, CA; *U.S. Public*, pg. 213
Kirkland, Linda, Dir.-Mktg.--Florida Medical Center South, Fort Lauderdale, FL; *U.S. Public*, pg. 1577
Kirkman, Paul, Exec. V.P.-Mktg. & Sls.--Beverage Canners International Corp., Miami, FL; *U.S. Private*, pg. 106
Kirkman, Paul, Mgr.-Mktg.--Naturalle Springs, Inc., Greeneville, TN; *U.S. Private*, pg. 106
Kirkowski, Michael, Exec. V.P.--Condor D.C. Power Supplies Inc., Oxnard, CA; *U.S. Public*, pg. 1419
Kirkpatrick, Raymond, Dir.-Mktg.--Hewlett Packard Product Division, Louisville, OH; *U.S. Public*, pg. 816

Kirkwood, Ronn, V.P. & Mktg. Res. Dir.--Cramer-Krasselt, Milwaukee, WI; *U.S. Private*, pg. 286
Kirman, Ivor, Mktg. Dir.--Inco Europe Limited, London, United Kingdom; *Int'l*, pg. 673
Kirpalani, John, V.P.-Mktg. & Sls.--Andrew Sports Club Inc., Secaucus, NJ; *U.S. Private*, pg. 73
Kirsch, Gary, Mgr.-Mktg.-Pressure Control--Hydril Company, Houston, TX; *U.S. Private*, pg. 551
Kirsch, Michael, V.P.-Mktg.--GoodTimes Entertainment Co., New York, NY; *U.S. Private*, pg. 464
Kirschgasler, Wayne, Dir.-Mktg. & Creative Services--Merrill Corporation, Saint Paul, MN; *U.S. Public*, pg. 1097
Kirshner, Hal, Pres., Chief Oper. Officer, V.P. & Acting Dir.-Mktg.--LORAD Corporation, Danbury, CT; *U.S. Public*, pg. 1595
Kirson, Mary W., Mgr.-Large Markets--PP&L Resources, Allentown, PA; *U.S. Public*, pg. 1244
Kish, Martin A., V.P.-Pub. Rels.--Valvoline Company, Lexington, KY; *U.S. Public*, pg. 139
Kish, Rich, Mgr.-Mktg.--Stein Inc., Sandusky, OH; *Int'l*, pg. 13
Kislevitz, David, Mng. Dir.-Sls.--Colorforms, Ramsey, NJ; *U.S. Public*, pg. 1625
Kislowski, Laura, V.P.-Mktg. & Managed Care--Paragon Health Network, Inc., Atlanta, GA; *U.S. Public*, pg. 1256
Kissela, G., Dir.-Mktg. Services--Mercury Marine, Fond Du Lac, WI; *U.S. Public*, pg. 265
Kissling, Mark, Plant Mgr.--A.C. Kissling, Inc., Philadelphia, PA; *U.S. Private*, pg. 624
Kitchen, Douglas O., Partner-Futures--J.C. Bradford & Co., Nashville, TN; *U.S. Private*, pg. 163
Kitchener, C., Mgr.-Mktg.--London International Group plc, London, United Kingdom; *Int'l*, pg. 815
Kitching, Andrew, Dir. Mktg./Dir. Response--Mirror Group plc, London, United Kingdom; *Int'l*, pg. 869
Kittleson, John G., Sec.--Bituminous Roadways, Inc., Inver Grove Heights, MN; *U.S. Private*, pg. 146
Kivits, Herman, Mgr.-Mktg. Communications--Royal Dutch/Shell Group of Companies, Hague, Netherlands; *Int'l*, pg. 1135
Kizer, C., Mgr.-Prod. Sls.--Gemtron Corporation, Sweetwater, TN; *Int'l*, pg. 1523
Kizielewicz, James, V.P.-Corp. Mktg.--Kronos Incorporated, Waltham, MA; *U.S. Public*, pg. 967
Kjellberg, Bengt, Mgr.-Mktg.--Interspiro Inc., Branford, CT; *Int'l*, pg. 1289
Kjellerup, Douglas L., V.P.-Mktg. & Devel.--Otter Tail Power Company, Fergus Falls, MN; *U.S. Public*, pg. 1234
Kjelmyr, John P., Mgr.-Oil & Gas Mktg.--Forest Oil Corporation, Denver, CO; *U.S. Public*, pg. 670
Klanac, Mike, Dir.-Sls. & Mktg.--Red Wings Inc., Fredonia, NY; *Int'l*, pg. 1398
Klanec, Mike, V.P.-Mktg.--Red Wings Inc., Fredonia, NY; *Int'l*, pg. 1398
Klapp, Bill, Mgr.-Training & Mktg. Communications--Verson Division, Chicago, IL; *U.S. Public*, pg. 48
Klass, Joe, Mgr.-Adv., Sls. & Mktg.-Plastics & Industrial--Raven Industries, Inc., Sioux Falls, SD; *U.S. Public*, pg. 1361
Klatt, David, V.P. & Gen. Mgr.-Consumer Power Tools--The Black & Decker Corporation, Towson, MD; *U.S. Public*, pg. 233
Klaus, Mike, Dir.-Direct Mktg.--North Shore Movers, Northbrook, IL; *U.S. Private*, pg. 805
Klaus, Walt, Mgr.-Mktg. Services--Giddings & Lewis, Inc., Fond Du Lac, WI; *Int'l*, pg. 1389
Klausing, Don, V.P.-Mktg.--I & K Distributors, Inc., Delphos, OH; *U.S. Private*, pg. 552
Klausing, Trisha, Dir.-Mktg. & Sls.--The Commercial Bank, Delphos, OH; *U.S. Public*, pg. 410
Klebanow, Andrew, V.P.-Mktg.--Santa Fe Gaming Corporation, Las Vegas, NV; *U.S. Public*, pg. 1432
Klee, Gary, Dir.-Mktg.--Noteworthy Industries Inc., Amsterdam, NY; *U.S. Private*, pg. 808
Kleger, Karen, V.P. & Mktg. Consulting--Mediaspot, Inc., Corona Del Mar, CA; *U.S. Private*, pg. 727
Kleiman, Bruce, V.P.-Mdsg. & Mktg.--A&E Stores, Inc., Teterboro, NJ; *U.S. Private*, pg. 1
Klein, Dick, Mgr.-Mktg. Programs--InterVoice, Inc., Dallas, TX; *U.S. Public*, pg. 910
Klein, Hemjoe, Dir.-Mktg.--Deutsche Lufthansa AG, Cologne, Germany; *Int'l*, pg. 407
Klein, Lew, Mgr.-Mktg. Communications--Paslode, Vernon Hills, IL; *U.S. Public*, pg. 867
Klein, Marlene, Coord.-Mktg. Projects--Enthone-OMI, Inc., West Haven, CT; *U.S. Public*, pg. 138
Kleinberg, Brian, Sr. V.P.-Mktg. & Business Devel.--American Express Company, New York, NY; *U.S. Public*, *pg. 73*
Kleinberg, Brian, Sr. V.P.-Optima Card Mktg.--American Express Travel Related Services Co., Inc., New York, NY; *U.S. Public*, pg. 73
Kleine, Mike, V.P.-Mktg. & Sls.--Bird Products Corporation, Palm Springs, CA; *U.S. Public*, pg. 1591
Kleinhenz, Allen, Dir.-Mktg.--Cramer Inc., Kansas City, KS; *U.S. Private*, pg. 285
Kleinquetl, Ed, V.P.-Mktg.--Philip Industrial Services Group, Houston, TX; *Int'l*, pg. 1050
Kleman, Wally, V.P.-Mktg.--Berlin Glove Company Ltd., Berlin, WI; *U.S. Private*, pg. 136
Kleman, Wally, V.P.-Mktg.--Mid-Western, Berlin, WI; *U.S. Private*, pg. 136
Klemencic, Joy, V.P.-Corp. Mktg.--Hill's Pet Nutrition, Topeka, KS; *U.S. Public*, pg. 397
Klene, Brian C., Exec. V.P.-Sls. & Mktg.--Micron Electronics, Inc., Nampa, ID; *U.S. Public*, pg. 1105
Klepinger, Lee, V.P.-Trng. & Mktg. Opers.--Wall Data Incorporated, Kirkland, WA; *U.S. Public*, pg. 1734
Klepner, Ron, V.P.-Mktg.-Angelica Image Apparell--Angelica Corporation, Chesterfield, MO; *U.S. Public*, pg. 113
Klepner, Ron, V.P.-Mktg.--Angelica Image Apparel, Saint Louis, MO; *U.S. Public*, pg. 113
Klevatt, Sydney, Sr. V.P.-Mktg.--The Sharper Image, San Francisco, CA; *U.S. Public*, pg. 1464
Klienfelter, John, Dir.-Mktg.--A.N. Deringer, Inc., Saint Albans, VT; *U.S. Private*, pg. 326
Klimm, Robert, Dir.-Mktg., Sls. & Service--Semiconductor Equipment Division, Beverly, MA; *U.S. Public*, pg. 557
Klinc Berg, Pat, Mgr.Mktg.--Sterling, Inc., Milwaukee, WI; *U.S. Private*, pg. 1041
Kline, Tom, Dir.-Mktg.--American Woodmark Corporation, Winchester, VA; *U.S. Public*, pg. 96
Kling, Herman V., Sr. V.P.-Mktg.--International Comfort Products, Franklin, TN; *U.S. Public*, pg. 898
Klinger, Daniel, Dir.-Mktg.--Ceras Johnson Ltda., Rio de Janeiro, Brazil; *U.S. Private*, pg. 593
Klink, Bodo B., V.P.-Mktg.--General Chemical Corporation, Parsippany, NJ; *U.S. Public*, pg. 707
Klipfell, John M., Sr. V.P.-Electronic Mktg.--American Greetings Corporation, Cleveland, OH; *U.S. Public*, pg. 77
Klippgen, Marcus, Mgr.-Mktg.--Blaupunkt-Werke GmbH, Hildesheim, Germany; *Int'l*, pg. 203
Klong, Lawrence A., Pres.--K & R Express Systems Inc., Hinsdale, IL; *U.S. Private*, pg. 602
Kloos, John A., Dir.-Mktg. & Sls.--E.V. Roberts & Associates, Inc., Culver City, CA; *U.S. Private*, pg. 935
Kloster, Dennis, V.P.-Mktg.--Unitary Products Group, York, PA; *U.S. Public*, pg. 1788
Klosterman, Bill, Mktg. & Communications--Crown Equipment Corporation, New Bremen, OH; *U.S. Private*, pg. 292
Klug, Susan, Sr. V.P.-Mktg.--The Vons Companies, Inc., Arcadia, CA; *U.S. Public*, pg. 1426
Klune, Paul, Dir.-Mktg.--Boury Enterprises, Wheeling, WV; *U.S. Private*, pg. 162
Klunp, Bill, V.P.-Mktg. & Retail Deli Sls.--Bil Mar Foods, Inc., Zeeland, MI; *U.S. Public*, pg. 1433
Kluska, John, V.P.-Mktg.--Cyborg Systems, Inc., Chicago, IL; *U.S. Private*, pg. 299
Klustner, Kevin, V.P.-Sls. & Mktg.--WRQ, Inc., Seattle, WA; *U.S. Private*, pg. 1145
Kment, Mike, Dir.-Corp. Mktg.--Lee Enterprises, Incorporated, Davenport, IA; *U.S. Public*, pg. 983
Knapp, Lori, Mgr.-Mktg. Services--Eaton Corporation, Engineered Fasteners Division, Brunswick, OH; *U.S. Public*, pg. 556
Knauff, Rhonda, Exec. Coord.-Retail Mktg.--Jimmy Dean Foods, Cordova, TN; *U.S. Public*, pg. 1433
Knauss, Paul E., V.P.-Mktg. & Opers.--Chrysler Financial Corporation, Southfield, MI; *U.S. Public*, pg. 354
Knaut, John M., Dir.-Mktg. & Sls.--United Receptical, Inc., Pottsville, PA; *U.S. Private*, pg. 1123
Knecht, Mark, V.P.-Mktg. & Bus. Devel.--Landmark Systems Corporation, Vienna, VA; *U.S. Private*, pg. 649
Knecht, Susan, Mgr.-Prof. Svcs.--TransNet Corporation, Somerville, NJ; *U.S. Public*, pg. 1631
Kneip, Dick F., Mgr.-Mktg.--Stahl Specialty Company, Kingsville, MO; *U.S. Private*, pg. 1029
Knibbe, Dave, V.P.-Sls. & Mktg.--Herman Miller, Inc., Zeeland, MI; *U.S. Public*, pg. 1111
Knierman, John, V.P.-Sls. & Mktg.--International Container Systems, Tampa, FL; *Int'l*, pg. 685
Knight, David E., Field Mktg. Services Dir. & Special Events Dir.--CheckMark Communications, Saint Louis, MO; *U.S. Private*, pg. 231
Knight, Ernest, Exec. V.P.-Sls.& Mktg.- Intl.--Miracle Recreation Equipment Company, Monett, MO; *U.S. Private*, pg. 752
Knight, Linda, Sr. V.P.-Mktg.--Foley's, Houston, TX; *U.S. Public*, pg. 1063
Knight, P., V.P.-Mktg.--BookCrafters U.S.A. Inc., Chelsea, MI; *U.S. Public*, pg. 70
Knight, Roger P., Sr. V.P.-North Asia Opers. & Pres.-China--CPC Asia Consumer Foods Division, Hong Kong, Hong Kong; *U.S. Public*, pg. 224
Knight, Tim, V.P.-Mktg.--Sherwin-Williams Diversified Brands, Inc., Solon, OH; *U.S. Public*, pg. 1466
Knightly, John H., Dir.-Corp. Mktg.--Brightware, Inc., Novato, CA; *U.S. Private*, pg. 168
Knipp, Kurt S., Exec. V.P.-Bankcard Services--National City Processing, Inc., Louisville, KY; *U.S. Public*, pg. 1154
Knirsch, Mister, Dir.-Mktg.--Castrol Austria GmbH, Wiener Neustadt, Austria; *Int'l*, pg. 235
Knittel, Mark, V.P.-Mktg.--Computer Network Technology Corporation, Minneapolis, MN; *U.S. Public*, pg. 421
Knizkey, Karen, Dir.-Mktg.--Charter Hospital of Mobile, Inc., Mobile, AL; *U.S. Public*, pg. 1034
Knoeller, Richard, Mgr.-Mktg.--Anaren Microwave Inc., East Syracuse, NY; *U.S. Public*, pg. 110
Knoll, Paul, V.P.-Mktg.--Universal Standard Healthcare, Inc., Southfield, MI; *U.S. Public*, pg. 1697
Knopke, Don, Dir.-Mktg. & Adv.--Contractors Supply Company, Inc., Kansas City, MO; *U.S. Private*, pg. 270
Knorr, Carol, Exec. V.P.-Mktg. & Devel.--GMAC Insurance Holdings, Detroit, MI; *U.S. Public*, pg. 719
Knorr, Carol J., V.P.-Mktg. & Devel.--General Motors Acceptance Corporation (GMAC), Detroit, MI; *U.S. Public*, pg. 719
Knott, Doug, V.P.-Sls. & Mktg.--Brooks Foods, Mount Summit, IN; *U.S. Private*, pg. 887
Knowles, Steve, Dir.-Mktg.--Integral Systems, Inc., Walnut Creek, CA; *Int'l*, pg. 242
Knox, Doug, V.P.-Mktg. & Assoc. Publisher--Tyndale House Publishers, Inc., Carol Stream, IL; *U.S. Private*, pg. 1112
Knox, Jerry, Mgr.-Retail Mktg. Services--Wayne Dalton of Sterling, Sterling, IL; *U.S. Private*, pg. 1155
Knudsen, Jim, V.P.-Mktg.--AEC/Application Automation, Inc., Wood Dale, IL; *U.S. Private*, pg. 1041
Knudsen, Kenneth, V.P.-Mktg.--Bruning Paint Company, Baltimore, MD; *U.S. Private*, pg. 176
Knudsen, Larry, V.P.-Sls. & Mktg.--Camp Healthcare, Jackson, MI; *Int'l*, pg. 1425
Knutson, Gary J., V.P.-Mktg.--Kenan Transport Company, Chapel Hill, NC; *U.S. Public*, pg. 949
Knutzen, Donald L., V.P.-Mktg. Services Div.--General Mills, Inc., Minneapolis, MN; *U.S. Public*, pg. 717
Ko, Jeffrey, Mgr.-Sls. & Mktg.--Superior Metal Printing Limited, Singapore, Singapore; *Int'l*, pg. 1322
Kobat, Randall, Roller Chain Mktg.--U.S. Tsubaki, Inc., Wheeling, IL; *Int'l*, pg. 1425
Kobayashi, Tsuneo, Gen. Mgr.-Grp. Mktg.--Yasuda Mutual Life Insurance Co., Tokyo, Japan; *Int'l*, pg. 1519
Kobel, Andrei, Dir.-Mktg.--Nihon Microtec Research, Tokyo, Japan; *U.S. Public*, pg. 1087
Kobliska, Julie A., V.P.-Mktg. Services--United Family Life Insurance Co., Atlanta, GA; *Int'l*, pg. 499
Kobori, Toshio, Dir.-Mktg.--Minolta Co., Ltd., Osaka, Japan; *Int'l*, pg. 869
Kocemba, John, V.P.-Mktg.--Peerless Carpet Corporation, Acton Vale, Canada; *Int'l*, pg. 1032
Koch, Bud, Mgr.-Mktg.--Radius Inc., Sunnyvale, CA; *U.S. Public*, pg. 1358
Koch, Glenn, Exec. V.P.--New Era Cap. Co., Derby, NY; *U.S. Private*, pg. 793
Koch, Ingo, Dir.-Mktg.--McBee Systems, Inc., Parsippany, NJ; *U.S. Private*, pg. 718
Koch, Jeremy, V.P.--People, New York, NY; *U.S. Public*, pg. 1613
Koch, John, V.P.-Prod. Mktg.--360 Degrees Communications Company, Chicago, IL; *U.S. Public*, pg. 1607
Koch, Stevan, Dir.-Mktg. & Sls.--General Motors do Brasil Ltda., Sao Caetano do Sul, Brazil; *U.S. Public*, pg. 722
Koch, Susan, Sr. V.P. & Dir.-Mktg.--Whitney Holding Corporation, New Orleans, LA; *U.S. Public*, pg. 1766
Koch, Susan, Sr. V.P. & Dir.--Whitney National Bank, New Orleans, LA; *U.S. Public*, pg. 1766
Koch, Tim, Mgr.-Mktg.-Consumer Prods.--Wagner Spray Tech Corp., Plymouth, MN; *U.S. Private*, pg. 1146
Koch, Uwe, Dir.-Mktg.--Schiess Moweg GmbH, Monchengladbach, Germany; *Int'l*, pg. 860
Koch, Walter, Pres. & Gen. Mgr.--Nestle Del Uruguay S.A., Montevideo, Uruguay; *Int'l*, pg. 921
Kochanski, John A., V.P.-Mktg. & Sls.--Pegasus International Corporation, Pennington, NJ; *U.S. Private*, pg. 1046
Kochi, Susumu, Mng. Dir.-Mktg. Div.--Dentsu Inc., Tokyo, Japan; *Int'l*, pg. 392
Kocon, Richard, V.P.-Mktg. & Adv.--Iams Company, Dayton, OH; *U.S. Private*, pg. 556
Kocsis, Maria, Dir.-Mktg.--Budapest Marriott Hotel, Budapest, Hungary; *Int'l*, pg. 232
Koehler, Eric W., V.P.-Mktg.--Bowles Fluidics Corporation, Columbia, MD; *U.S. Public*, pg. 248
Koehler, Karen, Mktg. Asst.--Cerberus Pyrotronics Inc., Cedar Knolls, NJ; *Int'l*, pg. 1246
Koehler, Steve, Mgr.-Mktg./Aerospace--MRC Bearings, Jamestown, NY; *Int'l*, pg. 1157
Koeller, Fred, V.P.-Mktg.--Andis Company, Sturtevant, WI; *U.S. Private*, pg. 73
Koelman, K., Mktg. Dir.--Clorox Professional Products Company, Oakland, CA; *U.S. Public*, pg. 387
Koeneman, Bradford W., Exec. V.P.-Investor Rels. & Mktg.--Magna Group, Inc., Saint Louis, MO; *U.S. Public*, pg. 1037
Koenig, Carol, Mgr.-Mktg.-Healthcare--Aladdin Synergetics, Inc., Nashville, TN; *U.S. Private*, pg. 31
Koenitzer, Jay G., V.P.-Mktg.--Helwig Carbon Products, Inc., Milwaukee, WI; *U.S. Private*, pg. 521
Koep, Steve, Dir.-Mktg. Services--Ag-Chem Equipment Co., Inc., Minnetonka, MN; *U.S. Public*, pg. 6
Koester, Jerry, Mng. Dir.-UADA Groups--PRO Group, Inc., Englewood, CO; *U.S. Private*, pg. 887
Koetje, Mark, V.P.-Sls. & Mktg.--Prime Technology, Inc., Grand Rapids, MI; *U.S. Private*, pg. 884
Kogod, Dennis L., V.P.-Sls. & Mktg.--Pilling Weck, Research Triangle Park, NC; *U.S. Public*, pg. 1569
Kohler, Liz, Mgr.-Mktg.--The O'Boise Corporation, Oak Brook, IL; *U.S. Private*, pg. 810
Kohley, Bill, Specialist-Mktg.--Spraying Systems Co., Wheaton, IL; *U.S. Private*, pg. 1026
Kohlmeier, Dave, V.P.-Mktg.--Data I/O Corporation, Redmond, WA; *U.S. Public*, pg. 486
Kohls, Kris, Exec. V.P.-Strategic Devel.--Dart Transit Company, Eagan, MN; *U.S. Private*, pg. 311
Kohn, Randolph L., V.P. & Dir.-Mktg.--Western Asset Management, Pasadena, CA; *U.S. Public*, pg. 985
Kohnstamm, Abby F., V.P.-Corp. Mktg.--International Business Machines Corporation, Armonk, NY; *U.S. Public*, pg. 895
Kohrs, Sherry, Dir.-Media & Mktg.--CPI Corp., Saint Louis, MO; *U.S. Public*, pg. 283
Kojima, Kazuto, Dir.-Mktg.--Fujitsu Limited, Tokyo, Japan; *Int'l*, pg. 525
Kok, Gary, Mgr.-Mktg.--Schumann Sasol (South Africa) Pty Ltd., Sasolburg, South Africa; *Int'l*, pg. 1197
Koksal, Jeff, Mgr.-Sls. & Mktg.--Diamond Power Specialty Co., Lancaster, OH; *U.S. Public*, pg. 1068
Kola, Laura Jean, Asst. Mktg.--Lender's Bagel Bakery, White Plains, NY; *U.S. Public*, pg. 1288
Kolb, David, Mgr.-Mktg.--Lightcraft, Jeannette, PA; *U.S. Private*, pg. 749
Kolb, James D., V.P.-Mktg.--EMCOR Group, Inc., Norwalk, CT; *U.S. Public*, pg. 571
Kolkebeck, W. Charles, V.P.-Mktg. & Sls.--Nuttall Gear Corporation, Niagara Falls, NY; *U.S. Private*, pg. 809
Koll, Leslie A., Sr. V.P.-Mktg.--Jenny Craig, Inc., La Jolla, CA; *U.S. Public*, pg. 926
Kollmeyer, Julie, Supvr.-Mktg. Commun.--Modernfold, Inc., New Castle, IN; *U.S. Private*, pg. 755
Kolter, William C., V.P.-Mktg.--Biomet, Inc., Warsaw, IN; *U.S. Public*, pg. 231
Komar, John, Mgr.-Mktg. Communications--In-Sink-Erator, Racine, WI; *U.S. Public*, pg. 573
Komar, Michael J., Mgr.-Mktg. Serv.--Thermo King Corporation, Minneapolis, MN; *U.S. Public*, pg. 877
Komline, Christopher L., V.P. & Dir.-Mktg--Komline-Sanderson Engineering Corp., Peapack, NJ; *U.S. Private*, *pg. 631*

Komoroski, Gourael, V.P.-Mktg.--OzEmail Limited, Sydney, Australia; *Int'l*, pg. 1019
Komschlies, Andrea, Dir.-Mktg.--Witcher Construction Co., Minneapolis, MN; *U.S. Private*, pg. 1185
Kon, Mitchell, V.P.-Mktg.--Elmer's Products, Inc., Columbus, OH; *U.S. Private*, pg. 158
Konczakowski, Peter, Sr. V.P.-Mktg.--National City Bank, Pennsylvania, Pittsburgh, PA; *U.S. Public*, pg. 1154
Koniuszek, Willem, Intl. Mktg. Mgr.--Inamed B.V., Breda, Netherlands; *U.S. Public*, pg. 874
Konowich, Abbey, Exec. V.P.-Mktg.--MCA Records, Inc., Universal City, CA; *Int'l*, pg. 1215
Konowitz, Thomas J., Sr. V.P.-Mktg.--New Jersey Natural Gas Co., Wall, NJ; *U.S. Public*, pg. 1172
Konyk, Beth, Dir.-Mktg.--Bayer Corporation, Pittsburgh, PA; *Int'l*, pg. 172
Koontz, Dave, V.P.-Mktg.--American Tourister, Inc., Warren, RI; *U.S. Public*, pg. 1430
Koop, Brian, Mgr.-Sls./Camera Division--Photo Control Corporation, Minneapolis, MN; *U.S. Public*, pg. 1292
Koos, Jeff, Mktg. Communications Admin.--Star Building Systems, Oklahoma City, OK; *U.S. Public*, pg. 1394
Kopacz, Bernadette, V.P.-Mktg.--Sea World of Texas, San Antonio, TX; *U.S. Public*, pg. 114
Kopchik, John, V.P.-Market Plng.--Northwest Airlines, Inc., Saint Paul, MN; *U.S. Public*, pg. 1200
Kopf, Jack, Dir.-Mktg. Services--Schering-Plough Animal Health, Union, NJ; *U.S. Public*, pg. 1438
Kopko, Wally, Sr. Dir.-Sls. & Mktg.-Home Impressions--HMI Industries, Cleveland, OH; *U.S. Public*, pg. 771
Kopp, Jurgen, Mgr.-Mktg.--KONE Aufzug GmbH, Hannover, Germany; *Int'l*, pg. 747
Kopp, Ken, V.P.-Mktg. Plus--Western Motivational Incentives Group, Inc., Los Angeles, CA; *U.S. Private*, pg. 1167
Kopp, Larry S., Mng. Dir.-Global Mktg.--Frank Russell Company, Tacoma, WA; *U.S. Private*, pg. 952
Koppen, Mark, Dir.-Mktg.--Beaulieu Vineyard, Rutherford, CA; *Int'l*, pg. 410
Koppenhofer, David, Dir.-Mktg. Strategy--Cummins Engine Company, Inc., Columbus, IN; *U.S. Public*, pg. 467
Koral, Mary, Mgr.-Mktg. Communications--Sanyo Energy (U.S.A.) Corporation, San Diego, CA; *Int'l*, pg. 1191
Korb, Susan, V.P.-Mktg. Communications--Tiffany & Co., New York, NY; *U.S. Public*, pg. 1608
Korb, Thomas, Dir.-Mktg.--Quest Technologies, Inc., Oconomowoc, WI; *U.S. Private*, pg. 900
Korbel, H., Mgr.-Mktg.--Olivetti Austria G.m.b.H., Vienna, Austria; *Int'l*, pg. 1003
Korenhof, R., Dir.-Intl. Mktg.--Van Melle N.V., Breda, Netherlands; *Int'l*, pg. 1450
Korlesky, John, Dir.-Mktg.--Eckerd Corporation, Largo, FL; *U.S. Public*, pg. 917
Korman, Paula, Mktg. Specialist--White Electrical Construction Co., Atlanta, GA; *U.S. Private*, pg. 1172
Kornfield, Dan, Dir.-Mktg. & Sls.--Sid Harvey Industries, Valley Stream, NY; *U.S. Private*, pg. 998
Kornhauser, Richard W., V.P.-Mktg.-Foot Care & Dental Care--Combe Incorporated, White Plains, NY; *U.S. Private*, pg. 257
Kornowa, Diane, Mgr.-Mktg. Services--Millar Elevator Industries, Inc., Holland, OH; *Int'l*, pg. 1205
Korper, Donna, Dir.-Mktg.--Optic Graphics, Inc., Glen Burnie, MD; *U.S. Private*, pg. 818
Kort, Raja, V.P.-Mktg. & Sls., Spirits--Austin Nichols & Co. Inc., New York, NY; *Int'l*, pg. 566
Kort, Raja, Dir.-Mktg.--Yoo Hoo Chocolate Beverage Corp., Carlstadt, NJ; *Int'l*, pg. 567
Korzen, Paul, Mgr.-Mktg.--Colad Group Inc., Buffalo, NY; *U.S. Private*, pg. 250
Kosanovich, Nick, V.P.-Mktg.--Norse Dairy Systems, Columbus, OH; *U.S. Private*, pg. 802
Koseki, Keinosuke, Mgr.-Mktg. Div.--Nippon Polaroid K.K., Tokyo, Japan; *U.S. Public*, pg. 1314
Koskelo, Kirsi-Marja, Mgr.-Mktg.--Berner Ltd., Helsinki, Finland; *Int'l*, pg. 189
Koski, Tina, Mgr.-Natl. Mktg.--Archway Cookies, Inc., Battle Creek, MI; *U.S. Private*, pg. 80
Koslow, Larry, V.P.-Mktg./Personal Care--Church & Dwight Co., Inc., Princeton, NJ; *U.S. Public*, pg. 355
Koslow, Larry, V.P.-Mktg. Personal Care--Arm & Hammer Consumer Products, Princeton, NJ; *U.S. Public*, pg. 356
Kosmowski, Walt, Mgr.-Mktg.--Electro Rent Corporation, Van Nuys, CA; *U.S. Public*, pg. 568
Kosobucki, Bob, V.P.-Worldwide Sls. & Mktg.--Optek Technology, Inc., Carrollton, TX; *U.S. Public*, pg. 1227
Kosoff, Steven, V.P.-Mktg. New Prod.--The Topps Company, Inc., New York, NY; *U.S. Public*, pg. 1621
Kostlin, Ulrich, Dr., Exec. Dir.-Mktg. & Sls.--Schering AG, Berlin, Germany; *Int'l*, pg. 1203
Kota, Brenda, Mktg. Coord.--LubeCon Systems, Inc., White Cloud, MI; *U.S. Private*, pg. 679
Kotas, William, Dir.-Mktg.--Aero Peru Corporation, Coral Gables, FL; *U.S. Private*, pg. 24
Kotcher, Michele, Dir.-Sls. & Mktg.--F.X. Coughlin Co., Taylor, MI; *U.S. Private*, pg. 278
Kottman, Michael, V.P.-Mktg. & Sls.--Clouth Gummiwerke AG, Cologne, Germany; *Int'l*, pg. 297
Kotz, Hans-Helmut, Dir.-Pub. Rels. & Mktg.--Deutsche Girozentrale-Deutsche Kommunalbank, Frankfurt/Main, Germany; *Int'l*, pg. 406
Koudelka, Pierre, V.P.-Sls. & Mktg.--Federal APD, Inc., Farmington, MI; *U.S. Public*, pg. 616
Kouwenhoven, Jacques, Mgr.-Mktg., Enclosures--Eldon AB, Nassjo, Sweden; *Int'l*, pg. 436
Kovacevich, Dee Dee, V.P.-Mktg.--Jazzercise, Inc., Carlsbad, CA; *U.S. Private*, pg. 584
Koval, M., Mgr.-Indus. Mktg.--Graymills Corp., Chicago, IL; *U.S. Private*, pg. 473
Kovalenko, Donna, V.P.-Mktg.--NBD Bank, Elkhart, IN; *U.S. Public*, pg. 628
Kowall, Tim, Gen. Mgr.-Sls. & Mktg.--Yamaha Motor Canada Ltd., North York, Canada; *Int'l*, pg. 1516
Kowalski, William, V.P.-Sls. & Mktg.--London House, Rosemont, IL; *U.S. Public*, pg. 1070
Kozak, Remy D., V.P.-Mktg.--Digital Courier International Inc., Burnaby, Canada; *Int'l*, pg. 413
Kozaki, Marge, Mgr.-Sls.--Howden Fluid Systems, Santa Barbara, CA; *U.S. Public*, pg. 1045
Kozel, Al, V.P.-Sls. & Mktg./Marine--Detroit Diesel Corp., Detroit, MI; *U.S. Private*, pg. 850
Koziel, John, Dir.-Sls. & Mktg.--Weldun International, Inc., Bridgman, MI; *Int'l*, pg. 205
Kozimor, George, Mgr.-Mktg.--E.J. Brooks Company, Newark, NJ; *U.S. Private*, pg. 172
Kozlow, P., V.P.-Mktg.-Somerset Vintage Cellars--Shieffelin Somerset Co., New York, NY; *Int'l*, pg. 412
Kozub, Gary, Dir.-Mktg.--HMI Industries, Cleveland, OH; *U.S. Public*, pg. 771
Kozuta, Kathy, Mktg. Services Specialist--Grace Cocoa/ Ambrosia Chocolate, Milwaukee, WI; *U.S. Public*, pg. 128
Kraaijeveld, G., Exec. Dir.-Bus. Unit Engrng.--Oce-van der Grinten N.V., Venlo, Netherlands; *Int'l*, pg. 993
Kraemer, Larry, Dir.-Mktg.--Harkins Builders, Inc., Silver Spring, MD; *U.S. Private*, pg. 502
Kraemer, Peter, Dir.-Mktg.--Mueller's Muehle GmbH, Gelsenkirchen, Germany; *Int'l*, pg. 896
Kraham, Stepehn, V.P.-Mktg.--The Education Publishing Group, Reading, MA; *Int'l*, pg. 1026
Kraham, Stephen, Mgr.-Mktg.--Educational Publishing, New York, NY; *U.S. Public*, pg. 1768
Kraham, Steve, V.P.-Mktg. College Group--John Wiley & Sons, Inc., New York, NY; *U.S. Public*, pg. 1768
Kraines, Brad, Dir.-Mktg. & Adv.--Kraco Enterprises, Inc., Compton, CA; *U.S. Private*, pg. 634
Kraisinger, Gary, V.P.-RichMix Products--Ritchie Corporation, Wichita, KS; *U.S. Private*, pg. 933
Krakoff, Reed, Sr. V.P. & Chief Mktg. Officer--Coach, New York, NY; *U.S. Public*, pg. 1433
Krakowski, Ron, Dir.-Mktg.--Turner Construction Company, Buffalo, NY; *U.S. Public*, pg. 1646
Kral, Peter, Mgr.-Mktg., Car Accessories--Eldon AB, Nassjo, Sweden; *Int'l*, pg. 436
Kramer, Debra, Mgr.-Sls. & Mktg.--BNA PLUS, Washington, DC; *U.S. Private*, pg. 182
Kramer, Donn P., Dir.-Mktg.-Commercial Tires-North America--The Goodyear Tire & Rubber Company, Akron, OH; *U.S. Public*, pg. 752
Kramer, Larry, V.P.-Mktg. & Sls.--Wilson Products Co., Salt Lake City, UT; *U.S. Private*, pg. 1181
Kramer, R.C., V.P.-Sls. & Mktg.--Fairmont Tamper, West Columbia, SC; *U.S. Public*, pg. 793
Krammer, Anja, Dir.-Mktg. & Channel Sls.--Key Tronic Corporation, Spokane, WA; *U.S. Public*, pg. 953
Krarec, Raphael, Dir.-Mktg.--Geoffrey Beene Fragrances, Miami, FL; *U.S. Public*, pg. 681
Krasiewich, Dave, V.P.-Sls. & Mktg.--Cochrane, Inc., King of Prussia, PA; *U.S. Public*, pg. 456
Krasnitz, Ron, Dir.-Mktg. & Adv.--Hirsch International Corp., Hauppauge, NY; *U.S. Public*, pg. 829
Krasnow, Todd J., Exec. V.P.-Mktg.--Staples, Inc., Westborough, MA; *U.S. Public*, pg. 1509
Krassenksy, Ron, Sr. V.P.-Sls. & Mktg.--Air Conditioning Co., Inc., Glendale, CA; *U.S. Private*, pg. 28
Kratsas, Nicholas, Dir.-Mktg.--Power Piping Company, Pittsburgh, PA; *U.S. Public*, pg. 1029
Kraus, Edward, Dir.-Mktg. Svcs.--Medusa Corporation, Cleveland, OH; *U.S. Public*, pg. 1084
Kraus, John R., Dir.-Mktg.--Wilmorite, Inc., Rochester, NY; *U.S. Private*, pg. 1180
Kraus, Tim, V.P.-Mktg. & Sls.--Manitowoc Ice, Inc., Manitowoc, WI; *U.S. Public*, pg. 1041
Krause, Beth, Dir.-Mktg.--IMPO Glaztile, Burr Ridge, IL; *Int'l*, pg. 1239
Krause, Gary W., V.P. & Dir.-Sls. & Mktg.--Laird & Company, Eatontown, NJ; *U.S. Private*, pg. 642
Krause, Laurie, Mgr.-Mktg. Communications-Business Machines Div.--Fellowes Manufacturing Co., Itasca, IL; *U.S. Private*, pg. 400
Krauss, Julie, V.P.-Mktg.--The Hartz Mountain Corp., Secaucus, NJ; *U.S. Private*, pg. 508
Krauss, Kyle, Dir.-EMS Mktg.--GenRad, Inc., Westford, MA; *U.S. Public*, pg. 731
Kraut, G., Dir.-Sls.--Riedel-de Haen AG, Seelze, Germany; *Int'l*, pg. 625
Krautkremer, Steve, Mgr.-Sls. & Mktg.--Old Town Canoe, Old Town, ME; *U.S. Public*, pg. 933
Krebs, Ann, Mktg. Specialist--OHM Corporation, Findlay, OH; *U.S. Public*, pg. 1207
Krecl, Robert, V.P.-Mktg. & Sls.--Seth Thomas, Norcross, GA; *U.S. Private*, pg. 445
Kreeft, Jan, Dir.-Sls., Mktg. & Adv.--ISS Servisystem B.V., Amersfoort, Netherlands; *Int'l*, pg. 657
Kregel, Jim, Dir.-Mktg.--Thomas Industries Inc., Sheboygan, WI; *U.S. Public*, pg. 1599
Kreger, Kate, Mgr.-Mktg. Commun. & Corp. Plng.--CPAC, Inc., Leicester, NY; *U.S. Public*, pg. 282
Kreinces, Melissa, Asst. Mgr.-Mktg.--Totes/Isotoner, Inc., New York, NY; *U.S. Public*, pg. 1433
Kreindler, Steven, Prod. Mgr.--Microtouch Systems, Inc., Methuen, MA; *U.S. Public*, pg. 1108
Kreiner, Fran, Mktg. Services--Cable & Wireless Communications Inc., Vienna, VA; *Int'l*, pg. 247
Kreisler, Dan, Dir.-Mktg.--Forest Laboratories, Inc., New York, NY; *U.S. Public*, pg. 670
Krekeler, Karen, Admin. Specialist Mktg.--Bank One, Cincinnati, Cincinnati, OH; *U.S. Public*, pg. 173
Kremer, Richard E., Exec. V.P.-Mktg.--Coast Savings Financial, Inc., Los Angeles, CA; *U.S. Public*, pg. 388
Kremers, Chuck, Sr. V.P.-Mktg.--Service Merchandise Company, Inc., Brentwood, TN; *U.S. Public*, pg. 1461
Kreple, Mark, V.P.-Intl. Sls. & Mktg.--Manitowoc Ice, Inc., Manitowoc, WI; *U.S. Public*, pg. 1041
Kreps, Robert W., V.P.-Mktg.--Ingersoll-Dresser Pump Company, Liberty Corner, NJ; *U.S. Public*, pg. 529
Kress, Luise, Mgr.-Mktg.-Fruit Drinks--Universal Flavors-U.S.A., Indianapolis, IN; *U.S. Public*, pg. 1696
Kressman, Jeff, Mgr.-Mktg. Projects--United Stationers Inc., Des Plaines, IL; *U.S. Public*, pg. 1689
Kreuk, Mary, V.P.-Mktg.--Peoples Jewellers Corporation, Don Mills, Canada; *Int'l*, pg. 1036
Kreusch, Leonard P., III, Pres.--Leonard Kreusch, Inc., Northvale, NJ; *U.S. Private*, pg. 635
Krevida, Linda, Sr., V.P.-Commun.--Indianapolis Life Insurance Co., Indianapolis, IN; *U.S. Private*, pg. 560
Kries, Harold, Pres. & Dir.-MKtg.--Humphrey, Inc., San Diego, CA; *U.S. Public*, pg. 1376
Krinsky, Peggy, Dir.-Adv. & Mktg. Svcs.--Sea World of Ohio, Aurora, OH; *U.S. Public*, pg. 114
Kristensen, J.E., Exec. V.P.-Sls. & Mktg.--APV Crepaco, Inc., Rosemont, IL; *Int'l*, pg. 1240
Kristiansson, Bengt, Mgr.-Mktg.--Atlet AB, Molnlycke, Sweden; *Int'l*, pg. 97
Kritzer, Andrew, Sr. Mgr.-Mktg. Communications--Samsung Electronics America, Inc., Ridgefield Park, NJ; *Int'l*, pg. 1183
Krivahee, Ken, Dir.-Sls. & Mktg.--Kaufman and Broad Utah Division, Midvale, UT; *U.S. Public*, pg. 945
Krivejko, Gary, V.P.-Mktg.--Puroflow Incorporated, Van Nuys, CA; *U.S. Public*, pg. 1345
Krizelman, Sheldon, Exec. V.P.-Mktg.--Quorum Health Resources, Inc., Brentwood, TN; *U.S. Public*, pg. 1354
Kroeber, Rita, Mgr.-Americas Grp. Mktg. Communications--Dow Jones Markets, Jersey City, NJ; *U.S. Public*, pg. 525
Kroener, Bix, Sr. V.P.-Mktg. & Sls.--Adaptive Information Systems, Mission Viejo, CA; *Int'l*, pg. 946
Kroetch, Jerry, V.P.-Sls. & Mktg.--Krofam Inc., Philip, SD; *U.S. Private*, pg. 636
Krokker, LeAnn, V.P. & Exec. Mktg. Officer--Pinnacle Financial Services Inc., Saint Joseph, MI; *U.S. Public*, pg. 1297
Krol, Bruce, Mgr.-Mktg. & Sls.--Vacudyne Inc., Chicago Heights, IL; *U.S. Private*, pg. 46
Krol, Joanne, Mgr.-Mktg.--Crowley, Milner & Company, Detroit, MI; *U.S. Public*, pg. 461
Krol, Joseph, V.P.-Sls. & Mktg.--P & F Industries, Inc., Farmingdale, NY; *U.S. Public*, pg. 1239
Krol, Joseph, V.P.-Sls. & Mktg--Embassy Industries, Inc., Farmingdale, NY; *U.S. Public*, pg. 1240
Kromer, Pam, Mgr.-Adv. & Mktg.--Rapid Power Technologies, Inc., Brookfield, CT; *U.S. Private*, pg. 910
Krone, Philip S., V.P.-Mktg.--Krone Casting Corp., North Chicago, IL; *U.S. Private*, pg. 636
Kroshinsky, Frances, V.P.-Mktg., Export Div.--Leviton Mfg. Co., Inc., Little Neck, NY; *U.S. Private*, pg. 663
Krueger, Eric, Dir.-Mktg.--Centex Construction Company, Dallas, TX; *U.S. Public*, pg. 322
Krueger, Eric, Dir.-Mktg.--Centex Construction Group, Inc., Dallas, TX; *U.S. Public*, pg. 322
Krueger, Jim, Dir.-Sls. & Mktg.--Mainship Corporation, Saint Augustine, FL; *U.S. Private*, pg. 697
Krueger, Larry, V.P.-Mktg.--Popeye's Chicken & Biscuits, Atlanta, GA; *U.S. Private*, pg. 5
Krueger, Richard G., V.P.-Sls. & Mgr.--The F.D. Lawrence Electric Co., Cincinnati, OH; *U.S. Private*, pg. 654
Krueger, Ted, Mgr.-Mktg. & Adv.--Rockford Acromatic Product Co., Rockford, IL; *U.S. Private*, pg. 938
Kruger, John, Exec. V.P.-Sls. & Mktg.--Hazel Bishop International, Englewood Cliffs, NJ; *U.S. Private*, pg. 514
Kruger, Roger, Dir.-Mktg.--AGRA Monenco, Inc., Houston, TX; *Int'l*, pg. 31
Krugler, Philip, Mgr.-Mktg. Svcs.--Penco Products, Oaks, PA; *U.S. Private*, pg. 848
Kruize, Midde, Mgr.-Mktg. & Adv.--N.V. Van Melle S.A., Berchem, Belgium; *Int'l*, pg. 1451
Krukowski, Richard P., V.P.-New Product Mktg.--Wallace Laboratories, Cranbury, NJ; *U.S. Public*, pg. 310
Krummel, Cardin, Dir.-Sls. & Mktg.--Carnival Creations, Linden, NJ; *U.S. Private*, pg. 213
Krump-Moss, Nan, Dir.-Mkt. Devel.--Hyatt Hotels Corporation, Chicago, IL; *U.S. Private*, pg. 551
Kruse, Duane, Mgr.-Mktg. Svcs.--Tyler Industries, Benson, MN; *U.S. Private*, pg. 1112
Kruse, Kelly, Mktg. Asst.--Check Technology Corporation, Minnetonka, MN; *U.S. Public*, pg. 342
Kruse, Sandy, Dir.-Mktg. Services--American Metal Products, Olive Branch, MS; *U.S. Public*, pg. 1053
Krzeminski, Jim, V.P.-Sls. & Mktg.--Bissell Inc., Grand Rapids, MI; *U.S. Private*, pg. 145
Krzynowek, John, V.P.-Mktg.--Tommy Armour Golf, Morton Grove, IL; *U.S. Public*, pg. 1683
Krzyżanski, Victor, Exec. V.P.-Mktg.--McCain Bindery Systems, Inc., Chicago, IL; *U.S. Private*, pg. 719
Kuchenmeister, Joseph P., Sr. V.P.-Dir. Mktg.--American Family Life Assurance Co. of Columbus, Columbus, GA; *U.S. Public*, pg. 28
Kuebler, Christopher A., V.P.-Mktg. & Sls.--Abbott Pharmaceutical Products Division, Abbott Park, IL; *U.S. Public*, pg. 13
Kuechenmeister, Joseph P., Sr. V.P. & Dir.-Mktg.--AFLAC Incorporated, Columbus, GA; *U.S. Public*, pg. 28
Kuecker, Tobey, Mgr.-Sls. & Svc.--Mosinee Converted Products, Columbus, WI; *U.S. Public*, pg. 1747
Kuehl, Terry, Mgr.-Sls./Lumber--Sierra Pacific Industries, Anderson, CA; *U.S. Private*, pg. 998
Kuendig, John, V.P.-Mktg. Devel.--Kraft Foods, Inc., Northfield, IL; *U.S. Public*, pg. 1287
Kuesma, David, Dir.-Mktg.--Fasson Films, Painesville, OH; *U.S. Public*, pg. 153
Kuester, Joe, Dir.-Mktg. & Sls.--Knudsen & Sons, Inc., Chico, CA; *U.S. Public*, pg. 1480
Kuhlei, Harold, Mgr.-Mktg.--Schumann Sasol GmbH & Co KG, Hamburg, Germany; *Int'l*, pg. 1197
Kuhn, Karen, Asst. V.P.-Mktg.--First Commerce Bancshares, Inc., Lincoln, NE; *U.S. Public*, pg. 629
Kuhn, Lori, Mgr.-Mktg.--Wolohan Lumber Co., Saginaw, MI; *U.S. Public*, pg. 1774
Kuhn, William, V.P.-Product Support--Grove WorldWide, Shady Grove, PA; *Int'l*, pg. 593

Kuhner, David L., Mgr.-Mktg. Communications--Pioneer-Standard Electronics, Inc., Cleveland, OH; *U.S. Public*, pg. 1300
Kuhnert, Ralph, V.P.-Opers./Asia Pacific--The Gleason Works, Rochester, NY; *U.S. Public*, pg. 746
Kuhns, Barbara, Mgr.-Mktg.--Steelox Systems Inc., Mason, OH; *U.S. Private*, pg. 1038
Kuisma, Maaret, Dir.-Mktg.--OY Stockmann AB, Helsinki, Finland; *Int'l*, pg. 1301
Kuisma, Maaret, Exec. V.P.-Mktg.--Stockmann Department Store Div., Helsinki, Finland; *Int'l*, pg. 1301
Kuk, Kenneth U., Sr. V.P.-Strategic Mktg.--ReliaStar Financial Corp., Minneapolis, MN; *U.S. Public*, pg. 1375
Kuklinski, Steve, V.P. & Mngmt. Supvr.--Periscope Marketing Communications, Minneapolis, MN; *U.S. Private*, pg. 853
Kula, Pat C., V.P.-Mktg. & Sls.--Diamond Electronics, Inc., Carroll, OH; *U.S. Public*, pg. 1663
Kulasa, Leon V., Dir.-Intl. Mktg.--GAI Consultants, Inc., Monroeville, PA; *U.S. Private*, pg. 433
Kulcsar, Edward, Dir.-Opers. & Mktg.--Associated Testing Laboratories, Inc., Wayne, NJ; *U.S. Public*, pg. 1341
Kulczycki, Bill, Dir.-Sls. & Mktg.--Lost Arrow Corporation, Ventura, CA; *U.S. Private*, pg. 676
Kulik, Paul J., Dir.-Sls. & Mktg.--Hennells, Inc., Ferndale, MI; *U.S. Private*, pg. 522
Kull, Michael J., Sr. Exec. V.P.-Mktg.--Dairy Queen Corporate Store, Louisville, KY; *U.S. Public*, pg. 220
Kullmann, Don, V.P.-Mktg. Procurement & Plng.--Prairie Farms Dairy, Inc., Carlinville, IL; *U.S. Private*, pg. 878
Kulvuari, Vic, V.P.-Mktg.--Avanti, Fremont, CA; *U.S. Public*, pg. 151
Kumar, Chuck, Dir.-Mktg.--Cherry Electrical Products Corporation, Waukegan, IL; *U.S. Public*, pg. 346
Kumm, Debora, V.P.-Mktg.--The West Bend Co., West Bend, WI; *U.S. Public*, pg. 1322
Kumm, Mark, Mgr.-Mkt. Plng. & Policy--Potomac Electric Power Company, Washington, DC; *U.S. Public*, pg. 1318
Kumraks, Apichart, 1st V.P.--Siam City Bank Public Company Limited, Bangkok, Thailand; *Int'l*, pg. 1239
Kunkel, Karen, Coord.-Mktg. Svcs.--Drew Industrial, Boonton, NJ; *U.S. Public*, pg. 139
Kunsch, Anders, Dir.-Mktg.--DSM Chemie Linz GmbH, Lienz, Austria; *Int'l*, pg. 356
Kunz, Hansruedi, Chief Oper. Officer--Metallica SA, Crissier, Switzerland; *Int'l*, pg. 1427
Kupferman, Spencer, Mgr.-Mktg.--Global Software, Inc., Raleigh, NC; *U.S. Private*, pg. 457
Kupiec, Dave, Dir.-Mktg.--Gourmet, New York, NY; *U.S. Private*, pg. 20
Kurharsky, Sergei, V.P.-Consumer Mktg.-Nickelodeon--Nickelodeon/Nick At Nite, New York, NY; *U.S. Private*, pg. 779
Kurinsky, Roger, V.P.-Sls. & Mktg./Specialty Prods.--Ivex Packaging Corporation, Lincolnshire, IL; *U.S. Public*, pg. 915
Kuriyama, Stanley, Mgr.-Mktg.--A & B Properties, Inc., Honolulu, HI; *U.S. Public*, pg. 39
Kurlancheck, Gary, V.P.-Mktg.--Fort James Corporation, Richmond, VA; *U.S. Public*, pg. 670
Kuroki, Sharon, Sr. V.P.-Music Club. Mktg.--Columbia House Music Club, New York, NY; *Int'l*, pg. 1281
Kuroski, Elizabeth, Mktg. & Adv. Specialist--Delphi Harrison Thermal Systems, Lockport, NY; *U.S. Public*, pg. 719
Kuroski, Rich, Dir.-Mktg.--Peerless Chain Company, Winona, MN; *U.S. Public*, pg. 1268
Kurth, Curtis, V.P.-Mktg.--Foremost Farms USA Cooperative, Baraboo, WI; *U.S. Private*, pg. 418
Kurtis, Bill, V.P.-Mktg. & Sls.--Lifetime Products Inc., Clearfield, UT; *U.S. Private*, pg. 667
Kurtz, W., Mgr.-Mktg.--KDI Precision Products, Inc., Cincinnati, OH; *U.S. Private*, pg. 603
Kurtze, Jack, Mgr.-Sls. & Mktg.--Maxcor Manufacturing, Inc., Colorado Springs, CO; *U.S. Private*, pg. 716
Kurvers, Craig, Mgr.-Mktg.--Lund International Holdings, Inc., Anoka, MN; *U.S. Public*, pg. 1020
Kurz, Rick, Chief Mktg. Officer & Sr. V.P.-Mktg.--ADVO, Inc., Windsor, CT; *U.S. Public*, pg. 23
Kurzman, Alan M., V.P.-Mktg.--Triangle Pacific Corporation, Dallas, TX; *U.S. Public*, pg. 1634
Kusek, Ed, Dir.-Mktg.--Turtle Wax, Inc., Chicago, IL; *U.S. Private*, pg. 1110
Kushner, E., Dir.-Mktg.--Frequency Electronics, Inc., Uniondale, NY; *U.S. Public*, pg. 681
Kushnerick, John L., Dir.-Mktg. & Sls.--American Camper, Tulsa, OK; *U.S. Public*, pg. 265
Kusnick, Drew, V.P.-Sls. & Mktg.--Kaufman and Broad of Northern California, Inc., San Ramon, CA; *U.S. Public*, pg. 945
Kusnick, Drew, V.P.-Sls. & Mktg.--Kaufman and Broad-South Bay Inc., Fremont, CA; *U.S. Public*, pg. 945
Kusserow, Paul B., Dir.-Mktg.--Colonial Williamsburg Foundation, Williamsburg, VA; *U.S. Private*, pg. 254
Kuster, Brian S., V.P.-Mktg.--Union Standard Insurance Company, Irving, TX; *U.S. Public*, pg. 216
Kuta, Al, Dir.-Mktg.--Lindsay Manufacturing Company, Lindsay, NE; *U.S. Public*, pg. 999
Kutchins, R., Mktg. Mgr.-Indus. Chemicals Div.--PQ Corporation, Berwyn, PA; *U.S. Private*, pg. 827
Kutchins, R., Mgr.-Mktg.--Industrial Chemicals Div., Valley Forge, PA; *U.S. Private*, pg. 827
Kuwahira, Karen, V.P.-Mktg. & Adv.--Ralston Purina Canada Inc., Mississauga, Canada; *U.S. Public*, pg. 1360
Kuypers, Bill, Dir.-Electronics Sls. & Mktg.--Tensolite Company, Saint Augustine, FL; *U.S. Public*, pg. 305
Kuypers, Tom, Dir.-Mktg.--Fabri-Centers of America, Inc., Hudson, OH; *U.S. Public*, pg. 609
Kuzmin, Gary, Dir.-Mktg.--Thermalloy, Inc., Farmers Branch, TX; *Int'l*, pg. 208
Kvicala, Michael, Mgr.-Adv.--Federal APD, Inc., Farmington, MI; *U.S. Public*, pg. 616
Kwinn, Dave, V.P.-Mktg.--CR Services, Elgin, IL; *Int'l*, pg. 1157
Kwinn, David, V.P.-Mktg.--Cooper Automotive Division, Chesterfield, MO; *U.S. Public*, pg. 443
Kwitoski, Stephen A., Sr. V.P.-Loan & Mktg. Admin.--Santa Monica Bank, Santa Monica, CA; *U.S. Public*, pg. 1757
Kwok, Lana V., Sr. Mktg. Specialist--Inter-Tel, Incorporated, Phoenix, AZ; *U.S. Public*, pg. 888
Kyle, G.G., Dir.-Mktg.--Tasty Baking Company, Philadelphia, PA; *U.S. Public*, pg. 1561
Kyrus, Diane, Dir.-Mktg.--Butterworths Asia, Singapore, Singapore; *Int'l*, pg. 1095
Kyser, Michael, V.P.-Mktg.--Badger Meter Industrial Div., Milwaukee, WI; *U.S. Public*, pg. 165
L'Heureux, Al, Mgr.-Sls. Promo. & Mktg.--Shivers Trading & Operating Co., Augusta, GA; *U.S. Private*, pg. 994
L'Heureux, Al, Mgr.-Sls. Promo. & Mktg.--Morris Communications Corporation, Augusta, GA; *U.S. Private*, pg. 995
L'Heureux, Jim, V.P.-Mktg.--Prodigy Inc., White Plains, NY; *U.S. Private*, pg. 888
La Monte, Steve, Sr. V.P.-Mktg.--Schering-Plough Healthcare Products Inc., Liberty Corner, NJ; *U.S. Public*, pg. 1438
La Vega, Francisco de, V.P.-Mktg.--Groupe Pernod Ricard, Paris, France; *Int'l*, pg. 566
LaBonte, Gordon J., Mktg. Dir.--Textron Automotive Interiors Company, Dover, NH; *U.S. Public*, pg. 1590
Laborowski, John V., V.P.-Sls. & Mktg.--Hammary Furniture Co., Lenoir, NC; *U.S. Public*, pg. 973
LaBroad, Mike, Dir.-Budweiser Mktg.--Anheuser-Busch Companies, Inc., Saint Louis, MO; *U.S. Public*, pg. 113
Lacey, Norman E., Dir.-Sls. & Mktg.--Thermo Black Clawson, Inc., Middletown, OH; *U.S. Public*, pg. 1593
Lachapelle, A.D., Sr. V.P.-Mktg. & Sls.--Reed & Barton Corporation, Taunton, MA; *U.S. Private*, pg. 916
Laconi, Joseph, Mgr.-Mktg.--Union Pen Company, Greenwich, CT; *U.S. Private*, pg. 1119
Lacy, Mary Beth, Mgr.-Mktg. Pub. Rels.--Lynx Golf, Inc., City of Industry, CA; *U.S. Private*, pg. 684
Lacy, Meg, Dir.-Mktg.--Federal Realty Investment Trust, Rockville, MD; *U.S. Public*, pg. 616
Lacy, Robert, V.P.-Mktg.--Plains Co-op Oil Mill, Lubbock, TX; *U.S. Private*, pg. 868
Lacy, Thomas, V.P.-Sls. & Mktg.--Bio-Logic Systems Corp., Mundelein, IL; *U.S. Public*, pg. 230
Ladden, Steven P., V.P.-Sls. & Mktg.--Yankee Energy System, Inc., Meriden, CT; *U.S. Public*, pg. 1787
Laden, Steven P., V.P.-Sls., Mktg. & External Rels.--Yankee Gas Services Company, Meriden, CT; *U.S. Public*, pg. 1788
Ladhoff, Don, V.P.-Mktg. & Sls.--The Lion Brewery, Inc., Wilkes-Barre, PA; *U.S. Public*, pg. 1000
Ladnier, Cheryl Jan, Sr. V.P.-Mktg. & Corp. Communication--The Bon Ton Stores, Inc., York, PA; *U.S. Public*, pg. 244
LaDoucer, Doug, V.P.-Mktg. & Sls.--E.D. Smith, Winona, Canada; *Int'l*, pg. 1263
Ladue, David, Gen. Mgr.-Sls.--Yale/Chase Materials Handling, Inc., City of Industry, CA; *U.S. Private*, pg. 1195
Ladwig, Roger, Dir.-Mktg.--DSP Technology Inc., Fremont, CA; *U.S. Public*, pg. 475
Laetz, Curtis J., V.P.-Mktg. & Devel.--OmniQuip International, Inc., Port Washington, WI; *U.S. Private*, pg. 500
Laezza, Joe, V.P.-Mktg. & Sls.--Falconbridge Limited, Toronto, Canada; *Int'l*, pg. 433
Laferriere, Rene, Mgr.-Mktg.--Precision Tools Div., North Kingstown, RI; *U.S. Public*, pg. 260
Laffoon, Heather, Mktg. Coord.--Signature Inns, Inc., Indianapolis, IN; *U.S. Public*, pg. 1473
LaFlamme, Mindy, Mgr.-Mktg.--Pace, Arlington Heights, IL; *U.S. Private*, pg. 919
Lafouta, Amoury, Mgr.-Mktg.--Sonauto S.A., Saint Ouen, France; *Int'l*, pg. 1063
Lafrennie, David, Grp. Mgr.-Mktg. Communications--LEGO Systems, Inc., Enfield, CT; *Int'l*, pg. 805
Lagana, Steve, Dir.-Mktg. Communications--PRC, Inc., Mc Lean, VA; *U.S. Public*, pg. 1003
Lagnado, Silvia, Dir.-Mktg.--Elida Faberge, Kingston upon Thames, United Kingdom; *Int'l*, pg. 1434
Lagny, Claude, Dir.-Corp. Communications--Elida Faberge, Paris, France; *Int'l*, pg. 1437
Lago, Marcelo, Dir.-Mktg.--L'Oreal Prodesca S.A., Buenos Aires, Argentina; *Int'l*, pg. 819
Lagosz, Christine, Mgr.-Mktg.--Trumpf Inc., Farmington, CT; *U.S. Private*, pg. 1108
LaGrace, Dick, Dir.-Mktg. & Sls.--Barry Controls Aerospace, Burbank, CA; *U.S. Public*, pg. 124
LaGrega, Andrew T., Sr. V.P.-Sls., Mktg. & Adv.--The Wilder Companies, Boston, MA; *U.S. Private*, pg. 1176
Laguette, Louisa, Supvr.-Mktg. & Pub. Rels.--Del Taco, Inc., Laguna Hills, CA; *U.S. Private*, pg. 321
Lahey, Kevin, V.P.-Mktg.--Buffalo Rock Company, Birmingham, AL; *U.S. Private*, pg. 179
Laidlaw, Frank, Dir.-Mktg. & Sls.--Berol Corp., Georgetown, KY; *U.S. Public*, pg. 1178
Lake, Carmen, Coord.-Mktg.--Aerolineas Argentinas, Miami, FL; *Int'l*, pg. 575
Lake, Charlie, Mgr.-Mktg.--Jomac, Inc., Warrington, PA; *U.S. Private*, pg. 595
Lake, Frank, Dir.-Mktg.--Boeing Helicopters, Ridley Park, PA; *U.S. Public*, pg. 241
Lal, Jagdish, Mgr.-Mktg., The Americas--Kuwait Airways, Canada, Toronto, Canada; *Int'l*, pg. 764
LaLiberty, Dennis, V.P.-Mktg.--Frank Consolidated Enterprises Inc., Des Plaines, IL; *U.S. Private*, pg. 423
Lamade, John, Dir.-Mktg.--Malco Products, Inc., Barberton, OH; *U.S. Private*, pg. 698
Lamar, Bill, V.P.-Natl. Mktg.--McDonald's Corporation, Oak Brook, IL; *U.S. Public*, pg. 1068
Lamb, Jay, Dir.-Mktg.--Smurfit Newsprint Corporation, Oregon City, OR; *Int'l*, pg. 1271
Lamb, Tim, V.P.-Mktg. & Sls.--Apex Precision Technology Inc., Indianapolis, IN; *U.S. Private*, pg. 77
Lambech, Arne, Dir.-Mktg.--Christiania Bank og Kreditkasse ASA, Oslo, Norway; *Int'l*, pg. 289
Lambert, Amy, Mktg. Asst.--Restaurants Unlimited, Seattle, WA; *U.S. Private*, pg. 925
Lambert, Bob, Supvr.-Mktg. Svcs.--Methode Electronics Inc., Chicago, IL; *U.S. Public*, pg. 1101
Lambert, Douglas, Mgr.-Mktg.--Red Kap Industries, Nashville, TN; *U.S. Public*, pg. 1702
Lambert, Jim, Dir.-Mktg.--Quintus Corporation, Fremont, CA; *U.S. Private*, pg. 901
Lambert, Kurt, Dir.-Mktg.-Milliken Textiles Yarn--Milliken & Company, Spartanburg, SC; *U.S. Private*, pg. 748
Lambert, Mark, Sr. V.P.-Sls. & Mktg.--Freightliner Corp., Portland, OR; *Int'l*, pg. 368
Lambert, Michael, V.P.-Mktg.--COMPAQ Computer Corporation, Houston, TX; *U.S. Public*, pg. 417
Lamer, Allan, V.P.-Mktg. & Adv. Mgr.--Kewaunee Engineering Corp., Kewaunee, WI; *U.S. Private*, pg. 703
Lamie, James, Dir.-Sports & Event Mktg.--The Gillette Company, Boston, MA; *U.S. Public*, pg. 743
Lammers, Henry P., V.P.-Mktg.--Marketing Communications, Lenexa, KS; *U.S. Public*, pg. 794
Lamone, Gene, V.P.-Sls. & Mktg. & Adv.--Capitol Manufacturing Co., Westerville, OH; *U.S. Public*, pg. 793
Lamparter, Jeff, Dir.-Mktg.--Systron Donner-Inertial Division, Concord, CA; *U.S. Public*, pg. 160
Lampen, Ron, V.P.-Sls. & Mktg.--Thermotron Industries, Holland, MI; *U.S. Private*, pg. 1136
Lampros, George, V.P.-Mktg.,Bread--Interstate Brands Corporation, Kansas City, MO; *U.S. Public*, pg. 909
Lanagan, Hope G., V.P. & Dir.-Mktg.--First Virginia Banks, Inc., Falls Church, VA; *U.S. Public*, pg. 641
Lanbot, Francoise, Dir.-Sls. & Mktg./Biotherm--L'Oreal Parfumerie, Brussels, Belgium; *Int'l*, pg. 819
Lancaster, Terry, Dir.-Mktg.--Email Limited, Waterloo, Australia; *Int'l*, pg. 450
Lancelot, Pascal, Dir.-Mktg.--Kone Corporation, Helsinki, Finland; *Int'l*, pg. 746
Land, Esther M., Mktg. Specialist--Rapistan Demag Corp., Grand Rapids, MI; *Int'l*, pg. 837
Landes, George, Jr., Dir.-Sls. & Mktg.--CMS Gilbreth Packaging Systems, Bensalem, PA; *U.S. Private*, pg. 558
Landini, Peggy, Dir.-Sls. & Customer Service--LG & E Energy Corp., Louisville, KY; *U.S. Public*, pg. 970
Landis, Dean, Treas. & Sec.--United Credit Corp. & Patroit Funding, New York, NY; *U.S. Private*, pg. 1121
Landreth, Dan, V.P.-Sales & Mktg.--SatCom Technologies Division, Duluth, GA; *U.S. Public*, pg. 424
Landrieu, Mike, Mgr.-Research Mktg.--Cracker Barrel Old Country Store, Inc., Lebanon, TN; *U.S. Public*, pg. 455
Landrum, Jennifer, Mgr.-Community Relations--Qual-Med, Inc., Pueblo, CO; *U.S. Public*, pg. 678
Landry, Brian, Dir.-Hospital Mktg.--Bergen Brunswig Medical Corporation, Montgomery, AL; *U.S. Public*, pg. 214
Landry, Steven J., Gen. Mgr.-Mktg.--Chrysler Canada Ltd., Windsor, Canada; *U.S. Public*, pg. 354
Landsman, Joshua, Mgr.-Mktg.--PC Quote, Inc., Chicago, IL; *U.S. Public*, pg. 1240
Landy, Marty, V.P.-Mktg.--Preston Trucking Company, Inc., Preston, MD; *U.S. Public*, pg. 1788
Landy, Michael, V.P.-Sls. & Mktg.--Sanmina Corporation, San Jose, CA; *U.S. Public*, pg. 1431
Lane, Edwin D., V.P.-Mktg.--Kerr-McGee Coal Corp., Oklahoma City, OK; *U.S. Public*, pg. 952
Lane, Jeff, V.P.-Mktg.--Miniature Precision Components, Walworth, WI; *U.S. Private*, pg. 750
Lane, Mike, Mgr.-Mktg. Opers.--3M Unitek Corporation, Monrovia, CA; *U.S. Public*, pg. 1606
Lane, W.R., Dir.-Sls. & Mktg.--Edward Barber & Co., London, United Kingdom; *U.S. Public*, pg. 1651
Laney, Gary, Gen. Mgr.-Spec. Prods. Mktg.--Ore-Ida Foods, Inc., Boise, ID; *U.S. Public*, pg. 805
Lang, Laurie, Sr. V.P.-Strategic Mktg.--The Walt Disney Company, Burbank, CA; *U.S. Public*, pg. 511
Lang, Marlen P., Admin.-Mktg. & Sales--Heckett MultiServ, Butler, PA; *U.S. Public*, pg. 793
Lang, Richard A., Jr., V.P.-Adv., Sls. & Mktg.--Dad's Products Co., Inc., Meadville, PA; *U.S. Private*, pg. 306
Lang, Richard J., V.P.-Intl. Sls. & Mktg.--DeVlieg-Bullard Inc., Westport, CT; *U.S. Public*, pg. 502
Lang, Robert P., V.P.--Valk Manufacturing Company, New Kingstown, PA; *U.S. Private*, pg. 1131
Lang, W., Mgr.-Mktg. Support--Eaton Corporation, Hydraulics Division, Eden Prairie, MN; *U.S. Public*, pg. 557
Langan, John, V.P.-Mktg. & Sls.--Clearly Canadian Beverage Corp., Vancouver, Canada; *Int'l*, pg. 297
Langbein, John, Mgr.-Mktg.--BHC Securities, Inc., Philadelphia, PA; *U.S. Public*, pg. 647
Langdon, Doug, Mgr.-Mktg. Research--Chattem, Inc., Chattanooga, TN; *U.S. Public*, pg. 341
Lange, Bill, V.P.-Mktg.--Mail Boxes Etc. USA, San Diego, CA; *U.S. Public*, pg. 1687
Lange, Bob, Mgr.-Mktg. Creative Services--San Antonio Express News, San Antonio, TX; *U.S. Private*, pg. 517
Lange, John, V.P.-Mktg.--GPD/Embraco North America, Inc., Norcross, GA; *U.S. Public*, pg. 1765
Lange, Ronald F., Dir.-Mktg.--QT Optoelectronics, Sunnyvale, CA; *U.S. Private*, pg. 897
Langford, Robert M., Chief Oper. Officer & Sr. Exec. V.P.--Shoney's, Inc., Nashville, TN; *U.S. Public*, pg. 1467
Langkabel, Jorg, Mgr.-Mktg.--Det Norske Veritas, Hamburg, Germany; *Int'l*, pg. 397
Langley, Frank A., V.P.-Mktg. & Prod. Devel.--Intercare Technologies, Inc., Waukesha, WI; *U.S. Public*, pg. 459
Langlois, B., Dir.-Mktg.--Maple Leaf Meats, Winnipeg, Canada; *Int'l*, pg. 841
Langlois, Dominique, V.P.-Mktg.--Environmental Fragrance Technologies, Ltd., New York, NY; *U.S. Private*, pg. 689
Langlois, Pierre, Mgr.-Mktg.--Faucher Industries Inc., Saint Leonard, Canada; *Int'l*, pg. 479
Langness, Irit, Dir.-Mktg.--Scenic Airlines Inc., Saint George, UT; *U.S. Public*, pg. 1476

Langridge, Jack, V.P.-Sls. & Mktg.--New Hampshire Ball Bearings, Inc., Peterborough, NH; *Int'l*, pg. 868
Langridge, Jane, Assoc. Dir.-Intl. Mktg.--Sequus Pharmaceuticals, Inc., Menlo Park, CA; *U.S. Public*, pg. 1460
Langston, Bruce, Mgr.-Prod. Mktg. & Sls. Promo.--Kelly-Moore Paint Company, Inc., San Carlos, CA; *U.S. Private*, pg. 613
Lanham, Larkin, V.P.-Mktg. & Sls.--CD Products, Inc., New Providence, NJ; *U.S. Public*, pg. 276
Lansworthy, Pamela, Dir.-Mktg.--Thorntons PLC, Darbyshire, United Kingdom; *Int'l*, pg. 1386
Lantz, Richard K., V.P.-Mktg.--Shenandoah Mfg. Co. Inc., Harrisonburg, VA; *U.S. Private*, pg. 992
Lanwermeyer, L.F., Exec. V.P.-Mktg.--Harris Bankcorp, Inc., Chicago, IL; *Int'l*, pg. 154
Lanzendorf, Bob, Prod. Mgr.--Marsh Company, Belleville, IL; *U.S. Private*, pg. 707
Lapides, James A., Exec. V.P.-Mktg. & Opers.--United Aluminum Corporation, North Haven, CT; *U.S. Private*, pg. 1120
Lapidus, Herbert, Dr., V.P.-New Product Devel.--Combe Incorporated, White Plains, NY; *U.S. Private*, pg. 257
Lapidus, Michael, Pres.-Retail Opers.--Jockey International, Inc., Kenosha, WI; *U.S. Private*, pg. 588
Lapin, Judi, V.P.-Mktg.--Donahue Schriber, Newport Beach, CA; *Int'l*, pg. 253
Lapine, Richard, V.P.-Sls. & Mktg.--Essex Specialty Products, Auburn Hills, MI; *U.S. Public*, pg. 523
LaPlante, David, V.P.-Sls. & Mktg.--Shurfine International, Inc., Northlake, IL; *U.S. Private*, pg. 997
Laplante, Lori C., Coord.-Mktg.--Edwards and Kelcey, Inc., Boston, MA; *U.S. Private*, pg. 364
LaPoff, Gary, V.P.-Sls.--The Manhattan Shirt Co., New York, NY; *U.S. Public*, pg. 1429
Lappin, Carol, Grp. V.P. & Mktg. Dir./Acct. Services--Ziccardi & Partners, Inc., New York, NY; *U.S. Private*, pg. 1205
Lapps, David M., V.P.-Opers.--Maaco Enterprises Inc., King of Prussia, PA; *U.S. Private*, pg. 689
LaQuintano, Tony, V.P.-Sls. & Mktg.--Dietzgen Corporation, Palatine, IL; *U.S. Private*, pg. 332
Laramy, John E., V.P.-Sls. & Mktg.--The Riverside Publishing Co., Chicago, IL; *U.S. Public*, pg. 841
Laraya, Rogelio G., Sr. V.P.-Fin. & Treas.--Benguet Corporation, Manila, Philippines; *Int'l*, pg. 186
Larcher, Patrice, Mgr.-Mktg. Services--Arianespace SA, Evry, France; *Int'l*, pg. 81
Lares, Rodolfo, Mgr.-Mktg.--Nuevo Federal S.A., Buenos Aires, Argentina; *Int'l*, pg. 990
Lariemar, Richard, V.P.-Mktg.-Automotive Div.--Hydro Aluminum Bohn, Inc., Farmington Hills, MI; *Int'l*, pg. 961
Larime, Michael W., V.P.-Sls. & Mktg.--Thetford Corporation, Ann Arbor, MI; *U.S. Private*, pg. 352
Lariviere, Louis F., V.P.-Promo. & Dir. Mktg.--Cossette Communication Marketing, Quebec, Canada; *Int'l*, pg. 335
Larney, M., Sr. V.P.-Mktg.--International Home Foods Inc., Parsippany, NJ; *U.S. Private*, pg. 526
Laroche, Louis J., Mgr.-Natl. Sls.--General Filters, Inc., Novi, MI; *U.S. Private*, pg. 444
Larocque, Greg, Mgr.-Mktg.--Gems Sensors, Plainville, CT; *U.S. Public*, pg. 481
Laroque, G., Mgr.-Mktg.--Measurement Systems, Inc., Fairfield, CT; *Int'l*, pg. 1431
LaRosa, Stephanie, V.P.-Sls. & Mktg.--Quantum Sport, New York, NY; *U.S. Private*, pg. 900
LaRose, Peter, V.P.--Nelson & Small Inc., Portland, ME; *U.S. Private*, pg. 790
Larrimore, David, V.P.-Mktg.--Wind River Systems, Inc., Alameda, CA; *U.S. Public*, pg. 1770
Larsen, J.A., V.P.-Mktg. & Sls.--CWC Textron Company, Muskegon, MI; *U.S. Public*, pg. 1590
Larsen, Jan, Mgr.-Mktg.--The Kent Company, Elkhart, IN; *Int'l*, pg. 440
Larsen, Johannes, Dir.-Mktg.--West Chemical Products, Inc., Princeton, NJ; *U.S. Private*, pg. 1158
Larsen, Larry E., V.P.-Mktg.--Williams Natural Gas Company, Tulsa, OK; *U.S. Public*, pg. 1769
Larsen, Richard, V.P.-Sls. & Mktg.--Arvida, Boca Raton, FL; *U.S. Private*, pg. 578
Larson, Chris, Dir.-Mktg.-Retail--Sanwa Bank California, Los Angeles, CA; *Int'l*, pg. 1189
Larson, Dan, Mgr.-Mktg.--Mrs. Baird's Bakeries, Inc., Fort Worth, TX; *U.S. Private*, pg. 765
Larson, Robert, V.P.-Mktg.--Nicholas Paper, Inc., Fitchburg, MA; *U.S. Private*, pg. 798
Larson, Stephen, Mgr.-Sls. & Mktg.--Oildyne, Minneapolis, MN; *U.S. Public*, pg. 411
Larson, T.A., Mgr.-Gas Mktg./N. America--Murphy Oil USA, Inc., El Dorado, AR; *U.S. Public*, pg. 1142
Larson, Thomas, V.P.-Mkts. Devel. & Info. Resources--United Power Association, Elk River, MN; *U.S. Private*, pg. 1123
Larsson, Kent A., Sr. V.P.-Mktg. & Sls. Promo.--Consolidated Stores Corp., Columbus, OH; *U.S. Public*, pg. 437
Larter, Dan, V.P.-Sls. & Mktg.--Burlington Motor Holdings Inc., Daleville, IN; *U.S. Private*, pg. 183
Larter, Paul, Dir.-Mktg. Communications--Du Pont (Australia) Ltd., Sydney, Australia; *U.S. Public*, pg. 532
Lasater, Gerald, V.P.-Wheat Starch Mktg.--Midwest Grain Products, Inc., Atchison, KS; *U.S. Public*, pg. 1111
Lasaur, Jim, Dir.-Mktg.--Restaurant Developers Corp., Independence, OH; *U.S. Private*, pg. 925
Laser, Leigh, Mgr.-Adv. & Mktg.--Books-A-Million, Inc., Birmingham, AL; *U.S. Public*, pg. 244
Laseter, Larry, V.P.-Sls. & Mktg.--Florida Power & Light Company, North Palm Beach, FL; *U.S. Public*, pg. 608
Lashley, Thomas, V.P.-Mktg.-Somerset Vintage Cellars--Shieffelin Somerset Co., New York, NY; *Int'l*, pg. 412
Laskauskas, Romas, Controller-Mktg. & Services--Kraft Foods Inc., Rye Brook, NY; *U.S. Public*, pg. 1288
Laskey, Christine, V.P.-Mktg. & Corp. Communications--National Trustco Inc., Toronto, Canada; *Int'l*, pg. 909
Laskowski, Joe, Dir.-Mktg. & Communications--Analog Devices, Santa Clara, CA; *U.S. Public*, pg. 108
Laskowski, Joseph, Dir.-Mktg. Communications--Analog Devices, Inc., Norwood, MA; *U.S. Public*, pg. 107
Lasnier, Eduardo Fernandez, Mgr.-Mktg.--Penaflor S.A., Buenos Aires, Argentina; *Int'l*, pg. 1032
Lassy, Ron, V.P.-Sls. & Mktg.--Vlier Engineering, Brighton, MA; *U.S. Public*, pg. 124
Laszlo, Matt, Mgr.-Corp. Mktg. Commun.--The Middleby Corporation, Rolling Meadows, IL; *U.S. Public*, pg. 1109
Latella, George J., Mgr.-Adv. & Mktg.--Tasty Baking Company, Philadelphia, PA; *U.S. Public*, pg. 1561
Later, Stewart, Dir.-Mktg.--BICC Brand-Rex, Willimantic, CT; *Int'l*, pg. 120
Latta, Brent A., V.P.-Mktg.--Landauer, Inc., Glenwood, IL; *U.S. Public*, pg. 977
Latta, John, V.P.--ElectroCom Automation L.P., Arlington, TX; *Int'l*, pg. 1244
Latta, R.M., V.P.-Sls. & Mtkg.--Chrysler Canada Ltd., Windsor, Canada; *U.S. Public*, pg. 354
Latuda, Suzanne, Dir.-Sls. & Mktg.--Wolverine Leather Div., Rockford, MI; *U.S. Public*, pg. 1775
Lau Costa, Constance, Dir.-Mktg.--Review Publishing Company Ltd., Hong Kong, Hong Kong; *U.S. Public*, pg. 525
Lau, B.H., V.P.-Sls. & Mktg.--Ph. Orth Co., Oak Creek, WI; *Int'l*, pg. 244
Lauber, A.L., Mgr.-Corp. Devel.--Organon Inc., West Orange, NJ; *Int'l*, pg. 48
Lauber, Dennis R., V.P.-Sls. & Mktg.--Grede Foundries, Inc., Milwaukee, WI; *U.S. Private*, pg. 476
Laudeman, Chuck, Dir.-Mktg.--Howell Gas Management Co., Houston, TX; *U.S. Public*, pg. 844
Lauderdale, Jim, V.P.-Mktg.-Dairy Foods Group--Mid-America Dairymen, Inc., Springfield, MO; *U.S. Private*, pg. 743
Laufer, Esther, Assoc. Publr. & Dir.-Mktg.--Cosmopolitan, New York, NY; *U.S. Private*, pg. 517
Laughlin, Daniel F., V.P.-Strategic Mktg.--Sears, Roebuck and Co., Hoffman Estates, IL; *U.S. Public*, pg. 1452
Laughlin, Thomas M., V.P. & Gen. Mgr.-Consumer Prods. Div.--Pharmacia & Upjohn, Kalamazoo, MI; *Int'l*, pg. 1048
Laughter, Barbara, Dir.-Mktg.--Everbrite, Inc., Greenfield, WI; *U.S. Private*, pg. 386
Lauletta, John, V.P.-Mktg. & Adv.--Gould Instrument Systems, Inc., Valley View, OH; *U.S. Public*, pg. 1592
Laura, Henry, V.P.-Sls., Mktg. & Adv./Agency Svcs.--The Arbitron Company, New York, NY; *U.S. Public*, pg. 331
Laurence, C., Dir.-Mktg.--Compass Group plc, Chertsey, United Kingdom,; *Int'l*, pg. 324
Laurenzi, Mark V., Exec. V.P.-Sls. & Mktg.--Marotta Scientific Controls, Inc., Montville, NJ; *U.S. Private*, pg. 706
Lauric, Jackie, Mgr.-Mktg. Commun.--Hypermedia Communications, Inc., San Mateo, CA; *U.S. Public*, pg. 851
Laurie, B.L., Dir.-Sls. & Mktg.--Coats Patons, Toronto, Canada; *Int'l*, pg. 300
Lauritzen, F.Q., Mgr.-European Mktg.--Wavin Bv, Zwolle, Netherlands; *Int'l*, pg. 1135
Lause, Steve, V.P.-Mktg.--Spartan Showcase, Inc., Union, MO; *U.S. Private*, pg. 904
Lausterer, Mary, Corp. Sec.--Hope's Architectural Products Inc., Jamestown, NY; *U.S. Private*, pg. 538
Lauteri, James, Asst. V.P. & Mgr.-Brand Mktg.--Mellon Bank Corporation, Pittsburgh, PA; *U.S. Public*, pg. 1084
Lauters, Gerald F., V.P.-Secondary Mktg.--First Financial Bank, FSB, Stevens Point, WI; *U.S. Public*, pg. 140
Lautzenhiser, Gary, Exec. V.P.-Sls., Mktg. & Bus. Devel.--Aristokraft, Inc., Jasper, IN; *U.S. Public*, pg. 675
LaValle, Joseph, Mgr.-Mktg. & Sls.--Washington Scientific Industries, Inc., Long Lake, MN; *U.S. Public*, pg. 1744
Lavelle, Barb, Mgr.-Sls. & Mktg.--Pennsylvania Cellular Telephone Corp., Williamsport, PA; *U.S. Public*, pg. 1708
Lavely, Anthony, Sr. V.P.-Sls. & Mktg.--Rally's Hamburgers, Inc., Louisville, KY; *U.S. Public*, pg. 1359
Lavely, Tony, Pres.-Consumer Mktg.--Creative Alliance, Inc., Louisville, KY; *U.S. Private*, pg. 287
Lavin, Chris, V.P.-Sls. & Mktg.--U.S. Filter, Lowell, MA; *U.S. Public*, pg. 1682
Lavin, Katherine, Dir.-Mktg. & Adv.--Dunmore Corporation, Newtown, PA; *U.S. Private*, pg. 346
Lavino, Sandy, V.P.-Mktg.--J.H. Baxter & Company, San Mateo, CA; *U.S. Private*, pg. 124
LaVite, Chris, Coord.-Mktg. Communications--Butler Manufacturing Company, Kansas City, MO; *U.S. Public*, pg. 271
Lavore, Tricia, Dir.-Mktg.--Casino Aztar, Evansville, IN; *U.S. Public*, pg. 158
Lavorgna, Anthony N., Mgr.-Mktg. & Sales--Airflex Div. Eaton Corp., Cleveland, OH; *U.S. Public*, pg. 556
Lavruhin, G., Chief Mktg. Officer--AutotractorExport, Moscow, Russia; *Int'l*, pg. 101
Law, Bob, Dir.-Sls. & Mktg.--Kenwood USA, Long Beach, CA; *Int'l*, pg. 730
Lawhorn, Mary Jane, Mgr.-Global Mktg.--Dell Computer Corporation, Round Rock, TX; *U.S. Public*, pg. 495
Lawler, A. Catherine, V.P.-Mktg.--Noma-International, Inc., Itasca, IL; *Int'l*, pg. 955
Lawless, Francis, V.P.-Mktg.--General Reinsurance Corp., Stamford, CT; *U.S. Public*, pg. 725
Lawrence, C. Philip, V.P.-Mktg.--InterLake Papers, Inc., Stamford, CT; *U.S. Public*, pg. 436
Lawrence, Charles, V.P.-Mktg. & Sls.--Zebco, Tulsa, OK; *U.S. Public*, pg. 265
Lawrence, Charles, V.P.-Mktg. & Sls.--Martin Reels, A Division of Zebco, Tulsa, OK; *U.S. Public*, pg. 265
Lawrence, Guy, Exec. V.P.-Intl. Distr. & Mktg.--MGM/UA Distribution Co., Santa Monica, CA; *U.S. Public*, pg. 1102
Lawrence, James L., V.P.-Mktg.--Hawaiian Independent Refinery, Inc., Honolulu, HI; *Int'l*, pg. 225
Lawrence, Larry, Mgr.-Mktg.--General Casualty Company of Wisconsin, Sun Prairie, WI; *Int'l*, pg. 345
Lawrence, Larry, Mgr.-Mktg.--General Casualty Company of Illinois, Freeport, IL; *Int'l*, pg. 346
Lawson, Chris, Dir.-Mktg. Communications--Grace Construction Products, Cambridge, MA; *U.S. Public*, pg. 755
Lawson, Damon, V.P.-Mktg. Commun.--Lawson Software, Minneapolis, MN; *U.S. Private*, pg. 654
Lawson, Heather, Dir.-Mktg./Software Div.--Dixons Group plc, Hemel Hempstead, United Kingdom,; *Int'l*, pg. 413
Lawson, Karmen, Mktg. Coord.--Kappler Safety Group, Inc., Guntersville, AL; *U.S. Private*, pg. 607
Lawson, Rodger A., Exec. V.P.-Mktg. & Plng.--The Prudential Insurance Company of America, Newark, NJ; *U.S. Private*, pg. 892
Lawton, John, V.P.-Sls. & Mktg.--Clean Harbors, Inc., Braintree, MA; *U.S. Public*, pg. 383
Lawton, Kristen, Coord.-Adv. & Mktg.--Hobie Cat Company, Oceanside, CA; *U.S. Private*, pg. 531
Lawton, Mike, Pres.-U.S. Baby Care--Gerber Products Company, Fremont, MI; *Int'l*, pg. 973
Lay, Sherry, Sr. V.P.-Mdsg. & Mktg.--Sunglass Hut International, Coral Gables, FL; *U.S. Public*, pg. 1535
Layman, Chris, Mgr.-Mktg.--Birmingham Steel Corp., Cleveland Div., Cleveland, OH; *U.S. Public*, pg. 232
Layman, Mark, Dir.-Mktg.-Data Mngmt.--Zoll Medical Corporation, Burlington, MA; *U.S. Private*, pg. 1207
Laymon, Eileen C., Sr. V.P.-Mktg.--GAB Robins North America, Inc., Parsippany, NJ; *Int'l*, pg. 1153
Layne, Stuart, Exec. V.P.-Mktg. & Sls.--Boston Celtics Limited Partnership, Boston, MA; *U.S. Public*, pg. 246
Lazar, Maureen, Coord.-Mktg. Communications--Safeskin Corporation, San Diego, CA; *U.S. Public*, pg. 1425
Lazarus, Denise, Mktg. Devel.--Farm Stores, Miami, FL; *U.S. Private*, pg. 394
Lazarus, Robert J., Dir.-Mktg.--L&R Manufacturing Co., Kearny, NJ; *U.S. Private*, pg. 638
Lazear, Scott, Sr. V.P.-Sls.--National Card Control, Inc., Crozier, VA; *U.S. Public*, pg. 321
Le Belle, Francois, Dir.-Mktg.--Bazar de L'Hotel de Ville, Paris, France; *Int'l*, pg. 181
Le Corre, Loic, Dir.-Mktg.-Novotel--Societe Internationale des Hotels Novotel, Evry, France; *Int'l*, pg. 21
Le Fevre, Paul, Chief Fin. Officer & Exec. V.P.-Strategic Plng. & Mktg.--Keyport Life Insurance Company, Boston, MA; *U.S. Private*, pg. 666
Le Gall, Karen, Mgr.-Mktg. Communications--Capintec Inc., Ramsey, NJ; *U.S. Private*, pg. 205
Le Jariel, Bertrand, Dir.-Mktg.--Bongrain S.A., Viroflay, France; *Int'l*, pg. 201
Lea, John, V.P.-Retail Sls. & Mktg.--Tyson Foods, Inc., Springdale, AR; *U.S. Public*, pg. 1652
Lea, Judy, Admin. Asst.-Mktg.--Tab Products Co., Palo Alto, CA; *U.S. Public*, pg. 1559
Lea, Melissa, V.P.-Mktg. & New Bus.--Arnold Communications, Inc., Boston, MA; *U.S. Private*, pg. 83
Leach, Brian, Mgr.-Mktg.--Salford Electrical Instruments Ltd., Heywood, United Kingdom; *Int'l*, pg. 545
Leach, David P., V.P.-Sls. & Mktg.--GH Hensley Industries, Inc., Dallas, TX; *U.S. Private*, pg. 439
Leach, Mike, Dir.-Mktg.--Carquest Corporation, Lakewood, CO; *U.S. Private*, pg. 215
Leach, Thomas, Dir.-Sls. & Mktg.--Horton Homes, Inc., Eatonton, GA; *U.S. Private*, pg. 540
Leahy, Robert B., Sr. V.P.-Sls. & Mktg.--Folger Nolan Fleming Douglas, Washington, DC; *U.S. Private*, pg. 416
Leaman, Donald H., Jr., Dir.-Adv. & Mktg.--Rystan Company, Inc., Little Falls, NJ; *U.S. Private*, pg. 436
Leamer, Jim, Exec. V.P.-Sls. & Mktg.--McSwain Carpets Inc., Cincinnati, OH; *U.S. Private*, pg. 725
Lear, Diane C., Admin.-Mktg. Services--Voith Hydro, Inc., York, PA; *Int'l*, pg. 1473
Learmonth, George M., Dir.-Mktg.--Lincoln Electric Mexicana S.A. de C.V., Mexico, Mexico; *U.S. Public*, pg. 997
Leary, Tim, Mgr.-Mktg.--Photo-Me International plc, Bookham, United Kingdom; *Int'l*, pg. 1055
Leasure, Kimberly, Dir.-Mktg. & Research--The Network of City Business Journals, Inc., Kansas City, MO; *U.S. Private*, pg. 19
Leavengood, Robert, V.P.-Sls. & Mktg.--UniSea Foods, Inc., Redmond, WA; *Int'l*, pg. 940
Leavitt, Adam, V.P.-Mktg.--Crystal Cruises, Inc., Los Angeles, CA; *Int'l*, pg. 941
Leavitt, John, Sr. V.P.-Sls. & Mktg.--Prime Hospitality Corp., Fairfield, NJ; *U.S. Public*, pg. 1326
Leavitt, Thomas, Sr. V.P.-Opers.--United Asset Management Corporation, Boston, MA; *U.S. Public*, pg. 1672
Leback, Elissa, Sr. V.P.-Mktg. Strategy--Viacom Enterprises, New York, NY; *U.S. Private*, pg. 779
LeBaron, Ron, Dir-Mktg.--American Nucleonics Corp., Westlake Village, CA; *U.S. Public*, pg. 556
LeBed, Orest, V.P.-Sls. & Mktg.--John Dusenbery Co., Inc., Randolph, NJ; *U.S. Private*, pg. 349
LeBlanc, Greg, V.P.-Mktg. & Sls.--CEM Corporation, Matthews, NC; *U.S. Public*, pg. 277
LeBlanc, Thomas C., Commercial Dir.-Alumina Prods.--LaRoche Industries Inc., Atlanta, GA; *U.S. Private*, pg. 651
Lechner, Michelle, Mktg. Specialist--Aubrey Manufacturing Company, Hartford, WI; *U.S. Public*, pg. 1193
Lecomte, Y.A., Dir.-Mktg.--TradeARBED S.A., Luxembourg, Luxembourg; *Int'l*, pg. 79
Leddy, Ed, Dir.-Mktg.--Pilot Corporation, Knoxville, TN; *U.S. Private*, pg. 865
Leddy, Kevin, Sr. V.P.-Mktg.--Time Warner Cable, Stamford, CT; *U.S. Public*, pg. 1610
Lederer, Steve, Mgr.-Mktg.--Harding Lawson Associates Group, Inc., Novato, CA; *U.S. Public*, pg. 785
Lederer, Steve, Dir.-Corp. Mktg. Grp.--Harding Lawson Associates, Novato, CA; *U.S. Public*, pg. 785
Lederman, John, Mgr.-Mktg. Communications--The BOC Group Inc. (Delaware), Murray Hill, NJ; *Int'l*, pg. 121

Ledger, Sarah, Mktg. Mgr.--Hawthorne Communications, Inc., Fairfield, IA; *U.S. Private*, pg. 512
Lee, Bill, Dir.-Mktg. Services--National Retail Hardware Assn., Indianapolis, IN; *U.S. Private*, pg. 786
Lee, Billy, Mgr.-Mktg.--Kvaerner Hong Kong R O for Kvaerner Singapore Pte Ltd, Sha Tin, Hong Kong; *Int'l*, pg. 772
Lee, Carole, Dir.-Mktg.--Conbraco Industries Inc., Matthews, NC; *U.S. Private*, pg. 261
Lee, Dani, Sls. & Mktg. Coord.--Gilliam Candy Brands, Edwardsville, KS; *U.S. Private*, pg. 454
Lee, Deana, Mgr.-Mktg.--Bessin Corporation, Chicago, IL; *U.S. Public*, pg. 1433
Lee, Deana, Mgr.-Mktg.--Best Kosher Sausage Co., Chicago, IL; *U.S. Public*, pg. 1433
Lee, Doo-Hwan, Pres.--Ssangyong Uni-Charm Co., Ltd., Kumi, Korea; *Int'l*, pg. 1291
Lee, Greg, Exec. V.P.-Sls., Mktg. & Tech. Svcs.--Tyson Foods, Inc., Springdale, AR; *U.S. Public*, pg. 1652
Lee, Howard, V.P.-Mktg.-Domestications Catalog--Hanover Direct, Inc., Weehawken, NJ; *U.S. Public*, pg. 782
Lee, Jack D., V.P.-Sls. & Mktg.--Associated Industrial Supply, Inc., Columbia, SC; *U.S. Private*, pg. 91
Lee, Jack R., Sr. V.P.-Mktg.--Domco Inc., Farnham, Canada; *Int'l*, pg. 415
Lee, Jae-Woong, Mgr.--Ssangyong Information & Communication Corporation, Seoul, Korea; *Int'l*, pg. 1292
Lee, James, Mgr.-Mktg.--China Ecotek Corporation, Kao-hsiung, Taiwan; *Int'l*, pg. 285
Lee, Jay, Mgr.-Mktg. Communications-Dodge Products--Rockwell Automation, Milwaukee, WI; *U.S. Public*, pg. 1397
Lee, Jenny, Mgr.-Mktg.--The Uncle Toby's Company Ltd., Richmond, Australia; *Int'l*, pg. 555
Lee, Joanna, Mgr.-Mktg.--Orchard Parade Holdings Limited, Singapore, Singapore; *Int'l*, pg. 1007
Lee, John A., Dir.-Product & Mktg. Svcs.--Halifax plc, Halifax, United Kingdom; *Int'l*, pg. 589
Lee, Kiwhan, Sr. V.P.-Sls. & Mktg.--American Tape Co., Secaucus, NJ; *Int'l*, pg. 685
Lee, Kwan-Sep, Chief Fin. Officer--Ssangyong Investment & Finance Co., Ltd., Inchon, Korea; *Int'l*, pg. 1292
Lee, Lelia, Mgr.-Mktg.--The Travel Channel, Atlanta, GA; *U.S. Private*, pg. 647
Lee, Michael, Dir.-Sls. & Mktg.--Zung Fu Company Ltd., Hong Kong, Hong Kong; *Int'l*, pg. 704
Lee, Nancy, Dir.-Mktg.-Instruments--GN Nettest Fiber Optic Division, Utica, NY; *Int'l*, pg. 536
Lee, Peter, V.P.-Mktg. & Admissions--Heald Colleges, San Francisco, CA; *U.S. Private*, pg. 514
Lee, Richard E., Dir.-Mktg.--The Lathrop Company, Toledo, OH; *U.S. Public*, pg. 1645
Lee, Robert S., V.P.--American Indemnity Financial Corp., Galveston, TX; *U.S. Public*, pg. 83
Lee, Robert S., Mgr.-Mktg.--American Fire & Indemnity Co., Galveston, TX; *U.S. Public*, pg. 83
Lee, Ronald C., Mktg. & Pub. Rels. Officer--Community First Bankshares, Inc., Fargo, ND; *U.S. Public*, pg. 416
Lee, Samuel Z., Dir.-Mktg. & Bus. Devel.--SmithKline Beecham Research Limited, Pasig, Philippines; *Int'l*, pg. 1266
Lee, Suk-Rae, Dir.-Mktg.--Dong-Suh Foods Corporation, Inchon, Korea; *Int'l*, pg. 416
Lee, Terry, V.P.-Mktg.--Zero-Max, Inc., Minneapolis, MN; *Int'l*, pg. 866
Lee, W. Bruce, Dir.-Corp. Mktg.--Gilbane Building Company, Providence, RI; *U.S. Private*, pg. 452
Lee, Yong-Hae, V.P.--Ssangyong Corporation, Seoul, Korea; *Int'l*, pg. 1291
Leech, W. Michael, V.P.-Sls. & Mktg.--W.G. Carroll, Inc., Atlanta, GA; *U.S. Public*, pg. 1071
Leek, John, Mgr.-Sls. & Mktg.--Baldwin (UK) Ltd., Dunstable, United Kingdom; *U.S. Public*, pg. 170
Leeming, John B., V.P.-Sls. & Mktg.--Nomaco, Inc., Zebulon, NC; *U.S. Private*, pg. 801
Leenerman, Sue, Dir.-Mktg.--Ciprico, Inc., Plymouth, MN; *U.S. Public*, pg. 370
Leeper, Frank, Mgr.-Channel Mktg.--Stanley Door Systems, Troy, MI; *U.S. Public*, pg. 1509
Leerink, J., Dir.-Sls. & Mktg.--Hak B.V., Giessen, Netherlands; *Int'l*, pg. 244
Leerskov, Metha S., Mgr.-Mktg.--GN Netcom A/S, Copenhagen, Denmark; *Int'l*, pg. 537
LeFebvre, Timothy, V.P.-Domestic Sls. & Mktg.--NESLAB Instruments, Inc., Newington, NH; *U.S. Public*, pg. 1595
LeFevre, Robert M., Sr. V.P.-Mktg. & Sls.--The United States Playing Card Company, Cincinnati, OH; *U.S. Private*, pg. 1125
Lefkowitz, Richard, Media & Mktg. Services Dir.--Emmerling Post, Inc., New York, NY; *U.S. Private*, pg. 374
Lefstedt, Jon, V.P.-Mktg.-Kinney--Kinney Shoe Corporation, New York, NY; *U.S. Public*, pg. 1777
Leftwich, John, V.P.-Europe Mktg.--Microsoft Corporation, Redmond, WA; *U.S. Public*, pg. 1107
LeGault, Sharon, Mgr.-Mktg.--Cooper Instrument Corp., Middlefield, CT; *U.S. Private*, pg. 274
Legerstrom, Leslie, Mktg. Coord.--Phillips Plastics Corporation, Phillips, WI; *U.S. Private*, pg. 862
Legros, Dick, V.P.-Religious Sls. & Mktg.--Standard Publishing, Cincinnati, OH; *U.S. Public*, pg. 1506
Legura, Mauro, Mgr.-Mktg. Communications--IBM Brasil-Industria Maquinas e Servicos Ltda., Rio de Janeiro, Brazil; *U.S. Public*, pg. 896
Lehmann, Daryl, Mgr.-Mktg. Product--Criticare Systems, Inc., Waukesha, WI; *U.S. Public*, pg. 459
Lehman, Mike, V.P.-Sls. & Mktg.--Bard Mfg. Co., Bryan, OH; *U.S. Private*, pg. 116
Lehman, Patti, Dir.-Mktg.--Rio Hotel & Casino Inc., Las Vegas, NV; *U.S. Public*, pg. 1390
Lehmbeck, Barney L., Sr. V.P.-Bus. Devel., Mktg. & Adv.--Liberty Bancorp, Inc., Oklahoma City, OK; *U.S. Public*, pg. 174
Lehmusto-Eranen, Kirsti, Mng. Dir.-Mktg.--Academic Bookstore, Helsinki, Finland; *Int'l*, pg. 1301
Lehning, Larry, Mgr.-Sls. & Mktg.--Liberty Precision Industries, Rochester, NY; *U.S. Private*, pg. 666
Lehr, Mike, Exec. Dir.-Broadcasting & Mktg.--The Orioles, Inc., Baltimore, MD; *U.S. Private*, pg. 819
Lehtinen, Olavi, Mng. Dir.-Mktg. & Buying--Sesto, Helsinki, Finland; *Int'l*, pg. 1301
Leibman, Carl, Dir.-Mktg.--ID Magazine, New York, NY; *Int'l*, *pg. 1446*
Leibman, Nora J., Dir.-Mkt. Res.--Pacific Enterprises, Los Angeles, CA; *U.S. Public*, pg. 1249
Leibowitz, Del, V.P.-Mktg.--Naturistics, Farmingdale, NY; *U.S. Public*, pg. 494
Leibowitz, Jennifer, Mktg., Commun., & Adv.--Medical Laboratory Automation, Inc., Pleasantville, NY; *U.S. Private*, pg. 727
Leicht, Ronald J., Sr. Mng. Dir.-Mktg.--Mazda Motor Corporation, Hiroshima, Japan; *Int'l*, pg. 849
Leier, Pam R., Mgr.-Mktg.--Lampert Yards, Inc., Saint Paul, MN; *U.S. Private*, pg. 645
Leigh, Carol, Mgr.-Mktg. Commun.--Midland Enterprises Inc., Cincinnati, OH; *U.S. Public*, pg. 549
Leighton, Steven E., V.P.-Mktg. Svcs.--Fingerhut Corp., Minnetonka, MN; *U.S. Public*, pg. 623
Leikauskis, Darryln, Dir.-Mktg.-Restaurant Division--Brigham's, Inc., Arlington, MA; *U.S. Private*, pg. 483
Leinart, Julia, V.P.-Mktg.--Kayser-Roth Corporation, New York, NY; *Int'l*, pg. 576
Leinfuss, Ellen, V.P.-Mktg. & Commun.--EA Engineering, Science & Technology, Inc., Hunt Valley, MD; *U.S. Public*, pg. 540
Leininger, Edward R., V.P.-Sls. & Mktg.--GSE, Inc., Farmington, MI; *U.S. Public*, pg. 1676
Leinwand, Benna, Asst. V.P.-Mktg.--Valley Bank & Trust, Brighton, CO; *U.S. Private*, pg. 1132
Leistritz, John P., V.P.-Mktg.--Paul Arpin Vanlines, Inc., West Warwick, RI; *U.S. Private*, pg. 85
Leland, Scott, Dir.-Mktg.--Bush Brothers & Company, Knoxville, TN; *U.S. Private*, pg. 189
LeMaster, Curt H., V.P.-Mktg. Pur. & Sys.--Wolohan Lumber Co., Saginaw, MI; *U.S. Public*, pg. 1774
LeMayo, Joan, Dir.-Sls. & Mktg./Crown Grp.--Random House, Inc., New York, NY; *U.S. Private*, pg. 20
Lemberger, Mark, Sr. V.P.-Sls. & Mktg.--Western States Envelope Co., Milwaukee, WI; *U.S. Private*, pg. 1168
Lemert, Paul, Gen. Mgr. & Dir.-Mktg.--Agri-Graphics, Inc., Pittsburg, KS; *U.S. Private*, pg. 46
Lemieux, Joceline, Mgr.-Mktg.--Gandalf Canada Ltd., Nepean, Canada; *Int'l*, pg. 540
Lemire, Roger, Mgr.-Mktg.--Calgary Flames Hockey Club, Calgary, Canada; *Int'l*, pg. 252
Lemke, T.F., Dir.-Mktg.--Inco Alloys International, Inc., Huntington, WV; *Int'l*, pg. 672
Lemm, Dick, V.P.-Mktg. & Adv.--Mini Mart, Inc., Casper, WY; *U.S. Public*, pg. 967
Lemmo, Mark, V.P. & Gen. Mgr.-Sls. & Mktg.--InterDigital Communications Corp., King of Prussia, PA; *U.S. Public*, pg. 889
Lemuigh, Henrik, Dir.-Mktg.--Dagbladet Boersen A/S, Copenhagen, Denmark; *Int'l*, pg. 359
Lenahan, Beth, Gen. Mgr.-Consumer Mktg.--Infoseek Corporaton, Sunnyvale, CA; *U.S. Public*, pg. 876
Lenandowski, Thomas, Sr. V.P.-Mktg.--Jones Medical Industries Inc., Saint Louis, MO; *U.S. Public*, pg. 933
Lenarz, Christy, Asst. Dir.-Mktg.--The Mighty Ducks of Anaheim, Anaheim, CA; *U.S. Public*, pg. 513
Lenci, Denise, Dir.-Bus. Communications--Engelhard Corporation, Iselin, NJ; *U.S. Public*, pg. 582
Lenhart, Betsy, Dir.-Mktg.--Waverly International, Baltimore, MD; *U.S. Public*, pg. 1748
Lennon, Chuck, Asst. V.P.-Mktg.--Sir Speedy, Inc., Mission Viejo, CA; *U.S. Private*, pg. 423
Lennon, John J., V.P.-Mktg.--Wisdom Imports Sales Co. Inc., Irvine, CA; *Int'l*, pg. 679
Lennox, Roy, Gen. Mgr.-Employee Benefits Actuarial Svcs. & Mktg.--Employee Benefits Div., Rondebosch, South Africa; *Int'l*, pg. 77
Lenny, Rick, V.P.-Mktg. & Sls.--Kraft Foods Inc., Rye Brook, NY; *U.S. Public*, pg. 1288
Lent, Martin, V.P.-Mktg.--Victor Technology, Addison, IL; *U.S. Private*, pg. 1139
Lentine, John, V.P.--Rex Lumber Company, Acton, MA; *U.S. Private*, pg. 926
Lentz, Thomas N., V.P.-Mktg.--Broyhill Furniture Industries, Inc., Saint Louis, MO; *U.S. Public*, pg. 688
Lenzi, David, Gen. Mgr.-Mktg.--Olympic Steel Inc., Cleveland, OH; *U.S. Public*, pg. 1221
Lenzo, Joe, Mgr.-Mktg.--Groschopp, Inc., Sioux Center, IA; *Int'l*, pg. 559
Leon del Rio, Jorge, Dir. Gen.-Mktg. & New Prods.--Grupo Elektra S.A. de C.V., Mexico, Mexico; *Int'l*, pg. 573
Leonard, Michael S., V.P.-Mktg. & Sls.--Continental Promotion Group, Tempe, AZ; *U.S. Private*, pg. 269
Leone, Chuck, V.P., Sales & Mktg.-Nissan--Nissan Forklift Corporation, North America, Marengo, IL; *Int'l*, pg. 944
Leone, Rick, V.P.-Sls. & Mktg.--Bonney Forge Corporation, Allentown, PA; *U.S. Private*, pg. 156
Leong, Kevin, Dir.-Convention Mktg.--Singapore Tourist Promotion Board, Singapore, Singapore; *Int'l*, pg. 1253
LePard, Gail, Dir.- Mkt. Res.--Computer Sciences Corporation, El Segundo, CA; *U.S. Public*, pg. 422
Leppert, Tom, Sr. V.P.-Sls. & Mktg.--Sargent & Greenleaf, Inc., Nicholasville, KY; *U.S. Private*, pg. 965
Leprince-Ringuet, Anne, Dir.-Mktg.-Novotel--Societe Internationale des Hotels Novotel, Evry, France; *Int'l*, pg. 21
LePrince, Lionel, Dir.-Mktg.--Kerlane, Courbevoie, France; *Int'l*, pg. 1176
Lerandeau, Michelle, V.P.-Retail Mktg.--McKesson U.S. Health Care, San Francisco, CA; *U.S. Public*, pg. 1073
Leshinski, Bruce A., Sr. V.P.-Sls. & Mktg.--Newly Weds Foods Inc., Chicago, IL; *U.S. Private*, pg. 796
LeSieur, Donald H., Exec. V.P. & Pres. Intl. Div.--Block Drug Company, Inc., Jersey City, NJ; *U.S. Public*, pg. 236
Lesko, Dennis, V.P.-Mktg.--Broadmoor Hotel, Inc., Colorado Springs, CO; *U.S. Private*, pg. 170
Less, Charles M., V.P.-Mktg.--Ferro Corporation, Cleveland, OH; *U.S. Public*, pg. 618
Lester, Cathy, Dir.-Lamp Mktg.--Angelo Brothers Co., Philadelphia, PA; *U.S. Private*, pg. 74
Lester, D. Nelson, V.P.-Mktg. & Sls.--Porcelain Products, Carey, OH; *U.S. Public*, pg. 308
Lester, Darrell, V.P.-Mktg. Services--Publishers Clearing House, Port Washington, NY; *U.S. Private*, pg. 893
Lester, Tricia, V.P.-Mktg.--Syntellect, Inc., Phoenix, AZ; *U.S.* Public, pg. 1550
Leu, Dennis T., V.P.-Business Mngmt.--Velsicol Chemical Corporation, Rosemont, IL; *U.S. Private*, pg. 1135
Leuchtenberger, Mark, V.P.-Mktg. & Sls.--Biogen, Inc., Cambridge, MA; *U.S. Public*, pg. 230
Leutas, Tony, Mgr.-Mktg. Commun.--Waters Corporation, Milford, MA; *U.S. Public*, pg. 1745
Leutenegger, Aldo, Chief Oper. Officer--Swissmetal Italia s.r.l., Milan, Italy; *Int'l*, pg. 1427
Leuthe, Paul, Mgr.-Corp. Mktg.--Sub-Zero Freezer Co., Inc., Madison, WI; *U.S. Private*, pg. 1048
LeVan, Jack A., Sr. V.P.-Mktg.--Zebra Technologies Corporation, Vernon Hills, IL; *U.S. Public*, pg. 1790
Levasseur, Martha, Dir.-Mktg.--Allen Telecom Inc., Solon, OH; *U.S. Public*, pg. 45
Levenson, Allen, V.P.-Mktg.--Petroleum Heat & Power Co., Stamford, CT; *U.S. Public*, pg. 1281
Lever, Edith, V.P.-Mktg.--Craftmatic Industries, Inc., Trevose, PA; *U.S. Private*, pg. 284
Levesque, Richard, V.P.-Mkt. Devel.--Walker Systems, Inc., Williamstown, WV; *U.S. Private*, pg. 1184
Levett, Alison, Dir.-Mktg.--Campbell Grocery Products Ltd., Kings Lynn, United Kingdom; *U.S. Public*, pg. 299
Levin, Bob, Mgr.-Mktg. Bus.--Lerner New York, New York, NY; *U.S. Public*, pg. 996
Levin, Diane, Dir.-Mktg. & Strategic Plng.--Brown and Caldwell, Pleasant Hill, CA; *U.S. Private*, pg. 173
Levin, Jackie, V.P.-Mktg.--Griffith Laboratories Worldwide, Inc., Alsip, IL; *U.S. Private*, pg. 481
Levin, Nancy, V.P.-Reg. Mktg.--Commerce Bancshares, Inc., Kansas City, MO; *U.S. Public*, pg. 409
Levin, Nancy E., Mgr.-Mktg.--Commerce Bank N.A., Kansas City, MO; *U.S. Public*, pg. 409
Levin, Peter R., Dir.-Strategic Mkt. Plng.--Cadillac Motor Car Division, Warren, MI; *U.S. Public*, pg. 720
Levin, Robert, Pres.-Worldwide Mktg., Sony Pictures--Columbia Pictures, Culver City, CA; *Int'l*, pg. 1281
Levin, Robert, Pres.-Worldwide Mktg.--Sony Pictures Entertainment, Culver City, CA; *Int'l*, pg. 1281
Levin, Robert J., Exec. V.P.-Mktg.--Federal National Mortgage Association (Fannie Mae), Washington, DC; *U.S. Public*, pg. 615
Levin, Stephen J., Exec. V.P.-Sls.--Telemundo Group, Inc., Hialeah, FL; *U.S. Public*, pg. 1570
Levine, D.S., V.P.-Sls. & Mktg., Indus. Prods. Grp.--Flowserve Corporation, Valve Div., Cookeville, TN; *U.S. Public*, pg. 658
Levine, Gary M., Sr. V.P.-Mktg.--Medicine Shoppe International, Inc., Saint Louis, MO; *U.S. Public*, pg. 304
Levine, Hy, Dir.-Print Mktg. (Motion Pictures)--The Walt Disney Company, Burbank, CA; *U.S. Public*, pg. 511
Levine, Jane, Publr.--Chicago Reader, Inc., Chicago, IL; *U.S. Private*, pg. 235
Levine, Larry, V.P.-Mktg.--Glenoit Mills, Inc., Tarboro, NC; *U.S. Private*, pg. 456
Levine, Mark, Exec. V.P. & Strategic Devel. Dir.--Wunderman Cato Johnson, New York, NY; *U.S. Private*, pg. 1197
Levine, Mark B., V.P.-Sls. & Mktg.--Watts Fluidair, Kittery, ME; *Int'l*, pg. 1243
Levine, Michael E., Exec. V.P.-Mktg. & Intl.--Northwest Airlines Corp., Saint Paul, MN; *U.S. Public*, pg. 1199
Levine, Michael E., Exec. V.P.-Mktg. & Intl.--Northwest Airlines, Inc., Saint Paul, MN; *U.S. Public*, pg. 1200
Levine, Steve, Exec. V.P.-Mktg.--Bel-Art Products, Pequannock, NJ; *U.S. Private*, pg. 130
Levine, Todd, V.P.-Mktg. & Sls.--Don Alleson, Inc., Rochester, NY; *U.S. Private*, pg. 339
Levinson, A.J., Mktg. Asst.--Centrifugal & Mechanical Industries, Saint Louis, MO; *U.S. Private*, pg. 370
Levinson, Adam, V.P.-Sls. & Mktg.--Sunroc Corporation, Dover, DE; *U.S. Private*, pg. 1053
Levinson, Lee, Dir.-Mktg.--General Housewares Corp., Terre Haute, IN; *U.S. Public*, pg. 715
Levis, Marcia, V.P.-Mktg.-Cosmed Div.--Beiersdorf, Inc., Norwalk, CT; *Int'l*, pg. 182
Levis, Michael, V.P.-Mktg.--Xicor, Inc., Milpitas, CA; *U.S. Public*, pg. 1785
Levitt, Wayne M., V.P.-Mktg.--Gate Petroleum Company, Jacksonville, FL; *U.S. Private*, pg. 441
Levoyer, A., Mgr.-Mktg.--Pernod, Creteil, France; *Int'l*, pg. 566
Levy, Carolyn J., Sr. V.P.-Mktg. & Sls. Information--Philip Morris U.S.A., New York, NY; *U.S. Public*, pg. 1289
Levy, Malcolm, V.P.-Sls. & Mktg.--Racal Instruments, Inc., Irvine, CA; *Int'l*, pg. 1083
Levy, Neal, Mgr.-Mktg. & Res.--Taco John's International, Inc., Cheyenne, WY; *U.S. Private*, pg. 1066
Levy, Sally, V.P.-Mktg.--U.S. Can Company, Newnan, GA; *U.S. Public*, pg. 1681
Levy, Steven E., V.P.-Sls. & Mktg.--Copperweld Bimetallics Products Co., Fayetteville, TN; *Int'l*, pg. 662
Lewenhagen, Stig, Mgr.-Mktg. & Pur.--Skanska Installation AB, Sundbyberg, Sweden; *Int'l*, pg. 1260
Lewin, Sandra, Dir.-Corp. Communications & Pub. Rels.--George Wimpey PLC, London, United Kingdom; *Int'l*, pg. 1510
Lewis, A.H., Mgr.-Intl. Mktg.--Krups GmbH & Co. KG, Solingen, Germany; *Int'l*, pg. 896
Lewis, Brad, V.P.-Mktg. Devel.--Joy Mining Machinery, Warrendale, PA; *U.S. Public*, pg. 789
Lewis, Carole, Dir.-Mktg.--American Marketing Industries, Inc., Kansas City, MO; *U.S. Private*, pg. 58

Lewis, Carole, Mgr.-Direct Mktg.--Swingster Company, Kansas City, MO; *U.S. Private*, pg. 58
Lewis, Crismon, Dir.-Mktg.--Landa, Inc., Portland, OR; *U.S. Private*, pg. 646
Lewis, David, Dir.-Mktg. Services--Lloyds TSB Group PLC, London, United Kingdom; *Int'l*, pg. 812
Lewis, Dick, Sr. V.P.-Mktg. & Sls.--Fortis Financial Group, Woodbury, MN; *Int'l*, pg. 499
Lewis, Don, Product Mgr.-Mktg.--Tekelec, Calabasas, CA; *U.S. Public*, pg. 1566
Lewis, Glynn, V.P.-Advanced Program--Planning Systems Inc., Mc Lean, VA; *U.S. Private*, pg. 869
Lewis, Jeanne, Sr. V.P.-Retail & Small Bus. Mktg.--Staples, Inc., Westborough, MA; *U.S. Public*, pg. 1509
Lewis, Jeff, V.P.-Hush Puppies Div.--Wolverine World Wide, Inc., Rockford, MI; *U.S. Public*, pg. 1775
Lewis, Julian B., V.P.-Mktg.--Fuller Company, Bethlehem, PA; *Int'l*, pg. 475
Lewis, Keith M., V.P.-Global Mktg. Porsche Design--Bausch & Lomb Incorporated, Rochester, NY; *U.S. Public*, pg. 194
Lewis, Kurt W., V.P.-Mktg. & Sls.--Fujisawa U.S.A. Inc., Deerfield, IL; *Int'l*, pg. 525
Lewis, Lon D., V.P.-Mktg. Bus. Devel.--Republic Group Incorporated, Hutchinson, KS; *U.S. Public*, pg. 1378
Lewis, Mark, Dir.-Mktg.--Planet Products Corp., Cincinnati, OH; *U.S. Private*, pg. 869
Lewis, Mary, Mgr.-Mktg. Communications--Greenlee Textron, Rockford, IL; *U.S. Public*, pg. 1589
Lewis, Melvin, V.P.-Mktg.--Maytag Company, Newton, IA; *U.S. Public*, pg. 1064
Lewis, Michael E., Mgr.-Sls. & Mktg.--Ekstrom Industries, Inc., Farmington Hills, MI; *U.S. Private*, pg. 172
Lewis, Mike, Mgr.-Mktg.-Electric Guitars--Fender Musical Instruments, Scottsdale, AZ; *U.S. Private*, pg. 400
Lewis, Robert B., V.P. & Gen. Mgr.--Asahi/America, Inc., Malden, MA; *U.S. Public*, pg. 137
Lewis, Roger L., 1st V.P.-Mktg.--Commercial Federal Corporation, Omaha, NE; *U.S. Public*, pg. 411
Lewis, Ron, Dir.-Mktg.--Myrick Construction Inc., Biscoe, NC; *U.S. Private*, pg. 771
Lewis, Samuel A., V.P.-Sls.--Elgar Corporation, San Diego, CA; *U.S. Public*, pg. 789
Lewis, Tommy, Dir.-Mktg.--The United Methodist Publishing House, Nashville, TN; *U.S. Private*, pg. 1122
Lewis, Tommy, Dir.-Mktg.--Abingdon Press, Nashville, TN; *U.S. Private*, pg. 1123
Lewis, Vern, Dir.-Mktg. & Mktg. Services--Medical Economics Company Inc., Montvale, NJ; *U.S. Public*, pg. 1601
Lewis, William, Dir.-Mktg. Professional Audio--Carver Corporation, Lynnwood, WA; *U.S. Public*, pg. 310
Lewtan, Elisabeth, Dir.-Mktg.--Lewtan Industries Corp., Hartford, CT; *U.S. Private*, pg. 666
Ley, George, Dir.-Mktg.--Acme Tube Inc., Somerset, NJ; *U.S. Private*, pg. 14
Lezin, Matt, V.P.--Salz Leathers, Inc., Santa Cruz, CA; *U.S. Private*, pg. 963
Li, Angelina H., V.P.-Mktg. Res.--Cox Communications, Inc., Atlanta, GA; *U.S. Public*, pg. 454
Li, Sung Taek, Dir.-Mktg.--Dong Bu Insurance Co., Seoul, Korea; *Int'l*, pg. 416
Liang, Tom, Mgr.-Mktg.--Litton Systems Canada Ltd., Etobicoke, Canada; *U.S. Public*, pg. 1005
Libit, Jordan M., V.P.-Mktg.--FileNet Corporation, Costa Mesa, CA; *U.S. Public*, pg. 622
Librizzi, Joseph A., Sr. V.P.-Mktg. & Sls.--Jevic Transportation, Inc., Delanco, NJ; *U.S. Public*, pg. 927
Librock, Ned T., V.P.-Sls. & Mktg.--Columbus McKinnon Corp., Amherst, NY; *U.S. Public*, pg. 405
Lichtendahl, Kathleen, Dir.-Mktg.--Hudepohl-Schoenling Brewing Company, Cincinnati, OH; *U.S. Private*, pg. 545
Lichtman, Howard, Exec. V.P.-Mktg. & Communications--Cineplex Odeon Corporation, Toronto, Canada; *Int'l*, pg. 292
Lichty, Craig, Dir.-Mktg./Terex Cranes--Terex Corporation, Westport, CT; *U.S. Public*, pg. 1581
Lichty, Craig, Mgr.-Mktg.--Terex Cranes, Conway, SC; *U.S. Public*, pg. 1581
Lickstein, Mark, Dir.-Mktg., Pub. Rels. & Commun.--Farmers & Merchants Bank of Central California, Lodi, CA; *U.S. Private*, pg. 394
Lieber, E., Dir.-Mktg. & Sls.--Presstek, Inc., Hudson, NH; *U.S. Public*, pg. 1324
Lieber, Murray, V.P.-Mktg.--Hercon Laboratories Corp., New York, NY; *U.S. Public*, pg. 802
Lieberman, Daniel, Pres.--A&W Restaurants, Inc.-Carousel Div., Minneapolis, MN; *U.S. Private*, pg. 2
Liebman, Paul, Mgr.-Mktg.--Coilcraft, Inc., Cary, IL; *U.S. Private*, pg. 250
Liebman, William, V.P.-Mktg.--Comtech PST Corp., Melville, NY; *U.S. Public*, pg. 425
Liebscher, Klaus, Dr., Dir.-Gen. Mngmt.--Raiffeisen Zentralbank Osterreich, Vienna, Austria; *Int'l*, pg. 1084
Liegeois, Paul J., Gen. Mgr.-Mktg. & Bus. Devel.--Wisconsin Public Service Corporation, Green Bay, WI; *U.S. Public*, pg. 1728
Lien, Grant, V.P.-Sls. & Mktg.--Tyler Industries, Benson, MN; *U.S. Private*, pg. 1112
Lieppe, Julia, Dir.-Mktg.--Western Farm Credit Bank, Sacramento, CA; *U.S. Private*, pg. 398
Liever, Damon, Sr. V.P.-Mktg. & Bus. Devel.--Uno Restaurant Corporation, West Roxbury, MA; *U.S. Public*, pg. 1698
Lifshitz, Uzi, V.P.-Mktg.--Mennen Medical Ltd., Rehovot, Israel; *Int'l*, pg. 858
Liggins, Darlene, Mgr.-Mktg. Communications--Owens Corning/Foamular, Parsippany, NJ; *U.S. Public*, pg. 1237
Light, Cynthia L., Second V.P.-Individual Mktg.--Shenandoah Life Insurance Company, Roanoke, VA; *U.S. Private*, pg. 992
Light, Kenneth B., Chief Fin. Officer, Chief Admin. Officer & Exec. V.P.--Allied Products Corporation, Chicago, IL; *U.S. Public*, pg. 48
Light, Michelle, Sr. V.P.-Sls. & Mktg.--Michael Anthony Jewelers, Inc., Mount Vernon, NY; *U.S. Public*, pg. 1103
Light, Ted, V.P.-Sls. & Mktg.--DuBois Chemicals, Cincinnati, OH; *Int'l*, pg. 1437
Lightbourne, Michael R., Sr. V.P.-Mktg.--Rentrak Corporation, Portland, OR; *U.S. Public*, pg. 1377
Lightfoot, Donald P., V.P.-Worldwide Mktg.--CalComp Technology, Inc., Anaheim, CA; *U.S. Public*, pg. 1007
Liistro, Brenda, V.P.-Mktg.-Infant Care--Playtex Beauty Care, Inc., Westport, CT; *U.S. Public*, pg. 1311
Lill, Geoff D., Gen. Mgr.-Mktg. & Transport Services--BHP Coal, Brisbane, Australia; *Int'l*, pg. 223
Lilley, Jackie, Dir.-Promo. & Event Mktg.--Nestle USA, Glendale, CA; *Int'l*, pg. 916
Lim, Cindy, Dir.-Intl Mktg-Div. II--Malaysia Tourism Promotion Board (MTPB), Kuala Lumpur, Malaysia; *Int'l*, pg. 832
Lim, George, V.P.-Mktg.--Philippine Long Distance Telephone Company, Manila, Philippines; *Int'l*, pg. 1051
Lim, K.S., Gen. Mgr.-Mktg.--Mobil Oil Singapore Pte. Ltd., Singapore, Singapore; *U.S. Public*, pg. 1119
Lim, Ron, Dir.-Mktg. & Sls.--Stonco Genlyte, Union, NJ; *U.S. Public*, pg. 730
Liman, Peter, V.P.-Mktg.--Tristar Corp., San Antonio, TX; *U.S. Public*, pg. 1640
Limata, Albert, Dir.-Mktg.--Gallo/Galileo Salame, San Lorenzo, CA; *U.S. Public*, pg. 1433
Limay, Luis A., Dir.-Mktg., Pur. & Sls.--San Sebastian Gold Mines, Inc., Milwaukee, WI; *U.S. Public*, pg. 410
Limebrook, David E., V.P.-Field Mktg.--Cox Communications, Inc., Atlanta, GA; *U.S. Public*, pg. 454
Limwattanakul, Suebpong, Asst. Mng. Dir.--Siam City-Showa Leasing Co., Ltd., Bangkok, Thailand; *Int'l*, pg. 1239
Lin, Ahwa, Mgr.-Sls. & Mktg.--Seika Electric Co., Ltd., Taipei, Taiwan; *Int'l*, pg. 1218
Lin, Frank, V.P.-Corp. Mktg.--Acer Incorporated, Taipei, Taiwan; *Int'l*, pg. 22
Lin, Ivan, Mktg. Dir.--Target Advertising Agency Limited, Taipei, Taiwan; *Int'l*, pg. 1355
Lin, Jia-Shyong, V.P.-Mktg./Sls., Sec. & Gen. Mgr.--Amspec Chemical Corporation, Gloucester City, NJ; *U.S. Private*, pg. 67
Linaman, Mary Ann, V.P.-Adv. & Mktg. Svcs.--King Koil Licensing Company Inc., Saint Paul, MN; *U.S. Private*, pg. 621
Linbeck, Leo, III, Dir.-Sls. & Mktg.--Linbeck Construction Corp, Houston, TX; *U.S. Private*, pg. 667
Linbrugger, Renee, Mktg. Specialist--Datum Inc., Irvine, CA; *U.S. Public*, pg. 488
Lincer, Walt, V.P.-Sls. & Mktg.--Citrus World Inc., Lake Wales, FL; *U.S. Private*, pg. 241
Lincoln, Jim, Dir.-Mktg.--Portec, Inc.-Construction Equipment Div., Yankton, SD; *U.S. Public*, pg. 1318
Lincoln, Thomas C., Dir.-Sls. & Mktg.--Cincinnati Industrial Machinery Div., Cincinnati, OH; *U.S. Private*, pg. 355
Lind, Ted, Corp. V.P.-Sls., Mktg. & Technology--The Bethlehem Corporation, Easton, PA; *U.S. Public*, pg. 225
Lind, Ted, Dir.-Mktg. & Sls.--The Bethlehem Corporation, Easton, PA; *U.S. Public*, pg. 225
Lind, William, Exec. V.P. & Gen. Mgr.--Barenbrug Northeast, Ogdensburg, NY; *Int'l*, pg. 167
Lindberg, Karl, Dir.-Sls. & Mktg.--Locust Street Securities, Inc., Des Moines, IA; *Int'l*, pg. 647
Linde, Ken, Mgr.-Mktg.--Smead Manufacturing Company, Hastings, MN; *U.S. Private*, pg. 1006
Lindemann, Sue, Mgr.-Comml. Mktg.--U.S. Electrical Motor Division, Saint Louis, MO; *U.S. Public*, pg. 573
Lindemulder, David, V.P.-Mktg.--MBT Architecture, San Francisco, CA; *U.S. Private*, pg. 686
Lindenboom, Gene, V.P.-Sls. & Mktg.--VAW of America, Inc., Ellenville, NY; *Int'l*, pg. 1466
Lindgren, G. Stephen, V.P.-Mktg.--G.R. Herberger's, Inc., Saint Cloud, MN; *U.S. Public*, pg. 1333
Lindley, C. Jane, Mgr.-Mktg.--C.J. Tower Inc., Buffalo, NY; *U.S. Public*, pg. 1071
Lindley, Harold, Dir.-Crude Oil & Mktg.--Apache Corporation, Houston, TX; *U.S. Public*, pg. 119
Lindley, Michael, Dir.-Mktg.--First of America Bank Corporation, Kalamazoo, MI; *U.S. Public*, pg. 636
Lindley, Nancy, Mgr.-Mktg.--Unistrut Corporation, Wayne, MI; *U.S. Public*, pg. 1651
Lindner, David, Dir.-Mktg.--United Dairy Farmers, Inc., Cincinnati, OH; *U.S. Private*, pg. 1121
Lindsay, Patrick J., V.P.-Mktg.--DuBois Chemicals, Cincinnati, OH; *Int'l*, pg. 1437
Lindsey, David, V.P.-Driving Simulation Sls.--Doron Precision Systems, Inc., Binghamton, NY; *U.S. Private*, pg. 341
Lindsey, David A., Sr. V.P.-Mktg. Div.--First Indiana Bank, A Federal Savings Bank, Indianapolis, IN; *U.S. Public*, pg. 1484
Lindsey, Francis, Sr. V.P.-World Mktg.--Conair Corporation, Stamford, CT; *U.S. Private*, pg. 261
Lindsey, Ralph, V.P.-Mktg. & Sls.--Barber Dairies, Inc., Birmingham, AL; *U.S. Private*, pg. 115
Lindstrom, Annette, Dir.-Adv. & Mktg. Svcs.--Home & Garden Television, Knoxville, TN; *U.S. Public*, pg. 1447
Lindstrom, Riitta-Leena, Dir.-Mktg. & Adv.--Masterfoods Oy, Helsinki, Finland; *U.S. Private*, pg. 707
Lineberry, Nan, Dir.-Mktg.--Lees Carpets, Greensboro, NC; *U.S. Public*, pg. 268
Lines, James, V.P.-Mktg.--Graham Manufacturing Co., Inc., Batavia, NY; *U.S. Public*, pg. 757
Ling, Kurt, Mgr.-Retail Adv.--Maytag Corporation, Newton, IA; *U.S. Public*, pg. 1064
Link, Gary F., V.P. & Dir.-Mktg. & Communication Services--HNTB Corporation, Kansas City, MO; *U.S. Private*, pg. 492
Link, James, Mgr.-Mktg.--Meadville Forging Co., Meadville, PA; *U.S. Private*, pg. 726
Linkowski, Bobbi, Dir.-Adv. & Mktg.--BioChem ImmunoSystems, Inc., Allentown, PA; *Int'l*, pg. 196
Linnan, James W., V.P.-Financial Markets--General Electric Capital Aviation Services, San Francisco, CA; *U.S. Public*, pg. 712
Linscott, Darlene, Dir.-Mktg.--Gitano Fashions Ltd., Bowling Green, KY; *U.S. Public*, pg. 686
Linsley, Patrick M., Exec. V.P.-Corp. Mktg.--The National Enquirer, New York, NY; *U.S. Public*, pg. 87
Linssen, Tony, Mgr.-Sls. & Mktg.--Barber Industries Ltd.-Service Center, Grande Prairie, Canada; *Int'l*, pg. 164
Lintz, Connie, Mgr.-Mktg.-Customer Service--Snyder Industries, Inc., Lincoln, NE; *U.S. Private*, pg. 1011
Linville, Christopher, V.P.-Sls. & Mktg.--Chattanooga Group, Inc., Hixson, TN; *U.S. Private*, pg. 231
Linville, Randal L., Pres.-Grain Mktg. Division--The Scoular Company, Omaha, NE; *U.S. Private*, pg. 977
Lionetta, William, Dir.-Mktg.--Chomerics Inc., Woburn, MA; *U.S. Public*, pg. 1262
Lipez, E., V.P.-Mktg.--Princess Hotels International Inc., New York, NY; *Int'l*, pg. 818
Lipinski, Paul, Mgr.-Mktg.--Noma-International, Inc., Itasca, IL; *Int'l*, pg. 955
Lipiro, Frank, Sr. V.P.-Licensing--Starter Corp., New Haven, CT; *U.S. Public*, pg. 1511
Lipka, Carole, Dir.-Mktg.--Keeney Manufacturing Co., Newington, CT; *U.S. Private*, pg. 611
Lipke, Neil E., Exec. V.P.--Gibraltar Steel Corp., Buffalo, NY; *U.S. Public*, pg. 742
Lippold, Larry J., V.P.-Sls. & Mktg.--Schlumberger Malco Inc., Owings Mills, MD; *Int'l*, pg. 1206
Lipscomb, Anne, Grp. V.P.-Mktg.--The Mills Corporation, Arlington, VA; *U.S. Public*, pg. 1113
Lipscomb, Robert, Mgr.-Marine Mktg.--Port of Portland, Portland, OR; *U.S. Private*, pg. 876
Lipscomb, William, V.P.-Sls. & Mktg.--Plastic Packaging, Inc., Hickory, NC; *U.S. Private*, pg. 871
Lis, Bob, Mgr.-Mktg.-Automotive Electronics Grp.--Philips Automotive Electronics, Cheshire, CT; *Int'l*, pg. 1054
Liscik, Raymond, V.P.-Adv., Mktg., Sls. & Pub. Rels.--JCI Data Processing, Inc., Cinnaminson, NJ; *U.S. Private*, pg. 577
Lishak, John, Jr., Pres.--Commercial Realty & Resources Corp., Wall, NJ; *U.S. Public*, pg. 1172
Lisi, Mary E., Dir.-Mktg. Communications--Komori America Corporation, Rolling Meadows, IL; *Int'l*, pg. 745
Liska, Patrick, Sr. Dir.-Mktg.-NonFoods, HBC, Pharmacy & Bakery--Big V Supermarkets, Inc., Florida, NY; *U.S. Private*, pg. 143
Lisker, Meshulam, Sec. & Dir.-Mktg.--Antwerp Diamond Distributors Inc., New York, NY; *U.S. Private*, pg. 76
Liston, Scott, V.P.-Mktg. & Sls.--Executive Jet Aviation, Inc., Columbus, OH; *U.S. Private*, pg. 388
Listwa, Les, V.P.-Mktg.--Computer Power Incorporated, High Bridge, NJ; *U.S. Public*, pg. 421
Listwin, Donald J., Sr. V.P.-Cisco IOS Devel. & Mktg.--Cisco Systems, Inc., San Jose, CA; *U.S. Public*, pg. 375
Lisy, Franz, Dir.-Mktg.--Gartenhilfe Ges.m.b.H., Lienz, Austria; *Int'l*, pg. 356
Litchfield, Nigel, Mgr.-Prod. Mktg.--Nokia Mobile Phones, Espoo, Finland; *Int'l*, pg. 951
Literski, Sally, Dir.-Mktg.--Malt-O-Meal Company, Minneapolis, MN; *U.S. Private*, pg. 699
Litrenta, Edward, V.P.-Mktg.--Sea World of Florida, Orlando, FL; *U.S. Public*, pg. 114
Littfin, Jack, Mgr.-Mktg. & Pur.--Littfin Lumber Company, Winsted, MN; *U.S. Private*, pg. 670
Little, Abbie G., Dir.-Mktg.--Crowley Frozen Desserts, Inc., Lancaster, PA; *Int'l*, pg. 752
Little, Ann, Dir.-Mktg. Communications--Wavetek Corporation, San Diego, CA; *U.S. Private*, pg. 1154
Little, Freda, Dir.-Mdsg.--Fairfax Lumber & Millwork Company Inc., Springfield, VA; *U.S. Private*, pg. 391
Little, Judy, Mgr.-Mktg.--Harley Ellington Design, Southfield, MI; *U.S. Private*, pg. 503
Little, Kenneth B., V.P.-Mktg. & Customer Service--New Brunswick Power Corporation, Fredericton, Canada; *Int'l*, pg. 923
Little, Lourdes, Dir.-Mktg.--Jan Bell Marketing Inc., Sunrise, FL; *U.S. Public*, pg. 207
Little, Rita, Dir.-Mktg.--Bed Bath & Beyond Inc., Union, NJ; *U.S. Public*, pg. 200
Little, Stephen, V.P.-Sls. & Mktg.--Ilco Unican Inc. (Electronic Access Controls Division), Montreal, Canada; *Int'l*, pg. 1432
Littleton, Tom, Dir.-Mktg.--Wigwam Resort, Litchfield Park, AZ; *Int'l*, pg. 721
Littley, Jack, Sr. V.P.-Plng. & Devel--BTG, Inc., Fairfax, VA; *U.S. Public*, pg. 164
Littmann, Debbie, Dir.-Mktg.--Eli's Cheese Cake Company, Chicago, IL; *U.S. Private*, pg. 371
Litwak, Jim, Exec. V.P.-Mdsg. & Mktg.--Trans World Entertainment Corporation, Albany, NY; *U.S. Public*, pg. 1629
Litzsinger, P.S., Sr. V.P.-Sls. & Mktg.--Carboline Co., Saint Louis, MO; *U.S. Public*, pg. 1357
Liu, R.Y., Mgr.-Mktg.--Tainan Spinning Co., Ltd., Tai-nan, Taiwan; *Int'l*, pg. 1347
Livecchi, Jim, Specialized Mktg. Dir.--SBC Advertising, Columbus, OH; *U.S. Private*, pg. 955
Livecchi, Jim, Specialized Mktg. Dir.--SBC Specialized Marketing, Columbus, OH; *U.S. Private*, pg. 955
Livermore, Russell, III, Mgr.-Mktg. Communications--ABT Building Products Corporation, Neenah, WI; *Int'l*, pg. 20
Livingston, Ingrid, Mgr.-Mktg. Commun.--Highway Equipment Company, Cedar Rapids, IA; *U.S. Private*, pg. 529
Llen, Joyce, Dir.-Sls. & Incentive Promotions--International Research & Evaluation, Eagan, MN; *U.S. Private*, pg. 571
Llewellyn, Robert, Sr. V.P.-Mktg.--Rothmans Benson & Hedges Inc., North York, Canada; *Int'l*, pg. 1130
Llopis, Glenn, Dir.-Sls. & Mktg.--Artichoke Industries, Inc., Castroville, CA; *U.S. Private*, pg. 86
Lloyd, Carol, Mgr.-Mktg.--Bacardi-Martini, USA, Inc., Miami, FL; *U.S. Private*, pg. 109

Lo Pinto, Richard, V.P.-Photo Mktg. Div.--Nikon Inc., Melville, NY; *Int'l*, pg. 931
Loarie, Susanne, V.P.-Mktg. & Bus. Devel.--Health Professionals, Inc., Fort Lauderdale, FL; *U.S. Public*, pg. 802
Lobban, John, Mgr.-Mktg.--Parker & Amchem, Etobicoke, Canada; *Int'l*, pg. 612
Lobue, Sherry, Mktg.--Regions Bank/Selma, Selma, AL; *U.S. Public*, pg. 1372
Locarno, John, Mgr.-Mktg. & Distr.--Barber-Colman Company, Rockford, IL; *Int'l*, pg. 1242
Lochen, Sandy, Mgr.-Mktg.--EMPI, Inc., Saint Paul, MN; *U.S. Public*, pg. 545
Lochner, Beth, Mgr.-Media Mktg.--Lenox Collections, Langhorne, PA; *U.S. Public*, pg. 261
Lock, Amy, Mgr.-Mktg. Svcs.--Eaton Corporation Commercial Controls Division, Selma, NC; *U.S. Public*, pg. 556
Lockard, Randy, Dir.-Mktg.--Tandy Brands Accessories, Inc., Arlington, TX; *U.S. Public*, pg. 1560
Lockard, Randy, Dir.-Mktg.--TBAC - Prince Gardner, Inc., Arlington, TX; *U.S. Public*, pg. 1560
Locke, Maureen, Mgr.-Mktg. Communications--Capintec Inc., Ramsey, NJ; *U.S. Private*, pg. 205
Locke, Ralph, V.P.-Mktg.--Syar Industries, Inc., Napa, CA; *U.S. Private*, pg. 1059
Locke, Todd, Mgr.-Sls. & Mktg.--Superior Dairy, Inc., Canton, OH; *U.S. Private*, pg. 1054
Lockhart, Frank L., Dir.-Mktg.-N. America--Ranco Inc., Plain City, OH; *Int'l*, pg. 1243
Lockhart, Frank L., Dir.-Mktg./North America--Ranco North America, Plain City, OH; *Int'l*, pg. 1243
Lockhart, Joan, Dir.-Corp. Mktg.--Avid Technology, Inc., Tewksbury, MA; *U.S. Public*, pg. 154
Lockley, Jim, V.P.-Sls. & Mktg.--Cramer Inc., Kansas City, KS; *U.S. Private*, pg. 285
Lockman-Brooks, Linda, Mgr.-Mktg., Adv. & Sls.--Duke Energy Corporation, Charlotte, NC; *U.S. Public*, pg. 534
Locus, Mimiam, Mgr.-Adv.- Fiat--Fiat Auto Belgio SA, Brussels, Belgium; *Int'l*, pg. 481
Lodato, August P., Dir.-Mktg.--J.L. Hammett Company, Braintree, MA; *U.S. Private*, pg. 498
Loden, Betty Jo, Mktg. Coord.--Reynolds Metals Co.-Can Division Headquarters, Richmond, VA; *U.S. Public*, pg. 1386
Lodge, Jean, Mgr.-Sls. & Mktg.--Salford Electrical Instruments Ltd., Heywood, United Kingdom; *Int'l*, pg. 545
Loebig, Gary L., Sr. V.P.-Market & Prod. Devel.--Stuart Entertainment Inc., Council Bluffs, IA; *U.S. Public*, pg. 1526
Loeffler, Bob, Mgr.-Mktg.--Miele Appliances, Inc., Somerset, NJ; *Int'l*, pg. 865
Loeffler, Dan, Mgr.-Sls. & Mktg.--Mafco Worldwide Corp., Camden, NJ; *U.S. Private*, pg. 690
Loehman, Mary, Dir.-Mktg. Services Chicago--Hart Schaffner & Marx Clothes, Chicago, IL; *U.S. Public*, pg. 795
Loehman, Mary, Dir.-Mktg. Services-Chicago--Hickey-Freeman/Bobby Jones, Rochester, NY; *U.S. Public*, pg. 795
Loehman, Mary, Dir.-Mktg. Services-Chicago--International Women's Apparel Group, Easton, PA; *U.S. Public*, pg. 796
Loehman, Mary L., Dir.-Mktg. Services--Hartmarx Corporation, Chicago, IL; *U.S. Public*, pg. 795
Loesch, MaryBeth, V.P.-Mktg.--CSG Systems International, Inc., Englewood, CO; *U.S. Public*, pg. 283
Loesel, Deborah, Mktg. Div.--Totes Incorporated, Loveland, OH; *U.S. Private*, pg. 111
Lofberg, Per G.H., Pres.-MEDCO Managed Care--MEDCO Containment Services, Inc., Montvale, NJ; *U.S. Public*, pg. 1091
Lofgren, Peter, V.P. & Dir.-Mktg.--Kymi Paper Mills Ltd., Kuusankoski, Finland; *Int'l*, pg. 1428
Loftus, William A., Exec. V.P.-Retail--Ace Hardware Corporation, Oak Brook, IL; *U.S. Private*, pg. 12
Logan, Colleen, Dir.-Mktg.--Icon Health & Fitness, Inc., Logan, UT; *U.S. Private*, pg. 556
Logan, Donald F., V.P.-Sls. & Mktg.--Russell Corp., Fabrics Div., Alexander City, AL; *U.S. Public*, pg. 1413
Logan, Gary, Dir.-Mktg.--Sax Arts & Crafts, Inc., New Berlin, WI; *U.S. Public*, pg. 1687
Logan, Judy, Dir.-Mktg. & Adv.--Netscape Communications Corp., Mountain View, CA; *U.S. Public*, pg. 1168
Logan, Matt, Dir.-Mktg.--Aquapore Moisture Systems, Inc., Phoenix, AZ; *Int'l*, pg. 1066
Logan, Robert, Sr. V.P.-European Sls. & Mktg.--R.R. Donnelley & Sons Company, Chicago, IL; *U.S. Public*, pg. 517
Logsdon, Linda, Sr. V.P.-Health Mktg. Svcs.--Express Scripts, Inc., Maryland Heights, MO; *U.S. Public*, pg. 600
Logue, George A., V.P.-Sls. & Mktg.--Houghton Mifflin School Division, Boston, MA; *U.S. Public*, pg. 841
Logue, Ken, V.P.-Sls. & Mktg.--Variform, Inc., Kearney, MO; *U.S. Public*, pg. 1193
Lohmann, Ed, V.P.-Mktg.--Alexander Doll Company, Inc., New York, NY; *U.S. Private*, pg. 33
Lohr, Cliff, V.P.-Intl. Sls.--Seco Warwick Corporation, Meadville, PA; *U.S. Private*, pg. 980
Lohse, Steen B., V.P.-Mktg.--Olicom A/S, Lyngby, Denmark; *Int'l*, pg. 1001
Lokitus, Tom, Mgr.-Commun.--Conestoga Wood Specialties Corp., East Earl, PA; *U.S. Private*, pg. 262
Lomazze, Chino, Mgr.-Mktg.--Akzo Chemicals S.p.A., Milan, Italy; *Int'l*, pg. 46
Lombard, Michael, Mgr.-Customer Svc.--Raffi & Swanson, Inc., Wilmington, MA; *U.S. Private*, pg. 907
Lombardi, J.R., V.P.-Mktg.--Wyman-Gordon Forgings, North Grafton, MA; *U.S. Public*, pg. 1782
Lombardi, J.V., V.P.-Mktg.--Wyman-Gordon Forgings, Inc., Houston, TX; *U.S. Public*, pg. 1782
Lombardi, James V., V.P.-Mktg.--Wyman-Gordon, North Grafton, MA; *U.S. Public*, pg. 1782
Lombardo, Carl R., Mgr.-Mktg.--Oasis Outsourcing, Inc., Palm Beach Gardens, FL; *U.S. Public*, pg. 1731
Lombardo, Tom, V.P.-Mktg. & Sls.--The Little Tikes Company, Hudson, OH; *U.S. Public*, pg. 1411
Lomenosoff, Jim, V.P.-Intl. Mktg.--Walt Disney Attractions-Walt Disney World, Lake Buena Vista, FL; *U.S. Public*, pg. 513
Lommel, John A., V.P.-Mktg. & Sls.--Kysor/Medallion, Spring Lake, MI; *U.S. Public*, pg. 968
Lommel, Ken, Mgr.-Wholesale Mktg.--Apex Oil Company, Inc., Saint Louis, MO; *U.S. Private*, pg. 77
London, Robert, V.P.-Mktg.--DAP Inc., Tipp City, OH; *Int'l*, pg. 1486
Lonergan, Mary, Dir.-Mktg./Silhouette Bus. Unit--Hunter Douglas, Inc., Upper Saddle River, NJ; *Int'l*, pg. 639
Long, Cheri, Mgr.-Mktg. Services--The Kerite Company, Seymour, CT; *U.S. Public*, pg. 844
Long, Doug, Mng. Dir.-PRO Hardware & Farm Mart--PRO Group, Inc., Englewood, CO; *U.S. Private*, pg. 887
Long, Gary, V.P.-Mktg.--J.R. Simplot Company, Minerals & Chemicals Group, Pocatello, ID; *U.S. Private*, pg. 1002
Long, Gary, V.P.-Mktg.--Public Service Company of New Hampshire, Manchester, NH; *U.S. Public*, pg. 1195
Long, J. Shane, V.P.-Sls. & Mktg.--STB Systems, Inc., Richardson, TX; *U.S. Public*, pg. 1421
Long, Jack, Dir.-Sls. & Mktg.--Holsum Bakery, Inc., Phoenix, AZ; *U.S. Private*, pg. 536
Long, James W., Dir.-Mktg. & Communications--The Atlantic Advertising Sales, New York, NY; *U.S. Private*, pg. 95
Long, Jeanette, Mgr.-Mktg. Commun.--American Standard Inc., Piscataway, NJ; *U.S. Public*, pg. 91
Long, Mark, Dir.-Mktg. Svcs.--Vanguard Cellular Systems, Inc., Greensboro, NC; *U.S. Public*, pg. 1707
Long, Roger, Dir.-Mktg.--KinderCare Learning Centers, Inc., Portland, OR; *U.S. Public*, pg. 961
Long, Sara J., Dir.-Mktg.--The News Tribune, Tacoma, WA; *U.S. Public*, pg. 1066
Long, Wayne, V.P. & Dir.-Mktg. & Broadcasting--Atlanta National League Baseball Club, Inc., Atlanta, GA; *U.S. Public*, pg. 1614
Long, Wayne, V.P.-Mktg.--Atlanta Braves, Inc., Atlanta, GA; *U.S. Public*, pg. 1614
Long, Yeo Khee, Asst. Chief Exec.-Corp. Svcs. & Mktg.--Singapore Tourist Promotion Board, Singapore, Singapore; *Int'l*, pg. 1253
Longo, Mark, V.P.-Mktg. & Sls.--Ohio Sealants Inc., Mentor, OH; *Int'l*, pg. 802
Longtin, Joel C., Pres.--Mr. Gatti's, Inc., Kerrville, TX; *U.S. Private*, pg. 639
Loomer, Tim, V.P.-Sls. & Mktg.--ScanTron Corporation, Tustin, CA; *U.S. Public*, pg. 786
Loomis, Richard A., V.P.-Mktg./Home Care Div.--Armor All Products Group, Oakland, CA; *U.S. Public*, pg. 387
Loos, William, V.P.-Mktg.--Loos & Co., Inc., Pomfret, CT; *U.S. Private*, pg. 675
Looyenga, R.L., Sr. V.P.-Mktg.--Auto-Owners Insurance, Lansing, MI; *U.S. Private*, pg. 100
Loperti, C., Dir.-Mktg.--Sangemini S.p.A., Rome, Italy; *Int'l*, pg. 1188
Lopes, Tim, Dir.-Mktg.--Emery Waterhouse Company, Portland, ME; *U.S. Private*, pg. 373
Lopez, Carmen, V.P. & Mng. Dir.-Sls.--The New Yorker Magazine, New York, NY; *U.S. Private*, pg. 795
Lopez, Cesar Vacchiano, Dir.-Mktg. & Sls.--Tabacalera, S.A., Madrid, Spain; *Int'l*, pg. 1345
Lopez, G., Sr. V.P.-Mktg.--International Home Foods Inc., Parsippany, NJ; *U.S. Private*, pg. 526
LoPresti, Michael, Dir.-Mktg.--Nautilus International, Independence, VA; *U.S. Public*, pg. 498
Lopuch, George Z., Sr. V.P.-Strategic Plng. & Res.--SuperValu, Inc., Eden Prairie, MN; *U.S. Public*, pg. 1540
Lorenze, A. John, V.P.-Mktg.--Standard-Knapp, Inc., Portland, CT; *U.S. Private*, pg. 1031
Lorenzon, Alfieri, Dir.-Mktg. & Sls.--McGraw-Hill Libri Italia, S.r.l., Milan, Italy; *U.S. Public*, pg. 1072
Losie, Paul M., V.P.-Mktg. & Adv.--Amwest Insurance Group, Inc., Calabasas, CA; *U.S. Public*, pg. 106
Losie, Paul M., Mgr.-Mktg.--Far West Insurance Company, Calabasas, CA; *U.S. Public*, pg. 106
Losier, John, Sr. V.P. & Gen. Mgr.-Worldwide Sls. & Mktg.--Tandem Computers Inc., Cupertino, CA; *U.S. Public*, pg. 417
Losthouse, Roy, Dr., Dir.-Sls. & Mktg.--Union Camp Chemicals, Durham, United Kingdom; *U.S. Public*, pg. 1666
Lot, Thierry, Dir.-Mktg.--Polive/Tricosteril, Courbevoie, France; *U.S. Public*, pg. 673
Loudon, James R.H., Dir.-Grp. Fin.--Blue Circle Industries PLC, London, United Kingdom; *Int'l*, pg. 197
Loughlin, Dena, Mktg. Communications Asst.--Condea Vista Company, Houston, TX; *Int'l*, pg. 325
Loughrey, Phil, V.P.-Mktg.--State Industries Inc., Ashland City, TN; *U.S. Private*, pg. 1036
Louie, Richard, Dir.-Creative Mktg.--Bon Appetit Magazine, New York, NY; *U.S. Private*, pg. 20
Louis, Jean, Mgr.-Mfr.--Bontex S.A., Stembert, Belgium; *U.S. Public*, pg. 734
Lounsberry, Fred, Exec. V.P.-Sls. & Mktg.--Universal Studios Music Australia, Sydney, Australia; *Int'l*, pg. 1216
Louvar, David, Dir.-Sls. & Mktg.-Saws--Wisconsin Automated Machinery Corp., Oshkosh, WI; *U.S. Private*, pg. 1184
Louw, Marjo, Mgr.-Mktg./Phenolics--Sasol Chemicals Pacific Limited, Wan Chai, Hong Kong; *Int'l*, pg. 1196
Love, Barbara, Mktg. Coord.--Tropicana Resort & Casino, Las Vegas, NV; *U.S. Public*, pg. 159
Love, Brian, V.P.-Strategic Mktg.--Griffin Bacal Volny, Toronto, Canada; *U.S. Private*, pg. 480
Love, Kelly, V.P.-Mktg.--Ohio Machinery Co., Cleveland, OH; *U.S. Private*, pg. 812
Lovelace, Angela, Dir.-Mktg.--Crain Communications, Inc., Chicago, IL; *U.S. Private*, pg. 284
Lovelace, Angela, Dir.-Mktg.--Automotive News, Detroit, MI; *U.S. Private*, pg. 284
Lovelace, Arlene, Coord.-Mktg. Communications--First Commercial Bank, N.A., Little Rock, AR; *U.S. Public*, pg. 630
Lovell, Mary S., Sr. V.P.-Utility Services--Atmos Energy Corporation, Dallas, TX; *U.S. Public*, pg. 145
Lovell, Robert B., V.P.-Mktg. & Adv.--Coca-Cola Bottling Co. United, Inc., Birmingham, AL; *U.S. Private*, pg. 248
Lovinger, Antonella, Dir.-Mktg.--Parmalat New Atlanta Dairies, Atlanta, GA; *Int'l*, pg. 1023
Lovold, Norton, Dir.-Sls. & Mktg.--Tone Commander Systems, Mukilteo, WA; *U.S. Private*, pg. 1090
Low, Jamie S., V.P. & Mgr.-Mktg.--Willis Corroon Corp. of Arizona, Phoenix, AZ; *Int'l*, pg. 1505
Low, Jeffrey B., V.P.-Mktg. & Bus. Devel.--Acacia Networks, Inc., Lowell, MA; *U.S. Private*, pg. 11
Lowe, Dominic, V.P.-Mktg. & Adv.--Schweppes Europe Limited, Watford, United Kingdom; *Int'l*, pg. 248
Lowe, Herbert, V.P.-Global Mktg.--The Athlete's Foot Group, Inc., Kennesaw, GA; *U.S. Private*, pg. 94
Lowe, Stacy, Mgr.-Mktg.--Acclaim Comics, New York, NY; *U.S. Public*, pg. 15
Lowe, Steve, Mgr.-Mktg.--Raleigh Industries Ltd., Nottingham, United Kingdom; *Int'l*, pg. 394
Lowentein, Leslie D., Mktg. Asst.--American Mathematical Society, Inc., Providence, RI; *U.S. Private*, pg. 59
Lowndes, Dan, V.P.-Sls. & Mktg.--Glentel Inc., Burnaby, Canada; *Int'l*, pg. 1336
Loyrews, Jon, Mgr.-Mktg.--Shirmax Leasing Ltd., Montreal, Canada; *Int'l*, pg. 1235
Lozanoff, Michael, Dir.-Mktg.--Newage Industries Inc., Plastics Technology Group, Willow Grove, PA; *U.S. Private*, pg. 796
Luboja, Ed, Mgr.-Mktg. Communications--V-Band Corporation, Elmsford, NY; *U.S. Public*, pg. 1701
Lubow, Adam, Mgr.-Mktg.--Kaufman and Broad Central Valley Div., Modesto, CA; *U.S. Public*, pg. 945
Lucas, Blair, Exec. V.P.-Mktg.--Jonathan Manufacturing Corp., Fullerton, CA; *U.S. Private*, pg. 595
Lucas, Brad, V.P.-Sls. & Mktg.--Toter Incorporated, Statesville, NC; *U.S. Private*, pg. 1092
Lucas, John, V.P.-Mktg.--CPC Latin American Consumer Foods Division, Englewood Cliffs, NJ; *U.S. Public*, pg. 447
Lucas, Scott, V.P.-Sls. & Mktg.--Dorner Manufacturing Corp., Hartland, WI; *U.S. Private*, pg. 340
Lucas, Stefanie, Adv. & Promo. Specialist--C-COR Electronics, Inc., State College, PA; *U.S. Public*, pg. 272
Lucas, Tom, V.P.-Mktg.--The Travel Channel, Atlanta, GA; *U.S. Private*, pg. 647
Lucchini, Genevieve, Dir.-Mktg.--Clarins SA, Les Plans, Switzerland; *Int'l*, pg. 295
Luce, Priscilla M., V.P.-Mktg. & Organization Communications--TRW Inc., Cleveland, OH; *U.S. Public*, pg. 1558
Lucenti, Janice, Mgr.-Project Mktg.--The Allstate Corporation, Northbrook, IL; *U.S. Public*, pg. 55
Lucey, Thomas J., Sr. Mng. Dir. & Chief of Inst. Mktg.--Putnam Investments, Inc., Boston, MA; *U.S. Public*, pg. 1049
Luchetta, Rodolfo, Div. Mgr.-Mktg.--Y.P.F., S.A., Buenos Aires, Argentina; *Int'l*, pg. 1515
Luchik, J. T., Mgr.-Mktg.--Lord Corp., Industrial Adhesives & Coatings Div., Erie, PA; *U.S. Private*, pg. 676
Luchs, Kenneth, Sr. V.P.-Mktg., Sls. & Adv.--Reliable Stores, Inc., Columbia, MD; *U.S. Private*, pg. 920
Luchtenberg, Daphne, Mktg. Mgr.- UK/Europe--Shandwick International Plc, London, United Kingdom; *Int'l*, pg. 1226
Luchtenberg, Daphne, Mktg. Mgr.-UK/Europe--Shandwick International Plc, London, United Kingdom; *Int'l*, pg. 1226
Luciano, Daniel, V.P.-Mktg.--Gardner Publications, Inc., Cincinnati, OH; *U.S. Private*, pg. 440
Lucky, Brad, V.P.-Mktg.--Pizza Inn, Inc., Dallas, TX; *U.S. Public*, pg. 1307
Ludgate, John, V.P.-Mktg.--International Paint Co., Inc., Union, NJ; *Int'l*, pg. 338
Ludh, William, Sr. V.P.-Mktg.--The Sportsman's Guide, Inc., Saint Paul, MN; *U.S. Public*, pg. 1499
Ludington, Callaway, Asst. V.P.-Mktg.--Enterprise Rent-A-Car Company, Saint Louis, MO; *U.S. Private*, pg. 377
Ludington, Deborah, Assoc. V.P.-Sls. & Mktg.--NESLAB Instruments, Inc., Newington, NH; *U.S. Public*, pg. 1595
Ludlow, Ted, V.P.-Sls. & Mktg.--Bedford Industries, Inc., Worthington, MN; *U.S. Private*, pg. 129
Ludwig, Kim, Mgr.-Communications--Energy Absorption Systems, Inc., Chicago, IL; *U.S. Public*, pg. 1353
Luebke, Richard, Gen. Sls. Mgr.--PACCAR Winch Division, Broken Arrow, OK; *U.S. Public*, pg. 1246
Luehrs, Susan J., V.P.-Mktg.--California State Bank, West Covina, CA; *U.S. Public*, pg. 294
Luhtanen, Andrea, Sr. V.P.-Mktg. Svcs.--Haworth Group Inc., Minneapolis, MN; *U.S. Private*, pg. 511
Luk, Philomena, Mgr.-Mktg. Svcs.--Veryfine Products, Inc., Westford, MA; *U.S. Private*, pg. 1137
Luke, Laura, Mgr.-Mktg. Communications--SRA International Inc., Arlington, VA; *U.S. Private*, pg. 957
Lukehart, Dean, V.P.-Mktg.--Grizzard, Atlanta, GA; *U.S. Private*, pg. 482
Luker, Mike, V.P.-Sls. & Mktg.--Sunny Fresh Foods, Monticello, MN; *U.S. Private*, pg. 210
Lukes, Tracy, Sr. Mgr.-Mktg.--FTD, Inc./Florists Transworld Delivery, Inc., Downers Grove, IL; *U.S. Private*, pg. 389
Lukeson, David, V.P.-Mktg. & Sls.--Grayson Electronics Corporation, Forest, VA; *U.S. Public*, pg. 46
Lukianov, Alexis V., V.P.-Mktg.--Danek Medical Inc., Memphis, TN; *U.S. Public*, pg. 1482
Lumbatis, David, Mgr.-Bus. Devel.--Gulf States, Inc., Freeport, TX; *U.S. Private*, pg. 487
Lumbatis, David, Mgr.-Mktg.--GSI of California, Pittsburg, CA; *U.S. Private*, pg. 487
Lumley, David R., Sr. V.P.-Sls. & Mktg.--Outboard Marine Corporation, Waukegan, IL; *U.S. Private*, pg. 478

Lumme, M., Mgr.-Mktg.--Kone Corporation, Helsinki, Finland; *Int'l*, pg. 746
Lummis, Larry, V.P.-Worldwide Sls.--Micronics Computers, Inc., Fremont, CA; *U.S. Public*, pg. 1106
Luna, Kathleen, Coord.-Mktg. Commun.--UVP, Inc., Upland, CA; *U.S. Private*, pg. 1115
Lunau, Mark L., V.P.-Mktg.--Peregrine Incorporated, Southfield, MI; *U.S. Private*, pg. 852
Lund, Jay, Mgr.-Business Devel.--Andersen Corporation, Bayport, MN; *U.S. Private*, pg. 71
Lund, Jerry, Mgr.-Sls. & Mktg.--Simmons Juvenile Products Co., Inc., New London, WI; *U.S. Private*, pg. 1001
Lund, Mindi, Mgr.-Mktg.--Time Inc. Health, New York, NY; *U.S. Public*, pg. 1613
Lund, Robert, Dir.-Mktg. & Prod. Distr.--Hamilton Co., Inc., Reno, NV; *U.S. Private*, pg. 497
Lundquist, E., Dir.-Mktg.--Flexible Products Company, Marietta, GA; *U.S. Private*, pg. 412
Lundstrom, Leif, Exec. V.P.-Mktg. Div.--FinnAir Oy, Helsinki, Finland; *Int'l*, pg. 485
Lundy, Dee, Dir.-Sls. & Mktg.--Family Inns of America, Inc., Pigeon Forge, TN; *U.S. Private*, pg. 392
Lunsford, Gretchen, Mgr.-Mktg. Services--Hazen Paper Company, Holyoke, MA; *U.S. Private*, pg. 514
Lunsford, Rick, Mgr.-Retail Mktg.--Ruiz Food Products, Inc., Dinuba, CA; *U.S. Private*, pg. 951
Lunt, Colby, V.P.-Mktg.--Rogers, Lunt & Bowlen Co., Greenfield, MA; *U.S. Private*, pg. 939
Lurati, Bruno, Dir.-Adv.--Robert Bosch AG, Otelfingen, Switzerland; *Int'l*, pg. 205
Lurio, David, Exec. V.P.--Elbeco Incorporated, Reading, PA; *U.S. Private*, pg. 367
Lush, David, V.P.-Mktg.--Midas-International Corp., Chicago, IL; *U.S. Public*, pg. 1766
Lusk, Kent R., Mgr.-Mktg.--360 Degrees Long Distance, Cary, NC; *U.S. Public*, pg. 1607
Lustenader, Jim, Sr. V.P.-Mktg. Svcs.--Dugan Valva Contess Inc., Morristown, NJ; *U.S. Private*, pg. 345
Lustig, Jane, V.P.-Mktg.--Vienna Sausage Mfg. Co., Chicago, IL; *U.S. Private*, pg. 1139
Lute, Graham, Dir.-Communications--Nestle S.A., Vevey, Switzerland; *Int'l*, pg. 915
Luter, Joseph W., IV, Sr. V.P.-Mktg. & Sls./Fresh Pork--The Smithfield Packing Co., Inc., Smithfield, VA; *U.S. Public*, pg. 1479
Luth, Klaus, Dir.-Sls.--Richardson G.m.b.H., Schwalbach, Germany; *U.S. Public*, pg. 1333
Luther, Deborah, Dir.-Mktg.--Fosters Freeze International, Inc., San Luis Obispo, CA; *U.S. Public*, pg. 677
Lutter, A.W. Jr., Sr. V.P.-Mktg. & Bus. Affairs--National Steel & Shipbuilding Company, San Diego, CA; *U.S. Private*, pg. 787
Lutz, Bob, Exec. Dir.-Pur.--Certified Grocers of California, Los Angeles, CA; *U.S. Private*, pg. 226
Lux, Steve, V.P.-Mktg.--Acclaim Entertainment, Inc., Glen Cove, NY; *U.S. Public*, pg. 15
Lux, W.A., V.P.-Mktg.--Rheem Air Conditioning Div., Fort Smith, AR; *Int'l*, pg. 1022
Lux, William, V.P.-Adv. & Mktg.--Rheem Manufacturing Co., New York, NY; *Int'l*, pg. 1022
Luxmore, Simon, Dir.-Sls. & Mktg.--Messier-Dowty Ltd., Gloucester, United Kingdom; *Int'l*, pg. 1340
Luxmore, Terry, Mgr.-Bus. Devel.--CTS Corp. Frequency Controls, Sandwich, IL; *U.S. Public*, pg. 285
Luzi, Armin L., Mgr.-Mktg.--Thetford Corporation, Ann Arbor, MI; *U.S. Private*, pg. 352
Lvehrs, Susan, V.P.-Mktg.--California State Bank-La Habra, La Habra, CA; *U.S. Public*, pg. 294
Lyall, David, Dir.-Sls. & Mktg.--Roush Industries Inc., Livonia, MI; *U.S. Private*, pg. 948
Lyden, John, Dir.-Mktg.-Best Buy--USA Weekend, New York, NY; *U.S. Public*, pg. 701
Lydic, John, Dir.-Mktg.--National Mine Service, Inc., Indiana, PA; *Int'l*, pg. 280
Lydy, Steve, V.P.-Bus. Devel.--Baker Concrete Construction, Inc., Monroe, OH; *U.S. Private*, pg. 111
Lygan, Doug, Mgr.-Mktg.--Jewel-Osco, Melrose Park, IL; *U.S. Public*, pg. 93
Lyle, Mark, Mgr.-Mktg.--Hopple Plastics, Inc., Florence, KY; *U.S. Private*, pg. 538
Lyles, Annis, Reg. Dir.-Mktg. Services--Coca-Cola Enterprises - Eastern Group/Southeast Region, Atlanta, GA; *U.S. Public*, pg. 393
Lyman, Kerry B., Mktg. Dir. & Pub. Rels. Dir.--CheckMark Communications, Saint Louis, MO; *U.S. Private*, pg. 231
Lyman, R. Yale, Mgr.-Business Devel.--Atkinson Construction, San Bruno, CA; *U.S. Public*, pg. 143
Lyman, Wendy, Dir.-Mktg.--National Food Stores, Inc., Edison, NJ; *U.S. Private*, pg. 783
Lynch, B., Mgr.-Passenger Mktg.--Aer Lingus, Melville, NY; *Int'l*, pg. 28
Lynch, Bill, V.P.-Sls. & Mktg.--Dukane Ultrasonics Div., Saint Charles, IL; *U.S. Private*, pg. 346
Lynch, Dan, V.P.-Mktg.--Thomas Nelson Inc., Nashville, TN; *U.S. Public*, pg. 1167
Lynch, Gerald A., V.P.-Intl. Sls. & Mktg.--Advanced Micro Devices, Inc., Sunnyvale, CA; *U.S. Public*, pg. 21
Lynch, Larry, Dir.-Mktg.--International Wine Accessories, Inc., Dallas, TX; *U.S. Private*, pg. 572
Lynch, Larry, Mgr.-Mktg.--Newspapers First, New York, NY; *U.S. Public*, pg. 964
Lynch, Lawrence R., Dir.-Mktg.--Pilgram Baxter & Associates, Wayne, PA; *U.S. Public*, pg. 1673
Lynch, Richard, V.P.-Mktg.--Penford Products Co., Cedar Rapids, IA; *U.S. Public*, pg. 1269
Lyndon, J., Mgr.-Adv., Pub. Rels. & Mktg. Communications--Aer Lingus, Melville, NY; *Int'l*, pg. 28
Lyndon, Leslie, Sr. V.P.-Creative & Dir.-Mktg.--Fox Broadcasting Company (FBC), Beverly Hills, CA; *Int'l*, pg. 926
Lynn, Gary L., V.P.-Sls. & Mktg.--Arrow Gear Company, Downers Grove, IL; *U.S. Private*, pg. 85
Lynn, Gary L., Mgr.-Sls. & Mktg.--Johnson Gear, Lincoln, NE; *U.S. Private*, pg. 85
Lyon, Arthur S., Jr., Chief Mktg. Officer & Sr. V.P.--Integon Corporation, Winston Salem, NC; *U.S. Public*, pg. 719
Lyon, John D., V.P.-Mktg. & Sls.--Safeguard Health Enterprises, Inc., Anaheim, CA; *U.S. Public*, pg. 1424
Lyon, Peter, Mgr.-Mktg.--GAI Consultants-Southeast, Inc., Orlando, FL; *U.S. Private*, pg. 434
Lyons, Bernie, V.P.-Mktg. & Sls.--Meadox Medicals, Inc., Oakland, NJ; *U.S. Public*, pg. 247
Lyons, Craig L., V.P.-Sls. & Mktg.--Flambeau Mill, Park Falls, WI; *Int'l*, pg. 434
Lyons, Debi, Mktg. Asst.--Western Interactive Media, Los Angeles, CA; *U.S. Private*, pg. 1166
Lyons, Ellis, Dir.-Sls. & Mktg.--W.H. Salisbury & Company, Skokie, IL; *Int'l*, pg. 1244
Lyons, John, Sr. V.P.-Sls. & Mktg.--Entex Information Services, Rye Brook, NY; *U.S. Private*, pg. 378
Lyons, Lynda, Dir.-Mktg.--Brooks Resources Corporation, Bend, OR; *U.S. Private*, pg. 172
Lyons, S.G., Mgr.-Gen. Mktg.--Lincoln-Mercury Division, Detroit, MI; *U.S. Public*, pg. 662
Lyons, Susanne, Exec. V.P.-Retail Mktg.--Charles Schwab & Co. Inc., San Francisco, CA; *U.S. Public*, pg. 1443
Lyons, Susanne D., Exec. V.P.-Retail Mktg.--The Charles Schwab Corporation, San Francisco, CA; *U.S. Public*, pg. 1442
Lysaught, Thomas F., V.P.-Mktg.--GTE Corporation, Stamford, CT; *U.S. Public*, pg. 696
Lyshaug, Hans-Petter, Mktg. Consultant--AS OSLO Sporveier, Oslo, Norway; *Int'l*, pg. 1012
Lyss, Steve, Dir.-Market Res.--Guidant Corporation-Vascular Intervention Group, Santa Clara, CA; *U.S. Public*, pg. 768
Lytle, Francine M., V.P. & Mktg. Dir.--Gianettino & Meredith Advertising, Short Hills, NJ; *U.S. Private*, pg. 450
Lytle, R.D., Chm. Bd., Pres. & Chief Exec. Officer--Star Bronze Company, Alliance, OH; *U.S. Private*, pg. 1034
Lytwynec, Brian P., Sr. V.P.-Mktg.--Utica Mutual Insurance Company, New Hartford, NY; *U.S. Private*, pg. 1129
Maag, Bob, V.P.-Mktg.--Osco Drug, Salt Lake City, UT; *U.S. Public*, pg. 93
Maas, Joe, Dir.-Mktg.-North America--NL Industries, Inc., Houston, TX; *U.S. Private*, pg. 270
Maas, Lori, Dir.-Mktg.--Parfums Van Cleef & Arpels, New York, NY; *Int'l*, pg. 445
Mabe, Keith, Dir.-Mktg.--Hanes Hosiery, Inc., Winston Salem, NC; *U.S. Public*, pg. 1434
Mabee, Peter, Mgr.-Prod. & Mktg.--Thomas Equipment Limited, Centreville, Canada; *Int'l*, pg. 850
Mabee, William H., Sr. V.P.--Manufacturers & Traders Trust Company, Buffalo, NY; *U.S. Public*, pg. 631
Maby, C., V.P.-Bus. & Mktg. Strategy, Consumer Parts--ICI Paints, Cleveland, OH; *Int'l*, pg. 664
Mac Donald, Ron, Sr. V.P.-Pricing & Mktg.--Manufacturers Consolidation Service, Inc., Memphis, TN; *U.S. Private*, pg. 700
MacAdam, Scott, Magazine Mktg. Dir.--Gillespie, Lawrenceville, NJ; *U.S. Private*, pg. 453
Macaluso, Carlos, Exec. V.P.-Sls. & Mktg.--Golden Eagle Group, Inc., Humble, TX; *U.S. Public*, pg. 749
Macapagal, Norman K., Grp. Mgr.-Mktg.--EEI Corporation, Manila, Philippines; *Int'l*, pg. 425
Macatavish, F.A., V.P.-Transmission & Distr.--Manitoba Hydro, Winnipeg, Canada; *Int'l*, pg. 834
MacBeth, Edward, V.P.-Mktg.--SCM Microsystems, Inc., Los Gatos, CA; *U.S. Public*, pg. 1417
MacBeth, Margaret, Mgr.-Mktg. Svcs.--Atlas Electric Devices Co., Chicago, IL; *U.S. Private*, pg. 96
MacCarthur, Twig, Exec. V.P.-Mktg.--Champion International Corp., Stamford, CT; *U.S. Public*, pg. 333
MacCausland, Kathy, Mgr.-Adv.--Viking Yacht Co., New Gretna, NJ; *U.S. Private*, pg. 1140
Macchi, Massimo, Prod. Mgr.-Sls. & Mktg.--Bulgari SPA, Rome, Italy; *Int'l*, pg. 232
MacConnell, Greg L., V.P.-Mktg. & Plng.--F.W. Myers & Co., Inc., Rouses Point, NY; *U.S. Private*, pg. 770
MacCord, G.W., V.P.-Sls. & Mktg.--Controlled Power (CPC), Canton, OH; *Int'l*, pg. 74
MacCormack, Bryna, Mgr.-Mktg. Support-Amphibious Aircraft--Bombardier Aerospace, Dorval, Canada; *Int'l*, pg. 200
Macdonald, A., V.P.-Sls. & Mktg.--ATCO Structures Inc., Calgary, Canada; *Int'l*, pg. 95
MacDonald, Bruce, Dir.-Mktg.--Darigold, Inc., Seattle, WA; *U.S. Private*, pg. 311
MacDonald, John, V.P.-Mktg.--Chrysler Corporation, Auburn Hills, MI; *U.S. Public*, pg. 352
MacDonald, Neil J., V.P.-Mktg./Western U.S.--Dassault Falcon Jet Corp., South Hackensack, NJ; *Int'l*, pg. 383
MacDonald, R. H., V.P.-Sls. & Dir.-Mktg.--Castrol Canada Inc., Toronto, Canada; *Int'l*, pg. 235
MacDonald, Rich, Dir.-Mktg. Plng.--Magna International Inc., Markham, Canada; *Int'l*, pg. 829
MacDonald, Robert, Mgr.-Mktg.--Noise & Vibration Systems, Cambridge, United Kingdom; *Int'l*, pg. 1431
MacDonnell, Amy, Mktg. Communications Specialist--Metrologic Instruments, Inc., Blackwood, NJ; *U.S. Public*, pg. 1102
MacDonough, John N., Exec. V.P.-Mktg.--Anheuser-Busch Europe, Inc., London, United Kingdom; *U.S. Public*, pg. 115
MacDougall, Bruce, V.P.-Mktg.--The Canadian Coleman Co., Ltd., Toronto, Canada; *U.S. Private*, pg. 691
Mace, Jack, Dir.-Mktg.--Stoneville Pedigreed Seed Co., Stoneville, MS; *U.S. Public*, pg. 1124
Macedo, Richard, V.P.-Mktg.--Kia Motors America, Inc., Irvine, CA; *Int'l*, pg. 733
Maceiras, Leonardo, Dir.-Mktg.--Business Mens Insurance Corporation, Coral Gables, FL; *U.S. Private*, pg. 189
Macekonis, Gerda, Sr. V.P.-Mktg.--Gilette Food Flavorings, Inc., Union, NJ; *U.S. Private*, pg. 453
Macewicz, Jane, V.P.-Mktg.--Putzmeister, Inc., Sturtevant, WI; *U.S. Private*, pg. 896
Macfarlane, Bud, V.P.-Sls. & Mktg.--Innovative Plastics Corporation, Orangeburg, NY; *U.S. Private*, pg. 565
MacFarlane, Deborah M., V.P.-Mktg.--Insight Health Services Corp., Newport Beach, CA; *U.S. Public*, pg. 880
Mach, Dick, Mgr.-Mktg.--Westchester Plastics, Nesquehoning, PA; *U.S. Public*, pg. 100
Machado, Marshall, V.P.-Sls. & Mktg.--AgrEvo USA Company, Wilmington, DE; *Int'l*, pg. 1203
Machenberg, Donald E., Sr. V.P. & Dir.-Bus. Devel. & Mktg.--ITT Fluid Technology Corporation, Midland Park, NJ; *U.S. Public*, pg. 860
Machlin, Bob, V.P.-Mktg.--Ascend Communications, Inc., Alameda, CA; *U.S. Public*, pg. 138
Machulak, Walter A., Sec. & Mgr.-Pur.--Homespan Realty Co., Inc., Milwaukee, WI; *U.S. Public*, pg. 410
Machuzick, John, V.P.-Consumer Foods Trade Mktg. & Promotion--General Mills, Inc., Minneapolis, MN; *U.S. Public*, pg. 717
MacIvor, P.J., Mgr.-Mktg. & Communications--CGC Inc., Mississauga, Canada; *U.S. Public*, pg. 1660
Mack, Lisbeth, V.P.-Adv. & Mktg. Programs--Trans World Airlines, Inc., Saint Louis, MO; *U.S. Public*, pg. 1629
Mack, Michael T., V.P.-Sls. & Mktg.--Mead Publishing Paper, Escanaba, MI; *U.S. Public*, pg. 1074
Mack, Ron, Mgr.-Mktg.--Hulman & Company, Terre Haute, IN; *U.S. Private*, pg. 547
Mack, Ruth, Exec. V.P.-Sls. & Mktg.--Wampler Foods, Timberville, VA; *U.S. Public*, pg. 1727
MacKenzie, Randy, Dir.-Mktg.-Furniture--Brodart Company, Williamsport, PA; *U.S. Private*, pg. 170
MacKenzie, Warren, V.P.-Sls. & Mktg.--Pittsburgh Tube Co., Moon Township, PA; *U.S. Private*, pg. 867
Mackey, Bruce W., Sr. V.P., Mktg. Services Dir. & Plng. Dir.--Northlich Stolley LaWarre, Cincinnati, OH; *U.S. Private*, pg. 806
Mackey, Patrick, Prod. Mgr.-Mkt. CIT--Executone Information Systems, Inc., Milford, CT; *U.S. Public*, pg. 599
Mackie, Jane, Mgr.-Mktg.--Sheraton Hotels (England) Limited, London, United Kingdom; *U.S. Public*, pg. 1512
Macko, Pat, Mktg. Admin.--Sherwin-Williams Diversified Brands, Inc., Solon, OH; *U.S. Public*, pg. 1466
MacLean, Clive, Exec. V.P. & Mktg. Dir.--CM Partners, Inc., Rolling Meadows, IL; *U.S. Private*, pg. 195
MacLean, Jennifer, V.P.-Mktg.--Metromail Corporation, Lombard, IL; *U.S. Public*, pg. 1102
MacLellan, Neil F., III, Exec. V.P.-Sls. & Mktg.--Mac-Gray Corporation, Cambridge, MA; *U.S. Public*, pg. 1029
Macleod, John A., V.P.-Mktg.--Sceptre Resources Limited, Calgary, Canada; *Int'l*, pg. 1203
MacLeod, Roxanne, Dir.-Mktg. & Sls.--Nova Scotia Power Inc., Halifax, Canada; *Int'l*, pg. 971
MacMasters, G. Greg, V.P.-Mktg.--Engineering Systems Co., Aston, PA; *U.S. Private*, pg. 313
MacMillan, Andrew J., Dir.-Pub. Rels.--Credit Suisse First Boston, Inc., New York, NY; *Int'l*, pg. 345
MacMillan, Kathie, V.P.-Corp. Mktg.--Bank of Montreal, Toronto, Canada; *Int'l*, pg. 153
Macnaughtan, John, Mgr.-Mktg.--Sturmey-Archer Limited, Nottingham, United Kingdom; *Int'l*, pg. 394
MacNulty, Samuel E., Sr. V.P.-Mktg. & Plng.--Inland Container-Container Division, Indianapolis, IN; *U.S. Public*, pg. 1575
Macros, Marcos Enrique, Supvr.-Mktg.--Acos Villares S.A., Sao Paulo, Brazil; *Int'l*, pg. 23
Macsuga, Joseph, V.P.-Oper. Divisions--Stebbins Engineering & Mfg. Co., Watertown, NY; *U.S. Private*, pg. 1037
MacWilliams, Dick, V.P.-Mktg. & Devel.--Bridge, New York, NY; *U.S. Private*, pg. 1162
Madden, Bruce, Exec. V.P.-Sls. & Mktg.--Maharam, Hauppauge, NY; *U.S. Private*, pg. 696
Madden, Katie, Mgr.-Mktg.--Barron's The Dow Jones Business & Financial Weekly, New York, NY; *U.S. Public*, pg. 524
Madden, Mike, Mgr.-Mktg. & Communications-Global Access Deposit--MasterCard International-Cirrus Brand, Purchase, NY; *U.S. Private*, pg. 714
Maddock, John P., Sr. V.P.-Mktg.--The Ailing & Cory Company, Rochester, NY; *U.S. Public*, pg. 1666
Maddox, Richard, Sr. V.P.-Sls. & Mktg.--Bachmann Industries, Inc., Philadelphia, PA; *U.S. Private*, pg. 109
Madenburg, Richard, Mgr.--Parsons Brinckerhoff Energy Services Inc., New York, NY; *U.S. Private*, pg. 841
Mader, M.R., V.P.-Mktg. Services--Consolidated Papers, Inc., Wisconsin Rapids, WI; *U.S. Public*, pg. 436
Madhauan, Philip, Mgr.-Mktg.--Silk Air, Singapore, Singapore; *Int'l*, pg. 1374
Madrigal, Renee, V.P.-Mktg.--New World Entertainment, Inc., Los Angeles, CA; *Int'l*, pg. 926
Madsen, Erik C., Dir.-Pricing, Mktg. & Process Redesign--IES Utilities Inc., Cedar Rapids, IA; *U.S. Public*, pg. 855
Madsen, Michael, V.P.-Mktg.--IMI Cornelius Inc. (MN), Anoka, MN; *Int'l*, pg. 646
Maenza, Drew, Asst. V.P. & Dir.-Mktg.--Crawford & Company, Atlanta, GA; *U.S. Public*, pg. 458
Maestri, Francesca, Dir.-Mktg.--D. Lazzaroni & C. S.p.A., Saronno, Italy; *Int'l*, pg. 804
Maffei, Nicholas, V.P.-Sls. & Product Devel.--Esquire Radio & Electronics Inc., Brooklyn, NY; *U.S. Private*, pg. 383
Magee, K.C., Gen. Mgr.-Mktg.--Ford Division, Detroit, MI; *U.S. Public*, pg. 662
Magee, Keith, V.P.-Sls. & Mktg., Europe--Lincoln-Mercury Division, Detroit, MI; *U.S. Public*, pg. 662
Magee, Steve, Dir.-Mktg.--Croft Metals, Inc., McComb, MS; *U.S. Private*, pg. 290
Magennis, Aidan, Dir.-Mktg.--Irish Biscuits, Dublin, Ireland; *Int'l*, pg. 688
Mager, Drew, Dir.-Mktg.--Molded Fiber Glass Co., Union City, PA; *U.S. Private*, pg. 756
Maggied, Brian, V.P.-Sls. & Mktg.--The Akro Corporation, Canton, OH; *U.S. Public*, pg. 399
Maghers, K., Dir.-Mktg.--Hepworth Heating Ltd., Belper, United Kingdom; *Int'l*, pg. 615
Magidson, Karen L., V.P. & Dir.-Corp. Mktg.--Citizens Banking Corporation, Flint, MI; *U.S. Public*, pg. 379

Maglia, Lou, V.P.-Mktg.--Elektra Entertainment, New York, NY; *U.S. Public*, pg. 1612
Magnani, Mario, Mgr.-Prod. Mktg.--Carrier Corp., Indianapolis, IN; *U.S. Public*, pg. 1690
Magnesen, Larry, Sr. V.P.--Old Kent Bank, Grand Rapids, MI; *U.S. Public*, pg. 1216
Magno, Mark, V.P.-Mktg.--Wheatland Tube Company, Collingswood, NJ; *U.S. Private*, pg. 1170
Magnuson, Brent A., Sr. V.P.-Mdse. & Mktg. (Interim)--The Bombay Company, Inc., Fort Worth, TX; *U.S. Public*, pg. 244
Magrill, Stephen, V.P.-Mktg. & Strategic Plng.--Interval International Inc., Miami, FL; *U.S. Public*, pg. 320
Maguire, Michael, V.P.-Mktg.--Time Warner Cable Liberty Division, Ferndale, NY; *U.S. Public*, pg. 1611
Mahaffey, C. Lloyd, Sr. V.P. & Gen. Mgr.-Mktg.--VeriFone, Inc., Redwood City, CA; *U.S. Public*, pg. 815
Maharam, Michael, Exec. V.P.-Design & Mktg.--Maharam, Hauppauge, NY; *U.S. Private*, pg. 696
Maher, Larry, Mgr.-Sls. & Mkg.--Zappa Plastics, Phillipsburg, NJ; *U.S. Private*, pg. 172
Maher, Tom, Mgr.-Mktg. Communications--Alcoa Building Products, Inc., Sidney, OH; *U.S. Public*, pg. 61
Mahoney, Neil J., Mgr.-Mktg. & Adv.--Evans Rule Co., Inc., Charleston, SC; *U.S. Public*, pg. 1511
Mahoney, Timothy, Dir.-Mktg.--Subaru of America, Inc., Cherry Hill, NJ; *Int'l*, pg. 523
Mahoney, Tom, V.P.-Mktg.--ITA Group Inc., West Des Moines, IA; *U.S. Private*, pg. 555
Mahony, Diane, Mgr.-Mktg.--Arby's Canada Inc., Mississauga, Canada; *U.S. Public*, pg. 1635
Maibach, Sheryl, Dir.-Mktg.--Barton Malow Enterprises, Inc., Southfield, MI; *U.S. Private*, pg. 120
Maicas, Carlos, Dir.-Mktg.--Kalifarma S.A., Barcelona, Spain; *Int'l*, pg. 1279
Maier, Karen F., V.P.-Mktg.--Frisch's Restaurants, Inc., Cincinnati, OH; *U.S. Public*, pg. 682
Maier, Kelley, V.P.-Mktg.-Fresh Vegetables--Dole Food Company, Inc., Westlake Village, CA; *U.S. Public*, pg. 515
Main, Peter, Exec. V.P.-Mktg. & Sls.--Nintendo of America, Redmond, WA; *Int'l*, pg. 932
Maines Simone, Kristi, Dir.-Mktg. Communications--Max & Erma's Restaurants, Columbus, OH; *U.S. Public*, pg. 1060
Mainolfi, Sylvio, Dir.-Mktg.--Branson Ultrasonics Corp.-Plastics Joining Div., Danbury, CT; *U.S. Public*, pg. 574
Mainolfi, Sylvio, Dir.-Mktg.--Branson Ultrasonics, Danbury, CT; *U.S. Public*, pg. 574
Mainzer, Bruce, Sr. V.P.-Mktg.--Vail Resorts, Inc., Vail, CO; *U.S. Public*, pg. 1704
Maire, F., Dir.-Mktg.-Sugar--Kraft Jacobs Suchard, Velizy-Villacoublay, France; *U.S. Public*, pg. 1290
Maiuccoro, Gary, Dir.-Sls. & Mktg.--Imperial Pools, Inc., Latham, NY; *U.S. Private*, pg. 558
Majestic, Dan, Mgr.-Mktg.--Matthews International Corp., Pittsburgh, PA; *U.S. Public*, pg. 1059
Majsak, Mike, Mgr.-Mktg.--Carhartt, Inc., Dearborn, MI; *U.S. Private*, pg. 210
Makabe, Mark, Sr. V.P.-Entertainment Sls. & Mktg.--Pioneer New Media Technologies, Long Beach, CA; *U.S. Private*, pg. 866
Makar, Janine, Mgr.-Mktg. Volleyball--Kaepa Inc., Greenville, SC; *U.S. Private*, pg. 604
Maki, Kash, Mgr.-Mktg.--Dayton Tire Company, Oklahoma City, OK; *Int'l*, pg. 213
Makomva, A.C.B., Mgr.-Mktg.--Zimbabwe Electricity Supply Authority, Harare, Zimbabwe; *Int'l*, pg. 1528
Makowski, Edward, V.P.-Market Dev.--AgrEvo USA Company, Wilmington, DE; *Int'l*, pg. 1203
Makrid, Mark, Dir.-Mktg.--Dairy Vale Co-op. Ltd., Adelaide, Australia; *Int'l*, pg. 372
Maksymyk, Dale, Dir.-Mktg.--Schneider Corp., Kitchener, Canada; *Int'l*, pg. 1207
Makuen, David, V.P.-Mktg.--Dana Perfumes Corp., New York, NY; *U.S. Private*, pg. 922
Maladra, Keith, Dir.-Mktg. & Adv.--PetCare Plus, Inc., Aurora, IL; *U.S. Private*, pg. 856
Malangone, Katherine, Dir.-Mktg. Services--F.W. Dodge Group, New York, NY; *U.S. Public*, pg. 1070
Malano, Darrell J., V.P.-Mktg.--The Franklin Life Insurance Company, Springfield, IL; *U.S. Public*, pg. 76
Malark, Greg, V.P.-Mktg.--Doubletree Corporation, Memphis, TN; *U.S. Public*, pg. 1335
Malarkey, Gregory B., Sr. V.P.-Sls. & Mktg., Tech. Svcs. & Warehouse Opers.--Herbert Malarkey Roofing Company, Portland, OR; *U.S. Private*, pg. 698
Malchin, Omer, V.P.-Mktg.--Pete's Brewing Company, Palo Alto, CA; *U.S. Public*, pg. 1280
Malcolm, Richard G., V.P.-Direct Mkts. Div.--Blue Cross & Blue Shield of Illinois, Chicago, IL; *U.S. Private*, pg. 151
Maldra, Keith, V.P.-Mktg.--Chernin's Shoes, Inc., Chicago, IL; *U.S. Private*, pg. 233
Maley, Patrick, V.P.-Sls. & Mktg.--Zoll Medical Corporation, Burlington, MA; *U.S. Private*, pg. 1207
Maley, Patrick J., V.P.-Mktg.--Norgren Co., Littleton, CO; *Int'l*, pg. 647
Malham, Joe, Mgr.-Sls. & Mktg.--Pennsylvania Cellular Telephone Corp., Bethlehem, PA; *U.S. Public*, pg. 1708
Malie, Robert L., Mgr.-Mktg.--Elkins Constructors, Inc., Jacksonville, FL; *U.S. Private*, pg. 372
Malin, Bob, V.P.-Mktg.--Serta, Inc., Itasca, IL; *U.S. Private*, pg. 985
Malitz, Michael, Natl. Mktg. Dir.--Creative Marketing International Corp., West Chicago, IL; *U.S. Private*, pg. 287
Mallamo, Reginald, V.P.-Mktg. Opers.--Harrah's Entertainment, Inc., Memphis, TN; *U.S. Public*, pg. 790
Mallamo, Reginald A., V.P.-Mktg.--Hampton Inns, Inc., Memphis, TN; *U.S. Public*, pg. 1335
Malling, James E., Sr. Exec. V.P.-Corp. Mktg. & Devel.--Municipal Bond Investors Assurance Corporation, Armonk, NY; *U.S. Public*, pg. 1023
Malloy, Michael, Sr. V.P.-Mktg.--Fair, Isaac and Company, Inc., San Rafael, CA; *U.S. Public*, pg. 609
Malloy, Terry, Sr. V.P.-Mktg. & Planning--Osco Drug, Salt Lake City, UT; *U.S. Public*, pg. 93
Malone, Eduardo, Chm. Bd. & Chief Exec. Officer--Chargeurs, Paris, France; *Int'l*, pg. 280
Malone, Marilyn, Mgr.-Mktg. Communications--Loctite Corp. North American Group, Rocky Hill, CT; *Int'l*, pg. 611
Malone, Molly, Mgr.-Reg. Mktg.--Bank One, Texas Corp., Dallas, TX; *U.S. Public*, pg. 173
Maloney, Carlene, Dir.-Mktg. Communications--Waterford Crystal, Inc., Wall, NJ; *Int'l*, pg. 1487
Maloney, Chip, V.P.-Mktg.--Xerox Imaging Systems, Inc., Palo Alto, CA; *U.S. Public*, pg. 1785
Maloney, Dennis, V.P.-Intl.--Jantzen, Portland, OR; *U.S. Public*, pg. 1702
Maloney, John, Exec. V.P.-Sls. & Mktg.--Tacony Corporation, Fenton, MO; *U.S. Private*, pg. 1066
Maloney, Mark A., V.P.-Mktg.--ULLICO Inc., Washington, DC; *U.S. Private*, pg. 1115
Maloney, Michael, Dir.-Mktg. & Sls.--Snappy Air Distribution Products, Detroit Lakes, MN; *U.S. Public*, pg. 1506
Maloy, Terry E., Sr. V.P.-Mktg. & Plng.--American Drug Stores Inc., Oak Brook, IL; *U.S. Public*, pg. 93
Mamas, Bill, V.P.-Mktg.--Sea World of Ohio, Aurora, OH; *U.S. Public*, pg. 114
Mammorella, Nancy, V.P.-Mktg. & Pub. Rels.--Mail Boxes Etc., San Diego, CA; *U.S. Public*, pg. 1687
Manak, George, Sr. Dir.-Mktg.--Griffith Laboratories Worldwide, Inc., Alsip, IL; *U.S. Private*, pg. 481
Manard, Conrad, Dir.-Mktg.--Lafarge Canada Inc., Montreal, Canada; *Int'l*, pg. 789
Mancuso, Kirt, Mgr.-Adv. & Mktg. Svcs.--Florsheim Group Inc., Chicago, IL; *U.S. Public*, pg. 656
Mancuso, Michael V., Dir.-Sls. & Mktg.--C.J. Tower Inc., Buffalo, NY; *U.S. Public*, pg. 1071
Mandala, Jim, Dir.-Sls. & Mktg.--Epson Canada Limited, Willowdale, Canada; *Int'l*, pg. 1219
Mandel, Lauren, V.P.-Mktg. & Sls.--The Napier Co., Meriden, CT; *U.S. Private*, pg. 774
Mandel, Mark D., V.P.-Mktg.--Health Management Systems, Inc., New York, NY; *U.S. Public*, pg. 802
Mandelbaum, Jay, Exec. V.P.-Mktg.--Salomon Smith Barney Holdings, Inc., New York, NY; *U.S. Public*, pg. 1633
Mandell, Jeanne M., Mgr.-Mktg.--Willis Corroon Corp. of Wash. D.C., Bethesda, MD; *Int'l*, pg. 1507
Mandell, Laura, Dir.-Mktg.--Hewitt Associates LLC, Lincolnshire, IL; *U.S. Private*, pg. 524
Mandell, Marshall S., Mgr.-Bus. Devel.--DynCorp, Reston, VA; *U.S. Private*, pg. 351
Manderscheid, Larry, V.P.-Sls. & Mktg.--Aerostar International, Sioux Falls, SD; *U.S. Public*, pg. 1361
Manenti, Thomas J., Sr. V.P.-Mktg. & Sls.--MiTek, Inc., Chesterfield, MO; *Int'l*, pg. 1106
Manero, Linda, Dir.-Mktg. Communications--Harleysville Group, Harleysville, PA; *U.S. Public*, pg. 786
Maneval, J.C., Mgr.-Mktg. Communications--Du Pont Chemicals, Wilmington, DE; *U.S. Public*, pg. 531
Maney, Bruna, Dir.-Mktg.--Fownes Brothers & Co., Inc., New York, NY; *U.S. Private*, pg. 422
Mang, Theo, Dr., Chief Tech. Officer--Fuchs Petrolub AG Oel + Chemie, Mannheim, Germany; *Int'l*, pg. 517
Mangan, James M., V.P.-Mktg. & Agency Opers.--Amerisure Companies, Farmington Hills, MI; *U.S. Private*, pg. 65
Mangan, Jim, V.P.-Mktg.--Bell Distributing, Sacramento, CA; *U.S. Private*, pg. 664
Mangiaracina, Vito, V.P.-Plastics Div.--Shoe Last Div., Walnut Ridge, AR; *U.S. Public*, pg. 1725
Mangine, Tony, V.P.-Sls. & Mktg.--FieldBrook Farms, Inc., Dunkirk, NY; *U.S. Private*, pg. 403
Mangione, Mike, Mktg. & Communications Specialist--Edwards High Vacuum, International, Grand Island, NY; *Int'l*, pg. 121
Mangione, Mike, Mktg. & Communications Specialist--Edwards High Vacuum International, Wilmington, MA; *Int'l*, pg. 121
Mangold, Bob, V.P. & Gen. Mgr.-Auto Warehouse Div.--STRAFCO, Inc., San Antonio, TX; *U.S. Private*, pg. 1046
Mangold, Ed, Sr. V.P.-Mktg.--Applied Communications, Inc., Omaha, NE; *U.S. Public*, pg. 1629
Manikowski, Tom, Dir.-Mktg.--Steelcase Wood Div., Kentwood, MI; *U.S. Private*, pg. 1038
Manion, Martin, V.P.-Mktg.--McIlhenny Company, Avery Island, LA; *U.S. Private*, pg. 722
Manjan, Thomas, Sr. V.P.-Sls. & Mktg.--Microlog Corporation, Germantown, MD; *U.S. Public*, pg. 1105
Mankamyer, Richard, Mgr.-Mktg. & Sls.--Schubert Industries Inc., Akron, OH; *U.S. Private*, pg. 973
Mankamyer, Richard, Mgr.-Mktg. & Sls.--The Springwall Mattress Co., Akron, OH; *U.S. Private*, pg. 973
Manly, Mark, Dir.-Mktg.--Freezer Queen Foods Inc., Buffalo, NY; *Int'l*, pg. 340
Mann B., Dir.-Mktg.--Scott National, Calgary, Canada; *Int'l*, pg. 1012
Mann, Al, V.P.-Pur. & Hardware--Ingram Micro Inc., Santa Ana, CA; *U.S. Public*, pg. 878
Mann, Christopher, V.P.-Mktg.--CVC Products, Inc., Rochester, NY; *U.S. Private*, pg. 197
Mann, Janet E., V.P.-Mktg.--ANGUS Chemical Company, Buffalo Grove, IL; *U.S. Private*, pg. 75
Mann, Raymond R., V.P.-Bus. Devel.--Analytical Surveys, Inc., Colorado Springs, CO; *U.S. Public*, pg. 110
Mannerkoski, Lauri, Vice Chm. & Exec. V.P.-Mktg.--Rautaruukki Oy, Helsinki, Finland; *Int'l*, pg. 1088
Manning, Dennis J., Chief Mktg. Officer & Sr. V.P.--The Guardian Life Insurance Company of America, New York, NY; *U.S. Private*, pg. 486
Manning, John, V.P.-Sls. & Mktg.--Crane Plastics Company, Columbus, OH; *U.S. Private*, pg. 286
Manning, Mary, Sr. V.P.-Mktg. & Devel.--Coty Inc., New York, NY; *Int'l*, pg. 185
Manning, Paul, Dir.-Mktg.--Springer-Verlag New York Inc., New York, NY; *Int'l*, pg. 1291
Manning, Terry J., V.P.-Mktg. & Sls.--Zoom Telephonics, Inc., Boston, MA; *U.S. Public*, pg. 1794
Mannion, Dennis, V.P.-Mktg.--The Phillies-A Limited Partnership, Philadelphia, PA; *U.S. Private*, pg. 861
Manns, D.M., Mgr.-Sls. & Mktg.--Linhas Corrente Ltda., Ipiranga, Brazil; *Int'l*, pg. 301
Manos, Bill, Dir.-Mktg. Cumberland Office--OCE-U.S.A., Itasca, IL; *Int'l*, pg. 994
Manos, Eric B., V.P.-Sls. & Mktg.--Buehler U.K. Ltd., Coventry, United Kingdom; *U.S. Public*, pg. 575
Manos, Steve, Mktg. Specialist--The Johnson Corporation, Three Rivers, MI; *U.S. Private*, pg. 591
Manson, Michelle, Mgr.-Mktg. Communications--Interpoint, Redmond, WA; *U.S. Public*, pg. 457
Mansouri, M., V.P.-Corp. Mktg.--UDT Sensors, Inc., Hawthorne, CA; *U.S. Private*, pg. 1112
Mansson, Ola, Pres.--Skanska Teknik AB, Malmo, Sweden; *Int'l*, pg. 1261
Mansur, Danilo M.C., Exec. V.P.-Middle Mkt.--Uniao de Bancos Brasileiros S.A. (Unibanco), Sao Paulo, Brazil; *Int'l*, pg. 1431
Mantellini, Ramon, Mgr.-Domestic Mktg.--Petroleos de Venezuela S.A., Caracas, Venezuela; *Int'l*, pg. 1045
Manual, Mary, Coord.-Mktg. Services--Industrial Coatings Group, Inc., Chicago, IL; *U.S. Private*, pg. 434
Manuel, Beth, Mktg. Services--Seco Warwick Corporation, Meadville, PA; *U.S. Private*, pg. 980
Manwarring, Mary, V.P.-Design Mktg.--Jerell, Inc., Dallas, TX; *U.S. Private*, pg. 586
Manz, Chris, Mgr.-Mktg.--Lectrodryer Div., Ajax Magnethermic Corp., Richmond, KY; *Int'l*, pg. 113
Manz, George, V.P.-Prod. Mktg., Kimball Office Grp.--Kimball International, Inc., Jasper, IN; *U.S. Public*, pg. 956
Mapes, Timothy W., Dir.-Worldwide Mktg. Communications--Delta Air Lines, Inc., Atlanta, GA; *U.S. Public*, pg. 497
Marabella, Angelo, Dir.-Mktg.--Jaco Electronics, Inc., Hauppauge, NY; *U.S. Public*, pg. 920
Marabuto, Marie, Mgr.-Corp. Mktg. Services--Troy Corporation, Florham Park, NJ; *U.S. Private*, pg. 1105
Marani, Erminio, Mgr.-Mktg.--Marcegaglia SpA, Mantova, Italy; *Int'l*, pg. 841
Marcadet, T., Mgr.-Adv. & Mktg.--Agfa-Gevaert S.A., Rueil-Malmaison, France; *Int'l*, pg. 174
Marcellus, Richard, Dir.-N. American Sls.--Simplicity Manufacturing, Inc., Port Washington, WI; *U.S. Private*, pg. 1002
Marchal, Gilles, Mgr.-Mktg.--Total S.A., Paris, France; *Int'l*, pg. 1408
Marchi, Graziano, Mgr.-Mktg.--Harold Leonard & Company, Inc., Union, NJ; *U.S. Private*, pg. 660
Marchione, John, Dir.-Mktg.--The Kelly-Springfield Tire Company, Cumberland, MD; *U.S. Public*, pg. 753
Marconi, Allan, V.P.-Sls. & Mktg.--Alpha Wire Company, Elizabeth, NJ; *U.S. Public*, pg. 201
Marconi, Deborah, Mgr.-Mktg.--Arbor Acres Farm, Inc., Glastonbury, CT; *Int'l*, pg. 202
Marconi, Frank, Mgr.-Adv. & Mktg.--Svedala Pumps & Process, Colorado Springs, CO; *Int'l*, pg. 1325
Marcotte, Richard, V.P.-Mktg. & Sls.--Nissan Canada Inc., Mississauga, Canada; *Int'l*, pg. 945
Marcucci, Tom, Dir.-Mktg.--Gonnella Baking Co., Chicago, IL; *U.S. Private*, pg. 463
Marcus, Paul, Exec. V.P.-Entertainment Mktg.--Simon Marketing, Inc., Los Angeles, CA; *U.S. Private*, pg. 1001
Marcus, Stanton C., Sls. & Mktg.--Coast Business Credit, Los Angeles, CA; *U.S. Public*, pg. 872
Marcus, Steven, V.P.-Mktg.- Personal Care--Del Laboratories, Inc., Farmingdale, NY; *U.S. Public*, pg. 494
Marcus, Steven, V.P.-Mktg./Personal Care--Sally Hansen, Farmingdale, NY; *U.S. Public*, pg. 494
Marden, David, Dir.-Product Devel.--Granite State Manufacturing Co., Manchester, NH; *U.S. Private*, pg. 36
Mardorf, Kevin C., Dir.-Mktg. Communications--U.S. Surgical Corp., Norwalk, CT; *U.S. Public*, pg. 1687
Marek, James, Dir.-Mktg.--C-Tech Systems, Plymouth, MN; *U.S. Public*, pg. 865
Marek, Joycelyn, V.P.-Mktg. & New Media--Houston Chronicle, Houston, TX; *U.S. Private*, pg. 517
Mareno, Rosita, V.P.-Food Service--Pepperidge Farm, Incorporated, Norwalk, CT; *U.S. Public*, pg. 299
Marfinowich, John, V.P.-Mktg.--United Water New Jersey, Inc., Harrington Park, NJ; *U.S. Public*, pg. 1692
Margaux, Andre, Mgr.-Sls. & Mktg.--Pacific Handy Cutter, Inc., Costa Mesa, CA; *U.S. Private*, pg. 831
Margin, Rick, V.P.-Mktg.--Prince Sports Group Inc., Bordentown, NJ; *U.S. Private*, pg. 884
Margin, Rick, V.P.-Mktg.--Ektelon, Bordentown, NJ; *U.S. Private*, pg. 884
Marici, Edward, V.P., Dir.-Mktg.--Porta Systems Co., Charlotte, NC; *U.S. Public*, pg. 1317
Mariconda, Christine, Dir.-Mktg. Svcs.--Brinkmann Instruments, Inc., Westbury, NY; *U.S. Private*, pg. 169
Marietti, Bill, Dir.-Mktg.--Ludington News Co. Inc., Detroit, MI; *U.S. Private*, pg. 679
Marigolis, Mike, V.P.-Mktg.--Ericsson, Inc., Richardson, TX; *Int'l*, pg. 1364
Marin, B., Dir.-Mktg.--Lucas Girling S.A., Pamplona, Spain; *Int'l*, pg. 820
Marinaro, Richard, V.P.-Mktg. & Sls.--Advanced Telemarketing Corp., Irving, TX; *U.S. Public*, pg. 11
Marinelli, Steve, Mgr.-Mktg.--National Welders Supply Co. Inc., Charlotte, NC; *U.S. Private*, pg. 788
Marino, J., Mgr.-Mktg.--FANUC Robotics North America, Inc., Rochester Hills, MI; *Int'l*, pg. 477
Marino, John, Dir.-Mktg.--FlightSafety Academy, Vero Beach, FL; *U.S. Public*, pg. 218
Marino, Vincenzo, Sr. V.P. & Dir.-Mktg.--Frederick Wildman & Sons Ltd., New York, NY; *U.S. Private*, pg. 1176
Marinosson, Orn, Dir.-Fin. & Mktg.--Landsvirkjun - The National Power Co., Reykjavik, Iceland; *Int'l*, pg. 801
Maritz, Doug, Bus. Devel. Dir.--Young & Rubicam South Africa, Johannesburg, South Africa; *U.S. Private*, pg. 1198

Marker, Cheryl, Dir.-Creative Svcs.--Self, New York, NY; *U.S. Private*, pg. 20

Marker, T., Dir.-Sales & Mktg.--Carbone of America, Commutation Components Div., Farmville, VA; *Int'l*, pg. 1028

Markert, John, V.P.-Mktg.--Shur-Lok Corporation, Irvine, CA; *U.S. Private*, pg. 997

Markl, Thomas L., Sr. V.P.--UTILX Corporation, Kent, WA; *U.S. Public*, pg. 1701

Markle, Paul, Dir.-Mktg.--Toronto Blue Jays Baseball Club, Inc., Toronto, Canada; *Int'l*, pg. 680

Markley, Roland, V.P.-Mktg.--Tork, Inc., Mount Vernon, NY; *U.S. Private*, pg. 1092

Marko, Ron, Dir.-Sls. Promo.--Saladmaster, Arlington, TX; *U.S. Private*, pg. 961

Markos, Ron, Mgr.-Sls. Promo.--Saladmaster, Inc., Arlington, TX; *U.S. Private*, pg. 917

Markovski, Mike, Dir.-Mktg.--U.S. Filter/Permutit, Warren, NJ; *U.S. Public*, pg. 1682

Markovski, Mike, V.P.-Mktg. & Corp. Communications--U.S. Filter/Arrowhead Inc., Rockford, IL; *U.S. Public*, pg. 1682

Markovsky, Mike, V.P.-Mktg. Communications--U.S. Filter, Palm Desert, CA; *U.S. Public*, pg. 61

Markovsky, Mike, V.P.-Mktg. & Corp. Communications--United States Filter Corporation, Palm Desert, CA; *U.S. Public*, pg. 1681

Markowski, Joseph, Sr. V.P.-Mktg.--Coty Inc., New York, NY; *Int'l*, pg. 185

Marks, Amy, Project Mgr.-Mktg.--Noville, South Hackensack, NJ; *U.S. Private*, pg. 808

Marks, Ann, V.P.-Mktg.--American Express Publishing Corporation, New York, NY; *U.S. Public*, pg. 74

Marks, Fabian, Mktg. Controller--Lever Brothers West Indies Ltd., Champs Fleurs, Trinidad & Tobago; *Int'l*, pg. 1437

Marks, Francis A., V.P.--Intelligent Systems Corp., Norcross, GA; *U.S. Public*, pg. 888

Marks, George V., Sr. V.P.-Transportation--Huitt-Zollars, Inc., Dallas, TX; *U.S. Private*, pg. 547

Marks, Jeffrey, Dir.-Mktg. & Communications--Epson America Inc., Torrance, CA; *Int'l*, pg. 1219

Marks, Lisa, Dir.-Mktg.--Ryka Incorporated, King of Prussia, PA; *U.S. Public*, pg. 1414

Marks, Tony J., Gen. Mgr.-Intl. Sls. & Mktg.--Air New Zealand Ltd., Auckland, New Zealand; *Int'l*, pg. 38

Markson, Peter, Pres.--Baar & Beards, New York, NY; *U.S. Private*, pg. 839

Markwart, Robert, V.P.-Mktg. & Sls.--The Chamberlain Group, Inc., Elmhurst, IL; *U.S. Private*, pg. 344

Markwell, Mary Ann, V.P.-Mktg.--The Fifth Third Bank of Kentucky, Louisville, Louisville, KY; *U.S. Public*, pg. 621

Marler, Larry, Gen. Mgr.-Dillard Express Stores--Dillard, A ResourceNet International Company, Greensboro, NC; *U.S. Public*, pg. 901

Marlo, Mike, Mgr.-Mktg.--Reilly Industries, Inc., Indianapolis, IN; *U.S. Private*, pg. 919

Marmion, Abby, V.P.-Mktg.--Bank One, Indiana, N.A., Indianapolis, IN; *U.S. Public*, pg. 173

Marmion, Bridget, Dir.-Sls. & Mktg./Random House Grp.--Random House, Inc., New York, NY; *U.S. Private*, pg. 20

Marmon, Larry, Exec. V.P.-Mktg. Opers.--Time-Life, Inc., Alexandria, VA; *U.S. Public*, pg. 1613

Marohl, Rudolph O., Pres.--Central Research Laboratories, Red Wing, MN; *U.S. Public*, pg. 521

Marques, Fatima de Jesus, Dir.-Mktg.--LPC Industrias Alimenticias S.A., Vila Jaguara, Brazil; *Int'l*, pg. 380

Marquez, Richard, Dir.-Channel Mktg.--Symantec Corporation - Beaverton Site, Beaverton, OR; *U.S. Public*, pg. 1545

Marquis, Doug, Pres. & Chief Exec. Officer--Handgards Inc., Northbrook, IL; *U.S. Private*, pg. 499

Marr, Cliff, V.P.-Sls. & Mktg.--Fiberesin Industries Inc., Oconomowoc, WI; *U.S. Private*, pg. 402

Marr, Daniel G., V.P.-Mktg.--Coca-Cola Enterprises Inc., Atlanta, GA; *U.S. Public*, pg. 393

Marra, Robert A., Sr. V.P.-Retail Mktg. & Prod. Devel.--John Hancock Mutual Life Insurance Company, Boston, MA; *U.S. Private*, pg. 589

Marrinucci, John, V.P.-Sls. & Mktg.--Gai-Tronics Corporation, Mohnton, PA; *U.S. Public*, pg. 1430

Marrone, Elizabeth, Dir.-Prod Devel.--Coty Inc., New York, NY; *Int'l*, pg. 185

Marrus, Allan J., Pres.--The Arlen Corporation, New York, NY; *U.S. Public*, pg. 131

Marsala, Lenard, Mgr.-Mktg.--Spectrum Control, Connecting Devices Div., Erie, PA; *U.S. Public*, pg. 1497

Marsden, Andrew, Dir.-Mktg.--Britvic Soft Drinks Ltd., Chelmsford, United Kingdom; *Int'l*, pg. 170

Marsden, R.H., Gen. Mgr.-Mktg.--Copeland Corporation Ltd., Thatcham, United Kingdom; *U.S. Public*, pg. 576

Marsden, Stephen T., Area Mgr.-Mktg.--KLM Royal Dutch Airlines, Elmsford, NY; *Int'l*, pg. 719

Marsh, Brooks, Dir.-Mktg.--SuperValu, Inc.-JM Jones Div., Champaign, IL; *U.S. Public*, pg. 1540

Marsh, Carmi M., V.P.-Retail Mktg. & Mgr.-Derby Office--Community National Bank, Derby, VT; *U.S. Public*, pg. 416

Marsh, Charles L., Sr. Exec. V.P.-Pur. & Mktg.--Southern Electronics Distributors International, Tucker, GA; *U.S. Public*, pg. 1490

Marsh, Daniel, V.P.-Sls. & Mktg.--Medical Action Industries Inc., Hauppauge, NY; *U.S. Public*, pg. 1079

Marsh, J., Mgr.-Prod.--Protective Closures Co., Inc., Buffalo, NY; *U.S. Public*, pg. 1045

Marsh, Jim, V.P.-Natl. Sls.--Atalanta Corporation, Elizabeth, NJ; *U.S. Private*, pg. 93

Marsh, Jim, Mgr.-Mktg. Communications--Graphic Controls Corporation, Buffalo, NY; *U.S. Private*, pg. 470

Marsh, Ron, V.P.-Sls. & Mktg.--Gwaltney of Smithfield, Ltd., Smithfield, VA; *U.S. Public*, pg. 1479

Marsh, Thomas, V.P.-Mktg.--Leslie - Locke, Inc., Atlanta, GA; *U.S. Public*, pg. 989

Marshall, Barbara, V.P. & Dir.-Mktg.--Anchor Financial Corporation, Myrtle Beach, SC; *U.S. Public*, pg. 111

Marshall, Bob, V.P.-OTC Mktg.--Chattem, Inc., Chattanooga, TN; *U.S. Public*, pg. 341

Marshall, Bob, V.P.-Mktg.-OTC--Chattem, Inc., Consumer Products Division, Chattanooga, TN; *U.S. Public*, pg. 341

Marshall, Bob, Dir.-Strategic Mktg.--Military Products Div., Sunnyvale, CA; *Int'l*, pg. 1054

Marshall, Brian, Mgr.-Mktg. Devel.--Spontex, Inc., Columbia, TN; *Int'l*, pg. 1409

Marshall, Doug, Mgr.-N.W. Retail Mktg.--Seafirst Corporation, Seattle, WA; *U.S. Public*, pg. 181

Marshall, Duff, Mgr.-Sls., Mktg. & Adv.--Marvin Lumber & Cedar Company, Warroad, MN; *U.S. Private*, pg. 710

Marshall, Geoffrey I., V.P.-Natl. Sls.--The Turner Corporation, New York, NY; *U.S. Public*, pg. 1645

Marshall, Gordon R., V.P.-Mktg.--The HON Co., Muscatine, IA; *U.S. Public*, pg. 772

Marshall, Jack, V.P.-Mktg.--Astro Dairy Products Ltd., Etobicoke, Canada; *Int'l*, pg. 95

Marshall, Laura, Mktg. Commun. Specialist--Zoll Medical Corporation, Burlington, MA; *U.S. Private*, pg. 1207

Marshall, Lisa A., Mktg. Officer--Associated Banc-Corp, Green Bay, WI; *U.S. Public*, pg. 140

Marshall, Richard J., V.P.-Mktg.--Maverik Country Stores, Inc., Salt Lake City, UT; *U.S. Private*, pg. 715

Marshall, Wayne T., Sr. Dir.-Mktg.-Produce, Meat, Seafood & Service Deli--Big V Supermarkets, Inc., Florida, NY; *U.S. Private*, pg. 143

Marshall, William, V.P.-Electrical Distr. & Mktg.--Leviton Mfg. Co., Inc., Little Neck, NY; *U.S. Private*, pg. 663

Marsigliano, Mike, Mgr.-Mktg. Communications--Thermo Electric Co., Inc., Saddle Brook, NJ; *U.S. Private*, pg. 1080

Marston, Barry, V.P.-Sls. & Mktg.--Medex Inc., Hilliard, OH; *U.S. Public*, pg. 689

Martel, Chris, Dir.-Mktg.--United Farm Tools, Mohawk, Oelwein, IA; *U.S. Private*, pg. 1122

Martel, Christopher W., Dir.-Mktg.--United Farm Tools, Inc., Glasgow, KY; *U.S. Private*, pg. 1122

Martel, Lynda, Mgr.-Mktg. Services--GTECH Corporation, West Greenwich, RI; *U.S. Public*, pg. 767

Martell, Dick, Mgr.-Grp. Mktg. & Design--People, New York, NY; *U.S. Public*, pg. 1613

Martens, John D., V.P.-Mkt. Plans--The Southern New England Telephone Company, New Haven, CT; *U.S. Public*, pg. 1491

Martens, Michael, Dir.-Mktg.--Dark Horse Comics, Inc., Milwaukie, OR; *U.S. Private*, pg. 311

Marti, David, Dir.-Database Mktg.--Big Y Foods Inc., Springfield, MA; *U.S. Private*, pg. 143

Martin, Andrew S., V.P.-Sls. & Mktg.--First Protective Insurance Group, Birmingham, AL; *U.S. Public*, pg. 1336

Martin, Andy, Mgr.-Mktg.--Lord Corporation, Cary, NC; *U.S. Private*, pg. 675

Martin, Bill, V.P.--Leader National Insurance Company, Dallas, TX; *U.S. Public*, pg. 75

Martin, Craig L., Sr. V.P.-Gen. Sls. & Mktg.--Jacobs Engineering Group Inc., Pasadena, CA; *U.S. Public*, pg. 921

Martin, Dale, Dir.-Mktg.--Mylan Laboratories, Inc., Pittsburgh, PA; *U.S. Public*, pg. 1143

Martin, Dale, Dir.-Mktg.--Mylan Pharmaceuticals Inc., Morgantown, WV; *U.S. Public*, pg. 1143

Martin, Gene, Dir.-Mktg.--South Carolina Electric & Gas Co. (SCE&G), Columbia, SC; *U.S. Public*, pg. 1436

Martin, Gordon, V.P.-Strategic Mktg.--Williams Telecommunications Systems, Inc., Houston, TX; *U.S. Public*, pg. 1769

Martin, J., Dir.-Mktg.--Charmilles Technologies SA, Meyrin, Switzerland; *Int'l*, pg. 489

Martin, James, V.P. & Marketplace Plng. Dir.--GSD&M, Austin, TX; *U.S. Private*, pg. 436

Martin, James, Mgr.-Mktg. Communications--Instron Corporation, Canton, MA; *U.S. Public*, pg. 882

Martin, James L., V.P.-Bleached Bd. Sls. & Mktg.--Westvaco Corporation, New York, NY; *U.S. Public*, pg. 1762

Martin, Jamie, V.P.-Retail Mktg.--Better Homes and Gardens Books, Des Moines, IA; *U.S. Public*, pg. 1094

Martin, Jerold M., V.P.-Mktg.--Pall Ultrafine Filtration Company, Greenvale, NY; *U.S. Public*, pg. 1254

Martin, Jim, Gen. Mgr.-Lubes--J.D. Streett & Co., Inc., Maryland Heights, MO; *U.S. Private*, pg. 1047

Martin, John, V.P.-Mktg. Services--The American Companies, Inc., Topeka, KS; *U.S. Private*, pg. 52

Martin, John B., Sr. Dir.-Mktg.--Coca-Cola Consolidated, Charlotte, NC; *U.S. Public*, pg. 392

Martin, John R., Jr., V.P.-Corp. Rels. & Mktg.--CBL & Associates Properties, Inc., Chattanooga, TN; *U.S. Public*, pg. 273

Martin, John S., Dir.-Mktg. Services & Pub. Rels.--Healthtex, Greensboro, NC; *U.S. Public*, pg. 1702

Martin, Jose Maria, Mgr.-Mktg.--Compania Espanola de Petroleos, S.A. (CEPSA), Madrid, Spain; *Int'l*, pg. 323

Martin, Kathy, Coord.-Mktg. Info.--Giddings & Lewis, Inc., Fond Du Lac, WI; *Int'l*, pg. 1389

Martin, Kent, Sr. V.P.--Servo Corporation of America, Westbury, NY; *U.S. Private*, pg. 987

Martin, Kevin, Dir.-Mktg.--Walbridge Aldinger Company, Detroit, MI; *U.S. Private*, pg. 1146

Martin, Mark A., V.P.-Mktg./Van Div.--Werner Enterprises, Inc., Omaha, NE; *U.S. Public*, pg. 1754

Martin, Michael, Dir.-Mktg. & Adv.--Martin Door Mfg., Inc., Salt Lake City, UT; *U.S. Private*, pg. 708

Martin, Michael S., Sr. V.P.-Mktg.--The Equitable Companies Incorporated, New York, NY; *U.S. Public*, pg. 588

Martin, Peter, V.P.-Sls. & Mktg.--Captive Plastics, Piscataway, NJ; *U.S. Private*, pg. 207

Martin, R. Steven, V.P.-Mktg.--Red Star Yeast & Products Div., Milwaukee, WI; *U.S. Public*, pg. 1695

Martin, Reginald, V.P.-Mktg. & Prod. Devel.--Bufkor, Inc., Clearwater, FL; *U.S. Private*, pg. 179

Martin, Robert, V.P.-Sls. & Mktg.--American Packaging Corporation, Philadelphia, PA; *U.S. Private*, pg. 60

Martin, Robert A., Exec. V.P.-Mktg.--Applebee's International, Inc., Overland Park, KS; *U.S. Public*, pg. 122

Martin, Ronald H., Sr. V.P.-Mktg.--Colorado National Bankshares, Inc., Denver, CO; *U.S. Public*, pg. 1680

Martin, Scott, V.P.-Sls. & Mktg.--Nodak Mutual Insurance Company, Fargo, ND; *U.S. Private*, pg. 800

Martin, Steve, Dir.-Mktg.--Duro Dyne Corporation, Farmingdale, NY; *U.S. Private*, pg. 349

Martin, Steve, Mgr.-Mktg. Svcs.--Hunter Fan Company, Memphis, TN; *U.S. Private*, pg. 549

Martin, Thomas O., V.P.-Mktg. & Sec.--Uniflow Manufacturing Co., Erie, PA; *U.S. Private*, pg. 1117

Martin, Thomas O., V.P.-Mktg. & Sls.--Kold Draft, Erie, PA; *U.S. Private*, pg. 1117

Martin, Tom, Dir.-Mktg. Communication--Dell Computer Corporation, Round Rock, TX; *U.S. Public*, pg. 495

Martin, Trish, Dir.-Mktg.--Sara Lee Hosiery, Winston Salem, NC; *U.S. Public*, pg. 1434

Martin, Trish, Dir.-Mktg.--L'eggs Products, Inc., Winston Salem, NC; *U.S. Public*, pg. 1434

Martine, Christine, Head-Mktg.--Bristol & West Building Society, Bristol, United Kingdom; *Int'l*, pg. 216

Martinengo, Massimo, Strategic Mktg. Dir.--Pirella Gottsche Lowe, Milan, Italy; *U.S. Private*, pg. 678

Martinez, Alicia, Dir.-Mktg. & Corp. Commun.--Metropolitan Transportation Authority, New York, NY; *U.S. Private*, pg. 739

Martinez, Celeste, Mgr.-Events & Corp. Mktg.--MacNeal-Schwendler Corp., Costa Mesa, CA; *U.S. Public*, pg. 1031

Martinez, Jerome, V.P.-Mktg.--American Furniture Company, Albuquerque, NM; *U.S. Private*, pg. 55

Martinez, Paul, V.P.-Sls. & Mktg.--Label-Aire Inc., Fullerton, CA; *U.S. Private*, pg. 641

Martinez, Ramon V., Dir.-Sls. & Mktg./Latin America--Ethyl Corporation, Richmond, VA; *U.S. Public*, pg. 595

Martino, Joe, Sr. Mktg. Exec.--The Stroh Brewery Company, Detroit, MI; *U.S. Private*, pg. 1047

Martino, Nicholas, V.P.-Mktg.--Checkpoint Systems Inc., Thorofare, NJ; *U.S. Public*, pg. 343

Martino, Silvio M., V.P.-Intl. Sls.--Goodman Equipment Corp., Bedford Park, IL; *U.S. Private*, pg. 464

Martinolich, Michael J., Dir.-Mktg.--Stiefel Laboratories, Inc., Coral Gables, FL; *U.S. Private*, pg. 1043

Martinowich, John, V.P.-New Bus. & External Affairs--United Water Resources, Harrington Park, NJ; *U.S. Public*, pg. 1691

Martinowich, John, Asst. V.P.-External Affairs & Mktg.--United Water Management & Services, Harrington Park, NJ; *U.S. Public*, pg. 1692

Martinsen, Tom, V.P.-Mktg. & Sls.--Tool & Hoist Division, Liberty Corner, NJ; *U.S. Public*, pg. 877

Martinson Kath, Kelly, Dir.-Mktg.--Capitol Construction Group, Inc., Wheeling, IL; *U.S. Private*, pg. 206

Martrenchar, Yves, Dir.-Mktg.--Banque Nationale de Paris, Paris, France; *Int'l*, pg. 163

Martz, Charles, V.P.-Mktg.--American Hardware Mutual Insurance Co., Columbus, OH; *U.S. Private*, pg. 764

Martz, Charles, V.P.-Mktg.--American Merchants Casualty Co., Columbus, OH; *U.S. Private*, pg. 764

Martz, West, V.P.-Mktg.--The Johnson Corporation, Three Rivers, MI; *U.S. Private*, pg. 591

Maruszak, Patricia, Mgr.-Mktg. Communications--Justrite Manufacturing Company, Des Plaines, IL; *U.S. Public*, pg. 617

Marvin, Susan I., Sr. V.P.- Sls. & Mktg.--Marvin Lumber & Cedar Company, Warroad, MN; *U.S. Private*, pg. 710

Marx, Kathryn, V.P.-Mktg.--Flint Ink Corp., Detroit, MI; *U.S. Private*, pg. 413

Marziali, Massimo, Mgr.-Mktg.--Mazzucchelli Polimeri Srl, Castiglione, Italy; *Int'l*, pg. 850

Marzol, Adolfo, Sr. V.P.-Capital Markets--Federal National Mortgage Association (Fannie Mae), Washington, DC; *U.S. Public*, pg. 615

Mascari, Cara, Dir.-Mktg.--County Seat Stores, Inc., Dallas, TX; *U.S. Private*, pg. 279

Masch, D.W., Mktg. Mgr.-Germany--Carpenter Technology (Deutschland) GmbH, Sindelfingen, Germany; *U.S. Public*, pg. 308

Maschio, Joseph, Sr. V.P.-Mktg.--Newspapers First, New York, NY; *U.S. Public*, pg. 964

Maschke, Peter C., Mgr.-Intl. Sls. & Mktg.--Bender Shipbuilding & Repair Company, Inc., Mobile, AL; *U.S. Private*, pg. 132

Masefield, Grace, Dir.-Mktg.--Isomedix Inc., Whippany, NJ; *U.S. Public*, pg. 1515

Maser, Barry, Mgr.-Intl. Mktg.--Aydin Displays (East), Horsham, PA; *U.S. Public*, pg. 158

Mashiter, Ian, Dir.-Mktg.--General DataComm Intl. Corp., Middlebury, CT; *U.S. Public*, pg. 708

Masi, J. Carl, V.P.-Mktg.--PictureTel, Andover, MA; *U.S. Public*, pg. 1294

Masingill, Joanne, V.P.-Software Bus. Unit--Microcom, Norwood, MA; *U.S. Public*, pg. 417

Maskal, Vanessa, V.P.-Mktg.--Drake Bakeries, Inc., Wayne, NJ; *Int'l*, pg. 349

Maslan, Brad, Mgr.-Mktg.--Ferrero U.S.A., Inc., Somerset, NJ; *Int'l*, pg. 480

Masline, Scott, V.P.-Mktg.--Galoob Toys, Inc., South San Francisco, CA; *U.S. Public*, pg. 698

Mason, Julie, Sls. & Mktg. Coordinator--Belcan Corporation, Cincinnati, OH; *U.S. Private*, pg. 131

Mason, Sharon, Corp. Sec.--Bliss-Salem, Inc., Salem, OH; *U.S. Private*, pg. 149

Mason, Steve, V.P.-Mktg.--American Classic Voyagers Company, New Orleans, LA; *U.S. Private*, pg. 380

Mason, Steve, V.P.-Mktg. Mdsg.--Homeland Stores, Inc., Oklahoma City, OK; *U.S. Public*, pg. 832

Mason, Steven M., V.P.-Mktg.--Homeland Holding Corp., Oklahoma City, OK; *U.S. Public*, pg. 832

Mason, Tim, V.P.-Mktg. & Sls.--Bridon Cordage Inc., Albert Lea, MN; *Int'l*, pg. 215

Mason, Tim, Dir.-Mktg. Opers.--Tesco PLC, Cheshunt, United Kingdom; *Int'l*, pg. 1376
Mason, Tom, Dir.-Sls. & Mktg.-Wausau--Wausau Homes, Inc., Rothschild, WI; *U.S. Private*, pg. 1154
Masquez, Richard, Dir.-Channel Mktg.--Symantec Corporation, Cupertino, CA; *U.S. Public*, pg. 1545
Mass, Harvey, Sr. V.P.-Sls. & Mktg.--First Central Financial Corporation, Lynbrook, NY; *U.S. Private*, pg. 406
Massa, William, V.P.-Mktg.--CasChem Inc., Bayonne, NJ; *U.S. Public*, pg. 297
Massart, G., Dir.-Mktg. & Europe Communications--Gates Europe, Erembodegem, Belgium; *Int'l*, pg. 1396
Masse, Julie, Mgr.-Mktg. Communications--Transportation Equipment Group-North America, Saint-Bruno, Canada; *Int'l*, pg. 200
Masselli, Michael, Sr. V.P.-Sls. & Mktg.--Jordan's Meats, Portland, ME; *U.S. Private*, pg. 599
Massey, Kristin, Dir.-Mktg.--Jackson MSC, Nashville, TN; *U.S. Private*, pg. 579
Massey, T.L., V.P.-Valve Sls., N. America--Flowserve Corporation, Valve Div., Cookeville, TN; *U.S. Public*, pg. 658
Massey, Wright, V.P.-Design Specialty Mktg.--Starbucks Coffee Company, Seattle, WA; *U.S. Public*, pg. 1510
Masson, Petur, Dir.-Mktg.--Coldwater Seafood Corporation, Rowayton, CT; *U.S. Private*, pg. 251
Mast, Larry L., Exec. V.P.-Sls. & Mktg.--The Penn Mutual Life Insurance Company, Philadelphia, PA; *U.S. Private*, pg. 849
Masterson, Jim, V.P.-Mktg. Services--Kraft Foods Inc., Rye Brook, NY; *U.S. Public*, pg. 1288
Mastorakis, V., Mgr.-Mktg.--Karelia Tobacco Company Inc., Kalamata, Greece; *Int'l*, pg. 724
Mastrandrea, Frank, Gen. Mgr.-Mktg.--DoFasco, Inc., Hamilton, Canada; *Int'l*, pg. 414
Mathes, Diane, Mgr.-Mktg. Communications--Vactor Mfg. Inc., Streator, IL; *U.S. Public*, pg. 617
Mathes, Johm, Dir.-Adv. & Mktg.--New York Carpet World, Dalton, GA; *U.S. Public*, pg. 1464
Mathews, Colin, Mgr.-Adv.--Abbey National Plc, London, United Kingdom; *Int'l*, pg. 19
Mathews, Dana, Dir.-Mktg.--Interface Electronics Corporation, Hopkinton, MA; *U.S. Private*, pg. 567
Mathews, James B., V.P.-Mktg.--Hunter Douglas, Inc., Upper Saddle River, NJ; *Int'l*, pg. 639
Mathews, Jim, Mgr.-Mktg. Com--Electronic Products Division, Austin, TX; *U.S. Public*, pg. 1605
Mathews, John W., V.P.-Southwest Reg. Sls.--EBP Life Insurnace Co., Minneapolis, MN; *U.S. Public*, pg. 635
Mathias, Howard, Plant Mgr. & Mktg.--Tank Division, Fremont, OH; *U.S. Public*, pg. 345
Mathios, Lori, Mgr.-Mktg.--Electronic Solutions, San Diego, CA; *U.S. Public*, pg. 1791
Mathison, Donald, Sr. V.P.-Sls. & Mktg.--Media General Cable of Fairfax County Inc., Chantilly, VA; *U.S. Public*, pg. 1078
Matias, Antonio Jacinto, Exec. Dir.-Mktg.--Banco Itau S.A., Sao Paulo, Brazil; *Int'l*, pg. 142
Matibag, Joe, Mktg.--Wavetek Corp., San Diego, CA; *U.S. Private*, pg. 1155
Matijevic, Angela, Mgr.-Mktg.(Midwest)--Almega Corporation, Bensenville, IL; *U.S. Public*, pg. 546
Matiya, Mary, Mgr.-Human Resources Services--A.E. Staley Manufacturing Co., Decatur, IL; *Int'l*, pg. 1356
Matkovich, Larry, Natl. Mktg. Dir.--Paslode, Vernon Hills, IL; *U.S. Public*, pg. 867
Matles, Hal, V.P.-Mktg.--M.H. Rhodes, Inc., Avon, CT; *U.S. Private*, pg. 927
Matlock, Gary, Mgr.-Bus. Devel.--Santa Fe Offshore Construction Co., Houston, TX; *Int'l*, pg. 765
Matlock, Kathy, Mgr.-Mktg.--Keller Graduate School of Management, Oak Brook Terrace, IL; *U.S. Public*, pg. 504
Matlock, Thomas P., V.P.-Sls. & Mktg.--The Brewer Company, Milford, OH; *U.S. Private*, pg. 167
Matos, Rob, V.P.-Mktg. & Branch Support--Commercial Union Assurance Company of Canada, Toronto, Canada; *Int'l*, pg. 308
Matsey, Raymond, Dir.-Mktg.--Advanced Metallurgy, Inc., Export, PA; *U.S. Public*, pg. 1564
Matsushita, Shinya, Mgr.-Adv.--Mizuno Corporation, Osaka, Japan; *Int'l*, pg. 884
Matsuura, Maiuyuui, Assoc. Dir.-Mkt. Research--SmithKline Beecham Pharmaceuticals, Tokyo, Japan; *Int'l*, pg. 1266
Matt, Alfred D., V.P.-Mktg. & Sls.--The F.X. Matt Brewing Co., Utica, NY; *U.S. Private*, pg. 714
Matteo, Maxine, Exec. V.P.-Adv., Mktg. & Bus. Devel.--INMC Mortgage Holdings, Inc., Pasadena, CA; *U.S. Public*, pg. 857
Matteo, Maxine, Mgr.-Mktg.--Indimac, Inc., Pasadena, CA; *U.S. Public*, pg. 857
Matter, John, V.P.-Sls. & Mktg.--Equitable Savings & Loan Association, Wauwatosa, WI; *U.S. Private*, pg. 380
Matteson, John, Exec. V.P.-Sls. & Mktg.--Fleischer Manufacturing, Inc., Columbus, NE; *U.S. Private*, pg. 410
Matteson, Patricia E., Sr. V.P.-Mktg.--People's Bank, Bridgeport, CT; *U.S. Public*, pg. 1274
Matthews, C.E., Mgr.-Mktg.--Morse Controls, Hudson, OH; *U.S. Public*, pg. 857
Matthews, D., Dir.-Mktg. Services--Princess Hotels International Inc., New York, NY; *Int'l*, pg. 818
Matthews, Don, V.P.-Sls. & Mktg.--Wahl Clipper Corp., Sterling, IL; *U.S. Private*, pg. 1146
Matthews, Gerard, Dir.-Mktg.--Lander Co., Inc., Englewood, NJ; *U.S. Private*, pg. 647
Matthews, John, Dir.-Mktg. (Glen Ellyn)--Clark Refining & Marketing Inc., Saint Louis, MO; *U.S. Private*, pg. 243
Matthews, Mary, Supvr.-Mktg.--Market Data Retrieval, Shelton, CT; *U.S. Public*, pg. 536
Matthews, Michael, Exec. V.P.-Worldwide Mktg.--Platinum Technology, Inc., Oak Brook Terrace, IL; *U.S. Public*, pg. 1309
Matthews, Minda, Coord.-Mktg.--LSI Industries, Inc., Cincinnati, OH; *U.S. Public*, pg. 971
Matthews, Paul, Mgr.-Mktg.--CAE Electronics plc, Burgess Hill, United Kingdom; *Int'l*, pg. 238
Matthews, Tanya C., Dir.-Mktg.--Dewberry & Davis, Fairfax, VA; *U.S. Private*, pg. 329
Matthews, Terry, Sr. V.P.-Sls. & Mktg.--J.B. Hunt Transport Services, Inc., Lowell, AR; *U.S. Public*, pg. 849
Matthews, W., V.P.-Mktg. & Contracts--Bristol Aerospace Limited, Winnipeg, Canada; *Int'l*, pg. 829
Matthews, W.A., Mgr.-Mktg.--Bristol Aerospace Ltd., Winnipeg, Canada; *Int'l*, pg. 1127
Matthies, Linda, Dir.-Corp. Mktg.--Doubletree Corporation, Memphis, TN; *U.S. Public*, pg. 1335
Matthys, Julius L., Mgr.-Mktg.--Long Products Division, Whyalla, Australia; *Int'l*, pg. 227
Mattina, Charles A., V.P.-Mktg.--Coyne Beahm Inc., Colfax, NC; *U.S. Private*, pg. 283
Mattingly, Gene, V.P.-Mktg.--Atmos Energy Corporation, Dallas, TX; *U.S. Public*, pg. 145
Mattke, John, Dir.-Adv. & Mktg.--Cold Spring Granite Company, Cold Spring, MN; *U.S. Private*, pg. 250
Mattoo, Sunil, V.P.-Mktg.--Praxair Inc., Danbury, CT; *U.S. Public*, pg. 1319
Mattoon, Richard D., Mktg. Mgr.--The Chantland Company Division, Humboldt, IA; *Int'l*, pg. 830
Mattos, William J., Mgr.-Promo. Svcs.--Spirol International Corp., Danielson, CT; *U.S. Private*, pg. 1026
Mattsson, Ingvar, Mgr.-Mktg.--Skanska Prefab AB, Malmo, Sweden; *Int'l*, pg. 1261
Maudgal, Vinod, Mgr.-Mktg.-CETAR LTD.--Philips Automotive Electronics, Cheshire, CT; *Int'l*, pg. 1054
Mauer, Todd, Dir.-Mktg.--Carlisle Food Service Products, Oklahoma City, OK; *U.S. Public*, pg. 305
Maulsby, Don, V.P.-Sls. & Mktg.--Interphase Corporation, Dallas, TX; *U.S. Public*, pg. 908
Maultasch, Myra, Dir.-Mktg./Del Pharmaceuticals--Del Laboratories, Inc., Farmingdale, NY; *U.S. Public*, pg. 494
Maupin, Patrick, Sr. V.P.-Sls. & Mktg.--Jaydon Incorporated, Rock Island, IL; *U.S. Private*, pg. 584
Maurer, M.A., V.P.-Convenience Stores--A&W Food Services of Canada Inc., North Vancouver, Canada; *Int'l*, *pg. 1*
Maurer, T., Dir.-Mktg. & Devel.--CorTec Company, Washington Court House, OH; *U.S. Public*, pg. 456
Mauser, Gerd E., Dir.-Corp. Mktg.--Porsche AG, Stuttgart, Germany; *Int'l*, pg. 1063
Mausshardt, Robert R., V.P.-Mktg., Tubular Products--Oregon Steel Mills Inc., Portland, OR; *U.S. Public*, pg. 1230
Mavers, Vaughn E., V.P.-Sls. & Mktg.--Peabody COALSALES Company, Saint Louis, MO; *Int'l*, pg. 594
Maves, Roger, Dir.-Mktg.--Graham, Milwaukee, WI; *Int'l*, pg. 377
Mavis, Todd, Exec. V.P.-Mktg. & Sls.--Mitchell International, San Diego, CA; *U.S. Public*, pg. 1601
Maxey, Tonya, Dir.-Mktg.--American Freightways Corporation, Harrison, AR; *U.S. Public*, pg. 75
Maxon, Jean, Dir.-Adv. & Mktg.--Technic Incorporated, Cranston, RI; *U.S. Private*, pg. 1071
Maxon, Lisa, Dir.-Mktg.--Deckers Outdoor Corporation, Goleta, CA; *U.S. Public*, pg. 491
Maxwell, Joseph D., V.P.-Mktg. & Sls.--Tractor Supply Co., Nashville, TN; *U.S. Public*, pg. 1627
May, Charles A., V.P.-Mktg.--Great River Insurance Company, Meridian, MS; *U.S. Public*, pg. 215
May, Hilary, Mgr.-Mktg. Svcs., Adv. & Pub. Rels.--Atalanta Corporation, Elizabeth, NJ; *U.S. Private*, pg. 93
May, Karen, Mgr.-Mktg., Automotive Aftermarket--Robertshaw Tennessee, Knoxville, TN; *Int'l*, pg. 1243
May, Ken, Mgr.-Mktg.--Brink Electric Construction Company, Rapid City, SD; *U.S. Private*, pg. 169
May, Thomas L., Chief Mktg. Officer & Exec. V.P.--Equitable Life Insurance Company of Iowa, Des Moines, IA; *Int'l*, pg. 647
May, Tom L., Exec. V.P.-Sls. & Chief Mktg. Officer--Equitable of Iowa Companies, Des Moines, IA; *Int'l*, pg. 647
May, William E., Jr., V.P.-Strategic Tech. Programs & Mktg. Svcs.--Nash Finch Company, Edina, MN; *U.S. Public*, pg. 1151
Mayer, Donald L., V.P.--Cole Hersee Company, Boston, MA; *U.S. Private*, pg. 251
Mayer, Ridgeley, Dir.-Mktg.--Young Stuff Apparel Group, Inc., New York, NY; *U.S. Private*, pg. 1202
Mayer, Robert G., V.P.-Mktg.--Madison Square Garden Corporation, New York, NY; *U.S. Public*, pg. 288
Mayers, Mike, Sr. V.P.-Mktg.--Keller Crescent Co., Evansville, IN; *U.S. Private*, pg. 612
Mayes, Dick, Dir.-Mktg.--Data I/O Corporation, Redmond, WA; *U.S. Public*, pg. 486
Mayfield, Stephen D., Grp. V.P.-Cement Mktg.--Texas Industries, Inc., Dallas, TX; *U.S. Public*, pg. 1585
Maynard, G.D., V.P.-Mktg.--Lear Corporation, Rochester Hills, MI; *U.S. Public*, pg. 982
Mayoras, Dave, V.P.-Sls. & Mktg./Hwy.--Detroit Diesel Corp., Detroit, MI; *U.S. Private*, pg. 850
Mazin, Rafael, Dir.-Mktg. Services & External Rels.--Procter & Gamble Espana S.A., Madrid, Spain; *U.S. Public*, pg. 1332
Mazo, Kelly Finn, Mgr.-Mktg.--P/A Industries, Inc., Bloomfield, CT; *U.S. Private*, pg. 825
Mazur, Jack, V.P.-Sls. & Mktg.--Johnstown Corporation, Johnstown, PA; *U.S. Private*, pg. 595
Mazzola, Ronald A., Exec. Dir.-Mktg. & Sls.--McNaughton & Gunn, Inc., Saline, MI; *U.S. Private*, pg. 724
Mazzucatto, Edson, Dir.-Mktg.--Fiat Automisveis S.A., Sao Paulo, Brazil; *Int'l*, pg. 483
McAdam, Robert C., Sr. V.P.-Mktg. & Sls.--Facemate Corporation, Chicopee, MA; *U.S. Private*, pg. 391
McAdaragh, Mary Beth, V.P.-Mktg. Services--CBS Enterprises Division, New York, NY; *U.S. Public*, pg. 274
McAffee, Russ, Dir.-Adv.--Team, Inc., Alvin, TX; *U.S. Public*, *pg. 1562*
McAffee, Russ, Dir.-Mktg.--Team Industrial Services, Inc., Alvin, TX; *U.S. Public*, pg. 1562
McAlear, Ronald J., V.P.-Adv. Programs & Mktg.--Avondale Industries, Inc., Avondale, LA; *U.S. Public*, pg. 156
McAleer, Tim, V.P.-Mktg.--Pittsburgh Brewing Company, Pittsburgh, PA; *U.S. Private*, pg. 619
McAlister, Linda, Dir.-Marcom--Western Staff Services, Walnut Creek, CA; *U.S. Public*, pg. 1760
McAlister, Phil, V.P. & Gen. Mgr.-Consumer Mktg. & Sls.--Technology Research Corporation, Clearwater, FL; *U.S. Public*, pg. 1564
McAllister, Arnold B., Dir.-Dealer Sls.--Monroe Systems For Business, Inc., Morris Plains, NJ; *U.S. Private*, pg. 757
McAllister, Tom, Mgr.-Mktg.--Alpha Microsystems, Santa Ana, CA; *U.S. Public*, pg. 57
McAlpine, John, Exec. V.P. & Sec.--The Crown Group, Inc., Warren, MI; *U.S. Private*, pg. 292
McAndrew, Thomas J., Mgr.-Mktg.--Rodney Hunt Company, Orange, MA; *U.S. Private*, pg. 549
McAndrews, Joy, V.P.-Mktg.--Nobel Education Dynamics, Inc., Media, PA; *U.S. Public*, pg. 1185
McAnsh, Craig, Sr. V.P.-Mktg.--The Cartoon Network, Atlanta, GA; *U.S. Public*, pg. 1614
McArthur, Lynne, Mgr.-Corp. Devel.--BFC Construction Corporation, Scarborough, Canada; *Int'l*, pg. 118
McAuliffe, Kevin, V.P.-Mktg. & Promo.--National Broadcasting Co., Inc., New York, NY; *U.S. Public*, pg. 712
McAvoy, Dale, Mgr.-Adv., Sls. & Mktg.-Flow Controls--Raven Industries, Inc., Sioux Falls, SD; *U.S. Public*, pg. 1361
McAvoy, Dale T., Mgr.-Sls. & Mktg.--Flow Control Division, Sioux Falls, SD; *U.S. Public*, pg. 1361
McAvoy, Philip, V.P.-Mktg.--Chadwick's of Boston, West Bridgewater, MA; *U.S. Public*, pg. 996
McBain, W.P., V.P.-Sls. & Mktg.--Daubert Coated Products, Inc., Westchester, IL; *U.S. Private*, pg. 313
McBean, Chris, Dir.-Global Bus.--Permabond International, Englewood, NJ; *Int'l*, pg. 1435
McBeth, Scott, Mgr.-Mktg.--CoreStates Bank, Lancaster, PA; *U.S. Public*, pg. 446
McBride, Kevin, Mgr.- Mktg.--Sunbeam Household Products, Schaumburg, IL; *U.S. Public*, pg. 1533
McBride, Kevin G., V.P.-Mktg. & Product Devel.--Sunbeam Corporation, Delray Beach, FL; *U.S. Public*, pg. 1533
McBride, Mary, V.P.-Mktg.--Pioneer Hi-Bred International, Inc., Des Moines, IA; *U.S. Public*, pg. 1298
McBride, Robert, Mktg. Communications-Voice Prods. & Svcs.--U S West Inc., Englewood, CO; *U.S. Public*, pg. 1688
McBride, Seamus, Dir.-Mktg.--Bass Brewers Ltd., Burton on Trent, United Kingdom; *Int'l*, pg. 170
McBride, Vince, Exec. V.P.-Sls. & Mktg.--The Selmer Co., Inc., Elkhart, IN; *U.S. Public*, pg. 1514
McBride, Vince, Exec. V.P.-Sales & Mktg.--Ludwig Industries, Monroe, NC; *U.S. Public*, pg. 1514
McCabe, Cory, Dir.-Product Mktg.--Shaklee Corporation, San Francisco, CA; *Int'l*, pg. 1518
McCabe, George, V.P.-Mktg. & Sls.--Mazda Motor of America, Inc., Irvine, CA; *Int'l*, pg. 849
McCabe, Joe, Dir.-Mktg.--GEC-Marconi Hazeltine Corporation, Greenlawn, NY; *Int'l*, pg. 544
McCabe, Logan, Dir.-Mktg.--Bristol Motor Speedway, Bristol, TN; *U.S. Public*, pg. 1498
McCabe, R.T., Dir.-Mktg.--Interplastic Corp., Saint Paul, MN; *U.S. Private*, pg. 572
McCadden, Michael, Sr. V.P.-Mktg.--The Gap, Inc., San Francisco, CA; *U.S. Public*, pg. 702
McCaffery, James, V.P.-Sales & Mktg.--Mitsumi Electronics Corp., Irving, TX; *Int'l*, pg. 884
McCaig, Donald, Mgr.-N. American Sls.--Ellicott Machine Corporation International, Baltimore, MD; *U.S. Private*, pg. 372
McCall, Carolyn, Dir.-Bus. Communications--Olin Microelectronic Materials, Inc., Norwalk, CT; *U.S. Public*, pg. 1219
McCamley, Steve, V.P.-Mktg.-Vehicles, Nerf, Tonka--Tonka Corporation, Pawtucket, RI; *U.S. Public*, pg. 797
McCammon, Kerry, Sr. V.P.-Home Elec. Mktg.--Pioneer Electronics (USA) Inc., Long Beach, CA; *Int'l*, pg. 1058
McCann, James B., Exec. V.P.--Maui Land & Pineapple Co., Inc., Kahului, HI; *U.S. Public*, pg. 1060
McCann, James B., Exec. V.P.-Sls. & Mktg.--Maui Pineapple Co., Ltd., Kahului, HI; *U.S. Public*, pg. 1060
McCarley, Bob, Mgr.-Mktg.--Electrical Insulation Suppliers, Atlanta, GA; *U.S. Private*, pg. 368
McCarrey, Patrick, V.P.-Mktg.--Holley Replacement Parts Division, Bowling Green, KY; *U.S. Public*, pg. 402
McCarron, Kira, V.P.-Mktg.--Toll Brothers, Inc., Huntingdon Valley, PA; *U.S. Public*, pg. 1620
McCarter, Judy, Dir.-Mktg.--Frost National Bank, San Antonio, TX; *U.S. Public*, pg. 467
McCarter, Judy D., Sr. V.P.-Mktg.--Cullen/Frost Bankers, Inc., San Antonio, TX; *U.S. Public*, pg. 467
McCarthy, Charlie, V.P.-Service Ctr., Merchant--Birmingham Steel Corporation, Birmingham, AL; *U.S. Public*, pg. 232
McCarthy, Francis J., V.P.-Mktg. & Sls.--A. Duda & Sons Inc., Oviedo, FL; *U.S. Private*, pg. 344
McCarthy, John, Grp. Dir.-Communications & Human Resources--Legal & General Group PLC, London, United Kingdom; *Int'l*, pg. 805
McCarthy, John, V.P.-Mktg. & Sls.--Amersham Corporation, Arlington Heights, IL; *Int'l*, pg. 992
McCarthy, Raymond, Asst. V.P.-Sls. & Mktg.--Hornor, Townsend & Kent, Philadelphia, PA; *U.S. Private*, pg. 849
McCarty, Brett, V.P.-Mktg.--Showtime Networks Inc., New York, NY; *U.S. Private*, pg. 779
McCarty, G. Craig, Sr. V.P.-Mktg.--UniCARE Financial Corp., Irvine, CA; *U.S. Private*, pg. 152
McCarty, Mike, Dir.-Mktg.--O.P. Link Handle Company, Salem, IN; *U.S. Private*, pg. 668
McCaslin, Marty, V.P.-Sls. & Mktg.--Siouxland Galvanizing Corp., Sioux City, IA; *U.S. Private*, pg. 656
McCatherine, Marsha, Coord.-Mktg.--ESPN, Inc., Bristol, CT; *U.S. Public*, pg. 512

McCaughey, Susan Dionne, Acct. Dir.-Mktg. Services-New York--Hickey-Freeman/Bobby Jones, Rochester, NY; *U.S. Public*, pg. 795
McCaughey, Susan Dionne, Acct. Dir.-Mktg. Services-New York--Intercontinental Branded Apparel, Buffalo, NY; *U.S. Public*, pg. 796
McCaughey, Susan Dionne, Dir.-Mktg. Services-New York--International Women's Apparel Group, Easton, PA; *U.S. Public*, pg. 796
McCaugley, Susan Dionne, Acct. Dir.-Mktg. Services-New York--Johnny Carson Apparel, Inc., Buffalo, NY; *U.S. Public*, pg. 796
McCauley, Jim, V.P.-Sls. & Mktg.--SaniServ Manufacturing Corp., Indianapolis, IN; *U.S. Private*, pg. 965
McCendon, Steve, Asst. V.P.-Sls. & Mktg.--Southwire Company, Carrollton, GA; *U.S. Private*, pg. 1019
McChesney, Timothy R., Dir.-Mktg.--Bell Mobility Cellular Inc., Etobicoke, Canada; *Int'l*, pg. 115
McClatchy, Janet, Mgr.-Mktg. Communications--Day & Zimmermann, Inc., Philadelphia, PA; *U.S. Private*, pg. 316
McClelland, Sue, V.P.-Media--E. & J. Gallo Winery, Modesto, CA; *U.S. Private*, pg. 438
McClelland, W. Allen, Mgr.-Mktg. Services & Adv.--Dayton Superior Corporation, Miamisburg, OH; *U.S. Private*, pg. 931
McClennon, Richard, Sr. V.P.-Mktg.--The Detroit News, Detroit, MI; *U.S. Public*, pg. 700
McClinton, Raymond, V.P.-Mktg.--Communications Instruments Inc., Fairview, NC; *U.S. Private*, pg. 259
McClory, Tom, Mgr.-Medical Prods. & Prod. Line--Mine Safety Appliances Co., Pittsburgh, PA; *U.S. Public*, pg. 1114
McCloskey, Daniel, V.P.-Sls. & Mktg.--Lifetime Hoan Corp., Westbury, NY; *U.S. Public*, pg. 992
McCloskey, William E., Mgr.-Mktg.--Instrument Specialties Company, Delaware Water Gap, PA; *U.S. Private*, pg. 565
McCloud, Michael, V.P.-Sls. & Mktg.--Cuisine Solutions, Inc., Alexandria, VA; *U.S. Public*, pg. 466
McClung, James A., V.P.-Worldwide Mktg.--FMC Corporation, Chicago, IL; *U.S. Public*, pg. 604
McCollam, Stephanie, Mktg. Communicatons--BAX Global, Irvine, CA; *U.S. Public*, pg. 1305
McCollough, Mary Ann, Gen. Mgr.-Mktg. Svcs.--Heinz U.S.A. Div., Pittsburgh, PA; *U.S. Public*, pg. 805
McCollum, Bruce, Exec. V.P.-Adv., Mktg. & Sls.--Tingley Rubber Corporation, South Plainfield, NJ; *U.S. Private*, pg. 1088
McComas, Gill, Dir.-Mktg./Buscuit Div.--United Biscuits (UK) Limited, West Drayton, United Kingdom; *Int'l*, pg. 1442
McComb, Dennis M., Chief Mktg. Officer--Bankers Life & Casualty Company, Chicago, IL; *U.S. Public*, pg. 433
McConaghy, Kathy, V.P.-Mkt. Devel.--John H. Harland Company, Decatur, GA; *U.S. Public*, pg. 785
McConaghy, Kathy, V.P.-Mktg. Devel.--The Check Store, Lakewood, CO; *U.S. Public*, pg. 785
McConnell, Paulette, Mktg. Consultant--Acxiom Corporation, Conway, AR; *U.S. Public*, pg. 18
McConnell, Peter R., V.P.-Mktg.--MCS, Inc., Pittsburgh, PA; *U.S. Public*, pg. 1099
McConnell, Rob, Mgr.-Mktg.--WRTV, Indianapolis, IN; *U.S. Public*, pg. 1070
McConnell, Scott, V.P.-Mktg.--Paramount Canada's Wonderland, Vaughan, Canada; *U.S. Private*, pg. 776
McCook, George M., V.P.-Sls. & Mktg.--Purcell Co., Inc., Diamondhead, MS; *U.S. Private*, pg. 895
McCormack, Dan, Sr. V.P.-Mktg.--The Pantry, Inc., Sanford, NC; *U.S. Private*, pg. 837
McCormack, John, V.P.-Sls. & Mktg.--McArthur Dairy, Inc., Sunrise, FL; *U.S. Public*, pg. 491
McCormey, William, Dir.-Corp. Communications--Shell Quimica de Venezuela, C.A., Caracas, Venezuela; *Int'l*, pg. 1142
McCormick, Antoinette, Mgr.-Mktg. Communications--Alfa Laval Separation Inc., Warminster, PA; *Int'l*, pg. 1378
McCormick, Chris, V.P.-Mktg.--L.L. Bean, Inc., Freeport, ME; *U.S. Private*, pg. 639
McCormick, Greg, V.P.-Mktg.--Storck U.S.A., L.P., Chicago, IL; *Int'l*, pg. 1304
McCormick, Jennifer, Mktg. Dir.-B.I.--The Peterson Group, New York, NY; *U.S. Public*, pg. 1642
McCormick, John, V.P.-Sls. & Mktg.--Stokely USA, Inc., Oconomowoc, WI; *U.S. Public*, pg. 1518
McCormick, Marcia E., Mktg. & Office Admin.--Williams, White & Co., Moline, IL; *U.S. Private*, pg. 1179
McCormick, Mariann, Mktg. Dir.--Jay Advertising, Inc., Rochester, NY; *U.S. Private*, pg. 583
McCormick, Molly, Mgr.-Mktg.--Freeport-McMoRan Inc., New Orleans, LA; *U.S. Public*, pg. 680
McCormick, Tom, Sec.--Kimray, Inc., Oklahoma City, OK; *U.S. Private*, pg. 620
McCormick, William G., Dir.-Domestic Branch System--Prudential Securities Inc., New York, NY; *U.S. Private*, pg. 892
McCourt, Robert D., Sr. Dir.-Mktg. & Creative Services--New Hampshire Insurance Group, New York, NY; *U.S. Public*, pg. 84
McCowan, Scott, V.P.-Mktg.--Heurikon Corporation, Madison, WI; *U.S. Public*, pg. 422
McCoy, Bill, Dir.-Sls. & Mktg.--The Fuller Brush Company, Great Bend, KS; *U.S. Public*, pg. 282
McCoy, Davy, Dir.-Mktg.--Feed Service Corp., Ohiowa, NE; *U.S. Private*, pg. 399
McCoy, Dennis, V.P.-Mktg.--Merchants Distributors, Inc., Hickory, NC; *U.S. Private*, pg. 657
McCracken, Pat, Dir.-Corp. Communications & Mktg. Programs-BMC Software, Inc., Houston, TX; *U.S. Public*, *pg. 162*
McCranie, Dan, V.P.-Mktg. & Sls.--Cypress Semiconductor Corporation, San Jose, CA; *U.S. Public*, pg. 470
McCrensky, Page, Mgr.-Mktg.--American Express Publishing Corporation, New York, NY; *U.S. Public*, pg. 74
McCroskey, Lee, Mgr.-Mktg.--Southwestern/Great American Inc., Nashville, TN; *U.S. Private*, pg. 1018
McCulla, Gary W., Pres. & Dir.-Sls. & Mktg.--Tel-Save Holdings, Inc., New Hope, PA; *U.S. Public*, pg. 1568
McCullar, Judy, Dir.-Mktg.--American Buildings Co., Eufaula, AL; *U.S. Public*, pg. 69
McCullen, Bob, V.P.-Mktg.--Helly-Hansen A/S, Moss, Norway; *Int'l*, pg. 1010
McCulloch, John, V.P.-Mktg.--HongKong Bank of Canada, Vancouver, Canada; *Int'l*, pg. 583
McCullough, Tom, Mgr.-Sls. & Mktg.--Cortland Line Co., Inc., Cortland, NY; *U.S. Private*, pg. 277
McCully, Duncan J., V.P.-Special Risks--Commercial Travelers Mutual Insurance Company, Utica, NY; *U.S. Private*, pg. 258
McCurach, Jeff, Dir.-Mktg.--The Andrew Jergens Company, Cincinnati, OH; *Int'l*, pg. 717
McCurdy, Jill, V.P.-Prod. Devel. & Mktg.--Koss Corporation, Milwaukee, WI; *U.S. Public*, pg. 966
McCurdy, Jill, Dir.-Prod. Devel. & Mktg.--Koss Classics Ltd., Milwaukee, WI; *U.S. Public*, pg. 966
McCutcheon, Linda, Dir.-Mktg., Time--Time Inc., New York, NY; *U.S. Public*, pg. 1612
McDaneld, Brent, Sr. V.P.-Mktg.--Gump's, San Francisco, CA; *U.S. Public*, pg. 782
McDaniel, Kelly, Dir.-Mktg. & Pur.--Al & Ed's Auto Sound Center, Monterey Park, CA; *U.S. Private*, pg. 30
McDannold, Doran E., V.P. & Dir.-Sls. & Mktg.--The Troy Savings Bank, Troy, NY; *U.S. Private*, pg. 1106
McDavid, David, Jr., V.P. & Mgr.-Opers.--David McDavid Auto Dealership, Irving, TX; *U.S. Private*, pg. 721
McDermott, Amy, Mgr.-Mktg.--The At-A-Glance Group, Sidney, NY; *U.S. Private*, pg. 295
McDermott, David, Creative Dir.--Rockett, Burkhead, Lewis & Winslow, Raleigh, NC; *U.S. Private*, pg. 938
McDermott, Donna, Mgr.-Mktg.--Bacardi-Martini, USA, Inc., Miami, FL; *U.S. Private*, pg. 109
McDermott, Michael, V.P.-Sls. & Mktg.--The Presmet Corp., Worcester, MA; *U.S. Private*, pg. 882
McDevitt, Bob, V.P.-Mktg.--Golden Corral Corporation, Raleigh, NC; *U.S. Private*, pg. 575
McDonagh, Jim, V.P.-Sls. & Mktg.--Riker Products, Inc., Toledo, OH; *U.S. Private*, pg. 300
McDonagh, Lucy, Asst. Mgr.-Mktg.--Reliable Automatic Sprinkler Co., Inc., Mount Vernon, NY; *U.S. Private*, pg. 920
McDonald, B.R., V.P.-Customer Mktg.--Wrigley Canada Inc., Don Mills, Canada; *U.S. Public*, pg. 1781
McDonald, Gerald, Mgr.-Mktg.--Conklin Instrument Corporation, Pleasant Valley, NY; *U.S. Private*, pg. 263
McDonald, John, Mgr.-Mktg.--Rapid Industries, Inc., Louisville, KY; *U.S. Private*, pg. 910
McDonald, John F., V.P.-Mktg.--Plaid Enterprises Inc., Norcross, GA; *U.S. Private*, pg. 352
McDonald, Ken J., V.P.-Mktg. N. America--Amway Corporation, Ada, MI; *U.S. Private*, pg. 69
McDonald, Kim, Dir.-Mktg.--Fairfield Branson, Branson, MO; *U.S. Public*, pg. 610
McDonald, L. Terry, Sr. V.P.-Mktg.--ShopKo Stores, Inc., Green Bay, WI; *U.S. Public*, pg. 1467
McDonald, Lloyd, V.P.-Mktg. & Client Services/Eckerd Health Services--Eckerd Corporation, Largo, FL; *U.S. Public*, pg. 917
McDonald, Margaret, V.P.-Mktg.--Federal Cartridge Co., Anoka, MN; *U.S. Public*, pg. 239
McDonald, Michele, Dir.-Promotions & Mktg.--The Calgary Sun, Calgary, Canada; *Int'l*, pg. 1320
McDonald, Rene, V.P.--Pharmacists Public Relations Bureau, Wichita, KS; *U.S. Private*, pg. 295
McDonald, Tim, Dir.-Mktg. Svcs.--Mechanics Tool Div., Dallas, TX; *U.S. Public*, pg. 1509
McDonnell, Gordon, Sr. Mgr.-Mktg./Office Paper--Boise Cascade Corporation, Boise, ID; *U.S. Public*, pg. 242
McDonnell, Joseph W., Sr. V.P.-Mktg. & External Affairs--Long Island Lighting Company, Hicksville, NY; *U.S. Public*, pg. 1013
McDonough, John, V.P.-Mktg. & Broadcasting--Chicago National League Ball Club, Inc. (Chicago Cubs), Chicago, IL; *U.S. Public*, pg. 1635
McDonough, Lynne, Mgr.-Mktg. Project--American Saw & Mfg. Company, East Longmeadow, MA; *U.S. Private*, pg. 61
McDonough, Robert T., Sr. V.P.-Mktg. & Sls.--Artistic Greetings, Inc., Elmira, NY; *U.S. Public*, pg. 136
McDougall, Sandy, Mgr.-Mktg. Sls. & Adv.--Air BC, Richmond, Canada; *Int'l*, pg. 36
McDowell, Charles T., V.P.-Sls. & Mktg.--First Protective Insurance Group, Birmingham, AL; *U.S. Public*, pg. 1336
McDowell, James, V.P.-Mktg.--BMW (US) Holding Corporation, Woodcliff Lake, NJ; *Int'l*, pg. 177
McDowell, Jerry, Mgr.-Pub. Rels.--Objective Systems Integrators, Inc., Folsom, CA; *U.S. Public*, pg. 1209
McDowell, Lesley, Coord.-Mktg.--Roquette America Inc., Keokuk, IA; *U.S. Private*, pg. 944
McDowell, Tony, Dir.-Mktg. Services--Champion International Corp., Stamford, CT; *U.S. Public*, pg. 333
McDuffee, Byron, Dir.-Consumer Mktg.--Spring-Green Lawn Care Corporation, Plainfield, IL; *U.S. Private*, pg. 1027
McElfresh, John, Dir.-Mktg. Communicatons--Schneider Automation, Inc., North Andover, MA; *Int'l*, pg. 1208
McElroy, Chris, Mktg. Commun. Specialist--Pella Corporation, Pella, IA; *U.S. Private*, pg. 848
McElroy, James J., Dir.-Mktg.--Brass-Craft Manufacturing Company, Southfield, MI; *U.S. Public*, pg. 1053
McElroy, Martin, Mng. Dir.-Devel.--Lester B. Knight & Associates, Inc., Chicago, IL; *U.S. Private*, pg. 626
McEvoy, Annette M., Sr. V.P.-Mktg.--Revlon International Corporation, New York, NY; *U.S. Private*, pg. 690
McFadden, Peggy, Mgr.-Mktg.--Herculite Products, Inc., York, PA; *U.S. Public*, pg. 802
McFall, Shaun, V.P.-Mktg.--Digital Microwave Corporation, San Jose, CA; *U.S. Public*, pg. 508
McFarland, Mary, Coord.-Mktg.--Multi-Ad Services, Incorporated, Peoria, IL; *U.S. Private*, pg. 766
McFarlane, Eric, Mgr.-Mktg.--Genova Products, Inc., Davison, MI; *U.S. Private*, pg. 447
McFarlane, Terry, Dir.-Mktg.--KLAS, Inc., Las Vegas, NV; *U.S. Private*, pg. 647
McFay, Michele, Dir.-Mktg.--David Weekley Homes, Houston, TX; *U.S. Private*, pg. 1158
McGannon, Thomas, V.P.-Mktg.--Chemtex International, Inc., New York, NY; *Int'l*, pg. 872
McGarrie, Karyn, Mgr.-Mktg.--Rodenstock USA, Inc., Danbury, CT; *Int'l*, pg. 1007
McGarrigle, Cynthia, V.P. & Mgr.-Area Mktg.--AmSouth Bank, Tampa, FL; *U.S. Public*, pg. 105
McGarry, M.J., Dir.-Intl. Mktg./Europe & U.K.--Carpenter Technology (U.K.) Limited, Redditch, United Kingdom; *U.S. Public*, pg. 308
McGarry, M.J., Dir.-Intl. Mktg., Europe--Carpenter Technology (Europe) S.A., Brussels, Belgium; *U.S. Public*, pg. 308
McGaw, William, V.P.-Mktg.--Viking Pump, Inc., Cedar Falls, IA; *U.S. Public*, pg. 862
McGee, Mike, Mgr.-Mktg./Carlsberg--Anheuser-Busch Companies, Inc., Saint Louis, MO; *U.S. Public*, pg. 113
McGee, Rick, V.P.-Sls. & Mktg.--Artisoft, Inc., Tucson, AZ; *U.S. Public*, pg. 136
McGhie, Andrew, Mgr.-Mktg.--George Philip Limited, London, United Kingdom; *Int'l*, pg. 1093
McGill, Timothy, Sr. V.P.-Grp. Mktg.--Mutual of Omaha Insurance Company, Omaha, NE; *U.S. Private*, pg. 769
McGinley, Michael B., V.P.-Mktg., Universal Resources--Celsius Energy Company, Salt Lake City, UT; *U.S. Public*, pg. 1352
McGinnis, M.J., Mgr.-Mktg.--Salt River Project Agricultural Improvement and Power District, Tempe, AZ; *U.S. Private*, pg. 962
McGivern, Daniel M., Dir.-Mktg.--DOALL Company, Des Plaines, IL; *U.S. Private*, pg. 337
McGlade, Tom, Sr. V.P.--Vienna Sausage Mfg. Co., Chicago, IL; *U.S. Private*, pg. 1139
McGlasson, Christine L., Dir.-Mktg.--Blue Diamond Growers, Sacramento, CA; *U.S. Private*, pg. 152
McGlaughin, Seth, Sr. Dir.-Mktg.--Lenscrafters, Cincinnati, OH; *Int'l*, pg. 822
McGlone, Brian, Dir.-Mktg & Sls.--Hubbell Premise Wiring, Inc., Stonington, CT; *U.S. Public*, pg. 844
McGlothlin, Lyle, Dir.-Mktg.--Bay West Paper Corp. Towel & Tissue Div., Middletown, OH; *U.S. Public*, pg. 1747
McGonigle, Tom, Dir.-Mktg. Services/Dresser Prods.--Komatsu America International Company, Vernon Hills, IL; *Int'l*, pg. 744
McGorrin, Michael, V.P.-Mktg.--Aramark Educational Resources Inc. Inc., Golden, CO; *U.S. Private*, pg. 79
McGouldrick, J., Dir.-Mktg.--American Foundry Group, Inc., Bixby, OK; *U.S. Private*, pg. 54
McGovern, Michael, Mgr.-Mktg.--Curtiss-Wright Corp., Lyndhurst, NJ; *U.S. Public*, pg. 469
McGovern, Michael, Mgr.-Mktg.--Curtiss-Wright Flight Systems, Inc., Fairfield, NJ; *U.S. Public*, pg. 469
McGovern, P.J., V.P.-Mktg.--Atwood & Morrill Co., Inc., Salem, MA; *Int'l*, pg. 1489
McGowan, Bret, Dir.-Mktg. & Adv.--Vicon Industries, Inc., Hauppauge, NY; *U.S. Public*, pg. 1719
McGowan, Michael, Mgr.-Corp. Adv.--Benjamin Moore & Co., Montvale, NJ; *U.S. Private*, pg. 133
McGowan, Scott, Dir.-Mktg.--Pre Finish Metals Incorporated, Elk Grove Village, IL; *U.S. Public*, pg. 1056
McGowan, Tom, Mgr.-Mktg.--Lever Brothers (Ireland) Ltd., Dublin, Ireland; *Int'l*, pg. 1437
McGowen-Carnes, Kathy, Dir.-Mktg.--Advertising Display Co., Englewood Cliffs, NJ; *U.S. Private*, pg. 23
McGrady, Steve, Dir.-Intl. Mktg.--SpeedFan International, Inc., Chandler, AZ; *U.S. Public*, pg. 1497
Mcgrane, Cathy F., Mgr.-Business Devel. & Civil Programs--SRA International Inc., Arlington, VA; *U.S. Private*, pg. 957
McGrane, Paul, Dir.-Mktg.--Prudential Corporation PLC, London, United Kingdom; *Int'l*, pg. 1073
McGrath, Caroline, Mgr.-Mktg. Communications--Epson Canada Limited, Willowdale, Canada; *Int'l*, pg. 1219
McGrath, Dennis P., V.P.-Mktg.--Weber Marking Systems, Inc., Arlington Heights, IL; *U.S. Private*, pg. 1157
McGrath, Michael, V.P.-Intl. Mktg.--Hillerich & Bradsby Co., Louisville, KY; *U.S. Private*, pg. 530
McGrath, Tom, Sr. V.P.-Boys Toys--Tonka Corporation, Pawtucket, RI; *U.S. Public*, pg. 797
McGraw, Gregory P., V.P.-Sls. & Mktg.--TIE/Communications, Inc., Overland Park, KS; *U.S. Private*, pg. 1085
McGregor, Andrew, Dir.-Mktg.--The Economist Group Limited., London, United Kingdom; *Int'l*, pg. 1026
McGregor, Marvin M., V.P. Mktg. & Bus. Devel.--Southwestern Electric Power Co., Shreveport, LA; *U.S. Public*, pg. 324
McGregor, Robert G., Mgr.-Sls. & Mktg.--Brookfield Engineering Laboratories, Inc., Stoughton, MA; *U.S. Private*, pg. 171
McGuff, Rick, Dir.-Sls. & Mktg.--Spalding Canada, Concord, Canada; *U.S. Private*, pg. 630
McGuiness, Tom, Sr. V.P.-Mktg.--Sony Music Entertainment, Inc., New York, NY; *Int'l*, pg. 1281
McGuire, Colleen, Dir.-Mktg. Services--NRI Schools, Washington, DC; *U.S. Public*, pg. 1071
McGuire, Garry K., Dir.-Mktg.--Northern Telecom Finance Corporation, Nashville, TN; *Int'l*, pg. 969
McGuire, Mac, Dir.-Mktg. & Sls.--Sangamon Industries, Taylorville, IL; *U.S. Private*, pg. 965
McGuire, Steve, Mgr.-Rels. Mktg.--The Saturn Corporation, Troy, MI; *U.S. Public*, pg. 721
McHenry, Brian, V.P.-Sls. & Mktg.--La France Corporation, Philadelphia, PA; *U.S. Private*, pg. 640
McHenry, Karen, Mgr.-Mktg.--Xtra Corporation, Boston, MA; *U.S. Public*, pg. 1786
McHenry, Scott, Sr. V.P.-Mktg. & Sls.--The Dial Corporation, Phoenix, AZ; *U.S. Public*, pg. 505

McHie, Stewart, Coord.-Adv. & Promo.--Exxon Company, U.S.A., Houston, TX; *U.S. Public*, pg. 601
McHugh, Eileen, Mktg. Asst.--Optimaxx International, Rockleigh, NJ; *U.S. Private*, pg. 818
McHugh, Patricia, Dir.-Mktg.--James McHugh Construction Co., Chicago, IL; *U.S. Private*, pg. 721
McHugh, Timothy, Mgr.-Sales & Mktg.--Access Corporation, Cincinnati, OH; *Int'l*, pg. 994
McIlguham, David, V.P.-Mktg.--Sealy Mattress Company of Memphis, Memphis, TN; *U.S. Private*, pg. 979
McIlquham, David J., V.P.-Mktg.--Sealy Corporation, Cleveland, OH; *U.S. Private*, pg. 978
McIlroy, Valerie, V.P.-Mktg., Swiss Chalet--Cara Operations Limited, Toronto, Canada; *Int'l*, pg. 266
McIlwain, Kary, Sr. V.P. & Mktg. & Strategic Plng. Dir.--Young & Rubicam Chicago, Chicago, IL; *U.S. Private*, pg. 1198
McIndoe, James, V.P.-Intl. Mktg.--Twin Disc, Incorporated, Racine, WI; *U.S. Public*, pg. 1646
McInerney, John J., V.P.-Sls. & Mktg.--McInerney Inc., Oak Park, MI; *U.S. Private*, pg. 722
McInnes, Mark, Dir.-Mktg.--David Jones Limited, Sydney, Australia; *Int'l*, pg. 714
McIntire, Judy, Asst. to Mktg. Dir.--Reed Business Information, Sutton, United Kingdom; *Int'l*, pg. 1094
McIntosh, Dick, V.P.-Sls. & Mktg.--Kyocera Canada, Inc., Mississauga, Canada; *Int'l*, pg. 776
McIntosh, Richard S., V.P.-Mktg.--Univex Corporation, Salem, NH; *U.S. Private*, pg. 1128
McIntyre, Anne, Mgr.-Mktg. Services--Springs Industries, Bedding Division, Charlotte, NC; *U.S. Public*, pg. 1500
McIntyre, Jeffrey, V.P.-Mktg. Affiliate Rels.--CBS Television Network, New York, NY; *U.S. Public*, pg. 274
McIntyre, Michael, V.P.-Mktg.--Killark Electric Manufacturing Co., Saint Louis, MO; *U.S. Public*, pg. 844
McKae, Darlo, Mktg.--Regions Bank/Talladega County, Talladega, AL; *U.S. Public*, pg. 1373
McKay, Alvin, Dir.-Mktg.--Cumberland Farms, Inc., Canton, MA; *U.S. Private*, pg. 295
McKay, Brad, Dir.-Mktg.--Parmalat Canada Ltd., Etobicoke, Canada; *Int'l*, pg. 1023
McKay, M., Mgr.-Mktg.--Walsworth Publishing Company, Inc., Marceline, MO; *U.S. Private*, pg. 1148
McKay, Rick, Dir.-Mktg.--McKinney & McKinney Advertising, Redondo Beach, CA; *U.S. Private*, pg. 723
McKeague, Marsha A., Mgr.-Woodlands--Great Northern Paper, Inc., Millinocket, ME; *U.S. Public*, pg. 248
McKechnie, Julia, Mgr.-Mktg.-U.K.--The Financial Times Ltd., London, United Kingdom; *Int'l*, pg. 1025
McKechnie, W.E., V.P.-Mktg.--Hostess Frito-Lay Co., Mississauga, Canada; *U.S. Public*, pg. 1277
McKee, John Patrick, Sr. Assoc.-Washington Mktg.--Cannon, Grand Island, NY; *U.S. Private*, pg. 205
McKeithen, Mack, V.P.- Mktg. Svc.--Union Underwear Co., Inc., Bowling Green, KY; *U.S. Public*, pg. 686
McKelvie, John, Dir.-Mktg.--Inductotherm Corp., Rancocas, NJ; *U.S. Private*, pg. 560
McKenna, Christine, Exec. V.P.-Mktg. & Adv.--Plasti-Kote Company Inc., Medina, OH; *U.S. Private*, pg. 870
McKenna, R. Renee, Second V.P.-Mktg.--American National Bank & Trust Co. of Chicago, Chicago, IL; *U.S. Public*, pg. 628
McKennedy, Michael P., Sr. V.P. & Chief Mktg. Officer--Sunset Life Insurance Co. of America, Olympia, WA; *U.S. Public*, pg. 943
McKenney, Bill, V.P.-Mktg.--Vicorp Restaurants, Inc., Denver, CO; *U.S. Public*, pg. 1719
McKenney, Bill, V.P.-Mktg.--Bakers Square Restaurants, Denver, CO; *U.S. Public*, pg. 1719
McKenney, J.K., Pres.--The Figaro Company, Inc., Mesquite, TX; *U.S. Private*, pg. 404
McKenzie, Duncan, Mgr.-Mktg. Info. Center--The Quaker Oats Company, Chicago, IL; *U.S. Public*, pg. 1347
McKenzie, Gary, V.P.-Mktg.--Calgary Flames Hockey Club, Calgary, Canada; *Int'l*, pg. 252
McKenzie, Preston, Mgr.-Mktg.--Antique Trader Publications, Dubuque, IA; *U.S. Private*, pg. 649
McKenzie, Ron, V.P.-Strategic Mktg.--FORE Systems, Inc., Warrendale, PA; *U.S. Public*, pg. 667
McKeough, Anne, V.P.-Mktg.--Mosby-Year Book, Inc., Saint Louis, MO; *U.S. Public*, pg. 1616
McKeown, Patrick, V.P.-Mktg.--Christy's Markets, Inc., Brockton, MA; *U.S. Private*, pg. 238
McKinley, John, V.P.-Engrng., Sls. & Mktg.--Varity Dayton Walther, Dayton, OH; *Int'l*, pg. 820
McKinley, Kay, Dir.-Mktg.--Christensen Products, Salt Lake City, UT; *U.S. Public*, pg. 981
McKinney, Mary, Exec. Dir.-Mktg. Communications & Innovation--Merck & Co., Inc., Whitehouse Station, NJ; *U.S. Public*, pg. 1090
McKinney, Mary, Exec. Dir.-Mktg., Communications & Innovation--Merck Human Health Division (U.S. Human Health), West Point, PA; *U.S. Public*, pg. 1091
McKinniss, Susan D., V.P.-Mktg.--Boeing Realty Corporation, Long Beach, CA; *U.S. Public*, pg. 241
McKinnon, Alan, V.P.-Sls. & Mktg.--Guilford Europe, Ltd., Derby, United Kingdom; *U.S. Public*, pg. 769
McKinstry, David, Mgr.-Commercial Sls. & Mktg.--IMO Pump, Monroe, NC; *U.S. Public*, pg. 857
McKissick, Larry, Mgr.-Sls. & Mktg.--Brunner & Lay, Inc., Springdale, AR; *U.S. Private*, pg. 176
McLain, Roger S., V.P.-Mktg.--Circuit Systems, Inc., Elk Grove Village, IL; *U.S. Public*, pg. 374
McLain, Virginia R., V.P. & Mgr.-Corp. Mktg.--Westvaco Corporation, New York, NY; *U.S. Public*, pg. 1762
McLane, Barbara, Mgr.-Mktg. Svcs.--Stonhard, Inc., Maple Shade, NJ; *U.S. Public*, pg. 1358
McLane, Peter C., Dir.-Mktg.--Daig Corporation, Minnetonka, MN; *U.S. Public*, pg. 1428
McLaren, E.A., Dir.-Global Mktg.--Bomford Turner Limited, Evesham, United Kingdom; *U.S. Public*, pg. 35
McLaughin, John G., V.P.-Sls. & Mktg.--Diagnostic Products Corporation, Los Angeles, CA; *U.S. Public*, pg. 505
McLaughlin, Ann, Mgr.-Mktg.--JSB Electrical PLC, Crewe, United Kingdom; *Int'l*, pg. 453
McLaughlin, Bill, Mgr.-Mktg. & Bus.--Scientific Imaging Systems, New Haven, CT; *U.S. Public*, pg. 550
McLaughlin, Bob, V.P.-Mktg.--Leblanc Communications, Inc., Richardson, TX; *U.S. Private*, pg. 656
McLaughlin, Doug, Dir.-Mktg.--Willis Corroon Property & Casualty Programs Div., Nashville, TN; *Int'l*, pg. 1508
McLaughlin, J. M., V.P.-Mktg.--Chicago Show Printing Co., Morton Grove, IL; *U.S. Private*, pg. 235
McLaughlin, John, Mgr.-Mktg.--Rumsey Electric Company, Conshohocken, PA; *U.S. Private*, pg. 951
McLaughlin, Martin, Dir.-Mktg.--BDO Seidman, LLP, Chicago, IL; *U.S. Private*, pg. 106
McLaughlin, Mike, V.P.-Mktg.--Draka U.S.A., Franklin, MA; *Int'l*, pg. 417
McLaughlin, Mike, V.P.-Mktg.--Chromatic Technologies, Inc., Franklin, MA; *Int'l*, pg. 417
McLaughlin, Mike, V.P.-Mktg.--Helix/Hi-Temp Cables, Inc., Franklin, MA; *Int'l*, pg. 417
McLaughlin, Mike, Dir.-Corp. Mktg.--Royal Insurance, Charlotte, NC; *Int'l*, pg. 1130
McLaughlin, Patty, Mgr.-Mktg.--Morton's of Chicago, Inc., Chicago, IL; *U.S. Public*, pg. 1136
McLean, Jill, Mktg.-Communications--DSM Sheffield Plastics, Sheffield, MA; *Int'l*, pg. 354
McLean, Thomas I., Sr. V.P.-Mktg. & Research--Kingsdown, Inc., Mebane, NC; *U.S. Private*, pg. 622
McLeish, Charles H., Dir.-Mktg. Services--LEGO Systems, Inc., Enfield, CT; *Int'l*, pg. 805
McMahon, Daniel J., Dir.-Mktg.--Network Services Company, Mount Prospect, IL; *U.S. Private*, pg. 791
McMahon, Frank, Mgr.-Sls. & Mktg.--OPT Industries, Inc., Phillipsburg, NJ; *U.S. Public*, pg. 1624
McMahon, Kevin, Dir.-Mktg. & Bus. Devel.--E.D. Bullard Company, Cynthiana, KY; *U.S. Private*, pg. 180
McMahon, Laura, Mgr.-Field Mktg.--Grandy's, Inc., Lewisville, TX; *U.S. Private*, pg. 61
McMahon, Patrick E., Dir.-Mkt. Devel.--CTS Corporation, Elkhart, IN; *U.S. Public*, pg. 285
McMahon, Paul, Mgr.-Mktg. & Communications--LoJack Corporation, Dedham, MA; *U.S. Public*, pg. 1012
McMahon, Sheldon, Grp. Mgr.-Mktg. Commun.--Nordson Corporation, Westlake, OH; *U.S. Public*, pg. 1188
McManaman, Robert, V.P.-Mktg. & Mdsg.--Mary Maxim, Inc., Port Huron, MI; *U.S. Private*, pg. 716
McManus, Dawn, Coord.-Mktg. Communications--Louisiana Gas Service Co., Harvey, LA; *U.S. Public*, pg. 380
McManus, Liz, Dir.-Mktg.--Media Recovery, Inc., Graham, TX; *U.S. Private*, pg. 726
McManus, M., Dir.-Mktg.--Barclays Bank PLC, London, United Kingdom; *Int'l*, pg. 164
McManus, Rich, Mgr.-Sls. & Mktg.--Huck International, Inc., Tucson, AZ; *U.S. Public*, pg. 1597
McMartin, Patricia, Dir.-Mktg.--The Mennen Company, New York, NY; *U.S. Public*, pg. 397
McMaster, D.W., Mgr.-Mktg. Services--Mine Safety Appliances Co., Pittsburgh, PA; *U.S. Public*, pg. 1114
McMath, Michael E., Exec. Dir.-Sls. & Mktg.--Lincoln National (UK) plc, Oxbridge, United Kingdom; *U.S. Public*, pg. 998
McMenemy, William, Exec. V.P.-Mktg., Cosmetics--Del Laboratories, Inc., Farmingdale, NY; *U.S. Public*, pg. 494
McMenemy, William, Exec. V.P.-Mktg.--Sally Hansen, Farmingdale, NY; *U.S. Public*, pg. 494
McMillan, Robert, Brand Process Leader--The Progressive Corporation, Cleveland, OH; *U.S. Public*, pg. 1334
McMillan, Suzanne, Sr. V.P.-Mktg.--Sotheby's Holdings Inc., New York, NY; *U.S. Public*, pg. 1487
McMillan, Wallace, Sr. V.P.-Mktg.--Deposit Guaranty National Bank, Jackson, MS; *U.S. Public*, pg. 500
McMillan, Wallace E., Sr., Sr. V.P.-Mktg.--Deposit Guaranty Corp., Jackson, MS; *U.S. Public*, pg. 500
McMullen, Dave, Supvr.-Mktg. Admin.--Yuasa-Exide, Inc., Reading, PA; *Int'l*, pg. 1522
McMurray, Michael, Dir.-Mktg.--The Bartell Drug Company, Seattle, WA; *U.S. Private*, pg. 118
McNally, Kathleen, V.P.-Mktg. Opers.--Richardson Electronics, Ltd., Lafox, IL; *U.S. Public*, pg. 1387
McNally, Monica M., V.P.-Mktg. & Underwriting--Willis Corroon Corp. of New Hampshire, Rochester, NH; *Int'l*, pg. 1506
McNamara, Ellen H., Dir.- Mkt. Devel.--TreeSource, Inc., Portland, OR; *U.S. Public*, pg. 1729
McNamara, J., Mgr.-Mktg.--Gentex Optics, Inc., Simpson, PA; *Int'l*, pg. 462
McNamara, John, Mgr.-Mktg.--Eaton Corporation Commercial Controls Division, Selma, NC; *U.S. Public*, pg. 556
McNamara, Michael, Exec. V.P. & Gen. Mgr.-Global Mktg. & U.S. Bus.--Neutrogena Corporation, Los Angeles, CA; *U.S. Public*, pg. 928
McNamee, David, Dir.-Mktg.--Jim Walter Homes, Inc., Tampa, FL; *U.S. Public*, pg. 1737
McNamee, Steve, V.P.-Mktg.--Aladdin Industries, Incorporated, Nashville, TN; *U.S. Private*, pg. 30
McNaught, Gerry, Dir.-Product Mktg.--AlliedSignal Canada Inc., Automotive Aftermarket, Stratford, Canada; *U.S. Public*, pg. 52
McNeill, Robin, V.P.-Prod. Mktg./Bus. Intelligence Tools--Cognos Inc., Ottawa, Canada; *Int'l*, pg. 305
McNicholas, Tom, V.P. & Gen. Mgr.-Consumer Grp.--Loctite Corp. North American Group, Rocky Hill, CT; *Int'l*, pg. 611
McNichols, Thomas A., Exec. V.P.-Mktg.--Barton Beers, Ltd., Chicago, IL; *U.S. Public*, pg. 300
McNiel, Bridget, V.P.-Mktg./Client Access--3Com Corporation, Santa Clara, CA; *U.S. Public*, pg. 1603
McNiven, Robert, Dir.-Mktg.--Matthew Clark Brands, Bristol, United Kingdom; *Int'l*, pg. 848
McNulty, John, Sr. V.P.-Sls. & Mktg.--Brunswick Bicyles Div., Bannockburn, IL; *U.S. Public*, pg. 265
McNulty, Thomas, V.P.-Mktg. Development--New England Confectionery Co., Cambridge, MA; *U.S. Private*, pg. 1113
McNulty, Tom, V.P.-Mktg. & Adv.--Super 8 Motels, Inc., Aberdeen, SD; *U.S. Public*, pg. 322
McOllough, Jeff, Mgr.-Adv., Sls., & Mktg.--Hagie Manufacturing Co., Clarion, IA; *U.S. Private*, pg. 493
McPherson, Ed, V.P.-Field Mktg.--Kentucky Fried Chicken Corporation (KFC), Louisville, KY; *U.S. Public*, pg. 1636
McPherson, Pat, V.P.-Mktg.--Kilovac Corporation, Carpinteria, CA; *U.S. Private*, pg. 259
McPike, Milton, Plant Mgr.--Rocco Quality Foods, Timberville, VA; *U.S. Private*, pg. 937
McQuaide, Helene, Dir.-Mktg.--Eat N Park Restaurants, Pittsburgh, PA; *U.S. Private*, pg. 358
McQueen, Edwin D., V.P.-Sls. & Mktg.--Steelox Systems Inc., Mason, OH; *U.S. Private*, pg. 1038
McQueen, James R., V.P.-Customer Service & Govt. Affairs--Connecticut Water Service, Inc., Clinton, CT; *U.S. Public*, pg. 431
McQueen, Jeff, V.P.-Sls. & Mktg.--Schwab Corp., Lafayette, IN; *U.S. Private*, pg. 974
McQuillin, David, V.P.-Mktg. & Sls.--Gunther Mele Limited, Brantford, Canada; *Int'l*, pg. 578
McQuiston, Bruce, Dir.-Mktg. & Sls.--Mentholatum Company, Buffalo, NY; *Int'l*, pg. 1126
McRae, Rick, Mgr.-Mktg.--Courtaulds Coatings Inc., Louisville, KY; *Int'l*, pg. 338
McRoa, Roy, Dir.-Mktg.--Smith Enterprises, Rock Hill, SC; *U.S. Private*, pg. 1007
McSpadden, Dan, Dir.-Mktg.--Citrus World Inc., Lake Wales, FL; *U.S. Private*, pg. 241
McStay, William J., Sr. V.P.-Mktg. Communication--Jiffy Lube International, Inc., Houston, TX; *U.S. Public*, pg. 1272
McSweeney, Patrick, Dir.-Mktg.--Atlanta Learning Center, College Park, GA; *U.S. Public*, pg. 218
McVeigh, Brian, V.P.-Mktg.--Kellwood Sportswear, Rutherford, TN; *U.S. Public*, pg. 948
McVicker, Jerry, V.P.-Wholesale Mktg.--Ultramar Diamond Shamrock Corporation, San Antonio, TX; *U.S. Public*, pg. 1663
McVicker, Linda, Dir.-Mktg.--Miltope Group, Inc., Hope Hull, AL; *U.S. Public*, pg. 1114
McWilliams, Scott G., V.P.-Mktg.--McWilliams Forge Co., Rockaway, NJ; *U.S. Private*, pg. 725
Mead, Richard J., V.P.-Fresh Fruit Mktg.--Sunkist Growers, Inc., Sherman Oaks, CA; *U.S. Private*, pg. 1052
Mead, Thom, V.P.-Mktg.--Affiliated Computer Services, Inc., Dallas, TX; *U.S. Public*, pg. 27
Meader, Diane E., V.P.--State Street Corporation, Boston, MA; *U.S. Public*, pg. 1513
Meadow, Scott, V.P.-Integrated Mktg.--Paradigm Communications, Tampa, FL; *U.S. Private*, pg. 838
Meadows, Jeff, V.P.-Shaw Retail Stores Devel.--Evans-Black Carpet Mills, Dalton, GA; *U.S. Public*, pg. 1464
Meads, Carlene, V.P.-Mktg.--Brookfield Homes, Del Mar, CA; *Int'l*, pg. 228
Meagher, Janice, Sr. V.P.-Mktg.-Universal Studios Hollywood & Univ. City Walk--Universal Studios Hollywood, Universal City, CA; *Int'l*, pg. 1216
Meakins, Ian, Dir.-Worldwide Mktg.--United Distillers PLC, Edinburgh, United Kingdom; *Int'l*, pg. 412
Meakins, Ian, Dir.-Worldwide Mktg.--United Distillers UK Plc, Perth, United Kingdom; *Int'l*, pg. 412
Meaney, Martin M., V.P.-Mktg. Communications--Wyeth-Ayerst Laboratories, Inc., Philadelphia, PA; *U.S. Public*, pg. 80
Mear, Christine, Coord.-Sls. Promo. & Sls. Admin.--Eversharp Pen Co., Franklin Park, IL; *U.S. Private*, pg. 386
Mears, Kirk, V.P.-Sls. & Mktg.--Carrington Laboratories, Inc., Irving, TX; *U.S. Public*, pg. 309
Meass, Kathy, Mktg. Asst.--Andes Candies Inc., Delavan, WI; *U.S. Private*, pg. 163
Mechanic, David M., Dir.-Sls. & Mktg.--Rubber Molding Division, Norwich, CT; *U.S. Private*, pg. 355
Mecklenburg, D., Mgr.-Mktg.--Melroe Company, Fargo, ND; *U.S. Public*, pg. 877
Meddock, Larry, V.P.-Mktg.--Correct Craft, Inc., Orlando, FL; *U.S. Private*, pg. 276
Medford, Mark O., Exec. V.P.-Customer Service Mktg.--Tennessee Valley Authority, Knoxville, TN; *U.S. Public*, pg. 1580
Medick, Keith, Gen. Mgr.-Mktg.--Joseph T. Ryerson & Son, Inc., Chicago, IL; *U.S. Public*, pg. 879
Meehan, Jack, Dir.-Mktg.--Harvey Industries, Inc., Waltham, MA; *U.S. Private*, pg. 508
Meehan, Lucy, Coord.-Mktg.--The Medical Protective Company, Fort Wayne, IN; *U.S. Private*, pg. 728
Meehan, Martha, V.P.-Mktg.--Watkins Incorporated, Winona, MN; *U.S. Private*, pg. 1153
Meehan, Michael, V.P.-Mktg. Supply Systems--Unisource (North East), Windsor, CT; *U.S. Public*, pg. 1671
Meehan, Rich, V.P.-Mktg. & Opers.--Heartland Express, Inc., Coralville, IA; *U.S. Public*, pg. 803
Meehan, Terry, V.P.-Mktg.--Periphonics Corp., Bohemia, NY; *U.S. Public*, pg. 1278
Meek, Chuck, Mgr.-Nat'l Accts.--Appleton Electric Co., Chicago, IL; *U.S. Public*, pg. 572
Megan, Phil, Dir.-Mktg.--MI-Jack Products, Inc., Hazel Crest, IL; *U.S. Private*, pg. 740
Mehallow, Michael, Exec. V.P.-Mktg.--Borg-Warner Protective Services Corporation, Parsippany, NJ; *U.S. Public*, pg. 245
Mehlem, Clas-Johan, Mgr.-Mktg.--Kaukas Sawn Goods Industry, Lappeenranta, Finland; *Int'l*, pg. 1428
Mehrlich, Richard W., Exec. V.P.-Sls & Mktg.--Medical Manager Corporation, Tampa, FL; *U.S. Public*, pg. 1080
Mehtlan, David L., V.P.-Sls. & Mktg.--American Stone-Mix, Inc., Towson, MD; *U.S. Private*, pg. 62
Meier, Jen, Mktg. Analyst--Boler Company, Itasca, IL; *U.S. Private*, pg. 155

Meier, Victor G., V.P.-Mktg./Premiere & Coronado--Premier Coatings, Inc., Elk Grove Village, IL; *Int'l*, pg. 1488
Meigboom, Kars, Mgr.-Mktg.--Sara Lee/DE, Utrecht, Netherlands; *U.S. Public*, pg. 1434
Meilinger, Joe, V.P.-Mktg.--Monfort, Inc., Greeley, CO; *U.S. Public*, pg. 427
Meinecke, Patricia J., Dir.-Corp. Commun. & Mktg.--Giddings & Lewis, Inc., Fond Du Lac, WI; *Int'l*, pg. 1389
Meinicke, Holger, Mgr.-Sls. & Mktg.--Degussa Corp., Dental Dept., South Plainfield, NJ; *Int'l*, pg. 388
Meis, John, V.P.-Sls. & Mktg.--Cross Creek Apparel, Inc., Mount Airy, NC; *U.S. Public*, pg. 1413
Meisenheimer, Danny, V.P.-Mktg.--Furr's/Bishops, Inc., Lubbock, TX; *U.S. Public*, pg. 689
Meister, Mark A., V.P.-Sls. & Mktg.--Post Glover Resistors Inc., Erlanger, KY; *Int'l*, pg. 590
Meizner, Art, Dir.-Mktg.--Advest, Inc., Hartford, CT; *U.S. Public*, pg. 23
Mekus, Tom, V.P.-Sls. & Mktg.--Diehl Specialties International, Defiance, OH; *U.S. Private*, pg. 332
Melancon, Pierre, V.P.-Mktg.--The Laurentian Group Corporation, Montreal, Canada; *Int'l*, pg. 396
Melancon, Rudy, Sls. & Service Mgr.--Varco BJ Oil Tools, New Iberia, LA; *U.S. Public*, pg. 1709
Melbourne, Dave, Dir.-Mktg.--Castleberry/Snow's Brands Inc., Augusta, GA; *U.S. Private*, pg. 219
Melby, Kurt, Mgr.-Mktg. Services--Monarch Cement Co., Humboldt, KS; *U.S. Public*, pg. 1123
Melien, Doug, V.P.-Mktg. & Sls.--GSW Water Heating Company, Fergus, Canada; *Int'l*, pg. 538
Melillo, J., Dir.-Mktg.- CHPG--Warner-Lambert K.K., Tokyo, Japan; *U.S. Public*, pg. 1739
Melling, Lawrence A., V.P.-Mktg.--IKOS Systems, Inc., Cupertino, CA; *U.S. Public*, pg. 864
Melloni, Carlo, Mgr.-Mktg. Programs--Fiat Auto Ireland Ltd., Dublin, Ireland; *Int'l*, pg. 481
Melum, Susan, Dir.-Mktg. Communications--Lanier Worldwide Inc., Atlanta, GA; *U.S. Public*, pg. 791
Melver, Bill, Dir.-Mktg.--National Engineering & Contracting Co., Strongsville, OH; *U.S. Private*, pg. 782
Melwid, David, Dir.-Sls. & Mktg.--PTS Electronics Corporation, Bloomington, IN; *U.S. Private*, pg. 828
Melyon, Jeff, Dir. -Field Mktg.--Pearle Inc., Dallas, TX; *U.S. Public*, pg. 396
Menard, Guy, Mgr.-Mktg.--Alcan Aluminium Limited, Montreal, Canada; *Int'l*, pg. 50
Menasce, Isaac, V.P.-Mktg. & Products--Merisel Latin America, Miami, FL; *U.S. Public*, pg. 1096
Mencher, Stuart, V.P.-Mktg. & Sls.--Teleport Communications Group, Staten Island, NY; *U.S. Public*, pg. 1572
Mendelsohn, Cheryl, Dir.-Mktg.--Wellington Regional Medical Center, West Palm Beach, FL; *U.S. Public*, pg. 1697
Mendelson, Peter, V.P.-Direct Mktg.--Gerber Life Insurance Co., White Plains, NY; *Int'l*, pg. 973
Mender, Karen, V.P. & Dir.-Mktg.--Dell Publishing, New York, NY; *Int'l*, pg. 191
Mendez, M. Alex, V.P.-Mktg. Enterprise Networking--Cisco Systems, Inc., San Jose, CA; *U.S. Public*, pg. 375
Mendius, L., V.P.-Sls. & Dir.-Mktg.--Silbrico Corporation, Hodgkins, IL; *U.S. Private*, pg. 1000
Mendoza, Andy, V.P.-Sls. & Mktg.--Nor-Cal Beverage Co., Inc., West Sacramento, CA; *U.S. Private*, pg. 801
Mendoza, Judy, Sr. V.P.-Mktg. & Sls. Promo.--Bergdorf Goodman, New York, NY; *U.S. Public*, pg. 785
Mendoza, Ray, V.P.-Natl. Accounts--Key Handling Systems, Inc., Moonachie, NJ; *U.S. Private*, pg. 618
Menezes, Ivan, V.P.-Grp. Mktg.--Whirlpool Europe B.V., Comerio, Italy; *U.S. Public*, pg. 1765
Menke, Lori, Mgr.-Mktg. Communications--Indiana Gas Company, Inc., Indianapolis, IN; *U.S. Public*, pg. 875
Menna, Christine, V.P.-Corp. Communications & Mktg.--Crown American Realty Trust, Johnstown, PA; *U.S. Public*, pg. 461
Menne, Gregory C., V.P.-Fixed-Income Mktg.--A.G. Edwards & Sons, Inc., Saint Louis, MO; *U.S. Public*, pg. 565
Mennis, Liam, 1st V.P.-Portfolio Mktg.--Countrywide Funding Corporation, Pasadena, CA; *U.S. Public*, pg. 453
Menpwich, Andreas, Mgr.-Mktg.--Maresi Markenartikelvertrieb Aktiengesellschaft, Vienna, Austria; *Int'l*, pg. 842
Mentrup, George, Mgr.-Market Assessment--Kansas City Power & Light Company, Kansas City, MO; *U.S. Public*, pg. 943
Menzies, D. Stephen, Sr. V.P.-Sls. & Mktg.--General American Transportation Corporation, Chicago, IL; *U.S. Public*, pg. 692
Meola, Linda S., Mgr.-Mktg.--The JPM Company, Lewisburg, PA; *U.S. Public*, pg. 919
Meola, Peter, V.P.-Mktg. & Sls.--Castrol North America, Wayne, NJ; *Int'l*, pg. 235
Meranda, Tim, Mgr.-Mktg., Sls. & Adv.--HCC Inc., Mendota, IL; *U.S. Private*, pg. 490
Mercadante, Blaise, Exec. V.P.-Mktg.--Universal Studios Music Australia, Sydney, Australia; *Int'l*, pg. 1216
Mercadante, Blaise, V.P.-Mktg.--Taco Bell Corp., Irvine, CA; *U.S. Public*, pg. 1637
Mercer, Bruce K., V.P.-Mktg., Sls. & Prod./Brand Mgr.--Swift Instruments, Inc., Dorchester, MA; *U.S. Private*, pg. 1058
Merchant, Debra, Mgr.-Mktg.--The Gorton Group, Gloucester, MA; *Int'l*, pg. 1434
Meredith, Craig, Coord.-Mktg. Support--Duff-Norton, Charlotte, NC; *U.S. Public*, pg. 406
Meredith, Russ, Dir-Mktg.--Steiner Corporation, Salt Lake City, UT; *U.S. Private*, pg. 1039
Meredith, Tony, Mgr.-Mktg.--New Zealand Milk Products (CIS) AO, Moscow, Russia; *Int'l*, pg. 923
Merion, Mike, V.P.-Mktg.--Dionex Corporation, Sunnyvale, CA; *U.S. Public*, pg. 510
Merkel, W. David, Jr., Mgr.-Mktg.--Harrington Hoists, Inc., Manheim, PA; *U.S. Private*, pg. 504
Merker, Dave, Dir.-Sls. & Mktg./Commercial Prods.--Cantex Inc., Mineral Wells, TX; *Int'l*, pg. 1312
Merkley, Dean, V.P.-Mktg. & Sls.--Litton Solid State, Santa Clara, CA; *U.S. Public*, pg. 1003
Merlo, Saverio, Sr. V.P.-Corp. Mktg.--Boole & Babbage, Inc., San Jose, CA; *U.S. Public*, pg. 244
Meroni, Giuliano, V.P.-Intl. Sls. & Mktg.--Advanced Micro Devices, Inc., Sunnyvale, CA; *U.S. Public*, pg. 21
Merrifield, C. Ann, V.P.-Mktg.--IG Laboratories, Inc., Framingham, MA; *U.S. Public*, pg. 733
Merrill, Dick, V.P.-Sls. & Mktg.--Mayfran International, Inc., Cleveland, OH; *Int'l*, pg. 1397
Merrill, Fred, V.P.-Sls. & Mktg.--Bristol Babcock, Inc., Watertown, CT; *Int'l*, pg. 472
Merrill, Robert L., Sr. V.P.-Mktg. & Sls.--Fraser Papers, Inc., Stamford, CT; *Int'l*, pg. 434
Merritt, Linda, Dir.-Mktg. & Bus. Devel.--Nadel Architects, Inc., Los Angeles, CA; *U.S. Private*, pg. 773
Merritt, Rebecca, Mktg. Asst.--Beaulieu Vineyard, Rutherford, CA; *Int'l*, pg. 410
Merry, Carol, Dir.-Corp. & Shareholder Commun.--Lexford Residential Trust, Columbus, OH; *U.S. Public*, pg. 991
Merryman, Jim, Mgr.-Mktg. & Indus. Ingredients--Oregon Freeze Dry, Inc., Albany, OR; *U.S. Private*, pg. 819
Merton, Oliver R.E., V.P.-Mktg.--Inmet Mining Corporation, Toronto, Canada; *Int'l*, pg. 678
Merton, Oliver R.E., V.P.-Mktg.--Metall Mining Corporation, Toronto, Canada; *Int'l*, pg. 862
Merwise, Norm, Sr. V.P.-Sls. & Mktg.--Scripto-Tokai Corp., Fontana, CA; *U.S. Private*, pg. 977
Mescher, Gary, V.P.-Mktg.--Georgia Tent & Awning Inc., Atlanta, GA; *U.S. Private*, pg. 448
Mescher, Gary, Dir.-Mktg.--General Trade Associates, Atlanta, GA; *U.S. Private*, pg. 448
Mesec, Susan, Sr. V.P.-Mktg. & Sls.--Stern's, Paramus, NJ; *U.S. Public*, pg. 618
Mesh, Leslie M., V.P.-Mktg. & Economic Devel.--APS, Phoenix, AZ; *U.S. Public*, pg. 1297
Messina, Michael, Mgr.-Mktg.--Plenum Publishing Corporation, New York, NY; *U.S. Public*, pg. 1311
Messinger, David G., Sr. V.P.-Sls. & Mktg.--Bush Industries Inc., Jamestown, NY; *U.S. Public*, pg. 270
Messinger, Steven, V.P.-Mktg.--Simi Winery, Healdsburg, CA; *Int'l*, pg. 781
Messitte, Anne, Dir.-Mktg.--Schocken Books, New York, NY; *U.S. Private*, pg. 21
Messmer, Daniel A., V.P.-Sls. & Mktg.--Escalade Sports, Evansville, IN; *U.S. Public*, pg. 591
Messmer, Peter J., Dir.-Mktg. & Adv.--Liqui-Box Corporation, Worthington, OH; *U.S. Public*, pg. 1000
Metcalf, Don, Mgr.-Mktg.--Rollins Truck Leasing Corp., Wilmington, DE; *U.S. Public*, pg. 1405
Metcalf, Donald K., Mgr.-Mktg.--Rollins Leasing Corp., Wilmington, DE; *U.S. Public*, pg. 1405
Metcalf, John, Mgr.-Mktg.--Sea Nymph Inc., Lebanon, MO; *U.S. Private*, pg. 478
Metcalf, Wendy, Dir.-Media--C S K Auto Inc., Phoenix, AZ; *U.S. Private*, pg. 1108
Metcalfe, David D., V.P.-Mktg.--Guarantee Electrical Company, Saint Louis, MO; *U.S. Private*, pg. 485
Metts, William, Dir.-Mktg.--Taylor Machine Works, Inc., Louisville, MS; *U.S. Private*, pg. 1070
Metz, Mike, Dir.-Mktg.--Titanium Metals Corporation, Denver, CO; *U.S. Private*, pg. 270
Metzer, Andreas, Exec. Dir.-Mktg., Buying & Store Opers.--Julius Meinl AG, Vienna, Austria; *Int'l*, pg. 856
Metzgar, Gary, Mgr.-Sls. & Mktg.--North American Products Corp., Jasper, IN; *U.S. Private*, pg. 803
Metzger, Daniel, Exec. V.P.-Mktg.--Lawson Software, Minneapolis, MN; *U.S. Private*, pg. 654
Metzger, Donna, Dir.-Mktg.--Contract Interiors Inc., Taylor, MI; *U.S. Private*, pg. 270
Metzker, Ruth, Mgr.-Mktg. Services--Pabst Brewing Co., San Antonio, TX; *U.S. Private*, pg. 954
Metzner, Richard, V.P.-Mktg. Programs--Continental Airlines, Houston, TX; *U.S. Public*, pg. 439
Meudt, Alan, V.P.-Sls. & Mktg.--MWCA, Rexburg, ID; *U.S. Public*, pg. 804
Meulemans, Greg, Mgr.-Promo., Direct & Database Mktg.--Stratton Corporation, Stratton Mountain, VT; *Int'l*, pg. 685
Meyer, Alan E., V.P.-Mktg.--American Family Mutual Insurance Co., Madison, WI; *U.S. Private*, pg. 53
Meyer, Angela, Dir.-Mktg. & Client Services--The Failure Group, Inc., Menlo Park, CA; *U.S. Public*, pg. 609
Meyer, Dennis J., V.P.-Mktg. & Plng.--Banta Corporation, Menasha, WI; *U.S. Public*, pg. 187
Meyer, Doug, V.P.-Mktg. & Adv.--Syms Corporation, Secaucus, NJ; *U.S. Public*, pg. 1547
Meyer, Douglas, V.P.-Mktg.--Miles Kimball Company, Oshkosh, WI; *U.S. Private*, pg. 745
Meyer, G. Fred, Dir.-Mktg. Research--Schlegel Corporation, Rochester, NY; *Int'l*, pg. 128
Meyer, Gerald L., V.P.-Mktg. & Dir.-Retail Branches--D.A. Davidson & Co., Great Falls, MT; *U.S. Private*, pg. 314
Meyer, Gregory, V.P.-Sls. & Mktg.--Fluor Daniel GTI, Inc., Norwood, MA; *U.S. Public*, pg. 660
Meyer, James, Exec. V.P.-Mktg. & Sls., Americas--Thomson Consumer Electronics Inc., Indianapolis, IN; *Int'l*, pg. 1383
Meyer, Marsha, Coord.-Mktg. Svcs.--Tokheim Corporation, Fort Wayne, IN; *U.S. Public*, pg. 1620
Meyer, Paula R., Pres. & Dir.-Mktg.--Piper Capital Management, Incorporated, Minneapolis, MN; *U.S. Public*, pg. 1303
Meyercord, Edward B., III, Exec. V.P.-Mktg. & Corp. Devel.--Tel-Save Holdings, Inc., New Hope, PA; *U.S. Public*, pg. 1568
Meyering, Robert, Exec. Dir.-Mktg.-Global Pharmaceuticals--Storz Instrument Co., Saint Louis, MO; *U.S. Public*, pg. 79
Meyers, Jeff, Mgr.-Mktg.--Tenney Environmental, Williamsport, PA; *U.S. Private*, pg. 1076
Mezeras, Kim, Mgr.-Residential Mktg.--Sierra Pacific Resources, Reno, NV; *U.S. Public*, pg. 1470
Mezeras, Kim, Mgr.-Residential Mktg.--Sierra Pacific Power Co., Reno, NV; *U.S. Public*, pg. 1470
Micallef, C., Gen. Mgr.-Mktg.--Johnson Yokogawa Corporation, Newnan, GA; *Int'l*, pg. 1521
Michael, Denny, V.P.-Mktg.--Alpha Microsystems, Santa Ana, CA; *U.S. Public*, pg. 57
Michaels, Tony, V.P.-Mktg.--Elias Brothers Restaurants, Inc., Warren, MI; *U.S. Private*, pg. 371
Michalek, Ron, V.P.-Mktg.--Dutton-Lainson Co., Hastings, NE; *U.S. Private*, pg. 350
Michaud, Jeffrey, Dir.-Mktg.--Cable Constructors, Inc., Iron Mountain, MI; *U.S. Private*, pg. 197
Michaud, Laura, V.P.-Sls. & Mktg.--Beltone Electronics Corporation, Chicago, IL; *U.S. Private*, pg. 132
Michaud, William J., V.P.-Sls. & Mktg.--Stocker & Yale, Inc., Salem, NH; *U.S. Public*, pg. 1518
Michel, Bill, V.P.-Mktg.--Eddie Bauer, Inc., Redmond, WA; *U.S. Public*, pg. 1499
Michel, Philip M., V.P.-Mktg.--The Cessna Aircraft Co., Wichita, KS; *U.S. Public*, pg. 1589
Michelin, Edouard, Mng. Dir. & Dir.-Mktg.--Compagnie Generale des Etablissements Michelin, Clermont, France; *Int'l*, pg. 322
Mick, Richard, V.P.-Sls. & Mktg.--IWI Holding Limited, Westmont, IL; *U.S. Public*, pg. 861
Mickle, J. Douglas, Dir.-Adv. & Mktg. Services--Reynolds Metals Co., Consumer Products Div., Richmond, VA; *U.S. Public*, pg. 1386
Middlebrook, Anthony, Mgr.-Adv. Svcs.--Procter & Gamble of Peru, Lima, Peru; *U.S. Public*, pg. 1332
Middleton, Lee, Dir.-Mktg.--Yashica, Inc., Somerset, NJ; *Int'l*, pg. 776
Middleton, Paul, Mgr.-Mktg. Services--The Marley Cooling Tower Co., Overland Park, KS; *U.S. Public*, pg. 1676
Middleton, Richard, Acct. Mgr.-Direct Mktg.--The Media Shop Limited, London, United Kingdom; *Int'l*, pg. 853
Middleton, Susan A., V.P.-Mktg.--Brothers Gourmet Coffees, Inc., Boca Raton, FL; *U.S. Public*, pg. 259
Midora, Kathleen, Dir.-Mktg. Svcs.--Angelo Brothers Co., Philadelphia, PA; *U.S. Private*, pg. 74
Miele, Arthur R., V.P.-Mktg. & Pres.-PD Sales Co.--Phelps Dodge Corporation, Phoenix, AZ; *U.S. Public*, pg. 1286
Mielecki, Max C., V.P.-Mktg. Communications--Grainger, Lincolnshire, IL; *U.S. Public*, pg. 758
Miellen, Richard, Dir.-Mktg. & Adv.--MFG Union City Operations, Union City, PA; *U.S. Private*, pg. 756
Migliaccio, Jack B., Dir.-Bus. Devel.--AIL Systems Inc., Deer Park, NY; *U.S. Public*, pg. 556
Mignault, Pierre L., V.P.-Corp. Devel.--Steinberg Inc., Montreal, Canada; *Int'l*, pg. 1272
Miguelon, Diane, Mgr.-Mktg.--Bank of Montreal, Toronto, Canada; *Int'l*, pg. 153
Mihalich, James M., V.P.-Sls. & Mktg.--Shakespeare Monofilament, Columbia, SC; *U.S. Public*, pg. 940
Mihatchuk, Bill, Dir.-Mktg.--Bayco Industries, Winnipeg, Canada; *Int'l*, pg. 395
Mikesell, Kelly, Dir.-Mktg.--Dayton Newspapers, Inc., Dayton, OH; *U.S. Private*, pg. 281
Mikkelsen, Alice, Mgr.-Adv. & Mktg.--Schumacher Electric Corporation, Mount Prospect, IL; *U.S. Private*, pg. 973
Miklavic, Jake, Mgr.-Mktg.--Meadowcraft, Inc., Birmingham, AL; *U.S. Private*, pg. 725
Miks, Marilyn, Asst. Mktg. Dir.--Blockbuster Music, Dallas, TX; *U.S. Private*, pg. 776
Miksta, Jim, V.P.-Mktg.--Daubert Coated Products, Inc., Westchester, IL; *U.S. Private*, pg. 313
Mikula, John, Div. V.P.-Mktg. & Customer Svcs.--Sonoco Products Company, Hartsville, SC; *U.S. Public*, pg. 1485
Mikulay, Robert L., Sr. V.P.-Mktg.--Philip Morris U.S.A., New York, NY; *U.S. Public*, pg. 1289
Milanello, Angelo, Mgr.-Fin. & Mktg.--Belfe S.p.A., Marostica, Italy; *Int'l*, pg. 185
Milanese, Bob, Dir.-Mktg.--Duracell International Inc., Bethel, CT; *U.S. Public*, pg. 743
Milbauer, Jerry, Dir.-Mktg. & Sls.--FWD/Seagrave Fire Apparatus, Inc., Clintonville, WI; *U.S. Private*, pg. 390
Mildner, Curtis A., V.P.-Mktg.--Central Maine Power Company, Augusta, ME; *U.S. Public*, pg. 325
Miles, Ana, Asst. V.P.-Mktg.--BankAtlantic Bancorp, Inc., Fort Lauderdale, FL; *U.S. Public*, pg. 183
Miles, David, Mgr.-Mktg.--Cyanamid of Great Britain Ltd., Gosport, United Kingdom; *U.S. Public*, pg. 81
Miles, Michelle T., Asst. V.P. & Dir.-Devel.--Hayes, Seay, Mattern & Mattern, Inc., Roanoke, VA; *U.S. Private*, pg. 513
Miles, Mike, Dir.-Mktg.--Alltel Information Services, Inc., Little Rock, AR; *U.S. Public*, pg. 56
Miles, Peter, Dir.-ADS Mktg.--GenRad, Inc., Westford, MA; *U.S. Public*, pg. 731
Miles, Ron, V.P.-Sls. & Mktg.-HVAC--White-Rodgers Div., Emerson Electric Co., Saint Louis, MO; *U.S. Public*, pg. 573
Miles, S., Mgr.-Mktg.-Marlboro & Raffles--Rothmans (UK) Ltd., Aylesbury, United Kingdom; *Int'l*, pg. 1130
Milewski, Bob, Dir.-Mktg.-Cheese & Cheese Powders--Kraft Food Ingredients Corp., Memphis, TN; *U.S. Public*, pg. 1288
Milhem, Janice, Mgr.-Mktg.--American Speedy Printing Centers, Inc., Troy, MI; *U.S. Private*, pg. 62
Millan, Vivian, Asst. Admin.-Mktg.--Casablanca Fan Company, Pomona, CA; *U.S. Private*, pg. 549
Millard, Cynthia, Mgr.-Mktg.--Medtech Inc., Jackson, WY; *U.S. Private*, pg. 728
Miller, Alton Wayne, Dir.-Sls. & Mktg.--Affiliated Foods Southwest, Little Rock, AR; *U.S. Private*, pg. 26
Miller, Barry, V.P.-Mktg.- LaCross--Del Laboratories, Inc., Farmingdale, NY; *U.S. Public*, pg. 494
Miller, Ben, V.P.-Mktg. & Sls.--Whaling Industries, Inc., Fall River, MA; *U.S. Private*, pg. 1170
Miller, Bill, Mgr.-Category--United Dairy Farmers, Inc., Cincinnati, OH; *U.S. Private*, pg. 1121
Miller, Bob, V.P.-Mktg.--East Kentucky Power Co-op, Winchester, KY; *U.S. Private*, pg. 356

Miller, Brenda, Mgr.-Mktg.--Today's Man, Inc., Moorestown, NJ; *U.S. Public*, pg. 1619
Miller, Bruce, V.P.-Mktg. & Sls.--E.A. Miller Company, Hyrum, UT; *U.S. Public*, pg. 428
Miller, Bud, V.P.-Business Devel.--AAI Corporation, Hunt Valley, MD; *U.S. Public*, pg. 1679
Miller, Christen, Mgr.-Communications & Mktg.--Elo TouchSystems, Inc., Fremont, CA; *U.S. Public*, pg. 1362
Miller, Craig, Dir.-Mktg.--Robin Hood Multifoods Inc., Markham, Canada; *U.S. Public*, pg. 901
Miller, Daniel, Pres.-Mktg.--Dexter Shoe Company, Dexter, ME; *U.S. Public*, pg. 217
Miller, Dave, Dir.-Worldwide Mktg.--Magnetrol International, Downers Grove, IL; *U.S. Private*, pg. 696
Miller, Dave, Mgr.-Mktg.--Introtek International, Edgewood, NY; *U.S. Private*, pg. 696
Miller, David, V.P.-Adv. & Mktg.--Multi-Local Media Corporation, Rockville Centre, NY; *U.S. Private*, pg. 767
Miller, David, V.P.-Mktg. & Sls.--Signature Inns, Inc., Indianapolis, IN; *U.S. Public*, pg. 1473
Miller, Diane, Mgr.-Mktg.--AGRA Earth & Environmental, Inc., Phoenix, AZ; *Int'l*, pg. 31
Miller, Doug, V.P.-Sls. & Mktg.--ComPair LeRoi, Sidney, OH; *Int'l*, pg. 1242
Miller, Ed, V.P.-Mktg.--The Wiremold Company, West Hartford, CT; *U.S. Private*, pg. 1184
Miller, Edward H., V.P.-Bus. Devel.--Frank Messer & Sons Construction Co., Cincinnati, OH; *U.S. Private*, pg. 734
Miller, Fred, Exec. V.P.-Mktg.--Kent Feeds Inc., Muscatine, IA; *U.S. Private*, pg. 1134
Miller, Gary, Mgr.-Sls. & Mktg.--Erlanger Tubular Corporation, Catoosa, OK; *U.S. Public*, pg. 1147
Miller, Graham, V.P.-Sls. & Mktg.--WD-40 Company, San Diego, CA; *U.S. Public*, pg. 1726
Miller, Greg, V.P.-Alternate Site Hospice--Manor Healthcare Corp., Gaithersburg, MD; *U.S. Public*, pg. 1041
Miller, Gregory D., V.P.-Mktg. & Strategic Plng.--Manor Care, Inc., Gaithersburg, MD; *U.S. Public*, pg. 1041
Miller, J. Carl, V.P.-Mktg.--Abolite Lighting Inc., Cincinnati, OH; *U.S. Public*, pg. 971
Miller, J.C., Jr., V.P.-Sls. & Mktg.--Hanna Corporation, Chicago, IL; *U.S. Private*, pg. 231
Miller, Jeff, Mgr.-Mktg. N.A.--Numetrix Inc., Norwalk, CT; *Int'l*, pg. 990
Miller, Jeff, V.P.-Sls. & Mktg.--Gilbert Paper, Menasha, WI; *U.S. Public*, pg. 1074
Miller, Jim, Exec. V.P.-Sls. & Mktg.--Sutter Home Winery, Inc., Saint Helena, CA; *U.S. Private*, pg. 1057
Miller, John, Mktg. Dir. & Res. Dir.--Leon Shaffer Golnick Advertising, Inc., Fort Lauderdale, FL; *U.S. Private*, pg. 463
Miller, June, Mgr.-Corp. Communications--Red Spot Paint & Varnish Co., Evansville, IN; *U.S. Private*, pg. 915
Miller, Lynda, Mgr.-Mktg.--KineticSystems Corporation, Lockport, IL; *U.S. Private*, pg. 620
Miller, Mark, Mgr.-Adv.--Hiniker Company, Mankato, MN; *U.S. Private*, pg. 530
Miller, Mark, Mgr.-Mktg.--Pride Health Care, Inc., Exeter, PA; *U.S. Private*, pg. 883
Miller, Mary M., V.P.-Mktg.--Signature Flight Support, Orlando, FL; *Int'l*, pg. 114
Miller, Maurice, V.P.-Member Svcs. & Mktg. Commun. & CENEX/Land O' Lakes--CENEX, Inc., Inver Grove Heights, MN; *U.S. Private*, pg. 221
Miller, Maurice, V.P.-Member Services & Mktg. Communications--Cenex/Land O'Lakes, Inc., Inver Grove Heights, MN; *U.S. Private*, pg. 222
Miller, Mercer, Dir.-Mktg./Appetizers--McCain Foods Inc., Oak Brook, IL; *Int'l*, pg. 850
Miller, Michael E., Mgr.-Prod. & Meetings Plng.--Milprint Inc., Oshkosh, WI; *U.S. Public*, pg. 210
Miller, Michael P., Sr. V.P.-Worldwide Oil & Gas Mktg.--Occidental Oil & Gas Corporation, Bakersfield, CA; *U.S. Public*, pg. 1210
Miller, Mike, Dir.-Sls. & Mktg. Svcs.--Beltone Electronics Corporation, Chicago, IL; *U.S. Private*, pg. 132
Miller, Mike, Natl. Mktg. Mgr.--Reynolds Metals Co.-Can Division Headquarters, Richmond, VA; *U.S. Public*, pg. 1386
Miller, Mira, V.P.-Sls. & Mktg.--Plastigage Corporation, Jackson, MI; *U.S. Private*, pg. 871
Miller, Nanci, V.P.-Mktg./Subscription Sls. & Series--The Reader's Digest Association, Inc., Pleasantville, NY; *U.S.* Public, pg. 1367
Miller, Nicholas J., V.P.-Mktg.--Jacor Communications, Inc., Covington, KY; *U.S. Public*, pg. 922
Miller, Pam, Mgr.-Mktg. Commun.--Simpson Dura-Vent Co., Inc., Vacaville, CA; *U.S. Public*, pg. 1474
Miller, Pam, Mktg. Communications-Wireless (Communications Grp.)--U S West Inc., Englewood, CO; *U.S. Public*, pg. 1688
Miller, R.S., Mgr.-Mktg.--Osmonics, Inc., Minnetonka, MN; *U.S. Public*, pg. 1233
Miller, Randy, Exec. V.P.-Mktg.--Waterhouse Investor Services, New York, NY; *Int'l*, pg. 1401
Miller, Ray, V.P.-Mktg.--Hoover Treated Wood Products, Inc., Thomson, GA; *U.S. Public*, pg. 1193
Miller, Raymond, V.P.-Sls. & Mktg.--National Seating Co., Vonore, TN; *U.S. Private*, pg. 786
Miller, Richard, V.P.-Mktg.--Standard Plywoods, Inc., Clinton, SC; *U.S. Private*, pg. 1032
Miller, Rick, Dir.-Strategic Mktg.--Mack Trucks, Inc., Allentown, PA; *Int'l*, pg. 1102
Miller, Robb, Dir.-Mktg.--Thermon Manufacturing Company, San Marcos, TX; *U.S. Private*, pg. 1080
Miller, Robert, Mgr.-Mktg.--Carolina Shoe Company, Morganton, NC; *U.S. Public*, pg. 217
Miller, Robert, V.P.--Glen Raven Marketing Corporation, New York, NY; *U.S. Private*, pg. 456
Miller, Robert, Ntl. Mgr.--APV Chemical Machinery, Inc., Process Systems Div., Saginaw, MI; *Int'l*, pg. 1240
Miller, Robert A., Gen. Dir.-Mktg.--Delco Electronics Corporation, Kokomo, IN; *U.S. Public*, pg. 720
Miller, Ron, V.P.-Mktg.--Butler Manufacturing Company, Kansas City, MO; *U.S. Public*, pg. 271
Miller, S.L., Coordinator-Supply & Mktg.--Royal Dutch/Shell Group of Companies, Hague, Netherlands; *Int'l*, pg. 1135
Miller, Scott, Mgr.-Mktg.--World Tableware, Inc., Dallas, TX; *Int'l*, pg. 1056
Miller, Sherlin, Coord.-Mktg.--Jayco Inc., Middlebury, IN; *U.S. Private*, pg. 583
Miller, Suzanne, Mgr.-Aviation Mktg.--Port of Portland, Portland, OR; *U.S. Private*, pg. 876
Miller, Thomas K., V.P.-Mktg. & Distrib.--HON Industries Inc., Muscatine, IA; *U.S. Public*, pg. 772
Miller, Thomas K., V.P.-Mktg. & Intl.--HON Export Limited, Muscatine, IA; *U.S. Public*, pg. 772
Miller, Tim, Natl. Sls. Mgr.-Fertilizer--Dempster Industries Inc., Beatrice, NE; *U.S. Private*, pg. 324
Miller, Timothy B., V.P.-Sls. & Mktg.--Cooper Hand Tools, Raleigh, NC; *U.S. Public*, pg. 444
Miller, Wayne, V.P.-Mktg. & Sls.--Micron Separations, Inc., Westborough, MA; *U.S. Private*, pg. 742
Miller, William G., Sr. V.P.-Mid-South Refining & Mktg.--Mapco Petroleum Inc., Tulsa, OK; *U.S. Public*, pg. 1042
Millican, Bryan, V.P.-Sls. & Mktg.--Con-Way Transportation Services, Palo Alto, CA; *U.S. Public*, pg. 281
Milliken, John, Mktg. Coord.--MacFarms of Hawaii, Inc., Sacramento, CA; *U.S. Public*, pg. 299
Milliran, Lee, Mgr.-Mktg. Support--Transkrit Corporation, Roanoke, VA; *U.S. Private*, pg. 782
Millman, Pam, Dir.-Mktg Services--Redbook, New York, NY; *U.S. Private*, pg. 517
Mills, David W., V.P.-Sls. & Adv.--PETsMART, Inc., Phoenix, AZ; *U.S. Public*, pg. 1281
Mills, Jerry A., V.P.-Mktg.--Northern Life Insurance Company, Seattle, WA; *U.S. Public*, pg. 1375
Mills, John, Dir.-Trade--Matthew Clark Taunton, Ltd., Bristol, United Kingdom; *Int'l*, pg. 848
Mills, Kelly, V.P.-Mktg.--A&M Records, Hollywood, CA; *Int'l*, pg. 1052
Mills, Ken, Dir.-Mktg.--Polaroid Corporation, Cambridge, MA; *U.S. Public*, pg. 1313
Mills, Paula, Mgr.-Mktg.--Woodward-Clyde Federal Services, Denver, CO; *U.S. Public*, pg. 1657
Mills, Valerie, Asst. Dir.-Mktg.--Eateries, Inc., Oklahoma City, OK; *U.S. Public*, pg. 555
Mills, Valerie, Asst. Dir.-Mktg.--Pepperoni Grill, Oklahoma City, OK; *U.S. Public*, pg. 555
Milone, Michael D., Chief Revenue Officer-Heinz Pet Prods.--Star-Kist Foods, Inc., Newport, KY; *U.S. Public*, pg. 806
Milsak, Frank, Dir.-Mktg.--EnviroSource-International Mill Service, Inc., Horsham, PA; *U.S. Public*, pg. 587
Minard, Aurelie, Asst. Dir.-Mktg.--NEC Electronics (France) S.A., Velizy-Villacoublay, France; *Int'l*, pg. 901
Minear, Donna M., Dir.-Mktg.--National Restaurant Supply Company, El Paso, TX; *U.S. Private*, pg. 786
Miner, John B., Mgr.-Mktg.--Alpha Associates, Inc., Woodbridge, NJ; *U.S. Private*, pg. 44
Minerman, Jennifer, Dir.-Mktg. Communications--Weider Nutrition Intl., Salt Lake City, UT; *U.S. Private*, pg. 1159
Minervino, Tara, Mgr.-Mktg.--Emson, Inc., Bridgeport, CT; *U.S. Private*, pg. 375
Mings, Chris, V.P.-Mktg.--Dean Foods Vegetable Company, Green Bay, WI; *U.S. Public*, pg. 490
Mink, M., Dir.-Mktg.--Nutricia BV, Zoetermeer, Netherlands; *Int'l*, pg. 991
Minkus, Sabra, Exec. V.P.--Transilwrap Company, Inc., Chicago, IL; *U.S. Private*, pg. 1097
Minnette, Jeff, V.P.-Mktg.--Rexam Closures, Evansville, IN; *Int'l*, pg. 1106
Minoque, Eve, Mgr.-Mktg.--Chicago Sun Times, Chicago, IL; *Int'l*, pg. 632
Minor, Bill, V.P.-Mktg.--Ohio Casualty Corporation, Hamilton, OH; *U.S. Public*, pg. 1214
Minor, Bill, V.P.-Mktg.--The Ohio Casualty Insurance Group, Hamilton, OH; *U.S. Public*, pg. 1214
Mintum, Brian, Exec. V.P.-Mktg.--Invesco Funds Group, Denver, CO; *Int'l*, pg. 685
Mintz, Charles E., Sr. V.P. & Dir.-Retail Mkts.--Scott & Stringfellow Financial, Inc., Richmond, VA; *U.S. Public*, pg. 1445
Mirabelli, Tony, V.P.-Mktg.--Uniden America Corporation, Fort Worth, TX; *Int'l*, pg. 1433
Miraglia, S.J., V.P.-North American Indus. & Super Precision--The Timken Company, Canton, OH; *U.S. Public*, pg. 1617
Miraglio, Laura, Mgr.-Mktg. Communications--Aetrium Inc., Saint Paul, MN; *U.S. Public*, pg. 27
Miramon, Philippe, Dir.-Mktg.--Quillet S.A., Levallois-Perret, France; *Int'l*, pg. 793
Miraselli, Anthony, Sr. V.P.-Mktg. & Sls.--Cobra Electronics Corporation, Chicago, IL; *U.S. Public*, pg. 391
Mirchin, Matt, V.P.-Mktg.--Champion Products Inc., Winston Salem, NC; *U.S. Public*, pg. 1433
Miriello, George, Dir.-Mktg.--Queen Carpet Corporation, Dalton, GA; *U.S. Private*, pg. 900
Mirlasseno, Giorgio, Dir.-Mktg.--Ferrero, Pino Torinese, Italy; *Int'l*, pg. 480
Misevicius, Milda, Exec. V.P. & New Bus. Devel. Dir.--Korey, Kay & Partners, New York, NY; *U.S. Private*, pg. 632
Mishler, Jim, V.P.-Sls. & Mktg.--Lennox International Inc., Richardson, TX; *U.S. Private*, pg. 659
Mishler, Jim, Mgr.-Mktg. & Sls.--Lennox Industries Inc., Richardson, TX; *U.S. Private*, pg. 659
Missry, Herbert, V.P.-Mktg.--Baby Togs, Inc., New York, NY; *U.S. Private*, pg. 108
Mitchael, Kevin, V.P.-Brand Mktg.--The William Carter Company, Morrow, GA; *U.S. Private*, pg. 217
Mitchell, Brian, Dir.-Sls. & Mktg.--Provident Music Group, Brentwood, TN; *Int'l*, pg. 1529
Mitchell, C.S., Dir.-Mktg.--The Branigar Organization, Inc., Savannah, GA; *U.S. Public*, pg. 1666
Mitchell, Debbie, V.P.-Mktg.--K-Swiss Inc., Chatsworth, CA; *U.S. Public*, pg. 937
Mitchell, Deborah, V.P.-Mktg.--20th Century Fox Home Entertainment, Los Angeles, CA; *U.S. Public*, pg. 275
Mitchell, Deborah, V.P.-Mktg.--20th Century Fox Home Entertainment, Los Angeles, CA; *Int'l*, pg. 926
Mitchell, James, Exec. V.P.-Mktg. & Prods.--IDS Financial Services, Inc., Minneapolis, MN; *U.S. Public*, pg. 73
Mitchell, James A., Exec. V.P.-Mktg. & Prods.--American Express Financial Advisor, Minneapolis, MN; *U.S. Public*, *pg. 73*
Mitchell, Jennifer L., Dir.-Mktg.--San Diego Gas & Electric Company, San Diego, CA; *U.S. Public*, pg. 584
Mitchell, Jim, Dir.-Mktg.--The NutraSweet Company, Deerfield, IL; *U.S. Public*, pg. 1125
Mitchell, Judy, Dir.-Adv. & Mktg.--Right Start, Inc., Westlake Village, CA; *U.S. Private*, pg. 930
Mitchell, Karen, Dir.-Mktg.--Mrs. Fields' Original Cookies, Inc., Salt Lake City, UT; *U.S. Private*, pg. 688
Mitchell, Mary, Mgr.-Mtkg. & Communications--Go-Video, Inc., Scottsdale, AZ; *U.S. Public*, pg. 748
Mitchell, Maura, Mktg. Team Leader-Roni Products--Golden Grain Company, Pleasanton, CA; *U.S. Public*, pg. 1348
Mitchell, Roy, V.P.-Sls. & Mktg.--American Furniture Company, Incorporated, Martinsville, VA; *U.S. Public*, pg. 974
Mitchell, Sam, Dir.-Mktg.-Valvoline--Valvoline Company, Lexington, KY; *U.S. Public*, pg. 139
Mitchell, William, Mgr.-Sls. & Services--Suntec Industries Inc., Rockford, IL; *U.S. Private*, pg. 1054
Mitome, Tsutomu, Dir.-Watch Mktg.--Seiko Corporation, Tokyo, Japan; *Int'l*, pg. 1218
Mitsuoka, Teruo, Sr. Mng. Dir.-Domestic Mktg. & Sls.--Mazda Motor Corporation, Hiroshima, Japan; *Int'l*, pg. 849
Mitten, Patrick, Dir.-Mktg.--Griffith Laboratories Worldwide, Inc., Alsip, IL; *U.S. Private*, pg. 481
Mittnick, Melvin, Mgr.-Division Mktg.--Textron Systems Corporation, Lowell, MA; *U.S. Public*, pg. 1589
Mixer, Charles, Sr. V.P.-Mktg. & Engrng.--Telephonics Corp., Farmington, NY; *U.S. Public*, pg. 766
Mixon, Marin, Mgr.-Mktg.--R.R. Bowker, New Providence, NJ; *Int'l*, pg. 1096
Miyamoto, Mikihiko, Pres. & Chief Mktg. Officer--Yasuda Mutual Life Insurance Co., Tokyo, Japan; *Int'l*, pg. 1519
Miyamoto, Mikihiko, Chief Mktg. Officer--Yasuda Mutual Life Insurance Co., Tokyo, Japan; *Int'l*, pg. 1519
Miyata, Keiichi, Exec. Dir. & Grp. Gen. Mgr.-Sls. & Mktg.--Sharp Corporation, Osaka, Japan; *Int'l*, pg. 1228
Mizell, Sidney C., Sr. V.P.-Sls. & Mktg.--Halter Marine Group, Inc., Gulfport, MS; *U.S. Public*, pg. 778
Mizunaga, Koji, Dep. Gen. Mgr.-Mktg.--Nishimatsu Construction Co., Ltd., Tokyo, Japan; *Int'l*, pg. 942
Mizuno, Toshiro, V.P.-Passenger Mktg. & Adv.--Japan Airlines American Region, New York, NY; *Int'l*, pg. 700
Moar, Jim, Dir.-Mktg. & Sls.--AlliedSignal Ocean Systems, Sylmar, CA; *U.S. Public*, pg. 50
Mobley, A. Scott, Chief Oper. Officer, Exec. V.P. & Sec.--Noble Roman's Inc., Indianapolis, IN; *U.S. Public*, pg. 1187
Moccia, Tom, Dir.-Mktg.--M.A. Hanna Engineered Materials, Bethlehem, PA; *U.S. Public*, pg. 781
Mock, Joe, Mgr.-Natl. Sls. & Mktg.--Douglas/Quikut, Walnut Ridge, AR; *U.S. Public*, pg. 217
Modlin, Bill, V.P.-Sls. & Mktg.--Hathaway Process Instrumentation, Carrollton, TX; *U.S. Public*, pg. 799
Moehling, Paul M., Mgr.-Sls.--Sommer Metalcraft Corporation, Crawfordsville, IN; *U.S. Private*, pg. 1013
Moeller, Mark, Dir.-Bus. Devel.--T.A. Loving Company, Goldsboro, NC; *U.S. Private*, pg. 677
Moen, Doug, V.P.-Sls. & Mktg.--Rea Magnet Wire Company, Inc., Fort Wayne, IN; *U.S. Private*, pg. 913
Moffat, John, V.P.-OEM Devel. & Mktg.--Code Alarm Security Systems, Madison Heights, MI; *U.S. Public*, pg. 394
Moffatt, Derek, Dir.-Mktg.--Texaco (Ireland) Ltd., Dublin, Ireland; *U.S. Public*, pg. 1584
Moffatt, W., Mgr.-Sls.--Standard Medical Imaging, Inc., Columbia, MD; *U.S. Private*, pg. 1032
Moffitt, Vicki, Dir.-Mktg.--KCI Communications, Inc, Mc Lean, VA; *U.S. Private*, pg. 784
Mogan, W.M., V.P.-Mktg.--Talley Defense Systems, Inc., Mesa, AZ; *U.S. Public*, pg. 308
Mogi, Kentaro, Dir.-Mktg.--Kikkoman Corporation, Chiba, Japan; *Int'l*, pg. 733
Mogol, Alan, V.P.-Sls. & Mktg.--Poly Pak America, Inc., Los Angeles, CA; *U.S. Private*, pg. 875
Mojica, Sergenti, Mgr.-Sls. & Mktg.--Eurocermex N.V., Brussels, Belgium; *U.S. Public*, pg. 115
Mokerlie, G., V.P.-Mktg.--Calgary Flames Hockey Club, Calgary, Canada; *Int'l*, pg. 252
Molesky, Mary Lou, Dir.-Mktg.--CLTV News, Oak Brook, IL; *U.S. Public*, pg. 1635
Molina, Philip G., Dir.-Mktg.--Family Smacks, Inc., Liberty, MO; *U.S. Private*, pg. 393
Molinari, M.V., V.P.-Sls. & Mktg.-North America--The Goodyear Tire & Rubber Company, Akron, OH; *U.S. Public*, pg. 752
Moliner, Agustin, V.P.-Mktg.--Banco Santander International Miami, Miami, FL; *Int'l*, pg. 143
Molkup, Kenneth, V.P.-Sls. & Mktg.--Premdor, Inc., Tampa, FL; *Int'l*, pg. 1067
Moll, Fredy, Dir.-Bus. Services--Von Roll AG, Gerlafingen, Switzerland; *Int'l*, pg. 1480
Moll, Kim, Mgr.-Mktg.--Pevely Dairy Company, Saint Louis, MO; *U.S. Private*, pg. 879
Moll, Laurie, Dir.-Mktg.--Encore Shoe Corporation, Rochester, NH; *U.S. Private*, pg. 375
Mollenhauer, Henry L., Dir.-Mktg.--S.D. Warren Co., Boston, MA; *Int'l*, pg. 1193
Mollner, Gerhard, Dir.-Mktg.--Henkel Austria Group, Vienna, Austria; *Int'l*, pg. 611
Molnar, Thomas, V.P.-Mktg. & Mfg.--Gibbs Wire & Steel Company, Inc., Southington, CT; *U.S. Private*, pg. 451
Moloney, Herbert W., Sr. V.P.-Mktg. & Sls.--Treasure Chest Advertising Co., Inc., Glendora, CA; *U.S. Public*, pg. 228

Moltner, Bill, Mgr.-Mktg. Resources--Lennox International Inc., Richardson, TX; *U.S. Private*, pg. 659

Momberger, Wolfgang, Dr., Dir.-Mktg.--Karstadt Aktiengesellschaft, Essen, Germany; *Int'l*, pg. 724

Monachino, Joseph J., V.P.-Sls. & Mktg.--Alarmguard Holdings, Inc., Orange, CT; *U.S. Public*, pg. 35

Monaco, Carmen, V.P.-Mktg.--Charming Shoppes, Inc., Bensalem, PA; *U.S. Public*, pg. 335

Monaco, Carmen, Sr. V.P.-Mktg. & Adv.--Goody's Family Clothing, Inc., Knoxville, TN; *U.S. Public*, pg. 753

Monaghan, Sandy, Mgr.-Mktg.-Airpax Protector Grp.--Philips Automotive Electronics, Cheshire, CT; *Int'l*, pg. 1054

Monaghan, Thomas, V.P.-Mktg./St. Ives--Alberto-Culver Company, Melrose Park, IL; *U.S. Public*, pg. 37

Monahan Rice, Beth, V.P.-Mktg. & Bus. Devel.--Hill, Holliday, Connors, Cosmopulos, Inc., Boston, MA; *U.S. Private*, pg. 529

Monahan, Mona, V.P.-Mktg.--The Princess Marcella Borghese, Inc., New York, NY; *U.S. Private*, pg. 690

Mongan, Michell E., Mkt. Res. Analyst--Paddock Publications, Inc., Arlington Heights, IL; *U.S. Private*, pg. 833

Mongeau, Jean, Gen. Mgr.-Sls. & Mktg.--Reseau de Television Quatre Saisons Inc., Montreal, Canada; *Int'l*, pg. 241

Mongiello, Patrick A., V.P.-Mktg. & Sls.--Brunschwig & Fils, Inc., White Plains, NY; *U.S. Private*, pg. 176

Monko, Cezary, Mgr.-Mktg.--Esselte Polska Sp.z.o.o., Kozienice, Poland; *Int'l*, pg. 461

Monocchio, Tony, V.P.-Sls. & Mktg.--The National Latex Products Co., Ashland, OH; *U.S. Private*, pg. 785

Monroe, Jane L., Mktg. Officer--AMCORE Bank, Rock River Valley, Dixon, IL; *U.S. Public*, pg. 64

Monsu, Philippe, Gen. Mgr.-Sls. & Mktg.--DynetCom, Guyancourt, France; *Int'l*, pg. 425

Montalvo, Michael A., V.P.-Mktg. & Sls.--Sierra Health Services, Inc., Las Vegas, NV; *U.S. Public*, pg. 1469

Montalvo, Mike, V.P.-Mktg. & Sls.--Sierra Health and Life Insurance Company, Inc., Las Vegas, NV; *U.S. Public*, pg. 1469

Montani, Rick, V.P.-Mktg.--Sika Corporation, Lyndhurst, NJ; *Int'l*, pg. 1249

Montanus, Gary G., Sr. V.P.-Worldwide Mktg.--Worldvision Enterprises, New York, NY; *U.S. Private*, pg. 776

Monteiro Alves, Jose Fernando, Dir.-Mktg.--Sadia Concordia S.A. Industria e Comercio, Concordia, Brazil; *Int'l*, pg. 1168

Monteiro, Frederico, Mgr.-Mktg. Intelligence--Souza Cruz, S.A., Rio de Janeiro, Brazil; *Int'l*, pg. 112

Monteith, Maggy, Dir.-Adv. & Mktg.--Columbia Tri-Star Films (UK), London, United Kingdom; *Int'l*, pg. 1281

Monteleone, Frank, Mgr.-Mktg.-Airpax Mechatronics Grp.--Philips Automotive Electronics, Cheshire, CT; *Int'l*, pg. 1054

Montgomery, James B., V.P.-Mktg.--Temple-Inland Forest Products Corp.-Bleached Paperboard Group, Evadale, TX; *U.S. Public*, pg. 1575

Montgomery, John A., V.P.-Mktg. & Communications--Texas-New Mexico Power Co., Fort Worth, TX; *U.S. Public*, pg. 1557

Montgomery, Mark, Mgr.-Mktg. & Plng. Devel.--AFG Industries, Inc., Kingsport, TN; *Int'l*, pg. 84

Monti, Cesare, Mgr.-Mktg.--Olivetti Corporation of Japan, Tokyo, Japan; *Int'l*, pg. 1003

Monty, Bill, Dir.-Mktg.--Wet-N-Wild, A Six Flags Water Park, Arlington, TX; *U.S. Public*, pg. 1612

Monzon, Medardo, Mgr.-Sls. & Mktg.--Arizona Chemical Div., Panama City, FL; *U.S. Public*, pg. 901

Moody, H.A., Dir.-Mktg. & Sls.--Ferguson Machine Co., Saint Louis, MO; *U.S. Public*, pg. 457

Moody, Mary, Dir.-Casino Mktg.--Silver City Casino, Las Vegas, NV; *U.S. Public*, pg. 375

Moody, R. Leon, III, V.P.-Mktg.--Batson-Cook Company, West Point, GA; *U.S. Private*, pg. 123

Mooibroek, Case, V.P.-Mktg.--Coleman Powermate, Inc., Omaha, NE; *U.S. Private*, pg. 691

Moon, John, V.P.-Mktg.--Alamo Group, Inc., Seguin, TX; *U.S. Public*, pg. 34

Moon, John, V.P.-Sls. & Mktg.--M&W, Gibson City, IL; *U.S. Public*, pg. 35

Moon, Robert V., Sr. V.P.-Casino Mktg.--MGM Grand Hotel, Inc., Las Vegas, NV; *U.S. Public*, pg. 1027

Moon, Ted, Dir.-Deli & Bakery Mdsg.--Winn-Dixie Stores, Inc., Jacksonville, FL; *U.S. Public*, pg. 1771

Moone, Robert H., V.P. & Dir.-Sls. & Mktg.--State Auto P & C, Columbus, OH; *U.S. Private*, pg. 1036

Mooney, Joan, Mgr.-Mktg. Services--Meto, USA, Morris Plains, NJ; *Int'l*, pg. 460

Mooney, Joan, Mgr.-Mktg. Svcs.--Esselte Meto Kimball Systems, Morris Plains, NJ; *Int'l*, pg. 460

Mooney, Kevin, Mgr.-Mktg.-Pizzas--UB Frozen & Chilled Limited, Grimsby, United Kingdom; *Int'l*, pg. 1442

Moore, Barbara, Mktg. & Sls. Coord.--Syseca Inc., Marina Del Rey, CA; *Int'l*, pg. 1384

Moore, Bob, V.P.-Mktg.--Marley Pump, Overland Park, KS; *U.S. Public*, pg. 1676

Moore, Bradley, Sr. V.P.-Systems--Munck Automation Technology, Newport News, VA; *U.S. Private*, pg. 767

Moore, C.E., V.P.-Contract Prods.--Beaird Industries, Inc., Shreveport, LA; *U.S. Public*, pg. 1639

Moore, Dan, V.P.-Mktg.--Southwestern/Great American Inc., Nashville, TN; *U.S. Private*, pg. 1018

Moore, Dan, V.P.-Sls. & Mktg.--Target Stamped Products Corp., Kinsman, OH; *U.S. Private*, pg. 1069

Moore, David, Dir.-Mktg.--Konica Business Machines USA, Inc., Windsor, CT; *Int'l*, pg. 748

Moore, Ed, Mgr.-Worldwide Mktg.--Hydraulic Valve Div., Hicksville, OH; *U.S. Public*, pg. 411

Moore, Ed, V.P.-Mktg.--Lundy Enterprises, Inc., New Orleans, LA; *U.S. Private*, pg. 681

Moore, Frank, Chief Oper. Officer & Exec. V.P.--McCall Oil & Chemical Corp., Portland, OR; *U.S. Private*, pg. 719

Moore, Gary, V.P.-Mktg.--Trico Industries, Inc., San Marcos, TX; *U.S. Public*, pg. 1247

Moore, Gerald, Mgr.-Mktg.--Fluids Handling Group, Springfield, OH; *U.S. Public*, pg. 1393

Moore, Greg, Dir.-Mktg. Poultry Group--Gold Kist, Inc., Atlanta, GA; *U.S. Private*, pg. 459

Moore, Jim, Mng. Dir.-Consumer Mktg.-STP--First Brands Corporation, Danbury, CT; *U.S. Public*, pg. 626

Moore, Jim, Mng. Dir.-Consumer Mktg. & Automotive Prods.--STP Corporation, Danbury, CT; *U.S. Public*, pg. 627

Moore, Katy, Mgr.-Direct Mktg.--Autodesk, Inc., San Rafael, CA; *U.S. Public*, pg. 148

Moore, Maureen, Dir.-Corp. Mktg. Communications--Fellowes Manufacturing Co., Itasca, IL; *U.S. Private*, pg. 400

Moore, Michael, V.P.-Strategic Svcs. & Mktg.--Memorex Telex Corp., Irving, TX; *Int'l*, pg. 857

Moore, Mike, V.P.-Svcs. Mktg.--Inacom Corp., Omaha, NE; *U.S. Public*, pg. 873

Moore, Mike, Dir.-Mktg. & Devel.--Reynolds Metals Co., Consumer Products Div., Richmond, VA; *U.S. Public*, pg. 1386

Moore, Pattye, Sr. V.P.-Mktg.--Sonic Corporation, Oklahoma City, OK; *U.S. Public*, pg. 1485

Moore, R., Dir.-Sls. & Mktg.--Dowty Aerospace, Wolverhampton, Wolverhampton, United Kingdom; *Int'l*, pg. 1337

Moore, Rick, Mgr.-Mktg.-East--Intermountain Gas Co., Boise, ID; *U.S. Private*, pg. 568

Moore, Ron, Mgr.-Mktg.--Thomas Built Buses, Inc., High Point, NC; *U.S. Private*, pg. 1082

Moore, William S., Sr. V.P.-Sls. & Mktg.--Rocky Shoes & Boots, Inc., Nelsonville, OH; *U.S. Public*, pg. 1402

Moorhead, John, V.P.-Bus. Mngmt. & Mktg. Services--Bestfoods, Englewood Cliffs, NJ; *U.S. Public*, pg. 223

Moot, Suzanne, Exec. V.P.-Mktg. & Retail Banking--UST Corporation, Boston, MA; *U.S. Public*, pg. 1660

Moot, Suzanne, Exec. V.P.-Retail Banking & Mktg.--USTrust, Boston, MA; *U.S. Public*, pg. 1660

Moquist, Paul A., Exec. V.P.-Sls. & Mktg.--Insignia Systems, Inc., Minnetonka, MN; *U.S. Public*, pg. 881

Moran, Amy, Mktg. Coord.--Competitive Media Reporting, New York, NY; *Int'l*, pg. 1447

Moran, Jack, Dir.-Mktg. Communications--Sulcus Computer Corp., Greensburg, PA; *U.S. Public*, pg. 1527

Moran, Laura, Mktg. Specialist-Consumer Contadina--Culinary Foods Group, Glendale, CA; *Int'l*, pg. 917

Moran, Michael, V.P.-Derivative Securities Mktg.--The American Stock Exchange, New York, NY; *U.S. Private*, pg. 62

Moran, Nancy, Mgr.-Mktg. Communications--American Meter Company, Horsham, PA; *Int'l*, pg. 1149

Moran, Victor, V.P.-Natl. Gas Mktg.--Swift Energy Company, Houston, TX; *U.S. Public*, pg. 1543

Morano, Jerry, Exec. V.P.-Mktg. & Commun.--Quality Bakers of America Cooperative, Inc., Greenwich, CT; *U.S. Private*, pg. 898

Morasca, Sam, V.P.-Mktg. Shell Oil Prods.--Shell Oil Company, Houston, TX; *Int'l*, pg. 1136

Mordecai, Mark, V.P.-Mktg.--Blauer Manufacturing Co., Inc., Boston, MA; *U.S. Private*, pg. 149

Morehouse, T.K., Sr. V.P.-Mktg.--Central Freight Lines, Inc., Waco, TX; *U.S. Private*, pg. 223

Morel, Fabrice, Dir.-Mktg.--Rail Europe Inc., Harrison, NY; *Int'l*, pg. 1165

Moreshead, Tracy, Dir.-Mktg.--Nationwide Building Society, Swindon, United Kingdom; *Int'l*, pg. 912

Moretensen, Nancy, V.P.-Mktg. & Services--Zions Co-operative Mercantile Institution, Salt Lake City, UT; *U.S. Public*, pg. 1793

Morgan, Ann, Dir.-Sls.--Accecones Ricci U.S.A., Inc., New York, NY; *Int'l*, pg. 445

Morgan, Jerry, Dir.-Mktg.--Halfords, Ltd., Redditch, United Kingdom; *Int'l*, pg. 203

Morgan, John, Dir.-Mktg.--Norman Levy Associates, Inc., Southfield, MI; *U.S. Private*, pg. 664

Morgan, Michael K., V.P.-Natl. Casino Mktg.--Harrah's Entertainment, Inc., Memphis, TN; *U.S. Public*, pg. 790

Morgan, Phil, Dir.-Mktg.--Rykoff-Sexton, Inc., Wilkes-Barre, PA; *U.S. Public*, pg. 918

Morgan, Raymond U., V.P.-Sls. & Mktg.--Barton Nelson Inc., Kansas City, MO; *U.S. Private*, pg. 120

Morgan, Rob, Sr. V.P.-Mktg., Sls. & Engrng.--Buck Knives, Inc., El Cajon, CA; *U.S. Private*, pg. 177

Morgan, Sue, V.P.-Mktg.--Church's Chicken, Inc., Atlanta, GA; *U.S. Private*, pg. 5

Morgan, Susan, V.P.-Mktg.--CAP Gemini America, New York, NY; *Int'l*, pg. 263

Morgan, Susan L., V.P.-Mktg.--Sybra, Inc., Atlanta, GA; *U.S. Private*, pg. 270

Morgenroth, Stefan, Dir.-Sls. & Mktg.--Georg Sahm GmbH & Co. KG Maschinenfabrik, Eschwege, Germany; *Int'l*, pg. 1169

Morgese, Chris, V.P.-Sls. & Mktg.--Titan Tool, Inc., Oakland, NJ; *U.S. Private*, pg. 500

Moriarty, Ken, Dir.-Audi Mktg.--Volkswagen of America, Inc., Auburn Hills, MI; *Int'l*, pg. 1474

Moriarty, Tim, V.P. & Database Mktg. Dir.--Arnold Information Technology, Boston, MA; *U.S. Private*, pg. 84

Morin-Reynolds, Jamie, Dir.-Mktg.--PG Vinyl Windows/PG Proglass Construction, Westbrook, ME; *U.S. Private*, pg. 826

Morin, Jean-Jacques, V.P.-Mktg.--Grocery Division, Montreal, Canada; *Int'l*, pg. 348

Morini, Christopher E., V.P.-Retail Sls. & Mktg.--Galaxy Food Company, Orlando, FL; *U.S. Public*, pg. 697

Moriondo, Alberto, Mgr.-Sls. & Mktg.--FMC FoodTech/Fran Rica, Stockton, CA; *U.S. Public*, pg. 605

Morissette, R.L., Mgr.-Mktg.--Firestone Textiles Company, Woodstock, Canada; *Int'l*, pg. 214

Moritz, Sandra, Mktg. Svcs. Supvr.--Revell-Monogram Inc., Morton Grove, IL; *U.S. Private*, pg. 926

Morman, Stacy, Mktg. Asst.--Restaurant Developers Corp., Independence, OH; *U.S. Private*, pg. 925

Morns, Diane, Mgr.-Mktg. Services--Milton Bradley Company, East Longmeadow, MA; *U.S. Public*, pg. 797

Morocco, David, V.P.-Mktg.--The Jean Coutu (PJC) USA Inc., Warwick, RI; *Int'l*, pg. 340

Moroz, Michael, Sr. V.P.-Mktg. Prods. & Svcs.--Damark International, Inc., Minneapolis, MN; *U.S. Public*, pg. 478

Morozowski, Jaime M., V.P.-Consumer Toiletries--Conair Corporation, Stamford, CT; *U.S. Private*, pg. 261

Morra, Jere, V.P.-Mktg.--Bandai America, Inc., Cypress, CA; *Int'l*, pg. 145

Morrell, Dave, Mgr.-Mktg.--Hawaiian Commercial & Sugar Co., Puunene, HI; *U.S. Public*, pg. 39

Morris, Anthony, Sr. V.P.--Long Island Bancorp, Inc., Melville, NY; *U.S. Public*, pg. 1013

Morris, Graham John, Dir.-Mktg. & Sls.--Audi AG, Ingolstadt, Germany; *Int'l*, pg. 1473

Morris, Karen, Dir.-Mktg.--Allied Capital Corporation, Washington, DC; *U.S. Public*, pg. 47

Morris, Kristin, Mktg. Mgr.-Graphics--Acorn Engineering Company, City of Industry, CA; *U.S. Private*, pg. 14

Morris, Kyla, Dir.-Mktg.--The Vacation Store, Virginia Beach, VA; *U.S. Private*, pg. 649

Morris, M. Stephen, Asst. V.P.-GA/MS Opers.--Alfa Insurance Corp., Montgomery, AL; *U.S. Public*, pg. 40

Morris, Marvin, V.P.-Mktg.--Alamo Group, Inc., Seguin, TX; *U.S. Public*, pg. 34

Morris, Pat, V.P.-Mktg. & Sls.-U.S.A.--Timex Corporation, Middlebury, CT; *U.S. Private*, pg. 1088

Morris, Ray, Consultant-Sls. & Mktg.--Bassick by Kaspar, Shiner, TX; *U.S. Private*, pg. 122

Morris, Roger, Dir.-Mktg. & Sls.--The Du Pont Merck Pharmaceutical Company, Wilmington, DE; *U.S. Public*, pg. 531

Morris, Sara, Sr. Dir.-Mktg. & Adv.--Polo/Ralph Lauren Corporation, New York, NY; *U.S. Private*, pg. 874

Morris, Shawn D., Sr. V.P.-Mktg.--National General Insurance Co., Earth City, MO; *U.S. Public*, pg. 721

Morrison, Fritz, Dir.-Mktg.--Americal Corporation, Henderson, NC; *U.S. Private*, pg. 49

Morrison, Mary, Sr. Mgr.-Mktg. Communications--Oki Semiconductor Group, Sunnyvale, CA; *Int'l*, pg. 1000

Morrison, Sylvia, Sr. V.P. & Gen. Mgr.-Direct Mktg.--Liggett-Stashower, Inc., Cleveland, OH; *U.S. Private*, pg. 667

Morrison, Tony, Dir.-Sls. & Mktg.--AmVestors Acquisition Subsidiary, Inc., Topeka, KS; *U.S. Private*, pg. 59

Morrissey, Christopher, Mgr.-Mktg. Commun.--Rogers Corporation, Rogers, CT; *U.S. Public*, pg. 1402

Morrissey, K., Mgr.-Mktg. Communications--Semiconductor Equipment Division, Beverly, MA; *U.S. Public*, pg. 557

Morro, Steve, V.P.-Mktg.--IGT North America, Reno, NV; *U.S. Public*, pg. 900

Morrow, David, V.P.-Sls. & Mktg.--Sanderson Plumbing Products Inc., Columbus, MS; *U.S. Private*, pg. 964

Morrow, David, Mktg. & Sls.--Beneke, Columbus, MS; *U.S. Private*, pg. 964

Morrow, Dennis, Dir.-Mktg. & Sls.--Enidine Incorporated, Orchard Park, NY; *U.S. Private*, pg. 377

Morrow, Garry R., Mgr.-Mktg.--Intermagnetics General Corporation, Latham, NY; *U.S. Public*, pg. 894

Morrow, Jef, Dir.-Corp. & Product Mktg.--Axiom Inc., Moorestown, NJ; *U.S. Public*, pg. 157

Morrow, Melinda R., Coord.-Mktg. & Adv.--Lectrodryer Div., Ajax Magnethermic Corp., Richmond, KY; *Int'l*, pg. 113

Morrow, Michael, V.P.-Mktg.--Kelly Services, Inc., Troy, MI; *U.S. Public*, pg. 949

Mortenson, Jim, Exec. V.P.-Sls. & Mktg.--Arrowhead Mills, Inc., Hereford, TX; *U.S. Private*, pg. 86

Mortimer, Justin, Mgr.-Mktg.--Telegenix Inc., Cherry Hill, NJ; *U.S. Private*, pg. 1073

Morton, Cindy, V.P.-Healthcare Mktg.--TMP Worldwide Recruitment Division, New York, NY; *U.S. Private*, pg. 1065

Morton, John, Sr. V.P.- Strategic Mktg. Services--Total Research Corporation, Princeton, NJ; *U.S. Public*, pg. 1625

Mosack, Cal C., V.P.-Sls. & Mktg.--Conbraco Industries Inc., Matthews, NC; *U.S. Private*, pg. 261

Moscardini, Luciano, Dir.-Mktg.--Recordati Industria Chimica e Farmaceutica S.p.A., Milan, Italy; *Int'l*, pg. 1090

Moscaroli, Aldo, Dir.-Mktg.--Rimoldi Necchi S.R.L., Milan, Italy; *Int'l*, pg. 1117

Moscoe, Frances, Sr. Dir.-Mktg. Commun.--Systems & Computer Technology Corporation, Malvern, PA; *U.S. Public*, pg. 1552

Moseley, Chris, Sr. V.P.-Adv. & Promo.--Discovery Communications, Inc., Bethesda, MD; *U.S. Private*, pg. 334

Moseley, Chris, Sr. V.P.-Adv. & Promo.--Discovery Networks, Inc., Bethesda, MD; *U.S. Private*, pg. 334

Moseley, Mark, V.P.-Mktg.--Rowe Furniture Corp., Mc Lean, VA; *U.S. Public*, pg. 1410

Moseneder, Reinhard, Dir.-Mktg.--Henkel Austria Group, Vienna, Austria; *Int'l*, pg. 611

Moser, Michael J., Exec. V.P.--Trans Financial, Inc., Bowling Green, KY; *U.S. Public*, pg. 1628

Moser, Michel, First V.P.-Mktg.--Banque Cantonale Vaudoise, Lausanne, Switzerland; *Int'l*, pg. 160

Moses, Senn, Exec. V.P.-Mktg.--Universal Studios Recreation Services Group, Universal City, CA; *Int'l*, pg. 1216

Mosey, Bill, V.P.-Sls. & Mktg.--K-D Lamp Company, Cincinnati, OH; *U.S. Private*, pg. 603

Mosher, Robert, Dir.-Mktg.-Devices--Storz Instrument Co., Saint Louis, MO; *U.S. Public*, pg. 79

Mosier, George O., V.P.-Sls. & Mktg., Intl. Div.--Foley-PLP Company, Rochester, NY; *U.S. Private*, pg. 416

Mosikili, M.S., Exec. Dir.-Mktg.--Eskom, Sandton, South Africa; *Int'l*, pg. 459

Moskowitz, Ilene, Head-Mktg. & Pub. Rels.--Bank Leumi Trust Company of New York, New York, NY; *Int'l*, pg. 150

Mosley, David A., V.P.-Admin.--American General Life & Accident Insurance Co., Nashville, TN; *U.S. Public*, pg. 76

Moss, Ann Mao, Dir.-Mktg.-Children's Books--Simon & Schuster Children's Publishing, New York, NY; *U.S. Private*, pg. 777
Moss, Dale, Exec. V.P.-Sls. & Mktg.--British Airways, Flushing, NY; *Int'l*, pg. 219
Moss, James E., V.P.-Mktg.--Entergy Gulf States, Inc., Beaumont, TX; *U.S. Public*, pg. 586
Moss, Scott, Dir.-Mktg.--House of White Birches, Inc., Berne, IN; *U.S. Private*, pg. 542
Moss, Wendy, Sr. V.P.-Mktg./Sony Wonder--Sony Music Entertainment, Inc., New York, NY; *Int'l*, pg. 1281
Mosser, Bart, V.P.-Mktg.--Hygrade Metal Moulding Mfg. Corp., Bethlehem, PA; *U.S. Private*, pg. 552
Mostek, Charles F., Exec. V.P.-Fresh Meats Sls. & Mktg.--IBP, Inc., Dakota City, NE; *U.S. Public*, pg. 852
Mostert, Adam, Mgr.-Mktg. & Logistics--Sasol Fertilizers, Randburg, South Africa; *Int'l*, pg. 1196
Mosthof, Albert, Dir.-Mktg.--Ed Miniat, Inc., Chicago, IL; *U.S. Private*, pg. 750
Mostin, Mike, V.P.-Sls. & Mktg.--J & R Film / Moviola Digital Co., Hollywood, CA; *U.S. Private*, pg. 576
Mostow, Mark R., Sr. V.P.-Sls. & Mktg.--Beverly Enterprises, Inc., Fort Smith, AR; *U.S. Public*, pg. 227
Motak, Sue, Mktg. Asst.--Columbus McKinnon Corp., Amherst, NY; *U.S. Public*, pg. 405
Mote, K.R., Mgr.--Dusenbery Europe Ltd., Bedford, United Kingdom; *U.S. Private*, pg. 350
Motsay, John M., V.P.-Sls. & Mktg.--Canton Drop Forge, Canton, OH; *U.S. Private*, pg. 205
Mott, Regina B., Dir.-Mktg. Services--Weider Publications, Inc., Woodland Hills, CA; *U.S. Private*, pg. 1159
Mott, Robert, V.P.-OEM Prod.--Cascade Corporation, Troutdale, OR; *U.S. Public*, pg. 310
Motush, Ken, Mgr.-Mktg.--Turtle Wax, Inc., Chicago, IL; *U.S. Private*, pg. 1110
Moudy, Larry, V.P.-Mktg.-Guitars--Fender Musical Instruments, Scottsdale, AZ; *U.S. Private*, pg. 400
Mountain, Maurice G., Mgr.-Mktg. Services--Indiana Glass Company, Cincinnati, OH; *U.S. Public*, pg. 976
Mountain, Patrick, Dir.-Sls. & Mktg. Consumer Audio--Carver Corporation, Lynnwood, WA; *U.S. Public*, pg. 310
Mourlon, Jacques, Gen. Mgr.-Intl. & Mktg. Strategy--Groupe SEB, Ecueille, France; *Int'l*, pg. 568
Mousiades, Hercules, V.P.-Mktg.--Appleton Papers Inc., Appleton, WI; *Int'l*, pg. 567
Mowell, Eric, Dir.-Mktg. & Sls.--James Burn International Limited, Esher, United Kingdom; *U.S. Public*, pg. 1507
Moya, Evelyn, Exec. Sec.--Woolworth Corporation, New York, NY; *U.S. Public*, pg. 1777
Moyer, Sandy, Dir.-Mktg.--International Envelope Company, Exton, PA; *U.S. Public*, pg. 70
Moylan, J., V.P.-Sales & Mktg.--Fleck Manufacturing Inc., Tillsonburg, Canada; *Int'l*, pg. 955
Mozak, Robert, V.P.-Sls. & Mktg.--Dey Laboratories Inc., Napa, CA; *Int'l*, pg. 812
Mruz, Michael J., Pres. & Chief Exec. & Oper. Officer--Nichols Research Corporation, Huntsville, AL; *U.S. Public*, pg. 1182
Msaka, Daniel, Dir.-Mktg.--SKF France S.A., Clamart, France; *Int'l*, pg. 1158
Mucci, Ron M., V.P.-Mktg.--Northwest Pipeline Corp., Salt Lake City, UT; *U.S. Public*, pg. 1769
Muckerman, John, Dir.-Mktg. & Adv.--Dierbergs Markets Inc., Chesterfield, MO; *U.S. Private*, pg. 332
Mudge, William A., V.P.-Global Mktg. Communications--McQuay International, Minneapolis, MN; *U.S. Private*, pg. 3
Mueller, Brett, Pres.-Magnum Div. & V.P.-Sls. & Mktg.--Mueller Sports Medicine, Inc., Prairie Du Sac, WI; *U.S. Private*, pg. 766
Mueller, D., V.P.-Mktg. Comm.--Carbone-Lorraine North America, Parsippany, NJ; *Int'l*, pg. 1028
Mueller, Mike, V.P.-Sls. & Mktg.--Columbus Show Case Company, Columbus, OH; *U.S. Private*, pg. 257
Mugno, Connie A., Mgr.-Mktg.--Simpson Gumpertz & Heger Inc., Arlington, MA; *U.S. Private*, pg. 1002
Muir, Chris, V.P.-Mktg.--C.H. Heist Corp., Clearwater, FL; *U.S. Public*, pg. 807
Muir, Mark L., V.P.-Mktg.--Viking Office Products, Torrance, CA; *U.S. Public*, pg. 1720
Muklevicz, Joe, V.P.-Mktg. & Sls.--AMI Industries, Inc., Colorado Springs, CO; *U.S. Public*, pg. 401
Mulder, John, V.P.-Automotive Mktg.--Gentex Corporation, Zeeland, MI; *U.S. Public*, pg. 731
Muldoon, Pat, V.P.-Mktg.--Sealright Company, Inc., De Soto, KS; *U.S. Public*, pg. 1451
Mule, Todd, Dir.-Mktg. & Industrial Rels.--River Parishes Hospital, La Place, LA; *U.S. Public*, pg. 1697
Mulhall, John F., V.P.-Sls. & Mktg.--Insituform East, Inc., Hyattsville, MD; *U.S. Public*, pg. 330
Mulhearn, Gina, Dir.-Mktg./Consumer Prods.--Thomaston Mills, Inc., Thomaston, GA; *U.S. Public*, pg. 1599
Mulinini, Mike, V.P.-Mktg.--National Welders Supply Co. Inc., Charlotte, NC; *U.S. Private*, pg. 788
Mulkey, Thomas J., V.P.-Mktg.--Apache Corporation, Houston, TX; *U.S. Public*, pg. 119
Mulki, Jay, Mgr.-Energy Services--Hawaiian Electric Company, Inc., Honolulu, HI; *U.S. Public*, pg. 800
Mullen, Kathleen, Sec.-Mktg.--Doubleday Direct, Garden City, NY; *Int'l*, pg. 191
Mullen, Larry J., Mgr.-Mktg., Treas. & Sec.--Terral Seed Co., Inc., Lake Providence, LA; *U.S. Private*, pg. 1077
Muller, Cindy, Coord.-Mktg. Communications--Rheem Water Heater, Montgomery, AL; *Int'l*, pg. 1022
Muller, E., Mgr.-Mktg.--Transbrasil S.A. Linhas Aereas, Sao Paulo, Brazil; *Int'l*, pg. 1416
Mulligan, Michael L., V.P.-Sls. & Mktg.--SuperValu, Inc., Eden Prairie, MN; *U.S. Public*, pg. 1540
Mulligan, Sharon, Mgr.-Mktg.--Chemical Engineering, New York, NY; *U.S. Public*, pg. 1071
Mullinex, Lonnie, Mktg.--Regions Bank/Anniston, Anniston, AL; *U.S. Public*, pg. 1371
Mullinix, George, V.P.-Mktg.--Brach & Brock Confections Inc., Chattanooga, TN; *U.S. Private*, pg. 163
Mullins, Kevin, V.P.-Sls. & Mktg.--LoJack Corporation, Dedham, MA; *U.S. Public*, pg. 1012
Mullins, Tom, Sr. V.P., Mktg. Services--EJL Advertising/Houston, Houston, TX; *U.S. Private*, pg. 673
Mullnix, Steve, V.P.-Sls. & Mktg.--The Todd-AO Corporation, Hollywood, CA; *U.S. Public*, pg. 1619
Mulroy, Barry, Sr. V.P.-Mktg.--Marquis Investments, New Orleans, LA; *U.S. Public*, pg. 629
Multari, Al, V.P.-Mktg.--Favorite Brands International, Inc., Lincolnshire, IL; *U.S. Private*, pg. 397
Mumma, J. Stephen, Sr. V.P.-Mktg. & Pub. Rels.--Atlas Van Lines, Inc., Evansville, IN; *U.S. Private*, pg. 97
Mumo, N., Dir.-Mktg.--Pentel of America, Ltd., Torrance, CA; *Int'l*, pg. 1035
Mumper-Dickerson, Melanie, V.P.-Mktg. Services & Pub. Rels.--NFO Research, Inc., Greenwich, CT; *U.S. Public*, pg. 1146
Munch, Bill, V.P.-Sls. & Mktg.--Pyramid Mouldings, Jacksonville, FL; *Int'l*, pg. 1335
Munchen, Paul, Dir.-Gen. Mktg., Sls. & Adv.--CLT-UFA, Luxembourg, Luxembourg; *Int'l*, pg. 561
Munck, G., V.P.-Mktg.--Kruger Pulp & Paper Sales, Inc., New York, NY; *Int'l*, pg. 762
Munday, Colin S., Mgr.-Mktg.--Intercool Energy Corporation, Latham, NY; *U.S. Public*, pg. 894
Mundee, Marsh, Dir.-Mktg.--Carquest Corp., Lakewood, CO; *U.S. Private*, pg. 445
Mundschau, John, Mgr.-Mktg.--Matec Corporation, Hopkinton, MA; *U.S. Public*, pg. 1056
Mundy, Basil, V.P.-Mktg.--MGI PHARMA INC., Minneapolis, MN; *U.S. Public*, pg. 1026
Munemitsu, Janice, V.P.-Mktg.--Wolf Brand Products, Fullerton, CA; *U.S. Public*, pg. 428
Munger, Bob, Mgr.-Mktg. & Sls.--Sakata Seed America, Inc., Morgan Hill, CA; *Int'l*, pg. 1178
Mungula, Roddfa, Dir.-Mktg.--McGraw-Hill/Interamericana de Mexico, S.A. de CV, Mexico, Mexico; *U.S. Public*, pg. 1072
Munich, Linda, Coord.-Leasing & Mktg./Apartments--New Plan Realty Trust, New York, NY; *U.S. Public*, pg. 1172
Munoz, Timothy F., V.P.-Relationship Mktg.--Comcast Cable Communications, Inc., Philadelphia, PA; *U.S. Public*, pg. 407
Munro, Deborah, Mgr.-Mktg.--Roltech, Cambridge, United Kingdom; *Int'l*, pg. 462
Munro, Laurie J., Sr. V.P.-Mktg.--Mackenzie Financial Corporation, Toronto, Canada; *Int'l*, pg. 828
Munroe, Pauline, Dir.-Mktg.--The Gillette Company, Personal Care Group, Boston, MA; *U.S. Public*, pg. 744
Munson, Andrea, Coord.-Mktg.--Gould Packaging, Inc., Vancouver, WA; *U.S. Private*, pg. 466
Muntean, Kirstin B., V.P.-Mktg., Consumer Prods.--Alberto-Culver USA, Inc., Melrose Park, IL; *U.S. Public*, pg. 38
Muntean, Kristin, V.P.-Trade Mktg.--Consumer Products Div., Melrose Park, IL; *U.S. Public*, pg. 37
Muntean, Kristin B., V.P.-Trade Mktg.--Alberto-Culver Company, Melrose Park, IL; *U.S. Public*, pg. 37
Murai, Kunihiro, V.P.-Mktg.--Yokogawa Electric Corporation, Tokyo, Japan; *Int'l*, pg. 1520
Murata, Akiya, Chief Fin. Officer & Gen. Mgr.-Sls. & Mktg.--Okazaki Golf Club KK, Okazaki, Japan; *Int'l*, pg. 1362
Murdoch, Douglas, Dir.-Sls. & Mktg.--Puritan-Bennett Canada Ltd., Pickering, Canada; *U.S. Public*, pg. 1040
Murdoch, Jack, V.P. & Gen. Mgr. North America Distrib.--AGCO Corporation, Duluth, GA; *U.S. Public*, pg. 28
Murdoch, Roger, Mgr.-Sls.--Miller-St. Nazianz, Inc., Saint Nazianz, WI; *U.S. Private*, pg. 748
Murdock, Ross, Mgr.-Mktg.--Telegenix Inc., Cherry Hill, NJ; *U.S. Private*, pg. 1073
Muro, John T., V.P.-Retail Mktg.--Northeast Utilities, Berlin, CT; *U.S. Public*, pg. 1194
Muro, John T., V.P.-Retail Mktg.--The Connecticut Light & Power Co., Berlin, CT; *U.S. Public*, pg. 1194
Murphy Scott, Kathleen, Asst. V.P.-Mktg.--General Reinsurance Corp., Stamford, CT; *U.S. Public*, pg. 725
Murphy, Cliff, V.P.-Mktg.--Ilco Unican Inc. (Dominion Lock Division), Montreal, Canada; *Int'l*, pg. 1432
Murphy, Dan, V.P.-Sls. & Mktg.--Iceland Seafood Corporation, Newport, VA; *U.S. Private*, pg. 556
Murphy, David, Mgr.-Mktg. & Pricing--Jersey Central Power & Light Co., Morristown, NJ; *U.S. Public*, pg. 695
Murphy, David, V.P.-Consumer Mktg. & Sls.--Chicago Tribune Co., Chicago, IL; *U.S. Public*, pg. 1635
Murphy, E.J., Dir.-Mktg.--Henry Ford & Son, Limited, Cork, Ireland; *U.S. Public*, pg. 665
Murphy, George, V.P.-Mktg.--Reily Foods Company, New Orleans, LA; *U.S. Private*, pg. 919
Murphy, Gerry, V.P.-Mktg.-Gen. Trade--Sifto Canada, Inc., Mississauga, Canada; *U.S. Private*, pg. 505
Murphy, Helen, Mgr.-Promo.--Crain's Chicago Business, Chicago, IL; *U.S. Private*, pg. 285
Murphy, Jim, Mgr.-Theatrical Distrb.--Coscient-Astral Distribution, Toronto, Canada; *Int'l*, pg. 335
Murphy, Joe, V.P.-Mktg.--Cooper Lighting Division, Elk Grove Village, IL; *U.S. Public*, pg. 443
Murphy, John, Dir.-Promo.--CFCF Inc., Montreal, Canada; *Int'l*, pg. 240
Murphy, John W., Dir.-Mktg.--Gaylord Container Corporation, Deerfield, IL; *U.S. Public*, pg. 704
Murphy, Karen, Coord.-Mktg. Promo.--Syracuse Supply Company, Syracuse, NY; *U.S. Private*, pg. 1060
Murphy, Kevin, V.P.-Sls. & Mktg., Fabric--Hoffman Laces, Ltd., Cobleskill, NY; *U.S. Public*, pg. 769
Murphy, Kevin J., V.P.-Mktg.--Recoton Corporation, Lake Mary, FL; *U.S. Public*, pg. 1369
Murphy, L.D., V.P.-Mktg. & Sls.--Marlite, Dover, OH; *U.S. Private*, pg. 705
Murphy, Martha, Sr. V.P.-Mktg.--Helen of Troy Corporation, El Paso, TX; *U.S. Public*, pg. 807
Murphy, Michael, V.P.-Sls. & Mktg.--Belden Inc., Saint Louis, MO; *U.S. Public*, pg. 200
Murphy, Michael, Dir.-Adv. & Mktg. (UK)--The Financial Times Ltd., London, United Kingdom; *Int'l*, pg. 1025
Murphy, Patrick, V.P.-Mktg. & Sls.--Coz Plastics Inc., Northbridge, MA; *U.S. Private*, pg. 827
Murphy, Richard D., V.P.-Sls. & Mktg.--Colonial Gas Company, Lowell, MA; *U.S. Public*, pg. 400
Murphy, Robert, V.P.-Sls. & Mktg.--David Clark Company Incorporated, Worcester, MA; *U.S. Private*, pg. 242
Murphy, Robert, Dir.-Channel Mktg. & Alliances--VeriFone, Inc., Redwood City, CA; *U.S. Public*, pg. 815
Murphy, Sharon, Mgr.-Adv. & Mktg.--ITC Learning Corp., Herndon, VA; *U.S. Public*, pg. 859
Murphy, Stephen E., Sr. V.P.-Mktg. Services--Buster Brown Apparel, Inc., Chattanooga, TN; *U.S. Private*, pg. 189
Murphy, Vincent A., Dir.-Mktg.--Vanguard Division, Farmington, CT; *Int'l*, pg. 917
Murphy, William, V.P. & Dir.-Customers Mktg.--Meredith Corporation, Des Moines, IA; *U.S. Public*, pg. 1094
Murphy, William, V.P. & Dir.-Mktg.--Country Home Magazine, Des Moines, IA; *U.S. Public*, pg. 1094
Murrah, Judy, Sr. V.P.-Mktg. Communicaitons--Symbol Technologies, Inc., Holtsville, NY; *U.S. Public*, pg. 1546
Murray, Asa G., V.P.-Sls. & Mktg.--Philadelphia Coca-Cola Bottling Co., Philadelphia, PA; *U.S. Private*, pg. 861
Murray, Bernadette, Dir.-Mktg.--Brooks Brothers, New York, NY; *Int'l*, pg. 843
Murray, Dave, Dir.-Mktg.--Premdor Inc., Mississauga, Canada; *Int'l*, pg. 1066
Murray, Douglas L., Sr. V.P.-Mktg. & Security Officer--First American Federal Savings Bank, Bristol, VA; *U.S. Public*, pg. 624
Murray, G., V.P.-Sls. & Mktg.--Prime Systems Group, Tampa, FL; *U.S. Public*, pg. 1329
Murray, Jennifer, V.P.-Mktg. Communications--Converse Inc., North Reading, MA; *U.S. Public*, pg. 441
Murray, Joe, Sr. V.P.-Sls. & Mktg.--Frank Industries, Inc., Brown City, MI; *U.S. Private*, pg. 423
Murray, Karen, Integrated Mktg. Dir.--Haworth Group Inc., Minneapolis, MN; *U.S. Private*, pg. 511
Murray, Liz, Coord.-Mktg.--Versa Services Ltd., Etobicoke, Canada; *U.S. Private*, pg. 79
Murray, Mark, Exec. V.P.-Mktg. & Sls.--FAG Bearings Corporation, Danbury, CT; *Int'l*, pg. 469
Murray, Michael J., Sr. V.P.-Sls. & Mktg.--Pilgrim's Pride Corporation, Pittsburg, TX; *U.S. Public*, pg. 1296
Murray, Mike, Mgr.-Mkt. Devel.--Seal Group, Irvine, CA; *U.S. Public*, pg. 1262
Murray, Nancy, V.P.-Public Relations & Mktg.--Treasure Chest Advertising Co., Inc., Glendora, CA; *U.S. Public*, pg. 228
Murray, R. J., V.P.-Mktg. & Sls.--Timec Company, Vallejo, CA; *U.S. Private*, pg. 1087
Murray, Robert W., V.P.-Communications--MagneTek, Inc., Nashville, TN; *U.S. Public*, pg. 1037
Murray, Sean, Sr. V.P.-Mktg.--U.S. Borax Inc., Valencia, CA; *Int'l*, pg. 1119
Murtaugh, Dave, Mgr.-Mktg. Commun./Michelin Brand--Michelin Americas Small Tires (MAST), Greenville, SC; *Int'l*, pg. 322
Murth, Gene, V.P.-Mktg.--Tyco Toys, Inc., Mount Laurel, NJ; *U.S. Public*, pg. 1058
Murzinski, Edward, V.P.-Mktg. & Sls.--Revcor, Inc., Carpentersville, IL; *U.S. Private*, pg. 925
Musarra, Patricia, Mktg. Rep.--Pollo Tropical, Inc., Miami, FL; *U.S. Public*, pg. 1315
Muscalino, T.L., Pres.-Home Furnishings Mktg.--Dan River Inc.-Home Furnishings & Related Prods., Div. I, Danville, VA; *U.S. Public*, pg. 479
Muscato, Dave, Dir.-Mktg.--The Perrier Group of America, Greenwich, CT; *Int'l*, pg. 919
Muscato, Dave, Dir.-Mktg.--Great Bear Spring Company, Greenwich, CT; *Int'l*, pg. 919
Muse, John, V.P.-Feed--Ag Processing Inc., A Cooperative, Omaha, NE; *U.S. Private*, pg. 26
Musgrove, Jack, V.P.-Mktg.--Digital Link Corporation, Sunnyvale, CA; *U.S. Public*, pg. 508
Mushkin, Albert S., Pres. & Chief Oper. Officer--Master Industries Corp., New York, NY; *U.S. Private*, pg. 713
Musial, Cheryl, V.P.-Sls. & Mktg.--Vitalink Pharmacy Services, Inc., Atlanta, GA; *U.S. Public*, pg. 1042
Musshafen, Gerhard, Dir.-Mktg.--Boehringer Mannheim GmbH, Mannheim, Germany; *Int'l*, pg. 331
Muto, Janet, V.P.-Mktg.--Microtouch Systems, Inc., Methuen, MA; *U.S. Public*, pg. 1108
Mutzl, Bob, Sr. Dir.-Mktg.--Catalina Marketing Corporation, Saint Petersburg, FL; *U.S. Public*, pg. 314
Muzika, Yahn, Dir.-Mktg.--BNP Arbitrage, Paris, France; *Int'l*, pg. 163
Muzyczko, T., Exec. V.P.--Samuel Bingham Co, Bloomingdale, IL; *U.S. Private*, pg. 144
Muzyka, Ray, Mgr.-Mktg.--Pressure Products Div., Dallas, TX; *U.S. Public*, pg. 1268
Myatt, Larry, V.P.-Mktg. & Admin.--SPS Payment Systems, Inc., Riverwoods, IL; *U.S. Public*, pg. 1132
Myatt, Paul, Dir.-Inside Sls. & Mktg.--Magnetrol International, Downers Grove, IL; *U.S. Private*, pg. 696
Mycock, Tony, Dir.-Sls. & Mktg.--Tate & Lyle PLC, London, United Kingdom; *Int'l*, pg. 1356
Myers, Carol, Coord.-Mktg.--Genfoot Inc., Montreal, Canada; *Int'l*, pg. 549
Myers, James H., V.P.-Intl. Sls. & Prod. Mngmt.--Simplicity Manufacturing, Inc., Port Washington, WI; *U.S. Private*, pg. 1002
Myers, Julianna, Coord.-Mktg.--Maine Yankee, Brunswick, ME; *U.S. Public*, pg. 325
Myers, Lynn C., Dir.-Pontiac Category--Pontiac-GMC Division, Detroit, MI; *U.S. Public*, pg. 720
Myers, Neil, Dir.-Mktg.--Lofts Seed, Inc., Winston Salem, NC; *U.S. Public*, pg. 29
Myers, Norman A., Vice Chm. & Chief Mktg. Officer--Browning-Ferris Industries, Inc., Houston, TX; *U.S. Public*, pg. 262
Myers, Raymond F., V.P. & Mgr.-Adv.--Southwest National Corporation, Greensburg, PA; *U.S. Public*, pg. 1493
Myers, Raymond F., V.P.-Mktg.--Southwest National Bank of Pennsylvania, Greensburg, PA; *U.S. Public*, pg. 1493

Myers, Reid, Mktg. Communications Specialist--Elo TouchSystems, Inc., Fremont, CA; *U.S. Public*, pg. 1362
Myers, Robert W., V.P.-Sls. & Mktg.--Morris Coupling Co., Erie, PA; *U.S. Private*, pg. 762
Myers, Ron, V.P.-Sls. & Mktg./OEM & BIC--Ameriwood Industries International Inc., Grand Rapids, MI; *U.S. Public*, pg. 98
Myers, Thomas C., V.P.-Mktg.--Dovatech, Ltd., Beecher, IL; *U.S. Public*, pg. 520
Myhra, Ken, Mktg. Specialist Supvr.--Seafirst Corporation, Seattle, WA; *U.S. Public*, pg. 181
Myland, Larry, Mgr.-Mktg.--Humphrey Products Company, Kalamazoo, MI; *U.S. Private*, pg. 547
Myrick, Tom, Mgr.-Mktg.--Scherer Bros. Lumber Company, Minneapolis, MN; *U.S. Private*, pg. 970
Nadeau, Clement E., V.P.-Mktg. & Plng.--Niagara Mohawk Power Corporation, Syracuse, NY; *U.S. Public*, pg. 1181
Nadel, Steven, Mgr.-Mktg.--Ferolie Group, Montvale, NJ; *U.S. Private*, pg. 401
Nadelberg, Michael, V.P.-Mktg. Svcs.--The Gillette Company, Boston, MA; *U.S. Public*, pg. 743
Nadelberg, Mike, V.P.-Mktg. Svcs.--The Gillette Company, Personal Care Group, Boston, MA; *U.S. Public*, pg. 744
Nadergard, Tove, V.P.-Mktg.--Sotheby's Inc., New York, NY; *U.S. Public*, pg. 1487
Nadolny, Gary, Dir.-Mktg.--Ansul Incorporated, Marinette, WI; *U.S. Public*, pg. 1648
Nagahata, Osamu, Mng. Dir.--All Nippon Airways Co. Ltd., Tokyo, Japan; *Int'l*, pg. 57
Nagel, Gayle, Coord.-Mktg.--Beaulieu Vineyard, Rutherford, CA; *Int'l*, pg. 410
Nagel, Greg S., Dir.-Mktg.--Spartech Corporation, Clayton, MO; *U.S. Public*, pg. 1495
Nagel, L. Wayne, Mgr.-Gas Mktg.--Anadarko Petroleum Corporation, Houston, TX; *U.S. Public*, pg. 107
Naggiar, Caroline, V.P.-Mktg. Communications--Tiffany & Co., New York, NY; *U.S. Public*, pg. 1608
Nagle, Andrew, V.P.-Sls. & Mktg.--A-B Emblem Div. of Conrad Industries, Inc., Weaverville, NC; *U.S. Private*, pg. 2
Nagle, W. Dan, V.P.-Sls. & Mktg.--Tasty Baking Company, Philadelphia, PA; *U.S. Public*, pg. 1561
Naibon, Yens, Dir.-Mktg.--Bang & Olufsen A/S, Struer, Denmark; *Int'l*, pg. 145
Naiderovich, Bill, V.P.-Mktg.--Lozier Corporation, Omaha, NE; *U.S. Private*, pg. 679
Naidoff, Mark, V.P.-Mktg.--Fellowes Manufacturing Co., Itasca, IL; *U.S. Private*, pg. 400
Najim, Edward L., Exec. V.P.-Sls. & Mktg.--Horace Mann Educators Corporation, Springfield, IL; *U.S. Public*, pg. 835
Nakagaki, Eisei, Exec. V.P.-Mktg.--Casio, Inc., Dover, NJ; *Int'l*, pg. 274
Nakagiri, Toshi, V.P.-Mktg. & Sls.--Permacel, New Brunswick, NJ; *Int'l*, pg. 950
Nakamatsu, M., Dir.-Mktg. & Mgr.-Personnel--Takagi Chokoku Co., Ltd.-Hamamatsu Factory, Hamamatsu, Japan; *Int'l*, pg. 1349
Nakamoto, Arlene M., Exec. V.P.-Sls. & Mktg.--American Savings Bank, F.S.B., Honolulu, HI; *U.S. Public*, pg. 800
Nakamura, Ken, V.P.-Mktg. Admin.--Komatsu America International Company, Vernon Hills, IL; *Int'l*, pg. 744
Nakamura, Tomofumi, Gen. Mgr.--OYO Corporation, Tokyo, Japan; *Int'l*, pg. 1019
Nakao, Atsushi, Assoc. Exec. Dir.-Ethical Pharmaceuticals Mktg.--Fujisawa Pharmaceutical Co. Ltd., Osaka, Japan; *Int'l*, pg. 525
Nalle, Linda, Dir.-Mktg. Commun.--Schnadig Corporation, Des Plaines, IL; *U.S. Private*, pg. 971
Nally, Chris, Mgr.-Sls.--Ultra Tool & Plastics, Inc., Amherst, NY; *U.S. Private*, pg. 1116
Namekawa, Nobutada, Mng. Dir. & Chief Exec.-Mktg.--Meiji Life Insurance Company, Tokyo, Japan; *Int'l*, pg. 854
Nano, Masufumi, Dir.-Mktg.--Nippon Express Co., Ltd., Tokyo, Japan; *Int'l*, pg. 933
Nanri, Masahiro, Mgr.-Hub-Mktg.--Nemic-Lambda KK, Tokyo, Japan; *Int'l*, pg. 1242
Nanson, Dave, V.P.-Sls. & Mktg.--Tollycraft Yacht Corporation, San Diego, CA; *U.S. Public*, pg. 1620
Nantell, Linda, Supvr.-Admin. Mktg.--Marathon Electric Manufacturing Corp., Wausau, WI; *U.S. Public*, pg. 1371
Napier, Angus, Mgr.-Sls. & Mktg.--Sasol Fibres, Reunion, South Africa; *Int'l*, pg. 1196
Napoli, Rand, Dir.-Mktg.--Leather Center, Inc., Carrollton, TX; *U.S. Private*, pg. 656
Napua, Josh, Jr., Sr. V.P.-Computer Prods. Mktg.--Wyle Electronics, Irvine, CA; *Int'l*, pg. 1457
Nardella, A.N., Sr. V.P.-Distribution--Hubbard Hall Inc., Waterbury, CT; *U.S. Private*, pg. 544
Nardi, Tom, V.P.-Mktg., Sls. & Treas.--Northern Illinois Gas Company, Naperville, IL; *U.S. Public*, pg. 1183
Nardizzi, Susan, V.P.-Mktg.-Shoney's--Shoney's, Inc., Nashville, TN; *U.S. Public*, pg. 1467
Nascimbene, Mario, Dir.-Mktg.--Davide Campari, Milan, Italy; *Int'l*, pg. 385
Nash, Cathleen H., Exec. V.P.-Mktg.--SunTrust, Orlando, FL; *U.S. Public*, pg. 1537
Nash, Charles J., Mgr.-Mktg., Kraft Paper--Kraft Paper Div., Memphis, TN; *U.S. Public*, pg. 903
Nash, Charlotte, Dir.-Trade Shows & Mktg. Communications-OEM--Leviton Mfg. Co., Inc., Little Neck, NY; *U.S. Private*, pg. 663
Nash, Mike, Dir.-Mktg.--Matthew Clark Taunton, Ltd., Bristol, United Kingdom; *Int'l*, pg. 848
Nask, Aleene, Dir.-Mktg.--Olin Corporation, Norwalk, CT; *U.S. Public*, pg. 1218
Nasky, Thomas G., Exec. V.P.-Mktg. & Sls.--Dualite Inc., Williamsburg, OH; *U.S. Private*, pg. 344
Nasky, Thomas G., Exec. V.P.-Sls. & Mktg.--Dualite Sales & Service, Inc., Williamsburg, OH; *U.S. Private*, pg. 344
Nass, James W., V.P.--Graham Paint and Varnish Company, Chicago, IL; *U.S. Private*, pg. 468
Nast, Bill, Exec. V.P.-Sls. & Mktg.--Tech Industries, Inc., Woonsocket, RI; *U.S. Private*, pg. 1071
Natale, James L., Pres.-Corp. Mktg. & Sls.--C.R. Bard, Inc., Murray Hill, NJ; *U.S. Public*, pg. 189
Natale, Lisa, Mgr.-Strategic Plng.--The Kendall-Betham Division, Piscataway, NJ; *U.S. Public*, pg. 1647
Nater, Antonio, Dir.-Mktg.--Prenatal, S.A., Barcelona, Spain; *Int'l*, pg. 1068
Nathan, Richard, Sr. V.P.-Opers. & Mktg.--Mason & Hanger Corporation, Inc., Lexington, KY; *U.S. Private*, pg. 711
Nathanson, Jerry, V.P.-Mktg. & Sls.--VARTA Batteries Inc., Elmsford, NY; *Int'l*, pg. 1452
Nattila, Robyn, Mgr.-Mktg.--New Hampshire Ball Bearings, Inc., Peterborough, NH; *Int'l*, pg. 868
Nau, Brian, Mgr.-Mktg.--Nestle Lyons Maid, York, United Kingdom; *Int'l*, pg. 918
Naughton, Beth, Mgr.-Mktg. Communications--Weiser Lock, Tucson, AZ; *U.S. Public*, pg. 1053
Nava, Frank, Dir.-Mktg.--Dana Canada Inc., Saint Catharines, Canada; *U.S. Public*, pg. 480
Navarro, Carmen E., Mgr.-Sls. & Export Mktg.--Benguet Corporation, Manila, Philippines; *Int'l*, pg. 186
Naviaux, J.C., Dir.-Mktg.--Radar Systems Group, Los Angeles, CA; *U.S. Public*, pg. 1364
Navota, Jim, Dir.-Mktg.--Sycamore Systems, Inc., Sycamore, IL; *U.S. Private*, pg. 638
Nawratil, Franz, V.P. & Mng. Dir.-Europe, Africa & Middle East Opers.--Hewlett-Packard Company, Palo Alto, CA; *U.S. Public*, pg. 813
Nazaruk, David, V.P.-Mktg.--R.R. Bowker, New Providence, NJ; *Int'l*, pg. 1096
Nazziola, Thomas E., V.P.-Mktg.--Ilco Unican Corp., Simplex Access Controls Division, Winston Salem, NC; *Int'l*, pg. 1432
Neal, Andy, Dir.-Mktg.--United Distillers PLC, Edinburgh, United Kingdom; *Int'l*, pg. 412
Neal, Bill G., Sr. V.P.-Sls. & Mktg.--Meco Corporation, Greeneville, TN; *U.S. Private*, pg. 726
Neal, Donna, Dir.-Mkt. Res.--Miller Brewing Company, Milwaukee, WI; *U.S. Public*, pg. 1289
Neale, J., Dir.-Mktg.--Doubleday Canada Ltd., Toronto, Canada; *Int'l*, pg. 192
Neale, Ronald, Dir.-Mktg.--Mazda Motor of America, Inc., Irvine, CA; *Int'l*, pg. 849
Neale'siemon, Betsy, Mgr.-Mktg. Communications--Bristol Babcock, Inc., Watertown, CT; *Int'l*, pg. 472
Neally, Joe, Mgr.-Mktg.--Ansco Photo-Optical Products Corp., Elk Grove Village, IL; *Int'l*, pg. 587
Neath, Sarah, Mgr.-Mktg. Svcs.--Thorntons PLC, Darbyshire, United Kingdom; *Int'l*, pg. 1386
Nebell, Bill, Mgr.-Mktg.--Psomas & Associates, Santa Monica, CA; *U.S. Private*, pg. 893
Neckameyer, Bill, V.P.-Mktg. & Sls.--California Offset Printers, Inc., Glendale, CA; *U.S. Private*, pg. 196
Nederlof, Gerhard B., Sr. V.P.-Mktg., Bus. Devel. & Svcs.--C-COR Electronics, Inc., State College, PA; *U.S. Public*, pg. 272
Neels, Henry, Sls. & Mktg. Mgr.--Whitehall Laboratoria B.V., Amsterdam, Netherlands; *U.S. Public*, pg. 82
Neely, Mike, V.P.-Mktg.--Tenneco Packaging, Consumer Products Group, Deerfield, IL; *U.S. Public*, pg. 1579
Negrini, Dario, Dir.-Corp. Sls. & Mktg.--Instrument Specialties Company, Delaware Water Gap, PA; *U.S. Private*, pg. 565
Neher, Erik, Dir.-Mktg.--The Family Circle, Inc., New York, NY; *Int'l*, pg. 190
Neher, Erik, Dir.-Mktg.--McCall's Magazine, New York, NY; *Int'l*, pg. 190
Neidhart, Thomas A., Jr., V.P.-Mktg.--Mrs. Baird's Bakeries, Inc., Fort Worth, TX; *U.S. Private*, pg. 765
Neil, M., Mktg. Asst.--Vishay Components (U.K.) Ltd., Sunderland, United Kingdom; *U.S. Public*, pg. 1722
Neiley, George F., III, V.P.-Sls. & Mktg.--Ring King Visibles, Inc., Muscatine, IA; *Int'l*, pg. 460
Neill, Eileen, Sr. Dir.-Global Mktg.--American Express Bank Ltd., New York, NY; *U.S. Public*, pg. 73
Neill, Terry H., V.P.-Strategic Mktg.--Cox Communications, Inc., Atlanta, GA; *U.S. Public*, pg. 454
Neilson, David L., V.P.-Sls. & Mktg.--Intermet Corporation, Troy, MI; *U.S. Public*, pg. 894
Neiman, Cathy, V.P.-Mktg.--ChubbHealth New York/New Jersey, New York, NY; *U.S. Public*, pg. 360
Nell, Michael P., V.P.-Corp. Mktg.--S3 Incorporated, Santa Clara, CA; *U.S. Public*, pg. 1415
Nelles, William A., V.P.-Sls. & Mktg.--Monex Deposit Co., Newport Beach, CA; *U.S. Private*, pg. 757
Nellums, Dana, V.P.-Mktg. Admin.--Riverside Manufacturing Co., Moultrie, GA; *U.S. Private*, pg. 934
Nelly, Eric, Mgr.-Mktg.--John B. Sanfilippo & Son, Inc., Elk Grove Village, IL; *U.S. Public*, pg. 1431
Nelson, Alden, Sr. Mgr.-Mktg.--Hochiki America Corporation, Huntington Beach, CA; *Int'l*, pg. 623
Nelson, Ann, Sr. V.P.-Opers. & Mktg. Svcs.--Marine Midland Bank, Buffalo, NY; *Int'l*, pg. 581
Nelson, Carl, V.P.-Mktg.--Nelson Photo Supplies, San Diego, CA; *U.S. Private*, pg. 791
Nelson, Carl, Dir.-Mktg.--Forest View Psychiatric Hospital, Grand Rapids, MI; *U.S. Public*, pg. 1697
Nelson, Dan, Exec. V.P.-Mktg.--CVS Corp., Woonsocket, RI; *U.S. Public*, pg. 287
Nelson, Glade, V.P.-Sls. & Mktg.--Ampco Metal Incorporated, Milwaukee, WI; *U.S. Private*, pg. 67
Nelson, Glen, V.P.-Sls. & Mktg.--Roll Forming Corporation, Shelbyville, KY; *U.S. Private*, pg. 941
Nelson, James E., Dir.-Sls. & Mktg.--Ederer Inc., Seattle, WA; *U.S. Private*, pg. 363
Nelson, Jeff, V.P.-Mktg.--ADAC Laboratories Inc., Milpitas, CA; *U.S. Public*, pg. 3
Nelson, Jim, Dir.-Sls. & Mktg.--Ederer Cranes, Seattle, WA; *U.S. Private*, pg. 363
Nelson, John, Sr. V.P.-Res. & Devel.--Waters Corporation, Milford, MA; *U.S. Public*, pg. 1745
Nelson, John L., V.P.-Sls. & Mktg.--Marlow Industries, Dallas, TX; *U.S. Private*, pg. 705
Nelson, Kimi, Mgr.-Sls. & Adv.--Westfall GMC Truck Inc., Kansas City, MO; *U.S. Private*, pg. 1169
Nelson, L.I., V.P.-Mktg.--Curtis 1000, Inc., Atlanta, GA; *U.S. Public*, pg. 70
Nelson, Matt, Mgr.-Mktg.-Electric Tools--Hitachi Koki U.S.A. Ltd., Norcross, GA; *Int'l*, pg. 620
Nelson, Melvin, Dir.-Mktg. & Pub. Rels.--Minnkota Power Cooperative, Inc., Grand Forks, ND; *U.S. Private*, pg. 751
Nelson, Murray A., V.P.-Retail Energy Mktg.--TransAlta Utilities, Calgary, Canada; *Int'l*, pg. 1416
Nelson, Phyllis, V.P.-Mktg. & Sls.--Clayton Industries Co., El Monte, CA; *U.S. Private*, pg. 245
Nelson, Ruth, V.P.-Mktg.--R.L. Polk & Co., Southfield, MI; *U.S. Private*, pg. 874
Nelson, Thomas, Dir.-Mktg. & Sls.--Athey Products Corporation, Wake Forest, NC; *U.S. Public*, pg. 142
Nemanic, Christina, Mgr.-Mktg.--Harris & Bank, Chicago, IL; *Int'l*, pg. 154
Nemeth, Al, Dir.-Sls. Collagen Products--Datascope Corp., Montvale, NJ; *U.S. Public*, pg. 487
Nemetz, Allen P., V.P.-Mktg. & Adv.--PIC Design, Middlebury, CT; *U.S. Private*, pg. 864
Nemetz, Mike, Dir.-Adv.--Talbots, Inc., Hingham, MA; *Int'l*, pg. 28
Nenniger, John, Dir.-Mktg.--Star Bank, N.A., Cincinnati, OH; *U.S. Public*, pg. 1510
Nerangis, Alex, Dir.-Mktg.--Columbia Medical Center Dallas Southwest, Dallas, TX; *U.S. Public*, pg. 404
Neri, Enrique Gasca, Dir.-Mktg. & Qualtiy--Altos Hornos de Mexico, S.A., Monclova, Mexico; *Int'l*, pg. 66
Nerlich, Bernie, Mgr.-Mktg.--Channellock, Inc., Meadville, PA; *U.S. Private*, pg. 229
Nesbit, Doug, V.P.-Mktg.--Sun Diamond Growers of California, Pleasanton, CA; *U.S. Private*, pg. 1051
Nesbit, Doug, Mgr.-Mktg.--Diamond Walnut Growers, Inc., Stockton, CA; *U.S. Private*, pg. 1051
Ness, Greg, V.P.-Retirement Plans Sls. & Mktg.--Standard Insurance Co., Portland, OR; *U.S. Private*, pg. 1031
Nestor, Linda, Mgr.-Mktg.--Rose's Stores, Inc., Henderson, NC; *U.S. Public*, pg. 1405
Nestor, Michael, V.P.-Mktg. & Sls., Pediatrics/Vaccines--Wyeth-Ayerst Laboratories, Inc., Philadelphia, PA; *U.S. Public*, pg. 80
Netzel, Jill, Mgr.-Mktg. Communications--Pentel of America, Ltd., Torrance, CA; *Int'l*, pg. 1035
Neubauer, Allyn, Dir.-Mktg. & Adv.--Amana Society, Inc., Amana, IA; *U.S. Private*, pg. 48
Neubauer, John, Dir.-Mktg. & Mgr.-Business Unit--Kraft Foods Inc., Rye Brook, NY; *U.S. Public*, pg. 1288
Neubauer, Mark E., V.P.-Sls. & Mktg.--Oriole Homes Corp., Delray Beach, FL; *U.S. Public*, pg. 1230
Neuberger, Klaus, Dir.-Mktg.--Margaret Astor GmbH, Mainz, Germany; *Int'l*, pg. 185
Neubert, Dick, Mgr.-Mktg.--Duro-Test Intl. Corp., Fairfield, NJ; *U.S. Private*, pg. 349
Neubert, Richard, Dir.-Mktg.--Duro-Test Corporation, Fairfield, NJ; *U.S. Private*, pg. 349
Neuchtelrlein, John, Dir.-Mktg.--Yardley of London, Inc., Memphis, TN; *Int'l*, pg. 819
Neuhoff, Clark, Dir.-Mktg.--Churny Company Inc., Northbrook, IL; *U.S. Public*, pg. 1288
Neuman, Norm, Sr. V.P.-Mktg.--Comshare, Incorporated, Ann Arbor, MI; *U.S. Public*, pg. 425
Neuman, Richard, Dir.-Special Mkt. Sls.--Hunter Fan Company, Memphis, TN; *U.S. Private*, pg. 549
Neumann, Mark C., V.P.-Sls.--Badger Paper Mills, Inc., Peshtigo, WI; *U.S. Public*, pg. 165
Neumann, Vivian F., V.P.-Sls. & Mktg.--St. Paul Metalcraft, Inc., Saint Paul, MN; *U.S. Private*, pg. 961
Neuwirth, Carol Ann, Mgr.-Mktg.--Unex Conveying Systems, Inc., Jackson, NJ; *U.S. Private*, pg. 1117
Neville, Richard S., Sr. V.P.-Mktg.--Western Petroleum Company, Eden Prairie, MN; *U.S. Private*, pg. 1168
Nevins, Joan M., V.P.-Mktg.--PictureTel, Andover, MA; *U.S. Public*, pg. 1294
Nevsimal, Charles J., Exec. V.P.-Sls. & Mktg--Wisconsin Pharmacal Co., Inc., Jackson, WI; *U.S. Private*, pg. 1185
Newberg, Anthony, V.P.-Mktg. & Data Processing--Dealers Electrical Supply Co., Waco, TX; *U.S. Private*, pg. 318
Newberry, Dee, Coord.-Adv. & Mktg.--Chris-Craft Boats, Sarasota, FL; *U.S. Private*, pg. 478
Newcomer, Randy M., Sr. V.P-Alaska Refining & Mktg.--Mapco Petroleum Inc., Tulsa, OK; *U.S. Public*, pg. 1042
Newell, Mark, Mgr.-Mktg.--Amtrak-National Railroad Passenger Corp., Washington, DC; *U.S. Private*, pg. 68
Newell, Michael, V.P.-Mktg.--Crystal Cream & Butter Company, Sacramento, CA; *U.S. Private*, pg. 294
Newell, Mitch, Mgr.-Corp. Prod.--Wyandot Inc., Marion, OH; *U.S. Private*, pg. 1193
Newell, Robert A., V.P.-Mktg.--NewTel Communications, Saint Johns, Canada; *Int'l*, pg. 115
Newham, D.H., Mng. Dir.--A.C. Labs (Pty.) Ltd., Sebenza, South Africa; *U.S. Public*, pg. 38
Newhouse, Debbie, Mgr.-Mktg. Services--Vermont American Tool Corp., Louisville, KY; *U.S. Public*, pg. 575
Newhouse, Steve, Dir.-Mktg., Sls. & Adv.--Atlantic Builders Group Inc., Baltimore, MD; *U.S. Private*, pg. 95
Newman, Cathy, Mktg. Coord.--Aromat Corporation, New Providence, NJ; *Int'l*, pg. 847
Newman, Dick, V.P.-Mktg.--Good Humor/Breyers Ice Cream, Green Bay, WI; *Int'l*, pg. 1435
Newman, Jeff, V.P.-Mktg. N. America--CiMatrix L.L.C., Canton, MA; *U.S. Public*, pg. 1395
Newman, Larry, Exec. V.P.-Mktg. & Sls.-Angelica Image Apparel--Angelica Corporation, Chesterfield, MO; *U.S. Public*, pg. 113
Newman, Larry, Exec. V.P.-Mktg. & Sls.--Angelica Image Apparel, Saint Louis, MO; *U.S. Public*, pg. 113
Newman, Mark, Dir.-Sls. & Mktg.--Bounty Books, London, United Kingdom; *Int'l*, pg. 1093
Newman, Monte, Exec. V.P.-Sls. & Mktg.-NBC TV Stations--National Broadcasting Co., Inc., New York, NY; *U.S. Public*, pg. 712
Newmeister, John, V.P.-Mktg.--Matrix Service Company, Tulsa, OK; *U.S. Public*, pg. 1057

Newton, Bill, Mgr.-Mktg.--Grain Processing Corp., Muscatine, IA; *U.S. Private*, pg. 1134
Newton, Dave, V.P.-Mktg.--Broadcast Programming, Seattle, WA; *U.S. Private*, pg. 531
Newton, Jeff, Dir.-Mktg. Communications--Eli Lilly and Company, Indianapolis, IN; *U.S. Public*, pg. 992
Newton, Ron, V.P.-Sls & Mktg.--Ammco Tools, Inc., La Vergne, TN; *U.S. Public*, pg. 480
Newton, Ron, V.P.-Sls. & Mktg.--Hennessy Industries, Inc., La Vergne, TN; *U.S. Public*, pg. 481
Neyer, Thomas L., Jr., V.P.-Mktg.--Al Neyer, Inc., Cincinnati, OH; *U.S. Private*, pg. 797
Neyzi, Mehmet Ali, Exec. V.P.-Mktg.--Arcelik A.S., Istanbul, Turkey; *Int'l*, pg. 741
Ng, James, Sr. V.P. & Dir. of Bus. Devel/Asia Pacific--Dentsu Young & Rubicam Partnerships, New York, NY; *U.S. Private*, pg. 325
Ngoh, Ng Sian, Mktg. Dir.--Dentsu Mandate Singapore Pte. Ltd., Singapore, Singapore; *Int'l*, pg. 393
Nibbe, Warner, V.P.-Sls. & Mktg.-Pacal Blades--Paper Calmenson & Co., Saint Paul, MN; *U.S. Private*, pg. 837
Nichol, Jeanne, Sr. Adv. Assoc.-Mktg. & Sls.--The Principal Financial Group, Des Moines, IA; *U.S. Private*, pg. 885
Nicholas, Gary A., V.P.-Opers. & Mktg.--Hope Gas, Inc., Clarksburg, WV; *U.S. Public*, pg. 435
Nicholas, John, Dir.-Mktg.--The Tetley Group Limited, Greenford, United Kingdom; *Int'l*, pg. 1377
Nicholas, Philip A., AIA, V.P.--Giffels Associates, Inc., Southfield, MI; *U.S. Private*, pg. 452
Nicholas, Philip A., AIA, Mgr.-Mktg--Giffels Associates Inc., Phoenix, AZ; *U.S. Private*, pg. 452
Nichols, Lynn, Dir.-Mktg.--Data Communications, New York, NY; *U.S. Public*, pg. 1070
Nicholson, Brett, Mgr.-Mktg.--Austral Bronze Crane Copper Limited, Wetherill Park, Australia; *Int'l*, pg. 340
Nicholson, Glenn D., Chief Mktg. Officer & Sr. V.P.--Manhattan Life Insurance Company, Cincinnati, OH; *U.S.* Private, pg. 1118
Nicholson, Mary, Specialist-Indus. Mktg.--Mallet & Co., Carnegie, PA; *U.S. Private*, pg. 698
Nicholson, Peter, V.P.-Adv. & Mktg. Services--Citizen Watch Co. of America, Inc., Lyndhurst, NJ; *Int'l*, pg. 294
Nicholson, Wendy, V.P. & Exec. Dir.-Public Relations--Simon & Schuster Trade Division, New York, NY; *U.S. Private*, pg. 777
Nichter, Harrold, Sr. V.P.-Customer Fulfillment--VWR Scientific Products, West Chester, PA; *U.S. Public*, pg. 1703
Nickel, E., Mgr.-Mktg.--Olivetti Germany, Frankfurt/Main, Germany; *Int'l*, pg. 1003
Nickle, Dwayne, V.P.-Mktg.--Fabwel Inc., Elkhart, IN; *U.S. Private*, pg. 390
Nickol, Anna, Mgr.-Mktg., Confections--Masterfoods Ltd., Dublin, Ireland; *U.S. Private*, pg. 707
Nicks, Pat, Mktg. Admin.--ConAgra Frozen Food Company, Omaha, NE; *U.S. Public*, pg. 427
Nicoll, Andrea, Mgr.-Mktg. Communications--The BOC Group Inc. (Delaware), Murray Hill, NJ; *Int'l*, pg. 121
Nicolson, John, Dir.-Mktg.--Scottish & Newcastle plc, Edinburgh, United Kingdom; *Int'l*, pg. 1211
Niderberg, Dave, Dir.-Mktg.--Therma-Tru Corp., Maumee, OH; *U.S. Private*, pg. 1079
Niebauer, Ron, Mgr.-Mktg.--SafetyMaster Corporation, Billings, MT; *U.S. Public*, pg. 1523
Niece, Toni, Reg. Mgr.-Mktg.--Landry's Seafood Restaurants Inc., Houston, TX; *U.S. Public*, pg. 977
Niedzielski, Kim, Mktg. Admin.--Hammel, Green & Abrahamson, Inc., Minneapolis, MN; *U.S. Private*, pg. 497
Niefield, Rick, Dir.-Mktg.--Houston Learning Center, Houston, TX; *U.S. Public*, pg. 218
Nielsen, Allen, Mgr.-Mktg.--Schottenstein Stores Corporation, Columbus, OH; *U.S. Private*, pg. 972
Nielsen, Mogens, Mgr.-Mktg.--Gyproc AB, Malmo, Sweden; *Int'l*, pg. 122
Nielsen, Rick, V.P.-Promotional Prods. Div.--Winthrop-Atkins Co., Inc., Middleboro, MA; *U.S. Private*, pg. 1183
Nielson, Norm, Dir.-Mktg. Commun.--Educational Insights, Inc., Carson, CA; *U.S. Public*, pg. 565
Nielson, Ray, V.P.-Mktg.--John Sterling Corporation, Richmond, IL; *U.S. Private*, pg. 1041
Nieman, David, V.P.-Sls. & Mktg. Tire Grp.--Titan International, Inc., Quincy, IL; *U.S. Public*, pg. 1618
Niemander, Leif, Dir.-Mktg.--SAB WABCO N.V., Zaventem, Belgium; *Int'l*, pg. 271
Niemeyer, Bart F., V.P.-Sls. & Mktg.--Koppel Steel Corp., Beaver Falls, PA; *U.S. Public*, pg. 1147
Niemi, Frank, Dir.-Mktg. & Sls.--Abbott Laboratories/Ashland, Ashland, OH; *U.S. Public*, pg. 13
Niemi, Kalevi, Dir.-Mktg.--Hagglunds Drives AB, Mellansel, Sweden; *Int'l*, pg. 670
Niemi, Kenneth A., V.P.-Mktg.--Weil-McLain, Michigan City, IN; *U.S. Public*, pg. 1676
Niemiec, Donald W., V.P.-Mktg.--Union Pacific Resources Company (UPRC), Fort Worth, TX; *U.S. Public*, pg. 1668
Nienhuyis, Winne, Mgr.-Sls. & Mktg./Access Control--Amtech International, Nanterre, France; *U.S. Public*, pg. 106
Nieto, Luis, Dir.-Ethnic Mktg. & Bus. Devel.--Kraft Foods, Inc., Northfield, IL; *U.S. Public*, pg. 1287
Nieves, John, Sr. V.P.-Mktg. & Sls.--New England Machinery, Inc., Bradenton, FL; *U.S. Private*, pg. 793
Niggli, Michael R., Sr. V.P.-Custom Accts. & V.P.-Sls. & Mktg.--Entergy Corporation, New Orleans, LA; *U.S. Public*, pg. 585
Niggli, Michael R., V.P.-Sls. & Mktg.--Entergy New Orleans, Inc., New Orleans, LA; *U.S. Public*, pg. 586
Nightingale, Peter, Dir.-Mktg.--ADT Phone & Modern Security, Northwood, United Kingdom; *U.S. Public*, pg. 1649
Nihalani, Suresh, V.P.-Product Mktg.--ACT Networks, Inc., Camarillo, CA; *U.S. Public*, pg. 3
Niklason, Donna, Mgr.-Mktg.--Butler Automatic, Inc., Canton, MA; *U.S. Private*, pg. 189
Niles, Carole, Mgr.-Mktg.--Hilb, Rogal and Hamilton Company of Arizona, Phoenix, AZ; *U.S. Public*, pg. 827
Niles, Gary J., Exec. V.P.-Mktg. & Product Acquisition--Galoob Toys, Inc., South San Francisco, CA; *U.S. Public*, *pg. 698*
Nilrat, Noppadol, V.P.--Siam City Factoring Co., Ltd., Bangkok, Thailand; *Int'l*, pg. 1239
Nimmo, Ian A., V.P.-Global Mktg.--Ethyl Corporation, Richmond, VA; *U.S. Public*, pg. 595
Nine, Jerry, V.P.-Sls. & Mktg.--National Education Training Group, Naperville, IL; *U.S. Public*, pg. 784
Nipper, Susan M., Gas Mktg./Acct.--Dugan Production Corp., Farmington, NM; *U.S. Private*, pg. 345
Nisbet, Betsy, Mgr.-Mktg.--Chancellor Corporation, Boston, MA; *U.S. Public*, pg. 335
Nishikawa, Morio, Mgr.-Mktg.-Consumer Prods.--Johnson Company, Ltd., Yokohama, Japan; *U.S. Private*, pg. 593
Nishimoto, Kohzo, Sr. Mng. Dir. & Chief Exec.-Corp. Mktg.--Meiji Life Insurance Company, Tokyo, Japan; *Int'l*, pg. 854
Nishioka, Art, V.P.-Mktg.--Kyocera International, Inc., San Diego, CA; *Int'l*, pg. 775
Niskala, Anita, Mktg. Asst.--Finland Travel Bureau Ltd., Helsinki, Finland; *Int'l*, pg. 485
Nissen, Bob, Mgr.-Mktg.--SL Waber, Nogales, AZ; *U.S. Public*, pg. 1419
Nissen, Robert E., V.P.-Mktg.--SL Waber, Inc., Mount Laurel, NJ; *U.S. Public*, pg. 1419
Nitchos, Peter, V.P.-Mktg.--Quebecor Printing MIL Inc., Don Mills, Canada; *U.S. Public*, pg. 1077
Nitsch, Gunter, V.P.-Mkt. Devel.--Vereinsbank Capital Corporation, New York, NY; *Int'l*, pg. 180
Nitz, Bruce E., V.P.-Sls. & Mktg.--Stanley Knight Corporation, New Troy, MI; *U.S. Private*, pg. 1033
Nix, P.R., Mktg. Services Dir.--Procter & Gamble Australia, Villawood, Australia; *U.S. Public*, pg. 1332
Nizam, J., Mgr.-Mktg.--Master Distributors, Santa Monica, CA; *U.S. Private*, pg. 714
Noack, Hans-Herbert, Mgr.-Sls. & Mktg.--Eagle-Picher Wolverine GmbH, Ohringen, Germany; *U.S. Private*, pg. 355
Noack, Hans-Herbert, Mgr.-Sls. & Mktg.--Eagle-Picher Wolverine Gmbh, Ohringen, Germany; *U.S. Private*, pg. 355
Noble, Lisa, V.P.-Mktg.--MJB Rice Company, Union City, CA; *Int'l*, pg. 917
Noble, Terry, Mgr.-Sls. & Customer Svc.--Pipetronix Ltd., Concord, Canada; *Int'l*, pg. 1071
Nodson, John, Mgr.-Mktg.--EIS Brake Parts Div., Berlin, CT; *U.S. Public*, pg. 1503
Noe, Brad, Exec. V.P.-Sls. & Mktg.--Henredon Furniture Industries, Inc., Morganton, NC; *U.S. Private*, pg. 432
Noecke, M., Mgr.-Mktg.--Sporlan Valve Company, Washington, MO; *U.S. Private*, pg. 1026
Noel, Michael, V.P.-Mktg.--AmeriTruck Refrigerated Transport, Inc., Waupaca, WI; *U.S. Private*, pg. 66
Noes, Don, Sr. V.P.-Sls. & Mktg.--Provident Music Group, Brentwood, TN; *Int'l*, pg. 1529
Noes, Don, Sr. V.P.-Sls. & Mktg.--Provident Music Distribution, Nashville, TN; *Int'l*, pg. 1529
Noetzli, Rolf, Dir.-European Devel.--Danzas Corporation, Bellevue, WA; *Int'l*, pg. 382
Nofsinger, Rowland, V.P.-Mktg. & Sls.--Nofsinger, Inc., Kansas City, MO; *U.S. Private*, pg. 187
Noga, Katie, Dir.-Mktg. Communications--Chicago Rawhide, Elgin, IL; *Int'l*, pg. 1157
Noga, Katie, Mgr.-Mktg. Services--CR Services, Elgin, IL; *Int'l*, pg. 1157
Nolan, Jim, Dir.-Mktg. & Sls.--Irish Cement Ltd., Stillorgan, Ireland; *Int'l*, pg. 242
Nolan, Tom, Dir.-Mktg. Plng. & Commun.--Medusa Corporation, Cleveland, OH; *U.S. Public*, pg. 1084
Nollman, Mitch, Mgr.-Home Audio Mktg.--Bose Corporation, Framingham, MA; *U.S. Private*, pg. 160
Noonan, George, Mgr.-Mktg.--Walter Drake, Inc., Colorado Springs, CO; *U.S. Private*, pg. 421
Noonan, Jeannie, Mgr.-Mktg.--Town & Country, New York, NY; *U.S. Private*, pg. 517
Nooney, Charles, Sr. V.P.-Sls. & Mktg.--The Disney Channel, Burbank, CA; *U.S. Public*, pg. 513
Norby, Mary, Dir.-Mktg.--Criticare Systems, Inc., Waukesha, WI; *U.S. Public*, pg. 459
Nordaby, Bill, Dir.-Sls. & Mktg.--Plastic Suppliers, Inc., Columbus, OH; *U.S. Private*, pg. 871
Nordell, Peter, V.P.-Mktg. & Sls.--Edlund Company, Inc., Burlington, VT; *U.S. Private*, pg. 364
Nordquist, Dale A., V.P.-Sls. & Mktg.--HEI, Inc., Victoria, MN; *U.S. Public*, pg. 770
Nordstrom, Jeff, Dir.-Mktg.--Whataburger, Inc., Corpus Christi, TX; *U.S. Private*, pg. 1170
Norfleet, Byron, V.P.-Mktg.--Johnston & Murphy Co., Nashville, TN; *U.S. Public*, pg. 728
Norha, Patrick R., V.P.-Mktg.--Northwest Paper Div., Cloquet, MN; *U.S. Public*, pg. 1318
Norman, Bruce E., V.P.-Mktg.--Mercury General Corporation, Los Angeles, CA; *U.S. Public*, pg. 1093
Norman, David, V.P.-Sls. & Mktg.--Kobelco Stewart Bolling, Inc., Hudson, OH; *Int'l*, pg. 740
Norman, H., Crumpton, V.P.-Sls. & Mktg.--H.H. Robertson Burford Plant, Hamilton, Canada; *U.S. Public*, pg. 1394
Norman, Ken, V.P.-Mktg.--National Spinning Co., Inc., New York, NY; *U.S. Private*, pg. 786
Norman, Missy, Dir.-Mktg.--First United Bancshares, Inc., El Dorado, AR; *U.S. Public*, pg. 641
Normandin, Marc, V.P.-Sls. & Mktg.--Nyltech North America Inc., Manchester, NH; *Int'l*, pg. 482
Normandin, Ray, Gen. Sls. & Mktg. Mgr.--Koyo Corporation of USA, Sales Division, Westlake, OH; *Int'l*, pg. 760
Noronha, S.S.B., V.P.-Mktg.--Esso Brasileira de Petroleo Limitada, Rio de Janeiro, Brazil; *U.S. Public*, pg. 602
Norquist, Tom, Dir.-Mktg. & Sls.--Game Time, Inc., Fort Payne, AL; *U.S. Public*, pg. 1543
Norris, J., V.P.-Mktg.--Mosler Inc., Hamilton, OH; *U.S. Private*, pg. 763
North, Frank A., V.P.-Mktg.--Chesapeake Insurance Division, Richmond, VA; *U.S. Public*, pg. 215
Northridge, Nigele, Mgr.-Sls. & Mktg.--Gallaher International Limited, Weybridge, United Kingdom; *Int'l*, pg. 539
Northup, Christopher, Dir.-Sls. & Mktg.--Keystone Automotive Industries, Inc., Pomona, CA; *U.S. Public*, pg. 955
Norton, Dave, Sr. V.P.-Retail--Eagle Food Centers, Inc., Milan, IL; *U.S. Public*, pg. 547
Norton, Joseph J., Supvr.-Energy Mktg.--St. Joseph Light & Power Co., Saint Joseph, MO; *U.S. Public*, pg. 1427
Norton, Larry P., Dir.-Mktg.--Concrete Technology Corp., Tacoma, WA; *U.S. Private*, pg. 262
Norton, Lynn, Dir.-Mktg.--Cinemark USA, Inc., Dallas, TX; *U.S. Private*, pg. 240
Norton, Patrick H., Sr. V.P.-Sls. & Mktg.--La-Z-Boy Incorporated, Monroe, MI; *U.S. Public*, pg. 972
Norton, Vic, Mgr.-Mktg.-Chemical--Bird Machine Company, South Walpole, MA; *U.S. Public*, pg. 166
Norvet, Dennis R., Dir.-Mktg.--Centex-Rodgers Construction Company, Nashville, TN; *U.S. Public*, pg. 322
Nosal, Bob, Dir.-Mktg., Adv. & Pub. Rels.--Unichema U.S.A., Chicago, IL; *Int'l*, pg. 1436
Nosbaum, LeRoy, V.P.-Mktg.--Itron Inc., Spokane, WA; *U.S.* Public, pg. 914
Nosek, Jim, Mgr.-Mktg. Svcs.--Edward Don & Company, North Riverside, IL; *U.S. Private*, pg. 339
Nost, Kirsti, Chief Info. Officer & Dir.-Mktg.--AS OSLO Sporveier, Oslo, Norway; *Int'l*, pg. 1012
Notarnicola, Jim, Exec. V.P.-Mktg.--Blockbuster Entertainment Group, Dallas, TX; *U.S. Private*, pg. 775
Nottingham, Tom, Mgr.-Mktg.--O-Seal Div., San Diego, CA; *U.S. Public*, pg. 1262
Nova, Gianluigi, Pres., Chief Exec. Officer & Controller--Itam Tech Italimplianti, Inc., Coraopolis, PA; *Int'l*, pg. 655
Novello, Debra, Mktg. Analyst--Urschel Labs Incorporated, Valparaiso, IN; *U.S. Private*, pg. 1129
Novinski, M., Dir.-Mktg.--Organon Inc., West Orange, NJ; *Int'l*, pg. 48
Novotny, Eva, Exec. V.P.-Sls. & Mktg.--Medstone International, Inc., Aliso Viejo, CA; *U.S. Public*, pg. 1082
Nowicki, Margaret, Mgr.-Adv. & Mktg.--Dale Electronics, Inc., Columbus, NE; *U.S. Public*, pg. 1722
Nowotarski, Mark, Mgr.-Mktg.--Aristokraft, Inc., Jasper, IN; *U.S. Public*, pg. 675
Noye, Kirby, Mgr.-Mktg. Admin.--Getinge/Castle Inc., Rochester, NY; *Int'l*, pg. 551
Nsamala, Isaac, Financial Controller & Dir.-Mktg.--National Bank of Malawi, Blantyre, Malawi; *Int'l*, pg. 1296
Nunamaker, Monique, Mgr.-Direct Mktg.--Avco Financial Services, Costa Mesa, CA; *U.S. Public*, pg. 1589
Nunes, Don, V.P.-Mktg.--Hawaii Newspaper Agency, Inc., Honolulu, HI; *U.S. Public*, pg. 701
Nusbaum, Dave, Dir.-Mktg.--Kampgrounds of America, Inc., Billings, MT; *U.S. Private*, pg. 603
Nuss, Kevin Marie, V.P.-Mktg.--Churchill Downs, Inc., Louisville, KY; *U.S. Public*, pg. 356
Nussbaum, Robert, V.P.-Sls. & Mktg.--The Lenson Coffee Co., Pleasantville, NJ; *U.S. Public*, pg. 351
Nussbaum, Bob, V.P.-Sls. & Mktg.--Ireland Coffee Tea, Inc., Pleasantville, NJ; *U.S. Public*, pg. 351
Nutt, Orval J., Chief Mktg. Officer & V.P.-Mktg.--Amdahl Corporation, Sunnyvale, CA; *Int'l*, pg. 527
Nuzzo, Philip F., Dir.-Mktg.--Novametrix Medical Systems Inc., Wallingford, CT; *U.S. Public*, pg. 1203
Nyblad, Mary Jo, Mgr.-Sls. & Mktg./Structural Panel Prods.--Boise Cascade Corporation, Boise, ID; *U.S. Public*, pg. 242
Nybo, Howard J., Pres.--Will & Baumer Incorporated, Liverpool, NY; *U.S. Private*, pg. 1176
Nyce, Jim, V.P.-Mktg. Svcs.--Tropicana Dole Beverages North America, Bradenton, FL; *Int'l*, pg. 1217
Nyiri, Kenneth F., Dir.-Mkt. Res.--Mississippi Chemical Corporation, Yazoo City, MS; *U.S. Public*, pg. 1117
Nyman, Lee, V.P.-Mfg. Brass Mngmt. Engrng.--Mueller Industries, Inc., Memphis, TN; *U.S. Public*, pg. 1141
Nysten, Thomas, Sr. V.P.-Mktg. Grp.--Metsa-Serla Corporation, Espoo, Finland; *Int'l*, pg. 863
Nystrom, Kris Baird, Dir.-Mktg. Svcs.--Mrs. Baird's Bakeries, Inc., Fort Worth, TX; *U.S. Private*, pg. 765
O'Boyle, D. D., Data Base Mktg. Dir.--Howard, Merrell & Partners, Inc., Raleigh, NC; *U.S. Private*, pg. 542
O'Brien, Chris J., Mgr.-Mktg.--Moore Products Co., Spring House, PA; *U.S. Public*, pg. 1128
O'Brien, Daniel A., V.P.--Harrop Industries, Inc., Columbus, OH; *U.S. Private*, pg. 506
O'Brien, Dennis, Sr. V.P.-Mktg.--Armstrong World Industries, Inc., Lancaster, PA; *U.S. Public*, pg. 131
O'Brien, Hugh, Exec. Dir.-Mktg. Services--Temerlin McClain, Irving, TX; *U.S. Public*, pg. 1642
O'Brien, John M., V.P.-Sls. & Mktg.--Federal Screw Works, Detroit, MI; *U.S. Public*, pg. 616
O'Brien, John R., V.P.-Mktg. & Program Mngmt.--COMSAT Mobile Communications, Clarksburg, MD; *U.S. Public*, pg. 424
O'Brien, Maureen, Mgr.-Mktg.--Frontier Insurance Company, Rock Hill, NY; *U.S. Public*, pg. 685
O'Brien, Maureen, Mgr.-Mktg.--Frontier Pacific Insurance Company, La Jolla, CA; *U.S. Public*, pg. 685
O'Brien, Michael T., V.P.-Sls. & Mktg./Precision & Indus.--Carsen Group Inc., Markham, Canada; *U.S. Public*, pg. 301
O'Brien, Ray, Sr. V.P.-Sls. & Mktg.-SkyTel--Mobile Telecommunications Technologies Corp., Jackson, MS; *U.S. Public*, pg. 1120
O'Brien, Richard, V.P.-Mktg.-Printing Paper--Unisource (North East), Windsor, CT; *U.S. Public*, pg. 1671
O'Brien, Robert, V.P.-Mktg.--Ceco Door Products, Brentwood, TN; *U.S. Public*, pg. 1676
O'Brien, Thomas W., V.P.-Sls. & Mktg.--Western Industries, Inc., Milwaukee, WI; *U.S. Private*, pg. 1165
O'Callaghan, Craig, V.P.--Universal Builders Supply, Inc., Mount Vernon, NY; *U.S. Private*, pg. 1126

O'Connell, Daniel, Mgr.-Mktg.--Tucson Learning Center, Tucson, AZ; *U.S. Public*, pg. 219

O'Connell, Kevin P., Exec. V.P. & Chief Mktg. Officer--UNUM Corporation, Portland, ME; *U.S. Public*, pg. 1699

O'Connell, Lisa, Coord.-Mktg. Services--Prudential Real Estate Affiliates Inc., Costa Mesa, CA; *U.S. Private*, pg. 892

O'Connor, Claude, Dir.-Mktg.--Snyder's of Hanover, Inc., Hanover, PA; *U.S. Private*, pg. 1011

O'Connor, Dan, V.P.-Sls. & Mtkg.--Northern Telecom - National Repair & Distribution Center, Nashville, TN; *Int'l*, pg. 970

O'Connor, Mary Lynn, Mgr.-Mktg.--Xebec Corporation, Kansas City, MO; *U.S. Private*, pg. 1194

O'Connor, Michael, Dir.-Mktg.--Circle Business Credit, Inc., Indianapolis, IN; *U.S. Public*, pg. 1785

O'Connor, Mike, V.P.-Sls. & Mktg.--Seitz Foods Inc., Saint Joseph, MO; *U.S. Public*, pg. 1434

O'Connor, Ron, Dir.-Mktg.--White Electrical Construction Co., Atlanta, GA; *U.S. Private*, pg. 1172

O'Connor, Terry, Dir.-Mktg. Svcs.--BASF Corporation, Mount Olive, NJ; *Int'l*, pg. 105

O'Connor, Tom, V.P.-Mktg.--Algonquin Gas Transmission Corporation, Boston, MA; *U.S. Public*, pg. 534

O'Connor, Tom, Dir.-Mktg.--TECO Energy, Inc., Tampa, FL; *U.S. Public*, pg. 1565

O'Dea, Bill, V.P.-Sls. & Mktg.--Azon Corporation, Johnson City, NY; *U.S. Private*, pg. 104

O'Dell, Blair, Mktg. Analyst--Bel-Art Products, Pequannock, NJ; *U.S. Private*, pg. 130

O'Dell, Pat, Natl. Mktg. Mgr.-Special Prods./White Cement--Lehigh Portland Cement Company, Allentown, PA; *Int'l*, pg. 605

O'Donnell, Christine, Dir.-Corp. Commun.--GAI Consultants, Inc., Monroeville, PA; *U.S. Private*, pg. 433

O'Donnell, Darren, V.P.-Mktg.--Milgray Electronics, Inc., Farmingdale, NY; *U.S. Public*, pg. 205

O'Donnell, Dennis, V.P.-Mktg.--Micro Vesicular Systems, Inc., Nashua, NH; *U.S. Public*, pg. 855

O'Donnell, Mike, Mgr.-Mktg. Research--Babcock & Wilcox Co., Barberton, OH; *U.S. Public*, pg. 1068

O'Flaherty, Thomas, Dir.-Mktg. & Sls.--Hercules Chemical Co., Inc., Passaic, NJ; *U.S. Private*, pg. 523

O'Grady, Anne, V.P.-Promo. Mktg. & Events--CBS Television Network, New York, NY; *U.S. Public*, pg. 274

O'Grady, Harry, V.P.-Mktg.--Becker Milk Co. Ltd., Scarborough, Canada; *Int'l*, pg. 182

O'Grady, Laura S., V.P.-Adv. & Mktg.--S & K Famous Brands, Inc., Glen Allen, VA; *U.S. Public*, pg. 1414

O'Hanlon, Rosemary, Coord.-Sls.--Times Fiber Communications, Inc., Wallingford, CT; *U.S. Private*, pg. 629

O'Hara, John, Dir.-Mktg.--Kodak Brasileira C.I.L., Sao Paulo, Brazil; *U.S. Public*, pg. 552

O'Hara, Kevin, Mgr.-Mktg. Communications--AlliedSignal Commercial Avionic Systems, Olathe, KS; *U.S. Public*, pg. 50

O'Hara, M., Dir.-Mktg.--Asahi Breweries Ltd., Tokyo, Japan; *Int'l*, pg. 83

O'Hare, William, Dir.-Levels & Tools Mktg.--Macklanburg-Duncan Co., Oklahoma City, OK; *U.S. Private*, pg. 692

O'Keane, Michael, Mgr.-Mktg.--Snap-Tite, Inc., Erie, PA; *U.S. Private*, pg. 1010

O'Keefe, Mary, Mgr.-Corp. Commun.--Veryfine Products, Inc., Westford, MA; *U.S. Private*, pg. 1137

O'Kelly, Noel, Mgr.-Mktg. Adm.--Liebert International B.V., Cork, Ireland; *U.S. Public*, pg. 577

O'Kray, Len, V.P.-Mktg. & Sls.--Elgin Sweeper Company, Elgin, IL; *U.S. Public*, pg. 617

O'Kronley, Theresa, Dir.-Mktg.--Winkelman Stores, Inc., Plymouth, MI; *U.S. Private*, pg. 858

O'Leary, E.J., V.P.-Sls. & Mktg.--Moog Automotive, Inc., Saint Louis, MO; *U.S. Public*, pg. 443

O'Leary, Jack, Mgr.-Mktg.--Lytron Incorporated, Woburn, MA; *U.S. Private*, pg. 684

O'Leary, John, Mgr.-Intl.--Forasol S.A., Velizy-Villacoublay, France; *Int'l*, pg. 496

O'Leary, John, V.P.-Worldwide Mktg.--Pride International, Inc., Houston, TX; *U.S. Public*, pg. 1324

O'Leary, Robert W., V.P.-Mktg., Sls. & Adv.--Scanforms, Inc., Bristol, PA; *U.S. Public*, pg. 228

O'Malley, Michael J., Gen. Mgr.-Mktg.--Buick Motor Div. General Motors Corp., Flint, MI; *U.S. Public*, pg. 720

O'Mara, Thomas K., Mgr.-Sls. & Mktg.--Autocam Corporation, Grand Rapids, MI; *U.S. Public*, pg. 148

O'Meara, John, Pres.--Telegenix Inc., Cherry Hill, NJ; *U.S. Private*, pg. 1073

O'Mera, Joe, Mgr.-Mktg./Tool Div.--Wilton Corporation, Palatine, IL; *U.S. Private*, pg. 1181

O'Neal, Peg, Mgr.-Mktg. Commun.--Avo International, Blue Bell, PA; *U.S. Private*, pg. 9

O'Neil, David C., V.P.-Mktg.--Southwest Gas Corporation, Las Vegas, NV; *U.S. Public*, pg. 1493

O'Neil, Deb, Mgr.-Mktg.--Labelon Corporation, Canandaigua, NY; *U.S. Private*, pg. 641

O'Neil, Evan J., V.P.-Bus. Devel. & Mktg.--Zeigler Coal Holding Company, Fairview Heights, IL; *U.S. Public*, pg. 1790

O'Neil, P.A., Dir.-Mktg.--W.E. O'Neil Construction Company, Chicago, IL; *U.S. Private*, pg. 817

O'Neill, Jeff J., V.P.-Mktg.--Federal-Mogul Corporation, Southfield, MI; *U.S. Public*, pg. 615

O'Neill, Jim, Sr. V.P.-Sls. & Mktg.--Alpine Electronics of America, Inc., Torrance, CA; *Int'l*, pg. 65

O'Neill, Jim, Dir.-Mktg. & Devel.--Dairyland Power Cooperative, La Crosse, WI; *U.S. Private*, pg. 307

O'Neill, Joyce, V.P.-Human Resources--Data Dimensions, Inc., Culver City, CA; *U.S. Public*, pg. 485

O'Neill, Kevin, V.P.-Mktg. & Sls.--Wilbur Chocolate Co., Inc., Lititz, PA; *U.S. Private*, pg. 210

O'Neill, Kevin M., Sr. V.P.-Bus. Devel. & Strategy--Anacomp, Inc., Indianapolis, IN; *U.S. Public*, pg. 106

O'Reagan, Richard, Sr. Dir.-Mktg.--Cybex International, Inc., Medway, MA; *U.S. Private*, pg. 1114

O'Reilly, Carole, Coord.-Mktg.--Bernina of America Inc., Aurora, IL; *Int'l*, pg. 189

O'Reilly, Frank, V.P.-Piece Dyed Fabrics--Graniteville Company, Graniteville, SC; *U.S. Private*, pg. 103

O'Reilly, Kelley, Pres.-Impact Adv. Inc. & V.P.-Mktg.--Big O Tires Incorporated, Englewood, CO; *U.S. Public*, pg. 1553

O'Reilly, Tom, Dir.-Sls. & Mktg.--Elida Faberge (Ireland) Ltd., Dublin, Ireland; *Int'l*, pg. 1437

O'Rourke, Patrick H., Dir.-Sls. & Mktg.--Selectone, Inc., Hayward, CA; *U.S. Private*, pg. 982

O'Rourke, Thomas J., Sr. V.P.-Mktg.--The CIT Group Holdings, Inc., New York, NY; *Int'l*, pg. 360

O'Shea, Tim, V.P.-Mktg.--Fresh Choice, Inc., Santa Clara, CA; *U.S. Public*, pg. 682

O'Shields, Betsy, Mgr.-Mktg.--Conso Products Company, Union, SC; *U.S. Public*, pg. 434

O'Sullivan, David, Mgr.-Mktg.--Warner-Lambert, Eastleigh, United Kingdom; *U.S. Public*, pg. 1739

O'Sullivan, John, V.P. & Dir.-Sls. & Mktg.--CBS Television Network, New York, NY; *U.S. Public*, pg. 274

O'Toole, Kathleen A., Asst. V.P. & Dir.-Mktg.--United Missouri Bank of St. Louis, Saint Louis, MO; *U.S. Public*, pg. 1655

O'Toole, Tom, V.P.-Mktg.--Hyatt Corporation, Chicago, IL; *U.S. Private*, pg. 551

Oakes, John C., II, Dir.-Retail Mktg.--Legg Mason, Inc., Baltimore, MD; *U.S. Public*, pg. 984

Oakes, Karin, Mgr.-Mktg. Communications--ESA, Inc., Chelmsford, MA; *U.S. Private*, pg. 354

Oakley, Brian M., Mgr.-Sls. & Mktg.--Fleet Industries, Fort Erie, Canada; *Int'l*, pg. 829

Oaks, Diane, Dir.-Mktg.--Sesame Place, Langhorne, PA; *U.S. Public*, pg. 114

Oates, Gordon, Jr., V.P.-Sls. & Mktg.--American Wyott Corporation, Cheyenne, WY; *U.S. Private*, pg. 1193

Oates, Randy, Dir.-Mktg.--Commercial National Bank, Shreveport, LA; *U.S. Public*, pg. 500

Obana, Mary, Dir.-Mktg. & Communications-Keds--The Stride Rite Corporation, Lexington, MA; *U.S. Public*, pg. 1524

Obana, Mary, V.P.-Mktg.--The Keds Corporation, Lexington, MA; *U.S. Public*, pg. 1525

Obey, David, Sr. V.P. & Dir.-Consumer Mktg.--Weider Publications, Inc., Woodland Hills, CA; *U.S. Private*, pg. 1159

Ochi, Gene, Sr. V.P.-Mktg.--Union-Transport Corporation, Rancho Dominguez, CA; *U.S. Private*, pg. 1119

Ochoe, Lynn, Dir.-Mktg.--San Miguel Corp., Manila, Philippines; *Int'l*, pg. 1183

Ochs, Roger C., Dir.-Mktg.--HD Vest Financial Services, Irving, TX; *U.S. Public*, pg. 770

Oda, Frances, V.P.-Mktg. Services--Mitsubishi Motor Sales of America, Inc., Cypress, CA; *Int'l*, pg. 875

Oddo, Jim, V.P.-Mktg., Adv. & Sls.--Atlas Hotels, Inc., San Diego, CA; *U.S. Private*, pg. 96

Odell, Stephen T., V.P.-Sls. & Mktg.--Jaguar Cars, Mahwah, NJ; *U.S. Public*, pg. 664

Odiseos, Susan, Dir.-Mktg. & Communications--Trigen Energy Corporation, White Plains, NY; *U.S. Public*, pg. 1637

Oeltjen, Ray, V.P.-Mktg.-Leupold--Leupold & Stevens, Inc., Beaverton, OR; *U.S. Private*, pg. 662

Oerehagen, Perge, Reg. Mgr.-Mktg. Europe--Luxo A/S, Oslo, Norway; *Int'l*, pg. 821

Oernfeldt, Sven, V.P.-Mktg.--Symbol Technologies, Inc., Holtsville, NY; *U.S. Public*, pg. 1546

Oertel, Jack, Dir.-Sls. & Mktg.--William A. Randolph, Inc., Morton Grove, IL; *U.S. Private*, pg. 909

Oftedahl, Kris, Mktg. Coord.--Don E. Williams Co., Rock Island, IL; *U.S. Private*, pg. 1177

Ogden, Dwaine, V.P.-Mktg.--Seradyn, Inc., Indianapolis, IN; *Int'l*, pg. 871

Ogden, Malcolm, Dir.-Mktg.--Leisure Resorts Management, Abiemore, United Kingdom; *Int'l*, pg. 168

Ogden, Tom, Supvr.-Mktg. Commun.--Magnetrol International, Downers Grove, IL; *U.S. Private*, pg. 696

Ogg, William C., Dir.-Comml. Market--Sentry Technology Corp., Hauppauge, NY; *U.S. Public*, pg. 1458

Oggero, Richard J., Chm. Bd.--The Weitz Company, Inc., Des Moines, IA; *U.S. Private*, pg. 1160

Oh, Dong-Hwee, Pres.--Ssangyong Research Institute, Seoul, Korea; *Int'l*, pg. 1292

Oh, John, V.P.-Mktg.--Young-Phillips Sales Co., Clemmons, NC; *U.S. Private*, pg. 1201

Ohannessian, Dikran, V.P.-Individual Mktg. & Services--Sun Life of Canada, Toronto, Canada; *Int'l*, pg. 1319

Ohl, D.W., V.P.-Sls. & Mktg.--Inco Alloys International, Inc., Huntington, WV; *Int'l*, pg. 672

Okamura, Bob, Mgr.-Mktg.--Lotte U.S.A., Inc., Battle Creek, MI; *Int'l*, pg. 819

Okano, Marilyn, Dir.-Relationship Mktg.--Nestle USA, Glendale, CA; *Int'l*, pg. 916

Okiyama, Gail, Mgr.-Mktg.--Precor, Inc., Bothell, WA; *U.S. Public*, pg. 1322

Okon, Joseph, V.P.-Adv. & Mktg. Communications--Marriott International, Inc., Washington, DC; *U.S. Public*, pg. 1047

Okon, Joseph, Sr. V.P.-Natl. Adv.--Fairfield Inn, Washington, DC; *U.S. Public*, pg. 1048

Okonski, Tracy, Sls. & Mkgt. Asst.--Surgical Specialties, Reading, PA; *U.S. Private*, pg. 1056

Okosky, Michael, V.P.-Sls. & Mktg.--PAXAR Corporation, White Plains, NY; *U.S. Public*, pg. 1266

Oksanen, Matti, Mgr.-Oil, Mktg. & Sls.--Neste Oy, Espoo, Finland; *Int'l*, pg. 912

Oktavec, Thomas, V.P.-Mktg.--Kocolene Oil Corp., Seymour, IN; *U.S. Private*, pg. 629

Oktela, Michael, Dir.-Mktg. & Sls.--Federal Signal Corporation, Signal Div., University Park, IL; *U.S. Public*, pg. 616

Okura, S., V.P.-Mktg.--Avon Products Co., Ltd., Tokyo, Japan; *U.S. Public*, pg. 156

Olander, R.R., V.P.--Foster-Miller, Inc., Waltham, MA; *U.S. Private*, pg. 421

Olausson, Ruth, Mgr.-Mktg.--Skanska International Building AB, Malmo, Sweden; *Int'l*, pg. 1260

Oldani, Michelle, Dir.-Mktg.-Company Opers.--Gingiss International, Addison, IL; *U.S. Private*, pg. 455

Oldham, Caryn, Mgr.-Mktg.-Hyperbarics--Sechrist Industries, Inc., Anaheim, CA; *U.S. Private*, pg. 980

Oldham, Laurance W., Sr. V.P.-Oper. & Marketing--Southern Hospitality Corporation, Nashville, TN; *U.S. Public*, pg. 488

Oldham, Mike, Sr. V.P. & Dir.-Sls. & Mktg.--Columbine JDS Systems, Inc., Denver, CO; *U.S. Public*, pg. 228

Olin, Scott, V.P.-Sls. & Mktg.--Columbia Paint & Coatings, Spokane, WA; *U.S. Private*, pg. 256

Olin, Thomas F. Jr., Pres.-Sls. & Mktg.--Archway Cookies, Inc., Battle Creek, MI; *U.S. Private*, pg. 80

Olinger, Jack, Exec. V.P.-Adv.--The Hammerblow Corp., Wausau, WI; *U.S. Private*, pg. 498

Olingy, Jeffrey F., Sr. V.P.-Sls. & Mktg.--Provident Companies, Inc., Chattanooga, TN; *U.S. Public*, pg. 1337

Olive, Nicholas, Dir.-Mktg./Mastercare--Dixons Group plc, Hemel Hempstead, United Kingdom,; *Int'l*, pg. 413

Olive, Paula D., Mktg.--Regions Bank/Mobile, Mobile, AL; *U.S. Public*, pg. 1372

Oliver, Kate, V.P.-Mktg.--The ServiceMaster Company, Downers Grove, IL; *U.S. Public*, pg. 1461

Oliver, Lloyd, Mgr.-Mktg.--The Imperial Life Assurance Co., Toronto, Canada; *Int'l*, pg. 396

Oliver, Roland O., V.P.-Mktg.--Comsearch, Inc., Reston, VA; *U.S. Public*, pg. 46

Olland, Cherie W., Dir.-Bus. Devel.--Jones, Day, Reavis & Pogue, Cleveland, OH; *U.S. Private*, pg. 596

Ollen, George, Dir.-Sls. & Mktg.--International Electronic Research Corp., Burbank, CA; *U.S. Public*, pg. 286

Oller, Otto, Dir.-Adv.--ITW Plastiglide, Rancho Dominguez, CA; *U.S. Public*, pg. 867

Olley, Peter H., V.P.-Sls. & Mktg.--Day-Glo Color Corp., Cleveland, OH; *U.S. Public*, pg. 1357

Olmo, Luis Del, Exec. V.P.-Mktg.--Sol Melia, Palma de Mallorca, Spain; *Int'l*, pg. 1277

Olschan, Brian S., Sr. V.P.-Mktg. & Sls.--Acme United Corporation, Fairfield, CT; *U.S. Public*, pg. 17

Olsen, Brett, Mgr.-Mktg. Svcs.--Utility Trailer Manufacturing Co., City of Industry, CA; *U.S. Private*, pg. 1130

Olsen, David, V.P.-Mktg.--Dryper's Corp., Vancouver, WA; *U.S. Private*, pg. 344

Olsen, Hans, V.P.-Mktg. & Worldwide Sls.--Trident Microsystems, Inc., Mountain View, CA; *U.S. Public*, pg. 1637

Olsen, K.E., V.P.-Mktg.--Roadway Express, Inc., Akron, OH; *U.S. Public*, pg. 1392

Olson-Graves, Sarah, V.P.-Mktg., New Line Home Video/Los Angeles--New Line Cinema Corporation, New York, NY; *U.S. Public*, pg. 1614

Olson, A. Eric, Dir.-Corp. Devel.--Battle Mountain Gold Company, Houston, TX; *U.S. Public*, pg. 193

Olson, Andy, Mktg. Asst.--Rite-Hite Corporation, Milwaukee, WI; *U.S. Private*, pg. 933

Olson, Andy, Mktg. Asst.--Rite-Hite Corporation (WI), Milwaukee, WI; *U.S. Private*, pg. 933

Olson, Charles R., V.P.-Sls. & Mktg.--Aspec Technology, Inc., Sunnyvale, CA; *U.S. Private*, pg. 89

Olson, Donald P., Mgr.-Mktg. & Employee Communications--Inland Steel Industries, Inc., Chicago, IL; *U.S. Public*, pg. 879

Olson, E. Whitney, V.P.-Mktg.--Foss Maritime Co., Portland, OR; *U.S. Private*, pg. 1092

Olson, Gregory G., V.P.-Mktg.--CBT Systems USA Ltd., Menlo Park, CA; *U.S. Public*, pg. 275

Olson, Larry D., Exec. V.P. & Pres.-Kent Components--Kent Electronics Corp., Houston, TX; *U.S. Public*, pg. 951

Olson, Mark, Mgr.-Sls. & Mktg.--Rodney Metals, New Bedford, MA; *U.S. Public*, pg. 43

Olson, Michael C., Sr. V.P.-Branch Opers. & Mktg. Svcs.--Ameriana Bank, New Castle, IN; *U.S. Public*, pg. 66

Olson, Terry, Exec. V.P.-Sls. & Mktg.--Brothers Gourmet Coffees, Inc., Boca Raton, FL; *U.S. Public*, pg. 259

Olson, Todd, Coord.-Mktg.--Burgess-Norton Mfg. Co., Geneva, IL; *U.S. Private*, pg. 68

Onn, Lee Wing, Dir.-Intl. Mktg.-Div. I--Malaysia Tourism Promotion Board (MTPB), Kuala Lumpur, Malaysia; *Int'l*, pg. 832

Ontoso, Isabel, Dir.-Corp. Mktg. & Adv.--Telefonica de Espana, S.A., Madrid, Spain; *Int'l*, pg. 1371

Onustock, Michael R., Exec. V.P.-Pulp & Fine Paper Mktg.--Willamette Industries, Inc., Portland, OR; *U.S. Public*, pg. 1768

Opet, William A., V.P.-Mktg. & Sls.--LIN Cellular Group, Kirkland, WA; *U.S. Public*, pg. 11

Oppenheimer, Deanna W., Exec. V.P.-Corp. Mktg. & Consumer Bank Div.--Washington Mutual Inc., Seattle, WA; *U.S. Public*, pg. 1741

Optyker, Fulber, Dir.-Mktg.--Facom, Morangis, France; *Int'l*, pg. 570

Orall, John F., V.P.-Mktg.--Winthrop Printing Company, Inc., Boston, MA; *U.S. Private*, pg. 1184

Orban, Rus, V.P.-Mktg.--Rutt Custom Cabinetry, Goodville, PA; *U.S. Private*, pg. 507

Orbe, Tom, V.P.-Mktg.--Nissan Motor Corporation in U.S.A., Gardena, CA; *Int'l*, pg. 945

Ordemann, Carl W., Sr. Partner & Dir.-Mktg.--HLW International LLP, New York, NY; *U.S. Private*, pg. 491

Ordman, Marty, Dir.-Promo. & Events--Dole Food Company, Inc., Westlake Village, CA; *U.S. Public*, pg. 515

Orem, Glen, Dir.-Mktg.--SouthCo. Inc., Concordville, PA; *U.S. Private*, pg. 1014

Orent, Jill, Dir.-Mktg.--Cuisinart Inc., Stamford, CT; *U.S. Private*, pg. 261

Orerby, Chip, Dir.-Mktg.--Old Dominion Freight Line, Inc., High Point, NC; *U.S. Public*, pg. 1216

Orfinik, Michael H., Pres.--Melnor Inc., Winchester, VA; *U.S.* Public, pg. 1234

Orinsi, Heidi, Mgr.- Mktg.--Bob Evans Farms, Inc. Restaurant Division, Columbus, OH; *U.S. Public*, pg. 596

Orlanda, Christina, Mgr.-Mktg. Programs--Broderbund Software, Inc., Novato, CA; *U.S. Public*, pg. 258
Orloff, Bradley, V.P.-Mktg.--United Retail Group, Inc., Rochelle Park, NJ; *U.S. Public*, pg. 1679
Orloff, Michael A., Sr. V.P.-Sls. & Mktg.--Roman, Inc., Roselle, IL; *U.S. Private*, pg. 942
Orman, Mary Jane, Mgr.-Mktg. Services & Production--Bryan Foods, West Point, MS; *U.S. Public*, pg. 1433
Ormes, Kevin, Grp. V.P.-Sls. & Mktg.--Mitsubishi Motor Sales of America, Inc., Cypress, CA; *Int'l*, pg. 875
Orr, Mark, V.P.-Mktg. Info. Systems--Ralphs Grocery Company, Compton, CA; *U.S. Private*, pg. 1202
Orr, Tom, Dir.-Mktg./Window Div.--Cameo Window Furnishings, New York, NY; *U.S. Private*, pg. 1094
Orsini, Edward R., V.P.-Mktg. (Cement-Ontario Div.)--St. Lawrence Cement Inc., Montreal, Canada; *Int'l*, pg. 628
Orsini, Thomas, Dir.-Mktg.--Becton Dickinson Infusion Therapy, Inc., Sandy, UT; *U.S. Public*, pg. 199
Ortal, Michele, Dir.-Mktg.--Clarins, Neuilly-sur-Seine, France; *Int'l*, pg. 295
Ortegon, Genny, V.P.-Mktg.--Advanced Logic Research, Inc., Irvine, CA; *U.S. Public*, pg. 703
Orth, David, V.P.-Mktg.--Breeze Eastern, Union, NJ; *U.S. Public*, pg. 1632
Orth, John, V.P.-Sls & Mktg.--Saab Cars USA, Inc., Norcross, GA; *Int'l*, pg. 687
Orth, Mark, Gen. Mgr.-Telecomm. & Mgr.-Sls.--Times Printing Company, Inc., Random Lake, WI; *U.S. Private*, pg. 1087
Ortiz, Elsa, Dir.-Mktg. & Promo.--Puerto Rico Tourism Company, San Juan, PR; *U.S. Private*, pg. 894
Ortiz, Hector, Exec. V.P. Sls. & Mktg.--Miller Products Company, Inc., North Bergen, NJ; *U.S. Private*, pg. 747
Ortiz, Lionel, Dir.-Mktg.--Cordis, a Johnson & Johnson Company, Miami, FL; *U.S. Public*, pg. 928
Ortueta, Antonio, Dir.-Sls. & Mktg., Trade--C.A. Cigarrera Bigott, Sucs., Caracas, Venezuela; *Int'l*, pg. 111
Ortyn, Andrew T., V.P.-Mktg.--Namico, Inc., Philadelphia, PA; *U.S. Private*, pg. 773
Osborn, Mike, Sr. V.P.-Mktg.--Robson Communities, Sun Lakes, AZ; *U.S. Private*, pg. 937
Osborne, Brian, V.P.-Mktg.--Sentinel Technologies Inc., Downers Grove, IL; *U.S. Private*, pg. 984
Osborne, Don, V.P.-Sls. & Mktg.--AMF Bakery Systems, Richmond, VA; *U.S. Private*, pg. 6
Osborne, Don, Mgr.-Mktg.--Spar Satellite Systems, Sainte-Anne-de-Bellevue, Canada; *Int'l*, pg. 1288
Osborne, Jim, Mgr.-Mktg.--Insurance Brokers & Managers, Inc., New Orleans, LA; *U.S. Public*, pg. 1677
Osborne, Jim, Mgr.-Mktg.--Lafayette Insurance Company, New Orleans, LA; *U.S. Public*, pg. 1677
Osborne, Joe C., Dir.-Mktg.--The Variable Annuity Life Insurance Co., Houston, TX; *U.S. Public*, pg. 76
Osborne, Marshall, Mgr.-Mktg.--DSM Engineering Plastic Products, Reading, PA; *Int'l*, pg. 354
Osburn, Dave, Dir.-Mktg.--Royal Rubber & Manufacturing Co., South Gate, CA; *U.S. Private*, pg. 949
Osherwitz, William, Chief Oper. Officer-Corp. Mktg.--Bessin Corporation, Chicago, IL; *U.S. Public*, pg. 1433
Osinski, Patrick, V.P.-Corp. Devel. & Govt. Affairs--Organon Inc., West Orange, NJ; *Int'l*, pg. 48
Osman, Stan, V.P.-Mktg.-Cake--Interstate Brands Corporation, Kansas City, MO; *U.S. Public*, pg. 909
Osos, Alan, Prod. Mgr.--Specialty Products Group, Niles, MI; *U.S. Public*, pg. 1160
Ostapowicz, Phil, V.P.-Mktg. & Sls.--Barry-Wehmiller Company, Saint Louis, MO; *U.S. Private*, pg. 118
Oster, Darren, Mgr.-Mktg.--Costa Cruise Lines, N.V., Miami, FL; *U.S. Private*, pg. 278
Osterman, L.B., V.P.-Mktg.-Steel--The Timken Company, Canton, OH; *U.S. Public*, pg. 1617
Ostern, Fred S., V.P.-Mktg.--FOTOBALL USA, Inc., San Diego, CA; *U.S. Public*, pg. 678
Ostroski, Carol, Mktg. & Sls. Acct. Exec.--Pegasus International Corporation, Pennington, NJ; *U.S. Private*, pg. 1046
Ostrow, Eric, V.P.-Mktg.--Ce De Candy, Inc., Union, NJ; *U.S. Private*, pg. 220
Osumi, T., Exec. V.P.-Mktg. & Sls.--Sumitomo Sitix Silicon, Inc., Fremont, CA; *Int'l*, pg. 1317
Oswald, Peter W., V.P.-Sls. & Mktg.--Akzo Nobel Fortafil Fibers Inc., Rockwood, TN; *Int'l*, pg. 48
Otelsberg, Barry L., Exec. V.P.-Commercial Mktg.--Pacific Crest Capital, Inc., Agoura Hills, CA; *U.S. Public*, pg. 1248
Oteri, Rosario, Dir.-Mktg.--Tri-K Industries, Inc., Northvale, NJ; *U.S. Private*, pg. 1100
Otis, William G., V.P.-Sls. & Mktg./Foodservice--Patrick Cudahy Inc., Cudahy, WI; *U.S. Public*, pg. 1479
Ott, J., Sr. Mgr.-Mktg.--CAE Elektronik GmbH, Stolberg, Germany; *Int'l*, pg. 238
Ott, Rick, Dir.-Mktg.--San Diego Union Tribune, San Diego, CA; *U.S. Private*, pg. 275
Ott, William F., Jr., Dir.-Corp. Mktg.--Watlow Electric Manufacturing Company, Saint Louis, MO; *U.S. Private*, pg. 1153
Ottaviani, David, Mgr.-Mktg.--Damascus Bishop Tube Co., Greenville, PA; *Int'l*, pg. 842
Ottaway, J.E., Dir.-Mktg.--Raytheon Support Systems, Long Beach, CA; *U.S. Public*, pg. 1364
Otte, Dick, Dir.-Commercial Mktg.--Curtiss-Wright Corp., Lyndhurst, NJ; *U.S. Public*, pg. 469
Otte, Dick, Dir.-Commercial Mktg.--Curtiss-Wright Flight Systems, Inc., Fairfield, NJ; *U.S. Public*, pg. 469
Otterbein, Gregory, Exec. V.P.-Mdse. & Mktg.--Sysco Food Services-Albany, Albany, NY; *U.S. Public*, pg. 1551
Otterstrom, Jim, V.P.-Mktg. Services--Brunswick Bowling & Billiards Corp., Muskegon, MI; *U.S. Public*, pg. 265
Ottestad, John O., Dir.-Refining & Mktg.--Norsk Hydro a.s, Oslo, Norway; *Int'l*, pg. 959
Ottie, Timothy W., Pres. & Gen. Mgr.--Thermal Transfer Corp., Monroeville, PA; *U.S. Public*, pg. 29
Otto, Dennis, V.P.-Mktg. & Opers.--Spartan Stores Inc., Grand Rapids, MI; *U.S. Private*, pg. 1021
Otto, Steve, Dir.-Mktg.--CTS Corporation-Connector Division, New Hope, MN; *U.S. Public*, pg. 285
Ottoson, Ulf, Mgr.-Mktg.--Esselte Sverige AB, Solna, Sweden; *Int'l*, pg. 459
Oueilette, Michael A., V.P.-Sls. & Mktg./Consumer Prods.--Carsen Group Inc., Markham, Canada; *U.S. Public*, pg. 301
Ouellette, Ray, Exec. V.P.-Sls. & Mktg.--IMI Cornelius Inc. (MN), Anoka, MN; *Int'l*, pg. 646
Ouellette, Ray, Exec. V.P.-Sls. & Mktg.--IMI Cornelius, Inc. (IA), Mason City, IA; *Int'l*, pg. 646
Oughterson, Mary, Dir.-Mktg.--Harden Furniture Company, McConnellsville, NY; *U.S. Private*, pg. 501
Outlaw, J. Thomas Jr., V.P. & Sls. Mgr.--Ingles Markets, Incorporated, Black Mountain, NC; *U.S. Public*, pg. 878
Overland, Dennis, Mgr.-Mktg. & Sls.-Fluid Power--Aro Fluid Products Division, Bryan, OH; *U.S. Public*, pg. 877
Overlock, Joan, V.P. & Dir.-Store Mktg.--The Limited, Inc., Columbus, OH; *U.S. Public*, pg. 995
Overly, Jere, Dir.-Mktg.--Lodgistix, Inc., Phoenix, AZ; *U.S. Public*, pg. 1527
Overweg, Ed, Mgr.-Intl. Mktg.--Thermotron Industries, Holland, MI; *U.S. Private*, pg. 1136
Owen, Michael E., V.P.-Mktg.--Robin Hood Multifoods Inc., Markham, Canada; *U.S. Public*, pg. 901
Owen, Rob, Dir.-Mktg.--Idahoan Foods, Lewisville, ID; *U.S. Private*, pg. 557
Owens, Leslie, Dir.-Mktg.--Pip Printing, Agoura Hills, CA; *U.S. Private*, pg. 423
Owens, Michael J., V.P.-Geographic & Ethnic Mktg.--Anheuser-Busch, Inc., Saint Louis, MO; *U.S. Public*, pg. 114
Owens, R. Harold, Pres. & Chief Oper. Officer--World Acceptance Corporation, Greenville, SC; *U.S. Public*, pg. 1778
Owens, Robert, V.P.-Mktg.--Sun Company, Inc., Philadelphia, PA; *U.S. Public*, pg. 1530
Owens, Robert, V.P.-Mktg.--Sun Company, Inc. (R&M), Philadelphia, PA; *U.S. Public*, pg. 1530
Owens, Sara, Mgr.-Mktg. Services--Churny Company Inc., Northbrook, IL; *U.S. Public*, pg. 1288
Owens, Stephen, V.P.-Sls. & Mktg.--Hofmann Industries, Inc., Sinking Spring, PA; *U.S. Private*, pg. 533
Oxby, Elizabeth, Mgr.-Mktg.--Letraset UK, London, United Kingdom; *Int'l*, pg. 462
Oxman, Michael, Sr. V.P. & Brand Mktg. Partner--DMB&B Detroit, Troy, MI; *U.S. Private*, pg. 302
Oyama, Eiji, Asst. V.P.-Mktg.--Sumitomo Bank of New York Trust Company, New York, NY; *Int'l*, pg. 1309
Oyaneder, Erwin, Dir.-Mktg.--Salvador Division, El Salvador, Chile; *Int'l*, pg. 302
Oyster, William, Pres., Chief Oper. Officer & Mgr.-Adv., Sls. & Mktg.--Dallas Gold & Silver Exchange, Inc., Dallas, TX; *U.S. Public*, pg. 478
Ozar, Bruce, V.P.-Sls.--Glen Oaks Industries, Inc., New York, NY; *U.S. Private*, pg. 456
Ozmun, John P., Dir.-Mktg.--20th Century Products Div., Los Angeles, CA; *U.S. Public*, pg. 153
Pacaro, Kirsten, Mgr.-Product Mktg.--Chi-Chi's Inc., Louisville, KY; *U.S. Private*, pg. 393
Pace, Don, Consultant-Sls. & Mktg.--Bassick by Kaspar, Shiner, TX; *U.S. Private*, pg. 122
Pace, Jane, Mgr.-Mktg.-Discus Athletic--Tultex Corporation, Martinsville, VA; *U.S. Public*, pg. 1644
Pacelli, Robert A., V.P.-Sls. & Mktg.--Weslock National, Inc., Los Angeles, CA; *U.S. Private*, pg. 1163
Pacenza, Lisa, Dir.-Mktg.--The CIT Group/Credit Finance, New York, NY; *Int'l*, pg. 360
Pacheco, Steve, Mgr.-Adv. & Mktg.--Hammermill Papers, Memphis, TN; *U.S. Public*, pg. 902
Pachi, Luigi, Mgr.-Mktg.--Datapoint Italia S.P.A., Milan, Italy; *Int'l*, pg. 384
Packer, Steven, V.P.-Mktg.--Comtech Communications Corp., Tempe, AZ; *U.S. Public*, pg. 425
Packshaw, Helena, Dir.-Mktg.--BHS Plc, London, United Kingdom; *Int'l*, pg. 1304
Pacyga, Robert, Dir.-Sls. & Mktg.--Minnesota Brewing Company, Saint Paul, MN; *U.S. Public*, pg. 1115
Padden, Roger M., Mgr.-Natl. Sls.--Hitox Corporation of America, Corpus Christi, TX; *U.S. Public*, pg. 829
Paddor, Kathy, Mgr.-Mktg.--Euromarket Designs, Inc., Northbrook, IL; *U.S. Private*, pg. 384
Padelford, Claire, Mgr.-Mktg. Communications--National Health Enhancement Systems, Inc., Phoenix, AZ; *U.S. Public*, pg. 1157
Padilla, Inger, Dir.-Mktg.--First American Real Estate Information Services, Inc., Saint Petersburg, FL; *U.S. Public*, pg. 625
Padnos, Mitchell W., V.P.-Sls. & Mktg.--Louis Padnos Iron & Metal Co., Holland, MI; *U.S. Private*, pg. 834
Pagano, Bill, Mgr.-Mktg. Svcs.--BASF Corporation, Mount Olive, NJ; *Int'l*, pg. 105
Pagano, Bob, V.P.-Mktg. & Product Plng.--Just Toys, New York, NY; *U.S. Private*, pg. 903
Pagano, Jim, Dir.-Mktg.--Florafax International, Inc., Vero Beach, FL; *U.S. Public*, pg. 654
Pagano, John, V.P.-Mkt. Res.--News America Marketing, Norwalk, CT; *Int'l*, pg. 925
Page, Eva, Dir.-Mktg.--Beverage Div., White Plains, NY; *U.S. Public*, pg. 1287
Page, Lou Ann, V.P. & Gen. Mgr.-Liquid Handling Div.--Medical Laboratory Automation, Inc., Pleasantville, NY; *U.S. Private*, pg. 727
Paggioli, Deborah, Dir.-Media--Gerber Scientific, Inc., South Windsor, CT; *U.S. Public*, pg. 740
Paglierani, Joan, Mgr.-Mktg. Communications--Unitrode Corporation, Merrimack, NH; *U.S. Public*, pg. 1694
Paguieri, Diego, Mgr.-Sls. & Mktg.--Ferrero Inc., Caguas, PR; *Int'l*, pg. 480
Paine, Bill, Mgr.-Commercial Mkts.--BC Gas Inc., Vancouver, Canada; *Int'l*, pg. 114
Paine, Jack, V.P.-Mktg.--Dayton Superior Corporation, Miamisburg, OH; *U.S. Private*, pg. 931
Painter, Pete, V.P.-Mktg.--Steering and Suspension Division, Saint Louis, MO; *U.S. Public*, pg. 443
Pajerski, Maureen, V.P.-Sls. & Mktg.--Rauland-Borg Corporation, Skokie, IL; *U.S. Private*, pg. 911
Pal, Sujit, Mgr.-Natl. Accts.--SunGard Financial Systems, Inc., Canoga Park, CA; *U.S. Public*, pg. 1534
Palante, Luke, V.P.-Sls. & Mktg.--Essex Grain Products, Inc., Frazer, PA; *U.S. Private*, pg. 383
Palasek, Hank, Dir.-Mktg. Svcs.--Packard BioScience Company, Meriden, CT; *U.S. Private*, pg. 833
Palazzolo, Piera, V.P.-Mktg.--Dale Carnegie Training, New York, NY; *U.S. Private*, pg. 308
Palczewski, Jorg, Dir.-Mktg.--McDonald's Deutschland GmbH, Munich, Germany; *U.S. Public*, pg. 1069
Palermo, Cynthia A., Mgr.-Mktg. Communications--The NutraSweet Kelco Company, San Diego, CA; *U.S. Public*, *pg. 1125*
Palfreeman, Neil, Dir.-Mktg.--MFI Furniture Center PLC, London, United Kingdom; *Int'l*, pg. 827
Palin, Nick, Sr. V.P.-Sls. & Mktg.--Rexall Sundown Inc., Boca Raton, FL; *U.S. Public*, pg. 1384
Palkiwala, Khrusheed, Mgr.-Mktg.--Alitalia Airlines, New York, NY; *Int'l*, pg. 652
Palko, Lorri M., Pres. & Chief Oper. Officer--Dorsey Trailers, Inc., Atlanta, GA; *U.S. Public*, pg. 520
Pallenik, Gary, V.P.-Sls & Mktg.--Comprehensive Behavioral Care, Inc., Tampa, FL; *U.S. Public*, pg. 419
Pallister, Tom, Dir.-Mktg.--Ford Motor Company Limited, Brentwood, United Kingdom; *U.S. Public*, pg. 666
Pallotta, Dino, V.P.-Relational Mktg.--Days Inns of America, Inc., Parsippany, NJ; *U.S. Public*, pg. 321
Palm, Mike, Dir.-N. America Mktg.--Berlitz International, Inc., Princeton, NJ; *U.S. Public*, pg. 221
Palma, Joseph J., V.P.-Sls. & Mktg.--E-Z-Em, Inc., Westbury, NY; *U.S. Public*, pg. 540
Palma, Joseph J., V.P.-Sls. & Mktg.--Enteric Products, Inc., Westbury, NY; *U.S. Public*, pg. 540
Palmer, Alan, Dir.-Mktg.--Cadbury Limited, Birmingham, United Kingdom; *Int'l*, pg. 248
Palmer, Cheryl, V.P.-Mktg.--Domecq Importers Inc., Old Greenwich, CT; *Int'l*, pg. 63
Palmer, Dave, Asst. V.P.-Mktg.--Alaska Airlines, Inc., Seattle, WA; *U.S. Public*, pg. 35
Palmer, Jeffrey H., V.P.-Sls. & Mktg.--Conmed Corporation, Utica, NY; *U.S. Public*, pg. 431
Palmer, Judy, Dir.-Mktg.--Holland America Line Westours, Seattle, WA; *U.S. Public*, pg. 306
Palmer, Steven, Dir.-Mktg. Svcs.--Guardian & Observer, London, United Kingdom; *Int'l*, pg. 577
Palmer, Zaleen, V.P.-Mktg.--Willis Corroon Corp. of Mobile, Mobile, AL; *Int'l*, pg. 1506
Palmieri, Gerardo, Dir.-Sls. & Mktg.--Scotsman Industries, Inc., Vernon Hills, IL; *U.S. Public*, pg. 1444
Palmieri, Gerardo, Dir.-Sls. & Mktg.--Frimont, S.p.A., Bettolino di Pogliano, Italy; *U.S. Public*, pg. 1445
Palmitier, Steve, Sr. V.P.-Mktg.--Midland National Life Insurance Co., Sioux Falls, SD; *U.S. Private*, pg. 963
Palo, Antero, Mgr.-Mktg.-The Americas--FINNAIR, New York, NY; *Int'l*, pg. 485
Palumbo, Daniel P., Chief Mktg. Officer & V.P.-Consumer Imaging--Eastman Kodak Company, Rochester, NY; *U.S. Public*, pg. 550
Paluzzi, Gina, Coord.-Mktg.--Stocker & Yale, Inc., Salem, NH; *U.S. Public*, pg. 1518
Paluzzi, Gina, Coord.-Mktg.--MFE Instruments, Salem, NH; *U.S. Public*, pg. 1518
Panagiotou, Elizabeth M., V.P. & Sr. Mktg. Officer--Elyria Savings & Trust National Bank, Elyria, OH; *U.S. Public*, pg. 646
Pancottine, Jeff, V.P.-Mktg.--Sequent Computer Systems, Inc., Beaverton, OR; *U.S. Public*, pg. 1459
Pando, Patrick, Dir.-Sls. & Mktg.--Lynch Machinery, Inc., Bainbridge, GA; *U.S. Public*, pg. 1022
Panebianco, James, Dir.-Mktg.--Conap Inc., Olean, NY; *U.S. Private*, pg. 261
Pang, Ark W., V.P.-Intl. Sls. & Mktg. & Gen. Mgr.-Equip. Div.--Ionics, Incorporated, Watertown, MA; *U.S. Public*, pg. 912
Panish, Tom Van, Mgr.-Mktg. Services--Cinergy, Plainfield, IN; *U.S. Public*, pg. 369
Pantelidis, James, Exec. V.P.--Petro-Canada, Calgary, Canada; *Int'l*, pg. 1041
Pantuso, Bill, Sr. V.P.-Mktg.--Chief Auto Parts, Dallas, TX; *U.S. Private*, pg. 236
Pao, Patti, Dir.-Mktg.--Guerlain, Inc., New York, NY; *Int'l*, pg. 780
Papa, Joseph, V.P.-Mktg. & Opers.--Novartis Pharmaceuticals, East Hanover, NJ; *Int'l*, pg. 973
Papa, T. Del, Dir.-Intl. & Asst. to Pres.--Benjamin Moore & Co., Montvale, NJ; *U.S. Private*, pg. 133
Papadellis, R.C., V.P.-Mktg.--Welch Foods Inc., A Cooperative, Concord, MA; *U.S. Private*, pg. 784
Papagni, Elizabeth, Mgr.-Mktg. Commun.--Industrial Electronic Engineers, Inc., Van Nuys, CA; *U.S. Private*, pg. 561
Papas, Claude, Dir.-Mktg.--Laboratoire LaChartre S.A., Blois, France; *U.S. Public*, pg. 1331
Papastavros, Theodore G., V.P.-Strategic Plng.--Ionics, Incorporated, Watertown, MA; *U.S. Public*, pg. 912
Pape, Gregory, Sr. V.P.-Sls. & Mktg.--American Shared Hospital Services, San Francisco, CA; *U.S. Public*, pg. 91
Pape, Janet, Mktg. Analyst--Schwab Corp., Lafayette, IN; *U.S. Private*, pg. 974
Pape, Robert R., Exec. V.P.--Neles-Jamesbury Corp., Worcester, MA; *Int'l*, pg. 1428
Papera, Richard D., V.P.-Sls. & Mktg.--Allstate Can Corporation, Parsippany, NJ; *U.S. Private*, pg. 44
Papermaster, Barry, V.P.-Mktg. Commun.--Best Power, Necedah, WI; *U.S. Private*, pg. 140
Papes, G.A., V.P.-Sls. & Mktg.--U.S. Can Company, Oak Brook, IL; *U.S. Public*, pg. 1681
Papesh, Patricia A., Sr. V.P.-Mktg.--American Greetings Corporation, Cleveland, OH; *U.S. Public*, pg. 77

Paping, R.V.M., Mgr.-Mktg.--Van Leeuwen Pipe and Tube Group B.V., Zwijndrecht, Netherlands; *Int'l*, pg. 1449

Papke, Brian J., V.P.-Mktg. & Sls.--WCI Machine Tools & Systems, Cincinnati, OH; *Int'l*, pg. 440

Papke, Charles, V.P.-Opers.--Harmony House Records & Tapes, Troy, MI; *U.S. Private*, pg. 503

Pappalardo, Frank S., Dir.-Corp. Mktg.--Environmental Services of America, Inc., Rahway, NJ; *U.S. Public*, pg. 546

Pappalardo, Joseph, V.P.-Mktg.--Unitrode Corporation, Merrimack, NH; *U.S. Public*, pg. 1694

Pappas, Danielle, Dir.-Mktg. & Pub. Rels.--Logo of the Americas, Fort Lauderdale, FL; *Int'l*, pg. 462

Paquette, M.W., Pres. & Reg. Dir.-Americas--Devro-Teepak, Inc., Westchester, IL; *Int'l*, pg. 408

Paquette, Nancy, Dir.-Channel Devel.--Tecmar Technologies, Inc., Longmont, CO; *Int'l*, pg. 1361

Paquette, Natalie, Mgr.-Mktg.--Uniboard Canada Inc., Laval, Canada; *Int'l*, pg. 1431

Para, Victor, V.P.-Sls. & Mktg.--Atalla Corporation, San Jose, CA; *U.S. Public*, pg. 417

Parco, Teodorico, Jr., Sr. Asst. V.P.-Mktg. & Ins.--Atlas Consolidated Mining & Development Corporation, Manila, Philippines; *Int'l*, pg. 95

Pardue, BethAnne N., Mgr.-Mktg.--Hackney and Sons, Inc., Washington, NC; *U.S. Private*, pg. 1097

Pardue, Murray, V.P.-Mktg.--The PBS&J Corporation, Miami, FL; *U.S. Private*, pg. 825

Pare, Anne, Mgr.-Mktg.--Union Industries, Inc., Providence, RI; *U.S. Private*, pg. 1119

Pare, Anne, Admin.-Sls. & Mktg.--Admiral Packaging, Inc., Providence, RI; *U.S. Private*, pg. 1119

Parham, Steve, V.P.-Mktg.--Healthsource Georgia, Atlanta, GA; *U.S. Public*, pg. 360

Parikh, Anand, V.P.-Mkt. Devel. & Bus. Plng.--Telco Systems, Inc., Norwood, MA; *U.S. Public*, pg. 1568

Paris, Jerry, Mgr.-Mktg.--Hobbs Corporation, Springfield, IL; *Int'l*, pg. 127

Parisse, Gabriella, Dir.-Mktg.--Johnson & Johnson S.p.A., Rome, Italy; *U.S. Public*, pg. 931

Park, Byung-Keun, Mng. Dir.--Ssangyong Shipping Co. Ltd., Seoul, Korea; *Int'l*, pg. 1292

Park, Chris S., Dir.-Mktg.-Korea, Japan & Micronesia--Grand Hyatt Seoul, Seoul, Korea; *U.S. Private*, pg. 551

Park, Chung-Il, Pres.--Bum-A Petroleum Co., Ltd., Seoul, Korea; *Int'l*, pg. 1292

Park, Hong-Jung, Dir.-Mktg.--Lotte Shopping Co. Ltd., Seoul, Korea; *Int'l*, pg. 819

Park, Hyo Sung, Sr. V.P.-Passenger Sls., Mktg. & Traffic--Korean Airlines Co., Ltd., Seoul, Korea; *Int'l*, pg. 758

Park, K.H., Coord.-Mktg. & Sls.--Hanjin Shipping Company Ltd., Seoul, Korea; *Int'l*, pg. 592

Park, Ken, Dir.-Mktg.--Facts on File News Services, New York, NY; *U.S. Public*, pg. 1327

Park, Linda, Grp. Mgr.-Natl. Mktg.--Amtrak-National Railroad Passenger Corp., Washington, DC; *U.S. Private*, pg. 68

Park, Young-Il, V.P.--Ssangyong Paper Co., Ltd., Seoul, Korea; *Int'l*, pg. 1292

Parker, Amy, V.P.-Mktg.--Smart & Final, Vernon, CA; *Int'l*, pg. 563

Parker, B.Z., Sr. V.P.-Refining, Mktg. & Transportation--Phillips Petroleum Company, Bartlesville, OK; *U.S. Public*, pg. 1290

Parker, Bruce, Sr. Exec. V.P. & Chief Merchant--Callaway Golf Company, Carlsbad, CA; *U.S. Public*, pg. 294

Parker, C.H., Dir.-Commercial Devel.--Charter plc, London, United Kingdom; *Int'l*, pg. 280

Parker, Jackie, Sr. Mktg. Analyst--Columbine JDS Systems, Inc., Denver, CO; *U.S. Public*, pg. 228

Parker, John, Dir.-Intl. Mktg.--Freudenberg Nonwovens, Durham, NC; *Int'l*, pg. 505

Parker, John, V.P.-Mktg. & Sls.--Woodmark Originals Inc., Archdale, NC; *U.S. Private*, pg. 747

Parker, John, V.P.-Mktg.--EnviroTech PumpSystems, Salt Lake City, UT; *Int'l*, pg. 1489

Parker, L. Edward, Exec. V.P.-Mktg.--Burlington Resources Inc., Houston, TX; *U.S. Public*, pg. 269

Parker, L. Edward, Exec. V.P.-Mktg.--Meridian Oil Holding Inc., Houston, TX; *U.S. Public*, pg. 269

Parker, Michael, V.P.-Commercial Mktg.--Encore Computer Corporation, Fort Lauderdale, FL; *U.S. Public*, pg. 580

Parker, Richard S., V.P.-Mktg.--Sundt Corp., Tucson, AZ; *U.S. Private*, pg. 1051

Parker, Steven, Sr. V.P.-Mktg. & Sls.--Red Roof Inns, Inc., Hilliard, OH; *U.S. Public*, pg. 1369

Parker, Susan, Dir.-Mktg. Programs--Southwest Airlines Co., Dallas, TX; *U.S. Public*, pg. 1493

Parker, Tom, V.P.-Sls. & Mktg.--Medeva Pharmaceuticals, Rochester, NY; *Int'l*, pg. 852

Parker, William S., V.P.-Mktg. & Sls.--American Dental Technologies, Southfield, MI; *U.S. Public*, pg. 70

Parkes, Bill, III, Dir.-Mktg.--Universal Construction Co., Huntsville, AL; *U.S. Public*, pg. 1646

Parkes, Susan, Dir.-Mktg.--Ladies' Home Journal, New York, NY; *U.S. Public*, pg. 1094

Parkhill, Jeff, Brand Mgr.--Everfresh Beverages Inc., Chicago, IL; *U.S. Public*, pg. 1153

Parkinson, D., V.P.-Sls. & Mktg.--Eureka Manufacturing Co., Inc., Norton, MA; *U.S. Private*, pg. 916

Parkinson, David, V.P.-Mktg.--Alberto-Culver Canada, Inc., Toronto, Canada; *U.S. Public*, pg. 38

Parkinson, Donald, Sr. V.P.-Franchising--Kentucky Fried Chicken Corporation (KFC), Louisville, KY; *U.S. Public*, pg. 1636

Parks, Carrie, Mktg. Mgr.--Ingalls, Boston, MA; *U.S. Private*, pg. 562

Parks, Ken, V.P.-Mktg.--Atols Tool and Mold Corp., Schiller Park, IL; *U.S. Private*, pg. 97

Parks, Kent R., Dir.-Adv.--Nasco International, Inc., Fort Atkinson, WI; *U.S. Private*, pg. 446

Parlak, Pamela, Mgr.-Mktg. & Adv.-Lenox Retail--Lenox Brands, Lawrenceville, NJ; *U.S. Public*, pg. 261

Parlette, J. Samuel, V.P.-Sls. & Mktg.--Cavco Industries, Inc., Phoenix, AZ; *U.S. Public*, pg. 323

Parmentier, Rob, Sr. V.P.-Domestic Sls. & Mktg.--Sea Ray, Knoxville, TN; *U.S. Public*, pg. 266

Paro, John J., V.P.-Mktg. & Sls.--The C.P. Hall Company, Chicago, IL; *U.S. Private*, pg. 495

Parr, Douglas, V.P.-Sls. & Mktg.--Dean Foods Company, Franklin Park, IL; *U.S. Public*, pg. 489

Parris, J.R., Dir.-Mktg.--Hobbs Corporation, Springfield, IL; *Int'l*, pg. 127

Parrish, Diana, Mgr.-Adv. & Mktg.--Thomasville Upholstery, Inc., Hickory, NC; *U.S. Public*, pg. 688

Parrish, Mark, Exec. V.P.-Sls. & Mktg.--Cardinal Health Inc., Dublin, OH; *U.S. Public*, pg. 304

Parrish, Mark W., Exec. V.P.-Sls. & Mktg.--Cardinal Distribution, Dublin, OH; *U.S. Public*, pg. 304

Parrish, Stephen Bennett, V.P.-Mktg. Supplies--American Mutual Life Holding Co., Des Moines, IA; *U.S. Private*, pg. 59

Parrot, Kenneth D., Dir.-Mktg.--Bank One, Kentucky, NA, Louisville, KY; *U.S. Public*, pg. 173

Parrotta, Linda, V.P.-Mktg.--Costa Cruise Lines, N.V., Miami, FL; *U.S. Private*, pg. 278

Parry, Keith, Mgr.-Mktg.--Adams Rite (Europe) Ltd., Swanley, United Kingdom; *U.S. Private*, pg. 17

Parry, Norma, Dir.-Mktg.--River Crest Hospital, San Angelo, TX; *U.S. Public*, pg. 1697

Parsanko, William, V.P.-Mktg.--C. B. Fleet Co., Inc., Lynchburg, VA; *U.S. Private*, pg. 410

Parsinen, Peter H., Sr. V.P.-Customer & Mktg. Support--Bell Helicopter Textron, Hurst, TX; *U.S. Public*, pg. 1588

Parsonage, Barry, Mgr.-Mktg. Powder Coatings--Jones Blair Company, Dallas, TX; *U.S. Private*, pg. 596

Parsons, Don, V.P.-Sls. & Mktg.--TNT Vacations, Boston, MA; *U.S. Private*, pg. 1065

Parsons, Richard, V.P.-Sls. & Mktg.--Westec Security Inc., Irvine, CA; *Int'l*, pg. 1217

Parsons, Terry N., Sr. V.P.-Mktg.--AMCORE Capital Management, Inc., Rockford, IL; *U.S. Public*, pg. 64

Partington, Roger, Dir.-Mktg.--Safeway PLC, Hayes, United Kingdom; *Int'l*, pg. 1169

Pas, Gregory, Jr., Mgr.-Mktg.--Aeros Instruments, Inc., Gurnee, IL; *U.S. Private*, pg. 1028

Pascale, Anthony, Gen. Mgr. & Mgr.-Mktg. & Sls.--Exsil, Inc., San Jose, CA; *Int'l*, pg. 802

Paschal, Bruce, Pres.-Duda Sls. Division--A. Duda & Sons Inc., Oviedo, FL; *U.S. Private*, pg. 344

Pascocello, Rick, Dir.-Adv.--Berkley Publishing Corp., New York, NY; *Int'l*, pg. 1027

Pasewark, Richard, Dir.-Mktg. & Pub. Relations--Edwards Super Food Stores, Carlisle, PA; *Int'l*, pg. 749

Pasewark, Richard, Dir.-Mktg. & Pub. Rels.--Edwards Super Food Stores, Long Island Div., Garden City, NY; *Int'l*, pg. 750

Pash, J., V.P.--Kathabar Incorporated, Somerset, NJ; *U.S. Private*, pg. 609

Pashley, A.R., Dir.-Household & Furnishing Mktg.--Bentalls plc, Kingston upon Thames, United Kingdom; *Int'l*, pg. 187

Pasqualina, Michael, Events Coord.--Discovery Communications, Inc., Bethesda, MD; *U.S. Private*, pg. 334

Passaglia, Ron, Sr. Exec. V.P.--Simmons Company, Atlanta, GA; *Int'l*, pg. 686

Passaro, Linda, V.P.-Mktg.--Baume Mercier, Inc., New York, NY; *U.S. Private*, pg. 124

Passe, Jennifer, Mgr.-Mktg.--AVC/Nu-Vision, Inc., Flint, MI; *U.S. Private*, pg. 9

Passey, Terrence, V.P.-Mktg.--Dowty Aerospace Aviation Services, Sterling, VA; *Int'l*, pg. 1337

Paszamant, David, Vice Chm., Exec. V.P. & Dir.-Mktg.--Adams Wine Co., Atlanta, GA; *U.S. Private*, pg. 17

Patane, Louis, Exec. Dir.-Motorsports Mktg.--Chrysler Corporation, Auburn Hills, MI; *U.S. Public*, pg. 352

Patano, Patricia, Dir.-Mktg. & Productions--J.D. Power and Associates, Agoura Hills, CA; *U.S. Private*, pg. 878

Patchen, James J., V.P.-Mktg. & Sls., Biological Prods.--Bayer Corporation/Pharmaceutical Division, West Haven, CT; *Int'l*, pg. 173

Pate, Jane A., Mktg. Coord.--D.C. Taylor Co., Cedar Rapids, IA; *U.S. Private*, pg. 1070

Pate, Mark A., Mgr.-Mktg.-Skin Care--Stanback Company, Salisbury, NC; *U.S. Private*, pg. 1030

Pate, Ronald O., Sr. V.P.-Sls. & Mktg.--Horace Small Apparel Company, Nashville, TN; *Int'l*, pg. 635

Pate, Tony, Dir.-Mktg.--Lazy Days R V Center, Inc., Seffner, FL; *U.S. Private*, pg. 655

Patel, Vinay, V.P.-Mktg.--Knights Franchise Systems, Inc., Parsippany, NJ; *U.S. Public*, pg. 321

Paterno, C.F., Div. V.P.-Indus. Prods. & Paper-Europe--Sonoco Products Company, Hartsville, SC; *U.S. Public*, pg. 1485

Paterson, Brian D., Sr. V.P.-Pur. & Mktg.--Southern Electronics Corporation, Tucker, GA; *U.S. Public*, pg. 1490

Paterson, Graham, V.P.-Sls. & Mktg.--Computer Corporation of America, Framingham, MA; *U.S. Private*, pg. 260

Pathan, M.A., Exec. Dir.-Mktg. Opers.--Indian Oil Corporation Limited, New Delhi, India; *Int'l*, pg. 673

Patire, Debbie, Dir.-Mktg.--Madison Square Garden Network, New York, NY; *U.S. Public*, pg. 288

Patmor, Roxanne, Mgr.-Mktg. Communications--Edison International, Rosemead, CA; *U.S. Public*, pg. 564

Patnode, Stephanie M., Coord.-Mktg.--Adams Express Co., Baltimore, MD; *U.S. Public*, pg. 1280

Paton, Jack, V.P.-Sls. & Mktg./Lotus--Columbus Mills, Inc., Columbus, GA; *U.S. Private*, pg. 256

Paton, Jack, V.P.-Sls. & Mktg.--Lotus Carpet Division, Phenix City, AL; *U.S. Private*, pg. 257

Paton, Michael, Dir.-Mktg.--Peter Pan Bus Lines, Inc., Springfield, MA; *U.S. Private*, pg. 856

Patrick, Debra R., Mgr.-Mktg.--Townsend & Bottum, Inc., Ann Arbor, MI; *U.S. Private*, pg. 146

Patrick, Jean A., Exec. V.P. & Dir.-Mktg.--The W.W. Williams Company, Columbus, OH; *U.S. Private*, pg. 1178

Patrick, Shelly, Mgr.-Mktg.--Willert Home Products, Inc., Saint Louis, MO; *U.S. Private*, pg. 1177

Patrone, Mary Jane, V.P.-Sls. & Mktg.--Globe Newspaper Company, Boston, MA; *U.S. Public*, pg. 1175

Patrone, Mary Jane, V.P.-Mktg.--The Boston Globe, Boston, MA; *U.S. Public*, pg. 1175

Patschke, Edwin L., Mgr.-Mktg.--NGL American Life, Menasha, WI; *U.S. Private*, pg. 784

Patterson, Barry, V.P.-Mktg.--Magruder Color Company, Inc., Elizabeth, NJ; *U.S. Private*, pg. 696

Patterson, Dennis M., Sr. V.P.-Mktg.--SunTrust Banks, Inc., Atlanta, GA; *U.S. Public*, pg. 1537

Patterson, Dick, V.P.-Mktg.--Aerospace Products, Inc., Wilmington, MA; *U.S. Public*, pg. 100

Patterson, Mike, Mgr.-Mktg.--Esselte Chrono AB, Solna, Sweden; *Int'l*, pg. 459

Patterson, Stephen, Dir.-Prod. Mgmnt. & Mktg.--Mercury Computer Systems, Inc., Chelmsford, MA; *U.S. Private*, pg. 732

Patti, Jeffrey, Dir.-Mktg.--The General Electric Company, p.l.c., London, United Kingdom; *Int'l*, pg. 543

Patton, Sarah, Dir.-Mktg.--Land-O-Sun Dairies, Inc., Johnson City, TN; *U.S. Private*, pg. 646

Patty, R. Bruce, V.P.-Mktg.--Burns & McDonnell Engineers-Architects-Consultants, Kansas City, MO; *U.S. Private*, pg. 187

Pattyjohn, Thad, V.P.-Sls.--Jamison Bedding, Inc., Franklin, TN; *U.S. Private*, pg. 581

Paul, Olivier, Mgr.-Mktg.--Beiersdorf S.A., Savigny-le-Temple, France; *Int'l*, pg. 183

Paul, Shari, Dir.-Mktg. Communications--CalComp Technology, Inc., Anaheim, CA; *U.S. Public*, pg. 1007

Pauler, Ingo, V.P.-Auto Lubricants Mktg./Americas/Southern Europe--Fuchs Petrolub AG Oel + Chemie, Mannheim, Germany; *Int'l*, pg. 517

Paull, Jim, Sr. V.P.-Sls. & Mktg.--Competitive Media Reporting, New York, NY; *Int'l*, pg. 1447

Paulson, Dave, V.P.-Sls. & Mktg.--Oceana Foods, Shelby, MI; *U.S. Private*, pg. 234

Paulson, David, V.P.-Mktg. & Sls.-Canned--Cherry Central Cooperative, Traverse City, MI; *U.S. Private*, pg. 233

Paulson, Duane, V.P.-Mktg.--Interactive Technologies, Inc., Saint Paul, MN; *U.S. Public*, pg. 888

Paulson, Randy, Mgr.-Mktg.--Woodward-Clyde, Portland, OR; *U.S. Public*, pg. 1656

Paulus, Michael S., Exec. V.P.-Mktg. Communications--Dix & Eaton Incorporated, Cleveland, OH; *U.S. Private*, pg. 336

Pavelski, Peggy, Mktg. Asst.--First Financial Bank, FSB, Stevens Point, WI; *U.S. Public*, pg. 140

Pawlik, Michael M., V.P.- Mktg.--Burr-Brown Corporation, Tucson, AZ; *U.S. Public*, pg. 270

Pawlik, Thomas, V.P.-Corp. Mktg.--Medline Industries, Inc., Mundelein, IL; *U.S. Private*, pg. 728

Paxton, Marion, Grp. Prod. Mgr.--Chicago Cutlery, Inc., Terre Haute, IN; *U.S. Public*, pg. 716

Paxton, Sol, Dir.-Mktg.--Today's Kids, Booneville, AR; *U.S. Private*, pg. 1020

Payne, Geneva, Mktg. Asst.--Sara Lee Knit Products, Winston Salem, NC; *U.S. Public*, pg. 1434

Payne, Michael, Dir.-Mktg.--Hillcross Pharmaceuticals, Runcorn, United Kingdom; *Int'l*, pg. 591

Payne, Michelle, Coord.-Communications--Freudenberg-NOK, Plymouth, MI; *U.S. Private*, pg. 427

Payne, Richard C., Dir.-Mktg.--Pierce National Life Insurance Co., Greenville, SC; *U.S. Public*, pg. 992

Payton, Billy, V.P.-Mktg.--Neiman Marcus Co., Dallas, TX; *U.S. Public*, pg. 785

Pazolt, Warren, V.P.-Sls. & Mktg.--Ernest Paper Products, Inc., Los Angeles, CA; *U.S. Private*, pg. 381

Peacock, Gary, Gen. Mgr.--Covington Foods, Inc., Covington, IN; *U.S. Private*, pg. 280

Pearce, Mike, V.P.-Sls. & Mktg.-Smith Diamond Tech.--Smith International, Inc., Houston, TX; *U.S. Public*, pg. 1478

Pearce, Richard A., Exec. V.P.-Mktg.--Purina Grocery Products Group, Saint Louis, MO; *U.S. Public*, pg. 1360

Pearce, Stan, Mgr.-Mktg. & Sls.--AGRA Plastics Inc., Mississauga, Canada; *Int'l*, pg. 30

Pearcy, W.J., V.P.-Mktg.--Houghton International Inc., Valley Forge, PA; *U.S. Private*, pg. 541

Pearsall, Roger, V.P.-North American--National Safety Associates, Memphis, TN; *U.S. Private*, pg. 786

Pearson, J.R., Mgr.-Mktg. Services--Vapor, Niles, IL; *U.S. Public*, pg. 1761

Pearson, John, V.P.-Mktg.--Casablanca Fan Company, Pomona, CA; *U.S. Private*, pg. 549

Pearson, John C., V.P.-Mktg.--Casablanca Fan Co., Inc., Memphis, TN; *U.S. Private*, pg. 549

Pearson, Scott, V.P.-Sls. & Mktg.--Digital Communications of America, Inc., Oklahoma City, OK; *U.S. Private*, pg. 872

Pearson, Tim, Dir.-Mktg.--KPMG LLP, New York, NY; *U.S. Private*, pg. 603

Pease, David H., III, V.P.-Engrng., Mfg. & Sec.--Pease Industries, Inc., Fairfield, OH; *U.S. Private*, pg. 845

Peavy, Mike, V.P.-Sls. & Mktg.--Cherokee Brick & Tile Co., Macon, GA; *U.S. Private*, pg. 233

Pecha, Robert O., V.P.-Sls. & Mktg.--Chemstone Corp., Strasburg, VA; *U.S. Private*, pg. 233

Peck, Chuck, Sr. V.P.-Mktg., Prods., Organization & Devel.--American Institute of C.P.A.'s Inc., New York, NY; *U.S. Private*, pg. 57

Peck, Don, V.P.-Sls. & Mktg.--Heat Controller, Inc., Jackson, MI; *U.S. Private*, pg. 518

Peck, Mike, Dir.-Mktg. Commun.--Modernfold, Inc., New Castle, IN; *U.S. Private*, pg. 755

Peck, Richard, V.P.-Sls. & Mktg.--Levlad, Inc., Chatsworth, CA; *U.S. Private*, pg. 663

Peckham, Terry, Mgr.-Marcom-Mktg.--Brown and Caldwell, Pleasant Hill, CA; *U.S. Private*, pg. 173

Pecorelli, Patrick, Mgr.-Mktg. Communications--M/A-COM Inc., Lowell, MA; *U.S. Public*, pg. 8

Pecori, Sergio A., Sr. V.P.--Hanson Engineers Inc., Springfield, IL; *U.S. Private*, pg. 500
Pecson, Reuben N., Asst. V.P.-Mktg. & Adv.--Philippine Airlines, Inc., Manila, Philippines; *Int'l*, pg. 1050
Peddicord, Herschel, Sr. V.P.-Mktg., Sls. & Engrng.--Criticare Systems, Inc., Waukesha, WI; *U.S. Public*, pg. 459
Pederon, Jim, Mgr.-Mktg. & Adv.--Lee Grocery Company, Everett, WA; *U.S. Private*, pg. 657
Pedersen, Alan, Mgr.-Mktg., Independent Fabricator Group--Hunter Douglas, Inc., Upper Saddle River, NJ; *Int'l*, pg. 639
Pederson, Gary, Mgr.-Mktg. & Sls.--Portec, Inc.-Construction Equipment Div., Yankton, SD; *U.S. Public*, pg. 1318
Pedlar, Bill, V.P.-Mktg.--Holland America Line Westours, Seattle, WA; *U.S. Public*, pg. 306
Pedler, Charles, Sr. Dir.-Mktg./Healthcare Div.--Executone Information Systems, Inc., Milford, CT; *U.S. Public*, pg. 599
Pee, Weldon, Dir.-Mktg.--Summit Performance Dist. Inc., Channelview, TX; *U.S. Public*, pg. 1233
Peel, Mark, V.P.-Mktg.--Maxwell Macmillan Professional & Business Reference Publishing, Englewood Cliffs, NJ; *U.S. Public*, pg. 1602
Peerbolte, Jerry D., V.P.-Mktg.--Baldor Electric Company, Fort Smith, AR; *U.S. Public*, pg. 168
Peeters, Johan, Dir.-Corp. Mktg.--Interbrew S.A., Leuven, Belgium; *Int'l*, pg. 679
Pefanis, Harry N., Sr. V.P.--Plains Resources Inc., Houston, TX; *U.S. Public*, pg. 1307
Peier, Heino, Mgr.-Communication--Coop Switzerland, Basel, Switzerland; *Int'l*, pg. 329
Peiring, Jeff, Dir.-Produce & Floral--The Food Emporium, Bronx, NY; *Int'l*, pg. 1375
Pelak, Dan, V.P.-Health Cares Systems Mktg.-Americas--Medtronic, Inc., Minneapolis, MN; *U.S. Public*, pg. 1082
Pelger, T.P., Mgr.-Mktg. Communications--Caterpillar Inc., Peoria, IL; *U.S. Public*, pg. 315
Pelham, Cindy, Mgr.-Field Mktg.--KinderCare Learning Centers, Inc., Portland, OR; *U.S. Public*, pg. 961
Pelizzari, Giovanni, Exec. Dir.-Bus. Unit Office Systems--Oce-van der Grinten N.V., Venlo, Netherlands; *Int'l*, pg. 993
Pellegrene, John, Exec. V.P.-Mktg.--Target Stores, Minneapolis, MN; *U.S. Public*, pg. 489
Pellegrinetti, Chris, Gen. Mgr.-Mktg.--Dun & Bradstreet (Australia) Pty. Ltd., Melbourne, Australia; *U.S. Public*, pg. 536
Pellegrini, Mary Ann, Mgr.-Mktg. & Adv.--Cablewave Systems, North Haven, CT; *U.S. Private*, pg. 197
Pelliccioni, David E., Mgr.-Corp. Mktg.--Toyota Motor Sales, U.S.A., Inc., Torrance, CA; *Int'l*, pg. 1412
Pellman, Mark, Mgr.-Mktg.--Multi-Arc Inc., Rockaway, NJ; *Int'l*, pg. 1198
Pelosi, M., V.P.-Sls. & Mktg.--Tranter, Inc., Augusta, GA; *U.S. Public*, pg. 521
Peltier, Art, Dir.-Product. Devel.--Schneider Automation, Inc., North Andover, MA; *Int'l*, pg. 1208
Peltola, Arlene, Mgr.-Grp. Mktg.--Just Born, Inc., Bethlehem, PA; *U.S. Private*, pg. 602
Peltola, Esa, V.P.-Mktg.--Bronto Skylift Oy AB, Tampere, Finland; *U.S. Public*, pg. 617
Pemberton, Brad, V.P.-Mktg.--Doublecoat, L.L.C., Jackson, MS; *U.S. Private*, pg. 266
Pena, Alexandra, Dir.-Mktg.--Merisel Latin America, Miami, FL; *U.S. Public*, pg. 1096
Pena, Oliver, V.P.-Mktg.--Johnson & Johnson de Argentina, S.A., Buenos Aires, Argentina; *U.S. Public*, pg. 930
Pendleton, Kip, Dir.-Mktg.--Mycogen Seeds, Saint Paul, MN; *U.S. Public*, pg. 1142
Pendleton, T., Sr. V.P.-Sls. & Mktg.--Corner Brook Pulp & Paper Limited, Corner Brook, Canada; *Int'l*, pg. 761
Pendleton, T.N., Sr. V.P.-Sls. & Mktg./Paper Prods.--Kruger Inc., Montreal, Canada; *Int'l*, pg. 761
Pendleton, T.N., Sr. V.P.-Sls. & Mktg./Paper Prods.--Bromptonville Mill, Bromptonville, Canada; *Int'l*, pg. 761
Pendleton, T.N., Sr. V.P.-Sls. & Mktg.--Kruger Inc., Montreal, Canada; *Int'l*, pg. 761
Pengelly, Eydie, Mgr.-Mktg.--Shell Chemical Co., Houston, TX; *Int'l*, pg. 1136
Penn, Richard, V.P.-Sls. & Mktg.--Hutchinson Technology Inc., Hutchinson, MN; *U.S. Public*, pg. 850
Penna, Sandra, Dir.-Mktg.--Enerfab Inc., Cincinnati, OH; *U.S. Private*, pg. 376
Pennacchio, John A., V.P. & Grp. Mktg. Dir.--Shieffelin Somerset Co., New York, NY; *Int'l*, pg. 412
Pennavaria, Russell, Dir.-Mktg. & Sls.-Medical Div.--Cincinnati Sub-Zero Products, Inc., Cincinnati, OH; *U.S. Private*, pg. 240
Pennell, Gary B., V.P.-Mktg., Sls. & Adv.--Diamond Chain Company, Indianapolis, IN; *U.S. Private*, pg. 68
Pennella, Mike, Exec. V.P.--Lamb-Weston, Inc., Kennewick, WA; *U.S. Public*, pg. 427
Penney, Jay, V.P.-Sls. & Mktg.--Frigidaire Home Products, Dublin, OH; *Int'l*, pg. 439
Pennington, Joe, V.P.-Estimating--George & Lynch, Inc., New Castle, DE; *U.S. Private*, pg. 448
Penny, Cindy, Coord.-Mktg.--Spaghetti Warehouse, Inc., Garland, TX; *U.S. Public*, pg. 1495
Penny, Jay, V.P.-Sls. & Mktg.--White Consolidated Industries, Inc., Cleveland, OH; *Int'l*, pg. 439
Penny, Jay, V.P.-Sls. & Mktg.-Appliances--Gibson Appliances, Dublin, OH; *Int'l*, pg. 439
Penny, Jay, V.P.-Sls. & Mktg.-Appliances--Kelvinator Appliances, Dublin, OH; *Int'l*, pg. 440
Pensinger, Larry, Dir.-Mktg.--Hardware Wholesalers, Inc., Fort Wayne, IN; *U.S. Private*, pg. 502
Peoples, Larry, Sr. V.P.-Mktg.--Riverside Manufacturing Co., Moultrie, GA; *U.S. Private*, pg. 934
Peoples, Thomas, V.P.-Mktg. Intl. Bus.--Aerojet, Sacramento, CA; *U.S. Public*, pg. 706
Pepin, Carolan, Dir.-Mktg.--Mikohn Gaming Corporation, Las Vegas, NV; *U.S. Public*, pg. 1111
Pepp, Denise, Dir.-Mktg. & Sls. Promo.--Stuart Anderson's Black Angus/Cattle Company Restaurants, Los Altos, CA; *U.S. Private*, pg. 61
Peppel, Alan S., Dir.-Mktg.--Russell Harrington Cutlery Inc., Southbridge, MA; *U.S. Private*, pg. 551
Pepper, Alan, Dir.-Prod. Mktg.--WEA Corp., Burbank, CA; *U.S. Public*, pg. 1612
Pepper, Kade, Rep.-Sls. & Customer Svcs.--New England Machinery, Inc., Bradenton, FL; *U.S. Private*, pg. 793
Pepper, Robert A., Asst. Gen. Mgr.-Mktg.--Derbyshire Building Society, Duffield, United Kingdom; *Int'l*, pg. 394
Peppercorn, Wayne, V.P.-Mktg.--LSI Industries, Inc., Cincinnati, OH; *U.S. Public*, pg. 971
Pepperton, Pat, Admin. Asst.-Mktg.--Stein Inc., Sandusky, OH; *Int'l*, pg. 13
Pepys Lowe, Renee, Exec. V.P.-Sls. & Mktg.--Noel Joanna, Inc., Rancho Santa Margarita, CA; *U.S. Public*, pg. 465
Pera, Jaime, Mgr.-Mktg.--Sensormatic E.C., S.A., Madrid, Spain; *U.S. Public*, pg. 1457
Peralta, Carlos, Sr. Mgr.-Mktg.--Bacardi-Martini, USA, Inc., Miami, FL; *U.S. Private*, pg. 109
Percenti, Don, Sr. V.P.-Sls. & Mktg./Balfour--Commemorative Brands, Inc., Austin, TX; *U.S. Private*, pg. 258
Percenti, Don, Sr. V.P.-Sls. & Mktg.--L.G. Balfour Co., Inc., Austin, TX; *U.S. Private*, pg. 258
Percovic, Branco, Mgr.-Mktg.--Helly-Hansen AB, Spanga, Sweden; *Int'l*, pg. 1010
Percy, Geoff, Dir.-Mktg.--Smith & Nephew Consumer Products Ltd., Birmingham, United Kingdom; *Int'l*, pg. 1263
Perdiguer, Miguel, Asst. Mgr.--Caixa d'Estalvis de Catalunya, Barcelona, Spain; *Int'l*, pg. 249
Perea, Kathy, Mgr.-Mrkt. Res.--Baskin-Robbins Incorporated, Glendale, CA; *Int'l*, pg. 63
Peres, Edward J., Div. Mgr.--Fuchs Lubricants, Midlantic Div., Baltimore, MD; *Int'l*, pg. 518
Peres, Jose Antonio, Mgr.-Mktg. Services--Johnson & Johnson Ltda., Sao Paulo, Brazil; *U.S. Public*, pg. 931
Perez, Eridania, V.P.-Mktg., Promotions & Sls.--Marcel Dekker, Inc., New York, NY; *U.S. Private*, pg. 321
Perez, Gabriel, Mgr.-Sls./Northeast--Iberia Air Lines of Spain, Miami, FL; *Int'l*, pg. 575
Perez, Jerry, Sr. V.P.-Mktg.--Fisher-Price, Inc., East Aurora, NY; *U.S. Public*, pg. 1058
Perez, Marcos, Mgr.-Mktg.--Bacardi-Martini, USA, Inc., Miami, FL; *U.S. Private*, pg. 109
Pericron, Pierre, Dir.-Mktg.--SmithKline Beecham Products France S.A., Nanterre, France; *Int'l*, pg. 1266
Perkalis, Barbara, Dir.-Mktg.--Carnrick Laboratories, Inc., Cedar Knolls, NJ; *U.S. Private*, pg. 436
Perkins, Cheryl, Mktg. Asst. & Trade Show Coord.--Prism Integrated Sanitation Management, Inc., Miami, FL; *U.S. Private*, pg. 592
Perkins, Jerry, Staff V.P.-Mktg.--Brunswick Corporation, Lake Forest, IL; *U.S. Public*, pg. 265
Perkins, Jim, Mgr.-Natl. Sls.--M & C Specialties Company, Southampton, PA; *U.S. Private*, pg. 684
Perkins, Kevin, Sr. Dir.-Cargo Sls. & Mktg.--America West Airlines, Inc., Phoenix, AZ; *U.S. Public*, pg. 67
Perkins, M.G., V.P.-Domestic Sls. & Mktg.--Morganite Inc., Dunn, NC; *Int'l*, pg. 891
Perkins, Paul K., V.P.-Mktg. & Corp. Plng.--Weyerhaeuser Canada Ltd., Vancouver, Canada; *U.S. Public*, pg. 1764
Perkins, Philip D., V.P.-Mktg.--Snyder's Drug Stores, Inc., Minnetonka, MN; *U.S. Private*, pg. 1011
Perkins, Robert, Mgr.-Mktg.--Jacobs Vehicle Equipment Company, Bloomfield, CT; *U.S. Public*, pg. 481
Perkins, Sharon, Sls. & Mktg. Asst.--Saunders Brothers, Westbrook, ME; *U.S. Private*, pg. 968
Perkins, Sherry, Dir.-Mktg. & Adv.--J.E. Higgins Lumber Co., Concord, CA; *U.S. Private*, pg. 527
Perks, Lachlan, V.P.-Mktg. & Sls.--Eclipse Inc., Rockford, IL; *U.S. Private*, pg. 360
Perl, Allen S., V.P.--T.L. Diamond Company, New York, NY; *U.S. Private*, pg. 330
Perlberg, Mark, Sr. V.P., Pres., Fin. Sls. Mktg. Division--The Check Store, Lakewood, CO; *U.S. Public*, pg. 785
Perlman, Milton, Consultant--Schott Brothers, Inc., Perth Amboy, NJ; *U.S. Private*, pg. 972
Perlmuter, Michael, Pres.--Perlmuter Printing Company, Cleveland, OH; *Int'l*, pg. 1177
Perman, Tim, Mgr.-Mktg.--Bristol Myers Co. Ltd., Ickenham, United Kingdom; *U.S. Public*, pg. 255
Pernas, Jim, Mgr.-Mktg.--Subaru Mid-America, Inc., Addison, IL; *Int'l*, pg. 523
Peroutka, Michael S., Exec. V.P.-Sls. & Mktg.--Faribault Foods Inc., Minneapolis, MN; *U.S. Private*, pg. 393
Peroutka, Michael S., Exec. V.P.-Sls. & Mktg.--Kuner-Empson Company, Brighton, CO; *U.S. Private*, pg. 393
Perrault, William, V.P.-Mktg.--Columbia Tri-Star Home Video, Burbank, CA; *Int'l*, pg. 1282
Perrier, Don, Mgr.-Pur.--Waterbury Farrel Technologies, Cheshire, CT; *U.S. Private*, pg. 461
Perrier, Gerald, V.P.-Mktg.--Welsco Inc., North Little Rock, AR; *U.S. Private*, pg. 1161
Perrine, Elizabeth, Mgr.-Mktg.--Time Systems, Inc., Phoenix, AZ; *U.S. Private*, pg. 1086
Perrone, Anthony, V.P.-Sls. & Mktg.--Refined Sugars, Inc., Yonkers, NY; *Int'l*, pg. 699
Perrotta, Mario, Mktg. Engr.--Norwalk Co., Inc., Norwalk, CT; *U.S. Private*, pg. 807
Perry, Daphne, Coord.-Mktg. Svcs.--H.J. Heinz Co. of Canada Ltd., North York, Canada; *U.S. Public*, pg. 806
Perry, Elisabeth L., Mgr.-Bus. Commun.--Consumers Water Company, Portland, ME; *U.S. Public*, pg. 438
Perry, Foster, Dir.-Bus. Devel.--Teledyne Brown Engineering, Huntsville, AL; *U.S. Public*, pg. 43
Perry, Joseph Z., V.P.-Sls. & Mktg.--ICL, Inc., Irvine, CA; *Int'l*, pg. 529
Perry, Mark, Dir.-Mktg.--Sierracin/Sylmar Corporation, Sylmar, CA; *U.S. Private*, pg. 999
Perry, Michele, Dir.-Communications--Molten Metal Technology, Inc., Fall River, MA; *U.S. Public*, pg. 1123
Perry, Ralph, V.P.-Consumer Mktg.--Rydelle Laboratories, Racine, WI; *U.S. Private*, pg. 592
Perry, Ralph D., V.P.-Consumer Mktg. Svcs.-Worldwide--S.C. Johnson & Son, Inc., Racine, WI; *U.S. Private*, pg. 592
Perry, Robert J., V.P.-Mktg.--Heath Consultants Incorporated, Houston, TX; *U.S. Private*, pg. 518
Perry, Sarah, Dir.- Mktg.--Desa International, Bowling Green, KY; *U.S. Private*, pg. 326
Perry, Thomas E., Mgr.-Mktg. Communications--Philips Components-Discrete Products Division, Slatersville, RI; *Int'l*, pg. 1054
Perry, William, Mgr.-Mktg.--National Machinery, Tiffin, OH; *U.S. Private*, pg. 785
Perryman, Don, Mgr.-Mktg.--Centocor Pharmaceutical Division, Malvern, PA; *U.S. Public*, pg. 323
Perschau, Rosemary, Staff V.P.-Corp. Plng.--Meredith Corporation, Des Moines, IA; *U.S. Public*, pg. 1094
Persons, Mark D., Dir.-New Prods. Devel.--Panel Publishers, Inc., New York, NY; *Int'l*, pg. 1513
Persson, Jan, Regional Product Mgr.--Sandvik South East Asia Ltd., Jurong, Singapore; *Int'l*, pg. 1187
Persson, Mats, Dir.-Mktg.-Catskill--Akzo Nobel AB, Stockholm, Sweden; *Int'l*, pg. 48
Persson, Tomas, Mgr.-Intl. Bus. Mktg.--Stabilator AB, Danderyd, Sweden; *Int'l*, pg. 1261
Peruccelli, Silvia, Mgr.-Mktg.--Caffaro S.p.A., Milan, Italy; *Int'l*, pg. 248
Pervin, Heidi, Mgr.-Integrated Mktg.--Chevron Corporation, San Francisco, CA; *U.S. Public*, pg. 347
Pesavento, Gilbert, Dir.-Sls. & Mktg.--American Specialties Inc., Yonkers, NY; *U.S. Private*, pg. 62
Pesch, William, V.P.-Mktg.--A.B. Dick Company, Niles, IL; *U.S. Private*, pg. 791
Pesci, Alexander, Dir.-Mktg.--Lemo SA, Ecublens, Switzerland; *Int'l*, pg. 806
Pesci, Paul, V.P.-Sls. & Mktg.--Ransomes-Cushman-Ryan, Lincoln, NE; *Int'l*, pg. 1088
Pesin, Larry, V.P.-Global Mktg. & Sls.--Concord Camera Corporation, Avenel, NJ; *U.S. Public*, pg. 429
Peskowitz, Jeff, Dir.-Mktg.--Alcoa Building Products, Inc., Sidney, OH; *U.S. Public*, pg. 61
Pester, Jack C., Sr. V.P.-Intl. Refining & Mktg.--The Coastal Corporation, Houston, TX; *U.S. Public*, pg. 389
Pester, Linda, Dir.-Mktg.Team-Strategic Planning--Busch Entertainment Corp., Clayton, MO; *U.S. Public*, pg. 114
Pestovic, Edward J., V.P.-Adv.--Crowley, Milner & Company, Detroit, MI; *U.S. Public*, pg. 461
Peter, Larry, Dir.-Sls. & Mktg.--Kinney Vacuum Company, Canton, MA; *U.S. Private*, pg. 1110
Peterka, Curt D., Mgr.-Mktg. Svcs.--Portec, Inc.-Construction Equipment Div., Yankton, SD; *U.S. Public*, pg. 1318
Peters, Carl, Corp. V.P.--The Failure Group, Inc., Menlo Park, CA; *U.S. Public*, pg. 609
Peters, Dave, V.P.-Mktg. & Sls.--Armstrong Air Conditioning Inc., Bellevue, OH; *U.S. Private*, pg. 659
Peters, David, Pres.--Peters Construction Corp., Waterloo, IA; *U.S. Private*, pg. 856
Peters, Rich, 2nd V.P.-Mktg. Svcs. & Pub. Rels.--Woodmen Accident & Life Co., Lincoln, NE; *U.S. Private*, pg. 1187
Peters, Susan, Sec.-Mktg. Controller--Lever Brothers West Indies Ltd., Champs Fleurs, Trinidad & Tobago; *Int'l*, pg. 1437
Peters, Walter, V.P.-Mktg.--Curtiss-Wright Corp., Lyndhurst, NJ; *U.S. Public*, pg. 469
Peters, Walter, V.P.-Mktg.--Curtiss-Wright Flight Systems, Inc., Fairfield, NJ; *U.S. Public*, pg. 469
Peters, William H., V.P.-Sls. & Mktg.--YSD Industries, Youngstown, OH; *U.S. Private*, pg. 1194
Petersen, Eric, Exec. Dir.-Sls. & Mktg.--Spartan International Inc., Holt, MI; *U.S. Private*, pg. 1020
Petersen, K.C., Pres. & Chief Oper. Officer--Schenectady International, Inc., Schenectady, NY; *U.S. Private*, pg. 969
Peterson, Brian, V.P.-Sls. & Mktg.--Haydon Switch & Instrument, Inc., Waterbury, CT; *U.S. Private*, pg. 513
Peterson, Charles S., V.P.-Mktg.--Investment Counselors of Maryland, Inc., Baltimore, MD; *U.S. Public*, pg. 1673
Peterson, Christye, V.P.-Mktg.--Niagara Frontier Hockey, L.P., Buffalo, NY; *U.S. Private*, pg. 798
Peterson, Duane, Natl. Sls. Mgr.-Mktg.--Gordon & Ferguson of Delaware, Inc., Plymouth, MN; *U.S. Private*, pg. 465
Peterson, Grant, Mgr.-Mktg.--Bridgestone Cycle (U.S.A.), Inc., San Leandro, CA; *Int'l*, pg. 213
Peterson, Helen R., Dir.-Mktg. Communications--COMSAT RSI, Inc., Sterling, VA; *U.S. Public*, pg. 424
Peterson, J., Dir.-Mktg.--Honeywell Defense Avionics Systems, Albuquerque, NM; *U.S. Public*, pg. 834
Peterson, Jeffrey H., Sr. V.P.-Mktg.--John Deere Industrial Equipment Company, Moline, IL; *U.S. Public*, pg. 492
Peterson, Joan, Coord-Mktg. Services--In-Sink-Erator, Racine, WI; *U.S. Public*, pg. 573
Peterson, John, Dir.-Mktg.--Air New Zealand Ltd. (U.S.A.), El Segundo, CA; *Int'l*, pg. 38
Peterson, John, V.P.-Mktg.--R.C. Willey Home Furnishings, Salt Lake City, UT; *U.S. Public*, pg. 221
Peterson, John T., Dir.-Sls. & Mktg.--Hunter Marine Corporation, Alachua, FL; *U.S. Private*, pg. 549
Peterson, Marco, V.P.-Mktg.--Datawatch Corporation, Wilmington, MA; *U.S. Public*, pg. 488
Peterson, Suzy, Admin.-Mktg.--Sealed-Sweet Growers, Inc., Vero Beach, FL; *U.S. Private*, pg. 978
Peterson, Wayne, Mgr.-Mktg. & Sls.--Amite Foundry and Machine, Inc., Amite, LA; *U.S. Public*, pg. 142
Petit, Brett, V.P.-Mktg.--Sesame Place, Langhorne, PA; *U.S. Public*, pg. 114
Petit, Brett, V.P.-Mktg.--Paramount Carowinds, Charlotte, NC; *U.S. Private*, pg. 776
Petit, Jean Claude, Dir.-Mktg.--Total S.A., Paris, France; *Int'l*, pg. 1408
Petit, Jean-Pierre, Dir.-Mktg.--McDonald's France SA, Guayancourt, France; *U.S. Public*, pg. 1069
Petite, Joe, V.P.-Mktg.--Hyponex Corporation, Marysville, OH; *U.S. Public*, pg. 1447

Petkash, Robert, Mgr.-Mktg. Devel.--Airflex Div. Eaton Corp., Cleveland, OH; *U.S. Public*, pg. 556
Petraitis, Paul, V.P.-Mktg.-Premiere Div.--Premier Coatings, Inc., Elk Grove Village, IL; *Int'l*, pg. 1488
Petrilli, Christian, Mgr.-Mktg.--Haydon Switch & Instrument, Inc., Waterbury, CT; *U.S. Private*, pg. 513
Petrillo, Joe, V.P.-Mktg.--Harding Lawson Associates Group, Inc., Novato, CA; *U.S. Public*, pg. 785
Petropoulos, Aris, V.P.-Diagnostic Mktg.--Centocor, Inc., Malvern, PA; *U.S. Public*, pg. 323
Petropoulous, Ari, Mgr.-Mktg.--Centocor Diagnostics Div., Malvern, PA; *U.S. Public*, pg. 323
Pettersen, M., Dir.-Applications Grp.--Shure Brothers Incorporated, Evanston, IL; *U.S. Private*, pg. 997
Petterson, Lorri, Mgr.-Mktg. Communications--Pentax Corporation, Englewood, CO; *Int'l*, pg. 85
Petti, Mark, Dir.-Mktg., Beverages--Kraft Foods Inc., Rye Brook, NY; *U.S. Public*, pg. 1288
Pettil, Donald, Mktg. Dir.-Clarion Prods.--Clarion Cosmetics, Hunt Valley, MD; *U.S. Public*, pg. 1330
Pettis, Edmund, V.P. & Mgr.-Mktg.--Roy F. Weston, Inc., West Chester, PA; *U.S. Public*, pg. 1761
Pettit, R. Michael, Mktg. Representative--Producers Gas Sales, Inc., Newark, OH; *U.S. Public*, pg. 1157
Peyse, Michael, Mgr.-Mktg. Services--AEC/Application Automation, Inc., Wood Dale, IL; *U.S. Private*, pg. 1041
Peyser, Michael, Mgr.-Mktg. Services--Nelmor Co., Inc., North Uxbridge, MA; *U.S. Private*, pg. 1041
Peyser, Michael, Mgr.-Mktg. Services--AEC/Application Engineering Corporation, Wood Dale, IL; *U.S. Private*, pg. 1041
Peyser, Michael J., Mgr.-Mktg. Services & Adv.--AEC, Inc., Wood Dale, IL; *U.S. Private*, pg. 500
Pezzelli, Kim, Mgr.-Mktg.--Frionor U.S.A. Inc., New Bedford, MA; *Int'l*, pg. 516
Pfeiffer, Ralph, V.P.-Sls. & Mktg.--Acorn Window Systems Inc., Quincy, MI; *U.S. Private*, pg. 14
Pfifer, Sharon, Dir.--Solid State Devices, Inc., La Mirada, CA; *U.S. Private*, pg. 1012
Pfister, Robert, V.P.-Sls. & Mktg.--General Office Environments Inc., Rochelle Park, NJ; *U.S. Private*, pg. 445
Pfister, Robert, V.P.-Sls. & Mktg.--General Office Environments Inc., Somerset, NJ; *U.S. Private*, pg. 445
Pfleger, Manfred, Mgr.-Mktg. & Logistics--Bayer AG, Leverkusen, Germany; *Int'l*, pg. 171
Pfluger, Anton, V.P.-Mktg.--Swissmetal Plant Dornach, Dornach, Switzerland; *Int'l*, pg. 1427
Pflugrad, Jim, V.P.-Sls. & Mktg./U.S.--GSW Pump Company, Fergus, Canada; *Int'l*, pg. 538
Phan, Quan, Mktg. Assoc.--Muratech America, Inc., Plano, TX; *Int'l*, pg. 897
Phaus, Chris, V.P.-Mktg. Svcs.--S-B Power Tool Company, Chicago, IL; *Int'l*, pg. 205
Phelan, J., V.P.-Intl. Sls. & Mktg.--Shure Brothers Incorporated, Evanston, IL; *U.S. Private*, pg. 997
Phelan, Kerry, Dir.-Mktg.-Youth Grp.--LEGO Systems, Inc., Enfield, CT; *Int'l*, pg. 805
Phelan, Kevin, V.P.-Telecommunications--B-Line Systems, Inc., Highland, IL; *U.S. Public*, pg. 1471
Phibbs, Diane, Sr. Mgr.-Mktg.--Popeye's Chicken & Biscuits, Atlanta, GA; *U.S. Private*, pg. 5
Philbin, J.W., Dir.-Mktg. & Adv.--Harvest Brands, Inc., Pittsburg, KS; *U.S. Private*, pg. 46
Philbin, John W., Dir.-Mktg. & Sls.--Altair Corporation, Lincolnshire, IL; *U.S. Private*, pg. 46
Philbrick, Chris, Mgr.-Sls. & Mktg.--Weir Floway Inc., Fresno, CA; *Int'l*, pg. 1489
Philips, Barbara, Grp. Mktg. Dir.--Coty Inc., New York, NY; *Int'l*, pg. 185
Philipson, Barry, Mgr.-Mktg.--National Sea Products Limited, Lunenburg, Canada; *Int'l*, pg. 909
Phillimore, J. Roger B., Grp. Comml. Dir.--Minorco, Luxembourg, Luxembourg; *Int'l*, pg. 77
Phillips, Bob, Mgr.-Mktg.--Phillips Service Industries, Inc., Livonia, MI; *U.S. Private*, pg. 862
Phillips, Bryant, V.P.-Sls. & Mktg.--Hatteras Yachts, New Bern, NC; *U.S. Private*, pg. 447
Phillips, Dennis, V.P.-Mktg.--Cox & Company, Inc., New York, NY; *U.S. Private*, pg. 281
Phillips, Jim, Dir.-Mktg., Mdsg. & Pub. Rels.--Control Systems Inc., Saint Paul, MN; *U.S. Private*, pg. 271
Phillips, Joe, Sr. V.P.-Mktg.--Champion Products Inc., Winston Salem, NC; *U.S. Public*, pg. 1433
Phillips, John, Dir.-Mktg.--Enterprise Service Solutions, Carrollton, TX; *U.S. Public*, pg. 729
Phillips, John B., V.P.-Sls. & Mktg.--Red Spot Paint & Varnish Co., Evansville, IN; *U.S. Private*, pg. 915
Phillips, John, Jr., V.P.-Mktg. & Sls.--McKee Foods Corporation, Collegedale, TN; *U.S. Private*, pg. 723
Phillips, Julie, Mgr.-Mktg.--Lucent Netcare Messaging Services, Dallas, TX; *U.S. Public*, pg. 1018
Phillips, Kurt, Dir.-Mktg.--Goodyear Jamaica Limited, Kingston, Jamaica; *U.S. Public*, pg. 753
Phillips, Mark, Dir.-Sls.--Maxon Corporation, Muncie, IN; *U.S. Private*, pg. 716
Phillips, Mark J., V.P.-Mktg. & Sls.--Barrister Information Systems Corporation, Buffalo, NY; *U.S. Public*, pg. 192
Phillips, Mary, Asst. V.P.-Mktg.--Capital Associates, Inc., Lakewood, CO; *U.S. Public*, pg. 302
Phillips, Robert, Dir.-Mktg.--Townsend Engineering Co., Des Moines, IA; *U.S. Private*, pg. 1094
Phillips, Scott, Mgr.-Mktg.--Fisher Gauge Limited, Peterborough, Canada; *Int'l*, pg. 491
Phillips, Scott, Mgr.-Mktg.--Fishercast, Peterborough, Canada; *Int'l*, pg. 491
Phillips, Scott, Mgr.-Sls. & Mktg.--Fishertech, Peterborough, Canada; *Int'l*, pg. 491
Phillips, Steve, Dir.-Mktg.-Bus. Aircraft--Bombardier Aerospace, Dorval, Canada; *Int'l*, pg. 200
Phillips, Steven D., Exec. V.P.-Consumer Div.--Countrywide Funding Corporation, Pasadena, CA; *U.S. Public*, pg. 453
Phillips, Wayne, Dir.-Retail Mktg.--Perdue Farms Incorporated, Salisbury, MD; *U.S. Private*, pg. 852
Phillips, William F., Dir.-Sls.--Spartech Corporation, Clayton, MO; *U.S. Public*, pg. 1495
Phillips, Wyatt, V.P.-Mktg.--QuikTrip Corporation, Tulsa, OK; *U.S. Private*, pg. 901
Phipps, Robin, Grp. Dir.-Sls. & Mktg.--Legal & General Group PLC, London, United Kingdom; *Int'l*, pg. 805
Phy, Ann, Coord.-Mktg.--NewAge Industries Inc., Willow Grove, PA; *U.S. Private*, pg. 796
Piar-Katter, Madalyn, Mgr.-Mktg. Communications--Cascade Corporation, Troutdale, OR; *U.S. Public*, pg. 310
Picard, Bruce, Dir.-Mktg.--Loomis, Sayles & Co., Boston, MA; *U.S. Private*, pg. 737
Picchetti, Diego, V.P.-Mktg.--Everest & Jennings, Inc., Earth City, MO; *U.S. Public*, pg. 758
Piccinini, Barbara, Mgr.-Mktg. Coord.--BS & B Process Systems, Inc., Houston, TX; *U.S. Private*, pg. 572
Piccolo, Philip J., Dir.-Corp. Mktg.--Escalade Sports, Evansville, IN; *U.S. Public*, pg. 591
Pickard, G. Carl, V.P.-Mktg.--Sanford Corporation, Bellwood, IL; *U.S. Public*, pg. 1178
Pickard, J. Duncan, V.P.-Mktg./Automotive--UAP, Inc., Montreal, Canada; *Int'l*, pg. 1426
Pickard, Tom, V.P.-Mktg.--Columbia Gas Distribution Companies, Columbus, OH; *U.S. Public*, pg. 402
Picker, Caryn, V.P.-Broadcast Media--Miramax Films, Inc., New York, NY; *U.S. Public*, pg. 514
Pickering, Arthur W., Sr. V.P.-Domestic Mktg.--National Western Life Insurance Company, Austin, TX; *U.S. Public*, pg. 1161
Pickert, Steve, V.P.-Sls. & Mktg.--M & S Systems, Inc., Dallas, TX; *U.S. Public*, pg. 1193
Picket, Howard, V.P.-Mktg.- Disney Cruiselines--Walt Disney Attractions-Walt Disney World, Lake Buena Vista, FL; *U.S. Public*, pg. 513
Pickett, Jo Ann, Dir.-Mktg.--Peerless Confection Company, Chicago, IL; *U.S. Private*, pg. 847
Pickett, Susan, V.P.-Mktg.--Pilot Air Freight Corp., Lima, PA; *U.S. Private*, pg. 865
Pico, Maria V., Dir.-Rums of Puerto Rico--Rums of Puerto Rico, New York, NY; *U.S. Private*, pg. 951
Picone, Thomas, V.P.-Sls. & Mktg.--Premier Mill Corp., Reading, PA; *U.S. Private*, pg. 881
Pieklo, Jim, Mgr.-Mktg. Communications--Goldbergs Marine Distributors, Edison, NJ; *U.S. Public*, pg. 1756
Piepenbring, Ray, Dir.-Aftermarket Sls. & Mktg.--Casco Products Corporation, Bridgeport, CT; *U.S. Public*, pg. 1458
Pieper, Roel, Sr. V.P. & Gen. Mgr.-Worldwide Sls. & Mktg.--Tandem Computers Inc., Cupertino, CA; *U.S. Public*, pg. 417
Pierce, Frank, V.P.-Communications--National Health Enhancement Systems, Inc., Phoenix, AZ; *U.S. Public*, pg. 1157
Pierce, Gale, Dir.-Mktg.--Speedy Car-X, Inc., Chicago, IL; *U.S. Public*, pg. 1578
Pierce, John, Gen. Mgr.-Sls. & Mktg.--Rosenbergers Dairies, Inc., Hatfield, PA; *U.S. Private*, pg. 945
Pierce, Marc, V.P.-Sls. & Mktg.--Pentax Precision Instrument Corp., Orangeburg, NY; *Int'l*, pg. 85
Pierce, Marie, Sec.-Mktg. Svcs.--Centeon, L.L.C., King of Prussia, PA; *Int'l*, pg. 626
Pierce, Michael G., V.P.-Mktg. & Sls.--The Austin Company, Cleveland, OH; *U.S. Private*, pg. 99
Pierce, Stacy, Mgr.-Exhibit Mktg.--Allen Telecom Inc., Solon, OH; *U.S. Public*, pg. 45
Pierce, Tom, Dir.-Mktg. Svcs.--Journal Communications Inc., Milwaukee, WI; *U.S. Private*, pg. 601
Piers, Andy, Dr., Dir.-Mktg.--Union Camp Chemicals, Durham, United Kingdom; *U.S. Public*, pg. 1666
Piersma, Craig, Mgr.-Mktg. Communications--Haworth, Inc., Holland, MI; *U.S. Private*, pg. 511
Pierson, Robert, V.P.-Sls. & Mktg.--Jervis B. Webb Company, Farmington Hills, MI; *U.S. Private*, pg. 1156
Piessens, Luc, Gen. Mgr.-Mktg.--Wisconsin Gas Company, Milwaukee, WI; *U.S. Public*, pg. 1767
Piete, Anne-Francoise, Dir.-Mktg.--Bacardi-Martini Belgium, Brussels, Belgium; *U.S. Private*, pg. 109
Pietrafesa, Michael, Exec. V.P.--Goldberger Doll Mfg. Company, Inc., Brooklyn, NY; *U.S. Private*, pg. 459
Pietrick, Robert, V.P.-Mktg. & Gasoline--Dairy Mart Convenience Stores, Inc., Cuyahoga Falls, OH; *U.S. Public*, pg. 476
Piggin, David, V.P.-Intl. Sls.--Circon Corporation, Santa Barbara, CA; *U.S. Public*, pg. 373
Piggott, L.L., Mktg. Mgr.--BestFriend Pet Foods Limited, Auckland, New Zealand; *U.S. Public*, pg. 807
Pike, Tina, Asst. V.P.-Creative Svcs. & Mktg.--First American Corporation, Nashville, TN; *U.S. Public*, pg. 624
Pikus, Carl, Dir.-Sls. & Mktg.--Fyrnetics, Inc., Roselle, IL; *Int'l*, pg. 1499
Pilgrim, Mike, V.P.-Mktg. & Sls.--Serco Company, Dallas, TX; *U.S. Public*, pg. 1676
Piliero, Zoe, Dir.-Corp. Communications--CVC Products, Inc., Rochester, NY; *U.S. Private*, pg. 197
Piliot, Dennis, V.P.-Sls. & Mktg.--Cherokee International LLC, Tustin, CA; *U.S. Private*, pg. 233
Pilnik, Richard D., Dir.-Pharmaceutical Mktg. & Opers.--Eli Lilly do Brasil Limitada, Sao Paulo, Brazil; *U.S. Public*, pg. 993
Pinchot, Roy, Dir.-Bus. Devel.--Biospherics Incorporated, Beltsville, MD; *U.S. Public*, pg. 232
Pinckney, Debbie, Dir.-Mktg.--Banner Associates Inc., Laramie, WY; *U.S. Private*, pg. 114
Pinda, Jane, V.P.-Mktg.--Bell Flavors & Fragrances, Northbrook, IL; *U.S. Private*, pg. 131
Pinder, Charlotte, Dir.-European Mktg.--Pepsi-Co. International, Surrey, United Kingdom; *U.S. Public*, pg. 1277
Pinder, Robert, Dir.-Mktg. & Sls.--Benzonia Manufacturing, Benzonia, MI; *U.S. Private*, pg. 753
Pinder, Robert, Dir.-Mktg.--Mitchell Corporation, Clare Div., Clare, MI; *U.S. Private*, pg. 753
Pinet, Paul, Dir.-Mktg.--Kimmins Corp., Tampa, FL; *U.S. Public*, pg. 960
Piniewski, Bob, Mgr.-Mktg.--United Eco Systems, High Point, NC; *Int'l*, pg. 74
Pinkard, Lee S., Natl. Dir.-Mktg. & Commun.--Coopers & Lybrand, New York, NY; *U.S. Private*, pg. 274
Pinkerton, Gary, Dir.-Mktg.--Keithley Instruments, Inc., Cleveland, OH; *U.S. Public*, pg. 946
Pinna, John, V.P.-Sls. & Mktg.--Roussel Corporation, Montvale, NJ; *Int'l*, pg. 625
Pinnell, R. M., Dir.-Mktg. & Communication--NatWest U.K., London, United Kingdom; *Int'l*, pg. 910
Pino, Michael A., V.P.-Mktg. & Opers.--Therapedic Associates, Inc., Middlesex, NJ; *U.S. Private*, pg. 1079
Pinoncely, Geoffroy, Exec. V.P.-Grocery Prods. Div.--Danone Group, Paris, France; *Int'l*, pg. 379
Pinto, Harold, V.P.-Sls. & Mktg.--Jacobsen Textron, Racine, WI; *U.S. Public*, pg. 1589
Pinto, Stephen F., Mgr.-Mktg. Svcs.--Southwestern Industries, Inc., Rancho Dominguez, CA; *U.S. Private*, pg. 1019
Piovesan, M., Mgr.-Sls.--Dynacast do Brazil Ltda., Sao Paulo, Brazil; *Int'l*, pg. 301
Piraino, J.V., V.P.-Mktg.--WESCO Distribution, Inc., Pittsburgh, PA; *U.S. Private*, pg. 244
Pirnat, Alan, Mgr.-Sls.--Metal Seal & Products, Inc., Willoughby, OH; *U.S. Private*, pg. 734
Pirnie, Douglas D., Jr., Sr. V.P.-Sls. & Mktg.--IMG, New York, NY; *U.S. Private*, pg. 555
Pirrone, Arthur, V.P.-Sls. & Mktg.--Inverness Corp., Fair Lawn, NJ; *U.S. Private*, pg. 574
Pirrone, Barbara, Dir.-Mktg.--The Langer Biomechanics Group, Inc., Deer Park, NY; *U.S. Public*, pg. 978
Pirrone, Barbara, Dir.-Mktg.--First Choice, Deer Park, NY; *U.S. Public*, pg. 978
Pirtle, William B., Sr. V.P.-Mktg. & Sls.--Barclay Furniture Company, Sherman, MS; *U.S. Public*, pg. 974
Pisano, Anthony, Natl. Dir.-Mktg.--Grant Thornton LLP, Chicago, IL; *U.S. Private*, pg. 470
Pisano, Wayne, Exec. Dir.-Market Mngmt.--Sandoz Pharmaceuticals Corp., East Hanover, NJ; *Int'l*, pg. 974
Pisano, Wayne, V.P.-Mktg.--Connaught Laboratories, Inc., Swiftwater, PA; *Int'l*, pg. 1109
Piscitelli, Francis M., V.P.-Mktg. & Sls.--Osram Sylvania Inc., Malvern, PA; *Int'l*, pg. 1245
Pistorese, Todd A., V.P.-Bus. Devel.--Tellus, Inc., Bellevue, WA; *U.S. Public*, pg. 1342
Pitcher, Sarah, V.P.-Corp. Commun.--Mesa Air Group, Las Vegas, NV; *U.S. Public*, pg. 1098
Pitcher, William M., Mgr.-Liquid Mktg.--Anadarko Petroleum Corporation, Houston, TX; *U.S. Public*, pg. 107
Pittman, David, Dir.-Mktg. Commun.--SPSS Inc., Chicago, IL; *U.S. Public*, pg. 1420
Pittman, Robert, Exec. V.P.--Trend Offset Printing Services, Los Alamitos, CA; *U.S. Private*, pg. 1099
Pittman, Rod, V.P.-Mktg. & Sls.--Lufkin Industries, Inc., Lufkin, TX; *U.S. Public*, pg. 1019
Pitts, Nancy, Mgr.-Mktg. Commun.--Witco Corporation, Greenwich, CT; *U.S. Public*, pg. 1773
Pitzer, Tim, Mgr.-Mktg.--Dark Horse Comics, Inc., Milwaukie, OR; *U.S. Private*, pg. 311
Pizzicaro, Elaine, Dir.-Mktg.--World Color-Chicago Div., Elk Grove Village, IL; *U.S. Public*, pg. 1778
Pizzo, Thomas V., Exec. V.P.--Century Business Credit Corporation, New York, NY; *U.S. Private*, pg. 225
Pizzuti, Michael, V.P.-Mktg.--Data Control Systems, Gaithersburg, MD; *U.S. Public*, pg. 420
Pla, Sebastian, Dir.-Mktg. & Adv.--Noblex Argentina S.A.C. e I., Buenos Aires, Argentina; *Int'l*, pg. 951
Pladna, D.L., V.P.-Sls. & Mktg.--A.Y. McDonald Supply Co. Inc., Dubuque, IA; *U.S. Private*, pg. 721
Plas, Raymond C., Exec. V.P.-Mktg. & Mdsg.--Gateway Apparel, Inc., Saint Louis, MO; *U.S. Private*, pg. 441
Plath, R., V.P.-Mktg.--Selecto-Flash, Inc., West Orange, NJ; *U.S. Private*, pg. 982
Platon, Romarico J., Mgr.-Mktg.--Benguet Management Corporation, Manila, Philippines; *Int'l*, pg. 186
Platt, Tony, V.P.-Mktg.--NextHealth Inc., Tucson, AZ; *U.S. Public*, pg. 1181
Playford, Alyson, Gen. Mgr.-Sls. & Mktg./Northern Europe--Utell International-United Kingdom, Sutton, United Kingdom; *Int'l*, pg. 1098
Pless, Judy, V.P.-Bus. Devel.-Viacom World Wide--Viacom Enterprises, New York, NY; *U.S. Private*, pg. 779
Pleszko, E.J., V.P.-Mktg.--Preformed Line Products, Cleveland, OH; *U.S. Public*, pg. 1321
Pletcher, Carl, Mgr.-Mktg.--Norcold, Sidney, OH; *U.S. Private*, pg. 352
Plocic, John, Dir.-Mktg.--Titan Tool, Inc., Oakland, NJ; *U.S. Private*, pg. 500
Plomske, T.I., Mgr.-Brand & Mdsg.--Shell Canada Ltd., Calgary, Canada; *Int'l*, pg. 1138
Ploss, Gus, V.P.-Sls., Mktg. & Bus. Devel.--Walbro Corporation, Cass City, MI; *U.S. Public*, pg. 1733
Plotica, Philip G., Mng. Dir.--ESAB Consumables, Hanover, PA; *Int'l*, pg. 281
Plotnick, David, Mgr.-Mktg.--Processed Plastic Company, Montgomery, IL; *U.S. Private*, pg. 888
Plowman, C. Bruce, V.P.-Corp. & Mktg. Communications--Computer Sciences Corporation, El Segundo, CA; *U.S. Public*, pg. 422
Pluijmakers, Jos, Dir.-Sls. & Mktg.--Pan European Publishing Co., Brussels, Belgium; *Int'l*, pg. 1099
Plumhoff, Todd, Mgr.-Cost Proposal--COMSAT RSI, Inc., Sterling, VA; *U.S. Public*, pg. 424
Plummer, Robert, Mgr.-Sls. & Mktg.--Dean Pump Division, Indianapolis, IN; *U.S. Public*, pg. 1100
Plummer, Terry, V.P.-Sls. & Mktg.--Boise Cascade Paper Div., Boise, ID; *U.S. Public*, pg. 243
Plummer, Terry M., V.P.-Mktg. & Sls./Paper Div.--Boise Cascade Corporation, Boise, ID; *U.S. Public*, pg. 242
Plummer, Tom, V.P.-Sls. & Mktg.--Kilgore Operations, Toone, TN; *U.S. Public*, pg. 47

Plush, Richard F., V.P.-Field Mktg. & Sls. Support--The Penn Mutual Life Insurance Company, Philadelphia, PA; *U.S. Private*, pg. 849
Poccio, Kathy, Mgr.-Mktg.--Acorn Structures, Acton, MA; *U.S. Private*, pg. 320
Poczobutt, Jan, V.P.-Mktg.--Unify Corporation, San Jose, CA; *U.S. Public*, pg. 1665
Poda, Jennifer, Mgr.-Mktg.--Rubber & Plastics News, Akron, OH; *U.S. Private*, pg. 285
Podracky, Steve, Mgr.-Mktg.--Schulze & Burch Biscuit Company, Chicago, IL; *U.S. Private*, pg. 973
Poduch, Julie, Dir.-Mktg.--Nalleys Fine Foods, Tacoma, WA; *U.S. Private*, pg. 887
Poe, Lisa, Mgr.-Mktg. Services--Jacuzzi Bros., Jacuzzi, Inc., Little Rock, AR; *U.S. Public*, pg. 1684
Poedens, Dr. B., Mgr.-Mktg. & Sls.--Mallinckrodt Medical B.V., Petten, Netherlands; *U.S. Public*, pg. 1040
Poehling, Jim, V.P.-Mktg. & Adv.--Greenfield Industries, Cleveland, OH; *U.S. Public*, pg. 950
Poertner, Hermann, V.P.-Worldwide Mktg. Communications--Apple Computer, Inc., Cupertino, CA; *U.S. Public*, pg. 121
Poeschel, Gordon P., Ph.D., Sr. V.P.-Mktg./Crop Protection Agriculture Div.--Bayer Corporation, Pittsburgh, PA; *Int'l*, pg. 172
Poesl, Wolfgang, Dir.-Mktg.--FAG Group, Schweinfurt, Germany; *Int'l*, pg. 468
Pogorzelski, Donald E., V.P.-Sls. & Mktg.-Diagnostics--Genzyme Corporation, Cambridge, MA; *U.S. Public*, pg. 733
Pohl, Henry, V.P.-Mktg.--Shiseido Cosmetics (America) Ltd., New York, NY; *Int'l*, pg. 1235
Pohl, John, V.P.-Mktg.--Cobra Electronics Corporation, Chicago, IL; *U.S. Public*, pg. 391
Poindexter, Laura, Dir.-Mktg.--Safeskin Corporation, San Diego, CA; *U.S. Public*, pg. 1425
Poindexter, Randy, Sr. V.P.-Mktg.--Bojangles' Restaraunts, Inc., Charlotte, NC; *U.S. Private*, pg. 154
Pokorny, J.J., Mgr.-Mktg.--Raytheon Engineers & Constructors, Inc., Englewood, CO; *U.S. Public*, pg. 1366
Polcyn, Mike, V.P.-Product Mktg. & Mngmt.--InterVoice, Inc., Dallas, TX; *U.S. Public*, pg. 910
Polera, Frank, Mgr.-Mktg. Commucications--Crouse-Hinds, Syracuse, NY; *U.S. Public*, pg. 444
Poles, Dave, V.P.-Mktg.--Clarke American Corp., San Antonio, TX; *Int'l*, pg. 267
Polich, Michael L., V.P.-Mktg. & Sls.--Doehler-Jarvis, Inc., Toledo, OH; *U.S. Public*, pg. 796
Polisseni, Eugene, V.P.-Mktg.--Paychex, Inc., Rochester, NY; *U.S. Public*, pg. 1267
Polke, Thomas P., V.P.-Sls. & Mktg.--Johnson Products Co., Inc., Chicago, IL; *U.S. Public*, pg. 915
Pollack, Janine, Dir.-Promo.--Crain's New York Business, New York, NY; *U.S. Private*, pg. 285
Pollack, Mark, Dir.-Mktg.--Savin Corporation, Stamford, CT; *Int'l*, pg. 1114
Pollan, Clifford M., V.P.-Sls. & Mktg.--NewsEdge Corporation, Burlington, MA; *U.S. Public*, pg. 1180
Pollis, John, V.P.-Mktg.--Fleetwood Enterprises, Inc., Riverside, CA; *U.S. Public*, pg. 650
Pollock, Mayer, II, Pres., Chief Exec. Officer & Chief Oper. Officer--The Pollock Corp., Pottstown, PA; *U.S. Private*, pg. 874
Pollyea, S.H., V.P.-Mktg.--Roto-Rooter, Cincinnati, OH; *U.S. Public*, pg. 344
Polowyk, George, Mgr.-Mktg. Services--Greenfield Industries, Cleveland, OH; *U.S. Public*, pg. 950
Polston, Peter, V.P.-Sls. & Mktg.--Cowden Metal Specialties, Inc., Chino, CA; *U.S. Private*, pg. 280
Poltenson, Frank, Mgr.-Mktg.--Vinings Industries Inc., Atlanta, GA; *U.S. Private*, pg. 1141
Polucha, J., Dir.-Mktg.--Valley Gas Co., Cumberland, RI; *U.S. Public*, pg. 1706
Polumbo, John, Pres.-Consumer Communications Services--Pacific Bell, San Ramon, CA; *U.S. Public*, pg. 1416
Pomerantz, Lee, Mgr.-Natl. Sls.--Otari Corporation, Foster City, CA; *Int'l*, pg. 1013
Pomeroy, Debra, Asst. Mgr.-Mktg.-Creative Services--DHL Worldwide Express, Redwood City, CA; *U.S. Private*, pg. 301
Pommer, Michael, V.P.-Mktg.--United Distillers USA, Inc., Stamford, CT; *Int'l*, pg. 412
Pomnean, Karen, Mgr.-Mktg.--Syncor International Corporation, Woodland Hills, CA; *U.S. Public*, pg. 1548
Pond, Dale C., Sr. V.P.-Mktg.--Lowe's Companies, Inc., North Wilkesboro, NC; *U.S. Public*, pg. 1015
Pond, Fred, Sr. V.P.-Mktg.--Ridge Tool Co., Elyria, OH; *U.S. Public*, pg. 574
Ponder, Michael H., V.P.-Sls. & Mktg.-Red Star BioProducts--Universal Foods Corporation, Milwaukee, WI; *U.S. Public*, pg. 1695
Pont, Neil, Mgr.-Sls.--Amwest Insurance Group, Inc., Calabasas, CA; *U.S. Public*, pg. 106
Ponticelli, Kevin, V.P.-Mktg., Tombstone Pizza--Kraft Foods Inc., Glenview, IL; *U.S. Public*, pg. 1288
Pontieri, Silvana, Mktg. Asst.--Henkel S/A. Industrias Quimicas, Sao Paulo, Brazil; *Int'l*, pg. 613
Pontin, Toby J., V.P.-Sls. & Mktg.--Kallista, Inc., San Leandro, CA; *U.S. Private*, pg. 630
Pontious, James C., V.P.-Sls. & Mktg.--Westinghouse Air Brake Company, Wilmerding, PA; *U.S. Public*, pg. 1760
Pool, Stanley L., V.P.-Sls. & Mktg. & Sec.--Mity-Lite, Inc., Orem, UT; *U.S. Public*, pg. 1118
Pool, William, Mgr.-Mktg.--Cargill Seed Div., Minneapolis, MN; *U.S. Private*, pg. 210
Poole, David J., Mgr.-Mktg. Services--Lister-Petter Ltd., Dursley, United Kingdom; *Int'l*, pg. 125
Poole, Rich, Dir.-Mktg.--Dykem Company, Saint Louis, MO; *U.S. Public*, pg. 866
Pooley, Grey, Dir.-Mktg.--Australian Guarantee Corporation Limited, Sydney, Australia; *Int'l*, pg. 1496
Pope, Julie, Coord.-Mktg.--Joern's Sunrise Medical, Stevens Point, WI; *U.S. Public*, pg. 1536
Pope, N.W., Exec. V.P.-Mktg. Grp.--First Hawaiian Bank, Honolulu, HI; *U.S. Public*, pg. 634
Popeil, Ron, Pres.--Ronco, Inventions. LLC, Chatsworth, CA; *U.S. Private*, pg. 943
Popelsky, Ellen, Dir.-Mktg./Kids R Us--Toys "R" Us, Inc., Paramus, NJ; *U.S. Public*, pg. 1626
Popovitch, Gary, Gen. Mgr.--Toledo Milk Processing, Inc., Toledo, OH; *U.S. Public*, pg. 1453
Popp, John B., V.P.-Mktg.--Perfection Bakeries Inc., Fort Wayne, IN; *U.S. Private*, pg. 852
Poppe, Dennis, V.P.-Mktg.--Catalina Lighting, Inc., Miami, FL; *U.S. Public*, pg. 314
Poppele, K., Mgr.-Sales & Mktg.--Carbone of America, Parsippany, NJ; *Int'l*, pg. 1028
Popplewell, Bill, Mgr.-Adv. & Coord.-Mktg.--Husky Oil Ltd., Calgary, Canada; *Int'l*, pg. 640
Portela, Daniel, Mgr.-Mktg.--Brastemp S.A., Sao Bernardo do Campo, Brazil; *U.S. Public*, pg. 1765
Porter, Allen, V.P.-Mktg.--Arizona Instrument Corporation, Phoenix, AZ; *U.S. Public*, pg. 129
Porter, Charles A., V.P.-Sls. & Mktg.--Peerless Pottery, Inc., Rockport, IN; *U.S. Private*, pg. 847
Porter, David J., Grp. Mgr.-Natl. Mktg.--Q.U.F. Industries Ltd., Brisbane, Australia; *Int'l*, pg. 1074
Porter, Glendon, V.P.-Mktg.--B & R Foods, Dover, FL; *U.S. Public*, pg. 1278
Porter, J.A., V.P.-Sls. & Mktg.--Solar Turbines Incorporated, San Diego, CA; *U.S. Public*, pg. 316
Porter, Jerry, Dir.-Mktg.--Klein Tools Inc., Skokie, IL; *U.S. Private*, pg. 625
Porter, Larry, Dir.-Mktg.--Van Leer Containers, Inc., Alsip, IL; *Int'l*, pg. 1146
Porter, Richard A., Pres.--Lamb-Weston, Inc., Kennewick, WA; *U.S. Public*, pg. 427
Portman, Jeff, Exec. V.P.-Sls. & Mktg.--AMC, Inc., Atlanta, GA; *U.S. Private*, pg. 6
Portnoy, Alice, Mgr.-Mktg. & Adv.--Neff (UK) Limited, Milton Keynes, United Kingdom; *Int'l*, pg. 912
Portnoy, Dan, V.P.-Mktg.--Cott Corporation, Pointe-Claire, Canada; *Int'l*, pg. 337
Porto, John, V.P.-Intl. Sls. & Mktg.--Dri-Print Foils Inc., Rahway, NJ; *U.S. Private*, pg. 343
Porvaznik, George, Commercial Dir.-Agricultural Nitrogen Prods.--LaRoche Industries Inc., Atlanta, GA; *U.S. Private*, pg. 651
Posch, Ellen, Dir.-CS/BMS/RMS Mktg.--Dun & Bradstreet Deutschland GmbH, Frankfurt/Main, Germany; *U.S. Public*, pg. 536
Posey, Bob, Dir.-Sls. & Mktg.--Aeroglide Corporation, Cary, NC; *U.S. Private*, pg. 24
Pospiech, Peter, Mgr.-Mktg.--Deutz AG, Cologne, Germany; *Int'l*, pg. 407
Post, Jeffrey, V.P.-Design & Mktg.--ATHOL Corporation, Butner, NC; *U.S. Private*, pg. 94
Post, Tony, Sr. V.P.-Mktg. & Gen. Mgr.--The Rockport Company, Marlborough, MA; *U.S. Public*, pg. 1370
Post, Virgil C., V.P.-Mktg., Sls. & Svcs.--Construction Equip. Div., Lubbock, TX; *U.S. Private*, pg. 355
Postel, Kristin, Dir.-Mktg.--Pizza Inn, Inc., Dallas, TX; *U.S. Public*, pg. 1307
Posten, William, Dir.-Mktg.--Turner Construction Company, Richmond, VA; *U.S. Public*, pg. 1646
Postlethwait, Jeff, Dir.-Sls. & Mktg.--Micro Networks Corp., Worcester, MA; *U.S. Private*, pg. 969
Potash, Jonathan, Dir.-Mktg.--Duty Free International, Inc., Ridgefield, CT; *Int'l*, pg. 103
Potempa, Louis E., V.P.-Devel.--Enron Corp., Houston, TX; *U.S. Public*, pg. 584
Potgieter, A., Dir.-Mktg.--CIBA-GEIGY (Pty.) Ltd., Isando, South Africa; *Int'l*, pg. 978
Potter, Alfred K. II, Sr. V.P.-Sls. & Mktg.--Gilbane Building Company, Providence, RI; *U.S. Private*, pg. 452
Potter, David, V.P.-Mktg.--Water Country USA, Williamsburg, VA; *U.S. Public*, pg. 114
Potter, Larry D., V.P. & Gen. Mgr.-Worldwide Field Opers., Test & Meas. Org.--Hewlett-Packard Company, Palo Alto, CA; *U.S. Public*, pg. 813
Potter, Muffie, V.P.-Mktg. & Pub. Rels.--Van Cleef & Arpels, Inc., New York, NY; *U.S. Private*, pg. 1132
Potter, Steve, Mgr.-N.A. Sports Mktg.--Mercedes-Benz of North America, Inc., Montvale, NJ; *Int'l*, pg. 368
Potts, Richard W., Pres.--Peerless Tube Company, Bloomfield, NJ; *U.S. Public*, pg. 1269
Poucher, Donald A., Dir.-Sls. & Mktg.--Deepwater Chemicals, Inc., Woodward, OK; *Int'l*, pg. 1395
Pouletty, Pierre, Dir.-Mktg.--Steelcase Strafor, Strasbourg, France; *Int'l*, pg. 569
Poulin, Marc, V.P.-Corp. Mktg.--Assurance vie Desjardins-Laurentienne, Levis, Canada; *Int'l*, pg. 396
Pouliot, Anatole, Dir.-Mktg.--Capital d'Amerique CDPQ, Montreal, Canada; *Int'l*, pg. 249
Pouliot, Anatole, Dir.-Mktg.--Capital Communications CDPQ, Montreal, Canada; *Int'l*, pg. 249
Pouliot, Anatole, Dir.-Mktg.--Capital International CDPQ, Montreal, Canada; *Int'l*, pg. 249
Pouliot, Anatole, Dir.-Mktg.--Sofinov, Montreal, Canada; *Int'l*, pg. 249
Poulos, Tom, V.P.-Mktg. & Sls.--American Paging, Inc., Minneapolis, MN; *U.S. Public*, pg. 1570
Pournaras, Dean, Product Mgr.-GFCI Residential--Pass & Seymour/Legrand, Syracuse, NY; *Int'l*, pg. 806
Pourteau, Enrique, V.P.-Refining & Mktg.--Y.P.F., S.A., Buenos Aires, Argentina; *Int'l*, pg. 1515
Pourzanjani, Cameron, V.P.-Mktg. & Sls.--Syseca Inc., Marina Del Rey, CA; *Int'l*, pg. 1384
Poussot, Bernard, Pres.--Wyeth-Ayerst International, Inc., Radnor, PA; *U.S. Public*, pg. 80
Pouzelt, Borns, V.P.-Mktg.--Colgate-Palmolive France, Courbevoie, France; *U.S. Public*, pg. 398
Povich, Denise, Mktg. Coord.--Tarlton Corporation, Saint Louis, MO; *U.S. Private*, pg. 1069
Powell, Angela, Mgr.-Reatil Mktg. & Pub. Rels.--Camping World, Inc., Bowling Green, KY; *U.S. Private*, pg. 204
Powell, Bob, Mktg. Dir.--PSI-Process Systems International, Inc., Cleveland, OH; *U.S. Public*, pg. 336
Powell, Doug, V.P.-Mktg.--Descente America Inc., Englewood, CO; *Int'l*, pg. 395
Powell, James R., Sr. V.P.-Sls. & Mktg.--Daisytek International Corporation, Plano, TX; *U.S. Public*, pg. 477
Powell, James R., Sr. V.P.-Sls. & Mktg.--Daisytek Incorporated, Plano, TX; *U.S. Public*, pg. 477
Powell, James R., Sr. V.P.-Sls. & Mktg.--Daisytek (Canada) Inc., Toronto, Canada; *U.S. Public*, pg. 477
Powell, James R., Sr. V.P.-Sls. & Mktg.--Daisytek Latin America, Miami, FL; *U.S. Public*, pg. 477
Powell, James R., Sr. V.P.-Sls. & Mktg.--Daisytek De Mexico S.A. de C.V., Mexico, Mexico; *U.S. Public*, pg. 477
Powell, James R., Sr. V.P.-Sls. & Mktg.--Priority Fulfillment Services, Inc., Plano, TX; *U.S. Public*, pg. 477
Powell, James R., Sr. V.P.-Sls. & Mktg.--Daisytek Australia Pty. Ltd., Alexandria, Australia; *U.S. Public*, pg. 477
Powell, Jeffrey E., Partner-Retail Sls. & Mktg.--J.C. Bradford & Co., Nashville, TN; *U.S. Private*, pg. 163
Powell, Jenny, Mgr.-Retail Mktg.--Starbanc Corporation, Cincinnati, OH; *U.S. Public*, pg. 1510
Powell, Jim, V.P.-Mktg. & Sls.--Sioux Honey Association, Sioux City, IA; *U.S. Private*, pg. 1003
Powell, Larry W., V.P.-Mktg.--Blue Ridge Insurance Co., Simsbury, CT; *Int'l*, pg. 345
Powell, Larry W., V.P.-Mktg.--Blue Ridge Indemnity Co., Simsbury, CT; *Int'l*, pg. 345
Powell, Larry W., V.P.-Mktg.--MassWest Insurance Company, West Springfield, MA; *Int'l*, pg. 345
Powell, Marilyn, Sr. V.P.-Mktg.--Atlantic Electric Co., Pleasantville, NJ; *U.S. Public*, pg. 430
Powell, Michelle, Dir.-Adv. & Mktg.--Mity-Lite, Inc., Orem, UT; *U.S. Public*, pg. 1118
Powell, Ruth, Mktg. Admin.--Malta Div.-Tomkins Industries, Inc., Malta, OH; *Int'l*, pg. 1398
Powell, Teresa M., Dir.-Bus. Devel.--AC Martin Partners, Los Angeles, CA; *U.S. Private*, pg. 708
Power, Robert, V.P.-Global Mktg.--American Home Products Corporation, Madison, NJ; *U.S. Public*, pg. 79
Powers, Dave, V.P.-Sls. & Mktg.--King Koil Licensing Company Inc., Saint Paul, MN; *U.S. Private*, pg. 621
Powers, Fred, Sr., Mktg. Partner--International Pin, Park Forest, IL; *U.S. Private*, pg. 269
Powers, John J., Exec. V.P.-Sls. & Mktg.--AEP Industries, Inc., South Hackensack, NJ; *U.S. Public*, pg. 4
Powers, Shaun, V.P.-Sls.--AGA Gas, Inc., Independence, OH; *Int'l*, pg. 13
Pradetto, Richard V., Sr. V.P.-Mktg.--Cincinnati Incorporated, Harrison, OH; *U.S. Private*, pg. 240
Pranger, Scott, V.P.-Sls. & Mktg.--Kurdziel Industries, Inc., Muskegon, MI; *U.S. Private*, pg. 637
Pranger, Scott, Mgr.-Sls.--Kurdziel Industries, Inc., Muskegon, MI; *U.S. Private*, pg. 637
Pranka, Tom, Mgr.-Mktg.& Sls.--ARDCO/Traverse Lift, Houston, TX; *U.S. Private*, pg. 859
Prasek, Karen, Mgr.-Mktg.--Zack Electronics, San Jose, CA; *U.S. Private*, pg. 1203
Prassack, Lisa, Mgr.-Mktg. Commun. & Bus. Printers--Lexmark International Group, Inc., Lexington, KY; *U.S. Public*, pg. 991
Prassack, Lisa, Mgr. Mktg Commun. & Bus. Printers--Lexmark International, Inc., Lexington, KY; *U.S. Public*, pg. 991
Prather, Douglas L., V.P.-Opers.--Kocolene Oil Corp., Seymour, IN; *U.S. Private*, pg. 629
Prazak, Joe, Mgr.-Farm-Lines Mktg.--Bou-Matic, Madison, WI; *U.S. Private*, pg. 301
Preble, Ryan R., V.P.-Mktg.--Reed Minerals, Highland, IN; *U.S. Public*, pg. 793
Preckel, Rick, Dir.-Mktg.--Maverick Tube Corporation, Chesterfield, MO; *U.S. Public*, pg. 1060
Predes, Guillermo Wolf, Dir.-Mktg. & Brand Mgr.-Laundry & Paper--Procter & Gamble of Peru, Lima, Peru; *U.S. Public*, pg. 1332
Preisel, Thomas G., V.P.-Opers., Sls. & Mktg.--Baltek Corporation, Northvale, NJ; *U.S. Public*, pg. 171
Prendergast, Kevin, Natl. Dir.-Consumer Mktg. & Adv.--Better Homes and Gardens Real Estate Service, Des Moines, IA; *U.S. Public*, pg. 1094
Prendergast, Sally, V.P.-Strategic Mktg.-Universal Strategic Mktg. Grp.--Universal Studios, Inc., Universal City, CA; *Int'l*, pg. 1215
Prentice, Mike, Dir.-Sls. & Mktg.--API Harowe, West Chester, PA; *U.S. Public*, pg. 90
Presca, Georgia, Dir.-Mktg.--Lotto S.p.A., Montebelluna, Italy; *Int'l*, pg. 819
Prescott, Dana C., Sr. V.P.-Mktg.--Sunrise Leasing Corporation, Golden Valley, MN; *U.S. Public*, pg. 1535
Prescott, Nadia, Dir.-Corp. Commun.--Numetrix Ltd., Toronto, Canada; *Int'l*, pg. 990
Presley, Rick, V.P.-Sls.--Cook Manufacturing Corporation, Duncan, OK; *U.S. Private*, pg. 272
Press, Terry, Head of Mktg.--DreamWorks SKG, Universal City, CA; *U.S. Private*, pg. 342
Pressman, Ronald R., V.P.-Mktg.--G.E. Power Systems, Schenectady, NY; *U.S. Public*, pg. 711
Presson, Stuart M., V.P.-Mktg.--Safety National Casualty Corp., Saint Louis, MO; *U.S. Public*, pg. 496
Preston, Anne P., Mktg. Services--Spire Corporation, Bedford, MA; *U.S. Public*, pg. 1499
Preston, Charlie, V.P.-Mktg.--First Security Corporation, Salt Lake City, UT; *U.S. Public*, pg. 637
Preston, Charlie, V.P.-Mktg.--First Security Bank of Idaho, N.A., Boise, ID; *U.S. Public*, pg. 637
Preston, Charlie, V.P.-Mktg.--First Security Bank of Utah, N.A., Salt Lake City, UT; *U.S. Public*, pg. 637
Preston, Michael L., Sr. V.P.-Sls. & Mktg.--APS Holding Corporation, Houston, TX; *U.S. Public*, pg. 10
Preston, Scott, Supvr.-Graphic Srvcs.--Mirro Company, Manitowoc, WI; *U.S. Public*, pg. 1177
Presutti, Mike, Mgr.-Mktg.--Mill-Rose Company, Mentor, OH; *U.S. Private*, pg. 746

Pretty, David A., Dir.-Sls. & Mktg.--Barratt Developments Plc, Newcastle upon Tyne, United Kingdom; Int'l, pg. 167

Prevatt, John W., V.P.-Sls. & Mktg.--Golden Gem Growers Inc., Umatilla, FL; U.S. Private, pg. 460

Prewitt-Wood, Ken, Sr. V.P.Mktg.--Blue Shield of California, San Francisco, CA; U.S. Private, pg. 153

Price, Beth, Mgr.-Mktg.--Bryce LLC Corporation, Memphis, TN; U.S. Private, pg. 177

Price, Bob, V.P.-Sls. & Mktg.--Thomas Built Buses, Inc., High Point, NC; U.S. Private, pg. 1082

Price, Brent, Mgr.-Mktg. Commun.--Desa International, Bowling Green, KY; U.S. Private, pg. 326

Price, Chad, Mgr.-Mktg.--Woodward Governor Company, Rockford, IL; U.S. Public, pg. 1776

Price, Chris, Prod. Mgr.-Casual Fabrics--Dickson Elberton Mills Inc., Elberton, GA; U.S. Private, pg. 331

Price, David A., V.P.-Adv. & Sls.--ACMAT Corporation, New Britain, CT; U.S. Public, pg. 16

Price, Denise, Dir.-Mktg.--Meridell Achievement Center, Liberty Hill, TX; U.S. Public, pg. 1697

Price, Jack, V.P.-Mktg.--Gear Products Inc., Tulsa, OK; U.S. Public, pg. 238

Price, Jack, V.P.-Mktg.--Philips Medical Systems North America Company, Shelton, CT; Int'l, pg. 1055

Price, Keith A., V.P.-Mktg.--The Hotsy Corporation, Englewood, CO; U.S. Private, pg. 500

Price, Kenneth, Sr. V.P.-Sls. & Mktg.--Toymax International Inc., Plainview, NY; U.S. Public, pg. 1626

Price, Kevin, V.P.-Sls. & Mktg.-Track Prods. Div.--ABC Rail Products Corp., Chicago, IL; U.S. Public, pg. 2

Price, Linda, Mgr.-Mktg.--Motion Industries, Inc., Irondale, AL; U.S. Public, pg. 732

Price, Mark, Sr. V.P.-New Bus. Devel.--Sterling Healthcare Group, Inc., Miami, FL; U.S. Public, pg. 608

Price, Marley, Dir.-Mktg.--Price Brothers Co., Dayton, OH; U.S. Private, pg. 883

Price, Richard, V.P.-Mktg.--Frederick's of Hollywood, Inc., Hollywood, CA; U.S. Private, pg. 424

Price, Richard, Dir.-Mktg.--Reed Business Information-East Grinstead, East Grinstead, United Kingdom; Int'l, pg. 1094

Price, Wayne, Dir.-Sls. & Mktg.--Amprobe Instrument, Lynbrook, NY; U.S. Public, pg. 1676

Price, William, Pres. & Mgr.-Adv. & Mktg.--Your Man Tours, Inc., Inglewood, CA; U.S. Private, pg. 1202

Prideaux, Michael, Dir.-Grp. Pub. Affairs--B.A.T Industries P.L.C., London, United Kingdom; Int'l, pg. 110

Pridemore, Stephen, Pres.--Bright of America, Inc., Summersville, WV; U.S. Public, pg. 223

Priem, Troy, Mgr.-Mktg. & Sls.--Nobles Mfg. Inc., Saint Croix Falls, WI; U.S. Private, pg. 800

Priestap, Linda, Sr. V.P.-Mktg.--First Data Corporation, Englewood, CO; U.S. Public, pg. 631

Prieto, Robert, Exec. V.P. & Dir.-Corp. Devel.--Parsons Brinckerhoff Inc., New York, NY; U.S. Private, pg. 841

Prillaman, L.I., Exec. V.P.-Mktg.--Norfolk Southern Corporation, Norfolk, VA; U.S. Public, pg. 1190

Primavera, John, V.P.-Mktg.--Red Devil Inc., Union, NJ; U.S. Private, pg. 915

Prince, D.R., Dir.-Mktg.--J. Hungerford Smith Company, Fullerton, CA; U.S. Public, pg. 428

Prince, John, Dir.-Mktg.--VeriBest Inc., Huntsville, AL; U.S. Public, pg. 891

Prince, Phil, V.P.- Sls. Promo. & Mktg. Services--Fieldcrest Cannon, Inc., Kannapolis, NC; U.S. Public, pg. 1296

Principe, Maria B., Mktg. Asst.--ABB Lummus Global Inc., Bloomfield, NJ; Int'l, pg. 4

Prine, Ken, Mgr.-Intl. Mktg.--Glen Raven Mills, Inc., Glen Raven, NC; U.S. Private, pg. 456

Prinz, Bill, V.P.-Sls. & Mktg.--Jayco Inc., Middlebury, IN; U.S. Private, pg. 583

Prinzi, Jim, V.P.-Mktg.--Monro Muffler/Brake, Inc., Rochester, NY; U.S. Public, pg. 1124

Prior, Heidi, Mgr.-Mktg. Opers.--Marketing Displays International, Farmington Hills, MI; U.S. Private, pg. 705

Prisco, Edward, V.P.-Mktg. & Adv.--San Antonio Express News, San Antonio, TX; U.S. Private, pg. 517

Pritchard, Randy L., V.P.-Mktg.--Boddie-Noell Enterprises Inc., Rocky Mount, NC; U.S. Private, pg. 154

Pritchard, Tom, Dir.-Mktg.--Empire of Carolina, Inc., Delray Beach, FL; U.S. Public, pg. 579

Pritchett, Irene, Dir.-Mktg.-Eye Products-Shades of You--Maybelline, Inc., New York, NY; Int'l, pg. 819

Pritt, Roger, V.P. & Gen. Mgr.-Auto Store Div.--STRAFCO, Inc., San Antonio, TX; U.S. Private, pg. 1046

Privette, John C., V.P.-Intl. Opers.--Hach Company, Loveland, CO; U.S. Public, pg. 773

Probst, Lud A., V.P.-Sls. & Mktg.--Jacobs Engineering Group Inc., Houston, TX; U.S. Public, pg. 921

Procha, Stephen, V.P.-Mktg.--Geonex Corporation, Saint Petersburg, FL; U.S. Private, pg. 447

Prock, Rosemary, Dir.-Mktg.--The Grandoe Corp., Gloversville, NY; U.S. Private, pg. 469

Proctor, Anthony G., V.P.- Sls. & Mktg. for HPG (UK)--Seal Products Incorporated, Naugatuck, CT; U.S. Public, pg. 849

Profaci, John A., V.P.-Mktg.--Colivita USA, Inc., Linden, NJ; U.S. Private, pg. 252

Prohodski, Alex, V.P.-Sls. & Mktg.--Novartis Seeds, Inc., Downers Grove, IL; Int'l, pg. 974

Prol, Robert, Dir.-Mktg.--Edwards Engineering Corporation, Pompton Plains, NJ; U.S. Private, pg. 365

Proost, Philippe, Dir.-Mktg. & Licences--UCB SA Pharma Sector, Braine-l'Alleud, Belgium; Int'l, pg. 1427

Prosser, Linda R., V.P.-Mktg. Commun.--EXAR Corporation, Fremont, CA; U.S. Public, pg. 597

Proto, Anthony, V.P.-Mktg. & Sls.--CEBCOR (Consolidated Employment Benefits Corp.), Chicago, IL; U.S. Private, pg. 220

Protzman, Robert, V.P.-Sls. & Mktg.--Schneider National, Inc., Green Bay, WI; U.S. Private, pg. 971

Proud, Caroline, Dir.-Sls. & Mktg.--Mitchell Beazley, London, United Kingdom; Int'l, pg. 1093

Proudfit, Donna, Dir.-Mktg.--Pickering Inc., Tacoma, WA; U.S. Private, pg. 864

Prounis, Charlene, Sr. V.P. & Mktg. Dir.-New Bus.--Grey Healthcare Group, New York, NY; U.S. Private, pg. 765

Provoost, Rudy, V.P.-Grp. Mktg./WEBV--Whirlpool Corporation, Benton Harbor, MI; U.S. Public, pg. 1764

Provost, Roy G., Dir.-Sls. & Mktg.-Indus. Div.--Bel-Ray Company, Inc., Farmingdale, NJ; U.S. Private, pg. 130

Prues, John, Mktg.--Dexol, Torrance, CA; U.S. Public, pg. 1390

Pruess, David, V.P.-Mktg.--Good Companies, Carson, CA; U.S. Private, pg. 463

Pruitt-Andrews, Katrina, Dir.-Mktg.--Micros Systems Inc., Beltsville, MD; U.S. Public, pg. 1106

Pruitt, Matt, V.P.-Mktg.--Cameron & Barkley Company, Charleston, SC; U.S. Private, pg. 203

Pryor, Chuck, V.P.-Bus. Devel.--Trumbull Corporation/P.J. Dick, Inc., West Mifflin, PA; U.S. Private, pg. 1107

Pryor, Ed, Gen. Mgr.-Mktg.--The Southern Life Association Limited, Cape Town, South Africa; Int'l, pg. 77

Pryor, John P., V.P.-Mktg. & Sls.--BGS Systems, Inc., Waltham, MA; U.S. Public, pg. 161

Pryor, Karin, Exec. Dir.-Mktg.--Dann Dee Display Fixtures, Niles, IL; U.S. Private, pg. 310

Psigoda, Mark, V.P.-Mktg.--Warner Cable Communications, Inc., Columbus, OH; U.S. Public, pg. 1611

Psota, Duane, Dir.-Mktg.--Earl May Seed & Nursery L.c., Shenandoah, IA; U.S. Private, pg. 356

Puccia, Vincent, V.P.-Sls. & Mktg.--American International Airways, Ypsilanti, MI; U.S. Private, pg. 57

Pucillo, John, Dir.-Mktg.--PAREXEL International Corporation, Waltham, MA; U.S. Public, pg. 1257

Puckett, L.H., Gen. Mgr.-Mktg. & Sls.--Union Camp Fine Paper Div., Franklin, VA; U.S. Public, pg. 1666

Puckett, Todd, Dir.-Mktg. & Adv.--Halter Marine Group, Inc., Gulfport, MS; U.S. Public, pg. 778

Puelz, Ann, Dir.-Mktg.--Shamrock Foods Company, Phoenix, AZ; U.S. Private, pg. 989

Puettner, Steven, Dir.-Mktg.--General Tours Inc., Keene, NH; U.S. Private, pg. 445

Pugatch, Gary, V.P.-Sls. & Mktg.--Williams Hospitality Group Inc., Carolina, PR; U.S. Public, pg. 1265

Pugh, William, Dir.-Mktg.--MEG, Cambridge City, IN; U.S. Private, pg. 686

Pugliese, Lou, Dir.-Mktg. Svcs.--Scholastic Inc., New York, NY; U.S. Public, pg. 1440

Pujalet, Marc, Sr. V.P.--Westin Hotels & Resorts, Seattle, WA; U.S. Public, pg. 1512

Pujol, Daniel, V.P.-Lambda European Opers.--Lambda Electronics Inc., Melville, NY; Int'l, pg. 1241

Puk, John J., Dir.-Mktg.--Monsey-Bakor, Kimberton, PA; U.S. Private, pg. 757

Pulichino, Enzo, Mgr.-Mktg.--Caleffi S.p.A., Viadana, Italy; Int'l, pg. 252

Pulk, David R., Sr. V.P.-Sls. & Mktg.--Golden Eagle Group, Inc., Humble, TX; U.S. Public, pg. 749

Pullen, Louis, Mgr.-Mktg.--Air New Zealand Ltd., Auckland, New Zealand; Int'l, pg. 38

Pully, Henry, Dir.-Mktg.--Lance, Inc., Charlotte, NC; U.S. Public, pg. 977

Pulner-Mihaly, Stacey, Dir.-Mktg.--Plan International USA, Inc., Warwick, RI; U.S. Private, pg. 869

Pulver, Kenneth, V.P.-Corp. Communications--Albany Mount Vernon Dryers, Greenville, SC; U.S. Public, pg. 36

Pung, Olga M., Asst. V.P. & Mktg. Officer--Independent Bank Corporation, Ionia, MI; U.S. Public, pg. 874

Purdie, R.D., V.P.-Mktg.--Imperial Oil Limited, Toronto, Canada; U.S. Public, pg. 602

Purdy, David, Mgr.-Mktg. Commun.--Racine Federated, Inc., Racine, WI; U.S. Private, pg. 906

Purdy, John W., Jr., V.P.-Mktg. & Pub. Affairs--Essex County Gas Company, Amesbury, MA; U.S. Public, pg. 593

Pure, Pamela, V.P.-Mktg.--IDX Systems Corporation, Burlington, VT; U.S. Public, pg. 854

Purigraski, M., Sr. V.P.-Mktg. & Sls.--Mead School & Office Products, Dayton, OH; U.S. Public, pg. 1074

Pursel, Harry, V.P.-Bus. Devel.--Litton Applied Technology, San Jose, CA; U.S. Public, pg. 1003

Pursell, Linda, V.P.-Mktg. Devel.--The Courier-Journal Louisville Times Co., Louisville, KY; U.S. Public, pg. 700

Purser, Bill L., V.P.-Mktg. & Natl. Accts.--Applied Industrial Technologies, Cleveland, OH; U.S. Public, pg. 122

Pursiano, Patty, Dir.-Mktg.--ADAP Inc., Brockton, MA; U.S. Private, pg. 4

Purtill, Tom, V.P.-Sls. & Mktg.--Baylor Company, Sugar Land, TX; Int'l, pg. 1134

Purul, Louis F., Sr. V.P.-Mktg. & Dir.-Mktg.--Midlantic Bank, N.A., Edison, NJ; U.S. Public, pg. 1242

Purvin, Jeffrey L., V.P.-Mktg., Oral Health Care Division--Block Drug Company, Inc., Jersey City, NJ; U.S. Public, pg. 236

Purvis, T.W., Exec. V.P.-Mktg. & Sls.--Appleton Electric Co., Chicago, IL; U.S. Public, pg. 572

Pusey, E., Dir.-Mktg.--GEC Plessey Semiconductors, Swindon, United Kingdom; Int'l, pg. 544

Puspok, Peter, Dir.-Commercial--Raiffeisen Zentralbank Osterreich, Vienna, Austria; Int'l, pg. 1084

Putnam, Roger G., Dir.-Sls. & Mktg.--Jaguar Cars Limited, Coventry, United Kingdom; U.S. Public, pg. 666

Putnicki, Patti, V.P.-Adv. & Mktg.--Dry Manufacturing Co., Winters, TX; U.S. Private, pg. 1795

Putt, Lisa, V.P.-Mktg.--Blue Cross and Blue Shield of Oklahoma, Tulsa, OK; U.S. Private, pg. 151

Putterman, Leland, V.P.-Worldwide Mktg.--BMC Software, Inc., Houston, TX; U.S. Public, pg. 162

Putvinski, Jim, V.P.-Sls. & Mktg.--Tecknit Incorporated, Cranford, NJ; U.S. Private, pg. 1072

Putz, Katherine, Sr. Dir.-Mktg. Commun.--Jones Medical Industries Inc., Saint Louis, MO; U.S. Public, pg. 933

Pyle, Roy, Dir.-Mktg. & Prod. Devel.--Industrial Distribution and OEM, North America, Dayton, OH; U.S. Public, pg. 1045

Qualman, Jay W., Jr., Gen. Dir.-Mktg. NAO--General Motors Corporation, Detroit, MI; U.S. Public, pg. 718

Quamme, Ralph, V.P.-Sls. & Mktg.--Long Equipment Co., Tarboro, NC; U.S. Private, pg. 675

Quarles, Judy, Mgr.-Mktg. Support--Puritan/Churchill Chemical Company, Atlanta, GA; U.S. Private, pg. 895

Quarles, Susan, Mgr.-Mktg.--Smith International, Inc., Houston, TX; U.S. Public, pg. 1478

Quarry, Adam, Dir.-Mktg.--3i Group plc, London, United Kingdom; Int'l, pg. 1386

Quartarone, Simone, Mgr.-Natl. Media--Quality Special Products, Scarborough, Canada; Int'l, pg. 1075

Queiros, Armando, Gen. Mgr.-Mktg.--Banco Totta & Acores, Lisbon, Portugal; Int'l, pg. 144

Quek, Karen, Reg. Mgr.-Mktg. Commun.--F.J. Benjamin Multimedia Pte Ltd., Singapore, Singapore; Int'l, pg. 187

Quenaudon, Deborah, Mgr.-Mktg.--Renault USA, Southfield, MI; Int'l, pg. 1102

Quenselle, George M., V.P. & Dir.- Medical Mktg.-Rx to OTC Switch--SmithKline Beecham Consumer Healthcare, U.S., Pittsburgh, PA; Int'l, pg. 1264

Queroli, Lauren, Dir.-Mktg.--Time Warner Cable Liberty Division, Ferndale, NY; U.S. Public, pg. 1611

Quertinmont, Tom, Mgr.-Mktg. Communications--Mettler-Toledo Inc., Worthington, OH; U.S. Private, pg. 4

Quesada, Juan, Exec. V.P.-Sls., Mktg. & Adv.--Cox Lumber Co., Saint Petersburg, FL; U.S. Private, pg. 283

Quevedo, Manny, V.P.-Mktg./Inacom Communications--Inacom Corp., Omaha, NE; U.S. Public, pg. 873

Quey, K., Dir.-Mktg.-USA--China Airlines Ltd., Los Angeles, CA; Int'l, pg. 284

Quick, Edgar A., Mgr.-Mktg. & Procurement--PowderTech Corporation, Valparaiso, IN; Int'l, pg. 878

Quick, Sidney W., V.P.-Mktg. Services--Alabama Gas Corporation, Birmingham, AL; U.S. Public, pg. 581

Quigg, Richard J., V.P.-Mktg.--Cannon-Muskegon Corp., Muskegon, MI; U.S. Public, pg. 1420

Quigley, Garrett, Mgr.-Mktg., Confections--Masterfoods Ltd., Dublin, Ireland; U.S. Private, pg. 707

Quigley, Sean, Mgr.-Mktg. & Time Information Prods.--Amano Cincinnati, Inc., Roseland, NJ; Int'l, pg. 70

Quimby, Edward D., Sr. V.P.-Sls. & Mktg.--The Turner Corporation, New York, NY; U.S. Public, pg. 1645

Quimby, Edward D., Sr. V.P.-Sls. & Mktg.--Turner Construction Company, New York, NY; U.S. Public, pg. 1645

Quinlan, Robert W., Mng. Dir.-Mktg.--Provident Bank of Maryland, Baltimore, MD; U.S. Public, pg. 1337

Quinley, John, Mgr.-LandPride Mktg. & Sls. Promo.--Great Plains Manufacturing, Inc., Salina, KS; U.S. Private, pg. 475

Quinn, Bruce, Dir.-Mktg.-Superconductors--Litton Solid State, Santa Clara, CA; U.S. Public, pg. 1003

Quinn, Chuck, V.P.-Mktg.--Franklin Sports, Inc., Stoughton, MA; U.S. Private, pg. 424

Quinn, Mike, Dir.-Regional Mktg.--Doubletree Corporation, Memphis, TN; U.S. Public, pg. 1335

Quinn, Pat, Mgr.-Mktg.--Esselte Meto Ltd., Bracknell, United Kingdom; Int'l, pg. 461

Quinn, Terry, Dir.-Mktg.--Hehr International Inc., Los Angeles, CA; U.S. Private, pg. 519

Quinones, Frankie, Admin.-Mktg.--Playmates Toys Inc., Costa Mesa, CA; Int'l, pg. 1060

Quint, Sharon, Mgr.-Mktg.--Aqua-Chem Inc., Milwaukee, WI; Int'l, pg. 824

Quinton, Linda, V.P. & Dir.-Mktg. Tourbook--St. Martins Press, Inc., New York, NY; Int'l, pg. 1479

Quirke, S., Mgr.-Mktg.--Gallaher (Dublin) Ltd., Tallaght, Ireland; Int'l, pg. 539

Quiter, George W., III, V.P.-Corp. Mktg.--Atkinson, San Bruno, CA; U.S. Public, pg. 143

Raab, Christopher, Mgr.-Natl. Mktg.--A&W Restaurants, Inc., Livonia, MI; U.S. Private, pg. 1

Raab, John, V.P.-Mktg.--Rapistan Demag Corp., Grand Rapids, MI; Int'l, pg. 837

Raasch, Jeff, Exec. V.P.-Sls. & Mktg.--Enerfab Inc., Cincinnati, OH; U.S. Private, pg. 376

Rabadan, William, V.P.-Mktg.--Spinnerin Inc., South Hackensack, NJ; U.S. Private, pg. 1025

Rabeno, Lou, Mgr.-Mktg.--Lawrence Metal Products, Inc., Bay Shore, NY; U.S. Private, pg. 654

Rabey, Wayne, Dir.-Sales & Mktg.--General Instrument of Canada Ltd., Mississauga, Canada; U.S. Public, pg. 716

Rabeyroux, Michel, Mgr.-Plng.--Calcia, Guerville, France; Int'l, pg. 292

Rabin, Hal, V.P.-Mktg.--Sonic Couriers of Arizona, Inc., Scottsdale, AZ; U.S. Private, pg. 1123

Rabinovitch, Donald, Pres.--AFP Imaging Corporation, Elmsford, NY; U.S. Public, pg. 6

Rable, Mary, Mktg. Mgr.-Hardware--Sandvik Saws & Tools Co., Throop, PA; Int'l, pg. 1185

Race, Peter, Mgr.-Mktg.--Naugatuck Glass Company, Naugatuck, CT; U.S. Private, pg. 789

Racher, Cora, Dir.-Mktg.--Nady Systems, Inc., Emeryville, CA; U.S. Private, pg. 773

Racicot, Nancy J., V.P.-Opers.--The Washington Water Power Company, Spokane, WA; U.S. Public, pg. 1744

Rackoff, Laurie, Dir.-Mktg.--Shonac Corporation, Columbus, OH; U.S. Private, pg. 996

Radaj, Trish, Mgr.-Mktg. Commun.--Richco Inc., Chicago, IL; U.S. Private, pg. 929

Radandt, Andre, V.P.-Mktg. & Production--Wm. Bolthouse Farms, Inc., Bakersfield, CA; U.S. Private, pg. 155

Radek, William F., V.P.-Mktg.--Sun Coast Closures of Florida, Inc., Sarasota, FL; U.S. Public, pg. 1530

Rademacher, Kent D., Sr. V.P.-Dental Office Opers., Sls & Mktg.--Safeguard Health Enterprises, Inc., Anaheim, CA; U.S. Public, pg. 1424

Rademacher, R.W., Mgr.-Mktg. Services--Beaird Industries, Inc., Shreveport, LA; U.S. Public, pg. 1639

Rademeyer, Ian, Mgr.-Mktg.--Tosas (Pty) Ltd., Wadeville, South Africa; Int'l, pg. 1197

Radford, G., Dir.-Mktg.--AHF-Ducommun Incorporated, Gardena, CA; U.S. Public, pg. 534

Radkowsky, Gerri, Mgr.-Mktg.--Molded Fiber Glass Companies, Ashtabula, OH; *U.S. Private*, pg. 755
Radler, Toni, Dir.-Mktg. & Adv.--Hohner/HSS Inc., Ashland, VA; *U.S. Private*, pg. 533
Radlin, David, Gen. Mgr. & Dir.-Mktg.--Jamaica Flour Mills, Ltd., Kingston, Jamaica; *Int'l*, pg. 411
Rado, Betsy, Dir.-Mktg--Smithfield Foods, Inc., Norfolk, VA; *U.S. Public*, pg. 1479
Radshaw, John, Mgr.-N. Amer. Sls. & Mktg.-Metallurgical Prods.--Hennepin Division, Exolon-Esk, Hennepin, IL; *U.S. Public*, pg. 600
Radwill, Scott, Pres., Chief Exec., Oper. & Fin. Officer--Master Appliance Corp., Racine, WI; *U.S. Private*, pg. 713
Rae, Bruce, V.P.-Mktg.--Medeco Security Locks, Inc., Salem, VA; *U.S. Public*, pg. 828
Raedepinet, Kathy, Mktg. Admin.--Therma-Tru Corp., Maumee, OH; *U.S. Private*, pg. 1079
Raffa, Connie L., Coord.-Mktg.--Giffels Associates, Inc., Southfield, MI; *U.S. Private*, pg. 452
Raffaelli, Richard, V.P.-Sls. & Mktg.--Muskin Leisure Products, Inc., Wilkes-Barre, PA; *U.S. Private*, pg. 768
Rafferty, Mary Katherine, Dir.-Mktg. & Pub. Rels.--Bulgari Corporation of America, New York, NY; *Int'l*, pg. 232
Rafferty, William S., Sr. V.P.-Mktg.--Mestek, Inc., Westfield, MA; *U.S. Public*, pg. 1099
Raffner, Bernard, V.P.-Sls. & Mktg.--Inductotherm Corp., Rancocas, NJ; *U.S. Private*, pg. 560
Raft, Steve, Exec. V.P.-Mktg.--Oshman's Sporting Goods, Inc., Houston, TX; *U.S. Public*, pg. 1233
Ragaenia, Roseana, Sec.-Mktg.--S.C. Johnson & Son de Argentina S.A.I.C., Buenos Aires, Argentina; *U.S. Private*, pg. 593
Ragatz, Jon, Dir.-Mktg. & Sls.--Alta-Dena Certified Dairy, City of Industry, CA; *Int'l*, pg. 201
Ragland, David, Pres. & Chief Exec. Officer--Duncan Equipment Company, Oklahoma City, OK; *U.S. Private*, pg. 346
Ragsdale, John, Dir.-Mktg.--Williamson-Dickie Mfg. Co., Fort Worth, TX; *U.S. Private*, pg. 1179
Rahim, Yaakob Bin Abdul, Mgr.-Seafreight Sls. & Mktg.--Kwe-Kintetsu World Express(S)Pte Ltd., Singapore, Singapore; *Int'l*, pg. 735
Raichle, Ellen, Mktg. Services--M & M Precision Systems Corporation, Carrollton, OH; *U.S. Public*, pg. 482
Raif, Joshua, V.P.-Mktg.--Laser Industries Ltd., Tel Aviv, Israel; *Int'l*, pg. 429
Raikes, Jeffrey S., Grp. V.P.-Sls. & Mktg.--Microsoft Corporation, Redmond, WA; *U.S. Public*, pg. 1107
Raines, Michelle, Dir.-Mktg.--Huntington National Bank, Morgantown, WV; *U.S. Public*, pg. 850
Rainey, Tom, V.P.-Mktg.--Dover Elevator Systems, Inc., Horn Lake, MS; *U.S. Public*, pg. 521
Rains, Lindsey, V.P.-Sls.--Heartland Express, Inc., Coralville, IA; *U.S. Public*, pg. 803
Rains, Sidney, V.P.-Sls. & Mktg.--Van Dorn Demag Corporation, Strongsville, OH; *Int'l*, pg. 837
Rainville, S., Mgr.-Mktg.--Hunter Douglas Canada Inc., Mississauga, Canada; *Int'l*, pg. 639
Rainville, Sue, Dir.-Mktg., Hunter Douglas Canada--Hunter Douglas, Inc., Upper Saddle River, NJ; *Int'l*, pg. 639
Rainwater, Thomas M., V.P.-Central Reg. Unit--Illinova Energy Partners, Inc., Oak Brook, IL; *U.S. Public*, pg. 870
Rajczi, Suzanne, V.P.-Mdsg.--Ginsberg's Institutional Foods, Inc., Hudson, NY; *U.S. Private*, pg. 455
Rajewski, Kurt, Supvr.-Mktg.--Kester Solder, Des Plaines, IL; *U.S. Public*, pg. 1003
Rajlis, Marcia, Dir.-Sls. & Mktg. Admin.--Columbian Mutual Life Insurance Co., Binghamton, NY; *U.S. Private*, pg. 256
Rak, Henry, V.P.-Mktg. Services--Kraft Foods Inc., Glenview, IL; *U.S. Public*, pg. 1288
Rakusin, Marshall, V.P.-Sls. & Mktg.--Fred V. Fowler Company, Inc., Newton, MA; *U.S. Private*, pg. 422
Ralston, Ronald, Exec. V.P.-Mktg. & Sls.--Parfums International Ltd., New York, NY; *Int'l*, pg. 1435
Ramaglia, Mary, V.P.-Sls. & Mktg.--Revco Scientific, Asheville, NC; *U.S. Public*, pg. 727
Ramalho, Americo, Dr., Mgr.-Pub. Rels.--Portuguese Railways (CP), Lisbon, Portugal; *Int'l*, pg. 1063
Rambaud, P., Sr. V.P.-Mktg. & Strategic Devel.--Danone Group, Paris, France; *Int'l*, pg. 379
Rambo, Virgil A., V.P.-Sls. & Mktg.--CorryHiebert Corporation, Corry, PA; *U.S. Public*, pg. 772
Ramer, Tim, Mgr.-Mktg. Commun.--Dana Corporation, Toledo, OH; *U.S. Public*, pg. 479
Ramey, A.J., V.P.-Sls. & Mktg.--Marley Mouldings Inc., Marion, VA; *Int'l*, pg. 843
Rammel, Ed, Dir.- Mktg.--Automotive Aftermarket, North America, Dayton, OH; *U.S. Public*, pg. 1045
Ramos de Souza, Cristiano, V.P.-Mktg.--Cervejarias Kaiser Brasil Ltda., Campinas, Brazil; *Int'l*, pg. 279
Ramos, Wendy, Mgr.-Mktg. & Adv.--Corcom, Inc., Libertyville, IL; *U.S. Public*, pg. 446
Ramsay, Dan, Mgr.-Mktg. Communications--Kenworth Truck Company, Kirkland, WA; *U.S. Public*, pg. 1246
Ramsbacher, Charles F., V.P.-Mktg.--Nash Finch Company, Edina, MN; *U.S. Public*, pg. 1151
Ramsby, Bob, Supvr.-Mktg. Communications--CTS Corporation-Connector Division, New Hope, MN; *U.S. Public*, pg. 285
Ramsby, Robert, Supvr.-Mktg. Communications--CTS Corporation, Elkhart, IN; *U.S. Public*, pg. 285
Ramsdale, Chris, Dir.-Mktg.--Computer Corporation of America, Framingham, MA; *U.S. Private*, pg. 260
Ramsdell, Robert, V.P.-Mktg. & Sls.-Lawn, Farm & Garden, Security Prods.--Universal Cooperatives, Inc., Minneapolis, MN; *U.S. Private*, pg. 1127
Ramsey, Christine, Dir.-Mktg. Mngmt.--Mobile Telecommunications Technologies Corp., Jackson, MS; *U.S. Public*, pg. 1120
Ramsey, Chuck, Mgr.-Mktg. Services--Magnetek Motors & Generators, Saint Louis, MO; *U.S. Public*, pg. 1037
Ramsey, Craig, V.P.-Mktg.--Quad Systems Corporation, Willow Grove, PA; *U.S. Private*, pg. 898
Ramsey, W. Knox, Exec. Dir.-Reg. Mktg. NAO--General Motors Corporation, Detroit, MI; *U.S. Public*, pg. 718
Rancak, Pam, Mktg. Services Admin.--Precision Twist Drill Co., Crystal Lake, IL; *Int'l*, pg. 1185
Rance, Michael J., V.P.-Sales & Mktg. Bus. Dev.--ICI Pharmaceuticals Group, Wilmington, DE; *Int'l*, pg. 664
Randall, Cindy, V.P.-Mktg.--Scott Forseman/Addison Wesley, Glenview, IL; *Int'l*, pg. 927
Randall, Mark, Dir.-Mktg.--Redland Roof Tiles Ltd., Reigate, United Kingdom; *Int'l*, pg. 1091
Randall, Robert, Dir.-Mktg.--Veda International, Inc., Alexandria, VA; *U.S. Private*, pg. 1136
Randall, Rod, V.P.-Worldwide Mktg.--Stratus Computer, Inc., Marlborough, MA; *U.S. Public*, pg. 1524
Randall, Wayne, Dir.-Mktg.--VP-Schickedanz AG, Nuremberg, Germany; *U.S. Public*, pg. 1333
Randazzo, Cindy, V.P.-Mktg.--May & Speh, Inc., Downers Grove, IL; *U.S. Public*, pg. 1063
Randazzo, Gary W., V.P.-Sls.--Houston Chronicle, Houston, TX; *U.S. Private*, pg. 517
Randle, William, Sr. V.P.-Mktg.--Huntington Bancshares Inc., Columbus, OH; *U.S. Public*, pg. 849
Randolph, Paula, Mgr.-Mktg.--Office Depot Inc., Delray Beach, FL; *U.S. Public*, pg. 1212
Rangel, Ramiro, V.P.-Mktg.--Louis Dreyfus Natural Gas Corp., Oklahoma City, OK; *U.S. Private*, pg. 342
Ranger, G., Dir.-Sls. & Mktg.--BBA Friction LTD., Cleckheaton, United Kingdom; *Int'l*, pg. 112
Ranieri, Joe, V.P.-Mktg.--Robotic Vision Systems, Inc., Hauppauge, NY; *U.S. Public*, pg. 1395
Raniszeski, Ed, Mgr.-Mktg. Communications--Rheem Air Conditioning Div., Fort Smith, AR; *Int'l*, pg. 1022
Rank, Bob, Mgr.-Mktg. Communications--Paragon Electric Co., Inc., Two Rivers, WI; *Int'l*, pg. 1243
Rankin, J.D., V.P.-Mktg. & Gov. Affairs--Lone Star Gas Co., Dallas, TX; *U.S. Public*, pg. 1587
Rankin, Owen, V.P.-Global Mktg.--Tambrands Inc., Cincinnati, OH; *U.S. Public*, pg. 1331
Rankin, Paul C., V.P.-Mktg. Retail--United Refining Company, Warren, PA; *U.S. Private*, pg. 915
Rannazzisi, Christine, Mgr.-Mktg.--Weider Publications, Inc., Woodland Hills, CA; *U.S. Private*, pg. 1159
Rano, John, Sr. V.P.-Mktg.--General Cigar Company, Inc., Bloomfield, CT; *U.S. Public*, pg. 708
Ransden, Glen, V.P.-Corp. Mktg.--Brigham's, Inc., Arlington, MA; *U.S. Private*, pg. 483
Ranslou, Robert, V.P.-Mktg.--SierraCom, Hopkinton, MA; *U.S. Private*, pg. 999
Ransom, H.L., V.P.-Mktg.--United States Pipe & Foundry Company, Inc., Birmingham, AL; *U.S. Public*, pg. 1736
Ransom, Mal, Sr. V.P.-Mktg.--Packard Bell NEC, Sacramento, CA; *U.S. Private*, pg. 833
Ranzinger, Rick, V.P.-Sls. & Mktg.--Lyman Products Corporation, Middletown, CT; *U.S. Private*, pg. 683
Rao, Kelly, Dir.-Mktg.--The Rao Group Inc., Sterling Heights, MI; *U.S. Private*, pg. 910
Rao, Kelly, Dir.-Mktg.--Metro 25 Tire Centers, Sterling Heights, MI; *U.S. Private*, pg. 910
Rapaport, Michael, Dir.-Mktg.--Bresler's Industries, Inc., Des Plaines, IL; *Int'l*, pg. 1520
Rappaport, Fran, Dir.-Mktg.--Restaurant Associates Corporation, New York, NY; *U.S. Private*, pg. 924
Rash, Edward, Dir.-Adv. & Pub. Rels.--Hannay Reels, Westerlo, NY; *U.S. Private*, pg. 499
Rashid, Osman, Mgr.-Mktg.--ATIO Corporation USA, Inc., Hopkins, MN; *U.S. Public*, pg. 1716
Rashkovsky, Gary, V.P.-Intl. Sls. & Mktg.--Del Global Technologies, Valhalla, NY; *U.S. Public*, pg. 493
Rasiq, Asmat, V.P.-Intl. Mktg. & Bus. Development--Craig Systems, Amesbury, MA; *U.S. Private*, pg. 284
Rask, Sharon, Dir.-Adv. & Mktg.--United HealthCare Corporation, Minnetonka, MN; *U.S. Public*, pg. 1677
Raskin, Larry, Grp. Prod. Mgr.-Prep. Foods--Hormel Grocery Prods. Div., Austin, MN; *U.S. Public*, pg. 840
Rasmusen, Ivan, Mgr.-Mktg.--C.G. Jensen A/S, Ballerup, Denmark; *Int'l*, pg. 1261
Rasmussen, Jann, V.P.-Mktg.--Teca Corporation, Pleasantville, NY; *Int'l*, pg. 1468
Rasmussen, Mark, Mgr.-Mktg.--Tennant Company, Minneapolis, MN; *U.S. Public*, pg. 1577
Rath, Charles W., Exec. V.P.-Mktg.--Wendy's International Inc., Dublin, OH; *U.S. Public*, pg. 1754
Rathburn, Gary J., V.P.-Mktg.--Mapco Coal Inc., Tulsa, OK; *U.S. Public*, pg. 1042
Ratkey, Ron, V.P.-Sls. & Mktg.--Access Industries, Grandview, MO; *U.S. Private*, pg. 11
Ratkus, Theodore S., Sr. V.P.-Sls. & Mktg.--Shorewood Packaging Corporation, New York, NY; *U.S. Public*, pg. 1468
Ratner, Mark, V.P.-Mktg.--Hawthorne Communications, Inc., Fairfield, IA; *U.S. Private*, pg. 512
Rattananit, Rangsan, Assoc. Mktg. Svcs. Dir.--Leo Burnett Ltd. Thailand, Bangkok, Thailand; *U.S. Private*, pg. 185
Rau, Jennifer, Mktg. Asst.--Good Humor/Breyers Ice Cream, Green Bay, WI; *Int'l*, pg. 1435
Rau, Rick, Dir.-Mktg.--Worlds of Fun & Oceans of Fun--Cedar Fair, L.P., Sandusky, OH; *U.S. Public*, pg. 319
Rauch, Ray, Sr. V.P.-Mktg.--Kraus-Anderson Construction Company, Minneapolis, MN; *U.S. Private*, pg. 635
Rauchwerger, Jerry, V.P.-Intl. Sls. & Mktg.--Inverness Corp., Fair Lawn, NJ; *U.S. Private*, pg. 574
Raulf, Hans-Otto, Dir.-Mktg.--Elektro Metall Export Gmbh, Ingolstadt, Germany; *U.S. Private*, pg. 313
Rausch, Anne, Mgr.-Direct Mktg.--Best Buy Co., Inc., Eden Prairie, MN; *U.S. Public*, pg. 223
Rauschenberg, Richard, Mgr.-Mktg.--Southern Guaranty Insurance Companies, Montgomery, AL; *Int'l*, pg. 346
Rauscher, Craig D., Mgr.-Mktg.--Stewart-Warner South Wind Corp., Indianapolis, IN; *Int'l*, pg. 127
Rauss, William G., V.P.-Sls. & Mktg.--Edwin B. Stimpson Company, Inc., Bayport, NY; *U.S. Private*, pg. 1043
Rawers, Mindy, Mgr.-Mktg. Svcs.--San Diego Union Tribune, San Diego, CA; *U.S. Private*, pg. 275
Rawlinson, John T., V.P.-Sls. & Mktg.--Renold, Inc., Westfield, NY; *Int'l*, pg. 1104
Ray, Donna, Mgr.-Mktg.--Astro-Med, Inc., West Warwick, RI; *U.S. Public*, pg. 141
Ray, Jennifer, Dir.-Mktg. & Pub. Rels.--Louisiana Downs, Bossier City, LA; *U.S. Private*, pg. 319
Ray, Kelly, First V.P.-Mktg.--Univest Financial Services, LLC, Atlanta, GA; *U.S. Private*, pg. 1128
Ray, Lisa D., Dir.-Sls. & Mktg.--Ray Communications, Inc., Kill Devil Hills, NC; *U.S. Private*, pg. 911
Ray, Peter, Mgr.-Mktg.--Automated Wagering, Hackensack, NJ; *U.S. Public*, pg. 1319
Ray, T.M., Mgr.-Mktg., U.K.--Stafford-Miller Limited, Welwyn Garden City, United Kingdom; *U.S. Public*, pg. 237
Ray, V.E., Dir.-Sls. & Mktg.--Flowserve Corporation, Foundry Div., Dayton, OH; *U.S. Public*, pg. 658
Raymond, Donald, V.P.-Mktg.--Uniboard Canada Inc., Laval, Canada; *Int'l*, pg. 1431
Raymond, G.J., V.P.-Mktg.--Kiwi Brands Pty. Ltd., Clayton, Australia; *U.S. Public*, pg. 1434
Raymond, Randy, V.P.-Mktg.--Cambridge Street Metal Co., Allston, MA; *U.S. Private*, pg. 203
Raz, Israel, Mgr.-Mktg.--Bio-Logic Systems Corp., Mundelein, IL; *U.S. Public*, pg. 230
Razek, Edward, Pres.-Mktg.--The Limited, Inc., Columbus, OH; *U.S. Public*, pg. 995
Read, J.D., National Sls. Mgr.--Canadian Timken Ltd., Saint Thomas, Canada; *U.S. Public*, pg. 1617
Read, Rosalie, Country Mgr.--Berlitz Schools of Languages Ltd., London, United Kingdom; *U.S. Public*, pg. 222
Reader, Marty, V.P.-Mktg.--G&K Services, Inc., Minnetonka, MN; *U.S. Public*, pg. 690
Ready, Jon E., V.P.-Sls. & Mktg.--Sunshine Biscuits, Inc., Woodbridge, NJ; *U.S. Private*, pg. 434
Ready, Jon E., V.P.-Sls. & Mktg.--Sunshine Biscuits, Inc., Woodbridge, NJ; *U.S. Public*, pg. 657
Reagan, Bruce M., V.P.-Mktg.--Turner Supply Company, Mobile, AL; *U.S. Private*, pg. 1110
Ream, Marcy, Mgr.-Mktg. Commun. & Adv.--Republic Storage Systems Company Inc., Canton, OH; *U.S. Private*, pg. 924
Reap, Jeff, Dir.-Sls. & Mktg.--Keith Smith Company, Hot Springs National Park, AR; *U.S. Private*, pg. 1008
Reaume, Jack, Coord.-Mktg.& Sls.--Air Control Products, Roxboro, NC; *U.S. Public*, pg. 556
Reay, Tim, V.P.-Mktg.--Tremco, Inc., Beachwood, OH; *U.S. Public*, pg. 1358
Rebello, Raul, Mgr.-Mkt. Res.--SmithKline Beecham Laboratorios Ltda., Rio de Janeiro, Brazil; *Int'l*, pg. 1266
Rebner, Cindy, Asst. Admin.-Mktg.--Minwax Company Div., Upper Saddle River, NJ; *U.S. Public*, pg. 1466
Rebull, Julio, Hispanic Mktg. Dir.--Beber & Silverstein & Partners, Inc., Miami, FL; *U.S. Private*, pg. 128
Recio, Tomas Garcia, Mgr.-Corp. Mktg.--Repsol S.A., Madrid, Spain; *Int'l*, pg. 1104
Recone, Max, V.P.-Mktg.--Playtex Beauty Care, Inc., Westport, CT; *U.S. Public*, pg. 1311
Rector, Harry, Sr. V.P.-Sls. & Mktg.--Southern Bag Corporation, Madison, MS; *U.S. Private*, pg. 1015
Reder, Thomas J., V.P.-Sls. & Mktg.--Fairbanks Morse Engine Division, Beloit, WI; *U.S. Public*, pg. 401
Redfeld, Jean, Asst. V.P.-Retail Mktg.--DTE Energy Company, Detroit, MI; *U.S. Public*, pg. 475
Redfern, Ron, Sr. V.P. & Adviser-Mktg.--The Orange County Register, Santa Ana, CA; *U.S. Private*, pg. 425
Redhouse, John W., V.P.-Sls. & Mktg.--Henkels & McCoy, Inc., Blue Bell, PA; *U.S. Private*, pg. 522
Redington, Brian, V.P.-Mktg.--Graycor Operating Companies, Homewood, IL; *U.S. Private*, pg. 472
Redlin, Martin N., Sr. V.P.-Mktg. & Sls.--Broan Mfg. Co., Inc., Hartford, WI; *U.S. Public*, pg. 1193
Redpath, Tim, Dir.-Mktg. & Commun.--Mitel Corporation, Kanata, Canada; *Int'l*, pg. 870
Redpath, Tim, Dir.-Mktg. Communications--Mitel, Inc., Herndon, VA; *Int'l*, pg. 870
Redshaw, John, V.P.-Sls. & Mktg.--Exolon-Esk Company, Tonawanda, NY; *U.S. Public*, pg. 600
Reece, Greg, V.P.-Sls.--Saladmaster, Inc., Arlington, TX; *U.S. Private*, pg. 917
Reece, Mike, Mgr.-Mktg.--Blackeyed Pea Restaurants Inc., Scottsdale, AZ; *U.S. Public*, pg. 498
Reece, Rozlyn, Mktg. Communications Project Coordinator--Science Applications International Corp., San Diego, CA; *U.S. Private*, pg. 975
Reeck, Larry, V.P.-Mktg. & Sls.--Dean Pickle & Specialty Products Co., Green Bay, WI; *U.S. Public*, pg. 490
Reed, Bob, V.P.-Mktg.--Harris Calorific Co., Gainesville, GA; *U.S. Public*, pg. 996
Reed, Catherine I., Sr. V.P. & Dir.-Mktg.--Brenton Banks, Inc., Des Moines, IA; *U.S. Public*, pg. 251
Reed, Charles L., Jr., Pres. & V.P.-Mktg.--Integra Technologies Corp., Waltham, MA; *U.S. Private*, pg. 565
Reed, James, Asst. V.P.-Mktg. Communications--Rockefeller Center Management Corporation, New York, NY; *Int'l*, pg. 873
Reed, Jennifer, V.P.-Adv. & Mktg.--Filene's Basement, Inc., Wellesley, MA; *U.S. Public*, pg. 622
Reed, John, V.P.-Mktg.--Capital Associates, Inc., Lakewood, CO; *U.S. Public*, pg. 302
Reed, Karen, V.P.-Catalog Mktg.--Coldwater Creek, Sandpoint, ID; *U.S. Public*, pg. 396
Reed, Kenneth, V.P.-Sls. & Mktg.--TriEnda Corporation, Portage, WI; *U.S. Private*, pg. 1103
Reed, Mark E., Sr. V.P.-Sls. & Mktg. Service--In Focus Systems, Inc., Wilsonville, OR; *U.S. Public*, pg. 873
Reed, Paul, Dir.-Mktg.--Norbest, Inc., Midvale, UT; *U.S. Private*, pg. 801
Reed, Robert, Dir.-Mktg.--Easy Day Manufacturing Company, Holliston, MA; *U.S. Private*, pg. 358
Reed, Vanessa, Dir.-Mktg., People--Time Inc., New York, NY; *U.S. Public*, pg. 1612

Reed, Vanessa, Dir.-Mktg.--People, New York, NY; *U.S. Public*, pg. 1613

Reed, William, V.P.-Sls. & Mktg.--C.P. Clare Corporation, Beverly, MA; *U.S. Public*, pg. 382

Reeder, Carol, Mktg. Sec.--Hartmann Luggage & Leather Goods Group, Lebanon, TN; *U.S. Public*, pg. 261

Reedy, Floyd, V.P.-Marketing--Charter Builders, Inc., Dallas, TX; *Int'l*, pg. 896

Reefman, Frank, V.P.-Intl. Mktg.--Sara Lee/DE, Utrecht, Netherlands; *U.S. Public*, pg. 1434

Reefman, R., Dir.-Sls. & Mktg.--Holmatro Industrial & Rescue Equipment, Raamsdonksveer, Netherlands; *Int'l*, pg. 632

Rees, P.K., Grp. Dir.-Mktg.--John Laing PLC, London, United Kingdom; *Int'l*, pg. 796

Reese, Anthony, Dir.-Strategic Mktg.--J. Sainsbury plc, London, United Kingdom; *Int'l*, pg. 1169

Reese, J. Barrett, Grp. V.P.-Sls. & Mktg./Expanded Shale & Clay--Texas Industries, Inc., Dallas, TX; *U.S. Public*, pg. 1585

Reese, Michele, V.P.-Adv. & Mktg.--Disneyland, Anaheim, CA; *U.S. Public*, pg. 511

Reese, Michele, Exec. V.P.-Mktg.--Universal Studios Hollywood, Universal City, CA; *Int'l*, pg. 1216

Reese, Monty A., V.P.-Mktg.--Michaels Stores, Inc., Irving, TX; *U.S. Public*, pg. 1104

Reese, Rob, Dir.-Mktg.--Ace Tank & Equipment Co., Seattle, WA; *U.S. Private*, pg. 12

Reese, Thomas J., Exec. V.P.-Commercial Div.--Continental General Tire, Inc., Charlotte, NC; *Int'l*, pg. 327

Reeser, Jacquelyn, V.P.-Mktg.--Briggs Industries, Inc., Tampa, FL; *U.S. Private*, pg. 168

Reeves, Dale, Dir.-Communications, Mktg. & Adv.--John Brown Plastics Machinery, Attleboro, MA; *Int'l*, pg. 773

Reeves, Ralph, Dir.-Mktg.--Kwal-Howells, Inc.(Denver), Denver, CO; *Int'l*, pg. 1501

Reeves, Sue, Dir.-Mktg. Communications--Dade Behring Inc., Westwood, MA; *U.S. Private*, pg. 110

Reeves, Susan, Mktg. Coord.--Sega of America Inc., Redwood City, CA; *Int'l*, pg. 1218

Regan, Annette, Mgr.-Trade Mktg.--McCormick Distilling Co., Weston, MO; *U.S. Private*, pg. 720

Regan, Joseph, Sr. V.P.-Sls. & Mktg.--Solectron Corporation, Milpitas, CA; *U.S. Public*, pg. 1483

Reguer, Rafi, V.P.-Electronic Mktg.--Waterhouse Investor Services, New York, NY; *Int'l*, pg. 1401

Reha, Christie M., Coord.-Mktg.--Wampole Laboratories, Cranbury, NJ; *U.S. Public*, pg. 310

Rehling, Louise, Sr. V.P.-Devel.--SPSS Inc., Chicago, IL; *U.S. Public*, pg. 1420

Rehman, Khalil Ur, Dir.-Mktg.--Organon Pakistan (Private) Limited, Karachi, Pakistan; *Int'l*, pg. 45

Reichbach, Joseph, Sr. V.P.-Sls. & Mktg.--Merix Corporation, Forest Grove, OR; *U.S. Public*, pg. 1096

Reichert, Laurie, Mktg. Asst.--Escalade Sports, Evansville, IN; *U.S. Public*, pg. 591

Reichert, Mark, V.P.-Mktg.--ABC Packaging Machine Corp., Tarpon Springs, FL; *U.S. Private*, pg. 3

Reichwald, William H., Exec. V.P.-Mktg.--Lutheran Brotherhood, Minneapolis, MN; *U.S. Private*, pg. 681

Reid, Bob, Exec. V.P.-Mktg. & Sls.--Outdoor Technologies Group, Spirit Lake, IA; *U.S. Private*, pg. 822

Reid, Clare, Mgr. Mktg.- Outdoor Heating--Desa International, Bowling Green, KY; *U.S. Private*, pg. 326

Reid, David, V.P.-Mktg.--Milcare, Inc., Grandville, MI; *U.S. Public*, pg. 1112

Reid, Don, Mgr.-Mktg.--Beaver Foods Limited, London, Canada; *Int'l*, pg. 266

Reid, Greg, Sr. V.P.-Mktg.--Yellow Corporation, Overland Park, KS; *U.S. Public*, pg. 1788

Reid, Greg, Sr. V.P.-Mktg.--Yellow Freight System, Inc., Overland Park, KS; *U.S. Public*, pg. 1788

Reid, J. William, V.P.-Sls. & Mktg.--Del Pharmaceuticals, Inc., Farmingdale, NY; *U.S. Public*, pg. 494

Reid, Jennifer, Mktg. Coord.--Fortune, New York, NY; *U.S. Public*, pg. 1613

Reid, Phil, V.P.-Res. Sls. & Mktg.--Season-All Industries, Inc., Indiana, PA; *Int'l*, pg. 267

Reid, Richard, Dir.-Sls. & Mktg.--Stadium Limited, Hartlepool, United Kingdom; *Int'l*, pg. 1293

Reid, Sheldon, V.P.-Mktg.--Norcen Energy Resources Limited, Calgary, Canada; *Int'l*, pg. 434

Reider, Thomas D., V.P.-Domestic Sls. & Mktg.--Ruslander & Sons, Inc., Buffalo, NY; *U.S. Private*, pg. 952

Reifeiss, Gary, V.P.-Mktg. & Consumer Prods.--Producers Rice Mill Inc., Stuttgart, AR; *U.S. Private*, pg. 888

Reifsnider, John L., V.P.--Scott & Stringfellow Capital Management, Inc., Richmond, VA; *U.S. Public*, pg. 1445

Reiland, Richard, V.P.-Sls. & Mktg.--Worcester Controls Corp., Marlborough, MA; *Int'l*, pg. 128

Reilly, Dave, Dir.-Mktg. & Sls.--Schleicher & Schuell, Inc., Keene, NH; *Int'l*, pg. 1206

Reilly, Ken, Dir.-Mktg.--Rohr, Inc., Chula Vista, CA; *U.S. Public*, pg. 751

Reilly, Michelle, Mgr.-Communications--Bird Products Corporation, Palm Springs, CA; *U.S. Public*, pg. 1591

Reilly, Thomas P., V.P.-Sls. & Mktg.--Rockbestos-Suprenant Cable Corp., Clinton, MA; *U.S. Private*, pg. 938

Reily, Brett, Mktg. Communications Specialist--Samuel Cabot, Inc., Newburyport, MA; *U.S. Private*, pg. 198

Reimenn, Kurt, Dir.-Mktg. & Adv.--Fonar Corporation, Melville, NY; *U.S. Public*, pg. 661

Reimer, Robert I., Mgr.-Mktg. & Sls.--Escast, Inc., Addison, IL; *U.S. Public*, pg. 612

Reinert, Christie, Dir.-Mktg.--WCI Communities, Inc., Bonita Springs, FL; *U.S. Private*, pg. 1144

Reingold, Jon, V.P.-Office Mktg.--Microsoft Corporation, Redmond, WA; *U.S. Public*, pg. 1107

Reinhard, Karen, Dir.-Mktg.--Communicolor Division, Newark, OH; *U.S. Public*, pg. 1505

Reis, Antonio C., Div. Mgr.-Natl Sls.--TAP Air Portugal, Newark, NJ; *Int'l*, pg. 1418

Reis, R.J., Exec. V.P.--Serigraph, Inc., West Bend, WI; *U.S. Private*, pg. 985

Reisinger, Phillip, Dir.-Prods. & Services--Carpeteria, Inc., Valencia, CA; *U.S. Private*, pg. 215

Reisner, M., Dir.-Mktg.--Alva/Amco Pharmacal Companies, Inc., Chicago, IL; *U.S. Private*, pg. 47

Reiss, Myrna, Dir.-Sls. & Mktg.--Value City Department Stores, Inc., Columbus, OH; *U.S. Private*, pg. 972

Reiss, W.A., V.P.-Mktg.--Camco Products & Services Company, Houston, TX; *U.S. Public*, pg. 298

Reissig, Robert, Gen. Mgr.--Genzyme Diagnostics, Medix Biotech, San Carlos, CA; *U.S. Public*, pg. 733

Reiter, Douglas, Sr. V.P.-Sls. & Mktg., Dallas--Safeguard Business Systems, Inc., Fort Washington, PA; *U.S. Private*, pg. 960

Reith, Ronald J., Exec. V.P.-Mktg. & Sls.--Merck Medco Managed Care, Independence, OH; *U.S. Public*, pg. 1091

Reitman, Bill, V.P.-Mktg.--Briggs & Stratton Corporation, Wauwatosa, WI; *U.S. Public*, pg. 252

Reitmeier, Debbie, Asst. V.P.-Mktg. & Sls.--Key Pharmaceuticals, Kenilworth, NJ; *U.S. Public*, pg. 1438

Reitz, Bonnie, Sr. V.P.-Mktg. & Sls. Distr.--Continental Airlines, Houston, TX; *U.S. Public*, pg. 439

Reitzner, James A., V.P. & Gen. Mgr.--Steenberg Homes, Inc., Fond Du Lac, WI; *U.S. Private*, pg. 1039

Reko, Brill, Mktg. Asst.--EAC Corporation, Saint Louis, MO; *U.S. Private*, pg. 353

Rella, Ina, Dir.-Mktg.--Triumph International, Sacavem, Portugal; *Int'l*, pg. 1424

Rem, Steen, V.P.-Sls. & Mktg.--International Pharmaceuticals, Oslo, Norway; *U.S. Public*, pg. 58

Rembeszewski, Jim, Dir.-Global Mktg.--British-American Tobacco Co. Ltd., Staines, United Kingdom; *Int'l*, pg. 111

Remensnyder, Gary, Dir.-Mktg.--Shakespeare Fishing Tackle, Columbia, SC; *U.S. Public*, pg. 940

Remtema, David, Mgr.-Mktg.--Windemuller Electric Inc., Wayland, MI; *U.S. Private*, pg. 1182

Remus, Ken, Mgr.-Mktg.--Symons Corporation, Des Plaines, IL; *U.S. Private*, pg. 932

Remus, Ken, Mgr.-Mktg., Adv. & Brandname--Symons Corporation, Centralia, IL; *U.S. Private*, pg. 932

Renalda, Roy, Exec. V.P.-Sls. & Mktg.--The Faxon Company, Inc., Westwood, MA; *Int'l*, pg. 385

Renaud, Ernie, Vice Chm.--Seed Restaurant Group, Inc., Lexington, KY; *U.S. Private*, pg. 981

Rench, Fred, Dir.-Mktg. & Plng./Container Opers.--Boise Cascade Corporation, Boise, ID; *U.S. Public*, pg. 242

Renich, Tom, Dir.-Sls. & Mktg.--Peabody TecTank, Inc., Parsons, KS; *U.S. Public*, pg. 1477

Rennels, Jack, V.P.-Mktg.--Emkay, Inc., Itasca, IL; *U.S. Private*, pg. 374

Rennie, D.M., Mgr.-Corp. Mktg.--General Motors of Canada Ltd., Oshawa, Canada; *U.S. Public*, pg. 722

Rennie, Sue, Mgr.-Mktg.--Dexion Group plc, Hemel Hempstead, United Kingdom; *U.S. Public*, pg. 893

Reno, David, Mgr.-Mktg.--Kern's Bakeries, Incorporated, Knoxville, TN; *U.S. Public*, pg. 547

Renouard, Ed S., Jr., Mgr.-Mktg. Communications--The Washington Water Power Company, Spokane, WA; *U.S. Public*, pg. 1744

Renshaw, Don, V.P.-Mktg.--Chemical Exchange Industries, Houston, TX; *U.S. Private*, pg. 232

Renshaw, John A., Dir.-Market Intelligence--J. Sainsbury plc, London, United Kingdom; *Int'l*, pg. 1169

Rent, John, Mgr.-Prod. Sls. & Mktg.--Lukens Steel Company, Coatesville, PA; *U.S. Public*, pg. 1020

Rentzel, Becky, Admin.-Sls. & Mktg.--York Wallcoverings Inc., York, PA; *U.S. Private*, pg. 1196

Resar, Carolyn, Dir.-Mktg., Commun. & Direct Mktg./Direct Response--Signature Brands USA, Inc., Solon, OH; *U.S. Public*, pg. 1472

Resendez, Gilbert, V.P.-Sls. & Mktg.--Monrovia Nursery Co., Azusa, CA; *U.S. Private*, pg. 757

Resh, Edward, Dir.-Mktg.--Lone Star Corrugated Container Corporation, Irving, TX; *U.S. Private*, pg. 674

Resnick, Dennis A., V.P.-Sls. & Mktg.--R & R Marketing, West Caldwell, NJ; *U.S. Private*, pg. 902

Resnik, Robert, Dir.-Mktg.--L. Powell Co., Inc., Culver City, CA; *U.S. Private*, pg. 877

Resusta, Luis, Mgr.-European Mktg.--FMC Food Machinery France, S.A., Aulnay-sous-Bois, France; *U.S. Public*, pg. 606

Resweber, Chris, Dir.-Mktg.- Jams, Jellies & Preserves--J.M. Smucker Company, Orrville, OH; *U.S. Public*, pg. 1480

Rettke, Ralph P., V.P.-Devel. & Tech.--W. Braun Company, Chicago, IL; *U.S. Private*, pg. 166

Retz, John R., V.P.-Mkt. Devel.--VASA Brougher, Inc., Indianapolis, IN; *Int'l*, pg. 464

Reubens, Simon, Mgr.-Mktg.--ANR Pipeline Co., Detroit, MI; *U.S. Public*, pg. 389

Reuland, Brenda, Dir.-Communications--American Eurocopter Corp., Grand Prairie, TX; *Int'l*, pg. 29

Reuland, Todd, V.P.-Mktg.--Reuland Electric Company, City of Industry, CA; *U.S. Private*, pg. 925

Reuning, Karl, Mktg. Communications--Frequency and Time Systems, Inc., Beverly, MA; *U.S. Public*, pg. 488

Reval, Wayne, Dir.-Mktg.- EMS--Zoll Medical Corporation, Burlington, MA; *U.S. Private*, pg. 1207

Rewey, Robert L., Jr., Grp. V.P.-Mktg., Sls. & Service--Ford Motor Company, Dearborn, MI; *U.S. Public*, pg. 661

Rewolinski, Ron, Mgr.-Mktg. Services--Tecumseh Products Co. Engine & Transmission Group, Grafton, WI; *U.S. Public*, pg. 1566

Reynar, Diana, Mgr.-Projects & Corp. Mktg.--Sierra Health Services, Inc., Las Vegas, NV; *U.S. Public*, pg. 1469

Reynolds, Carrie, V.P.-Mktg. Services--Prudential Real Estate Affiliates Inc., Costa Mesa, CA; *U.S. Private*, pg. 892

Reynolds, Curt, V.P.-Mktg. & Sls.--Comlinear Corporation, Fort Collins, CO; *U.S. Public*, pg. 1160

Reynolds, Gary, Sr. V.P.-Sls. & Mktg.--General Electric Capital Railcar Services, Chicago, IL; *U.S. Public*, pg. 712

Reynolds, James, V.P.-Mktg.--Albertson's, Inc., Boise, ID; *U.S. Public*, pg. 38

Reynolds, Jean M., V.P.-Sls. & Mktg.--BPI Inc., Kent, WA; *U.S. Public*, pg. 772

Reynolds, Kate, Mgr.-Mktg.--Laura Ashley (USA) Inc., Boston, MA; *Int'l*, pg. 804

Reynolds, Kathy, Pres.-Womens Div.--Jockey International, Inc., Kenosha, WI; *U.S. Private*, pg. 588

Reynolds, Laurence E., V.P.-Mktg.--R.J. Palmer, Inc., New York, NY; *U.S. Private*, pg. 835

Reynolds, Rick, V.P.-Mktg., N. America--Trimac Transportation System, Calgary, Canada; *Int'l*, pg. 1424

Reynolds, Robert D., V.P.-Mktg. & Electric Transmission--Illinois Power Company, Decatur, IL; *U.S. Public*, pg. 869

Reznick, Greg, V.P.-Mktg.--Micronics Computers, Inc., Fremont, CA; *U.S. Public*, pg. 1106

Rhee, Thomas, Dir.-Mktg. Communications & Research--Samsung Electronics America, Inc., Ridgefield Park, NJ; *Int'l*, pg. 1183

Rheinberg, A.C., Mgr.-Mktg.--Qualitas Bathrooms Ltd., Burton on Trent, United Kingdom; *Int'l*, pg. 197

Rhoades, Kay, Mgr.-Customer Service--Integrated Metal Technologies, Inc., Spring Lake, MI; *U.S. Public*, pg. 1112

Rhoades, Mark, V.P.-Mktg.--Jami, Inc., Shawnee Mission, KS; *U.S. Private*, pg. 581

Rhoades, Terence J., V.P.-Mktg. & Fin.--M.A.R.C.O., Ann Arbor, MI; *U.S. Private*, pg. 355

Rhodes, Amy, V.P. & Dir.-Mktg. & Sls.--Little, Brown & Co., New York, NY; *U.S. Public*, pg. 1612

Rhodes, Brenda, Mgr.-Mktg. (DMSD)--I.C. System, Inc., Vadnais Heights, MN; *U.S. Private*, pg. 553

Rhodes, David L., Jr., Sr. V.P.-Sls. & Mktg.--Unisource Worldwide, Inc., Berwyn, PA; *U.S. Public*, pg. 1670

Rhodes, Paul, V.P.-Mktg.--Industrial Dielectrics, Inc., Noblesville, IN; *U.S. Private*, pg. 560

Rhodes, Steve, V.P.-Mktg. & Sls.--Paramount Fitness Corp., Los Angeles, CA; *U.S. Private*, pg. 838

Rhone, Sylvia, Dir.-Mktg. & Special Mktg.--Elektra Entertainment, New York, NY; *U.S. Public*, pg. 1612

Riazzi, Richard, V.P.-Mktg. & Sls.--Idaho Power Company, Boise, ID; *U.S. Public*, pg. 861

Ribalta, Gail, V.P.-Mktg.--R.G. Barry Corporation, Pickerington, OH; *U.S. Public*, pg. 192

Ribe, Carl C., Mgr.-Mktg.--Frionor A/S, Lysaker, Norway; *Int'l*, pg. 516

Ricarte, Ramon Ferraz, Mng. Dir.-Strategic Mktg., Studies & Organization--Caja de Madrid Group, Madrid, Spain; *Int'l*, pg. 251

Ricat, Nicholas, Dir.-Mktg. & Communications--Societe Hoteliere Paris Vanves, Evry, France; *Int'l*, pg. 20

Ricci, Jim, V.P.-Mktg.--Stationery Products Division, Boston, MA; *U.S. Public*, pg. 744

Ricci, R., V.P.-Sls. & Mktg.--National Vendors, Bridgeton, MO; *U.S. Public*, pg. 457

Riccioli, Fred, Mgr.-Adv.--Neles-Jamesbury Corp., Worcester, MA; *Int'l*, pg. 1428

Rice, Dennis, Sr. V.P.-Mktg.--Buena Vista Home Video, Burbank, CA; *U.S. Public*, pg. 513

Rice, Dennis, Mgr.-Customer Programs--Omaha Public Power District, Omaha, NE; *U.S. Private*, pg. 815

Rice, Douglas F., V.P.-Mktg. & Tech. Services--Central Sprinkler Company, Lansdale, PA; *U.S. Public*, pg. 327

Rice, Gerald, Dir.-Sls. & Mktg.--Danfoss Fluid Power, Racine, WI; *Int'l*, pg. 377

Rice, Harold E., Jr., V.P.-Admin. & Fin.--Pittway Real Estate, Wesley Chapel, FL; *U.S. Public*, pg. 1306

Rice, John, Sr. V.P. & Gen. Mgr.-Personnel--Lever Brothers Co., New York, NY; *Int'l*, pg. 1435

Rice, John, V.P.-Mktg.--ShowBiz Pizza Time, Inc., Irving, TX; *U.S. Public*, pg. 1468

Rice, John F., V.P.-Mktg. & Sls.--Kevlin Corporation, Wilmington, MA; *U.S. Public*, pg. 953

Rich, Gerry, Pres.-Worldwide Mktg.--Metro-Goldwyn-Mayer Inc., Santa Monica, CA; *U.S. Public*, pg. 1101

Rich, Joan, Coord.-Mktg.--Tafa Incorporated, Concord, NH; *U.S. Public*, pg. 866

Rich, Paul, Dir.-Mktg.--H.O. Trerice Company, Oak Park, MI; *U.S. Private*, pg. 1099

Richard, J.L., Mktg. Dir.--Skis Dynastar S.A., Salindres, France; *Int'l*, pg. 1127

Richard, Mark, V.P.-Sls. & Mktg.--J.W. Allen & Company, Wheeling, IL; *U.S. Private*, pg. 37

Richards, A.C., V.P.-Business Devel.--Teledyne Ryan Aeronautical, San Diego, CA; *U.S. Public*, pg. 43

Richards, Barbara, Exec. V.P.-Mktg.--Chicago Mercantile Exchange, Chicago, IL; *U.S. Private*, pg. 235

Richards, Craig, Sr. V.P.-Sls. & Mktg.--Proteon, Inc., Westborough, MA; *U.S. Public*, pg. 1336

Richards, David, Sr. V.P.-Mktg.--Lenscrafters, Cincinnati, OH; *Int'l*, pg. 822

Richards, Doug, V.P.-Mktg. & Sls.--Weibel Winery, Lodi, CA; *U.S. Private*, pg. 1159

Richards, F. Timothy, Gen. Dir.-Mktg. & Bus. Ventures--Delphi Harrison Thermal Systems, Lockport, NY; *U.S. Public*, pg. 719

Richards, George, Sr. V.P.-Mktg. Customers & Clients--Damark International, Inc., Minneapolis, MN; *U.S. Public*, pg. 478

Richards, J.C., V.P.-Mktg. & Sls.--Frog Switch & Manufacturing Company, Carlisle, PA; *U.S. Private*, pg. 429

Richards, John, Exec. V.P.-Mktg.--Four Seasons Hotels Inc., Don Mills, Canada; *Int'l*, pg. 502

Richards, M.A., Mgr.-Natl. Sls. & Mktg.--Crane Australia Pty. Ltd., Saint Marys, Australia; *U.S. Public*, pg. 457

Richards, M.A., V.P.-Mktg.--Highway Equipment Company, Cedar Rapids, IA; *U.S. Private*, pg. 529

Richards, Paul, Mgr.-Corp. Communications--American Hardware Mutual Insurance Co., Columbus, OH; *U.S. Private*, pg. 764

Richards, R.A., Mgr.-Mktg.--Bluebird Foods Ltd, Manukau, New Zealand; *Int'l*, pg. 556

Richardson, Andrew, Dir.-Mktg.--Reed Elsevier Legal Division, London, United Kingdom; *Int'l*, pg. 1095

Richardson, Betsy, Sr. V.P.-Direct Corp. Mktg.--Fleet Financial Group, Inc., Boston, MA; *U.S. Public*, pg. 648
Richardson, Brian, V.P.- Mktg.--Canadian Pacific Hotels & Resorts Inc., Toronto, Canada; *Int'l*, pg. 258
Richardson, Cantey, Sr. V.P.-Sls & Mktg.--Diversco, Inc., Spartanburg, SC; *U.S. Private*, pg. 336
Richardson, Cary, V.P.-Wholesale Club Mktg.--Tyson Foods, Inc., Springdale, AR; *U.S. Public*, pg. 1652
Richardson, Danny, V.P.-Mktg.--Marine Drilling Companies, Inc., Sugar Land, TX; *U.S. Public*, pg. 1044
Richardson, Ed, Mgr.-Mktg.--Furon Co., Bristol, RI; *U.S. Public*, pg. 689
Richardson, J.W., Div. Mgr.-Mktg.--Meadow Lea Foods Ltd., Mascot, Australia; *Int'l*, pg. 555
Richardson, James R., Sr. V.P.-Mktg.--Flexsteel Industries, Inc., Dubuque, IA; *U.S. Public*, pg. 653
Richardson, Jim, V.P.-Sls. & Mktg.--Richardson Bros. Co. Div., Sheboygan Falls, WI; *U.S. Private*, pg. 929
Richardson, Jim, V.P.-Sls. & Mktg.--Richardson's Furniture Emporium, Sheboygan Falls, WI; *U.S. Private*, pg. 929
Richardson, Julie, Mgr.-Mktg.--Hatteras Yachts, New Bern, NC; *U.S. Private*, pg. 447
Richardson, Lee, Sr. V.P.-Mktg.--Rich's/Lazarus/Goldsmith's, Atlanta, GA; *U.S. Public*, pg. 618
Richardson, Lindy B., Sr. V.P.-Mktg. & Public Affairs--Columbia/HCA Healthcare Corporation, Nashville, TN; *U.S. Public*, pg. 403
Richardson, Lori, Sr. Dir.-Mktg.--Snap-On Tools Corporation, Kenosha, WI; *U.S. Public*, pg. 1480
Richardson, Mary, Mgr.-Mktg. & Detergent Soap--Lever Pond's Limited, Toronto, Canada; *Int'l*, pg. 1438
Richardson, Paul, V.P.-Mktg.--Consolidated Industries Corp., Lafayette, IN; *Int'l*, pg. 188
Richardson, Traci, Mgr.-Mktg.--The Apogee Companies, Inc., Lake Oswego, OR; *U.S. Private*, pg. 77
Richebacher, Tom, V.P.-Mktg.--Weiss Group., Palm Beach Gardens, FL; *U.S. Private*, pg. 1160
Richey, Alvan E., Jr., V.P.-Sls. & Mktg.--NCI Building Systems, Inc., Houston, TX; *U.S. Public*, pg. 1145
Richey, Cindy, Dir.-Mktg. Devel. & Res.--Kansas City Life Insurance Co., Kansas City, MO; *U.S. Public*, pg. 942
Richfield, Mark, Mgr.-Mktg. Svcs.--Vilter Manufacturing Corporation, Cudahy, WI; *U.S. Private*, pg. 1140
Richman, David, Mktg. Analyst--Tipper Tie, Inc., Apex, NC; *U.S. Public*, pg. 520
Richman, Joshua V., Pres. & Chief Exec. Officer--Straw Hat Cooperative Corp., Dublin, CA; *U.S. Private*, pg. 1046
Richman, Steve, V.P.-Mktg. & Sls.--The Murray Ohio Mfg. Co., Brentwood, TN; *Int'l*, pg. 1397
Richmond, Robert, Mgr.-Mktg.--Warn Industries, Inc., Clackamas, OR; *U.S. Private*, pg. 1150
Richter, George, V.P.-Sls. & Mktg./Meats Grp.--Farmland Industries, Inc., Kansas City, MO; *U.S. Private*, pg. 395
Richter, George, V.P.-Mktg.--Farmland Foods, Inc., Kansas City, MO; *U.S. Private*, pg. 396
Richter, Hans Joachim, Dir.-Mktg.--Philip Morris Gmbh, Munich, Germany; *U.S. Public*, pg. 1290
Rickborn, Chris, V.P.-Mktg. & Prod. Plng.--Equitrac Corporation, Coral Gables, FL; *U.S. Public*, pg. 590
Ricketts, Steve, Dir.-Mktg.--Xerox Imaging Systems, Inc., Peabody, MA; *U.S. Public*, pg. 1785
Ricky, Darleen, Dir.-Mktg.--Keeler Motor Car Company, Inc., Latham, NY; *U.S. Private*, pg. 611
Riddle, James R., Exec. V.P.-Mktg.--Heilig-Meyers Company, Richmond, VA; *U.S. Public*, pg. 804
Riddle, Larry, V.P.-Sls. & Mktg.--Ikegami Electronics (U.S.A.), Inc., Maywood, NJ; *Int'l*, pg. 660
Riddle, Richard, Mgr.-Mktg. & Sls.--TFX Medical Inc., Jaffrey, NH; *U.S. Public*, pg. 1570
Ridenour, David, V.P.-Mktg. Therapeutics--Wyeth-Ayerst Laboratories, Inc., Philadelphia, PA; *U.S. Public*, pg. 80
Ridge, Colman, Reg. Dir.-Sls. & Mktg.--DHL International (Singapore) Pte. Ltd., Singapore, Singapore; *U.S. Private*, pg. 302
Ridgway, John B., V.P.-Mktg.--Royal Doulton USA Inc., Somerset, NJ; *Int'l*, pg. 1135
Ridlehuber, Ronald H., Sr. V.P.-Independent Mktg.--Jefferson-Pilot Life Insurance Co., Greensboro, NC; *U.S. Public*, pg. 926
Ridley, Dave, V.P.-Sls. & Mktg.--Southwest Airlines Co., Dallas, TX; *U.S. Public*, pg. 1493
Ridley, Steve M., Dir.-Sls. & Mktg.--Dowty Aerospace Hydraulics, Cheltenham, Cheltenham, United Kingdom; *Int'l*, pg. 1337
Ridolfi, Steve A., V.P.-Mktg.--Bombardier Regional Aircraft Division, Downsview, Canada; *U.S. Public*, pg. 242
Ridulfo, S., Mgr.-Pub. Rels. & Mktg.--Olivetti Australia Pty. Ltd., Silverwater, Australia; *Int'l*, pg. 1003
Riebe, Ron, Dir.-Mktg.--Fleming Company, Waukesha, WI; *U.S. Public*, pg. 653
Riecks, Bob, Mgr.-Mktg.--Ansco Photo-Optical Products Corp., Elk Grove Village, IL; *Int'l*, pg. 587
Riedel, Hans, Exec. V.P.-Sls. & Mktg.--Porsche AG, Stuttgart, Germany; *Int'l*, pg. 1063
Riedel, James F., V.P.-Mktg. & Sls.--Webster Industries Inc., Tiffin, OH; *U.S. Private*, pg. 1157
Riedel, Nancy, Mgr.-Mktg.--AGRA Earth & Environmental, Inc., Albuquerque, NM; *Int'l*, pg. 31
Rieder, Raymond J., Chief Mktg. Officer & Sr. V.P.--Hudson General Corporation, Great Neck, NY; *U.S. Public*, pg. 845
Riediger, Joachim, Dir.-Risk Mngmt. Sls.--Dun & Bradstreet Deutschland GmbH, Frankfurt/Main, Germany; *U.S. Public*, pg. 536
Riefel, M.A., Coord.-Mktg.--Ferry-Morse Seed Company, Modesto, CA; *Int'l*, pg. 566
Riefler, Scott, Dir.-Sls. & Mktg.--T.L. Smith Machine, Springville, NY; *U.S. Private*, pg. 1009
Riegel, Dawn, Sr. Mktg. Analyst--Lancaster Colony Automotive Group, Dublin, OH; *U.S. Public*, pg. 977
Riegel, E. Thomas, V.P.-Mktg.--O'Sullivan Industries Holdings, Lamar, MO; *U.S. Public*, pg. 1234
Riegel, Mike, V.P.-Mktg. (Canada)--Bombardier, Learjet Inc., Wichita, KS; *Int'l*, pg. 200
Riegel, William S., V.P.-Sls. & Mktg.--The Pacific Lumber Company, Scotia, CA; *U.S. Public*, pg. 1062
Riehle, Peter, V.P.-Mktg. & Sls.--Trumpf Inc., Farmington, CT; *U.S. Private*, pg. 1108
Rieser, Mark, Grp. Mgr.-Mktg.--Caradco, Rantoul, IL; *U.S. Public*, pg. 61
Riesman, Lance, V.P.-Mktg.--Kwikset Corporation, Irvine, CA; *U.S. Public*, pg. 233
Rieson, Dean A., Pres. & Chief Exec. Officer--Carlson Real Estate Company, Minnetonka, MN; *U.S. Private*, pg. 212
Rietdyk, Helen, Mgr.-Mktg.--Osprey, London, United Kingdom; *Int'l*, pg. 1093
Riffey, Roger L., Mgr.-Mktg.--Kerr-McGee Coal Corp., Oklahoma City, OK; *U.S. Public*, pg. 952
Riffle, Don, Sr. V.P.-Sls. & Mktg.--Sea Watch International, Ltd., Easton, MD; *Int'l*, pg. 928
Riffner, Linda, Sr. V.P.-Mktg.--Commercial Federal Corporation, Omaha, NE; *U.S. Public*, pg. 411
Rigas, Denny A., Sr. V.P.-Mktg., Tech. & Sls.--Innovative Valve Technology, Inc., Houston, TX; *U.S. Public*, pg. 880
Rigertve, Steve, V.P.-Mktg.--Michelin Americas Small Tires (MAST), Greenville, SC; *Int'l*, pg. 322
Rigg, Don, Mgr.-Mktg. & Sls. Support--Champion Laboratories, Inc., Albion, IL; *U.S. Private*, pg. 1113
Riggon, Mike, Exec. V.P.-Mktg. & Mdse.--PetCare Plus, Inc., Aurora, IL; *U.S. Private*, pg. 856
Rigler, Gail, Dir.-Mktg.--Electronic Data Systems Corporation, Plano, TX; *U.S. Public*, pg. 569
Riipinen, J., Mgr.-Mktg.--Olivetti (Suomi) OY, Espoo, Finland; *Int'l*, pg. 1003
Riley, Bud, Mgr.-Mktg.--Koncor Industries Div., Wauseon, OH; *U.S. Public*, pg. 1617
Riley, Dennis, Sr. V.P.-Sls.--Superior Coffee and Foods, Bensenville, IL; *U.S. Public*, pg. 1434
Riley, John, V.P.-Mktg.--Great Lakes Confectionery, Cleveland, OH; *Int'l*, pg. 865
Riley, Lisa, Dir.-Mktg.--Storehouse PLC, London, United Kingdom; *Int'l*, pg. 1304
Riley, Margaret, V.P.-Mktg.--Hygrade Food Products Corporation, Southfield, MI; *U.S. Public*, pg. 1433
Riley, Michael R., Sr. V.P.-Property Mngmt.--SouthTrust Corporation, Birmingham, AL; *U.S. Public*, pg. 1491
Riley, Michael T., Sr. V.P.-Mktg., Infosvcs. & Opers.--First Financial Bancorp, Hamilton, OH; *U.S. Public*, pg. 632
Riley, Robert, Mktg. Mgr.-Indus.--Sandvik Saws & Tools Co., Throop, PA; *Int'l*, pg. 1185
Riley, Tom, V.P.-Acq. & Mktg.--Petroleum Development Corporation, Bridgeport, WV; *U.S. Public*, pg. 1280
Rinaldo, Carolyn, V.P.-Mktg. & Sls.--Marilyn Miglin, L.P., Chicago, IL; *U.S. Private*, pg. 745
Rinehart, Steven T., Mgr.-Mktg.--FirstEnergy Corp., Akron, OH; *U.S. Public*, pg. 644
Riner, Carla, Mgr.-Mktg. Publicity--American Packaging Corporation, Philadelphia, PA; *U.S. Private*, pg. 60
Riner, Henry, V.P.-Mktg.--Institute For Scientific Information, Philadelphia, PA; *U.S. Public*, pg. 1600
Ringler, David E., V.P.-Mktg.--Andres Wines Ltd., Winona, Canada; *Int'l*, pg. 75
Rinkle, Ron, V.P.-Mktg.--AirTouch Cellular - Western Region, Bellevue, WA; *U.S. Public*, pg. 34
Riordan, Charlotte Hart, V.P.-Prod. Strategy & Mktg.--Programart Corporation, Cambridge, MA; *U.S. Private*, pg. 890
Rios, Steven, Mgr.-Mktg. Svcs.--E.J. Brooks Company, Newark, NJ; *U.S. Private*, pg. 172
Ripa, John, V.P.-Sls.--Database America Companies, Montvale, NJ; *U.S. Private*, pg. 312
Ripoll, Jose, Mgr.-Mktg.--Hispano Olivetti Office, Barcelona, Spain; *Int'l*, pg. 1003
Rippeth, John, Mgr.-Mktg.--L&J Technologies, Hillside, IL; *U.S. Private*, pg. 638
Ripple, Louis J., Dir.-Sls. & Mktg./Worldwide--Allen-Edmonds Shoe Corp., Port Washington, WI; *U.S. Private*, pg. 36
Rishman, John, Dir.-Mktg./White Goods--Dixons Group plc, Hemel Hempstead, United Kingdom,; *Int'l*, pg. 413
Rising, Trish, Mgr. Mktg.--Thomson Company, Inc., Atlanta, GA; *U.S. Public*, pg. 1429
Riskin, Gregg, Mgr.-Mktg.--Samuel Cabot, Inc., Newburyport, MA; *U.S. Private*, pg. 198
Rissier, Henry, Sr. V.P.-Sls. & Mktg.--Anchor Continental Incorporated, Columbia, SC; *U.S. Private*, pg. 70
Ristaino, Robert A., V.P.-Sls., Mktg. & Service--New England Coffee Company, Malden, MA; *U.S. Private*, pg. 792
Ritchey, Mike, V.P.--Austin Quality Foods, Cary, NC; *U.S. Private*, pg. 100
Ritchie, Doug, V.P.-Mktg.--Cole-Haan, Yarmouth, ME; *U.S. Public*, pg. 1184
Ritchie, James, V.P.-Mktg.--Tridel Enterprises Inc., Downsview, Canada; *Int'l*, pg. 1423
Ritchie, John, Sr. V.P.-Sls. & Mktg.--KLLM Transport Services, Inc., Jackson, MS; *U.S. Public*, pg. 939
Ritchie, Joseph, V.P.-Sls. & Mktg.--Griffin Envelope, Inc., Seattle, WA; *U.S. Public*, pg. 1038
Ritchie, Roger, Dir.-Communications--FlightSafety International Inc., Flushing, NY; *U.S. Public*, pg. 218
Ritter, Leslie, Dir.-Mktg.--Muzak Limited Partnership, Seattle, WA; *U.S. Private*, pg. 222
Ritter, P.C., Sr. V.P.-Sls.--Mack Trucks, Inc., Allentown, PA; *Int'l*, pg. 1102
Ritterbush, Richard, V.P.-Mktg.--Autologic Information International, Inc., Thousand Oaks, CA; *U.S. Public*, pg. 1724
Ritze, Lee, Dir.-Mktg.--National Education Training Group, Naperville, IL; *U.S. Public*, pg. 784
Ritzman, Chris, Supvr.-Mktg.--Andis Company, Sturtevant, WI; *U.S. Private*, pg. 73
Rivard, Jill, V.P.-Adv. & Mktg.--Paul A. Schmitt Music Company, Minneapolis, MN; *U.S. Private*, pg. 971
Rivard, Michael, Exec. V.P.-Mktg.--Miracle Recreation Equipment Company, Monett, MO; *U.S. Private*, pg. 752
Rivas, Osvaldo, Mgr.-Mktg.--General Motors Chile S.A., Industria Automotriz, Santiago, Chile; *U.S. Public*, pg. 721
Rivera, Angela, Mgr.-Corp. Communications--FPA Medical Management, Inc., San Diego, CA; *U.S. Public*, pg. 608
Rivera, Lissette, Mktg. Admin.--United States Realty & Investment Co., New York, NY; *U.S. Private*, pg. 1125
Rivers, David P., V.P.-Mktg. & Sls.--E-Z-GO Textron, Augusta, GA; *U.S. Public*, pg. 1589
Rives, Chip, Pres.-Sports & Entertainment Mktg.--Woolf Associates, Boston, MA; *U.S. Private*, pg. 84
Riviello, John, Mng. Dir.--Kruger Recycling Inc., Albany, NY; *Int'l*, pg. 762
Riviere, Donald, V.P.-Strategic Devel.--Menasha Corporation, Neenah, WI; *U.S. Private*, pg. 731
Rizzi, Rich, Dir.-Adv.--Imprint Newpapers, Bristol, CT; *U.S. Public*, pg. 935
Rizzo, Joseph, Dir.-Mktg.--Altec Lansing Technologies, Inc., Milford, PA; *U.S. Private*, pg. 479
Rizzo, Rob, Coord.-Mktg.--American Speedy Printing Centers, Inc., Troy, MI; *U.S. Private*, pg. 62
Rizzuto, Joseph W., Dir.-Bus. Comm.--Rohm and Haas Company, Philadelphia, PA; *U.S. Public*, pg. 1403
Roach, Alfred R., Jr., Exec. V.P.-Mktg., Sls. & Prod. Support--Group Maintenance America Corp., Houston, TX; *U.S. Public*, pg. 766
Roach, Don H., V.P.-Mktg.--Snorkel, Saint Joseph, MO; *U.S. Private*, pg. 500
Roach, James, V.P.-Mktg., Sls. & Adv.--TII Industries, Inc., Copiague, NY; *U.S. Public*, pg. 1556
Roach, James, V.P.-Mktg. & Sls.--Vulcan Materials Company, Birmingham, AL; *U.S. Public*, pg. 1725
Roach, Kathleen, Dir.-Mktg.--Harman Consumer Group, Woodbury, NY; *U.S. Public*, pg. 787
Roache, Kathryn, Mgr.-Pub. Rels.--Bright National Bank, Flora, IN; *U.S. Public*, pg. 633
Roan, Larry A., Dir.-Mktg. & Adv.--F.A. Wilhelm Construction Co., Inc., Indianapolis, IN; *U.S. Private*, pg. 1176
Roark, Tanya, Mktg. Coord.--Lee's Famous Recipe Restaurant, Nashville, TN; *U.S. Private*, pg. 906
Robb, Ken, Dir.-Sls. & Mktg.--The Gates Rubber Company Ltd., Dumfries, United Kingdom; *Int'l*, pg. 1397
Robbins, Bob, Dir.-Mktg. Services & Corp. Communications--Mentor Corporation, Santa Barbara, CA; *U.S. Public*, pg. 1086
Robbins, Bruce, Mgr.-Sls. & Mktg.--Svedala Bulk Materials Handling Engineered Products, Pittsburgh, PA; *Int'l*, pg. 1326
Robbins, Carol, Sr. V.P.-Mktg.--Prudential Securities Inc., New York, NY; *U.S. Private*, pg. 892
Robbins, Clinton, Dir.-Mktg. & Sls.--General Motors Chile S.A., Industria Automotriz, Santiago, Chile; *U.S. Public*, pg. 721
Robbins, Don, V.P.-Sls. & Mktg.--Orange-Co., Inc., Bartow, FL; *U.S. Public*, pg. 1229
Robbins, Ken, Mgr.-Mktg.-Pneumatic Tools & Fasteners--Hitachi Koki U.S.A. Ltd., Norcross, GA; *Int'l*, pg. 620
Robbins, Susan, Mgr.-Mktg. & Commun.--Digital Sound Corporation, Carpinteria, CA; *U.S. Public*, pg. 508
Robbins, Terrie, V.P.-Mktg.--Pulitzer Publishing Company, Saint Louis, MO; *U.S. Public*, pg. 1343
Robbins, Tom, Sr. V.P.-Mktg.--Delchamps, Inc., Mobile, AL; *U.S. Private*, pg. 588
Robbins, Wayne, V.P.-Mktg./R&D--DEZurik, Sartell, MN; *U.S. Public*, pg. 726
Robellard, Jim, Dir.-Mktg. & Adv.--The Valspar Corporation, Minneapolis, MN; *U.S. Public*, pg. 1707
Roberson, Donald, Dir.-Mktg. & Sls.--Theradyne Corporation, Jordan, MN; *U.S. Private*, pg. 637
Robert, Dick, V.P.-Sls. & Mktg.--Griswold Industries, Inc., Costa Mesa, CA; *U.S. Private*, pg. 482
Roberts, Dale R., Dir.-Mktg.--Veda Incorporated, Alexandria, VA; *U.S. Private*, pg. 1136
Roberts, Dan, Exec. V.P.-Sls. & Mktg.--Wellington Industries Inc., Madison, GA; *U.S. Private*, pg. 1161
Roberts, Deborah, Dir.-Mktg. Communications--Overnite Transportation Co., Richmond, VA; *U.S. Public*, pg. 1668
Roberts, Dennis, Dir.-Mktg.--Gaylord Chemical Corporation, Slidell, LA; *U.S. Public*, pg. 704
Roberts, Douglas C., V.P.-Mktg.--Dekalb Genetics Corporation, De Kalb, IL; *U.S. Public*, pg. 493
Roberts, Ed, Mgr.-Mktg. & Sls.--American Marine Pte. Ltd., Jurong, Singapore; *Int'l*, pg. 531
Roberts, Evan J., V.P.-Mktg. & Product Devel.--BMY-Wheeled Vehicles, Marysville, OH; *U.S. Public*, pg. 793
Roberts, Graham, Dir.-Mktg. & Adv.--Unisys Limited, Uxbridge, United Kingdom; *U.S. Public*, pg. 1671
Roberts, James, Grp. V.P.-Mktg.--Blue Cross and Blue Shield of Oklahoma, Tulsa, OK; *U.S. Private*, pg. 151
Roberts, Jane, V.P.-Mktg.--LeFebure Corp., Cedar Rapids, IA; *Int'l*, pg. 387
Roberts, Janice M., Sr. V.P.-Mktg. & Bus. Devel.--3Com Corporation, Santa Clara, CA; *U.S. Public*, pg. 1603
Roberts, Jerry, Sr. V.P.-Network Bus. Devel.--BBDO Worldwide Inc., New York, NY; *U.S. Public*, pg. 1223
Roberts, John F., Dir.-Corp. Admin.--Morrison Knudsen Corporation, Boise, ID; *U.S. Public*, pg. 1133
Roberts, Pam, Mktg. Asst.--THORN Americas, Wichita, KS; *Int'l*, pg. 1385
Roberts, Patricia J., Gen. Dir.-Mktg.--General Motors of Canada Ltd., Oshawa, Canada; *U.S. Public*, pg. 722
Roberts, R.J., Dir.-Mktg.--Fuller, Smith & Turner Plc, London, United Kingdom; *Int'l*, pg. 529
Roberts, Wendy, Dir.-Adv.--Blue Cross and Blue Shield of Massachusetts, Boston, MA; *U.S. Private*, pg. 151
Roberts, William J., V.P.-Mktg.--Houston Engineers, Houston, TX; *U.S. Private*, pg. 1181
Roberts, Wyman, Exec. V.P.--Red Lobster USA, Orlando, FL; *U.S. Public*, pg. 484
Robertson-Mack, Vicky, Dir.-Mktg.--Cole Taylor Bank, Wheeling, IL; *U.S. Private*, pg. 1070
Robertson, B., Dir.-Intl. Sls. & Mktg.--Renold PLC, Manchester, United Kingdom; *Int'l*, pg. 1103

Robertson, Bill, Dir.-Mktg.--West Mill Clothes, Inc., Woodside, NY; *U.S. Private*, pg. 1163
Robertson, C. Frank, V.P.-Mktg.--Osmose Wood Preserving, Inc., Buffalo, NY; *U.S. Private*, pg. 821
Robertson, Dave, Dir.-Mktg.--Dayton Rogers Mfg. Co., Blaine, MN; *U.S. Private*, pg. 318
Robertson, Jeff, Mktg. Dir. & New Bus. Dir.--Caldwell VanRiper, Inc., Indianapolis, IN; *U.S. Private*, pg. 200
Robertson, Jennifer, Controller.-Intl;. Sls. & Mktg.--The Gates Rubber Company Ltd., Dumfries, United Kingdom; *Int'l*, pg. 1397
Robertson, Jerry, Mgr.-Mktg. Retail--Tultex Corporation, Martinsville, VA; *U.S. Public*, pg. 1644
Robertson, Paul W., Sr. V.P.-Mktg.--Baton Broadcasting Incorporated, Scarborough, Canada; *Int'l*, pg. 170
Robertson, Steve, Sr. V.P.-Sls. & Mktg.--The Keller Manufacturing Co., Inc., Corydon, IN; *U.S. Private*, pg. 612
Robicaux, D., V.P.-Mktg. & Sls.--Bank Building, Manchester, MO; *U.S. Private*, pg. 407
Robicaux, David, V.P.-Natl. Sls. & Mktg.--First Financial Building Corporation, Manchester, MO; *U.S. Private*, pg. 407
Robida, Annie, Mktg. Specialist--CF & I Steel, L.P., Pueblo, CO; *U.S. Public*, pg. 1230
Robidoux, Roy, Sr. V.P.-Mktg. & Sls.--The Cerplex Group, Inc., Tustin, CA; *U.S. Public*, pg. 332
Robinius, Vern, V.P.-Mktg.--Q & B Foods, Inc., Irwindale, CA; *Int'l*, pg. 1074
Robins, Bernard, Sr. V.P.-Mktg.--West Coast Life Insurance Co., San Francisco, CA; *U.S. Public*, pg. 1336
Robins, Christopher, Mgr.-Mktg. Retail--PAXAR Corporation, White Plains, NY; *U.S. Public*, pg. 1266
Robins, Peter, Mgr.-Adv. & Product Mktg.--Cincinnati Milacron U.K. Limited, Birmingham, United Kingdom; *U.S. Public*, pg. 368
Robins, R.D., V.P.-Segment Mngmt.--The Lubrizol Corporation, Wickliffe, OH; *U.S. Public*, pg. 1016
Robinson, Caren, Sr. V.P. & Dir.-Mktg.--City National Corporation, Beverly Hills, CA; *U.S. Public*, pg. 380
Robinson, Craig, Dir.-Mktg.-Canada--Speedy Muffler King, Inc., Toronto, Canada; *U.S. Public*, pg. 1578
Robinson, Craig, V.P.-Mktg.--Speedy Car-X, Inc., Chicago, IL; *U.S. Public*, pg. 1578
Robinson, Dan, Dir.-Mktg.--Top Flight, Inc., Chattanooga, TN; *U.S. Private*, pg. 1091
Robinson, David, Mgr.-Mktg.--Canadian Locker Co., Ltd., Scarborough, Canada; *U.S. Public*, pg. 86
Robinson, Heather, Dir.-Mktg.--Phil Long Ford, Colorado Springs, CO; *U.S. Private*, pg. 675
Robinson, Jeff, V.P.-Sls. & Mktg.--Amerford International Corporation, Atlanta, GA; *Int'l*, pg. 1388
Robinson, John A., V.P.-Mktg.--Techalloy Co., Inc., Mahwah, NJ; *Int'l*, pg. 572
Robinson, John H., Grp. Chief Exec. Officer--Smith & Nephew PLC, London, United Kingdom; *Int'l*, pg. 1263
Robinson, Joseph P., V.P.-Mktg.--Steel Technologies Inc., Louisville, KY; *U.S. Public*, pg. 1513
Robinson, Kate, Customer Svcs. & Sls.--March Manufacturing Inc., Glenview, IL; *U.S. Private*, pg. 702
Robinson, Linda, V.P.-Mktg.--F.W. Dodge Group, New York, NY; *U.S. Public*, pg. 1070
Robinson, Martin, Dir.-Mktg.--Scottish & New Castle Retail, Northampton, United Kingdom; *Int'l*, pg. 1212
Robinson, Melanie, Mgr.-Mktg.--Heery International, Inc., Atlanta, GA; *U.S. Private*, pg. 519
Robinson, N.M.F., Dir.-Mktg. & Sls.--Gallaher (Dublin) Ltd., Tallaght, Ireland; *Int'l*, pg. 539
Robinson, Roy J., V.P.-Mktg.--White Cap, Inc., Downers Grove, IL; *Int'l*, pg. 1207
Robinson, S., Mgr.-Mktg.-Rothmans & Dunhill--Rothmans (UK) Ltd., Aylesbury, United Kingdom; *Int'l*, pg. 1130
Robinson, Steven A., Sr. V.P.-Mktg.--Chick-fil-A, Inc., Atlanta, GA; *U.S. Private*, pg. 236
Robinson, Stuart, V.P.-Mktg.--Greyhound Lines, Inc., Dallas, TX; *U.S. Public*, pg. 765
Robinson, Stuart N., V.P.-Mktg.--Greyhound Lines, Inc., Dallas, TX; *U.S. Public*, pg. 765
Robinson, Susan, Asst. Admin.-Mktg.--W.R. Case & Sons Cutlery Company, Bradford, PA; *U.S. Private*, pg. 1207
Robinson, William B., Sr. V.P.-Mktg.--United Family Life Insurance Co., Atlanta, GA; *Int'l*, pg. 499
Robison, D.P., Dir.-Mktg.--Service Parts Operations, Flint, MI; *U.S. Public*, pg. 720
Robison, David, Mgr.-Sls. & Mktg.--Milton Roy Company, Ivyland, PA; *U.S. Public*, pg. 1534
Robison, Jeannie, Mgr.-Mktg. Communication--Intergraph Corporation, Huntsville, AL; *U.S. Public*, pg. 890
Robitaille, Jada, V.P.-Mktg.--Sechrist Industries, Inc., Anaheim, CA; *U.S. Private*, pg. 980
Roblard, Jim, Dir.-Adv. & Mktg.--Colony Paints, Kansas City, MO; *U.S. Public*, pg. 1707
Robles, Emilio, Dir.-Mktg. Communications--Philips Semiconductors, Sunnyvale, CA; *Int'l*, pg. 1054
Robling, Chris, Dir.-Commun.--Regional Transportation Authority (RTA), Chicago, IL; *U.S. Private*, pg. 918
Robling, Sally Genster, Dir.-Mktg.--Desserts Div., White Plains, NY; *U.S. Public*, pg. 1287
Robson, David, Mgr.-Mktg.--Dawson Holdings PLC, Folkestone, United Kingdom; *Int'l*, pg. 385
Rocafort, Irene C., Coord.-Mktg. Svcs.--Royal Olympic Cruises, New York, NY; *U.S. Public*, pg. 1411
Rocca, Frank H., V.P.-Mktg. & Sls.--Neapco, Inc., Pottstown, PA; *U.S. Private*, pg. 1113
Rocca, Graziella, Dir.-Mktg.--Monarimport S.p.A., Villanova di Castenaso, Italy; *Int'l*, pg. 295
Roche, Alexander, Exec. V.P.-Sls. & Mktg.--Fishery Products International Ltd., Saint Johns, Canada; *Int'l*, pg. 492
Roche, Mark, V.P.-Mktg.--LIVE Entertainment Inc., Van Nuys, CA; *U.S. Private*, pg. 671
Rochester, Ralph G., Sr. V.P.-Sls. & Mktg.--Comcast Cable Communications, Inc., Philadelphia, PA; *U.S. Public*, pg. 407
Rock, Ed, Dir.-Prod. Mtkg.--Scott Forseman/Addison Wesley, Glenview, IL; *Int'l*, pg. 927
Rock, Stephen, Dir.-Prod. Mktg.--Wherehouse Entertainment, Inc., Torrance, CA; *U.S. Private*, pg. 1171
Rockafellow, Allen, V.P. & Dir.-Mktg.--Aluma Shield Industries, Inc., Daytona Beach, FL; *U.S. Private*, pg. 47
Rodas, Lisa, Coord.-Mktg.--Spec's Music, Inc., Miami, FL; *U.S. Public*, pg. 1497
Roddy, David, V.P.-Mktg. Svcs.--Deluxe Corporation, Shoreview, MN; *U.S. Public*, pg. 498
Roddy, Larry, Mgr.-Natl. Sls.--National Cabinet Lock, Inc., Mauldin, SC; *U.S. Private*, pg. 270
Rodefeld, James A., Sr. V.P.-Mktg.--Jacobson Stores Inc., Jackson, MI; *U.S. Public*, pg. 922
Roden, Bob, Mgr.-Research--Pennzoil Products Co., Houston, TX; *U.S. Public*, pg. 1272
Rodenberg, Clinton F., Sr. V.P.-Mktg.--Schieffelin & Somerset Co., New York, NY; *Int'l*, pg. 412
Rodenmayer, Nelson, Dir.-Mktg.--Thriftway, Inc., Louisville, KY; *U.S. Public*, pg. 1771
Roder, Carol, Mgr.-Mktg.--Coleman Spas, Inc., Chandler, AZ; *U.S. Private*, pg. 691
Roderique, Bob, Mgr.-Mktg. Svcs.--Bussmann Division, Ellisville, MO; *U.S. Public*, pg. 443
Rodgers, Art, V.P.-Mktg.--Hyde Athletic Industries, Inc., Peabody, MA; *U.S. Public*, pg. 851
Rodgers, Caryn, Mgr.-Mktg.--Lundy Enterprises, Inc., New Orleans, LA; *U.S. Private*, pg. 681
Rodich, Michael E., V.P.-Mktg.--Stevens-Lee Company, Minneapolis, MN; *U.S. Private*, pg. 1042
Rodigues, Ronald, Dir.-Mktg.--Industrias Gessy Lever Ltda., Sao Paulo, Brazil; *Int'l*, pg. 1437
Rodriguez, Algirson Varagas, Mgr.-Mktg.--Rhodia S.A., Sao Paulo, Brazil; *Int'l*, pg. 1112
Rodriguez, Angelica, Mktg. Specialist--Hilton International Co., Coral Gables, FL; *Int'l*, pg. 787
Rodriguez, Eduardo A., Sr. V.P.-Customer & Corp. Svcs.--El Paso Electric Company, El Paso, TX; *U.S. Public*, pg. 567
Rodriguez, Luis Fernando, Sr. V.P.-Mktg.--Banco Popular de Puerto Rico, San Juan, PR; *U.S. Public*, pg. 175
Rodriguez, Sonia, V.P.--Mason Distributors, Inc., Hialeah, FL; *U.S. Private*, pg. 712
Rodriguez, Susan, Mktg.-Specialist--Infinicom, Chatham, NJ; *U.S. Private*, pg. 561
Roebuck, Richard, Mgr.-Mktg.--Pneumatic Div., Cannock, United Kingdom; *U.S. Public*, pg. 1264
Roeder, Gil M., Dir.-Mktg. Communications--APL Limited, Oakland, CA; *Int'l*, pg. 912
Roeder, J. Thomas, V.P.-Mktg. & Sls.--Symtron Systems, Inc., Fair Lawn, NJ; *U.S. Public*, pg. 1679
Roedig, Cynthia, Mgr.-Mktg. Commun.--Burr-Brown Corporation, Tucson, AZ; *U.S. Public*, pg. 270
Roeglin, Ginnie, V.P. & Natl. Mktg. Mgr.--Costco Wholesale, Issaquah, WA; *U.S. Public*, pg. 451
Roehl, Karen, Coord.-Mktg.--Shannon & Wilson, Inc., Seattle, WA; *U.S. Private*, pg. 989
Roehricht, Hans, V.P.-Bus. Opers.--AirSensors, Inc., Seattle, WA; *U.S. Public*, pg. 33
Roesle, Jack, V.P.-Sls. & Mktg.--Alpha/Owens Corning LLC, Collierville, TN; *U.S. Private*, pg. 45
Roessle, Erwin H., V.P.-Mktg.--Dreis & Krump Manufacturing Company, Chicago, IL; *U.S. Private*, pg. 342
Rogal, Steve, Dir.-Mktg.--Attwood Corporation, Lowell, MI; *U.S. Private*, pg. 1038
Rogalski, J.A., V.P.-Mktg.--J.M. Huber, Wood Products Div., Charlotte, NC; *U.S. Private*, pg. 545
Rogers, Bob, Dir.-Mktg.--Pharmacia & Upjohn Inter-American Corporation, Auckland, New Zealand; *Int'l*, pg. 1048
Rogers, Candice W., Sr. Exec. V.P.-Consumer Banking & Mktg. Div.--AmSouth Bancorporation, Birmingham, AL; *U.S. Public*, pg. 105
Rogers, Clint, Specialist-Mktg.--Cashco, Inc., Ellsworth, KS; *U.S. Private*, pg. 218
Rogers, David A., V.P.-U.S. Sls. & Mktg.--A.T. Cross Co., Lincoln, RI; *U.S. Public*, pg. 460
Rogers, Deborah, Dir.-Mktg.--Payco American Corporation, Brookfield, WI; *U.S. Public*, pg. 1267
Rogers, Desiree, Div. V.P.-Mktg. & Bus. Devel.--Peoples Energy Corporation, Chicago, IL; *U.S. Public*, pg. 1274
Rogers, Don D., Dir.-Sls. & Mktg.--Krause Plow Corp., Hutchinson, KS; *U.S. Private*, pg. 635
Rogers, Douglas C., Exec. V.P.-Mktg.--Whitehall-Robins Healthcare, Madison, NJ; *U.S. Public*, pg. 80
Rogers, Frank K., Dir.-Mktg. & Sls.--Providence and Worcester Railroad Company, Worcester, MA; *U.S. Public*, pg. 1336
Rogers, Fred, Dir.-Appliance Div.--Rangaire Inc., Cleburne, TX; *U.S. Public*, pg. 1193
Rogers, John, Dir.-Mktg.--John Fairfax Holdings Limited, Sydney, Australia; *Int'l*, pg. 477
Rogers, Ken, Exec. V.P.-Mktg. & Sls. (Canada)--Intertape Polymer Group, Green Bay, WI; *Int'l*, pg. 685
Rogers, Lura L., Asst. V.P.-Domestic Mktg.--National Western Life Insurance Company, Austin, TX; *U.S. Public*, pg. 1161
Rogers, Peter J., Jr., Dir.-Investor Rels. & Bus. Devel.--Micros Systems Inc., Beltsville, MD; *U.S. Public*, pg. 1106
Rogers, Phillip R., Mgr.-Mktg.--Flavorite Laboratories, Horn Lake, MS; *U.S. Private*, pg. 1090
Rogers, Richard, Dir.-Mktg.--Winchell's Donut Houses, L.P., Santa Ana, CA; *Int'l*, pg. 1230
Rogers, Susan, Mgr.-Pub. Rels.--Horizon Enterprises Group LLC, Taylor, MI; *U.S. Private*, pg. 539
Rogers, Thomas W., Sr. V.P.-Sls. & Mktg.--IMCO Recycling Inc., Irving, TX; *U.S. Public*, pg. 870
Rognoni, Bruno, Dir.-Strategic Mktg.--Metropolitana Milanese S.P.A., Milan, Italy; *Int'l*, pg. 863
Rohde, David, Sr. Mgr.-Mktg.--Thomas Industries, Consumer Lighting Division, Louisville, KY; *U.S. Public*, pg. 1599
Rohde, Mark R., Sr. V.P.-Sls. & Mktg.--Cincinnati Bell Information Systems Inc., Cincinnati, OH; *U.S. Public*, pg. 367
Rohlke, Gary, Dir.-Mktg.--Wandel & Goltermann Inc., Research Triangle Park, NC; *Int'l*, pg. 1486
Rohloff, Winfried, Sr. V.P.-Worldwide Sls., Mktg. & Services--CalComp Technology, Inc., Anaheim, CA; *U.S. Public*, pg. 1007
Rohnke, Elke Bennig, Member-Bd. of Mngmt.--Wella Group, Darmstadt, Germany; *Int'l*, pg. 1489
Roid, Hahns, Exec. V.P.-Sls. & Mktg.--Premier Cruises, Miami, FL; *U.S. Private*, pg. 293
Rojnica, Kruno, V.P.-Intl. Sls. & Mktg.--The Wm. Powell Company, Cincinnati, OH; *U.S. Private*, pg. 877
Rokowski, Carol, Creative Mktg. Services--ATAPCO Office Products Group, Saint Louis, MO; *U.S. Private*, pg. 64
Roland-Michaels, Starr, V.P.-Mktg.--National Card Control, Inc., Crozier, VA; *U.S. Public*, pg. 321
Rolim, Raquel, Mktg. Asst.--Fiat Automisveis S.A., Sao Paulo, Brazil; *Int'l*, pg. 483
Rolle, Michelle, Mgr.-Mktg. Communications--Orbotech Inc., Billerica, MA; *Int'l*, pg. 1007
Rollins, Donna, V.P.-Adv. & Creative--Marchon Eyewear, Melville, NY; *U.S. Private*, pg. 702
Rolls, D., Exec. V.P.-Mktg. & Sls.--The Chamberlain Group, Inc., Elmhurst, IL; *U.S. Private*, pg. 344
Rom, Carlos, Jr., Exec. V.P.-Caribbean & Latin American Expansion--Banco Popular de Puerto Rico, San Juan, PR; *U.S. Public*, pg. 175
Roma, Gary, V.P.-Sls. & Mktg.--Riverside Cement Co., Diamond Bar, CA; *Int'l*, pg. 1293
Romaine, Edward, Mgr.-Mktg. Communications--White Systems, Incorporated, Kenilworth, NJ; *U.S. Private*, pg. 866
Roman, David, V.P.-Corp. Adv. & Brand Mktg.--Apple Computer, Inc., Cupertino, CA; *U.S. Public*, pg. 121
Roman, Patti, V.P.-Mktg.--Aerolyte Systems, Washington, MO; *U.S. Private*, pg. 24
Roman, Spencer M., Sr. V.P.-Home Office Opers.--Harleysville Group, Harleysville, PA; *U.S. Public*, pg. 786
Romanach, Celio, Sr. Mgr.-Mktg.--Bacardi-Martini, USA, Inc., Miami, FL; *U.S. Private*, pg. 109
Romanies, Michael, V.P.-Mktg.--Number Nine Visual Technology, Lexington, MA; *U.S. Public*, pg. 1206
Rombouts, A., Dir.-Sls. & Mktg.--Holmatro Industrial & Rescue Equipment, Raamsdonksveer, Netherlands; *Int'l*, pg. 632
Romeis, Chris, V.P.-Mktg.--A.P.S., Memphis, TN; *U.S. Public*, pg. 10
Romero, Mike, V.P.-Mktg.--Louisville Bedding Company, Louisville, KY; *U.S. Private*, pg. 677
Rommel, Herbert, Mgr.-Mktg.--Alno AG, Pfullendorf, Germany; *Int'l*, pg. 65
Ron, Renes, Dir.-Mktg.--Colgate-Palmolive A/S, Glostrup, Denmark; *U.S. Public*, pg. 398
Ronbinson, Charles, Mng. Dir.--Progress International Limited, Plainview, NY; *U.S. Public*, pg. 141
Rondinelli, Karen, Dir.-Adv. & Mktg.--Allen-Edmonds Shoe Corp., Port Washington, WI; *U.S. Private*, pg. 36
Roney, Reid, V.P.-Sls. & Mktg.--Martin Industries, Inc. (AL), Florence, AL; *U.S. Private*, pg. 709
Roniger, Marc, Dir.-Mktg.--Scholl AG, Reinach, Switzerland; *Int'l*, pg. 1209
Ronis, Marty, V.P.-Mktg.--Michigan Wheel Corporation, Grand Rapids, MI; *U.S. Private*, pg. 741
Ronnebaum, Linda, Coord.-Mktg. Communications--Batesville Casket Company, Inc., Batesville, IN; *U.S. Public*, pg. 828
Ronning, Bruce, Dir.-Sls. & Mktg.--Hays Fluid Controls-Division of Romac Industries, Dallas, NC; *U.S. Private*, pg. 942
Roof, James F., V.P.-Worldwide Sls. & Mktg., Microelectronic Prods.--Shipley Co., LLC, Marlborough, MA; *U.S. Public*, pg. 1403
Rooke, Chris, V.P.-Mktg.--Tandem Computers Inc., Cupertino, CA; *U.S. Public*, pg. 417
Rooney, Jack, V.P.-Mktg.--Miller Brewing Company, Milwaukee, WI; *U.S. Public*, pg. 1289
Rooney, Robert, Mgr.-Mktg. & Sls.--Taylor & Francis Philadelphia, Bristol, PA; *Int'l*, pg. 1358
Roos, Scott, Dir.-Mktg.--Alkco Lighting Company, Franklin Park, IL; *Int'l*, pg. 821
Root, Steve, V.P.-Sls. & Mktg. Wheel Grp.--Titan International, Inc., Quincy, IL; *U.S. Public*, pg. 1618
Rooyakkers, Mark, Dir.-Mktg. & Adv.--Klipsch, Inc., Hope, AR; *U.S. Private*, pg. 626
Roozendaal-Verkerk, W., Mgr.-Mktg.--Bakery Ingredients Division, Delft, Netherlands; *Int'l*, pg. 1142
Roozendaal, H., Dir.-Mktg.--Pluspoint, Rotterdam, Netherlands; *Int'l*, pg. 750
Rorschach, Carol, Dir.-Mktg.--John Zink Co., Tulsa, OK; *U.S. Private*, pg. 628
Rosa, Scott, Exec. V.P.-Sls. & Mktg.--Cannon Equipment, Chattanooga, TN; *Int'l*, pg. 646
Rosas, Julio, Dir.-Mktg.--BYK Gulden, S.A. de C.V., Mexico, Mexico; *Int'l*, pg. 66
Rosas, Kathy, Mktg.--National Financial Insurance Company, Fort Worth, TX; *U.S. Private*, pg. 782
Rosati, Jamie, Sr. Mgr.-Mktg.--Swanson, Camden, NJ; *U.S. Public*, pg. 299
Rose, Bill, V.P.-Mktg. & Sls.--SRC Vision, Medford, OR; *U.S. Public*, pg. 20
Rose, Harry, Asst. V.P.-Mktg. & Corp. Communications--Atlantic Gulf Communities Corporation, Miami, FL; *U.S. Public*, pg. 144
Rose, Herbert A., V.P.-Sls, Mktg. & Consumer Prods.--Trion, Inc., Sanford, NC; *U.S. Public*, pg. 1639
Rose, Jim, Dir.-Sls. & Mktg.--John Crane Asia Pacific, Singapore, Singapore; *Int'l*, pg. 1339
Rose, Keith, Dir.-Mktg. & Adv.--Dain Rauscher Incorporated, Minneapolis, MN; *U.S. Public*, pg. 476
Rose, Ken, V.P.-Corp. Mktg.--CompuCom Systems, Inc., Dallas, TX; *U.S. Public*, pg. 1424

Rose, Stephen, Dir.-Mktg. Services--McGraw-Hill Healthcare Publications Group, Minneapolis, MN; *U.S. Public*, pg. 1071

Rose, Stephen, Dir.-Mktg. Sls.--The Physician and Sportsmedicine, Minneapolis, MN; *U.S. Public*, pg. 1071

Roselli, Eleni, V.P.-Mktg. & Adv.--Bon Jour International Ltd., New York, NY; *U.S. Private*, pg. 156

Rosello, Josianne, Mgr.-Mktg. & Pub. Rels.--First Leasing & Rental Corporation, Toa Baja, PR; *U.S. Public*, pg. 644

Rosello, Jossiane, Sr. V.P.-Mktg. & Pub. Rels.--Firstbank Puerto Rico, Santurce, PR; *U.S. Public*, pg. 644

Rosello, Jossiane, Mgr.-Mktg. & Pub. Prels.--First Federal Finance Corporation, Santurce, PR; *U.S. Public*, pg. 644

Rosen, Bernie, Dir.-Mktg.--Norlight Telecommunications Inc., Brookfield, WI; *U.S. Private*, pg. 601

Rosen, Dave, Dir.-Art Mktg.--G. Joannou Cycle Co. Inc., Northvale, NJ; *U.S. Private*, pg. 588

Rosen, David, Pres. & Chief Exec. Officer--CB North America, Inc., Saratoga Springs, NY; *U.S. Private*, pg. 192

Rosen, David, V.P.-Leasing, Mktg. & Adv.--Rosen Associates Management Corp., Jericho, NY; *U.S. Private*, pg. 945

Rosen, Mike, Chief Exec. Officer & Exec. V.P.-Corp Devel Mktg.--Herbalife International of America, Inc., Century City, CA; *U.S. Public*, pg. 809

Rosenberg, Andrew, Sr. V.P.-Mktg.--General Textiles, San Diego, CA; *U.S. Private*, pg. 445

Rosenberg, Frank B., Sr. V.P.-Mktg.--Crown Central Petroleum Corporation, Baltimore, MD; *U.S. Public*, pg. 462

Rosenberg, Gerald B., Sr. V.P.-Mktg. & Sls.--Bayer Corporation/Pharmaceutical Division, West Haven, CT; *Int'l*, pg. 173

Rosenberg, Hillary, Mgr.-Mktg.--Orval Kent Food Co., Wheeling, IL; *U.S. Private*, pg. 820

Rosenberg, Linda, V.P.-Mktg.--STV Group, Inc., Douglassville, PA; *U.S. Public*, pg. 1421

Rosenberg, Michael, First V.P.-Mktg.--LaSalle National Bank, Chicago, IL; *Int'l*, pg. 10

Rosenblatt, Steve, V.P.-Mktg.--Capitol Records, Inc., Hollywood, CA; *Int'l*, pg. 428

Rosenfeld, Jim, Dir.-Mktg. & Sls.--Fishman & Tobin, Inc., Conshohocken, PA; *U.S. Private*, pg. 408

Rosenstein, Sharon, Mgr.-Consumer Mktg.--Rust-Oleum Corporation, Vernon Hills, IL; *U.S. Public*, pg. 1358

Rosenthal, Josh, V.P.-Alternative Music Mktg.--Sony Music Entertainment, Inc., New York, NY; *Int'l*, pg. 1281

Rosenthal, Matt, Dir.-Mktg.--Faygo Beverages, Inc., Detroit, MI; *U.S. Public*, pg. 1153

Rosenthall, Robert, Dir.-Mktg.--Nicolet Analytical, Madison, WI; *U.S. Public*, pg. 1593

Rosenwald, James B., V.P.-OEM Mktg. & Sls.--Leviton Mfg. Co., Inc., Little Neck, NY; *U.S. Private*, pg. 663

Rosenzweig, Carey, Dir.-Mktg.--The Kingsford Products Company, Oakland, CA; *U.S. Public*, pg. 387

Rosner, Roy, V.P.-Mktg.--Telematics Inc., Fort Lauderdale, FL; *Int'l*, pg. 643

Rosquete, Noel, Mktg. Specialist--Republic National Bank of Miami, Miami, FL; *U.S. Private*, pg. 924

Ross-Sirola, Heather, Mgr.-Mktg. & Corp Adv.--Partek Corporation, Helsinki, Finland; *Int'l*, pg. 1024

Ross, Alan, V.P.-New Bus. Devel.--Cyborg Systems, Inc., Chicago, IL; *U.S. Private*, pg. 299

Ross, Arthur S., V.P.-Mktg. Communications--The Lincoln National Life Insurance Co., Fort Wayne, IN; *U.S. Public*, *pg. 998*

Ross, Brad, Dir.-Mktg.--Consumer Products Div., Hartsville, SC; *U.S. Public*, pg. 1486

Ross, Dave, Mgr.-Mktg. Communications--Richardson Electronics, Ltd., Lafox, IL; *U.S. Public*, pg. 1387

Ross, David, Sr. Mgr.-Mktg., Core Brands--The United States Playing Card Company, Cincinnati, OH; *U.S. Private*, pg. 1125

Ross, Ed, V.P.-Sls. & Mktg.--Anderson, Greenwood & Co., Stafford, TX; *U.S. Public*, pg. 1650

Ross, Jacqueline, V.P.-Mktg--Check Point Software Technologies Inc., Redwood City, CA; *U.S. Public*, pg. 342

Ross, Janine, Mgr.-Adv.--Dielectric Polymers, Inc., Holyoke, MA; *U.S. Public*, pg. 1258

Ross, Jeff, Mgr.-Mktg. & Promo.--Fox Net, Los Angeles, CA; *Int'l*, pg. 926

Ross, JoAnn, V.P.-Primetime, Late Night & Olympic Sls.--CBS Television Network, New York, NY; *U.S. Public*, pg. 274

Ross, Ken, Dir.-Sls. & Mktg.--Elkem Aluminium ANS, Oslo, Norway; *Int'l*, pg. 446

Ross, Kenneth L., V.P.-Mktg. & Gen. Mgr.-CBS Video--CBS Enterprises Division, New York, NY; *U.S. Public*, pg. 274

Ross, Lezlea, Mgr.-Mktg.--Hygeia Dairy Co., Inc., Harlingen, TX; *U.S. Private*, pg. 552

Ross, Lucille, Dir.-Mktg.-Haircolor--Clairol Canada Inc., Montreal, Canada; *U.S. Public*, pg. 254

Ross, Michael, V.P.-Mktg.--Palisades Media Group, Inc., Santa Monica, CA; *U.S. Private*, pg. 834

Ross, Pamela, Dir.-Mktg. Services--The Genie Company, Alliance, OH; *U.S. Private*, pg. 823

Ross, Steve, Pres.-Reseller Div. & Corp. Mktg.--Inacom Corp., Omaha, NE; *U.S. Public*, pg. 873

Ross, Vincent C., Dir.-Mktg.--The C.P. Hall Company, Chicago, IL; *U.S. Private*, pg. 495

Rossi, Dom, V.P.-Corp. Intergrated Mktg.--Reader's Digest Publications-US Sales Div., New York, NY; *U.S. Public*, pg. 1367

Rossi, Endvar, V.P.-Mktg. Sls. & Customer Svc.--Dow Corning Corporation, Midland, MI; *U.S. Public*, pg. 523

Rossi, Francesca, Dir.-Mktg. & Mgr.-Adv.--I.B.I.S.-S.p.A., Busseto, Italy; *Int'l*, pg. 642

Rossi, John, V.P.-Adv. & Mktg.--American Trouser, Inc., Columbus, MS; *U.S. Private*, pg. 64

Rossignol, Jacques, V.P. & Gen. Mgr.-SEP--SNECMA - Societe Nationale d'Etude et de Construction de Moteurs d'Aviation, Paris, France; *Int'l*, pg. 1165

Rossini, Ronald, Sr. Mktg. Officer--Northeast Marketing-Philadelphia Business Center, Philadelphia, PA; *U.S. Public*, pg. 649

Rosskam, Steve, Exec. V.P.-Sls. & Mktg.--David Michael & Co. Inc., Philadelphia, PA; *U.S. Private*, pg. 740

Rossler, Mark, V.P.- Mktg.--Baker Material Handling Corp., Summerville, SC; *Int'l*, pg. 810

Rossman, Marty, Dir.-Mktg.--Alliant Foodservice, Bensenville, IL; *U.S. Private*, pg. 244

Rossouw, Willie, Gen. Mgr.-Mktg.--Sasol Oil (Pty) Ltd., Randburg, South Africa; *Int'l*, pg. 1197

Rost, Jordan, Sr. V.P.-Mktg.--Warner Music Group, Inc., New York, NY; *U.S. Public*, pg. 1612

Rota, Ray E., Dir.-Mktg.--Pontiac-GMC Truck Division, Pontiac, MI; *U.S. Public*, pg. 720

Rotchford, Robert, V.P.- Sls. & Mktg.--Massachusetts Envelope Co., Somerville, MA; *U.S. Private*, pg. 712

Roth Rogers, Sheryl, V.P.-Mktg.--Swanson, Camden, NJ; *U.S. Public*, pg. 299

Roth, Alan D., V.P.-Mktg.--Voith Hydro, Inc., York, PA; *Int'l*, pg. 1473

Roth, David J., Dir.-Mktg. Services--Sofamor Danek Group, Inc., Memphis, TN; *U.S. Public*, pg. 1482

Roth, Richard, Sr. V.P.-Sls. & Mktg.--Queens Group, Inc., Long Island City, NY; *U.S. Private*, pg. 900

Rothenbach, R.C., V.P.-Bus. Mktg.--Bell Atlantic-PA, Philadelphia, PA; *U.S. Public*, pg. 203

Rotherham, Greg, V.P.-Mktg.--Humana Inc., Louisville, KY; *U.S. Public*, pg. 847

Rothfuss, Robert K., V.P.-Sls. & Mktg.--Buckhorn Material Handling Group Inc., Milford, OH; *U.S. Public*, pg. 1143

Rothkopf, Robert H., Pres.-Formed Prod. Grp.--Elco Textron, Rockford, IL; *U.S. Public*, pg. 1590

Rothman, Robin, Head-Mktg. Svcs.--Geffen Records, Los Angeles, CA; *Int'l*, pg. 1215

Rothnie, James B., Sr. V.P.-Mktg.--EMC Corporation, Hopkinton, MA; *U.S. Public*, pg. 545

Rothrock, William A., V.P.-Mktg. Devel.--Sanifill, Inc., Houston, TX; *U.S. Public*, pg. 1686

Roths, Jim, Mgr.-Mktg.--Telex Communication Div., Lincoln, NE; *U.S. Private*, pg. 1074

Rothschild, Martin, V.P.-Mktg.-Healthcare--Aladdin Synergetics, Inc., Nashville, TN; *U.S. Private*, pg. 31

Rotman, Selma, V.P.-Mktg.--Winners Apparel Ltd., Toronto, Canada; *U.S. Public*, pg. 1557

Rottering, Quintin, V.P.-Sls. & Mktg.--Beam Industries, Webster City, IA; *Int'l*, pg. 440

Rotunda, Joe, V.P.-Mktg. & Mdsg.--Rent-A-Center, Inc., Wichita, KS; *Int'l*, pg. 1385

Rotunno, Dave, Dir.-Mktg. & Adv.--Dean Foods Company, Franklin Park, IL; *U.S. Public*, pg. 489

Rouce, Phillip J., Gen. Mgr.-Mktg.--J & L Specialty Products Corp., Pittsburgh, PA; *Int'l*, pg. 572

Roudebush, James R., Chm. Bd.--Caldwell VanRiper, Inc., Indianapolis, IN; *U.S. Private*, pg. 200

Rougeau, Jean-Pierre, V.P.-Mktg. & Sls.--COGEMA - Compagnie Generale des Matieres Nucleaires, Velizy-Villacoublay, France; *Int'l*, pg. 304

Rouse, Bill, Dr., Dir.-Mktg. & Sls.--Cargill Seed Div., Minneapolis, MN; *U.S. Private*, pg. 210

Rouse, Rob, V.P.-Sls. & Mktg.--Hipotronics, Inc., Brewster, NY; *U.S. Public*, pg. 844

Routhier, Dominique, Dir.-Mktg.--Tefal S.A., Rumilly, France; *Int'l*, pg. 569

Rovekamp, F.H., Sr. V.P.-Mktg.--KLM Royal Dutch Airlines, Amstelveen, Netherlands; *Int'l*, pg. 719

Rovekamp, F.H., V.P.-Passenger Mktg.--KLM Royal Dutch Airlines, Elmsford, NY; *Int'l*, pg. 719

Row, Mike, Dir.-Mktg.--USSI, Carter Lake, IA; *U.S. Public*, pg. 1629

Rowan, Nile, V.P.-Mkt. Research--Pilkington Barnes Hind (PBH), San Diego, CA; *U.S. Private*, pg. 111

Rowan, Randy, V.P.-Sls. & Mktg.--G & W Electric Co., Blue Island, IL; *U.S. Private*, pg. 433

Rowe, Frank, V.P.-Opers./Europe--The Gleason Works, Rochester, NY; *U.S. Public*, pg. 746

Rowe, Jeffrey A., V.P.-Sls. & Mktg.--Xtek, Inc., Cincinnati, OH; *U.S. Private*, pg. 1194

Rowland, Charles, V.P.-Mktg.--ABB Industrial Systems, Inc., Columbus, OH; *Int'l*, pg. 4

Rowland, Ric, Dir.-Mktg.--C-COR Electronics, Inc., State College, PA; *U.S. Public*, pg. 272

Rowley, Ellen, Mgr.-Mktg. & Communications--Modcomp, Fort Lauderdale, FL; *U.S. Public*, pg. 283

Roy, Alan, Asst. V.P.-Gas Supply--Valley Resources, Inc., Cumberland, RI; *U.S. Public*, pg. 1706

Roy, Michel L., Dir.-Mktg.--Gaz Metropolitain & Company, Montreal, Canada; *Int'l*, pg. 541

Roy, Mike, Dir.-Sls. & Mktg.--Kohler Ltd., Etobicoke, Canada; *U.S. Private*, pg. 631

Roy, Terri, Mgr.-Sls. & Adv.--Installation Products Div., Lancaster, PA; *U.S. Public*, pg. 132

Royce, Charles, Mgr.-Sls.--Oceaneering International, Inc., Houston, TX; *U.S. Public*, pg. 1211

Royce, Charles A., Mgr.-Mktg.--Oilfield Marine Services-Americas Region, Morgan City, LA; *U.S. Public*, pg. 1211

Roz, Michelle, Coord.-Sls. & Mktg.--Luxor, Waukegan, IL; *U.S. Private*, pg. 359

Rozelle, Daniel, Sr. V.P. & Corp. Mktg. Dir.--Fort Wayne National Corporation, Fort Wayne, IN; *U.S. Public*, pg. 673

Rozzi, S.J., Mgr.-Dealer Rels.--Benjamin Moore & Co., Montvale, NJ; *U.S. Private*, pg. 133

Ruane, Brian, Dir.-Mktg.--Willis Corroon Corp. of New York, New York, NY; *Int'l*, pg. 1506

Ruano, Eleanor, Dir.-Mktg.--Western Multiplex Corporation, Sunnyvale, CA; *U.S. Public*, pg. 747

Rubin, Dorrie, V.P.-Mktg.--Chase Bank of Maryland, Baltimore, MD; *U.S. Public*, pg. 338

Rubin, Fred, Interactive Mktg. Dir.--TBWA Chiat/Day New York, New York, NY; *U.S. Private*, pg. 1062

Rubin, Ron, Dir.-Prod. Mktg.--V-Band Corporation, Elmsford, NY; *U.S. Public*, pg. 1701

Rubino, Bill, Pres.--Jofco Inc., Jasper, IN; *U.S. Private*, pg. 588

Rubinstein, Helena, Dir.-Sls. & Mktg.--L'Oreal Parfumerie, Brussels, Belgium; *Int'l*, pg. 819

Rubio, Fernando Vallar, Dir.-Mktg.--Neumaticos Goodyear SA, Buenos Aires, Argentina; *U.S. Public*, pg. 753

Ruby, Robert, Mktg.-Colored Prods.--Lehigh Portland Cement Company, Allentown, PA; *Int'l*, pg. 605

Rubzin, Todd, Dir.-Mktg.--Tiffany Extruders, Inc., Paterson, NJ; *U.S. Private*, pg. 1085

Rucidlo, Martin, Dir.-Mktg.--Superior Label Systems, Inc., Mason, OH; *U.S. Private*, pg. 1055

Ruddell, Brad, V.P.-Sls. & Mktg.--Weatherby, Inc., Atascadero, CA; *U.S. Private*, pg. 1155

Ruddick, I.W., Dir.-Commercial Adv.--Ranks Hovis McDougall Limited, Marlow, United Kingdom; *Int'l*, pg. 1395

Ruddock, Jennifer, Mgr.-Investor Rels.--Catellus Development Corporation, San Francisco, CA; *U.S. Public*, pg. 314

Ruder, Brian, Exec. V.P.-Global Mktg.--Citibank N.A., Long Island City, NY; *U.S. Public*, pg. 377

Rudnick, Jill, Dir.-Mktg.--Mirabella, New York, NY; *Int'l*, pg. 795

Rudolfo, Cheri, Sr. V.P.-Corp. Mktg.--Time Insurance, Milwaukee, WI; *Int'l*, pg. 499

Rudolph, Allen, V.P.-Mktg.--Rudolph and Sletten, Inc., Foster City, CA; *U.S. Private*, pg. 950

Rudolph, Dana, Dir.-Sls., Mktg. & Adv.--Rough Brothers, Inc., Cincinnati, OH; *U.S. Private*, pg. 947

Rudolph, Richard M., Exec. V.P.-Sls. & Mktg.--Rudolph Foods Company, Lima, OH; *U.S. Private*, pg. 950

Ruediger, Bernt E., V.P.-Mktg.--Troy Mills, Inc., Troy, NH; *U.S. Private*, pg. 1106

Ruff, John, Gen. Mgr.-Commodity Mktg.--Riceland Foods, Inc., Stuttgart, AR; *U.S. Private*, pg. 928

Ruffo, Lorraine, Coord.-Mktg.--Amersham Corporation, Arlington Heights, IL; *Int'l*, pg. 992

Ruffo, Lorraine, Coord.-Mktg.--Amersham Healthcare, Arlington Heights, IL; *Int'l*, pg. 992

Rufo, Dina, Dir.-Mktg.--Europa Cruises Corporation, Saint Petersburg, FL; *U.S. Public*, pg. 595

Ruhatter, Todd, V.P.-Mktg., Audio/Video, Toy & EMI Div.--Casio, Inc., Dover, NJ; *Int'l*, pg. 274

Ruhl, John, Dir.-Mktg.--Dedert Corporation, Olympia Fields, IL; *U.S. Private*, pg. 320

Ruhter, Don, Mktg. & Commun. Officer--Kemper Insurance Companies, Long Grove, IL; *U.S. Private*, pg. 614

Ruiz, Gliberto, V.P.-Consumer Banking--U.S. Operations Div., Hato Rey, PR; *U.S. Public*, pg. 176

Ruiz, Yolanda, Mgr.-Mktg. Communications--Electroglas, Inc., Santa Clara, CA; *U.S. Public*, pg. 727

Rullo, Stephen, Sr. V.P.-ARCO Prods. Co.--Atlantic Richfield Company, Los Angeles, CA; *U.S. Public*, pg. 144

Rullo, Steve, Sr. V.P.-Mktg.--ARCO Products Co., Los Angeles, CA; *U.S. Public*, pg. 144

Ruman, Nicole, Mgr.-Devel. Coord.--American Enterprise Institute for Public Policy Research, Washington, DC; *U.S. Private*, pg. 53

Rumer, Robert, Dir.-Mktg.--Vitesse Semiconductor Corporation, Camarillo, CA; *U.S. Public*, pg. 1723

Rumgay, Ian, Intl. Mktg. Dir.--Shandwick International Plc, London, United Kingdom; *Int'l*, pg. 1226

Rumgay, Ian, International Mktg. Dir.--Shandwick International Plc, London, United Kingdom; *Int'l*, pg. 1226

Rumley, Kieran, Dir.-Mktg.--Batchelors (Ireland) Ltd., Dublin, Ireland; *Int'l*, pg. 968

Runager, Michael E., Chief Mktg. Officer--Burnham, Atlanta, GA; *Int'l*, pg. 686

Runde, Sara, Mktg. Specialist--Archibald Candy Company, Chicago, IL; *U.S. Private*, pg. 597

Runk, John, Mng. Dir.-Mktg. & Sls.--Directory Distributing Associates, Inc., Scarborough, Canada; *U.S. Private*, pg. 334

Runstedler, Ronald L., V.P. & Dir.-Sls. & Mktg.--Union City Chair Co., Union City, PA; *U.S. Private*, pg. 170

Rupert, Gordon, V.P.-Sls. & Service--Bailey, Fischer & Porter Company, Warminster, PA; *Int'l*, pg. 449

Rupprecht, C., Mgr.-Natl. Sls. & Mktg.--Marsh Bellofram Corp., Newell, WV; *U.S. Private*, pg. 707

Ruprecht, Martine, Mgr.-Mktg. Communications--Beckman Instruments International, S.A., Nyon, Switzerland; *U.S. Public*, pg. 199

Rusbarsky, Joseph M., Mng. Dir.-Mktg.--OppenheimerFunds Distributor, Inc., New York, NY; *U.S. Private*, pg. 818

Rusch, Don, Mgr.-Mktg.--Midwest Industries, Inc., Ida Grove, IA; *U.S. Private*, pg. 744

Ruschak, William S., Exec. V.P.-Mktg. & Company Rels.--Willis Corroon Corp. of Michigan, Livonia, MI; *Int'l*, pg. 1506

Rush, Mark, V.P.-Mktg. Admin.--West Coast Life Insurance Co., San Francisco, CA; *U.S. Public*, pg. 1336

Rushmore, Richard, V.P.-Mktg.--Canadian American Railroad Company, Bangor, ME; *U.S. Private*, pg. 575

Rushmore, Richard, V.P.-Mktg.--Bangor & Aroostook Railroad Co., Bangor, ME; *U.S. Private*, pg. 575

Rushton, M.A.C., Dir.-Mktg.--Chemetics International Company Ltd Vancouver Operations, Vancouver, Canada; *Int'l*, pg. 774

Rusling, Robert, Dir.-Mktg.--Dollar Rent A Car, Tulsa, OK; *U.S. Public*, pg. 354

Russ, Charles J., Mgr.-Mktg. Devel.--Unitary Products Group, York, PA; *U.S. Public*, pg. 1788

Russ, Dennis, Mgr.-Mktg. & Communications--AAF-International, Louisville, KY; *U.S. Private*, pg. 3

Russel, Jay, Dir.-Mktg.--Castelazo & Associates, Los Angeles, CA; *U.S. Public*, pg. 1071

Russell, Douglas W., Chief Fin. Officer, Treas. & Asst. Sec.--Rotonics Manufacturing Inc., Gardena, CA; *U.S. Public*, pg. 1406

Russell, J.V., V.P.-Sls. & Mktg.-Blackhawk Collision Repair--Blackhawk Collision Repair Inc., Waukesha, WI; *U.S. Public*, pg. 805

Russell, Jason, Dir.-Mktg.--Carhartt, Inc., Dearborn, MI; *U.S. Private*, pg. 210
Russell, Kristine, Dir.-Mktg.--Grandy's, Inc., Lewisville, TX; *U.S. Private*, pg. 61
Russell, Mike, V.P.-Mktg.--Ultramar Diamond Shamrock Corporation, San Antonio, TX; *U.S. Public*, pg. 1663
Russell, Ray, V.P.-Sls. & Mktg.--Renfro Corp., Mount Airy, NC; *U.S. Private*, pg. 922
Russell, Richard R., Pres., Chief Exec. Officer & Mng. Dir.--The General Chemical Group, Inc., Hampton, NH; *U.S. Public*, pg. 707
Russo, Daniel, Dir.-Mktg.--Horizon Air Industries, Seattle, WA; *U.S. Public*, pg. 35
Russo, Hal, Dir.-Mktg. & New Prods.--Bayer Corporation/ Consumer Care Division, Morristown, NJ; *Int'l*, pg. 173
Russo, James, Mgr.-Mktg.--Genovese Drug Stores, Inc., Melville, NY; *U.S. Public*, pg. 730
Russo, Kenneth, V.P.-Professional Sls.--Conair Corporation, Stamford, CT; *U.S. Private*, pg. 261
Rustem, Donna, Dir.-Mktg.--Gantos Inc., Stamford, CT; *U.S. Public*, pg. 702
Rustigan, Dale, V.P.-Retail Mktg. & Dir.-Sls.--Leviton Mfg. Co., Inc., Little Neck, NY; *U.S. Private*, pg. 663
Ruta, Barry, Mgr.-Natl. Ornamental Mktg.--Speedling Incorporated, Sun City, FL; *U.S. Private*, pg. 1024
Ruter. Don, Mgr.-Mktg.--The Wm. Powell Company, Cincinnati, OH; *U.S. Private*, pg. 877
Rutherford, Dan, V.P.-Mktg. Dev.--ServiceMaster International, Downers Grove, IL; *U.S. Public*, pg. 1462
Rutherford, Joan, Dir.-Adv. & Mktg. Services--Fuji Photo Film U.S.A., Inc., Elmsford, NY; *Int'l*, pg. 524
Rutherford, Nathan R., V.P.-Mktg.--The Coe Manufacturing Company, Painesville, OH; *U.S. Private*, pg. 249
Rutledge, Elaine, Mgr.-Media Mktg.--Builders Square, Inc., San Antonio, TX; *U.S. Private*, pg. 477
Rutledge, Mark, Dir.-Mktg.--Shakertown 1992, Inc., Winlock, WA; *Int'l*, pg. 296
Rutledge, Scott, Mgr.-Mktg.--The Wooster Brush Company, Wooster, OH; *U.S. Private*, pg. 1188
Ruud, Richard, Dir.-Mktg.--Straw Hat Cooperative Corp., Dublin, CA; *U.S. Private*, pg. 1046
Ryan, Becky, Dir.-Mktg.-Bel Brands--Bel/Kaukauna USA, Little Chute, WI; *U.S. Private*, pg. 130
Ryan, D., Dir.-Mktg.-Canadian Airlines Saddledome--Calgary Flames Hockey Club, Calgary, Canada; *Int'l*, pg. 252
Ryan, Ed, Dir.-Mktg.--The Hanover Insurance Company, Worcester, MA; *U.S. Public*, pg. 54
Ryan, Kristen, Mgr.-Mktg.--Perry's Ice Cream Co., Inc., Akron, NY; *U.S. Private*, pg. 855
Ryan, Lisa, Mgr.-Mktg.--Furr's/Bishops, Inc., Lubbock, TX; *U.S. Public*, pg. 689
Ryan, M.T., Dir.-Sls. & Mktg.--Chemtronics Inc., Kennesaw, GA; *Int'l*, pg. 892
Ryan, Mary Pat, Sr. V.P.-Mktg.--United States Satellite Broadcasting, Co., Saint Paul, MN; *U.S. Private*, pg. 544
Ryan, Nancy E., Dir.-Communications & Media--Klockner Pentaplast of America, Inc., Gordonsville, VA; *Int'l*, pg. 737
Ryan, Pat, Dir.-Mktg./Gas--LG & E Energy Corp., Louisville, KY; *U.S. Public*, pg. 970
Ryan, Richard E., Mgr.-Grp. Mktg.--Just Born, Inc., Bethlehem, PA; *U.S. Private*, pg. 602
Ryan, Robert, Dir.-Mktg.--Richco Inc., Chicago, IL; *U.S. Private*, pg. 929
Ryan, Robert, V.P.-Mktg.--ZD Press, Emeryville, CA; *Int'l*, pg. 1276
Ryan, Robert E., Jr., V.P.-Sls. & Mktg.--Mike Albert Leasing, Inc., Cincinnati, OH; *U.S. Private*, pg. 32
Ryan, Robert M., V.P. & Dir.-Mktg.--Gooch Foods, Inc., Lincoln, NE; *U.S. Public*, pg. 128
Ryan, Thomas, Mgr.-Mktg.--Hatfield Quality Meats, Hatfield, PA; *U.S. Private*, pg. 510
Ryan, Todd J., V.P.-Sls. & Mktg.--Ag Services of America, Inc., Cedar Falls, IA; *U.S. Public*, pg. 6
Ryanczak, Anthony J., Sr. V.P.-Sls. & Mktg.--Griffin Technology Incorporated, Farmington, NY; *U.S. Public*, pg. 506
Rycroft, J.J., Dir.-Mktg.--BNFL, Warrington, United Kingdom; *Int'l*, pg. 120
Ryder, Duncan, V.P. & Dir.-Sls. & Mktg.--CBS Television Network, New York, NY; *U.S. Public*, pg. 274
Rydin, Craig, Pres.--Godiva Chocolatier, Inc., New York, NY; *U.S. Public*, pg. 299
Rygiel, Edward K., Sr. V.P.-Corp. Devel. & Pres.-MDS Capital Corp.--MDS Inc., Etobicoke, Canada; *Int'l*, pg. 826
Rylee, J., Mgr.-Mktg. Communications--Cutler-Hammer Eaton Corporation, Milwaukee, WI; *U.S. Public*, pg. 556
Rymeski, Robert, V.P.-Mktg. & Adv.--The Hilsinger Co. L.P., Plainville, MA; *U.S. Private*, pg. 530
Rynberg, Thomas, Mgr.-Mktg.--La-Co Industries Markal Company, Elk Grove Village, IL; *U.S. Private*, pg. 640
Rynd, John, V.P.-Mktg.--Noble Offshore Corporation, Houston, TX; *U.S. Public*, pg. 1186
Rynd, John T., V.P.-Mktg.--Noble Drilling Corporation, Houston, TX; *U.S. Public*, pg. 1186
Rytting, Susan, Sr. V.P.- Secondary Mktg.--Deposit Guaranty Mortgage Co., Jackson, MS; *U.S. Public*, pg. 501
Sabah, Ali Jaber Al-Ali Al, Mng. Dir.-Mktg.--Kuwait Petroleum Corporation, Safat, Kuwait; *Int'l*, pg. 764
Sabin, Kevin, Dir.-Mktg.--First Commercial Bank, N.A., Little Rock, AR; *U.S. Public*, pg. 630
Sabiston, Larry T., V.P.-Mktg.--Rosser International, Inc., Atlanta, GA; *U.S. Private*, pg. 946
Sabo, Stephen, Mgr.-Mktg. & Sls.--Allied Construction Products, Inc., Cleveland, OH; *U.S. Public*, pg. 1339
Sabol, Jim, Dir.-Mktg.--Krautkramer-Branson, Inc., Lewistown, PA; *U.S. Public*, pg. 574
Sabol, Ken, Mgr.-Mktg.--Babcock & Wilcox ST Company, Little Rock, AR; *U.S. Public*, pg. 1068
Sabol, Richard, Mgr.-Mktg.--Springer-Verlag New York Inc., New York, NY; *Int'l*, pg. 1291
Sacchetti, Christian, Dir.-Mktg.--Lafarge Aluminates, Paris, France; *Int'l*, pg. 789
Sacco, Frances, Dir.-Mktg. Communications--Microcom, Norwood, MA; *U.S. Public*, pg. 417
Sack, Deborah, V.P.-Mktg.--MasterCard International-Cirrus Brand, Purchase, NY; *U.S. Private*, pg. 714
Sadai, Kenichiro, Mgr.-Sls. & Mktg.--Sapporo U.S.A., Inc., New York, New York, NY; *Int'l*, pg. 1193
Sadauskas, Michele, Mgr.-Adv. & Mktg.--Guess ?, Inc., Los Angeles, CA; *U.S. Public*, pg. 768
Saddler, I.E., Dir.-Mktg. & Sls.--Kent Meters Ltd., Luton, United Kingdom; *Int'l*, pg. 2
Sadler, Catherine, Exec. V.P.-Mktg.--AnnTaylor, Inc., New York, NY; *U.S. Public*, pg. 116
Saeger, Bob, Exec. V.P.-Mktg. & Adv. Services--Visa U.S.A. Inc., San Francisco, CA; *U.S. Private*, pg. 1141
Saegesser, Paul, Dir.-Mktg.--Nordson Schweiz AG, Munchenstein, Switzerland; *U.S. Public*, pg. 1189
Saenz, John, V.P.-Mktg. & Bus. Devel.--Central and South West Corporation, Dallas, TX; *U.S. Public*, pg. 324
Saffer, David, V.P.-Mktg.--Colonial Metals Co., Columbia, PA; *U.S. Private*, pg. 253
Safier, Robert S., V.P.-Mktg.--Patent Construction Systems, Paramus, NJ; *U.S. Public*, pg. 793
Safranek, H., V.P. & Dir.-Mktg.--Timken do Brasil S.A. Comercio e Industria Limitada, Sao Paulo, Brazil; *U.S. Public*, pg. 1618
Sagara, Jiro, Mng. Dir. & Sr. V.P.-Acctg.--Japan Airlines Company, Ltd., Tokyo, Japan; *Int'l*, pg. 699
Sage, M., Mgr.-Sls. & Mktg.--GF International Limited, Alexandria, Australia; *Int'l*, pg. 555
Sagendorf, Martin C., Mgr.-Mktg.-Grinding Systems--Moore Tool Company, Inc., Bridgeport, CT; *U.S. Private*, pg. 889
Sager, Richard, V.P.-Mktg.--Williams Advanced Materials, Inc., Buffalo, NY; *U.S. Public*, pg. 266
Sahertian, Pat, Dir.-Mktg. & Adv.--Austin Productions, Inc., Holbrook, NY; *U.S. Private*, pg. 100
Sahlin, Sven Ake, Mgr.-Mktg.--Stora Billerud AB, Skoghall, Sweden; *Int'l*, pg. 1302
Saifer, Bill, V.P.-Sls. & Mktg.--Invacare Health Care Furnishings, Chesterfield, MO; *U.S. Public*, pg. 911
Saiki, Marcos, Mgr.-Mktg.--Badger Meter, Inc., Milwaukee, WI; *U.S. Public*, pg. 164
Saiki, Marcos, V.P.-Mktg.--Badger Meter Industrial Div., Milwaukee, WI; *U.S. Public*, pg. 165
Saito, Akio, V.P.-Mktg.--Northern Telecom Japan Inc., Tokyo, Japan; *Int'l*, pg. 970
Saito, Masaru, Dir. & Chief Mktg. Officer--Asahi Advertising Inc., Tokyo, Japan; *Int'l*, pg. 81
Saji, Nobutado, Exec. V.P.-Mktg. Tokyo--Suntory Ltd., Osaka, Japan; *Int'l*, pg. 1321
Sajonc, Ed, Dir.-Mktg. & Govt. Rels.--Todd Pacific Shipyards Corp., Seattle, WA; *U.S. Public*, pg. 1619
Sakai, Sale, V.P.-Mktg.--Active Software, Inc., Santa Clara, CA; *U.S. Private*, pg. 15
Sakharoff, Albert, V.P.-Sls. & Mktg.--Weiss Sheet Metal Company, Gardena, CA; *U.S. Private*, pg. 1160
Sakoutis, Steve, V.P.-Sls. & Mktg.--P & F Industries, Inc., Farmingdale, NY; *U.S. Public*. pg. 1239
Sakowski, Ray, Sr. V.P.-Mktg.--Voyager Service Warranties, Inc., Fort Worth, TX; *U.S. Public*, pg. 68
Salant, Laura, Dir.-Mktg.--Scientific American, Inc., New York, NY; *Int'l*, pg. 1479
Salat, Alain, Dir.-Mktg.--Leclerc, Issy-les-Moulineaux, France; *Int'l*, pg. 805
Salazar, Chris, V.P.-Sls. & Mktg.--Karnak Corporation, Clark, NJ; *U.S. Private*, pg. 607
Salazar, Nick, Dir.-Canadian Mktg.--Weiser Lock, Tucson, AZ; *U.S. Public*, pg. 1053
Salcedo, Eduardo A., Dir.-Mktg.--Procter & Gamble Venezuela, C.A., Caracas, Venezuela; *U.S. Public*, pg. 1332
Salcedo, Rick, Sr. V.P.-Mktg. & Creative Services--CNN (Cable News Network), Atlanta, GA; *U.S. Public*, pg. 1614
Salditt, Phil, Dir.-Mktg., Intl. Div.--Graco Inc., Golden Valley, MN; *U.S. Public*, pg. 756
Saldivar, Margaret, Communication Specialist--Mettler-Toledo Inc., Worthington, OH; *U.S. Private*, pg. 4
Saleeby, Caroline, Mgr.-Bus. & Circulation--Business Journals of North Carolina, LLC, Raleigh, NC; *U.S. Private*, pg. 19
Salemi, Hank, V.P.-Mktg.--Six Flags Great America, Inc., Gurnee, IL; *U.S. Public*, pg. 1611
Salemi, Hank, Dir.-Mktg.--Six Flags St. Louis, Eureka, MO; *U.S. Public*, pg. 1612
Salerno, Robert J., Exec. V.P.-Sls. & Mktg.--ServiceMaster Business & Industry Group, Downers Grove, IL; *U.S. Public*, pg. 1462
Sales, B.E., Gen. Mgr.-Mktg.--Murco Petroleum Ltd., London, United Kingdom; *U.S. Public*, pg. 1142
Sales, Wayne C., Sr. V.P.-Mktg.--Canadian Tire Corporation Limited, Toronto, Canada; *Int'l*, pg. 259
Saless, Bijan S., Exec. V.P.-Sls. & Mktg.--EA Engineering, Science & Technology, Inc., Hunt Valley, MD; *U.S. Public*, pg. 540
Salgado, Sherry, Dir.-Mktg.--GLENFED Insurance Services, Inc., Glendale, CA; *U.S. Public*, pg. 747
Saliba, John, Grp. Head-Pub. Rels. & Mktg.--Air Malta Co. Ltd., Luqa, Malta; *Int'l*, pg. 37
Salika, Jim, Dir.-Mktg. & Instrument Prod.--Hamilton Co., Inc., Reno, NV; *U.S. Private*, pg. 497
Sallaz, Terri, Dir.-Mktg.--Houlihan's Restaurant Group, Kansas City, MO; *U.S. Public*, pg. 841
Sallstrom, Goran, V.P.-Intl. Sls. & Mktg.--Pharmacia & Upjohn Deltec, Inc., Arden Hills, MN; *Int'l*, pg. 1049
Salminen, Susan, Mgr.-Mktg. Communications--Cylink Corp., Sunnyvale, CA; *U.S. Public*, pg. 1306
Salmon, Isabelle, Dir.-Sls. & Mktg.--Sofamor Danek Group, Inc., Memphis, TN; *U.S. Public*, pg. 1482
Salmon, Jack, V.P.-Sls. & Mktg.--Family Smacks, Inc., Liberty, MO; *U.S. Private*, pg. 393
Salmon, Robert, V.P.-Mktg.--Holder Corporation, Atlanta, GA; *U.S. Private*, pg. 533
Salmon, Robert, V.P.-Sls. & Mktg.--Spirit Cruises, Inc., Norfolk, VA; *Int'l*, pg. 1274
Salopek, D.F., Mgr.-Mktg.--Firestone Synthetic Rubber & Latex Co., Akron, OH; *Int'l*, pg. 214
Salovaara, Katherine P., Dir.-Consumer Mktg.--Life Magazine, New York, NY; *U.S. Public*, pg. 1613
Salyers, David, Sr. Dir.-Mktg.--Chick-fil-A, Inc., Atlanta, GA; *U.S. Private*, pg. 236
Salyers, Donald E., V.P.-Mktg. & Sls.--The Kelly-Springfield Tire Company, Cumberland, MD; *U.S. Public*, pg. 753
Salzberger, Paul C., Dir.-Mktg. Services--International Nickel, Inc., Saddle Brook, NJ; *Int'l*, pg. 672
Samborski, Ken, Dir.-Mktg.--Armada Corporation, Detroit, MI; *U.S. Private*, pg. 82
Sambuchi, Stephany, Coord.-Mktg. Projects--Deck House Inc., Acton, MA; *U.S. Private*, pg. 320
Samelman, Irv, V.P.-Mktg.--Jones Apparel Group, Inc., Bristol, PA; *U.S. Public*, pg. 933
Samet, Marcy, Mng. Dir. & Direct Mktg.--Gillespie, Lawrenceville, NJ; *U.S. Private*, pg. 453
Sammis, Elizabeth, Sr. Dir.-Communications--Mid Atlantic Medical Services, Inc., Rockville, MD; *U.S. Public*, pg. 1109
Sammon, Karen E., Dir.-Mktg.--PAR Technology Corporation, New Hartford, NY; *U.S. Public*, pg. 1256
Samojedny, Marty, Dir.-Advanced Bus. Devel.--Tellabs Operations, Inc., Lisle, IL; *U.S. Public*, pg. 1572
Sample, Joe K., V.P.-Mktg.--Temple-Inland Forest Products Corp.-Building Products Group, Diboll, TX; *U.S. Public*, pg. 1575
Sampson, Bob, Mgr.-Technical Sls. & Mktg. Mgr.--Wasco Products, Inc., Sanford, ME; *U.S. Private*, pg. 1152
Sampson, Elliot, Sr. Mgr.-Mktg.--Tafa Incorporated, Concord, NH; *U.S. Public*, pg. 866
Sampson, Richard, V.P.-Mktg. & Sls.--Valmont Industries, Inc., Valley, NE; *U.S. Public*, pg. 1706
Sampson, Tom, V.P.-Mktg.--Tombstone Pizza Corporation, Northfield, IL; *U.S. Public*, pg. 1288
Samsel, Richard, Dir.-Mktg.--Delta Consolidated Industries, Inc. (Co. Headquarters), Jonesboro, AR; *U.S. Public*, pg. 481
Samsing, Robert, Sr. V.P.-Sls. & Mktg.--Briggs Industries, Inc., Tampa, FL; *U.S. Private*, pg. 168
Samson, Roger, Sr. V.P.-Mktg. & Devel.--Sico Inc., Longueuil, Canada; *Int'l*, pg. 1239
Samuelson, Michael, Dir.-Mktg.--Apria Healthcare Group Inc., Costa Mesa, CA; *U.S. Public*, pg. 125
San Miguel, Francisco J., V.P.-Mktg.-Former Soviet Union & Europe--McDermott International, Inc., New Orleans, LA; *U.S. Public*, pg. 1067
Sanchez, Adriana, Corp. Librarian--Interbath, Inc., City of Industry, CA; *U.S. Private*, pg. 566
Sanchez, Fernando, Exec. V.P.-Admin. Mktg.--Leather Center, Inc., Carrollton, TX; *U.S. Private*, pg. 656
Sanchez, Jan, Dir.-Product Mktg.--Nu Horizons Electronics Corp., Melville, NY; *U.S. Public*, pg. 1205
Sanchez, Jeffrey, Mgr.-Mktg.--Teledyne Laars/Jandy Products, Novato, CA; *U.S. Public*, pg. 43
Sandeoni, Raffaele, Mgr.-Sls. & Mktg.--Vickers Systems, Milan, Italy; *U.S. Public*, pg. 25
Sander, Nancy, Mgr.-Mktg.--Brown & Haley, Tacoma, WA; *U.S. Private*, pg. 173
Sanders, A. Brian, Chief Mktg. Officer & Sr. V.P.--ADVO, Inc., Windsor, CT; *U.S. Public*, pg. 23
Sanders, Janet S., Mgr.-Mktg.--Sverdrup Civil, Inc., Maryland Heights, MO; *U.S. Private*, pg. 1057
Sanders, Mark, Dir.-Mktg. & Prod. Supt.--PACCAR Winch Division, Broken Arrow, OK; *U.S. Public*, pg. 1246
Sanders, Mary Brady, Dir.-Governmental Affairs & Mktg. Communications--The Homestead L.C., Hot Springs, VA; *U.S. Private*, pg. 247
Sanders, Mike, Mgr.-MarCom--Micropolis Corporation, Chatsworth, CA; *U.S. Private*, pg. 742
Sanders, Tom, Sr. V.P.-Mktg.--Information & Engineering Technology, Fairfax, VA; *U.S. Private*, pg. 351
Sanders, Travis, Gen. Mgr.-Aviation Mktg.--PS Trading, Inc., Dallas, TX; *U.S. Public*, pg. 1245
Sanders, Vernon C., V.P.-Sls. & Mktg.--Hydro-Aire, Burbank, CA; *U.S. Public*, pg. 457
Sanderson, Bill, Dir.-Mktg.--Sanderson Farms, Inc., Laurel, MS; *U.S. Public*, pg. 1430
Sanderson, Brian, V.P.-Mktg.-Home Prods. Div.--Wellington Home Products, Madison, GA; *U.S. Private*, pg. 1161
Sanderson, George, Sls. Mgr.-Mktg.--Wirth Howden--Howden Group Plc, Renfrew, United Kingdom; *Int'l*, pg. 636
Sanderson, Mark, Dir.-Mkt. Res. & Devel.--Sandoz Pharmaceuticals Corp., East Hanover, NJ; *Int'l*, pg. 974
Sandore, Jeff, V.P.-Mktg.--Tyson Foods, Inc., Springdale, AR; *U.S. Public*, pg. 1652
Sandow, Kenneth L., V.P.-Mktg. Devel.--American & Efird, Inc., Mount Holly, NC; *U.S. Public*, pg. 1412
Sandrik, Karen, Asst. Mktg. Dir.--Cherokee Inc., Van Nuys, CA; *U.S. Public*, pg. 345
Sands, Ken, V.P.-Mktg.--Cameron & Barkley Company, Charleston, SC; *U.S. Private*, pg. 203
Sandvig, Dave, Exec. V.P.-Mktg.--Fort Dodge Animal Health, Overland Park, KS; *U.S. Public*, pg. 79
Sandy, John, Corp. Mktg. Mgr.--High Industries, Inc., Lancaster, PA; *U.S. Private*, pg. 528
Sandzer-Bell, Ben, V.P.-Mktg.--Wilcox Electric, Inc., Kansas City, MO; *Int'l*, pg. 1384
Sanelli, Steven G., Grp. V.P.--The Eastern Company, Naugatuck, CT; *U.S. Public*, pg. 548
Sanford, Frank W., V.P.-Pur. & Mktg.--Sanford & Hawley, Inc., Unionville, CT; *U.S. Private*, pg. 965
Sanford, William, Exec. V.P.-Airgas Direct Indus.--Airgas, Inc., Radnor, PA; *U.S. Public*, pg. 33
Sangis, Georges, V.P. & Gen. Mgr.-Comml. Engines--SNECMA - Societe Nationale d'Etude et de Construction de Moteurs d'Aviation, Paris, France; *Int'l*, pg. 1165
Sanna, James, V.P.-Mktg.--Radio City Productions, New York, NY; *Int'l*, pg. 873

Sansone, Shannon V., Mktg. Rep.--Alimak Elevator Company, Bridgeport, CT; *U.S. Private*, pg. 34
Santamaria, Hector, Mgr.-Intl. Bus. Devel.--Wilcox Electric, Inc., Kansas City, MO; *Int'l*, pg. 1384
Santambrogio, Rita, V.P.-Mktg.--Cassina, Milan, Italy; *Int'l*, pg. 570
Santangelo, Steven J., Sr. V.P.-Strategic Mktg. & Res. Consultation--Tierney & Partners, Philadelphia, PA; *U.S. Public*, pg. 1641
Santauzzo, Victor, Mktg. Dir.--Young & Rubicam de Buenos Aires, Buenos Aires, Argentina; *U.S. Private*, pg. 1200
Santello, Rich, V.P.-Mktg. & Sls.--EnviroSource, Inc., Horsham, PA; *U.S. Public*, pg. 587
Santo, Frank, V.P.-Mktg.--Helm, Inc., Detroit, MI; *U.S. Private*, pg. 520
Santo, Jane Di, Dir.-Mktg.--Bulova Corporation, Woodside, NY; *U.S. Public*, pg. 1010
Santora, Karla, Dir.-Mktg.--Rodenstock USA, Inc., Danbury, CT; *Int'l*, pg. 1007
Santori, M., Mgr.-Mktg.--Tuthill Pump, Alsip, IL; *U.S. Private*, *pg. 1111*
Santoro, Richard G., V.P.-Sls. & Mktg.--Carpenter Technology Corporation, Reading, PA; *U.S. Public*, pg. 307
Santos, Richard, Dir.-Mktg.--A-P-A Transport Corp., North Bergen, NJ; *U.S. Private*, pg. 2
Santourian, Hrayr, Dir.-Mktg.--Stanley Home Products, Easthampton, MA; *U.S. Public*, pg. 282
Sanz, Robert, V.P.-Supply & Mktg.--Wickland Oil Company, Inc., Sacramento, CA; *U.S. Private*, pg. 1175
Sanzen, Robert, V.P.-Sls. & Mktg.--Mylan Laboratories, Inc., Pittsburgh, PA; *U.S. Public*, pg. 1143
Sanzone, Vito, Dir.-Mktg.--Iwerks Entertainment, Sarasota, FL; *U.S. Public*, pg. 915
Sapp, Karen, Dir.-Mktg.--Dominion Homes, Dublin, OH; *U.S. Public*, pg. 516
Saras, Amy, Mgr.-Mktg. Communications--The Kendall Company, Mansfield, MA; *U.S. Public*, pg. 1647
Sarauer, Lori, Exec. Sec.-Consumer Mktg.--The Pillsbury Company, Minneapolis, MN; *Int'l*, pg. 411
Sarauer, Lori, Exec. Sec.-Consumer Mktg.--Pillsbury Co., Minneapolis, MN; *Int'l*, pg. 411
Saretsky, Gregg A., V.P.-Passenger Mktg.--Canadian Airlines Corporation, Calgary, Canada; *Int'l*, pg. 255
Sargent, Jeannine Perchard, V.P.-Mktg.--GaSonics International, San Jose, CA; *U.S. Public*, pg. 703
Sargent, Michael J., V.P.-Mktg.--Inter-Tel, Incorporated, Phoenix, AZ; *U.S. Public*, pg. 888
Sargent, Sallie, Dir.-Event Mktg.--America West Airlines, Inc., Phoenix, AZ; *U.S. Public*, pg. 67
Sargento, Romain, Dir.-Mktg.--Sara Lee Hosiery, Winston Salem, NC; *U.S. Public*, pg. 1434
Sargento, Romaine, Dir.-Mktg.--L'eggs Products, Inc., Winston Salem, NC; *U.S. Public*, pg. 1434
Sarik, Dan, Dir.-Mktg.--Reed Tool Company, Houston, TX; *U.S. Public*, pg. 298
Sarkany, Tom, Dir.-Mutual Fund Mktg.--Value Line, Inc., New York, NY; *U.S. Private*, pg. 137
Sarkesion, Suzanne, Mgr.-Mktg.--AutoWeek, Detroit, MI; *U.S. Private*, pg. 284
Sarner, Steve, V.P.-Mktg. & Sls.--RenoAir Inc., Reno, NV; *U.S. Private*, pg. 922
Sartini, Ray, V.P.-Mktg.-Heat Transfer Div.--Hydro Aluminum Bohn, Inc., Farmington Hills, MI; *Int'l*, pg. 961
Sartorius, John, Dir.-Mktg. Team-Communications--Busch Entertainment Corp., Clayton, MO; *U.S. Public*, pg. 114
Sarvary, Mark, V.P.-Mktg., Nestle Frozen Food Co.--Nestle Frozen, Refrigerated, and Ice Cream Companies, Solon, OH; *Int'l*, pg. 918
Sas, John A., Dir.-Mktg.--Peacock Inc., La Salle, Canada; *Int'l*, pg. 1489
Sas, John A., Dir.-Mktg.--Brian Controls, Mississauga, Canada; *Int'l*, pg. 1489
Saslow, Seymour, Dir.-Sls. & Engrng.--Espey Mfg. & Electronics Corp., Saratoga Springs, NY; *U.S. Public*, pg. 592
Sass, George, Mgr.-Adv.--GB Holdings, Jurong, Singapore; *Int'l*, pg. 531
Sass, George, Mgr.-Mktg.--American Marine Pte. Ltd., Jurong, Singapore; *Int'l*, pg. 531
Sass, George, Dir.-Mktg.--Grand Banks Yachts, Ltd., Southport, CT; *Int'l*, pg. 531
Sass, Harvey, V.P.-Mktg.--Minwax Company Div., Upper Saddle River, NJ; *U.S. Public*, pg. 1466
Sasser, Bob L., Sr. V.P.-Mdsg. & Mktg.--Rose's Stores, Inc., Henderson, NC; *U.S. Public*, pg. 1405
Sasserath, Jay, V.P.-Strategic Mktg.--Plasma-Therm, Inc., Saint Petersburg, FL; *U.S. Public*, pg. 1308
Sater, Barbara, V.P., Mktg. Dir. & Res. Dir.--The Stephenz Group, Inc., San Jose, CA; *U.S. Private*, pg. 1040
Saterbo, Bryan, Sr. V.P. & Treas.--Colorado Boxed Beef Co., Auburndale, FL; *U.S. Private*, pg. 254
Saterbo, Stephen, Sr. V.P.-Fin. & Mktg.--Colorado Boxed Beef Co., Auburndale, FL; *U.S. Private*, pg. 254
Satow, Phillip M., Exec. V.P.-Mktg.--Forest Laboratories, Inc., New York, NY; *U.S. Public*, pg. 670
Satre, Curt, Mgr.-Mktg.--Canadian Occidental Petroleum Ltd., Calgary, Canada; *U.S. Public*, pg. 1210
Satterwhite, Kerry, Mgr.-Mktg.--The Stiffel Company, Chicago, IL; *U.S. Private*, pg. 1043
Satti, Marie, Dir.-Mktg. & Prod. Devel.--Supercuts, Inc., San Francisco, CA; *U.S. Public*, pg. 1373
Sattizahn, Ed, Exec. V.P.-Mktg.--The Learning Co., Inc., Cambridge, MA; *U.S. Public*, pg. 982
Sauder, Kevin, V.P.-Sls. & Mktg.--Sauder Woodworking Co., Archbold, OH; *U.S. Private*, pg. 967
Sauer, Elise, Dir.-Mktg.--Nevada Power Company, Las Vegas, NV; *U.S. Public*, pg. 1169
Saulino Blatt, Norma, Assoc. Publr.--Time Inc. Health, New York, NY; *U.S. Public*, pg. 1613
Saussy, Gordon, V.P.-Mktg.--3Com Corporation, Southborough, MA; *U.S. Public*, pg. 1604
Savage, Bob, V.P.-Sls. & Mktg.- Thermal Prods.--The Bergquist Company, Minneapolis, MN; *U.S. Private*, pg. 135
Savage, David K., Mgr.-Sls. & Mktg.--Schweizer Aircraft Corporation, Big Flats, NY; *U.S. Private*, pg. 975
Savage, Timothy M., V.P.-Mktg.--Troy Corporation, Florham Park, NJ; *U.S. Private*, pg. 1105
Savage, Tom, Product Mgr.-Mktg.--Jaco Electronics, Inc., Hauppauge, NY; *U.S. Public*, pg. 920
Savel, Mark, Mgr.-Sls. & Mktg.--Lee Myles Associates Corporation, Paramus, NJ; *U.S. Private*, pg. 657
Saveswein, Rick, Mgr.-Mktg.--Contico International, Inc., Saint Louis, MO; *U.S. Private*, pg. 267
Saville, Jim, V.P.-Sls. & Mktg.--Horsehead Resource Development Company, Inc., Palmerton, PA; *U.S. Private*, pg. 540
Savino, Steve, V.P.-Mktg.--Six Flags Theme Parks Inc., Parsippany, NJ; *U.S. Public*, pg. 1611
Savoie, Susan, V.P.-Sls. & Mktg./Medical Div.--Beiersdorf, Inc., Norwalk, CT; *Int'l*, pg. 182
Sawamura, Fumio, Sr. Mng. Dir.--Hosokawa Micron Corporation, Osaka, Japan; *Int'l*, pg. 635
Sawhney, Navin, Sr. V.P.-Mktg.--Cunard Line Ltd., New York, NY; *Int'l*, pg. 773
Sawicki, Craig, V.P. & Dir.-Natl. Mktg. & Gen. Mgr.-Midwest Region--W. Braun Company, Chicago, IL; *U.S. Private*, pg. 166
Sawyer, Louis, Exec. V.P.-Strategic Mktg.--Sawyer Riley Compton Inc., Atlanta, GA; *U.S. Private*, pg. 969
Sawyer, Matt, Dir.-Mktg.--The Chinet Co., Norwalk, CT; *Int'l*, *pg. 1146*
Saxberg, Catherine, Dir.-Marketing Services--Canadian Broadcast Sales, Toronto, Canada; *Int'l*, pg. 1482
Saxenmeyer, Susan J., V.P.-Commun.--TCA Cable TV, Inc., Tyler, TX; *U.S. Public*, pg. 1553
Saxenmeyer, Susan J., V.P.-Mktg.--TCA Management Company, Tyler, TX; *U.S. Public*, pg. 1553
Saxton, William, Mgr.-Grp. Mktg.--Quality Bakers Australia Ltd., Eastwood, Australia; *Int'l*, pg. 555
Sayre, Steve, V.P.-Mktg.--Lotus Development Corporation, Cambridge, MA; *U.S. Public*, pg. 896
Sbezzi, Carmen, V.P.-Sls. & Mktg.--J.A. Sexauer, Inc., Scarsdale, NY; *U.S. Private*, pg. 352
Scager, Robert, Sr. V.P.-Sls. & Mktg.--Comdisco Canada Ltd., Toronto, Canada; *U.S. Public*, pg. 408
Scala, Lou, V.P.-Mktg.-China & Dinnerware--Lenox Brands, Langhorne, PA; *U.S. Public*, pg. 261
Scalia, Janice, Mgr.-Mktg. Svcs.--Datascope Corp., Montvale, NJ; *U.S. Public*, pg. 487
Scalunberger, Laurent, Mgr.-Commercial--Au Bon Marche, Paris, France; *Int'l*, pg. 97
Scangas, Nicholas A., Exec. V.P.-Mktg. & Sls.--Scangas Brothers Holdings, Inc., Lynn, MA; *U.S. Private*, pg. 969
Scanlon, John, V.P.-Mktg./Telecomm.--Stratus Computer, Inc., Marlborough, MA; *U.S. Public*, pg. 1524
Scapelliti, Joe, Mgr.-Mktg.--Detrex Corporation, Southfield, MI; *U.S. Public*, pg. 501
Scarangella, Frank, Sr. V.P.--The Bank of New York Company, Inc., New York, NY; *U.S. Public*, pg. 178
Scarangella, Frank, Mgr.-Mktg.--The Bank of New York, New York, NY; *U.S. Public*, pg. 178
Scarborough, Elizbeth, V.P.-Sls. & Mktg., Healthcare Products--Mentor Urology, Inc., Santa Barbara, CA; *U.S. Public*, pg. 1086
Scarborough, Frank, V.P.-Sls. & Mktg.--Up-Right, Inc., Selma, CA; *U.S. Private*, pg. 1128
Scarbrough, Bill, Mktg.--Regions Bank/Troy, Troy, AL; *U.S. Public*, pg. 1373
Scarlett, M., Dir.-Sls. & Mktg.--Cincinnati Milacron U.K. Limited, Birmingham, United Kingdom; *U.S. Public*, pg. 368
Scarpinato, Stephen, Mgr.-Natl. Mktg.--Tamms Industries, Mentor, OH; *Int'l*, pg. 803
Scenna, Angela, Mktg. Services--Qualex Inc., Durham, NC; *U.S. Public*, pg. 551
Schaaf, Sue, Dir.-Mktg.--Developers Diversified Realty Corporation, Moreland Hills, OH; *U.S. Public*, pg. 502
Schachter, Rozalie, Dr., V.P.-Bus. Devel.--General Microwave Corporation, Amityville, NY; *U.S. Public*, pg. 717
Schaefer, Alan, Mgr.-Sls. & Mktg.--Weatherford, Houston, TX; *U.S. Public*, pg. 1749
Schaefer, Bob, Dir.-Mktg.--Warner-Jenkinson Co., Saint Louis, MO; *U.S. Public*, pg. 1696
Schaefer, Jeffrey N., V.P.-Sls.--Diebel Manufacturing Co., Morton Grove, IL; *U.S. Private*, pg. 331
Schaefer, Lesly, Sr. V.P.-Mktg. & Promotions--VH-1/Video Hits One, New York, NY; *U.S. Private*, pg. 779
Schaefer, Susie, Mgr.-Mktg. & Adv.--Midwest Grain Products, Inc., Atchison, KS; *U.S. Public*, pg. 1111
Schaeffer, Herbert, Mgr.-Logistics--Agrolinz Melamin GmbH, Lienz, Austria; *Int'l*, pg. 356
Schaeffer, Raymond, V.P.-New Bus.--Fay, Spofford & Thorndike, Inc., Burlington, MA; *U.S. Private*, pg. 397
Schaffer, Richard, V.P.-Sls. & Mktg.--Los Angeles Smoking & Curing Company, Los Angeles, CA; *U.S. Private*, pg. 810
Schaller, Paul, V.P.-Mktg.--Alantec Corp., San Jose, CA; *U.S. Public*, pg. 667
Schaller, Scott, V.P.-New Bus. Devel.--Vision-Ease Lens Inc., Brooklyn Park, MN; *U.S. Public*, pg. 162
Schankland, Joe, Sr. V.P.-Sls. & Mktg.--Select Beverages, Inc., Darien, IL; *U.S. Private*, pg. 982
Schanzer, Dave, V.P.-Mktg.-Healthy Choice--Armour Swift Eckrich, Downers Grove, IL; *U.S. Public*, pg. 426
Scharf, Edward W., Dir. & Coord.-Sls.--Southern States Cooperative, Inc., Richmond, VA; *U.S. Private*, pg. 1017
Scharfman, Paul, Mgr.-Mktg.--Louis Kemp Seafood Company, Duluth, MN; *U.S. Public*, pg. 1652
Schatz, David, V.P.-Corp. Devel.--Cognex Corporation, Natick, MA; *U.S. Public*, pg. 394
Schauer, William R., V.P.-Mktg.--Wisconsin Central Transportation Corporation, Rosemont, IL; *U.S. Public*, pg. 1772
Scheel, Rian, Mgr.-Natl. Sls. & Mktg.--Lockformer Company, Lisle, IL; *U.S. Public*, pg. 1100
Scheer-Ettinger, Robin, Dir.-Strategic Mktg.--Liz Claiborne, Inc., New York, NY; *U.S. Public*, pg. 1005
Scheer-Ettinger, Robin, Dir.-Strategic Mktg.--Liz Claiborne Cosmetics, Inc., New York, NY; *U.S. Public*, pg. 1006
Scheffers, Todd, Dir.-Mktg. & Sls.--Goodheart-Willcox Publisher, Tinley Park, IL; *U.S. Private*, pg. 464
Scheffler, Eldon, Mgr.-Mktg.--Midwest Vision Centers, Sauk Rapids, MN; *U.S. Private*, pg. 745
Scheidemantel, Carrie, Dir.-Mktg.--Schawkgraphics, Des Plaines, IL; *U.S. Public*, pg. 1437
Scheider, Jacquie, Dir.-Domestic Mktg.--CNN Headline News, Atlanta, GA; *U.S. Public*, pg. 1614
Scheider, Jacquie, Dir.-Domestic Mktg.--CNN (Cable News Network), Atlanta, GA; *U.S. Public*, pg. 1614
Scheidt, Dawn, Mktg. Asst.--Hitachi Instruments, Inc., San Jose, CA; *Int'l*, pg. 622
Schein, Cecilia, Mgr.-Mdsg.-Concord Miniatures--Cardinal Inc., Rahway, NJ; *U.S. Private*, pg. 208
Scheininger, Manette, V.P.-Mktg.--Maidenform Worldwide, New York, NY; *U.S. Private*, pg. 697
Scheininger, Manette, V.P.-Mktg.--True Form Intimate Apparel, New York, NY; *U.S. Private*, pg. 697
Schellenger, Norman D., V.P.-Sales & Mktg.--Whitby, Inc., Richmond, VA; *Int'l*, pg. 1427
Schenck, John, Dir.-Mktg. & Creative Services--Petersen Publishing Company, L.L.C., Los Angeles, CA; *U.S. Private*, pg. 856
Schenk, Ad, Dir.-Mktg.--British-American Tobacco (Germany) GmbH, Hamburg, Germany; *Int'l*, pg. 111
Schenk, Mike, Dir.-Mktg.--Hutch Sports USA, Inc., Hebron, KY; *U.S. Public*, pg. 1354
Schenk, Richard, Dir.-Bus. Devel.--Ingalls Shipbuilding, Pascagoula, MS; *U.S. Public*, pg. 1003
Schenks, Gary, V.P.-Mktg. & Sls.--J.W. Aluminum Company, Mount Holly, SC; *U.S. Public*, pg. 1736
Schepp, James, Mgr.-Sls. & Mktg.--Beckman Coulter, Miami, FL; *U.S. Public*, pg. 199
Scherbarth, Steven, V.P.-Mktg.--American Enterprise Investment Services, Inc., Minneapolis, MN; *U.S. Public*, pg. 73
Schere, Jay, Mgr.-Category--United Dairy Farmers, Inc., Cincinnati, OH; *U.S. Private*, pg. 1121
Scherer, Richard P., Sr. V.P.-Mktg. & Bus. Devel.--Laser Power Corporation, San Diego, CA; *U.S. Private*, pg. 652
Scherkenback, Wayne, Dir.-Mktg.--Turbine Engine Components Textron, Santa Fe Springs, CA; *U.S. Public*, *pg. 1588*
Scherz, Jurg C., Dir.-Mktg.--Brauerei AG, Zurich, Switzerland; *Int'l*, pg. 479
Scheske, Jan, Mgr.-Adv. & Mktg. Devel.--Johnson Outboards Marine Corp., Waukegan, IL; *U.S. Private*, pg. 478
Scheving, Scott, Mgr.-Mktg.--Minnkota Power Cooperative, Inc., Grand Forks, ND; *U.S. Private*, pg. 751
Schiek, Frederick A., Chief Oper. Officer & Exec. V.P.--EMC Insurance Group, Inc., Des Moines, IA; *U.S. Public*, pg. 545
Schiele, Patty, Supvr.-Pub. Rels.--CCH Incorporated, Riverwoods, IL; *Int'l*, pg. 1513
Schieppati, Giorgio, Dir.-Mktg.--ANIE-Associazione Nazionale Industrie Elettrotecniche ed Elettroniche, Milan, Italy; *Int'l*, pg. 16
Schiering, Dave, Mgr.-Mktg.--Spectra-Tech, Shelton, CT; *U.S. Public*, pg. 1593
Schiesel, R. L., V.P.-Mktg.--Marigold Foods, Inc., Minneapolis, MN; *Int'l*, pg. 752
Schieve, Jessica, Dir.-Mktg.--PowerTV, Inc., Cupertino, CA; *U.S. Public*, pg. 1443
Schifrin, Kevin, Exec. V.P.-Sls. & Mktg.--Stegner Food Products Co., Cincinnati, OH; *U.S. Private*, pg. 1039
Schillaci, Dina, Dir.-Mktg.--Bigsby & Kruthers Companies, Chicago, IL; *U.S. Private*, pg. 143
Schiller, John, V.P.-Mktg.--Concordia Publishing House, Saint Louis, MO; *U.S. Private*, pg. 261
Schilling, Allan, Exec. V.P.-Sls. & Mktg.--Pannier Corporation, Pittsburgh, PA; *U.S. Private*, pg. 837
Schilling, Lee, Sr. V.P.-Sls. & Mktg.--Collins & Aikman Floorcoverings, Inc., Dalton, GA; *U.S. Private*, pg. 192
Schillinger, Chuck, Dir.-Mktg. & Sls.--Amecom Div., College Park, MD; *U.S. Public*, pg. 1002
Schimelman, Joan K., Sr. V.P.-H.R. & Mktg./Adv.--Republic Security Financial Corporation, West Palm Beach, FL; *U.S. Public*, pg. 1381
Schinasi, Peter, Dir.-Mktg.-North America--Austrian Airlines, Whitestone, NY; *Int'l*, pg. 101
Schindler, Dana, Asst. Dir.-Mktg. & Communications--Great Lakes Window, Inc., Toledo, OH; *U.S. Public*, pg. 1193
Schindler, Tom, Mgr.-Sls. & Mktg.--West Virginia Cellular Telephone Corp., Ashland, KY; *U.S. Public*, pg. 1708
Schinsing, Terri, Mktg. Coord.--Crosman Airguns, East Bloomfield, NY; *U.S. Private*, pg. 291
Schirmer, James, Dir.-Brand Strategy, Media Group--U S West Inc., Englewood, CO; *U.S. Public*, pg. 1688
Schirmer, Robert, V.P.-Mktg.--Masco Corporation, Taylor, MI; *U.S. Public*, pg. 1052
Schissler, Robert E., V.P.-Mktg.--Logan Corporation, Huntington, WV; *U.S. Private*, pg. 672
Schlafer, Mike, Dir.-Mktg.--Rally's Hamburgers, Inc., Louisville, KY; *U.S. Public*, pg. 1359
Schlaker, Scott, Mgr.-Mktg. Projects--Royal Appliance Mfg. Co., Cleveland, OH; *U.S. Public*, pg. 1410
Schlanger, Cara, Circulation Dir.--Time Inc. Health, New York, NY; *U.S. Public*, pg. 1613
Schleier, Richard L., V.P.-Group Mkts. Specialty Prods.--Blue Cross & Blue Shield of Illinois, Chicago, IL; *U.S. Private*, pg. 151
Schleiter, Astrid, Asst.-Pub. Rels. & Mktg.--Wurzner Dauerbackwaren GmbH, Wurzen, Germany; *Int'l*, pg. 1514
Schlenker, Wolfgang, Mktg. Svcs.--Wandel & Goltermann GmbH & Co., Elektronische Messtechnik, Eningen, Germany; *Int'l*, pg. 1485

Schlinsog, B., Mgr.-Mktg. Programs--McQuay International, Minneapolis, MN; *U.S. Private*, pg. 3
Schlon, Teresa A., Dir.-Mktg.--Putman Publishing Co., Itasca, IL; *U.S. Private*, pg. 896
Schloss, James D., V.P.-Adv. & Mktg.--Smithfield Foods, Inc., Norfolk, VA; *U.S. Public*, pg. 1479
Schloss, James D., V.P.-Mktg.--The Smithfield Packing Co., Inc., Smithfield, VA; *U.S. Public*, pg. 1479
Schlosser, Rodney, Dir.-Mktg.--Southwestern Bell Mobile Systems, Inc., Dallas, TX; *U.S. Public*, pg. 1415
Schlotfeldt, Ken, Chief Oper. Officer, V.P. & Dir.-Mktg.--Badger Air Brush Company, Franklin Park, IL; *U.S. Private*, pg. 110
Schlueter, Roy, Mgr.-Special Mkts.--First Alert, Inc., Aurora, IL; *U.S. Private*, pg. 406
Schmabruch, H.C., V.P.-Freight Car & Mktg. Sls.--Thrall Car Mfg. Co., Chicago Heights, IL; *U.S. Private*, pg. 344
Schmadel, D.J., Dir.-Mktg. Devel,--Roto-Rooter, Cincinnati, OH; *U.S. Public*, pg. 344
Schmale, Jeff, Mgr.-Natl. Sls. & Mktg.--Durst Div., Beloit, WI; *U.S. Public*, pg. 1370
Schmatz, Rudolph J., V.P.-Sls. & Mktg.--Crown Crafts, Inc., Atlanta, GA; *U.S. Public*, pg. 465
Schmeidler, Norbert, Dir.-Mktg. & Sls.--Novo Nordisk (Pty) Ltd., Woodmead, South Africa; *Int'l*, pg. 988
Schmelzer, Dean, Exec. V.P.-Mktg. & Sls.--Fiserv, Inc., Brookfield, WI; *U.S. Public*, pg. 647
Schmid, Bill, V.P.-Mktg.--Williams & Company, Inc., Pittsburgh, PA; *U.S. Private*, pg. 1055
Schmid, Josef A., Dir.-Adv. & Mktg.--Mazda Austria GmbH, Klagenfurt, Austria; *Int'l*, pg. 849
Schmidt, Al, V.P.-Mktg. & Sls.--Tulip Corporation, City of Industry, CA; *U.S. Private*, pg. 1109
Schmidt, James B., Dir.-Mktg.--National Micronetics, Inc., Kingston, NY; *Int'l*, pg. 1347
Schmidt, Joachim, Dr., Dir.-Passenger Car Mktg.--Mercedes-Benz AG, Stuttgart, Germany; *Int'l*, pg. 368
Schmidt, Kemi, Dir.-Traffic Svcs. Mktg.--AmeriTruck Refrigerated Transport, Inc., Waupaca, WI; *U.S. Private*, pg. 66
Schmidt, Klaus, Dir.-Mktg.--Koenig & Bauer-Albert AG, Wurzburg, Germany; *Int'l*, pg. 742
Schmidt, Mark, Dir.-Mktg--Metrologic Instruments, Inc., Blackwood, NJ; *U.S. Public*, pg. 1102
Schmidt, Mike, V.P.-Mktg.--Milwaukee Electric Tool Corp., Brookfield, WI; *Int'l*, pg. 96
Schmidt, Richard, Sr. V.P.-Sls. & Mktg.--Federal Process Corp., Cleveland, OH; *U.S. Private*, pg. 399
Schmitt, Karl A., Dir.-Mktg.--Sherwin-Williams Paint Stores Group, Cleveland, OH; *U.S. Public*, pg. 1466
Schmittenberg, Horst, Dir.-Mktg.--Washington Specialty Metals, Buffalo Grove, IL; *U.S. Public*, pg. 1020
Schmitz, Delbert J., V.P.-Sls. & Mktg.--Superior Industries International, Inc., Van Nuys, CA; *U.S. Public*, pg. 1539
Schmoll, Donald, Dir.-Mktg.--House Beautiful, New York, NY; *U.S. Private*, pg. 517
Schnabel, Richard F., Exec. V.P.--Book of the Month Club, New York, NY; *U.S. Public*, pg. 1612
Schneid, Nancy, V.P.-Mktg.--Outback Steakhouse Inc., Tampa, FL; *U.S. Public*, pg. 1235
Schneider, Doug, Dir.-Mktg. Specialty Tools--Desa International, Bowling Green, KY; *U.S. Private*, pg. 326
Schneider, Edward, V.P.-Field Opers./Mktg.--Beech Aerospace Services, Inc., Madison, MS; *U.S. Public*, pg. 1365
Schneider, Lori, Mgr.-Production & Commun.--Grease Monkey International Inc., Denver, CO; *U.S. Public*, pg. 759
Schneider, Phil E., Sr. V.P.-Mktg.--Pier 1 Imports, Inc., Fort Worth, TX; *U.S. Public*, pg. 1295
Schneider, R. Douglas, V.P.-Mktg. & Consulting Services--Access Corporation, Cincinnati, OH; *Int'l*, pg. 994
Schneider, Rachel, Dir.-Mktg.--The Arbour Hospital, Boston, MA; *U.S. Public*, pg. 1696
Schneider, Robert R., V.P.-Sls. & Mktg.--White Mop Wringer Company, Tampa, FL; *U.S. Private*, pg. 1172
Schneider, Robert R., V.P.-Mtkg.--Pullman/Holt Corp., Tampa, FL; *U.S. Private*, pg. 1173
Schneider, Steve L., V.P.-Sls. & Mktg.--Lowrance Electronics, Inc., Tulsa, OK; *U.S. Public*, pg. 1015
Schneider, Steven L., Sr. V.P.-Sls. & Mktg.--Eagle Electronics, Catoosa, OK; *U.S. Public*, pg. 1016
Schneider, Steven L., Sr. V.P.-Sls. & Mktg.--Lowrance Avionics, Tulsa, OK; *U.S. Public*, pg. 1016
Schneider, Tom, Gen. Mgr.--Royal Waterbeds, Maryland Heights, MO; *U.S. Private*, pg. 949
Schneidewind, Art, V.P.-Sls. & Mktg.--Blue M Electric Co., Watertown, WI; *U.S. Public*, pg. 726
Schnepper, Howard, Sls. & Mktg. Mgr.--Chipico Pickles, Chicago, IL; *U.S. Private*, pg. 1140
Schnese, Kent A., V.P.-Sls. & Mktg.--Naz-Dar Company, Chicago, IL; *U.S. Private*, pg. 1084
Schnieders, Bob, Exec. V.P.-Sls. & Mktg.--Universal Studios, Inc., Universal City, CA; *Int'l*, pg. 1215
Schnitzer, Bruce, Mgr.-Mktg.--Telegenix Inc., Cherry Hill, NJ; *U.S. Private*, pg. 1073
Schnurr, Rodney, V.P.- Mktg.--Snyder's of Hanover, Inc., Hanover, PA; *U.S. Private*, pg. 1011
Schnurstein, Nancy, V.P.-Mktg. & Sls.--Fremont Indemnity Co./Medical Professional Liab. Div., Santa Monica, CA; *U.S. Public*, pg. 681
Schoberwalter, Carmen, Dir.-Mktg.--K & P Leykam Austria, Gratkorn, Austria; *Int'l*, pg. 757
Schoenbacher, Robert N., V.P.-Sls. & Mktg.--Newhouse Newspapers Metro-Suburbia, Inc., New York, NY; *U.S. Private*, pg. 20
Schoenberger, Diana L., V.P.-Mktg. Commun. & Investor Rels.--CitFed Bancorp, Inc., Dayton, OH; *U.S. Public*, pg. 376
Schoener, H., V.P.--Detecto Scale Company, Webb City, MO; *U.S. Private*, pg. 209
Schoenherr, Russell W., V.P.-Mktg.--Coltec Automotive Division, Troy, MI; *U.S. Public*, pg. 401
Schoenherr, Scott, Sr. Mgr.-Mktg./Printing & Converting Paper--Boise Cascade Corporation, Boise, ID; *U.S. Public*, pg. 242
Schoenhers, Deanna, Dir.-Mktg.--BAT Office Products, Zion, IL; *U.S. Public*, pg. 1686
Schoenholzer, Andrea, Coord.-Mktg. Communications--Jelmoli AG, Zurich, Switzerland; *Int'l*, pg. 705
Schoenig, Karl, Mgr.-Prods., Mktg. & Sls.--Medtronic GmbH, Bad Homburg, Germany; *U.S. Public*, pg. 1083
Schofield, Bob, V.P.-Mktg.--Progress Casting Group, Inc., Plymouth, MN; *U.S. Private*, pg. 890
Schofield, Colin, V.P.-Mktg.--Avedis Zildjian Company, Norwell, MA; *U.S. Private*, pg. 1206
Schofield, Dee, Coord.-Mktg.--Westat Inc., Rockville, MD; *U.S. Private*, pg. 1163
Scholl, Tom, V.P.-Sls.--Philway Products, Inc., Ashland, OH; *U.S. Private*, pg. 862
Schollman, Dave, Mgr.-Sls.--Waters Instruments, Inc., Rochester, MN; *U.S. Public*, pg. 1745
Schon, Joe, V.P.-Mktg. & Sls.--Agromac International, Inc., Gering, NE; *U.S. Private*, pg. 27
Schonauer, Tom, V.P.-Mktg. & Gen. Mgr.--Federal Signal Corporation, Signal Div., University Park, IL; *U.S. Public*, pg. 616
Schoonmaker, Randy, Mgr.-Village Mktg.--Mount Snow Resort, Mount Snow, VT; *U.S. Private*, pg. 61
Schoonover, Philip J., Sr. V.P.-Mktg./Consumer Electronics & Appliances--Best Buy Co., Inc., Eden Prairie, MN; *U.S. Public*, pg. 223
Schori, Tom, Dir.-Mktg. & Consumer Res.--Country Life Insurance Company, Bloomington, IL; *U.S. Private*, pg. 278
Schostaco, John, Mgr.-Mktg.--Schlosser Casting Company, Redmond, OR; *U.S. Private*, pg. 970
Schott, Roz, V.P.-Mktg. & Sls.--Schott Brothers, Inc., Perth Amboy, NJ; *U.S. Private*, pg. 972
Schouten, Peter, V.P.-Adv. & Mktg.--Vision-Ease Lens Inc., Brooklyn Park, MN; *U.S. Public*, pg. 162
Schouten, Pieter, Dir.-Mktg.--Optical Products Group, Brooklyn Park, MN; *U.S. Public*, pg. 162
Schrader, Frank D., V.P.-Central Reg. Sls.--EBP Life Insurance Co., Minneapolis, MN; *U.S. Public*, pg. 635
Schrage, Cal, Mgr.-Mktg.--Lincoln Steel, Lincoln, NE; *U.S. Private*, pg. 824
Schrage, Paul D., Sr. Exec. V.P. & Chief Mktg. Officer--McDonald's Corporation, Oak Brook, IL; *U.S. Public*, pg. 1068
Schram, John, Mgr.-Particleboard Sls. & Mktg.--Boise Cascade Timber & Wood Products Division, Boise, ID; *U.S. Public*, pg. 243
Schramm, John, Mgr.-Sls. & Mktg./Particleboard--Boise Cascade Corporation, Boise, ID; *U.S. Public*, pg. 242
Schrank, Charles, V.P.-Mktg./Consumer Prods. Div.--Block Drug Company, Inc., Jersey City, NJ; *U.S. Public*, pg. 236
Schreiber, Gary, Dir.-Sls. & Mktg.--Power Contracting & Engineering Corp., Schaumburg, IL; *U.S. Private*, pg. 877
Schreibmaier, Emanuel, Mgr.-Mktg. & Sls.--Sol Melia America, Miami, FL; *Int'l*, pg. 1277
Schreier, Leslie, V.P.-Mktg.--Elgin Watch Company, Long Island City, NY; *U.S. Private*, pg. 371
Schreiner, David G., V.P.-Mktg.--Del Webb Corporation, Phoenix, AZ; *U.S. Public*, pg. 494
Schreitmueller, Robert, Dir.-Mktg.--Electrovert, Grand Prairie, TX; *Int'l*, pg. 328
Schrier, Joe, V.P.-Mktg.--Golden West Baseball Club, Anaheim, CA; *U.S. Private*, pg. 461
Schroeder, Connie, Dir.-Promo.--Crain's Cleveland Business, Cleveland, OH; *U.S. Private*, pg. 285
Schroeder, Donald R., V.P.-Sls. & Mktg.--CTS Corporation, Elkhart, IN; *U.S. Public*, pg. 285
Schroeder, Jim, Mgr.-Mktg. Tech. Svcs.--S-B Power Tool Company, Chicago, IL; *Int'l*, pg. 205
Schroeder, Lisa, Mgr.-Mktg. Communications--Philips Electronics Instruments Company, Mahwah, NJ; *Int'l*, pg. 1054
Schroeder, Michael, V.P.-Sls. & Mktg.--Code-Alarm, Inc., Madison Heights, MI; *U.S. Public*, pg. 393
Schroeder, Robert W., V.P. & Gen. Mgr.-McCormick/Schilling Div.--McCormick & Company, Incorporated, Sparks, MD; *U.S. Public*, pg. 1066
Schroeder, S., Dir.-Microphone Prods.--Shure Brothers Incorporated, Evanston, IL; *U.S. Private*, pg. 997
Schroering, Tim, Mgr.-Mktg.--Badger Equipment Co., Winona, MN; *U.S. Private*, pg. 102
Schrowangen, Don, Mgr.-Sls. Oper.--Tech Spray, Inc., Amarillo, TX; *U.S. Private*, pg. 1071
Schubach, John J., V.P.-Strategic Mngmt. & Continuous Improvement--The Timken Company, Canton, OH; *U.S. Public*, pg. 1617
Schubert, Robert, Dir.-Sls. & Mktg.--Sermatech International, Inc., Limerick, PA; *U.S. Public*, pg. 1569
Schuetz, Gary A., V.P.-Mktg.--Amurol Confections Co., Yorkville, IL; *U.S. Public*, pg. 1781
Schuh, Don, Specialist-Mktg.--Neenah Foundry Company, Neenah, WI; *U.S. Private*, pg. 790
Schukai, Charles J., Sr. V.P.-Customer Svcs.--AmerenUE, Saint Louis, MO; *U.S. Public*, pg. 66
Schuler, Dale E., V.P.-Sls. & Mktg.--Veterinary Medicine Publishing Co., Inc., Lenexa, KS; *U.S. Public*, pg. 1600
Schuler, Edmund W., V.P.-Mktg. & Sls.--Werner & Pfleiderer Corporation, Ramsey, NJ; *Int'l*, pg. 511
Schuler, Ellen, Dir.-Mktg.-Sally Hansen Bleach & Depilatories--Del Laboratories, Inc., Farmingdale, NY; *U.S. Public*, pg. 494
Schulert, Sanford, Dir.-Mktg. Communications--Amoco Chemicals, Chicago, IL; *U.S. Public*, pg. 102
Schulist, Stacy, Dir.-Mktg.--Lyon's Restaurants, Inc., Foster City, CA; *U.S. Private*, pg. 684
Schulte, Lynn M., V.P.-Mktg.--Fuddruckers, Inc., Danvers, MA; *Int'l*, pg. 325
Schulte, Ralph, Dir.-Mktg.--The Barbers, Hairstyling for Men & Women, Inc., Minneapolis, MN; *U.S. Private*, pg. 115
Schultheis, Edward, Dir.-Sls. & Mktg.--Healthcare Management Group, New York, NY; *U.S. Public*, pg. 1071
Schultz, Bob, Exec. V.P.-Mktg.--Marine World Africa USA, Vallejo, CA; *U.S. Private*, pg. 703
Schultz, Bradford C., Sr. V.P.-Sls. & Mktg.--Accuride Corp., Henderson, KY; *U.S. Public*, pg. 1286
Schultz, Chuck A., V.P.-Sls. & Mktg.--Huck International Industrial Fastener Division, Waco, TX; *U.S. Public*, pg. 1597
Schultz, Harry, Controller--Trimfit, Inc., Bristol, PA; *U.S. Private*, pg. 1103
Schultz, K.R., Mgr.-Prod./Tobacco--Conwood Company L.P., Memphis, TN; *U.S. Private*, pg. 272
Schultz, Lisa, Dir.-Mktg.--The Keyes Company Realtors, Miami, FL; *U.S. Private*, pg. 618
Schultz, Michael, V.P.-Mktg. & Sls.--Hughes Family Markets, Inc., Irwindale, CA; *U.S. Public*, pg. 1349
Schultz, Robert G., V.P.-Mktg.--Plibrico Co., Chicago, IL; *U.S. Private*, pg. 872
Schultz, Thomas A., V.P.-Mktg.--Great Lakes Lithograph Co., Cleveland, OH; *U.S. Private*, pg. 474
Schulz, Bob, Mgr.-Mktg. Services--AGA Gas, Inc., Independence, OH; *Int'l*, pg. 13
Schulz, Donna, Asst V.P.-Grp. Mktg.--Standard Insurance Co., Portland, OR; *U.S. Private*, pg. 1031
Schumacher, Mark, V.P.-Mktg., Fisher-Rosemount Inc.--Rosemount Measurement Division, Eden Prairie, MN; *U.S. Public*, pg. 574
Schumacher, Robert W., Mktg. Coord.--Hughes Research Laboratories, Malibu, CA; *U.S. Public*, pg. 721
Schumacher, Rocky, Gen. Mgr.-Sls. & Mktg.--Agsco, Inc., Grand Forks, ND; *U.S. Private*, pg. 27
Schumer, William, Sr. V.P. & Dir.-Mktg.--Bank One, Cincinnati, Cincinnati, OH; *U.S. Public*, pg. 173
Schunmann, William C., V.P.-Intl. Mktg.--Rogers Corporation, Rogers, CT; *U.S. Public*, pg. 1402
Schurte, Ernst, Dir.-Mktg.--Deutsche Unilever Gmbh, Hamburg, Germany; *Int'l*, pg. 1436
Schustack, Margie, V.P.-Mktg./Prof. & Trade Grp.--John Wiley & Sons, Inc., New York, NY; *U.S. Public*, pg. 1768
Schuster, Dan, V.P.-Mktg.--SPD Technologies, Philadelphia, PA; *U.S. Private*, pg. 957
Schuster, Kurt, Mgr.-Mktg.--Intervet America, Inc., Millsboro, DE; *Int'l*, pg. 48
Schutes, Karen, Mgr.-Mktg. Communications--Kawneer Company, Norcross, GA; *U.S. Public*, pg. 60
Schutz, John, Exec. V.P.-Sls. & Mktg.--Strombecker Corporation, Chicago, IL; *U.S. Private*, pg. 1047
Schutz, Valerie, Mgr.-Mktg.--MBT Architecture, San Francisco, CA; *U.S. Private*, pg. 686
Schvanich, Luke M., V.P.-Mktg.--AGR International, Inc., Butler, PA; *U.S. Private*, pg. 5
Schwab, John, V.P.-Quality & Mktg.--Tenneco Packaging, Evanston, IL; *U.S. Public*, pg. 1579
Schwab, Mark, V.P.-Hallmark/Strategy & Mktg.--Hallmark Cards, Inc., Kansas City, MO; *U.S. Private*, pg. 495
Schwabenlender, Ron, Mgr.-Pub. Rels.--Okuma America Corporation, Charlotte, NC; *Int'l*, pg. 1001
Schwain, David G., V.P.-Mktg.--Land O'Lakes Fluid Dairy Division, Arden Hills, MN; *U.S. Private*, pg. 646
Schwall, Lawrence E., III, V.P.-Sls. & Mktg.--Karts International Inc., Covington, LA; *U.S. Public*, pg. 944
Schwanter, Jim, Pres. & Chief Mktg. Officer--Wickersham Hunt Schwantner, Boston, MA; *U.S. Private*, pg. 84
Schwantes, David L., Dir.-Mktg. & Sls.--Worthington Foods Inc., Worthington, OH; *U.S. Public*, pg. 1780
Schwartz, Ben, V.P.-Mktg.--Nu Horizons Electronics Corp., Melville, NY; *U.S. Public*, pg. 1205
Schwartz, Bruce, V.P.-Mktg. & Sls.--Boulevard Distillers and Importers Inc., Lawrenceburg, KY; *Int'l*, pg. 567
Schwartz, Fred, Sr. V.P., Creative Dir., Mktg.--Ammirati, Puris & Lintas, Inc., New York, NY; *U.S. Private*, pg. 66
Schwartz, Marc, V.P.-Mktg.--Handleman Company, Troy, MI; *U.S. Public*, pg. 779
Schwartz, Margaret, Dir.-Mktg.--Argo Instruments Inc., Winchester, VA; *Int'l*, pg. 839
Schwartz, Melissa, V.P.-Mktg.--Crystal Clear Industries, Ridgefield Park, NJ; *U.S. Private*, pg. 293
Schwartz, Nancy, V.P.-Adv. & Pub. Rels.--Medicine Shoppe International, Inc., Saint Louis, MO; *U.S. Public*, pg. 304
Schwartz, R., Dir.-Mktg.--Monarch Luggage Co. Inc., Brooklyn, NY; *U.S. Private*, pg. 757
Schwarz, Ken, V.P.-Sls. & Mktg.--Industrial Coated Fabrics Group, Spartanburg, SC; *U.S. Private*, pg. 507
Schwarz, Michael, Mgr.-Sls. & Mktg.--Electronic Systems Div., Sioux Falls, SD; *U.S. Public*, pg. 1361
Schwebel, Richard A., V.P.-Mktg. No. America--Construction Equipment Div., Racine, WI; *U.S. Public*, pg. 311
Schweber, Dennis, V.P.-Mktg.--Jaco Electronics, Inc., Hauppauge, NY; *U.S. Public*, pg. 920
Schweers, Mark E., Mgr.-Sls. & Mktg.--The International Metals Reclamation Company, Inc., Ellwood City, PA; *Int'l*, pg. 672
Schweig, John A., V.P.-Mktg.--Grainger, Lincolnshire, IL; *U.S. Public*, pg. 758
Schweikhart, K.A., Dir.-Corp. Commun.--Celotex Corporation, Tampa, FL; *U.S. Private*, pg. 221
Schweitzer, Bruce, Sr. V.P.-Sls. & Mktg.--Jennie-O Foods, Inc., Willmar, MN; *U.S. Public*, pg. 840
Schweitzer, George, Exec. V.P.-Mktg. & Communications--CBS Television Network, New York, NY; *U.S. Public*, pg. 274
Schwellyer, David, Mgr.-Mktg.--Wilbur-Ellis Agricultural, Sparta, MI; *U.S. Private*, pg. 1176
Schwetz, Phil, V.P.-Mktg.--Wittnauer International, Inc., New Rochelle, NY; *U.S. Public*, pg. 273
Schwickert, Karen, Mgr.-Sls.--Blu-Ray, Middletown, CT; *U.S. Private*, pg. 142
Schwiebert, Kirk, Mgr.-Mktg. & Sls.--Ohmite Manufacturing Company, Skokie, IL; *U.S. Private*, pg. 813
Schwieger, Dennis, V.P.-Mktg. & Sls.-Irrigation--Valmont Industries, Inc., Valley, NE; *U.S. Public*, pg. 1706

Schwinder, Marvin, Dir.-Mktg.--B&G Foods, Inc., Roseland, NJ; *U.S. Private*, pg. 105
Scibetta, Lisa, Mgr.-Mktg. & Adv.--Ultimate Technology Corporation, Victor, NY; *U.S. Public*, pg. 1637
Scocozzo, Robert, Dir.-Mktg.--Standard Tag Mfg. Co., Jersey City, NJ; *U.S. Public*, pg. 1038
Scothan, Chuck, V.P.-Mktg.-Power Wheels--Mattel Power Wheels, Fort Wayne, IN; *U.S. Public*, pg. 1058
Scott, Cathy, Dir.-Mktg. Communications--Western Digital Corporation, Irvine, CA; *U.S. Public*, pg. 1758
Scott, Craig, Mgr.-Mktg.--House of White Birches, Inc., Berne, IN; *U.S. Private*, pg. 542
Scott, David Maxwell, Dir.-Sls. & Mktg.--The Highland Distilleries Company plc, Glasgow, United Kingdom; *Int'l, pg. 619*
Scott, Debbie, Dir.-Mktg.--Hosokawa Micron Powder Systems, Summit, NJ; *Int'l*, pg. 636
Scott, Deborah, Dir.-Mktg.--Hosokawa Micron International Inc., New York, NY; *Int'l*, pg. 635
Scott, Elaine, Dir.-Mktg. & Adv.--Henry I. Siegel Company, Inc., New York, NY; *U.S. Private*, pg. 998
Scott, Gary A., Dir.-Mktg.--Golden Valley Microwave Foods, Inc., Edina, MN; *U.S. Public*, pg. 427
Scott, Harry, V.P.-Sls.--Mayer Myers Paper Company, Memphis, TN; *U.S. Private*, pg. 718
Scott, Heather, Mgr.-Mktg. Services--Temco Fireplace Products, Inc., Nashville, TN; *U.S. Public*, pg. 1576
Scott, James A., Mgr.-Mktg.--Alkota Cleaning Systems, Inc., Alcester, SD; *U.S. Private*, pg. 34
Scott, Jeffrey, V.P.-Mktg.--Crown Holdings, Inc., Roseville, MN; *U.S. Private*, pg. 293
Scott, John, Dir.-Mktg. & Communication--Allsteel, Inc., Aurora, IL; *U.S. Public*, pg. 772
Scott, John B., Grp. V.P.-Corp. Mktg. & Research & Devel.--Andrew Corporation, Orland Park, IL; *U.S. Public*, pg. 112
Scott, Kathy, Mktg. Asst.--Great Plains Companies, Inc., Roseville, MN; *U.S. Private*, pg. 475
Scott, Mary Jo, Dir.-Retail Sls.--See's Candy Shops, Inc., South San Francisco, CA; *U.S. Public*, pg. 221
Scott, Michel E., V.P.-Mktg. & Bus. Devel.--Numac Energy Inc., Calgary, Canada; *Int'l*, pg. 990
Scott, Mike, V.P.-Mktg.--Alabama Power Co., Birmingham, AL; *U.S. Public*, pg. 1489
Scott, Newton, Dir.-Mktg. & Sls.--Scottish Widows' Fund & Life Assurance Society, Edinburgh, United Kingdom; *Int'l, pg. 1212*
Scott, Paul, V.P.-Sls. & Mktg.--Richtex Corporation, Columbia, SC; *Int'l*, pg. 699
Scott, Robert, V.P.-Mktg.--Smith & Wesson Corp., Springfield, MA; *Int'l*, pg. 1397
Scott, Robert L., V.P.-Sls. & Mktg.--Cosmo Communications Corporation, Miami, FL; *U.S. Public*, pg. 451
Scott, Rodney, Dir.-Sls.--April Hill, Inc., Grand Rapids, MI; *U.S. Private*, pg. 483
Scott, Ronald D., Mgr.-Sls.--McDonald Equipment Co., Willoughby, OH; *U.S. Private*, pg. 721
Scott, Sherilyn, Dir.-Mktg.--Datasouth Computer Corporation, Charlotte, NC; *U.S. Public*, pg. 267
Scott, Sue, Dir.-Mktg.--Medeva Pharmaceuticals, Rochester, NY; *Int'l*, pg. 852
Scott, Wilbur L., V.P.-Mktg. Svcs./Ryder Public Transportation Svcs.--Ryder System, Inc., Miami, FL; *U.S. Public*, pg. 1413
Scotti, M., Mgr.-Mktg.--Solplant, Milan, Italy; *Int'l*, pg. 1524
Scovel, Edward, V.P.-Mktg.--Lightalarms Electronics Corporation, Baldwin, NY; *Int'l*, pg. 725
Scowsill, D., Sr. V.P.-Sls. & Mktg.--Hilton International Co., Coral Gables, FL; *Int'l*, pg. 787
Scudder, Bob, Prod. Mgr.--Martin Reels, A Division of Zebco, Tulsa, OK; *U.S. Public*, pg. 265
Scuderi, Sue, Mktg. Asst.--Ford, Bacon & Davis Companies Inc., Duluth, GA; *Int'l*, pg. 401
Sculfort, Ray, Sr. V.P.-Mktg.--Better Homes and Gardens Real Estate Service, Des Moines, IA; *U.S. Public*, pg. 1094
Scully, David, Dir.-Retail--Be-Lo Markets Inc., Norfolk, VA; *U.S. Private*, pg. 203
Scully, Edward, Dir.-Mktg.--Paisano Publications, Inc., Agoura, CA; *U.S. Private*, pg. 834
Sczcepaniak, Joe, V.P.-Sls. & Mktg./North America--Software Publishing Corporation, Fairfield, NJ; *U.S. Public*, pg. 1483
Seaglione, Jules, Mgr.-Mktg.--Arrow Fluid Power, Broadview, IL; *U.S. Private*, pg. 85
Seale, Donald W., V.P.-Mdse. Mktg.--Norfolk Southern Corporation, Norfolk, VA; *U.S. Public*, pg. 1190
Seals, Lindsay C., Sr. V.P.-Mktg., Insurance--United Companies Financial Corporation, Baton Rouge, LA; *U.S. Public*, pg. 1675
Searight, Bruce, Mgr.-Mktg., Sls. & Adv.--Energy Systems Industries, Inc., Boston, MA; *U.S. Private*, pg. 376
Searl, Craig A., Dir.-Mktg. & Adv.--Bee Line Company, Bettendorf, IA; *U.S. Private*, pg. 129
Searle, Gregg A., V.P.-U.S. Sls. & Mktg.--InterBold, Canton, OH; *U.S. Public*, pg. 506
Searle, Heather, V.P.-Mktg.--Michael Foods, Inc., Minneapolis, MN; *U.S. Public*, pg. 1103
Sears, Ed, Dir.-Mktg.--The Long & Foster Companies, Inc., Fairfax, VA; *U.S. Private*, pg. 674
Seaver, James M., Exec. V.P.-Sls. & Mktg. Grp.--AGCO Corporation, Duluth, GA; *U.S. Public*, pg. 28
Seaver, Peter R., V.P.-Healthcare Policy & Professional Rels.--Pharmacia & Upjohn, Kalamazoo, MI; *Int'l*, pg. 1048
Seawell, William L., II, Sr. V.P.-Ordinary Mktg.--Jefferson-Pilot Life Insurance Co., Greensboro, NC; *U.S. Public*, pg. 926
Seay, Steve, V.P.-Mktg.--InterBio Inc., Woodlands, TX; *U.S. Private*, pg. 566
Sebastian, Felix, V.P.-Mktg. & Sls.--Megapulse, Inc., Bedford, MA; *U.S. Private*, pg. 729
Sebastiao, A. Buddy, Mgr.-Mktg. & Intl. Sls.--Centrifugal & Mechanical Industries, Saint Louis, MO; *U.S. Private*, pg. 370
Sechrist, Mary, Dir.-Mktg. & Adv.--Alba-Waldensian, Inc., Valdese, NC; *U.S. Public*, pg. 35
Secrest, Mary, V.P.-Mktg.--Consumer Products Div., Valdese, NC; *U.S. Public*, pg. 36
Sedberry, Steven R., V.P.-Sls. & Mktg.--Century Aluminum Company, Monterey, CA; *U.S. Public*, pg. 328
Sedder, Shirley, Dir.-Mktg., Sec., Treas.--Andy's Restaurants Inc., Little Rock, AR; *U.S. Private*, pg. 74
Seddon, Thomas L., V.P.-Mktg. & Special Projects--Archway Cookies, Inc., Battle Creek, MI; *U.S. Private*, pg. 80
Seddon, Tom, V.P.-Mktg., Holiday Inn Express--Holiday Inn Worldwide, Atlanta, GA; *Int'l*, pg. 170
See, Gary H., Grp. V.P.-Mktg.--International Dairy Queen, Inc., Minneapolis, MN; *U.S. Public*, pg. 220
Seeburger, Stacy, Dir.-Mktg.--Jacmar Companies, Inc., Alhambra, CA; *U.S. Private*, pg. 580
Seeger, David, V.P.-Sls. & Mktg.--Welded Tube, Chicago, IL; *Int'l*, pg. 101
Seelbach, William H., Dir.-Mktg.--Cardinal Aluminum Co., Louisville, KY; *U.S. Private*, pg. 208
Seeliger, Michael, V.P.-Investor Rels. & Corp. Rels.--Horizon/CMS Healthcare Corporation, Albuquerque, NM; *U.S. Public*, pg. 836
Seely, Blaine, V.P.-Mktg. Svcs.--North American Van Lines, Inc., Fort Wayne, IN; *U.S. Public*, pg. 1191
Seffren, Randy, V.P.-Mktg.--D.P. Fitness, Opelika, AL; *U.S. Public*, pg. 1354
Seger, Charles F., III, V.P.-Sls. & Mktg. & Sec.--Dennis Chemical Co., Inc., Saint Louis, MO; *U.S. Private*, pg. 324
Seibert, Dane, Sr. V.P.-Sls. & Mktg.--Glacier Water Services Inc., Carlsbad, CA; *U.S. Public*, pg. 745
Seidel, Bill, Dir.-Mktg.--Justin Industries, Inc., Fort Worth, TX; *U.S. Public*, pg. 936
Seidl, Robert, Dir.-Mktg.--Solo Cup Company, Highland Park, IL; *U.S. Private*, pg. 1013
Seif, Richard, V.P.-Mktg.--The Lincoln Electric Company, Cleveland, OH; *U.S. Public*, pg. 996
Seigler, Dana, Mktg. Asst.--Intervet America, Inc., Millsboro, DE; *Int'l*, pg. 48
Seinfeld, Robert, V.P.-Bus. Devel.--Astronautics Corporation of America, Milwaukee, WI; *U.S. Private*, pg. 93
Seitz, Mark, Mgr.-Sls., Mktg., Adv. & Pub. Rels.--Service Supply Co. Inc. of Indiana, Indianapolis, IN; *U.S. Private*, pg. 987
Seitz, Thomas, Dir.-Sls. & Mktg.--MPS Corporation, Pittsburgh, PA; *U.S. Private*, pg. 687
Sejonds, George, Dir.-Mktg. & Bus. Plng.--Compagnie des Machines Bull, Louveciennes, France; *Int'l*, pg. 315
Sekaran, M.C., Mgr.-Mktg. Opers.--Mobil Oil Singapore Pte. Ltd., Singapore, Singapore; *U.S. Public*, pg. 1119
Selby, David, V.P.-Mktg. Svcs.--Sears, Roebuck and Co., Hoffman Estates, IL; *U.S. Public*, pg. 1452
Seldin, James, Pres.--Miss Elaine Inc., Saint Louis, MO; *U.S. Private*, pg. 752
Self, Linda, Dir.-Mktg.--Litton Systems, Inc. Advanced Circuitry Div., Springfield, MO; *U.S. Public*, pg. 1003
Self, Terri, Mktg. Coordinator--Alco Chemical, Chattanooga, TN; *Int'l*, pg. 1435
Selig, Cindy, Coord.-Mktg.--Super Sky Products, Inc., Mequon, WI; *U.S. Private*, pg. 1054
Selig, Phil A., Mgr.-Mktg. Svcs.--American Cast Iron Pipe Co., Birmingham, AL; *U.S. Private*, pg. 51
Sell, Madeline, V.P.-Adv. & Mktg. Support--Sanwa Bank California, Los Angeles, CA; *Int'l*, pg. 1189
Selleck, Michael, V.P.-Mktg.--Simon & Schuster, New York, NY; *U.S. Private*, pg. 777
Sellers, Dan, V.P.-Mktg.--QUALCOMM, San Diego, CA; *U.S. Public*, pg. 1348
Sellers, Gerald, V.P.-Mktg.--Shapell Industries, Inc., Beverly Hills, CA; *U.S. Private*, pg. 990
Sellers, Richard W., V.P.-Mktg.--SPS Aerospace Products Div., Jenkintown, PA; *U.S. Public*, pg. 1420
Sellers, William, Dir.-Mktg.--Mohawk Paper Mills, Inc., Cohoes, NY; *U.S. Private*, pg. 755
Sellwood, Peter, Reg. Dir.-Sls. & Mktg.--Willis Corroon South Limited, Maidstone, United Kingdom; *Int'l*, pg. 1503
Selsor, Jill, Mgr.-Distributor Rels.--Hobart Brothers Co., Troy, OH; *U.S. Public*, pg. 866
Selzler, James, Mgr.-Sls. & Mktg.--McAnally Enterprises, Inc., Yucaipa, CA; *U.S. Private*, pg. 718
Semen, Barbara, V.P.-Mktg.--Fabri-Centers of America, Inc., Hudson, OH; *U.S. Public*, pg. 609
Sementilli, Don, Mgr.-Mktg. Communications--O-Z/Gedney Co., Farmington, CT; *U.S. Public*, pg. 727
Semler, David, Dir.-Mktg.--McGraw-Hill Financial Information Services Group, New York, NY; *U.S. Public*, pg. 1071
Semmelhack, Gene, V.P.-Mktg.--Nightingale-Conant Corp., Niles, IL; *U.S. Private*, pg. 799
Senecal, Linda, V.P.-Mktg.--Sunrise Healthcare Corporation, Newton, MA; *U.S. Public*, pg. 1531
Senechal, Pascal, V.P. & Gen. Mgr.-Military Engines--SNECMA - Societe Nationale d'Etude et de Construction de Moteurs d'Aviation, Paris, France; *Int'l*, pg. 1165
Sener, Walt, Dir.-Sls. & Mktg.--The Crown Divisions, Wooster, OH; *U.S. Public*, pg. 1631
Seng, Leong Kwok, Gen. Mgr.--International Factors (Singapore) Ltd., Singapore, Singapore; *Int'l*, pg. 684
Senkbell, Robert C., V.P.-Mktg.--Eclipse Manufacturing Company, Sheboygan, WI; *U.S. Private*, pg. 361
Sens, Sharon, Dir.-Mktg. Svcs.--Norcraft Companies, Inc., Saint Paul, MN; *U.S. Private*, pg. 801
Sepancy, Jean-Maire, V.P. & Integrated Mktg. Dir.--Korey, Kay & Partners, New York, NY; *U.S. Private*, pg. 632
Sera, L.J., Mktg. Communications Specialist--Solar Turbines Incorporated, San Diego, CA; *U.S. Public*, pg. 316
Serafin, Daniel, V.P.-Sls. & Mktg.--Wolverine Gasket & Manufacturing Co., Inkster, MI; *U.S. Private*, pg. 355
Serafini, Randy, Dir.-Mktg. Commun.--Zitel Corporation, Fremont, CA; *U.S. Public*, pg. 1793
Sernoff, Elizabeth, Coord.-Mktg.--MasterCard International-Cirrus Brand, Purchase, NY; *U.S. Private*, pg. 714
Serracini, Carlo, Dir.-Mktg.--Electrolux San Jose, Pordenone, Italy; *Int'l*, pg. 442
Seshan, N.V., Mgr.-Mktg.--Tata McGraw-Hill Publishing Co., Private Limited, New Delhi, India; *U.S. Public*, pg. 1072
Sessler, Mark, V.P.-Mktg.--The Rival Company, Kansas City, MO; *U.S. Public*, pg. 1391
Sessler, Mark, V.P.-Mktg.--Pollenex, Kansas City, MO; *U.S. Public*, pg. 1391
Sessman, Bernie, Sr. V.P.-Sls. & Mktg.--L&R Manufacturing Co., Kearny, NJ; *U.S. Private*, pg. 638
Sessoms, Glenn D., V.P.-Retail Mktg. & Opers.--FDX Corporation, Memphis, TN; *U.S. Public*, pg. 603
Setian, Rick, V.P.-Sls. & Mktg.--Isolyser Company, Inc., Norcross, GA; *U.S. Public*, pg. 914
Setta, Salli, Dir.-Field Mktg.--Olive Garden Italian Restaurants, Orlando, FL; *U.S. Public*, pg. 484
Setubal, Alfredo Egydio, Exec. Dir.-Capital Mkt.--Banco Itau S.A., Sao Paulo, Brazil; *Int'l*, pg. 142
Sevde, Clem W., V.P. & Dir.-Consumer Mktg.--Meredith Corporation, Des Moines, IA; *U.S. Public*, pg. 1094
Severen, Randy, V.P.-Mktg.--Konami Corporation of America Inc., Buffalo Grove, IL; *Int'l*, pg. 746
Severence, Mark, Dir.-Mktg. & Mkt. Res.--Horner Rausch Optical Company East, Inc., Nashville, TN; *U.S. Private*, pg. 540
Severn, Gene, Prod. Mgr.-Mktg.--Executone Information Systems, Inc., Milford, CT; *U.S. Public*, pg. 599
Sewell, Robert, V.P.-Mktg. & Sls.--Telephonics Command Systems Div., Farmingdale, NY; *U.S. Public*, pg. 558
Sexton, Rod, Exec. V.P.-Mktg.--ICEE-USA Corp., Ontario, CA; *U.S. Public*, pg. 916
Seyk, George, Mgr.-Sls.--Littelfuse, Inc., Des Plaines, IL; *U.S. Public*, pg. 1001
Seymour, Mark, Mgr.-Mktg.--Powermatic, McMinnville, TN; *U.S. Public*, pg. 502
Seymour, Michael, Dir.-Mktg. & Admin. Svcs.--Production Management Companies, Inc., Harvey, LA; *U.S. Private*, pg. 888
Sgno, Sam, Mgr.-Mktg.--ACCO Canada Inc., Willowdale, Canada; *U.S. Public*, pg. 674
Shadbolt, T., V.P.-Mktg.--Jay-El Products, Inc., Carson, CA; *U.S. Public*, pg. 534
Shade, Robert, Jr., Pres.--Sierra Coating Technologies, De Pere, WI; *U.S. Private*, pg. 998
Shadgett, Alan, Mgr.-Communication Services--Cegelec AEG Automation Systems Corp., Canonsburg, PA; *Int'l*, pg. 52
Shadrach, William S., III, Dir.-Mktg.--Martin Industries, Inc. (AL), Florence, AL; *U.S. Private*, pg. 709
Shaeffer, Richard A., V.P.-Mktg.--Cereal Partners Worldwide, Morges, Switzerland; *U.S. Public*, pg. 718
Shaeffer, Richard A., V.P.-Mktg.--Cereal Partners Worldwide, Morges, Switzerland; *Int'l*, pg. 916
Shafer, Alice, V.P.-Corp. Mktg.--Alimed, Inc., Dedham, MA; *U.S. Private*, pg. 34
Shaffer, Adam, Sr. V.P.-Prod. & Mktg.--Micro Warehouse, Inc., Norwalk, CT; *U.S. Public*, pg. 1104
Shaheen, Gerald L., V.P.-Engine Mktg. & Admin.--Caterpillar Inc., Peoria, IL; *U.S. Public*, pg. 315
Shahidi, Majid, Mgr.-Mktg. & Promo.--Pratt & Whitney Canada Inc., Longueuil, Canada; *U.S. Public*, pg. 1690
Shakespear, George, V.P.-Corp. Mktg. Communications & Adv.--J.P. Morgan Co. Incorporated, New York, NY; *U.S.* Public, pg. 1129
Shallcross, Deanne, V.P.-Mktg.--Teachers Insurance and Annuity Association, New York, NY; *U.S. Private*, pg. 1071
Shalvoy, James J., V.P.-Sls. & Mktg.-Siding Div.--ABT Building Products Corporation, Neenah, WI; *Int'l*, pg. 20
Shamaly, John, V.P.-Mktg. & New Bus. Devel.--Silicon Valley Group, Inc., San Jose, CA; *U.S. Public*, pg. 1474
Shambora, Peter, V.P.-Mktg.--Mylex Corporation, Fremont, CA; *U.S. Public*, pg. 1143
Shamsey, John, Mgr.-Mktg.--Barnett International/PAREXEL, Media, PA; *U.S. Public*, pg. 1258
Shamyer, Bob, V.P. & Mktg. Services Dir.--Mintz & Hoke Inc., Avon, CT; *U.S. Private*, pg. 751
Shanes, Robert, Dir.-Mktg. & Sls.--Talk-A-Phone Co., Chicago, IL; *U.S. Private*, pg. 1067
Shanesy, Steve, V.P.-Mktg., Oscar Mayer Foods Corp.--Kraft Foods Inc., Glenview, IL; *U.S. Public*, pg. 1288
Shank, Meredith, Mgr.-Mktg. Communications--Novartis Seeds, Inc., Downers Grove, IL; *Int'l*, pg. 974
Shankar, Srinivasan, V.P.-Mktg., Turbine Systems--Sermatech Klock, Manchester, CT; *U.S. Public*, pg. 1570
Shanks, Bob, Sr. Dir.-Mktg.--Zenith Goldline Pharmaceuticals, Miami, FL; *U.S. Public*, pg. 915
Shannon, Barbara, Mgr.-Mktg.--The W.E. Bassett Company, Shelton, CT; *U.S. Private*, pg. 122
Shannon, Dave, Mng. Dir.-Sls. & Mktg.--Toyota Motor Distributors (Ireland) Ltd., Dublin, Ireland; *Int'l*, pg. 1413
Shannon, Mike, V.P.-Opers.--Truevision, Inc., Santa Clara, CA; *U.S. Public*, pg. 1642
Shannon, Steve, Gen. Mgr.-Mktg. Services--Oldsmobile Div. General Motors Corp., Lansing, MI; *U.S. Public*, pg. 720
Shapiro, Alan, V.P.-Mktg.--Jacques Moret, Inc., New York, NY; *U.S. Private*, pg. 580
Shapiro, Arthur, Exec. V.P.-Mktg.--Joseph E. Seagram & Sons, Inc., New York, NY; *Int'l*, pg. 1215
Shapiro, Arthur, Exec. V.P.-Mktg.--Seagram Chateau & Estate Wines Co., New York, NY; *Int'l*, pg. 1215
Shapiro, Arthur, Exec. V.P.- Mktg.--The House of Seagram, New York, NY; *Int'l*, pg. 1217
Shapiro, Dan, Sr. V.P.-Mktg.--George Weston Limited, Toronto, Canada; *Int'l*, pg. 1494
Shapiro, I. Joseph, V.P.-Sls. & Mktg.--ECI Telecom Ltd., Petah Tiqwa, Israel; *Int'l*, pg. 643
Shapiro, Karen, V.P.-Mktg. & Pub. Rels. Dir.--Hill, Holliday/Altschiller, New York, NY; *U.S. Private*, pg. 529
Shapiro, L.R., Dir.-Sls. & Mktg.--Union Camp Folding Carton Div., Clifton, NJ; *U.S. Public*, pg. 1666

Shapiro, Marc, V.P.-Mktg.--The Wackenhut Corporation, Palm Beach Gardens, FL; *U.S. Public*, pg. 1731

Shapiro, Marty, Mgr.-Mktg.--Drug Guild Div., Secaucus, NJ; *U.S. Public*, pg. 1169

Shapiro, Reid, Mgr.-Kid's Mktg.--L.A. Gear, Inc., Santa Monica, CA; *U.S. Public*, pg. 969

Sharkey, William, Sr. V.P.-Mktg.--CNA Insurance Companies, Chicago, IL; *U.S. Public*, pg. 1010

Sharkey, William H., Jr., Sr. V.P. & Chief Mktg. Officer--Continental Assurance Company, Chicago, IL; *U.S. Private*, pg. 267

Sharma, Rakesh, Dir.-Mktg.--Ultra Electronics Sonar & Communications Systems, Greenford, United Kingdom; *Int'l*, pg. 1431

Sharp, Carolyn L., Dir.-Mktg.--Virginia Metal Industries, Inc., Orange, VA; *U.S. Private*, pg. 1141

Sharp, David, Dir.-Intl. Mktg.--Ederer Inc., Seattle, WA; *U.S. Private*, pg. 363

Sharp, Tim, Dir.-Corp. Communications--BICC plc, London, United Kingdom; *Int'l*, pg. 120

Sharpe, George, V.P.-New Prod. Devel. & Dir.-Mktg. Res./ Window Fashions Div.--Hunter Douglas, Inc., Upper Saddle River, NJ; *Int'l*, pg. 639

Sharpe, Jean, Mgr.-Mktg.--BASF Corporation Fiber Products Division, Charlotte, NC; *Int'l*, pg. 105

Sharpe, Louis K., Chm. Bd. & Pres.--Sharpe Dry Goods Co., Inc., Checotah, OK; *U.S. Private*, pg. 990

Sharples, Jennifer, Mktg. Writer--Instron Corporation, Canton, MA; *U.S. Public*, pg. 882

Sharples, Richard J., V.P.-Mktg.--Anadarko Petroleum Corporation, Houston, TX; *U.S. Public*, pg. 107

Shattgen, C.F., V.P.-Sls. & Mktg.--Specialty Products and Insulation Company, Lancaster, PA; *U.S. Public*, pg. 913

Shattuck, James A., Exec. V.P.-Mktg. & Sls.--Union Pacific Railroad Company, Omaha, NE; *U.S. Public*, pg. 1668

Shattuck, Jim, V.P.-Mktg. & Sls.--Southern Pacific Rail Corporation, San Francisco, CA; *U.S. Public*, pg. 1668

Shaughnessy, James, Asst. V.P.-Mktg., Sls. & Retail Bus.--Wyeth-Ayerst Laboratories, Inc., Philadelphia, PA; *U.S. Public*, pg. 80

Shaw, Christine, Mktg. Coord.--FTD, Inc./Florists Transworld Delivery, Inc., Downers Grove, IL; *U.S. Private*, pg. 389

Shaw, Doug, V.P.-Wines & Treas.--M.S. Walker, Inc., Somerville, MA; *U.S. Private*, pg. 1147

Shaw, Ed, Dir.-Mktg.--Condor Pacific Industries, Inc., Westlake Village, CA; *U.S. Private*, pg. 262

Shaw, John, V.P.-Mktg.--Summa Four, Inc., Manchester, NH; *U.S. Public*, pg. 1527

Shaw, Kim, Mktg. & Analysis Dept.--Capital One Financial Corporation, Falls Church, VA; *U.S. Public*, pg. 302

Shaw, Mark, V.P.-Commercial Aircraft Mktg.--Transportation Equipment Corporation, San Francisco, CA; *U.S. Public*, pg. 1241

Shaw, Michael S., V.P.-Sls. & Mktg.--Peabody COALSALES Company, Saint Louis, MO; *Int'l*, pg. 594

Shaw, Nat, Mgr.-Mktg.--Pioneer/Eclipse Corp., Sparta, NC; *Int'l*, pg. 71

Shaw, Robbie, V.P.-Mktg. & Customer Service--Nova Scotia Power Inc., Halifax, Canada; *Int'l*, pg. 971

Shaw, Ronald K., Dir.-Adv. & Mktg.--Pinnacle Bank, Jasper, AL; *U.S. Public*, pg. 1297

Shaw, Steve, Dir.- Mktg.--Cincom Systems, Inc., Cincinnati, OH; *U.S. Private*, pg. 240

Shaw, Terry, Dir.-Mktg.--Acrison, Inc., Moonachie, NJ; *U.S. Private*, pg. 14

Shawe, Larry, V.P.-Sls. & Mktg.--Engle Homes, Inc., Boca Raton, FL; *U.S. Public*, pg. 583

Shawver, Todd A., V.P.-Sls. & Mktg.--Union Pump Company, Battle Creek, MI; *U.S. Private*, pg. 1119

Shay, Michael A., V.P.-Sls. & Mktg.--Hauck Mfg. Co., Cleona, PA; *U.S. Private*, pg. 510

Shea, Chip, Corp. Dir.-Adv.--Hunter Marine Corporation, Alachua, FL; *U.S. Private*, pg. 549

Shea, Chip, Dir.-Mktg.--Luhrs Corporation, Saint Augustine, FL; *U.S. Private*, pg. 680

Shea, Chip, Dir.-Mktg.--Mainship Corporation, Saint Augustine, FL; *U.S. Private*, pg. 697

Shea, Chip, Dir.-Corp. Mktg.--Silverton Marine Corporation, Millville, NJ; *U.S. Private*, pg. 1000

Shea, Christopher M., V.P.-Mktg.--Busch Entertainment Corp., Clayton, MO; *U.S. Public*, pg. 114

Shea, Fred, Dir.-Midwest Div. Sls. & Mktg.--Hyatt Hotels Corporation, Chicago, IL; *U.S. Private*, pg. 551

Shea, Michael, Sr. V.P.-Sls. & Mktg.--Daw Technologies, Inc., Salt Lake City, UT; *U.S. Public*, pg. 489

Shea, William H., Jr., Exec. V.P.--Buckeye Partners, L.P., Allentown, PA; *U.S. Public*, pg. 266

Sheairs, Robert, Mgr.-Mktg.--Edmund Scientific Company, Barrington, NJ; *U.S. Private*, pg. 364

Shealy, Dennis G., V.P.-Bus. Devel.--McCrory Construction Co., Inc., Columbia, SC; *U.S. Private*, pg. 720

Shearer, Jeff, V.P.-Mktg.--Toronto Star Newspapers Ltd., Toronto, Canada; *Int'l*, pg. 1402

Shears, Tom, Mktg.-Sls.--Wilsey Foods, Inc., Fort Worth, TX; *Int'l*, pg. 879

Shearson, Greg, V.P.-Mktg.--Sara Lee Bakery, Chicago, IL; *U.S. Public*, pg. 1433

Shecter, Amy, V.P. & Gen. Mgr.-Mdsg. Kids Foot Locker--Foot Locker, New York, NY; *U.S. Public*, pg. 1777

Sheehan, Chris, V.P.-Mktg.--Labelon Corporation, Canandaigua, NY; *U.S. Private*, pg. 641

Sheehan, David, Dir.-Mktg.--The Dreyfus Corporation, New York, NY; *U.S. Public*, pg. 1085

Sheehan, Jack, V.P.-Sls. & Mktg.--Wagner Lighting Products, Chesterfield, MO; *U.S. Public*, pg. 442

Sheehan, Jack, V.P.-Sls. & Mktg.--Cooper Automotive Division, Chesterfield, MO; *U.S. Public*, pg. 443

Sheehan, Jack, V.P.-Mktg.--Joern's Sunrise Medical, Stevens Point, WI; *U.S. Public*, pg. 1536

Sheehy, JoAnne, Exec. Asst. V.P.-Mktg.--Guinness Import Company, Stamford, CT; *Int'l*, pg. 412

Sheetz, Randall A., Exec. V.P.-Mktg.--Sheetz, Inc., Altoona, PA; *U.S. Private*, pg. 991

Sheidemantel, Carrie, Dir.-Mktg.--Process Color Plate, Chicago, IL; *U.S. Public*, pg. 1437

Sheilds, David, Mgr.-Grp. Circulation--The National Magazine Company Ltd., London, United Kingdom; *U.S. Private*, pg. 518

Sheill, Dana, V.P.-Mktg.--Sasson Licensing Corp., New York, NY; *U.S. Private*, pg. 967

Sheldon, John, V.P.-Mktg.--Players International, Inc., Atlantic City, NJ; *U.S. Public*, pg. 1310

Shell, Susan, Dir.-Mktg.--Englewood Community Hospital, Inc., Englewood, FL; *U.S. Public*, pg. 404

Shelow, William J., Jr., Dir.-Mktg.--Harleysville Life Insurance Co., Harleysville, PA; *U.S. Public*, pg. 787

Shelton, Jack, Sr. V.P.-Mktg.--Fender Musical Instruments, Scottsdale, AZ; *U.S. Private*, pg. 400

Shemesh, Jacob, Exec. V.P.-Sls.--IIS Intelligent Information Systems Ltd., Yokneam, Israel; *Int'l*, pg. 645

Shenk, Michael, Dir.-Mktg.--Holiday RV Superstores of New Mexico Inc., Las Cruces, NM; *U.S. Public*, pg. 830

Shepherd, Becky, Dir.-Commercial Mktg.--Da-Lite Screen Company, Inc., Warsaw, IN; *U.S. Private*, pg. 306

Shepherd, Bill, Dir.-Mktg. & Sls. Promo.--Calumet Carton Company, South Holland, IL; *U.S. Private*, pg. 201

Shepherd, Doug, V.P.-Mktg. & Bus.--Gilmore Envelope Corp., Los Angeles, CA; *U.S. Private*, pg. 454

Shepherd, Jan, Mgr.-Mktg. Food Service Div.--Novartis Nutrition Corporation, Saint Louis Park, MN; *Int'l*, pg. 974

Shepherd, Malcolm H., Mgr.-Sls. & Mktg.--Arrow Gear Company, Downers Grove, IL; *U.S. Private*, pg. 85

Shepherd, Nick, Gen. Mgr.-Coffee & Food--Kraft Jacobs Suchard, Cheltenham, United Kingdom; *U.S. Public*, pg. 1290

Shepherd, Ted, Pres.--Archibald Candy Company, Chicago, IL; *U.S. Private*, pg. 597

Shepherdson, Don, Sr. Master Counselor-Adv.--Ace Novelty Company, Inc., Woodinville, WA; *U.S. Public*, pg. 1309

Sheppard, S., Mgr.-Mktg.--The Sharper Image, San Francisco, CA; *U.S. Public*, pg. 1464

Sher, M., Mgr.-Mktg.-Laundry & Hard Surface--Kiwi Brands Pty. Ltd., Clayton, Australia; *U.S. Public*, pg. 1434

Sheridan, Gary, Dir.-Mktg.--Trumpf Inc., Farmington, CT; *U.S. Private*, pg. 1108

Sheridan, Rosemary, Asst. Exec. Dir.-Mktg. & Commun.--NJ Transit, Newark, NJ; *U.S. Private*, pg. 794

Sheriff, Karen, Dir.-Corp. Mktg. & Branding--Ameritech Corporation, Chicago, IL; *U.S. Public*, pg. 97

Sheriff, Karen, Dir.-Corp. Mktg. & Branding--Ameritech Corp., Chicago, IL; *U.S. Public*, pg. 98

Sherliker, Lorraine, Mgr.-Mktg. & Adv.--Camden Motors Ltd., Leighton Buzzard, United Kingdom; *Int'l*, pg. 165

Sherlock, Mike, Sr. V.P. & Gen. Mgr.--Gitano Fashions Ltd., Bowling Green, KY; *U.S. Public*, pg. 686

Sherman, Bill, Sr. V.P.-Institutional Prod.--Riddell Sports, Inc., New York, NY; *U.S. Public*, pg. 1389

Sherman, Cary, Mgr.-Mktg.--Fraser Papers, Inc., Stamford, CT; *Int'l*, pg. 434

Sherman, Cheryl, V.P.-Mktg.--IL USA, Inc., Stratford, CT; *U.S. Public*, pg. 856

Sherman, Dale A., V.P.-Mktg.--Walbar Turbine Components Division, Peabody, MA; *U.S. Public*, pg. 402

Sherman, Earl, Sr. V.P.-Bus. Devel.--Aerovox Inc., New Bedford, MA; *U.S. Public*, pg. 25

Sherman, Leigh I., Sr. V.P.-Mktg.--Old Kent Financial Corporation, Grand Rapids, MI; *U.S. Public*, pg. 1216

Sherman, Nancy, V.P.-Mktg.--Clarion Corporation of America, Gardena, CA; *Int'l*, pg. 296

Sherman, Natalie, Mgr.-Mktg.--Grindmaster Corporation, Louisville, KY; *U.S. Private*, pg. 482

Sherman, R.J., Gen. Dir.-Sls. & Mktg., U.S.--Service Parts Operations, Flint, MI; *U.S. Public*, pg. 720

Sherman, Thomas M., V.P.-Mktg.--Michigan Gas Company, Three Rivers, MI; *U.S. Public*, pg. 1489

Sherman, Tom, V.P.-Sls & Mktg.--Sunnyland Inc., Thomasville, GA; *U.S. Public*, pg. 1479

Sherman, Vikki, Dir.-Mktg.--Brim, Inc., Portland, OR; *U.S. Private*, pg. 168

Sherod, Steve, Mgr.-Sls. & Promo.--Andersen Corporation, Bayport, MN; *U.S. Private*, pg. 71

Sherwood, Judy, V.P.-Mktg.--Anoka Electric Cooperative, Ramsey, MN; *U.S. Private*, pg. 75

Sheske, Jan, Mgr.-Adv. & Mktg. Devel.--Outboard Marine Corporation, Waukegan, IL; *U.S. Private*, pg. 478

Sheth, Arun, Dir.-Intl. Sls. & Mktg.--KineticSystems Corporation, Lockport, IL; *U.S. Private*, pg. 620

Shewmaker, Steve, Dir.-Mktg.--Revenue Collection Group, San Diego, CA; *U.S. Public*, pg. 466

Shewmaker, Steve O., V.P.-Mktg.--Revenue Collection Group World Headquarters, San Diego, CA; *U.S. Public*, pg. 466

Sheya, James P., V.P.-Mktg.--Masland, Carlisle, PA; *U.S. Public*, pg. 981

Shield, Hank, Dir.-Buying & Mktg.--Associated Grocers of the South, Inc., Birmingham, AL; *U.S. Private*, pg. 91

Shields, Kevin J., V.P.-Mktg.--American Travellers Corporation, Bensalem, PA; *U.S. Public*, pg. 433

Shields, Kevin J., Dir.-Mktg.--American Travellers Life Insurance Company, Bensalem, PA; *U.S. Public*, pg. 433

Shields, Kevin J., Dir.-Mktg.--American Travellers Insurance Services, Bensalem, PA; *U.S. Public*, pg. 433

Shields, Kevin J., Dir.-Mktg.--United General Life Insurance, Bensalem, PA; *U.S. Public*, pg. 433

Shields, Nancy, V.P.-Mktg.--Astrex, Inc., Plainview, NY; *U.S. Public*, pg. 141

Shifflet, Fairy J., Mktg. Admin.--Na-Churs Plant Food Company, Marion, OH; *U.S. Private*, pg. 1096

Shigemura, Barton Y., V.P.-Mktg. & Services--Premisys Communications, Inc., Fremont, CA; *U.S. Public*, pg. 1323

Shikama, Yoji, V.P.-Mktg.--Mita Copystar America Inc., Fairfield, NJ; *Int'l*, pg. 870

Shiller, Linda, V.P.-Mktg., Sls. & Reservations--Imperial Hotels, El Segundo, CA; *U.S. Private*, pg. 558

Shiller, Linda, V.P.-Adv., Mktg. & Sls.--The Vagabond Inns, San Diego, CA; *U.S. Private*, pg. 558

Shimazaki, Kazuhiro, Exec. Dir.-Intl. Watch Mktg. & Mdsg.--Seiko Corporation, Tokyo, Japan; *Int'l*, pg. 1218

Shimazu, Hiro, Dir.-Mktg.--Kyowa Hakko U.S.A., Inc., New York, NY; *Int'l*, pg. 778

Shimizu, Yoko, Dir.-Mktg.--Clarins KK, Tokyo, Japan; *Int'l*, pg. 295

Shimmel, Hilli M., Mktg. & Communication Assoc.--Barber-Colman Company, Rockford, IL; *Int'l*, pg. 1242

Shimomura, Kei, Mgr.-Mktg. & Sls.--Japan Travel Bureau International, Inc., New York, NY; *U.S. Private*, pg. 582

Shiner, Donald, V.P.--Deluxe Homes Of PA., Inc., Berwick, PA; *U.S. Private*, pg. 323

Shingu, Michio, Dir.-New Product Plng. Div.--Rohto Pharmaceutical Co., Osaka, Japan; *Int'l*, pg. 1126

Shinnon, Fellina, Dir.-Mktg.--Philip Morris Limited, Moorabbin, Australia; *U.S. Public*, pg. 1290

Shinoda, Hiroshi, Sr. V.P.-Sls. & Mktg.--Pentel of America, Ltd., Torrance, CA; *Int'l*, pg. 1035

Shipe, Steve, Dir.-Mktg.--Liggett Group Inc., Durham, NC; *U.S. Public*, pg. 259

Shipley, L.C., V.P.-Mktg.--Coastal Lumber Company, Weldon, NC; *U.S. Private*, pg. 248

Shipley, Martina, Mktg. Coord.--Belvedere Company, Belvidere, IL; *U.S. Private*, pg. 1008

Shipley, Michael, Dir.-OTC Pur. & Mktg.--Neuman Distributors, Inc., Ridgefield, NJ; *U.S. Public*, pg. 1169

Shipp, Adrian, Dir.-Mktg.--Japan Airlines, Zurich, Switzerland; *Int'l*, pg. 700

Shipper, Aaron, V.P.-Mktg.--The Loewen Group, Inc., Burnaby, Canada; *Int'l*, pg. 814

Shirashi, Yasuji, Mgr.-Mktg. & Communicaitons--Kirin USA, Inc., New York, NY; *Int'l*, pg. 736

Shiraz, Asad, Dir.-Destination Mktg.--Singapore Tourist Promotion Board, Singapore, Singapore; *Int'l*, pg. 1253

Shirilla, John, Mgr.-Gen. Sls.--Photogenic Machine Company, Inc., Youngstown, OH; *U.S. Private*, pg. 864

Shirley, Dennis A., Sr. V.P. & Dir.-Mktg.--Great Western Financial Corporation, Chatsworth, CA; *U.S. Public*, pg. 1741

Shively, Terry, Dir.-Mktg.--Wix Div., Gastonia, NC; *U.S. Public*, pg. 479

Shiwanov, Ernest, Mgr.-Mktg. & Adv.--Turntec, Irvine, CA; *U.S. Private*, pg. 62

Shjefte, Paula, Dir.-PGP Marketing--Medtronic, Inc., Minneapolis, MN; *U.S. Public*, pg. 1082

Shockman, Robert, Dir.-Mktg.--Onan Corporation, Minneapolis, MN; *U.S. Public*, pg. 468

Shoe, Richard L., V.P.-Mktg. & Sls.--Carolina Biological Supply Co., Burlington, NC; *U.S. Private*, pg. 213

Shoemaker, Bruce, Mkt. Res.--U-Haul International, Inc., Phoenix, AZ; *U.S. Private*, pg. 49

Shoemaker, Jill, Mgr.-Base Brands Grp. Mktg.--Dreyer's Grand Ice Cream, Inc., Oakland, CA; *U.S. Public*, pg. 529

Shoen, Mark, Pres.-Mktg.--U-Haul International, Inc., Phoenix, AZ; *U.S. Private*, pg. 49

Shollenberger, Randy, Gen. Mgr.--Holiday RV Superstores, Inc.-Tampa, Tampa, FL; *U.S. Public*, pg. 830

Shomake, Beth, Mgr.-Corp. Communication--Reeves Southeastern Corporation, Tampa, FL; *U.S. Private*, pg. 916

Shone, Thomas, Dir.-Mktg.--The Cooper Companies, Inc., Irvine, CA; *U.S. Public*, pg. 442

Shook, Gregory R., Sr. V.P.-Admin. & Sec.--Branford Savings Bank, Branford, CT; *U.S. Public*, pg. 250

Shope, Lissa, Mgr.-Mktg. & Sls.--LINC Quantum Analytics, Foster City, CA; *U.S. Public*, pg. 996

Shore, Jeffrey, V.P.-Sls. & Mktg.--Kaufman and Broad Home Corporation, Los Angeles, CA; *U.S. Public*, pg. 944

Short, Bob, Sr. Dir.-Mktg.--C S K Auto Inc., Phoenix, AZ; *U.S. Private*, pg. 1108

Short, Brian, Dir.-Mktg.--Dayco Products Inc., Miamisburg, OH; *U.S. Public*, pg. 1045

Short, Dean, Mgr.-Sls. & Mktg./Laminated Beams & Decking--Boise Cascade Corporation, Boise, ID; *U.S. Public*, pg. 242

Short, R.G., V.P.-Mktg.--Wacker Silicones Corporation, Adrian, MI; *Int'l*, pg. 625

Shortal, T. Michael, V.P.-Mktg.--Kastle Systems LLC, Arlington, VA; *U.S. Private*, pg. 608

Shostack, John, Dir.-Brand Mktg.--Remco America, Inc., Wichita, KS; *Int'l*, pg. 1385

Shou, Wan, Reg. Mgr.-Mktg.--Motorola Singapore Pte., Ltd., Singapore, Singapore; *U.S. Public*, pg. 1140

Showers, Jacqui, Mgr.-Mktg. & Pub. Rels.--National Electrical Manufacturers Association, Arlington, VA; *U.S. Private*, pg. 782

Showich, Nick, V.P. & Dir.-Mktg.--Seton Company, Norristown, PA; *U.S. Private*, pg. 987

Showlater, Rick, Dir.-Mktg. & sls.--The Van Metres Companies, Burke, VA; *U.S. Private*, pg. 1132

Shrader, Charles, V.P.-Mktg.--Berg Electronics, Saint Louis, MO; *U.S. Public*, pg. 212

Shrigley, David A., Exec. V.P.-Sls., Service & Mktg.--Bay Networks, Inc., Santa Clara, CA; *U.S. Public*, pg. 196

Shriver, Debra, Sr. V.P.-Mktg. Communications--Hearst Magazines Division, New York, NY; *U.S. Private*, pg. 516

Shubat, Tom, Mgr.-Mktg.--Superior Linkage Division, New Haven, IN; *U.S. Private*, pg. 1111

Shuck, Michael, Pres.--Overholtzer Church Furniture, Inc., Modesto, CA; *U.S. Private*, pg. 823

Shuff, Bonnie, Mgr.-Mktg. Programs--AP North American Aftermarket Division, Goldsboro, NC; *U.S. Private*, pg. 230

Shugart, James, Dir.-Mktg.--Petroleum Helicopters, Inc., Metairie, LA; *U.S. Public*, pg. 1281

Shui, San Shang, Mgr.-Mktg.--DBS Computer Services Pte. Ltd., Singapore, Singapore; *Int'l*, pg. 350

Shull, Dennis, V.P.-Mktg.--Gardner Denver Machinery Inc., Quincy, IL; *U.S. Public*, pg. 703

Shultis, Beth, Dir.-Passenger Mktg.--Northwest Airlines, Inc., Saint Paul, MN; *U.S. Public*, pg. 1200

Shultis, Beth, V.P.-Mktg.--MLT Vacations, Inc., Minnetonka, MN; *U.S. Public*, pg. 1200
Shumway, Howard E., Mgr.-Mktg. Services--Shepard Niles, Inc., Montour Falls, NY; *U.S. Private*, pg. 992
Shusterman, Dan, Dir.-Mktg. & Adv.--Superior Industries International, Inc., Van Nuys, CA; *U.S. Public*, pg. 1539
Shutt, Buffy, Pres.-Mktg.--Universal Pictures, Universal City, CA; *Int'l*, pg. 1216
Shutty, Karen, Mgr.-Mktg.--The Popcorn Factory, Lake Forest, IL; *U.S. Private*, pg. 421
Sibbick, Bill, Sr. V.P.-Sls.--Stanley Furniture Co. Inc., Stanleytown, VA; *U.S. Public*, pg. 1508
Sick, Wilson W., 111, Exec. V.P.-Bus. Devel. & Mktg.--Cambridge Industries Inc., Madison Heights, MI; *U.S. Private*, pg. 202
Sickles, Paul, Mgr.-Mktg.--Nashua Corporation, Nashua, NH; *U.S. Public*, pg. 1152
Sidebottom, Kevin, Mgr.-Mktg.--Cerner Arabia Ltd., Riyadh, Saudi Arabia; *U.S. Public*, pg. 331
Sidman, Ken, V.P.-Mktg.--Norton Performance Plastics, Wayne, NJ; *Int'l*, pg. 1174
Sido, John, Mgr.-Prod. Mktg.-Crawlers, Loaders & Trucks--Komatsu America International Company, Vernon Hills, IL; *Int'l*, pg. 744
Sidwell, Bill, Dir.-Mktg.--Hutch Sports USA, Inc., Hebron, KY; *U.S. Public*, pg. 1354
Siebens, Chris, Mgr.-Efficiency Programs--Jersey Central Power & Light Co., Morristown, NJ; *U.S. Public*, pg. 695
Siebert, Don, Dir.-Mktg. Research--Fruit of the Loom, Inc., Chicago, IL; *U.S. Public*, pg. 685
Siebrecht, Frank, V.P.-Client Mktg. Plng.--Bader Rutter & Assoc., Inc., Brookfield, WI; *U.S. Private*, pg. 110
Sieck, Ron, Dir.-Mktg.--Honeywell's Micro Switch Division, Freeport, IL; *U.S. Public*, pg. 834
Sieckman, Debra, V.P.-Sls. & Mktg.--National Van Lines, Inc., Broadview, IL; *U.S. Private*, pg. 788
Siegel, Cary, V.P.-Mktg.--Catalina Marketing Corporation, Saint Petersburg, FL; *U.S. Public*, pg. 314
Siegel, Fred, Sr. V.P.-Mktg.--QVC, Inc., West Chester, PA; *U.S. Private*, pg. 897
Siegel, Jeff, Exec. V.P.-Sls. & Mktg.--Lifetime Hoan Corp., Westbury, NY; *U.S. Public*, pg. 992
Siegert, Elfriede, Dir.-Mktg.--Henkel Austria Group, Vienna, Austria; *Int'l*, pg. 611
Siegman, Earl H., V.P.-Mktg.--South Jersey Gas Co., Folsom, NJ; *U.S. Public*, pg. 1488
Siemens, Mike, Mgr.-Customer Devel.--Camping World, Inc., Bowling Green, KY; *U.S. Private*, pg. 204
Sieracki, Ed, Dir.-Mktg.--J.J. Keller & Associates, Inc., Neenah, WI; *U.S. Private*, pg. 612
Siewert, Monica, Mgr.-Media & Mktg. Svcs.--Sacramento Municipal Utility District, Sacramento, CA; *U.S. Private*, pg. 959
Siewert, Patrick T., Chief Oper. Officer-Mktg. & Sls.--Eastman Kodak Company, Rochester, NY; *U.S. Public*, pg. 550
Siewertz, Liselotte, Mgr.-Mktg.--Spintab, Stockholm, Sweden; *Int'l*, pg. 1328
Sigler, Dwayne, V.P.-Mktg. & Creative Services--General Nutrition Centers, Pittsburgh, PA; *U.S. Public*, pg. 725
Sigmund, Rolf, Dir.-Selective Beauty--Selective Beauty International Div., Brussels, Belgium; *Int'l*, pg. 819
Signorelli, Pat, Dir.-Media--Hunt-Wesson, Inc., Fullerton, CA; *U.S. Public*, pg. 428
Sigvardt, Ole, V.P.-Sls. & Mktg.--Danfoss Fluid Power, Racine, WI; *Int'l*, pg. 377
Sikora, Mike, Mgr.-Mktg. & Sls.-Fluid Handling--Aro Fluid Products Division, Bryan, OH; *U.S. Public*, pg. 877
Sikorski, T.J., V.P.-Mktg.--Bradford-White Corporation, Ambler, PA; *U.S. Private*, pg. 164
Siladi, Joseph, Sr. Assoc.-New York City Mktg.--Cannon, Grand Island, NY; *U.S. Private*, pg. 205
Silberman, Joe, Mgr.-Mktg./Pub. Rels.--Baker & McKenzie, Attorneys At Law, Chicago, IL; *U.S. Private*, pg. 111
Silberman, Robert, Mgr.-Mktg.--The Pilot Pen Corp. of America, Trumbull, CT; *Int'l*, pg. 1057
Silberman, Steve V., Exec. V.P.--Framesi USA, Inc./Roffler Industries, Inc./Casa di Colore, Inc., Coraopolis, PA; *U.S. Private*, pg. 419
Silcox, James, V.P.-Mktg.--Lincoln Foodservice Products, Inc., Fort Wayne, IN; *Int'l*, pg. 188
Siler, Melvin, Dir.- Mktg.--Great Lakes Media, Inc., Pontiac, MI; *U.S. Public*, pg. 513
Sillers, Coby, Sr. V.P.-Sls. & Mktg.--Oki Telecom Group, Suwanee, GA; *Int'l*, pg. 1000
Silva, Geoffrey W., Dir.-Mktg. & Bus. Devel.--Principal Marques Meat Co., Etobicoke, Canada; *Int'l*, pg. 841
Silva, Ken, Dir.-Mktg.--PECO Energy Company, Philadelphia, PA; *U.S. Public*, pg. 1268
Silvani, Marco, Dir.-Mktg.--Banca Commerciale Italiana, Milan, Italy; *Int'l*, pg. 135
Silver, Bertram R., Pres.--Jenkins Spirits Corp. Ltd., Londonderry, NH; *U.S. Private*, pg. 585
Silver, Lawrence A., Sr. V.P.-Investor Rels.--Raymond James Financial, Inc., Saint Petersburg, FL; *U.S. Public*, pg. 923
Silver, Richard L., Chm. Bd. & Chief Fin. Officer--Akrochem Corporation, Akron, OH; *U.S. Private*, pg. 30
Silver, Robert, V.P.-Mktg.--American Country Insurance Co., Chicago, IL; *U.S. Private*, pg. 1030
Silver, Robert C., Sr. V.P. & Dir.-H.R.--Sierra West Bancorp, Truckee, CA; *U.S. Public*, pg. 1470
Silver, Sandy, Exec. V.P.-Global Mktg.--Simon Marketing, Inc., Oak Brook Terrace, IL; *U.S. Private*, pg. 1001
Silverberg, Michael, Sr. V.P.--Moyer Packing Company, Souderton, PA; *U.S. Private*, pg. 765
Silverhart, Gary, Mktg. Analyst--Therma-Tru Corp., Maumee, OH; *U.S. Private*, pg. 1079
Silverman, Mark F., Dir.-Mktg.--Caja de Madrid Group, Madrid, Spain; *Int'l*, pg. 251
Silvers, Jerry, V.P.-Mktg. Devel.--The Cincinnati Enquirer, Inc., Cincinnati, OH; *U.S. Public*, pg. 700
Silverstein, Jay, Chief Mktg. Officer & V.P.--Oxford Health Plans Inc., Norwalk, CT; *U.S. Public*, pg. 1238
Silverstein, Marc, Mgr.-Mktg.--Friendship Dairies, Inc., Jericho, NY; *U.S. Private*, pg. 429
Silvestri, Dan, Mgr.-Mktg.--Aldan Industries, Philadelphia, PA; *U.S. Private*, pg. 33
Silvestri, Greg, Mgr.-Mktg.--Mazda Motor of America, Inc. Gulf Region, Sugar Land, TX; *Int'l*, pg. 849
Silvire, Ricardo, Dir.-Sls. & Mktg.--Swedish Match do Brasil S/A, Rio de Janeiro, Brazil; *Int'l*, pg. 1328
Sim, Anthony, Gen. Mgr.-Mktg.--Singapore Land Limited, Singapore, Singapore; *Int'l*, pg. 1252
Sim, John H., V.P.-Mktg.-Pulp Grp.--Avenor, Inc., Montreal, Canada; *Int'l*, pg. 101
Simard, Maude, Dir.-Mktg.--Clairol Canada Inc., Montreal, Canada; *U.S. Public*, pg. 254
Simariut, Wichian, Mgr.-Bus.--Bangkok Athletic Co., Ltd., Bangkok, Thailand; *Int'l*, pg. 146
Simkins, Wayne, Mgr.-Mktg.--Babcock Lumber Company, Pittsburgh, PA; *U.S. Private*, pg. 108
Simmon, Jimmy, Dir.-Store Devel.--Affiliated Foods Southwest, Little Rock, AR; *U.S. Private*, pg. 26
Simmon, Rena, Dir.-Mktg.--Yogen Fruz Worldwide Inc., Markham, Canada; *Int'l*, pg. 1520
Simmons, Don, V.P.-Sls. & Mktg.--Mountain Valley Spring Company, Hot Springs National Park, AR; *U.S. Private*, pg. 963
Simmons, G. Tom, V.P.-Mktg.--Siliconix, Inc., Santa Clara, CA; *Int'l*, pg. 367
Simmons, J.K., Dir.-Mktg. & Sls.--Kemlite Company, Joliet, IL; *U.S. Public*, pg. 457
Simmons, Jack, Mgr.-Mktg.--The R.J. Marshall Co., Southfield, MI; *U.S. Private*, pg. 708
Simmons, Patrick E., Dir.-Mktg. & Sls.--Yoplait USA, Minneapolis, MN; *U.S. Public*, pg. 718
Simmons, Rod, Mgr.-Mktg.--Bacardi-Martini, USA, Inc., Miami, FL; *U.S. Private*, pg. 109
Simmons, Victoria L., Mktg. Administrator--NavCom Defense Electronics, Inc., El Monte, CA; *U.S. Private*, pg. 789
Simms-Brown, Judy, Mgr.-Mktg. Commun.--Watlow Electric Manufacturing Company, Saint Louis, MO; *U.S. Private*, pg. 1153
Simms-Brown, Judy, Dir.-Sls. & Mktg.--Watlow Gordon, Richmond, IL; *U.S. Private*, pg. 1153
Simms, Mike, Dir.-Mktg.--Imperial Bancorp, Inglewood, CA; *U.S. Public*, pg. 871
Simms, Robert, Mgr.-Mktg.-Powder--Stanback Company, Salisbury, NC; *U.S. Private*, pg. 1030
Simolin, Botho, Dir.-Communications--Kemira Oy, Helsinki, Finland; *Int'l*, pg. 727
Simon, Cheri, V.P.-Mktg. & Adv. (Indianapolis)--The Edward J. DeBartolo Corporation, Youngstown, OH; *U.S. Private*, *pg. 319*
Simon, Christopher, V.P. & Dir.-Sls. & Mktg.--CBS Television Network, New York, NY; *U.S. Public*, pg. 274
Simon, Craig, Dir.-Mktg. Devel.--MAN Roland, Inc., Groton, CT; *Int'l*, pg. 825
Simon, Dieter, Dir.-Mktg.--Maul-Belser GmbH, Nuremberg, Germany; *Int'l*, pg. 849
Simon, Don, Dir.-Mktg. Services--Avis Rent A Car System, Inc., Garden City, NY; *U.S. Public*, pg. 321
Simon, Evelyn, V.P.-Plng.--United Technologies Automotive, Dearborn, MI; *U.S. Public*, pg. 1691
Simon, Gladys, Coord.-Mktg.--Trafalgar House Construction Ltd., Croydon, United Kingdom; *Int'l*, pg. 773
Simon, Jeremy, V.P.-Sls. & Mktg.--Del Global Technologies, Valhalla, NY; *U.S. Public*, pg. 493
Simon, Martin, Pres.--Triangle Brass Manufacturing, Los Angeles, CA; *U.S. Private*, pg. 1101
Simon, Rick, Dir.-Mktg.--DPR Construction, Inc., Redwood City, CA; *U.S. Private*, pg. 305
Simonelli, Julie, Mktg. Dept.--Packard Bell NEC, Sacramento, CA; *U.S. Private*, pg. 833
Simonelli, Maureen, Dir.-Mktg.--Motor Boating & Sailing, New York, NY; *U.S. Private*, pg. 517
Simonetti, Randall A., V.P.-Adv. & Mktg. Communications--Frontier Corporation, Rochester, NY; *U.S. Public*, pg. 683
Simono, Mike, Dir.-Sls.--Paragon Electric Co., Inc., Two Rivers, WI; *Int'l*, pg. 1243
Simons, Craig, V.P.-Sls. & Mktg.--IMI Cash Valve, Inc., Cullman, AL; *Int'l*, pg. 646
Simons, Jane, Mgr.-Mktg.--Merisel Europe, Brentford, United Kingdom; *U.S. Public*, pg. 1096
Simons, John, Mgr.-Mktg.--Robertet Flavors, South Plainfield, NJ; *Int'l*, pg. 1119
Simons, Sally, Chief Mktg. Officer--Sacramento Kings, Sacramento, CA; *U.S. Private*, pg. 959
Simonsen, M., Dir.-Sls. & Mktg.--Simonsen & Sons Limited, Nykobing, Denmark; *Int'l*, pg. 894
Simonson, Kip, Dir.-Mktg.--Cox Communications-Jefferson Parish Office, Harahan, LA; *U.S. Public*, pg. 455
Simpkins, C. M., V.P.-Mktg. & Sls.--Compaction America, Kewanee, IL; *U.S. Public*, pg. 1676
Simpson, David, Capital Mktg. Dir.--Dewe Rogerson Limited, London, United Kingdom; *Int'l*, pg. 408
Simpson, Kathy, Dir.-Mktg.--The Kansas City Southern Railway Co., Kansas City, MO; *U.S. Public*, pg. 944
Sims, Greg, Dir.-Mktg.--Michelin North America (Canada) Inc., Laval, Canada; *Int'l*, pg. 322
Sims, Mark, Dir.-Mktg. & Adv.--Kellogg Company of Great Britain Ltd., Manchester, United Kingdom; *U.S. Public*, pg. 947
Sims, Stewart C., Sr. V.P.-Mktg.--Tiger Electronics, Inc., Vernon Hills, IL; *U.S. Private*, pg. 1086
Sims, T. Pinckney, Exec. V.P. & Gen. Mgr.--Kleinert's, Inc., of Alabama, Elba, AL; *U.S. Private*, pg. 625
Sinclair, Ken A., V.P.-Mktg.--SHL Systemhouse - Canada/Asia, Ottawa, Canada; *Int'l*, pg. 1154
Sinclair, Larry B., Dir.-Mktg. Svcs.--Churchill Downs, Inc., Louisville, KY; *U.S. Public*, pg. 356
Sinclair, Nancy, V.P. & Dir.-Mktg. & Plng.--CVB Financial Corp., Ontario, CA; *U.S. Public*, pg. 286
Siney, Bruce, Dir.-External Rels. & Mktg.--Foster's Brewing Group Limited, Southbank, Australia; *Int'l*, pg. 500
Singer, Bill, Dir.-Mktg.--Perfecseal Company, Philadelphia, PA; *U.S. Public*, pg. 210
Singer, David, Mgr.-Adv. & Mktg.--Westwood Computer Corporation, Springfield, NJ; *U.S. Private*, pg. 1170
Singer, Ellen, Mgr.-Corp. Mktg.--Benjamin Moore & Co., Montvale, NJ; *U.S. Private*, pg. 133
Singfield, Mark, Reg. Dir.-Sls. & Mktg.--Willis Corroon South Limited, Maidstone, United Kingdom; *Int'l*, pg. 1503
Singson, Katherine, Dir.-Mktg.--Pixar Animation Studios, Richmond, CA; *U.S. Public*, pg. 1307
Sinicrode, Bryan, Dir.-Mktg.--ABC Packaging Machine Corp., Tarpon Springs, FL; *U.S. Private*, pg. 3
Sipe, Alan W., V.P.-Sls. & Mktg.--Klein Tools Inc., Skokie, IL; *U.S. Private*, pg. 625
Siravo, Karen, Mktg. Admin.--Steiner Co., Inc., Chicago, IL; *U.S. Private*, pg. 1039
Siri, Mary, Mgr.-Special Events--Town & Country, New York, NY; *U.S. Private*, pg. 517
Sirkin, Samuel, Sec. & Dir.-Mktg.--Clay-Park Labs, Inc., Bronx, NY; *Int'l*, pg. 30
Sirvoy, Loel J., Sr. V.P.-Opers. & Outboard Mktg.--Hach Company, Loveland, CO; *U.S. Public*, pg. 773
Sisson, Warren, Dir.-Mktg.--U.S. Intec, Inc., Port Arthur, TX; *U.S. Private*, pg. 433
Siswick, Dale, Sr. V.P.-Mktg.--Milton Bradley Company, East Longmeadow, MA; *U.S. Public*, pg. 797
Sitarz, Jim, V.P.-Sls. & Mktg.--Prospect Foundry, Inc., Minneapolis, MN; *U.S. Public*, pg. 142
Sivayathorn, Kulathida, Sr. V.P. & Gen. Mgr.--Bangkok Bank Public Company Limited, Bangkok, Thailand; *Int'l*, pg. 146
Siwak, Jeff, Mgr.-Mktg.--Express Scripts, Inc., Maryland Heights, MO; *U.S. Public*, pg. 600
Siwek, Paul, V.P.-Sls. & Mktg.--ELE International, Inc./Soiltest, Lake Bluff, IL; *Int'l*, pg. 1287
Sjamaar, R., Mgr.-Sls. & Mktg.--Honig Merkartikelen B.V., Koog aan de Zaan, Netherlands; *Int'l*, pg. 244
Sjoberg, Claes, Mgr.-Mktg.--Sektionsbyggarna AB, Anneberg, Sweden; *Int'l*, pg. 1260
Skarvan, Paul, Mgr.-Mktg. Commun.--Hutchinson Technology Inc., Hutchinson, MN; *U.S. Public*, pg. 850
Skebba, Bill, Jr., Sr. V.P.-Sls. & Mktg.--M.W. Kasch Company, Mequon, WI; *U.S. Private*, pg. 608
Skelly, John, V.P.-Intl. Sls. & Mktg.--Haarmann & Reimer Food Ingredients Div., Elkhart, IN; *Int'l*, pg. 173
Skelly, Wendy, Dir.-Casualty Mktg.--Willis Corroon Corp. of Los Angeles, Glendale, CA; *Int'l*, pg. 1506
Skelton, Brenda, Sr. V.P.-Mktg. & Customer Svc.--Midwest Express Airlines, Inc., Oak Creek, WI; *U.S. Public*, pg. 1111
Skelton, Brenda F., Sr. V.P.-Mktg. & Customer Svcs.--Midwest Express Holdings, Inc., Oak Creek, WI; *U.S. Public*, pg. 1111
Skelton, Don, Sr. V.P.-Mktg. & Sls.--Illinois Central Corporation, Chicago, IL; *U.S. Public*, pg. 864
Skene, Jerry A., V.P.-Sls. & Mktg.--Peter Pan Seafoods, Inc., Seattle, WA; *Int'l*, pg. 928
Skene, Susan, V.P.-Mktg.--Hershey Canada Inc., Mississauga, Canada; *U.S. Public*, pg. 812
Skenes, Ronald P., Mgr.-Mktg. Services--E-Z-GO Textron, Augusta, GA; *U.S. Public*, pg. 1589
Skeoch, Don, Sr. V.P.-Mktg.--Baskin-Robbins Incorporated, Glendale, CA; *Int'l*, pg. 63
Skeoch, Don, Dir.-Reg. Mktg.--Baskin-Robbins Incorporated, Glendale, CA; *Int'l*, pg. 63
Skibinski, Betsy, Mgr.-Mktg.& Sls.--Ansco Photo-Optical Products Corp., Elk Grove Village, IL; *Int'l*, pg. 587
Skibo, Andrew D., Exec. V.P.-Sls. & Mktg.--Life Sciences International, Philadelphia, PA; *U.S. Private*, pg. 317
Skidmore, Dennis W., V.P.-Mktg.--Independent Cement Corporation, Albany, NY; *Int'l*, pg. 629
Skiest, Steve, Mgr.-Mktg.--Toko America, Inc., Mount Prospect, IL; *Int'l*, pg. 1393
Skillings, Pamela, Mgr.-Mktg.--MasterCard International-Cirrus Brand, Purchase, NY; *U.S. Private*, pg. 714
Skinner, Charles, V.P.-Bus. Devel.--Betac International Corporation, Alexandria, VA; *U.S. Private*, pg. 140
Skinner, E.R., V.P.-Mktg.--Auto-Owners Insurance, Lansing, MI; *U.S. Private*, pg. 100
Skinner, Murray, V.P.-Mktg. & Sls.--Metroland Printing & Distributing, Mississauga, Canada; *Int'l*, pg. 1402
Skog, Bary L., Chief Mktg. Officer--Harley Ellington Design, Southfield, MI; *U.S. Private*, pg. 503
Skoler, Joanna, V.P.-Mktg.--Sotheby's Inc., New York, NY; *U.S. Public*, pg. 1487
Skomoroh, Ed, V.P.-Sls. & Mktg.--Polaris Industries, Inc., Minneapolis, MN; *U.S. Public*, pg. 1313
Skop, Francis E., Sr., V.P.-Mktg.--Sherwood, Lockport, NY; *U.S. Public*, pg. 793
Skorpinski, Casey J., V.P.-Sls. & Mktg.--Whiting Corporation, Harvey, IL; *U.S. Private*, pg. 1173
Skorupski, Richard, Dir.-Product Devel.-Giftware--Cardinal Inc., Rahway, NJ; *U.S. Private*, pg. 208
Skwara, Joe, V.P.-Technical Services & Devel.--Comstock Michigan Fruit, Rochester, NY; *U.S. Private*, pg. 887
Skyba, Kirsten, Mgr.-Mktg. Svcs.--Oshkosh Truck Corporation, Oshkosh, WI; *U.S. Public*, pg. 1233
Skyrmes, Smokey, V.P.-Sls. & Mktg.--Harcros Chemicals Inc., Kansas City, KS; *Int'l*, pg. 598
Slade, Barry, Dir.-Sls. & Mktg./Intl.--Fountain Powerboat Industries, Inc., Washington, NC; *U.S. Public*, pg. 678
Slade, Vicki, Dir.-Mktg.--Bank One, Wisconsin, Milwaukee, WI; *U.S. Public*, pg. 174
Slagle, Jim, V.P.-Sls. & Mktg.--Servico, Inc., West Palm Beach, FL; *U.S. Public*, pg. 1462
Slagle, Paula, Dir.-Mktg.--Alloy Technology International Inc., West Nyack, NY; *U.S. Private*, pg. 42
Slaney, Mary, V.P.-Sales & Mktg.--Delcar Digital, New York, NY; *U.S. Public*, pg. 1642
Slangen, Louis F.J., Sr. V.P.-Sls. & Mktg.--Invacare Corporation, Elyria, OH; *U.S. Public*, pg. 911
Slankard, Marilyn, Dir.-Mktg. & Sls.--Borders, Inc., Ann Arbor, MI; *U.S. Public*, pg. 245

Slark, D., Dir.-Comml.--Robertson Tooling Ltd., Kempston, United Kingdom; *Int'l*, pg. 449

Slater, Jeff, Dir.-Snacks Mktg.--GoodMark Foods, Inc., Raleigh, NC; *U.S. Public*, pg. 751

Slater, Kelly, Dir.-Mktg. Communications--Apertus Technologies Incorporated, Eden Prairie, MN; *U.S. Public*, pg. 119

Slater, Roger, Mgr.-Mktg. Services--Young Radiator Company, Racine, WI; *U.S. Private*, pg. 1201

Slater, Scott, V.P.-Mktg.--Intercraft Company, Taylor, TX; *U.S. Public*, pg. 1177

Slaugenhaupt, Lori, Dir.-Mktg.--Furman Foods, Inc., Northumberland, PA; *U.S. Private*, pg. 431

Slaughter, Joe, V.P. & Gen. Mgr.-Scholastic--Herff Jones Inc., Indianapolis, IN; *U.S. Private*, pg. 523

Slaughter, Michael, V.P.-Mktg.--Lawrence Division, Lawrence, MA; *U.S. Public*, pg. 27

Slaughter, Richard G., V.P.-Plng. & Sec.--U.S. Home Corporation, Houston, TX; *U.S. Public*, pg. 1682

Slaughter, Susan, Mgr.-Mktg. Communications--Wavetek Corporation, San Diego, CA; *U.S. Private*, pg. 1154

Slaunwhite, Gloria, Mgr.-Mktg.--Navistar International Corporation Canada, Hamilton, Canada; *U.S. Public*, pg. 1167

Slavens, Jimmy, Dir.-Prod. Mktg.--Komatsu America International Company, Vernon Hills, IL; *Int'l*, pg. 744

Slavin, E.A., V.P.-Sls. & Mktg.--NVF Company, Yorklyn, DE; *U.S. Private*, pg. 772

Slayton, Mark, Dir.-Mktg. Opers.--International Correspondence Schools, Inc., Scranton, PA; *U.S. Public*, pg. 783

Slezak, Eric, V.P.-Mktg.--Kester Solder, Des Plaines, IL; *U.S. Public*, pg. 1003

Slezak, Robert, Exec. V.P.-Tech. & Mktg.--Comverse Network Systems, Wakefield, MA; *U.S. Public*, pg. 425

Slinger, Grant, V.P.-Relationship Mktg. & Acct. Dir.--Mezzina/Brown Inc., New York, NY; *U.S. Private*, pg. 739

Slipz, John, Dir.-Corp. Mktg.--Novell Inc., San Jose, CA; *U.S. Public*, pg. 1203

Sload, Michael, Mgr.-Mktg.--The Mennen Company, New York, NY; *U.S. Public*, pg. 397

Sloan, Don, Dir.-Mktg.--W.H. Smith Group plc, London, United Kingdom; *Int'l*, pg. 1264

Sloan, Gurney, V.P.-Direct Mktg.--Ackerman McQueen, Inc., Colorado Springs, CO; *U.S. Private*, pg. 13

Sloan, Randy M., V.P.-Mktg.--PolyMedica Industries, Inc., Woburn, MA; *U.S. Public*, pg. 1315

Sloane, G. Michael, Exec. V.P. & Chief Mktg. Officer--American Reliable Insurance Company, Scottsdale, AZ; *U.S. Public*, pg. 67

Sloane, Robert, Supvr.-Mktg.--Tsumura International, Secaucus, NJ; *Int'l*, pg. 1426

Sloane, Todd, Dir.-Mktg. Devel.--Publishers Clearing House, Port Washington, NY; *U.S. Private*, pg. 893

Slocumb, Michael, V.P.-UKI Mktg. & New Prods.--Dyersburg Corporation, Dyersburg, TN; *U.S. Public*, pg. 538

Slocumb, Michael, V.P.-Mktg. & New Prods.--United Knitting, Inc., Cleveland, TN; *U.S. Public*, pg. 538

Slone, Carl J., V.P.-Mktg. & Sls.--Trigon Blue Cross & Blue Shield, Richmond, VA; *U.S. Public*, pg. 1637

Slone, Jim, Dir.-Mktg. & Prod. Mngmt.--Robert Bosch Fluid Power Corporation, Racine, WI; *Int'l*, pg. 204

Slone, R., Sr. V.P. & Dir.-Mktg.--Shieffelin Somerset Co., New York, NY; *Int'l*, pg. 412

Sloneker, Debbie, V.P.-Mktg.--Mar-Hyde Corporation, Cincinnati, OH; *U.S. Public*, pg. 1357

Slove, Martin L., Dir.-Mktg.--Takeda USA Inc., Orangeburg, NY; *Int'l*, pg. 1350

Sluder, Russell W., V.P.-Mktg.--Sentry Polymers, Inc., Freeport, TX; *U.S. Public*, pg. 1357

Slusarick, John, Mgr.-Mktg.--S.E. Huffman Corp., Clover, SC; *U.S. Private*, pg. 546

Sluss, Greg, Dir.-Sls. & Mktg.--Republic Storage Systems Company Inc., Canton, OH; *U.S. Private*, pg. 924

Slutzky, Elliot, Exec. V.P.-Sls.--LIVE Film & Mediaworks, Van Nuys, CA; *U.S. Private*, pg. 671

Small, Lee, V.P.-Mktg.--Continental Circuits Corp., Phoenix, AZ; *U.S. Public*, pg. 440

Smalley, Amanda, Mgr.-Mktg.--Matthew Clark Taunton, Ltd., Bristol, United Kingdom; *Int'l*, pg. 848

Smallman-Tew, Peter, Natl. Mgr.-Mktg.--Yamaha Motor Canada Ltd., North York, Canada; *Int'l*, pg. 1516

Smart, David E., Mgr.-Mktg.--Fiduciary Trust International Limited, London, United Kingdom; *U.S. Public*, pg. 621

Smeall, Janice, Mgr.-Sls.--Electro Dynamics Crystal Corporation, Overland Park, KS; *U.S. Private*, pg. 368

Smedsted, Michael, Dir.-Mktg.--Wenger Corporation, Owatonna, MN; *U.S. Private*, pg. 1162

Smelley, Bill, Mgr.-Mktg. Services--Valvoline Instant Oil Change, Inc., Lexington, KY; *U.S. Public*, pg. 139

Smeltzer, Dave, Prod. Mgr.--Welding Products Group, Niles, MI; *U.S. Public*, pg. 1161

Smette, Darryl G., V.P.-Mktg. & Admin. Plng.--Devon Energy Corporation, Oklahoma City, OK; *U.S. Public*, pg. 503

Smetts, Stewart, Exec. V.P.-Mktg.--La Rosa's, Inc., Cincinnati, OH; *U.S. Private*, pg. 640

Smidt, Mike, Mgr.-Mktg. Communications--Garst Seed Company, Slater, IA; *Int'l*, pg. 1524

Smikle, Deborah A., Dir.-Mktg. Communications--F.W. Dodge Group, New York, NY; *U.S. Public*, pg. 1070

Smiley, Doreen, Mgr.-Mktg.--Laserscope Surgical Systems, San Jose, CA; *U.S. Public*, pg. 979

Smillie, Cameron, Supvr.-Mktg. Services--Ascolectric Limited, Brantford, Canada; *U.S. Public*, pg. 575

Smit, G.C., Dir.-Mktg.--Astra Pharmaceutica B.V., Zoetermeer, Netherlands; *Int'l*, pg. 94

Smit, Jack, Mgr.-Mktg. & Sls.--Miracle Feeds Inc., London, Canada; *U.S. Private*, pg. 432

Smit, Ton, V.P.-Mktg. & Sls.--Wedco Holland B.V., s Gravendeel, Netherlands; *U.S. Public*, pg. 854

Smith Cox, Carrie, Exec. Dir.-Mktg. (Female Health Care)--Wyeth-Ayerst Laboratories, Inc., Philadelphia, PA; *U.S. Public*, pg. 80

Smith-Berry, Holly, Dir.-Mktg.--Toastmaster, Inc., Columbia, MO; *U.S. Public*, pg. 1619

Smith, A., Dir.-Mktg.--CV Home Furnishings Limited, Manchester, United Kingdom; *Int'l*, pg. 299

Smith, A.G., Dir.-Mktg. & Defence Sls.--Chloride Industrial Batteries Ltd., Manchester, United Kingdom; *Int'l*, pg. 125

Smith, Aileen, Mgr.-Circulation & Bus.--The Seattle Business Journal, Inc., Seattle, WA; *U.S. Private*, pg. 20

Smith, Andrea, Mgr.-Corp. & Mktg. Communications--Concurrent Computer Corporation, Fort Lauderdale, FL; *U.S. Public*, pg. 430

Smith, Angela, Dir.-Sls. & Mktg.--Moran Industries, Inc., Midlothian, IL; *U.S. Private*, pg. 760

Smith, Anne, Mgr.-Mktg. Communications--LORAD Corporation, Danbury, CT; *U.S. Public*, pg. 1595

Smith, Ashley, Mgr.-Promo. & Mdsg.-Southern Accents--Southern Progress Corporation, Birmingham, AL; *U.S. Public*, pg. 1612

Smith, Barbara, Mgr.-Sls.--Minerallac Co., Addison, IL; *U.S. Private*, pg. 750

Smith, Barry L., Sr. V.P.-Mktg.--Choice Hotels International, Inc., Silver Spring, MD; *U.S. Public*, pg. 351

Smith, Bill, V.P.-Adv. & Mktg.--Meijer, Inc., Grand Rapids, MI; *U.S. Private*, pg. 729

Smith, Bill, V.P.-Mktg.--Huffy Bicycle Company, Celina, OH; *U.S. Public*, pg. 846

Smith, Bruce W., V.P.-Mktg.--Smith Industries, Inc., Montgomery, AL; *U.S. Private*, pg. 1008

Smith, Bryden, V.P.-Mktg.--Whitin Roberts Co., Sanford, NC; *U.S. Private*, pg. 309

Smith, C.E., V.P.-Sls. & Mktg.--The American Group, Ferndale, WA; *U.S. Private*, pg. 56

Smith, Cameron, Mgr.-Mktg. Communications--Barry Controls, Brighton, MA; *U.S. Public*, pg. 124

Smith, Carl, V.P.-Mktg.--City Gas Company of Florida, Hialeah, FL; *U.S. Public*, pg. 1147

Smith, Carrie, Mgr.-Mktg.--Big O Tires Incorporated, Englewood, CO; *U.S. Public*, pg. 1553

Smith, Clarence, V.P.-Mktg.--Tree of Life, Inc., Saint Augustine, FL; *Int'l*, pg. 752

Smith, Craig, V.P.-Sls. & Mktg.--Leone Food Service Corp., Livonia, MI; *U.S. Private*, pg. 244

Smith, Craig, V.P. & Dir.-Mktg.--FirstFed Financial Corp., Santa Monica, CA; *U.S. Public*, pg. 645

Smith, Craig, V.P.-Mktg.--First Federal Bank of California, FSB, Santa Monica, CA; *U.S. Public*, pg. 646

Smith, Craig, Asst. Mktg. Mgr.--Plibrico Co., Chicago, IL; *U.S. Private*, pg. 872

Smith, D.C., Dir.-Mktg. & Sls.--Griffin Manufacturing Co., Muskogee, OK; *U.S. Private*, pg. 481

Smith, David, Dir.-Mktg.--Getko Group Inc., Westbury, NY; *U.S. Public*, pg. 320

Smith, David, V.P.-Mktg.--Metabo Corporation, West Chester, PA; *U.S. Private*, pg. 734

Smith, Debbie, Mktg. Communications Specialist--Power-One, Inc., Camarillo, CA; *U.S. Private*, pg. 878

Smith, Debbie, Dir.-Adv.--Earl Scheib, Inc., Beverly Hills, CA; *U.S. Public*, pg. 1437

Smith, Dennis H., Sr. V.P.-Mktg.--Fiduciary Management Associates, Inc., Chicago, IL; *U.S. Public*, pg. 1673

Smith, Don, Dir.-Sls. & Mktg.--Chris-Craft Boats, Sarasota, FL; *U.S. Private*, pg. 478

Smith, Don, V.P.-Mktg.--Huffy Sports Company, Sussex, WI; *U.S. Public*, pg. 846

Smith, Donald F., V.P.-Mktg. & Sls.--The Guttman Group, Belle Vernon, PA; *U.S. Private*, pg. 488

Smith, Donna J., Mgr.-Commun.--Tuboscope Incorporated, Houston, TX; *U.S. Public*, pg. 1643

Smith, Douglas, V.P.-Sls. & Mktg.--Davox Corp., Westford, MA; *U.S. Public*, pg. 488

Smith, Douglas, V.P.-Channel Sls. & Mktg.--Tecmar Technologies, Inc., Longmont, CO; *Int'l*, pg. 1361

Smith, E.T., Grp. V.P.--Industrial Americas Group, Maumee, OH; *U.S. Public*, pg. 24

Smith, Elena, Dir.-Mktg.--Arrow Shirt Company, New York, NY; *Int'l*, pg. 194

Smith, Elizabeth, Mktg. Specialist--Popeye's Chicken & Biscuits, Atlanta, GA; *U.S. Private*, pg. 5

Smith, Gary, Sr. V.P. & Dir.-Mktg.--Safeway Inc., Pleasanton, CA; *U.S. Public*, pg. 1426

Smith, George H., Supvr.-Mktg. Services--Cargill, Wayzata, MN; *U.S. Private*, pg. 210

Smith, Gerry, V.P.-Mktg.--Gold Eagle Company, Chicago, IL; *U.S. Private*, pg. 459

Smith, Ginger, Dir.-Mktg.--Compass Group-USA Division, Charlotte, NC; *Int'l*, pg. 324

Smith, Greg, Mgr.-Mktg. Svcs.--Allied Construction Products, Inc., Cleveland, OH; *U.S. Public*, pg. 1339

Smith, H.J., V.P.-Sls. & Mktg.--Ravarino & Freschi, Inc., Saint Louis, MO; *U.S. Private*, pg. 158

Smith, Harold, Dir.-Sls. & Mktg.--MTD Products Limited, Kitchener, Canada; *U.S. Private*, pg. 688

Smith, Heather, Admin. Asst.-Mktg.--Cole-Haan, Yarmouth, ME; *U.S. Public*, pg. 1184

Smith, Howard, Mgr.-Mktg.--Jordon Commercial Refrigerator Co., Philadelphia, PA; *U.S. Private*, pg. 599

Smith, Howard, V.P.-Nick Recreation Mktg.--Nickelodeon/Nick At Nite, New York, NY; *U.S. Private*, pg. 779

Smith, J., Gen. Mgr.-Mktg.--British Airways Cargo, London, United Kingdom; *Int'l*, pg. 219

Smith, J., Dir.-Mktg.--SmithKline Beecham Farma B.V., Rijswijk, Netherlands; *Int'l*, pg. 1266

Smith, James U., V.P.-Sls. & Mktg.--Ruetgers-Nease Corporation, State College, PA; *Int'l*, pg. 1148

Smith, Jay, V.P.-Sls. & Mktg.--Voit Sports, Inc., Carlsbad, CA; *U.S. Private*, pg. 1143

Smith, Jim, Exec. V.P.-Mktg.--Shadow Broadcast Services, Bala Cynwyd, PA; *U.S. Public*, pg. 1763

Smith, Jimmy, V.P.-Mktg & Sls.--Alden Electronics, Inc., Westborough, MA; *U.S. Private*, pg. 872

Smith, Joseph H., Pres.--40 Fort Eye Associates, Forty Fort, PA; *U.S. Private*, pg. 420

Smith, Kathy, Dir.-Mktg. Communications--Browning-Ferris Industries, Inc., Houston, TX; *U.S. Public*, pg. 262

Smith, Keith, V.P.-Mktg.--Hercules Incorporated, Wilmington, DE; *U.S. Public*, pg. 809

Smith, Ken, Mgr.-Mktg. Communications--Lista International Corporation, Holliston, MA; *Int'l*, pg. 812

Smith, Ken, Dir.-Mktg.--Torcon, Inc., Westfield, NJ; *U.S. Private*, pg. 1092

Smith, Kristi August, Dir.-Mktg.--Saab Cars USA, Inc., Norcross, GA; *Int'l*, pg. 687

Smith, Larry, V.P.-Mktg.--The Berkline Corporation, Morristown, TN; *U.S. Private*, pg. 432

Smith, Larry, Mgr.-Natl. Sls./RV--Kit Manufacturing Company, Long Beach, CA; *U.S. Public*, pg. 962

Smith, Lawrence W., Sr. V.P.-Sls. & Mktg./N. America--FCA International Ltd., Westmount, Canada; *Int'l*, pg. 470

Smith, Lisa, Asst. V.P.-Mktg. Communications--Old Kent Bank, Grand Rapids, MI; *U.S. Public*, pg. 1216

Smith, Lorraine, Mgr.-Mktg. Communications--Dacon Electronics Plc., Hemel Hempstead, United Kingdom; *U.S. Public*, pg. 395

Smith, Marc, Exec. V.P.-Sls. & Mktg.--The Stop & Shop Companies, Inc., Quincy, MA; *Int'l*, pg. 750

Smith, Mark, V.P.-Mktg. & Adv.--Mott's Inc., Stamford, CT; *Int'l*, pg. 248

Smith, Matthew, Dir.-Mktg.--Rieter Automotive North America Inc, Farmington Hills, MI; *Int'l*, pg. 1117

Smith, Matthew C., Mgr.- Mktg.--United States Ceramic Tile Co., East Sparta, OH; *U.S. Private*, pg. 1124

Smith, Maureen, Mktg. Coord.--Petrie Retail, Inc., Secaucus, NJ; *U.S. Private*, pg. 858

Smith, Mel, Mgr.-Mktg.--Airfoil Technologies International LLC, Cincinnati, OH; *U.S. Public*, pg. 1569

Smith, Michael, Mgr.-Mktg. Communications--Parker Hannifin Corp., Quick Coupling Div., Minneapolis, MN; *U.S. Public*, pg. 1260

Smith, Morris, Dir.-Mktg. Communications--Fujitsu Systems of America, Inc., La Jolla, CA; *Int'l*, pg. 526

Smith, Murray, V.P.-Devel.--Starrett HRH, New York, NY; *U.S. Private*, pg. 1035

Smith, Patti, Supvr.-Mktg. Res.--Michaels Stores, Inc., Irving, TX; *U.S. Public*, pg. 1104

Smith, Patti L., Dir.-Mktg.--A & S Building Systems, Inc., Caryville, TN; *U.S. Public*, pg. 1146

Smith, Philip, V.P.-Sales & Mktg.--A.H. Hoffman, Inc., Landisville, PA; *U.S. Private*, pg. 532

Smith, Philip, Pres.--AGEMA Infrared Systems, Inc., Secaucus, NJ; *Int'l*, pg. 1289

Smith, Randol, V.P.-Mktg.--Universal Furniture Industries, Inc., High Point, NC; *U.S. Private*, pg. 432

Smith, Randy, Dir.-Sls.--General Shale Products Corp., Johnson City, TN; *Int'l*, pg. 843

Smith, Randy, Dir.-Sls.--General Shale Products Corp., Elizabethton, TN; *Int'l*, pg. 843

Smith, Randy, V.P.-Mktg.--Virco Mfg. Corporation, Torrance, CA; *U.S. Public*, pg. 1721

Smith, Rebecca J., V.P.-Mktg.--The Disston Co., Greensboro, NC; *U.S. Public*, pg. 950

Smith, Rhonda, Admin.-Mktg.--Perkins Family Restaurants, Memphis, TN; *U.S. Private*, pg. 925

Smith, Richard, V.P.-Mktg.--Aurora Casket Company, Aurora, IN; *U.S. Private*, pg. 99

Smith, Richard, Mgr.-Mktg. Communications--The Lincoln Electric Company, Cleveland, OH; *U.S. Public*, pg. 996

Smith, Rick, Mgr.-Mktg. Commun./BFGoodrich Brand--Michelin Americas Small Tires (MAST), Greenville, SC; *Int'l*, pg. 322

Smith, Robert, Head-Mktg.--Geffen Records, Los Angeles, CA; *Int'l*, pg. 1215

Smith, Robert L., Dir.-Mktg.--Florida Public Utilities Company, West Palm Beach, FL; *U.S. Public*, pg. 655

Smith, Rod, Dir.-Mktg.-Primary Bks.--Reed Educational and Professional Publishing, Oxford, United Kingdom; *Int'l*, pg. 1094

Smith, Roger, Dir.-Mktg.--Glynwed Pipe Systems, Coleshill, United Kingdom; *Int'l*, pg. 554

Smith, Ron, Mgr.-Sls. & Mktg.--GAI Consultants, Inc., Fort Wayne, IN; *U.S. Private*, pg. 434

Smith, Ron, Mgr.-Mktg. Communications-Reliance Products--Rockwell Automation, Milwaukee, WI; *U.S. Public*, pg. 1397

Smith, S. Kerr, Dir.-Mktg.--Willis Corroon Corp. of Louisiana, New Orleans, LA; *Int'l*, pg. 1506

Smith, Sandra Clingan, V.P.-Mktg.--Captain D's Restaurant, Nashville, TN; *U.S. Public*, pg. 1467

Smith, Scott, Dir.-Mktg. Svcs.--Rawlings Sporting Goods Company, Fenton, MO; *U.S. Public*, pg. 1361

Smith, Sondra, Dir.-Mktg. Service, Europe--Dictaphone Co. U.K. Ltd., Royal Leamington Spa, United Kingdom; *U.S. Private*, pg. 1045

Smith, Stephen R., Exec. V.P.-Mktg.--Excel Communications, Inc., Dallas, TX; *U.S. Public*, pg. 598

Smith, Steven, Mgr.-Mktg.--Courtaulds Aerospace, Littleborough, United Kingdom; *Int'l*, pg. 338

Smith, Steven J., V.P.-Mktg.--Pawling Corporation, Pawling, NY; *U.S. Private*, pg. 844

Smith, Sue, Admin. Asst.-Mktg.--Brown-Forman Beverages Worldwide, Louisville, KY; *U.S. Public*, pg. 261

Smith, Sue, Dir.-Intl. Mktg.--Laserscope Surgical Systems, San Jose, CA; *U.S. Public*, pg. 979

Smith, Susan, Adm. Asst.-Mktg.--Ardell Industries Inc., Union, NJ; *U.S. Private*, pg. 597

Smith, T.W., Pres.--Calcot, Ltd., Bakersfield, CA; *U.S. Private*, pg. 200

Smith, Terryll R., V.P.-European Sls. & Mktg.--Advanced Micro Devices, Inc., Sunnyvale, CA; *U.S. Public*, pg. 21

Smith, Thomas M., Exec. V.P.-Mktg. & Sales--CPS Direct, Inc., Woburn, MA; *U.S. Private*, pg. 196

Smith, Tiffani, Coord.-Adv. Programs--Knouse Foods Inc., Peach Glen, PA; *U.S. Private*, pg. 627

Smith, Tim, Mgr.-Mktg. Services--The HON Co., Muscatine, IA; *U.S. Public*, pg. 772

Smith, W.E., Jr., V.P.-Mktg.--The Amalgamated Sugar Company LLC, Ogden, UT; *U.S. Private*, pg. 48

Smith, Wayne A., Exec. V.P.--George & Lynch, Inc., New Castle, DE; *U.S. Private*, pg. 448
Smith, William, V.P.-Mktg.--Vacation Break USA, Fort Lauderdale, FL; *U.S. Public*, pg. 611
Smith, William, V.P.-Reg. Salisbury--Tristate Electrical Supply Co., Inc., Hagerstown, MD; *U.S. Private*, pg. 1104
Smith, William J., Sr. V.P.-Sls. & Mktg.--Premisys Communications, Inc., Fremont, CA; *U.S. Public*, pg. 1323
Smits, Bert, Member-Bd. of Mngmt.--Wella Group, Darmstadt, Germany; *Int'l*, pg. 1489
Smolen, Leslie, Dir.-Mktg.--Tastee Freez International Inc., Utica, MI; *U.S. Private*, pg. 1069
Smorgon, Robert, Dir.-Mktg.--Smorgon A.R.C., Sunshine, Australia; *Int'l*, pg. 1269
Smurfit, D.F., Deputy Chm. & Exec. V.P.-Worldwide Sls. & Mktg.--Jefferson Smurfit Group p.l.c., Dublin, Ireland; *Int'l*, pg. 1269
Smusz, Robert, V.P.-Mktg. & Mdsg.--Arvey Paper & Office Products, Chicago, IL; *U.S. Public*, pg. 903
Smutny, Chuck, Exec. V.P.-Sls. & Mktg.--Agripac Inc., Salem, OR; *U.S. Private*, pg. 26
Smyth, Greg, Dir.-Mktg. & Sls.--Robert E. Bayley Construction, Seattle, WA; *U.S. Private*, pg. 125
Smyth, Patrick, V.P.-Worldwide Mktg.--Tandem Computers Inc., Cupertino, CA; *U.S. Public*, pg. 417
Smythe, Karen, V.P.-Mktg.--The Dannon Co., Tarrytown, NY; *Int'l*, pg. 379
Smythe, Robert A., V.P. & Dir.-Sls. & Mktg.--Zygo Corporation, Middlefield, CT; *U.S. Public*, pg. 1795
Snay, Dennis, V.P.-Retail Mktg.--New England Electric System, Westborough, MA; *U.S. Public*, pg. 1171
Snediker, James M., Pres., Chief Exec. Officer & Chief Oper. Officer--Chicago Show Printing Co., Morton Grove, IL; *U.S. Private*, pg. 235
Sneed, Amy, Dir.-New Mkt. Devel.--J. Crew Group, Inc., New York, NY; *U.S. Private*, pg. 1078
Sneed, Collette, Mktg. & Special Projects--American Business Advertising, Omaha, NE; *U.S. Private*, pg. 51
Sneed, Paula A., Sr. V.P.-Mktg. Services--Kraft Foods, Inc., Northfield, IL; *U.S. Public*, pg. 1287
Snelgrove, Linda, Mgr.-Mktg.--MasterCard International-Cirrus Brand, Purchase, NY; *U.S. Private*, pg. 714
Snell, David J., V.P.-Sls. & Mktg.--Data General (Canada) Ltd., Mississauga, Canada; *U.S. Public*, pg. 485
Snell, Greg, V.P.-Mktg.--ATMI Ecosys Corp., San Jose, CA; *U.S. Public*, pg. 12
Snell, Ken, V.P.-Mktg.--Vitality Foodservice, Inc., Zephyrhills, FL; *U.S. Private*, pg. 682
Snell, Phyllis, Mgr.-Sls. & Mktg.--Dimco-Gray Company, Centerville, OH; *U.S. Private*, pg. 333
Snider, Alan, V.P.-Sls. & Mktg.--Gussco Manufacturing, Inc., Brooklyn, NY; *U.S. Private*, pg. 488
Snider, Larry D., Dir.-Mktg. Commun.--Eastman Chemical Company, Kingsport, TN; *U.S. Public*, pg. 550
Snider, Richard, V.P.-Corp. Affairs--Thornton Oil Corp., Louisville, KY; *U.S. Private*, pg. 1084
Snider, Terrence Q., V.P.-Sls. & Mktg.--Merck Medco Managed Care, Des Moines, IA; *U.S. Public*, pg. 1091
Snitgen, Eric, V.P. & Gen. Mgr.-Ariel Prods.--Hendrix Wire & Cable, Milford, NH; *U.S. Public*, pg. 1598
Snoozy, Robert S., V.P.-Sls. & Mktg.--Lindsay Manufacturing Company, Lindsay, NE; *U.S. Public*, pg. 999
Snow, Clare, Mgr.-Mktg.--Mark IV Automotive Canada Inc., Weston, Canada; *U.S. Public*, pg. 1045
Snow, James, Mgr.-Mktg. Communications--International Lottery & Totalizator Systems, Inc., Carlsbad, CA; *U.S. Public*, pg. 900
Snyder, Daniel C., Sr. V.P.-Mktg. Information--National Liberty Corporation, Frazer, PA; *Int'l*, pg. 26
Snyder, Donna, Sr. Mktg. & Comm. Rep.--Du Pont Printing & Publishing, Wilmington, DE; *U.S. Public*, pg. 531
Snyder, Jim, V.P.-Mktg./Plastics--Clopay Corporation, Cincinnati, OH; *U.S. Public*, pg. 766
Snyder, Joseph T., Dir.-Sls. & Mktg.--J.T. Slocomb Company, South Glastonbury, CT; *U.S. Private*, pg. 1006
Snyder, Terri, Sr. V.P.-Mktg.--Ponderosa Steakhouse, Dallas, TX; *U.S. Private*, pg. 736
Snyder, Terry, V.P.-Mktg.--Bonanza Restaurants, Dallas, TX; *U.S. Private*, pg. 736
Snyder, Thomas D.., V.P.-Mktg.--Janesville Products, Norwalk, OH; *U.S. Public*, pg. 924
Snyder, Vickie, Mktg. & Communications Specialist--Farinon Div. Harris Corp., Redwood City, CA; *U.S. Public*, pg. 791
Soady, Kevin, Capital Mktg. Dir.--Dewe Rogerson Limited, London, United Kingdom; *Int'l*, pg. 408
Soares, Antonio, Sls. & Mktg. Mgr.--Whitehall Portugal, Lisbon, Portugal; *U.S. Public*, pg. 81
Sobel, Susan, Assoc. V.P.-Mktg.--ECI Telecom Ltd., Petah Tiqwa, Israel; *Int'l*, pg. 643
Soden, Richard, Mgr.-Mktg.--Transico Incorporated, Santa Ana, CA; *U.S. Public*, pg. 1630
Soderberg, Olle, Sr. V.P.-Adv.--Skandinaviska Enskilda Banken, Stockholm, Sweden; *Int'l*, pg. 1258
Soehnlen, Greg, Mgr.-Sls.--Superior Dairy, Inc., Canton, OH; *U.S. Private*, pg. 1054
Soennichsen, Torbin, Dir.-Sls. & Mktg.--Vestjyske Slagterier, Struer, Denmark; *Int'l*, pg. 1464
Sofhauser, Soren, V.P.-Sls. Admin.--Childcraft Education Corporation, Lancaster, PA; *U.S. Public*, pg. 513
Soh, K., Dir.-Mktg.- Confectionery--Warner-Lambert K.K., Tokyo, Japan; *U.S. Public*, pg. 1739
Sohm, Woo-Heon, Pres.--Ssangyong Investment Management Co., Ltd., Seoul, Korea; *Int'l*, pg. 1292
Sokoloff, Steven, V.P.-Mktg.--Milgray Electronics, Inc., Farmingdale, NY; *U.S. Public*, pg. 205
Sokoloff, Steven, V.P.-Mktg. & Sls.-Milgray/Toronto, Inc., Mississauga, Canada; *U.S. Public*, pg. 207
Sokoloff, Steven, V.P.-Mktg. & Pur.--Milgray/Montreal, Pointe-Claire, Canada; *U.S. Public*, pg. 207
Sokolowski, George, Sr. V.P.-Corp. Mktg.--The TJX Companies, Inc., Framingham, MA; *U.S. Public*, pg. 1556
Solan, Veronica, Mktg. Specialist--VG Laboratory Systems Ltd., Altrincham, United Kingdom; *U.S. Public*, pg. 1595
Sole, Ian, V.P.-Sls. & Mktg.--American Woodmark Corporation, Winchester, VA; *U.S. Public*, pg. 96
Solel, Avner, Mgr.-Mktg.--American Israeli Paper Mills Ltd., Hadera, Israel; *Int'l*, pg. 74
Solip, Lelian, Mgr.-Mktg.--Icicle Seafoods, Inc., Seattle, WA; *U.S. Private*, pg. 556
Solnass, Ananda, Coord.-Natl. Mktg.--Shiseido (Australia) Pty. Limited, Pyrmont, Australia; *Int'l*, pg. 1235
Solomita, Anthony P., V.P.-Consumer Electronics Mktg.--Conair Corporation, Stamford, CT; *U.S. Private*, pg. 261
Solomon, Bonnie, V.P.-Adv. & Mktg.--Barneys Inc., New York, NY; *U.S. Private*, pg. 116
Solomon, Robert, Exec. V.P., Mng. & Mktg. Dir.--Ammirati, Puris & Lintas, Inc., New York, NY; *U.S. Private*, pg. 66
Solomon, Susan Snell, Mgr.-Mktg. Services--CSP Inc., Billerica, MA; *U.S. Public*, pg. 283
Solomon, Tom, V.P.-Sls. & Mktg.--Uniblend Spinners, Inc., Conway, SC; *U.S. Private*, pg. 1117
Solomons, Phil, Dir.-Mktg.--nVIEW Corporation, Newport News, VA; *U.S. Public*, pg. 1206
Solon, Rich, Dir.-Mktg. Res.--Swanson, Camden, NJ; *U.S. Public*, pg. 299
Solon, Tony, Mgr.-Mktg. Commun.--AGCO Corporation, Duluth, GA; *U.S. Public*, pg. 28
Solter, Lance, V.P.-Opers. & Production--Warner-Jenkinson Co., Saint Louis, MO; *U.S. Public*, pg. 1696
Soltis, Karen, Mgr.-Mktg. & Commun.--Bacharach Inc., Pittsburgh, PA; *U.S. Private*, pg. 109
Somerdyk, Harry, Sr. V.P.-Mktg. & Brand Devel.--Business Week, New York, NY; *U.S. Public*, pg. 1069
Somerville, Anne, Mktg. Commun.--Carl Zeiss Optical, Inc., Petersburg, VA; *Int'l*, pg. 1523
Somma, Rande, V.P.-Sls. & Mktg.--Johnson Controls, Inc., Plymouth, MI; *U.S. Public*, pg. 932
Sommer, Barbara, Exec. V.P.-Mktg.--Letraset Nielsen & Bainbridge, Paramus, NJ; *Int'l*, pg. 460
Sommer, Daniel, Dir.-Mktg.--The CIT Group/Equipment Financing, Livingston, NJ; *Int'l*, pg. 360
Sommer, John, Exec. V.P.-Sls. & Mktg.--Kidron Inc., Kidron, OH; *U.S. Private*, pg. 619
Sommer, Steve, V.P.-Indus. Mktg.--Informix Software, Menlo Park, CA; *U.S. Public*, pg. 876
Sommers-Reilly, Mary Anne, V.P.-Adv., Magazine Dev.--Women's Magazines Group, New York, NY; *Int'l*, pg. 190
Sommers, Gerald, Exec. V.P.-Sls. & Mktg.--Allied Printing Services, Inc., Manchester, CT; *U.S. Private*, pg. 40
Sommovigo, Susan, Dir.-Mktg.--President Baking Company, Atlanta, GA; *Int'l*, pg. 1069
Songer, Jim, V.P.-Worldwide Sls. & Mktg.--Esco Corporation, Portland, OR; *U.S. Private*, pg. 382
Sonnino, Reuben, Dir.-Special Projects--SGS-Thomson Microelectronics, Inc., Carrollton, TX; *Int'l*, pg. 1153
Sonntag, Inge, Dir.-Mktg.--Clarins GmbH, Starnberg, Germany; *Int'l*, pg. 295
Soofi, Madjid, V.P.-Mktg.--Magneco/Metrel, Inc., Addison, IL; *U.S. Private*, pg. 695
Sophocleus, James, Dir.-Mktg.--Malt-O-Meal Company, Minneapolis, MN; *U.S. Private*, pg. 699
Sorbraten, Inger, Information Mgr.-Corp. Communication--Aker Raj Asa, Oslo, Norway; *Int'l*, pg. 41
Sorem, Dave, Dir.-Sls. & Mktg./Oil Centrifuges--Reuter Manufacturing Inc., Hopkins, MN; *U.S. Public*, pg. 1383
Sorensen, Ib, Mgr.-Mktg.--KONE Elevator A/S, Copenhagen, Denmark; *Int'l*, pg. 747
Sorenson, Dave, Natl. Sls. Mgr.--Fairmont Snack Group, Inc., Independence, OH; *U.S. Private*, pg. 392
Sorese, Phyliss, Mgr.-Mktg.-Silhouettes--Hanover Direct, Inc., Weehawken, NJ; *U.S. Public*, pg. 782
Sorkenn, Elizabeth, Assoc. Mgr.-Mktg.--France Telecom Inc., New York, NY; *Int'l*, pg. 504
Sornson, Amy, Sr. Mktg. Coord.--American Business Advertising, Omaha, NE; *U.S. Private*, pg. 51
Soroka, Matthew, Dir.-Mktg. & Art Dir.--Charles Atlas, Ltd., New York, NY; *U.S. Private*, pg. 229
Sorrazin, Raymond, V.P.-Distr. & Logistics--Provigo Inc., Montreal, Canada; *Int'l*, pg. 1072
Sorrentino, Ross, Mgr.-Petroleum Mkt.--Liquid Controls LLC, Lake Bluff, IL; *U.S. Private*, pg. 669
Sosville, Dick, V.P.-Sls. & Mktg.--The Dow Chemical Company, Midland, MI; *U.S. Public*, pg. 522
Sosville, Richard E., V.P.-Mktg. & Sls.--Dow Chemical North America, Midland, MI; *U.S. Public*, pg. 522
Sotak, Michael A., V.P.-Mktg.--Lesco, Inc., Rocky River, OH; *U.S. Public*, pg. 989
Sotir, Mark, Sr. V.P.-Mktg.--Budget Rent A Car Corporation, Lisle, IL; *U.S. Private*, pg. 178
Soto, Barabra Ann, Asst. Admin.-Mktg.--Casio Phone-Mate, Inc., Torrance, CA; *Int'l*, pg. 274
Sottile, J., Sr. V.P.-Mktg.--International Home Foods Inc., Parsippany, NJ; *U.S. Private*, pg. 526
Soucy, Mark, Mgr.-Mktg.--Schrader Bellows Division, Cuyahoga Falls, OH; *U.S. Public*, pg. 1261
Soufleris, Mark, V.P.-Mktg.--Nabi, Boca Raton, FL; *U.S. Public*, pg. 1148
Souter, J. Murray, V.P.-Sls. & Mktg.-Canada--Bauer Sports Inc., Montreal, Canada; *U.S. Public*, pg. 1184
Southerland, Michael, Exec. V.P.-Mktg.--Automobile Protection Corporation-APCO, Atlanta, GA; *U.S. Public*, pg. 150
Sowa, Monica, Mgr.-Adv. & Mktg.--Cruises Only Inc., Orlando, FL; *U.S. Private*, pg. 293
Sowal, Patricia, Mgr.-Mktg. Svcs.--Woodstream Corporation, Lititz, PA; *U.S. Public*, pg. 566
Sowder, Jules, V.P.-Mktg.--Promus Hotel Corporation, Memphis, TN; *U.S. Public*, pg. 1335
Sowell, Jeff, V.P.-Mktg.--Shoney's Restaurant Div., Nashville, TN; *U.S. Public*, pg. 1467
Sowell, Lee, V.P.-Sls. & Mktg.--Frigidaire Home Products-Specialty Power Equipment, Shreveport, LA; *Int'l*, pg. 440
Soysal, Turgut, Asst. Gen. Mgr.-Mktg.--Beko Elektronik A.S., Istanbul, Turkey; *Int'l*, pg. 741
Sozonoff, Alex, V.P. & Gen. Mgr.-Sls. & Mktg./Computer Org.--Hewlett-Packard Company, Palo Alto, CA; *U.S. Public*, pg. 813
Spaan, L.P.A., Mgr.-Mktg. & Sls.--Quality Bakers Nederland B.V., Gouda, Netherlands; *Int'l*, pg. 555
Spackman, G. Lawrence, Pres.-Gas Mktg. Group & Transcanada Energy Mngmnt.--Transcanada Pipelines Limited, Calgary, Canada; *Int'l*, pg. 1416
Spadone, Jay, Chief Info. Officer & Dir.-Mktg.--Spadone Inc., Norwalk, CT; *U.S. Private*, pg. 1019
Spaeth, Sandy, Sr. V.P.-Mktg.--Parade Publications Inc., New York, NY; *U.S. Private*, pg. 20
Spagnoletto, Patrizio, V.P.-Mktg.--Parmalat USA Corporation, Teaneck, NJ; *Int'l*, pg. 1023
Spagnou, Frederic, V.P.-Enterprise & Bus. Mktg, Apple Europe--Apple Computer, Inc., Cupertino, CA; *U.S. Public*, pg. 121
Spain, Leo, Mgr.-Mktg. & Sales--Eaton Corp. Div., Athens, AL; *U.S. Public*, pg. 556
Spalding, Jan, Sr. V.P. & Dir.-Mktg.--Harcourt Brace & Company - Elementary Div., Orlando, FL; *U.S. Public*, pg. 783
Spalding, Jim, Mgr.-Mktg.--Charmilles Technologies Corp., Lincolnshire, IL; *Int'l*, pg. 489
Spalteholz, Bianca, Gen. Mgr.Sls. & Mktg./Germany, Austria & Central/Eastern Europe--Utell International-Germany, Frankfurt, Germany; *Int'l*, pg. 1098
Spangler, C.L., V.P.-Mktg.--Handy & Harman Tube Co., Inc., Norristown, PA; *U.S. Public*, pg. 780
Spangler, Cheryl S., Dir.-Mktg.--Star Fine Foods, Inc., Fresno, CA; *U.S. Private*, pg. 1034
Spangler, David B., Pres. & Chief Exec. Officer--Jefferson Mills, Inc., Pulaski, VA; *U.S. Private*, pg. 584
Spangler, Larry, Gen. Mgr. & Adv. & Mktg. Services--Thomasville Furniture Industries, Inc., Thomasville, NC; *U.S. Public*, pg. 688
Spannlong, Janice, Mktg.--Regions Bank/Decatur/Hartselle, Decatur, AL; *U.S. Public*, pg. 1372
Spano, John W., V.P.-Sls. & Mktg.--Twin Disc, Incorporated, Racine, WI; *U.S. Public*, pg. 1646
Sparks, Jan, Dir.-Mktg.--Totes Incorporated, Loveland, OH; *U.S. Private*, pg. 111
Sparks, Jason, Dir.-Mktg. & Sls.--MAG Innovision Co., Inc., Santa Ana, CA; *U.S. Private*, pg. 694
Sparks, Kelly, Coord.-Mktg.--Baker's Supermarkets, Inc., Omaha, NE; *U.S. Public*, pg. 652
Sparks, Steve, Dir.-Mktg./Packaged Water--McKesson Water Products Company, Pasadena, CA; *U.S. Public*, pg. 1073
Spataro, John, V.P.-Mktg.--Ensoniq, Malvern, PA; *U.S. Private*, pg. 377
Spear, Gary, Dir.-Mktg. Communications--Finnigan Corporation, San Jose, CA; *U.S. Public*, pg. 1591
Spearman, Don, Dir.-Bus. Devel.--Vent-Axia Ltd., Crawley, United Kingdom; *Int'l*, pg. 1267
Spears, Debra, Mgr.-Mktg. Svcs.--PAXAR Corporation, White Plains, NY; *U.S. Public*, pg. 1266
Spears, James, V.P.-Mktg. & Adv.--AT&T Business Communications Services, Bridgewater, NJ; *U.S. Public*, pg. 10
Spears, Jimmy, Dir.-Mktg. & Sls.--Darlington Veneer Company, Darlington, SC; *U.S. Private*, pg. 311
Speciale, Phil, Dir.-Mktg.--AT&T Language Line Services, Monterey, CA; *U.S. Public*, pg. 11
Spector, David, Sr. V.P.-Secondary Mktg./Loan Sales--Countrywide Funding Corporation, Pasadena, CA; *U.S. Public*, pg. 453
Speed, Kevin, Mgr.-Mktg. Commun.--Richards Industries, Inc., Cincinnati, OH; *U.S. Private*, pg. 929
Speerstra, Stan, Dir.-Mktg.--Alsons Corporation, Hillsdale, MI; *U.S. Public*, pg. 1053
Speicher, Nevin, V.P.-Mktg.--Hobart Brothers Co., Troy, OH; *U.S. Public*, pg. 866
Speirs, John R., V.P.-Mktg.--Lever Brothers Household Products Div., New York, NY; *Int'l*, pg. 1436
Speirs, Joseph A., V.P.-Mktg.--Nature's Sunshine Products, Inc., Provo, UT; *U.S. Public*, pg. 1166
Spelleri, Richard J., V.P.-Mktg.--Echlin Inc., Branford, CT; *U.S. Public*, pg. 560
Spellman, Ray, Mgr.-Mktg. Communications--GEC-Marconi Hazeltine Corporation, Greenlawn, NY; *Int'l*, pg. 544
Spence, Chester E., V.P.-Mktg. & Sls.--American Technical Ceramics Corp., Huntington Station, NY; *U.S. Public*, pg. 93
Spencer, Floyd, Mgr.-Mktg. Services--Media General, Inc., Richmond, VA; *U.S. Public*, pg. 1077
Spencer, James, Dir.-Mktg., Ventures, Plng. & Sls.--Delphi Saginaw Steering Systems, Saginaw, MI; *U.S. Public*, pg. 719
Spencer, Jeff, Dir.-Mktg.-Royal Crown--Triarc Companies, Inc., New York, NY; *U.S. Public*, pg. 1634
Spencer, Martin G., V.P.-Sls. & Mktg.--Schwitzer, Inc., Indianapolis, IN; *U.S. Public*, pg. 968
Spencer, Mary, Mgr.-Adv. & Sls.--Little Giant Pump Company, Oklahoma City, OK; *U.S. Public*, pg. 1566
Spencer, Merlee, Dir.-Mktg.--Bushwhacker Associates, Inc., Texas City, TX; *U.S. Private*, pg. 141
Spencer, Paul, V.P.-Sls. & Mktg.--Cooper Power Tools Division, Lexington, SC; *U.S. Public*, pg. 444
Spencer, Thomas, Gen. Mgr.-Mktg.--Jaguar Cars, Mahwah, NJ; *U.S. Public*, pg. 664
Spengler, Peter J., V.P.-Mktg. Services--Bristol-Myers Squibb Company, New York, NY; *U.S. Public*, pg. 253
Speranza, Ernest V., Sr. V.P.-Adv. & Mktg. Worldwide--Toys "R" Us, Inc., Paramus, NJ; *U.S. Public*, pg. 1626
Speranza, Ernest V., Sr. V.P.-Adv./Mktg.--Toys "R" Us United States, Paramus, NJ; *U.S. Public*, pg. 1626
Spessard, Rob, Jr., V.P.-Mktg. & Professional Svcs.--Sun Data Inc., Norcross, GA; *U.S. Private*, pg. 1050
Spielman, Eli, Natl. Dir-Mktg.--Ernst & Young, LLP, New York, NY; *U.S. Private*, pg. 381
Spier, Chris, V.P.-Sls. & Mktg.--Bucyrus Blades Inc., Bucyrus, OH; *U.S. Private*, pg. 383

Spink, Ronald O., Dir.-Interactive Mktg. Services--BPA International, New York, NY; *U.S. Private*, pg. 107

Spinks, Jeff, Gen. Mgr.-EmployeeBenefits Customer Legal & Fin. Svcs.--Employee Benefits Div., Rondebosch, South Africa; *Int'l*, pg. 77

Spinks, Pam, Mtkg. Asst.--Givaudan-Roure Corporation-Flavors Division, Clifton, NJ; *Int'l*, pg. 1119

Spira, Paul, Dir.-Mktg.--Auto Glass Specialists, Madison, WI; *U.S. Private*, pg. 100

Spivey, Bill, Dir.-Mktg.--Quincy Corp., Quincy, FL; *U.S. Public*, pg. 1545

Spivey, Doug, V.P.-Mktg.--Packerland Packing Co., Green Bay, WI; *U.S. Private*, pg. 833

Splawski, Dennis, Dir.-Mktg. Services--Sandoz Agro, Inc., Des Plaines, IL; *Int'l*, pg. 974

Spoel, A., Mgr.-Mktg.--Steelmark-Eagle & Globe, Auburn, Australia; *Int'l*, pg. 100

Spoerle, Steve, Asst. V.P.-Corp. Mktg.--BetzDearborn Inc., Trevose, PA; *U.S. Public*, pg. 226

Spolane, David A., Exec. V.P.--Sterling Electronics Corporation, Houston, TX; *U.S. Public*, pg. 1051

Spoldi, Franco, Mgr.-Mktg.--Thermo Separation Products, San Jose, CA; *U.S. Public*, pg. 1594

Spore, Eric, V.P.-Mktg.--Alpha Olefins North America Inc., Houston, TX; *Int'l*, pg. 1196

Spotts, Steve, V.P.-Mktg. & Applications Support--Pharmacia & Upjohn Biotech Inc., Piscataway, NJ; *Int'l*, pg. 1047

Sprague, Dominique, Mktg. Supvr.--HBO & Company/Cycare Business Group, Scottsdale, AZ; *U.S. Public*, pg. 770

Sprimont, Roger, Exec. V.P.-Mktg.--Celsius AB, Stockholm, Sweden; *Int'l*, pg. 276

Spring, Tony, Sr. V.P.-Mktg.--Bloomingdale's, New York, NY; *U.S. Public*, pg. 617

Springer, Hugh, Grp. Mgr.-Clinical Prods. Div.--Novartis Nutrition Corporation, Saint Louis Park, MN; *Int'l*, pg. 974

Springer, Richard N., Mgr.-Mktg. Commun.--Wyle Electronics, Irvine, CA; *Int'l*, pg. 1457

Springer, Vic, V.P.-Mktg.--Morgan Distribution, Mechanicsburg, PA; *U.S. Public*, pg. 1132

Sproul, Susan W., Mgr.-Mktg.--BNA Books Div., Washington, DC; *U.S. Private*, pg. 181

Sprunger, Steve, Mgr.-Sls. & Mktg.--Kelley Company, Inc., Milwaukee, WI; *U.S. Private*, pg. 612

Sprunk, Sue, Dir.-MKtg.--Caldor, Inc., Norwalk, CT; *U.S. Public*, pg. 292

Sprunt, Julia W., V.P.-Mktg. & Communictions--Turner Broadcasting System Inc., Atlanta, GA; *U.S. Public*, pg. 1614

Squires, Troy, V.P.--Southwest Recreational Industries Inc., Leander, TX; *U.S. Private*, pg. 1018

Srednicki, Joyce, V.P.-Mktg./Household Prods.--Church & Dwight Co., Inc., Princeton, NJ; *U.S. Public*, pg. 355

Srndberh, Goran, Dir.-Mktg.--Jarnia AB, Ulricehammn, Sweden; *Int'l*, pg. 188

St. Clair, James, V.P.-Mktg.--Challenger Electrical Equipment Corp., Pittsburgh, PA; *U.S. Public*, pg. 558

St. Claire, Maggie, Dir.-Mktg. & Community Affairs--KSL Radio, Salt Lake City, UT; *U.S. Private*, pg. 327

St. Clari-Miller, Jane, Gen. Mgr.-Mktg.--H.J. Heinz Company, Limited, Hayes, United Kingdom; *U.S. Public*, pg. 806

St. Jean, Sheila, Mgr.-Mktg. Communications--IRD Mechanalysis, Inc. (U.S.A.), Columbus, OH; *U.S. Public*, pg. 789

St. John, Erin, Mgr.-Mktg. Services--Snappy Car Rental, Inc., Tulsa, OK; *U.S. Private*, pg. 1010

St. John, Norbert, Exec. V.P.-Mktg.--Richey Electronics, Inc., Garden Grove, CA; *U.S. Public*, pg. 1388

Sta, Jan J.A., Mgr.-Mktg. Communications--Quest International, Naarden, Netherlands; *Int'l*, pg. 1438

Staack, Craig F., Sr. V.P.-Mktg.--Heilig-Meyers Company, Richmond, VA; *U.S. Public*, pg. 804

Stabile, Jeffrey, Pres. & Chief Exec. Officer--Aero Systems Aviation Corp., Miami, FL; *U.S. Private*, pg. 24

Stablein, Larry, Sr. V.P.-Mktg.--Jewel-Osco, Melrose Park, IL; *U.S. Public*, pg. 93

Stacey, Colleen, Mktg. Assoc.--Circle Business Credit, Inc., Indianapolis, IN; *U.S. Public*, pg. 1785

Stachurski, Terri, Mgr.-Corp. Mktg.--OmniQuip International, Inc., Port Washington, WI; *U.S. Private*, pg. 500

Stack, Fred, V.P.-Mktg.--U.S. Electrical Motor Division, Saint Louis, MO; *U.S. Public*, pg. 573

Stack, Nathan, Mktg. & Corp. Communications--UBS Management North America, New York, NY; *Int'l*, pg. 1440

Stack, Pat, Sr. V.P.-Mktg.--BTI Americas, Inc., Northbrook, IL; *U.S. Private*, pg. 108

Stacy, Ron, V.P.-Mktg. & Sls.--American Flange & Manufacturing Co. Inc., Carol Stream, IL; *Int'l*, pg. 1146

Stad, Geller, Dir.-Mktg.--Du Pont de Nemours International S.A., Geneva, Switzerland; *U.S. Public*, pg. 532

Stadlen, Diane E., Sr. V.P. & Mktg. Analysis & Media Services Dir.--Creswell, Munsell, Fultz & Zirbel, L.P., Cedar Rapids, IA; *U.S. Private*, pg. 1197

Stafford, John, V.P.-Sls. & Mktg.--Systech Computer Corporation, San Diego, CA; *U.S. Private*, pg. 1061

Stager, Robert, Mgr.-Sls.--Sheffield Steel Corporation-Joliet, Joliet, IL; *U.S. Private*, pg. 991

Stai, Harlan C., Exec. V.P.-Opers.--Owen Health Care, Inc., Houston, TX; *U.S. Public*, pg. 304

Stainer, Dan, Mgr.-Mktg. Svcs.--Group 1 Software, Inc., Lanham, MD; *U.S. Public*, pg. 417

Stake, Randy J., Mgr.-Mktg. Commun.--Weber Marking Systems, Inc., Arlington Heights, IL; *U.S. Private*, pg. 1157

Staller, Chris, Dir.-Indus. Sls., Mktg. & Adv.--Vibro-Meter Corp., Long Beach, CA; *U.S. Private*, pg. 1138

Stamp, Carl, V.P.-Mktg.--Wright Medical Technology, Arlington, TN; *U.S. Private*, pg. 1192

Stamp, Jeffrey, Ph.D., Dir.-Mktg.--JII/Sales Promotion Associates, Inc., Coshocton, OH; *U.S. Private*, pg. 598

Stamper, Debbie, Mgr.-Mktg.--Gator Freightways, Inc., Wilmington, OH; *U.S. Private*, pg. 441

Stamper, Robert, V.P.-Mktg. & Wood Mdsg.--Drexel Heritage Furnishings Inc., Drexel, NC; *U.S. Private*, pg. 432

Stampfli, Urs, V.P.-Mktg. (Photo)--AGFA Division of Bayer Corporation, Ridgefield Park, NJ; *Int'l*, pg. 172

Stanbury, Robert G., V.P.-Res./Devel. & Mktg.--Flowserve Corporation, Rotating Equipment Grp., Dayton, OH; *U.S. Public*, pg. 658

Standen, Bill, Mgr.-Sls. & Mktg.--Abbott Electronics, Inc., Los Angeles, CA; *U.S. Private*, pg. 9

Standig, David L., V.P.-Mktg.--Comcast Cellular Communications, Inc., Wayne, PA; *U.S. Public*, pg. 407

Standridge, Gary, Mgr.-Bus. Devel. Services--The News Tribune, Tacoma, WA; *U.S. Public*, pg. 1066

Stanek, Bill, Mgr.-Mktg.-Filtration--Tetko, Inc., Briarcliff Manor, NY; *U.S. Private*, pg. 1078

Stang, Gary, V.P.-Sls. & Mktg.--Scoville Press, Inc., Minneapolis, MN; *U.S. Private*, pg. 977

Stangel, Michael, Sr. V.P.-Professional Div.--Alberto-Culver Company, Melrose Park, IL; *U.S. Public*, pg. 37

Stangel, Michael, V.P.-Professional Div.--Alberto-Culver Company, Melrose Park, IL; *U.S. Public*, pg. 37

Stanland, Mark H., Dir.- Mktg. Programs & Services--Dillard, A ResourceNet International Company, Greensboro, NC; *U.S. Public*, pg. 901

Stanley, David, Dir.-Mktg.--Physician Sales & Services Inc., Beaumont, TX; *U.S. Public*, pg. 1294

Stanley, Helen, Mgr.-Mktg.--LTB, Houston, TX; *U.S. Private*, *pg. 668*

Stanley, John H., Dir.-Commerical Mktg.--Public Service Company of North Carolina, Inc., Gastonia, NC; *U.S. Public*, pg. 1340

Stanley, Rick, Mktg. Coord.--Berkel Incorporated, La Porte, IN; *Int'l*, pg. 545

Stansfield, Jerry, Dir.-Mktg.--U.S. Marine Div., Everett, WA; *U.S. Public*, pg. 266

Stanton, F. Ronald, V.P. & Gen Mgr.-Sls. & Mktg.--Allen & Hanburys, Research Triangle Park, NC; *Int'l*, pg. 552

Staple, Ed, V.P.-Sls. & Mktg.--Greenlee Textron, Rockford, IL; *U.S. Public*, pg. 1589

Staples, Patricia J., Sr. V.P.-Mktg.--Community First Bankshares, Inc., Fargo, ND; *U.S. Public*, pg. 416

Stapleton, Charles D., V.P.-Mktg. Div.--Motorists Mutual Insurance Co., Columbus, OH; *U.S. Private*, pg. 764

Stare, Christina, Mgr.-Mktg. Svcs.--Travel U.K., London, United Kingdom,; *U.S. Private*, pg. 647

Stark, Jim, Sr. V.P.-RV Sls. & Mktg.--The Coast Distribution System, San Jose, CA; *U.S. Public*, pg. 388

Stark, Joel, Sr. V.P.-Mktg. & Devel.--Providence Journal-Bulletin, Providence, RI; *U.S. Public*, pg. 209

Stark, Steve, Exec. Dir.-Mktg. & Bus. Devel.--Citizens Gas & Coke Utility, Indianapolis, IN; *U.S. Private*, pg. 241

Starks, Richard, Sr. V.P.-Sls. & Mktg.--The Dallas Morning News, Inc., Dallas, TX; *U.S. Public*, pg. 209

Starkweather, Jeff, Dir.-Mktg.--WOKR-TV, Rochester, NY; *U.S. Private*, pg. 439

Starnes, Wayne, Exec. V.P.-Sls. & Mktg.--Stainless Ice-Tainer Co. (SITCO), Roswell, GA; *Int'l*, pg. 646

Starrett, Frederick D., III, Pres. & Treas.--Penobscot Frozen Foods, Inc., Belfast, ME; *U.S. Private*, pg. 850

Starrett, K.E., Dir.-Mktg.--American Excelsior Company, Arlington, TX; *U.S. Private*, pg. 53

Starzer, Mike R., V.P.-Corp. Devel.--Berry Petroleum Company, Taft, CA; *U.S. Public*, pg. 223

Stashkiw, Walter, V.P.-Mktg., Sls. & Adv.--The Will-Burt Company, Orrville, OH; *U.S. Private*, pg. 1177

Stasyszen, Bill, Dir.-Adv.--C.R. Anthony Company, Oklahoma City, OK; *U.S. Private*, pg. 1029

Staszkow, Myron, V.P.-Mktg. & Sls.--OMRON Systems, Inc., Schaumburg, IL; *Int'l*, pg. 1005

Stathers, Richard N., Sr. V.P.-Sls. & Mktg.--Centennial Technologies, Inc., Wilmington, MA; *U.S. Public*, pg. 322

Staudt, Michael, Dir.-Mktg. & Sls.--Sunkist Growers, Processed Products, Ontario, CA; *U.S. Private*, pg. 1052

Stauffer, Jeff, V.P.-Mktg.--Old World Industries, Inc., Northbrook, IL; *U.S. Private*, pg. 814

Stauffer, Michael G., Dir.-Sls. & Mktg.--Keystone Powdered Metal Company, Saint Marys, PA; *U.S. Private*, pg. 619

Stautzenbach, Edward G., V.P.-Mktg.--Mercury Finance Co., Lake Forest, IL; *U.S. Public*, pg. 1093

Stavely, Raymond E., Mgr.-Mktg. Svcs.--Delta Circuit Protection & Controls Ltd., Birmingham, United Kingdom; *Int'l*, pg. 390

Staven, Carolyn, Mgr.-Mktg. Communications--John Crane Mechanical Seals, Morton Grove, IL; *Int'l*, pg. 1339

Stavropoulos, Nickolas, Chief Fin. Officer & Exec. V.P.-Fin. & Mktg.--Colonial Gas Company, Lowell, MA; *U.S. Public*, pg. 400

Stead, Dominic, Mktg. Dir.--Mediapolis, London, United Kingdom; *Int'l*, pg. 853

Stealey, Lorrie, Mgr.-Mktg. Svcs.--Eva-Tone Inc., Clearwater, FL; *U.S. Private*, pg. 384

Stealey, Sarah, Mktg. Opers. Mgr.--American Television Time, Inc., Austin, TX; *U.S. Private*, pg. 63

Stearns, Doug, Dir.-Sls. & Mktg.--Seneca Wire & Manufacturing Co., Fostoria, OH; *U.S. Private*, pg. 984

Stebbins, Byron H., Sr. V.P.-Market Devel.--Newell Co., Freeport, IL; *U.S. Public*, pg. 1176

Stebbins, Liz, Dir.-Mktg.--Sterling Financial Corporation, Spokane, WA; *U.S. Public*, pg. 1516

Stebbins, Mark, V.P. & Secondary Mktg.--Sierra West Bank, Truckee, CA; *U.S. Public*, pg. 1470

Steefer, Shelley, Mgr.-Mktg.--United Artists Theatre Circuits Incorporated, Englewood, CO; *U.S. Private*, pg. 1120

Steel, Marion, Mgr.-Mktg. Services--PACCAR Australia Pty. Ltd., Bayswater, Australia; *U.S. Public*, pg. 1247

Steele, Carl, Mgr.-Mktg.--Municipal & Food--Bird Machine Company, South Walpole, MA; *U.S. Public*, pg. 166

Steele, Chris, Gen. Mgr.-Mktg.--Cheltenham & Gloucester plc, Gloucester, United Kingdom; *Int'l*, pg. 283

Steele, Cling, V.P.-Mktg.--Todd & Sargent, Inc., Ames, IA; *U.S. Private*, pg. 1089

Steele, George, Sr. V.P.-Mktg.--Rollerblade, Inc., Minnetonka, MN; *U.S. Private*, pg. 941

Steele, John W., Dir.-Sls. & Mktg.--The Uhlmann Co., Kansas City, MO; *U.S. Private*, pg. 1115

Steele, Richard A., Sr. V.P.-Sls. & Mktg.--Printronix, Inc., Irvine, CA; *U.S. Public*, pg. 1329

Steelman, Sheila, Mktg. Communications--Atlas/Soundolier, Fenton, MO; *U.S. Private*, pg. 64

Steer, B.E., Dir.-Mktg.--Britains Petite Ltd., Nottingham, United Kingdom; *U.S. Public*, pg. 789

Stefan, Mark R., Mgr.-Prod.--Ravarino & Freschi, Inc., Saint Louis, MO; *U.S. Private*, pg. 158

Stefanic, Sean, Mgr.-Mktg.--TV Host Inc., Harrisburg, PA; *U.S. Private*, pg. 1066

Stefanski, Larry, V.P.-Sls. & Mktg.--Cattleman's, Inc., Detroit, MI; *U.S. Public*, pg. 318

Steffes, Edward J., V.P.-Mktg.--DeVry Institutes, Oak Brook Terrace, IL; *U.S. Public*, pg. 503

Stefik, Lynn, Mgr.-Mktg. Communications--Pitney Bowes Software Systems, Glen Ellyn, IL; *U.S. Public*, pg. 1304

Stefkovich, Joe, Sr. Mgr.-Mktg.--Whatman Inc., Clifton, NJ; *Int'l*, pg. 1498

Stegall, Robert, Sr. V.P.-Sls. & Mktg.--SGI Integrated Graphic Systems, Houston, TX; *U.S. Public*, pg. 971

Steichen, Curt, Dir.-Mktg.--Hoffman Engineering Company, Anoka, MN; *U.S. Public*, pg. 1273

Steidl, Richard, Dir.-Mktg.--Otter Tail Power Company, Fergus Falls, MN; *U.S. Public*, pg. 1234

Steigerwald, Ed, Dir.-Mktg.--PCC Airfoils, Inc., Beachwood, OH; *U.S. Public*, pg. 1320

Stein, Alan, V.P.-Mktg.--Rockefeller Center Management Corporation, New York, NY; *Int'l*, pg. 873

Stein, David, V.P.-Mktg.--Integrated Brands Inc., Ronkonkoma, NY; *U.S. Public*, pg. 883

Stein, Joyce, Dir.-Mktg.--Primedia Inc., Mahwah, NJ; *U.S. Public*, pg. 1328

Stein, Joyce, Dir.-Mktg.--The World Almanac, Mahwah, NJ; *U.S. Public*, pg. 1328

Stein, Marshall, V.P.-Mktg.--Powerine Oil Company, Santa Fe Springs, CA; *U.S. Public*, pg. 314

Stein, Tim, V.P.-Sls. & Mktg.--Abex Friction Products, Winchester, VA; *U.S. Public*, pg. 443

Steinberg, Stephen, Dir.-Mktg.--Spaulding & Slye, Boston, MA; *U.S. Private*, pg. 1021

Steinbrook, Vicki, Mgr.-Sls. & Mktg.--White Castle Distributing, Inc., Columbus, OH; *U.S. Private*, pg. 1172

Steiner, Alan, Mgr.-Sls., Mktg., Adv. & Distr.--ITW Switches, Chicago, IL; *U.S. Public*, pg. 867

Steiner, Irene, Dir.-Mktg. & Sls.--The Vermont Teddy Bear Company, Inc., Shelburne, VT; *U.S. Public*, pg. 1716

Steiner, Jeff, Mgr.-Mktg Communications--Johnson Controls, Inc., Plymouth, MI; *U.S. Public*, pg. 932

Steinhart, Conrad, Controller, Treas. & Sec.--Happy Holiday Tree Farms, Sheridan, MI; *U.S. Private*, pg. 254

Steinhouse, Eric, Sr. V.P.-Mktg.--H & R Block, Inc., Kansas City, MO; *U.S. Public*, pg. 770

Steinkamp, Mark, Coord.-Pub. Rels & Adv.--Daktronics, Inc., Brookings, SD; *U.S. Public*, pg. 478

Steinke, James E., V.P.-Sls. & Mktg./Retail--Patrick Cudahy Inc., Cudahy, WI; *U.S. Public*, pg. 1479

Steinman, Andrew, V.P.-Mktg. & Sls.--Falcon Safety Products Inc., Somerville, NJ; *U.S. Private*, pg. 392

Steinmetz, Allan, Sr. V.P. & Corp. Dir.-Mktg.--Arthur D. Little, Inc., Cambridge, MA; *U.S. Private*, pg. 670

Steinmeyer, Jim, Sr. V.P.-Mktg.--Oakwood Homes Corporation, Greensboro, NC; *U.S. Public*, pg. 1209

Steinmiller, John, V.P.-Bus. Opers. & Mktg.--Milwaukee Bucks, Inc., Milwaukee, WI; *U.S. Private*, pg. 749

Steinstein, Gloria, Dir.-Mktg. Services--Pentland Group PLC, London, United Kingdom; *Int'l*, pg. 1035

Stella, Joe, Mgr.-Mktg. & Sls.--Dacor Corporation, Northfield, IL; *U.S. Private*, pg. 306

Stembridge, John C., V.P.-Sls. & Mktg.--WTD Industries, Inc., Portland, OR; *U.S. Public*, pg. 1729

Stemper, John, V.P.-Mktg.--Malt-O-Meal Company, Minneapolis, MN; *U.S. Private*, pg. 699

Stenberg, Michael, Dir.-Pulmonary & Bariatrics--Kinetic Concepts, Inc., San Antonio, TX; *U.S. Private*, pg. 620

Stencel, Mark, Dir.-Adv.--Frigid Coil West, Santa Fe Springs, CA; *U.S. Public*, pg. 1789

Stengel, Eva, Mgr.-Mktg. Services--VARTA AG, Hannover, Germany; *Int'l*, pg. 1451

Stennett, Cheryl, Dir.-Mktg.--Cargill Flour Div., Minneapolis, MN; *U.S. Private*, pg. 210

Stensby, Robert, V.P.-Mktg.--Lynx Golf, Inc., City of Industry, CA; *U.S. Private*, pg. 684

Stephan, R., Dir.-Mktg.--Moore Formularios Limitada, Bauru, Brazil; *Int'l*, pg. 889

Stephen, Jennifer, V.P.-Mktg.--The Stiffel Company, Chicago, IL; *U.S. Private*, pg. 1043

Stephens, Arnie, Mgr.-Mktg.--TELUS Mobility, Calgary, Canada; *Int'l*, pg. 1374

Stephens, Bonnie, Mgr.-Mktg. Commun.--Branson Ultrasonics Corp.-Plastics Joining Div., Danbury, CT; *U.S. Public*, pg. 574

Stephens, Bonnie, Mgr.-Mktg. Communications--Branson Ultrasonics, Danbury, CT; *U.S. Public*, pg. 574

Stephens, Buddy, V.P. & Dir.-Mktg.--Hale-Halsell Company, Tulsa, OK; *U.S. Private*, pg. 494

Stephens, Dana, Coord.-Sls. & Mktg.--Royston Laboratories, Pittsburgh, PA; *U.S. Public*, pg. 337

Stephens, John, Dir.-Mktg.--Anchor Inc., Orange Park, FL; *U.S. Public*, pg. 903

Stephensen, Tom, V.P.-Mktg.--VTEL Corporation, Austin, TX; *U.S. Public*, pg. 1703

Stephenson, Catherine, Mgr.-Mktg.--Scan-Optics, Inc., Manchester, CT; *U.S. Public*, pg. 1436

Stephenson, R.L., Sr. V.P.-Sls. & Mktg.--Resco Products, Inc., Conshohocken, PA; *U.S. Private*, pg. 924

Stephenson, Sandy, V.P.--Stephenson, Inc., Alexandria, VA; *U.S. Private*, pg. 1040

Sterling, T.J., Mgr.-Mktg.--Thomas Lighting-C&I Accent Division, Los Angeles, CA; *U.S. Public*, pg. 1599

Stern, Andrew, Sr. V.P.-Strategic Plng. & Corp. Mktg.--United States Fidelity & Guaranty Company, Baltimore, MD; *U.S. Public*, pg. 1659

Stern, Dan, Dir.-Mktg. & Sls.--Global Motor Sport Group, Inc., Morgan Hill, CA; *U.S. Public*, pg. 748
Stern, Joel, Mgr.-Info. Research--Candle Corporation, Santa Monica, CA; *U.S. Private*, pg. 204
Sterrett, Bob, Dir.-Mktg.--Litton Poly-Scientific, Blacksburg, VA; *U.S. Public*, pg. 1003
Sterrett, James E., Mgr.-Lumber/Plywood Sls. & Mktg.--Boise Cascade Timber & Wood Products Division, Boise, ID; *U.S. Public*, pg. 243
Steur, N.J., Mgr.-Mktg.--KTI Group B.V., Zoetermeer, Netherlands; *Int'l*, pg. 837
Stevens, Adrienne, V.P.-Sls. & Mktg.--BF Goodrich Avionic Systems, Inc., Grand Rapids, MI; *U.S. Public*, pg. 751
Stevens, Andrew E., Chm. Bd., Pres. & Dir.-Mktg. & Pub. Rels.--GWP, Inc., Los Angeles, CA; *U.S. Private*, pg. 437
Stevens, Ann, Dir.-Corp. Communications--Harte-Hanks Communications, Inc., San Antonio, TX; *U.S. Public*, pg. 793
Stevens, C.G., Dir.-Pub. Rels.--The Ziegler Companies, Inc., West Bend, WI; *U.S. Public*, pg. 1791
Stevens, C.G., V.P.-Mktg. Dir.--B.C. Ziegler & Co., West Bend, WI; *U.S. Public*, pg. 1792
Stevens, Dave, V.P.-Mktg.--Candle Corporation, Santa Monica, CA; *U.S. Private*, pg. 204
Stevens, David, Mgr.-Prod.--Setzer Forest Products, Sacramento, CA; *U.S. Private*, pg. 987
Stevens, Frank, V.P.-Sls. & Mktg.--Boler Company, Itasca, IL; *U.S. Private*, pg. 155
Stevens, Garry, Sr. Dir.-Mktg.-Grocery, DSD, Dairy & Frozen Foods--Big V Supermarkets, Inc., Florida, NY; *U.S. Private*, pg. 143
Stevens, Glenn, V.P.--GWP, Inc., Los Angeles, CA; *U.S. Private*, pg. 437
Stevens, Mark, Dir.-WW Direct Mktg. & Sls. Promo.--International Business Machines Corporation, Armonk, NY; *U.S. Public*, pg. 895
Stevens, Paul E., Mgr.-Mktg.--Alexander & Baldwin, Inc., Honolulu, HI; *U.S. Public*, pg. 39
Stevens, Paul E., Sr. V.P.-Mktg.--Matson Navigation Company, Inc., San Francisco, CA; *U.S. Public*, pg. 39
Stevens, Peter, Mgr.-Mktg.--United News & Media plc, London, United Kingdom; *Int'l*, pg. 1443
Stevens, Richard, Dir.-Natl. Prods.--Bergen Brunswig Corporation, Orange, CA; *U.S. Public*, pg. 213
Stevens, Tina, Mgr.-Mktg.--Blockbuster Entertainment Corporation Limited (U.K.), Uxbridge, United Kingdom; *U.S. Private*, pg. 776
Stevenson, Bruce, Dir.-Mktg.--Hill Phoenix, Colonial Heights, VA; *U.S. Public*, pg. 521
Stevenson, John, V.P.-Sls. & Mktg.--Health Economics Corporation, Dallas, TX; *U.S. Public*, pg. 588
Stevenson, John, Database Mktg. Dir.--The Chapman Agency, New York, NY; *U.S. Private*, pg. 1197
Stevenson, Lloyd, V.P.-Mktg. & Sls.--Abbott Ball Company, West Hartford, CT; *U.S. Private*, pg. 9
Stevenson, R.H., Sr. V.P.-Sls. & Mktg.--North State Pyrophyllite, Greensboro, NC; *U.S. Private*, pg. 924
Stevenson, Richard, Dir.-Mktg.--Control Laser Corporation, Orlando, FL; *U.S. Public*, pg. 599
Stevenson, Robert, V.P.-Sls. & Mktg.--Pioneer Plastics Corporation, Auburn, ME; *U.S. Private*, pg. 867
Steward, Hugh, Mgr.-Natl.-Mktg.--Ferrari North America, Hasbrouck Heights, NJ; *Int'l*, pg. 483
Stewart, C. Jim III, V.P.-Mktg.--Stewart & Stevenson Services, Inc., Houston, TX; *U.S. Public*, pg. 1517
Stewart, Danny, Exec. V.P.-Sls. & Mktg.--Catalina Lighting, Inc., Miami, FL; *U.S. Public*, pg. 314
Stewart, Doug, Mgr. Sales--The Amalgamated Sugar Company LLC, Ogden, UT; *U.S. Private*, pg. 48
Stewart, Glen L., V.P.-Transpacific & S. Pacific Mktg.--Hawaiian Airlines, Inc., Honolulu, HI; *U.S. Public*, pg. 799
Stewart, Jacque, Mgr.-Mktg.--Cerprobe Corporation, Gilbert, AZ; *U.S. Public*, pg. 332
Stewart, Jeanette, Mgr.-Mktg. Admin.--McGraw-Hill Information Systems Co. of Canada Ltd., North York, Canada; *U.S. Public*, pg. 1072
Stewart, Jeff, Gen. Mgr.-Professional Components Div.--Philips Components, Jupiter, FL; *Int'l*, pg. 1054
Stewart, Jerry, V.P.-Sls. & Mktg., Poultry Group--Gold Kist, Inc., Atlanta, GA; *U.S. Private*, pg. 459
Stewart, Joe, V.P.-Mktg.--Bar-S Foods Co., Phoenix, AZ; *U.S. Private*, pg. 114
Stewart, John, V.P.-Sls. & Mktg.--Schmidt Baking Co., Inc., Baltimore, MD; *U.S. Private*, pg. 970
Stewart, Linda, Dir.-Mktg.--Greenbull Inc., Louisville, KY; *U.S. Private*, pg. 477
Stewart, Mark, Asst. V.P.-Mktg.--Academy Insurance Group, Inc., Alpharetta, GA; *Int'l*, pg. 27
Stewart, Maurice L., V.P.-Mktg.--Sun Life Assurance Company of Canada (U.S.), Wellesley Hills, MA; *Int'l*, pg. 1319
Stewart, Rob, Dir.-Sls.--Stadelman Fruit L.L.C., Yakima, WA; *U.S. Private*, pg. 1028
Stewart, Roy J., Mgr.-Mktg. Services--Osborn Manufacturing, Cleveland, OH; *U.S. Public*, pg. 924
Stewart, Shirley, Dir.-Personnel & Mktg.--Modern Concrete Septic Tank Company, Ottsville, PA; *U.S. Private*, pg. 754
Stewart, Thomas, V.P.-Sls. & Mktg.--Gaymar Industries, Inc., Orchard Park, NY; *U.S. Private*, pg. 442
Stiger, Marc, Dir.-Books--Brodart Company, Williamsport, PA; *U.S. Private*, pg. 170
Stight, Richard, V.P.-Sls. & Mktg.--Columbian Rope Company, Guntown, MS; *U.S. Private*, pg. 256
Stigi, Peter, Sr. V.P.-Sls. & Mktg.--Tuscan/Lehigh Dairies LP, Union, NJ; *U.S. Private*, pg. 1110
Stillings, Robert, V.P.-Opers., Sls., Mktg. & Dir.-Personnel--Presto Food Stores, Inc., Plant City, FL; *U.S. Private*, pg. 882
Stillitano, P.J., Mgr.-Mktg. & Communications--Babcock & Wilcox Co., Barberton, OH; *U.S. Public*, pg. 1068
Stillman, Thomas, Mgr.-Mktg.-Food Ingredients--Universal Flavors-U.S.A., Indianapolis, IN; *U.S. Public*, pg. 1696
Stimac, Tom, Prod. Mgr.--De-Sta-Co, A Dover Resources Co., Troy, MI; *U.S. Public*, pg. 521
Stine, Tim, Dir.-Sls. Plng.-Retail & Food Svcs.--Tri Valley Growers, San Ramon, CA; *U.S. Private*, pg. 1101
Stinnett, Gary, V.P.-Mktg. & Mdsg.--Cole Vision Corporation, Cleveland, OH; *U.S. Public*, pg. 396
Stinson, Greg, Sr. V.P.-Mktg.--Ruppman Marketing Technologies, Inc., Peoria, IL; *U.S. Private*, pg. 951
Stith, Andrew W., Sr. V.P.-Sls. & Mktg.--NovaCare Employee Services, Inc., Norristown, PA; *U.S. Public*, pg. 1203
Stober, Jerry, Dir.-Mktg. & Mgr.-Prod.--Medrad, Inc., Indianola, PA; *Int'l*, pg. 1204
Stock, Mike, Visual Design Specialist--Cadillac Plastic & Chemical Co., Troy, MI; *U.S. Public*, pg. 781
Stockett, Peter, V.P.-Adv., Sls. & Mktg.--Sun Bancorp, Inc., Selinsgrove, PA; *U.S. Public*, pg. 1529
Stockett, Peter C., V.P.-Mktg.--Sun Bank d/b/a Snyder County Trust Company, Selinsgrove, PA; *U.S. Public*, pg. 1529
Stockham, Jim, Mgr.-Mktg. & Sls.--Zacky Farms, Inc., South El Monte, CA; *U.S. Private*, pg. 1203
Stocking, Janice, Mgr.-Mktg. Admin.--Miniature Precision Components, Walworth, WI; *U.S. Private*, pg. 750
Stockstill, Raymond W., V.P.-Mktg.--Smith Environmental Technologies Corp., Plymouth Meeting, PA; *U.S. Public*, pg. 1477
Stockton, Charles, V.P.-Mktg.--The Chinet Co., Norwalk, CT; *Int'l*, pg. 1146
Stoddard, John, V.P.-Mktg. & Communications--The Butcher Company, Marlborough, MA; *U.S. Private*, pg. 189
Stoebner, Tom, Mgr.-Adv., Sls. & Mktg.-Films--Raven Industries, Inc., Sioux Falls, SD; *U.S. Public*, pg. 1361
Stoebner, Tom, V.P.-Sls. & Mktg.--Engineered Films Div., Flexible Films Dept., Sioux Falls, SD; *U.S. Public*, pg. 1361
Stoeckel, Howard, Sr. V.P.-Mktg.--Wawa, Inc., Media, PA; *U.S. Private*, pg. 1155
Stoeckl, Wilhelm, Dir.-Mktg.--Novartis-Pharma GmbH, Vienna, Austria; *Int'l*, pg. 984
Stoffregen, Debbie, Mgr.-Mktg. Services--Selfix, Inc., Chicago, IL; *U.S. Public*, pg. 832
Stoffregen, Paul, Dir.-Mktg.--Bryan Foods, West Point, MS; *U.S. Public*, pg. 1433
Stohler, L. Gene, V.P.-Automotive Mktg. & Plng.--MascoTech, Inc., Taylor, MI; *U.S. Public*, pg. 1055
Stokely, Gregg, V.P.-Commercial Mktg.--BEI Sensors and Systems Company, Sylmar, CA; *U.S. Public*, pg. 160
Stokes, Jackie, Mgr.-Sls.--Dean Operations Inc., Kansas City, MO; *U.S. Private*, pg. 318
Stokes, Nick, Mgr.-Mktg. & Sls./Bldg. Matls.--Boise Cascade Corporation, Boise, ID; *U.S. Public*, pg. 242
Stokes, Nick, Mgr.-Division Sls. & Mktg.--Boise Cascade Building Materials Distribution Div., Boise, ID; *U.S. Public*, pg. 243
Stokes, Paul, Mgr.-Mktg.--Staveley Sensors Division, East Hartford, CT; *Int'l*, pg. 1299
Stokes, Ron, Mgr.-Intl. Mktg.--Glen Raven Mills, Inc., Glen Raven, NC; *U.S. Private*, pg. 456
Stokes, Terry, Dir.-Mktg.--Ultra Electronics Command & Control Systems, High Wycombe, United Kingdom; *Int'l*, pg. 1431
Stokey, Jeff, Dir.-Mktg.--Seaboard Farms, Athens, GA; *U.S. Public*, pg. 1449
Stolakis, Steve, Dir.-Prod. Mktg.--Oki Telecom Group, Suwanee, GA; *Int'l*, pg. 1000
Stoltman, Pat, Mgr.-Mktg. & Sls.--Farm Press, Clarksdale, MS; *U.S. Public*, pg. 1328
Stolz, Pascal, V.P.-Mktg.--Cobra Golf Incorporated, Carlsbad, CA; *U.S. Public*, pg. 675
Stone, Arnie, Dir.-Mktg.--Food Service Division, Hunt Valley, MD; *U.S. Public*, pg. 1066
Stone, Arthur L., V.P.-Intermodal Mktg./Mark VII Transportation Co.--Mark VII, Inc., Memphis, TN; *U.S. Public*, pg. 1046
Stone, Arthur L., V.P.-Intermodal Mktg.--Mark VII Transportation Company, Inc., Greenwood, IN; *U.S. Public*, pg. 1046
Stone, C.B., V.P.-Mktg.--Computerized Medical Systems, Inc., Saint Louis, MO; *U.S. Private*, pg. 260
Stone, David B., Exec. V.P.-Sls. & Mktg.--Merit Behavioral Care Corp., Park Ridge, NJ; *U.S. Public*, pg. 1036
Stone, Harold, Dir.-Mktg.--Radica USA Limited, Dallas, TX; *U.S. Private*, pg. 906
Stone, Harold, Jr., V.P.-Sls. & Mktg.--Renfro Corp., Mount Airy, NC; *U.S. Private*, pg. 922
Stone, Ira N., Sr. V.P.-Mktg., Communications & Pub. Affairs--Stone Container Corporation, Chicago, IL; *U.S. Public*, pg. 1520
Stone, Julia A., Dir.-Mktg.--WTVF, Nashville, TN; *U.S. Private*, pg. 647
Stone, Larry, Dir.-Natl. Mktg.--Heil Environmental Industries, Chattanooga, TN; *U.S. Public*, pg. 520
Stone, Tom, V.P.-Mktg. & Sls.--Crane Pumps & Systems Inc., Piqua, OH; *U.S. Public*, pg. 457
Stone, Tom, V.P.-Sales & Mktg.--Barnes Pumps, Inc., Mansfield, OH; *U.S. Public*, pg. 457
Stonehouse, Kate, Mgr.-Adv., Mktg. & Communications--SLM Holding Corp., Washington, DC; *U.S. Public*, pg. 1419
Stonum, Alan, Mgr.-Mktg. Communications--Commerce Bancshares, Inc., Kansas City, MO; *U.S. Public*, pg. 409
Stordeur, Gary, Product Mgr.-Mktg.--Jaco Electronics, Inc., Hauppauge, NY; *U.S. Public*, pg. 920
Storey, David, Dir.-Adv. & Mktg.--The Gazette Company, Cedar Rapids, IA; *U.S. Private*, pg. 442
Storey, Tom, Exec. V.P.-Sales & Mktg.--Doubletree Corporation, Memphis, TN; *U.S. Public*, pg. 1335
Stork, David, Mgr.-Mktg. Services--Eagle Window & Door, Inc., Dubuque, IA; *U.S. Public*, pg. 67
Stork, Jeffrey M., Pres.--Stonhard, Inc., Maple Shade, NJ; *U.S. Public*, pg. 1358
Stork, Thom, V.P.-Mktg.--Adventure Island, Tampa, FL; *U.S.* Public, pg. 114
Stormont, James, V.P.-Sls. & Mktg.--Bodine Electric Company, Chicago, IL; *U.S. Private*, pg. 154
Storms, Russ, V.P.-Mktg.--Bergen Brunswig Medical Corporation, Orange, CA; *U.S. Public*, pg. 214
Stotler, Bill, Dir.-Sls.--Marine World Africa USA, Vallejo, CA; *U.S. Private*, pg. 703
Stotts, Dennis, Mgr.-Mktg.--Didde Web Press, Emporia, KS; *U.S. Private*, pg. 331
Stotts, John, V.P.-Sls. & Mktg.--Conmed Corporation, Utica, NY; *U.S. Public*, pg. 431
Stotts, John, Dir.-Sls. & Mktg.--Conmed Andover Medical, Inc., Haverhill, MA; *U.S. Public*, pg. 431
Stoudt, Craig, Pres.-Ampad Div.--American Pad and Paper Company, Dallas, TX; *U.S. Public*, pg. 88
Stout, Carl A., V.P.-Sls. & Dir.-Mktg.--Morgan Foods, Inc., Austin, IN; *U.S. Private*, pg. 761
Stout, Donna, Mgr.-Mktg.-Food Service--Cains Foods, L.P., Ayer, MA; *U.S. Private*, pg. 199
Stout, Harry Lee, Pres.-Natural Gas Mktg. & Transportation--KCS Energy Inc., Edison, NJ; *U.S. Public*, pg. 938
Stout, R.M., V.P.-Land & Mktg.--Rio Algom Mining Corp., Oklahoma City, OK; *Int'l*, pg. 1118
Stovall, Juli, Mgr.-Mktg. & Commun.--Paul Mueller Company, Springfield, MO; *U.S. Public*, pg. 1141
Stover, Kim R., Dir.-Devel.--T.D. Williamson, Inc., Tulsa, OK; *U.S. Private*, pg. 1179
Stowe, Vicki, V.P.-Promotional Mktg.--Wonderware Corporation, Irvine, CA; *U.S. Public*, pg. 1775
Stracham, Jeremy, Exec. Dir.-Legal & Corp. Affairs--Glaxo Wellcome plc, London, United Kingdom; *Int'l*, pg. 552
Stracner, S.D., V.P.-Commun. & Pub. Affairs--Ameron International Corporation, Pasadena, CA; *U.S. Public*, pg. 98
Strader, David, Dir.-Mktg.--The Medical Protective Company, Fort Wayne, IN; *U.S. Private*, pg. 728
Strader, Mike, Dir.-Sls. & Mktg.--GEC Precision Corp., Wellington, KS; *Int'l*, pg. 545
Strafalace, Dan, V.P.-Gas Detection--Bacharach Inc., Pittsburgh, PA; *U.S. Private*, pg. 109
Strahan, Vicki, Dir.-Mktg.--Blumberg Communications Inc., Minneapolis, MN; *U.S. Public*, pg. 305
Strahman, Cora, Sec. & Mgr.-Mktg.--Strahman Valves, Inc., Florham Park, NJ; *U.S. Private*, pg. 1046
Straim, Paul, Dir.-Mktg.--Maxicare Health Plans, Inc., Los Angeles, CA; *U.S. Public*, pg. 1061
Strain, Dawn, V.P.-Mktg.--Provident Financial Group, Inc., Cincinnati, OH; *U.S. Public*, pg. 1338
Straly, Mark, Dir.-Mktg.--Bayer Corporation/Diagnostics Division, Tarrytown, NY; *Int'l*, pg. 173
Stranathan, Lee, V.P.-Mktg.--Igloo Products Corporation, Houston, TX; *U.S. Public*, pg. 265
Strand, James W., Exec. V.P.-Mktg. & Customer Service--Aliant Communications Co., Lincoln, NE; *U.S. Public*, pg. 40
Strand, Ron, Exec. V.P.-Banking Grp.--Community First Bankshares, Inc., Fargo, ND; *U.S. Public*, pg. 416
Strange, Jeanne, Dir.-Mktg. & Adv.--First Southwest Company, Dallas, TX; *U.S. Private*, pg. 407
Stratford, Ray, V.P.-Mktg.--Travel Ports of America Inc., Rochester, NY; *U.S. Public*, pg. 1632
Stratton, Maureen, Dir.-Mktg., Pub. Rels. & Trade Rels.--American Greetings Corporation, Cleveland, OH; *U.S. Public*, pg. 77
Stratton, S.M., Mgr.-Mktg. Communications--Solar Turbines Incorporated, San Diego, CA; *U.S. Public*, pg. 316
Strauss, Amy, V.P.-Strategic Mktg.--Sony Music Entertainment, Inc., New York, NY; *Int'l*, pg. 1281
Strauss, John, Mgr.-Natl. Mktg.--Fuji Medical Systems USA, Inc., Stamford, CT; *Int'l*, pg. 524
Strauss, Julie, Dir.-Mktg.--Golden Flake Snack Foods, Inc., Birmingham, AL; *U.S. Public*, pg. 750
Strauss, Karen L., Dir.-Mktg. Commun.--Owens Corning, Toledo, OH; *U.S. Public*, pg. 1236
Strauss, Robert, Dir.-Mktg. & Sls.--Fastenal Company, Winona, MN; *U.S. Public*, pg. 614
Strauss, Steve, Sr. V.P.-Mktg.--Baldwin Steel Company, Jersey City, NJ; *Int'l*, pg. 401
Straw, John E., V.P.-Sls. & Mktg.--Jefferson Smurfit Corporation, Saint Louis, MO; *Int'l*, pg. 1269
Strazella, Frances, Dir.-Mktg.--Stroehmann Bakeries, L.C., Horsham, PA; *Int'l*, pg. 1495
Strecker, William S., V.P.-Sls. & Mktg.--Kingsbury, Inc., Philadelphia, PA; *U.S. Private*, pg. 622
Streeter, Butch, V.P.-Sls. & Mktg.--Amarillo Hardware Company, Amarillo, TX; *U.S. Private*, pg. 335
Streets, Heather, Agency Mktg.--Miller/Kadanoff/Huber Direct & Interactive, San Francisco, CA; *U.S. Private*, pg. 747
Streff, Bill, Dir.-Mktg.--H.C. Miller Company, Milwaukee, WI; *U.S. Private*, pg. 747
Stricker, Karla, V.P.-Mktg.--Coram Healthcare Corporation, Denver, CO; *U.S. Public*, pg. 446
Strickland, Candace, Mktg.--Regions Bank/Sumter County, Livingston, AL; *U.S. Public*, pg. 1373
Strickland, J.C., Mgr.-Mktg.--Ericsson, Inc., Richardson, TX; *Int'l*, pg. 1364
Strickland, J.C., Mgr.-Mktg. Communications--Ericsson North America, Inc., Richardson, TX; *Int'l*, pg. 1364
Striegel, Dave, Dir.-Mktg. Svcs.--Growmark, Inc., Bloomington, IL; *U.S. Private*, pg. 484
Strine, Peggy E., Dir.-Mktg.--Mellon Bank (DE) National Association, Wilmington, DE; *U.S. Public*, pg. 1085
Stringer, R.J., Mktg. Dir.--The Oxford Collection Ltd., Oxford, United Kingdom; *Int'l*, pg. 807
Strode, N., Mgr.-Mktg. Svcs.--Philip Morris Limited, Moorabbin, Australia; *U.S. Public*, pg. 1290
Stroh, Richard, Mktg. & Communications Specialist--Anaren Microwave Inc., East Syracuse, NY; *U.S. Public*, pg. 110
Strohmeier, Doug, V.P.-Mktg.--The Kendall Company, Mansfield, MA; *U.S. Public*, pg. 1647
Strom, Barb, Sr. V.P.-Mktg. Strategy & Mdsg.--Things Remembered, Inc., Highland Heights, OH; *U.S. Public*, pg. 397

Strom, Tag, Dir.-Mktg.--Rosenthal U.S.A. Limited, Carlstadt, NJ; *Int'l*, pg. 1127
Stroman, Randy, Dir.-Mktg. Communications--Stainless Incorporated, Deerfield Beach, FL; *U.S. Private*, pg. 1029
Stroman, Randy, Dir.-Mktg. Communications--Charter House Incorporated, Holland, MI; *U.S. Private*, pg. 1029
Stromberg-Wise, Linnea, V.P.-Mktg., Valleyfair--Cedar Fair, L.P., Sandusky, OH; *U.S. Public*, pg. 319
Stromberg, Greg, V.P.-Mktg.--INX International, Milwaukee, WI; *Int'l*, pg. 1311
Stromberg, Linnea, V.P.-Mktg.--Valleyfair, Shakopee, MN; *U.S. Public*, pg. 319
Strong, Brian, Mgr.-Adv. & Mktg.--F.W. Woolworth Co. Limited, Canada, Weston, Canada; *U.S. Public*, pg. 1778
Strong, William, V.P.-Mktg. & Broadcasting--Dallas Stars, Irving, TX; *U.S. Private*, pg. 309
Stroud, Chris, V.P.-Pension Mktg.--FDP Corp., Miami, FL; *U.S. Public*, pg. 603
Stroud, Mickey, V.P.-Mktg. & Adv.--Old America Stores, Howe, TX; *U.S. Public*, pg. 1215
Stroud, N., V.P.-Mktg. & Sls.--Sumitomo Sitix Silicon, Inc., Fremont, CA; *Int'l*, pg. 1317
Struble, Robert J., Mgr.-Mktg. Communications--Harbison-Walker Refractories, Pittsburgh, PA; *U.S. Public*, pg. 748
Struller, Andrea, Mgr.-Mktg.--Maul-Belser GmbH, Nuremberg, Germany; *Int'l*, pg. 849
Strunk, Gary A., V.P.-Sls. & Mktg.--Peterson American Corp., Southfield, MI; *U.S. Private*, pg. 857
Strunk, Merrit, Mgr.-Mktg.--Ryobi Outdoor Products, Chandler, AZ; *Int'l*, pg. 1151
Strunk, Merrit A., Dir.-Mktg.--Ryobi America Corp., Anderson, SC; *Int'l*, pg. 1151
Strunk, Russell, V.P.-Mktg.--Tiger Direct, Inc., Miami, FL; *U.S. Public*, pg. 747
Strunk, Russell, Dir.-Mktg.--Tiger Direct, Inc. (d/b/a Tiger Software, Inc.), Miami, FL; *U.S. Public*, pg. 747
Stuart, James, V.P.-Mktg.--Coca-Cola Bottling Co. Consolidated, Charlotte, NC; *U.S. Public*, pg. 391
Stuart, William, V.P.-Mktg. & Sls.--Schulze & Burch Biscuit Company, Chicago, IL; *U.S. Private*, pg. 973
Stubbe, Allen, Mgr.-Sls. & Mktg.--Wagner Casters and Wheels, Hustisford, WI; *U.S. Private*, pg. 1146
Stuber, Paul, Dir.-Adv. & Mktg.--Rolex Watch Co. SA, Geneva, Switzerland; *Int'l*, pg. 1126
Stuckert, Bill, Mgr.-Govt. Mktg.--Comdisco, Inc., Rosemont, IL; *U.S. Public*, pg. 407
Stucki, Connie, Mgr.-Mktg. & Export--U.S. Safety, Lenexa, KS; *U.S. Private*, pg. 1125
Studer, Eric, V.P.-Mktg. Services--Motel 6 Operating L.P., Dallas, TX; *Int'l*, pg. 21
Studer, Evan, V.P.-Sls. & Mktg.--Sunstone Hotel Investors, Inc., San Clemente, CA; *U.S. Public*, pg. 1536
Stugrin, Mike, V.P.-Mktg.--Pinkerton's Inc., Encino, CA; *U.S. Public*, pg. 1296
Stuhlman, Dennis, Dir.-Sls. & Mktg./Commercial Prods.--Cantex Inc., Mineral Wells, TX; *Int'l*, pg. 1312
Stuhr, David, Mgr.-Mktg.--Minnesota Electric Supply Company, Willmar, MN; *U.S. Private*, pg. 750
Stull, Walt, Mgr.-Corp. Mktg Commun.--ADC Telecommunications, Inc., Minnetonka, MN; *U.S. Public*, pg. 4
Stump, Kirk V., Dir.-Mktg. & Adv.--Quick & Reilly, Inc., New York, NY; *U.S. Public*, pg. 650
Stuntz, Susan M., V.P.-Mktg. Commun. & Pub. Rels.--Colonial Williamsburg Foundation, Williamsburg, VA; *U.S. Private*, pg. 254
Stunyl, Maryann, Coord.-Mktg. & Communications--CAP Gemini America, New York, NY; *Int'l*, pg. 263
Stupinski, Eric, V.P.-Mktg.--DonTech, Chicago, IL; *U.S. Public*, pg. 98
Stuppy, Mark F., V.P.-Mktg.--Erie Scientific Co., Portsmouth, NH; *U.S. Public*, pg. 1545
Sturgell, Brian, V.P.-Sls. & Mktg.--Alcan Rolled Products Division, Cleveland, OH; *Int'l*, pg. 50
Sturgeon, Karen A., Sr. V.P.-Sls. & Mdse.--Lucky Stores Northern California Division, San Leandro, CA; *U.S. Public*, pg. 93
Sturgis, Bob, V.P.-Mktg.--Hickson Corporation, Smyrna, GA; *Int'l*, pg. 619
Sturm, H., V.P.-Mktg. Services--Midwesco Filter Resources Inc., Winchester, VA; *U.S. Public*, pg. 1026
Sturm, Richard, Sr. V.P.-Mktg. & Entertainment--MGM Grand Hotel, Inc., Las Vegas, NV; *U.S. Public*, pg. 1027
Sturtevant, Nancy B., Mgr.-Mktg.--Bradley Corporation, Menomonee Falls, WI; *U.S. Private*, pg. 164
Stutin, Jeffery M., V.P.-Mktg.--Commodore Holdings, Hollywood, FL; *U.S. Public*, pg. 414
Stutsman, Lori, Dir.-Mktg.--PACCAR Automotive Inc., Renton, WA; *U.S. Public*, pg. 1247
Styl, Alain, Mgr.-Intl. Mktg.--Guerlain S.A., Paris, France; *Int'l*, pg. 780
Su, Tommy, Mgr.-Mktg./Far East Containerboard & Fine Paper--Weyerhaeuser (Far East) Ltd., Wan Chai, Hong Kong; *U.S. Public*, pg. 1764
Subul, Freddy, Dir.-Mktg. & Commercial--Manoir Industries, Paris, France; *Int'l*, pg. 570
Succio, James E., V.P.-Mktg.--Elopak, Inc., New Hudson, MI; *Int'l*, pg. 1390
Succoso, Marian, V.P.-Adv. & Mktg. Programs--Loews Corporation, New York, NY; *U.S. Public*, pg. 1010
Suchordt, Volkert, Chief Oper. Officer--Busch-Jaeger Ludenscheider Metallwerk GmbH, Ludenscheid, Germany; *Int'l*, pg. 1427
Sudduth, Scott, Dir.-Mktg.--Quality Foods Inc., Little Rock, AR; *U.S. Private*, pg. 898
Suder, Pam, Mgr.-Mktg.--Ogden Aviation Services, New York, NY; *U.S. Public*, pg. 1213
Suer, Bernard P., V.P.-Mktg. & Devel.--Frank Messer & Sons Construction Co., Cincinnati, OH; *U.S. Private*, pg. 734
Suer, Myles F., Dir.-Mktg.--Irvine Sensors Corporation, Costa Mesa, CA; *U.S. Public*, pg. 913
Suessmilch, Wieland, Dir.-Sls. & Mktg.--Cherry Mikroschalter GmbH, Auerbach, Germany; *U.S. Public*, pg. 346
Suezawa, Jiro, Dir.-Mktg.--Kyowa Hakko U.S.A., Inc., New York, NY; *Int'l*, pg. 778
Sugar, David C., V.P., Sec. & Dir.-Mktg.--National Guardian Life Insurance Company, Madison, WI; *U.S. Private*, pg. 784
Sugarman, Arleen, Mktg. Dir.-AMS Travel--Active International, Pearl River, NY; *U.S. Private*, pg. 15
Suhocki, Raymond F., V.P.-Mktg. & Econ. Devel.--PP&L Resources, Allentown, PA; *U.S. Public*, pg. 1244
Sullivan, Celine, V.P.-Mkt. Devel.--Cowles Enthusiast Media, Inc., Stamford, CT; *U.S. Private*, pg. 281
Sullivan, Floyd, Mgr.-Adv.--Noritake Co., Inc., Secaucus, NJ; *Int'l*, pg. 959
Sullivan, Frank B., Sr. V.P.-Sls. & Mktg.--Square D Company, Palatine, IL; *Int'l*, pg. 1208
Sullivan, Gary, Exec. V.P.-Sls. & Mktg.--EMPI, Inc., Saint Paul, MN; *U.S. Public*, pg. 545
Sullivan, George, Sr. V.P.-Mktg.--Genmar Holdings, Inc., Minneapolis, MN; *U.S. Private*, pg. 447
Sullivan, George, V.P.-Mktg.--Hudson Life Reassurance Corporation, Shelton, CT; *Int'l*, pg. 1257
Sullivan, Jack, Mgr.-Consumer Mktg.--IGI, Inc., Buena, NJ; *U.S. Public*, pg. 855
Sullivan, Joan, Mgr.-Mktg. Div.--Wilmington Trust Corporation, Wilmington, DE; *U.S. Public*, pg. 1770
Sullivan, John J., V.P.-Sls.--SmarTrunk Systems, Inc., Hayward, CA; *U.S. Private*, pg. 1006
Sullivan, Kevin P., V.P.-Home Theater Div.--Go-Video, Inc., Scottsdale, AZ; *U.S. Public*, pg. 748
Sullivan, Marion, V.P.-Mktg.--Roundy's, Inc., Pewaukee, WI; *U.S. Private*, pg. 948
Sullivan, Mark, Dir.-Mktg.--MIC Technology Corporation, North Andover, MA; *U.S. Public*, pg. 24
Sullivan, Mark, Mgr.-Mktg. Communications (Graphic Systems)--AGFA Division of Bayer Corporation, Ridgefield Park, NJ; *Int'l*, pg. 172
Sullivan, Mark, V.P.-Mktg.--Tyco Toys, Inc., Mount Laurel, NJ; *U.S. Public*, pg. 1058
Sullivan, P., V.P.-Laundry Mktg.--Dexter Company, Fairfield, IA; *U.S. Private*, pg. 329
Sullivan, Pat, V.P.-Specialty Prods.--William M. Bird & Co., Inc., Charleston, SC; *U.S. Private*, pg. 145
Sullivan, Raymond P., V.P.-Mktg.--Sonoma Valley Bank, Sonoma, CA; *U.S. Public*, pg. 1487
Sullivan, Robert R., V.P.-Sls. & Mktg.--Southwire Company, Carrollton, GA; *U.S. Private*, pg. 1019
Sullivan, Sean, Dir.-Mktg.--Good Housekeeping, New York, NY; *U.S. Private*, pg. 517
Sullivan, Stephen G., Sr. V.P. & Mgr.-Commun. Svcs.--Liberty Mutual Insurance Co., Boston, MA; *U.S. Private*, pg. 666
Sullivan, Thomas J., V.P.-Sls. & Mktg.--DuBois Chemicals, Cincinnati, OH; *Int'l*, pg. 1437
Sullivan, Tim, V.P.-Mktg.--TDK Electronics Corporation, Port Washington, NY; *Int'l*, pg. 1336
Sullivan, Tim W., V.P.-Sls. & Mktg.--Bucyrus International, South Milwaukee, WI; *U.S. Private*, pg. 177
Sullivan, Will, Chief Mktg. Officer--Imation Corporation, Oakdale, MN; *U.S. Public*, pg. 870
Sulman, David L., V.P. & Gen. Mgr.--Teradyne, Inc., Boston, MA; *U.S. Public*, pg. 1580
Sultenfuss, John H., Sr. V.P.-Mktg. & Sls.--CF Industries, Inc., Long Grove, IL; *U.S. Private*, pg. 193
Sumdberg, Berhl, Mgr.-Mktg.--Atlas Copco Rockdrilling Equipment, Stockholm, Sweden; *Int'l*, pg. 96
Summer, Tammy, Dir.-Communications--Ryder System, Inc., Miami, FL; *U.S. Public*, pg. 1413
Summerford, George, Mktg.--Regions Bank/Dothan, Dothan, AL; *U.S. Public*, pg. 1372
Summers, Karl, V.P.-Sls. & Mktg.--Feintool U.S. Operations Inc., White Plains, NY; *Int'l*, pg. 479
Summers, Mindy, Mgr.-Mktg.--Houlihan's Restaurant Group, Kansas City, MO; *U.S. Public*, pg. 841
Summerville, Jared, Mktg. Specialist--Atlas Weathering DSET Laboratories, Phoenix, AZ; *U.S. Private*, pg. 96
Sun, T.C., Dir.--Taiwan Power Company, Taipei, Taiwan; *Int'l*, pg. 1348
Sunaway, A., Dir.-Div. Sls. & Mktg.--Ransomes Plc, Ipswich, United Kingdom; *Int'l*, pg. 1087
Sundblad, Johan, Dir.-Mktg.--IL Returpapper, Stockholm, Sweden; *Int'l*, pg. 646
Sundblad, Johan, Dir.-Mktg.--IL Sekretess, Stockholm, Sweden; *Int'l*, pg. 646
Sunderman, Bernd, Dir.-Mktg.--AGIE AG (Fur Industrielle Elektronik), Lausanne, Switzerland; *Int'l*, pg. 488
Sundermeyer, Ron, Exec. V.P.--S.A.S.I. Corporation, Collinsville, IL; *U.S. Private*, pg. 955
Sundquist, J.W., V.P.-Underwriting & Mgr.-Adv.--Bituminous Casualty Corp., Rock Island, IL; *U.S. Public*, pg. 1218
Sundstrom, Chris E., V.P.-Corp. Devel.--Wm. Wrigley Jr. Company, Chicago, IL; *U.S. Public*, pg. 1781
Sundwick, Robert, V.P.-Sls. & Mktg.--Grote Industries, Madison, IN; *U.S. Private*, pg. 483
Sung, N.J., Mgr.-Mktg. Communications--Kodak Korea Ltd., Seoul, Korea; *U.S. Public*, pg. 555
Supachaiyakit, Panthep, Mgr.-Mktg.--The Siam Cement Public Company Limited, Bangkok, Thailand; *Int'l*, pg. 1237
Suprenant, Becky, Dir.-Mktg. Services--The Pyramid Life Insurance Co., Mission, KS; *U.S. Public*, pg. 1694
Suprick, Mike, Mgr.-Mktg.--Jerome Foods Inc., Barron, WI; *U.S. Private*, pg. 586
Suptic, Dave, Dir.-Adv. & Mktg.--The Marley Cooling Tower Co., Overland Park, KS; *U.S. Public*, pg. 1676
Surago, Laurie, V.P.-Mktg.--Nematron Corp., Ann Arbor, MI; *U.S. Private*, pg. 791
Surgner, William H., V.P.-Mktg.--Barclay White Incorporated, Berwyn, PA; *U.S. Private*, pg. 115
Surma, Jean, Mgr.-Mktg. Communications--DEZurik, Sartell, MN; *U.S. Public*, pg. 726
Surrette, Jack, V.P.-Mktg. & Product Devel.--Tanning Research Labs., Inc., Ormond Beach, FL; *U.S. Private*, pg. 1068
Sustak, Carole L., Mgr.-Mktg. Svcs.--Essex International, Inc., Fort Wayne, IN; *U.S. Public*, pg. 593
Sustello, Rick, V.P.-Mktg. & Diversification--Uvex Safety, Inc., Smithfield, RI; *Int'l*, pg. 132
Sutherland, Hamish, Gen. Mgr.-Mktg.--Quality Bakers New Zealand Ltd., Auckland, New Zealand; *Int'l*, pg. 556
Sutherland, Mark, V.P.-Mktg.--Superior Coffee and Foods, Bensenville, IL; *U.S. Public*, pg. 1434
Sutherland, Robert W., Dir.-Sls. & Mktg.--Therm, Inc., Ithaca, NY; *U.S. Private*, pg. 1079
Suto, Shinzo, Sr. Mng. Dir. & Sr. V.P.-Intl. Passenger Mktg. Div.--Japan Airlines Company, Ltd., Tokyo, Japan; *Int'l*, pg. 699
Sutta, Arnold, V.P.-Mktg.--Bel Fuse Inc., Jersey City, NJ; *U.S. Public*, pg. 200
Sutter, Debbie, V.P.-Mktg. & Retail Sls.--Clear Shield National, Inc., Wheeling, IL; *U.S. Public*, pg. 586
Suttle, Phil, V.P.-Consumer Mktg.--United States Satellite Broadcasting Co., Saint Paul, MN; *U.S. Private*, pg. 544
Suttler, Goodloe, V.P.-Mktg., Quality & Plng.--Analog Devices, Inc., Norwood, MA; *U.S. Public*, pg. 107
Suttles, Chuck, Dir.-Mktg. & Sls.--Duff-Norton, Charlotte, NC; *U.S. Public*, pg. 406
Sutton, A., Mgr.-Mktg.--Swish Products Ltd., Tamworth, United Kingdom; *Int'l*, pg. 925
Sutton, David, Dir.-U.S. Mktg.--Weiser Lock, Tucson, AZ; *U.S. Public*, pg. 1053
Sutton, Don, Dir.-Mktg. & Adv.--Benjamin Franklin Literary & Medical Society, Inc., Indianapolis, IN; *U.S. Private*, pg. 133
Sutton, Mark, Mgr.-Mktg. & Sls.--Thilmany Division, Kaukauna, WI; *U.S. Public*, pg. 903
Sutton, Michael T., V.P.-Mktg.--General Shale Products Corp., Johnson City, TN; *Int'l*, pg. 843
Sutton, Teresa, V.P.-Mktg.--Compar, New York, NY; *Int'l*, pg. 1073
Suydam, Mark, V.P.-Sls. & Mktg.--Kirkwood Industries, Inc., Cleveland, OH; *U.S. Private*, pg. 623
Suzanski, Mike, V.P.-Mktg. & Sls.--Monier Inc., Irvine, CA; *Int'l*, pg. 1091
Suzio, Paul, V.P.-Mktg.--Edwards Systems Tech, Cheshire, CT; *U.S. Public*, pg. 726
Svenson, Bo, Mgr.-Mktg.--Karlshamns AB, Karlshamn, Sweden; *Int'l*, pg. 718
Svensonssom, Pelle, Dir.-Mktg.--Scandinavian Airlines System (SAS), Solna, Sweden; *Int'l*, pg. 1201
Svrcek, Rudy, V.P.-Sls. & Mktg.--The Irvine Company, Newport Beach, CA; *U.S. Private*, pg. 575
Swafford, Larry P., V.P.-Sls. & Mktg.--Smithfield Foods, Inc., Norfolk, VA; *U.S. Public*, pg. 1479
Swan, Alex, Gen. Mgr.--ITOCHU Building Products Co., Inc., Miami, FL; *Int'l*, pg. 694
Swan, Bob, Mgr.-Mktg.--The Euclid Chemical Company, Cleveland, OH; *U.S. Public*, pg. 1358
Swan, Tom, Dir.-New Prod. Devel.--R.J. Corr Naturals, Inc., Posen, IL; *U.S. Private*, pg. 276
Swann, Kate, Dir.-Mktg. Currys--Dixons Group plc, Hemel Hempstead, United Kingdom,; *Int'l*, pg. 413
Swann, Kate, Dir.-Mktg.--Currys Group plc, Hemel Hempstead, United Kingdom; *Int'l*, pg. 414
Swanson, Bob, V.P.-Mktg. & Devel.--Hickory Farms Catalogues of America, Inc., Maumee, OH; *U.S. Private*, pg. 525
Swanson, Robert, V.P.-Direct Mktg.--Hickory Farms, Inc., Maumee, OH; *U.S. Private*, pg. 525
Swart, Dirk F., V.P.-Sls. & Mktg.--United Sugars Corp., Bloomington, MN; *U.S. Private*, pg. 52
Swarts, Al, Dir.-Sls. & Mktg.--Amgen Inc., Thousand Oaks, CA; *U.S. Public*, pg. 100
Swartz, Michael, Sr. V.P.-Mktg.--JLG Industries, Inc., McConnellsburg, PA; *U.S. Public*, pg. 918
Swaynie, Karen, Adv. Administrator--Benjamin Franklin Literary & Medical Society, Inc., Indianapolis, IN; *U.S. Private*, pg. 133
Sweat, Gail, Mgr.-Reg. Mktg.--Blockbuster Music, Marietta, GA; *U.S. Private*, pg. 776
Swedberg, Joe, Dir.-Mktg./Meat Prods.--Hormel Foods Corp., Austin, MN; *U.S. Public*, pg. 840
Swedeen, John, V.P.-Sls. & Mktg.--Weiser Lock, Tucson, AZ; *U.S. Public*, pg. 1053
Sweeney, John E., V.P.-Mktg.--Avemco Corporation, Frederick, MD; *U.S. Public*, pg. 151
Sweeny, Brad, Dir.-Mktg.--Dominick & Dominick, Incorporated, New York, NY; *U.S. Private*, pg. 338
Sweet, Karen, Mgr.-Mktg.--Tyton Corporation, Milwaukee, WI; *Int'l*, pg. 208
Sweger, Debra E., Dir.-Mktg.--Taylor Company, Rockton, IL; *U.S. Public*, pg. 1496
Sweigart, Michelle, Coord.-Sls. & Mktg.-Aircrew Trng. Systems Div.--Environmental Tectonics Corporation (ETC), Southampton, PA; *U.S. Public*, pg. 587
Swenson, Ken, Dir.-Special Makes--Converse Inc., North Reading, MA; *U.S. Public*, pg. 441
Swenson, Margaretha, Mgr.-Mktg.--ESAB Welding Equipment AB, Laxa, Sweden; *Int'l*, pg. 281
Swetlik, Don, V.P.-Mktg. & Sls.--Bird Products Corporation, Palm Springs, CA; *U.S. Public*, pg. 1591
Swett, John P., Sr. V.P.-Sls., Mktg. & Tech. Services/ Rubber Div.--Bayer Corporation, Pittsburgh, PA; *Int'l*, pg. 172
Swette, Brian, Exec. V.P.-Mktg.--Pepsi-Cola Company, Somers, NY; *U.S. Public*, pg. 1277
Swiatkiewicz, Rosemarie, V.P.-Mktg.--First Federal Savings, East Hartford, CT; *U.S. Public*, pg. 632
Swift, Judy D., Reg. V.P.-Mktg.--Arbor Health Care Company, Lima, OH; *Int'l*, pg. 468
Swift, Parker, Mgr.-Mktg.--Lotus Carpet Division, Phenix City, AL; *U.S. Private*, pg. 257
Swinnerton, B.R.G., Dir.-Mktg.--Morganite Electrical Carbon Limited, Morriston, United Kingdom; *Int'l*, pg. 891

Swinskey, Bruce, V.P.-Gen Mgr. Gillette USA--The Gillette Company, Personal Care Group, Boston, MA; *U.S. Public*, pg. 744

Swisher, Dan, V.P.-Mktg.--ALZA International, Palo Alto, CA; *U.S. Public*, pg. 62

Swiskow, Jonathan D, Sr. V.P.-Sls. & Mktg.--Hickory Specialties, Inc., Brentwood, TN; *U.S. Public*, pg. 596

Swithenbank, Gene W., Exec. V.P.-Sls. & Mktg.--CommScope, Inc., Hickory, NC; *U.S. Public*, pg. 415

Swords, Mary Patricia, V.P. & Dir.-Sls. & Mktg.--The Bureau of National Affairs, Inc., Washington, DC; *U.S. Private*, pg. 181

Sykes, Lori, Coord.-Mktg. Commun.--New Brunswick Scientific Co., Inc., Edison, NJ; *U.S. Public*, pg. 1169

Sylvester, Jeff, V.P.-Sls. & Mktg./Construction & Industrial--Detroit Diesel Corp., Detroit, MI; *U.S. Private*, pg. 850

Sylvester, Patrick P., V.P.-Mktg.--IGA, Inc. (Independent Grocers Alliance), Chicago, IL; *U.S. Private*, pg. 555

Sylvia, Kenneth A., Sr. V.P., Grp. Publr. & Publr. Consultant--Cliggott Publishing, Greenwich, CT; *U.S. Private*, pg. 246

Symonds, Curtis N., Exec. V.P.-Affiliate Sls. & Mktg.--Black Entertainment Television Holdings Inc., Washington, DC; *U.S. Public*, pg. 235

Symons, Dawn, Mgr.-Mktg., EDI--CIS Technologies, Inc., Tulsa, OK; *U.S. Public*, pg. 1155

Synnott, Steve, Mng. Dir.-Garden Master/Proven Groups--PRO Group, Inc., Englewood, CO; *U.S. Private*, pg. 887

Sytsma, James A., Sr. V.P.-Mktg. & New Prod. Devel.--Altec Industries, Inc., Birmingham, AL; *U.S. Private*, pg. 47

Szakal, Eva I., V.P.-Market Devel.--New Jersey Resources Corporation, Wall, NJ; *U.S. Public*, pg. 1172

Sze, Patricia, Dir.-Worldwide Mktg.--Berlitz International, Inc., Princeton, NJ; *U.S. Public*, pg. 221

Szile, Donna, Admin.-Sls. & Mktg.--Kirkwood Industries, Inc., Cleveland, OH; *U.S. Private*, pg. 623

Szlemp, Maureen, Mgr.-Mktg. Communications & Svcs.--Norand Mobile Systems Div., Cedar Rapids, IA; *U.S. Public*, pg. 1699

Szollosi, Peter, Dir.-Creative Mktg.--Equity Group Investments, Chicago, IL; *U.S. Private*, pg. 380

Szomora, Sandor, Dir.-Mktg.--Aeroplex of Central Europe Ltd., Budapest, Hungary; *Int'l*, pg. 834

Szomora, Sandor, Dir.-Mktg.--Aeroplex of Central Europe Ltd., Budapest, Hungary; *U.S. Public*, pg. 1006

Szostak, Michael J., V.P.-Mktg. & Sls.--Douglas Steel Fabricating Corporation, Lansing, MI; *U.S. Private*, pg. 341

Szostek, John, V.P.-Mktg. & Sls.--BLH Electronics, Inc., Canton, MA; *Int'l*, pg. 1289

Szostek, John J., V.P.-Sls. & Mktg.--BIF, North Wales, PA; *U.S. Public*, pg. 726

Tabaksblat, Israel, V.P.-Mktg. & Sls.--Allomatic Products Company, Sullivan, IN; *U.S. Public*, pg. 1363

Taber, Robert M., Jr., V.P.-Worldwide Sls.--QT Optoelectronics, Sunnyvale, CA; *U.S. Private*, pg. 897

Tabisz, Stefan, Mgr.-Mktg.--The Gates Rubber Company Ltd., Dumfries, United Kingdom; *Int'l*, pg. 1397

Tachuk, Ron, V.P.-Mktg. & Sls.--Breed Technologies, Sterling Heights, MI; *U.S. Public*, pg. 251

Tack, Johan, Mng. Dir.-Mktg.--Generale de Banque S.A., Brussels, Belgium; *Int'l*, pg. 546

Taffet, Bruce, Mgr.-Mktg.--United Artists Theatre Circuits Incorporated, Englewood, CO; *U.S. Private*, pg. 1120

Taggart, David, Mgr.-Sls. & Mktg.--Aer Lingus, Paris, France; *Int'l*, pg. 28

Tahinos, Pete, Mgr.-Regional Mktg.--Precision Tune Autocare Inc., Leesburg, VA; *U.S. Public*, pg. 1321

Tai, E., Sr. Exec.- Mktg. & Plng. Personal Banking--The Hongkong and Shanghai Banking Corporation Limited (HongkongBank), Central, Hong Kong; *Int'l*, pg. 583

Tairoriol, Denise, Mktg. Coordinator--Zyan, Inc., King of Prussia, PA; *U.S. Private*, pg. 421

Tait, Nancy, Sr. V.P.-Stratagic Plng. & Mktg. Communications--Olsten Health Services, Melville, NY; *U.S. Public*, pg. 1221

Tait, Nancy, Dir.-Mktg.--Bear Creek Corporation, Medford, OR; *Int'l*, pg. 1518

Takahashi, Hideo, Dir.--Sakata Seed Corporation, Yokohama, Japan; *Int'l*, pg. 1178

Takahashi, Kumiko, Sr. Mng. Dir.-Mktg. Svcs.--Asatsu Inc., Tokyo, Japan; *Int'l*, pg. 85

Takahashi, Yasuyuki, Mgr. Sls. & Mktg.--Sapporo U.S.A., Inc., New York, New York, NY; *Int'l*, pg. 1193

Takasaki, Edwina, Dir.-Mktg.--The Shidler Group, Honolulu, HI; *U.S. Private*, pg. 994

Takemura, Masahiro, Sr. Mgr.-Intl. Marketing--Wako Securities Co., Ltd., Tokyo, Japan; *Int'l*, pg. 1485

Takenaka, Shusuke, Sr. Exec. Dir.-Mktg.--Seiko Corporation, Tokyo, Japan; *Int'l*, pg. 1218

Takeuchi, Kiichiro, Exec. Mng. Dir.--Fujikura Ltd., Tokyo, Japan; *Int'l*, pg. 525

Takkuren, Philip, Dir.-Intl. Mktg.--3M Unitek Corporation, Monrovia, CA; *U.S. Public*, pg. 1606

Talarico, L., Dir.-Mktg.-Western Canada--Andres Wines (B.C.) Ltd., Port Moody, Canada; *Int'l*, pg. 76

Talbert, William L., Exec. V.P.-Mktg.--Clark Construction Group, Inc., Bethesda, MD; *U.S. Private*, pg. 242

Talbot, Steve, Dir.-Mktg.--MapInfo Corp., Troy, NY; *U.S. Public*, pg. 1042

Talbott, Barbara, V.P.-Mktg.--Four Seasons Hotels Inc., Don Mills, Canada; *Int'l*, pg. 502

Talbott, Brian, Dir.-Prods.--Merle Norman Cosmetics, Inc., Los Angeles, CA; *U.S. Private*, pg. 733

Taliaferro, Mike, Exec. V.P.-Consumer Mkts. Div./Sls. & Mktg.--Countrywide Home Loans Inc., Pasadena, CA; *U.S. Public*, pg. 452

Talley, Lucy, Dir.-Adv.--Evening Post Publishing Co., Charleston, SC; *U.S. Private*, pg. 385

Talmadge, John, DVM, Dir.-Veterinary Mktg.--Iams Company, Dayton, OH; *U.S. Private*, pg. 556

Talon, Christine, Mgr.-Consumer Mktg.--Anchor Foods Limited, Swindon, United Kingdom; *Int'l*, pg. 923

Talovich, Michael, Sr. V.P. & Brand Mktg. Partner--DMB&B Detroit, Troy, MI; *U.S. Private*, pg. 302

Talreja, Prem, Dir.-Mktg. & Pub. Rels.--Sigma Designs, Inc., Fremont, CA; *U.S. Public*, pg. 1472

Talwin, Bernie, Gen. Mgr.-Aluminum Capacitors Div.--Philips Components, Jupiter, FL; *Int'l*, pg. 1054

Tam, Gilbert K.T., Sr. V.P.-Mkt. & Community Svcs. Division--Bank of Hawaii, Honolulu, HI; *U.S. Public*, pg. 1248

Tamayo, Peter, V.P.-Mktg. & Sls.--UHP Healthcare, Inglewood, CA; *U.S. Private*, pg. 1113

Tamura, A., V.P.-Mktg. & Sls.--Sumitomo Sitix Silicon, Inc., Fremont, CA; *Int'l*, pg. 1317

Tan, Esther, V.P.-Mktg.--Sun Life of Canada, Manila, Philippines; *Int'l*, pg. 1319

Tan, Jimmy, Mgr.-Mktg.--GP Batteries International Ltd., Singapore, Singapore; *Int'l*, pg. 537

Tan, Louis, Mgr.-Mktg. & Matls.--G.E. (U.S.A.) Aviation Service Operation Pte. Ltd., Singapore, Singapore; *U.S. Public*, pg. 713

Tan, Simon Y., Sr. V.P.-Individual Mkt. Devel. & Prod.--Phoenix Home Life Mutual Insurance Company, Hartford, CT; *U.S. Private*, pg. 863

Tan, Simon Y., Sr. V.P.-Individual Mkt. Devel.--Phoenix Home Life Mutual Insurance Co., Hartford, CT; *U.S. Private*, pg. 863

Tanaka, Fori, Sr. V.P.-Domestic Passenger Mktg.--Japan Airlines Company, Ltd., Tokyo, Japan; *Int'l*, pg. 699

Tanaka, Toshio, Sr. Exec. Dir.-Mktg. & Sls./Ethical Prods. Mktg. Div.--Tanabe Seiyaku Co., Ltd., Osaka, Japan; *Int'l*, pg. 1354

Tanaka, Yasuo, Sr. Mng. Dir.-Acct. Service & Promo.--Sogei Inc., Tokyo, Japan; *Int'l*, pg. 1277

Tangen, Chris, V.P.-Mktg.--North America Foods, Minnetonka, MN; *U.S. Public*, pg. 901

Tangren, Dag Olav, Mgr.-Mktg.--Norcem a.s., Oslo, Norway; *Int'l*, pg. 1199

Tank, Linda, Dir.-Mktg. Commun.--CENEX, Inc., Inver Grove Heights, MN; *U.S. Private*, pg. 221

Tankerlsey, Bobby, V.P.-Mktg. & Sls.--Young Pecan Company (A Partnership), Florence, SC; *U.S. Private*, pg. 1201

Tanksy, Larry, Dir.-Mktg.--Landry's Seafood Restaurants Inc., Houston, TX; *U.S. Public*, pg. 977

Tannenbaum, Lisa, V.P.-Mktg.--Home Shopping Network, Inc., Saint Petersburg, FL; *U.S. Public*, pg. 1685

Tanner, Carl, Dir.- Sls. & Mktg.--LiphaTech, Inc., Milwaukee, WI; *Int'l*, pg. 812

Tanner, Carroll, Dir.-Mktg.--Public Health Software Systems, Norcross, GA; *U.S. Public*, pg. 888

Tanner, Robert, V.P.-Mktg. & Sls.--Lapp Insulator Company, Le Roy, NY; *U.S. Private*, pg. 473

Tannnenbaum, Lisa, V.P.-Mktg & Mail Order--America's Store, Saint Petersburg, FL; *U.S. Public*, pg. 1685

Tanny, Lauren S., V.P.-Mktg.--Broderbund Software, Inc., Novato, CA; *U.S. Public*, pg. 258

Tanouye, Kimberly, Coord.-Mktg.--Robert Englekirk, Inc., Los Angeles, CA; *U.S. Private*, pg. 377

Tansini, Ernesto, Mgr.-Mktg. & Devel.--Cassa di Risparmio delle Provincie Lombarde SpA (CARIPLO), Milan, Italy; *Int'l*, pg. 274

Tansky, Larry, Dir.-Mktg. Services--Bonanza Restaurants, Dallas, TX; *U.S. Private*, pg. 736

Tansley, Marvin, Dir.-Mktg.--Schlumberger Industries, Owenton, KY; *U.S. Public*, pg. 1439

Tanzman, Linn, V.P. & Dir.-Mktg. Communications--Rolling Stone Magazine, New York, NY; *U.S. Private*, pg. 1162

Tapscott, Judy, Dir. Mtg./Dir. Response, Asst. Dir.-Sls.--National Banner Company, Inc., Dallas, TX; *U.S. Private*, *pg. 780*

Taragen, R.J., Exec. V.P.-Mktg.--Nielsen Media Research, New York, NY; *U.S. Public*, pg. 395

Tarantine, Dan, Mgr.-Sls. & Mktg.--White Microelectronics, Phoenix, AZ; *U.S. Public*, pg. 248

Taraze, Juan, V.P.-Sls.--Puerto Rican Cement Co., Inc., Guaynabo, PR; *U.S. Public*, pg. 1341

Tarbell, Joseph W., Exec. V.P. & Dir.-Mktg.--Willis Corroon Corp. of Massachusetts, Boston, MA; *Int'l*, pg. 1506

Tardiff, George, V.P.-Gen. Mktg.--Ford Motor Co. of Canada Ltd, Oakville, Canada; *U.S. Public*, pg. 666

Tareuko, Tonja, Mgr.-Mktg.--Jacobs Vehicle Equipment Company, Bloomfield, CT; *U.S. Public*, pg. 481

Tarin, S. M., Dir.-Mktg.--Pakistan International Airlines Corporation, Karachi, Pakistan; *Int'l*, pg. 1021

Tarka, Zbig, Dir.-Sls. & Mktg.--Valtek/Australia, Scoresby, Australia; *U.S. Public*, pg. 659

Tarkanish, Tom, V.P.-Sls. & Mktg./N. America--Greenwich Air Services, Miami, FL; *U.S. Public*, pg. 710

Tarlow, Paul, Mgr.-Electronic Mktg.--Group 1 Software, Inc., Lanham, MD; *U.S. Public*, pg. 417

Tarrant, Roger, V.P.-Sls. & Mktg.--M/A-COM Inc., Lowell, MA; *U.S. Public*, pg. 8

Tasser, Donald J., Dir.-Mktg.--AGC Life Insurance Co., Nashville, TN; *U.S. Public*, pg. 76

Tasser, Donald J., Sr. V.P. & Chief Mktg. Officer--American General Life & Accident Insurance Co., Nashville, TN; *U.S. Public*, pg. 76

Tassi, Susan, Coord.-Mktg. & Mdsg.--Key Industries, Inc., Fort Scott, KS; *U.S. Private*, pg. 618

Tativiolik, Patty, Mgr.-Mktg.--Concord Fabrics Inc., New York, NY; *U.S. Public*, pg. 429

Tatsutomi, Yasuo, Mng. Dir.-Quality , Cost Plng. & Domestic Mktg. & Sls.--Mazda Motor Corporation, Hiroshima, Japan; *Int'l*, pg. 849

Taunton, JT, Jr., Exec. V.P.-Sls. & Mktg.--Russell Corporation, Alexander City, AL; *U.S. Public*, pg. 1413

Tauresa, Prem, Mktg. Coord.--Sigma Designs, Inc., Fremont, CA; *U.S. Public*, pg. 1472

Taute, Harry, V.P.-Sls. & Mktg.--Communications Systems, Inc., Hector, MN; *U.S. Public*, pg. 415

Taverna, Richard, V.P.-Sls. & Mktg.--Par Industries, Inc., Medina, OH; *U.S. Private*, pg. 838

Taweel, Ramsey, V.P.-Mktg.--Textilease Corporation, Beltsville, MD; *U.S. Private*, pg. 1079

Taylor, Al, Dir.-Mktg.--Harris & Bank, Chicago, IL; *Int'l*, pg. 154

Taylor, Andy, Dir.-Mktg.--Paterno Imports Limited, Lake Bluff, IL; *U.S. Private*, pg. 843

Taylor, Bruce, Dir.-Pharmacy Mktg.--Rite Aid Corporation, Camp Hill, PA; *U.S. Public*, pg. 1390

Taylor, David P. Jr., V.P.-Mktg.--Capital Industries, Inc., Seattle, WA; *U.S. Private*, pg. 206

Taylor, Edgar, Dir.-Segment Mktg.--Nestle USA, Glendale, CA; *Int'l*, pg. 916

Taylor, Eileen, Exec. V.P. & Mktg. Dir.--The McClure Group, Wayne, PA; *U.S. Private*, pg. 719

Taylor, F. Bruce, V.P.-Mktg.--Cambior Inc., Montreal, Canada; *Int'l*, pg. 253

Taylor, Fran, Market Devel. Administrator--Keeneland Assoc., Inc., Lexington, KY; *U.S. Private*, pg. 611

Taylor, Gerry, Dir.-Mktg.--Varity Kelsey Hayes, Livonia, MI; *Int'l*, pg. 820

Taylor, Greg, Mgr.-Mktg.--Christensen Products, Salt Lake City, UT; *U.S. Public*, pg. 981

Taylor, Henry L., V.P.-Intl. Sls. & Mktg.--Accuride Corp., Henderson, KY; *U.S. Public*, pg. 1286

Taylor, J., V.P.-Mktg.-Intl. Mkts.--Labatt Breweries of Canada, Toronto, Canada; *Int'l*, pg. 679

Taylor, James A., Sr. V.P.-Global Mktg.--Gateway 2000, North Sioux City, SD; *U.S. Public*, pg. 703

Taylor, James M., V.P.-Mktg.--Robert Half International Inc., Menlo Park, CA; *U.S. Public*, pg. 774

Taylor, John C., Exec. V.P.-Sls. & Mktg.--John B. Sanfilippo & Son, Inc., Elk Grove Village, IL; *U.S. Public*, pg. 1431

Taylor, John C., Jr., V.P.-Sls. & Mktg.--John B. Sanfilippo & Son, Inc., Elk Grove Village, IL; *U.S. Public*, pg. 1431

Taylor, K., Mgr.-Mktg.--Moore Business Forms & Systems Ltd., Auckland, New Zealand; *Int'l*, pg. 889

Taylor, K.E., Mgr.-Mktg. Res. & Animal Research--Elanco Animal Health, Indianapolis, IN; *U.S. Public*, pg. 993

Taylor, Karen, Mgr.-MarCom--Encore Computer Corporation, Fort Lauderdale, FL; *U.S. Public*, pg. 580

Taylor, Karla, Mgr.-Mktg. & Adv.--Pearlstine Distributors Inc., Charleston, SC; *U.S. Private*, pg. 845

Taylor, Kevin, Dir.-Mktg. Services & Communications--Steering and Suspension Division, Saint Louis, MO; *U.S. Public*, pg. 443

Taylor, Kevin, Dir.-Mktg.--KONE Lifts Ltd., Hounslow, United Kingdom; *Int'l*, pg. 747

Taylor, Meredith, Sr. V.P.-Fin. & Mktg.--Stuart Anderson's Black Angus/Cattle Company Restaurants, Los Altos, CA; *U.S. Private*, pg. 61

Taylor, Mike, V.P.-Sls. & Mktg.--Vanner, Inc., Hilliard, OH; *Int'l*, pg. 449

Taylor, Peter, Dir.-Mktg., Communications & Human Relations--Royal & Sun Alliance Insurance Group plc, London, United Kingdom; *Int'l*, pg. 1130

Taylor, Regina, V.P.-Mktg.--Coldwell Banker Real Estate Corporation, Parsippany, NJ; *U.S. Public*, pg. 321

Taylor, Sasha, V.P.-Sls. & Mktg.--Sorbee International Ltd., Philadelphia, PA; *U.S. Private*, pg. 1014

Tcha, L.H., Dir.-Mktg.--Kodak Korea Ltd., Seoul, Korea; *U.S. Public*, pg. 555

Teale, C., Mgr.-Mktg.-Personal Care--Kiwi Brands Pty. Ltd., Clayton, Australia; *U.S. Public*, pg. 1434

Teasdale, Lyse, Mgr.-Canadian Mktg.--Cognos Inc., Ottawa, Canada; *Int'l*, pg. 305

Teasley, Dot, V.P.-Mktg.--Russell Corporation, Alexander City, AL; *U.S. Public*, pg. 1413

Teat, James, V.P.-Mktg.--Alamo Industrial Group, San Antonio, TX; *U.S. Private*, pg. 31

Teck, Tan Siew, Sr. Mgr.-Mktg. & Bus. Devel.--Singapore Technologies Shipbuilding & Engineering Limited, Singapore, Singapore; *Int'l*, pg. 1253

Tedesco, Anthony, V.P.-Mktg., Fantagraph Div.--Standard Textile Co., Inc., Cincinnati, OH; *U.S. Private*, pg. 1032

Teed, Ray, V.P.-Mktg.--Astoria Financial Corporation, Lake Success, NY; *U.S. Public*, pg. 141

Teel, Steve, Dir.-Mktg.--Raytheon Electronics Systems, Marlborough, MA; *U.S. Public*, pg. 1364

Teeple, Andrew R., V.P.-Sls. & Mktg.--Haddon Craftsmen, Inc., Scranton, PA; *U.S. Public*, pg. 518

Teer, Diane, V.P.-Mktg.--Campbell Soup Company Ltd., Toronto, Canada; *U.S. Public*, pg. 299

Tegt, Robert, V.P.-Mktg.--Jennie-O Foods, Inc., Willmar, MN; *U.S. Public*, pg. 840

Teich, Robert, Mgr.-Sls. & Mktg.--Duall Division, Owosso, MI; *U.S. Public*, pg. 1100

Teich, Tim, V.P.-Sls. & Mktg.--Advanced Input Devices, Inc., Coeur D'Alene, ID; *U.S. Private*, pg. 21

Teichgreeber, Jurgen, Mgr.-Sls.--Dr. Th. Boehme KG Chem. Fabrik GmbH & Co., Geretsried, Germany; *Int'l*, pg. 199

Teichner, Evelyn, Asst. Mgr.-Mktg.--Thai Airways Intl. Ltd.-U.S. Office, El Segundo, CA; *Int'l*, pg. 1381

Teifer, C.G., Dir.-Mktg.--Eight O'Clock Coffee, Hyattsville, MD; *Int'l*, pg. 1375

Teixeira, F., Mkt. Dir.--Richardson-Vicks do Brasil Quimica e Farmaceutica Ltda., Rio de Janeiro, Brazil; *U.S. Public*, pg. 1333

Tellegrene, John, Exec. V.P.-Mktg.--Dayton Hudson Corporation, Minneapolis, MN; *U.S. Public*, pg. 489

Teller, Bill, V.P.-Mktg.--Bunn-O-Matic Corporation, Springfield, IL; *U.S. Private*, pg. 180

Telles, Paulo R., Dir.-Mktg.--Apolo Produtos de Aco S.A., Rio de Janeiro, Brazil; *Int'l*, pg. 78

Temple, Cathy, Dir.-Sls. & Mktg.--Conran Octopus Limited, London, United Kingdom; *Int'l*, pg. 1093

Temple, Ian, Head-Mktg. & Press--British Film Institute, London, United Kingdom; *Int'l*, pg. 219

Temple, Mike, Exec. Dir.-Mktg. Plng.--Wyeth-Ayerst Laboratories, Inc., Philadelphia, PA; *U.S. Public*, pg. 80

Templeman, Miles, Mng. Dir.-Beer Co.--Whitbread PLC, London, United Kingdom; *Int'l*, pg. 1498

Templer, Audrey, V.P.-Mktg.--Kelley Dock Systems, Milwaukee, WI; *U.S. Private*, pg. 612

Templeton, John, Dir.-Corp. Brand Mktg.--Safeway Inc., Pleasanton, CA; *U.S. Public*, pg. 1426

Templin, J.M., V.P.-Sls. & Mktg.--Mayville Metal Products Division, Mayville, WI; *U.S. Private*, pg. 264

Tennehouse, Donald L., Dir.-Mktg.--Yosemite Insurance Co., Evansville, IN; *U.S. Public*, pg. 77

Tennenhouse, Don, Sr. V.P.-Mktg. & Bus. Devel.--American General Finance, Inc., Evansville, IN; *U.S. Public*, pg. 76

Tennison, Bob J., V.P.-Continuous Improvement--Hillenbrand Industries, Inc., Batesville, IN; *U.S. Public*, pg. 828

Tenzillo, Jim, V.P.-Mktg. Devel. & Plng.--W.W. Grainger, Inc., Lincolnshire, IL; *U.S. Public*, pg. 758

Tepp, Lia Kay, Dir.-Bus. Devel.--California Offset Printers, Inc., Glendale, CA; *U.S. Private*, pg. 196

Teran, Natalie, Mgr.-Mktg.-Cosmetics & Treatment--Guerlain, Inc., New York, NY; *Int'l*, pg. 780

Terem, Meral, Mgr.-Mktg.--Arcelik A.S., Istanbul, Turkey; *Int'l*, pg. 741

Terhune, Carolyn, Dir.-Mktg.--The Topeka Capital-Journal, Topeka, KS; *U.S. Private*, pg. 995

Terpstra, J. Scott, V.P.-West Reg. Sls.--EBP Life Insurnace Co., Minneapolis, MN; *U.S. Public*, pg. 635

Terraconi, Michael, Mgr.-Intl. Mktg.--Fuji Medical Systems USA, Inc., Stamford, CT; *Int'l*, pg. 524

Terry, Eric, Dir.-Mktg.--Hollywood Casino Corp, Atlantic City, NJ; *U.S. Public*, pg. 830

Terry, Howard, Dir.-Mktg.--Metromedia Steakhouses, Inc., Vandalia, OH; *U.S. Private*, pg. 736

Terry, Sherrie, V.P.-Mktg.--Chiquita Brands International, Inc., Cincinnati, OH; *U.S. Public*, pg. 349

Terry, Sherrie, V.P.-Mktg.--Chiquita Banana North America, Cincinnati, OH; *U.S. Public*, pg. 349

Tersigni, Phillip, V.P.-Sls. & Mktg.--Giant Industries, Toledo, OH; *U.S. Private*, pg. 451

Tertenik, Pete, Mgr.-Natl. Sls.--Flambeau Products-Columbus, Columbus, IN; *U.S. Private*, pg. 410

Tesch, Gary, Mgr.-Mktg.--HMT Inc., Houston, TX; *U.S. Public*, pg. 914

Tesh, Theresa, Dir.-North American Sls. Opers.--SAS Institute Inc., Cary, NC; *U.S. Private*, pg. 966

Tessitore, Joseph, Mktg. & Sls.--Childrens Press Inc., Danbury, CT; *Int'l*, pg. 794

Testa, Justin, V.P.-Mktg.--Cognex Corporation, Natick, MA; *U.S. Public*, pg. 394

Tevis, G. Phillip, Sr. V.P. & Pres.-Global Marketing Group--Dresser Industries, Inc., Dallas, TX; *U.S. Public*, pg. 528

Thacher, Fandy, Mgr.-Mktg.-Underground Prods.--Hendrix Wire & Cable, Milford, NH; *U.S. Public*, pg. 1598

Thacker, Louise, Mgr.-Mktg.--Hart Graphics Inc., Austin, TX; *U.S. Private*, pg. 507

Thacker, Robert, V.P.-Mktg.--Target Stores, Minneapolis, MN; *U.S. Public*, pg. 489

Thain, Clare, V.P.-Mktg.--Williams Worldwide, Santa Monica, CA; *U.S. Private*, pg. 1179

Thaler, Cathryn, V.P. & Dir.-Mktg.--Shoreline Financial Corp., Benton Harbor, MI; *U.S. Public*, pg. 1467

Thalmann, Craig, V.P.-Mktg. & Sls.--National Utility Service, Inc., Park Ridge, NJ; *U.S. Private*, pg. 787

Thamtham, Pascale, Dir.-Mktg.--Casino-Guichard Perrachon & Cie, Saint Etienne, France; *Int'l*, pg. 562

Tharp, James C., Sr. V.P.-Film & Mktg.--General Cinema Theatres, Inc., Chestnut Hill, MA; *U.S. Public*, pg. 693

Tharp, Ronald J., Dir.-Mktg.--Imaging Technologies Corp., San Diego, CA; *U.S. Public*, pg. 870

Thasarathar, Sue, Coord.-Mktg.--Toyota (Great Britain) Limited, Redhill, United Kingdom; *Int'l*, pg. 1414

Thatcher, Stephanie, Dir.-Mktg.--Fossil Inc., Richardson, TX; *U.S. Private*, pg. 420

Thather, Kathy, V.P.-Sls. & Mktg.--Broadcast Supply Worldwide, Inc., Tacoma, WA; *U.S. Private*, pg. 170

Thawley, Kay, Head-Mktg.--Michigan National Bank, N.A., Farmington Hills, MI; *Int'l*, pg. 906

Thaxton, William, Dir.-Mktg./WFS--Westcorp, Irvine, CA; *U.S. Public*, pg. 1756

Theeman, Klaus, Dir.-Mktg. & Sls.--Krups GmbH & Co. KG, Solingen, Germany; *Int'l*, pg. 896

Theis, H.E., V.P.-Mktg. & Sls.--Herr-Voss Corp., Callery, PA; *U.S. Private*, pg. 961

Theiss, Robert J., Mgr.-Growth--Snyder Berlin, Berlin, PA; *U.S. Private*, pg. 887

Thelemann, Sheila, Mgr.-Mktg. Services--OPUS Corp., Minnetonka, MN; *U.S. Private*, pg. 818

Theriot, Mark, Mgr.-Mktg.--Sun Electric, Lincolnshire, IL; *U.S. Public*, pg. 1480

Thesing, Wilhelm, Div. Mgr.--Durkopp Adler AG, Bielefeld, Germany; *Int'l*, pg. 468

Theune, Robert, V.P.-Sls. & Mktg.--Dunbarton Corporation, Dothan, AL; *U.S. Private*, pg. 194

Thia, Anthony, V.P.-Mktg.--Televideo, Inc., San Jose, CA; *U.S. Public*, pg. 1572

Thibault, Pierre, Dir.-Mktg.--Agropur, Granby, Canada; *Int'l*, pg. 31

Thibodeau, Kevin, Pres.-Waverly, N.A.--Waverly, Inc., Baltimore, MD; *U.S. Public*, pg. 1748

Thiel, Michael van, Dir.-Mktg.--Rexam Inc., Charlotte, NC; *Int'l*, pg. 1106

Thiel, Sally, Mgr.-Corp. Communications--C-COR Electronics, Inc., State College, PA; *U.S. Public*, pg. 272

Thiele, Ralf, Dir.-Domestic Mktg.--A. Racke GmbH, Bingen, Germany; *Int'l*, pg. 1083

Thielen, Dale, Mgr.-Mktg.--United Power Association, Elk River, MN; *U.S. Private*, pg. 1123

Thielen, Lenore J., Mgr.-Mktg. & Pub. Rels.--Dillingham Construction Corporation, Pleasanton, CA; *U.S. Private*, pg. 333

Thies, Len R., V.P.-Domestic Nitrogen--International Chemical Company, Tulsa, OK; *U.S. Private*, pg. 568

Thill, Dave, V.P.-Mktg.--Edwards Baking Co., Norcross, GA; *U.S. Private*, pg. 365

Thkelkeld, Kay, Dir.-Mktg.--Glendale Memorial Hospital and Medical Center, Glendale, CA; *U.S. Private*, pg. 1118

Thoel, Bryan, Dir.-Mktg.--Great Western Malting Co., Vancouver, WA; *U.S. Public*, pg. 428

Tholen, J. David, Exec. V.P.-Sls. & Mktg.--Hycor Biomedical, Inc., Irvine, CA; *U.S. Public*, pg. 851

Thoma, Michael, Sr. V.P.-Worldwide Mktg.--Brightware, Inc., Novato, CA; *U.S. Private*, pg. 168

Thomas, Bill, Sr. V.P.-Mktg.--Sea World of California, San Diego, CA; *U.S. Public*, pg. 114

Thomas, Brad, V.P.-Intl. Mktg.--International Chemical Company, Tulsa, OK; *U.S. Private*, pg. 568

Thomas, Brent, Gen. Mgr.-Non Chocolate--Hershey Chocolate U.S.A., Hershey, PA; *U.S. Public*, pg. 812

Thomas, Chris, Mgr.-Mktg.--ADD, Inc., Waupaca, WI; *U.S. Private*, pg. 601

Thomas, Cindy, V.P.-Direct Response Mktg.--BankAmerica Corporation, San Francisco, CA; *U.S. Public*, pg. 179

Thomas, Dalen D., Sr. V.P.-Sls., Mktg. & Strategic Plng.--Amtran, Inc., Indianapolis, IN; *U.S. Public*, pg. 106

Thomas, Damian A., V.P.-Mktg. & Sls.--PECO Energy Company, Philadelphia, PA; *U.S. Public*, pg. 1268

Thomas, Diane, Mktg. Admin. Asst.--Carlson Wagonlit Travel, Minneapolis, MN; *U.S. Private*, pg. 212

Thomas, Gene P., V.P.--Micron Electronics, Inc., Nampa, ID; *U.S. Public*, pg. 1105

Thomas, Geoff, Dir.-Mktg. & Sls.--Bostik Ltd., Leicester, United Kingdom; *Int'l*, pg. 1409

Thomas, George, V.P.-Sls. & Mktg.--R.A. Jones & Co. Inc., Covington, KY; *U.S. Private*, pg. 597

Thomas, Gil, V.P.-Sls. & Mktg.--Double-Cola Co.-USA, Chattanooga, TN; *U.S. Private*, pg. 341

Thomas, J. Fredric, Gen. Mgr.-Sls. Mktg.--Copperweld Miami Division, Piqua, OH; *Int'l*, pg. 662

Thomas, J.R., V.P.-Sls. & Mktg.--Kaufman Footwear, Kitchener, Canada; *Int'l*, pg. 725

Thomas, Janis P., Exec. V.P.-Mktg. & Mdse.--Black Entertainment Television Holdings Inc., Washington, DC; *U.S. Public*, pg. 235

Thomas, John E., Sr. V.P.-Mktg. & Creative Services--Mutual of Omaha Insurance Company, Omaha, NE; *U.S. Private*, pg. 769

Thomas, Julie, Mktg. Asst.--Detroit Stoker Co., Monroe, MI; *U.S. Public*, pg. 1679

Thomas, Linda, Dir.-Investor Rels.--Unit Corporation, Tulsa, OK; *U.S. Public*, pg. 1672

Thomas, Mary Ellen, Mgr.-Mktg. Commun.--Security Plastics, Inc., Hialeah, FL; *U.S. Private*, pg. 981

Thomas, N., Gen. Mgr.-Mktg. & Tech.--Peters & Brownes Foods Ltd., Balcatta, Australia; *Int'l*, pg. 1040

Thomas, Nigel, Mgr.-Mktg. & Tech.--Peters & Brownes Foods Ltd., Balcatta, Australia; *Int'l*, pg. 1040

Thomas, Paul, Dir.-Mktg.--Production Tool Supply Co., Warren, MI; *U.S. Private*, pg. 889

Thomas, Peter, V.P.-Mktg. & Sls.--Kennecott Holdings Corporation, Magna, UT; *Int'l*, pg. 1119

Thomas, Stanley A., Sr. Exec. V.P.-Mktg.--Shoppers Drug Mart, Ltd., Toronto, Canada; *Int'l*, pg. 112

Thomas, Stephen K., V.P.-Mktg.--Zions Bancorporation, Salt Lake City, UT; *U.S. Public*, pg. 1792

Thomas, Tristan, Mktg. Asst.--Maytag International, Inc., Chicago, IL; *U.S. Public*, pg. 1065

Thomason, John, V.P.-Mktg.--MTL Inc., Plant City, FL; *U.S. Public*, pg. 1028

Thomason, John, Mgr.-Mktg.--Montgomery Tank Lines, Inc., Plant City, FL; *U.S. Public*, pg. 1028

Thomason, Scott L., Pres. & Chief Exec. Officer--Thomason Auto Group, Gladstone, OR; *U.S. Private*, pg. 1083

Thomason, William P., Dir.-Mktg.--Policy Management Systems Corporation, Blythewood, SC; *U.S. Public*, pg. 1314

Thompson, Andrew M., V.P.-Southeast Reg. Sls.--EBP Life Insurnace Co., Minneapolis, MN; *U.S. Public*, pg. 635

Thompson, Ann, Mgr.-Mktg. Communications--Guidant Corporation-Vascular Intervention Group, Santa Clara, CA; *U.S. Public*, pg. 768

Thompson, Anthony, Grp. V.P.-Mktg.--Proudfoot USA Company, West Palm Beach, FL; *Int'l*, pg. 1072

Thompson, Bobbie, Sr. Mgr.-Mktg. & Communications--American Tourister, Inc., Warren, RI; *U.S. Public*, pg. 1430

Thompson, Brad, Mgr.-Mktg.--Laboratory Supply Company, Inc., Louisville, KY; *U.S. Private*, pg. 641

Thompson, Byl, Dir.-Mktg.--Esprit de Corp., San Francisco, CA; *U.S. Private*, pg. 383

Thompson, Carla, Mgr.-Mktg. Svcs.--Hart Crowser, Inc., Seattle, WA; *U.S. Private*, pg. 507

Thompson, Carol, Exec. Dir.-Mktg.--Christianity Today, Inc., Carol Stream, IL; *U.S. Private*, pg. 238

Thompson, D.J., Mgr.-Mktg. Services--Cat Pumps Corporation, Minneapolis, MN; *U.S. Private*, pg. 336

Thompson, Ernest E., III, V.P.-Sls. & Mktg.--CPAC, Inc., Leicester, NY; *U.S. Public*, pg. 282

Thompson, Ernest E., III, V.P.-Sls. & Mktg.--CPAC Equipment Division, Leicester, NY; *U.S. Public*, pg. 282

Thompson, George, Dir.-Mktg.--Hardaway Construction Corp. of Tennessee, Inc., Nashville, TN; *U.S. Private*, pg. 501

Thompson, James, Mktg. Svcs. Admin.--Ludlow Composites Corporation, Fremont, OH; *U.S. Private*, pg. 680

Thompson, Janelle, V.P.-Mktg.--Chateau St. Jean Winery, Kenwood, CA; *Int'l*, pg. 1321

Thompson, Janelle E., V.P.-Mktg. & Adv.--Wine World Estates Company, Saint Helena, CA; *Int'l*, pg. 917

Thompson, Janelle E., V.P.-Mktg.--Beringer Wine Estates Holdings, Inc., Saint Helena, CA; *U.S. Private*, pg. 1078

Thompson, John, V.P.-Sls. & Mktg.--Mays Chemical Company, Indianapolis, IN; *U.S. Private*, pg. 718

Thompson, John S., Pres. & Chief Exec.--BTR, Inc., Stamford, CT; *Int'l*, pg. 127

Thompson, Kevin, Dir.-Strtg. Partnerships & Event Mktg. NAO--General Motors Corporation, Detroit, MI; *U.S. Public*, pg. 718

Thompson, Lee, V.P. & Dir.-Grp. Mktg./Professional Reference & Trade Grp.--John Wiley & Sons, Inc., New York, NY; *U.S. Public*, pg. 1768

Thompson, M. G., Dir.-Mktg.-Microelectronic Chemicals--Mallinckrodt Baker Inc., Phillipsburg, NJ; *U.S. Public*, pg. 1039

Thompson, Norman J., Sr. V.P.--Air New Zealand Ltd. (U.S.A.), El Segundo, CA; *Int'l*, pg. 38

Thompson, R.I.F., V.P.-Mktg.--Camco Inc., Mississauga, Canada; *U.S. Public*, pg. 713

Thompson, Rick, V.P.-Sls. & Mktg.--Burlington Basket Co., Burlington, IA; *U.S. Private*, pg. 183

Thompson, Robin, Dir.-Mktg.--Patcraft Commercial Carpet, Chatsworth, GA; *U.S. Private*, pg. 900

Thompson, Sarah, Dir.-Mktg. Res.--The Dreyfus Corporation, New York, NY; *U.S. Public*, pg. 1085

Thompson, Scott, Mgr.-Mktg.--Fisher Broadcasting Inc., Seattle, WA; *U.S. Public*, pg. 648

Thompson, Thomas, Sr. V.P.-Sls. & Mktg.--Friedman Industries, Inc., Houston, TX; *U.S. Public*, pg. 682

Thompson, Walt, Natl. Program Mgr.-Special Events--Xerox Business Services, Rochester, NY; *U.S. Public*, pg. 1784

Thompson, William, V.P.-Mktg. & Devel.--Select Sires, Inc., Plain City, OH; *U.S. Private*, pg. 982

Thorn, Nancy, Mgr.-Mktg. Services--The Morning Star Group, Dallas, TX; *U.S. Public*, pg. 1527

Thorn, Nancy, Mgr.-Mktg. Services--Presto Food Products, Inc., City of Industry, CA; *U.S. Public*, pg. 1527

Thorne, Dan, Mgr.-Mktg.--Gilster Mary Lee Corp., Chester, IL; *U.S. Private*, pg. 455

Thorne, Kristi, Dir.-Mktg. Consumer Div.--ICI Paints, Cleveland, OH; *Int'l*, pg. 664

Thorneycroft-Smith, Christopher, Dir.-Mktg. Support--Iveco-Ford Truck Ltd., Watford, United Kingdom; *Int'l*, pg. 484

Thornhill Jones, Lisa, Dir.-Mktg. Communications Trusted Div.--CyberGuard Corporation, Fort Lauderdale, FL; *U.S. Public*, pg. 470

Thornton, Daniel P., Sr. V.P.-Sls. & Mktg.--Progress Printing Company, Lynchburg, VA; *U.S. Private*, pg. 890

Thornton, John, V.P.-Mktg. & Sls.--IRD Mechanalysis, Inc. (U.S.A.), Columbus, OH; *U.S. Public*, pg. 789

Thornton, Suzanne, Mgr.-Mktg.--Educational Development Corporation, Tulsa, OK; *U.S. Public*, pg. 564

Thornton, Terry, V.P.-Mktg. Plng.--Carnival Corporation, Miami, FL; *U.S. Public*, pg. 306

Thornton, Thomas, V.P.-Mktg.--Klockner-Moeller Corp., Franklin, MA; *Int'l*, pg. 736

Thorpe, John, Dir.-Mktg.--Tarmac plc, Wolverhampton, United Kingdom; *Int'l*, pg. 1355

Thorup, Henrik, Mgr.-Mktg.--ISS-International Service System A/S, Holte, Denmark; *Int'l*, pg. 656

Thrasher, Scott, Sr. V.P.-Sls. & Mktg.--Toastmaster, Inc., Columbia, MO; *U.S. Public*, pg. 1619

Thresher, Laurie, Mktg. Consultant--National Life Insurance Company, Montpelier, VT; *U.S. Private*, pg. 785

Thurman, Jimmy, V.P.-Sls. & Mktg.--Harrington & King, Chicago, IL; *U.S. Private*, pg. 504

Thurman, Mark, Dir.-Mktg.--Pepper Construction Company, Irvine, CA; *U.S. Private*, pg. 851

Thurstone, Peter, Mgr.-Sls.--Radix Wire Company, Cleveland, OH; *U.S. Private*, pg. 907

Thwaites, R., Sls., Mktg. & Comml. Mgr.--Ultra Electrics, Cheltenham, United Kingdom; *Int'l*, pg. 1431

Thybony, James D., Pres.--Thybony Wall Coverings Co., Chicago, IL; *U.S. Private*, pg. 1084

Thyen, John, Sr. Exec. V.P.-Mktg. & Sls.--Kimball International, Inc., Jasper, IN; *U.S. Public*, pg. 956

Tibbetts, Ivana, Dir.-Mktg. Commun.--Union Carbide Corporation, Danbury, CT; *U.S. Public*, pg. 1666

Tibbits, Rolland, V.P.-Sls. & Mktg.--Hill & Griffith Company, Cincinnati, OH; *U.S. Private*, pg. 529

Tiberi, John J., Dir.-Sls. & Mktg.--Medusa Aggregate Co., Cleveland, OH; *U.S. Public*, pg. 1084

Ticco, John A., Mgr.-Mktg.--Louis P. Ciminelli Construction Co. Inc., Buffalo, NY; *U.S. Private*, pg. 239

Ticknor, Richard, V.P.-Mktg.--Sugar Foods Corp, New York, NY; *U.S. Private*, pg. 1049

Tidwell, Robert H., V.P.-Mktg.--Genetics Institute, Inc., Cambridge, MA; *U.S. Public*, pg. 79

Tieger, Jeffrey, Mgr.-Mktg.--Kinpak, Inc., Montgomery, AL; *U.S. Public*, pg. 1211

Tienanelli, Patrick, V.P.-Mktg.--Domestic Uniform Rental Co., Farmington Hills, MI; *U.S. Private*, pg. 338

Tierman, Pam, Mktg. Asst.--Rite-Hite Corporation (WI), Milwaukee, WI; *U.S. Private*, pg. 933

Tieszen, Lori, Dir.-Mktg.--Domecq Importers Inc., Old Greenwich, CT; *Int'l*, pg. 63

Tietjen, Tom, V.P.-Mktg. & Sls.--Xerxes Corporation, Minneapolis, MN; *U.S. Private*, pg. 1194

Tietz, David, Gen. Mgr.--Holiday RV Superstores, Inc.-Ft. Myers, Fort Myers, FL; *U.S. Public*, pg. 830

Tiffin, Mark A., V.P.-Mktg.--Mackenzie Financial Corporation, Toronto, Canada; *Int'l*, pg. 828

Tighe Gaye, Kathleen, Partner-Direct Mktg. Services--Eric Mower and Associates, Rochester, NY; *U.S. Private*, pg. 765

Tighe, Larry, Exec. V.P.-Mktg.--Grand Holdings, Inc., Edina, MN; *U.S. Private*, pg. 468

Tilby, Peter, Reg. Dir.-Mktg.--DHL International (Hong Kong) Ltd., Wan Chai, Hong Kong; *U.S. Private*, pg. 302

Tilghman, Richard H., Sr V.P.-Mktg.--Pepper Construction Co., Chicago, IL; *U.S. Private*, pg. 851

Tilis, Jerome S., V.P.-Mktg.--Knight-Ridder, Inc., Miami, FL; *U.S. Public*, pg. 963

Tilk, Gunther, Dir.-Mktg.--Kali-Chemie Aktiengesellschaft, Hannover, Germany; *Int'l*, pg. 1278

Tillis, Arlen, V.P.-Sls. & Mktg.--Cox Lumber Co., Saint Petersburg, FL; *U.S. Private*, pg. 283

Tillman, Wesley, Mgr.-Mktg. Communications--W.M. Barr & Co., Inc., Memphis, TN; *U.S. Private*, pg. 117

Tillmann, Catherine, Dir.-Mktg. Services--Four Seasons Hotels Inc., Don Mills, Canada; *Int'l*, pg. 502

Tillson, Peter S., V.P.-Worksite MKtg.--Boston Mutual Life Insurance Co., Canton, MA; *U.S. Private*, pg. 161

Tilly, Maureen, Mktg. Svcs.--The Flood Company, Hudson, OH; *U.S. Private*, pg. 414

Tilney, Elizabeth A., Sr. V.P.-Corp. Mktg.--Enron Corp., Houston, TX; *U.S. Public*, pg. 584

Tilstone, A. David, V.P. & Dir.-Global Mktg.--Kennametal Inc., Latrobe, PA; *U.S. Public*, pg. 950

Timber, Jeanne, V.P.-Mktg. & Sls.--AR Accessories Group, Inc., Milwaukee, WI; *U.S. Private*, pg. 7
Timbie, Mark, V.P.-Mktg.--McCormick & Company, Incorporated, Sparks, MD; *U.S. Public*, pg. 1066
Timbie, Mark, V.P.-Sls. & Mktg.--McCormick/Schilling, Hunt Valley, MD; *U.S. Public*, pg. 1066
Timko, Joseph R., V.P.-Circulation--Yankee Publishing Incorporated, Dublin, NH; *U.S. Private*, pg. 1195
Timmes, Jim, Dir.-Mktg.--Cargill Salt Inc., Minneapolis, MN; *Int'l*, pg. 48
Timmons, Shirley A., Sr. V.P. & Mgr.-Mktg.--Willis Corroon Corp. of Kansas, Wichita, KS; *Int'l*, pg. 1506
Timner, Hans-Jorg, Dir.-Mktg.--AgrEvo GmbH, Berlin, Germany; *Int'l*, pg. 624
Timpanelli, Peter, Dir.-Sls. & Mktg.--Skinner Valve Division, New Britain, CT; *U.S. Public*, pg. 1260
Tinghitella, John, V.P.-Sls. & Mktg.--Marinco/AFI, Napa, CA; *U.S. Public*, pg. 1705
Tippery, Kenneth, V.P.-Mktg.--Ameripride Service Company, Minneapolis, MN; *U.S. Private*, pg. 65
Tipps, Bill, Sr. V.P.-Sls. & Mktg.--Universal-Rundle Corp., New Castle, PA; *U.S. Public*, pg. 1193
Tipton, Dick, V.P.-Sls. & Mktg.--Thermador, Los Angeles, CA; *U.S. Public*, pg. 1053
Tipton, Don, V.P.-Mktg.--Holm Industries, Inc., Scottsburg, IN; *U.S. Public*, pg. 1504
Tipton, Jim, Mgr.-Adv. & Mktg.--Beer Nuts, Inc., Bloomington, IL; *U.S. Private*, pg. 130
Tipton, Merry, Dir.-Mktg.--Sea Island Company, Sea Island, GA; *U.S. Private*, pg. 977
Tischler, Michael, V.P.-Mktg.--Epitronics, Inc., Mesa, AZ; *U.S. Public*, pg. 12
Titley, Patricia B., Dir.-Mktg.--Britrail Travel International Inc., New York, NY; *Int'l*, pg. 1165
Tjerandsen, Tom, Pres. & Gen. Mgr.--California Fresh Apricot Council, San Francisco, CA; *U.S. Private*, pg. 200
Tobak, Steve, V.P.-Corp. Mktg.--Cyrix Corporation, Richardson, TX; *U.S. Public*, pg. 1160
Tobey, Bill, Mgr.-Mktg. Communicaitons--Eimco Process Equipment Co., Salt Lake City, UT; *U.S. Public*, pg. 166
Todd, Hank, V.P.-Mktg.--Carlson Wagonlit Travel, Minneapolis, MN; *U.S. Private*, pg. 212
Todd, Jack, Mgr.-Mktg. Comm.--COMPAQ Computer Corporation, Houston, TX; *U.S. Public*, pg. 417
Todd, John, Mgr.-Customer Support & Engrng.--Yarway Corporation, Blue Bell, PA; *U.S. Public*, pg. 1650
Todd, Julian, Dir.-Mktg. Svcs.--H.P. Bulmer Holdings Plc, Hereford, United Kingdom; *Int'l*, pg. 232
Todd, Tom, Mgr.-Mktg.--Subaru of America Southeast Region, Austell, GA; *Int'l*, pg. 523
Todd, Tosha, Mgr.-Mktg.--IXL Cabinets, Dallas, TX; *U.S. Public*, pg. 1634
Toengi, Ferdi, Mng. Dir.-Mktg. & European Sls.--AGIE AG (Fur Industrielle Elektronik), Lausanne, Switzerland; *Int'l*, pg. 488
Toepker, Sarah, Mgr.-Mktg.--John G. Shedd Aquarium, Chicago, IL; *U.S. Private*, pg. 991
Togawa, T., Gen. Mktg.--Otto Sumisho Inc., Tokyo, Japan; *Int'l*, pg. 1015
Togher, Renee, Dir.-Mktg. & Sls.--Azteca Foods, Incorporated, Chicago, IL; *U.S. Private*, pg. 104
Tolar, James E., Mgr.-Mktg./Florida--Checkers Drive-In Restaurants, Inc., Clearwater, FL; *U.S. Public*, pg. 342
Tolbert, Robert, Dir.-Mktg.--Moore-Handley, Inc., Pelham, AL; *U.S. Public*, pg. 1128
Tolensky, Steven M., Pres.-Men's & Intl. Divisions--Jockey International, Inc., Kenosha, WI; *U.S. Private*, pg. 588
Tolfree, Richard, Mgr.-Mktg.--Hedsorboard Ltd., Surbiton, United Kingdom; *Int'l*, pg. 864
Tollefsrud, Curt, V.P.-Mktg. & Sls.--The Stolle Corporation, Sidney, OH; *U.S. Public*, pg. 61
Tollefsrud, Curt, V.P.-Mktg. & Sls.--Alcoa Building Products, Inc., Sidney, OH; *U.S. Public*, pg. 61
Tolman, Larry, V.P.-Mktg.--Merit Medical Systems, Inc., South Jordan, UT; *U.S. Public*, pg. 1096
Tolson, Adrian, V.P.-Mktg.--Chemoil, San Francisco, CA; *U.S. Private*, pg. 233
Tomack, John K., Sr. V.P.-Mktg. Communications--First Chicago NBD Corporation, Chicago, IL; *U.S. Public*, pg. 627
Tomack, John K., Sr. V.P.-Mktg. Communications--First National Bank of Chicago, Chicago, IL; *U.S. Public*, pg. 627
Tomasetti, Elissa, Dir.-Mktg.--Billboard Magazine, New York, NY; *Int'l*, pg. 1446
Tomb, Gordon, Dir.-Communications/Reading--GPU Energy, Johnstown, PA; *U.S. Public*, pg. 695
Tomczyk, Frederick A., Mgr.-Mktg. Services--Thetford Corporation, Ann Arbor, MI; *U.S. Private*, pg. 352
Tomeck, Edward M., V.P. & Mgr.-Mktg.--NBT Bancorp Inc., Norwich, NY; *U.S. Public*, pg. 1144
Tomimoto, Lynn, Dir.-Mktg.--Teleflora, LLC, Los Angeles, CA; *U.S. Private*, pg. 941
Tomlinson, Mack, Sr. V.P.-Sls. & Mktg.--Carfel, Inc., Miami, FL; *U.S. Private*, pg. 210
Tomlinson, S., Gen. Mgr.-Systems Mktg.--Johnson Yokogawa Corporation, Newnan, GA; *Int'l*, pg. 1521
Tomlinson, Scott, Dir.-Mktg.--Aero Electronics Incorporated, Memphis, TN; *U.S. Private*, pg. 731
Tomlinson, Steve, V.P.-Mktg.--Cegelec AEG Automation Systems Corp., Canonsburg, PA; *Int'l*, pg. 52
Tompkins, Brian, Dir.-Mktg.--Personal Communications Div., Fort Worth, TX; *Int'l*, pg. 1433
Tompkins, C.M., Dir.-Domestic Adv. & Mktg.--Sunkist Growers, Inc., Sherman Oaks, CA; *U.S. Private*, pg. 1052
Tompkins, Jim, Exec. V.P.-Sls. & Mktg.--New Balance Athletic Shoe, Inc., Boston, MA; *U.S. Private*, pg. 792
Tompkins, Towle, Dir.-Mktg.--WGME-TV, Portland, ME; *U.S. Private*, pg. 439
Tompkins, William, Jr., V.P.-Mktg.--The Washington Post, Washington, DC; *U.S. Public*, pg. 1743
Toms, Paul, Sr. V.P.-Mktg.--Hooker Furniture Corporation, Martinsville, VA; *U.S. Private*, pg. 538
Tonarely, J.F., V.P.-Mktg. Services--Best Foods Caribbean, Inc., Santurce, PR; *U.S. Public*, pg. 224
Tong, Richard, V.P.-Mktg. & Desktop & Bus. Sys.--Microsoft Corporation, Redmond, WA; *U.S. Public*, pg. 1107
Tonjum, James F., Sr. V.P.-Mktg. & Sls.--Wine World Estates Company, Saint Helena, CA; *Int'l*, pg. 917
Tonkin, Cheryl, Mgr.-Adv. & Mktg.--Utah Power & Light, Salt Lake City, UT; *U.S. Public*, pg. 1251
Toombs, Chuck, V.P.-Mktg.& Sls.--Cadet Manufacturing Company, Vancouver, WA; *U.S. Private*, pg. 198
Toomey, Rodger, Sr. V.P.-Mktg. & Bus. Devel.--Food Services of America, Seattle, WA; *U.S. Private*, pg. 987
Toor, Jon, V.P.-Mktg.--Micropolis Corporation, Chatsworth, CA; *U.S. Private*, pg. 742
Toplin, Irving, Mgr.-Mktg. Services--Carl Zeiss, Inc., Thornwood, NY; *Int'l*, pg. 1523
Torbert, Martin, Dir.-Mktg. Communications & Pub. Rels.--National Starch and Chemical Company, Bridgewater, NJ; *Int'l*, pg. 1435
Torek, David, Mktg. Analyst--Delphi Packard Electric Systems, Beachwood, OH; *U.S. Public*, pg. 719
Torgeson, Ernie, Asst. V.P.--John Burnham & Co., San Diego, CA; *U.S. Private*, pg. 186
Torhusebr, Tor, Dir.-Mktg.--AGA Progas A/S, Oslo, Norway; *Int'l*, pg. 13
Torneden, Roger, Sr. V.P. & Chief Mktg. Officer--TIG Holdings, Inc., New York, NY; *U.S. Public*, pg. 1555
Tornetta, Joe, V.P.-Sls. & Mktg.--Automatic Timing & Controls, Inc., New Holland, PA; *U.S. Private*, pg. 327
Torok, Steven, Exec. Dir.-Sls. & Mktg. Opers.--Chrysler Corporation, Auburn Hills, MI; *U.S. Public*, pg. 352
Torrant, Don, Mgr.-Mktg. Commun.--The Wiremold Company, West Hartford, CT; *U.S. Private*, pg. 1184
Torres, Edwin O., V.P.-Production & Mktg.--Westernbank of Puerto Rico, Mayaguez, PR; *U.S. Public*, pg. 1760
Torres, X. Guillamet, Dir.-Mktg. & Sls.--Howard S.A., Barcelona, Spain; *Int'l*, pg. 1387
Tortell, Brian, Mgr.-Mktg.--Air Malta Co. Ltd., Luqa, Malta; *Int'l*, pg. 37
Tosi, Mark, Pres.--The Pastene Companies Ltd., Canton, MA; *U.S. Private*, pg. 842
Totaro, David J., Chief Mktg. Officer & Exec. V.P.--The Dime Savings Bank of New York, New York, NY; *U.S. Public*, pg. 509
Toth, Doug, Mgr.-Mktg.-Vertical & Titan--U.S. Electrical Motor Division, Saint Louis, MO; *U.S. Public*, pg. 573
Toth, Ron, Mgr.-Sls.--Dearborn Gage Company, Garden City, MI; *U.S. Private*, pg. 319
Toth, Rusty, Mgr.-Mktg. & Sls.--Fosbel, Inc., Berea, OH; *Int'l*, pg. 234
Totten, Tracy, V.P.-Sls. & Mktg.--Totten Tubes, Inc., Los Angeles, CA; *U.S. Private*, pg. 1093
Tough, G.G., Dir.-Sls. & Mktg.-Diagnostic--Becton Dickinson Canada Inc., Mississauga, Canada; *U.S. Public*, pg. 200
Tourtellott, Thomas E., Sr. V.P.-Mktg. & Admin.--Nielsen Dillingham Builders, Inc., San Diego, CA; *U.S. Private*, pg. 333
Tousigntant, Tim, Dir.-Sls. & Mktg.--The Toro Company Irrigation Products, Riverside, CA; *U.S. Public*, pg. 1624
Towers, Megan, Mgr.-Mktg.--TMP Worldwide Ltd., Toronto, Canada; *U.S. Private*, pg. 1065
Towers, Russell A., Real Estate Analyst-NC, SC & GA--United Dominion Realty Trust, Inc., Richmond, VA; *U.S. Public*, pg. 1677
Towne, Andy, Mgr.-Mktg. Services--Adidas (UK) Ltd., Stockport, United Kingdom; *Int'l*, pg. 25
Townsen, Michael E., Sr. V.P.-Mktg.-Car Electronics--Pioneer Electronics (USA) Inc., Long Beach, CA; *Int'l*, pg. 1058
Townsend, Ann, Dir.-Mktg.--Analytic TSA Global Asset Management Inc., Los Angeles, CA; *U.S. Public*, pg. 1672
Townsend, Todd, Mgr.-Mktg. Services--Rockford International Group, Rockford, IL; *U.S. Private*, pg. 938
Toy, Bill, Dir.-Mktg. Recreational Vehicles Grp.--Fleetwood Enterprises, Inc., Riverside, CA; *U.S. Public*, pg. 650
Trach, John P., V.P.-Sls. & Mktg.--Daily Express, Inc., Carlisle, PA; *U.S. Private*, pg. 307
Tracy, Kerry, Coord.-Mktg.--George T. Schmidt, Niles, IL; *U.S. Private*, pg. 970
Tracy, Laurie, Dir.-Wholesale Admin. Sls. & Mktg.--DFI/Inflight, Inc., Ridgefield, CT; *Int'l*, pg. 103
Tracy, Steve, Assoc. V.P.-Mktg.--The PBS&J Corporation, Miami, FL; *U.S. Private*, pg. 825
Trads, Carsten, V.P.-Mktg. & Sls.--GN Danavox A/S, Taastrup, Denmark; *Int'l*, pg. 537
Traidman, Michael, V.P.-Sls. & Mktg.--Printco Group, Greenville, MI; *U.S. Public*, pg. 228
Trainor, Ann, Telemarketing Mgr.--SSD&W Integrated Marketing Communications, Montville, NJ; *U.S. Private*, pg. 958
Trainor, Michael, V.P.-Mktg. & Adv.--Century 21 Real Estate Corp., Parsippany, NJ; *U.S. Public*, pg. 321
Trangmar, Don, Exec. Dir.-Menswear & Gen. Merchandise Tech.--Marks & Spencer PLC, London, United Kingdom; *Int'l*, pg. 842
Trani, Anthony C., V.P.-Mktg. & Institutional Bus.--Metropolitan Life Insurance Co., New York, NY; *U.S. Private*, pg. 737
Transeth, Don, V.P.-EA Sports Mktg.--Electronic Arts, San Mateo, CA; *U.S. Public*, pg. 569
Trapnell, Britt, Sr. V.P. & Dir.-Mktg.--Caribbean American Life Assurance Company, Hato Rey, PR; *U.S. Public*, pg. 67
Trapolino, Kay, Mktg. Coord.--The Accor Group, Inc., Corona Del Mar, CA; *Int'l*, pg. 21
Trapolino, Peter, V.P.-Devel.--The Accor Group, Inc., Corona Del Mar, CA; *Int'l*, pg. 21
Trapp, Steve, V.P.-Sls. & Mktg.--G.I. Plastek, Elyria, OH; *U.S. Private*, pg. 435
Trautschold, Michael J., V.P.-Mktg. Services--ConAgra, Inc., Omaha, NE; *U.S. Public*, pg. 425
Travers, Michael, Sls. Mgr.-Indus.--Industrials Division, Belcamp, MD; *U.S. Private*, pg. 195
Trawinski, Eileen, First V.P.-Mktg.--Emigrant Savings Bank, New York, NY; *U.S. Private*, pg. 373
Trebek, Elaine, Sr. V.P.-MKtg.--Arcade Inc., Chattanooga, TN; *U.S. Private*, pg. 79
Trebilcock, Jim, V.P.-Corp. Mktg. Svcs.--Dr Pepper/Seven Up No. America, Dallas, TX; *Int'l*, pg. 248
Trebilcock, Jim, V.P.-Corp. Mktg. Svcs.--Dr. Pepper Co., Dallas, TX; *Int'l*, pg. 248
Treen, Ray, V.P.-Pur.--Hardware Wholesalers, Inc., Fort Wayne, IN; *U.S. Private*, pg. 502
Trehin, Jean, Mgr.-Mktg.--C.M.C. SA, Saint Quentin-en-Yvelines, France; *Int'l*, pg. 792
Treis, James F., V.P.-Mktg.--Arandell Corporation, Menomonee Falls, WI; *U.S. Private*, pg. 79
Treleaven, Jim, V.P.-Mktg.--Moore Document Solutions, Lake Forest, IL; *Int'l*, pg. 890
Tremoulis, James, V.P.-Sls. & Mktg.--O'Sullivan Corporation, Winchester, VA; *U.S. Public*, pg. 1234
Trendowicz, Julie, V.P.-Sls. & Mktg.--Copley Pharmaceuticals, Inc., Canton, MA; *U.S. Public*, pg. 446
Trent, Jeff, Coord.-Coupon Plus--O'Malia Food Markets Inc., Carmel, IN; *U.S. Private*, pg. 816
Treul, Nancy H., V.P.-Mktg.--Foremost Corporation of America, Caledonia, MI; *U.S. Public*, pg. 667
Trevisan, Jane D., V.P.-Mktg. & Sls.--SLM Holding Corp., Washington, DC; *U.S. Public*, pg. 1419
Triantafellou, Michael, V.P.-Retail Opers.--FFP Marketing Company, Inc., Fort Worth, TX; *U.S. Public*, pg. 604
Trick, Chris, Dir.-Natl. Mktg.--La Quinta Inns, Inc., San Antonio, TX; *U.S. Public*, pg. 972
Triffaux, Roland, V.P.-European Sls. & Mktg.--Xilinx, Inc., San Jose, CA; *U.S. Public*, pg. 1786
Trige, Peter, Mgr.-Mktg.--Sonofon, Horsholm, Denmark; *Int'l, pg. 537*
Trilling, Howard, V.P.-Mktg. & Commun.--American Marketing Industries, Inc., Kansas City, MO; *U.S. Private, pg. 58*
Trimble, Derek, V.P.-Mktg.--Cardkey Systems, Inc., Simi Valley, CA; *U.S. Public*, pg. 105
Trimble, Tom, V.P.-Bus. Devel.--The Titan Corporation, San Diego, CA; *U.S. Public*, pg. 1618
Trimble, Tom, Dir.-Mktg.--Titan Linkabit, San Diego, CA; *U.S. Public*, pg. 1618
Trimmer, Gord, V.P.-North American Sls. & Mktg.--A. Schulman, Inc., Akron, OH; *U.S. Public*, pg. 1441
Trimmer, P.J., Dir.-Intl. Mktg. & Program Plng.--Chrysler Corporation, Auburn Hills, MI; *U.S. Public*, pg. 352
Trinder, Chuck, Mgr.-Mktg.--A & S Tribal Industries, Poplar, MT; *U.S. Private*, pg. 1
Tringle, Terry, V.P.-Mktg.--American Color Graphics, Brentwood, TN; *U.S. Public*, pg. 1132
Triplett, Robert, Mgr.-Mktg. Svcs.--Taylor Machine Works, Inc., Louisville, MS; *U.S. Private*, pg. 1070
Tripp, Martha, V.P.-Mktg. Services--Holland Mark Martin, Boston, MA; *U.S. Private*, pg. 534
Tritt, Jeff, Dir.-Mktg. Communications--The Sherwin-Williams Company, Cleveland, OH; *U.S. Public*, pg. 1465
Tritt, Jeff, Dir.-Mktg. Communications--Sherwin-Williams Consumer Brands Division, Cleveland, OH; *U.S. Public*, pg. 1466
Tritt, Jeff, Dir.-Mktg. Communications--Pratt & Lambert United, Inc., Cleveland, OH; *U.S. Public*, pg. 1466
Trocher, John A., V.P.-Mktg. & Sls.--American Credit Indemnity, Baltimore, MD; *Int'l*, pg. 464
Trocke, Theresa, Mgr.-Mktg.--Land O'Lakes Fluid Dairy Division, Arden Hills, MN; *U.S. Private*, pg. 646
Troise, Fred, V.P.-Mktg.--Geraghty & Miller, Inc., Denver, CO; *Int'l*, pg. 607
Trongeay, Kas, V.P.-Mktg.--Tyco Toys, Inc., Mount Laurel, NJ; *U.S. Public*, pg. 1058
Trostel, Otto P., V.P.-Mktg.--Penn Security Bank and Trust Co., Scranton, PA; *U.S. Public*, pg. 1270
Troup, Daniel, V.P.-Mktg.--National Fruit Product Company, Winchester, VA; *U.S. Private*, pg. 783
Troxell, Gerald, Dir.-Mktg.--Media Incorporated, New York, NY; *U.S. Private*, pg. 726
Troxell, Gerald, Mktg. Dir.--Media Direct Partners, Incorporated, New York, NY; *U.S. Private*, pg. 726
Troy, Heidi, Mgr.-Sls. & Mktg.--Luxor, Waukegan, IL; *U.S. Private*, pg. 359
Troyer, Darrel, V.P.-Sls. & Adv.--Troyer Potato Products, Inc., Waterford, PA; *U.S. Private*, pg. 1106
Troyer, Paul E., V.P.-Sls., Mktg. & Adv.--Hanover Wire Cloth, Hanover, PA; *U.S. Private*, pg. 193
Truatschold, Mike, V.P.-Mktg. Svcs.--ConAgra Fruen Milling Co., Omaha, NE; *U.S. Public*, pg. 428
Trudeau, Michael, Mgr.-Mktg. Res. & Information--Toronto Star Newspapers Ltd., Toronto, Canada; *Int'l*, pg. 1402
Trudel, Brian, M., V.P.-Sls. & Mktg.--Carrier Vibrating Equipment, Inc., Louisville, KY; *U.S. Private*, pg. 215
True, James, Dir.-Mktg.--Osicom Technologies Inc., Annapolis Junction, MD; *U.S. Public*, pg. 1233
Truettner, Jerry, Dir.-Mktg.--Heresite Protective Coatings Inc., Manitowoc, WI; *U.S. Private*, pg. 523
Trujillo, Robert R., Exec. V.P. & Dir.-Franchise Mngmt.--Glendale Federal Bank, F.S.B., Glendale, CA; *U.S. Public*, pg. 747
Trumbo, Kirby, Sr. V.P.-Mktg. & Product Mngmt.--First American Corporation, Nashville, TN; *U.S. Public*, pg. 624
Trumbore, John, Sr. V.P.--Harris, Baio & McCullough Inc., Philadelphia, PA; *U.S. Private*, pg. 504
Trusty, David L., V.P.-Mktg.--Piedmont Natural Gas Co., Inc., Charlotte, NC; *U.S. Public*, pg. 1295
Trybus, Tom, Sr. V.P.-Mktg. & Sls.--Belvedere Company, Belvidere, IL; *U.S. Private*, pg. 1008
Tsay, Imad, Mgr.-Natl. Sls. & Mktg.--Miyano Machinery, Inc., Wood Dale, IL; *U.S. Private*, pg. 754
Tschanz, Tom, Dir.-Mktg.--Liquid Controls LLC, Lake Bluff, IL; *U.S. Private*, pg. 669
Tschich, Wilfried, Mgr.-Mktg.--O&K Orenstein & Koppel Aktiengesellschaft, Dortmund, Germany; *Int'l*, pg. 516
Tsujita, Hikaru, Sr. Mng. Dir.-Sls.--Sapporo Breweries Ltd., Tokyo, Japan; *Int'l*, pg. 1193

Tucker, Debbie, Dir.-Mktg.--International Dairy Queen, Inc., Minneapolis, MN; *U.S. Public*, pg. 220
Tucker, Debbie, Dir.-Mktg.--American Dairy Queen Corporation, Minneapolis, MN; *U.S. Public*, pg. 220
Tucker, Debbie, Dir.-Mktg.--Orange Julius of America, Edina, MN; *U.S. Public*, pg. 220
Tucker, Gary, Mgr.-Mktg.--The Paty Company, Piney Flats, TN; *U.S. Private*, pg. 844
Tucker, Hugh, V.P.-Sls. & Mktg.--Dataram Corporation, Princeton, NJ; *U.S. Public*, pg. 487
Tucker, James E., V.P.-Sls. & Mktg.--R.M. Palmer Company, Reading, PA; *U.S. Private*, pg. 835
Tucker, Jim, V.P.-Mktg. & Sls.--Denison Hydraulics, Inc., Marysville, OH; *U.S. Private*, pg. 324
Tucker, John W., V.P.-Mktg. & Sls.--ACT Networks, Inc., Camarillo, CA; *U.S. Public*, pg. 3
Tucker, Kevin, V.P.-Sls. & Retail--Suntory Water Group, Inc., Marietta, GA; *Int'l*, pg. 1321
Tucker, Michael, V.P.-Sls. & Mktg.--Hackney and Sons, Inc., Washington, NC; *U.S. Private*, pg. 1097
Tucker, Nancy, Dir.-Mktg.--The H.T. Hackney Co., Knoxville, TN; *U.S. Private*, pg. 493
Tucker, Valerie, Mktg.--Applied Biosystems, Foster City, CA; *U.S. Public*, pg. 1279
Tucker, William, Mgr.-Mktg.--Quaker State Corporation, Irving, TX; *U.S. Public*, pg. 1348
Tudor, L. C., Mgr.-Mktg. Services--WCI Machine Tools & Systems, Cincinnati, OH; *Int'l*, pg. 440
Tuerff, Tim, V.P.-Mktg.--Esselte Meto, Morris Plains, NJ; *Int'l*, pg. 460
Tuit, Debbie, Asst.-Sls. & Mktg.--Koch Otto H. York Co., Inc., Parsippany, NJ; *U.S. Private*, pg. 628
Tumasz, Matt, Dir.-Mktg.--Cytogen Corporation, Princeton, NJ; *U.S. Public*, pg. 471
Tumy, Julie, Exec. V.P. & Chief Mktg. Officer--Noble & Associates, Springfield, MO; *U.S. Private*, pg. 800
Tupa, Ed, V.P.-Sls. & Mktg.--Roxane Laboratories, Inc., Columbus, OH; *Int'l*, pg. 199
Turbow, Ilene, V.P.-Mktg.--Ryan's Family Steak Houses, Inc., Greer, SC; *U.S. Public*, pg. 1413
Turff, Martin, Mgr.-Mktg.--Esselte Europe, London, United Kingdom; *Int'l*, pg. 460
Turissini, James, Mgr.-Bus. Devel.--Ghafari Associates, Inc., Dearborn, MI; *U.S. Private*, pg. 450
Turko, Henry, Dir.-Mktg.--Network Peripherals Inc., Milpitas, CA; *U.S. Public*, pg. 1169
Turley, Dominic, Dir.-Mktg. & New Bus. Mgr.--Oak Grigsby, Sugar Grove, IL; *U.S. Public*, pg. 1209
Turley, G.A., Acting Dir.-Grp. Mktg.--Ground Systems Group, Fullerton, CA; *U.S. Public*, pg. 1364
Turlukowski, Paul, Product Mktg. Specialist--Faraday, Inc., Tecumseh, MI; *Int'l*, pg. 1246
Turman, Del, Mgr.-Mktg. Commun.--Computer Language Research, Inc., Carrollton, TX; *U.S. Public*, pg. 421
Turnbull, Andy, Mktg. Res. Dir.--Poulter Communications PLC, Leeds, United Kingdom; *Int'l*, pg. 1065
Turnbull, Mike, Sr. V.P.-Mktg.--AMC, Inc., Atlanta, GA; *U.S. Private*, pg. 6
Turner, A.D., Dir.-Mktg.--AAH Pharmaceuticals Limited, Runcorn, United Kingdom; *Int'l*, pg. 591
Turner, Brandon, Mgr.-Mktg.--JBL Div., Spartanburg, SC; *U.S. Public*, pg. 1262
Turner, Bruce, Dir.-Mktg.--Madison Industries, Los Angeles, CA; *U.S. Private*, pg. 428
Turner, Curtis L., V.P.-Propane Mktg.--Mapco Inc., Tulsa, OK; *U.S. Public*, pg. 1042
Turner, Curtis L., Sr. V.P.-Mktg. & Devel.--Mapco Natural Gas Liquids Inc., Tulsa, OK; *U.S. Public*, pg. 1042
Turner, Frank, Sr. V.P.-Sls. & Mktg.--Mighty Distributing System, Norcross, GA; *U.S. Private*, pg. 745
Turner, J. Timothy, Sr. V.P.-Sls. & Mktg.--Old Dominion Freight Line, Inc., High Point, NC; *U.S. Public*, pg. 1216
Turner, Jackie, Dir.-Mktg.--Carolina Builders Corporation, Marietta, GA; *Int'l*, pg. 1512
Turner, Jeff, V.P.-Mktg.--Swiss Army Brands, Inc., Shelton, CT; *U.S. Public*, pg. 1544
Turner, John A., V.P.-Sls. & Mktg.--Hatfield Quality Meats, Hatfield, PA; *U.S. Private*, pg. 510
Turner, Kevin, Mgr.--Geupel DeMars, Inc., Indianapolis, IN; *U.S. Private*, pg. 449
Turner, Lisa, Mgr.-Mktg. Communications--Bergen Brunswig Medical Corporation, Orange, CA; *U.S. Public*, pg. 214
Turner, Mitch, V.P.-Mktg. & Sls.--Corinthian Media, Inc., New York, NY; *U.S. Private*, pg. 275
Turner, R., Dir.-Mktg.--Northern Telecom, London, United Kingdom; *Int'l*, pg. 970
Turner, Richard T., Dir.-Grp. Mktg.--Rolls-Royce plc, London, United Kingdom; *Int'l*, pg. 1126
Turner, Ritay, Sr. V.P.-Mktg.--NationsBank of Texas, N.A., Dallas, TX; *U.S. Public*, pg. 1163
Turner, Rob, Gen. Mgr.-Mktg.--Sasol Mining (Pty.) Ltd., Secunda, South Africa; *Int'l*, pg. 1197
Turner, Robert J., Dir.-Mktg.--Glynwed Metals Processing Ltd., Wednesbury, United Kingdom; *Int'l*, pg. 554
Turner, Ron L., Sr. V.P.--Kurtz Bros., Inc., Clearfield, PA; *U.S. Private*, pg. 637
Turner, Stan, V.P.-Bus. Devel.--Davis Electrical Constructors, Inc., Greenville, SC; *U.S. Private*, pg. 315
Turner, Steve, Mgr.-Mktg. & Adv.--Turner Holding LLC, Covington, TN; *U.S. Private*, pg. 1109
Turny, Julie, Sr. V.P., Chief Mktg. Officer-Bus.-to-Bus. & Dir.--Noble & Associates Promotion Group, Springfield, MO; *U.S. Private*, pg. 800
Turrin, Phyllis, Dir.-Mktg.--Georgette Klinger, Inc., New York, NY; *U.S. Private*, pg. 626
Turrisi, Jeff, Dir.-Mktg.--Greater New York Mutual Insurance Company, New York, NY; *U.S. Private*, pg. 476
Turse, Bill, V.P.-Mktg. & Sls., Dir.-Adv.--Ferraz Corporation, Parsippany, NJ; *Int'l*, pg. 1028
Turton, James, Mgr.-Mktg.-Vegetarian/Non-Meats--UB Frozen & Chilled Limited, Grimsby, United Kingdom; *Int'l, pg. 1442*
Turunen, Eero, Sr. V.P.-Sls. & Mktg.--Valmet Corporation, Helsinki, Finland; *Int'l*, pg. 1447
Tusa, Philip, V.P.-Mktg. Patient Monitoring Div.--Datascope Corp., Montvale, NJ; *U.S. Public*, pg. 487
Tusinac, Edda, Mgr.-Intl. Marketing--Caere Corporation, Los Gatos, CA; *U.S. Public*, pg. 291
Tuthill, James G., Jr., Pres. & Chief Exec. Officer--Tuthill Corporation, Hinsdale, IL; *U.S. Private*, pg. 1110
Tutini, Peter, V.P.-Sls. & Mktg.--Perstorp Analytical Inc. Division NIRSystems, Silver Spring, MD; *Int'l*, pg. 1039
Tutt, Davina, Mgr.-Mktg. Communications--Dynex Technologies, Chantilly, VA; *U.S. Public*, pg. 1591
Twardowski, Jerry, V.P.-Mktg.--Atwood & Morrill Co., Inc., Salem, MA; *Int'l*, pg. 1489
Tweedt, Barbara, Mgr.-Mktg. Commun.--Schweizer Aircraft Corporation, Big Flats, NY; *U.S. Private*, pg. 975
Twining, Robert, V.P.-Sls., Mktg. & Bus. Plng.--COMSAT World Systems, Bethesda, MD; *U.S. Public*, pg. 424
Twinkle, William, Mgr.-Mktg.--Comstream, A Spar Company, Beijing, China; *Int'l*, pg. 1288
Twoby, John, Sr. V.P.-Mktg.--Interval International Inc., Miami, FL; *U.S. Public*, pg. 320
Twombly, Angus, V.P.-Mktg.--The Portland Newspapers, Portland, ME; *U.S. Private*, pg. 439
Twyble, William J., Sr. V.P.-Res. & Devel. Mktg. & Customer Satisfaction--The Lincoln Electric Company, Cleveland, OH; *U.S. Public*, pg. 996
Tyler, Mick, V.P.-Retail Mktg.--Ore-Ida Foods, Inc., Boise, ID; *U.S. Public*, pg. 805
Tyler, Robert E., Mgr.-Bulk Power Mktg.--Unicom Corporation, Chicago, IL; *U.S. Public*, pg. 1664
Tyler, Tim, Mktg. Commun. Specialist--Viking Range Corp., Greenwood, MS; *U.S. Private*, pg. 1140
Tyler, William A., V.P.-Sls. & Mktg.--Miller Fluid Power Corp., Bensenville, IL; *U.S. Private*, pg. 747
Tyndall, Donna, Sr. Dir.-Grocery Pur.--Arden-Mayfair, Inc., Compton, CA; *U.S. Public*, pg. 129
Tyneman, Harold, Dir.-Mktg., Independent Dealer Div.--ICI Paints, Cleveland, OH; *Int'l*, pg. 664
Tyreman, Harold, Dir.-Mktg. & Mgr.-Independent Dealers--ICI Paints, Cleveland, OH; *Int'l*, pg. 663
Tzavos, Bill, Sr. V.P.--Beardsley & Piper, L.L.C., Chicago, IL; *U.S. Private*, pg. 859
Tzetzo, Chris, Dir.-Mktg.--Clark Gum Company, Buffalo, NY; *U.S. Private*, pg. 243
Tzi, Helena Tsalki, Sec.-Mktg.--Henkel Hellas, Moschato, Greece; *Int'l*, pg. 612
Uchiyama, Akio, Mng. Dir.-Creative & Mktg.--Nippo Corporation, Tokyo, Japan; *Int'l*, pg. 932
Uchiyama, Hitoshi, Mgr.-Mktg.--Yamato Transport Co., Ltd., Tokyo, Japan; *Int'l*, pg. 1519
Udvance, Susan, Mgr.-Mktg.--Trans Leasing International Inc., Northbrook, IL; *U.S. Public*, pg. 1628
Ueki, Satoshi, Gen. Mgr.--Chiyoda Mutual Life Insurance Company, Tokyo, Japan; *Int'l*, pg. 286
Ueno, Seishi, V.P.-Sls. & Mktg.--Suntory International Corp., New York, NY; *Int'l*, pg. 1321
Uhl, Chuck, V.P.-Sls. & Mktg.--Satellite Technology Group, Fort Worth, TX; *Int'l*, pg. 1433
Uhl, Robin L., Dir.-Mktg.--Butler International, Inc., Montvale, NJ; *U.S. Public*, pg. 270
Uhlen, Bjorn, Dir.-Sls. & Mktg.--Korsnas AB, Gavle, Sweden; *Int'l*, pg. 759
Uhlin, Lars, Mgr.-Mktg. Devel.--Masterfoods Oy, Helsinki, Finland; *U.S. Private*, pg. 707
Uhrenbacher, Michael, Dir.-Mktg. & Adv.--Bierbrauerei Fohrenburg, Bludenz, Austria; *Int'l*, pg. 194
Ulbrich, Chris, V.P.- Mktg. & Sls.--Ulbrich Stainless Steels & Special Metals, Inc., North Haven, CT; *U.S. Private*, pg. 1115
Ullal, Jayshree, V.P.-Mktg. Workgroup Bus. Unit--Cisco Systems, Inc., San Jose, CA; *U.S. Public*, pg. 375
Ullman, Diana, Dir.-Adv. & Mktg.--Tops Appliance City, Edison, NJ; *U.S. Public*, pg. 1622
Ullman, Harriet, Mgr.-Mktg.--Copley Pharmaceuticals, Inc., Canton, MA; *U.S. Public*, pg. 446
Ulrich, Frank, Dir.-Mktg.--Sauder Manufacturing Corporation, Archbold, OH; *U.S. Private*, pg. 967
Ulrich, J., Mgr.-Mktg.--Golf Grip Division, Laurinburg, NC; *U.S. Public*, pg. 557
Ulrich, Keith, Sr. V.P. & Brand Mktg. Partner--DMB&B Detroit, Troy, MI; *U.S. Private*, pg. 302
Umans, Donald S., Dir.-Mktg.--Value Line Publishing, New York, NY; *U.S. Private*, pg. 137
Umbach, Maria, V.P.-Mktg.--Bankers Life Insurance Co. of New York, Woodbury, NY; *U.S. Private*, pg. 560
Underhill, Jerry D., Sr. V.P.-Sls. & Mktg.--Morrison Health Care Inc., Smyrna, GA; *U.S. Public*, pg. 1133
Underwood, Debbie, V.P.-Mktg.--Piggly Wiggly Co., Memphis, TN; *U.S. Public*, pg. 653
Unell, Murray, Dir.-Mktg.--Mail-Well Inc., Englewood, CO; *U.S. Public*, pg. 1037
Unell, Murry, Dir.-Mktg.--American Mail-Well Envelope, Englewood, CO; *U.S. Public*, pg. 1038
Ungar, Andrew T., V.P.-Mktg.--Great Lakes Construction Co., Independence, OH; *U.S. Private*, pg. 474
Unger, John, Gen. Mgr. & Dir.-Mktg.--United Aircraft Products, Forest, OH; *U.S. Public*, pg. 1262
Unrue, Bill, V.P.-Mktg.--The Thermos Company, Schaumburg, IL; *Int'l*, pg. 938
Unsworth, Teri E., V.P.-Mktg.--Guest Supply, Inc., Monmouth Junction, NJ; *U.S. Public*, pg. 768
Unterberger, Mr., Dir.-Mktg.--TA Triumph-Adler Vertriebs GmbH, Nuremberg, Germany; *Int'l*, pg. 1004
Unterwiener, H., V.P.-Mktg. & Sls.--Farrell Lines Incorporated, New York, NY; *U.S. Private*, pg. 397
Updike, Steven, V.P.-Food & Beverage Opers.--Ocean Properties, Ltd., Delray Beach, FL; *U.S. Private*, pg. 811
Updyke, Jerry, V.P.-Sls. & Mktg.--Lance Industries, Sylmar, CA; *U.S. Private*, pg. 645
Upgaard, E. Terrence, V.P.-Sls. & Mktg.--Slocan Forest Products Ltd., Richmond, Canada; *Int'l*, pg. 1263
Urban, Mike, V.P.--MAGVS, Inc., Cleveland, OH; *U.S. Private*, pg. 696
Urban, Pat, Dir.-Mktg.--Chace Precision Metals, Inc., Reidsville, NC; *U.S. Public*, pg. 1564
Urbaniak, Al, Dir.-Mktg--Steelcraft Manufacturing Company, Cincinnati, OH; *U.S. Public*, pg. 877
Urbas, Eytan, Dir.-Mktg. Commun.--Guthy-Renker Corp., Palm Desert, CA; *U.S. Private*, pg. 488
Urch, James, Mgr.-Adv. & Mktg.--Telescope Casual Furniture, Inc., Granville, NY; *U.S. Private*, pg. 1074
Ure, Kent, V.P.-Mktg. & Sls.--Milk Specialties Company, Dundee, IL; *U.S. Private*, pg. 746
Urman, Mike, V.P.--M.L. Stern & Company, Inc., Beverly Hills, CA; *U.S. Private*, pg. 1041
Ursini, Silvio, Exec. Dir.-Corp. Mktg.--Bulgari SPA, Rome, Italy; *Int'l*, pg. 232
Urushisako, Toshiaki, Dir. & Deputy Grp. Gen. Mgr.-Intl. Mktg.--Sharp Corporation, Osaka, Japan; *Int'l*, pg. 1228
Usina, Mike, Dir.-Sls. & Mktg.--Silverton Marine Corporation, Millville, NJ; *U.S. Private*, pg. 1000
Usquin, B., Mgr.-Strategic Mktg.--Groupe GAN, Paris, France; *Int'l*, pg. 563
Utal, Judi, V.P.-Mktg.--General Automation, Inc., Irvine, CA; *U.S. Public*, pg. 706
Utchell, Rick, V.P.-Sls. & Promo.--Dole Food Company, Inc., Westlake Village, CA; *U.S. Public*, pg. 515
Utley, John E., Sr. V.P.-Strategic Mktg.--LucasVarity Inc., Buffalo, NY; *Int'l*, pg. 820
Utley, John E., Sr. V.P.-Strategic Mktg.--Varity Kelsey Hayes, Livonia, MI; *Int'l*, pg. 820
Utteridge, M.A., Dir.-Sls. & Customer Svcs.--Britvic Soft Drinks Ltd., Chelmsford, United Kingdom; *Int'l*, pg. 170
Uttermohlen, Dee, Mgr.-Mktg., Adv. & Pub. Rels.--Safelite AutoGlass, Columbus, OH; *U.S. Private*, pg. 960
Utton, Nicholas A., Sr. V.P.-Mktg.--Mastercard International, Inc., Purchase, NY; *U.S. Private*, pg. 714
Vacca, Thomas A., Exec. V.P.-Mktg.--Midland Title Security, Inc., Cleveland, OH; *U.S. Public*, pg. 626
Vaccerelli, Vincent, Dir.-Mktg.--Leica, Inc., Depew, NY; *Int'l*, pg. 806
Vachon, Jean-Roch, Pres. & Chief Oper. Officer--Steinberg Inc., Montreal, Canada; *Int'l*, pg. 1272
Vagts, Bill, Mgr.-Mktg.--Mico Inc., North Mankato, MN; *U.S. Private*, pg. 741
Vain, William C., V.P.-Mktg. & Sls.--Penco Products, Oaks, PA; *U.S. Private*, pg. 848
Valaitis, Robert J., 1st V.P. & Dir.-Mktg.--St. Paul Bancorp, Inc., Chicago, IL; *U.S. Public*, pg. 1428
Valdez, Paul, Dir.-Mktg.--Bristol Myers Co. Ltd., Ickenham, United Kingdom; *U.S. Public*, pg. 255
Vale, Larry, Dir.-Mktg. Commun.--Keane, Inc., Boston, MA; *U.S. Public*, pg. 946
Valeiras, Luis, V.P.-Sls., Mktg. & Adv.--Gator Industries Inc., Hialeah, FL; *U.S. Private*, pg. 441
Valencia, Phaedra, Dir.-Mktg.--Tucson Realty & Trust Co., Tucson, AZ; *U.S. Private*, pg. 1109
Valenti-Thornton, Kathryn, V.P.-Sls. & Mktg.--VV Publishing Corp., New York, NY; *U.S. Private*, pg. 1131
Valentine, Dann, Mgr.-Mktg.--Delphi Packard Electric Systems, Beachwood, OH; *U.S. Public*, pg. 719
Valentine, Dave, V.P.-Mktg.--Luntz Corporation, Canton, OH; *U.S. Private*, pg. 681
Valentine, Donald G., Sr. V.P.-Mktg.--Continental Airline Holdings, Inc., Houston, TX; *Int'l*, pg. 1202
Valentine, Ellen, V.P.-Mktg.--American Software, Inc., Atlanta, GA; *U.S. Public*, pg. 91
Valentine, John, V.P.-Mktg. & Sls.--Belden Inc., Saint Louis, MO; *U.S. Public*, pg. 200
Valentine, John, Dir.-Mktg.--Belden Wire & Cable Company, Richmond, IN; *U.S. Public*, pg. 201
Valentino, James A., Sr. V.P.-Corp. Mktg.--Metropolitan Life Insurance Co., New York, NY; *U.S. Private*, pg. 737
Valentino, Tom, Dir.-Sls. & Mktg.--Mokon, Buffalo, NY; *U.S. Public*, pg. 1045
Valk, G. Lindsay, Sr. V.P. & Dir. of Circulation Mktg.--Hearst Magazines Division, New York, NY; *U.S. Private*, pg. 516
Valk, G. Lindsay, V.P.-Circulation & Mktg.--Hearst Magazines Division, New York, NY; *U.S. Private*, pg. 516
Valladeres, Veronica, V.P.-Mktg.--The Dress Barn, Inc., Suffern, NY; *U.S. Public*, pg. 528
Valles, Adrea, Dir.-Adv. & Mktg.--CPC Spain, S.A., Barcelona, Spain; *U.S. Public*, pg. 225
Vallieres, Jules, V.P.-Contract--Peerless Carpet Corporation, Acton Vale, Canada; *Int'l*, pg. 1032
Vallillo, Anthony J., Grp. V.P.-Client Services--United Illuminating Company, New Haven, CT; *U.S. Public*, pg. 1678
Valvo, Gary, V.P.-Sls. & Mktg.--Quincy Compressor Division Coltec Industries, Quincy, IL; *U.S. Public*, pg. 402
Valvo, Thomas J., Mgr.-Mktg.--MiTek, Inc., Chesterfield, MO; *Int'l*, pg. 1106
van Adrichem, H.J., Mgr.-Sls. & Mktg.--Algemene Sein Industrie B.V., Utrecht, Netherlands; *Int'l*, pg. 1194
van Amerongen, R., Dir.-Mktg. & Sls.--Red Band Venco, Breda, Netherlands; *Int'l*, pg. 244
Van Anken, Richard A., Pres. & Chief Exec. Officer--Jennings & Churella Construction Company, Wellington, OH; *U.S. Private*, pg. 586
Van Buhler, Allan, V.P. & Product Mgr.--Frontier Communications Services, Bingham Farms, MI; *U.S. Public*, pg. 684
Van Cauter, S., Dir.-Mktg.--Packard Instrument Co., Inc., Meriden, CT; *U.S. Private*, pg. 833
van de Wetering, H., Dir.-Mktg.--Hoogovens Ijmuiden Verkoopkantoor B.V., Ijmuiden, Netherlands; *Int'l*, pg. 754
van Dell, Ron, V.P.-Mktg.--Harris Semiconductor, Melbourne, FL; *U.S. Public*, pg. 792
van der Meer, Jaap, V.P.-Strategic Devel. & Worldwide Sls. & Mktg.--Alpnet Inc., Salt Lake City, UT; *U.S. Public*, pg. 58
van der Schoot, W.P.M., Sr. Exec. V.P.-Retail Banking--ABN-AMRO Holding N.V., Amsterdam, Netherlands; *Int'l, pg. 8*
van der Wal, G., Mgr.-Mktg. & Communications--NORIT N.V., Amersfoort, Netherlands; *Int'l*, pg. 958

van der Zwan, Arie Jacobs James, Exec. Dir. & Dir.-Legal, Mktg., Human Res., Tax Services & Plng.--The Southern Life Association Limited, Cape Town, South Africa; *Int'l*, pg. 77
Van Dine, Jim, Exec. V.P.-Sls., Mktg. & Customer Services--Deckers Outdoor Corporation, Goleta, CA; *U.S. Public*, pg. 491
Van Doren, Richard, V.P.-Mktg.--See's Candy Shops, Inc., South San Francisco, CA; *U.S. Public*, pg. 221
Van Dover, Joe, Mgr.-Mktg.--Madison Industries Inc. of Georgia, Conyers, GA; *U.S. Private*, pg. 428
Van Dyke, Paul, Sr. V.P.--Forever Living Products International, Inc., Scottsdale, AZ; *U.S. Private*, pg. 418
Van Dyne, Denese D., V.P.-Corp. Communications--Landmark Graphics Corporation, Houston, TX; *U.S. Public*, pg. 776
van Elst, Harry, Intl. Mktg. Mgr.--Inamed B.V., Breda, Netherlands; *U.S. Public*, pg. 874
Van Ex, Rene, Mgr.-Sls.--National Utility Service, S.A., Brussels, Belgium; *U.S. Private*, pg. 788
Van Gasse, Greg, V.P.-Mktg.--Florsheim Group Inc., Chicago, IL; *U.S. Public*, pg. 656
Van Gendt, G., Dir.-Mktg.--Bac Color Franseweg, Steenbergen, Netherlands; *Int'l*, pg. 131
Van Horn, Lucy, Dir.-Mktg.--American Recreation Centers, Inc., Sacramento, CA; *U.S. Public*, pg. 90
Van Kalsbeek, David, Dir.-Mktg. & Sls.--ITT Sheraton Corporation, Boston, MA; *U.S. Public*, pg. 1512
van Kralingen, C. A., Dir.-Opers-Northern Reg.--South African Breweries, Ltd., Johannesburg, South Africa; *Int'l, pg. 1286*
Van Kralingen, Tony, Dir.-Mktg.--South African Breweries, Ltd., Johannesburg, South Africa; *Int'l*, pg. 1286
van Moorleghem, William, Chief Oper. Officer--Advanced Materials and Technologies N.V., Herk-de-Stad, Belgium; *Int'l*, pg. 1427
Van Name, Christopher K., Dir.-Mktg. & Adv.--Goodway Technologies Corporation, Stamford, CT; *U.S. Private*, pg. 464
Van Natta, Nancy, V.P.-Mktg.--Mindscape, Inc., Novato, CA; *Int'l*, pg. 1026
Van Nevel, Bradley, Mkt. Develop Officer--Community First Bankshares, Inc., Fargo, ND; *U.S. Public*, pg. 416
Van Norman, Jim, V.P.-Mktg. Svcs.--Jamison Door Company, Hagerstown, MD; *U.S. Private*, pg. 581
Van Noy, Paul, Mng. Dir.-NPD Group--PRO Group, Inc., Englewood, CO; *U.S. Private*, pg. 887
van Ooyen, H., Mgr.-Mktg.--CSM Food Division, Diemen, Netherlands; *Int'l*, pg. 243
Van Ord, Norman, Pres.--Blue Seal Feeds, Inc., Londonderry, NH; *U.S. Private*, pg. 1134
van Pelt, Barbara, V.P.-Mktg.--A.H. Belo Corporation, Dallas, TX; *U.S. Public*, pg. 209
van Pelt, Bert, Chief Exec. Officer & Dir.-Mktg.--Elsevier Opleidingen BV, Zwijndrecht, Netherlands; *Int'l*, pg. 1094
van Pelt, J., Mgr.-Mktg.--Holmatro Industrial & Rescue Equipment, Raamsdonksveer, Netherlands; *Int'l*, pg. 632
van Prooijen, W., Mng. Dir.--Honig Foods-B.V., Koog aan de Zaan, Netherlands; *Int'l*, pg. 244
Van Remortel, Steve, Mgr.-Natl. Sls. & Mktg.--Enzopac, Inc., Sheboygan, WI; *U.S. Private*, pg. 379
Van Someren, Barb, Dir.-Mktg. Svcs.--Beltone Electronics Corporation, Chicago, IL; *U.S. Private*, pg. 132
Van Steemburg, Kurt, V.P.--Hudson Valley Paper Company, Albany, NY; *U.S. Private*, pg. 546
Van Tassel, S., Sr. V.P.-Mktg.--International Home Foods Inc., Parsippany, NJ; *U.S. Private*, pg. 526
Van Treese, Richard, Mgr.-Mktg.--Polyfibron Technologies Corp., Billerica, MA; *U.S. Private*, pg. 875
Van Valkenburg, Gina, Dir.-Mktg.--Charter-Provo School, Inc., Provo, UT; *U.S. Public*, pg. 1035
Van Valkenburgh, Deborah, Sr. V.P.-Sls. & Mktg.--First Maryland Bancorp, Baltimore, MD; *Int'l*, pg. 64
Van Vechton, Kathy, Dir.-Mktg.--Four Seasons Resorts, Kihei, HI; *Int'l*, pg. 502
Van Vuren, Darcy, Dir.-Corp. Mktg.--Connectix Corporation, San Mateo, CA; *U.S. Private*, pg. 264
Van Wechel, Jerry, Mgr.-Mktg.--Subaru of America Western, Inc., Portland, OR; *Int'l*, pg. 523
Van Wel, J., Mgr.-Mktg. & Sls.--McCain Alimentari (Italia) Srl, Bergamo, Italy; *Int'l*, pg. 850
Van Wezel, Leendert, Mgr.-Mktg.--Littelfuse B.V., Utrecht, Netherlands; *U.S. Public*, pg. 1001
Van Wunster, Massimo, Dir.-Mktg. & Sls.--Interbrew Italia S.p.A., Comun Nuovo, Italy; *Int'l*, pg. 679
Van-Deemer, Harry, Dir.-Mktg. & Adv.--NORDX/CDT, Rolling Meadows, IL; *U.S. Public*, pg. 287
Van, Jerry, V.P.-Mktg.--Candle-Lite, A Lancaster Colony Co., Cincinnati, OH; *U.S. Public*, pg. 976
Vanacker, Greg, Dir.-Adv. & Mktg. Communications--Okidata Group, Mount Laurel, NJ; *Int'l*, pg. 1000
VanAlstne, Gary, V.P.- Sales & Mktg.--PrimeCare Health Plan, Inc., Milwaukee, WI; *U.S. Public*, pg. 1678
Vanasse, Tanya, V.P.-Mktg.--Bank of the Hudson, Poughkeepsie, NY; *U.S. Public*, pg. 1319
Vance, Bill, Dir.-Mktg.--Rent-Way, Inc., Erie, PA; *U.S. Public, pg. 1377*
Vance, David, Dir.-Corp. Mktg. & Communications--Austin Industries, Inc., Dallas, TX; *U.S. Private*, pg. 99
VanCleave, Ken, V.P.-Grp. Mktg. & Managed Care--Ameritas Life Insurance Corp., Lincoln, NE; *U.S. Private*, pg. 65
Vandall, Sandy, Mgr.-Mktg.--The Genie Company, Alliance, OH; *U.S. Private*, pg. 823
Vandemore, Steve, Dir.-Mktg.--Woods Equipment Company, Oregon, IL; *U.S. Private*, pg. 249
Vanden Eynden, Jerry, Pres.--Indiana Glass Company, Cincinnati, OH; *U.S. Public*, pg. 976
Vanden Heuvel, Mike, V.P.-Mktg.--Miller Electric Manufacturing Co., Appleton, WI; *U.S. Public*, pg. 867
Vander Zee, J. Dirk, V.P.-Sls. & Mktg.--Mooney Aircraft Corporation, Kerrville, TX; *U.S. Private*, pg. 759
Vanderfleet-Scott, Jill, Dir.-Mktg.--Kimball International, Inc., Jasper, IN; *U.S. Public*, pg. 956
VanderWeele, Julie, Sr. V.P.-Mktg.--Mesirow Financial, Chicago, IL; *U.S. Private*, pg. 733
Vann, Gary, Sr. V.P.-Sls. & Mktg.--Mighty Distributing System, Norcross, GA; *U.S. Private*, pg. 745
Vanosdall, David, V.P.-Sls. & Mktg.--CENTRIA, Moon Township, PA; *U.S. Private*, pg. 225
Vansetegem, B., Mgr.-Mktg.--Spadel SA, Brussels, Belgium; *Int'l*, pg. 1287
VantHul, Randy, Dir.-Sls. & Mktg.--Sackner Products, Grand Rapids, MI; *U.S. Public*, pg. 924
Varela, Patricia, Sec.-Mktg.--Sancor Cooperativas Unidas Limitadas, Buenos Aires, Argentina; *Int'l*, pg. 1183
Varian, M., Dir.-New Bus. & Medical Mktg.--Stafford-Miller Limited, Welwyn Garden City, United Kingdom; *U.S. Public*, pg. 237
Varjan, George L., Dir.-Mktg. Services--Sandoz Pharmaceuticals Corp., East Hanover, NJ; *Int'l*, pg. 974
Varpahle, Larry, Dir.-Mktg./Grocery Prods.--Hormel Foods Corp., Austin, MN; *U.S. Public*, pg. 840
Vasalech, Debra, Mgr.-Mktg.--Univision Ltd. Partnership, New York, NY; *U.S. Private*, pg. 230
Vasconcelos, Avelar, Mgr.-Mktg. Services--Nestle Industrial e Commercial Ltda., Sao Paulo, Brazil; *Int'l*, pg. 921
Vashistha, Atul, V.P.-Mktg.--Rural Metro Corporation, Scottsdale, AZ; *U.S. Public*, pg. 1412
Vasques, Gary, Exec. V.P.-Mktg.--Kohl's Corporation, Menomonee Falls, WI; *U.S. Public*, pg. 965
Vaughan, Ronald D., V.P.-Mktg.--Grolier Interstate, Inc., Danbury, CT; *Int'l*, pg. 794
Vaughan, Vaughn V., V.P.--American Indemnity Company, Galveston, TX; *U.S. Public*, pg. 83
Vaughn, Chris, Dir.-Sls. & Mktg./Ventilation Prods.--Coppus Murray Group, Tuthill Corporation, Millbury, MA; *U.S. Private*, pg. 1110
Vaughn, Jack, Dir.-Domestic Sls. & Mktg.--Midcoast Aviation, Inc., Saint Louis, MO; *U.S. Private*, pg. 959
Vaughn, Jack L., Dir.-Domestic Sls. & Mktg.--Sabreliner Corporation, Saint Louis, MO; *U.S. Private*, pg. 959
Vaughn, Mary Ann, Coord.-Adv. & Mktg.--Anchor Industries Inc., Evansville, IN; *U.S. Private*, pg. 71
Vauthier, J. Philippe, Dir.-Mktg.--Facom, Morangis, France; *Int'l*, pg. 570
Vavra, John, Sr. V.P.-Sls. & Mktg.--Ascom Hasler Mailing Systems, Inc., Shelton, CT; *Int'l*, pg. 86
Veale, Ernest, V.P.-Sls., Mktg., Mdse. & Adv.--The Stellar Group Inc., Jacksonville, FL; *U.S. Private*, pg. 1040
Vehr, Eric, Mgr.-Mktg. Services & Inside Sls.--Automax, Inc., Cincinnati, OH; *U.S. Public*, pg. 658
Veirs, William, V.P.-Sls. & Mktg.--AmeriServe of Grand Rapids, Grand Rapids, MI; *U.S. Private*, pg. 533
Veit, Charles, V.P.-Mktg.--Office Electronics, Inc., Itasca, IL; *U.S. Private*, pg. 812
Veitenheimer, Lynette, Mktg. Communications-DIRECT Yellow Pages--U S West Inc., Englewood, CO; *U.S. Public*, pg. 1688
Velasquez, Andrea, V.P.-Mktg.--A. Epstein and Sons, Intl., Inc., Chicago, IL; *U.S. Private*, pg. 379
Velasquez, Andrea, Mgr.-Mktg.--Epstein Civil Engineering, Inc., Chicago, IL; *U.S. Private*, pg. 379
Veldhuizen, Brian, V.P.-Sls. & Mktg.--Freeman Energy Corporation, Springfield, IL; *U.S. Public*, pg. 709
Vella, Mark, Dir.-Mktg.--Fields Stores, Richmond, Canada; *Int'l*, pg. 637
Vella, Suzanne, Dir.-Mktg. Info. Svcs.--Olsten Corporation, Melville, NY; *U.S. Public*, pg. 1220
Veltkamp, Lara, Mgr.-Mktg.--Humphrey Fluid Power Ltd., Markham, Canada; *U.S. Private*, pg. 548
Veltri, Joseph A., V.P.-Trade Mktg. & Consumer Svcs.--Ekco Housewares, Inc., Franklin Park, IL; *U.S. Public*, pg. 566
Venable, Roger H., V.P.-Antiknock Mktg.--Ethyl Corporation, Richmond, VA; *U.S. Public*, pg. 595
Venema, John, Sr. V.P.-Mktg. & Mktg. Devel.--Overhead Door Corporation, Dallas, TX; *U.S. Private*, pg. 822
Venema, John, V.P.-Mktg.--The Genie Company, Alliance, OH; *U.S. Private*, pg. 823
Veneziano, Betsy, V.P.-Mktg. Opers.--Memorex Telex Corp., Irving, TX; *Int'l*, pg. 857
Venie, Michael S., V.P.-Mktg. & Sls.--Northwestern Steel & Wire Co., Sterling, IL; *U.S. Public*, pg. 1201
Veon, Gregory, V.P.-Mktg.--Lee Enterprises, Incorporated, Davenport, IA; *U.S. Public*, pg. 983
Verbkel, Bert, Dir.-Mktg.--Eli Lilly Nederland B.V., Nieuwegein, Netherlands; *U.S. Public*, pg. 994
Verbrugge, Noreen, V.P.-Mktg.--Personal Products Co., Skillman, NJ; *U.S. Public*, pg. 929
Verdickt, Jean-Jacques, Mng. Dir.-Information Svcs., Opers., Facility & Mktg.--Generale de Banque S.A., Brussels, Belgium; *Int'l*, pg. 546
Verdonck, Caroline, Mgr.-Sls. & Mktg./Benelux--Utell International-Benelux, Hilversum, Netherlands; *Int'l*, pg. 1098
Verdult, P.L.M., Sr. V.P.-Mktg. & Sales--Van Melle N.V., Breda, Netherlands; *Int'l*, pg. 1450
Verdurme, Philippe, Exec. V.P.-Sls. & Mktg.--Rail Europe Inc., Harrison, NY; *Int'l*, pg. 1165
Vere, Phil, Gen. Mgr.-Sls. & Mktg./Germany--Instron Schenck Testing Systems Limited, High Wycombe, United Kingdom; *U.S. Public*, pg. 883
Verger, Jaime, Dir.-Mktg.--Stafford-Miller De Espana, Madrid, Spain; *U.S. Public*, pg. 237
Vergoni, Paul R., V.P. & Dir.-Insurance Sls. & Mktg.--The Troy Savings Bank, Troy, NY; *U.S. Private*, pg. 1106
Verhelst, M., Dir.-Mktg.--L'Oreal Belgilux SA, Brussels, Belgium; *Int'l*, pg. 819
Verkinoren, G., Dir.-Mktg.--Vandemoortele N.V., Izegem, Belgium; *Int'l*, pg. 1451
Verley, Roger, Dir.-Strategy & Mktg.--Clestra Hauserman, Strasbourg, France; *Int'l*, pg. 569
Vermeulen, Theo, Mgr.-Sls. & Mktg.--MoDo Van Gelder, Amsterdam, Netherlands; *Int'l*, pg. 886
Vermillion, Douglas, Mgr.-Mktg.--Alpine Packing Company, Stockton, CA; *U.S. Private*, pg. 45
Vermylen, Robert A., V.P.-Sls. & Mktg.--A. Zeregas Sons, Inc., Fair Lawn, NJ; *U.S. Private*, pg. 1204
Vernon, Chris, Exec. V.P.-Mktg. & Sls.--The Vernon Company, Newton, IA; *U.S. Private*, pg. 1137
Vernon, Larry, Dir.-Mktg. Support--Evans & Sutherland Computer Corporation, Salt Lake City, UT; *U.S. Public*, pg. 595
Verschueren, R., Dir.-Mktg.--Boon Edam Inc., Salt Lake City, UT; *Int'l*, pg. 202
Verson, Richard N., Mgr.-Mktg. Communications--Everpure Inc., Westmont, IL; *U.S. Public*, pg. 467
Veru, Jean Paul, Mgr.-Mktg.--Credit Lyonnais Suisse SA, Geneva, Switzerland; *Int'l*, pg. 344
Verviele, C., Dir.-Mktg.--Moore Business Forms de Mexico S.A. de C.V., Tlalnepantla, Mexico; *Int'l*, pg. 889
Veseley, Radim, Mgr.-Mktg.--CGG Geophysics Canada Ltd., Calgary, Canada; *Int'l*, pg. 241
Vesterstad, Goran, Mgr.-Mktg.--Skanska Syd, Malmo, Sweden; *Int'l*, pg. 1260
Vesto, Kjell, Mgr.- Mktg. Devel.--Oy Nautor AB, Pietarsaari, Finland; *Int'l*, pg. 1428
Vetrone, Susan, Mgr.-Mktg.--Grinnell Fire Protection Systems, Westlake, OH; *Int'l*, pg. 1386
Vetrone, Susan, Mgr.-Mktg.--Grinnell Fire Protection Systems, Westlake, OH; *U.S. Public*, pg. 1647
Vetterli, Michael O., V.P.-Sls. & Mktg.--The Flecto Co., Inc., Oakland, CA; *U.S. Private*, pg. 410
Veyrines, Jacques, Exec. V.P.-Loans & Credits--Credit Nationale, Paris, France; *Int'l*, pg. 344
Vezeau, Claude, Dr., Dir.-Mktg.--Searle Canada Inc., Oakville, Canada; *U.S. Public*, pg. 1126
Viana, Mariano Garcia, Mgr.-Corp. Mktg. & Adv.--Telefonica de Espana, S.A., Madrid, Spain; *Int'l*, pg. 1371
Vicarelli, Sergio, Dir.-Mktg.--Dateo Import S.P.A., Milan, Italy; *Int'l*, pg. 385
Vichengrad, Jared A., Mktg. Specialist--Infinicom, Chatham, NJ; *U.S. Private*, pg. 561
Vick, Joe, V.P.-Mktg.--Alloy Products Corp, Waukesha, WI; *U.S. Private*, pg. 42
Vickery, Robert, Sr. V.P.-Mktg.--Hawthorne Adv., Inc., Philadelphia, PA; *U.S. Private*, pg. 512
Vickery, Robert, Sr. V.P.-Mktg.--Colonial Penn Group, Inc., Wilmington, DE; *U.S. Public*, pg. 990
Videau, Mrs., Dir.-Communication--Lafarge Refractaires Monolithiques, Montrouge, France; *Int'l*, pg. 789
Videla, Nicolas, Mgr.-Intl. & Mktg.--Noblex Argentina S.A.C. e I., Buenos Aires, Argentina; *Int'l*, pg. 951
Vidmar, William J., V.P.-Wholesale Sls.--Snyder's Drug Stores, Inc., Minnetonka, MN; *U.S. Private*, pg. 1011
Vien, Diane, Mgr.-Mktg.--Sheaffer Inc., Fort Madison, IA; *Int'l*, pg. 542
Vierling, Philip, V.P.-Mktg.--EMPI, Inc., Saint Paul, MN; *U.S. Public*, pg. 545
Vierthaler, A. F., Mgr.-Mktg Communications--Electrical Controls Sector, Stamford, CT; *U.S. Public*, pg. 726
Vignovic, Rade, V.P.-Mktg.--Transtar Holdings, L.P., Monroeville, PA; *U.S. Private*, pg. 1097
Vij, Sandeep, V.P.-Mktg.--Xilinx, Inc., San Jose, CA; *U.S. Public*, pg. 1786
Vikner, Paul L., Exec. V.P.-Sls. & Mktg.--Mack Trucks, Inc., Allentown, PA; *Int'l*, pg. 1102
Vila, Raul, Dir.-Mktg. Continental Opers., USA & Canada--Puerto Rico Tourism Company, San Juan, PR; *U.S. Private*, pg. 894
Villamil, Alberto, V.P.-Mktg. & Sls.--La Hacienda S.A. de C.V., Mexico, Mexico; *U.S. Public*, pg. 901
Villano, Glen J., V.P.-Sls. & Mktg.--Eaglemark Financial Services, Inc., Chicago, IL; *U.S. Public*, pg. 786
Villanueva, Rafael, Dir.-MKtg.--Tropicana Resort & Casino, Las Vegas, NV; *U.S. Public*, pg. 159
Villarin, Neal, Admin.-Mktg. Programs--SK Hand Tool Corp., Chicago, IL; *Int'l*, pg. 570
Villeneuve, Francois, V.P.-Mktg. & Human Resources-Eastern Canada Region--Costco Wholesale, Issaquah, WA; *U.S. Public*, pg. 451
Vincent, Daniele, Mktg. Dir.--TBWA Belgium, Brussels, Belgium; *U.S. Private*, pg. 1063
Vincent, David, Dir.-Sls. & Mktg.--Johnson Matthey Inc., Wayne, PA; *Int'l*, pg. 713
Vincent, Jami, Mgr.-Mktg.--Sunstone Hotel Investors, Inc., San Clemente, CA; *U.S. Public*, pg. 1536
Vincent, Scott, Dir.-Mktg. & Adv.--Flying J. Inc., Brigham City, UT; *U.S. Private*, pg. 415
Vinck, Alex, V.P.-Sls. & Mktg.--Southwest Marine, Inc., San Diego, CA; *U.S. Private*, pg. 213
Viner, Kim, Mgr.-Mktg.--Colorado Business Bank, Denver, CO; *U.S. Private*, pg. 255
Vinet, Daniel, V.P.-Mktg.--EnRoute Card Inc., Montreal, Canada; *Int'l*, pg. 36
Vinez, Dixie, V.P. & Mgr.-Corp. Mktg.--FirstMerit Corporation, Akron, OH; *U.S. Public*, pg. 646
Vining, Kevin, Mgr.-Mktg.--W.C. Bradley Co., Columbus, GA; *U.S. Private*, pg. 164
Vinnik, Sharon W., Dir.-Mktg.--Hoxan America Incorporated, Piscataway, NJ; *Int'l*, pg. 363
Vinzant, S. Benton, V.P.-Sls. & Mktg.--Newport Steel Corporation, Newport, KY; *U.S. Public*, pg. 1147
Viola, Richard, Dir.-Mktg.--Furman Lumber Company, Inc., Billerica, MA; *U.S. Private*, pg. 431
Viragh, Leslie, Opers. Dir. & Bus. Devel. Dir.--Resource Marketing, Inc., Columbus, OH; *U.S. Private*, pg. 924
Virdone, Joseph F., V.P.-U.S. Commercial Opers.--Quaker Chemical Corporation, Conshohocken, PA; *U.S. Public*, pg. 1346
Virene, Peter, Exec. V.P. & Dir.-Sls. & Mktg.--American Modular Technologies, Liberty, NC; *U.S. Public*, pg. 69
Virgo, Paul, Dir.-Mktg. & Adv.--Pro-Log Corporation, Monterey, CA; *U.S. Private*, pg. 887
Viscomi, A.J., Dir.-Mktg. Communications--ADT Security Services, Inc., Aurora, CO; *U.S. Public*, pg. 1649
Vitale, Frank, Dir.-Mktg.--Country Home Magazine, Des Moines, IA; *U.S. Public*, pg. 1094
Vitali, Carlo, Dir.-Mktg.--Olivetti SpA, Turin, Italy; *Int'l*, pg. 1002

Vitali, Cheryl, V.P.-Mktg.--Playtex Apparel, Inc., Stamford, CT; *U.S. Public*, pg. 1433
Vitello, Lynn, Mktg. Supvr.--The DIALOG Corporation, New York, NY; *Int'l*, pg. 412
Vittorio, David, Mktg. Specialist--New England Coffee Company, Malden, MA; *U.S. Private*, pg. 792
Vivian, Beth, V.P.-Field Mktg.--Account Specific Marketing, Inc. (ASM), Morristown, NJ; *U.S. Private*, pg. 345
Vivian, Ken, Dir.-Dental & Consumer Sls. & Mktg.--Stafford-Miller Limited, Welwyn Garden City, United Kingdom; *U.S. Public*, pg. 237
Vizzini, Paul, V.P.-Mktg. & Sls.--Lifeline Systems, Inc., Cambridge, MA; *U.S. Public*, pg. 992
Vleeskruijer, Dick, Dir.-Mktg.--NIFE B.V., Haarlem, Netherlands; *Int'l*, pg. 53
Vlk, Leroy F., Exec. Sec.--The Florists Assn. of Greater Cleveland, Inc., Cleveland, OH; *U.S. Private*, pg. 415
Vogel, Bob, V.P.-Technology Mktg.--Devon Direct Marketing & Advertising, Inc., Berwyn, PA; *U.S. Private*, pg. 329
Vogel, Kerri A., Mgr.-Mktg. Services--Carver Boat Corp., Pulaski, WI; *U.S. Private*, pg. 447
Vogel, Robert, V.P.-Mktg./Household Prods. Div.--Block Drug Company, Inc., Jersey City, NJ; *U.S. Public*, pg. 236
Vogelsang, Stanley B., V.P.-Natl. Acct. & Customer Rels.--Washington Inventory Service, San Diego, CA; *U.S. Public*, pg. 846
Vogler, Roxana, Mktg. Asst.--Marie Brizard Wines & Spirits USA, North Miami, FL; *U.S. Private*, pg. 702
Vogt, James, V.P.-Mktg.--Claremont Flock Corporation, Claremont, NH; *U.S. Private*, pg. 241
Vogus, John, Dir.-Mkt. Sls.--Knape & Vogt Mfg. Co., Grand Rapids, MI; *U.S. Public*, pg. 963
Vogus, John W., V.P.-Sls. & Mktg.--Knape & Vogt Mfg. Co., Grand Rapids, MI; *U.S. Public*, pg. 963
Vohs, Cheree, Mgr.-Mktg. Communications--The West Bend Co., West Bend, WI; *U.S. Public*, pg. 1322
Voisin, Bret, V.P.-Mktg.--Mears Transportation Group, Orlando, FL; *U.S. Private*, pg. 726
Volbracht, Anastasia, Dir.-Mktg.--Rainbow Technologies, GmbH, Unterschleissheim, Germany; *U.S. Public*, pg. 1359
Volk, Stephen, V.P.-Mktg.--The Acacia Group - Acacia Life Insurance Co., Bethesda, MD; *U.S. Private*, pg. 10
Volker, M.J., V.P.-Sls. & Mktg.--Merchants Home Delivery Service Inc., Oxnard, CA; *Int'l*, pg. 901
Volkwein, Ed, Sr. V.P.-Mktg. & Sls.--Philips Consumer Electronics, Knoxville, TN; *Int'l*, pg. 1054
Volpone, April, Mktg. Communs. Mgr.--Continental Promotion Group, Tempe, AZ; *U.S. Private*, pg. 269
Volza, Mike, Dir.-Mktg.--Mele Manufacturing Co., Inc., Utica, NY; *U.S. Private*, pg. 730
Von Aspern, Dieter, Dir.-Mktg. & Sls.--Hertie Waren-und Kaufhaus GmbH, Frankfurt/Main, Germany; *Int'l*, pg. 724
Von Boch, Oliver, Mgr.-Prod. Devel. & Mktg.--Villeroy & Boch Tableware, Ltd., Princeton, NJ; *Int'l*, pg. 1468
von Cozart, Betsy, Sr. Mktg. Analyst--Culinary Foods Group, Glendale, CA; *Int'l*, pg. 917
Von Der Bruegge, Karen, V.P.-Strategic Mktg.--Harrah's Entertainment, Inc., Memphis, TN; *U.S. Public*, pg. 790
von der Heydt, J.R., V.P. & Dir.-Dog Food Mktg.--Purina Grocery Products Group, Saint Louis, MO; *U.S. Public*, pg. 1360
Von Gruben, Brian G., Exec. V.P. & Dir.-Admin. Svcs.--Piccadilly Cafeterias, Inc., Baton Rouge, LA; *U.S. Public*, pg. 1294
Von Kaenel, Bob, V.P.-Mktg., Healthcare Div.--Getinge/Castle Inc., Rochester, NY; *Int'l*, pg. 551
Von Karhan, Udo, V.P.-Mktg./Europe, Middle East & Africa--Imax Corporation, Mississauga, Canada; *Int'l*, pg. 661
Von Ohaim, Wolfram, Dir.-Mktg.--Gaggenau USA Corporation, Norwood, MA; *U.S. Private*, pg. 437
Von Seggern, Walter, Sr. V.P.-Mktg.--Kulicke & Soffa Industries, Inc., Willow Grove, PA; *U.S. Public*, pg. 968
Vonnegut, Mary G., Sr. V.P.-Mktg.--Hanover Direct, Inc., Weehawken, NJ; *U.S. Public*, pg. 782
Vos, M.J., Mgr.-Mktg. & Sls.--Meneba Meel B.V., Rotterdam, Netherlands; *Int'l*, pg. 555
Vos, Thomas J., V.P.-Mktg.--Bowne & Co., Inc., New York, NY; *U.S. Public*, pg. 248
Voss, Dietmar, Sr. V.P.-Sls. & Mktg. Worldwide--Columbian Chemicals Company, Atlanta, GA; *U.S. Public*, pg. 1286
Voss, Janet, Dir.-Mktg.--Bank One, Texas Corp., Dallas, TX; *U.S. Public*, pg. 173
Voves, Joseph, Pres. & Mgr.-Mktg.--Metric & Multistandard Components, Hawthorne, NY; *U.S. Private*, pg. 736
Voyles, Mike, Dir.-Mktg.--Camping World, Inc., Bowling Green, KY; *U.S. Private*, pg. 204
Vreeland, R. F., Exec. V.P.-Mktg. & Sls.--Shieffelin Somerset Co., New York, NY; *Int'l*, pg. 412
Vrlicak, Ronald E., V.P.-South Reg. Sls.--EBP Life Insurnace Co., Minneapolis, MN; *U.S. Public*, pg. 635
Vuduris, James T., V.P.-Mktg.--Kysor Panel Systems, Fort Worth, TX; *U.S. Public*, pg. 1445
Vuillaume, Jean Claude, Dir.-Mktg.--Entremont S.A., Annecy, France; *Int'l*, pg. 458
Vujnovich, Michael L., Dir.-Natl. Sls. & Mktg.--Ascom Hasler Mailing Systems, Inc., Shelton, CT; *Int'l*, pg. 86
Vukmanic, Frank, Sr. V.P.-Sls. & Mktg.--Amperif Corporation, Chatsworth, CA; *U.S. Public*, pg. 1523
Vulcano, Diane, Dir.-Mktg.--Market Data Retrieval, Shelton, CT; *U.S. Public*, pg. 536
Vuolo, Katie, Mktg. Mgr.-Berlitz Publishing, Direct Response--Berlitz International, Inc., Princeton, NJ; *U.S. Public*, pg. 221
Vuolo, Steve, Dir.-Mktg.--Grist Mill Company, Lakeville, MN; *U.S. Public*, pg. 766
Wachob, Robert D., V.P.-Sls. & Mktg.--Rogers Corporation, Rogers, CT; *U.S. Public*, pg. 1402
Wachs, Hartmut, Gen. Mgr.-Intl. & Mktg. Strategy--Groupe SEB, Ecueille, France; *Int'l*, pg. 568
Wachter, Christopher, Supvr.-Mktg. Services--BPA International - Torrance, Torrance, CA; *U.S. Private*, pg. 107
Wackerlin, Jim, Exec. V.P.--American Seating Company, Grand Rapids, MI; *U.S. Private*, pg. 61
Waddicor, John, Mgr.-Mktg.--Colin Stewart Minchem Limited, Winsford, United Kingdom; *Int'l*, pg. 858
Wade, Beth, Mgr.-Electronic Documentation Prods.--Group 1 Software, Inc., Lanham, MD; *U.S. Public*, pg. 417
Wade, Birgitta, Dir.-Adv.--Empire Kosher Poultry, Inc., Mifflintown, PA; *U.S. Private*, pg. 374
Wade, Jeffrey, Exec. V.P.-Sls. & Mktg.--Showtime Networks Inc., New York, NY; *U.S. Private*, pg. 779
Wade, Jim, V.P.-Sls. & Mktg.--Crane Carrier Company, Tulsa, OK; *U.S. Private*, pg. 286
Wade, Stewart H., V.P.-Mktg. & Adv.--American Bureau of Shipping, New York, NY; *U.S. Private*, pg. 51
Wadsworth, Martha, Dir.-Adv. & Mktg.--Thonet, Statesville, NC; *U.S. Public*, pg. 1465
Waelbreck-Rocha, Elisabeth, Mktg. Principal-European Industry Service--DRI Europe, Inc., Brussels, Belgium; *U.S. Public*, pg. 1072
Wagahoff, Kenneth, V.P.-Mktg.--Top Air Manufacturing, Inc., Cedar Falls, IA; *U.S. Public*, pg. 1621
Wager, Deidra, Exec. V.P.-Retail Mktg. & Opers.--Starbucks Coffee Company, Seattle, WA; *U.S. Public*, pg. 1510
Waggett, James A., V.P.-Mktg.--CSP Inc., Billerica, MA; *U.S. Public*, pg. 283
Wagner, Albert J., V.P. & Grp. Mktg. Dir.-Bourbons--Shieffelin Somerset Co., New York, NY; *Int'l*, pg. 412
Wagner, Dale, V.P.-Sls. & Mktg., Home Fashions--Hoffman Laces, Ltd., Cobleskill, NY; *U.S. Public*, pg. 769
Wagner, Eugene M., V.P.-Mktg. & Sls./Rhinelander--Wausau Papers - Printing & Writing Div., Brokaw, WI; *U.S. Public*, pg. 1747
Wagner, Eugene M., V.P.-Mktg. & Sls.--Wausau-Mosinee Papers Specialty Papers Group, Rhinelander, WI; *U.S. Public*, pg. 1747
Wagner, James, V.P.-Strategic Projects/Mktg.--ContiMortgage Corporation, Horsham, PA; *U.S. Public*, pg. 439
Wagner, Jeff, Mgr.-Sls. & Mktg.--Barber-Colman Company, Rockford, IL; *Int'l*, pg. 1242
Wagner, Jill, Mgr.-Mktg.--Parlex Corporation, Methuen, MA; *U.S. Public*, pg. 1264
Wagner, John, Dir.-Mktg.--Mentholatum Company, Buffalo, NY; *Int'l*, pg. 1126
Wagner, K., V.P.-Mktg. & Sls. Foundry--Brillion Iron Works, Inc., Brillion, WI; *U.S. Public*, pg. 933
Wagner, Karen, V.P.-Mktg.--El Torito Restaurants Inc., Irvine, CA; *U.S. Private*, pg. 393
Wagner, Karsten, Dir.-Sls. & Mktg.--Nordsten, Skive, Denmark; *Int'l*, pg. 1386
Wagner, Karyn, V.P.-Mktg. & Adv.--Family Restaurants, Inc., Irvine, CA; *U.S. Private*, pg. 393
Wagner, Robert W., V.P.-Land & Mktg.--Plains Petroleum Operating Co., Lakewood, CO; *U.S. Public*, pg. 191
Wagner, Rodger, V.P.-Sls. & Mktg.--KYB Corporation of America, Lombard, IL; *Int'l*, pg. 727
Wagner, Ron, Supvr.-Retail Adv. & Mktg.--GMAC Mortgage Corporation, Horsham, PA; *U.S. Public*, pg. 720
Wagner, Steve, V.P.-Mktg., Carrier Sls. & Bus. Devel.--USLD Communications Corp., San Antonio, TX; *U.S. Public*, pg. 969
Wagner, Yves, Dir.-Economic Analysis & Intl. Mktg.--Banque Generale du Luxembourg SA, Luxembourg, Luxembourg; *Int'l*, pg. 161
Wagnor, Ben, Mgr.-Mktg. & Admin. Opers.--Radix Corporation, Salt Lake City, UT; *U.S. Private*, pg. 906
Wahan, Mike, V.P.-Mktg.--Taylor Made Golf Co. Inc., Carlsbad, CA; *Int'l*, pg. 1181
Wahlin, Helena, Mgr.-Mktg. & Sls.--Foga Systems, Oxnard, CA; *Int'l*, pg. 496
Wahn, Mathew, Grp. Mktg. Dir.--TMP Worldwide/Recruitment Division, New York, NY; *U.S. Private*, pg. 1065
Wahn, Matt, Grp. Mktg. Dir.--TMP Worldwide Recruitment Division, New York, NY; *U.S. Private*, pg. 1065
Wahtola, Charles H., Exec. V.P.-Bus. Devel--Woodward-Clyde Group, Inc., Denver, CO; *U.S. Public*, pg. 1655
Wain, Hans, Gen. Mgr. & Mgr. Mktg.--Jinwoong Inc., San Jose, CA; *Int'l*, pg. 707
Wain, Tracy, Mktg. Asst.--Spencer Gifts, Inc., Egg Harbor Township, NJ; *Int'l*, pg. 1216
Waite, Rick, Mgr.-Sls. & Mktg.--Burke Engineering Company, South El Monte, CA; *U.S. Private*, pg. 183
Waite, Robert E., V.P.-Corp. Rels. & Mktg.--CAE Inc., Toronto, Canada; *Int'l*, pg. 237
Waitkus, Letitia, Mgr.-Field Mktg.--A&W Restaurants, Inc., Livonia, MI; *U.S. Private*, pg. 1
Wakowski, Lisa, Dir.-Mktg.--Little Switzerland, Inc., Charlotte Amalie, VI; *U.S. Public*, pg. 1001
Walack, Molly, Dir.-Mktg. Communications--Leica Inc., Deerfield, IL; *Int'l*, pg. 806
Walberg, Mats, Mgr.-Mktg. & Sls.--Iggesund Paperboard AB, Iggesund, Sweden; *Int'l*, pg. 886
Walden, Daniel J., Dir.-Mktg. Communications--Consolidated Edison Company of New York, Inc., New York, NY; *U.S. Public*, pg. 434
Waldoch, Terri, V.P.-Sls. & Mktg.--Fritz Co. Inc., Newport, MN; *U.S. Private*, pg. 429
Waldon, Mike, V.P.-Sls. & Mktg.--Johanna Foods Inc., Flemington, NJ; *U.S. Private*, pg. 589
Waldron, Robert F., Dir.-Mktg.--International Dessert Partners, Miami, FL; *U.S. Public*, pg. 447
Waldvogel, Lynn, Sr. V.P. & Mgr.-Mktg.--PaineWebber Group Incorporated, New York, NY; *U.S. Public*, pg. 1252
Waldvogel, Lynn, Sr. V.P. & Mgr.-Mktg.--PaineWebber Incorporated, New York, NY; *U.S. Public*, pg. 1252
Wale, Andrew, Dir.-Mktg.--Thomas & Betts Electronics Division, Memphis, TN; *U.S. Public*, pg. 1597
Walen, Tom, Mgr.-Mktg.--Heat Bath Park Metallurgical Corp., Indian Orchard, MA; *U.S. Private*, pg. 518
Walker, Ann, Mgr.-Mktg.--Professional/First Travelcorp, Dalton, GA; *U.S. Private*, pg. 408
Walker, Bill, Dir.-Sls. & Mktg.--Superior Machine Systems, Mason, OH; *U.S. Private*, pg. 1055
Walker, Bob, V.P.-Mktg.--Bayer Corporation, Pittsburgh, PA; *Int'l*, pg. 172
Walker, Bob, V.P.-Mktg. Opers.--The Wine Group, San Francisco, CA; *U.S. Private*, pg. 1182
Walker, Brent, V.P.-Mktg.--American Fuel Cell & Coated Fabrics Co. (Amfuel), Magnolia, AR; *U.S. Private*, pg. 55
Walker, Brian, Mgr.-Mktg.--Thrige Electric, Odense, Denmark; *Int'l*, pg. 1387
Walker, Chuck, V.P.-Mktg. & Adv.--Spaghetti Warehouse, Inc., Garland, TX; *U.S. Public*, pg. 1495
Walker, Craig, Sr. V.P.-Mktg.--Pic'n Pay Stores, Inc., Matthews, NC; *U.S. Private*, pg. 864
Walker, Dianne, Mgr.-Mktg.--Thomas Engineering Inc., Hoffman Estates, IL; *U.S. Private*, pg. 1082
Walker, F.B., Sr. V.P.-Refining & Mktg.--Amerada Hess Corporation, New York, NY; *U.S. Public*, pg. 65
Walker, G.M.A., Dir.-Mktg. & Controller--Cussons (U.K.) LTD., Cheadle, United Kingdom; *Int'l*, pg. 1024
Walker, Greg, Dir.-Mktg.--Maker's Mark Distillery, Inc., Louisville, KY; *Int'l*, pg. 63
Walker, J. Philip, Sr. V.P.-Sls. & Mktg.--Interface Europe B.V., Scherpenzeel, Netherlands; *U.S. Public*, pg. 889
Walker, James, V.P.-Mktg.--Koger Equity Inc., Jacksonville, FL; *U.S. Public*, pg. 965
Walker, Ken, Mgr.-Corp. Sls. & Mktg.--Wangner Systems Corporation, Greenville, SC; *Int'l*, pg. 1418
Walker, Lisa, Mgr.-Mktg. Serv.--Vance Industries, Inc., Chicago, IL; *U.S. Private*, pg. 1133
Walker, Marty, Sr. V.P.-Sls. & Mktg.--Iams Company, Dayton, OH; *U.S. Private*, pg. 556
Walker, Michael, V.P.-Bus. Devel. & Mktg.--Delaware North Companies, Inc., Buffalo, NY; *U.S. Private*, pg. 321
Walker, R.C., Bus. Unit Mgr.--Peerless Faucet Corporation, Indianapolis, IN; *U.S. Public*, pg. 1053
Walker, Ruth, Mktg.--Regions Bank/Montgomery/Alexander City, Montgomery, AL; *U.S. Public*, pg. 1372
Walker, Scott, Dir.-Western Div. Sls. & Mktg.--Hyatt Hotels Corporation, Chicago, IL; *U.S. Private*, pg. 551
Walker, Scott, Chief Tech. Officer & Sr. V.P.--Delco Electronics Corporation, Kokomo, IN; *U.S. Public*, pg. 720
Walker, Susan, V.P.-Mktg.--Sally Beauty Company, Inc., Denton, TX; *U.S. Public*, pg. 38
Walker, Wells, V.P.-Mktg.-Tweeds--Hanover Direct, Inc., Weehawken, NJ; *U.S. Public*, pg. 782
Wall, Brad, Mgr.-Mktg.--ANESCO, Kingston, PA; *U.S. Private*, pg. 74
Wall, Jack, Pres.--Al Larson Boat Shop, Inc., Terminal Island, CA; *U.S. Private*, pg. 652
Wall, John, Sr. V.P.-Sls. & Mktg.--Owsley & Sons, Inc., Fort Mill, SC; *U.S. Private*, pg. 824
Wall, Kathy, V.P.-Mktg.--Lexington Furniture Industries, Lexington, NC; *U.S. Private*, pg. 432
Wallace, Forrest, V.P.-Mktg.--Provident Financial Group, Inc., Cincinnati, OH; *U.S. Public*, pg. 1338
Wallace, Forrest, V.P.-Mktg.--The Provident Bank, Cincinnati, OH; *U.S. Public*, pg. 1338
Wallace, Iain, Dir.-Mktg.--Rainbow Technologies, Neuilly-sur-Seine, France; *U.S. Public*, pg. 1359
Wallace, Jack, V.P.-Mktg.--Tapco International Corporation, Plymouth, MI; *U.S. Private*, pg. 1068
Wallace, Jeffrey J., Mgr.-Sls. & Mktg.--Besser Company, Alpena, MI; *U.S. Private*, pg. 139
Wallace, Rose, Mgr.-Mktg.--Transitions Optical, Inc., Pinellas Park, FL; *U.S. Public*, pg. 1245
Wallace, Scott C., V.P.-Mainland Mktg. & Sls.--Mauna Loa Macadamia Nut Corporation, Hilo, HI; *U.S. Private*, pg. 190
Wallace, Thomas J., Dir.-Mktg.--Sunniland Corporation, Sanford, FL; *U.S. Private*, pg. 1053
Wallace, Thomas T., Pres.--Johnston, Lemon & Co. Inc., Washington, DC; *U.S. Private*, pg. 595
Wallace, Tracy, Mktg. Mgr.--Holland Mark Martin, Boston, MA; *U.S. Private*, pg. 534
Wallace, Wendy, Dir.-Mktg. Services--The Times Publishing Co., Saint Petersburg, FL; *U.S. Private*, pg. 1087
Wallace, William, Dir.-Mktg.--CH2M Hill, Inc., Greenwood Village, CO; *U.S. Private*, pg. 195
Wallden, Erik J., V.P.-Worldwide Mktg.--PerSeptive Biosystems, Inc., Framingham, MA; *U.S. Public*, pg. 1279
Waller, H., V.P.-Mktg.--Eaton Corporation, Defense Valve and Actuator Division, El Segundo, CA; *U.S. Public*, pg. 556
Waller, Mark, Sr. V.P.-Mktg.--Schieffelin & Somerset Co., New York, NY; *Int'l*, pg. 412
Waller, Peter, Mktg. Dir.-Europe, Africa & Middle East--Kentucky Fried Chicken (Great Britain) Ltd., Camberley, United Kingdom; *U.S. Public*, pg. 1637
Walling, Sonja, Mgr.-Mktg.--Zynolyte Products Company, Carson, CA; *Int'l*, pg. 663
Wallis, John, V.P.-Sls. & Mktg.--Hyatt International Corporation, Chicago, IL; *U.S. Private*, pg. 551
Wallner, Collette, V.P.-Mktg.--Associated Bank, National Association, Neenah, WI; *U.S. Public*, pg. 140
Wallock, Dawn, V.P.-Mktg.--Del Taco, Inc., Laguna Hills, CA; *U.S. Private*, pg. 321
Walser, Val, Div. V.P.-Adv. Opers.--The Bon Marche, Inc., Seattle, WA; *U.S. Public*, pg. 617
Walsh, Betsy A., Mgr.-Mktg. Support--Packard Instrument Co., Inc., Meriden, CT; *U.S. Private*, pg. 833
Walsh, Brian A., V.P.-Sls. & Mktg.--Fort James Canada, Inc., Toronto, Canada; *U.S. Public*, pg. 672
Walsh, D., V.P.-Mktg.--Moore Data Management Services Div., Saint Louis Park, MN; *Int'l*, pg. 890
Walsh, Donna, Mgr.-Mktg.--Damart, Rollinsford, NH; *Int'l*, pg. 376
Walsh, Ellie, Dir.-Admin. Services--ABM Industries, San Francisco, CA; *U.S. Public*, pg. 2
Walsh, Harry, Mktg.--Calico Corners, Kennett Square, PA; *U.S. Private*, pg. 386
Walsh, James, Dir.-Prod. Mktg.--North Central AMPI, Inc., New Ulm, MN; *U.S. Private*, pg. 804

Walsh, James F., Sr. V.P.-Direct Mkts.--Blue Cross & Blue Shield of Illinois, Chicago, IL; *U.S. Private*, pg. 151
Walsh, Janet, Mktg. Support--Altron Incorporated, Wilmington, MA; *U.S. Public*, pg. 59
Walsh, Jim, V.P.-Mktg., Sls. & Technology--Slater Steels Corporation, Fort Wayne, IN; *Int'l*, pg. 1263
Walsh, John, V.P.-Consumer Mktg.--The Orange County Register, Santa Ana, CA; *U.S. Private*, pg. 425
Walsh, John, V.P.-Mktg.--Fremont Premium Finance Corp., Santa Monica, CA; *U.S. Public*, pg. 681
Walsh, Kenneth, Mgr.-Mktg. Services--Lincoln Industrial, Saint Louis, MO; *U.S. Public*, pg. 1273
Walsh, Matt, Deputy Grp. Mng. Dir. & Mgr.-Mktg.--Avonmore Waterford Group plc, Killkenny, Ireland; *Int'l*, pg. 102
Walsh, Ned, Dir.-Mktg.-Walsh Prods.--Litton Solid State, Santa Clara, CA; *U.S. Public*, pg. 1003
Walsh, Patrick J., Dir.-Field Svcs.--Ferrellgas Partners, L.P., Liberty, MO; *U.S. Public*, pg. 618
Walsh, Richard J., V.P.-Corp. Devel. & Mktg.--Cytogen Corporation, Princeton, NJ; *U.S. Public*, pg. 471
Walsh, Stan, Exec. V.P.-Mdsg. & Mktg.--Builders Square, Inc., San Antonio, TX; *U.S. Private*, pg. 477
Walter, Maureen, Dir.-Mktg.--The Royal China & Porcelain Companies Inc., Moorestown, NJ; *U.S. Private*, pg. 948
Walter, Reed, Dir.-Mktg.--Jack Young Associates, Hazleton, PA; *U.S. Private*, pg. 1201
Waltham, Susan, Mgr.-Mktg.--Ibstock Plc, Lutterworth, United Kingdom; *Int'l*, pg. 658
Walton, Kim, Mgr.-Mktg.--Hanover Wire Cloth, Hanover, PA; *U.S. Private*, pg. 193
Waluszko, Alex, V.P.-Mktg. & Sls.--UVP, Inc., Upland, CA; *U.S. Private*, pg. 1115
Wan, Kathy, Dir.-Mktg.--Casa Bonita, Inc., Carrollton, TX; *U.S. Public*, pg. 278
Wandell, Andrew, V.P.-Mktg. & Adv.--Knapp Shoes Inc., Penn Yan, NY; *U.S. Private*, pg. 401
Wandishin, John, Dir.-Mktg./Printers--Brother International Corporation, Somerset, NJ; *Int'l*, pg. 229
Wang, James, Mgr.-Mktg.--China Steel Chemical Corp., Kao-hsiung, Taiwan; *Int'l*, pg. 286
Wankmiller, Albert, V.P.-Sls. & Mktg.--Print-O-Stat, Inc., York, PA; *U.S. Private*, pg. 830
Wanko, James E., V.P.-Mktg.--USA Floral Products, Inc., Washington, DC; *U.S. Public*, pg. 1685
Wanner, Ken, V.P.-Sls. & Mktg.--Accra Pac Group, Elkhart, IN; *U.S. Private*, pg. 11
Wansley, Keith, Mgr.-Mktg.--Raytheon Marine, Manchester, NH; *U.S. Public*, pg. 1366
Waradzin, Michael E., Mgr.-Mkt. Knowledge--Learning International, Stamford, CT; *U.S. Public*, pg. 1617
Waraska, John, Dir.-Mktg.--ESA, Inc., Chelmsford, MA; *U.S. Private*, pg. 354
Ward-Zinski, John, Mktg. Controller - U.K.--Burmah Castrol plc, Swindon, United Kingdom; *Int'l*, pg. 234
Ward, Brian, V.P.-Sls. & Mktg.--Spectrum Control, Inc., Erie, PA; *U.S. Public*, pg. 1497
Ward, Doug, Pres. & Dir.-Mktg.--Amcor, Inc., Bountiful, UT; *Int'l*, pg. 242
Ward, Edward, V.P.-Mktg.--GEICO Corporation, Washington, DC; *U.S. Public*, pg. 219
Ward, John, Sr. V.P.-Sls. & Mktg.--Boston Whaler, Inc., Edgewater, FL; *U.S. Private*, pg. 689
Ward, Lauren, Dir.-Mktg.--Prentice Hall Humanities & Social Sciences, Upper Saddle River, NJ; *U.S. Private*, pg. 778
Ward, Lauren, V.P.- Direct Mktg.--Wadsworth Publishing co., Belmont, CA; *U.S. Public*, pg. 1600
Ward, Martin, Dir.-Mktg.--Alliance UniChem PLC, Chessington, United Kingdom; *Int'l*, pg. 57
Ward, Mike, Mgr.-Mktg.--North American Capacitor Co., Indianapolis, IN; *U.S. Private*, pg. 803
Ward, Peter A., Mgr.-Mktg.--Ward Trucking Corp., Altoona, PA; *U.S. Private*, pg. 1149
Ward, R., Dir.-Power & Energy Bus. Unit--Wyman-Gordon Investment Castings, Inc., Groton, CT; *U.S. Public*, pg. 1782
Ward, Richard, V.P.-Processing--Peterson Farms, Decatur, AR; *U.S. Private*, pg. 857
Ward, Robert, Dir.-Mktg.--Pawling Savings Bank, Pawling, NY; *U.S. Public*, pg. 1334
Warden, Dick, V.P.-Sls. & Mktg.--Structron Corporation, San Marcos, CA; *U.S. Private*, pg. 988
Warden, V.A., V.P.-Customer Services & Mktg.--Manitoba Hydro, Winnipeg, Canada; *Int'l*, pg. 834
Wardwell, Robert, V.P.-Sls. & Mktg.--Filter Products Division, Richmond, VA; *U.S. Public*, pg. 620
Ware, Buddy, Mgr.-Mktg. Services--Spontex, Inc., Columbia, TN; *Int'l*, pg. 1409
Ware, Dexter, V.P.-Sls. & Mktg.--Courtaulds Fibers Inc., Axis, AL; *Int'l*, pg. 339
Warford, Bud, Dir.-Mktg.--Star Building Systems, Oklahoma City, OK; *U.S. Public*, pg. 1394
Warkentin, Paul, Mktg. Communications Specialist--Etec Systems, Inc., Hayward, CA; *U.S. Public*, pg. 594
Warner, Ann, Mgr.-Mktg.--Clestra Hauserman, Inc., Solon, OH; *Int'l*, pg. 569
Warner, Barton, Dir.-Adv. & Mktg.--Johnson & Johnson Limited, Maidenhead, United Kingdom; *U.S. Public*, pg. 930
Warner, Bob, Dir.-Mktg. Communications--Freightliner Corp., Portland, OR; *Int'l*, pg. 368
Warner, Donald G., Dir.-Mktg.--NewAge Industries Inc., Willow Grove, PA; *U.S. Private*, pg. 796
Warner, James J., Pres.--Warner Vineyards, Paw Paw, MI; *U.S. Private*, pg. 1151
Warner, Jonathan P., V.P.-Mid-Atlantic Reg. Sls.--EBP Life Insurnace Co., Minneapolis, MN; *U.S. Public*, pg. 635
Warnock, James M., Sr. V.P.-Intl. Distr. Grp. & Mktg. Srvcs.--Aluma Systems Corp., Toronto, Canada; *Int'l*, pg. 1423
Warren, Adrienne, Coord.-Mktg.--Systron Donner-Inertial Division, Concord, CA; *U.S. Public*, pg. 160
Warren, Betsey, Mgr.-Mktg. Communications--Loctite Corp. North American Group, Rocky Hill, CT; *Int'l*, pg. 611
Warren, Bob, Dir.-Mktg.--Minor Rubber Co., Inc., Bloomfield, NJ; *U.S. Private*, pg. 751
Warren, Hal, Real Estate Analyst-FL--United Dominion Realty Trust, Inc., Richmond, VA; *U.S. Public*, pg. 1677
Warren, Linda, Sr. V.P.-Mktg.--Walt Disney Attractions-Walt Disney World, Lake Buena Vista, FL; *U.S. Public*, pg. 513
Warren, Polly C., Dir.-Communications--Pepper, Hamilton & Scheetz, Philadelphia, PA; *U.S. Private*, pg. 851
Warren, Robert D., V.P.-Bus. Mngmt. & Bus. Solutions--New England Business Service, Inc., Groton, MA; *U.S. Public*, pg. 1170
Warren, Robert E., V.P.-Intl. Mktg.--Pride International, Inc., Houston, TX; *U.S. Public*, pg. 1324
Warren, Tom, Mgr.-Sls. Opers.--Micromatic Textron, Holland, MI; *U.S. Public*, pg. 1589
Warren, Walter, Mgr.-Sls. & Mktg.--Salwasser Manufacturing Company, Inc., Reedley, CA; *U.S. Private*, pg. 963
Wash, M.R., Asst. Dir.-Grp. Mktg.--Hughes Space & Communications Group, Los Angeles, CA; *U.S. Public*, pg. 721
Washington, George, Mgr.-Mktg. Commun.--The Flood Company, Hudson, OH; *U.S. Private*, pg. 414
Wasikowski, Ronald R., Sr. V.P.-Mktg. & Sls.--World Airways, Inc., Herndon, VA; *U.S. Public*, pg. 1780
Wasp, Timothy H., Dir.-Mkt. Analysis & Plng.--The M.W. Kellogg Company, Houston, TX; *U.S. Public*, pg. 528
Wassarman, Beth, Dir.-Mktg.--Monet Jewelers, New York, NY; *U.S. Private*, pg. 757
Wasserman, Barbara, V.P. & Mktg. Dir.-Medicine & Science College--Oxford University Press, Inc., New York, NY; *Int'l*, pg. 1019
Wasserstrom, Edward, Supvr.-Mktg. Support--S & C Electric Company, Chicago, IL; *U.S. Private*, pg. 954
Wassmuth, Sallyann, Category Mgr.-Energy--Agway Energy Products (AEP), Syracuse, NY; *U.S. Private*, pg. 27
Wasson, Catherine L., V.P.-Mktg. Services--Merck Medco Managed Care, Des Moines, IA; *U.S. Public*, pg. 1091
Wasson, Pam, Dir.-Mktg.--Monrovia Nursery Co., Azusa, CA; *U.S. Private*, pg. 757
Watanabe, Satoshi, Mng. Dir.-Sls. & Mktg.--Yamaha Motor Co., Ltd., Iwata, Japan; *Int'l*, pg. 1516
Waterman, Win, V.P.-Mktg. & Sls.--Spotnails, Rolling Meadows, IL; *U.S. Private*, pg. 845
Waters, Phillip E., V.P.-Mktg. & Leasing--Prime Group Realty Trust, Chicago, IL; *U.S. Public*, pg. 1326
Waterson, David, Sr. V.P.-Res. & Devel. & Mktg.--Icon Health & Fitness, Inc., Logan, UT; *U.S. Private*, pg. 556
Watkins, David, Dir.-Product Mngmt.--INSO Corporation, Boston, MA; *U.S. Public*, pg. 882
Watkins, Harry B., V.P.-Tech. Mktg. & Tubular Grp.--RMI Titanium Company, Niles, OH; *U.S. Public*, pg. 1662
Watkins, Jim, V.P.-Pet Mktg.--Hill's Pet Nutrition, Topeka, KS; *U.S. Public*, pg. 397
Watkins, Jim, Sr. V.P.-Worldwide Mktg.--Burger King Corporation, Miami, FL; *Int'l*, pg. 411
Watkins, Peg, Grp. Mgr.-Mktg. Commun.--Nordson Corporation, Westlake, OH; *U.S. Public*, pg. 1188
Watkinson, D.J., Mgr.-Mktg.--AAH Pharmaceuticals Limited, Runcorn, United Kingdom; *Int'l*, pg. 591
Watson, Allen, Dir.-Mktg.--SAS Institute Inc., Cary, NC; *U.S. Private*, pg. 966
Watson, Bill, V.P. Mktg.-/Steak & Ale--Bennigan's, Dallas, TX; *U.S. Private*, pg. 736
Watson, Bill, V.P.-Mktg.-Steak & Ale--Steak and Ale Restaurants, Dallas, TX; *U.S. Private*, pg. 736
Watson, Brian, V.P.-Mktg./Patterson Dental Supply, Inc.--Patterson Dental Company, Saint Paul, MN; *U.S. Public*, pg. 1265
Watson, Carlton, Sr. V.P. & Dir.-Mktg.--Burdines, Miami, FL; *U.S. Public*, pg. 618
Watson, John, Sr. V.P.-Strategic Mktg.--Reebok International Ltd., Stoughton, MA; *U.S. Public*, pg. 1369
Watson, John P., Gen. Mgr.-Mktg. & Intl.--Matco Tools, Stow, OH; *U.S. Public*, pg. 482
Watson, Lisa, Reg. Acct. Mgr.--Utell International-San Francisco, San Francisco, CA; *Int'l*, pg. 1098
Watson, Pamela, Dir.-Direct Mktg.--Bose Corporation, Framingham, MA; *U.S. Private*, pg. 160
Watson, Peter, Mgr.-Mktg.--Esselte Australia Pty. Ltd., Wetherill Park, Australia; *Int'l*, pg. 461
Watson, Philip P., V.P.-Mktg.--Glit, Wrens, GA; *U.S. Public*, pg. 944
Watson, Rob, Dir.-Mktg., Printing--Dillard, A ResourceNet International Company, Greensboro, NC; *U.S. Public*, pg. 901
Watson, Robert, Dir.-Mktg.--Time Warner Cable of New York City, New York, NY; *U.S. Public*, pg. 1611
Watson, Russell A., Dir.-Mktg.--The Pepper Companies, Inc., Chicago, IL; *U.S. Private*, pg. 851
Watt, R.C., V.P. & Dir.-Cat Food Mktg.--Purina Grocery Products Group, Saint Louis, MO; *U.S. Public*, pg. 1360
Watt, William F., Sr. V.P.-Portfolio Mktg.--Countrywide Funding Corporation, Pasadena, CA; *U.S. Public*, pg. 453
Watt, William F., Exec. V.P. & Dir.-Mktg./Retail Banking--FirstFed Financial Corp., Santa Monica, CA; *U.S. Public*, pg. 645
Wattel, Bob, Exec. V.P.-Mktg.--Lettuce Entertain You Enterprises, Inc., Chicago, IL; *U.S. Private*, pg. 661
Watters, Geoff, V.P. & Interactive Mktg. Dir.--Laughlin/Constable, Inc., Milwaukee, WI; *U.S. Private*, pg. 653
Watts, Cynthia M., Mktg. Officer--SouthTrust Bank of Charleston, Charleston, SC; *U.S. Public*, pg. 1492
Waugh, James S., V.P.-Mktg.--FlightSafety International Inc., Flushing, NY; *U.S. Public*, pg. 218
Wavra, Pat, Sec.-Mktg. Services--Jaguar Cars, Mahwah, NJ; *U.S. Public*, pg. 664
Wawrykow, David, Mktg. Supvr.--Fisher Gauge Limited, Peterborough, Canada; *Int'l*, pg. 491
Way, Chet, Dir.-Mktg.--Healthsource Connecticut, Farmington, CT; *U.S. Public*, pg. 360
Wayne, Jeff, V.P.-Mktg.--Galderma Laboratories, Inc., Fort Worth, TX; *Int'l*, pg. 819
Wayne, Michael, Dir.-Sls. & Mktg.--Pool Energy Services Co., Houston, TX; *U.S. Public*, pg. 1316
Waytula, Carol, Mgr.-Mktg. Communications--OMRON Systems, Inc., Schaumburg, IL; *Int'l*, pg. 1005
Wdowiak, Walter, V.P.-Corp. Mktg.--United States Fidelity & Guaranty Company, Baltimore, MD; *U.S. Public*, pg. 1659
Wearne, J.R., V.P.-Mktg.--Amerimark Inc., Raleigh, NC; *U.S. Public*, pg. 1237
Weary, Brent, V.P.-Sls. & Mktg.--Rentway Inc., Etobicoke, Canada; *Int'l*, pg. 1424
Weatherall, Mathis, V.P.-Sls. & Mktg.--TABS Direct (Operating Div.), Stafford, TX; *U.S. Private*, pg. 482
Weatherby, Adam, Mgr.-Mktg.--Weatherby, Inc., Atascadero, CA; *U.S. Private*, pg. 1155
Weaver, Bruce, Dir.-Tech. Mktg. Services--Nature's Sunshine Products, Inc., Provo, UT; *U.S. Public*, pg. 1166
Weaver, Donald, Mgr.-Mktg. Communications--Worcester Controls Corp., Marlborough, MA; *Int'l*, pg. 128
Weaver, Paul E., Vice Chm.-Natl. Priority Indus. & Mkt.--Price Waterhouse L.L.P. - U.S., New York, NY; *U.S. Private*, pg. 883
Weaver, Robert, V.P.-Sls. & Key Accts.--Windmere-Durable Holdings, Hialeah, FL; *U.S. Public*, pg. 1771
Web, Charles, Mgr.-Export & Intl. Mktg.--Battenfeld Gloucester Engineering Co. Inc., Gloucester, MA; *U.S. Private*, pg. 123
Weba, Richard S., Dr., Dir.-Sls. & Mktg.--Electro-Science Laboratories, Inc., King of Prussia, PA; *U.S. Private*, pg. 369
Webb, Alan, Dir.-Food & Mktg.--SavaCentre Limited, London, United Kingdom; *Int'l*, pg. 1170
Webb, Caryl, Dir.-Mktg.--E. Moss Limited, Feltham, United Kingdom; *Int'l*, pg. 58
Webb, Dennis, V.P.-Mktg.--Liebert Corporation, Columbus, OH; *U.S. Public*, pg. 573
Webb, Don, V.P.-Sls. & Mktg.--Central Transport, Archdale, NC; *U.S. Private*, pg. 225
Webb, Graham, Dir.-Mktg.--Bell Sports Corp., San Jose, CA; *U.S. Public*, pg. 207
Webb, Ian, Dir.-Sls. & Mktg.--Fermec Holdings, Ltd., Manchester, United Kingdom; *U.S. Public*, pg. 312
Webb, J.F., V.P.-Sls. & Mktg.--Jaguar Canada Inc., Bramalea, Canada; *U.S. Public*, pg. 667
Webb, Kathy, Dir.-Mktg.--River Oaks Hospital, New Orleans, LA; *U.S. Public*, pg. 1697
Webb, Mary Sue, Mktg. Communications--Evenflo Company, Inc., Piqua, OH; *U.S. Private*, pg. 629
Webb, Robert, V.P.-Sls. & Mktg.--Saunders Brothers, Westbrook, ME; *U.S. Private*, pg. 968
Webb, Vince, V.P.-Mktg.--Management Recruiters International, Inc., Cleveland, OH; *U.S. Public*, pg. 277
Webb, Warren, V.P.-Sls. & Mktg.--Tri-State Armature & Electric Works, Memphis, TN; *U.S. Private*, pg. 1100
Webber, Sandy, V.P.-Sls. & Mktg.--Watsco, Inc., Coconut Grove, FL; *U.S. Public*, pg. 1745
Webber, W. Scott, Sr. V.P.-Mktg.--Trivoli Systems, Indianapolis, IN; *U.S. Public*, pg. 896
Weber-Conradt, Martha, Dir.-Corp. Mktg. Svcs.--UtiliCorp United Inc., Kansas City, MO; *U.S. Public*, pg. 1700
Weber, Barbara, Dir.-Mktg. & Sls.--El Paso Energy, Houston, TX; *U.S. Public*, pg. 567
Weber, Barbara, Supvr.-Mktg. Svcs.--Pierce Manufacturing, Inc., Appleton, WI; *U.S. Public*, pg. 1233
Weber, Dick H., V.P.-Sls. & Mktg.--Doane Products Co., Branded Sales Div., Joplin, MO; *U.S. Private*, pg. 337
Weber, Holly, Mktg. Coord.--Camosy, Inc., Russell, IL; *U.S. Private*, pg. 203
Weber, John, Dir.-N. American Sls.--Vernay Laboratories, Inc., Yellow Springs, OH; *U.S. Private*, pg. 1137
Weber, Marta, Dir.-Mktg. & Sls.--Swedish Match do Brasil S/A, Rio de Janeiro, Brazil; *Int'l*, pg. 1328
Weber, Richard, Dir.-Mktg.--Victoria Regional Medical Center, Victoria, TX; *U.S. Public*, pg. 1697
Weber, Stephen, V.P.-Mktg.--Aurora Electronics, Inc., Irvine, CA; *U.S. Public*, pg. 147
Weber, Trish, Dir.-Adv.--U.S. Borax Inc., Valencia, CA; *Int'l*, pg. 1119
Webster, Helen, Mgr.-Mktg./Solvents--Sasol Chemicals Europe Limited, Solihull, United Kingdom; *Int'l*, pg. 1196
Webster, Rachel, Asst. Mktg.--Martin Industries, Inc. (AL), Florence, AL; *U.S. Private*, pg. 709
Weddell, Sarah, Asst.-Bus. Affairs--WIC Entertainment Ltd., Vancouver, Canada; *Int'l*, pg. 1482
Wedeward, Jeff, V.P.-Indus. Grp.--Bader Rutter & Assoc., Inc., Brookfield, WI; *U.S. Private*, pg. 110
Wee, Alex, Mgr.-Mktg. Services--Mobil Oil Singapore Pte. Ltd., Singapore, Singapore; *U.S. Public*, pg. 1119
Weed, Joe K., V.P.-Mktg. & Commun.--EBSCO Industries, Inc., Birmingham, AL; *U.S. Private*, pg. 358
Weedman, Sidney, V.P.-Mktg. & Govt. Rels.--National City Bank, Indiana, Indianapolis, IN; *U.S. Public*, pg. 1154
Weekis, Jack, V.P.-Mktg.-North America--Benckiser Consumer Products Inc., Greenwich, CT; *Int'l*, pg. 185
Weeks, Dean, Mgr.-Mktg.-U.K.--Carpenter Technology (U.K.) Limited, Redditch, United Kingdom; *U.S. Public*, pg. 308
Weeks, Richard S., V.P.-Sls. & Mktg.--Automax, Inc., Cincinnati, OH; *U.S. Public*, pg. 658
Weeks, Robert, V.P.-Sls. & Mktg.--Battenfeld Gloucester Engineering Co. Inc., Gloucester, MA; *U.S. Private*, pg. 123
Wegener, Carl, V.P.-Dealer Mktg.--United States Satellite Broadcasting Co., Saint Paul, MN; *U.S. Private*, pg. 544
Wegener, S.M., Sr. V.P.-Programs & Mktg.--Talley Defense Systems, Inc., Mesa, AZ; *U.S. Public*, pg. 308
Weggeland, Ed M., V.P.-Sls. & Mktg.--Richmond Technology Inc., Redlands, CA; *U.S. Private*, pg. 929
Wegner, Jerre Lee, Dir.-Mktg. Communications--Computer Sciences Corporation, El Segundo, CA; *U.S. Public*, pg. 422
Wegrvyn, Karen, Mktg. Assoc.--Beverly Bancorporation Inc., Chicago, IL; *U.S. Public*, pg. 227
Wehberg, Keith, Chief Oper. Officer & V.P.-Mktg.--Shillcraft, Inc., Baltimore, MD; *U.S. Private*, pg. 994

Wehler, Trever, Mgr.-Mktg.--The Chase Manhattan Bank, N.A., London, United Kingdom; *U.S. Public*, pg. 339
Wehling, Robert, V.P.-Mktg.--Richardson-Vicks, Inc., Cincinnati, OH; *U.S. Public*, pg. 1331
Wehling, Robert, Sr. V.P.-Mktg. Research & Govt. Rels.--Richardson-Vicks, Inc., Health Care Products, Cincinnati, OH; *U.S. Public*, pg. 1331
Wehrly, James, V.P.-Sls. & Mktg.--The School Division, Menlo Park, CA; *Int'l*, pg. 1026
Wehrly, Pete, V.P.-Mktg.--DePuy, Inc., Warsaw, IN; *Int'l*, pg. 331
Weibler, Klaus P., Mng. Dir.-Gentex GmbH--Gentex Corporation, Zeeland, MI; *U.S. Public*, pg. 731
Weidman, Bill K., Dir.-Mktg. & Sls.--Kentucky-Tennessee Clay Co., Mayfield, KY; *U.S. Public*, pg. 804
Weigel, Joe, Dir.-Mktg. & Corp. Communications--Batesville Casket Company, Inc., Batesville, IN; *U.S. Public*, pg. 828
Weigel, Mark, V.P.-Sls. & Mktg.--Perry's Ice Cream Co., Inc., Akron, NY; *U.S. Private*, pg. 855
Weiland, William, V.P.--Carter Chambers Supply, Inc., Baton Rouge, LA; *U.S. Private*, pg. 216
Weiler, Chris, Brand Mgr.--Widmer's Wine Cellars, Inc., Naples, NY; *U.S. Public*, pg. 300
Weiler, Jane, Dir.-Mktg.--Peyton Meats, El Paso, TX; *U.S. Public*, pg. 75
Weill, Sheldon, V.P.-Mktg. & Sls.--Universal Folding Box Company, Inc., Hoboken, NJ; *U.S. Private*, pg. 1127
Weimer, Lynnette, Mgr.-Mktg. & Sls.--Group Dekko, Kendallville, IN; *U.S. Private*, pg. 484
Weinberg, Dennis, Dir.-Mktg./Communications--Howmedica, Inc., Rutherford, NJ; *U.S. Public*, pg. 1282
Weinberger, Robert, V.P.-Corp. Mktg.--Open Market, Inc., Burlington, MA; *U.S. Public*, pg. 1226
Weiner, Tina C., Dir.-Mktg.--Yale University Press, New Haven, CT; *U.S. Private*, pg. 1195
Weingardt, G. Greg, Mgr.-Mktg. Commun.--Union Carbide Corporation, Danbury, CT; *U.S. Public*, pg. 1666
Weinreb, Pam, Dir.-Mktg. Services--Pony U.S.A., Nashville, TN; *Int'l*, pg. 1036
Weinreb, Pam, Dir.-Mktg.--Mitre Sports (U.S.), Nashville, TN; *Int'l*, pg. 1036
Weinstein, Laura, Mgr.-Mktg.--Cellular One Buffalo, Cheektowaga, NY; *U.S. Public*, pg. 1415
Weinstein, Mark, Supvr.-Mktg.--BPA International - McLean, Mc Lean, VA; *U.S. Private*, pg. 107
Weintraub, William H., Sr. V.P.-Mktg.--Coors Brewing Company, Golden, CO; *U.S. Public*, pg. 445
Weir, J.D., V.P.-Mktg.--Futuro Inc., Milford, OH; *Int'l*, pg. 182
Weir, Wendy, Mgr.-Residential Mkts.--BC Gas Inc., Vancouver, Canada; *Int'l*, pg. 114
Weirather, Bob, Dir.-Strategic Mktg.--Harris Corp. Broadcast Div., Quincy, IL; *U.S. Public*, pg. 791
Weirback, Terry, Mgr.-Sls. & Mktg.--Perkasie Industries Corporation, Perkasie, PA; *U.S. Private*, pg. 854
Weisberg, Ira, V.P.-Mfg.--Interferon Sciences, Inc., New Brunswick, NJ; *U.S. Public*, pg. 694
Weisbruck, Craig, V.P.-Sls. & Mktg.--National Gypsum Company, Charlotte, NC; *Int'l*, pg. 790
Weischer, Carsten, Mgr.-Pub. Rels.--Knurr AG, Munich, Germany; *Int'l*, pg. 739
Weisenauer, Sandy, V.P.-Mktg.--Video Treasures, Troy, MI; *U.S. Public*, pg. 780
Weisert, Marvin, V.P.-Mktg.--Growmark, Inc., Bloomington, IL; *U.S. Private*, pg. 484
Weisman, Bob, Dir.-Mktg.--Custom Accessories Inc., Niles, IL; *U.S. Private*, pg. 298
Weisner, Ulf, Dir.-Mktg.--McCain GmbH (Germany), Frankfurt, Germany; *Int'l*, pg. 850
Weiss, Christine, Coord.-Electronic Mktg.--Florsheim Group Inc., Chicago, IL; *U.S. Public*, pg. 656
Weiss, Ed, Dir.-Mktg.--Monarch Avalon, Inc., Baltimore, MD; *U.S. Public*, pg. 1123
Weiss, Ellen R., Sr. V.P.-Mktg. & Communications--Binswanger, Philadelphia, PA; *U.S. Private*, pg. 144
Weiss, Jeffrey, Mgr.-Mktg.--Domestic Uniform Rental Co., Farmington Hills, MI; *U.S. Private*, pg. 338
Weiss, Robert M., V.P.-Mktg.--Poco Petroleums Ltd., Calgary, Canada; *Int'l*, pg. 1061
Weiss, Thomas, Mgr.-Mktg.--Spar Handels AG, Schenefeld, Germany; *Int'l*, pg. 1288
Weisser, Wolfgang, V.P.-Mktg.--Sauer Sundstrand Gmbh & Co., Neumunster, Germany; *Int'l*, pg. 1198
Weisshahn, Kari, Mktg. Asst.--Miller Electric Manufacturing Co., Appleton, WI; *U.S. Public*, pg. 867
Weissler, Mindy, Dir.-Mktg.--Advertising Checking Bureau Incorporated, New York, NY; *U.S. Private*, pg. 23
Weissman, Jay, Dir.-Mktg.--Paper Enterprises, Inc., Bronx, NY; *U.S. Private*, pg. 837
Weisz, Stephen P., Sr. V.P.-Lodging Brands--Marriott Hotels, Resorts, and Suites, Washington, DC; *U.S. Public*, pg. 1048
Weitl, Jim, Dir.-Mktg. & Sls.--Superior Bank, Chicago, IL; *U.S. Private*, pg. 1054
Weitz, Eric T., Pres. & Chief Exec. Officer--Robby Len Fashions, New York, NY; *U.S. Public*, pg. 121
Weitzell, Roy, Mgr.-Mktg.--ComSonics, Inc., Harrisonburg, VA; *U.S. Private*, pg. 260
Welch, Edward J., V.P.-Mktg.--Transkrit Corporation, Roanoke, VA; *U.S. Private*, pg. 782
Welch, James, Sr. V.P.-Mktg.--M.S. Carriers, Inc., Memphis, TN; *U.S. Public*, pg. 1027
Welch, Michael T., V.P.-Opers., Mktg., Restaurant Support Services & Res. & Devel.--Checkers Drive-In Restaurants, Inc., Clearwater, FL; *U.S. Public*, pg. 342
Welch, Richard, V.P.-Alliance Mktg.--Days Inns of America, Inc., Parsippany, NJ; *U.S. Public*, pg. 321
Welch, Victoria C., Mgr.-Mktg. Srvcs., Pub. Rels. & Media--Reynolds Metals Co.-Flexible Packaging Products Division, Richmond, VA; *U.S. Public*, pg. 1386
Welfelt, Dave, Dir.-Sls. & Mktg.--Excel Industries, Inc., Hesston, KS; *U.S. Private*, pg. 387
Welk, Tom, Dir.-Sls. & Mktg.--Lyke Corporation, Ripon, WI; *U.S. Private*, pg. 682
Wellington, Sue, V.P.-Mktg.--Gatorade Worldwide Division, Chicago, IL; *U.S. Public*, pg. 1347
Wellott, Harry, V.P. & Direct Mktg. Dir.--Mullen Advertising, Inc., Wenham, MA; *U.S. Private*, pg. 766
Wells, John, Dir.-Sls. & Mktg.--The Bakersfield Californian, Bakersfield, CA; *U.S. Private*, pg. 112
Wells, John, Mgr.-Mktg. Communications--Fisher Controls International, Inc., Marshalltown, IA; *U.S. Public*, pg. 573
Wells, John, Mgr.-Mktg. Conmmunications--Fisher Controls International, Inc., North Stonington, CT; *U.S. Public*, pg. 573
Wellzahn, Nancy, Mgr.-Mktg.--Niagara Frontier Transit & Metro System, Buffalo, NY; *U.S. Private*, pg. 798
Welsch, C., Mgr.-Mktg.--NIDEC, Canton, MA; *Int'l*, pg. 933
Welter, K., Mgr.-Mktg.--Ferrolegeringar AG, Dubendorf, Switzerland; *U.S. Private*, pg. 735
Welters, Heiko, Mgr.-Mktg.--Groschopp & Co. GmbH EMW Elektromotoren-Feinbauwerk, Viersen, Germany; *Int'l*, pg. 559
Weltman, Amy L., V.P.-Mktg.--Toymax International Inc., Plainview, NY; *U.S. Public*, pg. 1626
Welton, Steve, V.P.-Individual Mktg.--Ameritas Life Insurance Corp., Lincoln, NE; *U.S. Private*, pg. 65
Welty, John, Chm. Bd., Pres. & Dir.-Mktg. & Adv.--Swensen's Ice Cream Co., Ronkonkoma, NY; *U.S. Public*, pg. 883
Wendler, John, V.P.-Mktg.--Fruit of the Loom, Inc., Chicago, IL; *U.S. Public*, pg. 685
Wendorf, Kathy, Mgr.-Sls. & Mktg.--Wausau Metals, Nanik Division, Wausau, WI; *U.S. Public*, pg. 1500
Wendroff, Michael, Dir.-Mktg.-Skin Care--Combe Incorporated, White Plains, NY; *U.S. Private*, pg. 257
Wendt, Solveig Vija, Mktg. Consultant--SAS Park Royal Hotel, Lysaker, Norway; *Int'l*, pg. 1202
Weng, Dieter, Mgr.-Mktg.--Reemtsma Cigarettenfabriken GmbH, Hamburg, Hamburg, Germany; *Int'l*, pg. 1100
Wenge, Marion, Dir.-Mktg.--3M Deutschland GmbH, Neuss, Germany; *U.S. Public*, pg. 1606
Weninger, M.M., Supvr.-Sls. Promo. & Mktg. Communications--Preformed Line Products, Cleveland, OH; *U.S. Public*, pg. 1321
Wenmoth, Maureen, Dir.-Mktg. Services--Moen Incorporated, North Olmsted, OH; *U.S. Public*, pg. 675
Wennlund, Lloyd, Sr. V.P.-Mktg. & Personal Fin. Services--Northern Trust Corporation, Chicago, IL; *U.S. Public*, pg. 1195
Wentraub, Bill, Sr. V.P.-Mktg.--Adolph Coors Company, Golden, CO; *U.S. Public*, pg. 445
Wenzel, Gary, Dir.-Mktg.--U.S. Electrical Motor Division, Saint Louis, MO; *U.S. Public*, pg. 573
Wenzinger, Donald E., Natl. Sls. Mgr.-Entertainment Simulation Sls.--Doron Precision Systems, Inc., Binghamton, NY; *U.S. Private*, pg. 341
Werden, Wendy Erica, Coord.-Mktg. Commun.--Tucson Electric Power Company, Tucson, AZ; *U.S. Public*, pg. 1670
Werner, Lloyd, Sr. V.P.-Sls. & Mktg.--Group W Satellite Communications, Stamford, CT; *U.S. Public*, pg. 275
Werner, Tom, V.P.-Mktg. & Sls.--Commonwealth Industries, Inc., Louisville, KY; *U.S. Public*, pg. 415
Werry, Jennifer, Mktg. Officer--CNB Bancshares, Inc., Evansville, IN; *U.S. Public*, pg. 280
Wersal, Jennifer, Coord.-Mktg.--Pangburn Candy Company, Fort Worth, TX; *U.S. Private*, pg. 836
Werschmidt, Greg, Dir.-Mktg.--Kipp Group, Ontario, CA; *U.S. Private*, pg. 623
Wertches, John, V.P.-Mktg.--Pacific Pride Bakeries, Escondido, CA; *Int'l*, pg. 575
Werwick, Pete, Dir.-Mktg. & Sls.--McCauley Propeller Systems, Vandalia, OH; *U.S. Public*, pg. 1589
Wesley, Charles, V.P.-Sls. & Mktg.--Hyer Industries Inc./Thayer Scale, Pembroke, MA; *U.S. Private*, pg. 552
Wessel, Jeffrey W., Mgr.-Sls. & Mktg.--Weiss Scientific Glass Blowing Co., Inc., Portland, OR; *Int'l*, pg. 1408
Wessman, John, V.P.-Mktg.-Relationship Segment--First American Corporation, Nashville, TN; *U.S. Public*, pg. 624
West, Cecily, Dir.-Mktg.--800-FLOWERS, Inc., Westbury, NY; *U.S. Private*, pg. 366
West, Cheryl, Mgr.-Mktg.--Lumex Medical Products, Bay Shore, NY; *U.S. Public*, pg. 758
West, Dennis D., Exec. V.P.-Mktg.& Sls.--Salem Manufacturing Facility, Salem, OR; *Int'l*, pg. 875
West, Elena F., Mgr.-Mktg. Svcs.--The Ohio Art Company, Inc., Bryan, OH; *U.S. Public*, pg. 1214
West, J.S., Dir.-Sls. & Mktg.-Consumer Prods.--Becton Dickinson Canada Inc., Mississauga, Canada; *U.S. Public*, pg. 200
West, Jim, Dir.-Consumer Mktg. & Sls.--Goddess Bra Company, East Boston, MA; *U.S. Private*, pg. 458
West, Lanny, Dir.-Mktg.--Plastics Research & Development Co., Fort Smith, AR; *U.S. Private*, pg. 359
West, Lynda, Coord.-Sls. & Mktg.--Exolon-Esk Company, Tonawanda, NY; *U.S. Public*, pg. 600
West, Robert E., Mgr.-Mktg.--Lindenmeyr Munroe, Purchase, NY; *U.S. Private*, pg. 224
West, Robert E., Mgr.-Mktg.--Lindenmeyr Munroe, North Reading, MA; *U.S. Private*, pg. 224
West, Ross D., Dir.-Mktg.--American Felt & Filter, Newburgh, NY; *U.S. Private*, pg. 54
West, Russ, Natl. OEM Sls. Mgr.--Carefree of Colorado, Broomfield, CO; *U.S. Public*, pg. 217
West, Susan, V.P.-Mktg.--Columbia Tri-Star International Television, Culver City, CA; *Int'l*, pg. 1281
West, W. Casey, V.P.-Sls. & Mktg.--Stanchem Inc., East Berlin, CT; *U.S. Private*, pg. 1030
Westall, Rich, Dir.-Mktg. Services & Adv.--Mayfran International, Inc., Cleveland, OH; *Int'l*, pg. 1397
Westbrock, Leon, Grp. V.P.-Petroleum Mktg.--Cenex/Land O'Lakes, Inc., Inver Grove Heights, MN; *U.S. Private*, pg. 222
Westbrook, Mark, Mgr.-Mktg. & Sls.--Proto Systems of Atlanta, Alpharetta, GA; *U.S. Private*, pg. 891
Westen, Sue, Dir.-Sls.--QualMed Plans for Health-Pueblo, Pueblo, CO; *U.S. Public*, pg. 678
Westerberg, Jacqueline, V.P.-Sls. & Mktg.--JRC Canida, Inc., Fort Worth, TX; *U.S. Private*, pg. 578
Westfield, Barbara, Dir.-Mktg. & Prod. Devel.--Salton/Maxim Housewares, Inc., Mount Prospect, IL; *U.S. Public*, pg. 1430
Westgate, Ward, V.P.-Mktg.--Motion Industries (Canada), Inc., Lethbridge, Canada; *U.S. Public*, pg. 732
Westhoff, Stacy, Dir.-Mktg. & Adv.--O'Keeffe's, Inc., San Francisco, CA; *U.S. Private*, pg. 813
Weston, B.W.F., V.P.-Mktg.--Morton Salt, Chicago, IL; *U.S. Public*, pg. 1135
Weston, Kevin, V.P.-Mktg.--Current, Inc., Colorado Springs, CO; *U.S. Public*, pg. 498
Westover, Craig, Dir.-Mktg.--Tricord Systems, Inc., Plymouth, MN; *U.S. Public*, pg. 1637
Westphal, Chris, Dir.-Mktg.--DataCard Plastic Card Services, Minnetonka, MN; *U.S. Private*, pg. 312
Wetterauer, Michael, Sr. V.P.-Sls. & Mktg.--Case-Swayne Co. Inc., Corona, CA; *U.S. Private*, pg. 218
Wetzel, Angela, Mgr.-Mktg. Communications--Broadband Networks Group, Hatboro, PA; *U.S. Public*, pg. 716
Whalen-Martinez, Laurie, Mgr.-Mktg.--Del Taco, Inc., Laguna Hills, CA; *U.S. Private*, pg. 321
Wharnsby, William J., V.P.-Sls. & Mktg.--Waterloo Furniture Components Limited, Kitchener, Canada; *U.S. Private*, pg. 270
Wheaton, Art, V.P.-Mktg. & Sls.--Remington Arms Company, Inc., Madison, NC; *U.S. Private*, pg. 921
Wheeler, Doug, V.P.-Corp. Mktg.--Tandem Computers Inc., Cupertino, CA; *U.S. Public*, pg. 417
Wheeler, G., Dir.-Sls. & Mktg.--Salford Electrical Instruments Ltd., Heywood, United Kingdom; *Int'l*, pg. 545
Wheeler, Gail, Dir.-Retail Mktg.--McCain Citrus Inc., Oak Brook, IL; *Int'l*, pg. 850
Wheeler, Kimberly, Mgr.-Mktg. Services--The New Piper Aircraft, Inc., Vero Beach, FL; *U.S. Private*, pg. 794
Wheeler, Lan, Dir.-Mktg.--Reed Travel Publishing, Dunstable, United Kingdom; *Int'l*, pg. 1097
Wheeling, Joe, Sr. V.P.-Opers. Support--Motel 6 Operating L.P., Dallas, TX; *Int'l*, pg. 21
Whelan, Gerard, Mgr.-Corp. Communications--IMI Plc, Witton, United Kingdom; *Int'l*, pg. 646
Whelan, James, Mgr.-Mktg.--Fuller, Smith & Turner Plc, London, United Kingdom; *Int'l*, pg. 529
Whelan, Veronica, Dir.-Mktg. & Communications--Bell Atlantic New England, Boston, MA; *U.S. Public*, pg. 202
Whiddon, David, Dir.-Mktg.--Betac International Corporation, Alexandria, VA; *U.S. Private*, pg. 140
Whipp, Jennifer, Dir.-Mktg.--Axent Technologies, Rockville, MD; *U.S. Public*, pg. 157
Whipple, Charles, V.P.-Sls. & Mktg.--The Chicago Faucet Co., Des Plaines, IL; *U.S. Private*, pg. 234
Whisenhunt, Randy, Adv. Coord.--Collingwood Grain, Inc., Hutchinson, KS; *U.S. Public*, pg. 128
Whistler, Mick, Mgr.-Mktg.--Ardell Industries Inc., Union, NJ; *U.S. Private*, pg. 597
Whitacre, R. Gregory, V.P.-College & University Prods.--SLM Holding Corp., Washington, DC; *U.S. Public*, pg. 1419
Whitaker, Amy, Coord.-Mktg.--Recaro North America, Inc., Clawson, MI; *U.S. Private*, pg. 914
Whitby, Donelle, Mgr.-Mktg.--Carolina Tractor & Equipment Co., Charlotte, NC; *U.S. Private*, pg. 214
White, Brian, Coord.-Mktg. Commun.--Hypermedia Communications, Inc., San Mateo, CA; *U.S. Public*, pg. 851
White, C., V.P.-Mktg.--Comprehensive Business Services Inc., Mission Viejo, CA; *U.S. Private*, pg. 423
White, Dean, Dir.-Mktg.--Reactor Experiments, Inc., Sunnyvale, CA; *U.S. Public*, pg. 1594
White, Diana, Mgr.-Natl. Sls. Plng.--The National Latex Products Co., Ashland, OH; *U.S. Private*, pg. 785
White, Dori, Asst. V.P.-Adv./Mktg.--Computer Associates International, Inc., Islandia, NY; *U.S. Public*, pg. 420
White, Douglas, V.P.-Mktg.--Broan Mfg. Co., Inc., Hartford, WI; *U.S. Public*, pg. 1193
White, Douglas, V.P.-Mktg.--Aubrey Manufacturing Company, Hartford, WI; *U.S. Public*, pg. 1193
White, Eileen A., Asst. Product Mgr.--Upstate Milk Cooperatives Inc., Le Roy, NY; *U.S. Private*, pg. 1129
White, Garrett, V.P. & Dir.-Sls. & Mktg. Services--Houghton Mifflin College Div., Boston, MA; *U.S. Public*, pg. 841
White, Gary D., Grp. V.P.--Builder Marts of America, Inc., Greenville, SC; *U.S. Private*, pg. 179
White, Gregory A., V.P.-Mktg. Light Oils--Holly Corporation, Dallas, TX; *U.S. Public*, pg. 830
White, James, V.P.-Bus. Devel.--Washington Gas Light Co., Springfield, VA; *U.S. Public*, pg. 1740
White, John, V.P.-Sls. & Mktg.-EP--AAF-International, Louisville, KY; *U.S. Private*, pg. 3
White, Keith, Mgr.-Mktg.--Fabreeka International, Inc., Stoughton, MA; *U.S. Private*, pg. 390
White, Lawrence A., Exec. V.P.-Corp. Devel.--Versar Inc., Springfield, VA; *U.S. Public*, pg. 1717
White, Lawrence D., Exec. V.P.-Mktg.--NFO Research, Inc., Greenwich, CT; *U.S. Public*, pg. 1146
White, Liz, Mktg. & Adv. Coord.--Ortel Corporation, Alhambra, CA; *U.S. Public*, pg. 1232
White, Martin, V.P.-Mktg. Services--US Airways Group, Inc., Arlington, VA; *U.S. Public*, pg. 1680
White, Martin, V.P.-Mktg. Services--US Airways, Inc., Arlington, VA; *U.S. Public*, pg. 1680
White, Michael, Dir.-Sls.--Sea World of Texas, San Antonio, TX; *U.S. Public*, pg. 114
White, Mike, V.P.-Sls. & Mktg.--Hutchens Industries Inc., Springfield, MO; *U.S. Private*, pg. 550
White, Patty, Dir.-Mktg.--Healthsource Maine, Inc., Freeport, ME; *U.S. Public*, pg. 360
White, Patty, Exec. Asst.-Mktg.--Computerworld, Inc., Framingham, MA; *U.S. Private*, pg. 569

White, R.J., V.P.-Mktg.--Montana-Dakota Utilities Co., Bismarck, ND; *U.S. Public*, pg. 1025

White, Richard A., V.P.-Worldwide Mktg.--Flexible Steel Lacing Company, Downers Grove, IL; *U.S. Private*, pg. 413

White, Richard E., Sr. V.P.-Mktg.--Marathon Ashland Petroleum LLC, Findlay, OH; *U.S. Public*, pg. 139

White, Richard E., V.P.-Mktg., U.S.--USX Corporation, Pittsburgh, PA; *U.S. Public*, pg. 1661

White, Richard E., V.P.-Mktg.--Marathon Oil Company, Houston, TX; *U.S. Public*, pg. 1661

White, Richard E., Sr. V.P.-Mktg.--Marathon Ashland Petroleum LLC, Findlay, OH; *U.S. Public*, pg. 1662

White, Rick, Sr. Dir.-Mktg.--Fujisawa U.S.A. Inc., Deerfield, IL; *Int'l*, pg. 525

White, Rosemary, Mgr.-Mktg.--Datapro Services, Maidenhead, United Kingdom; *U.S. Public*, pg. 1072

White, Stephen, Dir.-Sls. & Mktg.--First National Mortgage Corporation, Glen Burnie, MD; *Int'l*, pg. 64

White, Steve, Dir.-Sls. & Mktg.--American Speedy Printing Centers, Inc., Troy, MI; *U.S. Private*, pg. 62

Whiteford, Russell E., Pres. & Chief Exec. Officer--DHP Limited Partnership, Chicopee, MA; *U.S. Private*, pg. 302

Whitehead, Reggie, V.P.-Mktg.-Special Mkt.--Walt Disney Attractions-Walt Disney World, Lake Buena Vista, FL; *U.S. Public*, pg. 513

Whitehead, Scott, Mgr.-Mktg. Svcs.--Colonial Williamsburg Foundation, Williamsburg, VA; *U.S. Private*, pg. 254

Whitehouse, Donald, Mgr.-Tech. Cmmunications--Emerson & Cuming Specialty Polymers, Lexington, MA; *Int'l*, pg. 1435

Whitehurst, William, Dir.-Mktg. & Sls.--Pac-Fab, Inc./East, Sanford, NC; *U.S. Public*, pg. 593

Whiteman, Derek, V.P.-Intl. Sls. & Mktg.--Christie Design, Chatsworth, CA; *U.S. Public*, pg. 1369

Whiteman, John F., V.P.-Sls. & Mktg.--Sentry Technology Corp., Hauppauge, NY; *U.S. Public*, pg. 1458

Whitescarver, Hunt, Mgr.-Mktg.-Retail--WLR Foods, Inc., Timberville, VA; *U.S. Public*, pg. 1727

Whitesell, Terry, Exec. V.P.-Sls. & Mktg.--Carpenter Industries, Inc., Richmond, IN; *U.S. Private*, pg. 215

Whitfield, Christy, Mgr.-Mktg.--Premier Parks Inc., Oklahoma City, OK; *U.S. Public*, pg. 1323

Whitfield, Ross, Dir.-Mktg.--Dow Hickam Pharmaceuticals Inc., Sugar Land, TX; *U.S. Public*, pg. 1143

Whithers, P., Dir.-Mktg. Devel.--British Gypsum Ltd., Loughborough, United Kingdom; *Int'l*, pg. 122

Whiting, Amy, Mktg. Asst.--Auto Glass Specialists, Madison, WI; *U.S. Private*, pg. 100

Whiting, David, V.P.-Mktg.--Glencoe/Mc-Graw Hill, Westerville, OH; *U.S. Public*, pg. 1070

Whitley, Lynn, V.P. & Dir.-Mktg.--South Trust Bank of Georgia, Atlanta, GA; *U.S. Public*, pg. 1492

Whitley, Steve A., Sr. V.P.-Retail Banking--Virginia First Savings Bank, F.S.B., Petersburg, VA; *U.S. Public*, pg. 1721

Whitlock, Janice L., Pres.-Dyersburg Mktg.--Dyersburg Corporation, Dyersburg, TN; *U.S. Public*, pg. 538

Whitlock, Todd, Dir.-Mktg.--Charles Pankow Builders, Ltd., Altadena, CA; *U.S. Private*, pg. 836

Whitmore, Rob, Dir.-Mktg. & Adv.--Alaska Industrial Hardware Inc., Anchorage, AK; *U.S. Private*, pg. 31

Whitmoyer, Ellen M., Sr. V.P.-Mktg.--Lebanon Valley Farmers Bank, Lebanon, PA; *U.S. Public*, pg. 688

Whitney, Fred, V.P.-Indus. Div.--Tesa Tuck Inc., Sparta, MI; *Int'l*, pg. 182

Whitney, Jim, V.P.-Sls. & Mktg.--Educational Insights, Inc., Carson, CA; *U.S. Public*, pg. 565

Whitney, Kenneth C., Mng. Dir.--The Blackstone Group, New York, NY; *U.S. Private*, pg. 147

Whitney, Philip R., Dir.-Consumer Mktg.--Money, New York, NY; *U.S. Public*, pg. 1613

Whitson, Jim, Assoc. Dir.-Grp. Mktg.--Eurodis Electron PLC, Reigate, United Kingdom; *Int'l*, pg. 1247

Whitt, John R., Sr. V.P.-Mktg., Sls. & Sec.--Sherman & Reilly, Inc., Chattanooga, TN; *U.S. Private*, pg. 993

Whittaker, Richard, Sr. V.P.-Strategic Devel. & Mktg. Opers.--Schering-Plough Healthcare Products Inc., Liberty Corner, NJ; *U.S. Public*, pg. 1438

Whittemore, Marianne, Dir.-Events Mktg.--Home & Garden Television, Knoxville, TN; *U.S. Public*, pg. 1447

Whittman, Bryan, V.P.-Promo., Publicity & Special Events--Disneyland, Anaheim, CA; *U.S. Public*, pg. 511

Whitwam, D., Dir.-Sls. & Mktg.--British Mohair Spinners Limited, Bradford, United Kingdom; *Int'l*, pg. 219

Wholley, Gina, V.P.-Mktg. & Human Resources--Lat Purser & Associates, Charlotte, NC; *U.S. Private*, pg. 896

Whooley, Bill, Dir.-Mktg.--Parsons Main, Inc., Boston, MA; *U.S. Private*, pg. 842

Whyte, Iain, Dir.-Mktg.--Glynwed Consumer & Construction Products Ltd., Royal Leamington Spa, United Kingdom; *Int'l*, pg. 554

Wiater, Lisa, Mgr.-Mktg.--Lancaster Colony Automotive Group, Dublin, OH; *U.S. Public*, pg. 977

Wichmann, Hans, Mgr.-Mktg.--Uniroyal Englebert Reifen GmbH, Aachen, Germany; *Int'l*, pg. 327

Wick, Alan, V.P.-Mktg.--Buffalo Hospital Supply Co., Inc., Buffalo, NY; *U.S. Private*, pg. 179

Wick, Arthur D., V.P.-Res. & Devel.--Lesco, Inc., Rocky River, OH; *U.S. Public*, pg. 989

Wick, Fred, V.P.-Mktg.--Cato Oil & Grease Co., Oklahoma City, OK; *Int'l*, pg. 1045

Wicker, Barry, Exec. V.P.-Sls. & Mktg.--Vital Signs, Inc., Totowa, NJ; *U.S. Public*, pg. 1723

Wicker, David, V.P.-Creative Svcs.--Things Remembered, Inc., Highland Heights, OH; *U.S. Public*, pg. 397

Wickstra, Gregg P., V.P.-Opers. Services--Peabody Holding Company, Inc., Saint Louis, MO; *Int'l*, pg. 594

Wickstrom, Wayne R., V.P. & Dir.-Mktg. & Sls./Furniture & Intl. Export Components--Leggett & Platt, Incorporated, Carthage, MO; *U.S. Public*, pg. 985

Widdis, Jonathan, Mgr.-Mktg.--ASCG, Inc., Anchorage, AK; *U.S. Private*, pg. 80

Widerkehr, R.L., V.P.-Vet. Sls. & Mktg.--SmithKline Beecham Laboratories, Bristol, TN; *Int'l*, pg. 1264

Widgodsky, John, Exec. V.P.-Sls. & Mktg.--Fruit of the Loom, Inc., Chicago, IL; *U.S. Public*, pg. 685

Widler, Niki, Sr. V.P.-Mktg.--Acceptance Insurance Co., Inc., Omaha, NE; *U.S. Public*, pg. 14

Widler, Niki, Sr. V.P.-Mktg.--Acceptance Insurance Companies, Inc., Omaha, NE; *U.S. Public*, pg. 15

Widmer, Fred, Gen. Mgr.-Mktg.--Coop Switzerland, Basel, Switzerland; *Int'l*, pg. 329

Wiechman, Duane, V.P.-Admin.--Chance Rides, Inc., Wichita, KS; *U.S. Private*, pg. 228

Wiecking, Carl, Dir.-Mktg.--DSM Sheffield Plastics, Sheffield, MA; *Int'l*, pg. 354

Wiedenfeld, Steve, Mgr.-Mktg.--Nordco, Inc., Milwaukee, WI; *U.S. Public*, pg. 1209

Wiela, Fred, Sr. V.P.-Sls. & Mktg.--Komag, Incorporated, San Jose, CA; *U.S. Public*, pg. 966

Wielgus, Wayne, V.P.-Worldwide Mktg. & Sls.--Best Western International, Inc., Phoenix, AZ; *U.S. Private*, pg. 140

Wielopolski, Mari Kroon, V.P.-Mktg. & Sls.--Awrey Bakeries, Inc., Livonia, MI; *U.S. Private*, pg. 103

Wien, Larry, Dir.-Mktg. & Adv.--Al & Ed's Auto Sound Center, Monterey Park, CA; *U.S. Private*, pg. 30

Wienholz, Ken, V.P.-Sls & Mktg.--Bell-Carter Foods, Inc., Lafayette, CA; *U.S. Private*, pg. 131

Wiese, Nancy J., Dir.-Worldwide Mktg. Communications--Xerox Corporation, Stamford, CT; *U.S. Public*, pg. 1783

Wiese, Virginia, Dir.-Strategic Plng.--American Banker Bond Buyer, New York, NY; *U.S. Public*, pg. 1600

Wiesemes, Kurt, V.P.-Mktg. & Sls.--Quality Packaging Products, Inc., Benton Harbor, MI; *U.S. Private*, pg. 899

Wiesmann, Patric, V.P.-Mktg. & Bus. Devel.--Mackie Designs, Inc., Woodinville, WA; *U.S. Public*, pg. 1030

Wigger, Tim, V.P.-Sls. & Mktg.--The Marley Cooling Tower Co., Overland Park, KS; *U.S. Public*, pg. 1676

Wiggers, Gray, V.P.-Mktg.--Trustmark National Bank, Jackson, MS; *U.S. Public*, pg. 1643

Wiggins, K.C., Mgr.-Domestic Sls.--Carver, Inc., Savannah, GA; *U.S. Private*, pg. 217

Wiggins, Morty, Sr. V.P.-Mktg.--A&M Records, Hollywood, CA; *Int'l*, pg. 1052

Wiggins, Theron, Dir.-Mktg.--Golden Sun Feeds, Inc., Estherville, IA; *U.S. Private*, pg. 895

Wiggonton, Adam, Sr. V.P.-Mktg.--OAG, Oak Brook, IL; *Int'l*, pg. 1097

Wightman, Randel L., V.P.-Mktg.--Radix Corporation, Salt Lake City, UT; *U.S. Private*, pg. 906

Wignall, David A., Sr. V.P. & Database Mktg. Grp. Dir.--Creswell, Munsell, Fultz & Zirbel, L.P., Cedar Rapids, IA; *U.S. Private*, pg. 1197

Wigodsky, John, Exec. V.P.-Mktg. & Sls.--Delta Apparel, Duluth, GA; *U.S. Public*, pg. 498

Wigodsky, John, Exec. V.P.-Mktg. & Sls.--Union Underwear Co., Inc., Bowling Green, KY; *U.S. Public*, pg. 686

Wigton, Nancy H., Sr. V.P.-Mktg.--Cambiar Investors, Inc., Englewood, CO; *U.S. Public*, pg. 1672

Wigzell, Steve, Grp. Dir.-Mktg.--Eagle Star, Cheltenham, United Kingdom; *Int'l*, pg. 110

Wilbur, Cheryl, Dir.-Mktg.--Conde Nast Traveler, New York, NY; *U.S. Private*, pg. 20

Wilbur, Laura, Mgr.-Mktg. Communications--American Tool Companies, Inc., Lincoln, NE; *U.S. Private*, pg. 63

Wilbur, Steve, Dir.-Sls. & Mktg.--David Michael & Co. Inc., Philadelphia, PA; *U.S. Private*, pg. 740

Wilcher, Charles, Mgr.-Mktg. Svcs.--Kemper Insurance Companies, Long Grove, IL; *U.S. Private*, pg. 614

Wilcox, Bonnie F., Mgr.-Mktg., Printing Papers & Business Products--Dillard, A ResourceNet International Company, Greensboro, NC; *U.S. Public*, pg. 901

Wilcox, Teresa, Mgr.-Mktg. Prod.--North American Van Lines, Inc., Fort Wayne, IN; *U.S. Public*, pg. 1191

Wildenberg, Michael, V.P.-Sls. & Mktg.--Bay West Paper Corp. Towel & Tissue Div., Middletown, OH; *U.S. Public*, pg. 1747

Wildenberg, Michael, V.P.-Sls. & Mktg.--Bay West Paper Corporation, Harrodsburg, KY; *U.S. Public*, pg. 1747

Wildenburg, Michael, V.P.-Mktg./Towel & Tissue--Wausau-Mosinee Paper Corporation, Mosinee, WI; *U.S. Public*, pg. 1747

Wildermuth, Ron E., Dir.-Corp. Rels.--Parsons Corporation, Pasadena, CA; *U.S. Private*, pg. 841

Wildey, Bob, V.P.-Mktg.--Six Flags Great Adventure Theme Park & Wild Safari Animal Park, Jackson, NJ; *U.S. Public*, pg. 1611

Wildman, John, V.P.-Mktg.--Bally Total Fitness Corporation, Chicago, IL; *U.S. Public*, pg. 171

Wileczka, Gary, Mgr.-Mktg.-Electronic Prods.--Partlow Corporation, New Hartford, NY; *U.S. Public*, pg. 482

Wilen, Tom V., Exec. V.P.-Worldwide Sls. & Mktg.--JBB Worldwide, Inc., Deerfield, IL; *U.S. Public*, pg. 675

Wilensky, Ron, V.P.-Bus. Devel.--TCI International Inc., Sunnyvale, CA; *U.S. Public*, pg. 1555

Wiley, Carl, Product & Mktg. Mgr.--Ney Dental International, Bloomfield, CT; *Int'l*, pg. 388

Wiley, M., Dir.-Mktg.--ABB Simcon, Inc., Bloomfield, NJ; *Int'l*, pg. 5

Wiley, Pat, Mgr.-Mktg.--Ziebart Corp., Troy, MI; *U.S. Private*, pg. 1205

Wiley, Pat, Mgr.-Mktg.--Ziebart Canada, Inc., Concord, Canada; *U.S. Private*, pg. 1205

Wiley, Patricia, Dir.-Mktg.--Ziebart International Corporation, Troy, MI; *U.S. Private*, pg. 1205

Wiley, Syl, Mgr.-Mktg.--Sturm, Ruger & Co., Inc., Southport, CT; *U.S. Public*, pg. 1526

Wilhelm, Bob, Sr. V.P.-Sls. & Mktg.--Unitog Company, Kansas City, MO; *U.S. Public*, pg. 1693

Wilhelm, Maria, Exec. Mktg. Asst.--Industrial Acoustics Company, Inc., Bronx, NY; *U.S. Public*, pg. 875

Wilhelm, Steven, Mgr.-Mktg.--Woodcraft Industries, Inc., Saint Cloud, MN; *U.S. Private*, pg. 1187

Wilka, Ann, Mgr.-Mktg.--Turtle Wax, Inc., Chicago, IL; *U.S. Private*, pg. 1110

Wilke, Jerry, V.P.-Sls., Worldwide Mkt. Devel.--Harley-Davidson, Inc., Milwaukee, WI; *U.S. Public*, pg. 786

Wilke, Michael, Sr. Dir.-Mktg.--Ampex Corporation, Redwood City, CA; *U.S. Public*, pg. 104

Wilkenson, John, Dir.-Mktg.--Grupo Iberia, Madrid, Spain; *Int'l*, pg. 574

Wilkerson, M. Tony, Sr. V.P.-Mktg.--Haverty Furniture Companies, Inc., Atlanta, GA; *U.S. Public*, pg. 799

Wilkie, Jack, V.P.-Mktg. & Franchise Devel.--Aamco Transmissions, Inc., Bala Cynwyd, PA; *U.S. Private*, pg. 9

Wilkinlok, William C., V.P.-Sls. & Mktg.--Metal Container Corporation, Saint Louis, MO; *U.S. Public*, pg. 114

Wilkins, Mark, V.P.-Mktg. Svcs.--Merle Norman Cosmetics, Inc., Los Angeles, CA; *U.S. Private*, pg. 733

Wilkins, Michael C., V.P.-Mkt. Devel.--Caesars World, Inc., Las Vegas, NV; *U.S. Public*, pg. 1512

Wilkinson-Barnhart, Michele, Mktg. Dir.-C.I.--The Peterson Group, New York, NY; *U.S. Public*, pg. 1642

Wilkinson, Dick, V.P.-Mktg.--Hussey Corporation, North Berwick, ME; *U.S. Private*, pg. 550

Wilkinson, Georgia, Mgr.-Mktg. Services--Cab-o-Sil Div. Cabot Corp., Tuscola, IL; *U.S. Public*, pg. 289

Wilkinson, Georgia, Mgr.-Mktg.-Fragrance--Guerlain, Inc., New York, NY; *Int'l*, pg. 780

Wilkinson, John E., Exec. V.P.-Mktg.--Track 'n Trail, El Dorado Hills, CA; *U.S. Public*, pg. 1626

Wilkinson, Nick, Mgr.-Media--Birds Eye Walls Ltd., Walton-on-Thames, United Kingdom; *Int'l*, pg. 1434

Wilkinson, Warren R., Dir.-Mktg. & Corp. Communications--Mesaba Holdings, Inc., Minneapolis, MN; *U.S. Public*, pg. 1099

Wilks, David, Pres.-Mktg. & Svcs.--New Century Energies, Inc., Denver, CO; *U.S. Public*, pg. 1170

Willcox-Jones, George, V.P.-Mktg.--Nepera Inc., Harriman, NY; *U.S. Public*, pg. 297

Willensky, Steven S., V.P.-Worldwide Mktg. & Product Mngmt.--G.E. Lighting Division, Cleveland, OH; *U.S. Public*, pg. 710

Willey, Glenn, V.P.-Sls.--Allfast Fastening Systems, Inc., City of Industry, CA; *U.S. Private*, pg. 37

Willey, John, V.P.--SL Surface Technology, Inc., Camden, NJ; *U.S. Public*, pg. 1419

Willey, Mark C., V.P.-Opers. & Mktg.--Atlantic Aviation Corp., New Castle, DE; *U.S. Private*, pg. 94

Williams, Andrew W., V.P.-Transmission & Mktg.--Potomac Electric Power Company, Washington, DC; *U.S. Public*, pg. 1318

Williams, Ann, Mgr.-Mktg.--G.S. Blodgett Corporation, Burlington, VT; *U.S. Public*, pg. 1064

Williams, Ann, V.P.-Sls. & Mktg.--Tollman/Hundley Hotels, Hopewell Junction, NY; *U.S. Private*, pg. 1090

Williams, Ann E., Mgr.-Mktg., Adv. & Pub. Rels.--The Blodgett Oven Co., Inc., Burlington, VT; *U.S. Public*, pg. 1064

Williams, Annie, Dir.-Mktg.--Newsweek, Inc., New York, NY; *U.S. Public*, pg. 1743

Williams, Beth, Mgr.-Mktg.--Telos Corporation, Ashburn, VA; *U.S. Public*, pg. 1573

Williams, Bob, V.P.-Sls. & Mktg.--G.D. Packaging Machinery Inc., Richmond, VA; *Int'l*, pg. 531

Williams, Brad, Mgr.-Mktg.--Levi Strauss & Co., San Francisco, CA; *U.S. Private*, pg. 662

Williams, Bradford J., V.P.-Intl. Mktg.--Osteonics Corp., Allendale, NJ; *U.S. Public*, pg. 1526

Williams, C. Garrett, Dir.-Sls. & Mktg.--Dewey Square Investors Corporation, Boston, MA; *U.S. Public*, pg. 1673

Williams, C.G., Sr. V.P.-Corp. Mktg.--AGRA Monenco, Oakville, Canada; *Int'l*, pg. 30

Williams, Chris, Mgr.-Ethnic Mktg.--Anheuser-Busch Companies, Inc., Saint Louis, MO; *U.S. Public*, pg. 113

Williams, Cristin, Coord.-Mktg.--Frozfruit Corporation, Gardena, CA; *U.S. Private*, pg. 430

Williams, Curtis, Mgr.-Mktg.--Tho-Ro Products, Inc., Carlstadt, NJ; *U.S. Private*, pg. 354

Williams, Dan, V.P.-Mktg./Formulted Dairy Foods Grp.--Mid-America Dairymen, Inc., Springfield, MO; *U.S. Private*, pg. 743

Williams, Dana, Dir.-Promo.--Southwest Airlines Co., Dallas, TX; *U.S. Public*, pg. 1493

Williams, David W., V.P.-Mktg., NAAG--Whirlpool Corporation, Benton Harbor, MI; *U.S. Public*, pg. 1764

Williams, Deb, Adv. & Mktg. Asst.--Webster Industries Inc., Tiffin, OH; *U.S. Private*, pg. 1157

Williams, Debbie, Dir.-Mktg. Communications--Johnson & Johnson Professional, Inc., Raynham, MA; *U.S. Public*, pg. 928

Williams, Ed, Sr. V.P.-Mktg.--Aladdin Mills, Dalton, GA; *U.S. Public*, pg. 1121

Williams, Elizabeth, Mgr.-Mktg.--Paramount Canada's Wonderland, Vaughan, Canada; *U.S. Private*, pg. 776

Williams, Frank, V.P.-Mktg.--Action Instruments, Inc., San Diego, CA; *U.S. Private*, pg. 15

Williams, Glenn, Sr. V.P. & Dir.-Mktg.--United American Insurance Co., Dallas, TX; *U.S. Public*, pg. 1623

Williams, I., Dir.-Mktg.--Coats Cucirini S.p.A., Milan, Italy; *Int'l*, pg. 300

Williams, Jana, Mgr.-Mktg.--Arthur Treacher's, Inc., Jacksonville, FL; *U.S. Public*, pg. 136

Williams, Jay, Pres.-Firstar, Illinois--Firstar Corporation, Milwaukee, WI; *U.S. Public*, pg. 642

Williams, Jay, Pres.-Firstar, Illinois--Firstar Milwaukee Bank, N.A., Milwaukee, WI; *U.S. Public*, pg. 643

Williams, John, V.P.-Mktg.--King & Prince Seafood Corporation, Brunswick, GA; *U.S. Private*, pg. 620

Williams, John, Mgr.-Mktg. Programs--Ford Motor Company Limited, Brentwood, United Kingdom; *U.S. Public*, pg. 666

Williams, Jonas, Dir.-Mktg.--Adams Rite Sabre International, Glendale, CA; *U.S. Private*, pg. 1203

Williams, Ken, V.P.-Mktg. & Opers.--Foodmaker, Inc., San Diego, CA; *U.S. Public*, pg. 661

Williams, Ken, Dir.-Mktg.--Smith Management Co., Inc., Shreveport, LA; *U.S. Private*, pg. 1009

Williams, Kenneth R., Exec. V.P.-Mktg. & Opers.--Foodmaker, Inc., San Diego, CA; *U.S. Public*, pg. 661
Williams, Larry P., V.P.-Logistics & Dedicated Fleets--Werner Enterprises, Inc., Omaha, NE; *U.S. Public*, pg. 1754
Williams, Linda G., V.P.-Corp. Mktg.--Epsilon, Burlington, MA; *U.S. Public*, pg. 74
Williams, Loren R., V.P.-Strategic Mktg. & New Bus. Devel.--Animal Health, Fort Lee, NJ; *U.S. Public*, pg. 58
Williams, Lori, Admin.-Sls. & Mktg.--Eaton Corporation, Pressure Sensors Division, Bethel, CT; *U.S. Public*, pg. 557
Williams, Lyle, V.P.-Mktg.--Western Extrusions, Carrollton, TX; *U.S. Private*, pg. 1165
Williams, Mike, Dir.-Mktg. & Sls.-ICI Paints--ICI Paints, Cleveland, OH; *Int'l*, pg. 663
Williams, Mike, Dir.-Mktg. & Sls-ICI Paints--Devoe Paint, Cleveland, OH; *Int'l*, pg. 663
Williams, Nicole, Dir.-Mktg.--Interactive Telecard Services, Inc. (ITS), Miami, FL; *U.S. Private*, pg. 566
Williams, Raymond R., Dir.-Mktg.--Barksdale, Inc., Los Angeles, CA; *U.S. Public*, pg. 457
Williams, Richard, Mgr.-Mktg.--Foseco Inc., Cleveland, OH; *Int'l*, pg. 234
Williams, Richard B., Vice Chm.--Alternative Resources Corporation, Lincolnshire, IL; *U.S. Public*, pg. 59
Williams, Roger D., Exec. V.P.-Food Products, Mktg., Pur., & Tech. Services--Bob Evans Farms, Inc., Columbus, OH; *U.S. Public*, pg. 596
Williams, Roger D., Exec. V.P.-Mktg.-Food Products--Bob Evans Farms, Inc. Sausage Division, Columbus, OH; *U.S. Public*, pg. 596
Williams, Ronald, Mgr.-Mktg.--Carter Products, Canada, Mississauga, Canada; *U.S. Public*, pg. 310
Williams, Scott, Mktg. Analyst--Baxter-Hyland, Glendale, CA; *U.S. Public*, pg. 196
Williams, Stephen E., V.P.-Mktg. & Sls.--Indiana Gas Company, Inc., Indianapolis, IN; *U.S. Public*, pg. 875
Williams, Stephen T., Exec. V.P.-Mktg. Dir.--American Bankers Insurance Co. of Florida, Miami, FL; *U.S. Public*, pg. 67
Williams, Steve, V.P.-Mktg. & Sls.--Macklanburg-Duncan Co., Oklahoma City, OK; *U.S. Private*, pg. 692
Williams, Suzanne, V.P.-Sls. & Mktg.--Ventura Coastal Corporation, Ventura, CA; *U.S. Private*, pg. 1136
Williams, Terrin, Mktg. Analyst--Lancaster Colony Automotive Group, Dublin, OH; *U.S. Public*, pg. 977
Williams, Tim, Dir.-Mktg.--Allied Building Products Corporation, East Rutherford, NJ; *U.S. Private*, pg. 38
Williams, Tim, Dir.-Worldwide Mktg.--Varity Kelsey Hayes, Livonia, MI; *Int'l*, pg. 820
Williams, Tom, Mgr.-Adv.-Texas--Six Flags Over Texas, Arlington, TX; *U.S. Public*, pg. 1612
Williams, Woody, V.P.-Sls.--Pennsylvania House Casegoods, Lewisburg, PA; *U.S. Public*, pg. 975
Williamson, Mark, Dir.-Mktg.--Britannia Music Co. Ltd., Ilford, United Kingdom; *Int'l*, pg. 1052
Williamson, Steve, Mgr.-Distr. Mktg.--Commonwealth Industries, Inc., Louisville, KY; *U.S. Public*, pg. 415
Willis, Joyce, Asst. V.P.-Pub. Rels.--The Hartford Financial Services Group Inc., Hartford, CT; *U.S. Public*, pg. 794
Willis, Mike, Dir.-Sls. & Mktg.-Indus.--Kappler Safety Group, Inc., Guntersville, AL; *U.S. Private*, pg. 607
Willis, Timothy, Asst. Mktg. Dir.--Peter Pan Bus Lines, Inc., Springfield, MA; *U.S. Private*, pg. 856
Willison, Blake, V.P.-Sls. & Mktg.--Unitech Industries, Inc., Tempe, AZ; *U.S. Public*, pg. 1672
Willison, Karen, V.P.-Mktg.--Rock Bottom Restaurants, Louisville, CO; *U.S. Public*, pg. 1396
Willoughby, Diana, Mgr.-Mktg.--Renaissance Publishing Co., Inc., Auburn, IN; *Int'l*, pg. 185
Willox, Bruce A., Mgr.-Mktg. Communications--A.T. Cross Co., Lincoln, RI; *U.S. Public*, pg. 460
Willox, Randy, Exec. V.P.-Consumer Mkts. Prod./Western Div.--Countrywide Home Loans Inc., Pasadena, CA; *U.S. Public*, pg. 452
Wills, Cathy, Sr. V.P.-Mktg.--Maybelline, Inc., New York, NY; *Int'l*, pg. 819
Wills, Roderick M., V.P.-Boston Traders Outlet/Mdsg.--Designs, Inc., Needham, MA; *U.S. Public*, pg. 501
Willsea, Lou, V.P.-Sls. & Mktg.--Racke USA, Sonoma, CA; *Int'l*, pg. 1083
Willsea, Louis, V.P.-Sls. & Mktg.--Buena Vista Winery, Sonoma, CA; *Int'l*, pg. 1083
Willson, Barry, Gen. Mgr. & Dir.-Mktg., Adv. & Sls.--Eberline Instrument Corporation, Santa Fe, NM; *U.S. Public*, pg. 1593
Willumsen, Anne Kathrine, V.P.-Sls. & Mktg.--Fine Chemicals, Oslo, Norway; *U.S. Public*, pg. 58
Wilmot, Gillian, V.P.-Mktg.--Avon Cosmetics Limited, Northampton, United Kingdom; *U.S. Public*, pg. 156
Wilmot, Louise, Deputy Exec. Dir.-Domestic Outreach--Catholic Relief Services, Baltimore, MD; *U.S. Private*, pg. 220
Wilner, Jeff, V.P.-Sls. & Mktg.--Mr. Christmas Inc., New York, NY; *U.S. Private*, pg. 765
Wilson-Gray, Sheri, Exec. V.P.--Saks Fifth Avenue, New York, NY; *U.S. Public*, pg. 1429
Wilson, A.H.R., Dir.-Sls. & Mktg.--Butler Newall Limited-Butler Machine Tool Div., Halifax, United Kingdom; *Int'l*, pg. 448
Wilson, Allan B., Exec. V.P.-Corp. Mktg.--Intergraph Corporation, Huntsville, AL; *U.S. Public*, pg. 890
Wilson, Bill, Mgr.-Intl. Mktg.--Centrilift, Claremore, OK; *U.S. Public*, pg. 167
Wilson, Campbell, Mgr.-Mktg.--PACCAR Automotive Inc., Renton, WA; *U.S. Public*, pg. 1247
Wilson, Chris, Mktg. Specialist-Consumer Contadina--Culinary Foods Group, Glendale, CA; *Int'l*, pg. 917
Wilson, Dan R., Sr. V.P.-Mktg.--Longs Drug Stores Corporation, Walnut Creek, CA; *U.S. Public*, pg. 1013
Wilson, Dave, V.P.-Non Stop Software Mktg.--Tandem Computers Inc., Cupertino, CA; *U.S. Public*, pg. 417
Wilson, David, Dir.-Mktg.--NCH Corporation, Irving, TX; *U.S. Public*, pg. 1145
Wilson, David G., Jr., Sr. V.P.-Sls. & Mktg--Cadmus Journal Services, Richmond, VA; *U.S. Public*, pg. 291
Wilson, Don, Mng. Dir.--Totes Canada Ltd., Etobicoke, Canada; *U.S. Private*, pg. 111
Wilson, James L., V.P.-Mktg. & Sales--First DataBank, San Bruno, CA; *U.S. Private*, pg. 515
Wilson, Jane, Coord.-Mktg. Svcs.--NVR, Inc., Mc Lean, VA; *U.S. Public*, pg. 1148
Wilson, Janet, Mgr.-Mktg.--McBride and Associates, Inc., Albuquerque, NM; *U.S. Private*, pg. 719
Wilson, Jeff, Dir.-Mktg.--Porcelanite, Inc., Lexington, NC; *Int'l*, pg. 573
Wilson, Jeffrey A., V.P.-Sls. & Mktg.--A.T. Massey Coal Company, Inc., Richmond, VA; *U.S. Public*, pg. 660
Wilson, Jill, Mgr.-Mktg.--James N. Gray Construction Co., Inc., Lexington, KY; *U.S. Private*, pg. 472
Wilson, Joe, Mgr.-Mktg.--Federal Signal Corporation, Signal Div., University Park, IL; *U.S. Public*, pg. 616
Wilson, John, Dir.-Mktg. Services--White Consolidated Industries, Inc., Cleveland, OH; *Int'l*, pg. 439
Wilson, John, Dir.-Sls. & Mktg.--IRPC Hinton Limited, Hinckley, United Kingdom; *Int'l*, pg. 1502
Wilson, Karin, Coord.-Sls. & Mktg.--Alra Laboratories, Inc., Gurnee, IL; *U.S. Private*, pg. 45
Wilson, Larry, V.P.-Sls. & Mktg./Canada--GSW Pump Company, Fergus, Canada; *Int'l*, pg. 538
Wilson, Lewis, Dir.-Mktg. & Grp. Research--Essence Communications Inc., New York, NY; *U.S. Private*, pg. 383
Wilson, Lon, Mgr.-Tech. Mktg.--Roquette America Inc., Keokuk, IA; *U.S. Private*, pg. 944
Wilson, Mark F., Dir.-Corp. Mktg.--Intermagnetics General Corporation, Latham, NY; *U.S. Public*, pg. 893
Wilson, Michael M., Exec. V.P.-Global Mktg. & Logistics--Methanex Corporation, Vancouver, Canada; *Int'l*, pg. 862
Wilson, Paula, Dir.-Mktg.& Communication--The Life Insurance Co. of Virginia, Richmond, VA; *U.S. Public*, pg. 712
Wilson, Robert G., V.P.-Rebar--Birmingham Steel Corporation, Birmingham, AL; *U.S. Public*, pg. 232
Wilson, Shelley, Dir.-Program Mktg.--Symantec Corporation, Cupertino, CA; *U.S. Public*, pg. 1545
Wilson, Shelley, Dir.-Program Mktg.--Symantec Corporation - Beaverton Site, Beaverton, OR; *U.S. Public*, pg. 1545
Wilson, Steven A., Dir.-Sls, Mktg. & Adv.--Music Sales Corporation, New York, NY; *U.S. Private*, pg. 768
Wilson, Ted, V.P.-Mktg.--Russell Corp., Jerzees Div., Alexander City, AL; *U.S. Public*, pg. 1413
Wilson, Thomas J., Sr. V.P.-Sls. & Mktg.--California & Hawaiian Sugar Company Inc., Crockett, CA; *U.S. Public*, pg. 39
Wilson, Tom, Mgr.-Sls.--Vile-Goller, Fine Art Printing & Lithography, Kansas City, KS; *U.S. Private*, pg. 1140
Wilson, Tom J., Mgr.-Mktg.--Alexander & Baldwin, Inc., Honolulu, HI; *U.S. Public*, pg. 39
Wilson, Wayne, V.P.-Sls. & Mktg.-Georgia/Northlake--Georgia/Durango Boot Company, Franklin, TN; *U.S. Public*, pg. 1684
Wilson, William L., Sr. V.P.-Mktg.--Data General Corporation, Westborough, MA; *U.S. Public*, pg. 485
Wilth, Barbara, Prod. Mgr.--Cruspi S.A., Dallikon, Switzerland; *Int'l*, pg. 348
Wiltshire, W.B., CLU, V.P.-Mktg.--Home Beneficial Corporation, Richmond, VA; *U.S. Public*, pg. 76
Wimbush, Frank A., Sr. V.P.-Mktg. & Branch Opers.--Noland Company, Newport News, VA; *U.S. Public*, pg. 1187
Wimmer, Friedrich, Mgr.-Fertilizer Mktg.--Agrolinz Melamin GmbH, Lienz, Austria; *Int'l*, pg. 356
Winberg, Fredrik, Mgr.-Mktg.--Cementa AB, Danderyd, Sweden; *Int'l*, pg. 1198
Winch, David, V.P.-Sls. & Mktg.--The Minster Machine Company, Minster, OH; *U.S. Private*, pg. 751
Windham, Elwanda, Mktg. Information Services Specialist--Hygrade Food Products Corporation, Southfield, MI; *U.S. Public*, pg. 1433
Windrum, Tracy T., Dir.-Production--People, New York, NY; *U.S. Public*, pg. 1613
Windsor, R., Mgr.-Mktg.--Eaton Corporation, Engineered Fasteners Division, Brunswick, OH; *U.S. Public*, pg. 556
Windsor, Ray, Mgr.-Sls. & Mktg.--Fujitsu Ten Corp. of America, Torrance, CA; *Int'l*, pg. 526
Wine, Melanie, Coord.-Sls. Promo.--WEN Products, Inc., Bensenville, IL; *U.S. Private*, pg. 1144
Winer, Stephen, Dir.-Mktg.--Jarchem Industries, Inc., Newark, NJ; *U.S. Private*, pg. 582
Winfrey, Jane, Dir.-Mktg./Bed & Bath Div.--Jakson-A CHF Company, New York, NY; *U.S. Private*, pg. 1094
Wing, Carol, Dir.-Mktg.--Number Nine Visual Technology, Lexington, MA; *U.S. Public*, pg. 1206
Wing, Sam, III, Mgr.-Mktg. & Adv.--Wing Industries, Inc., Greenville, TX; *U.S. Private*, pg. 1183
Wing, Steve, Mgr.-Global Mktg.--Masoneilan North American Operations, Houston, TX; *U.S. Public*, pg. 528
Wing, Steve, Dir.-Mktg.-Insulation Grp.--Johns Manville Corporation, Denver, CO; *U.S. Public*, pg. 927
Winget, A. Knox, III, Sr. V.P.-Mktg.--American & Efird, Inc., Mount Holly, NC; *U.S. Public*, pg. 1412
Wingrt, Randy, Mgr.-Mktg./Auto--Turtle Wax, Inc., Chicago, IL; *U.S. Private*, pg. 1110
Wink, Kathy, Mgr.-Graphics & Communications--Borden Decorative Products, Saint Louis, MO; *U.S. Private*, pg. 158
Winkelspecht, H. Brian, Mgr.--The JCM Group, Los Angeles, CA; *U.S. Private*, pg. 846
Winking, Kim, Mgr.-Mktg. Svcs.--Broadcast Electronics, Inc., Quincy, IL; *U.S. Private*, pg. 531
Winkler, Patricia, Dir.-Mktg. Commun.--The Fairmont Hotels, San Francisco, CA; *U.S. Private*, pg. 391
Winkler, Wolf, Exec. Mgr.-Mktg.--CAE Elektronik GmbH, Stolberg, Germany; *Int'l*, pg. 238
Winn, Mary, V.P.-Mktg.--Uno Restaurant Corporation, West Roxbury, MA; *U.S. Public*, pg. 1698
Winning, Cynthia A., Grp. V.P.-Mktg.--Jones Intercable, Inc., Englewood, CO; *U.S. Public*, pg. 597
Winston, Mark, Mgr.-Mktg.-Consumer Prods.--Wagner Spray Tech Corp., Plymouth, MN; *U.S. Private*, pg. 1146
Winston, Steve, V.P.-Mktg.--Guardian Products, Inc., Simi Valley, CA; *U.S. Public*, pg. 1535
Winter, Jay, Sr. Mgr.-Mktg. Svcs.--Wise Foods, Inc., Parsippany, NJ; *U.S. Private*, pg. 157
Winter, Phil, Mgr.-Mktg.--Natural Gas Liquids Marketing, Storage & Distribution, Houston, TX; *U.S. Public*, pg. 1663
Winters, Jim, Dir.-Mktg.--Vogue Magazine, New York, NY; *U.S. Private*, pg. 20
Wintz, Lester M., Sr. V.P.-Mktg.--Great Western Bank, Chatsworth, CA; *U.S. Public*, pg. 1741
Wipson, Dave, Dir.-Mktg.--Hypro Corporation, New Brighton, MN; *U.S. Public*, pg. 1767
Wiroth, Jean-Jaques, Dir.-Mktg.-Consumer Tires-North America Tires--The Goodyear Tire & Rubber Company, Akron, OH; *U.S. Public*, pg. 752
Wirt, Kenneth R., V.P.-Corp. Mktg.--Diamond Multimedia Systems, Inc., San Jose, CA; *U.S. Public*, pg. 505
Wirth, Donald J., Mgr.-Product Mktg.--Hardman Division of Harcros Chemicals, Inc., Belleville, NJ; *Int'l*, pg. 598
Wise, Bill, Mgr.-Mktg. Commun.--Sun Data Inc., Norcross, GA; *U.S. Private*, pg. 1050
Wise, Doug, Sr. V.P.-Mktg.--Players International, Inc., Atlantic City, NJ; *U.S. Public*, pg. 1310
Wise, Jeff, Dir.-Mktg.--Titanium Metals Corporation, Denver, CO; *U.S. Private*, pg. 270
Wise, Tom, Coord.-Mktg.--Heath Company, Benton Harbor, MI; *Int'l*, pg. 317
Wise, V.K., Dir.-Program Office Mktg.--Lockheed Space Operations Co., Titusville, FL; *U.S. Public*, pg. 1009
Wisely, Robert W., Exec. V.P.-Mktg.--CKE Restaurants Inc., Anaheim, CA; *U.S. Public*, pg. 278
Wisely, Robert W., V.P.-Mktg.--Carl Karcher Enterprises, Inc., Anaheim, CA; *U.S. Public*, pg. 278
Wisenbaker, Dan, Mgr.-Mktg.--Bettis Corporation, Waller, TX; *U.S. Public*, pg. 482
Wishart, Janet, Admin.-Mktg.--Nestle Lyons Maid, York, United Kingdom; *Int'l*, pg. 918
Wisinski, Tom, V.P.-Sls. & Mktg.--Interform Corporation, Bridgeville, PA; *U.S. Public*, pg. 333
Wismer, Faith, Mgr.-Mktg. Commun.--Koh-I-Noor, Inc., Bloomsbury, NJ; *U.S. Private*, pg. 629
Wisniewski, Michael, Dir.-Mktg.--AJC International, Inc., Atlanta, GA; *U.S. Private*, pg. 6
Witcher, Alan, V.P.-Sls. & Mktg.--Star Fine Foods, Inc., Fresno, CA; *U.S. Private*, pg. 1034
Witcher, Jimmy, Mgr.-Mktg.--Tech Spray, Inc., Amarillo, TX; *U.S. Private*, pg. 1071
Witherspoon, John, V.P.-Mktg. & Trng.--ABB Industrial Systems, Inc., Columbus, OH; *Int'l*, pg. 4
Withka, Thomas F., Pres.-Electric Energy Mktg.--KCS Energy Inc., Edison, NJ; *U.S. Public*, pg. 938
Witkowski, Maria, Dir.-Mktg.--Foster Wheeler Environmental Corporation, Livingston, NJ; *U.S. Public*, pg. 677
Witt, Becky, Dir.-Mktg.--Physician Sales and Services Inc., Jacksonville, FL; *U.S. Public*, pg. 1293
Witt, Melissa, Coord.-Mktg.--Essex Industries, New Haven, CT; *Int'l*, pg. 18
Witt, Melissa, Coord.-Mktg.--Sargent Manufacturing Company, New Haven, CT; *Int'l*, pg. 18
Witt, O., Dir.-Mktg. & Adv.--Battenfeld GmbH, Meinerzhagen, Germany; *Int'l*, pg. 825
Witt, Rick, Dir.-Mktg. Information--Borden Foods Corporation, Columbus, OH; *U.S. Private*, pg. 157
Witt, Rob, Mgr.-Sls.--Bibler Brothers, Inc., Russellville, AR; *U.S. Private*, pg. 142
Witte, Bob, V.P.-Domestic Sls. & Mktg.--Dri-Print Foils Inc., Rahway, NJ; *U.S. Private*, pg. 343
Wittig, Detlef, Dir.-Sls. & Mktg.--SKODA, Automobilova a.s., Mlada Boleslav, Czech Republic; *Int'l*, pg. 1475
Witty, Andrew, V.P. & Gen. Mgr.-Mktg.--Glaxo Wellcome Inc., Research Triangle Park, NC; *Int'l*, pg. 552
Witzerman, Dave, Dir.-Mktg.--Wheaton Van Lines, Inc., Indianapolis, IN; *U.S. Private*, pg. 1171
Witzgall, Annemarie, Gen. Mgr.-Sls. & Mktg.--Essex County Gas Company, Amesbury, MA; *U.S. Public*, pg. 593
Witzling, Mark, Dir.-Mktg.--Golden Cat Corporation, Saint Louis, MO; *U.S. Public*, pg. 1360
Wodzinski, Dale M., V.P.-Mktg. & Adv.--ESAB Welding & Cutting Products, Hanover, PA; *Int'l*, pg. 281
Woelfle, Cyndee, Dir.-Mktg.--Elkay Plastics Company, Inc., Los Angeles, CA; *U.S. Private*, pg. 372
Woh, Lawrence, Dir.-Intl. Mktg.--Emco Limited, London, Canada; *Int'l*, pg. 452
Wohlrab, Richard, Dir.-Mktg.--La Touraine Coffee Company, Secaucus, NJ; *U.S. Public*, pg. 351
Wohlrab, Richie, Dir.-Mktg.--Chock Full O' Nuts - Food Service Div., Secaucus, NJ; *U.S. Public*, pg. 351
Wohlschlaeger, Rick, Dir.-Mktg.--Doane Products Co., Joplin, MO; *U.S. Private*, pg. 337
Woitach, Paul, Dir.-Mktg.--Mettler-Toledo, Inc., Hightstown, NJ; *U.S. Private*, pg. 4
Wojnowiak, Mark, Dir.-Mktg.--Electronic Tele-Communications, Inc., Waukesha, WI; *U.S. Public*, pg. 570
Wolbers, Todd, Mgr.-Media--Top Brands, Inc., Oshkosh, WI; *U.S. Private*, pg. 1091
Wold-Olsen, Per, V.P.-Intl. Human Health Mktg.--Merck Human Health Division, Rahway, NJ; *U.S. Public*, pg. 1090
Wolf, Barbara, Mgr.-Mktg. Svcs.--Wesley-Jessen, Des Plaines, IL; *U.S. Private*, pg. 111
Wolf, Barbara, Dir.-Mktg. & Sls.--Merco/Savory Inc., Lakewood, NJ; *Int'l*, pg. 189
Wolf, Brian, Mgr.-Admin. & Mktg.--Basin Telecommunication, Inc., Bismarck, ND; *U.S. Private*, pg. 121
Wolf, Carol, Dir.-Mktg.-Food--The NutraSweet Kelco Company, San Diego, CA; *U.S. Public*, pg. 1125

Wolf, Dolores, Mgr.-Consumer Svcs.--The Food Emporium, Bronx, NY; *Int'l*, pg. 1375
Wolf, Janet, V.P.-Mktg.--Doubleday Direct, Garden City, NY; *Int'l*, pg. 191
Wolf, Jennifer, Dir.-Mktg.--Smith Corona Corp., Cortland, NY; *U.S. Private*, pg. 1007
Wolf, Steve, V.P.-Mktg.-Highway & Chemical--Sifto Canada, Inc., Mississauga, Canada; *U.S. Private*, pg. 505
Wolf, Terry G., V.P.-Mktg.--HBE Corporation/Design Build Divisions, Saint Louis, MO; *U.S. Private*, pg. 489
Wolfarth, Ronald, Mgr.-Sales & Mktg.--Axle and Brake Div., Henderson, KY; *U.S. Public*, pg. 556
Wolfe, Brain, Dir.-Consumer Mktg.--Sports Illustrated, New York, NY; *U.S. Public*, pg. 1613
Wolfe, Brian D., Dir.-Consumer Mktg.--Fortune, New York, NY; *U.S. Public*, pg. 1613
Wolfe, Eric, Dir.-Mktg.-Adult Grp.--LEGO Systems, Inc., Enfield, CT; *Int'l*, pg. 805
Wolfe, Karen, Coord.-Mktg. Media--Airflex Div. Eaton Corp., Cleveland, OH; *U.S. Public*, pg. 556
Wolfer, Carolyn, Coord.-Mktg.--Accu-Sort Systems, Inc., Telford, PA; *U.S. Private*, pg. 11
Wolfert, Steve, Asst. Dir.-Mktg. Services--American International Group, Inc., New York, NY; *U.S. Public*, pg. 83
Wolff, Jeff, Mgr.-Mkt. Res.--The Gazette Company, Cedar Rapids, IA; *U.S. Private*, pg. 442
Wolff, Paul, Gen. Mgr.-Mktg. Devel. & Quality Control--Banque Generale du Luxembourg SA, Luxembourg, Luxembourg; *Int'l*, pg. 161
Wolff, Roland C., Exec. V.P.-Mktg.--Vallen Safety Supply Company, Houston, TX; *U.S. Public*, pg. 1705
Wolfson, Alan D., Sr. V.P.-Market Intelligence--CT Financial Services, Inc., Toronto, Canada; *Int'l*, pg. 112
Wolk, Doug, Dir.-Natl. Sls.--Sentry Group, Rochester, NY; *U.S. Private*, pg. 984
Wolka, Wendell, Dir.-Mktg.--Ranco North America, Plain City, OH; *Int'l*, pg. 1243
Woll, Alan, Mgr.-Mktg., Automotive Aftermarket--Robertshaw Tennessee, Knoxville, TN; *Int'l*, pg. 1243
Wolner, Odd Erik, Mgr.-Mktg.--Esselte A/S, Oslo, Norway; *Int'l*, pg. 460
Wolpert, Marie, Dir.-Mktg.--The New Yorker Magazine, New York, NY; *U.S. Private*, pg. 795
Wolszon, Beth, V.P.-Mktg. & Strategic Plng.--Safelite AutoGlass, Columbus, OH; *U.S. Private*, pg. 960
Woltering, Mark, V.P.-Sls. & Mktg.--Amot Controls Corporation, Richmond, CA; *U.S. Public*, pg. 1405
Womack, Clydette, Mgr.-Mktg.--The Daily & Sunday Oklahoman, Oklahoma City, OK; *U.S. Private*, pg. 813
Wonar, Charlene, Coord.-Mktg.--Intercosmetics, Inc., New York, NY; *Int'l*, pg. 1489
Wong, Audrey, Sr. Mgr.-Mktg. Commun.--F. J. Benjamin Holdings Ltd., Singapore, Singapore; *Int'l*, pg. 187
Wong, Audry, Sr. Mgr.-Mktg. Commun.--F.J. Benjamin Multimedia Pte Ltd., Singapore, Singapore; *Int'l*, pg. 187
Wong, Colleen, Mgr.-Prod. Mktg.--Teleflora, LLC, Los Angeles, CA; *U.S. Private*, pg. 941
Wong, Dennis, Mgr.-Mktg.--California & Hawaiian Sugar Company Inc., Crockett, CA; *U.S. Public*, pg. 39
Wong, Katherine, Mgr.-Mktg. Svcs.--F.J. Benjamin Fashions (HK) Ltd., Causeway Bay, Hong Kong; *Int'l*, pg. 187
Wong, Michael, Dir.-Mktg.--Sanwa Foods, Inc., City of Industry, CA; *U.S. Public*, pg. 299
Wonsik, R. J., V.P. & Grp. Mktg. Dir.-Johnnie Walker Brands--Shieffelin Somerset Co., New York, NY; *Int'l*, pg. 412
Woo-Nelson, Yeanna, Sr. V.P.-Mktg./Men's--Jay Jacobs, Inc., Seattle, WA; *U.S. Public*, pg. 922
Woo, Monica, V.P.-Private Bank Mktg.--Citicorp, New York, NY; *U.S. Public*, pg. 376
Woo, Seok-Keun, Mgr.-Mktg.--Ssangyong Heavy Industries Co., Ltd., Seoul, Korea; *Int'l*, pg. 1292
Wood, A., Mktg. Mgr.--Scholl (Asia) Limited, Wan Chai, Hong Kong; *Int'l*, pg. 1209
Wood, Brian, Dir.-Mktg.--Johnson & Johnson Hemisferica, Caguas, PR; *U.S. Public*, pg. 928
Wood, Carol, Dir.-Mktg. & Affiliate Rels.--The Sports Network (TSN), Willowdale, Canada; *Int'l*, pg. 1343
Wood, Greg, V.P.-Mktg.--Supercuts, Inc., San Francisco, CA; *U.S. Public*, pg. 1373
Wood, James, V.P.-Sls. & Mktg.--Evans Tempcon Inc., Grand Rapids, MI; *U.S. Private*, pg. 7
Wood, Jan, V.P.-Mktg. & Commun.--Credit Union National Association, Madison, WI; *U.S. Private*, pg. 288
Wood, John, V.P.-Mktg. & Sls.--Clark Detroit-Diesel Allison, Cincinnati, OH; *U.S. Private*, pg. 242
Wood, John, Mgr.-Mktg.-Gear Products--U.S. Electrical Motor Division, Saint Louis, MO; *U.S. Public*, pg. 573
Wood, Ken, V.P. & Sec.--Barringer Technologies Inc., New Providence, NJ; *U.S. Public*, pg. 191
Wood, Lelitia Locker, Dir.-Mktg.--Stuart Circle Hospital Corporation, Atlanta, GA; *U.S. Public*, pg. 1036
Wood, Nicholas, V.P.-Mktg.--ATMI, Inc., Danbury, CT; *U.S. Public*, pg. 12
Wood, Ray, Mgr.-Mktg. & Sls.--Whitecable, Liverpool, United Kingdom; *Int'l*, pg. 462
Wood, Steve, Dir.-Mktg.--Husqvarna Forest & Garden Products, Charlotte, NC; *Int'l*, pg. 440
Wood, Tim, Mktg. Asst.--Lebanon Seaboard Corporation, Lebanon, PA; *U.S. Private*, pg. 656
Woodall, James, Mgr.-Opers.--Beechmont Investments Inc., Cincinnati, OH; *U.S. Private*, pg. 129
Woodard, C., Gen. Mgr.-Natl. Sls. & Mktg.--Australian Poultry Ltd., Beresfield, Australia; *Int'l*, pg. 555
Woodard, Robert, Mgr.-Mktg.--Tupperware U.S., Inc., Orlando, FL; *U.S. Public*, pg. 1644
Woodbury, Dan, Partner & Mktg. Services Dir.--Martin/Williams Advertising Inc., Minneapolis, MN; *U.S. Private*, pg. 710
Woodcox, Sandra, Mgr.-Mktg. Admin.--Elopak, Inc., New Hudson, MI; *Int'l*, pg. 1390
Woodford, Bill, Dir.-Sls. & Mktg.--Land O'Lakes Dairy Foods, Clear Lake, WI; *U.S. Private*, pg. 646
Woodgate, Derek, Dir.-Mktg.--Lee Europe N.V., Brussels, Belgium; *U.S. Public*, pg. 1702
Woodhouse, Rachel, Mgr.-Mktg.--Esselte NV Produktion, Saint-Niklaas, Belgium; *Int'l*, pg. 461
Wooding, J.M., Exec. V.P.-Defense Mktg. Directorate--British Aerospace Defence Limited (Military Aircraft), Preston, United Kingdom; *Int'l*, pg. 217
Woodington, Tad, Mgr.-Indus. Mktg.--Commonwealth Industries, Inc., Louisville, KY; *U.S. Public*, pg. 415
Woodley, Janice, Sr. V.P.-Mktg. & Mdsg.--George Weston Limited, Toronto, Canada; *Int'l*, pg. 1494
Woodley, Janice, Dir.-Mktg.--Weston Bakeries Limited, Etobicoke, Canada; *Int'l*, pg. 1495
Woodley, Janice, Sr. Dir.-Adv. & Mktg.--Loblaw Companies Limited, North York, Canada; *Int'l*, pg. 1495
Woodley, Janice, Sr. Dir.-Adv. & Mktg.--Loblaw Supermarkets Inc., North York, Canada; *Int'l*, pg. 1495
Woodring, Lee, Dir.-Mktg.--Hitachi Home Electronics, Norcross, GA; *Int'l*, pg. 621
Woodrow, Gary, Dir.-Mktg.--Williams Telecommunications Systems, Inc., Houston, TX; *U.S. Public*, pg. 1769
Woods, Djuna, Coord.-Mktg. Commun.--Advanced Logic Research, Inc., Irvine, CA; *U.S. Public*, pg. 703
Woods, Donald B., V.P.-Sls. & Mktg./Western Canada--Andres Wines Ltd., Winona, Canada; *Int'l*, pg. 75
Woods, Joe, V.P.-Mktg.--StacoEnergy Products Co., Dayton, OH; *U.S. Private*, pg. 260
Woods, Kay, Mktg. Sec.--Westat Inc., Rockville, MD; *U.S. Private*, pg. 1163
Woods, Nicole, Mktg. Events--Brock International Inc., Atlanta, GA; *U.S. Public*, pg. 258
Woods, Shelly, Mgr.-Mktg.--Premdor, Inc., Tampa, FL; *Int'l*, pg. 1067
Woodward, Lee, Mgr.-Mktg. Communications--AM General Corporation, South Bend, IN; *U.S. Private*, pg. 922
Woodward, Tony, Dir.-Mktg.--Selix F. Schoeller Ltd., High Wycombe, United Kingdom; *Int'l*, pg. 1209
Woodward, W.P., Sr. V.P.-Mktg.--Kerr-McGee Chemical Corp., Oklahoma City, OK; *U.S. Public*, pg. 952
Woolf, David, Mktg.--American International Industries, City of Commerce, CA; *U.S. Private*, pg. 57
Woollen, Edmund B., V.P.-Govt. Mktg.--Raytheon Company, Lexington, MA; *U.S. Public*, pg. 1364
Woolner, Ken, V.P.--Morrison Petroleums Ltd., Calgary, Canada; *Int'l*, pg. 895
Wooten, Sidney C., Jr., V.P.-Mktg. & Sls.--Lane Limited, Tucker, GA; *Int'l*, pg. 1129
Wooton, Heather, Sr. Assoc.-Mktg.--Number Nine Visual Technology, Lexington, MA; *U.S. Public*, pg. 1206
Wor, Tham Khai, Grp. Gen. Mgr.-Mktg.--Singapore Press Holdings Ltd., Singapore, Singapore; *Int'l*, pg. 1253
Worcester, Tim, Sr. V.P.-Mktg.--Bradlees Inc., Braintree, MA; *U.S. Public*, pg. 249
Word, Nancy, V.P.-Mktg. Communications--CSC Financial Services Group, Austin, TX; *U.S. Public*, pg. 422
Worley, Tom, Mgr.-Mktg.--Antenna Products Corp., Mineral Wells, TX; *U.S. Public*, pg. 289
Worley, Wade, Mgr.-Mktg.--B/E Aerospace, Inc./In Flight Entertainment Group, Irvine, CA; *U.S. Public*, pg. 159
Worrall, Charles, Mgr.-Mktg.-Lecithin--Central Soya Company, Inc., Fort Wayne, IN; *Int'l*, pg. 324
Worrall, Sandra E., Mgr.-Mktg.--N.G. Bailey & Co. Ltd., Ilkley, United Kingdom; *Int'l*, pg. 132
Worthington, Kristen, Asst. V.P.-Sls Promo & Consumer Mktg.--Associates Financial Services Corporation, Dallas, TX; *U.S. Public*, pg. 663
Worthman, Sandy, V.P.-Mktg.--Kitchell Corporation, Phoenix, AZ; *U.S. Private*, pg. 624
Wortman, Frederick, V.P.-Mktg. Admin.--Security Mutual Life Insurance Co. of New York, Binghamton, NY; *U.S. Private*, pg. 981
Wortmann, Tom, Mgr.-Mktg. Svcs.--Littelfuse, Inc., Des Plaines, IL; *U.S. Public*, pg. 1001
Worton, Geoffrey, V.P.-Sls. & Mktg.--The H.W. Wilson Co., Bronx, NY; *U.S. Private*, pg. 1180
Wortsmith, Dena, Dir.-Mktg.--Putt Putt Golf Courses of America, Inc., Fayetteville, NC; *U.S. Private*, pg. 896
Wovrosh, Rick, Dir.-Internal Art & Admin.-Mktg. Communications--Namco Controls Corporation, Highland Heights, OH; *U.S. Public*, pg. 482
Wozniak, Dennis, Sr. V.P.-Pur. & Mktg.--Arbor Drugs, Inc., Troy, MI; *U.S. Public*, pg. 126
Wraga, W., V.P.-Mktg.--Curtiss-Wright Flight Systems, Inc., Fairfield, NJ; *U.S. Public*, pg. 469
Wrath, Julie, Mgr.-Mktg.--Daiichi Fine Chemicals, Lincolnshire, IL; *Int'l*, pg. 879
Wray, Michael D., V.P.-Mktg.--John Crane Mechanical Seals, Morton Grove, IL; *Int'l*, pg. 1339
Wrenn, Tim, Mgr.-Sls. & Mktg.--Winchester Electronics, Watertown, CT; *U.S. Public*, pg. 1003
Wrentshler, Kathy, Coord.-Human Resources--A.E. Staley Manufacturing Co., Decatur, IL; *Int'l*, pg. 1356
Wrieth, Donald, Mgr.-Bus. Devel.--Peter Kiewit Sons Inc., Omaha, NE; *U.S. Private*, pg. 619
Wright, David, Mgr.-Sls.--WBBB, Burlington, NC; *U.S. Private*, pg. 297
Wright, David, Pres.-Sls. & Mktg. Div.--Duraliner U.S.A., Lapeer, MI; *U.S. Public*, pg. 537
Wright, David P., Exec. V.P.-Sls. & Mktg.--MedImmune, Inc., Gaithersburg, MD; *U.S. Public*, pg. 1081
Wright, Elizabeth B., Sr. V.P.-Strategic Plng. & Mktg.--National Trustco Inc., Toronto, Canada; *Int'l*, pg. 909
Wright, Elizabeth B., Sr. V.P.-Strategic Plng. & Mktg.--National Trust Company, Stratford, Canada; *Int'l*, pg. 910
Wright, F.J., V.P.-Mktg.--Pratt & Whitney Canada Inc., Longueuil, Canada; *U.S. Public*, pg. 1690
Wright, Gail, Dir.-Mktg. Communications--SunAmerica Inc., Los Angeles, CA; *U.S. Public*, pg. 1532
Wright, Gary, Mgr.-Corp. Commun.--RLI Corp., Peoria, IL; *U.S. Public*, pg. 1356
Wright, Jay, V.P.-Mktg.--Borden Foods Canada, Etobicoke, Canada; *U.S. Private*, pg. 159
Wright, John, Dir.-Mktg.--Rosemount Analytical, Uniloc Div., Irvine, CA; *U.S. Public*, pg. 574
Wright, Laurie, Dir.-Mktg.--Advance Business Graphics, Mira Loma, CA; *U.S. Private*, pg. 18
Wright, Lowell, V.P.-Mktg. & Sls.--Caremark International Inc, Northbrook, IL; *U.S. Public*, pg. 1082
Wright, Simon, Dir.-Mktg.--Interwood Marketing Group, Concord, Canada; *Int'l*, pg. 685
Wright, Steve, Dir.-Mktg.--Macklanburg-Duncan Co., Oklahoma City, OK; *U.S. Private*, pg. 692
Wright, Tim, Pres.--Mr. Wright's Amazing Coffee Factory, San Jose, CA; *U.S. Private*, pg. 765
Wright, Trish, V.P.-Mktg.--Interplay Productions, Inc., Irvine, CA; *U.S. Private*, pg. 572
Wright, W.H., Dir.-Sls. & Mktg.--Redland Tile & Brick, Crumlin, United Kingdom; *Int'l*, pg. 1091
Wrightman, Julie, Mktg. Asst.--Keating Building Corp., Bala Cynwyd, PA; *U.S. Private*, pg. 610
Write, Cheryl, Dir.-Mktg.--Doctors Hospital of Shreveport, Shreveport, LA; *U.S. Public*, pg. 1697
Wroblewski, Tom, Mgr.-Mktg.--Diemakers, Inc., Monroe City, MO; *U.S. Private*, pg. 332
Wruskyj, Peter, Mgr.-Mktg.--CTS Corp. Frequency Controls, Sandwich, IL; *U.S. Public*, pg. 285
Wu, Tzy-Chiang, V.P.--The International Commercial Bank of China, Taipei, Taiwan; *Int'l*, pg. 683
Wuebbens, Dave, Mgr.-Adv.--Prime Hospitality Corp., Fairfield, NJ; *U.S. Public*, pg. 1326
Wullschleger, Kurt, Dir.-Mktg.--Data Transmission Network Corporation, Omaha, NE; *U.S. Public*, pg. 486
Wurster, Hans C., Exec. V.P.-Mktg. & Sls.--Bel/Kaukauna USA, Little Chute, WI; *U.S. Private*, pg. 130
Wyatt, Jan, V.P.-Sls. & Mktg.--Interval International Inc., Miami, FL; *U.S. Public*, pg. 320
Wyatt, W.J., V.P.-Mktg.--Williams Scotsman, Inc., Baltimore, MD; *U.S. Private*, pg. 976
Wyckoff, Paul, Exec. V.P.-Sls. & Mktg.--Maharam, Hauppauge, NY; *U.S. Private*, pg. 696
Wyker, Ken, Dir.-Mktg./M.V.P.--Food Lion, Inc., Salisbury, NC; *Int'l*, pg. 463
Wyman, Dell, Sr. V.P.-Mktg.--Farm Family Casualty Insurance Co., Glenmont, NY; *U.S. Private*, pg. 394
Wynn, Pat, Mgr.-Mktg.--Greyhound Lines of Canada Ltd., Calgary, Canada; *Int'l*, pg. 559
Wypasek, Paul, Mgr.-Mktg.--Erico International, Solon, OH; *U.S. Private*, pg. 381
Wyrwa, Charles J., Sr. Mktg. Officer--Northeast Marketing-Boston Business Center, Boston, MA; *U.S. Public*, pg. 649
Wysocki, Sandra, Dir.-Res. & Mktg. Svcs.--Journal Communications Inc., Milwaukee, WI; *U.S. Private*, pg. 601
Wysocki, Verna, Mgr.-Adv. & Mktg.--Beaver Lumber Company Limited, Markham, Canada; *Int'l*, pg. 887
Wysong, Jennifer, Dir.-Mktg.--Cartwright Communications Co., Cincinnati, OH; *U.S. Public*, pg. 1582
Yabu, Kazuya, Sr. Mng. Dir. & Gen. Mgr.-Mktg.--Mitsubishi Electric Corporation, Tokyo, Japan; *Int'l*, pg. 872
Yacovonc, Rose, Mgr.-Mktg.--The Hibbert Company, Trenton, NJ; *U.S. Private*, pg. 525
Yale, D., V.P.-Mktg.--Labatt U.S.A., Darien, CT; *Int'l*, pg. 679
Yamada, Satoshi, Sr. Mng. Dir.-Intl. Bus. Devel. & Overseas Mktg. & Sls.--Mazda Motor Corporation, Hiroshima, Japan; *Int'l*, pg. 849
Yamaguchi, Richard, Mgr.-Mktg. & Pub. Rels.--Tropitone Furniture Co. Inc., Irvine, CA; *U.S. Private*, pg. 1105
Yamakoshi, Warren, Pres.--Nobart, Inc., Chicago, IL; *U.S. Private*, pg. 800
Yamamoto, Katsuaki, Mng. Dir.-Pur. & Domestic Mktg. & Sls.--Mazda Motor Corporation, Hiroshima, Japan; *Int'l*, pg. 849
Yamanaka, Kuniaki, Dir.-Tire Mktg. & Sls. Div.--Bridgestone Corporation, Tokyo, Japan; *Int'l*, pg. 213
Yamane, Hisao, Sr. Mng. Dir.-Petroleum Retail Mktg.--Japan Energy Corporation, Tokyo, Japan; *Int'l*, pg. 702
Yamane, Hisao, Mng. Dir.-Petroleum Retail Mktg.--Japan Energy Corporation, Tokyo, Japan; *Int'l*, pg. 702
Yan, Leonila R., Mgr.-Promo.--Philippine Long Distance Telephone Company, Manila, Philippines; *Int'l*, pg. 1051
Yanagisawa, Wataru, Mgr.-Lubricant Mktg. & Prod. Engrng.--Nippon Oil Company, Limited (NiSSEKI), Tokyo, Japan; *Int'l*, pg. 936
Yando, Fred, V.P.-Sls. & Mktg.--Christie Design, Chatsworth, CA; *U.S. Public*, pg. 1369
Yang, Richard, V.P.-Mktg. & Sls.--Garland Commercial Industries, Inc., Freeland, PA; *Int'l*, pg. 188
Yanofsky, Marc, Sr. V.P.-Mktg.--Hyatt Hotels Corporation, Chicago, IL; *U.S. Private*, pg. 551
Yara, Ronald T., Sr. V.P.-Strategic Mktg. & Sec.--S3 Incorporated, Santa Clara, CA; *U.S. Public*, pg. 1415
Yarborough, W. Glen, V.P.--Allied Research Corporation, Vienna, VA; *U.S. Public*, pg. 48
Yardley, C., V.P.-Mktg.--The New Home Sewing Machine Co., Mahwah, NJ; *Int'l*, pg. 699
Yardley, James C., V.P.-Mktg. & Bus. Devel.--Southern Natural Gas Company, Birmingham, AL; *U.S. Public*, pg. 1485
Yardley, Johnathan, Dir.-Mktg.--Windsor Healthcare Ltd., Bracknell, United Kingdom; *Int'l*, pg. 199
Yarns, Terry, Dir.-Sls. & Mktg.--Art's-Way Manufacturing Co., Inc., Armstrong, IA; *U.S. Public*, pg. 136
Yarson, Donald D., V.P.-Mktg. & Sls.--The Liposome Company, Inc., Princeton, NJ; *U.S. Public*, pg. 1000
Yasharian, Carl, V.P.-Mktg.--Rockefeller Group Telecommunications Services, Inc., New York, NY; *Int'l*, pg. 873
Yashiro, Hiroyuki, Mgr.-Hub-Mfg.--Nemic-Lambda KK, Tokyo, Japan; *Int'l*, pg. 1242
Yasuba, Shoichi, Gen. Mgr.-Sls. & Mktg--Okuma Corporation, Niwa, Japan; *Int'l*, pg. 1000
Yates, Guy W., Sr. V.P.-Supply & Mktg.--Giant Industries Arizona, Inc., Scottsdale, AZ; *U.S. Public*, pg. 742
Yates, Isaac, V.P.-Mktg.--Iveco Trucks Of North America Inc., Bensalem, PA; *Int'l*, pg. 484
Yates, Isaac, V.P.-Strategic Mktg.--Jostens, Minneapolis, MN; *U.S. Public*, pg. 934

Yates, R.C., Dir.-Mktg. & Bus. Devel.--Moore Europe, Lausanne, Switzerland; *Int'l*, pg. 889
Yaw, William R., Jr., Sr. V.P.--Standard Federal Bank, Troy, MI; *Int'l*, pg. 10
Ydiainen, Hu, Dir.-Mktg.--Opel Oy, Espoo, Finland; *U.S. Public*, pg. 723
Yeager, Tracy, Dir.-Commun.--People's Choice TV Corp., Shelton, CT; *U.S. Public*, pg. 1274
Yeandel, Victor F., V.P.--Consolidated Products, Inc., Indianapolis, IN; *U.S. Public*, pg. 436
Yegani, Jody, Mgr.-Mktg.--Anixter Inc., Skokie, IL; *U.S. Public*, pg. 115
Yeldin, Mary, V.P.-Mktg.--Warner Bros. Consumer Products, Burbank, CA; *U.S. Public*, pg. 1610
Yelen, Dennis, V.P.-Mktg. & Adv.--Coats & Clark Inc., Greenville, SC; *Int'l*, pg. 300
Yelland, John, Mgr.-Mktg.--Hewlett-Packard Ltd., Bracknell, United Kingdom; *U.S. Public*, pg. 821
Yenkner, Charles E., Jr., V.P.-Sls. & Mktg.--Ney Dental International, Bloomfield, CT; *Int'l*, pg. 388
Yenkner, Chuck, Sr. V.P.-Sls. & Mktg.--Ney Dental International, Bloomfield, CT; *Int'l*, pg. 388
Yenochochick, Mary Anne, Mktg. Asst.--CSC, Ltd., Warren, OH; *U.S. Private*, pg. 924
Yeo, Jimmy, V.P.-Mktg.--Hong Fok Corporation Ltd., Singapore, Singapore; *Int'l*, pg. 635
Yevoli, Vince, Mgr.-Mktg. & Sls.-Lithium--Yardney Technical Products, Inc., Pawcatuck, CT; *U.S. Private*, pg. 376
Yglesias, Joe, V.P.-Mktg. & Sls.--Victory Refrigeration Co. LC, Cherry Hill, NJ; *U.S. Private*, pg. 1139
Yiatchos, Gary, Sr. V.P.-Mktg. & Sls. Promo.--The Bon Marche, Inc., Seattle, WA; *U.S. Public*, pg. 617
Ying, Ho Sau, Mgr.-Mktg. & Prod. Devel.--Tiger Medicals Ltd., Singapore, Singapore; *Int'l*, pg. 603
Yocom, Joel, Dir.-Mktg. & Sls.--Flexible Circuit Products Division, Methuen, MA; *U.S. Public*, pg. 1264
Yoder, Del, Dir.-Mktg.--Supreme Corporation, Goshen, IN; *U.S. Public*, pg. 1542
Yoho, Franklin H., Sr. V.P.-Mktg. & Gas Supply--Public Service Company of North Carolina, Inc., Gastonia, NC; *U.S. Public*, pg. 1340
Yokley, Edward, Dir.-Mktg.--Security Plastics, Inc., Hialeah, FL; *U.S. Private*, pg. 981
Yokokawa, Norio, Chief Exec. Officer & V.P.--Skylark Co., Ltd., Tokyo, Japan; *Int'l*, pg. 1262
Yokota, Sunao, Exec. V.P.-Domestic Mktg. & Sls. & Parts & Accessories--Mazda Motor Corporation, Hiroshima, Japan; *Int'l*, pg. 849
Yonavick, P.A., Gen. Mgr.-Mktg. Services--Carpenter Specialty Alloys Operations, Reading, PA; *U.S. Public*, pg. 307
Yonekura, Hidekazu, Sr. Mng. Dir.-Corp. Communication & Domestic Mktg. & Sls.--Mazda Motor Corporation, Hiroshima, Japan; *Int'l*, pg. 849
Yonekura, Shuji, Sr. V.P.-Sls. & Mktg.--Sanden International (U.S.A.), Inc., Wylie, TX; *Int'l*, pg. 1184
Yong, P.C., Mgr.-Mktg.--QT Optoelectronics, Sunnyvale, CA; *U.S. Private*, pg. 897
Yoon, Cheol-Gu, Mgr.--Ssangyong Motor Company, Seoul, Korea; *Int'l*, pg. 1292
York, Andrew, Dir.-Mktg.--Nicklaus Golf Company, L.C., West Palm Beach, FL; *U.S. Private*, pg. 799
York, Betsy, V.P.-Mktg.--Ennis Business Forms, Inc., Ennis, TX; *U.S. Public*, pg. 583
York, Brett, V.P.-Sls. & Mktg.--Hopple Plastics, Inc., Florence, KY; *U.S. Private*, pg. 538
Yoshikami, Sandy, V.P.-Mktg.--International Plastics Company, New York, NY; *U.S. Private*, pg. 571
Yost, Gary, Dir.-Mktg.--Valassis Communications, Inc., Livonia, MI; *U.S. Public*, pg. 1704
Yost, Roger W., V.P.-Adv. & Event Mktg.--Jantzen, Portland, OR; *U.S. Public*, pg. 1702
Youmans, Bruce, Mgr.-Mktg. Communications & Adv.--TDK Electronics Corporation, Port Washington, NY; *Int'l*, pg. 1336
Younanpour, Ailen, Asst. Corp. Sec.--Pacific Scientific Company, Newport Beach, CA; *U.S. Public*, pg. 1250
Young, Donald C., III, Dir.-Mktg.--Checkers Drive-In Restaurants, Inc., Clearwater, FL; *U.S. Public*, pg. 342
Young, Donald E., V.P.-Mktg. & Sls.--E.H. Titchener & Company, Binghamton, NY; *U.S. Private*, pg. 1089
Young, Donald W., Sr. V.P.-Mktg.--Willis Corroon Corp. of Northern Ohio, Cleveland, OH; *Int'l*, pg. 1506
Young, Edward S., Chm. Bd.--Ken-Mac Metals, Inc., Cleveland, OH; *Int'l*, pg. 1388
Young, Ellen, Sr. Mgr.-Mktg., New Prods.--The United States Playing Card Company, Cincinnati, OH; *U.S. Private*, pg. 1125
Young, Galen, Mgr.-Mktg.--FRL, Inc., Los Banos, CA; *U.S. Public*, pg. 396
Young, James H., Chief Oper. Officer & Exec. V.P.--Reactive Metals & Alloys Corporation (REMACOR), West Pittsburg, PA; *U.S. Private*, pg. 913
Young, Joseph, V.P.-Sls. & Mktg./North America--Gundle/SLT Environmental, Inc., Houston, TX; *U.S. Public*, pg. 769
Young, Mark, Dir.-Mktg.--Ruby Tuesday, Inc., Mobile, AL; *U.S. Public*, pg. 1411
Young, Mark, Dir.-Mktg.--Ruby Tuesday Restaurants, Mobile, AL; *U.S. Public*, pg. 1412
Young, R. James, V.P.-Customer Mktg.--The Allstate Corporation, Northbrook, IL; *U.S. Public*, pg. 55
Young, Renee, Admin. Asst.-Mktg.--Clairson International Corp., Ocala, FL; *U.S. Public*, pg. 575
Young, Ryan, Dir.-Mktg.--Daw Technologies, Inc., Salt Lake City, UT; *U.S. Public*, pg. 489
Younkin, Timothy D., Sr. V.P. & Chief Mktg. Officer--Brown-Forman Beverages Worldwide, Louisville, KY; *U.S. Public*, pg. 261
Ypma, John, V.P.-Mktg.--AlliedSignal, Automotive Aftermarket, Rumford, RI; *U.S. Public*, pg. 51
Yu, Diane, Mgr.-Mktg.--Pip Printing, Agoura Hills, CA; *U.S. Private*, pg. 423
Yudis, Charles S., Exec. V.P.-Sls. & Mktg.--Capp, Inc., Clifton Heights, PA; *U.S. Private*, pg. 207
Yung, Steve, V.P.-Mktg./McCain Foods (Canada)--McCain Foods Limited, Florenceville, Canada; *Int'l*, pg. 850
Yuracko, Ellen, Sr. V.P.-Mktg. & Sec.--Gerber Life Insurance Co., White Plains, NY; *Int'l*, pg. 973
Yurcisin, John, Mgr.-Mktg.--Hyatt International Corporation, Chicago, IL; *U.S. Private*, pg. 551
Yurechko, Olga, V.P.-Mktg.--Hampshire Designers Inc., Anderson, SC; *U.S. Public*, pg. 778
Yurechko, Olga, V.P.-Mktg.--Designers Knitting Mills, New York, NY; *U.S. Public*, pg. 778
Yvan, Jo, V.P.-Sls. & Mktg.--Pride Products, Inc., Elizabeth, NJ; *U.S. Private*, pg. 883
Zabel, Lutz, Mgr.-Mktg. Indus. Adhesives--Sika Finanz AG, Baar, Switzerland; *Int'l*, pg. 1248
Zabetakis, David B., Asst. V.P.-Market Devel.--Unitil Corporation, Hampton, NH; *U.S. Public*, pg. 1692
Zabrocky, Stanley, Mgr.-Mktg. Services--Enthone-OMI, Inc., West Haven, CT; *U.S. Public*, pg. 138
Zaccaria, Joe, Dir.-Mktg. Communications--Leviton Mfg. Co., Inc., Little Neck, NY; *U.S. Private*, pg. 663
Zachwieja, Pat, V.P.-Mktg. & Plng.--Horizon Air Industries, Seattle, WA; *U.S. Public*, pg. 35
Zade, Larry, Gen. Mgr. & Dir.-Sls. & Mktg.-Wood Working--Wisconsin Automated Machinery Corp., Oshkosh, WI; *U.S. Private*, pg. 1184
Zagar, Alain, Mgr.-Mktg.--Schneider Group, Mississauga, Canada; *Int'l*, pg. 1208
Zager, Tom V., Mgr.-Sls. & Mktg.--Metron Steel Corp., Chicago, IL; *U.S. Private*, pg. 736
Zakzeski, Jim, V.P.-Mktg.--Cubix Corporation, Carson City, NV; *U.S. Private*, pg. 294
Zaldavar, Michael, V.P.-Sls. & Mktg.--Whessoe Varec, Cypress, CA; *Int'l*, pg. 1498
Zalewski, Gerald P., Mgr.-Sls. & Mktg.--Ruhle Companies, Inc., Valhalla, NY; *U.S. Private*, pg. 950
Zalewski, Gerald P., Mgr.-Sls. & Mktg.--Farrand Controls, Valhalla, NY; *U.S. Private*, pg. 951
Zall, Raymond F., V.P.-Mktg.--HDS Services, Farmington Hills, MI; *U.S. Private*, pg. 490
Zaloum, John, Dir.-Mktg.--Strombecker Corporation, Chicago, IL; *U.S. Private*, pg. 1047
Zamarin, Dave, V.P.-Mktg.--Showboat, Incorporated, Las Vegas, NV; *U.S. Public*, pg. 1469
Zambelli, Jean-Claude, V.P.-Sls. & Mktg.--Semtech Corporation, Newbury Park, CA; *U.S. Public*, pg. 1456
Zambini, Jerry, Dir.-Sls. & Mktg.--Rolland Inc., Saint-Jerome, Canada; *Int'l*, pg. 273
Zamora, Elan, Dir.-Mktg.--Barnes & Noble Direct, Rockleigh, NJ; *U.S. Public*, pg. 189
Zampini, Gerry, Dir.-Mktg.--Rolland Inc., Fine Papers Division, Saint-Jerome, Canada; *Int'l*, pg. 274
Zandamme, Etienne, Sr. V.P.-Mktg.--AGFA EPS Division, Wilmington, MA; *Int'l*, pg. 172
Zander, Stanley R., Dir.-Mktg.--Zander's Creamery Inc., Cross Plains, WI; *U.S. Private*, pg. 1203
Zandron, Daniel D., V.P.-Mktg.--Badger Meter Utility Div., Milwaukee, WI; *U.S. Public*, pg. 165
Zane, Barry, Mgr.-Market Devel.--PRS, Inc., Leicester, NY; *U.S. Public*, pg. 282
Zangardi, J. Michael, Dir.-Sls. & Mktg.--Simplex Industries, Inc., Scranton, PA; *U.S. Private*, pg. 1001
Zanitsch, Jerry, Sr. V.P.-Mktg.--New World Entertainment, Inc., Los Angeles, CA; *Int'l*, pg. 926
Zanzal, Andrew, Dir.-Mktg.--Photronics, Inc., Brookfield, CT; *U.S. Public*, pg. 1293
Zapciz, David, Dir.-Mktg. Commun.--The First Years Inc., Avon, MA; *U.S. Public*, pg. 642
Zarabara, Connie, Mgr.-Mktg. Svcs.--Hunt Corporation, Philadelphia, PA; *U.S. Public*, pg. 848
Zarenkim, Lior, Exec. V.P.-Mktg. & Customer Rels.--The Israel Electric Corporation Ltd., Haifa, Israel; *Int'l*, pg. 690
Zaring, John, Dir.-Mktg.--Turner Construction Co., Cincinnati, OH; *U.S. Public*, pg. 1645
Zaroda, Jim, Mgr.-Mktg.--Emcee Broadcast Products, Inc., White Haven, PA; *U.S. Public*, pg. 570
Zarookian, Paul A., Sr. V.P.-Sls. & Mktg.--A.I. Credit Corp., New York, NY; *U.S. Public*, pg. 85
Zarrella, Ronald L., V.P. & Grp. Exec.-North American Sls., Svc. & Mktg.--General Motors Corporation, Detroit, MI; *U.S. Public*, pg. 718
Zastrow, William L., Div. V.P.-Imaging Business Unit--Data General Corporation, Westborough, MA; *U.S. Public*, pg. 485
Zatz, Cheryl, Mgr.-Mktg.--Hammacher, Schlemmer & Co., Inc., Chicago, IL; *U.S. Private*, pg. 497
Zavadsky, Tom, Exec. V.P.-Sls. & Mktg.--Noel Olson Group, Stevens Point, WI; *U.S. Private*, pg. 800
Zebarth, Mike, V.P.-Sls. & Mktg.--Packard BioScience Company, Meriden, CT; *U.S. Private*, pg. 833
Zeckmeister, Rick, Dir.-Mktg.--Briggs & Stratton Corporation, Wauwatosa, WI; *U.S. Public*, pg. 252
Zefares, Camille, Dir.-Mktg. Services--Litton Applied Technology, San Jose, CA; *U.S. Public*, pg. 1003
Zehr, Dwain, Mgr.-Mktg.--IEC Arab Alabama Operations, Arab, AL; *U.S. Public*, pg. 855
Zeidler, Don, Mgr.-Dir. Mktg. Programs--W. Atlee Burpee Co., Warminster, PA; *U.S. Private*, pg. 187
Zeilman, Harold, Dir.-Sls. & Industrial Mktg.--Cincinnati Sub-Zero Products, Inc., Cincinnati, OH; *U.S. Private*, pg. 240
Zeiner, Wendy, Dir.-Corp. Mktg.--Open Market, Inc., Burlington, MA; *U.S. Public*, pg. 1226
Zelencik, Stephen, Chief Mktg. Exec. & Sr. V.P.--Advanced Micro Devices, Inc., Sunnyvale, CA; *U.S. Public*, pg. 21
Zemick, M., Exec. V.P.-Sls. & Mktg.--Industrial Steel & Wire Company, Chicago, IL; *U.S. Private*, pg. 561
Zemke, D.E., Sr. V.P.-Sls. & Mktg.--Cincinnati Bell Telephone, Cincinnati, OH; *U.S. Public*, pg. 367
Zemmin, Richard W., V.P.-Mktg. & Sls.--MichCon, Detroit, MI; *U.S. Public*, pg. 1025
Zenner, Nico, Asst. Gen. Mgr.--Sabena Belgian World Airlines, Manhasset, NY; *Int'l*, pg. 1168
Zepp, Alison, Dir.-Mktg. Commun.--W.W. Grainger, Inc., Lincolnshire, IL; *U.S. Public*, pg. 758
Zeratsky, J. Bur, Mgr.-Sls. & Mktg.--The Shaler Company, Waupun, WI; *U.S. Private*, pg. 786
Zerbe, Mark A., Exec. V.P.--Kent Electronics Corp., Houston, TX; *U.S. Public*, pg. 951
Zerkus, Marian, Mgr.-Residential Mktg.--Oglethorpe Power Corp., Tucker, GA; *U.S. Private*, pg. 812
Zerrer, Jeff, Sr. V.P.-Mktg.--American Finance Group, Inc., Boston, MA; *U.S. Public*, pg. 1241
Zetsche, Dieter, Dr., Dir.-Sls. & Mktg.--Daimler-Benz Aktiengesellschaft, Stuttgart, Germany; *Int'l*, pg. 366
Zibel, Mike, V.P.-Mktg.--Bob's Stores, Inc., Meriden, CT; *U.S. Public*, pg. 287
Zibits, Michael, Mgr.-Mkt.-Coating--Troy Corporation, Florham Park, NJ; *U.S. Private*, pg. 1105
Zickuhr, Keith, Sr. V.P.-Mktg.--Magna Group, Inc., Saint Louis, MO; *U.S. Public*, pg. 1037
Zieger, Henning, Dir.-Mktg. & Adv.--Interbath, Inc., City of Industry, CA; *U.S. Private*, pg. 566
Ziegler, Mike, V.P.-Mktg.--AGA Gas, Inc., Independence, OH; *Int'l*, pg. 13
Ziegler, Read, Dir.-Mktg.--MCI Systemhouse, Atlanta, GA; *U.S. Public*, pg. 1024
Zielfelt, Hennk, Dir.-Commercial Perfume--L'Oreal Parfumerie, Brussels, Belgium; *Int'l*, pg. 819
Zielinski, Bella P., Dir.-Mktg. Communications--The Inland Group, Inc., Oak Brook, IL; *U.S. Private*, pg. 564
Zielinski, Mark, Dir.Mktg.--Dunn-Edwards Corporation, Los Angeles, CA; *U.S. Private*, pg. 347
Zielinski, Pat, Dir.-Mktg.--CompuDyne Corporation, Willimantic, CT; *U.S. Public*, pg. 419
Zielinski, Ronald A., V.P.-Mktg./Intl. & Military--Dassault Falcon Jet Corp., South Hackensack, NJ; *Int'l*, pg. 383
Zielke, Bill, V.P.-Mktg.--Hardware Wholesalers, Inc., Fort Wayne, IN; *U.S. Private*, pg. 502
Ziering, Marilyn, V.P.-Mktg. Communications & Sec.--Diagnostic Products Corporation, Los Angeles, CA; *U.S. Public*, pg. 505
Zierten, Mark W., Dir.-Mktg.--Georgia Casualty & Surety Company, Atlanta, GA; *U.S. Public*, pg. 143
Zimmer, D., Dir.-Mktg.--Calberson, Paris, France; *Int'l*, pg. 1163
Zimmer, Tim, Mgr.-Mktg. & Sls.--Atchison/St. Joe Division, Atchison, KS; *U.S. Public*, pg. 142
Zimmerman, Beth, Admin. Asst.-Mktg.--Pioneer Hi-Bred International, Inc., Des Moines, IA; *U.S. Public*, pg. 1298
Zimmerman, Dale, Mgr.-Mktg.--Plains Petroleum Operating Co., Lakewood, CO; *U.S. Public*, pg. 191
Zimmerman, Ken, V.P.-Sls. & Mktg.--Alumacraft Boat Co., Saint Peter, MN; *U.S. Private*, pg. 1088
Zimmerman, Kent, Sr. V.P.-Mktg.--Kampgrounds of America, Inc., Billings, MT; *U.S. Private*, pg. 603
Zimmerman, Laurie, Mgr.-Mktg. Svcs.--A.H. Hoffman, Inc., Landisville, PA; *U.S. Private*, pg. 532
Zimmerman, Michael, Group Mgr.-Mktg.-Automotive Products--First Brands Corporation, Danbury, CT; *U.S. Public*, pg. 626
Zimmerman, Michael, Group Mgr.-Mktg./Automotive Products--STP Corporation, Danbury, CT; *U.S. Public*, pg. 627
Zimmerman, Ron, Sr. V.P.-Mktg. & Bus. Devel.--Leach International, Buena Park, CA; *U.S. Private*, pg. 655
Zimmermann, Don, V.P.-Opers.--Ferguson Manufacturing & Equipment Company, Inc., Dallas, TX; *U.S. Private*, pg. 401
Zimmermann, Keith, Jr., V.P.-Sls.--Whitney Blake Company of Vermont, Inc., Bellows Falls, VT; *U.S. Private*, pg. 148
Zimmermann, Steve, Mgr.-Mktg. Communications--Rockwell Automation, Milwaukee, WI; *U.S. Public*, pg. 1397
Zimmet, Jane, Dir.-Mktg.--Colfax Envelope Corporation, Buffalo Grove, IL; *U.S. Private*, pg. 252
Zindel, Al, V.P.-Sls. & Mktg.--Woolrich, Inc., Woolrich, PA; *U.S. Private*, pg. 1188
Zingale, Anthony, Sr. V.P.-Worlwide Mktg.--Cadence Design Systems, Inc., San Jose, CA; *U.S. Public*, pg. 290
Zinke, Bill, Dir.-Brand Mktg.--Baskin-Robbins Incorporated, Glendale, CA; *Int'l*, pg. 63
Zinone, Paul, Dir.-Sls.--S & P Comstock, Harrison, NY; *U.S. Public*, pg. 1071
Zinsou, Lionel, Sr. V.P.-Pasta & Ready-to-Serve Dishes Div.--Danone Group, Paris, France; *Int'l*, pg. 379
Zinter, Barb, Mgr.-Mktg. Services--Strippit, Inc., Akron, NY; *U.S. Public*, pg. 862
Zirkle, Steven, Gen. Mgr.-Sales--Eaton Corporation, Engine Components Division, Marshall, MI; *U.S. Public*, pg. 556
Ziskin, Bruce, V.P.-Mktg. & Mdsg.--Aid Auto Stores, Inc., Westbury, NY; *U.S. Public*, pg. 29
Zitel, Michelle, Mgr.-Mktg. Communications--CEM Corporation, Matthews, NC; *U.S. Public*, pg. 277
Zitzewitz, W.V., Mgr.-Plant Protection Mktg.--Agrolinz Melamin GmbH, Lienz, Austria; *Int'l*, pg. 356
Zlocki, Stan, Dir.-Mktg.--Farm Stores, Miami, FL; *U.S. Private*, pg. 394
Zlotnik, Arnold, Pres.--Surco Products, Inc., Pittsburgh, PA; *U.S. Private*, pg. 1056
Zlotolow, Jonathan, Mktg. Mgr.--MRI UK, London, United Kingdom; *U.S. Private*, pg. 727
Zobel, Kim, Mgr.-Customer Svcs., Sls. & Mktg.--Midwest Industries, Inc., Ida Grove, IA; *U.S. Private*, pg. 744
Zobel, Mike, Dir.-Sls. & Mktg.--Vacu-Dry Company, Sebastopol, CA; *U.S. Public*, pg. 1704
Zoehfeld, Robert, Dir.-Corp. Mktg.--Howe Furniture Corporation, Trumbull, CT; *U.S. Private*, pg. 543
Zolan, John, Dir.-Mktg.--Kohler Co. Generator Div., Sheboygan, WI; *U.S. Private*, pg. 630
Zona, Toni, Mktg. Asst.--Camillus Cutlery Co., Camillus, NY; *U.S. Private*, pg. 203
Zonars, S., V.P.-Mktg.--Dispatch Consumer Services, Westerville, OH; *U.S. Private*, pg. 335
Zook, John, Dir.-Mktg.--Atmos Energy Corporation, Dallas, TX; *U.S. Public*, pg. 145
Zook, Tony, V.P.-Mktg.--Astra USA, Inc., Westborough, MA; *Int'l*, pg. 93

Zoral, Mike, Dir.-Mktg.--M-I L.L.C., Houston, TX; *U.S. Public, pg. 776*
Zoukis, Paul, Sr. V.P.-Mktg. & Sls.--Hogan Systems, Inc., Dallas, TX; *U.S. Public*, pg. 422
Zove, Janet, Coord.-Mktg.--EMCOR Group, Inc., Norwalk, CT; *U.S. Public*, pg. 571
Zubrod, Stephen, V.P.-Mktg.--Baker's Supermarkets, Inc., Omaha, NE; *U.S. Public*, pg. 652
Zuch, Sallie F., V.P.-Mktg. & Oper.--Showtime Networks Inc., New York, NY; *U.S. Private*, pg. 779
Zucht, Earle, Sr. V.P.-Semiconductor Mktg.--Wyle Electronics, Irvine, CA; *Int'l*, pg. 1457
Zucker, Hans, Sr. V.P. & Mktg. Services Dir.--Korey, Kay & Partners, New York, NY; *U.S. Private*, pg. 632
Zugschwert, John F., V.P.-Govt. Mktg.--Textron Inc., Providence, RI; *U.S. Public*, pg. 1588
Zuissler, Susan, Mgr.-Mktg. Commun.--Morrison Health Care Inc., Smyrna, GA; *U.S. Public*, pg. 1133
Zukley, Sharon, Mgr.-Mktg. Communications--TEC Incorporated, Palatine, IL; *U.S. Public*, pg. 687
Zurcher, Frederic, V.P.-Mktg.--Hamilton Lamp Corp., North Kansas City, MO; *U.S. Public*, pg. 1354
Zwei, Doug, Dir.-Mktg.--Spectris Technologies, Inc., Decatur, GA; *Int'l*, pg. 14
Zwicker, Bruce, V.P.-Mktg. & Sls.--Millennium Inorganic Chemicals, Hunt Valley, MD; *Int'l*, pg. 593
Zyman, Sergio, Chief Mktg. Officer & Sr. V.P.--The Coca-Cola Company, Atlanta, GA; *U.S. Public*, pg. 392
Zyngier, Leonildo, Dir.-Sls. & Mktg.--Schwitzer, Inc., Indianapolis, IN; *U.S. Public*, pg. 968

PLANNING & DEVELOPMENT

Abshire, Richard B., V.P.-Fin. & Treas.--Adams Resources & Energy, Inc., Houston, TX; *U.S. Public*, pg. 18
Abzug, Barry M., V.P. & Dir.-Bus. Devel.--ITT Aerospace/Communications Div., Fort Wayne, IN; *U.S. Public*, pg. 859
Ackerman, Roy A., Chief Exec. Officer--Astre Corporate Group, Alexandria, VA; *U.S. Private*, pg. 93
Adams, David, V.P.-Training & Devel.--Barry's Jewelers, Inc., Monrovia, CA; *U.S. Public*, pg. 192
Adams, George F., V.P.-Bus. Devel.--Phoenix Technologies Ltd., San Jose, CA; *U.S. Public*, pg. 1292
Adams, John, Sr. V.P.-Prod. Plng. & Devel.--Hatteras Yachts, New Bern, NC; *U.S. Private*, pg. 447
Adams, John B., V.P.-Corp. Devel.--American Home Products Corporation, Madison, NJ; *U.S. Public*, pg. 79
Adams, K.C., Gen. Mgr.-Plng.--The Broken Hill Proprietary Company Limited, Melbourne, Australia; *Int'l*, pg. 223
Adams, Richard F., Jr., V.P.-Bus. Plng. & Analysis--AutoZone, Inc., Memphis, TN; *U.S. Public*, pg. 150
Adams, Robert E., Chief Oper. Officer & Exec. V.P.--Spencer Companies Inc., Huntsville, AL; *U.S. Private*, pg. 1024
Aeilli, Karen, Dir.-Plng. & Admin.--DuBois Chemicals, Cincinnati, OH; *Int'l*, pg. 1437
Agan, Gordan, V.P. & Strategic Plng. Dir.--Carat ICG, Los Angeles, CA; *U.S. Private*, pg. 207
Agathen, Paul A., Sr. V.P.-Energy Supply Services--AmerenUE, Saint Louis, MO; *U.S. Public*, pg. 66
Agnese, Carlos E., Exec. V.P.-Bus. Devel., Mktg., Estimating & Contract Admin.--Norfolk Shipbuilding & Drydock Corporation, Norfolk, VA; *U.S. Private*, pg. 802
Ahart, J.F., Chief Fin. Officer, V.P., Treas. & Sec.--Powell Industries, Inc., Houston, TX; *U.S. Public*, pg. 1319
Ahlborn, Brian, V.P.-Strategic Plng.--A.G. Simpson Co. Limited, Scarborough, Canada; *Int'l*, pg. 1252
Aho, Timothy, Sr. V.P.-Devel.--Prime Hospitality Corp., Fairfield, NJ; *U.S. Public*, pg. 1326
Ahrenhoerstrabaellmen , Dennis, Dir.-Bus. Devel.--The Western Group, Saint Louis, MO; *U.S. Private*, pg. 1165
Airikkala, Reino, Mgr.-Corp. Plng.--Kemira Oy, Helsinki, Finland; *Int'l*, pg. 727
Aitken, Chris, Dir.-Devl. Funding & Environment--Scottish Enterprise, Glasgow, United Kingdom; *Int'l*, pg. 1212
Aizawa, Hiroshi, Chief Fin. Officer & Div. Mgr.--Sumitomo Bank of California, San Francisco, CA; *Int'l*, pg. 1309
Ajram, Elie, Sr. V.P.-Strategic Plng.--Shoppers Drug Mart, Ltd., Toronto, Canada; *Int'l*, pg. 112
Albrecht, Steven, Chm. Bd., Pres. & Chief Exec. Officer--The Fred W. Albrecht Grocery Co., Akron, OH; *U.S. Private*, pg. 32
Alcaro, Len, Mgr.-Sls. Training--Jaguar Cars, Mahwah, NJ; *U.S. Public*, pg. 664
Alepin, Linda T., V.P.-Strategic Plng.--Amdahl Corporation, Sunnyvale, CA; *Int'l*, pg. 527
Alexander, I.R., Chief Fin. Officer & Exec. V.P.--Purina Mills, Inc., Saint Louis, MO; *U.S. Private*, pg. 895
Alexander, Leigh, Sr. V.P.-Mktg. & Bus. Devel.--Paging Network, Inc., Plano, TX; *U.S. Public*, pg. 1252
Alexander, Mark A., V.P.-Aquisitions & Corp. Devel.--Hanson North America, Woodbridge, NJ; *Int'l*, pg. 593
Aley, Paul N., Pres. & Chief Exec. Officer--National Machinery, Tiffin, OH; *U.S. Private*, pg. 785
Alford, Jim D., V.P.-Corp. Devel.--Pace Industries, Inc., Fayetteville, AR; *U.S. Public*, pg. 986
Allen, Bob D., Pres. & Chief Exec. Officer--Consolidated-Tomoka Land Co., Daytona Beach, FL; *U.S. Public*, pg. 437
Allen, Ed, V.P.-Strategic Communications--Reliance Electric, Cleveland, OH; *U.S. Public*, pg. 1397
Allen, J., Sec.--Babcock International Group PLC, Amersham, United Kingdom; *Int'l*, pg. 130
Allen, Jerry M., V.P.-Telephone Grp., Fin. & Plng.--Century Telephone Enterprises, Inc., Monroe, LA; *U.S. Public*, pg. 329
Allen, Kristina, Mng. Partner, Strategic Plng. Dir. & Media Delr.--Kovel Kresser & Partners, Santa Monica, CA; *U.S. Private*, pg. 634
Allen, Steve, Mgr.-Mkt. Devel.--Subaru Northwest Region, Portland, OR; *Int'l*, pg. 523
Allen, Thomas F., Business Devel. Officer--Southwest Marketing-Dallas Business Center, Dallas, TX; *U.S. Public*, pg. 650
Aller, Alfredo Vallina, Dir.-Devel. & Diversified--Hulleras Del Norte, S.A. (HUNOSA), Asturias, Spain; *Int'l*, pg. 639
Aller, Robert L., Sr. V.P.-Fin.--Loctite Corporation, Rocky Hill, CT; *Int'l*, pg. 611
Alligood, David L., V.P.-Engrng. & Plng.--Welded Tube, Chicago, IL; *Int'l*, pg. 101
Alliot, Jean, V.P.-Plng. & Economics--Elf Aquitane, Paris, France; *Int'l*, pg. 444
Allison, Elizabeth K., Sr. V.P.-Planning & Dev.--McGraw-Hill Publications Services Group, New York, NY; *U.S. Public*, *pg. 1071*
Allonen, Heikki, Sr. V.P.-Plng. Devel.--Metra Corporation, Helsinki, Finland; *Int'l*, pg. 862
Allschul, Alfred S., Chief Fin. Officer & V.P.-Fin. & Plng.--Amtrak-National Railroad Passenger Corp., Washington, DC; *U.S. Private*, pg. 68
Allweiss, Allan, Sr. Bus. Devel. Officer--Central Marketing-Chicago Business Center, Chicago, IL; *U.S. Public*, pg. 649
Alperi, Eero, Dir.-Plng. & Devel.--Amer Group Ltd., Helsinki, Finland; *Int'l*, pg. 72
Alperin, Robert P., V.P.-Bus. Devel.--Arch Communications Group, Inc., Westborough, MA; *U.S. Public*, pg. 127
Alvarez, Antonio C., Chm. Bd. & Pres.--Long MFG. NC, Inc., Tarboro, NC; *U.S. Private*, pg. 674
Alvarez, William, V.P.-Branch Banking Bus. Devel.--Firstbank Puerto Rico, Santurce, PR; *U.S. Public*, pg. 644
Amann, Julie, V.P.--Dain Rauscher Corporation, Minneapolis, MN; *U.S. Public*, pg. 476
Ambrus, Jozsef, Sr. V.P.-Strategic Plng.--TVX Gold Inc., Toronto, Canada; *Int'l*, pg. 1345
Ames, Richard S., Chm. Bd., Pres. & Chief Exec. Officer--Command Plastic Corporation, Akron, OH; *U.S. Private*, pg. 257
Amira, Jorge, Dir.-Plng.--Andina Division, Los Andes, Chile; *Int'l*, pg. 302
Anderson, Bruce K., Grp. Dir.-Fin. & Plng.--Varity Perkins, Peterborough, United Kingdom; *Int'l*, pg. 820
Anderson, Gerry, V.P.-Plng.--Sara Lee Bakery, Chicago, IL; *U.S. Public*, pg. 1433
Anderson, J.I.W., Dir.-Corp. Devel. & Medical Prods.--Unilever N.V., Rotterdam, Netherlands; *Int'l*, pg. 1434
Anderson, R.J., V.P.-Plng.--Thomas Publishing Company, New York, NY; *U.S. Private*, pg. 1082
Anderson, Robert E., III, Exec. V.P.-Plng. & Devel.--Owens & Minor Inc., Glen Allen, VA; *U.S. Public*, pg. 1236
Andreani, Joseph L., V.P.-New Bus. Devel.--Reflectone, Inc., Tampa, FL; *Int'l*, pg. 218
Andretta, Vincent J., Pres., Chief Exec. Officer & Treas.--Colony Liquor Distributors, Inc., Kingston, NY; *U.S. Private*, pg. 254
Andrews, Duane P., Exec. V.P.-Corp. Devel.--Science Applications International Corp., San Diego, CA; *U.S. Private*, pg. 975
Angeles, Lourdes C., V.P.-Corp. Plng.--Philippine Airlines, Inc., Manila, Philippines; *Int'l*, pg. 1050
Angelini, Carlo Giuseppe, Dir.-Budget & Controller--Istituto Mobiliare Italiano, Rome, Italy; *Int'l*, pg. 692
Angelo, Ray, Pres.--Angelo Brothers Co., Philadelphia, PA; *U.S. Private*, pg. 74
Annes, Michael D., V.P.-Bus. Devel./Counsel Law--The Quaker Oats Company, Chicago, IL; *U.S. Public*, pg. 1347
Anness, Lisa, V.P.-Plng.--Atlantic Gulf Communities Corporation, Miami, FL; *U.S. Public*, pg. 144
Anthony, James M., Sr. Dir.-Plng. & Analysis--Checkers Drive-In Restaurants, Inc., Clearwater, FL; *U.S. Public*, pg. 342
Antink, Grant S., Pres. & Chief Exec. Officer--Technical Image Products, Inc./DGI, Elk Grove Village, IL; *U.S. Private*, pg. 1072
Antonazzo, Nicholas O., Esq., Exec. V.P.-Real Estate Devel.--Crown American Realty Trust, Johnstown, PA; *U.S. Public*, pg. 461
Aquino, Ianthe, Sr. Asst. V.P.-Corp. Plng. & Devel.--Philippine Airlines, Inc., Manila, Philippines; *Int'l*, pg. 1050
Arango, Carlos Felipe, Bus. Devel. & Info.--Sancho S.A., Bogota, Colombia; *U.S. Public*, pg. 1422
Arikan, Necati, Pres.-Corp. Plng. Grp.--Koc Holding A.S., Istanbul, Turkey; *Int'l*, pg. 741
Armstrong, Robert J., V.P.-Design & Construction--Insight Health Services Corp., Newport Beach, CA; *U.S. Public*, pg. 880
Armstrong, Theodore M., Chief Fin. Officer & Sr. V.P.-Fin. & Admin.--Angelica Corporation, Chesterfield, MO; *U.S. Public*, pg. 113
Arnold, Richard E., V.P. & Dir.-Bus. Devel.--SmithKline Beecham Consumer Healthcare, U.S., Pittsburgh, PA; *Int'l*, pg. 1264
Arnskov, Thorkil M., Mgr.-Fin. & Plng.--GN Great Northern Telegraph Company, Copenhagen, Denmark; *Int'l*, pg. 536
Arone, Anne, Sr. V.P.-Corp. Devel.--EdperBrascan Corporation, Toronto, Canada; *Int'l*, pg. 433
Aronson, Lewis, Sr. V.P.-Org. Devel. & Strategic Plng.--Bush Industries Inc., Jamestown, NY; *U.S. Public*, pg. 270
Aronson, Louis V., II, Pres. & Chief Exec. Officer--Ronson Corporation, Somerset, NJ; *U.S. Public*, pg. 1405
Arpey, Gerard J., Chief Fin. Officer & Sr. V.P.--AMR Corporation, Fort Worth, TX; *U.S. Public*, pg. 9
Arriaga, Gloria, Mgr.-Corp. Plng.--Y.P.F., S.A., Buenos Aires, Argentina; *Int'l*, pg. 1515
Arvantinos, S.C., Sr. V.P. & Treas.--Hope's Architectural Products Inc., Jamestown, NY; *U.S. Private*, pg. 538
Asad, Mohammed Khalid, Prod. Devel. Mgr.--Utell International-United Arab Emirates, Dubai, United Arab Emirates; *Int'l*, pg. 1099
Asch, Peter, Pres. & Chief Exec. Officer--Twincraft, Inc., Winooski, VT; *U.S. Private*, pg. 1111
Asch, Robert, Chm. Bd.--Twincraft, Inc., Winooski, VT; *U.S. Private*, pg. 1111
Ashby, Alan, Dir.-Bus. Devel.--Missiles & Space Division, Huntsville, AL; *U.S. Public*, pg. 241
Askar, Ralph, V.P.-Franchise Devel.--Mail Boxes Etc. USA, San Diego, CA; *U.S. Public*, pg. 1687
Askins, Steve, Mgr.-Bus. Devel.--John Crane Polymer Division, Abingdon, United Kingdom; *Int'l*, pg. 1338
Asshauer, Juergen, Dr., Dir.-Devel.--AgrEvo GmbH, Berlin, Germany; *Int'l*, pg. 624
Asteljoki, Jussi, Sr. V.P.-Res. & Devel.--Outokumpu Oyj, Espoo, Finland; *Int'l*, pg. 1015
Astolfi, Jose, Mgr.-Bus. Devel.--Y.P.F., S.A., Buenos Aires, Argentina; *Int'l*, pg. 1515
Aston, R.C.M., Dir.-Strategy--NatWest U.K., London, United Kingdom; *Int'l*, pg. 910
Astrom, Hakan, Sr. V.P.-Strategic Plng. & Investor Rels.--Pharmacia & Upjohn, Inc., Windsor, United Kingdom; *Int'l*, pg. 1047
Atic, Esadeta, Div. V.P.-MIO Planning--The Bon Marche, Inc., Seattle, WA; *U.S. Public*, pg. 617
Atkin, Douglas, Exec. V.P. & Plng. Dir.--Wells BDDP, Inc., New York, NY; *Int'l*, pg. 117
Atwood, Robert T., Chief Fin. Officer & Exec. V.P.--First Union Corporation, Charlotte, NC; *U.S. Public*, pg. 639
Aubin, Christian, Sr. Exec. V.P.-Strategy, Acctg., Control & Strategy--Banque Nationale de Paris, Paris, France; *Int'l*, *pg. 163*
Augurt, Dr. Tom, V.P.-Product Plng. & Devel.--Propper Manufacturing Co., Inc., Long Island City, NY; *U.S. Private*, pg. 891
Austriaco, Rogelio C., V.P.-Network Plng. & Devel.--Philippine Long Distance Telephone Company, Manila, Philippines; *Int'l*, pg. 1051
Averett, Devron, Sr. V.P.-Res. & Devel.--ICN Pharmaceuticals, Inc., Costa Mesa, CA; *U.S. Public*, pg. 853
Avery, James R., Exec. V.P.-Opers. Plng. & Control--The Stroh Brewery Company, Detroit, MI; *U.S. Private*, pg. 1047
Ayer, William S., V.P.-Mktg. & Plng.--Alaska Air Group, Inc., Seattle, WA; *U.S. Public*, pg. 35
Ayers, Jonathan W., V.P.-Strategic Plng.--United Technologies Corporation, Hartford, CT; *U.S. Public*, pg. 1689
Ayres, John E., Exec. V.P.-Bus. Devel.--GZA GeoEnvironmental Technologies, Inc., Newton, MA; *U.S.* Public, pg. 697
Azuma, Shuji, Gen. Mgr.-Bus. Plng. & Promo. Div. & Dir.--The Nanto Bank, Ltd., Nara, Japan; *Int'l*, pg. 905
Bachman, Jay S., Sr. V.P., Treas. & Mgr.-Corp. Devel.--First Security Corporation, Salt Lake City, UT; *U.S. Public*, pg. 637
Back, Gregory, Exec. V.P.-Corp. Plng. & Devel.--American Business Information, Inc., Omaha, NE; *U.S. Public*, pg. 69
Backeland, Gerald H., V.P.-Plng. & Devel.--Westcoast Energy Inc., Vancouver, Canada; *Int'l*, pg. 1492
Backer, Richard I., Exec. V.P.-Devel. & Asst. Sec.--Carlyle & Co. Jewelers, Greensboro, NC; *U.S. Private*, pg. 213
Bacon, John W., V.P.-Plng. & Bus. Devel.--Potlatch Corporation, Spokane, WA; *U.S. Public*, pg. 1318
Badagliacca, Mark, Sr. V.P.-Plng.--Paramount Pictures Corporation, Los Angeles, CA; *U.S. Private*, pg. 776
Bader, Burke B., Pres.--Bader & Co., Ipava, IL; *U.S. Private, pg. 110*
Bagorro, Joaquim A.R., Sr. Mgr.-Plng. & Acctg.--Caixa Geral de Depositos, Lisbon, Portugal; *Int'l*, pg. 250
Bagwe, Suhas, V.P.-Strategic Plng. & Bus. Devel.--EXAR Corporation, Fremont, CA; *U.S. Public*, pg. 597
Bailey, Don S., Mgr.-Corp. Devel.--Marley PLC, Sevenoaks, United Kingdom; *Int'l*, pg. 843
Baird, Anthony H., V.P.-Strategic Plng. & External Affairs--BHP Petroleum Pty Ltd., Melbourne, Australia; *Int'l*, pg. 225
Baker, Robert, V.P.-Strategic Plng.--Dean Foods Company, Franklin Park, IL; *U.S. Public*, pg. 489
Baker, Robert L., Pres.--Plant Maintenance Service Corporation, Memphis, TN; *U.S. Private*, pg. 869
Baker, Timothy J., V.P.-Plng.--Blair Corporation, Warren, PA; *U.S. Public*, pg. 236
Baldauf, William P., V.P.-Fin. & Bus. Mngmt.--Tecstar Inc., City of Industry, CA; *U.S. Private*, pg. 1072
Baldwin, David, Dir.-Engrng., Mktg., Plng. & Program Mngmt.--Delphi Saginaw Steering Systems, Saginaw, MI; *U.S. Public*, pg. 719
Baldwin, Richard O., Jr., Exec. V.P. & Pres.-Corp. Devel. Div.--Stewart Enterprises, Inc., Metairie, LA; *U.S. Public*, pg. 1518
Balemian, Robert, Pres. & Chief Fin. Officer--Griffon Corp., Jericho, NY; *U.S. Public*, pg. 766
Balkins, Jim, V.P.-Corp. Plng. & Devel.--Boise Cascade Corporation, Boise, ID; *U.S. Public*, pg. 242
Ballow, Michael, Sr. V.P.-Devel.--Crown American Realty Trust, Johnstown, PA; *U.S. Public*, pg. 461
Balmat, Robert E., V.P.-Corp. Plng.--Rockwell International Corporation, Costa Mesa, CA; *U.S. Public*, pg. 1397
Balten, Ovid, Dir.-Bus. Devel.--Breeze Eastern, Union, NJ; *U.S. Public*, pg. 1632
Balzano, Vincent, Dir.-Media & Plng.--Carter Products Div., Cranbury, NJ; *U.S. Public*, pg. 310
Bannon, Larry C., V.P.-Prod. Plng.--Thomas Built Buses, Inc., High Point, NC; *U.S. Private*, pg. 1082
Bar-Tov, Moshe, V.P.-Corp. Strategic Plng.--ECI Telecom Ltd., Petah Tiqwa, Israel; *Int'l*, pg. 643
Barada, Robert, V.P.-Corp. Strategy--Pacific Telesis Group, San Francisco, CA; *U.S. Public*, pg. 1415
Barbarosa, Gilberto R., Mgr.-Plng. & Prod. Control--Acos Villares Mechanical Engineering Unit, Sao Paulo, Brazil; *Int'l*, pg. 23
Barber, Bruce M., V.P.-Stategic Studies--American Electric Power Service Corp., Columbus, OH; *U.S. Public*, pg. 72

Barbier, Remi, V.P.-Corp. Devel. & Strategic Plng.--XOMA Corporation, Berkeley, CA; *U.S. Public*, pg. 1786
Barclay, Rupert, Grp. Dir.-Strategy--Allied Domecq PLC, London, United Kingdom; *Int'l*, pg. 62
Barker, Ray, V.P.-Bus. Devel.--Cubic Corporation, San Diego, CA; *U.S. Public*, pg. 466
Barkley, Diane, V.P.-Bus. Devel.--La Petite Academy Inc., Overland Park, KS; *U.S. Private*, pg. 640
Barnard, Andrew A., Exec. V.P.-Bus. Plng. & Devel.--Transatlantic Holdings Inc., New York, NY; *U.S. Public*, pg. 84
Barnard, Laura F., V.P.-Corp. Devel.--Pacific Coast Producers, Lodi, CA; *U.S. Private*, pg. 830
Barneich, David, V.P.-Bus. Devel. & Sls. Oper.--American Isuzu Motors Inc., Whittier, CA; *Int'l*, pg. 692
Barnes, Andrew, Exec. V.P.-Strategic Bus. Devel.--Mycogen Corporation, San Diego, CA; *U.S. Public*, pg. 1142
Barnes, John R., Chm. Bd., Pres. & Chief Exec. Officer--Kaneb Services, Inc., Richardson, TX; *U.S. Public*, pg. 942
Barnet, Bruce, Exec. V.P. & Dir.-Real Estate & Devel.--Long Island Bancorp, Inc., Melville, NY; *U.S. Public*, pg. 1013
Barnett, Mike, Dir.-Plng. & Residential Mktg.--Energen Corporation, Birmingham, AL; *U.S. Public*, pg. 581
Baron, Rene, Exec. V.P.-Plng. & Devel.--N. Schlumberger & Cie, Guebwiller, France; *Int'l*, pg. 1206
Barr, David, V.P.-Pur. & Plng.--Bollinger Industries Inc., Grand Prairie, TX; *U.S. Public*, pg. 243
Barrett, Dr. Peter, V.P.-Corp. Plng. & Devel.--The Perkin-Elmer Corporation, Norwalk, CT; *U.S. Public*, pg. 1279
Barrett, Pete, Sr. V.P.-Affil. Mktg. & Stragic Plng.--ABC Television Network Group, New York, NY; *U.S. Public*, pg. 511
Barron, John J., V.P.-Bus. Devel.--Day-Timers, Inc., East Texas, PA; *U.S. Public*, pg. 674
Barry, Ken, Dir.-Adv. & Plng.--Pharmacia & Upjohn, Kalamazoo, MI; *Int'l*, pg. 1048
Bartholet, Tom, V.P.-Corp. Devel.--Odetics Inc., Anaheim, CA; *U.S. Public*, pg. 1212
Barwick, Allen, Pres. & Chief Exec. Officer--Shuford Mills, Inc., Hickory, NC; *U.S. Private*, pg. 996
Bashara, Tim, V.P.-Bus. Devel.--Electrospace Systems, Inc., Richardson, TX; *U.S. Public*, pg. 1365
Bateman, Michael K., V.P.-Corp. Devel.--Tandem Computers Inc., Cupertino, CA; *U.S. Public*, pg. 417
Battistella, Jacques, Corp. V.P.-Indus. Strategy--Aerospatiale, Paris, France; *Int'l*, pg. 28
Baughn, Phil, V.P.-Bus. Strategies--James N. Gray Construction Co., Inc., Lexington, KY; *U.S. Private*, pg. 472
Baulig, George L., Treas. & Sec.--South Jersey Industries, Inc., Folsom, NJ; *U.S. Public*, pg. 1488
Bauman, B. Kent, Pres. & Chief Fin. Officer--Condon Oil Company, Inc., Ripon, WI; *U.S. Private*, pg. 262
Bauman, James R., Sr. V.P.-Bus. Devel.--Apache Corporation, Houston, TX; *U.S. Public*, pg. 119
Beafore, Frank, Dir.-New Prod. Devel.--Vernay Laboratories, Inc., Yellow Springs, OH; *U.S. Private*, pg. 1137
Beal, G.W., V.P.-Strategy & Devel.--Kraft Canada Inc., Don Mills, Canada; *U.S. Public*, pg. 1288
Bean, Richard E., Chief Fin. Officer, Exec. V.P. & Sec.--Pearce Industries Inc., Houston, TX; *U.S. Private*, pg. 845
Bear, Stephen C., Sr. V.P.-Strategic Plng.--Bristol-Myers Squibb Consumer Products Group, New York, NY; *U.S. Public*, pg. 254
Bearomore, B., Mgr.-Planning--Philip Morris Limited, Moorabbin, Australia; *U.S. Public*, pg. 1290
Bearse, Richard, Sr. V.P.-Plng. & Devel.--United Dominion Industries, Ltd., Charlotte, NC; *U.S. Public*, pg. 1675
Beartl, Luis J., Sr. V.P.-South American Corp. Devel.--Barrick Gold Corporation, Toronto, Canada; *Int'l*, pg. 168
Beatty, Dennis, Dir.--ElectroCom Automation L.P., Arlington, TX; *Int'l*, pg. 1244
Beaulieu, Doris, V.P.-Corp. Devel.--Ultramar Diamond Shamrock Corporation, San Antonio, TX; *U.S. Public*, pg. 1663
Beck, Douglas J., Sr. V.P.-Bus. Devel.--ICF Kaiser International Inc., Fairfax, VA; *U.S. Public*, pg. 852
Beck, James A., Dir.-Plng. & Analysis--IMC Global, Bannockburn, IL; *U.S. Public*, pg. 856
Beck, Michael R., V.P.-Devel.--Blockbuster Entertainment Group, Dallas, TX; *U.S. Private*, pg. 775
Becker, Hazel B., Mgr.-Prod. Devel.--Tax Management, Inc., Washington, DC; *U.S. Private*, pg. 182
Becker, Larry K., Chief Fin. Officer & Exec. V.P.--Horace Mann Educators Corporation, Springfield, IL; *U.S. Public*, *pg. 835*
Beckert, William J., Sr. V.P.-Corp. Plng. & Economics--Citgo Petroleum Corporation, Tulsa, OK; *Int'l*, pg. 1045
Beckwith, F.W., Chm. Bd. & Chief Exec. Officer--Fareway Stores, Inc., Boone, IA; *U.S. Private*, pg. 393
Beckwith, G. Nicholas, III, Pres. & Chief Exec. Officer--Beckwith Machinery Company, Murrysville, PA; *U.S. Private*, pg. 129
Bedell-Pearce, Keith, Dir.-Intl. Devel.--Prudential Corporation PLC, London, United Kingdom; *Int'l*, pg. 1073
Bedford, Steve, Dir.-Grp. Devel.--Storehouse PLC, London, United Kingdom; *Int'l*, pg. 1304
Beecher, Brad P., Dir.-Plng. & Devel.--The Empire District Electric Company, Joplin, MO; *U.S. Public*, pg. 579
Beedie, R. Craig, Mgr.-Bus. Devel.--Delta Circuit Protection & Controls Ltd., Birmingham, United Kingdom; *Int'l*, pg. 390
Behrman, Russell, V.P.-Sls. Plng.--CBS Television Network, New York, NY; *U.S. Public*, pg. 274
Belgrad, D.A., Chm. Bd., Pres. & Chief Exec. Officer--Schnadig Corporation, Des Plaines, IL; *U.S. Private*, pg. 971
Bell, Joann, V.P.-Prod. Plng.--TNT Vacations, Boston, MA; *U.S. Private*, pg. 1065
Bell, Paul, Mgr.-Devel.--Lat Purser & Associates, Charlotte, NC; *U.S. Private*, pg. 896
Bell, R.M., Dir.-Plng.--Delta Air Lines, Inc., Atlanta, GA; *U.S. Public*, pg. 497
Bellows, H. Arthur, Jr., Pres. & Chief Oper. Officer--Audits & Surveys Worldwide, New York, NY; *U.S. Public*, pg. 147
Benefield, Michael E., V.P.-Plng. & Bus. Devel.--Questar Pipeline Company, Salt Lake City, UT; *U.S. Public*, pg. 1352
Benigno, Michael J., V.P.-Plng. & Budgeting--NorAm Energy Corp., Houston, TX; *U.S. Public*, pg. 843
Benito, Richard, V.P.-New Product Devel.--Peoples Telephone Company, Inc., Miami, FL; *U.S. Public*, pg. 1275
Bennett, Ronald G., Pres.--Calavo Growers of California, Santa Ana, CA; *U.S. Private*, pg. 199
Bennyhoff, George R., Sr. V.P.-Human Resources & Pub. Affairs--The West Company, Incorporated, Lionville, PA; *U.S. Public*, pg. 1755
Benozzo, Sergio, Dir.-Plng.--Fiamm S.p.A., Montecchio Maggiore, Italy; *Int'l*, pg. 480
Bensdorp, W.L., Sr. Dir.-Strategy & Bus. Devel.--Koninklijke Hoogovens N.V., Ijmuiden, Netherlands; *Int'l*, pg. 753
Benton, William B., Chm. Bd., Chief Exec. Officer & Chief Fin. Officer--Mid South Sales, Helena, AR; *U.S. Private*, pg. 744
Berardi, Louis, Sr. V.P.-New Bus. Devel. & Strategic Plng.--Roberts Pharmaceutical Corporation, Eatontown, NJ; *U.S. Public*, pg. 1393
Beren, S.O., Chm. Bd., Pres. & Chief Exec. Officer--Misco Industries, Wichita, KS; *U.S. Private*, pg. 752
Beres, William, V.P.-Strategic Plng.--John O. Butler Co., Chicago, IL; *Int'l*, pg. 1320
Berg, David, V.P.-Bus. Devel.--American Crystal Sugar Company, Moorhead, MN; *U.S. Private*, pg. 52
Berg, Guy, Dir.-Corp. Devel.--Gelco Information Network, Inc., Eden Prairie, MN; *U.S. Private*, pg. 442
Bergendorf, Karen, Mgr.-Plng. & Devel.--Jacobsen Textron, Racine, WI; *U.S. Public*, pg. 1589
Berger, Richard, Mgr.-Corp. Plng.--Coop Switzerland, Basel, Switzerland; *Int'l*, pg. 329
Bergrall, Lars, Sr. V.P.-Bus. & Strategic Devel.--Scandinavian Airlines System (SAS), Solna, Sweden; *Int'l*, pg. 1201
Berkeley, Frederick D., Chm. Bd. & Chief Exec. Officer--Graham Corporation, Batavia, NY; *U.S. Public*, pg. 757
Berling, Henry, Exec. V.P.-Partnership Devel.--Owens & Minor Inc., Glen Allen, VA; *U.S. Public*, pg. 1236
Berman, Barry H., Chm. Bd. & Pres.--CRN International, Inc., Hamden, CT; *U.S. Private*, pg. 197
Berman, Betsy, Sr. V.P.-Promo. Devel.--Dugan Valva Contess Inc., Morristown, NJ; *U.S. Private*, pg. 345
Bernadotte, Christian C., V.P.-Corp. Devel.--Nordson Corporation, Westlake, OH; *U.S. Public*, pg. 1188
Bernal, Enrique G., Dir.-Corp. Devel.--Galileo Corp., Sturbridge, MA; *U.S. Public*, pg. 698
Bernhard, Urs, Mng. Dir.-Mngmt. Devel.--Landis & Staefa AG, Zug, Switzerland; *Int'l*, pg. 800
Berry, Bill, Mgr.-Store Plng. & Mdsg.--Kelly-Moore Paint Company, Inc., San Carlos, CA; *U.S. Private*, pg. 613
Berry, Howard, Dir.-Strategic Devel.--HBO & Company/Cycare Business Group, Scottsdale, AZ; *U.S. Public*, pg. 770
Berry, William S., Exec. V.P.-Forest Resources & Corp. Devel.--Rayonier Inc., Stamford, CT; *U.S. Public*, pg. 1363
Bertelli, David, V.P.-Organization Devel.--Mercury Computer Systems, Inc., Chelmsford, MA; *U.S. Private*, pg. 732
Berthoud, John D., V.P.-Mktg. & Quality Mngmt.--Nalco Chemical Company, Naperville, IL; *U.S. Public*, pg. 1150
Bertman, Roger, V.P.-Corp. Devel.--VeriFone, Inc., Redwood City, CA; *U.S. Public*, pg. 815
Bescoby, Janet, Sr. V.P. & Grp. Plng. Dir.--Western International Media Corporation, Los Angeles, CA; *U.S. Private*, pg. 1165
Beseda, Jane, Mgr.-Strategic Plng.--Toyota Motor Sales, U.S.A., Inc., Torrance, CA; *Int'l*, pg. 1412
Betbeze, Jean-Paul, Mgr.-Economic & Fin. Res.--Credit Lyonnais S.A., Paris, France; *Int'l*, pg. 343
Beudeker, R.F., Mgr.-Business Devel.--Food Specialties Division, Delft, Netherlands; *Int'l*, pg. 1142
Bezpa, Bruce, V.P.-Strategic Devel.--Bowne & Co., Inc., New York, NY; *U.S. Public*, pg. 248
Bhardwaj, Sunil, V.P.-Admin. & Plng.--Consolidated Freightways Corp., Menlo Park, CA; *U.S. Public*, pg. 435
Biamo, Adrian, Dr., Exec. V.P.-Planning, Devel. & Tech.--The Israel Electric Corporation Ltd., Haifa, Israel; *Int'l*, pg. 690
Biel, Howard S., Sr. V.P. & Mng. Dir.-Devel.--Federal Realty Investment Trust, Rockville, MD; *U.S. Public*, pg. 616
Bierer, William, Chm. Bd. & Chief Exec. Officer--Essex Grain Products, Inc., Frazer, PA; *U.S. Private*, pg. 383
Bies, Susan Schmidt, Exec. V.P.-Risk Mngmt. & ALCO--First Tennessee National Corporation, Memphis, TN; *U.S. Public*, pg. 638
Biggs, J.D., Dir.-People Devel.--American Freightways Corporation, Harrison, AR; *U.S. Public*, pg. 75
Bignell, Allan, V.P.-Bus. Devel.--CAE Inc., Toronto, Canada; *Int'l*, pg. 237
Billingsly, Bob, Dir.-Processing & Devel.--Sanderson Farms, Inc., Laurel, MS; *U.S. Public*, pg. 1430
Bird, R. Craig, Chief Fin. Officer, Exec. V.P.-Fin. & Devel. & Admin.--Showboat, Incorporated, Las Vegas, NV; *U.S. Public*, pg. 1469
Bird, Terrence C., V.P.-Corp. Devel.--McCain Foods Limited, Florenceville, Canada; *Int'l*, pg. 850
Birdsall, Douglas, V.P.-Mktg. Affiliates & Strategic Plng.--Northwest Airlines, Inc., Saint Paul, MN; *U.S. Public*, pg. 1200
Birmingham, Joseph K., Sr. V.P.-Property Devel.--The TJX Companies, Inc., Framingham, MA; *U.S. Public*, pg. 1556
Birmingham, Joseph K., Sr. V.P.-Property Devel.--T.J. Maxx, Framingham, MA; *U.S. Public*, pg. 1557
Bischoff, J. Michael, V.P.-Corp. Devel.--Marsh & McLennan Companies, Inc., New York, NY; *U.S. Public*, pg. 1048
Bishop, Laura M., Chief Fin. Officer & Sr. V.P.--Luby's Cafeterias, Inc., San Antonio, TX; *U.S. Public*, pg. 1017
Bishop, Paul, V.P.-Corp. Plng.--Dana Corporation, Toledo, OH; *U.S. Public*, pg. 479
Bisser, Ben, Chief Fin. Officer & V.P.-Fin.--Tomkins Industries Inc., Dayton, OH; *Int'l*, pg. 1397
Bissett, Wm. J., V.P.-Govt. Affairs & Community Rel.--Delaware North Companies, Inc., Buffalo, NY; *U.S. Private*, pg. 321
Bissonnette, Bruce, Dir.-Devel.--Buffets, Inc., Eden Prairie, MN; *U.S. Public*, pg. 267
Bjornson, Dana, V.P.-Strategic Plng., Mergers & Acquisitions--American Mutual Life Holding Co., Des Moines, IA; *U.S. Private*, pg. 59
Black, Randy, Mgr.-Prod. Devel.--Rawlings Sporting Goods Company, Fenton, MO; *U.S. Public*, pg. 1361
Blackwell, Daria, Mng. Partner & Client Svcs. Dir.-Strategic Planning--Dugan/Farley Communications, Upper Saddle River, NJ; *U.S. Public*, pg. 1642
Blagge, Timothy J., Pres. & Chief Exec. Officer--Blagge Enterprises, Rancho Cordova, CA; *U.S. Private*, pg. 148
Blair, Michael D., Chm. Bd. & Chief Exec. Officer--Cyborg Systems, Inc., Chicago, IL; *U.S. Private*, pg. 299
Blanc, Claude H., V.P.-Strategic Procurement--Quebecor Printing, Inc., Montreal, Canada; *Int'l*, pg. 1076
Blanchard, Robert T., V.P.-Worldwide Strategic Plng.--Procter & Gamble Health & Personal Care Div., Cincinnati, OH; *U.S. Public*, pg. 1331
Blanck, Mike, V.P.-Strategic Plng. & Res.--Laughlin/Constable, Inc., Milwaukee, WI; *U.S. Private*, pg. 653
Blanco, Eduardo, Mgr.-Strategic Plng.--Petroleos de Venezuela S.A., Caracas, Venezuela; *Int'l*, pg. 1045
Blank, Werner J., V.P.-Res. & Devel.--King Industries, Inc., Norwalk, CT; *U.S. Private*, pg. 620
Blann, Jerry M., Pres.--Jackson Hole Ski Resort, Teton Village, WY; *U.S. Private*, pg. 579
Blay, Abby, Sr. V.P.-Trng.--Ross Roy Communications, Inc., Bloomfield Hills, MI; *U.S. Private*, pg. 946
Blitzer, Charles N., Pres. & Chief Exec. Officer--MGI PHARMA INC., Minneapolis, MN; *U.S. Public*, pg. 1026
Blizman, Wayne, V.P.-Corp. Plng. & Devel.--Durakon Industries, Inc., Lapeer, MI; *U.S. Public*, pg. 537
Bloemendaal, P.M.A., Mgr.-Strategy & Plng.--Royal Nedlloyd Group N.V., Rotterdam, Netherlands; *Int'l*, pg. 1143
Blood, Edward L., V.P.-Strategic Plng.--The Times Mirror Company, Los Angeles, CA; *U.S. Public*, pg. 1615
Bloodworth, Donald A., V.P.-Bus. Process Svcs.--PacifiCorp, Portland, OR; *U.S. Public*, pg. 1251
Bloom, Donald, Pres. & Chief Exec. Officer--Bloom Electric Services, Inc., Oklahoma City, OK; *U.S. Private*, pg. 150
Blouin, Bob, Strategic Plng. Dir.--Jordan Tamraz Caruso Advertising, Inc., Chicago, IL; *U.S. Private*, pg. 599
Blount, Ben B., Jr., Chief Fin. Officer & Exec. V.P.-Plng., Admin. & Fin.--Oxford Industries, Inc., Atlanta, GA; *U.S. Public*, pg. 1239
Blume, Dennis A., V.P.-Investment Strategy--Lincoln Investment Management Inc., Fort Wayne, IN; *U.S. Public*, pg. 998
Bodman, James W., Co-Chm. & Chief Exec. Officer--Vienna Sausage Mfg. Co., Chicago, IL; *U.S. Private*, pg. 1139
Boele, Fred, Plng. & Media Dir.--Benjamens, Van Doorn EURO RSCG, Amstelveen, Netherlands; *Int'l*, pg. 602
Boggess, W.T., V.P.-Strategic Plng.--Emerson Power Transmission Corporation, Ithaca, NY; *U.S. Public*, pg. 573
Bohanon, Mike, Mgr.-MIS & Strategic Plng.--Varity Dayton Walther, Dayton, OH; *Int'l*, pg. 820
Bohmann, James R., Sr. V.P. Corp. Devel. & Treas.--Payco American Corporation, Brookfield, WI; *U.S. Public*, pg. 1267
Bolan, Michael, V.P.-Mktg. & Prod. Devel.--Dallas Semiconductor Corporation, Dallas, TX; *U.S. Public*, pg. 478
Boland, David, Chm. Bd., Pres. & Chief Exec. Officer--David Boland, Inc., Titusville, FL; *U.S. Private*, pg. 154
Bold, Jesse, V.P.-Plng. & Dir. Response--Kovel Kresser & Partners, Santa Monica, CA; *U.S. Private*, pg. 634
Bolduc, Pierre, Exec. V.P.-New Business Devel. & Intl. Affairs--Hydro-Quebec, Montreal, Canada; *Int'l*, pg. 640
Bolger, Bernard J., Dr., V.P.-New Bus. Devel.--Loctite Corporation, Rocky Hill, CT; *Int'l*, pg. 611
Bollinger, Richard, Pres.--Bollinger Shipyards, Inc., Lockport, LA; *U.S. Private*, pg. 155
Bologna, Karen, Mgr.-Mktg. Communications--Hexcel Corporation, Pleasanton, CA; *U.S. Public*, pg. 824
Boltz, Ronald R., V.P.-Strategy & Regulatory Affairs & Gen. Mgr.-Large Cars--Chrysler Corporation, Auburn Hills, MI; *U.S. Public*, pg. 352
Bonaker, David A., V.P.-Plng. & Logistics--Diamond Multimedia Systems, Inc., San Jose, CA; *U.S. Public*, pg. 505
Boni, Thomas, V.P.-Systems Devel.--Liechtenstein Global Trust Limited, Vaduz, Liechtenstein; *Int'l*, pg. 809
Bonn, Joseph A., V.P.-Plng. & Admin.--Kaiser Aluminum Corporation, Houston, TX; *U.S. Public*, pg. 1062
Bonnate, Jean-Louis, Head-Plng. & Devel.--Banque Nationale de Paris, Paris, France; *Int'l*, pg. 163
Bonnette, Dennis, Chief Oper. Officer & Exec. V.P.--Advanced Circuit Technology, Nashua, NH; *U.S. Private*, *pg. 21*
Bonsal, Richard I., Pres.--Joshua L. Baily Co., Inc., Hoboken, NJ; *U.S. Private*, pg. 110
Bonsall, Mark B., Chief Fin. Officer & Assoc. Gen. Mgr.--Salt River Project Agricultural Improvement and Power District, Tempe, AZ; *U.S. Private*, pg. 962
Bonsey, Colin, Dir.-Plng.--Siebe plc, Windsor, United Kingdom; *Int'l*, pg. 1240
Boone, Sydney K., Jr., V.P.-Acquisitions & Devel.--Paragon Health Network, Inc., Atlanta, GA; *U.S. Public*, pg. 1256
Borrell, Gordon, V.P.-Corp. Devel.--Infinet Operations, Norfolk, VA; *U.S. Private*, pg. 649
Boryenace, Charles, Exec. V.P.-Strategic Plng.--American Waste Services, Inc., Warren, OH; *U.S. Public*, pg. 94

Boscaccy, Martin P., V.P.-Devel.--Harrah's Entertainment, Inc., Memphis, TN; *U.S. Public*, pg. 790
Boskey, William, Dir.-Intl. Sls., Mktg. & Joint Ventures--GM Powertrain Group, Pontiac, MI; *U.S. Public*, pg. 719
Boucher, Nicholas A., Mgr.-Plng. & Devel.--Glynwed International PLC, Birmingham, United Kingdom; *Int'l*, pg. 554
Boucher, Thomas C., V.P.-Energy Resources & Plng.--Green Mountain Power Corporation, South Burlington, VT; *U.S. Public*, pg. 761
Bouffard, Gaston, Sr. V.P./Sls. & Mktg./Paper & Bus. Devel.--Donohue Inc., Quebec, Canada; *Int'l*, pg. 1075
Bouhet, Jacques, Dir.-Intl. Devel.--Societe Generale, Paris, France; *Int'l*, pg. 1273
Bourez, Joel, Mng. Dir.-Business Devel./Intl. Projects--Landis & Staefa AG, Zug, Switzerland; *Int'l*, pg. 800
Bovis, George S., Sr. V.P.-Devel. & Growth Plng.--White Hen Pantry, Inc., Elmhurst, IL; *U.S. Private*, pg. 1172
Bowditch, Eric, Dir.-Bus. Devel.--Ohmeda, Liberty Corner, NJ; *Int'l*, pg. 121
Bowen, Rick A., V.P.-Bus. Devel., N. America & Latin America--Destec Energy, Inc., Houston, TX; *U.S. Public*, pg. 1146
Bowen, Steve, Bus. Devel. Dir.--Merkley Newman Harty, New York, NY; *U.S. Public*, pg. 1224
Bowser, James F., V.P.-New Prod. Devel.--Three-Five Systems, Tempe, AZ; *U.S. Public*, pg. 1604
Boyd, Dennis, Pres. & Chief Exec. Officer--Royal Waterbeds, Maryland Heights, MO; *U.S. Private*, pg. 949
Brack, George, V.P.-Corp. Devel.--Placer Dome Inc., Vancouver, Canada; *Int'l*, pg. 1060
Brackett, David, Dir.-Plng. & Fin.--Easco Inc., Girard, OH; *U.S. Public*, pg. 548
Braddock, James L., Chm. Bd., Pres. & Treas.--Fastec Industrial, Elkhart, IN; *U.S. Private*, pg. 397
Bradley, J. Douglas, Mng. Dir.-Corp. Devel.--TrizecHahn Corporation, Toronto, Canada; *Int'l*, pg. 1424
Brady, Frank, Pres. & Chief Exec. Officer--Brady Marketing Company, Pacheco, CA; *U.S. Private*, pg. 165
Brady, Paul, Dir.-Fin. & Plng.--Scottish Enterprise, Glasgow, United Kingdom; *Int'l*, pg. 1212
Brady, William J., V.P.-Plng., Resources & Fin.--Mobil Mining & Minerals Company, Ashland, VA; *U.S. Public*, pg. 1118
Brakeman, Brian F., V.P.-Plng.--The East Ohio Gas Co., Cleveland, OH; *U.S. Public*, pg. 435
Braley, Scott W., AIA, V.P.-Plng. & Devel.--Heery International, Inc., Atlanta, GA; *U.S. Private*, pg. 519
Bramblett, Michael T., Exec. V.P.--Jones Medical Industries Inc., Saint Louis, MO; *U.S. Public*, pg. 933
Brandstatter, Leo, Res. Dir. & Strategic Plng. Dir.--Rubin Ehrenthal & Associates, New York, NY; *U.S. Private*, pg. 949
Brandt, Roden A., Sr. V.P.-Plng. & Mktg.--Trans World Airlines, Inc., Saint Louis, MO; *U.S. Public*, pg. 1629
Branman, M. Jeffrey, Sr. V.P.-Corp. Devel.--Woolworth Corporation, New York, NY; *U.S. Public*, pg. 1777
Brasca, Luigi, Dir.-Plng. & Strategy--Eridania Beghin-Say Group, Neuilly-sur-Seine, France; *Int'l*, pg. 324
Braun, James K., V.P.-Corp. Devel.--Hubbell Incorporated, Orange, CT; *U.S. Public*, pg. 844
Braun, Mary Jo, V.P.-Corp. Plng. & Devel.--MCN Energy Group, Inc., Detroit, MI; *U.S. Public*, pg. 1024
Bray, John J., Chm.-Forum Europe Ltd.--The Forum Corporation, Boston, MA; *U.S. Private*, pg. 420
Brayman, John A., Exec. V.P.-Bus. Devel.--Entergy Corporation, New Orleans, LA; *U.S. Public*, pg. 585
Brazier, Lee, V.P.-Tech.--Milprint Inc., Oshkosh, WI; *U.S. Public*, pg. 210
Bready, Richard L., Chm. Bd. & Chief Exec. Officer--Nortek, Inc., Providence, RI; *U.S. Public*, pg. 1192
Bregman, Marlene, V.P.-Plng.--Leo Burnett Publicidade, Ltda., Sao Paulo, Brazil; *U.S. Private*, pg. 185
Breitenbach, E. Allen, Dr., Chm. Bd. & Chief Exec. Officer--Scientific Software-Intercomp, Inc., Denver, CO; *U.S. Public*, pg. 1443
Brennan, Charles M., III, Chm. Bd. & Chief Exec. Officer--MYR Group Inc., Rolling Meadows, IL; *U.S. Public*, pg. 1029
Brennan, Robert T., V.P.-Fin.--The Okonite Company, Ramsey, NJ; *U.S. Private*, pg. 813
Brent, John, Chief Fin. Officer & V.P.--Mac Papers, Inc., Jacksonville, FL; *U.S. Private*, pg. 689
Bresnahan, William J., Pres.--Hynes Industries Inc., Youngstown, OH; *U.S. Private*, pg. 552
Brewer, Montie R., V.P.-Resource Plng.--UAL Corporation, Elk Grove Village, IL; *U.S. Public*, pg. 1652
Brickner, Louis C., V.P.-Engrng. & Prod. Devel.--Delta International Machinery Corp., Pittsburgh, PA; *U.S. Public*, pg. 1273
Bridendall, John P., Sr. V.P.-Corp. Devel.--Brown-Forman Corporation, Louisville, KY; *U.S. Public*, pg. 261
Bridges, Brad, Gen. Mgr.-Plng.--James Hardie Industries Ltd., Sydney, Australia; *Int'l*, pg. 596
Bridgford, Barbara, Credit Officer--Harris Broadcast Division, Richmond, IN; *U.S. Public*, pg. 791
Bright, Todd, Dir.-Plng. Analysis--Eckerd Corporation, Largo, FL; *U.S. Public*, pg. 917
Brisco, Robert N., Sr. V.P.-Mktg. & New Bus. Devel.--Los Angeles Times, Los Angeles, CA; *U.S. Public*, pg. 1616
Britton, Bill, V.P.-Bus. Devel.--Outsource International, Deerfield Beach, FL; *U.S. Public*, pg. 1236
Brochu, Mike, Dir.-Bus. Dev.--Beckman Coulter, Miami, FL; *U.S. Public*, pg. 199
Brochu, Sophie, V.P.-Bus. Devel.--Gaz Metropolitain & Company, Montreal, Canada; *Int'l*, pg. 541
Brochu, Suzanne, Dir.-Bus. Networks--Capital International CDPQ, Montreal, Canada; *Int'l*, pg. 249
Brock, Gerald E., V.P. & Sr. Dir.-Devel.--Rouse Office & Community Development Div., Columbia, MD; *U.S. Public*, pg. 1407
Brolick, Emil J., Sr. V.P.-Strategic Plng. & Res.--Wendy's International Inc., Dublin, OH; *U.S. Public*, pg. 1754
Brooker, Peter, V.P.-Plng. & Sec.--The Great Atlantic & Pacific Tea Company, Inc., Montvale, NJ; *Int'l*, pg. 1375
Brookfield, Rowe, PharmD, Exec. Dir.-Res. & Devel.--MET Solutions, LLC, Raleigh, NC; *U.S. Public*, pg. 1642
Brooks, Charles F., V.P.-Project Devel./Opers. Entertainment Center Div.--Blockbuster Entertainment Group, Dallas, TX; *U.S. Private*, pg. 775
Brooks, Gary, Asst. Reg. Mng. Dir.-Bus. Devel.--Willis Corroon South Limited, Bristol, United Kingdom; *Int'l*, pg. 1503
Brooks, Greg, V.P.-Corp. Strategic Plng.--Allergan, Inc., Irvine, CA; *U.S. Public*, pg. 46
Brooks, Paul W., Sr. V.P.-Corp. & Mngmt. Devel.--Koch Industries, Incorporated, Wichita, KS; *U.S. Private*, pg. 628
Brookshire, Brad, Exec. V.P.-Corp. Devel.--Brookshire Grocery, Tyler, TX; *U.S. Private*, pg. 172
Brophy, Margaret M., Sr. V.P.-Strategic Plng. & Res. Dir.--Young & Rubicam Detroit, Detroit, MI; *U.S. Private*, pg. 1198
Brotherton, John, Sr. V.P.-Devel.--Players International, Inc., Atlantic City, NJ; *U.S. Public*, pg. 1310
Brown, Charles, Chm. Bd., Pres. & Chief Exec. Officer--Bayou State Oil Corporation, Shreveport, LA; *U.S. Private*, pg. 125
Brown, Chris M., Mgr.-Strategic Devel.--BHP Iron Ore, Perth, Australia; *Int'l*, pg. 224
Brown, Jeff, V.P.-Store Planning--The Elder-Beerman Stores Corp., Dayton, OH; *U.S. Private*, pg. 367
Brown, O. Carl, V.P.-Fin. Plng.--Atmos Energy Corporation, Dallas, TX; *U.S. Public*, pg. 145
Brown, Paul A., V.P.-Bus. Devel.--Fort Dodge Animal Health, Overland Park, KS; *U.S. Public*, pg. 79
Brown, Scott, V.P.-Corp. Devel.--Jabil Circuit, Inc., Saint Petersburg, FL; *U.S. Public*, pg. 919
Brown, Terrance J., V.P.-Corp. Growth & Devel.--General Mills, Inc., Minneapolis, MN; *U.S. Public*, pg. 717
Brown, W. Ronald, V.P.-Bus. Devel.--Intercontinental Mfg. Co., Garland, TX; *U.S. Private*, pg. 313
Browne, Christina, Bus. Devel. Coord.--SSB Advertising Sydney, Sydney, Australia; *Int'l*, pg. 394
Brownlee, Wayne R., Sr. V.P.-Expansion & Devel.--Potash Corporation of Saskatchewan Inc., Saskatoon, Canada; *Int'l*, pg. 1064
Bruce, Joseph, Exec. V.P.-Strategic Plng.--Eisner & Associates, Inc., Baltimore, MD; *U.S. Private*, pg. 366
Bruhn, Michael D., V.P.-Corp. Devel.--UtiliCorp United Inc., Kansas City, MO; *U.S. Public*, pg. 1700
Bruner, Gerald, Dir.-Business Devel.--Public Service Company of Oklahoma, Tulsa, OK; *U.S. Public*, pg. 324
Brunner, Rodolfo, Head-Corp. Plng.--Georg Fischer Ltd., Schaffhausen, Switzerland; *Int'l*, pg. 488
Brutt, Bob, V.P.-Franchising--Long John Silver's, Inc., Lexington, KY; *U.S. Private*, pg. 674
Brydges, W.T., Dr., V.P.-Bus. Devel.--Stackpole Ltd., Newton, MA; *U.S. Private*, pg. 1028
Bryson, Michael A., Sr. V.P.-Strategic Plng.--Mellon Bank Corporation, Pittsburgh, PA; *U.S. Public*, pg. 1084
Buccarelli, Richard A., V.P.-Corp. Devel.--U.S. Industries, Inc., Iselin, NJ; *U.S. Public*, pg. 1683
Bucher, Larry C., Pres.--Lloyd Properties, Los Angeles, CA; *U.S. Private*, pg. 672
Buckmeier, Ronald, V.P.-Prod. Devel.--Winnebago Industries, Inc., Forest City, IA; *U.S. Public*, pg. 1772
Budhraja, Vikram S., Sr. V.P.-Power Grid Bus. Unit--Southern California Edison Company, Rosemead, CA; *U.S. Public*, pg. 564
Buechner, Barry L., Sr. V.P.-Bus. Plng. & Systems--Day & Zimmermann, Inc., Philadelphia, PA; *U.S. Private*, pg. 316
Buecken, Lutz, Dr., Gen Counsel--Heidelberger Druckmaschinen A.G., Heidelberg, Germany; *Int'l*, pg. 604
Bullock, Sheri, Sr. Mgr.-Acctg. & Fin. Plng.--American Honda Motor Co., Inc., Torrance, CA; *Int'l*, pg. 634
Bulyk, J., V.P.-Corp. Devel.--Ulbrich Stainless Steels & Special Metals, Inc., North Haven, CT; *U.S. Private*, pg. 1115
Bunch, Doyle, Sr. V.P.-Corp. Plng. & Devel.--New Century Energies, Inc., Denver, CO; *U.S. Public*, pg. 1170
Bunnell, Dale, V.P.-Bus. Devel.--Mark Andy, Inc., Chesterfield, MO; *U.S. Public*, pg. 521
Buns, Tom, V.P.-Fin. & Treas.--Corcom, Inc., Libertyville, IL; *U.S. Public*, pg. 446
Burch, Miriam, V.P. & Assoc. Plng. Dir.--Western International Media Corporation, Los Angeles, CA; *U.S. Private*, pg. 1165
Burfeind, David, V.P.-Plng. & Devel.--Guy Gannett Communications, Portland, ME; *U.S. Private*, pg. 439
Burger, Richard, Exec. V.P.--Sulzer Ltd., Winterthur, Switzerland; *Int'l*, pg. 1305
Burk, Richard, V.P.-Strategic Plng.--USLD Communications Corp., San Antonio, TX; *U.S. Public*, pg. 969
Burke, Kevin M., V.P.-Corp. Plng.--Consolidated Edison Company of New York, Inc., New York, NY; *U.S. Public*, pg. 434
Burke, Larry W., Pres. & Chief Exec. Officer--Robinson Nugent, Inc., New Albany, IN; *U.S. Public*, pg. 1394
Burke, Roger L., V.P.-Managed Care Bus. Devel.--Tenet Healthcare Corporation, Santa Barbara, CA; *U.S. Public*, pg. 1576
Burlinghton, Brett, Sr. V.P.-Strategic Devel.--Excite, Inc., Redwood City, CA; *U.S. Public*, pg. 599
Burnett, Raymond N., Dir.-Labor Rels.--PG Publishing Co., Pittsburgh, PA; *U.S. Private*, pg. 147
Burnison, Gary D., Sr. V.P. & Dir.-Bus. Analysis & Plng.--Jefferies & Company, Inc., Los Angeles, CA; *U.S. Public*, *pg. 925*
Burns, Ron, Chief Fin. Officer, V.P. & Sec.--Grede Foundries, Inc., Milwaukee, WI; *U.S. Private*, pg. 476
Burr, Steven M., V.P.-Plng. & Engrng.--Snyder Oil Corporation, Fort Worth, TX; *U.S. Public*, pg. 1481
Burris, Paula, Mgr.-Corp. Analysis--General Electric Investment Corp., Stamford, CT; *U.S. Public*, pg. 712
Burrows, S.G., Sr. Mgr.-Plng.--The Hongkong and Shanghai Banking Corporation Limited (HongkongBank), Central, Hong Kong; *Int'l*, pg. 583
Busacca, Salvatore, Pres.--ScotiaMocatta, New York, NY; *Int'l*, pg. 156
Busam, S. James, Sr. V.P.-Bus. Devel.--ADP Marshall Contractors Inc., Rumford, RI; *U.S. Public*, pg. 660
Bush, Dwight L., V.P.-Bus. Devel.--SLM Holding Corp., Washington, DC; *U.S. Public*, pg. 1419
Bush, Howard J., V.P.-Mktg. & Sls.--Brenco, Inc., Petersburg, VA; *U.S. Public*, pg. 1710
Bushey, A. Scott, Exec. V.P.-Strategic Plng.--USLIFE Corporation, New York, NY; *U.S. Public*, pg. 77
Bushman, J.M., V.P.-Recruiting & Trng. Coord.--B.C. Ziegler & Co., West Bend, WI; *U.S. Public*, pg. 1792
Busto, Richard, V.P.-Strategy, Bus. Devel. & Network Services--Gandalf Technologies Inc., Nepean, Canada; *Int'l*, pg. 540
Butensky, Irwin S., Sr. V.P.-Res. & Devel.--Playtex Products Inc., Westport, CT; *U.S. Public*, pg. 1310
Butler, Thomas S., V.P.-Corp. Devel.--Republic Industries, Inc., Fort Lauderdale, FL; *U.S. Public*, pg. 1378
Butler, Todd, Dir.-Pur.--Ultrak Inc., Lewisville, TX; *U.S. Public*, pg. 1663
Butler, William, Chm. Bd., Pres. & Chief Exec. Officer--Corporex Companies, Inc., Cincinnati, OH; *U.S. Private*, pg. 276
Butterfield, Leslie, Chm. Bd., Plng Dir. & New Bus. Contact--Butterfield Day Devito Hockney Ltd., London, United Kingdom; *Int'l*, pg. 237
Buttolph, John, V.P.-Franchising & Devel.--Sholodge, Inc., Hendersonville, TN; *U.S. Public*, pg. 1467
Butz, Greg R., V.P.-Bus. Devel.--Comcast Cellular Communications, Inc., Wayne, PA; *U.S. Public*, pg. 407
Bybee, Gary A., Chief Fin. Officer & V.P.-Glass Recycling--Anheuser-Busch Recycling Corporation, Saint Louis, MO; *U.S. Public*, pg. 114
Byck, Joseph S., V.P.-Strategic Plng., Investor Rels. & Pub. Affairs--Union Carbide Corporation, Danbury, CT; *U.S. Public*, pg. 1666
Byczynski, Ed, V.P.-Plng. & Devel.--Life-Like Products, Inc., Baltimore, MD; *U.S. Private*, pg. 666
Byron, Carla A., V.P.-Corp. Plng.--Chiquita Brands International, Inc., Cincinnati, OH; *U.S. Public*, pg. 349
Cadden, Dee, Coord.-Trng.--Buckman Laboratories Inc., Memphis, TN; *U.S. Private*, pg. 180
Cado, Rene, Mgr.-Strategy--Groupe GAN, Paris, France; *Int'l*, pg. 563
Caffrey, Tom, Sr. V.P.-Bus. Devel.--Jordan Industries, Inc., Deerfield, IL; *U.S. Private*, pg. 598
Cagle, J. Douglas, Chm. Bd. & Chief Exec. Officer--Cagle's Inc., Atlanta, GA; *U.S. Public*, pg. 291
Calafati, Gabriel R., Chm. Bd., Pres. & Treas.--Frank Briscoe Co. Inc., Kenilworth, NJ; *U.S. Private*, pg. 169
Calafell, Robert C., Sr. V.P.-Plng. & Devel.--GTE Corporation, Stamford, CT; *U.S. Public*, pg. 696
Calderon, Zayra F., Sr. V.P.-Strategic Prod. Devel.--Cigna Healthcare, Inc., Bloomfield, CT; *U.S. Public*, pg. 359
Caldwell, David A., V.P.-Plng. & Devel.--Sun Life Assurance Company of Canada, Toronto, Canada; *Int'l*, pg. 1318
Call, William, Chm., Pres. & Chief Exec. Officer--Maverik Country Stores, Inc., Salt Lake City, UT; *U.S. Private* pg. 715
Callahan, Chris, V.P.-New Bus. Devel.--American Pad and Paper Company, Dallas, TX; *U.S. Public*, pg. 88
Calleja, Tomas, Mng. Dir.-Corp. Devel. & Chief Information Officer--Iberdrola, S.A., Bilbao, Spain; *Int'l*, pg. 657
Camacho, P. Bruce, Exec. V.P.-Investor Rels. & Dir.-Internal Devel.--American Bankers Life Assurance Co. of Florida, Miami, FL; *U.S. Public*, pg. 67
Camalo, Craig, Controller--Code-Alarm, Inc., Madison Heights, MI; *U.S. Public*, pg. 393
Cameron, Donald, V.P.-Design--Deck House Inc., Acton, MA; *U.S. Private*, pg. 320
Cameron, Donald, V.P.-Design--Acorn Structures, Acton, MA; *U.S. Private*, pg. 320
Campbell, W. Patrick, Exec. V.P.-Corp. Strategy & Bus. Dev.--Ameritech Corporation, Chicago, IL; *U.S. Public*, pg. 97
Campopiano, David G., V.P.-Corp. Devel.--Ferro Corporation, Cleveland, OH; *U.S. Public*, pg. 618
Cantin, Norman, V.P.-Plng. & Inventory Control--T.J. Maxx, Framingham, MA; *U.S. Public*, pg. 1557
Cantwell, Dennis M., V.P.-Fin. & Devel.--Chrysler Financial Corporation, Southfield, MI; *U.S. Public*, pg. 354
Capelao, Carlos, Dir.-Refineries Plng. & Control--Petrogal, s.a., Lisbon, Portugal; *Int'l*, pg. 1044
Capps, W. Lee, III, Dir.-Corp. Devel.--Kellwood Company, Chesterfield, MO; *U.S. Public*, pg. 948
Carballo, Gerardo Ulate, Dir.-Plng. & Design--Grupo Situr SA de CV, Guadalajara, Mexico; *Int'l*, pg. 576
Carlos, Michael C., Chm. Bd. & Chief Exec. Officer--National Distributing Co., Inc., Atlanta, GA; *U.S. Private*, pg. 781
Carlson, Gary L., Sr. V.P.-Strategic Devel.--Avatar Holdings Inc., Coral Gables, FL; *U.S. Public*, pg. 151
Carlson, Gary L., Sr. V.P.-Strategic Devel.--Avatar Properties Inc., Miami, FL; *U.S. Public*, pg. 151
Carlson, Kenneth J., Jr., Sec. & Dir.-Bus. Plng.--DSM Engineering Plastic Products, Reading, PA; *Int'l*, pg. 354
Carlson, Tom, Dir-Reg. Devel. (Asia Pacific)--Ramsey Technology, Inc., Minneapolis, MN; *U.S. Public*, pg. 1592
Carmi, Ilan, V.P.-Engrng.--3Com Corporation, Southborough, MA; *U.S. Public*, pg. 1604
Carnwath, Richard K., V.P.-Plng. & Devel.--Vulcan Materials Company, Birmingham, AL; *U.S. Public*, pg. 1725
Carovano, Rickard J., Dir.-Corp. Devel.--Esterline Technologies Corporation, Bellevue, WA; *U.S. Public*, pg. 594
Carpenter, Marshall L., Chief Fin. Officer & V.P.--MTS Systems Corporation, Eden Prairie, MN; *U.S. Public*, pg. 1028

Carpenter, Michael A., Vice Chm. & Exec. V.P.-Strategic Plng.--Travelers Group, New York, NY; *U.S. Public*, pg. 1632
Carpenter, Sarah, Dir.-Grp. Bus. Devel.--Dixons Group plc, Hemel Hempstead, United Kingdom,; *Int'l*, pg. 413
Carr, David, Chief Fin. Officer, Sr. V.P. & Sec.--Latshaw Enterprises, Inc., Wichita, KS; *U.S. Public*, pg. 979
Carr, P.S., Chief Mgr.-Strategy & Devel.--Australian Mutual Provident, Sydney, Australia; *Int'l*, pg. 100
Carrington, Christian A., V.P.-Strategic Plng. & Devel.--Alumax Inc., Atlanta, GA; *U.S. Public*, pg. 59
Carroll, Marie C., V.P.-Corp. Fin. Plng.--Anheuser-Busch Companies, Inc., Saint Louis, MO; *U.S. Public*, pg. 113
Carruthers, George, Pres., Chief Exec. & Chief Fin. Officer--Polycoat Systems, Inc., Hudson Falls, NY; *U.S. Private*, pg. 875
Carson, Ralph, Reg. V.P.-Strategic Plng. & Implementation, Team 1--Scott Forseman/Addison Wesley, Glenview, IL; *Int'l*, pg. 927
Carter, Bruce, V.P.-Health Care Discovery & Devel.--Novo Nordisk A/S, Bagsvaerd, Denmark; *Int'l*, pg. 987
Carter, Donald J., Chief Exec. Officer--Home Interiors & Gifts, Inc., Dallas, TX; *U.S. Private*, pg. 536
Carter, Georgia B., V.P.-Mktg. & Customer Svc.--CNG Transmission Corporation, Clarksburg, WV; *U.S. Public*, pg. 435
Carter, Sam R., Chief Fin. Officer & Treas.--Farmers Co-op Market Inc., Frisco City, AL; *U.S. Private*, pg. 395
Carton, Margaret, V.P.-Investor Rels. & Plng.--Coca-Cola Enterprises Inc., Atlanta, GA; *U.S. Public*, pg. 393
Cashion, Herschell A., Jr., Sr. V.P.-Bus. Devel.--The North American Coal Corporation, Dallas, TX; *U.S. Public*, pg. 1149
Casner, T., Dir.-Bus. Devel. & Aerospace Programs--United Technologies, Chemical Systems Div., San Jose, CA; *U.S. Public*, pg. 1690
Casper, Steven, Dir.-Bus. Devel.--AmeriPath, Inc., Riviera Beach, FL; *U.S. Public*, pg. 96
Cass, Susan M., V.P.-Invester Rels. & Fin. Plng.--The Ryland Group, Inc., Columbia, MD; *U.S. Public*, pg. 1414
Cassese, Patrick J., Chm. Bd., Pres. & Chief Exec. Officer--Antares Group Inc., Cleveland, OH; *U.S. Private*, pg. 76
Cassetty, Fred, Chm. Bd., Pres. & Chief Exec. Officer--Alley-Cassetty Coal Co., Nashville, TN; *U.S. Private*, pg. 37
Cassidy, John F., Jr., V.P.-Res. Ctr.--United Technologies Corporation, Hartford, CT; *U.S. Public*, pg. 1689
Cassity, G.M., V.P.-Strategic Mngmt.--BellSouth Telecommunications, Inc., Atlanta, GA; *U.S. Public*, pg. 209
Castillo, Bruce, Sr. Dir.-Plng. & Allocation--Gantos Inc., Stamford, CT; *U.S. Public*, pg. 702
Cate, Tom, Dir.-Strategic Plng.--Analog Devices, Santa Clara, CA; *U.S. Public*, pg. 108
Cauley, Bruce, Sr. V.P.-Devel.--The Dyson-Kissner-Moran Corporation, New York, NY; *U.S. Private*, pg. 351
Cawdron, P.E.B., Grp. Dir.-Strategy Devel.--Grand Metropolitan Plc, London, United Kingdom; *Int'l*, pg. 408
Celentano, Domenick, Chm. Bd. & Pres.--Celentano Bros. Inc., Verona, NJ; *U.S. Private*, pg. 221
Cetti, Carlo, V.P.-Strategic Plng.--Foodmaker, Inc., San Diego, CA; *U.S. Public*, pg. 661
Chadwick, Richard, Dir.-Bus. Devel.--J. Sainsbury plc, London, United Kingdom; *Int'l*, pg. 1169
Chaffin, Sam, V.P.-Fin.--Goodpasture, Inc., Brownfield, TX; *U.S. Private*, pg. 464
Chaigneau, Alain, Sr. V.P.-Strategic Plng.--Compagnie de Suez, Paris, France; *Int'l*, pg. 313
Chambliss, Charles W., V.P.-Prod. Devel. & Engrng.--Skyline Corporation, Elkhart, IN; *U.S. Public*, pg. 1476
Chan, Shufan, V.P.-Devel.--Linfinity Microelectronics Inc., Garden Grove, CA; *U.S. Public*, pg. 1547
Chan, Thomas, Exec. Dir.-Project Plng.--Sun Hung Kai Properties Ltd., Wan Chai, Hong Kong; *Int'l*, pg. 1318
Chandler, Darlene, V.P.-Organization Plng. & Devel.--SunAmerica Inc., Los Angeles, CA; *U.S. Public*, pg. 1532
Chandler, James, V.P.-Planning & Devel.--PLM International, Inc., San Francisco, CA; *U.S. Public*, pg. 1241
Chandler, W.S., Jr., V.P.-Devel.--Glen Raven Mills, Inc., Glen Raven, NC; *U.S. Private*, pg. 456
Chapman, B.P., Dir.-Plng. & Indus. Affairs--Air UK Ltd., Stansted, United Kingdom; *Int'l*, pg. 38
Chapman, Brad, V.P.-Human Resources Devel.--Peter Kiewit Sons Inc., Omaha, NE; *U.S. Private*, pg. 619
Charbin, Jacques, Dir.-Corp. Plng.--Cambridge Shopping Centres Limited, Toronto, Canada; *Int'l*, pg. 253
Charters, James, Mgr.-Trng. & Devel.--Paslode, Vernon Hills, IL; *U.S. Public*, pg. 867
Chase, Stephen G., Dir.-Corp. Plng. & Analysis--CF Industries, Inc., Long Grove, IL; *U.S. Private*, pg. 193
Chaudoin, Elaine, V.P.-Org. Plng. & Devel.--J.B. Hunt Transport Services, Inc., Lowell, AR; *U.S. Public*, pg. 849
Chazen, Stephen I., Exec. V.P.-Corp. Devel.--Occidental Petroleum Corporation, Los Angeles, CA; *U.S. Public*, pg. 1210
Chemers, Joel W., Dir.-Corp. Plng.--Juno Lighting, Inc., Des Plaines, IL; *U.S. Public*, pg. 935
Chen, C.C., Gen. Mgr.-Corp. Plng.--China Steel Corporation, Kao-hsiung, Taiwan; *Int'l*, pg. 285
Chenard, Pierre D., V.P.-Corp. Devel. & Gen. Counsel--Cambior Inc., Montreal, Canada; *Int'l*, pg. 253
Chernow, David S., Chief Devel. Officer & V.P.--American Oncology Resources, Inc., Houston, TX; *U.S. Public*, pg. 88
Cherry, Peter B., Chm. Bd. & Pres.--Cherry Electrical Products Corporation, Waukegan, IL; *U.S. Public*, pg. 346
Chesney, Michael K., V.P.-Corp. Devel.--Telephone and Data Systems, Inc., Chicago, IL; *U.S. Public*, pg. 1570
Chestnut, E. Randall, V.P.-Corp. Devel.--Crown Crafts, Inc., Atlanta, GA; *U.S. Public*, pg. 465
Chestnut, Kathie T., Sr. V.P.-Res. & Devel., Quality Assurance & Pur.--Wendy's International Inc., Dublin, OH; *U.S. Public*, pg. 1754
Chew, Peter, Sr. Mgr.-Corp. Devel.--Orchard Parade Holdings Limited, Singapore, Singapore; *Int'l*, pg. 1007
Chicharro, Pedro, Exec. V.P.-Plng. & Res.--Banco Santander, Madrid, Spain; *Int'l*, pg. 143
Childers, Mark V., Sr. V.P.-Organizational Devel. & Human Resources--Champion International Corp., Stamford, CT; *U.S. Public*, pg. 333
Childress, J. Milton, II, V.P.-Plng. & Devel.--United Dominion Industries, Ltd., Charlotte, NC; *U.S. Public*, pg. 1675
Chin, George, V.P.-Sls., Mktg. & Bus. Devel.--Pharmaceutical Formulations, Inc., Edison, NJ; *U.S. Public*, pg. 1284
Chisholm, Thomas, V.P.-Res. & Devel.--CiMatrix L.L.C., Canton, MA; *U.S. Public*, pg. 1395
Chittick, S. Woodworth, V.P.-Plng. & Bus. Devel.--Ocean Spray Cranberries, Inc., Middleboro, MA; *U.S. Private*, pg. 811
Chmara, Harold J., V.P.-Plng. & Tax--Hudson's Bay Company, Toronto, Canada; *Int'l*, pg. 637
Choi, Won Y., Mgr.-Plng. & Devel.--Crown Confectionery Co., Ltd., Seoul, Korea; *Int'l*, pg. 348
Choquette, Paul J., Jr., Chm. Bd. & Chief Exec. Officer--Gilbane Building Company, Providence, RI; *U.S. Private*, pg. 452
Christensen, Eric D., V.P.-Plng.--SkyWest Inc., Saint George, UT; *U.S. Public*, pg. 1476
Christensen, Eric D., V.P.-Plng.--SkyWest Airlines, Inc., Saint George, UT; *U.S. Public*, pg. 1476
Christensen, J.A., Mgr.-Bus. Devel.--Industrial Electronics Group, Torrance, CA; *U.S. Public*, pg. 1364
Christian, Chip, V.P.-Human Resources--Rocco Inc., Harrisonburg, VA; *U.S. Private*, pg. 937
Christian, David F., Mgr.-Tech. & Devel.--Sheet & Coil Products Division, Port Kembla, Australia; *Int'l*, pg. 227
Christie, William J., V.P.-Corp. Plng. & Taxation--Tridel Enterprises Inc., Downsview, Canada; *Int'l*, pg. 1423
Christmann, John J., IV, Mgr.-Bus. Devel.--Apache Corporation, Houston, TX; *U.S. Public*, pg. 119
Christopher, David A., V.P.-Prod. Devel.--United Family Life Insurance Co., Atlanta, GA; *Int'l*, pg. 499
Chu, Jennifer, V.P.-Fin. Plng. & Analysis--K-III Media Group, New York, NY; *U.S. Public*, pg. 1328
Clark, Bernie S., V.P.-Geo. Information Systems--MacDonald Dettwiler & Associates Ltd., Richmond, Canada; *U.S. Public*, pg. 1229
Clark, Burt, V.P.-Fin.--Champion Ignition Products, Chesterfield, MO; *U.S. Public*, pg. 442
Clark, Donald R., Chm. Bd.--Atlantic Builders Group Inc., Baltimore, MD; *U.S. Private*, pg. 95
Clark, James R., Chief Plng. Officer--American Stores Company, Salt Lake City, UT; *U.S. Public*, pg. 92
Clark, Janet F., Chief Fin. Officer & V.P.--Santa Fe Energy Resources, Inc., Houston, TX; *U.S. Public*, pg. 1431
Clark, Kristin, Exec. V.P.-Bus. Devel. & Customer Rels.--Seattle Pacific Industries, Inc., Seattle, WA; *U.S. Private*, *pg. 980*
Clark, Major L., III, Corp. Sr. V.P.-Corp. Dev. & Admin.--The Maxima Corporation, Lanham, MD; *U.S. Private*, pg. 716
Clark, Stuart L., V.P.-Bus. Devel./DOE Programs--IT Corp., Wilmington, CA; *U.S. Public*, pg. 908
Clark, Tom, V.P.--PCI, Austin, TX; *U.S. Private*, pg. 826
Clarke, Robert G., Mgr.-Business Devel.--Jacobs Engineering Group Inc., Houston, TX; *U.S. Public*, pg. 921
Clarkson, Lawrence W., Sr. V.P.-Plng. & Intl. Devel.--The Boeing Company, Seattle, WA; *U.S. Public*, pg. 239
Clausen, Dick, Chm. Bd., Pres. & Chief Exec. Officer--Verbatim Tape Corporation, San Diego, CA; *Int'l*, pg. 872
Clay, Larry D., Pres. & Chief Exec. Officer--Pacific Coast Producers, Lodi, CA; *U.S. Private*, pg. 830
Clegg, Dennis, Dir.-Plng.--North West Water Limited, Warrington, United Kingdom; *Int'l*, pg. 1444
Clement, Chris, V.P.-Corp. Plng. & Gen. Mgr.-Franchises--Searle & Co., Skokie, IL; *U.S. Public*, pg. 1125
Clement, Chris, V.P.-Corp. Plng. & Gen. Mgr.-Franchises--Searle Laboratories, Skokie, IL; *U.S. Public*, pg. 1125
Clements, Janice, Exec. V.P. & Strategy & Bus. Devel. Dir.--Zenith Media Services, Inc., New York, NY; *U.S. Private*, *pg. 1204*
Clements, M., Dir.-Bus. Devel.--Quadrastat Corp., City of Industry, CA; *U.S. Private*, pg. 17
Clerkin, Tom, V.P. & Dir.-Plng. & Res.--JC Penney Company, Inc., Plano, TX; *U.S. Public*, pg. 916
Clessuras, George J., V.P.-Bus. Devel.--McDermott International, Inc., New Orleans, LA; *U.S. Public*, pg. 1067
Cleveland, C.E. Thomas, Pres.--H.O. Penn Machinery Co. Inc., Poughkeepsie, NY; *U.S. Private*, pg. 849
Clevinger, Norman R., V.P.-Devel. & Plng.--Wolverine Tube Inc., Huntsville, AL; *U.S. Public*, pg. 1774
Cline, Robert T., V.P.-Organization & Plng.--Crowley Foods, Inc., Binghamton, NY; *Int'l*, pg. 752
Close, Edwin, Dir.-Plng. & Construction--Universal Health Services, Inc., King of Prussia, PA; *U.S. Public*, pg. 1696
Clothier, G.S., Sr. V.P.-Fin. & Plng.--The Phillies-A Limited Partnership, Philadelphia, PA; *U.S. Private*, pg. 861
Coady, Todd M., Chm. Bd., Pres. & Chief Exec. Officer--Hicks Oil-Hicks Gas, Inc., Roberts, IL; *U.S. Private*, pg. 526
Coates, Gary, V.P.-Bus. Devel.--Geraghty & Miller, Inc., Denver, CO; *Int'l*, pg. 607
Coblitz, Mark A., V.P.-Strategic Plng.--Comcast Corporation, Philadelphia, PA; *U.S. Public*, pg. 406
Cochran, John E., V.P.-Bus. Devel.--Miltope Corporation, Montgomery, AL; *U.S. Public*, pg. 1114
Cochran, Julie, V.P.-Business Devel.--Total System Services, Inc., Columbus, GA; *U.S. Public*, pg. 1550
Cochran, Mark A., V.P.-H.R. & Org. Strategy--Systems & Computer Technology Corporation, Malvern, PA; *U.S. Public*, pg. 1552
Cochrane, James, Exec. Dir.-Comml. Devel.--Glaxo Wellcome plc, London, United Kingdom; *Int'l*, pg. 552
Coffey, Joseph D., Dr., V.P.-Economics & Strategic Initiatives--Southern States Cooperative, Inc., Richmond, VA; *U.S. Private*, pg. 1017
Coffin, D.M., V.P. & Dir. Business Devel.--Irex Corporation, Lancaster, PA; *U.S. Public*, pg. 913
Coffman, Franklin E., Sr. V.P.-DOE Programs & Corp. Bus. Devel.--International Technology Corporation, Monroeville, PA; *U.S. Public*, pg. 907
Cohen, Donald, Chm. Bd., Pres., Chief Exec. Officer & Chief Fin. Officer--Tool King, Denver, CO; *U.S. Private*, pg. 1091
Cohen, Jon, Dir.-Strategic Plng.--Cowen & Company, New York, NY; *U.S. Private*, pg. 280
Cohen, Lewis M., Pres. & Chief Exec. Officer--Acme Canvas Co., Inc., Malden, MA; *U.S. Private*, pg. 13
Cohen, Richard, Vice Chm.--Norstan, Inc., Plymouth, MN; *U.S. Public*, pg. 1192
Coimbra, Rafael, V.P. & Assoc. Plng. Dir.--Western International Media Corporation, Los Angeles, CA; *U.S. Private*, pg. 1165
Colas, Gilles, Dir.-Corp. Plng.--Saint-Gobain, Courbevoie, France; *Int'l*, pg. 1170
Colbert, Donald W., Pres. & Chief Oper. Officer--S & K Famous Brands, Inc., Glen Allen, VA; *U.S. Public*, pg. 1414
Cole, James D., Chm. Bd., Pres., & Chief Exec. Officer--Newpark Resources, Inc., Metairie, LA; *U.S. Public*, pg. 1179
Collesano, Steven, Dir.-Res. & Devel.--American International Group, Inc., New York, NY; *U.S. Public*, pg. 83
Collette, Bill, V.P.-Engrng. & Devel. & Sec.--Computer Network Technology Corporation, Minneapolis, MN; *U.S.* Public, pg. 421
Collins, David P., Dir.-Fin. Plng.--Nash Finch Company, Edina, MN; *U.S. Public*, pg. 1151
Collins, Don L., Chm. Bd., Pres., Chief Exec. & Oper. Officer--Collins Industries, Inc., Hutchinson, KS; *U.S. Public*, pg. 399
Collins, J. Robert, Dr., V.P.-Strategic Plng. & Devel.--Raytheon E-Systems, Greenville, TX; *U.S. Public*, pg. 1365
Collins, Michael J., Dr., Pres. & Chief Exec. Officer--CEM Corporation, Matthews, NC; *U.S. Public*, pg. 277
Collins, Patrick, V.P.- Bus. Devel.--Rubin Postaer & Associates, Santa Monica, CA; *U.S. Private*, pg. 949
Columbus, Paul, V.P. & Dir.-Plng. & Investor Rels.--NVR, Inc., Mc Lean, VA; *U.S. Public*, pg. 1148
Colvin, Kerry J., Asst. V.P.-Plng.--Blair Corporation, Warren, PA; *U.S. Public*, pg. 236
Comas, Daniel L., V.P.-Corp. Devel.--Danaher Corporation, Washington, DC; *U.S. Public*, pg. 480
Comer, Clarence C., Pres. & Chief Exec. Officer--Southdown, Inc., Houston, TX; *U.S. Public*, pg. 1488
Comer, William T., Ph. D., Sr. V.P.-Strategic Mngmt.--Bristol-Myers Squibb U.S. Pharmaceutical Group, Evansville, IN; *U.S. Public*, pg. 254
Como, John, V.P.-Opers. Analyst & Plng. Resource Mngmt.--Greyhound Lines, Inc., Dallas, TX; *U.S. Public*, pg. 765
Condos, George, Exec. V.P.-Devel.--Wendy's International Inc., Dublin, OH; *U.S. Public*, pg. 1754
Coneval, William, Dir.-Bus. Devel.--Gores Technology Group, Sherman Oaks, CA; *U.S. Private*, pg. 465
Conklin, Carroll, Exec. V.P. & Strategic Services Dir.--Lord, Sullivan & Yoder Inc. Marketing Communications, Columbus, OH; *U.S. Private*, pg. 676
Conlon, Denis P., V.P.-Devel.--Berwind Corporation, Philadelphia, PA; *U.S. Private*, pg. 138
Connell, David W., V.P.-Plng.--Consolidated Natural Gas Company, Pittsburgh, PA; *U.S. Public*, pg. 435
Connell, David W., V.P.-Corp. Plng.--Consolidated Natural Gas Service Co., Inc., Pittsburgh, PA; *U.S. Public*, pg. 435
Connell, Rosemary, Corp. Plng. Exec.--Unigate PLC, London, United Kingdom; *Int'l*, pg. 1433
Connelly, Thomas S., Chm. Bd., Pres., Chief Exec. Officer--Connelly Containers, Inc., Bala Cynwyd, PA; *U.S. Private*, pg. 264
Conrad, John R., Chm. Bd.--S & C Electric Company, Chicago, IL; *U.S. Private*, pg. 954
Constantin, Gus, Chm. Bd., Pres. & Chief Exec. Officer--Phoenix American Incorporated, San Rafael, CA; *U.S. Private*, pg. 862
Conway, James F., III, Chm. Bd., Pres., Chief Oper. & Exec. Officer--Courier Corporation, North Chelmsford, MA; *U.S.* Public, pg. 453
Coogan, Kevin, Plng. Dir.-East Coast--Western Direct, New York, NY; *U.S. Private*, pg. 1166
Cook, Greg, Pres. & Chief Oper. Officer--Cook Manufacturing Corporation, Duncan, OK; *U.S. Private*, pg. 272
Cook, Owen, Dir.-Corp. Plng.--Mississippi Chemical Corporation, Yazoo City, MS; *U.S. Public*, pg. 1117
Cook, Robert E., Pres.--Frigidaire Home Products, Augusta, GA; *Int'l*, pg. 439
Cook, Stephani, Exec. V.P. & Strategic Plng. Dir.--Lowe & Partners/SMS, New York, NY; *U.S. Private*, pg. 678
Cook, William S., Jr., V.P.-Strategic Plng. & Acq.--L.B. Foster Company, Pittsburgh, PA; *U.S. Public*, pg. 675
Cooley, Charles, V.P.-Bus. Devel.--Browning-Ferris Industries, Inc., Houston, TX; *U.S. Public*, pg. 262
Cooley, Harold E., V.P.--G B Stores, Columbus, OH; *U.S. Private*, pg. 972
Coon, Howard A., IV, V.P.-Corp. Devel.--UNUM Corporation, Portland, ME; *U.S. Public*, pg. 1699
Cooper, Byron T., V.P.-Construction & Plng.--Ridgewood Properties, Inc., Atlanta, GA; *U.S. Public*, pg. 1389
Cooper, Marshall Y., Jr., Chm. Bd., Chief Exec. Officer & Pres.--Harriet & Henderson Yarns, Inc., Henderson, NC; *U.S. Private*, pg. 504
Cooper, Myron, V.P.-Devel.--Westbrae Natural Foods, Inc., Carson, CA; *U.S. Public*, pg. 774

Cooper, Russell L., Sr. V.P.-Franchising & Devel.--Shoney's, Inc., Nashville, TN; *U.S. Public*, pg. 1467
Cooper, Steven D., Sr. V.P.-Plng., Gen. Counsel & Sec.--Electrolux Corporation, Atlanta, GA; *U.S. Private*, pg. 369
Corbin, Karen C., Sr. V.P.-Programming & Devel.--Tribune Entertainment Company, Los Angeles, CA; *U.S. Public*, pg. 1636
Cordes, Eckhard, Dr., Dir.-Corp. Rail & Microelectronics--Daimler-Benz Aktiengesellschaft, Stuttgart, Germany; *Int'l*, pg. 366
Corfield, James, Mgr.-Corp. Devel.--Novartis Seeds, Inc., Downers Grove, IL; *Int'l*, pg. 974
Corley, L., Gen. Mgr.-Fin. & Plng./Housewares Div.--McPherson's Limited, Mulgrave, Australia; *Int'l*, pg. 852
Cornell, Ed, Exec. V.P.-New Bus. Devel.--OfficeMax, Shaker Heights, OH; *U.S. Public*, pg. 1212
Cornell, Linda, V.P.-Plng. & Res.--Sive/Young & Rubicam L.P., Cincinnati, OH; *U.S. Private*, pg. 1197
Cornely, Joseph H., III, 1st Sr. V.P., Dir.-Store Plng. & Mgr.-Real Estate--J. Baker, Inc., Canton, MA; *U.S. Public*, pg. 167
Corradded, P., Mgr.-Bus. Devel.--ANTEA SA, Orleans, France; *Int'l*, pg. 607
Corrias, Alberto, Assoc. Mgr.-Intl. & Devel.--IRI Istituto Ricostruzione Industriale, Rome, Italy; *Int'l*, pg. 652
Corso, Thomas, Dir.-Prod. Devel. & Plng.--Skinner Valve Division, New Britain, CT; *U.S. Public*, pg. 1260
Cortesi, Giuseppe, Dir.-New Initiatives & Devel.--Agusta S.P.A., Varese, Italy; *Int'l*, pg. 32
Corty, Andrew, V.P.-Affiliates & Plng.--The Times Publishing Co., Saint Petersburg, FL; *U.S. Private*, pg. 1087
Cosbey, Rick, Mgr.-Corp. Devel.--Dunn-Edwards Corporation, Los Angeles, CA; *U.S. Private*, pg. 347
Coster, Malcom, Sr. V.P.-Strategic Bus. Devel.--Unisys Corporation, Blue Bell, PA; *U.S. Public*, pg. 1671
Cothran, Larry, Sr. V.P.-Plng.--Huitt-Zollars, Inc., Dallas, TX; *U.S. Private*, pg. 547
Cotman, Roger, Chemist--Berryman Products, Inc., Arlington, TX; *U.S. Private*, pg. 138
Cotter, John, Sr. V.P.-Bus. Devel.--Paul Arpin Vanlines, Inc., West Warwick, RI; *U.S. Private*, pg. 85
Cottle, Gail, Exec. V.P.-Prod. Devel.--Nordstrom, Inc., Seattle, WA; *U.S. Public*, pg. 1190
Coulter, John, V.P.-Plng. & Tech.--MTA Long Island Rail Road, Jamaica, NY; *U.S. Private*, pg. 739
Countryman, Peter J., Chief Fin. Officer & Treas.--Sabin Robbins Paper Co., Cincinnati, OH; *U.S. Private*, pg. 959
Courtoy, Jean-Francois, V.P.-Res. & Devel.--Domco Inc., Farnham, Canada; *Int'l*, pg. 415
Couvert, J., Dir.-Civil Engrng., Real Estate & Land Devel.--SNCF, Paris, France; *Int'l*, pg. 1163
Coventry, Mary, V.P.-Corp. Devel.--Sealed Air Corporation, Saddle Brook, NJ; *U.S. Public*, pg. 1450
Cowan, Keith O., V.P.-Corp. Dev.--BellSouth Corporation, Atlanta, GA; *U.S. Public*, pg. 207
Cowart, D.R., Pres.--The Wm. Powell Company, Cincinnati, OH; *U.S. Private*, pg. 877
Cowart, Jim C., Chm. Bd. & Chief Exec. Officer--Aurora Electronics, Inc., Irvine, CA; *U.S. Public*, pg. 147
Cowart, Lawrence R., V.P. & Dir.-Bus. Devel.--The Coca-Cola Company, Atlanta, GA; *U.S. Public*, pg. 392
Cowles, Alfred L., III, Chief Fin. Officer, Treas. & Controller--Bluff City Distributing Co., Inc., Memphis, TN; *U.S. Private*, pg. 153
Cox, Alistair R., Dir.-Grp. Strategy--Blue Circle Industries PLC, London, United Kingdom; *Int'l*, pg. 197
Cragg, Bernard, Chief Fin. Officer & Dir.-Strategy & Devel.--Carlton Communications Plc, London, United Kingdom; *Int'l*, pg. 272
Craig, Maureen, Sr. V.P. & Strategic Plng. Dir.--DMB&B Los Angeles, Los Angeles, CA; *U.S. Private*, pg. 303
Cramer, Clifford S., V.P.-Plng. & Devel.--Merck & Co., Inc., Whitehouse Station, NJ; *U.S. Public*, pg. 1090
Crandell, Donnie, Sr. V.P.-Corp. Devel. & Pres.-MP/Real Estate Holdings--Minnesota Power, Duluth, MN; *U.S. Public*, pg. 1116
Cravens, Neal, V.P.-Plng. & Analysis--Joseph E. Seagram & Sons, Inc., New York, NY; *Int'l*, pg. 1215
Crawford, Gary, V.P.-Major Projects Div.--East Kentucky Power Co-op, Winchester, KY; *U.S. Private*, pg. 356
Cray, Cloud L., Jr., Chm. Bd.--Midwest Grain Products, Inc., Atchison, KS; *U.S. Public*, pg. 1111
Cribb, Ray, Mgr.-Res. & Devel.--Brush Wellman Inc., Cleveland, OH; *U.S. Public*, pg. 266
Crispin, George, V.P.-Industrial & Domestic Bus. Devel.--Agripac Inc., Salem, OR; *U.S. Private*, pg. 26
Criss, Barry E., Asst. V.P.-Store Devel.--Rite Aid Corporation, Camp Hill, PA; *U.S. Public*, pg. 1390
Crittenden, Gary L., Pres.-Hardware Stores--Sears, Roebuck and Co., Hoffman Estates, IL; *U.S. Public*, pg. 1452
Crocker, Will, Pres. & Chief Exec. Officer--Arnot Controls Corporation, Richmond, CA; *U.S. Public*, pg. 1405
Crockrom, Duane M., Mgr.-Corp. Devel.--Parker Hannifin Corporation, Cleveland, OH; *U.S. Public*, pg. 1259
Croft, James J., V.P.-Res. & Devel.--Carver Corporation, Lynnwood, WA; *U.S. Public*, pg. 310
Crombie, Brian H., V.P.-Plng. & Corp. Devel.--The Molson Companies Limited, Toronto, Canada; *Int'l*, pg. 887
Crotty, Brian, Exec. V.P.-Bus. Plng.--Elan Corporation Plc, Dublin, Ireland; *Int'l*, pg. 435
Crouch, Ron, Dir.-Design & Construction--W.M. Grace Development, Phoenix, AZ; *U.S. Private*, pg. 468
Crovetto, Mario, Dir.-Corp. Devel.--Recordati Industria Chimica e Farmaceutica S.p.A., Milan, Italy; *Int'l*, pg. 1090
Crovitz, Charles K., Sr. V.P.-Strategic Plng. & Bus. Devel.--The Gap, Inc., San Francisco, CA; *U.S. Public*, pg. 702
Crowe, Peter, Dir.-Sys. Devel.--Dixons Group plc, Hemel Hempstead, United Kingdom,; *Int'l*, pg. 413
Crozer, Robert P., Vice Chm.--Flowers Industries, Inc., Thomasville, GA; *U.S. Public*, pg. 656
Crum, David H., Pres., Chief Exec. & Chief Fin. Officer--Crum Electric Supply Co., Inc., Casper, WY; *U.S. Private*, *pg. 293*
Crummet, Stephen, Mgr.-Corp. Devel.--McKechnie PLC, Walsall, United Kingdom; *Int'l*, pg. 851
Cucchi, Gregory A., V.P.-Plng. & Devel.--PECO Energy Company, Philadelphia, PA; *U.S. Public*, pg. 1268
Cummins, Andrew, Grp. Dir.-Strategic Devel.--Inchcape PLC, London, United Kingdom; *Int'l*, pg. 671
Cuneo, Ngaire E., Exec. V.P.-Corp. Devel.--Conseco Inc., Carmel, IN; *U.S. Public*, pg. 432
Curling, Kay, Assoc. Dir.-Plng. & Opers.--SRA International Inc., Arlington, VA; *U.S. Private*, pg. 957
Curran, Brian, Acting V.P.-Bus. Devel.--SaskPower Commercial, Regina, Canada; *Int'l*, pg. 1196
Curran, Timothy J., Exec. V.P. & Gen. Counsel--Curran Group, Inc., Crystal Lake, IL; *U.S. Private*, pg. 297
Currey, Russell M., Sr. V.P.-Mktg. & Plng.--Rock-Tenn Company, Norcross, GA; *U.S. Public*, pg. 1396
Curry, Gael A., V.P.-Corp. Devel.--Sequent Computer Systems, Inc., Beaverton, OR; *U.S. Public*, pg. 1459
Curvale, Jean, Dir.-Corp. Devel.--Alcatel N.V., Amsterdam, Netherlands; *Int'l*, pg. 55
Cusimano, Louis, Dir.-Bus. Devel.--Power Contracting & Engineering Corp., Schaumburg, IL; *U.S. Private*, pg. 877
Cutts, Crawford L., V.P.-Bus. Devel.--SpecTran Corporation, Sturbridge, MA; *U.S. Public*, pg. 1497
Cutwright, Brenda F., Chief Fin. Officer & Sr. V.P.-Fin. & Plng.--Island Air, Honolulu, HI; *U.S. Private*, pg. 44
Cyr, Jean-Claude, V.P.-Devel. & Planning--Caisse de depot et placement du Quebec, Montreal, Canada; *Int'l*, pg. 249
D'Alessandro, Richard, Dir.-Strategic Plng. & Projects--National Forge Company, Irvine, PA; *U.S. Private*, pg. 783
D'Amico, Joe, V.P.-Devel.--Swift Energy Company, Houston, TX; *U.S. Public*, pg. 1543
D'Entreves, Jean-Claude, Dir.-Intl. Devel. & Europe--Societe BIC S.A., Clichy, France; *Int'l*, pg. 1272
da Cruz, Marques, Dr., Dir. Gen.-Corp. Plng.--Transportes Aereos Portugueses, Lisbon, Portugal; *Int'l*, pg. 1418
Daar, Dennis, V.P.-Devel.--Hausted, Medina, OH; *U.S. Private*, pg. 1001
Dack, Jerilyn, Sr. V.P., Media Dir. & Consumer Plng. Dir.--Hill, Holliday/Altschiller, New York, NY; *U.S. Private*, pg. 529
Dahl, Cheri, Dir.-Devel.--Christian Children's Fund, Inc., Richmond, VA; *U.S. Private*, pg. 238
Dahlberg, Burton F., Pres. & Chief Oper. Officer--Kraus-Anderson, Incorporated, Minneapolis, MN; *U.S. Private*, pg. 635
Dai, W.Y., Dir.-Plng. Div.--Chinese Petroleum Corporation, Taipei, Taiwan; *Int'l*, pg. 286
Dalal, Rajen K., V.P.-Corp. Plng. & Bus. Devel.--Chiron Corporation, Emeryville, CA; *U.S. Public*, pg. 349
Dalbeck, Richard W., Exec. V.P., Chief Fin. Officer & Sec.--The Guber Peters Entertainment Company, Los Angeles, CA; *Int'l*, pg. 1283
Dalby, Michael T., V.P.-Strategic Plng.--McKesson Corporation, San Francisco, CA; *U.S. Public*, pg. 1072
Dallas, Keith B., Dir.-Bus. Devel.--R.R. Donnelley, Limited-York, York, United Kingdom; *U.S. Public*, pg. 519
Dalton, Robb, Sr. V.P.-Bus. & Program Devel.--CBS Enterprises Division, New York, NY; *U.S. Public*, pg. 274
Daly, Julie L., V.P.-Strategic Plng.--United Retail Group, Inc., Rochelle Park, NJ; *U.S. Public*, pg. 1679
Daly, Leo A., Chm. Bd., Pres. & Treas.--Leo A. Daly Company, Omaha, NE; *U.S. Private*, pg. 309
Dana, Charles H., Exec. V.P.-Devel., Plng. & Sourcing--Owens Corning, Toledo, OH; *U.S. Public*, pg. 1236
Daniel, E. Leaon, Exec. V.P.-Intl. EOR & Bus. Devel.--Occidental Oil & Gas Corporation, Bakersfield, CA; *U.S. Public*, pg. 1210
Daniels, Dennis, Exec. V.P.-Domestic Devel.--United Artists Theatre Circuits Incorporated, Englewood, CO; *U.S. Private*, pg. 1120
Daniels, John, Mgr.-Bus. Devel.--Banner Aerospace, Inc., Washington, DC; *U.S. Public*, pg. 187
Daniels, Lawrence S., V.P.-Strategic Plng.--Biogen, Inc., Cambridge, MA; *U.S. Public*, pg. 228
Danzer, Dave, V.P.-Corp. Plng.--Toyota Motor Sales, U.S.A., Inc., Torrance, CA; *Int'l*, pg. 1412
Danzer, David, Mgr.-Corp. Plng.--Toyota Motor Sales, U.S.A., Inc., Torrance, CA; *Int'l*, pg. 1412
Darbaz, Tufan, Dir.-Plng. & Investment--Sabanci Holding A.S., Istanbul, Turkey; *Int'l*, pg. 1167
Darroman, Jean-Baptiste, V.P.-Strategy & Plng.--Elf Aquitane, Paris, France; *Int'l*, pg. 444
Dauer, John L., Exec. Dir.-Plng. & Devel.--Campbell-Ewald Advertising, Warren, MI; *U.S. Public*, pg. 908
Dauger, Jean-Marie, Exec. V.P.-Corp. Plng. & Control--Gaz de France, Paris, France; *Int'l*, pg. 541
Davey, Keith, Dir.-Business Devel.--Sifto Canada, Inc., Mississauga, Canada; *U.S. Private*, pg. 505
Davidson, Brian, Exec. V.P.-Devel.--Integrated Health Services, Inc., Owings Mills, MD; *U.S. Public*, pg. 884
Davidson, Stephen A., Sr. V.P.-Org. Devel.--GTECH Corporation, West Greenwich, RI; *U.S. Public*, pg. 767
Davidson, Wesley, V.P.-Corp. Devel.--Alberto-Culver Company, Melrose Park, IL; *U.S. Public*, pg. 37
Davies, Simon, Dir.-Plng. & Analysis--Dixons Group plc, Hemel Hempstead, United Kingdom,; *Int'l*, pg. 413
Davis, Cindy, Sr. V.P.-Bus. Devel.--The Arnold Palmer Golf Company, Ooltewah, TN; *U.S. Public*, pg. 132
Davis, David, Dir.-Bus. Devel.--Dowty Aerospace, Abingdon, United Kingdom; *Int'l*, pg. 1337
Davis, Gary B., Chief Fin. Officer & Treas.--Polk Audio, Inc., Baltimore, MD; *U.S. Public*, pg. 1315
Davis, Joel P., Sr. V.P.-Plng. & Devel.--The Gillette Company, Boston, MA; *U.S. Public*, pg. 743
Davis, Kenneth A., Pres., Chief Exec. Officer & Chief Oper. Officer--PharmHouse, Inc., New York, NY; *U.S. Public*, pg. 1286
Davis, Minda, Corp. V.P.-Organization, Devel. & Communications--The Canada Life Assurance Company, Toronto, Canada; *Int'l*, pg. 254
Dawahare, Joe, Dir.-Govt. Affairs & Gen. Counsel--Dawahares, Inc., Lexington, KY; *U.S. Private*, pg. 316
De Biaso, Carlos E., Mgr.-Devel.--Bundy Argentina SA, Victoria, Argentina; *Int'l*, pg. 1342
De Blasio, Michael P., Chief Fin. Officer & Sr. V.P.--Loral Space & Communications, New York, NY; *U.S. Public*, pg. 1014
de Burckhart, Maria Isabel, Exec. V.P.-Corp. Plng. & Fin.--Banco Popular de Puerto Rico, San Juan, PR; *U.S. Public*, pg. 175
de Crook, Roger, Mng. Dir.-Oper. & Devel.--STAHLwerke Bremen GmbH, Bremen, Germany; *Int'l*, pg. 79
de Eca, Isabel, Mgr.-Corp. Plng.--Central de Cervejas, S.A., Lisbon, Portugal; *Int'l*, pg. 279
de Koning, Ph.J., Gen. Mgr.-Mgmnt. Devel.--ING Groep N.V., Amsterdam, Netherlands; *Int'l*, pg. 647
De Macchi, Alberto, Dir.-Strategic Studies--Olivetti SpA, Turin, Italy; *Int'l*, pg. 1002
De Mange, Lorraine Petit, Mgr.-Mktg. Devel.--Transnet Group, London, United Kingdom; *Int'l*, pg. 1418
De Montfalcon, Xavier, V.P.-Strategy--Schneider S.A., Boulogne-Billancourt, France; *Int'l*, pg. 1207
De Simone, Lawrence E., V.P.-Strategic Planning--Central and South West Corporation, Dallas, TX; *U.S. Public*, pg. 324
Dean, Alan, Dir.-Business Devel.--United Utilities plc, Warrington, United Kingdom; *Int'l*, pg. 1444
Dean, Jay, Exec. V.P., Strategic Planning Dir. & Digital Branding Dir.--Young & Rubicam San Francisco, San Francisco, CA; *U.S. Private*, pg. 1198
DeAngelo, Thomas J., Chief Fin. Officer, Treas. & Sec.--Isomedix Inc., Whippany, NJ; *U.S. Public*, pg. 1515
Dearman, Charles, Dir.-Bus. Devel.--IEC Electronics Corp., Newark, NY; *U.S. Public*, pg. 854
DeChandt, John F., V.P.-Tech. Svcs. & New Prods.--Herbert Malarkey Roofing Company, Portland, OR; *U.S. Private*, pg. 698
DeCou, Dave, V.P.-Corp. Devel.--Bass Pro Shops, Inc., Springfield, MO; *U.S. Private*, pg. 122
Decyk, Roxanne J., V.P.-Plng.--Amoco Corporation, Chicago, IL; *U.S. Public*, pg. 101
Deegan, Donald, V.P.-Corp. Devel. & Plng.--Oil-Dri Corporation of America, Chicago, IL; *U.S. Public*, pg. 1214
Deering, Jeremy, Mgr.-Inv. Rels & Plng.--United Utilities plc, Warrington, United Kingdom; *Int'l*, pg. 1444
Dees, Steve, Exec. V.P.-Corp. Rels., Commun. & Intl. Svcs.--Farmland Industries, Inc., Kansas City, MO; *U.S. Private*, *pg. 395*
Defenbach, Byron, Mgr.-Program Devel. & Planning--Intermountain Gas Co., Boise, ID; *U.S. Private*, pg. 568
Deiter, Jon, Chief Fin. Officer & V.P.--Gerber Plumbing Fixtures Corporation, Chicago, IL; *U.S. Private*, pg. 449
Del Sontro, Rick, Sr. V.P.-Franchise Sls. & Devel.--Century 21 Real Estate Corp., Parsippany, NJ; *U.S. Public*, pg. 321
DeLaurentiis, John, Deputy Exec. Dir.-Plng. & Devel.--Regional Transportation Authority (RTA), Chicago, IL; *U.S. Private*, pg. 918
Delisle, Andre, Chief Fin. Officer & Exec. V.P.-Corp. Plng.--Hydro-Quebec, Montreal, Canada; *Int'l*, pg. 640
Dellamano, Patricia, Pres. & Chief Exec. & Chief Fin. Officer--Patson's Press, Sunnyvale, CA; *U.S. Private*, pg. 843
DeMartini, Michael J., Dir.-Corp. Devel.--K2 Inc., Los Angeles, CA; *U.S. Public*, pg. 940
Demere, Robert H., Jr., Pres. & Chief Exec. Officer--Colonial Oil Industries, Savannah, GA; *U.S. Private*, pg. 253
DeMesquita, Brent P., V.P.-Organizational Plng. & Mngmt. Devel.--Buffets, Inc., Eden Prairie, MN; *U.S. Public*, pg. 267
Demetter, Richard, Chief Fin. Officer & V.P.-Fin.--Sifco Industries, Inc., Cleveland, OH; *U.S. Public*, pg. 1470
Deming, Thomas, V.P. & Dir.-Fin., Plng. & Opers.--McDougal/Littell, Evanston, IL; *U.S. Public*, pg. 841
DeMoulas, Telemachus A., Pres. & Chief Exec. Officer--Demoulas Market Basket, Tewksbury, MA; *U.S. Private*, pg. 324
Deneka, Charles W., Sr. V.P.-Science & Tech.--Corning Incorporated, Corning, NY; *U.S. Public*, pg. 448
Dennison, John, Reg. Dir.-Bus. Devel.--Messier-Dowty International Marketing, Saint Louis, MO; *Int'l*, pg. 1340
Denny, Dwight D., Exec. V.P.-Devel.--Ryder System, Inc., Miami, FL; *U.S. Public*, pg. 1413
Dent, Doug, Dir.-Bus. Devel.--Weaver Popcorn Company, Inc., Van Buren, IN; *U.S. Private*, pg. 1156
Denton, Donald H., Jr., Sr. V.P. & Chief Plng. Officer--Duke Energy Corporation, Charlotte, NC; *U.S. Public*, pg. 534
DePaul, John D., Chm. Bd., Pres. & Chief Exec. Officer--The Lehigh Press, Inc., Cherry Hill, NJ; *U.S. Private*, pg. 658
DeSeta, Alfred, V.P.-Devel.--Primedia Inc., Mahwah, NJ; *U.S. Public*, pg. 1328
DeSimone, Samuel, Jr., V.P.-Corp. Devel.--Merix Corporation, Forest Grove, OR; *U.S. Public*, pg. 1096
DeSio, Robert J., V.P.-Franchise Support--Mail Boxes Etc. USA, San Diego, CA; *U.S. Public*, pg. 1687
Detz, Lewis W., Dir.-Bus. Devel.--ARGOSystems, Inc., Sunnyvale, CA; *U.S. Public*, pg. 240
Devereux, Paul, Gen. Mgr.-Bus. Devel.--Pacific Dunlop Limited, Melbourne, Australia; *Int'l*, pg. 1021
Devitre, Dinyar, Sr. V.P.-Corp. Plng.--Philip Morris Companies Inc., New York, NY; *U.S. Public*, pg. 1287
DeVittorio, Joseph M., V.P.-Corp. Plng.--Shaw Industries, Inc., Dalton, GA; *U.S. Public*, pg. 1464
Devlin, R., Sr. V.P.-Devel.--Hilton International Co., Coral Gables, FL; *Int'l*, pg. 787
Dews, N., Mgr.-New Bus. Devel.--John Fairfax Holdings Limited, Sydney, Australia; *Int'l*, pg. 477
Deyhimy, Ira, V.P.-Prod. Devel.--Vitesse Semiconductor Corporation, Camarillo, CA; *U.S. Public*, pg. 1723

Dickens, Jackie, Reg. Dir.-Strategic Plng.--Leo Burnett Worldwide Asia/Pacific Hdqtrs., Hong Kong, Hong Kong; *U.S. Private*, pg. 186
Dickerson, A. Lee, Sr. V.P.-Provider Networks--First Health Group Corp., Downers Grove, IL; *U.S. Public*, pg. 635
Dickerson, Frank M., Chief Fin. Officer, V.P., Gen. Counsel & Sec.--Harza Engineering Co., Chicago, IL; *U.S. Private, pg. 509*
Dickinson, Jeff, Exec. Dir.-Planning--GM Powertrain Group, Pontiac, MI; *U.S. Public*, pg. 719
Dickson, David N., Grp. V.P.-Intl. & Corp. Devel.--Hormel Foods Corp., Austin, MN; *U.S. Public*, pg. 840
Dienes, George L., V.P.-Corp. Devel.--Telephone and Data Systems, Inc., Chicago, IL; *U.S. Public*, pg. 1570
Diesen, M., Dir.-Plng.--Enso Oyj, Helsinki, Finland; *Int'l*, pg. 455
Dikkers, G.J.O.D., Dir.-Plng. & Information--Wavin Bv, Zwolle, Netherlands; *Int'l*, pg. 1135
Dikshit, B.N., Dir.-Tech. Plng. & Projects--Central Coalfields Limited, Ranchi, India; *Int'l*, pg. 298
Dillon, Adrian T., Chief Fin. Officer, Plng. Officer & Exec. V.P.--Eaton Corporation, Cleveland, OH; *U.S. Public*, pg. 555
Dilworth, Robert H., V.P.-Bus. Devel.--Computer Language Research, Inc., Carrollton, TX; *U.S. Public*, pg. 421
Dingley, A.J., Dir.-Plng. & Bus. Devel.--Ranger Oil (U.K.) Ltd., Guildford, United Kingdom; *Int'l*, pg. 1086
DiNicola, Joseph A., Exec. V.P.--Payless Car Rental System, Inc., Saint Petersburg, FL; *U.S. Private*, pg. 844
Dinsmore, Gerald K., Sr. V.P.-Fin. & Plng.--GTE North Incorporated, Irving, TX; *U.S. Public*, pg. 696
Dinsmore, Gerald K., Sr. V.P.-Fin. & Plng.--GTE South Incorporated, Irving, TX; *U.S. Public*, pg. 697
DiStefano, William, V.P.-Bus. Devel.--Autotote Corporation, Newark, DE; *U.S. Public*, pg. 150
Divelbiss, Ernie, Mgr.-Market Res.--Bush Hog Division, Selma, AL; *U.S. Public*, pg. 48
Dixon, Debra, Strategic Plng. Dir.--Italia Advertising, Dallas, TX; *U.S. Private*, pg. 576
Dmohowski, David, V.P.-Land Plng.--Tejon Ranch Company, Lebec, CA; *U.S. Public*, pg. 1566
Dobbs-Melton, Diana, V.P.-Plng. & Distr.--Gymboree Corporation, Burlingame, CA; *U.S. Public*, pg. 770
Dodds, William R., Sr. V.P.-Strategic Plng.--Northern Trust Corporation, Chicago, IL; *U.S. Public*, pg. 1195
Dodson, Bill D., V.P.-Fin. & Treas.--Marathon Electric Manufacturing Corp., Wausau, WI; *U.S. Public*, pg. 1371
Doenges, Peter K., Dir.-Strategic Tech.--Simulation Division, Salt Lake City, UT; *U.S. Public*, pg. 596
Doerfler, Ronald J., Chief Fin. Officer & Sr. V.P.--ABC, Inc, New York, NY; *U.S. Public*, pg. 511
Doerle, Duane, V.P.-Corp. Devel.--Federal Signal Corporation, Oak Brook, IL; *U.S. Public*, pg. 616
Dolbec, Michael, V.P.-Bus. Devel.--3Com Corporation, Santa Clara, CA; *U.S. Public*, pg. 1603
Dolce, Howard, V.P.-Retail Bus. Devel.--SNE Enterprises, Inc., Mosinee, WI; *U.S. Public*, pg. 1193
Dolle, Guy, Exec. V.P.--Groupe Usinor, Paris, France; *Int'l*, pg. 570
Dommel, Norbert, Strategic Plng. & Res. Dir.-Germany--DMB&B Frankfurt, Frankfurt/Main, Germany; *U.S. Private*, pg. 303
Don, Steve R., V.P.-Plng. & Devel.--Edward Don & Company, North Riverside, IL; *U.S. Private*, pg. 339
Donald, David, V.P.-Fin. & Plng.--Cooper Power Tools Division, Lexington, SC; *U.S. Public*, pg. 444
Donaldson, Darrell, Pres. & Chief Exec. Officer--Hot Shot Delivery Inc., Houston, TX; *U.S. Private*, pg. 541
Donaldson, William H., Sr. Advisor--Donaldson, Lufkin, & Jenrette, Inc., New York, NY; *U.S. Public*, pg. 589
Donlin, Bill, Sr. V.P.-Strategic Devel.--Dugan Valva Contess Inc., Morristown, NJ; *U.S. Private*, pg. 345
Dooley, Thomas E., Dep. Chm. & Exec. V.P.-Fin., Corp. Devel. & Communications--Viacom Inc., New York, NY; *U.S. Private*, pg. 775
Dooley, Thomas E., Sr. V.P.-Corp. Devel.--Viacom Broadcasting Inc., New York, NY; *U.S. Private*, pg. 778
Dooley, Thomas E., Sr. V.P.-Corp Devel.--Viacom Entertainment, Universal City, CA; *U.S. Private*, pg. 778
Doolin, Wallace, Exec. V.P.-Franchise & Corp. Devel.--TGI Friday's, Inc., Addison, TX; *U.S. Private*, pg. 212
Doordan, John M., V.P.-Sls./Bus. Devel.--QAD Inc, Carpinteria, CA; *U.S. Public*, pg. 1345
Doppstadt, William K., V.P.-Personnel Rels.--Newell Co., Freeport, IL; *U.S. Public*, pg. 1176
Dorfman, Robert M., Sr. V.P.-Mktg. & Bus. Devel.--Marriott Distribution Services (MDS), Washington, DC; *U.S. Public*, pg. 1048
Dorme, Patrick J., Chief Fin. Officer & V.P.-Fin.--Dynamics Corporation of America, Greenwich, CT; *U.S. Public*, pg. 286
Dorn, William Jennings B., Jr., Dir.-Bus. Devel.--Cox Enterprises, Inc., Atlanta, GA; *U.S. Private*, pg. 281
Dornbush, Dave, Chief Strategic Officer--Nesco Ameican Harvest Inc., Chaska, MN; *U.S. Private*, pg. 735
Douglass, John P., V.P.-Plng. & Control--Pest Elimination, Grand Forks, ND; *U.S. Public*, pg. 562
Douin, Georges, Exec. V.P.-Strategic Plng. & Intl. Opers.--Renault, Boulogne-Billancourt, France; *Int'l*, pg. 1102
Douma, J., Mgr.-Mktg. & Prod. Devel.--National Electrical Carbon Canada, Mississauga, Canada; *Int'l*, pg. 892
Dow, Kevin D., V.P.-Treas., Corp. Devel. & Admin.--HMI Industries, Cleveland, OH; *U.S. Public*, pg. 771
Dowling, Richard P., Sr. V.P.-Corp. Devel.--General Communication, Inc., Anchorage, AK; *U.S. Public*, pg. 708
Downey, J. Michael, Pres.--Downey Printing, Waukee, IA; *U.S. Private*, pg. 342
Doyle, William H.W., Sr. V.P.-Devel.--TrizecHahn Centers Inc., San Diego, CA; *Int'l*, pg. 1425
Drake, D. Robert, Dir.-Plng. & Devel.--North Carolina Mutual Life Insurance Co., Durham, NC; *U.S. Private*, pg. 804
Draper, Brian, Dir.-Devel.--Willis Corroon Midlands Limited, Birmingham, United Kingdom; *Int'l*, pg. 1502
Dreher, Joel, Mgr.-Plng & Devel.--Sound Advice, Inc., Dania, FL; *U.S. Public*, pg. 1488
Dresser, W. Donald, Exec. V.P., Dir.-Devel. & Asst. Sec.--United Foods, Inc., Bells, TN; *U.S. Public*, pg. 1677
Drezner, Stephen M., Sr. V.P.-Plng. & Special Programs--RAND, Santa Monica, CA; *U.S. Private*, pg. 908
Driscoll, Lisa Clark, V.P.--National Health Care Affiliates, Inc., Buffalo, NY; *U.S. Private*, pg. 784
Driver, Timothy S., Dir.-Corp. Devel.--Driver-Harris Company, Harrison, NJ; *U.S. Public*, pg. 530
du Bois, M.D., Dir.-Bus. Devel.--Spadel SA, Brussels, Belgium; *Int'l*, pg. 1287
Dubois, Michel, Corp. V.P.-Strategy, Quality & Innovation--Sodexho S.A., Montigny-le-Bretonneux, France; *Int'l*, pg. 1274
Duck, J., Dir.-Strategic Plng.--Bass Brewers Ltd., Burton on Trent, United Kingdom; *Int'l*, pg. 170
Ducote, Jere E., Mgr.-Business Devel.--Jacobs Engineering Group Inc., Houston, TX; *U.S. Public*, pg. 921
Dudchenko, Peter, V.P.-Corp. Devel. & Asst. Sec.--Citation Corporation, Birmingham, AL; *U.S. Public*, pg. 376
Duff, James K., V.P.-Bus. Devel.--Coeur D'Alene Mines Corporation, Coeur D'Alene, ID; *U.S. Public*, pg. 394
Duffield, Jeremy G., Sr. V.P.-Plng. & Devel.--The Vanguard Group, Inc., Valley Forge, PA; *U.S. Private*, pg. 1133
Duffy, Dennis J., Sr. V.P.-Customer Service Plng. & Delivery--Union Pacific Railroad Company, Omaha, NE; *U.S. Public*, pg. 1668
Duffy, Raymond G., V.P.-Plng.--Jefferson Smurfit Corporation, Saint Louis, MO; *Int'l*, pg. 1269
Dunbar, David, Dir.-Bus. Devel.--Weir Group PLC, Glasgow, United Kingdom; *Int'l*, pg. 1488
Dunham, Michael D., Pres. & Chief Exec. Officer--Effective Management Systems, Milwaukee, WI; *U.S. Public*, pg. 565
Dunivant, Noel, Dr., Sr. V.P.-Res. & Strategic Plng.--FGI Inc., Chapel Hill, NC; *U.S. Private*, pg. 389
Dunleavy, Michael F., V.P.-Bus. Devel.--Crown Cork & Seal Company, Inc., Philadelphia, PA; *U.S. Public*, pg. 462
Dunn, Robert J., Sr. V.P. & Dir.-Bus. Devel.--Willis Corroon Melling Inc., Montreal, Canada; *Int'l*, pg. 1509
Dunning, Judith, Sr. V.P.-Plng. & Allocation--Bradlees Inc., Braintree, MA; *U.S. Public*, pg. 249
Dupuis, Robert E., V.P.-Mktg. & Business Plng.--COMSAT World Systems, Bethesda, MD; *U.S. Public*, pg. 424
Durity, Harry, G., V.P.-Devel.--Automatic Data Processing, Inc., Roseland, NJ; *U.S. Public*, pg. 150
Durret, Louis-Francois, V.P.-Corp. Strategy & Intl. Devel.--COGEMA - Compagnie Generale des Matieres Nucleaires, Velizy-Villacoublay, France; *Int'l*, pg. 304
Dutta, Rono, Sr. V.P.-Plng.--United Air Lines, Inc., Elk Grove Village, IL; *U.S. Public*, pg. 1653
Dutta, Rono J., Sr. V.P.-Plng.--UAL Corporation, Elk Grove Village, IL; *U.S. Public*, pg. 1652
Duval, Daniel W., Pres. & Chief Exec. Officer--Robbins & Myers, Inc., Dayton, OH; *U.S. Public*, pg. 1393
Dweller, David S., V.P.-Strategic Bus. Devel.--Raytheon Company, Lexington, MA; *U.S. Public*, pg. 1364
Eales, V. Richard, V.P.-Corp. Devel.--Union Pacific Resources Company (UPRC), Fort Worth, TX; *U.S. Public*, pg. 1668
Eamer, Robert J., V.P.-Tech. Devel.--Domtar Inc., Montreal, Canada; *Int'l*, pg. 416
Early, Robert C., Exec. V.P.-Corp. Devel.--May & Speh, Inc., Downers Grove, IL; *U.S. Public*, pg. 1063
Earnshaw, Antonia, Sr. V.P. & Acct. Plng. Dir.-Insights Grp.--Young & Rubicam New York, New York, NY; *U.S. Private*, pg. 1198
Eason, Paul, V.P.-Bus. Devel.--Century Telephone Enterprises, Inc., Monroe, LA; *U.S. Public*, pg. 329
Easterbrook, Hugh, V.P.-Intl. Bus. Devel.--Rubbermaid Incorporated, Wooster, OH; *U.S. Public*, pg. 1411
Eaton, G.D., Plng. & Devl.--Ranks Hovis McDougall Limited, Marlow, United Kingdom; *Int'l*, pg. 1395
Ebert, Bernard F., V.P.-Global Plng., Procurement & Quality Control--Gateway 2000, North Sioux City, SD; *U.S. Public*, pg. 703
Ebert, M. Virginia, Asst. V.P.-Asset Devel.--Conrail, Inc., Philadelphia, PA; *U.S. Public*, pg. 431
Eberwine, Craig G., V.P.-Corp. Plng. & Devel.--Motorists Mutual Insurance Co., Columbus, OH; *U.S. Private*, pg. 764
Eckardt, Carl R., Exec. V.P.-Corp. Devel.--G-I Holdings Inc., Wilmington, DE; *U.S. Private*, pg. 433
Eckrosh, Fred, Plng. Supvr.--Western International Media Corporation, Portland, OR; *U.S. Private*, pg. 1167
Edgell, Gregory A., V.P.-Strategic Plng.--WSMP, Inc., Claremont, NC; *U.S. Public*, pg. 1729
Edleman, Thomas J., Chm. Bd.--Lomak Petroleum Inc., Fort Worth, TX; *U.S. Public*, pg. 1012
Edwards, Eric, Mgr.-Project Analysis--TVX Gold Inc., Toronto, Canada; *Int'l*, pg. 1345
Edwards, Jim, Dir.-Bus. Devel.--Countermeasures Div., Nashua, NH; *U.S. Public*, pg. 1008
Eells, Gwen J., Sr. V.P. & Gen. Counsel-Secondary Mktg.--INMC Mortgage Holdings, Inc., Pasadena, CA; *U.S. Public*, pg. 857
Egan, Don E., Mgr.-Plng. & Devel.--BHP Copper, San Francisco, CA; *Int'l*, pg. 227
Egan, Kay E., V.P. & Dir.-Mdse. Devel., Home & Leisure Div.--JC Penney Company, Inc., Plano, TX; *U.S. Public*, pg. 916
Egan, Robert W., Mgr.-Strategic Analysis--Boise Cascade Corporation, Boise, ID; *U.S. Public*, pg. 242
Eggenberger, Hans, Sr. V.P.-Res. & Devel.--Bobst S.A., Lausanne, Switzerland; *Int'l*, pg. 198
Eglin, Robin, V.P.-Corp. Dev.--Nobel Education Dynamics, Inc., Media, PA; *U.S. Public*, pg. 1185
Egyud, Jules, Dir.-Software Devel.--Franklin Electronic Publishers, Inc., Burlington, NJ; *U.S. Public*, pg. 679
Ehner, William J., Sr. V.P.-Strategic Plng.--Johns Manville Corporation, Denver, CO; *U.S. Public*, pg. 927
Eichner, John, Controller--Harold M. Pitman Co., Inc., Totowa, NJ; *U.S. Private*, pg. 867
Eilender, A., Exec. V.P.-Corp. Devel.--Sybron Chemicals Inc., Birmingham, NJ; *U.S. Public*, pg. 1544
Eisenberg, Kenneth, Chm. Bd. & Chief Exec. Officer--Kenwal Products Corp., Dearborn, MI; *U.S. Private*, pg. 615
Eisner, Dean H., V.P.-Bus. Plng. & Devel.--Cox Enterprises, Inc., Atlanta, GA; *U.S. Private*, pg. 281
Elgueta, Rogelio, Dir.-Expansion--Andina Division, Los Andes, Chile; *Int'l*, pg. 302
Ellberger, Larry, Chief Fin. Officer & Sr. V.P.-Strategic Plng. & Devel.--W.R. Grace & Co., Boca Raton, FL; *U.S. Public*, pg. 754
Eller, Bruno, V.P.-Store Planning--Reitmans (Canada) Limited, Montreal, Canada; *Int'l*, pg. 1102
Ellington, Stanley E., Jr., Chief Fin. Officer, V.P.-Fin. & Treas.--Production Management Companies, Inc., Harvey, LA; *U.S. Private*, pg. 888
Elliot, David W., Jr., Dir.-Corp. Devel.--St. Jude Medical, Inc., Saint Paul, MN; *U.S. Public*, pg. 1427
Elliot, Tom, Exec. V.P.-Intl. Devel.--United Artists Theatre Circuits Incorporated, Englewood, CO; *U.S. Private*, pg. 1120
Elliott, Noel, V.P.-Information Services & Logistics--Chapters Inc., Etobicoke, Canada; *Int'l*, pg. 280
Ellis, Barry W., Sr. V.P.-Devel., Real Estate & Environment--Cooper Communities, Inc., Bella Vista, AR; *U.S. Private*, pg. 273
Ellis, C. Lee, Sr. V.P.-Investments--Alfa Corporation, Montgomery, AL; *U.S. Public*, pg. 40
Ellis, David R., Corp. Mgr.-Bus. Devel.--J.J. Keller & Associates, Inc., Neenah, WI; *U.S. Private*, pg. 612
Ellis, Peter B.S., V.P.-Strategic Plng.--Textron Inc., Providence, RI; *U.S. Public*, pg. 1588
Ellwein, Michael D., V.P.-Corp. Devel. & Assoc. Gen. Counsel--Medtronic, Inc., Minneapolis, MN; *U.S. Public*, pg. 1082
Emery, Frank E., Mgr.-Plng. & Information--Watkins-Johnson Company, Palo Alto, CA; *U.S. Public*, pg. 1745
Emorey, Martha A., Dir.-Corp. Fin. & Trusts--Fortune Brands, Inc., Old Greenwich, CT; *U.S. Public*, pg. 674
Eng, Gloria, V.P.-Bus. Devel.--The McGraw-Hill Companies, New York, NY; *U.S. Public*, pg. 1069
Eng, Tan Ching, Sr. Mgr.-Design--Singapore Technologies Shipbuilding & Engineering Limited, Singapore, Singapore; *Int'l*, pg. 1253
Engel, Roger K., Dr., Sr. V.P.-Bus. Devel.--California Microwave, Inc.-Government Grp., Sunnyvale, CA; *U.S. Public*, pg. 293
Englar, John D., Sr. V.P.-Corp. Devel. & Law--Burlington Industries, Inc., Greensboro, NC; *U.S. Public*, pg. 268
Englefield, F.W., IV, Co-Pres., Chief Exec., Chief Fin. Officer & Sec.--Englefield, Inc., Newark, OH; *U.S. Private*, pg. 377
Engles, Charles R., Sr. V.P.-Corp. Devel.--Johns Manville Corporation, Denver, CO; *U.S. Public*, pg. 927
English, Paul, Sr. V.P.-Prod. Devel.--Interleaf, Inc., Waltham, MA; *U.S. Public*, pg. 893
Engstrom, Lennart, V.P.-Strategic Plng. & Analysis--AB Industrivarden, Stockholm, Sweden; *Int'l*, pg. 678
Ennis, Michael, V.P.-Real Estate & Store Devel.--Dollar General Corporation, Nashville, TN; *U.S. Public*, pg. 515
Epstein, Mark R., V.P.-Devel.--QUALCOMM, San Diego, CA; *U.S. Public*, pg. 1348
Epstein, Sidney, Chm. Bd.--A. Epstein and Sons, Intl., Inc., Chicago, IL; *U.S. Private*, pg. 379
Ericson, Roy W., V.P.-Plng. & Regulatory Compliance--North Carolina Natural Gas Corporation, Fayetteville, NC; *U.S. Public*, pg. 1194
Ernest, E. Robert, V.P.-Corp. Plng. & Devel.--C.R. Bard, Inc., Murray Hill, NJ; *U.S. Public*, pg. 189
Ernster, Peter G., V.P.-Bus. Plng., Economics & Devel.--Merck Human Health Division, Rahway, NJ; *U.S. Public*, pg. 1090
Errett, John, V.P.-Strategic Services--Conair Corporation, Stamford, CT; *U.S. Private*, pg. 261
Eschrich, Glenn, V.P.-Improvement Sys.--Publix Supermarkets Inc., Lakeland, FL; *U.S. Private*, pg. 893
Essman, Alyn, Dir.-Plng. & Devel., Merger/Acquisition Contact--CPI Corp., Saint Louis, MO; *U.S. Public*, pg. 283
Estey, John W., Pres. & Chief Exec. Officer--S & C Electric Company, Chicago, IL; *U.S. Private*, pg. 954
Ethans, H.T., V.P.-Bus. Devel.--Federal Industries Industrial Group, Inc., Winnipeg, Canada; *Int'l*, pg. 1150
Etter, Steve, Sr. Business Devel. Officer--Western Marketing-Oakland Region, Oakland, CA; *U.S. Public*, pg. 650
Ettinger, Deborah J., V.P.-Bus. Devel./Western Division--Tenet Healthcare Corporation, Santa Barbara, CA; *U.S. Public*, pg. 1576
Eugenio, Joao Eduardo, Mgr.-Commercial Plng. & Control--Central de Cervejas, S.A., Lisbon, Portugal; *Int'l*, pg. 279
Eustace, Royston K., V.P.-Strategic Plng.--TECO Energy, Inc., Tampa, FL; *U.S. Public*, pg. 1565
Evangelista, Thomas E., V.P.-Corp. Devel. & Commun.--Stanhome Inc., Westfield, MA; *U.S. Public*, pg. 1508
Evangelsta, Claro B., Asst. Gen. Mgr.--Benguet Corporation, Manila, Philippines; *Int'l*, pg. 186
Evans, Adrian O., Sr. V.P.-Construction & Maintenance--The Southland Corporation, Dallas, TX; *Int'l*, pg. 693
Evans, David, V.P.-Opers. & Plng.--Warner Bros. Consumer Products, Burbank, CA; *U.S. Public*, pg. 1610
Evans, David V., Sr. V.P. & Dir.-Plng. & Information Systems--JC Penney Company, Inc., Plano, TX; *U.S. Public*, pg. 916
Evans, Jeff, Mgr.-Plng. & Devel.--The Will-Burt Company, Orrville, OH; *U.S. Private*, pg. 1177
Evans, Joanne, V.P.-Plng. & Client Services--Kelly, Scott And Madison, Inc., Chicago, IL; *U.S. Private*, pg. 613
Evans, Lawrence E., Exec. V.P.-Store Devel.--AutoZone, Inc., Memphis, TN; *U.S. Public*, pg. 150
Evans, Lucy, Sr. V.P.-Fin. & Bus. Devel.--Swift Textiles, Inc., Atlanta, GA; *Int'l*, pg. 415

Evans, Melphine, V.P.-Strategic Plng. & Control--Alyeska Pipeline Service Company, Anchorage, AK; *U.S. Private*, pg. 47
Evatt, James W., V.P.-Bus. Devel.--Boeing Defense & Space Group, Kent, WA; *U.S. Public*, pg. 240
Everett, Scott, V.P.-New Prods., Mktg. & Strategic Plng.--Bayer Corporation/Consumer Care Division, Morristown, NJ; *Int'l*, pg. 173
Everton, Marsha, V.P.-Strategic Plng.--The Pfaltzgraff Co., York, PA; *U.S. Private*, pg. 860
Eymery, Jean-Pierre, V.P.-Strategy, Devel. & Indus. Alliances--Ciments Francais, Paris, France; *Int'l*, pg. 292
Eymery, Pierre, Mng. Dir.-Strategic Plng.--Groupe SEB, Ecueille, France; *Int'l*, pg. 568
Ezaki, Takeshi, Gen. Mgr.-Plng. & Devel--Okuma Corporation, Niwa, Japan; *Int'l*, pg. 1000
Faber, Charles P., V.P.-Corp. Devel.--Belden & Blake Corporation, Canton, OH; *U.S. Private*, pg. 1078
Fagel, Harold, Chief Exec. Officer--Aurora Packing Co., Inc., North Aurora, IL; *U.S. Private*, pg. 99
Fain, John H., Chm. Bd., Pres., Chief Exec. Officer & Chief Oper. Officer--Metro Information Services, Virginia Beach, VA; *U.S. Public*, pg. 1102
Fairbairn, S.G., Mgr.-Plng., Information & Control--CIBA-GEIGY (Pty.) Ltd., Isando, South Africa; *Int'l*, pg. 978
Faithfull, Wayne H., V.P.-Intl. Devel.--Sun Life of Canada, Manila, Philippines; *Int'l*, pg. 1319
Falaro, Martin, V.P.-Bus. Devel.--VideoServer, Inc., Burlington, MA; *U.S. Public*, pg. 1720
Falkenberg, Eric N., V.P.-Bus. Devel. & Strategic Plng.--Pacesetter Inc., Sylmar, CA; *U.S. Public*, pg. 1428
Fantelli, Paul F., V.P.-Bus. Devel.--The Lincoln Electric Company, Cleveland, OH; *U.S. Public*, pg. 996
Fantine, Jose, Dir.-Plng.--Petrobras - Petroleo Brasileiro S.A., Rio de Janeiro, Brazil; *Int'l*, pg. 1041
Faran, Ellen W., V.P. & Dir.-Fin. & Plng.--Houghton Mifflin Trade & Reference Div., Boston, MA; *U.S. Public*, pg. 841
Farella, Anne B., Mgr.-Plng. & Prod.--Telmark, Inc., Syracuse, NY; *U.S. Private*, pg. 27
Faridi, Hamed, V.P.-Res. & Devel.--McCormick & Company, Incorporated, Sparks, MD; *U.S. Public*, pg. 1066
Farisei, U., Gen. Mgr.-Mktg. & Bus. Devel.--Nuovo Pignone S.p.a., Florence, Italy; *Int'l*, pg. 990
Farkas, Steve, V.P.-Strategic Devel.--3Com Personal Communications Div., Skokie, IL; *U.S. Public*, pg. 1604
Farlie, Craig L., V.P.-Corp. Devel.--Republic Industries, Inc., Fort Lauderdale, FL; *U.S. Public*, pg. 1378
Farlsei, U., Mgr.-Mktg. & Bus. Devel.--Nuovo Pignone S.p.a., Florence, Italy; *Int'l*, pg. 990
Farnell, Gail, Mgr.-Media & Plng.--Carter Products Div., Cranbury, NJ; *U.S. Public*, pg. 310
Farrand, Christopher G., V.P.-Corp. Affairs--Peabody Holding Company, Inc., Saint Louis, MO; *Int'l*, pg. 594
Farrell, Robert, V.P.-Bus. Devel.--E.T. Browne Drug Co., Inc., Englewood Cliffs, NJ; *U.S. Private*, pg. 175
Farrill, Craig, F., V.P.-Strategic Tech.--AirTouch Communications, Inc., San Francisco, CA; *U.S. Public*, pg. 34
Faulkner, Robert, Gen. Mgr.--Effingham-Clay Service Co., Effingham, IL; *U.S. Private*, pg. 365
Fauve, Jean-Michel, Sr. Exec. V.P.-Devel.--Electricite de France, Paris, France; *Int'l*, pg. 437
Faveau, Alain, V.P.-Devel.--Rexel, S.A., Paris, France; *Int'l*, pg. 1107
Fawcett, Harland K., V.P.-Plng.--BNI Coal, Ltd., Bismarck, ND; *U.S. Public*, pg. 1116
Fawls, James F., Dir.-Plng. & Analysis--Blount International, Inc., Montgomery, AL; *U.S. Public*, pg. 237
Fawls, James F., Dir.-Plng. & Analysis--Blount, Inc., Montgomery, AL; *U.S. Public*, pg. 238
Fearon, R., V.P.-Plng. & Controller--Kruger Inc., Montreal, Canada; *Int'l*, pg. 761
Feather, Harold E., Exec. V.P.-Strategic Plng.--Rykoff-Sexton, Inc., Wilkes-Barre, PA; *U.S. Public*, pg. 918
Fedor, Robert J., Sr. V.P.-Corp. Strategic Devel.--Gould Electronics Inc., Eastlake, OH; *U.S. Public*, pg. 1591
Feigin, Barbara S., Exec. V.P. & Strategic Svcs. Dir.--Grey Advertising Inc., New York, NY; *U.S. Public*, pg. 764
Feinberg, Robert, V.P.-Corp. Dev.--GP Strategies Corporation, New York, NY; *U.S. Public*, pg. 694
Feld, Larry, V.P.-Store Devel. & Sec.--Today's Man, Inc., Moorestown, NJ; *U.S. Public*, pg. 1619
Feldman, Jerome I., Pres. & Chief Exec. Officer--GP Strategies Corporation, New York, NY; *U.S. Public*, pg. 694
Feldman, Michael D., Dir.-Bus. Devel.--GP Strategies Corporation, New York, NY; *U.S. Public*, pg. 694
Feldman, Thomas, V.P.-Strategic Plng. & New Bus. Devel.--Staples, Inc., Westborough, MA; *U.S. Public*, pg. 1509
Felger, Hugh, V.P.-Bus. & Tech. Devel.--Aerco International Inc., Northvale, NJ; *U.S. Private*, pg. 23
Felsenthal, Robert M., Sr. V.P.-Bus. Devel.--IMC Global, Bannockburn, IL; *U.S. Public*, pg. 856
Felton, Dean P., Sr. V.P.-Bus. Devel.--Willis Corroon Financial Services Corp., New York, NY; *Int'l*, pg. 1507
Felton, Susann D., V.P.-Generation Fuels & Bus. Plng.--Potomac Electric Power Company, Washington, DC; *U.S. Public*, pg. 1318
Fenning, Andrew, Exec. V.P., Strategic Devel. Dir.--J. Walter Thompson Company, New York, NY; *Int'l*, pg. 1483
Ferdegue, Roland, V.P.-Business Devel.--Lafarge S.A., Paris, France; *Int'l*, pg. 788
Ferguson, Robert G., V.P.-Bus. Devel.--UES, Inc., Dayton, OH; *U.S. Private*, pg. 1112
Fernandez Horcasitas, Jaime, Mgr.-Plng.--Grupo Cementos de Chihuahua S.A. de C.V., Chihuahua, Mexico; *Int'l*, pg. 573
Fernandez, James N., Chief Fin. Officer & Sr. V.P.-Fin.--Tiffany & Co., New York, NY; *U.S. Public*, pg. 1608
Fernandez, S.R., Dir.-Production & Logistics--Erven Lucas Bols S.A., Buenos Aires, Argentina; *Int'l*, pg. 451
Fernlock, Doug, Dir.-Res. & Strategic Plng.--J.W. Messner, Inc., Grand Rapids, MI; *U.S. Private*, pg. 734
Ferrantino, John, Dir.-Bus. Devel.--Yankee Gas Services Company, Meriden, CT; *U.S. Public*, pg. 1788
Ferrell, Miranda L., V.P.-Plng. & Bus. Devel.--Sonat Exploration Company, Houston, TX; *U.S. Public*, pg. 1485
Feys, Edwin, V.P. & Sec.--H.O. Trerice Company, Oak Park, MI; *U.S. Private*, pg. 1099
Field, Barbara A., Dir.-Fin. Plng.--Bytex Corporation, Westborough, MA; *U.S. Public*, pg. 1522
Field, Benjamin R., III, Chief Fin. Officer, Sr. V.P. & Treas.--Bemis Company, Inc., Minneapolis, MN; *U.S. Public*, pg. 210
Field, Culver, Sr. V.P.-Corp. Plng. & Devel.--Morgan Foods, Inc., Austin, IN; *U.S. Private*, pg. 761
Field, Donald M., Mgr.-Fin. Plng. & Cash Mngmt.--Peoples Energy Corporation, Chicago, IL; *U.S. Public*, pg. 1274
Fielder, James, V.P.-Acq. & Devel.--Robert B. Aikens & Associates LLC., Troy, MI; *U.S. Private*, pg. 28
Fields, P. Lamar, V.P.-Devel.--Carmike Cinemas, Inc., Columbus, GA; *U.S. Public*, pg. 305
Fifer, Michael O., V.P.-Corp. Devel.--Watts Industries, Inc., North Andover, MA; *U.S. Public*, pg. 1746
Files, Alton, V.P.-Devel.--TCBY Systems, Inc., Little Rock, AR; *U.S. Public*, pg. 1554
Findlay, Konstance J.K., Sr. V.P.-Bus. Devel. & Sec.--Conso Products Company, Union, SC; *U.S. Public*, pg. 434
Findling, Gary J., Asst. Treas.--Aeroquip-Vickers, Inc., Maumee, OH; *U.S. Public*, pg. 24
Fine, D., V.P.-Planning--Federal Industries Metals Group, Etobicoke, Canada; *Int'l*, pg. 1150
Fine, Jeff, Market Res. & Plng. Dir.--Mintz & Hoke Inc., Avon, CT; *U.S. Private*, pg. 751
Fink, Richard A., Sr. Exec. V.P. & Chief Credit Officer--Glendale Federal Bank, F.S.B., Glendale, CA; *U.S. Public*, pg. 747
Finley, Wayne, Sr. V.P. & Dir.-Devel.--TrizecHahn Centers Inc., San Diego, CA; *Int'l*, pg. 1425
Finn, Brian, Mgr.-Plng. & Srvcs.--Bil Mar Foods, Inc., Zeeland, MI; *U.S. Public*, pg. 1433
Finney, Bill, Dir.-Prod. Devel.--Mark III Industries, Ocala, FL; *U.S. Private*, pg. 704
Finocchi, Richard A., V.P.-Corp. Devel.--Comdisco, Inc., Rosemont, IL; *U.S. Public*, pg. 407
Fish, Gary R., V.P.-Corp. Devel.--Black Hills Corporation, Rapid City, SD; *U.S. Public*, pg. 235
Fishman, Gary, V.P.-Technical Opers. Admin. & Plng.--Northwest Airlines, Inc., Saint Paul, MN; *U.S. Public*, pg. 1200
Fitzgerald, Elizabeth, V.P.-Bus. Devel. & Strategy--Allegiance Healthcare Corp., McGaw Park, IL; *U.S. Public*, pg. 44
Fixter, D.G., Sr. V.P.-Org. & Bus. Devel.--GSW Inc., Guelph, Canada,; *Int'l*, pg. 538
Flaim, Theresa A., V.P.-Corp. Strategic Plng.--Niagara Mohawk Power Corporation, Syracuse, NY; *U.S. Public*, pg. 1181
Flanigan, Joseph G., Chm. Bd., Pres. & Chief Exec. Officer--Flanigan's Enterprises, Inc., Fort Lauderdale, FL; *U.S. Public*, pg. 648
Flannigan, Mike, Gen. Mgr.-Strategic Plng.--Air New Zealand Ltd., Auckland, New Zealand; *Int'l*, pg. 38
Fleischer, Jay, V.P.-Prod. Devel.--Crystal Clear Industries, Ridgefield Park, NJ; *U.S. Private*, pg. 293
Fleischman, Marvin H., Pres.--Peerless Distributing Co., Southfield, MI; *U.S. Private*, pg. 847
Fleming, Bruce E., V.P.-Corp. Devel.--Nortek, Inc., Providence, RI; *U.S. Public*, pg. 1192
Flesher, Robert, Mgr.-Plng. & Devel.--Phillips Petroleum Company, Bartlesville, OK; *U.S. Public*, pg. 1290
Fletcher, B. Lee, V.P.-Corp. Devel.--Heilig-Meyers Company, Richmond, VA; *U.S. Public*, pg. 804
Fletcher, William D., Sr. V.P.-Tech. & Bus. Devel.--Rockwell International Corporation, Costa Mesa, CA; *U.S. Public*, pg. 1397
Flint, H. Howard, II, Chm. Bd. & Chief Exec. Officer--Flint Ink Corp., Detroit, MI; *U.S. Private*, pg. 413
Flood, Thomas, Chief Fin. Officer, V.P.-Admin. & Fin. & Treas.--Tractor Supply Co., Nashville, TN; *U.S. Public*, pg. 1627
Flores, Julio, Dir.-Corp. Plng.--Taca International Airlines, S. A., San Salvador, El Salvador; *Int'l*, pg. 1346
Flores, Rene, Dir.-Plng. & Devel.--Puerto Rico Tourism Company, San Juan, PR; *U.S. Private*, pg. 894
Floyd, Lisa A., V.P.-Bus. Devel.--Apache Corporation, Houston, TX; *U.S. Public*, pg. 119
Fly, John, V.P.-Strategic Plng.--Milliken & Company, Spartanburg, SC; *U.S. Private*, pg. 748
Flynn, Dennis T., V.P.-Corp. Devel.--DVI Financial Services Inc., Newport Beach, CA; *U.S. Public*, pg. 476
Flynn, John J., Dir.-Corp. Devel.--First Brands Corporation, Danbury, CT; *U.S. Public*, pg. 626
Flynn, William T., Sr. V.P. & Chief Corp. Plng.--USAA (United Services Automobile Association), San Antonio, TX; *U.S. Private*, pg. 1114
Fogg, F.W., Pres. & Chief Exec. Officer--Southeastern Medequip, Inc., Jacksonville Beach, FL; *U.S. Private*, pg. 1015
Folwell, Ronald L., Sr., Chief Fin. Officer & V.P.-Fin., Leasing, Plng/Devel. & Real Est.--GSC Enterprises, Inc., Sulphur Springs, TX; *U.S. Private*, pg. 436
Fonts, Carlos E., V.P.-Corp. Devel.--Texas Industries, Inc., Dallas, TX; *U.S. Public*, pg. 1585
Foote, Robert T., Jr., V.P.-Plng. & Devel.--Applied Power Inc., Butler, WI; *U.S. Public*, pg. 124
Forbes, Alan, Gen. Mgr.-Corp. Devel. & Sec.--Standard Life Assurance, Edinburgh, United Kingdom; *Int'l*, pg. 1297
Forbis, John L., V.P.-Strategic Plng. & Corp. Devel.--Campbell Soup Company, Camden, NJ; *U.S. Public*, pg. 298
Ford, Bernard R., V.P.-Intl. Mktg. & Corp. Bus. Devel.--The Scotts Company, Marysville, OH; *U.S. Public*, pg. 1446
Ford, Brendan A., Sr. V.P.-Corp. Devel.--Cardinal Health Inc., Dublin, OH; *U.S. Public*, pg. 304
Ford, Gary, V.P.-Plng. & Res.--Shelter Mutual Insurance Company, Columbia, MO; *U.S. Private*, pg. 992
Foreman, R., Mgr.-Corp. Plng.--Ladbroke Group Plc, London, United Kingdom; *Int'l*, pg. 787
Forester, David E., V.P. & Sr. Dir.-Devel.--Rouse Office & Community Development Div., Columbia, MD; *U.S. Public*, pg. 1407
Forman, Fred L., Chief Info. Officer & Exec. V.P.--American Management Systems, Inc., Fairfax, VA; *U.S. Public*, pg. 86
Forman, Willis M., Pres., Chief Exec. Officer & Treas.--Paper Calmenson & Co., Saint Paul, MN; *U.S. Private*, pg. 837
Formeca, Bill, V.P. & Assoc. Plng. Dir.--Western International Media Corporation, Los Angeles, CA; *U.S. Private*, pg. 1165
Fornaro, Robert L., Sr. V.P.-Plng.--US Airways Group, Inc., Arlington, VA; *U.S. Public*, pg. 1680
Fornaro, Robert L., Sr. V.P.-Planning--US Airways, Inc., Arlington, VA; *U.S. Public*, pg. 1680
Fornella, Norman G., Chief Fin. Officer, Exec. V.P., Treas. & Sec.--Morse Diesel International, Inc., New York, NY; *U.S. Private*, pg. 762
Forshay, Paul, Dir.-Corp Devel.--Telephone and Data Systems, Inc., Chicago, IL; *U.S. Public*, pg. 1570
Fortmuller, George A., Chief Fin. Officer, V.P., Treas. & Sec.--Edwin B. Stimpson Company, Inc., Bayport, NY; *U.S. Private*, pg. 1043
Foss, John H., Chief Fin. Officer, V.P. & Treas.--Tecumseh Products Company, Tecumseh, MI; *U.S. Public*, pg. 1565
Fournier, Larry, V.P.-Devel.--Max & Erma's Restaurants, Columbus, OH; *U.S. Public*, pg. 1060
Fowler, Donald R., Sr. Dir.-Plng. & Procurement--U.S. Surgical Corp., Norwalk, CT; *U.S. Public*, pg. 1687
Fox, Lawrence A., Dir.-Corp. Devel.--JPE, Inc., Ann Arbor, MI; *U.S. Public*, pg. 919
Fox, Michael M., V.P.-Corp. Devel.--SRA International Inc., Arlington, VA; *U.S. Private*, pg. 957
Fox, Phil, V.P.-Corp. Plng.--The Andersons Incorporated, Maumee, OH; *U.S. Public*, pg. 111
Foyle, Gary, Dir.-Planning & Analysis--Metra Commuter Rail, Chicago, IL; *U.S. Private*, pg. 919
Frampton, Jack, V.P.-Franchise Devel.--Comprehensive Business Services Inc., Mission Viejo, CA; *U.S. Private*, pg. 423
Francis, Bob, Mgr.-Store Devel.--Dierbergs Markets Inc., Chesterfield, MO; *U.S. Private*, pg. 332
Francis, W. Curtis, V.P.-Opers. & Plng.--Advanced Micro Devices, Inc., Sunnyvale, CA; *U.S. Public*, pg. 21
Francis, William, Chief Fin. Officer, Treas. & Controller--Captive-Aire Systems, Inc., Youngsville, NC; *U.S. Private*, pg. 207
Frank, Bob, V.P.-Opers.--BGF Industries Inc., Greensboro, NC; *U.S. Private*, pg. 106
Franklin, Marc S., Sr. V.P.-Strategic Plng. & Devel.--Pacific Life Insurance Company, Newport Beach, CA; *U.S. Private*, pg. 831
Fraser, Richard, V.P.-Corp. & Proj. Devel.--Sandwell Inc., Vancouver, Canada; *Int'l*, pg. 1188
Fratangelo, Robert D., V.P.-Taxes & Strategic Fin. Plng.--Consolidated Natural Gas Company, Pittsburgh, PA; *U.S. Public*, pg. 435
Fratangelo, Robert D., V.P.-Taxes & Strategic Fin. Plng.--Consolidated Natural Gas Service Co., Inc., Pittsburgh, PA; *U.S. Public*, pg. 435
Frede, Jim, Dir.-Logistics--Mercantile Stores Company, Inc., Fairfield, OH; *U.S. Public*, pg. 1089
Freeman, G., Dir.-Devel.--Northern Rock Homes Limited, Newcastle upon Tyne, United Kingdom; *Int'l*, pg. 968
Freeman, John A., V.P.-Bus. Devel.--Newbridge Networks Corporation, Kanata, Canada; *Int'l*, pg. 923
Freeman, Peter R., Mgr.-Bus. Devel. & Strategic Plng.--Gasco, Inc., Honolulu, HI; *Int'l*, pg. 225
Freitag, Joan C., Mgr.-Bus. Devel.--Hanson Engineers Inc., Springfield, IL; *U.S. Private*, pg. 500
Freriks, Donald, Chief Fin. Officer & Exec. V.P.--O'Neal Steel Inc., Birmingham, AL; *U.S. Private*, pg. 817
Fresquez, Luis, Chief Info. Officer & Sr. V.P.--American Automobile Association, Heathrow, FL; *U.S. Private*, pg. 50
Friedman, Louis, Treas.--E. & J. Gallo Winery, Modesto, CA; *U.S. Private*, pg. 438
Friedson, David M., Pres. & Chief Exec. Officer--Windmere-Durable Holdings, Hialeah, FL; *U.S. Public*, pg. 1771
Fritsch, Jim, V.P.-Strategic Plng./CMC Steel Grp.--Structural Metals, Inc., Seguin, TX; *U.S. Public*, pg. 412
Frock, John, Exec. V.P. & Asst. Sec.--Nobel Education Dynamics, Inc., Media, PA; *U.S. Public*, pg. 1185
Froemming, Neil R., Mgr.-Devel.--BNA Software, Washington, DC; *U.S. Private*, pg. 182
Frohlinger, Debra, Plng. & Res.--Hampel/Stefanides, New York, NY; *U.S. Private*, pg. 498
Fromme, William R., V.P.-Strategic Plng.--Arinc Inc. (Consolidated), Annapolis, MD; *U.S. Private*, pg. 81
Frommer, Elmar, Dr., Div. Head.-Plng. & Controlling--BASF AG, Ludwigshafen, Germany; *Int'l*, pg. 103
Fryland, Sonnich, V.P.-Corp. Devel.--Novo Nordisk A/S, Bagsvaerd, Denmark; *Int'l*, pg. 987
Fu, Cary, Chief Fin. Officer & Exec. V.P.--Benchmark Electronics Inc., Angleton, TX; *U.S. Public*, pg. 210
Fuchs, David, Chm. Bd. & Chief Exec. Officer--Hampton Industries, Inc., Kinston, NC; *U.S. Public*, pg. 779
Fuchs, Manfred, Dr., Chm. Bd.--Fuchs Petrolub AG Oel + Chemie, Mannheim, Germany; *Int'l*, pg. 517
Fuentes, D. Tamez, Asst. Dir.-Commercial--Petroleos Mexicanos, Mexico, Mexico; *Int'l*, pg. 1046
Fujawa, Tom, Dir.-Bus. Devel.--Avionics, Nashua, NH; *U.S. Public*, pg. 1008
Fulks, Gary, Dir.-Engrng., Opers. & Plng.--Associated Electric Co-op Inc., Springfield, MO; *U.S. Private*, pg. 89
Fultz, Larry L., Sr. V.P.-Bus. Devel.--LEXIS-NEXIS, Miamisburg, OH; *Int'l*, pg. 1096
Funk, Tommy, Pres.--Sebastian Cotton & Grain Corp., Sebastian, TX; *U.S. Private*, pg. 980

Fuortes, Beverly, Dir.-Corp. Devel.--Amtech Corporation, Dallas, TX; *U.S. Public*, pg. 105
Furukawa, Kiyoshi, Mng. Dir.-Corp. Plng. & Intl. Projects--Sumitomo Metal Industries, Ltd., Tokyo, Japan; *Int'l*, pg. 1315
Fusarini, L., Mgr.-Tech. & Devel.--Solplant, Milan, Italy; *Int'l*, pg. 1524
Fusco, Tony, Sr. V.P.-Devel.--Lackman Food Service, Woodbury, NY; *U.S. Private*, pg. 642
Futami, Yasuhiko, Gen. Mgr.-Business Devel.--Terumo Corporation, Tokyo, Japan; *Int'l*, pg. 1375
Gabille, Jean-Pierre, V.P.-Corp. Devel.--The Loewen Group, Inc., Burnaby, Canada; *Int'l*, pg. 814
Gabler, Robert, Dir.-New Products--MBI Inc., Norwalk, CT; *U.S. Private*, pg. 685
Gaffney, Joseph M., Sr. V.P.-Corp. Plng. & Devel.--Olin Corporation, Norwalk, CT; *U.S. Public*, pg. 1218
Gaffrey, Mike, Exec. V.P. & Dir.-Corp. Devel.--ICF Kaiser International Inc., Fairfax, VA; *U.S. Public*, pg. 852
Gailius, Gilbert K., Chief Fin. Officer & V.P.-Fin.--American Biltrite Inc., Wellesley Hills, MA; *U.S. Public*, pg. 68
Gaines, Lisa, Dir.-Fin. & Plng.--Seed Restaurant Group, Inc., Lexington, KY; *U.S. Private*, pg. 981
Gaither, John F., Jr., V.P.-Corp. Devel. & Strategy--Baxter International Inc., Deerfield, IL; *U.S. Public*, pg. 196
Galati, Frank, V.P.-Corp. Affairs & Strategic Plng.--Cott Corporation, Pointe-Claire, Canada; *Int'l*, pg. 337
Gallagher, C. J., Mgr.-Tax & Corp. Devel.--Carter Holt Harvey Limited, Auckland, New Zealand; *U.S. Public*, pg. 904
Galldin, Hans, V.P.-Bus. Devel.--Cognos Inc., Ottawa, Canada; *Int'l*, pg. 305
Galvin, Hal, Mgr.-Corp. Devel.--MTS Systems Corporation, Eden Prairie, MN; *U.S. Public*, pg. 1028
Gambrill, Anthony, Chief Exec. Officer & Bus. Devel./Information--CGR Communications, Kingston, Jamaica; *U.S. Public*, pg. 1422
Gamel, Wendell W., Chm. Bd., Pres. & Chief Exec. Officer--Tech-Sym Corporation, Houston, TX; *U.S. Public*, pg. 1563
Gansler, Martin, Bd. Member, Res. & Devel., Sourcing)--Puma AG Rudolf Dassler Sport, Herzogenaurach, Germany; *Int'l*, pg. 1072
Garand, John J., V.P.-Plng. & Control--The Walt Disney Company, Burbank, CA; *U.S. Public*, pg. 511
Garcia Segovia, Armando J., Exec. V.P.-Devel.--Cemex, S.A. de C.V., Monterrey, Mexico; *Int'l*, pg. 278
Gardhouse, J. Mark, V.P.-Corp. Devel.--ARC International Corporation, Downsview, Canada; *Int'l*, pg. 17
Garoklanian, Charles F., Sr. Bus. Devel. Officer--Northeast Marketing-New York Business Center, New York, NY; *U.S. Public*, pg. 649
Garriott, Richard, Co-Founder, V.P. & Dir.-Devel.--Origin Systems, Inc., Austin, TX; *U.S. Public*, pg. 569
Garrison, Lynda, V.P.-Mktg.--Falcon Products, Inc., Saint Louis, MO; *U.S. Public*, pg. 611
Garver, Thomas K., V.P.-Bus. Devel.--Medeva Pharmaceuticals, Rochester, NY; *Int'l*, pg. 852
Garvey, Richard A., Pres.-Corp. Plng. & New Bus. Devel.--The Reader's Digest Association, Inc., Pleasantville, NY; *U.S. Public*, pg. 1367
Garville, Gregory J., V.P.-Corp. Devel.--Mickelberry Communications, Inc., New York, NY; *U.S. Private*, pg. 741
Gassman, Christine, Corp. Travel Planner--Pennaco Hosiery, New York, NY; *U.S. Public*, pg. 483
Gassner, Kathleen, Dir.-Franchise Devel.--Payless Car Rental System, Inc., Saint Petersburg, FL; *U.S. Private*, pg. 844
Gaston, Thomas A., V.P. & Bus. Devel. Officer--Elyria Savings & Trust National Bank, Elyria, OH; *U.S. Public*, pg. 646
Gates, Richard D., Sr. V.P.-Investor Rels. & Bus. Devel.--Rubbermaid Incorporated, Wooster, OH; *U.S. Public*, pg. 1411
Gaube, Jerold, V.P.-New Bus. Devel.--Azon Corporation, Johnson City, NY; *U.S. Private*, pg. 104
Gauntt, William A., V.P.-Bus. Devel./DOD Programs--IT Corp., Wilmington, CA; *U.S. Public*, pg. 908
Gaus, Hermann, Dir.-Devel. Passenger Cars--Mercedes-Benz AG, Stuttgart, Germany; *Int'l*, pg. 368
Gauthier, Daniel, Gen. Mgr.-Strategy & Devel.--S.A. Cimenteries CBR, Brussels, Belgium; *Int'l*, pg. 605
Gauvreau, Paul R., V.P.-Fin. & Treas.--Pittway Corporation, Chicago, IL; *U.S. Public*, pg. 1305
Gavzer, Charles A., Exec. V.P.-Devel. & Acquisitions--Hostmark Management Group, Rolling Meadows, IL; *U.S. Private*, pg. 541
Gay, Lawrence W., Sr. V.P.-Sls. & Bus. Devel.--GTECH Corporation, West Greenwich, RI; *U.S. Public*, pg. 767
Gaylord, Edson I., Chm. Bd.--Ingersoll International Inc., Rockford, IL; *U.S. Private*, pg. 562
Gaylord, Edward L., Pres. & Publisher--Oklahoma Publishing Company, Oklahoma City, OK; *U.S. Private*, pg. 813
Gebelein, Christopher, V.P.-Bus. Devel.--Borg Warner Automotive, Inc., Chicago, IL; *U.S. Public*, pg. 245
Geick, Paul D., Dir.-Corp. Plng.--MCN Energy Group, Inc., Detroit, MI; *U.S. Public*, pg. 1024
Geldmacher, Horst, V.P.-Overseas Bus. Devel.--The Dexter Corporation, Windsor Locks, CT; *U.S. Public*, pg. 504
Geller, Rachel, Sr. V.P. & Intl. Strategic Plng. Dir.--Saatchi & Saatchi Kid Connection, New York, NY; *U.S. Public*, pg. 1422
Gendron, Tom, Mgr.-Customer Support & Bus. Devel.--Woodward Governor Company, Rockford, IL; *U.S. Public*, pg. 1776
Gentelia, John, V.P.-Advanced Technology--Conmed Corporation, Utica, NY; *U.S. Public*, pg. 431
Gentine, Louis P., Chief Exec. Officer--Sargento Foods Inc., Plymouth, WI; *U.S. Private*, pg. 966
Gentine, Paul, V.P.-Organizational Devel.--Ross Roy Communications, Inc., Bloomfield Hills, MI; *U.S. Private*, pg. 946
George, Jim, V.P.-Market Devel.--Hawaii Newspaper Agency, Inc., Honolulu, HI; *U.S. Public*, pg. 701
Georgoulis, Stratton, Chm. Bd., Pres. & Chief Exec. Officer--TIC United Corporation, Dallas, TX; *U.S. Private*, pg. 1063
Gerard, Stephen, Pres., Chief Exec. Officer & Treas.--Bolliger, Inc., Stamford, CT; *U.S. Private*, pg. 155
Gerber, Jim, Dir.-Prod. & Mktg. Devel.--AP North American Aftermarket Division, Goldsboro, NC; *U.S. Private*, pg. 230
Gerety, Michael A., V.P.-Store Plng.--Toys "R" Us, Inc., Paramus, NJ; *U.S. Public*, pg. 1626
Germek, A.J., V.P.-Plng. & Devel.--Objective Systems Integrators, Inc., Folsom, CA; *U.S. Public*, pg. 1209
Gernert, Douglas P., Mgr.-Corp. Plng. & Devel.--Robertson-Ceco Corporation, San Ramon, CA; *U.S. Public*, pg. 1394
Gerty, Michael A., V.P.-Store Plng.--Toys "R" Us United States, Paramus, NJ; *U.S. Public*, pg. 1626
Gfeller, Werner, Mgr.-Planning & Devel.--GE Hydro, Lachine, Canada; *U.S. Public*, pg. 713
Ghins, Bernhard, Dir.-Strategy & Devel.--S.A. Cimenteries CBR, Brussels, Belgium; *Int'l*, pg. 605
Giancaspro, Michael W., V.P.-Corp. Plng.--Tredegar Industries Inc., Richmond, VA; *U.S. Public*, pg. 1633
Giangiulio, Joseph, Sr. V.P.-Bus. Devel.--Southwest National Bank of Pennsylvania, Greensburg, PA; *U.S. Public*, pg. 1493
Giarrusso, Laurel, V.P.-Strategic Plng.--Kronos Incorporated, Waltham, MA; *U.S. Public*, pg. 967
Gibbons, James T., V.P. & Dir.-Plng. & Devel.--WHX Corporation, New York, NY; *U.S. Public*, pg. 1726
Gibbs, James R., Pres. & Chief Exec. Officer--Wainoco Oil Corporation, Houston, TX; *U.S. Public*, pg. 1732
Gibbs, Richard L., Exec.V.P.-Fin. & Plng.--Teachers Insurance and Annuity Association, New York, NY; *U.S. Private*, pg. 1071
Gibson, Scott C., V.P.-Corp. Affairs & Strategy--Trans World Airlines, Inc., Saint Louis, MO; *U.S. Public*, pg. 1629
Gibson, Sidney, V.P.-Facility Plng.--UHP Healthcare, Inglewood, CA; *U.S. Private*, pg. 1113
Gies, Larry W., Chief Fin. Officer & Exec. V.P.--Pettibone Corporation, Lisle, IL; *U.S. Private*, pg. 859
Gil, Miguel Angel Remon, Dir.-Planning & Systems & Intl. Activities--Repsol S.A., Madrid, Spain; *Int'l*, pg. 1104
Gilbert, A. Donald, Jr., V.P.-Fin., Plng. & Key Accts.--Vermont Gas Systems, Inc., South Burlington, VT; *Int'l*, pg. 542
Gilbert, Bruno, Mgr.-Plng., Audit & Acctg.--Groupe GAN, Paris, France; *Int'l*, pg. 563
Gillenwater, James H., Jr., Sr. V.P.-Plng. & Devel.--Vencor, Inc., Louisville, KY; *U.S. Public*, pg. 1711
Gillespie, Robert J., Exec. V.P.-Strategy Plng. & Bus. Devel.--Bestfoods, Englewood Cliffs, NJ; *U.S. Public*, pg. 223
Gillis, John, Exec. V.P. & Res./Devel. Dir.--Ross Roy Communications, Inc., Bloomfield Hills, MI; *U.S. Private*, pg. 946
Gilman, Richard, Consultant--Gilrichco, Inc., Oxnard, CA; *U.S. Private*, pg. 454
Gilmour, Norman, Gen. Mgr.-Bus. Devel.--Sun Life and Provincial Holdings plc, London, United Kingdom; *Int'l*, pg. 1318
Ginn, David R., Exec. V.P.--Thiele Kaolin Co., Sandersville, GA; *U.S. Private*, pg. 1081
Ginoccio, Andy, Corp. Planning--Sanwa Business Credit Corporation, Chicago, IL; *Int'l*, pg. 1189
Ginsberg, Sheldon, Chief Fin. Officer & Exec. V.P.--Lazare Kaplan Intl., Inc., New York, NY; *U.S. Public*, pg. 981
Girouard, Marvin, Pres. & Chief Oper. Officer--Pier 1 Imports, Inc., Fort Worth, TX; *U.S. Public*, pg. 1295
Gish, Rollin, V.P., Strategist & Designer-Mktg. Communications--Ross Roy Communications, Inc., Bloomfield Hills, MI; *U.S. Private*, pg. 946
Glaske, Paul E., Chm. Bd., Pres. & Chief Exec. Officer--Blue Bird Corporation, Macon, GA; *U.S. Private*, pg. 151
Glass, Robert W., Sr. V.P.-Corp. Devel.--Robert Half International Inc., Menlo Park, CA; *U.S. Public*, pg. 774
Glass, Terry, Mgr.-Prod. Plng.--A.O. Smith Electrical Products Company, Tipp City, OH; *U.S. Public*, pg. 1477
Glassman, Brad, Mgr.-Corp. Devel.--Bradley Pharmaceuticals, Fairfield, NJ; *U.S. Public*, pg. 249
Glassman, Brad, Mgr.-Corp. Devel.--Doak Dermatologics, Westbury, NY; *U.S. Public*, pg. 250
Gleason, John H., Sr. V.P.-Project Plng. & Devel.--Del Webb Corporation, Phoenix, AZ; *U.S. Public*, pg. 494
Gledhill, Andrew, Plng. Dir.--Ground Zero, Santa Monica, CA; *U.S. Private*, pg. 484
Glen, Douglas, Sr. V.P.-Bus. Devel. & Strategic Plng.--Mattel, Inc., El Segundo, CA; *U.S. Public*, pg. 1057
Glenn, Gloria A., V.P.-Plng.--The Newhall Land And Farming Company, Valencia, CA; *U.S. Public*, pg. 1178
Glidden, Dan, V.P.-Water & Air Filtration--Teledyne Water Pik, Fort Collins, CO; *U.S. Public*, pg. 44
Gloudeman, Tom, Mgr.-Recruitment & Devel.--Lands' End, Inc., Dodgeville, WI; *U.S. Public*, pg. 977
Glover, Glenn H., Dir.-Plng.--Gold Kist, Inc., Atlanta, GA; *U.S. Private*, pg. 459
Glover, Richard, V.P.-Prod. Devel.--Cosco, Inc., Columbus, IN; *U.S. Private*, pg. 277
Gluesenkamp, Richard, Dir.-Bus. Devel.--Patterson Dental Company, Saint Paul, MN; *U.S. Public*, pg. 1265
Godfrey, William R., Exec. V.P.-Admin. Svcs.--Sierra Health Services, Inc., Las Vegas, NV; *U.S. Public*, pg. 1469
Godin, Paul, Exec. V.P. & Head-Econ. Forecasting--Electricite de France, Paris, France; *Int'l*, pg. 437
Goding, Keith L, Chief Devel. Officer & Exec. V.P.--RehabCare Group, Inc., Saint Louis, MO; *U.S. Public*, pg. 1373
Goedeker, Del E., V.P.-Corp. Devel.--Tuscarora Incorporated, New Brighton, PA; *U.S. Public*, pg. 1646
Goedkoop, R.J., Dir.-Bus. Devel. & Analysis--VNU Verenigde Nederlandse Uitgeversbedrijven B.V., Haarlem, Netherlands; *Int'l*, pg. 1445
Goins, Dixie E., V.P.-Res. & Devel.--Albemarle Corporation, Richmond, VA; *U.S. Public*, pg. 37
Goldbath, Raymond, Chm. Bd. & Chief Exec. Officer--Marathon Cheese Corp., Marathon, WI; *U.S. Private*, pg. 701
Goldberg, Michael C., Chm. Bd., Pres. & Chief Exec. Officer--FDP Corp., Miami, FL; *U.S. Public*, pg. 603
Golden, Michael, Pres.--Stephen Gould Paper Co., Inc., Whippany, NJ; *U.S. Private*, pg. 467
Goldfarb, Andrew, Pres. & Chief Exec. Officer--HCC Industries, Rosemead, CA; *U.S. Private*, pg. 490
Goldsmith, J. Wickliffe, Jr., Exec. V.P. & Dir.-Training--Piccadilly Cafeterias, Inc., Baton Rouge, LA; *U.S. Public*, pg. 1294
Goldsmith, Russell, Chief Exec. Officer--City National Corporation, Beverly Hills, CA; *U.S. Public*, pg. 380
Goldstein, Gary P., V.P.-New Bus. Devel.--Matthew Bender & Company, Incorporated, New York, NY; *U.S. Public*, pg. 1616
Golisano, B. Thomas, Chm. Bd., Pres. & Chief Exec. Officer--Paychex, Inc., Rochester, NY; *U.S. Public*, pg. 1267
Gollnick, Jerry F., Sr. V.P. & Gen. Mgr.-Bus. Devel.--Williams Field Services, Tulsa, OK; *U.S. Public*, pg. 1769
Golsen, Jack E., Chm. Bd., Pres. & Chief Exec. Officer--LSB Industries, Inc., Oklahoma City, OK; *U.S. Public*, pg. 970
Gomes, Tony, V.P.-Corp. Plng.--Big Y Foods Inc., Springfield, MA; *U.S. Private*, pg. 143
Gomez, William M., V.P.-Bus. Devel.--Syntex, Palo Alto, CA; *Int'l*, pg. 1120
Gonzalez Bonilla, Juan Manuel, Dir.-Plng.--Transportacion Maritima Mexicana S.A. de C.V., Mexico, Mexico; *Int'l*, pg. 1418
Gonzalez, Jaime, Exec. V.P.-Plng. & Devel.--Puerto Rico Tourism Company, San Juan, PR; *U.S. Private*, pg. 894
Gonzalez, Mario Garza, Pres.-Human Rels. & Plng. Div.--Vitro, Sociedad Anonima, Garza Garcia, Mexico; *Int'l*, pg. 1469
Good, Alexander H., V.P.-Strategic Plng. & Devel.--Bell Atlantic Corporation, New York, NY; *U.S. Public*, pg. 201
Goodman, John, V.P.-Corp. Devel.--Block Drug Company, Inc., Jersey City, NJ; *U.S. Public*, pg. 236
Goodman, Robert H., V.P.-Corp. Devel. & Plng.--ENSERCH Corporation, Dallas, TX; *U.S. Public*, pg. 1587
Goodrich, Philip, Sr. V.P.-Corp. Devel.--AMETEK, Inc., Paoli, PA; *U.S. Public*, pg. 99
Gorder, Mark S., Pres. & Chief Exec. Officer--Resistance Technology Inc., Arden Hills, MN; *U.S. Public*, pg. 1455
Gordon, Howard, Sr. V.P.-Bus. Devel. & New Ventures--Cheesecake Factory Incorporated, Calabasas Hills, CA; *U.S. Public*, pg. 343
Gordon, Russell L., Dir.-Corp. Devel.--RPM, Inc., Medina, OH; *U.S. Public*, pg. 1356
Gore, Raymond, Sr. Bus. Devel. Officer--Southwest Marketing-Dallas Business Center, Dallas, TX; *U.S. Public*, pg. 650
Gore, S. Tony, III, Exec. V.P.-Acq. & Corp. Devel.--Vanguard Cellular Systems, Inc., Greensboro, NC; *U.S. Public*, pg. 1707
Gorman, Kirk E., Chief Fin. Officer & Sr. V.P.--Universal Health Services, Inc., King of Prussia, PA; *U.S. Public*, pg. 1696
Gorman, Leon A., Pres.--L.L. Bean, Inc., Freeport, ME; *U.S.* Private, pg. 639
Gose, Gunther, Exec. V.P.--Zurich Insurance Company, Zurich, Switzerland; *Int'l*, pg. 1529
Goslee, Dwight J., Chief Info. Officer, Sr. V.P.-Bus. Systems & Devel.--ConAgra, Inc., Omaha, NE; *U.S. Public*, pg. 425
Goss, Lawrence A., Sr. V.P.-Bus. Devel.--California Microwave, Inc.-Wireless Products Grp., Sunnyvale, CA; *U.S. Public*, pg. 293
Goss, Michael F., V.P.-Corp. Devel. & Treas.--Oak Industries Inc., Waltham, MA; *U.S. Public*, pg. 1209
Gottwald, William M., V.P.-Corp. Strategy--Albemarle Corporation, Richmond, VA; *U.S. Public*, pg. 37
Goudis, Richard, V.P.-Investor Rels. & Corp. Plng.--Sunbeam Corporation, Delray Beach, FL; *U.S. Public*, pg. 1533
Gould, Fred, Dir.-Bus. Devel.--COMSAT Laboratories, Clarksburg, MD; *U.S. Public*, pg. 424
Goulding, Barry W., V.P.-Mktg. & Lender Prods.--SLM Holding Corp., Washington, DC; *U.S. Public*, pg. 1419
Govindarajan, P.S., Gen. Mgr.-Plng.--Indian Oil Corporation Limited, New Delhi, India; *Int'l*, pg. 673
Graber, Lee A., V.P.-Corp. Devel.--Homestake Mining Company, San Francisco, CA; *U.S. Public*, pg. 832
Graf, James, Mgr.-Bus. Plng.--American Bureau of Shipping, New York, NY; *U.S. Private*, pg. 51
Graham, C., Production, Plng. & Matls. Mgr.--Senior Conflow, Nottingham, United Kingdom; *Int'l*, pg. 1220
Graham, Gordon, Pres., Chief Exec. Officer & Chief Oper. Officer--Bell Industries, Inc., El Segundo, CA; *U.S. Public, pg. 204*
Grammenopoulos, Danny, Dir.-Bus. Devel.--Yogen Fruz Worldwide Inc., Markham, Canada; *Int'l*, pg. 1520
Grand, T., Plng. Dir.--Crispin Porter & Bogusky, Miami, FL; *U.S. Private*, pg. 290
Granger, Randy, Mgr.-Bus. Res.--San Antonio Express News, San Antonio, TX; *U.S. Private*, pg. 517
Grau, Stuart, Res. & Acct. Plng. Dir.--Avrett, Free & Ginsberg, Inc., New York, NY; *U.S. Private*, pg. 103
Graubart, Barry, V.P.-Database Devel. & Mktg.--Nelson Publications, Port Chester, NY; *U.S. Public*, pg. 1328
Graves, Kim, Legal Mgr.-Devel--North Limited, Melbourne, Australia; *Int'l*, pg. 967
Gray, John, V.P.-Network & Corp. Devel.--Southern Pacific Rail Corporation, San Francisco, CA; *U.S. Public*, pg. 1668
Gray, William J., Sr. V.P.-Mktg. & Supply--Holly Corporation, Dallas, TX; *U.S. Public*, pg. 830

Greaney, Patrick J., Sr. V.P.-Corp. Plng. & Bus. Devel.--Philips Electronics North America Corporation, New York, NY; *Int'l*, pg. 1053
Greaves, Kristin, Sr. V.P. & H.R./Devel. Dir.--Deutsch, Inc., New York, NY; *U.S. Private*, pg. 328
Greaves, Kristin, Sr. V.P. & H.R./Devel. Dir.--Deutsch LA, Santa Monica, CA; *U.S. Private*, pg. 328
Greco, Robert, Chief Tech. Officer, Treas. & Sec.--Active Voice Corporation, Seattle, WA; *U.S. Public*, pg. 17
Green, Andrew F., V.P.-Corp. Plng. & Controller--Advantica Restaurant Group, Inc., Spartanburg, SC; *U.S. Public*, pg. 22
Green, Andy, Dir.-Strategy & Bus. Mngmt.--British Telecommunications plc, London, United Kingdom; *Int'l*, pg. 222
Green, Leslie H., V.P.-Bus. Devel.--Swiss Army Brands, Inc., Shelton, CT; *U.S. Public*, pg. 1544
Green, Stanley, Pres. & Chief Exec. Officer--DAQ Electronics Inc., Piscataway, NJ; *U.S. Private*, pg. 300
Green, Stanley D., Chief Fin. Officer & Exec. V.P.-Fin. & Corp. Devel.--Southwestern Energy Company, Fayetteville, AR; *U.S. Public*, pg. 1494
Green, Thomas W., V.P.-Mngmt. Devel. & Compensation, GTE Service Corp.--GTE Corporation, Stamford, CT; *U.S. Public*, pg. 696
Greenberg, Catherine, Dir.-Mktg. & Stategic Devel.--The Roanoke Times, Roanoke, VA; *U.S. Private*, pg. 649
Greenberg, Daniel, Chm. Bd. & Chief Exec. Officer--Electro Rent Corporation, Van Nuys, CA; *U.S. Public*, pg. 568
Greene McChesney, Cynthia, Bus. Devel. Dir.--Fogarty Klein & Partners, Houston, TX; *U.S. Private*, pg. 415
Greene, Cheryl, Mng. Partner & Chief Strategy Officer--Deutsch, Inc., New York, NY; *U.S. Private*, pg. 328
Greenwald, Gerald, Chm. Bd. & Chief Exec. Officer--UAL Corporation, Elk Grove Village, IL; *U.S. Public*, pg. 1652
Greenwell, W., Dir.-Programs--United Technologies, Chemical Systems Div., San Jose, CA; *U.S. Public*, pg. 1690
Greer, Barton, Jr., Chm. Bd.--Autry Greer & Sons, Inc., Prichard, AL; *U.S. Private*, pg. 479
Greer, Kimberly, V.P.-Strategic Plng. & Brand Devel.--Business Week, New York, NY; *U.S. Public*, pg. 1069
Gregory, Mark, Mgr.-Product Design & Devel.--Master Appliance Corp., Racine, WI; *U.S. Private*, pg. 713
Greif, Martin A., V.P.-Market Devel.--INSO Corporation, Boston, MA; *U.S. Public*, pg. 882
Gresov, Boris, Chm. Bd., Pres. & Chief Exec. Officer--Standard Metals Corporation, New York, NY; *U.S. Public*, *pg. 1502*
Griffin, Robert G., V.P. & Dir.-Mergers, Acquisitions & Strategic Plng.--Leggett & Platt, Incorporated, Carthage, MO; *U.S. Public*, pg. 985
Griffin, Toni L., V.P.-Corp. Commun.--American Arbitration Association, New York, NY; *U.S. Private*, pg. 50
Griffith, Bill, V.P.-Real Estate--Rhodes, Inc., Atlanta, GA; *U.S. Public*, pg. 805
Grimmer, Rebecca N., V.P.-Strategic Information--Temple-Inland Forest Products Corp.-Bleached Paperboard Group, Evadale, TX; *U.S. Public*, pg. 1575
Grinstead, Phil, V.P.-Fin. Planning & Analysis--DHL Worldwide Express, Redwood City, CA; *U.S. Private*, pg. 301
Grisham, Sher, Mgr.-H.R.--Novellus Systems, Inc., San Jose, CA; *U.S. Public*, pg. 1204
Grodzins, Lee, V.P.-Advanced Devel.--American Science & Engineering, Inc., Billerica, MA; *U.S. Public*, pg. 90
Gronstedt, Lars O., Exec. V.P.-Bus. Devel.--Svenska Handelsbanken, Stockholm, Sweden; *Int'l*, pg. 1327
Grose, J. David, Chief Fin. Officer & V.P.-Fin.--Basic Construction Company, Newport News, VA; *U.S. Private*, *pg. 121*
Grossbard, Elliott B., M.D., Sr. V.P.-Devel.--Scios Inc., Mountain View, CA; *U.S. Public*, pg. 1444
Grossman, Arnold J., V.P.-Intl. Affairs--American Airlines, Inc., Fort Worth, TX; *U.S. Public*, pg. 9
Grove, Ronald C., Sr. V.P.-Logistics Plng.--PETsMART, Inc., Phoenix, AZ; *U.S. Public*, pg. 1281
Groves, George H., Exec. V.P.-Banking Services--Keystone Financial Inc., Harrisburg, PA; *U.S. Public*, pg. 956
Gubinelli, Sandro, Asst. V.P.-Res. & Devel.--Bobst S.A., Lausanne, Switzerland; *Int'l*, pg. 198
Guburnat, John, V.P.-Bus. Devel.--Atlantic Mutual Companies, New York, NY; *U.S. Private*, pg. 95
Guil, Julie, Mgr.-Plng.--Clothestime Stores, Inc., Anaheim, CA; *U.S. Public*, pg. 387
Guingnard, Robert J., V.P.-Strategic Plng.--Rogers Cantel Mobile Communications Inc., Saint-Laurent, Canada; *Int'l*, pg. 1122
Guitano, Anton, V.P.-Fin. & Plng.--KPIX-TV, San Francisco, CA; *U.S. Public*, pg. 275
Gullersoy, Gurbuz, Mgr.-Strategic Plng.--Arcelik A.S., Istanbul, Turkey; *Int'l*, pg. 741
Gulley, Joan L., Sr. V.P.-Strategic Plng.--PNC Bank Corp., Pittsburgh, PA; *U.S. Public*, pg. 1242
Guloien, Donald, Sr. V.P.-Bus. Devel.--Manulife Financial (The Manufacturers Life Insurance Company), Toronto, Canada; *Int'l*, pg. 840
Gunn, Scott, V.P.-Bus. Devel./U.S. & the Americas--GTECH Corporation, West Greenwich, RI; *U.S. Public*, pg. 767
Gunn, Thomas M., Sr. V.P.-Bus. Devel.--McDonnell Aircraft & Missile Systems Div., Berkeley, MO; *U.S. Public*, pg. 241
Gunter, Hubert, Sr. V.P.-Fund Mngmt. & Res.--Liechtenstein Global Trust Limited, Vaduz, Liechtenstein; *Int'l*, pg. 809
Gunter, John R., V.P.-Network Strategic Plng. & Support--BellSouth Telecommunications, Inc., Atlanta, GA; *U.S. Public*, pg. 209
Gupta, Satish K., V.P.-Corp. Mktg. & Bus. Devel.--Cirrus Logic, Inc., Fremont, CA; *U.S. Public*, pg. 375
Gupta, Vinod, Chm. Bd.--American Business Information, Inc., Omaha, NE; *U.S. Public*, pg. 69
Gurdy, Mike, Sr. V.P.-Bus. Devel.--Associates Financial Services Corporation, Dallas, TX; *U.S. Public*, pg. 663
Gurin, Ron, V.P.-Pur. & Prod. Devel.--Pressman Toy Corp., New York, NY; *U.S. Private*, pg. 882
Gustafsson, Lennart, V.P.-Corp. Strategy--SAS Service Partner A/S, Copenhagen, Denmark; *Int'l*, pg. 1202
Guzikowski, T.J., Mgr.-Plng. & Bus. Devel.--Colonial Pipeline Company, Atlanta, GA; *U.S. Private*, pg. 254
Haave, Luther, V.P.-Devel.--WIC Western International Communications Ltd., Vancouver, Canada; *Int'l*, pg. 1481
Habig, Brian, Exec. V.P.-Sls. & Mktg., Kimball--Kimball International, Inc., Jasper, IN; *U.S. Public*, pg. 956
Haddix, David D., Treas. & Dir.-Plng.--Therma-Tru Corp., Maumee, OH; *U.S. Private*, pg. 1079
Hagen, Edward L., V.P.-Bus. Devel.--Uniroyal Chemical Company, Inc., Middlebury, CT; *U.S. Public*, pg. 460
Hagen, Jerry, Controller--Symbol Technologies, Portable Systems Division, Costa Mesa, CA; *U.S. Public*, pg. 1546
Haig, Alan T., V.P.-Corp. Devel.--Republic Industries, Inc., Fort Lauderdale, FL; *U.S. Public*, pg. 1378
Hairston, William O., Jr., V.P.-Lending & Bus. Devel.--Pinnacle Bank, Jasper, AL; *U.S. Public*, pg. 1297
Hale, Terry L., V.P.-Food Svcs. & New Prod. Devel.--Uni-Marts, Inc., State College, PA; *U.S. Public*, pg. 1664
Hale, Roger L., Chm. Bd., Pres. & Chief Exec. Officer--Tennant Company, Minneapolis, MN; *U.S. Public*, pg. 1577
Haley, Eugene T., Sr. V.P.-Customer Satisfaction--Qualex Inc., Durham, NC; *U.S. Public*, pg. 551
Hall, A. Lee, V.P.--AAR Corp., Wood Dale, IL; *U.S. Public*, pg. 1
Hall, Alison, Mgr.-Adv. & Plng.--Guardian & Observer, London, United Kingdom; *Int'l*, pg. 577
Hall, Bradley C., V.P.-New Bus. Devel.--UGI Corporation, King of Prussia, PA; *U.S. Public*, pg. 1653
Hall, C.L., Pres. & Chief Exec. Officer--Graybar Electric Company, Inc., Clayton, MO; *U.S. Private*, pg. 472
Hall, J. Robert, Sr. V.P.-Strategic Plng.--Nabisco Inc., Parsippany, NJ; *U.S. Public*, pg. 1355
Hallam, Howard, Pres. & Chief Oper. Officer--Ben E. Keith Company, Fort Worth, TX; *U.S. Private*, pg. 611
Halversen, David, Sr. V.P.-Bus. Devel. & Commun.--Tupperware Corporation, Orlando, FL; *U.S. Public*, pg. 1644
Halverson, Bruce E., V.P.-Plng. & Allocation--Goody's Family Clothing, Inc., Knoxville, TN; *U.S. Public*, pg. 753
Hamachek, Ross F., V.P.- Plng. & Devel.--The Washington Post Company, Washington, DC; *U.S. Public*, pg. 1742
Hambleton, Peter, V.P.-Bus. Devel.--Hunter Douglas, Inc., Upper Saddle River, NJ; *Int'l*, pg. 639
Hamblett, Stephen, Chm. Bd. & Publr.--Providence Journal-Bulletin, Providence, RI; *U.S. Public*, pg. 209
Hamilburg, Maurice J., Pres. & Chief Exec. Officer--Plymouth Rubber Company, Inc., Canton, MA; *U.S. Public*, pg. 1311
Hamilton, W. Mark, V.P.-Corp. Devel.--Service Corporation International, Houston, TX; *U.S. Public*, pg. 1460
Hammel, Ron, Dir.-Devel.--Cousins Submarines, Menomonee Falls, WI; *U.S. Private*, pg. 280
Hammond, William I., V.P.-New Prod. Devel.--World Book, Inc., Columbus, OH; *U.S. Public*, pg. 218
Hampton, E. Kay, V.P.-Mkt. Devel.--Computer Language Research, Inc., Carrollton, TX; *U.S. Public*, pg. 421
Hancock, Michael, Exec. V.P.-Restaurant Devel.--Boddie-Noell Enterprises Inc., Rocky Mount, NC; *U.S. Private*, pg. 154
Hancox, William T., V.P.-Strategic Devel.--Atomic Energy of Canada Ltd., Mississauga, Canada; *Int'l*, pg. 97
Hankins, Steven, Sr. V.P.-Fin. Plng. & Shared Services--Tyson Foods, Inc., Springdale, AR; *U.S. Public*, pg. 1652
Hannon, Michael G., V.P.-Corp. Devel.--Allied Waste Industries, Scottsdale, AZ; *U.S. Public*, pg. 49
Hanrahan, Denis, V.P.-Corp. Devel.--Bank of Ireland, Dublin, Ireland; *Int'l*, pg. 152
Hanrahan, Timothy J., Sr. V.P.--Meridian Insurance Group, Inc., Indianapolis, IN; *U.S. Public*, pg. 1095
Hansen, Jens, V.P.-Res. & Devel.--International Pharmaceuticals, Oslo, Norway; *U.S. Public*, pg. 58
Hansen, R. Eric, V.P.-Sys. Plng. & Opers.--Carolina Power & Light Company, Raleigh, NC; *U.S. Public*, pg. 306
Hanson, Dan, V.P.-Plng.--Land O'Lakes, Inc., Arden Hills, MN; *U.S. Private*, pg. 645
Hanson, Michael D., V.P.-Corp. Plng.--Dentsply International Inc., York, PA; *U.S. Public*, pg. 498
Harden, Timothy S., V.P.-Broadband Devel.--Pacific Bell, San Ramon, CA; *U.S. Public*, pg. 1416
Hardin, Donald M., Chief Fin. Officer & V.P.--CCI Corporation, Tulsa, OK; *U.S. Private*, pg. 193
Hardison, Robert E., V.P.-Acquisitions & Devel.--Community Health Systems, Inc., Brentwood, TN; *U.S. Private*, pg. 419
Hare, Ed, V.P.-Plng. & Analysis--AK Steel Corporation, Middletown, OH; *U.S. Public*, pg. 7
Harf, Alfred, Asst. Exec. Dir.-Plng.--NJ Transit, Newark, NJ; *U.S. Private*, pg. 794
Harkins, William A., V.P.-Plng. & Inter-Utility Affairs--Consolidated Edison Company of New York, Inc., New York, NY; *U.S. Public*, pg. 434
Harkness, Glenn, V.P. & Dir.-Bus. Devel.--TRC Companies, Inc., Windsor, CT; *U.S. Public*, pg. 1557
Harling, Brian, V.P.-Corp. Affairs--MDS Inc., Etobicoke, Canada; *Int'l*, pg. 826
Harmon, Raymond, V.P.-Bus. Plng.--CBS Sports Div., New York, NY; *U.S. Public*, pg. 274
Haroldson, Stephen A., V.P. & Res. Asst.--CUNA Mutual Insurance Society, Madison, WI; *U.S. Private*, pg. 296
Harp, Sharon, V.P.-Plng. & Distr.--United Retail Group, Inc., Rochelle Park, NJ; *U.S. Public*, pg. 1679
Harper, Mike, Assoc. Plng. Dir.--TBWA Chiat/Day Toronto, Toronto, Canada; *U.S. Private*, pg. 1063
Harrell, Samuel M., Chm. Bd., Pres. & Chief Exec. Officer--EDI International, Inc., Cincinnati, OH; *U.S. Private*, pg. 353
Harrill, Donald L., Sr. V.P.-Vacation Ownership Opers.--Hilton Hotels Div., Beverly Hills, CA; *U.S. Public*, pg. 829
Harris, Henry C., Sr. V.P.-Strategic Plng. & Alliance--Zitel Corporation, Fremont, CA; *U.S. Public*, pg. 1793
Harris, James Wesley, V.P.-Devel.--Speedway Motorsports, Inc., Concord, NC; *U.S. Public*, pg. 1498
Harris, M.J., Dir.-Markets for Devel.--Redland PLC, Reigate, United Kingdom; *Int'l*, pg. 1090
Harris, Ralph A., V.P.-Corp. Devel.--Campbell Soup Company, Camden, NJ; *U.S. Public*, pg. 298
Harris, Richard, V.P.-Resource Plng. & Admin.--Sealaska Corporation, Juneau, AK; *U.S. Private*, pg. 978
Harris, William E., Sr. V.P.-Corp. Devel.--The Home Depot, Inc., Atlanta, GA; *U.S. Public*, pg. 831
Harrison, M., Dir.-Devel.--Princess Hotels International Inc., New York, NY; *Int'l*, pg. 818
Harriton, Lorraine, Sr. V.P.-Mktg. & Bus. Devel.--Network Computing Devices, Inc., Mountain View, CA; *U.S. Public*, pg. 1168
Harrold, Lewis N., V.P.-Engrng.--Waters Instruments, Inc., Rochester, MN; *U.S. Public*, pg. 1745
Harslem, Eric F., Sr. V.P.-Prod. & Tech. Strategy--Dell Computer Corporation, Round Rock, TX; *U.S. Public*, pg. 495
Hart, Steve, V.P.-Market Development--SkyWest Inc., Saint George, UT; *U.S. Public*, pg. 1476
Harta, P.I., Dir.-Bus. Devel.--Morgan Crucible Co. Plc, Windsor, United Kingdom; *Int'l*, pg. 890
Hartfield, Carl R., V.P.-Plng. & Devel.--Danfoss Fluid Power, Racine, WI; *Int'l*, pg. 377
Hartman, Carl C., Pres., Chief Exec. Officer & Chief Oper. Officer--Trinidad/Benham Corp., Denver, CO; *U.S. Private*, pg. 1103
Hartwick, R. Dean, V.P.-Corp. Devel.--Logicon, Inc., Torrance, CA; *U.S. Public*, pg. 1198
Harvey, Peter R., Pres.--Artra Group Incorporated, Northfield, IL; *U.S. Public*, pg. 136
Hasler, Harald, Dr., Mgr.-Corp. Devel.--Melitta Unternehmensgruppe Bentz KG, Minden, Germany; *Int'l*, *pg. 856*
Hassman, Rommey, Res. & Strategic Plng. Dir.--Gitam/BBDO, Ramat Gan, Israel; *Int'l*, pg. 552
Hatmaker, J.W., Dir.-Bus. Mngmt.-Specialty & New Products--Kerr-McGee Chemical Corp., Oklahoma City, OK; *U.S. Public*, pg. 952
Hattas, Dave, Mgr.-Bus. Devel.--Panasonic Factory Automation Co., Elgin, IL; *Int'l*, pg. 847
Hattier, Serge, Dir.-Devel.-Mercure--Societe Internationale des Hotels Novotel, Evry, France; *Int'l*, pg. 21
Hauser, Martin, Dr., V.P.-New Bus. Devel.--Loctite Corporation, Rocky Hill, CT; *Int'l*, pg. 611
Haverty, Rawson, Chm. Bd.--Haverty Furniture Companies, Inc., Atlanta, GA; *U.S. Public*, pg. 799
Hawkins, Thomas W., Sr. V.P.-Corp. Devel.--Republic Industries, Inc., Fort Lauderdale, FL; *U.S. Public*, pg. 1378
Hawley, Edmund, Chief Exec. Officer & Sr. V.P.--Skyway Freight Systems, Inc., Watsonville, CA; *U.S. Private*, pg. 1005
Hayashi, Toshio, Gen. Mgr.-Planning & Devel.--Tekken Corporation, Tokyo, Japan; *Int'l*, pg. 1362
Hayden, Donald J., Jr., Sr. V.P.-Bus. Devel., Worldwide Pharmaceuticals Grp.--Bristol-Myers Squibb Company, New York, NY; *U.S. Public*, pg. 253
Hayes, John E. Jr., Chm. Bd. & Chief Exec. Officer--Western Resources, Inc., Topeka, KS; *U.S. Public*, pg. 1759
Hazelip, Ace, Dir.-Prod. Devel.--Churchill Downs, Inc., Louisville, KY; *U.S. Public*, pg. 356
Hazen, Thomas L., Pres.-New Bus. Devel.--Texaco Worldwide Exploration & Production, Scroggins, TX; *U.S.* Public, pg. 1583
Healy, James P., V.P.-Energy Services Plng.--The Southern Connecticut Gas Company, Bridgeport, CT; *U.S. Public*, pg. 431
Heath, H. Anthony, V.P.-Plng. & Communications--Sun Life Assurance Company of Canada (U.K.) Limited, Basingstoke, United Kingdom; *Int'l*, pg. 1319
Heatherly, David A., Exec. V.P.-Prod. Devel./Claims--Foremost Corporation of America, Caledonia, MI; *U.S. Public*, pg. 667
Heether, Ernest, Sr. V.P.-Mdse. Opers., Plng. & Devel.--Kmart Corporation, Troy, MI; *U.S. Public*, pg. 963
Heffernan, Bill, V.P.-Real Estate & Construction--Staples, Inc., Westborough, MA; *U.S. Public*, pg. 1509
Heffernan, Eileen, Sr. Dir.-Bus. Devel.--Aquila Biopharmaceuticals, Inc., Worcester, MA; *U.S. Public*, pg. 126
Hefner, Christie, Chm. Bd. & Chief Exec. Officer--Playboy Enterprises, Inc., Chicago, IL; *U.S. Public*, pg. 1309
Heiding, Sven, Sr. V.P.-Comml. Devel.--Scandinavian Airlines System (SAS), Solna, Sweden; *Int'l*, pg. 1201
Heilman, David R., V.P.-Strategic Plng. & Corp. Devel.--General Nutrition, Inc., Pittsburgh, PA; *U.S. Public*, pg. 725
Heinemann, Jack E., V.P.-Devel.--Federal Realty Investment Trust, Rockville, MD; *U.S. Public*, pg. 616
Heiner, Clyde M., Sr. V.P.--Questar Corporation, Salt Lake City, UT; *U.S. Public*, pg. 1352
Heinrich, Donald M., V.P.-Bus. Devel.--A.O. Smith Corporation, Milwaukee, WI; *U.S. Public*, pg. 1476
Heithaus, John, V.P.-Corp. Devel.--Grindmaster Corporation, Louisville, KY; *U.S. Private*, pg. 482
Hekman, Edward W., Mgr.-Corp. Plng.--Autocam Corporation, Grand Rapids, MI; *U.S. Public*, pg. 148
Helbling, John K., Dir.-Economic Devel.--IES Industries Inc., Cedar Rapids, IA; *U.S. Public*, pg. 855
Hella, Yvan, Gen. Mgr.-Plng. & Transmission--Electrabel S.A., Brussels, Belgium; *Int'l*, pg. 436
Heller, William J., Sr. V.P.-Strategic Plng. & New Bus. Deve.--Edison International, Rosemead, CA; *U.S. Public*, pg. 564
Helm, Ellen, Mgr.-New Prod. Devel. & Prod. Mgmnt.--Simpson Electric Co., Elgin, IL; *U.S. Private*, pg. 1002
Henderson, Dan, V.P.-Mfg.--H. R. Kaminsky & Sons, Inc., Fitzgerald, GA; *U.S. Private*, pg. 606

Hendler, Dale B., V.P.-Corp. Devel.--Matson Navigation Company, Inc., San Francisco, CA; *U.S. Public*, pg. 39
Hendon, Barry T., Mgr.-Business Devel.--Jacobs Engineering Group Inc., Houston, TX; *U.S. Public*, pg. 921
Hendricks, Richard C., V.P. & Dir.-Corp. Business Devel.--Kennametal Inc., Latrobe, PA; *U.S. Public*, pg. 950
Hendrickson, Thomas N., Chm. Bd. & Chief Exec. Officer--CPAC, Inc., Leicester, NY; *U.S. Public*, pg. 282
Henley, A.B., Jr., Chm. Bd., Pres. & Chief Exec. Officer--Henley Paper Company, Greensboro, NC; *U.S. Private*, pg. 522
Henner, Dennis J., Ph.D., V.P.-Res. & Devel.--Genentech, Inc., South San Francisco, CA; *Int'l*, pg. 1120
Hennessy, Michael, Pres. & Chief Exec. Officer--Munro & Company, Inc., Hot Springs National Park, AR; *U.S. Private*, pg. 767
Henning, Alyson, Chief Bus. Devel. Officer--Ammirati Puris Lintas Worldwide, New York, NY; *U.S. Public*, pg. 908
Henning, Alyson B., Sr. V.P., Bus. Devel. Dir.--Ammirati, Puris & Lintas, Inc., New York, NY; *U.S. Private*, pg. 66
Henricks, Jon, V.P.-Corp. Affairs--DOALL Company, Des Plaines, IL; *U.S. Private*, pg. 337
Henriquez, Jaime, Gen. Superintendent-Mine Plng.--El Teniente Division, Rancagua, Chile; *Int'l*, pg. 302
Henry, Terry, Mgr.-Corp. Plng.--OGE Energy Corp., Oklahoma City, OK; *U.S. Public*, pg. 1207
Hensley, Tom, Chief Fin. Officer & V.P.--Fieldale Corporation, Baldwin, GA; *U.S. Private*, pg. 403
Herasimchuk, David A., V.P.-Mktg. Devel.--Global Marine Inc., Houston, TX; *U.S. Public*, pg. 748
Herbits, Stephen E., Exec. V.P.-Corp. Policy & External Affairs--The Seagram Company Ltd., Montreal, Canada; *Int'l*, pg. 1214
Herbst, H.R., V.P.-Strategic Plng.--Gulf Canada Resources Ltd., Calgary, Canada; *Int'l*, pg. 577
Hermosillo, Alberto Cabal, V.P.-Mktg. & Plng.--Grupo Synkro, S.A. de C.V., Mexico, Mexico; *Int'l*, pg. 576
Hernandez, Carlos, Mgr.-Fin. Plng.--C.A. Cigarrera Bigott, Sucs., Caracas, Venezuela; *Int'l*, pg. 111
Hershberger, Troy W., Dir.-Prod. Devel.--Biomet, Inc., Warsaw, IN; *U.S. Public*, pg. 231
Herzgsell, Willi, Mgr.-Plng., Info. & Control--CIBA-GEIGY Australia Ltd., Pendle Hill, Australia; *Int'l*, pg. 976
Hess, C. Frederick, V.P.--BC Gas Inc., Vancouver, Canada; *Int'l*, pg. 114
Hester, Hilliard H., V.P.-Mngmt. Contracts Division--Allied Clinical Laboratories, Inc., Nashville, TN; *U.S. Public*, pg. 973
Hester, Jim G., Mgr.-Bus. Devel. & Acq.--Plains Resources Inc., Houston, TX; *U.S. Public*, pg. 1307
Hetu, Daniel, Dr., V.P.-Corp. Devel.--BioChem Pharma Inc., Laval, Canada; *Int'l*, pg. 196
Heuer, Volker, Dir.-Devel. Vans--Mercedes-Benz AG, Stuttgart, Germany; *Int'l*, pg. 368
Heusdens, J.J., Mng. Dir.-Personnel, Environment & Physical Plng.--Hoogovens Ijmuiden, Ijmuiden, Netherlands; *Int'l*, pg. 753
Hickey, William M., Pres. & Chief Exec. Officer--Lapham-Hickey Steel Corp., Chicago, IL; *U.S. Private*, pg. 651
Hickman, Roy, V.P.-Prod. Devel.--Lotus Carpet Division, Phenix City, AL; *U.S. Private*, pg. 257
Higbie, Henry, Sr. V.P.-Fin. Plng.--Westpac Banking Corporation, Sydney, Australia; *Int'l*, pg. 1495
Higgs, Stacey, Reg. Planning Supvr.--Carat ICG, Raleigh, NC; *U.S. Private*, pg. 207
Higham, Jay, V.P.-Mktg. & Devel.--IntegraMed America, Purchase, NY; *U.S. Public*, pg. 883
Highet, Mac, Exec. V.P.-Corp. Devel.--Reed Elsevier Inc., New York, NY; *Int'l*, pg. 1095
Hightower, Sr., Neil H., Pres. & Chief Exec. Officer--Thomaston Mills, Inc., Thomaston, GA; *U.S. Public*, pg. 1599
Hill, D.B, Dir.-Intl. Route Devel.--Delta Air Lines, Inc., Atlanta, GA; *U.S. Public*, pg. 497
Hill, Marcy, Designer--American Uniform Co., Cleveland, TN; *U.S. Private*, pg. 1039
Hill, Roger W., Pres. & Chief Exec. Officer--Holly Sugar Corporation, Sugar Land, TX; *U.S. Public*, pg. 872
Hill, Sam I., Vice Chm. & DMB&B Strategic Plng. & Bus. Devel. Dir.--DMB&B Communications, New York, NY; *U.S. Private*, pg. 302
Hilsinger, Richard, V.P.-Devel. & Plng.--Alpha Metals, Inc., Jersey City, NJ; *Int'l*, pg. 328
Hinderberger, Stephen J., V.P.-Plng. & Analysis--The May Department Stores Company, Saint Louis, MO; *U.S. Public*, pg. 1063
Hindman, Don J., Chm. Bd., Pres. & Chief Exec. Officer--Clark Foodservice, Inc., Elk Grove Village, IL; *U.S. Private*, pg. 242
Hinnant, Darrell, Chief Oper. Officer--Radiator Specialty Company, Charlotte, NC; *U.S. Private*, pg. 906
Hinton, John R., Chief Fin. Officer, Sr. V.P.-Admin.--Kellogg Company, Battle Creek, MI; *U.S. Public*, pg. 947
Hipple, Richard J., Sr. V.P.-Pur., Engrng. & Strategic Plng.--The LTV Corporation, Cleveland, OH; *U.S. Public*, pg. 971
Hirai, Hajimu, Dir.-Corp. Plng.--Oji Paper Co., Ltd., Tokyo, Japan; *Int'l*, pg. 998
Hirata, Edward Y., V.P.-Regulatory Affairs--Hawaiian Electric Company, Inc., Honolulu, HI; *U.S. Public*, pg. 800
Hitchcock, James R., V.P.-Bus. Devel. & Tech. Services--Comptek Federal Systems, Inc., Buffalo, NY; *U.S. Public*, *pg. 419*
Hitomi, Akihiko, Gen. Mgr.--Sumikin Bussan Corporation, Osaka, Japan; *Int'l*, pg. 1308
Ho, Frank F., V.P.-Res. & Devel.--Tecstar Inc., City of Industry, CA; *U.S. Private*, pg. 1072
Hobbs, E. David, V.P.-Pur. & Plng.--Interface Flooring Systems Inc., La Grange, GA; *U.S. Public*, pg. 889
Hodnett, Bill M., Sr. V.P.-Cash Mngmt./U.S.--Brink's, Inc., Darien, CT; *U.S. Public*, pg. 1305
Hoeschen, Dave, Dir.-Real Estate--Holiday Companies, Bloomington, MN; *U.S. Private*, pg. 534
Hoffman, Barbara, Dir.-Bus. Devel.--Amgen Boulder, Inc., Boulder, CO; *U.S. Public*, pg. 101
Hoffman, Ebba C., Chm. Bd., Pres., Chief Exec. Officer & Chief Fin. Officer--Smead Manufacturing Company, Hastings, MN; *U.S. Private*, pg. 1006
Hofstaetter, Thomas, V.P.-Bus. Devel. & Strategic Plng.--Hoechst Marion Roussel, Inc., Bridgewater, NJ; *Int'l*, pg. 624
Hoguet, Karen M., Chief Fin. Officer--Federated Department Stores, Inc., Cincinnati, OH; *U.S. Public*, pg. 617
Hoit, Kenneth R., V.P.-Plng. & Budgets--Parker Drilling Company, Tulsa, OK; *U.S. Public*, pg. 1259
Holborn, Donald C., Sr. V.P.-Natl. Sls. Plng.--FMR Corp., Boston, MA; *U.S. Private*, pg. 403
Holcomb, Jim, V.P.-Mktg. & Strategic Plng.--Royal Appliance Mfg. Co., Cleveland, OH; *U.S. Public*, pg. 1410
Holcomb, Philo, Dir.-Corp. Plng.--USX Corporation, Pittsburgh, PA; *U.S. Public*, pg. 1661
Holding, R.E., Pres. & Chief Exec. Officer--Sinclair Oil Corp., Salt Lake City, UT; *U.S. Private*, pg. 1003
Holen, Helge, Sr. V.P.-Matls. & Bus. Devel.--Elkem ASA, Oslo, Norway; *Int'l*, pg. 446
Holland, James T., Pres. & Chief Exec. Officer--O'Sullivan Corporation, Winchester, VA; *U.S. Public*, pg. 1234
Holler, W.E., V.P.-Fin. & Treas.--The Deutsch Company, Santa Monica, CA; *U.S. Private*, pg. 328
Hollingsworth, Dennis L., Asst. V.P.-Corp. Devel.--Minnesota Power, Duluth, MN; *U.S. Public*, pg. 1116
Holt, Jim, Sr. V.P.-Global Mktg.--Telxon Corporation, Akron, OH; *U.S. Public*, pg. 1573
Holtz, Harry L., Pres. & Chief Exec. Officer--Great Northern Iron Ore Properties, Saint Paul, MN; *U.S. Public*, pg. 760
Holub, Mark C., Sr. V.P.-Visual Mdsg. & Store Plng.--Younkers, Inc., Des Moines, IA; *U.S. Public*, pg. 1334
Hong, William, Asst. Mgr.-Corp. Plng. & Investments--Sun Hung Kai Properties Ltd., Wan Chai, Hong Kong; *Int'l*, pg. 1318
Hongler, Georg, Dir.-Corp. Strategy--Von Roll AG, Gerlafingen, Switzerland; *Int'l*, pg. 1480
Hontzas, Thomas H., Exec. V.P.--Deposit Guaranty Corp., Jackson, MS; *U.S. Public*, pg. 500
Hood, Kathy, Mgr.-Fin. Plng.--El Paso Electric Company, El Paso, TX; *U.S. Public*, pg. 567
Hope, Stan, Mgr.-Opers.--Progress Paint Mfg. Co., Louisville, KY; *U.S. Private*, pg. 890
Hopkins, Grahme, Mng. Dir.-The Strategic Grp.--EvansGroup, Dallas, TX; *U.S. Private*, pg. 385
Hopkins, Peter D., V.P.-Plng. & Corp. Devel.--Suncor Inc., Calgary, Canada; *Int'l*, pg. 1320
Hoppe, Martin C., V.P.-Fin. & Bus. Plng.--GTE Mobile Communications Incorporated, Atlanta, GA; *U.S. Public*, pg. 696
Hopper, Preston D., Sr. V.P.-Plng. & Acctg. & Controller--CMS Energy Corporation, Dearborn, MI; *U.S. Public*, pg. 279
Horn, Paul, Dir.-Res.--International Business Machines Corporation, Armonk, NY; *U.S. Public*, pg. 895
Horrocks, William L., III, V.P.-Plng. & Sys.--Comcast Cable Communications, Inc., Philadelphia, PA; *U.S. Public*, pg. 407
Hotarek, Brian W., Chief Fin. Officer & Exec. V.P.--The Stop & Shop Companies, Inc., Quincy, MA; *Int'l*, pg. 750
Hotchkin, H.F., Treas.--Inductotherm Industries, Inc., Rancocas, NJ; *U.S. Private*, pg. 560
Houet-Dutruge, Gerald, V.P.-Corp. Devel.--SGS Societe Generale de Surveillance Holding S.A., Geneva, Switzerland; *Int'l*, pg. 1153
Houghton, Charles B., Jr., V.P.-Bus. Devel.--Lukens Inc., Coatesville, PA; *U.S. Public*, pg. 1019
Houlihan, Lawrence M., Chm. Bd., Pres., Chief Exec. & Chief Fin. Officer, Treas. & Sec.--Frank B. Ross Co. Inc., Jersey City, NJ; *U.S. Private*, pg. 946
Housen, Charles B., Chm. Bd., Pres. & Chief Exec. Officer--Erving Industries, Inc., Erving, MA; *U.S. Private*, pg. 382
Howell, C.S., Dir.-Plng. & Devel.--Union Camp Corporation, Wayne, NJ; *U.S. Public*, pg. 1665
Howell, Robert, Sr. V.P.-Corp. Devel.--UtiliCorp United Inc., Kansas City, MO; *U.S. Public*, pg. 1700
Howeth, Robert W., Chief Fin. Officer & Sr. V.P.--Fairfield Communities, Inc., Little Rock, AR; *U.S. Public*, pg. 610
Hrabina, Michael C., V.P.-Bus. Devel.--Accu-Sort Systems, Inc., Telford, PA; *U.S. Private*, pg. 11
Huang, Raymond, Asst. Gen. Mgr.-Corp. Devel.--CWT Distribution Limited, Singapore, Singapore; *Int'l*, pg. 246
Hubbard, Samuel T., Jr., Pres. & Chief Exec. Officer--The Ailing & Cory Company, Rochester, NY; *U.S. Public*, pg. 1666
Huber, Guntram, Dir.-Devel. Passenger Car Components--Mercedes-Benz AG, Stuttgart, Germany; *Int'l*, pg. 368
Hudis, Martin, Sr. V.P.-Tech. Devel.--Aerovox Inc., New Bedford, MA; *U.S. Public*, pg. 25
Hudson, James S., V.P.-Corp. Fin. Plng.--FDX Corporation, Memphis, TN; *U.S. Public*, pg. 603
Hudson, Mary Swatek, V.P.-Mktg. & Plng.--AMBI Inc., Tarrytown, NY; *U.S. Public*, pg. 7
Hudson, Thomas L., V.P.-Bus. Devel.--Avemco Corporation, Frederick, MD; *U.S. Public*, pg. 151
Huerta, Alfonson, Asst. Mgr.-Mine Plng.--Chuquicamata Division, Chuquicamata, Chile; *Int'l*, pg. 302
Huet, A., Inspector Gen.-Plng.& Org.--Banque Nationale de Belgique, Brussels, Belgium; *Int'l*, pg. 162
Huff, John R., Chm. Bd., Pres. & Chief Exec. Officer--Oceaneering International, Inc., Houston, TX; *U.S. Public*, pg. 1211
Hufford, James N., V.P.-Res., Devel. & Engrng.--CTS Corporation, Elkhart, IN; *U.S. Public*, pg. 285
Hughes, D., Dir.-Information & Business Plng.--Gallaher Tobacco Ltd., Weybridge, United Kingdom; *Int'l*, pg. 539
Hughes, Elaine, Dir.-Bus. Devel.--MYR Group Inc., Rolling Meadows, IL; *U.S. Public*, pg. 1029
Hughes, John B., V.P.-Strategic Plng.--Revenue Collection Group World Headquarters, San Diego, CA; *U.S. Public*, pg. 466
Hull, Stephen E., V.P.-Corp. Expansion--Heilig-Meyers Company, Richmond, VA; *U.S. Public*, pg. 804
Hulseman, Robert L., Pres.--Solo Cup Company, Highland Park, IL; *U.S. Private*, pg. 1013
Hultman, Per, Dir.-Res. & Strategic Devel.--Scandinavian Leisure Group A.B., Stockholm, Sweden; *Int'l*, pg. 39
Hume, William J., Chm. Bd.--Basic American Foods, Walnut Creek, CA; *U.S. Private*, pg. 121
Humphries, M., V.P.-Bus. Devel.--Momentum, Seattle, WA; *U.S. Public*, pg. 1329
Hunnicutt, Hal, Dir.-Plng.--Glen Raven Mills, Inc., Glen Raven, NC; *U.S. Private*, pg. 456
Hunt, Bruce W., Pres. & Chief Exec. Officer--Petro-Hunt Corporation, Dallas, TX; *U.S. Private*, pg. 858
Hunter, Richard, Sr. V.P.-Intl. Opers. & Devel.--Williams-Sonoma, Inc., San Francisco, CA; *U.S. Public*, pg. 1770
Huntley, Peter W., Exec. V.P.-Business Devel.--Matthew Clark Taunton, Ltd., Bristol, United Kingdom; *Int'l*, pg. 848
Huppi, Rolf, Chm. Bd. & Chief Exec. Officer--Zurich Insurance Company, Zurich, Switzerland; *Int'l*, pg. 1529
Hurley, Richard B., Dir.-Corp. Devel.--The Dexter Corporation, Windsor Locks, CT; *U.S. Public*, pg. 504
Hurtig, Gunnar, III, V.P.-Corp.-Strategic Plng.--National Semiconductor Corporation, Santa Clara, CA; *U.S. Public*, pg. 1159
Hurwitz, Steve, Dir.-Employee Devel.--Macromedia Incorporated, Hackensack, NJ; *U.S. Private*, pg. 693
Husain, Altaf, Treas., Sec. & Mgr.-Fin. & Plng.--National Refinery Limited, Karachi, Pakistan; *Int'l*, pg. 909
Hutaserani, Krisda, Sr. V.P.--Siam City Bank Public Company Limited, Bangkok, Thailand; *Int'l*, pg. 1239
Hutcheson, H. Ian, Mgr.-Plng. & Admin.--Ocelot Energy Inc., Calgary, Canada; *Int'l*, pg. 996
Hutchinson, Katherine, V.P.-Corp. Devel.--CyberGuard Corporation, Fort Lauderdale, FL; *U.S. Public*, pg. 470
Hutchinson, Sally Ford, Global Planning Dir.--DMB&B/London, London, United Kingdom; *U.S. Private*, pg. 304
Hutton, David A., Exec. V.P.-Exploration & Devel.--Rayrock Yellowknife Resources Inc., Toronto, Canada; *Int'l*, pg. 1089
Huy, Rose Gerrit, Dir.-Strategic Plng.--Mercedes-Benz AG, Stuttgart, Germany; *Int'l*, pg. 368
Hyde, Douglas W., Chm. Bd., Pres. & Chief Exec. Officer--OshKosh B'Gosh, Inc., Oshkosh, WI; *U.S. Public*, pg. 1232
Hylland, Richard R., Exec. V.P.--Northwestern Public Service, Huron, SD; *U.S. Public*, pg. 1200
Hyser, Wendy, Dir.-Plng. & Budgeting--Rite Aid Corporation, Camp Hill, PA; *U.S. Public*, pg. 1390
Iauco, David N., Sr. V.P.-Worldwide Bus. Devel.--R.J. Reynolds Tobacco Company, Winston Salem, NC; *U.S. Public*, pg. 1355
Idell, Cheryl, Pres.-Res. & Strategic Plng.--Western International Media Corporation, Los Angeles, CA; *U.S. Private*, pg. 1165
Idiaquez, James O., Mgr.-Corp. Plng.--The Louisiana Land and Exploration Company, New Orleans, LA; *U.S. Public*, *pg. 269*
Igual, David, Head-Comml. Plng.--Caixa d'Estalvis de Catalunya, Barcelona, Spain; *Int'l*, pg. 249
Ikeda, Kazuo, Dir.-Corp. Plng. Div.--Tokuyama Corporation, Tokyo, Japan; *Int'l*, pg. 1393
Ikegami, Fumio, Mng. Dir. & Gen. Mgr.-Admin.--Hokuriku Electric Industry Co., Ltd., Toyama, Japan; *Int'l*, pg. 627
Ikuta, Kohei, Exec. V.P.-Fin., Plng., Admin. & Mktg.--Diamond Star Motors, Normal, IL; *Int'l*, pg. 875
Ingraham, David W., Sr. V.P.-Fin., Plng. & Admin.--McGraw-Hill Broadcasting Co., Inc., New York, NY; *U.S. Public*, pg. 1070
Ippensen, Curt, V.P. & Strategic Plng. Dir.--Rhea & Kaiser Marketing Communications, Naperville, IL; *U.S. Private*, pg. 927
Iqbal, I., V.P. & Treas.-Tax & Plng.--Murphy Eastern Oil Co., London, United Kingdom; *U.S. Public*, pg. 1142
Iqbal, I., Treas. & Mgr.-Tax & Plng.--Murco Petroleum Ltd., London, United Kingdom; *U.S. Public*, pg. 1142
Iqbal, I., Treas. & Mgr.-Tax & Plng.--Murphy Petroleum Ltd., London, United Kingdom; *U.S. Public*, pg. 1142
Ishiwara, Yoshitsugu, Dir.-Devel. Div.--Mitsumi Electric Co., Ltd., Tokyo, Japan; *Int'l*, pg. 884
Ishizawa, Tatsuya, Dir.-Corp. Plng. & Govt. Affairs--Matsushita Electric Works, Ltd., Osaka, Japan; *Int'l*, pg. 847
Isler, Peter, Sr. V.P.-Res. & Devel.--UMS Swiss Metalworks Holding Ltd, Dornach, Switzerland; *Int'l*, pg. 1427
Isoherranen, Seppo, Sr. V.P.-Comml. Affairs--Outokumpu Oyj, Espoo, Finland; *Int'l*, pg. 1015
Isozaki, Valerie, Strategic Plng. Dir.--Alcone Marketing Group, Irvine, CA; *U.S. Public*, pg. 1223
Itkin, Lawrence, Treas.--Furniture Consultants, New York, NY; *U.S. Public*, pg. 1686
Itoi, Nobuo, Mng. Dir.-Corp. Plng., Pub. Rels., Environmental Affairs & Opers.--Nikon Corporation, Tokyo, Japan; *Int'l*, pg. 931
Iverson, Steven R., V.P.-Plng. & Fin.--Metal Container Corporation, Saint Louis, MO; *U.S. Public*, pg. 114
Ivy, Conway G., V.P.-Corp. Plng. & Devel.--The Sherwin-Williams Company, Cleveland, OH; *U.S. Public*, pg. 1465
Iwai, M., Mgr.-Plng.--Fanuc Ltd., Yamanashi, Japan; *Int'l*, pg. 477
Jabbar, Masood A., Chief Fin. Officer & V.P.-Fin.--Sun Microsystems Computer Corporation, Mountain View, CA; *U.S. Public*, pg. 1531
Jackson, Brian D., Dir.-Corp. Devel.--RPM, Inc., Medina, OH; *U.S. Public*, pg. 1356
Jackson, Robert W., V.P.-Prod. Devel.--SLM Holding Corp., Washington, DC; *U.S. Public*, pg. 1419
Jacobs, Paula M., Ph.D., V.P.-Devel.--Advanced Magnetics, Inc., Cambridge, MA; *U.S. Public*, pg. 20
Jacobson, Eric, V.P.-Bus. Devel.--Intertec Publishing, Overland Park, KS; *U.S. Public*, pg. 1327
Jacobson, Pat, Mgr.-Mktg.--MSI Insurance Companies, Arden Hills, MN; *U.S. Private*, pg. 688

Jaffe, David, Sr. V.P.-Bus. Devel. & Admin.--The Dress Barn, Inc., Suffern, NY; *U.S. Public*, pg. 528

Jakelich, Jeanine, Bus. Devel. Dir.--Jordan Tamraz Caruso Advertising, Inc., Chicago, IL; *U.S. Private*, pg. 599

James, J. Bradford, Exec. V.P.-Corp. Devel. & Distr.--USG Corporation, Chicago, IL; *U.S. Public*, pg. 1660

James, Richard E., V.P.-Corp. Plng.--WPS Resources Corp., Green Bay, WI; *U.S. Public*, pg. 1728

Jamis, Mary, Ph.D., Sr. V.P.-Plng.--Long Haymes Carr, Inc., Winston Salem, NC; *U.S. Public*, pg. 909

Janoff, Andrew S., V.P.-Res.--The Liposome Company, Inc., Princeton, NJ; *U.S. Public*, pg. 1000

Jansen, Jerry, Sr. Bus. Devel. Officer--Southeast Marketing-Atlanta Business Center, Atlanta, GA; *U.S. Public*, pg. 649

Jarman, Mark W., Mgr.-Corp. Commun. & New Bus. Devel.--Dynamic Materials Corporation, Lafayette, CO; *U.S. Public*, pg. 539

Jarowey, Peter M., Dir.-Bus. Analysis--Cabot Corporation, Boston, MA; *U.S. Public*, pg. 288

Jarpa, Sergio, Asst. Mgr.-Mining/Metalurgical Devel.--Chuquicamata Division, Chuquicamata, Chile; *Int'l*, pg. 302

Jartz, John G., Sr. V.P.-Law & Bus. Devel./Corp. Sec.--The Quaker Oats Company, Chicago, IL; *U.S. Public*, pg. 1347

Jartz, John G., V.P.-Bus. Devel.--The Quaker Oats Company, Chicago, IL; *U.S. Public*, pg. 1347

Jaso, Robert J., V.P.-Mktg. & Bus. Devel.--Harleysville Group, Harleysville, PA; *U.S. Public*, pg. 786

Javier, Rey M., V.P.-Corp. Dev.--EEI Corporation, Manila, Philippines; *Int'l*, pg. 425

Jay, Lonny J., Sr. V.P.-Plng. & Reporting--The May Department Stores Company, Saint Louis, MO; *U.S. Public*, pg. 1063

Jay, Morton, Chm. Bd.--Campmor Inc., Upper Saddle River, NJ; *U.S. Private*, pg. 204

Jefferies, Robert A., Jr., Sr. V.P.-Mergers, Acquisitions & Strategic Plng.--Leggett & Platt, Incorporated, Carthage, MO; *U.S. Public*, pg. 985

Jefferson, Robert F., V.P.-Mktg.--Arinc Inc. (Consolidated), Annapolis, MD; *U.S. Private*, pg. 81

Jeffries, Patrick W., Chief Devel. Officer & Exec. V.P.--Salick Health Care, Inc., Los Angeles, CA; *Int'l*, pg. 1524

Jehl, Louis, Dir.-Plng. & Devel.--Perkins Family Restaurants, Memphis, TN; *U.S. Private*, pg. 925

Jemas, Jr., William, V.P.-Entertainment & Bus. Devel.--Fleer-Skybox International Inc., Mount Laurel, NJ; *U.S. Public*, pg. 1052

Jennings, Edmon R., V.P.-Corp. Devel.--Genentech, Inc., South San Francisco, CA; *Int'l*, pg. 1120

Jennings, Ronald M., V.P.-Corp. Devel.--SBC Communications Inc., San Antonio, TX; *U.S. Public*, pg. 1415

Jensen, Kenneth L., Sr. V.P.-Corp. Devel. & Investor Rels.--Johns Manville Corporation, Denver, CO; *U.S. Public*, pg. 927

Jensen, Richard, V.P.-Mktg.--Thomas & Betts/Amerace, Brooksville, FL; *U.S. Public*, pg. 1598

Jensen, Robert K., Pres.--Fleischli Oil Company, Inc., Cheyenne, WY; *U.S. Private*, pg. 410

Jeppesen, Jon A., V.P.-Offshore--Apache Corporation, Houston, TX; *U.S. Public*, pg. 119

Jessen, Mogens, V.P.-Logistics--LEGO Systems, Inc., Enfield, CT; *Int'l*, pg. 805

Jewell, Everett G., Chm. Bd., Pres., Chief Exec. Officer & Treas.--Jewell Building Systems, Dallas, NC; *U.S. Private*, pg. 587

Jewett, Lee C., V.P.-Plng. & Design--Cedar Fair, L.P., Sandusky, OH; *U.S. Public*, pg. 319

Jiskoot, W.J., Sr. Exec. V.P.-New Issues, Corp. Fin., Venture Capital--ABN-AMRO Holding N.V., Amsterdam, Netherlands; *Int'l*, pg. 8

Jobin, Luc, V.P.-Bus. Devel.--Imasco Limited, Montreal, Canada; *Int'l*, pg. 112

John, T. Grant, Sr. V.P.-Plng.--Lukens Inc., Coatesville, PA; *U.S. Public*, pg. 1019

Johnsen, Terje Sunde, Sr. V.P.-Bus. & Strategic Devel.--Scandinavian Airlines System (SAS), Solna, Sweden; *Int'l*, pg. 1201

Johnson-Fogg, Rosalie, V.P.-Strategy/Business Devel.--Hobart Corporation, Troy, OH; *U.S. Public*, pg. 1322

Johnson, Crawford, III, Chm. Bd.--Coca-Cola Bottling Co. United, Inc., Birmingham, AL; *U.S. Private*, pg. 248

Johnson, David E., V.P.-Corp. Plng. & Devel.--Zions Bancorporation, Salt Lake City, UT; *U.S. Public*, pg. 1792

Johnson, David S., V.P.-Strategig Plng.--Hawker Siddeley Canada Inc., Mississauga, Canada; *Int'l*, pg. 604

Johnson, Edward F., V.P.-Mfg. Resource Devel.--Fruit of the Loom, Inc., Chicago, IL; *U.S. Public*, pg. 685

Johnson, Grant W., Chief Fin. Officer & Sr. V.P.--Dep Corporation, Rancho Dominguez, CA; *U.S. Public*, pg. 500

Johnson, Harold R., Sr. V.P.-Bus. Devel.--The Fairchild Corporation, Chantilly, VA; *U.S. Public*, pg. 610

Johnson, John T., Sr. V.P.-Bus. Devel.--Oceaneering International, Inc., Houston, TX; *U.S. Public*, pg. 1211

Johnson, John T., Sr. V.P.-Bus. Devel.--Oilfield Marine Services-Americas Region, Morgan City, LA; *U.S. Public*, *pg. 1211*

Johnson, Mark A., V.P.-Bus. Devel.--SLM Holding Corp., Washington, DC; *U.S. Public*, pg. 1419

Johnson, Michael P., Dir.-Inventory Plng. & Distr.--Bumble Bee Seafoods Inc., San Diego, CA; *U.S. Private*, pg. 526

Johnson, Steven M., V.P.-Corp. Devel. & Pres.-Tredegar Investments--Tredegar Industries Inc., Richmond, VA; *U.S. Public*, pg. 1633

Johnston, Ed, Mgr.-Land Devel.--Devon Energy Canada Corporation, Calgary, Canada; *U.S. Public*, pg. 503

Johnston, Ken, Sr. V.P.-Franchise Devel.--Triarc Restaurant Group, Fort Lauderdale, FL; *U.S. Public*, pg. 1635

Johnstone, D., Mgr.-Plng. Analysis & Mkt. Res.--Becton Dickinson Canada Inc., Mississauga, Canada; *U.S. Public*, pg. 200

Jolliffe, Mike, Mgr.-Bus. Devel.--AGRA International Limited, Oakville, Canada; *Int'l*, pg. 30

Jollymore, Peter, V.P.-Plng. & Mktg.--The New Brunswick Telephone Company, Limited (NBTel), Saint John, Canada; *Int'l*, pg. 230

Jones, Annabel, Mgr.-Corp. Devel.--Coats Viyella plc, Manchester, United Kingdom; *Int'l*, pg. 299

Jones, Arthur L., Sr. V.P.-Retail Devel. & Sls.--Associated Grocers, Inc., Seattle, WA; *U.S. Private*, pg. 90

Jones, Bill, Dir.-Bus. Devel.--Microwave Electronics Div., Nashua, NH; *U.S. Public*, pg. 1008

Jones, Bob, Chief Fin. Officer & Sr. V.P.-Opers.--Koh-I-Noor, Inc., Bloomsbury, NJ; *U.S. Private*, pg. 629

Jones, Charles L., Jr., Chief Strategic Plng. Officer & V.P.--Northrop Grumman Corporation, Los Angeles, CA; *U.S. Public*, pg. 1197

Jones, Ian, Div. Mgr.-Fin. & Plng.--The National Mutual Life Association of Australia Limited, Melbourne, Australia; *Int'l*, pg. 909

Jones, J. Burton, V.P.-Bus. Devel.--Western Gas Resources, Inc., Denver, CO; *U.S. Public*, pg. 1758

Jones, Landon Y., Jr., V.P.-Strategic Plng.--Time Inc., New York, NY; *U.S. Public*, pg. 1612

Jones, Michael F., V.P.-Opers. & Plng.--Homeowners Group, Inc., Sunrise, FL; *U.S. Public*, pg. 832

Jones, Rene, V.P.--First Empire State Corporation, Buffalo, NY; *U.S. Public*, pg. 631

Jones, Roger L., Dir.-Plng. & Analysis--Cooper Communities, Inc., Bella Vista, AR; *U.S. Private*, pg. 273

Jones, T., Dir.-Fin. & Plng.--Britvic Soft Drinks Ltd., Chelmsford, United Kingdom; *Int'l*, pg. 170

Jones, Walt, V.P.-Res. & Devel.--Farmers Mutual Hail Insurance Co. of Iowa, Des Moines, IA; *U.S. Private*, pg. 395

Jones, William R., V.P.-Bus. Devel.--Columbian Chemicals Company, Atlanta, GA; *U.S. Public*, pg. 1286

Jonglez, Antoine, Sr. V.P.-Business Devel.--Elf Aquitane, Paris, France; *Int'l*, pg. 444

Jordan, David A., Sr. V.P.-Bus. Devel.--Shoney's, Inc., Nashville, TN; *U.S. Public*, pg. 1467

Jorgensen, Lauri, Dir.-Mktg. Services--BPA International, New York, NY; *U.S. Private*, pg. 107

Josephson, Edward H., V.P.-Communications & Plng.--Textron Systems, Wilmington, MA; *U.S. Public*, pg. 1589

Joshi, Krishan K., Pres. & Chief Exec. Officer--UES, Inc., Dayton, OH; *U.S. Private*, pg. 1112

Juilfs, George, Pres. & Chief Exec. Officer--SENCORP, Newport, KY; *U.S. Private*, pg. 983

Jun, Lee, Exec. Mng. Dir.-Housing Devel. Projects--Daewoo Corporation, Seoul, Korea; *Int'l*, pg. 357

Jungers, Charles S., V.P.-Bus. Devel.--Sanders, A Lockheed Martin Company, Nashua, NH; *U.S. Public*, pg. 1008

Junk, Keith N., V.P.-Corp. Devel.--MascoTech, Inc., Taylor, MI; *U.S. Public*, pg. 1055

Juraw, Robert, V.P.-Bus. Plng. & Acquisitions--ICI Paints, Cleveland, OH; *Int'l*, pg. 664

Jurgens, Richard, Chief Admin. Officer & Sr. V.P.--Hy-Vee Food Stores Incorporated, West Des Moines, IA; *U.S. Private*, pg. 550

Justiss, James F., Jr., Chm. Bd., Pres. & Chief Exec. Officer--Justiss Oil Co., Inc., Jena, LA; *U.S. Private*, pg. 602

Kafadar, Ahmed D., Chm. Bd. & Chief Exec. Officer--OEA, Inc., Aurora, CO; *U.S. Public*, pg. 1206

Kagan, Irving, Chm. Bd.--Penobscot Shoe Company, Old Town, ME; *U.S. Public*, pg. 1273

Kahan, James S., Sr. V.P.-Corp. Devel.--SBC Communications Inc., San Antonio, TX; *U.S. Public*, pg. 1415

Kahn, Judy, V.P.-Publ. Rels. & Strategic Devel.--Shafer, Irvine, CA; *U.S. Private*, pg. 988

Kahn, Seymour, Chm. Bd. & Chief Exec. Officer--Mercury Air Group Inc., Los Angeles, CA; *U.S. Public*, pg. 1092

Kaila, Tapani, V.P.-Corp. Plng.--Metsa-Serla Corporation, Espoo, Finland; *Int'l*, pg. 863

Kaila, Tapani, Mgr.-Bus. Devel.--Metsa-Serla Corporation, Espoo, Finland; *Int'l*, pg. 863

Kakiuchi, Tsuyoshi, Dir. & Gen. Mgr.-Plng. Dept.--West Japan Railway Company, Osaka, Japan; *Int'l*, pg. 1490

Kalff, D.J.A., Sr. V.P.-Corp. Devel.--KLM Royal Dutch Airlines, Amstelveen, Netherlands; *Int'l*, pg. 719

Kalim, Khadija, Dir.-New Prod. Devel.--Butterworths Asia, Singapore, Singapore; *Int'l*, pg. 1095

Kaltenbacher, Philip D., Chm. Bd. & Chief Exec. Officer--Seton Company, Norristown, PA; *U.S. Private*, pg. 987

Kamber, Martin, V.P.-Bus. Devel. & Stategic Plng.--ITT Automotive, Inc., Auburn Hills, MI; *U.S. Public*, pg. 859

Kames, Kenneth, V.P.-New Bus. Devel.--The Gillette Company, Boston, MA; *U.S. Public*, pg. 743

Kane, Bradley P., V.P.-Strategic Acquisitions--Sensormatic Electronics Corporation, Boca Raton, FL; *U.S. Public*, pg. 1457

Kane, Patrick, Sr. V.P., Corp. Devel. & New Bus. Contact--CRN International, Inc., Hamden, CT; *U.S. Private*, pg. 197

Kane, Sam, Chm. Bd. & Chief Exec. Officer--Sam Kane Beef Processors, Inc., Corpus Christi, TX; *U.S. Private*, pg. 607

Kaneko, Nobuo, Gen. Mgr.-Intl. Plng.--The Yasuda Trust and Banking Co., Ltd., Tokyo, Japan; *Int'l*, pg. 1520

Kanner, Robert H., Chm. Bd., Pres., Chief Exec./Fin. Officer & Treas.--Pubco Corporation, Cleveland, OH; *U.S. Public*, pg. 1339

Kanwal, Amrit, V.P.-Corp. Devel.--Sequa Corporation, New York, NY; *U.S. Public*, pg. 1458

Kaplan, Samuel, Pres., Chief Exec. Officer, Sec. & Dir.-Sls. & Pur.--Admiration Hosiery Mills, Inc., Charlotte, NC; *U.S. Private*, pg. 528

Kappler, George, Chm. Bd., Pres. & Chief Exec. Officer--Kappler Safety Group, Inc., Guntersville, AL; *U.S. Private*, pg. 607

Karjalahti, Kyosti, V.P.-Strategic Plng.--Rautaruukki Oy, Helsinki, Finland; *Int'l*, pg. 1088

Karman, James B., Pres. & Chief Exec. Officer--Spaulding & Slye, Boston, MA; *U.S. Private*, pg. 1021

Karst, Brian G., First V.P.-Corp. Plng.--The Fifth Third Bank of Kentucky, Louisville, Louisville, KY; *U.S. Public*, pg. 621

Kaschner, Peter, Dir.-Emerging Business--AB SKF, Goteborg, Sweden; *Int'l*, pg. 1156

Kasdagly, Dino G., Sr. V.P.-Devel.--Digi International Inc., Minnetonka, MN; *U.S. Public*, pg. 506

Kassler, P., Coordinator-Grp. Plng.--Royal Dutch/Shell Group of Companies, Hague, Netherlands; *Int'l*, pg. 1135

Kassouf, James, Pres., Chief Exec. Officer & Treas.--Metropolitan Properties Systems, Cleveland, OH; *U.S. Private*, pg. 739

Kato, Hideo, Gen. Mgr.-Fin. & Investment Plng.--Sumitomo Life Insurance Company, Osaka, Japan; *Int'l*, pg. 1315

Katz, Martin, Sr. V.P.-Bus. Plng. & Mktg.--WSFS Financial Corporation, Wilmington, DE; *U.S. Public*, pg. 1728

Katz, William D., V.P.-Corp. Devel.--UGI Corporation, King of Prussia, PA; *U.S. Public*, pg. 1653

Katz, William D., V.P.-Corp. Devel.--AmeriGas Partners, L.P., Valley Forge, PA; *U.S. Public*, pg. 1653

Katzen, Cyrus, Dr., Pres. & Chief Exec. Officer--Mozel Development Corp., Baileys Crossroads, VA; *U.S. Private*, pg. 765

Kauffeld, Richard W., V.P.-Business Plng.--R.J. Reynolds Tobacco Company, Winston Salem, NC; *U.S. Public*, pg. 1355

Kaufmann, Mark, Assoc. Dir.-Strategic Plng. & Investor Rels.--MedImmune, Inc., Gaithersburg, MD; *U.S. Public*, pg. 1081

Kavanaugh, Paul K., Dir.-Hardware Devel.--Franklin Electronic Publishers, Inc., Burlington, NJ; *U.S. Public*, pg. 679

Kaye, Stephen F., Sr. V.P.-Corp. Plng.--The McGraw-Hill Companies, New York, NY; *U.S. Public*, pg. 1069

Keenan, Craig J., Dir.-Strategic Plng.--Food Lion, Inc., Salisbury, NC; *Int'l*, pg. 463

Keenan, Joe, Mgr.-Sls. & Mktg.--Hughes-Peters, Inc., Cincinnati, OH; *U.S. Private*, pg. 546

Kehaya, Mark W., V.P.-Plng.--Standard Commercial Corporation, Wilson, NC; *U.S. Public*, pg. 1501

Kehm, Roger, V.P.-Devel.--The Athlete's Foot Group, Inc., Kennesaw, GA; *U.S. Private*, pg. 94

Keillor, Sharon A., V.P.-Fin. & Plng.--Telecommunications Group, Gaithersburg, MD; *U.S. Public*, pg. 1745

Kellenberger, Paul, V.P.-Plng. & Bus. Devel.--Inacom Corp., Omaha, NE; *U.S. Public*, pg. 873

Keller, Cindy, V.P.-Client Devel.--Total System Services, Inc., Columbus, GA; *U.S. Public*, pg. 1550

Keller, James, Dir.-Bus. Devel.--NavCom Defense Electronics, Inc., El Monte, CA; *U.S. Private*, pg. 789

Kelley, Gary L., Chm. Bd., Pres. & Chief Exec. Officer--Kelley Bean Co., Inc., Morrill, NE; *U.S. Private*, pg. 612

Kellstrom, William H., Sr. V.P.-Strategic Planning--NorAm Energy Corp., Houston, TX; *U.S. Public*, pg. 843

Kelly, Edward J., Sr. V.P.-Corp. Devel.--CalMat Co., Los Angeles, CA; *U.S. Public*, pg. 295

Kelly, Richard C., Chief Fin. Officer, Exec. V.P.-Fin. & Treas.--Public Service Company of Colorado, Denver, CO; *U.S. Public*, pg. 1170

Kelly, Stephen J., Chm. Bd., Pres. & Chief Exec. Officer--SouthCo. Inc., Concordville, PA; *U.S. Private*, pg. 1014

Kelly, Thomas F., Mgr.-Mktg. & Devel.--GMAC Insurance Holdings, Detroit, MI; *U.S. Public*, pg. 719

Kelsky, Steven E., Sr. V.P.-Strategic Plng. & Devel.--Physician Computer Network, Inc., Morris Plains, NJ; *U.S. Public*, pg. 1293

Kennedy, Bernard D., Pres. & Chief Oper. Officer--King Kullen Grocery Co., Inc., Westbury, NY; *U.S. Private*, pg. 621

Kennedy, Richard G., Dir.-Corp. Devel.--MCN Energy Group, Inc., Detroit, MI; *U.S. Public*, pg. 1024

Kenney, Jerome P., Exec. V.P.-Corp. Strategy & Research--Merrill Lynch & Co., Inc., New York, NY; *U.S. Public*, pg. 1097

Kenny, Raymond P., V.P.- Strategic Plng.--American Greetings Corporation, Cleveland, OH; *U.S. Public*, pg. 77

Kenny, Raymond P., V.P.-Plng. & Res.--American Greetings U.S. Greeting Card Division, Cleveland, OH; *U.S. Public*, pg. 78

Kent, Ginger, Pres.-Brands & Prod. Devel. Grp.--Hasbro, Inc., Pawtucket, RI; *U.S. Public*, pg. 797

Kent, James L., V.P.-Planning & Logistics--McLane Company, Inc., Temple, TX; *U.S. Public*, pg. 1733

Kepf, Mark, Mgr.-Fin. Plng. & Analysis--Plasti-Line, Inc., Knoxville, TN; *U.S. Public*, pg. 1308

Kerckhoff, Richard D., Jr., Gen. Mgr.--Pevely Dairy Company, Saint Louis, MO; *U.S. Private*, pg. 879

Kerr, Howard J., Chm. Bd., Pres. & Chief Exec. Officer--Consolidated Pipe & Supply Company, Birmingham, AL; *U.S. Private*, pg. 266

Kerr, S.A., Grp. Corp. Planner--Jefferson Smurfit Group p.l.c., Dublin, Ireland; *Int'l*, pg. 1269

Kerr, Steven, V.P.-Leadership Devel.--General Electric Company, Fairfield, CT; *U.S. Public*, pg. 709

Kessler, Richard J., Chief Fin. Officer & V.P.-Fin. & Devel.--Oglebay Norton Company, Cleveland, OH; *U.S. Public*, pg. 1213

Ketterling, Wayne R., V.P.-Altimetry Programs--NavCom Defense Electronics, Inc., El Monte, CA; *U.S. Private*, pg. 789

Kettle, Franklin H., Exec V.P.-Aquisitions & Dir.-Corp. Devel.--United Asset Management Corporation, Boston, MA; *U.S. Public*, pg. 1672

Khim, Jay W., Dr., Chm. Bd., Pres. & Chief Exec. Officer--JWK International Corp., Annandale, VA; *U.S. Private*, pg. 579

Khoon, Quak Ser, Mgr.-Strategic Plng.--Singapore Petroleum Company Ltd., Singapore, Singapore; *U.S. Public*, pg. 102

Kiat, Gan Juay, V.P.-Bus. Devel.--Times Publishing Limited, Singapore, Singapore; *Int'l*, pg. 1390

Kida, Haruo, Sr. Mng. Dir.-Sls., Mktg. & Prod. Devel.--Nisshin Steel Co., Ltd., Tokyo, Japan; *Int'l*, pg. 946
Kieffer, D.A., V.P.-Fin., Treas. & Sec.--McCall Oil & Chemical Corp., Portland, OR; *U.S. Private*, pg. 719
Kierlin, Robert A., Chm. Bd., Pres. & Chief Exec. Officer--Fastenal Company, Winona, MN; *U.S. Public*, pg. 614
Kies, A.K., Mgr.-Prod. Devel.--Food Specialties Division, Delft, Netherlands; *Int'l*, pg. 1142
Kiggen, James D., Chm. Bd. & Chief Exec. Officer--Xtek, Inc., Cincinnati, OH; *U.S. Private*, pg. 1194
Killgallon, William C., Chm. Bd. & Chief Exec. Officer--The Ohio Art Company, Inc., Bryan, OH; *U.S. Public*, pg. 1214
Killian, William P., V.P.-Corp. Devel. & Strategy--Johnson Controls, Inc., Milwaukee, WI; *U.S. Public*, pg. 932
Kilpin, Mark, Mgr.-Pur. & Plng.--Benjamin Obdyke, Inc., Warminster, PA; *U.S. Private*, pg. 810
Kim, Edward, Pres., Chief Oper. & Chief Exec. Officer--Pantech Construction Co., Lanham, MD; *U.S. Private*, pg. 837
Kim, Young Ho, V.P.-Plng.--Korean Airlines Co., Ltd., Seoul, Korea; *Int'l*, pg. 758
Kimura, Kaoru, Dir.-Corp. Plng.--Yamanouchi Pharmaceutical Co. Ltd., Tokyo, Japan; *Int'l*, pg. 1518
Kimura, Mikihiko, Mng. Dir.-Corp. Plng.--Diamond Lease Co., Ltd., Tokyo, Japan; *Int'l*, pg. 413
Kimura, Yaichi, Dir. & Gen. Mgr.--Cosmo Oil Co., Ltd., Tokyo, Japan; *Int'l*, pg. 335
Kindsvater, John H., V.P.-Corp. Devel.--Zebra Technologies Corporation, Vernon Hills, IL; *U.S. Public*, pg. 1790
King, Christine, Sr. V.P.-Prod. Devel.--Brite Voice Systems, Inc., Heathrow, FL; *U.S. Public*, pg. 257
King, David, Sr. V.P.-Prod. Devel.--Comshare, Incorporated, Ann Arbor, MI; *U.S. Public*, pg. 425
King, G. Holman, V.P.-Corp. Devel.--Central and South West Services, Inc., Dallas, TX; *U.S. Public*, pg. 324
King, James M., V.P.-Plng. & Devel.--Aloha Airgroup, Inc., Honolulu, HI; *U.S. Private*, pg. 44
King, Olin B., Chm. Bd. & Chief Exec. Officer--SCI Systems, Inc., Huntsville, AL; *U.S. Public*, pg. 1416
King, Robert, Sr. V.P.-Strategic Plng. & Acquisitions--King World Productions, Inc., New York, NY; *U.S. Public*, pg. 961
King, Timothy, Sr. V.P.-Plng. & Devel.--John Wiley & Sons, Inc., New York, NY; *U.S. Public*, pg. 1768
Kinneberg, Eric E., V.P.-Plng.--Pegasus Gold Corporation, Spokane, WA; *U.S. Public*, pg. 1269
Kinschner, William H., V.P.-Mngmt. Support Services--Health Care & Retirement Corporation, Toledo, OH; *U.S.* Public, pg. 801
Kinugawa, Motonori, Gen. Mgr.-Plng. & Res.--Meiji Life Insurance Company, Tokyo, Japan; *Int'l*, pg. 854
Kinzler, Morton H., Chm. Bd., Pres. & Chief Exec. Officer--Barnwell Industries, Inc., Honolulu, HI; *U.S. Public*, pg. 190
Kipping, Arthur, Chm. Bd. & Pres.--Ray-Carroll County Grain Co-op, Richmond, MO; *U.S. Private*, pg. 911
Kirch, Peggy, V.P.-Commercial Devel.--Suncor Development Company, Phoenix, AZ; *U.S. Public*, pg. 1298
Kirchner, William E., Sr. V.P.-Prod. Devel. & Adv.--Department 56 Inc., Eden Prairie, MN; *U.S. Public*, pg. 500
Kirkpatrick, John, Mgr.-Plng. & Bus. Devel.--Condea Vista Company, Houston, TX; *Int'l*, pg. 325
Kirksey, T. Scott, V.P.-Fin. Plng. & Reporting--Greyhound Lines, Inc., Dallas, TX; *U.S. Public*, pg. 765
Kirschner, Robert A., V.P.-Planning & Rural Economic Devel.--TDS Telecommunications Corporation, Madison, WI; *U.S. Public*, pg. 1570
Kishida, Seiji, Sr. Mng. Dir.-Corp. Plng.--Settsu Corporation, Amagasaki, Japan; *Int'l*, pg. 1225
Kittine, Bob, V.P.-Specialty Sls. & New Product Devel.--Industrial & Retail Bag Division, Chicago, IL; *U.S. Public*, pg. 1521
Kivimaki, Mikko, Chm. Bd., Pres. & Chief Exec. Officer--Rautaruukki Oy, Helsinki, Finland; *Int'l*, pg. 1088
Kkoykka, John S., V.P.-Fin. & Plng.--Anheuser-Busch Europe, Inc., London, United Kingdom; *U.S. Public*, pg. 115
Klaisle, William J., V.P.-Corp. Devel.--Stone Container Corporation, Chicago, IL; *U.S. Public*, pg. 1520
Klas, Shirley, Mgr.--Times Printing Company, Inc., Random Lake, WI; *U.S. Private*, pg. 1087
Klaus, Robert, Pres. & Chief Exec. Officer--Klaus Radio Inc., Peoria, IL; *U.S. Private*, pg. 625
Klausby, Jes, Sr. V.P.-Plng. & Devel.--Nykredit, Copenhagen, Denmark; *Int'l*, pg. 993
Klebine, David, V.P.-Bus. Devel.--Apollo Colors Inc., Northbrook, IL; *U.S. Private*, pg. 77
Klein, Frederick, Sr. V.P.-Bus. Devel. & Professional Services--MEDCO Containment Services, Inc., Montvale, NJ; *U.S. Public*, pg. 1091
Kleinberg, Brian, Sr. V.P.-Mktg. & Business Devel.--American Express Company, New York, NY; *U.S. Public, pg. 73*
Klem, Richard H., V.P.-Corp. Strategy--CSX Corporation, Richmond, VA; *U.S. Public*, pg. 284
Klick, Don, V.P.-Strategic Devel--Omniflight, Inc., Dallas, TX; *U.S. Private*, pg. 816
Klick, Don, V.P.-Strategic Devel.--Omniflight Helicopters, Inc., Dallas, TX; *U.S. Private*, pg. 817
Klingbeil, Mark, Dir.-Fin. & Asst. Treas.--Medusa Corporation, Cleveland, OH; *U.S. Public*, pg. 1084
Kluempke, Patrick, Sr. V.P.-Corp. Plng. & Devel.--Harvest States Cooperatives, Saint Paul, MN; *U.S. Private*, pg. 508
Kneip, Robert C., Sr. V.P.-Corp. Plng. & Devel.--The Wackenhut Corporation, Palm Beach Gardens, FL; *U.S. Public*, pg. 1731
Knight, Allen M., V.P.-Corp. Devel.--Canadian Natural Resources Limited, Calgary, Canada; *Int'l*, pg. 258
Knight, Richard, Exec. Gen. Mgr.-Devel.--North Limited, Melbourne, Australia; *Int'l*, pg. 967
Knoblauch, Kathleen L., V.P.-Org. Plng. & Mngmt. Devel.--Kaufman and Broad Home Corporation, Los Angeles, CA; *U.S. Public*, pg. 944
Knoepfel, Hanspeter, Dir.-Strategic Plng.--Clariant International Ltd., Muttenz, Switzerland; *Int'l*, pg. 624
Knoepke, Eckhard, V.P.-Research & Devel.--Converse Inc., North Reading, MA; *U.S. Public*, pg. 441
Knoop, Stephen J., Dir.-Corp. Devel.--RPM, Inc., Medina, OH; *U.S. Public*, pg. 1356
Knopf, Leigh, V.P.-Plng. & Devel.--American Institute of C.P.A.'s Inc., New York, NY; *U.S. Private*, pg. 57
Knorr, Carol, Exec. V.P.-Mktg. & Devel.--GMAC Insurance Holdings, Detroit, MI; *U.S. Public*, pg. 719
Knueppel, Henry W., Exec. V.P.-Opers.--Regal-Beloit Corporation, Beloit, WI; *U.S. Public*, pg. 1370
Kobayashi, Isao, Sr. Mng. Dir.-Gen. Store Devel.--Ito-Yokado Co., Ltd., Tokyo, Japan; *Int'l*, pg. 693
Kobos, Michael, Dir.-New Product Planning--Galderma Laboratories, Inc., Fort Worth, TX; *Int'l*, pg. 819
Koch, Charles John, Chm. Bd., Pres. & Chief Exec. Officer--Charter One Financial, Inc., Cleveland, OH; *U.S. Public*, pg. 336
Koch, Harold O., Sr. V.P.-Bus. Devel.--Akorn, Inc., Lincolnshire, IL; *U.S. Public*, pg. 34
Koebel, Wayne R., Chief Fin. Officer, Exec. V.P., Treas. & Sec.--Shoreline Financial Corp., Benton Harbor, MI; *U.S. Public*, pg. 1467
Kogan, Eric D., Sr. V.P.-Corp. Devel.--Triarc Companies, Inc., New York, NY; *U.S. Public*, pg. 1634
Kohne, Gerard, V.P.-Bus. Devel.--OzEmail Limited, Sydney, Australia; *Int'l*, pg. 1019
Kollman, Karl, Dr., Dir.-Passenger Car Devel.--Mercedes-Benz AG, Stuttgart, Germany; *Int'l*, pg. 368
Kolodzieski, Edward, V.P.-Strategic Plng.--Ingles Markets, Incorporated, Black Mountain, NC; *U.S. Public*, pg. 878
Kolp, Timothy D., V.P.-Real Estate, Toy Div.--Consolidated Stores Corp., Columbus, OH; *U.S. Public*, pg. 437
Komesaroff, Michael, V.P.-Strategic Analysis & Plng. Services--Comalco Limited, Brisbane, Australia; *Int'l*, pg. 307
Kondas, Nicholas F., V.P.-Plng., Sys. & Profit Improvement--Farrell Lines Incorporated, New York, NY; *U.S. Private*, pg. 397
Kondo, Akira, Pres.--Japan Airlines Company, Ltd., Tokyo, Japan; *Int'l*, pg. 699
Kondo, Koichi, Exec. V.P.-Engrng. & Real Estate Devel.--Japan Tobacco Inc., Tokyo, Japan; *Int'l*, pg. 703
Kontogouris, Venetia, V.P.-Venture Devel.--D & B Enterprises inc, Wilton, CT; *U.S. Public*, pg. 535
Koontz, James L., Pres. & Chief Exec. Officer--Kingsbury Corporation, Keene, NH; *U.S. Private*, pg. 621
Korab, John J., Jr., V.P.-Corp. Devel.--Isco, Inc., Lincoln, NE; *U.S. Public*, pg. 913
Kordyback, Michael R., Exec. V.P.-Stategy, Fin. & Devel.--Jannock Limited, Toronto, Canada; *Int'l*, pg. 698
Korn, Bill, Exec. V.P.-Strategic Plng., Bus. Devel. & Brdcst. Opers.--CBS, New York, NY; *U.S. Public*, pg. 273
Korney, Arthur, V.P.-Res.--Crane Plastics Company, Columbus, OH; *U.S. Private*, pg. 286
Koss, Michael J., Pres., Chief Exec., Oper. & Fin. Officer--Koss Corporation, Milwaukee, WI; *U.S. Public*, pg. 966
Kotecha, Mahesh K., Mng. Dir.-Asia Bus. Devel.--Capital Markets Assurance Corporation, New York, NY; *U.S. Public*, pg. 1023
Kowalczyk, Barbara S., Sr. V.P. & Dir.-Corp. Plng. & Devel.--Lincoln National Corporation, Fort Wayne, IN; *U.S. Public*, pg. 997
Kowalsky, William, Chief Fin. Officer & V.P.-Fin.--Advertising Checking Bureau Incorporated, New York, NY; *U.S. Private*, pg. 23
Koykka, John S., V.P.-Intl. Devel.--Anheuser-Busch Companies, Inc., Saint Louis, MO; *U.S. Public*, pg. 113
Koykka, John S., V.P.-Fin. & Plng.--Anheuser-Busch European Trade Ltd., London, United Kingdom; *U.S. Public*, pg. 115
Kozen, Raymond E., V.P.-Plng. & Analysis--General Dynamics Corporation, Falls Church, VA; *U.S. Public*, pg. 708
Krakaver, Leonard, Pres.--Pall Rai, Inc., Hauppauge, NY; *U.S. Public*, pg. 1254
Kramer, Earl, Pres., Chief Exec. & Chief Oper. Officer--Concord Fabrics Inc., New York, NY; *U.S. Public*, pg. 429
Krasne, Charles A., Chm. Bd., Pres. & Chief Exec. Officer--Krasdale Foods Inc., White Plains, NY; *U.S. Private*, pg. 635
Krasne, Cynthia M., V.P.-Strategic Plng. & Analysis--Woolworth Corporation, New York, NY; *U.S. Public*, pg. 1777
Kraus, Peter, Ph.D., Sr. V.P.-Res. & Devel./Crop Protection--Bayer Corporation, Pittsburgh, PA; *Int'l*, pg. 172
Krawczuk, John, V.P.-Bus. Devel. & Plng.--Kearfott Guidance & Navigation Corp., Wayne, NJ; *U.S. Private*, pg. 93
Kreger, Kate, Mgr.-Mktg. Commun. & Corp. Plng.--CPAC, Inc., Leicester, NY; *U.S. Public*, pg. 282
Kreutzjans, Michael J., Sr. V.P.-Systems Devel.--PC Quote, Inc., Chicago, IL; *U.S. Public*, pg. 1240
Krueger, John D., V.P.-Plng. & Bus. Devel.--McDermott International, Inc., New Orleans, LA; *U.S. Public*, pg. 1067
Kruse, F.H., Mgr.-Global Plng. & Coordination--Procter & Gamble Pharmaceuticals, Inc., Cincinnati, OH; *U.S. Public*, pg. 1331
Kruse, P., Dr., Chief Officer-Corp. Devel.--Kuehne & Nagel International AG, Schindellegi, Switzerland; *Int'l*, pg. 763
Kubera, Gary L., V.P.-Corp. Devel.--McWhorter Technologies, Inc., Carpentersville, IL; *U.S. Public*, pg. 1074
Kuipers, A.S.F., Dir.-Bus. Devel.--Wolters Kluwer N.V., Amsterdam, Netherlands; *Int'l*, pg. 1512
Kuli, Amiel (Mike), V.P.-Bus. Devel.--ABX Air, Inc., Wilmington, OH; *U.S. Public*, pg. 33
Kumar, Ram N., V.P.-Distr. Bus. Devel.--The Toro Company, Bloomington, MN; *U.S. Public*, pg. 1623
Kunzier, R.A., Dir.-Strategic Planning--Kearfott Guidance & Navigation Corp., Wayne, NJ; *U.S. Private*, pg. 93
Kuriyama, Stanley M., V.P.-Land Plng. & Entitlements--A & B-Hawaii, Inc., Honolulu, HI; *U.S. Public*, pg. 39
Kurtz, David J., V.P.-Bus. Devel.--Enogex Inc., Oklahoma City, OK; *U.S. Public*, pg. 1207
Kwangsukstith, Chitrapongse, Dr., Asst. Governor-Policy & Plng.--Petroleum Authority of Thailand, Bangkok, Thailand; *Int'l*, pg. 1046
L'Allier, James J., V.P.-Prod. Devel.--National Education Training Group, Naperville, IL; *U.S. Public*, pg. 784
Labarre, Georges, V.P. & Dir.-Devel. & Diversification--Societe d'Applications Generales d'Electricite et de Mechanique, Paris, France; *Int'l*, pg. 1273
Lacher, Richard, Dir.-Plng. & Devel.--Commercial Metals Company, Dallas, TX; *U.S. Public*, pg. 411
Lackey, Jay, Reg. V.P.-Strategic Plng. & Implementation, Team 2--Scott Forseman/Addison Wesley, Glenview, IL; *Int'l*, pg. 927
Ladau, Drew, Dir.-Bus. Devel.--SPX Corporation, Muskegon, MI; *U.S. Public*, pg. 1420
Ladd, William, Sr. V.P.-Bus. Devel.--Sithe Energies, Inc., New York, NY; *U.S. Private*, pg. 1004
Laffon, Glen A., Exec. V.P.-Prod. Devel.--Central Reserve Life Corporation, Strongsville, OH; *U.S. Public*, pg. 326
Laino, Lauro, Mgr.-Plng. & Devel.--La Nacion S.A., Buenos Aires, Argentina; *Int'l*, pg. 785
Lakey, Ron G., V.P.-Fin. Plng.--ADT Security Systems, Inc., Carmel, IN; *U.S. Public*, pg. 1649
Laliberte, Antonio M., Vice Chm.-Plng. Res. & Devel.--Ernst & Young, LLP, New York, NY; *U.S. Private*, pg. 381
LaMay, Francis, Dir.-Plng. & Devel.--Cigna Corp., Philadelphia, PA; *U.S. Public*, pg. 356
Lamb, Bob, V.P.-Community Devel.--Arkansas Western Gas Co., Fayetteville, AR; *U.S. Public*, pg. 1494
Lambert, Keith M., Sr. V.P.-Strategy & Devel.--Foster's Brewing Group Limited, Southbank, Australia; *Int'l*, pg. 500
Lamoureux, Carole, V.P.-Acctg. & Internal Control--Hydro-Quebec, Montreal, Canada; *Int'l*, pg. 640
Landgren, Berne, Exec. V.P.-Grp. Devel.--Telia AB, Farsta, Sweden; *Int'l*, pg. 1373
Lane, Jim, Sr. V.P.-New Bus. Devel.--Kaiser Permanente, Oakland, CA; *U.S. Private*, pg. 605
Lane, Richard T., Exec. V.P.-Strategic Devel.--World Color Press, Inc., Greenwich, CT; *U.S. Public*, pg. 1778
Lang, Henry S., Chm. Bd. & Chief Exec. Officer--Home Juice Co., Melrose Park, IL; *U.S. Private*, pg. 537
Lange, Cheryl, Dir.-Human Resources--Sun Electric, Lincolnshire, IL; *U.S. Public*, pg. 1480
Langford, Robert M., Chief Oper. Officer & Sr. Exec. V.P.--Shoney's Inc., Nashville, TN; *U.S. Public*, pg. 1467
Langford, Thomas L., Chief Fin. Officer & Exec. V.P.--Stone & Webster, Incorporated, Boston, MA; *U.S. Public*, pg. 1519
Langley, John, Dir.-Res. & Devel.--Kappler Safety Group, Inc., Guntersville, AL; *U.S. Private*, pg. 607
Lanier, Thomas, Exec. V.P., Chief Fin. Officer & Sec.--Salem Carpet Mills, Inc., Winston Salem, NC; *U.S. Public*, pg. 1464
LaPlante, Larry E., V.P.-Fin. & Treas.--Maine Public Service Company, Presque Isle, ME; *U.S. Public*, pg. 1038
Laputz, Leslie J., V.P.-Strategic Plng.--Keyport Life Insurance Company, Boston, MA; *U.S. Private*, pg. 666
Larew, Garry, V.P.-Bus. Devel.--Engine Division, Fort Collins, CO; *U.S. Public*, pg. 1776
Larson, Arlyn J., V.P.-Corp. Plng. & Devel.--Pinnacle West Capital Corporation, Phoenix, AZ; *U.S. Public*, pg. 1297
Larson, Carl, V.P.-New Bus. Devel.--General Nutrition, Inc., Pittsburgh, PA; *U.S. Public*, pg. 725
Lasher, Christopher J., Sr. V.P.-Strategic Pharmacy Devel.--MEDCO Containment Services, Inc., Montvale, NJ; *U.S. Public*, pg. 1091
Latella, Robert N., Chief Oper. Officer & Exec. V.P.--Genesee Corporation, Rochester, NY; *U.S. Public*, pg. 728
Laughlin, J. Rodney, Exec. V.P.-Devel.--Magellan Health Services, Inc., Atlanta, GA; *U.S. Public*, pg. 1033
Laurent, Jean, Deputy Chief Exec. Officer-Devel. & Mkts.--Credit Agricole, Bonvin, France; *Int'l*, pg. 341
Lausen, D.M., Mgr.-Plng. & Devel.--BTR plc, London, United Kingdom; *Int'l*, pg. 124
Lautzenhiser, Gary, Exec. V.P.-Sls., Mktg. & Bus. Devel.--Aristokraft, Inc., Jasper, IN; *U.S. Public*, pg. 675
LaVetri, Melanie, Dir.-Bus. Devel.--Autodesk, Inc., San Rafael, CA; *U.S. Public*, pg. 148
Lavin, Cathy, Asst. V.P.-Corp. Plng.--Regence BlueCross BlueShield of Oregon, Portland, OR; *U.S. Private*, pg. 917
Lavin, Joseph, Sr. V.P.-Devel.--Choice Hotels International, Inc., Silver Spring, MD; *U.S. Public*, pg. 351
Law, Wing, Dir.-Fin. Plng.--The Topps Company, Inc., New York, NY; *U.S. Public*, pg. 1621
Lawrence, William B., Exec. V.P.-Corp. Devel. & Intl. & Govt. Rels., Gen. Counsel & Sec--TRW Inc., Cleveland, OH; *U.S. Public*, pg. 1558
Lawson, William, Pres. & Chief Exec. Officer--Lawson Software, Minneapolis, MN; *U.S. Private*, pg. 654
Lawson, William P., Chief Info. Officer & V.P.--AMETEK, Inc., Paoli, PA; *U.S. Public*, pg. 99
Lay, Joe L., Jr., Chm. Bd., Pres. & Chief Exec. Officer--Lay's Fine Foods, Knoxville, TN; *U.S. Private*, pg. 655
Layefsky, Jerry, Sr. V.P. & Strategic Plng. Dir.--DMB&B New York, New York, NY; *U.S. Private*, pg. 302
Layton, Mel, V.P.-Home Video Acquisitions & Devel.--Republic Entertainment, Inc., Los Angeles, CA; *U.S. Private*, pg. 776
Le Bel, Dominique, V.P.-Tech. & Devel.--Uniboard Canada Inc., Laval, Canada; *Int'l*, pg. 1431
Le Fevre, Paul, Chief Fin. Officer & Exec. V.P.-Strategic Plng. & Mktg.--Keyport Life Insurance Company, Boston, MA; *U.S. Private*, pg. 666

Leal, Fernando A., Sr. V.P.-Strategic Planning & Business Devel.--Pharmacia & Upjohn, Kalamazoo, MI; *Int'l*, pg. 1048
Leasure, George, Pres., Chief Exec. Officer, Chief Fin. Officer & Treas.--Ghent Manufacturing, Inc., Lebanon, OH; *U.S. Private*, pg. 450
Leblanc, Marcel, V.P.-Engnrg. & Devel.--Kruger Inc., Montreal, Canada; *Int'l*, pg. 761
Lechene, Jean, V.P.-Cement Strategy--Lafarge S.A., Paris, France; *Int'l*, pg. 788
Lechtenberger, Richard L., V.P.-Res. & Dev.--Protective Life Corporation, Birmingham, AL; *U.S. Public*, pg. 1336
Leclair, Daniel, V.P.-Fin. & Treas.--Hydro-Quebec, Montreal, Canada; *Int'l*, pg. 640
Lederer, David, Chief Oper. Officer & Exec. V.P.--Detection Systems, Inc., Fairport, NY; *U.S. Public*, pg. 501
Ledesma, Eduardo B., Asst. V.P.-Strategy--Philippine Long Distance Telephone Company, Manila, Philippines; *Int'l*, pg. 1051
Lee, George L, III, V.P.-Plng. & Devel.--Red Devil Inc., Union, NJ; *U.S. Private*, pg. 915
Lee, John K., Exec. V.P.--Everex Systems Inc., Fremont, CA; *Int'l*, pg. 498
Lee, Larry, Dir.-Devel.--Accor North America, Scarsdale, NY; *Int'l*, pg. 21
Lee, Lily, V.P.-Biostatistics, Medical & Regulatory Affairs--The Liposome Company, Inc., Princeton, NJ; *U.S. Public*, *pg. 1000*
Lee, Robert R., Exec. V.P.--Progressive Driver Services, Inc., Jacksonville, FL; *U.S. Private*, pg. 890
Leedom, John N., Sr., Chm. Bd., Chief Exec. Officer--Wholesale Electronic Supply, Dallas, TX; *U.S. Private*, pg. 1174
Leeper, Jerry, V.P.-Sys. Strategic Plng.--Farmland Industries, Inc., Kansas City, MO; *U.S. Private*, pg. 395
LeFrak, Samuel J., Chm. Bd.--Lefrak Organization Inc., Rego Park, NY; *U.S. Private*, pg. 658
Legband, Linda, V.P.-Org. Devel.--Inacom Corp., Omaha, NE; *U.S. Public*, pg. 873
Lehman, Dan, Mgr.-Mkt. Devel.-North--Subaru Western Region, Irvine, CA; *Int'l*, pg. 523
Leibbrandt, Hans Jurgen, Mgr.-Comml. Devel.--CODELCO Chile (Corporacion Nacional Del Cobre De Chile), Santiago, Chile; *Int'l*, pg. 302
Leibovitz, Mitchell G., Chm. Bd., Pres. & Chief Exec. Officer--The Pep Boys-Manny, Moe & Jack, Philadelphia, PA; *U.S. Public*, pg. 1276
Leibowitz, George, Sr. V.P.-Fin. & Corp. Devel.--Petroleum Heat & Power Co., Stamford, CT; *U.S. Public*, pg. 1281
Leiden, Cathy, V.P.-Client Services & Strategic Plng.--LVL Advertising, Palo Alto, CA; *U.S. Private*, pg. 640
Leland, John M., Jr., Dir.-Investor & Banking Rels.--Lukens Inc., Coatesville, PA; *U.S. Public*, pg. 1019
Leo, Frank N., V.P.-New Prods.--Automatic Liquid Packaging, Inc., Woodstock, IL; *U.S. Private*, pg. 101
LeRoy, Michael D., V.P.-Corp. Devel.--Zero Corporation, Los Angeles, CA; *U.S. Public*, pg. 1791
Lervick, Arne T., Chm. Bd. & Chief Exec. Officer--Twin City Foods, Inc., Stanwood, WA; *U.S. Private*, pg. 1111
Leslie, James, Sr. V.P.-Sustainable Devel.--Transalta Corporation, Calgary, Canada; *Int'l*, pg. 1416
Lester, C. Jackson, Mng. Dir.-Europe Bus. Devel.--Capital Markets Assurance Corporation, New York, NY; *U.S. Public*, pg. 1023
Lester, Peter, Gen. Mgr.-Bus. Devel.--North Limited, Melbourne, Australia; *Int'l*, pg. 967
Leu, Dennis T., V.P.-Business Mngmt.--Velsicol Chemical Corporation, Rosemont, IL; *U.S. Private*, pg. 1135
Levari, Henry, Sr. V.P.- External Affairs--Atlantic Electric Co., Pleasantville, NJ; *U.S. Public*, pg. 430
Levesque, Camil, V.P.-Strategic Plng.--Assurance vie Desjardins-Laurentienne, Levis, Canada; *Int'l*, pg. 396
Levi, Jean-Daniel, Dir.-Intl. Matters & Commercial Devel.--Framatome SA, Paris, France; *Int'l*, pg. 502
Levin, Richard C., Chief Oper. Officer & V.P.-Plng.--Biospherics Incorporated, Beltsville, MD; *U.S. Public*, pg. 232
Levine, Mark J., Mgr.-Bus. Devel.--Geo-Centers, Inc., Newton, MA; *U.S. Private*, pg. 447
Levinson, Jack, Mgr.-Retail Services--Lat Purser & Associates, Charlotte, NC; *U.S. Private*, pg. 896
Levitan, Jeff, Sr. V.P.-Strategic Plng. & Bus. Devel.--Staples, Inc., Westborough, MA; *U.S. Public*, pg. 1509
Levitt, David, Sr. V.P. & DMB&B Worldwide Dir.-Training & Devel.--DMB&B Communications, New York, NY; *U.S. Private*, pg. 302
Levy, David, Dir.-Plng.--Angelica Corporation, Chesterfield, MO; *U.S. Public*, pg. 113
Levy, David, V.P.-Strategy & Plng.--COGEMA - Compagnie Generale des Matieres Nucleaires, Velizy-Villacoublay, France; *Int'l*, pg. 304
Levy, Irvin L., Pres.--NCH Corporation, Irving, TX; *U.S. Public*, pg. 1145
Levy, J. David, V.P.-Plng.--Angelica Image Apparel, Saint Louis, MO; *U.S. Public*, pg. 113
Levy, Mark A., Pres. & Chief Oper. Officer--Oriole Homes Corp., Delray Beach, FL; *U.S. Public*, pg. 1230
Levy, R.M., Asst. V.P.-Devel.--Emerson Electric Co., Saint Louis, MO; *U.S. Public*, pg. 572
Levy, Steven A., Exec. V.P. & Treas.--The Titan Industrial Corp., New York, NY; *U.S. Private*, pg. 1089
Lewis, Bradley, V.P.-Global Mktg. Devel.--Joy Mining Machinery, Warrendale, PA; *U.S. Public*, pg. 790
Lewis, Harry A., V.P.-Fin. Strategy & Plng.--Chrysler Corporation, Auburn Hills, MI; *U.S. Public*, pg. 352
Lewis, J.E., Exec. Gen. Mgr.-Corp. Plng. & Admin.--The Broken Hill Proprietary Company Limited, Melbourne, Australia; *Int'l*, pg. 223
Lewis, Ralph M., Chm. Bd.--Lewis Homes Management Corp., Upland, CA; *U.S. Private*, pg. 665
Lewis, Tom, V.P.-Bus. Devel.--Sermatech International, Inc., Limerick, PA; *U.S. Public*, pg. 1569
Liberati, Anthony W., Sr. V.P.-Corp. Plng. & Fin.--The Edward J. DeBartolo Corporation, Youngstown, OH; *U.S. Private*, pg. 319
Liebowitz, Leo, Chm. Bd. & Chief Exec. Officer--Getty Petroleum Marketing Inc., Jericho, NY; *U.S. Public*, pg. 740
Liebscher, Klaus, Dr., Dir.-Gen. Mngmt.--Raiffeisen Zentralbank Osterreich, Vienna, Austria; *Int'l*, pg. 1084
Lietzau, Petty J., Coord.-Plng.--Hutchinson Technology Inc., Hutchinson, MN; *U.S. Public*, pg. 850
Liever, Damon, Sr. V.P.-Mktg. & Bus. Devel.--Uno Restaurant Corporation, West Roxbury, MA; *U.S. Public*, pg. 1698
Lievonen, Mark J., Sr. V.P.-Admin. & Devel.--Connaught Laboratories Limited, Willowdale, Canada; *Int'l*, pg. 1109
Liistro, Brenda O., V.P. & Mgr.-Bus. Devel.--Playtex Products Inc., Westport, CT; *U.S. Public*, pg. 1310
Lilenthal, Stephen W., Exec. V.P.-Field Devel. & Opers.--USF&G Corporation, Baltimore, MD; *U.S. Public*, pg. 1659
Lim Swee Choon, David, Gen. Mgr.-Devel.--Singapore Land Limited, Singapore, Singapore; *Int'l*, pg. 1252
Lindahl, Herbert W., Pres. & Chief Oper. Officer--State Industries Inc., Ashland City, TN; *U.S. Private*, pg. 1036
Lindsey, David, V.P.-Store Plng.--Nordstrom, Inc., Seattle, WA; *U.S. Public*, pg. 1190
Link, Teriann, V.P. & Assoc. Plng. Dir.--Western International Media Corporation, Los Angeles, CA; *U.S. Private*, pg. 1165
Linscott, Karen, Admin. Asst.-Bus. Devel.--Electrospace Systems, Inc., Richardson, TX; *U.S. Public*, pg. 1365
Linsky, Barry R., Sr. V.P.-Plng. & Bus. Devel.--The Interpublic Group of Companies, Inc., New York, NY; *U.S. Public*, pg. 908
Lippert, Robert L., V.P.-Strategic Plng.--The Seibels Bruce Group, Inc., Columbia, SC; *U.S. Public*, pg. 1453
Lipson, Robin, V.P.-Strategic Plng.--Blue Cross and Blue Shield of Massachusetts, Boston, MA; *U.S. Private*, pg. 151
Lissner, Lance M., V.P.-Corp. Plng. & Devel.--Honeywell-Measurex Corporation, Cupertino, CA; *U.S. Public*, pg. 833
Litow, Joel, V.P.-Strategic Plng.--Elf Atochem North America, Inc., Philadelphia, PA; *Int'l*, pg. 445
Littlejohn, Gail H., V.P.-Data Devel.--LEXIS-NEXIS, Miamisburg, OH; *Int'l*, pg. 1096
Littleton, Paul A., V.P.-Individual Distr. Devel.--Sun Life Assurance Company of Canada (U.K.) Limited, Basingstoke, United Kingdom; *Int'l*, pg. 1319
Littley, Jack, Sr. V.P.-Plng. & Devel--BTG, Inc., Fairfax, VA; *U.S. Public*, pg. 164
Litzinger, Robert A., V.P.-Fin.--Provident Financial Group, Inc., Cincinnati, OH; *U.S. Public*, pg. 1338
Liu, Joseph, Chief Fin. Officer & V.P.-Opers.--Diodes Incorporated, Westlake Village, CA; *U.S. Public*, pg. 510
Loadman, David, Sr. V.P.-Global Prod. & Systems Devel.--Telxon Corporation, Akron, OH; *U.S. Public*, pg. 1573
Loarie, Susanne, V.P.-Mktg. & Bus. Devel.--Health Professionals, Inc., Fort Lauderdale, FL; *U.S. Public*, pg. 802
Locke, R. Howard, Mgr.-Strategic Plng. & Quality Mngmt.--Memphis Light, Gas & Water, Memphis, TN; *U.S. Private*, pg. 731
Loepp, Fred E., V.P.-Prod. Mngmt.--W.W. Grainger, Inc., Lincolnshire, IL; *U.S. Public*, pg. 758
Loesby, Rex E., Dir.-Investor Rels.--Nord Resources Corporation, Albuquerque, NM; *U.S. Public*, pg. 1188
Loftin, Nancy C., Chief Legal Counsel, V.P. & Sec.--APS, Phoenix, AZ; *U.S. Public*, pg. 1297
Logan, David J., Dir.-Corp. Devel.--Hewlett-Packard Company, Palo Alto, CA; *U.S. Public*, pg. 813
Lohman, Dave, Dir.-Policy & Plng.--Port of Portland, Portland, OR; *U.S. Private*, pg. 876
Lohr, Jim, Exec. V.P.-Plng. & Devel.--Aydin Displays (East), Horsham, PA; *U.S. Public*, pg. 158
London, G.H., V.P. & G.M.-Bus. Opers. & Project Devel.--Airport Group International, Inc., Glendale, CA; *U.S. Public*, pg. 1009
Long, James H., Chief Oper. Officer & V.P.--Long MFG. NC, Inc., Tarboro, NC; *U.S. Private*, pg. 674
Long, Jonathan R., Pres., Chief Exec. Officer & Chief Fin. Officer--J.E. Higgins Lumber Co., Concord, CA; *U.S. Private*, pg. 527
Long, Robert, Corp. Devel. Dir.--Leo Burnett Kyodo Co. Ltd., Tokyo, Japan; *U.S. Private*, pg. 185
Longtin, Cheryl J., V.P.-Bus. Devel. & Stategic Plng.--ITT Automotive, Inc., Auburn Hills, MI; *U.S. Public*, pg. 859
Longworth, T.J., Sr. V.P.-Strategic Business Devel.--Canfor Corporation, Vancouver, Canada; *Int'l*, pg. 260
Lopez, Adolfo, Dir.-Business Plng. & Devel.--Chuquicamata Division, Chuquicamata, Chile; *Int'l*, pg. 302
Lopez, Jorge, V.P.-Strategic Plng. & Corp. Devel.--Symix Systems, Inc., Columbus, OH; *U.S. Public*, pg. 1546
Lopuch, George Z., Sr. V.P.-Strategic Plng. & Res.--SuperValu, Inc., Eden Prairie, MN; *U.S. Public*, pg. 1540
Loraine, J., Exec. Gen. Mgr.-Bus. Devel.--M.I.M. Holdings Ltd., Brisbane, Australia; *Int'l*, pg. 827
Lord, Douglas, V.P.-Logistics & Supply--Xerox Canada Ltd., North York, Canada; *U.S. Public*, pg. 1785
Lorenz, Donald N., Chief Fin. Officer & V.P.-Fin.--Price Brothers Co., Dayton, OH; *U.S. Private*, pg. 883
Lorenzen, Larry, V.P.-Corp. Devel.--Taylor Corporation, Mankato, MN; *U.S. Private*, pg. 1070
Love, Jimmy, V.P.-Corp. Devel.--Printpack Inc., Atlanta, GA; *U.S. Private*, pg. 886
Lovejoy, David R., Vice Chm.-Fin. Markets & Corp. Devel.--Mellon Bank Corporation, Pittsburgh, PA; *U.S. Public*, pg. 1084
Lowe, Peter S., Exec. Dir.-Business & Financial Plng.--Foster's Brewing Group Limited, Southbank, Australia; *Int'l*, pg. 500
Lowery, John W., V.P.-Store Plng.--Richfood Holdings, Inc., Glen Allen, VA; *U.S. Public*, pg. 1388
Lowry, Art, V.P.-Corp. Devel.--Wedco Technology, Bloomsbury, NJ; *U.S. Public*, pg. 854
Lowry, Gary W., V.P. & Controller--Duckwall-Alco Stores, Inc., Abilene, KS; *U.S. Public*, pg. 533
Loy, Robert W., Exec. V.P.-Opers.--Roberts Pharmaceutical Corporation, Eatontown, NJ; *U.S. Public*, pg. 1393
Lozano Cerda, Arturo, Dir.-Plng. & Fin.--Organizacion Soriana S.A. de C.V., Monterrey, Mexico; *Int'l*, pg. 1008
Lozowski, Joseph P., V.P.-Sls., Construction & Bus. Devel.--Contract Interiors Inc., Taylor, MI; *U.S. Private*, pg. 270
Lu, Zhou, Gen. Mgr.-Coord. & Plng.--Bank of China, Beijing, China; *Int'l*, pg. 152
Lucas, Keith E., V.P.-Global Customer Bus.--Crown Cork & Seal Company, Inc., Philadelphia, PA; *U.S. Public*, pg. 462
Lucas, Sarah H., Chief Strategic Officer & V.P.--GenRad, Inc., Westford, MA; *U.S. Public*, pg. 731
Lucas, Thomas H., V.P.-Corp. Devel.--The May Department Stores Company, Saint Louis, MO; *U.S. Public*, pg. 1063
Luce, Rebecca, V.P.-Corp. Devel.--One Price Clothing Stores, Inc., Duncan, SC; *U.S. Public*, pg. 1225
Luke, Albert G., Staff V.P.-Strategic Devel.--Dresser Industries, Inc., Dallas, TX; *U.S. Public*, pg. 528
Luke, James P., Chief Fin. Officer & Exec. V.P.--Blessings Corporation, Newport News, VA; *U.S. Private*, pg. 1179
Luker, Robert C., Chief Fin. Officer & V.P.--Kokomo Sanitary Pottery Corp., Kokomo, IN; *U.S. Private*, pg. 449
Lund, Vic, V.P.-Fin. & Acctg.--Sioux Honey Association, Sioux City, IA; *U.S. Private*, pg. 1003
Lunden, John F., V.P., Fin. & Bus. Devel.--Semiconductor Equipment Group, Scotts Valley, CA; *U.S. Public*, pg. 1745
Lundevall, Brent, Grp. V.P.-Projects--Daw Technologies, Inc., Salt Lake City, UT; *U.S. Public*, pg. 489
Luskin, Meyer, Chm. Bd., Pres. & Chief Exec. Officer--Scope Industries, Santa Monica, CA; *U.S. Public*, pg. 1444
Lutz, Emil, Exec. V.P.--Sulzer Ltd., Winterthur, Switzerland; *Int'l*, pg. 1305
Lutz, Robert, Dir.-Business Planning--Knoll Pharmaceutical Company, Whippany, NJ; *Int'l*, pg. 105
Lutz, Sheldon H., V.P.-Devel.--Columbia/HCA Healthcare Corporation, Nashville, TN; *U.S. Public*, pg. 403
Luzuriaga, Francesca, Exec. V.P.-Worldwide Bus. Plng. & Resources--Mattel, Inc., El Segundo, CA; *U.S. Public*, pg. 1057
Lyden, Michael, Sr. V.P.-Bus. Devel.--Tyco Toys, Inc., Mount Laurel, NJ; *U.S. Public*, pg. 1058
Lynam, Niall, Chief Tech. Officer & Sr. V.P.-Res. & Devel.--Donnelly Corporation, Holland, MI; *U.S. Public*, pg. 519
Lynn, Michael, Sr. V.P. & Central Region Plng. Dir.--Western International Media Corporation, Chicago, IL; *U.S. Private*, pg. 1167
Lyons, G. Duane, V.P.-Bus. Devel.--TransAlta Energy Corporation, Calgary, Canada; *Int'l*, pg. 1416
Lyons, Wayne, Pres. & Chief Exec. Officer--Lafarge Construction Materials, Canfield, OH; *Int'l*, pg. 788
Lytle, James, V.P.-Product Plng. & Dev.--International Correspondence Schools, Inc., Scranton, PA; *U.S. Public*, pg. 783
Ma, John, V.P.-Plng. & Opers.--Acclaim Entertainment, Inc., Glen Cove, NY; *U.S. Public*, pg. 15
Macaulay, Andrew, Sr. V.P. & Strategic Plng. Dir.--Roche Macaulay & Partners, Toronto, Canada; *U.S. Private*, pg. 678
MacCormack, G. Ross, V.P.-Corp. Strategy--Air Canada, Saint-Laurent, Canada; *Int'l*, pg. 36
MacDonald, Bill, Exec. V.P.-Strategic Plng.--ICN Pharmaceuticals, Inc., Costa Mesa, CA; *U.S. Public*, pg. 853
Macdonald, N.A., Dir.-Fin. & Devel.--Firth-Rixson Plc, Sheffield, United Kingdom; *Int'l*, pg. 487
MacDonald, Terrance F., V.P.-Systems Plng. & Environment--Nova Scotia Power Inc., Halifax, Canada; *Int'l*, pg. 971
Macey, James, Dir.-Res. & Devel.--Raytech Corporation, Shelton, CT; *U.S. Public*, pg. 1363
Machenberg, Donald E., Sr. V.P. & Dir.-Bus. Devel. & Mktg.--ITT Fluid Technology Corporation, Midland Park, NJ; *U.S. Public*, pg. 860
Machulak, Edward A., Exec. V.P., Sec. & Mktg., Sls. Promo, Adv. Dir.--Commerce Group Corp., Milwaukee, WI; *U.S. Public*, pg. 410
Macias, Jessy, Mgr.-Admin. & Fin. Plng.--Gilmore Envelope Corp., Los Angeles, CA; *U.S. Private*, pg. 454
MacIntyre, S.A., V.P.-Restaurant Devel.--A&W Food Services of Canada Inc., North Vancouver, Canada; *Int'l*, *pg. 1*
Macken, Tony, Mgr.-Grp. Plng.--CRH, plc, Dublin, Ireland; *Int'l*, pg. 242
Mackie, J. James, V.P.-Bus. Devel.--Newbridge Networks Corporation, Kanata, Canada; *Int'l*, pg. 923
MacKinlay, David, Dir.-Corp. Devel.--Vickers PLC, London, United Kingdom; *Int'l*, pg. 1466
Macnow, Joseph, Chief Fin. Officer & V.P.--Vornado Realty Trust, Saddle Brook, NJ; *U.S. Public*, pg. 1725
MacNulty, Samuel E., Sr. V.P.-Mktg. & Plng.--Inland Container-Container Division, Indianapolis, IN; *U.S. Public*, pg. 1575
Macomber, Kimberley, Mgr.-Bus. Devel.--W.G. Mills, Inc., Sarasota, FL; *U.S. Private*, pg. 749
MacVittie, Paula R., Pres. & Chief Exec. Officer--Caldwell VanRiper, Inc., Indianapolis, IN; *U.S. Private*, pg. 200
Madar, Jean, Dir.-Plng., Devel., Mergers & Acq.--Jean Philippe Fragrances, Inc., New York, NY; *U.S. Public*, pg. 924
Madero, Eugenio, V.P.-Fin. Plng. & Control--Corporacion Industrial Sanluis, Mexico, Mexico; *Int'l*, pg. 332
Madsen, Adam M., Sr. V.P.-Corp. & Strategic Plng.--Long Island Lighting Company, Hicksville, NY; *U.S. Public*, pg. 1013
Mady, Charlene, V.P.-Area Mdse. Plng.--Toys "R" Us, Inc., Paramus, NJ; *U.S. Public*, pg. 1626

Madzikanda, D.D., Chief Mgr.-Plng.--Zimbabwe Electricity Supply Authority, Harare, Zimbabwe; *Int'l*, pg. 1528

Maestrono, Mario, Dir.-Bus. Plng. & Devel.--SASIB SpA, Bologna, Italy; *Int'l*, pg. 1194

Magee, Bill, Mgr.-Bus. & Fin. Plng.--Duty Free International, Inc., Ridgefield, CT; *Int'l*, pg. 103

Magliocco, John, Chm. Bd. & Chief Exec. Officer--Peerless Importers, Inc., Brooklyn, NY; *U.S. Private*, pg. 847

Magnus, Tom, V.P., Res. Dir. & Strategic Plng. Dir.--The Sawtooth Group, Woodbridge, NJ; *U.S. Private*, pg. 969

Magnuson, Kristen L., V.P.-Fin. & Plng.--Michaels Stores, Inc., Irving, TX; *U.S. Public*, pg. 1104

Magrill, Stephen, V.P.-Mktg. & Strategic Plng.--Interval International Inc., Miami, FL; *U.S. Public*, pg. 320

Magruder, Logan, V.P.-Corp. Rels. & Bus. Devel.--Barrett Resources Corporation, Denver, CO; *U.S. Public*, pg. 191

Magsood, Saj, V.P.-Corp. Devel.--Methanex Corporation, Vancouver, Canada; *Int'l*, pg. 862

Maguire, Dan, V.P.-Store Plng. & Construction--Fabri-Centers of America, Inc., Hudson, OH; *U.S. Public*, pg. 609

Mahal, Mark G., V.P.-Plng. & Control--Ecolab Institutional Group, Saint Paul, MN; *U.S. Public*, pg. 562

Mahar, Michael C., Sr. V.P.--The Troy Savings Bank, Troy, NY; *U.S. Private*, pg. 1106

Mahin, Doug, V.P.-Strategic Plng. & New Bus. Devel.--Raytheon Aircraft Company, Wichita, KS; *U.S. Public*, pg. 1365

Mahmood, Asif, V.P.-Plng.--Texaco Worldwide Exploration & Production, Scroggins, TX; *U.S. Public*, pg. 1583

Mahoney, James R., Sr. V.P.-Consulting, Ventures & Corp. Devel.--International Technology Corporation, Monroeville, PA; *U.S. Public*, pg. 907

Maier, Craig F., Pres. & Chief Exec. Officer--Frisch's Restaurants, Inc., Cincinnati, OH; *U.S. Public*, pg. 682

Maier, F., Sr. V.P.-Devel.--Enserch Development Inc., Florham Park, NJ; *U.S. Public*, pg. 1587

Main, Timothy L., Sr. V.P.-Bus. Devel.--Jabil Circuit, Inc., Saint Petersburg, FL; *U.S. Public*, pg. 919

Mainelli, Michael R., Jr., V.P.-Bus. Devel.--Stryker Corporation, Kalamazoo, MI; *U.S. Public*, pg. 1525

Majcher, Thomas M., V.P.-Corp. Devel.--Rochester & Pittsburgh Coal Company, Indiana, PA; *U.S. Public*, pg. 1395

Makinen, Kalervo, Mgr.-Bus. Devel. & Strategic Plng.--Neste Oy, Espoo, Finland; *Int'l*, pg. 912

Malanga, Michael E., Sr. V.P.-Devel.--Family Restaurants, Inc., Irvine, CA; *U.S. Private*, pg. 393

Malinsky, Aaron, Exec. V.P.-Devel. & Strategic Plng.--The Great Atlantic & Pacific Tea Company, Inc., Montvale, NJ; *Int'l*, pg. 1375

Mallory, Kevin E., Sr. V.P. & Hotel Bus. Devel.--Starwood Hotels & Resorts, Phoenix, AZ; *U.S. Public*, pg. 1512

Malloy, Dennis, Dir.-Bus. Devel.--Binney & Smith Inc., Easton, PA; *U.S. Private*, pg. 496

Malmuth, David L., Sr. V.P.-Devel.--TrizecHahn Centers Inc., San Diego, CA; *Int'l*, pg. 1425

Malone, Thomas J., V.P.-Intl. Bus. Devel.--Wolverine Tube Inc., Huntsville, AL; *U.S. Public*, pg. 1774

Maloy, Terry E., Sr. V.P.-Mktg. & Plng.--American Drug Stores Inc., Oak Brook, IL; *U.S. Public*, pg. 93

Maltz, Scott, Exec. V.P.-TSL--Brite Voice Systems, Inc., Heathrow, FL; *U.S. Public*, pg. 257

Manberg, Ed, Chief Fin. Officer & V.P.--Byer California, San Francisco, CA; *U.S. Private*, pg. 191

Mandell, Andrew J., V.P.-Opers. Plng.--The Walt Disney Company, Burbank, CA; *U.S. Public*, pg. 511

Mandell, Marshall S., V.P.-Business Devel.--DynCorp, Reston, VA; *U.S. Private*, pg. 351

Mandro, Henry, Dir.-Bus. Devel. & Regulatory Affairs--Qual-Med, Inc., Pueblo, CO; *U.S. Public*, pg. 678

Mangum, Mylle, Dir.-Strategic Mngmt.--Holiday Inn Worldwide, Atlanta, GA; *Int'l*, pg. 170

Manion, Jerry, Dir.-Devel.--Motel 6 Operating L.P., Dallas, TX; *Int'l*, pg. 21

Mann, Gareth J., V.P.-Bus. Devel., Europe, Africa, Middle-East & Asia--Destec Energy, Inc., Houston, TX; *U.S. Public*, pg. 1146

Mansfield, Kirby A., V.P.-Bus. Devel.--INSO Corporation, Boston, MA; *U.S. Public*, pg. 882

Manvell, Elizabeth A., Mgr.-Fin. Plng.--Cambridge Shopping Centres Limited, Toronto, Canada; *Int'l*, pg. 253

Maor, Dov, Dr., Chief Scientist--Elscint Ltd., Haifa, Israel; *Int'l*, pg. 450

Marcalus, Nicholas R., Pres. & Chief Exec. Officer--Marcal Paper Mills, Inc., Elmwood Park, NJ; *U.S. Private*, pg. 701

Marcus, Stephen, Chm. Bd., Pres. & Chief Exec. Officer--The Marcus Corporation, Milwaukee, WI; *U.S. Public*, pg. 1044

Marcusson, Reese, Sr. V.P.-Corp. Plng. & Communications--WTTW (Channel 11), Chicago, IL; *U.S. Private*, pg. 1145

Margalith, Ethan Harold, Chm. Bd., Chief Exec. Officer & Treas.--Starving Students, Inc., Los Angeles, CA; *U.S. Private*, pg. 1035

Margolin, Barry, V.P.-Fin. & Plng. & Controller--Ha-Lo Industries, Inc., Niles, IL; *U.S. Public*, pg. 773

Markovitz, Philip D., Sr. V.P.-Store Devel.--Rite Aid Corporation, Camp Hill, PA; *U.S. Public*, pg. 1390

Marks, Francis A., V.P.--Intelligent Systems Corp., Norcross, GA; *U.S. Public*, pg. 888

Marotta, Thomas S., Chm. Bd., Pres. & Chief Exec. Officer--Marotta Scientific Controls, Inc., Montville, NJ; *U.S. Private*, pg. 706

Marsden, Charles J., Chief Fin. Officer & V.P.-Fin.--Crompton & Knowles Corporation, Stamford, CT; *U.S. Public*, pg. 459

Marsh, C. Alan, Vice Chm. & Sr. V.P.-Corp. Devel.--Marsh Supermarkets, Inc., Indianapolis, IN; *U.S. Public*, pg. 1049

Marshall, Clarence G., V.P.-Corp. Plng.--Century Telephone Enterprises, Inc., Monroe, LA; *U.S. Public*, pg. 329

Marshall, Isabel, Mgr.-Studies & Strategic Mngmnt.--CODELCO Chile (Corporacion Nacional Del Cobre De Chile), Santiago, Chile; *Int'l*, pg. 302

Marshall, Kelvin A.A., V.P.-Planning & Development--NewTel Enterprises Limited, Saint Johns, Canada; *Int'l*, pg. 115

Marshall, Ken, Sr. V.P.-Mfg., Res., Design & Devel.--The Rockport Company, Marlborough, MA; *U.S. Public*, pg. 1370

Marshall, Quintin G., Sr. V.P.-Corp. Devel.--Ogden Corporation, New York, NY; *U.S. Public*, pg. 1213

Marshall, R.J., Pres.--The R.J. Marshall Co., Southfield, MI; *U.S. Private*, pg. 708

Marshall, Robin L., Pres. & Chief Exec. Officer--Great Lakes Technologies Corp., Kalamazoo, MI; *U.S. Private*, pg. 475

Marshall, Walter, V.P.-Logistics & Plng.--New England Confectionery Co., Cambridge, MA; *U.S. Private*, pg. 1113

Marta, Robert, V.P.-Fin. & Plng.--Cooper Lighting Division, Elk Grove Village, IL; *U.S. Public*, pg. 443

Martin, Barry, Exec. V.P. & Acct. Plng. Dir.--Partners & Shevack, Inc., New York, NY; *U.S. Private*, pg. 842

Martin, Robert, Dir.-Bus. Devel.--Ferolie Group, Montvale, NJ; *U.S. Private*, pg. 401

Martin, W.R., V.P.-Bus. Devel.--Alliant Techsystems (Aerospace Division), Wilmington, DE; *U.S. Public*, pg. 47

Martin, Wayne, Pres. & Chief Exec. Officer--Plains Co-op Oil Mill, Lubbock, TX; *U.S. Private*, pg. 868

Martindale, Lucy G., V.P. & Dir.-Fin., Res. & Devel.--Glaxo Wellcome Inc., Research Triangle Park, NC; *Int'l*, pg. 552

Martinkovic, David, V.P.-Bus. Devel.--Reflectone, Inc., Tampa, FL; *Int'l*, pg. 218

Martonen, Ari, Sr. V.P.-Bus. Devel.--Tamrock Corp., Tampere, Finland; *Int'l*, pg. 1352

Mascott, G. Theodore, V.P.-Bus. Plng. & Admin.--Merck & Co., Inc., Whitehouse Station, NJ; *U.S. Public*, pg. 1090

Maser, H. Barry, V.P.-Bus. Devel. & Intl. Sls.--Aydin Corporation, Horsham, PA; *U.S. Public*, pg. 158

Mashimo, Tsugio, Mng. Dir. & Gen. Mgr.-Plng.--Gunze Sangyo, Inc., Tokyo, Japan; *Int'l*, pg. 578

Mason, David D. S., Pres., Chief Exec. & Chief Fin. Officer & Treas.--Toms Sierra Company, Ione, CA; *U.S. Private*, pg. 1090

Mason, Linda, V.P.-Public Affairs Programming--CBS News, New York, NY; *U.S. Public*, pg. 274

Mason, Murray, Dir.-Engrng. & Devel.--VARI-FORM, Woodstock, Canada; *Int'l*, pg. 1341

Mason, Ron, V.P.-Corp. Devel.--Oak Industries Inc., Waltham, MA; *U.S. Public*, pg. 1209

Mastic, Peter J., V.P.-Bus. Devel.--CMS Generation Co., Dearborn, MI; *U.S. Public*, pg. 280

Mastro, Mildred, Dir.-Training & Devel.--General Binding Corporation, Northbrook, IL; *U.S. Public*, pg. 707

Masugata, Masaru, Dir.-Tech. Devel. & Res. & Corp. Plng. & Safety Res. Lab.--East Japan Railway Company, Tokyo, Japan; *Int'l*, pg. 431

Mathers, Stephen R., V.P.-Corp. Devel.--Binks Sames Corporation, Franklin Park, IL; *U.S. Public*, pg. 229

Mathews, Curtis, Sr. V.P.-Corp. Devel.--ICO, Inc., Houston, TX; *U.S. Public*, pg. 853

Mathews, J.C. Ogier, V.P.-Corp. Devel.--The Loewen Group, Inc., Burnaby, Canada; *Int'l*, pg. 814

Mathews, Janice, Mgr.-Real Estate--Jan-Co., Inc., Cranston, RI; *U.S. Private*, pg. 581

Matrenza, R.F., Grp. Gen. Mgr.-Strategic Devel.--National Australia Bank Limited, Melbourne, Australia; *Int'l*, pg. 906

Matsumoto, Arata, Exec. V.P.-Plng. & Control--Kawasaki Heavy Industries, Ltd., Kobe, Japan; *Int'l*, pg. 725

Matsumoto, Hiroshi, V.P.-Bus. & Strategic Plng.--National Steel Corporation, Mishawaka, IN; *Int'l*, pg. 902

Matsumura, Akio, Mng. Dir.-Plng. & Admin.--UBE Industries Ltd., Tokyo, Japan; *Int'l*, pg. 1426

Matteo, Maxine, Exec. V.P.-Adv., Mktg. & Bus. Devel.--INMC Mortgage Holdings, Inc., Pasadena, CA; *U.S. Public*, pg. 857

Matthews, F. Luke, V.P.-Bus. Devel.--Global Marine Drilling Co., Houston, TX; *U.S. Public*, pg. 748

Mattson, Frank, V.P.-Distr. & Strategic Plng.--Ingram Entertainment Inc., La Vergne, TN; *U.S. Private*, pg. 563

Maughan, Rex, Chm. Bd., Pres. & Chief Exec. Officer--Forever Living Products International, Inc., Scottsdale, AZ; *U.S. Private*, pg. 418

Maurer, Christian, Dir.-Strategic Plng.--Alcatel N.V., Amsterdam, Netherlands; *Int'l*, pg. 55

May, Allan W., V.P.-Strategic Devel., Gen. Counsel & Sec.--OEC Medical Systems, Inc., Salt Lake City, UT; *U.S. Public*, pg. 1207

May, Jon, V.P.-Concept Devel.--Triarc Restaurant Group, Fort Lauderdale, FL; *U.S. Public*, pg. 1635

May, Van, Pres. & Chief Exec. Officer--Plains Cotton Co-op Association, Lubbock, TX; *U.S. Private*, pg. 868

Mayfield, Richard D., V.P.-Quality & Org. Analysis--The Acacia Group - Acacia Life Insurance Co., Bethesda, MD; *U.S. Private*, pg. 10

Maziarka, Donald, Pres., Chief Exec. & Chief Oper. Officer--George Sollitt Construction, Wood Dale, IL; *U.S. Private*, pg. 1013

McAlhaney, W. Hardee, Chief Fin. Officer & V.P.--Holiday RV Superstores, Inc., Orlando, FL; *U.S. Public*, pg. 829

McArthur, John E., V.P.-Devel.--Urban Group, Toronto, Canada; *Int'l*, pg. 253

McBride, Terry, Dir.-Coord. Devel. Div.--Healthcare America, Inc., Austin, TX; *U.S. Private*, pg. 515

McCarry, Gregory M., V.P.-Devel.--Pope Resources, Poulsbo, WA; *U.S. Public*, pg. 1317

McCarvel, John P., V.P.-Strategic Bus. Devel.--Micron Custom Manufacturing Services, Inc., Nampa, ID; *U.S. Public*, pg. 1105

McCellon-Allen, Venita, Sr. V.P.-Corp. Devel.--Central and South West Corporation, Dallas, TX; *U.S. Public*, pg. 324

McClellan, James W., V.P.-Strategic Plng.--Norfolk Southern Corporation, Norfolk, VA; *U.S. Public*, pg. 1190

McClelland, Norman P., Chief Exec. Officer--Shamrock Foods Company, Phoenix, AZ; *U.S. Private*, pg. 989

Mcclung, K. Gene, V.P.-Plng. Logistics & Bus. Devel.--Southern States Cooperative, Inc., Richmond, VA; *U.S. Private*, pg. 1017

McComas, R. Doss, V.P.-Bus. Devel.--COMSAT RSI, Inc., Sterling, VA; *U.S. Public*, pg. 424

McCormack, Maryanne, Pres.--Visible Changes, Houston, TX; *U.S. Private*, pg. 1141

McCormick, Louise L., V.P.-Corp. Plng.--Aetna Inc., Hartford, CT; *U.S. Public*, pg. 26

McCrady, David W., V.P.-Information Systems Plng.--Sun Life Assurance Company of Canada, Toronto, Canada; *Int'l*, pg. 1318

McCrady, Kenneth A., Chm. Bd.--Ennis Business Forms, Inc., Ennis, TX; *U.S. Public*, pg. 583

McCurdy, Charles G., Pres.--Primedia Inc., New York, NY; *U.S. Public*, pg. 1327

McDearmon, Ron, Sr. V.P.-Plng. & Devel.--Minyard Food Stores, Inc., Coppell, TX; *U.S. Private*, pg. 752

McDonnell, Bernard J., Exec. V.P.-Real Estate & Corp. Devel.--Provigo Inc., Montreal, Canada; *Int'l*, pg. 1072

McDonough, Phil S., Gen. Mgr.-Export & Plng.--International Division, Melbourne, Australia; *Int'l*, pg. 226

McEwen, Joseph, Chm. Bd. & Chief Exec. Officer--Modern Group Ltd., Bristol, PA; *U.S. Private*, pg. 754

McFalls, R. Alan, V.P.-Corp. Devel. & Planning--J.M. Smucker Company, Orrville, OH; *U.S. Public*, pg. 1480

McFarlane, Michael, Exec. Dir.-Strategic Plng.--Standard Chartered Bank PLC, London, United Kingdom; *Int'l*, pg. 1294

McFarlane, R. Bruce, V.P.-Bus. Devel.--Poco Petroleums Ltd., Calgary, Canada; *Int'l*, pg. 1061

McFarquhar, A.M., Dir.-Plng. & Nutrition--Bernard Matthews PLC, Norwich, United Kingdom; *Int'l*, pg. 189

McGee, Pat, Mgr.-Bus. Devel.--Sasol Ammonia, Johannesburg, South Africa; *Int'l*, pg. 1196

McGill, Charles H., Sr. V.P.-Corp. Devel.--Fortune Brands, Inc., Old Greenwich, CT; *U.S. Public*, pg. 674

McGill, John R., V.P. & Dir.-Dev.--Developers Diversified Realty Corporation, Moreland Hills, OH; *U.S. Public*, pg. 502

McGlade, Pete, V.P.-Schedule Plng.--Southwest Airlines Co., Dallas, TX; *U.S. Public*, pg. 1493

McGonagle, Patrick J., Pres. & Chief Exec. Officer--National Gas & Oil Company, Newark, OH; *U.S. Public*, pg. 1156

McGowan, Kevin, Dir.-Plng. & Analysis--Duty Free International, Inc., Ridgefield, CT; *Int'l*, pg. 103

McGowen, Bill, Dir.-Strategic Plng.--Field Container Company, L.P., Elk Grove Village, IL; *U.S. Private*, pg. 403

McGrath, William J., V.P.-Inventory Plng. & Control--QVC, Inc., West Chester, PA; *U.S. Private*, pg. 897

McGregor, Douglas A., Exec. V.P.-Oper. Devel.--The Rouse Company, Columbia, MD; *U.S. Public*, pg. 1407

McGregor, Marvin M., V.P. Mktg. & Bus. Devel.--Southwestern Electric Power Co., Shreveport, LA; *U.S. Public*, pg. 324

McGregor, Ronald J., V.P.-Opers. & Devel.--Vista Gold Corp., Denver, CO; *U.S. Public*, pg. 1723

McGuigan, Bill, V.P.-Prod. Devel.--Columbus Mills, Inc., Columbus, GA; *U.S. Private*, pg. 256

McHugh, M. Joseph, Pres. & Chief Oper. Officer--Triangle Pacific Corporation, Dallas, TX; *U.S. Public*, pg. 1634

McIlwain, Kary, Sr. V.P. & Mktg. & Strategic Plng. Dir.--Young & Rubicam Chicago, Chicago, IL; *U.S. Private*, pg. 1198

McIntyre, Greg, Dir.-Bus. Devel. & Plng.--CH2M Hill Companies, Ltd., Greenwood Village, CO; *U.S. Private*, pg. 195

McKeller, Joseph, Dir.-New Bus. & Devel. Programs--Boeing Helicopters, Ridley Park, PA; *U.S. Public*, pg. 241

McKenna, Mindi K., V.P.-Bus. Plng. & Devel.--Cerner Corporation, Kansas City, MO; *U.S. Public*, pg. 331

McKnight, Andrew D., Chm. Bd., Pres. & Chief Exec. Officer--Tri-Chem, Inc., Harrison, NJ; *U.S. Private*, pg. 1100

McKnight, P.E., V.P.-Organization Plng.--Emerson Electric Co., Saint Louis, MO; *U.S. Public*, pg. 572

McLain, Susan S., Dir.-Strategic Plng.--Puget Sound Energy, Inc., Bellevue, WA; *U.S. Public*, pg. 1342

McLoughlin, John, Dir.-Bus. Devel.--Jacobs International Limited, Inc., Dublin, Ireland; *U.S. Public*, pg. 922

McManus, John V., V.P.-Fin. & Asst. Sec.--Sheldahl, Inc., Northfield, MN; *U.S. Public*, pg. 1465

McMichael, Robert, Dir.-Plng.--McClatchy Newspapers Inc., Sacramento, CA; *U.S. Public*, pg. 1065

McMorris, Jeff, V.P.-Indus. Devel.--NW Transport Service, Inc., Denver, CO; *U.S. Private*, pg. 772

McNair, James, V.P.-Business Devel.--J2, Inc., Deerfield, IL; *U.S. Private*, pg. 598

McNally, Michael W., V.P.-Opers., Plng. & Devel.--Coca-Cola Enterprises Inc., Atlanta, GA; *U.S. Public*, pg. 393

McNatt, Robert M., V.P.-Devel.--Kapalua Land Co., Ltd., Lahaina, HI; *U.S. Public*, pg. 1060

McNeel, Clayton W., Pres. & Chief Oper. Officer--McNeel International Corp., Tampa, FL; *U.S. Private*, pg. 724

McNeeley, Donald R., Pres. & Chief Oper. Officer--Chicago Tube & Iron Co., Chicago, IL; *U.S. Private*, pg. 235

McNeil, John E., V.P.-Corp. Devel.--Royal Insurance Company of Canada, Toronto, Canada; *Int'l*, pg. 1131

McPhail, Douglas J., Pres., Chief Exec. & Fin. Officer & Treas.--Indiana Records Managers, Fishers, IN; *U.S. Private*, pg. 560

McPhearson, J.R., Jr., Pres.--Strachan Shipping Co., Garden City, GA; *U.S. Private*, pg. 1045

McPherson, John M., V.P.-Protein Devel.--Genzyme Corporation, Cambridge, MA; *U.S. Public*, pg. 733

McQueen, Josh, Exec. V.P. & Worldwide Plng. Dir.--Leo Burnett Company, Inc., Chicago, IL; *U.S. Private*, pg. 183

McShane, John, Exec. V.P.-Devel.--Koo Koo Roo, Inc., Los Angeles, CA; *U.S. Public*, pg. 966

McVey, James R., Mgr.-Area Devel.--Providence Energy Corporation, Providence, RI; *U.S. Public*, pg. 1337

McWilliams, James K., V.P.-Fuel Supply & Civil & Mining Engrng.--American Electric Power Service Corp., Columbus, OH; *U.S. Public*, pg. 72

Meader, Peggy, Pres. & Chief Exec. Officer--Inland Associates, Olathe, KS; *U.S. Private*, pg. 563

Meadows, Allen, V.P.-Corp. Plng.--Great Western Financial Corporation, Chatsworth, CA; *U.S. Public*, pg. 1741

Meagher, Mike, Mgr.-Bus. Devel.--James McHugh Construction Co., Chicago, IL; *U.S. Private*, pg. 721

Medeiros, Otavio R., Mgr.-Plng. & Devel.--Acos Villares S.A., Sao Paulo, Brazil; *Int'l*, pg. 23

Medina, Hector, Exec. V.P.-Plng. & Fin.--Cemex, S.A. de C.V., Monterrey, Mexico; *Int'l*, pg. 278

Meguro, Sumio, Exec. Dir.-Auditing--Seiko Corporation, Tokyo, Japan; *Int'l*, pg. 1218

Meitzner, Carl F., Dr., V.P.-Plng.--Bethlehem Steel Corporation, Bethlehem, PA; *U.S. Public*, pg. 226

Mello, Becky, Mgr.-Customer Rels.--Galpin Motors, North Hills, CA; *U.S. Private*, pg. 438

Meloni, Daniel, Mgr.-Corp. Plng. & Res.--Kemper Insurance Companies, Long Grove, IL; *U.S. Private*, pg. 614

Menard, Robert, V.P.-Projects & Construction--Cambior Inc., Montreal, Canada; *Int'l*, pg. 253

Mendelson, Steven, Sr. V.P.-Comedy Devel.--Columbia TriStar Television, Culver City, CA; *Int'l*, pg. 1282

Mengelt, Jurg, Mng. Dir.-Plng. & Control--Landis & Staefa AG, Zug, Switzerland; *Int'l*, pg. 800

Mercurio, Joe, Dir.-Plng. & Res.--Walgreen Co., Deerfield, IL; *U.S. Public*, pg. 1733

Merenoff, Barry N., Dir.-Plng. Svcs.--Harley Ellington Design, Southfield, MI; *U.S. Private*, pg. 503

Merland, J., Exec. V.P.-Innovation, Res. & Industrialization--Compagnie Generale de Geophysique, Massy, France; *Int'l*, pg. 241

Mertens, Don, Mgr.-Plng. & Devel.--Volkswagen Canada, Inc., Ajax, Canada; *Int'l*, pg. 1475

Mertes, Wayne M., Pres. & Chief Exec. Officer--National R.V., Inc., Perris, CA; *U.S. Public*, pg. 1159

Mervin, Jeff, Dir.-Bus. Devel.--Operations & Maintenance Division, Cleveland, OH; *U.S. Public*, pg. 1134

Metcalf, Dennis L., V.P.-Corp. Devel.--IDEX Corporation, Northbrook, IL; *U.S. Public*, pg. 862

Metropoulos, Jim, M.D., Sr. V.P. & Chief Strategic Officer--Lowe McAdams Healthcare, New York, NY; *U.S. Private*, *pg. 678*

Metrosky, Joseph, Mgr.-Fin. & Bus. Plng.--IMO Pump, Monroe, NC; *U.S. Public*, pg. 857

Metzger, J.R., V.P. & Gen. Mgr.-Corp. Plng.--Texaco Inc., White Plains, NY; *U.S. Public*, pg. 1582

Meyer, Brian E., V.P.-Applications Devel.--Berkley Information Services, Luverne, MN; *U.S. Public*, pg. 216

Meyer, Dennis J., V.P.-Mktg. & Plng.--Banta Corporation, Menasha, WI; *U.S. Public*, pg. 187

Meyers, Eric, Grp. V.P.-Corp. Restructuring/Implementation--Witco Corporation, Greenwich, CT; *U.S. Public*, pg. 1773

Meyers, Howard M., Chm. Bd., Pres. & Chief Exec. Officer--Quexco Incorporated, Dallas, TX; *U.S. Private*, pg. 900

Mezzanotte, Renee, V.P.-Bus. Devel.--Devon Direct Marketing & Advertising, Inc., Berwyn, PA; *U.S. Private*, pg. 329

Michalak, Michael, First V.P.-Plng. & Devel.--Comerica Incorporated, Detroit, MI; *U.S. Public*, pg. 408

Michaud, Mark, Dir.-Corp. Plng. & Devel.--Collins & Aikman Corporation, Charlotte, NC; *U.S. Public*, pg. 399

Michelet, J.L., Grp. V.P.--CAP Gemini S.A., Paris, France; *Int'l*, pg. 263

Mikkelson, James, V.P.-Tech. Devel.--Vitesse Semiconductor Corporation, Camarillo, CA; *U.S. Public*, pg. 1723

Miles, Rae, V.P.-New Prod. Devel.--Credit Union National Association, Madison, WI; *U.S. Private*, pg. 288

Miley, John, Exec. V.P. & Corp. Plng. Dir.--G2 Advertising, Huntington Beach, CA; *U.S. Public*, pg. 764

Miller, Augustus C., Chm. Bd., Pres., & Chief Exec. Officer--Miller Oil Co., Inc., Norfolk, VA; *U.S. Private*, pg. 747

Miller, Avram, V.P. & Dir.-Bus. Devel.--Intel Systems Group, Santa Clara, CA; *U.S. Public*, pg. 887

Miller, Avram C., V.P.-Corp. Bus. Dev. & Dir.-Bus. Dev.--Intel Corporation, Santa Clara, CA; *U.S. Public*, pg. 886

Miller, Charles D., Chm. Bd. & Chief Exec. Officer--Avery Dennison Corporation, Pasadena, CA; *U.S. Public*, pg. 152

Miller, D.J., V.P.-Corp. Devel. & Fin. Plng.--Northwest Natural Gas Company, Portland, OR; *U.S. Public*, pg. 1200

Miller, David P., Pres. & Chief Exec. Officer--Columbia National Group, Inc., Cleveland, OH; *U.S. Private*, pg. 255

Miller, Donald, Chief Fin. Officer--Schwan's Sales Enterprises, Marshall, MN; *U.S. Private*, pg. 974

Miller, Donald R., Jr., V.P.-Mkt. Devel.--Michaels Stores, Inc., Irving, TX; *U.S. Public*, pg. 1104

Miller, George, Sr. V.P.-Admin.--CD Products, Inc., New Providence, NJ; *U.S. Public*, pg. 276

Miller, Gregory D., V.P.-Mktg. & Strategic Plng.--Manor Care, Inc., Gaithersburg, MD; *U.S. Public*, pg. 1041

Miller, Jon, Mgr.-Development-Munition Systems--Thomson-CSF, Inc., Arlington, VA; *Int'l*, pg. 1384

Miller, Joseph, Sr. V.P.-Prod. Devel.--Sega of America Inc., Redwood City, CA; *Int'l*, pg. 1218

Miller, R.L., V.P.-Admin.--P.H. Glatfelter Company, Spring Grove, PA; *U.S. Public*, pg. 746

Miller, Rick, Dir.-Strategic Mktg.--Mack Trucks, Inc., Allentown, PA; *Int'l*, pg. 1102

Miller, Rusty, Dir.-Devel.--Motel 6 Operating L.P., Dallas, TX; *Int'l*, pg. 21

Miller, Sandy LaFleur, V.P. & Strategic Plng. Dir.--Italia/Gal Advertising, Los Angeles, CA; *U.S. Private*, pg. 576

Miller, Steven, Chm. Bd., Pres. & Chief Exec. Officer--Miller Resources International, Inc., North Brunswick, NJ; *U.S. Private*, pg. 748

Miller, Walter M., Sr. V.P.-Strategy & Devel.--Becton Dickinson & Company, Franklin Lakes, NJ; *U.S. Public*, pg. 199

Mills, Bradford A., Exec. V.P.-Bus. Plng. & Devel.--BHP Copper North America, Tucson, AZ; *Int'l*, pg. 224

Mills, P. Gerald, Chm. Bd., Pres. & Chief Exec. Officer--Jacobson Stores Inc., Jackson, MI; *U.S. Public*, pg. 922

Millsap, James M., Sr. V.P.-Corp. Devel.--IVAX Corporation, Miami, FL; *U.S. Public*, pg. 914

Milos, V.P.-Bus. Devel. & Human Resources--Schering Berlin Inc., Cedar Knolls, NJ; *Int'l*, pg. 1204

Miniat, Ronald, Chm., Pres. & Chief Exec. Officer--Ed Miniat, Inc., Chicago, IL; *U.S. Private*, pg. 750

Minnaugh, Mark, V.P.-Fin. & Acctg.--Giant Eagle, Inc., Pittsburgh, PA; *U.S. Private*, pg. 450

Minnihan, Richard L., V.P.-Bus. Devel.--Medical Laboratory Automation, Inc., Pleasantville, NY; *U.S. Private*, pg. 727

Mireur, J. Pete, Mgr.-Business Devel.--Jacobs Engineering Group Inc., Houston, TX; *U.S. Public*, pg. 921

Miron, Michael, V.P.-Corp. Strategy & Devel.--AirTouch Communications, Inc., San Francisco, CA; *U.S. Public*, pg. 34

Mitchell, Dean, V.P.-Bus. Devel. & Plng. & Gen. Mgr.-Specialty Div.--Glaxo Wellcome Inc., Research Triangle Park, NC; *Int'l*, pg. 552

Mitchell, Nigel, Exec. Mgr.-External Policy & Plng.--New Zealand Dairy Board, Wellington, New Zealand; *Int'l*, pg. 923

Mitchen, James P., V.P.-Bus. Devel.--Cliffs Drilling Company, Houston, TX; *U.S. Public*, pg. 386

Miura, Yuichi, Mng. Dir.-Corp. Plng.--Tokuyama Corporation, Tokyo, Japan; *Int'l*, pg. 1393

Miwa, Lawrence F., V.P. & Mgr.-Bus. Devel.--Central Pacific Bank, Honolulu, HI; *U.S. Public*, pg. 283

Mixtacki, Steven B., Chief Fin. Officer & V.P.--American TV & Appliance of Madison, Inc., Madison, WI; *U.S. Private*, pg. 64

Miyahara, Kenji, Exec. V.P.-Plng., Credit, Investments, Acctng. & Controller--Sumitomo Corporation, Tokyo, Japan; *Int'l*, pg. 1312

Miyamoto, Mikihiko, Pres. & Chief Mktg. Officer--Yasuda Mutual Life Insurance Co., Tokyo, Japan; *Int'l*, pg. 1519

Miyamoto, Mikihiko, Chief Mktg. Officer--Yasuda Mutual Life Insurance Co., Tokyo, Japan; *Int'l*, pg. 1519

Mladiner, Miro P., Mgr.-Corp. Devel.--Illinois Power Company, Decatur, IL; *U.S. Public*, pg. 869

Moberg, David, Sr. V.P.-Author Devel. Word Publishing--Thomas Nelson Inc., Nashville, TN; *U.S. Public*, pg. 1167

Moebius, Gordon, Dir.-Corp. Devel.--American Trans Air Execujet, Inc., Indianapolis, IN; *U.S. Public*, pg. 106

Moeller, Mark, Dir.-Bus. Devel.--T.A. Loving Company, Goldsboro, NC; *U.S. Private*, pg. 677

Moffat, G. Michael, V.P.-Bus. Plng.--The Oshawa Group Limited, Etobicoke, Canada; *Int'l*, pg. 1012

Moffat, John, V.P.-OEM Devel. & Mktg.--Code Alarm Security Systems, Madison Heights, MI; *U.S. Public*, pg. 394

Mogas, V. Louis, Pres. & Chief Exec. Officer--Mogas Industries, Inc., Houston, TX; *U.S. Private*, pg. 755

Mohrman, LeRoy, Chm. Bd., Pres. & Chief Exec. Officer--Handling Systems Engineering, Jacksonville, FL; *U.S. Private*, pg. 499

Moilanen, Thomas A., Pres. & Chief Exec. Officer--Cloverdale Equipment Co., Oak Park, MI; *U.S. Private*, pg. 247

Mokgatle, D.D., Exec. Dir.-Growth & Devel.--Eskom, Sandton, South Africa; *Int'l*, pg. 459

Monaghan, David G., Jr., V.P.-Fin.--GTE Government Systems Corporation, Needham, MA; *U.S. Public*, pg. 696

Mondello, Mark, V.P.-Bus. Devel.--Jabil Circuit, Inc., Saint Petersburg, FL; *U.S. Public*, pg. 919

Moneta, Jack, Sr. V.P.-Strategic Plng. & Tech. Devel.--Photronics, Inc., Brookfield, CT; *U.S. Public*, pg. 1293

Mongeau, C., V.P.-Strategic & Fin. Plng.--Canadian National Railway Company, Montreal, Canada; *Int'l*, pg. 258

Monie, Nat, Mgr.-Bus. Devel.--Dowty Aerospace, New Delhi, India; *Int'l*, pg. 1337

Montagner, Philippe, Grp. Dir.-Telecomm.& Devel.--Bouygues, Saint Quentin-en-Yvelines, France; *Int'l*, pg. 206

Monteyne, Guido, V.P.-Bus. Devel.--Sidmar N.V., Gent, Belgium; *Int'l*, pg. 79

Montgomery, Susan, V.P. & Assoc. Plng. Dir.--Western International Media Corporation, Los Angeles, CA; *U.S. Private*, pg. 1165

Moore, Alice C., Mgr.-Prod. Plng.--Ocean Spray Cranberries-Bordentown Plant, Bordentown, NJ; *U.S. Private*, pg. 811

Moore, C. Harold, V.P.-Plng.--Fruit of the Loom, Inc., Chicago, IL; *U.S. Public*, pg. 685

Moore, Fred, Client Services Dir. & Devel. Dir.--The Arnold Agency, Richmond, VA; *U.S. Private*, pg. 84

Moore, Fred, V.P.-Strategic Plng.--Storage Technology Corporation, Louisville, CO; *U.S. Public*, pg. 1522

Moore, Glenn R., Pres. & Chief Oper. Officer--Maynard Oil Co., Dallas, TX; *U.S. Public*, pg. 1064

Moore, Joe, V.P.-Corp. Plng.--Wedco Technology, Bloomsbury, NJ; *U.S. Public*, pg. 854

Moore, John O., Mng. Dir.--Duncan Equipment Company, Oklahoma City, OK; *U.S. Private*, pg. 346

Moore, M.A., Dr., Dir.-Tech. & Mkt. Devel.--Morganite Thermal Ceramics Limited, Norton, United Kingdom; *Int'l*, *pg. 893*

Moore, Patrick Q., Mgr.-Grp. Plng.--Borders Group, Inc., Ann Arbor, MI; *U.S. Public*, pg. 245

Moore, Sam, Chm. Bd., Pres. & Chief Exec. Officer--Thomas Nelson Inc., Nashville, TN; *U.S. Public*, pg. 1167

Moore, T. Jerald, Exec. V.P.-Bus. Devel. & Plng.--Beverly Enterprises, Inc., Fort Smith, AR; *U.S. Public*, pg. 227

Moore, William B., Vice Chm. & Chief Tech. Officer--Moore Products Co., Spring House, PA; *U.S. Public*, pg. 1128

Morache, Fred, V.P.-Bus. Devel.--Mail Boxes Etc. USA, San Diego, CA; *U.S. Public*, pg. 1687

Morales, Juan Enrique, V.P.-Devel.--CODELCO Chile (Corporacion Nacional Del Cobre De Chile), Santiago, Chile; *Int'l*, pg. 302

Moran, James G., Sr. V.P.-Corp. Admin.--Regal Ware, Inc., Kewaskum, WI; *U.S. Private*, pg. 917

Morberg, Per Ove, Exec. V.P.-Strategic Bus. Devel.--Celsius AB, Stockholm, Sweden; *Int'l*, pg. 276

Morel, Ernie, Sr. V.P.-Plng. & Projects--Bank of Montreal - Winnipeg, Winnipeg, Canada; *Int'l*, pg. 153

Morgan, Joseph W., V.P.-Strategic Plng.--Blimpie International, Inc., Atlanta, GA; *U.S. Public*, pg. 236

Morgan, Phillip R., Pres. & Chief Exec. Officer--Morgan Construction Co., Worcester, MA; *U.S. Private*, pg. 761

Morgan, R.A., V.P.-Strategic Plng.--Kelley Advertising Inc., Hamilton, Canada; *U.S. Public*, pg. 765

Morgan, Thomas M., V.P.-Indian Gaming Devel.--Harrah's Entertainment, Inc., Memphis, TN; *U.S. Public*, pg. 790

Mori, Masaru, Gen. Mgr.-Real Estate--Cosmo Oil Co., Ltd., Tokyo, Japan; *Int'l*, pg. 335

Morin, George E., V.P.-Devel. (Natl.)--Cossette Communication Marketing, Quebec, Canada; *Int'l*, pg. 335

Morioka, Eizo, Gen. Mgr.-Tech. Devel. & Plng.--Sumitomo Corporation, Tokyo, Japan; *Int'l*, pg. 1312

Morlock, Bryan, Dir.-Resource Plng.--Otter Tail Power Company, Fergus Falls, MN; *U.S. Public*, pg. 1234

Mormann, Stephen A., Dir.-Fin. & Bus. Devel.--Constellation Energy Projects & Services, Inc., Baltimore, MD; *U.S. Public*, pg. 172

Moro, Anthony, Sr. V.P.-Devel.--Tridel Enterprises Inc., Downsview, Canada; *Int'l*, pg. 1423

Morris, Bryan, V.P.-Business Devel.--Cominco, Ltd., Vancouver, Canada; *Int'l*, pg. 307

Morris, Cheryl L., V.P.-Aeroquip Plng. & Control--Aeroquip-Vickers, Inc., Maumee, OH; *U.S. Public*, pg. 24

Morris, G. Eryl, Dir.-Plng. & Opers. Devel., Information Technology & Packaging--Courtaulds plc, London, United Kingdom; *Int'l*, pg. 338

Morris, John H., Exec. V.P.--RPM, Inc., Medina, OH; *U.S. Public*, pg. 1356

Morris, Michael F., V.P.-Store Devel.--Rite Aid Corporation, Camp Hill, PA; *U.S. Public*, pg. 1390

Morrison, Charles E., Partner, Exec. V.P., Strategic Plng. Dir. & New Bus. Contact--Don Coleman Advertising, Inc., Southfield, MI; *U.S. Private*, pg. 251

Morrow, John W., Jr., Exec. V.P.-Corp. Devel.--Service Corporation International, Houston, TX; *U.S. Public*, pg. 1460

Morsky, Matti, V.P.-Plng. & Devel.--Metsa-Serla Corporation, Espoo, Finland; *Int'l*, pg. 863

Mortier, Denis, Exec. V.P.-Equity Fin.--Credit Nationale, Paris, France; *Int'l*, pg. 344

Moses, Thomas J., Exec. Asst.-Admin. Affairs--Holstein Association USA, Inc., Brattleboro, VT; *U.S. Private*, pg. 536

Moss, J. Cameron, V.P.-Corp. Plng.--Hillenbrand Industries, Inc., Batesville, IN; *U.S. Public*, pg. 828

Moss, John L., V.P.-Devel.--NewsEdge Corporation, Burlington, MA; *U.S. Public*, pg. 1180

Moynihan, Brian T., Mng. Dir.-Corp. Strategy & Devel.--Fleet Financial Group, Inc., Boston, MA; *U.S. Public*, pg. 648

Moynihan, Stephen H., V.P. & Treas.--Clean Harbors, Inc., Braintree, MA; *U.S. Public*, pg. 383

Mueller, David R., Chm. Bd. & Chief Exec. Officer--Comair Holdings, Inc., Erlanger, KY; *U.S. Public*, pg. 406

Mueller, Hans, Ph.D., Sr. V.P.-Bus. Devel.--Wyeth-Ayerst Laboratories, Inc., Philadelphia, PA; *U.S. Public*, pg. 80

Mueller, Robert J., Exec. V.P.-External Affairs & Bus. Devel.--International Rectifier Corporation, El Segundo, CA; *U.S. Public*, pg. 906

Muir, Chris, V.P.-Mktg.--C.H. Heist Corp., Clearwater, FL; *U.S. Public*, pg. 807

Mullen, Thomas W., Exec. V.P.-Strategic Planning--Trustmark Corporation, Jackson, MS; *U.S. Public*, pg. 1643

Mullen, Thomas W., Exec. V.P.-Strategic Plng.--Trustmark National Bank, Jackson, MS; *U.S. Public*, pg. 1643

Mullins, Roy L., Jr., Pres. & Chief Exec. Officer--Beacon Sales Corporation, Jacksonville, FL; *U.S. Private*, pg. 126

Mundt, Thomas P., V.P.-Strategic Plng., Investor Rels. & Communications--Wolverine World Wide, Inc., Rockford, MI; *U.S. Public*, pg. 1775

Munoz, Sandra, Planner Supvr.--Young & Rubicam de Buenos Aires, Buenos Aires, Argentina; *U.S. Private*, pg. 1200

Munroe, J.F., V.P.-Organization Devel.--Glaxo Wellcome PLC, Research Triangle Park, NC; *Int'l*, pg. 553

Mura, H., V.P.-Joint Ventures & Plng.--Centeon, L.L.C., King of Prussia, PA; *Int'l*, pg. 626

Murnane, William, V.P.--Innovex, Inc., Hopkins, MN; *U.S. Public*, pg. 880

Murphy, Jim, Sr. V.P.--BankAmerica Corporation, San Francisco, CA; *U.S. Public*, pg. 179

Murphy, John J., Chief Fin. Officer, Exec. V.P. & Treas.--Arrow Financial Corporation, Glens Falls, NY; *U.S. Public*, pg. 135

Murphy, Peter, Jr., Chm. Bd., Pres. & Chief Exec. Officer--Murphy Company, Eugene, OR; *U.S. Private*, pg. 768

Murray, P.C., Gen. Mgr.-Corp. Devel.--LASMO plc, London, United Kingdom; *Int'l*, pg. 803

Murray, R.W., Chief Fin. Officer, Sr. V.P., Treas., Controller & Sec.--Webb, Murray & Associates, Houston, TX; *U.S. Private*, pg. 1157

Murro, John M., V.P.-Strategic Plng.--Lebhar-Friedman, Inc., New York, NY; *U.S. Private*, pg. 656

Muscat, Leslie, Grp. Head-Plng. & Devel.--Air Malta Co. Ltd., Luqa, Malta; *Int'l*, pg. 37

Muse, Charles H., Jr., Chief Fin. Officer & Treas.--Crown Coal & Coke Co. Inc., Pittsburgh, PA; *U.S. Private*, pg. 292

Musgrave, Stephen T., Dir.-Plng. & Control--Alamco, Inc., Charleston, WV; *U.S. Public,* pg. 403
Myers, Norman S., Pres., Chief Exec. & Fin. Officers & Treas.--IDM Controls, Houston, TX; *U.S. Private,* pg. 554
Myers, Ron, Dir.-Corp. Plng. & Budgets--F. Schumacher & Co., New York, NY; *U.S. Private,* pg. 973
Nadkarni, Ravi, V.P.-Research & Dev.--Stern-Leach Company, Attleboro, MA; *Int'l,* pg. 329
Naffah, Karim, Dir.-Strategic Planning--Bass PLC, London, United Kingdom; *Int'l,* pg. 169
Nagano, Sunao, Exec. V.P.--Marubeni Corporation, Osaka, Japan; *Int'l,* pg. 844
Nagel, David C., V.P.-Plng. & Admin.--Amoco Production Company, Chicago, IL; *U.S. Public,* pg. 102
Nagy, Ed, Sr. V.P.-Store Plng.--Wal-Mart Stores, Inc., Bentonville, AR; *U.S. Public,* pg. 1732
Nahum, Eitan, V.P.-Strategic Plng. & Bus. Devel.--U.S. Surgical Corp., Norwalk, CT; *U.S. Public,* pg. 1687
Nai Meng, Yeo, Sr. Dir.-Opers. & Plng.--Singapore Tourist Promotion Board, Singapore, Singapore; *Int'l,* pg. 1253
Naito, Tsuneo, Mng. Dir.-Mngmt. Strategy--Sega Enterprises Ltd., Tokyo, Japan; *Int'l,* pg. 1218
Nakagawa, Jean H., Exec. V.P.-Corp.--Servco Pacific Inc., Honolulu, HI; *U.S. Private,* pg. 986
Nakagawa, Teruyuki, Dir.-Bus. Devel.--Showpla Asia Limited, Singapore, Singapore; *Int'l,* pg. 1237
Nakai, Yuzo, Mgr.-Plng.--The Chugoku Electric Power Co., Inc., Hiroshima, Japan; *Int'l,* pg. 291
Nakamachi, Yoshiyuki, Sr. Mng. Dir.--All Nippon Airways Co. Ltd., Tokyo, Japan; *Int'l,* pg. 57
Nakamae, Takashi, Gen. Mgr.-Corp. Plng.--Maruha Corporation, Tokyo, Japan; *Int'l,* pg. 845
Nakamura, Katsu, Sr. V.P.-Plng.--SEIKO Corporation of America, Mahwah, NJ; *Int'l,* pg. 1218
Napper, Bill, Mgr.-Corp. Devel.--Methode Electronics Inc., Chicago, IL; *U.S. Public,* pg. 1101
Nardi, Thomas A., Sr. V.P.-Non-Utility Oper. & Bus. Devel.--NICOR Inc., Naperville, IL; *U.S. Public,* pg. 1182
Nardulli, Gino, Mgr.-Sls. Promo., Communications & Devel.--Imperial Bondware Corp., Montvale, NJ; *U.S. Public,* pg. 903
Nash, Garrett J., V.P.-Mkt. Planning & Dealer Support--Mitsubishi Motor Sales of America, Inc., Cypress, CA; *Int'l,* pg. 875
Naso, Robert B., Sr. V.P.-Res. & Devel.--Nabi, Boca Raton, FL; *U.S. Public,* pg. 1148
Natale, Lisa, Mgr.-Strategic Plng.--The Kendall-Betham Division, Piscataway, NJ; *U.S. Public,* pg. 1647
Natathanapat, Chutima, Sr. V.P.-Policy & Plng.--The Industrial Finance Corporation of Thailand, Bangkok, Thailand; *Int'l,* pg. 677
Neale, Allen R., V.P.-Supply Plng.--Essex County Gas Company, Amesbury, MA; *U.S. Public,* pg. 593
Neaton, Daniel A., V.P.-Plng., Devel. & Strategic Plng.--Aquarion Company, Bridgeport, CT; *U.S. Public,* pg. 126
Nebenzahl, Paul, V.P.-Development--WTTW (Channel 11), Chicago, IL; *U.S. Private,* pg. 1145
Needham, Thomas R., Dir.-Plng. & Devel.--Allen & Hoshall, Inc., Memphis, TN; *U.S. Private,* pg. 36
Neely, Gerald L., V.P.-Bus. Devel.--Tracor Aerospace, Inc., Austin, TX; *U.S. Public,* pg. 1627
Negrete, Mauro, Mgr.-Systems Devel.--Sao Paulo Alpargatas S.A., Sao Paulo, Brazil; *Int'l,* pg. 1193
Neisel, Peter, Chief Exec. Officer--Schwab Corp., Lafayette, IN; *U.S. Private,* pg. 974
Nelson, Peter, V.P.-Corp. Plng.--Horsehead Industries, Inc., New York, NY; *U.S. Private,* pg. 540
Nelson, Ronald A., V.P.-Machine Res. & Devel.--The Lincoln Electric Company, Cleveland, OH; *U.S. Public,* pg. 996
Nelson, Ronald I., V.P.-Bus. Devel.--Integrated Marketing Services, Omaha, NE; *U.S. Public,* pg. 631
Nelson, Ted, Sr. V.P. & Plng. Dir.--Mullen Advertising, Inc., Wenham, MA; *U.S. Private,* pg. 766
Nemke, Jane, Dir.-Bus. Devel.--Wausau Metals, Nanik Division, Wausau, WI; *U.S. Public,* pg. 1500
Ness, Ben, Sr. V.P.-Strategic Plng. & Credit Services--AnnTaylor, Inc., New York, NY; *U.S. Public,* pg. 116
Nethercutt, J.B., Chm. Bd.--Merle Norman Cosmetics, Inc., Los Angeles, CA; *U.S. Private,* pg. 733
Neuman, Werner E., Pres.--Corcom, Inc., Libertyville, IL; *U.S. Public,* pg. 446
Neville, Robert J., Chm. Bd., Pres. & Chief Exec. Officer--The North American Manufacturing Co., Cleveland, OH; *U.S. Private,* pg. 803
Newman, Jane, Strategic Plng. Dir.--Merkley Newman Harty, New York, NY; *U.S. Public,* pg. 1224
Newman, William, Chm. Bd. & Chief Exec. Officer--New Plan Realty Trust, New York, NY; *U.S. Public,* pg. 1172
Newton, Dennis, Dir.-Strategic Res.--Nextel Communications, Mc Lean, VA; *U.S. Public,* pg. 1180
Newton, Jeffrey N., V.P.-Bus. Devel.--CBT Systems USA Ltd., Menlo Park, CA; *U.S. Public,* pg. 275
Nicholas, Philip A., AIA, V.P.--Giffels Associates, Inc., Southfield, MI; *U.S. Private,* pg. 452
Nicholson, David C., Chief Fin. Officer & Sr. V.P.--Rock-Tenn Company, Norcross, GA; *U.S. Public,* pg. 1396
Nickerson, Melody, Strategic Plng. Dir.--Hell-Brice Retail Advertising, Newport Beach, CA; *U.S. Private,* pg. 519
Nicol, Andrew, V.P.-Corp. Devel.--Delaware North Companies, Inc., Buffalo, NY; *U.S. Private,* pg. 321
Nicoletti, Thomas, V.P.-Investor Rels. & Bus. Devel.--Altera Corporation, San Jose, CA; *U.S. Public,* pg. 59
Niedel, James, Dr., Exec. Dir.-Res. & Devel.--Glaxo Wellcome plc, London, United Kingdom; *Int'l,* pg. 552
Niekamp, Cynthia A., V.P.-Strategy & Plng.--The Mead Corporation, Dayton, OH; *U.S. Public,* pg. 1074
Nielsen, Erik H.P., V.P.-Bus. Devel.--GN Nettest Holding, Brondby, Denmark; *Int'l,* pg. 536
Nilsson, David O., Mgr.-Plng. & Analysis--Pamida Holdings Corporation, Omaha, NE; *U.S. Public,* pg. 1255
Ninsananda, Bunyaraks, Sr. V.P. & Gen. Mgr.--Bangkok Bank Public Company Limited, Bangkok, Thailand; *Int'l,* pg. 146
Nishimura, Hiroshi, Mng. Dir.-New Business Admin., Res. Labs, New Matls. & Biomed.--Sumitomo Metal Industries, Ltd., Tokyo, Japan; *Int'l,* pg. 1315
Nishizawa, Tetsuro, V.P.-Bus. Plng. & Fin.--Subaru of America, Inc., Cherry Hill, NJ; *Int'l,* pg. 523
Nissen, Robert, Sr. Dir.-Bus. Devel.--Schering-Plough Healthcare Products Inc., Liberty Corner, NJ; *U.S. Public,* pg. 1438
Niwore, Roberta, Mgr.-Sls. Planning--Bayer Corporation/ Pharmaceutical Division, West Haven, CT; *Int'l,* pg. 173
Noar, Stephen, Dir.-Subsidiaries & Dev.--PPP hc, Tunbridge Wells, United Kingdom; *Int'l,* pg. 1020
Noble, Chris M., V.P.-Plng. & Control--ARCO Products Co., Los Angeles, CA; *U.S. Public,* pg. 144
Nobles, Hinton F., Jr., Exec. V.P.--Barnett Banks, Inc., Jacksonville, FL; *U.S. Public,* pg. 1162
Nolan, Christopher W., Dir.-Investor Rels.--International Specialty Products, Inc., Wayne, NJ; *U.S. Public,* pg. 858
Nomiyama, Akihiko, Gen. Mgr.-Tokyo Branch--Japan Energy Corporation, Tokyo, Japan; *Int'l,* pg. 702
Noon, Chris J., Mgr.-Plng.--Rod & Bar Products Division, Port Waratah, Australia; *Int'l,* pg. 227
Norris, David G., Exec. V.P.-Fin. & Bus. Devel.--Fishery Products International Ltd., Saint Johns, Canada; *Int'l,* pg. 492
Norris, Robin G., Exec. V.P.-Strategic Plng.--Zellers Inc., Toronto, Canada; *Int'l,* pg. 637
North, Bill, V.P.-Bus. Devel.--Mylex Corporation, Fremont, CA; *U.S. Public,* pg. 1143
North, Gita, Dir.-Mdse. Plng.--Dixons Group plc, Hemel Hempstead, United Kingdom,; *Int'l,* pg. 413
Norton, Mike, Dir.-Investor Rels., Strategic Plng. & Budget--UCAR International Inc., Danbury, CT; *U.S. Public,* pg. 1662
Norton, Robert R., Chm. Bd., Pres. & Chief Exec. Officer--BeefAmerica Operating Co., Inc., Omaha, NE; *U.S. Private,* pg. 130
Norton, William W., V.P.-Res. & Devel.--Culligan International Company, Northbrook, IL; *U.S. Public,* pg. 467
Novaes S. Bastos, Carlos Alberto, Dir.-Organizational Devel.--Petrobras - Petroleo Brasileiro S.A., Rio de Janeiro, Brazil; *Int'l,* pg. 1041
Novak, Helena, V.P.-Plng.--General Tours Inc., Keene, NH; *U.S. Private,* pg. 445
Novello, Joseph, Dir.-Planning & Analysis--ADT Security Services, Inc., Aurora, CO; *U.S. Public,* pg. 1649
Novelly, P. A., Chief Exec. Officer--Apex Oil Company, Inc., Saint Louis, MO; *U.S. Private,* pg. 77
Novogrebelski, Eduardo, Plng. Dir.--DPZ-Duailibi, Petit, Zaragoza, Propaganda S.A., Sao Paulo, Brazil; *Int'l,* pg. 352
Nye, Bruce, Sr. V.P.-Corp. Devel.--The Cerplex Group, Inc., Tustin, CA; *U.S. Public,* pg. 332
Nygaard, Brian, V.P.-Retail--Principal Mutual Life Insurance Co., Des Moines, IA; *U.S. Private,* pg. 886
Nygard, Bjarne, V.P.-Bus. Devel.--Kymi Paper Mills Ltd., Kuusankoski, Finland; *Int'l,* pg. 1428
O'Brien, Kevin P., V.P.-Corp. Devel.--United Asset Management Corporation, Boston, MA; *U.S. Public,* pg. 1672
O'Brien, Patrick, Chief Fin. Officer, V.P. & Dir.-Bus. Fin.--The Associated Press, New York, NY; *U.S. Private,* pg. 92
O'Brien, Patrick, V.P., Treas. & Dir.-Strategic Planning--Wide World Photos, Inc., New York, NY; *U.S. Private,* pg. 92
O'Brien, S.R., Sec. & Dir.-Plng. & Devel.--Redland PLC, Reigate, United Kingdom; *Int'l,* pg. 1090
O'Connor, J.F., Chief Exec.-Corp. Devel.--BBA Group plc, London, United Kingdom; *Int'l,* pg. 112
O'Gorman, Peter J., Exec. V.P.-Intl. Store & Prod. Devel.--The Great Atlantic & Pacific Tea Company, Inc., Montvale, NJ; *Int'l,* pg. 1375
O'Grady, Daniel, V.P.-Franchise Devel.--Pollo Tropical, Inc., Miami, FL; *U.S. Public,* pg. 1315
O'Hagan, Ken, Dir.-Corp. Devel.--Emco Limited, London, Canada; *Int'l,* pg. 452
O'Halloran, Brad S., Dir.-Corp. Devel.--The Sports Section Inc., Chicago, IL; *Int'l,* pg. 103
O'Hara, Kevin M., V.P.-Corp. Plng.--Piedmont Natural Gas Co., Inc., Charlotte, NC; *U.S. Public,* pg. 1295
O'Leary, John, Mgr.-Intl.--Forasol S.A., Velizy-Villacoublay, France; *Int'l,* pg. 496
O'Leary, Patrick, V.P.-Application Devel. Tools/4GL Prods.--Cognos Inc., Ottawa, Canada; *Int'l,* pg. 305
O'Reilly, Cormac, Dir.-Devel.--Costain Engineering & Construction Limited, London, United Kingdom; *Int'l,* pg. 336
O'Reilly, Jim, V.P.-Prod. Devel.--Proxima Corporation, San Diego, CA; *U.S. Public,* pg. 1339
O'Rourke, Eileen, Mgr.-Devel.--Bel-Art Products, Pequannock, NJ; *U.S. Private,* pg. 130
O'Toole, James E., V.P.-Prod. Devel.--Micron Communications, Inc., Boise, ID; *U.S. Public,* pg. 1105
Oatman, David C., V.P.-Investor Rels. & Corp. Devel.--Pool Energy Services Co., Houston, TX; *U.S. Public,* pg. 1316
Oberauer, Heinrich, Mng. Dir.-Store Devel. & Construction--Julius Meinl AG, Vienna, Austria; *Int'l,* pg. 856
Oberle, Edwin F., V.P.-Real Estate & Store Devel.--Food Lion, Inc., Salisbury, NC; *Int'l,* pg. 463
Obst, J.C., Treas.--Schenectady International, Inc., Schenectady, NY; *U.S. Private,* pg. 969
Ocampo, Oscar L., V.P.-Business Development--EEI Corporation, Manila, Philippines; *Int'l,* pg. 425
Ochsner, P.D., V.P.-Plng. & Strategic Devel.--Guarantee Life Insurance Co., Omaha, NE; *U.S. Public,* pg. 768
Oddi, Vincnet J., V.P.-Devel.--Morgan's Foods, Inc., Beachwood, OH; *U.S. Public,* pg. 1133
Odquist, Olle, Dir.-Grp. Projects & Strategies--Stena Line AB, Goteborg, Sweden; *Int'l,* pg. 1300
Oeler, Richard H., V.P.-Energy & Matls.--Air Products and Chemicals, Inc., Allentown, PA; *U.S. Public,* pg. 30
Oerehagen, Perge, Reg. Mgr.-Mktg. Europe--Luxo A/S, Oslo, Norway; *Int'l,* pg. 821
Offereins, Otto, V.P.-Devel. & Support--Symix Systems, Inc., Columbus, OH; *U.S. Public,* pg. 1546
Ofner, C.R., Sr. V.P.-Bus. Devel.--Reading & Bates Corporation, Houston, TX; *U.S. Public,* pg. 1354
Ogawa, Shuji, Mng. Dir.-Planning & New Business Dev.--Nippon Shinpan Co., Ltd., Tokyo, Japan; *Int'l,* pg. 939
Ogilvie, George, Dir.-Facilities--American Mathematical Society, Inc., Providence, RI; *U.S. Private,* pg. 59
Oh, S.B., Gen. Mgr.-Corp. Plng.--Sunkyong America, Inc., New York, NY; *Int'l,* pg. 1320
Ohi, Masami, V.P.-Corp. Plng.--Henningsen Foods, Inc., White Plains, NY; *Int'l,* pg. 1074
Ohinata, Kaz, Gen. Mgr.-Corp. Plng.--Sanden International (U.S.A.), Inc., Wylie, TX; *Int'l,* pg. 1184
Ohkawa, Yoshihiko, Mng. Dir.-Plng.--Japan Tobacco Inc., Tokyo, Japan; *Int'l,* pg. 703
Ohnuki, Yoshiaki, Exec. Mng. Dir. & Gen. Mgr.-Corp. Plng.--Mitsui & Co., Ltd., Tokyo, Japan; *Int'l,* pg. 877
Oiwa, Kazuhiko, Grp. Head-Plng. & Controller--The Long-Term Credit Bank of Japan, Limited, Tokyo, Japan; *Int'l,* pg. 815
Olavarria, Armando, Dir.-Strategic Plng.--El Teniente Division, Rancagua, Chile; *Int'l,* pg. 302
Oleszczuk, Andrew J., V.P.-Devel.--Tribune Company, Chicago, IL; *U.S. Public,* pg. 1635
Olivera, A.J., V.P.-Power Delivery--Florida Power & Light Company, North Palm Beach, FL; *U.S. Public,* pg. 608
Olsen, Alan H., Mgr.-Devel.--BHP Manganese, Melbourne, Australia; *Int'l,* pg. 224
Olson, Jody B., V.P.-Corp. Devel.--TJ International, Inc., Boise, ID; *U.S. Public,* pg. 1556
Olson, Rodney E., Chief Fin. Officer & Sr. V.P.-Fin. & Corp. Devel.--Sabreliner Corporation, Saint Louis, MO; *U.S. Private,* pg. 959
Olsrud, Sherman, Pres.--Sherms Thunderbird Market, Medford, OR; *U.S. Private,* pg. 993
Onody, Stephen, V.P.-New Bus. Devel.--Vital Signs, Inc., Totowa, NJ; *U.S. Public,* pg. 1723
Ophey, Lothar, Dr. Ing., Exec. V.P.-Prod.--Traub AG, Reichenbach, Germany; *Int'l,* pg. 1419
Oram, John, Pres.--ICC Industries, Inc., New York, NY; *U.S. Private,* pg. 553
Orban, David, Dir.-Bus. Devel.--Adams Rite Manufacturing Co., City of Industry, CA; *U.S. Private,* pg. 17
Oren, John R., Chm. Bd. & Chief Exec. Officer--Corporate Express Delivery Systems Southwest, Inc., Houston, TX; *U.S. Public,* pg. 449
Oria y Barros, Jorge, Exec. V.P.-Corp. Devel. & Fin. Plng.--Grupo Casa Autrey, Mexico, Mexico; *Int'l,* pg. 573
Orito, Hisanao, Sr. Mng. Dir.-Res. & Devel.--Makita Corporation, Anjo, Japan; *Int'l,* pg. 831
Orleans, Jeffery P., Chm. & Chief Exec. Officer--FPA Corporation, Bensalem, PA; *U.S. Public,* pg. 608
Orr, Graham, Exec. V.P.-Corp. Develop.--Magna International Inc., Markham, Canada; *Int'l,* pg. 829
Osborne, John M., Exec. V.P.-Franchise Sls. & Devel.--HFS, Incorporated, Parsippany, NJ; *U.S. Public,* pg. 321
Oster, Wolfgang, M.D., Sr. V.P.-Worldwide Clinical Res.--U.S. Bioscience, Inc., Conshohocken, PA; *U.S. Public,* pg. 1681
Osterman, John C., Pres., Chief Oper. Officer & Treas.--Chicago Rivet & Machine Company, Naperville, IL; *U.S. Public,* pg. 348
Ostrow, Gene J., V.P.-Corp. Devel.--OHM Corporation, Findlay, OH; *U.S. Public,* pg. 1207
Ott, James H., Chm. Bd.--Novar Electronics, Barberton, OH; *U.S. Private,* pg. 808
Overcast, H. Edwin, V.P.-Strategic Plng. & Rates--AGL Resources, Atlanta, GA; *U.S. Public,* pg. 6
Overturf, Thomas A., V.P.-Devel.--Boeing Realty Corporation, Long Beach, CA; *U.S. Public,* pg. 241
Owe-Larsson, Jan, Dir.-Property Devel. Opers.--L E Lundbergforetagen AB, Stockholm, Sweden; *Int'l,* pg. 820
Owen, David P., V.P.-Strategy & Tech.--Network Equipment Technologies, Inc., Redwood City, CA; *U.S. Public,* pg. 1168
Owen, Edward, V.P.-Plng. & Devel.--360 Degrees Communications Company, Chicago, IL; *U.S. Public,* pg. 1607
Oza, J., V.P.-Corp. Plng.--Public Service Electric & Gas Co., Newark, NJ; *U.S. Public,* pg. 1340
Ozmun, Robert, Chief Fin. Officer & Controller--Grocers Supply Co. Inc., Houston, TX; *U.S. Private,* pg. 483
Pace, Louis M., Mgr.-Fin. Analysis & Plng.--Sovereign Specialty Chemical, Inc., Chicago, IL; *U.S. Private,* pg. 1019
Paddon, Patrick E., Chm. Bd., Pres. & Chief Exec. Officer--Amplicon, Inc., Santa Ana, CA; *U.S. Public,* pg. 104
Pagan, Angie, Dir.-Prod. Devel.--Puerto Rico Tourism Company, San Juan, PR; *U.S. Private,* pg. 894
Page, Henry C., Jr., V.P.-H.R. & External Affairs--Ethyl Corporation, Richmond, VA; *U.S. Public,* pg. 595
Page, Peter, Dr., Dir.-Software Devel.--Siemens-Nixdorf Informationssysteme AG, Paderborn, Germany; *Int'l,* pg. 1245
Palazzolo, Barbara, V.P.-Creative & Strategic Bus. Devel.--DMB&B Public Relations, Troy, MI; *U.S. Private,* pg. 303
Pall, Brian, Sr. V.P.-Devel.--The Great Atlantic & Pacific Tea Company, Inc., Montvale, NJ; *Int'l,* pg. 1375
Palmer, C. Robert, Chm. Bd., Pres. & Chief Exec. Officer--Rowan Companies, Inc., Houston, TX; *U.S. Public,* pg. 1409
Palmer, R.J., V.P.-Mktg. & Strategic Plng.--Dresser-Rand Co. (Wellsville), Wellsville, NY; *U.S. Public,* pg. 529
Pamplin, Robert B., Jr., Dr., Pres., Chief Oper. Officer & Sec.--R.B. Pamplin Corp., Portland, OR; *U.S. Private,* pg. 835
Pantazelos, Peter G., Exec. V.P.-Devel.--Thermo Electron Corporation, Waltham, MA; *U.S. Public,* pg. 1591
Pape, Eldon C., Chief Fin. & Plng. Officer & Exec. V.P.--Omaha Public Power District, Omaha, NE; *U.S. Private,* pg. 815

Papesh, Patricia A., Sr. V.P.-Prod. Devel.--American Greetings U.S. Greeting Card Division, Cleveland, OH; *U.S. Public*, pg. 78
Parete, Anthony, V.P.-Franchise Devel.--Swensen's Ice Cream Co., Ronkonkoma, NY; *U.S. Public*, pg. 883
Parikh, Anand, V.P.-Mkt. Devel. & Bus. Plng.--Telco Systems, Inc., Norwood, MA; *U.S. Public*, pg. 1568
Park, Drew E., V.P.-Intl. & Corp. Devel.--International Technology Corporation, Monroeville, PA; *U.S. Public*, pg. 907
Park, R. F., Head-Grp. Strategy--National Westminster Bank PLC, London, United Kingdom; *Int'l*, pg. 910
Parker, A. Joseph, Sr. V.P.-Retail Bus. Line Mngmt.--National City Corporation, Cleveland, OH; *U.S. Public*, pg. 1154
Parker, Barry J.C., Pres. & Chief Exec. Officer--Luby's Cafeterias, Inc., San Antonio, TX; *U.S. Public*, pg. 1017
Parker, D. Michael, Chief Fin. Officer, V.P.-Fin., Sec. & Treas.--Kewaunee Scientific Corporation, Statesville, NC; *U.S. Public*, pg 953
Parker, David H., Chm. Bd., Pres. & Chief Exec. Officer--Pelican Products, Torrance, CA; *U.S. Private*, pg. 848
Parker, Richard, Pres. & Chief Exec. Officer--Artco-Bell Corporation, Temple, TX; *U.S. Private*, pg. 86
Parker, Tom, V.P.-Mktg. & Plng.--Sierra Pacific Resources, Reno, NV; *U.S. Public*, pg. 1470
Parker, William M., Exec. V.P.-Bus. Devel.--CACI International Inc, Arlington, VA; *U.S. Public*, pg. 272
Parrish, Danny B., V.P.-Fin., Asst. Treas. & Asst. Sec.--James N. Gray Construction Co., Inc., Lexington, KY; *U.S. Private*, pg. 472
Parrish, James O., V.P.-Fin. & Treas.--Twin Disc, Incorporated, Racine, WI; *U.S. Public*, pg. 1646
Parrish, Ronald L., V.P.-Corp. Dev.--Tandy Corporation, Fort Worth, TX; *U.S. Public*, pg. 1560
Parry, David, Mgr.-Plng. & Devel.--Nationwide Building Society, Swindon, United Kingdom; *Int'l*, pg. 912
Parry, Richard M., V.P.-Mktg.-Hawaii--BHP Hawaii, Inc., Honolulu, HI; *Int'l*, pg. 225
Parry, Richard M., V.P.-Opers. Planning Supply--Gasco, Inc., Honolulu, HI; *Int'l*, pg. 225
Pasqual, Dorrie, Asst. Dir.-Bus. Plng.--Cara Operations Limited, Toronto, Canada; *Int'l*, pg. 266
Pasquarello, Theodore, Pres. & Chief Exec. Officer--Chiswick Trading Inc., Sudbury, MA; *U.S. Private*, pg. 237
Pasquasy, F., Dir.-Sys. Plng.--Cockerill Sambre, Brussels, Belgium; *Int'l*, pg. 301
Pasquerilla, Nicholas J., Sr. V.P.-Facilities Plng. Dept.--Crown American Realty Trust, Johnstown, PA; *U.S. Public*, pg. 461
Patalita, David, V.P.-Devel.--Saul Centers Inc., Chevy Chase, MD; *U.S. Public*, pg. 1435
Pathanaporn, Pratin, Deputy Governor-Policy & Plng.--Petroleum Authority of Thailand, Bangkok, Thailand; *Int'l*, *pg. 1046*
Patlove, Abram E., Sr. V.P.-Plng. & Devel./Intl.--Comcast Corporation, Philadelphia, PA; *U.S. Public*, pg. 406
Paton, John E., V.P.-Real Estate Opers. & Devel.--Manulife Financial (The Manufacturers Life Insurance Company), Toronto, Canada; *Int'l*, pg. 840
Patton, John S., Dir.-Strategic Plng.--Ethyl Corporation, Richmond, VA; *U.S. Public*, pg. 595
Paul, Douglas A., V.P.-Strategic Plng.--American International Group, Inc., New York, NY; *U.S. Public*, pg. 83
Paull, Irene, Dir.-Sys. Devel--Dixons Group plc, Hemel Hempstead, United Kingdom,; *Int'l*, pg. 413
Pavlenko, Linda, V.P. & Grp. Dir.-Media Res.--Ralston Purina Company, Saint Louis, MO; *U.S. Public*, pg. 1359
Payne, Ronald D., V.P.-Bus. Devel.--ALLTEL Corporation, Little Rock, AR; *U.S. Public*, pg. 55
Pearlman, Bruce M., V.P.-Fin. Plng. & Analysis--SLM Holding Corp., Washington, DC; *U.S. Public*, pg. 1419
Peck, Douglas E., Pres. & Gen. Counsel--Renosol Corp., Saline, MI; *U.S. Private*, pg. 922
Peck, Roger, Sr. V.P.-Devel.--Levy Real Estate Partners, Chicago, IL; *U.S. Private*, pg. 664
Peck, Steve, Dir.-Plng. & Analysis--Ellwood City Forge, Ellwood City, PA; *U.S. Private*, pg. 373
Peckham, Rod J., Exec. V.P.-Fin. & Admin. & Strategic Plng.--Forstmann & Company, Inc., New York, NY; *U.S. Public*, pg. 670
Pecko, Carl A., V.P.-Plng.--Ashland, Inc., Russell, KY; *U.S. Public*, pg. 138
Pecoraro, Gerald, V.P.-Sls., Household Prods. Div.--Block Drug Company, Inc., Jersey City, NJ; *U.S. Public*, pg. 236
Pedersen, Steinar, V.P.-Res. & Devel.--Fine Chemicals, Oslo, Norway; *U.S. Public*, pg. 58
Pekkanen, Kauko T., V.P.-Bus. Devel. & Information Systems--Metsa-Serla Corporation, Espoo, Finland; *Int'l*, pg. 863
Pelanda, Raymond, Mgr.-Bus.--Arrow Oilfield Service Company, Canton, OH; *U.S. Private*, pg. 1078
Pena, Victor, V.P.-Bus. Devel.--Sierra Pacific Resources, Reno, NV; *U.S. Public*, pg. 1470
Peng, Chia Choon, Gen. Mgr.-Plng. & Audit--Keppel Corporation Limited, Singapore, Singapore; *Int'l*, pg. 731
Peninon, Dominique, Exec. V.P.-Dev.--Financiere Saint Dominique, Paris, France; *Int'l*, pg. 344
Penner, Larry, V.P.-Corp. Admin.--Leblanc Communications, Inc., Richardson, TX; *U.S. Private*, pg. 656
Peponis, Klein, V.P.-Strategic Plng. & Bus. Devel.--Toys "R" Us, Inc., Paramus, NJ; *U.S. Public*, pg. 1626
Pereira, Wagner Celeste, Mgr.-Plng. & Devel.--Cervejarias Kaiser Brasil Ltda., Campinas, Brazil; *Int'l*, pg. 279
Perkins, J.B., V.P.-Corp. Plng. & Devel.--Houston Industries Incorporated, Houston, TX; *U.S. Public*, pg. 842
Perkins, Paul K., V.P.-Mktg. & Corp. Plng.--Weyerhaeuser Canada Ltd., Vancouver, Canada; *U.S. Public*, pg. 1764
Perrin, Charles H., Gen. Mgr.-Bus. Devel.--Apache Corporation, Houston, TX; *U.S. Public*, pg. 119
Perry, J., Mgr.-Bus. Devel.--Meyer International PLC, London, United Kingdom; *Int'l*, pg. 864
Perry, Victor A., III, V.P.-Corp. Devel.--The Times Mirror Company, Los Angeles, CA; *U.S. Public*, pg. 1615
Perschau, Rosemary, Staff V.P.-Corp. Plng.--Meredith Corporation, Des Moines, IA; *U.S. Public*, pg. 1094
Peru, Ramiro G., Sr. V.P.-Org. Devel. & Info. Tech.--Phelps Dodge Corporation, Phoenix, AZ; *U.S. Public*, pg. 1286
Peters, Donald H., V.P.-Plng.--EG & G, Inc., Wellesley, MA; *U.S. Public*, pg. 542
Peters, Robert L., Chm. Bd., Pres. & Chief Exec. Officer--Holmquist Grain & Lumber Co., Oakland, NE; *U.S. Private*, pg. 535
Peterson, Shirley V., V.P.-Organizational Devel.--Northrop Grumman Corporation, Los Angeles, CA; *U.S. Public*, pg. 1197
Petit, Francois, Dir.-Bus. Devel.--Alcatel N.V., Amsterdam, Netherlands; *Int'l*, pg. 55
Petrello, Anthony, Plng. & Devel.--Nabors Industries, Inc., Houston, TX; *U.S. Public*, pg. 1148
Petrillo, Alfred B., Jr., Sr. V.P.-Store Plng.--Ames Department Stores, Inc., Rocky Hill, CT; *U.S. Public*, pg. 99
Petrino, Richard A., V.P.-H.R. & Plng. & Devel.--Comcast Corporation, Philadelphia, PA; *U.S. Public*, pg. 406
Pettersson, Mats, Sr. V.P.-Bus. Devel.--Pharmacia & Upjohn, Inc., Windsor, United Kingdom; *Int'l*, pg. 1047
Petty, Carole, Mgr.-Corporate Planning--T.D. Williamson, Inc., Tulsa, OK; *U.S. Private*, pg. 1179
Pfistner, Stephen, V.P.-H.R. & Org. Devel.--FiberMark Inc., Brattleboro, VT; *U.S. Public*, pg. 620
Phelan, Dan, V.P.-Personnel--SmithKline Beecham Corporation, Philadelphia, PA; *Int'l*, pg. 1264
Phelps, Greg, Sr. V.P.--Genzyme Corporation, Cambridge, MA; *U.S. Public*, pg. 733
Phelps, Thomas E., V.P.-Investments & Strategic Planning--Noranda Inc., Toronto, Canada; *Int'l*, pg. 433
Phillip, Chuck, V.P.-New Bus.--RELA, Inc., Boulder, CO; *U.S. Public*, pg. 401
Phillips-Parker, Rebecca, V.P.-Communications & Bus. Devel.--Indian Head Industries Inc., Charlotte, NC; *U.S. Private*, pg. 559
Phillips, John, V.P.-Business Devel.--Gould Electronics Inc., Shawmut Circuit Protection Division, Newburyport, MA; *U.S. Public*, pg. 1592
Phillips, Michelle, Planner Supvr. & Media Buyer--Don Coleman Advertising, Inc., Southfield, MI; *U.S. Private*, pg. 251
Phillips, Richard B., Sr. V.P.-Tech.--International Paper Company, Purchase, NY; *U.S. Public*, pg. 901
Phillips, Thomas L., Chm. Bd., Pres. & Chief Exec. Officer--Phillips Publishing International, Inc., Potomac, MD; *U.S. Private*, pg. 862
Piccinini, Robert M., Chm. Bd., Chief Exec. Officer & Pres.--Save Mart Supermarkets, Modesto, CA; *U.S. Private*, pg. 968
Picknelly, Peter A., Jr., Pres. & Chief Exec. Officer--Peter Pan Bus Lines, Inc., Springfield, MA; *U.S. Private*, pg. 856
Piekos, Frank, V.P.-Corp. Devel.--Philip Industrial Services Group, Houston, TX; *Int'l*, pg. 1050
Pierce, James L., Chm. Bd. & Chief Exec. Officer--Arinc Inc. (Consolidated), Annapolis, MD; *U.S. Private*, pg. 81
Pierce, Robert C., V.P.-Res. & Devel./Personal Care--Colgate-Palmolive Company, New York, NY; *U.S. Public*, *pg. 397*
Pierquet, Bill, V.P.-Devel.--Del Taco, Inc., Laguna Hills, CA; *U.S. Private*, pg. 321
Pieschel, Paul B., V.P.-Franchise Devel.--Moto Photo, Inc., Dayton, OH; *U.S. Public*, pg. 1136
Piette, Daniel, V.P.-Opers. & Strategic Plng.--LVMH Moet Hennessy Louis Vuitton, Paris, France; *Int'l*, pg. 779
Pignatelli, James N., Chief Oper. Officer & Sr. V.P.-Bus. Devel.--Tucson Electric Power Company, Tucson, AZ; *U.S. Public*, pg. 1670
Pike, Raymond D., Exec. V.P.-Intl. Corp. Devel.--International Game Technology, Reno, NV; *U.S. Public*, pg. 900
Pilling, Bill, V.P.-Prod. Devel.--Pilling Weck, Fort Washington, PA; *U.S. Public*, pg. 1569
Pillsbury, Warren L., V.P.-Bus. Devel.--Network Systems Corporation, Minneapolis, MN; *U.S. Public*, pg. 1522
Pilz, Allen, V.P.-Adv.--The Lathrop Company, Toledo, OH; *U.S. Public*, pg. 1645
Pineda, Antonio J., Asst. V.P.-Strategic Planning--Atlas Consolidated Mining & Development Corporation, Manila, Philippines; *Int'l*, pg. 95
Pingeon, Jean, Dir.-Strategy & Devel.--Promodes SA, Mondeville, France; *Int'l*, pg. 1071
Pinsley, Sol, Chm. Bd., Pres., Chief Exec. & Chief Oper. Officer--Espey Mfg. & Electronics Corp., Saratoga Springs, NY; *U.S. Public*, pg. 592
Pipes, Raymond D., V.P.-Corp. Devel.--American Standard Inc., Piscataway, NJ; *U.S. Public*, pg. 91
Pistorese, Todd A., V.P.-Bus. Devel.--Tellus, Inc., Bellevue, WA; *U.S. Public*, pg. 1342
Pita, George L., V.P.-Fin. & Intl. Devel.--Sunglass Hut International, Coral Gables, FL; *U.S. Public*, pg. 1535
Pitts, Preston, Pres. & Chief Oper. Officer--Legacy Marketing Group, Petaluma, CA; *U.S. Private*, pg. 658
Pizzani, Paul, V.P.-Fin. & Bus. Plng.--COMSAT International Ventures, Bethesda, MD; *U.S. Public*, pg. 425
Platek, Stanley W., V.P.-Res. & Devel.--Commonwealth Industries, Inc., Louisville, KY; *U.S. Public*, pg. 415
Platt, T. Gregory, V.P.-Systems Devel.--Berkley Information Services, Luverne, MN; *U.S. Public*, pg. 216
Plaza, Juan F., Dir.-Plng. & Systems--Grupo Synkro, S.A. de C.V., Mexico, Mexico; *Int'l*, pg. 576
Pliska, Peter M., Sr. Business Devel. Officer--Western Marketing-Oakland Region, Oakland, CA; *U.S. Public*, pg. 650
Plomgren, Ronald A., Chief Fin. Officer & Sr. V.P.--Longs Drug Stores Corporation, Walnut Creek, CA; *U.S. Public*, *pg. 1013*
Ploss, Gus, V.P.-Sls., Mktg. & Bus. Devel.--Walbro Corporation, Cass City, MI; *U.S. Public*, pg. 1733
Pocapalia, Dan, Chm. Bd., Pres. & Chief Exec. Officer--Kit Manufacturing Company, Long Beach, CA; *U.S. Public*, pg. 962
Poe, John D., Pres. & Chief Exec. Officer--Semtech Corporation, Newbury Park, CA; *U.S. Public*, pg. 1456
Pollack, Jordan, Dir.-New Bus. Devel.--Knoll Pharmaceutical Company, Whippany, NJ; *Int'l*, pg. 105
Polson, D.L., V.P.-Fin.--Anschutz Corporation, Denver, CO; *U.S. Private*, pg. 75
Poltrack, David, Exec. V.P.-Plng. & Res.--CBS Television Network, New York, NY; *U.S. Public*, pg. 274
Pompeo, A. Mario, V.P.-Fin.--Banfi Vintners, Old Brookville, NY; *U.S. Private*, pg. 113
Poncins, Eric de, V.P.-Devel.--Groupe Pernod Ricard, Paris, France; *Int'l*, pg. 566
Popkin, Greg, V.P.-Corp. Admin. Plng.--Helmsley-Spear Inc., New York, NY; *U.S. Private*, pg. 521
Porritt, G., Mgr.-Corp. Devel.--Senior Engineering Group, plc., Rickmansworth, United Kingdom; *Int'l*, pg. 1220
Porta, Xavier Seguro, Head-Strategical Plng.--Caixa d'Estalvis de Catalunya, Barcelona, Spain; *Int'l*, pg. 249
Porter, Kevin P., V.P.-Strategic Plng.--Best Buy Co., Inc., Eden Prairie, MN; *U.S. Public*, pg. 223
Porth, Dieter, Dir.-Heavy Commercial Vehicle Devel.--Mercedes-Benz AG, Stuttgart, Germany; *Int'l*, pg. 368
Portman, Robert G., V.P.-Retail Devel.--American Greetings U.S. Greeting Card Division, Cleveland, OH; *U.S. Public*, pg. 78
Posinski, Frank J., Pres. & Chief Oper. Officer--Cincinnati Gear Company, Cincinnati, OH; *U.S. Private*, pg. 240
Poste, George, Chm. Bd.-Res. & Devel.--SmithKline Beecham Corporation, Philadelphia, PA; *Int'l*, pg. 1264
Postle, Richard C., Pres.-St. Louis Bread Co.--Au Bon Pain Co., Inc., Boston, MA; *U.S. Public*, pg. 146
Potempa, Louis E., V.P.-Devel.--Enron Corp., Houston, TX; *U.S. Public*, pg. 584
Potter, C. Nicholas, V.P.-Strategic Plng.--J.P. Morgan Co. Incorporated, New York, NY; *U.S. Public*, pg. 1129
Potts, Sherry, Dir., V.P.-Bus. Coord. & Acquisition--Planning Systems Inc., Mc Lean, VA; *U.S. Private*, pg. 869
Powell, H. Verne, Exec. V.P.-Corp. Devel. & External Affairs--Shaw's Supermarkets, Inc., East Bridgewater, MA; *Int'l*, pg. 1170
Powell, Steve, Dir.-New Prod. Devel.--Richard Young Office Products, Inc., Deerfield Beach, FL; *U.S. Public*, pg. 450
Powell, Teresa M., Dir.-Bus. Devel.--AC Martin Partners, Los Angeles, CA; *U.S. Private*, pg. 708
Powers, Doug, Dir.-Plng.--Media Incorporated, New York, NY; *U.S. Private*, pg. 726
Pradas, Francisco, Mgr.-Exploration & Prod.--Petroleos de Venezuela S.A., Caracas, Venezuela; *Int'l*, pg. 1045
Prater, R.E., V.P.-Strategic Plng.--American Electric Power Service Corp., Columbus, OH; *U.S. Public*, pg. 72
Prater, Ronald, Sec.--Owensboro Grain Co., Inc., Owensboro, KY; *U.S. Private*, pg. 824
Prato, Maurizio, Mgr.-Planning & Control--IRI Istituto Ricostruzione Industriale, Rome, Italy; *Int'l*, pg. 652
Pratt, Robert N., Chm. Bd., Pres. & Chief Oper. & Chief Exec. Officer--Alta Gold Co., Henderson, NV; *U.S. Public*, pg. 58
Preiss, David, V.P.-Bus. Devel. & Plng.--COMSAT World Systems, Bethesda, MD; *U.S. Public*, pg. 424
Prentice, Latona, Dir.-Budget & Rates--Citizens Gas & Coke Utility, Indianapolis, IN; *U.S. Private*, pg. 241
Prescott, William, V.P.-Admin.--Packerland Packing Co., Green Bay, WI; *U.S. Private*, pg. 833
Prest, Carole Y., V.P.-Strategic Plng.--Manor Care, Inc., Gaithersburg, MD; *U.S. Public*, pg. 1041
Preston, Jean F., Mgr.-Systems Devel.--Noland Company, Newport News, VA; *U.S. Public*, pg. 1187
Pretorius, Quintin, Gen. Mgr.-Broker Div. & Devel.--Life Division, Rondebosch, South Africa; *Int'l*, pg. 77
Price, Ben, V.P.-Prod. Devel.--Kaepa Inc., Greenville, SC; *U.S. Private*, pg. 604
Prieto, Robert, Exec. V.P. & Dir.-Corp. Devel.--Parsons Brinckerhoff Inc., New York, NY; *U.S. Private*, pg. 841
Probst, David S., V.P.-Bus. Devel.--Indianapolis Water Company, Indianapolis, IN; *U.S. Public*, pg. 1185
Proctor, Alistair, Dir.-Network Services--Scottish Enterprise, Glasgow, United Kingdom; *Int'l*, pg. 1212
Proudfit, Donna, Dir.-Mktg.--Pickering Inc., Tacoma, WA; *U.S. Private*, pg. 864
Proulx, Robert, V.P.-Computer Services--Hydro-Quebec, Montreal, Canada; *Int'l*, pg. 640
Prow, Enoch J., Exec. V.P. & Sec.--NationsBank South, Atlanta, GA; *U.S. Public*, pg. 1163
Pruchinsky, Diane E., V.P.-Acctg. & Fin. Analyst Mgr.--FirstMerit Corporation, Akron, OH; *U.S. Public*, pg. 646
Pryor, Chuck, V.P.-Bus. Devel.--Trumbull Corporation/P.J. Dick, Inc., West Mifflin, PA; *U.S. Private*, pg. 1107
Pulido, Adreienne, V.P., Res. Dir. & Strategic Plng. Dir.--Bromley, Aguilar & Associates, San Antonio, TX; *U.S. Private*, pg. 692
Purcell, Robert C., Mgr.-Plng. & Devel.--GM Powertrain Group, Pontiac, MI; *U.S. Public*, pg. 719
Purnell, John H., V.P. & Grp. Exec.--Anheuser-Busch Companies, Inc., Saint Louis, MO; *U.S. Public*, pg. 113
Pursell, Linda, V.P.-Mktg. Devel.--The Courier-Journal Louisville Times Co., Louisville, KY; *U.S. Public*, pg. 700
Purves, Norman W.V., V.P.-Devel.--TrizecHahn Corporation, Toronto, Canada; *Int'l*, pg. 1424
Putnam, Spencer, Chief Oper. Officer & Sec.--The Vermont Teddy Bear Company, Inc., Shelburne, VT; *U.S. Public*, pg. 1716
Pyle, Roy, Dir.-Mktg. & Prod. Devel.--Industrial Distribution and OEM, North America, Dayton, OH; *U.S. Public*, pg. 1045
Quadros, Peter, Gen. Mgr.-Research/Corp. Plng. & Devl.--Coles Myer Ltd., Tooronga, Australia; *Int'l*, pg. 306
Quinn, Roger, Mgr.-Production Plng.--Newport Steel Corporation, Newport, KY; *U.S. Public*, pg. 1147

Quinton, Cathy, Plng. Dir.--Western International Media Corporation, Toronto, Canada; *U.S. Private*, pg. 1168
Quirke, S., Dir.-Material Plng.--ChemPump, Warrington, PA; *U.S. Public*, pg. 456
Race, Mark, Sr. V.P.-Store Plng.--OfficeMax, Shaker Heights, OH; *U.S. Public*, pg. 1212
Raduchel, William J., Chief Info. Officer & V.P.-Corp. Plng. & Devel.--Sun Microsystems, Inc., Palo Alto, CA; *U.S. Public*, pg. 1531
Rafael, Manuel M., V.P.-Network Plng. & Devel.--Philippine Long Distance Telephone Company, Manila, Philippines; *Int'l*, pg. 1051
Raffensberger, Ann, V.P.-Plng. & Controlling--Knoll Pharmaceutical Company, Whippany, NJ; *Int'l*, pg. 105
Raibagkar, D.G., Dir.-Project & Plng.--Northern Coalfields Limited, Sidhi, India; *Int'l*, pg. 299
Ramalhete, Manuel, Dr., Dir.-Plng. & Control--Petrogal, s.a., Lisbon, Portugal; *Int'l*, pg. 1044
Ramat, Charles, Chm. Bd., Pres., Chief Exec. Officer & Asst. Sec.--Aris Industries, Inc., New York, NY; *U.S. Public*, pg. 129
Rambaud, P., Sr. V.P.-Mktg. & Strategic Devel.--Danone Group, Paris, France; *Int'l*, pg. 379
Ramirez, Armando, Sr. V.P.-Strategic Plng. & Mergers & Acq.--National City Corporation, Cleveland, OH; *U.S. Public*, pg. 1154
Ranang, Olle, Dir.-Total Quality Devel.--AB SKF, Goteborg, Sweden; *Int'l*, pg. 1156
Randholm, Bengt, Head-Bus. Devel.--Eldon AB, Nassjo, Sweden; *Int'l*, pg. 436
Rangel, Antonio Luis Ferre, V.P.-Opers.--Puerto Rican Cement Co., Inc., Guaynabo, PR; *U.S. Public*, pg. 1341
Ranshaw, John R., V.P.-Bus. Devel., Dir.-Export & Intl. Mgr.--E & A Industries, Inc., Indianapolis, IN; *U.S. Private*, pg. 352
Rapp, Barry L., V.P.-Plng. & Devel.--Bachman Company, Reading, PA; *U.S. Private*, pg. 109
Ratcliffe, Clyde H., III, Dir.-Diversification Plng.--Universal Leaf Tobacco Company, Inc., Richmond, VA; *U.S. Public*, pg. 1694
Rath, Ulli E.G., V.P.-Corp. Devel.--Rio Algom Limited, Toronto, Canada; *Int'l*, pg. 1118
Ratner, Brian J., Sr. V.P.-Devel.--Forest City Enterprises, Inc., Cleveland, OH; *U.S. Public*, pg. 667
Ray, Bradford T., Pres. & Chief Oper. Officer--Steel Technologies Inc., Louisville, KY; *U.S. Public*, pg. 1513
Ray, E. Wayne, Jr., Chief Fin. Officer, V.P. & Treas.--Riviana Foods Inc., Houston, TX; *U.S. Public*, pg. 1392
Ray, Terry D., V.P.-Bus. Devel.--Eastern Enterprises, Weston, MA; *U.S. Public*, pg. 548
Raymond, Gary, Pres.-Resort Devel. Grp.--Intrawest Corporation, Vancouver, Canada; *Int'l*, pg. 685
Raymond, John, V.P.-Corp. Devel.--Orkin Exterminating Co., Inc., Atlanta, GA; *U.S. Public*, pg. 1404
Razon, Jacob, Exec. V.P.--The Israel Electric Corporation Ltd., Haifa, Israel; *Int'l*, pg. 690
Read, Randolph C., Chief Fin. Officer-Fin. & Plng. & Sr. V.P.--Stone Container Corporation, Chicago, IL; *U.S. Public*, pg. 1520
Read, W.E., V.P.-Bus. Devel.--Walk, Haydel & Associates, Inc., New Orleans, LA; *Int'l*, pg. 624
Reagan, Thomas N., Pres.--Reagan Equipment Company, Inc., Gretna, LA; *U.S. Private*, pg. 913
Ream, Michael D., V.P.-Plng.--Up-Right, Inc., Selma, CA; *U.S. Private*, pg. 1128
Reasor, Mark, V.P.-Logistical Plng.--Signal Apparel Company, Inc., Chattanooga, TN; *U.S. Public*, pg. 1472
Reavley, Martin, Dir.-Fin. & Plng.--Bass PLC, London, United Kingdom; *Int'l*, pg. 169
Rebensdorf, John H., V.P.-Strategic Plng.--Union Pacific Railroad Company, Omaha, NE; *U.S. Public*, pg. 1668
Record, Chris, V.P.-Bus. Devel.--Carrington Laboratories, Inc., Irving, TX; *U.S. Public*, pg. 309
Redlinger, Richard, V.P.-Corp. Devel. & Treas.--Dravo Corporation, Pittsburgh, PA; *U.S. Public*, pg. 527
Redlinger, Richard, V.P.-Fin. & Planning--Dravo Lime Company, Pittsburgh, PA; *U.S. Public*, pg. 527
Redman, LaJuan, Exec. V.P.-Admin.--The Windham Company, Pensacola, FL; *U.S. Private*, pg. 1182
Redon, Benoit, Dir.-Strategy & Devel.--AGF Assurances, Paris, France; *Int'l*, pg. 14
Reed, Andrew E., V.P.-Corp. Devel.--Geraghty & Miller, Inc., Denver, CO; *Int'l*, pg. 607
Reed, Carol, V.P.-Prod. Devel.--Bradlees Inc., Braintree, MA; *U.S. Public*, pg. 249
Reed, W. Earl, III, Chief Fin. Officer & Exec. V.P.--Vencor, Inc., Louisville, KY; *U.S. Public*, pg. 1711
Rees, Michael, V.P.-Corp. Plng.--The Braas Group, Oberursell, Germany; *Int'l*, pg. 1091
Reeves, Dennis S., V.P.-Planning--Hawaiian Independent Refinery, Inc., Honolulu, HI; *Int'l*, pg. 225
Regent, Aaron W., Sr. V.P.-Corp. Devel.--EdperBrascan Corporation, Toronto, Canada; *Int'l*, pg. 433
Regnell, Thomas L., V.P.-Acq.--Washington Real Estate Investment Trust, Kensington, MD; *U.S. Public*, pg. 1743
Rego, Thomas A., Sr. V.P.-Store Devel. & Sec.--Riser Foods, Inc., Bedford, OH; *U.S. Private*, pg. 450
Reherman, Ronald G., Chm. Bd., Pres. & Chief Exec. Officer--SIGCORP, Inc., Evansville, IN; *U.S. Public*, pg. 1471
Reich, Richard M., V.P.-Prod. Plng. & Devel. & Tech. Support--Lifeline Systems, Inc., Cambridge, MA; *U.S. Public*, pg. 992
Reichenbach, Jean-Pierre, Mgr.-Bus. Devel.--Alcatel N.V., Amsterdam, Netherlands; *Int'l*, pg. 55
Reid, Ian, Mgr.-Grp. Plng.--Scottish Widows' Fund & Life Assurance Society, Edinburgh, United Kingdom; *Int'l*, pg. 1212
Reid, Odis, V.P.-Franchise Devel.--Mitsubishi Motor Sales of America, Inc., Cypress, CA; *Int'l*, pg. 875
Reidelbach, Heinrich, Dir.-Corp. Plng.--Mercedes-Benz AG, Stuttgart, Germany; *Int'l*, pg. 368
Rein, R. Joseph, V.P.-Corp. Plng.--Deposit Guaranty Corp., Jackson, MS; *U.S. Public*, pg. 500
Reinberg, Jeffrey, Sr. Exec. V.P.-Admin.--Maritz Inc., Fenton, MO; *U.S. Private*, pg. 703
Reineke, Klaus, Dir.-Risk Mngmt. & Risk Policy--IKB Deutsche Industriebank AG, Dusseldorf, Germany; *Int'l*, pg. 645
Reinfried, Rolf H., V.P.-Corp. Devel.--Lonza Inc., Fair Lawn, NJ; *Int'l*, pg. 67
Reinke, William F., V.P.-System Plng. & Oper.--Duke Energy Corporation, Charlotte, NC; *U.S. Public*, pg. 534
Reisenbach, Sanford E., Exec. V.P.-Mktg. & Plng.--Warner Bros. Studios, Inc., Burbank, CA; *U.S. Public*, pg. 1611
Reisner, Franz, Mng. Dir.-Store Devel. & Construction--Julius Meinl AG, Vienna, Austria; *Int'l*, pg. 856
Reiter, William M., M.D., Chm. Bd., Pres. & Chief Exec. Officer--Health Professionals, Inc., Fort Lauderdale, FL; *U.S. Public*, pg. 802
Reitman, Robert S., Chm. Bd., Pres. & Exec. Officer--The Tranzonic Companies, Pepper Pike, OH; *U.S. Public*, pg. 1632
Remes, Scott, Dir.-New Prod. Devel.--CAIRE, Inc., Burnsville, MN; *U.S. Private*, pg. 751
Renaud, Paul, V.P.-Devel./Bus. Intelligence Tools--Cognos Inc., Ottawa, Canada; *Int'l*, pg. 305
Renzulli, Patricia L., Dir.-Plng.--Sun Company, Inc., Philadelphia, PA; *U.S. Public*, pg. 1530
Reppert, Daniel A., Mgr.-Planning & Research--Royal Insurance, Charlotte, NC; *Int'l*, pg. 1130
Resinger, Scott, Sr. V.P.-Devel.--Leiner Health Products, Inc., Carson, CA; *U.S. Private*, pg. 659
Retcher, M.F., Chief Fin. Officer & Treas.--Art Iron, Inc., Toledo, OH; *U.S. Private*, pg. 86
Revhaug, Omund, Exec. V.P.-Corp. Devel.--Norske Skogindustrier A.S, Skogn, Norway; *Int'l*, pg. 965
Rexford, John, Sr. V.P.-Corp. Devel.--Affiliated Computer Services, Inc., Dallas, TX; *U.S. Public*, pg. 27
Reyelts, Paul C., V.P.-Fin.--The Valspar Corporation, Minneapolis, MN; *U.S. Public*, pg. 1707
Reynolds, Randall J., V.P.-Plng. & Bus. Devel.--BCE Mobile Communications Inc., Saint-Laurent, Canada; *Int'l*, pg. 115
Reynolds, Randall J., V.P.-Plng. & Devel.--Bell Mobility Paging Inc., Downsview, Canada; *Int'l*, pg. 115
Reynolds, Thomas G., V.P.-Plng. & Devel.--DIMON, Incorporated, Danville, VA; *U.S. Public*, pg. 509
Rheem, Richard, Dir.-Plng. & Business Devel.--Freedom Forge Corporation, Burnham, PA; *U.S. Private*, pg. 425
Rheinheimer, Ron, V.P.-Enterprise Acct. Plng.--Inacom Corp., Omaha, NE; *U.S. Public*, pg. 873
Rice, Andrew, Sr. V.P.-Corp. Devel.--Jordan Industries, Inc., Deerfield, IL; *U.S. Private*, pg. 598
Rice, Andrew W., V.P.-Corp. Planning--J2, Inc., Deerfield, IL; *U.S. Private*, pg. 598
Rice, David, Dir.-Architecture & Plng.--Zoological Society of San Diego, San Diego, CA; *U.S. Private*, pg. 1207
Rice, Dennis K., V.P.-Plng.--Northrop Grumman Corporation, Los Angeles, CA; *U.S. Public*, pg. 1197
Rich, Marvin P., Exec. V.P.-Strategic Plng., Fin. & Admin.--Kmart Corporation, Troy, MI; *U.S. Public*, pg. 963
Richard, Chuck, V.P.-Strategic Plng.--Reed Elsevier Business Information, Newton, MA; *Int'l*, pg. 1095
Richard, John P., V.P.-Bus. Devel.--Genome Therapeutics Corporation, Waltham, MA; *U.S. Public*, pg. 730
Richards, George G., V.P.-Devel. & Fin.--Ragazzis, Inc., Raleigh, NC; *U.S. Private*, pg. 575
Richards, Rick L., V.P.-Plng. & Prods.--Commonwealth Industries, Inc., Louisville, KY; *U.S. Public*, pg. 415
Richards, Wesley D., V.P.-Devel.--MicroAge, Inc., Tempe, AZ; *U.S. Public*, pg. 1104
Richardson, Dan, V.P.-Fin. & Plng. & Treas.--Great Salt Lake Minerals Corp., Overland Park, KS; *U.S. Private*, pg. 505
Richardson, Dave, Grp. Gen. Mgr.-Corp. Devel.--Australia & New Zealand Banking Group Limited, Melbourne, Australia; *Int'l*, pg. 98
Richardson, John G., Pres., Chief Exec. & Chief Fin. Officer--Sugar Creek Packing Co., Washington Court House, OH; *U.S. Private*, pg. 1049
Richardson, Joy S., Mng. Dir.-Latin America Bus. Devel.--Capital Markets Assurance Corporation, New York, NY; *U.S. Public*, pg. 1023
Richey, Van L., Pres. & Chief Exec. Officer--American Cast Iron Pipe Co., Birmingham, AL; *U.S. Private*, pg. 51
Richmond, Patrick, Exec. V.P.-Corp. Devel.--Primark Corporation, Waltham, MA; *U.S. Public*, pg. 1325
Richter, Irvin E., Chm. Bd. & Chief Exec. Officer--Hill International Inc., Willingboro, NJ; *U.S. Private*, pg. 529
Rickborn, Chris, V.P.-Mktg. & Prod. Plng.--Equitrac Corporation, Coral Gables, FL; *U.S. Public*, pg. 590
Ricker, Charles W., Jr., Pres.-Plng. & Network Grp.--TDS Telecommunications Corporation, Madison, WI; *U.S. Public*, pg. 1570
Rieger, Glenn T., Sr. V.P.--Safeguard Scientifics, Inc., Wayne, PA; *U.S. Public*, pg. 1424
Riehl, T.F., V.P.-Res. & Devel.--Brown & Williamson Tobacco Corp., Louisville, KY; *Int'l*, pg. 111
Riemersma, Jim K., V.P.-Strategic Plng.--BHP Petroleum Ltd., London, United Kingdom; *Int'l*, pg. 225
Rienstra, Thys, V.P.-New Bus. Devel.--Instrument Specialties Company, Delaware Water Gap, PA; *U.S. Private*, pg. 565
Rietz, Ake, Chief Fin. Officer & Exec. V.P.--Svenska Cellulosa Aktiebolaget (SCA), Stockholm, Sweden; *Int'l*, pg. 1326
Rigg, D.J.K., Dir.-Commercial Devel.--De La Rue plc, London, United Kingdom; *Int'l*, pg. 386
Riley, Chris, Acct. Plng. Dir.--Wieden & Kennedy, Inc., Portland, OR; *U.S. Private*, pg. 1175
Ringel, Barbara A., Ph.D., Sr. V.P. & Strategic Plng. Dir.--Pedone & Partners Adv., Inc., New York, NY; *U.S. Private*, pg. 846
Rinne, Risto, V.P.-Corp. Plng. & Sec.--Neste Oy, Espoo, Finland; *Int'l*, pg. 912
Riopel, Louis M., Sr. V.P.-Devel.--Societe Generale de Financement du Quebec, Montreal, Canada; *Int'l*, pg. 1274
Riordan, Dan, V.P.-Bus. Devel.--TelCom Semiconductor, Inc., Mountain View, CA; *U.S. Public*, pg. 1569
Riskedal, Steve, Pres.--La Salle County Farm Supply, Ottawa, IL; *U.S. Private*, pg. 640
Riskind, Kenneth J., Pres. & Chief Exec. Officer--Fullerton Metals Co., Northbrook, IL; *U.S. Private*, pg. 431
Ritchason, Marvin, Chief Exec. Officer--Ray-Carroll County Grain Co-op, Richmond, MO; *U.S. Private*, pg. 911
Ritter, A. Wayne, V.P.-Acquisitions--The Wiser Oil Company, Dallas, TX; *U.S. Public*, pg. 1773
Ritter, Douglas R., V.P.-Bus. Plng.--Paging Network, Inc., Plano, TX; *U.S. Public*, pg. 1252
Riviere, Donald, V.P.-Strategic Devel.--Menasha Corporation, Neenah, WI; *U.S. Private*, pg. 731
Rix, Nigel, Dir.-Devel.--Amtech Europe Limited, Cambridge, United Kingdom; *U.S. Public*, pg. 106
Rizzo, John F., V.P.-Corp. Devel.--Republic Industries, Inc., Fort Lauderdale, FL; *U.S. Public*, pg. 1378
Rizzo, John R., V.P.-Corp. Devel.--Perini Corporation, Framingham, MA; *U.S. Public*, pg. 1278
Roberson, Mark, Dir. Plng. & Devel.--Central and South West Corporation, Dallas, TX; *U.S. Public*, pg. 324
Roberts, Evan J., V.P.-Mktg. & Product Devel.--BMY-Wheeled Vehicles, Marysville, OH; *U.S. Public*, pg. 793
Roberts, Janice, V.P.-Plng. & Allocation--Designs, Inc., Needham, MA; *U.S. Public*, pg. 501
Roberts, Janice M., Sr. V.P.-Mktg. & Bus. Devel.--3Com Corporation, Santa Clara, CA; *U.S. Public*, pg. 1603
Roberts, Jeannette, Dir.-Corp. Devel.--Kaiser Ventures, Inc., Ontario, CA; *U.S. Public*, pg. 941
Roberts, John F., Dir.-Corp. Admin.--Morrison Knudsen Corporation, Boise, ID; *U.S. Public*, pg. 1133
Roberts, John P., Sr. Business Devel. Officer--Western Marketing-Los Angeles Region, Sherman Oaks, CA; *U.S.* Public, pg. 650
Roberts, Stephen M., Pres., Chief Exec. Officer & Treas.--F.L. Roberts & Co. Inc., Springfield, MA; *U.S. Private*, pg. 935
Roberts, Thomas A., V.P.-Retail Devel.--Rio Hotel & Casino Inc., Las Vegas, NV; *U.S. Public*, pg. 1390
Robertson, Peter W., Mgr.-Opers Plng. & Bus. Systems--Sheet & Coil Products Division, Port Kembla, Australia; *Int'l*, pg. 227
Robertson, Scott V., Pres. & Chief Exec. Officer--Robertson's Auto Salvage, Wareham, MA; *U.S. Private*, pg. 936
Robins, Christopher, Mgr.-Mktg. Retail--PAXAR Corporation, White Plains, NY; *U.S. Public*, pg. 1266
Robinson, Connie, Sr. V.P. & Grp. Plng. Dir.--Western International Media Corporation, Los Angeles, CA; *U.S. Private*, pg. 1165
Robinson, J.H., Chief Devel. Officer--Black & Veatch, Kansas City, MO; *U.S. Private*, pg. 146
Robinson, P.B., V.P.-School & Office Prods.--The Mead Corporation, Dayton, OH; *U.S. Public*, pg. 1074
Robinson, Steve, Bus. Mgr.--Cetrk USA, Limerick, PA; *U.S. Public*, pg. 1569
Robinson, Thomas A., Dir.-Corp. Devel. & Strategy--Varlen Corporation, Naperville, IL; *U.S. Public*, pg. 1710
Robles, Fernando Quiroz, Deputy Pres.--Grupo Financiero Banamex/Accival, S.A. de C.V., Mexico, Mexico; *Int'l*, pg. 574
Rocca, G., Mgr.-Fin. Plng.--Fiatallis North America, Inc., Carol Stream, IL; *Int'l*, pg. 483
Roch, Roger, Asst. V.P.-Res. & Devel.--Bobst S.A., Lausanne, Switzerland; *Int'l*, pg. 198
Rockwood-Fulton, Elizabeth, V.P.-New Bus. Devel. & Media Plng. Rels.--CBS Television Network, New York, NY; *U.S. Public*, pg. 274
Rodgers, J. Scott, V.P.-Devel.--First Worthing Company, Dallas, TX; *U.S. Private*, pg. 408
Rodgers, Mark, V.P.-Bus. Devel.--Mobile Telecommunications Technologies Corp., Jackson, MS; *U.S. Public*, pg. 1120
Rodrigues, Chris, Strategic Plng. Dir.--TTA/Newport, Inc., Newport Beach, CA; *U.S. Private*, pg. 1083
Rodriguez, Antonio, Sr. V.P.-Fin. & Plng.--The Seagram Spirits and Wine Group, New York, NY; *Int'l*, pg. 1217
Roe, James L., Dir.-Strategic Devel.--TI Group plc, Abingdon, United Kingdom; *Int'l*, pg. 1337
Roels, J.A., Dir.-Strategy--Royal Gist-Brocades N.V., Delft, Netherlands; *Int'l*, pg. 1142
Roels, J.A., Mgr.-Strategy--Corporate New Business Development Div., Delft, Netherlands; *Int'l*, pg. 1142
Roest, Marius, Gen. Mgr.-Intl. Bus. Devel.--Akzo Coatings B.V., Hoofddorp, Netherlands; *Int'l*, pg. 42
Rogers, Mark C., Dr., Chief Tech. Officer & Sr. V.P.-Corp. Devel.--The Perkin-Elmer Corporation, Norwalk, CT; *U.S.* Public, pg. 1279
Rohling, Edward J., Sr. V.P.-Corp. Devel.--Bristol Hotels & Resorts, Dallas, TX; *U.S. Public*, pg. 253
Rohrmann, Guenter, Pres. & Chief Exec. Officer--Air Express International Corporation, Darien, CT; *U.S. Public*, pg. 30
Rokoff, June L., Sr. V.P.-Spreadsheet Tech.--Lotus Development Corporation, Cambridge, MA; *U.S. Public*, pg. 896
Roland, E.J., V.P.-Opers., Plng. & Transportation--Amoco Oil Company, Chicago, IL; *U.S. Public*, pg. 102
Roland, William F., Pres.--Megapulse, Inc., Bedford, MA; *U.S. Private*, pg. 729
Roley, Surinder, Dir.-Fin. Plng.--Centigram Communications Corporation, San Jose, CA; *U.S. Public*, pg. 323
Rolle, Ilse, Mgr.-Staff Support--Coop Switzerland, Basel, Switzerland; *Int'l*, pg. 329
Roloff, Jeffrey J., Chm. Bd. & Chief Exec. Officer--Central Data Corporation, Champaign, IL; *U.S. Private*, pg. 223
Romeyer, Daniel, Dir.-Strategy & Devel./Central Europe--S.A. Cimenteries CBR, Brussels, Belgium; *Int'l*, pg. 605
Ronchi, Adello, Dir.-Prod. Plng.--Rimoldi Necchi S.R.L., Milan, Italy; *Int'l*, pg. 1117

Roney, Patrick E., Chm. Bd., Pres. & Chief Exec. Officer--Electro Mechanical Design Services, Inc., Gaithersburg, MD; *U.S. Private*, pg. 369
Roney, William C., III, Partner & Dir.-Bus. Devel.--Roney & Co., Detroit, MI; *U.S. Private*, pg. 943
Ronsin, Philippe, Dir.-Devel. & European Affairs--Ciments Francais, Paris, France; *Int'l*, pg. 292
Roper, Kevin, V.P.-Plng.--BancTec, Inc., Dallas, TX; *U.S. Public*, pg. 176
Rose, Stuart, Dir.-Strategic Plng.--The Body Shop International, Littlehampton, United Kingdom; *Int'l*, pg. 199
Roseman, Robert A., V.P.-Bus. Devel.--TCA Management Company, Tyler, TX; *U.S. Public*, pg. 1553
Rosen, Jack, Chm. Bd., Pres. & Chief Exec. Officer--Continental Health Affiliates, Inc., Englewood Cliffs, NJ; *U.S. Public*, pg. 440
Rosenberg, Edward L., Exec. V.P.-Supply & Transportation--Crown Central Petroleum Corporation, Baltimore, MD; *U.S. Public*, pg. 462
Rosendale, Henry, V.P.-Bus. Devel.--AAI/ACL Technologies, Santa Ana, CA; *U.S. Public*, pg. 1679
Rosenhek, Allan, V.P.-Corp. Devel.--Glentel Inc., Burnaby, Canada; *Int'l*, pg. 1336
Ross, Gerald, Pres., Chief Exec. & Chief Fin. Officer--MGR Equipment Corp., Inwood, NY; *U.S. Private*, pg. 687
Ross, Mark, Dir.-Natl. Tournaments & PPA Commissioner--Professional Putters Association, Fayetteville, NC; *U.S. Private*, pg. 896
Rosson, W.M., Chm. Bd.--Conwood Company L.P., Memphis, TN; *U.S. Private*, pg. 272
Rotenberry, William J., Dir.-Corp. Devel. & Asst. Sec.--Joslyn Corporation, Chicago, IL; *U.S. Public*, pg. 481
Roth, Daniel, Exec. V.P. & Chief Strategic Officer--Western International Media Corporation, Los Angeles, CA; *U.S. Private*, pg. 1165
Roth, W.R., Pres.--SJW Corp., San Jose, CA; *U.S. Public*, pg. 1418
Rothstein, Harvey, Sr. Exec. V.P.-Real Estate & Devel.--Davco Restaurants Inc., Crofton, MD; *U.S. Public*, pg. 488
Rothwell, Bernard J., III, Chm. Bd.--Bay State Milling Co., Quincy, MA; *U.S. Private*, pg. 124
Rotival, L., Gen. Mgr.-Sys., Pub. Rels. & Bus. Devel.--Nuovo Pignone S.p.a., Florence, Italy; *Int'l*, pg. 990
Roumeguere, P., V.P. & Dep. Gen. Mgr.-Devel.--SNCF, Paris, France; *Int'l*, pg. 1163
Round Turner, Sheena, Chief Exec. Officer--MCL, Nairobi, Kenya; *U.S. Public*, pg. 1422
Roux, David, Exec. V.P.-Corp. Devel.--Oracle Corporation, Redwood City, CA; *U.S. Public*, pg. 1227
Rowe, Allan D., Chief Fin. Officer & Sr. V.P.-Fin.--Empire Company Limited, Stellarton, Canada; *Int'l*, pg. 453
Rowe, Stanton, V.P.-Bus. Devel.--Datascope Corp., Montvale, NJ; *U.S. Public*, pg. 487
Rowny, Michael, Exec. V.P.-Alliances & Ventures--MCI Communications Corp., Atlanta, GA; *U.S. Public*, pg. 1023
Rowse, Steve, V.P.-Bus. Devel.--Veryfine Products, Inc., Westford, MA; *U.S. Private*, pg. 1137
Roy, Antonio Sacristan, Coord.-Corp. Plng.--Petroleos Mexicanos, Mexico, Mexico; *Int'l*, pg. 1046
Roy, Michel L., Dir.-Mktg.--Gaz Metropolitain & Company, Montreal, Canada; *Int'l*, pg. 541
Rubin, Alan, V.P.-Res. & Devel.--HBOC, Atlanta, GA; *U.S. Public*, pg. 770
Rubin, John, V.P.-Bus. Devel.--News America Marketing, Norwalk, CT; *Int'l*, pg. 925
Ruck, John W., V.P.-Plng.--Earle M. Jorgensen Company, Brea, CA; *U.S. Private*, pg. 600
Ruder, Brian, Dir.-Brand Plng. & Strategic Devel.--Citibank Credit Card Marketing, Long Island City, NY; *U.S. Public*, pg. 377
Rudovsky, Paul, Chief Fin. Officer & Exec. V.P.-Fin. & Plng.--Atlantis Plastic, Inc., Atlanta, GA; *U.S. Public*, pg. 145
Rudy, Ronald, Sr. V.P.-Opers.--International Aluminum Corporation, Monterey Park, CA; *U.S. Public*, pg. 894
Rued, Scott D., V.P.-Corp. Devel.--Tower Automotive, Inc., Grand Rapids, MI; *U.S. Public*, pg. 1625
Ruelle, Luc, Market Res. Dir. & New Bus. Contact--Leo Burnett Brussels, Brussels, Belgium; *U.S. Private*, pg. 185
Ruggerello, Peter, V.P.-Systems Devel.--Bergen Brunswig Corporation, Orange, CA; *U.S. Public*, pg. 213
Ruiz-Clavijo, Juan Villena, Exec. V.P.-Corp. Planning & Control--Sepi, Madrid, Spain; *Int'l*, pg. 1224
Rusk, John A., V.P.-Pur. & Plng.--Conair Corporation, Stamford, CT; *U.S. Private*, pg. 261
Russak, Michael A., Ph.D., V.P.-Res. & Devel.--HMT Technology Corporation, Fremont, CA; *U.S. Public*, pg. 771
Russo, Elio P., Plng. Dir.--DPZ-Duailibi, Petit, Zaragoza, Propaganda S.A., Sao Paulo, Brazil; *Int'l*, pg. 352
Russo, Paul W., V.P.-Corp. Devel. & Strategy--The Stanley Works, New Britain, CT; *U.S. Public*, pg. 1508
Ruybal, Jim, Exec. V.P.-New Bus. Dept.--United Artists Theatre Circuits Incorporated, Englewood, CO; *U.S. Private*, pg. 1120
Ryan, Edward R., Pres. & Chief Exec. Officer--Sandusky International Inc., Sandusky, OH; *U.S. Private*, pg. 964
Rydin, Wes, Chief Fin. Officer & V.P.--Malden Mills Industries, Inc., Lawrence, MA; *U.S. Private*, pg. 698
Ryno, H. Bruce, V.P.-Fin., Plng. & Devel. & Publication Services--Science & Technology Group, New York, NY; *U.S. Public*, pg. 1071
Sack, Burton M., Exec. V.P.-New Bus. Devel.--Applebee's International, Inc., Overland Park, KS; *U.S. Public*, pg. 122
Sadler, Roger W., V.P.-Bus. Devel.--Tracor, Inc., Austin, TX; *U.S. Public*, pg. 1627
Sagara, Jiro, Mng. Dir. & Sr. V.P.-Acctg.--Japan Airlines Company, Ltd., Tokyo, Japan; *Int'l*, pg. 699
Saint-Sauver, Herve, Dir.-Fin.--Societe Generale, Paris, France; *Int'l*, pg. 1273
Sakurai, Daizaburo, Mng. Dir.-Mngmt. Strategy--Sega Enterprises Ltd., Tokyo, Japan; *Int'l*, pg. 1218
Sakurai, Koichi, Mng. Dir. & Gen. Mgr.-Tech. Devel.--West Japan Railway Company, Osaka, Japan; *Int'l*, pg. 1490
Saldivar, Juan Ludlow, Dir.-Systems Plng. & Integration--Telefonos de Mexico S.A. de C.V., Mexico, Mexico; *Int'l*, pg. 1373
Salinger, Jeffrey W., V.P.-Product Mgmt. & Bus. Devel.--SLM Holding Corp., Washington, DC; *U.S. Public*, pg. 1419
Salto, Leon, Sr. Exec. V.P.-Bus. Devel.--Promodes SA, Mondeville, France; *Int'l*, pg. 1071
Salver, Henry A., Sr. V.P.--GAI Consultants, Inc., Monroeville, PA; *U.S. Private*, pg. 433
Sampson, Ronald, Sr. V.P.-Corp. Devel.--Burrell Communications Group Inc., Chicago, IL; *U.S. Private*, pg. 188
Samson, Roger, Sr. V.P.-Mktg. & Devel.--Sico Inc., Longueuil, Canada; *Int'l*, pg. 1239
Sanchez, Oscar J., V.P.-Engrng. Devel.--Chad Therapeutics, Chatsworth, CA; *U.S. Public*, pg. 332
Sanderson, K.L., V.P.-Plng., Tech. & Devel.--Duraco Products, Inc., Streamwood, IL; *U.S. Private*, pg. 348
Sanford, Randy, Dir.-Prod. Devel.--Galaxy Carpet Mills, Inc., Chatsworth, GA; *U.S. Public*, pg. 1121
Sangster, R. Hugh B., Sr. V.P.-Corp. Devel.--IPL Energy Inc., Calgary, Canada; *Int'l*, pg. 651
Sanquini, Richard L., Sr. V.P.-Business Devel.--National Semiconductor Corporation, Santa Clara, CA; *U.S. Public*, pg. 1159
Santamaria, Hector, Mgr.-Intl. Bus. Devel.--Wilcox Electric, Inc., Kansas City, MO; *Int'l*, pg. 1384
Santillana, Ignacio, Sr. V.P.-Intl. Bus. Devel.--GTE Corporation, Stamford, CT; *U.S. Public*, pg. 696
Saranga, Mike, Sr. V.P.-Product Mngmt. & Devel.--Informix Software, Menlo Park, CA; *U.S. Public*, pg. 876
Sarik, Dan, V.P.-Corp. Devel.--Daniel Industries, Inc., Houston, TX; *U.S. Public*, pg. 482
Sarnow, Beatrice, Pub. Rels. Dir.--American Television Time, Inc., Austin, TX; *U.S. Private*, pg. 63
Sasayama, Hisao, V.P. & Gen. Mgr.-Corp. Planning Div.--Sumitomo Corporation of America, New York, NY; *Int'l*, pg. 1312
Sasayama, Shinya, Dir.-New Business Devel.--Nikon Corporation, Tokyo, Japan; *Int'l*, pg. 931
Saslow, Seymour, Dir.-Sls. & Engrng.--Espey Mfg. & Electronics Corp., Saratoga Springs, NY; *U.S. Public*, pg. 592
Sasso, Greg W., V.P.-Corp. Devel. & Commun.--Biomet, Inc., Warsaw, IN; *U.S. Public*, pg. 231
Sato, Nobutake, Exec. V.P.-Plng.--Ito-Yokado Co., Ltd., Tokyo, Japan; *Int'l*, pg. 693
Saunders, Gary, Dir.-Reg. Devel. (Central & S. America)--Ramsey Technology, Inc., Minneapolis, MN; *U.S. Public*, pg. 1592
Saunders, Neil, V.P. & Plng. Dir.--Citron Haligman Bedecarre, San Francisco, CA; *U.S. Private*, pg. 241
Saunders, R. Reed, Sr. V.P.-Corp. Strategy & Devel.--American Express Financial Advisor, Minneapolis, MN; *U.S. Public*, pg. 73
Sava, Katerina, Res. Dir. & Plng. Dir.--Leo Burnett Athens, Athens, Greece; *U.S. Private*, pg. 184
Savaglio, Ted, V.P.-Program Plng.--CBS News, New York, NY; *U.S. Public*, pg. 274
Saveliev, Michael, V.P.-Enrng. & Bus. Devel.--Shurflo Pump Manufacturing Co., Santa Ana, CA; *U.S. Public*, pg. 1767
Sawin, Craig B., V.P.-Plng. & Analysis--Harcourt General, Inc., Chestnut Hill, MA; *U.S. Public*, pg. 782
Sawka, Richard, Pres.-Plng. Div.--Allright Corporation, Houston, TX; *U.S. Private*, pg. 42
Sawyer, Tim, Assoc. Dir.-Sls. Admin. & Bus. Devel.--Barr Laboratories Inc., Pomona, NY; *U.S. Public*, pg. 191
Sayer, H.G., V.P.-Resource Plng. & Devel.--Canal Electric Co., Cambridge, MA; *U.S. Public*, pg. 415
Scarbough, Steven, Pres.--Standard Pacific Corp., Costa Mesa, CA; *U.S. Public*, pg. 1503
Scavo, Alton J., Sr. V.P. & Dir.-Community Devel., Gen. Mgr.-Columbia--The Rouse Company, Columbia, MD; *U.S. Public*, pg. 1407
Scavuzzo, Michael, V.P.-Agency Services & Devel.--Atlas Van Lines, Inc., Evansville, IN; *U.S. Private*, pg. 97
Schacht, Sylvia, Strategic Plng. Dir.--Lowe & Partners, Dusseldorf, Germany; *U.S. Private*, pg. 678
Schachter, Rozalie, Dr., V.P.-Bus. Devel.--General Microwave Corporation, Amityville, NY; *U.S. Public*, pg. 717
Schaeffer, Jean, Mgr.-Bus. Plng.--Seattle City Light, Seattle, WA; *U.S. Private*, pg. 979
Schaeffer, R.A., V.P.-Prod. Devel.--R.A. Jones & Co. Inc., Covington, KY; *U.S. Private*, pg. 597
Schaeffer, Scott, Pres.--Plibrico Co., Chicago, IL; *U.S. Private*, pg. 872
Schafer, Lee, V.P.-Corp. Plng.--Aetrium Inc., Saint Paul, MN; *U.S. Public*, pg. 27
Schaffhauser, Robert J., V.P.-Tech. Corp. Devel.--Engelhard Corporation, Iselin, NJ; *U.S. Public*, pg. 582
Schaller, Scott, V.P.-New Bus. Devel.--Vision-Ease Lens Inc., Brooklyn Park, MN; *U.S. Public*, pg. 162
Schatz, David, V.P.-Corp. Devel.--Cognex Corporation, Natick, MA; *U.S. Public*, pg. 394
Schecter, Leroy, Chm. Bd. & Chief Exec. Officer--American Strip Steel Inc., Kearny, NJ; *U.S. Private*, pg. 62
Schell, Theodore H., Sr. V.P.-Strategic Plng. & Corp. Devel.--Sprint Corporation, Westwood, KS; *U.S. Public*, pg. 1500
Schenk, James A., Staff V.P. & Dir.-Plng.--Brunswick Corporation, Lake Forest, IL; *U.S. Public*, pg. 265
Scherer, Gilbert, Pres.--American Passage Media Corporation, Seattle, WA; *U.S. Private*, pg. 60
Scherer, Richard P., Sr. V.P.-Mktg. & Bus. Devel.--Laser Power Corporation, San Diego, CA; *U.S. Private*, pg. 652
Schiavone, Ronald, Chief Exec. Officer--Schiavone Construction Co., Secaucus, NJ; *U.S. Private*, pg. 970
Schiciano, Jason C., Pres.--The Coon-De Visser Co., Royal Oak, MI; *U.S. Private*, pg. 273
Schicker, Thomas, Dir.-Plng.--Montgomery Tank Lines, Inc., Plant City, FL; *U.S. Public*, pg. 1028
Schiff, E.A., V.P.-New Mkt. Devel.--Technology Research Corporation, Clearwater, FL; *U.S. Public*, pg. 1564
Schiller, Edward E., V.P.-Res. & Devel.--CPAC, Inc., Leicester, NY; *U.S. Public*, pg. 282
Schiller, Leonard M., Owner & Dir.-Acq.--The Dearborn Group, Chicago, IL; *U.S. Private*, pg. 319
Schipper, Christopher G., V.P.-Strategic Planning--PepsiCo, Inc., Purchase, NY; *U.S. Public*, pg. 1276
Schittler, Franz-Michael, Dir.-Engine Devel.--Mercedes-Benz AG, Stuttgart, Germany; *Int'l*, pg. 368
Schlittler, Charles E., Dir.-Environ. Tech.& Plng.--Kerr-McGee Chemical Corp., Oklahoma City, OK; *U.S. Public*, pg. 952
Schlotmann, Mike, V.P. & Controller--The Kroger Co., Cincinnati, OH; *U.S. Public*, pg. 967
Schmid, James A., Chief Exec. Officer--Crescent Electric Supply Co., East Dubuque, IL; *U.S. Private*, pg. 289
Schmidt, Peter G., Pres. & Chief Exec. Officer--Marine Construction & Design Co., Seattle, WA; *U.S. Private*, pg. 703
Schmidt, Robert, Sr. Bus. Devel. Officer--Northeast Marketing-New York Business Center, New York, NY; *U.S. Public*, pg. 649
Schneeberger, R. Louis, Chief Fin. Officer--Olympic Steel Inc., Cleveland, OH; *U.S. Public*, pg. 1221
Schneider, Forrest M., Chief Fin. Officer & Sr. V.P.--Lane Industries, Inc., Northbrook, IL; *U.S. Private*, pg. 649
Schneider, Karl, Mgr.-Import--Griffin Transport Services, Inc., Sparks, NV; *U.S. Private*, pg. 481
Schnewlin, Frank, Exec. V.P.--Zurich Insurance Company, Zurich, Switzerland; *Int'l*, pg. 1529
Schoenfeld, Barry, Sr. V.P. & Strategic Plng. Dir.--Asher/Gould Advertising, Inc., Los Angeles, CA; *U.S. Private*, pg. 88
Schoettner, Manfred, Dir.-Bus. Devel. & Personnel--Cherry Mikroschalter GmbH, Auerbach, Germany; *U.S. Public*, pg. 346
Schottenstein, Jay, Chm. Bd. & Chief Exec. Officer--Value City Department Stores, Inc., Columbus, OH; *U.S. Private*, pg. 972
Schrager, Phillip G., Chm. Bd. & Chief Exec. Officer--Pacesetter Corporation, Omaha, NE; *U.S. Private*, pg. 830
Schrems, Rainer, Mng. Dir.-Strategic Devel.--Julius Meinl AG, Vienna, Austria; *Int'l*, pg. 856
Schrum, E.P., Pres., Chief Exec. Officer & Treas.--Carolina Mills, Inc., Maiden, NC; *U.S. Private*, pg. 214
Schubach, John J., V.P.-Strategic Mngmt. & Continuous Improvement--The Timken Company, Canton, OH; *U.S. Public*, pg. 1617
Schubert, William C., Pres., Chief Exec. Officer & Treas.--Kitchell Corporation, Phoenix, AZ; *U.S. Private*, pg. 624
Schulte, Bernd A., V.P.-Corp. Devel.--W.R. Grace & Co., Boca Raton, FL; *U.S. Public*, pg. 754
Schulte, Fred C., Chief Exec. Officer--Elgin National Industries, Inc., Downers Grove, IL; *U.S. Private*, pg. 370
Schultz, James D., Chief Fin. Officer, Sr. V.P., Treas. & Sec.--Old America Stores, Howe, TX; *U.S. Public*, pg. 1215
Schultz, Steven T., Sr. V.P.-Devel.--La Quinta Inns, Inc., San Antonio, TX; *U.S. Public*, pg. 972
Schulze, Richard M., Chm. Bd., Founder & Chief Exec. Officer--Best Buy Co., Inc., Eden Prairie, MN; *U.S. Public*, pg. 223
Schutte, E.J., Mgr.-Prod. Devel. & Quality Control--Bakery Ingredients Division, Delft, Netherlands; *Int'l*, pg. 1142
Schwalbach, Glen R., Asst. V.P.-Corp. Plng.--WPS Resources Corp., Green Bay, WI; *U.S. Public*, pg. 1728
Schwalbe, Martin, Strategy & Convergence Dir.--Fahlgren, Dublin, OH; *U.S. Private*, pg. 391
Schwartz, David, Pres. & Chief Exec. Officer--Bio-Rad Laboratories, Inc., Hercules, CA; *U.S. Public*, pg. 230
Schwartz, Jeanne M., V.P.-New Prod. Devel.--United Family Life Insurance Co., Atlanta, GA; *Int'l*, pg. 499
Schweig, John A., V.P.-Bus. Devel. & Intl.--W.W. Grainger, Inc., Lincolnshire, IL; *U.S. Public*, pg. 758
Sciame, Frank, Pres., Treas., Chief Exec. & Chief Fin. Officer--F.J. Sciame Construction Co. Inc., New York, NY; *U.S. Private*, pg. 975
Sciera, Tamara D., Dir.-Strategic Plng.--Marietta Corporation, Cortland, NY; *U.S. Private*, pg. 702
Scolaro, Anthony C., V.P.-Plng. & Bus. Devel.--Premark International, Inc., Deerfield, IL; *U.S. Public*, pg. 1321
Scolaro, Michael, Sr. Bus. Devel. Officer--Central Marketing-Chicago Business Center, Chicago, IL; *U.S. Public*, pg. 649
Scott, Bryan, Grp. Gen. Mgr.-Bus. Devel.--Australian National Industries Limited, Pyrmont, Australia; *Int'l*, pg. 100
Scott, C. Wes, Exec. V.P.-Corp.--Northern Telecom Limited, Brampton, Canada; *Int'l*, pg. 968
Scott, F. Andrerw, Sr. V.P.-Corp. Devel.--The Loewen Group, Inc., Burnaby, Canada; *Int'l*, pg. 814
Scott, John W., V.P.-Investor Rels.--Bestfoods, Englewood Cliffs, NJ; *U.S. Public*, pg. 223
Scott, Kevin, Dir.-Strategy--Tombstone Pizza Corporation, Northfield, IL; *U.S. Public*, pg. 1288
Scott, Norman A., V.P. & Dir.-New Bus. Devel.--ARGOSystems, Inc., Sunnyvale, CA; *U.S. Public*, pg. 240
Scotton, William P., Pres.--Custom Decor, Inc., Smyrna, DE; *U.S. Private*, pg. 298
Seabrook, Raymond J., V.P.-Plng. & Control--Ball Corporation, Muncie, IN; *U.S. Public*, pg. 170
Sean Minning, Dir.-Bus. Plng.--Christian Dior Perfumes Inc., New York, NY; *Int'l*, pg. 781
Searle, Stewart A., III, Sr. V.P.-Plng. & Devel.--National Service Industries, Inc., Atlanta, GA; *U.S. Public*, pg. 1160
Searson, H.M., Dir.-Plng. & Devel.--Pilkington Plc, Saint Helens, United Kingdom; *Int'l*, pg. 1056

Seay, Larry M., V.P.-Mkt. Devel.--American & Efird, Inc., Mount Holly, NC; *U.S. Public*, pg. 1412

Sechler, Henry J., V.P.-Intl. Bus. Devel.--General Dynamics Corporation, Falls Church, VA; *U.S. Public*, pg. 708

Segal, Michael B., V.P.-Res. & Devel.--Bondo/Mar-Hyde Corporation, Cleveland, OH; *U.S. Public*, pg. 1357

Seiler, Stephen R., Exec. V.P.-Plng., Investment & Devel.--Elan Corporation Plc, Dublin, Ireland; *Int'l*, pg. 435

Sejonds, George, Dir.-Mktg. & Bus. Plng.--Compagnie des Machines Bull, Louveciennes, France; *Int'l*, pg. 315

Sekiguchi, Hidetoshi, Mgr.-Plng.--Nippon Oil Company, Limited (NISSEKI), Tokyo, Japan; *Int'l*, pg. 936

Selbach, Scott, V.P.-Corp. Devel.--Carlisle Companies Incorporated, Syracuse, NY; *U.S. Public*, pg. 305

Seligman, Scott J., Pres.--Seligman & Associates, Inc., Southfield, MI; *U.S. Private*, pg. 982

Sellyn, Laurence G., Chief Fin. Officer & Sr. V.P.-Fin. & Corp. Devel.--Wajax Limited, Delta, Canada; *Int'l*, pg. 1484

Semadeni, Thomas, V.P.-Banking Relations & New Business Devel.--Liechtenstein Global Trust Limited, Vaduz, Liechtenstein; *Int'l*, pg. 809

Semones, Lewis F., Jr., Sr. Mng. Dir.-Strategic Plng. & Bus. Devel.--Interstate/Johnson Lane Corporation, Charlotte, NC; *U.S. Public*, pg. 910

Sender, Robert, V.P.-Fin. Plng. & Intl. Analysis--Columbia Tri-Star Home Video, Burbank, CA; *Int'l*, pg. 1282

Seng, Teo Eu, Mgr.-Bus. Devel.--Singapore Petroleum Company Ltd., Singapore, Singapore; *U.S. Public*, pg. 102

Serafino, Steven, V.P.-Corp. Devel.--Republic Industries, Inc., Fort Lauderdale, FL; *U.S. Public*, pg. 1378

Seregny, Jeffrey T., Exec. V.P. & Plng./Devel. Dir.--Campbell-Ewald Advertising, Warren, MI; *U.S. Public*, pg. 908

Serrano, Ronald M., Sr. V.P.-Corp. Devel.--Southern New England Telecommunications Corporation, New Haven, CT; *U.S. Public*, pg. 1490

Sesnewicz, Richard W., V.P.-Bus. Devel.--American Science & Engineering, Inc., Billerica, MA; *U.S. Public*, pg. 90

Seth, Donald W., Dir.-Strategic Plng.--Electromagnetic Systems Div., Goleta, CA; *U.S. Public*, pg. 1364

Sevick, Daniel M., Chief Fin. Officer & Treas.--Environmental Resources Management, Exton, PA; *U.S. Private*, pg. 378

Shah, Kumar, Dir.-Plng., Bus. Devel. & Investor Rels.--Cytec Industries Inc., West Paterson, NJ; *U.S. Public*, pg. 471

Shah, S. Mir Muhammad, Dr., Deputy Mng. Dir.--Pakistan International Airlines Corporation, Karachi, Pakistan; *Int'l*, *pg. 1021*

Shah, Sanjay N., V.P.-Corp. Strategy, Plng. & Bus. Devel.--Wyman-Gordon, North Grafton, MA; *U.S. Public*, pg. 1782

Shaharun, Mohamed Zohari Mohamed, V.P.-Exploration & Prod.--Petroliam Nasional Berhad (Petronas), Kuala Lumpur, Malaysia; *Int'l*, pg. 1046

Shalit, Michael, V.P.-New Bus. Devel.--ECI Telecom Ltd., Petah Tiqwa, Israel; *Int'l*, pg. 643

Shanks, David C., V.P.-Human Resources--Sun Company, Inc., Philadelphia, PA; *U.S. Public*, pg. 1530

Shapell, Nathan, Chm. Bd., Pres. & Chief Exec. Officer--Shapell Industries, Inc., Beverly Hills, CA; *U.S. Private*, pg. 990

Shapiro, Jay M., Sr. V.P.-Devel.--General Cinema Theatres, Inc., Chestnut Hill, MA; *U.S. Public*, pg. 693

Shapiro, Richard B., Chm. Bd., Pres. & Chief Exec. Officer--Charles River Data Systems, Inc., Framingham, MA; *U.S.* Private, pg. 230

Shapland, Dave, Chief Fin. Officer & V.P.-Plng.--Bryan Foods, West Point, MS; *U.S. Public*, pg. 1433

Sharfstein, Marvin, V.P.-Corp. Devel.--Cabot Medical Corporation, Langhorne, PA; *U.S. Public*, pg. 373

Sharland, T.T., Exec. Dir.-Corp. Strategy--English China Clays Plc, Theale, United Kingdom; *Int'l*, pg. 455

Sharma, Amit, V.P.-Strategic Plng. & Bus. Devel.--G.E. Capital Commercial Real Estate Financing, Stamford, CT; *U.S. Public*, pg. 712

Sharpe, George, V.P.-New Prod. Devel. & Dir.-Mktg. Res./Window Fashions Div.--Hunter Douglas, Inc., Upper Saddle River, NJ; *Int'l*, pg. 639

Shaw, James C., Pres.--Spirol International Corp., Danielson, CT; *U.S. Private*, pg. 1026

Shawlis, Bruce, Dir.-Prod. Devel.--Craftex Mills Inc. of Pennsylvania, Blue Bell, PA; *U.S. Private*, pg. 284

Shea, B.F., Chief Fin. Officer & V.P.-Fin.--Dan River Inc., Danville, VA; *U.S. Public*, pg. 478

Shea, Thomas, Dir.-Strategic Plng.--General Datacomm Industries, Inc., Middlebury, CT; *U.S. Public*, pg. 708

Sheble, Ronald W., Dir.-Plng.--MasterBrand Industries, Inc., Lincolnshire, IL; *U.S. Public*, pg. 675

Sheehan, John J., Jr., V.P.-Devel.--Nationwide Health Properties Inc., Newport Beach, CA; *U.S. Public*, pg. 1166

Sheil, David R., V.P.-Personnel--Cooper Industries, Inc., Houston, TX; *U.S. Public*, pg. 442

Shelem, Avner, V.P. & Gen. Mgr.--GaSonics International, San Jose, CA; *U.S. Public*, pg. 703

Shellenberger, Ronald G., Mgr.-New Bus. Devel.--Rogers N.K. Seed Co., Boise, ID; *Int'l*, pg. 974

Shelton, Paul G., Chief Fin. Officer, Sr. V.P. & Pres.-Americo Carriers--AMCOL International Corp., Arlington Heights, IL; *U.S. Public*, pg. 63

Shephard, James B., Sr. V.P.-Corp. Bus. Devel.--Landstar Holding, Shelton, CT; *U.S. Public*, pg. 978

Shepherd, Steven, V.P. & Dir.-Inventory--Crum Electric Supply Co., Inc., Casper, WY; *U.S. Private*, pg. 293

Sherf, David A., Sr. V.P.-Devel.--Doubletree Corporation, Memphis, TN; *U.S. Public*, pg. 1335

Sherman, Thomas W., Chief Fin. Officer, Exec. V.P. & Treas.--Bay State Gas Company, Westborough, MA; *U.S.* Public, pg. 196

Sherry, Libby, V.P., Res. Dir. & Brand Plng. Dir.--The Weightman Group, Philadelphia, PA; *U.S. Private*, pg. 1159

Sherwood, Simon M.C., V.P.-Strategy & Latin America/Iberia--Sea Containers Ltd., Hamilton, Bermuda; *Int'l*, pg. 1213

Shewmake, C.B., Chm. Bd. & Chief Exec. Officer--Algernon Blair International, Montgomery, AL; *U.S. Private*, pg. 33

Shiel, William A., Sr. V.P.-Facilities Devel.--Walgreen Co., Deerfield, IL; *U.S. Public*, pg. 1733

Shield, Hank, Dir.-Buying & Mktg.--Associated Grocers of the South, Inc., Birmingham, AL; *U.S. Private*, pg. 91

Shimizu, C., V.P.-Plng.--Sharp Electronics Corporation, Mahwah, NJ; *Int'l*, pg. 1228

Shingu, Michio, Dir.-New Product Plng. Div.--Rohto Pharmaceutical Co., Osaka, Japan; *Int'l*, pg. 1126

Shipley, Larry, Exec. V.P.-Corp. Devel.--IBP, Inc., Dakota City, NE; *U.S. Public*, pg. 852

Shipley, William S. II, Chm. Bd. & Chief Exec. Officer--Shipley Companies, York, PA; *U.S. Private*, pg. 994

Shipper, David J., V.P.-Corp. Devel.--The Loewen Group, Inc., Burnaby, Canada; *Int'l*, pg. 814

Shirakawa, Kazuo, Dir.-Strategic Plng.--Hawaiian Electric Industries, Inc., Honolulu, HI; *U.S. Public*, pg. 799

Shivamber, Leon, V.P.-Plng.--Arrow Electronics, Inc., Melville, NY; *U.S. Public*, pg. 133

Shober, Ralph, Dir.-Corp. Devel.--BioWhittaker, Inc., Walkersville, MD; *U.S. Public*, pg. 297

Shoemaker, John C., V.P.-Worldwide Opers.--Sun Microsystems Computer Corporation, Mountain View, CA; *U.S. Public*, pg. 1531

Shoen, E.J., Chm. Bd. & Pres.--Amerco, Reno, NV; *U.S. Private*, pg. 48

Shore, Jerry, Chm. Bd. & Chief Exec. Officer--Park Electrochemical Corporation, Lake Success, NY; *U.S. Public*, pg. 1258

Shultz, Gerald, Chm. Bd., Pres. & Chief Exec. Officer--Micro-Met L Corp., Indianapolis, IN; *U.S. Private*, pg. 742

Shumaker, Fred, V.P.-Bus. Devel.--Oceaneering Production Systems, Houston, TX; *U.S. Public*, pg. 1211

Sibisa, Jorge, Dir.-Business Devel.--CODELCO Chile (Corporacion Nacional Del Cobre De Chile), Santiago, Chile; *Int'l*, pg. 302

Sibthorpe, Ronald F., Dir.-Admin. & Plng.--Lincoln Assurance Limited, Uxbridge, United Kingdom; *U.S. Public*, pg. 998

Siebenales, Rick, V.P.-Devel.--CyberGuard Corporation, Fort Lauderdale, FL; *U.S. Public*, pg. 470

Silles, Victor, Chief Fin. Officer & Treas.--Thetford Corporation, Ann Arbor, MI; *U.S. Private*, pg. 352

Sills, John, Dir.-Plng./Mastercare--Dixons Group plc, Hemel Hempstead, United Kingdom,; *Int'l*, pg. 413

Sills, Lawrence I., Pres. & Chief Exec. & Oper. Officer--Standard Motor Products Inc., Long Island City, NY; *U.S.* Public, pg. 1503

Sills, Milton D., V.P.-Engrng.--The Cessna Aircraft Co., Wichita, KS; *U.S. Public*, pg. 1589

Silverman, Nicole, V.P.-Strategic Plng.--PHP Healthcare Corporation, Reston, VA; *U.S. Public*, pg. 1241

Simmons, Duane, V.P.-Plng.--Kaibab Industries, Phoenix, AZ; *U.S. Private*, pg. 605

Simmons, Victoria L., Mktg. Administrator--NavCom Defense Electronics, Inc., El Monte, CA; *U.S. Private*, pg. 789

Simon, Anthony, Sr. V.P.-Bus. Devel.--CPC Europe Consumer Foods Division, Brussels, Belgium; *U.S. Public*, pg. 224

Simon, Nicholas J., V.P.-Bus. & Corp. Devel.--Genentech, Inc., South San Francisco, CA; *Int'l*, pg. 1120

Simon, Peter, V.P.-Bus. Devel.--National Information Services (NIS), Bethesda, MD; *Int'l*, pg. 1096

Simonson, Karl D., V.P. & Dir.-Plng. & Devel.--Genesee Corporation, Rochester, NY; *U.S. Public*, pg. 728

Simpson, Phil, Chm. Bd., Pres. & Chief Exec. Officer--Republic Group Incorporated, Hutchinson, KS; *U.S. Public*, pg. 1378

Sims, Karen, Dir.-Plng.--U.S. Home Corporation, Houston, TX; *U.S. Public*, pg. 1682

Sinclair, Bob, V.P.-Bus. Devel.--Mennen Medical Inc., Clarence, NY; *Int'l*, pg. 858

Sinclair, Nancy, V.P. & Dir.-Mktg. & Plng.--CVB Financial Corp., Ontario, CA; *U.S. Public*, pg. 286

Sipila, A., Dir.-Plng.--Nokia Telecommunications, Espoo, Finland; *Int'l*, pg. 952

Siqueira, Edwin Natan, Finance Plng. & Devel.--SmithKline Beecham Laboratorios Ltda., Rio de Janeiro, Brazil; *Int'l*, *pg. 1266*

Sisois, Mikes, V.P.-Plng. & Information Systems--Atmel Corporation, San Jose, CA; *U.S. Public*, pg. 145

Skarbek, Joe, Sr. V.P.-Plng. & Admin.--Frankel & Company, Chicago, IL; *U.S. Private*, pg. 424

Skarie, David P., V.P. & Dir.-Customer Devel.--Ralcorp Holdings Inc., Saint Louis, MO; *U.S. Public*, pg. 1359

Skene, Jeremy, V.P.-Business Devel.--Coherent Communications Systems Corp., Ashburn, VA; *U.S. Public*, pg. 1424

Skibski, Richard, V.P.-Res. & Tech.--Cyborg Systems, Inc., Chicago, IL; *U.S. Private*, pg. 299

Skinner, William L., Sr. V.P.-Admin. & Corp. Devel.--Alltrista Corporation, Muncie, IN; *U.S. Public*, pg. 56

Skomba, John, V.P.-Corp. Devel.--FTI Foodtech International Inc., Don Mills, Canada; *Int'l*, pg. 476

Skwara, Joe, V.P.-Technical Services & Devel.--Comstock Michigan Fruit, Rochester, NY; *U.S. Private*, pg. 887

Slatkine, Michael, V.P.-Business Devel.--Laser Industries Ltd., Tel Aviv, Israel; *Int'l*, pg. 429

Slaughter, Richard G., V.P.-Plng. & Sec.--U.S. Home Corporation, Houston, TX; *U.S. Public*, pg. 1682

Sledd, Robert C., Chm. Bd. & Chief Exec. Officer--Performance Food Group Company, Richmond, VA; *U.S.* Public, pg. 1278

Slifka, Alfred A., Pres. & Chief Exec. Officer--Global Petroleum Corp., Waltham, MA; *U.S. Private*, pg. 457

Sloan, Kenneth H., Chief Exec. Officer & Sr. Exec. V.P.-Fin., Plng.--Shoppers Drug Mart, Ltd., Toronto, Canada; *Int'l*, pg. 112

Slocum, Terry, Sr. V.P.-Corp. Devel.--Western Staff Services, Walnut Creek, CA; *U.S. Public*, pg. 1760

Slosberg, Karl, Sr. Bus. Devel. Officer--Northeast Marketing-Cleveland Business Center, Cleveland, OH; *U.S. Public*, pg. 649

Slovin, Bruce, Pres.--MacAndrews & Forbes Holdings Inc., New York, NY; *U.S. Private*, pg. 689

Small, A. Francis, Mgr.-Devel.--Tranzrail Limited, Willington, New Zealand; *U.S. Public*, pg. 1773

Smalley, Jerome D., Sr. V.P. & Dir.-Commercial & Office Devel.--The Rouse Company, Columbia, MD; *U.S. Public*, *pg. 1407*

Smalley, Robert A., Jr., Chief Oper. Officer & Exec. V.P.--Cruise America, Inc., Mesa, AZ; *U.S. Private*, pg. 178

Smead, H.J., Chm. Bd., Chief Exec. & Chief Fin. Officer & Sec.--Kaiser Aerospace & Electronics Corp., Foster City, CA; *U.S. Private*, pg. 605

Smeltzer, Steve, V.P.-Corp. Plng.--Noteworthy Industries Inc., Amsterdam, NY; *U.S. Private*, pg. 808

Smette, Darryl G., V.P.-Mktg. & Admin. Plng.--Devon Energy Corporation, Oklahoma City, OK; *U.S. Public*, pg. 503

Smith, Brian L., Sr. V.P.-Mngmt. Liability, Claims Consulting & Prod. Devel.--Willis Corroon Financial Services Corp., New York, NY; *Int'l*, pg. 1507

Smith, Claibourne D., V.P.-Corp. Plng.--Du Pont (E.I. Du Pont De Nemours & Co.), Wilmington, DE; *U.S. Public*, pg. 530

Smith, Clarence H., V.P.-Opers. & Devel.--Haverty Furniture Companies, Inc., Atlanta, GA; *U.S. Public*, pg. 799

Smith, David, V.P. & Bus. Devel. Officer--Elyria Savings & Trust National Bank, Elyria, OH; *U.S. Public*, pg. 646

Smith, David, V.P.-Bus. Devel.--Placer Dome Inc., Vancouver, Canada; *Int'l*, pg. 1060

Smith, F., Mng. Dir.-Asia & Market Devel.--United Biscuits (Holdings) Plc, West Drayton, United Kingdom; *Int'l*, pg. 1442

Smith, Fred, V.P.-Corp. Devel.--Pettibone Corporation, Lisle, IL; *U.S. Private*, pg. 859

Smith, Gerard, Sr. V.P. & Plng. Dir.-North America--DMB&B Communications, New York, NY; *U.S. Private*, pg. 302

Smith, Jeffrey A., Gen. Mgr.-Plng. & Acquisition--Western Mining Corporation Holdings Limited, Southbank, Australia; *Int'l*, pg. 1494

Smith, Jeffrey M., Sr. V.P.-Plng. & Devel.--Churchill Downs, Inc., Louisville, KY; *U.S. Public*, pg. 356

Smith, K.L., Mgr.-Water Customer Service & Planning--Salt River Project Agricultural Improvement and Power District, Tempe, AZ; *U.S. Private*, pg. 962

Smith, Kent B., V.P.-Strategic Plng.--Rayonier Inc., Stamford, CT; *U.S. Public*, pg. 1363

Smith, Kevin R., V.P.-Comml. Bus. Devel., Engrng. & Construction--IT Corp., Wilmington, CA; *U.S. Public*, pg. 908

Smith, Murray, V.P.-Devel.--Starrett HRH, New York, NY; *U.S. Private*, pg. 1035

Smith, Patrick, Bus. Devel. Dir.--Sampson Tyrrell Enterprise, London, United Kingdom; *Int'l*, pg. 1482

Smith, Randall G., V.P.-Grp. Videoconferencing Systems--PictureTel, Andover, MA; *U.S. Public*, pg. 1294

Smith, Robert S., V.P.-Business Devel.--General Datacomm Industries, Inc., Middlebury, CT; *U.S. Public*, pg. 708

Smith, Robert W., V.P. & Gen. Counsel--DEC International, Inc., Madison, WI; *U.S. Private*, pg. 301

Smith, Robert W., Sr. V.P.-Store Devel. & Plng.--Fleming Companies, Inc., Oklahoma City, OK; *U.S. Public*, pg. 652

Smith, W.T., Pres. & Gen. Mgr.--Tidelands Oil Production Co., Long Beach, CA; *U.S. Private*, pg. 1084

Smith, Willis D., V.P.-Plng. & Admin.--Boeing Defense & Space Group, Kent, WA; *U.S. Public*, pg. 240

Smithshoek, Roy L., V.P.-Corp. Devel.--Renaissance Energy Ltd., Calgary, Canada; *Int'l*, pg. 1102

Smolik, T. James, Sr. V.P.-Project Devel.--Placer Dome Inc., Vancouver, Canada; *Int'l*, pg. 1060

Snoke, D.W., V.P.-Plng. & Devel.--ESCO Electronics Corporation, Saint Louis, MO; *U.S. Public*, pg. 546

Snowden, Philip F., Mgr.-Organisation Devel.--Slab & Plate Products Division, Wollongong, Australia; *Int'l*, pg. 227

Snyder, Dennis C., V.P.-Pulp Services & Plng.--Rayonier Inc., Stamford, CT; *U.S. Public*, pg. 1363

Snyder, Gary, Sr. V.P.-Plng.--Analysis & Technology, Inc., North Stonington, CT; *U.S. Public*, pg. 109

Snyder, Gary, Asst. V.P.-Strategic Plng.--Citizens Utilities Company, Stamford, CT; *U.S. Public*, pg. 379

Snyder, Michael I., V.P.-Plng.--Toll Brothers, Inc., Huntingdon Valley, PA; *U.S. Public*, pg. 1620

Snyder, R. Kent, Sr. V.P.-Comml. Affairs--Agouron Pharmaceuticals, Inc., La Jolla, CA; *U.S. Public*, pg. 28

Snyers, Etienne, Mgr.-Strategy--Electrabel S.A., Brussels, Belgium; *Int'l*, pg. 436

Soble, David S., Pres. & Chief Exec. Officer--Interstate Steel Co. Inc., Des Plaines, IL; *Int'l*, pg. 572

Solari, Marco, Dir.-Plng. & Devel.--Migros, Zurich, Switzerland; *Int'l*, pg. 865

Solender, T. Jeff, V.P.-Devel. & Plng.--Grey Asia Pacific, Quarry Bay, Hong Kong; *U.S. Public*, pg. 765

Solenthaler, Bart, V.P.-Fin. & Plng.--Crouse-Hinds, Syracuse, NY; *U.S. Public*, pg. 444

Solombrino, Scott, Chm. Bd., Pres. & Chief Exec. Officer--Dav-El Worldwide, Chelsea, MA; *U.S. Private*, pg. 314

Solomon, William T., Chm. Bd. & Chief Exec. Officer--Austin Industries, Inc., Dallas, TX; *U.S. Private*, pg. 99

Song, Seung-Hyo, Exec. V.P. & Dir.--Cho Hung Bank, Seoul, Korea; *Int'l*, pg. 287

Soon, Vincent Tan Cheh, Sr. Mgr.-Bus. Devel.--DBS Card Centre Pte. Ltd., Singapore, Singapore; *Int'l*, pg. 350

Soto, Francisco Murillo, Dir.-Plng.--Vitromex, S.A., Saltillo, Mexico; *Int'l*, pg. 1469

Sottile, John H., Pres. & Chief Exec. Officer--The Goldfield Corporation, Melbourne, FL; *U.S. Public*, pg. 750

Southworth, Joe, V.P.-Prod. Devel. & Support--Ross Systems, Inc., Atlanta, GA; *U.S. Public*, pg. 1406

Spackler, J. Keith, Mgr.-Fin.--Ag Processing Inc., A Cooperative, Omaha, NE; *U.S. Private*, pg. 26

Speck, Robert A., Sr. V.P.-Strategic Plng.--Shoney's, Inc., Nashville, TN; *U.S. Public*, pg. 1467

Speed, Robert, Dir.-Corp. Devel.--Agra Inc., Calgary, Canada; *Int'l*, pg. 30

Spellman, R., Dir.-Distribution--Halifax plc, Halifax, United Kingdom; *Int'l*, pg. 589

Spencer, Lori L., V.P.-Strategic Plng.--The Lamson & Sessions Co., Cleveland, OH; *U.S. Public*, pg. 976

Spencer, Richard D., Chief Info. Officer & V.P.-Plng.--Equitable Resources, Inc., Pittsburgh, PA; *U.S. Public*, pg. 589

Spencer, Terry S., Exec. V.P.-Devel.--First American Corporation, Nashville, TN; *U.S. Public*, pg. 624

Spinoy, Bernadette, Mgr.-Corp. Plng.--Petrofina S.A., Brussels, Belgium; *Int'l*, pg. 1043

Spoehel, Ronald R., V.P.-Corp. Devel.--Harris Corporation, Melbourne, FL; *U.S. Public*, pg. 791

Sponseller, Bob, V.P., Gen. Mgr. & Controller--Golden West Broadcasters, Los Angeles, CA; *U.S. Private*, pg. 461

Sprang, Clark E., V.P.-Bus. Devel.--The Goodyear Tire & Rubber Company, Akron, OH; *U.S. Public*, pg. 752

Sprenger, Thomas A., V.P.-Store Devel./Residential--La-Z-Boy Incorporated, Monroe, MI; *U.S. Public*, pg. 972

Springer, Stephen R., V.P.-Bus. Devel./Intl.--Williams Field Services, Tulsa, OK; *U.S. Public*, pg. 1769

Spyker, L., Asst. Dir.-Plng.--Siebe plc, Windsor, United Kingdom; *Int'l*, pg. 1240

Stacey, Gary, Sr. V.P.-Res. & Devel. & Tech. Assessment--Haemonetics Corporation, Braintree, MA; *U.S. Public*, pg. 773

Stafford, C. Richard, V.P.-Corp. Devel.--Carter-Wallace, Inc., New York, NY; *U.S. Public*, pg. 309

Stafford, Randy, Pres. & Chief Exec. Officer--The Court Company, Memphis, TN; *U.S. Private*, pg. 279

Staggs, Thomas O., Sr. V.P.-Strategic Plng.--The Walt Disney Company, Burbank, CA; *U.S. Public*, pg. 511

Stagliano, Adam, Pres. & Acct. Plng. Dir.--Weiss, Whitten, Stagliano Inc., New York, NY; *U.S. Private*, pg. 1160

Stalnaker, Horace, V.P.-Planning--Columbus Mills, Inc., Columbus, GA; *U.S. Private*, pg. 256

Stalzer, Robert J., Sr. V.P.-Admin., Fin., Treas. & Asst. Sec.--Servo Corporation of America, Westbury, NY; *U.S. Private*, pg. 987

Stamps, W. Kennedy, Asst. Dir.-Site Plng.--Harley Ellington Design, Southfield, MI; *U.S. Private*, pg. 503

Standen, Craig C., Sr. V.P.-Corp. Devel.--The E.W. Scripps Company, Cincinnati, OH; *U.S. Public*, pg. 1447

Standing, Richard, Mgr.-Bus. Devel.--Simpson International (UK) Ltd., Huddersfield, United Kingdom; *U.S. Public*, pg. 1475

Standing, Richard, Mgr.-Bus. Devel.--Simpson International (UK) Ltd., West Yorkshire, United Kingdom; *U.S. Public*, pg. 1475

Stang, Richard, Sr. Bus. Devel. Officer--Northeast Marketing-New York Business Center, New York, NY; *U.S. Public*, pg. 649

Stannard, Charles I., Sr. V.P. & Plng. Dir.--DMB&B Detroit, Troy, MI; *U.S. Private*, pg. 302

Stanoch, Annette, V.P.-Plng.--TransNet Corporation, Somerville, NJ; *U.S. Public*, pg. 1631

Stanton, Carey, V.P.-Bus. Devel.--Corel Corporation, Ottawa, Canada; *Int'l*, pg. 331

Stanton, Jim L., V.P.-Plng.--Lightnin Mixers, Rochester, NY; *U.S. Public*, pg. 726

Stark, Eliot R., Sr. V.P.-Mergers & Acquistions & Strategic & Corp. Plng.--Compuware Corporation, Farmington Hills, MI; *U.S. Public*, pg. 423

Stark, Steve, Exec. Dir.-Mktg. & Bus. Devel.--Citizens Gas & Coke Utility, Indianapolis, IN; *U.S. Private*, pg. 241

Stattin-Jellheden, Birgit A., Sr. V.P.-Worldwide Prod. Devel.--Pharmacia & Upjohn, Inc., Windsor, United Kingdom; *Int'l*, pg. 1047

Staynk, Ed J., V.P.-Devel.--Shopping Centre Group, Toronto, Canada; *Int'l*, pg. 253

Stearns, Eric, V.P.-Exploration & Devel.--Petroleum Development Corporation, Bridgeport, WV; *U.S. Public*, pg. 1280

Stebbins, Byron H., Sr. V.P.-Market Devel.--Newell Co., Freeport, IL; *U.S. Public*, pg. 1176

Steel, Jon, Vice Chm. & Strategic Plng. Dir.--Goodby, Silverstein & Partners, San Francisco, CA; *U.S. Public*, pg. 1224

Stein, Robert, V.P.-Bus. Devel.--FiberMark Inc., Brattleboro, VT; *U.S. Public*, pg. 620

Stein, Steven B., Pres. & Chief Oper. Officer--Allied Security, Inc., Pittsburgh, PA; *U.S. Private*, pg. 40

Steinback, Michael, Pres.--Communications Instruments Inc., Fairview, NC; *U.S. Private*, pg. 259

Steinborn-Reetz, Lothar, Mgr.-Plng. & Devel.--Landesbank Hessen-Thuringen Girozentrale, Frankfurt/Main, Germany; *Int'l*, pg. 798

Steiner, Lawrence G., Chief Exec. Officer--Ameripride Service Company, Minneapolis, MN; *U.S. Private*, pg. 65

Steir, Michael, Dir.-Contracts & Intl. Plng.--Cognex Corporation, Natick, MA; *U.S. Public*, pg. 394

Stenitzer, George, Dir.-Corp. Positioning--Ameritech Corporation, Chicago, IL; *U.S. Public*, pg. 97

Stephens, G. Martin, Sr. V.P.--Golden Gem Growers Inc., Umatilla, FL; *U.S. Private*, pg. 460

Stephens, J.T., Pres. & Chief Exec. Officer--EBSCO Industries, Inc., Birmingham, AL; *U.S. Private*, pg. 358

Stephens, Rod, Dir.-Pur. & Production Plng.--Sun-Maid Growers of California, Kingsburg, CA; *U.S. Private*, pg. 1051

Stephens, W. Lackey, Pres.--R.L. Zeigler Co. Inc., Tuscaloosa, AL; *U.S. Private*, pg. 1204

Stephenson, William A., V.P.-Mdse. Allocation & Plng.--Toys "R" Us, Inc., Paramus, NJ; *U.S. Public*, pg. 1626

Stepp, Don, Dir.-Bus. Devel.--Electrospace Systems, Inc., Richardson, TX; *U.S. Public*, pg. 1365

Sterling, Marcia, V.P.-Bus. Devel. & Gen. Counsel--Autodesk, Inc., San Rafael, CA; *U.S. Public*, pg. 148

Stern, Andrew, Exec. V.P.-Strategic Corp. Plng.--USF&G Corporation, Baltimore, MD; *U.S. Public*, pg. 1659

Stern, Andrew, Sr. V.P.-Strategic Plng. & Corp. Mktg.--United States Fidelity & Guaranty Company, Baltimore, MD; *U.S. Public*, pg. 1659

Stern, Bill, V.P.-Sls. & Bus. Devel.--Recon/Optical, Inc., Barrington, IL; *U.S. Private*, pg. 914

Stern, Kenneth, V.P.-Adv. & Corp. Devel.--Axsys Technologies, Inc., New York, NY; *U.S. Public*, pg. 157

Stevens, Craig B., V.P.-Admin. & Plng.--Bowater Coated Paper & Pulp Div., Catawba, SC; *U.S. Public*, pg. 248

Stevens, Mary, Mgr.-Plng.--Herman Miller, Inc., Zeeland, MI; *U.S. Public*, pg. 1111

Stevenson, Philip H., Dir.-New Prod. Devel.--HMI Industries, Cleveland, OH; *U.S. Public*, pg. 771

Stewart, David R., Dir.-Pub. Rels.--Stewart & Stevenson Services, Inc., Houston, TX; *U.S. Public*, pg. 1517

Still, John T., III, Sr. V.P.-Corp. Devel.--Jefferson-Pilot Corporation, Greensboro, NC; *U.S. Public*, pg. 925

Stillman, Larry, Pres. & Chief Exec. Officer--Ingram Paper Company, City of Industry, CA; *U.S. Public*, pg. 904

Stinson, Thomas, V.P.-Strategic Plng. & Sec.--Noranda Forest Inc., Toronto, Canada; *Int'l*, pg. 434

Stobaugh, Bill H., V.P.-Plng.--Murphy Oil Corporation, El Dorado, AR; *U.S. Public*, pg. 1141

Stockdale, Mark, Plng.--Leo Burnett Limited, London, United Kingdom; *U.S. Private*, pg. 185

Stoffel, James, Dir.-Fin. & Plng.--Carson Pirie Scott & Co., Milwaukee, WI; *U.S. Public*, pg. 309

Stoilen, Sheldon T., Grp. V.P.-Corp. Services & Plng. & Public Affairs--Canfor Corporation, Vancouver, Canada; *Int'l*, pg. 260

Stokes, T. Andrew, Sr. V.P.-Corp. Devel.--Nationwide Health Properties Inc., Newport Beach, CA; *U.S. Public*, pg. 1166

Stoltz, Jon T., Sr. V.P.-Plng. & Rates--Cascade Natural Gas Corporation, Seattle, WA; *U.S. Public*, pg. 311

Stone, L., Mgr.-Plng. & Devel.--LucasVarity plc, London, United Kingdom; *Int'l*, pg. 819

Storat, Richard E., V.P.-Corp. Affairs--Gaylord Container Corporation, Deerfield, IL; *U.S. Public*, pg. 704

Storch, Gerald L., Sr. V.P.-Strategic Plng.--Dayton Hudson Corporation, Minneapolis, MN; *U.S. Public*, pg. 489

Storm, David J., V.P.-Plng., Logistics & Info. Svcs.--Harley-Davidson Motor Company, Milwaukee, WI; *U.S. Public*, pg. 786

Stott, Mark D., V.P.-Plng. & Devel.--Global Industrial Technologies, Dallas, TX; *U.S. Public*, pg. 747

Stougaard, Gary, V.P.-Devel.--The Woodfin Suite Hotels, San Diego, CA; *U.S. Private*, pg. 1187

Stout, Everett E., Pres., Chief Exec. Officer, Chief Fin. Officer & Controller--Metaltech, Inc., Kirkwood, MO; *U.S.* Private, pg. 735

Stout, Gene E., Exec V.P.-Corp. Devel.--Coachmen Industries, Inc., Elkhart, IN; *U.S. Public*, pg. 387

Stover, Bruce H., V.P.-Worldwide Bus. Devel.--Anadarko Petroleum Corporation, Houston, TX; *U.S. Public*, pg. 107

Stover, James, V.P.-Engrng & Res. & Devel.--Jayco Inc., Middlebury, IN; *U.S. Private*, pg. 583

Strasma, Edward J., Chief Fin. Officer, Exec. V.P. & Controller--Interstate Producers Livestock Association, Peoria, IL; *U.S. Private*, pg. 573

Straus, David J., Chm. Bd. & Chief Exec. Officer--STRAFCO, Inc., San Antonio, TX; *U.S. Private*, pg. 1046

Strecansky, James F., V.P. & Gen. Mgr.-Process Systems & Equipment Div.--Air Products and Chemicals, Inc., Allentown, PA; *U.S. Public*, pg. 30

Strickland, T.L., Sr. V.P.-Intl. Devel.--Morganite Inc., Dunn, NC; *Int'l*, pg. 891

Strite, Jack, Dir - Strategic Plng. & Bus. Computing--AlliedSignal Aerospace, Stratford, CT; *U.S. Public*, pg. 50

Stroup, Harry B., V.P.-Devel.--Applebee's International, Inc., Overland Park, KS; *U.S. Public*, pg. 122

Stuart, Timothy R., Pres. & Chief Oper. Officer--Stuart Entertainment Inc., Council Bluffs, IA; *U.S. Public*, pg. 1526

Stumpf, Charles T., Owner--Financial Associates, Overland Park, KS; *U.S. Private*, pg. 404

Stuntz, William, Pres.--Dranetz-BMI, Edison, NJ; *U.S. Private*, pg. 1144

Sturman, Jon M., V.P.-Corp. Devel.--The Pittston Company, Glen Allen, VA; *U.S. Public*, pg. 1305

Suer, Bernard P., V.P.-Mktg. & Devel.--Frank Messer & Sons Construction Co., Cincinnati, OH; *U.S. Private*, pg. 734

Suffa, William P., V.P.-Strategic Devel.--Jacor Communications, Inc., Covington, KY; *U.S. Public*, pg. 922

Sufferini, F., Grp. Mgr.-Corp. Affairs & Plng.--Australian National Industries Limited, Pyrmont, Australia; *Int'l*, pg. 100

Suhocki, Raymond F., V.P.-Mktg. & Econ. Devel.--PP&L Resources, Allentown, PA; *U.S. Public*, pg. 1244

Sullivan, David C., Sr. V.P.-Devel. & Opers.--Hampton Inns, Inc., Memphis, TN; *U.S. Public*, pg. 1335

Sullivan, Douglas B., Pres. & Chief Oper. Officer--Michaels Stores, Inc., Irving, TX; *U.S. Public*, pg. 1104

Sullivan, Kevin, Sr. Bus. Devel. Officer--Northeast Marketing-St. Louis Business Center, Saint Louis, MO; *U.S. Public*, pg. 649

Sullivan, William H., Jr., Chm. Bd.--National Gas & Oil Company, Newark, OH; *U.S. Public*, pg. 1156

Sultan, Nader Hamad, Dep. Chm. & Mng. Dir.-Plng.--Kuwait Petroleum Corporation, Safat, Kuwait; *Int'l*, pg. 764

Suman, Dan, V.P.-New Bus. Devel.--Gentex Corporation, Zeeland, MI; *U.S. Public*, pg. 731

Sumic, Zarko, V.P.-Prod. Devel.--Tellus, Inc., Bellevue, WA; *U.S. Public*, pg. 1342

Summers, C. Richard, Sr. V.P.-Plng. & Devel.--Texas Commerce Bank, Houston, TX; *U.S. Public*, pg. 339

Sumrall, Thomas D., V.P.-Mngmt. Plng.--Rockwell International Corporation, Costa Mesa, CA; *U.S. Public*, pg. 1397

Sunderland, Charles T., V.P.-Corp. Devel.--Ash Grove Cement Company, Shawnee Mission, KS; *U.S. Private*, pg. 87

Sundstrom, Chris E., V.P.-Corp. Devel.--Wm. Wrigley Jr. Company, Chicago, IL; *U.S. Public*, pg. 1781

Surrette, Jack, V.P.-Mktg. & Product Devel.--Tanning Research Labs., Inc., Ormond Beach, FL; *U.S. Private*, pg. 1068

Susor, Robert J., Sr. V.P.-Mkt. Devel.--Genuine Parts Company, Atlanta, GA; *U.S. Public*, pg. 732

Sussman, Gerald, Sr. V.P.-Plng. & Admin.--Oxford University Press, Inc., New York, NY; *Int'l*, pg. 1019

Sutphen, John C., Sr. V.P.-Intl. Bus. Devel.--American Express Travel Related Services Co., Inc., New York, NY; *U.S. Public*, pg. 73

Suurtamm, Peter, V.P.-Business Plng. & Analysis--Cara Operations Limited, Toronto, Canada; *Int'l*, pg. 266

Suzuki, Eisuke, Mgr.-Gen. Affairs & Plng.--Ashikaga Bank-International Division, Tokyo, Japan; *Int'l*, pg. 88

Suzuki, Kazuo, Gen. Mgr.-Plng.--Yasuda Mutual Life Insurance Co., Tokyo, Japan; *Int'l*, pg. 1519

Suzuki, Koji, Gen. Mgr.-Agency Plng.--Yasuda Mutual Life Insurance Co., Tokyo, Japan; *Int'l*, pg. 1519

Suzuki, Yukuo, Mng. Dir.-Plng. & Pur., Logistics & Pur., Fertilizer--UBE Industries Ltd., Tokyo, Japan; *Int'l*, pg. 1426

Svedahl, Reidar, Dir.-Bus. Devel.--Scandinavian Leisure Group A.B., Stockholm, Sweden; *Int'l*, pg. 39

Swanson, Stephen L., Sr. V.P.-Strategic Plng.--PNC Bank Corp., Pittsburgh, PA; *U.S. Public*, pg. 1242

Sweatt, Blaine, III, Exec. V.P. & Pres.-New Bus. Devel.--Darden Restaurants, Inc., Orlando, FL; *U.S. Public*, pg. 483

Sweeney, Dennis A., V.P.-Corp. & System Plng.--Citation Insurance Group, San Jose, CA; *U.S. Public*, pg. 376

Sweeney, William E., Exec. V.P.--BDM International, Inc., Mc Lean, VA; *U.S. Public*, pg. 1558

Swift, Asa, V.P.-Market Devel.--Columbus Mills, Inc., Columbus, GA; *U.S. Private*, pg. 256

Swift, M. Allen, Chm. Bd., Pres. & Treas.--M. Swift & Sons Inc., Hartford, CT; *U.S. Private*, pg. 1059

Swift, Virgil N., Exec. V.P.-Bus. Devel.--Swift Energy Company, Houston, TX; *U.S. Public*, pg. 1543

Swinehart, Keith, II, Pres.--Vanguard Plastics, Inc., Mc Pherson, KS; *U.S. Private*, pg. 1134

Swinehart, Keith, Sr., Chm. Bd., Chief Exec. Officer & Chief Fin. Officer--Vanguard Plastics, Inc., Mc Pherson, KS; *U.S. Private*, pg. 1134

Syar, C.M., Chm. Bd.--Syar Industries, Inc., Napa, CA; *U.S. Private*, pg. 1059

Synder, John W., V.P.-Corp. Plng.--Du Pont (E.I. Du Pont De Nemours & Co.), Wilmington, DE; *U.S. Public*, pg. 530

Szapor, Stephen J., V.P.-Strategic Plng.--Greate Bay Casino Corporation, Atlantic City, NJ; *U.S. Public*, pg. 760

Szmulewitz, Armend, V.P.-Plng. & Prod. Dev.--Rexall Sundown Inc., Boca Raton, FL; *U.S. Public*, pg. 1384

Tabar, Klaus, Sr. V.P.-Devel., Store Plng. & Construction--Krause's Furniture Inc., Brea, CA; *U.S. Public*, pg. 967

Tada, Hideo, Exec. Dir.-Plng. & Internal Audit--Japan Tobacco Inc., Tokyo, Japan; *Int'l*, pg. 703

Tahmahkera, Virginia, Mgr.-Org. Devel. & Plng.--Zoological Society of San Diego, San Diego, CA; *U.S. Private*, pg. 1207

Tai, E., Sr. Exec.- Mktg. & Plng. Personal Banking--The Hongkong and Shanghai Banking Corporation Limited (HongkongBank), Central, Hong Kong; *Int'l*, pg. 583

Takimoto, Kaichi, Deputy Gen. Mgr.-Plng. & Coordination Div.--Sumitomo Corporation, Tokyo, Japan; *Int'l*, pg. 1312

Taku, Yasuo, Mgr.-Res. Grp., Corp. Plng.--The Kansai Electric Power Co., Inc., Osaka, Japan; *Int'l*, pg. 722

Talley, David, V.P.-Bus. Affairs--Fox Broadcasting Company (FBC), Beverly Hills, CA; *Int'l*, pg. 926

Tallis, Alan, Exec. V.P.-Corp. Devel.--Red Roof Inns, Inc., Hilliard, OH; *U.S. Public*, pg. 1369

Tan, Thian H., V.P. & Mng. Dir-Mfg./Plng.--Komag, Incorporated, San Jose, CA; *U.S. Public*, pg. 966

Tanabe, Makoto, Sr. Mng. Dir.-Corp. Planning--Nippon Shinpan Co., Ltd., Tokyo, Japan; *Int'l*, pg. 939

Tanaka, Masahiro, Gen. Mgr.-Consumer Prods. Business Div.--Terumo Corporation, Tokyo, Japan; *Int'l*, pg. 1375

Tanchico, Emiliano R., Asst. V.P.-Personnel Mgmnt. & Devel.--Philippine Long Distance Telephone Company, Manila, Philippines; *Int'l*, pg. 1051

Tang, Cyrus, Chm. Bd., Pres., & Chief Exec. Officer--Tang Industries Inc., Las Vegas, NV; *U.S. Private*, pg. 1068

Tanzer, Mark W., V.P.-Prod. Devel.--Cracker Barrel Old Country Store, Inc., Lebanon, TN; *U.S. Public*, pg. 455

Tarantino, Robert V., Pres. & Chief Exec. Officer--Dataram Corporation, Princeton, NJ; *U.S. Public*, pg. 487

Tarbox, Richard C., V.P.-Corp. Devel.--SunGard Data Systems Inc., Wayne, PA; *U.S. Public*, pg. 1534

Tardif, Daniel, V.P.-Corp. Devel.--Tembec Inc., Montreal, Canada; *Int'l*, pg. 1374

Tarrant, R. Lane, Chm. Bd., Pres. & Chief Exec. Officer--Tarrant Service, Inc., Louisville, KY; *U.S. Private*, pg. 1069

Tauber, Orner J., Jr., Pres. & Chief Exec. Officer--Tauber Oil Company, Houston, TX; *U.S. Private*, pg. 1069

Taunt, Robin J., Dir.-Bus. Devel.--Smiths Industries plc, London, United Kingdom; *Int'l*, pg. 1266

Taunton, Michael J., Asst. Mgr.--Brooklyn Union, Brooklyn, NY; *U.S. Public*, pg. 259

Taylor, Colin, Dir.-Project Devel.--Sacramento Municipal Utility District, Sacramento, CA; *U.S. Private*, pg. 959

Taylor, James, Pres. & Chief Exec. & Fin. Officers--Reuter Manufacturing Inc., Hopkins, MN; *U.S. Public*, pg. 1383

Taylor, James M., Mgr.-Bus. Devel.--Bundy Asia Pacific, Adelaide, Australia; *Int'l*, pg. 1341

Taylor, Jeffrey, Dir.-Res. & Devel.--Standard Textile Co., Inc., Cincinnati, OH; *U.S. Private*, pg. 1032

Taylor, Karl, Sr. V.P.-Strategic & Mdse. Plng.--Montgomery Ward & Co., Inc., Chicago, IL; *U.S. Private*, pg. 758

Taylor, Kenneth, Pres.--Ohio Machinery Co., Cleveland, OH; *U.S. Private*, pg. 812

Taylor, Natalie, Dir.-Diversity Plng.--Food Lion, Inc., Salisbury, NC; *Int'l*, pg. 463

Taylor, Rod, V.P.-Corp. Strategies & Devel.--Ontario Hydro, Toronto, Canada; *Int'l*, pg. 1007

Taylor, Stephen C., V.P.-Professional Development--AON Corporation, Chicago, IL; *U.S. Public*, pg. 117

Taylor, Walter J., Dir.-Intl Bus. Devel.--Best Foods Exports, Englewood Cliffs, NJ; *U.S. Public*, pg. 224

Teck, Tan Siew, Sr. Mgr.-Mktg. & Bus. Devel.--Singapore Technologies Shipbuilding & Engineering Limited, Singapore, Singapore; *Int'l*, pg. 1253

Tedbury, Steve, Mng. Dir.-Strategic Plng.--Tate & Lyle PLC, London, United Kingdom; *Int'l*, pg. 1356

Telbin, Michael, Asst. V.P.-Res. & Devel.--LeaRonal, Inc., Freeport, NY; *U.S. Public*, pg. 982

ten Berg, W.M., Sr. Exec. V.P.-Plng., Control Acctg. & Taxation--ABN-AMRO Holding N.V., Amsterdam, Netherlands; *Int'l*, pg. 8

Tenhundfeld, A.H., Jr., V.P.-Admin. & Plng.--Mobile Gas Service Corp., Mobile, AL; *U.S. Public*, pg. 1120

Tennenhouse, Don, Sr. V.P.-Mktg. & Bus. Devel.--American General Finance, Inc., Evansville, IN; *U.S. Public*, pg. 76

Tennison, Bob J., V.P.-Continuous Improvement--Hillenbrand Industries, Inc., Batesville, IN; *U.S. Public*, pg. 828

Tenzillo, Jim, V.P.-Mktg. Devel. & Plng.--W.W. Grainger, Inc., Lincolnshire, IL; *U.S. Public*, pg. 758

Terl, Stewart, V.P.-Plng. & Admin.--Ausherman Construction Company, Frederick, MD; *U.S. Private*, pg. 99

Testwuide, Thomas R., Pres. & Chief Exec. Officer--Schreier Malting Co., Sheboygan, WI; *U.S. Private*, pg. 972

Thal, David, V.P.-Prod. Devel.--Aetna Industries, Inc., Center Line, MI; *U.S. Private*, pg. 25

Thalmann, Diane L., V.P.-Mktg. & Bus. Plng.--Waukesha Cherry-Burrell, Delavan, WI; *U.S. Public*, pg. 1677

Tharpe, Larry, Dir.-Pur., Plng. & Inventory Control--Heckethorn Mfg. Company, Inc., Dyersburg, TN; *U.S. Private*, pg. 519

Theodores, Theodore P., V.P.-Bus. Devel.--EG & G, Inc., Wellesley, MA; *U.S. Public*, pg. 542

Thies, Dennis M., Sr. V.P.-Corp. Devel.--Southdown, Inc., Houston, TX; *U.S. Public*, pg. 1488

Thies, Mark T., V.P.-Devel. & Controller--Black Hills Corporation, Rapid City, SD; *U.S. Public*, pg. 235

Thoma, Edward W., Sr. V.P.-Fin.--Oneida Ltd., Oneida, NY; *U.S. Public*, pg. 1225

Thomas, G.N., Chm. Bd., Pres., & Chief Exec. Officer--A. Levy & J. Zentner Co., Sacramento, CA; *U.S. Private*, pg. 663

Thomas, J. Alun, V.P.-Corp. Plng. & Devel./Asia Pacific--The Lubrizol Corporation, Wickliffe, OH; *U.S. Public*, pg. 1016

Thomas, Lawrence J., V.P.-Strategic Plns.--Technical Products Division, Sterling, VA; *U.S. Public*, pg. 424

Thomas, Mark W., Exec. V.P.-Prod. Devel.--National Cattlemen's Beef Association, Chicago, IL; *U.S. Private*, pg. 780

Thompson, Clyde W., V.P.-Admin. & Plng.--Stant Corporation, Denver, CO; *Int'l*, pg. 1396

Thompson, David D., V.P.-Hardware Research & Devel.--Cray Research, Eagan, MN; *U.S. Public*, pg. 1473

Thompson, John D., Sr. V.P.-Strategic & Bus. Devel.--The Dexter Corporation, Windsor Locks, CT; *U.S. Public*, pg. 504

Thompson, Len, V.P.-Corp. Policies--Burrell Communications Group Inc., Chicago, IL; *U.S. Private*, pg. 188

Thompson, Mark D., Chief Fin. Officer & Exec. V.P.--Lexford Residential Trust, Columbus, OH; *U.S. Public*, pg. 991

Thompson, Michael D., Pres. & Chief Exec. Officer--Thompson Tractor Company, Birmingham, AL; *U.S. Private*, pg. 1083

Thompson, Paul, Dir.-Business Devel.--LG & E Energy Corp., Louisville, KY; *U.S. Public*, pg. 970

Thompson, Robert L., Comptroller & Dir.-Corp. Planning--Oryx Energy, Dallas, TX; *U.S. Public*, pg. 1232

Thompson, William, V.P.-Mktg. & Devel.--Select Sires, Inc., Plain City, OH; *U.S. Private*, pg. 982

Thoren, Kaj, Dir.-Business Devel.--AB SKF, Goteborg, Sweden; *Int'l*, pg. 1156

Thorngren, Bertil, Sr. V.P.-Corp. Strategy--Telia AB, Farsta, Sweden; *Int'l*, pg. 1373

Thornley, Mark, V.P.-Plng.--Imax Corporation, Mississauga, Canada; *Int'l*, pg. 661

Thrash, H. Lee, III, Chief Fin. Officer & V.P.-Planning & Devel.--Caraustar Industries, Inc., Austell, GA; *U.S. Public*, pg. 303

Throop, Robert S., Chm. Bd. & Chief Exec. Officer--Anthem Electronics Inc., San Jose, CA; *U.S. Public*, pg. 134

Thrush, Robert A., V.P.-Prod. Mngmt.--W.W. Grainger, Inc., Lincolnshire, IL; *U.S. Public*, pg. 758

Thune, Nelson F., Sr. V.P.-Opers. & Plng.--Hycor Biomedical, Inc., Irvine, CA; *U.S. Public*, pg. 851

Tiasayakorn, Santi, Mgr.-Bus. Devel. & Project Div.--The Siam Cement Public Company Limited, Bangkok, Thailand; *Int'l*, pg. 1237

Tietjen, John, V.P.-Bus. Devel./Household Surface Care--Colgate-Palmolive Company, New York, NY; *U.S. Public*, *pg. 397*

Tietz, Adrienne, V.P.-Corp. Dev.--National Computer Systems, Eden Prairie, MN; *U.S. Public*, pg. 1155

Timmons, Michael, Dir.-Org. Devel.--Dominion Textile Inc., Montreal, Canada; *Int'l*, pg. 415

Tinmouth, WilliamW., Sr. V.P.-Corp. Affairs & Law--Cambridge Shopping Centres Limited, Toronto, Canada; *Int'l*, pg. 253

Tobey, Robert F., V.P.-Corp. Devel.--Echlin Inc., Branford, CT; *U.S. Public*, pg. 560

Tobin, Charles, V.P.-Plng. & Devel.--Western Waste Industries, Torrance, CA; *U.S. Public*, pg. 1686

Tobison, John, Chief Info. Officer & V.P.-Strategic Plng.--MapInfo Corp., Troy, NY; *U.S. Public*, pg. 1042

Tockarshewsky, Joseph B., Chm. Bd., Pres. & Chief Exec. Officer--Bank of the Hudson, Poughkeepsie, NY; *U.S. Public*, pg. 1319

Todd, Henry R., V.P.-Bus. Devel., Govt. & Tourism--Carlson Companies, Inc., Minnetonka, MN; *U.S. Private*, pg. 211

Todd, Rick, V.P.-Corp. Devel.--Silver Dollar City, Inc., Branson, MO; *U.S. Private*, pg. 1000

Toledano, Salomon, Exec. V.P.-Devel., Mergers & Aquisitions--Club Mediterranee SA, Paris, France; *Int'l*, pg. 298

Tomizawa, Hiroshi, Sr. Exec. V.P.--Japan Tobacco Inc., Tokyo, Japan; *Int'l*, pg. 703

Tomlin, Eugene B., Pres. & Chief Exec. Officer--I.H. French & Co. Inc., Champaign, IL; *U.S. Private*, pg. 427

Tomlinson, Lynn, Dir.-Prod. Devel.--Dresher, Inc., Carthage, MO; *U.S. Public*, pg. 986

Tompkins, J. Richard, Chm. Bd. & Pres.--Middlesex Water Company, Iselin, NJ; *U.S. Public*, pg. 1110

Toomey, Rodger, Sr. V.P.-Mktg. & Bus. Devel.--Food Services of America, Seattle, WA; *U.S. Private*, pg. 987

Torchia, Eugene, Jr., V.P.-Store Plng.--The Gap, Inc., San Francisco, CA; *U.S. Public*, pg. 702

Torcivia, Bryan, V.P.-Plng. & Pur.--The Earthgrains Company, Clayton, MO; *U.S. Public*, pg. 547

Torond, R.E., Grp. Mgr.-Plng.--Johnson Matthey Public Limited Company, London, United Kingdom; *Int'l*, pg. 713

Towle, C., Dir.-Plng. & Devel.--Seven Seas Limited, Hull, United Kingdom; *Int'l*, pg. 593

Towler, Robert A., Sr. V.P.-Bus. Devel.--Alberta Energy Company, Ltd., Calgary, Canada; *Int'l*, pg. 48

Toyama, Eisuke, V.P.-Strategy & Prod. Plng.--Nissan Motor Corporation in U.S.A., Gardena, CA; *Int'l*, pg. 945

Tracol, Pierre, Dir.-Intl. Devel.--Saint-Gobain, Courbevoie, France; *Int'l*, pg. 1170

Traub, Seth, Dir.-Bus. Devel.--L3 Communications Hycor Div., Woburn, MA; *U.S. Private*, pg. 638

Traylor, Linda G., V.P.-H.R. & Plng & Devel.--Advantica Restaurant Group, Inc., Spartanburg, SC; *U.S. Public*, pg. 22

Treichel, Steve, V.P.-Plng.--Lund International Holdings, Inc., Anoka, MN; *U.S. Public*, pg. 1020

Treinen, David J., Sr. V.P.-Plng. & Analysis--First Data Corporation, Hackensack, NJ; *U.S. Public*, pg. 630

Treinen, Mark E., V.P.-Bus. Devel.--Valmont Industries, Inc., Valley, NE; *U.S. Public*, pg. 1706

Trela, Timothy W., V.P.-Plng., Logistics & Systems Tech./ISFPC--Inland Steel Products Company, East Chicago, IN; *U.S. Public*, pg. 879

Trewella, Robert, Mgr.-Strategic & Bus. Plng.--AGA Gas, Inc., Independence, OH; *Int'l*, pg. 13

Trice, Robert H., Jr., V.P.-Intl. Bus. Devel.--Lockheed Martin Corporation, Bethesda, MD; *U.S. Public*, pg. 1006

Tripathi, Praveen, Assoc. Reg. Dir.-Media & Strategic Plng.--Chaitra Leo Burnett Private Ltd., Mumbai, India; *U.S. Private*, pg. 184

Tropp, Art, V.P.-Real Estate & Store Devel.--Williams-Sonoma, Inc., San Francisco, CA; *U.S. Public*, pg. 1770

Trub, Aaron D., V.P., Treas. & Sec.--Smithfield Foods, Inc., Norfolk, VA; *U.S. Public*, pg. 1479

Trubisky, Ronald J., Dir.-Indus. & Plng.--The Dispatch Printing Company, Columbus, OH; *U.S. Private*, pg. 334

Truchi, James, Chief Fin. Officer, Controller & Treas.--Trucchis Markets, Raynham, MA; *U.S. Private*, pg. 1107

Truesdell, J.E., Jr., Pres. & Sec.--Austin Group, Flint, MI; *U.S. Private*, pg. 99

Trumble, Marian, Dir.-Admin. Planning--Carson Pirie Scott & Co., Milwaukee, WI; *U.S. Public*, pg. 309

Tsim, Paul, Mgr.-Bus. Devel.--Sun Hung Kai Properties Ltd., Wan Chai, Hong Kong; *Int'l*, pg. 1318

Tsuchiya, Takashi, Mng. Dir.--Tosoh Corporation, Tokyo, Japan; *Int'l*, pg. 1407

Tsuchiya, Yoshihiro, Mng. Dir.-Admin. Div., Corp. Plng. & Acctg.--Nippo Corporation, Tokyo, Japan; *Int'l*, pg. 932

Tsuruta, Tadao, Exec. V.P.-Tech. & New Enterprises--Nikon Corporation, Tokyo, Japan; *Int'l*, pg. 931

Tuck, Joel, Sr. V.P.-Devel.--Mr. Gatti's, Inc., Kerrville, TX; *U.S. Private*, pg. 639

Turf, Barbara, Pres.--Euromarket Designs, Inc., Northbrook, IL; *U.S. Private*, pg. 384

Turgyan, Mark, V.P.--Right Management Consultants, Inc., Philadelphia, PA; *U.S. Public*, pg. 1390

Turnbull, G. Keith, Exec. V.P.-Strategic Analysis/Plng. & Information--Aluminum Company of America, Pittsburgh, PA; *U.S. Public*, pg. 60

Turner, Curtis L., Sr. V.P.-Mktg. & Devel.--Mapco Natural Gas Liquids Inc., Tulsa, OK; *U.S. Public*, pg. 1042

Turner, H. Allen, V.P.-Corp. Devel.--Devon Energy Corporation, Oklahoma City, OK; *U.S. Public*, pg. 503

Turner, Martin, Dir.-Corp. Plmg.--Ansell International, Glen Waverley, Australia; *Int'l*, pg. 1021

Turner, Stan, V.P.-Bus. Devel.--Davis Electrical Constructors, Inc., Greenville, SC; *U.S. Private*, pg. 315

Twining, Robert, V.P.-Sls., Mktg. & Bus. Plng.--COMSAT World Systems, Bethesda, MD; *U.S. Public*, pg. 424

Twomey, Sean M., V.P.-Business Devel.--Quebecor Printing, Inc., Montreal, Canada; *Int'l*, pg. 1076

Tyson, Andrew R., Sr. V.P.-Corp. Devel.--Keycorp, Cleveland, OH; *U.S. Public*, pg. 954

Tyson, Don, Sr. Chm.-Exec. & Fin. Committee--Tyson Foods, Inc., Springdale, AR; *U.S. Public*, pg. 1652

Uchiyama, Kensuke, Mng. Dir.-Res. & Devel.--Japan Tobacco Inc., Tokyo, Japan; *Int'l*, pg. 703

Uddir, Jalal, Dir.-Corp. Plng.--Pakistan International Airlines Corporation, Karachi, Pakistan; *Int'l*, pg. 1021

Ueda, Koichi, Mng. Dir.-Customer Service, Office Systems Plng. & Admn.--Yasuda Mutual Life Insurance Co., Tokyo, Japan; *Int'l*, pg. 1519

Ueki, Satoshi, Gen. Mgr.--Chiyoda Mutual Life Insurance Company, Tokyo, Japan; *Int'l*, pg. 286

Uhlman, Tom, Sr. V.P.-Corp. Strategy, Devel. & Pub. Affairs--Lucent Technologies Inc., Murray Hill, NJ; *U.S. Public*, pg. 1017

Uhlmann, Eberhard, Mgr.-Treas./Plng. & Disbursements--European Investment Bank, Luxembourg, Luxembourg; *Int'l*, pg. 465

Ulmer, Simon W., V.P. & Gen. Mgr.-Bus. Devel.--Johns Manville Corporation, Denver, CO; *U.S. Public*, pg. 927

Ulrichsen, Borre B., Dir.-Bus. Devel.--Tiedemanns - Joh.H.Andresen ANS, Oslo, Norway; *Int'l*, pg. 1389

Underhill, Susan, Mgr.-Training & Devel.--Oglebay Norton Company, Cleveland, OH; *U.S. Public*, pg. 1213

Updyke, Rick, Mgr.-Plng.--The Southland Corporation, Dallas, TX; *Int'l*, pg. 693

Urquiaga Blanco, Jose, V.P.-Plng. & Devel.--Industrias Penoles S.A. de C.V., Cuauhtemoc, Mexico; *Int'l*, pg. 677

Uthoff, Steve J., V.P.-Plng. & Analysis--Browning-Ferris Industries, Inc., Houston, TX; *U.S. Public*, pg. 262

Utley, John E., Sr. V.P.-Strategic Mktg.--Varity Kelsey Hayes, Livonia, MI; *Int'l*, pg. 820

Vadasz, Leslie L., Sr. V.P. & Dir.-Corp. Bus. Devel.--Intel Corporation, Santa Clara, CA; *U.S. Public*, pg. 886

Vaish, A., Dir. Plng. & Quality Enhancement--Air India, Mumbai, India; *Int'l*, pg. 37

Valencia de Freitas, Luciano, Dir.-Mfg.--Sao Paulo Alpargatas S.A., Sao Paulo, Brazil; *Int'l*, pg. 1193

Valerio, Martha M., V.P.-Corp. Devel.--Northwestern Mutual Life Insurance Co., Milwaukee, WI; *U.S. Private*, pg. 807

Valk, G. Lindsay, V.P.-Circulation & Mktg.--Hearst Magazines Division, New York, NY; *U.S. Private*, pg. 516

Vallieres, Jules, V.P.-Bus. Devel.--Uniboard Canada Inc., Laval, Canada; *Int'l*, pg. 1431

Valvano, Nick, V.P.-Bus. Devel.--Olsy North America Inc., Liberty Lake, WA; *Int'l*, pg. 1002

Van Adel, R.E., V.P.-Devel. & Project Fin.--Agra Inc., Calgary, Canada; *Int'l*, pg. 30

Van Bronkhorst, Jon, V.P.-Bus. Devel.--HMT Technology Corporation, Fremont, CA; *U.S. Public*, pg. 771

Van Cura, Robert, Mgr.-Plng. & Devel.--ULLICO Inc., Washington, DC; *U.S. Private*, pg. 1115

van der Laan, W., Dir.-Organizational Devel.--CSM N.V., Diemen, Netherlands; *Int'l*, pg. 243

van der Meer, Jaap, V.P.-Strategic Devel. & Worldwide Sls. & Mktg.--Alpnet Inc., Salt Lake City, UT; *U.S. Public*, pg. 58

van der Puil, Jan, Dir.-Grp. Devel.--CRH, plc, Dublin, Ireland; *Int'l*, pg. 242

van Haeringen, A.C., Dir.-Strategic Plng. & Investor Rels.--Ballast Nedam NV, Amstelveen, Netherlands; *Int'l*, pg. 133

Van Hoesen, Richard H., Chief Fin. Officer & V.P.-Fin.--Wall Data Incorporated, Kirkland, WA; *U.S. Public*, pg. 1734

van Hooff, Peter, Dir.-Corp. Strategy--Reed Elsevier plc, London, United Kingdom; *Int'l*, pg. 1093

Van Hooser, David G., Sr. V.P. & Dir.-Corp. Strategy--Owens-Illinois, Inc., Toledo, OH; *U.S. Public*, pg. 1238

Van Horn, Bob, Exec. V.P. & Strategic Plng. Dir.--Crispin Porter & Bogusky Advertising, Miami, FL; *U.S. Private*, pg. 290

van Melle, H.P., Sr. V.P.-Production & Logistics & Planning--Van Melle N.V., Breda, Netherlands; *Int'l*, pg. 1450

van Remoortere, Francois P., V.P.-Res.--W.R. Grace & Co., Boca Raton, FL; *U.S. Public*, pg. 754

van Straten, M.C., Global Planner & Asst. Prod. Mgr.--Industrial Pharmaceutical Products Division, Delft, Netherlands; *Int'l*, pg. 1142

Van Tiem, James D., Chief Fin. Officer & Treas.--The Cypress Companies, Akron, OH; *U.S. Private*, pg. 299

Van Vleck, Richard, V.P.-Corp. Strategy & Devel.--LEXIS-NEXIS, Miamisburg, OH; *Int'l*, pg. 1096

van Wezel, J., Mgr.-Plng. & Organization--Bols International B.V., Nieuw-Vennep, Netherlands; *Int'l*, pg. 751

Vandenbergh, Henry J., Jr., Chief Fin. Officer & Treas.--Rose Packing Company, Barrington, IL; *U.S. Private*, pg. 945

VandenBrand, Rene M.J., V.P.-Corp. Devel. & Sec.--Veritas DGC Inc., Houston, TX; *U.S. Private*, pg. 1136

VanHook, Marvin, V.P.-Plng.--Petroleum Heat & Power Co., Stamford, CT; *U.S. Public*, pg. 1281

Vanzura, Cedric J., V.P.-Grp. Plng. & Resource Mngmt.--Borders Group, Inc., Ann Arbor, MI; *U.S. Public*, pg. 245

Varga, Robert C., V.P.-Corp. Devel. & Govt. Rels.--Equifax Inc., Atlanta, GA; *U.S. Public*, pg. 588

Vaux, Robert G., Sr. V.P.-Fin. & Corp. Devel.--Labatt Brewing Company Limited, Toronto, Canada; *Int'l*, pg. 679

Veghte, Robert I., Pres. & Chief Exec. Officer--Wheaton Inc., Millville, NJ; *Int'l*, pg. 67

Veldhuizen, Brian, V.P.-Sls. & Mktg.--Freeman Energy Corporation, Springfield, IL; *U.S. Public*, pg. 709

Velins, Eriks, Gen. Mgr.-Plng.--BHP Petroleum, Melbourne, Australia; *Int'l*, pg. 224

Vella, George J., V.P.-Chemical Res. & Devel.--PerSeptive Biosystems, Inc., Framingham, MA; *U.S. Public*, pg. 1279

Venema, John, Sr. V.P.-Mktg. & Mktg. Devel.--Overhead Door Corporation, Dallas, TX; *U.S. Private*, pg. 822

Verkroost, Fredrik C., Dr., Mng. Dir.-Corp. Devel.--Landis & Staefa AG, Zug, Switzerland; *Int'l*, pg. 800

Vermillion, Michael R., V.P.-Plng. & Devel.--Salient 3 Communications, Inc., Reading, PA; *U.S. Public*, pg. 1429

Vidaurrazaga, Juan J., Sr. V.P.-Engrng. & Plng.--Dataproducts Corporation, Simi Valley, CA; *Int'l*, pg. 620

Viera, Mercedes, Mgr.-Personnel Plng. & Devel.--C.A. Cigarrera Bigott, Sucs., Caracas, Venezuela; *Int'l*, pg. 111

Vieth, George W., Jr., V.P.-Devel. & Plng.--Humana Inc., Louisville, KY; *U.S. Public*, pg. 847

Virrankoski, Risto, Deputy Pres.--Outokumpu Oyj, Espoo, Finland; *Int'l*, pg. 1015

Visscher, Herbert B.H., Sr. V.P.-Grp. Bus. Devel.--AEGON N.V., Hague, Netherlands; *Int'l*, pg. 25

Voelte, Donald R., Sr. V.P.-Plng.--Atlantic Richfield Company, Los Angeles, CA; *U.S. Public*, pg. 144

Vogt, Carl, 1st Sr. V.P. & Dir.-Mdse. Plng. & Distr., Licensed Discount Div.--J. Baker, Inc., Canton, MA; *U.S. Public*, pg. 167
Volpentesta, Frank, Chief Oper. Officer & V.P.--Bearing Headquarters Co., Broadview, IL; *U.S. Private*, pg. 127
von Boetticher, Gotthard, Dir.-Tech. Plng. & Logistics--Mercedes-Benz AG, Stuttgart, Germany; *Int'l*, pg. 368
Von Lehman, John I., Chief Fin. Officer, V.P. & Treas.--The Midland Company, Cincinnati, OH; *U.S. Public*, pg. 1110
von Pierer, Heinrich, Dr., Pres. & Chief Exec. Officer--Siemens AG, Munich, Germany; *Int'l*, pg. 1244
Vossen, Curt, V.P.--Cargill Ltd., Winnipeg, Canada; *U.S. Private*, pg. 210
Vovis, Gerald F., Sr. V.P.-Res. & Devel.--Genome Therapeutics Corporation, Waltham, MA; *U.S. Public*, pg. 730
Vyas, Dilip S., V.P.-Bus. Devel. & Treas.--Circuit Systems, Inc., Elk Grove Village, IL; *U.S. Public*, pg. 374
Wade, Danny, V.P.-Prod. Devel.--World Carpets, Inc., Dalton, GA; *U.S. Private*, pg. 1190
Waggoner, Donald, Sr. V.P.-Corp. Devel.--Leupold & Stevens, Inc., Beaverton, OR; *U.S. Private*, pg. 662
Wagner, Janice E., V.P.-Customer Service Plng.--Rogers Cantel Mobile Communications Inc., Saint-Laurent, Canada; *Int'l*, pg. 1122
Wagner, Paul, Dir.-Planning--American International Airways, Ypsilanti, MI; *U.S. Private*, pg. 57
Wagner, Steve, V.P.-Mktg., Carrier Sls. & Bus. Devel.--USLD Communications Corp., San Antonio, TX; *U.S. Public*, pg. 969
Wagstaff, Robert S., Second V.P.-Individual Prod. Devel.--Shenandoah Life Insurance Company, Roanoke, VA; *U.S. Private*, pg. 992
Wainick, Jerome B., V.P.-Research & Devel.--Tambrands Inc., Cincinnati, OH; *U.S. Public*, pg. 1331
Walch, Gerhard, V.P.-Client Relations & New Business Devel.--Liechtenstein Global Trust Limited, Vaduz, Liechtenstein; *Int'l*, pg. 809
Waldorf, Robert, Chm. Bd. & Pres.--Idea Man, Inc., Los Angeles, CA; *U.S. Private*, pg. 557
Wale, Kevin E., Dir.-Fin. & Strategic Plng.--General Motors-Holden's Automotive Limited, Melbourne, Australia; *U.S. Public*, pg. 723
Walker, R.A., V.P.-Planning--Grand Trunk Corporation (GTC), Detroit, MI; *Int'l*, pg. 258
Walker, Robert, Dir.-Plng. & Devel.--Raytheon Systems Co., Kirkwood, NY; *U.S. Public*, pg. 1364
Walker, Robert L., Chief Fin. Officer & Sr. V.P.-Fin.--AEGON USA, Inc., Louisville, KY; *Int'l*, pg. 26
Walkoviak, Joe W., V.P.-Strategic Plng.--SBC Communications Inc., San Antonio, TX; *U.S. Public*, pg. 1415
Wall, Terrence D., Chm. Bd., Pres. & Chief Exec. Officer--Vital Signs, Inc., Totowa, NJ; *U.S. Public*, pg. 1723
Wallace, Leonard E., V.P.-Engrng. & New Ventures--Kerr-McGee Petroleum Exploration & Production Division, Oklahoma City, OK; *U.S. Public*, pg. 952
Wallace, Scott R., V.P.-Corp. Devel.--Monitor Liability Managers, Inc., Rolling Meadows, IL; *U.S. Public*, pg. 215
Wallach, James, Pres. & Chief Exec. Officer--Central National-Gottesman Inc., Purchase, NY; *U.S. Private*, pg. 224
Wallas, Nancy, V.P. & Assoc. Plng. Dir.--DeWitt Media, Inc., New York, NY; *U.S. Private*, pg. 329
Wallenburg, Marcus, Exec. V.P.-Bus. Devel.--Investor AB, Stockholm, Sweden; *Int'l*, pg. 686
Walsh, Kevin J.F., V.P.-Fin. & Plng.--Sun Microsystems Computer Corporation, Mountain View, CA; *U.S. Public*, pg. 1531
Walsh, Richard J., V.P.-Corp. Devel. & Mktg.--Cytogen Corporation, Princeton, NJ; *U.S. Public*, pg. 471
Walsh, William J., Jr., Chief Oper. Officer, Exec. V.P. & Sec.--Consumers Financial Corporation, Camp Hill, PA; *U.S. Public*, pg. 437
Walter, Philip S., V.P. & Gen. Mgr.-New Bus. devel.--American Woodmark Corporation, Winchester, VA; *U.S. Public*, pg. 96
Walter, Richard A., Chm. Bd. & Chief Exec. Officer--Scicom Data Services, Ltd., Minnetonka, MN; *U.S. Private*, pg. 975
Wan, David, Exec. V.P.-Strategic Plng. & Devel.--Simon & Schuster, New York, NY; *U.S. Private*, pg. 777
Wang, I.L., Dir.--Taiwan Power Company, Taipei, Taiwan; *Int'l*, pg. 1348
Wantula, Peter, Sr. V.P.-Strategic Plng & New Bus.--Optima Direct, Inc., Vienna, VA; *U.S. Public*, pg. 1224
Ward, Bruce, Ph.D., V.P.-New Prod. Devel. Process--Respironics, Inc., Pittsburgh, PA; *U.S. Public*, pg. 1383
Ward, David K., Pres.--Ward Trucking Corp., Altoona, PA; *U.S. Private*, pg. 1149
Ward, Simon, Dir.-Plng. & Devel.--Whitbread PLC, London, United Kingdom; *Int'l*, pg. 1498
Warf, Alben W., Sr. V.P.-Electronic Systems Devel.--Diebold, Incorporated, Canton, OH; *U.S. Public*, pg. 506
Warren, Jeffrey H., V.P.-Land & Minerals & Asst. Sec.--Tejon Ranch Company, Lebec, CA; *U.S. Public*, pg. 1566
Warren, Lori, Brand Plng. Dir.--Hoffman/Lewis, San Francisco, CA; *U.S. Private*, pg. 532
Warren, Toney C., V.P.-Strategic Plng.--Telecom Solutions, San Jose, CA; *U.S. Public*, pg. 1547
Watanabe, Hajime, Mgr.-Corp. Plng.--The Bank of Tokyo-Mitsubishi, Ltd., Tokyo, Japan; *Int'l*, pg. 157
Watanabe, Hideo, Mng. Dir. & Mgr.-Corp. Plng.--Mitsubishi Chemical Corporation, Tokyo, Japan; *Int'l*, pg. 870
Water, Bernard, Gen. Mgr.-Strategy Corp.--Coles Myer Ltd., Tooronga, Australia; *Int'l*, pg. 306
Watson, Bill, V.P. Mktg.-/Steak & Ale--Bennigan's, Dallas, TX; *U.S. Private*, pg. 736
Watson, James E., Dir.-Intl. Business Admin.--The Ohio Art Company, Inc., Bryan, OH; *U.S. Public*, pg. 1214
Watts, David H., Pres. & Chief Exec. Officer--Granite Construction Incorporated, Watsonville, CA; *U.S. Public*, pg. 759
Waugh, Dick, V.P.-Securities Analysis & Strategy--Principal Mutual Life Insurance Co., Des Moines, IA; *U.S. Private*, pg. 886
Wax, Ben, Mgr.-Corp. Facilities--Webcraft Technologies, Inc., North Brunswick, NJ; *U.S. Public*, pg. 228
Webb, Dennis W., Grp. V.P.-Intl. Opers. & Bus. Devel.--Navistar International Transportation Corp., Chicago, IL; *U.S. Public*, pg. 1167
Webb, Jervis C., Chm. Bd. Emeritus--Jervis B. Webb Company, Farmington Hills, MI; *U.S. Private*, pg. 1156
Webb, Michael G., Sr. V.P.-Plng. & Devel.--Kerr-McGee Corporation, Oklahoma City, OK; *U.S. Public*, pg. 952
Webber, G.J., Reg. Dir.-Bus. Devel.--New Zealand Milk Products (North Asia) Ltd, Tokyo, Japan; *Int'l*, pg. 923
Webber, Stephanie, Ph.D., V.P.-Devel. Pharmacology--Agouron Pharmaceuticals, Inc., La Jolla, CA; *U.S. Public*, pg. 28
Weber, Bill, Pres.-ISC Grp. & V.P.-Bus. Plng.--Esco Corporation, Portland, OR; *U.S. Private*, pg. 382
Weber, Craig, V.P.-Prod. Devel.--Normark Corporation, Minnetonka, MN; *U.S. Private*, pg. 802
Weber, Mark, Sr. V.P.-Bus. Devel.--Reed Exhibition Companies-North America, Norwalk, CT; *Int'l*, pg. 1096
Weber, Pedro Cerisola y, Dir.-Planning--Telefonos de Mexico S.A. de C.V., Mexico, Mexico; *Int'l*, pg. 1373
Webster, David, Mgr.-DRI Bus. Devel.--BHP Iron Ore, Perth, Australia; *Int'l*, pg. 224
Weger, Steven J., V.P.-Plng. & Devel.--Abbott Laboratories, Abbott Park, IL; *U.S. Public*, pg. 12
Wegman, Daniel R., Pres.--Wegmans Food Markets, Inc., Rochester, NY; *U.S. Private*, pg. 1158
Wehber, Wayne, Mgr.-Prod. Devel.--Vilter Manufacturing Corporation, Cudahy, WI; *U.S. Private*, pg. 1140
Wehrle, Henry B., III, Pres. & Chief Exec. Officer--McJunkin Corporation, Charleston, WV; *U.S. Private*, pg. 722
Weiler, Richard J., V.P.-Corp. Devel.--Carpenter Technology Corporation, Reading, PA; *U.S. Public*, pg. 307
Weinberg, David, V.P.-Corp. Devel. & Strategy--Hyperion Software, Stamford, CT; *U.S. Public*, pg. 851
Weingold, Joel, V.P.-Bus. Affairs--Queens Group, Inc., Long Island City, NY; *U.S. Private*, pg. 900
Weinstein, Joel B., V.P.-Bus. Devel.--Hologic, Inc., Waltham, MA; *U.S. Public*, pg. 831
Weir, Donald, Dr., Mng. Dir.-Corp. Tech. Strategy--Landis & Staefa AG, Zug, Switzerland; *Int'l*, pg. 800
Weis, Alice, Dir.-Membership Devel. Admin.--Best Western International, Inc., Phoenix, AZ; *U.S. Private*, pg. 140
Weis, Bob, Dir.-New Product Devel.--Master Lock Company, Milwaukee, WI; *U.S. Public*, pg. 675
Welch, Jon, Mgr.-Corp. Plng.--AGCO Corporation, Duluth, GA; *U.S. Public*, pg. 28
Welch, Steven K., V.P.-Intl. Bus. Devel.--Amoco Corporation, Chicago, IL; *U.S. Public*, pg. 101
Wells, Alan, V.P.-Corp. Devel.--MidAmerican Energy Holdings, Des Moines, IA; *U.S. Public*, pg. 1109
Wells, Jerry, V.P.-Oper. & Strategic Plng.--Knouse Foods Inc., Peach Glen, PA; *U.S. Private*, pg. 627
Wendel, W. Hall, Jr., Chm. Bd. & Chief Exec. Officer--Polaris Industries, Inc., Minneapolis, MN; *U.S. Public*, pg. 1313
Wenstrup, H.D., Pres. & Chief Exec. Officer--CHEMCENTRAL Corporation, Bedford Park, IL; *U.S. Private*, pg. 231
Wentler, G.E., Dir.-Product Devel.--Procter & Gamble Pharmaceuticals, Inc., Cincinnati, OH; *U.S. Public*, pg. 1331
Werner, Douglas, Sr. V.P.-Strategic Plng. & Bus. Devel.--Foundation Health Systems, Inc., Pueblo, CO; *U.S. Public*, pg. 678
Werner, Raymond, Controller--Siliconix, Inc., Santa Clara, CA; *Int'l*, pg. 367
Wertheimer, Kim, V.P.-Plng. & Devel.--Circle International, Dallas, TX; *U.S. Public*, pg. 372
Wertz, Byron A., V.P.-Corp. Devel.--Telephone and Data Systems, Inc., Chicago, IL; *U.S. Public*, pg. 1570
Wessinger, John, Mgr.-Bus. Devel.--Wolverine Tube Inc., Huntsville, AL; *U.S. Public*, pg. 1774
Whalen, H.F., V.P. & Dir.-Corp. Devel.--PQ Corporation, Berwyn, PA; *U.S. Private*, pg. 827
Wheeler, Edward, V.P.-Research--Lapp Insulator Company, Le Roy, NY; *U.S. Private*, pg. 473
Wheeler, Robert V., Mgr.-Corp. Devel.--Landauer, Inc., Glenwood, IL; *U.S. Public*, pg. 977
Wheen, Ivan, Mng. Dir.-Strategic Plng.--Bankers Trust International (Asia) Ltd., Singapore, Singapore; *U.S. Public*, pg. 186
Wheiler, Ken, Mgr.-Planning & Admin.--Weyerhaeuser Japan Ltd., Tokyo, Japan; *U.S. Public*, pg. 1764
Whepley, Harry, V.P.-Fin.--Tekra Corporation, New Berlin, WI; *U.S. Private*, pg. 1073
Whitacre, David, V.P.-Devel.--Sandoz Agro, Inc., Des Plaines, IL; *Int'l*, pg. 974
Whitacre, R. Gregory, V.P.-College & University Prods.--SLM Holding Corp., Washington, DC; *U.S. Public*, pg. 1419
White, Brad, Dir.-Bus. Devel.--The Sharper Image, San Francisco, CA; *U.S. Public*, pg. 1464
White, Charlene, Mgr.-Res. & Devel.--AEP Industries, Inc., South Hackensack, NJ; *U.S. Public*, pg. 4
White, David A., Jr., Sr. V.P.-Corp. Plng. & Devel.--Cooper Industries, Inc., Houston, TX; *U.S. Public*, pg. 442
White, Diana, Mgr.-Natl. Sls. Plng.--The National Latex Products Co., Ashland, OH; *U.S. Private*, pg. 785
White, Eric, V.P.-Corp. Devel.--Glenayre Technologies, Inc., Charlotte, NC; *U.S. Public*, pg. 746
White, G.A., Gen. Engr. & Plng. Mgr.--Oldsmobile Div. General Motors Corp., Lansing, MI; *U.S. Public*, pg. 720
White, J. Spratt, Sr. V.P.-Growth & Devel. & Human Resources--Springs Industries, Inc., Fort Mill, SC; *U.S. Public*, pg. 1499
White, James C., Mgr.-Plng. & Communications--Danfoss Fluid Power, Racine, WI; *Int'l*, pg. 377
White, Jeffrey S., Jr., Sr. Dir.-Corp. Devel.--U.S. Surgical Corp., Norwalk, CT; *U.S. Public*, pg. 1687
White, Kevin R., Exec. V.P.-Corp. Devel. & Strategic Plng.--Louis Dreyfus Natural Gas Corp., Oklahoma City, OK; *U.S. Private*, pg. 342
White, Martin A., Sr. V.P.-Corp. Devel.--MDU Resources Group, Inc., Bismarck, ND; *U.S. Public*, pg. 1025
White, Warren, Chief Information Officer & V.P.-Plng.--Dominion Textile Inc., Montreal, Canada; *Int'l*, pg. 415
Whiteling, M., Dir.-Fin. Control & Plng.--Berisford plc, London, United Kingdom; *Int'l*, pg. 188
Whiteside, Ralph T., V.P.-Devel.--Sprint Corporation, Westwood, KS; *U.S. Public*, pg. 1500
Whitfield, William, V.P.-Bus. Devel. & Analysis--Tyson Foods, Inc., Springdale, AR; *U.S. Public*, pg. 1652
Whitlow, Maurice, Pres. & Chief Exec. Officer--General Processors, Inc., Oxford, NC; *U.S. Public*, pg. 1502
Whitman, John, Dir.-Grp. Plng.--Inchcape PLC, London, United Kingdom; *Int'l*, pg. 671
Whitman, William F., Jr., Chm. Bd.--The Middleby Corporation, Rolling Meadows, IL; *U.S. Public*, pg. 1109
Whiton, A.E., V.P. & Controller--Ionics, Incorporated, Watertown, MA; *U.S. Public*, pg. 912
Whitsell, Helen J., Chm. Bd., Chief Exec. Officer & Treas.--Copeland Lumber Yard, Inc., Portland, OR; *U.S. Private*, pg. 274
Whitt, David, Pres. & Chief Oper. Officer--Elixir Industries, Gardena, CA; *U.S. Private*, pg. 371
Whyte, Marcella, Mgr.-Prod. Devel.--Dakotah, Inc., Webster, SD; *U.S. Public*, pg. 477
Wick, Arthur D., V.P.-Res. & Devel.--Lesco, Inc., Rocky River, OH; *U.S. Public*, pg. 989
Wick, Jeff, Pres. & Chief Exec. Officer--Wick Building Systems, Mazomanie, WI; *U.S. Private*, pg. 1174
Wick, John F., Chm. Bd.--Wick Building Systems, Mazomanie, WI; *U.S. Private*, pg. 1174
Wicker, William M., Sr. V.P.-Corp. Devel.--Texaco Inc., White Plains, NY; *U.S. Public*, pg. 1582
Widmann, Nancy, Sr. V.P.-Mkt. Devel.--CBS Enterprises Division, New York, NY; *U.S. Public*, pg. 274
Wiedenhaupt, Kurt, Chm. Bd & Pres.--American Precision Industries Inc., Buffalo, NY; *U.S. Public*, pg. 90
Wiggin, Roger C., V.P.-Exploration & Devel.--Tipperary Corporation, Denver, CO; *U.S. Public*, pg. 1618
Wilder, Lawrence, V.P.-Prod. Devel.--Kleinert's, Inc., Plymouth Meeting, PA; *U.S. Private*, pg. 625
Wilder, Lawrence M., V.P.-Special Projects--Kleinert's, Inc., of Alabama, Elba, AL; *U.S. Private*, pg. 625
Wilder, Robert A., Dir.-Corp. Devel.--Telephone and Data Systems, Inc., Chicago, IL; *U.S. Public*, pg. 1570
Wilding, George, Dir.-Store Design & Devel.--Dixons Group plc, Hemel Hempstead, United Kingdom,; *Int'l*, pg. 413
Wilen, Glenn, V.P.-Fin. Plng.--The House of Seagram, New York, NY; *Int'l*, pg. 1217
Wilen, John C., V.P.-Corp. Strategic Planning--PepsiCo, Inc., Purchase, NY; *U.S. Public*, pg. 1276
Wilensky, Ron, V.P.-Bus. Devel.--TCI International Inc., Sunnyvale, CA; *U.S. Public*, pg. 1555
Wilhelm, George, Mgr.-Mining Devel. & Construction--TVX Gold Inc., Toronto, Canada; *Int'l*, pg. 1345
Wilkins, Alex M., Mgr.-Plng. Exploration & Devel.--BHP Coal, Brisbane, Australia; *Int'l*, pg. 223
Willard, Dean M., Chief Exec. Officer--Courtaulds Aerospace, Glendale, CA; *Int'l*, pg. 339
Willensky, David R., Sr. V.P.-Corp. Plng. & Devel.--ConAgra, Inc., Omaha, NE; *U.S. Public*, pg. 425
Williams, Ben, V.P.-Business Devel.--PAR Technology Corporation, New Hartford, NY; *U.S. Public*, pg. 1256
Williams, Bruce, V.P.-Plng. & Tech.--Western International Media Corporation, New York, NY; *U.S. Private*, pg. 1166
Williams, Cathy, V.P.-Client Devel.--Total System Services, Inc., Columbus, GA; *U.S. Public*, pg. 1550
Williams, Clarke M., Chm. Bd.--Century Telephone Enterprises, Inc., Monroe, LA; *U.S. Public*, pg. 329
Williams, Clay C., V.P.-Corp. Devel.--Tuboscope Incorporated, Houston, TX; *U.S. Public*, pg. 1643
Williams, David L., Mgr.-Bus. Devel., Europe--Rockwell International Corporation, Costa Mesa, CA; *U.S. Public*, pg. 1397
Williams, Frank R., V.P.-Tech. Assessment--Conmed Corporation, Utica, NY; *U.S. Public*, pg. 431
Williams, Judith A., V.P.-Corp. Plng.--Alexander & Baldwin, Inc., Honolulu, HI; *U.S. Public*, pg. 39
Williams, Kathryn L., V.P.-Strategic Devel.--Simpson Industries, Inc., Plymouth, MI; *U.S. Public*, pg. 1474
Williams, Loren R., V.P.-Strategic Mktg. & New Bus. Devel.--Animal Health, Fort Lee, NJ; *U.S. Public*, pg. 58
Williams, Nicole S., Chief Fin. Officer, Exec. V.P.-Fin. & Sec.--R.P. Scherer Corporation, Troy, MI; *U.S. Public*, pg. 1437
Williams, Richard, Dir.-Bus. Devel.--Safeway PLC, Hayes, United Kingdom; *Int'l*, pg. 1169
Williams, Robin, Mgr.-Plng. & Scheduling--Parkdale Mills, Gastonia, NC; *U.S. Private*, pg. 840
Williams, Ronald, Pres. & Chief Exec. Officer--Gary-Williams Energy Corporation, Denver, CO; *U.S. Private*, pg. 440
Williams, Tony, V.P.-Fin. & Plng.--Varity Kelsey Hayes, Livonia, MI; *Int'l*, pg. 820
Williams, Trevor, Mgr.-Bus. Devel./Canada--Apache Corporation, Houston, TX; *U.S. Public*, pg. 119
Williams, Wade, Sr. V.P.-Corp. Devel.--Smith's Food & Drug Centers, Inc., Salt Lake City, UT; *U.S. Public*, pg. 1103
Williams, William J., V.P.-Business Devel.--Jacobs Engineering Group Inc., Houston, TX; *U.S. Public*, pg. 921
Williamson, Daniel E., Dir.-Bus. Devel.--Biomet, Inc., Warsaw, IN; *U.S. Public*, pg. 231
Williamson, Pat, Exec. V.P.-Devel.--Pizza Hut, Inc., Dallas, TX; *U.S. Public*, pg. 1636
Willingham, Don, Mgr.-New Bus. Devel.--Boise Cascade Corporation, Boise, ID; *U.S. Public*, pg. 242

Willingham, Jack W., Exec. V.P.-Restaurant Devel.--Perkins Family Restaurants, Memphis, TN; *U.S. Private*, pg. 925
Williome, Jack H., Pres. & Chief Exec. Officer--Kaufman and Broad of Texas, Ltd., San Antonio, TX; *U.S. Public*, pg. 945
Willis, Donald E., V.P.-Strategic Plng.--Alliant Techsystems, Hopkins, MN; *U.S. Public*, pg. 47
Willis, Gary, Chief Fin. Officer, V.P.-Fin. & Treas.--Eddins-Walcher Company, Midland, TX; *U.S. Private*, pg. 362
Wilson, Michael, Dir.-Fin. Regulation & Plng.--Severn Trent Water Ltd., Birmingham, United Kingdom; *Int'l*, pg. 1225
Winfrey, Timothy, Dir.-Corp. Devel.--Owens Corning, Toledo, OH; *U.S. Public*, pg. 1236
Winger, Kenneth W., Sr. V.P.-Corp. Devel.--Laidlaw Inc., Burlington, Canada; *Int'l*, pg. 259
Winninghoff, Albert C.M., Corp. Vice Chm., Chief Oper. Officer & Corp. Plng. Dir.--Leo Burnett Company, Inc., Chicago, IL; *U.S. Private*, pg. 183
Winter, Irwin W., Chief Fin. Officer & Exec. V.P.--Phillips-Van Heusen Corporation, New York, NY; *U.S. Public*, pg. 1291
Winters, Bob, V.P.- Franchise Devel.--Perkins Family Restaurants, Memphis, TN; *U.S. Private*, pg. 925
Winters, Steve D., Chm. Bd. & Pres.--Bepco, Inc., Winston Salem, NC; *U.S. Private*, pg. 134
Wirth, B.A., V.P.-Bus. Devel.--BHP Petroleum (Americas) Inc., Houston, TX; *Int'l*, pg. 225
Wisdon, Bob, Mgr.-Plng.--Schlosser Forge Company, Rancho Cucamonga, CA; *U.S. Private*, pg. 970
Wise, Ted, Exec. V.P.--O'Reilly Automotive Inc., Springfield, MO; *U.S. Public*, pg. 1230
Witt, Tom, V.P.-Devel.--SunBridge Assisted Living, Albuquerque, NM; *U.S. Public*, pg. 1531
Wittman, Peter, Exec. V.P.-New Bus. Devel.--WWF Paper Corporation, Bala Cynwyd, PA; *U.S. Private*, pg. 1145
Wohlert, Doug, V.P.-Devel.--Sea World of California, San Diego, CA; *U.S. Public*, pg. 114
Wolf, Roger J., Chief Fin. Officer, Sr. V.P., Sec. & Treas.--Hurco Companies, Inc., Indianapolis, IN; *U.S. Public*, pg. 850
Wolff, Paul, Gen. Mgr.-Mktg. Devel. & Quality Control--Banque Generale du Luxembourg SA, Luxembourg, Luxembourg; *Int'l*, pg. 161
Wolk, Joel, V.P.-Strategic Plng.--Corinthian Media, Inc., New York, NY; *U.S. Private*, pg. 275
Wolters, J., Mgr.-Plng. & Devel.--DSM N.V., Heerlen, Netherlands; *Int'l*, pg. 352
Womble, Edgar, Gen. Mgr.--Perryton Equity, Perryton, TX; *U.S. Private*, pg. 855
Wong, Byron, Dir.-Texaco Europe Bus. Devel.--Texaco Inc., White Plains, NY; *U.S. Public*, pg. 1582
Wood, Bill J., V.P.-Res. & Devel.--RELA, Inc., Boulder, CO; *U.S. Public*, pg. 401
Wood, James H., V.P.-Information Systems, Plng. & Tech.--Springs Industries, Inc., Fort Mill, SC; *U.S. Public*, pg. 1499
Wood, Steve, Dir.-Store Plng. & Design--Ross Stores, Inc., Newark, CA; *U.S. Public*, pg. 1405
Wood, Wayne W., V.P.-Corp. Plng.--Commercial Union Assurance Company of Canada, Toronto, Canada; *Int'l*, pg. 308
Woodard, Larry, V.P.-Strategic Plng.--Uniworld Group, Inc., New York, NY; *U.S. Private*, pg. 1128
Woodbeck, Thomas M., Exec. V.P.--Overhead Conveyor Co., Ferndale, MI; *U.S. Private*, pg. 822
Woodruff, J. David, Jr., V.P.-Legal & Corp. Devel. & Asst. Sec.--Energen Corporation, Birmingham, AL; *U.S. Public*, *pg. 581*
Woods, Edward G., V.P.-Bus. Devel.--Albemarle Corporation, Richmond, VA; *U.S. Public*, pg. 37
Woodward, Sam, Sr. V.P.-Opers. & Plng.--Yellow Corporation, Overland Park, KS; *U.S. Public*, pg. 1788
Woodworth, Pat, Chm. Bd., Pres. & Chief Exec. Officer--Winona Knits, Winona, MN; *U.S. Private*, pg. 1183
Woolf, Jonathan, Mgr.-Mkt. Devel.-South--Subaru Western Region, Irvine, CA; *Int'l*, pg. 523
Worner, Ernst, Div. Mgr.--Durkopp Adler AG, Bielefeld, Germany; *Int'l*, pg. 468
Worthan, R.L., V.P.-Reg. & Resource Plng.--Intermountain Gas Co., Boise, ID; *U.S. Private*, pg. 568
Wotherspoon, G., Dir.-Property & Devel.--Safeway PLC, Hayes, United Kingdom; *Int'l*, pg. 1169
Wrem, Jeffrey, Dir.-Fin.--New Cooperative Inc., Fort Dodge, IA; *U.S. Private*, pg. 792
Wren, Marcy, Special Event Mgr.--CMI-Atlanta, Atlanta, GA; *U.S. Private*, pg. 287
Wrieth, Donald, Mgr.-Bus. Devel.--Peter Kiewit Sons Inc., Omaha, NE; *U.S. Private*, pg. 619
Wright, Albert B. III, V.P.-Corp. Plng.--Welch Foods Inc., A Cooperative, Concord, MA; *U.S. Private*, pg. 784
Wright, C.A., Dir.-New Bus.--LASMO plc, London, United Kingdom; *Int'l*, pg. 803
Wright, Elizabeth B., Sr. V.P.-Strategic Plng. & Mktg.--National Trustco Inc., Toronto, Canada; *Int'l*, pg. 909
Wright, Elizabeth B., Sr. V.P.-Strategic Plng. & Mktg.--National Trust Company, Stratford, Canada; *Int'l*, pg. 910
Wright, Richard C., V.P.-Devel.--Universal Health Services, Inc., King of Prussia, PA; *U.S. Public*, pg. 1696
Wright, Rick, Dir.-New Bus. Devel.--Product Information Network, Englewood, CO; *U.S. Private*, pg. 597
Wright, Samuel G., Chief Fin. Officer & Exec. V.P.--Eckerd Corporation, Largo, FL; *U.S. Public*, pg. 917
Wu, Randy L., V.P.-Energy Devel.--El Paso Natural Gas Co., Houston, TX; *U.S. Public*, pg. 567
Wu, Tzy-Chiang, V.P.--The International Commercial Bank of China, Taipei, Taiwan; *Int'l*, pg. 683
Wyckaert, Luke, Chm. Bd., Pres. & Chief Exec. Officer--Intertrade Industries, Huntington Beach, CA; *U.S. Private*, pg. 573
Wyle, Stephen, Sr. V.P.-Strategic Plng.--Investors Services Group, Boston, MA; *U.S. Public*, pg. 631
Wynne, Michael W., Sr. V.P.-Intl. Plng. & Devel.--General Dynamics Corporation, Falls Church, VA; *U.S. Public*, pg. 708
Xiaowei, Mao, Gen. Mgr.-Strategic Devel.--Bank of China, Beijing, China; *Int'l*, pg. 152
Yamaguchi, Kenji, Deputy Pres., Dir.-Plng., Pub. Rels., Gen. Affairs & Sec.--Yasuda Mutual Life Insurance Co., Tokyo, Japan; *Int'l*, pg. 1519
Yamamoto, Hideo, Dir.-Plng. & Control--UBE Industries Ltd., Tokyo, Japan; *Int'l*, pg. 1426
Yamamoto, Hiroshi, Exec. Dir.-Corp. Information Plng.--Fujisawa Pharmaceutical Co. Ltd., Osaka, Japan; *Int'l*, pg. 525
Yamazaki, Koji, Mgr.-Overseas Plng.--Fujikura Ltd., Tokyo, Japan; *Int'l*, pg. 525
Yamazaki, Masao, Sr. Exec. V.P.--Japan Tobacco Inc., Tokyo, Japan; *Int'l*, pg. 703
Yamazaki, Takashi, Mgr.-Plng.--Wako Securities Co., Ltd., Tokyo, Japan; *Int'l*, pg. 1485
Yardley, James C., V.P.-Mktg. & Bus. Devel.--Southern Natural Gas Company, Birmingham, AL; *U.S. Public*, pg. 1485
Yates, Christopher, Sr. V.P.-Bus. Devel.--Daisytek International Corporation, Plano, TX; *U.S. Public*, pg. 477
Yates, Christopher, Sr. V.P.-Bus. Devel.--Daisytek Incorporated, Plano, TX; *U.S. Public*, pg. 477
Yates, Christopher, Sr. V.P.-Bus. Devel.--Daisytek (Canada) Inc., Toronto, Canada; *U.S. Public*, pg. 477
Yates, Christopher, Sr. V.P.-Bus. Devel.--Daisytek Latin America, Miami, FL; *U.S. Public*, pg. 477
Yates, Christopher, Sr. V.P.-Bus. Devel.--Daisytek De Mexico S.A. de C.V., Mexico, Mexico; *U.S. Public*, pg. 477
Yates, Christopher, Sr. V.P.-Bus. Devel.--Priority Fulfillment Services, Inc., Plano, TX; *U.S. Public*, pg. 477
Yates, Christopher, Sr. V.P.-Bus. Devel.--Daisytek Australia Pty. Ltd., Alexandria, Australia; *U.S. Public*, pg. 477
Yates, Jim R., V.P.-Corp. Devel.--Gasco, Inc., Honolulu, HI; *Int'l*, pg. 225
Yates, R.C., Dir.-Mktg. & Bus. Devel.--Moore Europe, Lausanne, Switzerland; *Int'l*, pg. 889
Yaw, Liu K, V.P.-Sls. & Plng.--China Airlines Ltd., Taipei, Taiwan; *Int'l*, pg. 284
Yeager, Frederick C., V.P.-Fin. & Devel.--Time Warner Inc., New York, NY; *U.S. Public*, pg. 1610
Yeager, Waldo E., Chief Fin. Officer & Treas.--Seaway Food Town, Inc., Maumee, OH; *U.S. Public*, pg. 1452
Yearly, Douglas, V.P.-Asset Devel.--Toll Brothers, Inc., Huntingdon Valley, PA; *U.S. Public*, pg. 1620
Yerly, Marcel, V.P.-Res. & Devel.--Bobst S.A., Lausanne, Switzerland; *Int'l*, pg. 198
Yi, Mo Soo, Mgr.-Bus. Devel.--DBS Factors Pte. Ltd., Singapore, Singapore; *Int'l*, pg. 350
Ying, Ho Sau, Mgr.-Mktg. & Prod. Devel.--Tiger Medicals Ltd., Singapore, Singapore; *Int'l*, pg. 603
Yokotsuka, Masaaki, Sr. Mng. Dir.-Corp. Plng. & Coordination--Sumitomo Chemical Company, Ltd., Tokyo, Japan; *Int'l*, pg. 1310
Yonekura, Hiromasa, Mng. Dir.-Plng. & Coordination--Sumitomo Chemical Company, Ltd., Tokyo, Japan; *Int'l*, pg. 1310
York, E. Malcolm, Chief Fin. Officer & Exec. V.P.--Paul Inman Associates Inc., Farmington, MI; *U.S. Private*, pg. 564
Yoshii, Masanori, Dir.-Res. & Devel.--Showpla Asia Limited, Singapore, Singapore; *Int'l*, pg. 1237
Yoshino, Kyohei, Dep. Mgr.-Plng. Dept.--The Chiba Bank, Ltd.-International Division, Tokyo, Japan; *Int'l*, pg. 283
Yoshino, Tohru, Exec. V.P.--Oji Paper Co., Ltd., Tokyo, Japan; *Int'l*, pg. 998
Yoshioka, Yusaku, Gen. Mgr.--Toyo Tire & Rubber Co., Ltd., Osaka, Japan; *Int'l*, pg. 1411
Young, Allan R., V.P.-Devel.--Sunshine Mining And Refining Company, Boise, ID; *U.S. Public*, pg. 1536
Young, B., Mgr.-Corp. Devel.--Australian Oil & Gas Corporation Limited, Sydney, Australia; *Int'l*, pg. 101
Young, Bob, V.P.-Engrng. & Res.--Outboard Marine Corporation, Waukegan, IL; *U.S. Private*, pg. 478
Young, David A., V.P.-Bus. Devel.--Health Care Property Investors, Inc., Newport Beach, CA; *U.S. Public*, pg. 801
Young, Jack, Strategic Plng. Dir.--Waring & LaRosa, Inc., New York, NY; *U.S. Private*, pg. 1150
Young, James H., Jr., Sr. V.P.-Bus. Development--South Carolina Electric & Gas Co. (SCE&G), Columbia, SC; *U.S. Public*, pg. 1436
Young, Richard F., Chm. Bd., Pres. & Chief Exec. Officer--Sues, Young & Brown Inc., Baldwin Park, CA; *U.S. Private*, pg. 1049
Young, Rob, Sr. V.P.-Plng. & Res.--Harrison, Young, Pesonen & Newell Inc., Toronto, Canada; *Int'l*, pg. 598
Young, Valeri Ann, V.P.-Bus Devel.--Ketchum Directory Advertising/Los Angeles, Los Angeles, CA; *U.S. Private*, pg. 616
Young, Vivian, Exec. V.P., Strategic Services Dir.--Ammirati, Puris & Lintas, Inc., New York, NY; *U.S. Private*, pg. 66
Younus, Mohammad, Mgr.-Budget & Plng.--National Refinery Limited, Karachi, Pakistan; *Int'l*, pg. 909
Yousefi, Cid, V.P.-Prod. Devel. & MIS--Equitrac Corporation, Coral Gables, FL; *U.S. Public*, pg. 590
Yu, Jonathan K., V.P.-Bus. Devel.--Lattice Semiconductor Corporation, Hillsboro, OR; *U.S. Public*, pg. 979
Yuen, Norman K.T., Mng. Dir.-Corp. Devel. & Opers.--Hong Kong Telecommunications Limited, Quarry Bay, Hong Kong; *Int'l*, pg. 247
Yuge, Yutaka, Exec. V.P. & Gen. Mgr.-Corp. Plng. & Coordination Grp.--Japan Energy Corporation, Tokyo, Japan; *Int'l*, pg. 702
Zacheis, Carleton F., Sr. V.P.-Plng. & Bus. Devel.--Maytag Corporation, Newton, IA; *U.S. Public*, pg. 1064
Zandman, Felix, Dr., Chm. Bd., Pres. & Chief Exec. Officer--Vishay Intertechnology, Inc., Malvern, PA; *U.S. Public*, pg. 1721
Zane, Barry, Mgr.-Market Devel.--PRS, Inc., Leicester, NY; *U.S. Public*, pg. 282
Zangerle, Niklaus, Asst. V.P.-Res. & Devel.--Bobst S.A., Lausanne, Switzerland; *Int'l*, pg. 198
Zapiola, Ernesto, Mgr.-H.R. & Devel.--Y.P.F., S.A., Buenos Aires, Argentina; *Int'l*, pg. 1515
Zarrow, Henry, Pres. & Chief Exec. Officer--Sooner Pipe & Supply Corp., Tulsa, OK; *U.S. Private*, pg. 1014
Zazuri, Stephen, Dir.-Prod. Devel.--R.H. Forschner Division, Shelton, CT; *U.S. Public*, pg. 1544
Zazuri, Stephen, Dir.-Prod. Devel.--Swiss Army Brands Ltd., Shelton, CT; *U.S. Public*, pg. 1544
Zekind, Diane, Dir.-Advanced Plng. & Admin.--CMI International Inc., Southfield, MI; *U.S. Private*, pg. 195
Ziegler, J., V.P.-Strategic Plng.--Bombardier, Learjet Inc., Wichita, KS; *Int'l*, pg. 200
Ziff, Joshua J., V.P.-Bus. Devel.--Medrad, Inc., Indianola, PA; *Int'l*, pg. 1204
Zimbalist, Efrem, III, V.P.-Strategic Dev.--The Times Mirror Company, Los Angeles, CA; *U.S. Public*, pg. 1615
Zimmerman, Derk, Sr. V.P.-New Ventures & Bus. Devel.--CBS, New York, NY; *U.S. Public*, pg. 273
Zinbarg, Benson, Pres., Chief Exec. Officer, Chief Fin. Officer & Treas.--Sun Hill Industries, Inc., Stamford, CT; *U.S. Private*, pg. 1051
Zinkin, Peter, Dir.-Plng. & Devel.--BICC plc, London, United Kingdom; *Int'l*, pg. 120
Zorkers, Walter S., Sr. V.P.-Devel.--Hvide Marine Incorporated, Fort Lauderdale, FL; *U.S. Public*, pg. 851
Zoukis, Paul, Sr. V.P.-Mktg. & Sls.--Hogan Systems, Inc., Dallas, TX; *U.S. Public*, pg. 422
Zurita, Guadalupe, Mgr.-Bus. Devel.--Arrow Internacional de Mexico S.A., Mexico, Mexico; *U.S. Public*, pg. 135

PRESIDENT

Aagaard, A. Kim, Pres. & Chief Exec. Officer--Synergistics Industries Limited, Mississauga, Canada; *U.S. Public*, pg. 734
Aagaard, A. Kim, Pres.--Synergistics Industries (NJ) Inc., Farmingdale, NJ; *U.S. Public*, pg. 734
Aagaard, A. Kim, Pres.--Synergistics Industries (TX) Inc., Conroe, TX; *U.S. Public*, pg. 734
Aagaard, A. Kim, Pres.--Synergistics Industries Limited, Lindsay, Canada; *U.S. Public*, pg. 734
Aagaard, A. Kim, Pres.--Synergistics Industries Limited, Orangeville, Canada; *U.S. Public*, pg. 734
Aagaard, A. Kim, Pres.--Synergistics Industries Limited, Valleyfield, Canada; *U.S. Public*, pg. 734
Aagaard, A. Kim, Pres.--Synergistics Industries Limited, Saint Remi-de-Napierville, Canada; *U.S. Public*, pg. 734
Aagaard, A.K., Pres.--Synergistics Chemicals, Inc., Mississauga, Canada; *U.S. Public*, pg. 734
Aagaard, Henrik, Pres.--Novo Nordisk of North America, Inc., New York, NY; *Int'l*, pg. 987
Aal, Irv, Pres. & Chief Exec. Officer--Tyler Industries, Benson, MN; *U.S. Private*, pg. 1112
Aalen, Gary, Pres.--Mountain Operations Land Division, Englewood, CO; *U.S. Public*, pg. 1683
Aamodt, Tor Arne, Pres.--Kvaerner Rosenberg a.s., Stavanger, Norway; *Int'l*, pg. 769
Aanderud, Stephen A., Pres. & Chief Exec. Officer--Thrustmaster, Inc., Hillsboro, OR; *U.S. Public*, pg. 1607
Aanenson, Vernon O., Pres. & Treas.--Old Dutch Foods, Inc., Roseville, MN; *U.S. Private*, pg. 814
Aaron, C.H., Pres. & Mgr.--Videk, Rochester, NY; *U.S. Public*, pg. 551
Aaron, Marcus, II, Pres. & Treas.--The Homer Laughlin China Company, Newell, WV; *U.S. Private*, pg. 653
Aaron, Marcus, II, Pres. & Treas.--The Newell Company, Newell, WV; *U.S. Private*, pg. 653
Aaron, Marcus, II, Pres. & Treas.--Newell Bridge & Railway Company, Newell, WV; *U.S. Private*, pg. 653
Aarons, Richard, Pres.--AFD Contract Furniture, New York, NY; *U.S. Private*, pg. 5
Aaronson, Michael, Pres. & Chief Oper. Officer--Rag Shops, Inc., Hawthorne, NJ; *U.S. Public*, pg. 1358
Abad, George, Pres.--General Trading Co., Carlstadt, NJ; *U.S. Private*, pg. 445
Abada, Rami, Pres. & Chief Oper. Officer--Jennifer Convertibles Inc., Woodbury, NY; *U.S. Public*, pg. 926
Abastar, Fernando, Pres.--Banco Central Hispano-U.S.A., New York, NY; *Int'l*, pg. 139
Abate, Joseph A., Pres. & Exec. Oper. Officer--Tilcon, Inc., New Britain, CT; *U.S. Private*, pg. 1086
Abbe, Charles J., Pres. & Chief Oper. Officer--Optical Coating Laboratory, Inc., Santa Rosa, CA; *U.S. Public*, pg. 1227
Abbell, Joseph J., Chm. Bd. & Pres.--Abbell Associates, Chicago, IL; *U.S. Private*, pg. 9
Abbey, Nelson D., III, Pres. & Chief Exec. Officer--Abbey Etna Machine Company, Perrysburg, OH; *U.S. Private*, pg. 9
Abbot, Jerry, Pres.--Metro Label Corp., Garland, TX; *U.S. Private*, pg. 736
Abbott, David L., Pres. & Chief Exec. Officer--Purina Mills, Inc., Saint Louis, MO; *U.S. Private*, pg. 895
Abbott, John R., Pres.--J.R. Abbott Construction, Inc., Seattle, WA; *U.S. Private*, pg. 9
Abbott, Michael E., Chm. Bd. & Chief Exec. Officer--American Republic Insurance Co., Des Moines, IA; *U.S. Private*, pg. 61
Abbott, Robert T., Chief Exec. & Chief Oper. Officer--NeoRx Corporation, Seattle, WA; *U.S. Private*, pg. 791
Abbott, Steven R., Pres. & Chief Exec. Officer--Essex International, Inc., Fort Wayne, IN; *U.S. Public*, pg. 593
Abbott, Steven R., Pres.--Wire & Cable Sector, Fort Wayne, IN; *U.S. Public*, pg. 593
Abbott, Tim, Pres.--Electro Dynamics Crystal Corporation, Overland Park, KS; *U.S. Private*, pg. 368
Abdalla, Gerald M., Pres. & Chief Oper. Officer--Croft Metals, Inc., McComb, MS; *U.S. Private*, pg. 290
Abdalla, Herbert A., Pres. & Chief Exec. Officer--Abdalla's Lafayette, Inc., Lafayette, LA; *U.S. Private*, pg. 10
Abdel-Malek, Refaat A., Pres. & Chief Exec. Officer--Harza Engineering Co., Chicago, IL; *U.S. Private*, pg. 509

Abdoo, Richard A., Chm. Bd., Pres. & Chief Exec. Officer--Wisconsin Energy Corporation, Milwaukee, WI; *U.S. Public*, pg. 1773

Abe, Hideo, Pres.--Chiyoda Life Asset Management of America Inc., New York, NY; *Int'l*, pg. 287

Abe, Hideo, Pres.--Chiyoda Life Realty of America, Inc., New York, NY; *Int'l*, pg. 287

Abe, Yoshitaka, Pres & Chief Exec. Officer--Dentsu Young & Rubicam Inc. (Tokyo), Tokyo, Japan; *U.S. Private*, pg. 325

Abehsera, Daniel, Pres. & Dir. Gen.--Rohr Europe, Toulouse, France; *U.S. Public*, pg. 752

Abel, Gary V., Pres.--C.R. Daniels, Inc., Ellicott City, MD; *U.S. Private*, pg. 310

Abel, Roger L., Pres. & Chief Oper. Officer--Occidental Oil & Gas Corporation, Bakersfield, CA; *U.S. Public*, pg. 1210

Abelman, Steve, Pres. & Chief Exec. Officer--Oxford Automotive, Inc., Troy, MI; *U.S. Private*, pg. 825

Abelmann, Ronald A., Pres. & Chief Exec. Officer--Wind River Systems, Inc., Alameda, CA; *U.S. Public*, pg. 1770

Abely, Joseph F., Pres. & Chief Oper. Officer--LoJack Corporation, Dedham, MA; *U.S. Public*, pg. 1012

Abene, Bill, Pres.--Panel Prints, Inc., Old Forge, PA; *U.S. Private*, pg. 836

Abernathy, Gary N., Pres. & Chief Exec. Officer--Saztec International, Inc., Billerica, MA; *U.S. Public*, pg. 1435

Abernathy, Jerry, Pres. & Chief Oper. Officer--Coty Inc., New York, NY; *Int'l*, pg. 185

Abernethy, Robert C., Pres. & Sec.--Carolina Glove Co., Newton, NC; *U.S. Private*, pg. 214

Ablon, R. Richard, Chm. Bd., Pres. & Chief Exec. Officer--Ogden Corporation, New York, NY; *U.S. Public*, pg. 1213

Ablon, R. Richard, Pres.--Ogden Entertainment, Inc., New York, NY; *U.S. Public*, pg. 1213

Ablon, R. Richard, Pres.--Ogden Aviation Services, New York, NY; *U.S. Public*, pg. 1213

Abouhamad, Emilio, Pres.--Maraven, S.A., Caracas, Venezuela; *Int'l*, pg. 1045

Abplanalp, John P., Pres.--Precision Valve Corporation, Yonkers, NY; *U.S. Private*, pg. 880

Abplanalp, Robert H., Chm. Bd., Pres. & Chief Exec. Officer--Precision Valve Corporation, Yonkers, NY; *U.S. Private*, pg. 880

Abraham, C.F., Pres.--Screw Conveyor Corp., Hammond, IN; *U.S. Private*, pg. 977

Abraham, Marc, Pres.--Beacon Communications, Los Angeles, CA; *U.S. Public*, pg. 138

Abraham, Otto W., Chm. Bd. & Pres.--Engineered Products, Inc., Pittsburgh, PA; *U.S. Private*, pg. 376

Abrahamsson, Roland, Pres.--Elitfonster AB, Vetlanda, Sweden; *Int'l*, pg. 678

Abrahamsson, Roland, Pres.--Elit Fonster AB, Vetlanda, Sweden; *Int'l*, pg. 1260

Abram, J. Adam, Pres. & Chief Exec. Officer--Front Royal, Inc., Morrisville, NC; *U.S. Private*, pg. 430

Abram, John, Pres.--In-Stat Incorporated, Scottsdale, AZ; *Int'l*, pg. 1096

Abram, Michael F., Pres.--Erskine House Group Plc, Sevenoaks, United Kingdom; *U.S. Public*, pg. 864

Abrams, Allan, Chm. Bd., Pres., Chief Exec. Officer & Chief Oper. Officer--Arrow Fastener Co., Inc., Saddle Brook, NJ; *U.S. Private*, pg. 85

Abrams, Donald L., Pres. & Chief Oper. Officer--Three D Departments, Inc., Costa Mesa, CA; *U.S. Public*, pg. 1604

Abrams, Ellen J., Pres. & Chief Exec. Officer--National City Trust Company, West Palm Beach, FL; *U.S. Public*, pg. 1154

Abrams, Heni, Mng. Partner--Hanft Byrne Raboy Abrams & Partners, Inc., New York, NY; *U.S. Private*, pg. 499

Abrams, Leigh J., Pres. & Chief Exec. Officer--Drew Industries Incorporated, White Plains, NY; *U.S. Public*, pg. 529

Abrams, Leigh J., Pres. & Chief Exec. Officer--Leslie Building Products, Inc., White Plains, NY; *U.S. Public*, pg. 989

Abrams, Lloyd R., Pres. & Chief Exec. Officer--Bentley International, Inc., Saint Louis, MO; *U.S. Public*, pg. 212

Abrams, Paul, Pres.--NeoRx Corporation, Seattle, WA; *U.S. Private*, pg. 791

Abrams, Ralph D., Pres.--Lea & Perrins, Inc., Fair Lawn, NJ; *Int'l*, pg. 380

Abrams, Richard, Pres.--Abrams & Co. Publishing Inc., Waterbury, CT; *U.S. Private*, pg. 10

Abramson, Earl, Chm. Bd. & Pres.--Rapid Mounting & Finishing Co., Chicago, IL; *U.S. Private*, pg. 910

Abramson, Larry, Pres.--Camerican International, Paramus, NJ; *U.S. Public*, pg. 426

Abramson, Morrie K., Chm. Bd., Pres. & Chief Exec. Officer--Kent Electronics Corp., Houston, TX; *U.S. Public*, pg. 951

Abromovic, A. Mark, Pres.--ERI Realty, Inc., Pittsburgh, PA; *U.S. Public*, pg. 589

Abruzzo, Cloyd J., Pres. & Chief Exec. Officer--Stoneridge, Inc., Warren, OH; *U.S. Private*, pg. 1044

Accardi, Larry J., Pres.--Sysco Food Services of Atlanta, Inc., College Park, GA; *U.S. Public*, pg. 1551

Accordino, Daniel, Pres.--Quanta Advertising Corporation, Syracuse, NY; *U.S. Private*, pg. 216

Acerbi, Giuliano, Pres.--Ferrero U.S.A., Inc., Somerset, NJ; *Int'l*, pg. 480

Ach, Roger W., II, Chm. Bd., Pres. & Chief Exec. Officer--Chicago West Pullman Corporation, Cincinnati, OH; *U.S. Private*, pg. 235

Achenbaum, Warren, Chm. Bd. & Pres.--Cox & Company, Inc., New York, NY; *U.S. Private*, pg. 281

Acker, Fred, Exec. V.P.-Sls. & Mktg.--Kleer-Vu Plastics Corp., Compton, CA; *U.S. Public*, pg. 962

Ackerley, Barry A., Co-Chm. Bd. & Chief Exec. Officer--The Ackerley Group, Seattle, WA; *U.S. Public*, pg. 15

Ackerley, William N., Pres. & Chief Oper. Officer--The Ackerley Group, Seattle, WA; *U.S. Public*, pg. 15

Ackerman, F. Duane, Pres. & Chief Exec. Officer--BellSouth Corporation, Atlanta, GA; *U.S. Public*, pg. 207

Ackerman, Robert, Pres.--Sheffield Steel Corporation-Joliet, Joliet, IL; *U.S. Private*, pg. 991

Acklen, Charles, Pres.--Perry Brothers, Inc., Lufkin, TX; *U.S. Private*, pg. 854

Ackley, Robert W., Pres.--Davis Standard Corporation, Pawcatuck, CT; *U.S. Public*, pg. 459

Ackmann, Steven C., Pres. & Chief Oper. Officer--BT Financial Corporation, Johnstown, PA; *U.S. Public*, pg. 163

Ackmann, Steven C., Pres.--Laurel Community Development Corporation, Johnstown, PA; *U.S. Public*, pg. 164

Acri, Anthony, Pres.--International Microwave Corporation, Norwalk, CT; *U.S. Private*, pg. 571

Acridge, James E., Chm. Bd., Pres. & Chief Exec. Officer--Giant Industries Inc., Scottsdale, AZ; *U.S. Public*, pg. 741

Adachi, Masakazu, Pres.--Japan Immunoresearch Laboratories Co., Ltd., Gunma, Japan; *Int'l*, pg. 1013

Adachi, Takeshi, Pres.--Daiko Advertising, Inc., Tokyo, Japan; *Int'l*, pg. 365

Adair, Danny J., Pres.--U.S. Intec, Inc., Port Arthur, TX; *U.S. Private*, pg. 433

Adalid, Antonio Gonzalez, Pres.--Repsol Quimica, Madrid, Spain; *Int'l*, pg. 1104

Adam, A., Pres. & Chief Exec. Officer--Algoma Steel Inc., Sault Sainte Marie, Canada; *Int'l*, pg. 56

Adam, Brian, Pres.--Passenger Railroad Insurance Ltd., Hamilton, Bermuda; *U.S. Private*, pg. 69

Adams, Alan, Pres.--Prime Cast, Inc., South Beloit, IL; *U.S. Public*, pg. 142

Adams, David, Pres.--Flowers USA, Uniondale, NY; *U.S. Private*, pg. 415

Adams, Donald E., Pres. & Chief Exec. Officer--SouthTrust Mobile Services, Birmingham, AL; *U.S. Public*, pg. 1492

Adams, Dorothy, Pres.--Gump's By Mail, Inc., San Francisco, CA; *U.S. Public*, pg. 782

Adams, Frank A., Pres. & Chief Exec. Officer--Grotech Capital Group, Inc., Timonium, MD; *U.S. Private*, pg. 483

Adams, Gerald, Pres.--Box USA Inc., Compton, CA; *U.S. Private*, pg. 421

Adams, Harold L., Chm. Bd., Pres. & Chief Exec. Officer--RTKL Associates Inc., Baltimore, MD; *U.S. Private*, pg. 906

Adams, Jacob, Chm. Bd., Pres. & Chief Exec. Officer--Arctic Slope Regional Corporation, Barrow, AK; *U.S. Private*, pg. 80

Adams, James L., Pres.--Energy Systems Group, Inc., Evansville, IN; *U.S. Public*, pg. 1471

Adams, John C., Chm. Bd., Pres. & Chief Exec. Officer--Russell Corporation, Alexander City, AL; *U.S. Public*, pg. 1413

Adams, John G., Pres. & Gen. Mgr.--Adams Extract Co., Inc., Austin, TX; *U.S. Private*, pg. 16

Adams, John S., Pres.--Construction Management Service, Wilmington, DE; *U.S. Private*, pg. 266

Adams, K.S., Jr., Chm. Bd., Pres. & Chief Exec. Officer--Adams Resources & Energy, Inc., Houston, TX; *U.S. Public*, pg. 18

Adams, Kenneth G., Pres.--Adams Investment Company, Bartlesville, OK; *U.S. Private*, pg. 16

Adams, Mark, Pres.--Adams Business Media, Cathedral City, CA; *U.S. Private*, pg. 16

Adams, Mark, Pres.--Adams Business Media, Arlington Heights, IL; *U.S. Private*, pg. 16

Adams, Michael A., Pres.--Commonwealth Communications, Princeton, NJ; *U.S. Public*, pg. 1354

Adams, Pelham E., Pres.--Adams Business Forms, Topeka, KS; *U.S. Private*, pg. 16

Adams, Peter S., Pres. & Treas.--UNUM Sales Corp., Portland, ME; *U.S. Public*, pg. 1700

Adams, R. Dale, Pres. & Chief Exec. Officer--First National Bank of Marshall, Marshall, IL; *U.S. Public*, pg. 634

Adams, R.E., Pres.--Dixie Electric Cooperative, Union Springs, AL; *U.S. Private*, pg. 337

Adams, R.L., Pres.--CNG Transmission Corporation, Clarksburg, WV; *U.S. Public*, pg. 435

Ades, Richard B., Pres., Chief Exec. Officer & Treas.--R.P. Adams Company, Inc., Tonawanda, NY; *U.S. Public*, pg. 19

Adams, Rick, Pres.--Parts Company of America, Northbrook, IL; *U.S. Public*, pg. 758

Adams, Rob, Pres.--United HealthCare of Oregon, Inc., Minnetonka, MN; *U.S. Public*, pg. 1678

Adams, Robert E., Pres. & Chief Exec. Officer--MidSouth Ice Co., Huntsville, AL; *U.S. Private*, pg. 1025

Adams, Rodney K., Pres.--Beneficial Canada Inc., Thornhill, Canada; *U.S. Public*, pg. 211

Adams, William A., Pres. & Chief Oper. Officer--Bliss Manufacturing Company, Youngstown, OH; *U.S. Public*, pg. 771

Adamson, James B., Chm. Bd., Pres. & Chief Exec. Officer--Advantica Restaurant Group, Inc., Spartanburg, SC; *U.S. Public*, pg. 22

Adderley, Terence E., Pres. & Chief Exec. Officer--Kelly Services, Inc., Troy, MI; *U.S. Public*, pg. 949

Addesso, Dominic J., Pres. & Treas.--Exchange Insurance Company, Buffalo, NY; *U.S. Public*, pg. 1455

Addison, John A., Jr., Pres.--Primerica Financial Services, Duluth, GA; *U.S. Public*, pg. 1633

Adell Garcia, D. Jose Antonio, Pres.--Telecomunicaciones Marinas, S.A. (Temasa), Madrid, Spain; *Int'l*, pg. 1372

Adelman, Jason, Pres.--A&Z Hayward, Inc., East Providence, RI; *U.S. Private*, pg. 2

Adelstein, Stanford M., Pres.--Northwestern Engineering Co., Rapid City, SD; *U.S. Private*, pg. 806

Adereth, Jonathan, Pres. & Chief Exec. Officer--Elscint Ltd., Haifa, Israel; *Int'l*, pg. 450

Ades, Alan, Chm. Bd., Pres. & Chief Exec. Officer--A&E Stores, Inc., Teterboro, NJ; *U.S. Private*, pg. 1

Adkins, William, Pres.--Southern California Auto Group, Torrance, CA; *U.S. Private*, pg. 1016

Adkins, William J., Pres.--Torrance Nissan, Inc., Torrance, CA; *U.S. Public*, pg. 1380

Adkinson, C. Wayne, Pres. & Chief Exec. Officer--Regions Investments, Inc., Birmingham, AL; *U.S. Public*, pg. 1371

Adkison, Peter, Pres. & Chief Exec. Officer--Wizards of the Coast, Renton, WA; *U.S. Private*, pg. 1185

Adkison, Peter, Pres. & Chief Exec. Officer--TSR, Inc., Renton, WA; *U.S. Private*, pg. 1185

Adler, Kevin, Pres. & Chief Oper. Officer--Cambridge Industries Inc., Madison Heights, MI; *U.S. Private*, pg. 202

Adler, Larry M., Pres. & Chief Exec. Officer--Adler Boschetto Peebles & Partners, Inc., New York, NY; *U.S. Private*, pg. 17

Adler, Myron, Pres. & Chief Exec. Officer--Myron Manufacturing Corporation, Maywood, NJ; *U.S. Private*, pg. 771

Adler, Richard J., Pres.--Fort Dearborn Company, Niles, IL; *U.S. Private*, pg. 419

Adler, Robert, Pres.--DeCorp, Carrollton, TX; *U.S. Public*, pg. 948

Adler, Robert, Pres. & Chief Exec. Officer--Vintage Blue, Arleta, CA; *U.S. Public*, pg. 948

Adler, Robert W., Pres. & Chief Exec. Officer--Halmode Apparel, Inc., New York, NY; *U.S. Public*, pg. 948

Adorjan, J. Joe, Chm. Bd., Pres. & Chief Exec. Officer--Borg-Warner Security Corporation, Chicago, IL; *U.S. Public*, pg. 245

Adrean, Lee, Pres. & Chief Exec. Officer--Peoples Security Insurance Company, Durham, NC; *Int'l*, pg. 27

Adrion, Robert, Ph.D., Pres.--Becton Dickinson Infusion Therapy, Inc., Sandy, UT; *U.S. Public*, pg. 199

Aebli, Robert J., Pres.--Heurikon Corporation, Madison, WI; *U.S. Public*, pg. 422

Affleck, John A., Pres.--Stratton Management Company, Plymouth Meeting, PA; *U.S. Private*, pg. 1046

Agarow, Uma N., Pres. & Chief Exec. Officer--Allied Healthcare Products, Inc., Saint Louis, MO; *U.S. Public*, pg. 48

Agathos, Louis, Chm. Bd., Pres. & Chief Exec. Officer--Belshaw Brothers, Inc., Seattle, WA; *Int'l*, pg. 188

Agee, H. Mike, Pres.--South Charleston Sewage Treatment Co., South Charleston, WV; *U.S. Public*, pg. 1667

Aginian, Richard D., Pres. & Chief Exec. Officer--HomeTown Communications Network, Inc., Livonia, MI; *U.S. Private*, pg. 537

Agler, Thomas S., Pres. & Chief Oper. Officer--Great Lakes Financial Resources, Inc., Matteson, IL; *U.S. Private*, pg. 474

Agne, Sue Wiegmann, Pres.--The Wiegmann Company, Freeburg, IL; *U.S. Public*, pg. 845

Agness, Terry, Pres.--Ford Meter Box Company, Wabash, IN; *U.S. Private*, pg. 418

Agnew, Patrick J., Pres. & Chief Oper. Officer--St. Paul Bancorp, Inc., Chicago, IL; *U.S. Public*, pg. 1428

Agranoff, Gerald N., Pres.--Datapoint Development Center, Inc., San Antonio, TX; *Int'l*, pg. 384

Agrawal, Raj, Pres.--LICOM, Inc., Herndon, VA; *U.S. Public*, pg. 1702

Agresti, Jack J., Pres. & Chief Exec. Officer--Atkinson, San Bruno, CA; *U.S. Public*, pg. 143

Agsten, Carl F., Pres.--Carlton, Inc., Charleston, WV; *U.S. Private*, pg. 694

Aguilar Romo, Marcos, Pres. & Chief Oper. Officer--Grupo Continental S.A., Tampico, Mexico; *Int'l*, pg. 573

Aguilar, Adolfo, Jr., Pres. & Chief Creative Officer--Bromley, Aguilar & Associates, San Antonio, TX; *U.S. Private*, pg. 692

Aguilar, Estuardo, Pres. & Chief Exec. Officer--Dos:Puntos, Guatemala, Guatemala; *U.S. Private*, pg. 304

Aguilar, Pedro, Pres. & Chief Exec. Officer-DMB&B/Spain--D'Arcy Masius Benton & Bowles, S.A., Madrid, Spain; *U.S. Private*, pg. 304

Aguirre, Carlos E., Chm. Bd., Pres. & Chief Exec. Officer--Oregon Metallurgical Corporation, Albany, OR; *U.S. Public*, pg. 43

Ahearn, Joseph M., Pres. & Chief Exec. Officer--Toy Biz, Inc., New York, NY; *U.S. Public*, pg. 1625

Ahearn, Lance W., Pres. & Chief Exec. Officer--ENSERV, Inc., Madison, WI; *U.S. Public*, pg. 1728

Ahern, John E., III, Pres. & Chief Oper. Officer--J.F. Ahern Co., Fond Du Lac, WI; *U.S. Private*, pg. 27

Ahern, Joseph M., Pres. & Chief Exec. Officer--Colorforms, Ramsey, NJ; *U.S. Public*, pg. 1625

Ahlmann, Kaj, Chm., Pres. & Chief Exec. Officer--Employers Reinsurance Corp., Overland Park, KS; *U.S. Public*, pg. 711

Ahlstrom, Krister, Pres. & Chief Exec. Officer--A. Ahlstrom Corporation, Helsinki, Finland; *Int'l*, pg. 32

Ahm, Jong-Won, Pres.--Ssangyong Corporation, Seoul, Korea; *Int'l*, pg. 1291

Ahmed, Iftikhar, Pres. & Chief Oper. Officer--The Singer Company, Hong Kong, Hong Kong; *Int'l*, pg. 1220

Ahrendt, Dieter, Dr., Pres.--NEUMAG-Neumunstersche Maschinen-und Anlagenbau GmbH, Neumunster, Germany; *Int'l*, pg. 399

Ahrens, Jay, Chm. Bd., Pres. & Chief Exec. Officer--Holly's Inc., Grand Rapids, MI; *U.S. Private*, pg. 535

Ahrens, Ronald A., Pres.--Bristol-Myers Squibb Consumer Products Group, New York, NY; *U.S. Public*, pg. 254

Ahrens, Ronald A., Pres.--Merck Consumer Healthcare Group, Iselin, NJ; *U.S. Public*, pg. 1090

Ahs, Bjorn, Pres. & Chief Exec. Officer--Kvaerner Pulping Technologies AB, Goteborg, Sweden; *Int'l*, pg. 768

Ahuja, Sanjiv, Pres.--Bellcore, Morristown, NJ; *U.S. Private*, pg. 976

Aiba, Noboru, Pres.--Yamaichi International (America) Inc., New York, NY; *Int'l*, pg. 1517

Aiba, Noboru, Pres.--Yamaichi (America) Holdings, Inc., New York, NY; *Int'l*, pg. 1517

Aida, Kenji, Pres.--Nippon Shokubai Co., Ltd., Osaka, Japan; *Int'l*, pg. 939

Aiken, Donald, Pres.--ABB Industrial Systems, Inc., Columbus, OH; *Int'l*, pg. 4

Aiken, Edward G., Pres. & Gen. Mgr.--KSTP-TV, Saint Paul, MN; *U.S. Private*, pg. 544
Aiken, Hugh H., Chm. Bd., Pres. & Chief Exec. Officer--Atchison Casting Corporation, Atchison, KS; *U.S. Public*, pg. 142
Aizawa, Takashi, Pres.--Asahi Chemical Industry - Brussels Office, Brussels, Belgium; *Int'l*, pg. 84
Akabori, Kazuo, Pres.--Dentsu Holdings B.V., Amsterdam, Netherlands; *Int'l*, pg. 393
Akama, Norifumi, Pres.--Bridgestone Cycle Co., Ltd., Tokyo, Japan; *Int'l*, pg. 213
Akasaka, Kazuo, Pres.--Isuzu Motors America Inc., Plymouth, MI; *Int'l*, pg. 692
Akashi, Katsumi, Pres.--Cordis-Japan, Ltd., Tokyo, Japan; *U.S. Public*, pg. 928
Akel, Dominique, Pres.--Sciaky S.A., Vitry-sur-Seine, France; *Int'l*, pg. 1211
Akers, William C., II, Pres. & Chief Exec. Officer--Akers Packaging Service Inc., Middletown, OH; *U.S. Private*, pg. 29
Akesson, Bo, Pres.--Betongindustri AB, Stockholm, Sweden; *Int'l*, pg. 1199
Akiksa, Fumiyuki, Gen. Mgr.--The Bank of Tokyo-Mitsubishi, Ltd. (Dusseldorf Branch), Dusseldorf, Germany; *Int'l*, pg. 158
Akimoto, Yumi, Pres.--Mitsubishi Materials Corp., Tokyo, Japan; *Int'l*, pg. 874
Akins, Bruce, Pres.--Catellus Residential Group, Irvine, CA; *U.S. Public*, pg. 315
Akioka, Hiroshi, Pres.--Kintetsu World Express (Benelux) B.V., Schiphol, Netherlands; *Int'l*, pg. 735
Akisadu, Yasuo, Pres.--Kawasaki Motors (UK) Ltd., Buckingham, United Kingdom; *Int'l*, pg. 726
Akiyama, Tomiichi, Pres.--Sumitomo Corporation, Tokyo, Japan; *Int'l*, pg. 1312
Akiyama, Yoshihisa, Pres.--The Kansai Electric Power Co., Inc., Osaka, Japan; *Int'l*, pg. 722
Akizawa, Takashi, Pres. & Chief Exec. Officer--Ishihara Sangyo Kaisha, Ltd., Osaka, Japan; *Int'l*, pg. 689
Akrami, Ahmad, Pres.--NexStar Automation, Inc., Longmont, CO; *U.S. Public*, pg. 1795
Aks, Lars, Pres.--Nokia General Communications Ltd., Swindon, United Kingdom; *Int'l*, pg. 954
Al Mishari, Ahmad, Chm. Bd. & Mng. Dir.--Kuwait Airways Corp., Safat, Kuwait; *Int'l*, pg. 764
Al Quraishi, Ali Zaid, Chm.--Teamwork Saudi Arabia Limited, Riyadh, Saudi Arabia; *Int'l*, pg. 1360
Al Zabin, Ahmed, Dir. Gen.--Kuwait Airways Corp., Safat, Kuwait; *Int'l*, pg. 764
Al-Barzinji, Jamal, Pres.--Mar-Jac Poultry Inc., Gainesville, GA; *U.S. Private*, pg. 701
Al-Mubarak, A.I., Pres.--Al-Jubail Petrochemical Company, Tareet, Saudi Arabia; *U.S. Public*, pg. 601
Ala-Pietila, Pekka, Pres.--Nokia Mobile Phones, Espoo, Finland; *Int'l*, pg. 951
Alagen, Beny, Chm. Bd., Pres. & Chief Exec. Officer--Packard Bell NEC, Sacramento, CA; *U.S. Private*, pg. 833
Alamo, Tony, Pres.--Luxor Hotel, Las Vegas, NV; *U.S. Public*, pg. 375
Alba, K., Pres.--NI Steel Products Co., Ltd., Tokyo, Japan; *Int'l*, pg. 946
Alban, James C., III, Pres.--Alban Tractor Co. Inc., Baltimore, MD; *U.S. Private*, pg. 32
Albani, Thomas, Pres. & Chief Exec. Officer--Electrolux Corporation, Atlanta, GA; *U.S. Private*, pg. 369
Albarelli, Michael, Jr., Chm. Bd. & Pres.--Amloid Corporation, Saddle Brook, NJ; *U.S. Private*, pg. 66
Albers, Murrey R., Pres.--United States Bakery, Portland, OR; *U.S. Private*, pg. 1124
Albers, Thomas, Pres.--Trek Bicycle Corporation, Waterloo, WI; *U.S. Private*, pg. 1099
Albert, Larry, Pres.--R.L. Albert & Son, Inc., Greenwich, CT; *U.S. Private*, pg. 32
Albert, Lawrence S., Gen. Mgr.--Ventura Foods, Omaha, NE; *U.S. Private*, pg. 508
Albert, Michael P., Chm. Bd. & Pres.--The Harodite Finishing Company Inc., North Dighton, MA; *U.S. Private*, pg. 503
Albertini, Steve, Partner--Earle Palmer Brown Public Relations, New York, NY; *U.S. Private*, pg. 174
Albertini, Steve, Partner--Earle Palmer Brown Public Relations, Philadelphia, PA; *U.S. Private*, pg. 174
Albertson, Ed, Div. Pres.--TMP Worldwide, Inc., Clawson, MI; *U.S. Private*, pg. 1064
Albino, John, Pres.--MacGREGOR (USA) Inc., Pine Brook, NJ; *Int'l*, pg. 670
Albornoz Bonet, Carlos Martinez de, Pres.--AESA Astilleros Espanoles, S.A., Madrid, Spain; *Int'l*, pg. 1223
Albornoz Bonet, Carlos Martinez de, Pres.--ASTANO - Astilleros y Talleres del Noroeste, S.A., Madrid, Spain; *Int'l*, pg. 1223
Albrecht, Arlin, Pres. & Chief Exec. Officer--Red Wing Publishing Company, Red Wing, MN; *U.S. Private*, pg. 915
Albrecht, Ivan, Pres.--Gilcrest Storage, Akron, OH; *U.S. Private*, pg. 32
Albrecht, Steven, Chm. Bd., Pres. & Chief Exec. Officer--The Fred W. Albrecht Grocery Co., Akron, OH; *U.S. Private*, pg. 32
Albrecht, William, Pres.--Barry Controls, Brighton, MA; *U.S. Public*, pg. 124
Albright, T. Rosie, Pres.--Carter Products Div., Cranbury, NJ; *U.S. Public*, pg. 310
Albus, Bob, Pres.--Premier, Inc., Greenwich, CT; *U.S. Private*, pg. 647
Alcock, G.L., Jr., Pres. & Chief Exec. Officer--S. Bent & Brothers, Inc., Gardner, MA; *U.S. Private*, pg. 134
Alcorn, Charles S., Pres., Chief Oper. Officer & Chief Fin. Officer--Donlee Technologies Inc., York, PA; *U.S. Private*, pg. 339
Alcorn, Terry, Pres.--Connors Brunswick, Inc., South Portland, ME; *U.S. Private*, pg. 264
Alcott, Charles, III, Pres.--Compass Bank of the South, N.A., Pensacola, FL; *U.S. Public*, pg. 419
Alderson, John W., Pres.-Casual Dining--Shoney's, Inc., Nashville, TN; *U.S. Public*, pg. 1467
Aldred, P.J., Pres. & Chief Exec. Officer--Enerflex Systems Ltd., Calgary, Canada; *Int'l*, pg. 1400
Aldrich, Bob, Pres.--Telechron of North Carolina, Inc., Leland, NC; *U.S. Private*, pg. 1073
Aldrich, David, Pres.--SAIC, Germantown, MD; *U.S. Private*, pg. 976
Aldridge, Edward C., Pres. & Chief Exec. Officer--Aerospace Corporation, El Segundo, CA; *U.S. Private*, pg. 24
Aldrighetti, Luigi, Pres.--Bastogi-S.p.A., Milan, Italy; *Int'l*, pg. 170
Alejos, Richard, Pres.--Holderness Supplies, Tucson, AZ; *U.S. Private*, pg. 534
Alesi, Charles, Pres.--O.S. Walker Co. Inc., Worcester, MA; *U.S. Private*, pg. 1147
Alesi, Pierre, Pres.--Corse Composites Aeronautiques, Ajaccio, France; *Int'l*, pg. 1166
Alessandrello, Rosario, Pres.--Tecnimont Spa, Milan, Italy; *Int'l*, pg. 324
Alewine, Betty C., Pres. & Chief Exec. Officer--COMSAT Corporation, Bethesda, MD; *U.S. Public*, pg. 424
Alexander, Andrew, Pres.--Weingarten Realty Investors, Houston, TX; *U.S. Public*, pg. 1751
Alexander, Don, Pres.--Skandia America Reinsurance Corporation, New York, NY; *Int'l*, pg. 1257
Alexander, G., Pres.--Devro International Plc, Chryston, United Kingdom; *Int'l*, pg. 408
Alexander, George, Pres.--Right Ideas Inc., Port Saint Lucie, FL; *U.S. Private*, pg. 930
Alexander, Helen, Pres. & Chief Exec. Officer--The Economist Group Limited., London, United Kingdom; *Int'l*, pg. 1026
Alexander, Herbert, Pres.--UPB of Jackson, Jackson, TN; *U.S. Public*, pg. 1669
Alexander, Kobi, Chm. Bd., Pres. & Chief Exec. Officer--Comverse Technology, Inc., Woodbury, NY; *U.S. Public*, pg. 425
Alexander, Marcellus, V.P. & Gen. Mgr.--WJZ-TV, Baltimore, MD; *U.S. Public*, pg. 275
Alexander, Neil, Pres. & Publr.--The United Methodist Publishing House, Nashville, TN; *U.S. Private*, pg. 1122
Alexander, Neil, Pres.--Abingdon Press, Nashville, TN; *U.S. Private*, pg. 1123
Alexy, R. James, Pres. & Chief Exec. Officer--Network Services Company, Mount Prospect, IL; *U.S. Private*, pg. 791
Aley, Paul N., Pres. & Chief Exec. Officer--National Machinery, Tiffin, OH; *U.S. Private*, pg. 785
Alfano, James C., Pres. & Chief Exec. Officer--Stelco Inc., Hamilton, Canada; *Int'l*, pg. 1299
Alford, Bill, Pres.--Covington Specialty Print, Covington, GA; *U.S. Public*, pg. 786
Alford, Brad, Pres.--Food Services Division, Glendale, CA; *Int'l*, pg. 917
Alford, Doug, Pres.--First Commerce Mortgage Company, Lincoln, NE; *U.S. Public*, pg. 629
Alfredsen, Hermod, Pres.--Kvaerner Kleven a.s., Ulsteinvik, Norway; *Int'l*, pg. 769
Alfson, Donald, Pres.--Dale Electronics, Inc., Columbus, NE; *U.S. Public*, pg. 1722
Alfson, Donald, Pres.--Vitramon, Incorporated, Monroe, CT; *U.S. Public*, pg. 1722
Alfter, Willi, Pres.--Volksfursorge Krankenversicherung AG, Hamburg, Germany; *Int'l*, pg. 16
Alger, David D., Pres. & Chief Exec. Officer--Castle Convertible Fund, Inc., New York, NY; *U.S. Public*, pg. 313
Algotsson, Alf, Pres.--NCC Civil Engineering, Solna, Sweden; *Int'l*, pg. 899
Ali, Tun Ismail Bin Mohamed, Chm.--The Guthrie Corporation, PLC, London, United Kingdom; *Int'l*, pg. 113
Alibrandi, Joseph F., Chm. Bd., Pres. & Chief Exec. Officer--Whittaker Corporation, Simi Valley, CA; *U.S. Public*, pg. 1766
Alicandu, Jose Rafael, Mgr.-Adv.--Banco Provincial S.A. Banco Universal, Caracas, Venezuela; *Int'l*, pg. 142
Alkis, H., Pres. & Chief Exec. Officer--Kusters Corporation, Spartanburg, SC; *U.S. Private*, pg. 637
Allard, Charles R., Pres.--Allarcom Pay Television Limited, Edmonton, Canada; *Int'l*, pg. 1481
Allard, Jean Marc, Chm. Bd., Pres. & Chief Exec. Officer--Hubbard Construction Co., Winter Park, FL; *U.S. Private*, pg. 544
Allard, John, Pres.--Allard Industries, Manchester, NH; *U.S. Private*, pg. 36
Allard, John R., Pres. & Chief Exec. Officer--The Jewell Electrical Instruments Co., Manchester, NH; *U.S. Private*, pg. 36
Allard, Michael E., Pres. & Chief Oper. Officer--Granite State Manufacturing Co., Manchester, NH; *U.S. Private*, pg. 36
Allbritton, Robert L., Pres.--Allfinco, Inc., Wilmington, DE; *U.S. Private*, pg. 854
Alleger, Robert, Pres.--Aerospace Technology, Fort Worth, TX; *U.S. Private*, pg. 351
Allegretti, Alfred, Pres.--Bayside Fuel Oil Depot Corp., Brooklyn, NY; *U.S. Private*, pg. 125
Allegretto, Paul, Pres.--North & Judd, Middletown, CT; *U.S. Private*, pg. 804
Allen, Bob D., Pres. & Chief Exec. Officer--Consolidated-Tomoka Land Co., Daytona Beach, FL; *U.S. Public*, pg. 437
Allen, Charles S., Pres. & Chief Exec. Officer--Sloan Valve Company, Franklin Park, IL; *U.S. Private*, pg. 1006
Allen, D. W., Pres.--IPC Power Resistors International Inc., Florence, KY; *Int'l*, pg. 590
Allen, Darryl F., Chm. Bd., Pres. & Chief Exec. Officer--Aeroquip-Vickers, Inc., Maumee, OH; *U.S. Public*, pg. 24
Allen, David, Chm. Bd., Pres., Chief Exec. Officer & Chief Fin. Officer--AMD Industries Inc., Cicero, IL; *U.S. Private*, pg. 6
Allen, Delbert E., Jr., Pres. & Chief Exec. Officer--Allen Canning Company, Siloam Springs, AR; *U.S. Private*, pg. 36
Allen, Donna M., Asst. to Pres. & Chief Oper. Officer--Willis Corroon Corp. of New Hampshire, Rochester, NH; *Int'l*, pg. 1506
Allen, Frank, Pres.--National-Arnold Magnetics Company, Adelanto, CA; *U.S. Public*, pg. 1420
Allen, Gail E., Pres.--Sysco Food Services-Albany, Albany, NY; *U.S. Public*, pg. 1551
Allen, Gary, Pres.--International Petroleum Corporation, Plant City, FL; *U.S. Public*, pg. 906
Allen, Gerald, Pres.--Avatar Utilities, Inc., Coral Gables, FL; *U.S. Public*, pg. 151
Allen, Gerald, Pres.--Gerald Group Inc., Rego Park, NY; *U.S. Private*, pg. 448
Allen, Harvey, Pres. & Chief Exec. Officer--M.S. Walker, Inc., Somerville, MA; *U.S. Private*, pg. 1147
Allen, Herbert A., Pres. & Chief Exec. Officer--Allen & Company Incorporated, New York, NY; *U.S. Private*, pg. 36
Allen, J. William Jr., Pres. & Chief Exec. Officer--J.W. Allen & Company, Wheeling, IL; *U.S. Private*, pg. 37
Allen, James, Pres. & Chief Oper. Officer--European Bakers, LTD, Tucker, GA; *U.S. Public*, pg. 657
Allen, Jefferson F., Pres.--Tosco Corporation, Stamford, CT; *U.S. Public*, pg. 1624
Allen, John, Pres.--Michael Curran & Associates, Houston, TX; *U.S. Private*, pg. 297
Allen, John E., Pres.--LincAm Properties, Inc., Chicago, IL; *U.S. Public*, pg. 997
Allen, Julian, Pres.--South Fresh Farms, Indianola, MS; *U.S. Private*, pg. 1014
Allen, Kristina, Mng. Partner, Strategic Plng. Dir. & Media Delr.--Kovel Kresser & Partners, Santa Monica, CA; *U.S. Private*, pg. 634
Allen, Randy, Pres.--Jaran Inc., San Francisco, CA; *U.S. Private*, pg. 582
Allen, Randy, Pres.--Lilli Ann Corporation, San Francisco, CA; *U.S. Private*, pg. 582
Allen, Rex, Pres.--Allen Communication, Salt Lake City, UT; *U.S. Public*, pg. 1616
Allen, Robert M., Pres.--Allens Of Hastings, Inc., Hastings, NE; *U.S. Private*, pg. 37
Allen, Ronald, Chm. Bd., Pres. & Chief Exec. Officer--American Foodservice Corp., King of Prussia, PA; *U.S. Private*, pg. 54
Allen, Stanley, Pres.--Allen Foods, Inc., Saint Louis, MO; *U.S. Private*, pg. 37
Allen, Terrence J., Chm. Bd & Pres.--Pemco Die Casting Corporation, Bridgman, MI; *U.S. Private*, pg. 848
Allen, Theodore M., Chm. & Pres.--United Grain Growers Ltd., Winnipeg, Canada; *Int'l*, pg. 1442
Allen, Thomas W., Pres. & Chief Exec. Officer--Vernay Laboratories, Inc., Yellow Springs, OH; *U.S. Private*, pg. 1137
Allen, Todd, Pres.--The Harry Alter Company, Lansing, IL; *U.S. Private*, pg. 1075
Allen, Wesley J., Pres.--Leprino Foods, Denver, CO; *U.S. Private*, pg. 660
Allen, William A., Pres.--Wells Mfg. Corp., Fond Du Lac, WI; *U.S. Private*, pg. 1113
Allen, William B., Pres.--Republic Alloys, Inc., Charlotte, NC; *U.S. Private*, pg. 923
Allen, William H., Pres.--Whitehall-Robins Laboratories Ltd., Mississauga, Canada; *U.S. Public*, pg. 82
Allender, Richard C., Chm. Bd., Pres. & Chief Exec. Officer--Farah Incorporated, El Paso, TX; *U.S. Public*, pg. 612
Allerd, Greg, Pres.--Smith Hardware Company, Goldsboro, NC; *U.S. Private*, pg. 335
Alles, Don, Mgr.-Mktg. Communications--Eaton Corporation, Truck Components Operations-North America, Galesburg, MI; *U.S. Public*, pg. 557
Alley, Michael J., Pres.--Fifth Third Bank of Central Indiana, Greensburg, IN; *U.S. Public*, pg. 621
Allison, Herbert M., Jr., Pres. & Chief Oper. Officer--Merrill Lynch & Co., Inc., New York, NY; *U.S. Public*, pg. 1097
Allison, Robert J., Jr., Chm. Bd., Pres. & Chief Exec. Officer--Anadarko Petroleum Corporation, Houston, TX; *U.S. Public*, pg. 107
Allocca, Michael A., Pres.--Ascom Hasler Mailing Systems, Inc., Shelton, CT; *Int'l*, pg. 86
Allread, Neal, Pres.--Kurz-Kasch, Inc., Wilmington, OH; *U.S. Private*, pg. 637
Allred, Barry L., Pres. & Chief Exec. Officer--Elkins Constructors, Inc., Jacksonville, FL; *U.S. Private*, pg. 372
Allred, C. Stephen, Pres.--Environmental/Government Group, Boise, ID; *U.S. Public*, pg. 1134
Allsup, Lonnie D., Chm. Bd. & Pres.--Allsups Convenience Stores Inc., Clovis, NM; *U.S. Private*, pg. 44
Almeida, Richard J., Chm. Bd., Pres. & Chief Exec. Officer--Heller International Corporation, Chicago, IL; *Int'l*, pg. 519
Almeida, Richard J., Chm. Bd., Pres. & Chief Exec. Officer--Heller International, Chicago, IL; *U.S. Private*, pg. 520
Almenteros, Pedro, Gen. Mgr.--Sein Mendez Laboratories, Inc., Rio Piedras, PR; *U.S. Public*, pg. 670
Almerfors, Arne, Pres.--Agema Infrared Systems AB, Danderyd, Sweden; *Int'l*, pg. 1289
Alois, Edward J., Pres.--Unifoil Corporation, Passaic, NJ; *U.S. Private*, pg. 1117
Alonso, Adolfo Castanon, Pres.--Minas de Figaredo, S.A., Oviedo, Spain; *Int'l*, pg. 1224
Alonso, Miguel Aguilo, Pres.--Iberia Lineas Aereas de Espana, S.A., Madrid, Spain; *Int'l*, pg. 1224
Alosa, Joseph R., Pres. & Treas.--Patsy's, Inc., Concord, NH; *U.S. Private*, pg. 843
Alossi, Mike, Pres.--Butler (Shanghai), Inc., Shanghai, China; *U.S. Public*, pg. 271
Alper, Martin, Pres. & Chief Exec. Officer--Virgin Interactive Entertainment Inc., Irvine, CA; *U.S. Private*, pg. 776

Alperson, Robert, Chm. Bd. & Pres.--Rolled Steel Products Corporation, Los Angeles, CA; *U.S. Private*, pg. 941
Alperson, Robert, Chm. Bd. & Pres.--E & E Steel, Inc., Los Angeles, CA; *U.S. Private*, pg. 941
Alpert, Janet A., Pres.--Lawyers Title Insurance Corporation, Richmond, VA; *U.S. Public*, pg. 981
Alpert, Norman R., Chm. Bd., Pres. & Chief Exec. Officer--Bio-Tek Instruments, Inc., Winooski, VT; *U.S. Private*, pg. 144
Alred, Ken, Pres.--Timpte, Inc., Council Bluffs, IA; *U.S. Private*, pg. 1088
Alsop, Joseph W., Pres.--Progress Software Corporation, Bedford, MA; *U.S. Public*, pg. 1334
Alt, Willis E., Jr., Pres. & Chief Exec. Officer--First National Bank of Warsaw, Warsaw, IN; *U.S. Public*, pg. 674
Alter, Robert A., Chm. Bd., Pres. & Sec.--Sunstone Hotel Investors, Inc., San Clemente, CA; *U.S. Public*, pg. 1536
Alterman, Sidney, Pres.--Alterman Transport Lines, Inc., Opa Locka, FL; *U.S. Private*, pg. 47
Altesane, Al, Pres.--Global Turnkey Systems Inc., Parsippany, NJ; *U.S. Private*, pg. 457
Altman, Murray, Pres.--May Department Stores International, Inc., Saint Louis, MO; *U.S. Public*, pg. 1064
Altman, Robert, Pres. & Chief Exec. Officer--General Media International Inc., New York, NY; *U.S. Private*, pg. 444
Altmeyer, John W., Pres.--Carlisle SynTec Inc., Carlisle, PA; *U.S. Public*, pg. 305
Alton, John W., Pres.--Minerallac Co., Addison, IL; *U.S. Private*, pg. 750
Altorfer, Rolf, Pres. & Chief Exec. officer--Panalpina, Inc., Jersey City, NJ; *Int'l*, pg. 1022
Altschuler, Samuel, Chm. Bd. & Pres.--Altron Incorporated, Wilmington, MA; *U.S. Public*, pg. 59
Alvarado, D., Pres.--Kaufel International Inc., Orocovis, PR; *Int'l*, pg. 725
Alvarez Perez, Angel, Pres. & Chief Exec. Officer--Firstbank Puerto Rico, Santurce, PR; *U.S. Public*, pg. 644
Alvarez, Antonio C., Chm. Bd. & Pres.--Long MFG. NC, Inc., Tarboro, NC; *U.S. Private*, pg. 674
Alvarez, Eduardo R., Pres. & Chief Exec. Officer--Consolidated ORIX Leasing and Finance Corporation, Manila, Philippines; *Int'l*, pg. 1009
Alvarez, Javier, Pres.--Iberia Air Lines of Spain, Miami, FL; *Int'l*, pg. 575
Alvarez, Rick, Pres.--Ruiz Food Products, Inc., Dinuba, CA; *U.S. Private*, pg. 951
Alvarez, Tony, Chm. Bd., Pres. & Chief Exec. Officer--Wherehouse Entertainment, Inc., Torrance, CA; *U.S. Private*, pg. 1171
Alvarrez, Isidoro, Pres.--El Corte Ingles SA, Madrid, Spain; *Int'l*, pg. 435
Alyea, G. Mark, Pres. & Chief Oper. Officer--Alro Group, Jackson, MI; *U.S. Private*, pg. 45
Alyward, Dan, Gen. Mgr.--Marine World Africa USA, Vallejo, CA; *U.S. Private*, pg. 703
Amacker, Jefferson Z., Div. Pres.--HTL/Kin-Tech Division, Duarte, CA; *U.S. Public*, pg. 1250
Amano, Ken, Pres.--Denso Sales California, Long Beach, CA; *Int'l*, pg. 1412
Amatangelo, Nicholas S., Pres.--Bowne of Chicago, Inc., Chicago, IL; *U.S. Public*, pg. 248
Amatavivadhana, Adul, Pres.--Berli Jucker Public Co. Ltd., Bangkok, Thailand; *Int'l*, pg. 487
Amato, Jay, Pres. & Chief Oper. Officer--Vanstar Corporation, Pleasanton, CA; *U.S. Public*, pg. 1708
Amatyakul, Damrongsuk, Pres.--The Mutual Fund Co., Ltd., Bangkok, Thailand; *Int'l*, pg. 677
Ambrose, Michael, Pres. & Gen. Mgr.--Cottman Transmission Systems, Inc., Fort Washington, PA; *U.S. Private*, pg. 278
Ambrosi, Nicholas, Pres.--ABD Group Inc., Chicago, IL; *U.S.* Public, pg. 503
Ambrosi, Nicholas, Pres.--Ambrosi & Associates, Inc., Chicago, IL; *U.S. Public*, pg. 503
Ambrosino, Allen, Pres. & Chief Oper. Officer--Database America Companies, Montvale, NJ; *U.S. Private*, pg. 312
Amedia, Frank, Pres.--American Architectural Products, Inc., Youngstown, OH; *U.S. Public*, pg. 67
Amemiya, Koichi, Pres.--American Honda Motor Co., Inc. Automobile Sales Division, Torrance, CA; *Int'l*, pg. 634
Amemiya, M., Chm. Bd. & Chief Exec. Officer--Interkal, Inc., Kalamazoo, MI; *Int'l*, pg. 759
Amerson, Robert, Pres. & Chief Exec. Officer--Flanders Corp., Washington, NC; *U.S. Public*, pg. 648
Ames, Richard S., Chm. Bd., Pres. & Chief Exec. Officer--Command Plastic Corporation, Akron, OH; *U.S. Private*, pg. 257
Amin, Ramesh, Pres.--CRT Div., Melrose Park, IL; *U.S. Public*, pg. 1790
Amin, Sam, Pres.--Beardsley & Piper, L.L.C., Chicago, IL; *U.S. Private*, pg. 859
Aminian, Gary, Pres. & Chief Exec. Officer--BIW Cable Systems, Inc., Franklin, MA; *Int'l*, pg. 417
Amiot, Alain, Pres.--Etablissements Vallaroche (SA), Paris, France; *Int'l*, pg. 1165
Amiot, Alain, Pres.--Societe de Reassurance Vallaroche SA (SOREVAL), Senningerberg, Luxembourg; *Int'l*, pg. 1165
Amman, Robert J., Chm., Pres. & Chief Exec. Officer--John H. Harland Company, Decatur, GA; *U.S. Public*, pg. 785
Amman, Robert S., Pres.--Western Union Financial Services, Inc., Paramus, NJ; *U.S. Public*, pg. 631
Ammer, Bonnie, Pres. & Publisher-Travel--Fodor's Travel Publications, Inc., New York, NY; *U.S. Private*, pg. 21
Amormino, Jack, Pres.--AMB Development Group LLC, Milwaukee, WI; *U.S. Private*, pg. 6
Amos, Daniel P., Pres. & Chief Exec. Officer--AFLAC Incorporated, Columbus, GA; *U.S. Public*, pg. 28
Amos, George H., III, Chm. Bd. & Pres.--Tucson Realty & Trust Co., Tucson, AZ; *U.S. Private*, pg. 1109
Amos, James H., Pres. & Chief Oper. Officer--Mail Boxes Etc., San Diego, CA; *U.S. Public*, pg. 1687
Amos, Stuart, Pres. & Chief Oper. Officer--Siebe plc, Windsor, United Kingdom; *Int'l*, pg. 1240
Ampula, Bob, Pres.--Total Beverage Corporation, Landover, MD; *U.S. Public*, pg. 484
Amsbaugh, Jeffry K., Pres. & Chief Exec. Officer--Nobel Insurance Limited, Hamilton, Bermuda; *Int'l*, pg. 951
Amster, Kirk, Pres.--A S H, Inc., Phoenix, AZ; *U.S. Private*, pg. 2
Amsterdam, Michael, Pres.--Steelworks, Inc. Dover Division, Dover, DE; *U.S. Private*, pg. 1039
Amstutz, Max D., Chm. Bd. & Pres.--Von Roll AG, Gerlafingen, Switzerland; *Int'l*, pg. 1480
Amtmann, James S., Pres. & Chief Oper. Officer--First Alert, Inc., Aurora, IL; *U.S. Private*, pg. 406
Amundson, Patty W., Pres.--M & I Bank of Janesville, Janesville, WI; *U.S. Public*, pg. 1050
Amundson, Wayne, Pres.--Finley Farmers Grain & Elevator Company, Finley, ND; *U.S. Private*, pg. 405
Anand, Jaggy, Pres.--Firestone Fibers & Textiles Co., Kings Mountain, NC; *Int'l*, pg. 214
Anchel, Edward, Chm. Bd. & Pres.--Altec Lansing Technologies, Inc., Milford, PA; *U.S. Private*, pg. 479
Anciro, Ernesto, Jr., Pres.--Ancira Enterprises Inc., San Antonio, TX; *U.S. Private*, pg. 71
Ancochea Soto, D. German, Pres.--Seguros De Vida Y Pensiones Antares, S.A., Madrid, Spain; *Int'l*, pg. 1371
Andal, B.J., Pres.--Interactive Market Systems, Inc., New York, NY; *Int'l*, pg. 1447
Andereck, Michael D., Pres. & Chief Exec. Officer--DocuCorp International, Dallas, TX; *U.S. Public*, pg. 1425
Andersen, Bent, Pres.--Astra Japan, Osaka, Japan; *Int'l*, pg. 94
Andersen, Douglas, Pres.--Allied Mutual Insurance Company, Des Moines, IA; *U.S. Private*, pg. 39
Andersen, Henning, Pres.--All Plast A-S, Havndal, Denmark; *Int'l*, pg. 460
Andersen, Kalle Braa, Pres.--Danapak A.m.b.a., Holte, Denmark; *Int'l*, pg. 826
Andersen, L.A., Pres.--Texaco Arabia Inc., Dhahran, Saudi Arabia; *U.S. Public*, pg. 1584
Andersen, Ole B. L., Pres.--Tri-Clover Inc., Kenosha, WI; *Int'l*, pg. 1379
Andersen, Sven Arild, Mng. Dir.--Pronova A/S, Lysaker, Norway; *Int'l*, pg. 961
Anderson, A. Scott, Pres. & Chief Exec. Officer--Zions First National Bank, Salt Lake City, UT; *U.S. Public*, pg. 1793
Anderson, Alan, Pres. & Chief Exec. Officer--Quintus Corporation, Fremont, CA; *U.S. Private*, pg. 901
Anderson, Basil, Pres.--Campbell Finance Corp., Newark, DE; *U.S. Public*, pg. 299
Anderson, Benny, Pres.--Machinery Stockholm, Jarfalla, Sweden; *Int'l*, pg. 899
Anderson, Bill, Sr. Partner & Exec. V.P.--Fleishman-Hillard Inc., Saint Louis, MO; *U.S. Private*, pg. 411
Anderson, Bill, Sr. Partner--Fleishman-Hillard, Saint Louis, MO; *U.S. Private*, pg. 411
Anderson, Bill, Pres. & Gen. Mgr.--WTWC-TV, Tallahassee, FL; *U.S. Private*, pg. 439
Anderson, Bradbury H., Pres. & Chief Oper. Officer--Best Buy Co., Inc., Eden Prairie, MN; *U.S. Public*, pg. 223
Anderson, Bruce, Pres.--Larkin, Meeder & Schweidel-Tulsa, Tulsa, OK; *U.S. Private*, pg. 651
Anderson, Bruce, Pres. & Chief Exec. Officer--IWI Holding Limited, Westmont, IL; *U.S. Public*, pg. 861
Anderson, Carl J., Pres.--Doremus & Company, New York, NY; *U.S. Public*, pg. 1223
Anderson, Charles M., Pres. & Chief Oper. Officer--Stamler Corporation, Millersburg, KY; *U.S. Private*, pg. 814
Anderson, Charlie, Mng. Partner & Chief Fin. Officer--Carmichael Lynch, Inc., Minneapolis, MN; *U.S. Private*, pg. 213
Anderson, Clifford I., Chm. Bd. & Pres.--Crown Holdings, Inc., Roseville, MN; *U.S. Private*, pg. 293
Anderson, Clyde, Pres. & Chief Exec. Officer--Books-A-Million, Inc., Birmingham, AL; *U.S. Public*, pg. 244
Anderson, Craig, Pres.--The Hercules Tire & Rubber Company, Findlay, OH; *U.S. Private*, pg. 523
Anderson, Curtis G., Pres. & Chief Oper. Officer--Kuhlman Corporation, Savannah, GA; *U.S. Public*, pg. 968
Anderson, D.J., Pres.--International Nickel, Inc., Saddle Brook, NJ; *Int'l*, pg. 672
Anderson, David, Pres.--Canatom Inc., Montreal, Canada; *Int'l*, pg. 31
Anderson, Donald V., Jr., Pres.--EF Data Corp., Tempe, AZ; *U.S. Public*, pg. 293
Anderson, Doug, Pres. & Chief Exec. Officer--Rent-A-Center, Inc., Wichita, KS; *Int'l*, pg. 1385
Anderson, Doug, Pres. & Chief Exec. Officer--Remco America, Inc., Wichita, KS; *Int'l*, pg. 1385
Anderson, Edward R., Pres. & Chief Exec. Officer--CompuCom Systems, Inc., Dallas, TX; *U.S. Public*, pg. 1424
Anderson, Edward, R., Chm. Bd., Pres. & Chief Exec. Officer--Rose's Stores, Inc., Henderson, NC; *U.S. Public*, pg. 1405
Anderson, Eric E., Pres. & Chief Exec. Officer--Aviall, Inc., Dallas, TX; *U.S. Public*, pg. 154
Anderson, Fred, Pres. & Chief Exec. Officer--Stewart Smith West, Inc., Los Angeles, CA; *Int'l*, pg. 1508
Anderson, G.D., Jr., Pres. & Chief Exec. Officer--Sherley Grain Company, Bovina, TX; *U.S. Private*, pg. 993
Anderson, Gary, Pres. & Chief Exec. Officer--IDS Trust Co., Minneapolis, MN; *U.S. Public*, pg. 73
Anderson, Gary, Pres.--Dow Corning Corporation, Midland, MI; *U.S. Public*, pg. 523
Anderson, Girard F., Pres. & Chief Oper. Officer--TECO Energy, Inc., Tampa, FL; *U.S. Public*, pg. 1565
Anderson, Glenn, Pres.--Dynamic Homes, Inc., Detroit Lakes, MN; *U.S. Public*, pg. 538
Anderson, Gregg A., Pres.--Monogram Aerospace Fasteners, Inc., Los Angeles, CA; *U.S. Public*, pg. 1054
Anderson, Harold E., Pres.--Anderson Trucking Service Inc., Saint Cloud, MN; *U.S. Private*, pg. 72
Anderson, Ivan V., Jr., Pres.--Evening Post Publishing Co., Charleston, SC; *U.S. Private*, pg. 385
Anderson, James, Chm. Bd., Chief Exec. Officer & Pres.--Anderson Brothers Construction Brainerd, Brainerd, MN; *U.S. Private*, pg. 72
Anderson, James N., Pres.--Builders Supply and Lumber Co., Inc., Frederick, MD; *U.S. Public*, pg. 1344
Anderson, James R., Pres.--Concrete Technology Corp., Tacoma, WA; *U.S. Private*, pg. 262
Anderson, Jeff, Pres. & Chief Exec. Officer--Gerry Sportswear Company, Mercer Island, WA; *U.S. Private*, pg. 449
Anderson, Jeff, Pres.--Mambosock, Mercer Island, WA; *U.S.* Private, pg. 449
Anderson, Jeff, Pres. & Gen. Mgr.--First American Title Insurance Agency of Yuma, Inc., Yuma, AZ; *U.S. Public*, pg. 626
Anderson, Jeff, Pres. & Gen. Mgr.--Williams Technologies, Inc., Summerville, SC; *U.S. Private*, pg. 1179
Anderson, John E., Pres.--Topa Equities Ltd, Inc., Los Angeles, CA; *U.S. Private*, pg. 1091
Anderson, Keith, Gen. Mgr.- Park Precision Div.--Ajax Services Inc., Warren, OH; *Int'l*, pg. 113
Anderson, Kenneth C., Pres.--Reed Minerals, Highland, IN; *U.S. Public*, pg. 793
Anderson, Kent T., Chm. Bd., Pres. & Chief Exec. Officer--B.B. Walker Company, Asheboro, NC; *U.S. Public*, pg. 1734
Anderson, Kjeld, Pres.--ALK Sverge AB, Kungsbacka, Sweden; *Int'l*, pg. 288
Anderson, Lavon N., Dr., Pres. & Chief Oper. Officer--Rexene Corporation, Dallas, TX; *U.S. Private*, pg. 549
Anderson, Lee, Pres.--Pentax Vision Inc., Minnetonka, MN; *Int'l*, pg. 85
Anderson, Lowell C., Chm. Bd., Pres. & Chief Exec. Officer--Allianz Life Insurance Company of North America, Minneapolis, MN; *Int'l*, pg. 58
Anderson, Melvern K., Pres.--Busch Agricultural Resources, Inc., Saint Louis, MO; *U.S. Public*, pg. 114
Anderson, Michael H., Chm. Bd., Pres. & Chief Exec. Officer--Hogan Systems, Inc., Dallas, TX; *U.S. Public*, pg. 422
Anderson, Michael J., Pres. & Chief Oper. Officer--The Andersons Incorporated, Maumee, OH; *U.S. Public*, pg. 111
Anderson, Milada F., Pres.--F&B Manufacturing Co., Phoenix, AZ; *U.S. Private*, pg. 388
Anderson, Neill, Pres.--Anderson-Barrows Metals Corp., Palmdale, CA; *U.S. Public*, pg. 1746
Anderson, Paul M., Pres. & Chief Oper. Officer--Duke Energy Corporation, Charlotte, NC; *U.S. Public*, pg. 534
Anderson, Paul M., Pres. & Chief Oper. Officer--Duke Energy International, L.L.C., Houston, TX; *U.S. Public*, pg. 534
Anderson, Peter John, Pres.--Banco Chase Manhattan S.A., Rio de Janeiro, Brazil; *U.S. Public*, pg. 339
Anderson, Ralph, Chm Bd., Pres., & Chief Exec. Officer--Belcan Corporation, Cincinnati, OH; *U.S. Private*, pg. 131
Anderson, Richard A., Pres.--BBS Holdings, Inc., Atlanta, GA; *U.S. Public*, pg. 209
Anderson, Robert, Pres.--Brambles USA Inc., Chicago, IL; *Int'l*, pg. 211
Anderson, Roland, Pres.--Lyndon Property Insurance Company, Saint Louis, MO; *U.S. Public*, pg. 685
Anderson, Ronald, Pres.--Southern Farm Bureau Casualty Insurance Company, Ridgeland, MS; *U.S. Private*, pg. 1016
Anderson, Ronald G., Pres. & Chief Exec. Officer--GretagMacbeth LLC, New Windsor, NY; *U.S. Public*, pg. 965
Anderson, Ross, Pres.--Lamson and Goodnow Mfg. Co., Shelburne Falls, MA; *U.S. Private*, pg. 940
Anderson, Roy, III, Pres.--Roy Anderson Corp., Gulfport, MS; *U.S. Private*, pg. 72
Anderson, Ruel L., Jr., Pres. & Chief Exec. Officer--Anco Insulations, Inc., Baton Rouge, LA; *U.S. Private*, pg. 71
Anderson, Steven, Pres.--Rax Restaurants, New Albany, OH; *U.S. Private*, pg. 911
Anderson, T.I., Pres. & Chief Exec. Officer--W.J. & Dennis Co., Elgin, IL; *U.S. Private*, pg. 1144
Anderson, Thomas G., Pres.--Gordy's, Inc., Worthington, MN; *U.S. Private*, pg. 465
Anderson, Thomas L., Pres.--U.S. Pharmaceuticals, Baltimore, MD; *U.S. Public*, pg. 58
Anderson, Tom, Pres.--Schwing America Inc., Saint Paul, MN; *Int'l*, pg. 1211
Anderson, William C., Pres.--Guyot-Hicks-Anderson & Associates, Traverse City, MI; *U.S. Public*, pg. 1217
Andersson, Christer, Mgr.--Edmeston AB, Goteborg, Sweden; *Int'l*, pg. 1185
Andersson, Goran, Pres.--Chr. Hansen AB, Goteborg, Sweden; *Int'l*, pg. 288
Andersson, Kennert, Pres.--Precon VA System AB, Vanersborg, Sweden; *Int'l*, pg. 1199
Andersson, Krister, Pres.--Ballast Ost AB, Linkoping, Sweden; *Int'l*, pg. 899
Andis, M. L., Chm. Bd. & Pres.--Andis Company, Sturtevant, WI; *U.S. Private*, pg. 73
Ando, June, Exec. V.P.--Kawai America Corporation, Compton, CA; *Int'l*, pg. 725
Ando, Koki, Pres.--Nissin Food Products Co., Ltd., Osaka, Japan; *Int'l*, pg. 949
Ando, Noriaki, Pres.--Rohm Fukuoka Co., Ltd., Fukuoka, Japan; *Int'l*, pg. 1125
Andonian, John K., Pres.--A K H Company, Inc., City of Commerce, CA; *U.S. Private*, pg. 2
Andos, Nick, Pres.--Centrifugal & Mechanical Industries, Saint Louis, MO; *U.S. Private*, pg. 370
Andrade, Armando, Exec. Pres.--Pragma/DMB&B, Lima, Peru; *U.S. Private*, pg. 305
Andras, O.S., Pres.--Enterprise Products Company, Houston, TX; *U.S. Private*, pg. 377
Andrasick, James S., Pres. & Chief Oper. Officer--C. Brewer & Company, Limited, Honolulu, HI; *U.S. Private*, pg. 190

Andraside, James S., Pres. & Chief Exec. Officer--Mauna Loa Macadamia Nut Corporation, Hilo, HI; *U.S. Private*, pg. 190
Andre, Benny, Pres.--Diamond Motors Inc., Baton Rouge, LA; *U.S. Private*, pg. 330
Andrea, Douglas, Co.-Pres.--Andrea Electronics Corporation, Long Island City, NY; *U.S. Public*, pg. 112
Andrea, John, Co.-Pres. & Chief Oper. Officer--Andrea Electronics Corporation, Long Island City, NY; *U.S. Public*, pg. 112
Andreae, Jan, Pres.--Albert Heijn B.V., Zaandam, Netherlands; *Int'l*, pg. 749
Andreae, Mark, Pres.--Clark Detroit-Diesel Allison, Cincinnati, OH; *U.S. Private*, pg. 242
Andreas, G. Allen, Pres. & Chief Exec. Officer--Archer Daniels Midland Company (ADM), Decatur, IL; *U.S. Public*, pg. 127
Andreas, George C., Chm. Bd. & Pres.--Lantzsch-Andreas Enterprises, Inc., Vienna, VA; *U.S. Private*, pg. 650
Andreoli, James M., Pres. & Chief Exec. Officer--Baker Commodities, Inc., Los Angeles, CA; *U.S. Private*, pg. 111
Andresen, Johan Henrik, Jr., Proprietor--Tiedemanns - Joh.H.Andresen ANS, Oslo, Norway; *Int'l*, pg. 1389
Andress, James N., Pres. & Chief Oper. Officer--Stern's, Paramus, NJ; *U.S. Public*, pg. 618
Andretta, Vincent J., Pres., Chief Exec. Officer & Treas.--Colony Liquor Distributors, Inc., Kingston, NY; *U.S. Private*, pg. 254
Andrews, Bruce, Pres.--Monitor Aerospace Corporation, Amityville, NY; *U.S. Private*, pg. 757
Andrews, Bruce I., Pres.--Animal Health, Fort Lee, NJ; *U.S. Public*, pg. 58
Andrews, Charles E., Pres. & Chief Exec. Officer--Sunbelt Beverages, Lutherville, MD; *U.S. Private*, pg. 1051
Andrews, Dayton T., Pres.--Dayton Andrews Inc., Clearwater, FL; *U.S. Private*, pg. 74
Andrews, George, Pres.--Wicks 'n Sticks, Ltd, Houston, TX; *U.S. Private*, pg. 1175
Andrews, George W., Chm. Bd. & Pres.--Keco Industry, Inc., Florence, KY; *U.S. Private*, pg. 611
Andrews, John, Pres.--CSX Technology, Inc., Jacksonville, FL; *U.S. Public*, pg. 284
Andrews, Mark G., Pres.--C & M Corporation, Wauregan, CT; *U.S. Private*, pg. 191
Andrews, R. Bruce, Pres. & Chief Exec. Officer--Nationwide Health Properties Inc., Newport Beach, CA; *U.S. Public*, pg. 1166
Andrews, S.J., V.P. & Gen. Mgr.--The Ohio Brass Co., Wadsworth, OH; *U.S. Public*, pg. 845
Andrews, Tom, Pres.--Lubriquip, Inc., Cleveland, OH; *U.S. Public*, pg. 862
Andringa, Mary, Pres. & Chief Oper. Officer--Vermeer Manufacturing Company, Pella, IA; *U.S. Private*, pg. 1137
Andrusterich, Thomas A., Pres. & Chief Exec. Officer--Henry Birks & Sons (1993) Inc., Montreal, Canada; *Int'l*, pg. 196
Andrzejewski, John R., Pres. & Chief Exec. Officer--Anson Industries, Inc., Melrose Park, IL; *U.S. Private*, pg. 76
Andrzejewski, John R., Pres.--Anning-Johnson Company, Melrose Park, IL; *U.S. Private*, pg. 76
Angeli, C., Pres.--Pacific Motor Transport Co., Burlingame, CA; *U.S. Public*, pg. 1668
Angelich, Mark S., Pres.--Amelco Industries, Gardena, CA; *U.S. Public*, pg. 65
Angelich, Samuel M., Chm. Bd. & Pres.--Amelco Corporation, Gardena, CA; *U.S. Public*, pg. 65
Angelillo, Tom, Pres. & Chief Exec. Officer--Southern Progress Corporation, Birmingham, AL; *U.S. Public*, pg. 1612
Angell, Charles T., Pres.--Newly Weds Foods Inc., Chicago, IL; *U.S. Private*, pg. 796
Angelo, Ray, Pres.--Angelo Brothers Co., Philadelphia, PA; *U.S. Private*, pg. 74
Angle, William S., III, Pres. & Chief Exec. Officer--Oak Industries Inc., Waltham, MA; *U.S. Public*, pg. 1209
Angott, Lawrence, Pres.--C.F. Burger Creamery Company, Detroit, MI; *U.S. Private*, pg. 182
Angus, Christopher, Pres.--Astro-Valcour Inc., Glens Falls, NY; *Int'l*, pg. 756
Annable, C.D., Pres. & Chief Oper. Officer--Canuck Engineering Inc., Calgary, Canada; *Int'l*, pg. 31
Annunziata, Robert, Pres.--Teleport Communications Group, Staten Island, NY; *U.S. Public*, pg. 1572
Anruh, James, Pres.--Unisys Limited, Uxbridge, United Kingdom; *U.S. Public*, pg. 1671
Anschutz, Philip, Pres.--Anschutz Corporation, Denver, CO; *U.S. Private*, pg. 75
Ansley, Samuel A., Pres.--Air Vent Inc., Peoria Heights, IL; *Int'l*, pg. 1170
Ansteeg, H.P., Pres.--Intochem B.V., Woerden, Netherlands; *Int'l*, pg. 682
Anstett, Joseph L., Pres. & Chief Fin. Officer--Silver State Disposal Service, Inc., Las Vegas, NV; *U.S. Public*, pg. 1380
Anstett, Joseph L., Pres.--Disposal Urban Maintenance Procession Co., Inc., Las Vegas, NV; *U.S. Public*, pg. 1380
Ant-Wuorinen, Jukka, Pres.--AMER TOBACCO Ltd., Tuusula, Finland; *Int'l*, pg. 72
Anthony, John E., Chm. Bd., Pres. & Chief Exec. Officer--Bearden Lumber Company, Inc., Bearden, AR; *U.S. Private*, pg. 127
Anthony, John Lee, Pres. & Chief Exec. Officer--Anthony Forest Products Co., Inc., El Dorado, AR; *U.S. Private*, pg. 76
Anthony, Michael, Pres. & Chief Exec. Officer--Brookstone Company, Inc., Nashua, NH; *U.S. Public*, pg. 259
Anthony, William H., Pres.--Daden-Anthony Associates, Inc., San Clemente, CA; *U.S. Public*, pg. 1563
Antink, Grant S., Pres. & Chief Exec. Officer--Technical Image Products, Inc./DGI, Elk Grove Village, IL; *U.S. Private*, pg. 1072
Antonelli, Alberto, Dir.--Dateo Import S.P.A., Milan, Italy; *Int'l*, pg. 385
Antonelli, Daniel, Pres.--A.C. Humko, Memphis, TN; *Int'l*, pg. 92
Antonellis, Domenic M., Pres. & Chief Oper. Officer--New England Confectionery Co., Cambridge, MA; *U.S. Private*, pg. 1113
Antonellis, Dominic, Pres.--Haviland Candy Inc., Cambridge, MA; *U.S. Private*, pg. 1113
Antonini, Richard L., Chm. Bd., Pres. & Chief Exec. Officer--Foremost Corporation of America, Caledonia, MI; *U.S. Public*, pg. 667
Anttonen, Risto, Pres.--Ahlstrom Alcore Ltd, Karhula, Finland; *Int'l*, pg. 32
Antunes, Wilber, Div. Mgr.--S.A. Nestle de Productos Alimenticios, Buenos Aires, Argentina; *Int'l*, pg. 921
Anundi, Sven, Pres.--NCC Building, Lulea, Sweden; *Int'l*, pg. 898
Anzai, Ichiro, Pres.--Showa Aluminum Corp., Sakai, Japan; *Int'l*, pg. 1236
Anzai, Kunio, Pres.--Tokyo Gas Co., Ltd., Tokyo, Japan; *Int'l*, pg. 1394
Anzaki, Satoru, Pres.--Komatsu Ltd., Tokyo, Japan; *Int'l*, pg. 743
Anzilotti, Michael G., Pres. & Chief Exec. Officer--First Virginia Bank, Falls Church, VA; *U.S. Public*, pg. 641
Anzola, Francisco, Pres.--Bariven, S.A., Caracas, Venezuela; *Int'l*, pg. 1045
Anzola, H., Pres.--Etoxyl, C.A., Caracas, Venezuela; *U.S. Public*, pg. 1219
Aoki, Akira, Pres. & Chief Exec. Officer--Japan Securities Finance Co. Ltd., Tokyo, Japan; *Int'l*, pg. 702
Aoki, Hirohisa, Pres.--Tokai Bank of California, Los Angeles, CA; *Int'l*, pg. 1391
Aoki, Tasuku, Deputy Pres.--The Mitsubishi Trust and Banking Corporation, Tokyo, Japan; *Int'l*, pg. 876
Aoki, Tatsuo, Pres.--The Meijiseimei Insurance Services of California, Inc., Los Angeles, CA; *Int'l*, pg. 854
Aoki, Yashimitsu, Pres.--Diamond Lease U.S.A. Inc., Greenwich, CT; *Int'l*, pg. 413
Aono, Y., Pres. & Chief Exec. Officer--Toshiba Display Devices, Inc., Horseheads, NY; *Int'l*, pg. 1405
Aoyagi, Kazuhiro, Pres.--Komatsu Europe International N.V., Vilvoorde, Belgium; *Int'l*, pg. 744
Aoyagi, Moriki, Pres.--Sumitomo Metal Mining Co., Ltd., Tokyo, Japan; *Int'l*, pg. 1316
Aoyagi, Susumu, Pres.--Quick Nikkei News, Inc., New York, NY; *Int'l*, pg. 929
Apkin, George, Co-owner--Butler Wholesale Products, Inc., Adams, MA; *U.S. Private*, pg. 190
Appel, John, Pres.--General Business Services, Inc., Waco, TX; *U.S. Public*, pg. 538
Appel, John, Pres.--E.K. Williams, Waco, TX; *U.S. Public*, pg. 538
Appel, John C., Pres. & Exec. V.P.-Network Opers.--GTE North Incorporated, Irving, TX; *U.S. Public*, pg. 696
Appel, John C., Pres.--GTE South Incorporated, Irving, TX; *U.S. Public*, pg. 697
Appelgren, Jim, Pres.--Automatic Signal/Eagle Signal, Austin, TX; *Int'l*, pg. 1245
Appelwick, Robert A., Jr., Pres.--New Apple Lines, Inc., Madison, SD; *U.S. Private*, pg. 792
Apperson, R.P., Chm. Bd & Pres.--Apperson Business Forms, Inc., Los Angeles, CA; *U.S. Private*, pg. 78
Apple, P. Jack, Pres.--Cummins Cumberland Inc., Louisville, KY; *U.S. Private*, pg. 295
Applebaum, Arnold N., Chm. Bd., Pres. & Chief Exec. Officer--Solid State Devices, Inc., La Mirada, CA; *U.S. Private*, pg. 1012
Applebaum, Eugene, Chm. Bd., Pres. & Chief Exec. Officer--Arbor Drugs, Inc., Troy, MI; *U.S. Public*, pg. 126
Applegate, L. Thomas, Pres. & Chief Oper. Officer--Surgical Appliance Industries, Inc., Cincinnati, OH; *U.S. Private*, pg. 1056
Applegate, Malcolm W., Pres. & Gen. Mgr.--Indianapolis Newspapers, Inc., Indianapolis, IN; *U.S. Public*, pg. 326
Applequist, Roy, Pres. & Chief Exec. Officer--Great Plains Manufacturing, Inc., Salina, KS; *U.S. Private*, pg. 475
Appleton, Steve, Chm. Bd., Pres. & Chief Exec. Officer--Micron Technology Inc., Boise, ID; *U.S. Public*, pg. 1105
Applewhite, Marvin, Pres.--Applications International Division, Sunbury-on-Thames, United Kingdom; *U.S. Public*, pg. 1516
Appold, James, Chm. Bd., Pres. & Chief Exec. Officer--Consolidated Biscuit Co., Mc Comb, OH; *U.S. Private*, pg. 265
Aprile, Joe, Pres.--Canteen Corporation, Charlotte, NC; *Int'l*, pg. 324
Apter, Allen D., Pres.--R.A. Industries, Inc., Lansdale, PA; *U.S. Private*, pg. 902
Aquilina, Benjamin, Pres.--Victoria Packing Corporation, Brooklyn, NY; *U.S. Private*, pg. 1139
Arabia, James R., Chm. Bd., Pres. & Chief Exec. Officer--I.C.H. Corporation, La Jolla, CA; *U.S. Public*, pg. 853
Arai, Hyoma, Pres.--PT Hanken Indonesia, Bekasi, Indonesia; *Int'l*, pg. 745
Arai, Kimio, Pres. & Chief Exec. Officer--Tokyu Agency Inc., Tokyo, Japan; *Int'l*, pg. 1394
Arai, Minoru, Pres.--Seiyo Corporation, Tokyo, Japan; *Int'l*, pg. 1178
Arai, Moasami, Sr. V.P.--Ryobi North America, Inc., Chicago, IL; *Int'l*, pg. 1151
Arai, Satoshi, Pres.--Kawasho International Canada Ltd., Vancouver, Canada; *Int'l*, pg. 727
Arai, Shuzo, Director & Pres.--Sanwa International (Ireland) PLC, Dublin, Ireland; *Int'l*, pg. 1190
Arai, Takao, Pres. & Chief Exec. Officer--Nippon Life Insurance Company of the Philippines, Inc., Makati, Philippines; *Int'l*, pg. 936
Arai, Takashi, Pres.--Daiko HWG Advertising Corp., Taipei, Taiwan; *Int'l*, pg. 366
Arakawa, Kazuo, Pres.--Sankosha Advertising Agency, Ltd., Tokyo, Japan; *Int'l*, pg. 1189
Arakawa, Minoru, Pres.-Nintendo of America, Inc.--Nintendo Company, Ltd., Kyoto, Japan; *Int'l*, pg. 932
Arakawa, Minoru, Pres.--Nintendo of America, Redmond, WA; *Int'l*, pg. 932
Arakelian, George H., Pres.--Standard Manufacturing Co., Inc., Troy, NY; *U.S. Private*, pg. 1031
Araki, Hiroshi, Pres.--The Tokyo Electric Power Co., Inc., Tokyo, Japan; *Int'l*, pg. 1394
Araki, Keisuke, Pres. & Chief Exec. Officer--Oki America Inc., Hackensack, NJ; *Int'l*, pg. 1000
Aramani, Ronald A., Pres. & Chief Exec. Officer--Allegheny Airlines, Inc., Middletown, PA; *U.S. Public*, pg. 1680
Arana, Jose Manuel Jimendez, Pres.--ENCASUR - E.N. Carbonifera del Sur, S.A., Madrid, Spain; *Int'l*, pg. 1224
Arango Correa, Alvaro, Pres.--Sancho S.A., Bogota, Colombia; *U.S. Public*, pg. 1422
Aranguren, Ignacio, Pres.--Productos de Maiz S.A., Guadalajara, Mexico; *U.S. Public*, pg. 448
Arata, Frank N., Jr, Pres.--Keyes Asset Managemet, Miami, FL; *U.S. Private*, pg. 618
Araya, Hector, Pres.--Barrick Gold, La Serena, Chile; *Int'l*, pg. 169
Arayama, Mitsu, Pres.--Nissin Foods (U.S.A.) Co. Ltd., Gardena, CA; *Int'l*, pg. 949
Arbuthnot, Paul, Pres.--Quality Chekd Dairies, Inc., Naperville, IL; *U.S. Private*, pg. 898
Arcadi, John, Pres.--Depew Development Inc., Lancaster, NY; *U.S. Private*, pg. 326
Arcara, James A., Pres. & Chief Oper. Officer--KRXY Holding Corporation, New York, NY; *U.S. Public*, pg. 512
Arcati, John, Pres.--Champion Aluminum Window Corporation, Syosset, NY; *U.S. Private*, pg. 227
Arcella, Frank, Pres.--AeroMet Corporation, Eden Prairie, MN; *U.S. Public*, pg. 1029
Archambault, Pierre, Pres.--Security Chimneys International Ltd., Laval, Canada; *Int'l*, pg. 1217
Archer, David, Pres.--Cello Bag Company, Inc., Renton, WA; *Int'l*, pg. 72
Archer, G. Rick, Pres. & Chief Exec. Officer--SouthTrust Bank of Middle Tennessee, Nashville, TN; *U.S. Public*, pg. 1492
Archer, Ken, Acting Pres.--European Business Development, Farnborough, United Kingdom; *U.S. Public*, pg. 423
Archibald, Nolan D., Chm. Bd., Pres. & Chief Exec. Officer--The Black & Decker Corporation, Towson, MD; *U.S. Public*, pg. 233
Archila, Guillermo A., Pres.--Corpoven, S.A., Caracas, Venezuela; *Int'l*, pg. 1045
Architas, Pauline, Acting Pres.--Europe Division, Paris, France; *U.S. Public*, pg. 1516
Archuleta, Celestino E., Pres. & Chief Exec. Officer--National Systems & Research Co., Colorado Springs, CO; *U.S. Private*, pg. 787
Archuleta, George, Chm., Pres. & Chief Exec. Officer--Alantec Corp., San Jose, CA; *U.S. Public*, pg. 667
Ardelt, Maximillian, Pres.--Kloeckner & Co. AG, Duisburg, Germany; *Int'l*, pg. 737
Ardia, Stephen V., Chm. Bd., Pres. & Chief Exec. Officer--Environment/One Corporation, Niskayuna, NY; *U.S. Public*, pg. 586
Arditi, David, Pres. & Chief Exec. Officer--Peerless Carpet Corporation, Acton Vale, Canada; *Int'l*, pg. 1032
Arduini, Giovanni, Chm. Bd., Pres., Chief Exec. & Oper. Officer--I.B.I.S.-S.p.A., Busseto, Italy; *Int'l*, pg. 642
Arena, George, Pres.--Microwave Data Systems, Inc., Rochester, NY; *U.S. Public*, pg. 293
Arenberg, William D., Pres. & Chief Exec. Officer--Columbia Pipe & Supply Company, Chicago, IL; *U.S. Private*, pg. 256
Argabright, Steve, Pres.--Nalco Fuel Tech, Naperville, IL; *U.S. Public*, pg. 1150
Argente, Faustino de Andres, Pres.--SODIEX - Sociedad Para el Desarrollo Industrial de Extremadura, S.A., Caceres, Spain; *Int'l*, pg. 1225
Argov, Gideon, Chm. Bd., Pres. & Chief Exec. Officer--Kollmorgen Corporation, Waltham, MA; *U.S. Public*, pg. 965
Arguetty, Isaac, Chm. Bd., Pres. & Chief Exec. Officer--Jan Bell Marketing Inc., Sunrise, FL; *U.S. Public*, pg. 207
Argyelan, Michael, Pres.--Whittaker, Clark & Daniels, Inc., South Plainfield, NJ; *U.S. Private*, pg. 1174
Arima, K., Pres.--Nippon Crown House Co., Ltd., Sasima, Japan; *Int'l*, pg. 946
Arimura, Katsuhiko, Pres.--Adaptive Information Systems, Mission Viejo, CA; *Int'l*, pg. 946
Ariyoshi, Koichi, Pres.--The Yasuda Fire & Marine Insurance Company Limited, Tokyo, Japan; *Int'l*, pg. 1519
Arkin, Moshe, Chm. Bd., Pres. & Chief Exec. Officer--Agis Industries Ltd., Bnei-Brak, Israel; *Int'l*, pg. 30
Arledge, David A., Chm. Bd, Pres. & Chief Exec. Officer--The Coastal Corporation, Houston, TX; *U.S. Public*, pg. 389
Arledge, Roone, Pres. & Chief Oper. Officer--ABC News Holding Company, Inc., New York, NY; *U.S. Public*, pg. 511
Arlen, John R., Pres. & Chief Exec. Officer--Thetford Corporation, Ann Arbor, MI; *U.S. Private*, pg. 352
Arlint, Tom, Opers. Mgr.--Willamette Industries, Inc., Eugene, OR; *U.S. Public*, pg. 1769
Armbrust, Rick, V.P.--Square D Automation Products, Milwaukee, WI; *Int'l*, pg. 1208
Armentrout, Eugene E., Pres.--Gradison Division, Cincinnati, OH; *U.S. Public*, pg. 1068
Armistead, John, Deputy Mng. Partner & Exec. Creative Dir.--DMB&B Los Angeles, Los Angeles, CA; *U.S. Private*, pg. 303
Armour, John, Pres.--Dormeyer Industries, Chicago, IL; *U.S.* Private, pg. 340
Armstrong, C. J., Jr., Pres. & Chief Exec. Officer--Omniflight Helicopters, Inc., Dallas, TX; *U.S. Private*, pg. 817
Armstrong, C.J., Jr., Pres. & Chief Exec. Officer--Omniflight, Inc., Dallas, TX; *U.S. Private*, pg. 816

Armstrong, Frank, III, Chm. Bd. & Pres.--National Fruit Product Company, Winchester, VA; U.S. Private, pg. 783
Armstrong, Greg L., Pres. & Chief Exec. Officer--Plains Resources Inc., Houston, TX; U.S. Public, pg. 1307
Armstrong, Greg L., Pres.--Calumet Florida, Inc., Immokalee, FL; U.S. Public, pg. 1308
Armstrong, Greg L., Pres. & Chief Exec. Officer--Plains Illinois, Inc., Bridgeport, IL; U.S. Public, pg. 1308
Armstrong, Jeff, Pres.--ASI Landmark, Inc., Cary, NC; U.S. Public, pg. 110
Armstrong, M.H., Chm., Pres. & Chief Exec. Officer--Armstrong International, Inc., Three Rivers, MI; U.S. Private, pg. 83
Armstrong, W. Charles, Chm. & Pres.--Bank of America Oregon, Portland, OR; U.S. Public, pg. 180
Armstrong, Wayne, Pres.--Lockheed Martin Tactical Defense Systems, Archbald, PA; U.S. Public, pg. 1009
Arnberg, Henry, Chm. Bd., Pres. & Chief Exec. Officer--Hirsch International Corp., Hauppauge, NY; U.S. Public, pg. 829
Arnerius, Sven, Group Mng. Dir.--Kalmar Industries AB, Kalmar, Sweden; Int'l, pg. 1420
Arneson, Jody, Partner--Potentia Healthcare Communications Partners, Chicago, IL; U.S. Public, pg. 1224
Arnett, E. James, Pres. & Chief Exec. Officer--The Molson Companies Limited, Toronto, Canada; Int'l, pg. 887
Arnette, F. Davis, Pres. & Chief Exec. Officer--Regions Bank/Elbert County, Elberton, GA; U.S. Public, pg. 1372
Arnhold, John P., Co-Pres.--Arnhold and S. Bleichroeder, Inc., New York, NY; U.S. Private, pg. 83
Arno, Raymond, Pres.--Airtex, Lancaster, NY; U.S. Private, pg. 1113
Arnof, Ian, Pres. & Chief Exec. Officer--First Commerce Corporation, New Orleans, LA; U.S. Public, pg. 629
Arnold-Baker, James, Chief Exec. Officer--Oxford University Press, Oxford, United Kingdom; Int'l, pg. 1018
Arnold, Barbara, Pres.--Optical Products Group, Brooklyn Park, MN; U.S. Public, pg. 162
Arnold, Barbara, Pres.--Vision-Ease Lens Inc., Brooklyn Park, MN; U.S. Public, pg. 162
Arnold, E.H., Chm. Bd., Pres. & Chief Exec. Officer--Arnold Industries, Inc., Lebanon, PA; U.S. Public, pg. 132
Arnold, Edward, Pres.--Lockheed Martin Librascope, Glendale, CA; U.S. Public, pg. 1008
Arnold, Greg, Pres. & Chief Oper. Officer--Truman Arnold Companies, Texarkana, TX; U.S. Private, pg. 84
Arnold, John B., Pres.--The Fifth Third Bank of Western Ohio, National Association, Piqua, OH; U.S. Public, pg. 622
Arnold, Paul N., Pres. & Chief Exec. Officer--CORT Business Services Corporation, Fairfax, VA; U.S. Public, pg. 451
Arnold, Phillip, Pres.--L.M. Scofield Company, Los Angeles, CA; U.S. Private, pg. 976
Arnold, Thomas, Pres.--North American Capacitor Co., Indianapolis, IN; U.S. Private, pg. 803
Arnold, William V., III, Pres.--M & I Central State Bank, Ripon, WI; U.S. Public, pg. 1050
Arnoldi, Geoff, Pres. & Gen. Mgr.--Publicis BCP Toronto Inc., Toronto, Canada; Int'l, pg. 116
Arnone, Miles, Pres.--Boston Digital Corp., Milford, MA; U.S. Private, pg. 161
Aronoff, Jack, Pres.--Gate City Beverage Distributors, San Bernardino, CA; U.S. Private, pg. 441
Aronson, Louis V., II, Pres. & Chief Exec. Officer--Ronson Corporation, Somerset, NJ; U.S. Public, pg. 1405
Arpin, David, Pres. & Chief Oper. Officer--Paul Arpin Vanlines, Inc., West Warwick, RI; U.S. Private, pg. 85
Arquilla, George, III, Pres.--Burnside Construction Co., Downers Grove, IL; U.S. Private, pg. 187
Arras, Richard, Pres.--The Restaurant Company, Itasca, IL; U.S. Private, pg. 925
Arras, Richard K., Pres. & Chief Oper. Officer--Perkins Family Restaurants, Memphis, TN; U.S. Private, pg. 925
Arrendale, Thomas A., Pres.--Best Aviation, Baldwin, GA; U.S. Private, pg. 403
Arrendale, Thomas A., Jr., Pres.--Fieldale Corporation, Baldwin, GA; U.S. Private, pg. 403
Arrieta, Edgar, Pres.--Consultores Occidentales, S.A. (COSA), Maracaibo, Venezuela; Int'l, pg. 31
Arrington, Michael B., Pres. & Chief Exec. Officer--Arrington Travel Center Inc., Chicago, IL; U.S. Private, pg. 85
Arrison, Craig, Pres.--Smith McDonald Corp., Buffalo, NY; U.S. Private, pg. 1009
Arrison, Craig, Pres.--Smith Metal Arts Company, Inc., Buffalo, NY; U.S. Private, pg. 1009
Arrowsmith, Peter D., Pres. & Chief Oper. Officer--Tetra Tech NUS, Inc., Gaithersburg, MD; U.S. Public, pg. 1582
Arst, Mike, Pres.--Goldsmiths, Inc., Wichita, KS; U.S. Private, pg. 462
Artandi, George, Pres. & Chief Oper. Officer--Book of the Month Club, New York, NY; U.S. Public, pg. 1612
Arthofer, Frank, Pres.--Nestle Chocolate & Confection, Glendale, CA; Int'l, pg. 917
Arthur, Ralph, Pres.--Burlington Motor Holdings Inc., Daleville, IN; U.S. Private, pg. 183
Arthur, Robert P., Pres.--Magellan International Trading, Northbrook, IL; U.S. Private, pg. 694
Arthur, Thomas D., Pres.--Havatampa, Inc., Tampa, FL; U.S. Private, pg. 510
Artinian, Garo, Pres.--Draka U.S.A., Franklin, MA; Int'l, pg. 417
Artinian, Garo G., Pres.--Delta Suprenant Wire & Cable Inc., Clinton, MA; Int'l, pg. 391
Arunanondchai, Suvit, Pres.--Thai Orix Leasing Co., Ltd., Bangkok, Thailand; Int'l, pg. 677
Arvin, Joseph L., Pres., Chief Oper. Officer & Chief Information Officer--Arrow Gear Company, Downers Grove, IL; U.S. Private, pg. 85
Asaba, Minoru, Pres.--Asahi America Inc., New York, NY; Int'l, pg. 85
Asaba, Minoru, Pres.--Asahi International Ltd., New York, NY; Int'l, pg. 85
Asabe, Hiroshi, Pres.--Pentel Co., Ltd., Tokyo, Japan; Int'l, pg. 1035
Asada, Hiroshi, Pres.--Tigerpoly Manufacturing, Inc., Grove City, OH; Int'l, pg. 1390
Asakura, Masa, Pres.--JAE Oregon, Inc., Tualatin, OR; Int'l, pg. 701
Asano, Tadanao, Pres.--Toray Textiles Europe Ltd., Nottingham, United Kingdom; Int'l, pg. 1400
Asaumi, Naoaki, Pres. & Chief Exec. Officer--The Sakura Bank (Canada), Toronto, Canada; Int'l, pg. 1180
Asberg, Thomas, Pres.--Kvaerner Turbin AB, Kristinehamn, Sweden; Int'l, pg. 770
Asbury, Neal, Pres.--Asbury Worldwide, Miramar, FL; U.S. Public, pg. 1110
Asch, Michael A., Pres., Chief Oper. Officer, Chief Fin. Officer & Treas.--Rexx Environmental Corp., New York, NY; U.S. Public, pg. 1384
Asch, Peter, Pres. & Chief Exec. Officer--Twincraft, Inc., Winooski, VT; U.S. Private, pg. 1111
Aschinger, Carl J., Jr., Chm. Bd., Pres. & Chief Exec. Officer--Columbus Show Case Company, Columbus, OH; U.S. Private, pg. 257
Aschinger, Carl J., Jr., Chm. Bd. & Pres.--Columbus Showcase, Ashland Division, Ashland, KY; U.S. Private, pg. 257
Aschkenasy, Herbert, Pres. & Chief Exec. Officer--Oregon Freeze Dry, Inc., Albany, OR; U.S. Private, pg. 819
Ash, Allie, Pres. & Chief Exec. Officer--National Information Corporation, Mc Lean, VA; U.S. Private, pg. 784
Ash, Paul J., Pres.--Sam Ash Music Corp., Hicksville, NY; U.S. Private, pg. 88
Ash, Roger P., Pres.--Wershow-Ash-Lewis, Tigard, OR; U.S. Private, pg. 1162
Ashberry, Bill, Pres.--Enco-Georgia, Albany, GA; U.S. Private, pg. 375
Ashby, Thomas W., Pres.--Brake Supply Co., Evansville, IN; U.S. Private, pg. 628
Ashcraft, Steven P., Pres.--Global Special Risks, Inc. of Texas, Dallas, TX; Int'l, pg. 1503
Ashe, Reid, Publisher--The Tampa Tribune, Tampa, FL; U.S. Public, pg. 1079
Asher, Russell, Pres.--Master Craft Corp., Kalamazoo, MI; Int'l, pg. 267
Ashkettle, Phillip D., Pres. & Chief Exec. Officer--Reichhold Chemicals, Inc., Durham, NC; Int'l, pg. 370
Ashkettle, Phillip D., Pres.--Reichhold Chemie AG, Hausen, Switzerland; Int'l, pg. 370
Ashkin, Michael, Pres.--Darby Group of Cos., Westbury, NY; U.S. Private, pg. 311
Ashley, Larry, Pres.--Lockheed Canada, Ottawa, Canada; U.S. Public, pg. 1009
Ashman, Stephen, Pres.--Capital Bank, N.A., Rockville, MD; U.S. Private, pg. 205
Ashour, Mamdouh, Pres.--Scubapro France S.A., Antibes, France; U.S. Public, pg. 933
Ashton, Harris J., Chm. Bd., Pres. & Chief Exec. Officer--General Host Corporation, Stamford, CT; U.S. Public, pg. 715
Asinari, Matthew, Pres. & Chief Exec. Officer--Dentsu Young & Rubicam brand communications (Network Center), Singapore, Singapore; U.S. Private, pg. 325
Askey, Dan, Pres.--Balkamp, Inc., Indianapolis, IN; U.S. Public, pg. 732
Askin, Richard H., Jr., Pres. & Chief Exec. Officer--Tribune Entertainment Company, Los Angeles, CA; U.S. Public, pg. 1636
Askinas, Milton, Pres. & Chief Exec. Officer--Glen Oaks Industries, Inc., New York, NY; U.S. Private, pg. 456
Asphahani, Aziz, Pres. & Chief Exec. Officer--Carus Chemical Company, Chemical Div., Peru, IL; U.S. Private, pg. 217
Asplundh, Christopher, Pres.--Asplundh Tree Expert Co., Willow Grove, PA; U.S. Private, pg. 89
Assard, David G., Pres.--Textron Lycoming, Williamsport, PA; U.S. Public, pg. 1589
Asselta, Alex, Pres.--Casa Di Bertacchi, Vineland, NJ; U.S. Private, pg. 928
Astrup, Leonard, Pres.--Astrup Drugs, Inc., Austin, MN; U.S. Private, pg. 93
Asuka, H., Pres.--The Chuo Woollen Mills, Ltd., Nagoya, Japan; Int'l, pg. 946
Atad, Effi, Pres.--New Media Communication, Tel Aviv, Israel; U.S. Public, pg. 788
Atanasoff, John V., II, Chm. Bd., Pres. & Chief Exec. Officer--Colorado MEDtech, Inc., Boulder, CO; U.S. Public, pg. 401
Atasoy, Faruk, Pres.--Birikim FCA!, Istanbul, Turkey; Int'l, pg. 470
Atchison, Robert, Pres.--Ampex Data Systems, Redwood City, CA; U.S. Public, pg. 104
Ates, Luther A., Pres. & Chief Exec. Officer--Regions Bank/Walton/Holmes County, De Funiak Springs, FL; U.S. Public, pg. 1373
Atkin, Jerry C., Chm. Bd., Pres. & Chief Exec. Officer--SkyWest Inc., Saint George, UT; U.S. Public, pg. 1476
Atkins, E. Larry, Pres. & Chief Exec. Officer--Insight Health Services Corp., Newport Beach, CA; U.S. Public, pg. 880
Atkinson, Basil, Pres.--Judson-Atkinson Candies, Inc., San Antonio, TX; U.S. Private, pg. 602
Atkinson, R. Jay, Pres. & Chief Exec. Officer--Jannock Limited, Toronto, Canada; Int'l, pg. 698
Atkinson, Richard, Dr., Pres.--Shandon Lipshaw Inc., Pittsburgh, PA; U.S. Public, pg. 1595
Atman, Robert, Pres. & Chief Exec. Officer--General Media Automotive Group Inc., New York, NY; U.S. Private, pg. 444
Atman, Robert, Pres. & Chief Exec. Officer--General Media Communications Group Inc., New York, NY; U.S. Private, pg. 444
Atman, Robert, Pres. & Chief Exec. Officer--General Media Entertainment Group Inc., New York, NY; U.S. Private, pg. 444
Atman, Robert, Pres. & Chief Exec. Officer--General Media Films Group Inc., New York, NY; U.S. Private, pg. 444
Atman, Robert, Pres. & Chief Exec. Officer--The General Media Group Inc., New York, NY; U.S. Private, pg. 444
Atols, Robert M., Pres.--Atols Tool and Mold Corp., Schiller Park, IL; U.S. Private, pg. 97
Attaway, Michael H., Pres.--M M Systems Corporation, Tucker, GA; U.S. Private, pg. 685
Atterio, Enrico, Dr., Pres.--D. Lazzaroni & C. S.p.A., Saronno, Italy; Int'l, pg. 804
Attwell, W. R., Pres.--Battlefield Equipment Rentals, Stoney Creek, Canada; Int'l, pg. 1400
Atwater, A.G., Jr., Pres. & Chief Exec. Officer--Amurol Confections Co., Yorkville, IL; U.S. Public, pg. 1781
Atwood, Gary A., Pres.--Atwood Distributing, Inc., Enid, OK; U.S. Private, pg. 98
Atwood, Robert G., Pres.--United Sugars Corp., Bloomington, MN; U.S. Private, pg. 52
Aube, Greg, Pres.--First Consumers National Bank, Beaverton, OR; U.S. Public, pg. 1499
Aucoin, Camille, Pres.--Sunbrand Div., Atlanta, GA; U.S. Private, pg. 1177
Audouze, Francois, Pres. & Dir. Gen.--Arus Group, Aubervilliers, France; Int'l, pg. 79
Auerbach, Zevin, Pres.--The Ad Team Of Florida Inc., Miami, FL; U.S. Private, pg. 16
Augello, Mike, Pres. & Chief Oper. Officer--Reeves Southeastern Corporation, Tampa, FL; U.S. Private, pg. 916
Auger, Paul, Pres.--Pine State Trading Company, Augusta, ME; U.S. Private, pg. 865
Augur, Christopher, Pres.--SpeedFam Corporation, Chandler, AZ; U.S. Public, pg. 1498
August, Albert, Pres.--Richmond Newspapers, Inc., Richmond, VA; U.S. Public, pg. 1079
Augustssen, Kurth, Pres.--Molnlycke AB, Goteborg, Sweden; Int'l, pg. 1326
Auhll, Richard A., Chm. Bd., Pres. & Chief Exec. Officer--Circon Corporation, Santa Barbara, CA; U.S. Public, pg. 373
Auray, Delbert L., Pres. & Treas.--Bridgeport Fittings, Inc., Stratford, CT; U.S. Private, pg. 168
Aurichio, Joseph L., Pres. & Chief Oper. Officer--The Dyson-Kissner-Moran Corporation, New York, NY; U.S. Private, pg. 351
Aurichio, Joseph L., Pres. & Chief Exec. Officer--Kearney-National, Inc., White Plains, NY; U.S. Private, pg. 351
Ausherman, Marvin E., Pres.--Ausherman Construction Company, Frederick, MD; U.S. Private, pg. 99
Austin, Aubrey L., Chm. Bd., Pres. & Chief Exec. Officer--Santa Monica Bank, Santa Monica, CA; U.S. Public, pg. 1757
Austin, C.T., Pres.--Photo Mechanical Services Inc., Minneapolis, MN; U.S. Private, pg. 891
Austin, George K., Jr., Pres.--A-Dec, Inc., Newberg, OR; U.S. Private, pg. 2
Austin, John, Pres.--Blue Ridge Electric Membership Corp., Lenoir, NC; U.S. Private, pg. 153
Austin, John T.,Sr., Pres.--James Austin Co., Mars, PA; U.S. Private, pg. 99
Austin, Michael, Pres. & Chief Exec. Officer--Haynes International, Inc., Kokomo, IN; U.S. Public, pg. 801
Austin, Ron, Pres.--Globelle Corporation, Mississauga, Canada; Int'l, pg. 554
Austin, T.G., Pres.--Gustafson, Inc., Plano, TX; U.S. Public, pg. 460
Auth, Thomas A., Pres.--Interactive Technologies, Inc., Saint Paul, MN; U.S. Public, pg. 888
Autrey Maza, Sergio M., Pres. & Chief Exec. Officer--Grupo Casa Autrey, Mexico, Mexico; Int'l, pg. 573
Autrey, H.E., Pres.--Miller Electric Company, Jacksonville, FL; U.S. Private, pg. 747
Autry, Gene, Chm. Bd., Pres. & Chief Exec. Officer--Golden West Broadcasters, Los Angeles, CA; U.S. Private, pg. 461
Auty, J. Donald, Pres.--The Pantene Co., Wilton, CT; U.S. Public, pg. 1330
Auvinen, Thomas, Pres.--The Pyramid Life Insurance Co., Mission, KS; U.S. Public, pg. 1694
Auyanet, Antonio Castellano, Pres.--UNELCO - Union Electrica de Canarias, S.A., Las Palmas, Spain; Int'l, pg. 1224
Avallone, A. Louis, Pres.--Alpha Associates, Inc., Woodbridge, NJ; U.S. Private, pg. 44
Avchen, Daniel L., Chief Exec. Officer--Hammel, Green & Abrahamson, Inc., Minneapolis, MN; U.S. Private, pg. 497
Avento, Joseph, Pres.--Bristol Metals, L.P., Bristol, TN; U.S. Public, pg. 1548
Averett, Joe N., Jr., Pres.--Crystal Oil Company, Shreveport, LA; U.S. Public, pg. 466
Aversano, John, Pres. & Chief Exec. Officer--Air Conditioning Co., Inc., Glendale, CA; U.S. Private, pg. 28
Aversenti, Candida C., Pres., Chief Oper. Officer & V.P.-Mktg.--General Magnaplate Corporation, Linden, NJ; U.S. Public, pg. 717
Avery, David, Pres.--Novellus Systems, Ltd., Horsham, United Kingdom; U.S. Public, pg. 1204
Avery, David, Pres.--Novellus Systems, B.V., Eindhoven, Netherlands; U.S. Public, pg. 1204
Avery, David, Pres.--Novellus Systems, Ltd., Lorgues, France; U.S. Public, pg. 1204
Avery, David, Pres.--Novellus Systems, Ltd., Falkirk, United Kingdom; U.S. Public, pg. 1204
Avery, Frederick F., Pres.--Ridg's Finer Foods, Garland, TX; U.S. Public, pg. 1288
Avery, John M., Pres. & Chief Exec. Officer--Government Employees Financial Corporation, Washington, DC; U.S. Public, pg. 220
Avery, Nathan M., Chm. Bd., Pres. & Chief Exec. Officer--Galveston-Houston Company, Houston, TX; U.S. Private, pg. 438
Avida, Dan, Pres. & Chief Exec. Officer--Electronics For Imaging, Inc., San Mateo, CA; U.S. Public, pg. 570
Avril, John G., Pres.--Sakrete, Inc., Cincinnati, OH; U.S. Private, pg. 961

Awad, Dennis, Pres.--Zack Electronics, San Jose, CA; *U.S. Private*, pg. 1203
Awad, Dennis J., Pres.--Zack Electronics/Tele-Com Products, Inc., Duarte, CA; *U.S. Private*, pg. 1203
Axelrod, Norman, Chm. Bd., Pres. & Chief Exec. Officer--Linens 'n Things, Inc., Clifton, NJ; *U.S. Private*, pg. 668
Axelson, Karl Axel, Pres.--Gambro AB Oy, Sahaajankatu, Finland; *Int'l*, pg. 667
Axelsson, Bygg Larry, Pres.--Byggs Sprutbetong AB, Malung, Sweden; *Int'l*, pg. 899
Ayer, Ramani, Pres. & Chief Oper. Officer--Hartford Fire Insurance Co., Hartford, CT; *U.S. Public*, pg. 794
Ayeroff, Jeff, Co-Pres.--Sony Music Entertainment, Inc., New York, NY; *Int'l*, pg. 1281
Ayling, John, Mng. Dir.--John Ayling and Associates Limited, London, United Kingdom; *Int'l*, pg. 103
Aylward, Scott, Pres.--Barkley & Evergreen Advertising, Inc., Kansas City, MO; *U.S. Private*, pg. 116
Ayotte, R. Lee, Pres.--Insurance Intermediaries, Inc., Columbus, OH; *U.S. Private*, pg. 789
Ayre, James, Pres.--Tab Products of Canada, Ltd., Willowdale, Canada; *U.S. Public*, pg. 1559
Ayres, James D., Pres. & Chief Oper. Officer--Harleysville Atlantic Insurance Company, Savannah, GA; *U.S. Public*, pg. 786
Ayres, Steve A., Pres.--Petron, Inc., Alexandria, LA; *U.S. Private*, pg. 859
Azevedo, Wagner Canhedo, Pres.--Viacao Aerea Sao Paulo S.A. (VASP), Sao Paulo, Brazil; *Int'l*, pg. 1464
Azoulay, Bernard, Pres. & Chief Exec. Officer--Elf Atochem North America, Inc., Philadelphia, PA; *Int'l*, pg. 445
Azria, Rene-Pierre, Pres.--Financiere Indosuez Inc., New York, NY; *Int'l*, pg. 314
Azrielant, Aya, Pres.--Andin International Inc., New York, NY; *U.S. Private*, pg. 73
Ba, L.D., Dir.--Ebara Hai Duong Company Ltd., Hai Duong, Vietnam; *Int'l*, pg. 432
Baan, C.G., Pres. & Dir.--DAF Trucks N.V., Eindhoven, Netherlands; *U.S. Public*, pg. 1247
Baba, Eizo, Pres.--Chiyoda Life Investment Luxemburg S.A., Luxembourg, Luxembourg; *Int'l*, pg. 287
Baba, Eizo, Pres.--Chiyoda Investment Cayman Limited, Georgetown, Cayman Islands; *Int'l*, pg. 287
Baba, Hisao, Pres. & Chief Exec. Officer--Oki Semiconductor Group, Sunnyvale, CA; *Int'l*, pg. 1000
Baba, Takayoshi, Pres.--Hochiki Corporation, Tokyo, Japan; *Int'l*, pg. 623
Baba, Y., Pres.--Foster Electric (U.S.A.) Inc., Schaumburg, IL; *Int'l*, pg. 500
Babb, Donald, Pres.--Hickham Industries Inc., La Porte, TX; *Int'l*, pg. 1305
Babcock, John B., Jr., Pres. & Chief Exec. Officer--BPI Communications Inc., New York, NY; *Int'l*, pg. 1446
Babcock, John Jr., Pres. & Chief Exec. Officer--A/S/M Communications, Inc., New York, NY; *Int'l*, pg. 1446
Babcock, Richard, Editor--New York Magazine, New York, NY; *U.S. Public*, pg. 1328
Babcock, Richard, Editor--Chicago Magazine, Chicago, IL; *U.S. Public*, pg. 1328
Babick, Don, Pres. & Publisher--The Province, Vancouver, Canada; *Int'l*, pg. 631
Babineaux, D.J., Pres.--American Valve & Hydrant Co., Beaumont, TX; *U.S. Private*, pg. 52
Babriele, Del Torchio, Pres.--FKI FAI Komatsu Industries, S.p.A., Este, Italy; *Int'l*, pg. 474
Baca, Eduardo, Pres.--Graffiti/DMB&B, Buenos Aires, Argentina; *U.S. Private*, pg. 304
Baccari, Vincent, Pres.--Darlene Jewelry Manufacturing Company, Pawtucket, RI; *U.S. Private*, pg. 311
Baccich, C.T., Pres.--Mineral Research & Development Corp., Charlotte, NC; *Int'l*, pg. 802
Bach, Andrew, Pres. & Chief Exec. Officer--AVO International, Dallas, TX; *Int'l*, pg. 1335
Bach, Bjorn, Pres.--Hydro Agri North America, Tampa, FL; *Int'l*, pg. 961
Bach, Kenneth W., Chm. Bd., Pres. & Chief Exec. Officer--Electro Metrics, Inc., Johnstown, NY; *U.S. Private*, pg. 369
Bachand, Stephen E., Pres. & Chief Exec. Officer--Canadian Tire Corporation Limited, Toronto, Canada; *Int'l*, pg. 259
Bacharach, Dov, Pres.--Wyle-Ginsbury Electronics, Oradell, NJ; *Int'l*, pg. 1458
Bachhuber, Carl, Chm. Bd., Pres. & Chief Exec. Officer--Mayville Engineering Co., Inc., Mayville, WI; *U.S. Private*, pg. 718
Bachman, Dale L., Pres.--Bachman's, Inc., Minneapolis, MN; *U.S. Private*, pg. 109
Bachmann, John W., Mng. Principal--Edward Jones, Saint Louis, MO; *U.S. Private*, pg. 597
Bachus, Charles R., Pres. & Chief Oper. Officer--Southern Missouri Containers Inc., Springfield, MO; *U.S. Private*, pg. 1017
Bacig, Louis, Vice Chm. & Mng. Partner--Carmichael Lynch, Inc., Minneapolis, MN; *U.S. Private*, pg. 213
Bacigalupo, Richard J., Exec. Dir.--Regional Transportation Authority (RTA), Chicago, IL; *U.S. Private*, pg. 918
Bacik, Brian, Pres.--GSW Thermoplastics Company, Barrie, Canada; *Int'l*, pg. 538
Backus, John C., Jr., Pres. & Chief Oper. Officer--InteliData, Herndon, VA; *U.S. Public*, pg. 1780
Bacon, David L., Pres. & Chief Oper. Officer--Schleicher & Schuell, Inc., Keene, NH; *Int'l*, pg. 1206
Bacon, Donald G., Chm. Bd., Pres. & Chief Exec. Officer--West Kootenay Power, Trail, Canada; *U.S. Public*, pg. 1701
Bacon, Eric, Pres.--CFA Holding Company, Charlotte, MI; *U.S. Private*, pg. 194
Bacus, Jim, Pres.--Diversitech, Inc., Gainesville, FL; *Int'l*, pg. 288
Badcock, Ben M., Chm. Bd., Pres. & Chief Exec. Officer--W.S. Badcock Corporation, Mulberry, FL; *U.S. Private*, pg. 109
Baddour, Sharon, Sr. Principal & Bus. Affairs Dir.--Publicis/Bloom, Dallas, TX; *Int'l*, pg. 469
Bader, Burke B., Pres.--Bader & Co., Ipava, IL; *U.S. Private*, pg. 110
Bader, Frank, Pres.--Air Techniques, Inc., Hicksville, NY; *U.S. Private*, pg. 28
Bader, Ronald L., Pres. & Chief Exec. Officer--Bader Rutter & Assoc., Inc., Brookfield, WI; *U.S. Private*, pg. 110
Badger, Susan, Pres. & Chief Exec. Officer--Wadsworth Publishing co., Belmont, CA; *U.S. Public*, pg. 1600
Badgett, Guy M., III, Pres.--Vulcan Materials Company-Southeast Div., Atlanta, GA; *U.S. Public*, pg. 1726
Badgley, Jeff, Pres.--Miller Industries, Inc., Ooltewah, TN; *U.S. Public*, pg. 1112
Badosa, Juan, Pres.--Repsol Butano S.A., Madrid, Spain; *Int'l*, pg. 1104
Badrick, John, Pres.--Turnkey Technologies, Inc., Edison, NJ; *U.S. Private*, pg. 1110
Badtke, Donald J., Chm. Bd. & Pres.--Stanley Knight Corporation, New Troy, MI; *U.S. Private*, pg. 1033
Baduy, Miguel, Pres.--Creacional/DMB&B, Guayaquil, Ecuador; *U.S. Private*, pg. 303
Badyna, Edward R., Pres.--Chesapeake Packaging Co./Scranton, Scranton, PA; *U.S. Public*, pg. 347
Bae, Jung Kyun, Pres.--Newmax Co., Ltd., Cheongju, Korea; *Int'l*, pg. 1347
Baer, Art, Pres.--Foster Management Co., King of Prussia, PA; *U.S. Private*, pg. 421
Baer, Art, Pres.--Zyan, Inc., King of Prussia, PA; *U.S. Private*, pg. 421
Baer, Richard, Chm. Bd. & Pres.--Nuevo Federal S.A., Buenos Aires, Argentina; *Int'l*, pg. 990
Baer, Robert E., Pres. & Chief Exec. Officer--Efficient Engineering Co., Troy, MI; *U.S. Private*, pg. 365
Baer, Robert J., Pres.--UniGroup, Inc., Fenton, MO; *U.S. Private*, pg. 1117
Baertz, Wolfgang A., Joint Acting Pres.--Dresdner Bank Luxembourg S.A., Luxembourg, Luxembourg; *Int'l*, pg. 419
Bagby, Steven, Pres.--Salomon-North America Inc., Georgetown, MA; *Int'l*, pg. 1181
Baggett, W. Les, Pres. & Chief Exec. Officer--LePage's, Inc., Pittsburgh, PA; *U.S. Private*, pg. 598
Baggott, Clifford D., Pres.--Cres-Cor, Cleveland, OH; *U.S. Private*, pg. 288
Bagley, George D., Pres. & Chief Exec. Officer--Horizon Air Industries, Seattle, WA; *U.S. Public*, pg. 35
Baglivo, Mary L., Pres. & Client ServicesDir.--EURO RSCG Tatham, Chicago, IL; *Int'l*, pg. 601
Bagnall, George, Pres.--Industrial Components Group, Shelton, CT; *Int'l*, pg. 127
Bago, Ernest G., Pres.--TSR Consulting Services, Inc., New York, NY; *U.S. Public*, pg. 1559
Bagwell, Larry, Pres. & Chief Exec. Officer--Rea Magnet Wire Company, Inc., Fort Wayne, IN; *U.S. Private*, pg. 913
Bahia-Guimaraes, Paulo F., Dir.-Pres.--Mineracao Marex Ltda., Rio de Janeiro, Brazil; *Int'l*, pg. 224
Bahre, Everett, Pres. & Chief Exec. Officer--Lambda Advanced Analog, Santa Clara, CA; *Int'l*, pg. 1241
Baia, Paul E., Pres.--Frequency and Time Systems, Inc., Beverly, MA; *U.S. Public*, pg. 488
Baich, Kevin, Pres.--Crown Shoe Company, L.L.C., Saint Louis, MO; *U.S. Private*, pg. 1089
Bailey, Albert C., Jr., Pres. & Chief Exec. Officer--Lavelle Company, Philadelphia, PA; *U.S. Private*, pg. 653
Bailey, C.A. Bud, Pres.--Bud Bailey Construction Inc., Salt Lake City, UT; *U.S. Private*, pg. 1059
Bailey, Colin, Pres., Chief Exec. Officer & V.P.--Calgon Carbon Corporation, Pittsburgh, PA; *U.S. Public*, pg. 292
Bailey, Dan I., Co-Pres.-Tech. Division--Tekgraf, Inc., Norcross, GA; *U.S. Private*, pg. 1073
Bailey, David E., Pres.--Norwest Bank Colorado N.A., Denver, CO; *U.S. Public*, pg. 1202
Bailey, Don M., Pres. & Chief Exec. Officer--Comarco, Inc., Yorba Linda, CA; *U.S. Public*, pg. 406
Bailey, Geoffrey D., Mng. Dir.--SmithKline Beecham Research Limited, Pasig, Philippines; *Int'l*, pg. 1266
Bailey, Harry J., Pres. & Chief Exec. Officer--Ameriana Bancorp, New Castle, IN; *U.S. Public*, pg. 66
Bailey, John, Chm. Bd., Pres., Chief Exec. & Fin. Officer & Treas.--Cal Emblem Labels, Inc., Fresno, CA; *U.S. Private*, pg. 199
Bailey, John H., Chm. Bd., Pres., Chief Exec. & Chief Oper. Officer--The Climatic Corp., Columbia, SC; *U.S. Private*, pg. 246
Bailey, Keith E., Chm. Bd., Pres. & Chief Exec. Officer--The Williams Companies, Inc., Tulsa, OK; *U.S. Public*, pg. 1769
Bailey, Kirk, Pres.-UPB Bank--Union Planters Bank, Memphis, TN; *U.S. Public*, pg. 1669
Bailey, L. Douglas, Pres.--Home Shopping Club, Inc., Clearwater, FL; *U.S. Public*, pg. 1685
Bailey, Mike, Pres.--Compass Group-USA Division, Charlotte, NC; *Int'l*, pg. 324
Bailey, Robert L., Pres. & Chief Exec. Officer--PMC Sierra, Inc., Burnaby, Canada; *U.S. Public*, pg. 1470
Bailey, Robert, III, Pres.--Mid American Elevator Co., Inc., Chicago, IL; *U.S. Private*, pg. 743
Bailey, Timothy P., Pres. & Chief Exec. Officer--TCF Bank Wisconsin, Milwaukee, WI; *U.S. Public*, pg. 1554
Baileys, Steven J., D.D.S., Chm. Bd., Pres. & Chief Exec. Officer--Safeguard Health Enterprises, Inc., Anaheim, CA; *U.S. Public*, pg. 1424
Bailin, Mark, Pres.--Rymer International Seafood Inc., Chicago, IL; *U.S. Public*, pg. 1414
Bailleres, Alberto, Pres.--Quimica del Rey S.A. de C.V., Mexico, Mexico; *Int'l*, pg. 677
Baillie, A. Charles, Pres. & Chief Exec. Officer--The Toronto Dominion Bank, Toronto, Canada; *Int'l*, pg. 1401
Bailly, Jeff, Pres. & Chief Exec. Officer--UFP Technology, Georgetown, MA; *U.S. Private*, pg. 1112
Baily, Lawrence, Pres.--New England Power Co., Westborough, MA; *U.S. Public*, pg. 1171
Bain, John H., Chm. Bd. & Pres.--Homewood Corporation, Columbus, OH; *U.S. Private*, pg. 537
Baines, Henry T., Pres.--Baines Management Co., Baltimore, MD; *U.S. Private*, pg. 111
Bainsfair, Paul, Joint Chm., Joint Chief Exec. Officer & Pres.--BST-BDDP, London, United Kingdom; *Int'l*, pg. 117
Bair, Daran, Pres.--Martin Universal Design, Inc., Detroit, MI; *U.S. Private*, pg. 709
Baird, Brent D., Pres.--Merchants Group, Inc., Buffalo, NY; *U.S. Public*, pg. 1090
Baird, Euan, Chm. Bd., Pres. & Chief Exec. Officer--Schlumberger Limited, New York, NY; *U.S. Public*, pg. 1439
Baird, Stephen W., Pres.--Baird & Warner Inc., Chicago, IL; *U.S. Private*, pg. 111
Baird, William J., Jr., Pres. & Chief Exec. Officer--Willis Corroon Corp. of Maryland, Hunt Valley, MD; *Int'l*, pg. 1506
Baird, William S., Pres. & Chief Exec. Officer--Alabama Metal Industries Corporation, Birmingham, AL; *U.S. Private*, pg. 30
Bak, Eugene, Pres.--Mooney Chemicals, Cleveland, OH; *U.S. Public*, pg. 1208
Bak, Per, Pres.--De danske Mejeriers Faellesindkeb amba, Kolding, Denmark; *Int'l*, pg. 826
Bakane, John L., Pres.--Cone Apparel Products, Greensboro, NC; *U.S. Public*, pg. 430
Bakehorn, C. Don, Pres.--American Stationery Co., Inc., Peru, IN; *U.S. Private*, pg. 62
Baker, Alton F., III, Editor, Publ. & Pres.--Guard Publishing Company, Eugene, OR; *U.S. Private*, pg. 485
Baker, Andrew H., Chm. Bd., Pres. & Chief Exec. Officer--Unilab Corporation, Tarzana, CA; *U.S. Public*, pg. 1352
Baker, Dale, Pres. & Chief Exec. Officer--Aviation Sales Company, Miami, FL; *U.S. Public*, pg. 154
Baker, Dan R., Pres.--Energy West Mining Company, Portland, OR; *U.S. Public*, pg. 1251
Baker, Daniel, Chm. Bd., Pres. & Chief Exec. Officer--Tate Access Floors, Inc., Jessup, MD; *U.S. Private*, pg. 1069
Baker, Daniel L., Chm. Bd. & Pres.--Baker Concrete Construction, Inc., Monroe, OH; *U.S. Private*, pg. 111
Baker, David, Chief Exec. Officer--AIS Media, Surrey Hills, Australia; *Int'l*, pg. 15
Baker, Dolph, Pres. & Chief Oper. Officer--Cal-Maine Foods, Inc., Jackson, MS; *U.S. Public*, pg. 292
Baker, Donna, Pres.--Outdoor Systems, Inc.-New York, New York, NY; *U.S. Public*, pg. 1235
Baker, Edward D., Pres.--Nieco Corporation, Burlingame, CA; *U.S. Private*, pg. 799
Baker, F. Gregory, Pres.--Westward Seafoods, Inc., Seattle, WA; *Int'l*, pg. 845
Baker, F. P., Deputy Chm. & Pres.--International Paints (Canada) Ltd., Montreal, Canada; *Int'l*, pg. 339
Baker, F.C. "Buzz", Pres. & Chief Exec. Officer--Creswell, Munsell, Fultz & Zirbel, L.P., Cedar Rapids, IA; *U.S. Private*, pg. 1197
Baker, Francis E., Pres. & Chief Exec. Officer--Andersen Group, Inc., Bloomfield, CT; *U.S. Public*, pg. 111
Baker, G. Thomas, Pres., Chief Oper. Officer & Chief Fin. Officer--International Game Technology, Reno, NV; *U.S. Public*, pg. 900
Baker, H. Gene, Pres.--Fort Worth Division, Fort Worth, TX; *U.S. Public*, pg. 509
Baker, James, Pres.--Electro-Matic Products Inc., Farmington, MI; *U.S. Private*, pg. 369
Baker, Jay, Pres.--Kohl's Corporation, Menomonee Falls, WI; *U.S. Public*, pg. 965
Baker, John, Pres.--Micro Electronics, Inc., Hilliard, OH; *U.S. Private*, pg. 742
Baker, John D. II, Pres. & Chief Exec. Officer--Florida Rock Industries, Inc., Jacksonville, FL; *U.S. Public*, pg. 655
Baker, Kenneth D., Pres. & Chief Exec. Officer--NewAge Industries Inc., Willow Grove, PA; *U.S. Private*, pg. 796
Baker, L.M., Jr., Pres. & Chief Exec. Officer--Wachovia Corporation, Winston Salem, NC; *U.S. Public*, pg. 1730
Baker, Maurice W., Pres. & Chief Exec. Officer--Madison Grocery Co., Inc., Richmond, KY; *U.S. Private*, pg. 694
Baker, R. Daniel, Pres.--TIE Systems Northern California, Hayward, CA; *U.S. Private*, pg. 1085
Baker, R. Daniel, Pres.--TIE Systems-Sacramento, Sacramento, CA; *U.S. Private*, pg. 1085
Baker, R. Daniel, Pres.--TIE Systems Colorado, Denver, CO; *U.S. Private*, pg. 1085
Baker, R. Daniel, Pres.--TIE Systems-Portland, Portland, OR; *U.S. Private*, pg. 1085
Baker, R. Daniel, Pres.--TIE Systems Utah, Salt Lake City, UT; *U.S. Private*, pg. 1085
Baker, Richard A., Pres.--Bernard Chaus, Inc., Secaucus, NJ; *U.S. Public*, pg. 342
Baker, Robert L., Pres.--Plant Maintenance Service Corporation, Memphis, TN; *U.S. Private*, pg. 869
Baker, Roland C., Pres.--First Penn-Pacific Life Insurance Co., Oak Brook Terrace, IL; *U.S. Public*, pg. 998
Baker, William, Pres.--Penn Machine Company, Johnstown, PA; *Int'l*, pg. 281
Baker, William L., Jr., Pres.--J B Labs, Inc., Holland, MI; *U.S. Private*, pg. 576
Bakke, Dennis W., Pres. & Chief Exec. Officer--AES Corporation, Arlington, VA; *U.S. Public*, pg. 5
Bakke, James, Pres.--Sub-Zero Freezer Co., Inc., Madison, WI; *U.S. Private*, pg. 1048
Bakke, Richard M., Pres. & Chief Exec. Officer--PG Vinyl Windows/PG Proglass Construction, Westbrook, ME; *U.S. Private*, pg. 826
Bakony, Andrew, Pres.--Reading & Bates Drilling Co., Houston, TX; *U.S. Public*, pg. 1354
Baladjanian, Greg, Pres. & Chief Oper. Officer--Chromalloy Gas Turbine Corp., San Antonio, TX; *U.S. Public*, pg. 1458
Balaz, Joe K., Pres. & Chief Exec. Officer--Flinn & Dreffein Engineering Co., Northbrook, IL; *U.S. Private*, pg. 413

Baldassari, Dennis, Pres. & Chief Oper. Officer--Jersey Central Power & Light Co., Morristown, NJ; *U.S. Public*, pg. 695
Baldassari, Dennis, Pres.--Pennsylvania Electric Company, Reading, PA; *U.S. Public*, pg. 695
Balderson, Clark, Pres.--Balderson Inc., Wamego, KS; *U.S. Public*, pg. 315
Balduino, Michael, Pres.--Imperial Bondware Corp., Montvale, NJ; *U.S. Public*, pg. 903
Baldwin, H. Furlong, Chm. Bd., Pres. & Chief Exec. Officer--Mercantile Bankshares Corporation, Baltimore, MD; *U.S. Public*, pg. 1088
Baldwin, John W., Pres.--Polyvinyl Films, Inc., Sutton, MA; *U.S. Private*, pg. 875
Baldwin, Mark E., Pres.--Keystone Valve (China) Ltd., Guangdong, China; *U.S. Public*, pg. 1650
Baldwin, Mike, Pres.--Market Data Retrieval, Shelton, CT; *U.S. Public*, pg. 536
Baldwin, Ralph L., Pres.--Community Credit Corporation, New Castle, DE; *U.S. Public*, pg. 1729
Baldwin, Richard F., Pres.--Lea Lumber & Plywood LLC, Windsor, NC; *U.S. Private*, pg. 655
Baldwin, Sandra Kaye, Pres. & Treas.--H & H Distributing Company, Inc., West Union, IA; *U.S. Private*, pg. 489
Baldwin, William, Pres.--Speedring, Inc., Cullman, AL; *U.S. Public*, pg. 158
Bale, Thomas M., Pres.--Bale Of Kentucky, Inc., Horse Cave, KY; *U.S. Private*, pg. 112
Balemian, Robert, Pres. & Chief Fin. Officer--Griffon Corp., Jericho, NY; *U.S. Public*, pg. 766
Balkanski, Alexandre A., Pres. & Chief Exec. Officer--C-Cube Microsystems, Milpitas, CA; *U.S. Public*, pg. 272
Balkema, Gary S., Exec. V.P. & Pres.--Consumer Care Division--Bayer Corporation, Pittsburgh, PA; *Int'l*, pg. 172
Balkenende, R.C., Pres.--Van Leeuwen Pipe & Tube Corp., Houston, TX; *Int'l*, pg. 1449
Ball, Anna C., Chm. Bd., Pres. & Chief Exec. Officer--Ball Horticultural Company, West Chicago, IL; *U.S. Private*, pg. 112
Ball, Christopher, Pres.--Panlabs International Operations, Bothell, WA; *Int'l*, pg. 827
Ball, John K., Pres. & Chief Oper. Officer--R.M. Shoemaker Co., West Conshohocken, PA; *U.S. Private*, pg. 996
Ball, Kenneth L., Pres. & Gen. Mgr.--Borden Decorative Products, Saint Louis, MO; *U.S. Private*, pg. 158
Ball, Larry, Pres.--Litton Poly-Scientific, Blacksburg, VA; *U.S. Public*, pg. 1003
Ball, Ray, Pres.--Pioneer Aluminum, Inc., Los Angeles, CA; *U.S. Private*, pg. 866
Ball, Robert L., Pres.--Alcan Aluminum Corporation, Cleveland, OH; *Int'l*, pg. 50
Ball, William A., Sr., Pres.--Air Power, Inc., High Point, NC; *U.S. Private*, pg. 28
Ballard, Dale H., Chm. Bd., Pres. & Chief Exec. Officer--Ballard Medical Products, Draper, UT; *U.S. Public*, pg. 171
Ballard, John W., Pres. & Chief Exec. Officer--TCI International Inc., Sunnyvale, CA; *U.S. Public*, pg. 1555
Ballengee, J.H., Pres. & Chief Oper. Officer--Union Camp Corporation, Wayne, NJ; *U.S. Public*, pg. 1665
Ballentine, James M., Pres. & Chief Exec. Officer--Detroit Stoker Co., Monroe, MI; *U.S. Public*, pg. 1679
Balletti, Robert, Pres.--Kvaerner Venture Inc., Stamford, CT; *Int'l*, pg. 770
Ballew, Glenn, Pres. & Chief Exec. Officer--Midwest Mutual Insurance Co., West Des Moines, IA; *U.S. Private*, pg. 881
Ballew, Glenn, Pres.--Equity Fire & Casualty Insurance Company, West Des Moines, IA; *U.S. Private*, pg. 881
Ballin, Robert, Pres. & Chief Exec. Officer--Willis Corroon Corp. of Eugene, Eugene, OR; *Int'l*, pg. 1505
Balloun, James S., Chm. Bd., Pres. & Chief Exec. Officer--National Service Industries, Inc., Atlanta, GA; *U.S. Public*, pg. 1160
Balmas, Bruce B., Pres. & Chief Exec. Officer--D & N Mortgage Corporation, Hancock, MI; *U.S. Public*, pg. 472
Baloun, Terry, Pres.--Norwest Bank Minnesota West, N.A., Moorhead, MN; *U.S. Public*, pg. 1202
Baloun, Terry, Pres.--Norwest Bank North Dakota, N.A., Fargo, ND; *U.S. Public*, pg. 1202
Balson, Patrick, Pres. & Chief Exec. Officer--Aetna Bearing Company, Chicago, IL; *U.S. Private*, pg. 25
Bamberger, Jonathon, Pres.--Canada Malting Co. Limited, Mississauga, Canada; *U.S. Public*, pg. 428
Bammer, Herbert, Co-Pres.--Austrian Airlines, Vienna, Austria; *Int'l*, pg. 101
Banach, Michael J., Pres.--Clark Specialty Co., Inc., Hammondsport, NY; *U.S. Private*, pg. 243
Bancroft, Charles, Pres. & Chief Exec. Officer--Citation Insurance Group, San Jose, CA; *U.S. Public*, pg. 376
Band, Robert, Pres.--Perini Management Services, Inc., Framingham, MA; *U.S. Public*, pg. 1278
Bandi, Lawrence E., Pres. & Chief Exec. Officer--Valley National Gasses Inc., Wheeling, WV; *U.S. Private*, pg. 1132
Bandolik, Keith A., Pres. & Chief Exec. Officer--Switchcraft, Inc., Chicago, IL; *U.S. Public*, pg. 1366
Bandy, George, Pres.--Horner Rausch Optical Company East, Inc., Nashville, TN; *U.S. Private*, pg. 540
Bane, Daniel T., Pres.--Grocers Capital Co., Los Angeles, CA; *U.S. Private*, pg. 227
Bane, Daniel T., Pres. & Chief Fin. Officer--Crown Grocers, Inc., Los Angeles, CA; *U.S. Private*, pg. 227
Bang, Chul, Pres.--Keystone Valve (Korea) Ltd., Kyonggi-do, Korea; *U.S. Public*, pg. 1650
Bang, Han-Woo, Pres.--Ssangyong Pacific, Diamond Bar, CA; *Int'l*, pg. 1292
Banghart, John F., Pres. & Chief Oper. Officer--The Worcester Insurance Co., Worcester, MA; *U.S. Public*, pg. 787
Banik, Bill, Pres.--Chris-Craft Boats, Sarasota, FL; *U.S. Private*, pg. 478
Bank, David, Pres.--M.F. Bank Restoration Co., Duluth, GA; *U.S. Private*, pg. 114
Bank, David L., Pres.--M.F. Bank & Company, Inc., Minneapolis, MN; *U.S. Private*, pg. 113
Bankard, James, Pres. & Chief Oper. Officer--Home Juice Co., Melrose Park, IL; *U.S. Private*, pg. 537
Bankes, James R., Pres. & Chief Exec. Officer--Samsill Corporation, Fort Worth, TX; *U.S. Private*, pg. 963
Banks, Allen, Pres.--The Program Exchange, New York, NY; *U.S. Public*, pg. 1422
Banks, Charles, Pres. & V.P.-Adv.--Energy & Process Corp., Tucker, GA; *Int'l*, pg. 1512
Banks, Charles A., Pres. & Chief Exec. Officer--Ferguson Enterprises, Inc., Newport News, VA; *Int'l*, pg. 1512
Banks, James, Pres.--International Rotex, Inc., Reno, NV; *Int'l*, pg. 460
Banks, Larry, Pres.--Household Life Insurance Co., Farmington, MI; *U.S. Public*, pg. 842
Banks, Wm. J., Pres.--Bearing Service Company, Pittsburgh, PA; *U.S. Private*, pg. 127
Bankuty, Geza E., Chm. Bd., Pres. & Chief Exec. Officer--New England Machinery, Inc., Bradenton, FL; *U.S. Private*, pg. 793
Bannister, Denise, Pres. & Publr.--Pensacola News-Journal, Inc., Pensacola, FL; *U.S. Public*, pg. 701
Bannon, George, Pres. & Chief Exec. Officer--Handex Environment Inc., Morganville, NJ; *U.S. Private*, pg. 498
Bannon, Robert G., Pres. & Chief Exec. Officer--First American Title Insurance Co. of N.Y., New York, NY; *U.S. Public*, pg. 626
Bansholt, Soren, Pres.--Scandinavian Division, Copenhagen, Denmark; *U.S. Public*, pg. 423
Bantoft, Chris, Pres.--ACC Long Distance U.K. Ltd., London, United Kingdom; *U.S. Public*, pg. 3
Banucci, Gene G., Ph.D., Chm. Bd., Pres. & Chief Exec. Officer--ATMI, Inc., Danbury, CT; *U.S. Public*, pg. 12
Banzet, Serge, Pres. & Chief Oper. Officer--Peugeot Motors of America Inc., Little Falls, NJ; *Int'l*, pg. 1020
Bapes, Peter C., Pres. & Chief Exec. Officer--Associated Leasing, Inc., Menomonee Falls, WI; *U.S. Public*, pg. 140
Baracos, Leon, Pres.--Weilwood Industries, Inc., New York, NY; *U.S. Private*, pg. 965
Baradarien, Diane, Pres.--Allegria Inc., Harrison, NJ; *U.S. Private*, pg. 565
Baranski, Dennis A., Chm. Bd., Pres. & Chief Exec. Officer--Barancorp, Lecompton, KS; *U.S. Private*, pg. 115
Barash, C., Pres.--OMI Bulk Management Co., New York, NY; *U.S. Public*, pg. 1208
Barba, J. Brendan, Chm. Bd., Pres. & Chief Exec. Officer--AEP Industries, Inc., South Hackensack, NJ; *U.S. Public*, pg. 4
Barber, Bruce, Pres. & Chief Oper. Officer--First National Bank, Palestine, Palestine, TX; *U.S. Public*, pg. 630
Barber, Hillard, Pres.--Barber Brothers Contracting Company, Baton Rouge, LA; *U.S. Private*, pg. 115
Barber, Irving K., Chm. Bd., Pres. & Chief Exec. Officer--Slocan Forest Products Ltd., Richmond, Canada; *Int'l*, pg. 1263
Barber, Joseph J., Jr., Pres.--Cine Magnetics, Inc., Armonk, NY; *U.S. Private*, pg. 240
Barber, Philip F., Pres.--Shenandoah Valley Land Development Div., Silver Spring, MD; *U.S. Public*, pg. 1683
Barber, Walter, Pres. & Chief Exec. Officer--Fluor Daniel GTI, Inc., Norwood, MA; *U.S. Public*, pg. 660
Barbero, Giorgio Pietro, Pres.--Barbero 1891 SpA, Canale, Italy; *Int'l*, pg. 164
Barbieux, Yves, Pres. & Mng. Dir.--Nestle France, Courbevoie, France; *Int'l*, pg. 921
Barbookles, James, Pres. & Chief Exec. Officer--Orion Research Inc., Boston, MA; *U.S. Public*, pg. 1592
Barbour, Alfred D., Pres.--Roessing Bronze Co., Mars, PA; *U.S. Private*, pg. 939
Barcellos, Sergio, Pres.--BS Continental S.A. Utilidades Domesticas, Sao Paulo, Brazil; *Int'l*, pg. 123
Barcik, Stephen J., Pres.--Interpak Terminals, Inc., Houston, TX; *Int'l*, pg. 724
Barclay, Richard D., Pres. & Chief Exec. Officer--First National Bank of Central Illinois, Springfield, IL; *U.S. Public*, pg. 644
Bard, I. Gary, Chm. Bd. & Chief Exec. Officer--Aydin Corporation, Horsham, PA; *U.S. Public*, pg. 158
Bard, James R., Pres.--Bard Mfg. Co., Bryan, OH; *U.S. Private*, pg. 116
Bard, Shannon, Pres. & Chief Exec. Officer--Aquapore Moisture Systems, Inc., Phoenix, AZ; *Int'l*, pg. 1066
Barder, D. Richard, Pres.--M & I Bank of Beloit, Beloit, WI; *U.S. Public*, pg. 1050
Bardis, Christo D., Pres.--Reynen, Bardis & Winn, Sacramento, CA; *U.S. Private*, pg. 926
Bardis, John A., Pres. & Chief Exec. Officer--Vencare, Incorporated, Alpharetta, GA; *U.S. Public*, pg. 1715
Bardo, Charles, Pres.--Ceramic Cooling Tower Co., Fort Worth, TX; *U.S. Private*, pg. 68
Bardwell, Darrell, Pres.--Biddulph Automotive Group, Glendale, AZ; *U.S. Private*, pg. 142
Bared, Joe, Pres.--Farm Stores, Miami, FL; *U.S. Private*, pg. 394
Barefoot, Gerald, Pres. & Chief Exec. Officer--Rieter Automotive North America Inc, Farmington Hills, MI; *Int'l*, pg. 1117
Barenbrug, Bert J.M., Pres.--Barenbrug Holland BV, Oosterhout, Netherlands; *Int'l*, pg. 166
Barents, Brian E., Pres.--Bombardier, Learjet Inc., Wichita, KS; *Int'l*, pg. 200
Bares, W.G., Chm. Bd., Pres. & Chief Exec. Officer--The Lubrizol Corporation, Wickliffe, OH; *U.S. Public*, pg. 1016
Barest, Bonnie, Exec. Principal & Exec. Dir.-Media Services--Publicis/Bloom, New York, NY; *Int'l*, pg. 470
Barger, John William, Sr., Pres. & Chief Exec. Officer--Barger Builders, Saint Petersburg, FL; *U.S. Private*, pg. 116
Bargeron, Walter N., Pres.--Bethlehem Steel-Burns Harbor Division, Chesterton, IN; *U.S. Public*, pg. 226
Barguirdjian, Henri, Pres. & Chief Exec. Officer--Van Cleef & Arpels, Inc., New York, NY; *U.S. Private*, pg. 1132
Bargum, Magnus, Mng. Dir.--Oy Algol AB, Espoo, Finland; *Int'l*, pg. 15
Barke, Bill, Pres.--Allyn & Bacon, Needham, MA; *U.S. Private*, pg. 778
Barker, David R., Pres.--Penn Virginia Oil & Gas Company, Kingsport, TN; *U.S. Public*, pg. 1271
Barker, G. Carlton, Chm. Bd., Pres. & Chief Exec. Officer--Regions Bank/Montgomery/Alexander City, Montgomery, AL; *U.S. Public*, pg. 1372
Barker, Mike, Pres. & Chief Oper. Officer--InterVoice, Inc., Dallas, TX; *U.S. Public*, pg. 910
Barker, Sam, Pres.-US Pharmaceutical Group--Bristol-Myers Squibb U.S Pharmaceutical Group, Plainsboro, NJ; *U.S. Public*, pg. 255
Barker, W.R., Pres.--Ravarino & Freschi, Inc., Saint Louis, MO; *U.S. Private*, pg. 158
Barkhurst, Ross, Pres. & Chief Exec. Officer--Vermont Yankee Nuclear Power Corp., Brattleboro, VT; *U.S. Public*, pg. 328
Barkley, Andy, Pres.--Six Flags Fiesta Texas, San Antonio, TX; *U.S. Public*, pg. 1611
Barkley, Rick, Pres.--Remcor Products Co., Glendale Heights, IL; *Int'l*, pg. 646
Barksdale, James L., Pres. & Chief Exec. Officer--Netscape Communications Corp., Mountain View, CA; *U.S. Public*, pg. 1168
Barletta, Anthony, Pres.--Barletta Materials & Construction, Hazleton, PA; *U.S. Private*, pg. 116
Barlow, Bruce, Mr., Pres.--Conida Farms, Hazelton, ID; *U.S. Private*, pg. 693
Barlow, J. Bruce, Pres.--Macristy Industries, Inc., New Britain, CT; *U.S. Private*, pg. 693
Barlow, John, Pres. & Chief Exec. Officer--Safelite AutoGlass, Columbus, OH; *U.S. Private*, pg. 960
Barlucchi, Claudio, Pres--EMTEC Magnetics Italia Spa, Cesano Maderno, Italy; *Int'l*, pg. 743
Barlup, Lou, Pres.--Crane Pumps & Systems Inc., Piqua, OH; *U.S. Public*, pg. 457
Barlup, Lou, Pres.--Sellers Cleaning Systems, Piqua, OH; *U.S. Public*, pg. 457
Barlup, Louis M., III, Pres.--ChemPump, Warrington, PA; *U.S. Public*, pg. 456
Barnaby, Richard G., Pres. & Chief Oper. Officer--Kaiser Permanente, Oakland, CA; *U.S. Private*, pg. 605
Barnard, Andrew, Pres.--Odyssey Reinsurance Corporation, New York, NY; *Int'l*, pg. 1258
Barnard, Glen, Pres.--Kaufman and Broad Colorado Division, Denver, CO; *U.S. Public*, pg. 945
Barnard, Glen, Pres.--Kaufman and Broad Utah Division, Midvale, UT; *U.S. Public*, pg. 945
Barnes, Chris, Pres. & Chief Oper. Officer--Spectrulite Consortium, Inc., Madison, IL; *U.S. Private*, pg. 1024
Barnes, Dallas, Pres.--Meherrin Agriculture & Chemical Co., Severn, NC; *U.S. Private*, pg. 729
Barnes, Donald, Jr., Pres.--Belle Tire Distributor Inc., Allen Park, MI; *U.S. Private*, pg. 132
Barnes, Galen, Pres. & Chief Oper. Officer--Employers Insurance of Wausau, Wausau, WI; *U.S. Private*, pg. 788
Barnes, Galen R., Pres.--Nationwide Insurance Enterprise, Columbus, OH; *U.S. Private*, pg. 788
Barnes, George, Pres.--Chesapeake Display and Packaging Co., Winston Salem, NC; *U.S. Public*, pg. 346
Barnes, James E., Chm. Bd., Pres. & Chief Exec. Officer--Mapco Inc., Tulsa, OK; *U.S. Public*, pg. 1042
Barnes, John, Mng. Dir.--Bain & Company Limited, Sydney, Australia; *Int'l*, pg. 406
Barnes, John R., Chm. Bd., Pres. & Chief Exec. Officer--Kaneb Services, Inc., Richardson, TX; *U.S. Public*, pg. 942
Barnes, L.L., Pres.--Cyantek Corporation, Fremont, CA; *Int'l*, pg. 802
Barnes, Larry B., Chm. Bd.--LB Industries Inc., Boise, ID; *U.S. Private*, pg. 639
Barnes, Richard A., Pres. & Chief Oper. Officer--Republic Fastener Products Corp., Great Falls, SC; *U.S. Private*, pg. 923
Barnes, Robert L., Pres. & Chief Oper. Officer--Knight Architects Engineers Planners, Inc., Chicago, IL; *U.S. Private*, pg. 626
Barnes, William, Pres.--Kansa Corporation, Emporia, KS; *U.S. Public*, pg. 170
Barnet, Bruce, Pres. & Chief Exec. Officer--Reed Elsevier Business Information, Newton, MA; *Int'l*, pg. 1095
Barnett, Cecil C., Chm. Bd., Pres. & Chief Exec. Officer--Algood Food Company, Louisville, KY; *U.S. Private*, pg. 34
Barnett, Daniel, Pres.-Wine Div.--Canandaigua Wine Company Div., Canandaigua, NY; *U.S. Public*, pg. 300
Barnett, Daniel C., Pres.--Canandaigua Wine Co., Canandaigua, NY; *U.S. Public*, pg. 300
Barnett, Dave, Pres.--F&F Foods, Chicago, IL; *U.S. Private*, pg. 388
Barnett, John, Pres. & Chief Exec. Officer--Molson Breweries, Toronto, Canada; *Int'l*, pg. 500
Barnett, John, Pres. & Chief Exec. Officer--Molson Breweries, Toronto, Canada; *U.S. Public*, pg. 1289
Barnett, Marilyn, Pres.--Mars Advertising Co., Southfield, MI; *U.S. Private*, pg. 706
Barnett, Marilyn, Pres.--Mars Public Relations Group, Southfield, MI; *U.S. Private*, pg. 707
Barnett, Paul S., Pres.--Barnett Millworks, Inc., Theodore, AL; *U.S. Private*, pg. 116
Barnett, Richard M., Chm. Bd., Pres. & Chief Exec. Officer--Reliable Stores, Inc., Columbia, MD; *U.S. Private*, pg. 920
Barnett, T. G., Pres.--Marsh Company M.C.S.A., Bellevue, Switzerland; *U.S. Private*, pg. 708
Barnett, T. G., Pres.--Marion 100, Inc., Marion, IL; *U.S. Private*, pg. 708
Barnett, Thomas G., Pres. & Chief Oper. Officer--Marsh Company, Belleville, IL; *U.S. Private*, pg. 707
Barney, R.L., Pres.--Carbon Products Operation Inc., East Stroudsburg, PA; *Int'l*, pg. 891

Barnhardt, T.L., Pres. & Chief Exec. Officer--Barnhardt Manufacturing Co., Charlotte, NC; *U.S. Private*, pg. 116

Barnhill, R.E., Jr., Pres.--Barnhill Contracting Company, Tarboro, NC; *U.S. Private*, pg. 117

Barnhill, Robert B., Jr., Chm. Bd., Pres. & Chief Exec. Officer--Tessco Technologies, Inc., Sparks, MD; *U.S. Public*, pg. 1582

Barnhill, Tim, Pres.--Central State Bank, Lexington, TN; *U.S. Public*, pg. 1669

Barnum, Scott, Pres. & Chief Oper. Officer--Pete's Brewing Company, Palo Alto, CA; *U.S. Public*, pg. 1280

Barnum, T.B., Chm. Bd., Pres. & Chief Exec. Officer--Max & Erma's Restaurants, Columbus, OH; *U.S. Public*, pg. 1060

Barocas, Martin, Pres.--Santee Print Works, Inc., New York, NY; *U.S. Private*, pg. 965

Baron, Carole, Pres.--Dell Publishing, New York, NY; *Int'l*, pg. 191

Baron, Ronald, Pres.--Winthrop-Atkins Co., Inc., Middleboro, MA; *U.S. Private*, pg. 1183

Baron, Sheri, Pres. & Strategic Plng. Dir.--Gotham Incorporated, New York, NY; *U.S. Private*, pg. 677

Barone, Elaine, Pres. & Treas.--Coken Company, Inc., Providence, RI; *U.S. Private*, pg. 250

Barr, Donald M., Pres.--Barr & Barr, Inc., New York, NY; *U.S. Private*, pg. 117

Barr, Emily, Pres. & Gen. Mgr.--WTVD-TV, Durham, NC; *U.S. Public*, pg. 512

Barr, J. James, Pres. & Chief Exec. Officer--American Water Works Company, Inc., Voorhees, NJ; *U.S. Public*, pg. 95

Barr, J. James, Pres.--Occoquan Land Corporation, Voorhees, NJ; *U.S. Public*, pg. 95

Barr, J. James, Pres.--American Commonwealth Company, Voorhees, NJ; *U.S. Public*, pg. 95

Barr, J. James, Pres.--American Water Works Service Company, Inc., Voorhees, NJ; *U.S. Public*, pg. 95

Barr, J. James, Pres.--Greenwich Water System, Inc., Voorhees, NJ; *U.S. Public*, pg. 95

Barr, J. James, Pres.--American International Water Services Company, Voorhees, NJ; *U.S. Public*, pg. 95

Barr, John, Pres. & Chief Oper. Officer--Quaker State Corporation, Irving, TX; *U.S. Public*, pg. 1348

Barr, Lynn E., Pres. & Chief Exec. Officer--Underground Construction Co., Inc., Benicia, CA; *U.S. Private*, pg. 1116

Barr, Michael, Pres. & Treas.--Barr Electric Corporation, Wheeling, IL; *U.S. Private*, pg. 117

Barr, Wallace, Pres. & Chief Oper. Officer-AC Hilton & Bally's Park Place--Atlantic City Hilton, Atlantic City, NJ; *U.S. Public*, pg. 829

Barragan, Napoleon, Pres. & Chief Exec. Officer--Dial A Mattress USA, Long Island City, NY; *U.S. Private*, pg. 330

Barrans, Terry, Pres. & Chief Exec. Officer--Fisher Mills, Inc., Seattle, WA; *U.S. Public*, pg. 648

Barre, Stephen A., Chm. Bd., Pres., Chief Exec. Officer & Sec.--Servo Corporation of America, Westbury, NY; *U.S. Private*, pg. 987

Barrett, Connie, Pres.--Tressa, Inc., Erlanger, KY; *U.S. Private*, pg. 1100

Barrett, Craig, Pres. & Chief Oper. Officer--Intel Corporation, Santa Clara, CA; *U.S. Public*, pg. 886

Barrett, Don, Pres.--Infobase Services, Conway, AR; *U.S. Public*, pg. 18

Barrett, James A., Jr., Pres.--Rio Hotel & Casino Inc., Las Vegas, NV; *U.S. Public*, pg. 1390

Barrett, James H., Pres. & Chief Exec. Officer--Duchesne Bank, Saint Peters, MO; *U.S. Public*, pg. 643

Barrett, John F., Pres. & Chief Exec. Officer--The Western and Southern Life Insurance Company, Cincinnati, OH; *U.S. Private*, pg. 1164

Barrett, John F., Pres. & Chief Exec. Officer--Western-Southern Life Assurance Co., Cincinnati, OH; *U.S. Private*, pg. 1164

Barrett, Marty, Pres.--Global Processing & Recycling Group, Shied-Tech Cambridge, Cambridge, Canada; *U.S. Public*, pg. 748

Barriga, Mauricio, Mng. Dir.--Leo Burnett Columbiana, S.A., Bogota, Colombia; *U.S. Private*, pg. 185

Barrington, Michael R., Vice Chm., Pres. & Chief Oper. Officer--AmeriCredit Corp., Fort Worth, TX; *U.S. Public*, pg. 96

Barrington, William J., Pres. & Chief Exec. Officer--Sea Ray, Knoxville, TN; *U.S. Public*, pg. 266

Barrios Sanchez, Luis, Pres. & Chief Exec. Officer--Grupo Posadas S.A. de C.V., Mexico, Mexico; *Int'l*, pg. 576

Barro, Tom, Pres.--Lamp Post Franchise Corporation, Tustin, CA; *U.S. Private*, pg. 644

Barrocas, Alberto, Pres. & Treas.--Injection Footwear Corp., Miami, FL; *U.S. Private*, pg. 563

Barron, Millard E., Pres.--Zellers Inc., Toronto, Canada; *Int'l*, pg. 637

Barron, Patricia, Pres.--Xerox Engineering Systems Division, Rochester, NY; *U.S. Public*, pg. 1784

Barrott, William E., III, Pres.--Aurora Casket Company, Aurora, IN; *U.S. Private*, pg. 99

Barry, David, Pres.--Vivra Renal Care, Aliso Viejo, CA; *U.S. Public*, pg. 1724

Barry, Edward W., Pres.--Oxford University Press, Inc., New York, NY; *Int'l*, pg. 1019

Barry, Frank, Pres.--The Sheridan Press, Inc., Hanover, PA; *U.S. Private*, pg. 993

Barry, Joseph A., Pres.--Cast-Matic Corporation, Stevensville, MI; *U.S. Public*, pg. 894

Barry, Ronald N., Jr., Pres.--Hopkinsville Elevator Company, Inc., Hopkinsville, KY; *U.S. Private*, pg. 538

Barry, Stephen, Pres.--January & Associates, Inc., Brentwood, TN; *U.S. Private*, pg. 287

Barry, Tom, Chm. Bd., Pres. & Chief Oper. Officer--Mighty Distributing System, Norcross, GA; *U.S. Private*, pg. 745

Barse, David M., Pres.--Danielson Holding Corporation, New York, NY; *U.S. Public*, pg. 483

Barsema, James A., Pres. & County Mgr.--First American Title Insurance Agency, Inc., Pinetop, AZ; *U.S. Public*, pg. 626

Barsema, James A., Pres. & Gen. Mgr.--First American Title Insurance Agency of Gila, Inc., Payson, AZ; *U.S. Public*, pg. 626

Barsoum, Khalil, Pres. & Chief Exec. Officer--IBM Canada Limited, Markham, Canada; *U.S. Public*, pg. 897

Barstead, Gregory, Pres.--Colonial Penn Group, Inc., Wilmington, DE; *U.S. Public*, pg. 990

Barstead, Gregory R., Pres.--Charter National Life Insurance Co., Saint Louis, MO; *U.S. Public*, pg. 990

Bartell, George D., Pres. & Chief Oper. Officer--The Bartell Drug Company, Seattle, WA; *U.S. Private*, pg. 118

Bartelli, James, Chm. Bd., Pres. & Chief Exec. Officer--Mercury Computer Systems, Inc., Chelmsford, MA; *U.S. Private*, pg. 732

Bartels, Bill, Pres. & Chief Exec. Officer--Spar Marketing Force, Inc., Rochester Hills, MI; *U.S. Public*, pg. 23

Bartelt, Kenneth H., Pres. & Chief Oper. Officer--PowderTech Corporation, Valparaiso, IN; *Int'l*, pg. 878

Bartenbach, Klaus G., Pres. & Chief Exec. Officer--Ford, Bacon & Davis Companies Inc., Duluth, GA; *Int'l*, pg. 401

Bartenbach, Klaus G., Pres. & Chief Exec. Officer--Ford, Bacon & Davis Companies, Inc., Duluth, GA; *Int'l*, pg. 401

Bartges, Hans, Pres. & Chief Exec. Officer--Auto Lenders Acceptance Corp., Atlanta, GA; *Int'l*, pg. 499

Barth, James, Pres. & Chief Exec. Officer--Shurfine International, Inc., Northlake, IL; *U.S. Private*, pg. 997

Barth, Jean Paul, Pres.--Hutchinson S.A., Paris, France; *Int'l*, pg. 1409

Barth, Steve, Pres. & Chief Exec. Officer--Challenger Electrical Equipment Corp., Pittsburgh, PA; *U.S. Public*, pg. 558

Bartholomae, Raymond E., Exec. V.P. & Gen. Mgr.--Symons Corporation, Des Plaines, IL; *U.S. Private*, pg. 932

Bartle, John, Joint Chief Exec.--Bartle Bogle Hegarty Limited, London, United Kingdom; *Int'l*, pg. 169

Bartles, Dean L., Pres.--G.D. International, Ltd., Charlotte Amalie, VI; *U.S. Public*, pg. 1219

Bartlett, Dennis M., Pres.--Chino Mines Company, Hurley, NM; *U.S. Public*, pg. 1287

Bartlett, Robert A., Jr., Pres. & Chief Oper. Officer--The F.A. Bartlett Tree Expert Co., Stamford, CT; *U.S. Private*, pg. 119

Bartlett, Tom, Pres. & Chief Exec. Officer--Grupo Iusacell SA de CV, Mexico, Mexico; *U.S. Public*, pg. 204

Bartlett, William P., Pres.--Callidus Technologies Inc., Tulsa, OK; *U.S. Public*, pg. 344

Bartley, Brain K., Pres.--Virginia Metal Industries, Inc., Orange, VA; *U.S. Private*, pg. 1141

Bartley, Lynn, Pres.--Riverside Millwork Company, Inc., Penacook, NH; *U.S. Private*, pg. 934

Bartling, John B., Pres. & Chief Exec. Officer--Lexford Residential Trust, Columbus, OH; *U.S. Public*, pg. 991

Bartolin, Stephan, Jr., Pres.--Broadmoor Hotel, Inc., Colorado Springs, CO; *U.S. Private*, pg. 170

Bartolome, Alberto, Pres.--EURO RSCG, Buenos Aires, Argentina; *Int'l*, pg. 602

Barton, A.P., Jr., Chm. Bd., Pres. & Chief Exec. Officer--Mutual Manufacturing & Supply Co., Cincinnati, OH; *U.S. Private*, pg. 769

Barton, Bob, Pres.--Alcoa Fujikura, Dearborn, MI; *U.S. Public*, pg. 60

Barton, John A., Pres. & Chief Exec. Officer--Southwestern Electric Service Co., Dallas, TX; *U.S. Public*, pg. 1588

Barton, Richard D., Pres. & Chief Exec. Officer--The Paper Magic Group, Inc., Scranton, PA; *U.S. Public*, pg. 284

Barton, Richard S., Pres. & Chief Exec. Officer--Xerox Canada Holdings Inc., North York, Canada; *U.S. Public*, pg. 1785

Barton, Robert, Pres. & Chief Exec. Officer--National Electric Coil, Columbus, OH; *U.S. Private*, pg. 782

Barton, Timothy A., Pres.--Network Long Distance, Inc., Baton Rouge, LA; *U.S. Public*, pg. 1169

Bartow, Bill, Pres.--Art Van Furniture Inc., Warren, MI; *U.S. Private*, pg. 86

Bartz, James W., Pres.--Columbia Lumber & Manufacturing Co., Columbia, SC; *U.S. Private*, pg. 255

Barwick, Allen, Pres. & Chief Exec. Officer--Shuford Mills, Inc., Hickory, NC; *U.S. Private*, pg. 996

Basey, Al, Pres.--CMI Corporation, Oklahoma City, OK; *U.S. Public*, pg. 278

Basham, B.H., Pres. & Chief Exec. Officer--Industrial Rubber Products Company, Charleston, WV; *U.S. Private*, pg. 561

Basham, Robert T., Pres. & Chief Oper. Officer--Outback Steakhouse Inc., Tampa, FL; *U.S. Public*, pg. 1235

Bashe, Jerry, Exec. V.P. & Gen. Mgr.--Dresser Valve & Controls Div., Woodlands, TX; *U.S. Public*, pg. 528

Basinait, Martin C., Pres. & Chief Exec. Officer--Western Regional Off Track Betting, Batavia, NY; *U.S. Private*, pg. 1168

Basing, M.P., Pres.--Swiss Bank Corporation (Canada), Toronto, Canada; *Int'l*, pg. 1331

Baskin, Scott, Pres.--Mark Shale, Burr Ridge, IL; *U.S. Private*, pg. 989

Baskind, Barry, Pres., Chief Exec. Officer & Dir.-Cash Mngmt.--Mott's Holdings, Inc., Glastonbury, CT; *U.S. Private*, pg. 764

Bassani, Darryl, Pres.--Bassani Manufacturing, Anaheim, CA; *U.S. Private*, pg. 122

Basserman, Peter P., Pres.--SNET Mobility, Inc., Rocky Hill, CT; *U.S. Public*, pg. 1491

Bassett, I. Jay, Pres.--Spectrum Industries, Grand Rapids, MI; *U.S. Private*, pg. 1024

Bassett, M. Glen, Pres.--Baker Petrolite Corporation, Houston, TX; *U.S. Public*, pg. 166

Bassett, Steve, Pres.--Contempri Homes, Inc., Taylor, PA; *U.S. Public*, pg. 439

Bassett, William A., Chm. Bd., Pres. & Chief Exec. Officer--Decorator Industries, Inc., Pembroke Pines, FL; *U.S. Public*, pg. 491

Bassett, William C., Pres.--The W.E. Bassett Company, Shelton, CT; *U.S. Private*, pg. 122

Bassi, Peter A., Pres.--Tricon Restaurants International, Dallas, TX; *U.S. Public*, pg. 1637

Bassi, Roger, Pres.--Fidelity & Surety Division, Schaumburg, IL; *U.S. Public*, pg. 215

Basso, Fred, Pres.--Power Designs, Inc., Danbury, CT; *U.S. Private*, pg. 878

Bassoul, Selim, Pres.--Southbend, Fuquay Varina, NC; *U.S. Public*, pg. 1110

Bast, Brian, Pres. & Treas.--Bast Chevrolet Inc., Seaford, NY; *U.S. Private*, pg. 122

Bast, Thomas R., Pres.--M & I First National Bank, West Bend, WI; *U.S. Public*, pg. 1050

Bastable, Colum P., Pres. & Chief Exec. Officer--Royal LePage Limited, Don Mills, Canada; *Int'l*, pg. 1143

Bastable, John, Sr. V.P.--Aer Lingus, Melville, NY; *Int'l*, pg. 28

Bastian, Michael, Pres. & Chief Exec. Officer--Royal Bank Action Direct Inc., Richmond Hill, Canada; *Int'l*, pg. 1131

Bastow, David, Pres.--F.R. Gross Company, Stow, OH; *U.S. Public*, pg. 103

Batchelor, David, Pres.--Lifestyle Brands, Ltd., Chicago, IL; *U.S. Public*, pg. 1310

Bateman, George, Pres.--Bateman Brothers Lumber Co., Inc., New Britain, PA; *U.S. Private*, pg. 122

Bateman, Mark, Sr. Principal & Client Services Dir.--Publicis/Bloom, Dallas, TX; *Int'l*, pg. 469

Bateman, Walter R., Pres. & Chief Exec. Officer--Harleysville Group, Harleysville, PA; *U.S. Public*, pg. 786

Bateman, Walter R., Chm. Bd. & Pres.--Harleysville Services Inc, Harleysville, PA; *U.S. Public*, pg. 787

Bateman, Walter R., Pres. & Chief Exec. Officer--Harleysville Mutual Insurance, Harleysville, PA; *U.S. Public*, pg. 787

Bateman, Walter R., Chm., Pres. & Chief Oper. Officer--Mainland Insurance Co., Harleysville, PA; *U.S. Public*, pg. 787

Bates, Ernest A., M.D., Chm. Bd., Pres., Chief Exec. & Oper. Officer--American Shared Hospital Services, San Francisco, CA; *U.S. Public*, pg. 91

Bates, Garth C., Jr., Pres.--Stewart & Stevenson de las Americas, Inc., Houston, TX; *U.S. Public*, pg. 1517

Bates, George G., Pres.--Ring Technologies, Inc., Warren, MI; *U.S. Private*, pg. 931

Bates, John C., Chm. of Bd., Pres. & Chief Exec. Officer--Heidtman Steel Products, Inc., Toledo, OH; *U.S. Private*, pg. 519

Bates, Mary K., Pres. & Gen. Mgr.--First American Title Co. of Spokane, Spokane, WA; *U.S. Public*, pg. 625

Bates, Robert D., Chm. Bd., Pres. & Chief Exec. Officer--Guarantee Life Insurance Co., Omaha, NE; *U.S. Public*, pg. 768

Bates, Thomas R., Pres. & Chief Exec. Officer--Weatherford Enterra Incorporated, Houston, TX; *U.S. Public*, pg. 1749

Bates, Thomas R., Pres.--Weatherford U.S., Inc., Houston, TX; *U.S. Public*, pg. 1749

Bates, Thomas R., Pres.--Weatherford Canada Limited, Calgary, Canada; *U.S. Public*, pg. 1750

Bates, Thomas R., Jr., Pres.--Weatherford US Inc., Santa Paula, CA; *U.S. Public*, pg. 1749

Bates, Wesley, Chm. Bd. & Pres.--Stanley Steemer International, Inc., Dublin, OH; *U.S. Private*, pg. 1033

Batinovich, Andrew, Pres. & Chief Oper. Officer--Glenborough Realty Trust Incorporated, San Mateo, CA; *U.S. Public*, pg. 747

Batisse, Jean-Paul, Pres.--Serpo France S.A., Nimes, France; *Int'l*, pg. 1200

Batt, James M., Pres., Chief Exec. Officer & Controller--Peck Spring Company, Plainville, CT; *U.S. Private*, pg. 846

Batt, Richard, Pres.--DH Compounding Co., Clinton, TN; *U.S. Public*, pg. 781

Battaglia, Joseph, Pres.--Telephonics Corp., Farmington, NY; *U.S. Public*, pg. 766

Batteast, Robert V., Chm. Bd., Pres. & Treas.--Batteast Construction Company, Inc., South Bend, IN; *U.S. Private*, pg. 123

Batterberg, J.T., Pres.--Delphi Packard Electric Systems, Beachwood, OH; *U.S. Public*, pg. 719

Battersby, John J., Pres.--Summit Food Service Distributors, London, Canada; *Int'l*, pg. 266

Batting, Robert T., Pres. & Chief Exec. Officer--Kenney Manufacturing Company, Warwick, RI; *U.S. Private*, pg. 615

Battista, Gabriel, Pres. & Chief Exec. Officer--Cable & Wireless Communications Inc., Vienna, VA; *Int'l*, pg. 247

Battitta, Mark, Partner--Media First International, Inc., New York, NY; *U.S. Private*, pg. 726

Batty, Mark J., Pres.--International Typeface Corporation (ITC), New York, NY; *Int'l*, pg. 460

Batz, H. D., Pres.--Shimadzu Europa GmbH, Duisburg, Germany; *Int'l*, pg. 1232

Bauchiero, Frank E., Pres. & Chief Oper. Officer--Walbro Corporation, Cass City, MI; *U.S. Public*, pg. 1733

Baucom, Mark, Pres.--Hickory Construction Company, Hickory, NC; *U.S. Private*, pg. 525

Bauer, Chris M., Chm. Bd. & Chief Exec. Officer--Firstar Milwaukee Bank, N.A., Milwaukee, WI; *U.S. Public*, pg. 643

Bauer, David J., Pres.--Mountain States Airgas, Charleston, WV; *U.S. Public*, pg. 33

Bauer, Elmer, Jr., Pres.--Dettra Flag Company, Oaks, PA; *U.S. Private*, pg. 328

Bauer, G.K., Pres.--CU Power International Ltd., Calgary, Canada; *Int'l*, pg. 95

Bauer, J.W., Pres.--M.A. Hanna Color, Suwanee, GA; *U.S. Public*, pg. 781

Bauer, John P., Pres.--Basic Food International Inc., Fort Lauderdale, FL; *U.S. Private*, pg. 121

Bauer, John P., Pres.--Global Food Corporation, Fort Lauderdale, FL; *U.S. Private*, pg. 121
Bauer, Stephen, Pres.--Prudential Real Estate Affiliates Inc., Costa Mesa, CA; *U.S. Private*, pg. 892
Bauer, Stephen C., Pres.--SAFECO Asset Management Company, Seattle, WA; *U.S. Public*, pg. 1423
Bauer, William C., Pres.--Empire Electric Association, Cortez, CO; *U.S. Private*, pg. 374
Baugh, Jim, Pres.--Wilson Sporting Goods Co., Chicago, IL; *Int'l*, pg. 73
Baugh, Michael A., Pres. & Gen. Mgr.--BHP Petroleum Pty Ltd., Melbourne, Australia; *Int'l*, pg. 225
Baugher, John O., Pres. & Treas.--Baugher Chevrolet-Buick Inc., Waynesboro, VA; *U.S. Private*, pg. 123
Baughman, Gary, Pres. & Chief Exec. Officer--Fisher-Price, Inc., East Aurora, NY; *U.S. Public*, pg. 1058
Baughman, Kathy, Pres.--HLB Communications, Inc., Chicago, IL; *U.S. Private*, pg. 491
Baughman, Walter, III, Pres. & Chief Oper. Officer--Plastomer Corp., Livonia, MI; *U.S. Private*, pg. 872
Baum, David, Chm. Bd., Pres. & Chief Exec. Officer--Arcon Construction Co., Inc., Harris, MN; *U.S. Private*, pg. 80
Baum, John C., Pres.--W.A. Baum Company, Inc., Copiague, NY; *U.S. Private*, pg. 124
Baum, Leonard M., Pres. & Chief Oper. Officer--Advanced Magnetics, Inc., Cambridge, MA; *U.S. Public*, pg. 20
Bauman, B. Kent, Pres. & Chief Fin. Officer--Condon Oil Company, Inc., Ripon, WI; *U.S. Private*, pg. 262
Bauman, James J., Co-President & Co-Chief Exec. Officer--Eastbridge Capital Inc., New York, NY; *Int'l*, pg. 933
Bauman, James R., Pres.--M & I Bank of Burlington, Burlington, WI; *U.S. Public*, pg. 1050
Bauman, Robert L., Chm. Bd., Pres. & Chief Exec. Officer--Hickok Incorporated, Cleveland, OH; *U.S. Public*, pg. 825
Bauman, W.A., Pres. & Treas.--Enger-Kress Company, West Bend, WI; *U.S. Private*, pg. 376
Baumann, Daniel E., Pres. & Chief Oper. Officer--Paddock Publications, Inc., Arlington Heights, IL; *U.S. Private*, pg. 833
Baumann, James, Pres.--Follett College Stores Corp., Elmhurst, IL; *U.S. Private*, pg. 417
Baumann, John, Pres.--The Swiss Colony, Inc, Monroe, WI; *U.S. Private*, pg. 1059
Baumgardner, J. Dwane, Ph.D., Chm. Bd., Pres. & Chief Exec. Officer--Donnelly Corporation, Holland, MI; *U.S. Public*, pg. 519
Baumgardner, Robert M., Pres.--Unisource, Gahanna, OH; *U.S. Public*, pg. 1671
Baumgartner, A.R., Dr., Pres.--Ayerst, McKenna & Harrison Inc., Saint-Laurent, Canada; *U.S. Public*, pg. 80
Baumgartner, James D., Pres.--Standard Property Corporation, Pittsburgh, PA; *U.S. Private*, pg. 529
Baumgartner, James W., Pres.--First USA Financial Services, Inc., Murray, UT; *U.S. Public*, pg. 174
Baumgartner, V.H., Pres.--Caterpillar Materiels Routiers, Rantigny, France; *U.S. Public*, pg. 316
Baumgartner, Werner, Pres.--Behr Systems, Inc., Auburn Hills, MI; *Int'l*, pg. 421
Baur, Victor W., Pres.--Transgas Inc., Lowell, MA; *U.S. Public*, pg. 401
Bause, Fred, Pres.--Ferrous Processing & Trading Co., Detroit, MI; *U.S. Private*, pg. 402
Bawden, Mark, Pres.--Bawden Corporation, Eldridge, IA; *U.S. Private*, pg. 124
Baxter, Brent A., Pres.--Hazelwood Farms Bakeries, Inc., Hazelwood, MO; *U.S. Public*, pg. 1541
Baxter, Frank E., Chm. Bd., Pres. & Chief Exec. Officer--Jefferies Group, Inc., Los Angeles, CA; *U.S. Public*, pg. 924
Baxter, Keith G., Pres. & Chief Exec. Officer--Cornerstone Propane G.P. Inc., Watsonville, CA; *U.S. Public*, pg. 1201
Baxter, Peter J., Pres. & Chief Exec. Officer--CFX Bank, Keene, NH; *U.S. Public*, pg. 277
Baxter, Raymond A., Pres. & Chief Oper. Officer--Interbake Foods Inc., Richmond, VA; *Int'l*, pg. 1495
Baxter, Rick, Pres. & Chief Exec. Officer--J.H. Baxter & Company, San Mateo, CA; *U.S. Private*, pg. 124
Bayer, Ian D., Pres. & Chief Exec. Officer--Battle Mountain Gold Company, Houston, TX; *U.S. Public*, pg. 193
Bayer, Robert, Chm. Bd., Pres. & Chief Exec. Officer--Bayer Clothing Group, New York, NY; *U.S. Private*, pg. 124
Bayers, William G., Pres.--President Baking-Louisville, Louisville, KY; *Int'l*, pg. 1069
Bayless, Charles E., Chm. Bd., Pres. & Chief Exec. Officer--UniSource Energy Corporation, Tucson, AZ; *U.S. Public*, pg. 1670
Bayley, Ronald, Pres.--Robert E. Bayley Construction, Seattle, WA; *U.S. Private*, pg. 125
Bayly, George V., Pres. & Chief Exec. Officer--Ivex Packaging Corporation, Lincolnshire, IL; *U.S. Public*, pg. 915
Bazet, James R., Pres., Chief Exec. Officer & Chief Oper. Officer--Cobra Electronics Corporation, Chicago, IL; *U.S. Public*, pg. 391
Bazie, Tracey A., Pres. & Mng. Dir.--Johnson & Johnson Hemisferica, Caguas, PR; *U.S. Public*, pg. 928
Bazzy, David, Pres. & Chief Oper. Officer--Kenwal Products Corp., Dearborn, MI; *U.S. Private*, pg. 615
Beach, William H., Chm. Bd., Pres., Chief Exec. & Oper. Officer--Beach Mold & Tool Inc., New Albany, IN; *U.S. Private*, pg. 125
Beadles, C. Victor, III, Pres.--Beadles Lumber Company, Inc., Moultrie, GA; *U.S. Private*, pg. 126
Beadley, James, Pres. & Chief Oper. Officer--Koppel Steel Corp., Beaver Falls, PA; *U.S. Public*, pg. 1147
Beahan, James F., Pres.--Rutland Plastic Technologies, Inc., Pineville, NC; *U.S. Private*, pg. 414
Beahm, Roger L., Pres., Chief Oper. Officer & New Bus. Contact--Coyne Beahm Inc., Colfax, NC; *U.S. Private*, pg. 283
Beale, Robert B., Pres.--Control Systems Inc., Saint Paul, MN; *U.S. Private*, pg. 271
Beale, Samuel E., Chm. Bd. & Chief Exec. Officer--Ruby Tuesday, Inc., Mobile, AL; *U.S. Public*, pg. 1411
Beall, Pamela K.M., Pres.--Environmental Treatment & Technologies Corp., Findlay, OH; *U.S. Public*, pg. 1208
Beam, Alan M., Pres. & Chief Exec. Officer--F.W. Woolworth Co. Limited, Canada, Weston, Canada; *U.S. Public*, pg. 1778
Beaman, Charles E., Pres.--Weston Paper & Manufacturing Co., Terre Haute, IN; *U.S. Private*, pg. 1169
Bean, Delcie D., Pres., Chief Exec. Officer & Treas.--D.D. Bean & Sons Co., Jaffrey, NH; *U.S. Private*, pg. 126
Bean, Richard A., Pres.--Mercantile Bank of Dubuque, N.A., Dubuque, IA; *U.S. Public*, pg. 1088
Bean, Ronald H., Pres.--Pizza Haven Inc., Bellevue, WA; *U.S. Private*, pg. 868
Beanon, Thomas, Pres.--MelloButtercup Ice Cream Inc., Wilson, NC; *U.S. Private*, pg. 730
Bear, Craig, Pres.--Alloy Products Corp, Waukesha, WI; *U.S. Private*, pg. 42
Bear, Lewis, Jr., Pres.--The Lewis Bear Company, Pensacola, FL; *U.S. Private*, pg. 127
Beard, A.D., Chm. Bd. & Pres.--Formation, Inc., Moorestown, NJ; *U.S. Private*, pg. 419
Beard, C. Randolph, Jr., Pres.--Annin & Company, Roseland, NJ; *U.S. Private*, pg. 75
Beard, Frederick K., Exec. V.P. & Chm. Bd., Pres. & Chief Exec. Officer-Mellon Bank--Mellon Bank Corporation, Pittsburgh, PA; *U.S. Public*, pg. 1084
Beard, Thomas G., Chm. Bd., Pres. & Chief Exec. Officer--Palmer Electric Co., Winter Park, FL; *U.S. Private*, pg. 834
Beardall, James C., Chm. Bd., Pres. & Chief Exec. Officer--Anderson Lumber Company, Ogden, UT; *U.S. Private*, pg. 72
Beardi, James, Pres.--M&T Mortgage Corp., Buffalo, NY; *U.S. Public*, pg. 631
Beardi, James, Pres.--M&T Credit Corporation, Buffalo, NY; *U.S. Public*, pg. 631
Beasley, Lawrence H., Pres.--Apache Plastics, L.P., Lodi, CA; *U.S. Private*, pg. 77
Beasley, Marvin E., Pres.--Keystone Valvtron, Inc., Houston, TX; *U.S. Public*, pg. 1650
Beasley, Robert E., Jr., Pres. & Chief Exec. Officer--Hunter Fan Company, Memphis, TN; *U.S. Private*, pg. 549
Beaston, Davis, Pres.--U.S. Furniture Industries, Inc., Archdale, NC; *U.S. Private*, pg. 1125
Beaton, Bradford, Chm. Bd., Pres. & Chief Exec. Officer--New England Newspaper Supply Company, Inc., Millbury, MA; *U.S. Private*, pg. 793
Beatrice, Joseph G., Pres.--Grybauskas Beatrice, New York, NY; *U.S. Private*, pg. 485
Beattie, Ted, Pres. & Chief Exec. Officer--John G. Shedd Aquarium, Chicago, IL; *U.S. Private*, pg. 991
Beatty, Fred F., Pres.--IKG Industries, Clark, NJ; *U.S. Public*, pg. 793
Beauchamp, Guy-R., Pres. & Chief Oper. Officer--CF Cable TV Inc., Montreal, Canada; *Int'l*, pg. 240
Beauchamp, Guy-R., Pres. & Chief Oper. Officer--Laurentien Cable TV Inc., Montreal, Canada; *Int'l*, pg. 241
Beauchamp, Guy-R., Pres. & Chief Oper. Officer--Northern Cable Holdings Ltd., Montreal, Canada; *Int'l*, pg. 241
Beauchamp, Patrick L., Chm. Bd., Pres. & Treas.--Beauchamp Distributing Company, Compton, CA; *U.S. Private*, pg. 127
Beaudet, Andre, Pres.--Hano Document Printers, Inc., Springfield, MA; *U.S. Public*, pg. 1686
Beaudet, Bevin, Pres.--American Water Works Association, Denver, CO; *U.S. Public*, pg. 94
Beaudoin, Pierre, Pres. & Chief Exec. Officer--Bombardier Motorized Consumer Products Group, Montreal, Canada; *Int'l*, pg. 200
Beaudoin, Pierre, Pres. & Chief Oper. Officer--Bombardier Recreational Products, Montreal, Canada; *Int'l*, pg. 200
Beaudry, Terry G., Pres. & Chief Admin. Officer--First Midwest Trust Company, N.A., Joliet, IL; *U.S. Public*, pg. 636
Beaumont, Ronald R., Pres. & Chief Exec. Officer--MFS Telecom Companies, Oak Brook, IL; *U.S. Public*, pg. 1779
Beausejour, D.F., Assoc. Gen. Mgr.--Procter & Gamble Australia, Villawood, Australia; *U.S. Public*, pg. 1332
Beauvais, Kenny, Pres.--HDW, Incorporated, Shreveport, LA; *U.S. Private*, pg. 335
Beavers, Shirley, Pres. & Chief Exec. Officer--First Virginia Life Insurance Company, Falls Church, VA; *U.S. Public*, pg. 642
Beban, Gary, Pres.--CB Commercial Real Estate, Los Angeles, CA; *U.S. Public*, pg. 272
Beban, Gary, Pres. & Gen. Mgr.--CB Commercial Real Estate Group, Inc., Los Angeles, CA; *U.S. Public*, pg. 272
Beban, Richard, Pres.--Capital Mercury Shirt, New York, NY; *U.S. Private*, pg. 206
Bebear, Claude, Chm. Bd. & Pres.--AXA-UAP, Paris, France; *Int'l*, pg. 18
Beben, Henry, Pres. & Chief Exec. Officer--Principal Marques Inc., Toronto, Canada; *Int'l*, pg. 599
Beber, Jennifer, Pres.--Beber & Silverstein & Partners, Inc., Miami, FL; *U.S. Private*, pg. 128
Bech, Tore, Pres.--Aker ExClay a.s., Oslo, Norway; *Int'l*, pg. 42
Bechen, Peter F., Pres. & Chief Exec. Officer--M & T Partners, Portland, OR; *U.S. Private*, pg. 684
Becher, F. James, Jr., Chm. Bd., Pres. & Chief Exec. Officer--Geneva Corporation, Greensboro, NC; *U.S. Private*, pg. 446
Bechtler, Thomas W., Dr., Pres.--Schiesser Eminence Holding AG, Stein, Switzerland; *Int'l*, pg. 618
Bechtold, Raymond, Owner--Trigon Adcotech, Fremont, CA; *U.S. Private*, pg. 1103
Beck, Catherine A., Pres.--Noma Industries Limited, North York, Canada; *Int'l*, pg. 954
Beck, Dan, Pres.--Sir Speedy, Inc., Mission Viejo, CA; *U.S. Private*, pg. 423
Beck, David A., Chm. Bd. & Pres.--Clark Grave Vault Co., Columbus, OH; *U.S. Private*, pg. 243
Beck, J. Edward, Jr., Pres.--Bitrek Corporation, Waynesboro, PA; *U.S. Private*, pg. 145
Beck, James A., Pres.--Seneca Resources Corp., Houston, TX; *U.S. Public*, pg. 1156
Beck, James A., Chm. Bd., Pres. & Chief Exec. Officer--SouthTrust Bank of North Carolina, Raleigh, NC; *U.S. Public*, pg. 1492
Beck, James R., Pres.--National Wine & Spirits Corp., Indianapolis, IN; *U.S. Private*, pg. 788
Beck, Scott, Co-Chm. & Pres.--Boston Chicken, Inc., Golden, CO; *U.S. Public*, pg. 247
Beck, Stuart J., Pres., Sec., Treas. & Dir.--Granite Broadcasting Corporation, New York, NY; *U.S. Public*, pg. 759
Becker, Al, Sr. V.P.-Opers.--Oscar Mayer Foods Corp., Madison, WI; *U.S. Public*, pg. 1288
Becker, Alan, Pres.--Woodard Inc., Owosso, MI; *U.S. Private*, pg. 192
Becker, Bernard, Pres.--Reed Exhibition Companies-Europe, Paris, France; *Int'l*, pg. 1096
Becker, Bernard, Pres.--Reed Expositions-France, Paris, France; *Int'l*, pg. 1097
Becker, Christopher, Pres. & Chief Exec. Officer--GeneTrace Systems, Inc., Menlo Park, CA; *U.S. Private*, pg. 958
Becker, Dan, Pres.--Aegis, Inc., New Bedford, MA; *U.S. Public*, pg. 1219
Becker, David M., Pres. & Chief Oper. Officer--Ward Lake Drilling, Inc., Gaylord, MI; *U.S. Private*, pg. 1078
Becker, Don C., Pres. and Publr.--Journal of Commerce, Inc., New York, NY; *Int'l*, pg. 1026
Becker, Douglas, Pres.--Sylvan Learning Systems Inc., Baltimore, MD; *U.S. Public*, pg. 1545
Becker, Ewald, Joint Pres.--Kohler Interconsult GmbH, Elmshorn, Germany; *Int'l*, pg. 1420
Becker, Jim, Pres. & Dir.-Adv. & Sls.--Speedrack Products Group, Ltd., Sparta, MI; *U.S. Private*, pg. 1024
Becker, John, Pres.--Greenbull Inc., Louisville, KY; *U.S. Private*, pg. 477
Becker, John A., Pres. & Chief Oper. Officer--Firstar Corporation, Milwaukee, WI; *U.S. Public*, pg. 642
Becker, John C., Pres., Chief Exec. Officer & Chief Oper. Officer--Axent Technologies, Rockville, MD; *U.S. Public*, pg. 157
Becker, Mr., Pres.--Neuebaum Woll-Spinnerei Und Weberei Hof A.G., Hof, Germany; *Int'l*, pg. 922
Becker, Norbert, Pres. & Chief Exec. Officer--Renaissance Cosmetics, Inc., New York, NY; *U.S. Private*, pg. 922
Becker, Phillip E., Pres. & Chief Exec. Officer--First National Bank in Massillon, Massillon, OH; *U.S. Public*, pg. 646
Becker, Richard, Pres. & Chief Exec. Officer--M & I Bank of Menomonee Falls, Menomonee Falls, WI; *U.S. Public*, pg. 1050
Becker, W. Marston, Pres.--J&H Marsh & McLennan Management Services (Guernsey) Ltd., Saint Peter Port, United Kingdom; *U.S. Public*, pg. 1049
Beckerman, David R., Pres. & Chief Exec. Officer--Polyfibron Technologies Corp., Billerica, MA; *U.S. Private*, pg. 875
Beckfield, Brad, Pres.--ConAgra Frozen Foods, Council Bluffs, IA; *U.S. Public*, pg. 427
Beckman, Jerry, Pres. & Mng. Dir.-Intl.--Simon Marketing, Inc., Los Angeles, CA; *U.S. Private*, pg. 1001
Beckman, Jim, Pres. & Gen. Mgr.--Glen Ellen Winery, Sonoma, CA; *U.S. Private*, pg. 455
Beckman, Richard, Publisher--Conde Nast Traveler, New York, NY; *U.S. Private*, pg. 20
Beckman, Robert J., Pres.--Intergen Company, Purchase, NY; *U.S. Private*, pg. 567
Beckstoffer, Henry G., Jr., Pres.--Saunders Oil Company, Inc., Richmond, VA; *U.S. Private*, pg. 968
Beckwith, Brian, Pres. & Chief Exec. Officer--Primedia Inc., Peoria, IL; *U.S. Public*, pg. 1328
Beckwith, G. Nicholas, III, Pres. & Chief Exec. Officer--Beckwith Machinery Company, Murrysville, PA; *U.S. Private*, pg. 129
Beckwith, Robert, Pres.--Sun Diamond Growers of California, Pleasanton, CA; *U.S. Private*, pg. 1051
Beckwith, Ronald, Pres.--Douglas Steel Fabricating Corporation, Lansing, MI; *U.S. Private*, pg. 341
Becquelin, Philippe, Co-Pres.--EURO RSCG D 10, Latresne, France; *Int'l*, pg. 600
Becraft, F. Joseph, Vice Chm., Pres. & Chief Oper. Officer--Valero Marketing & Supply Company, San Antonio, TX; *U.S. Public*, pg. 1704
Becraft, F. Joseph, Vice Chm., Pres. & Chief Oper. Officer--Valero Refining Company, San Antonio, TX; *U.S. Public*, pg. 1704
Becraft, Joe, Pres.--Aquila Gas Pipeline Corporation, San Antonio, TX; *U.S. Public*, pg. 1701
Bedell, Thomas, Chm. Bd. & Pres.--Outdoor Technologies Group, Spirit Lake, IA; *U.S. Private*, pg. 822
Bedell, Thomas, Pres.--Berkley, Inc., Spirit Lake, IA; *U.S. Private*, pg. 822
Bedford, Bryan K., Pres. & Chief Exec. Officer--Mesaba Holdings, Inc., Minneapolis, MN; *U.S. Public*, pg. 1099
Bedford, C., V.P.-Calgary--McKim Advertising Ltd., Calgary, Canada; *U.S. Private*, pg. 104
Bedford, N. Clark, Pres.--Beckwith Elevator Co., Boston, MA; *U.S. Private*, pg. 128
Bednorz, John, Exec. V.P.--Saw Drilling, Inc., Victoria, TX; *U.S. Public*, pg. 1519
Beebe, Stephen A., Pres. & Chief Exec. Officer--J.R. Simplot Company, Boise, ID; *U.S. Private*, pg. 1002
Beecham, R. Thomas, Pres. & Chief Oper. Officer--Jernberg Industries, Inc., Chicago, IL; *U.S. Private*, pg. 586
Beel, Ken, Pres.--Derlan Aerospace Canada Limited, Milton, Canada; *Int'l*, pg. 395

Beers, John, Pres. & Chief Exec. Officer--World Finer Foods, Inc., Bloomfield, NJ; *U.S. Private*, pg. 1190
Beeston, Paul, Pres. & Chief Exec. Officer--Toronto Blue Jays Baseball Club, Inc., Toronto, Canada; *Int'l*, pg. 680
Begel, Thomas, Pres.--Truck Components Inc., Rockford, IL; *U.S. Public*, pg. 933
Begel, Thomas M., Chm. Bd., Pres, & Chief Exec. Officer--Johnstown America Industries, Chicago, IL; *U.S. Public*, pg. 933
Begg, James, Pres.--BLD Europe S.A., Brussels, Belgium; *Int'l*, pg. 394
Beghini, Victor G., Pres.--Marathon Oil Company, Houston, TX; *U.S. Public*, pg. 1661
Begin, Brad, Pres.--MetalWest LLC, Brighton, CO; *U.S. Private*, pg. 817
Begin, Richard, Pres.--Charcuterie la Tour Eiffel Inc., Ville Vanier, Canada; *Int'l*, pg. 850
Begley, Patrick, Pres.--Alcom Printing Group, Inc., Bethlehem, PA; *U.S. Private*, pg. 33
Beh, Paul, Pres.--Reed Exhibition Companies-South Asia/Pacific, Singapore, Singapore; *Int'l*, pg. 1097
Behan, Patrick J., Pres. & Chief Exec. Officer--Hill-Behan Lumber Company, Saint Louis, MO; *U.S. Private*, pg. 529
Behler, A. Donald, Chm. Bd. & Pres.--Blue Ridge Pressure Castings, Inc., Lehighton, PA; *U.S. Private*, pg. 153
Behm, Brian, Pres.--Power Team Division, Owatonna, MN; *U.S. Public*, pg. 1421
Behnke, Bruce I., Pres. & Gen. Mgr.--Stanley Fastening Systems, East Greenwich, RI; *U.S. Public*, pg. 1509
Behr, Richard, Pres. & Chief Exec. Officer--Joseph Behr & Sons Inc., Rockford, IL; *U.S. Private*, pg. 130
Behrakis, George D., Pres., Chief Exec. Officer & Treas.--Muro Pharmaceutical, Inc., Tewksbury, MA; *U.S. Private*, pg. 767
Behrendt, Peter D., Chm. Bd., Pres. & Chief Exec. Officer--Exabyte Corporation, Boulder, CO; *U.S. Public*, pg. 597
Behrens, Klaus Hermann, Pres.--Henkel S/A. Industrias Quimicas, Sao Paulo, Brazil; *Int'l*, pg. 613
Beidler, Reed, Pres.--CR LLC, Evanston, IL; *U.S. Private*, pg. 196
Beirne, Patrick, Pres.--Pulte Illinois Division, Hoffman Estates, IL; *U.S. Public*, pg. 1344
Beiser, John W., Pres.--Atlantic Southeast Airlines Inc., Atlanta, GA; *U.S. Public*, pg. 144
Beissinger, Frederick W., Chm. Bd., Pres. & Chief Exec. Officer--American General Finance, Inc., Evansville, IN; *U.S. Public*, pg. 76
Beitter, John, Principal--Jackhammer, Dallas, TX; *U.S. Private*, pg. 929
Bekkers, John, Pres. & Chief Oper. Officer--Gold Kist, Inc., Atlanta, GA; *U.S. Private*, pg. 459
Belan, Robert D., Pres.--Badger Meter Utility Div., Milwaukee, WI; *U.S. Public*, pg. 165
Beland, Claude, Pres.--Confederation Des Caisses Des Jardins, Levis, Canada; *Int'l*, pg. 325
Belanger, Bernard, Pres. & Chief Exec. Officer--Premier CDN Enterprises Ltd., Dorval, Canada; *Int'l*, pg. 1067
Belanger, Charles, Vice Chm., Pres. & Chief Exec. Officer--Reseau de Television Quatre Saisons Inc., Montreal, Canada; *Int'l*, pg. 241
Belanger, Jean, Pres.--Premier Tech Ltee, Riviere-du-Loup, Canada; *Int'l*, pg. 1068
Belanger, Leo, Pres.--SunGard Financial Systems, Inc., Canoga Park, CA; *U.S. Public*, pg. 1534
Belbin, Mike, Gen. Mgr.--Beckman Instruments International, S.A., Nyon, Switzerland; *U.S. Public*, pg. 199
Belcaster, Robert, Pres.--Chicago Transit Authority, Chicago, IL; *U.S. Private*, pg. 919
Belcher, Donald D., Chm. Bd., Pres. & Chief Exec. Officer--Banta Corporation, Menasha, WI; *U.S. Public*, pg. 187
Belda, Alain, Pres. & Chief Oper. Officer--Aluminum Company of America, Pittsburgh, PA; *U.S. Public*, pg. 60
Belda, Alain, Pres.--Alcoa Aluminio S.A., Pocos de Caldas, Brazil; *U.S. Public*, pg. 61
Belda, Ricardo E., Pres.--Alcoa Nederland Holding B. V., Drunen, Netherlands; *U.S. Public*, pg. 62
Belden, Sanford A., Pres. & Chief Exec. Officer--Community Bank System, Inc., De Witt, NY; *U.S. Public*, pg. 416
Belden, Sanford A., Pres. & Chief Exec. Officer--Community Bank N.A., De Witt, NY; *U.S. Public*, pg. 416
Beldham, Paul, Pres.--Knight Equipment International Inc., Costa Mesa, CA; *U.S. Public*, pg. 862
Belfus, Linda, Pres.--Hanley & Belfus, Inc., Philadelphia, PA; *Int'l*, pg. 1479
Belgrad, D.A., Chm. Bd., Pres. & Chief Exec. Officer--Schnadig Corporation, Des Plaines, IL; *U.S. Private*, pg. 971
Belk, Irwin, Chm. Bd. & Pres.--Monroe Hardware Co., Monroe, NC; *U.S. Private*, pg. 335
Bell, A. Quinn, Pres. & Chief Exec. Officer--The Suddath Companies, Jacksonville, FL; *U.S. Private*, pg. 1049
Bell, Alan R., Pres. & Chief Exec. Officer--Dakota Mining Corporation, Denver, CO; *U.S. Public*, pg. 477
Bell, David, Pres. & Chief Exec. Officer-Bozell Worldwide--True North Communications Inc., Chicago, IL; *U.S. Public*, pg. 1641
Bell, David, Pres. & Chief Exec. Officer--Bozell Worldwide, Inc., New York, NY; *U.S. Public*, pg. 1642
Bell, Dennis, Pres.--Wisconsin Label Corporation, Algoma, WI; *U.S. Private*, pg. 1184
Bell, Gene, Pres. & Chief Exec. Officer--San Diego Union Tribune, San Diego, CA; *U.S. Private*, pg. 275
Bell, George, Pres. & Chief Exec. Officer--Excite, Inc., Redwood City, CA; *U.S. Public*, pg. 599
Bell, George L., Pres.--Star Food Products, Inc., Burlington, NC; *U.S. Private*, pg. 1034
Bell, Jerry, Pres.--Minnesota Twins Baseball Club, Minneapolis, MN; *U.S. Private*, pg. 750
Bell, John, Pres.--CPS Direct, Inc., Woburn, MA; *U.S. Private*, pg. 196
Bell, Larry, Pres. & Chief Exec. Officer--Shato Holdings Ltd., Vancouver, Canada; *Int'l*, pg. 1230
Bell, Ray, Pres.--Ray Bell Construction Co. Inc., Brentwood, TN; *U.S. Private*, pg. 131
Bell, Ray L., Pres. & Chief Exec. Officer--Bell Gas, Inc., Roswell, NM; *U.S. Private*, pg. 131
Bell, Richard E., Pres. & Chief Exec. Officer--Riceland Foods, Inc., Stuttgart, AR; *U.S. Private*, pg. 928
Bell, Richard R., Pres. & Chief Exec. Officer--HDR Engineering, Inc., Omaha, NE; *Int'l*, pg. 207
Bell, Thomas D., Jr., Pres. & Chief Exec. Officer (New York)--Burson-Marsteller, New York, NY; *U.S. Private*, pg. 1197
Bellin, J.M., Pres. & Gen. Mgr.--Eli Lilly Italia, S.p.A., Sesto Fiorentino, Italy; *U.S. Public*, pg. 994
Bellin, Jacques, Pres.-Pullman-Sofitel--Societe Hoteliere Paris Vanves, Evry, France; *Int'l*, pg. 20
Bellini, Francesco, Ph.D., Pres. & Chief Exec. Officer--BioChem Pharma Inc., Laval, Canada; *Int'l*, pg. 196
Bello, Paul S., Pres.& Chief Oper. Officer--Prism Integrated Sanitation Management, Inc., Miami, FL; *U.S. Private*, pg. 592
Bellows, H. Arthur, Jr., Pres. & Chief Oper. Officer--Audits & Surveys Worldwide, New York, NY; *U.S. Public*, pg. 147
Bellringer, Stephen, Pres. & Chief Exec. Officer--BC Gas Inc., Vancouver, Canada; *Int'l*, pg. 114
Belmont, Henry John, Pres.--Jaeger-Le Coultre, Le Sentier, Switzerland; *Int'l*, pg. 697
Belmonte, Dennis R., Pres. & Chief Exec. Officer--Benguet Corporation, Manila, Philippines; *Int'l*, pg. 186
Belmonte, Dennis R., Chm. & Pres.--Benguet Management Corporation, Manila, Philippines; *Int'l*, pg. 186
Belot, Thomas G., Pres. & Chief Exec. Officer--The Vollrath Company, L.L.C., Sheboygan, WI; *U.S. Private*, pg. 1143
Belsaas, Scott, Pres.--Johnson Brothers Wholesale Liquor, Saint Paul, MN; *U.S. Private*, pg. 591
Belsky, Stanley, Pres. & Chief Oper. Officer--Assembly Component Systems, Inc., Burr Ridge, IL; *U.S. Public*, pg. 980
Belsky, Stanley, Pres. & Chief Oper. Officer--Automatic Screw Machines Products Company, Decatur, AL; *U.S. Public*, pg. 980
Belson, Ross A., Pres. & Chief Oper. Officer--General Datacomm Industries, Inc., Middlebury, CT; *U.S. Public*, pg. 708
Beltrame, Jim, Pres.--Successories, Inc., Aurora, IL; *U.S. Private*, pg. 1049
Belz, Martin S., Co-Pres. & Chief Oper. Officer--Belz Enterprises, Memphis, TN; *U.S. Private*, pg. 132
Belz, Ronald A., Co-Pres.--Belz Enterprises, Memphis, TN; *U.S. Private*, pg. 132
Belzberg, Brent S., Pres. & Chief Exec. Officer--Harrowston Corporation, Toronto, Canada; *Int'l*, pg. 599
Belzer, Alan, Pres. & Chief Oper. Officer--AlliedSignal Inc., Morristown, NJ; *U.S. Public*, pg. 49
Belzer, John D., Pres. & Chief Oper. Officer--TCI Aluminum, Gardena, CA; *U.S. Private*, pg. 1063
Belzer, John D., Pres.--E-Z Lok, Gardena, CA; *U.S. Private*, pg. 1063
Bement, John, Pres. & Gen. Mgr.--Six Flags Over Georgia, Austell, GA; *U.S. Public*, pg. 1612
Ben-Horian, Yaron, Pres.--Randy International, Jamaica, NY; *U.S. Private*, pg. 909
Benacin, Philippe, Vice Chm. & Pres.--Jean Philippe Fragrances, Inc., New York, NY; *U.S. Public*, pg. 924
Benante, Martin R., Pres. & Gen. Mgr.--Target Rock Corp., Farmingdale, NY; *U.S. Public*, pg. 470
Benaroya, Raphael, Chm. Bd., Pres. & Chief Exec. Officer--United Retail Group, Inc., Rochelle Park, NJ; *U.S. Public*, pg. 1679
Benassi, Peter, Pres. & Chief Exec. Officer--MRI Los Angeles, Santa Monica, CA; *U.S. Private*, pg. 727
Benassi, Peter M., Pres. & Chief Exec. Officer--Media Resources International, New York, NY; *U.S. Private*, pg. 727
Benchley, Richard, Pres.--Fechheimer Bros. Co., Cincinnati, OH; *U.S. Public*, pg. 217
Benda, Victor C., Pres.--AIC-FSS Advertising, Minneapolis, MN; *U.S. Private*, pg. 5
Benda, Victor C., Pres. & Chief Oper. Officer--Analysts International Corporation, Minneapolis, MN; *U.S. Public*, pg. 110
Bende, Andrea B., Pres.--Sprint International, Westwood, KS; *U.S. Public*, pg. 1500
Bendel, Gerry, Pres.--Clairol, Inc., Stamford, CT; *U.S. Public*, pg. 254
Bendele, Gerald E., Pres.--Knoll Pharmaceutical Company, Whippany, NJ; *Int'l*, pg. 105
Bendell, Bruce, Pres.--Major Automotive Group, Long Island City, NY; *U.S. Private*, pg. 697
Bender, A. Thomas, Pres. & Chief Exec. Officer--The Cooper Companies, Inc., Irvine, CA; *U.S. Public*, pg. 442
Bender, Miles, Pres. & Chief Exec. Officer--National Energy Group, Inc., Dallas, TX; *U.S. Public*, pg. 1156
Bender, Robert, Pres.--Pentax Technologies Corp., Broomfield, CO; *Int'l*, pg. 85
Bender, Thomas B., Jr., Chm. Bd., Pres. & Chief Exec. Officer--Bender Shipbuilding & Repair Company, Inc., Mobile, AL; *U.S. Private*, pg. 132
Bender, Thomas C., Pres.--The Cretex Companies, Elk River, MN; *U.S. Private*, pg. 289
Bender, Thomas J., Pres.-Behavioral Health--Universal Health Services, Inc., King of Prussia, PA; *U.S. Public*, pg. 1696
Benderson, Randall, Pres. & Chief Exec. Officer--Benderson Development Co., Inc., Buffalo, NY; *U.S. Private*, pg. 132
Bendheim, J.C., Pres.--Philipp Brothers Chemicals, Inc., Fort Lee, NJ; *U.S. Private*, pg. 861
Bendix, Selina, Pres.--Bendix Environmental Research, Berkeley, CA; *U.S. Public*, pg. 51
Bendowski, Joseph, Pres.--Van Son Holland Ink Corp. of America, Mineola, NY; *U.S. Private*, pg. 1133
Benecki, Walter, Pres.--The Arnold Engineering Company, Marengo, IL; *U.S. Public*, pg. 1420
Benedetti, Gianpietro, Pres. & Chief Exec. Officer--Danielli & C. Officine Meccaniche S.p.A., Udine, Italy; *Int'l*, pg. 378
Benenson, James, Jr., Chm. Bd. & Pres.--Arrowhead Holding Corporation, Brecksville, OH; *U.S. Private*, pg. 86
Benenson, James, Jr., Chm. Bd. & Pres.--Vesper Corporation, Brecksville, OH; *U.S. Private*, pg. 86
Benetton, Luciano, Chm. Bd. & Pres.--Benetton Group S.p.A., Ponzano Veneto, Italy; *Int'l*, pg. 186
Benfield, Ron, Chm. Bd. & Pres.--Central Lincoln People's Utility District, Newport, OR; *U.S. Private*, pg. 223
Benhamou, Eric A., Chm. Bd., Pres. & Chief Exec. Officer--3Com Corporation, Santa Clara, CA; *U.S. Public*, pg. 1603
Benhamou, Guy, Chm. Bd., Pres. & Chief Exec. Officer--Oroamerica, Inc., Burbank, CA; *U.S. Public*, pg. 1232
Beni, John J., Pres. & Chief Oper. Officer--Parade Publications Inc., New York, NY; *U.S. Private*, pg. 20
Beningson, Robert M., Chm. Bd., Pres. & Chief Exec. Officer--York Research Corporation, New York, NY; *U.S. Public*, pg. 1789
Beningson, Robert M., Pres.--Cogeneration Technologies Inc., New York, NY; *U.S. Public*, pg. 1789
Benjamin, Floyd, Pres.--Akorn Manufacturing, Inc., Decatur, IL; *U.S. Public*, pg. 34
Benjamin, Frank, Pres. & Chief Exec. Officer--F. J. Benjamin Holdings Ltd., Singapore, Singapore; *Int'l*, pg. 187
Benjamin, Larry, Pres. & Chief Exec. Officer--Stella Foods, Inc., Green Bay, WI; *U.S. Private*, pg. 1040
Benjamin, Lawrence, Pres. & Chief Exec. Officer--Specialty Foods Corporation, Deerfield, IL; *U.S. Private*, pg. 1022
Benjamin, Lawrence, Pres.--Stella Foods Inc., Lincolnshire, IL; *U.S. Private*, pg. 1040
Benjamin, Mark, Pres. & Chief Exec. Officer--Morley Builders, Santa Monica, CA; *U.S. Private*, pg. 761
Benjamin, Mark, Pres. & Chief Exec. Officer--Benchmark Contractors, Inc., Santa Monica, CA; *U.S. Private*, pg. 761
Benjamin, Mark E., Pres.--Benjamin Metals Company, Gardena, CA; *U.S. Private*, pg. 133
Benjamins, John L., Mng. Dir.--John Benjamins BV, Amsterdam, Netherlands; *Int'l*, pg. 187
Bennack, Frank, Pres. & Chief Exec. Officer-Hearst Corp.--Cosmopolitan, New York, NY; *U.S. Private*, pg. 517
Bennack, Frank A., Jr., Pres. & Chief Exec. Officer--The Hearst Corporation, New York, NY; *U.S. Private*, pg. 515
Bennack, Frank A., Jr., Pres. & Chief Exec. Officer--Hearst Realty Development Co., Inc., New York, NY; *U.S. Private*, pg. 515
Benner, Rick, Pres.--Sacramento Kings, Sacramento, CA; *U.S. Private*, pg. 959
Bennerdt, Staffan, Pres.--NCC Finans, Solna, Sweden; *Int'l*, pg. 899
Bennet, Richard W., III, Pres. & Chief Exec. Officer--Kaufmann's, Pittsburgh, PA; *U.S. Public*, pg. 1063
Bennett, Avi, Pres.--McClelland & Stewart, Toronto, Canada; *Int'l*, pg. 851
Bennett, Bill, Pres.-Geffen & DGC Records--Geffen Records, Los Angeles, CA; *Int'l*, pg. 1215
Bennett, Gail Kirk, Sr., Pres.--Bennett Brothers, Inc., Chicago, IL; *U.S. Private*, pg. 133
Bennett, Gary P., Chm. Bd., Pres. & Chief Exec. Officer--Analysis & Technology, Inc., North Stonington, CT; *U.S. Public*, pg. 109
Bennett, Harold C., Pres.--Utility Trailer Manufacturing Co., City of Industry, CA; *U.S. Private*, pg. 1130
Bennett, James P., Pres. & Chief Oper. Officer--Healthsouth Corporation, Birmingham, AL; *U.S. Public*, pg. 803
Bennett, Jeffrey, Pres. & Chief Exec. Officer--Nature's Recipe Pet Foods, Corona, CA; *U.S. Private*, pg. 789
Bennett, Michael F., Pres.--Emtex Leasing Corp., Roswell, GA; *U.S. Private*, pg. 1177
Bennett, Richard W., Pres.--Market Facts of Canada, Ltd., Toronto, Canada; *U.S. Public*, pg. 1047
Bennett, Robert R., Pres. & Chief Exec. Officer--Liberty Media Corporation, Englewood, CO; *U.S. Public*, pg. 1555
Bennett, Ronald, Pres.--Service Tire Truck Centers, Inc., Bethlehem, PA; *U.S. Private*, pg. 987
Bennett, Ronald G., Pres.--Calavo Growers of California, Santa Ana, CA; *U.S. Private*, pg. 199
Bennett, Stanley T., Pres.--Oakhurst Dairy, Portland, ME; *U.S. Private*, pg. 809
Bennett, Stephen D., Pres. & Chief Exec. & Oper. Officer--Acme Metals Incorporated, Riverdale, IL; *U.S. Public*, pg. 16
Bennett, Thomas Bert, Pres. & Chief Oper. Officer--Wayne Dalton Corporation, Mount Hope, OH; *U.S. Private*, pg. 1155
Benninger, Edward C., Pres.--Valero Energy Corporation, San Antonio, TX; *U.S. Public*, pg. 1704
Bennion, Richard E., Pres. & Chief Exec. Officer--The Rowe Corporation, Charlotte, NC; *U.S. Private*, pg. 948
Bennis, Kevin J., Pres.--Frontier Communications Services, Bingham Farms, MI; *U.S. Public*, pg. 684
Benoit, Steve, Pres.--Mountain States Constructors, Inc., Albuquerque, NM; *U.S. Private*, pg. 764
Benosik, Doris D., Pres. & Chief Oper. Officer--Datapoint Corporation, Paris, France; *Int'l*, pg. 384
Bensabat, Paul, Pres. & Chief Exec. Officer--Sorrento Cheese Company, Inc., Buffalo, NY; *Int'l*, pg. 323
Bensimon, Jack, Pres. & Chief Exec. Officer--Bensimon Byrne DMB&B Toronto, Toronto, Canada; *U.S. Private*, pg. 303
Bensimon, Raquel, Pres. & Chief Fin. Officer--Dearden's, Los Angeles, CA; *U.S. Private*, pg. 319
Bensinger, Steven J., Pres.--Chartwell Re Corporation, Stamford, CT; *U.S. Public*, pg. 336
Bensinger, Steven J., Pres.--The Insurance Corp. of New York, New York, NY; *U.S. Public*, pg. 336
Benson, Alan, Pres.--Linzer Products Corp., Flushing, NY; *U.S. Private*, pg. 669

Benson, Buzz, Pres.--Piper Jaffray Ventures Inc., Minneapolis, MN; *U.S. Public*, pg. 1303
Benson, David F., Pres. & Treas.--Meditrust Corporation, Needham, MA; *U.S. Public*, pg. 1081
Benson, Donald W., Pres. & Chief Exec. Officer--Associated Grocers, Inc., Seattle, WA; *U.S. Private*, pg. 90
Benson, Jack D., Pres.--Old Kent Bank of Cadillac, Cadillac, MI; *U.S. Public*, pg. 1216
Benson, Jerry S., Jr., Pres. & Chief Oper. Officer--VTEL Corporation, Austin, TX; *U.S. Public*, pg. 1703
Benson, John A., Pres.--Nelson, Benson & Zellmer, Inc., Denver, CO; *U.S. Public*, pg. 1673
Benson, Keith, Pres.--Suncoast Motion Picture Co., Minnetonka, MN; *U.S. Public*, pg. 1142
Benson, Kevin E., Pres., Chief Exec. & Fin. Officer--Canadian Airlines Corporation, Calgary, Canada; *Int'l*, pg. 255
Benson, Kevin E., Pres. & Chief Exec. Officer--Canadian Airlines International Ltd., Calgary, Canada; *Int'l*, pg. 256
Benson, Larry R., Pres.--Benson's, Inc., Bogart, GA; *U.S. Private*, pg. 134
Benson, Thomas, Pres.--Atlanta Gas Light Company, Atlanta, GA; *U.S. Public*, pg. 7
Benson, Thomas, Publ.--Midwest Living Magazine, Des Moines, IA; *U.S. Public*, pg. 1094
Benson, W. Arthur, Pres.--MG Electric Power, Inc., New York, NY; *Int'l*, pg. 862
Benstock, Michael, Co-Pres.--Superior Surgical Mfg. Co., Inc., Seminole, FL; *U.S. Public*, pg. 1539
Bensussen, Gale, Pres.--Leiner Health Products, Inc., Carson, CA; *U.S. Private*, pg. 659
Bentas, Lilly, Chm. Bd. & Pres.--Cumberland Farms, Inc., Canton, MA; *U.S. Private*, pg. 295
Benter, George H., Pres. & Chief Oper. Officer--City National Corporation, Beverly Hills, CA; *U.S. Public*, pg. 380
Bentley, Greg, Chm. Bd. & Pres.--Bentley Systems, Inc., Exton, PA; *U.S. Private*, pg. 134
Bentley, Peter, Pres.--Parker Pen PLC, Newhaven, United Kingdom; *U.S. Public*, pg. 745
Benton, A.E., Chm. Bd. & Pres.--Benton Oil & Gas Company, Carpinteria, CA; *U.S. Public*, pg. 212
Bentson, Steve, Pres.--Century Manufacturing, Bloomington, MN; *U.S. Public*, pg. 1273
Bentzinger, Susan E., Partner & Sr. V.P.--Media That Works, Cincinnati, OH; *U.S. Private*, pg. 727
Benua, P.L., Pres.--Oasis Corp., Columbus, OH; *U.S. Private*, pg. 810
Benun, Ronald, Pres.--Bentex Kiddie Corporation, New York, NY; *U.S. Private*, pg. 134
Benz, Thomas, Pres.--Alois Zettler Elecktrotechnische Fabrik GmbH, Munich, Germany; *Int'l*, pg. 1528
Beom-Dae Park, In-Hee, Pres.--Jinwoong Lanka (Pvt) Ltd., Ja-Ela, Sri Lanka; *Int'l*, pg. 707
Berard, Dailey J., Chm. Bd., Pres. & Chief Exec. Officer--Unifab International Inc., New Iberia, LA; *U.S. Public*, pg. 1665
Berberian, Paul, Pres.--Link-VTC, Inc., Boulder, CO; *U.S. Public*, pg. 684
Berberian, Ronald, Chm. Bd. & Pres.--Bank of Agriculture & Commerce, Stockton, CA; *U.S. Private*, pg. 114
Berdass, Daniel M., Pres.--Bermo, Inc., Circle Pines, MN; *U.S. Private*, pg. 136
Bere, David, Pres. & Chief Exec. Officer--McCain Foods Inc., Oak Brook, IL; *Int'l*, pg. 850
Beren, Peter H., Pres.--Mountain Iron & Supply Company, Wichita, KS; *U.S. Private*, pg. 764
Beren, S.O., Chm. Bd., Pres. & Chief Exec. Officer--Misco Industries, Wichita, KS; *U.S. Private*, pg. 752
Berenato, Joseph C., Pres., Chief Fin. Officer & Chief Oper. Officer--Ducommun Incorporated, Carson, CA; *U.S. Public*, pg. 533
Berenfield, Leonard, Pres.--Berenfield Containers, Inc., Mason, OH; *U.S. Private*, pg. 135
Berens, James R., Pres. & Chief Oper. Officer--Norwest Financial, Inc., Des Moines, IA; *U.S. Public*, pg. 1202
Beres, Dennis, Dr., Pres.--Frequency Engineering Laboratories, Farmingdale, NJ; *U.S. Private*, pg. 427
Beres, Gary S., Pres.--Crafty Beaver Home Center, Skokie, IL; *U.S. Private*, pg. 284
Beretta, Ugo Gussalli, Pres.--P. Beretta S.P.A., Gardone Riviera, Italy; *Int'l*, pg. 187
Berg, Al, Co-Pres.--Marchon Eyewear, Melville, NY; *U.S. Private*, pg. 702
Berg, Bruce, Pres.-Southern Reg.--The Home Depot, Inc., Atlanta, GA; *U.S. Public*, pg. 831
Berg, Carl E., Pres. & Chief Exec. Officer--Mission West Properties, Cupertino, CA; *U.S. Public*, pg. 1117
Berg, Christopher B., Pres.--The McGuire Furniture Company, San Francisco, CA; *U.S. Private*, pg. 630
Berg, Harris, V.P. & Gen. Mgr.--Wick Bldg. Systems Inc. Manufactured Homes Div., Marshfield, WI; *U.S. Private*, pg. 1174
Berg, Jack H., Pres., Chief Exec. Officer & Treas.--Serfilco, Ltd., Northbrook, IL; *U.S. Private*, pg. 985
Berg, Jeffrey, Pres. & Chief Exec. Officer--ICM Holdings Inc., New York, NY; *U.S. Private*, pg. 554
Berg, Jeffrey K., Pres.--Suttle Apparatus Corporation, Hector, MN; *U.S. Public*, pg. 416
Berg, John, Pres.--Norwest Bank Minnesota South, N.A., Rochester, MN; *U.S. Public*, pg. 1202
Berg, John A., Pres.--Norwest Bank Red Wing, N.A., Red Wing, MN; *U.S. Public*, pg. 1202
Berg, Kory L., Pres.--Arrosto Coffee Company, Los Angeles, CA; *U.S. Public*, pg. 966
Berg, Lars, Pres. & Chief Exec. Officer--Telia AB, Farsta, Sweden; *Int'l*, pg. 1373
Berg, N.A., Pres.--American Steel Foundries, Chicago, IL; *U.S. Private*, pg. 68
Berg, Richard M., Pres.--A.J. Oster Company, Warwick, RI; *U.S. Public*, pg. 1219
Berg, Rick, Pres.--Dowty Aerospace, Los Angeles, Duarte, CA; *Int'l*, pg. 1337
Berg, Ronald, Pres.--Alpha Shirt Co., Inc., Philadelphia, PA; *U.S. Private*, pg. 45
Bergami, Frank, Pres.--Rolock, Inc., Fairfield, CT; *U.S. Private*, pg. 942
Berge, D. Ramon Encisco, Pres.--Estrategias Telefonicas, S.A. (Estratel), Madrid, Spain; *Int'l*, pg. 1371
Bergeman, Carl T., Pres.--Computer Knowledge, Mountain Lakes, NJ; *U.S. Public*, pg. 421
Bergenudd, Ulf, Pres.--Axel Johnson Servicehandelsgruppen AB, Stockholm, Sweden; *Int'l*, pg. 709
Berger, Charles M., Chm. Bd., Pres. & Chief Exec. Officer--The Scotts Company, Marysville, OH; *U.S. Public*, pg. 1446
Berger, Chris, Pres. & Gen. Mgr.--Hazelwood Farms Bakeries, Inc., McMinnville, OR; *U.S. Public*, pg. 1541
Berger, Donald, Pres.--Pony Express Delivery Services, Inc, Atlanta, GA; *U.S. Public*, pg. 245
Berger, John, Pres.--Dreison International, Inc., Cleveland, OH; *U.S. Private*, pg. 342
Berger, John, Pres.--Eagle Engineering & Manufacturing, Inc., Cleveland, OH; *U.S. Private*, pg. 342
Berger, John R., Pres.--F&G Re, Inc., Morristown, NJ; *U.S. Public*, pg. 1659
Berger, Lee, Pres.--First Interstate Bank of Montana, N.A., Kalispell, MT; *U.S. Public*, pg. 1753
Berger, R.I., Pres.--Berel Industries Inc., Cerritos, CA; *U.S. Private*, pg. 135
Berger, Ron, Chm. Bd., Pres., Chief Exec. Officer--Rentrak Corporation, Portland, OR; *U.S. Public*, pg. 1377
Berger, Steve, Pres.--Promotional Broadcast Services, Los Angeles, CA; *U.S. Private*, pg. 1166
Berger, Steve, Pres.--Western Product Placement, Los Angeles, CA; *U.S. Private*, pg. 1167
Berger, Steven, Pres.--Nationwide Communications, Inc., Columbus, OH; *U.S. Private*, pg. 789
Berger, Walter Z., Pres.--LG & E Energy Systems Inc., Louisville, KY; *U.S. Public*, pg. 970
Berger, Wes, Div. Pres.--Hi-Profit Distributors, Inc., Sun Valley, CA; *Int'l*, pg. 752
Bergeron, Albert A., Pres.--PartyLite Gifts, Inc., Plymouth, MA; *U.S. Public*, pg. 239
Bergeron, Edmond, Pres.--GWC Health, Inc., Cedar Knolls, NJ; *U.S. Private*, pg. 436
Bergeron, Edmond, Pres.--Carnrick Laboratories, Inc., Cedar Knolls, NJ; *U.S. Private*, pg. 436
Bergersen, Tore, Pres.--Aker Oil and Gas Technology, Oslo, Norway; *Int'l*, pg. 41
Bergeson, Rolly, Pres.--Westair Commuter Airlines, Inc., Fresno, CA; *U.S. Public*, pg. 1099
Berghash, David, Pres.--Brimms Inc., Tonawanda, NY; *U.S. Private*, pg. 169
Berglass, Robert, Chm. Bd. & Pres.--Dep Corporation, Rancho Dominguez, CA; *U.S. Public*, pg. 500
Berglin, Vern, Pres.--Alumacraft Boat Co., Saint Peter, MN; *U.S. Private*, pg. 1088
Berglund, Thomas R., M.D., Chm. Bd. & Pres.--Michigan Physicians Mutual Liability Inc., East Lansing, MI; *U.S. Private*, pg. 741
Bergman, David R., Pres. & Treas.--Processed Plastic Company, Montgomery, IL; *U.S. Private*, pg. 888
Bergman, Donald A., Pres.--Bulldog Co., Memphis, TN; *U.S. Public*, pg. 1176
Bergman, Stanley M., Chm. Bd., Pres. & Chief Exec. Officer--Henry Schein, Inc., Melville, NY; *U.S. Public*, pg. 1437
Bergmann, Harry, Dr., Pres. & Creative Dir.--Demner, Merlicek & Bergmann Werbegesellschaft mbH, Vienna, Austria; *Int'l*, pg. 392
Bergmann, Horst A., Chm. Bd., Pres. & Chief Exec. Officer--Jeppesen Sanderson, Englewood, CO; *U.S. Public*, pg. 1616
Bergmann, Horst A., Chm. Bd., Pres. & Chief Exec. Officer--Jeppesen and Co. GmbH, Frankfurt/Main, Germany; *U.S. Public*, pg. 1617
Bergmann, Horst A., Chm., Pres. & Chief Exec. Officer--Achieve Global, Tampa, FL; *U.S. Public*, pg. 1617
Bergonzi, Albert J., Pres. & Co-Chief Oper. Officer--HBOC, Atlanta, GA; *U.S. Public*, pg. 770
Bergquist, Carl R., Jr., Chm. Bd., Pres. & Chief Exec. Officer--The Bergquist Company, Minneapolis, MN; *U.S. Private*, pg. 135
Bergsma, David P., Pres. & Chief Oper. Officer--Levy Security Corp., Chicago, IL; *U.S. Private*, pg. 664
Bergsten, Gunnar, Pres.--Husdjurforsakrings AB Sleipner, Stockholm, Sweden; *Int'l*, pg. 1256
Bergstrom, James D., Pres.--Ragnar Benson, Inc., Park Ridge, IL; *U.S. Private*, pg. 99
Bergstrom, Jan-Eric, Pres.--Perstorp Surface Materials, Perstorp, Sweden; *Int'l*, pg. 1038
Bergstrom, Robert, Pres.--Real Decisions Corp., Stamford, CT; *U.S. Public*, pg. 395
Bergstrom, Steve W., Pres. & Chief Oper. Officer--NGC Corporation, Houston, TX; *U.S. Public*, pg. 1146
Bergstrom, Ulf, Pres.--NCC Linkoping, Linkoping, Sweden; *Int'l*, pg. 899
Berk, Alexander, Pres. & Chief Oper. Officer--Barton Incorporated, Chicago, IL; *U.S. Public*, pg. 300
Berk, Fred, Pres., & Chief Exec. Officer--Huffman Koos, River Edge, NJ; *U.S. Private*, pg. 546
Berk, James G., Pres.--Hard Rock Cafe International Inc., Wilmington, DE; *Int'l*, pg. 1087
Berkbigler, Dale T., Pres.--Qual-Med, Inc., Pueblo, CO; *U.S. Public*, pg. 678
Berke, Kenneth, Pres.--The Sperry & Hutchinson Company, Inc., New York, NY; *U.S. Public*, pg. 990
Berke, Steve, Pres.--Cincinnati Sub-Zero Products, Inc., Cincinnati, OH; *U.S. Private*, pg. 240
Berkeley, Virginia K., Pres. & Chief Exec. Officer--Colorado Business Bank, Denver, CO; *U.S. Private*, pg. 255
Berkley, Allen, Pres.--Berkliff Corporation, New York, NY; *U.S. Private*, pg. 135
Berkley, William, Pres. & Chief Exec. Officer--Tension Envelope Corp., Kansas City, MO; *U.S. Private*, pg. 1077
Berkman, Mehmet Ali, Pres.--Arcelik A.S., Istanbul, Turkey; *Int'l*, pg. 741
Berkowitz, Arthur M., Pres.--J.E. Berkowitz, LP, Westville, NJ; *U.S. Private*, pg. 135
Berkowitz, Donald A., Pres.--Central Lewmar, Newark, NJ; *U.S. Private*, pg. 223
Berkson, E.J., Pres.--Locust Street Securities, Inc., Des Moines, IA; *Int'l*, pg. 647
Berkson, Howard, Pres.--Stanbee Company, Inc., Carlstadt, NJ; *U.S. Private*, pg. 1030
Berlin, Charles L., Pres.--Old Kent Bank of Gaylord, Gaylord, MI; *U.S. Public*, pg. 1217
Berlin, David N., Chm. Bd. & Pres.--Metalloy Corporation, Hudson, MI; *U.S. Private*, pg. 735
Berlin, John E., Pres.--Tensolite Company, Saint Augustine, FL; *U.S. Public*, pg. 305
Berlind, Jeff, Pres.-RBI--Foodservice Director, New York, NY; *Int'l*, pg. 1446
Berman, Barry H., Chm. Bd. & Pres.--CRN International, Inc., Hamden, CT; *U.S. Private*, pg. 197
Berman, Larry S., Chm. Bd. & Pres.--MNP Corp., Utica, MI; *U.S. Private*, pg. 687
Berman, Milton I., Chm. Bd., Pres. & Treas.--Avibank Mfg., Inc., Burbank, CA; *U.S. Private*, pg. 101
Berman, Richard N., Chm. Bd., Pres. & Chief Exec. Officer--R&B, Inc., Colmar, PA; *U.S. Public*, pg. 1354
Berman, Robert A., Pres. & Chief Exec. Officer--Hospitality Worldwide Services, Inc., New York, NY; *U.S. Public*, pg. 841
Bern, Dorrit J., Chm. Bd., Pres. & Chief Exec. Officer--Charming Shoppes, Inc., Bensalem, PA; *U.S. Public*, pg. 335
Bernacchi, James P., Pres. & Chief Oper. Officer--Universal Coach Parts, Inc., Des Plaines, IL; *Int'l*, pg. 326
Bernal, Ronald, Pres.--MIPS Technologies, Inc., Mountain View, CA; *U.S. Public*, pg. 1473
Bernard, Rob, Pres.--Limited Stores, Columbus, OH; *U.S. Public*, pg. 996
Bernard, Thomas E., Pres.--B & G Wholesalers, Inc., Nashville, TN; *U.S. Private*, pg. 105
Bernardini, Allen, Pres.--Winchester Electronics, Watertown, CT; *U.S. Public*, pg. 1003
Bernards, Douglas, Chm. Bd., Pres. & Chief Exec. Officer--Bernards Brothers, Inc., San Fernando, CA; *U.S. Private*, pg. 136
Bernasconi, Leo, Pres.--Tufira S.r.l., Milan, Italy; *Int'l*, pg. 490
Berner, George, Pres.--Berner Ltd., Helsinki, Finland; *Int'l*, pg. 189
Bernes, I. Robert, Pres.--Triple A Specialty Company, Chicago, IL; *U.S. Private*, pg. 1103
Bernhard, Barney, Pres.--Reed MIDEM Organisation Inc., New York, NY; *Int'l*, pg. 1096
Bernhardt, Andrew B., Pres.--Harris Bank Frankfort, Frankfort, IL; *Int'l*, pg. 154
Bernick, Howard B., Pres. & Chief Exec. Officer--Alberto-Culver Company, Melrose Park, IL; *U.S. Public*, pg. 37
Bernick, Howard B., Pres. & Chief Exec. Officer--Alberto-Culver USA, Inc., Melrose Park, IL; *U.S. Public*, pg. 38
Bernique, Michael, Pres.--Satellite Data Networks, San Diego, CA; *U.S. Public*, pg. 716
Bernitt, Charles F., Pres.--IPAC, Inc., Niagara Falls, NY; *U.S. Private*, pg. 555
Bernon, Alan J., Pres.--Garelick Farms, Inc., Franklin, MA; *U.S. Public*, pg. 1527
Bernstein, Allen J., Chm. Bd., Pres. & Chief Exec. Officer--Morton's Restaurant Group, Inc., New Hyde Park, NY; *U.S. Public*, pg. 1136
Bernstein, Daniel, Pres.--Bel Fuse Inc., Jersey City, NJ; *U.S. Public*, pg. 200
Bernstein, George, Pres. & Chief Exec. Officer--AVC/Nu-Vision, Inc., Flint, MI; *U.S. Private*, pg. 9
Bernstein, Harvey, Pres. & Chief Exec. Officer--Spirite Industries, Inc., Englewood, NJ; *U.S. Private*, pg. 1026
Bernstein, Mark, Pres.--Manhattan Brass & Copper Co., Maspeth, NY; *U.S. Private*, pg. 699
Bernstein, Michael H., Pres. & Chief Exec. Officer--Crown Crafts, Inc., Atlanta, GA; *U.S. Public*, pg. 465
Bernstein, Philip L., Pres.--Jacob Stern & Sons, Inc., Santa Barbara, CA; *U.S. Private*, pg. 1041
Bernstein, Robert, Chm. Bd., Pres. & Chief Exec. Officer--Bernstein-Rein Advertising, Inc., Kansas City, MO; *U.S. Private*, pg. 137
Bero, Robert D., Pres. & Chief Exec. Officer--Menasha Corporation, Neenah, WI; *U.S. Private*, pg. 731
Berolzheimer, Philip, Pres.--California Cedar Products, Inc., Stockton, CA; *U.S. Private*, pg. 200
Berrard, Steven R., Pres. & Co-Chief Exec. Officer--Republic Industries, Inc., Fort Lauderdale, FL; *U.S. Public*, pg. 1378
Berris, Brian, Partner-Private Client--Brown Brothers Harriman & Co., New York, NY; *U.S. Private*, pg. 173
Berry, Claude A., Jr., Chm. Bd. & Pres.--Wehr Constructors Inc., Louisville, KY; *U.S. Private*, pg. 1159
Berry, Dan W., Chm. Bd., Pres. & Chief Exec. Officer--American Trouser, Inc., Columbus, MS; *U.S. Private*, pg. 64
Berry, David J., Pres.--Bank of America Texas, Dallas, TX; *U.S. Public*, pg. 180
Berry, Kenneth L., Pres.--Berry Contracting, Corpus Christi, TX; *U.S. Private*, pg. 137
Berry, L.W., Jr., Pres.--Texaco Refining & Marketing, Inc., Tulsa, OK; *U.S. Public*, pg. 1583
Berry, Michael, Pres.--Flexitallic LP, Deer Park, TX; *U.S. Private*, pg. 413
Berry, Walter T., Pres.--Berry Companies, Inc., Wichita, KS; *U.S. Private*, pg. 137
Berry, William K., Pres.--Goody Products, Inc., Peachtree City, GA; *U.S. Public*, pg. 1177
Berry, William K., Pres.--Duray, Inc., Kearny, NJ; *U.S. Public*, pg. 1177
Berry, William K., Pres.--Ace Comb Company Inc., Booneville, AR; *U.S. Public*, pg. 1177

Berry, William S., Pres.--Rayonier New Zealand Limited, Auckland, New Zealand; *U.S. Public*, pg. 1363
Berryman, David H., Pres.--Gibson Musical Instruments, Inc., Nashville, TN; *U.S. Private*, pg. 451
Bersett, Gerald W., Pres. & Chief Oper. Officer--Sturm, Ruger & Co., Inc., Southport, CT; *U.S. Public*, pg. 1526
Bersoff, Edward H., Dr., Chm. Bd., Pres. & Chief Exec. Officer--BTG, Inc., Fairfax, VA; *U.S. Public*, pg. 164
Berson, Paul, Pres.--B & B Motor & Control Corporation, Long Island City, NY; *U.S. Private*, pg. 105
Berta, Michael A., Ph.D., Pres. & Chief Exec. Officer--RMS Information Systems, Inc., Lanham, MD; *U.S. Public*, pg. 1425
Berta, Mike, Pres. & Chief Exec. Officer--RMS Techs, Inc., Lanham, MD; *U.S. Private*, pg. 905
Berta, Vince A., Pres. & Chief Exec. Officer--Trans Financial, Inc., Bowling Green, KY; *U.S. Public*, pg. 1628
Bertani, Gigi, Pres.--B Communications/GGK, Milan, Italy; *Int'l*, pg. 1335
Berthelot, Barry F., Pres. & Chief Exec. Officer--The First National Bank of Lafayette, Lafayette, LA; *U.S. Public*, pg. 630
Berthelsen, Bruce, Pres. & Chief Exec. Officer--Willis Corroon Corp. of Georgia, Atlanta, GA; *Int'l*, pg. 1506
Berthelsen, Lee, Pres.--Marc Plaza Corp., Milwaukee, WI; *U.S. Public*, pg. 1044
Berthiaume, Douglas A., Chm. Bd., Pres. & Chief Exec. Officer--Waters Corporation, Milford, MA; *U.S. Public*, pg. 1745
Berthold, James K., Chm. Bd. & Pres.--Sunnen Products Company, Saint Louis, MO; *U.S. Private*, pg. 1053
Bertino, Fred, Pres. & Creative Dir.--Hill, Holliday, Connors, Cosmopulos, Inc., Boston, MA; *U.S. Private*, pg. 529
Bertolini, Enzo, Pres.--Chr. Hansen Biosystems S.p.A., Vedano al Lambro, Italy; *Int'l*, pg. 289
Bertuccioli, Giorgio, Pres.--Bristol Italiana (Sud), S.p.A., Rome, Italy; *U.S. Public*, pg. 255
Bertuch, Michael, Pres.--Via Tech Publishing Solutions, Bay Shore, NY; *U.S. Private*, pg. 1138
Besche, Michael, Pres.--Besche Oil Company, Inc., Waldorf, MD; *U.S. Private*, pg. 139
Besecke, Edmund E., Pres.--Wurzner Dauerbackwaren GmbH, Wurzen, Germany; *Int'l*, pg. 1514
Besenyei, M., Pres.--Repeelacki Sajtyre, Budapest, Hungary; *Int'l*, pg. 201
Beshouri, Peter, Chm. Bd., Pres. & Chief Exec. Officer--Sound Advice, Inc., Dania, FL; *U.S. Public*, pg. 1488
Besse, John, Pres.--Northern Michigan Veneers, Inc., Gladstone, MI; *U.S. Private*, pg. 805
Besse, Stephen, Pres.--Gravymaster Inc., Branford, CT; *U.S. Private*, pg. 471
Besse, William C., Chief Exec. Officer--Coleman Powermate Compressors, Springfield, MN; *U.S. Private*, pg. 691
Bessen, Ted, Pres.--Potamkin Manhattan, New York, NY; *U.S. Private*, pg. 876
Bessert, Gregory P., Pres.--Cadet Manufacturing Company, Vancouver, WA; *U.S. Private*, pg. 198
Besserud, Roland A., Pres.--Economy Mechanical Industries, Inc., Wheeling, IL; *U.S. Private*, pg. 602
Bessinger, Dan, Pres. & Gen. Mgr.--Black Clawson Converting Machinery Company, Fulton, NY; *U.S. Private*, pg. 147
Besson, Michel L., Pres.--CertainTeed Corporation Foundation, Valley Forge, PA; *Int'l*, pg. 1171
Best, Arthur C., Pres. & Chief Oper. Officer--C.B. Ragland Company, Nashville, TN; *U.S. Private*, pg. 907
Best, David, Dr., Pres.--BESTMED, Inc., New York, NY; *U.S. Public*, pg. 1422
Best, James W, Pres. & Gen. Mgr.--CAE Machinery Ltd., Vancouver, Canada; *Int'l*, pg. 237
Best, Rhys J., Pres.--Lone Star Technologies, Inc., Dallas, TX; *U.S. Public*, pg. 1012
Best, Russell, Pres. & Chief Exec. Officer--Best Access Systems, Indianapolis, IN; *U.S. Public*, pg. 223
Beswick, William F., Pres.--Graham Vacuum & Heat Transfer Ltd., Congleton,, United Kingdom; *U.S. Public*, pg. 757
Betagole, Robert, Pres.--Mike Albert Leasing, Inc., Cincinnati, OH; *U.S. Private*, pg. 32
Betcher, Rich, Pres.--Inland Die Casting, Wheeling, IL; *U.S. Private*, pg. 903
Bete, Michael, Pres.--Channing L. Bete Co., Inc., South Deerfield, MA; *U.S. Private*, pg. 140
Bethards, Brandon, Pres. & Chief Oper. Officer--Kvaerner Pulping Inc., Charlotte, NC; *Int'l*, pg. 770
Bethune, David R., Pres. & Chief Oper. Officer--IVAX Corporation, Miami, FL; *U.S. Public*, pg. 914
Bethurum, George M., Chm. Bd., Pres. & Chief Exec. Officer--Bethurum Research & Development, Inc., Texas City, TX; *U.S. Private*, pg. 141
Betke, Bill, Pres.--Revco Scientific, Asheville, NC; *U.S. Public*, pg. 727
Betlem, Dick, Pres. & Chief Oper. Officer--Albemarle Corporation, Richmond, VA; *U.S. Public*, pg. 37
Betra, Ashok, Owner--Interplast Universal Industries, Inc., Lodi, NJ; *U.S. Private*, pg. 572
Bettacchi, Robert J., Pres.--Grace Construction Products, Cambridge, MA; *U.S. Public*, pg. 755
Bettendorf, Larry, Pres. & Chief Exec. Officer--ECP Incorporated, Westchester, IL; *U.S. Private*, pg. 313
Bettendorf, Larry, Pres.--The Protector Corporation, Elmhurst, IL; *U.S. Private*, pg. 891
Bettini, Mario, Pres.--Georg Fischer Sloane Inc., Little Rock, AR; *Int'l*, pg. 490
Betts, William, Pres.--Johnstown Corporation, Johnstown, PA; *U.S. Private*, pg. 595
Bettwy, Teo, Pres.--Mykotronx, Torrance, CA; *U.S. Public*, pg. 1359
Beuchler, Bruce, Pres. & Gen. Mgr.--Richtex Corporation, Columbia, SC; *Int'l*, pg. 699
Beutlich, F. Jack, Gen. Partner--Beutlich, L.P., Waukegan, IL; *U.S. Private*, pg. 141
Bevan, Bob, Pres.--SofTechnics Inc., Garland, TX; *U.S. Private*, pg. 1012
Bever, Jay Andrew, Jr., Pres. & Chief Oper. Officer--B&B Corporate Holdings, Inc., Tampa, FL; *U.S. Private*, pg. 104
Beveridge, Crawford, Pres. & Chief Exec. Officer--Scottish Enterprise, Glasgow, United Kingdom; *Int'l*, pg. 1212
Bevilacqua, Michael, Pres.--CPC Foodservice Group, Franklin Park, IL; *U.S. Public*, pg. 224
Bevilaqua, Steven K., Pres. & Chief Exec. Officer--KLLM Transport Services, Inc., Jackson, MS; *U.S. Public*, pg. 939
Bevilocqua, Michael, Pres.-Amgen Boulder--Amgen Boulder, Inc., Boulder, CO; *U.S. Public*, pg. 101
Bewkes, Jeffrey L, Chm. Bd., Pres. & Chief Exec. Officer--Home Box Office, Inc., New York, NY; *U.S. Public*, pg. 1612
Beyer, C., Pres.--C.A. Cigarrera Bigott, Sucs., Caracas, Venezuela; *Int'l*, pg. 111
Bezak, Sharon, Pres. & V.P.-Sls. & Mktg.--Sharon Concepts, Millburn, NJ; *U.S. Private*, pg. 990
Bezos, Jeffrey P., Chm. Bd., Pres. & Chief Exec. Officer--Amazon.com, Inc., Seattle, WA; *U.S. Public*, pg. 62
Bhagat, Jai, Pres.--SkyTel Corp., Washington, DC; *U.S. Public*, pg. 1120
Bhah, Prakash, Pres.--VF Factory Outlet Stores, Hempstead, TX; *U.S. Public*, pg. 1702
Bhargava, P., Pres.--Kalyani Sharp India Limited, Sirur, India; *Int'l*, pg. 1229
Bhargava, Rai P.K., Pres. & Chief Exec. Officer--MCN Investment, Detroit, MI; *U.S. Public*, pg. 1025
Bhutani, Raj, Dr., Pres. & Chief Exec. Officer--Alra Laboratories, Inc., Gurnee, IL; *U.S. Private*, pg. 45
Bianchi, S.A., Pres. & Chief Exec. Officer--Livernois Engineering Company, Dearborn, MI; *U.S. Private*, pg. 672
Bianco, James S., Sr., Chm. Bd. & Pres.--Control Module, Inc., Enfield, CT; *U.S. Private*, pg. 271
Biblowitz, Joshua, Pres. & Chief Oper. Officer--Masters, Inc., Westbury, NY; *U.S. Private*, pg. 714
Biciher, Gary R., Pres. & Chief Oper. Officer--Louis P. Ciminelli Construction Co. Inc., Buffalo, NY; *U.S. Private*, pg. 239
Bickes, Thomas, Pres. & Chief Oper. Officer--Staffing Solutions, Boulder, CO; *U.S. Private*, pg. 1028
Bickman, James, Pres.--Stocker & Yale, Inc., Salem, NH; *U.S. Public*, pg. 1518
Biddinger, Clay M., Pres. & Chief Exec. Officer--Sun Financial Group, Inc., Tampa, FL; *U.S. Public*, pg. 691
Biddle, James, Sr, Pres. & Chief Exec. Officer--Mader Construction Corp, Elma, NY; *U.S. Private*, pg. 693
Biddle, Willing L., Pres. & Chief Oper. Officer--Urstadt Biddle Properties, Inc., Greenwich, CT; *U.S. Public*, pg. 1700
Bidermann, Maurice, Chm.--Bidermann International S.A., Paris, France; *Int'l*, pg. 194
Bidwell, Donald, Sr., Pres. & Chief Exec. Officer--Bidwell Industrial Group, Inc., Middletown, CT; *U.S. Private*, pg. 142
Bidwell, Donald, Sr., Pres.--Magnagrip, Middletown, CT; *U.S. Private*, pg. 142
Bidwell, Donald, Sr., Pres. & Chief Exec. Officer--Power-Dyne, Middletown, CT; *U.S. Private*, pg. 142
Bidwell, Donald, Sr., Pres. & Chief Exec. Officer--Rapid Print, Middletown, CT; *U.S. Private*, pg. 142
Bidwell, F., Pres.--Malone Advertising, Inc., Akron, OH; *U.S. Private*, pg. 698
Bidwell, Mike, Pres.--Rainbow International Carpet Dyeing & Cleaning Co., Waco, TX; *U.S. Public*, pg. 538
Bidwill, William V., Pres.--Arizona Cardinals, Phoenix, AZ; *U.S. Private*, pg. 81
Biedenharn, Hank, Pres.--Ouachita Coca-Cola Bottling Company, Monroe, LA; *U.S. Public*, pg. 393
Bielinski, Donald E., Grp. Pres.--W.W. Grainger, Inc., Lincolnshire, IL; *U.S. Public*, pg. 758
Bienenfeld, Marvin, Pres.--Bestform Foundations, Inc., Long Island City, NY; *U.S. Private*, pg. 140
Bierer, Alice, Pres. & Chief Fin. Officer--Essex Grain Products, Inc., Frazer, PA; *U.S. Private*, pg. 383
Bierich, H.C. Marcus, Dr., Chm.-Supervisory Bd.--J.M. Voith, GmbH, Heidenheim, Germany; *Int'l*, pg. 1472
Biever, Barton R., Jr., Pres.--Alpha Mills Corp., Schuylkill Haven, PA; *U.S. Private*, pg. 45
Bigden, Julian V., Pres.--Fenner Drives, Manheim, PA; *U.S. Private*, pg. 400
Biggar, Bill, Partner--Potentia Healthcare Communications Partners, Chicago, IL; *U.S. Public*, pg. 1224
Biggar, James M., Pres. & Chief Exec. Officer--Nestle Holdings, Inc., Stamford, CT; *Int'l*, pg. 916
Biggs, James P., Pres.--People's Bank, Bridgeport, CT; *U.S. Public*, pg. 1274
Biggs, John H., Chm. Bd., Pres. & Chief Exec. Officer--Teachers Insurance and Annuity Association, New York, NY; *U.S. Private*, pg. 1071
Bijapurkar, Ashoke, Pres.--Rediffusion-DY&R Pvt. Ltd., Mumbai, India; *U.S. Private*, pg. 326
Bijou, Thomas, Pres.--Advanced Telemarketing Corp., Irving, TX; *U.S. Public*, pg. 11
Bijur, Arthur W., Pres. & Exec. Creative Dir.--Cliff Freeman & Partners, New York, NY; *U.S. Public*, pg. 1422
Bijvoet, B., Pres.--Campina Melkunie BV, Zaltbommel, Netherlands; *Int'l*, pg. 254
Bileti, Michael, Pres.--Peter A. Basile Sons Inc., Livonia, MI; *U.S. Private*, pg. 121
Bileydi, Sumer, Sr. Partner & Media Dir.--Carmichael Lynch, Inc., Minneapolis, MN; *U.S. Private*, pg. 213
Biller, Leslie S., Pres. & Chief Oper. Officer--Norwest Corporation, Minneapolis, MN; *U.S. Public*, pg. 1201
Billeter, H.A., Pres. & Chief Exec. Officer--Johnny Appleseed's, Inc., Beverly, MA; *U.S. Private*, pg. 590
Billett, Geoffrey J., Pres. & Sec.--Ecophon CertainTeed, Inc., Valley Forge, PA; *Int'l*, pg. 1171
Billett, James F., Jr., Chm. Bd., Pres. & Chief Exec. Officer--Trenwick Group Inc., Stamford, CT; *U.S. Public*, pg. 1634
Billing, Grant D., Pres. & Chief Exec. Officer--Norcen Energy Resources Limited, Calgary, Canada; *Int'l*, pg. 434
Billmaier, James A., Pres. & Chief Exec. Officer--Asymetrix Learning Systems, Inc., Bellevue, WA; *U.S. Private*, pg. 93
Billock, John K., Pres.-Sls. & Mktg.--Home Box Office, Inc., New York, NY; *U.S. Public*, pg. 1612
Bilodeau, Paul, Pres. & Gen. Mgr.--Wyeth Ltd., North York, Canada; *U.S. Public*, pg. 82
Biltekoff, James, Pres.--Astro Dairy Products Ltd., Etobicoke, Canada; *Int'l*, pg. 95
Biltekoff, James, Pres.--Elan Foods, Buffalo, NY; *U.S. Private*, pg. 484
Bin Ahmad, Haji Yahaya, Pres.--Automotive Manufacturers (Malaysia) Sdn. Bhd., Pekan, Malaysia; *Int'l*, pg. 692
Bindel, Edward, Pres.--MiniData Services, Inc., Pine Brook, NJ; *U.S. Public*, pg. 331
Binder, Herbert R., Pres. & Chief Oper. Officer--Shoppers Drug Mart, Ltd., Toronto, Canada; *Int'l*, pg. 112
Binder, Stanley S., Chm. Bd., Pres & Chief Exec. Officer--Barringer Technologies Inc., New Providence, NJ; *U.S. Public*, pg. 191
Binswanger, David R., Pres. & Chief Exec. Officer--Binswanger, Philadelphia, PA; *U.S. Private*, pg. 144
Biosca, Fernando Vela, Pres.--INITEC - E.N. de Ingenieria y Tecnologia, S.A., Madrid, Spain; *Int'l*, pg. 1225
Birch, Eric N., Pres. & Chief Exec. Officer--Intertek Testing Services, Andover, MA; *Int'l*, pg. 672
Bird, David, Pres.--Malta Div.-Tomkins Industries, Inc., Malta, OH; *Int'l*, pg. 1398
Bird, Robert H., Pres.--Blue Chip Stamps, Los Angeles, CA; *U.S. Public*, pg. 217
Bird, Thomas, Pres. & Chief Oper. Officer--Nepera Inc., Harriman, NY; *U.S. Public*, pg. 297
Birdsong, George, Pres.--Birdsong Corporation, Suffolk, VA; *U.S. Private*, pg. 145
Birk, Tom, Partner--Houston Herstek Favat, Boston, MA; *U.S. Private*, pg. 542
Birkhauser, Robert R., III, Chm. Bd. & Pres.--Auto Glass Specialists, Madison, WI; *U.S. Private*, pg. 100
Birkholz, Ray, Pres. & Chief Exec. Officer--Republic Storage Systems Company Inc., Canton, OH; *U.S. Private*, pg. 924
Birkin, Michael, Pres.-Intl.--Diversified Agency Services, New York, NY; *U.S. Public*, pg. 1223
Birmingham, Bruce R., Pres.--The Bank of Nova Scotia, Toronto, Canada; *Int'l*, pg. 155
Birmingham, Norm, Pres.--Westmark Group Holdings Inc., Delray Beach, FL; *U.S. Public*, pg. 1761
Birnbach, Gerald, Chm. Bd., Pres. & Chief Exec. Officer--Rowe Furniture Corp., Mc Lean, VA; *U.S. Public*, pg. 1410
Birndorf, Harold, Pres.--Atlas Lift Truck Rentals & Sales, Inc., Schiller Park, IL; *U.S. Private*, pg. 96
Bisasky, Louis W., Pres. & Chief Oper. Officer--Schlumberger Malco Inc., Owings Mills, MD; *Int'l*, pg. 1206
Bisballe, Bruce, Pres. & Chief Oper. Officer--Manufacturers Products Company, Warren, MI; *U.S. Private*, pg. 701
Bishop, Del, Pres.--SDL Construction, Bellevue, WA; *U.S. Private*, pg. 719
Bishop, Dennis, Pres. & Gen. Mgr.--Stanley Hydraulic Tools Div., Milwaukie, OR; *U.S. Public*, pg. 1509
Bishop, Eugene D., Pres. & Chief Oper. Officer--California State Bank, West Covina, CA; *U.S. Public*, pg. 294
Bishop, Frank, Gen. Mgr.--Atlas Cylinder, Eugene, OR; *U.S. Public*, pg. 1261
Bishop, Katherine, Pres. & Chief Oper. Officer--Lebanon Seaboard Corporation, Lebanon, PA; *U.S. Private*, pg. 656
Bishop, Robert D., Chm. & Pres.--SunTrust Bank, Northeast Georgia, N.A., Athens, GA; *U.S. Public*, pg. 1538
Bishop, Thomas A., Gen. Mgr.--Arizona Auction Services, Inc., Chandler, AZ; *U.S. Private*, pg. 282
Bishop, William L., Pres. & Chief Oper. Officer--The Western Group, Saint Louis, MO; *U.S. Private*, pg. 1165
Bissell, J.R., Pres.--Venturi Inc., Traverse City, MI; *U.S. Private*, pg. 1136
Bissell, Mark J., Pres. & Chief Exec. Officer--Bissell Inc., Grand Rapids, MI; *U.S. Private*, pg. 145
Bissell, Robin, Pres. & Chief Oper. Officer--Esskay, Riderwood, MD; *U.S. Public*, pg. 1479
Bisson, Edwin, Pres. & Chief Exec. Officer--Crowe Rope Industries L.L.C., Waterville, ME; *U.S. Private*, pg. 291
Biswell, Stephen, Pres.--Nash DeCamp Company, Visalia, CA; *U.S. Public*, pg. 1152
Bitensky, Samson, Chm. Bd. & Pres.--Fab Industries, Inc., New York, NY; *U.S. Public*, pg. 603
Bither, Richard A., PE, Chm. Bd., Pres. & Chief Exec. Officer--Giffels Associates, Inc., Southfield, MI; *U.S. Private*, pg. 452
Bither, Richard A., PE, Pres.--Giffels Technologies, Inc., Southfield, MI; *U.S. Private*, pg. 452
Bitter, Adriana Scalamandre, Pres.--Scalamandre, Inc., Long Island City, NY; *U.S. Private*, pg. 969
Bittner, Clarence J., Pres. & Chief Oper. Officer--Shook National Corporation, Dayton, OH; *U.S. Private*, pg. 996
Bittner, Gary W., Pres. & Chief Oper. Officer--Richfood, Inc., Mechanicsville, VA; *U.S. Public*, pg. 1389
Bittner, Thomas, Pres. & Chief Exec. Officer--Polychrome Corp. Div., Fort Lee, NJ; *Int'l*, pg. 370
Bivins, William, Pres.--Stahmann Farms, Inc., La Mesa, NM; *U.S. Private*, pg. 1029
Bixby, Edward K., Pres.--General Mills, Consumer Foods Sales Div., Minneapolis, MN; *U.S. Public*, pg. 718
Bixby, Edward K., Pres.--General Mills Sales, Inc., Minneapolis, MN; *U.S. Public*, pg. 718
Bixby, Walter E., Vice Chm., Pres. & Chief Exec. Officer--Kansas City Life Insurance Co., Kansas City, MO; *U.S. Public*, pg. 942
Bixby, Walter E., III, Pres. & Chief Oper. Officer--Old American Insurance Co., Kansas City, MO; *U.S. Public*, pg. 943

Bixler, Phyllis, Pres.--Ranch-Way Feed Inc., Fort Collins, CO; *U.S. Private*, pg. 908
Bize, Pierre, Pres. & Chief Exec. Officer--CSE Insurance Group, San Francisco, CA; *U.S. Private*, pg. 197
Bjork, Claes, Pres. & Grp. Chief Exec. Officer--Skanska AB, Danderyd, Sweden; *Int'l*, pg. 1260
Bjork, Claes, Pres.--Beers Construction Company, Atlanta, GA; *Int'l*, pg. 1261
Bjorklund, Hakan, Pres.--Astra Lakemedal AB, Sodertalje, Sweden; *Int'l*, pg. 93
Bjorkman, Joseph R., Pres.--Alkota Cleaning Systems, Inc., Alcester, SD; *U.S. Private*, pg. 34
Bjorkman, Nils, Pres.--Tetra Laval Food, Lund, Sweden; *Int'l*, pg. 1378
Blaauw, A.C.W., Chm. Bd. & Pres.--Meco Development Limited, Hong Kong, Hong Kong; *Int'l*, pg. 852
Blachere, Francois, Pres.--EURO RSCG Gregoire, Blachere, Huard & Roussel, Levallois-Perret, France; *Int'l*, pg. 601
Black, C. Robert, Chm. & Pres.--Texaco Overseas Holdings Inc., White Plains, NY; *U.S. Public*, pg. 1583
Black, C. Robert, Pres.--Texaco Worldwide Exploration & Production, Scroggins, TX; *U.S. Public*, pg. 1583
Black, Cathleen, Pres.--Hearst Magazines Division, New York, NY; *U.S. Private*, pg. 516
Black, David, V.P. & Gen. Mgr.--Admiral Heintz, Inc., Wadsworth, OH; *U.S. Public*, pg. 1143
Black, Frank C., Chm. Bd. & Pres.--Vogler Motor Company, Inc., Carbondale, IL; *U.S. Private*, pg. 1143
Black, James, Chm. Bd. & Pres.--Johnson County Farm Bureau Co-op, Franklin, IN; *U.S. Private*, pg. 591
Black, James, Sr. Partner & Exec. Creative Dir.--EURO RSCG Tatham, Chicago, IL; *Int'l*, pg. 601
Black, James W., Pres.--Protection Mutual Insurance Co., Park Ridge, IL; *U.S. Private*, pg. 891
Black, Jeff, Pres. & Treas.--Black & Co., Decatur, IL; *U.S. Private*, pg. 146
Black, L. David, Chm. Bd., Pres., & Chief Exec. Officer--JLG Industries, Inc., McConnellsburg, PA; *U.S. Public*, pg. 918
Black, Stanley D., Pres.--Trend-Lines Inc., Revere, MA; *U.S. Private*, pg. 1099
Black, William H., III, Pres.--Black Cadillac Olds, Inc., Greensboro, NC; *U.S. Private*, pg. 146
Blackburn, J.M., Pres. & Chief Exec. Officer--Halifax plc, Halifax, United Kingdom; *Int'l*, pg. 589
Blackburn, Wilson, Pres.--Cross Pointe Paper Corporation, Saint Paul, MN; *Int'l*, pg. 434
Blacker, Stanley, Pres.--Stanley Blacker, Inc., New York, NY; *U.S. Private*, pg. 147
Blackfan, John, Pres.--Chemionics Corporation, Tallmadge, OH; *U.S. Private*, pg. 234
Blackwell, Daria, Mng. Partner & Client Svcs. Dir.-Strategic Planning--Dugan/Farley Communications, Upper Saddle River, NJ; *U.S. Public*, pg. 1642
Blackwell, E. Scott, Pres. & Chief Exec. Officer--eMerge Vision Systems, Sebastian, FL; *U.S. Public*, pg. 1425
Blackwell, James A., Pres.--Lockheed Aeronautical Systems Company, Marietta, GA; *U.S. Public*, pg. 1007
Blackwell, Katrina, Pres.--Red Ball Corporation, Seattle, WA; *U.S. Private*, pg. 97
Blackwell, William E., Pres.--Jefferson-Pilot Communications Company, Greensboro, NC; *U.S. Public*, pg. 925
Blackwood, Jason T., Pres.--Physiotherapy Associates, Inc., Kalamazoo, MI; *U.S. Public*, pg. 1526
Blaeser, Jack, Pres. & Chief Exec. Officer--Concord Communications, Inc., Marlborough, MA; *U.S. Public*, pg. 429
Blagge, Timothy J., Pres. & Chief Exec. Officer--Blagge Enterprises, Rancho Cordova, CA; *U.S. Private*, pg. 148
Blaikie, Peter M., Pres. & Chief Oper. Officer--Unican Security Systems Ltd., Montreal, Canada; *Int'l*, pg. 1432
Blair, Douglas, Pres. & Chief Exec. Officer--The Thermos Company, Schaumburg, IL; *Int'l*, pg. 938
Blair, Ed A., Pres. & Gen. Mgr.--BHP Petroleum (Americas) Inc., Houston, TX; *Int'l*, pg. 225
Blair, Greg, Pres.--Escort, Inc., West Chester, OH; *U.S. Private*, pg. 383
Blair, Jack, Pres.--Smith & Nephew North America, Memphis, TN; *Int'l*, pg. 1263
Blair, Jerrold, Pres.--International Recovery Corp., Miami Springs, FL; *U.S. Public*, pg. 906
Blair, Michael D., Chm. Bd. & Chief Exec. Officer--Cyborg Systems, Inc., Chicago, IL; *U.S. Private*, pg. 299
Blair, R. Cary, Chm. Bd., Pres. & Chief Exec. Officer--Westfield Companies, Westfield Center, OH; *U.S. Private*, pg. 1169
Blajsczak, Richard J., Pres. & Chief Exec. Officer--RCB Baking Company, Fargo, ND; *U.S. Public*, pg. 1354
Blake, Jeffrey, Pres.-Domestic Dist.--Columbia Pictures, Culver City, CA; *Int'l*, pg. 1281
Blake, Norman P., Jr., Chm. Bd., Pres. & Chief Exec. Officer--USF&G Corporation, Baltimore, MD; *U.S. Public*, pg. 1659
Blake, Phil, Publr.-Wisconsin State Journal--Madison Newspapers, Inc., Madison, WI; *U.S. Public*, pg. 984
Blake, Ronald L., Pres.--Ameritech Enhanced Business Services, Chicago, IL; *U.S. Public*, pg. 98
Blakeley, Paul, Pres.--Tupman Thurlow Co. Inc., Avon, CT; *U.S. Private*, pg. 1109
Blanchard, Charles H., Pres. & Chief Exec. Officer--First National Bank of Russellville, Russellville, AR; *U.S. Public*, pg. 630
Blanchard, J.A.(Gus), III, Chm. Bd., Pres. & Chief Exec. Officer--Deluxe Corporation, Shoreview, MN; *U.S. Public*, *pg. 498*
Blanchard, Kenneth E., Chm. Bd., Pres. & Chief Exec. Officer--Phonetics, Inc., Aston, PA; *U.S. Private*, pg. 863
Blanchard, Richard F., Pres.--Wm. Blanchard Co., Springfield, NJ; *U.S. Private*, pg. 148
Blanchard, Robert T., Pres.--Procter & Gamble Beauty Care Div., Cincinnati, OH; *U.S. Public*, pg. 1330
Blanchard, Roy, Pres.--Geo. H. Lehleitner & Co., Inc., Kenner, LA; *U.S. Private*, pg. 659
Blanco, Rafael, Esq., Pres., Chief Exec. & Oper. Officer--PonceBank, F.S.B., Ponce, PR; *U.S. Public*, pg. 1316
Bland, W. Greg, Pres. & Chief Exec. Officer--Tasco Sales Inc., Miramar, FL; *U.S. Private*, pg. 928
Blank, Arthur M., Pres., Chief Exec. Officer & Chief Oper. Officer--The Home Depot, Inc., Atlanta, GA; *U.S. Public*, pg. 831
Blankemeyer, Robert H., Pres.--Storz Instrument Co., Saint Louis, MO; *U.S. Public*, pg. 79
Blankenmeyer, Gerald, Jr., Pres.--Lasting Products, Inc., Dallas, TX; *U.S. Private*, pg. 652
Blankenship, Don L., Chm. Bd., Pres. & Chief Exec. Officer--A.T. Massey Coal Company, Inc., Richmond, VA; *U.S. Public*, pg. 660
Blankenship, Joseph M., Pres. & Chief Exec. Officer--National Bank of Summers, Hinton, WV; *U.S. Public*, pg. 836
Blankenship, Truman, Pres., Chief Exec. Officer & Chief Oper. Officer--Berryman Products, Inc., Arlington, TX; *U.S. Private*, pg. 138
Blann, Jerry M., Pres.--Jackson Hole Ski Resort, Teton Village, WY; *U.S. Private*, pg. 579
Blashill, Tom, Pres.--Dynagear Inc., Downers Grove, IL; *U.S. Private*, pg. 350
Blasius, Donald, Pres.--National Union Electric Corp., Cleveland, OH; *Int'l*, pg. 440
Blatt, Sid, Pres.--Columbus Steel Drum, Inc., Blacklick, OH; *U.S. Private*, pg. 385
Blattner, Scott, Pres.--D.H. Blattner & Sons, Inc., Avon, MN; *U.S. Private*, pg. 148
Blauer, Charles, Chm. Bd., Pres.,Chief Exec. Officer & Treas.--Blauer Manufacturing Co., Inc., Boston, MA; *U.S. Private*, pg. 149
Blaugrund, Lee S., Pres. & Chief Exec. Officer--American Furniture Company, Albuquerque, NM; *U.S. Private*, pg. 55
Blechman, Michael S., Pres.--PAMCO Printed Tape & Label Company, Inc., Des Plaines, IL; *U.S. Private*, pg. 598
Bleil, James S., Pres. & Gen. Mgr.--Williams Detroit Diesel-Allison S.W., Inc., Phoenix, AZ; *U.S. Private*, pg. 1179
Bletas, James D., Pres.--California Microwave-TeleCom Transmission Systems, Inc., Fremont, CA; *U.S. Public*, pg. 293
Blethen, Roger W., Pres. & Chief Exec. Officer--LTX Corporation, Westwood, MA; *U.S. Public*, pg. 972
Bleuler, Brigitte, Co-Pres.--EURO RSCG D 10, Toulouse, France; *Int'l*, pg. 600
Bleusteen, Jeffrey L., Pres.--H-D Michigan, Inc., Ann Arbor, MI; *U.S. Public*, pg. 786
Bleustein, Jeffrey, Pres. & Chief Exec. Officer--Harley-Davidson, Inc., Milwaukee, WI; *U.S. Public*, pg. 786
Blevins, James W., Pres. & Chief Exec Officer--Blevins Inc., Nashville, TN; *U.S. Private*, pg. 149
Blevins, Kenneth W., Pres.--Alcoa Electronic Packaging, Inc., San Diego, CA; *U.S. Public*, pg. 60
Blevins, Tony C., Pres.--Texaco Brasil S. A.-Produtos de Petroleo, Rio de Janeiro, Brazil; *U.S. Public*, pg. 1584
Bliss, David C., Chm. Bd., Pres. & Chief Exec. Officer--Quality Stores Inc., Muskegon, MI; *U.S. Private*, pg. 899
Blissenbach, Henry, Pres. & Chief Oper. Officer--Chronimed Inc., Minnetonka, MN; *U.S. Public*, pg. 352
Blissenbach, Henry, Pres.--Diversified Pharmaceutical Services, Inc., Edina, MN; *Int'l*, pg. 1265
Blitzer, Charles N., Pres. & Chief Exec. Officer--MGI PHARMA INC., Minneapolis, MN; *U.S. Public*, pg. 1026
Blitzer, Mike, Pres.--Van Heusen Retail Division, Bridgewater, NJ; *U.S. Public*, pg. 1291
Bloch, Federico, Pres. & Chief Exec. Officer--Taca International Airlines, S. A., San Salvador, El Salvador; *Int'l*, pg. 1346
Bloch, Martin B., Pres. & Chief Scientist--Frequency Electronics, Inc., Uniondale, NY; *U.S. Public*, pg. 681
Bloch, Michael, Pres.--Bloch/New England, Inc., Worcester, MA; *U.S. Private*, pg. 149
Bloch, Thomas, Pres.--The CIT Group/Business Credit, New York, NY; *Int'l*, pg. 360
Blocha, John, Pres. & Chief Oper. Officer--Coburn Optical Industries Inc., Tulsa, OK; *U.S. Private*, pg. 248
Block, Edward L., Pres. & Chief Exec. Officer--Block Distributing Company, San Antonio, TX; *U.S. Private*, pg. 149
Block, George P., Pres.--Carstens Inc., Chicago, IL; *U.S. Private*, pg. 216
Block, Leonard, Pres.--Block Drug Corporation Dental Products Co., Jersey City, NJ; *U.S. Public*, pg. 237
Block, Richard, Pres.--AGI Inc., Melrose Park, IL; *U.S. Private*, pg. 5
Block, Sam, Jr., Pres.--Ideal Chemical & Supply Company, Memphis, TN; *U.S. Private*, pg. 557
Block, Thomas R., Pres. & Treas.--Block Drug Company, Inc., Jersey City, NJ; *U.S. Public*, pg. 236
Block, William, Jr., Pres.--Blade Communications, Inc., Toledo, OH; *U.S. Private*, pg. 147
Block, William, Jr., Pres. & Co-Publr.--Toledo Blade Co., Toledo, OH; *U.S. Private*, pg. 147
Block, William, Jr., Pres. & Co-Publisher--PG Publishing Co., Pittsburgh, PA; *U.S. Private*, pg. 147
Bloebaum, William D., Jr., Pres.--Mead Pulp Sales, Inc., Dayton, OH; *U.S. Public*, pg. 1074
Bloem, Anthero, Pres. & Gen. Mgr.--Valvulas Keystone de Mexico, S.A. de C.V., Guadalajara, Mexico; *U.S. Public*, pg. 1650
Blommer, Joseph, Pres. & Treas.--Blommer Chocolate Co., Chicago, IL; *U.S. Private*, pg. 150
Blomqvist, Thomas, Pres.--Ikea Svenska AB, Almhult, Sweden; *Int'l*, pg. 660
Bloodwell, Daniel, Pres.--Bickford's Family Restaurants, Brighton, MA; *U.S. Public*, pg. 545
Bloom, Donald, Pres. & Chief Exec. Officer--Bloom Electric Services, Inc., Oklahoma City, OK; *U.S. Private*, pg. 150
Bloom, Jack, Pres.--Baldi, Bloom & Whelan Advertising, New York, NY; *U.S. Private*, pg. 112
Bloom, Jonathan O., Pres.--Resource Net International, New York, NY; *U.S. Public*, pg. 903
Bloom, Robert H., Chm. Bd. & Chief Exec. Officer--Publicis/Bloom Inc., New York, NY; *Int'l*, pg. 470
Bloom, Ron, Pres.--Think New Ideas, Inc., New York, NY; *U.S. Public*, pg. 1224
Bloomberg, Lawrence S., Pres. & Chief Exec. Officer--First Marathon Inc., Toronto, Canada; *Int'l*, pg. 486
Bloomberg, Michael, Pres. & Founder--Bloomberg L.P., New York, NY; *U.S. Private*, pg. 150
Bloomfield, Robert M., Pres.--Enteric Products, Inc., Westbury, NY; *U.S. Public*, pg. 540
Blose, Thomas R., Jr., Pres.--United Cities Gas Company, Brentwood, TN; *U.S. Public*, pg. 146
Bloss, David, Pres. & Chief Oper. Officer--Watts Industries, Inc., North Andover, MA; *U.S. Public*, pg. 1746
Blossom, Donald M., Pres. & Chief Exec. Officer--The First National Bank of Ottawa, Ottawa, OH; *U.S. Public*, pg. 1413
Blossom, John, Pres.--Small, Parker & Blossom, Peoria, IL; *U.S. Public*, pg. 280
Blossom, Rick L., Pres. & Chief Oper. Officer--First National Bank of Southwestern Ohio, Hamilton, OH; *U.S. Public*, pg. 633
Blouch, Gerald B., Pres. & Chief Oper. Officer--Invacare Corporation, Elyria, OH; *U.S. Public*, pg. 911
Blow, Warner C., Pres. & Chief Exec. Officer--Sterling Commerce, Inc., Dublin, OH; *U.S. Public*, pg. 1515
Blue, Dale, Pres. & Chief Exec. Officer--The Chase Manhattan Bank of Canada, Toronto, Canada; *U.S. Public*, pg. 340
Blue, David S., Pres. & Chief Exec. Officer--Louisville Scrap Material Co., Inc., Louisville, KY; *U.S. Private*, pg. 677
Blue, David W., Pres. & Chief Oper. Officer--The O'Boise Corporation, Oak Brook, IL; *U.S. Private*, pg. 810
Blue, J. Charles, Pres. & Chief Oper. Officer--United Agri Products Co., Greeley, CO; *U.S. Public*, pg. 426
Blue, J. Neal, Chm. Bd., Pres. & Chief Exec. Officer--General Atomics, San Diego, CA; *U.S. Private*, pg. 443
Bluestein, David G., Pres.--Chesebrough-Pond's Household Products Div., Jacksonville, FL; *Int'l*, pg. 1435
Bluestone, Stanton, Chm. Bd. & Pres.--Boston Store, Milwaukee, WI; *U.S. Public*, pg. 309
Bluhm, Neil G., Pres.--JMB Realty Corporation, Chicago, IL; *U.S. Private*, pg. 577
Blum, Brad, Pres.--Olive Garden Italian Restaurants, Orlando, FL; *U.S. Public*, pg. 484
Blum, Richard J., Pres.--The Kirk & Blum Mfg. Co., Cincinnati, OH; *U.S. Private*, pg. 623
Blum, Robert M., Pres.--Craftex Mills Inc. of Pennsylvania, Blue Bell, PA; *U.S. Private*, pg. 284
Blumberg, Armin W., Pres. & Chief Exec. Officer--Nautilus Insurance Company, Scottsdale, AZ; *U.S. Public*, pg. 216
Blumberg, Armin W., Pres. & Chief Exec. Officer--Great Divide Insurance Company, Scottsdale, AZ; *U.S. Public*, pg. 216
Blumberg, David, Pres. & Chief Exec. Officer--Blumberg Communications Inc., Minneapolis, MN; *U.S. Public*, pg. 305
Blume, Robert L., Pres. & Chief Exec. Officer--Capital Development Co., Lacey, WA; *U.S. Private*, pg. 205
Blumenfeld, Peter, Pres. & Chief Oper. Officer--Sport Supply Group, Inc., Dallas, TX; *U.S. Public*, pg. 1499
Blumenfeld, Seth D., Pres. & Grp. Exec.--MCI International Inc., Rye Brook, NY; *U.S. Public*, pg. 1024
Blumenthal, Alan, Pres. & Mgr.-Sls.--Radiator Specialty Company, Charlotte, NC; *U.S. Private*, pg. 906
Blumenthal, Arthur H., Pres.--SL Waber, Inc., Mount Laurel, NJ; *U.S. Public*, pg. 1419
Blumenthal, Arthur H., Pres.--SL Waber, Nogales, AZ; *U.S. Public*, pg. 1419
Blumenthal, Harry J., Jr., Pres.--Blumenthal Print Works, Inc., New Orleans, LA; *U.S. Private*, pg. 153
Blumenthal, Isidor, Pres.--Lion Brand Yarn Co., New York, NY; *U.S. Private*, pg. 669
Blumenthal, Thomas A., Chm. Bd, Pres. & Chief Exec. Officer--Norwalk Powdered Metals, Inc., Norwalk, CT; *U.S. Private*, pg. 808
Blumenthal, Warren S., Pres.--DG Foods, LLC, Chicago, IL; *U.S. Private*, pg. 301
Blystone, John B., Chm. Bd., Pres. & Chief Exec. Officer--SPX Corporation, Muskegon, MI; *U.S. Public*, pg. 1420
Blyth, Peter, Pres.-Radisson Hotels Worldwide--Radisson Hotel Corporation, Minneapolis, MN; *U.S. Private*, pg. 212
Boardman, Elaine, Pres. & Chief Oper. Officer--Patient Care, Inc., West Orange, NJ; *U.S. Public*, pg. 344
Boatwright, Ken, Pres.--Woodbury Business Forms, Inc., La Grange, GA; *U.S. Private*, pg. 1186
Bobbins, Chuck, Pres.--R.F. Technology, Inc., Norwalk, CT; *Int'l*, pg. 1289
Bober, David, Pres. & Chief Exec. Officer--American Beverage Corp. Inc., Akron, OH; *Int'l*, pg. 752
Bobin, Alan, Pres. & Chief Exec. Officer--The Generra Company, Seattle, WA; *U.S. Private*, pg. 446
Bobinchuck, Michael, Pres.--Par Industries, Inc., Medina, OH; *U.S. Private*, pg. 838
Bobins, Norman, Pres. & Chief Exec. Officer--LaSalle National Bank, Chicago, IL; *Int'l*, pg. 10
Bobit, Ty F., Pres. & Chief Oper. Officer--Bobit Publishing Company, Torrance, CA; *U.S. Private*, pg. 154
Boccardi, Louis D., Pres. & Chief Exec. Officer--The Associated Press, New York, NY; *U.S. Private*, pg. 92
Boches, Edward, Principal & Co-Creative Dir.--Mullen Advertising, Inc., Wenham, MA; *U.S. Private*, pg. 766
Bock, Warren, Pres.--International Relocation Insurance Services Inc., Vienna, VA; *Int'l*, pg. 1503
Bockerstette, Joe, Pres. & Chief Exec. Officer--Seyfert Foods, Inc., Fort Wayne, IN; *U.S. Private*, pg. 988
Bockstanz, David, Pres.--Frank Industries, Inc., Brown City, MI; *U.S. Private*, pg. 423
Bodager, Brian R., Pres. & Chief Exec. Officer--Banc Life Insurance Corporation, Phoenix, AZ; *U.S. Public*, pg. 140
Bodaken, Bruce, Pres. & Chief Oper. Officer--Blue Shield of California, San Francisco, CA; *U.S. Private*, pg. 153

Boddie, William L., Pres. & Chief Exec. Officer--Boddie-Noell Enterprises Inc., Rocky Mount, NC; U.S. Private, pg. 154

Bode, Henry J., Pres.--Videojet Systems International, Inc., Wood Dale, IL; Int'l, pg. 545

Bodine, John R., Pres. & Chief Exec. Officer--Bodine Electric Company, Chicago, IL; U.S. Private, pg. 154

Bodine, Stanley A., Pres. & Chief Oper. Officer--Funco, Inc., Eden Prairie, MN; U.S. Public, pg. 688

Bodnar, J. Michael, Pres. & Chief Exec. Officer--Shoney's, Inc., Nashville, TN; U.S. Public, pg. 1467

Bodziony, Dennis, Pres.--Tempo Products Company, Solon, OH; U.S. Private, pg. 870

Boeckmann, Herbert F., II, Pres.--Galpin Motors, North Hills, CA; U.S. Private, pg. 438

Boedeker, Theodore R., Co-Pres.--Tricon Industries, Inc., Lisle, IL; U.S. Private, pg. 1102

Boehm, Josef F., Pres. & Chief Oper. Officer--Alaska Industrial Hardware Inc., Anchorage, AK; U.S. Private, pg. 31

Boehm, William J., Chm. Bd., Pres. & Chief Exec. Officer--Connector Manufacturing Company, Hamilton, OH; U.S. Private, pg. 264

Boel, Guus, Pres.--Applied Power Inc., Butler, WI; U.S. Public, pg. 124

Boel, Guus, Pres.--Enerpac U.S., Butler, WI; U.S. Public, pg. 124

Boender, Rene, Mng. Partner--Bercum Boender Cardozo & Werkendam B.V., Amsterdam, Netherlands; U.S. Private, pg. 1198

Boerger, Dick G., Pres. & Chief Exec. Officer--Southwestern Bell Printing Company, Houston, TX; U.S. Public, pg. 1415

Bogard, Richard, Pres. & Gen. Mgr.--Cherry Central Cooperative, Traverse City, MI; U.S. Private, pg. 233

Bogle, Donald E., Pres. & Chief Exec. Officer--Moore Products Co., Spring House, PA; U.S. Public, pg. 1128

Bognanno, P. F., Pres. & Chief Exec. Officer--Principal Residential Mortgage, Inc., Des Moines, IA; U.S. Private, pg. 886

Bogusky, Alex, Vice Chm., Partner & Creative Dir.--Crispin Porter & Bogusky, Miami, FL; U.S. Private, pg. 290

Boh, Robert S., Pres. & Chief Exec. Officer--Boh Bros. Construction Co., LLC, New Orleans, LA; U.S. Private, pg. 154

Bohan, Gloria, Pres. & Chief Exec. Officer--Omega World Travel, Inc., Fairfax, VA; U.S. Private, pg. 816

Bohannan, Robert, Pres.--Marine Midland Mortgage Corporation, Buffalo, NY; Int'l, pg. 581

Bohannon, Robert H., Chm. Bd., Pres. & Chief Exec. Officer--Viad Corp, Phoenix, AZ; U.S. Public, pg. 1718

Bohman, Staffan, Pres.--Alfa Laval Agri AB, Lund, Sweden; Int'l, pg. 1378

Bohman, Terrance, Pres. & Chief Exec. Officer--Universal Cooperatives, Inc., Minneapolis, MN; U.S. Private, pg. 1127

Bohn, David G., Pres.--Preferred Utilities Manufacturing Corp., Danbury, CT; U.S. Private, pg. 881

Bohn, David G., Pres.--Preferred Instruments, Danbury, CT; U.S. Private, pg. 881

Bohn, David G., Pres.--W.N. Best, Danbury, CT; U.S. Private, pg. 881

Bohn, Robert G., Pres. & Chief Exec. Officer--Oshkosh Truck Corporation, Oshkosh, WI; U.S. Public, pg. 1233

Bohon, Roger L., Pres.--ENCAP Systems, Inc., Roanoke, VA; U.S. Private, pg. 513

Bohren, Kevin, Pres. & Chief Exec. Officer--Traveling Software Inc., Bothell, WA; U.S. Private, pg. 1098

Bohringer, Werner, Pres.--Terrot Strickmaschinen GmbH, Stuttgart, Germany; Int'l, pg. 1307

Boies, Jeffery E., Pres.--VSA, Inc., Denver, CO; U.S. Public, pg. 901

Boire, John, Pres.--Byers Industries, Inc., Portland, OR; U.S. Private, pg. 191

Boire, John L., Pres.--Byers Portland Willamette, Portland, OR; U.S. Private, pg. 191

Boissinot, Tim, Pres. & Gen. Mgr.--Quebecor Printing Edmonton, Edmonton, Canada; Int'l, pg. 1077

Boissonneault, Roger M., Pres. & Chief Oper. Officer--Warner-Chilcott Laboratories, Inc., Rockaway, NJ; Int'l, pg. 436

Boisvert, Bill, Pres. & Chief Fin. Officer--Attachmate, Bellevue, WA; U.S. Private, pg. 98

Boivin, Daniel W., Pres.--Nova Chemicals Ltd., Calgary, Canada; Int'l, pg. 971

Boivir, Pierre C., Pres.--Bauer Sports Inc., Montreal, Canada; U.S. Public, pg. 1184

Bok, Wayne, Pres.--North Central AMPI, Inc., New Ulm, MN; U.S. Private, pg. 804

Bokor, James, Pres.--Robert James Sales Inc., Buffalo, NY; U.S. Private, pg. 935

Bokser, Stephen R., Pres. & Chief Oper. Officer--White Rose Food, Carteret, NJ; U.S. Private, pg. 330

Bolafanti, Matthew, Pres.--Marine Midland Business Loans, Inc., Norwalk, CT; Int'l, pg. 581

Boland, David, Chm. Bd., Pres. & Chief Exec. Officer--David Boland, Inc., Titusville, FL; U.S. Private, pg. 154

Boland, John A., III, Pres. & Chief Exec. Officer--Dominion Textile Inc., Montreal, Canada; Int'l, pg. 415

Boland, Michael, Pres.--Maritz Travel Co., Fenton, MO; U.S. Private, pg. 704

Bolander, Glen S., Pres. & Chief Exec. Officer--Grist Mill Company, Lakeville, MN; U.S. Public, pg. 766

Boler, John, Chm. Bd. & Pres.--Boler Company, Itasca, IL; U.S. Private, pg. 155

Bolger, Patrick K., Pres. & Chief Oper. Officer--TransTechnology Corporation, Liberty Corner, NJ; U.S. Public, pg. 1632

Bolgiani, Francesco, Deputy Chm. & Pres.--Banca del Gottardo, Lugano, Switzerland; Int'l, pg. 1310

Bolin, James H., Pres.--Rural Metro Corporation, Scottsdale, AZ; U.S. Public, pg. 1412

Bolinger, Robert S., Pres. & Chief Exec. Officer--Susquehanna Bancshares, Inc., Lititz, PA; U.S. Public, pg. 1542

Bollenbach, Stephen F., Pres. & Chief Exec. Officer--Hilton Hotels Corporation, Beverly Hills, CA; U.S. Public, pg. 828

Boller, Claude, Pres.--Genetic Design Inc., Greensboro, NC; U.S. Public, pg. 733

Bollier, Sherwood, Pres.--Niagara Cutter, Inc., Amherst, NY; U.S. Private, pg. 798

Bolling, Thomas J., Pres. & Exec. Creative Dir.--Wolf Mansfield Bolling Advertising Inc., Buffalo, NY; U.S. Private, pg. 1185

Bollinger, Bobby D., Vice Chm. & Pres.--Bollinger Industries Inc., Grand Prairie, TX; U.S. Public, pg. 243

Bollinger, Richard, Pres.--Bollinger Shipyards, Inc., Lockport, LA; U.S. Private, pg. 155

Bollinger, Ron, Pres. & Chief Exec. Officer--N.B.F. Bollinger Industries, Americus, GA; U.S. Public, pg. 243

Bologna, Thomas A., Pres. & Chief Exec. Officer--Gen-Probe Inc., San Diego, CA; Int'l, pg. 291

Bolster, William, Pres.--CNBC, Fort Lee, NJ; U.S. Public, pg. 712

Bolthouse, William J., Pres.--Wm. Bolthouse Farms, Inc., Bakersfield, CA; U.S. Private, pg. 155

Bolton, Rod, Pres.--Electronic Solutions, San Diego, CA; U.S. Public, pg. 1791

Bomberg, Frank, Pres.--Complast, Inc., Bloomington, MN; U.S. Private, pg. 259

Bonahoom, A. James, Jr., Pres. & Sec.--Wolverine Packing Co., Detroit, MI; U.S. Private, pg. 1186

Bonanno, Salvatore J., Pres.--Foamex International Inc., Linwood, PA; U.S. Private, pg. 1094

Bonanno, Salvatore J., Pres.--Foamex, L.P., Linwood, PA; U.S. Private, pg. 1094

Boncosky, William A., Pres.--HPS, Inc., Indianapolis, IN; U.S. Private, pg. 492

Bond, Henry M., Pres.--Ikon Office Solutions-Baltimore, Baltimore, MD; U.S. Public, pg. 863

Bond, James H., Pres. & Chief Oper. Officer--Central Parking Corp., Nashville, TN; U.S. Public, pg. 326

Bond, Robert, Gen. Mgr.--Parker Hannifin Corp., Quick Coupling Div., Minneapolis, MN; U.S. Public, pg. 1260

Bond, Roger, Pres.--Abbott Ball Company, West Hartford, CT; U.S. Private, pg. 9

Bondi, Enrico, Pres.--Edison S.p.A., Milan, Italy; Int'l, pg. 324

Bondioli, Edy, Pres.--Bondioli & Pavesi S.p.A., Suzzara, Italy; Int'l, pg. 201

Bonelli, Anthony, Pres. & Chief Oper. Officer--Neuman Distributors, Inc., Ridgefield, NJ; U.S. Public, pg. 1169

Bonetti, Alessandro, Pres.--Antibioticos S.A., Madrid, Spain; Int'l, pg. 324

Bonfante, Michael, Pres. & Chief Exec. Officer--Nob Hill General Store, Inc., Gilroy, CA; U.S. Private, pg. 799

Bonfiglio, Frank J., Pres.--Vanguard Financial Services, Lombard, IL; U.S. Public, pg. 1216

Bongers, P. Frank, Pres.--SmithKline Beecham Farma B.V., Rijswijk, Netherlands; Int'l, pg. 1266

Bongrain, Jean Noel, Pres.--Bongrain S.A., Viroflay, France; Int'l, pg. 201

Bonica, Steven, Pres.--Panasonic Broadcast & Television Systems Company, Secaucus, NJ; Int'l, pg. 847

Boniface, William, Pres.--Bonland Industries, Inc., Wayne, NJ; U.S. Private, pg. 156

Bonilla, Predo P., Pres.--Trebla Chemical Company, Saint Louis, MO; U.S. Public, pg. 282

Bonk, James E., Pres. & Chief Exec. Officer--Camelot Music, Inc., Canton, OH; U.S. Private, pg. 203

Bonn, Neal F., Pres. & Chief Exec. Officer--F.H. Bonn Company, Springfield, OH; U.S. Private, pg. 156

Bonnaud, J.J., Pres.--Gan Sa, Paris, France; Int'l, pg. 565

Bonnaud, J.J., Pres.--Gan Vie, Paris, France; Int'l, pg. 565

Bonnefoi, Jean Claude, Pres.--Parbel Inc., Miami, FL; Int'l, pg. 818

Bonner, Eric N., Pres.--Permacel Tape, North Brunswick, NJ; U.S. Public, pg. 153

Bonner, Stephen B., Pres.--McGraw-Hill Construction Information Group, New York, NY; U.S. Public, pg. 1070

Bonnet, William A., Pres.--Maui Electric Co., Ltd., Kahului, HI; U.S. Public, pg. 800

Bonnetti, Alessandro, Pres.--Antibioticos S.p.A., Milan, Italy; Int'l, pg. 324

Bono, Al J., Pres. & Chief Exec. Officer--Favorite Brands International, Inc., Lincolnshire, IL; U.S. Private, pg. 397

Bono, Vincent, Pres.--Clearpoint Enterprises, Milford, MA; U.S. Private, pg. 245

Bonsal, Richard I., Pres.--Joshua L. Baily Co., Inc., Hoboken, NJ; U.S. Private, pg. 110

Bontrager, John, Chm. Bd. & Pres.--Signature Inns, Inc., Indianapolis, IN; U.S. Public, pg. 1473

Bonus, Bob, Pres.--Corporate Foods Ltd., Etobicoke, Canada; Int'l, pg. 841

Booker, Noel, Pres.--Progress Paint Mfg. Co., Louisville, KY; U.S. Private, pg. 890

Booker, Noel, Pres. & Chief Exec. Officer--K.C.I. Coatings, Inc., Louisville, KY; U.S. Private, pg. 890

Bookmyer, Bruce, Pres.--Hess & Clark Company, Ashland, OH; U.S. Public, pg. 426

Bookstaver, Thomas, Pres. & Publr.--The Herald-Dispatch, Huntington, WV; U.S. Public, pg. 701

Boomer, Walter E., Pres. & Chief Exec. Officer--Rogers Corporation, Rogers, CT; U.S. Public, pg. 1402

Boomsma, Wouter, Pres.--NCT Holland B.V., Breda, Netherlands; Int'l, pg. 914

Boone, Charles E., Pres.--Con-Way Western Express, Inc., Buena Park, CA; U.S. Public, pg. 281

Boone, Florence, Chm. Bd.--Pace, Arlington Heights, IL; U.S. Private, pg. 919

Boonstra, C., Chm. Bd. & Pres.--Philips Electronics N.V., Eindhoven, Netherlands; Int'l, pg. 1051

Boonstra, Cor, Pres.--Philips International B.V., Eindhoven, Netherlands; Int'l, pg. 1051

Boonstra, John, Pres.--Dempster Equipment, Toccoa, GA; U.S. Private, pg. 1089

Booth, John J., Acting Chm. Bd., Pres. & Chief Exec. Officer--INCSTAR Corporation, Stillwater, MN; Int'l, pg. 483

Booth, Judith A., Pres.--Courier Connection, Inc., Westford, MA; U.S. Public, pg. 453

Booth, Rodger, Pres.--Bemrose Corporation, Humberside, United Kingdom; Int'l, pg. 185

Booth, William H., Pres.--Hammacher, Schlemmer & Co., Inc., Chicago, IL; U.S. Private, pg. 497

Borba, George, Pres.--California Milk Producers, Artesia, CA; U.S. Private, pg. 201

Borchardt, Robert L., Co-Chm. Bd, Pres. & Chief Exec. Officer--Recoton Corporation, Lake Mary, FL; U.S. Public, pg. 1369

Borck, Judith L., Pres. & Chief Exec. Officer--Country Home Bakery, Inc., Bridgeport, CT; U.S. Private, pg. 278

Bord, Michel, Pres. & Chief Exec. Officer--Austin Nichols & Co. Inc., New York, NY; Int'l, pg. 566

Bordage, Real, Pres.--H.B. Fuller, Canada Inc., Mississauga, Canada; U.S. Public, pg. 687

Bordages, William, Pres.--Azon Corporation, Johnson City, NY; U.S. Private, pg. 104

Bordelon, Noreen Hogg, Pres.--Trend Line Corporation, Jackson, MS; U.S. Private, pg. 1099

Borden, Lorraine, Chm. Bd., Chief Exec. Officer, Chief Fin. Officer, Pres.--Great Scott Advertising Co. Inc., New York, NY; U.S. Private, pg. 475

Bordenape, Philippe, Pres.--BNP Finance, Paris, France; Int'l, pg. 163

Borders, Elzie Z., Pres.--Noranda Aluminium, Brentwood, TN; Int'l, pg. 434

Bordoni, Nuccio, Pres.--Leo Burnett Co., S.r.l., Milan, Italy; U.S. Private, pg. 185

Boren, Leland E., Chm. Bd., Pres. & Chief Exec. Officer--Avis Industrial Corporation, Upland, IN; U.S. Private, pg. 102

Borer, Mel, Pres.--Share Technologies - Fairchild, South Hackensack, NJ; U.S. Public, pg. 1568

Bores, Stephen J., Pres. & Chief Oper. Officer--Therma-Tru Corp., Maumee, OH; U.S. Private, pg. 1079

Borg, Malcolm A., Chm. Bd., Pres. & Chief Exec. Officer--Macromedia Incorporated, Hackensack, NJ; U.S. Private, pg. 693

Borgen, Knut, Pres.--Aker Engineering plc (AE), London, United Kingdom; Int'l, pg. 42

Borges, Felix R., Grp. Pres.--Rochester Midland Corporation, Rochester, NY; U.S. Private, pg. 937

Borghese, Francesco, Chm. Bd. & Pres.--Orlane, Inc., New York, NY; Int'l, pg. 1011

Borghorst, Bob, Pres.--Arthur A. Pozzi Co., Inc., Portland, OR; U.S. Private, pg. 878

Borgkrantz, Anders, Pres.--Sparbanken Finans, Stockholm, Sweden; Int'l, pg. 1328

Borick, Louis L., Chm. Bd. & Pres.--Superior Industries International, Inc., Van Nuys, CA; U.S. Public, pg. 1539

Borjesson, Anders, Pres. & Chief Exec. Officer--Bergman & Beving AB, Stockholm, Sweden; Int'l, pg. 188

Bork, William J., Pres. & Chief Oper. Officer--Penn National Gaming, Inc., Wyomissing, PA; U.S. Public, pg. 1270

Borland, Paul C., Pres. & Chief Oper. Officer--NS Group, Inc., Newport, KY; U.S. Public, pg. 1147

Born, Harmon M., Pres.--Beaudry Ford, Inc., Atlanta, GA; U.S. Private, pg. 127

Born, Harmon M., Pres.--B&M Equipment, Inc., Atlanta, GA; U.S. Private, pg. 127

Born, Rik, Pres.--Installation Products Div., Lancaster, PA; U.S. Public, pg. 132

Born, Ross J., Co-Pres.--Just Born, Inc., Bethlehem, PA; U.S. Private, pg. 602

Borne, Mike, Pres.--Phillips & Jacobs/North, Lititz, PA; U.S. Public, pg. 1329

Borowsky, Ned S., Pres. & Chief Oper. Officer--North American Publishing Company, Philadelphia, PA; U.S. Private, pg. 803

Borreca, John P., Pres.--Celotex Corporation, Tampa, FL; U.S. Private, pg. 221

Borregales, Carlos, Pres.--Bitumenes Orinoco, S.A. (BITOR), Caracas, Venezuela; Int'l, pg. 1045

Borror, Doug, Pres.--Dominion Homes, Dublin, OH; U.S. Public, pg. 516

Borsch, Norbert, Chm.--Borsch, Stengel & Partner GmbH, Frankfurt/Main, Germany; Int'l, pg. 203

Borst, Dennis, Pres.--Western Motivational Incentives Group, Inc., Los Angeles, CA; U.S. Private, pg. 1167

Bortz, Neil K., Partner--Towne Properties, Cincinnati, OH; U.S. Private, pg. 1093

Boruch, John, Pres.--Amkor Electronics, Inc., West Chester, PA; U.S. Private, pg. 66

Borzino, Leo, Pres. & Chief Exec. Officer--Petite Sophisticate Outlet, Enfield, CT; U.S. Private, pg. 219

Bosau, Robert D., Pres.--Tribune Education, Chicago, IL; U.S. Public, pg. 1636

Bosca, C.B., Pres.--Hugo Bosca Co., Inc., Springfield, OH; U.S. Private, pg. 160

Boscamp, Jim, Pres.--Nautica Footwear, Nashville, TN; U.S. Public, pg. 728

Bosch, Fred, Pres.--Barenbrug Northeast, Ogdensburg, NJ; Int'l, pg. 167

Boschell, Greg, Chm. Bd. & Pres.--Wattyl, Canada Bay, Australia; Int'l, pg. 1488

Boschetto, Andrew, Pres.--Quebecor Printing Modern Inc., Brookfield, CT; Int'l, pg. 1078

Boscia, Jon A., Pres.--Lincoln Financial Group, Inc., Fort Wayne, IN; U.S. Public, pg. 997

Bosco, Jerry, Pres.--Relief Printing, Baldwin Park, CA; U.S. Private, pg. 921

Boshi, Edward, Pres.--Legal & General Holdings (France) S.A., Paris, France; Int'l, pg. 805

Bosken-Diebels, Paul, Dr., Pres.--Diebels Private Brewery, Issum, Germany; Int'l, pg. 413

Bosley, James R., Pres. & Chief Exec. Officer--First Parke State Bank, Rockville, IN; U.S. Public, pg. 634

Bosquez, Ramon, Pres.--UETA, Inc., Laredo, TX; *Int'l*, pg. 103
Boss, Russell A., Pres. & Chief Exec. Officer--A.T. Cross Co., Lincoln, RI; *U.S. Public*, pg. 460
Bossidy, Bruce, Pres.--EGA, Seymour, CT; *Int'l*, pg. 436
Bossier, Albert L., Jr., Chm. Bd., Pres. & Chief Exec. Officer--Avondale Industries, Inc., Avondale, LA; *U.S. Public*, pg. 156
Bost, Robert G., Pres.--Petroleum Products Corp., Middletown, PA; *U.S. Private*, pg. 859
Bostic, Sid, Pres.--Norwest Bank Indiana, N.A., Fort Wayne, IN; *U.S. Public*, pg. 1202
Bostic, Sid A., Pres. & Chief Oper. Officer--FirstMerit Corporation, Akron, OH; *U.S. Public*, pg. 646
Boston, Larry D., Pres.--UMB First State Bank of Morrisonville, Morrisonville, IL; *U.S. Public*, pg. 1654
Boswell, E.F., Pres. & Chief Oper. Officer--Eddy Paper Company Limited, Ottawa, Canada; *Int'l*, pg. 1495
Boswell, Rob, Pres.--Moroch & Assoc., Inc., Dallas, TX; *U.S. Private*, pg. 762
Boswell, Robert S., Pres. & Chief Exec. Officer--Forest Oil Corporation, Denver, CO; *U.S. Public*, pg. 670
Bosworth, Michael F., Chm. Bd., Pres. & Chief Exec. Officer--OrCAD Inc., Beaverton, OR; *U.S. Public*, pg. 1230
Botelho, Mauricio, Pres. & Chief Exec. Officer--Embraer-Empresa Brasileira de Aeronautica S.A., Sao Jose dos Campos, Brazil; *Int'l*, pg. 452
Bothwell, David, Pres. & Chief Exec. Officer--Howtek, Inc., Hudson, NH; *U.S. Public*, pg. 844
Botsford, David, Pres.--The Botsford Group, Atlanta, GA; *U.S. Private*, pg. 409
Bottoms, Jack, Pres.--FOCAS, Alpharetta, GA; *Int'l*, pg. 329
Bottorff, Dennis C., Chm. Bd., Pres. & Chief Exec. Officer--First American Corporation, Nashville, TN; *U.S. Public*, pg. 624
Botts, William W., Chm. Bd., Pres. & Chief Exec. Officer--O.I. Corporation, College Station, TX; *U.S. Public*, pg. 1208
Bouchard, John E., III, Chm. Bd. & Pres.--John Bouchard & Sons Company, Nashville, TN; *U.S. Private*, pg. 161
Bouchard, Michel, Pres.--Beauticontrol Cosmetics Canada Ltd., Burlington, Canada; *U.S. Public*, pg. 199
Boucher, George, Pres.--Marine Exhibition Corporation, Miami, FL; *U.S. Private*, pg. 1186
Bouchez, Jacques, Pres. & Chief Oper. Officer--The Crispin Company, Houston, TX; *U.S. Private*, pg. 290
Bouchie, L. Kirk, Reg. Pres.--Citizens Bank, Vincennes Region, Vincennes, IN; *U.S. Public*, pg. 281
Bouchon, Antoine, Honorary Pres.--Generale Sucriere SNC, Paris, France; *Int'l*, pg. 548
Bouckaert, Carl, Pres. & Chief Exec. Officer--Beaulieu Group, Dalton, GA; *U.S. Private*, pg. 127
Bouffard, Richard, Pres.--Truelove & Maclean Inc., Waterbury, CT; *U.S. Private*, pg. 1107
Bougie, Jacques, Pres. & Chief Exec. Officer--Alcan Aluminium Limited, Montreal, Canada; *Int'l*, pg. 50
Boujo, Patrick, Pres.--IPC Peripherals Pte Ltd., Singapore, Singapore; *Int'l*, pg. 651
Boulet, Jean-Claude, Pres. & Chief Exec. Officer-BDDP S.A.--BDDP Group, Paris, France; *Int'l*, pg. 116
Boulis, Gus, Chm. Bd., Pres. & Chief Exec. Officer--Miami Subs Corporation, Fort Lauderdale, FL; *U.S. Public*, pg. 1103
Boulot, Jean-Pierre, Pres. & Gen. Mgr.--Bazar de L'Hotel de Ville, Paris, France; *Int'l*, pg. 181
Boultinghouse, Marlan, Pres.--ARCO Aluminum, Russellville, KY; *U.S. Public*, pg. 144
Bourgeois, Steven J., Pres. & Chief Exec. Officer--Franklin-Lamoille Bank, Saint Albans, VT; *U.S. Public*, pg. 724
Bourke, Thomas J., Pres. & Chief Exec. Officer--Tele-Direct (Publications) Inc., Montreal, Canada; *Int'l*, pg. 116
Bourland, Curtis F., Chm. Bd., Pres. & Chief Exec. Officer--Continental Graphics Holdings, Inc., Los Angeles, CA; *U.S. Private*, pg. 268
Bourne, J.P., Pres.--Warner-Lambert K.K., Tokyo, Japan; *U.S. Public*, pg. 1739
Bourns, Gordon L., Chm. Bd. & Pres.--Bourns, Inc., Riverside, CA; *U.S. Private*, pg. 161
Bourque, Robert V., Pres.--Alaron Inc., Auburn Hills, MI; *U.S. Private*, pg. 31
Bours Castelo, Eduardo, Pres.--Industrias Bachoco S.A. de C.V., Celaya, Mexico; *Int'l*, pg. 677
Boushie, Ray, Pres.--Hydro-Aire, Burbank, CA; *U.S. Public*, pg. 457
Bouton, Daniel, Dir. Gen--Societe Generale, Paris, France; *Int'l*, pg. 1273
Boutonnet, Edward, Chm. Bd. & Pres.--Ocean Mist Farms Corp., Castroville, CA; *U.S. Private*, pg. 811
Boutwell, Wayne A., Pres. & Chief Exec. Officer--Southern States Cooperative, Inc., Richmond, VA; *U.S. Private*, pg. 1017
Bouvette, Bill, Pres.--Media Duplication International, Calgary, Canada; *Int'l*, pg. 852
Bouw, P., Pres.--KLM Royal Dutch Airlines, Amstelveen, Netherlands; *Int'l*, pg. 719
Bouw, Pieter, Pres.--KLM Royal Dutch Airlines, Elmsford, NY; *Int'l*, pg. 719
Bouysset, A., Pres.--Laboratoires Merck Sharp & Dohme S.A., Paris, France; *U.S. Public*, pg. 1092
Bova, Anthony F., Pres. & Chief Exec. Officer--Atlantis Plastic, Inc., Atlanta, GA; *U.S. Public*, pg. 145
Bovaird, W.J., Chm. Bd., Pres. & Chief Exec. Officer--Bovaird Supply Co., Tulsa, OK; *U.S. Private*, pg. 162
Bovender, Jack O., Jr., Pres. & Chief Oper. Officer--Columbia/HCA Healthcare Corporation, Nashville, TN; *U.S. Public*, pg. 403
Bowden, Al, Pres. & Chief Exec. Officer--Sencore, Inc., Sioux Falls, SD; *U.S. Private*, pg. 983
Bowden, Ashley E., Pres. & Chief Oper. Officer--QST Communications, Inc., Peoria, IL; *U.S. Public*, pg. 367
Bowden, Bill R., Pres.--Hardin's-Sysco Food Services, Inc., Memphis, TN; *U.S. Public*, pg. 1551
Bowden, Del, Pres.--First Mortgage Corporation, Omaha, NE; *U.S. Public*, pg. 501
Bowden, G.E., Gen. Mgr.--PACCAR Winch Division, Broken Arrow, OK; *U.S. Public*, pg. 1246
Bowden, Travis J., Pres. & Chief Exec. Officer--Gulf Power Company, Pensacola, FL; *U.S. Public*, pg. 1490
Bowe, Peter A., Pres. & Chief Exec. Officer--Ellicott Machine Corporation International, Baltimore, MD; *U.S. Private*, pg. 372
Bowen, Jeffrey A., Pres.--Flo-Pac Corporation, Minneapolis, MN; *U.S. Private*, pg. 414
Bowen, John, Pres.--The Robert E. Morris Company, Farmington, CT; *U.S. Private*, pg. 762
Bowen, Kevin C., Pres. & Chief Exec. Officer--K-Tron America, Inc., Pitman, NJ; *U.S. Public*, pg. 938
Bowen, Robert, Pres. & Chief Exec. Officer--COMNET Corporation, Lanham, MD; *U.S. Public*, pg. 416
Bowen, Stephen T., Pres. & Chief Exec. Officer--Polymer Composites Inc., Winona, MN; *Int'l*, pg. 624
Bowers, Alan J., Pres. & Chief Exec. Officer--MBL Life Assurance Corporation, Newark, NJ; *U.S. Private*, pg. 685
Bowers, Christopher D., Pres.--United GHS Inc., Elk Grove Village, IL; *U.S. Public*, pg. 1653
Bowers, D.D., Pres. & Chief Exec. Officer--Makino Inc., Mason, OH; *Int'l*, pg. 831
Bowers, David A., Pres.--National Cabinet Lock, Inc., Mauldin, SC; *U.S. Private*, pg. 270
Bowers, John, Pres. & Chief Exec. Officer--Southwestern Financial Services Corp., Dallas, TX; *U.S. Private*, pg. 1018
Bowie, Robert A., II, Pres.--First USA Capital Markets, Inc., Dallas, TX; *U.S. Public*, pg. 174
Bowis, John, Pres.--Chevy Chase Cars & Geo, Bethesda, MD; *U.S. Private*, pg. 234
Bowles, Crandall C., Pres. & Chief Oper. Officer--Springs Industries, Inc., Fort Mill, SC; *U.S. Public*, pg. 1499
Bowles, Robert L., Pres. & Chief Exec. Officer--D.C. Chartered Health Plan, Washington, DC; *U.S. Public*, pg. 1241
Bowlin, John, Pres.--Lender's Bagel Bakery, White Plains, NY; *U.S. Public*, pg. 1288
Bowlin, John D., Pres. & Chief Exec. Officer--Kraft Foods International, Rye Brook, NY; *U.S. Public*, pg. 1288
Bowlus, Brad, Pres.--PacifiCare of Washington, Seattle, WA; *U.S. Public*, pg. 1251
Bowlus, Brad A., Pres. & Chief Exec. Officer--PacifiCare of California, Cypress, CA; *U.S. Public*, pg. 1251
Bowman, A. Blaine, Pres. & Chief Exec. Officer--Dionex Corporation, Sunnyvale, CA; *U.S. Public*, pg. 510
Bowman, Bob, Pres.--MGM Grand Merchandising, Inc., Las Vegas, NV; *U.S. Public*, pg. 1027
Bowman, C. Don, Pres.--Hilb, Rogal & Hamilton Company of McAllen, McAllen, TX; *U.S. Public*, pg. 827
Bowman, Donald E., Pres.--Redland Genstar Stone Products Company, Hunt Valley, MD; *Int'l*, pg. 1091
Bowman, Harry W., Chm. Bd., Pres. & Chief Exec. Officer--Outboard Marine Corporation, Waukegan, IL; *U.S. Private*, pg. 478
Bowman, John, Pres.--Clover Club Foods, Inc., Kaysville, UT; *U.S. Private*, pg. 469
Bowman, John E., Pres.--Saunders Brothers, Westbrook, ME; *U.S. Private*, pg. 968
Bowman, Robert A., Pres. & Chief Oper. Officer--ITT Corporation, New York, NY; *U.S. Public*, pg. 1512
Bowman, William F., Pres.--Associated Company, Inc., Wichita, KS; *U.S. Private*, pg. 89
Box, L. Richard, Pres.--Bourns Sensors & Controls Division, Ogden, UT; *U.S. Private*, pg. 161
Box, Sam W., Chm. Bd., Pres. & Chief Exec. Officer--Foster Wheeler Environmental Corporation, Livingston, NJ; *U.S. Public*, pg. 677
Boxberger, Michael, Pres.--Korn/Ferry International, New York, NY; *U.S. Private*, pg. 633
Boxberger, Michael D., Pres.--Korn/Ferry International, Los Angeles, CA; *U.S. Private*, pg. 632
Boxer, S.J., Pres.--Unitary Products Group, York, PA; *U.S. Public*, pg. 1788
Boyadjieff, George, Pres. & Chief Exec. Officer--Varco International, Inc., Orange, CA; *U.S. Public*, pg. 1709
Boyan, William L., Jr., Pres. & Chief Oper. Officer--John Hancock Mutual Life Insurance Company, Boston, MA; *U.S. Private*, pg. 589
Boyce, Donald N., Chm. Bd., Pres. & Chief Exec. Officer--IDEX Corporation, Northbrook, IL; *U.S. Public*, pg. 862
Boyce, G. H., Pres. & Chief Exec. Officer--Kennecott Energy and Coal Company, Salt Lake City, UT; *Int'l*, pg. 1119
Boyce, Michael, Pres.--Harris Chemical Group, Inc., New York, NY; *U.S. Private*, pg. 505
Boyd, Dennis, Pres. & Chief Exec. Officer--Royal Waterbeds, Maryland Heights, MO; *U.S. Private*, pg. 949
Boyd, Dennis, Pres. & Chief Exec. Officer--Boyd Flotation, Inc, Maryland Heights, MO; *U.S. Private*, pg. 949
Boyd, Ed, Pres.--Harman Speaker Manufacturing, Northridge, CA; *U.S. Public*, pg. 787
Boyd, Michael L., Pres. & Chief Exec. Officer--San Angelo National Bank, San Angelo, TX; *U.S. Public*, pg. 633
Boyd, Ralph E., Pres. & Chief Oper. Officer--Cascade Natural Gas Corporation, Seattle, WA; *U.S. Public*, pg. 311
Boyd, Robert M., Pres. & Chief Admin. Officer--First Virginia Bank of Tidewater, Norfolk, VA; *U.S. Public*, pg. 642
Boyea, Bruce W., Pres. & Chief Exec. Officer--Security Mutual Life Insurance Co. of New York, Binghamton, NY; *U.S. Private*, pg. 981
Boyer, David S., Pres. & Chief Exec. Officer--Teleflex Incorporated, Plymouth Meeting, PA; *U.S. Public*, pg. 1569
Boyer, L.E., Pres.--Polyloom Corp. of America, Dayton, TN; *U.S. Private*, pg. 875
Boyer, Rahn, Pres. & Chief Exec. Officer--Gem-Dandy, Inc., Madison, NC; *U.S. Private*, pg. 442
Boyer, Richard, Pres. & Chief Exec. Officer--Stoneville Furniture Co. Inc., Stoneville, NC; *U.S. Private*, pg. 1045
Boyers, Pat, Pres.--Executive Software, Glendale, CA; *U.S. Private*, pg. 388
Boyette, John V., Pres. & Mng. Dir.--Geraghty & Miller, Inc., Denver, CO; *Int'l*, pg. 607
Boykin, Edward P., Pres.--CSC Pinnacle Alliance, New York, NY; *U.S. Public*, pg. 423
Boykin, Robert W., Pres.--Boykin Lodging Co., Cleveland, OH; *U.S. Public*, pg. 249
Boylan, Michael J., Pres.--The National Enquirer, New York, NY; *U.S. Public*, pg. 87
Boylan, Michael J., Pres.--NDSI, Inc., Lantana, FL; *U.S. Public*, pg. 87
Boylan, Michael J., Pres.--Weekly World News, Inc., Lantana, FL; *U.S. Public*, pg. 87
Boylan, Michael J., Pres.--Country Weekly, Inc., Lantana, FL; *U.S. Public*, pg. 87
Boyle, Jim, Pres.--United Dairymen of Arizona, Tempe, AZ; *U.S. Private*, pg. 1121
Boyle, Kevin, Pres.--Schulze & Burch Biscuit Company, Chicago, IL; *U.S. Private*, pg. 973
Boyle, Matt, Pres. & Chief Exec. Officer--Tech/Ops Sevcon, Inc., Boston, MA; *U.S. Public*, pg. 1563
Boyle, R.E., Chm. Bd., Pres. & Chief Exec. Officer--Ormet Corporation, Wheeling, WV; *U.S. Private*, pg. 820
Boyle, Richard A., Pres.--Patton Management, Inc., Atlanta, GA; *U.S. Private*, pg. 843
Boyle, Richard A., Pres.--Wright & Lopez, Inc., Atlanta, GA; *U.S. Private*, pg. 843
Boyle, Richard A., Pres.--Wright & Lopez of Alabama, Inc., Birmingham, AL; *U.S. Private*, pg. 844
Boyle, William, Pres.--Cardio Data Services, Haddonfield, NJ; *U.S. Private*, pg. 1114
Boyles, Robert M., Pres.--Mellon Capital Management Corporation (MFSC 1085
Boyman, Russell, Mng. Partner-Brdcst.--Mediapolis, London, United Kingdom; *Int'l*, pg. 853
Boze, Jimmy R., Chm. Bd., Pres. & Chief Exec. Officer--The Security Bank, Harrison, Harrison, AR; *U.S. Public*, pg. 630
Bozniak, Murray, Pres.--Home Depot Canada, Scarborough, Canada; *U.S. Public*, pg. 832
Bozuwa, Paul, Pres.--Capital City Press, Inc., Berlin, VT; *U.S. Private*, pg. 205
Bozym, Charles P., Pres.--Somat Corporation, Coatesville, PA; *U.S. Public*, pg. 1322
Bozzuto, Michael A., Pres., Chief Exec. Officer & Treas.--Bozzuto's Inc., Cheshire, CT; *U.S. Public*, pg. 249
Braam, Ronald, Pres.--Manufacturers Soap & Chemical Co., Cleveland, TN; *U.S. Public*, pg. 1548
Bracewell, Joseph S., Chm. Bd., Pres. & Chief Exec. Officer--Century Bancshares, Inc., Washington, DC; *U.S. Public*, pg. 328
Brach, Robert W., Pres.--Central Florida Press L.C., Orlando, FL; *U.S. Public*, pg. 291
Brachman, Merom, Pres.--Yenkin-Majestic Paint Corporation, Columbus, OH; *U.S. Private*, pg. 1195
Bracken, Frank D., Pres. & Chief Oper. Officer--Haggar Corporation, Dallas, TX; *U.S. Public*, pg. 774
Bradbury, Christopher, Pres.--Contaminant Recovery Systems, Centredale, RI; *U.S. Public*, pg. 592
Bradbury, David, Chm. Bd. & Pres.--Bradbury Company, Inc., Moundridge, KS; *U.S. Private*, pg. 163
Bradbury, Richard F., Pres.--Ceco Door Products, Oklahoma City, OK; *U.S. Public*, pg. 1676
Braddock, James L., Chm. Bd., Pres. & Treas.--Fastec Industrial, Elkhart, IN; *U.S. Private*, pg. 397
Bradfield, William S., Pres. & Sr. V.P.--Sathers Inc., Round Lake, MN; *U.S. Private*, pg. 397
Bradford, Greg, Pres.--Aerospatiale Inc., Washington, DC; *Int'l*, pg. 29
Bradford, Gregory R., Pres.-Mktg. Systems Grp. & Mng. Dir.-CACI Ltd.--CACI International Inc, Arlington, VA; *U.S.* Public, pg. 272
Bradford, J.W., Jr., Pres.--AFG Industries, Inc., Kingsport, TN; *Int'l*, pg. 84
Bradley, Bruce, Pres. & Publr.--The Virginian-Pilot, Norfolk, VA; *U.S. Private*, pg. 649
Bradley, C.C., Pres.--Sharp Laboratories of Europe, Ltd., Oxford, United Kingdom; *Int'l*, pg. 1230
Bradley, Charles E., Chm. Bd., Pres. & Chief Exec. Officer--Reunion Industries, Inc., Stamford, CT; *U.S. Public*, pg. 1383
Bradley, David R. Jr., Editor & Publisher--News-Press & Gazette Company, Saint Joseph, MO; *U.S. Private*, pg. 797
Bradley, Kirk J., Pres.--Lee-Moore Oil Co., Inc., Sanford, NC; *U.S. Private*, pg. 657
Bradley, Richard, Pres.--Missouri Medical Insurance Company, Saint Louis, MO; *U.S. Public*, pg. 1080
Bradshaw, David L., Chm. Bd., Pres. & Chief Exec. Officer--Tipperary Corporation, Denver, CO; *U.S. Public*, pg. 1618
Bradshaw, Robert, Pres.--Boon Edam Inc., Salt Lake City, UT; *Int'l*, pg. 202
Bradstock, John, Pres.-N. & Central America--DDB Needham Worldwide Inc., New York, NY; *Int'l*, pg. 357
Bradstock, John, Pres.-N. & Central America--DDB Needham Worldwide Inc., New York, NY; *U.S. Public*, pg. 1223
Brady, Brian J., Chm. Bd., Pres. & Chief Exec. Officer--Dominguez Services Corporation, Long Beach, CA; *U.S. Public*, pg. 516
Brady, Francis P., Pres. & Sr. V.P.-Television Division--Viacom Broadcasting Inc., New York, NY; *U.S. Private*, pg. 778
Brady, Frank, Pres. & Chief Exec. Officer--Brady Marketing Company, Pacheco, CA; *U.S. Private*, pg. 165
Brady, Jack D., Chm. Bd., Pres. & Chief Exec. & Oper. Officer--Crown Andersen Inc., Peachtree City, GA; *U.S. Public*, pg. 462
Brady, John, Pres.--Brady Enterprises, Inc., East Weymouth, MA; *U.S. Private*, pg. 165

Brady, John, Chief Exec. Officer & Pres.--Excelsior Manufacturing & Supply Corp., Itasca, IL; *U.S. Private*, pg. 387
Brady, Joseph F., Pres.--Centrilift, Claremore, OK; *U.S. Public*, pg. 167
Brady, Larry D., Pres.--FMC Corporation, Chicago, IL; *U.S. Public*, pg. 604
Brady, Patrick J., Pres. & Chief Exec. Officer--Semiconductor Equipment Group, Scotts Valley, CA; *U.S. Public*, pg. 1745
Brady, Philip, Pres.--Thomas G. Ferguson Associates, Inc., Parsippany, NJ; *Int'l*, pg. 1483
Brady, Robert, Pres. & Chief Exec. Officer--First NH Mortgage Corp., Hooksett, NH; *Int'l*, pg. 153
Brady, Robert T., Chm. Bd., Pres. & Chief Exec. Officer--Moog Incorporated, East Aurora, NY; *U.S. Public*, pg. 1127
Brady, Rodney, Pres.--Deseret Management Corporation, Salt Lake City, UT; *U.S. Private*, pg. 327
Bragdon, Serge, Pres. & Chief Exec. Officer--Uniboard Canada Inc., Laval, Canada; *Int'l*, pg. 1431
Bragg, Paul A., Pres. & Chief Oper. Officer--Pride International, Inc., Houston, TX; *U.S. Public*, pg. 1324
Bragg, Russ, Pres.--ConAgra Poultry Co., Duluth, GA; *U.S. Public*, pg. 427
Bragiel, Jerry, Pres. & Chief Exec. Officer--Champion Parts, Inc., Glen Ellyn, IL; *U.S. Public*, pg. 334
Braginsky, Sidney, Pres.--Olympus America Inc., Melville, NY; *Int'l*, pg. 1005
Brainin, Garry, Chm. Bd. & Pres.--Altair Corporation, Lincolnshire, IL; *U.S. Private*, pg. 46
Braithwaite, J. Lorne, Pres. & Chief Exec. Officer--Cambridge Shopping Centres Limited, Toronto, Canada; *Int'l*, pg. 253
Braka, Ivor, Chm. Bd. & Pres.--United States Realty & Investment Co., New York, NY; *U.S. Private*, pg. 1125
Brakhan, Andrew, Pres.--Sennheiser Electronic Corp., Old Lyme, CT; *U.S. Private*, pg. 984
Braksick, N.A., Pres.--Asgrow Seed Company, Kalamazoo, MI; *Int'l*, pg. 1048
Braman, Norman, Pres.--Braman World Car Center, Miami, FL; *U.S. Private*, pg. 165
Bramble, David C., Pres. & Chief Oper. Officer--David A. Bramble, Inc., Chestertown, MD; *U.S. Private*, pg. 165
Bramble, Frank P., Pres. & Chief Exec. Officer--First Maryland Bancorp, Baltimore, MD; *Int'l*, pg. 64
Bramer, Kurt R., Pres.--Kinney Vacuum Company, Canton, MA; *U.S. Private*, pg. 1110
Bramley, B.D., Chm. Bd.--British-American Tobacco Co. Ltd., Staines, United Kingdom; *Int'l*, pg. 111
Bramley, Christopher, Pres. & Chief Exec. Officer--Safety Fund National Bank, Fitchburg, MA; *U.S. Public*, pg. 278
Bramsen, James, Pres.--Spraying Systems Co., Wheaton, IL; *U.S. Private*, pg. 1026
Branch, Malcolm, Pres.--Abitec, Columbus, OH; *Int'l*, pg. 92
Branchaude, Michel, Pres.--Infradev International, Montreal, Canada; *Int'l*, pg. 249
Branche, Francois, Pres. & Chief Exec. Officer--Calberson, Paris, France; *Int'l*, pg. 549
Branco, Joao Paulo Castel, Pres. & Creative Dir.--Cineponto/Leo Burnett Publicidade Lda., Lisbon, Portugal; *U.S. Private*, pg. 184
Brande, Marybeth, Partner-Creative Copy--Lewis Gace Bozell Healthcare Worldwide, Fort Lee, NJ; *U.S. Public*, pg. 1642
Brandenberg, Frank, Pres. & Chief Exec. Officer--EA Industries, West Long Branch, NJ; *U.S. Public*, pg. 541
Brandenberg, Frank, Pres.--Tanon Manufacturing, Inc., West Long Branch, NJ; *U.S. Public*, pg. 541
Brandfon, Bruce L., Pres.--SuperValu, Inc.-Quincy Div., Quincy, FL; *U.S. Public*, pg. 1540
Brandli, Hanspeter, Chm. Bd. & Pres.--Danzas Holding Ltd., Basel, Switzerland; *Int'l*, pg. 382
Brandon, David A., Chm. Bd., Pres. & Chief Exec. Officer--Valassis Communications, Inc., Livonia, MI; *U.S. Public*, pg. 1704
Brandt, Brad, Pres.--William Bayley/Folger Adam Security, Inc., Springfield, OH; *U.S. Private*, pg. 125
Brandt, David N., Pres. & Chief Exec. Officer--Dresdner Bank Canada, Toronto, Canada; *Int'l*, pg. 419
Brandt, Steve, Pres. & Publr.--Democrat & Chronicle, Rochester, NY; *U.S. Public*, pg. 699
Brandt, Tom, Pres.--Bivona Inc., Gary, IN; *Int'l*, pg. 818
Brandt, William A., Jr., Pres. & Chief Exec. Officer--Mercury Finance Co., Lake Forest, IL; *U.S. Public*, pg. 1093
Braniff, Thomas M, Pres.--Texas Instruments Consulting, Houston, TX; *U.S. Public*, pg. 1586
Branjord, Gregory A., Pres.--The Jones Store Co., Kansas City, MO; *U.S. Public*, pg. 1090
Brant, James, Pres.--Ampco Auto System Parking, Los Angeles, CA; *U.S. Public*, pg. 2
Brant, Peter, Pres.--Brant Allen Industries, Inc., Greenwich, CT; *U.S. Private*, pg. 165
Branthoover, Kim, Partner & Grp. Acct. Dir.--TLPartnership, Dallas, TX; *U.S. Public*, pg. 1224
Brantley, L. Wayne, Pres.--Lanier Clothes, Atlanta, GA; *U.S. Public*, pg. 1239
Branyan, Bruce H., Pres.--Business Markets Organization, Overland Park, KS; *U.S. Public*, pg. 1500
Bras, Robert W., Pres.--Menu Foods, Inc., Pennsauken, NJ; *U.S. Private*, pg. 731
Braswell, Gary, Pres. & Chief Exec. Officer--MPD, Inc., Owensboro, KY; *U.S. Private*, pg. 687
Bratter, Robert, Pres.--SVG Track Systems, San Jose, CA; *U.S. Public*, pg. 1474
Braud, Marcel, Chm. Bd. & Pres.--Manitou BF, Ancenis, France; *Int'l*, pg. 834
Brauer, Bernie, Pres.--Unocal Canada Limited, Calgary, Canada; *U.S. Public*, pg. 1698
Brauer, Kevin E., Pres.--National Integrated Services, Overland Park, KS; *U.S. Public*, pg. 1500
Brault, Lionel, Pres.--Kendo, Puteaux, France; *Int'l*, pg. 601
Brault, Philippe, Pres.--Banque Francaise Commerciale, Paris, France; *Int'l*, pg. 313
Braum, William H., Pres. & Chief Exec. Officer--Braum Ice Cream Stores Inc., Oklahoma City, OK; *U.S. Private*, pg. 166
Brauman, Murray, Partner--Yesawich, Moss & Brown, New York, NY; *U.S. Private*, pg. 1196
Braun, Edward H., Pres. & Chief Exec. Officer--Veeco Instruments, Inc., Plainview, NY; *U.S. Public*, pg. 1711
Braun, John A., Pres.--Amprobe Instrument, Lynbrook, NY; *U.S. Public*, pg. 1676
Braun, Ron, Pres.--PsyCare, Atlanta, GA; *U.S. Public*, pg. 888
Braun, Stanley, Pres., Chief Exec. Officer & Chief Oper. Officer--Pac Rim Holding Corporation, Woodland Hills, CA; *U.S. Public*, pg. 1246
Braunheim, Stephen, Pres.--California Manufacturing Enterprises, Corona, CA; *U.S. Private*, pg. 201
Braunlich, Heiko, Pres.--Kvaerner Ships Equipment GmbH, Bremen, Germany; *Int'l*, pg. 768
Braunlich, Heiko, Pres.--Kvaerner Brug (Deutschland) GmbH, Bremen, Germany; *Int'l*, pg. 771
Brauns, Jurgen, Pres.--Babcock Textilmaschinen GmbH, Seevetal, Germany; *Int'l*, pg. 399
Brause, Eckard, Pres.--Berkshire Industries, Inc., Westfield, MA; *U.S. Private*, pg. 136
Brausel, W., Pres. & Chief Exec. Officer--Fisk Electric Company, Houston, TX; *Int'l*, pg. 16
Bravo, Juan, Pres.--Harbison-Walker Refractories, Pittsburgh, PA; *U.S. Public*, pg. 748
Brawner, E.I., Pres.--ICI Canada Inc., North York, Canada; *Int'l*, pg. 664
Bray, Jack, Pres.--R.A. Briggs & Co., Lake Zurich, IL; *U.S. Private*, pg. 536
Bray, Michael E., Pres.--Deutsche Babcock-Riley International Inc., Worcester, MA; *Int'l*, pg. 401
Bray, Michael E., H., Pres. & Chief Oper. Officer--Riley Consolidated, Inc., Worcester, MA; *Int'l*, pg. 401
Brayton, Roswell, Jr., Pres., Chief Exec. Officer & Chief Fin. Officer--Woolrich, Inc., Woolrich, PA; *U.S. Private*, pg. 1188
Brazell, Carl, Co-Pres.--Metromedia International Telecommunications, Inc., Stamford, CT; *U.S. Public*, pg. 1103
Brazier, Robert G., Pres. & Chief Oper. Officer--Airborne Freight Corporation, Seattle, WA; *U.S. Public*, pg. 32
Braznell, Gerald, Pres. & Chief Exec. Officer--Heritage Inks International, Edison, NJ; *U.S. Private*, pg. 524
Breakstone, Ronald, Pres.--Refrigiwear, Inc., Dahlonega, GA; *U.S. Private*, pg. 917
Brearley, Charles T., Pres.--John O. Butler Co., Chicago, IL; *Int'l*, pg. 1320
Brecht, Robert P., Pres. & Chief Exec. Officer--Peoples Savings Bank of Ashtabula, Ashtabula, OH; *U.S. Public*, pg. 647
Breed, Johnnie Cordell, Pres. & Chief Oper. Officer--Breed Technologies, Inc., Lakeland, FL; *U.S. Public*, pg. 251
Breen, Donald D., Pres. & Chief Exec. Officer--Brothers Gourmet Coffees, Inc., Boca Raton, FL; *U.S. Public*, pg. 259
Breen, Edward, Pres.--Broadband Networks Group, Hatboro, PA; *U.S. Public*, pg. 716
Breen, Neil, Pres. & Chief Oper. Officer--Callaghan & Company, Deerfield, IL; *U.S. Public*, pg. 1601
Bregou, Christian, Chm. & Chief Exec. Officer--C.E.P. Communication Group, Paris, France; *Int'l*, pg. 239
Brehm, Bill, Jr., Pres.--Brehm Communications Inc., San Diego, CA; *U.S. Private*, pg. 166
Breiner, James, Pres.--Baltimore Business Publications, Inc., Baltimore, MD; *U.S. Private*, pg. 19
Breitzka, Steve, Pres.--Fisher Pierce Division, Weymouth, MA; *U.S. Public*, pg. 1250
Brem, Michael M., Pres.--Gilroy Foods, Inc., Gilroy, CA; *U.S. Public*, pg. 428
Breme, Herald, Pres.--Schumag AG, Aachen, Germany; *Int'l*, pg. 399
Bremner, Ron, Pres. & Chief Exec. Officer--Calgary Flames Hockey Club, Calgary, Canada; *Int'l*, pg. 252
Bremond, John H., Pres.--Kaufman and Broad-Monterey Bay, Inc., Salinas, CA; *U.S. Public*, pg. 945
Brenan, Michael R., Chm. Bd., Pres. & Chief Exec. Officer--MainStreet BankGroup Incorporated, Martinsville, VA; *U.S. Public*, pg. 1038
Brennan, J., Pres.--Crane Valves/North American, Joliet, IL; *U.S. Public*, pg. 457
Brennan, J.H., Pres. & Chief Exec. Officer--Commemorative Brands, Inc., Austin, TX; *U.S. Private*, pg. 258
Brennan, John J., Chm., Pres. & Chief Exec. Officer--The Vanguard Group, Inc., Valley Forge, PA; *U.S. Private*, pg. 1133
Brennan, Michael J., Pres.--Micromatic Textron, Holland, MI; *U.S. Public*, pg. 1589
Brennan, Michael P., Pres. & Chief Exec. Officer--Deer Park Federal Savings and Loan Association, Cincinnati, OH; *U.S. Public*, pg. 66
Brennan, Robert B., Pres. & Chief Exec. Officer--Manitoba Hydro, Winnipeg, Canada; *Int'l*, pg. 834
Brennan, Robert J., Pres. & Chief Oper. Officer--American Institute for Foreign Study, Greenwich, CT; *U.S. Private*, pg. 56
Brennan, Terrence, Pres.--Research Data Corp, Haddonfield, NJ; *U.S. Private*, pg. 1114
Brenneman, Gregory D., Pres. & Chief Oper. Officer--Continental Airlines, Houston, TX; *U.S. Public*, pg. 439
Brenner, Beth Fuchs, Publisher--Self, New York, NY; *U.S. Private*, pg. 20
Brenner, Stanley, Pres.--CV Reit, Inc., West Palm Beach, FL; *U.S. Public*, pg. 286
Brenninkmeyer, Roland, Pres. & Chief Exec. Officer--American Retail Group, New York, NY; *U.S. Private*, pg. 61
Bresge, Les, Pres.--Kamro Lighting Products Ltd., Rexdale, Canada; *Int'l*, pg. 725
Bresky, Harry, Pres.--Seaboard Flour Corporation, Newton, MA; *U.S. Public*, pg. 1449
Breslawsky, Marc C., Pres. & Chief Oper. Officer--Pitney Bowes Inc., Stamford, CT; *U.S. Public*, pg. 1303
Breslin, Thomas J., Pres. & Gen. Mgr.--Martin Electronics, Inc., Perry, FL; *U.S. Private*, pg. 709
Bresnahan, William J., Pres.--Hynes Industries Inc., Youngstown, OH; *U.S. Private*, pg. 552
Bressanelli, Jerome P., Pres.--Canton Drop Forge, Canton, OH; *U.S. Private*, pg. 205
Bresser, N. de Ronde, Pres.-Bd. of Mngmt.--Hollandsche Beton Groep NV, Rijswijk, Netherlands; *Int'l*, pg. 630
Breton, Mike, Pres.--Mapa Pioneer Corporation, Willard, OH; *Int'l*, pg. 1409
Brettschneider, Stan, Pres.--Green Bus Lines, Inc., Jamaica, NY; *U.S. Private*, pg. 476
Breuer, Linda S., Pres. & Chief Exec. Officer--Breuer/Tornado, Chicago, IL; *U.S. Private*, pg. 167
Brevard, J. Rolan, Pres.--Professional Food Systems, El Dorado, AR; *U.S. Public*, pg. 427
Brevenik, John R., Pres. & Chief Oper. Officer--Herberts-O'Brien Inc., Houston, TX; *Int'l*, pg. 626
Brewer, C. James, Pres.--Burgess-Norton Mfg. Co., Geneva, IL; *U.S. Private*, pg. 68
Brewer, Don, Pres.--Brewer Oil Co., Artesia, NM; *U.S. Private*, pg. 167
Brewer, Mark, Pres.--Falley's Inc., Topeka, KS; *U.S. Private*, pg. 1202
Brewer, Patrick, Pres.--Grandville Printing Company, Grandville, MI; *U.S. Private*, pg. 469
Brewer, Pinckney W., Pres.--The Brewer Company, Milford, OH; *U.S. Private*, pg. 167
Brewer, William, Pres.--Cornell Forge Company, Chicago, IL; *U.S. Private*, pg. 276
Brewton, Kenneth, Jr., Pres. & Chief Exec. Officer--Clariant Corporation, Charlotte, NC; *Int'l*, pg. 624
Breyer, Robert, Pres. & Chief Oper. Officer--Alkeremes, Cambridge, MA; *U.S. Public*, pg. 41
Brian, Steven, Pres. & Chief Oper. Officer--Home Products International, Inc., Chicago, IL; *U.S. Public*, pg. 832
Brian, William A., Pres. & Chief Exec. Officer--Brian Unlimited Distribution Company, Inc., Detroit, MI; *U.S. Private*, pg. 167
Brice, Hal, Pres. & Creative Dir.--Heil-Brice Retail Advertising, Newport Beach, CA; *U.S. Private*, pg. 519
Brick, Bill, Pres. & Chief Oper. Officer--Suiza Foods Corporation, Dallas, TX; *U.S. Public*, pg. 1526
Brick, Frank E., Pres., Chief Oper. Officer & Chief Exec. Officer--Telxon Corporation, Akron, OH; *U.S. Public*, pg. 1573
Brickel, Jack W., Pres., Chief Exec. & Chief Oper. Officer--BEC Inc., Richmond, MI; *U.S. Private*, pg. 106
Brickley, James A., Pres. & Chief Exec. Officer--Federal Farm Credit Banks Funding Corporation, Jersey City, NJ; *U.S. Private*, pg. 398
Bridge, Gordon, Pres.--AT&T Strategy & New Service Innovations, Parsippany, NJ; *U.S. Public*, pg. 11
Bridge, Larry, Pres.--Pacificare of Utah, Salt Lake City, UT; *U.S. Public*, pg. 1251
Bridges, L. Michael, Pres.--Columbia Atlantic Trading Corporation, Wilmington, DE; *U.S. Public*, pg. 402
Bridges, Paul, Pres. & Treas.--Bridges & Company, Inc., Pittsburgh, PA; *U.S. Private*, pg. 168
Bridgewater, B.A., Jr., Chm. Bd., Pres., & Chief Exec. Officer--Brown Group, Inc., Saint Louis, MO; *U.S. Public*, pg. 262
Bridgman, Larry W., Pres.--Simmons Outdoor Corporation, Tallahassee, FL; *U.S. Public*, pg. 238
Bridgman, Tim, Pres. & Chief Exec. Officer--United States Cold Storage, Inc., Cherry Hill, NJ; *U.S. Private*, pg. 1124
Briere, Denis, Pres.--Scierie Parent Inc., Trois Rivieres, Canada; *Int'l*, pg. 761
Brierley, Harold M., Chm. Bd. & Pres.--Brierley & Partners, Dallas, TX; *U.S. Private*, pg. 168
Brierley, Ron, Sir, Pres.--Brierley Investments Limited, Wellington, New Zealand; *Int'l*, pg. 215
Brierley, Sir. Ronald Alfred, Chm. Bd.--BIL (Far East Holdings) Ltd., Hong Kong, Hong Kong; *Int'l*, pg. 215
Brigante, David F., Pres.--Nu-Kote International, Dallas, TX; *U.S. Public*, pg. 1205
Briggs, Douglas S., Pres.--QVC, Inc., West Chester, PA; *U.S. Public*, pg. 407
Briggs, Douglas S., Pres.--QVC, Inc., West Chester, PA; *U.S. Private*, pg. 897
Briggs, Douglas S., Pres.--QVC, Inc., West Chester, PA; *U.S. Public*, pg. 1555
Briggs, K. Douglas, Pres. & Treas.--Quincy Mutual Fire Insurance Company, Quincy, MA; *U.S. Private*, pg. 901
Briggs, R. Stephen, Pres.--Empire General Life Assurance Corporation, Birmingham, AL; *U.S. Public*, pg. 1336
Briggs, Robert S., Chm. Bd., Pres. & Chief Exec. Officer--Bangor Hydro-Electric Company, Bangor, ME; *U.S. Public*, pg. 178
Briggs, Thomas, Pres.--B-Line Systems, Inc., Highland, IL; *U.S. Public*, pg. 1471
Brigham, James R., Jr., Pres.--Diagraph Corporation, Earth City, MO; *U.S. Private*, pg. 330
Bright, Harvey W., Pres. & Chief Exec. Officer--Engineered Specialty Plastics, Hot Springs National Park, AR; *U.S. Public*, pg. 583
Bright, Stanley J., Pres. & Chief Exec. Officer--MidAmerican Energy Holdings, Des Moines, IA; *U.S. Public*, pg. 1109
Brightbill, William R., Pres. & Treas.--Ritter Bros., Inc., Harrisburg, PA; *U.S. Private*, pg. 933
Brill, Edward T., Pres.--GS Electric, Carlisle, PA; *U.S. Public*, pg. 726
Brill, Martin, Pres.--Tweeds, Inc., Weehawken, NJ; *U.S. Public*, pg. 782
Brilliant, Dave, Pres.--Sporto Corp., Boston, MA; *U.S. Private*, pg. 1026
Brindle, A.W., Pres. & Chief Exec. Officer--Wards Cove Packing Company, Seattle, WA; *U.S. Private*, pg. 1149
Brining, David R., Pres., Chief Oper. & Chief Exec. Officer--Valley Forge Corporation, San Rafael, CA; *U.S. Public*, pg. 1705

Brink, Douglas, Pres.--Brink Electric Construction Company, Rapid City, SD; *U.S. Private*, pg. 169
Brink, John, Assoc. Publisher--Mother Earth News, New York, NY; *U.S. Private*, pg. 1056
Brinkley, Bert, Pres.--Plastic Packaging, Inc., Hickory, NC; *U.S. Private*, pg. 871
Brinkley, George T., Pres.--W.R. Case & Sons Cutlery Company, Bradford, PA; *U.S. Private*, pg. 1207
Brinkman, Lloyd D., Chm. Bd., Chief Exec. & Chief Oper. Officer--LDB Corporation, Kerrville, TX; *U.S. Private*, pg. 639
Brinkman, Martha, Pres.--Furniture In Parts, Inc., New York, NY; *U.S. Private*, pg. 432
Brinkmeyer, Marc A., Pres.--Riley Creek Lumber Company, Laclede, ID; *U.S. Private*, pg. 931
Brinson, A. Vernon, Pres.--Royal Oldsmobile Mazda, Inc., Metairie, LA; *U.S. Private*, pg. 948
Brinson, Danny, Pres.--Bunny Bread Co., Inc., New Orleans, LA; *U.S. Public*, pg. 657
Brinzo, John S., Pres. & Chief Exec. Officer--Cleveland-Cliffs Inc, Cleveland, OH; *U.S. Public*, pg. 386
Brisbon, Eric, Pres.--Ambac International Corp., Columbia, SC; *U.S. Private*, pg. 48
Brisebois, Mark F., Pres.--Excelis, Inc., Dallas, TX; *U.S. Public*, pg. 625
Briskie, Julius, Pres.--Pace Press, Inc., Moonachie, NJ; *U.S. Private*, pg. 829
Briskin, Bernard, Chm. Bd., Pres. & Chief Exec. Officer--Arden Group, Inc., Los Angeles, CA; *U.S. Public*, pg. 128
Britt, William R., Chm. Bd., Pres. & Chief Exec. Officer--Palmer-American National Bank, Danville, IL; *U.S. Public*, pg. 1217
Brittelle, Douglas J., Pres.--Compool Corporation, Mountain View, CA; *U.S. Public*, pg. 592
Brittingham, James L., Pres.--Rollex Corporation, Elk Grove Village, IL; *U.S. Private*, pg. 941
Britzke, Robert W., Pres.--Rogers Tool Works, Inc., Rogers, AR; *U.S. Public*, pg. 950
Brizzolara, Bruce J., Pres. & Chief Exec. Officer--Eversharp Pen Co., Franklin Park, IL; *U.S. Private*, pg. 386
Brletich, Frank, Pres.--LinkUSA Corporation, Cedar Rapids, IA; *U.S. Private*, pg. 684
Broad, Eli, Chm. Bd., Pres. & Chief Exec. Officer--SunAmerica Inc., Los Angeles, CA; *U.S. Public*, pg. 1532
Broad, John W., Pres. & Chief Exec. Officer--Broad, Vogt & Conant, Inc., Detroit, MI; *U.S. Private*, pg. 170
Broad, Robert C., Pres.--CCL Label, Burlington, Canada; *Int'l*, pg. 238
Broad, Robert C., Pres.--CCL Label, Winnipeg, Canada; *Int'l*, pg. 238
Broadbent, Peter C., Pres.--Wahlstrom & Company, Stamford, CT; *U.S. Public*, pg. 1641
Broadhead, Michael, Mng. Dir.--Heywood Williams Group PLC, Huddersfield, United Kingdom; *Int'l*, pg. 618
Broadhurst, Joseph D., Pres.--Integrated Material Handling Company, Oshkosh, WI; *Int'l*, pg. 1397
Broady, George, Pres. & Chief Exec. Officer--Ultrak Inc., Lewisville, TX; *U.S. Public*, pg. 1663
Broas, Matthew, Pres.--Harbour Island, Inc., Tampa, FL; *U.S. Public*, pg. 211
Brochart, J., Pres.--Van Leer Singapore Pte. Ltd., Jurong, Singapore; *Int'l*, pg. 1147
Brock, Gary, Pres.--Symplex Communications Corp., Ann Arbor, MI; *U.S. Private*, pg. 1060
Brock, Gunnar, Pres.--Tetra Pak, Lund, Sweden; *Int'l*, pg. 1378
Brock, J. Don, Chm. Bd. & Pres.--Astec Industries, Inc., Chattanooga, TN; *U.S. Public*, pg. 141
Brock, Jerry, Pres.--Jacobs Applied Technology, Inc., Orangeburg, SC; *U.S. Public*, pg. 921
Brock, Scott T., Pres.--E.W. Blanch Wholesale Insurance Services Inc., Minneapolis, MN; *U.S. Public*, pg. 236
Brock, Steve G., Pres. & Gen. Mgr--WCIV, LLC, Mount Pleasant, SC; *U.S. Private*, pg. 854
Brocke, Dean, Pres.--George F. Brocke & Sons, Inc., Kendrick, ID; *U.S. Private*, pg. 170
Brockman, Ron, Pres.--Stegner Food Products Co., Cincinnati, OH; *U.S. Private*, pg. 1039
Brod, Irven J., Chm. Bd. & Pres.--Empire Diamond Corporation, New York, NY; *U.S. Private*, pg. 374
Brodd, Ulf K., Pres--Bensons, Gloucester, United Kingdom; *Int'l*, pg. 460
Brode, Michael, Pres. & Treas.--Broder Bros. Co., Plymouth, MI; *U.S. Private*, pg. 170
Broderick, John J., Pres.--Judd's Incorporated, Washington, DC; *U.S. Private*, pg. 855
Brodeur, A.W., Chm. Bd., Pres. & Chief Exec. Officer--Cassidy's Ltd., Brossard, Canada; *Int'l*, pg. 275
Brodey, Larry, Pres.--Durst Corporation, Mountainside, NJ; *U.S. Private*, pg. 349
Brodey, Larry, Pres.--Jaclo Inc., Mountainside, NJ; *U.S. Private*, pg. 349
Brodie, Nancy S., Pres.--Independence Square Properties, Philadelphia, PA; *U.S. Private*, pg. 849
Brody, Marvin D., Chm. Bd., Pres. & Chief Exec. Officer--Employee Solutions, Inc., Phoenix, AZ; *U.S. Public*, pg. 579
Broekema, Dirk, Jr., Pres.--Centennial Federal Savings Bank F.S.B., Durango, CO; *U.S. Public*, pg. 1793
Brogan, R. Alan, Pres. & Chief Exec. Officer--North American Van Lines, Inc., Fort Wayne, IN; *U.S. Public*, pg. 1191
Brojack, William, Owner--William Brojack Lumber Company, Olyphant, PA; *U.S. Private*, pg. 171
Brolin, Anders, Pres.--Stora Project, Solna, Sweden; *Int'l*, pg. 899
Brolin, Anders, Pres.--NCC Stora Projelet, Solna, Sweden; *Int'l*, pg. 899
Bromberg, Sam, Partner-Creative Copy--Lewis Gace Bozell Healthcare Worldwide, Fort Lee, NJ; *U.S. Public*, pg. 1642
Bromley, D.E.G., Pres.--TriWaste Reduction Services Inc., Calgary, Canada; *Int'l*, pg. 1424
Bromley, Peter, Pres.-Agrichemicals--Elf Atochem North America, Agrichemicals Div., Philadelphia, PA; *Int'l*, pg. 446
Bromley, Wayne L., Jr., Pres. & Chief Exec. Officer--Giles & Ransome, Inc., Bensalem, PA; *U.S. Private*, pg. 453
Broms, Edward, Pres.--AGA Gas C.A., Caracas, Venezuela; *Int'l*, pg. 13
Bronchetti, Robert J., Pres., Chief Exec. Officer & Chief Oper. Officer--National Auto Credit Inc., Solon, OH; *U.S. Public*, pg. 1152
Bronfman, Edgar, Jr., Pres. & Chief Exec. Officer--The Seagram Company Ltd., Montreal, Canada; *Int'l*, pg. 1214
Bronfman, Sam, II, Pres.--Seagram Chateau & Estate Wines Co., New York, NY; *Int'l*, pg. 1215
Bronstein, Gerald M., Pres.--Bomaine Corporation, Santa Monica, CA; *U.S. Private*, pg. 155
Brookfield, David A., Pres.--Brookfield Engineering Laboratories, Inc., Stoughton, MA; *U.S. Private*, pg. 171
Brookman, Amber M., Pres. & Chief Exec. Officer--Brookwood Companies Inc., New York, NY; *U.S. Public*, pg. 777
Brooks, Barlow W., Jr., Pres. & Chief Exec. Officer--Roll Forming Corporation, Shelbyville, KY; *U.S. Private*, pg. 941
Brooks, Craig, Pres. & Chief Exec. Officer--Key Mortgage Services, Inc., Cleveland, OH; *U.S. Public*, pg. 954
Brooks, David R., Pres.--American Airlines Cargo, Fort Worth, TX; *U.S. Public*, pg. 9
Brooks, Diana D., Pres. & Chief Exec. Officer--Sotheby's Holdings Inc., New York, NY; *U.S. Public*, pg. 1487
Brooks, Diana D., Pres. & Chief Exec. Officer--Sotheby's Inc., New York, NY; *U.S. Public*, pg. 1487
Brooks, Heather, Pres.--Atlas Pen & Pencil Corporation, Hollywood, FL; *U.S. Private*, pg. 96
Brooks, J.O., Pres.--Bay Area Bancshares, Redwood City, CA; *U.S. Private*, pg. 124
Brooks, James R., Pres. & Chief Exec. Officer--Global Special Risks, Inc. Holdings, Metairie, LA; *Int'l*, pg. 1503
Brooks, James R., Pres. & Chief Exec. Officer--Global Special Risks, Inc. of Houston, Houston, TX; *Int'l*, pg. 1503
Brooks, Jay W., Pres.--Brooks, Montague & Associates, Inc., Chattanooga, TN; *U.S. Public*, pg. 1155
Brooks, Kim, Pres.--Kaufman and Broad New Mexico Division, Albuquerque, NM; *U.S. Public*, pg. 945
Brooks, Landon E., Pres.--Gits Manufacturing Company, Inc., Creston, IA; *U.S. Public*, pg. 1705
Brooks, Mike, Chm. Bd., Pres. & Chief Exec. Officer--Rocky Shoes & Boots, Inc., Nelsonville, OH; *U.S. Public*, pg. 1402
Brooks, Richard E.T., Chm., Pres. & Chief Exec. Officer--ChemDesign Corporation, Fitchburg, MA; *Int'l*, pg. 173
Brooks, Roger, Pres. & Chief Exec. Officer--American Mutual Life Holding Co., Des Moines, IA; *U.S. Private*, pg. 59
Brooks, Wendell, Pres. & Sec.--Wood Group Pressure Control, Houston, TX; *U.S. Public*, pg. 1775
Brookshire, R. A., Chm. Bd. & Pres.--Brookshire Bros., Ltd., Lufkin, TX; *U.S. Private*, pg. 172
Brophy, George T., Chm. Bd., Pres. & Chief Exec. Officer--ABT Building Products Corporation, Neenah, WI; *Int'l*, pg. 20
Brophy, Thomas J., Pres.--Universal Fidelity Life Insurance Company, Duncan, OK; *U.S. Private*, pg. 1127
Brosig, Thomas, Pres.--Grand Casinos, Inc., Minnetonka, MN; *U.S. Public*, pg. 758
Brosius, Andy, Pres., Chief Oper. Officer--Midwest Industries, Inc., Ida Grove, IA; *U.S. Private*, pg. 744
Brosnahan, William P., Pres.--Colad Group Inc., Buffalo, NY; *U.S. Private*, pg. 250
Brost, Jay, Pres. & Chief Exec. Officer--Miniature Precision Components, Walworth, WI; *U.S. Private*, pg. 750
Brotsky, Aaron, Pres.--Al & Ed's Auto Sound Center, Monterey Park, CA; *U.S. Private*, pg. 30
Brotzman, Rich, Pres. & Dir. Gen.--Hallmark Mexicana, S. de R.I. de C.V., Mexico, Mexico; *U.S. Private*, pg. 496
Broughton, T. Gary, Pres.--GPU Nuclear Corp., Parsippany, NJ; *U.S. Public*, pg. 695
Brouse, John S., Pres. & Chief Exec. Officer--Highmark Inc., Pittsburgh, PA; *U.S. Private*, pg. 528
Broussaud, Charles-Henri, Pres.--Calberson, Paris, France; *Int'l*, pg. 1163
Browder, Edward H., Pres.--Unitrode Corporation, Merrimack, NH; *U.S. Public*, pg. 1694
Brower, William R., Pres.--Brower Products, Cincinnati, OH; *U.S. Private*, pg. 172
Brown, Andy, Pres. & Chief Oper. Officer--El Paso Baking Co., Inc., El Paso, TX; *U.S. Public*, pg. 657
Brown, Arthur, Chm. Bd., Pres. & Chief Exec. Officer--Hecla Mining Company, Coeur D'Alene, ID; *U.S. Public*, pg. 803
Brown, Arthur V., V.P.-Opers. & Tech. Services--The Jim Dandy Co., Inc., Atlanta, GA; *Int'l*, pg. 918
Brown, Betty L., Pres.--Meldrum & Fewsmith Directory Marketing, Cleveland, OH; *U.S. Private*, pg. 730
Brown, Bill, Pres.--Mezzina/Brown Inc., New York, NY; *U.S. Private*, pg. 739
Brown, Bruce, Pres.--Vertel, Woodland Hills, CA; *U.S. Public*, pg. 1717
Brown, C. Terry, Pres. & Chief Exec. Officer--Atlas Hotels, Inc., San Diego, CA; *U.S. Private*, pg. 96
Brown, Carter, Pres. & Chief Exec. Officer--Omega Performance Group, Sausalito, CA; *U.S. Private*, pg. 816
Brown, Charles, Chm. Bd., Pres. & Chief Exec. Officer--Bayou State Oil Corporation, Shreveport, LA; *U.S. Private*, pg. 125
Brown, Christopher A., Pres. & Chief Oper. Officer--Rotelle, Inc., West Point, PA; *U.S. Public*, pg. 1389
Brown, D., Pres.--Tempo Instrument Inc., Commack, NY; *Int'l*, pg. 208
Brown, Dale, Pres. & Chief Exec. Officer--Sive/Young & Rubicam L.P., Cincinnati, OH; *U.S. Private*, pg. 1197
Brown, David J., Pres.--Morgan Distribution, Mechanicsburg, PA; *U.S. Public*, pg. 1132
Brown, Denis, Pres. & Chief Exec. Officer--Pinkerton's Inc., Encino, CA; *U.S. Public*, pg. 1296
Brown, Donald, Pres. & Chief Oper. Officer--Slant/Fin Corporation, Greenvale, NY; *U.S. Private*, pg. 1005
Brown, Douglas R., Pres. & Chief Exec. Officer--Advent International, Boston, MA; *U.S. Private*, pg. 22
Brown, Douglas W., Pres.--Pace Industries Puget Division, Inc., Tacoma, WA; *U.S. Public*, pg. 986
Brown, Duncan, Pres.--Epitronics, Inc., Mesa, AZ; *U.S. Public*, pg. 12
Brown, E. H., Chm. Bd. & Partner--Brown Marketing Communications, Chicago, IL; *U.S. Private*, pg. 174
Brown, Earle Palmer, Founder--Earle Palmer Brown, New York, NY; *U.S. Private*, pg. 173
Brown, Eddie R., Pres.--Landstar Ranger, Inc., Jacksonville, FL; *U.S. Public*, pg. 978
Brown, Edward C., Pres. & Treas.--Bill Brown Ford Inc., Livonia, MI; *U.S. Private*, pg. 173
Brown, Edwin C., Pres.--Feed Service Corp., Ohiowa, NE; *U.S. Private*, pg. 399
Brown, Eric, Pres.--Pro-Line Corporation, Dallas, TX; *U.S. Private*, pg. 887
Brown, Franklin, Pres.--BHP Trading Inc., Long Beach, CA; *Int'l*, pg. 226
Brown, Franklin D., Pres. & Chief Exec. Officer--Pharmacia & Upjohn Deltec, Inc., Arden Hills, MN; *Int'l*, pg. 1049
Brown, Franklin, Sr., Pres.--F.M. Brown Sons, Inc., Birdsboro, PA; *U.S. Private*, pg. 174
Brown, Glenn, Pres.--Contract Freighters, Inc., Joplin, MO; *U.S. Private*, pg. 270
Brown, Greg, Pres.--Ameritech Custom Business Services, Chicago, IL; *U.S. Public*, pg. 98
Brown, Greg, Pres.-Suntec USA--Suntec Industries Inc., Rockford, IL; *U.S. Private*, pg. 1054
Brown, Henry E., Pres.--Brown & Brown Venture Group, LLC, Mesa, AZ; *U.S. Private*, pg. 172
Brown, Hyatt, J., Chm. Bd., Pres. & Chief Exec. Officer--Poe & Brown, Inc., Daytona Beach, FL; *U.S. Public*, pg. 1312
Brown, I. Larry, Pres. & Chief Exec. Officer--Rollins Leasing Corp., Wilmington, DE; *U.S. Public*, pg. 1405
Brown, J. Bruce, Chm. Bd. & Chief Exec. Officer--Lambert Smith Hampton, London, United Kingdom; *Int'l*, pg. 797
Brown, J.S., III, Pres.--Bruce Foods Corp., Cade, LA; *U.S. Private*, pg. 175
Brown, Jack, Pres.--Stater Brothers Holdings, Colton, CA; *U.S. Public*, pg. 456
Brown, Jack W., Chm. Bd., Pres. & Chief Exec. Officer--Gish Biomedical, Inc., Irvine, CA; *U.S. Public*, pg. 745
Brown, Jack W., Pres.--Gish International, Inc., Irvine, CA; *U.S. Public*, pg. 745
Brown, James, Pres. & Chief Exec. Officer--Union Planters Bank of Mississippi, Grenada, MS; *U.S. Public*, pg. 1669
Brown, Jay W., Pres. & Chief Exec. Officer--Du Pont Protein Technologies International, Saint Louis, MO; *U.S. Public*, pg. 531
Brown, Jeremy E., Sr. Mng. Partner--Earle Palmer Brown, New York, NY; *U.S. Private*, pg. 173
Brown, John W., Chm. Bd., Pres. & Chief Exec. Officer--Stryker Corporation, Kalamazoo, MI; *U.S. Public*, pg. 1525
Brown, Joseph W., Chm. Bd., Pres. & Chief Exec. Officer--Talegen Corporation, Seattle, WA; *U.S. Public*, pg. 1784
Brown, Joseph W., Jr., Chm.--San Francisco Insurance Company (U.K.) Ltd., London, United Kingdom; *Int'l*, pg. 59
Brown, Kathye W., Pres., Chief Exec. Officer, V.P. & Corp. Sec.--Brown Evans Distributing Co., Mesa, AZ; *U.S. Private*, pg. 174
Brown, Marvin P., Pres. & Chief Exec. Officer--Mace Security International, Inc., Bennington, VT; *U.S. Public*, pg. 1030
Brown, Marvin R., M.D., Pres.--Alanex Corporation, San Diego, CA; *U.S. Public*, pg. 28
Brown, Mel, Pres.--Square D Canada, Mississauga, Canada; *Int'l*, pg. 1209
Brown, Michael, Pres. & Chief Oper. Officer--Litton Industries, Inc., Woodland Hills, CA; *U.S. Public*, pg. 1002
Brown, Michael, Pres.--Wayne Wire Cloth Products, Inc., Kalkaska, MI; *U.S. Private*, pg. 1155
Brown, Michael C., Pres.--Ryland Mortgage Co., Columbia, MD; *U.S. Public*, pg. 1414
Brown, Michael S., Pres. & Chief Oper. Officer--Wometco Enterprises, Inc., Coral Gables, FL; *U.S. Private*, pg. 1186
Brown, Milton R., Chm. Bd., Pres. & Chief Exec. Officer--Suntec Industries Inc., Rockford, IL; *U.S. Private*, pg. 1054
Brown, Nicholas M., Jr., Pres. & Chief Oper. Officer--NAC Re Corp., Greenwich, CT; *U.S. Public*, pg. 1144
Brown, Nicholas M., Jr., Pres. & Chief Exec. Officer--NAC Reinsurance Corporation, Greenwich, CT; *U.S. Public*, pg. 1144
Brown, Paul, Pres.--Liquid Molding Systems, Inc., Midland, MI; *U.S. Public*, pg. 125
Brown, Paul, Pres.--Wedge Energy Group Inc., Houston, TX; *U.S. Private*, pg. 1158
Brown, Peter C., Pres. & Chief Fin. Officer--AMC Entertainment, Inc., Kansas City, MO; *U.S. Private*, pg. 6
Brown, Phil, Pres.--Noble House Hotels and Resorts, Kirkland, WA; *U.S. Private*, pg. 800
Brown, R. Donald, Chm. Bd., Pres. & Chief Exec. Officer--Imperial Tobacco Limited, Montreal, Canada; *Int'l*, pg. 112
Brown, R. Frank, Pres. & Chief Exec. Officer--Arthur Treacher's, Inc., Jacksonville, FL; *U.S. Public*, pg. 136
Brown, R.W., Pres.--Baymont Technologies Inc., Clearwater, FL; *Int'l*, pg. 31
Brown, Randy, Pres. & Chief Exec. Officer--Agsco, Inc., Grand Forks, ND; *U.S. Private*, pg. 27
Brown, Richard J., Pres.--HGC Bank, Chicago, IL; *Int'l*, pg. 154

Brown, Richard L., Pres.--Rockford Mercantile Agency, Rockford, IL; *U.S. Public*, pg. 65

Brown, Richard L., Pres. & Chief Exec. Officer--Houston General Insurance Co., Fort Worth, TX; *Int'l*, pg. 1392

Brown, Richard M., Pres. & Chief Exec. Officer--Golden West Baseball Club, Anaheim, CA; *U.S. Private*, pg. 461

Brown, Robert E., Pres. & Chief Oper. Officer--Bombardier Aerospace, Dorval, Canada; *Int'l*, pg. 200

Brown, Ronald A., Pres. & Chief Exec. Officer--Calcor Space Facility, Inc., Whittier, CA; *U.S. Private*, pg. 200

Brown, Ronald D., Pres. & Chief Exec. Officer--Sales Technologies, Atlanta, GA; *U.S. Public*, pg. 395

Brown, Stanton F., Pres.--Windsor Shade Tobacco Company, Inc., Hartford, CT; *U.S. Private*, pg. 1182

Brown, Stewart, Chief Exec. Officer & Mng. Dir.--BWI Plc, Altrincham, United Kingdom; *Int'l*, pg. 130

Brown, Suzanne, Mng. Partner-Fin. & Opers.--Gillespie Public Relations, Princeton, NJ; *U.S. Private*, pg. 454

Brown, Thomas G., Chm., Pres. & Chief Exec. Officer--Duncanson & Holt, New York, NY; *U.S. Public*, pg. 1699

Brown, Thomas V., Pres. & Chief Exec. Officer--Caraustar Industries, Inc., Austell, GA; *U.S. Public*, pg. 303

Brown, Timothy C., Chm. Bd., Pres. & Chief Exec. Officer--Thomas Industries Inc., Louisville, KY; *U.S. Public*, pg. 1598

Brown, W.C., Pres. & Chief Exec. Officer--B C Sugar Refinery, Ltd., Vancouver, Canada; *Int'l*, pg. 103

Brown, W.M., Pres.--Thomson U.S. Inc., Stamford, CT; *U.S. Public*, pg. 1601

Brown, Wayne W., Pres. & Chief Exec. Officer--Willis Corroon Corp. of Louisiana, New Orleans, LA; *Int'l*, pg. 1506

Brown, Willis E., Jr., Pres.--Brown Motors, Toledo, OH; *U.S. Private*, pg. 174

Brown, Woods R., Pres., Chief Exec. Officer & Treas.--Kingsbury, Inc., Philadelphia, PA; *U.S. Private*, pg. 622

Browne, David M., Pres. & Chief Exec. Officer--Lenscrafters, Cincinnati, OH; *Int'l*, pg. 822

Browne, Gregg, Pres. & Gen. Mgr.--Loga Athletic/Headwear Inc., Mattapoisett, MA; *U.S. Public*, pg. 1644

Browne, Stephen B., Pres. & Chief Exec. Officer--All American Bottling Corp., Oklahoma City, OK; *U.S. Private*, pg. 34

Browne, Stephen B., Pres. & Chief Exec. Officer--All-American Bottling Financial Corp., Oklahoma City, OK; *U.S. Private*, pg. 34

Brownell, Jon, Pres.--Monte Vista Co-Op Association, Inc., Monte Vista, CO; *U.S. Private*, pg. 758

Browning, Frederick M., Pres.--Browning Chemical Corporation, White Plains, NY; *U.S. Private*, pg. 175

Browning, James R., Pres.--Elk Supply Company, Clinton, OK; *U.S. Private*, pg. 371

Browning, Peter C., Pres. & Chief Oper. Officer--Sonoco Products Company, Hartsville, SC; *U.S. Public*, pg. 1485

Browsky, Dick, Pres.--Bando America, Inc., Itasca, IL; *Int'l*, pg. 145

Broyles, Joseph R., Pres. & Chief Oper. Officer--Indianapolis Water Company, Indianapolis, IN; *U.S. Public*, pg. 1185

Brozman, Jack L., Chm. Bd., Pres. & Chief Exec. Officer--Concorde Career Colleges, Inc., Kansas City, MO; *U.S. Public*, pg. 430

Brualdi, Ulysses J., Jr., Pres. & Chief Exec. Officer--ADT Security Services, Inc., Aurora, CO; *U.S. Public*, pg. 1649

Brubaker, Bob, Pres.--Clark Filter, Lancaster, PA; *U.S. Public*, pg. 381

Brubaker, Robert P., Chm. Bd., Pres. & Chief Exec. Officer--King & Prince Seafood Corporation, Brunswick, GA; *U.S. Private*, pg. 620

Bruce, Jim, Pres. & Publisher--The Windsor Star, Windsor, Canada; *Int'l*, pg. 632

Bruce, Rick, Pres.--Puritan/Churchill Chemical Company, Atlanta, GA; *U.S. Private*, pg. 895

Bruce, Robert, Pres.--International Correspondence Schools (Australasia) Limited, Lane Cove, Australia; *U.S. Public*, pg. 784

Bruce, Tom B., Pres.--Bruce Industries, Inc., Dayton, NV; *U.S. Private*, pg. 175

Bruce, William B., Pres.--BB&T Savings Bank, Elkin, NC; *U.S. Public*, pg. 160

Bruch, Karl F., III, Pres.--Sherwood, Lockport, NY; *U.S. Public*, pg. 793

Brucker, Gerald, Pres.--AlliedSignal Controls & Accessories, South Bend, IN; *U.S. Public*, pg. 50

Bruder, Thomas A., Pres.--M.A.B. Paints, Terre Haute, IN; *U.S. Private*, pg. 175

Bruder, Thomas A., Jr., Pres.--M.A. Bruder & Sons, Incorporated, Broomall, PA; *U.S. Private*, pg. 175

Bruell, Pierre, Pres. & Chief Exec. Officer--Polarome International, Jersey City, NJ; *U.S. Private*, pg. 874

Bruenger, M.W., Pres.--M. Bruenger & Co., Inc., Wichita, KS; *U.S. Private*, pg. 175

Bruggeman, Steven, Pres.-Cat Pumps Div.--Diversified Dynamics Corporation, Minneapolis, MN; *U.S. Private*, pg. 336

Bruggeman, Steven, Pres.--Cat Pumps Corporation, Minneapolis, MN; *U.S. Private*, pg. 336

Bruggeman, Thomas, Pres.-Homeright Div.--Diversified Dynamics Corporation, Minneapolis, MN; *U.S. Private*, pg. 336

Bruggeting, Johannes S., Pres.--Boole & Babbage Europe, Foxrock, Ireland; *U.S. Public*, pg. 245

Bruggisser, Philipppe, Pres. & Chief Exec. Officer--The Swissair Group, Zurich, Switzerland; *Int'l*, pg. 1333

Bruijn, F.J.A.N., Pres.--Spaarbeleg N.V., Nieuwegein, Netherlands; *Int'l*, pg. 26

Bruk, Manuel, Pres. & Gen. Mgr.--Cyanamid Mexico, Mexico, Mexico; *U.S. Public*, pg. 81

Brum, Roger, Pres.--Southwest Aerospace, Tustin, CA; *Int'l*, pg. 853

Brumback, Emerson L., Pres. & Chief Exec. Officer--Bank One, Cincinnati, Cincinnati, OH; *U.S. Public*, pg. 173

Brumley, Jimmy, Pres.--SouthTrust Bank of Marion County, Hamilton, AL; *U.S. Public*, pg. 1492

Brun, Henry, Pres.--Amsco School Publications, Inc., New York, NY; *U.S. Private*, pg. 67

Brunell, Charles A., Mng. Dir.--Novo Nordisk Bioindustrials, Inc., Danbury, CT; *Int'l*, pg. 987

Brunell, Val E., Pres.--Janssen/Ortho Inc., North York, Canada; *U.S. Public*, pg. 930

Brunet, Pierre, Pres.--Bourgey Montreuil, Mery-sur-Seine, France; *Int'l*, pg. 549

Brunetti, Wayne H., Pres. & Chief Oper. Officer--New Century Energies, Inc., Denver, CO; *U.S. Public*, pg. 1170

Brunetti, Wayne H., Pres. & Chief Exec. Officer--Public Service Company of Colorado, Denver, CO; *U.S. Public*, pg. 1170

Brunetti, Wayne H., Pres.--1480 Welton, Inc., Denver, CO; *U.S. Public*, pg. 1170

Brunetti, Wayne H., Pres.--P.S.R. Investments, Inc., Denver, CO; *U.S. Public*, pg. 1170

Brunetti, Wayne H., Pres.--P.S. Colorado Credit Corp., Denver, CO; *U.S. Public*, pg. 1170

Brunner, M. F., Pres.--Brunner & Lay, Inc., Springdale, AR; *U.S. Private*, pg. 176

Bruno, Joseph M., Chm. Bd. & Chief Exec. Officer--Dixie Brewing Co., Inc., New Orleans, LA; *U.S. Private*, pg. 336

Bruno, Kendra Elliott, Pres.--Dixie Brewing Co., Inc., New Orleans, LA; *U.S. Private*, pg. 336

Bruno, Mark, Pres.--All Seasons Services, Inc., Braintree, MA; *U.S. Private*, pg. 35

Bruno, Robert, Pres.--Reily Electrical Supply, Inc., Metairie, LA; *U.S. Private*, pg. 919

Brunton, John C., Pres. & Gen. Mgr.--Kysor Panel Systems, Portland, OR; *U.S. Public*, pg. 1445

Brunton, Richard, Pres.--JMCT Publicidad, New York, NY; *U.S. Private*, pg. 599

Brunton, Tim, Pres.--Chr. Hansen Limited (Canada), Mississauga, Canada; *Int'l*, pg. 288

Brush, Douglas, Pres.--Sentry Group, Rochester, NY; *U.S. Private*, pg. 984

Brust, Tom, Pres.--Micropure Medical, Inc., White Bear Lake, MN; *U.S. Private*, pg. 743

Brutger, Larry, Chm. Bd. & Pres.--Brutger Equities, Inc., Saint Cloud, MN; *U.S. Private*, pg. 176

Brutsche, H.R., III, Chm. Bd., Pres. & Chief Exec. Officer--Vari-Lite International, Dallas, TX; *U.S. Public*, pg. 1709

Bruzelius, Jan, Pres. & Chief Exec. Officer--IL Returpapper, Stockholm, Sweden; *Int'l*, pg. 646

Bruzelius, Jan, Pres. & Chief Exec. Officer--IL Sekretess, Stockholm, Sweden; *Int'l*, pg. 646

Bryan, F. Sibley, Jr., Pres. & Chief Exec. Officer--Chipman-Union, Inc., Union Point, GA; *U.S. Private*, pg. 237

Bryan, J. Stewart, III, Chm. Bd., Pres. & Chief Exec. Officer--Media General, Inc., Richmond, VA; *U.S. Public*, pg. 1077

Bryan, J.P., Pres. & Chief Exec. Officer--Gulf Canada Resources Ltd., Calgary, Canada; *Int'l*, pg. 577

Bryan, John H., III, Pres. & Chief Exec. Officer--Bryan Foods, West Point, MS; *U.S. Public*, pg. 1433

Bryan, L. Merill, Jr., Pres. & Chief Exec. Officer--Union Pacific Technologies, Saint Louis, MO; *U.S. Public*, pg. 1668

Bryan, W. Lester, Pres. & Chief Oper. Officer--The Washington Water Power Company, Spokane, WA; *U.S. Public*, pg. 1744

Bryant, C. Edward, Jr., Pres.--Continental Conveyor & Equipment Company, Winfield, AL; *U.S. Private*, pg. 791

Bryant, Chuck, Pres.--UPB of East Tennessee, Knoxville, TN; *U.S. Public*, pg. 1669

Bryant, Douglas E., Dr., Pres.--Foseco Holding Inc., Cleveland, OH; *Int'l*, pg. 234

Bryant, Dudley E., Pres. & Chief Exec. Officer--Advanced Separation Technologies Incorporated, Lakeland, FL; *U.S. Public*, pg. 655

Bryant, Harry M., Sr., Pres.--Bryant Electric Supply Company, Inc., Lowell, NC; *U.S. Private*, pg. 177

Bryant, Matthew C., Pres.--Carat MBS, New York, NY; *U.S. Private*, pg. 208

Bryant, Robert, Pres.--Bryant, Fulton & Shee, Vancouver, Canada; *U.S. Private*, pg. 678

Bryant, Ronald D., Pres.--Masters Inc., Gaithersburg, MD; *U.S. Private*, pg. 714

Bryant, Stephen D., World Editor--The Upper Room, Nashville, TN; *U.S. Private*, pg. 1129

Bryant, Warren, Pres.--Dillon Companies, Inc., Hutchinson, KS; *U.S. Public*, pg. 967

Bryce, John D., Pres.--Bryce LLC Corporation, Memphis, TN; *U.S. Private*, pg. 177

Bryfonski, Dedria, Pres. & Chief Exec. Officer--Gale Research Inc., Detroit, MI; *U.S. Public*, pg. 1600

Brymer, Bob, Pres.-Air Filtration Prods.--AAF-International, Louisville, KY; *U.S. Private*, pg. 3

Bryson, Tom, Pres.--WJRT-TV, Flint, MI; *U.S. Public*, pg. 984

Brzezinski, Francis, Pres. & Chief Oper. Officer--Wisvest Corporation, Milwaukee, WI; *U.S. Public*, pg. 1773

Buccellato, Carl, Chm. Bd., Pres. & Chief Exec. Officer--Homeowners Group, Inc., Sunrise, FL; *U.S. Public*, pg. 832

Bucci, Anthony L., Pres. & Chief Exec. Officer--MARC, Pittsburgh, PA; *U.S. Private*, pg. 701

Buchan, William S., Pres.--Terex Trucks, Tulsa, OK; *U.S. Public*, pg. 1581

Buchanan, D.M., Pres.--Long Reach Holdings Inc., Houston, TX; *U.S. Private*, pg. 675

Buchanan, David R., Chm. Bd., Pres. & Chief Exec. Officer--Three-Five Systems, Tempe, AZ; *U.S. Public*, pg. 1604

Buchanan, James, Pres.--Concord Specialty Corp., Batesville, AR; *U.S. Private*, pg. 177

Buchanan, James K., Pres.--Super Food Services, Inc., Miamisburg, OH; *U.S. Public*, pg. 1152

Buchanan, Robert C., Pres. & Chief Exec. Officer--Fox Valley Corporation, Appleton, WI; *U.S. Private*, pg. 422

Buchanan, W.F., Pres.--MHI Lithograph Printing, Lincolnshire, IL; *Int'l*, pg. 874

Buchel, Andre P., Pres. & Chief Exec. Officer--Sulzermedica USA Inc., Angleton, TX; *Int'l*, pg. 1307

Bucher, Larry C., Pres.--Lloyd Properties, Los Angeles, CA; *U.S. Private*, pg. 672

Buchwald, Per, Pres.--Granzow A/S, Glostrup, Denmark; *Int'l*, pg. 678

Buck, Charles B., Pres.--County Tool & Abrasive, Santee, CA; *U.S. Private*, pg. 177

Buck, Charles T., Chm. Bd., Pres. & Chief Exec. Officer--Buck Knives, Inc., El Cajon, CA; *U.S. Private*, pg. 177

Buck, Manfred, Pres. & Chief Exec. Officer--Maison Mathieu, S.A., Antwerp, Belgium; *Int'l*, pg. 846

Buck, Stephen, Chief Oper. Officer--Container Tooling Corporation, Neptune, NJ; *U.S. Public*, pg. 617

Buckee, James W., Dr., Pres. & Chief Exec. Officer--Talisman Energy Inc., Calgary, Canada; *Int'l*, pg. 1352

Buckland, Arthur R., Pres. & Chief Exec. Officer--C.P. Clare Corporation, Beverly, MA; *U.S. Public*, pg. 382

Buckler, Steven N., Pres. & Sec.--ACS Industries, Inc., Woonsocket, RI; *U.S. Private*, pg. 3

Buckler, Steven N., Pres.--ACS Industries, Inc., Fiber Operation, Woonsocket, RI; *U.S. Private*, pg. 4

Buckley, Bob, Pres. & Chief Exec. Officer--Meridian Neuro Care, Newport Beach, CA; *U.S. Public*, pg. 839

Buckley, Charles, Pres. & Chief Exec. Officer--John Brown Plastics Machinery, Attleboro, MA; *Int'l*, pg. 773

Buckley, George, Pres.--U.S. Electrical Motor Division, Saint Louis, MO; *U.S. Public*, pg. 573

Buckley, James J., Pres. & Chief Exec. Officer--CBT Systems USA Ltd., Menlo Park, CA; *U.S. Public*, pg. 275

Buckley, Maurice, Pres. & Chief Exec. Officer--Pamarco Technologies, Inc., New Providence, NJ; *U.S. Private*, pg. 835

Buckley, Susan, Partner & Sr. V.P.--Media That Works, Cincinnati, OH; *U.S. Private*, pg. 727

Buckley, Walter W., III, Pres. & Chief Exec. Officer--Internet Capital Group, Wayne, PA; *U.S. Public*, pg. 1425

Buckman, Frederick W., Pres. & Chief Exec. Officer--PacifiCorp, Portland, OR; *U.S. Public*, pg. 1251

Buckman, Leonard C., Pres.--Meritor Wabco Vehicle Control Systems, Troy, MI; *U.S. Public*, pg. 1096

Buckman, Robert H., Pres. & Chief Exec. Officer--Bulab Holdings, Inc., Memphis, TN; *U.S. Private*, pg. 180

Buckwalter, Alan R., III, Vice Chm. & Pres.--Texas Commerce Bank, Houston, TX; *U.S. Public*, pg. 339

Buda, Frank, Pres. & Gen. Mgr.--Santa Rosa Steel Forming, Inc., Santa Rosa, CA; *U.S. Private*, pg. 965

Budd, Kenneth R., Pres.--Lofts Seed, Inc., Winston Salem, NC; *U.S. Public*, pg. 29

Buddemeyer, David, Pres., Chief Exec. Officer & Chief Oper. Officer--Servico, Inc., West Palm Beach, FL; *U.S. Public*, pg. 1462

Buddig, William C., Pres.--Carl Buddig & Company, Homewood, IL; *U.S. Private*, pg. 178

Budig, George J., Pres.--George E. Fern Company, Cincinnati, OH; *U.S. Private*, pg. 178

Budig, Otto M., Jr., Pres.--Budco Group Inc., Cincinnati, OH; *U.S. Private*, pg. 178

Budney, Albert J., Jr., Pres. & Chief Oper. Officer--Niagara Mohawk Power Corporation, Syracuse, NY; *U.S. Public*, pg. 1181

Budolfsen, Elsebeth, Pres.--ALK A/S, Horsholm, Denmark; *Int'l*, pg. 288

Bue, Robert L., Pres.--Norwest Bank La Crosse, N.A., La Crosse, WI; *U.S. Public*, pg. 1202

Buechler, Bradley B., Pres. & Chief Exec. Officer--Spartech Corporation, Clayton, MO; *U.S. Public*, pg. 1495

Buell, Erik, Pres.--Buell Motorcycle Company, East Troy, WI; *U.S. Public*, pg. 786

Buenger, C. G., Pres.--Modern Equipment Co., Inc., Port Washington, WI; *U.S. Private*, pg. 33

Buerkle, Howard, Pres.--Melru Corporation, Ramsey, NJ; *U.S. Public*, pg. 933

Buerkle, W.W., Pres.--Buerkle Buick-Honda Co., Saint Paul, MN; *U.S. Private*, pg. 178

Buettner, Thomas W., Dr., Chm. Bd., Pres. & Chief Exec. Officer--Ruetgers-Nease Corporation, State College, PA; *Int'l*, pg. 1148

Buff, Helen, Pres.--Penny Plate, Inc., Cherry Hill, NJ; *U.S. Private*, pg. 850

Buffett, Warren E., Chm. Bd. & Chief Exec. Officer--Berkshire Hathaway Inc., Omaha, NE; *U.S. Public*, pg. 217

Buffington, Douglas A., Pres., Chief Oper. & Fin. Officer & Treas.--Square Two Golf Incorporated, Fairfield, NJ; *U.S. Public*, pg. 1501

Buford, E.R., Pres. & Chief Exec. Officer--Temtex Industries Inc., Dallas, TX; *U.S. Public*, pg. 1575

Buford, E.R., Pres. & Chief Exec. Officer--Temco Fireplace Products, Inc., Nashville, TN; *U.S. Public*, pg. 1576

Buha, Stephen, Pres.--Great Lakes Peterbilt, GMC, Portage, IN; *U.S. Private*, pg. 475

Buhler, Alfred P., Chm., Pres. & Chief Exec. Officer--Bank of America Canada, Toronto, Canada; *U.S. Public*, pg. 182

Buhler, Michael O., Pres. & Chief Oper. Officer--Old Dominion Box Co., Inc., Madison Heights, VA; *U.S. Private*, pg. 814

Buhr, Dale R., Pres.--Industrial Powder Coatings, Inc., Norwalk, OH; *U.S. Public*, pg. 894

Buis, Mike, Pres.--Goshen Rubber Co., Inc., Goshen, IN; *U.S. Private*, pg. 465

Buitoni, G.L.L., Pres. & Chief Exec. Officer--Ferrari North America, Inc., Englewood Cliffs, NJ; *Int'l*, pg. 483

Bujold, Remi, Pres.--GPC Government Policy Consultants (Quebec), Quebec, Canada; *U.S. Public*, pg. 1225

Bukaty, Michael E., Pres. & Chief Oper. Officer--Latshaw Enterprises, Inc., Wichita, KS; *U.S. Public*, pg. 979

Bukowick, P.A., Pres.--Alliant Techsystems (Aerospace Division), Wilmington, DE; *U.S. Public*, pg. 47

Bulcao, Gilberto, Pres.--Becton Dickinson Ind. Cirurgicas, S.A., Sao Paulo, Brazil; *U.S. Public*, pg. 200

Bulduc, John, Partner--HIG Capital Management, Miami, FL; *U.S. Private*, pg. 490

Bull, Marshall R., Chm. Bd. & Pres.--Industrial Wire Products Corporation, Pomona, CA; *U.S. Private*, pg. 561
Bull, Matthew, Creative Partner--Bull Calvert Pace, Cape Town, South Africa; *U.S. Private*, pg. 678
Bull, Stewart, Chm.-UK & Europe--CME KHBB, London, United Kingdom; *Int'l*, pg. 241
Bull, William H., Pres. & Chief Exec. Officer--McNaughton-McKay Electric Co., Madison Heights, MI; *U.S. Private*, pg. 724
Bullard, Edward D., Pres. & Chief Exec. Officer--E.D. Bullard Company, Cynthiana, KY; *U.S. Private*, pg. 180
Bullock, B.L., Pres. & Chief Exec. Officer--Intera Information Technologies Corp., Calgary, Canada; *Int'l*, pg. 1424
Bullock, James R., Jr., Pres. & Treas.--Environmental Air Systems, Inc., Greensboro, NC; *U.S. Private*, pg. 378
Bullock, Jim, Pres. & Chief Exec. Officer--Laidlaw Inc., Burlington, Canada; *Int'l*, pg. 259
Bullock, Lester, Pres.--Europa Cruises Corporation, Saint Petersburg, FL; *U.S. Public*, pg. 595
Bullock, R.C., Chm. Bd. & Pres.--Curt Bullock Builders, Inc., Danville, IL; *U.S. Private*, pg. 180
Bullock, Thomas, Pres. & Chief Exec. Officer--Ocean Spray Cranberries, Inc., Middleboro, MA; *U.S. Private*, pg. 811
Bulthaup, Gerd, Pres.--Bulthaup GmbH & Co., Aich, Germany; *Int'l*, pg. 1410
Bulych, Sam, Pres.--Torchinsky Engineering Ltd, Calgary, Canada; *Int'l*, pg. 31
Buma, Toshinori, Deputy Pres.--The Hokkaido Takushoku Bank, Ltd., Sapporo, Japan; *Int'l*, pg. 626
Bumby, Edward W., Pres. & Chief Exec. Officer--Ripon Foods, Inc., Ripon, WI; *U.S. Private*, pg. 931
Bumenauer, Leo, Pres.--Advanced Distribution System, Inc., Columbus, OH; *U.S. Public*, pg. 911
Bump, Milo, Pres.--Texas Copy Systems, Inc., Austin, TX; *U.S. Public*, pg. 864
Bunce, John, Pres.--SATEC Systems Inc., Grove City, PA; *U.S. Private*, pg. 967
Bundrant, Charles, Pres.--Trident Seafood Corporation, Seattle, WA; *U.S. Public*, pg. 429
Bundy, Terry L., Pres. & Chief Exec. Officer--Lincoln Electric Systems, Lincoln, NE; *U.S. Private*, pg. 668
Bunn, Arthur H., Pres. & Chief Exec. Officer--Bunn-O-Matic Corporation, Springfield, IL; *U.S. Private*, pg. 180
Bunnell, H. Dean, Pres.--Maxtech, Inc., State College, PA; *U.S. Public*, pg. 1718
Buntin, Jeffrey W., Pres. & Chief Exec. Officer--The Buntin Group, Nashville, TN; *U.S. Private*, pg. 181
Buonaiuto, Val, Pres.--Hitachi Instruments, Inc., San Jose, CA; *Int'l*, pg. 622
Burbach, Jeffrey J., Pres.--EZ Paintr Corp., Saint Francis, WI; *U.S. Public*, pg. 1177
Burbage, Roger T., Pres.--Landstar Poole, Inc., Evergreen, AL; *U.S. Public*, pg. 978
Burch, Jeffrey I., Publisher--House Beautiful, New York, NY; *U.S. Private*, pg. 517
Burch, R.L., Chm. Bd. & Pres.--Jonathan Manufacturing Corp., Fullerton, CA; *U.S. Private*, pg. 595
Burd, Steve, Pres. & Chief Exec. Officer--Safeway Inc., Pleasanton, CA; *U.S. Public*, pg. 1426
Burdick, Norman H., Pres.--Agronaut Great Central Insurance Co., Peoria, IL; *U.S. Public*, pg. 129
Burdick, Richard L., Chm. Bd., Pres. & Chief Exec. Officer--Thermon Manufacturing Company, San Marcos, TX; *U.S. Private*, pg. 1080
Burdsall, John, Pres.--Heraeus Inc., New York, NY; *Int'l*, pg. 616
Burellis, Leo W., Pres.--Ultra Building Systems, Inc., South Hackensack, NJ; *U.S. Private*, pg. 194
Burello, A., Pres.--Zanussi Elettrodomestici S.p.A., Pordenone, Italy; *Int'l*, pg. 442
Burenga, Kenneth, Pres.--Barron's The Dow Jones Business & Financial Weekly, New York, NY; *U.S. Public*, pg. 524
Burenga, Kenneth L., Pres., Chief Exec. Officer & Chief Oper. Officer-Dow Jones Market--Dow Jones & Company, Inc., New York, NY; *U.S. Public*, pg. 524
Burford, Jeffrey, Pres. & Chief Exec. Officer--Fibrebond Corporation, Minden, LA; *U.S. Private*, pg. 402
Burg, H. Peter, Pres., Chief Oper. & Fin. Officer--FirstEnergy Corp., Akron, OH; *U.S. Public*, pg. 644
Burg, H. Peter, Pres.--Ohio Edison Company, Akron, OH; *U.S. Public*, pg. 645
Burgdorff, Peter, Pres. & Chief Exec. Officer--ERA Real Estate, Parsippany, NJ; *U.S. Public*, pg. 321
Burgert, Werner, Dr., Pres.--BASF Corporation Fiber Products Division, Charlotte, NC; *Int'l*, pg. 105
Burgess, Malcolm S., Jr., Chm. Bd. & Pres.--Burgess Pigment Co., Sandersville, GA; *U.S. Private*, pg. 182
Burgess, Robert K., Pres. & Chief Exec. Officer--Pulte Corporation, Bloomfield Hills, MI; *U.S. Public*, pg. 1344
Burgess, Robert K., Pres.--Alias Wavefront, New York, NY; *U.S. Public*, pg. 1474
Burgett, W. Brian, Pres. & Chief Exec. Officer--Kokosing Construction Company, Inc., Fredericktown, OH; *U.S. Private*, pg. 631
Burgin, Jim, Pres.-Sls.--Bollinger Industries Inc., Grand Prairie, TX; *U.S. Public*, pg. 243
Burgland, Steve, Pres.--Spectra-Physics Laserplane Inc., Dayton, OH; *U.S. Public*, pg. 1594
Burgo, Ray, Pres. & Chief Oper. Officer--Giant Eagle, Inc., Pittsburgh, PA; *U.S. Private*, pg. 450
Burgoyne, James F., Pres.--Burgoyne, Inc., Philadelphia, PA; *U.S. Private*, pg. 182
Burhmaster, Robert C., Pres. & Chief Exec. Officer--Jostens, Minneapolis, MN; *U.S. Public*, pg. 934
Burke, Andrew J., Pres. & Chief Exec. Officer--Degussa Corporation, Ridgefield Park, NJ; *Int'l*, pg. 388
Burke, Colette, Pres.--Mott's Inc., Stamford, CT; *Int'l*, pg. 248
Burke, Gary W., Pres. & Chief Exec. Officer--Burke Engineering Company, South El Monte, CA; *U.S. Private*, *pg. 183*
Burke, Gerry, Pres.--Astra Pharmaceuticals (Ireland) Ltd., Dublin, Ireland; *Int'l*, pg. 94
Burke, J. Gary, Pres.--Truck World Inc., Hubbard, OH; *U.S. Private*, pg. 1107
Burke, James R., Pres.--Enterra Petroleum Equipment Group, Inc., Houston, TX; *U.S. Public*, pg. 1749
Burke, Jeffrey A., Pres. & Chief Oper. Officer--Osco Industries Inc., Portsmouth, OH; *U.S. Private*, pg. 820
Burke, Larry W., Pres. & Chief Exec. Officer--Robinson Nugent, Inc., New Albany, IN; *U.S. Public*, pg. 1394
Burke, Michael J., Pres.--Buffalo Hospital Supply Co., Inc., Buffalo, NY; *U.S. Private*, pg. 179
Burke, Paul B., Chm. Bd., Pres. & Chief Exec. Officer--BMC Industries, Inc., Minneapolis, MN; *U.S. Public*, pg. 162
Burke, R. James, Pres.--Drive Train Industries, Denver, CO; *U.S. Private*, pg. 343
Burke, Richard, Pres.--Main Brothers Oil Company, Inc., Albany, NY; *U.S. Private*, pg. 697
Burke, Richard, Pres.--Moffet, Larson, & Johnson, Arlington, VA; *U.S. Public*, pg. 1743
Burke, Richard A., Pres.--Trek Corporation, Waterloo, WI; *U.S. Private*, pg. 1099
Burke, W.R., Pres. & Chief Exec. Officer--White Cap, Inc., Downers Grove, IL; *Int'l*, pg. 1207
Burke, William J., Chm. Bd. & Chief Exec. Officer--Osco Industries Inc., Portsmouth, OH; *U.S. Private*, pg. 820
Burke, William T., Pres.--Hopper Soliday & Co., Inc., Lancaster, PA; *Int'l*, pg. 65
Burkett, Ron, Pres.--Southeast Fire Sprinkler Company, Longwood, FL; *U.S. Private*, pg. 462
Burkett, Ronald, Pres.--S.I. Goldman Co., Longwood, FL; *U.S. Private*, pg. 461
Burkett, Thomas, Pres.--Goodman Manufacturing, Houston, TX; *U.S. Private*, pg. 464
Burkhardt, Edward A., Chm. Bd., Pres. & Chief Exec. Officer--Wisconsin Central Transportation Corporation, Rosemont, IL; *U.S. Public*, pg. 1772
Burkhardt, Edward A., Pres.--Wisconsin Central International, Inc., Rosemont, IL; *U.S. Public*, pg. 1773
Burkhardt, Martin E., Pres.--A.C. Scanning, Inc., Bedford, MA; *U.S. Public*, pg. 1735
Burkhardt, William C., Pres. & Chief Exec. Officer--Austin Quality Foods, Cary, NC; *U.S. Private*, pg. 100
Burkhead, Scott, Pres., Chief Oper. Officer & New Bus. Contact--Rockett, Burkhead, Lewis & Winslow, Raleigh, NC; *U.S. Private*, pg. 938
Burkle, Ronald, Mng. Partner--The Yucaipa Companies, Los Angeles, CA; *U.S. Private*, pg. 1202
Burleigh, William R., Pres. & Chief Exec. Officer--The E.W. Scripps Company, Cincinnati, OH; *U.S. Public*, pg. 1447
Burleson, Milt, Pres.--Monterey Mechanical Company, Oakland, CA; *U.S. Private*, pg. 758
Burner, David L., Chm. Bd., Pres. & Chief Exec. Officer--The B.F. Goodrich Company, Richfield, OH; *U.S. Public*, pg. 751
Burnes, Kennett F., Pres. & Chief Oper. Officer--Cabot Corporation, Boston, MA; *U.S. Public*, pg. 288
Burnett, George, Mng. Dir.--Ashtead Group PLC, Leatherhead, United Kingdom; *Int'l*, pg. 88
Burnett, Hugh T., Pres.--Cash Bases Incorporated, Westport, CT; *U.S. Public*, pg. 1637
Burney, Derek H., Chm., Pres. & Chief Exec. Officer--Bell Canada International, Inc., Montreal, Canada; *Int'l*, pg. 115
Burnham, Daniel P., Pres.--AlliedSignal Aerospace, Torrance, CA; *U.S. Public*, pg. 50
Burns, Bruce, Pres.--Burns Bros. Inc., Portland, OR; *U.S. Private*, pg. 187
Burns, C. Robert, Jr., Pres. & Mng. Dir.--Fencourt Reinsurance Co. Ltd., Hamilton, Bermuda; *U.S. Public*, pg. 795
Burns, Dennis, Pres.--Marsh Bellofram Corp., Newell, WV; *U.S. Private*, pg. 707
Burns, Gregory L., Chm. Bd., Pres. & Chief Exec. Officer--O'Charley's Inc., Nashville, TN; *U.S. Public*, pg. 1211
Burns, Harry A., Pres. & Chief Exec. Officer--Cargill Salt Inc., Minneapolis, MN; *Int'l*, pg. 48
Burns, James, Pres.--ATMI Ecosys Corp., San Jose, CA; *U.S. Public*, pg. 12
Burns, John J., Jr., Pres. & Chief Exec. Officer--Alleghany Corporation, New York, NY; *U.S. Public*, pg. 42
Burns, Jordan, Pres.--Tussenderlo Kerley Inc., Phoenix, AZ; *Int'l*, pg. 619
Burns, Jullius, Pres. & Chief Exec. Officer--MMI Products, Inc., Houston, TX; *U.S. Private*, pg. 687
Burns, M. Anthony, Chm. Bd., Pres. & Chief Exec. Officer--Ryder System, Inc., Miami, FL; *U.S. Public*, pg. 1413
Burns, R. Howard, Pres.--Windsor Door, Little Rock, AR; *U.S. Public*, pg. 69
Burns, R. Patrick, Pres. & Chief Exec. Officer--The Vermont Teddy Bear Company, Inc., Shelburne, VT; *U.S. Public*, pg. 1716
Burns, Richard, Pres.--Central Commissary, Inc., Phoenix, AZ; *U.S. Private*, pg. 276
Burns, Russ, Pres.--Universal Construction Co., Huntsville, AL; *U.S. Public*, pg. 1646
Burnside, Barry L., Pres.--Clairol Canada Inc., Montreal, Canada; *U.S. Public*, pg. 254
Burnstad, Victor, Pres.--Burnstad Brothers, Inc., Tomah, WI; *U.S. Private*, pg. 187
Burnstead, Frederick H., Pres.--Burnstead Construction Company, Bellevue, WA; *U.S. Private*, pg. 187
Burr, Brian, Pres.--The Upper Deck Company, LLC, Carlsbad, CA; *U.S. Private*, pg. 1129
Burr, Christopher D., Pres. & Gen. Mgr.--Johnson & Johnson K.K., Tokyo, Japan; *U.S. Public*, pg. 930
Burr, Christopher D., Pres. & Mng. Dir.--Johnson & Johnson Medical K.K., Tokyo, Japan; *U.S. Public*, pg. 931
Burrell, Paul M., Chm. Bd., Pres. & Chief Exec. Officer--Outsource International, Deerfield Beach, FL; *U.S. Public*, pg. 1236
Burri, Ernst A., Pres. & Gen. Mgr.--Compania Dominicana de Telefonos, C. por A., Santo Domingo, Dominican Republic; *U.S. Public*, pg. 697
Burris, Robert D., Pres. & Chief Oper. Officer--Burris Foods, Inc., Milford, DE; *U.S. Private*, pg. 188
Burriss, J.D., Chm. Bd., Pres. & Chief Exec. & Oper. Officer--The Alpha Corporation Of Tennessee, Collierville, TN; *U.S. Private*, pg. 44
Burriss, J.D., Chm. Bd. & Pres.--Chroma-Tek, Collierville, TN; *U.S. Private*, pg. 45
Burriss, John H., Pres.--Burriss Corp., Columbia, SC; *U.S. Private*, pg. 188
Burroughs, James R., Pres. & Chief Oper. Officer--First Gray Line Corporation, Beverly Hills, CA; *U.S. Private*, pg. 407
Burroughs, Ken, Pres.--Skeeter Products, Inc., Kilgore, TX; *U.S. Private*, pg. 689
Burroughs, Sarah, Pres. & Chief Oper. Officer--Burrell Communications Group Inc., Chicago, IL; *U.S. Private*, pg. 188
Burrow, Brian D., Pres.--Campbell Oil Co., Massillon, OH; *U.S. Private*, pg. 204
Burrow, Grady, Pres. & Chief Exec. Officer--National Computer Print, Inc., Birmingham, AL; *U.S. Private*, pg. 780
Burrows, Donald E., Pres.--Anarad, Inc., Santa Barbara, CA; *U.S. Public*, pg. 1563
Burrows, John, Pres. & Chief Exec. Officer--SPI Polyols, Inc., New Castle, DE; *Int'l*, pg. 599
Burrows, K.F., Pres.--Bristol Aerospace Ltd., Winnipeg, Canada; *Int'l*, pg. 1127
Burrows, Penny, Pres.--Sunwest Bank of Sandoval County, N.A., Rio Rancho, NM; *U.S. Public*, pg. 1165
Burrows, R.W., Jr., Chm. Bd. & Pres.--Burrows Paper Corporation, Little Falls, NY; *U.S. Private*, pg. 188
Burrus, Michael C., Pres.--Multimedia Cablevision, Co., Wichita, KS; *U.S. Public*, pg. 699
Bursch, Dean, Pres.--Consolidated Electrical Distributors, Westlake Village, CA; *U.S. Private*, pg. 265
Bursma, Albert, Jr., Pres.--Great Source Education Group, Wilmington, MA; *U.S. Public*, pg. 841
Burson, Bill, Pres.--Halstead Industries, Inc., Greensboro, NC; *U.S. Private*, pg. 496
Burson, Bill, Pres.--Halstead Industrial Prods. Div., Wynne, AR; *U.S. Private*, pg. 497
Burstein, David, Pres.--Harland Bartholomew & Associates Inc., Memphis, TN; *U.S. Private*, pg. 841
Burstein, David, Pres.--Parsons Engineering Science, Inc., Pasadena, CA; *U.S. Private*, pg. 842
Burstein, David, Pres.--Harland Bartholomew & Associates Inc., Sacramento, CA; *U.S. Private*, pg. 842
Burstein, David, Pres.--Harland Bartholomew & Associates Inc., Jacksonville, FL; *U.S. Private*, pg. 842
Burstein, David, Pres.--Harland Bartholomew & Associates Inc., Chesterfield, MO; *U.S. Private*, pg. 842
Burt, James, Pres. & Chief Exec. Officer--Wisconsin Pharmacal Co., Inc., Jackson, WI; *U.S. Private*, pg. 1185
Burt, John R., Chm. Bd. & Pres.--Duro-Last Roofing, Inc., Saginaw, MI; *U.S. Private*, pg. 349
Burt, Richard L., Pres.--Comtech Systems, Inc., Saint Cloud, FL; *U.S. Public*, pg. 425
Burt, Robert N., Pres.--FMC Corp., Agricultural Products Group, Philadelphia, PA; *U.S. Public*, pg. 605
Burtman, Charles, Pres. & Chief Exec. Officer--Burtman Iron Works, Inc., Readville, MA; *U.S. Private*, pg. 188
Burton, J.C., Pres.--Amoco Services, Inc., London, United Kingdom; *U.S. Public*, pg. 103
Burton, J.L., Pres.--Nacan Products Ltd., Brampton, Canada; *Int'l*, pg. 1436
Burton, L. Grant, Pres.--Starcan Corporation, Toronto, Canada; *Int'l*, pg. 1297
Burton, Raymond C., Jr., Pres. & Chief Exec. Officer--TTX Co., Chicago, IL; *U.S. Private*, pg. 1066
Burton, Robert G., Chm. Bd., Pres. & Chief Exec. Officer--World Color Press, Inc., Greenwich, CT; *U.S. Public*, pg. 1778
Burton, T. Roy, Pres.-Electronics/OEM Div.--Thomas & Betts Corporation, Memphis, TN; *U.S. Public*, pg. 1597
Burtraw, Roger L., Pres.--Harvard Industries, Inc., Tampa, FL; *U.S. Public*, pg. 796
Burtraw, Roger L., Pres.--Kingston Warren, Farmington Hills, MI; *U.S. Public*, pg. 796
Burts, Stephen L., Jr., Pres.--Synovus Financial Corp., Columbus, GA; *U.S. Public*, pg. 1548
Burwell, Bruce, Dir.--Joslyn Research & Development Corporation, Woodstock, IL; *U.S. Public*, pg. 482
Burzin, Klaus, Pres. & Chief Oper. Officer--Huls America Inc., Somerset, NJ; *Int'l*, pg. 1455
Busacca, Salvatore, Pres.--ScotiaMocatta, New York, NY; *Int'l*, pg. 156
Busby, Don C., Pres.--Huck International Industrial Fastener Division, Waco, TX; *U.S. Public*, pg. 1597
Busby, Jack W., Jr., Pres. & Chief Oper. Officer--Hancock Fabrics, Inc., Tupelo, MS; *U.S. Public*, pg. 779
Busby, Jheryl, Pres. & Chief Exec. Officer--Motown Record Company, J.P., New York, NY; *Int'l*, pg. 1052
Busby, Robert L., Pres.--NWL Investments, Inc., Austin, TX; *U.S. Public*, pg. 1161
Busby, Robert L., III, Pres.--NWL 806 Main, Inc., Austin, TX; *U.S. Public*, pg. 1161
Busby, Robert L., III, Pres.--NWL Properties, Inc., Austin, TX; *U.S. Public*, pg. 1161
Busby, Robert L., III, Pres.--NWL Financial, Inc., Austin, TX; *U.S. Public*, pg. 1161
Busby, Robert L., III, Pres.--NWL Services, Inc., Austin, TX; *U.S. Public*, pg. 1161
Busch, August A., III, Chm. Bd & Pres. & V.P.-Mktg.--Anheuser-Busch Companies, Inc., Saint Louis, MO; *U.S. Public*, pg. 113
Busch, Len, Pres.--Matrix Technologies Inc., Maumee, OH; *U.S. Private*, pg. 714
Busch, Paul L., Dr., Chm. Bd., Pres. & Chief Exec. Officer--Malcolm Pirnie, Inc., White Plains, NY; *U.S. Private*, pg. 867
Buser, Raoul C., Pres. & Chief Oper. Officer--Alcell Technologies Inc., Newcastle, Canada; *Int'l*, pg. 1104
Bush, David, Pres.--Sechrist Industries, Inc., Anaheim, CA; *U.S. Private*, pg. 980

Bush, Paul S., Chm. Bd., Pres. & Chief Exec. Officer--Bush Industries Inc., Jamestown, NY; *U.S. Public*, pg. 270

Bush, Robert, Pres.--First Ameritas Life Insurance Corp. of New York, Suffern, NY; *U.S. Private*, pg. 65

Bush, Ronald, Pres.--DeVry Institute of Technology, Decatur, GA; *U.S. Public*, pg. 504

Bushen, David A., Pres.--Old Kent Brokerage Services, Inc., Grand Rapids, MI; *U.S. Public*, pg. 1216

Buskirk, Glen, Pres.--Rock Hill Materials Company, Catasauqua, PA; *U.S. Private*, pg. 938

Bustillo, Oscar, Jr., Chm. Bd., Pres. & Chief Exec. Officer--Republic National Bank of Miami, Miami, FL; *U.S. Private*, pg. 924

Busto, Richard, Pres. & Chief Oper. Officer--Gandalf Technologies Inc., Nepean, Canada; *Int'l*, pg. 540

Bustos, Luis, Pres.--Allied Domecq Brasil Industria e Comercio Ltda., Rio de Janeiro, Brazil; *Int'l*, pg. 63

Butcher, Jonathan, Chm. Bd. & Pres.--Butcher & Co., Inc., Philadelphia, PA; *U.S. Private*, pg. 189

Butcher, Jonathan, Pres.--Butcher Energy, Philadelphia, PA; *U.S. Private*, pg. 189

Butel, Jean-Luc, Pres.--Nippon Becton Dickinson Company Ltd., Tokyo, Japan; *U.S. Public*, pg. 200

Butera, Joseph, Pres.--Butera Finer Foods Inc., Elgin, IL; *U.S. Private*, pg. 189

Buterbaugh, Noel L., Pres. & Chief Exec. Officer--BioWhittaker, Inc., Walkersville, MD; *U.S. Public*, pg. 297

Buterbaugh, Noel L., Pres.--Clonetics, Inc., Walkersville, MD; *U.S. Public*, pg. 297

Butler, Andrew, Pres.--Butler Automatic, Inc., Canton, MA; *U.S. Private*, pg. 189

Butler, Bruce, Pres. & Gen. Mgr.--EMC Test System, L.P., Austin, TX; *U.S. Public*, pg. 546

Butler, Chris, Pres.--Interactive Solutions, Boston, MA; *U.S. Public*, pg. 1224

Butler, Clifford E., Vice Chm. & Exec. Pres.--Pilgrim's Pride Corporation, Pittsburg, TX; *U.S. Public*, pg. 1296

Butler, Edward F., Chm. Bd., Pres. & Chief Exec. Officer--Regions Bank/Southern Louisiana, New Orleans, LA; *U.S. Public*, pg. 1373

Butler, Eugene W., Pres.--Harris Bank St. Charles, Saint Charles, IL; *Int'l*, pg. 154

Butler, Frank E., Pres. & Gen. Mgr.--Sherwin-Williams Coatings Division, Cleveland, OH; *U.S. Public*, pg. 1466

Butler, Frank W., Pres.--Catalina Yachts, Inc., Woodland Hills, CA; *U.S. Private*, pg. 219

Butler, Fred M., Pres. & Chief Exec. Officer--The Manitowoc Company, Inc., Manitowoc, WI; *U.S. Public*, pg. 1040

Butler, Gilbert, Pres.--Butler Capital Corp., New York, NY; *U.S. Private*, pg. 190

Butler, Lester, Chm. Bd., Pres. & Chief Exec. Officer--SouthTrust Bank of Charleston, Charleston, SC; *U.S. Public*, pg. 1492

Butler, Norton L., Pres. & Chief Oper. Officer--Chittenden & Eastman Co., Burlington, IA; *U.S. Private*, pg. 237

Butler, Norton L., Pres. & Chief Oper. Officer--Eastman House Of California, Inc., Burlington, IA; *U.S. Private*, pg. 238

Butler, Norton L., Pres. & Chief Oper. Officer--Eastman House Of Alabama, Inc., Burlington, IA; *U.S. Private*, pg. 238

Butler, Robert F., Pres. & Chief Exec. Officer--Holtzman's Little Folk Shop, Inc., City of Industry, CA; *U.S. Public*, pg. 1777

Butler, Thomas R., Pres. & Chief Oper. Officer-Novus Services, Inc.--Dean Witter, Discover & Co., New York, NY; *U.S. Public*, pg. 1132

Butler, Thomas R., Pres.--NOVUS Services, Inc., Riverwoods, IL; *U.S. Public*, pg. 1132

Butler, Tom, Pres.--Monarch Construction Company, Cincinnati, OH; *U.S. Private*, pg. 757

Butler, Viggo, Pres.--Airport Group International, Inc., Glendale, CA; *U.S. Public*, pg. 1009

Butler, William, Chm. Bd., Pres. & Chief Exec. Officer--Corporex Companies, Inc., Cincinnati, OH; *U.S. Private*, pg. 276

Butryn, G.L., Pres.--Escanaba Paper Co., Escanaba, MI; *U.S. Public*, pg. 1076

Buttacavoli, Ciro, Publr.--Industrial Equipment News, New York, NY; *U.S. Private*, pg. 1082

Butters, Brian, Pres. & Publisher--The Kamloops Daily News, Kamloops, Canada; *Int'l*, pg. 631

Butterworth, Edward L., Pres. & Chief Exec. Officer--Fedco, Inc., Santa Fe Springs, CA; *U.S. Private*, pg. 398

Buttner, Jean B., Chm. Bd. & Chief Exec. Officer--Arnold Bernhard & Co., New York, NY; *U.S. Private*, pg. 137

Buttner, Jean Bernhard, Chm. Bd., Pres. & Chief Exec. Officer--Value Line, Inc., New York, NY; *U.S. Private*, pg. 137

Buttrill, W. Shelly, Pres.--Lockheed Martin Aeronutronic, Santa Margarita, CA; *U.S. Public*, pg. 1008

Butvilas, George J., Pres. & Chief Exec. Officer--D & N Financial Corporation, Hancock, MI; *U.S. Public*, pg. 472

Butz, John, Pres.--Allomatic Products Company, Sullivan, IN; *U.S. Public*, pg. 1363

Butz, Terry, Pres.--Kelso-Burnett Company, Rolling Meadows, IL; *U.S. Private*, pg. 613

Butz, Wayne D., Pres., Chief Oper. Officer & Actuary--Harleysville Life Insurance Co., Harleysville, PA; *U.S. Public*, pg. 787

Butzer, Bart, Pres.--Mervyn's California, Hayward, CA; *U.S. Public*, pg. 489

Buxton, Andrew R.W., Chm. Bd. & Pres.--Barclays Bank PLC, London, United Kingdom; *Int'l*, pg. 164

Buxton, W.H., Chm. Bd. & Chief Exec. Officer--McNeil (Ohio) Corporation, Saint Paul, MN; *U.S. Public*, pg. 1273

Buxton, Winslow H., Chm. Bd., Pres. & Chief Exec. Officer--Pentair, Inc., Saint Paul, MN; *U.S. Public*, pg. 1273

Byer, Allan G., Chm. Bd. & Pres.--Byer California, San Francisco, CA; *U.S. Private*, pg. 191

Byer, Robert S., Pres.--Byer & McGuggart, Inc., New York, NY; *Int'l*, pg. 117

Byers, Norman P., Pres.--Telos International Corp., Ashburn, VA; *U.S. Public*, pg. 1573

Byers, Ronald G., Chief Oper. Officer--Evans Tempcon Inc., Grand Rapids, MI; *U.S. Private*, pg. 7

Byrd, David M., Pres.--Southern Beverage Packers, Inc., Harlem, GA; *U.S. Private*, pg. 1015

Byrd, Jeff, Pres.--Bristol Motor Speedway, Bristol, TN; *U.S. Public*, pg. 1498

Byrd, Robert, Chm. Bd., Pres. & Chief Exec. Officer--The Keller Manufacturing Co., Inc., Corydon, IN; *U.S. Private*, pg. 612

Byrkit, Larry, Pres.--UPB of the Tennessee Valley, Harriman, TN; *U.S. Public*, pg. 1669

Byrne, Arthur, Chm. Bd., Pres. & Chief Exec. Officer--The Wiremold Company, West Hartford, CT; *U.S. Private*, pg. 1184

Byrne, J. Dixon, Mng. Partner--Hanft Byrne Raboy Abrams & Partners, Inc., New York, NY; *U.S. Private*, pg. 499

Byrne, John F., Sr., Pres.--Jack Byrne Ford & Mercury, Inc., Mechanicville, NY; *U.S. Private*, pg. 191

Byrne, Joseph, Pres.--Property Development Associates, Oakland, CA; *U.S. Public*, pg. 1426

Byrne, M.A., Joint Pres.--Janus Elevator Products Inc., Hauppauge, NY; *Int'l*, pg. 590

Byrne, Patrick F., Pres.--Global Power Company, Waverly, TN; *Int'l*, pg. 74

Byrnes, Bruce L., Pres.--Procter & Gamble Cleaning & Paper Products Div., Cincinnati, OH; *U.S. Public*, pg. 1330

Byrnes, Edward G., Pres. & Chief Exec. Officer--Byrnes & Kiefer Company, Callery, PA; *U.S. Private*, pg. 191

Byrnes, James J., Chm. Bd., Pres. & Chief Exec. Officer--Tompkins County Trust Company, Ithaca, NY; *U.S. Public*, pg. 1621

Byrnes, John T., Pres.--M & I Brokerage Services, Inc., Milwaukee, WI; *U.S. Public*, pg. 1050

Byrnes, Robert J., Pres. & Chief Oper. Officer--FFP Marketing Company, Inc., Fort Worth, TX; *U.S. Public*, pg. 604

Bysiek, Edward J., Pres.--ABB Air Preheater Inc., Wellsville, NY; *Int'l*, pg. 3

Bytnar, Michael W., Pres.--Nooter Fabricators, Inc., Saint Louis, MO; *U.S. Private*, pg. 801

Byun, D.S., Pres.--Simpson Industries, Inc., Seoul, Korea; *U.S. Public*, pg. 1475

Caballero, Dennis P., Pres.--Security Industrial Insurance Co., Inc., Donaldsonville, LA; *Int'l*, pg. 814

Caballero, Killko, Pres.--White Pine Software, Nashua, NH; *U.S. Private*, pg. 1173

Cabana, Charles, Pres.--Mark Chevrolet Inc., Wayne, MI; *U.S. Private*, pg. 704

Caberlotto, Albert, Pres.--Lotto S.p.A., Montebelluna, Italy; *Int'l*, pg. 819

Cabot, Samuel, III, Pres. & Chief Exec. Officer--Samuel Cabot, Inc., Newburyport, MA; *U.S. Private*, pg. 198

Cabrey, John, Pres. & Gen. Mgr.--Sequa Chemicals, Inc., Chester, SC; *U.S. Public*, pg. 1459

Cacciato, Richard, Pres.--Frederick Wildman & Sons Ltd., New York, NY; *U.S. Private*, pg. 1176

Cacciatore, William C., Chm. Bd., Pres. & Chief Exec. Officer--Richey Electronics, Inc., Garden Grove, CA; *U.S. Public*, pg. 1388

Caccini, Gian Paolo, Vice Chm., Pres., Chief Exec. & Chief Oper. Officer--CertainTeed Corporation, Valley Forge, PA; *Int'l*, pg. 1170

Caddock, Richard E. Sr., Pres.--Caddock Electronics, Inc., Riverside, CA; *U.S. Private*, pg. 198

Cadelo, Leo, Pres.--The Eureka Company, Bloomington, IL; *Int'l*, pg. 440

Cadena, Alvaro, Pres. & Chief Oper. Officer--Graham Corporation, Batavia, NY; *U.S. Public*, pg. 757

Cadena, Alvaro, Pres. & Chief Oper. Officer--Graham Manufacturing Co., Inc., Batavia, NY; *U.S. Public*, pg. 757

Cadieux, Chester, Chm. Bd., Pres. & Chief Exec. Officer--QuikTrip Corporation, Tulsa, OK; *U.S. Private*, pg. 901

Cadogan, William J., Chm. Bd., Pres. & Chief Exec. Officer--ADC Telecommunications, Inc., Minnetonka, MN; *U.S. Public*, pg. 4

Cadwell, Marvin S., Pres. & Chief Exec. Officer--Shared Medical Systems Corporation, Malvern, PA; *U.S. Public*, pg. 1463

Cady, Lyle, Pres. & Chief Exec. Officer--Jouan, Inc., Winchester, VA; *U.S. Private*, pg. 601

Cady, Lyle E., Jr., Pres.--Precision Scientific Inc., Winchester, VA; *U.S. Private*, pg. 601

Cafaro, Al, Pres.--A&M Records, Hollywood, CA; *Int'l*, pg. 1052

Cafaro, Anthony M., Pres.--The Cafaro Co., Youngstown, OH; *U.S. Private*, pg. 198

Caffarone, Douglas P., Pres. & Chief Oper. Officer--Geyer-McAllister Publications, Inc., New York, NY; *U.S. Private*, pg. 450

Cafferata, Patricia A., Pres. & Chief Exec. Officer--Young & Rubicam Chicago, Chicago, IL; *U.S. Private*, pg. 1198

Caffery, Patrick, Pres. & Chief Exec. Officer--Edgewater Steel Company, Oakmont, PA; *U.S. Private*, pg. 364

Caffey, Guy H., III, Pres.--SouthTrust Bank of Marshall County, Boaz, AL; *U.S. Public*, pg. 1492

Caffrey, Hugh R., Pres. & Chief Exec. Officer--Hilb, Rogal and Hamilton Company of Atlanta, Inc., Atlanta, GA; *U.S. Public*, pg. 827

Cahill, Larry, Pres. & Treas.--Larken Inc., Cedar Rapids, IA; *U.S. Private*, pg. 651

Cahill, Robert V., Pres.--Chartwell Partners, Los Angeles, CA; *U.S. Private*, pg. 230

Cahouet, Frank V., Chm. Bd., Pres. & Chief Exec. Officer--Mellon Bank Corporation, Pittsburgh, PA; *U.S. Public*, pg. 1084

Caille, Andre, Pres.& Dir. Gen.--Hydro-Quebec, Montreal, Canada; *Int'l*, pg. 640

Cain, Paul W., Pres.--Mesa Environmental, Fort Worth, TX; *U.S. Public*, pg. 1300

Cairney, Len, Pres. & Gen. Mgr.--Beaulieu Vineyard, Rutherford, CA; *Int'l*, pg. 410

Caizza, Donald, Pres. & Chief Exec. Officer--CSC, Ltd., Warren, OH; *U.S. Private*, pg. 924

Calabrese, Frank, Pres.--F C L Graphics, Harwood Heights, IL; *U.S. Private*, pg. 389

Calabrese, P.J., Pres.--The Grieve Corporation, Round Lake, IL; *U.S. Private*, pg. 480

Calabrese, Wayne H., Pres. & Chief Oper. Officer--Wackenhut Corrections Corporation, Palm Beach Gardens, FL; *U.S. Public*, pg. 1731

Calabro, Joseph A., Pres. & Chief Exec. Officer--Artistic Greetings, Inc., Elmira, NY; *U.S. Public*, pg. 136

Calafati, Gabriel R., Chm. Bd., Pres. & Treas.--Frank Briscoe Co. Inc., Kenilworth, NJ; *U.S. Private*, pg. 169

Calamari, Joseph, Pres. & Chief Oper. Officer--Marvel Entertainment Group, New York, NY; *U.S. Public*, pg. 1052

Calandra, T.M., Pres.--Starcrest Products of California, Perris, CA; *U.S. Private*, pg. 1035

Calandra, T.M., Pres.--Signatures, Perris, CA; *U.S. Private*, pg. 1035

Calandra, T.M., Pres.--Starcrest of California, Perris, CA; *U.S. Private*, pg. 1035

Calandra, T.M., Pres.--Handsome Rewards, Perris, CA; *U.S. Private*, pg. 1035

Calarco, Vincent A., Chm. Bd., Pres. & Chief Exec. Officer--Crompton & Knowles Corporation, Stamford, CT; *U.S. Public*, pg. 459

Calarco, Vincent A., Pres. & Chief Exec. Officer--Uniroyal Chemical Company, Inc., Middlebury, CT; *U.S. Public*, pg. 460

Calcattera, Paul, Pres.--Cowtown Boot Company, El Paso, TX; *U.S. Private*, pg. 281

Caldarone, Anthony J., Chm., Pres. & Chief Exec. Officer--Calton, Inc., Manalapan, NJ; *U.S. Public*, pg. 296

Calder, Clive, Chm. Bd. & Pres.--Zomba Recording Corp., London, United Kingdom; *Int'l*, pg. 1529

Caldwell, Donald R., Pres. & Chief Oper. Officer--Safeguard Scientifics, Inc., Wayne, PA; *U.S. Public*, pg. 1424

Caldwell, Geanne, Pres.--AEW Partners, L.P., Boston, MA; *U.S. Private*, pg. 5

Caldwell, James D., Pres.--Omni Hotels, Irving, TX; *U.S. Private*, pg. 1065

Caldwell, John, Pres.--Swing-N-Slide Corp., Janesville, WI; *U.S. Public*, pg. 1543

Caldwell, John E., Pres. & Chief Exec. Officer--CAE Inc., Toronto, Canada; *Int'l*, pg. 237

Caldwell, Kenneth A., Pres.--Aker Omega Inc. (AE), Houston, TX; *Int'l*, pg. 42

Caldwell, Max, Pres.--NAPCO, Inc., Terryville, CT; *U.S. Public*, pg. 1592

Caldwell, Royce S., Pres.--Customer Services, Saint Louis, MO; *U.S. Public*, pg. 1416

Caleffi, Odilio, Pres.--Caleffi S.p.A., Viadana, Italy; *Int'l*, pg. 252

Calengor, Jerry, Pres.--Normark Corporation, Minnetonka, MN; *U.S. Private*, pg. 802

Calerno, Catherine, Pres. & Chief Exec. Officer--Rainoldi, Kerzner & Radcliffe, San Francisco, CA; *U.S. Public*, pg. 1224

Calhoun, David, Pres. & Chief Exec. Officer--G.E. Lighting Division, Cleveland, OH; *U.S. Public*, pg. 710

Calhoun, David L., Pres. & Chief Exec. Officer--GE Transportation Systems, Erie, PA; *U.S. Public*, pg. 711

Calhoun, Lynn, Pres. & Chief Fin. Officer--Prime Technology, Inc., Grand Rapids, MI; *U.S. Private*, pg. 884

Calhy, Ronald B., Chm., Pres. & Chief Exec. Officer--United HealthCare Insurance Company, Hartford, CT; *U.S. Public*, pg. 1678

Caliari, Roberto, Pres.--Vetrotex International, Chambery, France; *Int'l*, pg. 1177

Calicchio, John, Chm. Bd. & Pres.--Delcal Enterprises, Inc., New York, NY; *U.S. Private*, pg. 322

Calkins, James E., Chm. Bd. & Pres.--The Calkins Manufacturing Company, Spokane, WA; *U.S. Private*, pg. 201

Calkins, Kim, Pres.--Princess Soft Toys, Minneapolis, MN; *U.S. Private*, pg. 884

Call, Harry M., Pres. & Chief Oper. Officer--Goody's Family Clothing, Inc., Knoxville, TN; *U.S. Public*, pg. 753

Call, Ralph, Pres. & Chief Exec. Officer--Dyna Technology Incorporated, Le Center, MN; *U.S. Private*, pg. 350

Call, William, Chm., Pres. & Chief Exec. Officer--Maverik Country Stores, Inc., Salt Lake City, UT; *U.S. Private*, pg. 715

Callaghan, Chris, Pres.--Prep - STAT/Spectrum, Franklin, KY; *U.S. Private*, pg. 882

Callaghan, Howard, Pres.--Plastic Suppliers, Inc., Columbus, OH; *U.S. Private*, pg. 871

Callahan-Guion, Kathleen, Pres. & Chief Oper. Officer--E-Z Serve Corp., Houston, TX; *U.S. Public*, pg. 540

Callahan-Guion, Kathleen, Pres. & Chief Oper. Officer--E-Z Serve Convenience Stores, Inc., Houston, TX; *U.S. Public*, pg. 540

Callahan, Dennis, Chm. Bd., Pres. & Chief Exec. Officer--Crowley, Milner & Company, Detroit, MI; *U.S. Public*, pg. 461

Callahan, Dennis, Pres. & Chief Exec. Officer--Steinbach Stores, Inc., Detroit, MI; *U.S. Public*, pg. 461

Callahan, James M., Pres.--Vistakon Johnson & Johnson Vision Products, Inc., Jacksonville, FL; *U.S. Public*, pg. 929

Callahan, Joseph, Pres.--Swagelok Company, Solon, OH; *U.S. Private*, pg. 1057

Callahan, Peter, Chm. Bd., Pres. & Chief Exec. Officer--American Media, Inc., Lake Worth, FL; *U.S. Public*, pg. 87

Callahan, Richard J., Pres. & Chief Oper. Officer--Greenwich Insurance Company, Greenwich, CT; *U.S. Public*, pg. 1144

Callahan, Richard J., Pres. & Chief Oper. Officer--Indian Harbor Insurance Company, Greenwich, CT; *U.S. Public*, pg. 1144

Callahan, Robert F., Pres.--ABC/Watermark, Inc., Los Angeles, CA; *U.S. Public*, pg. 511
Callas, Chris, Sr. Principal & Grp. Mngmt. Supvr.--Publicis/Bloom, New York, NY; *Int'l*, pg. 470
Callaway, Edward C., Pres.--Crested Butte Mountain Resort, Inc., Crested Butte, CO; *U.S. Private*, pg. 289
Callaway, James R., Pres.--Microflect Company, Inc., Salem, OR; *U.S. Public*, pg. 1707
Callaway, Roy, Publr.--The Garden Island, Lihue, HI; *U.S. Public*, pg. 1343
Calley, John, Pres. & Chief Oper. Officer--Sony Pictures Entertainment, Culver City, CA; *Int'l*, pg. 1281
Calligaris, A.E., Chm. Bd., Pres. & Chief Exec. Officer--Stebbins Engineering & Mfg. Co., Watertown, NY; *U.S. Private*, pg. 1037
Callon, Fred L., Pres. & Chief Exec. Officer--Callon Petroleum Company, Natchez, MS; *U.S. Public*, pg. 295
Callon, John S., Pres.--Wilcox Energy Company, Natchez, MS; *U.S. Public*, pg. 295
Calloway, Steve, Pres.--Six Flags Over Texas, Arlington, TX; *U.S. Public*, pg. 1612
Calton, Renneth J., Chm. Bd & Pres.--North Carolina Equipment Co., Raleigh, NC; *U.S. Private*, pg. 804
Calvert, Horace A., Pres.--Exsol, Inc., Houston, TX; *U.S. Public*, pg. 1454
Calvet, Jacques, Pres.--PSA Peugeot Citroen, Paris, France; *Int'l*, pg. 1020
Camacho, Ernest M., Pres.--Pacifica Services, Inc., Pasadena, CA; *U.S. Private*, pg. 832
Cambre, Ronald C., Chm. Bd., Pres. & Chief Exec. Officer--Newmont Mining Corporation, Denver, CO; *U.S. Public*, pg. 1178
Camden, J., Pres.--RMC Group p.l.c., Egham, United Kingdom; *Int'l*, pg. 1078
Camelio, Cosmo, Pres. & Chief Exec. Officer--Freudenberg Nonwovens, Durham, NC; *Int'l*, pg. 505
Cameron, Alan, Pres.--Epic Technical Group, Auburn Hills, MI; *U.S. Public*, pg. 560
Cameron, Donald, Pres.--Lawtons Drug Stores Limited, Dartmouth, Canada; *Int'l*, pg. 454
Cameron, Duane H., Pres.--Systems Parking, Inc., Los Angeles, CA; *U.S. Private*, pg. 1061
Cameron, Ewen R., Pres.--Teltronics Inc., Sarasota, FL; *U.S. Public*, pg. 1573
Cameron, Gerald T., Jr., Pres.--Amray, Inc., Bedford, MA; *U.S. Private*, pg. 67
Cameron, William M., Pres. & Chief Exec. Officer--American Fidelity Corp., Oklahoma City, OK; *U.S. Private*, pg. 54
Camino, Louis D., Pres. & Chief Oper. Officer--Rouge Steel Company, Dearborn, MI; *U.S. Public*, pg. 1406
Cammarata, Bernard, Pres. & Chief Exec. Officer--The TJX Companies, Inc., Framingham, MA; *U.S. Public*, pg. 1556
Camosy, Raymond J., Pres. & Chief Exec. Officer--Camosy, Inc., Russell, IL; *U.S. Private*, pg. 203
Camp, Glen B., Pres.--Mono Pumps Ltd., Manchester, United Kingdom; *U.S. Public*, pg. 529
Camp, J., Pres.--Penny & Giles Drives Technology Inc., Arcadia, CA; *Int'l*, pg. 208
Campanaro, Leonard A., Pres. & Chief Oper. Officer--Harsco Corporation, Camp Hill, PA; *U.S. Public*, pg. 792
Campbell, Argyle, Chm. Bd. & Pres.--Cambro Manufacturing Company, Huntington Beach, CA; *U.S. Private*, pg. 203
Campbell, Brian P., Pres.--TriMas Corporation, Ann Arbor, MI; *U.S. Public*, pg. 1054
Campbell, Brice, Principal & Mngmt. Supvr.--Publicis/Bloom, Dallas, TX; *Int'l*, pg. 469
Campbell, Calvin A., Jr., Chm. Bd., Pres. & Chief Exec. Officer--Goodman Equipment Corp., Bedford Park, IL; *U.S. Private*, pg. 464
Campbell, Carl L., Pres. & Chief Exec. Officer--Keystone Financial Inc., Harrisburg, PA; *U.S. Public*, pg. 956
Campbell, Charles J., Chm. Bd., Pres. & Chief Exec. Officer--Florsheim Group Inc., Chicago, IL; *U.S. Public*, pg. 656
Campbell, David, Pres. & Chief Exec. Officer--Master Lock Company, Milwaukee, WI; *U.S. Public*, pg. 675
Campbell, David, Pres.--Benjamin Obdyke, Inc., Warminster, PA; *U.S. Private*, pg. 810
Campbell, David D., Pres.--Milwaukee Lock Company, Milwaukee, WI; *U.S. Public*, pg. 675
Campbell, David J., Pres. & Chief Exec. Officer--The Detroit Medical Center, Detroit, MI; *U.S. Private*, pg. 328
Campbell, Dugald, Pres.--Tower Automotive, Inc., Grand Rapids, MI; *U.S. Public*, pg. 1625
Campbell, Duncan, Jr., Pres.--The Campbell Group, Inc., Portland, OR; *U.S. Public*, pg. 1672
Campbell, Edward P., Pres. & Chief Exec. Officer--Nordson Corporation, Westlake, OH; *U.S. Public*, pg. 1188
Campbell, Edward P., Pres. & Chief Oper. Officer--Nordson Corporation, Amherst, OH; *U.S. Public*, pg. 1188
Campbell, George M., Pres. & Chief Exec. Officer--Regions Bank/North Louisiana, Monroe, LA; *U.S. Public*, pg. 1372
Campbell, Gordon W., Pres.--R.P. Scherer K.K., Tokyo, Japan; *U.S. Public*, pg. 1438
Campbell, Howard F., Pres.--Emco Distribution, Mississauga, Canada; *Int'l*, pg. 453
Campbell, J.H., Jr., Pres. & Chief Exec. Officer--Associated Grocers, Inc., Baton Rouge, LA; *U.S. Private*, pg. 90
Campbell, J.S., Pres.--IPC Resistors Inc., Mississauga, Canada; *Int'l*, pg. 590
Campbell, Jack, Pres.--Minigrip Zip-Pak, Orangeburg, NY; *U.S. Public*, pg. 867
Campbell, James, Chm. Bd., Pres. & Chief Exec. Officer--First Community Bank of Saltville, Saltville, VA; *U.S. Public*, pg. 1039
Campbell, James, Pres.--Trans Financial Bank, N.A., Bowling Green, KY; *U.S. Public*, pg. 1628
Campbell, James R., Pres.--Norwest Bank Faribault, N.A., Faribault, MN; *U.S. Public*, pg. 1202
Campbell, Joel, Pres.--Cooper Automotive Division, Chesterfield, MO; *U.S. Public*, pg. 443
Campbell, John, Pres.--J.E. Goold & Company, Portland, ME; *U.S. Public*, pg. 229
Campbell, John J., III, Chm. Bd. & Pres.--John J. Campbell Co., Inc., Memphis, TN; *U.S. Private*, pg. 204
Campbell, Jon R., Pres. & Chief Exec. Officer--Norwest Bank Arizona, N.A., Phoenix, AZ; *U.S. Public*, pg. 1202
Campbell, Ken, Pres.--Sunwest Bank of Santa Fe, Santa Fe, NM; *U.S. Public*, pg. 1165
Campbell, Kenneth L., Mrs., Chm. Bd. & Pres.--Dover Industries Limited, Burlington, Canada; *Int'l*, pg. 417
Campbell, Lewis B., Pres. & Chief Oper. Officer--Textron Inc., Providence, RI; *U.S. Public*, pg. 1588
Campbell, Michael, Pres.--Wolf-Campbell Public Relations, Toronto, Canada; *U.S. Private*, pg. 1186
Campbell, Michael L., Chm. Bd., Pres. & Chief Exec. Officer--Regal Cinemas Inc., Knoxville, TN; *U.S. Public*, pg. 1371
Campbell, Morgan, Pres.--Stockham Valves & Fittings, Inc., Birmingham, AL; *U.S. Private*, pg. 1043
Campbell, Neil, Pres.--Lab Products, Inc., Seaford, DE; *U.S. Private*, pg. 641
Campbell, P.D., Pres. & Chief Exec. Officer--Dunlop Tire Corporation, Buffalo, NY; *Int'l*, pg. 1317
Campbell, R.S., Pres. & Chief Exec. Officer--Marlite, Dover, OH; *U.S. Private*, pg. 705
Campbell, Richard, Pres.--BP Exploration (Alaska) Inc., Anchorage, AK; *Int'l*, pg. 220
Campbell, Robert, Mng. Dir.--Blackwell Science, Oxford, United Kingdom; *Int'l*, pg. 197
Campbell, Robert H., Chm. Bd., Chief Exec. Officer & Pres.--Sun Company, Inc., Philadelphia, PA; *U.S. Public*, pg. 1530
Campbell, Robert S., Pres. & Chief Exec. Officer--Henry Vogt Machine Co., Louisville, KY; *U.S. Private*, pg. 1143
Campbell, T. Scott, Pres.--T. Bruce Sales, Inc., West Middlesex, PA; *U.S. Private*, pg. 175
Campbell, Thomas R., Pres.--AC Products, Inc., Placentia, CA; *U.S. Public*, pg. 1346
Campbell, William, Pres.--Allmetal Screw Products Corp., Deer Park, NY; *U.S. Private*, pg. 41
Campbell, William, Pres.--Allmetal Screw Products Corp, Cleveland, OH; *U.S. Private*, pg. 41
Campbell, William, Pres.--Allmetal Screw Products Corp, Baltimore, MD; *U.S. Private*, pg. 41
Campbell, William M., Chm. Bd. & Pres.--Camalloy, Incorporated, Washington, PA; *U.S. Private*, pg. 202
Campbell, William V., Pres. & Chief Exec. Officer--Intuit, Inc., Mountain View, CA; *U.S. Public*, pg. 911
Camperi, S., Pres.--SAE Engineering, Inc., Santa Clara, CA; *U.S. Private*, pg. 955
Campino, Pedro B., Pres.--Compania Minera Cerro Colorado Limitada, Santiago, Chile; *Int'l*, pg. 1118
Campos, Antonio, Pres.--Banco Central Canada, Toronto, Canada; *Int'l*, pg. 140
Campos, Rafael del Riego, Pres.--SODICAMAN - Sociedad Para el Desarrollo Industrial de Castilla-La Mancha, S.A., Guadalajara, Spain; *Int'l*, pg. 1225
Camunas, D. Julio, Pres.--Compania Gestora de Servicio Mensatel, S.A., Madrid, Spain; *Int'l*, pg. 1372
Canaan, David, Sr. Mng. Partner--SBG Enterprise, San Francisco, CA; *Int'l*, pg. 1483
Canale, John D., Pres.--D. Canale Food Services, Inc., Memphis, TN; *U.S. Private*, pg. 204
Candela, John A., Pres. & Chief Exec. Officer--The First National Bank of St. Mary's, Leonardtown, MD; *U.S. Public*, pg. 1089
Candela, Peter R., Pres. & Chief Exec. Officer--Pinnacle Bank, Valparaiso, IN; *U.S. Public*, pg. 1297
Candell, Thomas M., Pres. & Chief Exec. Officer--Rocor Transportation Companies Inc., Oklahoma City, OK; *U.S. Private*, pg. 938
Canet, Gerardo, Chm. Bd., Pres. & Chief Exec. Officer--IntegraMed America, Purchase, NY; *U.S. Public*, pg. 883
Canfield, Arthur J., III, Pres.--Select Canfield, Chicago, IL; *U.S. Private*, pg. 982
Canino, Joel, Pres.--CNF Industries Inc., Meriden, CT; *U.S. Public*, pg. 950
Cankes, Robert, Pres. & Chief Exec. Officer--Christian Dior Perfumes Inc., New York, NY; *Int'l*, pg. 781
Cannen, John, Pres.--First National Bank, Kearney, NE; *U.S. Public*, pg. 629
Canning, Simon, Pres. & Chief Oper. Officer--SBC Warburg Dillon Read, Stamford, CT; *Int'l*, pg. 1329
Canning, Simon, Pres. & Chief Exec. Officer--SBC Warburg Dillon Read Inc., Boston, MA; *Int'l*, pg. 1329
Canning, Simon, Pres. & Chief Exec. Officer--SBC Warburg Dillon Read Inc., New York, NY; *Int'l*, pg. 1329
Canno, Jonathon S., Chm. Bd., Pres. & Chief Oper. Officer--Equitable Bag Company, Inc., Florence, KY; *U.S. Private*, pg. 380
Cannon, Brown, Pres.--Cody Company, Denver, CO; *U.S. Private*, pg. 249
Cannon, Dean G., Chm. Bd. & Pres.--Cannon Express Inc., Springdale, AR; *U.S. Public*, pg. 301
Cannon, Douglas, Pres.--ITT Controls & Instruments Division, Midland Park, NJ; *U.S. Public*, pg. 860
Cannon, Francis, Pres.--DeVRY Institute of Technology, Irving, TX; *U.S. Public*, pg. 504
Cannon, Kent, Pres.--Beneficial Life Insurance, Salt Lake City, UT; *U.S. Private*, pg. 327
Cannon, Russell, Publr.--The Daily Journal, Park Hills, MO; *U.S. Public*, pg. 1343
Cannova, Carl S., Pres.--Sysco Food Services of West Coast Florida, Inc., Palmetto, FL; *U.S. Public*, pg. 1552
Cantalupo, James R., Pres. & Chief Exec. Officer-Intl.--McDonald's Corporation, Oak Brook, IL; *U.S. Public*, pg. 1068
Cantor, Paul G.S., Pres. & Chief Exec. Officer--Confederation Life Insurance Company, Toronto, Canada; *Int'l*, pg. 325
Cantrell, Ronald, Pres.--Miller Fluid Power Corp., Bensenville, IL; *U.S. Private*, pg. 747
Cantrell, Wesley, Pres. & Chief Exec. Officer--Lanier Worldwide Inc., Atlanta, GA; *U.S. Public*, pg. 791
Cantrell, William, Pres.--Peoples Gas System, Inc., Tampa, FL; *U.S. Public*, pg. 1565
Cantu, Carlos H., Pres. & Chief Exec. Officer--The ServiceMaster Company, Downers Grove, IL; *U.S. Public*, pg. 1461
Cantwell, Jim N., Pres.--SCANA Petroleum Resources, Inc., Houston, TX; *U.S. Public*, pg. 1436
Capaldini, Mark, Pres. & Chief Exec. Officer--Congressional Information Service (CIS), Bethesda, MD; *Int'l*, pg. 1096
Capell, Peter, Pres.--Snacks Unlimited Division, Minneapolis, MN; *U.S. Public*, pg. 718
Caplan, James A., Chm. Bd., Pres., Treas., Prod. Mgr. & Chief Engr.--Capp, Inc., Clifton Heights, PA; *U.S. Private*, pg. 207
Capon, James, Pres.--Dockers Brand, San Francisco, CA; *U.S. Private*, pg. 663
Capone, Daniel J., Jr., Pres. & Chief Exec. Officer--Proteon, Inc., Westborough, MA; *U.S. Public*, pg. 1336
Caponecchi, August J., Pres.--Tactair Fluid Controls Corp., Liverpool, NY; *U.S. Private*, pg. 1196
Caporella, Nick A., Chm. Bd., Pres., Chief Exec. Officer & Chief Fin. Officer--National Beverage Corp., Plantation, FL; *U.S. Public*, pg. 1153
Cappelletti, John M., Jr., Pres.--Putman Publishing Co., Itasca, IL; *U.S. Private*, pg. 896
Cappola, Dave, Pres.--Globe Mortgage America, LLC., River Edge, NJ; *U.S. Private*, pg. 458
Capps, Thomas E., Chm. Bd., Pres. & Chief Exec. Officer--Dominion Resources, Inc., Richmond, VA; *U.S. Public*, pg. 516
Capriotti, Laurence, Pres. & Chief Exec. Officer--Intercounty Title Co. of Illinois, Chicago, IL; *U.S. Private*, pg. 567
Caputo, Anthony, Pres.--Spar Aviation Services, Mississauga, Canada; *Int'l*, pg. 1288
Caraballo, Malcolm J., Pres.--Wireless Products Group, Palo Alto, CA; *U.S. Public*, pg. 1745
Carabini, Louis E., Chm. Bd. & Pres.--Monex Deposit Co., Newport Beach, CA; *U.S. Private*, pg. 757
Caraci, Philip D., Pres.--Saul Centers Inc., Chevy Chase, MD; *U.S. Public*, pg. 1435
Caravia, Manuel, Pres.--Komfort Corporation, Milwaukie, OR; *U.S. Public*, pg. 1602
Carberry, Robert L., Chm. Bd., Pres. & Chief Exec. Officer--CyberGuard Corporation, Fort Lauderdale, FL; *U.S. Public*, pg. 470
Carbonari, Frank, Pres.--Kilgore Operations, Toone, TN; *U.S. Public*, pg. 47
Carbonell, Robert J., Pres. & Chief Exec. Officer--Tetley USA Inc., Shelton, CT; *Int'l*, pg. 1377
Carbonne, S., Pres. & Dir.-Foto Division--Agfa-Gevaert S.A., Rueil-Malmaison, France; *Int'l*, pg. 174
Carbonnier, Jean Claude, Pres.--Zimmer S.A., Vitry-sur-Seine, France; *U.S. Public*, pg. 257
Carcelle, Yves, Pres.--LVMH Moet Hennessy Louis Vuitton, Paris, France; *Int'l*, pg. 779
Carcich, James J., Pres.--BMCA Insulation Products, Inc., Ontario, CA; *U.S. Private*, pg. 433
Carcieri, Donald, Pres.--Cookson America Inc., Providence, RI; *Int'l*, pg. 328
Card, Wesley R., Pres.--Jones Investment Co., Inc., Wilmington, DE; *U.S. Public*, pg. 933
Cardarelli, Donald P., Pres. & Chief Exec. Officer--Agway, Inc., De Witt, NY; *U.S. Private*, pg. 27
Cardenas, Francisco, Pres.--Leo Burnett S.A. de C.V., Mexico, Mexico; *U.S. Private*, pg. 185
Carder, John, Pres.--Carder, Inc., Lamar, CO; *U.S. Private*, pg. 208
Carder, John, Pres.--Ranchers Supply Company, Inc., Lamar, CO; *U.S. Private*, pg. 908
Carderas, Rafael, Pres.--Carvel Print Grupo Serigraph, Queretaro, Mexico; *U.S. Private*, pg. 985
Cardillo, Harry M., Pres.--Habisat Globe Inc., Buffalo, NY; *Int'l*, pg. 585
Cardillo, Michael J., Pres.--U.S. Healthcare, Inc., Blue Bell, PA; *U.S. Public*, pg. 26
Cardin, R. Larry, Pres. & Chief Exec. Officer--Regions Bank/Columbus, Columbus, GA; *U.S. Public*, pg. 1372
Cardinal, Claus, Pres. & Chief Exec. Officer--Jefferson Insurance Company of New York, Jersey City, NJ; *Int'l*, pg. 59
Cardis, Don, Pres.--Schneller, Inc., Kent, OH; *U.S. Private*, pg. 971
Cardon, William R., Pres.--Kaufman and Broad Coastal, Newport Beach, CA; *U.S. Public*, pg. 945
Cardoro, John J., Pres.--Entergy Louisiana, Inc., New Orleans, LA; *U.S. Public*, pg. 586
Cardwell, Harvey, Pres.--Robin's Foods Inc., Thunder Bay, Canada; *Int'l*, pg. 1195
Cardy, Robert W., Chm., Pres. & Chief Exec. Officer--Carpenter Technology Corporation, Reading, PA; *U.S. Public*, pg. 307
Carey, D.J., Pres.--Noville, South Hackensack, NJ; *U.S. Private*, pg. 808
Carey, D.L., Pres.--Knouse Foods Inc., Peach Glen, PA; *U.S. Private*, pg. 627
Carey, Don, Pres.--Ohio Valley Aluminum Company, Shelbyville, KY; *U.S. Private*, pg. 567
Carey, Francis J., Pres. & Mng. Dir.--W.P. Carey & Co., Inc., New York, NY; *U.S. Private*, pg. 209
Carey, Gene E., Pres. & Chief Oper. Officer--Spencer Gifts, Inc., Egg Harbor Township, NJ; *Int'l*, pg. 1216
Carfora, Alfred, Pres. & Chief Exec. Officer--Duty Free International, Inc., Ridgefield, CT; *Int'l*, pg. 103
Cargile, David L., Chm. Bd., Pres. & Chief Exec. Officer--Centris Group Inc., Costa Mesa, CA; *U.S. Public*, pg. 328
Cargiulo, Ralph J., Pres. & Chief Exec. Officer--The United States Life Ins. Co. In the City of New York, New York, NY; *U.S. Public*, pg. 77
Cariani, Paul R., Pres. & Chief Exec. Officer--Maine Public Service Company, Presque Isle, ME; *U.S. Public*, pg. 1038
Carideo, Frank, Pres.--Fire Control Instruments, Inc., Waltham, MA; *U.S. Private*, pg. 406
Carideo, Frank H., Pres.--Fire Controls Instruments, Waltham, MA; *U.S. Public*, pg. 1306

Caridis, Tony, Chm. Bd. & Pres.--Heat & Control, Inc., Hayward, CA; *U.S. Private*, pg. 518
Carifa, John D., Pres., Chief Oper. Officer & Chief Fin. Officer--Alliance Capital Management Corp., New York, NY; *U.S. Public*, pg. 589
Carl, Fred, Jr., Chm. Bd., Pres. & Chief Exec. Officer--Viking Range Corp., Greenwood, MS; *U.S. Private*, pg. 1140
Carlberg, Anders G., Pres.--Axel Johnson International AB, Kista, Sweden; *Int'l*, pg. 709
Carlberg, W. Charles, Pres. & Chief Exec. Officer--Rives Carlberg, Houston, TX; *U.S. Private*, pg. 934
Carlbom, Chuck, Pres., Chief Exec. Officer & Sec.--United Grocers Inc., Portland, OR; *U.S. Private*, pg. 1122
Carlen, Hilean, Pres.--NCC Eskilstuna, Eskilstuna, Sweden; *Int'l*, pg. 899
Carley, Stephen, Pres. & Chief Oper. Officer--Universal Studios Hollywood, Universal City, CA; *Int'l*, pg. 1216
Carlile, Rex, Pres.--Trim Trends, Farmington Hills, MI; *U.S. Public*, pg. 796
Carlin, Carlo Graf, Pres.--Allianz RAS Argentina, Buenos Aires, Argentina; *Int'l*, pg. 60
Carlisle, Brian, Chm. Bd. & Chief Exec. Officer--Adept Technology, Inc., San Jose, CA; *U.S. Public*, pg. 19
Carlisle, Brian, Mng. Dir.--Kraft Jacobs Suchard, Cheltenham, United Kingdom; *U.S. Public*, pg. 1290
Carlisle, Van, Pres. & Chief Exec. Officer--Fire King International, Inc., New Albany, IN; *U.S. Private*, pg. 406
Carlisle, Wayne, Pres.--Carlisle Equipment Company, Wilder, KY; *U.S. Private*, pg. 211
Carlson, Cynthia, Pres. & Chief Exec. Officer--American Enterprise Investment Services, Inc., Minneapolis, MN; *U.S. Public*, pg. 73
Carlson, D.A., Jr., Pres., Chief Exec. Officer & Treas.--Ziegler Securities Division, Chicago, IL; *U.S. Public*, pg. 1792
Carlson, Donald, Pres.--Carlson Systems, Omaha, NE; *U.S. Private*, pg. 212
Carlson, Gary E., Pres. & Mng. Dir.--Cyanamid Canada Inc., Markham, Canada; *U.S. Public*, pg. 80
Carlson, Greg, Pres.--Marco Sales Co., Saint Louis, MO; *U.S. Private*, pg. 628
Carlson, H. Gary, Dr., Chm. Bd., Pres. & Chief Exec. Officer--ElecSys Inc., Peoria, IL; *U.S. Private*, pg. 367
Carlson, John, Pres.--Bunzl Distribution USA Inc., Saint Louis, MO; *Int'l*, pg. 233
Carlson, LeRoy T., Jr., Pres. & Chief Exec. Officer--Telephone and Data Systems, Inc., Chicago, IL; *U.S. Public*, pg. 1570
Carlson, Lisa, Principal--The PowerBase Marketing Group, Dallas, TX; *U.S. Private*, pg. 651
Carlson, Robert F., Jr., Pres.--Seabeam Instruments, Inc., Walpole, MA; *U.S. Private*, pg. 228
Carlson, Robert F., Sr., Pres.--Channel Technologies, Inc., Santa Barbara, CA; *U.S. Private*, pg. 228
Carlson, Sandra, Pres. & Creative Dir.--Carlson & Partners, Inc., New York, NY; *U.S. Private*, pg. 211
Carlson, Scott, Pres. & Chief Oper. Officer--Westin, Inc., Omaha, NE; *U.S. Private*, pg. 1169
Carlson, Victor E., Pres., Chief Oper. Officer, Chief Exec. Officer--Foga Systems, Oxnard, CA; *Int'l*, pg. 496
Carlsson, Leif E., Pres.--ITT Flygt AB, Solna, Sweden; *U.S. Public*, pg. 860
Carlstrom, Errol, Pres. & Chief Oper. Officer--Sunrise Leasing Corporation, Golden Valley, MN; *U.S. Public*, pg. 1535
Carlton, Donald M., Pres. & Chief Exec. Officer--Radian International LLC, Austin, TX; *U.S. Public*, pg. 522
Carlton, Edward, Jr., Pres. & Chief Exec. Officer--Corrugated Metals, Inc., Bedford Park, IL; *U.S. Private*, pg. 277
Carmack, Terry, Pres.--New Horizons LLC, Cincinnati, OH; *U.S. Private*, pg. 794
Carmazzi, Frank, Pres. & Chief Exec. Officer--Persingers, Inc., Charleston, WV; *U.S. Private*, pg. 855
Carmichael, Jr., Robert L., Pres.--Commercial Bank and Trust Company of Troup County, La Grange, GA; *U.S. Public*, pg. 1549
Carmody, James M., Pres.--Operations & Maintenance Division, Cleveland, OH; *U.S. Public*, pg. 1134
Carmody, Thomas R., Chm. Bd., Pres. & Chief Exec. Officer--American Business Products, Inc., Atlanta, GA; *U.S. Public*, pg. 70
Carnahan, Carolyn W., Pres.--Woodfin Pontiac-Isuzu, Baton Rouge, LA; *U.S. Private*, pg. 1187
Carnevale, A.R., Pres. & Chief Exec. Officer--Bradford-White Corporation, Ambler, PA; *U.S. Private*, pg. 164
Carney, John D., Pres.--Blackstone Valley Electric Co., Lincoln, RI; *U.S. Public*, pg. 549
Carney, John D., Pres.--Newport Electric Corporation, Middletown, RI; *U.S. Public*, pg. 550
Carney, John J., Pres.--Spectra-Physics USA, Inc., Blue Bell, PA; *Int'l*, pg. 1289
Carney, Peter Roy, Pres.--Superior Graphite Co., Chicago, IL; *U.S. Private*, pg. 1054
Carni, Giora, Pres. & Chief Exec. Officer--Clay-Park Labs, Inc., Bronx, NY; *Int'l*, pg. 30
Carns, Charles E., Pres.--Mears Transportation Group, Orlando, FL; *U.S. Private*, pg. 726
Carollo, Jerome, Pres.--Kaiser Electro Optics, Carlsbad, CA; *U.S. Private*, pg. 605
Carota, Richard J., Chm. Bd., Pres. & Chief Exec. Officer--Finch, Pruyn & Co., Inc., Glens Falls, NY; *U.S. Private*, pg. 405
Carothers, W. Jay, Pres. & Chief Oper. Officer--Filene's Basement, Inc., Wellesley, MA; *U.S. Public*, pg. 622
Carozza, E.J., Pres.--Certech International Ltd., Corby, United Kingdom; *U.S. Public*, pg. 308
Carp, Daniel A., Pres. & Chief Oper. Officer--Eastman Kodak Company, Rochester, NY; *U.S. Public*, pg. 550
Carpenter, Alvin R., Pres. & Chief Exec. Officer--CSX Transportation, Inc., Jacksonville, FL; *U.S. Public*, pg. 284
Carpenter, Dave, Pres. & Chief Exec. Officer--UniHealth, Burbank, CA; *U.S. Private*, pg. 1117
Carpenter, David O., Pres.--Great Lakes Carbon Corp., Houston, TX; *U.S. Private*, pg. 540
Carpenter, George E., Pres.--Semac Industries Inc., Millersburg, OH; *U.S. Private*, pg. 983
Carpenter, K.M., Pres.--Curtis-Toledo, Inc., Saint Louis, MO; *U.S. Private*, pg. 298
Carpenter, Larry, Pres. & Chief Exec. Officer--Spring Arbor Distributors, Belleville, MI; *U.S. Private*, pg. 563
Carpenter, Richard, Pres.--Wyatt Energy Incorporated, New Haven, CT; *U.S. Private*, pg. 1193
Carpenter, Richard W., Pres. & Chief Exec. Officer--Leisure Technology, Inc., Atlanta, GA; *U.S. Private*, pg. 659
Carpenter, Terry R., Pres. & Chief Exec. Officer--Indiana Lawrence Bank, North Manchester, IN; *U.S. Public*, pg. 633
Carpenter, W.R., V.P. & Gen. Mgr.--Killark Electric Manufacturing Co., Saint Louis, MO; *U.S. Public*, pg. 844
Carpenter, William D., Pres.--Teal Electronics, San Diego, CA; *U.S. Public*, pg. 1419
Carpenter, William M., Pres. & Chief Exec. Officer--Bausch & Lomb Incorporated, Rochester, NY; *U.S. Public*, pg. 194
Carper, Howell P., Pres. & Chief Exec. Officer--Iceland Seafood Corporation, Newport, VA; *U.S. Private*, pg. 556
Carr, Andrew D., Pres.--J&H Marsh & McLennan Management Services (Bermuda) Ltd., Hamilton, Bermuda; *U.S. Public*, pg. 1049
Carr, Jay F., Pres.--Hershey Pasta and Grocery Group, Hershey, PA; *U.S. Public*, pg. 812
Carr, Jay F., Pres.--Hershey International, Hershey, PA; *U.S. Public*, pg. 812
Carr, John, III, Pres. & Chief Exec. Officer--Central Supply Co., Inc., Indianapolis, IN; *U.S. Private*, pg. 225
Carr, Michael T., Pres. & Chief Exec. Officer--Weider Publications, Inc., Woodland Hills, CA; *U.S. Private*, pg. 1159
Carr, Robert O., Chm. Bd. & Pres.--Carr Real Estate Services, Washington, DC; *U.S. Public*, pg. 309
Carr, Robin, Sr. V.P. & Brand Mktg. Partner--DMB&B Detroit, Troy, MI; *U.S. Private*, pg. 302
Carr, Thomas A., Pres. & Chief Exec. Officer--CarrAmerica Realty, Washington, DC; *U.S. Public*, pg. 308
Carrafiello, Gerald A., Pres.--Carrafiello, Diehl & Associates, Inc., Irvington, NY; *U.S. Private*, pg. 215
Carraher, Richard, Pres. & Chief Exec. Officer--Fragrance Resources, Inc., Clifton, NJ; *U.S. Private*, pg. 423
Carrara, G., Pres.--Italimpianti of America, Incorporated, Coraopolis, PA; *Int'l*, pg. 655
Carrera-Justiz, Francisco, Pres.--Bacardi-Martini Product Development Inc., Jacksonville, FL; *Int'l*, pg. 131
Carrera-Justiz, Francisco, Pres.--Bacardi-Martini Product Quality Americas Inc., Jacksonville, FL; *Int'l*, pg. 131
Carrington, Beth R., Pres.--Acutex Division, Whitehall, MI; *U.S. Public*, pg. 1421
Carrion, Richard L., Chm. Bd., Pres. & Chief Exec. Officer--Banco Popular de Puerto Rico, San Juan, PR; *U.S. Public*, pg. 175
Carrion, Richard L., Chm. Bd., Pres. & Chief Exec. Officer--BanPonce Corporation, Hato Rey, PR; *U.S. Public*, pg. 176
Carris, William, Pres.--Carris Financial Group, Rutland, VT; *U.S. Private*, pg. 215
Carrizosa, Fernando, Pres.--Wackenhut Intl., Inc., Coral Gables, FL; *U.S. Public*, pg. 1731
Carroll, Bill J., Pres.--Saginaw Overseas Corporation, Detroit, MI; *U.S. Public*, pg. 723
Carroll, Charles A., Pres. & Chief Oper. Officer--Rubbermaid Incorporated, Wooster, OH; *U.S. Public*, pg. 1411
Carroll, David M., Pres.--First Union National Bank of Florida, Jacksonville, FL; *U.S. Public*, pg. 640
Carroll, Esme, Pres. & Chief Exec. Officer--Ambrose Carr Linton Carroll Inc., Toronto, Canada; *Int'l*, pg. 71
Carroll, James E., Pres. & Chief Oper. Officer--Bradley Corporation, Menomonee Falls, WI; *U.S. Private*, pg. 164
Carroll, Michael P., Pres.--Millipore Asia Limited, Kowloon, Hong Kong; *U.S. Public*, pg. 1113
Carroll, Philip J., Pres. & Chief Exec. Officer--Shell Oil Company, Houston, TX; *Int'l*, pg. 1136
Carroll, Richard, Pres.--Sommer & Maca Industries, Inc., Cicero, IL; *U.S. Private*, pg. 1013
Carroll, Thomas, Partner--Messner Vetere Berger McNamee Schmetterer/EURO RSCG, New York, NY; *Int'l*, pg. 602
Carroll, Thomas, Pres.--McCain Bindery Systems, Inc., Chicago, IL; *U.S. Private*, pg. 719
Carroll, Thomas E., Pres. & Chief Exec. Officer--MEDIQ Incorporated, Pennsauken, NJ; *U.S. Public*, pg. 1081
Carruthers, George, Pres., Chief Exec. & Chief Fin. Officer--Polycoat Systems, Inc., Hudson Falls, NY; *U.S. Private*, pg. 875
Carse, Wayne L., Pres.--Carse Oil Co. Inc., Orlando, FL; *U.S. Private*, pg. 216
Carson, Bruce M., Pres.--Dot Printer, Inc., Irvine, CA; *U.S. Private*, pg. 341
Carson, Charles E., Jr., Pres.--Minarik Corp, Glendale, CA; *U.S. Private*, pg. 749
Carson, Susan, Pres.--Herman Miller, Ltd., Toronto, Canada; *U.S. Public*, pg. 1112
Carson, Terry, Pres.--Arkansas State Bank, Clarksville, AR; *U.S. Public*, pg. 630
Carson, W. Howard, Pres.--Peabody Western Coal Company, Flagstaff, AZ; *Int'l*, pg. 594
Carson, W. Pierce, Ph.D., Pres. & Chief Exec. Officer--Nord Resources Corporation, Albuquerque, NM; *U.S. Public*, pg. 1188
Carstarphen, J.M., Chm. Bd., Pres. & Chief Exec. Officer--Stowe-Pharr Mills, Inc., Mc Adenville, NC; *U.S. Private*, pg. 1045
Carstens, Matthew, Pres.--United Steel & Wire Co., Battle Creek, MI; *U.S. Private*, pg. 1126
Carstens, Robert, Sr. Partner & MIS Dir.--EURO RSCG Tatham, Chicago, IL; *Int'l*, pg. 601
Carstens, Tom, Pres.--ATHOL Corporation, Butner, NC; *U.S. Private*, pg. 94
Carstensen, Teri, Pres.--Fiserv Fresno, Inc., Fresno, CA; *U.S. Public*, pg. 647
Carswell, Charles, Pres.--Lytron Incorporated, Woburn, MA; *U.S. Private*, pg. 684
Carter, Arthur L., Pres.--Shepaug Corporation, New York, NY; *U.S. Private*, pg. 993
Carter, Bryan, Pres.--Carter-Jones Companies, Inc., Kent, OH; *U.S. Private*, pg. 217
Carter, Charles A., Pres. & Chief Oper. Officer--MET Solutions, LLC, Raleigh, NC; *U.S. Public*, pg. 1642
Carter, Donald, Pres.--DC Company, Fresno, CA; *Int'l*, pg. 736
Carter, Frank H., Pres. & Chief Exec. Officer--Wellington Industries Inc., Madison, GA; *U.S. Private*, pg. 1161
Carter, J., Pres.--Keystone Thermometrics Corporation, Saint Marys, PA; *Int'l*, pg. 208
Carter, J. Wesley, Pres. & Chief Oper. Officer--Extendicare Inc., Markham, Canada; *Int'l*, pg. 468
Carter, Jerry, Pres.--Marta Technologies, Inc., Nashville, TN; *U.S. Public*, pg. 46
Carter, Joan, Pres., Chief Oper. Officer & Corp. Sec.--U.M. Holding Limited, Haddonfield, NJ; *U.S. Private*, pg. 1113
Carter, Joan, Acting Pres.--Life Extension Institute, New York, NY; *U.S. Private*, pg. 1114
Carter, John, Jr., Pres.--Thermometrics, Inc., Edison, NJ; *Int'l*, pg. 208
Carter, Jud, Pres.--Bell-Carter Foods, Inc., Lafayette, CA; *U.S. Private*, pg. 131
Carter, Mike, Pres.--Passat Laundry Systems, Grand Prairie, TX; *U.S. Private*, pg. 842
Carter, P., Pres.--Metro Brewery, Etobicoke, Canada; *Int'l*, pg. 679
Carter, Robert E., Pres.--Ketchum, Inc., Pittsburgh, PA; *U.S. Private*, pg. 617
Carter, Sam, Chm. Bd. & Pres.--Carter Companies, Kansas City, MO; *U.S. Private*, pg. 216
Carter, Stephen, Pres. & Chief Exec. Officer--Concordia Publishing House, Saint Louis, MO; *U.S. Private*, pg. 261
Carter, Stephen M., Pres. & Chief Exec. Officer--Southwestern Bell Telecom, Dallas, TX; *U.S. Public*, pg. 1416
Carter, Thomas F., Jr., Pres. & Chief Oper. Officer--QST Environmental Inc., Peoria, IL; *U.S. Public*, pg. 367
Carter, Wayne S., Pres.--Chesapeake Insurance Division, Richmond, VA; *U.S. Public*, pg. 215
Cartwright, J. David, Pres.--Cooper Hand Tools, Raleigh, NC; *U.S. Public*, pg. 444
Cartwright, Peter, Chm. Bd., Pres. & CHief Exec. Officer--Calpine Corporation, San Jose, CA; *U.S. Public*, pg. 296
Carty, Donald J., Pres.--AMR Corporation, Fort Worth, TX; *U.S. Public*, pg. 9
Carty, Donald J., Pres.--American Airlines, Inc., Fort Worth, TX; *U.S. Public*, pg. 9
Caruso, John E., Chm. Bd. & Pres.--Regency Dodge Inc., Jacksonville, FL; *U.S. Private*, pg. 918
Caruso, Joseph A., Pres.--Jordan Tamraz Caruso Advertising, Inc., Chicago, IL; *U.S. Private*, pg. 599
Caruso, Paul, Pres.--Oildyne, Minneapolis, MN; *U.S. Public*, pg. 411
Carvelli, A.J., Vice Chm. & Chief Exec. Officer--Pannier Corporation, Pittsburgh, PA; *U.S. Private*, pg. 837
Carver, Martin G., Chm. Bd., Pres. & Chief Exec. Officer--Bandag, Incorporated, Muscatine, IA; *U.S. Public*, pg. 177
Casados, Tony, Pres.--Plains Electric Generation Transmission Co-Op, Inc., Albuquerque, NM; *U.S. Private*, pg. 868
Caschette, Gerard, Pres. & Treas.--Genesee Metal Stampings, Inc., West Henrietta, NY; *U.S. Private*, pg. 446
Caschette, Jack, Pres.--Genesee Wester, Englewood, CO; *U.S. Private*, pg. 446
Case, Stephen M., Chm. Bd., Pres, Chief Exec. & Oper. Officer--America Online Incorporated, Dulles, VA; *U.S. Public*, pg. 66
Case, Steven K., Pres.--CyberOptics Corporation, Golden Valley, MN; *U.S. Public*, pg. 470
Casebeer, Scott, Pres. & Chief Exec. Officer--Capitol Chevrolet Cadillac GEO Subaru Inc., Salem, OR; *U.S. Private*, pg. 206
Casella, John W., Chm. Bd., Pres. & Chief Exec. Officer--Casella Waste Systems, Inc., Rutland, VT; *U.S. Public*, pg. 312
Caserta, Frank N., Pres.--CDI Telecommunications, Inc., Scottsdale, AZ; *U.S. Public*, pg. 277
Casey, Brian T., Pres.--Thomas Engineering Inc., Hoffman Estates, IL; *U.S. Private*, pg. 1082
Casey, Donald P., Pres. & Chief Tech. Officer--Wang Laboratories, Inc., Billerica, MA; *U.S. Public*, pg. 1737
Casey, Edward F., Pres. & Chief Exec. Officer--Stewart Smith Group, Inc., Nashville, TN; *Int'l*, pg. 1508
Casey, Kerry, Sr. Partner & Exec. Creative Dir.--Carmichael Lynch, Inc., Minneapolis, MN; *U.S. Private*, pg. 213
Casey, Richard L., Chm. Bd., Pres. & Chief Exec. Officer--Scios Inc., Mountain View, CA; *U.S. Public*, pg. 1444
Casey, Shawn M., Vice Chm., Pres. & Chief Exec. Officer--Success Development International, Jacksonville, FL; *U.S. Private*, pg. 1048
Cash, Francis W., Chm. Bd., Pres. & Chief Exec. Officer--Red Roof Inns, Inc., Hilliard, OH; *U.S. Public*, pg. 1369
Cash, R.D., Chm. Bd., Pres. & Chief Exec. Officer--Questar Corporation, Salt Lake City, UT; *U.S. Public*, pg. 1352
Caskey, Rich, Pres.--Sioux Tools, Inc., Sioux City, IA; *U.S. Public*, pg. 1480
Casner, Paul G., Jr., Pres.--Electronic Systems Group, Gaithersburg, MD; *U.S. Public*, pg. 474
Cass, Ronald A., Chm. Bd., Pres., Chief Exec. Officer & Treas.--Hospital Staffing Services, Inc., Fort Lauderdale, FL; *U.S. Public*, pg. 840
Cass, William J., Pres.--De Nooyer Chevrolet Inc., Albany, NY; *U.S. Private*, pg. 318
Cassady, Kenneth, Pres.--Monarch Marking Systems, Miamisburg, OH; *U.S. Public*, pg. 1266

Cassese, John J., Chm. Bd., Pres., Chief Oper. & Chief Exec. Officer--Computer Horizons Corp., Mountain Lakes, NJ; *U.S. Public*, pg. 421
Cassese, Patrick J., Chm. Bd., Pres. & Chief Exec. Officer--Antares Group Inc., Cleveland, OH; *U.S. Private*, pg. 76
Cassetty, Fred, Chm. Bd., Pres. & Chief Exec. Officer--Alley-Cassetty Coal Co., Nashville, TN; *U.S. Private*, pg. 37
Cassina, Franco, Pres.--Cassina, Milan, Italy; *Int'l*, pg. 570
Cassner, Alvin B., Pres. & Chief Exec. Officer--Rotary Forms Press, Inc., Hillsboro, OH; *U.S. Private*, pg. 947
Castagha, Gary, Pres.--Chemdal Corporation, Palatine, IL; *U.S. Public*, pg. 64
Castagna, Patrick J., Pres.--Carlos R. Leffler Inc., Richland, PA; *U.S. Private*, pg. 658
Castaldo, Nicholas, Pres. & Chief Oper. Officer--Pollo Tropical, Inc., Miami, FL; *U.S. Public*, pg. 1315
Castellana, Peter, Jr., Pres.--Western Beef, Inc., Ridgewood, NY; *U.S. Public*, pg. 1758
Castellani, Lawrence, Pres. & Chief Exec. Officer--Tops Markets, Inc., Amherst, NY; *Int'l*, pg. 750
Castellano, Robert J., Pres.--Cucina Classica Italiana, Inc., Lakewood, NJ; *U.S. Public*, pg. 1435
Castellano, Steve, Pres.--Todd-AO Studios/East, New York, NY; *U.S. Public*, pg. 1619
Castellini, Clateo, Chm. Bd., Pres. & Chief Exec. Officer--Becton Dickinson & Company, Franklin Lakes, NJ; *U.S. Public*, pg. 199
Castello, John L., Chm. Bd., Chief Exec. Officer & Pres.--XOMA Corporation, Berkeley, CA; *U.S. Public*, pg. 1786
Casten, Thomas R., Pres. & Chief Exec. Officer--Trigen Energy Corporation, White Plains, NY; *U.S. Public*, pg. 1637
Castle, A.M., Pres.--Astro Homes, Shippenville, PA; *U.S. Public*, pg. 318
Castle, A.M., Pres.--Brigadier Homes of North Carolina, Nashville, NC; *U.S. Public*, pg. 318
Castle, A.M., Pres.--Mansion Homes, Robbins, NC; *U.S. Public*, pg. 318
Castle, Frank E., Pres. & Chief Exec. Officer--Components Corporation Of America, Dallas, TX; *U.S. Private*, pg. 259
Castle, Jim, Pres. & Chief Exec. Officer--D.A. Stuart Company, Warrenville, IL; *U.S. Private*, pg. 1048
Castle, Joseph L., Chm. Bd., Pres. & Chief Exec. Officer--Castle Energy Corporation, Radnor, PA; *U.S. Public*, pg. 313
Castle, Robert L., Pres. & Chief Exec. Officer--VideoServer, Inc., Burlington, MA; *U.S. Public*, pg. 1720
Castonguay, Lee, Pres. & Gen. Mgr.--Hubacher, Cadillac & Landrover Inc., Sacramento, CA; *U.S. Private*, pg. 543
Castor, Joe D., Pres. & Chief Exec. Officer--Westco Products, Inc., Pico Rivera, CA; *Int'l*, pg. 244
Castro, Adolfo, Chief Exec. Officer--Lowe MBAC, Barcelona, Spain; *U.S. Private*, pg. 678
Castro, Antonio, Pres.--Aceromex Atlas, S.A. de C.V., Tlalnepantla, Mexico; *U.S. Public*, pg. 308
Castro, J.H., Pres. & Gen. Mgr.--R.P. Scherer Argentina S.A.I.C., Buenos Aires, Argentina; *U.S. Public*, pg. 1438
Castro, John W., Pres. & Chief Exec. Officer--Merrill Corporation, Saint Paul, MN; *U.S. Public*, pg. 1097
Castrucci, Mike, Pres.--Mike Castrucci Chevrolet, Milford, OH; *U.S. Private*, pg. 219
Casty, Ronald, Pres.--Webster Industries Div., Peabody, MA; *U.S. Private*, pg. 231
Casty, Ronald G., Chm. Bd., Pres., Chief Exec. & Oper. Officer--Chelsea Industries, Inc., Peabody, MA; *U.S. Private*, pg. 231
Casullo, Frank, Pres.--Parsons Precision Products, Inc., Parsons, KS; *U.S. Private*, pg. 598
Cataldo, Robert J., Pres. & Chief Oper. Officer--Hostmark Management Group, Rolling Meadows, IL; *U.S. Private*, pg. 541
Catapole, Steven, Mgr.--Laporte Fluorides, Rotherham, United Kingdom; *Int'l*, pg. 802
Catenacci, Carlo J., Pres.--John Carlo Inc., Clinton Township, MI; *U.S. Private*, pg. 211
Cater, John T., Pres.--Compass Bank Houston, Houston, TX; *U.S. Public*, pg. 419
Cates, Steven T., Pres. & Chief Exec. Officer--Texas Life Insurance Company, Waco, TX; *U.S. Private*, pg. 738
Cathey, Peter, Pres. & Chief Exec. Officer--DFI/Inflight, Inc., Ridgefield, CT; *Int'l*, pg. 103
Cation, Kenneth L., Grp. Pres.--Atlas/Soundolier, Fenton, MO; *U.S. Private*, pg. 64
Catlin, Tucker, Pres.--Juliana Vineyards, Pope Valley, CA; *U.S. Public*, pg. 1383
Cato, Glenn P., Pres. & Chief Exec. Officer--Maxum Health Corp., Dallas, TX; *U.S. Public*, pg. 881
Caton, Robert J., Chm. Bd. & Pres.--Fay, Spofford & Thorndike, Inc., Burlington, MA; *U.S. Private*, pg. 397
Catsimatidis, John, Chm. Bd.--United Acquisition Corporation, New York, NY; *U.S. Private*, pg. 915
Caughman, Gerald W., Pres.--Power Sources, Inc., Charlotte, NC; *U.S. Public*, pg. 344
Caughran, Carl W., Pres. & Chief Exec. Officer--Nalleys Fine Foods, Tacoma, WA; *U.S. Private*, pg. 887
Causey, C.R., Pres.--Puget Western, Inc., Bellevue, WA; *U.S. Public*, pg. 1342
Causey, Jerry L., Pres.--Virginia Natural Gas, Inc., Norfolk, VA; *U.S. Public*, pg. 436
Causley, James F., Jr., Pres.--James Chevrolet Inc., Clinton Township, MI; *U.S. Private*, pg. 580
Causley, Richard, Pres.--Jim Causley Pontiac GMC Inc., Clinton Township, MI; *U.S. Private*, pg. 220
Cavalier, John C., Pres. & Chief Exec. Officer--MapInfo Corp., Troy, NY; *U.S. Public*, pg. 1042
Cavaliere, Phyllis, Pres. & Chief Exec. Officer--Metropolitan Sunday Newspapers, Inc., New York, NY; *U.S. Private*, pg. 739
Cavaliere, Phyllis, Pres. & Chief Exec. Officer--Sunday Magazine Network, New York, NY; *U.S. Private*, pg. 739
Cavalli, Jim I., Pres.--Banner Associates Inc., Laramie, WY; *U.S. Private*, pg. 114
Cavanaugh, Jim, Chm. Bd., Pres., Chief Exec. Officer & Sec.--Jani King International, Inc., Dallas, TX; *U.S. Private*, pg. 581
Cavanaugh, William, III, Pres. & Chief Exec. Officer--Carolina Power & Light Company, Raleigh, NC; *U.S. Public*, pg. 306
Cavanough, Glen, Pres.-Multi-Media Group--Telex Communications, Inc., Minneapolis, MN; *U.S. Private*, pg. 1074
Cavazza, Claudio, Pres. & Mng. Dir.--Sigma-Tau Finanziaria S.p.A., Rome, Italy; *Int'l*, pg. 1248
Cavell, Charles G., Pres. & Chief Exec. Officer--Quebecor Printing, Inc., Montreal, Canada; *Int'l*, pg. 1076
Cavell, Charles G., Pres.--Quebecor Printing Hazleton Inc., Hazleton, PA; *Int'l*, pg. 1076
Cavender, Lea, Chm. Bd. & Pres.--E-Z Bowz, Inc., Sevierville, TN; *U.S. Private*, pg. 352
Caveney, John J., Pres.-Domestic--Panduit Corp., Tinley Park, IL; *U.S. Private*, pg. 836
Cavens, Leonard W., Pres.--Pease Industries, Inc., Fairfield, OH; *U.S. Private*, pg. 845
Cavitt, Jerry, Pres. & Chief Oper. Officer--President Baking Company, Atlanta, GA; *Int'l*, pg. 1069
Cawley, Charles M., Pres.--MBNA Corporation, Wilmington, DE; *U.S. Public*, pg. 1023
Cawley, Charles M., Chm. Bd., Pres. & Chief Exec. Officer--MBNA America Bank N.A., Wilmington, DE; *U.S. Public*, pg. 1023
Cawley, Timothy J., Pres.--Ameritech Small Business Services, Hoffman Estates, IL; *U.S. Public*, pg. 98
Cawly, Robert H., Pres. & Chief Exec. Officer--Sentry Technology Group, Westborough, MA; *U.S. Public*, pg. 1425
Caye, Charles G., Jr., Pres.--W.C. Caye & Company, Inc., Augusta, GA; *U.S. Private*, pg. 220
Cayne, James E., Pres., Chief Exec. Officer & Sr. Mng. Dir.--The Bear Stearns Companies Inc., New York, NY; *U.S. Public*, pg. 197
Cebrian Sanchez, Juan Jose, Pres.--Proyeparsons, C.A., Caracas, Venezuela; *U.S. Private*, pg. 842
Cecchi, Giuseppe, Pres. & Chief Exec. Officer--The IDI Group Companies, Arlington, VA; *U.S. Private*, pg. 554
Cecil, Robert S., Chm. Bd., Pres. & Chief Exec. Officer--Plantronics Inc., Santa Cruz, CA; *U.S. Public*, pg. 1308
Cei, Jay, Pres. & Chief Oper. Officer--Ulbrich Wire, Inc., North Haven, CT; *U.S. Private*, pg. 1115
Ceiley, Glen, Pres. & Chief Exec. Officer--Bisco Industries, Inc, Orange, CA; *U.S. Private*, pg. 145
Ceitlin, Michael Lenn, Pres.--Zivi S.A. Cutelaria, Porto Alegre, Brazil; *Int'l*, pg. 1529
Celauro, John, Pres.--4C Foods Corporation, Brooklyn, NY; *U.S. Private*, pg. 421
Celentano, Domenick, Chm. Bd. & Pres.--Celentano Bros. Inc., Verona, NJ; *U.S. Private*, pg. 221
Celentano, E., Pres.--Getty Oil (Guatemala), Inc., Coral Gables, FL; *U.S. Public*, pg. 1583
Celentano, E., Pres.--Lubricantes y Tambores del Ecuador, C.A., Guayaquil, Ecuador; *U.S. Public*, pg. 1584
Celentano, E., Pres.--Texaco Chile S.A.C., Santiago, Chile; *U.S. Public*, pg. 1584
Celentano, E., Pres.--Texaco Cote d'Ivorie, Abidjan, Cote d'Ivoire; *U.S. Public*, pg. 1584
Celentano, E., Pres.--Texaco Overseas (Nigeria) Petroleum Co., Lagos, Nigeria; *U.S. Public*, pg. 1584
Celentano, E., Pres.--Texaco Uruguay Sociedad Anonima, Montevideo, Uruguay; *U.S. Public*, pg. 1584
Cella, Frank C., Pres. & Chief Exec. Officer--Nestle Canada Inc., North York, Canada; *Int'l*, pg. 921
Centanni, Ross, Pres. & Chief Exec. Officer--Gardner Denver Machinery Inc., Quincy, IL; *U.S. Public*, pg. 703
Centofanti, Louis F., Dr., Chm. Bd., Pres. & Chief Exec. Officer--Perma-Fix Environmental Services, Inc., Gainesville, FL; *U.S. Public*, pg. 1279
Cerasini, Jim, Pres.--Impact Communications Group, Chicago, IL; *U.S. Public*, pg. 1641
Cerbins, Victor, Pres.--Universal Boilers Corp., Galva, IL; *U.S. Private*, pg. 1126
Cereda, Gianni, Pres.--GenCorp Printworld, Monroe, NC; *U.S. Public*, pg. 706
Ceresa, Attilio, Pres.-Italy Opers. & Gen. Mgr.--Biffi Italia S.r.l., Piacenza, Italy; *U.S. Public*, pg. 1650
Ceriana, Carlo, Pres.--Ferrero Inc., Caguas, PR; *Int'l*, pg. 480
Cerillo, Peter, Pres. & Chief Exec. Officer--Shape Inc., Kennebunk, ME; *U.S. Private*, pg. 990
Cerini, F. Brian, Pres. & Chief Exec. Officer--Sierra Capital Management, Northridge, CA; *U.S. Public*, pg. 1742
Cernibori, Livio, Pres.--Neo Abello S.p.A., Ospiate di Bollate, Italy; *Int'l*, pg. 289
Cerny, Ronald, Pres.--The J.M. Ney Company, Bloomfield, CT; *U.S. Public*, pg. 111
Cervellero, Paul B., Pres.--Inductotherm Corp., Rancocas, NJ; *U.S. Private*, pg. 560
Cesarini, Francesco, Chm. Bd.--Banca Popolare di Milano, Milan, Italy; *Int'l*, pg. 137
Cevoli, Vic, Pres.--Cipriani Kremer Design, Boston, MA; *U.S. Private*, pg. 84
Chadha, Xin, Pres.--Osicom Technologies Inc., Santa Monica, CA; *U.S. Public*, pg. 1233
Chadourne, A.P., Bus. Dir.--Sterno, Inc., New York, NY; *U.S. Public*, pg. 397
Chadronnier, J. M., Pres. & Dir. Gen.--Grands Terroirs Associes BV, Nieuw-Vennep, Netherlands; *Int'l*, pg. 751
Chadronnier, J. M., Pres. & Dir. Gen.--Consortium Vinicole de Bordeaux et de la Gironde SA, Parempuyre, France; *Int'l*, pg. 752
Chadronnier, J.M., Pres. & Gen. Dir.--C.V.B.G. (Consortium Vinicole de Bordeaux et de la Gironde), Blanquefort, France; *Int'l*, pg. 751
Chadwick, William, Pres.--Chadwick-Helmuth Company, Inc., El Monte, CA; *U.S. Private*, pg. 227
Chadwick, William H., Pres. & Chief Exec. Officer--Banknorth Group Inc., Burlington, VT; *U.S. Public*, pg. 186
Chadwick, Winslow, Jr., Pres.--Consolidated Companies Inc. (CONCO), Metairie, LA; *U.S. Private*, pg. 265
Chae, Yoon-Byung, Pres.--Ssangyong Developments Pte. Ltd., Singapore, Singapore; *Int'l*, pg. 1292
Chaffee, John, Jr., Pres.--Malrite Communications Group, Inc., Cleveland, OH; *U.S. Private*, pg. 698
Chaffin, R.C., Pres.--Capital Assurance Company, Inc., Coral Gables, FL; *Int'l*, pg. 1257
Chaffin, Richard, Pres.--Gillette Dairy of the Black Hills, Inc., Rapid City, SD; *U.S. Public*, pg. 1152
Chaffin, Richard, Pres.--Nebraska Dairies, Inc., Norfolk, NE; *U.S. Public*, pg. 1152
Chaiken, Eugene B., Chm., Pres. & Chief Exec. Officer--Almo Corp., Philadelphia, PA; *U.S. Private*, pg. 44
Chaikin, Scott, Pres. & Chief Oper. Officer--Dix & Eaton Incorporated, Cleveland, OH; *U.S. Private*, pg. 336
Chaimowitz, Ronald, Pres. & Chief Exec. Officer--GT Interactive Software Corp., New York, NY; *U.S. Public*, pg. 696
Chais, Khom, Pres.--JMP Newcor Holdings Inc., Northbrook, IL; *Int'l*, pg. 1025
Chakkaphak, Pin, Pres. & Chief Exec. Officer--Finance One Public Company Limited, Bangkok, Thailand; *Int'l*, pg. 484
Chaldecott, Axel, Mng. Partner--Howell Henry Chaldecott Lury & Partners, London, United Kingdom; *Int'l*, pg. 637
Chalhoub, Joseph, Pres. & Chief Oper. Officer--Safety-Kleen Corp., Elgin, IL; *U.S. Public*, pg. 1425
Chalmers, A., Pres.--Digitron, West Columbia, SC; *U.S. Private*, pg. 333
Chalmers, Bernie, Pres.--NBS Imprinter, Kitchener, Canada; *Int'l*, pg. 898
Chalmers, David B., Chm. Bd., Pres., Chief Exec. Officer & Treas.--Coral Oil & Gas Inc., Houston, TX; *U.S. Private*, pg. 275
Chaloux, Leonard, Pres.--Taylor Hobson Pneumo, Rolling Meadows, IL; *Int'l*, pg. 1087
Chalsty, John S., Chm. Bd. & Chief Exec. Officer--Donaldson, Lufkin, & Jenrette, Inc., New York, NY; *U.S. Public*, pg. 589
Chaltiel, Victor M.G., Chm. Bd., Pres. & Chief Exec. Officer--Total Renal Care Holdings, Inc., Torrance, CA; *U.S. Public*, pg. 1625
Chamberlain, Robin, Pres.--Snapper Power Equipment, Mc Donough, GA; *U.S. Public*, pg. 1103
Chambers, Chris, Pres.--Continental Homes of California, San Diego, CA; *U.S. Public*, pg. 441
Chambers, Dale, Gen. Mgr.--Empire Livestock Marketing Inc., Syracuse, NY; *U.S. Private*, pg. 308
Chambers, Glenn, Pres.--Heil Environmental Industries, Chattanooga, TN; *U.S. Public*, pg. 520
Chambers, Herb, Pres. & Treas.--Herb Chambers Cos., Somerville, MA; *U.S. Private*, pg. 227
Chambers, John T., Pres. & Chief Exec. Officer--Cisco Systems, Inc., San Jose, CA; *U.S. Public*, pg. 375
Chambers, Raymond, Co-Chief Exec. Officer--Dryper's Corp., Vancouver, WA; *U.S. Private*, pg. 344
Chamides, Ronald H., Pres.--Fleet Capital Leasing, Providence, RI; *U.S. Public*, pg. 650
Champagne, Gilles, Pres. & Chief Exec. Officer--Oceanex, Montreal, Canada; *Int'l*, pg. 924
Champel, Louis, Pres.--Rhodia-Merieux Chile, Santiago, Chile; *Int'l*, pg. 1112
Champion, James K., Pres. & Chief Exec. Officer--Riverdale Chemical Co., Glenwood, IL; *U.S. Private*, pg. 934
Champness, G., Pres. & Chief Exec. Officer--Svedala Industries Inc., York, PA; *Int'l*, pg. 1325
Chan, Matthew, Pres.--Novellus Singapore Pte Ltd., Singapore, Singapore; *U.S. Public*, pg. 1204
Chan, Matthew, Pres.--Intraco Asia Singapore, Singapore, Singapore; *U.S. Public*, pg. 1205
Chan, Matthew, Pres.--Novellus Systems Taiwan, Hsin-chu, Taiwan; *U.S. Public*, pg. 1205
Chan, Matthew, Pres.--Novellus Systems Shanghai, Shanghai, China; *U.S. Public*, pg. 1205
Chan, P.K., Pres.--Hayes Corporation, Norcross, GA; *U.S. Public*, pg. 800
Chance, Richard G., Pres.--Chance Industries, Inc., Wichita, KS; *U.S. Private*, pg. 228
Chandler, J. Harold, Pres. & Chief Exec. Officer--Provident Companies, Inc., Chattanooga, TN; *U.S. Public*, pg. 1337
Chandler, Jeanne, Pres.--Benchmark Appraisal Group, Columbia, MD; *U.S. Public*, pg. 1089
Chandler, Richard H., Chm. Bd.,Pres. & Chief Exec. Officer--Sunrise Medical, Inc., Carlsbad, CA; *U.S. Public*, pg. 1535
Chandler, Scott C., Pres. & Chief Exec. Officer--C-COR Electronics, Inc., State College, PA; *U.S. Public*, pg. 272
Chandler, T.F., Pres. & Chief Exec. Officer--The Western Sugar Company, Denver, CO; *Int'l*, pg. 1357
Chandonnet, Peter, Pres.--SPS Aerospace Products Div., Jenkintown, PA; *U.S. Public*, pg. 1420
Chandran, Robert V., Pres. & Chief Exec. Officer--Chemoil, San Francisco, CA; *U.S. Private*, pg. 233
Chaney, William R., Pres.--Tiffany & Co. International, New York, NY; *U.S. Public*, pg. 1609
Chang, Jack, Pres.--CWI International China, Ltd., Fujian, China; *U.S. Public*, pg. 1749
Chang, Jack, Pres.--TWI International, Inc., Cleveland, OH; *U.S. Public*, pg. 1749
Chang, Tom, Chm. Bd. & Pres.--H. Salt of Southern California, Inc., Monterey Park, CA; *U.S. Private*, pg. 489
Changying, Tong, Pres.--China National Technical Import & Export Corporation (CNTIC), Beijing, China; *Int'l*, pg. 285
Chanoki, Futoshi, Pres.--Murata Electronics North America, Inc., Smyrna, GA; *Int'l*, pg. 897
Chantrakantanond, Phinyavat, Pres.--Krung Thai IBJ Leasing Co., Bangkok, Thailand; *Int'l*, pg. 676
Chao, Allen Y., Ph.D., Pres.--Watson Laboratories, Inc., Corona, CA; *U.S. Public*, pg. 1746
Chao, Donald K.L., Pres.--China Steel Express Corporation, Kao-hsiung, Taiwan; *Int'l*, pg. 286
Chapin, Melville, Pres.--H.B. Smith Co., Inc., Westfield, MA; *U.S. Private*, pg. 1008

Chaplin, Wayne, Pres. & Chief Oper. Officer--Southern Wine & Spirits of America Inc., Miami, FL; *U.S. Private*, pg. 1017

Chapman, Andrew, Pres.--Elizabethtown Water Company, Westfield, NJ; *U.S. Public*, pg. 540

Chapman, Andrew M., Pres.--E'Town Corporation, Westfield, NJ; *U.S. Public*, pg. 540

Chapman, Christopher, Pres. & Chief Exec. Officer--North Central Life Insurance Company, Saint Paul, MN; *U.S. Private*, pg. 404

Chapman, Gordon R., Pres.--Wellstream Company, Panama City, FL; *U.S. Public*, pg. 528

Chapman, Hugh M., Pres. & Chief Exec. Officer--NationsBank South, Atlanta, GA; *U.S. Public*, pg. 1163

Chapman, James K., Pres.--M.A. Hanna Engineered Materials, Bethlehem, PA; *U.S. Public*, pg. 781

Chapman, Jeff C., Pres. & Treas.--Primesouth, Inc., Columbia, SC; *U.S. Public*, pg. 1436

Chapman, Jim, Pres.--M.A. Hanna Engineered Materials, Corona, CA; *U.S. Public*, pg. 781

Chapman, L.A., Pres.--Rohr Credit Corporation, Chula Vista, CA; *U.S. Public*, pg. 751

Chapman, Lawrence, Pres. & Chief Exec. Officer--Manna Pro Corporation, Saint Louis, MO; *U.S. Private*, pg. 700

Chapman, Lynn, Pres. & Chief Exec. Officer--Netrix, Corp., Herndon, VA; *U.S. Private*, pg. 791

Chapman, Paul, Pres. & Chief Exec. Officer--Chattanooga Group, Inc., Hixson, TN; *U.S. Private*, pg. 231

Chapman, R.P., Pres.--Rose Bearings Ltd., Lincoln, United Kingdom; *Int'l*, pg. 869

Chapman, Richard P., Jr., Pres.--Brookline Savings Bank, Brookline, MA; *U.S. Private*, pg. 171

Chapman, Rick, Pres.--Finnigan Corporation, San Jose, CA; *U.S. Public*, pg. 1591

Chapman, Robert H., Chm. Bd. & Pres.--Barry-Wehmiller Company, Saint Louis, MO; *U.S. Private*, pg. 118

Chapman, Robert H., III, Chm. Bd., Pres., Chief Exec. Officer & Treas.--Inman Mills, Inman, SC; *U.S. Private*, pg. 564

Chapman, Steven G., Pres. & Chief Exec. Officer--ITA Group Inc., West Des Moines, IA; *U.S. Private*, pg. 555

Chapman, Thomas F., Pres. & Chief Oper. Officer--Equifax Inc., Atlanta, GA; *U.S. Public*, pg. 588

Chapman, Wilford, Chm. Bd., Pres. & Chief Exec. Officer--Idaho Supreme Company, Firth, ID; *U.S. Private*, pg. 557

Chappell, Richard, Pres.--Chappell Agency Inc., Richmond, VA; *Int'l*, pg. 736

Charbonneau, Peter D., Pres. & Chief Oper. Officer--Newbridge Networks Corporation, Kanata, Canada; *Int'l*, pg. 923

Chardavoyne, David E., Pres.--United Water New York, West Nyack, NY; *U.S. Public*, pg. 1692

Chardavoyne, David E., Pres.--United Water Works, Harrington Park, NJ; *U.S. Public*, pg. 1692

Charkiewicz, Thomas, Pres.--Manufacturers Technologies, Inc., West Springfield, MA; *U.S. Private*, pg. 701

Charlebois, Dennis, Pres.--Xetron, West Chicago, IL; *U.S. Public*, pg. 1306

Charlton-Perrin, Geoffrey, Pres. & Chief Exec. Officer--DFM/TATHAM, Chicago, IL; *Int'l*, pg. 601

Charlton, Peter A.M., Partner & Chief Creative Officer--Kupper Parker Communications Inc., Saint Louis, MO; *U.S. Private*, pg. 637

Charlton, Russell T., Pres. & Chief Exec. Officer--Transamerica Real Estate Information Companies, Dallas, TX; *U.S. Public*, pg. 1630

Charmorro, Luis, Pres.--AGA-FANO S.A., Bogota, Colombia; *Int'l*, pg. 13

Charnay, Jean-Pierre, Pres. & Dir.-Gen.--Witco S.A., Paris, France; *U.S. Public*, pg. 1774

Charnley, Hal, Pres. & Chief Exec. Officer--Artel Video Systems, Inc., Marlborough, MA; *U.S. Private*, pg. 86

Charpentier, Albert J., Chm. Bd., Pres. & Chief Exec. Officer--Ensoniq, Malvern, PA; *U.S. Private*, pg. 377

Charrier, John P., Jr., Pres. & Chief Exec. Officer--Atlantic Bank, Ocean City, MD; *U.S. Public*, pg. 642

Charro, Jose Ignacio Encinas, Pres.--Defex, S.A., Madrid, Spain; *Int'l*, pg. 1224

Charron, Celine, Pres.--Touch Infopublicite Inc. (Infomercials), Montreal, Canada; *Int'l*, pg. 116

Chartier, Guy, Pres. & Dir. General--Banque Parisienne de Credit, Paris, France; *Int'l*, pg. 548

Charton, Steve, Chm. Bd., Pres & Chief Exec. Officer--Don Miguel Mexican Foods, Inc., Anaheim, CA; *U.S. Private*, pg. 339

Chartrand, Sandra, Office Mgr.--Kintetsu World Express Inc., Mirabel, Canada; *Int'l*, pg. 735

Chartrau, Doyne, Pres.--Ward Manufacturing, Inc., Blossburg, PA; *U.S. Private*, pg. 1149

Chase, Eric T., Chm. Bd., Pres., Chief Exec. Officer & Founder--QC Optics, Inc., Wilmington, MA; *U.S. Public*, pg. 1345

Chase, Howard E., Pres. & Chief Exec. Officer--Trident Rowand Group, Inc., Somerset, NJ; *U.S. Private*, pg. 1103

Chase, J.B., V.P. & Gen. Mgr.--WCPO-TV, Cincinnati, OH; *U.S. Public*, pg. 1448

Chase, John W., Pres.--Chase Chevrolet Co., Inc., Stockton, CA; *U.S. Private*, pg. 230

Chase, Michael R., Pres. & Chief Oper. Officer--Interstate Power Company, Dubuque, IA; *U.S. Public*, pg. 910

Chase, Peter, Pres.--Humiseal Div., Woodside, NY; *U.S. Public*, pg. 337

Chase, Peter R., Pres. & Chief Exec. Officer--Chase Corporation, Braintree, MA; *U.S. Public*, pg. 337

Chase, Shirley, Pres.--EFG Technologies Inc., Saint Paul, MN; *U.S. Public*, pg. 1679

Chasen, Melvin, Chm. Bd., Pres. & Chief Exec. Officer--Transmedia Network Inc., Miami, FL; *U.S. Public*, pg. 1631

Chastain, J.D., Pres.--Redburn Tire Company, Phoenix, AZ; *U.S. Private*, pg. 915

Chastain, Roger W., Pres. & Chief Oper. Officer--Mount Vernon Mills, Inc., Greenville, SC; *U.S. Private*, pg. 835

Chatt, Joseph R., Sr., Pres.--Caribe Express, Aguadilla, PR; *U.S. Private*, pg. 211

Chattman, Martin E., Pres.--NorVal, Inc., Lafayette, NJ; *Int'l*, pg. 1201

Chaudet, Marc-Henri, Pres.--Orior Holding S.A., Vevey, Switzerland; *Int'l*, pg. 1008

Chaufty, William L., Pres.--Hilb, Rogal and Hamilton Company of Oklahoma, Oklahoma City, OK; *U.S. Public*, pg. 827

Chavez, Lloyd G., Pres. & Chief Exec. Officer--LGC Management, Englewood, CO; *U.S. Private*, pg. 639

Chavez, Robert B., Pres. & Chief Exec. Officer--Etienne Aigner, New York, NY; *U.S. Private*, pg. 384

Chavkin, Robert, Pres. & Chief Oper. Officer--Biddle Sawyer Corporation, New York, NY; *U.S. Private*, pg. 142

Cheatley, H.W., Pres.--Bunn-O-Matic Corp. of Canada Ltd., Aurora, Canada; *U.S. Private*, pg. 181

Cheaure, Alfred, Pres.--American Kennel Club, Inc., New York, NY; *U.S. Private*, pg. 58

Checketts, David W., Pres. & Chief Exec. Officer--Madison Square Garden Corporation, New York, NY; *U.S. Public*, pg. 288

Checketts, David W., Pres. & Chief Exec. Officer--Madison Square Garden Network, New York, NY; *U.S. Public*, pg. 288

Chedraui Obeso, Antonio, Pres.--Grupo Comercial Chedraui S.A. de C.V., Veracruz, Mexico; *Int'l*, pg. 573

Chedraui Obeso, Antonio, Pres.--Tiendas Chedraui S.A. de C.V., Veracruz, Mexico; *Int'l*, pg. 573

Cheema, Jasse, Chm. Bd. & Pres.--Theodore Barry & Associates, Los Angeles, CA; *U.S. Private*, pg. 118

Chehebar, J., Pres. & Chief Exec. Officer--Rainbow Apparel Distribution Center, Brooklyn, NY; *U.S. Private*, pg. 907

Chellgren, Paul, Pres.--Nokia Mobile Phones Inc., Tampa, FL; *Int'l*, pg. 952

Chelminski, Andrew, Pres.--The Bentley Agnew Group Inc., London, Canada; *Int'l*, pg. 187

Chelminski, Andrew, Pres.--Bentley Leathers Inc., Dollard des Ormeaux, Canada; *Int'l*, pg. 187

Chen, Bryon, Pres.--Astra Pharmaceuticals (Taiwan) Ltd., Taipei, Taiwan; *Int'l*, pg. 94

Chen, F., Pres.--Sampo Corporation (Taipei), Taipei, Taiwan; *Int'l*, pg. 1229

Chen, H.H., Pres.--China Ecotek Corporation, Kao-hsiung, Taiwan; *Int'l*, pg. 285

Chen, J.Y., Pres.--China Steel Corporation, Kao-hsiung, Taiwan; *Int'l*, pg. 285

Chen, Jeffrey C., Chm. Bd., Pres. & Chief Exec. Officer--General Sciences Corp., Laurel, MD; *U.S. Private*, pg. 976

Chen, Joe, Dr., Pres. & Chief Exec. Officer--Micropolis Corporation, Chatsworth, CA; *U.S. Private*, pg. 742

Chen, John S., Pres. & Chief Oper. Officer--Sybase, Inc., Emeryville, CA; *U.S. Public*, pg. 1544

Chen, K.Y., Pres.--Chinese Petroleum Corporation, Taipei, Taiwan; *Int'l*, pg. 286

Chen, Pao Yuan, Pres.--China Steel Chemical Corp., Kao-hsiung, Taiwan; *Int'l*, pg. 286

Chen, Pehong, Dr., Chm. Bd., Pres. & Chief Exec. Officer--BroadVision, Inc., Redwood City, CA; *U.S. Public*, pg. 258

Chen, Sai-Sin, Pres., Chief Exec. Officer & Dir.-Fin.--Seika Electric Co., Ltd., Taipei, Taiwan; *Int'l*, pg. 1218

Chenard, Pierre, Interim Pres.--Cambinex Exploration, Montreal, Canada; *Int'l*, pg. 253

Chenault, Kenneth I., Pres. & Chief Oper. Officer--American Express Company, New York, NY; *U.S. Public*, pg. 73

Cheney, Peter, Pres.--Kal Kan Foods, Inc., Vernon, CA; *U.S. Private*, pg. 707

Cheng, Theodore S.S., Pres. & Mng. Dir.--The International Commercial Bank of China, Taipei, Taiwan; *Int'l*, pg. 683

Cheng, Xin, Pres.--Merat Optical Communications, Santa Monica, CA; *U.S. Public*, pg. 1233

Cheng, Xin, Chm. Bd., Pres. & Chief Exec. Officer--Meret Communications, San Diego, CA; *U.S. Public*, pg. 1233

Cheong, Gerry, Pres.--KE-Burgmann Singapore Pte. Ltd., Singapore, Singapore; *Int'l*, pg. 234

Cher, Ronald, Pres.--Elder Manufacturing Company, Creve Coeur, MO; *U.S. Private*, pg. 367

Cherlouche, Y., Pres. & Chief Exec. Officer--Scitex Corporation Ltd., Holon, Israel; *Int'l*, pg. 644

Chernin, Peter, Pres.--The News Corporation Limited, Sydney, Australia; *Int'l*, pg. 925

Cherocci, Jim, Pres.--Courtesy Chevrolet & Imports Inc., Ithaca, NY; *U.S. Private*, pg. 279

Cheron, Daniel, Pres.--Pain Jacquet S.A., Evry, France; *Int'l*, pg. 1021

Cherone, Patrick F., Pres. & Chief Exec. Officer--Wisconsin Machine and Tool Corporation, Milwaukee, WI; *U.S. Private*, pg. 1185

Cherry, Jim, Pres. & Chief Oper. Officer--CAE Electronics, Ltd., Saint-Laurent, Canada; *Int'l*, pg. 237

Cherry, Peter B., Chm. Bd. & Pres.--Cherry Electrical Products Corporation, Waukegan, IL; *U.S. Public*, pg. 346

Chertkow, Louis, Pres. & Chief Exec. Officer--Elkay Plastics Company, Inc., Los Angeles, CA; *U.S. Private*, pg. 372

Chertow, Brent, Co-Pres.--Kidd Creek Division, Timmins, Canada; *Int'l*, pg. 433

Cherubini, Juilian, Pres.--Alimed, Inc., Dedham, MA; *U.S. Private*, pg. 34

Chesebro, R.E., Jr., Pres.--Wigwam Mills, Inc., Sheboygan, WI; *U.S. Private*, pg. 1175

Chesebro, Stephen D., Pres. & Chief Oper. Officer--Pennzoil Company, Houston, TX; *U.S. Public*, pg. 1272

Cheshire, Michael J., Pres. & Chief Oper. Officer--Gerber Scientific, Inc., South Windsor, CT; *U.S. Public*, pg. 740

Chesire, Michael J., Pres.--O-Z/Gedney, Nelson Firestop Products, Tulsa, OK; *U.S. Public*, pg. 726

Chesney, David H., Pres. & Gen. Mgr.--Nestaway, Cleveland, OH; *U.S. Private*, pg. 103

Chesonis, Arunas A., Pres. & Chief Oper. Officer--ACC Corp., Rochester, NY; *U.S. Public*, pg. 2

Chess, David, Pres.--Superior Pool Products, Inc., Anaheim, CA; *U.S. Public*, pg. 1219

Chessin, James L., Pres.--Bondo/Mar-Hyde Corporation, Cleveland, OH; *U.S. Public*, pg. 1357

Chesterman, Kenneth W., Pres.--Omnicare Pharmacy Services, Cincinnati, OH; *U.S. Public*, pg. 1223

Chesterton, James D., Pres. & Chief Exec. Officer--A.W. Chesterton Company, Stoneham, MA; *U.S. Private*, pg. 234

Chestnov, Robert, Pres. & Chief Exec. Officer--Jaclyn, Inc., West New York, NJ; *U.S. Public*, pg. 920

Chestnutt, Jim, Pres.--National Spinning Co., Inc., New York, NY; *U.S. Private*, pg. 786

Cheung, Shirley S., Pres.--Heinz-UFE Ltd., Guangzhou, China; *U.S. Public*, pg. 807

Cheung, Steve, Pres.--Georg Fischer Disa Inc., Oswego, IL; *Int'l*, pg. 382

Chevrier, Robert, Vice Chm., Pres. & Chief Exec. Officer--Westburne Inc., Montreal, Canada; *Int'l*, pg. 1491

Chevrier, Robert, Chm. Bd., Pres. & Chief Exec. Officer--Westburne Industrial Enterprises, Ltd., Ville Saint Laurent, Canada; *Int'l*, pg. 1492

Chi, Steven Y., Pres.--Mining Group, San Antonio, TX; *U.S. Public*, pg. 1134

Chi, Y.K., Pres.--C.S. Aluminium Corporation, Kao-hsiung, Taiwan; *Int'l*, pg. 285

Chiaraluce, Marshall T., Pres. & Chief Exec. Officer--Connecticut Water Service, Inc., Clinton, CT; *U.S. Public*, pg. 431

Chiaraluce, Marshall T., Pres.--The Connecticut Water Company, Clinton, CT; *U.S. Public*, pg. 431

Chiba, Koji, Pres. & Chief Exec. Officer--Duskin Co., Ltd., Osaka, Japan; *Int'l*, pg. 422

Chibata, Ichiro, Ph.D., Chm. Bd., Pres. & Chief Exec. Officer--Tanabe Seiyaku Co., Ltd., Osaka, Japan; *Int'l*, pg. 1354

Chicon, Maida, Mng. Partner & Client Services Dir.--Fova, Inc., New York, NY; *U.S. Public*, pg. 764

Chigi, Yoshitara, Pres.--Yumex/ILC, Himeji, Japan; *U.S. Public*, pg. 856

Chikli, Rene-Marc, Pres.--Jet Tours, Ivry-sur-Seine, France; *Int'l*, pg. 560

Child, Kent, Pres.--Kwal-Howells, Inc.(Denver), Denver, CO; *Int'l*, pg. 1501

Child, Sheldon F., Pres.--R.C. Willey Home Furnishings, Salt Lake City, UT; *U.S. Public*, pg. 221

Child, Wayne, Pres.--Basin Electric Power Cooperative, Bismarck, ND; *U.S. Private*, pg. 121

Childerhose, Ken, Pres.--Powell Equipment Ltd., Winnipeg, Canada; *Int'l*, pg. 1066

Childers, Charles E., Chm. Bd., Pres. & Chief Exec. Officer--Potash Corporation of Saskatchewan Inc., Saskatoon, Canada; *Int'l*, pg. 1064

Childress, Brad, Pres.--Plastomer Products Div., Newtown, PA; *U.S. Public*, pg. 402

Childress, Gary, Pres.--MWCA, Rexburg, ID; *U.S. Public*, pg. 804

Childs, John, Pres.--J.W. Childs Associates, L.P., Boston, MA; *U.S. Private*, pg. 237

Childs, T. Bruce, Pres.--First Franklin Financial Corp., Toccoa, GA; *U.S. Private*, pg. 407

Chiles, James B., Pres.--Canadian Mist Distillers Ltd., Collingwood, Canada; *U.S. Public*, pg. 262

Chilton, Nick, Pres. & Chief Oper. Officer--Wyandot Inc., Marion, OH; *U.S. Private*, pg. 1193

Chin, Daniel J., Pres.--Dress Division, New York, NY; *U.S. Public*, pg. 1239

Chin, Lee, V.P. & Gen. Mgr.--CBM America Corp., Fort Lee, NJ; *U.S. Private*, pg. 192

Ching, Chew Lee, Chm. & Pres.--Dentsu Mandate Singapore Pte. Ltd., Singapore, Singapore; *Int'l*, pg. 393

Ching, Ho, Pres. & Chief Exec. Officer--Singapore Technologies Pte. Ltd., Singapore, Singapore; *Int'l*, pg. 1253

Chino, Tasuku, Pres.--Skylark Co., Ltd., Tokyo, Japan; *Int'l*, pg. 1262

Chiste, R., Pres. & Chief Exec. Officer--Philip Industrial Services Group, Houston, TX; *Int'l*, pg. 1050

Chitayat, Amir, Pres.--Anorad Corporation, Hauppauge, NY; *U.S. Private*, pg. 75

Chitty, Charles R., Chm. Bd., Pres. & Chief Exec. Officer--IQ Software Corporation, Norcross, GA; *U.S. Public*, pg. 858

Chiu, Y.T., Pres.--OPICOIL Houston, Inc., Houston, TX; *Int'l*, pg. 286

Chivari, George A., Pres. & Chief Exec. Officer--Bil Mar Foods, Inc., Zeeland, MI; *U.S. Public*, pg. 1433

Chlebowski, John F., Jr., Pres.--GATX Terminals Corporation, Chicago, IL; *U.S. Public*, pg. 692

Cho, Kook-pil, Pres.--Ssangyong Resources Pty., Ltd., Sydney, Australia; *Int'l*, pg. 1293

Cho, Kuk-Pil, Pres.--Jinbang Steel Co., Ltd., Pohang, Korea; *Int'l*, pg. 1291

Cho, Yang-Ho, Pres. & Chief Oper. Officer--Korean Airlines Co., Ltd., Seoul, Korea; *Int'l*, pg. 758

Chocola, J. Christopher, Pres. & Chief Exec. Officer--CTB International Corp., Milford, IN; *U.S. Public*, pg. 284

Choe, Ng Kee, Deputy Pres. & Chief Oper. Officer--DBS Bank Ltd., Singapore, Singapore; *Int'l*, pg. 350

Choel, Patrick J., Pres. & Chief Exec. Officer--Chesebrough-Pond's USA Co., Greenwich, CT; *Int'l*, pg. 1435

Choi, James K.C., Pres. & Chief Exec. Officer--Renaissance Hotel Group N.V., Central, Hong Kong; *U.S. Public*, pg. 1048

Choi, Tan, Pres.--Ssangyong Engineering Co., Ltd., Seoul, Korea; *Int'l*, pg. 1292

Chokwatana, Boonkiet, Dep. Chm. & Pres.--International Cosmetics Co., Ltd., Bangkok, Thailand; *Int'l*, pg. 684

Chokwatana, Boonsithi, Pres.--Thai Sports Garment Co., Ltd., Bangkok, Thailand; *Int'l*, pg. 885

Chokwatana, Narong, Chm. Bd. & Pres.--Bangkok Athletic Co., Ltd., Bangkok, Thailand; *Int'l*, pg. 146

Chomeau, James W., Pres.--Capitol County Mutual Fire Insurance Co., Houston, TX; *U.S. Public*, pg. 1374

Choo, J.S., Pres.--Hyosung-Ebara Environment Engineering Co., Ltd., Seoul, Korea; *Int'l*, pg. 432
Choo, Yoon H., Dr., Chm. Bd., Pres. & Chief Exec. Officer--National Micronetics, Inc., Kingston, NY; *Int'l*, pg. 1347
Chopra, Deepak, Chm. Bd., Pres. & Chief Exec. Officer--UDT Sensors, Inc., Hawthorne, CA; *U.S. Private*, pg. 1112
Chopra, Deepak, Chm. Bd., Pres. & Chief Exec. Officer--OSI Systems, Inc., Hawthorne, CA; *U.S. Public*, pg. 1208
Choquette, Pierre, Pres. & Chief Exec. Officer--Methanex Corporation, Vancouver, Canada; *Int'l*, pg. 862
Chorbajian, Herbert G., Chm. Bd., Pres. & Chief Exec. Officer--Albank Financial Corporation, Albany, NY; *U.S. Public*, pg. 36
Chorengel, Bernd, Pres.--Hyatt International Corporation, Chicago, IL; *U.S. Private*, pg. 551
Chormann, Richard F., Chm. Bd., Pres. & Chief Exec. Officer--First of America Bank Corporation, Kalamazoo, MI; *U.S. Public*, pg. 636
Chouinard, Yvon, Pres.--Lost Arrow Corporation, Ventura, CA; *U.S. Private*, pg. 676
Chouinard, Yvon, Pres.--Patagonia, Ventura, CA; *U.S. Private*, pg. 677
Choulet, Robert, Pres.--AlliedSignal Engines, Phoenix, AZ; *U.S. Public*, pg. 50
Chouraqui, R., Pres.--Hydrochim, S.A., Amboise, France; *U.S. Public*, pg. 1219
Choy, I.J., Pres.--American Tape Co., Secaucus, NJ; *Int'l*, pg. 685
Christ, Clifford C., Pres. & Chief Exec. Officer--NavCom Defense Electronics, Inc., El Monte, CA; *U.S. Private*, pg. 789
Christen, Peter, Pres. & Chief Exec. Officer--Blue Ridge Insurance Co., Simsbury, CT; *Int'l*, pg. 345
Christen, Peter, Chm. Bd., Pres. & Chief Exec. Officer--Blue Ridge Indemnity Co., Simsbury, CT; *Int'l*, pg. 345
Christensen, David A., Pres. & Chief Exec. Officer--Raven Industries, Inc., Sioux Falls, SD; *U.S. Public*, pg. 1361
Christensen, Gary M., Pres. & Chief Exec. Officer--Pella Corporation, Pella, IA; *U.S. Private*, pg. 848
Christensen, Jeff, Pres.--Zee Medical, Inc., Irvine, CA; *U.S. Public*, pg. 1073
Christensen, Lief, Pres.--Manistique Papers, Inc., Manistique, MI; *Int'l*, pg. 762
Christensen, Mahlon, Pres. & Chief Exec. Officer--Muska Electric Company, Roseville, MN; *U.S. Private*, pg. 768
Christenson, Joseph C., Pres.--PPT Vision, Inc., Eden Prairie, MN; *U.S. Public*, pg. 1245
Christian, Betty S., Chm. Bd., Pres. & Chief Exec. Officer--Central Coca-Cola Bottling Company, Inc., Richmond, VA; *U.S. Private*, pg. 222
Christian, Dennis W., Pres.--Mississippi Marketing, Inc., Natchez, MS; *U.S. Public*, pg. 295
Christian, Nathan, Pres. & Chief Exec. Officer--Norwest Bank El Paso, N.A., El Paso, TX; *U.S. Public*, pg. 1201
Christiansen, Olav K., Pres.--Aker Oil & Gas Technology, Inc., Houston, TX; *Int'l*, pg. 42
Christiansen, Ron, Mng. Partner--CF2GS, Seattle, WA; *U.S. Private*, pg. 194
Christianson, Finn Normann, Pres.--Burmeister & Wain Energi A/S, Virum, Denmark; *Int'l*, pg. 398
Christianson, Robert D., Pres.--Burton Medical Products Corporation, Chatsworth, CA; *Int'l*, pg. 821
Christie, Cary, Pres.--Christie Design, Chatsworth, CA; *U.S. Public*, pg. 1369
Christie, Guy, Pres.--Descente Canada Inc., Vancouver, Canada; *Int'l*, pg. 396
Christie, Jane M., Pres. & Chief Exec. Officer--General Automation, Inc., Irvine, CA; *U.S. Public*, pg. 706
Christie, Robert S., Pres.--McGraw-Hill College Division, New York, NY; *U.S. Public*, pg. 1070
Christmas, James W., Pres. & Chief Exec. Officer--KCS Energy Inc., Edison, NJ; *U.S. Public*, pg. 938
Christmas, James W., Pres.--Proliq, Inc., Edison, NJ; *U.S. Public*, pg. 939
Christmas, James W., Pres.--National Enerdrill, Edison, NJ; *U.S. Public*, pg. 939
Christofferson, Randy L., Pres.--First USA Bank, Wilmington, DE; *U.S. Public*, pg. 174
Christopher, Brian, Pres.--Christenson Electric, Inc., Portland, OR; *U.S. Private*, pg. 238
Christopher, Brian H.E., Chm. Bd.--Astec International Limited, Wan Chai, Hong Kong; *Int'l*, pg. 92
Christopher, Doris, Pres.--The Pampered Chef, Ltd., Addison, IL; *U.S. Private*, pg. 835
Christopher, S.M., Pres.--Security Life of Denver Insurance Company, Denver, CO; *Int'l*, pg. 648
Christopher, Thomas, Pres.--Bookstop, Inc., New York, NY; *U.S. Public*, pg. 189
Christopher, William F., Pres.--Alcoa Forged Products, Cleveland, OH; *U.S. Public*, pg. 60
Chronis, Peter W., Pres.--Reece-Campbell, Inc., Cincinnati, OH; *U.S. Private*, pg. 916
Chryst, Steven L., Pres. & Chief Exec. Officer--Anchor Financial Corporation, Myrtle Beach, SC; *U.S. Public*, pg. 111
Chun-fan, Fu, Pres.--China Airlines Ltd., Taipei, Taiwan; *Int'l*, pg. 284
Chun-Hak, Ahn, Pres.--Korea Heavy Industries & Construction Co., Ltd., Seoul, Korea; *Int'l*, pg. 758
Chun, Gao Hai, Pres.--China Otsuka Pharmaceutical Co., Ltd., Tianjin, China; *Int'l*, pg. 1014
Chun, Rupert K., Pres.--Mutual Welding Co., Ltd, Honolulu, HI; *U.S. Private*, pg. 770
Chun, Yang Xiao, Pres.--Shanghai Bao Tai Long Concrete Products Co., Ltd., Shanghai, China; *Int'l*, pg. 1293
Chunbai, Zhu, Pres. & Dir.--China Kang Fu International Leasing Co., Ltd., Beijing, China; *Int'l*, pg. 521
Chung, Kang-Hwan, Pres.--Tai-Il Media Co., Seoul, Korea; *Int'l*, pg. 1347
Chung, Nak-Kyung, Pres.--Novellus Systems Korea, Seoul, Korea; *U.S. Public*, pg. 1204
Chung, W.S., Pres.--Hyosung-Ebara Company Ltd., Seoul, Korea; *Int'l*, pg. 432
Church, D.A., Pres.--Seibert-Oxidermo, Inc., Romulus, MI; *U.S. Public*, pg. 502
Church, John F., Jr., Pres. & Chief Exec. Officer--The Cincinnati Cordage & Paper Company, Cincinnati, OH; *U.S. Private*, pg. 239
Church, Kenneth E., Pres.--Clayton-Marcus Company, Inc., Hickory, NC; *U.S. Public*, pg. 975
Church, Walter G., Sr., Pres. & Chief Exec. Officer--BB&T Savings Bank, SSB, Valdese, NC; *U.S. Public*, pg. 160
Church, William R., Pres.--Church & Church Inc., Auburn Hills, MI; *U.S. Private*, pg. 239
Chute, Robert A., Chm. Bd., Pres. & Chief Exec. Officer--The Gage Company, Pittsburgh, PA; *U.S. Private*, pg. 437
Chwang, Ronald, Pres. & Chief Exec. Officer--Acer America Corporation, San Jose, CA; *Int'l*, pg. 22
Ciak, Kenneth, Pres.--IDS Property Casualty Insurance Company, Minneapolis, MN; *U.S. Public*, pg. 73
Ciamarro, Roberto, Pres. & Gen. Mgr.--Canagex Investments Limited, Montreal, Canada; *Int'l*, pg. 396
Cianci, Giovanni, Pres.--Quaker-Chiari & Forti S.P.A., Silea, Italy; *U.S. Public*, pg. 1348
Ciardella, Robert L., Pres.--Asymtek, Carlsbad, CA; *U.S. Public*, pg. 1188
Cibran, Bert, Pres. & Chief Oper. Officer--Ramsay Health Care, Inc., Coral Gables, FL; *U.S. Public*, pg. 1360
Ciccarelli, John A., Pres. & Chief Exec. Officer--Dayton Superior Corporation, Miamisburg, OH; *U.S. Private*, pg. 931
Cichy, J.S., Pres.--White-Rodgers Div., Emerson Electric Co., Saint Louis, MO; *U.S. Public*, pg. 573
Ciepiel, Anthony M., Pres. & Chief Oper. Officer--Realty One, Cleveland, OH; *U.S. Private*, pg. 914
Ciesla, Robert, High Chief Ranger--Catholic Order of Foresters, Naperville, IL; *U.S. Private*, pg. 220
Ciffone, Donald L., Jr., Pres. & Chief Exec. Officer--EXAR Corporation, Fremont, CA; *U.S. Public*, pg. 597
Cigarran, Thomas G., Chm. Bd., Pres. & Chief Exec. Officer--American Healthcorp Inc., Nashville, TN; *U.S. Public*, pg. 78
Cignarella, Robert, Pres. & Chief Exec. Officer--BMW, Flushing, NY; *U.S. Private*, pg. 107
Cillo, Larry J., Pres.--Harris Investors Direct, Inc., Chicago, IL; *Int'l*, pg. 154
Cilurzo, Joseph W., Pres. & Chief Exec. Officer--Mobile Technology Inc., Los Angeles, CA; *U.S. Private*, pg. 754
Cimino, Jay, Pres. & Chief Exec. Officer--Phil Long Ford, Colorado Springs, CO; *U.S. Private*, pg. 675
Cims, Donald V., Pres.--Nuarc Company, Inc., Niles, IL; *U.S. Private*, pg. 808
Cinnamon, Barry A., Chm. Bd., Pres. & Chief Exec. Officer--Software Publishing Corporation, Fairfield, NJ; *U.S. Public*, pg. 1483
Ciola, Tom, Pres.--National Health Products, Orlando, FL; *U.S. Private*, pg. 784
Ciolino, Paul, Pres.--Unit Rail Anchor Company, Atchison, KS; *U.S. Public*, pg. 1711
Ciprut, Aydin Toni, Pres.--Peyma Chr. Hansen's A.S., Istanbul, Turkey; *Int'l*, pg. 289
Circo, Dennis P., Pres. & Chief Exec. Officer--Precision Industries, Omaha, NE; *U.S. Private*, pg. 879
Cirilli, Dante, Pres. & Dir.-Mktg. Div.--Grolier Inc., Danbury, CT; *Int'l*, pg. 794
Cirka, Lawrence P., Pres.--Integrated Health Services, Inc., Owings Mills, MD; *U.S. Public*, pg. 884
Cirona, James, Pres.--Western Farm Credit Bank, Sacramento, CA; *U.S. Private*, pg. 398
Cisneros, Henry, Pres. & Chief Oper. Officer--Univision Ltd. Partnership, New York, NY; *U.S. Private*, pg. 230
Cissell, Mary, Publr.--Democrat News, Fredericktown, MO; *U.S. Public*, pg. 1343
Citron, Kirk, Pres.--Citron Haligman Bedecarre, San Francisco, CA; *U.S. Private*, pg. 241
Clack, Ian, Chief Exec. Officer & Mng. Dir.--Burns, Philp & Company Limited, Sydney, Australia; *Int'l*, pg. 236
Cladianos, Pete, Jr., Pres. & Chief Exec. Officer--The Sands Regent, Reno, NV; *U.S. Public*, pg. 1431
Clague, Clive, Chm. Bd.--Stadium Limited, Hartlepool, United Kingdom; *Int'l*, pg. 1293
Clain, G., Pres. & Chief Exec. Officer--J. Gerber & Co. Inc., New York, NY; *U.S. Private*, pg. 449
Clancey, John, Pres. & Chief Exec. Officer--Sea-Land Service, Inc., Charlotte, NC; *U.S. Public*, pg. 284
Clapp, William A., Pres.--Mayville Metal Products Division, Mayville, WI; *U.S. Private*, pg. 264
Claprood, Pierre, Pres. & Chief Exec. Officer--Natrel Inc., Longueuil, Canada; *Int'l*, pg. 32
Clarity, Tim B., Pres. & Chief Exec. Officer--Clarity Coverdale Fury Advertising, Minneapolis, MN; *U.S. Private*, pg. 242
Clark, A. James, Chm. Bd & Pres.--Clark Enterprises, Inc., Bethesda, MD; *U.S. Private*, pg. 242
Clark, Al, Pres.--Southeastern Realty Group Inc., Orlando, FL; *U.S. Private*, pg. 1015
Clark, Cyrus, III, Pres. & Chief Exec. Officer--Cyrus Clark Co., Inc., New York, NY; *U.S. Private*, pg. 242
Clark, D.L., Pres.--Smiths Industries Aerospace & Defense Systems Inc.-Clearwater, Clearwater, FL; *Int'l*, pg. 1268
Clark, David, Chm. Bd., Pres. & Chief Exec. Officer--Homeland Holding Corp., Oklahoma City, OK; *U.S. Public*, pg. 832
Clark, David, Pres. & Chief Exec. Officer--Homeland Stores, Inc., Oklahoma City, OK; *U.S. Public*, pg. 832
Clark, David, Pres. & Chief Oper. Officer--WSMP, Inc., Claremont, NC; *U.S. Public*, pg. 1729
Clark, David R., Pres.--Thomas & Howard Co., Columbia, SC; *U.S. Private*, pg. 1081
Clark, Dick, Pres.--Dick Clark Corporate Productions, Inc., Burbank, CA; *U.S. Public*, pg. 382
Clark, Don, Pres. & Chief Exec. Officer--Mid America Steel, Inc., Fargo, ND; *U.S. Private*, pg. 743
Clark, Douglas, Pres.--Smiths Industries Aerospace & Defense Systems Inc.-Malvern, Malvern, PA; *Int'l*, pg. 1268
Clark, E. Roger, Chm. Bd., Pres. & Chief Exec. Officer--National Forge Company, Irvine, PA; *U.S. Private*, pg. 783
Clark, Ed, Pres. & Gen. Mgr.--Atlanta Motor Speedway, Hampton, GA; *U.S. Public*, pg. 1498
Clark, Edward, Chm. Bd., Pres. & Chief Exec. Officer--American Seating Company, Grand Rapids, MI; *U.S. Private*, pg. 61
Clark, Fred, Pres. & Chief Exec. Officer--The Clark Group, Mission, Canada; *Int'l*, pg. 296
Clark, G.J., Pres. & Gen. Mgr.--John Deere Ltd., Grimsby, Canada; *U.S. Public*, pg. 493
Clark, Gary, Pres. & Chief Exec. Officer--Indimac Third Party Construction Lending Division, Pasadena, CA; *U.S. Public*, pg. 857
Clark, George A., Chm. Bd., Pres. & Chief Exec. Officer--Snap-Tite, Inc., Erie, PA; *U.S. Private*, pg. 1010
Clark, Grahame N., Jr., Chm., Pres. & Chief Exec. Officer--BancTec, Inc., Dallas, TX; *U.S. Public*, pg. 176
Clark, H., Pres.--Trade Dimensions, Stamford, CT; *Int'l*, pg. 1447
Clark, J. Thomas, Pres.--Dubin-Clark & Company, Greenwich, CT; *U.S. Private*, pg. 344
Clark, James, Gen. Mgr.--Clark Pacific, Sacramento, CA; *U.S. Private*, pg. 243
Clark, Jeff C., Pres.--Covington Foods, Inc., Covington, IN; *U.S. Private*, pg. 280
Clark, Jimmie D., Pres.--Sysco/Louisville Food Services Co., Louisville, KY; *U.S. Public*, pg. 1552
Clark, John N., Pres.--Smith & Nephew Rehabilitation Inc., Germantown, WI; *Int'l*, pg. 1263
Clark, Joseph T., Pres. & Chief Exec. Officer--Response Oncology, Inc., Memphis, TN; *U.S. Public*, pg. 1449
Clark, Katherine K., Pres. & Chief Exec. Officer--Landmark Systems Corporation, Vienna, VA; *U.S. Private*, pg. 649
Clark, Kenneth J., Pres.--Lincoln National Reinsurance Company (Bermuda) Limited, Fort Wayne, IN; *U.S. Public*, pg. 998
Clark, Kenneth J., Pres.--Lincoln National Structured Settlement, Inc., Fort Wayne, IN; *U.S. Public*, pg. 998
Clark, Kenneth J., Pres.--Old Fort Insurance Co., Ltd. (Bermuda), Hamilton, Bermuda; *U.S. Public*, pg. 998
Clark, L. Hill, Pres. & Chief Oper. Officer--Crane Co., Stamford, CT; *U.S. Public*, pg. 456
Clark, Louis, Pres. & Chief Oper. Officer--The Clark Group, Mission, Canada; *Int'l*, pg. 296
Clark, O.B., Pres.--Associated Electric Co-op Inc., Springfield, MO; *U.S. Private*, pg. 89
Clark, Phil, Pres.--Six Flags Astroworld/Six Flags Waterworld/Six Flags Houston, Houston, TX; *U.S. Public*, pg. 1611
Clark, R. Kerry, Pres.--Procter & Gamble Laundry Products Division, Cincinnati, OH; *U.S. Public*, pg. 1331
Clark, Robert, Pres.--Great Salt Lake Minerals Corp., Overland Park, KS; *U.S. Private*, pg. 505
Clark, Robert G., Chm., Pres. & Chief Exec. Officer--International Capital Equipment Limited, Hamilton, Bermuda; *Int'l*, pg. 683
Clark, Robert W., Pres. & Chief Exec. Officer--Shenandoah Life Insurance Company, Roanoke, VA; *U.S. Private*, pg. 992
Clark, Robert W., Pres.--Old Dominion Life Insurance Co., Roanoke, VA; *U.S. Private*, pg. 992
Clark, Scott, Pres.--Shakertown 1992, Inc., Winlock, WA; *Int'l*, pg. 296
Clark, Stephen S., Pres. & Chief Exec. Officer--Dwyer Instruments Inc., Michigan City, IN; *U.S. Private*, pg. 350
Clark, Stephen S., Pres.--Love Controls Corporation, Michigan City, IN; *U.S. Private*, pg. 350
Clark, Stephen W., Pres.--Galderma Laboratories, Inc., Fort Worth, TX; *Int'l*, pg. 819
Clark, Steven, Pres. & Chief Exec. Officer--Taco Cabana, San Antonio, TX; *U.S. Public*, pg. 1559
Clark, Stuart, Pres.--Interactive Data Corporation, Lexington, MA; *Int'l*, pg. 1025
Clark, T. Daniel, Sr. Div. Pres.--Dexter Packaging Products, Waukegan, IL; *U.S. Public*, pg. 504
Clark, Thomas B., Pres. & Chief Exec. Officer--Alltrista Corporation, Muncie, IN; *U.S. Public*, pg. 56
Clark, Thomas H., Pres.--Guaranty Income Life Insurance Co., Baton Rouge, LA; *U.S. Private*, pg. 485
Clark, Thomas L., Pres. & Chief Exec. Officer--Carver Federal Savings Bank, New York, NY; *U.S. Public*, pg. 310
Clark, W. Roger, Pres.--United Companies Lending Corporation, Baton Rouge, LA; *U.S. Public*, pg. 1675
Clark, Wayne, Pres.--Pure Pulse Technologies, Inc., San Diego, CA; *U.S. Public*, pg. 1062
Clark, Wesley M., Grp. Pres.--W.W. Grainger, Inc., Lincolnshire, IL; *U.S. Public*, pg. 758
Clark, William S., Pres. & Chief Exec. Officer--First Bank of Stuart, Stuart, VA; *U.S. Public*, pg. 1039
Clarke, Bruce E., Pres. & Mng. Dir.--PanAgora Asset Managment, Inc., Boston, MA; *Int'l*, pg. 935
Clarke, Bruce E., Pres. & Mng. Dir.--PanAgora Asset Managment, Inc., Boston, MA; *U.S. Public*, pg. 987
Clarke, C. Boyd, Pres. & Chief Oper. Officer--U.S. Bioscience, Inc., Conshohocken, PA; *U.S. Public*, pg. 1681
Clarke, D.F., Pres.--Nova Chemicals, Inc., Monaca, PA; *Int'l*, pg. 971
Clarke, David, Pres.--CSR America Inc., Atlanta, GA; *Int'l*, pg. 245
Clarke, Gareth, Pres.--London International, U.S. Holdings Inc., Norcross, GA; *Int'l*, pg. 815
Clarke, Jeffrey, Chm. Bd., Pres. & Chief Exec. Officer--Coho Energy, Inc., Dallas, TX; *U.S. Public*, pg. 396
Clarke, John, Pres.--Monier Inc., Irvine, CA; *Int'l*, pg. 1091
Clarke, John M., Pres.--SmithKline Beecham Canada, Inc., Oakville, Canada; *Int'l*, pg. 1265
Clarke, M.B., Pres.--Glens Falls Cement Co., Glens Falls, NY; *Int'l*, pg. 423
Clarke, Nathan, Pres.--Trademark Research Corporation, New York, NY; *Int'l*, pg. 1513

Clarke, Robert F., Chm. Bd., Pres. & Chief Exec. Officer--Hawaiian Electric Industries, Inc., Honolulu, HI; *U.S. Public*, pg. 799
Clarke, Robert F., Chm. Bd. & Pres.--Pacific Energy Conservation Services, Inc., Honolulu, HI; *U.S. Public*, pg. 800
Clarke, Thomas E., Pres. & Chief Oper. Officer--Nike, Inc., Beaverton, OR; *U.S. Public*, pg. 1184
Clarke, William A., Pres.--Johnson & Johnson Medical, Inc., Arlington, TX; *U.S. Public*, pg. 928
Clarkson, Malcolm, Pres.--Falmer Press Ltd., London, United Kingdom; *Int'l*, pg. 1358
Clarkson, William E., Pres.--Clarkson Construction Companies, Kansas City, MO; *U.S. Private*, pg. 244
Clary, John P., Pres. & Chief Exec. Officer--Modcomp, Fort Lauderdale, FL; *U.S. Public*, pg. 283
Classon, Rolf A., Exec. V.P. & Pres.-Diagnostics Div.--Bayer Corporation, Pittsburgh, PA; *Int'l*, pg. 172
Claudon, Ronald C., Sr., Pres. & Chief Oper. Officer--Valley Pontiac Buick GMC, Inc., Auburn, WA; *U.S. Private*, pg. 1132
Clausen, Dick, Chm. Bd., Pres. & Chief Exec. Officer--Verbatim Tape Corporation, San Diego, CA; *Int'l*, pg. 872
Clausen, Jorgen M., Pres. & Chief Exec. Officer--Danfoss A/S, Nordborg, Denmark; *Int'l*, pg. 376
Claussen, Georg, Pres.--Tesa Tuck Inc., Sparta, MI; *Int'l*, pg. 182
Claussen, John H., Pres.--TRC Environmental Corporation, Windsor, CT; *U.S. Public*, pg. 1558
Clauster, Brendan R., Pres.--Liberty Programming Corporation, Englewood, CO; *U.S. Public*, pg. 1555
Clay, John, Pres.--Practitioners Publishing Co., Fort Worth, TX; *U.S. Public*, pg. 1601
Clay, John W., Jr., Chm. Bd., Pres. & Chief Exec. Officer--SunTrust Banks of Tennessee, Inc., Nashville, TN; *U.S. Public*, pg. 1538
Clay, Larry D., Pres. & Chief Exec. Officer--Pacific Coast Producers, Lodi, CA; *U.S. Private*, pg. 830
Clay, Robert Earl, Owner--Pridgeon & Clay, Inc., Grand Rapids, MI; *U.S. Private*, pg. 883
Clay, Robert Edwin, Pres.--Pridgeon & Clay, Inc., Grand Rapids, MI; *U.S. Private*, pg. 883
Clay, Robert W., Pres.--Town & Country Supermarket, Hardy, AR; *U.S. Private*, pg. 1093
Clayton, Donnie, Sec.--Professional Putters Association, Fayetteville, NC; *U.S. Private*, pg. 896
Clayton, F.O., Pres. & Chief Exec. Officer--Shand Mining Inc., Indianapolis, IN; *Int'l*, pg. 281
Clayton, Joseph P., Pres. & Chief Oper. Officer--Frontier Corporation, Rochester, NY; *U.S. Public*, pg. 683
Clayton, Kevin T., Pres.--Clayton Homes, Inc., Knoxville, TN; *U.S. Public*, pg. 382
Clayton, Paul, Pres.--Burger King Corporation, Miami, FL; *Int'l*, pg. 411
Clayton, Richard R., Pres. & Chief Oper. Officer--Eastern Enterprises, Weston, MA; *U.S. Public*, pg. 548
Clayton, William, Jr., Pres.--Clayton Industries Co., El Monte, CA; *U.S. Private*, pg. 245
Cleary, Mark, Pres.--Aerolyte Systems, Washington, MO; *U.S. Private*, pg. 24
Cleary, Martin J., Pres. & Chief Oper. Officer--The Richard E. Jacobs Group, Westlake, OH; *U.S. Private*, pg. 580
Cleary, Thomas, Pres.--Alumax Foils, Inc., Saint Louis, MO; *U.S. Public*, pg. 60
Cleary, William T., Founding Sr. Partner--CKS Group, Cupertino, CA; *U.S. Private*, pg. 195
Cleave, James H., Pres. & Chief Exec. Officer--HSBC Americas, Buffalo, NY; *Int'l*, pg. 580
Cleave, James H., Pres. & Chief Exec. Officer--Marine Midland Bank, Buffalo, NY; *Int'l*, pg. 581
Cleberg, Harry C., Pres. & Chief Exec. Officer--Farmland Industries, Inc., Kansas City, MO; *U.S. Private*, pg. 395
Clegg, Jack, Chm. Bd., Pres. & Chief Exec. Officer--Nobel Education Dynamics, Inc., Media, PA; *U.S. Public*, pg. 1185
Clem, Roy J., Pres. & Gen. Mgr.--WSET Incorporatd, Lynchburg, VA; *U.S. Private*, pg. 854
Clemens, Jack S., Pres. & Chief Exec. Officer--Clemens Markets Inc., Kulpsville, PA; *U.S. Private*, pg. 245
Clemens, Philip A., Pres. & Chief Exec. Officer--Hatfield Quality Meats, Hatfield, PA; *U.S. Private*, pg. 510
Clemens, Richard E., Pres. & Chief Exec. Officer--The Monarch Machine Tool Company, Sidney, OH; *U.S. Public*, pg. 1123
Clement, Dan, Pres.--Martino's Bakery, Inc., Burbank, CA; *U.S. Private*, pg. 710
Clement, Gale W., Chm. Bd. & Pres.--Idahoan Foods, Lewisville, ID; *U.S. Private*, pg. 557
Clement, James W., Pres. & Chief Exec. Officer--Bank of Carroll, Hillsville, VA; *U.S. Public*, pg. 1038
Clemente, Robert, Pres.--Secom General Corporation, Novi, MI; *U.S. Public*, pg. 1453
Clements, Donald M., Jr., Pres.--AEP Resources Service Company, Columbus, OH; *U.S. Public*, pg. 72
Clements, Edward B., Pres. & Chief Exec. Officer--Clements Foods Co., Oklahoma City, OK; *U.S. Private*, pg. 245
Clements, Jeffrey K., Pres.--Zebra Technologies Corporation, Vernon Hills, IL; *U.S. Public*, pg. 1790
Clements, Robert, Pres.--K. Hovnanian Investment Properties, Inc., Red Bank, NJ; *U.S. Public*, pg. 843
Clemons, Luther F., Pres.--Associated Equipment Company of Delaware, Mobile, AL; *U.S. Private*, pg. 90
Clemons, Philip J., Pres.--CorryHiebert Corporation, Corry, PA; *U.S. Public*, pg. 772
Clemons, V. Gordon, Chm. Bd., Pres. & Chief Exec. Officer--CorVel Corporation, Irvine, CA; *U.S. Public*, pg. 451
Clerval, Pierre, Pres. & Chief Exec. Officer--Hutchenson Seal Corporation, Downey, CA; *U.S. Private*, pg. 550
Clerval, Pierre, Pres. & Chief Exec. Officer--Stillman Seal, Carlsbad, CA; *U.S. Private*, pg. 550
Cleveland, C.E. Thomas, Pres.--H.O. Penn Machinery Co. Inc., Poughkeepsie, NY; *U.S. Private*, pg. 849
Cleveland, James R., Jr., Pres. & Chief Exec. Officer--Cleveland Group, Inc., Atlanta, GA; *U.S. Private*, pg. 246
Cleveland, Jay W., Sr., Pres. & Chief Exec. Officer--Cleveland Brothers Equipment Co., Inc., Harrisburg, PA; *U.S. Private*, pg. 245
Clevenger, J.G., Pres.--Cyprus Bagdad Copper Corporation, Bagdad, AZ; *U.S. Public*, pg. 471
Clevenger, J.G., Pres.--Cyprus Sierrita, Green Valley, AZ; *U.S. Public*, pg. 471
Clevenger, J.G., Pres.--Cyprus Tohono Corporation, Casa Grande, AZ; *U.S. Public*, pg. 471
Clevenger, J.G., Pres.--Cyprus Miami Mining Corporation, Claypool, AZ; *U.S. Public*, pg. 471
Clevenger, J.G., Pres.--Cyprus Rod Chicago Corporation, Chicago, IL; *U.S. Public*, pg. 471
Clevenger, J.G., Pres.--Cyprus Climax Metals Company, Tempe, AZ; *U.S. Public*, pg. 471
Cleverly, A. Bruce, Pres.--Oral-B Laboratories, Belmont, CA; *U.S. Public*, pg. 743
Clifford, James R., Pres. & Chief Oper. Officer--Sears Canada, Inc., Toronto, Canada; *U.S. Public*, pg. 1452
Clifford, John, Pres. & Chief Exec. Officer--Clifford Paper Inc., Upper Saddle River, NJ; *U.S. Private*, pg. 246
Clift, Mark F., Pres.--Marithe and Francois Girbaud N.A., Greensboro, NC; *U.S. Public*, pg. 1702
Clifton, M.A., Pres.--Sunbelt Mining Co., Inc., Albuquerque, NM; *U.S. Public*, pg. 1340
Clifton, Matthew P., Pres.--Holly Corporation, Dallas, TX; *U.S. Public*, pg. 830
Clifton, Paul H., Jr., Pres.--BenefitAmerica, Columbia, SC; *U.S. Public*, pg. 1699
Cliggott, Richard T., Sr., Chief Exec. Officer--Cliggott Publishing, Greenwich, CT; *U.S. Private*, pg. 246
Cline, Peter J., Exec. V.P. & Pres.-Handleman Entertainment Resources--Handleman Company, Troy, MI; *U.S. Public*, pg. 779
Cline, Phil, Pres.--Broughton Foods Company, Marietta, OH; *U.S. Public*, pg. 259
Clingman, Fully, Pres.--H.E. Butt Grocery Co., San Antonio, TX; *U.S. Private*, pg. 190
Clinton, Jeffrey M., Pres.--Grey Eagle Distributors Inc., Maryland Heights, MO; *U.S. Private*, pg. 480
Clinton, Stephen P., Pres.--HSMM Facilities, Inc., Roanoke, VA; *U.S. Private*, pg. 513
Clipez, Patrice, Pres.--Synergie, Puteaux, France; *Int'l*, pg. 601
Clode, P.M., Pres. & Chief Exec. Officer--Grosvenor Marketing Ltd., Paramus, NJ; *Int'l*, pg. 92
Clodfelter, Gary N., Pres. & Chief Exec. Officer--White Electrical Construction Co., Atlanta, GA; *U.S. Private*, pg. 1172
Cloney, Richard M., Pres.--Susque-Bancshares Leasing Co., Inc., Lititz, PA; *U.S. Public*, pg. 1542
Clore, Larry, Pres.--Multi-Ad Services, Incorporated, Peoria, IL; *U.S. Private*, pg. 766
Close, Allyn D., Pres., Chief Exec. Officer & Mgr.-Sls. & Mktg.--Interpacific Investors Services, Seattle, WA; *U.S. Private*, pg. 572
Close, Carl Zane, Pres. & Chief Exec. Officer--Cerprobe Corporation, Gilbert, AZ; *U.S. Public*, pg. 332
Close, R.C., Pres.--Kodak Electronic Printing Systems, Billerica, MA; *U.S. Public*, pg. 551
Close, Robert, Pres.--Magnedyne Div., Vista, CA; *U.S. Private*, pg. 999
Closson, Steven A., Pres.--Androscoggin Savings Bank, Lewiston, ME; *U.S. Private*, pg. 74
Cloud, Ronald E., Pres. & Chief Exec. Officer--E.V. Roberts & Associates, Inc., Culver City, CA; *U.S. Private*, pg. 935
Cloud, Stephen R., Pres. & Chief Exec. Officer--IBT, Inc., Merriam, KS; *U.S. Private*, pg. 553
Clough, Stephen K., Pres. & Chief Exec. Officer--Kaydon Corporation, Clearwater, FL; *U.S. Public*, pg. 945
Clouston, Robert A.R., Pres. & Gen. Mgr., Consumer Prods--Warner-Lambert Canada, Inc., Scarborough, Canada; *U.S. Public*, pg. 1739
Cloutier, Alain, Pres.--Publicis BCP Promotion Inc., Montreal, Canada; *Int'l*, pg. 116
Cloward, Steven, Pres. & Chief Exec. Officer--Big O Tires Incorporated, Englewood, CO; *U.S. Public*, pg. 1553
Clowe, Tom, Pres. & Chief Exec. Officer--Missouri Gas Energy, Kansas City, MO; *U.S. Public*, pg. 1491
Cloyd, G.G., V.P.-Pharmaceuticals-U.S.--Procter & Gamble Pharmaceuticals, Inc., Cincinnati, OH; *U.S. Public*, pg. 1331
Clune, Michael T., Pres.--Clune Construction Limited, Chicago, IL; *U.S. Private*, pg. 247
Cluss, Chris, Pres. & Chief Exec. Officer--O.C. Cluss Lumber Co., Uniontown, PA; *U.S. Private*, pg. 248
Coackley, Robert, Pres.--General Signal Networks, Shelton, CT; *U.S. Public*, pg. 727
Coady, Michael F., Pres.--Fairchild Publications, New York, NY; *U.S. Public*, pg. 513
Coady, Todd M., Chm. Bd., Pres. & Chief Exec. Officer--Hicks Oil-Hicks Gas, Inc., Roberts, IL; *U.S. Private*, pg. 526
Coate, John P., Sr., Pres.--Flowers Baking Co. of Bradenton, Inc., Sarasota, FL; *U.S. Public*, pg. 657
Coates, Jon P., Pres. & Chief Exec. Officer--Key Bank of Colorado, Fort Collins, CO; *U.S. Public*, pg. 954
Coath, J. Douglas, Jr., Pres. & Chief Exec. Officer--Frank W. Winne & Son, Inc., Philadelphia, PA; *U.S. Private*, pg. 1183
Coatney, Doyle, Pres. & Chief Exec. Officer--Acme Truck Line, Inc., Harvey, LA; *U.S. Private*, pg. 14
Cobb, Timothy S., Chm. Bd., Pres. & Chief Exec. Officer--Salient 3 Communications, Inc., Reading, PA; *U.S. Public*, pg. 1429
Coblentz, Joanne, V.P. & Gen. Mgr.--WAXY (FM), Fort Lauderdale, FL; *U.S. Public*, pg. 925
Coburn, Ronald, Pres. & Chief Exec. Officer--Savage Arms Inc., Westfield, MA; *U.S. Private*, pg. 968
Coccari, Greg, Pres. & Chief Exec. Officer--Teleflora, LLC, Los Angeles, CA; *U.S. Private*, pg. 941
Cocchiola, Mark, Chm. Bd., Pres. & Chief Exec. Officer--Suprema Specialties, Inc., Paterson, NJ; *U.S. Public*, pg. 1541
Cocheteux, Jean-Bernard, Pres.--Turbomeca Microturbo Division, Bordes, France; *Int'l*, pg. 786
Cochran, G. Moffet, Pres.--Wood, Struthers & Winthrop Management Corp., New York, NY; *U.S. Public*, pg. 589
Cochran, R. E., Pres.--809
Cochran, Robert P., Pres. & Chief Exec. Officer--Financial Security Assurance Holdings Ltd., New York, NY; *U.S. Public*, pg. 622
Cochrane, Jr., Haywood D., Pres. & Chief Exec. Officer--Allied Clinical Laboratories, Inc., Nashville, TN; *U.S. Public*, pg. 973
Cochrane, Kevin, Pres.--Texon Materials Inc., Russell, MA; *U.S. Private*, pg. 1079
Cochrane, Len, Pres. & Chief Oper. Officer--The Family Channel Inc., Toronto, Canada; *Int'l*, pg. 1482
Cockaerts, Marcel, Pres.--Kredietbank N.V., Brussels, Belgium; *Int'l*, pg. 760
Cockayne, Jim D., Pres.--Weiss Sheet Metal Company, Gardena, CA; *U.S. Private*, pg. 1160
Cockerill, Bob, Pres.--Batten Graphics, Toronto, Canada; *U.S. Public*, pg. 1437
Cockwell, Ian G., Pres.--Unicorp Canada Corporation, Toronto, Canada; *Int'l*, pg. 1433
Cockwell, Jack L., Pres. & Chief Exec. Officer--EdperBrascan Corporation, Toronto, Canada; *Int'l*, pg. 433
Cocquyt, Marie-Jose, Pres. & Chief Exec. Officer--Kompass International Neuenschwander SA, Cruet, France; *Int'l*, pg. 745
Coder, P. Jerry, Pres.--EKC Technology, Inc., Hayward, CA; *U.S. Public*, pg. 344
Coder, Stephen, Pres.--Ring King Visibles, Inc., Muscatine, IA; *Int'l*, pg. 460
Cody, John T., Jr., Pres. & Chief Oper. Officer-Domestic--JC Penney Company, Inc., Plano, TX; *U.S. Public*, pg. 916
Cody, Kevin, Pres.--Pace Mechanical Services, Inc, Westland, MI; *U.S. Public*, pg. 572
Coe, Dennis R., Pres. & Chief. Exec. Officer--Lois/EJL Los Angeles, Los Angeles, CA; *U.S. Public*, pg. 1011
Coffeng, Hans, Pres. & Chief Exec. Officer--Fremont Indemnity Corp., Santa Monica, CA; *U.S. Public*, pg. 681
Coffey, Larry R., Pres.--Landmark Community Newspapers, Inc., Shelbyville, KY; *U.S. Private*, pg. 648
Coffey, R.L., Pres.--Vigortone AG Products, Inc., Cedar Rapids, IA; *Int'l*, pg. 1357
Coffman, C. Morris, Chm. Bd., Pres. & Chief Exec. Officer--Farmers Bank & Trust Co., Madisonville, KY; *U.S. Public*, *pg. 1217*
Coffman, Kenneth M., Pres.--K & G of Wisconsin, Inc., Milwaukee, WI; *U.S. Private*, pg. 602
Cofield, Charles D., Pres.--American Emulsions Co., Inc., Dalton, GA; *U.S. Public*, pg. 1357
Cofield, Charles D., Pres.--Chemical Specialties Manufacturing Corp., Baltimore, MD; *U.S. Public*, pg. 1357
Cogan, John F., Jr., Chm. Bd. & Pres.--The Pioneer Group, Inc., Boston, MA; *U.S. Public*, pg. 1298
Coggin, James A., Pres. & Chief Oper. Officer--Proffitt's, Inc., Alcoa, TN; *U.S. Public*, pg. 1333
Coggin, Luther, Pres. & Chief Exec. Officer--Coggin Automotive Group, Jacksonville, FL; *U.S. Private*, pg. 250
Coghlan, John, Pres.--Beam Industries, Webster City, IA; *Int'l*, pg. 440
Coghlin, John F., Pres.--Dock Foundry Company, Three Rivers, MI; *U.S. Private*, pg. 337
Cogliati, Carlo, Pres.--Ausimont S.p.A., Bollate, Italy; *Int'l*, pg. 324
Cogswell, Gary, Pres.--JEOL (U.S.A.), Inc., Peabody, MA; *Int'l*, pg. 697
Cogswell, Steve, Pres.--Prime Matrix Wireless Communications, Calabasas, CA; *U.S. Private*, pg. 884
Cohan, Norman H., Pres. & Chief Exec. Officer--Security Plastics, Inc., Hialeah, FL; *U.S. Private*, pg. 981
Cohen Tervaert, Dirk G., Chm. Bd. & Pres.--N.V. Deli-Universal, Rotterdam, Netherlands; *U.S. Public*, pg. 1695
Cohen, Alan, Pres.--Andal Corp., New York, NY; *U.S. Public*, pg. 111
Cohen, Alan, Chm. Bd., Pres. & Chief Exec. Officer--Finish Line, Inc., Indianapolis, IN; *U.S. Public*, pg. 623
Cohen, Andrew, Pres.--Chorus Line Corporation, Vernon, CA; *U.S. Private*, pg. 238
Cohen, Betty, Pres.--The Cartoon Network, Atlanta, GA; *U.S. Public*, pg. 1614
Cohen, C. Anders, Chm. Bd.--A. Cohen & Co. P.L.C., London, United Kingdom; *Int'l*, pg. 306
Cohen, Donald, Chm. Bd., Pres., Chief Exec. Officer & Chief Fin. Officer--Tool King, Denver, CO; *U.S. Private*, pg. 1091
Cohen, Gadi, Pres.--PNY Technologies, Inc., Parsippany, NJ; *U.S. Private*, pg. 827
Cohen, Gary B., Pres.--ACI Telecentrics, Inc., Minneapolis, MN; *U.S. Public*, pg. 3
Cohen, Gerald D., Pres.--Information Builders, New York, NY; *U.S. Private*, pg. 561
Cohen, Harry, Pres.--First Computer Corporation, Los Angeles, CA; *U.S. Private*, pg. 406
Cohen, Howard, Pres.--Caddy Corp. of America, Bridgeport, NJ; *U.S. Private*, pg. 198
Cohen, Howard, Pres.--Host Apparel, Inc., New York, NY; *U.S. Private*, pg. 540
Cohen, Ian N., Partner & Acct. Plng. Dir.--Kupper Parker Communications Inc., Saint Louis, MO; *U.S. Private*, pg. 637
Cohen, Ira D., Pres.--TransCor Waste Service, Inc., Tampa, FL; *U.S. Public*, pg. 960
Cohen, James, Pres. & Chief Exec. Officer--Hudson County News Company, North Bergen, NJ; *U.S. Private*, pg. 545
Cohen, Larry, Pres.--The Hotsy Corporation, Englewood, CO; *U.S. Private*, pg. 500
Cohen, Larry H., Pres.--Accurate Perforating Co., Chicago, IL; *U.S. Private*, pg. 12
Cohen, Leonard, Pres. & Chief Exec. Officer--Kelly, Scott And Madison, Inc., Chicago, IL; *U.S. Private*, pg. 613

Cohen, Lewis M., Pres. & Chief Exec. Officer--Acme Canvas Co., Inc., Malden, MA; *U.S. Private*, pg. 13
Cohen, Louis D., Pres. & Chief Exec. Officer--Sheplers, Inc., Wichita, KS; *U.S. Private*, pg. 993
Cohen, Maryjo, Pres., Chief Exec. Officer & Chief Fin. Officer--National Presto Industries, Inc., Eau Claire, WI; *U.S. Public*, pg. 1159
Cohen, Melvin S., Pres.--Presto Export Ltd., Saint Croix, VI; *U.S. Public*, pg. 1159
Cohen, Millard S., Pres.--Nixdorff Krein Industries Inc., Saint Louis, MO; *U.S. Private*, pg. 799
Cohen, Milton L., Chm. Bd. & Pres.--Lifetime Hoan Corp., Westbury, NY; *U.S. Public*, pg. 992
Cohen, Peter J., Chm. Bd., Pres. & Chief Exec. Officer--Periphonics Corp., Bohemia, NY; *U.S. Public*, pg. 1278
Cohen, Philip E., Partner--Harris Drury Cohen, Fort Lauderdale, FL; *U.S. Private*, pg. 505
Cohen, Richard, Pres.--C & S Wholesale Grocery Inc., Brattleboro, VT; *U.S. Private*, pg. 192
Cohen, Robert H., Chm. Bd. & Pres.--Beauty Enterprises Inc., Hartford, CT; *U.S. Private*, pg. 128
Cohen, Robert N., Pres.--Daycon Products Company, Inc., Lanham, MD; *U.S. Private*, pg. 317
Cohen, Ronnie, Pres.--AyerDirect, New York, NY; *U.S. Private*, pg. 104
Cohen, Sam, Pres.--Service Packing Company-United Food Group, Los Angeles, CA; *U.S. Private*, pg. 986
Cohen, Steven, Pres. & Chief Exec. Officer--Hasselblad USA, Inc., Fairfield, NJ; *Int'l*, pg. 1468
Cohen, Warren, Pres.--All-Luminum Products, Inc., Philadelphia, PA; *U.S. Private*, pg. 34
Cohen, Warren, Pres.--Eagle Electric Mfg. Co., Inc., Long Island City, NY; *U.S. Private*, pg. 354
Cohen, William L., Chm. Bd., Pres. & Chief Exec. Officer--Andover Togs, Inc., New York, NY; *U.S. Public*, pg. 112
Cohenca, Philip, Pres.--Jason Industrial, Inc., Fairfield, NJ; *U.S. Private*, pg. 583
Cohlst, C.G., Pres.-Mktg. & Sls.--UBO Verzekeringen, Utrecht, Netherlands; *Int'l*, pg. 26
Cohn, Gerald, Pres.--E.J. Footwear Corp., Endicott, NY; *U.S. Public*, pg. 1684
Cohn, Gerald M., Pres.--Georgia/Durango Boot Company, Franklin, TN; *U.S. Public*, pg. 1684
Cohn, Jeffrey, Chief Exec. Officer & Pres.--Decorative Crafts, Inc., Greenwich, CT; *U.S. Private*, pg. 320
Cohn, Mark, Pres.--Texas Telemarketing, Inc., Minneapolis, MN; *U.S. Public*, pg. 478
Cohn, Mark, Pres.--Damark Financial Services, Inc., Minneapolis, MN; *U.S. Public*, pg. 478
Cohn, Mark A., Chm. Bd. & Chief Exec. Officer--Damark International, Inc., Minneapolis, MN; *U.S. Public*, pg. 478
Cohn, Richard, Pres.--Sigmund Cohn Corp., Mount Vernon, NY; *U.S. Private*, pg. 250
Cohn, Richard, Pres.--Pyrofuse, Mount Vernon, NY; *U.S. Private*, pg. 250
Cohn, Richard, Pres.--Medwire, Mount Vernon, NY; *U.S. Private*, pg. 250
Coil, Lawrence, Pres. & Chief Exec. Officer--Pinkerton & Laws Inc., Atlanta, GA; *U.S. Private*, pg. 865
Coimbra, Roberto, Exec. V.P., Pres. & CEO-JWT/Venezuela--J. Walter Thompson Company, New York, NY; *Int'l*, pg. 1483
Cojuangco, Antonio, Pres. & Chief Exec. Officer--Philippine Long Distance Telephone Company, Manila, Philippines; *Int'l*, pg. 1051
Colangelo, Larry A., Pres. & Chief Exec. Officer--SPD Technologies, Philadelphia, PA; *U.S. Private*, pg. 957
Colasacco, Domenic, Chm. Bd. & Pres.--United States Trust Company, Boston, MA; *U.S. Public*, pg. 1660
Colbert, Christopher M., Pres.--Holland Mark Martin, Boston, MA; *U.S. Private*, pg. 534
Colbert, Donald W., Pres. & Chief Oper. Officer--S & K Famous Brands, Inc., Glen Allen, VA; *U.S. Public*, pg. 1414
Colbert, Jack L., Pres.--United Southwest Bank, Washington, IN; *U.S. Public*, pg. 1217
Colbran, Scott, Pres.--Rogers Cable Systems, Etobicoke, Canada; *Int'l*, pg. 1123
Colby, Donald L., Pres. & Chief Exec. Officer--BNY Holdings (New Jersey) Corp., West Paterson, NJ; *U.S. Public*, pg. 178
Colcolough, Ted, Pres.--Greenwood Mills, Inc., Greenwood, SC; *U.S. Private*, pg. 479
Cole, Bruce, Pres.--National Insurance Group, South San Francisco, CA; *U.S. Public*, pg. 1157
Cole, C. David, Pres.--Aquion, Elk Grove Village, IL; *U.S. Private*, pg. 78
Cole, Chris, Pres.--The Buschman Company, Cincinnati, OH; *U.S. Private*, pg. 866
Cole, Crawford, Pres. & Chief Exec. Officer--West Marine, Inc., Watsonville, CA; *U.S. Public*, pg. 1756
Cole, Eddie, Pres.--Answer Products, Inc., Valencia, CA; *U.S. Private*, pg. 639
Cole, Gary, Pres.--Playboy Models, Inc., Beverly Hills, CA; *U.S. Public*, pg. 1310
Cole, Gregory W., Pres. & Chief Exec. Officer--Inland Detroit Diesel Allison Co., Butler, WI; *U.S. Private*, pg. 564
Cole, Jack, Pres.--Lance Camper Manufacturing Corporation, Lancaster, CA; *U.S. Private*, pg. 645
Cole, James D., Chm. Bd., Pres., & Chief Exec. Officer--Newpark Resources, Inc., Metairie, LA; *U.S. Public*, pg. 1179
Cole, John, Pres.--PolyPhaser Corporation, Minden, NV; *Int'l*, pg. 1268
Cole, Kenneth, Chm. Bd. & Pres.--Kenneth Cole Productions, New York, NY; *U.S. Public*, pg. 951
Cole, Louis C., Chm. Bd., Pres. & Chief Exec. Officer--Legato Systems, Inc., Palo Alto, CA; *U.S. Public*, pg. 984
Cole, Nick, Pres.--Spicer Off-Highway Axle Div., Fort Wayne, IN; *U.S. Public*, pg. 479
Cole, Tom, Pres.--Federated Logistics, Secaucus, NJ; *U.S. Public*, pg. 618
Colebrook, Miles, Exec. V.P., Grp. Pres.-JWT/Intl., & Global Bus. Dir.-Nestle--J. Walter Thompson Company, New York, NY; *Int'l*, pg. 1483
Colehower, William S., Chm. Bd. & Pres.--Jomac, Inc., Warrington, PA; *U.S. Private*, pg. 595
Coleman, Debi, Chm. Bd., Pres. & Chief Exec. Officer--Merix Corporation, Forest Grove, OR; *U.S. Public*, pg. 1096
Coleman, Donald A., Pres. & Chief Exec. Officer--Don Coleman Advertising, Inc., Southfield, MI; *U.S. Private*, pg. 251
Coleman, James R., Pres.--Coleman Cadillac Inc., Bethesda, MD; *U.S. Private*, pg. 251
Coleman, Jim, Pres. & Chief Exec. Officer--Coleman Cable Systems, Inc., North Chicago, IL; *U.S. Public*, pg. 968
Coleman, John, Pres.--Snyder Tank Corp., Buffalo, NY; *U.S. Private*, pg. 1011
Coleman, John P., Pres.--Sussex Publishers, Inc., New York, NY; *U.S. Private*, pg. 1056
Coleman, Lonzo, Chm. Bd., Pres. & Chief Exec. Officer--ColeJon Corporation, Cleveland, OH; *U.S. Private*, pg. 251
Coleman, Mike, Pres.--North Star Steel Co., Wayzata, MN; *U.S. Private*, pg. 210
Coleman, P. Michael, Chm. Bd., Pres. & Chief Exec. Officer--Integrity Incorporated, Mobile, AL; *U.S. Public*, pg. 886
Coleman, Robert E., Sr., Pres. & Owner--Coleman Oldsmobile, Inc., Baton Rouge, LA; *U.S. Private*, pg. 252
Coleman, Rogers K., Pres.--Blue Cross & Blue Shield of Texas, Inc., Richardson, TX; *U.S. Private*, pg. 152
Coleman, Tom, Pres.--E-Z Mart Stores, Inc., Texarkana, TX; *U.S. Private*, pg. 353
Coleon, Yves, Pres. & Chief Exec. Officer--Lalique North America, Carlstadt, NJ; *Int'l*, pg. 797
Coler, Gregory, Pres.-Govt. Transactions--Transactive Corporation, Austin, TX; *U.S. Public*, pg. 767
Coles, Bruce, Pres.--Law Engineering, Inc., Atlanta, GA; *U.S. Private*, pg. 653
Coley, Bill A., Pres.--Tower Printing Company, Atlanta, GA; *U.S. Public*, pg. 1736
Coley, Tom H., Pres.--South Trust Bank of Georgia, Atlanta, GA; *U.S. Public*, pg. 1492
Colgan, Paul, Chm. Bd. & Pres.--Waldo Bros. Company, Boston, MA; *U.S. Private*, pg. 1147
Coliccino, Frank, Pres.--Dairy Mart East, Inc., East Providence, RI; *U.S. Public*, pg. 476
Colin, Lawrence, Pres.--Colin Service Systems, Inc., White Plains, NY; *U.S. Private*, pg. 252
Collette, Craig D., Pres. & Chief Exec. Officer--California State Bank-La Habra, La Habra, CA; *U.S. Public*, pg. 294
Collier, Barry, Pres.--Video City Inc., Bakersfield, CA; *U.S. Public*, pg. 1719
Collier, Barry D., Pres.--Peter Pan Seafoods, Inc., Seattle, WA; *Int'l*, pg. 928
Collin, Andre, Pres. & Chief Oper. Officer--Cadim, Montreal, Canada; *Int'l*, pg. 249
Collins, Arthur D., Jr., Pres. & Chief Oper. Officer--Medtronic, Inc., Minneapolis, MN; *U.S. Public*, pg. 1082
Collins, Bert, Pres. & Chief Exec. Officer--North Carolina Mutual Life Insurance Co., Durham, NC; *U.S. Private*, pg. 804
Collins, C.A., Pres. & Chief Exec. Officer--Adams Rite Sabre International, Glendale, CA; *U.S. Private*, pg. 1203
Collins, Charles F., Pres. & Chief Exec. Officer--Industrial Maintenance Overflow Corporation, Fletcher, NC; *U.S. Private*, pg. 561
Collins, Christopher C., Chm. Bd., Pres. & Chief Exec. Officer--Nuttall Gear Corporation, Niagara Falls, NY; *U.S. Private*, pg. 809
Collins, Don L., Chm. Bd., Pres., Chief Exec. & Oper. Officer--Collins Industries, Inc., Hutchinson, KS; *U.S. Public*, pg. 399
Collins, Duane E., Pres. & Chief Exec. Officer--Parker Hannifin Corporation, Cleveland, OH; *U.S. Public*, pg. 1259
Collins, Edward, Pres.--Morse Diesel International, Inc., New York, NY; *U.S. Private*, pg. 762
Collins, Francis A., Pres. & Chief Exec. Officer--The Imperial Electric Company, Akron, OH; *U.S. Private*, pg. 598
Collins, Francis A., Pres.--The Scott Motors Company, Alamogordo, NM; *U.S. Private*, pg. 598
Collins, James L. S., Pres.--Chick-fil-A, Inc., Atlanta, GA; *U.S. Private*, pg. 236
Collins, John, Pres.--Steering and Suspension Division, Saint Louis, MO; *U.S. Public*, pg. 443
Collins, John A. III, Pres.--American Marking Systems, Clifton, NJ; *U.S. Private*, pg. 58
Collins, John A., III, Pres.--Paterson Stamp Works, Clifton, NJ; *U.S. Private*, pg. 59
Collins, John F., Pres.--Moog Automotive, Inc., Saint Louis, MO; *U.S. Public*, pg. 443
Collins, Larry, Pres.--Enterprise Electronics Corp., Enterprise, AL; *U.S. Public*, pg. 1563
Collins, Marshall J., Jr., Pres. & Chief Exec. Officer--BI-LO Inc., Greenville, SC; *Int'l*, pg. 749
Collins, Michael J., Dr., Pres. & Chief Exec. Officer--CEM Corporation, Matthews, NC; *U.S. Public*, pg. 277
Collins, Mike, Pres.--American Marine Holdings Inc., Sarasota, FL; *U.S. Private*, pg. 58
Collins, Pat, Pres. & Publisher--The Spectator, Hamilton, Hamilton, Canada; *Int'l*, pg. 631
Collins, Richard B., Pres. & Chief Exec. Officer--First Massachusettes Bank, N.A., Worcester, MA; *U.S. Public*, pg. 187
Collins, Robert T., Pres. & Publisher--Asbury Park Press, Inc., Neptune, NJ; *U.S. Public*, pg. 699
Collins, Ron, Pres. & Chief Exec. Officer--Stone Fort National Bank, Nacogdoches, Nacogdoches, TX; *U.S. Public*, pg. 630
Collins, Russell A., Pres. & Chief Exec. Officer--Fattal & Collins (F&C), Marina Del Rey, CA; *U.S. Public*, pg. 765
Collins, Steve, Partner & Mngmt. Supvr.--Martin/Williams Advertising Inc., Minneapolis, MN; *U.S. Private*, pg. 710
Collins, Vernon E., Chm. Bd., Pres. & Chief Exec. Officer--Bliss-Salem, Inc., Salem, OH; *U.S. Private*, pg. 149
Collins, W., III, Chm. Bd. & Pres.--Warren E. Collins, Inc., Braintree, MA; *U.S. Private*, pg. 253
Collins, Wayne, Pres. & Chief Exec. Officer--Pennock, Philadelphia, PA; *U.S. Private*, pg. 850
Collins, William, Pres. & Chief Exec. Officer--Bill Collins Ford Inc., Louisville, KY; *U.S. Private*, pg. 253
Collins, William A., Pres.--Collins Electric Company, Inc., Chicopee, MA; *U.S. Private*, pg. 253
Collins, William L., III, Pres. & Chief Exec. Officer--Metrocall, Inc., Alexandria, VA; *U.S. Public*, pg. 1102
Colliver, Danielle, Pres.--N.W. Ayer & Partners Detroit, Detroit, MI; *U.S. Private*, pg. 104
Collman, Nicholas J., Chm. Bd., Pres. & Chief Exec. Officer--Collman Graphics, Inc., Baltimore, MD; *U.S. Private*, pg. 253
Collura, Sam, Pres.--TIE Systems Arkansas/Gulfcoast, Little Rock, AR; *U.S. Private*, pg. 1085
Colman, James A., Pres. & Chief Exec. Officer--Acme Mills Co. Inc., Detroit, MI; *U.S. Private*, pg. 13
Colman, John, Chief Exec. Officer--Mother Earth News, New York, NY; *U.S. Private*, pg. 1056
Colne, Nigel, Pres.--Marks & Spencer US Holdings Inc., New York, NY; *Int'l*, pg. 843
Colonna, Peter, Pres., Chief Exec. Officer & Mng. Dir.--Colonna Bros., Inc., North Bergen, NJ; *U.S. Private*, pg. 254
Coltart, Michael, Pres. & Chief Exec. Officer--Andes Candies Inc., Delavan, WI; *U.S. Private*, pg. 163
Coltman, David A., Chm. Bd. & Pres.--Covia, LLC, Elk Grove Village, IL; *U.S. Public*, pg. 1653
Coltman, David A., Chm. Bd. & Pres.--United Vacations, Inc., Elk Grove Village, IL; *U.S. Public*, pg. 1653
Colton, Bruce L., Pres. & Chief Exec. Officer--Domestic Uniform Rental Co., Farmington Hills, MI; *U.S. Private*, pg. 338
Colwell, J. Bart, Pres. & Chief Exec. Officer--First State Bank, Brazil, IN; *U.S. Public*, pg. 634
Colwell, John G., Jr., Pres.--Colwell Industries, Inc., Minneapolis, MN; *U.S. Private*, pg. 257
Combe, Christopher B., Pres.--Combe Incorporated, White Plains, NY; *U.S. Private*, pg. 257
Combe, Jean-Francois, Pres.--SKF France S.A., Clamart, France; *Int'l*, pg. 1158
Combs, Charles S., Pres. & Chief Exec. Officer--Merchants National Bank, Terre Haute, IN; *U.S. Public*, pg. 1217
Combs, William H., III, Pres. & Chief Exec. Officer--Tamaqua Cable Products Corp., Schuylkill Haven, PA; *Int'l*, pg. 417
Comeau, Robert, Pres.--PacifiCare Life & Health Insurance Co., Costa Mesa, CA; *U.S. Public*, pg. 1251
Comer, Clarence C., Pres. & Chief Exec. Officer--Southdown, Inc., Houston, TX; *U.S. Public*, pg. 1488
Comey, Dale R., Chm. & Pres.--First State Insurance Company, Boston, MA; *U.S. Public*, pg. 794
Comment, Jeffrey W., Chm. Bd., Pres. & Chief Exec. Officer--Helzberg's Diamond Shops, Inc., Kansas City, MO; *U.S. Public*, pg. 220
Commerot, Gerard, Pres. & New Bus. Contact--Ketchum Advertising France, Paris, France; *U.S. Private*, pg. 617
Commes, Thomas A., Pres. & Chief Oper. Officer--The Sherwin-Williams Company, Cleveland, OH; *U.S. Public*, pg. 1465
Commette, William, Pres.--Middlesex Insurance, Westford, MA; *U.S. Private*, pg. 985
Commette, William E., Pres.--Middlesex Insurance Co., Stevens Point, WI; *U.S. Private*, pg. 985
Como, John, Sr., Pres.--Amco Folding Cartons, Inc., Towaco, NJ; *U.S. Private*, pg. 48
Comora, Owen, Pres.--Owen Comora Associates, New York, NY; *U.S. Private*, pg. 985
Compean, J., Pres. & Sec.--Grupo Video Visa S.A. de C.V., Mexico, Mexico; *Int'l*, pg. 577
Comper, F. Anthony, Pres. & Chief Oper. Officer--Bank of Montreal, Toronto, Canada; *Int'l*, pg. 153
Compitelo, Joseph, Pres.--International Envelope Company, Exton, PA; *U.S. Public*, pg. 70
Compton, Franklin, Pres., Chief Exec. Officer & New Bus. Contact--Sawyer Riley Compton Inc., Atlanta, GA; *U.S. Private*, pg. 969
Compton, James, Pres. & Chief Exec. Officer--Stewart Smith Southeast, Inc., Tampa, FL; *Int'l*, pg. 1508
Compton, Ned, Pres. & Chief Oper. Officer--Community First Bank & Trust, Celina, OH; *U.S. Public*, pg. 633
Compton, Thomas A., Pres. & Chief Exec. Officer--EnviroSource-International Mill Service, Inc., Horsham, PA; *U.S. Public*, pg. 587
Compton, William F., Pres. & Chief Oper. Officer--Trans World Airlines, Inc., Saint Louis, MO; *U.S. Public*, pg. 1629
Comstock, Harwood B., Chm. Bd. & Pres.--Pratt-Read Corporation, Bridgeport, CT; *U.S. Private*, pg. 879
Comtois, Claude, Pres.--AGRA Monenco Quebec, Inc., Montreal, Canada; *Int'l*, pg. 30
Conacher, J.C., Pres.--Halma Holdings Inc., Cincinnati, OH; *Int'l*, pg. 590
Conant, Mark, Pres.--USA Petroleum Corporation, Agoura Hills, CA; *U.S. Private*, pg. 1125
Conant, Victor, Pres. & Chief Exec. Officer--Nightingale-Conant Corp., Niles, IL; *U.S. Private*, pg. 799
Conaty, James R., Pres.--H.B. Fuller Automotive Products, Madison Heights, MI; *U.S. Public*, pg. 687
Concato, Andrea, Partner & Creative Dir.--Eurocom Concato di Pace Srl, Milan, Italy; *Int'l*, pg. 603
Condo, Koiege, Pres.--Honda Motor do Brasil Ltda., Sao Paulo, Brazil; *Int'l*, pg. 635
Condo, Patrick C., Pres. & Chief Exec. Officer--Excalibur Technologies Corporation, Vienna, VA; *U.S. Public*, pg. 598
Condon, Fred, Pres.--F.G. Montabert, Midland Park, NJ; *U.S. Private*, pg. 758

Condon, Pierre, Pres.--Interavia Publishing Group, Geneva, Switzerland; *U.S. Public*, pg. 1601

Condron, Kevin, Pres.--Granite Group Wholesale LLC, Manchester, NH; *U.S. Private*, pg. 469

Cone, G. Hollis, Chm. Bd., Pres. & Chief Exec. Officer--Defender Services, Inc., Columbia, SC; *U.S. Private*, pg. 320

Cone, George W., Pres. & Chief Oper. Officer--Virtual Vision, Inc., Redmond, WA; *U.S. Public*, pg. 1573

Conforti, Fred, Pres. & Chief Exec. Officer--Pittway Systems Technology Grp., Naperville, IL; *U.S. Public*, pg. 1306

Congdon, David S., Pres. & Chief Oper. Officer--Old Dominion Freight Line, Inc., High Point, NC; *U.S. Public*, pg. 1216

Congel, Robert J., Mng. Partner--The Pyramid Companies, Syracuse, NY; *U.S. Private*, pg. 896

Conger, H.M., Pres.--Phelps Dodge Morenci Inc., Morenci, AZ; *U.S. Public*, pg. 1287

Coniglio, Michel, Pres.--Carbone-Lorraine North America, Parsippany, NJ; *Int'l*, pg. 1028

Conine, Mike, Pres.--Stewart & Stevenson Holdings, Inc., Houston, TX; *U.S. Public*, pg. 1517

Conklin, Charles E., Pres. & Chief Exec. Officer--Conklin Instrument Corporation, Pleasant Valley, NY; *U.S. Private*, pg. 263

Conklin, Keith H., Pres.--Nestle Foodservice Canada, Markham, Canada; *Int'l*, pg. 922

Conlan, Don R., Pres.--The Capital Group Companies Inc., Los Angeles, CA; *U.S. Private*, pg. 206

Conley, J., Pres.--Photo Mechanix Inc., Carpentersville, IL; *U.S. Private*, pg. 891

Conley, Joseph H., Jr., Pres. & Chief Exec. Officer--Cook Moving Systems, Inc., Buffalo, NY; *U.S. Private*, pg. 272

Conley, Michael E., Pres. & Chief Exec. Officer--General Life Insurance Company Of America, Edwardsville, IL; *U.S. Private*, pg. 443

Conlin, Kelly P., Pres.--International Data Group, Boston, MA; *U.S. Private*, pg. 569

Conlon, Harry B., Chm. Bd., Pres. & Chief Exec. Officer--Associated Banc-Corp, Green Bay, WI; *U.S. Public*, pg. 140

Conlon, Thomas, Pres.--D.L. Blair Inc., Garden City, NY; *U.S. Private*, pg. 148

Conlon, Timothy L., Pres. & Chief Oper. Officer--Berg Electronics, Saint Louis, MO; *U.S. Public*, pg. 212

Connally, John H., Pres., Chief Fin. Officer & Dir.--States, Inc., Breckenridge, TX; *U.S. Private*, pg. 1037

Connavino, Nicholas A., Pres.--SuperValu, Inc.-Northeastern Reg., Burlington, MA; *U.S. Public*, pg. 1540

Connell, Grover, Chm. Bd. & Pres.--Connell Co., Westfield, NJ; *U.S. Private*, pg. 264

Connell, William F., Chm. Bd. & Chief Exec. Officer--Connell Limited Partnership, Boston, MA; *U.S. Private*, pg. 264

Connelly, James G., III, Pres. & Chief Oper. Officer--Caremark International Inc, Northbrook, IL; *U.S. Public*, pg. 1082

Connelly, Jerry, Pres. & Chief Exec. Officer--Pfaudler, Inc., Rochester, NY; *U.S. Public*, pg. 1393

Connelly, Stephen, Pres. & Exec. Creative Dir.--Ingalls, Boston, MA; *U.S. Private*, pg. 562

Connelly, Thomas S., Chm. Bd., Pres., Chief Exec. Officer--Connelly Containers, Inc., Bala Cynwyd, PA; *U.S. Private*, pg. 264

Conner, Richard W., Pres.--Rennoc Corporation, Vineland, NJ; *U.S. Private*, pg. 922

Conners, Jack, Pres. & Gen. Mgr.--WICS-TV, Springfield, IL; *U.S. Private*, pg. 439

Connolly, John D., Pres.--LTCB-MAS Investment Management, Inc., Conshohocken, PA; *Int'l*, pg. 816

Connolly, Kevin, Pres.--Excerpta Medica Inc., Belle Mead, NJ; *Int'l*, pg. 1100

Connolly, Michael, Pres.-U.S. Opers.--Waterford Foods USA, Inc., Wilmington, DE; *Int'l*, pg. 102

Connor, Joseph, Pres.--Fiberlock Technologies, Inc., Cambridge, MA; *U.S. Private*, pg. 201

Connor, Richard J., Gen. Mgr.--Macwhyte Co., Kenosha, WI; *U.S. Private*, pg. 68

Connors, Chester L., Pres. & Chief Fin. Officer--Magneco/Metrel, Inc., Addison, IL; *U.S. Private*, pg. 695

Connors, James J., Pres. & Chief Exec. Officer--Century Products Co., Macedonia, OH; *U.S. Private*, pg. 226

Conomikes, John G., Pres. & Co-Chief Exec. Officer--Hearst-Argyle Television Incorporated, New York, NY; *U.S. Private*, pg. 516

Conover, Donald E., Pres. & Chm. Bd.--Greystone Realty Corporation, Greenwich, CT; *U.S. Private*, pg. 795

Conrad, Bernhard, Pres.--A-B Emblem Div. of Conrad Industries, Inc., Weaverville, NC; *U.S. Private*, pg. 2

Conrad, Carlton J., Jr., Pres. & Chief Exec. Officer--E.H. Titchener & Company, Binghamton, NY; *U.S. Private*, pg. 1089

Conrad, Phil, Pres.--Endevco Corporation, San Juan Capistrano, CA; *Int'l*, pg. 853

Conrad, William C., Pres. & Chief Exec. Officer--First American Capital Management, Inc., Newport Beach, CA; *U.S. Public*, pg. 625

Conrades, George H., Chm. Bd., Pres. & Chief Exec. Officer--GTE Internetworking, Cambridge, MA; *U.S. Public*, pg. 696

Conroy, Michael, Pres.--FCAIBMZ CID, Madrid, Spain; *Int'l*, pg. 469

Conroy, Patrick T., Pres.--GENXON Power Systems LLC, Mountain View, CA; *U.S. Public*, pg. 1776

Conroy, T.F., Pres.--Security Life of Denver Reinsurance Company, Denver, CO; *Int'l*, pg. 648

Consonni, Marcello, Pres.--Hagglunds Drives Srl, Milan, Italy; *Int'l*, pg. 670

Constable, John, Partner & Creative Dir.--Laughlin/Constable, Inc., Milwaukee, WI; *U.S. Private*, pg. 653

Constantin, Gus, Chm. Bd., Pres. & Chief Exec. Officer--Phoenix American Incorporated, San Rafael, CA; *U.S. Private*, pg. 862

Constantino, Carol L., Pres.--Noteworthy Industries Inc., Amsterdam, NY; *U.S. Private*, pg. 808

Contadino, Joseph, Chm. Bd., Pres. & Treas.--Del Webb's Coventry Homes, Phoenix, AZ; *U.S. Public*, pg. 495

Contalini, Carl, Pres.--Waterbury Companies, Inc., Waterbury, CT; *U.S. Public*, pg. 308

Conte, Leo, Pres. & Chief Exec. Officer--Montebello Brands Inc., Baltimore, MD; *U.S. Private*, pg. 758

Conte, Pierre, Pres.-Europe--Johnson & Johnson Professional Products Ltd., Bracknell, United Kingdom; *U.S. Public*, pg. 931

Conterno, Francesco Michele, Dr., Chm. Bd. & Pres.--Lati Industria Termoplastici S.p.A., Vedano Olona, Italy; *Int'l*, pg. 804

Contess, Neil, Principal & Sr. Mng. Partner--Dugan Valva Contess Inc., Morristown, NJ; *U.S. Private*, pg. 345

Conthe Gutierrez, D. Julian, Pres.--Maptel, S.A, Madrid, Spain; *Int'l*, pg. 1372

Contino, Frederic L., Pres.--Plastics, Inc., Saint Paul, MN; *U.S. Public*, pg. 1177

Contino, Frederic L., Pres.--Anchor Hocking Plastics, Saint Paul, MN; *U.S. Public*, pg. 1177

Contino, Frederic L., Pres.--Jareen Co., Saint Paul, MN; *U.S. Public*, pg. 1177

Contino, Rick, Pres.--Game Time, Inc., Fort Payne, AL; *U.S. Public*, pg. 1543

Contorakes, Evan, Pres.--Evans & Fitzgerald Advertising, Coral Gables, FL; *U.S. Private*, pg. 701

Contos, Larry D., Pres.--Pay Less Super Markets, Inc., Anderson, IN; *U.S. Private*, pg. 844

Conver, Tim, Pres.--Aerovironment, Inc., Monrovia, CA; *U.S. Private*, pg. 25

Conway, Dennis, Owner--Commerical Roofers Inc., Las Vegas, NV; *U.S. Private*, pg. 258

Conway, Dick, Pres.--TSI Holdings, Inc., Kansas City, KS; *U.S. Private*, pg. 1066

Conway, J.M., Pres.--PTI Technolgies, Inc., Newbury Park, CA; *U.S. Public*, pg. 546

Conway, James F., III, Chm. Bd., Pres., Chief Oper. & Exec. Officer--Courier Corporation, North Chelmsford, MA; *U.S. Public*, pg. 453

Conway, John, Pres.--Data Business Forms Limited, Brampton, Canada; *Int'l*, pg. 384

Conway, John W., Pres.--Crown Cork & Seal, Americas Division, Philadelphia, PA; *U.S. Public*, pg. 463

Conway, Ronald J., Pres.--TCV, Inc., Philadelphia, PA; *U.S. Public*, pg. 432

Conway, William E., Jr., Mng. Dir.--Carlyle Holding Corporation, Washington, DC; *U.S. Private*, pg. 213

Cook, Brian, Pres.--Famous Footwear, Madison, WI; *U.S. Public*, pg. 262

Cook, C. Thomas, Pres. & Chief Exec. Officer--First Security Information Technology, Inc., Salt Lake City, UT; *U.S. Public*, pg. 637

Cook, Charlie, Pres.--UPB of Middle Tennessee, Nashville, TN; *U.S. Public*, pg. 1669

Cook, Daniel L., Pres.--Overland Transportation System, Inc., Indianapolis, IN; *Int'l*, pg. 1469

Cook, David G., Pres.--Stearns Manufacturing Company, Sauk Rapids, MN; *U.S. Public*, pg. 940

Cook, E. Gary, Chm. Bd., Pres. & Chief Exec. Officer--Witco Corporation, Greenwich, CT; *U.S. Public*, pg. 1773

Cook, Gordon, Pres.--Genfoot Inc., Montreal, Canada; *Int'l*, pg. 549

Cook, Greg, Pres. & Chief Oper. Officer--Cook Manufacturing Corporation, Duncan, OK; *U.S. Private*, pg. 272

Cook, J. Mark, Pres.--Cyprus Foote Mineral Co., Kings Mountain, NC; *U.S. Public*, pg. 471

Cook, Jack E., Pres.--National Concrete Products Company, Plymouth, MI; *U.S. Private*, pg. 781

Cook, John J., Jr., Pres.--UAM Investment Services, Inc., Boston, MA; *U.S. Public*, pg. 1674

Cook, Kenneth C., Pres. & Chief Exec. Officer--Potomac Valley Bank, Gaithersburg, MD; *U.S. Public*, pg. 1089

Cook, Richard W., Pres.--Buena Vista Pictures Distribution Inc., Burbank, CA; *U.S. Public*, pg. 513

Cook, Robert E., Pres.--Frigidaire Home Products, Augusta, GA; *Int'l*, pg. 439

Cook, Ron A., Pres.--Boykin Management Co., Cleveland, OH; *U.S. Private*, pg. 162

Cook, Thomas A., Pres. & Chief Oper. Officer--Healthcare Services Group, Inc., Huntingdon Valley, PA; *U.S. Public*, pg. 803

Cook, Thomas W., Pres.--Gunite Corporation, Rockford, IL; *U.S. Public*, pg. 933

Cook, Warren C., Pres.--Sugarloaf/USA, Kingfield, ME; *U.S. Private*, pg. 62

Cook, William R., Chm. Bd., Pres. & Chief Exec. Officer--BetzDearborn Inc., Trevose, PA; *U.S. Public*, pg. 226

Cook, William R., Chm. Bd., Pres. & Chief Exec. Officer--Jenkins & Associates, Shawnee Mission, KS; *U.S. Private*, pg. 585

Cooke, A. Curts, Pres. & Chief Oper. Officer--Russ Berrie and Company, Inc., Oakland, NJ; *U.S. Public*, pg. 222

Cooke, Gordon R., Pres. & Chief Exec. Officer--DM Management Company, Hingham, MA; *U.S. Public*, pg. 473

Cooke, J.P. Blase, Chm. Bd., Pres. & Chief Exec. Officer--Harkins Builders, Inc., Silver Spring, MD; *U.S. Private*, pg. 502

Cooke, Jack Kent, Pres.--Jack Kent Cooke, Inc., Middleburg, VA; *U.S. Private*, pg. 273

Cooke, Mike, Pres.--Weaver Construction, LLC, Greensboro, NC; *U.S. Private*, pg. 1156

Cooley, D.R., Pres.--Tollycraft Yacht Corporation, San Diego, CA; *U.S. Public*, pg. 1620

Coombs, Janet, Pres.--Wunderman Cato Johnson, New York, NY; *U.S. Private*, pg. 1197

Coon, Max A., Chm. Bd. & Pres.--Maxco, Inc., Lansing, MI; *U.S. Public*, pg. 1061

Cooney, Robert J., Pres. & Chief Oper. Officer--X.L. Insurance Company, Ltd., Hamilton, Bermuda; *Int'l*, pg. 467

Coopat, E. Thomas, Pres., Chief Exec. Officer & Rep. Dir.--Avon Products Co., Ltd., Tokyo, Japan; *U.S. Public*, pg. 156

Cooper, B. E., Pres. & Chief Exec. Officer--Kennecott Holdings Corporation, Magna, UT; *Int'l*, pg. 1119

Cooper, Benny, Pres.--Affiliated Foods, Inc., Amarillo, TX; *U.S. Private*, pg. 25

Cooper, Benny R., Pres.--Affiliated Finance Inc., Amarillo, TX; *U.S. Private*, pg. 25

Cooper, Charles B., Pres. & Chief Oper. Officer--American Income Holding, Inc., Wilmington, DE; *U.S. Public*, pg. 1622

Cooper, Donald M., Chm. Bd., Pres. & Chief Exec. Officer--CoreStates Bank, Lancaster, PA; *U.S. Public*, pg. 446

Cooper, Frederick, Pres.--Quality Bakers of America Cooperative, Inc., Greenwich, CT; *U.S. Private*, pg. 898

Cooper, Ian G., Pres.--Bayex Incorporated, Albion, NY; *Int'l*, pg. 1170

Cooper, J. Patterson, Pres.--Bankers Trust Co. of Florida, N.A., West Palm Beach, FL; *U.S. Public*, pg. 185

Cooper, Jerry A., Pres. & Chief Exec. Officer--Defiance, Inc., Cleveland, OH; *U.S. Public*, pg. 493

Cooper, John A., Jr., Pres.--Cooper Communities, Inc., Bella Vista, AR; *U.S. Private*, pg. 273

Cooper, John S., Sr. V.P. & Grp. Exec.-Railroad Group--Portec Inc., Railway Maintenance Products Div., Pittsburgh, PA; *U.S. Public*, pg. 1318

Cooper, Jonathan, Pres.--Spectronics Corporation, Westbury, NY; *U.S. Private*, pg. 1024

Cooper, Jonathan, Pres.--Tracer Products, Westbury, NY; *U.S. Private*, pg. 1024

Cooper, Joseph V., Chm. Bd & Pres.--C. Weaver Chevrolet, Inc., New York Mills, NY; *U.S. Private*, pg. 1156

Cooper, M. Lynn, Chm. Bd., Pres. & Chief Exec. Officer--Citizens Bank of Illinois, Mount Vernon, IL; *U.S. Public*, pg. 280

Cooper, Marshall Y., Jr., Chm. Bd., Chief Exec. Officer & Pres.--Harriet & Henderson Yarns, Inc., Henderson, NC; *U.S. Private*, pg. 504

Cooper, Martin, Pres. & Gen. Mgr.--AAR Cooper Aviation, Elk Grove Village, IL; *U.S. Public*, pg. 1

Cooper, Michael, Pres.--Pitney Bowes Software Systems, Glen Ellyn, IL; *U.S. Public*, pg. 1304

Cooper, Ned, Pres. & Div. Mgr.--Batavia Wine Cellars, Batavia, NY; *U.S. Public*, pg. 300

Cooper, Ned, Pres.-Batavia Wine Cellars--Canandaigua Wine Co., Canandaigua, NY; *U.S. Public*, pg. 300

Cooper, Norton J., Pres. & Chief Exec. Officer--Charles Jacquin et Cie, Inc., Philadelphia, PA; *U.S. Private*, pg. 580

Cooper, Philip D., Pres.--ORIX Commercial Alliance Corporation, Secaucus, NJ; *Int'l*, pg. 1009

Cooper, R. G., Pres.--Kirkland & Rose Ltd., Richmond, Canada; *Int'l*, pg. 244

Cooper, Ric, Pres.--HMS Partners, Columbus, OH; *U.S. Private*, pg. 491

Cooper, Richard, Pres.--Finnfeeds International Ltd., Marlborough, United Kingdom; *Int'l*, pg. 349

Cooper, Robert A., Jr., Pres.-Pargo's--Shoney's, Inc., Nashville, TN; *U.S. Public*, pg. 1467

Cooper, Roger A., Pres.--Target Oilfield Pipe & Supply Company (TOPS), Canton, OH; *U.S. Private*, pg. 1078

Cooper, Ronald, Pres. & Chief Exec. Officer--Delta Foremost Chemical Corp., Memphis, TN; *U.S. Private*, pg. 322

Cooper, Stephen E., Chm., Pres. & Chief Exec. Officer--Etec Systems, Inc., Hayward, CA; *U.S. Public*, pg. 594

Cooper, William, Chm. Bd & Pres.--Allied Industrial Group, Inc., Saint Louis, MO; *U.S. Private*, pg. 39

Cooperman, Samuel, Pres.-Stolt Parcel Tankers--Stolt-Nielsen S.A., London, United Kingdom; *Int'l*, pg. 1301

Cooperrider, Stu, Partner--Houston Herstek Favat, Boston, MA; *U.S. Private*, pg. 542

Coopersmith, Jeff, Pres.--HMS-Direct Columbus, Columbus, OH; *U.S. Private*, pg. 492

Cooperstone, Elliot S., Pres. & Chief Exec. Officer--Alexander & Alexander Inc., New York, NY; *U.S. Public*, pg. 117

Coors, Jeffrey H., Co-Pres. & Co-Chief Exec. Officer--ACX Technologies Inc., Golden, CO; *U.S. Public*, pg. 3

Coors, Jeffrey H., Pres.--Graphic Packaging Corporation, Wayne, PA; *U.S. Public*, pg. 3

Coors, Joseph, Jr., Co-Pres. & Co-Chief Exec. Officer--ACX Technologies Inc., Golden, CO; *U.S. Public*, pg. 3

Coors, Joseph, Jr., Pres. & Chief Exec. Officer--Coors Ceramics Company, Golden, CO; *U.S. Public*, pg. 3

Coors, William K., Chm. Bd. & Pres.--Adolph Coors Company, Golden, CO; *U.S. Public*, pg. 445

Copacia, Timothy, Pres.--Ross Roy Communications, Inc., Bloomfield Hills, MI; *U.S. Private*, pg. 946

Cope, Larry W., Pres. & Chief Exec. Officer--Clear Springs Foods, Inc., Buhl, ID; *U.S. Private*, pg. 245

Cope, Thomas L., Pres.--John Copes Food Products, Inc., Rheems, PA; *U.S. Private*, pg. 274

Copeland, Claire, Pres.--Mappins Jewelers, Don Mills, Canada; *Int'l*, pg. 1036

Copeland, Claire, V.P.-Opers.--Peoples Jewelers, Don Mills, Canada; *Int'l*, pg. 1036

Copeland, Clare, Pres. & Chief Exec. Officer--Peoples Jewellers Corporation, Don Mills, Canada; *Int'l*, pg. 1036

Copeland, F.C., Pres. & Chief Exec. Officer--Citibank Canada, Toronto, Canada; *U.S. Public*, pg. 378

Copeland, James E., Mng. Partner--Deloitte & Touche LLP, Wilton, CT; *U.S. Private*, pg. 322

Copland, James R., III, Pres., Chief Exec. Officer & Treas.--Copland Fabrics, Inc., Burlington, NC; *U.S. Private*, pg. 274

Copley, David C., Pres. & Chief Exec. Officer--The Copley Press, Inc., La Jolla, CA; *U.S. Private*, pg. 275

Copley, Helen K., Publisher--San Diego Union Tribune, San Diego, CA; *U.S. Private*, pg. 275

Coppage, Robert, Pres.--VF Jeanswear-Europe, Brussels, Belgium; *U.S. Public*, pg. 1702

Copping, Harold, Pres. & Gen. Mgr.--Teleflex (Canada) Ltd., Vancouver, Canada; *U.S. Public*, pg. 1570
Coppinger, Jack, Pres. & Chief Exec. Officer--Super Discount Markets, Inc., Lithia Springs, GA; *Int'l*, pg. 463
Coppinger, Jack, Pres. & Chief Exec. Officer--Super Discount Markets, Inc., Lithia Springs, GA; *U.S. Public*, pg. 1540
Copple, Frank, Pres.--Stinnes Interoil Inc., Red Bank, NJ; *Int'l*, pg. 1459
Coppola, Alfred C., Pres. & Chief Oper. Officer--The Okonite Company, Ramsey, NJ; *U.S. Private*, pg. 813
Coppola, Arthur, Pres. & Chief Exec. Officer--The Macerich Company, Santa Monica, CA; *U.S. Public*, pg. 1030
Coppola, Carl, Pres. & Sec.--Mark Lighting Fixture Co., Inc., Edison, NJ; *U.S. Private*, pg. 704
Coppola, Ralph, Pres.--Hill Phoenix, Colonial Heights, VA; *U.S. Public*, pg. 521
Copps, Timothy J., Pres.--The Copps Corp., Stevens Point, WI; *U.S. Private*, pg. 275
Corasanti, Eugene R., Chm. Bd., Pres. & Chief Exec. Officer--Conmed Corporation, Utica, NY; *U.S. Public*, pg. 431
Corbel, Gary, Pres.--Welenco, Inc., Bakersfield, CA; *Int'l*, pg. 1019
Corbero, Miguel Cucurull, Pres.--Agropecuaria de Guissona, S. Coop. Ltda., Guisona, Spain; *Int'l*, pg. 31
Corbet, Tim, Pres.--Trimfoot Company, Farmington, MO; *U.S. Public*, pg. 1684
Corbett, Donald, Pres.--MDI Management Inc., Hickory, NC; *U.S. Private*, pg. 657
Corbett, E.M., Jr., Chm. Bd., Pres. & Chief Exec. Officer--Harwick Standard Distribution Corporation, Akron, OH; *U.S. Private*, pg. 509
Corbett, Luke R., Pres.--Kerr-McGee Oil (U.K.) PLC, London, United Kingdom; *U.S. Public*, pg. 952
Corbett, Richard, Pres.--Crane Manufacturing, Cudahy, WI; *U.S. Private*, pg. 286
Corbo, V.J., Dr., Pres. & Chief Oper. Officer--Hercules Incorporated, Wilmington, DE; *U.S. Public*, pg. 809
Corcoran, David, Pres. & Mng. Exec.--Northern Trust Bank of Florida, N.A., Bradenton, FL; *U.S. Public*, pg. 1196
Corcoran, E. Thomas, Pres.--Fort Dodge Animal Health, Overland Park, KS; *U.S. Public*, pg. 79
Corcoran, Jim, Pres.--Systems Tax Service, Inc., Fountain Valley, CA; *U.S. Public*, pg. 331
Corcoran, John E., Pres.--Corcoran Trucking Company, Billings, MT; *U.S. Private*, pg. 275
Corcoran, Thomas A., Pres.--Lockheed Martin Electronics Group, Bethesda, MD; *U.S. Public*, pg. 1006
Cordaro, Robert, Pres.--VF Asia Limited, Kowloon, Hong Kong; *U.S. Public*, pg. 1702
Corder, Sidney, Pres. & Chief Exec. Officer--MSC Corporation, Indianapolis, IN; *U.S. Public*, pg. 110
Corder, Sidney V., Chm. Bd., Pres. & Chief Exec. Officer--Analytical Surveys, Inc., Colorado Springs, CO; *U.S. Public*, pg. 110
Cordes, Eugene H., Dr., Pres.--Sanofi Research Division, Malvern, PA; *Int'l*, pg. 445
Cordes, Jeffrey D., Pres. & Chief Oper. Officer--Pillowtex Corporation, Dallas, TX; *U.S. Public*, pg. 1296
Cordido Valery, Carlos G., Pres. & Gen. Mgr.--Componentes Delfa, C.A., Caracas, Venezuela; *U.S. Public*, pg. 724
Cordova, Randy M., Pres.--World Dryer Corp., Berkeley, IL; *U.S. Public*, pg. 1497
Corell, David, Pres.--Aerofin Corp., Lynchburg, VA; *U.S. Public*, pg. 103
Corelli, John, Pres.--Petals, White Plains, NY; *U.S. Private*, pg. 856
Corey, Allen, Pres. Chief Exec. Officer--Big River Grille & Brewery Works, Chattanooga, TN; *U.S. Public*, pg. 1396
Corey, John, Pres.--Mechanics Tool Div., Dallas, TX; *U.S. Public*, pg. 1509
Corey, John, Pres.--National Hand Tools, Dallas, TX; *U.S. Public*, pg. 1509
Corey, R.L., Pres.--Molson Sports and Entertainment, Montreal, Canada; *Int'l*, pg. 887
Cormier, Andy, Pres.--NB Coal Company Limited, Minto, Canada; *Int'l*, pg. 923
Cormier, Leonard L., III, Pres.--Cormier Chevrolet Company, Inc., Carson, CA; *U.S. Private*, pg. 276
Corn, Larry, Pres.--Roadrunner Trucking, Inc., Albuquerque, NM; *U.S. Public*, pg. 911
Corn, Larry, Pres.--Roadrunner Distribution Systems, Inc., Indianapolis, IN; *U.S. Public*, pg. 911
Corn, Robert, Pres.--Roush Industries Inc., Livonia, MI; *U.S.* Private, pg. 948
Cornelius, Charles, Pres. & Chief Exec. Officer--Atlanta Life Insurance Company, Atlanta, GA; *U.S. Private*, pg. 94
Cornelius, Niles S., Pres.--Therapedic Associates, Inc., Middlesex, NJ; *U.S. Private*, pg. 1079
Cornell, Alan D., Pres.--Korry Electronics Co., Seattle, WA; *U.S. Public*, pg. 594
Cornell, Andrew, Pres. & Chief Exec. Officer--Cornell Iron Works, Inc., Mountain Top, PA; *U.S. Private*, pg. 276
Cornell, William E., Pres.--Sea-3, Inc., Houston, Houston, TX; *U.S. Private*, pg. 1096
Cornella, Rick L., Pres.--Hevi-Duty Electric, Goldsboro, NC; *U.S. Public*, pg. 726
Cornett, Ben, Pres.--Ademco Sensor Company, Louisville, KY; *U.S. Public*, pg. 1306
Cornille, John, Pres.--Bracco Diagnostics, Inc., Princeton, NJ; *Int'l*, pg. 210
Cornish, D. Samuel, Pres.--Collegeville/Imagineering L.P., Collegeville, PA; *U.S. Private*, pg. 252
Cornog, R., Pres.--Broderick & Bascom Rope Co., Sedalia, MO; *U.S. Private*, pg. 68
Cornog, Robert A., Chm. Bd., Pres. & Chief Exec. Officer--Snap-On Tools Corporation, Kenosha, WI; *U.S. Public*, pg. 1480
Cornwall, John R., Pres. & Chief Exec. Officer--MetLife Capital Holdings, Inc., Bellevue, WA; *U.S. Private*, pg. 737
Cornwell, Kevin L., Chm. Bd., Pres. & Chief Exec. Officer--Utah Medical Products, Inc., Midvale, UT; *U.S. Public*, pg. 1700
Cornwell, William J., Pres.--Electroglas, Inc., Santa Clara, CA; *U.S. Public*, pg. 727
Corogin, Peter J., Pres. & Chief Exec. Officer--Lake Erie Electric, Inc., Westlake, OH; *U.S. Private*, pg. 643
Corozza, Eugene J., Pres.--Certech, Inc., Wood Ridge, NJ; *U.S. Public*, pg. 307
Corp, William, Pres. & Chief Exec. Officer--Comstock Canada Ltd., Burlington, Canada; *U.S. Public*, pg. 572
Corr, Robert, Pres.--R.J. Corr Naturals, Inc., Posen, IL; *U.S. Private*, pg. 276
Corr, Thomas L., Pres. & Chief Exec. Officer--George E. Warren Corporation, Vero Beach, FL; *U.S. Private*, pg. 1151
Corral, Frank, Pres.--Chicago Heights Steel, Chicago Heights, IL; *U.S. Private*, pg. 234
Corrallo, Orazio, Dir.-North American Opers.--Alitalia Airlines, New York, NY; *Int'l*, pg. 652
Corrao, Michael J., Pres. & Chief Exec. Officer--Gingiss International, Addison, IL; *U.S. Private*, pg. 455
Correnti, John D., Co-Vice Chm., Pres. & Chief Exec. Officer--Nucor Corporation, Charlotte, NC; *U.S. Public*, pg. 1205
Correra, Francis X., Pres.--Town & Country Corporation, Chelsea, MA; *U.S. Public*, pg. 1625
Corrigan-Davis, Mary Ann, Pres.--Summit Division, Cleveland, OH; *U.S. Public*, pg. 78
Corrigan, Dennis, Pres.--Corrigan Bros., Inc., Saint Louis, MO; *U.S. Private*, pg. 277
Corrigan, Patton, Pres.--Stamford Capital, Stamford, CT; *U.S. Private*, pg. 1029
Corriveau, Alfred N., Pres.--Bombardier Real Estate Ltd., Montreal, Canada; *Int'l*, pg. 200
Corriveau, David O., Co-Chief Exec. Officer & Pres.--Dave & Buster's, Dallas, TX; *U.S. Public*, pg. 488
Corsentino, Charles J., Pres. & Chief Exec. Officer--Exhibitgroup/Giltspur, Roselle, IL; *U.S. Public*, pg. 1718
Corsiglia, Robert, Pres. & Chief Exec. officer--Hyre Electric Company of Indiana, Inc., Highland, IN; *U.S. Public*, pg. 572
Corsini, John M., Pres., Chief Exec. Officer & Treas.--Uncas Manufacturing Company, Providence, RI; *U.S. Private*, pg. 1116
Corso, Joseph D., Pres.--Birmingham Southeast, Cartersville, GA; *U.S. Public*, pg. 232
Corson, Keith D., Pres. & Chief Oper. Officer--Coachmen Industries, Inc., Elkhart, IN; *U.S. Public*, pg. 387
Corti, Oscar, Pres.--Syremont S.p.A., Novara, Italy; *Int'l*, pg. 324
Corvin, Joe, Pres.--CF & I Steel, L.P., Pueblo, CO; *U.S. Public*, pg. 1230
Cosgrove, Howard E., Chm. Bd., Pres. & Chief Exec. Officer--Delmarva Power & Light Company, Wilmington, DE; *U.S. Public*, pg. 430
Cosgrove, Jack D., Pres.--Avionics & Communications, Cedar Rapids, IA; *U.S. Public*, pg. 1397
Cosgrove, T.J., Pres.--M-B Companies Inc. of Wisconsin, Chilton, WI; *U.S. Private*, pg. 684
Cosner, J. L., Pres.--American Ingredients Company, Grandview, MO; *Int'l*, pg. 244
Cosner, Melvin, Pres. & Chief Exec. Officer--Lady Baltimore Foods, Inc., Kansas City, KS; *U.S. Public*, pg. 975
Coss, Lawrence M., Chm. Bd., Pres. & Chief Exec. & Oper. Officer--Green Tree Financial Corporation, Saint Paul, MN; *U.S. Public*, pg. 761
Cosslett, Andrew, Pres.--Cottee's Foods, Liverpool, Australia; *Int'l*, pg. 248
Cosson, Jean-Pierre, Co-Pres.--EURO RSCG D 10, Latresne, France; *Int'l*, pg. 600
Cosson, Jean-Pierre, Co-Pres.--EURO RSCG D 10, Toulouse, France; *Int'l*, pg. 600
Costa, Frank J., Pres. & Chief Oper. Officer--Active Voice Corporation, Seattle, WA; *U.S. Public*, pg. 17
Costa, Harry, Pres.--United Parking Services, Inc., Toronto, Canada; *U.S. Public*, pg. 326
Costa, Jose Maria, Pres.--Young & Rubicam C.A., Chuao, Venezuela; *U.S. Private*, pg. 1200
Costa, Jose Maria, Pres.--J.M.C./Young & Rubicam, Caracas, Venezuela; *U.S. Private*, pg. 1200
Costa, Michael A., Pres.--Kaufman and Broad Multi-Housing Group, Long Beach, CA; *U.S. Public*, pg. 945
Costa, Nicola, Pres.--Costa Container Lines S.p.A., Genoa, Italy; *Int'l*, pg. 336
Costa, Pat V., Chm. Bd., Pres. & Chief Exec. Officer--Robotic Vision Systems, Inc., Hauppauge, NY; *U.S. Public*, pg. 1395
Costa, Paulo, Pres. & Chief Oper. Officer--Janssen Pharmaceutica, Inc., Titusville, NJ; *U.S. Public*, pg. 928
Costello, Albert J., Chm. Bd., Pres. & Chief Exec. Officer--W.R. Grace & Co., Boca Raton, FL; *U.S. Public*, pg. 754
Costello, Mike, Pres.--B.C. Hydro, Vancouver, Canada; *Int'l*, pg. 114
Costello, Paul, Pres.--Continental PIR Communications, Inc., Toronto, Canada; *Int'l*, pg. 1226
Costello, Robert L., Pres., Chief Exec. & Chief Oper. Officer--URS Greiner Engineering, Inc., Denver, CO; *U.S.* Public, pg. 1658
Costides, Nick, Pres.--Cosco, Inc., Columbus, IN; *U.S. Private*, pg. 277
Costley, Gary E., Ph.D., Chm. Bd., Pres. & Chief Exec. Officer--International Multifoods Corporation, Minneapolis, MN; *U.S. Public*, pg. 900
Costley, Greg, Pres.--Dole Citrus & Dole Deciduous, Bakersfield, CA; *U.S. Public*, pg. 515
Cote, David M., Pres. & Chief Exec. Officer--G.E. Appliances, Louisville, KY; *U.S. Public*, pg. 710
Cotherman, Scott, Pres. & Chief Oper. Officer--Corbett HealthConnect, A Frank J. Corbett, Inc., Company, Chicago, IL; *U.S. Public*, pg. 1223
Cothren, H. Bobby, Pres.--The Stellar Group Inc., Jacksonville, FL; *U.S. Private*, pg. 1040
Cotterill, D., Chief Exec. Officer--Renold PLC, Manchester, United Kingdom; *Int'l*, pg. 1103
Cottier, Marius, Dr., Pres. & Chief Exec. Officer--Schweizer Verband der Raiffeisenbanken, Saint Gallen, Switzerland; *Int'l*, pg. 1211
Cottone, Basilio, Pres.--Agusta S.P.A., Varese, Italy; *Int'l*, pg. 32
Couch, John C., Chm. Bd., Pres. & Chief Exec. Officer--Alexander & Baldwin, Inc., Honolulu, HI; *U.S. Public*, pg. 39
Couch, John C., Chm. Bd. & Pres.--A & B-Hawaii, Inc., Honolulu, HI; *U.S. Public*, pg. 39
Couch, Ken, Pres.--Smith Wholesale Drug Div., Spartanburg, SC; *U.S. Private*, pg. 1008
Coughlan, Dermot G., Chm. & Chief Exec. Officer--Derlan Industries Limited, Toronto, Canada; *Int'l*, pg. 395
Coughlin, Christopher J., Pres.--Nabisco International Incorporated, New York, NY; *U.S. Public*, pg. 1355
Coughlin, John, Pres. & Chief Exec. Officer--Benthos, Inc., North Falmouth, MA; *U.S. Public*, pg. 212
Coughlin, Joseph, Pres.--F.X. Coughlin Co., Taylor, MI; *U.S. Private*, pg. 278
Coughlin, Michael, Pres. & Chief Oper. Officer--Brooks Beverage Management, Inc., Columbus, OH; *U.S. Private*, pg. 142
Coughlin, Michael D., Pres.--Concord Litho Co., Inc., Concord, NH; *U.S. Private*, pg. 261
Cougill, Dan, Pres. & Chief Oper. Officer--Riddell Sports, Inc., New York, NY; *U.S. Public*, pg. 1389
Cougill, Dan, Pres. & Chief Oper. Officer--Riddell Sports, Inc., Chicago, IL; *U.S. Public*, pg. 1389
Couglin, T.C., Pres.--Riggs National Corporation, Washington, DC; *U.S. Public*, pg. 1389
Couillaud, Bernard J., Ph.D., Pres. & Chief Exec. Officer--Coherent, Inc., Santa Clara, CA; *U.S. Public*, pg. 395
Couling, Gary, Pres.--E.R. Probyn Export Ltd., New Westminster, Canada; *Int'l*, pg. 1071
Coulombe, Dennis N., Pres. & Chief Oper. Officer--White Rock Distilleries Inc., Lewiston, ME; *U.S. Private*, pg. 1173
Coulon, Jules, Chm. Bd. & Pres.--Moulinex S.A., Bagnolet, France; *Int'l*, pg. 896
Coultas, Jeffrey B., Pres. & Chief Exec. Officer--Elliott State Bank, Jacksonville, IL; *U.S. Public*, pg. 643
Coultas, William H., Pres.--Old Kent Bank-Lansing, Lansing, MI; *U.S. Public*, pg. 1216
Coulter, David A., Pres. & Chief Exec. Officer--Bank of America NT&SA, San Francisco, CA; *U.S. Public*, pg. 180
Coulter, David A., Pres. & Chief Exec. Officer--Bank of America California, San Francisco, CA; *U.S. Public*, pg. 180
Coulter, Robert, Pres. & Chief Oper. Officer--Shelby Williams Industries, Inc., Morristown, TN; *U.S. Public*, pg. 1464
Councilor, T., Pres.--Black Millwork Co., Inc., Allendale, NJ; *U.S. Private*, pg. 147
Coupe, C., Pres.--Haden Engineering Pty, Rosebery, Australia; *Int'l*, pg. 586
Couperthwaite, Larry, Pres.--Atlet, Inc., Schaumburg, IL; *Int'l*, pg. 97
Couri, Ronald J., Pres. & Chief Exec. Officer--Couristan Inc., Fort Lee, NJ; *U.S. Private*, pg. 279
Couric, Charles, Pres.--Brita (USA), Inc., Oakland, CA; *U.S. Public*, pg. 387
Courtemanche, Jack, Pres.--Country Coach, Inc., Junction City, OR; *U.S. Public*, pg. 1159
Courtney, Eugene W., Pres. & Chief Exec. Officer--HEI, Inc., Victoria, MN; *U.S. Public*, pg. 770
Courtney, Lawrence, Pres.--Greenhorne & O'Mara, Inc., Greenbelt, MD; *U.S. Private*, pg. 477
Courville, Leon, Pres. & Chief Oper. Officer--National Bank of Canada, Montreal, Canada; *Int'l*, pg. 907
Cousins, Dean, Pres.--Ferraz Corporation, Parsippany, NJ; *Int'l*, pg. 1028
Coutroulis, Peter, Partner--Messner Vetere Berger McNamee Schmetterer/EURO RSCG, New York, NY; *Int'l*, pg. 602
Coutu, Francois-Jean, Pres. & Chief Oper. Officer--The Jean Coutu Group (PJC) Inc., Longueuil, Canada; *Int'l*, pg. 340
Coutu, Michel, Pres.--The Jean Coutu (PJC) USA Inc., Warwick, RI; *Int'l*, pg. 340
Covalt, Robert B., Chm. Bd., Pres. & Chief Exec. Officer--Sovereign Specialty Chemical, Inc., Chicago, IL; *U.S. Private*, pg. 1019
Covalt, Robert B., Pres.--Morton International Inc., Chicago, IL; *U.S. Public*, pg. 1135
Covarrubias, Carlos Levy, Pres.--Acciones y Valores de Mexico, S.A. de C.V., Mexico, Mexico; *Int'l*, pg. 574
Covey, Timothy, Pres.--Wenger Corporation, Owatonna, MN; *U.S. Private*, pg. 1162
Covington, Edward H., Pres. & Treas.--Harriss & Covington Hosiery Mills, High Point, NC; *U.S. Private*, pg. 506
Cowan, Brian C., Pres.--Chr. Hansen (UK) Ltd., Reading, United Kingdom; *Int'l*, pg. 289
Cowan, James R., Chm. Bd., Pres. & Chief Exec. Officer--Stonecutter Mills Corp., Spindale, NC; *U.S. Private*, pg. 1044
Cowan, R. Douglas, Chm. Bd., Pres. & Chief Exec. Officer--The Davey Tree Expert Company, Kent, OH; *U.S. Private*, pg. 314
Cowart, D.R., Pres.--The Wm. Powell Company, Cincinnati, OH; *U.S. Private*, pg. 877
Cowie, Bruce E., Pres. & Chief Oper. Officer-Broadcast Group--Electrohome Ltd., Kitchener, Canada; *Int'l*, pg. 438
Cowin, John J., Chm. Bd., Pres. & Treas.--Cowin & Company, Inc., Birmingham, AL; *U.S. Private*, pg. 280
Cowles, Alfred, Jr., Pres. & Chief Exec. Officer--Bluff City Distributing Co., Inc., Memphis, TN; *U.S. Private*, pg. 153
Cowpland, Michael, Chm. Bd., Pres. & Chief Exec. Officer--Corel Corporation, Ottawa, Canada; *Int'l*, pg. 331

Cox, Anne H., Founding Partner--Chicago Creative Partnership, Chicago, IL; *U.S. Private*, pg. 234

Cox, Barrie R., Pres.--ADM Food Additives Division, Decatur, IL; *U.S. Public*, pg. 127

Cox, Basil, Pres. & Chief Oper. Officer--Eat N Park Restaurants, Pittsburgh, PA; *U.S. Private*, pg. 358

Cox, Charles, Pres. & Chief Fin. Officer--Cox Furniture, Maxton, NC; *U.S. Private*, pg. 283

Cox, David C., Pres. & Chief Exec. Officer--Cowles Media Company, Minneapolis, MN; *U.S. Private*, pg. 280

Cox, Ed, Pres.--Lithograph Printing Company, Inc., Memphis, TN; *U.S. Private*, pg. 713

Cox, Frank, Pres. & Chief Exec. Officer--Cranford Johnson Robinson Woods, Little Rock, AR; *U.S. Private*, pg. 286

Cox, M., Chief Exec. Officer--American Carbon Industries, Birmingham, AL; *Int'l*, pg. 891

Cox, Neil, Pres.--Ameritech Information Systems Inc., Chicago, IL; *U.S. Public*, pg. 98

Cox, Ralph, Pres. & Gen. Mgr.--Primark Tool Group, Louisville, KY; *U.S. Public*, pg. 575

Cox, Robert G., Pres.--Summit Bancorp, Princeton, NJ; *U.S.* Public, pg. 1527

Cox, Robert G., Pres.--Summit Bank, Chatham, NJ; *U.S. Public*, pg. 1528

Cox, Ron, Pres. & Chief Exec. Officer--Learning International, Stamford, CT; *U.S. Public*, pg. 1617

Cox, Walter G., Jr., Pres.--Xaloy, Inc., Pulaski, VA; *U.S. Private*, pg. 1194

Cox, William B., Jr., Pres. & Chief Exec. Officer--Cox Wood Preserving Co., Orangeburg, SC; *U.S. Private*, pg. 283

Coxe, Donald G.M., Pres. & Chief Investment Officer--Harris Investment Management, Inc., Chicago, IL; *Int'l*, pg. 154

Coxwell, David, Pres.--J.B. Coxwell Contract, Inc., Jacksonville, FL; *U.S. Private*, pg. 283

Coyle, Michael J., Pres.--Daig Corporation, Minnetonka, MN; *U.S. Public*, pg. 1428

Coyne, Frank J., Pres. & Chief Oper. Officer--The Camden Fire Insurance Assn., Philadelphia, PA; *Int'l*, pg. 543

Coyne, Frank J., Pres. & Chief Oper. Officer--General Assurance Company, Melville, NY; *Int'l*, pg. 543

Cozzani, Gian Carlo, Pres. & Chief Exec. Officer--Vesuvius U.S.A., Champaign, IL; *Int'l*, pg. 329

Cracken, John R.W., Partner--Cracken, Harkey, Street & Co., LLC, Dallas, TX; *U.S. Private*, pg. 283

Craig, A. Gordon, Pres.--TSN Communications, North York, Canada; *Int'l*, pg. 1343

Craig, George, Pres. & Chief Exec. Officer--HarperCollins Publishers, New York, NY; *Int'l*, pg. 926

Craig, Jenny, Vice Chm. & Pres.--Jenny Craig, Inc., La Jolla, CA; *U.S. Public*, pg. 926

Craig, Robert J., Pres.--P.F. Collier & Son Ltd., Etobicoke, Canada; *Int'l*, pg. 433

Crain, C. William, Pres. & Chief Oper. Officer--London Fog Industries, Inc., New York, NY; *U.S. Private*, pg. 673

Crain, Keith E., Publr. & Dir.-Editorial--Automotive News, Detroit, MI; *U.S. Private*, pg. 284

Crain, Rance, Pres. & Editor-in-Chief--Advertising Age, Chicago, IL; *U.S. Private*, pg. 284

Crain, Rance E., Pres.--Crain Communications, Inc., Chicago, IL; *U.S. Private*, pg. 284

Cram, Scott W., Pres.--CRSS Constructors, Inc., Denver, CO; *U.S. Public*, pg. 922

Cramer, James D., Chm. Bd., Pres. & Chief Exec. Officer--Science & Engineering Associates, Albuquerque, NM; *U.S. Private*, pg. 975

Cramer, Larry, Pres. & Chief Exec. Officer--Laser Diode Products, New Brunswick, NJ; *Int'l*, pg. 892

Cramer, Robert, Pres.--Fareway Stores, Inc., Boone, IA; *U.S. Private*, pg. 393

Crandall, Robert M., Pres. & Chief Oper. Officer--Mentholatum Company, Buffalo, NY; *Int'l*, pg. 1126

Crandell, D.R., Div. Pres.--Solvents & Environmental Services Div., Southfield, MI; *U.S. Public*, pg. 502

Crane, Ann B., Pres. & Chief Exec. Officer--Crane Plastics Company, Columbus, OH; *U.S. Private*, pg. 286

Crane, James R., Chm. Bd., Pres. & Chief Exec. Officer--Eagle USA Airfreight, Houston, TX; *U.S. Public*, pg. 547

Crane, Jeffrey D., Pres.--Crane Construction Co., Northbrook, IL; *U.S. Private*, pg. 286

Crane, Jonathan C., Pres. & Chief Exec. Officer--Bogen Communications, Inc., Ramsey, NJ; *U.S. Public*, pg. 739

Crane, Jonathan C., Chm. Bd., Pres. & Chief Exec. Officer--Marcam Solutions, Inc., Newton, MA; *U.S. Public*, pg. 1042

Crane, Lawrence L., Jr., Pres.--Piggly Wiggly Co., Memphis, TN; *U.S. Public*, pg. 653

Crane, Thomas R., Jr., Pres.--Castrol North America, Wayne, NJ; *Int'l*, pg. 235

Cranor, John M., III, Chm. Bd., Pres. & Chief Exec. Officer--Long John Silver's, Inc., Lexington, KY; *U.S. Private*, pg. 674

Crawford, Brook, Pres.--Hilb, Rogal and Hamilton Company of Dallas, Dallas, TX; *U.S. Public*, pg. 827

Crawford, Edward, Chm. Bd., Pres & Chief Exec. & Oper. Officer--Park-Ohio Industries, Inc., Cleveland, OH; *U.S. Public*, pg. 1258

Crawford, James W., Pres.--Continental Dynamics, Inc., Herndon, VA; *U.S. Public*, pg. 110

Crawford, Kathy, Pres.-Western Direct--Western Direct, Phoenix, AZ; *U.S. Private*, pg. 1166

Crawford, Mac, Chm. Bd., Pres. & Chief Exec. Officer--Magellan Health Services, Inc., Atlanta, GA; *U.S. Public*, pg. 1033

Crawford, Michael, Pres.--GTE Data Services Incorporated, Temple Terrace, FL; *U.S. Public*, pg. 696

Crawford, Paul, III, Pres. & Chief Exec. Officer--Interstate Billing Service, Inc., Decatur, AL; *U.S. Public*, pg. 1373

Crawford, Randy, Pres. & Treas.--Adair Feed & Grain Company, Adair, IA; *U.S. Private*, pg. 16

Crawford, Randy, Pres.--Crawford & Crawford, Inc., Adair, IA; *U.S. Private*, pg. 16

Crawford, William, Pres.--Steelcase Design Partnership, Kentwood, MI; *U.S. Private*, pg. 1038

Crawford, Wista, Pres.--Cosmolab Div., Lewisburg, TN; *U.S. Private*, pg. 629

Creach, Dale, Pres. & Chief Oper. Officer--MFA Oil Company, Columbia, MO; *U.S. Private*, pg. 687

Creech, Jack, Pres.--Color-Box, Inc., Richmond, IN; *U.S. Public*, pg. 347

Creeden, Joseph M., Pres.--Intertrace Technology, Inc., Rancho Cucamonga, CA; *U.S. Public*, pg. 1101

Creedon, Robert J., Pres.--Senator Ford, Sacramento, CA; *U.S. Private*, pg. 983

Crehalet, Yves, Mng. Partner--Crehalet Pouget Poussielgues, Paris, France; *U.S. Private*, pg. 1152

Creighton, John W., Pres. & Chief Exec. Officer--Weyerhaeuser Company, Federal Way, WA; *U.S. Public*, pg. 1764

Cremer, Robert, Pres.--Marta Cooperative of America Inc., Scottsdale, AZ; *U.S. Private*, pg. 708

Cremin, Robert W., Pres. & Chief Oper. Officer--Esterline Technologies Corporation, Bellevue, WA; *U.S. Public*, pg. 594

Crenshaw, Bruce, Pres. & Chief Exec. Officer--Royal Rubber & Manufacturing Co., South Gate, CA; *U.S. Private*, pg. 949

Cresci, Robert, Chm. Bd., Pres. & Chief Exec. Officer--Serv-Tech, Inc., Houston, TX; *U.S. Public*, pg. 1460

Crespo-Setien, Adolfo, Pres.--Koipe S.A., San Sebastian, Spain; *Int'l*, pg. 324

Crespo, J.R., Chm. Bd., Pres. & Chief Exec. Officer--Connecticut Energy Corporation, Bridgeport, CT; *U.S. Public*, pg. 431

Cretegny, Raymond, Pres.--Norfoods, Inc., Overland Park, KS; *U.S. Private*, pg. 802

Creten, Andre, Pres.--Mann & Hummel Hydromation N.V., Tongeren, Belgium; *Int'l*, pg. 484

Creten, Andre, Pres.--Hydromation France S.A.R.L., Paris, France; *Int'l*, pg. 484

Cretors, Phyllis, Pres.--The Popcorn Factory, Lake Forest, IL; *U.S. Private*, pg. 421

Crettex, Philipe, Mng. Dir.--CIBA-GEIGY Uruguaya S.A., Montevideo, Uruguay; *Int'l*, pg. 980

Crevoiserat, Jeffrey B., Pres.--Octagon Process Inc., Edgewater, NJ; *U.S. Private*, pg. 811

Crew, Drummond, Pres.--Empire Candle, Inc., Kansas City, MO; *U.S. Private*, pg. 330

Crews, Don, Pres.--First Tennessee Bank - Dyersburg, Dyersburg, TN; *U.S. Public*, pg. 639

Crews, Hilliard, Chm. Bd., Pres., Chief Exec. & Chief Fin. Officer--Shelby Group International, Inc., Memphis, TN; *U.S. Private*, pg. 991

Criadis, Michalis, Pres. & Mng. Dir.--Vitamin, Athens, Greece; *Int'l*, pg. 1377

Crichfield, Douglas, Pres. & Chief Exec. Officer--Concord Savings Bank, Concord, NH; *U.S. Public*, pg. 278

Crichley, Keith, Pres. & Chief Exec. Officer--Printwest Communications Ltd., Regina, Canada; *Int'l*, pg. 1195

Crifasi, Samuel J., Pres.--Hi Nabor Supermarket Inc., Baton Rouge, LA; *U.S. Private*, pg. 525

Crilly, John H., Pres.--Sun Data Inc., Norcross, GA; *U.S. Private*, pg. 1050

Crim, Jack C., Pres. & Chief Oper. Officer--Talley Industries, Inc., Phoenix, AZ; *U.S. Public*, pg. 307

Crim, Randy B., Pres.--Old Kent Bank of Petoskey, Petoskey, MI; *U.S. Public*, pg. 1217

Crimmins, Timothy P., Jr., Pres.--Bank of Western Massachusetts, Springfield, MA; *U.S. Public*, pg. 351

Cringan, Drew, Pres. & Chief Exec. Officer--McKim Communications Limited, Winnipeg, Canada; *U.S. Private*, pg. 104

Crisafulli, Frank, Pres.--United Alliant Food Service, Albany, NY; *U.S. Private*, pg. 244

Crisanti, Kimberly V., Partner--Chicago Creative Partnership, Chicago, IL; *U.S. Private*, pg. 234

Criscolo, Charles, Pres.--Red Apple Companies, New York, NY; *U.S. Private*, pg. 914

Crisman, Craig D., Chm. Bd., Pres., Chief Exec. & Fin. Officer--Applied Magnetics Corporation, Goleta, CA; *U.S.* Public, pg. 123

Crisp, Donald W., Pres. & Chief Exec. Officer--Caroline Hunt Trust Estate, Dallas, TX; *U.S. Private*, pg. 548

Crispino, Ralph, Chm. Bd. & Pres.--Plasticrete Block & Supply Corp., North Haven, CT; *U.S. Private*, pg. 871

Crist, Robert, Pres. & Chief Exec. & Chief Oper. Officer--American Recreation Centers, Inc., Sacramento, CA; *U.S. Public*, pg. 90

Cristiano, Joseph P., Pres. & Chief Exec. Officer--Kelly-Moore Paint Company, Inc., San Carlos, CA; *U.S. Private*, pg. 613

Cristovao, Joao Henrique de, Pres.--Banco de Montreal S.A., Rio de Janeiro, Brazil; *Int'l*, pg. 155

Croatti, Ronald D., Vice Chm., Pres. & Chief Exec. Officer--UniFirst Corporation, Wilmington, MA; *U.S. Public*, pg. 1665

Crocker, Charles, Chm. Bd., Pres. & Chief Exec. Officer--BEI Technologies, Inc., San Francisco, CA; *U.S. Public*, pg. 160

Crocker, Douglas, II, Pres.--First Capital Financial Corp., Troy, MI; *U.S. Private*, pg. 473

Crocker, Douglas, II, Pres. & Chief Exec. Officer--Equity Residential Properties Trust, Chicago, IL; *U.S. Public*, pg. 590

Crocker, Will, Pres. & Chief Exec. Officer--Amot Controls Corporation, Richmond, CA; *U.S. Public*, pg. 1405

Crockett, R.J., Pres. & Chief Exec. Officer--Dexter Company, Fairfield, IA; *U.S. Private*, pg. 329

Croen, Ronald A., Pres. & Chief Exec. Officer--Nuance Communications, Menlo Park, CA; *U.S. Private*, pg. 958

Crofutt, Tom, Pres.--Dayton Tire Company, Oklahoma City, OK; *Int'l*, pg. 213

Croggon, Jeremy, Pres.--Omya, Inc., Proctor, VT; *Int'l*, pg. 1061

Croll, Samuel W., III, Pres.--Croll-Reynolds Company, Inc., Westfield, NJ; *U.S. Private*, pg. 290

Crom, J. Oliver, Pres. & Chief Exec. Officer--Dale Carnegie Training, New York, NY; *U.S. Private*, pg. 308

Cromie, Scott J., Pres.--American Home Shield Corporation, Memphis, TN; *U.S. Public*, pg. 1461

Cronin, Edmund B., Jr., Pres. & Chief Exec. Officer--Washington Real Estate Investment Trust, Kensington, MD; *U.S. Public*, pg. 1743

Cronin, Robert J., Pres. & Chief Exec. Officer--Wallace Computer Services, Inc., Lisle, IL; *U.S. Public*, pg. 1735

Cronin, Timothy C., Pres.--Hilton Active Apparel, Lincolnwood, IL; *U.S. Public*, pg. 940

Cronin, Timothy E., Co-Pres. & Co-Chief Exec. Officer--The Nikko Securities Co. International Inc., New York, NY; *Int'l*, pg. 930

Cronk, William F., III, Pres.--Dreyer's Grand Ice Cream, Inc., Oakland, CA; *U.S. Public*, pg. 529

Crook, J. Mitchell, Pres.--First Maryland Leasecorp, Baltimore, MD; *Int'l*, pg. 64

Crook, Kent W., Pres. & Treas.--The Burton Company, North Haven, CT; *U.S. Public*, pg. 826

Crooke, Edward A., Pres. & Chief Oper. Officer--Baltimore Gas and Electric Company, Baltimore, MD; *U.S. Public*, pg. 172

Crooks, Thomas, Pres.--Fahlgren, Dublin, OH; *U.S. Private*, pg. 391

Croom, Judson H., Pres. & Chief Exec. Officer--CTX Mortgage Co., Inc., Dallas, TX; *U.S. Public*, pg. 323

Cropper, Stephen L., Pres. & Chief Exec. Officer--Williams Pipe Line Co., Tulsa, OK; *U.S. Public*, pg. 1769

Crosby, Mike, Pres.-Automotive Components Div.--Freudenberg-NOK, Plymouth, MI; *U.S. Private*, pg. 427

Cross, Geoffrey, Pres. & Chief Oper. Officer--Petroferm Inc., Fernandina Beach, FL; *U.S. Private*, pg. 858

Cross, Jim, Pres. & Chief Exec. Officer--Thaw & Walrus, Inc., Seattle, WA; *U.S. Private*, pg. 914

Cross, Joe D., Jr., Pres.--Cross Motors Corp., Louisville, KY; *U.S. Private*, pg. 291

Cross, Les, Pres.--Smith & Nephew DonJoy Inc., Carlsbad, CA; *Int'l*, pg. 1263

Cross, Mike, Exec. V.P. & Gen. Mgr.--Sea World of California, San Diego, CA; *U.S. Public*, pg. 114

Cross, Ray, Chm. Bd., Pres. & Chief Exec. Officer--Krone Casting Corp., North Chicago, IL; *U.S. Private*, pg. 636

Cross, Rick, Pres.--Mr. Electric Corporation, Waco, TX; *U.S.* Public, pg. 538

Cross, Rick, Pres.--Aire Serve Heating & Air Conditioning, Inc., Waco, TX; *U.S. Public*, pg. 538

Cross, Rick, Pres.--Mr. Rooter Corporation, Waco, TX; *U.S. Public*, pg. 538

Cross, Timothy E., Pres. & Chief Exec. Officer--M & I Bank of Shawano, N.A., Shawano, WI; *U.S. Public*, pg. 1050

Cross, Wilbur J., Chm. Bd., Pres. & Chief Exec. Officer--Catskill Savings Bank, Catskill, NY; *U.S. Public*, pg. 318

Crossen, Mark, Pres. & Chief Exec. Officer--Amrion Inc., Boulder, CO; *U.S. Public*, pg. 1767

Crosser, Richard H., Pres. & Chief Oper. Officer--Crossmann Communities, Inc., Indianapolis, IN; *U.S. Public*, pg. 461

Crossingham, James H., Jr., Chm. Bd. & Pres.--Spencer's Inc., Mount Airy, NC; *U.S. Private*, pg. 1025

Crossman, R.E., Pres. & Gen. Mgr.--Bryant Grinder Corp., Springfield, VT; *U.S. Private*, pg. 461

Crossman, Richard, Pres.--Vermont USA Machine Tool Group, North Springfield, VT; *U.S. Private*, pg. 461

Croteau, Edmond, Pres.--Spiegel Meats, Inc., Miami, FL; *U.S. Private*, pg. 1025

Crotty, Daniel W., Pres. & Chief Oper. Officer--Van Dyne-Crotty, Inc., Dayton, OH; *U.S. Private*, pg. 1132

Crouch, B.G., Dr., Pres.--Elf Sanofi Inc., New York, NY; *Int'l*, *pg. 445*

Crouch, Michael A., Pres.--DAC International, Inc., Austin, TX; *U.S. Public*, pg. 187

Crow, William, Pres. & Chief Oper. Officer--Friedman Industries, Inc., Houston, TX; *U.S. Public*, pg. 682

Crowder, Otis A., Pres. & Chief Exec. Officer--Crowder Construction Co., Charlotte, NC; *U.S. Private*, pg. 291

Crowe, A Derrill, Pres.--Mutual Assurance, Inc., Birmingham, AL; *U.S. Public*, pg. 1080

Crowe, A. Derrill, M.D., Chm. Bd. & Pres.--Medical Assurance, Inc., Birmingham, AL; *U.S. Public*, pg. 1079

Crowe, James Q., Pres. & Chief Exec. Officer--Kiewit Construction Group, Inc., Omaha, NE; *U.S. Private*, pg. 619

Crowe, Jeffrey C., Chm. Bd., Pres. & Chief Exec. Officer--Landstar Holding, Shelton, CT; *U.S. Public*, pg. 978

Crowe, Maureen, Pres. & Chief Exec. Officer--Carl Byoir & Associates, Inc., New York, NY; *Int'l*, pg. 1483

Crowe, S.J., Pres.--Chevron Capital U.S.A. Inc., San Francisco, CA; *U.S. Public*, pg. 348

Crowell, Donald W., Mng. Partner--Crowell, Weedon & Co., Los Angeles, CA; *U.S. Private*, pg. 291

Crowell, Ralph, Pres.--Glines & Rhodes, Inc., Attleboro, MA; *U.S. Private*, pg. 457

Crowell, Steven H., Pres., Chief Oper. Officer, Chief Exec. Officer & Treas.--East Coast Steel, Inc., Claremont, NH; *U.S. Private*, pg. 356

Crowley, Frank J., Pres. & Chief Oper. Officer--Commercial Union Life Assurance Company of Canada, Scarborough, Canada; *Int'l*, pg. 308

Crowley, Ralph D., Jr., Pres.--Polar Beverages, Worcester, MA; *U.S. Private*, pg. 873

Crowley, Thomas, Jr., Chm. Bd., Pres. & Chief Exec. Officer--Crowley Maritime Corporation, Oakland, CA; *U.S.* Private, pg. 292

Crown, Fred S., Jr., Pres.--Lee, Robinson & Steine, Inc., Nashville, TN; *U.S. Public*, pg. 624

Crown, William, Pres. & Chief Exec. Officer--CC Industries, Inc., Chicago, IL; *U.S. Private*, pg. 192

Crowson, Niel, Chm. Bd., Pres. & Chief Exec. Officer--E.C. Barton & Company, Jonesboro, AR; *U.S. Private*, pg. 119

Crozier, J., Chm. Bd.--Riley Advertising Limited, London, United Kingdom; *Int'l*, pg. 1117

Crozier, William M., Jr., Chm. Bd. & Pres.--BayBanks, Inc., Boston, MA; *U.S. Public*, pg. 184

Crudup, Kent, Pres.--Coleman Spas, Inc., Chandler, AZ; *U.S. Private*, pg. 691
Cruger, Melvin E., Pres.--Teledyne Water Pik, Fort Collins, CO; *U.S. Public*, pg. 44
Cruikshank, Bruce, Pres.--Sealed Air Food Packaging Division, Patterson, NC; *U.S. Public*, pg. 1451
Cruiscshanks, Douglas, Pres. & Chief Exec. Officer--NationsBank Virginia, Richmond, VA; *U.S. Public*, pg. 1163
Crum, David H., Pres., Chief Exec. & Chief Fin. Officer--Crum Electric Supply Co., Inc., Casper, WY; *U.S. Private*, pg. 293
Crum, Franklin W., Pres. & Chief Exec. Officer--The Jim Dandy Co., Inc., Atlanta, GA; *Int'l*, pg. 918
Crum, Gary T., Pres.-Aim Capitol--Aim Family of Funds, Houston, TX; *Int'l*, pg. 685
Crum, Niles D., Publr.--ID Magazine, New York, NY; *Int'l*, pg. 1446
Crumley, James, Pres.--Proof Positive/Farrowlyne Associates, Inc., Evanston, IL; *U.S. Public*, pg. 503
Crump, John, Pres.--Sensall, Div. of Rosemount, Inc., Hauppauge, NY; *U.S. Public*, pg. 574
Crutchfield, Bill, Chm. Bd., Pres. & Chief Exec. Officer--State First National Bank, Texas, Texarkana, TX; *U.S. Public*, pg. 630
Crutchfield, K.S., Pres.--Cyprus Cumberland Coal Corporation, Middlesboro, KY; *U.S. Public*, pg. 471
Crutchfield, K.S., Pres.--Cyprus Mountain Coals Corporation, Bulan, KY; *U.S. Public*, pg. 471
Crutchfield, K.S., Pres.--Cyprus Kanawha Corporation, Powellton, WV; *U.S. Public*, pg. 471
Crutchfield, Kevin, Pres.--Cannelton Industries, Inc., Charleston, WV; *U.S. Public*, pg. 471
Crutchfield, Kevin, Pres.--Cannelton Inc., Charleston, WV; *U.S. Public*, pg. 471
Cruz, Eduardo, Pres.--Crown Cork de Chile, S.A.I., Santiago, Chile; *U.S. Public*, pg. 464
Cruz, Eduardo, Pres.--Crown Cork de Chile S.A., Santiago, Chile; *U.S. Public*, pg. 464
Cruz, Joe, Pres.--Consolidated Foundries, Cudahy, CA; *U.S. Private*, pg. 265
Cruz, Lamberto, Mng. Partner, Chief Fin. Officer & Admin. Services--Fova, Inc., New York, NY; *U.S. Public*, pg. 764
Cruz, William R., Co-Chm. Bd., Pres. & Co-Chief Exec. Officer--Omega Research Inc., Miami, FL; *U.S. Public*, pg. 1222
Csiszar, Ernst N., Pres. & Chief Exec. Officer--The Seibels Bruce Group, Inc., Columbia, SC; *U.S. Public*, pg. 1453
Csiszar, Ernst N., Pres. & Chief Exec. Officer--Consolidated American Insurance Co., Columbia, SC; *U.S. Public*, pg. 1454
Csiszar, Ernst N., Pres. & Chief Exec. Officer--Catawba Insurance Co., Columbia, SC; *U.S. Public*, pg. 1454
Csiszar, Ernst N., Pres. & Chief Exec. Officer--Investors National Life Insurance Co., Columbia, SC; *U.S. Public*, pg. 1454
Csiszar, Ernst N., Pres. & Chief Exec. Officer--Kentucky Insurance Co., Louisville, KY; *U.S. Public*, pg. 1454
Csiszar, Ernst N., Pres. & Chief Exec. Officer--Seibels, Bruce & Co., Columbia, SC; *U.S. Public*, pg. 1454
Csiszar, Ernst N., Pres. & Chief Exec. Officer--Agency Specialty Inc., Columbia, SC; *U.S. Public*, pg. 1454
Csiszar, Ernst N., Pres. & Chief Exec. Officer--Forest Lake Travel Service, Inc., Columbia, SC; *U.S. Public*, pg. 1454
Cuadra Chamberlain, Vicente, Pres.--Publiciaa Cuadra Chamberlain, Managua, Nicaragua; *U.S. Private*, pg. 186
Cuatrecasas, Pedro, Pres.--COFIR (Corporacion Financiera Reunida), Madrid, Spain; *Int'l*, pg. 240
Cubria, Raphael, Pres.--Video Electronics de S.A., Garza Garcia, Mexico; *U.S. Public*, pg. 1720
Cucuz, Ron, Pres. & Chief Exec. Officer--Hayes Wheels International, Inc., Romulus, MI; *U.S. Private*, pg. 513
Cuddihy, Rita, Pres.--US Airways Shuttle, Flushing, NY; *U.S. Private*, pg. 1124
Cuello, Rafael, Pres.--Caribe Freight, Santo Domingo, Dominican Republic; *U.S. Private*, pg. 211
Cuesta, Armando, Pres.--ECI Telecom Americas Inc., Fort Lauderdale, FL; *Int'l*, pg. 643
Culberson, Scott, Pres.--Chance Rides, Inc., Wichita, KS; *U.S. Private*, pg. 228
Culbertson, James F., Jr., Pres.--Temp-Control Mechanical Corp., Portland, OR; *U.S. Private*, pg. 1075
Culea, J.D., Chm., Pres. & Chief Exec. Officer--Northern Labs, Inc., Manitowoc, WI; *U.S. Private*, pg. 805
Cullen, J. Russell, Jr., Pres. & Chief Exec. Officer--Nason and Cullen Group Incorporated, King of Prussia, PA; *U.S. Private*, pg. 775
Cullen, Thomas, Pres.--Duferco Steel Inc., Laurence Harbor, NJ; *U.S. Private*, pg. 345
Cullen, Tom, Pres.--Sterling Steel Service Ltd., Chicago, IL; *U.S. Private*, pg. 345
Cullman, Edgar M., Jr., Pres. & Chief Exec. Officer--General Cigar Holdings Inc, New York, NY; *U.S. Public*, pg. 707
Cullman, Lewis B., Pres.--Cullman Ventures, Inc., Norwalk, CT; *U.S. Private*, pg. 294
Cullman, Lewis B., Pres.--Cullman Ventures, Inc., New York, NY; *U.S. Private*, pg. 295
Cullum, John D., Pres.--PHH Vehicle Management Services, United Kingdom, Swindon, United Kingdom; *U.S. Public*, pg. 322
Culp, H. Lawrence, Pres.--Veeder-Root Company, Simsbury, CT; *U.S. Public*, pg. 482
Culp, Perry, Pres.--Texas Metal Works, Inc., Beaumont, TX; *U.S. Private*, pg. 1078
Culp, Robert G., III, Chm. Bd. & Chief Exec. Officer--Culp, Inc., High Point, NC; *U.S. Public*, pg. 467
Culver, Curt S., Pres. & Chief Oper. Officer--Mortgage Guaranty Insurance Corporation, Milwaukee, WI; *U.S. Public*, pg. 1026
Cummings, Gerry, Pres.--B.G. Industries, Taylor, MI; *U.S. Private*, pg. 106
Cummings, Robert, Mng. Dir.--Windpoint Partners, Southfield, MI; *U.S. Private*, pg. 1182
Cummings, Robert S., Pres.--SAIC Engineering, Inc., Lakeville, MA; *U.S. Private*, pg. 976
Cummings, Terry M., Pres. & Chief Exec. Officer--Bremer Financial Corporation, Saint Paul, MN; *U.S. Private*, pg. 167
Cummings, Thomas L., III, Pres. & Chief Exec.--Cummings Inc., Nashville, TN; *U.S. Private*, pg. 295
Cummins, Bob, Pres.--Wellborn - DE Corp., Albuquerque, NM; *U.S. Private*, pg. 347
Cuneo, Ronald E., Pres.--Wang Fed Inc., Mc Lean, VA; *U.S. Public*, pg. 1737
Cunningham, A. Patrick, Pres.--Dovatech, Ltd., Beecher, IL; *U.S. Public*, pg. 520
Cunningham, C. Baker, Chm. Bd., Pres. & Chief Exec. Officer--Belden Inc., Saint Louis, MO; *U.S. Public*, pg. 200
Cunningham, C. Baker, Chm. Bd., Pres. & Chief Exec. Officer--Belden Wire & Cable Company, Richmond, IN; *U.S. Public*, pg. 201
Cunningham, C. Joseph, III, Chm. Bd., Pres. & Chief Exec. Officer--The Fidelity Bank, Frostburg, MD; *U.S. Public*, pg. 1089
Cunningham, Douglas L., Pres. & Chief Exec. Officer--Rexair, Inc., Troy, MI; *U.S. Public*, pg. 1684
Cunningham, Gerel C., Pres.--Essex Corporation, New York, NY; *U.S. Public*, pg. 320
Cunningham, Gordon, Pres.--London Life Insurance Group, London, Canada; *Int'l*, pg. 435
Cunningham, James, Pres.--The Stiffel Company, Chicago, IL; *U.S. Private*, pg. 1043
Cunningham, Joe, Pres. & Publr.--The Rockdale Citizen Publishing Company, Conyers, GA; *U.S. Public*, pg. 759
Cunningham, John P., Pres. & Chief Oper. Officer--International Aluminum Corporation, Monterey Park, CA; *U.S. Public*, pg. 894
Cunningham, John W., Pres.--Crown Litometal, S.A., Medellin, Colombia; *U.S. Public*, pg. 465
Cunningham, Larry, Pres.--Gooch Foods, Inc., Lincoln, NE; *U.S. Public*, pg. 128
Cunningham, Larry H., Pres.--ADM Corn Processing Division, Decatur, IL; *U.S. Public*, pg. 127
Cunningham, Larry H., Pres.--ADM Protein Specialties, Decatur, IL; *U.S. Public*, pg. 128
Cunningham, Maston N., Pres. & Gen. Mgr.--Occidental Exploration and Production Company, Quito, Ecuador; *U.S. Public*, pg. 1210
Cunningham, Michael, Sr. Partner, Exec. Creative Dir.--Eric Mower and Associates, Inc., Syracuse, NY; *U.S. Private*, pg. 765
Cunningham, Phil, Pres.--Networking Products, Alexandria, VA; *U.S. Public*, pg. 1105
Cunningham, Philip T., Pres. & Chief Exec. Officer--Microdyne Corporation, Alexandria, VA; *U.S. Public*, pg. 1105
Cunningham, Ralph S., Pres. & Chief Exec. Officer--Citgo Petroleum Corporation, Tulsa, OK; *Int'l*, pg. 1045
Cunningham, Theodor R., Pres. & Mng. Dir.--Chrysler de Mexico S.A., Mexico, Mexico; *U.S. Public*, pg. 354
Cunningham, Theodore R., Pres. & Mng. Dir.--Chrysler de Mexico, Ramos Arizpe, Mexico; *U.S. Public*, pg. 354
Cuny, John D., Pres.--Anthem Health Plans of Florida Inc., Jacksonville, FL; *U.S. Private*, pg. 76
Cuomo, Tom, Grp. V.P.--Drew Industrial, Boonton, NJ; *U.S. Public*, pg. 139
Curiel, Juan Carlos Lasa, Pres.--Juliana Constructora Gijonesa, S.A., Gijon, Spain; *Int'l*, pg. 1223
Curlander, Paul J., Dr., Pres. & Chief Oper. Officer--Lexmark International Group, Inc., Lexington, KY; *U.S. Public*, pg. 991
Curlander, Paul J., Dr., Pres. & Chief Oper. Officer--Lexmark International, Inc., Lexington, KY; *U.S. Public*, pg. 991
Curleigh, James, Pres.--Taylor Made (Great Britain) Ltd., Basingstoke, United Kingdom; *Int'l*, pg. 1181
Curler, Jeffrey H., Pres.--Bemis Company, Inc., Minneapolis, MN; *U.S. Public*, pg. 210
Curley, Dwight G., Pres.--Granite State Gas Transmission, Inc., Portsmouth, NH; *U.S. Public*, pg. 197
Curley, Thomas, Pres., Publr. & Chief Oper. Officer--USA Today, Arlington, VA; *U.S. Public*, pg. 700
Curran, Denis, Pres.--Bank of Ireland Asset Management Limited, Greenwich, CT; *Int'l*, pg. 152
Curran, J.J., Pres.--Mizuno Canada Limited, Mississauga, Canada; *Int'l*, pg. 885
Curran, Mark, Pres.--Shakey's Incorporated, Irvine, CA; *U.S. Private*, pg. 989
Curran, Robert, Pres.--Wheel Tronic Inc., Mississauga, Canada; *U.S. Public*, pg. 1481
Curran, William, Pres. & Chief Exec. Officer--Curran Group, Inc., Crystal Lake, IL; *U.S. Private*, pg. 297
Currence, Anna, Pres. & Chief Oper. Officer--Crown Books Corporation, Landover, MD; *U.S. Public*, pg. 484
Currie, Doug A., Pres.--EFCO Inc., Erie, PA; *U.S. Private*, pg. 353
Currie, Jerry N., Pres. & Chief Exec. Officer--Curries Company, Mason City, IA; *Int'l*, pg. 18
Currie, R.J., Pres.--Loblaw Companies Limited, North York, Canada; *Int'l*, pg. 1495
Currie, Richard J., Pres.--George Weston Limited, Toronto, Canada; *Int'l*, pg. 1494
Curry, Bernard F., Jr., Pres.--The Curry Corporation, Scarsdale, NY; *U.S. Private*, pg. 297
Curry, Craig, Pres.--POST Buckley Schuh & Jernigan, Dallas, TX; *U.S. Private*, pg. 826
Curry, James, Pres.--South Florida Land Division, Fort Myers, FL; *U.S. Public*, pg. 1683
Curry, Keys A., Jr., Pres. & Chief Oper. Officer--Destec Energy, Inc., Houston, TX; *U.S. Public*, pg. 1146
Curry, Steven, Pres.--Knutson Construction Co., Minneapolis, MN; *U.S. Private*, pg. 627
Curry, Thomas, Pres.--MacNeal-Schwendler Corp., Costa Mesa, CA; *U.S. Public*, pg. 1031
Curry, Thomas C., Pres. & Chief Exec. Officer--The Macneal-Schwendler Corp., Los Angeles, CA; *U.S. Public*, pg. 1030
Curry, W. Roger, Pres. & Chief Exec. Officer--Consolidated Freightways Corp., Menlo Park, CA; *U.S. Public*, pg. 435
Curtin, Frank T., Chm. Bd., Pres. & Chief Exec. Officer--Brown & Sharpe Manufacturing Company, North Kingstown, RI; *U.S. Public*, pg. 260
Curtin, John D., Jr., Chm. Bd., Pres. & Chief Exec. Officer--Aearo Company, Boston, MA; *U.S. Private*, pg. 23
Curtin, Joseph, Pres.--Tube City Inc., Glassport, PA; *U.S. Private*, pg. 1108
Curtis, Charlie, Pres. & Chief Exec. Officer--Nana Regional Corporation, Inc., Anchorage, AK; *U.S. Private*, pg. 774
Curtis, Charlie, Pres.--Nana Development Corporation, Kotzebue, AK; *U.S. Private*, pg. 774
Curtis, Chuck, Chm. Bd., Pres. & Chief Exec. Officer--Valentine Radford, Inc., Kansas City, MO; *U.S. Private*, pg. 1131
Curtis, Donald, Pres.--Curtis Media Group, Raleigh, NC; *U.S. Private*, pg. 297
Curtis, George, Pres.--Kern's Bakeries, Incorporated, Knoxville, TN; *U.S. Public*, pg. 547
Curtis, Jay, Chm. Bd. & Pres.--Curtis Lumber Company, Ballston Spa, NY; *U.S. Private*, pg. 297
Curtis, Jonathan G., Pres.--CDM Federal Programs Corporation, Fairfax, VA; *U.S. Private*, pg. 204
Curtis, Lawrence, Pres.--Partlow Corporation, New Hartford, NY; *U.S. Public*, pg. 482
Curtis, Paul F., Pres., Chief Oper. Officer & Treas.--L.N. Curtis & Sons, Oakland, CA; *U.S. Private*, pg. 297
Curtius, Michael D., Pres. & Chief Oper. Officer--Mercury General Corporation, Los Angeles, CA; *U.S. Public*, pg. 1093
Curto, Richard S., Pres. & Chief Exec. Officer--Prime Group Realty Trust, Chicago, IL; *U.S. Public*, pg. 1326
Cusack, Thomas J., Pres. & Chief Exec. Officer--Transamerica Life Companies, Los Angeles, CA; *U.S. Public*, pg. 1630
Cusano, Michael R., Pres.--Deepwater Chemicals, Inc., Woodward, OK; *Int'l*, pg. 1395
Cushing, James E., Jr., Pres. & Chief Oper. Officer--Wright Group Publishing, Inc., Bothell, WA; *U.S. Public*, pg. 1636
Cushing, Robert, Pres. & Chief Exec. Officer--Pepsi-Cola General Bottlers, Inc., Rolling Meadows, IL; *U.S. Public*, pg. 1277
Cusick, C. Robert, Vice Chm., Pres. & Chief Exec. Officer--International Murex Technologies Corporation, Guelph, Canada; *Int'l*, pg. 684
Custer, Patrick A., Chm. Bd., Pres. & Chief Exec. Officer--Curtis Mathes Holding Corp., Dallas, TX; *U.S. Public*, pg. 1057
Cusumano, Gary M., Pres. & Chief Oper. Officer--The Newhall Land And Farming Company, Valencia, CA; *U.S. Public*, pg. 1178
Cuteri, Frank, Pres.--Brown Automotive Group, Fairfax, VA; *U.S. Private*, pg. 173
Cutillas, Mamuel Jorge, Pres.--Bacardi Limited, Pembroke, Bermuda; *Int'l*, pg. 131
Cutini, Jerauld J., Pres.--OnTrak Systems, Inc., San Jose, CA; *U.S. Public*, pg. 975
Cutler, Alexander M., Pres. & Chief Oper. Officer--Eaton Corporation, Cleveland, OH; *U.S. Public*, pg. 555
Cutler, Jay, Pres.--Educational Insights, Inc., Carson, CA; *U.S. Public*, pg. 565
Cutler, Joel Bernard, Pres.--National Leisure Group, Boston, MA; *U.S. Public*, pg. 320
Cutter, W.R., Chm. Bd. & Pres.--Cutter Aviation Albuquerque, Inc, Albuquerque, NM; *U.S. Private*, pg. 298
Cuvelier, Joseph, Pres. & Chief Exec. Officer--Gie ETEX Gestion, Vernouillet, France; *Int'l*, pg. 430
Cuyegkeng, Paul, Pres.--Dole Asia, Tokyo, Japan; *U.S. Public*, pg. 515
Cvengros, William D., Pres. & Chief Exec. Officer--PIMCO Advisors, Stamford, CT; *U.S. Public*, pg. 1296
Cypher, Victor, Pres. & Chief Exec. Officer--Caldwell Manufacturing Company, Rochester, NY; *U.S. Private*, pg. 200
Cyphers, Cray, Partner & Creative Dir.--Eric Mower and Associates/Buffalo, Inc., Buffalo, NY; *U.S. Private*, pg. 765
Cyrenne, R.O., Pres. & Chief Oper. Officer--Kruger Urban Forest Products, Inc., Bromptonville, Canada; *Int'l*, pg. 761
Cyrenne, Roland O., Pres. & Chief Oper. Officer--Kruger Inc., Montreal, Canada; *Int'l*, pg. 761
Cyrenne, Roland O., Pres. & Chief Oper. Officer--Trois-Rivieres Mill, Trois-Rivieres, Canada; *Int'l*, pg. 761
Cyrenne, Roland O., Pres. & Chief Oper. Officer--Place Turcot Mill, Montreal, Canada; *Int'l*, pg. 761
Cyrenne, Roland O., Pres. & Chief Oper. Officer--Ville LaSalle Plant, La Salle, Canada; *Int'l*, pg. 761
Cyrenne, Roland O., Pres. & Chief Oper. Officer--Rexdale Plant, Rexdale, Canada; *Int'l*, pg. 761
Czaus, Walt, Pres.--Otis Merla Systems, Garland, TX; *U.S. Public*, pg. 776
Czeban, S.J., Pres.--Murray Canada, Brampton, Canada; *Int'l*, pg. 1397
Czechowski, Claude, Pres.--French Division, Boulogne-Billancourt, France; *U.S. Public*, pg. 423
Czerwinski, Connie, Pres.--Cerwin Vega, Inc., Simi Valley, CA; *U.S. Private*, pg. 227
Czerwinski, Mike, Pres.--Eatelcorp Inc., Gonzales, LA; *U.S. Private*, pg. 358
Cziraky, Debra Adray, Pres. & Chief Exec. Officer--Adray Appliance & Photo Center, Inc., Dearborn, MI; *U.S. Private*, pg. 18
Czura, Antony, Pres. & Chief Exec. Officer--SGS North America Inc., New York, NY; *Int'l*, pg. 1153
Czyzyk, Joseph A., Pres. & Chief Oper. Officer--Mercury Air Group Inc., Los Angeles, CA; *U.S. Public*, pg. 1092

D-Alonzo, Thomas, Pres.--PPD Pharmaco, Inc., Wilmington, NC; *U.S. Public*, pg. 1285
D'Agostino, J., Pres.--Lehrer McGovern Bovis Inc., New York, NY; *Int'l*, pg. 1035
D'Agostino, James, Pres.--American General Corporation, Houston, TX; *U.S. Public*, pg. 76
D'Alessandro, Dominic, Pres. & Chief Exec. Officer--Manulife Financial (The Manufacturers Life Insurance Company), Toronto, Canada; *Int'l*, pg. 840
D'Alessandro, Dominic, Pres. & Chief Exec. Officer--Manulife Financial, Toronto, Canada; *Int'l*, pg. 840
D'Aloia, Paul, Pres. & Gen. Mgr.--Huffy Sports Company, Sussex, WI; *U.S. Public*, pg. 846
D'Alonzo, Thomas, M.D., Pres. & Chief Oper. Officer--Pharmaceutical Product Development, Inc., Wilmington, NC; *U.S. Public*, pg. 1285
d'Amade, J., Pres.--Agences Maritime Associes, Le Havre, France; *Int'l*, pg. 682
d'Amade, J., Pres.--Agence Maritime et Conteneurs, Boulogne-Billancourt, France; *Int'l*, pg. 682
D'Ambra, Michael, Pres.--Birmingham Cable Communications, Inc., Birmingham, AL; *U.S. Public*, pg. 1610
D'Amelio, Yvonne, Principal & Chief Fin. Officer--Vox Medica Corporation, Philadelphia, PA; *U.S. Private*, pg. 1143
D'Amour, Gerald E., Pres.--Big Y Foods Inc., Springfield, MA; *U.S. Private*, pg. 143
D'Andrea, Paul, Pres. & Chief Exec. Officer--Mystic Color Lab, Inc., Mystic, CT; *Int'l*, pg. 501
d'Angeac, Gilles Dupuy, Pres.--Alcatel USA Corp, New York, NY; *Int'l*, pg. 55
D'Angelo, Mr., Pres.--Avions de Transport Regional - ATR, Blagnac, France; *Int'l*, pg. 654
D'Anna, Vito, Pres.--Mars Super Markets, Inc., Baltimore, MD; *U.S. Private*, pg. 707
d'Anterroches, Ph., Pres.--SBS Valeurs S.A., Paris, France; *Int'l*, pg. 1331
D'Antoni, David J., Pres.--Ashland Chemical, Dublin, OH; *U.S. Public*, pg. 139
D'Antuono, M., Pres.--Parsons Constructors Inc., Pasadena, CA; *U.S. Private*, pg. 842
D'Arcy, Thomas P., Pres. & Chief Exec. Officer--Bradley Real Estate, Inc., Northbrook, IL; *U.S. Public*, pg. 250
D'Augostino, Vincent, Pres.--Benefit Consultants, Inc. (CT), San Carlos, CA; *U.S. Public*, pg. 320
D'Urso, Giorgio, Pres. & Chief Exec. Officer--Diamedix Corporation, Miami, FL; *U.S. Public*, pg. 914
D'Urso, Giorgio, Pres.--Delta Biologicals, S.r.l., Rome, Italy; *U.S. Public*, pg. 915
Da Costa Noble, Christian, Pres.--Tailleur Industrie, Paris, France; *Int'l*, pg. 549
da Costa, M., Pres.--Tyton Hellermann do Brasil Industria e Comercio Ltda., Sao Paulo, Brazil; *Int'l*, pg. 209
da Costa, Vera Nobre, Pres.--Young & Rubicam (Portugal), Lisbon, Portugal; *U.S. Private*, pg. 1199
da Cruz, Rui Monteiro, Dir. Gen.-North America--TAP Air Portugal, Newark, NJ; *Int'l*, pg. 1418
da Silva, Antonio Carlos R., Pres.--Cervejarias Kaiser Brasil Ltda., Campinas, Brazil; *Int'l*, pg. 279
Dabrowski, Steve, Pres. & Dir. Gen.--Lowe & Partners/SMS de Mexico, Mexico, Mexico; *U.S. Private*, pg. 678
Dacey, Mark, Pres.--A/S/M Communications, Inc., New York, NY; *Int'l*, pg. 1446
Dachowski, Peter, Pres.-Insulation Div.--Isover Saint-Gobain, Courbevoie, France; *Int'l*, pg. 1176
Dachowski, Peter R., Pres.--CertainTeed International, Inc., Valley Forge, PA; *Int'l*, pg. 1171
Dachowski, Peter R., Pres.--CertainTeed Manatee Insulation Ltd., Montreal, Canada; *Int'l*, pg. 1176
Dachs, A.M., Pres.--The Fremont Group, San Francisco, CA; *U.S. Private*, pg. 427
Dack, Lee, Div. Pres.--Kaynar/K-Fast/APS, Fullerton, CA; *U.S. Public*, pg. 940
Dackow, Orest T., Pres. & Chief Exec. Officer--The Great-West Life Assurance Company, Winnipeg, Canada; *Int'l*, pg. 557
Dadd, Ronald F., Pres. & Chief Exec. Officer--Construction Specialties, Inc., Cranford, NJ; *U.S. Private*, pg. 266
Daetwyler, Willy Peter, Chm.--Zuercher Lagerhaus AG, Zurich, Switzerland; *Int'l*, pg. 1529
Dagnaed, John Philip, Pres.-L'oreal Technique Professional--L'Oreal Technique Professional Div., Brussels, Belgium; *Int'l*, pg. 819
Dahan, Andre, Pres.--Dun & Bradstreet, Murray Hill, NJ; *U.S. Public*, pg. 535
Dahan, Daniel, Pres.-Paris Agency--DMB&B Paris, Asnieres-sur-Seine, France; *U.S. Private*, pg. 304
Dahl, H. Douglas, Pres.--Eastern Associated Coal Corp., Charleston, WV; *Int'l*, pg. 594
Dahl, H. Douglas, Pres.--Peabody Coal Co., Charleston, WV; *Int'l*, pg. 594
Dahl, Richard J., Pres. & Chief Oper. Officer--Pacific Century Financial Corporation, Honolulu, HI; *U.S. Public*, pg. 1248
Dahl, Robert, Pres.--Curtis 1000, Inc., Atlanta, GA; *U.S. Public*, pg. 70
Dahlback, Claes, Pres.--ABB AB, Stockholm, Sweden; *Int'l*, pg. 7
Dahlback, Claes, Pres.--Investor AB, Stockholm, Sweden; *Int'l*, pg. 686
Dahlberg, A.W., Chm. Bd., Pres. & Chief Exec. Officer--Southern Company, Atlanta, GA; *U.S. Public*, pg. 1489
Dahlberg, Burton, Pres. & Chief Oper. Officer--Kraus-Anderson Incorporated, Minneapolis, MN; *U.S. Private*, pg. 635
Dahlberg, Burton F., Pres. & Chief Oper. Officer--Kraus-Anderson, Incorporated, Minneapolis, MN; *U.S. Private*, pg. 635
Dahlberg, Burton F., Pres.--Kraus-Anderson Mortgage Company, Minneapolis, MN; *U.S. Private*, pg. 635
Dahlem, Charles, Pres.--Dahlem Company, Inc., Louisville, KY; *U.S. Private*, pg. 306
Dahlem, Jim, Pres.--Dahlem Company, Inc., Louisville, KY; *U.S. Private*, pg. 306
Dahlin, John D., Pres.--EURO RSCG Dahlin Smith White, LLC, Salt Lake City, UT; *U.S. Private*, pg. 384
Dahlin, Richard L., Pres.--Henry & Henry, Inc., Lancaster, NY; *Int'l*, pg. 244
Dahlke, James, Pres.--Harrow Industries, Grand Rapids, MI; *U.S. Private*, pg. 506
Dahlmann, David S., Pres. & Chief Exec. Officer--Southwest National Corporation, Greensburg, PA; *U.S. Public*, pg. 1493
Dahlsten, Larry, Pres.--Mid-Kansas Co-op Association, Moundridge, KS; *U.S. Private*, pg. 743
Dahlsten, Larry, Pres.--Lubrication Consultants, L.L.C., Moundridge, KS; *U.S. Private*, pg. 743
Dahlstrom, Christer, Pres.--Skandia Investment AB, Stockholm, Sweden; *Int'l*, pg. 1256
Dahlstrom, Ossi, Mng. Dir.--Interrent OY, Helsinki, Finland; *Int'l*, pg. 684
Daidone, John, Pres.--Daidone Electrical Inc., Newark, NJ; *U.S. Private*, pg. 307
Daigle, Richard, Pres.--Daigle Oil Co., Fort Kent, ME; *U.S. Private*, pg. 307
Daikubara, Izumi, Pres.--GSI Exim America Inc., New York, NY; *Int'l*, pg. 578
Dailey, Peter, Chm., Pres. & Chief Exec. Officer--Memorex Telex N.V., Amsterdam, Netherlands; *Int'l*, pg. 857
Daillance, Jean-Marc, Pres.--Muskin Leisure Products, Inc., Wilkes-Barre, PA; *U.S. Private*, pg. 768
Daily, Curtis E., Pres. & Grp. V.P.--Flowserve Corporation, Rotating Equipment Grp., Dayton, OH; *U.S. Public*, pg. 658
Daisy, Edward, Pres.--Adhesive Research, Inc., Glen Rock, PA; *U.S. Private*, pg. 1091
Dake, William P., Pres.--Stewart's Ice Cream Co., Inc., Saratoga Springs, NY; *U.S. Private*, pg. 1043
Dalborg, Hans, Pres. & Chief Exec. Officer--Nordbanken AB, Stockholm, Sweden; *Int'l*, pg. 957
Dale, Bruce, Pres.--Aaron Brothers, Inc., City of Commerce, CA; *U.S. Public*, pg. 1104
Dale, Michael H., Pres.--Jaguar Cars, Mahwah, NJ; *U.S. Public*, pg. 664
Dale, Robert, Pres.--Windy Hill Pet Food Co., Brentwood, TN; *U.S. Private*, pg. 1182
Dale, Robert, Pres.--Windy Hill Pet Food Co., Perham, MN; *U.S. Private*, pg. 1182
Dalia, Muhammad Younus, Chm. Bd. & Pres.--Habib Bank Ltd., Karachi, Pakistan; *Int'l*, pg. 584
Dalinsky, Frank J., Pres.--Philadelphia Reserve Supply Company, Croydon, PA; *U.S. Private*, pg. 861
Dallinger, Curtis C., Pres.--Natural Fuels Corporation, Denver, CO; *U.S. Public*, pg. 1170
Dalman, Melody, Partner--Suarez Corporation Industries, Canton, OH; *U.S. Private*, pg. 1048
Dalquist, H. David, III, Pres.--Northland Aluminum Products, Inc., Minneapolis, MN; *U.S. Private*, pg. 805
Dalquist, H. David, III, Pres.--Nordic Ware, Minneapolis, MN; *U.S. Private*, pg. 806
Dalquist, H. David, III, Pres.--Nordic Ware Direct, Inc., Saint Louis Park, MN; *U.S. Private*, pg. 806
Dalsgaard, Carl-Johan, Pres.--Astra Pain Control AB, Sodertalje, Sweden; *Int'l*, pg. 93
Dalsgaard, Erik, Gen. Mgr.--BancTec Danmark A/S, Herlev, Denmark; *U.S. Public*, pg. 177
Dalton, Charles E., Pres. & Chief Exec. Officer--Blue Ridge Electric Cooperative Inc., Pickens, SC; *U.S. Private*, pg. 153
Dalton, James E., Jr., Pres. & Chief Exec. Officer--Quorum Health Group, Inc., Brentwood, TN; *U.S. Public*, pg. 1353
Dalton, Michaael J., Pres.--Concord Electric Company, Hampton, NH; *U.S. Public*, pg. 1692
Dalton, Michael J., Pres. & Chief Oper. Officer--Unitil Corporation, Hampton, NH; *U.S. Public*, pg. 1692
Dalton, Michael J., Pres.--Exeter & Hampton Electric Co., Hampton, NH; *U.S. Public*, pg. 1692
Dalton, Michael J., Pres.--Fitchburg Gas and Electric Light Co., Fitchburg, MA; *U.S. Public*, pg. 1692
Dalton, William R.P., Pres. & Chief Exec. Officer--HongKong Bank of Canada, Vancouver, Canada; *Int'l*, pg. 583
Daltoso, Joseph M., Chm. Bd., Pres. & Chief Exec. Officer--Micron Electronics, Inc., Nampa, ID; *U.S. Public*, pg. 1105
Daly, Andy, Pres.--Vail Resorts, Inc., Vail, CO; *U.S. Public*, pg. 1704
Daly, Andy, Pres.--Vail Associates, Inc., Vail, CO; *U.S. Public*, pg. 1704
Daly, Ann, Pres.--Buena Vista Home Video, Burbank, CA; *U.S. Public*, pg. 513
Daly, James G., Pres.--UNITIL Power Corporation, Hampton, NH; *U.S. Public*, pg. 1692
Daly, James G., Pres.--UNITIL Resources, Inc., Hampton, NH; *U.S. Public*, pg. 1692
Daly, Kevin, Chm. Bd., Pres. & Chief Exec. Officer--ATL Products, Inc., Anaheim, CA; *U.S. Public*, pg. 1212
Daly, Leo A., Chm. Bd., Pres. & Treas.--Leo A. Daly Company, Omaha, NE; *U.S. Private*, pg. 309
Daly, Terry, Pres.--Hermes Precisa Australia Pty Ltd., Sydney, Australia; *Int'l*, pg. 579
Dalyai, Steve, Pres. & Chief Oper. Officer--QEI, Inc., Springfield, NJ; *U.S. Private*, pg. 897
Damadian, Raymond, Chm. Bd. & Pres.--Fonar Corporation, Melville, NY; *U.S. Public*, pg. 661
Dambra, Barton, Pres. & Chief Exec. Officer--Markin Tubing, Inc., Wyoming, NY; *U.S. Private*, pg. 705
Dame, Reed, Pres.--Woodgrain Millwork, Fruitland, ID; *U.S. Private*, pg. 1187
Damico, Joseph F., Pres. & Chief Oper. Officer--Allegiance Healthcare Corp., McGaw Park, IL; *U.S. Public*, pg. 44
Damico, Joseph F., Pres. & Chief Oper. Officer--Allegiance Healthcare International, McGaw Park, IL; *U.S. Public*, pg. 45
Dammeier, Kurt B., Pres.--Print Northwest Company, L.P., Fife, WA; *Int'l*, pg. 1076
Dammeyer, Rod F., Pres. & Chief Exec. Officer--Great American Management & Investment, Inc., Chicago, IL; *U.S. Private*, pg. 473
Damschroder, Robert L., Chm. Bd. & Pres.--Hickman, Williams & Co. Inc., Cincinnati, OH; *U.S. Private*, pg. 525
dan Hartog, C., Deputy Pres.--KLM Royal Dutch Airlines, Amstelveen, Netherlands; *Int'l*, pg. 719
Dan, Michael T., Pres. & Chief Exec. Officer--The Pittston Company, Glen Allen, VA; *U.S. Public*, pg. 1305
Dan, Michael T., Pres. & Chief Exec. Officer--Brink's, Inc., Darien, CT; *U.S. Public*, pg. 1305
Danaher, B., Pres.--Phillips & Temro Industries Inc., Eden Prairie, MN; *Int'l*, pg. 1388
Danahy, J. Patrick, Pres. & Chief Exec. Officer--Cone Mills Corporation, Greensboro, NC; *U.S. Public*, pg. 430
Danahy, James M., Pres.--Sysco Food Services of Connecticut, Rocky Hill, CT; *U.S. Public*, pg. 1551
Dancheck, Joseph M., Pres.--Harris Life Insurance Company, Scottsdale, AZ; *Int'l*, pg. 154
Dando, David C., Pres.--MCDR, Inc., Memphis, TN; *U.S. Private*, pg. 686
Dandurand, Richard A., Pres.--Stanley Access Technologies, Farmington, CT; *U.S. Public*, pg. 1509
Dane, John, III, Chm. Bd., Pres. & Chief Exec. Officer--Halter Marine Group, Inc., Gulfport, MS; *U.S. Public*, pg. 778
Danehy, R. James, Pres.--Centocor Diagnostics Div., Malvern, PA; *U.S. Public*, pg. 323
Danforth, Robert, Pres.--Litecontrol Corporation, Hanson, MA; *U.S. Private*, pg. 669
Dangar, E., Chief Exec. Officer--Fortune Communication Holdings Ltd., Sydney, Australia; *Int'l*, pg. 500
Daniel, Charles, Pres. & Chief Exec. Officer--UPB of Girardeau Co., Cape Girardeau, MO; *U.S. Public*, pg. 1669
Daniel, Josef, Pres.--AGA GAS spol.s r.o., Prague, Czech Republic; *Int'l*, pg. 13
Daniel, Josef, Pres.--AGA GAS Spol.s r.o., Bratislava, Slovakia; *Int'l*, pg. 13
Daniell, James, Pres. & Chief Oper. Officer--American Strip Steel Inc., Kearny, NJ; *U.S. Private*, pg. 62
Daniels, George F., Pres.--McCord Winn Textron Company, Manchester, NH; *U.S. Public*, pg. 1590
Daniels, George G., Pres.--Daniels Manufacturing Corporation, Orlando, FL; *U.S. Private*, pg. 310
Daniels, Grover B., Pres.--Daniels Printing Company, Everett, MA; *U.S. Private*, pg. 310
Daniels, Jim A., Pres.--Plunkett-Webster, Inc., New Rochelle, NY; *U.S. Private*, pg. 872
Daniels, Lyndon R., Pres. & Chief Oper. Officer--Arch Communications Group, Inc., Westborough, MA; *U.S. Public*, pg. 127
Daniels, Mike, Pres.--SCT Government Systems, Lexington, KY; *U.S. Public*, pg. 1552
Daniels, Norman, Pres.--G.I. Joe's Inc., Wilsonville, OR; *U.S. Private*, pg. 435
Danielsson, Erik, Pres. & Chief Exec. Officer--Pharmacia & Upjohn Biosystems AB, Uppsala, Sweden; *Int'l*, pg. 1047
Danilson, Ron, Pres. & Chief Exec. Officer--Delaware Charter Guarantee & Trust Co., Wilmington, DE; *U.S. Private*, pg. 885
Danio, John R., Pres.--CR Kendall Corporation, Hilger, MT; *U.S. Public*, pg. 302
Danis, Peter G., Jr., Pres. & Chief Exec. Officer-Boise Cascade Office Prods.--Boise Cascade Corporation, Boise, ID; *U.S. Public*, pg. 242
Dann, Earl, Pres.--Dann Dee Display Fixtures, Niles, IL; *U.S. Private*, pg. 310
Dannemiller, John C., Chm. Bd., Pres. & Chief Exec. Officer--Applied Industrial Technologies, Cleveland, OH; *U.S. Public*, pg. 122
Dannenhauer, Daniel g., Pres.--Hilb, Rogal and Hamilton Company of Fort Myers, Fort Myers, FL; *U.S. Public*, pg. 827
Danner-Duroc, Bernard J., Pres. & Chief Exec. Officer--EVI, Inc., Houston, TX; *U.S. Public*, pg. 547
Danner, Dean W., Pres. & Chief Exec. Officer--Electronic Tele-Communications, Inc., Waukesha, WI; *U.S. Public*, pg. 570
Danner, Paul, Pres. & Chief Exec. Officer--Regions Bank/Citrus County, Inverness, FL; *U.S. Public*, pg. 1372
Dannin, Mick, Pres.--Nomaco, Inc., Zebulon, NC; *U.S. Private*, pg. 801
Danter, Phil, Mng. Partner-Strategy--Mediapolis, London, United Kingdom; *Int'l*, pg. 853
Dantzler, Dan, Gen. Mgr. & Pres.-RF Communications--Telex Communications, Inc., Minneapolis, MN; *U.S. Private*, pg. 1074
Danza, John, Partner--Messner Vetere Berger McNamee Schmetterer/EURO RSCG, New York, NY; *Int'l*, pg. 602
Danzinger, Eric A., Pres. & Chief Exec. Officer-Corp.--Starwood Hotels & Resorts, Phoenix, AZ; *U.S. Public*, pg. 1512
Dapper, G. Steven, Pres. & Chief Exec. Officer--Rapp Collins Worldwide, New York, NY; *U.S. Public*, pg. 1224
DaPra, Dennis, Pres. & Chief Oper. Officer--ACO Inc., Farmington Hills, MI; *U.S. Private*, pg. 3
Darazsdi, Frank J., Pres. & Sr. Partner--Bourton Group, Rockford, IL; *U.S. Private*, pg. 162
Darbelnet, Robert L., Pres. & Chief Exec. Officer--American Automobile Association, Heathrow, FL; *U.S. Private*, pg. 50
Darby, Christopher, Pres. & Chief Exec. Officer--Caronet LLC, Raleigh, NC; *U.S. Public*, pg. 307
Darby, Fred W., Pres.--Niagara Transformer Corp., Buffalo, NY; *U.S. Private*, pg. 798
Darby, Kenneth M., Pres. & Chief Exec. & Oper. Officer--Vicon Industries, Inc., Hauppauge, NY; *U.S. Public*, pg. 1719
Darby, Warren A., Pres.--ServiceCare, Inc., Columbia, SC; *U.S. Public*, pg. 1436
Darch, S.T., Pres.--ING Baring Sociedad de Bolsa (Argentina), Buenos Aires, Argentina; *Int'l*, pg. 649

Darcy, John M., Pres. & Gen. Mgr.--Penford Food Ingredients Company, Englewood, CO; *U.S. Public*, pg. 1269
Darcy, Jon J., Pres., Chief Exec. Officer & Treas.--Thermo-Mizer Environmental Corp., Rahway, NJ; *U.S. Public*, pg. 1596
Darcy, Randy G., Pres.--General Mills Operations, Inc., Minneapolis, MN; *U.S. Public*, pg. 718
Darcy, Tom, Pres.--Engineer Control Intl., Elon College, NC; *U.S. Private*, pg. 376
Dardaud, Jacques, Pres.--Laboratoires Bristol S.A., Paris, France; *U.S. Public*, pg. 256
Dare, Carl M., Pres.--Dare Foods Limited, Kitchener, Canada; *Int'l*, pg. 383
Dare, Larry, Chief Exec. Officer--Richardson G.m.b.H., Schwalbach, Germany; *U.S. Public*, pg. 1333
Darehshori, Nader, Chm. Bd., Pres. & Chief Exec. Officer--Houghton Mifflin Company, Boston, MA; *U.S. Public*, pg. 841
Dargatz, K.C., Pres.--Nim-Cor, Inc., Auburn Hills, MI; *Int'l*, pg. 586
Dariano, Leonard, Pres.--Metro Ford Sales, Inc., Schenectady, NY; *U.S. Private*, pg. 736
Darkes, V.M. Kempston, Pres. & Gen. Mgr.--General Motors of Canada Ltd., Oshawa, Canada; *U.S. Public*, pg. 722
Darling, Albert, Jr., Pres.--Darling Envelope Corporation, Shawnee Mission, KS; *U.S. Private*, pg. 311
Darling, Darrell, Pres. & Chief Exec. Officer--First National Bank of Crossville, Crossville, TN; *U.S. Public*, pg. 1669
Darling, John B., Pres.--Darling's, Bangor, ME; *U.S. Private*, pg. 311
Darling, Robert M., Pres. & Chief Exec. Officer--Ampco Metal Incorporated, Milwaukee, WI; *U.S. Private*, pg. 67
Darling, W., Pres. & Chief Exec. Officer--General Railway Signal Corp., Rochester, NY; *Int'l*, pg. 1194
Darlow, Richard A., Div. Pres.--HIAC/ROYCO Division, Silver Spring, MD; *U.S. Public*, pg. 1250
Darnall, Robert J., Chm. Bd., Pres. & Chief Exec. Officer--Inland Steel Industries, Inc., Chicago, IL; *U.S. Public*, pg. 879
Darragh, Kent J., Pres.--Cadillac Plastic & Chemical Co., Troy, MI; *U.S. Public*, pg. 781
Darrow, Russell M., Jr., Pres. & Treas.--Russ Darrow Group, West Bend, WI; *U.S. Private*, pg. 311
Dart, L.K., Gen. Mgr.--ITT Jabsco, Costa Mesa, CA; *U.S. Public*, pg. 860
Dart, Robert, Pres.--Dart Container Corp., Mason, MI; *U.S. Private*, pg. 311
Dartnell, David, Pres.--David Dart, Chatsworth, CA; *U.S. Public*, pg. 948
Darvish, John, Pres. & Chief Exec. Officer--Darcars Ltd., Lanham, MD; *U.S. Private*, pg. 311
Darwin, Allen, Pres.--Cardinal Inc., Rahway, NJ; *U.S. Private*, pg. 208
Darwin, Allen, Pres.--Concord Miniatures, Rahway, NJ; *U.S. Private*, pg. 209
Dasburg, John H., Pres. & Chief Exec. Officer--Northwest Airlines Corp., Saint Paul, MN; *U.S. Public*, pg. 1199
Dassas, Pierre, Pres.--Dassas Communication, Courbevoie, France; *Int'l*, pg. 383
Dattilo, Tom, Pres.--Victor Products, Lisle, IL; *U.S. Public*, pg. 480
Dattoli, Joseph, V.P. & Gen. Mgr.--Perugina Brands of America, Saddle Brook, NJ; *Int'l*, pg. 917
Dauch, Richard E., Pres. & Chief Exec. Officer--American Axle & Manufacturing, Detroit, MI; *U.S. Private*, pg. 51
Daugherty, Mike, Pres.--Mike Daugherty's Chevrolet Geo, Inc., Sacramento, CA; *U.S. Private*, pg. 313
Daunhauer, Gregory, Pres.--Byerly Ford-Nissan Inc., Louisville, KY; *U.S. Private*, pg. 191
Davatzes, Nicholas, Pres. & Chief Exec. Officer--The History Channel, New York, NY; *U.S. Public*, pg. 512
Davatzes, Nickolas, Pres. & Chief Exec. Officer--Arts & Entertainment Network/ABC/NBC, New York, NY; *U.S. Public*, pg. 512
Davatzes, Nickolas, Pres. & Chief Exec. Officer--A&E Television Networks, New York, NY; *U.S. Private*, pg. 515
Davatzes, Nickolas, Pres. & Chief Exec. Officer--Arts & Entertainment Network/ABC/NBC, New York, NY; *U.S. Private*, pg. 516
Davenport, Glenn A., Pres. & Chief Exec. Officer--Morrison Health Care Inc., Smyrna, GA; *U.S. Public*, pg. 1133
Davenport, John, Pres.--Photogenic Machine Company, Inc., Youngstown, OH; *U.S. Private*, pg. 864
Davenport, Timothy A., Pres. & Chief Exec. Officer--Best Software, Inc., Reston, VA; *U.S. Public*, pg. 223
Davenport, Tommy, Pres.--J.T. Davenport & Sons, Inc., Sanford, NC; *U.S. Private*, pg. 314
Davenzo, Richard, Pres.--American Frozen Foods, Inc., Stratford, CT; *U.S. Private*, pg. 55
David, George A., Pres. & Chief Exec. Officer--United Technologies Corporation, Hartford, CT; *U.S. Public*, pg. 1689
David, Popplewell, Pres.--Cincinnati Life Insurance Co., Fairfield, OH; *U.S. Public*, pg. 368
Davidson, Charles T., Chm. Bd., Pres. & Chief Exec. Officer--J.A. Jones, Inc., Charlotte, NC; *Int'l*, pg. 633
Davidson, Charles T., Chm. Bd., Pres. & Chief Exec. Officer--J. A. Jones Construction Company, Charlotte, NC; *Int'l*, pg. 633
Davidson, Deborah, Pres.--Generation Metals Corp., Hauppauge, NY; *U.S. Private*, pg. 446
Davidson, Denis H., Pres. & Chief Exec. Officer--Clear Shield National, Inc., Wheeling, IL; *U.S. Public*, pg. 586
Davidson, F. Lee, Pres. & Chief Exec. Officer--Parks Corporation, Fall River, MA; *U.S. Private*, pg. 840
Davidson, Janice G., Dr., Pres.--Davidson & Associates, Inc., Torrance, CA; *U.S. Public*, pg. 320
Davidson, Jeff, Chm. Bd. & Pres.--Michael Weinig, Inc., Statesville, NC; *Int'l*, pg. 1488
Davidson, John, Pres.--Ericsson Components, Inc., Richardson, TX; *Int'l*, pg. 1364
Davidson, Kenneth W., Chm. Bd. & Pres.--Maxxim Medical, Inc., Clearwater, FL; *U.S. Public*, pg. 1063
Davidson, Lawrence J., Jr., Pres., Chief Exec.,Oper. & Fin. Officer--The Weathervane Retail Corp., New Britain, CT; *U.S. Private*, pg. 1156
Davidson, Paul, Pres.--Tridon Inc., Nashville, TN; *U.S. Public*, pg. 11
Davidson, Richard K., Chm. Bd., Pres. & Chief Exec. Officer--Union Pacific Corporation, Dallas, TX; *U.S. Public*, pg. 1667
Davidson, Rick, Pres. & Chief Oper. Officer--O'Sullivan Industries Holdings, Lamar, MO; *U.S. Public*, pg. 1234
Davidson, Spencer, Pres. & Chief Exec. Officer--General American Investors Company, Inc., New York, NY; *U.S. Public*, pg. 706
Davidson, Wayne A., Pres.--Bristol-Myers Squibb Pharmaceutical & Nutritional Group, New York, NY; *U.S. Public*, pg. 254
Davidson, William, Chm. Bd., Pres., Chief Exec. & Chief Oper. Officer--Guardian Industries Corp., Auburn Hills, MI; *U.S. Private*, pg. 485
Davidsson, Lars, Pres.--Kvaerner Kamfab AB, Karlstad, Sweden; *Int'l*, pg. 767
Davies, C.W., Jr., Pres. & Chief Exec. Officer--Tultex Corporation, Martinsville, VA; *U.S. Public*, pg. 1644
Davies, C.W., Jr., Pres.--Akom Ltd., Montego Bay, Jamaica; *U.S. Public*, pg. 1644
Davies, Craig E., Pres. & Chief Exec. Officer--UTILX Corporation, Kent, WA; *U.S. Public*, pg. 1701
Davies, George P., Chm. Bd. & Pres.--Trico Electric Co-Op, Tucson, AZ; *U.S. Private*, pg. 1102
Davies, Gregory T.H., Pres.--Jacobs Vehicle Equipment Company, Bloomfield, CT; *U.S. Public*, pg. 481
Davies, Gregory T.H., Pres. & Chief Oper. Officer--Westinghouse Air Brake Company, Wilmerding, PA; *U.S. Public*, pg. 1760
Davies, J.A., Mng. Dir.--British Steel Seamless Tubes-Wednesfield Works, Wolverhampton, United Kingdom; *Int'l*, pg. 220
Davies, Jim, Pres.--J.J. Kenny Co., Inc., New York, NY; *U.S.* Public, pg. 1070
Davies, John H., Pres.--Barringer Research Limited, Mississauga, Canada; *U.S. Public*, pg. 192
Davies, Paul T., Pres. & Chief Exec. Officer--F.W. Woolworth Co., New York, NY; *U.S. Public*, pg. 1777
Davies, Robert A., III, Pres. & Chief Exec. Officer--Church & Dwight Co., Inc., Princeton, NJ; *U.S. Public*, pg. 355
Davis, Al, Pres.--Oakland Raiders, Alameda, CA; *U.S. Private*, pg. 809
Davis, Albert E., Pres.--Diemakers, Inc., Monroe City, MO; *U.S. Private*, pg. 332
Davis, Allen L., Pres. & Chief Exec. Officer--Provident Financial Group, Inc., Cincinnati, OH; *U.S. Public*, pg. 1338
Davis, Allen V.C., Chm. Bd & Pres.--Custom Control Sensors, Inc., Chatsworth, CA; *U.S. Private*, pg. 298
Davis, Brian, Pres. & Chief Exec. Officer--Nationwide Building Society, Swindon, United Kingdom; *Int'l*, pg. 912
Davis, Charles E., Sr., Chm. Bd., Pres. & Treas.--Laboratory Supply Company, Inc., Louisville, KY; *U.S. Private*, pg. 641
Davis, Charles H., Pres.--Midwestern Holdings, Inc., Chicago, IL; *Int'l*, pg. 155
Davis, Clay M., Pres.--Hollywood Supply Company, Hollywood, CA; *U.S. Public*, pg. 1619
Davis, Clive, Pres.-Arista Records--Bertelsmann Music Group, Wilmington, DE; *Int'l*, pg. 191
Davis, Clyde P., Pres., Treas. & Creative Dir.--Cline, Davis & Mann, Inc., New York, NY; *U.S. Private*, pg. 246
Davis, D.R., Pres.--Hoffman-Miller Engineers, Inc., Tempe, AZ; *U.S. Private*, pg. 842
Davis, Darrell L., Pres.--Chrysler Financial Corporation, Southfield, MI; *U.S. Public*, pg. 354
Davis, Dennis, Pres.--Argosy Electronics, Inc., Eden Prairie, MN; *U.S. Private*, pg. 81
Davis, Don, Pres.--Wolfe Nursery, Fort Worth, TX; *U.S. Public*, pg. 715
Davis, Don H., Jr., Pres. & Chief Oper. Officer--Rockwell International Corporation, Costa Mesa, CA; *U.S. Public*, pg. 1397
Davis, Donald W., Pres. & Chief Exec. Officer--Sunbelt Nursery Group Inc., Fort Worth, TX; *U.S. Public*, pg. 715
Davis, Dwight, Pres.--Employers Insurance of Wausau, Wausau, WI; *U.S. Private*, pg. 788
Davis, Edward, Pres.--Bernard Johnson Young Inc., Houston, TX; *U.S. Private*, pg. 136
Davis, Erroll B. Jr., Pres. & Chief Exec. Officer--WPL Holdings, Inc., Madison, WI; *U.S. Public*, pg. 1727
Davis, G., Pres.--BookCrafters U.S.A. Inc., Chelsea, MI; *U.S.* Public, pg. 70
Davis, Gary, Pres.--BookCrafters U.S.A. Inc., Fredericksburg, VA; *U.S. Public*, pg. 70
Davis, Gene, Pres.--National Distributing Co., Inc., Tampa, FL; *U.S. Private*, pg. 781
Davis, Gerald, Pres.--Merchants Distributors, Inc., Hickory, NC; *U.S. Private*, pg. 657
Davis, Glen, Pres.--Addison Steel Inc., Albany, GA; *U.S. Private*, pg. 17
Davis, Hank, Pres.--Jimmy Davis Enterprises, Inc., Madison, FL; *U.S. Private*, pg. 315
Davis, J. Roy, Jr., Pres.--S&D Coffee Inc., Concord, NC; *U.S. Private*, pg. 954
Davis, J.B., Pres.--Klaussner Corporation, Asheboro, NC; *U.S. Private*, pg. 625
Davis, J.R., Pres.--The Lakefront Dock & Railroad Terminal Co., Baltimore, MD; *U.S. Public*, pg. 432
Davis, Jack, Pres. & Chief Exec. Officer--Ventura Foods LLC, City of Industry, CA; *Int'l*, pg. 879
Davis, James, Pres.--Nichols-Homeshield, Davenport, IA; *U.S. Public*, pg. 1350
Davis, James C., Pres. & Chief Exec. Officer--FFG Trust, Inc., Springfield, IL; *U.S. Public*, pg. 644
Davis, James S., Pres. & Chief Exec. Officer--TAD Resources International, Inc., Cambridge, MA; *U.S. Private*, pg. 1062
Davis, James, Jr., Pres.--BCIS Services, Inc., Sherman Oaks, CA; *U.S. Public*, pg. 175
Davis, Jay M., Pres. & Chief Exec. Officer--National Distributing Co., Inc., Atlanta, GA; *U.S. Private*, pg. 781
Davis, Jeffrey G., Chm. Bd., Pres. & Chief Exec. Officer--Aetna Plywood, Inc., Barrington, IL; *U.S. Private*, pg. 25
Davis, Jeffrey J., Pres.--Joseph Davis, Inc., Buffalo, NY; *U.S. Private*, pg. 315
Davis, Jerry, Pres.--Thermo Energy Systems Corporation, Waltham, MA; *U.S. Public*, pg. 1593
Davis, Jerry B., Pres. & Chief Exec. Officer--Halliburton Energy Services, Carrollton, TX; *U.S. Public*, pg. 776
Davis, Jerry R., Pres. & Chief Oper. Officer--Union Pacific Railroad Company, Omaha, NE; *U.S. Public*, pg. 1668
Davis, John, Pres. & Chief Exec. Officer--Thomson Book/Reference Group, Stamford, CT; *U.S. Public*, pg. 1600
Davis, John H., Pres.--First Community Bank of Tifton, Tifton, GA; *U.S. Public*, pg. 1549
Davis, John L., Pres. & Chief Oper. Officer--The Wing Group, Woodlands, TX; *U.S. Public*, pg. 1760
Davis, John S., Pres. & Chief Exec. Officer--Mobile Gas Service Corp., Mobile, AL; *U.S. Public*, pg. 1120
Davis, Kenneth A., Pres., Chief Exec. Officer & Chief Oper. Officer--PharmHouse, Inc., New York, NY; *U.S. Public*, pg. 1286
Davis, Kim A., Pres. & Chief Oper. Officer--Gelman Sciences, Inc., Ann Arbor, MI; *U.S. Public*, pg. 1253
Davis, Kim E., Pres.-DATEC Ind., Inc.--Davis Industries Inc., Plymouth, MI; *U.S. Private*, pg. 315
Davis, Kindle, Pres.--Bud Davis Cadillac, Inc., Memphis, TN; *U.S. Private*, pg. 314
Davis, Larry D., Pres.--U.S. Turbine Corporation, Maineville, OH; *Int'l*, pg. 1127
Davis, Marc C., Pres.--Davis Wood Products, Inc., Hudson, NC; *U.S. Private*, pg. 315
Davis, Mark, Pres.--Creekside Industrial, Houston, TX; *U.S. Private*, pg. 288
Davis, Marvin, Pres.--Davis Companies, Los Angeles, CA; *U.S. Private*, pg. 315
Davis, Nigel, Pres.--Dover Elevator International, Inc., Memphis, TN; *U.S. Public*, pg. 521
Davis, Pat, Pres. & Chief Exec. Officer--UPB of Northeast MS, New Albany, MS; *U.S. Public*, pg. 1669
Davis, Randall K., Pres.--Operations Management Division, Reston, VA; *U.S. Public*, pg. 1516
Davis, Richard, Pres.-Intl. Opers.--The Cerplex Group, Inc., Tustin, CA; *U.S. Public*, pg. 332
Davis, Richard A., Pres. & Chief Exec. Officer--Treibacher Schleifmittel Corp., Niagara Falls, NY; *U.S. Private*, pg. 1099
Davis, Richard A., Pres. & Chief Exec. Officer--Pentzer Corporation, Spokane, WA; *U.S. Public*, pg. 1744
Davis, Richard L., II, Pres.--Davis Industries Inc., Plymouth, MI; *U.S. Private*, pg. 315
Davis, Robert, Pres.--Hayward Industrial Products, Elizabeth, NJ; *U.S. Private*, pg. 513
Davis, Robert J., Pres.--Sysco Food Services of Charlotte, Inc., Concord, NC; *U.S. Public*, pg. 1551
Davis, Roland J., Pres.--Executive Productivity Systems, Inc., Chesapeake, VA; *U.S. Private*, pg. 388
Davis, Ronald D., Pres. & Chief Exec. Officer--Monroc, Inc., Salt Lake City, UT; *U.S. Public*, pg. 1124
Davis, Shelby M.C., Chm. Bd., Pres. & Chief Exec. Officer--Davis Selected Advisors, L.P., Santa Fe, NM; *U.S. Private*, pg. 315
Davis, Stephen A., Pres. & Chief Oper. Officer--American Saw & Mfg. Company, East Longmeadow, MA; *U.S. Private*, pg. 61
Davis, T. Grant, Jr., Pres.--Davis-Moore Oldsmobile, Inc., Wichita, KS; *U.S. Private*, pg. 315
Davis, Thomas, Pres.--North Carolina Mutual Wholesale Drug Co., Durham, NC; *U.S. Private*, pg. 804
Davis, Thomas A., Pres., Chief Exec. Officer & Asst. Sec.--United HealthCare of Utah, Salt Lake City, UT; *U.S. Public*, pg. 1678
Davis, Thomas D., Pres. & Chief Oper. Officer--The Smithfield Packing Co., Inc., Smithfield, VA; *U.S. Public*, pg. 1479
Davis, Tim L., Pres.--Bird Machine Company, South Walpole, MA; *U.S. Public*, pg. 166
Davis, Tom, Pres.-Resilient--Mannington Resilient Floors, Salem, NJ; *U.S. Private*, pg. 700
Davis, W. Donald, Chm. Bd., Pres. & Chief Exec. Officer--SouthTrust Bank, Cullman County, Cullman, AL; *U.S. Public*, pg. 1491
Davis, Wes, Pres. & Chief Exec. Officer--Microtouch Systems, Inc., Methuen, MA; *U.S. Public*, pg. 1108
Davis, William, Pres. & Chief Exec. Officer--Uniroyal Goodrich Canada Inc., Kitchener, Canada; *Int'l*, pg. 322
Davis, William Jack, Chm. Bd. & Pres.--Davis Mining & Manufacturing, Coeburn, VA; *U.S. Private*, pg. 315
Davisson, W. Gene, Pres. & Chief Exec. Officier--Bank of Hundred, Hundred, WV; *U.S. Public*, pg. 850
Daw, Ronald W., Chm. Bd., Pres. & Chief Exec. Officer--Daw Technologies, Inc., Salt Lake City, UT; *U.S. Public*, pg. 489
Dawahare, A.F., Pres. & Dir.-Sls. & Mktg.--Dawahares, Inc., Lexington, KY; *U.S. Private*, pg. 316
Dawdy, Richard A., Pres. & Chief Oper. Officer--UMB First National Bank, Collinsville, IL; *U.S. Public*, pg. 1654
Dawe, Donald J., Pres.--AVA, Atlanta, GA; *U.S. Private*, pg. 8
Dawkins, Peter, Pres.--Enco Materials, Inc., Nashville, TN; *U.S. Private*, pg. 375
Dawson, Gaynor W., Pres. & Gen. Mgr.--EG & G Environmental, Inc., Pittsburgh, PA; *U.S. Public*, pg. 543
Dawson, Jack, Pres.--First State Bank of Fayette Co., Somerville, TN; *U.S. Public*, pg. 1669
Dawson, James A., Pres. & Chief Exec. Officer--Quebecor Printing (USA) Corp., Boston, MA; *Int'l*, pg. 1076

Dawson, James A., Pres.--Quebecor Printing Kingsport Inc., Kingsport, TN; *Int'l*, pg. 1076

Dawson, James A., Pres.--The Webb Company, Dover, DE; *Int'l*, pg. 1078

Dawson, James A., Pres.--Quebecor Printing Richmond Inc., Richmond, VA; *Int'l*, pg. 1078

Dawson, James A., Pres.--Quebecor Printing Buffalo Inc., Depew, NY; *Int'l*, pg. 1078

Dawson, James A., Pres.--Quebecor Printing Dickson Inc., Dickson, TN; *Int'l*, pg. 1078

Dawson, James A., Pres.--Quebecor Printing St. Paul Inc., Saint Paul, MN; *Int'l*, pg. 1078

Dawson, L. Decker, Pres.--Dawson Geophysical Company, Midland, TX; *U.S. Public*, pg. 489

Dawson, Laurence A., Jr., Pres. & Co.-Chief Exec. Officer--American Homestar Corporation, League City, TX; *U.S. Public*, pg. 83

Dawson, Tom, Chm. Bd., Pres. & Chief Exec. Officer--Dawson Construction Co., Inc., Gadsden, AL; *U.S. Private*, pg. 316

Day-Harper, Melinda, Pres. & Chief Oper. Officer--Wise & Associates/S&W Technical Services, San Antonio, TX; *U.S. Public*, pg. 1161

Day, Frank, Chm. Bd., Pres. & Chief Exec. Officer--Rock Bottom Restaurants, Louisville, CO; *U.S. Public*, pg. 1396

Day, James D., Chm. Bd., Pres. & Chief Exec. Officer--Noble Drilling Corporation, Houston, TX; *U.S. Public*, pg. 1186

Day, John T., Pres. & Chief Exec. Officer--Mining Services International, Inc., Sandy, UT; *U.S. Public*, pg. 1115

Day, Joseph C., Pres. & Chief Exec. Officer--Freudenberg-NOK, Plymouth, MI; *U.S. Private*, pg. 427

Day, Ken, Pres.--Signal Science, Santa Clara, CA; *U.S. Public*, pg. 46

Day, Kevin, Pres.--Vincennes Steel Corp., Vincennes, IN; *U.S. Private*, pg. 1141

Day, Kim, Pres.--Zenith Products Corp., New Castle, DE; *U.S. Public*, pg. 1054

Day, Larry, Pres. & Chief Oper. Officer--Monro Muffler/Brake, Inc., Rochester, NY; *U.S. Public*, pg. 1124

Dayan, Charles, Pres. & Chief Exec. Officer--Bon Jour International Ltd., New York, NY; *U.S. Private*, pg. 156

Dayan, Charles, Pres. & Chief Exec. Officer--Licensing Div., New York, NY; *U.S. Private*, pg. 156

de Aguilar, Milagros Plaza, Pres.--Creativity/Young & Rubicam Asociados, Lima, Peru; *U.S. Private*, pg. 1200

de Aguirre, Ignacio Maria Garcia, Pres.--SODIAN - Sociedad Para el Desarrollo Industrial de Analucia, S.A., Seville, Spain; *Int'l*, pg. 1225

de Albornoz Bonet, Carlos Martinez, Pres.--Empresa Auxiliar de la Industria, Auxini, S.A., Madrid, Spain; *Int'l*, pg. 1224

De Andrade, Flavio, Pres.--Souza Cruz, S.A., Rio de Janeiro, Brazil; *Int'l*, pg. 112

de Andres, Felix Llorente, Pres.--T.G.I. - Tecnologia del Grupo INI, S.A., Madrid, Spain; *Int'l*, pg. 1225

De Angelo, Joseph A., Pres.--Curtis Bay Towing Company Of Virginia, Greenwich, CT; *U.S. Private*, pg. 760

De Angelo, Joseph A., Pres.--Curtis Bay Towing Company Of Pennsylvania, Greenwich, CT; *U.S. Private*, pg. 760

De Angelo, Joseph A., Pres.--Florida Towing Company, Greenwich, CT; *U.S. Private*, pg. 760

De Angelo, Lawrence, Pres.--EMS Asia Pacific, Lan Tau Island, Hong Kong; *U.S. Public*, pg. 566

de Athayde, Augusto, Pres.--Banco Espirito Santo do Oriente SARL (Besor), Macau, Macau; *Int'l*, pg. 142

de Beauvoir, Philippe, Pres.--Au Bon Marche, Paris, France; *Int'l*, pg. 97

De Biase, Dean, Pres. & Chief Exec. Officer--The Imagination Network, Burlingame, CA; *U.S. Public*, pg. 66

de Boer, Edward, Pres.--EnviroTech PumpSystems, Salt Lake City, UT; *Int'l*, pg. 1489

De Boers, Joop, Creative Dir. & Partner--HLPB, Amsterdam, Netherlands; *Int'l*, pg. 1377

De Bouvere, L., Pres & Gen. Mgr.--N.V. Kodak S.A., Vilvoorde, Belgium; *U.S. Public*, pg. 554

De Bree, Simon, Chm. Bd. & Pres.--DSM N.V., Heerlen, Netherlands; *Int'l*, pg. 352

de Buhr, Ted, Pres. & Chief Exec. Officer--Fox Photo, Inc., Saint Louis, MO; *U.S. Public*, pg. 283

de Caceres, Javier Monzon, Pres.--Ceselsa-Inisel, S.A., Madrid, Spain; *Int'l*, pg. 1224

de Carvalho Dias, Roberto Marques, Pres. & Chief Exec. Officer--LPC Industrias Alimenticias S.A., Vila Jaguara, Brazil; *Int'l*, pg. 380

de Castro Esteves, Ivan, Pres.--Cobra-Computadores e Sistemas Brasileiros, Rio de Janeiro, Brazil; *Int'l*, pg. 142

de Castro, James, Pres. & Chief Oper. Officer--Chancellor Media Corporation, Irving, TX; *U.S. Public*, pg. 335

de Chalendar, Pierre Andre, Chm. Bd., Pres. & Chief Exec. Officer--Norton Company, Worcester, MA; *Int'l*, pg. 1173

de Champfleury, Pierre, Pres.--Yves Saint Laurent Parfums S.A., Neuilly-sur-Seine, France; *Int'l*, pg. 445

de Cima, Ernesto Zaragoza, Pres. & Chief Exec. & Chief Fin. Officer--Inversiones De Guaymas S.A. De C.V., Guaymas, Mexico; *Int'l*, pg. 685

de Entrambasaguas, Guillermo Serrano, Pres.--Viva, Vuelos Internacionales de Vacaciones, S.A., Madrid, Spain; *Int'l*, *pg. 1225*

De Forrest, Sean B., Pres. & Chief Exec. Officer--American Security Distribution, Anaheim, CA; *U.S. Private*, pg. 61

De Graffenreidt, James H., Jr., Pres. & Chief Exec. Officer--Washington Gas Light Co., Springfield, VA; *U.S. Public*, pg. 1740

De Gregorio, Anthony, Pres. & Chief Creative Exec.-New York--Publicis/Bloom Inc., New York, NY; *Int'l*, pg. 470

de Jesus Valdez, Jose, Pres.--Alpek, S.A. de C.V., Garza Garcia, Mexico; *Int'l*, pg. 56

De Jonge, Max, Pres. & Chief Exec. Officer--O'Neal Steel Inc., Birmingham, AL; *U.S. Private*, pg. 817

De Kertanguy, Loic, Pres.--J.B. Martin Company, New York, NY; *U.S. Private*, pg. 709

De Kock, David L., Pres.--Sysco Food Services of Grand Rapids, Inc., Grand Rapids, MI; *U.S. Public*, pg. 1551

de la Cruz, Rene, Pres. & Chief Exec. Officer--de la Cruz & Associates, San Juan, PR; *U.S. Private*, pg. 318

de la Guardia, Ruben, Pres.--Phillips Petroleum International Corporation, Bartlesville, OK; *U.S. Public*, pg. 1291

de la Parra, Miguel Blesa, Chm., Pres. & Chief Exec. Officer--Caja de Madrid Group, Madrid, Spain; *Int'l*, pg. 251

De la Peza, Pablo, Pres.--Seguros Banamex-Aegon, S.A. de C.V., Mexico, Mexico; *Int'l*, pg. 574

de La Roer, Hubert, Pres.--Minnesota Rubber Europe S.A., Evreux, France; *U.S. Private*, pg. 898

de Labouchere, Pierre, Pres. & Chief Exec. Officer--R.J. Reynolds Tobacco Intl., Inc., Geneva, Switzerland; *U.S. Public*, pg. 1355

de Ladoucette, Philip, Pres. & Chief Mng. Officer--Charbonnages de France, Rueil-Malmaison, France; *Int'l*, *pg. 280*

de Lange, J., Pres.--Nicholas Turkey Breeding Farms, Sonoma, CA; *Int'l*, pg. 202

de Launoit, Jean-Pierre, Pres.--RTL TVi, Brussels, Belgium; *Int'l*, pg. 562

de Maio, Mike, Pres.--EJL Advertising/Chicago, Chicago, IL; *U.S. Private*, pg. 673

de Maio, Mike, Pres. & Chief Oper. Officer--Lois/EJL Chicago, Chicago, IL; *U.S. Public*, pg. 1011

de Maio, Mike, Pres.--Lois/EJL Advertising/Chicago, Chicago, IL; *U.S. Public*, pg. 1011

De Marco, Nicholas, Pres.--International Apparel Marketing Corp., New York, NY; *U.S. Public*, pg. 498

De Mattos, Carlos D., Chm. Bd. & Pres.--Matthews Studio Equipment, Burbank, CA; *U.S. Public*, pg. 1060

de Meeus d'Argenteuil , Daniel, Pres.--G-Securities, Brussels, Belgium; *Int'l*, pg. 547

de Mello Brandao, Lazaro, Chm. Bd. & Pres.--Banco Bradesco S.A., Sao Paulo, Brazil; *Int'l*, pg. 139

De Mento, Biagio, Sr., Pres. & Chief Exec. Officer--Brooks Provisions Inc., Philadelphia, PA; *U.S. Private*, pg. 172

de Miguel, F., Dir.--Van Leer Embalagens Industriais do Brasil Ltda, Sao Paulo, Brazil; *Int'l*, pg. 1146

De Neve, J., Pres.--Bekaert Corporation, Rogers, AR; *Int'l*, pg. 184

de Nora, Niccolo, Pres.--Caffaro S.p.A., Milan, Italy; *Int'l*, pg. 248

De Nouyer, Susan, Mng. Partner-Opers.--Gillespie, Lawrenceville, NJ; *U.S. Private*, pg. 453

de Ocio, Daniel, Pres.--Chr. Hansen-Lacta S.L., Madrid, Spain; *Int'l*, pg. 289

De Oliveira, Ararino Sallum, Pres.--Allianz-Bradesco Cia. Brasileira de Seguros, Sao Paulo, Brazil; *Int'l*, pg. 59

de Prat, Luis Perez, Pres.--Made Sistemas Electricos, S.A., Vicalvaro, Spain; *Int'l*, pg. 1224

de Priede, Javier Gimeno, Pres.--Cabinas Telefonicas, S.A. (Cabitel), Madrid, Spain; *Int'l*, pg. 1371

de Puzo, Julio J., Jr., Pres. & Chief Exec. Officer--Source Capital, Inc., Los Angeles, CA; *U.S. Public*, pg. 1488

de Rassin, Jean Marc, Pres.--S.O.C.A.T.A.(Societe de Construction d'Avions de Tourismes et d'Affaires), Tarbes, France; *Int'l*, pg. 29

De Schutter, Richard U., Chm. Bd. & Pres.--Searle & Co., Skokie, IL; *U.S. Public*, pg. 1125

De Simone, Lawrence E., Pres.--CSW Communications, Inc., Dallas, TX; *U.S. Public*, pg. 324

De Stefano, Daniel, Pres.--Deerskin Trading Post, Inc., North Bergen, NJ; *U.S. Public*, pg. 879

De Stigter, Glenn H., Pres. & Chief Exec. Officer--The Weitz Company, Inc., Des Moines, IA; *U.S. Private*, pg. 1160

de Vink, Lodewijk J.R., Pres. & Chief Oper. Officer--Warner-Lambert Company, Morris Plains, NJ; *U.S. Public*, pg. 1738

De Vito, Robert A., Chm. Bd., Pres., Chief Exec. & Chief Oper. Officer--Cyber Systems, Inc., Anaheim, CA; *U.S. Private*, pg. 299

de Vlugt, W., Chm. Bd. & Chief Exec. Officer--Royal Packaging Industries Van Leer B.V., Amstelveen, Netherlands; *Int'l*, pg. 1145

De Voto, Richard, Chm. Bd. & Pres.--Canyon Resources Corporation, Golden, CO; *U.S. Public*, pg. 301

De Vries, Henry, Pres.--Midwest Fasteners Corporation, Kalamazoo, MI; *U.S. Private*, pg. 744

De-Cardenas, Gilbert, Pres.--Cacique, City of Industry, CA; *U.S. Public*, pg. 995

Deal, Frederick A., Pres. & Chief Exec. Officer--Society First Federal Savings Bank, Fort Myers, FL; *U.S. Public*, pg. 954

Deal, Steven C., Pres. & Chief Exec. Officer--Hilb, Rogal and Hamilton Company of Virginia, Glen Allen, VA; *U.S. Public*, pg. 827

Dean, Art, Pres.--Evergreen Mills Inc., Ada, OK; *U.S. Private*, pg. 1134

Dean, Henry, Pres.--Monticello Drug Co., Jacksonville, FL; *U.S. Private*, pg. 759

Dean, Henry E., III, Pres. & Chief Exec. Officer--The Monticello Companies, Inc., Jacksonville, FL; *U.S. Private*, pg. 759

Dean, Herbert, M.D., Pres.--Fallon Community Health Plan, Worcester, MA; *U.S. Private*, pg. 392

Dean, Howard M., Pres.--McArthur Dairy, Inc., Sunrise, FL; *U.S. Public*, pg. 491

Dean, Jerry, Pres.--Keystone Foods Corporation, Bala Cynwyd, PA; *U.S. Private*, pg. 619

Dean, Jim, Pres.--Four Corners Aviation, Inc., Farmington, NM; *U.S. Public*, pg. 1099

Deane, Jill, Pres.--Lane Bryant, Reynoldsburg, OH; *U.S. Public*, pg. 995

Dearden, Douglas E., Chief Exec. Officer--Dearden's, Los Angeles, CA; *U.S. Private*, pg. 319

Deardoff, R.B., Pres.--Island Lincoln-Mercury, Merritt Island, FL; *U.S. Private*, pg. 576

Deardorff, T.D., Chm. Bd. & Pres.--Deardorff-Jackson Company, Oxnard, CA; *U.S. Private*, pg. 319

Dearlove, A. James, Pres. & Chief Exec. Officer--Penn Virginia Corporation, Radnor, PA; *U.S. Public*, pg. 1271

DeArment, W.S., Pres. & Chief Exec. Officer--Hold-E-Zee, Ltd., Meadville, PA; *U.S. Private*, pg. 229

DeArment, William S., Pres. & Chief Exec. Officer--Channellock, Inc., Meadville, PA; *U.S. Private*, pg. 229

Deary, Grant, Co.-Chm. Bd. & Pres.--Nor-Cal Beverage Co., Inc., West Sacramento, CA; *U.S. Private*, pg. 801

Deasy, William J., Vice Chm., Pres. & Chief Exec. Officer--T.L. James & Company, Ruston, LA; *U.S. Private*, pg. 580

DeBari, Brien, Pres.--ALK Laboratories, Inc., Wallingford, CT; *Int'l*, pg. 288

DeBartolo, Edward J., Jr., Pres. & Chief Exec. Officer--The Edward J. DeBartolo Corporation, Youngstown, OH; *U.S.* Private, pg. 319

DeBartolo, Lou, Pres.--Power Conversion-North America West, Fremont, CA; *U.S. Public*, pg. 422

DeBelser, Keith, Pres.--Leblanc Communications, Inc., Richardson, TX; *U.S. Private*, pg. 656

Debenedictis, Nicholas, Chm. Bd., Pres. & Chief Exec. Officer--Philadelphia Suburban Corporation, Bryn Mawr, PA; *U.S. Public*, pg. 1287

deBest, Cess, Pres. & Chief Exec. Officer--Verkerke Reprodukties, N.V., Ede, Netherlands; *U.S. Private*, pg. 496

DeBoer, Randall D., Pres.--Ikon Office Solutions-Michigan, Grand Rapids, MI; *U.S. Public*, pg. 863

DeBolt, Marion L., Pres. & Gen. Mgr.--All American Homes, Inc., Decatur, IN; *U.S. Public*, pg. 388

DeBone, Louis J., Pres.--Bertek, Inc., Saint Albans, VT; *U.S.* Public, pg. 1143

Debonny, Mike, Pres. & Chief Exec. Officer--OMNI Products, Inc., Portland, OR; *U.S. Private*, pg. 816

Decaillet, Pierre, Pres.--Sakata Seed Europe B.V., Rijssen, Netherlands; *Int'l*, pg. 1178

DeCamp, D.A., Pres. & Chief Exec. Officer--Flexfab Horizons International, Inc., Hastings, MI; *U.S. Private*, pg. 412

DeCardenas, Gilbert L., Pres. & Chief Fin. Officer--Cacique, Inc., City of Industry, CA; *U.S. Private*, pg. 198

DeCarion, Philip, Pres.--Cornucopia, Inc., Irvine, CA; *U.S. Private*, pg. 276

DeCarlo, Anthony J., Pres. & Chief Exec. Officer--Lumbermens Merchandising Corporation, Wayne, PA; *U.S. Private*, pg. 680

DeCarlo, D.J., Pres.--Matthews International Memorial Division, Pittsburgh, PA; *U.S. Public*, pg. 1059

DeCaro, Angelo A., Jr., Pres.--Xetel Corporation, Austin, TX; *Int'l*, pg. 1125

DeCesaris, Geaton A., Jr., Pres. & Chief Exec. Officer--Washington Homes, Inc., Landover, MD; *U.S. Public*, pg. 1741

DeCesaris, Geaton A., Sr., Chm. Bd.--Washington Homes, Inc., Landover, MD; *U.S. Public*, pg. 1741

Dechamps, Daniel, Pres. & Treas.--Trumpf Inc., Farmington, CT; *U.S. Private*, pg. 1108

Decherd, Robert W., Chm. Bd., Pres. & Chief Exec. Officer--A.H. Belo Corporation, Dallas, TX; *U.S. Public*, pg. 209

Deck, N., Pres.--Claritas, Inc., Arlington, VA; *Int'l*, pg. 1447

Decker, C. David, Pres.--GTE Laboratories Incorporated, Waltham, MA; *U.S. Public*, pg. 697

Decker, Thomas A., Pres.--CertainTeed Foreign Sales Corp., Valley Forge, PA; *Int'l*, pg. 1171

Decker, W. Patrick, Pres. & Chief Oper. Officer--Kronos Incorporated, Waltham, MA; *U.S. Public*, pg. 967

Deckman, Joe, Pres.--Window Fabrication Div., Wausau, WI; *U.S. Public*, pg. 120

DeCoene, Thomas, Pres.--LTCB Latin America, Inc. (LLA), New York, NY; *Int'l*, pg. 816

deCorderoy, M., Pres.--Beiersdorf S.A., Savigny-le-Temple, France; *Int'l*, pg. 183

Dedert, Thomas W., Pres.--Dedert Corporation, Olympia Fields, IL; *U.S. Private*, pg. 320

Dedman, Robert H., Jr., Pres. & Chief Oper. Officer--Club Corporation International, Dallas, TX; *U.S. Private*, pg. 247

Dee, John T., Pres. & Chief Exec. Officer--Service America Corporation, Stamford, CT; *U.S. Private*, pg. 986

Dee, Jonathan, Pres.--Ce De Candy, Inc., Union, NJ; *U.S. Private*, pg. 220

Deel, Jerry, Pres.--Portec, Inc.-Construction Equipment Div., Yankton, SD; *U.S. Public*, pg. 1318

Deems, T.F., Pres.--United Clays, Inc., Brentwood, TN; *Int'l*, *pg. 1487*

Deen, Danny, Pres.--Deen Wholesale Meat Company, Inc., Fort Worth, TX; *U.S. Private*, pg. 320

Deering, Anthony W., Chm. Bd., Pres. & Chief Exec. Officer--The Rouse Company, Columbia, MD; *U.S. Public*, pg. 1407

Deering, Joseph W., Pres.--Hobart Corporation, Troy, OH; *U.S. Public*, pg. 1322

Deets, Max, Pres.--National Cattlemen's Beef Association, Greenwood Village, CO; *U.S. Private*, pg. 780

DeFabis, Mike, Pres. & Chief Exec. Officer--Associated Wholesale Grocers, Inc., Kansas City, KS; *U.S. Private*, pg. 93

DeFeo, Neil, Pres.--Remington Products Company, L.L.C., Bridgeport, CT; *U.S. Private*, pg. 921

DeFeo, Ronald J., Pres.--Wholesale Glass Fabricators Inc., Wilmington, NC; *Int'l*, pg. 616

DeFeo, Ronald M., Pres. & Chief Exec. Officer--Terex Corporation, Westport, CT; *U.S. Public*, pg. 1581

Deferrari, Ronald S., Pres. & Chief Oper. Officer--Plasma-Therm, Inc., Saint Petersburg, FL; *U.S. Public*, pg. 1308

Defibaugh, Patricia J., Chm. Bd., Chief Exec. Officer, & Treas.--Aloette Cosmetics, Inc., West Chester, PA; *U.S. Public*, pg. 57

DeFlorio, Victor, Pres.--Bridgestone/Firestone de la Argentina S.A.I.C., Buenos Aires, Argentina; *Int'l*, pg. 214

DeFosset, Don, Pres.--Navistar International Corporation, Chicago, IL; *U.S. Public*, pg. 1167

Defranco, John, Sr. Partner & Acct. Grp. Head--Lewis Gace Bozell Healthcare Worldwide, Fort Lee, NJ; *U.S. Public*, pg. 1642

Dega, Gerard, Chm. Bd. & Pres.--Alcatel Cit (S.A.), Velizy-Villacoublay, France; *Int'l*, pg. 56
Degan, Robert A., Pres. & Chief Exec. Officer--Summa Four, Inc., Manchester, NH; *U.S. Public*, pg. 1527
Degelman, Wilfred, Chm. Bd. & Pres.--Degelman Industries Ltd., Regina, Canada; *Int'l*, pg. 388
Degen, A.P., Pres.--Vamco, Cumberland, RI; *U.S. Public*, pg. 1706
Degen, A.P., Pres.--Valley Gas Co., Cumberland, RI; *U.S. Public*, pg. 1706
Degen, Alfred P., Chm. Bd., Pres. & Chief Exec. Officer--Valley Resources, Inc., Cumberland, RI; *U.S. Public*, pg. 1706
DeGennaro, Michael, Pres.--Matrix Essentials, Inc., Solon, OH; *U.S. Public*, pg. 254
DeGiglio, Michael A., Pres. & Chief Exec. Officer--EcoScience Corporation, East Brunswick, NJ; *U.S. Public*, pg. 563
Degler, Sandra C., Pres.--Tax Management, Inc., Washington, DC; *U.S. Private*, pg. 182
Degnan, Gerard A., Pres.--ADM Arkady, Olathe, KS; *U.S. Public*, pg. 127
Degnan, John J., Pres.--The Chubb Corporation, Warren, NJ; *U.S. Public*, pg. 354
Degradt, William, Pres.--Surgical Specialties, Reading, PA; *U.S. Private*, pg. 1056
DeGrandchamp, Joseph, Pres.--Michigan Blueberry Growers Assn., Grand Junction, MI; *U.S. Private*, pg. 740
DeGregorio, Anthony, Pres. & Chief Creative Officer--Publicis/Bloom, New York, NY; *Int'l*, pg. 470
DeGregorio, Richard, Pres.--Pioneer Flour Mills, San Antonio, TX; *U.S. Private*, pg. 866
Dehague, Jerry, Pres.--Total Petroleum, Inc., Wichita, KS; *U.S. Public*, pg. 1663
DeHahn, Mary L., Partner & Chief Oper. Officer--Kupper Parker Communications Inc., Saint Louis, MO; *U.S. Private*, pg. 637
DeHaven, Bud, Pres.--Electronica Condor De Mexico, S.A., Cuauhtemoc, Mexico; *U.S. Public*, pg. 1419
Dehmlow, Steven L., Pres., Chief Exec. & Chief Oper. Officer--GLS Corporation, Arlington Heights, IL; *U.S. Private*, pg. 435
Dehne, John S., Pres.--Lockheed Martin Infared Imaging Systems, Lexington, MA; *U.S. Public*, pg. 1008
Deierlein, J.N., Jr., Pres.--Republic Contracting Corp., Columbia, SC; *U.S. Private*, pg. 923
Deieso, Donald A., Pres.--EA Global, Inc., Hunt Valley, MD; *U.S. Public*, pg. 541
Deieso, Donald A., Ph.D., Pres. & Chief Exec. Officer--EA Engineering, Science & Technology, Inc., Hunt Valley, MD; *U.S. Public*, pg. 540
Deikel, Theodore, Chm. Bd., Pres. & Chief Exec. Officer--Fingerhut Corp., Minnetonka, MN; *U.S. Public*, pg. 623
Deinus, Dmitry, Pres.--Shoe Pavilion, Richmond, CA; *U.S. Private*, pg. 996
Deisenroth, Clint, Pres.--Whittaker Electronic Systems, Simi Valley, CA; *U.S. Public*, pg. 1767
Deitsch, David, Pres.--Deitsch Plastics Company, West Haven, CT; *U.S. Private*, pg. 320
Deitzer, Harry J., Pres.--Besser Canada, Ltd., Bramalea, Canada; *U.S. Private*, pg. 139
DeJaeger, K.L., Pres.--Industrial Plastics Company, Fort Smith, AR; *U.S. Public*, pg. 56
deJaray, Steven A.W., Pres. & Chief Exec. Officer--AIM Safety Company Inc., Delta, Canada; *Int'l*, pg. 36
Dejardin, Pierre, Pres.-Exec. Bd.--Banque Piguet & Cie S.A., Yverdon, Switzerland; *Int'l*, pg. 160
DeJoris, John Paul, Chm. Bd. & Pres.--John Paul Mitchell Systems, Santa Clarita, CA; *U.S. Private*, pg. 753
del Castillo, Pedro Gamero, Deputy Chm. & Pres.--Vallehermoso, S.A., Madrid, Spain; *Int'l*, pg. 1447
del Cueto Legaspi, Roberto, Pres.--Banco Nacional de Mexico, S.A. (Banamex), Mexico, Mexico; *Int'l*, pg. 574
Del Dotto, Reno, Pres.--Tri-K Industries, Inc., Northvale, NJ; *U.S. Private*, pg. 1100
Del Guidice, Fred, Pres.--Del American Properties, Inc., Maitland, FL; *U.S. Private*, pg. 321
Del Mar, Bruce, Pres. & Treas.--Del Mar Avionics, Irvine, CA; *U.S. Private*, pg. 321
del Peral, Javier Revuelta, Pres.--Telefonica Publicidad e Informac., Madrid, Spain; *Int'l*, pg. 1372
del Rivero, Eduardo, Pres. & Chief Exec. Officer--del Rivero Messianu Advertising, Ltd., Coral Gables, FL; *U.S. Private*, pg. 321
del Rosal, Roberto, Pres. & Chief Exec. Officer--Bacardi Corporation, San Juan, PR; *Int'l*, pg. 131
Del Rossi, Paul R., Pres.--GC International, Inc., Chestnut Hill, MA; *U.S. Public*, pg. 693
Del Valle, Thomas, Pres.--Executive Airlines, San Juan, PR; *U.S. Public*, pg. 9
Del Vecchio, Claudio, Pres. & Chief Exec. Officer--Casual Corner Group, Inc., Enfield, CT; *U.S. Private*, pg. 219
Del Vecchio, Claudio, Pres. & Chief Exec. Officer--Petite Sophisticate Outlet, Enfield, CT; *U.S. Private*, pg. 219
Del Vecchio, Claudio, Pres. & Chief Exec. Officer--Casual Corner Outlet, Enfield, CT; *U.S. Private*, pg. 219
Del Vecchio, Claudio, Pres. & Chief Exec. Officer--Casual Corner Woman, Enfield, CT; *U.S. Private*, pg. 219
Del Vecchio, Leonardo, Chm. Bd. & Pres.--Luxottica Group S.p.A., Agordo, Italy; *Int'l*, pg. 822
Del Vecchio, Leonardo, Prof., Chm. Bd & Pres.--GS Societa Generale Supermercati, Milan, Italy; *Int'l*, pg. 186
Delahaut, Robert J., Chm. Bd. & Pres.--M K Diamond Products, Inc., Torrance, CA; *U.S. Private*, pg. 684
Delaney, Jay, Pres.--McMaster Carr Supply Co. Inc., Elmhurst, IL; *U.S. Private*, pg. 724
Delaney, Kathy, Partner & Creative Dir.--Deutsch, Inc., New York, NY; *U.S. Private*, pg. 328
DeLaney, Tom, Pres.--Premier Metal Products Company, Bronx, NY; *U.S. Private*, pg. 881
Delano, Warren, Pres.--Lexington Precision Corporation, New York, NY; *U.S. Public*, pg. 991
DeLap, Mike, Pres. & Chief Exec. Officer--Schlosser Forge Company, Rancho Cucamonga, CA; *U.S. Private*, pg. 970
Delavan, John P., Pres. & Chief Exec. Officer--Intrenet, Inc., Milford, OH; *U.S. Public*, pg. 910
Delaye, Dennis, Pres.--UniSea Foods, Inc., Redmond, WA; *Int'l*, pg. 940
DeLellis, Bob, Pres.--20th Century Fox Home Entertainment, Los Angeles, CA; *U.S. Public*, pg. 275
DeLellis, Bob, Pres.--20th Century Fox Home Entertainment, Los Angeles, CA; *Int'l*, pg. 926
DeLeo, Richard, Pres.--Countrywide Title Corporation, Pasadena, CA; *U.S. Public*, pg. 453
Deleye, A.H.C., Chm. Bd.--Royal Begemann Group, Breda, Netherlands; *Int'l*, pg. 1133
Delgadillo, Joseph L., Pres. & Chief Oper. Officer--M & I Data Services, Inc., Brown Deer, WI; *U.S. Public*, pg. 1050
Delgado, Jose Carlos March, Chm. Bd. & Pres.--Banca March S.A., Palma de Mallorca, Spain; *Int'l*, pg. 136
Delgado, Juan March, Pres.--Corporacion Financiera Alba S.A., Madrid, Spain; *Int'l*, pg. 136
Delian, Lu, Pres.--Casco Signal Ltd., Shanghai, China; *Int'l*, pg. 1195
DeLibero, Shirley A., Exec. Dir.--NJ Transit, Newark, NJ; *U.S. Private*, pg. 794
DeLisle, Richard H., Pres.--Scott Aviation, Lancaster, NY; *U.S. Public*, pg. 622
Dell'Oca, Conrad J., Ph.D., Pres. & Chief Exec. Officer--Aspec Technology, Inc., Sunnyvale, CA; *U.S. Private*, pg. 89
Della Noce, Joseph, Pres. & Chief Oper. Officer--Richfood Pennsylvania, Harrisburg, PA; *U.S. Public*, pg. 1389
Della Penta, David T., Pres. & Chief Exec. Officer--Nalge Company, Rochester, NY; *U.S. Public*, pg. 1545
Dellamano, Patricia, Pres. & Chief Exec. & Chief Fin. Officer--Patson's Press, Sunnyvale, CA; *U.S. Private*, pg. 843
Dellepiane, F., Pres.--Hotel Cipriani S.p.A., Venice, Italy; *Int'l*, pg. 1214
DelliBovi, Alfred A., Pres. & Chief Exec. Officer--Federal Home Loan Bank of New York, New York, NY; *U.S. Private*, pg. 399
Dellinger, Bob, Pres.-Sls. & Mktg./Bed Div.--Fieldcrest Cannon, Inc., Kannapolis, NC; *U.S. Public*, pg. 1296
Delmar, Jack, Pres. & Chief Oper. Officer--Brascan Brazil, Rio de Janeiro, Brazil; *Int'l*, pg. 435
DeLoache, William E., III, Pres.--Shealy Electrical Wholesalers, Greenville, SC; *U.S. Private*, pg. 991
Delobel, Jean-Claude, Pres.--Cockerill Sambre, Brussels, Belgium; *Int'l*, pg. 301
DeLong, Dan, Pres. & Chief Exec. Officer--Triplett Corporation, Bluffton, OH; *U.S. Private*, pg. 1104
DeLong, R., Pres.--Krug International Technology/Scientific Services, Inc., Dayton, OH; *U.S. Public*, pg. 968
DeLorenzo, David A., Pres. & Chief Oper. Officer--Dole Food Company, Inc., Westlake Village, CA; *U.S. Public*, pg. 515
Delorey, Paul J., Pres.--JanSport, Appleton, WI; *U.S. Public*, pg. 1702
Delorme, J.P., Pres. & Chief Exec. Officer--U.S. Divers Co., Inc., Santa Ana, CA; *U.S. Private*, pg. 1125
Delp, R. Lee, Pres. & Chief Exec. Officer--Moyer Packing Company, Souderton, PA; *U.S. Private*, pg. 765
Delsol, Robert J., Pres. & V.P.--Pacific Steel Casting Co., Berkeley, CA; *U.S. Private*, pg. 832
DeLuca, Anthony J., Pres. & Chief Exec. Officer--International Technology Corporation, Monroeville, PA; *U.S. Public*, pg. 907
DeLuca, Robert, Chm. Bd., Pres. & Chief Exec. Officer--Aero Data Metal Crafters, Ronkonkoma, NY; *U.S. Private*, pg. 23
DeLue, Robert S., Pres. & Chief Exec. Officer--ACSIA, Burlingame, CA; *Int'l*, pg. 499
Delusinne, Philippe, Pres., Mng. Dir. & Chief Exec. Officer--Young & Rubicam Belgium S.A., Brussels, Belgium; *U.S. Private*, pg. 1199
DelZotto, Elvio, Pres. & Chief Oper. Officer--Tridel Enterprises Inc., Downsview, Canada; *Int'l*, pg. 1423
DeMaria, Richard J., Pres.--DeMaria Building Co. Inc., Novi, MI; *U.S. Private*, pg. 323
DeMarines, Victor A., Pres. & Chief Exec. Officer--Mitre Corporation, Bedford, MA; *U.S. Private*, pg. 753
DeMarle, Richared, Gen. Mgr.--Watts Fluidair, Kittery, ME; *Int'l*, pg. 1243
DeMartini, David P., Pres.-Chief Oper. Officer & Merger/Acquisitions Contact--Mitsui Foods, Inc., Norwood, NJ; *Int'l*, pg. 879
DeMartino, F.A., Pres.--Parsons Infrastructure & Technology Group Inc., Pasadena, CA; *U.S. Private*, pg. 842
DeMatteo, Daniel A., Pres. & Chief Oper. Officer--Babbage's Etc. LLC, Grapevine, TX; *U.S. Private*, pg. 108
Dembinski, Jan A., Pres., Chief Exec. Officer & Treas.--M.J. Daly & Sons, Inc., Waterbury, CT; *U.S. Private*, pg. 309
Demere, Robert H., Jr., Pres. & Chief Exec. Officer--Colonial Oil Industries, Savannah, GA; *U.S. Private*, pg. 253
DeMerritt, Ted C., Chief Exec. Officer--Olsy North America Inc., Liberty Lake, WA; *Int'l*, pg. 1002
Demetrieus, John, Pres.--Sunkyong America, Inc., New York, NY; *Int'l*, pg. 1320
DeMeulenaere, Robert L., Pres. & Chief Exec. Officer--Brenton Banks, Inc., Des Moines, IA; *U.S. Public*, pg. 251
DeMicco, Frank J., Pres.--United Water New Jersey, Inc., Harrington Park, NJ; *U.S. Public*, pg. 1692
DeMichiei, J.M., Pres.--Cyprus Emerald Resources Corporation, Waynesburg, PA; *U.S. Public*, pg. 471
DeMichiei, J.M., Pres.--Cyprus Empire Corporation, Craig, CO; *U.S. Public*, pg. 471
DeMichiei, J.M., Pres.--Cyprus Plateau Mining Corporation, Price, UT; *U.S. Public*, pg. 471
DeMichiei, J.M., Pres.--Cyprus Shoshone Coal Corporation, Hanna, WY; *U.S. Public*, pg. 471
DeMiecoo, Frank J., Pres.--United Water Mid-Atlantic, Succasunna, NJ; *U.S. Public*, pg. 1692
Deming, Claiborne P., Pres. & Chief Exec. Officer--Murphy Oil Corporation, El Dorado, AR; *U.S. Public*, pg. 1141
Demko, Don, Pres.--The Holden Group, Los Angeles, CA; *Int'l*, pg. 435
Demmer, William J., Pres.--Jack Demmer Ford, Inc., Wayne, MI; *U.S. Private*, pg. 323
Demms, Terry D., Pres. & Chief Exec. Officer--CSW Energy, Inc., Dallas, TX; *U.S. Public*, pg. 324
Demone, Henry E., Pres. & Chief Exec. Officer--National Sea Products Limited, Lunenburg, Canada; *Int'l*, pg. 909
Demone, Henry E., Pres. & Chief Exec. Officer--National Sea Products Incorporated, Portsmouth, NH; *Int'l*, pg. 909
Demorest, Robert L., Pres.--Modern Controls, Inc., Minneapolis, MN; *U.S. Public*, pg. 1120
DeMorette, Don, Pres.--TL Systems Corporation, Minneapolis, MN; *Int'l*, pg. 205
DeMoulas, Telemachus A., Pres. & Chief Exec. Officer--Demoulas Market Basket, Tewksbury, MA; *U.S. Private*, pg. 324
DeMoura, Brian, Pres.--Guilford of Maine, Inc., Guilford, ME; *U.S. Public*, pg. 889
Dempsey, Charles, Pres.--Buccaneer Homes, Inc., Hamilton, AL; *U.S. Public*, pg. 318
Dempsey, Kenneth L., Pres.--Masland Carpets, Inc., Saraland, AL; *U.S. Public*, pg. 514
Demura, Sachio, Pres.--Dentsu Oceania Pty. Ltd., Sydney, Australia; *Int'l*, pg. 394
DeMuth, Christopher, Pres.--American Enterprise Institute for Public Policy Research, Washington, DC; *U.S. Private*, pg. 53
den Ouden, Jaap, Pres.--Mercon Steel Structures B.V., Gorinchem, Netherlands; *Int'l*, pg. 858
Denardo, Donna, Pres. & Chief Oper. Officer--Vitalink Pharmacy Services, Inc., Naperville, IL; *U.S. Public*, pg. 1041
Denburg, Edmund, Pres. & Chief Exec. Officer--Barton Press, Inc., West Orange, NJ; *U.S. Private*, pg. 120
Denenberg, Alfred H., Pres.--Adelphia Lamp & Shade Inc., Philadelphia, PA; *U.S. Private*, pg. 17
Denend, Leslie G., Pres.--Network Associates, Inc., Santa Clara, CA; *U.S. Public*, pg. 1168
Denhof, Dan, Pres.--Lester Coggins Trucking, Okahumpka, FL; *U.S. Private*, pg. 250
Denig, Thomas H., Pres.--Trus Joist MacMillan Limited, Surrey, Canada; *Int'l*, pg. 829
Denig, Thomas H., Pres. & Chief Exec. Officer--TJ International, Inc., Boise, ID; *U.S. Public*, pg. 1556
Denig, Thomas H., Pres.--Trus Joist MacMillan Limited, Surrey, Canada; *U.S. Public*, pg. 1556
Denig, Thomas H., Pres.--Trus Joist (Western) Ltd., Surrey, Canada; *U.S. Public*, pg. 1556
Denig, Thomas H., Pres.--Norco Windows, Inc., Boise, ID; *U.S. Public*, pg. 1556
Denis Thomas, S., Pres.--Textilease Corporation, Beltsville, MD; *U.S. Private*, pg. 1079
Denis, Jacques, Pres.--Atotech U.S.A. Inc., Rock Hill, SC; *U.S. Private*, pg. 97
Denisco, Ralph, Pres. & Chief Exec. Officer--Norse Dairy Systems, Columbus, OH; *U.S. Private*, pg. 802
Denisco, Ralph A., Pres.--NDS, Columbus, OH; *Int'l*, pg. 918
Denise, Robert, Chm. Bd., Pres., Chief Exec. Officer & Chief Fin. Officer--Bucilla Corporation, Hazleton, PA; *U.S. Private*, pg. 352
Denison, Calvin, Pres. & Chief Oper. Officer--Divi Hotels, Inc., Chapel Hill, NC; *U.S. Private*, pg. 336
Denkl, Heinz, Pres.--Services Conseils Dowell, Montrouge, France; *U.S. Public*, pg. 1439
Denley, James H., Pres. & Editor--Birmingham Post-Herald Company, Birmingham, AL; *U.S. Public*, pg. 1447
Denne, Donald, Pres.--Alba-Waldensian Health Products Div., Valdese, NC; *U.S. Public*, pg. 36
Denney, Christopher, Pres.--Kolmar Laboratories, Inc., Port Jervis, NY; *Int'l*, pg. 239
Dennis, Aaron S., Pres. & Treas.--Dennis Chemical Co., Inc., Saint Louis, MO; *U.S. Private*, pg. 324
Dennis, Daniel R., Jr., Chm. Bd., Pres. & Chief Exec. Officer--Norwich Financial Corp., Norwich, CT; *U.S. Public*, pg. 1203
Dennis, David M., Pres.--SBC Advertising, Columbus, OH; *U.S. Private*, pg. 955
Dennis, Jim W., Pres.--Pacesetter Inc., Sylmar, CA; *U.S. Public*, pg. 1428
Dennis, Ron, Pres.--Kash N Karry Food Stores, Inc., Tampa, FL; *Int'l*, pg. 463
Denny, Robert M., Pres.--CSC Credit Services, Inc., Houston, TX; *U.S. Public*, pg. 423
Denrich, Louis, Pres.--So-Lo-Food, Inc., Baltimore, MD; *U.S. Private*, pg. 1011
Densen, Lawrence, Pres.--Eastco Industrial Safety Corp., Huntington Station, NY; *U.S. Public*, pg. 548
Densmore, Marty D., Pres. & Chief Oper. Officer--Steelox Systems Inc., Mason, OH; *U.S. Private*, pg. 1038
Dent, Frederick B., Jr., Pres.--Mayfair Mills, Inc., Arcadia, SC; *U.S. Private*, pg. 718
Dent, James R., Chm. Bd & Pres.--Crosby & Overton, Inc., Long Beach, CA; *U.S. Private*, pg. 290
Denton, John, Pres.--Snyder's of Hanover, Inc., Hanover, PA; *U.S. Private*, pg. 1011
Denton, Leet E., Pres.--Denton Enterprises Inc., Grosse Pointe Woods, MI; *U.S. Private*, pg. 325
Denton, Leet E., Pres.--Denton Concrete Services Inc., Grosse Pointe Woods, MI; *U.S. Private*, pg. 325
Dentz, David, Gen. Mgr.--Diamonair, Cedar Knolls, NJ; *U.S. Public*, pg. 1003
DeNuccio, Jeanette, Pres.--Plastic Engineering Co. Inc., Haverhill, MA; *U.S. Private*, pg. 871

DePaul, John D., Chm. Bd., Pres. & Chief Exec. Officer--The Lehigh Press, Inc., Cherry Hill, NJ; *U.S. Private*, pg. 658
Depoil, Francois, Pres.--Laboratoires Fumouze S.A., Saint Denis, France; *U.S. Public*, pg. 310
DePriest, Karin, Pres.--PSR, Kirkland, WA; *U.S. Private*, pg. 828
DeRamus, William H., Pres.--Miller & Co., Selma, AL; *U.S. Private*, pg. 746
DeRemigis, Joseph, Dr., Pres.--Hughes Leitz Optical Technologies, Ltd., Vancouver, Canada; *U.S. Public*, pg. 722
Derham Cato, John P., Vice Chm., Pres. & Chief Oper. Officer--The Cato Corporation, Charlotte, NC; *U.S. Public*, pg. 318
Derhofer, George, Pres.--Bassett-Walker, Martinsville, VA; *U.S. Public*, pg. 1702
DeRoeck, Walter A., Pres.--Palladin Financial, Inc., Austin, TX; *U.S. Public*, pg. 1554
DeRoeck, Walter A., Pres.--Barton Creek Capital, Inc., Austin, TX; *U.S. Public*, pg. 1554
DeRosa, Patricia, Pres. & Chief Oper. Officer--AnnTaylor Stores Corporation, New York, NY; *U.S. Public*, pg. 116
DeRosa, Patricia, Pres. & Chief Oper. Officer--AnnTaylor, Inc., New York, NY; *U.S. Public*, pg. 116
DeRosa, Patricia, Pres.--GapKids Division, San Bruno, CA; *U.S. Public*, pg. 702
DeRosa, Paul R., Pres. & Chief Exec. Officer--Eastbridge Holdings Inc., New York, NY; *Int'l*, pg. 933
DeRosa, Paul R., Pres.--Eastbridge Asset Management Inc., New York, NY; *Int'l*, pg. 933
Derr, Kenneth T., Chm. Bd. & Chief Exec. Officer--Chevron Corporation, San Francisco, CA; *U.S. Public*, pg. 347
Derrick, John M., Jr., Pres. & Chief Exec. Officer--Potomac Electric Power Company, Washington, DC; *U.S. Public*, pg. 1318
Derrick, Mark E., Pres. & Chief Exec. Officer--Perry & Derrick Co., Cincinnati, OH; *U.S. Private*, pg. 854
Derst, Edward J., III, Pres. & Chief Exec. Officer--Derst Baking Company, Inc., Savannah, GA; *U.S. Private*, pg. 326
des Dorides, Philippe, Chief Opers. Officer & Gen. Mgr.--SAFA, Madrid, Spain; *Int'l*, pg. 1114
Desai, Dinesh, Pres.--Western Sky Industries, Inc., Philadelphia, PA; *U.S. Private*, pg. 1168
Desai, Rohit M., Chm. Bd. & Pres.--Desai Capital Management Incorporated, New York, NY; *U.S. Private*, pg. 326
DeSantis, Gerry, Pres.--Honeywell Leeds & Northrup International, Horsham, PA; *U.S. Public*, pg. 834
Desbiens, Michel, Pres. & Chief Exec. Officer--Donohue Inc., Quebec, Canada; *Int'l*, pg. 1075
Descarpentries, Jean Mark, Pres.--Bull S.A., Louveciennes, France; *Int'l*, pg. 315
Desfosos, Theresa, Pres. & Gen. Mgr.--Park Manufacturing, Inc., Oxford, ME; *U.S. Private*, pg. 840
Desmarais, Rene, Pres. & Chief Oper. Officer--CFCF 12, Montreal, Canada; *Int'l*, pg. 241
Desmond, Dermot, Chm. Bd. & Pres.--International Investment & Underwriting Ltd., Dublin, Ireland; *Int'l*, pg. 684
Despres, Germain L., Pres.--Danisco Ingredients Canada Inc., Rexdale, Canada; *Int'l*, pg. 378
Desprez, Martin, Chm. Bd., Pres., Chief Exec. Officer & Dir. General--Editions du Juris-Classeur, Paris, France; *Int'l*, pg. 1095
Desroche, Eric, Pres.--Measurement Science, Inc., Englewood, CO; *U.S. Private*, pg. 826
DeStefano, James L., Pres. & Chief Exec. Officer--Emcee Broadcast Products, Inc., White Haven, PA; *U.S. Public*, pg. 570
Detampel, Donald, Pres.--ConferTech International, Westminster, CO; *U.S. Public*, pg. 683
Deters, Roger E., Pres.--Norcostco, Inc., Minneapolis, MN; *U.S. Private*, pg. 801
Detjen, Larry L., Pres.--Valvoline Instant Oil Change, Inc., Lexington, KY; *U.S. Public*, pg. 139
Detlef, Vernon A., Pres.--Thomas & Skinner, Inc., Indianapolis, IN; *U.S. Private*, pg. 1082
Detsch, Hanspeter, Chief Exec. Officer--Impuls Advertising AG, Kusnacht, Switzerland; *Int'l*, pg. 666
Detter, Gerald L., Pres. & Chief Exec. Officer--Con-Way Transportation Services, Palo Alto, CA; *U.S. Public*, pg. 281
Deulofeu, Julio, Pres.--EvansGroup, San Francisco, CA; *U.S. Private*, pg. 385
Deuster, Robert G., Chm. Bd., Pres. & Chief Exec. Officer--Newport Corporation, Irvine, CA; *U.S. Public*, pg. 1179
Deutch, Andrew, Pres.--Grey Direct, New York, NY; *U.S. Public*, pg. 764
Deutsch, Carl, Pres.--The Deutsch Company, Santa Monica, CA; *U.S. Private*, pg. 328
Deutsch, Jeffrey A., Pres.--Machinery Acceptance Corp., Houston, TX; *U.S. Public*, pg. 1517
Deutsch, Jeffrey A., Pres.--Machinery Acceptance Corporation, Houston, TX; *U.S. Public*, pg. 1517
Deutsch, Richard J., Pres.--IMPO Glaztile, Burr Ridge, IL; *Int'l*, pg. 1239
Deutschman, Leo, Pres.--Iroquois Die & Mfg. Co., Warren, MI; *U.S. Private*, pg. 575
Devanna, Leonard R., Pres. & Chief Oper. Officer-COM/Energy Enterprises, Inc.--Commonwealth Energy System, Cambridge, MA; *U.S. Public*, pg. 414
Devanna, Leonard R., Pres. & Chief Oper. Officer--COM/Energy Resources Inc., Cambridge, MA; *U.S. Public*, pg. 414
Devanna, Leonard R., Pres. & Chief Oper. Officer--COM/Energy Enterprises, Cambridge, MA; *U.S. Public*, pg. 414
Devening, R. Randolph, Chm. Bd., Pres. & Chief Exec. Officer--Foodbrands America, Inc., Oklahoma City, OK; *U.S. Public*, pg. 852
Dever, Michael L., Pres.--Performance Automotive Network, Fairfield, OH; *U.S. Private*, pg. 853
Devereaux, Lance, Pres.--Wausau Metals, Nanik Division, Wausau, WI; *U.S. Public*, pg. 1500
Devereaux, Lance W., Pres.--Springs Window Fashions Division, Middleton, WI; *U.S. Public*, pg. 1500
Deverell, Thomas J., Pres.--Ikon Office Solutions-San Diego, San Diego, CA; *U.S. Public*, pg. 864
Devereux, John, Jr., Pres.--Flowers of Hawaii, Pasadena, CA; *U.S. Private*, pg. 415
DeVesto, Thomas J., Pres. & Chief Exec. Officer--Cambridge Soundworks, Inc., Newton, MA; *U.S. Private*, pg. 202
DeVille, Paul, Pres., Chief Oper. Officer & Sec.--Persis Corporation, Honolulu, HI; *U.S. Private*, pg. 855
Devine, C.R., Pres.--KCS Resources, Inc., Houston, TX; *U.S. Public*, pg. 939
DeVito, Vince, Pres.--Adam Technology Co., Union, NJ; *U.S. Public*, pg. 1101
Devlin, Mike, Pres. & Chief Exec. Officer--Rational Software Corporation, Cupertino, CA; *U.S. Public*, pg. 1361
Devlin, Philip D., Pres.--Sunrise Energy Services, Inc., Dallas, TX; *U.S. Private*, pg. 1053
DeVore, Ron, Pres.--Terumo Medical Corp., Somerset, NJ; *Int'l*, pg. 1376
DeVos, Richard, Jr., Pres.--Amway Corporation, Ada, MI; *U.S. Private*, pg. 69
DeVoto, Richard H., Pres.--CR Briggs Corporation, Trona, CA; *U.S. Public*, pg. 302
DeVries, William L., Pres. & Chief Exec. Officer-Athletic Footwear & Apparel--Woolworth Corporation, New York, NY; *U.S. Public*, pg. 1777
Dew, Donald H., Chm. Bd., Pres. & Chief Exec. Officer--Diemolding Corp., Canastota, NY; *U.S. Private*, pg. 332
Dewald, Steven E., Pres.--Peoples Electric Contractor, Inc., Saint Paul, MN; *U.S. Private*, pg. 851
Dewan, Derek E., Chm. Bd., Pres. & Chief Exec. Officer--AccuStaff Incorporated, Jacksonville, FL; *U.S. Public*, pg. 15
Dewberry, Sidney O., Mng. Partner--Dewberry & Davis, Fairfax, VA; *U.S. Private*, pg. 329
DeWeerd, LaVerne, Pres.--Dickinson Press, Inc., Grand Rapids, MI; *U.S. Private*, pg. 331
DeWinter, C. Mark, Chm. Bd., Pres. & Chief Exec. Officer--Woodhead Industries, Inc., Buffalo Grove, IL; *U.S. Public*, pg. 1776
DeWitt, Gene, Pres.--DeWitt Media, Inc., New York, NY; *U.S. Private*, pg. 329
DeWitt, Larry, Pres.--Cargill Flour Div., Minneapolis, MN; *U.S. Private*, pg. 210
Dexeus, C., Chm. & Pres.--SBS Espanan S.A., Madrid, Spain; *Int'l*, pg. 1331
Dexter, Richard, Pres.--Dexter Axle Div., Elkhart, IN; *Int'l*, pg. 1396
DeYager, Peter W., Pres.--The Foreign Candy Co., Inc., Hull, IA; *U.S. Private*, pg. 418
Dezio, John, Pres.--Captive Plastics, Piscataway, NJ; *U.S. Private*, pg. 207
Dhar, Subhash K., Pres. & Chief Oper. Officer--Ovonic Battery Company, Inc., Troy, MI; *U.S. Public*, pg. 581
Di Meana, Vittorio Ripa, Pres.--SASIB SpA, Bologna, Italy; *Int'l*, pg. 1194
Di Zazzo, James G., Pres.--Oomphies, Inc., Lawrence, MA; *U.S. Private*, pg. 817
Dial, Walter David, III, Chm. Bd., Pres. & Chief Exec. Officer--Plymouth Creameries, Inc., Plymouth, WI; *U.S. Private*, pg. 872
Diamantis, George, Pres.--National Print Group, Inc., Chattanooga, TN; *U.S. Private*, pg. 785
Diamond, Abraham L., Pres. & Chief Exec. Officer--Diamond Chemical Co., Inc., East Rutherford, NJ; *U.S. Private*, pg. 330
Diamond, Chris, Pres., Chief Oper. Officer & Chief Exec. Officer--Haystack Ski Resort at Mount Snow, Wilmington, VT; *U.S. Private*, pg. 61
Diamond, Deborah, V.P. & Partner--Ayer Public Relations, New York, NY; *U.S. Private*, pg. 104
Diamond, Gerald, Chm. Bd., Chief Exec. Officer & Pres.--Southern Electronics Distributors International, Tucker, GA; *U.S. Public*, pg. 1490
Diamond, Lawrence, Chm. Bd., Pres., Chief Exec. & Chief Oper. Officer & Dir.-Pur.--Triangle Marketing Corp., New York, NY; *U.S. Private*, pg. 1102
Diamond, Russell, Pres., Chief Oper. Officer & Dir.-Mktg. & Treas.--Snyder-Diamond, Santa Monica, CA; *U.S. Private*, pg. 1011
Diamond, Thedore L., Pres.--T.L. Diamond Company, New York, NY; *U.S. Private*, pg. 330
Diaz, Fausto, Jr., Pres.--American International Container, Inc., Miami, FL; *U.S. Private*, pg. 57
Diaz, Gonzalo E., Pres.--Med-Lab Supply Company, Inc., Miami, FL; *U.S. Private*, pg. 726
Diaz, Peter, Pres. & Gen. Mgr.--KHOU-TV Inc., Houston, TX; *U.S. Public*, pg. 209
DiBenedetto, George, Pres.--Hiram Walker, Southfield, MI; *Int'l*, pg. 63
DiBui, William J., Pres., Chief Exec. Office & Chief Oper. Officer--Rumsey Electric Company, Conshohocken, PA; *U.S. Private*, pg. 951
DiCamillo, Gary T., Chm. & Chief Exec. Officer--Polaroid Corporation, Cambridge, MA; *U.S. Public*, pg. 1313
Dick, Douglas P., Pres.--Dick Corporation, Large, PA; *U.S. Private*, pg. 331
Dick, Robbie, Pres.--Casey Co., Long Beach, CA; *U.S. Private*, pg. 218
Dicke, James, II, Pres.--Crown Equipment Corporation, New Bremen, OH; *U.S. Private*, pg. 292
Dickelman, James H., Chm. Bd., Pres. & Chief Exec. Officer--Schultz Sav-O Stores, Inc., Sheboygan, WI; *U.S. Public*, pg. 1442
Dickens, Kevin, Pres.--ACC Long Distance, Ltd., Etobicoke, Canada; *U.S. Public*, pg. 3
Dickenson, J.T., Pres. & Chief Oper. Officer--Justin Industries, Inc., Fort Worth, TX; *U.S. Public*, pg. 936
Dickerman, George, Pres.--Spalding Sports Worldwide, Chicopee, MA; *U.S. Private*, pg. 630
Dickerson, Arthur J., Chm. Bd., Pres. & Chief Exec. Officer--Southwestern Petroleum Corporation, Fort Worth, TX; *U.S. Private*, pg. 1019
Dickerson, Michael A., Pres. & Chief Exec. Officer--High Point Financial Corp., Branchville, NJ; *U.S. Public*, pg. 826
Dickey, Boh A., Pres. & Chief Oper. Officer--SAFECO Corporation, Seattle, WA; *U.S. Public*, pg. 1423
Dickieson, C.W., Pres.--Indiana Harbor Belt Railroad Co., Hammond, IN; *U.S. Public*, pg. 432
Dickinson, Gary W., Pres. & Chief Exec. Officer--Delco Electronics Corporation, Kokomo, IN; *U.S. Public*, pg. 720
Dickinson, John F., Pres.--Compac Corporation, Netcong, NJ; *U.S. Public*, pg. 1054
Dickinson, Roy, Pres.--Bayco Industries, Winnipeg, Canada; *Int'l*, pg. 395
Dickinson, Walter, Pres.--Walter Dickinson Inc., Jacksonville, FL; *U.S. Private*, pg. 331
Dickson, Bruce, Pres.--Continental Homes of Austin, L.P., Austin, TX; *U.S. Public*, pg. 441
Dickson, Charles, Mgr.--Burson-Marsteller, Brisbane, Australia; *U.S. Private*, pg. 1198
Dickson, Harold A., Jr., Chm. Bd., Pres. & Chief Exec. Officer--SouthTrust Bank, Sylacauga, Sylacauga, AL; *U.S. Public*, pg. 1492
Dickson, John H., Pres. & Chief Oper. Officer--AllEnergy Marketing Company, L.L.C., Waltham, MA; *U.S. Public*, pg. 549
Dickson, Thomas W., Pres.--Ruddick Corporation, Charlotte, NC; *U.S. Public*, pg. 1412
Dickten, Erich, Chm. Bd.--Dickten & Masch Manufacturing Co., Nashotah, WI; *U.S. Private*, pg. 331
DiCola, Frank E., Pres.--Atlantic Thermal Systems, Inc., Pleasantville, NJ; *U.S. Public*, pg. 430
Didde, David C., Pres.--Didde Corporation, Overland Park, KS; *U.S. Private*, pg. 331
Diddle, L.E., Pres.--Bulab Realty Of Missouri, LLC, Memphis, TN; *U.S. Private*, pg. 180
DiDominicis, Dennis F., Pres.--Ryka Incorporated, King of Prussia, PA; *U.S. Public*, pg. 1414
Diedrick, G. Vern, Pres.--Allied Carbi-Tech, Inc., Topeka, IN; *U.S. Private*, pg. 38
Diego, Guillermo, Chm., Pres. & Chief Exec. Officer-Y&R Spain--Young & Rubicam, S.A., Madrid, Spain; *U.S. Private*, pg. 1199
Diehl, Peter, Pres. & Chief Exec. Officer--Diehl Inc., Defiance, OH; *U.S. Private*, pg. 332
Diehl, Peter A., Pres.--Diehl Specialties International, Defiance, OH; *U.S. Private*, pg. 332
Diem, John R., Pres.--Southern Agricultural Insecticides, Inc., Palmetto, FL; *U.S. Private*, pg. 1015
Diemer, Edmund, Pres. & Treas.--Metal Seal & Products, Inc., Willoughby, OH; *U.S. Private*, pg. 734
Diener, I. Howard, Pres. & Chief Oper. Officer--The Cosmetic Center Inc., Columbia, MD; *U.S. Private*, pg. 689
Dienes, John D., Pres. & Chief Oper. Officer--United Companies Financial Corporation, Baton Rouge, LA; *U.S. Public*, pg. 1675
Dienes, John R., Pres. & Chief Fin. Officer--Hercules Engine Company, Canton, OH; *U.S. Private*, pg. 523
Dierberg, James, Chm. Bd., Pres. & Chief Exec. Officer--First Banks America, Inc., Clayton, MO; *U.S. Public*, pg. 626
Dierberg, Robert J., Chm. Bd. & Pres.--Dierbergs Markets Inc., Chesterfield, MO; *U.S. Private*, pg. 332
Dietrich, E. Joy, Pres.--Vidar, Inc., New London, MN; *U.S. Private*, pg. 1139
Dietrich, Thomas W., Pres. & Chief Exec. Officer--Dietrich's Milk Products, Inc., Reading, PA; *U.S. Private*, pg. 332
DiFebo, Val, Partner & Grp. Dir.--Deutsch, Inc., New York, NY; *U.S. Private*, pg. 328
Diffley, Robert G., Pres.--Malama Pacific Corp., Honolulu, HI; *U.S. Public*, pg. 800
DiFillippo, Thomas D., Chm. Bd. & Pres.--DeVault Foods, Devault, PA; *U.S. Private*, pg. 329
Diggins, John, Pres. & Chief Exec. Officer--Foresight Software, Inc., Atlanta, GA; *U.S. Private*, pg. 872
Diggins, Vance, Pres.--Gores Technology Group, Sherman Oaks, CA; *U.S. Private*, pg. 465
DiGioia, Anthony M., Jr., Chm. Bd. & Pres.--GAI Consultants, Inc., Monroeville, PA; *U.S. Private*, pg. 433
DiGiovanna, Charles, Pres. & Chief Exec. Officer--Continental Plastic Containers, Inc., Norwalk, CT; *U.S. Public*, pg. 440
DiGiusto, Walter, Pres., Chief Exec. Officer & Treas.--ESA, Inc., Chelmsford, MA; *U.S. Private*, pg. 354
DiJohn, Joseph, Exec. Dir.--Pace, Arlington Heights, IL; *U.S.* Private, pg. 919
Dik, W., Pres.--KPN Koninklyke PTT Nederland NV, Groningen, Netherlands; *Int'l*, pg. 720
Dilacqua, John, Pres.--Philip Metals Inc., Cleveland, OH; *Int'l*, pg. 1050
Dilda, E.C., Pres.--Stancom Home Center, Inc., Wilson, NC; *U.S. Public*, pg. 1502
Dilda, Roland, Pres. & Chief Exec. Officer--Aero Systems Engineering Inc., Saint Paul, MN; *Int'l*, pg. 276
Dill, John, Pres. & Chief Exec. Officer--McGraw-Hill Ryerson, Ltd., Whitby, Canada; *U.S. Public*, pg. 1072
Dillard, Henry, III, Chm. Bd. & Pres.--Electronic Drives and Controls, Parsippany, NJ; *U.S. Private*, pg. 370
Dillard, William T., Pres.--Pipeco Services, Houston, TX; *U.S. Private*, pg. 867
Dillard, William, II, Pres. & Chief Oper. Officer--Dillard's, Inc., Little Rock, AR; *U.S. Public*, pg. 509
Dille, Steven B., Pres. & Chief Oper. Officer--Scicom Data Services, Ltd., Minnetonka, MN; *U.S. Private*, pg. 975
Dillon, Daniel P., Pres. & Chief Exec. Officer--Welch Foods Inc., A Cooperative, Concord, MA; *U.S. Private*, pg. 784
Dillon, David B., Pres. & Chief Oper. Officer--The Kroger Co., Cincinnati, OH; *U.S. Public*, pg. 967
Dillon, Donald F., Pres.--Information Technology, Inc., Lincoln, NE; *U.S. Public*, pg. 647

Dillon, Gary G., Chm. Bd., Pres. & Chief Exec. Officer--Schwitzer, Inc., Indianapolis, IN; *U.S. Public*, pg. 968

Dillon, George F., Pres. & Chief Oper. Officer--Nicholas Paper, Inc., Fitchburg, MA; *U.S. Private*, pg. 798

Dillon, John, Pres. & Chief Oper. Officer--Arbor Software Corporation, Sunnyvale, CA; *U.S. Public*, pg. 127

Dillon, Mark, Pres.--Tampa Bay Steel, Tampa, FL; *U.S. Private*, pg. 1067

DiLorenzo, James E., Chm. Bd., Pres. & Chief Exec. Officer--Quality Pontiac GMC Buick, Albuquerque, NM; *U.S. Private*, pg. 899

Dilworth, Ed, Pres.--LVL Advertising, Palo Alto, CA; *U.S. Private*, pg. 640

Dilworth, John R., Pres.--The Psychological Corp., San Antonio, TX; *U.S. Public*, pg. 784

Dimacopoulos, Gregory, Pres.--Astra Hellas S.A., Athens, Greece; *Int'l*, pg. 93

DiMaria, Peter, Chief Oper. Officer & Pres.--Accu-Time System, Ellington, CT; *U.S. Private*, pg. 11

DiMartino, George, Pres.--Piher International Corporation, Mount Prospect, IL; *Int'l*, pg. 853

DiMartino, Joseph S., Pres. & Chief Oper. Officer--The Dreyfus Corporation, New York, NY; *U.S. Public*, pg. 1085

DiMeglio, Mario, Pres.--Process & Industrial Division, Philadelphia, PA; *U.S. Private*, pg. 317

Dimeling, William, Partner--Dimeling, Schreiber & Park, Philadelphia, PA; *U.S. Private*, pg. 333

Dimeo, Thomas P., Pres. & Chief Exec. Officer--Dimeo Construction Company, Providence, RI; *U.S. Private*, pg. 333

Dimling, John A., Pres. & Chief Oper. Officer--Nielsen Media Research, New York, NY; *U.S. Public*, pg. 395

Dimon, James, Pres. & Chief Oper. Officer--Travelers Group, New York, NY; *U.S. Public*, pg. 1632

Dinardi, James, Pres.--Foster Refrigerator Corporation, Hudson, NY; *U.S. Private*, pg. 421

Dindorf, Joseph L., Chm. Bd., Pres. & Chief Exec. Officer--Hein-Werner Corporation, Waukesha, WI; *U.S. Public*, pg. 805

Dineen, Pat, Pres.--Harrison Baking Co., Harrison, NJ; *U.S. Private*, pg. 65

Dines, Paul, Chm. Bd., Pres. & Chief Exec. Officer--Reyco Industries, Inc., Springfield, MO; *U.S. Private*, pg. 926

Dinesen, Vagn A., Pres.--Extract-oil, S.A., Santa Ana, Spain; *Int'l*, pg. 288

Dinesen, Vagn A., Pres.--Xantoflor, S.A., Tudela, Spain; *Int'l*, pg. 289

Dinetz, Steven, Pres. & Chief Exec. Officer--Chancellor Radio Broadcasting Co., Dallas, TX; *U.S. Public*, pg. 335

Dinger, William S., Pres. & Sec.--William H. Sadlier, Inc., New York, NY; *U.S. Public*, pg. 1422

DiNicola, Robert J., Chm. Bd., Pres. & Chief Exec. Officer--Zale Corporation, Irving, TX; *U.S. Public*, pg. 1789

Dinsdale, Chris, Pres.--Tillamook Food Sales, Tigard, OR; *U.S. Private*, pg. 1086

Dintaman, James L., Pres.--Food Division, Solon, OH; *Int'l*, pg. 916

Dintaman, James L., Pres.--Nestle Frozen, Refrigerated, and Ice Cream Companies, Solon, OH; *Int'l*, pg. 918

Dinzole, John W., Pres. & Chief Oper. Officer--Devon Group, Inc., Stamford, CT; *U.S. Public*, pg. 503

Dion, Philip J., Chm. Bd. & Chief Exec. Officer--Del Webb Corporation, Phoenix, AZ; *U.S. Public*, pg. 494

Dionne, Denis, Pres.--Capital Communications CDPQ, Montreal, Canada; *Int'l*, pg. 249

Dionne, Denis, Pres.--Sofinov, Montreal, Canada; *Int'l*, pg. 249

DiPaolo, Tony, Pres.--Jos. M. Herman Shoe Co., Armonk, NY; *U.S. Private*, pg. 524

DiPasqua, Louis S., Pres. & Chief Exec. Officer--TBC Corporation, Memphis, TN; *U.S. Public*, pg. 1553

DiPietro, F., Pres.--Morganite AG, Kloten, Switzerland; *Int'l*, pg. 891

DiPietro, Robert, Pres.-Marine Group--TFX Marine, Hagerstown, MD; *U.S. Public*, pg. 1570

DiPietro, Robert M., Pres.--Teleflex Marine, Limerick, PA; *U.S. Public*, pg. 1569

DiPippo, Gerry, Pres.--Volt Directory Services, Blue Bell, PA; *U.S. Public*, pg. 1724

Dircks, William, Chm. Bd. & Pres.--Berger Transfer & Storage, Inc., Saint Paul, MN; *U.S. Private*, pg. 135

DiRosa, Richard, Pres.--Block Industries, Inc., Wilmington, NC; *U.S. Private*, pg. 150

Disbrow, Bruce, Pres. & Chief Exec. Officer--DonTech, Chicago, IL; *U.S. Public*, pg. 98

Dischler, Ralph, Pres. & Chief Exec. Officer--Maplehurst Farms, Inc., Indianapolis, IN; *U.S. Public*, pg. 490

Dishman, Charles H., Pres. & Chief Exec. Officer--Tri-City Oldsmobile Inc., Louisville, KY; *U.S. Private*, pg. 1100

DiSibio, Ralph R., Pres.--Parsons Development Company, Pasadena, CA; *U.S. Private*, pg. 842

Dittmer, Thomas, Pres.--Refco Inc., Chicago, IL; *U.S. Private*, pg. 917

Ditto, Arthur H., Pres. & Chief Oper. Officer--Kinross Gold Corporation, Toronto, Canada; *Int'l*, pg. 734

Divane, William T., Jr., Pres. & Treas.--Divane Bros. Electric Co., Franklin Park, IL; *U.S. Private*, pg. 336

Divin, Rolland, Pres. & Chief Exec. Officer--Tom's Foods, Inc., Columbus, GA; *U.S. Private*, pg. 1090

Divird, D. Thomas, Pres. & Chief Exec. Officer--Anchor Continental Incorporated, Columbia, SC; *U.S. Private*, pg. 70

Dix, Jan F., Pres. & Chief Exec. Officer--OCE USA, Inc., Chicago, IL; *Int'l*, pg. 994

Dixon, Dennis E., Pres.--International Bancshares Corp, Laredo, TX; *U.S. Private*, pg. 568

Dixon, Donna, Pres.--The Hair Cuttery, Falls Church, VA; *U.S. Private*, pg. 287

Dixon, Gene, Jr., Pres.--Kyanite Mining Corporation, Dillwyn, VA; *U.S. Private*, pg. 638

Dixon, J. E., Pres.--JE Merit Constructors, Inc., Houston, TX; *U.S. Public*, pg. 921

Dixon, John, Pres. & Chief Exec. Officer--Mutual Service Corporation, North Palm Beach, FL; *U.S. Private*, pg. 831

Dixon, Stephen, Pres. & Chief Exec. Officer--Martin Luther Hospital Anaheim, Anaheim, CA; *U.S. Private*, pg. 1118

Doak, Robert, Gen. Mgr.--Chattanooga Choo-Choo Holiday Inn, Chattanooga, TN; *U.S. Private*, pg. 231

Doak, William R., Pres.--Bent Tube, Inc., Fowlerville, MI; *U.S. Private*, pg. 134

Dobbin, Alvin, Pres. & Chief Exec. Officer--Giant of Salisbury, Inc., Hyattsville, MD; *U.S. Public*, pg. 741

Dobbin, Alvin, Pres. & Chief Exec. Officer--Shaw Community Supermarket, Hyattsville, MD; *U.S. Public*, pg. 741

Dobbin, Alvin, Pres.--Giant of Cherry Hill, Inc., Hyattsville, MD; *U.S. Public*, pg. 741

Dobloug, Mikkel, Pres.--Swix Sport, Lillehammer, Norway; *Int'l*, pg. 1390

Dobosz, Ed, Pres.--Consolidated Metal Products, Inc., Cincinnati, OH; *U.S. Private*, pg. 265

Dobrez, John G., Pres.--Dober Chemical Corp., Midlothian, IL; *U.S. Private*, pg. 337

Dobrez, John G., Pres.--Industrial Laundry Group of Amerclean, Midlothian, IL; *U.S. Private*, pg. 337

Dobson, Thomas, Pres. & Chief Exec. Officer--Whataburger, Inc., Corpus Christi, TX; *U.S. Private*, pg. 1170

Dockheer, Anthony, Pres.--Astra Pharmaceutica B.V., Zoetermeer, Netherlands; *Int'l*, pg. 94

Dockter, James E., Pres. & Chief Exec. Officer--PBD, Inc., Alpharetta, GA; *U.S. Private*, pg. 825

Dockweiler, Thomas L., Pres. & Chief Exec. Officer--First National Bank of Blue Island, Blue Island, IL; *U.S. Private*, pg. 474

Doctor, Louis J., Pres. & Chief Exec. Officer--Truevision, Inc., Santa Clara, CA; *U.S. Public*, pg. 1642

Dodd, David A., Pres. & Chief Exec. Officer--Solvay Pharmaceuticals, Inc., Marietta, GA; *Int'l*, pg. 1278

Dodd, James R., Pres.--Citizens Trust Company of Indiana, N.A., Evansville, IN; *U.S. Public*, pg. 280

Dodds, Douglas W., Vice Chm., Pres. & Chief Exec. Officer--Schneider Corp., Kitchener, Canada; *Int'l*, pg. 1207

Dodge, Arthur B., III, Pres. & Chief Exec. Officer--Dodge Regupol, Inc., Lancaster, PA; *U.S. Private*, pg. 337

Dodge, E.V., Pres. & Chief Exec. Officer--Canadian Pacific Railway, Minneapolis, MN; *Int'l*, pg. 259

Dodge, James H., Chm. Bd., Pres. & Chief Exec. Officer--Providence Energy Corporation, Providence, RI; *U.S. Public*, pg. 1337

Dodig, Victor G., Pres. & Chief Exec. Officer--Atlas Asset Management Inc., Toronto, Canada; *Int'l*, pg. 865

Dodson, David, Chm. Bd. & Chief Exec. Officer--ADAP Inc., Brockton, MA; *U.S. Private*, pg. 4

Dodson, Edmond O., Pres.--Farmers State Bank, Liberty, IN; *U.S. Public*, pg. 633

Dodson, Garry, Pres.--Sealing Equipment Products Co., Inc., Pelham, AL; *U.S. Private*, pg. 978

Doelder, Jay L., Pres.--Pak-Sak Industries, Inc., Sparta, MI; *U.S. Public*, pg. 1061

Doellinger, Steve, Pres.--Don E. Williams Co., Rock Island, IL; *U.S. Private*, pg. 1177

Doeren, William B., Pres. & Chief Exec. Officer--General Cinema Theatres, Inc., Chestnut Hill, MA; *U.S. Public*, pg. 693

Doerr, Harvey, Pres.--Murphy Oil Co., Ltd., Calgary, Canada; *U.S. Public*, pg. 1142

Doerr, Jack A., Pres., Chief Fin. Officer & Treas.--F.B. Wright Co., Dearborn, MI; *U.S. Private*, pg. 1192

Doherty, John P., Pres.--American Southern Financial Group, Miami, FL; *U.S. Private*, pg. 618

Doherty, Phillip H., Pres. & Chief Exec. Officer--Star Data Systems Inc., Markham, Canada; *U.S. Public*, pg. 1077

Dohmen, John, Pres. & Chief Exec. Officer--The F. Dohmen Company, Germantown, WI; *U.S. Private*, pg. 338

Dohring, Ed, Pres.--SVG Lithography Systems, Wilton, CT; *U.S. Public*, pg. 1474

Dohrman, Fred, Pres. & Chief Exec. Officer--Winnebago Acceptance Corp., Forest City, IA; *U.S. Public*, pg. 1772

Doi, Kazunari, Pres.--The Green Cross Corporation, Osaka, Japan; *Int'l*, pg. 558

Doi, Utaro, Pres.--Chugai Boyeki Co., Ltd., Tokyo, Japan; *Int'l*, pg. 290

Doig, George, Pres. & Chief Exec. Officer--Johnson Yokogawa Corporation, Newnan, GA; *Int'l*, pg. 1521

Doka, Michael, Pres.--Rehrig Pacific Company, Los Angeles, CA; *U.S. Private*, pg. 919

Dokmo, Harold B., Jr., Chm. Bd., Pres., Owner, Treas. & Sec.--Norcraft Companies, Inc., Saint Paul, MN; *U.S. Private*, pg. 801

Dolan, John F., Pres.--Fairfax Lumber & Millwork Company Inc., Springfield, VA; *U.S. Private*, pg. 391

Dolan, Paul, Pres.--Fetzer Vineyards California Wines, Hopland, CA; *U.S. Public*, pg. 261

Dolan, Robert E., Chm. & Pres.--Lynch Capital Corporation, Greenwich, CT; *U.S. Public*, pg. 1021

Dollens, Ronald W., Pres. & Chief Exec. Officer--Guidant Corporation, Indianapolis, IN; *U.S. Public*, pg. 768

Dolson, Robert A., Pres. & Chief Exec. Officer--Continental Water Company, Saint Louis, MO; *U.S. Private*, pg. 269

Doman, H.S., Chm. Bd., Pres. & Chief Exec. Officer--Doman Industries Limited, Duncan, Canada; *Int'l*, pg. 414

Dombek, Gerard M., Pres. & Gen. Mgr.--Precoat Metals Division, Saint Louis, MO; *U.S. Public*, pg. 1458

Domey, Alice K., Controller--Sunhill Food Of Vermont, Inc., Swanton, VT; *Int'l*, pg. 1464

Dominioni, Angelo M., Pres. & Chief Exec. Officer--Cucina Classica Italiana Inc., Lakewood, NJ; *U.S. Public*, pg. 1435

Domino, Richard J., Pres.--Tropical Sportswear International, Tampa, FL; *U.S. Private*, pg. 1105

Domo, James F., Pres.--Joslyn Hi-Voltage Corporation, Cleveland, OH; *U.S. Public*, pg. 481

Domont, John J., Pres.--Symbol, Santa Fe, NM; *U.S. Public*, *pg. 1546*

Domuracki, Mary Ann, Pres. & Chief Exec. Officer--Pennaco Hosiery, New York, NY; *U.S. Public*, pg. 483

Dona, J.C., Pres.--Brabant Pers bv, s Hertogenbosch, Netherlands; *Int'l*, pg. 1445

Donaghy, James E., Pres.--Sheldahl, Inc., Northfield, MN; *U.S. Public*, pg. 1465

Donahue-Dalton, Ellen, Pres.-Game Design--GameScape, Inc., Coventry, RI; *U.S. Public*, pg. 767

Donahue, Dennis, Pres. & Chief Exec. Officer & Chief Oper. Officer--The Will-Burt Company, Orrville, OH; *U.S. Private*, pg. 1177

Donahue, Dennis, Pres.--Enviromental Products Inc., Orrville, OH; *U.S. Private*, pg. 1177

Donahue, Tim, Pres.--Nextel Communications, Mc Lean, VA; *U.S. Public*, pg. 1180

Donahue, William L., Chm. Bd., Pres., Chief Exec. & Chief Oper. Officer--Dixon Paper Co., Denver, CO; *U.S. Public*, *pg. 902*

Donald, James L., Chm. Bd., Pres. & Chief Exec. Officer--DSC Communications Corporation, Plano, TX; *U.S. Public*, pg. 475

Donald, Jim, Chm. Bd., Pres. & Chief Exec. Officer--Pathmark Stores Incorporated, Woodbridge, NJ; *U.S. Private*, pg. 843

Donald, Odie C., Pres.--BellSouth Mobility, Inc., Atlanta, GA; *U.S. Public*, pg. 208

Donaldson, Bennett, Pres.--Cunningham-Limp Development Co., Farmington Hills, MI; *U.S. Private*, pg. 297

Donaldson, Darrell, Pres. & Chief Exec. Officer--Hot Shot Delivery Inc., Houston, TX; *U.S. Private*, pg. 541

Donaldson, J. Harold, Pres. & Chief Exec. Officer--Regions Bank/Marianna, Marianna, FL; *U.S. Public*, pg. 1372

Donaldson, John H., Pres.--1838 Bond-Debenture Trading Fund, Radnor, PA; *U.S. Public*, pg. 566

Donaldson, Nigel, Chm. & Pres.--United Advertising Publications, Inc., Dallas, TX; *Int'l*, pg. 1443

Donegan, James, Chm. Bd., Pres., Chief Exec. & Oper. Officer--Sipex Corporation, Billerica, MA; *Int'l*, pg. 1415

Donley, Terrance K., Pres.--Donley's, Inc., Cleveland, OH; *U.S. Private*, pg. 340

Donlon, John, Pres.--Four Media Companies, Burbank, CA; *U.S. Private*, pg. 422

Donnell, Thomas, Pres.--Cain's Coffee Co., Oklahoma City, OK; *U.S. Public*, pg. 351

Donnelly, Clifford W., Pres.--PCA Life Reinsurance, Miami, FL; *U.S. Public*, pg. 1293

Donnelly, James C., Pres. & Chief. Exec. Officer--Sta-Rite Industries, Inc., Delavan, WI; *U.S. Public*, pg. 1767

Donnelly, John J., Pres.--L.F. Driscoll Co., Bala Cynwyd, PA; *U.S. Private*, pg. 343

Donnelly, John J., Pres.--DRS Laurel Technologies, Johnstown, PA; *U.S. Public*, pg. 475

Donnelly, Thomas, Pres. & Chief Exec. Officer--Camping World, Inc., Bowling Green, KY; *U.S. Private*, pg. 204

Donner, Michael, Chm. Bd., Pres. & Chief Exec. Officer--Barco of California, Gardena, CA; *U.S. Private*, pg. 115

Donohoe, James A., III, Pres. & Chief Exec. Officer--The Donohoe Companies, Inc., Washington, DC; *U.S. Private*, *pg. 340*

Donohoo, Richard G., Pres.--The Gibson Group Inc., Cincinnati, OH; *U.S. Private*, pg. 451

Donohue, Michael, Pres.--Associated Sand & Gravel Co., Inc., Everett, WA; *Int'l*, pg. 245

Donohue, Thomas J., Pres. & Chief Exec. Officer--Nation's Business, Washington, DC; *U.S. Private*, pg. 788

Donovan, Nancy S., Pres.--NOVUS Financial Corporation, Riverwoods, IL; *U.S. Public*, pg. 1132

Donovan, Raymond J., Pres. & Chief Fin. Officer--Schiavone Construction Co., Secaucus, NJ; *U.S. Private*, *pg. 970*

Donovan, Stephen P., Jr., Pres.--Procter & Gamble Food Products Div., Cincinnati, OH; *U.S. Public*, pg. 1331

Donovan, Thomas A., Pres.--Capitol Construction Group, Inc., Wheeling, IL; *U.S. Private*, pg. 206

Donovan, William T., Pres. & Chief Fin. Officer--Christiana Companies, Inc., Milwaukee, WI; *U.S. Public*, pg. 352

Doo, Burton, Pres. & Treas.--Altron Systems Corporation, Fremont, CA; *U.S. Public*, pg. 59

Doolan, Victor H., Pres.--BMW (US) Holding Corporation, Woodcliff Lake, NJ; *Int'l*, pg. 177

Dooley, Joseph F., Pres.--Duracell Canada Inc., Mississauga, Canada; *U.S. Public*, pg. 743

Dooley, Larry W., Pres. & Chief Exec. Officer--Regions Bank-Cedartown/Rockmart, Cedartown, GA; *U.S. Public*, *pg. 1372*

Doolittle, James H., Pres. & Chief Oper. Officer--Time Warner Cable, Stamford, CT; *U.S. Public*, pg. 1610

Doonan, Wendell M., Pres.--Doonan & Sons, Inc., Great Bend, KS; *U.S. Private*, pg. 340

Doran, Daniel J., Pres.--Ace Doran Hauling & Rigging Company, Cincinnati, OH; *U.S. Private*, pg. 340

Doran, Daniel J., Pres.--Ace Doran Brokerage, Cincinnati, OH; *U.S. Private*, pg. 340

Doran, Ed, Pres.--Nutmeg Mills Inc., Tampa, FL; *U.S. Public*, pg. 1702

Doran, Lindsay, Pres.--United Artists Pictures, Inc., Santa Monica, CA; *U.S. Public*, pg. 1102

Dore, Kathleen, Pres.--Bravo Network, Woodbury, NY; *U.S. Public*, pg. 288

Dore, William J., Chm. Bd., Pres. & Chief Exec. Officer--Global Industries, Ltd., Lafayette, LA; *U.S. Public*, pg. 748

Doretti, Robert L., Pres. & Chief Exec. Officer--Thinking Machines Corporation, Burlington, MA; *U.S. Private*, pg. 1081

Dorfi, Klaus G., Pres. & Chief Oper. Officer--Atlantic Mutual Companies, New York, NY; *U.S. Private*, pg. 95

Dorfman, Joel, Pres. & Chief Exec. Officer--Thorn Apple Valley, Inc., Southfield, MI; *U.S. Public*, pg. 1602

Dorfman, Larry I., Pres. & Chief Exec. Officer--Automobile Protection Corporation-APCO, Atlanta, GA; *U.S. Public*, pg. 150

Dorfman, Robert, Pres.--King Wire Inc., North Chicago, IL; *U.S. Private*, pg. 621

Dorhmann, R.W., Pres.--FryeTech, Inc., Des Moines, IA; *U.S. Private*, pg. 430

Doria, Joseph, Pres. & Chief Exec. Officer--The Lincoln Electric Co. of Canada Ltd., Toronto, Canada; *U.S. Public*, pg. 997

Doriga, Ramon Eduardo Garcia Lopez, Pres.--CTE - Compania Trasatlantica Espanola, S.A., Madrid, Spain; *Int'l*, pg. 1224

Dorigo, Rob, Pres.--Ferrero, Pino Torinese, Italy; *Int'l*, pg. 480

Dorio, Martin, Pres. & Chief Exec. Officer--Clark Material Handling Company, Lexington, KY; *U.S. Private*, pg. 243

Doris, Kevin, Pres. & Chief Exec. Officer--Gerland Corp., Houston, TX; *U.S. Private*, pg. 449

Dorkin, John, Pres. & Gen. Mgr.--Independence Television Co., Louisville, KY; *U.S. Private*, pg. 147

Dorman, John A., Pres. & Chief Oper. Officer--Broad National Bancorporation, Newark, NJ; *U.S. Public*, pg. 257

Dormer, Michael, Pres.--DePuy, Inc., Warsaw, IN; *Int'l*, pg. 331

Dorn, Ernst W., II, Pres.--Ernst W. Dorn Co., Inc., Gardena, CA; *U.S. Private*, pg. 340

Dorn, J.M., Jr., Chm. Bd. & Pres.--Aiken Electric Cooperative Inc., Aiken, SC; *U.S. Private*, pg. 28

Dorn, J.M., Jr., Chm. Bd. & Pres.--Aiken Electric Satellite, Aiken, SC; *U.S. Private*, pg. 28

Dornau, Peter, Pres.--Kinpak, Inc., Montgomery, AL; *U.S. Public*, pg. 1211

Dornau, Peter, Pres.--Starbrite Corp., Fort Lauderdale, FL; *U.S. Public*, pg. 1510

Dornau, Peter G., Chm. Bd. & Pres.--Ocean Bio-Chem Inc., Fort Lauderdale, FL; *U.S. Public*, pg. 1211

Dorner, Werner, Pres.--Dorner Manufacturing Corp., Hartland, WI; *U.S. Private*, pg. 340

Dorris, Al, Pres. & Chief Exec. Officer--Xerxes Corporation, Minneapolis, MN; *U.S. Private*, pg. 1194

Dorris, Joe M., Pres.--Futaba Corporation of America, Irvine, CA; *Int'l*, pg. 531

Dorsa, Peter A., Pres.--Epoxylite Corporation-Resin Div., Irvine, CA; *U.S. Private*, pg. 379

Dorsy, Claude, Pres.--First Florida Equities, Inc., Miami, FL; *U.S. Private*, pg. 407

Dorwart, Paul, Pres.--Linear Products Inc., Vancouver, WA; *U.S. Public*, pg. 687

Dosho, Koichi, Pres.--NMB Minebea GmbH, Langen, Germany; *Int'l*, pg. 868

Dosho, Koichi, Pres.--Precision Motors - Deutsche Minebea GmbH, Spaichingen, Germany; *Int'l*, pg. 869

Dotson, John L. Jr., Pres. & Publisher--The Beacon Journal Publishing Company, Akron, OH; *U.S. Public*, pg. 963

Dott, Jackson Y., Pres.--Monarch Avalon, Inc., Baltimore, MD; *U.S. Public*, pg. 1123

Dotter, Helmut, Mng. Dir.--Goldwell A.G., Darmstadt, Germany; *Int'l*, pg. 717

Dotterweich, Helmut, Pres. & Chief Exec. Officer--Spar Handels AG, Schenefeld, Germany; *Int'l*, pg. 1288

Dottori, Frank A., Pres. & Chief Exec. Officer--Tembec Inc., Montreal, Canada; *Int'l*, pg. 1374

Douay, Michel, Pres.--Clestra Hauserman, Strasbourg, France; *Int'l*, pg. 569

Doub, David M., Pres.--Florida Division, Saint Petersburg, FL; *U.S. Public*, pg. 509

Doubles, James E., Pres. & Chief Exec. Officer--TSI Incorporated, Shoreview, MN; *U.S. Public*, pg. 1559

Douce, Patrice, Pres. & Chief Oper. Officer--Sodexho S.A., Montigny-le-Bretonneux, France; *Int'l*, pg. 1274

Doucet, John, Pres. & Chief Oper. Officer--Day & Ross Inc., Hartland, Canada; *Int'l*, pg. 850

Douek, Joseph, Pres. & Gen. Mgr.--Willoughby's, New York, NY; *U.S. Private*, pg. 1180

Dougan, J., Pres.--BFC Buildings, Scarborough, Canada; *Int'l*, pg. 118

Dougan, J., Pres.--BFC Frontier, Lynnwood, WA; *Int'l*, pg. 118

Dougan, Paul M., Pres. & Chief Exec. Officer--Equity Oil Company, Salt Lake City, UT; *U.S. Public*, pg. 590

Dougan, Paul M., Pres.--Symskaya Exploration, Inc., Salt Lake City, UT; *U.S. Public*, pg. 590

Doughan, James, Pres. & Chief Exec. Officer--Abitibi-Consolidated Inc., Montreal, Canada; *Int'l*, pg. 19

Dougherty, David F., Pres. & Chief Exec. Officer--MATRIXX Marketing Inc., Cincinnati, OH; *U.S. Public*, pg. 368

Dougherty, R.L., Pres.--Fischbach & Dougherty, Inc., Atlanta, GA; *U.S. Private*, pg. 408

Dougherty, Robert J., Jr., Pres. & Chief Oper. Officer--Enterprise Diversified Holdings Incorporated, Newark, NJ; *U.S. Public*, pg. 1340

Doughty, David, Pres.--Clark Boardman Company, Ltd., New York, NY; *U.S. Public*, pg. 1602

Douglas, Barry, Pres.--New York Wire Co., Mount Wolf, PA; *U.S. Private*, pg. 795

Douglas, Herbert, Pres. & Chief Exec. Officer--Weiners Stores, Inc., Houston, TX; *U.S. Private*, pg. 1160

Douglas, J. Scott, Pres.--Dancker, Sellew & Douglas, Inc., New York, NY; *U.S. Private*, pg. 309

Douglas, James, Pres.-Regional--Citizens Bank of Kentucky, Morganfield, KY; *U.S. Public*, pg. 280

Douglas, T. O'Neal, Chm. Bd., Pres. & Chief Exec. Officer--First Colonial Insurance Company, Jacksonville, FL; *U.S. Public*, pg. 79

Douglas, Walter E., Sr., Chm. Bd. & Pres.--Avis Ford Inc., Southfield, MI; *U.S. Private*, pg. 101

Dourney, Martin W., Pres.--Omaha Property and Casualty Insurance Co., Omaha, NE; *U.S. Private*, pg. 770

Doutre, P., Pres.--Racal Filter Technologies, Inc., Brockville, Canada; *Int'l*, pg. 1083

Douville, Arthur J., Pres.--Unisource (North East), Windsor, CT; *U.S. Public*, pg. 1671

Douville, Jean, Chm. Bd., Pres. & Chief Exec. Officer--UAP, Inc., Montreal, Canada; *Int'l*, pg. 1426

Dover, J.D., Pres.--Zeolyst International, Houston, TX; *U.S. Private*, pg. 827

Dowd, Chuck, Chief Oper. Officer--Delta Faucet Corporation, Indianapolis, IN; *U.S. Public*, pg. 1053

Dowd, Kevin P., Pres., Chief Exec. Officer & Chief Oper. Officer--Checkpoint Systems Inc., Thorofare, NJ; *U.S. Public*, pg. 343

Dowd, William, Pres. & Chief Oper. Officer--Fleming Companies, Inc., Oklahoma City, OK; *U.S. Public*, pg. 652

Dowdell, Rodger B., Jr., Chm. Bd., Pres. & Chief Exec. Officer--American Power Conversion Corporation, West Kingston, RI; *U.S. Public*, pg. 89

Dowden, Dan, Pres.--Ouimet Corp., Nashville, TN; *U.S. Private*, pg. 821

Dowdle, James C., Pres. & Chief Exec. Officer--CLTV News, Oak Brook, IL; *U.S. Public*, pg. 1635

Dowdy, William C., Pres.--ServiceMaster Healthcare Management Services, Inc., Downers Grove, IL; *U.S. Public*, pg. 1462

Dowell, Gary R., Pres. & Chief Exec. Officer--Reistertown Federal Savings Bank, Baltimore, MD; *U.S. Public*, pg. 1543

Dowes, Richard, Pres.--Etablissements Bez S.A., Paris, France; *Int'l*, pg. 62

Dowling, James H., Chm. Emeritus, Pres. & Chief Exec. Officer-Lat. Amer. (Miami)--Burson-Marsteller, New York, NY; *U.S. Private*, pg. 1197

Dowling, John, Pres.--Sunwest Bank of Gallup, Gallup, NM; *U.S. Public*, pg. 1165

Dowling, Michael, Pres.--Sawgrass Electronics Group Inc., Coral Springs, FL; *U.S. Private*, pg. 968

Dowling, Steven A., Pres.--Macmillan/McGraw-Hill School Publishing Company, New York, NY; *U.S. Public*, pg. 1070

Dowling, Tim, Pres.--Sunwest Bank of Raton, N.A., Raton, NM; *U.S. Public*, pg. 1165

Downes, Laurence M., Chm. Bd., Pres. & Chief Exec. Officer--New Jersey Resources Corporation, Wall, NJ; *U.S. Public*, pg. 1172

Downes, Laurence M., Pres.--NJR Energy Services Corporation, Wall, NJ; *U.S. Public*, pg. 1172

Downey, Bruce L., Chm. Bd., Pres. & Chief Exec. Officer--Barr Laboratories Inc., Pomona, NY; *U.S. Public*, pg. 191

Downey, G. Lowell, Pres.--Collingwood Grain, Inc., Hutchinson, KS; *U.S. Public*, pg. 128

Downey, J. Michael, Pres.--Downey Printing, Waukee, IA; *U.S. Private*, pg. 342

Downey, Paul, Pres., Treas. & Sec.--Advanced Circuit Technology, Nashua, NH; *U.S. Private*, pg. 21

Downey, Richard T., Pres.--Hypertronics Corporation, Hudson, MA; *Int'l*, pg. 1268

Downing, Donald S., Pres.--SunTrust Mortgage Inc., Atlanta, GA; *U.S. Public*, pg. 1538

Downing, Gary R., Pres.--Medtech Inc., Jackson, WY; *U.S. Private*, pg. 728

Downing, Kathryn, Pres. & Chief Exec. Officer--Matthew Bender & Company, Incorporated, New York, NY; *U.S. Public*, pg. 1616

Downing, Kathryn M., Pres. & Chief Exec. Officer--Mosby-Year Book, Inc., Saint Louis, MO; *U.S. Public*, pg. 1616

Downing, Lowell Morris, Jr., Pres.--Lowell Packing Company, Fitzgerald, GA; *U.S. Private*, pg. 679

Dowsett, Patrick W., Pres. & Chief Exec. Officer--East Moline Metal Products Company, East Moline, IL; *U.S. Private*, pg. 357

Doxsee, Tucker, Pres.--Heraeus Instruments Inc., South Plainfield, NJ; *Int'l*, pg. 616

Doyle White, R., Chm. Bd., Pres. & Chief Exec. Officer--U.S. Filter/Davis Water & Waste Industries, Inc., Thomasville, GA; *U.S. Public*, pg. 1682

Doyle, Brian K., Pres. & Treas.--King Milling Company, Lowell, MI; *U.S. Private*, pg. 621

Doyle, Buzz, Pres. & Chief Oper. Officer--Furr's Supermarkets, Albuquerque, NM; *U.S. Private*, pg. 432

Doyle, James F., Pres.--Stokely-Van Camp, Inc., Chicago, IL; *U.S. Public*, pg. 1348

Doyle, Joseph, Pres.--BGM Health Communications, Inc., Los Angeles, CA; *U.S. Public*, pg. 1223

Doyle, Kevin, Pres.--Wassall USA Inc., Southport, CT; *Int'l*, pg. 1486

Doyle, Lawrence P., Pres. & Chief Exec. Officer--ASC Incorporated, Southgate, MI; *U.S. Private*, pg. 8

Doyle, Mary, Pres. & Principal--HSC Securities Corporation, Dallas, TX; *U.S. Public*, pg. 778

Doyle, Patrick J., Pres. & Chief Exec. Officer--Willis Corroon Corp. of Missouri, Saint Louis, MO; *Int'l*, pg. 1506

Doyle, Thomas D., Pres.--Trans Mountain Pipeline Company Ltd., Vancouver, Canada; *Int'l*, pg. 114

Doyle, Wayne, Pres.--Peterson Tractor Company, San Leandro, CA; *U.S. Private*, pg. 858

Doyle, William A., Pres.--InterDigital Communications Corp., King of Prussia, PA; *U.S. Public*, pg. 889

Dozier, Michael, Pres. & Chief Oper. Officer--TIE/Communications, Inc., Overland Park, KS; *U.S. Private*, pg. 1085

Draba, Roman A., Pres.--Southeastern Michigan Gas Company, Port Huron, MI; *U.S. Public*, pg. 1489

Drabinsky, C.R., Pres.--Deluxe Toronto Limited, Toronto, Canada; *Int'l*, pg. 1087

Drabinsky, Cyril, Pres.--Deluxe Laboratories, Inc., Hollywood, CA; *Int'l*, pg. 1087

Draeger, Kenneth, Pres.--AGFA EPS Division, Wilmington, MA; *Int'l*, pg. 172

Drago, Franklin J., Pres.--Bison Canning Co., Inc., Angola, NY; *U.S. Private*, pg. 468

Drago, Joseph A., Pres. & Chief Oper. Officer--The Dartnell Corporation, Chicago, IL; *U.S. Private*, pg. 312

Dragon, William, Jr., Pres.--Pacific Trail Inc., Seattle, WA; *U.S. Private*, pg. 673

Dragoti, Stan, Pres.--Moss/Dragoti, New York, NY; *Int'l*, pg. 117

Draheim, Edward R., Chief Exec. Officer--Faultless Caster, Evansville, IN; *Int'l*, pg. 473

Drake, Dave, Pres.--SMC Mining Company, Fairview Heights, IL; *U.S. Public*, pg. 1790

Drake, Edward, Pres.--Designers Knitting Mills, New York, NY; *U.S. Public*, pg. 778

Drake, J. Michael, Pres.--Econocom-USA Inc., Memphis, TN; *U.S. Private*, pg. 361

Drake, John E., Pres.--Crest Ridge Homes, Inc., Breckenridge, TX; *U.S. Public*, pg. 333

Drakesmith, John, Pres.--Heintzelman's Truck Center Inc., Orlando, FL; *U.S. Private*, pg. 519

Drakoulias, Peter, Partner & Bus. Devel. Dir.--Deutsch, Inc., New York, NY; *U.S. Private*, pg. 328

Drakoulias, Peter, Partner & Bus. Devel. Dir.--DirectDeutsch, New York, NY; *U.S. Private*, pg. 328

Drakoulias, Peter, Partner & Bus. Devel. Dir.--Interactive Deutsch, New York, NY; *U.S. Private*, pg. 329

Draper, E. Linn, Jr., Dr., Chm. Bd., Pres. & Chief Exec. Officer--American Electric Power Company, Inc., Columbus, OH; *U.S. Public*, pg. 71

Draper, E. Linn, Jr., Dr., Chm. Bd., Pres. & Chief Exec. Officer--American Electric Power Service Corp., Columbus, OH; *U.S. Public*, pg. 72

Draper, E.L., Dr., Pres.--Ohio Valley Electric Corporation, Piketon, OH; *U.S. Private*, pg. 813

Draper, Michael, Pres.--Sauer-Sundstrand Company, Ames, IA; *Int'l*, pg. 1198

Dray, Patrick Michael, Pres.--Columbia Corporation, Brentwood, TN; *U.S. Private*, pg. 255

Drayer, Phillip M., Chm. Bd., Pres. & Chief Exec. Officer--TelCom Semiconductor, Inc., Mountain View, CA; *U.S. Public*, pg. 1569

Drazen, Mike, Mng. Partner & Chief Creative Officer--Earle Palmer Brown, New York, NY; *U.S. Private*, pg. 173

Drebes, Charles F., Pres. & Chief Exec. Officer--Gaylord Printing, Inc., Detroit, MI; *U.S. Private*, pg. 441

Drecoll, J. Cameron, Pres. & Gen. Mgr.--Brad Foote Gear Works, Inc., Cicero, IL; *U.S. Private*, pg. 417

Dreher, Donald D., Chm. Bd., Pres. & Chief Exec. Officer--DMI Furniture Inc., Louisville, KY; *U.S. Public*, pg. 473

Dreier, R. Chad, Chm. Bd., Pres. & Chief Exec. Officer--The Ryland Group, Inc., Columbia, MD; *U.S. Public*, pg. 1414

Dreimann, Leonhard, Pres. & Chief Exec. Officer--Salton/Maxim Housewares, Inc., Mount Prospect, IL; *U.S. Public*, pg. 1430

Drendel, Gene, Pres.--Capitol Group, Springfield, IL; *U.S. Private*, pg. 206

Drennan, Robert, Pres.--Unichema U.S.A., Chicago, IL; *Int'l*, pg. 1436

Drennen, Felix, III, Pres. & Chief Exec. Officer--Brice Building Co., Inc., Birmingham, AL; *U.S. Private*, pg. 167

Dresen, William, Pres.--TriEnda Corporation, Portage, WI; *U.S. Private*, pg. 1103

Dressler, Abbott, W., Pres.--Colfax, Inc., Pawtucket, RI; *U.S. Private*, pg. 252

Dressler, Robert, Chm. Bd., Pres. & Chief Exec. Officer--Century Door U.S.A. Inc., Tampa, FL; *Int'l*, pg. 1067

Drew, Robert, Pres.--Lockheed Martin Fairchild Imaging Sensors, Milpitas, CA; *U.S. Public*, pg. 1008

Drexler, Michael, Pres.--BJK&E Media Group, New York, NY; *U.S. Public*, pg. 1642

Drexler, Millard S., Pres. & Chief Exec. Officer--The Gap, Inc., San Francisco, CA; *U.S. Public*, pg. 702

Drexler, Millard S., Pres. & Chief Exec. Officer--Old Navy Stores, San Francisco, CA; *U.S. Public*, pg. 703

Drexler, Richard A., Chm. Bd., Pres. & Chief Exec. Officer--Allied Products Corporation, Chicago, IL; *U.S. Public*, pg. 48

Dreyer, Alec G., Pres.--Illinova Generating Co., Decatur, IL; *U.S. Public*, pg. 870

Dreyer, John W., Chm. Bd., Pres. & Chief Exec. Officer--Harold M. Pitman Co., Inc., Totowa, NJ; *U.S. Private*, pg. 867

Dreyer, Kris, Chm. Bd., Pres. & Chief Exec. Officer--South Bend Stamping, South Bend, IN; *U.S. Private*, pg. 1014

Dreyfus-Cloarec, Claire, Pres.--Groupe Servair (Compagnie d'Exploitation des Services Auxiliaires Aeriens), Roissy, France; *Int'l*, pg. 560

Driesse, Henry J., Pres. & Gen. mgr.--ITT Avionics Division, Clifton, NJ; *U.S. Public*, pg. 859

Driggers, Gary, Pres. & Chief Oper. Officer--Midcoast Aviation, Inc., Saint Louis, MO; *U.S. Private*, pg. 959

Driggs, Dick, Pres.--Addison Products Company, Orlando, FL; *U.S. Private*, pg. 518

Drimal, Charles E., Jr., Pres., Chief Exec. Officer & Chief Oper. Officer--PrimeEnergy Corporation, Stamford, CT; *U.S. Public*, pg. 1328

Drinkall, Austin M., Chm. Bd., Pres. & Chief Exec. Officer--South Bend Plastics, Inc., Mishawaka, IN; *U.S. Private*, pg. 1014

Drinkward, Robert, Pres. & Sec.--Bergelectric Corporation, Los Angeles, CA; *U.S. Private*, pg. 135

Drinkward, Wayne, Pres.--Hoffman Corporation, Portland, OR; *U.S. Private*, pg. 532

Driscoll, Susan, Pres.--Worth Publisher Inc., New York, NY; *Int'l*, pg. 1479

Driscoll, W. Michael, Pres. & Chief Exec. Officer--Smith Corona Corp., Cortland, NY; *U.S. Private*, pg. 1007

Driver, Adrian, Pres.--CSR Central, Houston, TX; *Int'l*, pg. 245

Driver, Frank L., IV, Pres. & Chief Exec. Officer--Driver-Harris Company, Harrison, NJ; *U.S. Public*, pg. 530

Driver, Philip L., Pres.--Berkley Care Network, Inc., Greensboro, NC; *U.S. Public*, pg. 216

Drnevich, Ronald J., Pres. & Chief Exec. Officer--Gannett Fleming Affiliates, Inc., Camp Hill, PA; *U.S. Private*, pg. 439

Drobis, David, Chm. & Sr. Partner--Prap Japan, Inc., Tokyo, Japan; *U.S. Private*, pg. 617

Drobis, David R., Chm., Sr. Partner & Chief Exec. Officer--Ketchum Public Relations Worldwide, New York, NY; *U.S. Private*, pg. 617

Droesch, E. Richard, Pres.--Florence Corporation, Huntington, NY; *U.S. Private*, pg. 414

Drohan, Gregory J., Pres.--Carter Products, Canada, Mississauga, Canada; *U.S. Public*, pg. 310

Droin, Michel, Reg. Pres.--Melitta Iberica S.A., Madrid, Spain; Int'l, pg. 857
Drosdick, John G., Pres. & Chief Oper. Officer--Sun Company, Inc., Philadelphia, PA; U.S. Public, pg. 1530
Drouillard, Neil R., Pres. & Chief Exec. Officer--F/N Group, Inc., Oak Park, MI; U.S. Public, pg. 84
Drower, Herbert, Pres.--Transilwrap Company, Inc., Chicago, IL; U.S. Private, pg. 1097
Droz, Henry, Pres.--WEA Corp., Burbank, CA; U.S. Public, pg. 1612
Drozeski, L.C., Jr., Pres. & Chief Oper. Officer--Bunzl Extrusion, Richmond, VA; Int'l, pg. 232
Druckenmiller, Robert, Pres.--Porter Novelli International, New York, NY; U.S. Public, pg. 1224
Druehl, Bradley P., Pres.--HRH Insurance Services of Northern California, Inc., San Rafael, CA; U.S. Public, pg. 827
Drum, Robert P., Pres.--Fleet Services Corp., Providence, RI; U.S. Public, pg. 650
Drumheller, Phillip M., Pres.--Lane Press, Inc., South Burlington, VT; U.S. Private, pg. 650
Drumm, Curtis, Pres.--Monarch Ware, Inc., Algoma, WI; U.S. Private, pg. 735
Drumm, Robert, Pres.--General Tours Inc., Keene, NH; U.S. Private, pg. 445
Drumm, Streuby L., Jr., Pres.--Drumm & Associates, Inc., New Orleans, LA; U.S. Private, pg. 343
Drumm, Wesley, Pres.--Nesco Ameican Harvest Inc., Chaska, MN; U.S. Private, pg. 735
Drumm, Wesley C., Chm. Bd., Pres. & Treas.--The Metal Ware Corp., Two Rivers, WI; U.S. Private, pg. 734
Drummond, Jere A., Pres. & Chief Exec. Officer--BellSouth Telecommunications, Inc., Atlanta, GA; U.S. Public, pg. 209
Drummond, Robert J., Pres. & Chief Exec. Officer--Epsilon, Burlington, MA; U.S. Public, pg. 74
Drury, Francis T., Pres.--Kathabar Incorporated, Somerset, NJ; U.S. Private, pg. 609
Druse, Loise, Pres.--Bristol-Myers S.A.E., Madrid, Spain; U.S. Public, pg. 255
Dryburg, Doug, Pres.--Izod, New York, NY; U.S. Public, pg. 1292
Dryburgh, R.H.R., Pres. & Chief Exec. Officer--Jannock Steel Fabricating Company, Oakville, Canada; Int'l, pg. 698
Dryburgh, R.H.R., Pres.--Jenisys Engineered Products, Oakville, Canada; Int'l, pg. 698
Dryburgh, R.H.R., Pres.--Jenisys Engineered Products, Inc., Louisville, KY; Int'l, pg. 698
Dryden, Lindsay D. III, Pres.--Dryden Oil Company, Inc., Baltimore, MD; Int'l, pg. 235
Dryden, Trip, Pres.--Dryden Oil of New England, Worcester, MA; Int'l, pg. 235
Drysdale, Robert H., Pres.--Crestar Securities Corporation, Richmond, VA; U.S. Public, pg. 458
du Chatelier, Bernard, Pres.--Cyanamid Iberica, S.A., Madrid, Spain; U.S. Public, pg. 81
Du Peloux, Cyrille, Pres. & Dir. Gen.--Multivision, Paris, France; Int'l, pg. 561
du Rudder, Thierry, Chm. Bd. & Pres.--American Cometra, Inc., Fort Worth, TX; Int'l, pg. 562
Du, Ben R., Pres.--Flojet Corporation, Irvine, CA; U.S. Private, pg. 414
Duailibi, Roberto, Mng. Partner--DPZ-Duailibi, Petit, Zaragoza, Propaganda S.A., Sao Paulo, Brazil; Int'l, pg. 352
Dubay, Eugene, Pres.--Kansas Gas Service, Overland Park, KS; U.S. Public, pg. 1226
Dubbeldeman, G., Pres.--KTI Belgium N.V., Mol, Belgium; Int'l, pg. 836
Dube, Jean-Marie, Pres.--Willis Corroon Aerospace of Canada Ltd., Montreal, Canada; Int'l, pg. 1509
Dubendorf, John, Pres.--Blue Anchor, Inc., Dinuba, CA; U.S. Private, pg. 150
Dubes, Michael J., Pres. & Chief Exec. Officer--Northern Life Insurance Company, Seattle, WA; U.S. Public, pg. 1375
Dubey, Prabhat K., Pres. & Chief Exec. Officer--MMC Networks, Inc., Sunnyvale, CA; U.S. Public, pg. 1027
Dubiel, Robert S., Pres. & Chief Exec. Officer--Cobra Golf Incorporated, Carlsbad, CA; U.S. Public, pg. 675
Dubin, Melvin, Chm. Bd.--Slant/Fin Corporation, Greenvale, NY; U.S. Private, pg. 1005
Dubin, Thomas G., Pres.--Manufacturers' News, Inc., Evanston, IL; U.S. Private, pg. 700
Dubinsky, Peter, Pres. & Chief Exec. Officer--Accurate Bushing Co., Inc., Garwood, NJ; U.S. Private, pg. 11
Dubois, Bernard C., Pres.--Haydon Switch & Instrument, Inc., Waterbury, CT; U.S. Private, pg. 513
Dubrule, Paul, Co.-Chm. & Co-Pres.--Accor S.A., Evry, France; Int'l, pg. 20
Duch-Pedersen, Alf, Pres. & Chief Exec. Officer--Danisco A/S, Copenhagen, Denmark; Int'l, pg. 378
Duchman, Mendel, Pres.--Allou Personal Care Corp., Saugus, CA; U.S. Public, pg. 55
Duchossois, Craig J., Pres. & Chief Exec. Officer--Duchossois Industries, Inc., Elmhurst, IL; U.S. Private, pg. 344
Duchoud, Gilbert, Pres.-Exec. Bd.--Banque Cantonale Vaudoise, Lausanne, Switzerland; Int'l, pg. 160
Duda, Ferdinand S., Pres. & Chief Exec. Officer--A. Duda & Sons Inc., Oviedo, FL; U.S. Private, pg. 344
Duda, Joseph A., Pres.-Duda land--A. Duda & Sons Inc., Oviedo, FL; U.S. Private, pg. 344
Dudas, Nicholas, Pres.--Klockner-Moeller Corp., Franklin, MA; Int'l, pg. 736
Dudek, Walter, Pres. & Chief Exec. Officer--Dudek & Bock Spring Manufacturing Company, Chicago, IL; U.S. Private, pg. 344
Dudley, Robert G., Pres.--First National Bank of El Dorado, El Dorado, AR; U.S. Public, pg. 641
Dueffert, Gregory, Pres. & Treas.--Lincoln Industries, Inc., Boonville, IN; U.S. Private, pg. 1207
Duerden, John, Chm. Bd. & Pres.--Stonington Partners Inc., New York, NY; U.S. Private, pg. 1045
Duerden, John, Chm. Bd., Pres. & Chief Exec. Officer--Dictaphone Corp., Stratford, CT; U.S. Private, pg. 1045
Duerr, David, Pres.-Grey Ink--Grey Direct, New York, NY; U.S. Public, pg. 764
Dueser, F. Scott, Pres. & Chief Exec. Officer--First National Bank of Abilene, Abilene, TX; U.S. Public, pg. 633
Duff, Charles, Chm. Bd. & Pres.--Farnam Companies, Inc., Phoenix, AZ; U.S. Private, pg. 396
Duff, Thomas M., Pres. & Chief Exec. Officer--Wellman, Inc., Shrewsbury, NJ; U.S. Public, pg. 1752
Duffield, David, Pres. & Chief Exec. Officer--PeopleSoft, Inc., Pleasanton, CA; U.S. Public, pg. 1276
Duffin, Iain, Pres.--ITT Cannon, Santa Ana, CA; U.S. Public, pg. 859
Dufford, Donn, Pres.--Dufford Marketing, Pasadena, CA; U.S. Private, pg. 345
Duffy, Brian, Pres.--C. B. Fleet Co., Inc., Lynchburg, VA; U.S. Private, pg. 410
Duffy, E. Patrick, Pres.--Bowater Coated Paper & Pulp Div., Catawba, SC; U.S. Public, pg. 248
Duffy, Kevin, Pres. & Chief Oper. Officer--Xyvision, Inc., Wakefield, MA; U.S. Public, pg. 1787
Dufour, Bruce, Pres. & Gen. Mgr.--Kysor Cooling Systems, Cadillac, MI; U.S. Public, pg. 968
Dufour, Robert M., Pres.--National Card Control, Inc., Crozier, VA; U.S. Public, pg. 321
Dugan, D.R., Pres.--American Finance Group, Inc., Boston, MA; U.S. Public, pg. 1241
Dugan, Frances, Pres.--Dugan & Meyers Construction Co., Cincinnati, OH; U.S. Private, pg. 345
Dugan, Rob, Pres.--McGavin Foods Ltd., Langley, Canada; Int'l, pg. 841
Dugan, Thomas A., Pres.--Anaheim Manufacturing Company, Anaheim, CA; U.S. Private, pg. 70
Dugan, Thomas A., Pres., Chief Exec. Officer & Chief Fin. Officer--Dugan Production Corp., Farmington, NM; U.S. Private, pg. 345
Duggan, Edwin L., Sr., Pres.--Duggan Industries, Inc., Dallas, TX; U.S. Private, pg. 345
Duggan, J., Pres.--NMB Precision Inc., Mississauga, Canada; Int'l, pg. 868
Duggan, Jackie, Pres.--Crankshaft Machine Group, Jackson, MI; U.S. Private, pg. 102
Duggan, Michael, Pres.--Melard Manufacturing Corporation, Passaic, NJ; U.S. Private, pg. 729
Dugger, Tom, Pres.--Firestone Tube Company, Russellville, AR; Int'l, pg. 214
Duggirala, Kamal, Pres.--Barra, Inc., Berkeley, CA; U.S. Public, pg. 191
Duke, Timothy R., Pres. & Chief Exec. Officer--Steel of West Virginia, Inc., Huntington, WV; U.S. Public, pg. 1513
Dull, David, Pres. & Chief Exec. Officer--Fluidrive Inc., Brookston, IN; U.S. Private, pg. 415
Dull, William H., Pres. & Chief Exec. Officer--Tamura Corporation of America, Temecula, CA; U.S. Private, pg. 1067
Dumas, Jean-Louis, Exec. Mgr.--Hermes International, Paris, France; Int'l, pg. 617
Dumont, Daniel, Pres. & Chief Oper. Officer--Joslyn Canada Inc., Lachine, Canada; U.S. Public, pg. 482
duMoulin, Richard T., Chm., Pres. & Chief Exec. Officer--Marine Transport Lines, Inc., Weehawken, NJ; U.S. Private, pg. 703
Dun, Richard H., Pres.--Transistor Devices Europe Ltd., Cork, Ireland; U.S. Private, pg. 1097
Dunah, Richard E., Pres.--Precision Lamp, Inc., Cotati, CA; U.S. Public, pg. 856
Dunavant, William B., III, Pres.--Dunavant Enterprises, Inc., Memphis, TN; U.S. Private, pg. 346
Dunaway, Mike, Pres.--POLESTAR Labs, Inc., Escondido, CA; U.S. Private, pg. 874
Dunbar, Bill, Pres. & Chief Exec. Officer--Northwestel Inc., Whitehorse, Canada; Int'l, pg. 115
Dunbar, Bill, Pres. & Chief Exec. Officer--CellularVision Canada Ltd., Vancouver, Canada; Int'l, pg. 1482
Dunbar, Jim, Pres.--GSW Pump Company, Fergus, Canada; Int'l, pg. 538
Dunbar, William F., Pres. & Chief Oper. Officer--Allied Capital Corporation II, Washington, DC; U.S. Public, pg. 47
Duncan, D. F., Pres.--Toromont Process Systems Inc., Houston, TX; Int'l, pg. 1401
Duncan, Dave, Pres.--Imprimerie Quebecor Canada, Woodbridge, Canada; Int'l, pg. 1077
Duncan, Gail, Pres.--Jerome-Duncan Ford, Sterling Heights, MI; U.S. Private, pg. 586
Duncan, Gregory A., Pres. & Chief Exec. Officer--Citizens National Bank of Southern Pennsylvania, Greencastle, PA; U.S. Public, pg. 1542
Duncan, Jay, Pres.--Duncan & Hill Division, Niles, IL; U.S. Public, pg. 773
Duncan, Jon, Pres.--Birdair, Inc., Amherst, NY; Int'l, pg. 1348
Duncan, M. David, Pres.--Physicians Insurance Company of Indiana, Indianapolis, IN; U.S. Public, pg. 1080
Duncan, Melvin D., Jr., Pres.--Red Ball Leasing, Inc., Indianapolis, IN; U.S. Private, pg. 97
Duncan, Ronald A., Pres. & Chief Exec. Officer--General Communication, Inc., Anchorage, AK; U.S. Public, pg. 708
Duncan, William W., Jr., Pres. & Chief Exec. Officer--St. Michaels Bank, Saint Michaels, MD; U.S. Public, pg. 1089
Dundon, Brian R., Pres.--Magnetek Motors & Generators, Saint Louis, MO; U.S. Public, pg. 1037
Dunford, Stanley, Chm. Bd. & Pres.--Contrans Corporation, Woodstock, Canada; Int'l, pg. 328
Dunham, Duane R., Pres.--Bethlehem Steel-Sparrows Point Division, Sparrows Point, MD; U.S. Public, pg. 226
Dunham, Michael D., Pres. & Chief Exec. Officer--Effective Management Systems, Milwaukee, WI; U.S. Public, pg. 565
Dunlap, Angela O., Pres.-MCI Consumer Markets--MCI Telecommunications Corp., Washington, DC; U.S. Public, pg. 1024
Dunlap, Edward B., Chm Bd., Pres. & Chief Exec. Officer--Centimark Corporation, Canonsburg, PA; U.S. Private, pg. 222
Dunlap, Frederick C., Pres.--United HealthCare of Florida, Inc., Coral Gables, FL; U.S. Public, pg. 1678
Dunlap, Rex H., Pres. & Chief Oper. Officer--First Financial Building Corporation, Manchester, MO; U.S. Private, pg. 407
Dunlap, Rex H., Pres.--Bank Building, Manchester, MO; U.S. Private, pg. 407
Dunmire, Cyril C., Jr., Pres.--Stabler Companies, Inc., Harrisburg, PA; U.S. Private, pg. 1028
Dunmire, Ron, Pres.--Standard Havens, Kansas City, MO; U.S. Public, pg. 1365
Dunn, Al, Pres.--Saint Augustine Foods, Inc., Claremont, NC; U.S. Public, pg. 1729
Dunn, Charles O., Pres. & Chief Exec. Officer--Mississippi Chemical Corporation, Yazoo City, MS; U.S. Public, pg. 1117
Dunn, Howard L. Jr., Pres. & Chief Oper. Officer--Culp, Inc., High Point, NC; U.S. Public, pg. 467
Dunn, James, Pres.--Heidelberg Canada Graphic Equipment Ltd., Etobicoke, Canada; Int'l, pg. 605
Dunn, James R., Pres.--Plaskolite Inc., Columbus, OH; U.S. Private, pg. 870
Dunn, James W., Pres. & Chief Exec. Officer--Willis Corroon Corp. of Florida, Tampa, FL; Int'l, pg. 1505
Dunn, Jim, Pres.--Lockheed Martin Fairchild Systems, Syosset, NY; U.S. Public, pg. 1008
Dunn, Mike, Pres.--Alliance America, Norcross, GA; U.S. Private, pg. 37
Dunn, Robert, Pres.--National Riggers & Erectors, Plymouth, MI; U.S. Private, pg. 511
Dunn, Terrence P., Pres. & Chief Exec. Officer--Dunn Industries Inc., Kansas City, MO; U.S. Private, pg. 347
Dunn, W. Byron, Pres.--Lone Star Steel Company, Dallas, TX; U.S. Public, pg. 1012
Dunning, Richard, Pres. & Chief Exec. Officer--VIMRx Pharmaceuticals, Inc., Wilmington, DE; U.S. Public, pg. 1702
Dunxun, Zheng, Pres.--Sinochem International Petroleum Co. Ltd., Beijing, China; Int'l, pg. 1254
Dupps, John A., Jr., Pres.--Dupps Company, Germantown, OH; U.S. Private, pg. 348
Dupuis, Pierre, Pres. & Chief Exec. Officer--Sico Inc., Longueuil, Canada; Int'l, pg. 1239
Dupuy, Yvan, Pres.--Benjamin Moore & Co., Montvale, NJ; U.S. Private, pg. 133
Durame, Jean, Pres.--Credit Industriel de Normandie, Rouen, France; Int'l, pg. 564
Duran, Alvaro Bilbao, Pres.--Bilbao/Y&R, Asuncion, Paraguay; U.S. Private, pg. 1200
Durant, James E., Pres. & Chief Exec. Officer--Trautman & Shreve, Inc., Denver, CO; U.S. Public, pg. 572
Durante, Jay, Partner--Messner Vetere Berger McNamee Schmetterer/EURO RSCG, New York, NY; Int'l, pg. 602
Durante, Raffaele, Pres.--Siemens S.p.A., Milan, Italy; Int'l, pg. 1248
Duren, D. Ronald, Pres. & Chief Oper. Officer--Telecom Solutions, San Jose, CA; U.S. Public, pg. 1547
Durfee, Jim, Partner--Messner Vetere Berger McNamee Schmetterer/EURO RSCG, New York, NY; Int'l, pg. 602
Durfee, John, Chm. Bd., Pres. & Treas.--Bethel Mills, Inc., Bethel, VT; U.S. Private, pg. 141
Durham, Larry, Pres.--Durham Transportation, Inc., Austin, TX; U.S. Private, pg. 348
Durham, Larry K., Pres.--Durham Transportation Inc., Rosemead, CA; U.S. Private, pg. 348
Durham, Michael J., Pres. & Chief Exec. Officer--The SABRE Group Holdings, Inc., Fort Worth, TX; U.S. Public, pg. 10
Durham, Timothy S., Pres. & Chief Exec. Officer--Carpenter Industries, Inc., Richmond, IN; U.S. Private, pg. 215
Durhan, Michael D., Chm., Pres. & Chief Exec. Officer--SunTrust Bank, West Florida, Pensacola, FL; U.S. Public, pg. 1538
Durhein, Rich, Pres.--McHugh Software International, Waukesha, WI; U.S. Private, pg. 866
Durkee, Ed, Pres.--Accudyne Corporation, Janesville, WI; U.S. Public, pg. 47
Durnin, Douglas K., Pres.--A.K. Durnin Chrysler Plymouth, Inc., Baton Rouge, LA; U.S. Private, pg. 348
Duroux, Axel, Pres.--RTL 2, Paris, France; Int'l, pg. 561
Durr, Heinz, Chm. Bd., Pres. & Chief Exec. Officer--Deutsche Bahn, Frankfurt/Main, Germany; Int'l, pg. 401
Durrett, R. Lamar, Pres. & Chief Exec. Officer--Air Canada, Saint-Laurent, Canada; Int'l, pg. 36
Durst, Larry, Sr. Partner--Einson Freeman Inc., Paramus, NJ; Int'l, pg. 1483
Durwood, Stanley H., Chm. Bd. & Chief Exec. Officer--AMC Entertainment, Inc., Kansas City, MO; U.S. Private, pg. 6
Dusa, Jerry A., Pres. & Chief Exec. Officer--Digi International Inc., Minnetonka, MN; U.S. Public, pg. 506
Dusa, Jerry A., Pres.--Eagle Technology, San Jose, CA; U.S. Public, pg. 1105
Dussart, Marc, Pres.--MACtac Europe S.A., Soignies, Belgium; U.S. Public, pg. 210
Dussault, C., Pres. & Chief Oper. Officer--Le Groupe Commerce, Saint-Hyacinthe, Canada; Int'l, pg. 650
Dustin, William, Pres.--Creative Card Co., Chicago, IL; U.S. Public, pg. 89
Duthie, David, Dr., Pres.--Courtaulds Fibers Inc., Axis, AL; Int'l, pg. 339
Dutia, Suren G., Chm. Bd., Pres. & Chief Exec. Officer--Photomatrix Corporation, San Diego, CA; U.S. Public, pg. 1292
Dutlinger, Robert P., Pres.--Medaes Incorporated, Norcross, GA; U.S. Private, pg. 287

Dutton, Christopher L., Pres. & Chief Exec. Officer--Green Mountain Power Corporation, South Burlington, VT; *U.S. Public*, pg. 761
Duval, Daniel W., Pres. & Chief Exec. Officer--Robbins & Myers, Inc., Dayton, OH; *U.S. Public*, pg. 1393
Duvall, Bill, Pres.--Lincoln Property Company, Dallas, TX; *U.S. Private*, pg. 668
Duwe, Brian, Pres.--Gilliam Candy Brands, Edwardsville, KS; *U.S. Private*, pg. 454
Dwelle, T.A., Partner--Nella Oil Company, Auburn, CA; *U.S. Private*, pg. 790
Dworkin, David, Pres. & Chief Exec. Officer-Uptons Inc.--American Retail Group, New York, NY; *U.S. Private*, pg. 61
Dworman, Alvin, Chm. Bd. & Pres.--Lee National Corporation, New York, NY; *U.S. Private*, pg. 658
Dwyer, James, Pres.--Wireless One Network LP, Fort Myers, FL; *U.S. Private*, pg. 1184
Dwyer, M.A., Pres. & Chief Exec. Officer--Daubert Chemical Company, Inc., Chicago, IL; *U.S. Private*, pg. 313
Dwyer, W., V.P.-Opers.--Litton Solid State, Santa Clara, CA; *U.S. Public*, pg. 1003
Dye, Donald H., Pres. & Chief Exec. Officer--Callaway Golf Company, Carlsbad, CA; *U.S. Public*, pg. 294
Dye, Michael H., Pres. & Chief Exec. Officer--The PBS&J Corporation, Miami, FL; *U.S. Private*, pg. 825
Dye, William, Pres. & Chief Exec. Officer--Unidigital Inc., New York, NY; *U.S. Public*, pg. 1664
Dye, William G., Pres.--Air Cargo Equipment Corporation, Rancho Dominguez, CA; *U.S. Public*, pg. 1791
Dyer, Bruce, Pres.--BFD Productions, Inc., Las Vegas, NV; *U.S. Public*, pg. 1321
Dyer, Cliff, Pres.--Merisel Latin America, Miami, FL; *U.S. Public*, pg. 1096
Dyer, Lex, III, Chm. Bd., Pres. & Chief Exec. Officer--International Airline Support Group, Inc., Atlanta, GA; *U.S. Public*, pg. 894
Dyment, F.J., Pres. & Chief Exec. Officer--Ranger Oil Limited, Calgary, Canada; *Int'l*, pg. 1086
Dymond, Robert C.J., Pres. & Chief Exec. Officer--ANGUS Chemical Company, Buffalo Grove, IL; *U.S. Private*, pg. 75
Dyott, Stephen, Pres.--American Color Graphics, Brentwood, TN; *U.S. Public*, pg. 1132
Dyson, Marvin, Pres.--WGCI-AM/FM, Chicago, IL; *U.S. Public*, pg. 335
Dyszkiewicz, Tom, Pres. & Chief Exec. Officer--The National Super Service Co., Toledo, OH; *U.S. Private*, pg. 787
Eaccarino, Lou, Pres.-Designers Knitting Mills--Hampshire Designers Inc., Anderson, SC; *U.S. Public*, pg. 778
Each, Thomas C., Pres.--Chemifax, Santa Fe Springs, CA; *U.S. Private*, pg. 774
Eacott, James H., III, Pres. & Treas.--Bartlett Brainard Eacott, Inc., Bloomfield, CT; *U.S. Private*, pg. 118
Eades, David C., Mng. Gen. Partner--Regency Associates Limited Partnership, Champaign, IL; *U.S. Private*, pg. 918
Eagle, Charles, Pres.--Budget Marketing, Inc., Des Moines, IA; *U.S. Private*, pg. 178
Eagle, John R., Pres. & Chief Oper. Officer--Eagle Lincoln Mercury Inc., Dallas, TX; *U.S. Private*, pg. 355
Eagon, Douglas, Pres.--Stiles Corporation, Fort Lauderdale, FL; *U.S. Private*, pg. 1043
Eaker, Alan C., Pres.--GTE Alaska Incorporated, Anchorage, AK; *U.S. Public*, pg. 697
Earhart, Donald M., Chm. Bd., Pres. & Chief Exec. Officer--I-Flow Corporation, Lake Forest, CA; *U.S. Public*, pg. 851
Earle, Randolph A., Pres. & Gen. Mgr.--Mrs. Giles Country Kitchens, Inc., Lynchburg, VA; *U.S. Public*, pg. 596
Earley, Anthony F., Jr., Pres. & Chief Oper. Officer--DTE Energy Company, Detroit, MI; *U.S. Public*, pg. 475
Earley, Pat, Pres.--Ameritech Communications, Inc., Rosemont, IL; *U.S. Public*, pg. 98
Earnhardt, Hal J., III, Pres. & Owner--Earnhardt's Motor Companies, Gilbert, AZ; *U.S. Private*, pg. 356
Earnheart, Aubrey, Pres. & Chief Exec. Officer--First State Bank, Brownsville, TN; *U.S. Public*, pg. 1669
Earp, Donald C., Pres.--Earp Distribution Center, Kansas City, KS; *U.S. Private*, pg. 356
Earwood, Dale C., Pres.--NorAm Field Services Corp., Shreveport, LA; *U.S. Public*, pg. 843
Easley, Dan, Pres.--Sunrise Medical Respiratory Products Division, Somerset, PA; *U.S. Public*, pg. 1536
Eason, J. Cliff, Pres.--Network Services, Saint Louis, MO; *U.S. Public*, pg. 1416
East, Charles, Pres. & Chief Exec. Officer--Regions Bank/Rockdale County, Conyers, GA; *U.S. Public*, pg. 1372
Easterly, David E., Pres. & Chief Oper. Officer--Cox Enterprises, Inc., Atlanta, GA; *U.S. Private*, pg. 281
Easterly, Thomas B., Pres.--Johnstown Knitting Mill Co., Johnstown, NY; *U.S. Private*, pg. 595
Eastham, Dennis, Pres. & Chief Oper. Officer--Blau Marketing Technologies, Inc., Wilton, CT; *U.S. Private*, pg. 148
Eastlake, R.W., Pres.--Kaw Pipeline Co., Houston, TX; *U.S. Public*, pg. 1584
Eastland, Woods E., Pres. & Chief Exec. Officer--Staple Cotton Cooperative Association, Greenwood, MS; *U.S. Private*, pg. 1033
Eastly, Arthur C., Pres.--Canadian Forest Oil Ltd., Calgary, Canada; *U.S. Public*, pg. 670
Easton, John J., Pres.--Raybestos Products Co., Crawfordsville, IN; *U.S. Public*, pg. 1363
Easton, Robert G., Pres. & Chief Exec. Officer--Stockton Holdings Limited, Hamilton, Bermuda; *Int'l*, pg. 1010
Eaton, Bruce C., Pres.--Eaton Office Supply Co., Inc., Amherst, NY; *U.S. Private*, pg. 358
Eaton, Henry F., Chm. & Chief Exec. Officer--Dix & Eaton Incorporated, Cleveland, OH; *U.S. Private*, pg. 336
Eaton, Robert J., Chm. Bd., Pres. & Chief Exec. Officer--Chrysler Corporation, Auburn Hills, MI; *U.S. Public*, pg. 352
Ebbers, Bernard J., Pres. & Chief Exec. Officer--WorldCom, Inc., Jackson, MS; *U.S. Public*, pg. 1779
Eberhardt, Urs, Founder & Pres.--Cash Werbeagentur AG/DMB&B Zurich, Zurich, Switzerland; *U.S. Private*, pg. 303
Ebersole, George D., Pres.--Energy Absorption Systems, Inc., Chicago, IL; *U.S. Public*, pg. 1353
Ebert, Donald E., Pres.--Roll Coater, Inc., Greenfield, IN; *U.S. Public*, pg. 137
Ebert, Larry, Pres.--Flowers Snack of Tennessee, Inc., Crossville, TN; *U.S. Public*, pg. 657
Ebrahimi, Fred, Pres. & Chief Exec. Officer--Quark Inc., Denver, CO; *U.S. Private*, pg. 900
Eby, Clifford C., Pres.--Barton-Aschman Associates, Inc., Evanston, IL; *U.S. Private*, pg. 841
Echols, Rebecca S., Pres. & Chief Exec. Officer--Regions Bank/Douglas County, Douglasville, GA; *U.S. Public*, pg. 1372
Echter, Michael, Mng. Partner--Gillespie Public Relations, Princeton, NJ; *U.S. Private*, pg. 454
Eckart, John E., Pres.--Indiana-American Water Co., Inc., Greenwood, IN; *U.S. Public*, pg. 95
Ecke, Paul, III, Chm. Bd., Pres. & Chief Exec. Officer--Paul Ecke Ranch, Encinitas, CA; *U.S. Private*, pg. 359
Ecker, William, US Pres.-Retail--Clairol, Inc., Stamford, CT; *U.S. Public*, pg. 254
Ecker, William, Pres.--Redmond Products, Inc., Chanhassen, MN; *U.S. Public*, pg. 254
Eckerle, David E., Pres. & Chief Exec. Officer--Dubois County Bank, Jasper, IN; *U.S. Public*, pg. 1217
Eckerling, Sanford, Pres. & Treas.--Universal Overall Company, Chicago, IL; *U.S. Private*, pg. 1127
Eckersmann, Dan, Pres.--Le Tourneau, Inc., Longview, TX; *U.S. Public*, pg. 1410
Eckert, Alfred C., III, Pres.--Greenwich Street Capital Partners, Inc., New York, NY; *U.S. Private*, pg. 479
Eckert, Michael J., Pres. & Chief Exec. Officer--Broadcast and Video Enterprises Div., Atlanta, GA; *U.S. Private*, pg. 647
Eckert, Wesley, Pres. & Chief Exec. Officer--Darigold, Inc., Seattle, WA; *U.S. Private*, pg. 311
Eckhoff, Bruce, Pres.--Telos Consulting Services, Santa Clara, CA; *U.S. Public*, pg. 1573
Eckhoff, Gilbert B., Pres. & Chief Exec. Officer--Henningsen Foods, Inc., White Plains, NY; *Int'l*, pg. 1074
Eckhouse, Shimon, Chm. Bd., Pres. & Chief Exec. Officer--ESC Medical Systems Ltd., Yokneam, Israel; *Int'l*, pg. 429
Eckloff, Richard, Pres.--BioChem ImmunoSystems, Inc., Allentown, PA; *Int'l*, pg. 196
Eckman, Amy, Pres.--Eckman Construction Company, Bedford, NH; *U.S. Private*, pg. 359
Eckstine, Ed, Co-Pres.--Polygram Records, Inc., New York, NY; *Int'l*, pg. 1052
Economos, John, Pres.--Atlanta Beverage Co., Atlanta, GA; *U.S. Private*, pg. 94
Eda, Minoru, Deputy Pres.--The Sanwa Bank Limited, Osaka, Japan; *Int'l*, pg. 1189
Edamoto, Kenzo, Pres. & Chief Exec. Officer--Sapporo Breweries Ltd., Tokyo, Japan; *Int'l*, pg. 1193
Edberg, UC, Pres.--IDAB Wamac International, Eksjo, Sweden; *Int'l*, pg. 643
Eddings, J. Carson, Pres. & Chief Exec. Officer--The William Cook Agency, Inc., Jacksonville, FL; *U.S. Private*, *pg. 273*
Eddington, Thomas, Pres.--Weststar Engineering Inc., San Diego, CA; *U.S. Public*, pg. 65
Eddins, Mark A., Pres. & Chief Exec. Officer--Friendly Chevrolet Co. Inc., Dallas, TX; *U.S. Private*, pg. 428
Eddis, Gerald, Pres.--Viking Electronics, Inc., Chatsworth, CA; *U.S. Private*, pg. 1184
Eddis, Gerald W., Pres.--Wire-Pro Inc., Salem, NJ; *U.S. Private*, pg. 1184
Ede, Terrence, Pres.--Vectron Labs, Inc., Norwalk, CT; *U.S. Public*, pg. 522
Edelbrock, O. Victor, Jr., Chm. Bd., Pres. & Chief Exec. Officer--Edelbrock Corp., Torrance, CA; *U.S. Public*, pg. 563
Edell, David, Pres. & Chief Exec. Officer--CCA Industries, Inc., East Rutherford, NJ; *U.S. Public*, pg. 276
Edelman, Dan, Pres. & Chief Oper. Officer--The Bon Marche, Inc., Seattle, WA; *U.S. Public*, pg. 617
Edelman, Leo, Pres.--Greater New York Box Co., Clifton, NJ; *U.S. Private*, pg. 476
Edelman, Murray R., Pres.--The Cleveland Electric Illuminating Company, Independence, OH; *U.S. Public*, pg. 645
Edelman, Richard, Pres. & Chief Exec. Officer--Edelman Public Relations Worldwide, Chicago, IL; *U.S. Private*, pg. 362
Edelman, Richard W., Pres. & Chief Exec. Officer--Edelman Worldwide, Inc., New York, NY; *U.S. Private*, pg. 362
Edelman, Thomas J., Chm. Bd., Pres. & Chief Exec. Officer--Patina Oil & Gas Corp., Denver, CO; *U.S. Public*, *pg. 1264*
Edelmann, John A., Pres.--Marketing Support, Incorporated, Chicago, IL; *U.S. Private*, pg. 705
Edelmann, Klaus, Pres. & Chief Oper. Officer--KHD Humboldt Wedag AG, Cologne, Germany; *Int'l*, pg. 408
Edelson, L., Pres.--Westchester Lace, Inc., North Bergen, NJ; *U.S. Private*, pg. 1163
Edelson, Norman, Pres.--Edelson & Sons Corporation, Mamaroneck, NY; *U.S. Private*, pg. 363
Edenfield, James C., Pres., Chief Exec. Officer & Treas.--American Software, Inc., Atlanta, GA; *U.S. Public*, pg. 91
Edens, Jim B., Chm. Bd. & Pres.--Huttig Sash & Door Co., Chesterfield, MO; *U.S. Public*, pg. 457
Edick, Fred W., Pres.--Dyke Industry, Inc., Little Rock, AR; *U.S. Private*, pg. 350
Edl, Jack, Pres.--Yorktowne, Inc., Red Lion, PA; *U.S. Private*, pg. 1196
Edman, William D., Pres.--Chevron Canada Resources Limited, Calgary, Canada; *U.S. Public*, pg. 348
Edmonson, Tim, Pres.-Tulsa Div.--Nabholz Construction Corp., Conway, AR; *U.S. Private*, pg. 772
Edwab, David, Pres.--Men's Wearhouse, Fremont, CA; *U.S. Public*, pg. 1086
Edward, David, Pres.--The Body Shop, Cedar Knolls, NJ; *Int'l*, pg. 199
Edwards, Alden, Pres.--Autologic Information International, Inc., Thousand Oaks, CA; *U.S. Public*, pg. 1724
Edwards, Annette, Pres.--Insulate LLC, Auburn, WA; *Int'l*, pg. 1171
Edwards, Barrie, Pres.--Music Sales Corporation, New York, NY; *U.S. Private*, pg. 768
Edwards, Benjamin F., III, Chm. Bd., Pres. & Chief Exec. Officer--A.G. Edwards, Inc., Saint Louis, MO; *U.S. Public*, *pg. 565*
Edwards, Brian, Mng. Dir.--St. Ives plc, London, United Kingdom; *Int'l*, pg. 1177
Edwards, Bryn, Pres. & Chief Exec. Officer--Automation Software, Inc., Farmington, MI; *U.S. Public*, pg. 110
Edwards, C. Webb, Pres.--Norwest Services, Inc., Minneapolis, MN; *U.S. Public*, pg. 1202
Edwards, David, Sr. Principal & Grp. Acct. Dir.--Publicis/Bloom, Dallas, TX; *Int'l*, pg. 469
Edwards, Ian F., Mng. Dir.--Capral Aluminium Limited, Granville, Australia; *Int'l*, pg. 266
Edwards, Jack, Pres. & Chief Exec. Officer--Danzas Corporation, Bellevue, WA; *Int'l*, pg. 382
Edwards, Jimmie R., Pres.--Vulcan Iron Works, Inc., Detroit, MI; *U.S. Private*, pg. 1144
Edwards, John K., Pres.--Onan Corporation, Minneapolis, MN; *U.S. Public*, pg. 468
Edwards, Joseph, Pres. & Chief Exec. Officer--Superior Federal Bank, Fort Smith, AR; *U.S. Private*, pg. 1054
Edwards, Kurt, Pres.--Odessa Exploration, Inc., Odessa, TX; *U.S. Public*, pg. 953
Edwards, Larry, Pres. & Chief Exec. Officer--Reliability Incorporated, Houston, TX; *U.S. Public*, pg. 1373
Edwards, Martin H., Chm. Bd. & Pres.--Edwards Brothers, Inc., Ann Arbor, MI; *U.S. Private*, pg. 365
Edwards, Merle W., Jr., Pres. & Chief Exec. Officer--Coastal Wholesale, Inc., Kinston, NC; *U.S. Private*, pg. 248
Edwards, Steve, Pres.--GES Inc., Marianna, AR; *U.S. Private*, pg. 434
Edwards, Tom, Pres.--Ruskin Div., Grandview, MO; *Int'l*, pg. 1398
Edwards, Tom, Pres.--Swartwout Industries, Grandview, MO; *Int'l*, pg. 1398
Edwards, W. Linton, III, Pres.--Benjamin Ansehl Company, Saint Louis, MO; *U.S. Private*, pg. 75
Edwards, William E., III, Pres. & Chief Oper. Officer--Cardinal Aluminum Co., Louisville, KY; *U.S. Private*, pg. 208
Edwards, William G., Pres.--Golden West Homes, Mesa, AZ; *U.S. Public*, pg. 1209
Edwards, William G., Pres.--Destiny Industries Inc., Moultrie, GA; *U.S. Public*, pg. 1209
Edwards, William H., Pres. & Chief Exec. Officer--Lockwood Greene Technologies, Oak Ridge, TN; *Int'l*, pg. 633
Edwardson, John A., Pres. & Chief Oper. Officer--UAL Corporation, Elk Grove Village, IL; *U.S. Public*, pg. 1652
Eeg, David A., Pres. & Chief Exec. Officer--Storage Dimensions, Inc., Milpitas, CA; *U.S. Public*, pg. 1522
Egan, Dave, Pres.--Ketchum Advertising/Pittsburgh, Pittsburgh, PA; *U.S. Private*, pg. 616
Egan, Gerald L., Pres. & Chief Exec. Officer--Egan Cos., Minneapolis, MN; *U.S. Private*, pg. 365
Egan, Jack, Pres. & Chief Exec. Officer--RehabWorks Inc., Clearwater, FL; *U.S. Public*, pg. 839
Egan, James J., Pres.--The CIT Group/Sales Financing, Inc., Livingston, NJ; *Int'l*, pg. 360
Egan, John M., Pres. & Chief Exec. Officer--The Antec Corporation, Rolling Meadows, IL; *U.S. Public*, pg. 116
Egan, Michael A., Pres. & Chief Exec. Officer--CheckRite International, Midvale, UT; *U.S. Public*, pg. 484
Egan, Raymond C., Pres.--Bristol-Myers Squibb U.S., Evansville, IN; *U.S. Public*, pg. 254
Egart, John J., Pres. & Chief Exec. Officer--First Team Sports Inc., Anoka, MN; *U.S. Public*, pg. 638
Egashira, Kunio, Pres.--Ajinomoto Company Inc., Tokyo, Japan; *Int'l*, pg. 40
Egawa, N., Pres.--Yamaha Corporation of America, Buena Park, CA; *Int'l*, pg. 1516
Eger, L.A., Pres.--Fulmer Company, Inc., Export, PA; *Int'l*, pg. 891
Eggert, Charles, Pres.--Pacific Foods, Inc., Kent, WA; *U.S. Private*, pg. 831
Egioff, Peter, Pres.--Sulzer Ruti Inc., Spartanburg, SC; *Int'l*, pg. 1307
Egizii, Robert, Pres. & Chief Exec. Officer--Egizii Electric, Inc., Springfield, IL; *U.S. Private*, pg. 366
Eglin, Bridger, Pres.--Guaranty Corporation, Baton Rouge, LA; *U.S. Private*, pg. 485
Eglin, Peter B., Chm. Bd., Pres. & Chief Exec. Officer--Mellon Bank, N.A.-Northeastern Region, Wilkes-Barre, PA; *U.S. Public*, pg. 1085
Egner, Bill, Pres.--Schutte Lumber Company, Kansas City, MO; *U.S. Private*, pg. 973
Egner, Dave, Pres.--Plymouth Industries, Inc., Plymouth, OH; *U.S. Private*, pg. 873
Egner, Dave, Pres.--Autolift Industrial Lift Trucks, Plymouth, OH; *U.S. Private*, pg. 873
Egnew, J.C., Pres. & Chief Oper. Officer--Outdoor Venture Corp., Stearns, KY; *U.S. Private*, pg. 822
Egstrand, Bjarne, Pres.--Saab Sweden AB, Nykoping, Sweden; *Int'l*, pg. 687
Ehler, Gene, Pres.--Energas Company, Lubbock, TX; *U.S. Public*, pg. 145
Ehlinger, Mark D., Pres.--Security Pacific Bank Canada, Vancouver, Canada; *U.S. Public*, pg. 183
Ehmke, Lane, Pres.--Bridgestone/Firestone Credit Services Company, Brook Park, OH; *Int'l*, pg. 213
Ehr, Robert, Pres.--Smiths Industries Aerospace & Defense Systems Inc.-Grand Rapids Operation, Grand Rapids, MI; *Int'l*, pg. 1268
Ehrenthal, Herb, Pres.--Rubin Ehrenthal & Associates, New York, NY; *U.S. Private*, pg. 949

Ehrlen, Olle, Pres.--NCC Building, Stockholm, Sweden; *Int'l, pg. 898*
Ehrlich, Donald J., Pres. & Chief Exec. Officer--Wabash National Corp., Lafayette, IN; *U.S. Public*, pg. 1730
Ehrlich, Paul, Chm. Bd. & Pres.--Wisconsin Automated Machinery Corp., Oshkosh, WI; *U.S. Private*, pg. 1184
Ehrlichman, Stephen M., Pres.--Stelar Inc., Chicago, IL; *U.S.* Private, pg. 1040
Ehrnrooth, Georg, Pres. & Chief Exec. Officer--Metra Corporation, Helsinki, Finland; *Int'l*, pg. 862
Eibl, Carlton, Pres.--Mycogen Corporation, San Diego, CA; *U.S. Public*, pg. 1142
Eibner, W.P., Pres. & Chief Exec. Officer--Fostoria Industries, Inc., Fostoria, OH; *U.S. Private*, pg. 421
Eichenfield, Samuel L., Chm. Bd., Pres. & Chief Exec. Officer--The FINOVA Group Inc., Phoenix, AZ; *U.S. Public*, pg. 624
Eichenfield, Samuel L., Chm. Bd., Pres. & Chief Exec. Officer--FINOVA Capital Corporation, Phoenix, AZ; *U.S. Public*, pg. 624
Eichhorn, Gary, Pres. & Chief Exec. Officer--Open Market, Inc., Burlington, MA; *U.S. Public*, pg. 1226
Eichler, Franklin R., Pres.--First Mount Joy Corporation, Mount Joy, PA; *U.S. Private*, pg. 407
Eichorn, Mark R., Pres.--Anchor Hocking Consumer Glass, Lancaster, OH; *U.S. Public*, pg. 1177
Eichorn, Mark R., Pres.--Anchor Hocking Corporation, Freeport, IL; *U.S. Public*, pg. 1177
Eickelman, R.J., Pres.--Pressed Steel Tank Co., Inc., Milwaukee, WI; *U.S. Private*, pg. 882
Eidel, Helmuth L., Pres.--Tri-City Electrical Contractors Inc., Altamonte Springs, FL; *U.S. Private*, pg. 1100
Eigruber, Horst, Pres.--American Maplan Corporation, Mc Pherson, KS; *Int'l*, pg. 825
Eihusen, Robert, Chm. Bd., Pres. & Chief Exec. Officer--Chief Industries, Inc., Grand Island, NE; *U.S. Private*, pg. 236
Eilingsen, Ken, Pres.--Aegis Safety Holdings, Inc., Weehawken, NJ; *U.S. Public*, pg. 782
Einstein, Ernst, Pres.--Einstein Moomjy Inc., Pine Brook, NJ; *U.S. Private*, pg. 366
Eio, Peter, Pres.--LEGO Systems, Inc., Enfield, CT; *Int'l*, pg. 805
Eischeid, Theodore J., Pres.--Revell-Monogram Inc., Morton Grove, IL; *U.S. Private*, pg. 926
Eisele, Ed, Pres. & Chief Exec. Officer--Holsum Bakery, Inc., Phoenix, AZ; *U.S. Private*, pg. 536
Eisele, George, Pres.--TMP Worldwide/Direct Marketing Services, Mount Olive, NJ; *U.S. Private*, pg. 1064
Eisele, Klaus, Pres.--Baden-Wurttemberg Branch, Stuttgart, Germany; *Int'l*, pg. 645
Eiseman, Thomas A., Pres.--Revere Electric Supply Co., Chicago, IL; *U.S. Private*, pg. 926
Eisen, Paul, Pres.--Jeans West, Inc., Saint Louis, MO; *U.S. Public*, pg. 563
Eisen, Paul, Pres.--Oaktree, Saint Louis, MO; *U.S. Public*, pg. 564
Eisenberg, Gregg M., Chm. Bd., Pres. & Chief Exec. Officer--Maverick Tube Corporation, Chesterfield, MO; *U.S. Public*, pg. 1060
Eisenburg, David, Chm. Bd., Pres. & Chief Exec. Officer--Chief Auto Parts, Dallas, TX; *U.S. Private*, pg. 236
Eisenstadt, Marvin Ernest, Pres.--Cumberland Packing Corp., Brooklyn, NY; *U.S. Private*, pg. 295
Eisner, Steven C., Pres. & Chief Exec. Officer--Eisner & Associates, Inc., Baltimore, MD; *U.S. Private*, pg. 366
Eistert, Michael, Pres.--Babcock Sempell AG, Korschenbroich, Germany; *Int'l*, pg. 399
Eiswerth, Leon R., Pres.--Park Drop Forge Div., Cleveland, OH; *U.S. Public*, pg. 1258
Eitel, Charles, Pres. & Chief Oper. Officer--Interface Inc., Atlanta, GA; *U.S. Public*, pg. 889
Eitzinger, Robert, Pres.--Mid-West Automation Systems, Inc., Buffalo Grove, IL; *U.S. Public*, pg. 475
Eizmende, Francisco C., Jr., Pres.--San Miguel Corp., Manila, Philippines; *Int'l*, pg. 1183
Ejabat, Mory, Pres. & Chief Exec. Officer--Ascend Communications, Inc., Alameda, CA; *U.S. Public*, pg. 138
Ekaireb, Errol, Pres. & Chief Oper. Officer--Remec, Inc., San Diego, CA; *U.S. Public*, pg. 1376
Ekas, Ronald, Pres.--Carco Electronics, Menlo Park, CA; *U.S. Private*, pg. 208
Ekberg Johnson, Judith, Pres. & Chief Exec. Officer--Meyer Broadcasting Company, Bismarck, ND; *U.S. Private*, pg. 739
Ekedahl, Rolf, Mng. Dir.--Munksjo AB, Jonkoping, Sweden; *Int'l*, pg. 1423
Ekholm, Markku, Mng. Dir.--Suomen Unipol Oy, Helsinki, Finland; *Int'l*, pg. 15
Ekins, W. Leo, Pres. & Chief Exec. Officer--AgrEvo USA Company, Wilmington, DE; *Int'l*, pg. 1203
Eklund, George, Pres. & Chief Exec. Officer--Digital Solutions, Inc., Somerset, NJ; *U.S. Public*, pg. 508
Eklund, Helge, Pres. & Chief Exec. Officer--Sodra Cell AB, Vaxjo, Sweden; *Int'l*, pg. 1275
Eklund, Henrik, Pres.--Sanitec Ltd. Oy, Ratingen, Germany; *Int'l*, pg. 863
Eklund, Wesley, Pres.--Fleet Engineers, Inc., Muskegon, MI; *U.S. Private*, pg. 410
Ekstrom, L.W., Chm. Bd. & Pres.--Samuel Bingham Co, Bloomingdale, IL; *U.S. Private*, pg. 144
Ekyamp, William, Pres.--Koch Membrane Systems, Wilmington, MA; *U.S. Private*, pg. 628
El Ganzouri, Mohamed, Pres.--Egypt Otsuka Pharmaceutical Co., S.A.E., Cairo, Egypt; *Int'l*, pg. 1014
Elbert, Paul A., Chm. Bd. & Pres.--Michigan Gas Storage Co., Jackson, MI; *U.S. Public*, pg. 280
Elder, Edwin W., III, Pres.--American Country Financial Services Corp., Chicago, IL; *U.S. Private*, pg. 1030
Elder, Irma, Pres.--Troy Motors, Troy, MI; *U.S. Private*, pg. 1106
Elen, Robert, Pres. & Chief Oper. Officer--DavisElen Advertising, Inc., Los Angeles, CA; *U.S. Private*, pg. 316
Elenbaas, Ronald A., Pres.--Stryker Corporation Endoscopy, San Jose, CA; *U.S. Public*, pg. 1526
Elfner, Anders, Pres.--Skanska Stockholm Malardalen, Danderyd, Sweden; *Int'l*, pg. 1260
Elford, John, Gen. Mgr.--Turtle Bay Hilton Golf & Tennis Resort, Kahuku, HI; *U.S. Public*, pg. 829
Elgas, Devere L., Pres., Chief Exec. Officer & Chief Oper. Officer--Citizens Gas Fuel Company, Adrian, MI; *U.S. Public*, pg. 1025
Elia, Claudio, Pres.--Anjou International Company, New York, NY; *Int'l*, pg. 321
Elia, Michael A., Pres. & Chief Exec. Officer--Sevenson Environmental Services, Inc., Niagara Falls, NY; *U.S. Public*, pg. 1462
Elias, Arthur G., Pres.--Hayhurst Elias Dudek, Inc., Winnipeg, Canada; *U.S. Public*, pg. 827
Elias, Richard, Pres.--Transitions Optical, Inc., Pinellas Park, FL; *U.S. Public*, pg. 1245
Eliasek, Thomas, Pres.--Harris Steel Co., Cicero, IL; *U.S. Private*, pg. 506
Elizalde, Javier, Pres. & Gen. Mgr.--Aeromexpress S.A. de C.V., Mexico, Mexico; *Int'l*, pg. 332
Elizando, Cesar, Pres.--Corporacion E.G., S.A. de C.V., Monterrey, Mexico; *Int'l*, pg. 395
Elizondo, Alejandro M., Pres.--Hylsamex, S.A. de C.V., San Nicolas, Mexico; *Int'l*, pg. 56
Elizondo, Cesar, Pres.--Ruhrpumpen GmbH, Witten, Germany; *Int'l*, pg. 395
Elkas, George, Pres. & Chief Oper. Officer--Flexi-Van Leasing, Inc., Kenilworth, NJ; *U.S. Private*, pg. 413
Elkas, George, Pres.--Flexi-Van Leasing, Inc., Kenilworth, NJ; *U.S. Private*, pg. 413
Elkhatib, Hasan M., Pres. & Chief Exec. Officer--Dena Corporation, Elk Grove Village, IL; *U.S. Private*, pg. 324
Elkin, Kenneth, Pres. & Chief Exec. Officer--SGS U.S. Testing Company, Inc., Fairfield, NJ; *Int'l*, pg. 1153
Elkin, Stephen C., Pres.--Bergdorf Goodman, New York, NY; *U.S. Public*, pg. 785
Elkington, John, Pres.--Performa Entertainment Real Estate, Inc., Memphis, TN; *U.S. Private*, pg. 853
Ellenberger, Richard G., Pres. & Chief Exec. Officer--Cincinnati Bell Telephone Company, Cincinnati, OH; *U.S. Public*, pg. 367
Eller, Scott, Pres. & Chief Oper. Officer--Eller Media Company, Phoenix, AZ; *U.S. Public*, pg. 383
Ellerbrook, Niel, Pres. & Chief Oper. Officer--IEI Services, LLC, Indianapolis, IN; *U.S. Public*, pg. 875
Ellerbrook, Niel C., Pres. & Chief Oper. Officer--Indiana Energy, Inc., Indianapolis, IN; *U.S. Public*, pg. 874
Ellerman, Mike, Pres.--Yuasa-Exide, Inc., Reading, PA; *Int'l*, pg. 1522
Ellett, Phil D., Pres. & Chief Exec. Officer--Gates/Arrow Commercial Systems Div., Greenville, SC; *U.S. Public*, pg. 133
Elliff, Mark J., Pres. & Chief Exec. Officer--United Missouri Bank of Boonville, Boonville, MO; *U.S. Public*, pg. 1654
Elliman, Donald M., Jr., Pres.--Sports Illustrated, New York, NY; *U.S. Public*, pg. 1613
Ellingsen, Ken, Pres.-Catalog--LWI Holdings Inc., Cleveland, OH; *U.S. Public*, pg. 782
Ellingson, Chester W., Jr., Chm. Bd. & Pres.--Reese Enterprises, Inc., Rosemount, MN; *U.S. Private*, pg. 916
Ellington, Suzanne, Partner--Chicago Creative Partnership, Chicago, IL; *U.S. Private*, pg. 234
Elliot, B., Pres.--Oland Breweries Limited, Halifax, Canada; *Int'l*, pg. 679
Elliot, Mike, Pres.--JSI, French Lick, IN; *U.S. Private*, pg. 583
Elliott, B.L., Pres.--Eastman Savings & Loan Association, Rochester, NY; *U.S. Public*, pg. 551
Elliott, Charles A., Chm. Bd., Pres. & Chief Exec. Officer--Crenlo, Inc., Rochester, MN; *U.S. Private*, pg. 288
Elliott, E.J., Chm. Bd. & Pres.--Gencor Industries, Inc., Orlando, FL; *U.S. Public*, pg. 705
Elliott, J. Mark, Pres. & Chief Oper. Officer--QST Enterprises Inc., Peoria, IL; *U.S. Public*, pg. 367
Elliott, James V., Pres. & Chief Exec. Officer--Investors Trust Company, Wyomissing, PA; *U.S. Public*, pg. 1159
Elliott, John E., Pres.--Thermotech Systems Corporation, Orlando, FL; *U.S. Public*, pg. 705
Elliott, Marc G., Pres.--General Combustion Corporation, Orlando, FL; *U.S. Public*, pg. 705
Elliott, Michael, Pres.--Jasper Seating Co., Inc., Jasper, IN; *U.S. Private*, pg. 583
Elliott, Neal M., Chm. Bd., Pres. & Chief Exec. Officer--Horizon/CMS Healthcare Corporation, Albuquerque, NM; *U.S. Public*, pg. 836
Elliott, Perry, Pres. & Chief Exec. Officer--Stephenville Bank & Trust Co., Stephenville, TX; *U.S. Public*, pg. 633
Elliott, Robert D., Pres. & Chief Exec. Officer--Aerovox Inc., New Bedford, MA; *U.S. Public*, pg. 25
Ellis, B. Herbert, Pres.--Barnes & Reinecke, Inc., Arlington Heights, IL; *U.S. Public*, pg. 49
Ellis, Barry, Pres. & Mngng. Dir.--Gardenwood Limited Partnership, Bella Vista, AR; *U.S. Private*, pg. 274
Ellis, Barry, Pres. & Mngng. Dir.--Highlands at Briarcliff Limited Partnership, Bella Vista, AR; *U.S. Private*, pg. 274
Ellis, Charles R., Pres. & Chief Exec. Officer--John Wiley & Sons, Inc., New York, NY; *U.S. Public*, pg. 1768
Ellis, E. Addison, III, Pres. & Chief Exec. Officer--Glencoe/McGraw Hill, Westerville, OH; *U.S. Public*, pg. 1070
Ellis, Fred K., Pres. & Chief Inv. Officer--Skandia Investment Management, Inc., New York, NY; *Int'l*, pg. 1257
Ellis, J. Ronald, Pres. & Chief Exec. Officer--Willis Corroon Corp. of Nashville, Nashville, TN; *Int'l*, pg. 1506
Ellis, Mark, Pres.--STAR Anchors & Fasteners, Mountainville, NY; *U.S. Private*, pg. 1033
Ellis, Paula Lynn, Pres. & Publr.--The Sun News, Myrtle Beach, SC; *U.S. Public*, pg. 964
Ellis, Paula Lynn, Pres. & Publr.--Sun Publishing Company, Inc., Myrtle Beach, SC; *U.S. Public*, pg. 964
Ellis, Robert, Pres.--Haviland Telephone Company, Inc., Haviland, KS; *U.S. Public*, pg. 1021
Ellis, Robert F., Pres.--Austron Inc., Austin, TX; *U.S. Public*, pg. 488
Ellis, Tim, Pres.--Dynex Technologies, Chantilly, VA; *U.S. Public*, pg. 1591
Ellis, Willen, Pres.--ATIO Corporation USA, Inc., Hopkins, MN; *U.S. Public*, pg. 1716
Ellison, Richard D., Pres.--TRC Environmental Solutions, Inc., Irvine, CA; *U.S. Public*, pg. 1558
Ellison, Richard D., Ph.D.,P.E., Chm. Bd., Pres. & Chief Exec. Officer--TRC Companies, Inc., Windsor, CT; *U.S. Public*, pg. 1557
Ellstrom, Olof W., Jr., Pres. & Chief Exec. Officer--Dearborn Gage Company, Garden City, MI; *U.S. Private*, pg. 319
Ellsworth, David K., Pres.--Underwriters & Management Services Inc., Indianapolis, IN; *U.S. Public*, pg. 998
Elmburg, John R., Pres.--Blitz USA, Inc., Miami, OK; *U.S. Private*, pg. 149
Elowitz, Norman, Chm. Bd., Pres. & Chief Exec. Officer--Honey Fashions Ltd., New York, NY; *U.S. Private*, pg. 537
Elsberry, Howard W., Chm. Bd., Pres. & Chief Exec. Officer--Westlake Hardware, Inc., Lenexa, KS; *U.S. Private*, pg. 1169
Elsey, John H., Pres.--Dairyland County Mutual Insurance Co., Austin, TX; *U.S. Private*, pg. 985
Elson, Irwin L., Pres.--JLK America Inc., Livonia, MI; *U.S. Public*, pg. 951
Elswick, Lloyd C, Pres.--Bendix Security Systems, Pasadena, MD; *U.S. Public*, pg. 51
Elton, Linda, Pres.--Sasson Licensing Corp., New York, NY; *U.S. Private*, pg. 967
Elwood, E.P., Pres.--Lever Pond's Limited, Toronto, Canada; *Int'l*, pg. 1438
Elwood, Peter, Pres.--Lipton, Toronto, Canada; *Int'l*, pg. 1438
Ely, Timothy, Pres.--Highfield Manufacturing Co., Bridgeport, CT; *Int'l*, pg. 127
Emami, Hamid, Pres.--Abbott Electronics, Inc., Los Angeles, CA; *U.S. Private*, pg. 9
Embere, Bob, Pres.--Smith Pipe & Steel Co., Phoenix, AZ; *U.S. Private*, pg. 1009
Emerson, Barry K., Chm. Bd., Pres. & Chief Exec. Officer--Texas National Bank, Southlake, TX; *U.S. Public*, pg. 633
Emerson, Bob, Country Mgr.--NBS Limited-Card Services Division, Weybridge, United Kingdom; *Int'l*, pg. 898
Emerson, Richard B., Mng. Partner & Chief Oper. Officer, Divisions--Arnold Communications, Inc., Boston, MA; *U.S. Private*, pg. 83
Emery, Merle, Pres.-Multi-Plex, Inc.--Davis Industries Inc., Plymouth, MI; *U.S. Private*, pg. 315
Emhiser, William, Pres.--Amicon, Inc., Beverly, MA; *U.S. Public*, pg. 1113
Emich, Fred, III, Pres. & Chief Exec. Officer--Emich Oldsmobile, Inc., Golden, CO; *U.S. Private*, pg. 373
Emison, James W., Pres.--Western Petroleum Company, Eden Prairie, MN; *U.S. Private*, pg. 1168
Emkes, Mark, Pres.--Bridgestone/Firestone de Mexico, S.A. de C.V., Mexico, Mexico; *Int'l*, pg. 214
Emma, Edward C., Pres. & Chief Oper. Officer--Jockey International, Inc., Kenosha, WI; *U.S. Private*, pg. 588
Emmens, Matthew W., Pres.--Astra Merck Inc., Wayne, PA; *Int'l*, pg. 93
Emmerling, John, Chm. Bd. & Chief Creative Officer--Emmerling Post, Inc., New York, NY; *U.S. Private*, pg. 374
Emmerson, A.A., Pres.--Sierra Pacific Industries, Anderson, CA; *U.S. Private*, pg. 998
Emmi, Michael J., Chm. Bd., Pres. & Chief Exec. Officer--Systems & Computer Technology Corporation, Malvern, PA; *U.S. Public*, pg. 1552
Emmons, Don, Pres.--Prescolite Moldcast Lighting Company, San Leandro, CA; *U.S. Public*, pg. 1684
Emrich, John A., Pres. & Chief Oper. Officer--Guilford Mills, Inc., Greensboro, NC; *U.S. Public*, pg. 768
Enders, A.T., Mng. Partner & Chief Exec. Officer--Brown Brothers Harriman & Co., New York, NY; *U.S. Private*, pg. 173
Enders, Larry J., Pres. & Chief Exec. Officer--Oliver Rubber Co., Athens, GA; *U.S. Public*, pg. 1504
Endoh, Shozo, Pres.--The Chuo Trust & Banking Co., Ltd., Tokyo, Japan; *Int'l*, pg. 291
Endung, Roar, Pres.--Kvaerner Ships Equipment a.s, Lier, Norway; *Int'l*, pg. 770
Endy, Eric P., Pres.--Paul-Son Gaming Corporation, Las Vegas, NV; *U.S. Public*, pg. 1265
Engel, Bruce L., Pres.--WTD Industries, Inc., Portland, OR; *U.S. Public*, pg. 1729
Engel, Clyde W., Chm. Bd. & Pres.--R D I S Corporation, Chicago, IL; *U.S. Private*, pg. 903
Engel, Philip L., Pres.--Continental Assurance Company, Chicago, IL; *U.S. Private*, pg. 267
Engel, Philip L., Pres.--CNA Insurance Companies, Chicago, IL; *U.S. Public*, pg. 1010
Engel, R.U., Pres.--F&S Incorporated, New York, NY; *Int'l*, pg. 1458
Engel, Susan, Chm. Bd., Pres. & Chief Exec. Officer--Department 56 Inc., Eden Prairie, MN; *U.S. Public*, pg. 500
Engelberger, John K., Gen. Mgr.--Eaton Corporation, Pressure Sensors Division, Bethel, CT; *U.S. Public*, pg. 557
Engelbrecht, Horst P., Pres.--Lightnin Mixers, Rochester, NY; *U.S. Public*, pg. 726
Engelke, George L., Chm. Bd., Pres. & Chief Exec. Officer--Astoria Financial Corporation, Lake Success, NY; *U.S. Public*, pg. 141
Engels, Karl G., Pres. & Chief Exec. Officer--Hoechst Marion Roussel, Inc., Bridgewater, NJ; *Int'l*, pg. 624
Engelsman, Tom, Pres. & Chief Oper. Officer--Beloit Corporation, Beloit, WI; *U.S. Public*, pg. 789

Engelson, Iris, Pres.--Interet Corporation, Millburn, NJ; *U.S. Private*, pg. 567

Engelstein, Alec, Chm. Bd., Pres. & Chief Exec. Officer--Engle Homes, Inc., Boca Raton, FL; *U.S. Public*, pg. 583

Enger, Ole, Pres. & Chief Exec. Officer--Elkem ASA, Oslo, Norway; *Int'l*, pg. 446

Engibous, Thomas J., Pres. & Chief Exec. Officer--Texas Instruments Incorporated, Dallas, TX; *U.S. Public*, pg. 1585

England, C.M., Pres. & Chief Exec. Officer--Logan Corporation, Huntington, WV; *U.S. Private*, pg. 672

England, Ed D., Pres.--C P Converters, Inc., York, PA; *U.S. Private*, pg. 192

England, Gordon, Pres.--Lockheed Fort Worth Company, Fort Worth, TX; *U.S. Public*, pg. 1007

England, Peter W., Pres. & Chief Exec. Officer--Elizabeth Arden Company, New York, NY; *Int'l*, pg. 1435

England, Rodney, Pres.--England/Corsair, New Tazewell, TN; *U.S. Public*, pg. 972

Engle, Clyde W., Chm. Bd., Pres. & Treas.--GSC Enterprises, Inc., Chicago, IL; *U.S. Private*, pg. 436

Engle, Clyde W., Chm. Bd., Pres. & Chief Exec. Officer--Telco Capital Corporation, Chicago, IL; *U.S. Private*, pg. 1073

Engle, Clyde Wm., Chm. Bd. & Pres.--Bank of Lincolnwood, Lincolnwood, IL; *U.S. Private*, pg. 436

Engle, Gary D., Pres. & Chief Exec. Officer--Equis Financial Group, Boston, MA; *U.S. Private*, pg. 379

Engle, Jerry R., Pres. & Chief Exec. Officer--Citizens Bank of Central Indiana, Greenwood, IN; *U.S. Public*, pg. 280

Engle, Phillip R., Pres.--Bergen Brunswig Drug Company, Orange, CA; *U.S. Public*, pg. 213

Englefield, Benjamin B., Co-Pres.--Englefield, Inc., Newark, OH; *U.S. Private*, pg. 377

Englefield, F.W., IV, Co-Pres., Chief Exec., Chief Fin. Officer & Sec.--Englefield, Inc., Newark, OH; *U.S. Private*, pg. 377

Englekirk, Robert E., Chm. Bd., Pres. & Chief Exec. Officer--Robert Englekirk, Inc., Los Angeles, CA; *U.S. Private*, pg. 377

Engler, Paul F., Chm. Bd. & Pres.--Cactus Feeders, Inc., Amarillo, TX; *U.S. Private*, pg. 198

Englert, Lawrence, Pres.--The May Apparel Group, Inc., Mebane, NC; *U.S. Private*, pg. 717

English, Floyd L., Chm. Bd., Pres. & Chief Exec. Officer--Andrew Corporation, Orland Park, IL; *U.S. Public*, pg. 112

English, J.M., Pres.--Idaho Forest Industry, Inc., Coeur D'Alene, ID; *U.S. Private*, pg. 556

English, James D., Pres.--Kal Grafx, Kentwood, MI; *U.S. Private*, pg. 387

English, John T., Pres. & Chief Oper. Officer--Florida Public Utilities Company, West Palm Beach, FL; *U.S. Public*, pg. 655

Engsted, Michael, Pres.--AGA Gas Ltd., Coventry, United Kingdom; *Int'l*, pg. 13

Engstrom, Erik, Pres.--Bantam Doubleday Dell Publishing Group, Inc., New York, NY; *Int'l*, pg. 191

Enichen, Robert C., Pres.--Exact Equipment Corporation, Langhorne, PA; *U.S. Private*, pg. 387

Ennen, Richard, Pres. & Chief Exec. Officer--Universal International, Inc., New Hope, MN; *U.S. Public*, pg. 1697

Ennerfelt, Goran, Pres. & Chief Exec. Officer--Axel Johnson AB, Stockholm, Sweden; *Int'l*, pg. 707

Ennis, B.M., Pres.--United Foods, Inc., Bells, TN; *U.S. Public*, pg. 1677

Eno, Julius Ralph, Pres.--Hamamatsu Corp., Bridgewater, NJ; *U.S. Private*, pg. 497

Enright, Patty, Sr. Partner & Human Resources Dir.--Ogilvy & Mather Worldwide, Inc., New York, NY; *Int'l*, pg. 1483

Enser, William, Pres.--Philips Electronics Instruments Company, Mahwah, NJ; *Int'l*, pg. 1054

Ensign, Bill, Pres.--Goldstrike Hotel, Jean, NV; *U.S. Public*, pg. 375

Ensor, Clyde F., Sr., Chm. Bd. & Pres.--Hesco Parts Corporation, Louisville, KY; *U.S. Private*, pg. 524

Ensor, Eric F., Pres.--Bellsouth Personal Communications, Inc., Atlanta, GA; *U.S. Public*, pg. 208

Entremont, M., Pres. & Dir. Gen.--Entremont S.A., Annecy, France; *Int'l*, pg. 458

Entringer, James W., Chm. Bd., Pres. & Chief Exec. Officer--Selective Insurance Group, Inc, Branchville, NJ; *U.S. Public*, pg. 1455

Entringer, James W., Chm. & Pres.--Niagara Exchange Corporation, Buffalo, NY; *U.S. Public*, pg. 1455

Eoff, Robert H., Pres.--WREG-TV, Memphis, TN; *U.S. Public*, pg. 1174

Eook, Robert E., Pres.--Frigidaire Home Products, Orangeburg, SC; *Int'l*, pg. 440

Epprecht, Hans, Pres. & Chief Exec. Officer--The Great Lakes Cheese Co., Newbury, OH; *U.S. Private*, pg. 473

Epstein, Abram, Pres.--A J M Packaging Corporation, Bloomfield Hills, MI; *U.S. Private*, pg. 2

Epstein, Alan L., Partner--Kupper Parker Communications Inc., Saint Louis, MO; *U.S. Private*, pg. 637

Epstein, Donald, Chm. Bd., Pres. & Chief Exec. Officer--Vesco Oil Corp., Southfield, MI; *U.S. Private*, pg. 1138

Epstein, Glenn, Pres. & Chief Oper. Officer--Intermagnetics General Corporation, Latham, NY; *U.S. Public*, pg. 893

Epstein, Glenn, Pres. & Chief Exec. Officer--Oxford Instruments-Nuclear Measurements Group, Oak Ridge, TN; *Int'l*, pg. 1018

Epstein, Greg, Pres.--Perry Machinery Corporation, Hainesport, NJ; *U.S. Private*, pg. 855

Epstein, Jerry, Sr. Partner & Exec. V.P.--Fleishman-Hillard Inc., Saint Louis, MO; *U.S. Private*, pg. 411

Epstein, Mark, Pres.--Robertet Flavors, South Plainfield, NJ; *Int'l*, pg. 1119

Erazim, John M., Pres.--Yarway Corporation, Blue Bell, PA; *U.S. Public*, pg. 1650

Erb, Fred A., Chm. Bd., Pres. & Chief Exec. Officer--Amurcon Corporation, Southfield, MI; *U.S. Private*, pg. 69

Erbes, William, Pres.--LINC Equipment Services, Lincolnshire, IL; *U.S. Public*, pg. 996

Erdeljan, Aleksandar, Chm. Bd., Pres. & Co-Chief Exec. Officer--R.P. Scherer Corporation, Troy, MI; *U.S. Public*, pg. 1437

Erdle, William J., III, Chm. Bd. & Pres.--Erdle Perforating Co., Rochester, NY; *U.S. Private*, pg. 380

Erdmann, David L., Chm. Bd., Pres. & Chief Exec. Officer--Outlook Group Corporation, Neenah, WI; *U.S. Public*, pg. 1235

Erenmalm, Stattan, Pres. & Chief Exec. Officer--Akerlund & Rausing, Leerdam, Netherlands; *Int'l*, pg. 33

Erennalm, Stattan, Pres. & Chief Exec. Officer--AB Akerlund & Rausing Group, Lund, Sweden; *Int'l*, pg. 33

Erfert, Reiner, Vice Chm.-Europe, Middle East & Africa--Michael Conrad & Leo Burnett GmbH, Frankfurt/Main, Germany; *U.S. Private*, pg. 184

Ergul, Necdet, Pres.--Microphase Corporation, Norwalk, CT; *U.S. Private*, pg. 742

Erhardt, Mary C., Pres. & Gen. Mgr.--Mark Antenna Products, Inc., Des Plaines, IL; *U.S. Public*, pg. 424

Erickson, Bill, Sr. V.P. & Pres.-Americas--Medtronic, Inc., Minneapolis, MN; *U.S. Public*, pg. 1082

Erickson, D.L., Pres.--Consolidated Communications, Mattoon, IL; *U.S. Public*, pg. 1073

Erickson, Donovan, Pres.--Holiday Station Stores, Inc., Minneapolis, MN; *U.S. Private*, pg. 534

Erickson, James W., Chm. Bd., Pres. & Chief Exec. Officer--Anderson Erickson Dairy Company, Des Moines, IA; *U.S. Private*, pg. 72

Erickson, John H., Pres.--Erickson Transport Corporation, Springfield, MO; *U.S. Private*, pg. 381

Erickson, Robert D., Chm. Bd. & Pres.--Amoco Canada Petroleum Company Ltd., Calgary, Canada; *U.S. Public*, pg. 103

Erickson, Robert M., Pres. & Chief Fin. Officer--Madison Acceptance Corporation, San Jose, CA; *U.S. Public*, pg. 376

Erickson, Sheldon, Chm. Bd., Pres. & Chief Exec. Officer--Cameron, Houston, TX; *U.S. Public*, pg. 298

Erickson, Steven, Pres.--Erickson's Diversified Corp., Hudson, WI; *U.S. Private*, pg. 381

Erickson, Terry C., Pres.--National Yellow Pages Monitor (NYPM), San Francisco, CA; *U.S. Public*, pg. 1146

Erickson, Theresa, Pres.--Old Kent Bank of Ludington, Ludington, MI; *U.S. Public*, pg. 1217

Ericson, James D., Pres. & Chief Exec. Officer--Northwestern Mutual Life Insurance Co., Milwaukee, WI; *U.S. Private*, pg. 807

Ericson, K.I., Pres.--ITT Flygt Corporation, Trumbull, CT; *U.S. Public*, pg. 860

Ericsson, Bjorn, Pres.--Astra Pharmaceuticals (HK) Ltd., Kwai Chung, Hong Kong; *Int'l*, pg. 94

Eriksen, Douglas, Pres.--Recaro North America, Inc., Clawson, MI; *U.S. Private*, pg. 914

Erikson, Robert W., Pres., Chief Fin. Officer & Treas.--CERBCO, Inc., Landover, MD; *U.S. Public*, pg. 330

Eriksson, Bengt, Pres.--Ballast Stockholm AB, Upplands Vasby, Sweden; *Int'l*, pg. 899

Eriksson, Orjan, Gen. Mgr.--Systems Support, Vaxjo, Sweden; *Int'l*, pg. 277

Eriksson, Peter, Pres.--Alnab Armatur AB, Partille, Sweden; *Int'l*, pg. 678

Erkeneff, Richard R., Pres. & Chief Exec. Officer--United Industrial Corporation, New York, NY; *U.S. Public*, pg. 1679

Erkeneff, Richard R., Pres. & Chief Exec. Officer--AAI Corporation, Hunt Valley, MD; *U.S. Public*, pg. 1679

Ermold, John D., Pres.--MD Pneumatics, Springfield, MO; *U.S. Private*, pg. 1111

Ernesto Solitto, Roberto Felix, Pres.--Independencia Compania Argentina de Seguros, S.A., Buenos Aires, Argentina; *U.S. Public*, pg. 216

Ernst, Paul W., Pres. & Chief Exec. Officer--Carter Day International, Minneapolis, MN; *U.S. Private*, pg. 216

Erokan, Dennis, Pres. & Editor-in-Chief--Bam Media, Pleasant Hill, CA; *U.S. Private*, pg. 113

Erskine, David, Pres. & Chief Exec. Officer--Scott Paper Limited, Mississauga, Canada; *Int'l*, pg. 762

Erskine, John E., Jr., Pres. & Chief Exec. Officer--Racine Federated, Inc., Racine, WI; *U.S. Private*, pg. 906

Erussard, Michel, Pres.--Renault USA, Southfield, MI; *Int'l*, pg. 1102

Ervesun, Enrique, Pres. & Gen. Mgr.--Cyanamid de Venezuela CA, Caracas, Venezuela; *U.S. Public*, pg. 80

Ervin, Robert E., Pres.--Consumers Service Company, Boardman, OH; *U.S. Public*, pg. 439

Erxleben, William, Pres. & Chief Exec. Officer--Data I/O Corporation, Redmond, WA; *U.S. Public*, pg. 486

Esak, J. Ronald, Pres. & Chief Exec. Officer--Nexus Plastics, Inc., Hawthorne, NJ; *U.S. Private*, pg. 797

Esaki, Kiyoshi, Pres.--GEOSTR Corporation, Tokyo, Japan; *Int'l*, pg. 763

Escande, J. P., Pres.--Societe Bordelaise de Cic, Bordeaux, France; *Int'l*, pg. 565

Escardo, Gustavo A. Garcia, Gen Mgr--Duracell Argentina S.A., Buenos Aires, Argentina; *U.S. Public*, pg. 743

Escarrer, Gabriel, Chm. Bd. & Pres.--Sol Melia, Palma de Mallorca, Spain; *Int'l*, pg. 1277

Eschrich, Robert W., Pres. & Chief Exec. Officer--WM Life Insurance Company, Seattle, WA; *U.S. Public*, pg. 1742

Eskildsen, John, Pres.--United States National Bank of Oregon, Portland, OR; *U.S. Public*, pg. 1681

Eskilson, Thomas T., Pres., Treas. & Sec.--Dixie Dairy Company, Gary, IN; *U.S. Private*, pg. 337

Espen, Robert W., Pres.--Miether Bearing Products, Inc., Odessa, TX; *U.S. Private*, pg. 33

Espino, Alberto N., Pres. & Chief Oper. Officer--Coastal Fuels Marketing, Inc., Miami, FL; *U.S. Public*, pg. 390

Espinosa, Herberto, Pres. & Chief Exec. Officer--Amtrade International Bank, Miami, FL; *U.S. Private*, pg. 68

Espinosa, Jacobo Hernandez, Pres.--Repsol Derivados, Madrid, Spain; *Int'l*, pg. 1104

Esposito, Chris, Pres.--Fisher Skylights, Inc., Holbrook, NY; *U.S. Private*, pg. 408

Esposito, Chris, Pres. & Chief Exec. Officer--Four Seasons Solar Products Corp., Holbrook, NY; *U.S. Private*, pg. 422

Esposito, Michael J., Chm., Pres. & Chief Exec. Officer--Exel Insurance Co. Ltd., Hamilton, Bermuda; *Int'l*, pg. 467

Esselborn, Bruce A., Pres.--Capsure Holdings Corp., Chicago, IL; *U.S. Public*, pg. 303

Essenburg, Sally, Pres.--CareerTrack Inc., Boulder, CO; *U.S. Public*, pg. 1555

Estadella, Antonio, Pres.--Sau-Sea Foods, Inc., Tarrytown, NY; *U.S. Private*, pg. 967

Estenfelder, L.G., Pres.--Gates Europe, Erembodegem, Belgium; *Int'l*, pg. 1396

Estenson, Noel, Pres. & Chief Exec. Officer--CENEX, Inc., Inver Grove Heights, MN; *U.S. Private*, pg. 221

Estes, Alexandra H., Chm. Bd. & Pres.--Haeger Industries, Inc., Dundee, IL; *U.S. Private*, pg. 493

Estes, Doug, Pres.--Moeller Products Co., Inc., Greenville, MS; *U.S. Private*, pg. 755

Estes, Robey W., Jr., Pres. & Treas.--Estes Express Lines, Inc., Richmond, VA; *U.S. Private*, pg. 384

Esteve Espinosa, D. Jose I., Pres.--Teleinformatica Y Comunicaciones, S.A., Madrid, Spain; *Int'l*, pg. 1372

Esteverena, Rolando, Chm. Bd. & Pres.--ADFlex Solutions, Inc., Chandler, AZ; *U.S. Public*, pg. 20

Estey, John W., Pres. & Chief Exec. Officer--S & C Electric Company, Chicago, IL; *U.S. Private*, pg. 954

Estok, John, Pres.--Firstcorp, Portland, OR; *U.S. Private*, pg. 408

Estrade, Javier de Ozamiz, Pres.--Defover, S.A., Panama, Panama; *Int'l*, pg. 1224

Eterovic, Cedomir, Pres.--Dana South American Operations, Fort Lauderdale, FL; *U.S. Public*, pg. 480

Etheredge, James, Pres.--Crescent Electric Supply Co., East Dubuque, IL; *U.S. Private*, pg. 289

Ethier, James B., Pres. & Chief Oper. Officer--Bush Brothers & Company, Knoxville, TN; *U.S. Private*, pg. 189

Ethridge, J.B., Pres.--Struthers Industries Inc., Gulfport, MS; *U.S. Private*, pg. 1048

Ethridge, J.B., Pres.--Struthers Wells Corp., Warren, PA; *U.S. Private*, pg. 1048

Eto, Terukazu, Pres.--JEOL, Ltd., Tokyo, Japan; *Int'l*, pg. 696

Etschmaier, Louis, Pres.--Hauck Mfg. Co., Cleona, PA; *U.S. Private*, pg. 510

Etter, Richard A., Chm. & Pres.--Bank of America Nevada, Reno, NV; *U.S. Public*, pg. 180

Ettie, Gordon, Pres.--Bepex Corporation, Minneapolis, MN; *Int'l*, pg. 636

Ettleson, Richard, Chm. Bd. & Pres.--Electro Brand, Inc., Chicago, IL; *U.S. Private*, pg. 368

Ettore, Joseph R., Pres. & Chief Exec. Officer--Ames Department Stores, Inc., Rocky Hill, CT; *U.S. Public*, pg. 99

Ettridge, Steven, Pres.--Temps & Company, Washington, DC; *U.S. Private*, pg. 1075

Eubanks, Gordon E., Jr., Pres. & Chief Exec. Officer--Symantec Corporation, Cupertino, CA; *U.S. Public*, pg. 1545

Eubanks, John, Pres.--Mesco Metal Buildings, Grapevine, TX; *U.S. Public*, pg. 1146

Euchukanonchai, Krairit, Pres.--Thana One Finance and Securities Limited, Bangkok, Thailand; *Int'l*, pg. 485

Eugster, Jack, Chm. Bd., Pres. & Chief Exec. Officer--Musicland Group Inc., Minnetonka, MN; *U.S. Public*, pg. 1142

Eulich, John, Pres.--Mark Andy, Inc., Chesterfield, MO; *U.S. Public*, pg. 521

Eunson, Jack T., Pres.--Zurn Balke-Durr, Inc., Tampa, FL; *Int'l*, pg. 401

Eureyecko, John, Pres. & Chief Oper. Officer--Piercing Pagoda, Inc., Bethlehem, PA; *U.S. Public*, pg. 1296

Eustace, Harry F., Pres.--California Microwave Navigation Systems, Inc., Washington, DC; *U.S. Public*, pg. 293

Evan, George, Pres.--Magnetics Data, Inc., Eden Prairie, MN; *U.S. Private*, pg. 696

Evangelio Rodriguez, D. Jesus V., Pres.--Sistemas Tecnicos Loterias Del Estado (S.T.L.), Madrid, Spain; *Int'l*, pg. 1372

Evangelista, Rose, Pres.--Just Toys, New York, NY; *U.S. Private*, pg. 903

Evans, Carol, Pres.--Stagebill, New York, NY; *U.S. Public*, pg. 1328

Evans, David S., Pres.--CBP Resources, Inc., Greensboro, NC; *U.S. Private*, pg. 192

Evans, Gary, Pres. & Chief Exec. Officer--Sioux Honey Association, Sioux City, IA; *U.S. Private*, pg. 1003

Evans, George W., Pres. & Chief Exec. Officer--Regions Bank/Banks County, Homer, GA; *U.S. Public*, pg. 1371

Evans, Gorton M., Pres. & Chief Exec. Officer--Consolidated Papers, Inc., Wisconsin Rapids, WI; *U.S. Public*, pg. 436

Evans, H. Malloy, Jr., Pres. & Treas.--Cheraw Yarn Mills, Inc., Cheraw, SC; *U.S. Private*, pg. 233

Evans, Jay H., Pres. & Chief Investment Officer--AMCORE Capital Management, Inc., Rockford, IL; *U.S. Public*, pg. 64

Evans, Jim, Pres. & Chief Exec. Officer--Evans, Hardy & Young, Inc., Santa Barbara, CA; *U.S. Private*, pg. 384

Evans, John, Pres. & Gen. Mgr.--Stu Evans Lincoln-Mercury Inc., Southgate, MI; *U.S. Private*, pg. 385

Evans, John, Pres.--Acme Industrial Company, Carpentersville, IL; *U.S. Private*, pg. 586

Evans, John, Pres.--First Union Securities Inc., Charlotte, NC; *U.S. Public*, pg. 640

Evans, John, Sr. V.P. & Dir.--Al Paul Lefton Co., Inc., Public Relations, Philadelphia, PA; *U.S. Private*, pg. 658

Evans, Larry J., Pres.--Western Cooperative Electric Association, Inc., Wa Keeney, KS; *U.S. Private*, pg. 1165

Evans, Leslie R., Pres.--Equipment Sales Division, Van Nuys, CA; *U.S. Public*, pg. 568

Evans, Mark E., Pres.--Wiltron Company, Morgan Hill, CA; *Int'l*, pg. 77
Evans, Mike, Pres.--Hopple Plastics, Inc., Florence, KY; *U.S. Private*, pg. 538
Evans, Morgan J., Pres. & Chief Oper. Officer--First Security Corporation, Salt Lake City, UT; *U.S. Public*, pg. 637
Evans, Richard H., Pres.--Florida Panthers Holdings, Inc., Fort Lauderdale, FL; *U.S. Public*, pg. 654
Evans, Ronald A., Pres. & Chief Exec. Officer--Best Western International, Inc., Phoenix, AZ; *U.S. Private*, pg. 140
Evans, Ronald C., Pres. & Chief Exec. Officer--Nationwide Homes, Inc., Martinsville, VA; *U.S. Private*, pg. 788
Evans, Ronald J., Pres.--Evans Industries, Inc., Harvey, LA; *U.S. Private*, pg. 385
Evans, Ronald J., Pres.--Kinark Corporation, Tulsa, OK; *U.S. Public*, pg. 960
Evans, Stuart M., Pres. & Chief Exec. Officer--Amtech Europe Limited, Cambridge, United Kingdom; *U.S. Public*, pg. 106
Evans, Thomas E., Pres.--Tenneco Automotive, Deerfield, IL; *U.S. Public*, pg. 1577
Evans, Thomas R., Pres.--The Atlantic Monthly Magazine, Boston, MA; *U.S. Private*, pg. 95
Evans, Thomas R., Pres. & Publr.--U.S. News & World Report, New York, NY; *U.S. Private*, pg. 1125
Evans, Tom, Pres.--Walker Manufacturing Co., Deerfield, IL; *U.S. Public*, pg. 1578
Evans, William, Pres.--Delta Industries, East Granby, CT; *U.S. Private*, pg. 322
Evans, William F., Jr., Pres. & Chief Oper. Officer--Columbus Mills, Inc., Columbus, GA; *U.S. Private*, pg. 256
Evans, William H., Chm. Bd., Pres. & Chief Exec. Officer--SunTrust Bank, North Central Florida, Ocala, FL; *U.S. Public*, pg. 1537
Evanson, Paul, Pres.--Florida Power & Light Company, North Palm Beach, FL; *U.S. Public*, pg. 608
Evenson, Jerry, Pres.--Northwest Pipe Fittings, Inc., Billings, MT; *U.S. Private*, pg. 806
Everett, Donald S., Pres. & Chief Oper. Officer--Interstate Steel Supply Company, Philadelphia, PA; *U.S. Public*, pg. 1100
Everist, Thomas, Pres.--L.G. Everist Inc., Sioux Falls, SD; *U.S. Private*, pg. 386
Everson, Lloyd K., M.D., Pres.--American Oncology Resources, Inc., Houston, TX; *U.S. Public*, pg. 88
Evert, James, Chm. Bd., Pres. & Chief Exec. Officer--Irvine Sensors Corporation, Costa Mesa, CA; *U.S. Public*, pg. 913
Everts, J.A., Pres.--Permatech, Inc., Graham, NC; *U.S. Public*, pg. 61
Evins, T.M., Pres.--W.A. Adams, Inc., Wilson, NC; *U.S. Public*, pg. 1502
Evon, Joe M., Pres. & Gen. Mgr.--BHP Petroleum Ltd., London, United Kingdom; *Int'l*, pg. 225
Ewell, Ken, Pres.--Proto-Power Corporation, Groton, CT; *U.S. Public*, pg. 965
Ewers, Gene, Pres.--King of the Road, Russell, KS; *U.S. Private*, pg. 236
Ewing, George, Jr., Pres.--A.H. Hoffman, Inc., Landisville, PA; *U.S. Private*, pg. 532
Ewing, George, Jr., Pres.--Hoffman Seeds, Inc., Landisville, PA; *U.S. Private*, pg. 532
Ewing, M., Pres.--Hood Corporation, Whittier, CA; *U.S. Private*, pg. 673
Ewing, Stephen E., Pres. & Chief Exec. Officer--MichCon, Detroit, MI; *U.S. Public*, pg. 1025
Exposito, Daisy, Pres. & Chief Creative Officer--The Bravo Group, New York, NY; *U.S. Private*, pg. 1197
Exum, James F., Jr., Pres. & Chief Oper. Officer--Krystal Company, Chattanooga, TN; *U.S. Private*, pg. 636
Eyler, John, Pres. & Chief Exec. Officer--F.A.O. Schwarz, New York, NY; *Int'l*, pg. 750
Ezell, Stan, Pres.--Purity Dairies Inc., Nashville, TN; *U.S. Private*, pg. 895
Ezoye, Shigeru, Pres.--Toto Ltd., Kitakyushu, Japan; *Int'l*, pg. 1410
Fabbri, Mark, Pres.--Kvaerner FSSL Ltd., London, United Kingdom; *Int'l*, pg. 767
Fabbri, Mark, Pres.--FSSL Ltd., London, United Kingdom; *Int'l*, pg. 772
Faber, N., Pres.--Neil Faber Media Inc., New York, NY; *U.S.* Private, pg. 390
Fabian, John M., Pres. & Chief Exec. Officer--ANSER (Analytic Services Inc.), Arlington, VA; *U.S. Private*, pg. 75
Fabiano, Anthony, Pres. & Chief Oper. Officer--Despatch Industries, Minneapolis, MN; *U.S. Private*, pg. 327
Fabick, Harry, Pres. & Chief Oper. Officer--John Fabick Tractor Company, Fenton, MO; *U.S. Private*, pg. 390
Fabre, Pierre, Mng. Dir.--Pierre Fabre S.A., Castres, France; *Int'l*, pg. 1056
Fabre, Roland, Pres.--Techlam SA, Cernay, France; *Int'l*, pg. 1166
Fabrikant, Charles, Chm. Bd., Pres. & Chief Exec. Officer--Seacor Smit Inc., Houston, TX; *U.S. Public*, pg. 1449
Fabris, James D., Pres.--Hurco Manufacturing Company, Indianapolis, IN; *U.S. Public*, pg. 850
Fabrizzi, Vincent J., Pres. & Chief Oper. Officer--Paradigm Communications, Tampa, FL; *U.S. Private*, pg. 838
Faccenda, Robin, Pres.--Hitchcock Chair Company LTD, New Hartford, CT; *U.S. Private*, pg. 531
Facchina, Robert, Pres. & Chief Exec. Officer--Johanna Foods Inc., Flemington, NJ; *U.S. Private*, pg. 589
Fadel, Ali A., Pres.--Associated Spring, Bristol, CT; *U.S. Public*, pg. 190
Fadel, Mitch, Pres. & Chief Exec. Officer--ColorTyme, Inc., Irving, TX; *U.S. Private*, pg. 255
Fadiga, Antonio, Pres. & Co-Exec. Officer--Young & Rubicam Brazil, Sao Paulo, Brazil; *U.S. Private*, pg. 1200
Faeller, Kurt, Pres. & Chief Exec. Officer--Rieter Holdings, Winterthur, Switzerland; *Int'l*, pg. 1116
Fagan, A.L., Pres.--Charterhouse Group International, Inc., New York, NY; *U.S. Private*, pg. 230
Fagan, R.J., Pres.--Quaker Chemical Corp., Wilmington, DE; *U.S. Public*, pg. 1346
Fagan, Robert D., Pres.--Power Markets Development Company, Allentown, PA; *U.S. Public*, pg. 1244
Fagel, Marvin, Pres.--Aurora Packing Co., Inc., North Aurora, IL; *U.S. Private*, pg. 99
Fagerholm, Stig H., Pres.--Opel Oy, Espoo, Finland; *U.S. Public*, pg. 723
Fagerlin, Mark, Pres.--Burns & Roe Services Corp., Oradell, NJ; *U.S. Private*, pg. 187
Faherty, Gregory T., Pres.--Siplast Inc., Irving, TX; *Int'l*, pg. 659
Fahey, John, Pres. & Chief Exec. Officer--National Geographic Society, Washington, DC; *U.S. Private*, pg. 783
Fahey, John M., Jr., Pres. & Chief Exec. Officer--Time-Life, Inc., Alexandria, VA; *U.S. Public*, pg. 1613
Fahlin, Roland, Pres. & Chief Exec. Officer--ICA Handlarnas AB, Solna, Sweden; *Int'l*, pg. 642
Fahrni, Fritz, Pres. & Chief Exec. Officer--Sulzer Ltd., Winterthur, Switzerland; *Int'l*, pg. 1305
Fahs, John C., Chm. Bd., Pres., Chief Exec. Officer & Treas.--California Panel & Veneer Company, Cerritos, CA; *U.S. Private*, pg. 201
Fain, John H., Chm. Bd., Pres., Chief Exec. Officer & Chief Oper. Officer--Metro Information Services, Virginia Beach, VA; *U.S. Public*, pg. 1102
Fain, Jonathan D., Pres.--Teknor Apex Company, Pawtucket, RI; *U.S. Private*, pg. 1073
Fair, C.B., III, Pres. & Chief Exec. Officer--Regions Bank/ Paulding County, Dallas, TX; *U.S. Public*, pg. 1372
Fairbank, C.E., Pres.--MC2 Inc., Lombard, IL; *U.S. Public*, pg. 1210
Fairbanks, J. Nelson, Pres. & Chief Exec. Officer--United States Corrulite Corporation, Clewiston, FL; *U.S. Private*, *pg. 1126*
Fairbanks, J. Nelson, Pres. & Chief Exec. Officer--South Central Florida Express, Inc., Clewiston, FL; *U.S. Private*, *pg. 1126*
Fairbanks, J. Nelson, Pres. & Chief Exec. Officer--Southern Garden Citrus Processing, Clewiston, FL; *U.S. Private*, pg. 1126
Fairchild, Ronald, Pres. & Chief Exec. Officer--Paul Inman Associates Inc., Farmington, MI; *U.S. Private*, pg. 564
Fairfield, Bill, Pres. & Chief Exec. Officer--Inacom Corp., Omaha, NE; *U.S. Public*, pg. 873
Faison, F.J., Jr., Pres.--Carroll's Foods, Inc., Warsaw, NC; *U.S. Private*, pg. 215
Fait, George A., Chm. Bd. & Pres.--Capitol Indemnity Corporation, Madison, WI; *U.S. Public*, pg. 302
Fait, George A., Chm. Bd. & Pres.--Capitol Specialty Insurance Corporation, Madison, WI; *U.S. Public*, pg. 302
Fait, George A., Pres.--Capitol Facilities Corp., Madison, WI; *U.S. Public*, pg. 302
Falk, Lloyd, Pres., Chief Exec. Officer & Chief Oper. Officer--Fort Lock Corporation, River Grove, IL; *U.S. Private*, pg. 419
Falk, Steve, Pres. & Chief Exec. Officer--San Francisco Newspaper Agency, San Francisco, CA; *U.S. Private*, pg. 239
Falkowski, Patricia A., Pres. & Chief Investment Officer--Fiduciary Management Associates, Inc., Chicago, IL; *U.S. Public*, pg. 1673
Fallarino, John, Pres.--Metpar Corp., Westbury, NY; *U.S. Private*, pg. 735
Fallon, Donald, Chm. Bd., Pres. & Chief Exec. Officer--S.A. Cimenteries CBR, Brussels, Belgium; *Int'l*, pg. 605
Faludy, Thomas, Pres.--Carefree of Colorado, Broomfield, CO; *U.S. Public*, pg. 217
Famalette, James, Pres. & Chief Oper. Officer--Gottschalks Inc., Fresno, CA; *U.S. Public*, pg. 754
Famalette, Joseph P., Pres. & Chief Exec. Officer--Tri Valley Growers, San Ramon, CA; *U.S. Private*, pg. 1101
Fanelli, Richard G., Pres. & Chief Exec. Officer--Enthone-OMI, Inc., West Haven, CT; *U.S. Public*, pg. 138
Fanning, John, Pres.--Comforce/Uniforce Staffing Services, Woodbury, NY; *U.S. Public*, pg. 409
Fanning, John, Pres.--PRO, Woodbury, NY; *U.S. Public*, pg. 409
Fanning, John, Pres.--THISCO, Woodbury, NY; *U.S. Public*, pg. 409
Fanning, John, Pres.--SOCO Thomasville, Inc., Fort Worth, TX; *U.S. Public*, pg. 1482
Fantegrossi, Vincent, Pres.--Cape Cod Potato Chip Company, Hyannis, MA; *U.S. Private*, pg. 205
Fantini, S., Pres.--AGIP Petroleum Co., Inc., Dover, DE; *Int'l*, *pg. 428*
Farace, Andrea, Pres.--Trace International Holdings, Inc., New York, NY; *U.S. Private*, pg. 1094
Farb, Martin N., Pres. & Chief Exec. Officer--Brinkmann Instruments, Inc., Westbury, NY; *U.S. Private*, pg. 169
Farber, Jack, Chm. Bd., Pres. & Chief Exec. Officer--CSS Industries, Inc., Philadelphia, PA; *U.S. Public*, pg. 283
Farge, J., Pres.--Pari Mutuel Urbain, Paris, France; *Int'l*, pg. 1023
Farha, James T., Pres. & Chief Exec. Officer--Standard Life & Accident Insurance Co., Galveston, TX; *U.S. Public*, pg. 88
Fariello, Frank A., Chm. Bd., Pres. & Chief Exec. Officer--EDO Corporation, New York, NY; *U.S. Public*, pg. 541
Farkas, Joseph, Pres.--Standard Products Industrial, Bezons, France; *U.S. Public*, pg. 1505
Farley, Claire S., Pres.--Getty Oil Exploration Co., Universal City, CA; *U.S. Public*, pg. 1583
Farley, Joseph J., Pres.--Teletrak Advanced Technology Systems, Inc., Greenwich, CT; *U.S. Public*, pg. 808
Farley, William F., Chm. Bd., Pres. & Chief Exec. Officer--Farley, Inc., Chicago, IL; *U.S. Private*, pg. 394
Farm, Kaj, Pres.--Oy Scan-Auto AB, Helsinki, Finland; *Int'l*, pg. 686
Farman, Richard D., Pres. & Chief Oper. Officer--Pacific Enterprises, Los Angeles, CA; *U.S. Public*, pg. 1249
Farmer, Bruce J., Pres. & Chief Exec. Officer--Four Winds Investment Corp., Galveston, TX; *U.S. Private*, pg. 422
Farmer, Chad, Pres. & Creative Dir.--Lambesis, Del Mar, CA; *U.S. Private*, pg. 644
Farmer, Donald, Pres.--Great Western Metals Inc., Houston, TX; *U.S. Private*, pg. 422
Farmer, Forest J., Pres.--Acustar, Inc., Troy, MI; *U.S. Public*, *pg. 353*
Farmer, Frank A., Pres.--Highland Propane Company, Roanoke, VA; *U.S. Public*, pg. 1393
Farmer, John R., Chm. Bd., Pres. & Chief Exec. Officer--SouthTrust Bank, Tuscaloosa County, Tuscaloosa, AL; *U.S. Public*, pg. 1492
Farmer, Larry E., Pres.--Brown & Root Energy Services, London, United Kingdom; *U.S. Public*, pg. 775
Farmer, Phillip W., Chm. Bd., Pres. & Chief Exec. Officer--Harris Corporation, Melbourne, FL; *U.S. Public*, pg. 791
Farmer, Roy F., Chm. Bd., Pres., Chief Exec. Officer & Chief Oper. Officer--Farmer Brothers Company, Torrance, CA; *U.S. Public*, pg. 613
Farmer, Scott D., Pres. & Chief Oper. Officer--Cintas Corporation, Mason, OH; *U.S. Public*, pg. 370
Farnsworth, Harold R., Pres.--E.J. Bartells Co., Renton, WA; *U.S. Private*, pg. 118
Farnsworth, Jack, Pres. & Chief Exec. Officer--Primedia Informatin Group, New York, NY; *U.S. Public*, pg. 1328
Farnsworth, Jack, Pres. & Chief Exec. Officer--Primedia Workplace Learning, Carrollton, TX; *U.S. Public*, pg. 1328
Farnsworth, Ken, Jr., Chm. Bd., Pres. & Exec. V.P.--Rhodes International, Inc., Salt Lake City, UT; *U.S. Private*, pg. 927
Farnsworth, Ross N., Pres.--Farnsworth Companies, Mesa, AZ; *U.S. Private*, pg. 397
Faron, M.J., Pres.--W.E. O'Neil Construction Company, Chicago, IL; *U.S. Private*, pg. 817
Farquhar, Robert, Div. Pres.--Movie Star Factory Outlet Stores, Poplarville, MS; *U.S. Public*, pg. 1141
Farr, Mel, Pres.--Mel Farr Automotive Group, Inc., Oak Park, MI; *U.S. Private*, pg. 729
Farrah, Pat, Chm. Bd., Pres. & Chief Exec. Officer--MG Products, San Antonio, TX; *U.S. Public*, pg. 1026
Farrar, John S., Pres.--Roper Bros. Lumber Co., Inc., Petersburg, VA; *U.S. Private*, pg. 944
Farrar, Roger L., Pres.--Vanguard Bank & Trust Company, Valparaiso, FL; *U.S. Public*, pg. 1549
Farrel, Mike, Pres.--SFX Broadcasting Incorporated, New York, NY; *U.S. Public*, pg. 1417
Farrell, Francis X., Publisher--The Sporting News Publishing Company, Saint Louis, MO; *U.S. Public*, pg. 1616
Farrell, Frank A., Jr., Chm. Bd., Pres. & Chief Exec. Officer--Hope's Architectural Products Inc., Jamestown, NY; *U.S. Private*, pg. 538
Farrell, Jerald F., Pres.--Hughes Communications, Inc., Long Beach, CA; *U.S. Public*, pg. 721
Farrell, John F.P., Pres.-DMB&B North America--D'Arcy Masius Benton & Bowles Communications, New York, NY; *U.S. Private*, pg. 303
Farrell, Michael J., Pres.--Wide-Lite, San Marcos, TX; *U.S. Public*, pg. 730
Farrell, Roger A., Pres. & Chief Exec. Officer--Enogex Inc., Oklahoma City, OK; *U.S. Public*, pg. 1207
Farrell, W. James, Chm. Bd., Pres. & Chief Exec. Officer--Illinois Tool Works Inc., Glenview, IL; *U.S. Public*, pg. 865
Farren, Owen, Pres. & Chief Exec. Officer--SL Industries, Inc., Mount Laurel, NJ; *U.S. Public*, pg. 1418
Farrington, Hugh G., Pres. & Chief Exec. Officer--Hannaford Bros. Co., Scarborough, ME; *U.S. Public*, pg. 781
Farris, Allen, Pres. & Chief Exec. Officer--United Missouri Bank N.A., Kansas City, MO; *U.S. Public*, pg. 1654
Farris, David J., Pres. & Chief Oper. Officer--Beneficial Corporation, Wilmington, DE; *U.S. Public*, pg. 211
Farris, David J., Pres. & Chief Exec. Officer--Beneficial Management Corporation, Peapack, NJ; *U.S. Public*, pg. 211
Farris, David J., Pres. & Chief Exec. Officer--Beneficial Management Corporation of America & Affiliated Corps., Wilmington, DE; *U.S. Public*, pg. 211
Farris, G. Stephen, Pres.--The Phoenix Resource Companies, Inc., Oklahoma City, OK; *U.S. Public*, pg. 119
Farris, G. Steven, Pres. & Chief Oper. Officer--Apache Corporation, Houston, TX; *U.S. Public*, pg. 119
Farris, Michael R., Pres. & Chief Exec. Officer--Lasersight Inc., Saint Louis, MO; *U.S. Public*, pg. 979
Farris, William P., Pres. & Chief Exec. Officer--Mattison Technologies, Inc., Rockford, IL; *U.S. Private*, pg. 714
Farro, Angelo, Pres.--Deutsch Metal Components, Gardena, CA; *U.S. Private*, pg. 328
Farver, Pat, Pres.--Blissfield Manufacturing Company, Blissfield, MI; *U.S. Private*, pg. 149
Farwell, I.S., Pres.--Rheem Water Heater, Montgomery, AL; *Int'l*, pg. 1022
Fascitelli, Michael D., Pres.--Vornado Realty Trust, Saddle Brook, NJ; *U.S. Public*, pg. 1725
Fasolo, Joseph, Pres.--Baum Printing House, Inc., Philadelphia, PA; *U.S. Public*, pg. 1735
Fassler, Joseph K., Pres. & Chief Exec. Officer--Restaura, Inc., Phoenix, AZ; *U.S. Public*, pg. 1718
Fast, Robert B., Pres.--Claims Service International, Inc., Portland, ME; *U.S. Public*, pg. 1699
Faucetta, Peter, Pres.--Applied Graphics, Los Angeles, CA; *U.S. Private*, pg. 1125
Faukner, Fred E., Jr., Pres.--Boston Acoustics, Inc., Peabody, MA; *U.S. Public*, pg. 246
Faulk, Richard D., Pres.--Indimac Manufactured Housing Division, San Diego, CA; *U.S. Public*, pg. 857
Fausett, Jeff, Pres.--GKN Westland Aerospace North America Inc., Compton, CA; *Int'l*, pg. 535
Favat, Peter, Pres., Partner--Houston Herstek Favat, Boston, MA; *U.S. Private*, pg. 542
Favereau-Forestier, Michel, Pres.--Chr. Hansen France S.A., Arpajon, France; *Int'l*, pg. 289

Favier, James G., Jr., Pres.--Olin Microelectronic Materials, Inc., Norwalk, CT; *U.S. Public*, pg. 1219
Favini, Carlo, Pres.--Elga Ronal S.r.l., Milan, Italy; *U.S. Public*, pg. 982
Favish, Michael, Pres. & Chief Exec. Officer--FOTOBALL USA, Inc., San Diego, CA; *U.S. Public*, pg. 678
Favre, Art E., Pres.--Performance Contractors Inc., Baton Rouge, LA; *U.S. Private*, pg. 853
Favre, Martin, Pres.--Bernina of America Inc., Aurora, IL; *Int'l*, pg. 189
Fawcett, Gerald A., Pres. & Chief Oper. Officer--Kaiser Ventures, Inc., Ontario, CA; *U.S. Public*, pg. 941
Faxon, Bradford J., Chm. Bd. & Pres.--Fall River Gas Company, Fall River, MA; *U.S. Public*, pg. 611
Fayet, Luc, Pres.--Schweppes France S.A., Levallois-Perret, France; *Int'l*, pg. 248
Fayfield, Robert, Chm. Bd., Pres. & Chief Exec. Officer--Banner Engineering Corp., Minneapolis, MN; *U.S. Private*, pg. 114
Fearday, Ken, Pres.--L.L. Olds Seed Company, Madison, WI; *U.S. Private*, pg. 814
Featherstone, Diane L., Pres.--Constellation Energy Source, Inc., Baltimore, MD; *U.S. Public*, pg. 172
Feaver, Ed, Pres.--Prescription Solutions, Costa Mesa, CA; *U.S. Public*, pg. 1251
Fecan, Ivan, Pres. & Chief Oper. Officer--Baton Broadcasting Incorporated, Scarborough, Canada; *Int'l*, pg. 170
Federman, Joseph R., Chm Bd., Pres. & Chief Exec. Officer--Victor Technology, Addison, IL; *U.S. Private*, pg. 1139
Fedrick, Dee, Pres.--C.R. Fedrick, Inc., Novato, CA; *U.S. Private*, pg. 1052
Fee, Frank J., III, Pres. & Treas.--Reliable Automatic Sprinkler Co., Inc., Mount Vernon, NY; *U.S. Private*, pg. 920
Fee, P.S., Pres. & Chief Exec. Officer--BOVAR Inc., Calgary, Canada; *Int'l*, pg. 1424
Fee, Robert E., Pres.--Turner Construction Company, New York, NY; *U.S. Public*, pg. 1645
Feehan, Daniel R., Pres. & Chief Oper. Officer--Cash America International, Inc., Fort Worth, TX; *U.S. Public*, pg. 312
Feehrer, E. Ross, Pres. & Chief Exec. Officer--F.N. Burt Company, Inc., Buffalo, NY; *U.S. Private*, pg. 188
Feeley, Edmund, Pres. & Chief Oper. Officer--Fleer-Skybox International Inc., Mount Laurel, NJ; *U.S. Public*, pg. 1052
Feely, Pat, Pres. & Chief Oper. Officer--Radica USA Limited, Dallas, TX; *U.S. Private*, pg. 906
Feeney, Ed, Pres.-Liebert North America--Liebert Corporation, Columbus, OH; *U.S. Public*, pg. 573
Feeney, James H., Pres. & Chief Exec. Officer--Trone Advertising, Inc., Greensboro, NC; *U.S. Private*, pg. 1104
Feeney, John E., Pres.--AGRA Cambrian Inc., Oakville, Canada; *Int'l*, pg. 30
Feeney, William, Pres.--Dole Europe, S.A., Paris, France; *U.S. Public*, pg. 515
Fees, John A., Pres.-B&W Federal Svcs., Inc.--Babcock & Wilcox Co., Barberton, OH; *U.S. Public*, pg. 1068
Fees, John A., Pres.--Diamond Power Specialty Co., Lancaster, OH; *U.S. Public*, pg. 1068
Fees, Samuel E., Pres. & Chief Exec. Officer--Woodstuff Manufacturing, Inc., Phoenix, AZ; *U.S. Private*, pg. 1187
Fegler, James T., Pres.--Equitable Resources Marketing Company, Pittsburgh, PA; *U.S. Public*, pg. 590
Fehr, Jeffrey F., Pres.--Warren Rupp, Inc., Mansfield, OH; *U.S. Public*, pg. 862
Fehr, Robert, Pres. & Chief Exec. Officer--Cox Lumber Co., Saint Petersburg, FL; *U.S. Private*, pg. 283
Fehrenbach, Dan, Pres. & Chief Exec. Officer--Citizens Bank of Western Indiana, Terre Haute, IN; *U.S. Public*, pg. 280
Fehrman, Roger A., Pres. & Chief Exec. Officer--The Felters Company, Roebuck, SC; *U.S. Private*, pg. 400
Feigenbutz, Gary, Pres. & Chief Exec. Officer--Miracle Recreation Equipment Company, Monett, MO; *U.S. Private*, pg. 752
Feighner, Mark S., Pres.--GTE Mobile Communications Incorporated, Atlanta, GA; *U.S. Public*, pg. 696
Feil, Bob, Pres.-Tencel Div.--Courtaulds Fibers Inc., Axis, AL; *Int'l*, pg. 339
Feinberg, Henry J., Chm. Bd., Pres. & Chief Exec. Officer--Rand McNally & Company, Skokie, IL; *U.S. Private*, pg. 908
Feinberg, Hill, Pres. & Chief Exec. Officer--First Southwest Company, Dallas, TX; *U.S. Private*, pg. 407
Feinberg, Martin, Pres.--Winner Communications, Inc., New York, NY; *U.S. Private*, pg. 1183
Feinstein, Alan, Pres.--Micro Slides Div., Hauppauge, NY; *U.S. Private*, pg. 125
Feinstein, Leonard, Pres. & Co-Chief Exec. Officer--Bed Bath & Beyond Inc., Union, NJ; *U.S. Public*, pg. 200
Feinstein, Martin D., Pres. & Chief Oper. Officer--Farmers Group, Inc., Los Angeles, CA; *Int'l*, pg. 110
Feinstein, Ronald, Pres.--Dennison Stationery Products Company, Holyoke, MA; *U.S. Public*, pg. 153
Feinstein, Ronald, Pres. & Chief Exec. Officer--Lifeline Systems, Inc., Cambridge, MA; *U.S. Public*, pg. 992
Feist, Edwin, Pres.--Mead Johnson Philippines, Inc., Manila, Philippines; *U.S. Public*, pg. 256
Felber, Ronald, Pres., Chief Exec. & Chief Oper. Officer--Oakite Products, Inc., Berkeley Heights, NJ; *Int'l*, pg. 861
Feld, Kenneth, Pres. & Chief Exec. Officer--Ringling Bros., Barnum & Bailey Combined Shows, Inc., Vienna, VA; *U.S. Private*, pg. 400
Feld, Kenneth, Pres.--Ice Follies & Holiday on Ice, Vienna, VA; *U.S. Private*, pg. 400
Feldenkreis, George, Pres.--Carfel, Inc., Miami, FL; *U.S. Private*, pg. 210
Feldenkreis, Oscar, Pres. & Chief Oper. Officer--Supreme International Corp., Miami, FL; *U.S. Public*, pg. 1542
Felder, G. Frank, Pres.--Bankhead Enterprises Inc., Atlanta, GA; *U.S. Private*, pg. 114
Feldman, Allan, Pres.--RGA and East End Accessories, New York, NY; *U.S. Private*, pg. 903
Feldman, Gerald, Pres. & Chief Exec. Officer--Allied Advertising Agency, Public Relations, Boston, MA; *U.S. Private*, pg. 38
Feldman, Jerome I., Pres. & Chief Exec. Officer--GP Strategies Corporation, New York, NY; *U.S. Public*, pg. 694
Feldman, Joseph, Pres. & Chief Exec. Officer--Isfel Company, Inc., Rahway, NJ; *U.S. Private*, pg. 576
Feldman, Lawrence H., Chm. Bd., Pres. & Chief Exec. Officer--Tower Realty Trust, Inc., New York, NY; *U.S. Public*, pg. 1625
Feldman, Robert, Pres. & Chief Exec. Officer-GCI Group, Inc.--GCI Group Inc., New York, NY; *U.S. Public*, pg. 764
Feldman, Steve, Pres.--Pulte Puerto Rican Operations, Bayamon, PR; *U.S. Public*, pg. 1345
Feldman, Steven M., Pres.--Totsy Manufacturing Company, Inc., Holyoke, MA; *U.S. Private*, pg. 1093
Felicella, Frank, Pres. & Chief Exec. Officer--Builders Square, Inc., San Antonio, TX; *U.S. Private*, pg. 477
Felker, G. Stephen, Chm. Bd., Pres. & Chief Exec. Officer--Avondale Incorporated, Monroe, GA; *U.S. Private*, pg. 102
Feller, Raymond, Pres.--Rowman & Littlefield Publishers, Inc., Lanham, MD; *U.S. Private*, pg. 1128
Fellowes, James E., Pres. & Chief Oper. Officer--Fellowes Manufacturing Co., Itasca, IL; *U.S. Private*, pg. 400
Fellows, George, Pres. & Chief Exec. Officer--Revlon, Inc., New York, NY; *U.S. Private*, pg. 689
Fellows, George, Pres. & Chief Oper. Officer--Revlon International Corporation, New York, NY; *U.S. Private*, pg. 690
Fellows, James, Pres. & Chief Exec. Officer--Evans Adhesive Corp., Columbus, OH; *U.S. Private*, pg. 384
Felsenthal, Peter, Pres.--Earle Industries, Inc., Earle, AR; *U.S. Private*, pg. 356
Felsinger, Donald E., Pres. & Chief Oper. Officer--Enova Corp, San Diego, CA; *U.S. Public*, pg. 583
Felsted, John, Pres.--Chr. Hansen Pty. Ltd., Greenacres, Australia; *Int'l*, pg. 289
Feltenstein, Sidney, Chm. Bd., Pres. & Chief Exec. Officer--A&W Restaurants, Inc., Livonia, MI; *U.S. Private*, pg. 1
Felton, Edgar C., Chm. & Pres.--Bank of Bermuda (New York) Limited, New York, NY; *Int'l*, pg. 151
Felts, Jeffrey E., Pres. & Chief Exec. Officer--Hamilton Mutual Insurance Company Of Cincinnati, Cincinnati, OH; *U.S. Private*, pg. 497
Fendrich, George, Div. Mgr.--Raven Industries Sportswear Div., Sioux Falls, SD; *U.S. Public*, pg. 1361
Fenelle, Donald, Pres.--Dee Paper Company, Chester, PA; *U.S. Private*, pg. 320
Feniger, William D., Chm. Bd., Pres. & Chief Exec. Officer--Meridian National Corporation, Toledo, OH; *U.S. Public*, pg. 1095
Fennie, Bruce W., V.P. & Gen. Mgr.--Harris Corp., RF Communications Group Marketing Division, Rochester, NY; *U.S. Public*, pg. 792
Fenster, Albert J., Pres.--Capucci Creations International, Inc., Beverly Hills, CA; *U.S. Private*, pg. 207
Fenton, Jim, Pres., Chief Exec. Officer & Treas.--Southeastern Steel Company, Florence, SC; *U.S. Private*, pg. 1015
Ferchat, Robert A., Chm., Pres. & Chief Exec. Officer--BCE Mobile Communications Inc., Saint-Laurent, Canada; *Int'l*, pg. 115
Ferdinandtsen, G.R., Chm. Bd. & Pres.--American National Life Insurance Co. of Texas, Galveston, TX; *U.S. Public*, pg. 87
Ferenbach, Richard S., Pres.--Leon-Ferenbach Inc., Hoboken, NJ; *U.S. Private*, pg. 660
Fergus, Dan, Pres.--Genesee Precision Fabricating, Grand Prairie, TX; *U.S. Private*, pg. 446
Fergus, Dan, Pres.--Genesee Stamping, Grand Prairie, TX; *U.S. Private*, pg. 446
Ferguson, C. David, Chm. Bd., Pres., Chief Exec. & Chief Oper. Officer--Gould Electronics Inc., Eastlake, OH; *U.S. Public*, pg. 1591
Ferguson, C. David, Pres.--Gould Electronics Inc., Foil Division, Eastlake, OH; *U.S. Public*, pg. 1592
Ferguson, Daryl A., Pres. & Chief Oper. Officer--Citizens Utilities Company, Stamford, CT; *U.S. Public*, pg. 379
Ferguson, Daryl A., Pres. & Chief Oper. Officer--Citizens Telecommunications, Stamford, CT; *U.S. Public*, pg. 380
Ferguson, David, Pres. & Chief Exec. Officer--McCourt Label Co., Lewis Run, PA; *U.S. Private*, pg. 720
Ferguson, Dwight, Pres. & Chief Oper. Officer--Florimex Worldwide, Inc., Danville, VA; *U.S. Public*, pg. 510
Ferguson, J.T., Pres. & Chief Exec. Officer--Cormier Rice Milling Company, Inc., De Witt, AR; *U.S. Private*, pg. 276
Ferguson, James, Pres. & Chief Exec. Officer--Span-America Medical Systems Inc., Greenville, SC; *U.S. Public*, pg. 1495
Ferguson, Lee, Pres. & Chief Oper. Officer--Bike Athletic Co., Knoxville, TN; *U.S. Private*, pg. 143
Ferguson, Mark H., Chm. Bd., Pres. & Chief Exec. Officer--Firstbank of Illinois Co., Springfield, IL; *U.S. Public*, pg. 643
Ferguson, Robert, Pres.--Bankers Trust Australia Limited, Sydney, Australia; *U.S. Public*, pg. 185
Ferguson, Robert, Pres.--Continental Airline Holdings, Inc., Houston, TX; *Int'l*, pg. 1202
Ferguson, Sam, Pres., Chief Exec. & Chief Oper. Officer--Ferguson International, Inc., Dallas, TX; *U.S. Private*, pg. 401
Ferguson, Thomas, Pres. & Chief Oper. Officer--Mirro Company, Manitowoc, WI; *U.S. Public*, pg. 1177
Ferguson, Thomas A., Jr., Pres. & Chief Oper. Officer--Newell Co., Freeport, IL; *U.S. Public*, pg. 1176
Ferguson, W.A. III, Pres. & Chief Exec. Officer--Setco, Cincinnati, OH; *U.S. Private*, pg. 987
Ferguson, Whitworth, Jr., Pres.--Ferguson Electric Construction Co., Inc., Buffalo, NY; *U.S. Private*, pg. 401
Ferland, E. James, Chm. Bd., Pres. & Chief Exec. Officer--Public Service Enterprise Group Incorporated, Newark, NJ; *U.S. Public*, pg. 1340
Ferlauto, Dominic, Pres.--The Keds Corporation, Lexington, MA; *U.S. Public*, pg. 1525
Ferman, James L., Jr., Pres.--Ferman Oldsmobile, Tampa, FL; *U.S. Private*, pg. 401
Fernandes Salgueiro, Joao Mauricio, Dr., Chm. Bd. & Pres.--Caixa Geral de Depositos, Lisbon, Portugal; *Int'l*, pg. 250
Fernandes, Jay, Pres.--Whittaker Controls, Inc., North Hollywood, CA; *U.S. Public*, pg. 1767
Fernandez Rodriguez, Antonio, Chm. & Pres.--Grupo Modelo S.A., Mexico, Mexico; *U.S. Public*, pg. 115
Fernandez Vidal, D. Guillermo, Pres.--T.S. Telefonica Sistemas, S.A., Madrid, Spain; *Int'l*, pg. 1372
Fernandez, Antonio, Pres.--EMTEC Magnetics Iberica S.A., Madrid, Spain; *Int'l*, pg. 743
Fernandez, Emanuel, Pres. & Chief Fin. Officer--Condal Distributors Inc., Bronx, NY; *U.S. Private*, pg. 262
Fernandez, Fernando Rubio, Pres.--INESPAL - Industria Espanola del Aluminio, S.A., Madrid, Spain; *Int'l*, pg. 1225
Fernandez, John Viney, Pres.--PDV Marina, S.A., Caracas, Venezuela; *Int'l*, pg. 1045
Fernandez, Jorge, Pres.--Fleck Controls, Milwaukee, WI; *U.S. Public*, pg. 1273
Fernandez, Joseph H., Chm. Bd., Pres. & Chief Exec. Officer--Buttrey Food & Drug Company, Great Falls, MT; *U.S. Public*, pg. 271
Fernandez, Luis Garza T., Pres.--Galvak S.A., San Nicolas, Mexico; *Int'l*, pg. 56
Fernandez, Nestor, Pres. & Chief Exec. Officer--Digitron Tool Co., Inc., Miamisburg, OH; *U.S. Private*, pg. 332
Fernee, Brian, Pres.--RNF Media Corporation Inc., Beverly Hills, CA; *U.S. Private*, pg. 905
Ferola, Frank F., Chm. Bd. & Pres.--The Stephan Company, Fort Lauderdale, FL; *U.S. Public*, pg. 1514
Feroz, Mehtabuddin, Pres.--Otsuka Pakistan Ltd., Karachi, Pakistan; *Int'l*, pg. 1014
Ferran, Xavier, Chm. Bd. & Pres.--Bacardi-Martini Belgium, Brussels, Belgium; *U.S. Private*, pg. 109
Ferrari, Giannantonio, Pres. & Chief Oper. Officer--Honeywell Inc., Minneapolis, MN; *U.S. Public*, pg. 833
Ferreira Lima, Manuel Branco, Chm. Bd. & Pres.--Transportes Aereos Portugueses, Lisbon, Portugal; *Int'l*, pg. 1418
Ferreira, Fernando Xavier, Chm. Bd., Pres. & Chief Exec. Officer--Telebras S.A., Brasilia, Brazil; *Int'l*, pg. 1362
Ferreira, K., Chief Exec. Officer--The Simba Group, Isando, South Africa; *Int'l*, pg. 496
Ferreiro, Juan, Pres.--Cronos/DMB&B, San Salvador, El Salvador; *U.S. Private*, pg. 303
Ferreiro, Maria H., Pres.--Union Carbide Argentina S.A.I.C.S., Buenos Aires, Argentina; *U.S. Public*, pg. 1667
Ferrell, John F., Pres. & Chief Creative Officer--FerrellCalvillo Communications, Inc., New York, NY; *U.S. Private*, pg. 401
Ferrentino, Michael, Pres.--Comforce Corporation, Lake Success, NY; *U.S. Public*, pg. 409
Ferrera, Kenneth G., Pres.--James Ferrera & Sons, Inc., Canton, MA; *U.S. Private*, pg. 401
Ferreras, Pedro, Pres.--SEPI, Madrid, Spain; *Int'l*, pg. 1223
Ferrero, Adolfo, Pres.--Sancor Cooperativas Unidas Limitadas, Buenos Aires, Argentina; *Int'l*, pg. 1183
Ferrier, A.A., Pres.--Redpath Industries Ltd., Toronto, Canada; *Int'l*, pg. 1357
Ferries, Chuck, Pres. & Chief Exec. Officer--Scott Sports Group, Ketchum, ID; *U.S. Private*, pg. 977
Ferris, Steve, Pres.--Apache Canada Ltd., Calgary, Canada; *U.S. Public*, pg. 119
Ferro, David R., Publr.--Argus-Courier, Petaluma, CA; *U.S. Public*, pg. 1343
Ferro, Jose, Pres.--EMTEC da Amazonia S.A., Sao Bernardo do Campo, Brazil; *Int'l*, pg. 743
Ferron, Rosendo, Pres. & Chief Exec. Officer--Halsey Drug Company, Brooklyn, NY; *U.S. Private*, pg. 496
Ferrone, Donald, Pres.--American Sightseeing International, San Francisco, CA; *U.S. Private*, pg. 61
Ferry, William, Pres. & Chief Exec. Officer--Banyan Systems Inc., Westborough, MA; *U.S. Public*, pg. 189
Fertitta, George A., Pres.--Margeotes/Fertitta & Partners Inc., New York, NY; *U.S. Private*, pg. 702
Fertitta, Tilman, Chm. Bd., Pres. & Chief Exec. Officer--Landry's Seafood Restaurants Inc., Houston, TX; *U.S. Public*, pg. 977
Feshbach, Andrew D., Pres. & Chief Exec. Officer--Big Dog Holdings Inc., Santa Barbara, CA; *U.S. Public*, pg. 227
Fesler, Daniel, Pres.--Lampert Yards, Inc., Saint Paul, MN; *U.S. Private*, pg. 645
Fesperman, John, Pres.--J.C. Penney Life Insurance Company, Plano, TX; *U.S. Public*, pg. 917
Festa, Angelo Carlo, Chm. Bd. & Pres.--Belfe S.p.A., Marostica, Italy; *Int'l*, pg. 185
Festa, John R., Pres.--Buypass Corporation, Atlanta, GA; *U.S. Public*, pg. 446
Fethke, Wayne G., Pres.--Fiskars Inc., Wausau, WI; *Int'l*, pg. 492
Fette, Joe, Pres.--Dover Chemical Corp., Dover, OH; *U.S. Private*, pg. 553
Fetterman, Bert M., Pres.--Kvaerner National, Inc. Canadian Division, Edmonton, Canada; *Int'l*, pg. 768
Fetterman, Lewis M., Jr., Pres.--Lundy Packing Co., Clinton, NC; *U.S. Private*, pg. 681
Fettig, Jeff M., Pres.--Whirlpool Europe B.V., Comerio, Italy; *U.S. Public*, pg. 1765
Fetxer, Brian, Pres.--Steelastic Co., Akron, OH; *U.S. Private*, pg. 860
Feuerstein, Aaron, Pres. & Chief Exec. Officer--Malden Mills Industries, Inc., Lawrence, MA; *U.S. Private*, pg. 698
Feuillat, Guy, Pres. & Dir. General--Banque de L'Aquitaine, Bordeaux, France; *Int'l*, pg. 548

Feury, Robert, Pres. & Chief Exec. Officer--Allied Building Products Corporation, East Rutherford, NJ; *U.S. Private*, pg. 38

Feyen, Pat, Pres.--PacifiCare of Oklahoma, Tulsa, OK; *U.S. Public*, pg. 1251

Feyen, Pat, Pres.--PacifiCare of Texas, Dallas, TX; *U.S. Public*, pg. 1251

Feys, Allan, Pres.--H.O. Trerice Company, Oak Park, MI; *U.S. Private*, pg. 1099

Fezzey, Michael D., Pres. & Gen. Mgr.--WJR-AM, Detroit, MI; *U.S. Public*, pg. 512

Fialkow, Frederick H., Chm. Bd., Pres. & Chief Exec. Officer--National Home Health Care Corp., Scarsdale, NY; *U.S. Public*, pg. 1157

Fiarman, Vicki, Partner & Production Mgr.--Dugan/Farley Communications, Upper Saddle River, NJ; *U.S. Public*, pg. 1642

Fiaschetti, Michael, Pres. & Chief Oper. Officer--HealthAmerica of Central Pennsylvania, Harrisburg, PA; *U.S. Public*, pg. 454

Fibery, Donald C., Pres. & Chief Exec. Officer--Central DuPage Health System, Winfield, IL; *U.S. Private*, pg. 223

Fickes, Steven W., Pres. & Chief Fin. Officer--PennCorp Financial Group, Inc., New York, NY; *U.S. Public*, pg. 1271

Fidler, Jay W., Pres. & Chief Exec. Officer--Hercules Chemical Co., Inc., Passaic, NJ; *U.S. Private*, pg. 523

Fiebiger, James R., Pres. & Chief Exec. Officer--Gatefield Corporation, Fremont, CA; *U.S. Public*, pg. 703

Fiedler, Lee F., Pres. & Chief Exec. Officer--The Kelly-Springfield Tire Company, Cumberland, MD; *U.S. Public*, pg. 753

Fiedler, Richard K., Chm. Bd. & Pres.--Admiral Maintenance Service L.P., Lincolnwood, IL; *U.S. Private*, pg. 17

Fiegehen, Allan G., Pres. & Chief Oper. Officer--Cubix Corporation, Carson City, NV; *U.S. Private*, pg. 294

Field, Arthur, Pres.--NCC Specialty Publications, Dartmouth, Canada; *Int'l*, pg. 924

Field, Joe, Pres.--Pony U.S.A., Nashville, TN; *Int'l*, pg. 1036

Field, Joseph, Pres.--Entertainment Communications, Bala Cynwyd, PA; *U.S. Private*, pg. 378

Field, Kenneth W., Pres. & Chief Exec. Officer--Continental Web Press, Inc., Itasca, IL; *U.S. Private*, pg. 269

Field, Kenneth W., Sr., Pres. & Chief Exec. Officer--Continental Web Press Of Kentucky, Walton, KY; *U.S. Private*, pg. 269

Field, Lawrence, Pres. & Chief Exec. Officer--Field Container Company, L.P., Elk Grove Village, IL; *U.S. Private*, pg. 403

Field, Thomas C., Pres.--Schlage Lock Company, Colorado Springs, CO; *U.S. Public*, pg. 876

Fielder, Jerry, Pres.--Exel Microelectronics, Inc., San Jose, CA; *Int'l*, pg. 1125

Fielding, Bill, Pres.--Excel Corp., Wichita, KS; *U.S. Private*, pg. 210

Fielding, Ronald, Pres.--Hormel International Corporation, Austin, MN; *U.S. Public*, pg. 840

Fielding, Ronald H., Pres., Portfolio Mgr. & Chief Strategist--Rochester Fund Municipals, Rochester, NY; *U.S. Private*, pg. 937

Fields, Catherine M., Pres. & Chief Exec. Officer--P.S. International Inc., Durham, NC; *U.S. Private*, pg. 827

Fields, F.W., Pres. & Chief Exec. Officer--The Coe Manufacturing Company, Painesville, OH; *U.S. Private*, pg. 249

Fields, Joe, Pres.--Mitre Sports (U.S.), Nashville, TN; *Int'l*, pg. 1036

Fields, Ronald, Pres.--Consolidated Beverages, Inc., Auburn, MA; *U.S. Private*, pg. 264

Fields, Wayne, Pres.--American Nursery Products, LLC, Tulsa, OK; *U.S. Private*, pg. 59

Fields, William R., Pres. & Chief Exec. Officer--Hudson's Bay Company, Toronto, Canada; *Int'l*, pg. 637

Fierman, Gerald Shea, Pres. & Chief Exec. Officer--ANESCO, Kingston, PA; *U.S. Private*, pg. 74

Fiers, Alan, Pres.--MEGTEC, De Pere, WI; *U.S. Public*, pg. 1459

Fiery, D.E., Pres.--Miller Chemical & Fertilizer Corp., Hanover, PA; *U.S. Private*, pg. 33

Fiesler, Emily, Pres.--Fort Worth Lumber Company, Fort Worth, TX; *U.S. Private*, pg. 419

Fife, Scott, Pres. & Chief Exec. Officer--Citizens First Bank, Fordyce, AR; *U.S. Public*, pg. 630

Fifield, Ralph E., Pres. & Chief Oper. Officer--United States Pipe & Foundry Company, Inc., Birmingham, AL; *U.S. Public*, pg. 1736

Figenshu, William R., Pres. & Sr. V.P.-Radio Division--Viacom Broadcasting Inc., New York, NY; *U.S. Private*, pg. 778

Figoff, Michael, Pres. & Chief Exec. Officer--Puroflow Incorporated, Van Nuys, CA; *U.S. Public*, pg. 1345

Fike, William, Pres.--Atoma International, Inc., Markham, Canada; *Int'l*, pg. 829

Fike, William T., Pres. & Chief Exec. Officer--Sierra West Bancorp, Truckee, CA; *U.S. Public*, pg. 1470

Filanowski, Mark, Pres.-MTL Mngmt.--Marine Transport Lines, Inc., Weehawken, NJ; *U.S. Private*, pg. 703

Filer, Jim, Pres.--Apex, Raleigh, NC; *U.S. Public*, pg. 1306

Filesi, Thomas R., Pres. & Chief Exec. Officer--Optek Technology, Inc., Carrollton, TX; *U.S. Public*, pg. 1227

Filho, Jose Ermirio de Moraes, Pres. & Dir.-Adv.--S.A. Industrias Votorantim, Sao Paulo, Brazil; *Int'l*, pg. 677

Filho, Walter Fontana, Pres. & Chief Exec. Officer--Sadia Group, Barueri, Brazil; *Int'l*, pg. 1168

Filipov, Fil, Pres.--Terex Cranes, Conway, SC; *U.S. Public*, pg. 1581

Filipowski, Andrew J., Chm. Bd., Pres. & Chief Exec. Officer--Platinum Technology, Inc., Oak Brook Terrace, IL; *U.S. Public*, pg. 1309

Filipps, Frank P., Pres. & Chief Exec. Officer--CMAC Investment Corporation, Philadelphia, PA; *U.S. Public*, pg. 278

Fillippo, Thomas A., Pres., Chief Exec. Officer & Corp. Sec.--DeVault Foods, Devault, PA; *U.S. Private*, pg. 329

Fillmer, Larry, Pres. & Chief Exec. Officer--Antares Alliance Group, Dallas, TX; *Int'l*, pg. 528

Filosa, Nicholas A., Pres. & Chief Exec. Officer--Union Bank & Trust Co., North Vernon, IN; *U.S. Public*, pg. 633

Filotas, William, Pres.--Crown Cork de Mexico, S.A., El Salto, Mexico; *U.S. Public*, pg. 464

Filter, Eunice M., Pres. & Chief Exec. Officer--Xerox Credit Corporation, Stamford, CT; *U.S. Public*, pg. 1785

Fimbel, Edward, Jr., Chm. Bd. & Pres.--Fimbel Door Corporation, Whitehouse, NJ; *U.S. Private*, pg. 404

Fimot, Luc, Pres.--Merinos, Saint Quentin-en-Yvelines, France; *Int'l*, pg. 858

Finch, David B., Pres. & Chief Exec. Officer--ATCOM, Inc., Research Triangle Park, NC; *U.S. Private*, pg. 94

Finch, Doug, Pres.--Plastigage Corporation, Jackson, MI; *U.S. Private*, pg. 871

Finch, John, Pres.--Wyoming Concrete Products Co., Casper, WY; *U.S. Private*, pg. 208

Finch, Kenneth J., Pres.--Edwards & Broughton Company, Raleigh, NC; *U.S. Public*, pg. 1735

Finch, Sam, Pres.--Blue Grass Quality Meats, Crescent Springs, KY; *U.S. Private*, pg. 152

Fincher, Jim V., Pres. & Chief Exec. Officer--Commercial Bank at Alma, Alma, AR; *U.S. Public*, pg. 641

Finden-Crofts, Alan J., Group Chief Exec.--Derby International Corporation S.A., Luxembourg, Luxembourg; *Int'l*, pg. 394

Findlay, J. Duncan, Pres.--Shannon & Wilson Intl., Seattle, WA; *U.S. Private*, pg. 989

Findlay, William, Pres. & Publisher--The Expositor, Brantford, Canada; *Int'l*, pg. 631

Fine, Allan H., Co-Pres.--M. Fine & Sons Manufacturing Co., Inc., New York, NY; *U.S. Private*, pg. 405

Fine, Lonnie, Pres.--Triangle Services, Inc., Valley Stream, NY; *U.S. Private*, pg. 1102

Fine, Martin L., Co-Pres.--M. Fine & Sons Manufacturing Co., Inc., New York, NY; *U.S. Private*, pg. 405

Fine, Michael, Pres.--Bakers/Leeds Shoe Stores, Saint Louis, MO; *U.S. Public*, pg. 563

Fine, Michael, Pres.--Size 5-7-9 Shops, Inc., Saint Louis, MO; *U.S. Public*, pg. 564

Fine, Michael, Pres.--The Wild Pair, Saint Louis, MO; *U.S. Public*, pg. 564

Fine, Robert W., Pres. & Chief Oper. Officer--Transworld Home Healthcare, Inc., New York, NY; *U.S. Public*, pg. 1632

Fine, S.A., Pres. & Chief Oper. Officer--The Biltrite Corporation, Waltham, MA; *U.S. Private*, pg. 144

Fine, Stephen L., Co-Pres.--M. Fine & Sons Manufacturing Co., Inc., New York, NY; *U.S. Private*, pg. 405

Finegood, David, Pres.--Good Companies, Carson, CA; *U.S. Private*, pg. 463

Fineman, Bernard S., Pres. & Treas.--Caldwell Tanks, Inc., Louisville, KY; *U.S. Private*, pg. 200

Finerty, Patrick, Pres.--Robert B. Aikens & Associates LLC., Troy, MI; *U.S. Private*, pg. 28

Finger, Robert, Pres.--Finger Furniture Company, Inc., Houston, TX; *U.S. Private*, pg. 405

Fingerle, John B., Pres.--Fingerle Lumber Co., Ann Arbor, MI; *U.S. Private*, pg. 405

Fingerlin, Mark, Pres.--HomeFed Trust, San Diego, CA; *U.S. Public*, pg. 1742

Fink, David, Pres.--Guilford Transportation Industries Inc., Nashua, NH; *U.S. Private*, pg. 487

Fink, Jean-Marie, Pres.--Roulement Service S.A., Strasbourg, France; *Int'l*, pg. 212

Fink, Marvin H., Pres. & Chief Exec. Officer--Teledyne Electronic Technologies, Los Angeles, CA; *U.S. Public*, pg. 43

Fink, Ruth G., Pres.--CGF Industries, Topeka, KS; *U.S. Private*, pg. 194

Finkell, Donald, Pres. & Chief Exec. Officer--Standard Plywoods, Inc., Clinton, SC; *U.S. Private*, pg. 1032

Finkelstein, David, Pres.--Leathers Best, Farmingdale, NY; *U.S. Private*, pg. 656

Finkelstein, James A., Pres.--New York Law Journal, New York, NY; *Int'l*, pg. 956

Finkelstein, Marc S., Pres.--Hughes-Treitler Manufacturing Corporation, Garden City, NY; *U.S. Private*, pg. 547

Finkelstein, Paul D., Pres. & Chief Exec. Officer--Regis Corporation, Minneapolis, MN; *U.S. Public*, pg. 1373

Finlason, Jack, Pres.--International Cold Storage Co., Inc., Andover, KS; *U.S. Private*, pg. 568

Finley, A.K., Pres.--Town & Country Homes, Fort Worth, TX; *U.S. Public*, pg. 319

Finley, Fred J., Pres. & Chief Oper. Officer--GTE Reinsurance Company Limited, Hamilton, Bermuda; *U.S. Public*, pg. 697

Finley, Jon L., Pres.--Gold Medal Div., Minneapolis, MN; *U.S. Public*, pg. 718

Finley, Peggy, Pres.--American Antenna Corp, Elgin, IL; *U.S. Private*, pg. 207

Finn, Jerome E., Pres.--P/A Industries, Inc., Bloomfield, CT; *U.S. Private*, pg. 825

Finn, Richard H., Pres. & Chief Exec. Officer--Transamerica Finance Group, Inc., Los Angeles, CA; *U.S. Public*, pg. 1630

Finnegan, John D., Pres.--General Motors Acceptance Corporation (GMAC), Detroit, MI; *U.S. Public*, pg. 719

Finnegan, Neal, Pres. & Chief Exec. Officer--UST Corporation, Boston, MA; *U.S. Public*, pg. 1660

Finney, Kevin M., Pres.-Bedding Div.--Fieldcrest/Cannon Bed Fashions Division, New York, NY; *U.S. Public*, pg. 1296

Finocchio, Robert, Pres. & Chief Exec. Officer--Informix Software, Menlo Park, CA; *U.S. Public*, pg. 876

Fiondella, Robert W., Chm. Bd., Pres. & Chief Exec. Officer--Phoenix Home Life Mutual Insurance Company, Hartford, CT; *U.S. Private*, pg. 863

Fiondella, Robert W., Chm. Bd., Pres. & Chief Exec. Officer--Phoenix Home Life Mutual Insurance Co., Hartford, CT; *U.S. Private*, pg. 863

Fiorentino, Carl F., Pres.--Tiger Direct, Inc. (d/b/a Tiger Software, Inc.), Miami, FL; *U.S. Public*, pg. 747

Fiorentino, Gilbert J., Chm. Bd., Pres. & Chief Exec. Officer--Tiger Direct, Inc., Miami, FL; *U.S. Public*, pg. 747

Fiorina, Carly, Jr., Pres.--Lucent Technologies, Consumer Products Div., Parsippany, NJ; *U.S. Public*, pg. 1017

Fiorini, Michael, Mng. Dir.--The East Asiatic Company Ltd. A/S, Copenhagen, Denmark; *Int'l*, pg. 430

Fireman, Paul, Chm. Bd., Pres. & Chief Exec. Officer--Reebok International Ltd., Stoughton, MA; *U.S. Public*, pg. 1369

Firesheets, William T., II, Pres.--Buquet & Le Blanc Inc., Baton Rouge, LA; *U.S. Private*, pg. 181

Firestone, Sue, Pres.--Sue Firestone & Assoc., Santa Barbara, CA; *U.S. Private*, pg. 406

Firm, Donald, Pres.--Davenport Machine Tool Div., Rochester, NY; *U.S. Public*, pg. 520

Firth, Nicholas, Pres.-BMG Music Publ.--Bertelsmann Music Group, Wilmington, DE; *Int'l*, pg. 191

Fisch, Michael J., Pres. & Chief Exec. Officer--The Bakersfield Californian, Bakersfield, CA; *U.S. Private*, pg. 112

Fischel, Dennis, Pres.--Discovision Associates, Irvine, CA; *Int'l*, pg. 1057

Fischer, C., Pres.--OWL AG Logistik-Systeme, Buchs, Switzerland; *Int'l*, pg. 490

Fischer, Charlotte G., Chm. Bd., Pres. & Chief Exec. Officer--Paul Harris Stores, Inc., Indianapolis, IN; *U.S. Public*, pg. 792

Fischer, Craig A., Pres.--American River Transportation Co., Decatur, IL; *U.S. Public*, pg. 128

Fischer, Daniel J., Pres., Chief Exec. Officer & Gen. Counsel--Manhattan Life Insurance Company, Cincinnati, OH; *U.S. Private*, pg. 1118

Fischer, Duane, Pres.--The Scoular Company, Omaha, NE; *U.S. Private*, pg. 977

Fischer, Earl, Pres.--Western Kentucky Gas Co., Owensboro, KY; *U.S. Public*, pg. 146

Fischer, Erwin, Pres.--Flender Austria Antriebstechnik AG, Spielberg, Austria; *Int'l*, pg. 400

Fischer, Irving, Pres. & Chief Oper. Officer--Starrett HRH, New York, NY; *U.S. Private*, pg. 1035

Fischer, Kelly, Pres.-Parachute Inc. & Sls. Promo. Dir.--Clarity Coverdale Fury Advertising, Minneapolis, MN; *U.S. Private*, pg. 242

Fischman, Meryl, Pres.--Harrison & Star, New York, NY; *U.S. Private*, pg. 506

Fiscus, Robert L., Pres. & Chief Fin. Officer--United Illuminating Company, New Haven, CT; *U.S. Public*, pg. 1678

Fishbein, Robert, Co-Pres. & Treas.--West Shore Envelope Company, Inc., New York, NY; *U.S. Private*, pg. 1163

Fisher, J.W., Pres.--Auto-Owners Insurance, Lansing, MI; *U.S. Private*, pg. 100

Fisher, James, Gen. Mgr.--Airflex Div. Eaton Corp., Cleveland, OH; *U.S. Public*, pg. 556

Fisher, Jeffrey, Pres. & Chief Exec. Officer--Pyramid Handbags Inc., New York, NY; *U.S. Private*, pg. 896

Fisher, John, Pres. & Chief Exec. Officer--Hyde Athletic Industries, Inc., Peabody, MA; *U.S. Public*, pg. 851

Fisher, Joseph V., Pres. & Chief Exec. Officer--Big V Supermarkets, Inc., Florida, NY; *U.S. Private*, pg. 143

Fisher, Rayburn J., Jr., Pres. & Chief Exec. Officer--Regions Bank/Atlanta, Sandy Springs, GA; *U.S. Public*, pg. 1371

Fisher, Stephen N., Jr., Pres.--Seagram Beverage Co., New York, NY; *Int'l*, pg. 1215

Fisher, Thomas L., Chm. Bd., Pres. & Chief Exec. Officer--NICOR Inc., Naperville, IL; *U.S. Public*, pg. 1182

Fisher, Thomas L., Chm. Bd., Pres. & Chief Exec. Officer--Northern Illinois Gas Company, Naperville. IL; *U.S. Public*, pg. 1183

Fisher, Vaughn C., Pres. & Chief Oper. Officer--Ingles Markets, Incorporated, Black Mountain, NC; *U.S. Public*, pg. 878

Fisher, William E., Pres.--Transaction Systems Architects, Inc., Omaha, NE; *U.S. Public*, pg. 1629

Fisher, William E., Pres. & Chief Exec. Officer--Applied Communications, Inc., Omaha, NE; *U.S. Public*, pg. 1629

Fisherkeller, Paul F., Pres. & Chief Exec. Officer--Taco John's International, Inc., Cheyenne, WY; *U.S. Private*, pg. 1066

Fishkellar, Paul, Pres.--Casa Bonita, Inc., Carrollton, TX; *U.S. Public*, pg. 278

Fishman, Jerald G., Pres. & Chief Exec. Officer--Analog Devices, Inc., Norwood, MA; *U.S. Public*, pg. 107

Fishman, Mark, Pres.--Fishman & Tobin, Inc., Conshohocken, PA; *U.S. Private*, pg. 408

Fishman, Steven S., Chm. Bd., Pres. & Chief Exec. Officer--Pamida Holdings Corporation, Omaha, NE; *U.S. Public*, pg. 1255

Fitch, Laura W., Chm. & Pres.--Bank of America New Mexico, Albuquerque, NM; *U.S. Public*, pg. 180

Fitzgerald, Barry, Pres.--American Nucleonics Corp., Westlake Village, CA; *U.S. Public*, pg. 556

Fitzgerald, D.F., Pres. & Treas.--Son Chief Electrics, Inc., Winsted, CT; *U.S. Private*, pg. 1014

Fitzgerald, David P., Pres.--Fitzgerald & Co., Atlanta, GA; *U.S. Private*, pg. 409

Fitzgerald, Duane D., Pres. & Chief Exec. Officer--Bath Iron Works Corporation, Bath, ME; *U.S. Public*, pg. 709

Fitzgerald, Francis A., Pres.--Saratoga Equine Sports Center, Saratoga Springs, NY; *U.S. Private*, pg. 965

Fitzgerald, Gwen, Pres.--TSI Washington Laboratories, Rockville, MD; *U.S. Public*, pg. 733

Fitzgerald, James W., Pres.--The New York Times Magazine Company Group, Trumbull, CT; *U.S. Public*, pg. 1174

Fitzgerald, Joseph P., Pres.--Landstar Ligon, Inc., Madisonville, KY; *U.S. Public*, pg. 978

Fitzgerald, Kelly, Pres.--Technology Solutions Inc., New York, NY; *U.S. Private*, pg. 1157

Fitzgerald, Mark, Pres. & Chief Exec. Officer--Willis Corroon Construction Services Corp., New Hyde Park, NY; *Int'l*, pg. 1504

Fitzgerald, Michael J., Pres.--The Riggs National Bank of Maryland, Rockville, MD; *U.S. Public*, pg. 1390
Fitzgerald, Peter D., Pres.--Qualex Inc., Durham, NC; *U.S. Public*, pg. 551
Fitzgerald, Robert, Pres.--Flavor House Products, Inc., Dothan, AL; *U.S. Private*, pg. 410
Fitzgerald, T.C., Pres.--Griffin Pipe Products Co., Downers Grove, IL; *U.S. Private*, pg. 68
FitzGibbon, David A., Pres.--Ilsco, Cincinnati, OH; *U.S. Private*, pg. 558
Fitzhugh, James, Branch Pres.--First State Bank N.A., Abilene, Abilene, TX; *U.S. Public*, pg. 874
Fitzpatrick, Barry J., Chm. Bd., Pres. & Chief Exec. Officer--First Virginia Banks, Inc., Falls Church, VA; *U.S. Public*, pg. 641
Fitzpatrick, Daniel B., Chm. Bd., Pres. & Chief Exec. Officer--Quality Dining Inc., Mishawaka, IN; *U.S. Public*, pg. 1349
Fitzpatrick, Gerard J., Pres.--Fitzpatrick & Weller, Inc., Ellicottville, NY; *U.S. Private*, pg. 409
Fitzpatrick, Richard J., Pres. & Chief Exec. Officer--The Howard Bank, N.A., Burlington, VT; *U.S. Public*, pg. 187
FitzSimons, Dennis J., Pres.--Tribune Broadcasting Company, Chicago, IL; *U.S. Public*, pg. 1636
Fix, Roger L., Pres.-John Crane N. America--John Crane North America, Morton Grove, IL; *Int'l*, pg. 1339
Fjelstul, Dean M., Pres. & Treas.--Jim Walter Computer Services, Inc., Tampa, FL; *U.S. Public*, pg. 1737
Flagg, Howard S., Pres.--PairGain Technologies Inc., Tustin, CA; *U.S. Public*, pg. 1253
Flahaux, Jose, Pres.--Supply Point, Inc., Fremont, CA; *U.S. Public*, pg. 541
Flakoll, Thomas J., Pres. & Chief Exec. & Oper. Officer--Technitrol, Inc., Trevose, PA; *U.S. Public*, pg. 1564
Flam, Seth, Dr., Pres. & Chief Exec. Officer--FPA Medical Management, Inc., San Diego, CA; *U.S. Public*, pg. 608
Flanagan, David T., Pres. & Chief Exec. Officer--Central Maine Power Company, Augusta, ME; *U.S. Public*, pg. 325
Flanagan, Dennis, Pres. & Chief Exec. Officer--Okidata Group, Mount Laurel, NJ; *Int'l*, pg. 1000
Flanagan, James P., Pres. & Client Services Dir.--Tinsley Advertising, Miami, FL; *U.S. Private*, pg. 1088
Flanagan, John, Chm. Bd., Pres. & Chief Exec. Officer--Goodheart-Willcox Publisher, Tinley Park, IL; *U.S. Private*, pg. 464
Flanagan, P.J., Pres.--Swift and Company Ltd., Sydney, Australia; *Int'l*, pg. 682
Flanagan, Paul, Site Mgr.--Quinlan Pretzel Co., Inc., Denver, PA; *U.S. Private*, pg. 158
Flanagan, Richard, Pres.--Borders, Inc., Ann Arbor, MI; *U.S. Public*, pg. 245
Flanagan, Richard L., Pres.--Planet Music, Inc., Ann Arbor, MI; *U.S. Public*, pg. 245
Flanders, Dudley K., Pres. & Chief Exec. Officer--Flanders Industries, Inc., Fort Smith, AR; *U.S. Private*, pg. 410
Flanders, Scott, Pres.--Macmillan Computer Publishing USA, Indianapolis, IN; *U.S. Private*, pg. 777
Flanigan, Joseph G., Chm. Bd., Pres. & Chief Exec. Officer--Flanigan's Enterprises, Inc., Fort Lauderdale, FL; *U.S. Public*, pg. 648
Flannery, Michael, Pres. & Chief Oper. Officer--Pope & Talbot, Inc., Portland, OR; *U.S. Public*, pg. 1316
Flaskamp, Antonius, Co-Pres.--Flaskamp GmbH, Berlin, Germany; *Int'l*, pg. 493
Flaskamp, Manuela, Co-Pres.--Flaskamp GmbH, Berlin, Germany; *Int'l*, pg. 493
Flaten, Alfred N., Pres.--T.J. U.S. Company, Statesboro, GA; *U.S. Public*, pg. 1152
Flaten, Alfred N., Pres.--Piggly Wiggly Northland Corp., Minneapolis, MN; *U.S. Public*, pg. 1152
Flatgard, Bjorn, Pres. & Chief Exec. Officer--Nycomed Pharma AS, Oslo, Norway; *Int'l*, pg. 993
Flatgard, Bjorn, Pres.--Elopak A/S, Lierstranda, Norway; *Int'l*, pg. 1389
Flatley, Thomas J., Pres.--The Flatley Company, Braintree, MA; *U.S. Private*, pg. 410
Flatow, Mike, Pres. & Chief Exec. Officer--Champion Products Inc., Winston Salem, NC; *U.S. Public*, pg. 1433
Flatt, J. Bruce, Pres. & Chief Oper. Officer--Brookfield Properties Corporation, Toronto, Canada; *Int'l*, pg. 228
Flaum, Sander A., Pres. & Chief Exec. Officer--Robert A. Becker, New York, NY; *Int'l*, pg. 601
Flechner, H., Pres--Bayer Argentina S.A., Munro, Argentina; *Int'l*, pg. 175
Flechtner, Richard D., Pres. & Chief Exec. Officer--Car-Freshner Corporation, Watertown, NY; *U.S. Private*, pg. 207
Fleckenstein, John, Acting Pres., Exec. V.P. & Gen. Mgr.--O-Z/Gedney Co., Farmington, CT; *U.S. Public*, pg. 727
Fleenor, Roger H., Pres.--Red Apple, Inc., Ontario, OR; *U.S. Private*, pg. 915
Fleetwood, Christopher J., Chief Exec. Officer--Whessoe Plc, Newton Aycliffe, United Kingdom; *Int'l*, pg. 1498
Fleischauer, Jack, Pres.--First Commercial Bank, N.A., Little Rock, AR; *U.S. Public*, pg. 630
Fleischer, Barry, Pres.--Aldan Industries, Philadelphia, PA; *U.S. Private*, pg. 33
Fleischer, Helmut, Pres.--H.F.&P. Munchen GmbH, Munich, Germany; *Int'l*, pg. 394
Fleischer, Morton H., Chm. Bd., Pres. & Chief Exec. Officer--Franchise Finance Corp. of America, Scottsdale, AZ; *U.S. Public*, pg. 679
Fleischhacker, Mark, Pres. & Chief Oper. Officer--Lake Region Manufacturing, Inc., Chaska, MN; *U.S. Private*, pg. 643
Fleischman, Marvin H., Pres.--Peerless Distributing Co., Southfield, MI; *U.S. Private*, pg. 847
Fleischmann, David, Pres.--Standard Manifold Company, Inc., Chicago, IL; *U.S. Private*, pg. 1031
Fleishman, Gene, Pres.--CRC Industries, Inc., Warminster, PA; *U.S. Private*, pg. 138
Fleishman, Marvin H., Pres.--Joy Service, Southfield, MI; *U.S. Private*, pg. 602
Fleming, Francis R., Pres. & Chief Oper. Officer--Chad Therapeutics, Chatsworth, CA; *U.S. Public*, pg. 332
Fleming, Hu, Pres.--Cochrane, Inc., King of Prussia, PA; *U.S. Public*, pg. 456
Fleming, Joseph L., Pres.--Golden Alaska Seafoods, Inc., Seattle, WA; *Int'l*, pg. 928
Fleming, Kenneth, Pres. & Chief Oper. Officer--World Publishing Company, Tulsa, OK; *U.S. Private*, pg. 1190
Fleming, Larry A., Pres. & Chief Exec. Officer--Knoxville Utilities Board, Knoxville, TN; *U.S. Private*, pg. 627
Fleming, M. Jack, Chm. Bd., Pres., Chief Exec. Officer & Treas.--Merchants Publishing Co., Kalamazoo, MI; *U.S. Private*, pg. 732
Fleming, P.J., Chm. & Pres.--Getty Gas Gathering, Inc., New Orleans, LA; *U.S. Public*, pg. 1583
Fleming, Paul J., Pres.--Monitor Surety Managers, Inc., New York, NY; *U.S. Public*, pg. 215
Fleming, Robert, Pres. & Chief Exec. Officer--Land-O-Sun Dairies, Inc., Johnson City, TN; *U.S. Private*, pg. 646
Fleming, Robert W., Pres. & Chief Exec. Officer--Folger Nolan Fleming Douglas, Washington, DC; *U.S. Private*, pg. 416
Flenniken, Tom, Pres. & Chief Exec. Officer--UPB of Chattanooga, Chattanooga, TN; *U.S. Public*, pg. 1669
Fletcher, Andrew, Pres. & Chief Exec. Officer--Tausche Martin Lonsdorf, Atlanta, GA; *U.S. Private*, pg. 1069
Fletcher, David A., Pres. & Chief Oper. Officer--Deposition Technologies, Inc., San Diego, CA; *U.S. Public*, pg. 1056
Fletcher, Donald J., Pres.--George S. May International Company, Park Ridge, IL; *U.S. Private*, pg. 717
Fletcher, Jerry, Pres.--Fletcher Cobre Tire Co. Inc., Phoenix, AZ; *U.S. Private*, pg. 411
Fletcher, Kenneth W., Chm. Bd., Pres. & Chief Exec. Officer--Roberds, Inc., Carrollton, OH; *U.S. Public*, pg. 1393
Fletcher, Phil, Pres.--ConAgra Fruen Milling Co., Omaha, NE; *U.S. Public*, pg. 428
Flicker, Warren, Pres. & Chief Oper. Officer--Homasote Company, Trenton, NJ; *U.S. Public*, pg. 831
Flickinger, William, Pres. & Chief Oper. Officer--HPM Corporation, Mount Gilead, OH; *U.S. Private*, pg. 492
Fligg, Loren L., Pres. & Chief Oper. Officer--Hawkeye Security Insurance Company, West Des Moines, IA; *Int'l*, pg. 543
Flinchbaugh, James D., Pres.--Weldon Machine Tool, Inc., York, PA; *U.S. Private*, pg. 1161
Flint, E.M., Pres. & Mng. Dir.--Esso Production Malaysia Inc., Kuala Lumpur, Malaysia; *U.S. Public*, pg. 602
Flippin, William S., Pres. & Publr.--Reading Eagle Company, Reading, PA; *U.S. Private*, pg. 913
Flischel, W., Pres. of Partners--Woolpert, Dayton, OH; *U.S. Private*, pg. 1188
Fliss, Michael C., Pres. & Chief Exec. Officer--AMCORE Bank N.A., Rock River Valley, Sterling, IL; *U.S. Public*, pg. 64
Flittie, John H., Vice Chm., Pres. & Chief Oper. Officer--ReliaStar Financial Corp., Minneapolis, MN; *U.S. Public*, pg. 1375
Flock, H.H., Pres.--Tuthill Pump, Alsip, IL; *U.S. Private*, pg. 1111
Flock, Michael, Pres.--Dun & Bradstreet Canada Ltd., Mississauga, Canada; *U.S. Public*, pg. 536
Floeckher, Peter W., Pres. & Chief Exec. Officer--The Citizens National Bank, Laurel, MD; *U.S. Public*, pg. 1089
Flom, Joseph H., Partner--Skadden, Arps, Slate, Meagher & Flom LLP, New York, NY; *U.S. Private*, pg. 1004
Flood, A.L., Chm. Bd. & Chief Exec. Officer--Canadian Imperial Bank of Commerce, Toronto, Canada; *Int'l*, pg. 256
Flood, Peter E., Pres. & Chief Exec. Officer--The Flood Company, Hudson, OH; *U.S. Private*, pg. 414
Florence, Leonard, Chm. Bd., Pres. & Chief Exec. Officer--Syratech Corporation, East Boston, MA; *U.S. Private*, pg. 1060
Florence, Leonard, Pres.--Towle Manufacturing Corporation, East Boston, MA; *U.S. Private*, pg. 1061
Florence, Leonard, Pres.--Leonard Florence Associates, East Boston, MA; *U.S. Private*, pg. 1061
Flores, Fernando, Pres.--Mexicana Airlines, Los Angeles, CA; *Int'l*, pg. 332
Flores, Jesus, Owner--4Day Tire Stores, Fountain Valley, CA; *U.S. Private*, pg. 421
Florescue, Barry, Pres. & Chief Exec. Officer--Marietta Corporation, Cortland, NY; *U.S. Private*, pg. 702
Flori, John R., Pres. & Chief. Exec. Officer--Flori Corp., Phoenix, AZ; *U.S. Private*, pg. 414
Florig, Edward, Pres. & Treas.--Florig Equipment Company, Inc., Conshohocken, PA; *U.S. Private*, pg. 415
Florio, Steven, Pres. & Chief Exec. Officer--The Conde Nast Publications Inc., New York, NY; *U.S. Private*, pg. 20
Florio, Thomas, Pres.--The New Yorker Magazine, New York, NY; *U.S. Private*, pg. 795
Florjancic, Frederick J., Pres.--Brunswick Bowling & Billiards Corp., Muskegon, MI; *U.S. Public*, pg. 265
Florsheim, Thomas W., Jr., Pres. & Chief Oper. Officer--Weyco Group, Inc., Milwaukee, WI; *U.S. Public*, pg. 1763
Flowers, F.W., Jr., Pres--Eager Beaver, Lake Wales, FL; *U.S. Private*, pg. 354
Floyd, James G., Pres. & Chief Exec. Officer--The Houston Exploration Company, Houston, TX; *U.S. Public*, pg. 259
Floyd, William R., Pres. & Chief Exec. Officer--Choice Hotels International, Inc., Silver Spring, MD; *U.S. Public*, pg. 351
Flynn, J., Chief Oper. Officer--Fred Perry Sportswear Ltd., London, United Kingdom; *Int'l*, pg. 620
Flynn, James F., Pres.--Union Carbide Inter-America, Inc., Danbury, CT; *U.S. Public*, pg. 1667
Flynn, James T., Pres. & Chief Oper. Officer--Long Island Lighting Company, Hicksville, NY; *U.S. Public*, pg. 1013
Flynn, Michael, Pres. & Chief Oper. Officer--Kimco Realty Corporation, New Hyde Park, NY; *U.S. Public*, pg. 960
Flynn, Patrick, Pres., Chief Exec. Officer, Chief Oper. Officer & Controller--Freeway Corporation, Cleveland, OH; *U.S. Private*, pg. 426
Flynn, Terence M., Pres.--Portal Publications, Ltd., Corte Madera, CA; *U.S. Public*, pg. 503
Focht, Michael H., Sr., Pres. & Chief Oper. Officer--Tenet Healthcare Corporation, Santa Barbara, CA; *U.S. Public*, pg. 1576
Focht, Michael H., Sr., Pres.--Tenet HealthSystem Medical, Inc., Dallas, TX; *U.S. Public*, pg. 1577
Focke, Heinz-Hermann, Chief Exec.--Focke & Co. (GmbH & Co.) Verpackungsmaschiner, Verden, Germany; *Int'l*, pg. 496
Foegele, George, Pres. & Chief Exec. Officer--Transamerica Life Insurance Co.-Canada, Scarborough, Canada; *U.S. Public*, pg. 1630
Fogarty, Robert S., Jr., Chm. Bd. & Pres.--Kindel Furniture Company, Grand Rapids, MI; *U.S. Private*, pg. 620
Fogarty, William, Principal--Fogarty Klein & Partners, Houston, TX; *U.S. Private*, pg. 415
Fogel, William, Chm. Bd., Pres. & Chief Exec. Officer--Jordon Commercial Refrigerator Co., Philadelphia, PA; *U.S. Private*, pg. 599
Fogelstrom, Lennert, Pres.--ABB Atom AB, Vasteras, Sweden; *Int'l*, pg. 7
Fogg, F.W., Pres. & Chief Exec. Officer--Southeastern Medequip, Inc., Jacksonville Beach, FL; *U.S. Private*, pg. 1015
Fogg, James W., Pres.--Banta Catalog Group, Saint Paul, MN; *U.S. Public*, pg. 188
Fogg, Larry, Pres.--Saskatchewan Government Insurance, SGI, Regina, Canada; *Int'l*, pg. 1195
Foglio, Anthony P., Pres. & Chief Exec. Officer--IDV North America, Fort Lee, NJ; *Int'l*, pg. 411
Fojtasek, Randall S., Pres. & Chief Exec. Officer--Atrium Companies, Inc., Dallas, TX; *U.S. Private*, pg. 98
Foley, Charles R., Pres. & Chief Exec. Officer--Ameriwood Industries International Inc., Grand Rapids, MI; *U.S. Public*, pg. 98
Foley, E. Wayne, Pres. & Gen. Mgr.--Stanley Air Tools Div., Cleveland, OH; *U.S. Public*, pg. 1509
Foley, Frank M., Pres. & Chief Exec. Officer--CHF Industries, Inc., New York, NY; *U.S. Private*, pg. 1094
Foley, J. Michael, Pres. & Chief Exec. Officer--Midwest Employer's Casualty Company, Maryland Heights, MO; *U.S. Public*, pg. 215
Foley, Michael, Pres.--Heineken USA Inc., White Plains, NY; *Int'l*, pg. 608
Foley, Paul, Jr., Pres.--Foley Holding Company, Inc., Wichita, KS; *U.S. Private*, pg. 416
Foley, Stephen X., Pres.--Steve Foley Cadillac, Northbrook, IL; *U.S. Private*, pg. 416
Foley, Thomas C., Chm. Bd.--NTC Group, Greenwich, CT; *U.S. Private*, pg. 772
Foley, William A., Chm. Bd., Pres. & Chief Exec. Officer--Lesco, Inc., Rocky River, OH; *U.S. Public*, pg. 989
Folger, Roger, Pres., Chief Exec. Officer & Chief Oper. Officer--Punch Press Products, Inc., Los Angeles, CA; *U.S. Private*, pg. 895
Folgner, Donald, Pres.--Wells/Bloomfield, Verdi, NV; *U.S. Public*, pg. 1497
Folino, Paul F., Pres. & Chief Exec. Officer--Emulex Corporation, Costa Mesa, CA; *U.S. Public*, pg. 579
Folk, James C., Pres.--SL Montevideo Technology, Inc., Montevideo, MN; *U.S. Public*, pg. 1419
Folkert, Rod, Pres. & Chief Exec. Officer--Grocers Baking Co., Grand Rapids, MI; *U.S. Private*, pg. 482
Follett, K.A., Pres.--Follett Educational Services, Chicago, IL; *U.S. Private*, pg. 417
Follett, R.C., Pres.--Follett Library Resources, Crystal Lake, IL; *U.S. Private*, pg. 417
Folz, Joseph L., Pres. & Chief Oper. Officer--Harleysville-Garden State Insurance Co., Marlton, NJ; *U.S. Public*, pg. 787
Folz, Theo, Pres. & Chief Exec. Officer--Consolidated Cigar Corp., Fort Lauderdale, FL; *U.S. Private*, pg. 690
Folz, Theo W., Pres. & Chief Exec. Officer--Mafco Consolidated Group Inc., New York, NY; *U.S. Private*, pg. 690
Folz, Theodore W., Pres. & Chief Exec. Officer--Consolidated Cigar Corporation, Fort Lauderdale, FL; *U.S. Private*, pg. 690
Fondow, Williams J., Pres.--Thermo Black Clawson, Inc., Middletown, OH; *U.S. Public*, pg. 1593
Fondren, William M., Jr., Pres.--Orgill Inc., Memphis, TN; *U.S. Private*, pg. 819
Fong, Ed, Partner & Art Dir.--Potentia Healthcare Communications Partners, Chicago, IL; *U.S. Public*, pg. 1224
Fong, Henry, Chm. Bd., Pres. & Chief Exec. Officer--RDM Sports Group, Atlanta, GA; *U.S. Public*, pg. 1354
Fontaine, George, Gen. Mgr.--Sandpiper Cove Div., Destin, FL; *U.S. Private*, pg. 895
Fontana, Cesar, Pres.--Cia. AGA del Peru S.A., Lima, Peru; *Int'l*, pg. 13
Fontana, Christine, Pres.--Communications International (NY), New York, NY; *U.S. Private*, pg. 259
Fontana, Omar, Chm. Bd. & Pres.--Transbrasil S.A. Linhas Aereas, Sao Paulo, Brazil; *Int'l*, pg. 1416
Fontanazza, William C., Pres.--Wisconsin Wire & Steel, Brookfield, WI; *U.S. Public*, pg. 1061
Fontenot, Al, Pres.--ATAPCO Office Products Group, Saint Louis, MO; *U.S. Private*, pg. 64
Fonville, Ken, Pres.--Pennsylvania House Casegoods, Lewisburg, PA; *U.S. Public*, pg. 975
Foot, Silas B., III, Pres.--S.B. Foot Tanning Co., Red Wing, MN; *U.S. Private*, pg. 915
Foote, Dale, Pres.--Straube Regional Center LLC, Pennington, NJ; *U.S. Private*, pg. 1046
Foote, J.D., Pres.--Pegasus International Corporation, Pennington, NJ; *U.S. Private*, pg. 1046
Foote, Robert, Pres. & Chief Exec. Officer--David White, L.L.C., Germantown, WI; *U.S. Public*, pg. 1765

Foote, Robert, Pres. & Chief Exec. Officer--David White, L.L.C., Germantown, WI; *U.S. Private*, pg. 1765
Forbes, Jack, Pres.--Nielsen & Bainbridge, Paramus, NJ; *Int'l*, pg. 460
Forbes, Jack, Pres.--Letraset Nielsen & Bainbridge, Paramus, NJ; *Int'l*, pg. 460
Forbes, James L., Pres. & Chief Exec. Officer--Badger Meter, Inc., Milwaukee, WI; *U.S. Public*, pg. 164
Forbes, Jim, Pres.--The American Meat Packing Corp., Chicago, IL; *U.S. Private*, pg. 575
Forbes, Malcolm S., Jr., Pres., Chief Exec. & Editor-in-Chief--Forbes, Inc., New York, NY; *U.S. Private*, pg. 417
Forbes, Samuel E., Chm. Bd. & Pres.--Peerless Tyre Co., Denver, CO; *U.S. Private*, pg. 847
Forbes, Timothy C., Pres. & Chief Oper. Officer--American Heritage Magazine, New York, NY; *U.S. Private*, pg. 417
Ford, Allyn, Pres.--Scott Timber Co., Dillard, OR; *U.S. Private*, pg. 905
Ford, Allyn C., Pres.--RLC Industries Co., Dillard, OR; *U.S. Private*, pg. 905
Ford, Allyn C., Pres.--Roseburg Forest Products Co., Dillard, OR; *U.S. Private*, pg. 905
Ford, Joe T., Chm. Bd., Pres. & Chief Exec. Officer--ALLTEL Corporation, Little Rock, AR; *U.S. Public*, pg. 55
Ford, John S., Jr., Pres.--Ford Steel Co., Inc., Maryland Heights, MO; *U.S. Private*, pg. 418
Ford, Nelson, Pres.--The Clinipad Corporation, Rocky Hill, CT; *U.S. Private*, pg. 246
Ford, Steve, Pres.--Knurr (UK) Ltd., Saint Ives, United Kingdom; *Int'l*, pg. 739
Ford, W. Douglas, Pres.--Amoco Oil Company, Chicago, IL; *U.S. Public*, pg. 102
Ford, William J., Pres.--National Truck Leasing System, Oak Brook Terrace, IL; *U.S. Private*, pg. 787
Fordham, Sharon, Pres.--LifeSavers Company, Parsippany, NJ; *U.S. Public*, pg. 1355
Fore, James R., Chm. Bd., Pres. & Chief Exec. & Oper. Officer--Communication Cable, Inc., Sanford, NC; *U.S. Public*, pg. 968
Foremberd, Christian, Pres.--Reifenhauser Ind. de Maquinas Ltda., Diadema, Brazil; *Int'l*, pg. 1101
Forese, James J., Pres.--IBM Credit Corporation, Stamford, CT; *U.S. Public*, pg. 896
Forester, Benjamin, Chm. Bd., Pres. & Chief Exec. Officer--Rex Lumber Company, Acton, MA; *U.S. Private*, pg. 926
Forgie, James L., Pres.--Waltec Components, Wallaceburg, Canada; *Int'l*, pg. 453
Forgie, James L., Pres.--Waltec American Forgings, Inc., Port Huron, MI; *Int'l*, pg. 453
Forgione, Anthony, Chm. Bd. & Pres.--Boyer Candy Company Inc., Altoona, PA; *U.S. Private*, pg. 162
Forguez, M. William, Pres.--Information Dimensions, Dublin, OH; *U.S. Private*, pg. 465
Forissier, Marie-Jose, Chm.-Initiative Media Worldwide & Pres.-Media Communs.--Ammirati Puris Lintas Worldwide, New York, NY; *U.S. Public*, pg. 908
Forlenza, Vincent A., Pres.--Becton Dickinson Microbiology Systems, Sparks, MD; *U.S. Public*, pg. 199
Forman, Barry, Pres.--Forman Brothers, Inc., Washington, DC; *U.S. Private*, pg. 418
Forman, Sam, Chm. Bd., Pres. & Chief Exec. Officer--County Seat Stores, Inc., Dallas, TX; *U.S. Private*, pg. 279
Forman, Willis M., Pres., Chief Exec. Officer & Treas.--Paper Calmenson & Co., Saint Paul, MN; *U.S. Private*, pg. 837
Formosa, Peter, Pres.--Frank Ix & Sons, Inc., New York, NY; *U.S. Private*, pg. 423
Fornataro, A.A., Pres. & Chief Exec. Officer--Salem Group, Inc., Pittsburgh, PA; *U.S. Private*, pg. 961
Fornataro, A.A., Pres.--Salem Asset Management Corp., Wilmington, DE; *U.S. Private*, pg. 961
Fornell, Karl-Valter, Pres.--Maskin AB Rapid, Varnamo, Sweden; *Int'l*, pg. 678
Forrest, B., Pres.--The Long Company, Chicago, IL; *U.S. Private*, pg. 674
Forrest, Jackie, Pres.--Flowers Baking Co. of Lynchburg, Inc., Lynchburg, VA; *U.S. Public*, pg. 657
Forrest, James, Mng. Dir.--Windpoint Partners, Southfield, MI; *U.S. Private*, pg. 1182
Forrester, Gary, Pres.--Aztex Enterprises, Knoxville, TN; *U.S. Private*, pg. 104
Forsee, Gary D., Pres.--Sprint's Long Distance Division, Dallas, TX; *U.S. Public*, pg. 1501
Forsgren, Jack, Pres.--Nobel Biocare, Goteborg, Sweden; *Int'l*, pg. 951
Forstmann, Theodore J., Partner--Forstmann Little & Co., New York, NY; *U.S. Private*, pg. 419
Forstmoser, Peter, Chm. Bd. & Pres.--Hesta Tex AG, Zug, Switzerland; *Int'l*, pg. 617
Forston, Marion, Pres.--Lisa Motor Lines, Inc., Fort Worth, TX; *U.S. Public*, pg. 685
Forston, Marion, Pres.--Middleton Transportation Co., Fort Worth, TX; *U.S. Public*, pg. 685
Forsyth, James G., III, Pres.--Moto, Inc., Belleville, IL; *U.S. Private*, pg. 764
Forsyth, Robert, Pres.--FKG Oil Company, Belleville, IL; *U.S. Private*, pg. 764
Forsythe, Daryl R., Pres. & Chief Exec. Officer--NBT Bancorp Inc., Norwich, NY; *U.S. Public*, pg. 1144
Forsythe, F.S., Pres.--Cliffs Mining Company, Cleveland, OH; *U.S. Public*, pg. 386
Forsythe, Gerald, Chm. Bd., Pres. & Chief Exec. Officer--Indeck Power Equipment Company, Wheeling, IL; *U.S. Private*, pg. 559
Forsythe, Gordon, Pres.--Ascom Canada Limited, Markham, Canada; *Int'l*, pg. 86
Fort, L., Pres.--Greening Donald Co. Ltd., Orangeville, Canada; *Int'l*, pg. 1389
Forter, Rod, Pres.--Nordberg-Read, Inc., Middleboro, MA; *Int'l*, pg. 1428
Fortgang, Mathew, Pres.--M. Fabrikant & Sons, Inc., New York, NY; *U.S. Private*, pg. 390
Fortgens, Henk, Pres.--AGA Gas B.V., Amsterdam, Netherlands; *Int'l*, pg. 13
Forti, Edwin, Pres.--Burrell/DFA Advertising, New York, NY; *U.S. Private*, pg. 188
Fortier, John A., Pres.--Bacco Construction Co., Iron Mountain, MI; *U.S. Private*, pg. 109
Fortier, Marc G., Chm. Bd., Pres. & Chief Exec. Officer--Societe Generale de Financement du Quebec, Montreal, Canada; *Int'l*, pg. 1274
Fortkiewicz, Victor A., Pres. & Chief Exec. Officer--Elizabethtown Gas Co., Union, NJ; *U.S. Public*, pg. 1147
Fortmann, Guenter, Mng. Dir.--Wyeth-Pharma GmbH, Munster, Germany; *U.S. Public*, pg. 82
Fortner, Richard, Pres.--AAR Landing Gear Center, Miami, FL; *U.S. Public*, pg. 1
Fortney, Jay, Pres. & Gen. Mgr.--Charles Town Races, Charles Town, WV; *U.S. Public*, pg. 1270
Fortson, Thomas N., Jr., Pres.--Terminix Service, Inc., Columbia, SC; *U.S. Private*, pg. 1077
Fortun, Wayne M., Pres., Chief Exec. Officer & Chief Oper. Officer--Hutchinson Technology Inc., Hutchinson, MN; *U.S. Public*, pg. 850
Fortunato, Bob, Pres.--CMI Holding Corp., Canton, MA; *U.S. Private*, pg. 195
Fortunato, Bob, Pres.--Chadwick-Miller Inc., Canton, MA; *U.S. Private*, pg. 195
Fortunoff, Alan, Pres.--Fortunoff, Uniondale, NY; *U.S. Private*, pg. 420
Forward, Gordon E., Pres. & Chief Exec. Officer--Chaparral Steel Co., Midlothian, TX; *U.S. Public*, pg. 1585
Foscolo, Ralph J., Jr., Pres.--Niagara Asset Corporation, Buffalo, NY; *U.S. Public*, pg. 955
Foshee, Douglas L., Pres. & Chief Exec. Officer--Nuevo Energy Company, Houston, TX; *U.S. Public*, pg. 1206
Fosket, Gene, Pres.--Plasma Technology, Inc., Torrance, CA; *U.S. Private*, pg. 870
Fosmire, John C., Pres. & Chief Exec. Officer--Anderson Lithograph Company, Los Angeles, CA; *U.S. Private*, pg. 72
Foss, Stephen W., Pres.--Foss Manufacturing Company Incorporated, Hampton, NH; *U.S. Private*, pg. 420
Fossati, Renzo, Pres.--Chr. Hansen S.p.A., Milan, Italy; *Int'l*, pg. 289
Fosse, Finn E., Pres.--Kvaerner Insurance A/S, Oslo, Norway; *Int'l*, pg. 769
Foster, Charles, Exec. Dir.--Port of Oakland, Oakland, CA; *U.S. Private*, pg. 876
Foster, Dennis, Pres. & Chief Exec. Officer--360 Degrees Communications Company, Chicago, IL; *U.S. Public*, pg. 1607
Foster, Gregg L., Pres.--Elyria Foundry Company, Elyria, OH; *U.S. Private*, pg. 373
Foster, John, Pres.--Foster Pontiac, Inc., Milwaukee, WI; *U.S. Private*, pg. 421
Foster, Kent, Pres.--GTE Corporation, Stamford, CT; *U.S. Public*, pg. 696
Foster, Lee B., II, Pres. & Chief Exec. Officer--L.B. Foster Company, Pittsburgh, PA; *U.S. Public*, pg. 675
Foster, Leland, Ph.D., Pres. & Chief Exec. Officer--HyClone Laboratories Inc., Logan, UT; *Int'l*, pg. 1037
Foster, Michael, Pres. & Chief Exec. Officer--Moorman's Inc., Quincy, IL; *U.S. Private*, pg. 760
Foster, Mike, Pres.--MoorMan's Feed Division, Quincy, IL; *U.S. Private*, pg. 760
Foster, Neil, Pres. & Chief Exec. Officer--Star Sales Co., Inc., Knoxville, TN; *U.S. Private*, pg. 1035
Foster, P. Wesley, Jr., Pres.--The Long & Foster Companies, Inc., Fairfax, VA; *U.S. Private*, pg. 674
Foster, Robert, Pres. & Gen. Mgr.--Medtronic Avalon Laboratories, Inc., Rancho Dominguez, CA; *U.S. Public*, pg. 1083
Foster, Steven L., Pres. & Chief Exec. Officer--Jillian's Entertainment Corporation, Boston, MA; *U.S. Private*, pg. 587
Foster, W. David, Pres. & Chief Oper. Officer--C.H. Heist Corp., Clearwater, FL; *U.S. Public*, pg. 807
Foster, W. Douglas, Chm. Bd., Pres. & Chief Exec. Officer--Salem Carpet Mills, Inc., Winston Salem, NC; *U.S. Public*, pg. 1464
Foster, Willett S., IV, Pres. & Chief Exec. Officer--Edlund Company, Inc., Burlington, VT; *U.S. Private*, pg. 364
Fote, Charles T., Pres.--First Data Corporation, Englewood, CO; *U.S. Public*, pg. 631
Foti, Samuel J., Pres. & Chief Oper. Officer--The Mutual Life Insurance Company of New York, New York, NY; *U.S. Private*, pg. 769
Fouad, Fouad Abdulla, Pres. & Chief Oper. Officer--Abdulla Fouad Co. Ltd., Dammam, Saudi Arabia; *Int'l*, pg. 501
Foucault, Jean-Charles, Pres.--Sodexi, Roissy, France; *Int'l*, pg. 560
Foudree, Charles M., Pres.--Harmon Industries-Lees Summit, Lees Summit, MO; *U.S. Public*, pg. 788
Foudree, Charles M., Pres.--Vale-Harmon Enterprises, Ltd., Montreal, Canada; *U.S. Public*, pg. 788
Fougere, Richard J., Pres.--Kollmorgen Virtual Motion Group, Blacksburg, VA; *U.S. Public*, pg. 965
Foulkes-Jones, Robert, Chief Exec. Officer--Brammer plc, Altrincham, United Kingdom; *Int'l*, pg. 212
Foullon, Dr. Hannes, Mng. Partner--Westag Werbeagentur, Cologne, Germany; *Int'l*, pg. 1491
Fountain, Jack, Pres.--Burgmann Seals America, Inc., Houston, TX; *Int'l*, pg. 233
Fountain, Larry, Pres. & Chief Exec. Officer--Stanley Stores, Inc., Vidor, TX; *U.S. Private*, pg. 1033
Fountain, Reginald M., Jr., Chm. Bd., Pres. & Chief Exec. & Oper. Officer--Fountain Powerboat Industries, Inc., Washington, NC; *U.S. Public*, pg. 678
Fourtean, Patrick, Pres.--St. Jude Medical Europe, Inc., Brussels, Belgium; *U.S. Public*, pg. 1428
Fourticq, Michael, Sr., Owner & Chief Exec. Officer--Brown Jordan Company, El Monte, CA; *U.S. Private*, pg. 174
Foust, David D., Pres. & Chief Exec. Officer--Seneca Wire & Manufacturing Co., Fostoria, OH; *U.S. Private*, pg. 984
Fowler, Frederick V., Jr., Chm. Bd., Pres. & Chief Exec. Officer--Fred V. Fowler Company, Inc., Newton, MA; *U.S. Private*, pg. 422
Fowler, George E., Pres. & Chief Oper. Officer--Hadron, Inc., Alexandria, VA; *U.S. Public*, pg. 773
Fowler, John, Pres.--Somerset Pontiac GMC Inc., Troy, MI; *U.S. Private*, pg. 1013
Fowler, Mark, Pres.--First Bank of Arkansas, Jonesboro, AR; *U.S. Public*, pg. 630
Fowler, Mark, Pres.--Systech Computer Corporation, San Diego, CA; *U.S. Private*, pg. 1061
Fowler, Robert E., Jr., Pres. & Chief Exec. & Oper. Officer--IMC Global, Bannockburn, IL; *U.S. Public*, pg. 856
Fowler, Robert E., Jr., Pres. & Chief Exec. Officer--The Vigoro Corporation, Chicago, IL; *U.S. Public*, pg. 856
Fowler, Walter B., Chm. Bd., Pres. & Chief Exec. Officer--The Carbide/Graphite Group, Inc., Pittsburgh, PA; *U.S. Public*, pg. 304
Fowlkers, Thomas, Pres.--The United Company, Bristol, VA; *U.S. Private*, pg. 1121
Fox, Bob, Pres. & Chief Exec. Officer--Foster Farms, Livingston, CA; *U.S. Private*, pg. 421
Fox, Brad, Pres.--GMB Sales, Setauket, NY; *U.S. Public*, pg. 1720
Fox, Ed, Pres.--North Star BHP Steel LLC, Delta, OH; *Int'l*, pg. 226
Fox, Herbert C., Pres. & Chief Exec. Officer--Active Electrical Supply Company, Chicago, IL; *U.S. Private*, pg. 15
Fox, Jeff, Pres. & Chief Exec. Officer--Alltel Information Services, Inc., Little Rock, AR; *U.S. Public*, pg. 56
Fox, Larry H., Pres.--Powder River Coal Company, Gillette, WY; *Int'l*, pg. 594
Fox, Martin, Pres.--Initio, Inc., Carson City, NV; *U.S. Public*, pg. 879
Fox, Michael P., Pres.--Naz-Dar Company, Chicago, IL; *U.S. Private*, pg. 1084
Fox, Murray L., Pres. & Chief Exec. Officer--Consolidated Carma Corporation, Calgary, Canada; *Int'l*, pg. 229
Fox, Sheila, Pres.--Chapman Warwick Inc., San Diego, CA; *U.S. Private*, pg. 1152
Fox, William A., Pres.--The Peoples Natural Gas Co., Pittsburgh, PA; *U.S. Public*, pg. 435
Fox, William A., Jr., Pres.--Hope Gas, Inc., Clarksburg, WV; *U.S. Public*, pg. 435
Foxworth, Walter L., Pres.--Foxworth-Galbraith Lumber Co., Dallas, TX; *U.S. Private*, pg. 423
Foxworthy, Michael, Pres.--Charles Dunn Company, Inc., Los Angeles, CA; *U.S. Private*, pg. 229
Foy, Thomas, Pres. & Chief Exec. Officer--Action Industries, Inc., Tupelo, MS; *U.S. Public*, pg. 688
Foyle, R.C., Pres.--Heraeus/Kulzer, Inc. - Dental Products Div., South Bend, IN; *Int'l*, pg. 616
Fraatz, Paul, Jr., Pres. & Treas.--Pacor, Inc., Philadelphia, PA; *U.S. Private*, pg. 833
Fracassi, Allen, Pres.--Philip Services Corp., Hamilton, Canada; *Int'l*, pg. 1050
Frachey, Enrico, Pres.--Fila USA, Sparks, MD; *Int'l*, pg. 484
Fradin, David W., Pres. & Chief Oper. Officer--IEC Electronics Corp., Newark, NY; *U.S. Public*, pg. 854
Fradin, Roger, Pres.-Mfg.--Alarm Device Manufacturing Company, Syosset, NY; *U.S. Public*, pg. 1306
Fraim, Richard, Pres. & Gen. Mgr.--KLAS, Inc., Las Vegas, NV; *U.S. Private*, pg. 647
Frakes, Larry A., Pres.--Everest National Insurance Co., Liberty Corner, NJ; *U.S. Public*, pg. 597
Frakes, Larry A., Pres.--Everest Indemnity Insurance Company, Liberty Corner, NJ; *U.S. Public*, pg. 597
Frame, Paul A., Pres. & Chief Exec. Officer--Seitel, Inc., Houston, TX; *U.S. Public*, pg. 1454
Frame, W. Douglas, Pres.--National-Oilwell/Dreco, Edmonton, Canada; *U.S. Public*, pg. 1158
France, B.E., Pres.--The H.T. Hackney Co., Knoxville, TN; *U.S. Private*, pg. 493
France, Jerry, Pres.--Intertec Presentations, Englewood, CO; *U.S. Public*, pg. 1328
Franceschi, Vincent, Pres. & Chief Oper. Officer--Vectra Technologies, Inc., San Ramon, CA; *U.S. Public*, pg. 1711
Francesconi, Joseph J., Pres. & Chief Exec. Officer--Network Equipment Technologies, Inc., Redwood City, CA; *U.S. Public*, pg. 1168
Francis, Dennis, Pres.--Patrician Associates, Inc., Des Moines, IA; *U.S. Private*, pg. 885
Francis, Dennis, Pres.--Petula Associates, Ltd., Des Moines, IA; *U.S. Private*, pg. 885
Francis, Dennis, Pres.--Principal Development Associates, Inc., Des Moines, IA; *U.S. Private*, pg. 885
Francis, Martin S., Co.-Pres.--LTX Corporation, Westwood, MA; *U.S. Public*, pg. 972
Francis, Peter T., Chm. Bd., Pres. & Chief Exec. Officer--J.M. Huber Corporation, Edison, NJ; *U.S. Private*, pg. 544
Francis, Philip L., Pres. & Chief Exec. Officer--Shaw's Supermarkets, Inc., East Bridgewater, MA; *Int'l*, pg. 1170
Francis, Thomas M., Pres.--Windsor Industries, Inc., Englewood, CO; *U.S. Private*, pg. 1182
Francisco, Roland C., Pres.--CSA Management Inc., Toronto, Canada; *Int'l*, pg. 243
Francisco, Rolando C., Pres.--Goldcorp Inc., Toronto, Canada; *Int'l*, pg. 243
Francisco, Rolando C., Pres.--Lexam Explorations Inc., Toronto, Canada; *Int'l*, pg. 243
Franck, Christian, Pres.--Bayernland Gmbh & Co. KG, Nuremberg, Germany; *Int'l*, pg. 181
Franco, Donna S., Pres. & Chief Oper. Officer--Melrose, Chatsworth, CA; *U.S. Public*, pg. 948
Franco, M., Pres.--SDI Technologies Inc., Rahway, NJ; *U.S. Private*, pg. 956
Francoeur, M., Pres. & Chief Exec. Officer--Stelco-McMaster Ltee, Contrecoeur, Canada; *Int'l*, pg. 1299
Francois, Emile, Pres. & Chief Exec. Officer--Poliet, Courbevoie, France; *Int'l*, pg. 1177

Francois, Yves-Paul, Pres.--Microturbo Division, Toulouse, France; *Int'l*, pg. 786
Franey, Bart H., Pres. & Chief Oper. Officer Milcare--Milcare, Inc., Grandville, MI; *U.S. Public*, pg. 1112
Frangenberg, Bernd, Pres. & Chief Exec. Officer--Continental General Tire, Inc., Charlotte, NC; *Int'l*, pg. 327
Franich, Steven, Pres. & Chief Exec. Officer--Marty Franich Auto Center, Watsonville, CA; *U.S. Private*, pg. 423
Frank, Cary, Pres.--Arrow Chevrolet, Inc., Midlothian, IL; *U.S. Private*, pg. 85
Frank, D.P., Pres. & Chief Exec. Officer--Ziegler Thrift Trading, Inc., Minneapolis, MN; *U.S. Public*, pg. 1792
Frank, George, Pres.--CNJ Distributing, Billings, MT; *U.S. Private*, pg. 196
Frank, H. Alan, Chm. Bd.--Union Industries, Inc., Providence, RI; *U.S. Private*, pg. 1119
Frank, Harley A., Pres. & Chief Oper. Officer--Union Industries, Inc., Providence, RI; *U.S. Private*, pg. 1119
Frank, J.L., Pres.--Marathon Ashland Petroleum LLC, Findlay, OH; *U.S. Public*, pg. 139
Frank, James S., Pres.--Frank Consolidated Enterprises Inc., Des Plaines, IL; *U.S. Private*, pg. 423
Frank, Jeffrey, Div. Pres.--Sanmark Group, New York, NY; *U.S. Public*, pg. 1141
Frank, Karl, Gen. Mgr.--Tucker Rocky Distributing, Portland, OR; *U.S. Private*, pg. 639
Frank, Louis, Pres.--Turnbull Enterprises, Inc., Baltimore, MD; *U.S. Private*, pg. 1109
Frank, Richard, Pres.--Walt Disney Pictures and Television, Burbank, CA; *U.S. Public*, pg. 513
Frank, Richard R., Pres. & Chief Exec. Officer--Lawry's Restaurants, Inc., Pasadena, CA; *U.S. Private*, pg. 654
Frank, Stephen E., Pres. & Chief Oper. Officer--Southern California Edison Company, Rosemead, CA; *U.S. Public*, pg. 564
Frankel, Alfred, Pres.--ICD Group International Inc., New York, NY; *U.S. Private*, pg. 554
Frankel, Robert, Pres.--Gerber Agri Inc., New York, NY; *U.S. Private*, pg. 449
Frankel, Steven T., Pres. & Chief Exec. Officer--Quidel Corporation, San Diego, CA; *U.S. Public*, pg. 1352
Frankenberg, Jay, Pres. & Chief Exec. Officer--Graphic Technology, Inc., New Century, KS; *Int'l*, pg. 950
Franklin, Beth, Pres. & Chief Exec. Officer--Star Transportation, Inc., Nashville, TN; *U.S. Private*, pg. 1035
Franklin, Bruce, Pres.--International Correspondence Schools (New Zealand) Limited, Wellington, New Zealand; *U.S. Public*, pg. 784
Franklin, Dick, Pres.--PT BHP Steel Building Products Indonesia, Jakarta, Indonesia; *Int'l*, pg. 226
Franklin, E. Thomas, Chm., Pres. & Treas.--Franklin Baking Co., Inc., Goldsboro, NC; *U.S. Private*, pg. 424
Franklin, Gary A., Pres. & Chief Fin. Officer--ServiceMaster of Canada Ltd., Mississauga, Canada; *U.S. Public*, pg. 1462
Franklin, H. Allen, Pres. & Chief Exec. Officer--Georgia Power Co., Atlanta, GA; *U.S. Public*, pg. 1490
Franklin, Larry, Pres.--Franklin Sports, Inc., Stoughton, MA; *U.S. Private*, pg. 424
Franklin, Larry, Pres. & Chief Exec. Officer--Harte-Hanks Communications, Inc., San Antonio, TX; *U.S. Public*, pg. 793
Frankovic, Richard, Pres. & Chief Oper. Officer--The Rugby Group, Inc., Rockville Centre, NY; *Int'l*, pg. 625
Franz, Elizabeth T., Pres. & Publr.--Great Falls Tribune, Great Falls, MT; *U.S. Public*, pg. 700
Franz, J.E., Pres.--Zephyer Properties, Inc., Dayton, OH; *U.S. Public*, pg. 1076
Franz, Wurm, Pres.--Agrolinz Melamin Italia S.r.l., Castellanza, Italy; *Int'l*, pg. 356
Franzke, John A., Pres.--Little Rock Division, Little Rock, AR; *U.S. Public*, pg. 509
Franzone, John B., Pres. & Chief Exec. Officer--Fawn Industries, Inc., Hunt Valley, MD; *U.S. Private*, pg. 397
Frasca, Giorgio, Pres. & Chief Exec. Officer--Iveco France S.A., Trappes, France; *Int'l*, pg. 696
Frascari, Dr. Giuliano, Mng. Dir.--SMET, Milan, Italy; *U.S. Private*, pg. 1065
Fraser, Alan, Pres. & Chief Exec. Officer--Digital Link Corporation, Sunnyvale, CA; *U.S. Public*, pg. 508
Fraser, Arthur W., Pres.--Peck Road Ford Truck Sales, Whittier, CA; *U.S. Private*, pg. 846
Fraser, Don C., Pres.--BHP Steel Canada Inc., Vancouver, Canada; *Int'l*, pg. 227
Fraser, Duncan, Pres.--Consolidated Graphic Communications, Bridgeville, PA; *U.S. Public*, pg. 333
Fraser, E. Russell, Pres.--Pacifica Real Estate Group, Santa Barbara, CA; *U.S. Private*, pg. 832
Frattaroli, Robert J., Pres. & Chief Oper. Officer--Pharmaceutical Marketing Services Inc., Phoenix, AZ; *U.S. Public*, pg. 1284
Frauenfelder, Lew, Pres. & Chief Exec. Officer--Fujitsu Computer Products of America, Inc., San Jose, CA; *Int'l, pg. 526*
Fravel, J.C., Chm., Pres. & Chief Exec. Officer--Syroco Inc., Peabody, MA; *Int'l*, pg. 844
Frawley, Steve, Pres. & Chief Exec. Officer--Emery Waterhouse Company, Portland, ME; *U.S. Private*, pg. 373
Fray, Earl, Pres. & Gen. Mgr.--EG & G Mound Applied Technologies, Miamisburg, OH; *U.S. Public*, pg. 543
Frazee, John P., Jr., Chm. Bd., Pres. & Chief Exec. Officer--Paging Network, Inc., Plano, TX; *U.S. Public*, pg. 1252
Frazier, Doug, Pres.--EQE International, San Francisco, CA; *U.S. Private*, pg. 354
Frazier, Edward C., Pres.--Liberty Sports, Inc., Englewood, CO; *U.S. Public*, pg. 1555
Frazier, James H., Pres. & Chief Exec. Officer--Building Plastics, Inc., Memphis, TN; *U.S. Private*, pg. 180
Freakley, Ed, Pres.--Worrell Enterprises, Inc., Boca Raton, FL; *U.S. Private*, pg. 1191
Frechette, Peter L., Pres. & Chief Exec. Officer--Patterson Dental Company, Saint Paul, MN; *U.S. Public*, pg. 1265
Frechette, Robert, Pres.--Safecard Services, Inc., Jacksonville, FL; *U.S. Public*, pg. 320
Frederick, Donald A., Pres.--Pennzoil Exploration & Production Co., Houston, TX; *U.S. Public*, pg. 1272
Frederick, Glenn, Pres.--CAE Vanguard, Inc., Minneapolis, MN; *Int'l*, pg. 237
Frederick, Rick, Pres.--Ikon Office Solutions, Oklahoma City, OK; *U.S. Public*, pg. 863
Frederick, Tom, Pres.--The Plexus Group, Sunnyvale, CA; *U.S. Public*, pg. 177
Frederick, William A., Pres.-Special Markets Div.--Thomas & Betts Corporation, Memphis, TN; *U.S. Public*, pg. 1597
Fredericks, Michael, Pres.--NCC Publishing, Tillsonburg, Canada; *Int'l*, pg. 924
Frederickson, A.D., Pres.--Road Machinery Company, Phoenix, AZ; *U.S. Private*, pg. 934
Frediani, Steve, Pres. & Chief Exec. Officer--Ancra International LLC, Hawthorne, CA; *U.S. Private*, pg. 71
Fredin, Ronald R., Pres.--Atlas Roofing Corp., Meridian, MS; *U.S. Private*, pg. 96
Fredrickson, Joseph, Pres.--Eldorado Chemical Company, San Antonio, TX; *U.S. Private*, pg. 367
Fredrickson, Tony, Pres.--Titan Research & Technology, San Diego, CA; *U.S. Public*, pg. 1618
Fredriksson, Ake, Pres. & Chief Exec. Officer--Perstorp AB, Perstorp, Sweden; *Int'l*, pg. 1036
Freed, Joseph, Chm. Bd. & Chief Exec. Officer--Capitol Construction Group, Inc., Wheeling, IL; *U.S. Private*, pg. 206
Freed, Robert, Pres.--Kaufman and Broad-South Bay Inc., Fremont, CA; *U.S. Public*, pg. 945
Freedhoff, Harry, Pres.--Tyco Canada Ltd., Mississauga, Canada; *U.S. Public*, pg. 1059
Freedman-Carmen, Miriam, Partner & Grp. Art Dir.--Lewis Gace Bozell Healthcare Worldwide, Fort Lee, NJ; *U.S. Public*, pg. 1642
Freedman, Gracie, Pres.--FMS Management Systems, Inc., Miami, FL; *U.S. Private*, pg. 389
Freedman, Mark, Pres.--S. Freedman & Sons, Inc., Landover, MD; *U.S. Private*, pg. 425
Freedman, Robert, Pres. & Chief Information Officer--John Hancock Advisers, Inc., Boston, MA; *U.S. Private*, pg. 589
Freeman, Benjamin H., II, Pres.--H. Freeman & Son, Inc., Philadelphia, PA; *U.S. Private*, pg. 426
Freeman, Bruce, Pres.--AEC, Inc., Wood Dale, IL; *U.S. Private*, pg. 500
Freeman, Bruce, Pres.--Nelmor Co., Inc., North Uxbridge, MA; *U.S. Private*, pg. 1041
Freeman, Bruce, Pres.--AEC/Application Engineering Corporation, Wood Dale, IL; *U.S. Private*, pg. 1041
Freeman, Edmund J., Pres.--Joy Energy Systems Inc., Charlotte, NC; *U.S. Public*, pg. 789
Freeman, Ellen S., Pres. & New Bus. Contact--Freeman Associates, Inc., Wellesley, MA; *U.S. Private*, pg. 425
Freeman, Gerald M., Pres. & Gen. Mgr.--Stone Forest Industries, Chicago, IL; *U.S. Public*, pg. 1521
Freeman, John, Pres.--N.B.M. Corp., McAlester, OK; *U.S. Private*, pg. 771
Freeman, John, Pres.--UPB of Northeast Arkansas, Jonesboro, AR; *U.S. Public*, pg. 1669
Freeman, Joshua M., Pres.--Carl M. Freeman Associates, Inc., Potomac, MD; *U.S. Private*, pg. 426
Freeman, Kenneth W., Chm. Bd., Pres. & Chief Exec. Officer--Quest Diagnostics, Inc., Teterboro, NJ; *U.S. Public*, pg. 1351
Freeman, Mark S., Pres. & Chief Exec. Officer--Freeman Cosmetic Corp., Los Angeles, CA; *U.S. Private*, pg. 426
Freeman, Marshall W., Chm. Bd., Pres. & Chief Exec. Officer--Miller Freeman Inc., San Francisco, CA; *Int'l*, pg. 1443
Freeman, Norman, Pres.--Associated Global Systems, New Hyde Park, NY; *U.S. Private*, pg. 90
Freeman, Terry, Pres.--Bibler Brothers, Inc., Russellville, AR; *U.S. Private*, pg. 142
Freeman, Walter, Pres.--Kentucky Indiana Lumber Co. Inc., Louisville, KY; *U.S. Private*, pg. 615
Freeman, William A., Pres.--Watkins Associated Industries Inc., Atlanta, GA; *U.S. Private*, pg. 1153
Freeman, William M., Pres. & Chief Exec. Officer--Bell Atlantic-Washington, D.C., Inc., Washington, DC; *U.S. Public*, pg. 203
Freeman, William M., Pres. & Gen. Mgr.--Mentor Opthalmics, Inc., Santa Barbara, CA; *U.S. Public*, pg. 1086
Freer, George, Pres.--SASIB Packaging North America, Skokie, IL; *Int'l*, pg. 1194
Freer, Kenneth, Pres.--The Fonda Group, Inc., Saint Albans, VT; *U.S. Private*, pg. 421
Frega, Ben, Pres. & Chief Exec. Officer--Comstock Michigan Fruit, Rochester, NY; *U.S. Private*, pg. 887
Frehner, Garth E., Pres.--Frehner Construction Company, Inc., North Las Vegas, NV; *U.S. Private*, pg. 426
Freibergs, Janis, Pres.--Talsi Building Materials Ltd., Talsi, Latvia; *Int'l*, pg. 1201
Freitag, Miles, Pres.--Solvay Animal Health, Inc., Mendota Heights, MN; *Int'l*, pg. 1277
Frelat, B., Pres.--Rail Europe Inc., Harrison, NY; *Int'l*, pg. 1165
Frem, Antoine N., Vice Chm. & Pres.--Interstate Resources, Inc., Rosslyn, VA; *U.S. Private*, pg. 573
French, Ed, Pres. & Chief Oper. Officer--Heatcraft Inc., Grenada, MS; *U.S. Private*, pg. 659
French, Gary L., Pres.--Timec Company, Vallejo, CA; *U.S. Private*, pg. 1087
French, Gary L., Pres.--UAM Fund Services Inc., Boston, MA; *U.S. Public*, pg. 1674
French, James S.M., Pres. & Chief Exec. Officer--Dunn Investment Co., Birmingham, AL; *U.S. Private*, pg. 347
French, John, Pres.--Shell Quimica de Venezuela, C.A., Caracas, Venezuela; *Int'l*, pg. 1142
French, Morton R., Jr., Pres., Chief Exec. Officer, Chief Fin. Officer & Treas.--Commercial Plastics & Supplies Corp., Richmond Hill, NY; *U.S. Private*, pg. 258
French, Theodore R., Pres. & Chief Fin. Officer--Case Corporation, Racine, WI; *U.S. Public*, pg. 311
Frenster, Hans, Pres.--Insulating Materials, Inc., Schenectady, NY; *U.S. Private*, pg. 565
Fresard, F. James, Pres.--Jim Fresard Pontiac Buick, Inc., Royal Oak, MI; *U.S. Private*, pg. 427
Frescoln, L.D., Pres. & Chief Oper. Officer--Flint Ink Corp., Detroit, MI; *U.S. Private*, pg. 413
Freske, Richard C., Pres.--Gerald H. Phipps, Inc., Denver, CO; *U.S. Private*, pg. 862
Fretag, Miles, Pres.--Salsbury Laboratories, Inc., Charles City, IA; *Int'l*, pg. 1277
Freulich, Howard, Pres.--Rokeach Food Distributing Inc., Newark, NJ; *U.S. Private*, pg. 940
Frew, Bud L., Pres. & Chief Exec Officer--MFA Incorporated, Columbia, MO; *U.S. Private*, pg. 686
Frey, Chuck, Gen. Mgr.--NuArc Co., Philadelphia, PA; *U.S. Private*, pg. 809
Frey, Dale F., Chm. Bd. & Pres.--General Electric Investment Corp., Stamford, CT; *U.S. Public*, pg. 712
Frey, J.R., Pres.--Alberta Power Limited, Edmonton, Canada; *Int'l*, pg. 95
Frey, John S., Chm. Bd. & Pres.--John S. Frey Enterprises, Los Angeles, CA; *U.S. Private*, pg. 428
Frey, Philip, Jr., Chm. Bd., Pres. & Chief Exec. Officer--Microsemi Corporation, Santa Ana, CA; *U.S. Public*, pg. 1107
Frey, Quintin F., Pres.--Turkey Hill Dairy, Inc., Conestoga, PA; *U.S. Private*, pg. 1109
Frey, Tom, Pres.--DEZurik, Sartell, MN; *U.S. Public*, pg. 726
Freyou, Ernest, Pres. & Chief Exec. Officer--Regions Bank/New Iberia, New Iberia, LA; *U.S. Public*, pg. 1372
Frezel, Jerrold A., Pres.--Premier Dental Products Company, King of Prussia, PA; *U.S. Private*, pg. 881
Frias, Fernan, Pres.--ARS/DMB&B, Caracas, Venezuela; *U.S. Private*, pg. 303
Fricchione, Henry, Pres.--Simplex Industries, Inc., Scranton, PA; *U.S. Private*, pg. 1001
Frick, Raymond A., Pres.--Specialties Bindery, Inc., Hyattsville, MD; *Int'l*, pg. 1078
Frick, Raymond A., Pres.--Quebecor Printing Semline Inc., Braintree, MA; *Int'l*, pg. 1078
Frick, Raymond A., Pres.--Quebecor Printing Federated Inc., Providence, RI; *Int'l*, pg. 1078
Frickel, Jack, Pres.--Stantron/PFT/EMI, Pacoima, CA; *U.S. Public*, pg. 1791
Friday, Tim, Pres.--TTA/Newport, Inc., Newport Beach, CA; *U.S. Private*, pg. 1083
Friebird, Paul, Pres.--Pyromet, Inc., Aston, PA; *U.S. Private*, pg. 897
Fried, R., Pres.--Monarch Luggage Co. Inc., Brooklyn, NY; *U.S. Private*, pg. 757
Friedberg, Thomas H., Chm Bd., Pres. & Chief Exec. Officer--ACCEL International Corporation, Dublin, OH; *U.S. Public*, pg. 14
Frieder, Israel, Pres. & Chief Oper. Officer--Telematics Inc., Fort Lauderdale, FL; *Int'l*, pg. 643
Friederich, Baldur, Pres.--Filtros Mann S.A. de C.V., Tlalnepantla, Mexico; *Int'l*, pg. 484
Friedheim, Louis, Pres. & Chief Exec. Officer--Cougle Commission Company, Inc., Chicago, IL; *U.S. Private*, pg. 278
Friedland, Scott, Pres. & Chief Exec. Officer--Friedland Jacobs Communications, Burbank, CA; *U.S. Private*, pg. 428
Friedland, Thomas S., Pres. & Chief Exec. Officer--Harcrest International, Ltd., Clark, NJ; *U.S. Private*, pg. 500
Friedman, Albert, Pres.--Banner Wholesale Grocers, Inc., Chicago, IL; *U.S. Private*, pg. 114
Friedman, Dr. Alan, Pres. & Chief Exec. Officer--Planning Systems Inc., Mc Lean, VA; *U.S. Private*, pg. 869
Friedman, Eric D., Pres. & Chief Oper. Officer--The Grandoe Corp., Gloversville, NY; *U.S. Private*, pg. 469
Friedman, Ernest L., Pres.--King Koil Licensing Company Inc., Saint Paul, MN; *U.S. Private*, pg. 621
Friedman, Ira, Pres.--Snell Acoustics, Peabody, MA; *U.S. Public*, pg. 246
Friedman, Irwin, Chm. Bd. & Mng. Partner--Friedman, Eisenstein, Raemer and Schwartz, LLP, Chicago, IL; *U.S.* Private, pg. 428
Friedman, Irwin, Pres.--International Components Corporation, Melville, NY; *U.S. Private*, pg. 569
Friedman, J. Roger, Pres. & Chief Exec. Officer--Lebhar-Friedman, Inc., New York, NY; *U.S. Private*, pg. 656
Friedman, Jack, Chm. Bd., Pres. & Chief Exec. Officer--JAKKS Pacific, Inc., Malibu, CA; *U.S. Public*, pg. 923
Friedman, Kurt, Pres.--Cincinnati Thermal Spray, Inc., Cincinnati, OH; *U.S. Private*, pg. 240
Friedman, Mark, Pres.--S. Rothchild & Co., Inc., New York, NY; *U.S. Private*, pg. 947
Friedman, Randolf J., Pres.--Great Lakes Wholesale Drugs, Livonia, MI; *U.S. Private*, pg. 475
Friedman, Ron, Pres. & Chief Oper. Officer--Group 1 Software, Inc., Lanham, MD; *U.S. Public*, pg. 417
Friedman, Seymour, Sr. V.P. & Exec. Production Mgr.--Columbia TriStar Television, Culver City, CA; *Int'l*, pg. 1282
Friedman, William S., Pres. & Chief Exec. Officer--National Income Realty Trust, New York, NY; *U.S. Public*, pg. 1157
Friedman, William S., Pres. & Chief Exec. Officer--Tarragon Realty Investors, Dallas, TX; *U.S. Public*, pg. 1561
Friedmann, Daniel E., Pres. & Chief Exec. Officer--MacDonald Dettwiler & Associates Ltd., Richmond, Canada; *U.S. Public*, pg. 1229
Friedmann, Kurt, Pres.--Polymet Corp., Cincinnati, OH; *U.S. Private*, pg. 875
Friedrich, Doug, Pres. & Chief Exec. Officer--Capital Graphics Inc., Wheeling, IL; *U.S. Private*, pg. 206
Friedrich, Jurgen, Pres.--GESTRA GmbH, Bremen, Germany; *Int'l*, pg. 549

Friedson, David M., Pres. & Chief Exec. Officer--Windmere-Durable Holdings, Hialeah, FL; *U.S. Public*, pg. 1771
Friend, Raymond G., Pres.--High Plains Corporation, Wichita, KS; *U.S. Public*, pg. 825
Friendly, Ian M., Pres.--Yoplait USA, Minneapolis, MN; *U.S. Public*, pg. 718
Friends, Barry G., Pres.--Deaktor/Sysco Food Services Co., Harmony, PA; *U.S. Public*, pg. 1551
Frierson, Daniel K., Chm. Bd., Pres. & Chief Exec. Officer--The Dixie Group, Inc., Chattanooga, TN; *U.S. Public*, pg. 514
Frierson, Phil, Pres.--MagnaView Inc., Dallas, TX; *U.S. Public*, pg. 1720
Fries, Randy, Pres.--Electro Methods Inc., South Windsor, CT; *U.S. Private*, pg. 369
Fries, Robert, Pres.--Stratton Corporation, Stratton Mountain, VT; *Int'l*, pg. 685
Friese, Marianne, Partner & Global Brand Mktg. Dir.--Ketchum Public Relations, GmbH, Munich, Germany; *U.S. Private*, pg. 617
Frigeri, Rodolfo A., Pres.--Banco de la Provincia de Buenos Aires, Buenos Aires, Argentina; *Int'l*, pg. 140
Frigerio, Fiorenzo, Pres.--A.I. Ocean, Novegro di Segrate, Italy; *Int'l*, pg. 14
Frigstad, David, Chm. Bd. & Pres.--Frost & Sullivan, Mountain View, CA; *U.S. Private*, pg. 430
Frima, Maija-Liisa, Pres.--Gyproc Oy, Kirkkonismmi, Finland; *Int'l*, pg. 1200
Friou, Roger P., Pres.--Jitney-Jungle Stores of America, Inc., Jackson, MS; *U.S. Private*, pg. 588
Frisch, Alfred, Pres.--Beaver Street Fisheries, Inc., Jacksonville, FL; *U.S. Private*, pg. 128
Frisell, William, Pres. & Chief Exec. Officer--Diners Club Inc., Chicago, IL; *U.S. Public*, pg. 377
Fristad, Kenneth A., Pres. & Gen. Mgr.--Boss Manufacturing Company, Kewanee, IL; *U.S. Private*, pg. 1142
Fristedt, Hans, Pres. & Chief Oper. Officer--American Trading and Production Corporation, Baltimore, MD; *U.S. Private*, pg. 63
Frith, Margaret, Pres.-Putnam & Grossett Group--The Putnam Berkley Group, Inc., New York, NY; *Int'l*, pg. 1027
Frith, Russell J., Chm. Bd., Pres. & Chief Exec. Officer--Lawn Doctor Inc., Holmdel, NJ; *U.S. Private*, pg. 653
Fritsch, Bill, Pres.--CF2GS, Seattle, WA; *U.S. Private*, pg. 194
Fritz, Don, Pres.--Kellogg Company of Great Britain Ltd., Manchester, United Kingdom; *U.S. Public*, pg. 947
Fritz, Jerry L., Pres.--Precision Foods, Inc., Saint Louis, MO; *U.S. Private*, pg. 1134
Fritz, Leonard, Pres.--Huron Valley Steel Corp., Belleville, MI; *U.S. Private*, pg. 549
Fritz, Michael, Pres.--Rugg Manufacturing Company, Greenfield, MA; *U.S. Private*, pg. 950
Fritz, Steve, Pres.--Jantzen, Portland, OR; *U.S. Public*, pg. 1702
Fritz, Wayne, Pres.--Saladmaster, Arlington, TX; *U.S. Private*, pg. 961
Fritz, William J., Pres.--Everbrite, Inc., Greenfield, WI; *U.S. Private*, pg. 386
Fritze, Kenneth, Pres.--Philip Fritze & Sons, Inc., Whippany, NJ; *U.S. Private*, pg. 429
Fritzke, Tom L., Pres.--Heresite Protective Coatings Inc., Manitowoc, WI; *U.S. Private*, pg. 523
Froeber, Joe, Pres.--Americal Corporation, Henderson, NC; *U.S. Private*, pg. 49
Froehlich, Virgil, Pres. & Gen. Mgr.--Affiliated Foods Cooperative Inc., Norfolk, NE; *U.S. Private*, pg. 25
Froemming, Herb, Pres. & Chief Oper. Officer--Brauns Fashions Corporation, Plymouth, MN; *U.S. Public*, pg. 251
Froh, Walter F., Pres.--Clarity Vision, Camp Hill, PA; *U.S. Private*, pg. 529
Frohnaple, David, Pres.--Collier-Keyworth, Inc., Liberty, NC; *U.S. Public*, pg. 985
Froissant, Andre, Pres. & Chief Exec. Officer--Credit Lyonnais Canada, Montreal, Canada; *Int'l*, pg. 344
Frojd, Tim, Partner & Fin. Dir.--Martin/Williams Advertising Inc., Minneapolis, MN; *U.S. Private*, pg. 710
Froman, John, Pres.--Circuit City Central Div., Richmond, VA; *U.S. Public*, pg. 374
Fromson, Howard A., Pres.--Ano-Coil Corporation, Rockville, CT; *U.S. Private*, pg. 75
Fromstein, Mitchell S., Chm. Bd., Pres. & Chief Exec. Officer--Manpower Inc., Milwaukee, WI; *U.S. Public*, pg. 1042
Frooman, Robert J., Pres.--Sysco Food Services, Cincinnati, OH; *U.S. Public*, pg. 1551
Frost, Chad, Pres.--Frost Inc., Grand Rapids, MI; *U.S. Private*, pg. 430
Frost, Howard, Pres.-Sls.--Bollinger Industries Inc., Grand Prairie, TX; *U.S. Public*, pg. 243
Frost, Michael, Pres.--Burner Systems International, Inc., Chattanooga, TN; *U.S. Private*, pg. 351
Frost, Mike, Pres. & Chief Exec. Officer--Cleveland Capital Holdings, Cliffside, NC; *U.S. Private*, pg. 246
Frost, Mike, Pres.--Petroleum World, Cliffside, NC; *U.S. Private*, pg. 246
Frost, Patrick, Pres.--Frost National Bank, San Antonio, TX; *U.S. Public*, pg. 467
Frost, Robert P., Pres.--Frost Company, Chattanooga, TN; *U.S. Private*, pg. 430
Fruchtenbaum, Edward, Pres. & Chief Oper. Officer--American Greetings Corporation, Cleveland, OH; *U.S. Public*, pg. 77
Frudakis, Darlene, Pres.--Pet Ag Inc., Elgin, IL; *U.S. Private*, *pg. 746*
Frump, J. Ronald, Pres. & Chief Oper. Officer--Vitality Foodservice, Inc., Zephyrhills, FL; *U.S. Private*, pg. 682
Fry, Jim, Pres. & Chief Oper. Officer--Tuscarora Yarns Inc., Mount Pleasant, NC; *U.S. Private*, pg. 1110
Fry, John, Pres.--Fry's Electronics, Inc., San Jose, CA; *U.S. Private*, pg. 430
Fry, John, Pres.--Dun & Bradstreet Ltd., High Wycombe, United Kingdom; *U.S. Public*, pg. 536
Fry, Keith A., Pres. & Chief Oper. Officer--Lake States Insurance Co., Traverse City, MI; *U.S. Public*, pg. 787
Fry, R.E., Pres.--IDenticard Systems, Inc., Lancaster, PA; *U.S. Private*, pg. 557
Fryling, Victor J., Pres. & Chief Oper. Officer--CMS Energy Corporation, Dearborn, MI; *U.S. Public*, pg. 279
Frymark, John R., Pres.--Guardian Products, Inc., Simi Valley, CA; *U.S. Public*, pg. 1535
Fryml, J.S., Pres. & Chief Exec. Officer--American Fast Print, Limited, Spartanburg, SC; *U.S. Private*, pg. 53
Fuchs, Eduard, Pres.--H. Krantz-TKT GmbH, Bergisch Gladbach, Germany; *Int'l*, pg. 399
Fuchs, Jay R., Pres.--American Bankers Insurance Co. of Florida, Miami, FL; *U.S. Public*, pg. 67
Fuchs, Jay R., Pres.--American Bankers Life Assurance Co. of Florida, Miami, FL; *U.S. Public*, pg. 67
Fuchs, Jay R., Pres.--Bankers American Life Assurance Company, Pearl River, NY; *U.S. Public*, pg. 68
Fuchs, Steven, Pres.--Hampton Industries, Inc., Kinston, NC; *U.S. Public*, pg. 779
Fuciu, George N., Pres.--Technology Services, Overland Park, KS; *U.S. Public*, pg. 1501
Fuelling, Thomas N., Pres. & Chief Exec. Officer--Lawry's Foods, Inc., Monrovia, CA; *Int'l*, pg. 1435
Fuerbach, W.F., Jr., Chm. Bd., Pres. & Treas.--S.M. Frank & Co., Inc., Peekskill, NY; *U.S. Private*, pg. 423
Fuerst, John, Pres. & Chief Oper. Officer--Continental/Midland, Inc., Park Forest, IL; *U.S. Private*, pg. 268
Fugazy, Roy, Pres.--Fugazy International Corporation, New York, NY; *U.S. Private*, pg. 430
Fugelsang, George N., Pres.--Dresdner Securities (USA) Inc., New York, NY; *Int'l*, pg. 418
Fugman, Max, Pres.--Gault Distributors Inc., Richmond, Canada; *Int'l*, pg. 541
Fuhrmann, Charles J., II, Pres., Chief Exec. Officer & Chief Fin. Officer--Lot$ Off Corporation, San Antonio, TX; *U.S. Public*, pg. 1014
Fuji, Harunosuk, Pres.--Mitsubishi Cable Industries, Ltd., Tokyo, Japan; *Int'l*, pg. 870
Fujii, Hideyuki, Pres.--Gigalex Co., Ltd., Osaka, Japan; *Int'l*, pg. 1125
Fujii, Hiro, Pres. & Chief Exec. Officer--Minolta Corporation, Ramsey, NJ; *Int'l*, pg. 869
Fujii, Hiroshi, Pres.--Nippon Paint Company Ltd., Osaka, Japan; *Int'l*, pg. 937
Fujii, K., Pres.--Sharp Electronica Espana S.A. (Barcelona), Barcelona, Spain; *Int'l*, pg. 1229
Fujii, Kimio, Pres.--Cirrus Logic K.K., Tokyo, Japan; *U.S. Public*, pg. 375
Fujii, Kunito, Pres.--Wako Electric Co., Ltd., Okayama, Japan; *Int'l*, pg. 1125
Fujimoto, Kuniaki, Pres.--Compaq Computer Japan KK, Tokyo, Japan; *U.S. Public*, pg. 418
Fujine, Junichi, Pres.--Phoenix Technologies K.K., Tokyo, Japan; *U.S. Public*, pg. 1292
Fujioka, Hiroshi, Pres.--Nanto Lease Co., Ltd., Nara, Japan; *Int'l*, pg. 906
Fujiseki, Katsuhiro, Pres.--Seiyo, Ltd., Tokyo, Japan; *Int'l*, pg. 1178
Fujita, Hiromichi, Pres.--Toppan Printing Company, Ltd., Tokyo, Japan; *Int'l*, pg. 1399
Fujita, Katsuhisa, Pres.--Diamond Lease Co., Ltd., Tokyo, Japan; *Int'l*, pg. 413
Fujita, Naohisa, Pres.--Mitsubishi Rayon America, Inc., New York, NY; *Int'l*, pg. 876
Fujita, Yuzuru, Pres.--Asahi Mutual Life Insurance Company, Tokyo, Japan; *Int'l*, pg. 85
Fujiwara, Kikuo, Pres. & Chief Exec. Officer--Shimadzu Corporation, Kyoto, Japan; *Int'l*, pg. 1232
Fujiyama, Akira, Pres. & Chief Exec. Officer--Fujisawa Pharmaceutical Co. Ltd., Osaka, Japan; *Int'l*, pg. 525
Fukai, Kiyoshi, Pres.--P.T. Otsuka Indonesia, Jakarta, Indonesia; *Int'l*, pg. 1014
Fukase, Masaru, Pres.--Komatsu do Brasil Ltda., Sao Paulo, Brazil; *Int'l*, pg. 744
Fukatsu, Seiji, Pres. & Chief Exec. Officer--All Nippon Airways Co. Ltd., Tokyo, Japan; *Int'l*, pg. 57
Fukawatase, Tohsifumi, Pres.--Minebea Onkyo Co., Ltd., Yamanashi, Japan; *Int'l*, pg. 868
Fukawatase, Toshifumi, Pres.--Hwan Chong Enterprise Co., Ltd., Kao-hsiung, Taiwan; *Int'l*, pg. 868
Fukaya, Y., Pres.--Mitsubishi Cable America, Inc., New York, NY; *Int'l*, pg. 870
Fukuchi, Hideo, Pres. & Chief Exec. Officer--Nikon Inc., Melville, NY; *Int'l*, pg. 931
Fukuda, Hidenori, Pres.--Dai Nippon Book Binding Co., Ltd., Tokyo, Japan; *Int'l*, pg. 363
Fukuda, Hiromu, Pres.--Hitachi Semiconductor (America), Inc., Irving, TX; *Int'l*, pg. 622
Fukuda, Junnosuke, Pres.--Dentsu West Japan Inc., Osaka, Japan; *Int'l*, pg. 393
Fukuda, K., Pres. & Chief Oper. Officer--Ikegami Electronics (U.S.A.), Inc., Maywood, NJ; *Int'l*, pg. 660
Fukuhara, Yoshiharu, Pres. & Chief Exec. Officer--Shiseido Company Ltd., Tokyo, Japan; *Int'l*, pg. 1235
Fukui, Kikuo, Pres.--Tiffany & Co. K.K. (Japan), Tokyo, Japan; *U.S. Public*, pg. 1609
Fukui, Kikuo, Pres.--Tiffany & Co. Japan Inc., New York, NY; *U.S. Public*, pg. 1609
Fukui, Kikuo, Pres.--Tiffany & Co. Japan Inc. - Japan Branch, New York, NY; *U.S. Public*, pg. 1609
Fukui, Sagorogei, Pres.--Renishaw K.K., Nagoya, Japan; *Int'l*, pg. 1103
Fukui, Sagurogei, Pres.--Renishaw K.K., Tokyo, Japan; *Int'l*, *pg. 1103*
Fukunaga, Eric S., Pres. & Chief Oper. Officer--Servco Pacific Inc., Honolulu, HI; *U.S. Private*, pg. 986
Fukunaga, Mr., Pres.--Tsubakimoto Chain Co., Osaka, Japan; *Int'l*, pg. 1425
Fukutsuji, Michio, Pres.--Central Automotive Products, Ltd., Osaka, Japan; *Int'l*, pg. 278
Fukuzawa, Takeshi, Pres.--Mitsubishi Estate Co., Ltd., Tokyo, Japan; *Int'l*, pg. 873
Fulchino, Paul E., Pres. & Chief Oper. Officer--B/E Aerospace, Inc., Wellington, FL; *U.S. Public*, pg. 159
Fuld, Jr., Richard S., Chm. Bd. & Chief Exec. Officer--Lehman Brothers Holdings Inc., New York, NY; *U.S. Public*, pg. 987
Fuld, Richard S., Pres. & Co-Chief Exec. Officer--Lehman Brothers, New York, NY; *U.S. Public*, pg. 987
Fuldner, Christopher T., Pres.--Efco Corporation, Monett, MO; *U.S. Private*, pg. 353
Fulenwider, Claire, Pres.--Heartland Energy Services, Inc., Madison, WI; *U.S. Public*, pg. 1728
Fulenwider, Claire, Pres.--Heartland Energy Group, Inc., Madison, WI; *U.S. Public*, pg. 1728
Fuller, Fred, Pres.--CIBA Seeds, Greensboro, NC; *Int'l*, pg. 973
Fuller, Fred D., Pres.--Novartis Seeds, Inc., Downers Grove, IL; *Int'l*, pg. 974
Fuller, Gary T., Pres. & Chief Exec. Officer--Woolworth Overseas Corp., New York, NY; *U.S. Public*, pg. 1778
Fuller, Gary W., Pres. & Treas.--Jamieson Film Company, Inc., Dallas, TX; *U.S. Public*, pg. 551
Fuller, Jack, Pres.--Tribune Publishing Company, Chicago, IL; *U.S. Public*, pg. 1636
Fuller, Jeffrey L., Pres. & Chief Oper. Officer--Transcrypt International, Lincoln, NE; *U.S. Public*, pg. 1630
Fuller, Lawrence R., Pres. & Publr.--The Honolulu Advertiser, Honolulu, HI; *U.S. Public*, pg. 701
Fuller, Michael, Pres. & Chief Exec. Officer--Management Dynamics, New Providence, NJ; *U.S. Public*, pg. 1040
Fuller, Michael B., Pres.--Sprint's Local Telecommunication Division, San Diego, CA; *U.S. Public*, pg. 1500
Fuller, Ned, Pres.--C & J Clark Retail, Inc., Kennett Square, PA; *Int'l*, pg. 297
Fuller, Richard S., Pres. & Chief Exec. Officer--The Smithfield Companies, Inc., Portsmouth, VA; *U.S. Public*, *pg. 1479*
Fuller, Yvonne, Div. Pres.--Midwest Natural Foods, Bloomington, IN; *Int'l*, pg. 752
Fullerton, James H., Pres. & Chief Exec. Officer--M & I Bank of LaCrosse, La Crosse, WI; *U.S. Public*, pg. 1050
Fullerton, Scott, Pres.--AMF Reece Incorporated, Mechanicsville, VA; *U.S. Private*, pg. 7
Fulton, Gary, Partner--Bryant, Fulton & Shee, Vancouver, Canada; *U.S. Private*, pg. 678
Fulton, J. Michael, Pres.--Comerica Bank California, San Jose, CA; *U.S. Public*, pg. 409
Fulton, James, Pres. & Chief Exec. Officer--FKI Industries. Inc., Fairfield, CT; *Int'l*, pg. 472
Fulton, John J., Chm. Bd. & Pres.--Delta Power Co., Rockford, IL; *U.S. Private*, pg. 322
Fulton, Rufus J., Jr., Pres. & Chief Exec. Officer--Fulton Financial Corp., Lancaster, PA; *U.S. Public*, pg. 687
Fulton, Sandy M., Pres. & Chief Exec. Officer-Pacific Forest Products Ltd.--Avenor, Inc., Montreal, Canada; *Int'l*, pg. 101
Fulton, Thomas M., Pres. & Chief Exec. Officer--Landauer, Inc., Glenwood, IL; *U.S. Public*, pg. 977
Fumagalli, Peppino, Pres.--Candy S.p.A., Brugherio, Italy; *Int'l*, pg. 259
Fumire, R.A., Pres.--Summit Corporation of America, Thomaston, CT; *U.S. Private*, pg. 1050
Funai, Tetsuro, Pres.--Funai Electric Co., Ltd., Osaka, Japan; *Int'l*, pg. 529
Funari, Robert, Pres. & Chief Exec. Officer--Syncor International Corporation, Woodland Hills, CA; *U.S. Public*, pg. 1548
Funk, Albert, Pres.--Modern Hilift Equipment Co., West Conshohocken, PA; *U.S. Private*, pg. 755
Funk, Joe, Pres. & Chief Exec. Officer--Allen-Rogers Co., Laconia, NH; *U.S. Private*, pg. 315
Funk, John, Pres.--TCR Corporation, Minneapolis, MN; *U.S. Public*, pg. 1632
Funk, Tommy, Pres.--Sebastian Cotton & Grain Corp., Sebastian, TX; *U.S. Private*, pg. 980
Fuqua, Jeffrey B., Pres.--Amick Construction Ltd., Orlando, FL; *U.S. Private*, pg. 66
Furbacher, Stephen A., Pres.--Warren Petroleum Company, Houston, TX; *U.S. Public*, pg. 1146
Furebotten, Tohan, Pres.--Kvaerner Kimek a.s., Kirkenes, Norway; *Int'l*, pg. 770
Furgal, James W., Pres.--Camillus Cutlery Co., Camillus, NY; *U.S. Private*, pg. 203
Furlong, Edward V., Jr., Pres. & Chief Exec. Officer--WWF Paper Corporation, Bala Cynwyd, PA; *U.S. Private*, pg. 1145
Furlong, Ralph D., Pres.--Industrial Steel & Wire Company, Chicago, IL; *U.S. Private*, pg. 561
Furlong, Sue, Mng. Partner & Exec. V.P.--Dugan Valva Contess Inc., Morristown, NJ; *U.S. Private*, pg. 345
Furman, Fred D., Pres.--PMR Corporation, San Diego, CA; *U.S. Public*, pg. 1242
Furman, Thomas D., Jr., Pres. & Chief Oper. Officer--Camp Dresser & McKee Inc., Cambridge, MA; *U.S. Private*, pg. 203
Furnari, Beverly, Pres.--Fairview Construction, Inc, Auburn Hills, MI; *U.S. Private*, pg. 392
Furnaro, Frank, Partner & Exec. V.P.--Stawasz & Partners/Health Care Communications, New York, NY; *U.S. Private*, pg. 599
Furness, Terence N., Pres.--Zimmer, Inc., Warsaw, IN; *U.S. Public*, pg. 254
Furness, Terence N., Pres.--Microtek Medical, Inc., Columbus, MS; *U.S. Public*, pg. 914
Furr, Randy W., Pres. & Chief Oper. Officer--Sanmina Corporation, San Jose, CA; *U.S. Public*, pg. 1431
Furry, Michael, Pres.--Reinhold Industries Inc., Santa Fe Springs, CA; *U.S. Private*, pg. 920
Furubayashi, T., Pres.--Feintool Japan Co. Ltd., Atsugi, Japan; *Int'l*, pg. 479
Furubayashi, T., Pres.--Feintool Engineering Co. Ltd., Atsugi, Japan; *Int'l*, pg. 479

Furuhashi, Satoru, Chm. Bd. & Pres.--Hosiden Corporation, Yao, Japan; *Int'l*, pg. 635
Furuhata, Masayoshi, Pres. & Chief Exec. Officer--Mitsui & Co. (U.S.A.), Inc., New York, NY; *Int'l*, pg. 879
Furuichi, Kimihisha, Pres.--Sumitomo Chemical Deutschland GmbH, Dusseldorf, Germany; *Int'l*, pg. 1312
Furuichi, Takeshi, Pres.--NLI International, New York, NY; *Int'l*, pg. 935
Furukawa, Junnosuke, Pres.--The Furukawa Electric Co., Ltd., Tokyo, Japan; *Int'l*, pg. 530
Furukawa, Suguru, Pres.--Kuroda Precision Industries Ltd., Kawasaki, Japan; *Int'l*, pg. 764
Furuya, Katsuhiko, Pres.--Matsuya Company Ltd., Tokyo, Japan; *Int'l*, pg. 848
Fusco, Edmund J., Sr., Pres.--The Fusco Corporation, New Haven, CT; *U.S. Private*, pg. 432
Fusco, Robert A., Pres.--Olsten Health Services, Melville, NY; *U.S. Public*, pg. 1221
Fuse, Takashi, Pres.--Nissho Iwai (Thailand) Limited Partnership, Bangkok, Thailand; *Int'l*, pg. 948
Fushita, Tom, Pres.--CIE Systems, Irvine, CA; *Int'l*, pg. 694
Fusilli, Donald P., Jr., Pres. & Gen. Mgr.--Baker/MO Services, Inc., Cypress, TX; *U.S. Public*, pg. 168
Fusz, Louis, Jr., Pres.--Lou Fusz Automotive Network, Saint Louis, MO; *U.S. Private*, pg. 432
Fuszard, Curtis J., Pres.--Associated Financial Center, Ltd., Menomonee Falls, WI; *U.S. Public*, pg. 140
Futagi, Hidenori, Pres.--AEON Group, Chiba, Japan; *Int'l*, pg. 28
Futagi, Hidenori, Pres.--JUSCO Co., Ltd., Chiba, Japan; *Int'l*, pg. 28
Futami, Tomio, Pres.--Hino Motors, Ltd., Tokyo, Japan; *Int'l*, pg. 620
Futchko, Andrew R., Pres.--Bethlehem Steel-PA Steel Technologies Inc., Steelton, PA; *U.S. Public*, pg. 226
Futerman, Eli N., Pres.--Hahn Automotive Warehouse, Inc., Rochester, NY; *U.S. Public*, pg. 774
Futerman, Eli N., Pres.--Professional Auto Warehouse, Rochester, NY; *U.S. Public*, pg. 774
Futter, Bernard, Pres. & Chief Exec. Officer--Futter Lumber Corporation, Rockville Center, NY; *U.S. Private*, pg. 432
Futterknecht, James O. Jr., Chm. Bd., Pres., & Chief Exec. Officer--Excel Industries, Inc., Elkhart, IN; *U.S. Public*, pg. 598
Fyfe, David, Pres. & Chief Oper. Officer--Thoro, Jacksonville, FL; *U.S. Private*, pg. 505
Fynes, D.M.S., Pres.--Castell Interlocks Inc., Erlanger, KY; *Int'l*, pg. 590
Gaard, Jens Maj, Pres.--Andelssmar A.m.b.a., Viby, Denmark; *Int'l*, pg. 826
Gaasche, Ted L., Pres.--SunGard Planning Solutions Inc., Wayne, PA; *U.S. Public*, pg. 1535
Gabayzadeh, Mehdi, Pres.--American Tissue, Inc., Mechanicville, NY; *U.S. Private*, pg. 63
Gabayzadehi, Mehdi, Pres.--American Tissue Corporation, Hauppauge, NY; *U.S. Private*, pg. 63
Gaboardi, Saverio, Dr., Pres.--Astra Veicoli Industriali S.p.A., Piacenza, Italy; *Int'l*, pg. 94
Gabrys, Gerard, Pres. & Chief Oper. Officer--Guest Services, Inc., Fairfax, VA; *U.S. Private*, pg. 486
Gaby, Barb, Pres.--Amway Hotel Corporation, Grand Rapids, MI; *U.S. Private*, pg. 69
Gaddis, William, V.P.-Fin. & Admin.--Murata of America, Inc., Charlotte, NC; *Int'l*, pg. 897
Gadow, Rainer, Dr., Pres.--euroflamm GmbH, Bremen, Germany; *Int'l*, pg. 400
Gadsden, Peter, Sir, Pres.--PPP hc, Tunbridge Wells, United Kingdom; *Int'l*, pg. 1020
Gaeng, J. Brian, Pres. & Chief Exec. Officer--Fredericktown Bank & Trust Co., Frederick, MD; *U.S. Public*, pg. 1089
Gaetz, Richard E., Pres. & Chief Oper. Officer--Vitran Corporation Inc., Toronto, Canada; *Int'l*, pg. 1469
Gaffney, Michael, Pres.--Snyder Berlin, Berlin, PA; *U.S. Private*, pg. 887
Gaffney, T.C., Pres.--Performance Products Division, New York, NY; *U.S. Public*, pg. 1500
Gage, Duncan, Pres.--Lafarge, Southfield, MI; *Int'l*, pg. 788
Gage, Patrick, Dr., Pres. & Chief Oper. Officer--Genetics Institute, Inc., Cambridge, MA; *U.S. Public*, pg. 79
Gagliano, John, Pres.--Alfa Romeo Distributors of North America, Orlando, FL; *Int'l*, pg. 481
Gagne, Paul E., Pres. & Chief Exec. Officer--Avenor, Inc., Montreal, Canada; *Int'l*, pg. 101
Gagne, Steve, Pres.--Dana Commercial Credit Corporation, Troy, MI; *U.S. Public*, pg. 479
Gagnier, Charles E., Pres. & Chief Exec. Officer--AMCORE Bank N.A., Rockford, Rockford, IL; *U.S. Public*, pg. 64
Gagnon, David, V.P.-Consulting--TRI-S Environmental Consulting, Brattleboro, VT; *U.S. Public*, pg. 546
Gagnon, Michael P., Pres.--Acacia Networks, Inc., Lowell, MA; *U.S. Private*, pg. 11
Gagnum, Hilge, Pres.--Greiter AG, Altstatten, Switzerland; *U.S. Public*, pg. 929
Gahm, W. Dwight, Chm. Bd., Pres. & Chief Exec. Officer--Kitchen Kompact, Inc., Jeffersonville, IN; *U.S. Private*, pg. 624
Gaillard, Charles W., Pres.--General Mills, Inc., Minneapolis, MN; *U.S. Public*, pg. 717
Gaines, Michael, Pres. & Chief Oper. Officer--Moore-Handley, Inc., Pelham, AL; *U.S. Public*, pg. 1128
Gainsburg, Roy, Pres.--St. Martins Press, Inc., New York, NY; *Int'l*, pg. 1479
Gainza, Xavier, Mng. Partner & Chief-Creative Services--Fova, Inc., New York, NY; *U.S. Public*, pg. 764
Gaites, Robert J., Pres.--The Strober Organization, Inc., Brooklyn, NY; *U.S. Private*, pg. 403
Gaither, Hugh, Pres. & Chief Oper. Officer--Ridgeview, Inc., Newton, NC; *U.S. Private*, pg. 930
Gaither, John S., Pres.--Reichhold Limited, Mississauga, Canada; *Int'l*, pg. 370
Gaither, Thomas A., Pres.--Sunlink Corporation, Atlanta, GA; *U.S. Public*, pg. 208
Gaither, William H., Pres.--J.H. Heafner Co. Inc., Lincolnton, NC; *U.S. Private*, pg. 514
Galamba, Richard I., Chm. Bd.--Galamba Metals, Inc., Kansas City, KS; *U.S. Private*, pg. 437
Galanis, Terry S., Jr., Pres.--Sealing Devices Inc., Lancaster, NY; *U.S. Private*, pg. 978
Galanski, Stan, Pres.--New Hampshire Insurance Group, New York, NY; *U.S. Public*, pg. 84
Galante, Joe, Pres.-RCA Records Label--Bertelsmann Music Group, Wilmington, DE; *Int'l*, pg. 191
Galarreta, Jesus Peralta, Pres.--SODICAL - Sociedad Para el Desarrollo Industrial de Castilla y Leon, S.A., Valladolid, Spain; *Int'l*, pg. 1225
Galbraith, Evan Griffith, Chm. Bd.--LVMH Moet Hennessy Louis Vuitton, New York, NY; *Int'l*, pg. 781
Gale, Andy, Pres. & Chief Oper. Officer--Landa, Inc., Portland, OR; *U.S. Private*, pg. 646
Galesi, Francesco, Chm. Bd. & Pres.--Galesi Group, Schenectady, NY; *U.S. Private*, pg. 437
Galizia, Paul, Pres.--Bealls Outlet Inc., Bradenton, FL; *U.S. Private*, pg. 126
Gall, James I., Pres.--Sudler & Hennessey: Gall Inc., Montreal, Canada; *U.S. Private*, pg. 1200
Gall, Jim, Pres.--Sudler & Hennessey/Gall Inc., Montreal, Canada; *U.S. Private*, pg. 1200
Gallagher, Bernard P., Pres. & Chief Oper. Officer--Century Communications Corp., New Canaan, CT; *U.S. Public*, pg. 329
Gallagher, Bob, Pres.--Six Flags Hurricane Harbor, Arlington, TX; *U.S. Public*, pg. 1611
Gallagher, Bob, Pres.--Wet-N-Wild, A Six Flags Water Park, Arlington, TX; *U.S. Public*, pg. 1612
Gallagher, J. Patrick, Jr., Pres. & Chief Exec. Officer--Arthur J. Gallagher & Co., Itasca, IL; *U.S. Public*, pg. 698
Gallagher, Jack, Pres.--Drake Bakeries, Inc., Wayne, NJ; *Int'l*, pg. 349
Gallagher, John E., Jr., Pres.--Arrow International, Cleveland, OH; *U.S. Private*, pg. 85
Gallagher, R.J., Pres.--R.J. Gallagher Co., Houston, TX; *U.S. Private*, pg. 438
Gallagher, Robert J., Pres. & Chief Oper. Officer--Acuson Corporation, Mountain View, CA; *U.S. Public*, pg. 18
Gallagher, Sean, Pres.--Ortho-Kinetics, Inc., Waukesha, WI; *U.S. Private*, pg. 820
Gallagher, Thomas C., Pres. & Chief Oper. Officer--Genuine Parts Company, Atlanta, GA; *U.S. Public*, pg. 732
Gallagher, Thomas J., Pres. & Chief Oper. Officer--Everest Reinsurance Holdings, Liberty Corner, NJ; *U.S. Public*, pg. 597
Gallagher, Thomas J., Pres. & Chief Oper. Officer--Everest Reinsurance Co., Liberty Corner, NJ; *U.S. Public*, pg. 597
Gallagher, 27804, Pres.--R.J. Gallagher Co., Houston, TX; *U.S. Private*, pg. 438
Gallaher, Edward W., Sr., Pres., Chief Exec. Officer & Treas.--Phoenix Medical Technology, Inc., Andrews, SC; *U.S. Public*, pg. 1292
Gallant, Ben J., Pres. & Chief Exec. Officer--American Dental Technologies, Southfield, MI; *U.S. Public*, pg. 70
Gallen, Herbert, Chm. Bd. & Pres.--Ellen Tracy Inc., New York, NY; *U.S. Private*, pg. 372
Galles, Rick, Pres.--Galles Chevrolet, Albuquerque, NM; *U.S. Private*, pg. 438
Galli, Joseph, Pres.--Black & Decker Inc., Towson, MD; *U.S. Public*, pg. 234
Galligan, Thomas J., III, Chm. Bd., Pres. & Chief Exec. Officer--Papa Gino's Inc., Dedham, MA; *U.S. Private*, pg. 837
Gallimore, David A., Pres.--Lancaster Glass Corporation, Lancaster, OH; *U.S. Public*, pg. 977
Gallivan, John P., Pres.--D. Waldner Company, Inc., Farmingdale, NY; *U.S. Private*, pg. 1147
Gallo, Dan, Pres.--Pen-Tab Industries, Inc., Front Royal, VA; *U.S. Private*, pg. 848
Gallo, Robert J., Pres.--Missouri-American Water Co., Saint Joseph, MO; *U.S. Public*, pg. 95
Gallo, Robert J., Pres.--Ohio-American Water Co., Marion, OH; *U.S. Public*, pg. 95
Gallo, Robert J., Pres.--Iowa-American Water Co., Davenport, IA; *U.S. Public*, pg. 95
Gallo, Robert J., Pres.--Michigan-American Water Company, Calumet, MI; *U.S. Public*, pg. 95
Gallogly, James J., Pres. & Chief Oper. Officer--Sofamor Danek Group, Inc., Memphis, TN; *U.S. Public*, pg. 1482
Gallois, Louis, Pres.--Aeroassurances, Paris, France; *Int'l*, pg. 29
Gallois, Louis, Pres. & Chief Exec. Officer--SNCF, Paris, France; *Int'l*, pg. 1163
Galloway, David, Chm. Bd.--Silhouette Books, New York, NY; *Int'l*, pg. 1402
Galloway, David A., Pres. & Chief Exec. Officer--Torstar Corporation, Toronto, Canada; *Int'l*, pg. 1402
Gallus, Gregory F., Chm. Bd. & Pres.--Foodland Distributors, Livonia, MI; *U.S. Public*, pg. 1541
Galotti, Ronald, Publisher--Vogue Magazine, New York, NY; *U.S. Private*, pg. 20
Galustian, Ralph, Exec. V.P.--Bayer Corp. Pharmaceuticals, Berkeley, CA; *Int'l*, pg. 173
Galustian, Ralph M., Pres.-Biological Prds.--Bayer Corporation/Pharmaceutical Division, West Haven, CT; *Int'l*, pg. 173
Galuten, Jerry, Chm. Bd. & Pres.--SGD International Corp., Riverdale, NY; *U.S. Private*, pg. 957
Galvin, R.E., Pres.--Chevron USA Production Co., Houston, TX; *U.S. Public*, pg. 348
Galvin, Stephen J., Pres.--Educational Finance Group, Hyannis, MA; *U.S. Public*, pg. 1679
Gamache, Brian, Pres. & Chief Oper. Officer--WHG Resorts & Casinos, Carolina, PR; *U.S. Public*, pg. 1265
Gamache, Robert, Pres.--Albert Trostel Packings Ltd., Lake Geneva, WI; *U.S. Private*, pg. 1105
Gambill, Ben S., Jr., Pres.--Braid Electric Company, Nashville, TN; *U.S. Private*, pg. 165
Gambill, Mark M., Pres.--Wheat First Butcher Singer, Inc., Richmond, VA; *U.S. Public*, pg. 640
Gamble, Paul, Pres.--AMI Group, Inc., Lanham, MD; *U.S. Private*, pg. 7
Gamble, Richard, Pres. & Grp. Chief Exec.--Royal & Sun Alliance Insurance Group plc, London, United Kingdom; *Int'l*, pg. 1130
Gambow, N.E., Pres.--Post Glover Resistors Inc., Erlanger, KY; *Int'l*, pg. 590
Gamby, Werner, Pres.--W. Gamby & Co., New York, NY; *U.S. Private*, pg. 439
Gamel, Thomas W., Pres.--Timpte Industries, Inc., Denver, CO; *U.S. Private*, pg. 1088
Gamel, Wendell W., Chm. Bd., Pres. & Chief Exec. Officer--Tech-Sym Corporation, Houston, TX; *U.S. Public*, pg. 1563
Gamper, Albert R., Jr., Pres. & Chief Exec. Officer--The CIT Group Holdings, Inc., New York, NY; *Int'l*, pg. 360
Ganahl, Peter, Pres.--Ganahl Lumber Company, Anaheim, CA; *U.S. Private*, pg. 439
Ganci, Paul J., Pres. & Chief Oper. Officer--Central Hudson Gas & Electric Corporation, Poughkeepsie, NY; *U.S. Public*, pg. 324
Gandrud, Robert P., Pres. & Chief Exec. Officer--Lutheran Brotherhood, Minneapolis, MN; *U.S. Private*, pg. 681
Gandy, Kartar, Pres. & Chief Fin. Officer--Signtech USA, Ltd., San Antonio, TX; *U.S. Private*, pg. 999
Ganger, Ira, Pres.--Amerex USA, Inc., New York, NY; *U.S. Private*, pg. 49
Gangwal, Rakesh, Pres. & Chief Oper. Officer--US Airways Group, Inc., Arlington, VA; *U.S. Public*, pg. 1680
Gangwal, Rakesh, Pres. & Chief Oper. Officer--US Airways, Inc., Arlington, VA; *U.S. Public*, pg. 1680
Ganin, Saul, Pres.--Ganin Tire Co., Inc., Brooklyn, NY; *U.S. Private*, pg. 439
Ganley, Jack, Pres.--Burlington House Fabrics Group, New York, NY; *U.S. Public*, pg. 268
Ganly, Neal J., Pres.--Bemis Polyethylene Packaging Div., Terre Haute, IN; *U.S. Public*, pg. 210
Gann, Kenneth W., Pres. & Chief Exec. Officer--CCAIR, Inc., Charlotte, NC; *U.S. Public*, pg. 276
Gannaway, Michael T., Pres.-Fragrance Grp.--Charles of the Ritz Group Ltd., New York, NY; *U.S. Private*, pg. 689
Gannon, John J., Pres.--Physician Practice Management, Northbrook, IL; *U.S. Public*, pg. 1082
Gannon, Robert P., Chm. Bd., Pres. & Chief Exec. Officer--Montana Power Company, Butte, MT; *U.S. Public*, pg. 1126
Gans, Leo, Pres.--Action Technology Company, Rockaway, NJ; *U.S. Private*, pg. 15
Ganster, Dennis G., Pres. & Chief Exec. Officer--Comshare, Incorporated, Ann Arbor, MI; *U.S. Public*, pg. 425
Gant, Allen E., Jr., Chm. Bd & Pres.--Glen Raven Mills, Inc., Glen Raven, NC; *U.S. Private*, pg. 456
Gant, Allen E., Jr., Pres.--Glen Raven Marketing Corporation, New York, NY; *U.S. Private*, pg. 456
Gantcher, Nathan, Pres. & Co-Chief Exec. Officer--CIBC Oppenheimer Corp., New York, NY; *Int'l*, pg. 257
Ganz, Susan, Pres.--Lion Brothers Company, Inc., Owings Mills, MD; *U.S. Private*, pg. 669
Gap-Suk, Yang, Pres.--KOHAP Group, Seoul, Korea; *Int'l*, pg. 742
Gaples, Harry S., Pres.--Kleinschmidt Inc., Deerfield, IL; *U.S. Private*, pg. 625
Garavoglia, Luca, Pres.--Davide Campari, Milan, Italy; *Int'l*, pg. 385
Garbacz, Gerald G., Chm. Bd., Pres. & Chief Exec. Officer--Nashua Corporation, Nashua, NH; *U.S. Public*, pg. 1152
Garbarski, Eddie, Pres.--Garbarski EURO RSCG, Brussels, Belgium; *Int'l*, pg. 603
Garbee, Richard E., Pres.--Hayward Pool Products, Inc., Elizabeth, NJ; *U.S. Private*, pg. 513
Garber, C. Stedman, Jr., Pres. & Chief Oper. Officer--Santa Fe International Corporation, Dallas, TX; *Int'l*, pg. 765
Garber, George E., Pres. & Chief Exec. Officer--The St. George Group, Inc., Pittsburgh, PA; *U.S. Private*, pg. 960
Garby, Gage, Pres.--Senetics, Boulder, CO; *U.S. Public*, pg. 1755
Garces, Jorge J., Pres.--John Crane Latin America, Codigo, Mexico; *Int'l*, pg. 1339
Garcia Hijonoso, Rene, Pres.--Protexa Industrias S.A. de C.V., Santa Catarina, Mexico; *Int'l*, pg. 576
Garcia, Angelo R., III, Pres.--Arrow Freight Corporation, Bulacan, Philippines; *Int'l*, pg. 186
Garcia, Antonio Valcarce, Pres.--ENCE - E.N. de Celulosas, S.A., Madrid, Spain; *Int'l*, pg. 1224
Garcia, Eduardo Abellan, Pres.--HUNOSA - E.N. Hulleras del Norte, S.A., Oviedo, Spain; *Int'l*, pg. 1224
Garcia, Francisci, Gen. Mgr.--Young & Rubicam C.A., Chuao, Venezuela; *U.S. Private*, pg. 1200
Garcia, John E., Pres.--Intermedics Inc., Angleton, TX; *Int'l*, pg. 1307
Garcia, Jose Antonio, Pres. & Chief Oper. Officer--Philippine Airlines, Inc., Manila, Philippines; *Int'l*, pg. 1050
Garcia, Jose Luis Alvarez, Pres.--Foarsa Forjas Y Aceros De Reinosa, S.A., Reynosa, Mexico; *Int'l*, pg. 1225
Garcia, Manuel Fernandez, Pres.--Productos Tubulares, S.A., Vizcaya, Spain; *Int'l*, pg. 1224
Garcia, Pete, Pres. & Chief Exec. Officer--University Mechanical & Engineering Contractors, Inc., San Diego, CA; *U.S. Public*, pg. 572
Gard, Russell M., Vice Chm., Pres. & Chief Oper. Officer--American Pad and Paper Company, Dallas, TX; *U.S. Public*, pg. 88
Gardehall, Hans, Pres.--NCC Prefab AB, Sollentuna, Sweden; *Int'l*, pg. 899
Gardella, David, Pres.--The Instant Web Companies, Chanhassen, MN; *U.S. Private*, pg. 565
Gardella, William T., Pres.--Rex Marine Center, Inc., Norwalk, CT; *U.S. Private*, pg. 926
Gardiner, Walter A., Pres.--Imperial Schrade Corp., Ellenville, NY; *U.S. Private*, pg. 559
Gardner, Bruce, Pres.--Datawatch Corporation, Wilmington, MA; *U.S. Public*, pg. 488
Gardner, David E., Pres. & Chief Exec. Officer--Alfred Nickles Bakery, Inc., Navarre, OH; *U.S. Private*, pg. 799

Gardner, George D., Pres. & Mng. Dir.--Grocers Specialty Co., Los Angeles, CA; *U.S. Private*, pg. 227
Gardner, George D., Pres.--Grocers General Merchandise Co., Los Angeles, CA; *U.S. Private*, pg. 227
Gardner, H. McIntyre, Pres. & Chief Oper. Officer--Helen of Troy Corporation, El Paso, TX; *U.S. Public*, pg. 807
Gardner, Herbert M., Chm. Bd. & Pres.--Supreme Industries, Inc., Goshen, IN; *U.S. Public*, pg. 1541
Gardner, J. S., Pres.--Principal Marketing Services, Inc., Des Moines, IA; *U.S. Private*, pg. 886
Gardner, Jean, Pres.--Penninsular Meat Company, Inc., Tampa, FL; *U.S. Private*, pg. 850
Gardner, John R., Pres.--Sun Life Assurance Company of Canada, Toronto, Canada; *Int'l*, pg. 1318
Gardner, K. Eric, Pres.--American Investment Bank, NA, Salt Lake City, UT; *U.S. Public*, pg. 990
Gardner, Lee M., Pres. & Chief Oper. Officer--MascoTech, Inc., Taylor, MI; *U.S. Public*, pg. 1055
Gardner, Mike, Pres.--Whittaker Communications, Inc., Santa Clara, CA; *U.S. Public*, pg. 1767
Gardner, Myrna, Pres.--Hudson Street Partners, New York, NY; *U.S. Public*, pg. 1422
Gardner, Richard E., Pres.--Calumet Construction Corporation, Hammond, IN; *U.S. Private*, pg. 201
Gardner, Terri, Pres. & Chief Exec. Officer--Soft Sheen Products, Inc., Chicago, IL; *U.S. Private*, pg. 1012
Gardner, William, Pres. & Chief Exec. Officer--Wisconsin & Southern Railroad Co., Milwaukee, WI; *U.S. Private*, pg. 1184
Garel, John R., Pres. & Chief Exec. Offcier--Cadmus Journal Services, Inc., Linthicum Heights, MD; *U.S. Public*, pg. 291
Garfield, Eugene, Ph.D., Chm. Bd. & Pres.--Institute For Scientific Information, Philadelphia, PA; *U.S. Public*, pg. 1600
Garfinkle, Mitchel, Pres.--Mitchel-Lincoln Packaging, Saint-Laurent, Canada; *Int'l*, pg. 870
Garfunkel, Margaret D., Pres.--MBIA Municipal Investors Service Corporation, Armonk, NY; *U.S. Public*, pg. 1023
Garges, Thomas W. Jr., Pres.--Rochester & Pittsburgh Coal Company, Indiana, PA; *U.S. Public*, pg. 1395
Gargiulo, James V., Pres.--Sofco-Mead, Inc., Scotia, NY; *U.S. Private*, pg. 1012
Gargiulo, James V., Pres.--D.J. Mead-Hubbs & Howe, Depew, NY; *U.S. Private*, pg. 1012
Garlick, Ralph W., Pres.--Old Kent Bank-East, Southfield, MI; *U.S. Public*, pg. 1216
Garlington, Dub, Pres. & Chief Oper. Officer--Affiliated Funding Inc., Amarillo, TX; *U.S. Private*, pg. 25
Garlock, John, Pres.--Porter-Cable Corporation, Jackson, TN; *U.S. Public*, pg. 1274
Garlock, Randy, Pres. & Chief Oper. Officer--J.I. Kislak Inc., Hialeah, FL; *U.S. Private*, pg. 624
Garlow, James F., Pres.--John W. Hancock Jr., Inc., Salem, VA; *U.S. Public*, pg. 1392
Garman, M. Lawrence, Pres. & Chief Exec. Officer--Daubert Industries, Inc., Westchester, IL; *U.S. Private*, pg. 313
Garner, Jack, Pres.--UPB of Central Mississippi, Jackson, MS; *U.S. Public*, pg. 1669
Garnett, William A., Pres.--Jones Capital Corporation, Charlotte, NC; *Int'l*, pg. 633
Garnham, Francisco, Pres.--AGA de Mexico S.A. de C.V., Tlalnepantla, Mexico; *Int'l*, pg. 13
Garnier, Anton C., Chm. Bd., Pres. & Chief Exec. Officer--Southwest Water Company, West Covina, CA; *U.S. Public*, pg. 1494
Garnier, Jean-Pierre, Pres.--SmithKline Beecham Pharmaceuticals, Philadelphia, PA; *Int'l*, pg. 1265
Garofalo, Donald R., Pres. & Chief Exec. Officer--Andersen Corporation, Bayport, MN; *U.S. Private*, pg. 71
Garrasso, Mario, Pres.--Exor America, New York, NY; *Int'l*, pg. 467
Garratt, Reginald G., Pres. & Chief Exec. Officer--Knowles Electronics, Inc., Itasca, IL; *U.S. Private*, pg. 627
Garrett, Brian D., Pres.--CommScope, Inc., Hickory, NC; *U.S. Public*, pg. 415
Garrett, E.P., Pres.--Welco Lumber Company, Marysville, WA; *U.S. Private*, pg. 1161
Garrett, John C., Pres.-Semiconductor Sector--Harris Corporation, Melbourne, FL; *U.S. Public*, pg. 791
Garrett, John C., Pres.--Harris Semiconductor, Melbourne, FL; *U.S. Public*, pg. 792
Garrett, Sam L., Pres.--Ikon Office Solutions-Dallas, Dallas, TX; *U.S. Public*, pg. 863
Garrett, Scott, Chm. Bd., Pres. & Chief Exec. Officer--Dade Behring Inc., Deerfield, IL; *U.S. Private*, pg. 110
Garrett, Scott, Chm. Bd., Pres. & Chief Exec. Officer--Dade Behring Inc., Deerfield, IL; *Int'l*, pg. 626
Garrett, Steve O., Pres.--Sunwest Bank of Farmington, Farmington, NM; *U.S. Public*, pg. 1165
Garrett, Todd A., Pres.--Procter & Gamble Health & Beauty Care Belgium, Brussels, Belgium; *U.S. Public*, pg. 1332
Garrett, Todd A., Pres.--Procter & Gamble Health & Beauty Care Germany, Mainz, Germany; *U.S. Public*, pg. 1332
Garrett, William, Pres.--Delta Mills Marketing Company, New York, NY; *U.S. Public*, pg. 498
Garrigues-Walker, Jose Miguel, Pres.--FCA!BMZ Madrid, Madrid, Spain; *Int'l*, pg. 470
Garrison, F.S., Chm. Bd., Pres. & Chief Exec. Officer--American Freightways Corporation, Harrison, AR; *U.S. Public*, pg. 75
Garrison, F.S., Pres. & Chief Exec. Officer--American Freightways, Inc., Harrison, AR; *U.S. Public*, pg. 76
Garrison, John, Pres. & Chief Exec. Officer--SBS Holdings, Inc., Saginaw, MI; *U.S. Private*, pg. 955
Garrott, Thomas M., Chm. Bd., Pres. & Chief Exec. Officer--National Commerce Bancorporation, Memphis, TN; *U.S. Public*, pg. 1154
Garry, G. R., Pres.--Fiber Optic Services, Inc., Melbourne, FL; *U.S. Public*, pg. 750
Garry, William, Pres.--Cavalier Corporation, Chattanooga, TN; *U.S. Private*, pg. 220
Garry, William J., Editor-in-Chief--Bon Appetit Magazine, New York, NY; *U.S. Private*, pg. 20
Garson, Donald, Pres.--Dakota Pork Industries, Green Bay, WI; *U.S. Private*, pg. 54
Gartlan, Ronald B., Pres. & Chief Fin. Officer--Godfather's Pizza, Inc., Omaha, NE; *U.S. Private*, pg. 458
Gartner, Pedro, Pres.--AGA Argentina SACIFIMR, Buenos Aires, Argentina; *Int'l*, pg. 13
Garton, Daniel P., Pres.--AMR Eagle, Inc., Fort Worth, TX; *U.S. Public*, pg. 9
Garvens, Kent, Pres.--Electro-Coatings, Inc., Berkeley, CA; *U.S. Private*, pg. 368
Garvey, John K., Chm. Bd. & Pres.--Petroleum Inc., Wichita, KS; *U.S. Private*, pg. 858
Garvey, Neil, Pres.--Simplex Technologies, Inc., Portsmouth, NH; *U.S. Public*, pg. 1648
Garvey, Willard W., Chm. Bd., Pres. & Chief Exec. Officer--Garvey Industries, Inc., Wichita, KS; *U.S. Private*, pg. 440
Garvin, Andrew P., Chm. Bd., Pres., Chief Exec. Officer & Treas.--Find/SVP, Inc., New York, NY; *U.S. Public*, pg. 623
Garvin, Thomas M., Pres. & Chief Exec. Officer--UB Foods U.S., Inc., Elmhurst, IL; *Int'l*, pg. 1442
Garza de la Garza, Jorge, Pres.--Compania Minera Las Cuevas S.A. de C.V., San Luis Potosi, Mexico; *Int'l*, pg. 575
Garza Delgado, Roberto, Pres.--Versax, S.A. de C.V., Garza Garcia, Mexico; *Int'l*, pg. 56
Garza Laguera, Eugenio, Chm. Bd.--Bancomer, S.A., Mexico, Mexico; *Int'l*, pg. 145
Garza, Jorge, Pres.--Aceros Camesa S.A. de C.V., Mexico, Mexico; *Int'l*, pg. 575
Gascoyne, John, Pres.--Hubbard Farms, Inc., Walpole, NH; *U.S. Public*, pg. 1092
Gascoyne, John, Pres.--Hubbard Farms, Inc., Walpole, NH; *Int'l*, pg. 1114
Gaslow, Lawrence L., Chm. Bd. & Pres.--Empire Office Equipment, Inc., New York, NY; *U.S. Private*, pg. 374
Gasper, Joseph J., Pres.--Nationwide Life Insurance Co., Columbus, OH; *U.S. Private*, pg. 789
Gasperson, Bill, Pres.--Flowers Baking Co. of West Virginia, Bluefield, WV; *U.S. Public*, pg. 657
Gassner, Rudi, Pres. & Chief Exec. Officer-BMG Intl.--Bertelsmann Music Group, Wilmington, DE; *Int'l*, pg. 191
Gasson, Anthony, Pres. & Dir.-Adv.--Swirl, II LTD, New York, NY; *U.S. Private*, pg. 1059
Gasson, R.G., Pres.--American Safety Technologies, Inc., Roseland, NJ; *Int'l*, pg. 892
Gast, Warren E., Pres., Chief Exec. Officer & Gen. Mgr.--Gast Mfg. Corp., Benton Harbor, MI; *U.S. Private*, pg. 440
Gaston, Gerald N., Vice Chm., Pres. & Chief Exec. Officer--American Bankers Insurance Group, Inc., Miami, FL; *U.S. Public*, pg. 67
Gaston, Gerald N., Chm. Bd.--Voyager Service Warranties, Inc., Fort Worth, TX; *U.S. Public*, pg. 68
Gatehouse, Richard A., Pres.--Elkay Manufacturing Company, Oak Brook, IL; *U.S. Private*, pg. 372
Gatehouse, Rihcard, Pres.--Halsey Taylor, Oak Brook, IL; *U.S. Private*, pg. 372
Gates, Cecil B., Pres.--Crown Fence Co., Long Beach, CA; *U.S. Private*, pg. 292
Gates, Robert W., Jr., Pres. & Chief Oper. Officer--Horace Small Apparel Company, Nashville, TN; *Int'l*, pg. 635
Gates, Robert W., Jr., Pres.--R & R Uniforms, Nashville, TN; *Int'l*, pg. 635
Gates, T.J., Chm. Bd. & Pres.--Spfco Erectors, Inc., Cincinnati, OH; *U.S. Private*, pg. 1017
Gates, Tim J., Pres.--Southern Ohio Fabricators, Inc., Batavia, OH; *U.S. Private*, pg. 1017
Gates, Walter, Pres. & Chief Exec. Officer--THORN Americas, Wichita, KS; *Int'l*, pg. 1385
Gathright, Richard E., Pres. & Chief Oper. Officer--TransMontaigne Oil Company, Denver, CO; *U.S. Public*, pg. 1631
Gattas, Andy, Pres.--Knowledge Tree Inc., Memphis, TN; *U.S. Private*, pg. 627
Gattis, Jerry, Pres. & Chief Oper. Officer--Cagle's Inc., Atlanta, GA; *U.S. Public*, pg. 291
Gaucher, Michel, Chm. Bd. & Pres.--Socanav Inc., Montreal, Canada; *Int'l*, pg. 1272
Gaudiani, Mike, Pres.--Teledyne Fluid Systems, Brecksville, OH; *U.S. Public*, pg. 43
Gaughn, Peter, Pres. & Chief Exec. Officer--Pip Printing, Agoura Hills, CA; *U.S. Private*, pg. 423
Gaulin, Jean, Vice Chm., Pres. & Chief Oper. Officer--Ultramar Diamond Shamrock Corporation, San Antonio, TX; *U.S. Public*, pg. 1663
Gaulke, Michael, Pres. & Chief Exec. Officer--The Failure Group, Inc., Menlo Park, CA; *U.S. Public*, pg. 609
Gaullier, J.P., Pres.--Gan Sante, Paris, France; *Int'l*, pg. 565
Gault, James, Pres.--Aqua-Aerobic Systems Inc., Rockford, IL; *U.S. Private*, pg. 78
Gaunt, Bobbie, Pres. & Chief Exec. Officer--Ford Motor Co. of Canada Ltd, Oakville, Canada; *U.S. Public*, pg. 666
Gaunt, Hugh, Pres.--Rothchild's Larry L., New York, NY; *U.S. Private*, pg. 947
Gaunt, James R., Pres.--The Fifth Third Bank of Kentucky, Paris, KY; *U.S. Public*, pg. 621
Gauss, Cal, Pres. & Chief Exec. Officer--Wm. E. Wright Limited Partnership, West Warren, MA; *U.S. Private*, pg. 1192
Gauss, Cal, Pres.--Boye Needle, Chicago, IL; *U.S. Private*, pg. 1192
Gauss, Cal, Pres.--EZ International, West Warren, MA; *U.S. Private*, pg. 1192
Gautherie, Jacques, Pres.--Dumez-GTM, Nanterre, France; *Int'l*, pg. 823
Gauthier, Henry E., Chm. Bd., Pres. & Chief Oper. Officer--Coherent, Inc., Santa Clara, CA; *U.S. Public*, pg. 395
Gauthier, Noel, Pres.--SNECMA Services International (SSI), Paris, France; *Int'l*, pg. 1166
Gautier, Jean Francois, Pres. & Chief Exec. Officer--Salomon S.A., Annecy, France; *Int'l*, pg. 1181
Gavazzi, Roberto, Pres.--Allianz Via Assurances, Charenton-le-Pont, France; *Int'l*, pg. 60
Gavazzi, Roberto, Dr., Pres.--Allianz Subalpina S.p.A., Turin, Italy; *Int'l*, pg. 60
Gavazzi, Roberto, Dr., Pres.--Allianz Via Vie-Compagnie d'Assurances sur la Vie, Charenton-le-Pont, France; *Int'l*, pg. 60
Gavazzi, Roberto, Dr., Pres. Dir. Gen.--Compagnie Generale de Prevoyance, Strasbourg, France; *Int'l*, pg. 60
Gavazzi, Roberto, Dr., Pres. Dir. Gen.--Rhin et Moselle Assurances Compagnie d' Assurances sur la vie Societe Anonyme, Strasbourg, France; *Int'l*, pg. 61
Gaver, Joseph C., Pres.--Trayer Products, Inc., Elmira, NY; *U.S. Private*, pg. 1098
Gavin, Michael P., Pres.--Atlantic Federal Savings Bank, Baltimore, MD; *U.S. Public*, pg. 1543
Gavois, Francis, Chm. Bd. & Pres.--Banque Francaise du Commerce Exterieur, Paris, France; *Int'l*, pg. 160
Gawlik, Mark A., Pres. & Chief Oper. Officer--Play by Play Toys & Novelties, Inc., San Antonio, TX; *U.S. Public*, pg. 1309
Gawlik, Rick, Pres.--SierraCom, Hopkinton, MA; *U.S. Private*, pg. 999
Gay, B.R., Pres.--Bard Interventional Products, Tewksbury, MA; *U.S. Public*, pg. 189
Gay, Tan Cheng, Pres.--Pacific Technology Private ltd., Singapore, Singapore; *Int'l*, pg. 1292
Gaylord, E.K., II, Pres.--The Daily & Sunday Oklahoman, Oklahoma City, OK; *U.S. Private*, pg. 813
Gaylord, Edward L., Pres. & Publisher--Oklahoma Publishing Company, Oklahoma City, OK; *U.S. Private*, pg. 813
Gaynor, Dan, Pres. & Publisher--The St. Catharines Standard, Saint Catharines, Canada; *Int'l*, pg. 631
Gburek, John, Pres.--Precision Imaged Products Group, Tully, NY; *U.S. Public*, pg. 162
Gealach, K., Pres.--Agfa-Gevaert N.V., Antwerp, Belgium; *Int'l*, pg. 174
Geary, E. Timothy, Pres.--National Surgery Centers, Inc., Chicago, IL; *U.S. Public*, pg. 1161
Geary, Ronald G., Pres. & Chief Exec. Officer--Res-Care Incorporated, Louisville, KY; *U.S. Public*, pg. 1382
Gebauer, Rüdiger, Pres. & Chief Exec. Officer--Springer-Verlag New York Inc., New York, NY; *Int'l*, pg. 1291
Gebhard, Carol, Pres. & Gen. Mgr.--Washington Inventory Service, San Diego, CA; *U.S. Public*, pg. 846
Gebhardt, Barbara, Pres.--Career Blazers Learning Center of Melville, Melville, NY; *U.S. Private*, pg. 209
Gebhardt, Christian, Pres.--Neuwiesen Immobilien AG, Winterthur, Switzerland; *Int'l*, pg. 1305
Gebhardt, Scott W., Pres. & Chief Exec. Officer--PG&E Energy Services, San Francisco, CA; *U.S. Public*, pg. 1241
Gebler, David B., Chm. Bd., Pres. & Chief Exec. Officer--Airlease Ltd., San Francisco, CA; *U.S. Public*, pg. 33
Gebo, Brenton T., Pres.--Gebo Distributing Co., Inc., Plainview, TX; *U.S. Private*, pg. 442
Gecz, Michael, Pres.--Gavin Anderson & Company, New York, NY; *U.S. Public*, pg. 1223
Gedge, D., Pres.--Deep Sea Clam Company Limited, Lunenburg, Canada; *Int'l*, pg. 909
Gee, David, Pres. & Chief Exec. Officer--Marsulex Inc., North York, Canada; *Int'l*, pg. 599
Gee, William, III, Pres.--Cloverhill Bakery, Chicago, IL; *U.S. Private*, pg. 247
Geer, P. Nicholas, Chm. Bd. & Pres.--Westar Group Ltd., Vancouver, Canada; *Int'l*, pg. 1491
Geffen, David, Partner--DreamWorks SKG, Universal City, CA; *U.S. Private*, pg. 342
Gehl, William D., Chm. Bd., Pres. & Chief Exec. Officer--Gehl Company, West Bend, WI; *U.S. Public*, pg. 704
Gehl, William D., Pres.--Gehl Power Products, Inc., Yankton, SD; *U.S. Public*, pg. 704
Geiger, Eugene G., Pres. & Treas.--Geiger Brothers, Lewiston, ME; *U.S. Private*, pg. 442
Geiger, Joe, Pres.--Leggett & Platt, Inc., Bedford Park, IL; *U.S. Public*, pg. 985
Geiger, Ron, Pres. & Chief Exec. Officer--Harker's Distribution, Inc., Le Mars, IA; *U.S. Private*, pg. 502
Geiger, Thomas B., Jr., Pres.--Capital Tire, Inc., Toledo, OH; *U.S. Private*, pg. 206
Geiger, W., Pres.--Carole Fabrics Corp., Martinez, GA; *Int'l*, pg. 639
Geijer, Reinhold, Pres. & Chief Exec. Officer--Swedbank, Stockholm, Sweden; *Int'l*, pg. 1328
Geis, Kevin Z., Pres.--Brenton Savings Bank, FSB, Ames, IA; *U.S. Public*, pg. 251
Geise, David N., Pres. & Chief Exec. Officer--Furman Foods, Inc., Northumberland, PA; *U.S. Private*, pg. 431
Geisler, Dick G., Pres.--Cowboy Oil Company, Pocatello, ID; *U.S. Private*, pg. 280
Geissinger, Frederick W., Chm. Bd., Pres. & Chief Exec. Officer--Yosemite Insurance Co., Evansville, IN; *U.S. Public*, pg. 77
Gelber, L.J., Pres.--ESI Energy, Inc., North Palm Beach, FL; *U.S. Public*, pg. 608
Gelder, Robert, Pres. & Treas.--Barden & Robeson Corporation, Middleport, NY; *U.S. Private*, pg. 116
Gelhaus, Paul, Pres.--Figi's, Inc., Marshfield, WI; *U.S. Public*, pg. 623
Gelinas, J. Arthur, Pres. & Chief Exec. Officer--Davie Industries Inc., Levis, Canada; *Int'l*, pg. 385
Geller, Larry, Pres. & Chief Exec. Officer--Rosauers Supermarkets, Inc., Spokane, WA; *U.S. Private*, pg. 944
Gellerman, Jay M., Chm. Bd, Pres. & Chief Exec. Officer--Jaydon Incorporated, Rock Island, IL; *U.S. Private*, pg. 584
Gellert, George G., Chm. Bd. & Pres.--Atalanta Corporation, Elizabeth, NJ; *U.S. Private*, pg. 93
Gellert, Jay M., Pres. & Chief Oper Officer--Foundation Health Systems, Inc., Pueblo, CO; *U.S. Public*, pg. 678
Gelles, Heinz, Pres.--The Phoenix Learning Group, Inc., Saint Louis, MO; *U.S. Private*, pg. 863
Gellin, Kirk, Co-Pres.--Land N Sea, Inc., New York, NY; *U.S. Private*, pg. 645

Gellis, Phil, Pres.--Kombi, Ltd., Essex Junction, VT; *U.S. Private*, pg. 631
Gelpi, John J., Pres.--Industrial Metals of the South, New Orleans, LA; *U.S. Private*, pg. 561
Gels, James V., Publr.--Duluth News-Tribune, Duluth, MN; *U.S. Public*, pg. 964
Gemunder, Joel F., Pres.--Omnicare, Inc., Covington, KY; *U.S. Public*, pg. 1223
Genasci, Bill, Pres.--Select Sires, Inc., Plain City, OH; *U.S. Private*, pg. 982
Gencarelli, Louis A., Sr., Pres. & Chief Exec. Officer--Bess Eaton Donut Flour Co., Inc., Westerly, RI; *U.S. Private*, pg. 139
Gendler, Paul, Dr., Pres.--Language Institute for English (L.I.F.E.), Madison, NJ; *U.S. Public*, pg. 221
Gendrano, Renato C., Pres.--Infocom Technologies, Inc., Pasig, Philippines; *Int'l*, pg. 1051
Genetempo, John, Pres.--ADT Security Systems Southwest, Dallas, TX; *U.S. Public*, pg. 1649
Gengenbach, Benno, Co-Pres.--Schroff, Straubenhardt, Germany; *U.S. Public*, pg. 1274
Genier, Bob, Pres.--Atwood & Morrill Co., Inc., Salem, MA; *Int'l*, pg. 1489
Genovese, Leonard, Chm. Bd., Pres. & Chief Exec. Officer--Genovese Drug Stores, Inc., Melville, NY; *U.S. Public*, pg. 730
Genovese, Rocco C., Chm. Bd., Pres. & Chief Exec. Officer--Burke Industries, Inc., San Jose, CA; *U.S. Private*, pg. 183
Genovese, Rocco C., Pres. & Chief Exec. Officer--Burke Flooring Products Div., San Jose, CA; *U.S. Private*, pg. 183
Genovese, Rocco C., Pres. & Chief Exec. Officer--Custom Process, San Jose, CA; *U.S. Private*, pg. 183
Genrich, Hans-Dieter, Pres.--EFEKA Friedrich & Kaufmann GmbH & Co., Isernhagen, Germany; *U.S. Public*, pg. 81
Gensen, Paul Arne, Pres. & Dir.-Fin. & Sls.--DAB-Silkeborg a/s, Silkeborg, Denmark; *Int'l*, pg. 350
Gentles, R.G., Pres. & Mng. Dir.--Blue Circle America Inc., Marietta, GA; *Int'l*, pg. 197
Gentner, Roland, Pres. & Chief Oper. Officer--Sodak Gaming, Inc., Rapid City, SD; *U.S. Public*, pg. 1482
Gentry, Frank, Pres.--Harbor Financial/New America, Walnut Creek, CA; *U.S. Public*, pg. 644
Gentry, John, Pres. & Treas.--Positronic Industries, Inc., Springfield, MO; *U.S. Private*, pg. 876
Gentry, Marvin D., Chm. Bd. & Pres.--New Fortis Corp., King, NC; *U.S. Public*, pg. 843
Gentry, Robert T., Pres. & Chief Exec. Officer--Penn Central National Bank, Huntingdon, PA; *U.S. Public*, pg. 1222
Genuardi, Charles A., Pres. & Chief Exec. Officer--Genuardi Family Markets Inc., Norristown, PA; *U.S. Private*, pg. 447
Geocaris, John T., Pres.--Little Lady Foods, Inc., Elk Grove Village, IL; *U.S. Private*, pg. 671
Geoga, Doug, Pres.--Hyatt Hotels Corporation, Chicago, IL; *U.S. Private*, pg. 551
Geoppinger, William A., Pres. & Chief Exec. Officer--Hillshire Farm & Kahn's, Cincinnati, OH; *U.S. Public*, pg. 1433
George, Bill, Pres. & Chief Oper. Officer--Groendyke Transports, Inc., Enid, OK; *U.S. Private*, pg. 483
George, Boyd L., Pres.--Capital Resources, Inc., Hickory, NC; *U.S. Private*, pg. 657
George, Boyd L., Pres.--Merchants Transport of Hickory, Hickory, NC; *U.S. Private*, pg. 657
George, Dan, Pres. & Treas.--Central United Life Insurance Co., Houston, TX; *U.S. Private*, pg. 225
George, Dennis, Pres. & Gen. Mgr.--Bridgestone/Firestone Information Services Company, Akron, OH; *Int'l*, pg. 213
George, Gordon, Mng. Dir.--Elida Faberge, Kingston upon Thames, United Kingdom; *Int'l*, pg. 1434
George, John W., Pres.--Autocon Technologies, Inc., Farmington, MI; *U.S. Public*, pg. 850
George, Michael J., Pres. & Chief Exec. Officer--Melody Foods, Inc., Farmington Hills, MI; *U.S. Private*, pg. 730
George, Richard L., Pres. & Chief Exec. Officer--Suncor Inc., Calgary, Canada; *Int'l*, pg. 1320
George, Richard W., Sir., Chm. & Mng. Dir.--Weetabix Limited, Kettering, United Kingdom; *Int'l*, pg. 1488
George, Robert C., Pres. & Chief Exec. Officer--Indian Rocks National Bank, Largo, FL; *U.S. Public*, pg. 608
George, Ross, Pres. & Chief Exec. Officer--Simonds Industries Inc., Fitchburg, MA; *U.S. Private*, pg. 1001
George, Thomas D., Pres.--Motorola Semiconductor Products Sector, Phoenix, AZ; *U.S. Public*, pg. 1137
Georgehead, Christopher W., II, Pres. & Chief Exec. Officer--Gateway Press, Inc., Louisville, KY; *U.S. Private*, pg. 441
Georgoulis, Stratton, Chm. Bd., Pres. & Chief Exec. Officer--TIC United Corporation, Dallas, TX; *U.S. Private*, pg. 1063
Geppi, Stephen A., Pres. & Chief Exec. Officer--Diamond Comic Distributors, Inc., Timonium, MD; *U.S. Private*, pg. 330
Geraghy, James A., Pres. & Chief Exec. Officer--Genzyme Transgenics, Framingham, MA; *U.S. Public*, pg. 733
Gerard, Hipolito, Pres.--Kaufman y Broad de Mexico SA de CV, Mexico, Mexico; *U.S. Public*, pg. 945
Gerard, Stephen, Pres., Chief Exec. Officer & Treas.--Bolliger, Inc., Stamford, CT; *U.S. Private*, pg. 155
Gerber, Charles J., Jr., Pres.--Alcor Envelope Co., Hamburg, NY; *U.S. Public*, pg. 1666
Gerber, Kirk B., Pres.--HSC Controls, Buffalo, NY; *U.S. Public*, pg. 1776
Gerbig, Robert L., Pres. & Chief Exec. Officer--Gerbig, Snell/Weisheimer & Assoc., Inc., Columbus, OH; *U.S. Private*, pg. 449
Gerborg, Bengt, Pres.--VWS, Inc., Cleveland, OH; *Int'l*, pg. 440
Gerchenson, Jeffery H., Pres. & Chief Oper. Officer--Alva/Amco Pharmacal Companies, Inc., Chicago, IL; *U.S. Private*, pg. 47
Gerdelman, John W., Pres.--NetworkMCI Services, Richardson, TX; *U.S. Public*, pg. 1024
Gerdes, Lawrence E., Pres.--Charlie Thomas Dealerships, Houston, TX; *U.S. Private*, pg. 1082
Gerdes, Mary, Pres.--Western Nebraska National Bank, North Platte, NE; *U.S. Public*, pg. 629
Gerdes, Thomas R., Pres.--Plastic Moldings Corp., Cincinnati, OH; *U.S. Private*, pg. 871
Gerdin, Russell A., Chm. Bd., Pres. Chief Exec. Officer, Chief Oper. Officer & Sec.--Heartland Express, Inc., Coralville, IA; *U.S. Public*, pg. 803
Gerdy, Harvey, Chm. Bd., Pres. & Chief Exec. Officer--International Seaway Trading Corporation, Boca Raton, FL; *U.S. Private*, pg. 572
Gergacz, David, Pres. & Chief Exec. Officer--Brite Voice Systems, Inc., Heathrow, FL; *U.S. Public*, pg. 257
Gergacz, David, Pres. & Chief Exec. Officer--Brite Voice Systems, Canton, MA; *U.S. Public*, pg. 257
Geringer, Steven I., Pres. & Chief Exec. Officer--PCS Health Systems, Inc., Scottsdale, AZ; *U.S. Public*, pg. 993
Gerken, Jim, Pres.--Norwalk Furniture Corporation, Norwalk, OH; *U.S. Private*, pg. 807
Gerlach, John B., Jr., Pres., Chief Exec. Officer, Chief Oper. Officer & Sec.--Lancaster Colony Corporation, Columbus, OH; *U.S. Public*, pg. 976
Gerlach, N. Erich, Pres.--The Braas Group, Oberursell, Germany; *Int'l*, pg. 1091
Germaine, Robert, V.P.-Opers.--Bickford's Family Restaurants, Brighton, MA; *U.S. Public*, pg. 545
Gernentz, Jeanne, Pres.--Odell State Bank, Odell, IL; *U.S. Public*, pg. 1316
Gerondeau, Jean Lewis, Pres. & Dir. Gen.--Groupe Zodiac, Issy-les-Moulineaux, France; *Int'l*, pg. 572
Gerry, Gordon R., Pres.--AGRA International Limited, Oakville, Canada; *Int'l*, pg. 30
Gersh, Gary, Pres.--Capitol Records, Inc., Hollywood, CA; *Int'l*, pg. 428
Gerson, Matthew, Chm. Bd & Pres.--Gerson & Gerson, Inc., New York, NY; *U.S. Private*, pg. 449
Gerstall, A. Frederick, Pres.--Hidden Valley Coal Company, Los Angeles, CA; *U.S. Public*, pg. 296
Gerstein, David B., Pres.--Thermwell Products Co., Inc., Paterson, NJ; *U.S. Private*, pg. 1081
Gerstein, Jorg, Pres.--Rudolf Muller & Co. G.m.b.H., Pohlheim, Germany; *Int'l*, pg. 289
Gerstell, A. Frederick, Pres.--CalMat Co. of Arizona, Los Angeles, CA; *U.S. Public*, pg. 295
Gerstell, A. Frederick, Pres.--Allied Concrete, Inc., Los Angeles, CA; *U.S. Public*, pg. 295
Gerstell, A. Frederick, Pres.--Azusa Rock, Inc., Los Angeles, CA; *U.S. Public*, pg. 295
Gerstell, A. Frederick, Pres.--Kirst Construction Co., Inc., Los Angeles, CA; *U.S. Public*, pg. 296
Gerstell, A. Frederick, Pres.--Rio Norte Este Co., Los Angeles, CA; *U.S. Public*, pg. 296
Gerstell, A. Frederick, Pres.--River Bend Corp., Los Angeles, CA; *U.S. Public*, pg. 296
Gerstell, A. Frederick, Pres.--Sanger Rock and Sand, Los Angeles, CA; *U.S. Public*, pg. 296
Gerstell, A. Frederick, Pres.--Triangle Rocks Products, Inc., Los Angeles, CA; *U.S. Public*, pg. 296
Gerster, Donald, Pres.--Protective Closures Co., Inc., Buffalo, NY; *U.S. Public*, pg. 1045
Gerstner, Louis V., Jr., Chm. Bd. & Chief Exec. Officer--International Business Machines Corporation, Armonk, NY; *U.S. Public*, pg. 895
Gertler, Leonard, Pres.--All American Home Center, Downey, CA; *U.S. Private*, pg. 34
Gertner, Jane S., Pres.--Chocolate Products Co. Ltd., Toronto, Canada; *Int'l*, pg. 1495
Gescheider, Bruce A., Pres. & Chief Exec. Officer--ACCO Brands, Inc., Wheeling, IL; *U.S. Public*, pg. 674
Geschke, Charles M., Pres. & Chief Fin. Officer--Adobe Systems Incorporated, San Jose, CA; *U.S. Public*, pg. 20
Geske, Larry D., Pres. & Chief Exec. Officer--Energy West Inc., Great Falls, MT; *U.S. Public*, pg. 581
Geske, Larry D., Pres.--Energy West Resources, Great Falls, MT; *U.S. Public*, pg. 581
Geslin, Philippe, Pres. & Chief Oper. Officer--Compagnie de Suez, Paris, France; *Int'l*, pg. 313
Gessner, Tom R., Chm. Bd. & Pres.--Al Johnson Construction Co., Bloomington, MN; *U.S. Private*, pg. 590
Getsey, Andy, Pres. & New Bus. Contact--Shafer, Irvine, CA; *U.S. Private*, pg. 988
Gette, Anthony R., Pres., Chief Oper. Officer & Sec.--Mentor Corporation, Santa Barbara, CA; *U.S. Public*, pg. 1086
Gette, Anthony R., Pres.--Mentor Urology, Inc., Santa Barbara, CA; *U.S. Public*, pg. 1086
Gettlefinger, Herman E., Pres.--Kelso Oil Company, Knoxville, TN; *U.S. Private*, pg. 613
Gettler, Benjamin, Chm. Bd., Pres., Chief Exec. Officer & Chief Fin. Officer--Vulcan International Corporation, Wilmington, DE; *U.S. Public*, pg. 1725
Gey, Robert, Pres.--Lincoln Automotive, Saint Louis, MO; *U.S. Public*, pg. 1273
Geyer, Richard D., Pres.--Williams Bridge Co., Manassas, VA; *U.S. Public*, pg. 1770
Ghaemmaghami, Nicky, Pres.--Hydraulics International, Inc., Chatsworth, CA; *U.S. Private*, pg. 551
Ghafari, Yousif B., Pres. & Chief Exec. Officer--Ghafari Associates, Inc., Dearborn, MI; *U.S. Private*, pg. 450
Ghaleb, Kahlil, Pres.--Hagglunds Drives SARL, Grenoble, France; *Int'l*, pg. 670
Ghassemian, Mojtaba, Pres.--U.K. Division, Farnborough, United Kingdom; *U.S. Public*, pg. 423
Ghelfi, Brent, Pres. & Chief Exec. Officer--Cavco Industries, Inc., Phoenix, AZ; *U.S. Public*, pg. 323
Ghelfi, Brent, Pres.--SunBuilt Homes, Inc., Phoenix, AZ; *U.S. Public*, pg. 323
Ghelfi, Gregg, Pres.--National Security Containers, Phoenix, AZ; *U.S. Public*, pg. 323
Gherty, John E., Pres. & Chief Exec. Officer--Land O'Lakes, Inc., Arden Hills, MN; *U.S. Private*, pg. 645
Ghiz, Lewis, Pres.--Paddock Pool Construction Co., Inc., Scottsdale, AZ; *U.S. Private*, pg. 833
Gholson, Robert L., Pres. & Chief Exec. Officer--Universal Life Insurance Company, Memphis, TN; *U.S. Private*, pg. 1127
Giacco, Alexander, Chm. Bd. & Pres.--Rheometric Scientific, Piscataway, NJ; *U.S. Public*, pg. 1387
Giambrone, Angelo, Pres.--Unimed Management Services, Burbank, CA; *U.S. Private*, pg. 1118
Giancamilli, Andrew A., Pres. & Gen. Mgr.-Mdse.--Kmart Corporation, Troy, MI; *U.S. Public*, pg. 963
Giancola, James, Pres. & Chief Exec. Officer--CNB Bancshares, Inc., Evansville, IN; *U.S. Public*, pg. 280
Giangreco, Michael, Publr.--The Napa Valley Register, Napa, CA; *U.S. Public*, pg. 1343
Giannelli, S.P., Pres.--Toromont Process Systems Inc., Malden, MA; *Int'l*, pg. 1401
Giannone, Richard, Pres.--D&Z Microelectronics, Philadelphia, PA; *U.S. Private*, pg. 317
Giannopoulos, A.L., Pres. & Chief Exec. Officer--Micros Systems Inc., Beltsville, MD; *U.S. Public*, pg. 1106
Gibara, Samir G., Chm. Bd., Pres. & Chief Exec. Officer--The Goodyear Tire & Rubber Company, Akron, OH; *U.S. Public*, pg. 752
Gibb, Richard G., Pres.--Federal Signal Corporation, Signal Div., University Park, IL; *U.S. Public*, pg. 616
Gibb, Robert, Jr., Chm. Bd. & Pres.--Robert Gibb & Sons, Inc., Fargo, ND; *U.S. Private*, pg. 451
Gibbons, Charles H., Chm. Bd., Pres. & Chief Exec. Officer--Intellisource, Fairfield, CT; *U.S. Public*, pg. 1425
Gibbons, John J., Chm. Bd., Pres. & Chief Exec. Officer--Tseng Labs, Norristown, PA; *U.S. Public*, pg. 1643
Gibbons, Robert J., Pres. & Chief Exec. Officer--The Franklin Life Insurance Company, Springfield, IL; *U.S. Public*, pg. 76
Gibbons, Ronald W., Pres. & Chief Exec. Officer--First National Bank, Harrisburg, IL; *U.S. Public*, pg. 1217
Gibbs, C.L., Pres.--Standard Pipe Line Co., San Ramon, CA; *U.S. Public*, pg. 348
Gibbs, David, Pres.--Todd-AO Filmatic Ltd., London, United Kingdom; *U.S. Public*, pg. 1619
Gibbs, Frank, Pres. & Chief Oper. Officer--Ryan Herco Products Corp., Burbank, CA; *U.S. Private*, pg. 953
Gibbs, H. Jarrell, Pres.--Texas Utilities Communications Inc., Dallas, TX; *U.S. Public*, pg. 1588
Gibbs, H. Jarrell, Pres.--Texas Utilities Properties Inc., Dallas, TX; *U.S. Public*, pg. 1588
Gibbs, James M., Pres.--Marley Pump, Overland Park, KS; *U.S. Public*, pg. 1676
Gibbs, James R., Pres. & Chief Exec. Officer--Wainoco Oil Corporation, Houston, TX; *U.S. Public*, pg. 1732
Gibbs, Nick, Pres.--Gibbs Die Casting Corp., Henderson, KY; *U.S. Private*, pg. 628
Gibbs, Wayne, Pres.--Gibbs Wire & Steel Company, Inc., Southington, CT; *U.S. Private*, pg. 451
Gibson, Chip, Pres. & Publr.--Crown Publishers, Inc., New York, NY; *U.S. Private*, pg. 21
Gibson, Daniel, Pres.--Wolcott & Lincoln, Inc., Kansas City, MO; *U.S. Private*, pg. 1185
Gibson, Dennis, Pres.--Secoroc Inc., Commerce City, CO; *Int'l*, pg. 96
Gibson, John R., Pres. & Chief Exec. Officer--American Pacific Corporation, Las Vegas, NV; *U.S. Public*, pg. 88
Gibson, John R., Pres.--AMPAC Development Company, Las Vegas, NV; *U.S. Public*, pg. 88
Gibson, John R., Pres.--Halotron, Inc., Cedar City, UT; *U.S. Public*, pg. 88
Gibson, John R., Jr., Pres.--American Azide Corporation, Cedar City, UT; *U.S. Public*, pg. 88
Gibson, Ralph M., Pres. & Treas.--Durrett-Sheppard Steel Co., Inc., Baltimore, MD; *U.S. Private*, pg. 349
Gibson, Tim, Pres.--New Zealand Milk Products (North Asia) Ltd, Tokyo, Japan; *Int'l*, pg. 923
Gibson, William M., Chm. Bd., Pres. & Chief Exec. Officer--Manugistics Group, Inc., Rockville, MD; *U.S. Public*, pg. 1042
Gidney, Lane, Pres.--First American Title Co. of Utah, Salt Lake City, UT; *U.S. Public*, pg. 625
Gidwitz, James G., Pres.--Continental Catalina, Inc., Chicago, IL; *U.S. Public*, pg. 441
Gidwitz, Ronald J., Pres. & Chief Exec. Officer--Helene Curtis Industries, Inc., Chicago, IL; *Int'l*, pg. 1434
Giedt, Ronel W., Pres. & Chief Oper. Officer--Juno Lighting, Inc., Des Plaines, IL; *U.S. Public*, pg. 935
Gieg, L. Frederick, Jr., Pres. & Chief Exec. Officer--RMI Titanium Company, Niles, OH; *U.S. Public*, pg. 1662
Giegerich, John R., Pres.--Kathryn Beich, Inc., Bloomington, IL; *Int'l*, pg. 917
Gierer, Vincent A., Jr., Chm. Bd., Pres. & Chief Exec. Officer--UST Inc., Greenwich, CT; *U.S. Public*, pg. 1660
Giermak, C.F., Pres.--Eriez Magnetics, Erie, PA; *U.S. Private*, pg. 381
Gies, Joe, Partner & Creative Dir.--Kupper Parker Communications Inc., Saint Louis, MO; *U.S. Private*, pg. 637
Gieske, Friedhelm, Mng. Dir.--RWE-DEA AG, Hamburg, Germany; *Int'l*, pg. 1081
Gieskes, Hans, Pres. & Chief Exec. Officer--LEXIS-NEXIS, Miamisburg, OH; *Int'l*, pg. 1096
Gietzen, Jeff, Pres. & Chief Exec. Officer--D & W Food Centers, Inc., Grand Rapids, MI; *U.S. Private*, pg. 300
Gifford, Gary L., Pres. & Chief Exec. Officer--Maui Land & Pineapple Co., Inc., Kahului, HI; *U.S. Public*, pg. 1060
Gifford, John F., Chm. Bd., Pres. & Chief Exec. Officer--Maxim Integrated Products, Inc., Sunnyvale, CA; *U.S. Public*, pg. 1061
Gifstad, Walther, Pres.--Aker Verdal a.s., Verdal, Norway; *Int'l*, pg. 42
Gigas, George, Pres.--Cablewave Systems, North Haven, CT; *U.S. Private*, pg. 197
Gignac, Kenneth, Chm. Bd. & Pres.--Elgin Dairy Foods, Inc., Chicago, IL; *U.S. Private*, pg. 370

Gignac, Louis P., Pres. & Chief Exec. Officer--Cambior Inc., Montreal, Canada; *Int'l*, pg. 253
Gignac, Pierre, Pres. & Chief Exec. Officer--Ultima Foods, Brossard, Canada; *Int'l*, pg. 32
Gigou, Michel, Pres. & Chief Exec. Officer--Mack Trucks, Inc., Allentown, PA; *Int'l*, pg. 1102
Gilbane, Thomas F., Jr., Pres. & Chief Oper. Officer--Gilbane Building Company, Providence, RI; *U.S. Private*, pg. 452
Gilbert, Bob, Pres.--Infinet Operations, Norfolk, VA; *U.S. Private*, pg. 649
Gilbert, Carl A., Pres. & Chief Exec. Officer--Dravo Corporation, Pittsburgh, PA; *U.S. Public*, pg. 527
Gilbert, Dave, Pres.--Golin/Harris Communications, Inc., Chicago, IL; *Int'l*, pg. 1226
Gilbert, Donald M., Pres.--Suffolk Capital Management, New York, NY; *U.S. Public*, pg. 1674
Gilbert, Jackson B., Pres.--Banco Espirito Santo Sa. (Bessa), Madrid, Spain; *Int'l*, pg. 142
Gilbert, John, Pres.--Bioplex Corp., Montvale, NJ; *U.S. Public*, pg. 487
Gilbert, John, Pres.--Datascope Collagen Products Division, Montvale, NJ; *U.S. Public*, pg. 487
Gilbert, John O., Pres. & Chief Oper. Officer--Aid Association for Lutherans, Appleton, WI; *U.S. Private*, pg. 27
Gilbert, Richard, Pres.--Quartet Manufacturing Co., Skokie, IL; *U.S. Public*, pg. 707
Gilbert, Richard, Pres.--MUDD Jeans, Inc., New York, NY; *U.S. Private*, pg. 766
Gilbert, Robert, Pres.--Bel/Kaukauna USA, Little Chute, WI; *U.S. Private*, pg. 130
Gilbert, Rodney C., Pres. & Chief Exec. Officer--Rust International Inc., Birmingham, AL; *U.S. Public*, pg. 1366
Gilbert, Roger, MD, Corp. Pres.--MeritCare Foundation, Fargo, ND; *U.S. Private*, pg. 733
Gilbert, Walter F., Chm. Bd., Pres., Chief Exec. Officer & Treas.--Semco Industries Inc., Stoughton, MA; *U.S. Private*, pg. 983
Gilbert, William B., Chm. Bd.--Lifetime Doors Inc., Farmington, MI; *U.S. Private*, pg. 666
Gilbertsen, Robert G., Pres. & Chief Exec. Officer--Network Computing Devices, Inc., Mountain View, CA; *U.S. Public*, pg. 1168
Gilbertson, Jay, Pres., Co-Chief Oper. Officer, Chief Fin. Officer, Treas. & Sec.--HBOC, Atlanta, GA; *U.S. Public*, pg. 770
Gilbertson, K., Pres.--Brown Shoe Co. of Canada Ltd., Perth, Canada; *U.S. Public*, pg. 262
Gilbertson, Roger, MD, Corp. Pres.--MeritCare Hospital, Fargo, ND; *U.S. Private*, pg. 733
Gilbertson, Roger, MD, Corp. Pres.--HealthCare Accessories, Fargo, ND; *U.S. Private*, pg. 733
Gilbertson, Roger, MD, Corp. Pres.--Health Ventures, Fargo, ND; *U.S. Private*, pg. 733
Gilbertson, Roger, MD, Corp. Pres.--MeritCare Medical Group, Fargo, ND; *U.S. Private*, pg. 733
Gilchrist, David M., Jr., Pres.--VP Buildings, Memphis, TN; *U.S. Public*, pg. 972
Gilchrist, David, Jr., Pres. & Chief Oper. Officer--Varco-Pruden Buildings, Memphis, TN; *U.S. Public*, pg. 1677
Giles, A.H., Pres.--Zinc Products Company, Greeneville, TN; *U.S. Public*, pg. 57
Giles, Don, Pres. & Chief Exec. Officer--Icicle Seafoods, Inc., Seattle, WA; *U.S. Private*, pg. 556
Gill, Emmanuel, Pres. & Chief Exec. Officer--Elbit Computers Ltd., Haifa, Israel; *Int'l*, pg. 644
Gill, H. Ross, III, Pres.--The National Latex Products Co., Ashland, OH; *U.S. Private*, pg. 785
Gill, Robert, Pres. & Chief Exec. Officer--Matec Corporation, Hopkinton, MA; *U.S. Public*, pg. 1056
Gill, Stephen E., Pres. & Chief Exec. Officer--M.C. Gill Corporation, El Monte, CA; *U.S. Private*, pg. 453
Gill, Stephen M., Pres.--Wilson USA Inc., Cranford, NJ; *Int'l*, pg. 124
Gillen, Richard, Chm. Bd., Pres. & Chief Exec. Officer--Harbor Financial Mortgage Corp., Houston, TX; *U.S. Public*, pg. 644
Gillenwater, Kelso, Pres. & Publr.--The News Tribune, Tacoma, WA; *U.S. Public*, pg. 1066
Gillespie, George E., Pres.--Pyron Corp., Niagara Falls, NY; *Int'l*, pg. 1524
Gillespie, George E., Pres.--Pyron Metal Powders, Inc., Greenback, TN; *Int'l*, pg. 1524
Gillespie, James J., Pres. & Chief Exec. Officer--Rally's Hamburgers, Inc., Louisville, KY; *U.S. Public*, pg. 1359
Gillespie, Lloyd, Pres.--Nacoma Products, Inc., Nacogdoches, TX; *U.S. Private*, pg. 773
Gillespie, Michael, Pres.-Asia--The Lincoln Electric Company (Asia Pacific) Pte. Ltd., Singapore, Singapore; *U.S. Public*, pg. 996
Gillespie, Richard J., Pres.--Gillespie, Lawrenceville, NJ; *U.S. Private*, pg. 453
Gillespie, Robert W., Chm., Pres. & Chief Exec. Officer--Keycorp, Cleveland, OH; *U.S. Public*, pg. 954
Gillette, E. Peter, Chm. Bd. & Pres.--Piper Trust Company, Minneapolis, MN; *U.S. Public*, pg. 1303
Gillette, James R., Pres.--Swinerton Inc., San Francisco, CA; *U.S. Private*, pg. 1059
Gilliam, John, Pres. & Chief Exec. Officer--Anderson Wholesale Company, Muskogee, OK; *U.S. Private*, pg. 73
Gilliam, Michael N., Pres.--Southwestern Bell Media Ventures, San Antonio, TX; *U.S. Public*, pg. 1415
Gilliatt, S.R., Pres.--RFL Electronics, Inc., Boonton, NJ; *U.S. Private*, pg. 903
Gillig, Stephen R., Pres., Chief Admin. Officer & Sec.--Fort Wayne National Corporation, Fort Wayne, IN; *U.S. Public*, pg. 673
Gilligan, Patrick J., Pres.-Nord Photo Engineering--Photo Control Corporation, Minneapolis, MN; *U.S. Public*, pg. 1292
Gillis, Daniel F., Pres. & Chief Exec. Officer--Software AG Americas, Inc., Reston, VA; *U.S. Public*, pg. 1482
Gillispie, C. Stephenson, Jr., Chm. Bd., Pres. & Chief Exec. Officer--Cadmus Communications Corporation, Richmond, VA; *U.S. Public*, pg. 290
Gillogly, Terry B., Pres.--Gillogly Chevrolet & Geo, Inc., West Seneca, NY; *U.S. Private*, pg. 454
Gilluly, C.W., Chm. Bd., Pres. & Chief Exec. Officer--Hadron, Inc., Alexandria, VA; *U.S. Public*, pg. 773
Gillum, Jack, Pres. & Chief Exec. Officer--BCS Wireless, New Glarus, WI; *U.S. Public*, pg. 609
Gilman, Alan B., Pres. & Chief Exec. Officer--Consolidated Products, Inc., Indianapolis, IN; *U.S. Public*, pg. 436
Gilman, Alan B., Pres.--SNS Investment Company, Indianapolis, IN; *U.S. Public*, pg. 436
Gilman, Alan B., Pres.--Steak 'n Shake, Inc., Indianapolis, IN; *U.S. Public*, pg. 437
Gilman, Bill, Pres. & Chief Oper. Officer--McLaughlin Manufacturing Company, Greenville, SC; *U.S. Private*, pg. 724
Gilman, Steven F., Chm. Bd., Pres. & Chief Exec. Officer--Gilrichco, Inc., Oxnard, CA; *U.S. Private*, pg. 454
Gilmartin, Raymond V., Chm. Bd., Pres. & Chief Exec. Officer--Merck & Co., Inc., Whitehouse Station, NJ; *U.S. Public*, pg. 1090
Gilmer, Ken, Pres.--Wing Industries, Inc., Greenville, TX; *U.S. Private*, pg. 1183
Gilotti, Stephen A., Pres.--Textron Financial Corporation, Providence, RI; *U.S. Public*, pg. 1590
Gilpatrick, Rick, Pres.--Gilpatrick Construction Company, Inc, Riverton, WY; *U.S. Private*, pg. 454
Gilroy, J.A., Pres. & Chief Oper. Officer--LucasVarity Inc., Buffalo, NY; *Int'l*, pg. 820
Gilson, Bob, Pres.--Anthracite Industries, Inc., Sunbury, PA; *U.S. Private*, pg. 87
Gin, Sue Ling, Pres., Chief Exec. Officer & Sole Dir.--Flying Food Fare, Inc., Chicago, IL; *U.S. Private*, pg. 415
Ginebra, Freddy, Chm. Bd & Pres.--Publicitaria Cumbre, Santo Domingo, Dominican Republic; *U.S. Public*, pg. 1422
Gingerich, John C., Pres. & Chief Oper. Officer--Honeywell-Measurex Corporation, Cupertino, CA; *U.S. Public*, pg. 833
Gingl, Manfred, Pres. & Chief Exec. Officer--Tesma International Inc., Concord, Canada; *Int'l*, pg. 830
Ginn, Julia, Pres.--The Presmet Corp., Worcester, MA; *U.S. Private*, pg. 882
Ginn, Robert M., Pres.--BPI Inc., Kent, WA; *U.S. Public*, pg. 772
Ginn, Russell, Chm. Bd., Pres. & Chief Exec. Officer--The Flexitallic Group, Inc., Houston, TX; *U.S. Private*, pg. 413
Ginn, William, Pres.--Sumitomo Bank Leasing & Finance, Inc., New York, NY; *Int'l*, pg. 1308
Ginsberg, Bruce C., Pres.--New England Frozen Foods, Inc., Southborough, MA; *U.S. Private*, pg. 793
Ginsberg, David M., Pres. & Chief Exec. Officer--Ginsberg's Institutional Foods, Inc., Hudson, NY; *U.S. Private*, pg. 455
Ginsberg, Randy, Pres.--George Rice & Sons, Los Angeles, CA; *U.S. Public*, pg. 1779
Giogio, Robert, Pres.--Day & Zimmermann International, Inc., Philadelphia, PA; *U.S. Private*, pg. 317
Gioia, Craig, Pres.--Zynolyte Products Company, Carson, CA; *Int'l*, pg. 663
Giordano, Andrew, Pres.--Graham-Field Health Products, Inc., Hauppauge, NY; *U.S. Public*, pg. 757
Giordano, Robert R., Pres. & Chief Exec. Officer--EnergyNorth, Inc., Manchester, NH; *U.S. Public*, pg. 581
Giordano, Ron, Pres.--H.S. Crocker Co., Inc., Huntley, IL; *U.S. Private*, pg. 290
Giordano, Sal, III, Pres.--Melcor Corporation, Trenton, NJ; *U.S. Public*, pg. 615
Giordano, Salvatore, Jr., Vice Chm., Pres. & Chief Exec. Officer--Fedders Corp., Liberty Corner, NJ; *U.S. Public*, pg. 614
Giorgio, Robert J., Pres.--Life Sciences International, Philadelphia, PA; *U.S. Private*, pg. 317
Giovannetti, Gary, Pres. & Chief Exec. Officer--Co-Steel Sayreville Inc., Sayreville, NJ; *Int'l*, pg. 298
Gipson, Gordon, Pres.--The Caxton Printers Ltd., Caldwell, ID; *U.S. Private*, pg. 220
Gipson, Hayward R., Pres. & Chief Exec. Officer--Playtex Apparel, Inc., Stamford, CT; *U.S. Public*, pg. 1433
Girard, Chris, Pres. & Chief Exec. Officer--Plaid Pantries, Inc., Beaverton, OR; *U.S. Private*, pg. 868
Girard, Francis E., Pres. & Chief Exec. Officer--Comverse Network Systems, Wakefield, MA; *U.S. Public*, pg. 425
Giraudi, Giancarlo, Dr., Pres. & Gen. Dir.--Orlane, Paris, France; *Int'l*, pg. 1011
Girdlestone, Brian A., Pres.-Hoover N.A.--Hoover Company, Canton, OH; *U.S. Public*, pg. 1065
Girouard, Marvin, Pres. & Chief Oper. Officer--Pier 1 Imports, Inc., Fort Worth, TX; *U.S. Public*, pg. 1295
Girsky, Joel H., Chm. Bd., Pres. & Treas.--Jaco Electronics, Inc., Hauppauge, NY; *U.S. Public*, pg. 920
Gist, Betty, Chm. Bd., Pres., & Chief Exec. Officer--Dairy Fresh Corp., Greensboro, AL; *U.S. Private*, pg. 307
Gisvold, Rune, Pres.--Kvaerner Venture a.s, Oslo, Norway; *Int'l*, pg. 770
Gitter, David J., Pres. & Chief Exec. Officer--M & I Bank Fox Valley, Appleton, WI; *U.S. Public*, pg. 1050
Giuffre, Frank, Pres.--Rexworks Inc., Milwaukee, WI; *U.S. Private*, pg. 926
Giugni, June, Pres.--Cosmetique, Inc., Vernon Hills, IL; *U.S. Private*, pg. 277
Giuliano, Louis J., Pres. & Chief Exec. Officer--ITT Defense & Electronics, Inc., Mc Lean, VA; *U.S. Public*, pg. 859
Giumarra, Sal, Chm. Bd. & Pres.--Giumarra Vineyards, Edison, CA; *U.S. Private*, pg. 455
Giuntini, Paul, Pres.--Carlsberg Financial Corp., Pasadena, CA; *U.S. Private*, pg. 211
Giuntini, Philip M., Pres.--American Management Systems, Inc., Fairfax, VA; *U.S. Public*, pg. 86
Giuria, Alfredo, Pres.--Viceversa/Young & Rubicam, Montevideo, Uruguay; *U.S. Private*, pg. 1200
Giusti, Luis E., Dr., Pres.--Petroleos de Venezuela S.A., Caracas, Venezuela; *Int'l*, pg. 1045
Given, J.B., Pres.--Thermal Ceramics Inc., Augusta, GA; *Int'l*, pg. 894
Gladchun, Marshall D., Pres. & Chief Exec. Officer--Advanced Accessories Systems, LLC., Sterling Heights, MI; *U.S. Private*, pg. 21
Gladstone, Christopher, Pres.--Quadrangle Development Corporation, Washington, DC; *U.S. Private*, pg. 898
Gladys, Kendall, Pres.--International Tool & Supply Company, Inc., Houston, TX; *Int'l*, pg. 684
Glancy, Alfred R., III, Chm. Bd., Pres. & Chief Exec. Officer--MCN Energy Group, Inc., Detroit, MI; *U.S. Public*, pg. 1024
Glander, Tom, Pres.--Super Cycle, Inc., Saint Paul, MN; *U.S. Private*, pg. 914
Glanville, Peter E., Pres.--Lowry Hill Investment Advisors, Inc., Minneapolis, MN; *U.S. Public*, pg. 1201
Glaske, Paul E., Chm. Bd., Pres. & Chief Exec. Officer--Blue Bird Corporation, Macon, GA; *U.S. Private*, pg. 151
Glass, Curtis, Pres.--Bollman Hat Co., Adamstown, PA; *U.S. Private*, pg. 155
Glass, Curtis, Pres.--Bailey Hats, Fort Worth, TX; *U.S. Private*, pg. 155
Glass, David D., Pres. & Chief Exec. Officer--Wal-Mart Stores, Inc., Bentonville, AR; *U.S. Public*, pg. 1732
Glass, Jeff, Pres.--The Taney Corporation, Taneytown, MD; *U.S. Private*, pg. 1067
Glass, Sherwin, Chm. Bd., Pres. & Chief Exec. Officer--Warehouse Home Furnishings Distributor, Dublin, GA; *U.S. Private*, pg. 1150
Glass, Wilbur H., Jr., Pres.--The Auchter Company, Jacksonville, FL; *U.S. Private*, pg. 98
Glassman, Daniel, Chm. Bd., Pres. & Chief Exec. Officer--Bradley Pharmaceuticals, Fairfield, NJ; *U.S. Public*, pg. 249
Glassman, Daniel, Chm. Bd., Pres. & Chief Exec. Officer--Doak Dermatologics, Westbury, NY; *U.S. Public*, pg. 250
Glatt, Jordan, Pres.--Magla Products, Morristown, NJ; *U.S. Private*, pg. 695
Glauberman, Stuart, Pres.--Malco Products, Inc., Barberton, OH; *U.S. Private*, pg. 698
Glave, Jan-Gunnar, Pres.--Skanska Anlaggning AB, Malmo, Sweden; *Int'l*, pg. 1260
Glazer, Avram A., Pres. & Chief Exec. Officer--Zapata Corporation, Houston, TX; *U.S. Public*, pg. 1789
Glazer, Bennett, Pres.--Glazer's Wholesale Drug Co. Inc., Dallas, TX; *U.S. Private*, pg. 455
Glazer, Michael L., Pres.--Consolidated Stores Corp., Columbus, OH; *U.S. Public*, pg. 437
Glazner, Wayne D., Pres. & Chief Exec. Officer--Valley National Bank of Cortez, Cortez, CO; *U.S. Public*, pg. 1793
Gleason, Alfred M., Pres.-Port of Portland Commission--Port of Portland, Portland, OR; *U.S. Private*, pg. 876
Gleason, Dana, Pres.--Dana Design, Bozeman, MT; *U.S. Public*, pg. 940
Gleason, David M., Pres.--Austin Powder Co., Cleveland, OH; *U.S. Private*, pg. 100
Gleason, James S., Chm. Bd. & Pres.--Gleason Corporation, Rochester, NY; *U.S. Public*, pg. 746
Gleason, Matthew S., Chm. Bd. & Pres.--Gleason/Calise/Associates, Inc., Dallas, TX; *U.S. Private*, pg. 455
Gleason, Robert, Pres.--Rottlund Homes of Florida, Inc., Fort Myers, FL; *U.S. Public*, pg. 1406
Gledhill, Robert, Pres.--Samuel Specialty Metals, Parsippany, NJ; *U.S. Private*, pg. 964
Gleeman, Marsha, Pres.--MGM/UA Music, Santa Monica, CA; *U.S. Public*, pg. 1102
Gleim, Richard, Pres.--Federated Fry Metals, Inc., Altoona, PA; *Int'l*, pg. 328
Glen, James, Pres.--Chem-Tainer Industries, North Babylon, NY; *U.S. Private*, pg. 231
Glendenning, Jack, Pres.--Inland Printing Co., Inc., La Crosse, WI; *U.S. Private*, pg. 564
Glendinning, Paul, Pres.--Glendinning Marine Products, Inc., Conway, SC; *U.S. Public*, pg. 1705
Glenn, Clyde A., Jr., Pres. & Treas.--Potter-Shackelford Construction Co., Greenville, SC; *U.S. Private*, pg. 877
Glenn, David W., Pres. & Chief Oper. Officer--Federal Home Loan Mortgage Corporation, Mc Lean, VA; *U.S. Public*, pg. 615
Glennon, Denis, Partner--Messner Vetere Berger McNamee Schmetterer/EURO RSCG, New York, NY; *Int'l*, pg. 602
Glick, Eugene B., Pres.--Gene B. Glick Company, Inc., Indianapolis, IN; *U.S. Private*, pg. 457
Glickman, Marshall L., Pres. & Chief Exec. Officer--Ruslander & Sons, Inc., Buffalo, NY; *U.S. Private*, pg. 952
Glickman, Marshall L., Pres. & Mng. Dir.--Jewett International Corp., Buffalo, NY; *U.S. Private*, pg. 952
Glickman, Stuart, Chm. Bd., Pres., Chief Exec. Officer & Chief Fin. Officer--Safe Alarm, Inc., Davie, FL; *U.S. Private*, pg. 960
Glime, Ronald, Pres.--Warrantech Automotive, Inc., Euless, TX; *U.S. Public*, pg. 1740
Glinka, Connie, Pres.--Sunflower Group In-Store Services, Des Plaines, IL; *U.S. Private*, pg. 1052
Glinn, John, Jr., Pres.--Superior Printing Co., Warren, OH; *U.S. Private*, pg. 1055
Glisenti, Giuseppi, Pres.--Finmeccanica S.p.A., Rome, Italy; *Int'l*, pg. 653
Glore, Jodie, Pres. & Chief Oper. Officer--Reliance Electric, Cleveland, OH; *U.S. Public*, pg. 1397
Glosser, Roy J., Pres. & Chief Oper. Officer--American Locker Group, Inc., Jamestown, NY; *U.S. Public*, pg. 85
Glosser, Roy J., Pres.--American Locker Co., Inc., Jamestown, NY; *U.S. Public*, pg. 86
Glosser, Roy J., Pres.--American Locker Security Systems, Inc., Jamestown, NY; *U.S. Public*, pg. 86
Glosser, Roy J., Pres.--American Locker Co. of Canada Ltd., Scarborough, Canada; *U.S. Public*, pg. 86
Glosser, Roy J., Pres.--Canadian Locker Co., Ltd., Scarborough, Canada; *U.S. Public*, pg. 86

Glover, Keith, Pres. & Gen. Mgr.--Producers Rice Mill Inc., Stuttgart, AR; *U.S. Private*, pg. 888

Glover, Vernon, Pres. & Chief Exec. Officer--Tennessee Farmers Co-op, La Vergne, TN; *U.S. Private*, pg. 1076

Glover, William, Pres. & Gen. Mgr.--TENERA Rocky Flats, LLC, Louisville, CO; *U.S. Public*, pg. 1576

Gluckman, Thomas, Pres.--Fownes Brothers & Co., Inc., New York, NY; *U.S. Private*, pg. 422

Glusac, William L., Pres.--Vulcan Materials Company-Midwest Div., Lombard, IL; *U.S. Public*, pg. 1726

Glynn, Robert D. Jr., Chm. Bd., Pres. & Chief Exec. Officer--PG&E Corporation, San Francisco, CA; *U.S. Public*, pg. 1240

Glynn, William C., Pres.--Intermountain Industries, Inc., Boise, ID; *U.S. Private*, pg. 568

Glynn, William C., Pres.--IGI Resources, Inc., Boise, ID; *U.S. Private*, pg. 568

Glynn, William C., Pres.--III Exploration Co., Boise, ID; *U.S. Private*, pg. 568

Goasguen, J., Pres.--Durkopp Adler France S.A., Paris, France; *Int'l*, pg. 469

Gobayzadeh, Mehdi, Pres.--American Tissue Mills of Greenwich, Middle Falls, NY; *U.S. Private*, pg. 63

Gobel, Andre, Pres.--Leaf Norway A/S, Skare, Norway; *Int'l*, pg. 638

Gobel, Don, Pres.--U.S. Repeating Arms Company, New Haven, CT; *U.S. Private*, pg. 1125

Gochnauer, Richard, Pres. & Chief Oper. Officer--Golden State Foods, Irvine, CA; *U.S. Private*, pg. 460

Goda, Kohei, Pres. & Chief Exec. Officer--Haseko Corporation, Tokyo, Japan; *Int'l*, pg. 599

Godard, Alain, Pres.--Rhone-Poulenc Agrochimie, Lyon, France; *Int'l*, pg. 1109

Godbold, Francis S., Pres.--Raymond James Financial, Inc., Saint Petersburg, FL; *U.S. Public*, pg. 923

Godbold, Wilford D., Jr., Pres. & Chief Exec. Officer--Zero Corporation, Los Angeles, CA; *U.S. Public*, pg. 1791

Goddard, John H., Jr., Pres. & Chief Exec. Officer--Momentum, Seattle, WA; *U.S. Public*, pg. 1329

Goddu, Roger, Chm. Bd., Pres. & Chief Exec. Officer--Montgomery Ward & Co., Inc., Chicago, IL; *U.S. Private*, pg. 758

Godfrey, James, Pres. & Mgr.-Mktg.--Marti Electronics, Cleburne, TX; *U.S. Private*, pg. 531

Godfrey, James R., Pres.--HealthGuard of Lancaster, Lancaster, PA; *U.S. Private*, pg. 529

Godfrey, Mark, Pres. & Gen. Mgr.--Felton Brush Inc., Manchester, NH; *U.S. Private*, pg. 400

Godfrey, Paul, Pres. & Chief Exec. Officer--Sun Media Corporation, Toronto, Canada; *Int'l*, pg. 1320

Godfrey, Paul, Pres.--The Calgary Sun, Calgary, Canada; *Int'l*, pg. 1320

Godfrey, William G., Chm. Bd., Pres. & Chief Exec. Officer--Tekra Corporation, New Berlin, WI; *U.S. Private*, pg. 1073

Godomski, Richard, Chm. Bd., Pres. & Chief Exec. Officer--Process Systems Inc., Memphis, TN; *U.S. Private*, pg. 888

Godsey, Edward P., Pres. & Gen. Mgr.--Chesapeake Packaging Co./Baltimore, Baltimore, MD; *U.S. Public*, pg. 346

Godwin, Jerry H., Pres. & Chief Oper. Officer--Murphy Family Farms, Rose Hill, NC; *U.S. Private*, pg. 768

Godwin, Jimmy D., Pres.--Forms & Supply, Inc., Charlotte, NC; *U.S. Private*, pg. 419

Godwin, Michael E., Pres.--Harris Bank Libertyville, Libertyville, IL; *Int'l*, pg. 154

Goebel, Christopher J., Pres. & Chief Exec. Officer--Star Lumber & Supply Company, Inc., Wichita, KS; *U.S. Private*, pg. 1034

Goebel, Robert L., Co-Chm. Bd.--Star Lumber & Supply Company, Inc., Wichita, KS; *U.S. Private*, pg. 1034

Goebel, William J., Co-Chm. Bd.--Star Lumber & Supply Company, Inc., Wichita, KS; *U.S. Private*, pg. 1034

Goebert, Donald F.U., Chm. Bd. & Pres.--Relm Wireless Corp., West Chester, PA; *U.S. Public*, pg. 1376

Goedecke, Otto E., Pres. & Treas.--Otto Goedecke, Inc., Houston, TX; *U.S. Private*, pg. 458

Goedeke, Edward R., Pres. & Chief Oper. Officer--Manufacturers Railway Company, Saint Louis, MO; *U.S. Public*, pg. 114

Goega, Douglas G., Pres.--Hyatt Corporation, Chicago, IL; *U.S. Private*, pg. 551

Goehring, Craig, Chm. Bd., Pres. & Chief Exec. Officer--Brown and Caldwell, Pleasant Hill, CA; *U.S. Private*, pg. 173

Goeing, Peter, Pres.--PTG Plasma-Oberflachentechnik GmbH, Horb am Neckar, Germany; *Int'l*, pg. 400

Goer, Alan, Pres.--Goer Manufacturing Co., Charleston, SC; *U.S. Private*, pg. 904

Goergen, Robert B., Chm. Bd., Pres. & Chief Exec. Officer--Blyth Industries, Greenwich, CT; *U.S. Public*, pg. 239

Goergen, Ronald M., Chm. Bd. & Pres.--American Appraisal Associates, Inc., Milwaukee, WI; *U.S. Private*, pg. 49

Goerner, Rick, Pres. & Chief Exec. Officer--Silicon Systems, Inc., Tustin, CA; *U.S. Public*, pg. 1585

Goers, Charles, Pres., Chief Exec. Officer & Treas.--T O Plastics, Inc., Minneapolis, MN; *U.S. Private*, pg. 1065

Goertz, Gary W., Pres.--FIL (U.S.) Inc., Solon, OH; *Int'l*, pg. 1151

Goethe, Robert A., Chm. Bd., Pres. & Chief Exec. Officer--Regions Mortgage, Inc., Montgomery, AL; *U.S. Public*, pg. 1373

Goetsch, Warren D., Pres.--Menard Electric Cooperative, Petersburg, IL; *U.S. Private*, pg. 731

Goetschel, Arthur, Pres.--Amsted Industries Incorporated, Chicago, IL; *U.S. Private*, pg. 68

Goetschel, Arthur W., Pres.--Griffin Wheel Co., Chicago, IL; *U.S. Private*, pg. 68

Goetschi, Pierre, Pres.--Switzerland Cheese Association, Inc., Valley Cottage, NY; *Int'l*, pg. 1211

Goetz, Lew, Pres. & Chief Exec. Officer--SOR Inc., Lenexa, KS; *U.S. Private*, pg. 957

Goff, Dick, Pres.--Rockford International Group, Rockford, IL; *U.S. Private*, pg. 938

Goforth, Rene, Pres., Treas. & Sec.--Hilb, Rogal and Hamilton Company of Victoria, Victoria, TX; *U.S. Public*, pg. 827

Gogan, James W., Pres. & Chief Exec. Officer--Empire Company Limited, Stellarton, Canada; *Int'l*, pg. 453

Gogel, Don J., Pres.--Clayton, Dubilier & Rice, Inc, New York, NY; *U.S. Private*, pg. 244

Goggin, Joseph P., Pres.--Red Wing Shoe Co., Inc., Red Wing, MN; *U.S. Private*, pg. 915

Goggins, Colleen A., Pres.--Johnson & Johnson Consumer Products, Skillman, NJ; *U.S. Public*, pg. 928

Goh, Hup Jin, Pres.--Sanwa Foods, Inc., City of Industry, CA; *U.S. Public*, pg. 299

Gohmann, J. Michael, Pres. & Chief Exec. Officer--Gohmann Asphalt & Construction Inc., Clarksville, IN; *U.S. Private*, pg. 459

Goity, Gregorio R., Pres.--Boston Inversora De Valores S.A., Buenos Aires, Argentina; *U.S. Public*, pg. 185

Gokal, Ramesh, Pres. & Chief Exec. Officer--Knights Franchise Systems, Inc., Parsippany, NJ; *U.S. Public*, pg. 321

Goksel, Attila, Pres.--Serpo AS, Istanbul, Turkey; *Int'l*, pg. 1200

Gold Frank, Jack C., Pres.--Mead Coated Board Division, Columbus, GA; *U.S. Public*, pg. 1074

Gold, Daniel, Pres.--Cable Television Division, New Canaan, CT; *U.S. Public*, pg. 329

Gold, Danny, Partner--Kombi, Ltd., Essex Junction, VT; *U.S. Private*, pg. 631

Gold, Matthew L., Chm. Bd., Pres. & Chief Exec. Officer--Precision Standard, Inc., Denver, CO; *U.S. Public*, pg. 1321

Gold, Stanley P., Pres.--Shamrock Holdings, Inc., Burbank, CA; *U.S. Private*, pg. 989

Gold, Stanley P., Pres.--Shamrock Holdings Of California, Inc., Burbank, CA; *U.S. Private*, pg. 989

Gold, Theodore S., Pres.--Hicks & Associates Inc., Mc Lean, VA; *U.S. Private*, pg. 976

Goldberg, Arthur, Chm. Bd., Pres. & Chief Exec. Officer--Di Giorgio Corporation, Carteret, NJ; *U.S. Private*, pg. 330

Goldberg, Bruce M., Pres. & Chief Oper. Officer--All American Semiconductor, Inc., Miami, FL; *U.S. Public*, pg. 41

Goldberg, Danny, Pres. & Chief Exec. Officer & Chm. Bd.-Mercury Grp.--Polygram N.V., Baarn, Netherlands; *Int'l*, pg. 1051

Goldberg, Edward, Pres.--Knomark, Inc., Aurora, IL; *U.S. Private*, pg. 627

Goldberg, Howard, Pres. & Chief Oper. Officer--Lillian Vernon Corporation, New Rochelle, NY; *U.S. Public*, pg. 1716

Goldberg, Howard A., Pres. & Chief Exec. Officer--Players International, Inc., Atlantic City, NJ; *U.S. Public*, pg. 1310

Goldberg, Leslie H., Pres.--Bowl America, Incorporated, Alexandria, VA; *U.S. Public*, pg. 248

Goldberg, Linda P., Pres. & Chief Exec. Officer--Dental Health Alliance, L.L.C., New York, NY; *Int'l*, pg. 499

Goldberg, Michael C., Chm. Bd., Pres. & Chief Exec. Officer--FDP Corp., Miami, FL; *U.S. Public*, pg. 603

Goldberg, Neil, Pres. & Chief Exec. Officer--Raymour and Flanigan Furniture Co., Liverpool, NY; *U.S. Private*, pg. 912

Goldberg, Norman, Pres.-Men's Div.--The Apparel Group, Ltd., Louisville, KY; *U.S. Private*, pg. 78

Goldberg, Richard H., Chm. Bd., Pres. & Chief Exec. Officer--Synon Corporation, Larkspur, CA; *U.S. Private*, pg. 1060

Goldberg, Stanley, Chm. Bd., Pres. & Chief Exec. Officer--Ringer Corporation, Bloomington, MN; *U.S. Public*, pg. 1390

Goldberger, Robert D., Pres. & Chief Exec. Officer--GFI America, Minneapolis, MN; *U.S. Private*, pg. 435

Goldberger, Seymour, Pres.--Goldberger Doll Mfg. Company, Inc., Brooklyn, NY; *U.S. Private*, pg. 459

Goldbloom, Michael, Pres. & Publisher--The Gazette, Montreal, Canada; *Int'l*, pg. 631

Goldby, Steven, Chm. Bd., Pres. & Chief Exec. Officer--MDL Information Systems, Inc., San Leandro, CA; *Int'l*, pg. 1100

Golde, William, Pres.--Michael Business Machines Corporation, Charleston, SC; *U.S. Private*, pg. 740

Golden, Ed, Pres.--Barton Brands, Ltd., Chicago, IL; *U.S. Public*, pg. 300

Golden, Michael, Pres.--Stephen Gould Paper Co., Inc., Whippany, NJ; *U.S. Private*, pg. 467

Golden, Richard S., Pres. & Chief Exec. Officer--D.O.C. Optics Corporation, Southfield, MI; *U.S. Private*, pg. 305

Golden, Stephen C., Pres.--New York Times Company Forest Products Group, New York, NY; *U.S. Public*, pg. 1174

Golden, Terence C., Pres., Chief Exec. Officer & Dir.--Cousins Properties Incorporated, Atlanta, GA; *U.S. Public*, pg. 453

Golden, Terence C., Pres. & Chief Exec. Officer--Host Marriott Corporation, Bethesda, MD; *U.S. Public*, pg. 841

Goldenberg, David R., Pres.--Goldenberg Candy Company, Philadelphia, PA; *U.S. Private*, pg. 461

Goldfarb, Abraham, Pres.--National Banner Company, Inc., Dallas, TX; *U.S. Private*, pg. 780

Goldfarb, Andrew, Pres. & Chief Exec. Officer--HCC Industries, Rosemead, CA; *U.S. Private*, pg. 490

Goldhirsh, Bernard A., Chm. Bd.--The Goldhirsh Group, Boston, MA; *U.S. Private*, pg. 461

Goldick, Stanley, Pres.--Lewis Frimel, New York, NY; *U.S. Public*, pg. 519

Goldin, Ken, Chm. Bd., Pres. & Chief Exec. Officer--The Score Board, Inc., Cherry Hill, NJ; *U.S. Public*, pg. 1444

Goldish, Marc, Pres.--Milton Industries, Inc., Chicago, IL; *U.S. Private*, pg. 749

Goldman, Benjamin D., Pres. & Chief Oper. Officer--FPA Corporation, Bensalem, PA; *U.S. Public*, pg. 608

Goldman, David, Pres. & Treas.--Goldman Financial Group, Boston, MA; *U.S. Private*, pg. 461

Goldman, James W., Pres.--JWG Associates, Inc., Wellesley, MA; *U.S. Private*, pg. 579

Goldman, Marc, Pres. & Chief Exec. Officer--Farmland Dairies, Wallington, NJ; *U.S. Private*, pg. 395

Goldman, Mark D., Pres. & Chief Exec. Officer--Galoob Toys, Inc., South San Francisco, CA; *U.S. Public*, pg. 698

Goldman, Myron, Pres.--Excelled Sheepskin & Leather Coat Corporation, New York, NY; *U.S. Private*, pg. 387

Goldman, Steve, Pres. & Chief Exec. Officer--Power-One, Inc., Camarillo, CA; *U.S. Private*, pg. 878

Goldman, Thomas, Pres.--Iowa Paint Mfg. Company, Inc., Des Moines, IA; *U.S. Private*, pg. 575

Goldmeier, Alan, Pres.--Ross Bicycles USA Ltd., Farmingdale, NY; *U.S. Private*, pg. 946

Goldpy, Willy, Pres.--Philips Danmark A/S, Copenhagen, Denmark; *Int'l*, pg. 1055

Goldring, Allen A., Pres.--Overseas Military Sales Corporation, Woodbury, NY; *U.S. Private*, pg. 823

Goldring, Jeff, Pres.--Republic Beverage Company, Houston, TX; *U.S. Private*, pg. 149

Goldring, Jeff, Pres.--Republic Beverage Co., Dallas, TX; *U.S. Private*, pg. 150

Goldsmith, Michael, Pres.--Metcal, Inc., Menlo Park, CA; *U.S. Private*, pg. 735

Goldstein, Arthur L., Chm. Bd., Pres. & Chief Exec. Officer--Ionics, Incorporated, Watertown, MA; *U.S. Public*, pg. 912

Goldstein, Bernie, Pres.--Phoenix Division, Tempe, AZ; *U.S. Public*, pg. 509

Goldstein, K.T., Pres. & Chief Exec. Officer--Universal Underwriters Insurance Co., Overland Park, KS; *Int'l*, pg. 1530

Goldstein, Mark E., Pres. & Chief Exec. Officer--Scott's Liquid Gold-Inc., Denver, CO; *U.S. Public*, pg. 1447

Goldstein, Marry, Pres. & Chief Exec. Officer--Alliance Gaming Corporation, Las Vegas, NV; *U.S. Public*, pg. 46

Goldstein, Richard A., Pres. & Chief Exec. Officer--Unilever United States Inc., New York, NY; *Int'l*, pg. 1435

Goldston, Mark, Pres. & Chief Exec. Officer--Einstein/Noah Bagel Corp., Golden, CO; *U.S. Public*, pg. 247

Goldstone, Steven F., Chm. Bd., Pres. & Chief Exec. Officer--RJR Nabisco Holdings Corp., New York, NY; *U.S. Public*, pg. 1354

Goldwater, Charles, Pres. & Chief Exec. Officer--Mann Theatres, Encino, CA; *U.S. Private*, pg. 239

Goldwater, Chuck, Pres.--Cinamerica Theatres, L.P., Encino, CA; *U.S. Private*, pg. 239

Goldworn, Jill, Pres.--Interplay OEM, Inc., Irvine, CA; *U.S. Private*, pg. 573

Goldwyn, John, Pres.--Paramount Pictures Corporation, Los Angeles, CA; *U.S. Private*, pg. 776

Golemme, Joe, Pres.--Federal Products Co., Providence, RI; *U.S. Public*, pg. 594

Golemo, Stanley M., Jr., Chm. Bd. & Pres.--Hood & Company, Hamburg, PA; *Int'l*, pg. 572

Golhofer, Jim, Pres.--Grolsch Importers Inc., Atlanta, GA; *Int'l*, pg. 559

Golias, Tipton L., Pres. & Chief Exec. Officer--Helena Laboratories Corporation, Beaumont, TX; *U.S. Private*, pg. 519

Golinelli, Marino, Pres.--Schiapparelli, Milan, Italy; *Int'l*, pg. 1204

Golisano, B. Thomas, Chm. Bd., Pres. & Chief Exec. Officer--Paychex, Inc., Rochester, NY; *U.S. Public*, pg. 1267

Gollek, Dieter, Pres.--Clausen & Bosse GmbH, Leck, Germany; *Int'l*, pg. 1478

Gollenbeck, Jurgen, Dr., Chm. Bd.--Howaldtswerke-Deutsche Werft AG, Kiel, Germany; *Int'l*, pg. 1069

Golm, Louis C., Pres.--AirTouch International, Walnut Creek, CA; *U.S. Public*, pg. 34

Golnick, Greg J., Pres.--Generations Gold, West Palm Beach, FL; *U.S. Private*, pg. 463

Golnick, H. Marshall, Pres.--Leon Shaffer Golnick Advertising, Inc., Fort Lauderdale, FL; *U.S. Private*, pg. 463

Golnick, Leon Shaffer, Chm. Bd.--Leon Shaffer Golnick Advertising, Inc., Fort Lauderdale, FL; *U.S. Private*, pg. 463

Golonski, Thomas W., Pres.--National City Bank, Pennsylvania, Pittsburgh, PA; *U.S. Public*, pg. 1154

Golsen, Barry, Pres. & Chief Oper. Officer--Climatemaster Corp., Santa Monica, CA; *U.S. Public*, pg. 970

Golsen, Jack E., Chm. Bd., Pres. & Chief Exec. Officer--LSB Industries, Inc., Oklahoma City, OK; *U.S. Public*, pg. 970

Golteus, Hans, Pres. & Chief Oper. Officer--Norwegian Cruise Line, Miami, FL; *U.S. Private*, pg. 808

Goltzman, Joseph L., Chm. Bd., Pres. & Chief Exec. Officer--Anheuser-Busch Recycling Corporation, Saint Louis, MO; *U.S. Public*, pg. 114

Golub, Neil, Pres. & Chief Oper. Officer--Price Chopper Operating Co., Inc., Schenectady, NY; *U.S. Private*, pg. 463

Golub, Neil M., Pres. & Chief Oper. Officer--Golub Corporation, Schenectady, NY; *U.S. Private*, pg. 463

Goluboff, Hal, Sr. Principal & Grp. Creative Dir.--Publicis/Bloom, New York, NY; *Int'l*, pg. 470

Gomer, David W., Pres. & Chief Exec. Officer--Cape Coral National Bank, Cape Coral, FL; *U.S. Public*, pg. 607

Gomes, Jim, Pres.--Danish Creamery Association, Fresno, CA; *U.S. Private*, pg. 310

Gomez, Louis, Plant Mgr.--Waterbury Companies, Inc.-Independence Div., Independence, LA; *U.S. Public*, pg. 308

Gommel, Richard, Pres.-North America--Safeguard Business Systems, Inc., Fort Washington, PA; *U.S. Private*, pg. 960

Gommori, Hiroshi, Pres.--Hitachi Koki Co., Ltd., Tokyo, Japan; *Int'l*, pg. 620

Gon Roell, Dr. Steinfan, Pres.--Zwick/Roell Group, Ulm, Germany; *Int'l*, pg. 1532
Goncalves, Jorge Basto, Dr., Pres.--Vercoope-Uniao Das Adegas Cooperativas da Regiao Dos Vinhoa Verdes, U.C.R.L., Santo Tirso, Portugal; *Int'l*, pg. 1463
Gongas, John C., Pres.--Nora Transmission Co., Pittsburgh, PA; *U.S. Public*, pg. 590
Gongas, John C., Jr., Pres.--ET Storage Company, Pittsburgh, PA; *U.S. Public*, pg. 590
Gongaware, Donald F., Pres. & Chief Exec. Officer--Bankers Life & Casualty Company, Chicago, IL; *U.S. Public*, pg. 433
Gonis, Arthur P., Pres. & Chief Exec. Officer--Ragu Foods, Inc., Trumbull, CT; *Int'l*, pg. 1436
Gonnella, Robert A., Chm. Bd. & Pres.--Gonnella Baking Co., Chicago, IL; *U.S. Private*, pg. 463
Gonye, Jeffrey, Mng. Dir.--Windpoint Partners, Southfield, MI; *U.S. Private*, pg. 1182
Gonzalez Nova, Carlos, Chm. Bd. & Pres.--Controladora Comercial Mexicana, S.A. de C.V., Mexico, Mexico; *Int'l*, pg. 328
Gonzalez, Daniel, Pres.--Union des Assurances Federales, Paris, France; *Int'l*, pg. 344
Gonzalez, Jesse, Pres.--Singleton Seafood Co., Tampa, FL; *U.S. Public*, pg. 427
Gonzalez, Jesse, Pres.--ConAgra Shrimp Company, Tampa, FL; *U.S. Public*, pg. 427
Gonzalez, Pablo de Bergia, Pres.--Casa Aircraft USA Incorporated, Chantilly, VA; *Int'l*, pg. 1224
Gonzalez, Rogelio A., Pres.--Astra Chemicals S.A., Mexico, Mexico; *Int'l*, pg. 93
Good, Brian, Pres.--OSI, Chicago, IL; *U.S. Private*, pg. 1068
Good, Chester G., Pres.--GM Allison Japan Limited, Tokyo, Japan; *U.S. Public*, pg. 721
Good, Richard L., Pres. & Chief Oper. Officer--NTS Development Company, Louisville, KY; *U.S. Private*, pg. 772
Good, Robert W., Pres.--Wolfer Printing Company, City of Commerce, CA; *U.S. Private*, pg. 1186
Good, Steven L., Pres.--Sheldon Good & Co., Chicago, IL; *U.S. Private*, pg. 463
Goodale, Paul R., Pres.--Walker Wire & Steel Company, Ferndale, MI; *U.S. Private*, pg. 1147
Goodall, Brian, Partner, Pres. & New Bus. Contact--Hampel/Stefanides, New York, NY; *U.S. Private*, pg. 498
Goodall, Brian, Pres.--Hampel/Stefanides, San Francisco, CA; *U.S. Private*, pg. 498
Goodall, Stephen, Pres.--J.D. Power and Associates, Agoura Hills, CA; *U.S. Private*, pg. 878
Goode, David R., Chm. Bd., Pres. & Chief Exec. Officer--Norfolk Southern Corporation, Norfolk, VA; *U.S. Public*, pg. 1190
Goode, Earl A., Pres.--GTE Information Services Incorporated, Dallas-Fort Worth Airport, TX; *U.S. Public*, pg. 696
Goode, R.C., Pres.--M.W. Kellogg Limited, Wembley, United Kingdom; *U.S. Public*, pg. 528
Gooden, C. Michael, Chm. Bd. & Pres.--Integrated Systems Analysts, Inc., Arlington, VA; *U.S. Private*, pg. 566
Gooden, Robert, Pres.--Seacore Limited, Helston, United Kingdom; *Int'l*, pg. 31
Gooding, Terence, Dr., Pres.--Wavetek Communications Div., Indianapolis, IN; *U.S. Private*, pg. 1155
Goodkin, Michael, Pres.--P.F. Collier LP, New York, NY; *Int'l*, pg. 433
Goodlick, William H., Pres.--SuperValu, Inc.-Food Marketing Div., Fort Wayne, IN; *U.S. Public*, pg. 1540
Goodman, Alan, Pres.--Park Distributors, Inc., Bridgeport, CT; *U.S. Private*, pg. 839
Goodman, Andrew, Pres.--Sherwood Lumber Corporation, Islandia, NY; *U.S. Private*, pg. 994
Goodman, Andrew P., Pres.--Minipack Systems Limited, Southampton, United Kingdom; *U.S. Public*, pg. 1067
Goodman, Hal, Partner-Fin.--Eric Mower and Associates, Inc., Syracuse, NY; *U.S. Private*, pg. 765
Goodman, Louis J., Pres. & Chief Exec. Officer--J.C. Higgins Corp., Stoughton, MA; *U.S. Public*, pg. 572
Goodman, Mark, Pres.--J. Josephson, Inc., South Hackensack, NJ; *U.S. Private*, pg. 601
Goodman, Marvin, Pres.--Apparel Ventures, Inc., Gardena, CA; *U.S. Private*, pg. 78
Goodman, Murray, Pres. & Treas.--Goodmans, Inc., Phoenix, AZ; *U.S. Private*, pg. 464
Goodmanson, Richard R., Pres.--America West Holdings Corporation, Phoenix, AZ; *U.S. Public*, pg. 66
Goodmanson, Richard R., Pres. & Chief Exec. Officer--America West Airlines, Inc., Phoenix, AZ; *U.S. Public*, pg. 67
Goodmon, James F., Pres. & Chief Exec. Officer--Capitol Broadcasting Co., Inc., Raleigh, NC; *U.S. Private*, pg. 206
Goodnight, James H., Pres., Chief Exec. Officer & Co-Founder--SAS Institute Inc., Cary, NC; *U.S. Private*, pg. 966
Goodrich, T.M., Pres. & Chief Exec. Officer--BE & K, Inc., Birmingham, AL; *U.S. Private*, pg. 106
Goodson, Kenneth, Pres.--Integrated Metal Technologies, Inc., Spring Lake, MI; *U.S. Public*, pg. 1112
Goodspeed, Richard E., Pres. & Chief Oper. Officer--The Vons Companies, Inc., Arcadia, CA; *U.S. Public*, pg. 1426
Goodwill, Dan, Pres.--Sunac America, Etobicoke, Canada; *Int'l*, pg. 924
Goodwin, Carl, Pres. & Chief Exec. Officer--Bijur Lubricating Corporation, Bennington, VT; *U.S. Private*, pg. 143
Goodwin, D.W., Pres.--Dealers Manufacturing Company, Minneapolis, MN; *U.S. Private*, pg. 318
Goodwin, Daniel L., Chm. Bd. & Chief Exec. Officer--The Inland Group, Inc., Oak Brook, IL; *U.S. Private*, pg. 564
Goodwin, H. Clark, Pres. & Chief Exec. Officer--Bank of Union, Monroe, NC; *U.S. Public*, pg. 627
Goodwin, John E., Pres.--Texas Homestead Mortgage Co., San Antonio, TX; *U.S. Public*, pg. 945
Goodwin, Morris, Pres. & Treas.--IDS Deposit Corp., Midvale, UT; *U.S. Public*, pg. 73
Goodwin, Peter J., Pres.--The Feldspar Corp., Atlanta, GA; *Int'l*, pg. 1523
Goodwin, Peter J., Pres.--Suzorite Mica Products Inc., Boucherville, Canada; *Int'l*, pg. 1523
Goodwin, Peter J., Pres.--Suzorite Mineral Products, Inc., Spruce Pine, NC; *Int'l*, pg. 1524
Goodyear, William M., Chm. & Pres.--Bank of America Illinois Trust Company of Florida, N.A., Boca Raton, FL; *U.S. Public*, pg. 181
Goolsby, John L., Pres. & Chief Exec. Officer--Howard Hughes Corporation, Las Vegas, NV; *U.S. Public*, pg. 1407
Gorak, Michael, Pres.--Martin/F. Weber Company, Philadelphia, PA; *U.S. Private*, pg. 710
Gorder, Mark S., Pres. & Chief Exec. Officer--Resistance Technology Inc., Arden Hills, MN; *U.S. Public*, pg. 1455
Gordon, Arthur, Chief Exec. Officer--E.N.C., City of Commerce, CA; *U.S. Public*, pg. 948
Gordon, Barry J., Chm. Bd. & Pres.--American Fund Advisors, Inc., Garden City, NY; *U.S. Private*, pg. 55
Gordon, Bernard M., Pres.--Anadventure II Corporation, Peabody, MA; *U.S. Public*, pg. 109
Gordon, Beth, Pres. & Mng. Dir.--The Media Edge, New York, NY; *U.S. Private*, pg. 1079
Gordon, Bradley, Pres.--Amcel Corp., Watertown, MA; *U.S. Private*, pg. 48
Gordon, Dan, Pres. & Chief Exec. Officer--Gordon Food Service Inc., Grand Rapids, MI; *U.S. Private*, pg. 465
Gordon, David G., Pres.--Dexter Nonwovens Division, Windsor Locks, CT; *U.S. Public*, pg. 504
Gordon, Ellen R., Pres. & Chief Oper. Officer--Tootsie Roll Industries, Inc., Chicago, IL; *U.S. Public*, pg. 1621
Gordon, Janine, Pres.--Waring LaRosa Gordon Public Relations, New York, NY; *U.S. Private*, pg. 1150
Gordon, Jerry A., Pres. & Chief Oper. Officer--Glacier Water Services Inc., Carlsbad, CA; *U.S. Public*, pg. 745
Gordon, M. J., Chm. Bd.--World Trade & Marketing, LTD., Chicago, IL; *U.S. Public*, pg. 1621
Gordon, Melvin S., Pres. & Chief Exec. Officer--Paradise, Inc., Plant City, FL; *U.S. Public*, pg. 1256
Gordon, Miles, Pres.--Financial Network Investment Corp, Torrance, CA; *U.S. Private*, pg. 404
Gordon, Peter, Pres.--Crystal Geyser Roxane Water L.P., Olancha, CA; *Int'l*, pg. 1013
Gordon, R.J., Pres. & Chief Oper. Officer-Ohio & Kentucky--Columbia Gas Distribution Companies, Columbus, OH; *U.S. Public*, pg. 402
Gordon, Richard, Pres. & Chief Exec. Officer--American Aircraft Parts Manufacturing Co., Fraser, MI; *U.S. Private*, pg. 49
Gordon, Robert D., Chm. Bd., Pres. & Chief Exec. Officer--Apertus Technologies Incorporated, Eden Prairie, MN; *U.S. Public*, pg. 119
Gordon, Robert D., Pres.--Systems Strategies, Inc., New York, NY; *U.S. Public*, pg. 120
Gordon, T.G., Pres.--Equifax National Decision Systems, Encinitas, CA; *U.S. Public*, pg. 588
Gordon, Tom, Pres.--Equifax Check Service, Brea, CA; *U.S. Public*, pg. 588
Gordonsmith, John, Pres.--Financial Collection Agencies (International) Inc., Westmount, Canada; *Int'l*, pg. 470
Gordonsmith, John, Pres.--Financial Collection Agencies (International) Inc., Mississauga, Canada; *Int'l*, pg. 470
Gordonsmith, John, Pres.--Financial Collection Agencies, Edmonton, Canada; *Int'l*, pg. 470
Gordonsmith, John, Pres.--Financial Collection Agencies (International) Inc., Brantford, Canada; *Int'l*, pg. 470
Gore, James L., Pres. & Chief Oper. Officer--Southern Health Services, Inc., Richmond, VA; *U.S. Public*, pg. 454
Gore, Jeff, Pres.--Franklin Press, San Bernardino, CA; *U.S. Private*, pg. 268
Gore, Robert W., Pres. & Chief Exec. Officer--W.L. Gore & Associates, Inc., Newark, DE; *U.S. Private*, pg. 465
Gore, Stephen J., Pres. & Chief Exec. Officer--DT Industries Inc., Springfield, MO; *U.S. Public*, pg. 475
Goree, Vickie, Pres.--Brance Krachy Company, Inc., Houston, TX; *U.S. Private*, pg. 165
Gorell, Frank, Pres.--Jamison Bedding, Inc., Franklin, TN; *U.S. Private*, pg. 581
Gorell, Wayne C., Pres.--Season-All Industries, Inc., Indiana, PA; *Int'l*, pg. 267
Gores, Tom, Pres. & Chief Exec. Officer--Platinum Equity Holdings, LLC, Los Angeles, CA; *U.S. Private*, pg. 872
Gorga, Joseph L., Pres.--CMI Industries Inc.-Finished Fabrics Division, Greensboro, NC; *U.S. Private*, pg. 195
Gorham, Brian L., Pres. & Chief Exec. Officer--Hilb, Rogal and Hamilton Insurance Services of Central California, Inc., Fresno, CA; *U.S. Public*, pg. 827
Gorin, Michael, Pres. & Chief Fin. Officer--Aeroflex Incorporated, Plainview, NY; *U.S. Public*, pg. 23
Gorin, Michael, Pres.--Aeroflex Systems Corp., Saint Leonard, MD; *U.S. Public*, pg. 24
Gorla, Carlo, Pres.--Computational Systems Inc., Knoxville, TN; *U.S. Public*, pg. 572
Gorman, James T., Pres.--Puma North America, Brockton, MA; *Int'l*, pg. 1072
Gorman, John, Pres.--Timberline Software Corporation, Beaverton, OR; *U.S. Public*, pg. 1609
Gorman, Kenneth, Chm. Bd., Pres., & Chief Exec. Officer--IDC Services, Inc., Chicago, IL; *U.S. Private*, pg. 554
Gorman, Kenneth F., Chm. Bd., Pres. & Chief Exec. Officer--Production Payments, Inc., Chicago, IL; *U.S. Private*, pg. 554
Gorman, Kirk E., Pres., Chief Oper. & Fin. Officer--Universal Health Realty Income Trust, King of Prussia, PA; *U.S. Public*, pg. 1697
Gorman, Leon A., Pres.--L.L. Bean, Inc., Freeport, ME; *U.S. Private*, pg. 639
Gorra, William, Chm. Bd., Pres. & Chief Exec. Officer--Simoniz USA, Inc., Bolton, CT; *U.S. Private*, pg. 1001
Gorski, Donald J., Pres. & Chief Oper. Officer--Devon Publishing Group, Novato, CA; *U.S. Public*, pg. 503
Gorski, P. Paul, Pres.--Siouxland Galvanizing Corp., Sioux City, IA; *U.S. Private*, pg. 656
Gortazar Landecho, Ignacio, Gen. Mgr.--Voith Tolosa S.A., Tolosa, Spain; *Int'l*, pg. 1473
Gosa, James J., Pres. & Chief Exec. Officer--American Woodmark Corporation, Winchester, VA; *U.S. Public*, pg. 96
Gosselink, Jerry D., Pres.-Natl. Div. & Chief Oper. Officer--The Weitz Company, Inc., Des Moines, IA; *U.S. Private*, pg. 1160
Gossman, Michael W., Pres.--Midwest Mechanical Contractors Inc., Overland Park, KS; *U.S. Private*, pg. 687
Gotliev, Meyer, Pres. & Chief Oper. Officer--The Samuel Goldwyn Company, Los Angeles, CA; *U.S. Private*, pg. 463
Goto, Masahiko, Pres. & Rep. Dir.--Makita Corporation, Anjo, Japan; *Int'l*, pg. 831
Gotschall, Jeffrey P., Pres. & Chief Exec. Officer--Sifco Industries, Inc., Cleveland, OH; *U.S. Public*, pg. 1470
Gottdenker, Michael I., Pres. & Chief Oper. Officer--Commonwealth Telephone Enterprises, Inc., Dallas, PA; *U.S. Public*, pg. 415
Gottdenker, Stu, Partner--Yesawich, Moss & Brown, New York, NY; *U.S. Private*, pg. 1196
Gottesman, Harold A., Pres.--Edison Parking Properties, LLC, Newark, NJ; *U.S. Private*, pg. 364
Gottlieb, Richard D., Pres. & Chief Exec. Officer--Lee Enterprises, Incorporated, Davenport, IA; *U.S. Public*, pg. 983
Gottlieb, Susan, Partner-Brdcst. Buying--Media First International, Inc., New York, NY; *U.S. Private*, pg. 726
Gottlieb, Terry, Pres. & Chief Exec. Officer--Talent Partners, Chicago, IL; *U.S. Private*, pg. 554
Gottwald, John D., Pres. & Chief Exec. Officer--Tredegar Industries Inc., Richmond, VA; *U.S. Public*, pg. 1633
Gottwald, Thomas E., Pres. & Chief Oper. Officer--Ethyl Corporation, Richmond, VA; *U.S. Public*, pg. 595
Goucher, Bob, Pres.--Starmark, Inc., Sioux Falls, SD; *U.S. Public*, pg. 1054
Goudard, Jean Pierre, Chm. Bd. & Chief Exec. Officer--Roussel UCLAF S.A., Romainville, France; *Int'l*, pg. 626
Gough, Leland, Pres.--Peoples Bank, Senatobia, MS; *U.S. Public*, pg. 639
Gough, Thomas L., Pres. & Chief Oper. Officer--Integral Systems, Inc., Lanham, MD; *U.S. Public*, pg. 883
Gougoux, Yves, Pres. & Chief Exec. Officer--Publicis BCP Montreal Inc., Montreal, Canada; *Int'l*, pg. 116
Gould, Fredric, Gen. Partner--Georgetown Partners, Inc., Great Neck, NY; *U.S. Private*, pg. 466
Gould, Fredric H., Gen. Partner--Gould Investors, L.P., Great Neck, NY; *U.S. Private*, pg. 466
Gould, Harry E., Jr., Chm. Bd. & Pres.--Gould Paper Corporation, New York, NY; *U.S. Private*, pg. 466
Gould, Peter J., Pres. & Chief Exec. Officer--Aldine Technologies Industries Inc., Carlstadt, NJ; *U.S. Private*, pg. 33
Gould, Robert R., Partner--Brown Brothers Harriman & Co., New York, NY; *U.S. Private*, pg. 173
Gould, Steven, Pres. & Chief Exec. Officer--Gould Packaging, Inc., Vancouver, WA; *U.S. Private*, pg. 466
Gould, William, Mgr.-Sls. & Mktg.--The William G. Bell Company, East Weymouth, MA; *U.S. Private*, pg. 165
Gould, William S., III, Pres.--Magnetic Analysis Corp., Mount Vernon, NY; *U.S. Private*, pg. 695
Gouldie, Peter J., Pres. & Mng. Dir.--Inco Pacific Sales Limited, Taipei, Taiwan; *Int'l*, pg. 673
Gourd, Alain, Pres. & Chief Exec. Officer--Canadian Satellite Communications Inc., Mississauga, Canada; *Int'l*, pg. 1481
Gourd, Alain, Pres. & Chief Exec. Officer--CSC, Ottawa, Ottawa, Canada; *Int'l*, pg. 1482
Gournay, Patrick, Pres. & Chief Exec. Officer--The Dannon Co., Tarrytown, NY; *Int'l*, pg. 379
Gouyou Beauchamps, Xavier, Pres.--Telediffusion de France, Paris, France; *Int'l*, pg. 503
Govenreuile, Jerry, Pres.--ECRM, Tewksbury, MA; *U.S. Private*, pg. 353
Gowan, Damon, Pres. & Chief Exec. Officer--Gowan, Inc., Houston, TX; *U.S. Public*, pg. 572
Gowan, Tim, Pres.--Community Cash Stores, Spartanburg, SC; *U.S. Private*, pg. 259
Gowdy, Bob G., Pres. & Chief Exec. Officer--Commercial Union Corporation, Boston, MA; *Int'l*, pg. 308
Gower, Dennis, Div. Pres.--SLACAN, Brantford, Canada; *Int'l*, pg. 1262
Gower, Roger, Chm. Bd., Pres. & Chief Exec. Officer--Micro Component Technology Inc., Saint Paul, MN; *U.S. Public*, pg. 1104
Gowland, Pablo Eduardo, Jr., Pres., Gen. Mgr., Exec. V.P., Opers. Dir.--Gowland Publicidad S.A., Buenos Aires, Argentina; *U.S. Public*, pg. 1642
Gowland, Pablo, Jr., Pres.--Gowland/ADD, Buenos Aires, Argentina; *U.S. Private*, pg. 1200
Gowlik, Mark, Pres.--Ace Novelty Company, Inc., Woodinville, WA; *U.S. Public*, pg. 1309
Grabel, Keith, Pres.--Westwood Computer Corporation, Springfield, NJ; *U.S. Private*, pg. 1170
Graber, Don R., Pres. & Chief Oper. Officer--Huffy Corporation, Miamisburg, OH; *U.S. Public*, pg. 846
Grabish, Richard F., Vice Chm. & Pres.--A.G. Edwards Trust Company, Saint Louis, MO; *U.S. Public*, pg. 565
Grabner, George J., Jr., Pres.--American Recreation Products, Inc., Saint Louis, MO; *U.S. Public*, pg. 948
Grabow, Steve, Pres.--Sally Lou Fashions Corporation, New York, NY; *U.S. Private*, pg. 962
Grabowski, Jerry W., Pres., Chief Exec. Officer, Chief Fin. Officer & Treas.--Waters Instruments, Inc., Rochester, MN; *U.S. Public*, pg. 1745
Grace, Barnett, Chm. Bd., Pres. & Chief Exec. Officer--First Commercial Corporation, Little Rock, AR; *U.S. Public*, pg. 630

Grace, W.M., Chm. Bd. & Pres.--W.M. Grace Development, Phoenix, AZ; U.S. Private, pg. 468
Grad, John, Pres.--Landis & Staefa, Inc., Buffalo Grove, IL; Int'l, pg. 800
Grad, John, Pres.--Landis & Staefa Inc., Buffalo Grove, IL; Int'l, pg. 800
Gradeen, Glenn D., Pres. & Chief Oper. Officer--Ocelot Energy Inc., Calgary, Canada; Int'l, pg. 996
Gradinger, J. Gary, Chm. Bd., Pres. & Chief Exec. Officer--Golden Star Inc., Kansas City, MO; U.S. Private, pg. 460
Graetzer, Anthony M., Partner & Grp. Acct. Dir.--Hampel/Stefanides, New York, NY; U.S. Private, pg. 498
Graf, A. Jay, Pres.--Guidant Corporation-Cardiac Rhythm Management Group, Saint Paul, MN; U.S. Public, pg. 768
Graf, John A., Pres.--Western National Corporation, Houston, TX; U.S. Public, pg. 76
Graf, Mel, Pres. & Chief Exec. Officer--Baris Shoe Company, Inc., New York, NY; U.S. Private, pg. 116
Graf, Paul E., Pres. & Chief Exec. Officer--Axel Johnson Inc., Stamford, CT; Int'l, pg. 709
Graf, Richard J., Pres.--Cohen Furniture Company, Peoria Heights, IL; U.S. Private, pg. 250
Graf, Rudy, Pres. & Chief Oper. Officer--Centennial Cellular Corp., New Canaan, CT; U.S. Public, pg. 329
Graff, Stewart, Pres.--Douglas Stephen Plastics, Inc., Paterson, NJ; U.S. Private, pg. 341
Graffeo, Christopher, Pres. & Chief Exec. Officer--National City Bank, Indiana, Indianapolis, IN; U.S. Public, pg. 1154
Graham, Alex, Pres.--Western Pool Terminals Limited, Vancouver, Canada; Int'l, pg. 1195
Graham, Bob, Pres.-Aim Distr.--Aim Family of Funds, Houston, TX; Int'l, pg. 685
Graham, Daniel J., Pres.--Berry Network, Inc., Dayton, OH; U.S. Private, pg. 137
Graham, Don A., Pres.-Rollform--Trinity-Structural Steel, Montgomery, AL; U.S. Public, pg. 1639
Graham, Edward J., Pres.--SJ EnerTrade, Folsom, NJ; U.S. Public, pg. 1488
Graham, Edward S., Pres.--Noramco, Inc., Athens, GA; U.S. Public, pg. 929
Graham, Gordon, Pres., Chief Exec. Officer & Chief Oper. Officer--Bell Industries, Inc., El Segundo, CA; U.S. Public, pg. 204
Graham, Gordon L., Pres.--Sysco Food Services of Southeast Florida, Inc., Riviera Beach, FL; U.S. Public, pg. 1552
Graham, J.D., Pres.--Canadian Western Natural Gas Company Limited, Calgary, Canada; Int'l, pg. 95
Graham, James, Pres. & Chief Exec. Officer--Versa Services Ltd., Etobicoke, Canada; U.S. Private, pg. 79
Graham, John, Pres. & Gen. Mgr.--Molded Fiber Glass Co., Union City, PA; U.S. Private, pg. 756
Graham, John D., Chm. & Chief Exec. Officer--Fleishman-Hillard Inc., Saint Louis, MO; U.S. Private, pg. 411
Graham, Mark, Pres.--Southern Division, Norcross, GA; U.S. Public, pg. 1255
Graham, Mike, Mng. Partner--RTCdirect, Washington, DC; Int'l, pg. 1483
Graham, Paul, Pres.--3 dbm, Inc., Camarillo, CA; U.S. Public, pg. 534
Graham, Stuart, Pres.--Slattery Associates Inc., Whitestone, NY; Int'l, pg. 1261
Graham, Stuart, Pres. & Chief Exec. Officer--Skanska E&C, Carmel, IN; Int'l, pg. 1261
Graham, Suzanne, Pres.--Rauland-Borg Corporation of Florida, Altamonte Springs, FL; U.S. Private, pg. 911
Grahn, Gary L., Pres. & Chief Exec. Officer--The Langer Biomechanics Group, Inc., Deer Park, NY; U.S. Public, pg. 978
Grainger, John R., Pres.--Laidlaw Transit, Inc, Van Nuys, CA; Int'l, pg. 259
Gralnick, Marvin, Chm. Bd., Pres. & Chief Exec. Officer--Chico's Fas Inc, Fort Myers, FL; U.S. Public, pg. 349
Gram, Torleif, Pres.--Aker Contracting a.s., Stavanger, Norway; Int'l, pg. 41
Granberry, William R., Pres. & Chief Oper. Officer--Tom Brown, Inc., Midland, TX; U.S. Public, pg. 262
Grand, Andre, Pres. & Chief Oper. Officer--Servirail, Paris, France; Int'l, pg. 560
Grandall, Arthur J., Pres.--Ikon Office Systems, Elmsford, NY; U.S. Public, pg. 864
Grande, Raymond E., Pres.--LFE Instruments, Chesterland, OH; U.S. Public, pg. 482
Grandin, Michael A., Pres. & Chief Exec. Officer--Sceptre Resources Limited, Calgary, Canada; Int'l, pg. 1203
Grandinetti, Anthony A., Pres.--Ball Packaging Holdings Corp., Westminster, CO; U.S. Public, pg. 171
Grandle, Ralph W., Co-Pres.--Tricon Industries, Inc., Lisle, IL; U.S. Private, pg. 1102
Grandy, Fred, Pres. & Chief Exec. Officer--Goodwill Industries International, Bethesda, MD; U.S. Private, pg. 464
Grandy, Richard, Pres.--Easy Gardener Inc., Waco, TX; U.S. Public, pg. 1682
Grandy, Richard, Pres.--Weatherly Consumer Products, Paris, KY; U.S. Public, pg. 1682
Granger, Alton, Chm. Bd. & Pres.--Granger Construction Co., Lansing, MI; U.S. Private, pg. 469
Granger, John, Pres.--APPX Software Inc., Richmond, VA; U.S. Public, pg. 1634
Granger, Ronald K., Chm. Bd., Pres. & Chief Exec. Officer--Granger Companies, Lansing, MI; U.S. Private, pg. 469
Granget, Michel, Pres.--FBFC, Paris, France; Int'l, pg. 503
Grangier, Jean-Claude, Deputy Pres.-Exec. Bd. & Exec. V.P.--Banque Cantonale Vaudoise, Lausanne, Switzerland; Int'l, pg. 160
Grann, Phillis, Pres.--Penguin Putnam Inc., New York, NY; Int'l, pg. 1027
Grannan, Ken, Pres. & Gen. Mgr.--Electromechanical Systems, Inc., Largo, FL; U.S. Public, pg. 424
Grano, Joseph, Jr., Pres.--PaineWebber Group Incorporated, New York, NY; U.S. Public, pg. 1252
Grant, Barry, Pres.--Phoenix Div., Tempe, AZ; U.S. Public, pg. 1683
Grant, Berl, Pres. & Chief Exec. Officer--Seymour Manufacturing Company, Seymour, IN; U.S. Private, pg. 988
Grant, David, Pres.--Sight Systems, Inc., Newbury Park, CA; U.S. Public, pg. 1795
Grant, David S., Pres. & Chief Oper. Officer--Voyager Emblems, Inc., Sanborn, NY; U.S. Private, pg. 1143
Grant, Donald W., Pres.--Western Reinsurance Brokers, Inc., Los Angeles, CA; U.S. Private, pg. 1168
Grant, Douglas M., Pres. & Chief Oper. Officer--Isco, Inc., Lincoln, NE; U.S. Public, pg. 913
Grant, Glenn E., Pres. & Chief Exec. Officer--Glastic Corporation, Cleveland, OH; Int'l, pg. 740
Grant, R. Douglas, Chm. Bd., Pres. & Chief Exec. Officer--Lakeland Financial Corporation, Warsaw, IN; U.S. Public, pg. 975
Grant, Ronald, Pres.--Ziniz Inc., Louisville, KY; U.S. Private, pg. 1206
Grant, Susan, Pres.--Turner Program Services, Inc., Atlanta, GA; U.S. Public, pg. 1615
Grant, Thomas W., Pres.--Pax World Fund Family, Portsmouth, NH; U.S. Public, pg. 1266
Grant, Thomas W., Jr., Pres.--Durex Consumer Products, Norcross, GA; Int'l, pg. 815
Grant, Thomas W., Jr., Pres.--Marigold Glove Division, Norcross, GA; Int'l, pg. 815
Grant, Tone, Pres.--Refco Group Ltd., Chicago, IL; U.S. Private, pg. 917
Grant, W. Thomas II, Chm. Bd., Pres. & Chief Exec. Officer--Lab One, Lenexa, KS; U.S. Public, pg. 1449
Grantham, H. Varley, Pres.--Grantham Distributing Company, Inc., Orlando, FL; U.S. Private, pg. 470
Grantmyre, William E., Pres.--Heater Utilities, Incorporated, Cary, NC; U.S. Public, pg. 1116
Gras, Dieter, Pres.--Werner & Pfleiderer Corporation, Ramsey, NJ; Int'l, pg. 511
Grasley, M.H., Pres.--Shell Chemical Co., Houston, TX; Int'l, pg. 1136
Grass, David, Pres.--Firestone Industrial Products Co., Carmel, IN; Int'l, pg. 214
Grassie, Dr. A., Pres.--Wyeth S.A. de C.V., Mexico, Mexico; U.S. Public, pg. 82
Grauman, Gary, Pres.--Rocco Quality Foods, Timberville, VA; U.S. Private, pg. 937
Graupman, Richard, Chm. Bd. & Pres.--South Central Co-Op, Fairfax, MN; U.S. Private, pg. 1014
Gravel, Michael M., Pres.--Baum USA, Sidney, OH; Int'l, pg. 1293
Gravenhorst, Ted, Sr., Pres. & Chief Exec. Officer--John Boos & Company, Effingham, IL; U.S. Private, pg. 156
Graves, B.J., Pres.--Jackson Paper Company, Jackson, MS; U.S. Private, pg. 579
Graves, Earl G., Chm. Bd. & Pres.--Earl G. Graves, Ltd., New York, NY; U.S. Private, pg. 471
Graves, J. Anthony, Pres.--Concord Computing Corp., Elk Grove Village, IL; U.S. Public, pg. 429
Graves, Matthew, Pres.--Medusa Minerals Co, Thomasville, PA; U.S. Public, pg. 1084
Graving, Bruce, Pres. & Gen. Mgr.--Horizon Coal Services, Inc., Butte, MT; U.S. Public, pg. 1127
Gravino, Richard R., Pres.--Provident Consumer Financial Services, Cincinnati, OH; U.S. Public, pg. 1338
Gravnick, Phil, Pres.--Attitash Bear Peak, Bartlett, NH; U.S. Private, pg. 61
Gravsam, Michael, Pres.--Grovenberg, Williamsport, PA; U.S. Private, pg. 1077
Gravsam, Mike, Pres.--Lunaire Environmental, Williamsport, PA; U.S. Private, pg. 1077
Grawert, Ronald R., Pres.--GTE Mobilnet Incorporated, Atlanta, GA; U.S. Public, pg. 696
Gray, Bill, Sr. Partner & Mng. Dir.-O&M NY--Ogilvy & Mather Worldwide, Inc., New York, NY; Int'l, pg. 1483
Gray, Bruce, Pres. & Chief Oper. Officer--Xicor, Inc., Milpitas, CA; U.S. Public, pg. 1785
Gray, C. Michael, Pres. & Chief Oper. Officer--Performance Food Group Company, Richmond, VA; U.S. Public, pg. 1278
Gray, C.C. Howard, Pres. & Chief Exec. Officer--James N. Gray Construction Co., Inc., Lexington, KY; U.S. Private, pg. 472
Gray, Dave, Pres.--Lyke Corporation, Ripon, WI; U.S. Private, pg. 682
Gray, David, Pres.--Astra Pharmaceuticals (Malaysia) Sdn Bhd., Kuala Lumpur, Malaysia; Int'l, pg. 94
Gray, David, Pres.--Enzopac, Inc., Sheboygan, WI; U.S. Private, pg. 379
Gray, Ed, Pres.--Gray Seifart & Co., New York, NY; U.S. Public, pg. 985
Gray, James E., Pres. & Chief Oper. Officer--Macy's East, New York, NY; U.S. Public, pg. 618
Gray, James H., Pres.-Regional--Citizens Bank of Kentucky, Madisonville, KY; U.S. Public, pg. 280
Gray, James K., Pres.--Canadian Hunter Exploration Ltd., Calgary, Canada; Int'l, pg. 433
Gray, John, S., Sr., Chm. Bd. & Pres.--Jack Gray Transport, Inc., Gary, IN; U.S. Private, pg. 471
Gray, Kal, Pres.--Crescive Die & Tool, Inc., Saline, MI; U.S. Private, pg. 289
Gray, Kelly, Pres.--St. John Knits, Irvine, CA; U.S. Private, pg. 960
Gray, Mike, Partner & Bus. Devel. Dir.--Martin/Williams Advertising Inc., Minneapolis, MN; U.S. Private, pg. 710
Gray, R. B., Pres.--Royal Bank Export Finance Co. Ltd. (REFCO), Toronto, Canada; Int'l, pg. 1131
Gray, Robert A., Pres. & Chief Exec. Officer--Gray Printing Co., Fostoria, OH; U.S. Private, pg. 472
Gray, Roger L., Pres. & Chief Exec. Officer--Gray Kirk/VanSant Advertising, Inc., Baltimore, MD; U.S. Private, pg. 472
Gray, Stephen, Pres. & Chief Oper. Officer--McLeodUSA Incorporated, Cedar Rapids, IA; U.S. Public, pg. 1073
Gray, Steven P., Pres.--Chi Systems Division, Ann Arbor, MI; U.S. Public, pg. 1539
Gray, Tracey L., Pres. & Chief Oper. Officer--Elcotel, Inc., Sarasota, FL; U.S. Public, pg. 568
Graybill, V. Lynn, Chm. Bd., Pres. & Chief Exec. Officer--Karts International Inc., Covington, LA; U.S. Public, pg. 944
Grayer, Jonathan, Pres. & Chief Oper. Officer--Kaplan Educational Centers Ltd., New York, NY; U.S. Public, pg. 1743
Graylis, William, Pres.--Cinergy Investments, Inc., Indianapolis, IN; U.S. Public, pg. 369
Graziado, George M., Chm. Bd., Pres. & Chief Exec. Officer--Imperial Bancorp, Inglewood, CA; U.S. Public, pg. 871
Grazier, George, Pres.--Farmland Foods, Inc., Kansas City, MO; U.S. Private, pg. 396
Grealis, William J., Pres.--Cinergy Investments, Inc., Indianapolis, IN; U.S. Public, pg. 369
Grealis, William J., Pres.--Power Equipment Supply Company, New Washington, IN; U.S. Public, pg. 369
Grealis, William J., Pres.--PSI Power Resource Development, Inc., Indianapolis, IN; U.S. Public, pg. 369
Grealis, William J., Pres.--PSI Power Resource Operations, Indianapolis, IN; U.S. Public, pg. 369
Grealis, William J., Pres.--CGE Eck, Inc., Cincinnati, OH; U.S. Public, pg. 369
Grealis, William J., Pres.--CG&E Resource Marketing, Inc., Cincinnati, OH; U.S. Public, pg. 369
Grealis, William J., Pres.--KO Transmission Company, Cincinnati, OH; U.S. Public, pg. 369
Grealis, William J., Pres.--Lawrenceburg Gas Co., Cincinnati, OH; U.S. Public, pg. 369
Grealis, William J., Pres.--Miami Power Corp., Cincinnati, OH; U.S. Public, pg. 369
Grealis, William J., Pres.--Tri-State Improvement Co., Cincinnati, OH; U.S. Public, pg. 369
Grealis, William J., Pres.--Union Light, Heat and Power Co., Cincinnati, OH; U.S. Public, pg. 369
Grealis, William J., Pres.--Cinergy Corp., Cincinnati, OH; U.S. Public, pg. 369
Greanias, Stanley L., Pres. & Chief Exec. Officer--Superior Coffee and Foods, Bensenville, IL; U.S. Public, pg. 1434
Greason, Robert J., Pres.--Hickman, Williams Canada, Inc., Cambridge, Canada; U.S. Private, pg. 525
Greathouse, Steve, Pres. & Chief Exec. Officer--Casino Electronics, Inc., Las Vegas, NV; U.S. Public, pg. 47
Greaves, Richard W., Dr., Chm. Bd. & Pres.--Vibro-Meter Corp., Long Beach, CA; U.S. Private, pg. 1138
Grebler, M.J., Pres.--Tony Lambert Company, New York, NY; U.S. Private, pg. 644
Grebow, Edward, Pres. & Chief Exec. Officer--Chyron Corp., Melville, NY; Int'l, pg. 1372
Greek, David N., Pres.--Hill & Griffith Company, Cincinnati, OH; U.S. Private, pg. 529
Greely, F.J., Jr., Pres. & Chief Exec. Officer--Regions Bank/Central Louisiana, New Roads, LA; U.S. Public, pg. 1372
Greely, William C., Pres. & Chief Exec. Officer--Keeneland Assoc., Inc., Lexington, KY; U.S. Private, pg. 611
Green-Armytage, Jock M., Chm. Bd.--Guthrie North America, Inc., Orlando, FL; Int'l, pg. 113
Green, B.J., Pres.--Solutia Inc., Foley, AL; U.S. Public, pg. 1484
Green, Bob, Pres.--Leone Food Service Corp., Livonia, MI; U.S. Private, pg. 244
Green, Clay S., Pres. & Chief Exec. Officer--First Midwest Mortgage Corporation, Joliet, IL; U.S. Public, pg. 636
Green, Dave, Pres.--Linotype-Hell Company, Hauppauge, NY; Int'l, pg. 604
Green, David, Pres.--Dole Northwest, East Wenatchee, WA; U.S. Public, pg. 515
Green, Frederick M., Pres. & Chief Exec. Officer--Ault Incorporated, Minneapolis, MN; U.S. Public, pg. 147
Green, Gary, Pres.--Comair Aviation Academy, Inc., Sanford, FL; U.S. Public, pg. 406
Green, George, Pres. & Exec V.P.-Hearst Magazines Intl.--Hearst Magazines Division, New York, NY; U.S. Private, pg. 516
Green, George J., Pres.--Hearst Magazines International, New York, NY; U.S. Private, pg. 517
Green, Henry, Pres. & Chief Exec. Officer--Physician Computer Network, Inc., Morris Plains, NJ; U.S. Public, pg. 1293
Green, J. B., Pres. & Chief Exec. Officer--Marigold Foods, Inc., Minneapolis, MN; Int'l, pg. 752
Green, Jack, Pres.--Tallapoosa River Electric Co-Op, Lafayette, AL; U.S. Private, pg. 1067
Green, James M., Pres. & Chief Exec. Officer--FWD/Seagrave Fire Apparatus, Inc., Clintonville, WI; U.S. Private, pg. 390
Green, Joan, Pres.--BT Brokerage Corporation, New York, NY; U.S. Public, pg. 185
Green, Johnathan D., Pres. & Chief Exec. Officer--Rockefeller Center Management Corporation, New York, NY; Int'l, pg. 873
Green, Judson, Pres.--Walt Disney Attractions Division, Anaheim, CA; U.S. Public, pg. 511
Green, Keith, Pres. & Dir.--Trak Auto Corporation, Landover, MD; U.S. Public, pg. 484
Green, Kenneth, Pres.--Revlon International Corporation, London, United Kingdom; U.S. Private, pg. 690
Green, Louis R., Pres. & Chief Opers. Officer--Conestoga Wood Specialties Corp., East Earl, PA; U.S. Private, pg. 262
Green, Michael P., Chm.--Carlton Communications Plc, London, United Kingdom; Int'l, pg. 272
Green, Mike, Pres. & Chief Exec. Officer-Inpower--Integral Systems, Inc., Walnut Creek, CA; Int'l, pg. 242
Green, Mike, Pres. & Chief Oper. Officer--InPower Inc., San Francisco, CA; Int'l, pg. 242
Green, Peter J., Pres.--John E. Green Co., Detroit, MI; U.S. Private, pg. 477

Green, R. Thomas, Jr., Chm. Bd., Pres. & Chief Exec. Officer--Oglebay Norton Company, Cleveland, OH; *U.S. Public*, pg. 1213

Green, Richard K., Pres. & Chief Oper. Officer--Blistex, Inc., Oak Brook, IL; *U.S. Private*, pg. 149

Green, Richard L., Chm. Bd., Pres. & Chief Exec. Officer--General Shale Products Corp., Johnson City, TN; *Int'l*, pg. 843

Green, Richard L., Chm. Bd., Pres. & Chief Exec. Officer--General Shale Products Corp., Elizabethton, TN; *Int'l*, pg. 843

Green, Robert K., Pres. & Chief Oper. Officer--UtiliCorp United Inc., Kansas City, MO; *U.S. Public*, pg. 1700

Green, Stanley, Pres. & Chief Exec. Officer--DAQ Electronics Inc., Piscataway, NJ; *U.S. Private*, pg. 300

Green, Steve, Pres.--Flowers Baking Co. of Tyler, Inc., Tyler, TX; *U.S. Public*, pg. 657

Greenbaum, Bruce, Pres.--Brice Manufacturing Company, Inc., Pacoima, CA; *U.S. Public*, pg. 534

Greenberg, Evan G., Pres. & Chief Oper. Officer--American International Group, Inc., New York, NY; *U.S. Public*, pg. 83

Greenberg, Frank, Pres.--Baltic Linen Company, Inc., Valley Stream, NY; *U.S. Private*, pg. 113

Greenberg, Lon R., Chm. Bd., Pres. & Chief Exec. Officer--UGI Corporation, King of Prussia, PA; *U.S. Public*, pg. 1653

Greenberg, Lon R., Chm. Bd., Pres. & Chief Exec. Officer--AmeriGas Partners, L.P., Valley Forge, PA; *U.S. Public*, pg. 1653

Greenberg, Mark, Pres.--Jay Instrument & Specialty Co., Cincinnati, OH; *U.S. Private*, pg. 583

Greenberg, Richard L., Pres.--Wadsworth Publishing Co., Belmont, CA; *U.S. Public*, pg. 1600

Greenberg, Steven, Pres.--Coscient-Astral Distribution, Toronto, Canada; *Int'l*, pg. 335

Greenblatt, Alfred A., Pres.-Apparel/Home/Industrial Fabrics & Sr. V.P.--Guilford Mills, Inc., Greensboro, NC; *U.S. Public*, pg. 768

Greenblatt, Sherwin, Pres. & Chief Oper. Officer--Bose Corporation, Framingham, MA; *U.S. Private*, pg. 160

Greenburg, Gary, Pres.--Sage Enterprises, Inc., Des Plaines, IL; *U.S. Private*, pg. 960

Greene, Cheryl, Mng. Partner & Chief Strategy Officer--Deutsch, Inc., New York, NY; *U.S. Private*, pg. 328

Greene, Edward, Pres.--Carl Zeiss Optical, Inc., Petersburg, VA; *Int'l*, pg. 1523

Greene, Marc J., Pres. & Chief Exec. Officer--Regions Bank/White County, Cleveland, GA; *U.S. Public*, pg. 1373

Greene, Robert E., Pres.--Opal Concepts, Inc., Anaheim, CA; *U.S. Private*, pg. 817

Greene, Ronald D., Principal & Pres.--Devon Direct Marketing & Advertising, Inc., Berwyn, PA; *U.S. Private*, pg. 329

Greene, Tim, Partner & Mngmt. Supvr.--Eric Mower and Associates, Inc., Syracuse, NY; *U.S. Private*, pg. 765

Greene, Warren E., Pres. & Chief Exec. Officer--Adair Greene Advertising, Atlanta, GA; *U.S. Private*, pg. 16

Greenfield, Albert M., III, Pres. & Treas.--Albert M. Greenfield & Company, Philadelphia, PA; *U.S. Private*, pg. 477

Greenfield, Dan, Pres.--Carco International, Inc., Fort Smith, AR; *U.S. Private*, pg. 208

Greenhill, Robert D., Pres. & Chief Oper. Officer--Texas, New Mexico & Oklahoma Coaches, Inc., Lubbock, TX; *U.S. Public*, pg. 766

Greenhouse, Martin, Pres. & Co-Creative Dir.--Berenter Greenhouse & Webster, Inc., New York, NY; *U.S. Private*, pg. 135

Greenlee, Donald W., Pres.--Circle Plastics Products, Inc., Circleville, OH; *U.S. Private*, pg. 240

Greenlee, Stewart M., Pres. & Chief Exec. Officer--The Fifth Third Bank of Southern Ohio, Hillsboro, OH; *U.S. Public*, pg. 622

Greenly, Duane, Pres.--Morgan Manufacturing, Oshkosh, WI; *U.S. Public*, pg. 1132

Greenman, John, Publisher--The Columbus Ledger & Enquirer, Columbus, GA; *U.S. Public*, pg. 964

Greenspun, Brian L., Pres. & Editor--Las Vegas Sun, Las Vegas, NV; *U.S. Private*, pg. 652

Greenstein, Scott, Co-Pres.--October Films, Inc., New York, NY; *Int'l*, pg. 1216

Greenwald, Martin W., Chm. Bd., Pres. & Chief Exec. Officer--Image Entertainment, Inc., Chatsworth, CA; *U.S. Public*, pg. 870

Greenwood, Lorne, Pres.-Davis Tool & Engrng. Co.--Davis Industries Inc., Plymouth, MI; *U.S. Private*, pg. 315

Greenwood, Nigel, Dr., Pres.--Buck Forkardt, Inc., Portage, MI; *Int'l*, pg. 1484

Greer, C. Scott, Pres.--United Technologies Automotive, Dearborn, MI; *U.S. Public*, pg. 1691

Greer, Carl C., Pres.--Martin Exploration Management Company, Alsip, IL; *U.S. Private*, pg. 709

Greer, Freddy C., Pres.--The Citizens Bank, Fort Valley, GA; *U.S. Public*, pg. 1549

Greer, G.L., Pres.--Gerard L. Greer Co., Fountain Valley, CA; *Int'l*, pg. 891

Greer, Henry H., Pres., Chief Oper. Officer & Chief Fin. Officer--SEI Investments, Oaks, PA; *U.S. Public*, pg. 1417

Greer, Jack V., Sr., Pres.--Autry Greer & Sons, Inc., Prichard, AL; *U.S. Private*, pg. 479

Greer, Jana Waring, Pres.-SunAmerica Mktg. Inc. & Sr. V.P. SunAmerica, Inc. Affairs--SunAmerica Inc., Los Angeles, CA; *U.S. Public*, pg. 1532

Greer, Mike, Pres.--Pinnacle Coating & Converting, Inc., Spartanburg, SC; *U.S. Private*, pg. 866

Greer, Paul, Pres.--D&Z Utility Services, Philadelphia, PA; *U.S. Private*, pg. 317

Greer, Robert J., Pres.--Michael's Development Company, Marlton, NJ; *U.S. Private*, pg. 740

Grefe, Peter, Pres.--Shur-Lok Corporation, Irvine, CA; *U.S. Private*, pg. 997

Gregerson, R.L., Chm. Bd. & Pres.--American Excelsior Company, Arlington, TX; *U.S. Private*, pg. 53

Gregg, Jeffrey L., Pres.--Bretlin, Inc., Calhoun, GA; *U.S. Public*, pg. 514

Gregg, Ray, Pres.--WCI Machine Tools & Systems, Cincinnati, OH; *Int'l*, pg. 440

Gregg, Robert C., Pres.--Gregg Industries, Inc., El Monte, CA; *U.S. Private*, pg. 480

Gregoire, Ronald, Pres.--Cerritos Ford, Inc., Cerritos, CA; *U.S. Private*, pg. 226

Gregor, Charles W., Pres.--Magnet Wire Insulation Sector, Fort Wayne, IN; *U.S. Public*, pg. 593

Gregor, Thomas C., Chm. Bd., Pres. & Chief Exec. Officer--United National Bancorp, Bridgewater, NJ; *U.S. Public*, pg. 1679

Gregory, Harry, Pres. & Gen. Mgr.--AAR Allen Aircraft, Elk Grove Village, IL; *U.S. Public*, pg. 1

Gregory, Jon, Pres.--Quarries Division, Barre, VT; *U.S. Public*, pg. 1396

Gregory, Kim, Pres.--Hansen Mechanical Contractors, Inc., Las Vegas, NV; *U.S. Public*, pg. 572

Gregory, Steven, Pres.--New England Technology Group, Inc., Cambridge, MA; *U.S. Private*, pg. 793

Gregory, William R., Pres. & Chief Exec. Officer--ESELCO, Inc., Sault Sainte Marie, MI; *U.S. Public*, pg. 591

Greinke, Bruce, Pres. & Gen. Mgr.--Magnetics International, Inc., Chesterton, IN; *U.S. Public*, pg. 879

Greisch, John J., Pres.--Interlake Material Handling Div., Naperville, IL; *U.S. Public*, pg. 893

Greisinger, James, Pres.--Dean Pickle & Specialty Products Co., Green Bay, WI; *U.S. Public*, pg. 490

Greisinger, Jim, Pres. & Chief Exec. Officer--Dean Pickles & Specialty Products, Cairo, GA; *U.S. Public*, pg. 490

Gremillion, Robert, Pres. & Chief Exec. Officer--Sun-Sentinel Company, Fort Lauderdale, FL; *U.S. Public*, pg. 1636

Gremmo, Piergiuseppe, Chief Oper. Officer--Bozzalla & Lesna S.p.A., Coggiola, Italy; *Int'l*, pg. 209

Grenon, Jean-Francois, Pres.-Digital Division--Microwave Radio Communications, Chelmsford, MA; *U.S. Public*, pg. 294

Gresov, Boris, Chm. Bd., Pres. & Chief Exec. Officer--Standard Metals Corporation, New York, NY; *U.S. Public*, pg. 1502

Gress, Ronald D., Pres.--Gress Foods Inc., Gainesville, GA; *U.S. Private*, pg. 480

Gressel, Alan, Chm. Bd., Pres., Chief Exec. Officer & Chief Oper. Officer--Research Environmental Industries, Inc., Cleveland, OH; *U.S. Private*, pg. 924

Gressier, C., Chm. Bd. & Mng. Dir.--CTT Sceta, Paris, France; *Int'l*, pg. 1163

Greulich, Joseph D., Pres.--D & S Plastics International, Auburn Hills, MI; *Int'l*, pg. 1277

Grey, Joel, Administrator--Sutter Auburn Faith Community Hospital, Auburn, CA; *U.S. Private*, pg. 1057

Griebel, James D., Pres.--Treated Water Outsourcing, Naperville, IL; *U.S. Public*, pg. 1150

Griebel, R. Nelson, Chm. Bd., Chief Exec. Officer & Pres.--Bank of Boston Connecticut, Hartford, CT; *U.S. Public*, pg. 184

Grier, James R., III, Pres. & Chief Exec. Officer--Eby Corporation, Wichita, KS; *U.S. Private*, pg. 359

Grier, James R., III, Pres. & Chief Exec. Officer--Martin K. Eby Construction Company, Inc., Wichita, KS; *U.S. Private*, pg. 359

Grierson, Patrick, Pres.--Canadian Broadcast Sales, Toronto, Canada; *Int'l*, pg. 1482

Gries, Louis, Pres.--James Hardie Building Products Inc., Fontana, CA; *Int'l*, pg. 597

Griesedieck, Chris R., Pres. & Chief Exec. Officer--Colonial Bank, Des Peres, MO; *U.S. Public*, pg. 643

Griessel, Richard, Pres.--Semikron Inc., Hudson, NH; *Int'l*, pg. 1220

Grife, Norman, Pres.--Randy International, Jamaica, NY; *U.S. Private*, pg. 909

Grife, Randy, Pres.--Randy International, Jamaica, NY; *U.S. Private*, pg. 909

Griffin, Ben Hill, III, Chm. Bd., Pres. & Chief Exec. Officer--Alico, Inc., La Belle, FL; *U.S. Public*, pg. 41

Griffin, Bobby I., Exec. V.P. & Pres.-Pacing Business--Medtronic, Inc., Minneapolis, MN; *U.S. Public*, pg. 1082

Griffin, Dennis B., Pres. & Chief Exec. Officer--Griffin Industries, Inc., Cold Spring, KY; *U.S. Private*, pg. 480

Griffin, Donald W., Chm. Bd., Pres. & Chief Exec. Officer--Olin Corporation, Norwalk, CT; *U.S. Public*, pg. 1218

Griffin, Jeff, Chm. Bd., Pres. & Chief Exec. Officer--Griffin Transport Services, Inc., Sparks, NV; *U.S. Private*, pg. 481

Griffin, Jerry, Pres.--Sewell Village Cadillac Co., Dallas, TX; *U.S. Private*, pg. 988

Griffin, Jerry, Pres.--United Service Equipment Company, Murfreesboro, TN; *U.S. Public*, pg. 1507

Griffin, John W., Chm. Bd., Pres. & Chief Exec. Officer--Griffin Manufacturing Co., Muskogee, OK; *U.S. Private*, pg. 481

Griffin, Leonard, Pres.--Key Plastics, Inc., Novi, MI; *U.S. Private*, pg. 618

Griffin, Mark, Chm. Bd., Pres. & Chief Exec. Officer--Ris Paper Company, Long Island City, NY; *U.S. Private*, pg. 932

Griffin, Mark E., Chm. Bd., Pres. & Chief Exec. Officer--Lewis Drug, Inc., Sioux Falls, SD; *U.S. Private*, pg. 665

Griffin, Marvin, Pres.--Daisy Manufacturing Company, Inc., Rogers, AR; *U.S. Private*, pg. 308

Griffin, Merv, Chm. & Chief Exec. Officer--Merv Griffin Enterprises, Beverly Hills, CA; *Int'l*, pg. 1282

Griffin, Randall M., Pres.--Constellation Real Estate Group Inc., Baltimore, MD; *U.S. Public*, pg. 172

Griffin, Rutledge A., Jr., Chm. Bd., Pres. & Chief Exec. Officer--Griffin Corporation, Valdosta, GA; *U.S. Private*, pg. 480

Griffin, William, Pres.--CNF Constructors Inc., Meriden, CT; *U.S. Public*, pg. 950

Griffins, Herbert R., Pres.--Preservative Paint Company, Seattle, WA; *U.S. Private*, pg. 613

Griffith, Dan, Pres.--Harig Products, Elgin, IL; *U.S. Public*, pg. 252

Griffith, Dan, Pres.--Harig Grinders, Elgin, IL; *U.S. Public*, pg. 252

Griffith, Dan L., Pres. & Chief Exec. Officer--Bridgeport Machines, Inc., Bridgeport, CT; *U.S. Public*, pg. 251

Griffith, David, Pres.--Modern Group Ltd., Bristol, PA; *U.S. Private*, pg. 754

Griffith, Dean L., Chm. Bd., Pres. & Chief Exec. Officer--Griffith Laboratories Worldwide, Inc., Alsip, IL; *U.S. Private*, pg. 481

Griffith, Gary R., Pres.--Acordia Northeast, Boston, MA; *Int'l*, pg. 671

Griffith, Gerald P., Pres. & Chief Exec. Officer--Alpha/Owens Corning LLC, Collierville, TN; *U.S. Private*, pg. 45

Griffith, Howard, Pres.--Vertex Computer Cable Products, Farmingdale, NY; *U.S. Public*, pg. 1718

Griffith, Sherman, Pres.--Fischer Companies, Memphis, TN; *U.S. Private*, pg. 408

Griffiths, William C., Pres.--Waukesha Cherry-Burrell, Delavan, WI; *U.S. Public*, pg. 1677

Grigelevich, Joseph, Pres. & Chief Exec. Officer--American Modular Technologies, Liberty, NC; *U.S. Public*, pg. 69

Grigg, Charles W., Chm. Bd., Pres. & Chief Exec. Officer--SPS Technologies, Inc., Jenkintown, PA; *U.S. Public*, pg. 1419

Grigg, Richard R., Jr., Pres. & Chief Oper. Officer--Wisconsin Energy Corporation, Milwaukee, WI; *U.S. Public*, pg. 1773

Grigg, Ted, Pres.--William Cook Direct Marketing, Inc., Jacksonville, FL; *U.S. Private*, pg. 273

Griggs, David, Pres., Chief Exec. & Chief Fin. Officer & Treas.--Jack Griggs Inc., Exeter, CA; *U.S. Private*, pg. 482

Griggs, Doyle, Pres.--Professional Aviation Associates, Inc., Atlanta, GA; *U.S. Public*, pg. 187

Grigsby, E.K., Pres.--Phillips Petroleum International Investment Company, Reno, NV; *U.S. Public*, pg. 1291

Grigsby, Sam, Pres.--Bank of East Tennessee, Morristown, TN; *U.S. Public*, pg. 1669

Grilli, Donald A., Pres.--Johnson & Johnson Professional, Inc., Raynham, MA; *U.S. Public*, pg. 928

Grillo, Steven G., Pres., Chief Exec. Officer & Chief Oper. Officer--General Office Environments Inc., Rochelle Park, NJ; *U.S. Private*, pg. 445

Grimaldi, Joseph M., Principal & Chief Oper. Officer--Mullen Advertising, Inc., Wenham, MA; *U.S. Private*, pg. 766

Grimes, James T., Pres.--Golden Eagle Distributors, Inc., Tucson, AZ; *U.S. Private*, pg. 460

Grimes, Thomas D., Pres. & Treas.--Puritan Bakery, Inc., Carson, CA; *U.S. Private*, pg. 895

Grimmer, Park, Pres.--Grimmer Realty Co. Inc., Birmingham, AL; *U.S. Private*, pg. 482

Grinberg, Efraim, Pres.--Movado Group, Inc., Lyndhurst, NJ; *U.S. Public*, pg. 1140

Grindstaff, Kurt, Pres. & Chief Oper. Officer--Seven-Up Bottling Co. of St. Louis, Hazelwood, MO; *U.S. Private*, pg. 142

Griner, Lyn, Pres.-Mktg. & Co. Communications--JC Penney Company, Inc., Plano, TX; *U.S. Public*, pg. 916

Grinstead, Steve R., Pres. & Chief Oper. Officer--Fresh America Corp., Dallas, TX; *U.S. Public*, pg. 681

Grinstead, Steve R., Pres.--Lone Star Produce Acquisition Corp., Austin, TX; *U.S. Public*, pg. 682

Grinzewitsch, George, Chm. Bd. & Pres.--Von Housen Motors, Sacramento, CA; *U.S. Private*, pg. 1143

Grinzewitsch, George, Chm. Bd. & Pres.--Sacramento Jaguar, Inc., Sacramento, CA; *U.S. Private*, pg. 1143

Grisanti, Eugene P., Chm. Bd., Pres. & Chief Exec. Officer--International Flavors & Fragrances, Inc., New York, NY; *U.S. Public*, pg. 898

Grisanti, Michael J., Pres. & Chief Exec. Officer--Grisanti, Inc., Louisville, KY; *U.S. Private*, pg. 482

Griver, Michael A., Pres. & Chief Exec. Officer--American Health and Life Insurance Co., Fort Worth, TX; *U.S. Public*, pg. 1633

Grize, William, Pres. & Chief Oper. Officer--The Stop & Shop Companies, Inc., Quincy, MA; *Int'l*, pg. 750

Grizzard, Claude H., Jr., Pres.--Grizzard, Atlanta, GA; *U.S. Private*, pg. 482

Groat, Jonathan M., Pres. & Chief Exec. Officer--Smith-Lee Co., Inc., Oneida, NY; *U.S. Private*, pg. 1009

Grob, J. Murray, Pres.--Caravan Products Company, Inc., Totowa, NJ; *U.S. Private*, pg. 208

Grob, J. Murray, Pres.--Caravan Brokay, Totowa, NJ; *U.S. Private*, pg. 208

Grobman, Frank, Pres. & Chief Exec. Officer--Dan's Supreme Super Markets Inc., Hempstead, NY; *U.S. Private*, pg. 310

Grodd, Clifford, Pres.--Paul Stuart, Inc., New York, NY; *U.S. Private*, pg. 844

Grodnitzky, Alan S., Pres.--The Penn Companies, Philadelphia, PA; *U.S. Private*, pg. 849

Groendyke, Jay, Pres. & Chief Exec. Officer--Synergis Technologies Group, Grand Rapids, MI; *U.S. Private*, pg. 1060

Groenevelt, Aat, Chm. Bd. & Pres.--Provimi Veal Corporation, Seymour, WI; *U.S. Private*, pg. 892

Grogan, David R., Chm., Pres. & Chief Exec. Officer--Toter Incorporated, Statesville, NC; *U.S. Private*, pg. 1092

Groh, James H., Pres. & Chief Oper. Officer--Nu-Kote International, Dallas, TX; *U.S. Public*, pg. 1205

Groh, Thomas M., Pres.--McAlpin's, Lexington, KY; *U.S. Public*, pg. 1090

Groh, Thomas N., Pres.--Root Dry Goods Company, Inc., Terre Haute, IN; *U.S. Public*, pg. 1090

Gromek, Josheph, Pres. & Chief Exec. Officer--Brooks Brothers, New York, NY; *Int'l*, pg. 843

Gronberg, Erik, Pres. & Chief Exec. Officer--Deminex (Canada) Ltd., Calgary, Canada; *Int'l*, pg. 1461

Gronda, Richard, Pres. & Chief Oper. Officer--Farrell Lines Incorporated, New York, NY; *U.S. Private*, pg. 397

Groner, Stanley, Pres.--Highland Industries Inc., Greensboro, NC; *U.S. Private*, pg. 528
Groom, John, Pres. & Chief Oper. Officer--Elan Corporation Plc, Dublin, Ireland; *Int'l*, pg. 435
Groome, Harry C., III, Pres.--SmithKline Beecham Clinical Laboratories, Inc., King of Prussia, PA; *Int'l*, pg. 1264
Grooms, David, Pres.--Kyocera America, Inc., San Diego, CA; *Int'l*, pg. 775
Grooms, Sam, Pres.--Hy-Tek Material Handling, Inc., Columbus, OH; *U.S. Private*, pg. 550
Gropp, Louis, Editor-in-Chief--House Beautiful, New York, NY; *U.S. Private*, pg. 517
Gros, Didier, Co-Pres.--Sphere SA, Courcouronnes, France; *Int'l*, pg. 21
Grosch, Greg, Chm. Bd., Pres. & Chief Exec. Officer--White Cap Industries, Inc., Costa Mesa, CA; *U.S. Public*, pg. 1765
Gross, John J., Partner--John Gross & Co., Baltimore, MD; *U.S. Private*, pg. 483
Gross, Louis E., Chm. & Pres.--Unity Manufacturing Co., Chicago, IL; *U.S. Private*, pg. 1126
Gross, Myron, Pres.--Pioneer Paper Corporation, Carlstadt, NJ; *U.S. Private*, pg. 867
Gross, Rick E., Pres.--Vindicator Technologies, Austin, TX; *U.S. Private*, pg. 1141
Grossblatt, Harvey, Pres.--Universal Security Instruments Inc., Owings Mills, MD; *U.S. Public*, pg. 1697
Grosse, Helmut, Pres.--Voigt & Co. Baugesellschaft GmbH, Berlin, Germany; *Int'l*, pg. 1261
Grossenburg, Barry, Pres.--Grossenburg Implements, Incorporated, Winner, SD; *U.S. Private*, pg. 483
Grossman, David, Pres.--Grossman Iron & Steel Company, Saint Louis, MO; *U.S. Private*, pg. 483
Grossman, Irving J., Chm. & Pres.--Beacon Container Corporation, Birdsboro, PA; *U.S. Private*, pg. 125
Grossman, Peter, Pres.--Nunn-Bush Shoe Co., Milwaukee, WI; *U.S. Public*, pg. 1763
Grossman, Robert, Chm. Bd., Pres. & Chief Exec. Officer--Emons Transportation Group, Inc., York, PA; *U.S. Public*, pg. 578
Grossman, Steven, Pres.--Massachusetts Envelope Co., Somerville, MA; *U.S. Private*, pg. 712
Grossman, Steven M., Pres.--Southern Container Corporation, Hauppauge, NY; *U.S. Private*, pg. 1016
Grossmann, Axel, Pres.--Filtros Mann Ltda., Indaial, Brazil; *Int'l*, pg. 484
Grosso, John, Pres. & Chief Exec. Officer--PCA International, Inc., Matthews, NC; *U.S. Public*, pg. 1240
Grot, John, Chm. Bd. & Pres.--Pascoe Building Systems, Inc., Columbus, GA; *U.S. Private*, pg. 842
Grote, William D., III, Pres.--Grote Industries, Madison, IN; *U.S. Private*, pg. 483
Grottke, Gary, Pres.--Amfac/JMB Hawaii, Inc., Honolulu, HI; *U.S. Private*, pg. 577
Grottke, Gary, Pres.--Amfac Agribusiness, Inc., Honolulu, HI; *U.S. Private*, pg. 578
Grottke, Gary, Pres.--Kekaha Sugar Company, Limited, Kekaha, HI; *U.S. Private*, pg. 578
Grottke, Gary, Pres.--The Lihue Plantation Company, Limited, Lihue, HI; *U.S. Private*, pg. 578
Grottke, Gary, Pres.--Kauai Sugar Storage Co., Lihue, HI; *U.S. Private*, pg. 578
Grottke, Gary, Pres.--Waiahole Irrigation Co., Ltd., Waipahu, HI; *U.S. Private*, pg. 578
Grottke, Gary, Pres.--Pioneer Mill Company, Ltd., Lahaina, HI; *U.S. Private*, pg. 578
Grottke, Gary, Pres. & Mgr.--Puna Sugar Co., Ltd., Keaau, HI; *U.S. Private*, pg. 578
Grottke, Gary, Pres.--Amfac Sugar and Agribusiness, Inc., Honolulu, HI; *U.S. Private*, pg. 578
Grouse, Charles, Pres.--L3 Communications Advanced Recorders Div., Sarasota, FL; *U.S. Private*, pg. 638
Grove, Deborah, Pres.--Old Dominion Systems of Maryland, Germantown, MD; *U.S. Public*, pg. 1105
Grove, Richard C., Pres.--Milwaukee Electric Tool Corp., Brookfield, WI; *Int'l*, pg. 96
Groven, Darrol N., Pres.--Heavy Civil Construction, Boise, ID; *U.S. Public*, pg. 1134
Grow, Daniel M., Pres.--Drexel Heritage Furnishings Inc., Drexel, NC; *U.S. Private*, pg. 432
Grow, Robert J., Pres. & Chief Oper. Officer--Geneva Steel, Vineyard, UT; *U.S. Public*, pg. 729
Growney, Robert L., Pres. & Chief Oper. Officer--Motorola, Inc., Schaumburg, IL; *U.S. Public*, pg. 1136
Grubbs, R., Pres. & Chief Exec. Officer--Anixter Inc., Skokie, IL; *U.S. Public*, pg. 115
Gruber, David, Pres.--MEPC American Properties, Dallas, TX; *U.S. Private*, pg. 686
Gruber, David P., Pres. & Chief Exec. Officer--Wyman-Gordon, North Grafton, MA; *U.S. Public*, pg. 1782
Gruber, Evan M., Pres. & Chief Exec. Officer--Modtech, Inc., Perris, CA; *U.S. Public*, pg. 1121
Grubman, John, Pres.--Media Printing Corporation, Pompano Beach, FL; *U.S. Private*, pg. 726
Gruenewald, David, Pres.--Arvey Paper & Office Products, Chicago, IL; *U.S. Public*, pg. 903
Grum, Clifford J., Chm. Bd., Pres. & Chief Exec. Officer--Temple-Inland Forest Products Corporation, Diboll, TX; *U.S. Public*, pg. 1575
Grun, William F., Pres.--Aerospace Systems & Equipment, Torrance, CA; *U.S. Public*, pg. 1127
Grundhofer, Jerry A., Chm. Bd., Pres. & Chief Exec. Officer--Starbanc Corporation, Cincinnati, OH; *U.S. Public*, pg. 1510
Grundhofer, Jerry A., Chm. Bd., Pres. & Chief Exec. Officer--Star Bank, N.A., Cincinnati, OH; *U.S. Public*, pg. 1510
Grundhofer, John F., Pres. & Chief Exec. Officer--U.S. Bancorp, Minneapolis, MN; *U.S. Public*, pg. 1680
Gruneisen, Jorg, Chm. Bd., Pres.--Villeroy & Boch AG, Mettlach, Germany; *Int'l*, pg. 1468
Grunewald, Fred, Pres. & Chief Oper. Officer--The Genie Company, Alliance, OH; *U.S. Private*, pg. 823
Grunewald, Fred S., Pres. & Chief Oper. Officer--Overhead Door Corporation, Dallas, TX; *U.S. Private*, pg. 822
Grunfeld, Ernie, Pres.--New York Knickerbockers, New York, NY; *U.S. Public*, pg. 288
Grunfeld, Tommy, Pres.--Sharplan Lasers GmbH, Freising, Germany; *Int'l*, pg. 429
Grunstein, Laurence R., Pres.--Citizen Watch Co. of America, Inc., Lyndhurst, NJ; *Int'l*, pg. 294
Grunsten, Richard, Pres.--GSP Marketing Services, Inc., Chicago, IL; *U.S. Private*, pg. 436
Grzelak, Dave, Pres. & Chief Exec. Officer--Komatsu America International Company, Vernon Hills, IL; *Int'l*, pg. 744
Grzybowski, J.R., Pres.--PDM Bridge, Wausau, WI; *U.S. Public*, pg. 1305
Grzybowski, J.R., Pres.--PDM Bridge, Eau Claire, WI; *U.S. Public*, pg. 1305
Gu, D.L., Pres.--Yantai Ebara Air Conditioning Equipment Co., Ltd., Yantai, China; *Int'l*, pg. 432
Guan, Ming-Der, Pres.--Heinz Win Chance Ltd., Samutprakan, Thailand; *U.S. Public*, pg. 807
Guarino, Walter F., Pres.--SSD&W Integrated Marketing Communications, Montville, NJ; *U.S. Private*, pg. 958
Gubala, Thomas J., Pres.--ARGOSystems, Inc., Sunnyvale, CA; *U.S. Public*, pg. 240
Gubesch, M.M., Pres.--Janesville Products, Norwalk, OH; *U.S. Public*, pg. 924
Gucci, Maurizio, Dr., Pres.--Guccio Gucci S.p.A., Milan, Italy; *Int'l*, pg. 686
Guccione, Kathy Keeton, Pres.--Omni Publications International Ltd., New York, NY; *U.S. Private*, pg. 444
Gudmundson, Crandall, Pres.--Odetics Inc., Anaheim, CA; *U.S. Public*, pg. 1212
Guenther, Lutz, Dr., Pres. & Chief Oper. Officer--Copper Range Company, White Pine, MI; *Int'l*, pg. 862
Guertin, Timothy E., Pres.--Oncology Systems, Palo Alto, CA; *U.S. Public*, pg. 1710
Guffey, John W., Jr., Chm. Bd., Pres. & Chief Exec. Officer--Coltec Holdings Inc, Charlotte, NC; *U.S. Public*, pg. 401
Gugelmann, Erich, Pres.--Schweizerische Kaseunion AG, Bern, Switzerland; *Int'l*, pg. 1211
Gugino, Carmelo, Jr., Pres. & Chief Exec. Officer--Dinaire Corp., Buffalo, NY; *U.S. Private*, pg. 334
Guichard, Antoine, Assoc. Generale & Mng. Partner--Casino-Guichard Perrachon & Cie, Saint Etienne, France; *Int'l*, pg. 562
Guida, Pedro, Gen. Mgr.--Banco Exterior, S.A., Montevideo, Uruguay; *Int'l*, pg. 81
Guido, R., Pres.--Inco United States Inc., New York, NY; *Int'l*, pg. 672
Guido, Sally A., Pres.--Lee Myles Associates Corporation, Paramus, NJ; *U.S. Private*, pg. 657
Guido, Umberto, Pres.--Promodes SA, Mondeville, France; *Int'l*, pg. 1071
Guiles, Edwin A., Pres.--San Diego Gas & Electric Company, San Diego, CA; *U.S. Public*, pg. 584
Guilfoyle, Dick, Pres.--USF Insurance Company, Philadelphia, PA; *U.S. Public*, pg. 328
Guiliano, Mireille, Pres.--Clicquot, Inc., New York, NY; *Int'l*, pg. 781
Guillen, L. Alejandro, Pres.--EA Engineering, Science & Technology de Mexico, S.A. de C.V., Colonia, Mexico; *U.S. Public*, pg. 541
Guillet, Denise, Sr. Principal & Grp. Mngmt. Supvr.--Publicis/Bloom, New York, NY; *Int'l*, pg. 470
Guillin, Pierre, Pres. & Chief Exec. Officer--Sanders, Athis-Mons, France; *Int'l*, pg. 459
Guimaraes Assedio, Joao Jose, Co.-Pres.--FIMA-Productos Alimentares, Lda, Lisbon, Portugal; *Int'l*, pg. 471
Guinasso, Vic, Pres. & Chief Oper. Officer--DHL Worldwide Express, Redwood City, CA; *U.S. Private*, pg. 301
Guinchord, Gilles, Pres. & Chief Exec. Officer--Rexel, Inc., Coral Gables, FL; *Int'l*, pg. 1107
Guindo, Julio Alcaide, Pres.--Cargosur, S.A., Madrid, Spain; *Int'l*, pg. 1225
Guinot, Francois, Pres.--Fine Inorganic Chemicals, Courbevoie, France; *Int'l*, pg. 1109
Guiry, Gordon, Pres.--TSC Film Distribution, Burnaby, Canada; *Int'l*, pg. 1343
Guis, J., Pres.--VNU Magazine Group International bv, Haarlem, Netherlands; *Int'l*, pg. 1445
Guiterrez, Edgar, Pres.--Banacol Marketing Corp., Coral Gables, FL; *U.S. Private*, pg. 113
Gula, Allen J., Jr., Pres. & Chief Exec. Officer--Key Services Corporation, Cleveland, OH; *U.S. Public*, pg. 954
Gulbas, Bruce, Pres. & Chief Exec. Officer--National Restaurant Supply Company, El Paso, TX; *U.S. Private*, pg. 786
Gulbas, Bruce, Pres.--Interfab, El Paso, TX; *U.S. Private*, pg. 786
Gulden, Frank, Acting Pres.--Avdel Textron, Hertford, United Kingdom; *U.S. Public*, pg. 1590
Gulett, Michael, Pres. & Chief Exec. Officer--Paradigm Technology, Inc., San Jose, CA; *U.S. Public*, pg. 1256
Gulhti, Pradep, Owner--Interplast Universal Industries, Inc., Lodi, NJ; *U.S. Private*, pg. 572
Gullickson, W.D., Jr., Pres. & Chief Exec. Officer--McLaughlin Gormley King Company, Minneapolis, MN; *U.S. Private*, pg. 723
Gulling, Daniel L., Pres. & Chief Exec. Officer--Marinette Marine Corporation, Marinette, WI; *U.S. Private*, pg. 703
Gullotti, Russell A., Chm. Bd., Pres. & Chief Exec. Officer--National Computer Systems, Eden Prairie, MN; *U.S. Public*, pg. 1155
Gummer, Charles L., Pres. & Chief Exec. Officer--Comerica Bank Texas, Dallas, TX; *U.S. Public*, pg. 409
Gumpertz, Donald G., Chm. Bd., Pres. & Chief Exec. Officer--Industrial Electronic Engineers, Inc., Van Nuys, CA; *U.S. Private*, pg. 561
Gumucio, Marcelo, Pres. & Chief Exec. Officer--Memorex Telex Corp., Irving, TX; *Int'l*, pg. 857
Gunji, Hiromi, Chm. Bd., Pres. & Chief Exec. Officer--Brother International Corporation, Somerset, NJ; *Int'l*, pg. 229
Gunlock, T.W., Pres.--Sabre Systems & Service Inc., Miamisburg, OH; *Int'l*, pg. 890
Gunn, G. James, Pres.--AMR Services Corporation, Dallas-Fort Worth Airport, TX; *U.S. Public*, pg. 9
Gunnoe, Larry R., Pres. & Chief Oper. Officer--Idaho Power Company, Boise, ID; *U.S. Public*, pg. 861
Gunst, Robert A., Pres. & Chief Exec. Officer--The Good Guys, Inc., Brisbane, CA; *U.S. Public*, pg. 750
Gunther, Stephen J., Pres.--AGL Energy Services, Inc., Atlanta, GA; *U.S. Public*, pg. 7
Guont, James R., Chm., Pres. & Chief Exec. Officer--The Fifth Third Bank of Kentucky, Louisville, Louisville, KY; *U.S. Public*, pg. 621
Gupta, Gautom, Pres.--IDEA Corporation, Bedford, MA; *U.S. Private*, pg. 557
Gupta, Rajat, Mng. Dir.--McKinsey & Company, Inc., New York, NY; *U.S. Private*, pg. 723
Guralnick, Miles, Pres.--Vespa Laboratories, Inc., Spring Mills, PA; *Int'l*, pg. 288
Gurewitz, Richard, Chm. Bd., Pres. & Chief Exec. Officer--Poly Pak America, Inc., Los Angeles, CA; *U.S. Private*, pg. 875
Gurgold, Carl, Pres.--Tiffany Extruders, Inc., Paterson, NJ; *U.S. Private*, pg. 1085
Gurgovits, Stephen J., Pres. & Chief Exec. Officer--First National Bank of Pennsylvania, Hermitage, PA; *U.S. Public*, pg. 607
Gurgui, Alex, Pres.--Olivetti Management of America, Inc., New York, NY; *Int'l*, pg. 1002
Gurian, Kenneth J., Chm. Bd. & Chief Exec. Officer--BGM Health Communications, Inc., Los Angeles, CA; *U.S. Public*, pg. 1223
Gurin, Richard S., Pres. & Chief Exec. Officer--Binney & Smith Inc., Easton, PA; *U.S. Private*, pg. 496
Gurley, Patrick J., Pres.--Gurley Motor Company, Gallup, NM; *U.S. Private*, pg. 488
Gurr, Danny, Pres.--DeWolfe & Fiske Inc., Canton, MA; *U.S. Private*, pg. 195
Gury, David J., Chm. Bd., Pres. & Chief Exec. Officer--Nabi, Boca Raton, FL; *U.S. Public*, pg. 1148
Guryan, George, Pres. & Chief Oper. Officer--The Excellence Group, Stamford, CT; *U.S. Private*, pg. 387
Gusick, Dennis, Chm. Bd., Pres. & Chief Exec. Officer--Helm, Inc., Detroit, MI; *U.S. Private*, pg. 520
Gussack, David, Pres.--General Bearing Corp., West Nyack, NY; *U.S. Public*, pg. 706
Gussman, Marvin, Pres.--Marvin Engineering Company, Inc., Inglewood, CA; *U.S. Private*, pg. 710
Gustaferro, Angelo, Chm. Bd., Pres. & Chief Exec. Officer--nVIEW Corporation, Newport News, VA; *U.S. Public*, pg. 1206
Gustafson, F. Edward, Chm. Bd., Pres. & Chief Exec. Officer--Envirodyne Industries, Inc., Oak Brook, IL; *U.S. Public*, pg. 586
Gustafson, James E., Pres. & Chief Oper. Officer--General Re Corporation, Stamford, CT; *U.S. Public*, pg. 725
Gustafson, James E., Pres.--GRC Realty Corp., Stamford, CT; *U.S. Public*, pg. 725
Gustafson, Ronald R., Pres. & Chief Oper. Officer--Coast Packing Company, Vernon, CA; *U.S. Private*, pg. 248
Gustafsson, Bengt, Pres.--Skanska Installation AB, Sundbyberg, Sweden; *Int'l*, pg. 1260
Gustafsson, Bengt, Pres.--Industriventilation Svenska AB, Vaxjo, Sweden; *Int'l*, pg. 1261
Gustafsson, Bernt, Pres.--Danisco Sugar AB, Malmo, Sweden; *Int'l*, pg. 378
Gustafsson, Claes, Pres.--Skanska Bygg AB, Danderyd, Sweden; *Int'l*, pg. 1260
Gustafsson, Lennart, Pres.--Euroclean, Itasca, IL; *Int'l*, pg. 440
Gustafsson, M., Pres.--Coldwater Seafood Corporation, Rowayton, CT; *U.S. Private*, pg. 251
Gustavsen, John C., Pres. & Chief Exec. Officer--Amspec Chemical Corporation, Gloucester City, NJ; *U.S. Private*, pg. 67
Gustin, Joseph A., Pres.--Mid-America Capital Resources, Inc., Indianapolis, IN; *U.S. Public*, pg. 913
Guston, Tim, Pres.--DecisionMark, Cedar Rapids, IA; *U.S. Private*, pg. 442
Guth, Albert E., Pres.--Astec Financial Services, Inc., Chattanooga, TN; *U.S. Public*, pg. 141
Guthrie, M. Philip, Chm. Bd., Pres. & Chief Exec. Officer--American Eagle Group, Inc., Dallas, TX; *U.S. Public*, pg. 71
Guthy, Bil, Co-Pres.--Guthy-Renker Corp., Santa Monica, CA; *U.S. Private*, pg. 488
Guthy, Bill, Co-Pres.--Guthy-Renker Corp., Palm Desert, CA; *U.S. Private*, pg. 488
Gutierrez, Juan J., Chm. Bd. & Pres.--Kemron Environmental Services, Inc., Vienna, VA; *U.S. Private*, pg. 614
Gutierrez, Tom, Pres. & Chief Exec. Officer--Exide Electronics Group, Inc., Raleigh, NC; *Int'l*, pg. 126
Gutkin, Michael, Mng. Partner & Media Services Dir.--Fova, Inc., New York, NY; *U.S. Public*, pg. 764
Gutmann, Rudolf, Pres.--Buhler Inc., Minneapolis, MN; *U.S. Private*, pg. 179
Gutterman, Arthur, Chm. Bd., Pres., Chief Exec. & Chief Oper. Officer--Jelmar Company, Lincolnwood, IL; *U.S. Private*, pg. 585
Guttman, James L., Pres.--Mon River Towing Inc., Belle Vernon, PA; *U.S. Private*, pg. 489
Guttman, Richard M., Pres.--Guttman Oil, Inc., Belle Vernon, PA; *U.S. Private*, pg. 489
Guttman, Steven J., Pres. & Chief Exec. Officer--Federal Realty Investment Trust, Rockville, MD; *U.S. Public*, pg. 616
Guy, Didier, Pres.--Ecole de Pilotage Amaury de la Grange, Merville, France; *Int'l*, pg. 560
Guyer, Ray, Pres. & Chief Exec. Officer--PetCare Plus, Inc., Aurora, IL; *U.S. Private*, pg. 856
Guyette, James M, Chm. Bd. & Pres.--Air Canada, New York, NY; *Int'l*, pg. 36
Guzman, Kathleen, Pres.--Christie's East, New York, NY; *Int'l*, pg. 290

Guzman, Samuel, Pres. & Chief Exec. Officer--Young & Rubicam Bogota, Bogota, Colombia; *U.S. Private,* pg. 1200
Guzzetti, Louis A., Jr., Pres. & Chief Exec. Officer--EnviroSource, Inc., Horsham, PA; *U.S. Public,* pg. 587
Guzzetti, William L., Pres. & Chief Oper. Officer--Hallwood Energy Partners, L.P., Denver, CO; *U.S. Public,* pg. 778
Guzzo, E.J., Pres.--Prime Bancshares Inc., Houston, TX; *U.S. Public,* pg. 1326
Gwinn, John C., Jr., Pres.--Congaree Construction Co., Inc., Columbia, SC; *U.S. Private,* pg. 263
Gyarfas, Tamas, Pres.--NAP-TV, Budapest, Hungary; *Int'l,* pg. 394
Gyde, Dick, Pres.--Childcraft Education Corporation, Lancaster, PA; *U.S. Public,* pg. 513
Gyenes, Peter, Pres. & Chief Exec. Officer--Ardent Software, Inc., Westborough, MA; *U.S. Public,* pg. 129
Gygi, Richard W., Pres.--CPS Corporation, Franklin, TN; *U.S. Private,* pg. 422
Gyllstrom, Gregory, Pres. & Chief Exec. Officer--Industrial Coatings Group, Inc., Chicago, IL; *U.S. Private,* pg. 434
Haab, Larry, Chm. Bd., Pres. & Chief Exec. Officer--Illinova Inc., Decatur, IL; *U.S. Public,* pg. 869
Haab, Larry D., Chm. Bd., Pres. & Chief Exec. Officer--Illinois Power Company, Decatur, IL; *U.S. Public,* pg. 869
Haag, Daniel S., Pres.--Major Sysco Food Services Inc., Modesto, CA; *U.S. Public,* pg. 1551
Haag, Herbert, Pres. & Chief Fin. Officer--PartnerRe Ltd., Pembroke, Bermuda; *Int'l,* pg. 1024
Haas-Wittmuess, Hans-Jurgen, Pres.--Banque Veuve Morin-Pons, Lyon, France; *Int'l,* pg. 419
Haas, B.K., Pres.--Bud Industries, Inc., Willoughby, OH; *U.S. Private,* pg. 178
Haas, Fred, Jr., Pres.--National Band & Tag Co., Newport, KY; *U.S. Private,* pg. 780
Haas, Kenneth H., Pres.--Intellicorp Inc., Mountain View, CA; *U.S. Public,* pg. 887
Haas, Marvin I., Pres. & Chief Exec. Officer--Chock Full O' Nuts Corporation, New York, NY; *U.S. Public,* pg. 351
Habecker, Eugene B., Pres., Chief Exec. Officer & Sec.--American Bible Society, New York, NY; *U.S. Private,* pg. 51
Habegger, Fred, Pres. & Chief Exec. Officer--The Habegger Corporation, Cincinnati, OH; *U.S. Private,* pg. 492
Habel, Michael, Mng. Principal--Baxter Hodell Donnelly Preston Inc., Cincinnati, OH; *U.S. Private,* pg. 124
Haber, Barry, Gen. Mgr.--Cuisinart Inc., Stamford, CT; *U.S. Private,* pg. 261
Haber, Edgar, M.D., Pres.--The Squibb Institute for Medical Research, Princeton, NJ; *U.S. Public,* pg. 254
Haberberger, Arthur A., Pres.--Horrigan American Inc., Reading, PA; *Int'l,* pg. 9
Habernickel, Duke, Pres.--The Haband Co., Prospect Park, NJ; *U.S. Private,* pg. 492
Hacart, Michel, Pres.--Circuit Foil Luxembourg S.A., Wiltz, Luxembourg; *Int'l,* pg. 80
Hach, Bruce J., Pres. & Chief Oper. Officer--Hach Company, Loveland, CO; *U.S. Public,* pg. 773
Hack, David, Partner & Grp. Art Dir.--Lewis Gace Bozell Healthcare Worldwide, Fort Lee, NJ; *U.S. Public,* pg. 1642
Hackenburg, P. Richard, Pres. & Chief Oper. Officer--Willis Corroon Advanced Risk Management Services, Nashville, TN; *Int'l,* pg. 1505
Hacker, Douglas A., Pres.--United Worldwide Corporation, Tumon, GU; *U.S. Public,* pg. 1653
Hackerman, Willard, Pres., Chief Exec. Officer & Treas.--The Whiting-Turner Contracting Co., Baltimore, MD; *U.S. Private,* pg. 1174
Hackett, James P., Pres. & Chief Exec. Officer--Steelcase Inc., Grand Rapids, MI; *U.S. Private,* pg. 1038
Hackett, John J., Pres.--TIE Systems, Inc. New England, Needham, MA; *U.S. Private,* pg. 1085
Hackett, Roger B., Chm. Bd., Pres., Chief Exec. & Chief Oper. Officer--Go-Video, Inc., Scottsdale, AZ; *U.S. Public,* pg. 748
Hackett, William F., Pres.--Barton Beers, Ltd., Chicago, IL; *U.S. Public,* pg. 300
Hackler, B.J., Pres.--Trans Louisiana Gas Co., Lafayette, LA; *U.S. Public,* pg. 145
Hackman, Daryl, Pres.--Farm & Home Oil Company, Telford, PA; *U.S. Private,* pg. 394
Hackney, F. Ray, Pres.--Duall Plastics, Inc., Athol, MA; *Int'l, pg. 233*
Hackney, Hodges, Pres.--Hackney International, Washington, NC; *U.S. Private,* pg. 1097
Hacksell, Uli, Pres.--Astra Draco AB, Lund, Sweden; *Int'l,* pg. 93
Hackworth, Michael L., Pres. & Chief Exec. Officer--Cirrus Logic, Inc., Fremont, CA; *U.S. Public,* pg. 375
Hadani, Ron, Pres.--DRS Medical Systems, Mahwah, NJ; *U.S. Public,* pg. 475
Hadden, E.M., Pres.--Standard Supply & Hardware Co., New Orleans, LA; *U.S. Private,* pg. 1032
Hadden, Richard, Pres.-Vancouver--Cossette Communication Marketing, Quebec, Canada; *Int'l,* pg. 335
Haddix, George, Pres.--CSG Systems International, Inc., Englewood, CO; *U.S. Public,* pg. 283
Haddock, Ron W., Pres. & Chief Exec. Officer--Fina, Inc., Dallas, TX; *Int'l,* pg. 1044
Haddrill, Richard M., Pres., Chief Exec. Officer & Treas.--Power House Technologies, Inc., Bozeman, MT; *U.S. Public,* pg. 1319
Hadeler, David, Pres., Chief Exec. Officer & Founder--Hadeler Sullivan Ewing, Dallas, TX; *U.S. Private,* pg. 493
Haderlein, Mary, Mng. Partner & Mngmt. Dir.--Grant/Jacoby, Inc., Chicago, IL; *U.S. Private,* pg. 470
Hadfield, Frederick W., Pres. & Chief Exec. Officer--Ingersoll-Dresser Pump Company, Liberty Corner, NJ; *U.S. Public,* pg. 529
Hadfield, Jay, Pres.--Utimaco Safeware, Inc., Windsor, CT; *Int'l,* pg. 1444
Hadfield, Mike, Pres.--Robert Bosch Fluid Power Corporation, Racine, WI; *Int'l,* pg. 204
Hadley, Bret, Pres.--Wham-O, Inc., San Francisco, CA; *U.S. Private,* pg. 1170
Haegele, Jack E., Chm. Bd. & Pres.--TBG Services, Inc., New York, NY; *Int'l,* pg. 1335
Haeger, M.R., Pres.--Abell-Howe Company, Forest Park, IL; *U.S. Private,* pg. 10
Haemmerle, Andre, Pres.--Intermedics S.A., Le Locle, Switzerland; *Int'l,* pg. 1307
Haessler, J., Pres.--Assurity Life Inc., Lincoln, NE; *U.S. Private,* pg. 1187
Haessler, John, Pres. & Chief Exec. Officer--Woodmen Accident & Life Co., Lincoln, NE; *U.S. Private,* pg. 1187
Hafer, Fred D., Chm. Bd., Pres. & Chief Exec. Officer--GPU, Inc., Morristown, NJ; *U.S. Public,* pg. 695
Hafner, F., Pres.--SBS Sociedad de Valores S.A., Madrid, Spain; *Int'l,* pg. 1331
Hafner, J.A., Jr., Pres. & Chief Exec. Officer--Riviana International Inc., Houston, TX; *U.S. Public,* pg. 1392
Hafner, Joseph A., Jr., Pres. & Chief Exec. Officer--Riviana Foods Inc., Houston, TX; *U.S. Public,* pg. 1392
Haft, Alfred, Pres.--Haywin Textile Products, Inc., Brooklyn, NY; *U.S. Private,* pg. 514
Haga, Tom, Pres.--Pioneer New Media Technologies, Long Beach, CA; *U.S. Private,* pg. 866
Hagadorn, Robert E., Pres.--Hazen & Sawyer, New York, NY; *U.S. Private,* pg. 514
Hagaman, John, Pres.--Dow Elanco, Indianapolis, IN; *U.S. Public,* pg. 522
Hagan, J. Michael, Chm. Bd. & Chief Exec. Officer--Furon Company, Laguna Niguel, CA; *U.S. Public,* pg. 688
Hageboeck, Leo, Pres.--Sperrholz Koch GmbH, Coesfeld, Germany; *Int'l,* pg. 1491
Hagelstein, Robert, Pres.--Greenwood Publishing Group Inc., Westport, CT; *Int'l,* pg. 1094
Hagen, Cliff, Pres. & Chief Exec. Officer--Cass-Clay Creamery, Fargo, ND; *U.S. Private,* pg. 218
Hager, J.L., Pres. & Chief Exec. Officer--WRR Environmental Services Co., Inc., Eau Claire, WI; *U.S. Public,* pg. 1792
Hagerty, Dean S., Pres.--Public Utility District No. 2 of Grant County, Ephrata, WA; *U.S. Private,* pg. 893
Haggarty, Michael C., Pres. & Chief Exec. Officer--The Auburn State Bank, Auburn, IN; *U.S. Public,* pg. 674
Haggerty, Charles A., Chm. Bd., Pres. & Chief Exec. Officer--Western Digital Corporation, Irvine, CA; *U.S. Public,* pg. 1758
Hagglund, Bjorn, Pres.--Stora Forest AB, Falun, Sweden; *Int'l,* pg. 1303
Hagie, John R., Pres.--Hagie Manufacturing Co., Clarion, IA; *U.S. Private,* pg. 493
Hagiwara, J., Pres.--The New Home Sewing Machine Co., Mahwah, NJ; *Int'l,* pg. 699
Hagiwara, Seiji, Pres.--The Yokohama Rubber Co., Ltd., Tokyo, Japan; *Int'l,* pg. 1521
Haglund, Mark, Pres.-Automotive--STP Corporation, Danbury, CT; *U.S. Public,* pg. 627
Haglund, Mark E., Pres.--STP Products, Inc., Danbury, CT; *U.S. Public,* pg. 627
Hagmeyer, R.W., Pres.--Convenience Plus Partners Ltd., Denver, CO; *U.S. Private,* pg. 271
Hagood D. Maybank, Pres.--William M. Bird & Co., Inc., Charleston, SC; *U.S. Private,* pg. 145
Hahn, George E., Pres.--Hahn Systems, Inc., Indianapolis, IN; *U.S. Private,* pg. 493
Hahn, Horst, Pres., Chief Exec. Officer & Gen. Mgr.--Multimatic Corporation, Northvale, NJ; *U.S. Private,* pg. 767
Hahn, Yea Sun, Pres.--Korea Development Leasing Corporation, Seoul, Korea; *Int'l,* pg. 1010
Hahnlee, Tim, Partner--Media That Works, Cincinnati, OH; *U.S. Private,* pg. 727
Hahs, Dwain L., Pres.--Eyewear Division, Rochester, NY; *U.S. Public,* pg. 194
Hai, Hong, Dr., Pres. & Chief Exec. Officer--Haw Par Brothers International Limited, Singapore, Singapore; *Int'l,* pg. 603
Hai, Hong, Dr., Pres. & Chief Exec. Officer--Tiger Medicals Ltd., Singapore, Singapore; *Int'l,* pg. 603
Haidinger, Robert N., Chm. Bd., Pres. & Chief Exec. Officer--JJI Lighting Group Inc., Greenwich, CT; *Int'l,* pg. 821
Haigh, Brian, Pres.--Organon Inc., West Orange, NJ; *Int'l,* pg. 48
Haile, William B., Pres. & Chief Exec. Officer--SunTrust Bank, Savannah, N.A., Savannah, GA; *U.S. Public,* pg. 1538
Haiman, Kurt, Pres.--Grey Design & Promotion, New York, NY; *U.S. Public,* pg. 764
Haimann, Emilio, Pres.--BDDP S.p.A, Milan, Italy; *Int'l,* pg. 117
Haimovitz, Jules, Pres. & Chief Oper. Officer--King World Productions, Inc., New York, NY; *U.S. Public,* pg. 961
Haines, Debby L., Pres.--Simian Company, Inc., Santa Cruz, CA; *U.S. Public,* pg. 1357
Haines, James S., Jr., Pres. & Chief Exec. Officer--El Paso Electric Company, El Paso, TX; *U.S. Public,* pg. 567
Haines, John B., IV, Pres.--Haines Kibblehouse, Skippack, PA; *U.S. Private,* pg. 494
Haines, Peter, Pres. & Chief Exec. Officer--Cybex International, Inc., Medway, MA; *U.S. Private,* pg. 1114
Haines, Terry L., Pres. & Chief Exec. Officer--A. Schulman, Inc., Akron, OH; *U.S. Public,* pg. 1441
Haines, W.K., Jr., Pres.--Haines & Co., Inc., Canton, OH; *U.S. Private,* pg. 494
Hainley, Gary, Pres.--The Shannon Group, Brentwood, TN; *U.S. Public,* pg. 1041
Haire, Larry, Pres. & Chief Oper. Officer--Kilgore First National Bank, Kilgore, TX; *U.S. Public,* pg. 630
Hakala, Heikki, Pres. & Chief Exec. Officer-Rauma Oy--UPM-Kymmene Corporation, Helsinki, Finland; *Int'l,* pg. 1427
Hakala, Heikki, Pres. & Chief Exec. Officer--Rauma Ltd., Helsinki, Finland; *Int'l,* pg. 1428
Hakanson, John, Pres.--System Sensor Division, Saint Charles, IL; *U.S. Public,* pg. 1306
Hakanson, Staffan, Pres.--SAB WABCO N.V., Zaventem, Belgium; *Int'l,* pg. 271
Hake, J.J., Pres.--Duke Manufacturing Co., Inc., Saint Louis, MO; *U.S. Private,* pg. 346
Hakim, B.H., Pres.--P.T. Caltex Pacific Indonesia, Jakarta, Indonesia; *U.S. Public,* pg. 348
Hakim, George N., Jr., Pres.--Crowntuft Manufacturing Co., New York, NY; *U.S. Public,* pg. 948
Hakkarainen, Ari, Pres.--TrioVing a.s., Hoyden, Norway; *Int'l, pg. 18*
Hakooz, Samir A., Pres.--Plasma Energy Corporation, Raleigh, NC; *U.S. Public,* pg. 344
Halamoda, Jurgen, Pres.--Astra Ges. m.b.H., Lienz, Austria; *Int'l,* pg. 93
Halamuda, Jerry, Pres. & Chief Oper. Officer--Color Spot Nursery, Inc., Pleasant Hill, CA; *U.S. Private,* pg. 254
Halbreich, Jeremy L., Pres. & Gen. Mgr.--The Dallas Morning News, Inc., Dallas, TX; *U.S. Public,* pg. 209
Halbrook, John A., Chm. Bd., Pres. & Chief Exec. Officer--Woodward Governor Company, Rockford, IL; *U.S. Public,* pg. 1776
Halcomb, Dr. Joseph, Pres.--Hall Surgical Division, Carpinteria, CA; *U.S. Public,* pg. 254
Hale, Elden A., Jr., Pres.--NYT Video Productions, Scranton, PA; *U.S. Public,* pg. 1174
Hale, Elden A., Jr., Pres.--WTKR-TV, Norfolk, VA; *U.S. Public,* pg. 1174
Hale, J.E., Pres.--Texaco Trinidad, Inc., Port of Spain, Trinidad & Tobago; *U.S. Public,* pg. 1584
Hale, Jeffrey, Pres.-Media Information Grp.--Competitive Media Reporting, New York, NY; *Int'l,* pg. 1447
Hale, John, Chm. Bd., Pres. & Chief Exec. Officer--Telex Communications, Inc., Minneapolis, MN; *U.S. Private,* pg. 1074
Hale, Roger L., Chm. Bd., Pres. & Chief Exec. Officer--Tennant Company, Minneapolis, MN; *U.S. Public,* pg. 1577
Hale, Roger W., Chm. Bd., Pres. & Chief Exec. Officer--LG & E Energy Corp., Louisville, KY; *U.S. Public,* pg. 970
Halef, Besim, Pres.--MM Industra, Ltd., Dartmouth, Canada; *Int'l,* pg. 74
Halenda, John, Pres.--Wynn's-Precision, Inc., Lebanon, TN; *U.S. Public,* pg. 1783
Hales, Antony J., Chief Exec.--Allied Domecq PLC, London, United Kingdom; *Int'l,* pg. 62
Haley, Jane Gosiger, Pres.--Gosiger Inc., Dayton, OH; *U.S. Private,* pg. 466
Haley, Larry W., Chm. Bd. & Pres.--Midwest Tire & Muffler, Inc., Rapid City, SD; *U.S. Private,* pg. 745
Haley, Michael P., Pres.--American Furniture Company, Incorporated, Martinsville, VA; *U.S. Public,* pg. 974
Haley, Regina, Pres.--Finnaren & Haley, Inc., Conshohocken, PA; *U.S. Private,* pg. 405
Haley, Robert G., Pres.--BellSouth Information Systems, Inc. (BIS), Atlanta, GA; *U.S. Public,* pg. 208
Haley, Roy W., Pres. & Chief Exec. Officer--WESCO Distribution, Inc., Pittsburgh, PA; *U.S. Private,* pg. 244
Haley, Thomas D., Pres. & Chief Oper. Officer--Centrex Corporation, Findlay, OH; *U.S. Private,* pg. 225
Hall, A. Stewart, Jr., Pres. & Chief Oper. Officer--Hughes Supply, Inc., Orlando, FL; *U.S. Public,* pg. 846
Hall, Alvin D., Pres. & Chief Exec. Officer--Miller & Smith, Inc., Mc Lean, VA; *U.S. Private,* pg. 746
Hall, Andrew J., Pres.--Phibro Division of Salomon Inc., Westport, CT; *U.S. Public,* pg. 1633
Hall, Bradley C., Pres.--UGI Enterprises, King of Prussia, PA; *U.S. Public,* pg. 1653
Hall, C.L., Pres. & Chief Exec. Officer--Graybar Electric Company, Inc., Clayton, MO; *U.S. Private,* pg. 472
Hall, Charles, Pres.--Elgin National Industries, Inc., Downers Grove, IL; *U.S. Private,* pg. 370
Hall, Conrad M., Pres. & Chief Exec. Officer--Trader Publishing Company, Norfolk, VA; *U.S. Private,* pg. 649
Hall, Dennis J., Pres.--Carlisle Companies Incorporated, Syracuse, NY; *U.S. Public,* pg. 305
Hall, Don, Div. Mgr.--ConAgra Broiler Co., Gainesville, GA; *U.S. Public,* pg. 427
Hall, Donald M., Pres.--Cannon Equipment, Chattanooga, TN; *Int'l,* pg. 646
Hall, Floyd, Chm. Bd., Pres. & Chief Exec. Officer--Kmart Corporation, Troy, MI; *U.S. Public,* pg. 963
Hall, Gail, Pres. & Gen. Mgr.--Lexington Co-Op Oil Co., Lexington, NE; *U.S. Private,* pg. 666
Hall, Graham, Pres.--Todd-AO U.K., London, United Kingdom; *U.S. Public,* pg. 1619
Hall, Graham, Pres.--Todd-AO Europe Holding Ltd., London, United Kingdom; *U.S. Public,* pg. 1619
Hall, J. Robert, Pres.-Lenox Brands--Lenox, Incorporated, Lawrenceville, NJ; *U.S. Public,* pg. 261
Hall, J.E., Jr., Pres.--Central Freight Lines, Inc., Waco, TX; *U.S. Private,* pg. 223
Hall, James C., Pres. & Chief Exec. Officer--Fidelity Federal Savings Bank, Marion, IN; *U.S. Public,* pg. 632
Hall, James N., Pres.--Dacco, Inc., Cookeville, TN; *U.S. Private,* pg. 598
Hall, K. Michael, Pres., Chief Exec. & Chief Oper. Officer--Hall Contracting Corp., Louisville, KY; *U.S. Private,* pg. 495
Hall, Larry D., Chm. Bd., Pres. & Chief Exec. Officer--K N Energy, Inc., Lakewood, CO; *U.S. Public,* pg. 937
Hall, Larry W., Pres.--Hall Sign, Inc., Bloomington, IN; *U.S. Private,* pg. 495
Hall, Laurence W., Jr., Pres.--Robbins Manufacturing Company, Tampa, FL; *U.S. Private,* pg. 935
Hall, Richard M., Jr., Pres.--Colorado Business Leasing, Inc., Denver, CO; *U.S. Private,* pg. 255
Hall, Richard N., Sr., Pres.--Tennessee Dressed Beef Company, Nashville, TN; *U.S. Private,* pg. 1076
Hall, Robert, Pres.--Lenox Brands, Lawrenceville, NJ; *U.S. Public,* pg. 261
Hall, Robert, Pres.--Lenox Brands, Langhorne, PA; *U.S. Public,* pg. 261

Hall, Robert, Publisher--Philadelphia Newspapers, Inc., Philadelphia, PA; *U.S. Public*, pg. 964
Hall, Robert J., Chm. & Publr.--Philadelphia Daily News, Philadelphia, PA; *U.S. Public*, pg. 964
Hall, Thomas D., Pres. & Treas.--Acme Design Technology, Co., Crozet, VA; *U.S. Private*, pg. 13
Hall, Thomas L., Pres. & Chief Exec. Officer--International Women's Apparel Group, Easton, PA; *U.S. Public*, pg. 796
Hall, Thomas. W., Pres.--GTE Southwest Incorporated, Irving, TX; *U.S. Public*, pg. 697
Hall, William, Pres.--Sight & Sound, Wilsonville, OR; *U.S. Public*, pg. 780
Hall, William E., Pres.--Parsons Process Group Inc., Houston, TX; *U.S. Private*, pg. 842
Hall, William K., Pres. & Chief Exec. Officer--Eagle Industries, Inc., Chicago, IL; *U.S. Private*, pg. 473
Halla, Brian, Chm. Bd., Pres. & Chief Exec. Officer--National Semiconductor Corporation, Santa Clara, CA; *U.S. Public*, pg. 1159
Hallam, Howard, Pres. & Chief Oper. Officer--Ben E. Keith Company, Fort Worth, TX; *U.S. Private*, pg. 611
Hallam, Mark, Pres.--Ceiling & Partitions, Inc., Landover, MD; *U.S. Private*, pg. 221
Hallberg, Per, Pres.--Optiroc AB, Sollentuna, Sweden; *Int'l*, pg. 1200
Halle, Bruce T., Pres.--Discount Tire, Scottsdale, AZ; *U.S. Private*, pg. 334
Halle, Bruce T., Jr., Pres.--Reinalt-Thomas Corp., Ann Arbor, MI; *U.S. Private*, pg. 919
Haller, Federico G., Pres.--ATS Omega de Mexico, S.A. de C.V., Tlalnepantla, Mexico; *U.S. Public*, pg. 1222
Haller, J., Pres. & Chief Exec. Officer--PNC Bank, Cincinnati, OH; *U.S. Public*, pg. 1242
Hallet, Jim, Pres. & Chief Exec. Officer--Adesa Inc., Indianapolis, IN; *U.S. Public*, pg. 1116
Hallgren, Kenneth, Pres. & Chief Oper. Officer--Hurd Millwork Company, Inc., Medford, WI; *U.S. Private*, pg. 1113
Halligan, Joe, Pres. & Chief Exec. Officer--PharmChem Laboratories, Inc., Menlo Park, CA; *U.S. Public*, pg. 1285
Hallman, Richard, Pres.--Electronic Data Magnetics, Inc., High Point, NC; *U.S. Private*, pg. 370
Hallock, Peter, Pres.--Allan Schneider Associates, Southampton, NY; *U.S. Private*, pg. 971
Halloway, Michael, Pres. & Chief Exec. Officer--American Credit Services Inc., Rochester, NY; *U.S. Public*, pg. 336
Halluitte, Blaise, Pres.--Rhodia Nordeste, Sao Paulo, Brazil; *Int'l*, pg. 1109
Halper, Norman A., Pres.--The First Republic Corporation of America, New York, NY; *U.S. Public*, pg. 637
Halperin, Thomas C., Chm Bd., Pres. & Chief Exec. Officer--Commercial Light Company, Hillside, IL; *U.S. Private*, pg. 258
Halpin, Denise, Partner & Sr. V.P.--Media That Works, Cincinnati, OH; *U.S. Private*, pg. 727
Halpin, James F., Pres. & Chief Exec. Officer--CompUSA, Dallas, TX; *U.S. Public*, pg. 420
Halsey, A.W., Pres.--Texaco Petroleos de Angola S.A.R.L., Luanda, Angola; *U.S. Public*, pg. 1584
Halton, Dale F., Chm. Bd., Pres. & Chief Exec. Officer--Pepsi-Cola Bottling Company of Charlotte Inc., Charlotte, NC; *U.S. Private*, pg. 852
Halvorson, William, Pres.--Prospect Motors, Inc., Jackson, CA; *U.S. Private*, pg. 891
Ham, John, Pres. & Gen. Mgr.--Metabo Corporation, West Chester, PA; *U.S. Private*, pg. 734
Hamada, Eiji, Pres.--Dentsu (Taiwan) Inc., Taipei, Taiwan; *Int'l*, pg. 394
Hamada, Yasuyuki, Pres. & Chief Exec. Officer--Nisshin Steel Co., Ltd., Tokyo, Japan; *Int'l*, pg. 946
Hamanaka, Shoichiro, Pres.--Nippon Express Co., Ltd., Tokyo, Japan; *Int'l*, pg. 933
Hamar, Gary, Pres.--Zipp Industries, Plainview, TX; *U.S. Private*, pg. 1207
Hamar, Gary, Pres.--Pax Company, Salt Lake City, UT; *U.S.* Private, pg. 1207
Hamaya, Mike, Pres.--Bridgestone/Firestone Technology Company, Akron, OH; *Int'l*, pg. 213
Hamberg, Goran, Pres.--Hercules Grandlaggning AB, Kista, Sweden; *Int'l*, pg. 899
Hamburger, John A., Pres.--Parliament Company, Southfield, MI; *U.S. Private*, pg. 840
Hamel, Gilles, Pres. & Gen. Mgr.--Faucher Industries Inc., Saint Leonard, Canada; *Int'l*, pg. 479
Hamilburg, Maurice J., Pres. & Chief Exec. Officer--Plymouth Rubber Company, Inc., Canton, MA; *U.S. Public*, pg. 1311
Hamill, John P., Pres.--Fleet Bank of Massachusetts, N.A., Boston, MA; *U.S. Public*, pg. 649
Hamilton, Charles W., Pres. & Chief Oper. Officer--Aristech Chemical Corporation, Pittsburgh, PA; *Int'l*, pg. 872
Hamilton, David L., Pres. & Chief Oper. Officer--George W. Auch Co., Pontiac, MI; *U.S. Private*, pg. 98
Hamilton, David R., Chm. Bd., Pres. & Chief Exec. Officer--Chemical Leaman Corporation, Exton, PA; *U.S. Private*, pg. 233
Hamilton, Jeff A., Pres.--PTS Electronics Corporation, Bloomington, IN; *U.S. Private*, pg. 828
Hamilton, Josh, Pres.--CMI Industries, Inc., Geneva, AL; *U.S. Private*, pg. 195
Hamilton, Judith H., Pres.--Dataquest Incorporated, San Jose, CA; *U.S. Public*, pg. 535
Hamilton, Robert J. Jr., Pres.--Hamilton Equipment, Inc., Ephrata, PA; *U.S. Private*, pg. 497
Hamilton, Steven, Pres.--Hamilton Co., Inc., Reno, NV; *U.S.* Private, pg. 497
Hamilton, Thomas M., Chm. Bd., Pres. & Chief Exec. Officer--EEX Corporation, Houston, TX; *U.S. Public*, pg. 542
Hamlin, Craig, Pres. & Chief Exec. Officer--ADM Milling Co., Overland Park, KS; *U.S. Public*, pg. 128
Hamlin, Craig, Pres.--ADM Milling Co. - Rice Division, Shawnee Mission, KS; *U.S. Public*, pg. 128
Hamlin, Craig, Pres.--ADM Milling Co. - Valley Grain, Overland Park, KS; *U.S. Public*, pg. 128
Hamlin, Craig L., Pres. & Chief Exec. Officer--ADM Milling Co., Overland Park, KS; *U.S. Public*, pg. 128
Hamlin, Mark, Pres.--The Reserve Group, Akron, OH; *U.S. Private*, pg. 924
Hamm, Charles S., Pres.--Bellsouth Mobile Systems Group, Atlanta, GA; *U.S. Public*, pg. 208
Hamm, Charles S., Pres.--Bellsouth Cellular National Marketing, Inc., Atlanta, GA; *U.S. Public*, pg. 208
Hamm, Jerry T., Pres.--Jerry Hamm Chevrolet Inc., Jacksonville, FL; *U.S. Private*, pg. 497
Hamm, John W., Pres.--Sprecher & Schuh N. America, Houston, TX; *U.S. Public*, pg. 1397
Hamm, Willi, Pres.--Canadian Energy Services, New Westminster, Canada; *Int'l*, pg. 74
Hamm, Willi, Pres.--Industra Thermal Service Corporation, New Westminster, Canada; *Int'l*, pg. 74
Hammachek, Todd, Pres. & Chief Exec. Officer--Penford Corp., Bellevue, WA; *U.S. Public*, pg. 1269
Hammarstedt, Jan, Pres.--GPA Plast AB, Hjarnarp, Sweden; *Int'l*, pg. 678
Hammell, Randy, Pres.--Peacock Inc., La Salle, Canada; *Int'l*, pg. 1489
Hammer, C. LaRoy, Pres.--Stewart & Stevenson Vehicle Services, Inc., Houston, TX; *U.S. Public*, pg. 1518
Hammer, Jeffrey R., Pres.--Crystal Cabinet Works, Inc., Princeton, MN; *U.S. Private*, pg. 293
Hammer, John, Pres.--Revlon-Realistic Professional Products, Inc., New York, NY; *U.S. Private*, pg. 690
Hammer, Thomas James, Pres.--Quail Piping Products, Inc., Magnolia, AR; *U.S. Public*, pg. 137
Hammerberg, David L., V.P.-Opers.--Reames Foods Inc., Clive, IA; *U.S. Public*, pg. 977
Hammergren, John, Pres.--McKesson Health Systems, San Francisco, CA; *U.S. Public*, pg. 1073
Hammerstein, Steve, Pres.--International Center for Entrepreneurial Development, Inc., Cypress, TX; *U.S. Private*, pg. 568
Hammill, Richard D., Chm. Bd., Pres. & Chief Exec. Officer--Hycor Biomedical, Inc., Irvine, CA; *U.S. Public*, pg. 851
Hammond, Barbara, Pres.--Home Interiors & Gifts, Inc., Dallas, TX; *U.S. Private*, pg. 536
Hammond, Craig, Pres., Chief Oper. Officer & Sec.--L. Perrigo Company, Allegan, MI; *U.S. Public*, pg. 1280
Hammond, Harvey K., Jr., Chm. Bd., Pres. & Chief Exec. Officer--HNTB Corporation, Kansas City, MO; *U.S. Private*, pg. 492
Hammond, P., Pres.--American Tech Manufacturing Corporation, Glenolden, PA; *Int'l*, pg. 590
Hammond, T.L., Pres.--Southern Graphics Systems, Louisville, KY; *U.S. Public*, pg. 1386
Hammond, Terry, Pres. & Chief Exec. Officer--Crown International, Inc., Elkhart, IN; *U.S. Private*, pg. 293
Hammond, Thomas L., Pres.--GSE, Inc., Farmington, MI; *U.S. Public*, pg. 1676
Hammond, Toby B., Chm. Bd & Pres.--Hancock Lumber, Inc., Casco, ME; *U.S. Private*, pg. 498
Hamner, Nathan, Pres.--Seward Inc., Petersburg, VA; *U.S. Private*, pg. 988
Hamnes, Kare Angel, Pres.--Kvaerner Fjellstrand (S) Pte Ltd., Singapore, Singapore; *Int'l*, pg. 771
Hampel, Bernard, Ph.D., Pres. & Chief Exec. Officer--Eon Labs Manufacturing, Inc., Laurelton, NY; *U.S. Private*, pg. 379
Hampel, Larry, Partner & Creative Dir.--Hampel/Stefanides, New York, NY; *U.S. Private*, pg. 498
Hampson, David G., Pres. & Chief Oper. Officer--Willis Corroon Corp. of New Hampshire, Rochester, NH; *Int'l*, pg. 1506
Hampton, Bruce, Pres.--Railroad Pass Casino, Henderson, NV; *U.S. Public*, pg. 375
Hampton, Bruce, Pres.--Value Priced Clothing Inc., Culver City, CA; *U.S. Public*, pg. 1086
Hampton, Charles, Pres. & Chief Exec. Officer--American Louver Co., Skokie, IL; *U.S. Private*, pg. 58
Hamrick, C. Rush, III, Pres.--Bindley Western, Kendall Division, Shelby, NC; *U.S. Public*, pg. 228
Hamway, Ezra, Pres.--Remco Toys, New York, NY; *U.S. Public*, pg. 923
Hamway, Ezra, Pres.--American Home Entertainment, New York, NY; *U.S. Public*, pg. 923
Hanada, Susumu, Pres.--Tokyo-Mitsubishi Derivative Products (USA), Inc., New York, NY; *Int'l*, pg. 157
Hanan, Steven, Pres.--Boscarale/Tom Togs, New York, NY; *U.S. Private*, pg. 160
Hanasaki, Takenori, Pres. & Chief Exec. Officer--Oki Telecom Group, Suwanee, GA; *Int'l*, pg. 1000
Hanawa, Yoshikazu, Pres.--Nissan Motor Co., Ltd., Tokyo, Japan; *Int'l*, pg. 943
Hancock, David, Pres.--Spectrum Industries, Inc., Chippewa Falls, WI; *U.S. Private*, pg. 1024
Hancock, Gary, Pres.--Helena Chemical Company, Memphis, TN; *Int'l*, pg. 845
Hancock, George, Pres. & Chief Exec. Officer--Pyramid Breweries, Inc.; *U.S. Public*, pg. 1345
Hancock, George, Pres.--Thomas Kemper Lager, Seattle, WA; *U.S. Public*, pg. 1345
Hancock, George, Pres.--Thomas Kemper Soda Company, Seattle, WA; *U.S. Public*, pg. 1345
Hancock, Steve, Pres.--TBWA Chiat/Day Toronto, Toronto, Canada; *U.S. Private*, pg. 1063
Hand, Kerry, Pres. & Chief Exec. Officer--Communicorp, Inc., Columbus, GA; *U.S. Public*, pg. 28
Hand, Kevin, Pres.--EMAP France, Paris, France; *Int'l*, pg. 451
Hand, Melvin R., Pres.--Los Angeles Die Casting, Los Angeles, CA; *U.S. Public*, pg. 142
Hand, Scott M., Pres.--Inco Limited, Toronto, Canada; *Int'l*, pg. 672
Handerhan, Kevin J., Pres.--Ellwood Group, Inc., Ellwood City, PA; *U.S. Private*, pg. 373
Handerhan, Kevin J., Pres.--Ellwood City Forge, Ellwood City, PA; *U.S. Private*, pg. 373
Handy, David G., Pres. & Chief Exec. Officer--Associated Bank, National Association, Neenah, WI; *U.S. Public*, pg. 140
Haney, David C., Pres. & Chief Exec.Officer--Willis Corroon Corp. of Penn., Radnor, PA; *Int'l*, pg. 1507
Haney, J. Whitney, Pres.--PAR Microsystems Corporation, New Hartford, NY; *U.S. Public*, pg. 1256
Haney, R. Lee, Pres.--Saddle River Holdings Corp., Pearl River, NY; *U.S. Public*, pg. 1229
Haney, William M., III, Chm. Bd., Pres. & Chief Exec. Officer--Molten Metal Technology, Inc., Fall River, MA; *U.S. Public*, pg. 1123
Hanft, Adam, Mng. Partner & Pres.--Hanft Byrne Raboy Abrams & Partners, Inc., New York, NY; *U.S. Private*, pg. 499
Hanggi, Rolf, Pres. & Co-Chief Exec. Officer--Zurich Insurance Company, Zurich, Switzerland; *Int'l*, pg. 1529
Hanika, Stephen D., Sr. Partner & Acct. Mngmt.--EURO RSCG Tatham, Chicago, IL; *Int'l*, pg. 601
Hanka, Erina, Pres.--Suspa, Inc., Grand Rapids, MI; *Int'l*, pg. 1322
Hankins, A. Burton, Pres.--Hankins Lumber Company, Inc., Elliott, MS; *U.S. Private*, pg. 499
Hankinson, James F., Pres. & Chief Exec. Officer--New Brunswick Power Corporation, Fredericton, Canada; *Int'l*, pg. 923
Hanley, Bryant M., Jr., Pres.--Barrow, Hanley, Mewhinney & Strauss, Inc., Dallas, TX; *U.S. Public*, pg. 1672
Hanley, Peter C., Pres.--Arnold Advertising, Mc Lean, VA; *U.S. Private*, pg. 84
Hanley, Tim, Pres.--Telephone Directory Advertising, Atlanta, GA; *U.S. Private*, pg. 1073
Hanley, William T., Pres. & Chief Exec. Officer--Galileo Corp., Sturbridge, MA; *U.S. Public*, pg. 698
Hanlin, Russell L., Pres., Chief Exec. & Chief Oper. Officer--Sunkist Growers, Inc., Sherman Oaks, CA; *U.S. Private*, pg. 1052
Hanlon, Jack, Pres. & Chief Oper. Officer--Gerber Plumbing Fixtures Corporation, Chicago, IL; *U.S. Private*, pg. 449
Hanlon, Jack, Pres. & Chief Oper. Officer--Kokomo Sanitary Pottery Corp., Kokomo, IN; *U.S. Private*, pg. 449
Hanlon, Jerry, Pres.--AGRA Marine Construction Limited, Richmond, Canada; *Int'l*, pg. 30
Hanlon, Jerry, Pres.--AGRA Foundations (Pacific) Limited, Richmond, Canada; *Int'l*, pg. 30
Hanlon, Jerry, Pres.--MCL Pile Driving, Richmond, Canada; *Int'l*, pg. 30
Hanman, Gary, Pres. & Chief Exec. Officer--Mid-America Dairymen, Inc., Springfield, MO; *U.S. Private*, pg. 743
Hann, S.A., Chm. Bd. & Pres.--Medicalodges, Inc., Coffeyville, KS; *U.S. Private*, pg. 728
Hanna, Allan C., Pres. & Chief Exec. Officer--Zephyr Inc., Muskegon, MI; *U.S. Private*, pg. 1204
Hanna, Dan, Pres.--Hanna-Sherman International, Inc., Portland, OR; *U.S. Private*, pg. 499
Hanna, Don, Pres.--Eberline Instrument Corporation, Santa Fe, NM; *U.S. Public*, pg. 1593
Hanna, Don, Pres.--National Nuclear Corporation, Sunnyvale, CA; *U.S. Public*, pg. 1594
Hanna, William W., Pres. & Chief Oper. Officer--Koch Industries, Incorporated, Wichita, KS; *U.S. Private*, pg. 628
Hannah, Bill, Pres.--Nabholz Construction Corp., Conway, AR; *U.S. Private*, pg. 772
Hannah, David H., Pres.--Reliance Steel & Aluminum Co., Los Angeles, CA; *U.S. Public*, pg. 1375
Hannah, James, Pres.--Karnak Corporation, Clark, NJ; *U.S. Private*, pg. 607
Hannah, Thomas E., Pres. & Chief Exec. Officer--Collins & Aikman Corporation, Charlotte, NC; *U.S. Public*, pg. 399
Hannay, Roger A., Pres., Chief Exec. Officer & Chief Fin. Officer--Hannay Reels, Westerlo, NY; *U.S. Private*, pg. 499
Hannell, Geoff, Publr.--Harper Audio, New York, NY; *Int'l*, pg. 926
Hannigan, Raymond R., Pres. & Chief Exec. Officer--Kinetic Concepts, Inc., San Antonio, TX; *U.S. Private*, pg. 620
Hanon, John, Pres. & Chief Exec. Officer--Berks Products Corporation, Reading, PA; *U.S. Private*, pg. 136
Hans, Jean-Pierre, Pres.--Astra Luxembourg S.A.R.L., Ehlange, Luxembourg; *Int'l*, pg. 94
Hansberger, James R., Pres. & Chief Exec. Officer--RAM Golf Corporation, Melrose Park, IL; *U.S. Private*, pg. 908
Hansel, Stephen A., Pres. & Chief Exec. Officer--Hibernia Corporation, New Orleans, LA; *U.S. Public*, pg. 825
Hansen, D.K., Pres.--Crystal Cream & Butter Company, Sacramento, CA; *U.S. Private*, pg. 294
Hansen, Darryl D., Chm. Bd., Pres. & Chief Exec. Officer--Preferred Risk Mutual Insurance, West Des Moines, IA; *U.S. Private*, pg. 880
Hansen, Darryl D., Pres. & Chief Exec. Officer--Central Property & Casualty Insurance Company, West Des Moines, IA; *U.S. Private*, pg. 880
Hansen, Don, Pres.--Northrock Resources Ltd., Calgary, Canada; *Int'l*, pg. 970
Hansen, Donald W., Chm. Bd. & Pres.--Delta Resins & Refractories, Inc., Milwaukee, WI; *U.S. Private*, pg. 323
Hansen, Egon Friis, Pres.--AGA A/S, Copenhagen, Denmark; *Int'l*, pg. 13
Hansen, James, Chm. Bd. & Pres.--VideoLabs, Inc., Minneapolis, MN; *U.S. Public*, pg. 1720
Hansen, Jerry, Pres.--Recomp, Inc., Sandy, UT; *U.S. Private*, pg. 914
Hansen, John, Pres.--MD Foods Sverige AB, Malmo, Sweden; *Int'l*, pg. 826
Hansen, John J., Pres.--Kwik Trip Inc., La Crosse, WI; *U.S. Private*, pg. 637
Hansen, Justin, Owner--A.L. Hansen Manufacturing Co., Waukegan, IL; *U.S. Private*, pg. 500
Hansen, Otto, Pres.--A/S Ruko, Herlev, Denmark; *Int'l*, pg. 18
Hansen, Paul, Pres. & Chief Exec. Officer--Penobscot Shoe Company, Old Town, ME; *U.S. Public*, pg. 1273

Hansen, Poul, Pres.--Chr. Hansen A/S, Horsholm, Denmark; *Int'l*, pg. 288

Hansen, W.E., Pres.--Brandywine Sports, Inc., Wilmington, DE; *U.S. Private*, pg. 165

Hansen, William, II, Owner--A.L. Hansen Manufacturing Co., Waukegan, IL; *U.S. Private*, pg. 500

Hanson, John N., Pres. & Chief Exec. Officer--Joy Mining Machinery, Warrendale, PA; *U.S. Public*, pg. 789

Hanson, John Nils, Pres. & Chief Oper. Officer--Harnischfeger Industries, Inc., Saint Francis, WI; *U.S. Public*, pg. 788

Hanson, Leroy, Dr., Pres. & Chief Oper. Officer--Triple F, Inc., Des Moines, IA; *U.S. Private*, pg. 1104

Hanson, Rick, Chm. Bd., Pres. & Chief Exec. Officer--Old Home Foods, Inc., Saint Paul, MN; *U.S. Private*, pg. 814

Hanson, Russell, Pres. & Gen. Mgr.--Flexible Assembly Systems Division, Bridgman, MI; *Int'l*, pg. 204

Hanson, Steven E., Pres.--Calcitek, Inc., Carlsbad, CA; *Int'l*, pg. 1307

Hantho, Charles H., Chm. Bd.--DoFasco, Inc., Hamilton, Canada; *Int'l*, pg. 414

Happel, Joe, Pres.--Ampco Saftey Tools, Dallas Div., Garland, TX; *U.S. Private*, pg. 67

Happel, R.W., V.P. & Gen. Mgr.--Electro-Motive Division, La Grange, IL; *U.S. Public*, pg. 719

Hara, Akira, Pres.--Baldwin Printing Control Equipment (Beijing) Company, Ltd., Beijing, China; *U.S. Public*, pg. 170

Hara, Akira, Pres.--Baldwin Asia Pacific Ltd., Hong Kong, Hong Kong; *U.S. Public*, pg. 170

Hara, Akira, Pres.--Baldwin Graphic Equipment Pty., Balmain, Australia; *U.S. Public*, pg. 170

Hara, Akira, Pres.--Baldwin Printing Control Equipment (Beijing) Co., Ltd., Shanghai, China; *U.S. Public*, pg. 170

Hara, Tadahiro, Pres.--Toyo Corporation, Tokyo, Japan; *Int'l*, pg. 1410

Hara, Takashi, Pres.--Toray Engineering Co., Ltd., Osaka, Japan; *Int'l*, pg. 1399

Hara, Yoshinari, Pres.--Daiwa Securities Co. Ltd., Tokyo, Japan; *Int'l*, pg. 374

Harada, Eiko, Pres.--Apple Computer Japan, Inc., Tokyo, Japan; *U.S. Public*, pg. 121

Harada, Hiroo, Pres. Dir.--P.T. IBJ Indonesia Bank, Jakarta, Indonesia; *Int'l*, pg. 676

Haraki, Shingo, Pres.--Dentsu East Japan Inc., Tokyo, Japan; *Int'l*, pg. 393

Harary, Joey, Pres.--Jacques Moret, Inc., New York, NY; *U.S. Private*, pg. 580

Haratunian, M., Pres. & Chief Exec. Officer--STV Architects, Douglassville, PA; *U.S. Public*, pg. 1421

Harbaugh, Rick, Pres.--The Overland National Bank, Grand Island, NE; *U.S. Public*, pg. 629

Harbert, Raymond J., Pres. & Chief Exec. Officer--Harbert Corporation, Birmingham, AL; *U.S. Private*, pg. 500

Harbing, Lars-Peter, Pres. & Chief Exec. Officer--Getinge/Castle Inc., Rochester, NY; *Int'l*, pg. 551

Harbour, Patrick C., Pres.--Harbour Contractors, Inc., Naperville, IL; *U.S. Private*, pg. 500

Harcourt, John P., Jr., Pres. & Chief Exec. Officer--Healthcare America, Inc., Austin, TX; *U.S. Private*, pg. 515

Harcourt, R., Pres.--Angus Fire Limited, Mississauga, Canada; *Int'l*, pg. 1500

Harcourt, R.M., Pres.--Flexline Hose Inc., Fuquay Varina, NC; *Int'l*, pg. 1500

Hard, Brian, Pres.--Penske Truck Leasing Company LP, Reading, PA; *U.S. Private*, pg. 850

Hard, Brian, Pres.--Penske Logistics, Reading, PA; *U.S. Private*, pg. 851

Hardage, Samuel A., Pres. & Chief Exec. Officer--The Woodfin Suite Hotels, San Diego, CA; *U.S. Private*, pg. 1187

Harder, Ronald R., Pres. & Chief Exec. Officer--Jewelers Mutual Insurance Company, Neenah, WI; *U.S. Private*, pg. 587

Hardesty, John D., Pres.--Maryland & Virginia Milk Producers Cooperative Association, Inc., Reston, VA; *U.S. Private*, pg. 711

Hardie, Graham, Pres.--Aker Contracting plc, Aberdeen, United Kingdom; *Int'l*, pg. 42

Hardin, James, Pres. & Chief Exec. Officer--Brookshire Grocery, Tyler, TX; *U.S. Private*, pg. 172

Hardin, Joseph, Jr., Pres. & Chief Exec. Officer--Kinko's Corporation, Ventura, CA; *U.S. Private*, pg. 622

Hardin, Leonard, Pres.--National City Bank, Kentucky, Louisville, KY; *U.S. Public*, pg. 1154

Hardin, Tom, Pres. & Chief Oper. Officer--Hub Group, Inc., Lombard, IL; *U.S. Public*, pg. 844

Harding, Christopher, Sir, Chm. Bd.--Legal & General Group PLC, London, United Kingdom; *Int'l*, pg. 805

Harding, Frank I., III, Pres.--Key Trust Company of Ohio, National Association, Cleveland, OH; *U.S. Public*, pg. 955

Harding, L.G., Pres.--Maple Leaf Meats, Winnipeg, Canada; *Int'l*, pg. 841

Hardison, Jerry, Pres.--Lone Star Corrugated Container Corporation, Irving, TX; *U.S. Private*, pg. 674

Hardison, Jerry, Pres.--Lone Star Container Sales Corp., Irving, TX; *U.S. Private*, pg. 674

Hardman, Gregory S., Pres.--Warsteiner Importers Agency, Lombard, IL; *Int'l*, pg. 1486

Hardt, David, Pres.--Data-Tronics Corp., Fort Smith, AR; *U.S. Public*, pg. 130

Hardt, Ralph, Pres.--Oberg Industries Corp., Freeport, PA; *U.S. Private*, pg. 810

Hardy-Magerko, Maggie, Pres. & Chief Oper. Officer--84 Lumber Company, Eighty Four, PA; *U.S. Private*, pg. 366

Hardy, Allan J., Pres.--Gemini Aluminum Corporation, Pomona, CA; *U.S. Private*, pg. 443

Hardy, E. Russell, Pres.--Services Division, Sunnyvale, CA; *U.S. Public*, pg. 293

Hardy, Thomas G., Pres. & Chief Oper. Officer--Trans Resources, Inc., New York, NY; *U.S. Private*, pg. 1096

Hare, Ronald, Pres. & Chief Oper. Officer--Petroleum Marketers, Inc., Roanoke, VA; *U.S. Private*, pg. 859

Haretakis, Catherine, Pres.--Spires Restaurants Inc., Orange, CA; *U.S. Private*, pg. 1026

Harf, Peter, Dr., Pres. & Chief Exec. Officer--Joh. A. Benckiser GmbH, Ludwigshafen, Germany; *Int'l*, pg. 185

Harford, Jim, Chm. Bd., Pres. & Chief Exec. Officer--Everfresh Beverages Inc., Chicago, IL; *U.S. Public*, pg. 1153

Hargrave, Robert L., Pres. & Treas.--Takumei Kumiai Holdings, Inc., Houston, TX; *U.S. Public*, pg. 1518

Hargraves, David, Pres.--DTC Communications, Inc., Nashua, NH; *U.S. Private*, pg. 306

Harjehausen, Ed, Pres.--ADM Ethanol Sales, Decatur, IL; *U.S. Public*, pg. 127

Harker, John V., Chm. Bd., Pres. & Chief Exec. Officer--In Focus Systems, Inc., Wilsonville, OR; *U.S. Public*, pg. 873

Harker, Roger, Pres.--Bently Nevada Corporation, Minden, NV; *U.S. Private*, pg. 134

Harkey, John D., Jr., Partner--Cracken, Harkey, Street & Co., LLC, Dallas, TX; *U.S. Private*, pg. 283

Harkins, Frank S., Jr., Pres. & Chief Exec. Officer--Bank of Raleigh, Beckley, WV; *U.S. Public*, pg. 836

Harl, R. Randall, Pres.--Brown & Root Industrial Services, Houston, TX; *U.S. Public*, pg. 775

Harlacher, Meredith I., Pres. & Chief Oper. Officer--Conectiv, Wilmington, DE; *U.S. Public*, pg. 430

Harlan, Leonard M., Pres.--Castle-Harlan, Inc., New York, NY; *U.S. Private*, pg. 219

Harless, Katharine J., Pres.--GTE Airfone Incorporated, Oak Brook, IL; *U.S. Public*, pg. 696

Harlev, Raphael, Pres.--El Al Airlines Ltd., Lod, Israel; *Int'l*, pg. 435

Harley, Hugh, Pres.--Rossignol Ski Co., Williston, VT; *Int'l*, pg. 1127

Harlin, James, Pres.--Mid-Continent Life Insurance Company, Oklahoma City, OK; *U.S. Public*, pg. 655

Harlow, John M., Pres.--Intervest-Mortgage Investment Company, Lake Oswego, OR; *U.S. Public*, pg. 1516

Harmala, Jukka, Chm. Bd., Pres. & Chief Exec. Officer--Enso Oyj, Helsinki, Finland; *Int'l*, pg. 455

Harman, Mike, Pres.--MW Manufacturers Inc., Rocky Mount, VA; *Int'l*, pg. 593

Harmel, Paul, Pres. & Chief Oper. Officer--Lifetouch, Portrait Studios, Eden Prairie, MN; *U.S. Private*, pg. 667

Harmon, David E., Chm. Bd., Pres., Chief Exec. & Chief Oper. Officer--El Camino Resources, Ltd., Woodland Hills, CA; *U.S. Private*, pg. 366

Harmon, Lowell D., Chm. Bd. & Pres.--Progressive Driver Services, Inc., Jacksonville, FL; *U.S. Private*, pg. 890

Harmon, Steven J., Pres. & Chief Exec. Officer--Twin City Die Castings Co., Minneapolis, MN; *U.S. Private*, pg. 1111

Harmon, W. Henry, Pres.--Columbia Coal Gasification Corp., Ashland, KY; *U.S. Public*, pg. 402

Harmon, W. Henry, Pres. & Chief Exec. Officer--Columbia Natural Resources, Inc., Charleston, WV; *U.S. Public*, pg. 403

Harms, Robert L., Pres. & Gen. Mgr.--3M Canada Inc., London, Canada; *U.S. Public*, pg. 1606

Harned, John, Pres.--Indian River Transport Co., Winter Haven, FL; *U.S. Private*, pg. 560

Harnett, Gordon D., Chm. Bd., Pres. & Chief Exec. Officer--Brush Wellman Inc., Cleveland, OH; *U.S. Public*, pg. 266

Harp, Gerald L., Chm. Bd. & Pres.--Harp's Food Stores, Inc., Springdale, AR; *U.S. Private*, pg. 504

Harper, Daniel R., Chm. Bd. & Pres.--Harper Bros., Inc., Fort Myers, FL; *U.S. Private*, pg. 504

Harper, Marvin, Chm. Bd. & Chief Exec. Officer--General Spring, Inc., Hartsville, TN; *U.S. Private*, pg. 445

Harper, Robert Y., Pres. & Chief Oper. Officer--Hopkinsville Milling Co., Hopkinsville, KY; *U.S. Private*, pg. 538

Harper, Ronald G., Chm. Bd., Pres. & Chief Exec. Officer--MPSI Systems Inc., Tulsa, OK; *U.S. Public*, pg. 1027

Harra, Robert V.A., Jr., Pres., Chief Oper. Officer & Treas.--Wilmington Trust Corporation, Wilmington, DE; *U.S. Public*, pg. 1770

Harrell, Edward H., Pres.--Tribune Review Publishing Co., Greensburg, PA; *U.S. Private*, pg. 1102

Harrell, Michael K., Pres.--Bellsouth Mobile Data, Inc., Atlanta, GA; *U.S. Public*, pg. 208

Harrell, Samuel M., Chm. Bd., Pres. & Chief Exec. Officer--EDI International, Inc., Cincinnati, OH; *U.S. Private*, pg. 353

Harrelson, Ronald S., Pres.--CFE Company, Phoenix, AZ; *U.S. Public*, pg. 51

Harries, David, Pres. & Chief Exec. Officer--DMB&B Montreal, Montreal, Canada; *U.S. Private*, pg. 304

Harrigan, W. Brian, Pres. & Chief Exec. Officer--United Insurance Companies, Inc., Dallas, TX; *U.S. Public*, pg. 1679

Harrington, Daniel M., Pres.--Allentown Cement Co. Inc., Blandon, PA; *Int'l*, pg. 1201

Harrington, David A., Pres.--Delta Rubber Company, Danielson, CT; *U.S. Private*, pg. 323

Harrington, Richard J., Pres., Chief Exec. & Oper. Officer--The Thomson Corporation, Stamford, CT; *U.S. Public*, pg. 1599

Harrington, Richard J., Pres. & Chief Exec. Officer--Thomson Professional Publishing, Stamford, CT; *U.S. Public*, pg. 1601

Harris, Ben, Pres.--Jarman Shoe Co., Nashville, TN; *U.S. Public*, pg. 728

Harris, Ben T., Pres. & Chief Exec. Officer--Genesco Inc., Nashville, TN; *U.S. Public*, pg. 728

Harris, Cynthia, Pres.--The Renovator's Supply, Inc., Conway, NH; *U.S. Private*, pg. 923

Harris, David J., Pres. & Chief Exec. Officer--M & I Bank Northeast, Green Bay, WI; *U.S. Public*, pg. 1050

Harris, Franco, Owner--Parks LLC, Baltimore, MD; *U.S. Private*, pg. 840

Harris, G. Dennis, Pres.--North Bros. Co., Atlanta, GA; *U.S. Private*, pg. 853

Harris, George, Pres. & Chief Fin. Officer--Harris, Baio & McCullough Inc., Philadelphia, PA; *U.S. Private*, pg. 504

Harris, George, Pres.--Evenflo Company, Inc., Piqua, OH; *U.S. Private*, pg. 629

Harris, George C., Chm. Bd. & Pres.--Lumber Group Inc., Dothan, AL; *U.S. Private*, pg. 680

Harris, Graeme, Partner--Goldsack Harris Thompson Advertising, Wellington, New Zealand; *U.S. Private*, pg. 184

Harris, James A., Pres. & Chief Exec. Officer--Eljer Plumbingware, Dallas, TX; *U.S. Public*, pg. 1794

Harris, Jerrold B., Pres. & Chief Exec. Officer--VWR Scientific Products, West Chester, PA; *U.S. Public*, pg. 1703

Harris, John, Pres. & Chief Oper. Officer--Harris Steel Group Inc., Willowdale, Canada; *Int'l*, pg. 597

Harris, John, Pres.--Harris Rebar, Stoney Creek, Canada; *Int'l*, pg. 598

Harris, Jordan, Co-Pres.--Sony Music Entertainment, Inc., New York, NY; *Int'l*, pg. 1281

Harris, Joseph R., Pres.--General Drug Co., Chicago, IL; *U.S. Private*, pg. 1007

Harris, King, Pres. & Chief Exec. Officer--Pittway Corporation, Chicago, IL; *U.S. Public*, pg. 1305

Harris, Leonard J., Pres.--Consolidated Viscount Resources Ltd., Vancouver, Canada; *Int'l*, pg. 326

Harris, Michael S., Pres. & Chief Exec. Officer--Deck House Inc., Acton, MA; *U.S. Private*, pg. 320

Harris, Michael S., Pres. & Chief Exec. Officer--Acorn Structures, Acton, MA; *U.S. Private*, pg. 320

Harris, Michael W., Pres.-Mfg.--World Color Press, Inc., Greenwich, CT; *U.S. Public*, pg. 1778

Harris, Randy, Pres.--Sunwest Bank of Clovis, N.A., Clovis, NM; *U.S. Public*, pg. 1165

Harris, Richard, Pres.--Western Indemnity Insurance Company, Houston, TX; *U.S. Public*, pg. 685

Harris, Richard M., Pres.--Predicasts, Cleveland, OH; *U.S. Public*, pg. 1600

Harris, Rob, Pres.--GSW Heating Products Company, Stoney Creek, Canada; *Int'l*, pg. 538

Harris, Rob, Pres.--GSW Jackes-Evans Manufacturing Co., Saint Louis, MO; *Int'l*, pg. 538

Harris, Robert D., Pres. & Chief Oper. Officer--Elastic Materials, Inc., Smithville, OH; *U.S. Private*, pg. 367

Harris, Robert M., Pres. & Chief Exec. Officer--GFA Brands, Inc., Cresskill, NJ; *U.S. Private*, pg. 435

Harris, Robert R., Pres.--Armtec Defense Products Co., Coachella, CA; *U.S. Public*, pg. 594

Harris, Ron R., Pres. & Chief Exec. Officer--Pervasive Software Inc., Austin, TX; *U.S. Public*, pg. 1280

Harris, Stan, Partner--Harris Drury Cohen, Fort Lauderdale, FL; *U.S. Private*, pg. 505

Harris, Steve, Pres.--Frontier Transport Corporation, Indianapolis, IN; *Int'l*, pg. 1469

Harris, Thomas E., Pres. & Chief Exec. Officer--Commonwealth Gas Services, Inc., Richmond, VA; *U.S. Public*, pg. 403

Harris, Tim, Pres.--Armour Food Company, Downers Grove, IL; *U.S. Public*, pg. 427

Harris, Tim, Pres.--Princess Cruise Lines, Los Angeles, CA; *Int'l*, pg. 1035

Harris, Tim, Pres. & Chief Oper. Officer--Witt Company, Cincinnati, OH; *U.S. Private*, pg. 1185

Harris, William B., Pres. & Chief Exec. Officer--Trevira, Charlotte, NC; *Int'l*, pg. 626

Harrison, A., Pres.--Racal NCS Inc., Houston, TX; *Int'l*, pg. 1083

Harrison, Angela E., Pres. & Chief Exec. Officer--Welsco Inc., North Little Rock, AR; *U.S. Private*, pg. 1161

Harrison, Barry W., Pres. & Chief Exec. Officer--Mark Resources Inc., Calgary, Canada; *Int'l*, pg. 842

Harrison, Carl, Pres.--McCain Refrigerated Foods Inc., Oakville, Canada; *Int'l*, pg. 850

Harrison, David, Pres. & Chief Exec. Officer--Harrison, Young, Pesonen & Newell Inc., Toronto, Canada; *Int'l*, pg. 598

Harrison, E. Hunter, Pres. & Chief Exec. Officer--Illinois Central Corporation, Chicago, IL; *U.S. Public*, pg. 864

Harrison, Gary, Pres. & Chief Oper. Officer--Mrs. Smith's Bakeries, Inc., Thomasville, GA; *U.S. Public*, pg. 657

Harrison, J. Dan, Pres. & Chief Oper. Officer--Schott's Bakery, Inc., Houston, TX; *U.S. Public*, pg. 658

Harrison, James W., Pres. & Exec. V.P.-Metal Chemicals North America--Henkel Surface Technologies, Madison Heights, MI; *Int'l*, pg. 610

Harrison, John, Pres. & Chief Exec. Officer--Chemical Bank Key State, Owosso, MI; *U.S. Public*, pg. 345

Harrison, John C., Jr., Pres. & Chief Exec. Officer--Harrison Construction Corp., Miami, FL; *U.S. Private*, pg. 506

Harrison, John J., Pres.--DiMark, Inc., Langhorne, PA; *U.S. Public*, pg. 793

Harrison, N.A., Pres. & Chief Exec. Officer--BFC Construction Corporation, Scarborough, Canada; *Int'l*, pg. 118

Harrison, Neil, Pres.--Weight Watchers Gourmet Food Company, Pittsburgh, PA; *U.S. Public*, pg. 806

Harrison, Richard, Pres.--Atlantic Auto Finance Corp., Fairport, NY; *U.S. Private*, pg. 1095

Harrison, Richard, Pres. & Chief Oper. Officer--Parametric Technology Corporation, Waltham, MA; *U.S. Public*, pg. 1257

Harrison, Richard, Pres.--Parametric Technology Corporation, Bedford, MA; *U.S. Public*, pg. 1257

Harrison, Ridgley W., III, Pres.--Minwax Company Div., Upper Saddle River, NJ; *U.S. Public*, pg. 1466

Harrison, Robert E., Pres., Chief Exec. & Fin. Officer--Standard Commercial Corporation, Wilson, NC; *U.S. Public*, pg. 1501

Harrison, Thomas, Principal--Hoak Capital, Dallas, TX; *U.S. Private*, pg. 531

Harrison, Thomas L., Pres.--Diversified Agency Services, New York, NY; *U.S. Public*, pg. 1223

Harrold, Orville R., Pres.--Providence and Worcester Railroad Company, Worcester, MA; *U.S. Public*, pg. 1336

Harshman, Richard R., Pres. & Chief Exec. Officer--Storck U.S.A., L.P., Chicago, IL; *Int'l*, pg. 1304

Hart, E. Thomas, Pres. & Chief Exec. Officer--QuickLogic Corporation, Sunnyvale, CA; *U.S. Private*, pg. 901

Hart, Edward, Pres.--Wabash Magnetics, Huntington, IN; *U.S. Private*, pg. 351

Hart, James W., Chm. Bd., Pres., Chief Exec. Officer & Chief Fin. Officer--Hart Holding Company, Inc., Norwalk, CT; *U.S. Private*, pg. 507

Hart, Kenneth A., Pres., Chief Oper. Officer & Sec.--First Trust and Savings Bank of Taylorville, Taylorville, IL; *U.S. Public*, pg. 644

Hart, Robert, Pres.--Sierracin/Sylmar Corporation, Sylmar, CA; *U.S. Private*, pg. 999

Hart, Ronald D., Pres. & Treas.--Hart Crowser, Inc., Seattle, WA; *U.S. Private*, pg. 507

Hart, Tom, Pres. & Chief Oper. Officer--The Crown Group, Inc., Warren, MI; *U.S. Private*, pg. 292

Hartery, John C., Pres.--Stora Forest Industries, Port Hawkesbury, Canada; *Int'l*, pg. 1304

Hartgraves, John, Pres.--Brazos Electric Power Cooperative, Inc., Waco, TX; *U.S. Private*, pg. 166

Hartke, Phillip, Pres.--Effingham-Clay Service Co., Effingham, IL; *U.S. Private*, pg. 365

Hartl, Richard, Chm. Bd., Pres. & Chief Exec. Officer--Calmar Inc., City of Industry, CA; *U.S. Private*, pg. 201

Hartman, Carl C., Pres., Chief Exec. Officer & Chief Oper. Officer--Trinidad/Benham Corp., Denver, CO; *U.S. Private*, pg. 1103

Hartman, David, Pres.--Midwest Products, Inc., Strafford, MO; *U.S. Public*, pg. 849

Hartman, Jack, Pres. & Chief Exec. Officer--SunTrust Bank, Southeast Georgia, N.A., Brunswick, GA; *U.S. Public*, pg. 1538

Hartman, John, Pres.--Chemung Ford, Inc., Elmira, NY; *U.S. Private*, pg. 233

Hartman, William R., Pres.--Bank One, Kentucky, NA, Louisville, KY; *U.S. Public*, pg. 173

Hartog, Larry, Pres.--Kentucky Manufacturing Co., Louisville, KY; *U.S. Private*, pg. 615

Harton, T. Dean, Pres.--Hawthorne Corp., Charleston, SC; *U.S. Private*, pg. 512

Hartsfield, Wayne, Pres.--First National Bank of Searcy, Searcy, AK; *U.S. Public*, pg. 630

Hartsock, Bob, Pres.--Danuser Machine Co., Fulton, MO; *U.S. Private*, pg. 310

Hartunian, Gordon, Pres.--A B C Appliance Inc., Pontiac, MI; *U.S. Private*, pg. 2

Hartwick, Winfried, Pres.--Karrena GmbH, Ratingen, Germany; *Int'l*, pg. 398

Hartzell, Richard, Chief Fin. Officer--Southbend, Fuquay Varina, NC; *U.S. Public*, pg. 1110

Hartzmark, Michael, Pres. & Chief Exec. Officer--Cragar Industries, Inc., Phoenix, AZ; *U.S. Public*, pg. 456

Haruta, Hiroshi, Pres.--Citizen Watch Company, Ltd., Tokyo, Japan; *Int'l*, pg. 293

Harvey, Claude, Pres.--Central Plants, Inc., Los Angeles, CA; *U.S. Public*, pg. 1249

Harvey, David E., Chm. Bd., Pres., Chief Oper. & Chief Exec. Officer--Rome Cable Corporation, Rome, NY; *U.S. Private*, pg. 942

Harvey, David R., Ph.D., Pres. & Chief Oper. Officer--Sigma-Aldrich Corporation, Saint Louis, MO; *U.S. Public*, pg. 1471

Harvey, F.L. Mike, Pres.--Applications Management Group, Plano, TX; *U.S. Public*, pg. 1516

Harvey, Joseph H. III, Pres. & Chief Oper. Officer--J.H. Harvey Company, Nashville, GA; *U.S. Private*, pg. 508

Harvey, Michael, Pres.--Gulfstar Energy, Inc., Houston, TX; *U.S. Public*, pg. 516

Harvey, Peter R., Pres.--Artra Group Incorporated, Northfield, IL; *U.S. Public*, pg. 136

Harzenski, Eugene S., Pres. & Chief Exec. Officer--Alloy Technology International Inc., West Nyack, NY; *U.S. Private*, pg. 42

Hascall, James G., Pres.--Olin Specialty Metals Corporation, East Alton, IL; *U.S. Public*, pg. 1219

Hasch, J. Bruce, Pres. & Chief Oper. Officer--Peoples Energy Corporation, Chicago, IL; *U.S. Public*, pg. 1274

Hasch, J. Bruce, Pres. & Chief Oper. Officer--North Shore Gas Co., Waukegan, IL; *U.S. Public*, pg. 1275

Hasch, J. Bruce, Pres. & Chief Oper. Officer--Peoples District Energy Corporation, Chicago, IL; *U.S. Public*, pg. 1275

Hasch, J. Bruce, Pres. & Chief Oper. Officer--Peoples Energy Services Corporation, Chicago, IL; *U.S. Public*, pg. 1275

Hasch, J. Bruce, Pres. & Chief Oper. Officer--Peoples NGV Corp., Chicago, IL; *U.S. Public*, pg. 1275

Hasegawa, Nobuhisa, Pres.--Banco Sumitomo Brasileiro S.A., Sao Paulo, Brazil; *Int'l*, pg. 1310

Hasegawa, Ryoichi, Pres. & Dir.--P.T. Bank Sumitomo Niaga, Jakarta, Indonesia; *Int'l*, pg. 1310

Hasegawa, Takehiko, Pres. & Representative Dir.--Yamaha Motor Co., Ltd., Iwata, Japan; *Int'l*, pg. 1516

Haseldonckx, Paul, Pres. & Chief Exec. Officer--Deminex-Deutsche GmbH, Essen, Germany; *Int'l*, pg. 1460

Haselton, Philip N., Pres.--Detex Corporation, New Braunfels, TX; *U.S. Private*, pg. 327

Haserjian, Bryan, Pres.--Carpeteria, Inc., Valencia, CA; *U.S. Private*, pg. 215

Hashagen, John D., Jr., Pres. & Chief Exec. Officer--Vermont Financial Services Corp., Brattleboro, VT; *U.S. Public*, pg. 1716

Hashimoto, A., Pres.--Nichimen America, Inc., New York, NY; *Int'l*, pg. 927

Hashimoto, Akira, Pres.--Micro-Mech. Inc., Ipswich, MA; *Int'l*, pg. 578

Hashimoto, Eiichi, Pres.--Corporate Software Ltd., KK, Tokyo, Japan; *U.S. Public*, pg. 519

Hashimoto, Takashi, Pres.--Mitsui Trust Bank (U.S.A.), New York, NY; *Int'l*, pg. 883

Hashimoto, Takayuki, Pres.--Toto (Beijing) Co., Ltd., Beijing, China; *Int'l*, pg. 1410

hashimoto, Tomoaki, Pres.--Amano Partners U.S.A. Inc. (A.P.U.), Roseland, NJ; *Int'l*, pg. 71

Hashimoto, Toru, Pres.--Haseko Development Inc., Osaka, Japan; *Int'l*, pg. 600

Hashizaki, J., Pres.--Sharp Electronics of Canada Ltd., Mississauga, Canada; *Int'l*, pg. 1230

Hasimoto, Shozo, Pres.--Nomura Research Institute, Ltd., Tokyo, Japan; *Int'l*, pg. 956

Haskell, George, Pres. & Chief Exec. Officer--Organizational Dynamics Inc., Burlington, MA; *U.S. Private*, pg. 819

Haskell, Gregory W., Pres. & Chief Oper. Officer--XL Vision Inc., Sebastian, FL; *U.S. Public*, pg. 1424

Haskins, John H., Chm. Bd., Pres. & Treas.--Arrow Tank & Engineering Co., Minneapolis, MN; *U.S. Private*, pg. 85

Haslam, William E., Pres.--Pilot Corporation, Knoxville, TN; *U.S. Private*, pg. 865

Haslehurst, Peter, Chief Exec.--EIS Group Plc, London, United Kingdom; *Int'l*, pg. 426

Hassan, Fred, Pres. & Chief Exec. Officer--Pharmacia & Upjohn, Inc., Windsor, United Kingdom; *Int'l*, pg. 1047

Hassanein, Richard C., Pres.--Todd-AO Studios West, Santa Monica, CA; *U.S. Public*, pg. 1619

Hassanein, Salah M., Pres. & Chief Exec. Officer--The Todd-AO Corporation, Hollywood, CA; *U.S. Public*, pg. 1619

Hassell, Bill, Pres.--Engineered Polymers Corporation, Mora, MN; *Int'l*, pg. 328

Hassinger, Hubert, Pres.--Perkasie Industries Corporation, Perkasie, PA; *U.S. Private*, pg. 854

Hassinger, Norman M., Jr., Chm. Bd., Pres., Chief Exec. & Chief Oper. Officer--The Hassinger Companies Hoffman Homes, Arlington Heights, IL; *U.S. Private*, pg. 510

Hasslocher, Robert C., Pres.--Hasslocher Enterprises, Inc., San Antonio, TX; *U.S. Private*, pg. 510

Hasten, Michael, Pres., Chief Exec. Officer & Chief Oper. Officer--Downey Designs International, Indianapolis, IN; *U.S. Private*, pg. 342

Hastey, Joe A., Pres.--Piedmont Olsen Hensley, Inc., Greenville, SC; *Int'l*, pg. 607

Hasting, John, Pres.--Litho-Krome Company, Columbus, GA; *U.S. Private*, pg. 496

Hastings, Barry G., Pres. & Chief Oper. Officer--Northern Trust Corporation, Chicago, IL; *U.S. Public*, pg. 1195

Hastings, F. Curtis, Pres.--J.H. Findorff & Son, Inc., Madison, WI; *U.S. Private*, pg. 405

Hasty, Alan E., Pres.--Sysco Food Services of Virginia, Inc., Harrisonburg, VA; *U.S. Public*, pg. 1552

Hata, Fumio, Pres.--Daihatsu America, Inc., Los Alamitos, CA; *Int'l*, pg. 365

Hata, Kenjiro, Pres.--Meiji Life Insurance Company, Tokyo, Japan; *Int'l*, pg. 854

Hatakeyama, Shigemitsu, Pres.--The Inctec Inc., Yokohama, Japan; *Int'l*, pg. 363

Hatanaka, Takeshi, Pres.--Sumikin Bussan International (Australia) Pty. Ltd., Melbourne, Australia; *Int'l*, pg. 1308

Hatchell, Dennis G., Pres.--Alex Lee, Inc., Hickory, NC; *U.S. Private*, pg. 657

Hatcher, Bob, Pres.--Marks & Morgan Jewelers Inc, Augusta, GA; *U.S. Private*, pg. 705

Hatcher, David E., Chm. Bd., Pres. & Chief Exec. Officer--Gamma Biologicals Inc., Houston, TX; *U.S. Public*, pg. 698

Hatfield, Rodney B., Pres.--Blue Grass Chrysler-Plymouth Inc., Lexington, KY; *U.S. Private*, pg. 152

Hathaway, Derek C., Corp. Chm., Pres. & Chief Exec. Officer--Heckett MultiServ, Butler, PA; *U.S. Public*, pg. 793

Hatsopoulos, John N., Pres. & Chief Fin. Officer--Thermo Electron Corporation, Waltham, MA; *U.S. Public*, pg. 1591

Hatt, James R.S., Chm. Bd., Pres. & Chief Exec. Officer--Petersburg Long Distance Inc., Toronto, Canada; *Int'l*, pg. 1040

Hattori, Hideaki, Pres. & Chief Exec. Officer--Pacific Guardian Life Insurance, Honolulu, HI; *Int'l*, pg. 854

Hattori, Kirk, Pres.--Canadian Kawasaki Motors Inc., Don Mills, Canada; *Int'l*, pg. 726

Hattori, Osamu, Pres.--Rohm Electronics (Philippines) Sales Corporation, Cavite, Philippines; *Int'l*, pg. 1125

Haub, Christian W.E., Pres. & Co-Chief Exec. Officer--The Great Atlantic & Pacific Tea Company, Inc., Montvale, NJ; *Int'l*, pg. 1375

Hauber, Earl, Pres.--Environmental Construction, Inc. (ECI), Plantation, FL; *Int'l*, pg. 607

Hauck, John C., Pres.--Tubular Steel Inc., Saint Louis, MO; *U.S. Private*, pg. 1108

Hauck, L. Christian, Pres. & Chief Exec. Officer--Sunflower Electric Power Corporation, Hays, KS; *U.S. Private*, pg. 1052

Hauck, Richard E., Pres.--Rodgard Corporation, Buffalo, NY; *U.S. Public*, pg. 142

Haueisen, Charles, Pres.--Continental Forge Company, Compton, CA; *U.S. Private*, pg. 268

Hauer, Frank, Pres.--O&Y Properties Corporation, Toronto, Canada; *Int'l*, pg. 993

Haugen, Donald, Pres.--Waterous Company, South Saint Paul, MN; *U.S. Private*, pg. 52

Hauner, Axel, Pres.--Telair International Cargo Systems, Oxnard, CA; *U.S. Public*, pg. 1570

Hauner, Axel H.R., Pres.--Telair International, Oxnard, CA; *U.S. Public*, pg. 1570

Haupenthal, John, Pres.--The Pervo Paint Company, Los Angeles, CA; *U.S. Private*, pg. 856

Hauser, Joshua A., Pres. & Chief Exec. Officer--Lambda Electronics Inc., Melville, NY; *Int'l*, pg. 1241

Hauslein, James N., Chm. Bd., Pres. & Chief Exec. Officer--Sunglass Hut International, Coral Gables, FL; *U.S. Public*, pg. 1535

Hausmann, Carl, Chm. Bd. & Pres.--Central Soya Company, Inc., Fort Wayne, IN; *Int'l*, pg. 324

Hauss, John, Pres. & Chief Exec. Officer--Lifetime Doors Inc., Farmington, MI; *U.S. Private*, pg. 666

Haussler, Manfred A., Pres.-Intl.--Reemtsma Cigarettenfabriken GmbH, Hamburg, Hamburg, Germany; *Int'l*, pg. 1100

Haux, Rick, Pres.--Bedroom Superstores, Phoenix, AZ; *U.S. Private*, pg. 129

Havener, Gary W., Pres. & Chief Exec. Officer--Cabre Corp., Wilmington, DE; *U.S. Public*, pg. 289

Haverkate, Mark, Pres. & Chief Exec. Officer--Cable Michigan, Inc., Princeton, NJ; *U.S. Public*, pg. 287

Haverland, Richard M., Chm. Bd., Pres. & Chief Exec. Officer--Highlands Insurance Co., Houston, TX; *U.S. Public*, pg. 826

Haversat, Robert A., Pres.--Sargent Manufacturing Company, New Haven, CT; *Int'l*, pg. 18

Haverty, Michael R., Pres. & Chief Exec. Officer--The Kansas City Southern Railway Co., Kansas City, MO; *U.S. Public*, pg. 944

Haveson, Brian, Pres. & Chief Oper. Officer--Nutri/System Inc., Horsham, PA; *U.S. Private*, pg. 859

Havill, Chuck, Pres. & Gen. Mgr.--Door Closer Division, Princeton, IL; *U.S. Public*, pg. 876

Haw, C.L.W., Pres.--National Farms Inc., Kansas City, MO; *U.S. Private*, pg. 782

Hawbaker, Daniel R., Pres.--Glenn O. Hawbaker, Inc., State College, PA; *U.S. Private*, pg. 511

Hawes, Howard H., Pres.--ALLTEL Telephone Services Corporation, Little Rock, AR; *U.S. Public*, pg. 56

Hawk, David W., Pres. & Chief Exec. Officer--Gertrude Hawk Chocolates, Inc., Dunmore, PA; *U.S. Private*, pg. 449

Hawk, Richard C., Chm. Bd., Pres. & Chief Exec. Officer--Hawk Management Corporation, Overland Park, KS; *U.S. Private*, pg. 511

Hawk, Robert, Pres. & Chief Exec. Officer--Hale-Halsell Company, Tulsa, OK; *U.S. Private*, pg. 494

Hawkes, James B., Chm. Bd., Pres. & Chief Exec. Officer--Eaton Vance Corp., Boston, MA; *U.S. Public*, pg. 559

Hawkey, Robert, Pres.--Leach International, Buena Park, CA; *U.S. Private*, pg. 655

Hawkins, Arthur M., Chm. Bd., Pres. & Chief Exec. Officer--Exide Corporation, Reading, PA; *U.S. Public*, pg. 600

Hawkins, Dan, Pres. & Chief Exec. Officer--Bank of Goodletsville, Goodlettsville, TN; *U.S. Public*, pg. 1669

Hawkins, Marvin J., Jr., Pres.--J.D. Diffenbaugh, Inc., Riverside, CA; *U.S. Private*, pg. 332

Hawkins, Phillip E., Pres. & Chief Exec. Officer--The Penn Traffic Company, Syracuse, NY; *U.S. Public*, pg. 1270

Hawkins, Russell B., Pres.--VM Software Division, Reston, VA; *U.S. Public*, pg. 1516

Hawkins, William, Pres.--Sherwood-Davis & Geck, Saint Louis, MO; *U.S. Public*, pg. 80

Hawkins, William A., Pres.--Ethicon Endo-Surgery, Inc., Cincinnati, OH; *U.S. Public*, pg. 928

Hawksley, Chris, Pres.--Flint Manufacturing Co., Burton, MI; *U.S. Private*, pg. 413

Hawksworth, Keith, Pres.--Parsons Brinckerhoff International, Pte. Ltd, Singapore, Singapore; *U.S. Private*, pg. 841

Hawley, Michael C., Pres. & Chief Oper. Officer--The Gillette Company, Boston, MA; *U.S. Public*, pg. 743

Haworth, Gordon, Pres.--Costain Process Inc., Dallas, TX; *Int'l*, pg. 337

Hay, Alec J., Pres.--Poly-Bond Inc., Waynesboro, VA; *Int'l*, pg. 415

Hayakawa, Katsumi, Pres.--Kumagai International USA Corporation, Irving, TX; *Int'l*, pg. 764

Hayakawa, Katsumi, Pres.--KG Land California Corporation, Belmont, CA; *Int'l*, pg. 764

Hayakawa, Susumu, Pres.--Marsiling Ltd., Kowloon, Hong Kong; *Int'l*, pg. 579

Hayashi, Hiroshi, Pres.--The Mitsubishi Trust and Banking Corporation, Tokyo, Japan; *Int'l*, pg. 876

Hayashi, Koji, Pres.--Kajima Engineering and Construction Inc., Pasadena, CA; *Int'l*, pg. 722

Hayashi, Stuart, Principal--Latitude, Dallas, TX; *U.S. Private*, pg. 929

Hayden, D.A., Pres.--Arnold Public Relations, Boston, MA; *U.S. Private*, pg. 84

Hayden, J. P., III, Pres. & Chief Oper. Officer--M/G Transportation Services, Inc., Amelia, OH; *U.S. Public*, pg. 1111

Hayden, Robert W., Pres. & Chief Exec. Officer--The Midland Company, Cincinnati, OH; *U.S. Public*, pg. 1110

Hayer, John, Pres.--Kulite Semiconductor Products, Inc., Leonia, NJ; *U.S. Private*, pg. 636

Hayes, Carl I., Jr., Pres.--C.I. Hayes, Inc., Cranston, RI; *U.S. Private*, pg. 513

Hayes, Carl R., Pres.--Amlings Flowerland, Hinsdale, IL; *U.S. Private*, pg. 66

Hayes, Forrest D., Pres.--Brittany Corporation, Cleveland, OH; *U.S. Private*, pg. 169

Hayes, Greg, Pres.--Southcorp U.S.A., Inc., Atlanta, GA; *Int'l*, pg. 1287

Hayes, Jeanne A., Pres.--Quality Education Data (QED), Denver, CO; *U.S. Private*, pg. 858

Hayes, John, Pres. & Chief Exec. Officer--Raycom Media, Inc., Montgomery, AL; *U.S. Private*, pg. 911

Hayes, John E. Jr., Chm. Bd. & Chief Exec. Officer--Western Resources, Inc., Topeka, KS; *U.S. Public*, pg. 1759

Hayes, Judith W., Pres.--Consumers Maine Water, Rockport, ME; *U.S. Public*, pg. 438

Hayes, Lacey L., III, Pres.--Pneumatic Products Corp., Ocala, FL; *U.S. Public*, pg. 1676

Hayes, Lacy L., III, Pres.--Flair Corporation, Ocala, FL; *U.S. Public*, pg. 1676

Hayes, Lacy L., III, Pres.--Dollinger Corporation, Rich Creek, VA; *U.S. Public*, pg. 1676

Hayes, Michael J., Pres. & Chief Exec. Officer--Fred's Inc., Memphis, TN; *U.S. Public*, pg. 680

Hayes, Philip M., Pres.--The Kent Company, Elkhart, IN; *Int'l*, pg. 440

Hayes, Roger H., Pres.--S.E. Huffman Corp., Clover, SC; *U.S. Private*, pg. 546

Hayes, Roger H., Pres.--Springfield Manufacturing LLC, Clover, SC; *U.S. Private*, pg. 546
Hayes, Todd S., Pres.--Interact Accessories, Inc., Hunt Valley, MD; *U.S. Public*, pg. 1369
Hayes, Vayle, Pres.--Dahlsten Truck Line, Inc., Clay Center, NE; *U.S. Private*, pg. 306
Hayes, W.J., Pres.--Permacel, New Brunswick, NJ; *Int'l*, pg. 950
Hayes, W.M., Pres.--Placer Dome Latin America, Santiago, Chile; *Int'l*, pg. 1060
Haymon, Monte R., Pres. & Chief Exec. Officer--S.D. Warren Co., Boston, MA; *Int'l*, pg. 1193
Haynes, Michael C., Pres. & Chief Exec. Officer--GT Bicycles, Inc., Santa Ana, CA; *U.S. Public*, pg. 695
Haynes, Peter, Pres. & Chief Exec. Officer--Consumers Water Company, Portland, ME; *U.S. Public*, pg. 438
Haynes, William E., Chm. Bd., Pres. & Chief Exec. Officer--Innovative Valve Technology, Inc., Houston, TX; *U.S. Public*, pg. 880
Haynes, William E., Pres. & Chief Exec. Officer--Lyondell-Citgo Refining Company, Ltd., Houston, TX; *U.S. Public*, pg. 1022
Hays, George G., Pres. & Chief Exec. Officer--Arizona Instrument Corporation, Phoenix, AZ; *U.S. Public*, pg. 129
Hays, Harry S., Chm. Bd. & Pres.--Allen & Ohara, Inc., Memphis, TN; *U.S. Private*, pg. 36
Hays, Michael D., Pres. & Chief Exec. Officer--National Research Corporation, Lincoln, NE; *U.S. Public*, pg. 1159
Hays, Patrick, Pres.--Blue Cross and Blue Shield Association, Chicago, IL; *U.S. Private*, pg. 151
Hays, William, Sr., Pres. & Chief Exec. Officer--Town & Country Ford Inc., Louisville, KY; *U.S. Private*, pg. 1093
Hayutin, Murray P., Pres.--Hilb, Rogal and Hamilton Company of Denver, Denver, CO; *U.S. Public*, pg. 827
Hayward-Surry, Jeremy, Pres., Chief Fin. Officer & Treas.--Pall Corporation, Greenvale, NY; *U.S. Public*, pg. 1253
Hayward, Allen, Co-Pres.--Kidd Creek Division, Timmins, Canada; *Int'l*, pg. 433
Hayward, John C., Pres.--Michael Baker, Jr., Inc., Beaver, PA; *U.S. Public*, pg. 168
Hayward, Lawrence, Pres. & Chief Exec. Officer--Carr Gottstein Foods, Anchorage, AK; *U.S. Public*, pg. 308
Haywood, Lee, Pres. & Gen. Mgr.--First American Title Insurance Agency of Mohave, Inc., Kingman, AZ; *U.S. Public*, pg. 626
Hazard, Glenn C., Pres. & Chief Exec. Officer--FTP Software Inc., Andover, MA; *U.S. Public*, pg. 609
Hazen, Richard C., Pres.--Green Bay Supply Co., Inc., Hatfield, PA; *U.S. Public*, pg. 307
Hazen, Thomas, Pres. & Chief Exec. Officer--Hazen Paper Company, Holyoke, MA; *U.S. Private*, pg. 514
Head, J. Michael, Pres.--Mark Risk Management, Inc., Kansas City, MO; *U.S. Public*, pg. 1046
Head, J. Michael, Pres.--Mark VII Transportation Solutions, Inc., Kansas City, MO; *U.S. Public*, pg. 1046
Head, Jack, Pres.--Head Distributing Co., Smyrna, GA; *U.S. Private*, pg. 514
Headbloom, Gust, Jr., Pres.--Apex Broach & Machine Co., Detroit, MI; *U.S. Private*, pg. 77
Heagerty, John D., Pres.--The Coakley Heagerty Advertising & Public Relations Co., San Jose, CA; *U.S. Private*, pg. 248
Heagle, Jim, Pres.--Calgon Corporation, Pittsburgh, PA; *Int'l*, pg. 455
Heagney, W. Dennis, Pres. & Chief Oper. Officer--Transocean Offshore, Inc., Houston, TX; *U.S. Public*, pg. 1631
Heald, Francis J., Pres.--Green Mountain Propane Gas Co., Burlington, VT; *U.S. Public*, pg. 761
Healey, Richard M., Pres.--Rockefeller Group Telecommunications Services, Inc., New York, NY; *Int'l*, pg. 873
Healey, William J., Pres. & Chief Exec. Officer--Viking Yacht Co., New Gretna, NJ; *U.S. Private*, pg. 1140
Healy, Denis J., Pres.--Turtle Wax, Inc., Chicago, IL; *U.S. Private*, pg. 1110
Healy, James T., Pres. & Chief Exec. Officer--Genus Inc., Sunnyvale, CA; *U.S. Public*, pg. 732
Healy, Joseph, Pres. & Chief Exec. Officer--Reckitt & Colman Inc., Montvale, NJ; *Int'l*, pg. 1090
Healy, Michael, Pres. & Chief Exec. Officer--Sordoni Skanska Construction Co., Parsippany, NJ; *Int'l*, pg. 1261
Healy, Stephen D., Pres.--Cochrane Furniture Co., Inc., Lincolnton, NC; *U.S. Public*, pg. 352
Healy, Thomas, Pres.--Owen-Ames-Kimball Co., Grand Rapids, MI; *U.S. Private*, pg. 823
Healy, Tim, Pres. & Chief Exec. Officer--Select Beverages, Inc., Darien, IL; *U.S. Private*, pg. 982
Heard, William, Pres.--Bill Heard Enterprises, Inc., Columbus, GA; *U.S. Private*, pg. 515
Hearn, Michael, Chm. Bd. & Pres.--MBT Architecture, San Francisco, CA; *U.S. Private*, pg. 686
Heath, Alan, Pres. & Chief Exec. Officer--The Vendo Company, Fresno, CA; *Int'l*, pg. 1184
Heath, Richard W., Pres. & Chief Exec. Officer--BeautiControl Cosmetics, Inc., Carrollton, TX; *U.S. Public*, pg. 198
Heaton, John, Pres.--Nanometrics Incorporated, Sunnyvale, CA; *U.S. Public*, pg. 1151
Heaton, Larry A., Pres. & Chief Exec. Officer--Bank of Ferrum, Ferrum, VA; *U.S. Public*, pg. 1038
Heavenridge, David L., Pres. & Chief Exec. Officer--Dominion Capital, Inc., Richmond, VA; *U.S. Public*, pg. 516
Heavenridge, David L., Pres.--Rincon Securities, Inc., Richmond, VA; *U.S. Public*, pg. 516
Hebe, James L., Pres. & Chief Exec. Officer--Freightliner Corp., Portland, OR; *Int'l*, pg. 368
Hebenstreit, James B., Pres.--Bartlett and Company, Kansas City, MO; *U.S. Private*, pg. 118
Hebert, Jacques, Pres.--FCA!BMZ Paris, Suresnes, France; *Int'l*, pg. 469
Hebert, Lawrence I., Pres. & Chief Oper. Officer--Perpetual Corporation, Washington, DC; *U.S. Private*, pg. 854
Hecht, Allen D., Pres. & Chief Oper. Officer--Health Resources International, West Hartford, CT; *U.S. Private*, pg. 514
Hecht, William F., Chm. Bd., Pres. & Chief Exec. Officer--Pennsylvania Power & Light Company-Lehigh Div., Allentown, PA; *U.S. Public*, pg. 1244
Heck, Gary, Chm. Bd. & Pres.--F. Korbel Bros. Inc., Guerneville, CA; *U.S. Private*, pg. 632
Heck, J.A., Pres.--ATT Network Sistems International, B.V., Hilversum, Netherlands; *Int'l*, pg. 1373
Heck, Raymond E., Pres.--Heck Industries, Baton Rouge, LA; *U.S. Private*, pg. 519
Heck, Warren, Pres.--Greater New York Mutual Insurance Company, New York, NY; *U.S. Private*, pg. 476
Hecker, U. Joseph, Pres.--Pike & Fischer, Bethesda, MD; *U.S. Private*, pg. 182
Heckmann, Dick, Pres. & Chief Exec. Officer--U.S. Filter, Palm Desert, CA; *U.S. Public*, pg. 61
Heckmann, Richard J., Pres. & Chief Exec. Officer--United States Filter Corporation, Palm Desert, CA; *U.S. Public*, pg. 1681
Hector, P. Holcomb, V.P. & Gen. Mgr.--Diamondhead Div., Diamondhead, MS; *U.S. Private*, pg. 895
Hedbecker, Robert, Pres.--Gotaverken Energy Systems Inc., Charlotte, NC; *Int'l*, pg. 770
Hedfors, Bo, Pres.--Ericsson North America, Inc., Richardson, TX; *Int'l*, pg. 1364
Hedges, Andrew, Pres.--Reckitt & Colman Canada Inc., Toronto, Canada; *Int'l*, pg. 1090
Hedges, Jay, Pres.--Champion Pneumatic Machinery Co., Inc., Princeton, IL; *U.S. Private*, pg. 228
Hedlund, Thomas, Pres.--Ballast Nord AB, Umea, Sweden; *Int'l*, pg. 899
Hednert, Lennart, Pres.--Celsius Invest AB, Eskilstuna, Sweden; *Int'l*, pg. 276
Hedrick, K.L., Pres. & Chief Exec. Officer--Phillips Gas Company, Bartlesville, OK; *U.S. Public*, pg. 1291
Hedstrom, Clas Ake, Pres. & Chief Exec. Officer--Sandvik AB, Sandviken, Sweden; *Int'l*, pg. 1185
Hedstrom, Jan, Pres. & Chief Exec. Officer--Gunnebo Industrier AB, Gunnebo, Sweden; *Int'l*, pg. 578
Hee, Lee Yeon, Pres.--The Panther Car Co., Ltd., Harlow, United Kingdom; *Int'l*, pg. 1292
Hee, Song Soon, Pres.--Burgmann Malaysia SDN BHD, Petaling Jaya, Malaysia; *Int'l*, pg. 233
Heenan, D.A., Pres. & Chief Exec. Officer--Theo. H. Davies & Co., Ltd, Honolulu, HI; *Int'l*, pg. 704
Heeringa, Donald G., Chm. Bd. & Pres.--Trendway Corporation, Holland, MI; *U.S. Private*, pg. 1099
Heffel, Jerry, Pres.-Southwestern Co.--Southwestern/Great American Inc., Nashville, TN; *U.S. Private*, pg. 1018
Heffelfinger, Richard E., Pres.--Eastern American Energy Corporation, Charleston, WV; *U.S. Private*, pg. 357
Heffer, John, Pres. & Chief Exec. Officer--Republic Factors Corp., New York, NY; *U.S. Public*, pg. 1380
Hefferman, Liam, Pres.--Timar (Culturas em Agua), Lda., Olhao, Portugal; *Int'l*, pg. 1390
Heflebower, Jeffrey N., Pres. & Chief Exec. Officer--The Peoples Bank of Maryland, Denton, MD; *U.S. Public*, pg. 1089
Hefner, Linda, Pres.--L'eggs Products, Inc., Winston Salem, NC; *U.S. Public*, pg. 1434
Hefner, Thomas L., Pres. & Chief Exec. Officer--Duke Realty Investments, Inc., Indianapolis, IN; *U.S. Public*, pg. 535
Hefter, Harry O., Chm. Bd. & Pres.--The HOH Organizations, Chicago, IL; *U.S. Private*, pg. 492
Hefter, Walter, Dr., Pres.--Feldschlosschen Hurlimann Holding, Rhaeninfelden, Switzerland; *Int'l*, pg. 479
Hefty, Thomas R., Chm. Bd., Pres. & Chief Exec. Officer--United Wisconsin Services, Inc., Milwaukee, WI; *U.S. Public*, pg. 1692
Hegarty, David J., Pres. & Chief Oper. Officer--Health and Retirement Properties Trust, Newton, MA; *U.S. Public*, pg. 801
Hegarty, Michael, Pres. & Chief Oper. Officer--The Equitable Companies Incorporated, New York, NY; *U.S. Public*, pg. 588
Hegde, A.R., Pres.--Astra-IDL Ltd., Bangalore, India; *Int'l*, pg. 93
Hegener, Peter W., Pres. & Chief Exec. Officer--Peterson's Guides, Inc., Princeton, NJ; *U.S. Private*, pg. 858
Heider, David, Pres. & Chief Exec. Officer--United Hardware Distributing Co., Plymouth, MN; *U.S. Private*, pg. 335
Heider, James B., Pres. & Chief Oper. Officer--Gilman Paper Co., Saint Marys, GA; *U.S. Private*, pg. 454
Heidrich, James K., Jr., Chm. Bd., Pres. & Chief Exec. Officer--The Miami Margarine Co., Cincinnati, OH; *U.S. Private*, pg. 740
Heidt, Larry P., Pres.--Nabors Drilling & Energy Services UK, Ltd., Aberdeen, United Kingdom; *U.S. Public*, pg. 1149
Heikkonen, Mikko, Pres.--Nokia Network and Access Systems, Espoo, Finland; *Int'l*, pg. 953
Heilbronner, Heinrich, Vice Chm., Pres. & Chief Oper. Officer--Semikron International, GmbH & Co. KG, Nuremberg, Germany; *Int'l*, pg. 1220
Heiler, Lynn, Publisher--Bon Appetit Magazine, New York, NY; *U.S. Private*, pg. 20
Heily, John M., Chm. Bd., Pres. & Chief Exec. Officer--Continental Mills, Inc., Tukwila, WA; *U.S. Private*, pg. 269
Heiman, Gary, Pres. & Chief Exec. Officer--Standard Textile Co., Inc., Cincinnati, OH; *U.S. Private*, pg. 1032
Heiman, Richard I., Pres.--Campbell Hausfeld Division of Scott Fetzer, Harrison, OH; *U.S. Public*, pg. 217
Heimark, Donald, Pres.--Triangle Distributing Company, Santa Fe Springs, CA; *U.S. Private*, pg. 1101
Heimbinder, Isaac, Pres., Co.-Chief Exec. Officer & Chief Oper. Officer--U.S. Home Corporation, Houston, TX; *U.S. Public*, pg. 1682
Heimbuch, Babette E., Pres. & Chief Exec. Officer--FirstFed Financial Corp., Santa Monica, CA; *U.S. Public*, pg. 645
Heimerbinger, Jefferey, Pres.--Office Electronics, Inc., Itasca, IL; *U.S. Private*, pg. 812
Hein, Larry, Pres.--FMC-Smith Meter Co., Erie, PA; *U.S. Public*, pg. 605
Heine, Chuck, Pres.--Dana Asia/Pacific, Hong Kong, Hong Kong; *U.S. Public*, pg. 480
Heine, Spencer, Acting Pres.--Credit Card Sentinel, Schaumburg, IL; *U.S. Private*, pg. 759
Heine, Spencer H., Acting Pres.--The Signature Group, Schaumburg, IL; *U.S. Private*, pg. 758
Heineman, Scott P., Pres.--Conway Import Co. Inc., Franklin Park, IL; *U.S. Private*, pg. 272
Heinen, Thomas J., Pres. & Chief Oper. Officer--Heinen's Inc., Cleveland, OH; *U.S. Private*, pg. 519
Heiner, Clyde M., Pres. & Chief Exec. Officer--Interstate Land Corp., Salt Lake City, UT; *U.S. Public*, pg. 1352
Heiner, Clyde M., Pres. & Chief Exec. Officer--Questar Development Corporation, Salt Lake City, UT; *U.S. Public*, pg. 1352
Heiner, Clyde M., Pres. & Chief Exec. Officer--Questar InfoComm, Salt Lake City, UT; *U.S. Public*, pg. 1352
Heiner, Dennis G., Pres.--Kwikset Corporation, Irvine, CA; *U.S. Public*, pg. 233
Heinio, Ari, Mng. Dir.--OY Stockmann AB, Helsinki, Finland; *Int'l*, pg. 1301
Heinle, Charles, Pres.--Heinle & Heinle Publishers, Inc., Boston, MA; *U.S. Public*, pg. 1600
Heinrich, John P., Pres.--Oncomembrane, Inc., Seattle, WA; *Int'l*, pg. 1013
Heinrich, John P., Pres.--Otsuka Electronics (U.S.A.) Inc., Fort Collins, CO; *Int'l*, pg. 1013
Heins, John, Pres. & Chief Exec. Officer--Gruner + Jahr USA Publishing, Inc., New York, NY; *Int'l*, pg. 190
Heins, John, Pres. & Chief Exec. Officer--Parents Magazine, New York, NY; *Int'l*, pg. 191
Heinson, R. Conrad, Pres.--Allied Oil & Supply, Inc., Omaha, NE; *U.S. Private*, pg. 39
Heinson, R. Conrad, Pres.--Allied Tire Co., Omaha, NE; *U.S. Private*, pg. 39
Heinz-Mann, L.C., Pres.--XKD Corporation, Los Gatos, CA; *U.S. Private*, pg. 1194
Heinz, James H., Pres.--Bell Flavors & Fragrances, Northbrook, IL; *U.S. Private*, pg. 131
Heinz, Terry J., Pres. & Chief Oper. Officer--Huntco Inc., Town and Country, MO; *U.S. Public*, pg. 849
Heinze, Pater R., Pres.--Building Materials Corporation of America, Wayne, NJ; *U.S. Private*, pg. 433
Heinze, Peter R., Pres. & Chief Oper. Officer--International Specialty Products, Inc., Wayne, NJ; *U.S. Public*, pg. 858
Heitt, James D., Pres. & Chief Oper. Officer--Met-Coil Systems Corp., Cedar Rapids, IA; *U.S. Public*, pg. 1099
Held, A. Peter, Pres.--Cooper Power Tools Division, Lexington, SC; *U.S. Public*, pg. 444
Held, James G., Pres. & Chief Exec. Officer--Home Shopping Network, Inc., Saint Petersburg, FL; *U.S. Public*, pg. 1685
Held, James G., Pres. & Chief Exec. Officer--America's Store, Saint Petersburg, FL; *U.S. Public*, pg. 1685
Held, Robert, Pres.--Seely Equipment & Supply Co., Inc., Wall, NJ; *U.S. Private*, pg. 755
Heldfond, Robert C., Pres.--EB5 Corporation, Portland, OR; *U.S. Private*, pg. 353
Heldman, Julie, Co-Chm. Bd. & Pres.--Signature Eyewear, Inc., Inglewood, CA; *U.S. Public*, pg. 1473
Heldman, Lou, Publisher--Centre Daily Times, Inc., State College, PA; *U.S. Public*, pg. 964
Heldrich, John, Pres. & Chief Exec. Officer--Swift Textiles, Inc., Atlanta, GA; *Int'l*, pg. 415
Heldt, Patti, Pres. & Sec.--Steven Manufacturing Co., Hermann, MO; *U.S. Private*, pg. 1042
Helgason, Sigurdur, Pres. & Chief Exec. Officer--Icelandair, Reykjavik, Iceland; *Int'l*, pg. 658
Helgason, Sigurdur, Pres. & Chief Exec. Officer--IceLandAir, Columbia, MD; *Int'l*, pg. 658
Helgeson, Donald P., Chm. Bd. & Pres.--JFC Inc., Saint Cloud, MN; *U.S. Private*, pg. 577
Helgeson, Donald P., Pres.--Gold'n Plump Poultry, Inc., Arcadia, WI; *U.S. Private*, pg. 577
Hell, Manfred, Pres.--Jack Wolfskin, Idstein, Germany; *U.S. Public*, pg. 933
Hellberg, Bengt, Pres.--Valmet Svenska AB, Eskilstuna, Sweden; *Int'l*, pg. 1449
Hellberg, Clifford W., Chm. Bd., Pres. & Chief Exec. Officer--Creative Productions, Pittsburgh, PA; *U.S. Private*, pg. 288
Heller, Chester M., Sr., Dr., Chm. Bd., Pres., Chief Exec. Officer & Chief Engr.--Marquette Coppersmithing Co., Inc., Philadelphia, PA; *U.S. Private*, pg. 706
Heller, Harvey R., Pres.--Heller Bros. Packing Corp., Winter Garden, FL; *U.S. Private*, pg. 520
Heller, Jeffrey M., Pres. & Chief Oper. Officer--Electronic Data Systems Corporation, Plano, TX; *U.S. Public*, pg. 569
Heller, Judy, Co-Chm. & Pres.--Cruises Only Inc., Orlando, FL; *U.S. Private*, pg. 293
Heller, Robert W., Pres. & Chief Exec. Officer--Advance Circuits, Inc., Minnetonka, MN; *Int'l*, pg. 713
Hellerman, Paul, Pres.--Bulley & Andrews Company, Chicago, IL; *U.S. Private*, pg. 180
Hellerman, Paul, Pres.--The Meyne Company, Chicago, IL; *U.S. Private*, pg. 180
Hellman, Bryce, Pres.--J. Hellman Produce, Inc., Los Angeles, CA; *U.S. Private*, pg. 520
Hellman, H. Carl, Pres.--Ceco Door Products, Brentwood, TN; *U.S. Public*, pg. 1676
Hellman, Peter S., Pres. & Chief Oper. Officer--TRW Inc., Cleveland, OH; *U.S. Public*, pg. 1558
Hellman, William, Chm. Bd., Pres & Chief Exec. Officer--JG Industries, Inc., Chicago, IL; *U.S. Public*, pg. 917
Hellstrom, Ron, Pres.--BetterBrands, Ltd., Waipahu, HI; *U.S. Private*, pg. 1202
Helm, G. William, Jr., Pres.--Work/Family Directions, Boston, MA; *U.S. Private*, pg. 1188

Helm, Greg J., Pres.--Houston Helm and Company, Los Angeles, CA; *U.S. Private*, pg. 542
Helm, Michael J., Pres.--Kaufman and Broad Central Valley Div., Modesto, CA; *U.S. Public*, pg. 945
Helmen, John R., Pres., Chief Exec. Officer & Chief Oper. Officer--Photo Control Corporation, Minneapolis, MN; *U.S. Public*, pg. 1292
Helmer, Paul J., Pres.--Paul J. Krez Company, Morton Grove, IL; *U.S. Private*, pg. 635
Helmerich, Hans, Pres. & Chief Exec. Officer--Helmerich & Payne, Inc., Tulsa, OK; *U.S. Public*, pg. 808
Helmetag, Carl, Pres. & Chief Exec. Officer--Head USA, Inc., Columbia, MD; *U.S. Private*, pg. 514
Helmick, David G., Pres.--Helmick Corporation, Fairmont, WV; *U.S. Private*, pg. 520
Helms, Carol A., Pres.--Edd Helms Electrical Contracting, Miami, FL; *U.S. Private*, pg. 520
Helms, Roger, Pres. & Chief Oper. Officer--The Arnold Palmer Golf Company, Ooltewah, TN; *U.S. Public*, pg. 132
Helpern, Joan, Pres.--Joan & David Helpern, Inc., New York, NY; *U.S. Private*, pg. 521
Helpern, Joan, Pres. & Chief Exec. Officer--Joan & David Helpern, Inc., Everett, MA; *U.S. Private*, pg. 521
Helppie, Richard D., Jr., Pres. & Chief Exec. Officer--Superior Consultant Holdings Corp., Southfield, MI; *U.S. Public*, pg. 1538
Helton, James E., Pres. & Chief Exec. Officer--M & M Precision Systems Corporation, Carrollton, OH; *U.S. Public*, pg. 482
Helton, James E., Pres.--Ball Screws & Actuators Co., Inc., San Jose, CA; *U.S. Public*, pg. 482
Helton, Raymond E., Pres. & Chief Exec. Officer--Sterling Electric, Inc., Irvine, CA; *U.S. Private*, pg. 1041
Helzer, James A., Pres. & Chief Exec. Officer--Unicover Corporation, Cheyenne, WY; *U.S. Private*, pg. 1117
Hembree, H. Lawson, IV, Pres. & Chief Oper. Officer--Merchants National Bank, Fort Smith, AR; *U.S. Public*, pg. 501
Hemer, Douglas L., Pres. & Chief Exec. Officer--San Diego Division, San Diego, CA; *U.S. Public*, pg. 27
Hemingway, Timothy, Pres.--The Holland Hitch Company, Holland, MI; *U.S. Private*, pg. 534
Hemmer, Paul W., Jr., Pres. & Chief Exec. Officer--Paul Hemmer Construction Company, Fort Mitchell, KY; *U.S. Private*, pg. 521
Hemmerle, Glenn, Pres. & Chief Exec. Officer--The Johnny Rockets Group, Inc, Irvine, CA; *U.S. Private*, pg. 222
Hemmerle, Glenn, Pres. & Chief Exec. Officer--Pearle Vision, Inc., Dallas, TX; *U.S. Public*, pg. 397
Hemphill, William J., Pres.--Bristol Laboratories International, S.A., Colon, Panama; *U.S. Public*, pg. 255
Hempt, George F., Chm. Bd. & Pres.--Hempt Brothers, Inc., Camp Hill, PA; *U.S. Private*, pg. 521
Hemstad, Bjorn, Pres.--Ericsson Network Systems, Inc., Richardson, TX; *Int'l*, pg. 1364
Hendel, M., Pres.--Commodore Aviation, Miami, FL; *Int'l*, pg. 690
Henderson, Bruce M., Pres.--Henderson Electric Co., Inc., Louisville, KY; *U.S. Private*, pg. 521
Henderson, Dan, Pres.--Peterson Farms, Decatur, AR; *U.S. Private*, pg. 857
Henderson, Don, Pres.--Contech Construction Products Inc., Middletown, OH; *U.S. Private*, pg. 267
Henderson, Donald, Chm. Bd., Pres. & Chief Exec. Officer--Citation National Insurance Company, San Jose, CA; *U.S. Public*, pg. 376
Henderson, Donald, Chm. Bd., Pres. & Chief Exec. Officer--Citation Insurance Company, San Jose, CA; *U.S. Public*, pg. 376
Henderson, Frederick A., Pres. & Mng. Dir.--General Motors do Brasil Ltda., Sao Caetano do Sul, Brazil; *U.S. Public*, pg. 722
Henderson, George W., Pres. & Chief Exec. Officer--Burlington Industries, Inc., Greensboro, NC; *U.S. Public*, pg. 268
Henderson, J.M., Mng. Dir.--MetalTech International PLC, Stourbridge, United Kingdom; *Int'l*, pg. 862
Henderson, James, Partner & Information Tech. Dir.--Eric Mower and Associates, Inc., Syracuse, NY; *U.S. Private*, pg. 765
Henderson, James A., Pres.--Atlas Copco Wagner Inc., Portland, OR; *Int'l*, pg. 96
Henderson, Jeffery, Pres.--Henderson Auctions, Livingston, LA; *U.S. Private*, pg. 577
Henderson, Jeffrey, Pres.--JAH Enterprises, Inc., Livingston, LA; *U.S. Private*, pg. 577
Henderson, Kevin, Pres.-Steakhouses--Shoney's, Inc., Nashville, TN; *U.S. Public*, pg. 1467
Henderson, Louis C., Jr., Pres. & Chief Exec. Officer--Wall Street Deli, Inc., Birmingham, AL; *U.S. Public*, pg. 1734
Henderson, Michael L., Pres. & Chief Exec. Officer--Joseph J. Henderson & Son, Inc., Gurnee, IL; *U.S. Private*, pg. 521
Henderson, Nina Z., Pres.--CPC Specialty Markets Group, Englewood Cliffs, NJ; *U.S. Public*, pg. 224
Henderson, Robert J., Sr., Chm. Bd., Pres. & Chief Exec. Officer--Ford Development Corporation, Cincinnati, OH; *U.S. Private*, pg. 418
Henderson, William, Pres.--Trimtex Co. Inc., Williamsport, PA; *U.S. Private*, pg. 1103
Hendres, Paul, Pres.--Philip Morris Gmbh, Munich, Germany; *U.S. Public*, pg. 1290
Hendrick, John D., Pres.--Okuma America Corporation, Charlotte, NC; *Int'l*, pg. 1001
Hendricks, Adele, Pres. & Retail Dir.--Dean's Photo Service, San Diego, CA; *U.S. Private*, pg. 319
Hendricks, Albert L., Pres.--Wisconsin Protective Coatings Corp., Green Bay, WI; *U.S. Public*, pg. 1358
Hendricks, Albert L., Pres.--Briner Paint Manufacturing Co., Inc., Corpus Christi, TX; *U.S. Public*, pg. 1358
Hendricks, Karen L., Chm. Bd., Pres. & Chief Exec. Officer--Baldwin Piano & Organ Company, Loveland, OH; *U.S. Public*, pg. 169
Hendricks, Kenneth A., Pres. & Chief Exec. Officer--ABC Supply Company, Inc., Beloit, WI; *U.S. Private*, pg. 3
Hendrickson, Boyd W., Pres. & Chief Oper. Officer--Beverly Enterprises, Inc., Fort Smith, AR; *U.S. Public*, pg. 227
Hendrickson, Leon, Pres.--Silver Towne L.P., Winchester, IN; *U.S. Private*, pg. 1000
Hendrikson, Eddie L., Pres.--SAFECO Properties, Inc., Seattle, WA; *U.S. Public*, pg. 1423
Hendrix, Tom E., Chm. Bd., Pres. & Chief Exec. Officer--Henco, Inc., Selmer, TN; *U.S. Private*, pg. 521
Hendry, Robert, Pres. & Chief Exec. Officer--Saab Automobile AB, Nykoping, Sweden; *Int'l*, pg. 687
Hendry, Robert, Pres. & Chief Exec. Officer--Saab Automobile AB, Nykoping, Sweden; *U.S. Public*, pg. 725
Henein, Rafick, Ph.D., Pres. & Chief Exec. Officer--Zenith Goldline Pharmaceuticals, Miami, FL; *U.S. Public*, pg. 915
Henel, Robert E., Jr., Pres. & Chief Exec. Officer--The Annapolis Banking & Trust Co., Annapolis, MD; *U.S. Public*, pg. 1088
Heningway, Jon, Pres.--Stevedoring Services Of America, Seattle, WA; *U.S. Private*, pg. 1042
Henkel, David R., Pres.--Johnson & Quin, Inc., Niles, IL; *U.S. Private*, pg. 590
Henkels, Dirk, Dr., Pres.--Stocko Metallwaren Fabriken Henkels & Sohn, Wuppertal, Germany; *Int'l*, pg. 1301
Henley, A.B., Jr., Chm. Bd., Pres. & Chief Exec. Officer--Henley Paper Company, Greensboro, NC; *U.S. Private*, pg. 522
Henley, Dale, Pres. & Chief Exec. Officer--Haggen, Inc., Bellingham, WA; *U.S. Private*, pg. 493
Henman, Gary, Chm. Bd. & Pres.--Dairy Farmers of America, Inc., Arlington, TX; *U.S. Private*, pg. 307
Henmi, Shinzo, Pres.--Liaoning Liao Bian Advanced Fashion Garments Co., Ltd., Dalian, China; *Int'l*, pg. 579
Henmi, Taekeshi, Pres.--Showa Shell Sekiyu KK, Tokyo, Japan; *Int'l*, pg. 1140
Hennecke, Hans Peter, Pres.--Dolomitwerke GmbH, Wulfrath, Germany; *Int'l*, pg. 1388
Hennecke, Hans Peter, Dr., Pres.--Rheinische Kalksteinwerke GmbH, Wulfrath, Germany; *Int'l*, pg. 1388
Hennessey, Mike J., Pres. & Chief Exec. Officer--Jumping Jacks, Monett, MO; *U.S. Private*, pg. 767
Hennessey, Robert J., Chm., Pres. & Chief Exec. Officer--Genome Therapeutics Corporation, Waltham, MA; *U.S. Public*, pg. 730
Hennessy, Mary R., Pres. & Chief Oper. Officer--TIG Holdings, Inc., New York, NY; *U.S. Public*, pg. 1555
Hennessy, Michael, Pres. & Chief Exec. Officer--Munro & Company, Inc., Hot Springs National Park, AR; *U.S. Private*, pg. 767
Hennessy, Michael W., Pres.--Lovejoy Inc., Downers Grove, IL; *U.S. Private*, pg. 677
Hennigan, George R., Pres.--Kerr-McGee Chemical Corp., Oklahoma City, OK; *U.S. Public*, pg. 952
Henning, Charles, Gen. Mgr.--Sonoma Mission Inn & Spa, Sonoma, CA; *U.S. Private*, pg. 1014
Henning, John J., Pres.--Symtron Systems, Inc., Fair Lawn, NJ; *U.S. Public*, pg. 1679
Henning, Peter H., Pres. & Chief Exec. Officer--Plano Molding Co., Plano, IL; *U.S. Private*, pg. 869
Henning, Robert V., Pres.--Belmont Metals, Inc., Brooklyn, NY; *U.S. Private*, pg. 132
Henricks, Dale, Pres.--University Book Store, Madison, WI; *U.S. Private*, pg. 1127
Henricks, Susan L., Pres. & Chief Exec. Officer--Metromail Corporation, Lombard, IL; *U.S. Public*, pg. 1102
Henriksen, Freddie, Dir.-Admin.--Castrol A/S, Copenhagen, Denmark; *Int'l*, pg. 235
Henry, Barbara A., Pres. & Publr.--Des Moines Register & Tribune Co., Des Moines, IA; *U.S. Public*, pg. 700
Henry, H.C., Jr., Pres.--BellSouth Resources, Inc., Atlanta, GA; *U.S. Public*, pg. 208
Henry, James C., III, Pres. & Chief Exec. Officer--E.P. Henry Corporation, Woodbury, NJ; *U.S. Private*, pg. 522
Henry, Jerry, Chm. Bd., Pres. & Chief Exec. Officer--Johns Manville Corporation, Denver, CO; *U.S. Public*, pg. 927
Henry, Roger P., Pres. & Chief Oper. Officer--Swingster Company, Kansas City, MO; *U.S. Private*, pg. 58
Henry, Steve, Creative Partner--Howell Henry Chaldecott Lury & Partners, London, United Kingdom; *Int'l*, pg. 637
Henry, William L., Pres. & Chief Exec. Officer--The Stroh Brewery Company, Detroit, MI; *U.S. Private*, pg. 1047
Henry, William L., III, Pres.--Linear Dynamics Inc., Parsippany, NJ; *U.S. Private*, pg. 668
Hensel, Neil, Pres.--Titan Systems, Inc., San Diego, CA; *U.S. Public*, pg. 1618
Hensler, Guenter, Pres.-BMG Classics--Bertelsmann Music Group, Wilmington, DE; *Int'l*, pg. 191
Hensley, James W., Pres.--Hensley & Co., Phoenix, AZ; *U.S. Private*, pg. 523
Hensley, Thomas L., Pres. & Chief Exec. Officer--Dairy Queen Corporate Store, Louisville, KY; *U.S. Public*, pg. 220
Henson, Edward, Pres.--JSB Financial, Lynbrook, NY; *U.S. Public*, pg. 919
Henson, J. Peter, Chm. Bd. Pres. & Chief Exec. Officer--Flexible Products Company, Marietta, GA; *U.S. Private*, pg. 412
Henson, Ted, Pres.--3ummit Performance Dist. Inc., Channelview, TX; *U.S. Public*, pg. 1233
Hentges, Richard J., Pres. & Chief Oper. Officer--Foley-Belsaw Company, Minneapolis, MN; *U.S. Private*, pg. 416
Hentschell, Carolyn, Partner & Client/Consumer Services--Kupper Parker Communications Inc., Saint Louis, MO; *U.S. Private*, pg. 637
Heraeus, Jurgen, Dr., Chm. Bd.--Heraeus Holding GmbH, Hanau, Germany; *Int'l*, pg. 615
Herbert, Allan, Pres.--Hollister Incorporated, Libertyville, IL; *U.S. Private*, pg. 535
Herbert, Jeffrey, Chief Exec. Officer--Charter plc, London, United Kingdom; *Int'l*, pg. 280
Herbert, Laurence, Pres.--Intertext Group, Ltd., Glasgow, United Kingdom; *U.S. Public*, pg. 784
Herbert, Laurence, Pres.--The School of Accountancy, Glasgow, United Kingdom; *U.S. Public*, pg. 784
Herbert, Lawrence, Pres.--International Correspondence Schools Ltd., Glasgow, United Kingdom; *U.S. Public*, pg. 784
Herbert, Richard K., Pres. & Chief Oper. Officer--Howell Corporation, Houston, TX; *U.S. Public*, pg. 843
Herbst, Thomas C., Pres.--Abello Deutschland Pharma GmbH, Bornheim, Germany; *Int'l*, pg. 288
Herbster, Charles, Chm. Bd., Pres. & Chief Exec. Officer--Conklin Co. Inc., Shakopee, MN; *U.S. Private*, pg. 263
Herche, David F., Chief Exec. Officer--Enerfab Inc., Cincinnati, OH; *U.S. Private*, pg. 376
Herd, James M., Pres.--Polk Audio, Inc., Baltimore, MD; *U.S. Public*, pg. 1315
Herder, Gary A., Pres. & Chief Exec. Officer--Prab, Inc., Kalamazoo, MI; *U.S. Public*, pg. 1319
Herdrich, William J., Pres. & Chief Exec. Officer--Poly-Seal Corporation, Baltimore, MD; *U.S. Private*, pg. 875
Herkstroter, C.A.J., Chm.-Bd. of Mngmt & Pres.--Royal Dutch/Shell Group of Companies, Hague, Netherlands; *Int'l*, pg. 1135
Herley, John W., Pres.--Atlas Wire Corporation, Schiller Park, IL; *U.S. Private*, pg. 97
Herlihy, Michael, Pres. & Chief Exec. Officer--Advest Bank, Hartford, CT; *U.S. Public*, pg. 23
Herlihy, Sylvester, Pres.--Channel Master, Smithfield, NC; *U.S. Private*, pg. 228
Herlihy, Tom, Pres.--Smith Technologies Corp., Portland, OR; *U.S. Public*, pg. 1478
Herlitz, Peter, Chm. Mngmt. Bd. & Pres.--Herlitz PBS Aktiengesellschaft, Berlin, Germany; *Int'l*, pg. 616
Herluf, Claus, Pres.--Scan-Ad Gruppen A/S, Arhus, Denmark; *Int'l*, pg. 1198
Herman, Alan, Jr., Pres.--Jabel, Inc., Irvington, NJ; *U.S. Private*, pg. 579
Herman, Bernard, Pres.--Star Video Entertainment, L.P., Jersey City, NJ; *U.S. Private*, pg. 1132
Herman, Jay A., Pres. & Chief Exec. Officer--Check Technology Corporation, Minnetonka, MN; *U.S. Public*, pg. 342
Herman, Mike, Pres.--Comdisco Electronics Group, San Diego, CA; *U.S. Public*, pg. 408
Herman, Mike, Pres.--Comdisco Laboratory & Scientific Group, Canton, MA; *U.S. Public*, pg. 408
Herman, Wes, Pres. & Gen. Mgr.--Chesapeake Packaging Co./North Tonawanda, North Tonawanda, NY; *U.S. Public*, pg. 347
Herman, Will, Pres.--Viewlogic Systems Group, Marlborough, MA; *U.S. Public*, pg. 1548
Hermance, Frank S., Pres & Chief Oper. Officer--AMETEK, Inc., Paoli, PA; *U.S. Public*, pg. 99
Hermann, Jesse, Pres.--Borg Warner Automotive-Alabama Div., Selma, AL; *U.S. Public*, pg. 245
Hermann, Jesse, Pres.--BWD Automotive, North Brunswick, NJ; *U.S. Public*, pg. 560
Hermanson, Terry, Pres.--Mr. Christmas Inc., New York, NY; *U.S. Private*, pg. 765
Hermanson, Terry, Pres.--Mr. Christmas Limited, Kowloon, Hong Kong; *U.S. Private*, pg. 765
Hermelin, Victor M., Chm.--KV Pharmaceutical Company, Saint Louis, MO; *U.S. Public*, pg. 941
Hermenet, E.W., Pres.--Brooks Foods, Mount Summit, IN; *U.S. Private*, pg. 887
Hermes, Charles, Pres.--Dutton-Lainson Co., Hastings, NE; *U.S. Private*, pg. 350
Hermoso, Jose Manuel Garcia, Pres.--A.H.V. Ensidesa Capital, S.A., Madrid, Spain; *Int'l*, pg. 1223
Hermoso, Jose Manuel Garcia, Pres.--C.S.I. Corporacion Siderurgia Integral, S.A., Madrid, Spain; *Int'l*, pg. 1224
Hernan, Fernando Guerrero, Pres.--TAUSA - Trasatlantica Agency USA Inc., New York, NY; *Int'l*, pg. 1224
Hernandez, James A. Jr., Pres. & Chief Exec. Officer--3 Score, Inc., Tucker, GA; *U.S. Public*, pg. 291
Hernandez, Mike Acosta, Pres. & Chief Exec. Officer--Camino Real Chevrolet & Geo, Monterey Park, CA; *U.S. Private*, pg. 203
Hernandez, Roland, Pres. & Chief Exec. Officer--Telemundo Group, Inc., Hialeah, FL; *U.S. Public*, pg. 1570
Herndon, Carl M., Pres.--Black Fin Yacht Corporation, Fort Lauderdale, FL; *U.S. Private*, pg. 147
Herndon, Hubert G., Pres. & Chief Exec. Officer--Bank of Morgan County, Madison, GA; *U.S. Public*, pg. 1371
Herndon, James L., Pres. & Chief Oper. Officer--Centex Construction Company, Dallas, TX; *U.S. Public*, pg. 322
Herndon, Vince, Pres. & Chief Oper. Officer--Holcomb & Hoke Mfg. Company, Inc., Indianapolis, IN; *U.S. Private*, pg. 533
Herr, Eric, Pres. & Chief Oper. Officer--Autodesk, Inc., San Rafael, CA; *U.S. Public*, pg. 148
Herr, Gary P., Pres.--Sysco Food Services of Iowa, Inc., West Des Moines, IA; *U.S. Public*, pg. 1551
Herran, Manuel, Pres.--Real Holding Management Corp., Miami, FL; *U.S. Private*, pg. 913
Herrbach, Ralph W., Pres.--Cedarapids, Inc., Cedar Rapids, IA; *U.S. Public*, pg. 1365
Herrera, Manuel O., Pres.--Molinas de Puerto Rico, San Juan, PR; *U.S. Public*, pg. 426
Herrick, Todd W., Pres. & Chief Exec. Officer--Tecumseh Products Company, Tecumseh, MI; *U.S. Public*, pg. 1565
Herriman, M. Davis, Pres.--Maryland Concession & Vending Company, Hyattsville, MD; *U.S. Public*, pg. 741
Herring, James, Pres. & Chief Exec. Officer--Friona Industries, L.P., Amarillo, TX; *U.S. Private*, pg. 429
Herring, Phil, Pres.--Herring Newman, Seattle, WA; *U.S. Private*, pg. 524
Herring, Sherwin, Pres.--Southco Distributing Company, Goldsboro, NC; *U.S. Private*, pg. 1014
Herrington, Douglas, Pres.--Chemical Bank Thumb Area, Caro, MI; *U.S. Public*, pg. 345
Herrman, Jim, Pres.--Gardner Abrasives, South Beloit, IL; *U.S. Public*, pg. 1699

Herrmann, Dick, Pres. & Chief Exec. Officer--Health Economics Corporation, Dallas, TX; *U.S. Public*, pg. 588
Herrmann, John A., Pres. & Chief Exec. Officer--The Bridgeford Group, New York, NY; *Int'l*, pg. 674
Hersch, Ronald G., Ph.D., Pres.--Comprehensive Behavioral Care, Inc., Tampa, FL; *U.S. Public*, pg. 419
Hersh, Harry, Pres. & Chief Exec. Officer--Suntory Water Group, Inc., Marietta, GA; *Int'l*, pg. 1321
Hersh, Robert, Chm. Bd., Pres. & Chief Exec. Officer--Catalina Lighting, Inc., Miami, FL; *U.S. Public*, pg. 314
Hershaft, Arthur, Chm. Bd., Pres. & Chief Exec. Officer--PAXAR Corporation, White Plains, NY; *U.S. Public*, pg. 1266
Hershaft, Judith, Pres.--Innovative Plastics Corporation, Orangeburg, NY; *U.S. Private*, pg. 565
Hershman, Leonard, Pres. & Chief Exec. Officer--Passport Travel, Inc., Overland Park, KS; *U.S. Private*, pg. 842
Herslow, John H., Pres. & Chief Exec. Officer--Sillcocks Plastics, Inc., Berkeley Heights, NJ; *U.S. Private*, pg. 63
Herson, Eugene E., Pres. & Chief Exec. Officer--EMCON, San Mateo, CA; *U.S. Public*, pg. 571
Herson, Gerald, Pres. & Chief Exec. Officer--Delair Group, L.L.C., Delair, NJ; *U.S. Private*, pg. 47
Herst, Douglas J., Chm. Bd. & Pres.--Peerless Lighting Corp., Berkeley, CA; *U.S. Private*, pg. 847
Herstek, Rich, Partner--Houston Herstek Favat, Boston, MA; *U.S. Private*, pg. 542
Herstrum, Al, Pres. & Chief Exec. Officer--Yazoo Power Equipment, LLC, Jackson, MS; *U.S. Private*, pg. 1195
Herter, Edward M., Pres.--Simpson Electric Co., Elgin, IL; *U.S. Private*, pg. 1002
Hertog, Roger, Pres. & Chief Oper. Officer--Sanford C. Bernstein & Co., Inc., New York, NY; *U.S. Private*, pg. 137
Hertwig, James R., Pres.--Landstar ITCO, Inc., Jacksonville, FL; *U.S. Public*, pg. 978
Hertwig, James R., Pres.--Landstar Logistics, Inc., Jacksonville, FL; *U.S. Public*, pg. 978
Hertz, Doug J., Pres. & Chief Oper. Officer--United Distributors, Inc., Smyrna, GA; *U.S. Private*, pg. 1121
Hertzke, Bruce D., Pres. & Chief Oper. Officer--Winnebago Industries, Inc., Forest City, IA; *U.S. Public*, pg. 1772
Herz, John, Pres.--PIC Design, Middlebury, CT; *U.S. Private*, *pg. 864*
Herzer, Richard K., Chm. Bd., Pres. & Chief Exec. Officer--IHOP Corp., Glendale, CA; *U.S. Public*, pg. 862
Herzig, Ron F., Pres. & Chief Exec. Officer--Fremont Indemnity Co./Medical Professional Liab. Div., Santa Monica, CA; *U.S. Public*, pg. 681
Hess, Blaine R., Pres. & Chief Exec. Officer--Thomas J. Lipton Company, Englewood Cliffs, NJ; *Int'l*, pg. 1435
Hess, Gary, Pres. & Chief Exec. Officer--Vacu-Dry Company, Sebastopol, CA; *U.S. Public*, pg. 1704
Hess, J. Daniel, Pres. & Chief Oper. Officer--Takatta Inc., Auburn Hills, MI; *U.S. Private*, pg. 528
Hess, J. Robert, Chm. Bd. & Pres.--Lancaster Malleable Castings Company, Lancaster, PA; *U.S. Private*, pg. 645
Hess, Norbert A., Jr., Pres. & Gen. Mgr.--Coachmen Automotive, Elkhart, IN; *U.S. Public*, pg. 388
Hess, Ronald G., Pres. & Chief Oper. Officer--W-B Supply Co., Pampa, TX; *U.S. Private*, pg. 1144
Hesse, D.R., Pres.--AT&T Network Systems International, Hilversum, Netherlands; *U.S. Public*, pg. 11
Hesse, Daniel, Pres.--AT&T Wireless Services, Kirkland, WA; *U.S. Public*, pg. 11
Hesse, Jay C., Pres. & Chief Exec. Officer--Automatic Equipment Mfg. Co., Pender, NE; *U.S. Private*, pg. 101
Hesselman, Parry, Pres.--Thomas Steel Strip Corp., Warren, OH; *Int'l*, pg. 756
Hessels, J.M., Chm. Bd. & Pres.--Vendex International N.V., Amsterdam, Netherlands; *Int'l*, pg. 1462
Hesser, Grant V., Pres. & Chief Exec. Officer--Maescher Industries, Inc., Cincinnati, OH; *U.S. Private*, pg. 694
Hession, C. E., Dir.-Opers.--Colgate-Palmolive, Dublin, Ireland; *U.S. Public*, pg. 398
Hessler, Kurt, Pres., Chief Exec. Officer & Chief Fin. Officer--Quarterdeck Corp., Marina Del Rey, CA; *U.S. Public*, pg. 1350
Hester, Evelyn, Pres.--Dover Handbag Co., Inc., New York, NY; *U.S. Private*, pg. 1042
Hester, Mark W., Pres.--Telos Field Engineering, Bountiful, UT; *U.S. Public*, pg. 1573
Hester, Mark W., Pres.--Telos Systems Solutions, Bountiful, UT; *U.S. Public*, pg. 1573
Hester, Philip L., Pres. & Chief Oper. Officer--Goldwell Cosmetics (USA) Inc., Linthicum Heights, MD; *Int'l*, pg. 718
Hester, Thomas R., Pres.--Rocky Rococo Corporation, Oconomowoc, WI; *U.S. Private*, pg. 938
Hetrick, C.N., Pres. & Chief Oper. Officer--Maxon Corporation, Muncie, IN; *U.S. Private*, pg. 716
Hettinga, Martin, Mng. Dir. & Partner--HLPB, Amsterdam, Netherlands; *Int'l*, pg. 1377
Heuser, Manfred, Joint Mng. Dir.--HM1, Heuser, Mayer & Partner Direct Marketing GmbH, Munich, Germany; *Int'l*, pg. 579
Heuze, J.C.P.R., Pres.--Prochimar S.A., Paris, France; *Int'l*, pg. 682
Hewett, Peter J., Pres.--MB America, Inc., Westport, CT; *Int'l*, pg. 267
Hewitt, Thomas F., Pres.--Carnival Hotels & Casinos, Miami, FL; *U.S. Public*, pg. 1265
Hewitt, William B., Pres. & Chief Oper. Officer--The Union Corporation, Greenwich, CT; *U.S. Public*, pg. 1667
Heydon, Douglas, Pres.--Arianespace, Inc., Washington, DC; *Int'l*, pg. 81
Heye, Donald R., Pres.--Hyspan Precision Products, Inc., Chula Vista, CA; *U.S. Private*, pg. 552
Heye, Willliam B., Jr., Chm. Bd., Pres. & Chief Exec. Officer--SBE, Inc., San Ramon, CA; *U.S. Public*, pg. 1416
Heyerdahl d.y., Jens P., Pres. & Chief Exec. Officer--Orkla A.S.A., Oslo, Norway; *Int'l*, pg. 1010
Heyman, Lawrence S., Pres. & Chief Exec. Officer--Heyman Corporation, Niles, IL; *U.S. Private*, pg. 524
Heyman, Michael, Pres.--Trans Leasing International Inc., Northbrook, IL; *U.S. Public*, pg. 1628
Heyn, Chris, Pres.-Manhattan Menswear--Salant Corporation, New York, NY; *U.S. Public*, pg. 1429
Heyward, Andrew, Pres.--DIC Entertainment, Burbank, CA; *U.S. Public*, pg. 513
Heyward, Westley M., Pres.--CalFarm Insurance Company, Sacramento, CA; *U.S. Public*, pg. 1791
Hiatt, Russ, Pres. & Chief Exec. Officer--The Citizens State Bank, Williamsport, IN; *U.S. Public*, pg. 1217
Hick, John W.W., Pres.--TVX Gold Inc., Toronto, Canada; *Int'l*, pg. 1345
Hickcox, W. Thomas, Pres. & Chief Oper. Officer--Continental Homes Holding Corp., Scottsdale, AZ; *U.S. Public*, pg. 440
Hickert, Thomas C., Pres.--WCI Machine Tools, Bridgeport, CT; *Int'l*, pg. 440
Hickey, Brian E., Pres. & Chief Exec. Officer--Harlequin Enterprises Ltd., Don Mills, Canada; *Int'l*, pg. 1402
Hickey, Dan, Pres.-Corp. Opers.--Smyth, Co., Saint Paul, MN; *U.S. Private*, pg. 1010
Hickey, Joel, Pres.--Dow Corning S.T.I., Plymouth, MI; *U.S. Public*, pg. 523
Hickey, John, Pres.--RPR Correspondant Clearing, Saint Louis, MO; *U.S. Public*, pg. 476
Hickey, John R., Pres. & Chief Oper. Officer--Advantage Learning Systems, Inc., Wisconsin Rapids, WI; *U.S. Public*, pg. 22
Hickey, William M., Pres. & Chief Exec. Officer--Lapham-Hickey Steel Corp., Chicago, IL; *U.S. Private*, pg. 651
Hickey, William V., Pres. & Chief Oper. Officer--Sealed Air Corporation, Saddle Brook, NJ; *U.S. Public*, pg. 1450
Hickey, William, III, Pres.-Corp. Opers.--Smyth, Co., Saint Paul, MN; *U.S. Private*, pg. 1010
Hickingbotham, Herren C., Pres. & Chief Oper. Officer--TCBY Enterprises Inc., Little Rock, AR; *U.S. Public*, pg. 1553
Hicks, Jeff, Pres.--Crispin Porter & Bogusky Advertising, Miami, FL; *U.S. Private*, pg. 290
Hicks, Jeffrey, Pres.--Crispin Porter & Bogusky, Miami, FL; *U.S. Private*, pg. 290
Hicks, Joseph D., Pres. & Chief Exec. Officer--Siecor Corporation, Saskatoon, Canada; *U.S. Public*, pg. 449
Hickson, Richard G., Pres. & Chief Exec. Officer--Trustmark Corporation, Jackson, MS; *U.S. Public*, pg. 1643
Hidaka, Toshiaki, Pres.--Toray Fibers (Thailand), Ltd., Bangkok, Thailand; *Int'l*, pg. 1400
Hiekintalo, Mauri, Pres.--Artek oy ab, Helsingfors, Finland; *Int'l*, pg. 1072
Higashio, Takeshi, Pres. & Chief Fin. Officer--Haseko (California) Inc., Los Angeles, CA; *Int'l*, pg. 600
Higashio, Takeshi, Pres.--Haseko (New York) Inc., New York, NY; *Int'l*, pg. 600
Higashiyama, Akiyuki, Pres.--Oversea Courier Service Co., Ltd., Tokyo, Japan; *Int'l*, pg. 929
Higbee, Ann, Mng. Partner--EMA Public Relations Services, Inc., Syracuse, NY; *U.S. Private*, pg. 765
Higbee, Ann G., Mng. Partner-EMA Pub. Rels. Services--Eric Mower and Associates, Inc., Syracuse, NY; *U.S. Private*, pg. 765
Higbee, Ann G., Mng. Partner-EMA Pub. Rels. Services--Eric Mower and Associates/Buffalo, Inc., Buffalo, NY; *U.S. Private*, pg. 765
Higbee, Ann G., Mng. Partner-EMA Pub. Rels.--Eric Mower & Associates, Albany, NY; *U.S. Private*, pg. 765
Higbee, Ann G., Mng. Partner-EMA Pub. Rels. Services--Eric Mower & Associates, Atlanta, GA; *U.S. Private*, pg. 765
Higbee, D., Pres.--Sawhill Tubular Div., Sharon, PA; *U.S. Public*, pg. 131
Higby, Lawrence M., Pres. & Chief Oper. Officer--Apria Healthcare Group Inc., Costa Mesa, CA; *U.S. Public*, pg. 125
Higdon, Ira, Jr., Pres.--Ira Higdon Grocery, Inc., Cairo, GA; *U.S. Private*, pg. 527
Higdon, Joe, Pres.--Stones, Inc., Bainbridge, GA; *U.S. Private*, pg. 1045
Higginbotham, Richard A., Pres. & Chief Exec. Officer--Fleet Bank, N.A., Hartford, CT; *U.S. Public*, pg. 649
Higginbotham, Richard A., Pres. & Chief Exec. Officer--Fleet National Bank of Connecticut, Hartford, CT; *U.S. Public*, pg. 649
Higginbotham, Steve F., Pres.--Ozark Motor Lines, Memphis, TN; *U.S. Private*, pg. 825
Higgins, Bill, Pres. & Chief Exec. Officer--Dillingham Construction Corporation, Pleasanton, CA; *U.S. Private*, pg. 333
Higgins, Glenn F., Pres.--Comtech Antenna Systems, Inc., Saint Cloud, FL; *U.S. Public*, pg. 425
Higgins, Harold, Publr.--Boulder Publishing, Inc., Boulder, CO; *U.S. Public*, pg. 1447
Higgins, James, Chm. Bd., Pres. & Chief Exec. Officer--Charter Builders, Inc., Dallas, TX; *Int'l*, pg. 896
Higgins, Kathy, Pres.--Sachs Holding Company, Chesterfield, MO; *U.S. Private*, pg. 959
Higgins, Larry B., Chm. Bd., Pres. & Chief Exec. Officer--H & H Tube & Manufacturing Co., Vanderbilt, MI; *U.S. Private*, pg. 489
Higgins, Robert J., Pres. & Chief Exec. Officer--Fleet National Bank, Providence, RI; *U.S. Public*, pg. 649
Higgins, Robert J., Chm. Bd., Pres. & Chief Exec. Officer--Trans World Entertainment Corporation, Albany, NY; *U.S. Public*, pg. 1629
Higgins, S.L., Chm. Bd. & Pres.--Air Industries Corporation, Garden Grove, CA; *U.S. Private*, pg. 28
Higgins, Walter M., Chm. Bd., Pres. & Chief Exec. Officer--Sierra Pacific Resources, Reno, NV; *U.S. Public*, pg. 1470
High, S. Dale, Chm. Bd. & Pres.--High Industries, Inc., Lancaster, PA; *U.S. Private*, pg. 528
Highland, Glenn, Pres. & V.P.--DataCard Corporation, Minnetonka, MN; *U.S. Private*, pg. 312
Highland, Glenn W., Pres. & Chief Exec. Officer--DataCard Corporation, Minnetonka, MN; *U.S. Private*, pg. 312
Hightower, Lloyd A., Pres. & Chief Exec. Officer--Williams Field Services, Tulsa, OK; *U.S. Public*, pg. 1769
Hightower, Sr., Neil H., Pres. & Chief Exec. Officer--Thomaston Mills, Inc., Thomaston, GA; *U.S. Public*, pg. 1599
Highum, P. Michael, Pres.--HS Resources, San Francisco, CA; *U.S. Public*, pg. 772
Higo, Yoshinari, Pres.--Kawasho International (H.K.) Ltd., Hong Kong, Hong Kong; *Int'l*, pg. 727
Higuchi, Koukei, Pres.--The Tokio Marine & Fire Insurance Company, Ltd., Tokyo, Japan; *Int'l*, pg. 1391
Higuchi, Takeshi, Pres.--Nikkei Research, Inc., Tokyo, Japan; *Int'l*, pg. 929
Higuchi, Tatsuo, Pres. & Chief Exec. Officer--Pharmavite Corp., Mission Hills, CA; *U.S. Private*, pg. 860
Higuchi, Tatsuo, Pres. & Chief Exec. Officer--Pharmavite Corporation, Mission Hills, CA; *Int'l*, pg. 1013
Higurashi, Takeshi, Chm. Bd., Pres. & Chief Exec. Officer--Subaru of America, Inc., Cherry Hill, NJ; *Int'l*, pg. 523
Hii, Peter, Pres.--Nemic-Lambda KK, Tokyo, Japan; *Int'l*, pg. 1242
Hikosaka, K., Pres.--Nissho Iwai Foods Corp., Tokyo, Japan; *Int'l*, pg. 946
Hilb, Robert H., Pres.--Hilb, Rogal and Hamilton Company of Canada, Limited, Winnipeg, Canada; *U.S. Public*, pg. 828
Hilbert, Steven C., Chm. Bd., Pres. & Chief Exec. Officer--Conseco Inc., Carmel, IN; *U.S. Public*, pg. 432
Hilbert, William M., Pres. & Chief Exec. Officer--PHB Die Casting, Fairview, PA; *U.S. Private*, pg. 826
Hilbert, William M., Sr., Pres. & Chief Exec. Officer--PHB Machining Division, Fairview, PA; *U.S. Private*, pg. 826
Hilbert, William M., Sr., Pres. & Chief Oper. Officer--PHB Tool & Die, Girard, PA; *U.S. Private*, pg. 826
Hilbert, William M., Sr., Pres. & Chief Exec. Officer--PHB Plastic & Rubber Molding Division, Fairview, PA; *U.S. Private*, pg. 826
Hildebrand, E.H., Pres.--CR Quality Services, Inc., Philadelphia, PA; *U.S. Public*, pg. 432
Hildebrand, W.R., Pres. & Chief Oper. Officer--Fiatallis North America, Inc., Carol Stream, IL; *Int'l*, pg. 483
Hildebrand, Willard R., Pres. & Chief Exec. Officer--Bucyrus International, South Milwaukee, WI; *U.S. Private*, pg. 177
Hildebrand, Willard R., Pres. & Chief Exec. Officer--Great Dane Trailers, Inc., Savannah, GA; *U.S. Private*, pg. 1030
Hildebrandt, Bernd, Pres.--CCC Steel, Inc., Rancho Dominguez, CA; *U.S. Public*, pg. 1375
Hildebrandt, Mel, Pres.--Linbeck Construction Corp, Houston, TX; *U.S. Private*, pg. 667
Hilding, Greg, Pres.--First American Bank & Trust, Willmar, MN; *U.S. Private*, pg. 167
Hiler, Larry, Pres.--Hiler Industries, La Porte, IN; *U.S. Private*, pg. 529
Hilkert, Tom, Pres. & Chief Exec. Officer--MEG, Cambridge City, IN; *U.S. Private*, pg. 686
Hill, Alan, Pres.--Lawrence Paper Company, Lawrence, KS; *U.S. Private*, pg. 654
Hill, Allen M., Pres. & Chief Exec. Officer--DPL Inc., Dayton, OH; *U.S. Public*, pg. 473
Hill, Allen M., Pres. & Chief Exec. Officer--Dayton Power & Light Co., Dayton, OH; *U.S. Public*, pg. 473
Hill, Brian, Pres.-Worldwide Seed--Cargill Seed Div., Minneapolis, MN; *U.S. Private*, pg. 210
Hill, Brice E., Pres. & Chief Exec. Officer--Centex Construction Group, Inc., Dallas, TX; *U.S. Public*, pg. 322
Hill, David F., Pres.--SAFECO Services Co., Seattle, WA; *U.S. Public*, pg. 1423
Hill, David F., Pres.-SAFECO Mutual Funds--SAFECO Asset Management Company, Seattle, WA; *U.S. Public*, pg. 1423
Hill, Dennis, Pres.--Nordic Systems, Ltd., Wauwatosa, WI; *U.S. Private*, pg. 410
Hill, Edward G., Jr., Pres. & Chief Exec. Officer--Abco Markets, Inc., Phoenix, AZ; *U.S. Private*, pg. 10
Hill, Elmer W., Pres. & Chief Exec. Officer--GEC Precision Corp., Wellington, KS; *Int'l*, pg. 545
Hill, Howard, Pres.--Keysor Century Corporation, Saugus, CA; *U.S. Private*, pg. 618
Hill, Ian, Pres.--Berendsen Fluid Power, Inc., Tulsa, OK; *Int'l*, pg. 1284
Hill, J. Donald, Chm. Bd., Pres. & Chief Exec. Officer--Excel Technology, Inc., New York, NY; *U.S. Public*, pg. 599
Hill, James, Pres.--Superior Emergency Vehicles, Ltd., Red Deer, Canada; *U.S. Public*, pg. 617
Hill, James, Pres.--Nitro Steel Div., Pleasant Prairie, WI; *U.S. Public*, pg. 1349
Hill, Julie, Pres.--Costain Homes Inc., Newport Beach, CA; *Int'l*, pg. 337
Hill, Kevin R., Pres.--Oxford Health Plans (IL), Inc., Rosemont, IL; *U.S. Public*, pg. 1239
Hill, Lewis, Pres.--First American Tax Valuation, Irving, TX; *U.S. Public*, pg. 625
Hill, Lloyd L., Pres. & Chief Oper. Officer--Applebee's International, Inc., Overland Park, KS; *U.S. Public*, pg. 122
Hill, Paul H., Pres.--Dryvit Systems, Inc., West Warwick, RI; *U.S. Public*, pg. 1357
Hill, R.L., Pres.--Amtech Logistics Corporation, Dallas, TX; *U.S. Public*, pg. 432
Hill, Richard S., Chm. Bd., Pres. & Chief Exec. Officer--Novellus Systems, Inc., San Jose, CA; *U.S. Public*, pg. 1204
Hill, Robert D., Pres. & Chief Exec. Officer--Davel Communications Group, Inc., Jacksonville, IL; *U.S. Public*, pg. 488
Hill, Robert D., Pres.--PST Vans, Inc., Salt Lake City, UT; *U.S. Public*, pg. 1246
Hill, Roger W., Pres. & Chief Exec. Officer--Holly Sugar Corporation, Sugar Land, TX; *U.S. Public*, pg. 872
Hill, Sam, Pres.--EAC-Embraer Aircraft Corporation, Fort Lauderdale, FL; *Int'l*, pg. 452

Hill, Stan, Pres.--Kaiser Aerospace & Electronics Corp., Foster City, CA; *U.S. Private*, pg. 605
Hill, Stephen R., Chm. & Pres.--Tone Commander Systems, Mukilteo, WA; *U.S. Private*, pg. 1090
Hill, William C., Pres.--The Monarch Company, Inc., Atlanta, GA; *U.S. Private*, pg. 756
Hill, William R., Pres. & Chief Exec. Officer--OAO Technology Solutions, Inc., Greenbelt, MD; *U.S. Public*, pg. 1425
Hillback, Elliott D., Jr., Pres. & Chief Exec. Officer--IG Laboratories, Inc., Framingham, MA; *U.S. Public*, pg. 733
Hillegass, Bonnie, Pres.--Family Healthcare Services, Inc., Las Vegas, NV; *U.S. Public*, pg. 1469
Hillen, C.A., Pres. & Gen. Mgr.--Olin Pantex, Inc, Saint Petersburg, FL; *U.S. Public*, pg. 1219
Hillenbrand, W August, Pres. & Chief Exec. Officer--Hillenbrand Industries, Inc., Batesville, IN; *U.S. Public*, pg. 828
Hiller, Rainald, Pres.--EMTEC Magnetics ECE GmbH, Vienna, Austria; *Int'l*, pg. 743
Hiller, Robert G., Pres.--Telecommunications Group, Gaithersburg, MD; *U.S. Public*, pg. 1745
Hillerich, John A., III, Pres. & Chief Exec. Officer--Hillerich & Bradsby Co., Louisville, KY; *U.S. Private*, pg. 530
Hilliard, Edie, Pres.--Broadcast Programming, Seattle, WA; *U.S. Private*, pg. 531
Hillis, Kelly, Pres. & Chief Exec. Officer--Regions Bank/Carroll County, Carrollton, GA; *U.S. Public*, pg. 1372
Hillman, Howard B., Chm. Bd., Pres. & Chief Exec. Officer--Auto-trol Technology Corporation, Denver, CO; *U.S. Public*, pg. 148
Hillman, Lee S., Pres. & Chief Exec. Officer--Bally Total Fitness Holdings Corporation, Chicago, IL; *U.S. Public*, pg. 171
Hilmes, Jerome B., Pres.--Applied Technology Division, Falls Church, VA; *U.S. Public*, pg. 423
Hilpert, Dale W., Pres. & Chief Oper. Officer--Woolworth Corporation, New York, NY; *U.S. Public*, pg. 1777
Hilsabeck, Frank H., Pres. & Chief Exec. Officer--Aliant Communications Inc., Lincoln, NE; *U.S. Public*, pg. 40
Hilton, Avery, Pres. & Gen. Mgr.--SMI Steel South Carolina, Cayce, SC; *U.S. Public*, pg. 412
Hilton, James C., Pres.-Wayne Div.--Dresser Industries Wayne Division, Austin, TX; *U.S. Public*, pg. 528
Hilyard, Jim, Vice Chm. & Pres.--Ludowici Roof Tile, Inc., New Lexington, OH; *Int'l*, pg. 1171
Hilz, Mark T., Pres. & Chief Exec. Officer--PC Service Source, Inc., Dallas, TX; *U.S. Public*, pg. 1240
Himelfarb, Donald M., Pres.--Thrifty Rent-a-Car System, Inc., Tulsa, OK; *U.S. Public*, pg. 354
Himes, Donald A., Pres.--Nordco, Inc., Milwaukee, WI; *U.S. Public*, pg. 1209
Hin, Chong Siong, Pres. & Gen. Mgr.--Xian-Janssen Pharmaceutical Ltd., Xian, China; *U.S. Public*, pg. 932
Hinchman, David F., Pres. & Chief Exec. Officer--U.S. Precision Lens Inc., Cincinnati, OH; *U.S. Public*, pg. 448
Hinckley, James, Pres. & Chief Oper. Officer--Club Resorts Holding, Inc., Dallas, TX; *U.S. Private*, pg. 247
Hinckley, Jim, Pres.--Club Corporation of America, Dallas, TX; *U.S. Private*, pg. 247
Hinden, Randy, Pres.--Duro Dyne Corporation, Farmingdale, NY; *U.S. Private*, pg. 349
Hinderager, Larry, Pres.--J.R. Simplot Company, Minerals & Chemicals Group, Pocatello, ID; *U.S. Private*, pg. 1002
Hindery, Leo, Jr., Pres. & Chief Exec. Officer--TCI Communications, Inc., Englewood, CO; *U.S. Public*, pg. 1554
Hindin, Richard J., Pres.--ADWORKS, Inc., Washington, DC; *U.S. Private*, pg. 23
Hindman, Don J., Chm. Bd., Pres. & Chief Exec. Officer--Clark Foodservice, Inc., Elk Grove Village, IL; *U.S. Private*, pg. 242
Hinds, Cameron, Pres.--First Commerce Investors, Lincoln, NE; *U.S. Public*, pg. 629
Hines, Edward, Pres. & Chief Exec. Officer--Edward Hines Lumber Co., Itasca, IL; *U.S. Private*, pg. 530
Hines, J.B., Pres.--SLI International Corp., Stamford, CT; *Int'l*, pg. 1268
Hines, Richard L., Pres.--Johnson & Johnson Finance Corporation, New Brunswick, NJ; *U.S. Public*, pg. 928
Hinfey, John K., Pres. & Chief Exec. Officer--United Planners' Financial Services of America, Scottsdale, AZ; *U.S. Private*, pg. 831
Hingst, Ronald A., Pres.--Carpenter Co., Richmond, VA; *U.S. Private*, pg. 214
Hinkaty, Charles, Pres.--Del Pharmaceuticals, Inc., Farmingdale, NY; *U.S. Public*, pg. 494
Hinman, Kirk, Pres., Chief Exec. Officer, Chief Fin. Officer & Treas.--Rome Strip Steel Co., Inc., Rome, NY; *U.S. Private*, pg. 942
Hinman, Stephen, Pres.--Waterloo Service Company, Waterloo, IA; *U.S. Private*, pg. 1152
Hinman, Wayne A., Pres.--Air Products Ref-fuel Holding Corp., Allentown, PA; *U.S. Public*, pg. 31
Hino, Tetsuya, Pres.--Noritake Co., Limited, Nagoya, Japan; *Int'l*, pg. 958
Hinshaw, W. Eric, Pres. & Chief Exec. Officer--Kingsdown, Inc., Mebane, NC; *U.S. Private*, pg. 622
Hinson, Charlie, Pres.--Limited Store Planning, Columbus, OH; *U.S. Public*, pg. 995
Hinson, Richard E., Pres. & Gen. Mgr.--Searle Canada Inc., Oakville, Canada; *U.S. Public*, pg. 1126
Hinterlong, B.J., Pres. & Gen. Mgr.--Thomas Conveyor Company, Burleson, TX; *U.S. Private*, pg. 1082
Hintikka, Martti, Pres.--ExClay Suomi Oy, Helsinki, Finland; *Int'l*, pg. 1200
Hintikka, Pentti-Juhani, Pres.--Wartsila Diesel International Ltd. Oy, Strasbourg, France; *Int'l*, pg. 863
Hintz, Donald, Pres.--Entergy Operations, Inc., Jackson, MS; *U.S. Public*, pg. 586
Hintz, Roger, Pres. & Gen. Mgr.--Winpower Inc., Saint Peter, MN; *U.S. Private*, pg. 350
Hipp, Frederick R., Pres. & Chief Exec. Officer--Houlihan's Restaurant Group, Kansas City, MO; *U.S. Public*, pg. 841
Hipp, Ray, Pres. & Chief Exec. Officer--ITI Marketing Services, Inc., Omaha, NE; *U.S. Private*, pg. 555
Hipp, W. Hayne, Chm. Bd., Pres. & Chief Exec. Officer--Liberty Corporation, Greenville, SC; *U.S. Public*, pg. 991
Hiraga, Kazutsugu, Pres.--Chichibu Onoda Cement Corporation, Tokyo, Japan; *Int'l*, pg. 284
Hirai, Katsuhiko, Pres. & Chief Exec. Officer--Toray Industries, Inc., Tokyo, Japan; *Int'l*, pg. 1399
Hirai, Yoshifumi, Pres.--Yamato Transport USA, Inc., Flushing, NY; *Int'l*, pg. 1519
Hiranandani, Hiro, Pres. & Chief Exec. Officer--Computer Power Incorporated, High Bridge, NJ; *U.S. Public*, pg. 421
Hirano, Kazuo, Pres.--Daido Life Insurance Company, Osaka, Japan; *Int'l*, pg. 363
Hirasawa, Sadaaki, Pres.--Bank of Yokohama, Yokohama, Japan; *Int'l*, pg. 158
Hirashima, Tomoyoshi, Pres.--Circle Freight International Japan Ltd., Funibashi, Japan; *U.S. Public*, pg. 372
Hirata, Nobuo, Pres.--Dentsu Kyushu, Fukuoka, Japan; *Int'l*, pg. 393
Hirata, Tadashi, Pres. & Chief Oper. Officer--Kyowa Hakko Kogyo Company, Ltd., Tokyo, Japan; *Int'l*, pg. 778
Hirayama, S., Chm. Bd. & Pres.--Nippon Fisher Company, Ltd., Tokyo, Japan; *U.S. Public*, pg. 1126
Hirayama, Shinji, Pres. & Chief Exec. Officer--The Fuji Bank & Trust Co., New York, NY; *Int'l*, pg. 519
Hirko, Joe, Pres.--Tule Hub Services Co., Portland, OR; *U.S. Public*, pg. 585
Hirl, J. Roger, Pres. & Chief Exec. Officer--Occidental Chemical Corporation, Dallas, TX; *U.S. Public*, pg. 1210
Hirose, Masashi, Pres.--Miura Boiler Co. Ltd., Northbrook, IL; *Int'l*, pg. 884
Hirota, Horoshi, Pres.--Kuraki Company Ltd., Nagaoka, Japan; *Int'l*, pg. 764
Hirsch, Charles L., Chm. Bd. & Pres.--Charles Leonard, Inc., Glendale, NY; *U.S. Private*, pg. 660
Hirsch, David, Pres.--Pawtucket Fasteners Inc., Pawtucket, RI; *U.S. Private*, pg. 844
Hirsch, Howard, Pres.--Forest Electric Corp., New York, NY; *U.S. Public*, pg. 571
Hirsch, Nathan, Pres. & Chief Exec. Officer--Junior Gallery Ltd., New York, NY; *U.S. Private*, pg. 602
Hirsch, Robert A., Pres.--Baldwin Steel Company, Jersey City, NJ; *Int'l*, pg. 401
Hirsch, Stanley, Pres.--Structural Industries, Inc., Hicksville, NY; *U.S. Private*, pg. 1048
Hirsch, Steven, Pres.-Camelot Entertainment Sls. Inc.--King World Productions, Los Angeles, CA; *U.S. Public*, pg. 961
Hirsch, William B., Pres. & Chief Exec. Officer--Keystone Powdered Metal Company, Saint Marys, PA; *U.S. Private*, pg. 619
Hirschauer, Tom, Pres.--EvansGroup, Indianapolis, IN; *U.S. Private*, pg. 385
Hirschboeck, John K., Pres.--Young & Rubicam Detroit, Detroit, MI; *U.S. Private*, pg. 1198
Hirschfeld, David L., Pres., Chief Exec. Officer & Treas.--Hirschfeld, Inc., San Angelo, TX; *U.S. Private*, pg. 530
Hirschmann, Joseph L., Pres.--First DataBank, San Bruno, CA; *U.S. Private*, pg. 515
Hirschorn, Martin, Pres. & Chief Exec. Officer--Industrial Acoustics Company, Inc., Bronx, NY; *U.S. Public*, pg. 875
Hirsh, Charles, Pres.--Accurate Box Co., Inc., Paterson, NJ; *U.S. Private*, pg. 11
Hirshman, Karl J., Pres. & Chief Oper. Officer--Doron Precision Systems, Inc., Binghamton, NY; *U.S. Private*, pg. 341
Hirsig, Alan R., Pres. & Chief Exec. Officer--ARCO Chemical Co., Newtown Square, PA; *U.S. Public*, pg. 144
Hirt, David J., Pres. & Chief Exec. Officer--Batesville Casket Company, Inc., Batesville, IN; *U.S. Public*, pg. 828
Hisai, Keinosuke, Pres.--Nichiro Corporation, Tokyo, Japan; *Int'l*, pg. 928
Hisano, Ryomin, Pres.--Shin-Wako Securities Investment Trust and Management Co., Ltd., Tokyo, Japan; *Int'l*, pg. 1485
Hiscock, Derek, Pres.--Robinson-Blackmore Express, Saint Johns, Canada; *Int'l*, pg. 924
Hishmeh, Basem L., Pres. & Chief Exec. Officer--Aerco International Inc., Northvale, NJ; *U.S. Private*, pg. 23
Hislop, Michael J., Pres. & Chief Oper. Officer--Il Fornaio America Corporation, Corte Madera, CA; *U.S. Public*, pg. 864
Hitchcock, Fritz, Pres. & Chief Exec. Officer--Hitchcock Automotive Resources, City of Industry, CA; *U.S. Private*, pg. 531
Hitchcock, Timothy R., Pres. & Chief Exec. Officer--Hitchcock Industries, Inc., Bloomington, MN; *U.S. Private*, pg. 531
Hite, R. Lee, Chm. Bd., Pres. & Chief Exec. Officer--The Hite Company, Altoona, PA; *U.S. Private*, pg. 531
Hitesman, Timothy E., Pres.--Osborn Manufacturing, Cleveland, OH; *U.S. Public*, pg. 924
Hjartland, Gunnar, Pres. & Chief Exec. Officer--Jotun A/S, Sandefjord, Norway; *Int'l*, pg. 714
Hjerpe, William, Pres.--Honeywell Europe S.A., Brussels, Belgium; *U.S. Public*, pg. 834
Hladky, Joe, Pres. & Publr.--The Gazette Company, Cedar Rapids, IA; *U.S. Private*, pg. 442
Hlobik, Lawrence S., Chm. Bd. & Pres.--Terra Nitrogen Company, L.P., Tulsa, OK; *U.S. Public*, pg. 1581
Ho, Kim Ki, Pres.--Ssangyong Heavy Industries Co., Ltd., Seoul, Korea; *Int'l*, pg. 1292
Hoag, Frank E., Pres. & Chief Oper. Officer--Campbell-Ewald Advertising, Warren, MI; *U.S. Public*, pg. 908
Hoag, Thomas R., Pres. & Chief Exec. Officer--ScanTron Corporation, Tustin, CA; *U.S. Public*, pg. 786
Hoagland, Robert, Pres.--H.B. Ives, Wallingford, CT; *U.S. Private*, pg. 506
Hoashi, Masahito, Pres.--Kibun Co. Ltd., Tokyo, Japan; *Int'l*, pg. 733
Hobbs, Eamonn P., Pres. & Chief Exec. Officer--AngioDynamics, Queensbury, NY; *U.S. Public*, pg. 540
Hobbs, Gerald S., Pres. & Chief Exec. Officer--VNU USA, Inc., New York, NY; *Int'l*, pg. 1447
Hobbs, Mixon, Pres.--Homestead Homes, Cordele, GA; *U.S. Public*, pg. 318
Hochberg, Mitchell C., Pres. & Chief Exec. Officer--Spectrum Skanska Inc., Greenwich, CT; *Int'l*, pg. 1261
Hochfelder, James Lawrence, Pres.--Beldoch Industries, West Hempstead, NY; *U.S. Public*, pg. 519
Hochreiter, E. Joseph, Pres. & Chief Oper. Officer--Bailey, Fischer & Porter Company, Warminster, PA; *Int'l*, pg. 449
Hockaday, Irvine O., Jr., Pres. & Chief Exec. Officer--Hallmark Cards, Inc., Kansas City, MO; *U.S. Private*, pg. 495
Hockenbrocht, David W., Pres. & Chief Oper. Officer--Sparton Corporation, Jackson, MI; *U.S. Public*, pg. 1496
Hocking, William G., Dr., Pres.--Marshfield Clinic, Marshfield, WI; *U.S. Private*, pg. 708
Hod, Nathan, Pres. & Chief Exec. Officer--DSP Communications Inc., Cupertino, CA; *U.S. Public*, pg. 475
Hodes, Bernard S., Pres.--Bernard Hodes Group, New York, NY; *U.S. Public*, pg. 1224
Hodge, Harry, Pres. & Dir. Gen.-Quiksilver Europe--Quiksilver, Inc., Costa Mesa, CA; *U.S. Public*, pg. 1353
Hodge, Luther H., Pres.--Fleet Trust Co. of Florida, N.A., Stuart, FL; *U.S. Public*, pg. 649
Hodgekins, Barry J., Pres.--Josam Company, Michigan City, IN; *U.S. Private*, pg. 600
Hodges, C.C., Chief Oper. Officer--Lincoln Big Three, Inc., Baton Rouge, LA; *Int'l*, pg. 37
Hodges, Jim, Pres.--Royal Paper Box of California, Montebello, CA; *U.S. Private*, pg. 949
Hodges, Larry, Pres.--Mrs. Fields' Original Cookies, Inc., Salt Lake City, UT; *U.S. Private*, pg. 688
Hodges, Larry, Pres. & Chief Exec. Officer--Pretzel Time Inc., Salt Lake City, UT; *U.S. Private*, pg. 688
Hodges, Ron, Pres. & Chief Oper. Officer--Volunteer Bank, Jackson, TN; *U.S. Public*, pg. 176
Hodgson, Marley, Chm. Bd. & Pres.--Trafalgar Ghurka Ltd., Norwalk, CT; *U.S. Private*, pg. 1095
Hodgson, R.J., Pres.--Technical Coatings Co., Flanders, NJ; *U.S. Private*, pg. 133
Hodgson, Thomas R., Pres. & Chief Oper. Officer--Abbott Laboratories, Abbott Park, IL; *U.S. Public*, pg. 12
Hodin, Donald, Pres.--Waltec Engineering, Wallaceburg, Canada; *Int'l*, pg. 453
Hodnik, David F., Pres. & Chief Exec. Officer--Ace Hardware Corporation, Oak Brook, IL; *U.S. Private*, pg. 12
Hodowal, John R., Chm. Bd. & Pres.--Ipalco Enterprises, Inc., Indianapolis, IN; *U.S. Public*, pg. 912
Hodson, Tom, Chm. Bd. & Pres.--Columbia Falls Aluminum Company, Columbia Falls, MT; *U.S. Private*, pg. 255
Hoeft, William L., Pres.--Ziegler Inc., Minneapolis, MN; *U.S. Private*, pg. 1205
Hoeksema, Timothy E., Chm. Bd., Pres. & Chief Exec. Officer--Midwest Express Holdings, Inc., Oak Creek, WI; *U.S. Public*, pg. 1111
Hoelzer, Dennis, Chm. Bd., Pres. & Chief Exec. Officer--Sentinel Technologies Inc., Downers Grove, IL; *U.S. Private*, pg. 984
Hoemann, Jamie, Sr. Principal & Grp. Creative Dir.--Publicis/Bloom, Dallas, TX; *Int'l*, pg. 469
Hoeper, Howard P., Chm. Bd. & Pres.--Packaging Resources, Incorporated, Lake Forest, IL; *U.S. Private*, pg. 833
Hoeppner, Tom, Pres.--Kraft Foods Inc., Glenview, IL; *U.S. Public*, pg. 1288
Hoerig, Jerry, Pres.--Syntex Chemicals, Inc., Boulder, CO; *Int'l*, pg. 1120
Hoesterey, R., Pres.--Para Systems Inc., Carrollton, TX; *U.S. Private*, pg. 260
Hoeven, John, Pres. & Chief Exec. Officer--Bank Of North Dakota, Bismarck, ND; *U.S. Private*, pg. 114
Hoey, John J., Pres. & Chief Exec. Officer--Hondo Oil & Gas Company, Roswell, NM; *Int'l*, pg. 818
Hofer, Judith K., Pres. & Chief Exec. Officer--Filene's, Boston, MA; *U.S. Public*, pg. 1063
Hofer, Thomas W., Pres.--Spring-Green Lawn Care Corporation, Plainfield, IL; *U.S. Private*, pg. 1027
Hoff, Randy, Pres.--Barnstead/Thermolyne Corporation, Dubuque, IA; *U.S. Public*, pg. 1545
Hoffbuhr, Jack, Exec. Dir.--American Water Works Association, Denver, CO; *U.S. Public*, pg. 94
Hoffer, Robert A., Sr., Pres. & Chief Exec. Officer--Hoffer Plastics Corporation, South Elgin, IL; *U.S. Private*, pg. 532
Hoffman, Allison, Partner & Sr. V.P.--Media That Works, Cincinnati, OH; *U.S. Private*, pg. 727
Hoffman, Bernard, Dr., Pres.--J. Dieffenbacher GmbH & Co., Eppingen, Germany; *Int'l*, pg. 413
Hoffman, Bruno, Pres.--Hoffman Laces, Ltd., Cobleskill, NY; *U.S. Public*, pg. 769
Hoffman, Charles, Pres.--Litton Applied Technology, San Jose, CA; *U.S. Public*, pg. 1003
Hoffman, Dave, Pres.--ALZA, Ltd., Palo Alto, CA; *U.S. Public*, pg. 62
Hoffman, David, Chm. Bd.--Freeman Products, Elmwood Park, NJ; *U.S. Private*, pg. 1105
Hoffman, Douglas A., Pres.--Branch Electric Supply Co., Inc., Boston, MA; *U.S. Private*, pg. 165
Hoffman, Ebba C., Chm. Bd., Pres., Chief Exec. Officer & Chief Fin. Officer--Smead Manufacturing Company, Hastings, MN; *U.S. Private*, pg. 1006
Hoffman, G.L., Chm. Bd., Pres., Chief Exec. Officer & Sec.--Insignia Systems, Inc., Minnetonka, MN; *U.S. Public*, pg. 881
Hoffman, Harvey, Pres. & Chief Exec. Officer--Fraenkel Company, Baton Rouge, LA; *U.S. Private*, pg. 423
Hoffman, Jerry V., Chm. Bd., Pres. & Chief Exec. Officer--Berry Petroleum Company, Taft, CA; *U.S. Public*, pg. 223

Hoffman, Kenneth A., Pres. & Chief Exec. Officer--Hart Schaffner & Marx Clothes, Chicago, IL; *U.S. Public,* pg. 795
Hoffman, Mark H., Pres.--Transport, Inc., Madison, AL; *U.S. Public,* pg. 482
Hoffman, Mark S., Pres. & Chief Exec. Officer--A.P.S., Memphis, TN; *U.S. Public,* pg. 10
Hoffman, Martin, Pres., Chief Exec. & Fin. Officer, Treas.--Designatronics, Inc., New Hyde Park, NY; *U.S. Private,* pg. 327
Hoffman, Richard R., Pres.--HAWG Hauling & Disposal, Inc., Buckhannon, WV; *U.S. Public,* pg. 403
Hoffman, Robert, Pres.--Crown Prince, Inc. (CA), City of Industry, CA; *U.S. Private,* pg. 293
Hoffman, Tom, Pres.--Kenneth O. Lester, Inc., Lebanon, TN; *U.S. Public,* pg. 1278
Hoffmann, David R., Pres. & Chief Fin. Officer--ALZA Development Corporation, Palo Alto, CA; *U.S. Public,* pg. 62
Hoffmann, Rolf, Pres.--Magdeburger Armaturenwerke MAW AG, Magdeburg, Germany; *Int'l,* pg. 400
Hofley, Norman H., Pres.--Hofley Manufacturing Company, Roseville, MI; *U.S. Private,* pg. 532
Hofman, George W., Pres. & Chief Oper. Officer--Teleflex Automotive, Troy, MI; *U.S. Public,* pg. 1569
Hofmann, C.B., Pres.--Amecom Div., College Park, MD; *U.S.* Public, pg. 1002
Hofmann, Herbert C., Pres. & Chief Exec. Officer--Bulova Corporation, Woodside, NY; *U.S. Public,* pg. 1010
Hofmann, John, Pres.--Frigid Products, Inc., Elizabeth, NJ; *U.S. Private,* pg. 883
Hofschulz, Robert, Pres.--Intercare Technologies, Inc., Waukesha, WI; *U.S. Public,* pg. 459
Hofstra, Johan, Pres.-DMB&B Eur., Mid. East, Africa, India, Pakistan& IMP Europe--DMB&B/Worldwide Communications Amsterdam, Amsterdam, Netherlands; *U.S. Private,* pg. 304
Hofstra, Johan, Pres.-Africa--DMB&B/Worldwide Communications, Amsterdam, Netherlands; *U.S. Private,* pg. 304
Hofvander, Per, Pres.--Skanska International Civil Engineering AB, Danderyd, Sweden; *Int'l,* pg. 1260
Hogan, Dan W., Pres. & Chief Exec. Officer--NBC Bank, FSB (Knoxville), Knoxville, TN; *U.S. Public,* pg. 1155
Hogan, Daug, Pres.--Teledyne Advanced Materials, Huntsville, AL; *U.S. Public,* pg. 43
Hogan, Frank, Chm. Bd. & Pres.--Sullivan Long & Hagerty, Inc., Birmingham, AL; *U.S. Private,* pg. 1050
Hogan, Frank J., Pres. & Chief Exec. Officer--Overseas Service Corporation, West Palm Beach, FL; *U.S. Private, pg. 823*
Hogan, Michael J.C., Pres.--SaskPower Commercial, Regina, Canada; *Int'l,* pg. 1196
Hogan, Robert F., Jr., Pres.--AmerCable, Eldorado, TX; *U.S.* Private, pg. 91
Hogan, Terrance J., Pres.--Alumitech, Inc., Streetsboro, OH; *Int'l,* pg. 1523
Hogan, Thomas J., Pres. & Chief Exec. Officer--Foley's, Houston, TX; *U.S. Public,* pg. 1063
Hogan, Timothy P., Chm. Bd., Pres. & Chief Exec. Officer--Warmington Homes, Costa Mesa, CA; *U.S. Private,* pg. 1150
Hogarty, Charles J., Pres. & Chief Oper. Officer--Keystone Automotive Industries, Inc., Pomona, CA; *U.S. Public,* pg. 955
Hogarty, Daniel J. Jr., Pres. & Chief Exec. Officer--The Troy Savings Bank, Troy, NY; *U.S. Private,* pg. 1106
Hoge, Ronald N., Pres. & Chief Exec. Officer--MagneTek, Inc., Nashville, TN; *U.S. Public,* pg. 1037
Hogenkamp, Timothy R., Pres. & Chief Oper. Officer--The Loewen Group, Inc., Burnaby, Canada; *Int'l,* pg. 814
Hogg, Robert H., III, Chief Exec. Officer & Pres.--Better Brands Of Atlanta, Inc., Atlanta, GA; *U.S. Private,* pg. 141
Hoggatt, Don, Pres.-Northeast Reg.--JC Penney Company, Inc., Plano, TX; *U.S. Public,* pg. 916
Hogge, Jack, Pres.--Northern Trust Securities, Inc., Chicago, IL; *U.S. Public,* pg. 1197
Hogrell, Rolf, Pres.--Jonkopings Lantman Ek. For., Jonkoping, Sweden; *Int'l,* pg. 714
Hohman, Jeffrey L., Pres.--Micropump Corporation, Vancouver, WA; *U.S. Public,* pg. 862
Hohman, Theodore, Pres.--TCH Industries Inc., Grand Rapids, MI; *U.S. Private,* pg. 1063
Hohmeier, John, Pres.--MTD Products Limited, Kitchener, Canada; *U.S. Private,* pg. 688
Hohorst, W., Pres.--WAGO Contact i.Gr, Wipperfurth, Germany; *Int'l,* pg. 209
Hoketsu, Hiroshi, Pres. & Mng. Dir.--Ortho Clinical Diagnostic Systems K.K., Tokyo, Japan; *U.S. Public,* pg. 931
Hokin, Myron, Pres. & Chief Exec. Officer--Century America Corporation, Chicago, IL; *U.S. Private,* pg. 225
Holahan, John M., Pres. & Chief Oper. Officer--Travel Ports of America Inc., Rochester, NY; *U.S. Public,* pg. 1632
Holas, Frank W., Pres. & Chief Exec. Officer--Rich SeaPak Corp., Saint Simons Island, GA; *U.S. Private,* pg. 928
Holbek, Karsten, Pres.--AGA Gas GmbH, Hamburg, Germany; *Int'l,* pg. 13
Holbrook, Dick R., Pres. & Chief Oper. Officer--AFC Enterprises, Atlanta, GA; *U.S. Private,* pg. 5
Holcomb, Benjamin F., Pres.--American Cellular Communications Corporation, Atlanta, GA; *U.S. Public,* pg. 208
Holcombe, Tony, Pres.--Comdata Corporation, Brentwood, TN; *U.S. Public,* pg. 331
Holden, John S., Jr., Pres.--Automatic Machine Products Company, Attleboro, MA; *U.S. Private,* pg. 101
Holden, Richmond Y., Jr., Chm. Bd. & Pres.--J.L. Hammett Company, Braintree, MA; *U.S. Private,* pg. 498
Holden, Stuart, Jr., Pres.--Keeney Manufacturing Co., Newington, CT; *U.S. Private,* pg. 611
Holder, George Hugh, Pres.--Hershey Creamery Company, Harrisburg, PA; *U.S. Private,* pg. 524
Holder, Hal, Jr., Pres.--Cutler Manufacturing Corporation, Lakeland, FL; *U.S. Private,* pg. 298
Holderith, Paul, Pres.--Risdon Corporation, Naugatuck, CT; *U.S. Public,* pg. 463
Holding, Frank B., Jr., Pres.--First Citizens Banc Shares, Inc., Raleigh, NC; *U.S. Public,* pg. 628
Holding, Frank, Jr., Pres.--First Citizens Bank & Trust Co., Raleigh, NC; *U.S. Public,* pg. 629
Holding, R.E., Pres. & Chief Exec. Officer--Sinclair Oil Corp., Salt Lake City, UT; *U.S. Private,* pg. 1003
Holdt, Terry N., Pres. & Chief Exec. Officer--S3 Incorporated, Santa Clara, CA; *U.S. Public,* pg. 1415
Holgate, Fred, Pres.--Prestige Stations Inc., Cerritos, CA; *U.S. Public,* pg. 144
Holiday, H. Roger, Pres.--Time Oil Company, Seattle, WA; *U.S. Private,* pg. 1086
Holland, Al, Pres.-Active Asset Recovery--Active International, Pearl River, NY; *U.S. Private,* pg. 15
Holland, Del, Pres.--Six Flags Magic Mountain & Six Flags Hurricane Harbor, Valencia, CA; *U.S. Public,* pg. 1611
Holland, Edward W., Pres.--HWC Distribution Corp., Houston, TX; *U.S. Public,* pg. 55
Holland, J. Daniel, Pres.--Papa John's International Inc., Louisville, KY; *U.S. Public,* pg. 1255
Holland, James T., Pres. & Chief Exec. Officer--O'Sullivan Corporation, Winchester, VA; *U.S. Public,* pg. 1234
Holland, John B., Chm. Bd. & Pres.--Durum Energy Corp., Vancouver, Canada; *Int'l,* pg. 422
Holland, John B., Chm. Bd. & Pres.--Durum Energy Corp., Sucursal Del Peru, Vancouver, Canada; *Int'l,* pg. 422
Holland, John B., Chm. Bd. & Pres.--Durum (Australia) Pty. Ltd., Vancouver, Canada; *Int'l,* pg. 422
Holland, John L., Pres.--BetzDearborn Water Management Group, Horsham, PA; *U.S. Public,* pg. 226
Holland, Michael C., Pres. & Chief Exec. Officer--Mojave Pipeline Company, Bakersfield, CA; *U.S. Public,* pg. 567
Holland, Richard F., Pres. & Chief Exec. Officer--D/B Cameras Microcheck Division, Fullerton, CA; *U.S. Private,* pg. 5
Holland, Richard F., Pres. & Chief Exec. Officer--Electro-Mechanical Instruments Div., Fullerton, CA; *U.S. Private,* pg. 5
Holland, Richard F., Pres. & Chief Exec. Officer--Precision Power Div., Fullerton, CA; *U.S. Private,* pg. 5
Holland, Terry M., Pres.--Trimin Enterprises, Inc., Vancouver, Canada; *Int'l,* pg. 1424
Holland, William, Pres.--AEI Holding Co., Inc., Fullerton, CA; *U.S. Private,* pg. 4
Hollander, Betty, Pres.--OMEGA Engineering, Inc., Stamford, CT; *U.S. Private,* pg. 816
Hollander, Ross H., Pres.--Hartford Distributors Inc., Manchester, CT; *U.S. Private,* pg. 507
Hollander, Theodore C., Jr., Pres.--Presray Corp., Pawling, NY; *U.S. Private,* pg. 844
Holleman, Matt, Chm. Bd. & Pres.--Capitol Street Corp., Jackson, MS; *U.S. Private,* pg. 207
Holleman, Matthew, Pres. & Chief Exec. Officer--Mississippi Valley Gas Co., Jackson, MS; *U.S. Private,* pg. 753
Hollenbeck, Richard, Pres.--National Brands, Inc., Phoenix, AZ; *U.S. Private,* pg. 780
Holler, J., Pres. & Chief Exec. Officer--PNC Bank, Cincinnati, OH; *U.S. Public,* pg. 1242
Holler, Roger, Pres.--Dodge of Winter Park, Winter Park, FL; *U.S. Private,* pg. 337
Holler, Roger W., Jr., Pres.--Roger Holler Chevrolet & GEO Co., Winter Park, FL; *U.S. Private,* pg. 534
Holleran, J.W., Pres.--Jefferson Square, Inc., Boise, ID; *U.S.* Public, pg. 243
Holleran, J.W., Pres.--JPB General Placerville Corporation, Boise, ID; *U.S. Public,* pg. 243
Holleran, J.W., Pres.--Voyageur Panel Limited, Boise, ID; *U.S. Public,* pg. 243
Holleran, Patrick, Pres.--Field Controls Co., Kinston, NC; *U.S. Private,* pg. 860
Hollern, Michael P., Chm. Bd. & Pres.--Brooks Resources Corporation, Bend, OR; *U.S. Private,* pg. 172
Hollern, Michael P., Pres.--Awbrey Glen Golf Club, Inc., Bend, OR; *U.S. Private,* pg. 172
Holley, Rick R., Pres. & Chief Exec. Officer--Plum Creek Timber Co., L.P., Seattle, WA; *U.S. Public,* pg. 1311
Holliday, Charles O., Pres. & Chief Exec. Officer--Du Pont (E.I. Du Pont De Nemours & Co.), Wilmington, DE; *U.S. Public,* pg. 530
Holliday, Jessica J., Pres.--Prodair Corporation, Wilmington, DE; *U.S. Public,* pg. 31
Hollidge, Ken, Pres.--ACR Industries Inc., Macomb Township, MI; *U.S. Private,* pg. 3
Hollier, Robert, Pres.--OSCA, Lafayette, LA; *U.S. Public,* pg. 760
Holliger, Frederic L., Pres. & Chief Exec. Officer--Giant Exploration & Production Co., Farmington, NM; *U.S. Public,* pg. 742
Holliman, W.G., Pres. & Chief Exec. Officer--Furniture Brands International Inc., Saint Louis, MO; *U.S. Public,* pg. 688
Hollingsworth, B.B., Jr., Chm. Bd., Pres. & Chief Exec. Officer--Group 1 Automotive, Inc., Houston, TX; *U.S. Public,* pg. 767
Hollingsworth, David, Pres.--Gates, McDonald & Co., Hilliard, OH; *U.S. Private,* pg. 789
Hollingsworth, J.D., Pres.--Hollingsworth Saco Lowell Corporation, Inc., Easley, SC; *U.S. Private,* pg. 535
Hollingsworth, Ronnie, Pres.--Hollingsworth Oil Co. Inc., Springfield, TN; *U.S. Private,* pg. 535
Hollingsworth, Tom, Pres.--Sun Bulb Company, Inc., Arcadia, FL; *U.S. Private,* pg. 1050
Hollingsworth, Valentine, III, Pres.--Hollingsworth & Vose Co., East Walpole, MA; *U.S. Private,* pg. 534
Hollister, Dean, Pres. & Chief Exec. Officer--Hollister Advertising, New Providence, NJ; *U.S. Public,* pg. 830
Holloway, Richard A., Pres.--Teledyne Brown Engineering, Huntsville, AL; *U.S. Public,* pg. 43
Holm, Magnus, Pres.--Optiroc Oy AB, Helsinki, Finland; *Int'l, pg. 1200*
Holman, Edwin J., Chm. Bd., Pres. & Chief Exec. Officer--Petrie Retail, Inc., Secaucus, NJ; *U.S. Private,* pg. 858
Holman, W.H., III, Pres.-Pump & Save--Jitney-Jungle Stores of America, Inc., Jackson, MS; *U.S. Private,* pg. 588
Holmes, David R., Chm., Pres. & Chief Exec. Officer--The Reynolds and Reynolds Company, Dayton, OH; *U.S. Public,* pg. 1384
Holmes, Edith, Pres.--FCW Publishing Corp., Falls Church, VA; *U.S. Private,* pg. 569
Holmes, George B., Pres., Chief Exec. & Chief Fin. Officer--Dombrowski & Holmes, Inc., Hammond, IN; *U.S. Private, pg. 338*
Holmes, Howdy, Pres.--Chelsea Milling Co., Chelsea, MI; *U.S. Private,* pg. 231
Holmes, John, Pres.--Roney Otman, Aurora, IL; *U.S. Private,* pg. 943
Holmes, John B., Jr., Pres.--Sonat Exploration GOM Inc., Houston, TX; *U.S. Public,* pg. 1485
Holmes, Martin, Pres. & Chief Exec. Officer--Belvedere Company, Belvidere, IL; *U.S. Private,* pg. 1008
Holmes, Ned, Chm. Bd.--Port of Houston Authority, Houston, TX; *U.S. Private,* pg. 876
Holmes, Ramsay R., Pres. & Chief Exec. Officer--The Bank of Nova Scotia Trust Company, Toronto, Canada; *Int'l,* pg. 155
Holmes, Warren, Pres.--Sudbury Division, Falconbridge, Canada; *Int'l,* pg. 433
Holmqvist, Bjarne, Pres.--Componenta Dynapac AB, Vastra Frolunda, Sweden; *Int'l,* pg. 1419
Holmsen, Cato A., Pres.--Scancem International ANS, Oslo, Norway; *Int'l,* pg. 1201
Holmstrom, Tom, Pres. & Chief Exec. Officer--Corporate Express Office Products, Arden Hills, MN; *U.S. Public,* pg. 449
Holmstrom, Tom, Pres. & Chief Exec. Officer--Corporate Express Office Products, Duluth, MN; *U.S. Public,* pg. 449
Holness, Gordon V.R., Pres. & Chief Exec. Officer--Albert Kahn Associates, Inc., Detroit, MI; *U.S. Private,* pg. 604
Holoubek, Verne R., Pres.--Holoubek Inc., Waukesha, WI; *U.S. Private,* pg. 536
Holsapple, Jerry L., Pres. & Chief Exec. Officer--Bright National Bank, Flora, IN; *U.S. Public,* pg. 633
Holst-Knudsen, C.T., Pres.--Industrial Equipment News, New York, NY; *U.S. Private,* pg. 1082
Holst-Knudsen, Carl T., Pres.--Thomas Publishing Company, New York, NY; *U.S. Private,* pg. 1082
Holstein, Richard, Pres.--Superior Die Tool And Machine Company, Columbus, OH; *U.S. Private,* pg. 1054
Holsworth, William C., Pres. & Chief Exec. Officer--FINAST, Maple Heights, OH; *Int'l,* pg. 750
Holt, Dennis F., Chm. Bd., Pres. & Chief Exec. Officer--Western International Media Corporation, Los Angeles, CA; *U.S. Private,* pg. 1165
Holt, Newell E., Pres.--Dillard, A ResourceNet International Company, Greensboro, NC; *U.S. Public,* pg. 901
Holt, Richard, Pres.--Carolina Mirror Company, North Wilkesboro, NC; *U.S. Private,* pg. 214
Holthaus, Gerard E., Pres. & Chief Oper. Officer--Scotsman Holding Inc., Baltimore, MD; *U.S. Private,* pg. 976
Holthaus, Gerard E., Pres. & Chief Oper. Officer--Williams Scotsman, Inc., Baltimore, MD; *U.S. Private,* pg. 976
Holthaus, J.J.C., Pres.--Lips United B.V., Drunen, Netherlands; *Int'l,* pg. 812
Holthouse, Michael H., Pres.--Sprint Paranet, Houston, TX; *U.S. Public,* pg. 1501
Holton, Earl, Pres.--Meijer, Inc., Grand Rapids, MI; *U.S. Private,* pg. 729
Holton, Earl, Pres.--Meijer Wholesale Inc., Lansing, MI; *U.S.* Private, pg. 729
Holtschlag, Steve, Pres. & Chief Exec. Officer--Consolidated Systems, Inc., Columbia, SC; *U.S. Private,* pg. 266
Holtz, Harry L., Pres. & Chief Exec. Officer--Great Northern Iron Ore Properties, Saint Paul, MN; *U.S. Public,* pg. 760
Holtzman, Bernard, Pres.--Harve Benard Ltd., Secaucus, NJ; *U.S. Private,* pg. 508
Holtzman, Bernard, Pres.--Harve Benard Ltd., New York, NY; *U.S. Private,* pg. 508
Holtzman, Seymour, Pres. & Chief Exec. Officer--Jewelcor Companies, Wilkes-Barre, PA; *U.S. Private,* pg. 587
Holub, William J., Pres.--Vineland Transit Mix Concrete Co., Inc., Marlton, NJ; *Int'l,* pg. 1201
Holubec, Henry, Pres.--Contractors Supplies, Inc., Lufkin, TX; *U.S. Private,* pg. 270
Holycross, Charles, Pres.--Armor Safe Technologies, Vista, CA; *U.S. Private,* pg. 861
Holzcheiter, Kenneth J., Pres. & Gen. Mgr.--A.N. Deringer, Inc., Saint Albans, VT; *U.S. Private,* pg. 326
Holzer, Dennis, Pres.--Hamburg Brothers, Pittsburgh, PA; *U.S. Private,* pg. 497
Holzer, Edwin H., Chm. Bd., Chief Exec. Officer & Mng. Dir.--Lois/EJL Chicago, Chicago, IL; *U.S. Public,* pg. 1011
Holzer, Henry, Pres. & Chief Exec. Officer--SGS Government Programs Inc., New York, NY; *Int'l,* pg. 1153
Homa, Joseph R., Pres.--J. Fegely Inc., Pottstown, PA; *U.S.* Private, pg. 399
Homa, Joseph R., Pres.--Carey Division, Baltimore, MD; *U.S. Private,* pg. 399
Homan, Charles I., Pres. & Chief Exec. Officer--Michael Baker Corporation, Pittsburgh, PA; *U.S. Public,* pg. 168
Homan, Hendrik, Pres.--AKG Acoustics, Vienna, Austria; *U.S. Public,* pg. 787
Homan, Paul M., Pres. & Chief Exec. Office--Riggs Bank N.A., Washington, DC; *U.S. Public,* pg. 1390
Homan, Robert W., Pres. & Treas.--Homan Lumber Mart, Inc., Elkhart, IN; *U.S. Private,* pg. 536
Homer, C.R., Pres. & Chief Exec. Officer--GSW Inc., Guelph, Canada,; *Int'l,* pg. 538
Homes, W.G., Chm. Bd., Pres. & Treas.--Homes & Son Contractors, Inc., Phoenix, AZ; *U.S. Private,* pg. 537

Homfray, Christopher, Partner & Sr. V.P.--Scotchbrook Communications Ltd., Wan Chai, Hong Kong; *U.S. Private*, pg. 411

Honda, Takao, Pres.--Johnson Company, Ltd., Yokohama, Japan; *U.S. Private*, pg. 593

Honderich, John, Publisher--Toronto Star Newspapers Ltd., Toronto, Canada; *Int'l*, pg. 1402

Hondros, Paul J., Pres. & Chief Oper. Officer--Pilgram Baxter & Associates, Wayne, PA; *U.S. Public*, pg. 1673

Hone, L. Michael, Pres. & Chief Exec. Officer--Centennial Technologies, Inc., Wilmington, MA; *U.S. Public*, pg. 322

Honegger, Arthur, Pres.--DRS Ahead Technology, Inc., San Jose, CA; *U.S. Public*, pg. 475

Honek, Joseph A., Pres.--Connecticut Drive Shaft, Inc., Milford, CT; *U.S. Private*, pg. 263

Honeycutt, V.B., Chm. Bd., Pres. & Chief Exec. Officer--Computer Sciences Corporation, El Segundo, CA; *U.S. Public*, pg. 422

Hong, Glenn K.Y., Pres.--Young Brothers, Ltd., Honolulu, HI; *U.S. Public*, pg. 800

Hong, Woo-Shik, Pres. & Chief Exec. Officer--Seoul DMB&B, Inc., Seoul, Korea; *U.S. Private*, pg. 305

Hong, Wooshik, Pres. & Chief Exec. Officer--Seoul DMB&B, Inc., Seoul, Korea; *Int'l*, pg. 1223

Honkamp, John A., Pres.--Hydrite Chemical Company, Brookfield, WI; *U.S. Private*, pg. 551

Honma, Masakazu, Pres.--Hitachi Consumer Products of America, Inc., Anaheim, CA; *Int'l*, pg. 622

Honoki, Koji, Pres.--Nikkei Media Marketing, Inc., Tokyo, Japan; *Int'l*, pg. 929

Honroth, Dale K., Pres. & Chief Exec. Officer--Kendale Industries, Inc., Valley View, OH; *U.S. Private*, pg. 614

Hood, A. Thomas, Pres. & Chief Exec. Officer--First Financial Holdings, Inc., Charleston, SC; *U.S. Public*, pg. 634

Hoog, Thomas W., Pres. & CEO-USA--Hill and Knowlton, Inc., New York, NY; *Int'l*, pg. 1483

Hooi, Teoh Tee, Sr. V.P.-Americas--Singapore Airlines, Los Angeles, CA; *Int'l*, pg. 1374

Hook, Claes, Pres.--Euronord WTM AB, Gavle, Sweden; *Int'l*, pg. 678

Hook, James B., Pres.--V.B. Hook & Co., Inc., Columbia, SC; *U.S. Private*, pg. 538

Hooker, A. Frank, Jr., Pres. & Chief Oper. Officer--Hooker Furniture Corporation, Martinsville, VA; *U.S. Private*, pg. 538

Hooker, David S., Pres.--Transnational Motors Inc., Grand Rapids, MI; *U.S. Private*, pg. 1097

Hooker, E. Stanton, Pres. & Chief Exec. Officer--Midland Paper Co., Elk Grove Village, IL; *U.S. Private*, pg. 744

Hooley, John H., Pres. & Chief Exec. Officer--Cub Foods Stores, Stillwater, MN; *U.S. Public*, pg. 1541

Hoon, Cho Choong, Chm. Bd.--Hanjin Shipping Company Ltd., Seoul, Korea; *Int'l*, pg. 592

Hoon, Soh Chee, Dr., Pres.--MMC-GTM Bina Sama, Kuala Lumpur, Malaysia; *Int'l*, pg. 823

Hoon, Soh Chee, Dr., Pres.--GTM Wan Soon Pte Ltd., Singapore, Singapore; *Int'l*, pg. 823

Hooper, Anthony W., Chm. Bd., Pres. & Chief Exec. Officer--Insituform Technologies, Inc., Chesterfield, MO; *U.S. Public*, pg. 881

Hooper, Lee, Pres.--Sharon Tube Company, Sharon, PA; *U.S. Private*, pg. 990

Hooper, Michael, Pres.--The Crown Divisions, Wooster, OH; *U.S. Public*, pg. 1631

Hooper, Robert, Pres.--Abbott Laboratories Ltd., Saint-Laurent, Canada; *U.S. Public*, pg. 13

Hooper, Steven, Pres.--Land Title Insurance Co. of St. Louis, Des Peres, MO; *U.S. Public*, pg. 626

Hoopis, Michael P., Pres.--Black & Decker Household Products Group, Shelton, CT; *U.S. Public*, pg. 234

Hoops, Alan, Pres. & Chief Exec. Officer--PacifiCare Health Systems, Inc., Cypress, CA; *U.S. Public*, pg. 1250

Hooykaas, Henricus, Pres.--Royal Nederland Levensverzekering N.V., Utrecht, Netherlands; *Int'l*, pg. 16

Hope, Michael, Pres.--Utell International, Brentford, United Kingdom; *Int'l*, pg. 1098

Hopkins, Jerry W., Pres. & Chief Oper. Officer--Texas Refinery Corp., Fort Worth, TX; *U.S. Private*, pg. 1078

Hopkins, Jim, Pres.--Chromatic Technologies, Inc., Franklin, MA; *Int'l*, pg. 417

Hopkins, Jim, Pres.--Helix/Hi-Temp Cables, Inc., Franklin, MA; *Int'l*, pg. 417

Hopkins, Michael B., Pres.--First American Equity Loan Services, Cleveland, OH; *U.S. Public*, pg. 625

Hoppe, David T., Chm. Bd. & Pres.--CORS, Itasca, IL; *U.S. Private*, pg. 196

Hoppenjans, A.J., Pres.--Turner Electric Corporation, Fairview Heights, IL; *U.S. Public*, pg. 1705

Hopper, David A., Pres.--Lincoln National Risk Management, Inc., Fort Wayne, IN; *U.S. Public*, pg. 998

Hopper, Duane B., Pres. & Chief Exec. Officer--Graphic Controls Corporation, Buffalo, NY; *U.S. Private*, pg. 470

Hopper, John, Sr. Partner--Einson Freeman Inc., Paramus, NJ; *Int'l*, pg. 1483

Hopsicker, Michael, Pres.--Agway Energy Products (AEP), Syracuse, NY; *U.S. Private*, pg. 27

Hopson, Andy, Pres.--EvansGroup (Public Relations), Salt Lake City, UT; *U.S. Private*, pg. 385

Hopson, Jim, Pres. & Chief Exec. Officer--The Advocate, Newark, OH; *U.S. Private*, pg. 23

Hoque, Jeffery C., Pres. & Mgr.-Sls. & Adv.--Charles Atlas, Ltd., New York, NY; *U.S. Private*, pg. 229

Hora, Charles, Pres.--Lord Corporation, Mechanical Products Division, Erie, PA; *U.S. Private*, pg. 676

Hora, Charles J., Jr., Dr., Pres.--Lord Corporation, Cary, NC; *U.S. Private*, pg. 675

Horan, Niall, Pres. & Gen. Mgr.--Royer Industries, Inc., Kingston, PA; *Int'l*, pg. 1066

Hord, Fenton N., Pres. & Chief Exec. Officer--Carolina Builders Corporation, Raleigh, NC; *Int'l*, pg. 1512

Hord, Noel, Pres. & Chief Oper. Officer--Nine West Group, Inc., Stamford, CT; *U.S. Public*, pg. 1185

Horein, James R., Pres.--Lincoln National Management Services, Inc., Fort Wayne, IN; *U.S. Public*, pg. 998

Hori, Tetsusaburo, Pres.--Sintyal Otsuka Pharmaceutical S.A., Buenos Aires, Argentina; *Int'l*, pg. 1014

Horiguchi, Hitoshi, Pres.--Sumitomo Sitix Europe Plc., London, United Kingdom; *Int'l*, pg. 1317

Hormer, Donald G., Pres.--First Hawaiian Insurance, Inc., Honolulu, HI; *U.S. Public*, pg. 635

Horn, Larry, Pres.--Quincy Soybean Co., Quincy, IL; *U.S. Private*, pg. 760

Horn, Ralph, Chm. Bd., Pres. & Chief Exec. Officer--First Tennessee National Corporation, Memphis, TN; *U.S. Public*, pg. 638

Horn, Ralph, Chm. Bd., Pres., Chief Exec. & Oper. Officer--First Tennessee Bank National Association, Memphis, TN; *U.S. Public*, pg. 639

Horn, Richard, Pres. & Treas.--Mulberry Metal Products, Inc., Union, NJ; *U.S. Private*, pg. 766

Horn, Robert E., Pres.--McCormick Pesa, S.A. de C.V., Mexico, Mexico; *U.S. Public*, pg. 1067

Horn, Russell E., Jr., Pres.--Pace Resources, Inc., York, PA; *U.S. Private*, pg. 829

Horn, William B., Pres.--Gorman-Rupp of Canada Ltd., Saint Thomas, Canada; *U.S. Public*, pg. 754

Hornady, Steve, Pres.--Hornady Manufacturing Company, Grand Island, NE; *U.S. Private*, pg. 539

Hornady, Steve, Pres.--Hornady Ammunition, Grand Island, NE; *U.S. Private*, pg. 540

Hornbacher, Dean P., Pres.--Hornbachers, Fargo, ND; *U.S. Public*, pg. 1541

Hornbaker, R.W., Pres.--Garlock Bearings Division, Thorofare, NJ; *U.S. Public*, pg. 402

Hornberger, Glenn, Pres. & Chief Oper. Officer--Mohawk Finishing Products, Inc., Amsterdam, NY; *U.S. Public*, pg. 1357

Hornberger, Glenn O., Pres.--Floquil-Polly S Color Corp., Amsterdam, NY; *U.S. Public*, pg. 1357

Hornberger, Glenn O., Pres.--Chemical Coatings, Inc., Hudson, NC; *U.S. Public*, pg. 1357

Hornberger, Glenn O., Pres.--Star Finishing Products, Inc., Hinsdale, IL; *U.S. Public*, pg. 1358

Hornbuckle, William J., Pres. & Chief Oper. Officer--Caesars Palace, Las Vegas, NV; *U.S. Public*, pg. 1512

Hornbuckley, William J., Pres. & Chief Exec. Officer--GNL, Corp., Laughlin, NV; *U.S. Public*, pg. 1116

Hornby, Darell, Pres.--Clarke Transport, Concord, Canada; *Int'l*, pg. 924

Horne, Bob, Mng. Partner--Griffin Bacal Inc., New York, NY; *U.S. Private*, pg. 480

Horne, Eugene B., Pres.--PH Holding, Sanford, NC; *U.S. Private*, pg. 837

Horne, F.L., Pres.--Gas-Fired Products, Inc., Charlotte, NC; *U.S. Private*, pg. 440

Horne, Jim, Pres. & Chief Oper. Officer--Ohmite Manufacturing Company, Skokie, IL; *U.S. Private*, pg. 813

Horne, Joseph A., Pres.--Rolane Factory Outlets, Greensboro, NC; *U.S. Private*, pg. 941

Horner, Donald G., Pres. & Chief Exec. Officer--Pacific One Dealer Center, Inc., Costa Mesa, CA; *U.S. Public*, pg. 635

Horner, Kenneth D., Pres.--North Pacific Insurance Company, Portland, OR; *Int'l*, pg. 543

Horner, Maurice O., Pres. & Chief Exec. Officer--Willis Corroon Corp. of Chattanooga, Chattanooga, TN; *Int'l*, pg. 1505

Horner, Nick, Pres. & Chief Exec. Officer--Citizens First Bank, El Dorado, AR; *U.S. Public*, pg. 630

Horngvist, Hans, Pres.--Skanska Norr AB, Sundsvall, Sweden; *Int'l*, pg. 1260

Hornick, Gerald C., Pres.--Advanced Structures, Inc., Escondido, CA; *U.S. Public*, pg. 592

Hornsten, Lawrence, Pres.--Sunwest Bank of El Paso, El Paso, TX; *U.S. Public*, pg. 1165

Hornung, Donald F., Pres. & Gen. Mgr.--Crustbuster, Inc., Dodge City, KS; *U.S. Private*, pg. 293

Hornyak, George T., Jr., Pres. & Chief Exec. Officer--Pulse Bancorp, Inc., South River, NJ; *U.S. Public*, pg. 1344

Hornyak, George T., Jr., Pres. & Chief Exec. Officer--Pulse Savings Bank, South River, NJ; *U.S. Public*, pg. 1344

Horowitz, DennisJ., Pres.--Philips Components-Discrete Products Division, Slatersville, RI; *Int'l*, pg. 1054

Horowitz, Joel J., Pres. & Chief Exec. Officer--Tommy Hilfiger Corporation, Kowloon, Hong Kong; *Int'l*, pg. 1398

Horowitz, Richard A., Chm. Bd., Pres. & Chief Exec. Officer--P & F Industries, Inc., Farmingdale, NY; *U.S. Public*, pg. 1239

Horowitz, Zach, Pres.--MCA Records, Inc., Universal City, CA; *Int'l*, pg. 1215

Horras, Doug, Gen. Mgr.--Hillshire Farm Company, New London, WI; *U.S. Public*, pg. 1433

Horrick, James, Pres. & Chief Exec. Officer--Reed Stenhouse Companies Ltd., Toronto, Canada; *U.S. Public*, pg. 118

Horrigan, D. Greg, Pres. & Co-Chief Exec. Officer--Silgan Corporation, Stamford, CT; *U.S. Public*, pg. 1473

Horsfman, Paul, Pres.--Industrial & Automotive Fasteners, Inc., Royal Oak, MI; *U.S. Public*, pg. 919

Horsley, R. Scott, Pres.--Ameritech Capital Services, Rolling Meadows, IL; *U.S. Public*, pg. 98

Horstmeyer, John, Pres. & Chief Oper. Officer--Independent Metals, Germantown, WI; *U.S. Private*, pg. 559

Hort, Michael, Pres.--Enterprise, New York, NY; *U.S. Private*, pg. 377

Hort, Robert, Pres.--Enterprise, New York, NY; *U.S. Private*, pg. 377

Horton, Adelaide, Pres. & Chief Oper. Officer--BDDP North America, Inc., New York, NY; *Int'l*, pg. 117

Horton, Darrell, Pres.--Big Horn Co-Op Marketing Association, Greybull, WY; *U.S. Private*, pg. 143

Horton, Donald R., Chm. Bd., Pres., Chief Exec. Officer & Chief Oper. Officer--D.R. Horton, Inc., Arlington, TX; *U.S. Public*, pg. 840

Horton, Duncan, Pres.--ASSA Ltd., Croydon, United Kingdom; *Int'l*, pg. 17

Horton, Gregory L., Chm. Bd., Pres. & Chief Exec. Officer--DDL Electronics, Inc., Newbury Park, CA; *U.S. Public*, pg. 473

Horton, Jim, Pres.--Hagglunds Drives Pty Ltd, Canning Vale, Australia; *Int'l*, pg. 670

Horton, Keith D., Pres.--Penn Virginia Coal Company, Duffield, VA; *U.S. Public*, pg. 1271

Horton, L. Thomas, Pres. & Chief Exec. Officer--Courtaulds Coatings Inc., Louisville, KY; *Int'l*, pg. 338

Horton, N.D., Jr., Pres.--Horton Homes, Inc., Eatonton, GA; *U.S. Private*, pg. 540

Horton, Richard B., Pres.--Edgerton Forge, Inc., Edgerton, OH; *U.S. Private*, pg. 102

Horwitz, Dan, Pres. & Chief Exec. Officer--Thompson Medical Company, Inc., West Palm Beach, FL; *U.S. Private*, pg. 1083

Horwitz, Lewis P., Pres.--The Lewis Horwitz Organization, Los Angeles, CA; *U.S. Private*, pg. 540

Horwitz, Louis B., Chm. Bd. & Pres.--Datum Inc., Irvine, CA; *U.S. Public*, pg. 488

Horwitz, Martin, Pres. & Chief Exec. Officer--Stewart Smith Mid America, Inc., Chicago, IL; *Int'l*, pg. 1508

Hosch, Robert F., Chm. Bd. & Pres.--Harris Contracting Co., Saint Paul, MN; *U.S. Private*, pg. 505

Hoser, Albert, Pres. & Chief Exec. Officer--Siemens Corporation, New York, NY; *Int'l*, pg. 1245

Hoshide, Masao, Pres.--Mikuni American Corporation, Northridge, CA; *Int'l*, pg. 867

Hoshino, Hiroaki, Pres.--Kajima International, Inc., Englewood Cliffs, NJ; *Int'l*, pg. 722

Hoshino, T., Pres. & Chief Exec. Officer--The Andrew Jergens Company, Cincinnati, OH; *Int'l*, pg. 717

Hoshino, Y., Pres.--Fujikura America Inc., Marietta, GA; *Int'l*, pg. 525

Hoskins, Gregory J., Pres. & Chief Exec. Officer--Refined Sugars, Inc., Yonkers, NY; *Int'l*, pg. 699

Hoskins, Tom, Pres.--The Dunlap Company, Fort Worth, TX; *U.S. Private*, pg. 346

Hoskins, W. Lee, Chm., Pres. & Chief Exec. Officer--Huntington National Bank, Columbus, OH; *U.S. Public*, pg. 850

Hosler, David, Pres. & Chief Exec. Officer--Old Guard Insurance Group, Lancaster, PA; *U.S. Public*, pg. 1216

Hosoda, Masayuki, Pres.--Otari, Inc., Tokyo, Japan; *Int'l*, pg. 1013

Hosokawa, Yoshio, Pres.--Hosokawa Micron Corporation, Osaka, Japan; *Int'l*, pg. 635

Hosomi, Kiyoshi, Pres.--Kayaba Industry Co., Ltd., Tokyo, Japan; *Int'l*, pg. 727

Hostetler, Robert D., Pres. & Chief Exec. Officer--American Telecasting, Inc., Colorado Springs, CO; *U.S. Public*, pg. 93

Hotaling, Reid, Pres.--K. Hovnanian Companies of Florida, Inc., West Palm Beach, FL; *U.S. Public*, pg. 843

Hotard, Edgar G., Pres.--Praxair Inc., Danbury, CT; *U.S. Public*, pg. 1319

Hothem, Steve F., Pres.--Landmark Systems Inc., Livonia, MI; *U.S. Private*, pg. 649

Hotopp, Thomas B., Pres.--Mine Safety Appliances Co., Pittsburgh, PA; *U.S. Public*, pg. 1114

Hotta, Michihisa, Pres.--Dongguan Sanxing Socks Co., Ltd., Tung Guan, China; *Int'l*, pg. 579

Hotta, Toshinobu, Pres.--Nikkeisha, Inc., Tokyo, Japan; *Int'l*, pg. 929

Houchens, Ruel, Pres.--Houchens Industries Inc., Bowling Green, KY; *U.S. Private*, pg. 541

Houck, J.C., Pres.--Texaco Development Corp., White Plains, NY; *U.S. Public*, pg. 1583

Houck, Peter, Pres. & Chief Exec. Officer--Houck Industries, Inc., Visalia, CA; *U.S. Private*, pg. 541

Houde, K., Pres.--Calumet Photographic, Inc., Bensenville, IL; *U.S. Private*, pg. 202

Hougen, Randall, Pres. & Chief Exec. Officer--Hougen Manufacturing Inc., Swartz Creek, MI; *U.S. Private*, pg. 541

Hough, Lawrence A., Pres. & Chief Exec. Officer--SLM Holding Corp., Washington, DC; *U.S. Public*, pg. 1419

Hough, Paul H., Pres.--Van Waters & Rogers Ltd., Richmond, Canada; *Int'l*, pg. 1147

Houghton, Peter E., Pres.--Fiduciary Trust International of the South, Miami, FL; *U.S. Public*, pg. 621

Houle, David C., Pres. & Chief Oper. Officer--IEA, Inc., Research Triangle Park, NC; *U.S. Public*, pg. 126

Houlihan, Kevin, Partner--Chicago Creative Partnership, Chicago, IL; *U.S. Private*, pg. 234

Houlihan, Lawrence M., Chm. Bd., Pres., Chief Exec. & Chief Fin. Officer, Treas. & Sec.--Frank B. Ross Co. Inc., Jersey City, NJ; *U.S. Private*, pg. 946

Hourselt, Gary L., Pres.--Huck International Aerospace Fastener Division, Carson, CA; *U.S. Public*, pg. 1597

House, David, Pres.--James Hardie Gypsum Washington, Seattle, WA; *Int'l*, pg. 597

House, David L., Chm. Bd., Pres. & Chief Exec. Officer--Bay Networks, Inc., Santa Clara, CA; *U.S. Public*, pg. 196

House, Don M., Pres. & Chief Oper. Officer--Venturian Corp., Hopkins, MN; *U.S. Public*, pg. 1716

House, H.D., Pres.--Centex American Gypsum Co., Albuquerque, NM; *U.S. Public*, pg. 322

House, James F., Pres. & Chief Exec. Officer--SouthTrust Bank, Dothan, Dothan, AL; *U.S. Public*, pg. 1491

Houseman, James E., Pres.--Harrop Industries, Inc., Columbus, OH; *U.S. Private*, pg. 506

Housen, Charles B., Chm. Bd., Pres. & Chief Exec. Officer--Erving Industries, Inc., Erving, MA; *U.S. Private*, pg. 382

Houser, George G., Pres.--Raytheon Systems Co., Kirkwood, NY; *U.S. Public*, pg. 1364

Houserman, Howard, Chm. Bd. & Pres.--Zetec, Inc., Issaquah, WA; *U.S. Private*, pg. 1205

Housey, John J., Jr., Pres.--Orleans Materials & Equipment Co., Inc., New Orleans, LA; *U.S. Private*, pg. 820

Housley, Mark, Chm. Bd., Pres. & Chief Exec. Officer--Radius Inc., Sunnyvale, CA; *U.S. Public*, pg. 1358

Housman, Charles J., Chm. Bd. & Pres.--Armatron International, Inc., Melrose, MA; *U.S. Public*, pg. 131
Housman, Edward L., Pres.--Automatic Radio International, Melrose, MA; *U.S. Public*, pg. 131
Housman, Kenneth L., Chief Oper. Officer--Echovision Division, Melrose, MA; *U.S. Public*, pg. 131
Houssein, Joe S., Chm. Bd., Pres. & Chief Exec. Officer--Intrawest Corporation, Vancouver, Canada; *Int'l*, pg. 685
Houssels, J. Kell, III, Pres. & Chief Exec. Officer--Showboat, Incorporated, Las Vegas, NV; *U.S. Public*, pg. 1469
Houssin, P., Pres.--Kraft Jacobs Suchard, Velizy-Villacoublay, France; *U.S. Public*, pg. 1290
Houston, David, Pres.--Hardel Mutual Plywood Corporation, Olympia, WA; *U.S. Private*, pg. 501
Houston, Doug, Partner--Houston Herstek Favat, Boston, MA; *U.S. Private*, pg. 542
Houston, Dwight, Pres.--Houston Products, Waverly, TN; *Int'l*, pg. 74
Houston, Paul A., Pres. & Chief Exec. Officer--Scott's Restaurants Inc., Markham, Canada; *Int'l*, pg. 1213
Houston, Paul A., Pres.--Scott's Management Services Inc., Markham, Canada; *Int'l*, pg. 1213
Houston, Robert A., V.P. & Gen. Mgr.--Hydrolectric Lift Trucks Inc., Wilmington, OH; *U.S. Public*, pg. 61
Houston, W. Tennent, Pres. & Chief Exec. Officer--Merry Land & Investment Company, Inc., Augusta, GA; *U.S. Public*, pg. 1098
Hovekamp, George D., Jr., Pres. & Chief Exec. Officer--The Kruse Company, Fairfield, OH; *U.S. Private*, pg. 636
Hovind, David J., Pres.--Paccar Inc., Bellevue, WA; *U.S. Public*, pg. 1246
Hovland, Bruce, Pres. & Gen. Mgr.--Interstate Payco Seed Company, West Fargo, ND; *U.S. Private*, pg. 573
Hovnanian, Ara K., Pres. & Chief Exec. Officer--Hovnanian Enterprises, Inc., Red Bank, NJ; *U.S. Public*, pg. 843
Howalt, F. Harvey, Jr., Pres. & Chief Exec. Officer--Textile Rubber & Chemical Company, Dalton, GA; *U.S. Private*, pg. 1079
Howard, Alfred J., Pres.--RehabCare Outpatient Services, Inc., Jacksonville, FL; *U.S. Public*, pg. 1373
Howard, Allen E., III, Pres. & Gen. Mgr.--KXTV Inc., Sacramento, CA; *U.S. Public*, pg. 209
Howard, Charles, Pres.--Howard Manufacturing, Kent, WA; *U.S. Private*, pg. 477
Howard, Clarisa F., Pres. & Chief Exec. Officer--bd Systems, Inc, Torrance, CA; *U.S. Private*, pg. 106
Howard, Elaine, Pres. & Chief Exec. Officer--Army Times Publishing Co., Springfield, VA; *U.S. Public*, pg. 699
Howard, Gary, Pres.--Bizzack Inc., Lexington, KY; *U.S. Private*, pg. 146
Howard, Gary L., Pres. & Chief Exec. Officer--McRae's, Inc., Jackson, MS; *U.S. Public*, pg. 1333
Howard, Gerald T., Pres., & Chief Exec. Officer--D.C.I., Inc., Saint Cloud, MN; *U.S. Private*, pg. 301
Howard, Ginger L., Pres.--Guidant Corporation-Vascular Intervention Group, Santa Clara, CA; *U.S. Public*, pg. 768
Howard, Gregory, Pres.--Polaris Pool Systems, Inc., San Marcos, CA; *U.S. Private*, pg. 873
Howard, James J., Chm. Bd., Pres. & Chief Exec. Officer--Northern States Power Company, Minneapolis, MN; *U.S. Public*, pg. 1195
Howard, Jerry A., Chm. Bd., Pres. & Chief Exec. Officer--Atrion Corporation, Arab, AL; *U.S. Public*, pg. 146
Howard, Kenneth, Pres.--Columbia Manufacturing Inc., Westfield, MA; *U.S. Private*, pg. 255
Howard, Richard R., Pres.--Genesis Health Ventures, Inc., Kennett Square, PA; *U.S. Public*, pg. 728
Howard, Richard R., Pres.--Genesis ElderCare, Philadelphia, PA; *U.S. Public*, pg. 728
Howard, Robert, Pres.--Alcoa Fujikura, Troy, MI; *U.S. Public*, pg. 61
Howard, Ronald A., Chief Exec. Officer--Hayes Corporation, Regional Office, Gaithersburg, MD; *U.S. Public*, pg. 801
Howard, Scott, Owner--Commerical Roofers Inc., Las Vegas, NV; *U.S. Private*, pg. 258
Howard, W.R., Pres. & Treas.--Saddlebag Lake Resorts, Inc., La Belle, FL; *U.S. Public*, pg. 41
Howe, Fletcher S., Jr., Pres.--Bancorp Investment Group, Ltd., Honolulu, HI; *U.S. Public*, pg. 1248
Howe, Hubbard C., Chm. Bd., Pres. & Chief Exec. Officer--A.P.S., Inc., Houston, TX; *U.S. Public*, pg. 10
Howe, Hubbard C., Chm. Bd. & Pres.--A.P.S., Memphis, TN; *U.S. Public*, pg. 10
Howe, Michael V., Pres.--Mileage Plus Holdings, Inc., Elk Grove Village, IL; *U.S. Public*, pg. 1653
Howe, Tom E., Pres.--Jays Foods LLC, Chicago, IL; *U.S. Private*, pg. 584
Howe, Willis E., Pres.--SuperValu, Inc.-Keene Div., Keene, NH; *U.S. Public*, pg. 1540
Howell, Ebert, Chm. Bd., Pres. & Chief Exec. Officer--Trippe Mfg. Co., Chicago, IL; *U.S. Private*, pg. 1104
Howell, Hilton H., Jr., Pres. & Chief Exec. Officer--Atlantic American Corporation, Atlanta, GA; *U.S. Public*, pg. 143
Howell, Rupert, Mng. Partner--Howell Henry Chaldecott Lury & Partners, London, United Kingdom; *Int'l*, pg. 637
Howell, William, Pres. & Chief Oper. Officer--Howell Instruments Inc., Fort Worth, TX; *U.S. Private*, pg. 543
Howells, Daniel P., Pres. & Chief Exec. Officer--Nature's Sunshine Products, Inc., Provo, UT; *U.S. Public*, pg. 1166
Howells, Robert L., Pres. & Chief Exec. Officer--Mendoza, Dillon & Asociados, Inc., Newport Beach, CA; *Int'l*, pg. 1483
Howenstein, William K., Pres.--Copper & Brass Sales, Inc., Eastpointe, MI; *Int'l*, pg. 1389
Howes, R., Pres.--Racal Canada Inc., Vancouver, Canada; *Int'l*, pg. 1083
Hoxsie, Frederick A., Pres.--Herlin Press Inc., West Haven, CT; *U.S. Private*, pg. 524
Hoy, Thomas L., Chm. Bd. & Pres.--Arrow Financial Corporation, Glens Falls, NY; *U.S. Public*, pg. 135
Hoy, Thomas L., Pres.--Glen Falls National Bank & Trust Company, Glens Falls, NY; *U.S. Public*, pg. 135
Hoyle, Donald A., Jr., Pres. & Chief Exec. Officer--Pioneer American Holding Company, Carbondale, PA; *U.S. Public*, pg. 1298
Hoyt, Everette E., Pres. & Chief Oper. Officer--Black Hills Corporation, Rapid City, SD; *U.S. Public*, pg. 235
Hoyt, James E., Pres.--Midway Products Corporation, Monroe, MI; *U.S. Private*, pg. 744
Hoyt, Seph, Pres.--Financial World Partners, New York, NY; *U.S. Private*, pg. 404
Hoyt, Steven B., Pres.--Hoyt Home Improvement, Bloomington, MN; *U.S. Private*, pg. 543
Hoz, Maria E., Broker--Century 21 Agmont Real Estate, Inc., Chicago, IL; *U.S. Private*, pg. 226
Hozik, John, Pres. & Chief Exec. Officer--The Philadelphia Bourse, Inc., Lanham, MD; *U.S. Private*, pg. 861
Hradecky, James, Pres., Chief Oper. Officer & Exec. Creative Dir.--Berry-Brown Advertising, Inc., Dallas, TX; *U.S. Private*, pg. 137
Hribar, Herb, Pres.--Ameritech Cellular and Paging Services, Hoffman Estates, IL; *U.S. Public*, pg. 98
Hroblak, Gerald, Pres. & Chief Exec. Officer--United Broadcasting L.P., Bethesda, MD; *U.S. Private*, pg. 1121
Hron, Ihor W., Chm. Bd., Pres. & Chief Exec. Officer--Midland Life Insurance Co., Columbus, OH; *U.S. Private*, pg. 744
Hsi, S.C., Chm. Bd.--Taiwan Power Company, Taipei, Taiwan; *Int'l*, pg. 1348
Hsien-Hsiung, Chang, Pres.--Tainan Spinning Co., Ltd., Tainan, Taiwan; *Int'l*, pg. 1347
Hsin, Lo Ta, Pres.--Mandarin Airlines, Taipei, Taiwan; *Int'l*, pg. 284
Hsu, Gerald C., Pres.--Avanti, Fremont, CA; *U.S. Public*, pg. 151
Hu, L.R., Pres.--Gains Investment Corporation, Kao-hsiung, Taiwan; *Int'l*, pg. 285
Hua, Yu Chi, Chm. Bd. & Pres.--Keng Hua Paper Products Co., Inc., Manila, Philippines; *Int'l*, pg. 729
Huang, Thomas Nan-Tu, Pres.--Wei-Chuan Foods Corporation, Taipei, Taiwan; *Int'l*, pg. 1488
Hubacker, Fred L., Pres.--Textron Automotive Company, Troy, MI; *U.S. Public*, pg. 1590
Hubbard, Allan B., Pres.--E & A Industries, Inc., Indianapolis, IN; *U.S. Private*, pg. 352
Hubbard, Allan B., Pres.--E & A Investors, L.P., Indianapolis, IN; *U.S. Private*, pg. 352
Hubbard, J.H., Mng. Dir.--Davies Shephard Pty. Ltd., Keon Park, Australia; *Int'l*, pg. 2
Hubbard, James W., Pres. & Chief Exec. Officer--Herff Jones Inc., Indianapolis, IN; *U.S. Private*, pg. 523
Hubbard, Jerry, Pres.--Marglen Industries, Rome, GA; *U.S. Private*, pg. 702
Hubbard, John D., Pres.--Hinderliter Heat Treating, Inc., Dallas, TX; *U.S. Private*, pg. 530
Hubbard, R.D., Pres. & Chief Exec. Officer--Turf Paradise, Inc., Phoenix, AZ; *U.S. Public*, pg. 831
Hubbard, Robert A., Chm. Bd. & Pres.--Wilbur Smith Associates, Columbia, SC; *U.S. Private*, pg. 1009
Hubbard, Robert W., Pres.--KOB-TV, Inc., Albuquerque, NM; *U.S. Private*, pg. 544
Hubbard, Robert W., Pres.-TV Grp.--KSTP-TV, Saint Paul, MN; *U.S. Private*, pg. 544
Hubbard, Stanley E., Pres. & Chief Exec. Officer--United States Satellite Broadcasting, Co., Saint Paul, MN; *U.S. Private*, pg. 544
Hubbard, Stanley S., Chm. Bd., Pres. & Chief Exec. Officer--Hubbard Broadcasting, Inc., Saint Paul, MN; *U.S. Private*, pg. 543
Hubbell, Richard A., Pres. & Chief Oper. Officer--RPC Incorporated, Atlanta, GA; *U.S. Public*, pg. 1356
Hubble, Don W., Chm. Bd., Pres. & Chief Exec. Officer--Angelica Corporation, Chesterfield, MO; *U.S. Public*, pg. 113
Hubble, Don W., Pres.--Zep Manufacturing, Dorval, Canada; *U.S. Public*, pg. 1160
Huber, John, Pres.--Phoenix Chemical Company, East Dubuque, IL; *U.S. Public*, pg. 856
Huber, John, Pres. & Chief Oper. Officer--Wynn's International, Inc., Orange, CA; *U.S. Public*, pg. 1782
Huber, Martin, Chief Exec. Officer & Pres.-Exec. Committee--Georg Fischer Ltd., Schaffhausen, Switzerland; *Int'l*, pg. 488
Huber, Paul, Pres.--Seco Warwick Corporation, Meadville, PA; *U.S. Private*, pg. 980
Huber, Richard L., Pres. & Chief Exec. Officer--Aetna Inc., Hartford, CT; *U.S. Public*, pg. 26
Huber, Rob, Dir.-Commercial--Boon Edam B.V., Edam, Netherlands; *Int'l*, pg. 202
Huber, Ron, Chm. Bd., Pres. & Chief Exec. Officer--Time Systems, Inc., Phoenix, AZ; *U.S. Private*, pg. 1086
Huberfield, David, Pres. & Chief Oper. Officer--Hunt Valve, Salem, OH; *U.S. Private*, pg. 549
Huberman Goldberg, Marilyn, Pres.--Museum Boutique Intercontinental, Ltd., New York, NY; *U.S. Private*, pg. 768
Hubermeier, Juergen, Pres. & Chief Oper. Officer--Hexcel Corporation, Pleasanton, CA; *U.S. Public*, pg. 824
Hubers, David, Chm. Bd., Chief Exec. Officer & Pres.--IDS Financial Services, Inc., Minneapolis, MN; *U.S. Public*, pg. 73
Hubers, David R., Pres. & Chief Exec. Officer--American Express Financial Advisor, Minneapolis, MN; *U.S. Public*, pg. 73
Hubert, Roger, Pres.--Manoir Industries, Paris, France; *Int'l*, pg. 570
Hubler, Howard, Pres.--Hubler Chevrolet Inc., Indianapolis, IN; *U.S. Private*, pg. 545
Hubner, C.E., Jr., Pres. & Chief Oper. Officer--Central/Shippee, Inc., Bloomingdale, NJ; *U.S. Private*, pg. 224
Hubner, Eric, Pres.--Allied Felt Group, Bloomingdale, NJ; *U.S. Private*, pg. 224
Hudak, Steve, Pres.--Kool Seal, Inc., Twinsburg, OH; *U.S. Private*, pg. 632
Hudd, Neil, Pres.--N.B.S. Inc., Lachine, Canada; *Int'l*, pg. 898
Huddleston, Ray, Pres. & Chief Exec. Officer--Citizens First Bank, Springhill, LA; *U.S. Public*, pg. 630
Hudler, Carol, Pres. & Publr.--Macon Telegraph Publishing Company, Macon, GA; *U.S. Public*, pg. 964
Hudler, Donald W., Chm. Bd. & Pres.--The Saturn Corporation, Troy, MI; *U.S. Public*, pg. 721
Hudson, Bill, Pres.--NVR Settlement Services, Pittsburgh, PA; *U.S. Public*, pg. 1148
Hudson, Chuck, Pres.--Brawn of California, Inc., San Diego, CA; *U.S. Public*, pg. 782
Hudson, Don, Pres.--Hathaway Process Instrumentation, Carrollton, TX; *U.S. Public*, pg. 799
Hudson, J. Clifford, Pres. & Chief Exec. Officer--Sonic Corporation, Oklahoma City, OK; *U.S. Public*, pg. 1485
Hudson, James E., Pres.--Jim Hudson, Pontiac, Oldsmobile GMC, Columbia, SC; *U.S. Private*, pg. 545
Hudson, John K., Pres.--Young Refining Corp., Douglasville, GA; *U.S. Private*, pg. 1202
Hudson, Kathy M., Pres. & Chief Exec. Officer--W.H. Brady Co., Milwaukee, WI; *U.S. Public*, pg. 250
Hudson, Kent O., Pres. & Chief Exec. Officer--SRS, Raleigh, NC; *U.S. Public*, pg. 307
Hudson, M.R., Chm. Bd. & Pres.--Fisca Oil Co., Inc., Westwood, KS; *U.S. Private*, pg. 408
Hudson, M.R., Chm. & Pres.--Meta Oil Inc., Westwood, KS; *U.S. Private*, pg. 408
Hudson, Mack, Pres.--Caltrol, Inc., Glendora, CA; *U.S. Private*, pg. 201
Hudson, Michael, Pres.--Bourns Integrated Technologies Division, Logan, UT; *U.S. Private*, pg. 161
Hudson, R., Pres.--BFC Industrial Nicholls-Radtke, Cambridge, Canada; *Int'l*, pg. 118
Hudson, R.J., Pres.--Mikropul Environmental Systems Div., Summit, NJ; *Int'l*, pg. 636
Hudson, Robert C., Jr., Pres. & Treas.--H.D. Hudson Manufacturing Company, Chicago, IL; *U.S. Private*, pg. 545
Hudson, S. Michael, Pres. & Chief Exec. Officer--Allison Engine Company Inc., Indianapolis, IN; *Int'l*, pg. 1127
Hudson, Stephen R., Pres. & Chief Exec. Officer--Nyltech North America Inc., Manchester, NH; *Int'l*, pg. 482
Hudson, Steven K., Pres. & Chief Exec. Officer--Newcourt Credit Group Inc., Toronto, Canada; *Int'l*, pg. 924
Hudson, Tom, Pres. & Chief Exec. Officer--Computer Network Technology Corporation, Minneapolis, MN; *U.S. Public*, pg. 421
Hudson, William A., Chm. Bd. & Pres.--Diversco, Inc., Spartanburg, SC; *U.S. Private*, pg. 336
Hudson, William J., Pres. & Chief Exec. Officer--AMP Incorporated, Harrisburg, PA; *U.S. Public*, pg. 7
Hudspeth, Peter, Mng. Partner--EURO RSCG Healthcare, London, United Kingdom; *Int'l*, pg. 603
Huebner, Margaret A., Pres.--Grocers Development Co., Los Angeles, CA; *U.S. Private*, pg. 227
Huelsbeck, Dave, Pres.--Whiteswan/Meta, Libertyville, IL; *U.S. Private*, pg. 342
Huelsbeck, David, Pres.--Dowling Textile Manufacturing Co., Mc Donough, GA; *U.S. Private*, pg. 341
Huelsman, Howare, Pres. & Gen. Mgr.--Casco Products Corporation, Bridgeport, CT; *U.S. Public*, pg. 1458
Huemme, Douglas W., Chm. Bd., Pres. & Chief Exec. Officer--Lilly Industries, Inc., Indianapolis, IN; *U.S. Public*, pg. 994
Huemme, Richard C., Chm. Bd., Pres. & Chief Exec. Officer--Pittsburgh Tube Co., Moon Township, PA; *U.S. Private*, pg. 867
Huete, Pedro Guardeno, Pres.--ASTANDER - Astilleros de Santander S.A., El Astillero, Spain; *Int'l*, pg. 1223
Huether, Richard D., Pres. & Chief Exec. Officer--Independent Can Company, Belcamp, MD; *U.S. Private*, pg. 559
Huey, David, Pres.--Buckeye Cablevision, Toledo, OH; *U.S. Private*, pg. 147
Huey, John, Mng. Editor--Fortune, New York, NY; *U.S. Public*, pg. 1613
Huff, Eric, Pres.--Call Interactive, Omaha, NE; *U.S. Public*, pg. 631
Huff, Jackson, Pres. & Chief Exec. Officer--UPB of Louisiana, Baton Rouge, LA; *U.S. Public*, pg. 1669
Huff, John R., Chm. Bd., Pres. & Chief Exec. Officer--Oceaneering International, Inc., Houston, TX; *U.S. Public*, pg. 1211
Huff, John R., Chm. Bd., Pres. & Chief Exec. Officer--Oceaneering International, Inc., Morgan City, LA; *U.S. Public*, pg. 1211
Huff, Marvin, Pres.--Citizens Information Systems, Inc., Evansville, IN; *U.S. Public*, pg. 281
Huff, Ronald E., Pres. & Chief Fin. Officer--Belden & Blake Corporation, Canton, OH; *U.S. Private*, pg. 1078
Huff, Wayne, Pres. & Chief Exec. Officer--Cegelec AEG Automation Systems Corp., Canonsburg, PA; *Int'l*, pg. 52
Huffer, Russell, Pres. & Chief Exec. Officer--Apogee Enterprises, Inc., Minneapolis, MN; *U.S. Public*, pg. 120
Huffman, David J., Pres.--Celebrity Incorporated, Tyler, TX; *U.S. Public*, pg. 319
Huffman, Neil, Pres. & Chief Oper. Officer--Neil Huffman Nissan Inc., Louisville, KY; *U.S. Private*, pg. 546
Huffman, Robert T., Pres. & Chief Exec. Officer--Vesta Insurance Group, Inc., Birmingham, AL; *U.S. Public*, pg. 1718
Hufford, Chuck, Pres.--Midwest Agri-Commodities, Corte Madera, CA; *U.S. Private*, pg. 53
Huget, Larry, Pres.--Bucyrus Blades Inc., Bucyrus, OH; *U.S. Private*, pg. 383
Huggins, Charles N., Pres.--See's Candy Shops, Inc., South San Francisco, CA; *U.S. Public*, pg. 221
Huggins, Frederick A., Jr., Pres. & Chief Exec. Officer--The Barbers, Hairstyling for Men & Women, Inc., Minneapolis, MN; *U.S. Private*, pg. 115
Huggins, Frederick A., Jr., Pres. & Chief Exec. Officer--We Care Hair, Minneapolis, MN; *U.S. Private*, pg. 115
Hughes, Charlie, Pres.--Land Rover North America, Lanham, MD; *Int'l*, pg. 177

Hughes, Christian T., Pres.--Torotel, Inc., Grandview, MO; *U.S. Public*, pg. 1624
Hughes, Christian T., Pres.--OPT Industries, Inc., Phillipsburg, NJ; *U.S. Public*, pg. 1624
Hughes, Christopher D., Pres.--Booth/Crystal Tips, Dallas, TX; *U.S. Public*, pg. 1445
Hughes, David H., Pres.--H. Venture Corp., Orlando, FL; *U.S. Public*, pg. 847
Hughes, Glenn E., Pres.--Hughes Construction, Inc., North Salt Lake, UT; *U.S. Private*, pg. 546
Hughes, H.D., Chm. Bd., Pres., Chief Exec. Officer & Dir.-Sls.--Diversified Group, Inc., Harahan, LA; *U.S. Private*, pg. 336
Hughes, John, Pres. & Chief Exec. Officer--AMCOL International Corp., Arlington Heights, IL; *U.S. Public*, pg. 63
Hughes, John, Pres. & Chief Exec. Officer--Volclay Standard Pty. Ltd., Geelong, Australia; *U.S. Public*, pg. 64
Hughes, Joseph F., Chm. Bd., Pres., Chief Exec. Officer & Treas.--TSR Inc., Hauppauge, NY; *U.S. Public*, pg. 1559
Hughes, Linda, Pres. & Publisher--The Edmonton Journal, Edmonton, Canada; *Int'l*, pg. 631
Hughes, Mark, Chm. Bd., Pres. & Chief Exec. Officer--Herbalife International of America, Inc., Century City, CA; *U.S. Public*, pg. 809
Hughes, Marvin B., Pres.-Railcar Repair--Trinity Railcar Leasing, Dallas, TX; *U.S. Public*, pg. 1639
Hughes, Mike, Pres. & Creative Dir.--The Martin Agency, Richmond, VA; *U.S. Private*, pg. 678
Hughes, Mike, Pres. & Creative Dir.--The Martin Agency, Richmond, VA; *U.S. Public*, pg. 909
Hughes, R., Pres.--Laporte Absorbents Europe, Widnes, United Kingdom; *Int'l*, pg. 802
Hughes, Stephen B., Pres. & Chief Exec. Officer--Celestial Seasonings, Boulder, CO; *U.S. Public*, pg. 319
Hughes, Terry, Pres. & Chief Exec. Officer--InfoWorks, Mississauga, Canada; *U.S. Public*, pg. 1225
Hughes, Thomas Bud, Pres.--Stoneville Pedigreed Seed Co., Stoneville, MS; *U.S. Public*, pg. 1124
Hughes, W.J., Pres.--American Life & Casualty Insurance Co., Des Moines, IA; *U.S. Public*, pg. 433
Hughey, Lee E., Pres.--Frog Switch & Manufacturing Company, Carlisle, PA; *U.S. Private*, pg. 429
Hugill, Herbert L., Pres.--R.P. Scherer North America, Saint Petersburg, FL; *U.S. Public*, pg. 1438
Hugo-Martinez, Albert J., Pres. & Chief Exec. Officer--GTI Corporation, San Diego, CA; *U.S. Public*, pg. 767
Hugo-Martinez, Albert J., Pres. & Chief Exec. Officer--Valor Electronics, Inc., San Diego, CA; *U.S. Public*, pg. 768
Huh, Suk-Beom, Pres.--Hokuryu Cement Corp., Hokkaido, Japan; *Int'l*, pg. 1291
Huisinga, Darrel, Pres. & Chief Exec. Officer--J.D. Streett & Co., Inc., Maryland Heights, MO; *U.S. Private*, pg. 1047
Huisman, Dick, Pres. & Chief Exec. Officer--Greyhound Lines of Canada Ltd., Calgary, Canada; *Int'l*, pg. 559
Huisman, Willem, Chm. Bd., Pres. & Chief Exec. Officer--Precision Systems, Inc., Saint Petersburg, FL; *U.S. Public*, pg. 1321
Huizenga, Donald, Pres. & Chief Exec. Officer--Kurdziel Industries, Inc., Muskegon, MI; *U.S. Private*, pg. 637
Hulber, Loren J., Pres. & Chief Exec. Officer--NovaCare Employee Services, Inc., Norristown, PA; *U.S. Public*, pg. 1203
Hulit, E. Addison, Pres.--Addison Insurance Company, Lombard, IL; *U.S. Public*, pg. 1677
Hulit, E. Addison, Pres.--Addison Insurance Agency, Lombard, IL; *U.S. Public*, pg. 1677
Hull, Dennis, Dir.-Mktg.--Butterball Turkey Company, Downers Grove, IL; *U.S. Public*, pg. 426
Hull, John, Pres.--Hanover Shoe Co., Hanover, PA; *Int'l*, pg. 297
Hull, John L., Pres.--Hull/Finmac, Inc., Warminster, PA; *U.S. Private*, pg. 547
Hull, Kenneth J., Pres. & Chief Exec. Officer--Follett Corporation, River Grove, IL; *U.S. Private*, pg. 416
Hull, Lewis W., Chm. Bd., Pres. & Chief Exec. Officer--Hull Corporation, Hatboro, PA; *U.S. Private*, pg. 547
Hull, Robert, Pres. & Publisher--The Nugget, North Bay, Canada; *Int'l*, pg. 631
Hullah, William A., Pres.--FTI Foodtech International Inc., Don Mills, Canada; *Int'l*, pg. 476
Hulse, W. Michael, Pres.--Murphy Eastern Oil Co., London, United Kingdom; *U.S. Public*, pg. 1142
Hulseman, Robert L., Pres.--Solo Cup Company, Highland Park, IL; *U.S. Private*, pg. 1013
Hultberg, Hans, Pres.--AB BINAB, Kista, Sweden; *Int'l*, pg. 899
Hultgren, Hilmer C., Pres.--Louisiana Utilities Supply Company, Baton Rouge, LA; *U.S. Private*, pg. 245
Humann, L. Phillip, Chm. Bd., Pres. & Chief Exec. Officer--SunTrust Banks, Inc., Atlanta, GA; *U.S. Public*, pg. 1537
Hume, Gary, Div. Pres.--Keene Distributors, Cleburne, TX; *Int'l*, pg. 752
Hume, George H., Pres.--Basic American Foods, Walnut Creek, CA; *U.S. Private*, pg. 121
Hume, John, Pres.--John Fyfe Ltd., Aberdeen, United Kingdom; *Int'l*, pg. 166
Humke, Ramon L., Pres. & Chief Oper. Officer--Indianapolis Power & Light Company, Indianapolis, IN; *U.S. Public*, pg. 913
Hummel, S. Gerald, Pres. & Chief Exec. Officer--The Russell National Bank, Lewistown, PA; *U.S. Public*, pg. 1222
Hummer, Paul F., Chm. Bd., Pres. & Chief Exec. Officer--A.P. Green Industries, Inc., Mexico, MO; *U.S. Public*, pg. 761
Hummers, William S., III, Pres.--CF Investment Company, Greenville, SC; *U.S. Public*, pg. 306
Humphrey, Robert P., Pres. & Gen. Mgr.--Humphrey Products Company, Kalamazoo, MI; *U.S. Private*, pg. 547
Humphrey, Stephen, Pres.--Bronner Slosberg Humphrey/Strategic Interactive Group, Boston, MA; *U.S. Private*, pg. 171
Humphrey, Stewart, Pres.--Scandinaviska Enskilda Banken London, London, United Kingdom; *Int'l*, pg. 1259
Humphreys, Johnny M., Pres. & Chief Exec. Officer--Itron Inc., Spokane, WA; *U.S. Public*, pg. 914
Humphreys, Roy, Pres.--Shea Homes, Walnut, CA; *U.S. Private*, pg. 990
Humphreys, Steven, Pres. & Chief Exec. Officer--SCM Microsystems, Inc., Los Gatos, CA; *U.S. Public*, pg. 1417
Humston, William L., Pres.--Standard Electronics, Inc., Amherst, NY; *U.S. Private*, pg. 1031
Hung, Edward, Pres.--Caswell-Massey Co. Ltd., Edison, NJ; *U.S. Private*, pg. 219
Hung, Philip, Pres. & V.P.-Mktg.--Braun, North America, Woburn, MA; *U.S. Public*, pg. 743
Hung, Wendell, Pres. & Chief Exec. Officer--Deltak Inc., Plymouth, MN; *U.S. Public*, pg. 924
Hunger, Walter, Pres.--Hunger DFE GmbH, Wurzburg, Germany; *Int'l*, pg. 639
Hunger, Walter, Pres.--Hunger Hydraulics, Limited, Rossford, OH; *Int'l*, pg. 639
Hunkin, J.S., Pres. & Chief Oper. officer--The CIBC Wood Gundy Corporation, Toronto, Canada; *Int'l*, pg. 256
Hunnell, Robert, Pres.--Allied Tire Sales, Orlando, FL; *U.S. Private*, pg. 41
Hunsinger, Peter King, Publisher--Gourmet, New York, NY; *U.S. Private*, pg. 20
Hunt, Bruce W., Pres. & Chief Exec. Officer--Petro-Hunt Corporation, Dallas, TX; *U.S. Private*, pg. 858
Hunt, Donald, Pres.--BRW, Inc., Minneapolis, MN; *U.S. Private*, pg. 107
Hunt, Donald K., Pres.--Sysco Food Services of Horseheads, Horseheads, NY; *U.S. Public*, pg. 1551
Hunt, Frank M., Chm. Bd. & Pres.--Citrus World Inc., Lake Wales, FL; *U.S. Private*, pg. 241
Hunt, Frank, III, Chm. Bd. & Pres.--Sealed-Sweet Growers, Inc., Vero Beach, FL; *U.S. Private*, pg. 978
Hunt, Joseph A., Pres.--Westat Inc., Rockville, MD; *U.S. Private*, pg. 1163
Hunt, Kevin, Pres.--Bremner, Inc., Saint Louis, MO; *U.S. Public*, pg. 1359
Hunt, Mitchell W., Jr., Chm. Bd., Pres. & Chief Exec. Officer--SouthTrust Bank of Columbus, Columbus, GA; *U.S. Public*, pg. 1492
Hunt, Robert G., Vice Chm. & Pres.--The Hunt Corporation, Indianapolis, IN; *U.S. Private*, pg. 548
Hunt, Robert L., II, Pres. & Chief Oper. Officer--Coast Savings Financial, Inc., Los Angeles, CA; *U.S. Public*, pg. 388
Hunt, Rocklyn, Pres. & Chief Exec. Officer--Regions Bank/Forsyth County, Cumming, GA; *U.S. Public*, pg. 1372
Hunt, Terrence M., Pres.--Futronix Systems, Houston, TX; *U.S. Public*, pg. 951
Hunt, Terrill E., Pres. & Chief Exec. Officer--Allied Security, International, Spokane, WA; *U.S. Private*, pg. 41
Hunt, V. William, Pres. & Chief Oper. Officer--Arvin Industries, Inc., Columbus, IN; *U.S. Public*, pg. 136
Hunt, W. Kenneth, III, Pres.--Liberty Life Insurance Company, Greenville, SC; *U.S. Public*, pg. 992
Hunt, W.L., Chm. Bd. & Pres.--Hunt Building Corporation, El Paso, TX; *U.S. Private*, pg. 548
Hunt, William, Chief Exec. Officer--Lundia Div. of MII, Inc., Jacksonville, IL; *U.S. Private*, pg. 680
Hunt, William O., Chm. Bd., Pres. & Chief Exec. Officer--Intellicall, Inc., Carrollton, TX; *U.S. Public*, pg. 887
Hunte, Henry F., Chm. Bd. & Pres.--H.G. Fenton Material Company, San Diego, CA; *U.S. Private*, pg. 400
Hunter, David, Pres.--Blaw-Knox Construction Equipment Corporation, Mattoon, IL; *U.S. Public*, pg. 877
Hunter, Herb, Pres.--Christian Memorial Cultural Center, Rochester Hills, MI; *U.S. Private*, pg. 238
Hunter, James L., Pres. & Chief Exec. Officer--Mackenzie Financial Corporation, Toronto, Canada; *Int'l*, pg. 828
Hunter, Jerry E., Chm. Bd., Pres. & Chief Exec. Officer--JPS Textile Group, Inc., Greenville, SC; *U.S. Private*, pg. 578
Hunter, John C., III, Pres. & Chief Oper. Officer--Solutia Inc., Saint Louis, MO; *U.S. Public*, pg. 1483
Hunter, John W., Chm. Bd, Pres. & Chief Exec. Officer--Adtec Detention Systems, San Antonio, TX; *U.S. Private*, pg. 18
Hunter, R. Alan, Pres. & Chief Oper. Officer--The Stanley Works, New Britain, CT; *U.S. Public*, pg. 1508
Hunter, Richard, Pres. & Chief Exec. Officer--Pace International L.P., Kirkland, WA; *U.S. Private*, pg. 829
Hunter, Samuel P., Pres. & Chief Exec. Officer--T.A. Loving Company, Goldsboro, NC; *U.S. Private*, pg. 677
Huntington, James F., Pres.--School Annual Publishing Co., Coshocton, OH; *U.S. Private*, pg. 598
Huntington, Jim, Pres.--Gitano Fashions Ltd., Bowling Green, KY; *U.S. Public*, pg. 686
Huntington, Jim, Pres.--Bushnell Corporation, Overland Park, KS; *U.S. Private*, pg. 1191
Huntoon, Kenneth H., Pres.--The Fibre-Metal Products Company, Concordville, PA; *U.S. Private*, pg. 402
Huntsman, Peter, Pres. & Chief Oper. Officer--Huntsman Corporation, Salt Lake City, UT; *U.S. Private*, pg. 549
Huntsman, Peter R., Pres. & Chief Oper. Officer--Huntsman Corporation, Salt Lake City, UT; *U.S. Private*, pg. 549
Huppertz, John, Ph.D., Mng. Partner-Mktg. & Res. Services--Eric Mower and Associates, Inc., Syracuse, NY; *U.S. Private*, pg. 765
Huppertz, John, Ph.D., Mng. Partner-Mktg. & Res. Services--Eric Mower and Associates/Buffalo, Inc., Buffalo, NY; *U.S. Private*, pg. 765
Huppertz, John, Ph.D., Mng. Partner-Mktg. & Res. Services--Eric Mower & Associates, Albany, NY; *U.S. Private*, pg. 765
Huppertz, John, Ph.D., Mng. Partner-Mkgt. & Res. Services--Eric Mower & Associates, Atlanta, GA; *U.S. Private*, pg. 765
Hurd, Fred, Pres.--Plascal Corporation, Farmingdale, NY; *U.S. Private*, pg. 870
Hurd, James, Pres.--Lyman Lumber Company, Excelsior, MN; *U.S. Private*, pg. 683
Hurford, Gary T., Pres.--Hunt Oil Company, Dallas, TX; *U.S. Private*, pg. 548
Hurley, Kevin, Pres.--Springhouse Corporation, Spring House, PA; *Int'l*, pg. 1100
Hurley, Mark, Pres.--Chr. Hansen Ireland Limited, Little Island, Ireland; *Int'l*, pg. 289
Hurley, Paul J., Pres.--International Turbine Engine Corporation (ITEC), Phoenix, AZ; *U.S. Public*, pg. 51
Hurlimann, Rene R., Co-Owner & Pres.--Eurad RSCG, Zurich, Switzerland; *Int'l*, pg. 602
Hurst, Mike D., Pres. & Chief Oper. Officer--McCarthy Building Companies, Saint Louis, MO; *U.S. Private*, pg. 719
Hurt, Michael L., Pres. & Chief Oper. Officer--TB Wood's Corporation, Chambersburg, PA; *U.S. Public*, pg. 1562
Hurvitz, Eli, Pres. & Chief Exec. Officer--Teva Pharmaceutical Industries Ltd., Petah Tiqwa, Israel; *Int'l*, pg. 1380
Husby, Paul, Pres.--3M Do Brasil Ltda., Sao Paulo, Brazil; *U.S. Public*, pg. 1606
Husein, Ahmad, Pres.--P.T. KADI International, Jakarta, Indonesia; *Int'l*, pg. 764
Husek, Vladimir, Pres.--Chr. Hansen Czech Republic, s.r.o, Prague, Czech Republic; *Int'l*, pg. 289
Huseth, Merle H., Pres.--K. Hovnanian Companies Northeast, Inc., Edison, NJ; *U.S. Public*, pg. 843
Hushovd, Oyvind, Pres.--Falconbridge Limited, Toronto, Canada; *Int'l*, pg. 433
Huskins, Walter E., Pres.--UST Leasing Corporation, Boston, MA; *U.S. Public*, pg. 1660
Hussain, Abdul Razzak Mohamad Mulla, Dep. Chm. & Mng. Dir.--Kuwait Petroleum Corporation, Safat, Kuwait; *Int'l*, pg. 764
Husseini, Tamer, Chm. Bd., Pres. & Chief Exec. Officer--Celeritek, Inc., Santa Clara, CA; *U.S. Public*, pg. 319
Hussey, Edward J., Pres.--Liberty Homes, Inc., Goshen, IN; *U.S. Public*, pg. 992
Hussey, Tim, Pres. & Chief Exec. Officer--Hussey Seating Company, North Berwick, ME; *U.S. Private*, pg. 550
Hussey, Timothy B., Pres. & Chief Exec. Officer--Hussey Corporation, North Berwick, ME; *U.S. Private*, pg. 550
Hussman, Walter E., Jr., Chm. Bd., Pres. & Publr.--Wehco Media, Inc., Little Rock, AR; *U.S. Private*, pg. 1159
Husson, Jean Claude, Pres.--Alcatel Espace, Nanterre, France; *Int'l*, pg. 55
Husson, Jean-Claude, Pres.--Alcatel Espace, Nanterre, France; *Int'l*, pg. 56
Huta, Henry N., Pres. & Chief Exec. Officer--Califia Company, San Diego, CA; *U.S. Public*, pg. 584
Hutchens, Jeff, Pres.--Hutchens Industries Inc., Springfield, MO; *U.S. Private*, pg. 550
Hutchens, Leon E., Pres.--Kaneb Pipe Line Partners, L.P., Richardson, TX; *U.S. Public*, pg. 942
Hutchens, Thomas D., Pres. & Chief Oper. Officer--JC Penney Company, Inc., Plano, TX; *U.S. Public*, pg. 916
Hutchins, Alma A., Pres.--Hutchins Manufacturing Company, Pasadena, CA; *U.S. Private*, pg. 550
Hutchinson, Lew C., Pres. & Chief Exec. Offcier--Co-Steel Inc., Toronto, Canada; *Int'l*, pg. 298
Hutchinson, Peter, Pres.--Onexa, S.A. de C.V., Garza Garcia, Mexico; *Int'l*, pg. 56
Hutchinson, Richard, Pres.--Consolidated Industries Corp., Lafayette, IN; *Int'l*, pg. 188
Hutchison, Craig, Pres. & Chief Exec. Officer--Perry Graphic Communications, Inc., Waterloo, WI; *U.S. Private*, pg. 855
Huts, Fernand, Pres.--Katoen Natie NV, Antwerp, Belgium; *Int'l*, pg. 724
Huttaporn, Preecha, Pres.--The Siam Sanitary Fittings Co., Ltd., Pathum Thani, Thailand; *Int'l*, pg. 1239
Huttaporn, Preecha, Pres.--The Siam Sanitary Fittings Co., Ltd., Bangkok, Thailand; *Int'l*, pg. 1410
Huttle, Larry, Pres.--Airstream, Inc., Jackson Center, OH; *U.S. Public*, pg. 1602
Hutton, Edward B., Jr., Pres. & Chief Exec. Officer--Waverly, Inc., Baltimore, MD; *U.S. Public*, pg. 1748
Hutton, Henry, Pres.--Chuck Hutton Chevrolet Company, Memphis, TN; *U.S. Private*, pg. 550
Hutts, Joseph C., Chm. Bd., Pres. & Chief Exec. Officer--Phycor, Inc., Nashville, TN; *U.S. Public*, pg. 1293
Huvers, C., Mng. Dir.--Internatio (Pty.) Ltd., Krugersdorp, South Africa; *Int'l*, pg. 682
Huwer, Doug, Pres.--Daimler-Benz Capital Inc., Wilmington, DE; *Int'l*, pg. 368
Huyghebaert, Jan, Chm. Bd. & Pres.--Almanij N.V., Antwerp, Belgium; *Int'l*, pg. 65
Hvistendahl, Finn A., Pres. & Cheif Exec. officer--Den norske Bank ASA, Oslo, Norway; *Int'l*, pg. 392
Hwa, Ong Choon, Sr. Partner--Hillard Scotchbrook Communications Pte. Ltd., Singapore, Singapore; *U.S. Private*, pg. 411
Hwan, Chang Ji, Pres.--Ssangyong Engineering & Construction Co., Ltd., Seoul, Korea; *Int'l*, pg. 1291
Hwang, Li-San, Dr., Chm. Bd., Pres. & Chief Exec. Officer--Tetra Tech, Inc., Pasadena, CA; *U.S. Public*, pg. 1582
Hyatt, Arnold, Pres. & Chief Exec. Officer--Stride Rite Footwear, Inc., Lawrence, MA; *U.S. Public*, pg. 1525
Hyatt, Gary, Pres.--Vesture Corporation, Asheboro, NC; *U.S. Public*, pg. 192
Hyatt, Kenneth E., Chm. Bd., Pres. & Chief Exec. Officer--Walter Industries, Inc., Tampa, FL; *U.S. Public*, pg. 1736
Hyatt, Kenneth E., Pres.--Mid-State Homes, Inc., Tampa, FL; *U.S. Public*, pg. 1736
Hyatt, Kenneth E., Pres.--Cardem Insurance Co., Ltd., Tampa, FL; *U.S. Public*, pg. 1736
Hyatt, T.L., Pres.--HyCon, Inc., Harpersville, AL; *U.S. Public*, pg. 1304
Hyde, Douglas W., Chm. Bd., Pres. & Chief Exec. Officer--OshKosh B'Gosh, Inc., Oshkosh, WI; *U.S. Public*, pg. 1232
Hyde, James R., Pres.--Grace Davison, Baltimore, MD; *U.S. Public*, pg. 755
Hyde, R., Pres.--Smith Engineering Co., Ontario, CA; *Int'l*, pg. 586

Hyder, Hartley, Pres.--J.W. Window Components, Inc., Elizabethton, TN; U.S. Public, pg. 1736
Hydorn, Vernon H., Pres. & Chief Exec. Officer--Barber Dairies, Inc., Birmingham, AL; U.S. Private, pg. 115
Hyer, Frank S., Pres.--Hyer Industries Inc./Thayer Scale, Pembroke, MA; U.S. Private, pg. 552
Hyjek, Ed, Pres.--Bridgestone/Firestone Canada, Inc., Mississauga, Canada; Int'l, pg. 214
Hyland, David, Pres.--Inner Ceramic USA, Garland, TX; U.S. Private, pg. 564
Hyland, Geoffrey F., Pres. & Chief Exec. Officer--Shaw Industries Ltd., Etobicoke, Canada; Int'l, pg. 1231
Hyland, Gregory, Pres.--Anderson, Greenwood & Co., Stafford, TX; U.S. Public, pg. 1650
Hylbert, Paul, Pres. & Co-Chief Exec. Officer--Prime Source Inc., Carrollton, TX; U.S. Private, pg. 884
Hylland, R.R., Pres. & Chief Oper. Officer--Northwestern Growth Corp., Sioux Falls, SD; U.S. Public, pg. 1201
Hylton, E., Pres.--Ebara International Corp., Sparks, NV; Int'l, pg. 431
Hylton, Tracy W., Pres.--WRM, Incoporated, Mabscott, WV; U.S. Private, pg. 1144
Hyman, Morton P., Pres.--Overseas Shipholding Group, Inc., New York, NY; U.S. Public, pg. 1236
Hyman, Steven, Pres.--Susie's Deals, City of Industry, CA; U.S. Private, pg. 1056
Hyon Won, Moo, Pres.--Hyosung Group, Seoul, Korea; Int'l, pg. 640
Hyslop, Charles N., Pres. & Chief Exec. Officer--Sybra, Inc., Atlanta, GA; U.S. Private, pg. 270
Hyun Ahn, Jung, Pres.--Dentsu Young & Rubicam/Seoul, Seoul, Korea; U.S. Private, pg. 325
Iacovelli, Guido, Chm. Bd. & Pres.--Italian Food Manufacturers, Inc., Vestal, NY; U.S. Private, pg. 576
Iafeliece, Jonathan, Partner & Chief Creative Officer--North Castle Partners Advertising, Inc., Stamford, CT; U.S. Private, pg. 804
Ialenti, Pascal, Pres.--Venmar Ventilation, Inc., Drummondville, Canada; U.S. Public, pg. 1194
Iammarino, Craig, Pres.--Welded Tube, Chicago, IL; Int'l, pg. 101
Iandoli, Michael, Pres.--Technical Aid Corporation, Newton, MA; U.S. Private, pg. 1072
Iason, John, V.P.--Balson-Hercules Ltd., New York, NY; Int'l, pg. 326
Ibarguen, Anthony A., Pres. & Chief Oper. Officer--Tech Data Corporation, Clearwater, FL; U.S. Public, pg. 1562
Ibos, Robert J., Chm. Bd., Pres. & Chief Exec. Officer--National Engineering & Contracting Co., Strongsville, OH; U.S. Private, pg. 782
Ibsen, Robert, Dr., Chm. Bd., Pres., Chief Exec. Officer & Treas.--Den-Mat Corporation, Santa Maria, CA; U.S. Private, pg. 324
Ichimura, Kentaro, Pres.--Kawasaki Motors Pty. Ltd., Rydalmere, Australia; Int'l, pg. 726
Ichinoki, Nori, Pres.--JAE Electronics, Inc., Irvine, CA; Int'l, pg. 701
Ickes, David, Pres.--Sky Bros. Inc., Allentown, PA; U.S. Public, pg. 918
Idei, Nobuyuki, Pres. & Chief Oper. Officer--Sony Corporation, Tokyo, Japan; Int'l, pg. 1280
Idelson, Charles K., Pres. & Chief Exec. Officer--SunTrust Bank, Southwest Florida, Fort Myers, FL; U.S. Public, pg. 1538
Idemitsu, Yuji, Pres.--Idemitsu Kosan Co., Ltd., Tokyo, Japan; Int'l, pg. 659
Ielmini, John, Pres.--Patterson Frozen Foods, Inc., Patterson, CA; U.S. Private, pg. 843
Ienaga, Takahiro, Pres.--Mitsui & Co. (Thailand) Ltd., Bangkok, Thailand; Int'l, pg. 882
Igarashi, Motoyuki, Pres.--K.G. System Construction Co., Ltd., Tokyo, Japan; Int'l, pg. 763
Igarashi, Sadaaki, Pres.--Beijing Toto Co., Ltd., Beijing, China; Int'l, pg. 1410
Iger, Robert A., Pres. & Chief Oper. Officer--ABC, Inc, New York, NY; U.S. Public, pg. 511
Iglesias, Enrique V., Pres.--InterAmerican Development Bank, Washington, DC; U.S. Private, pg. 566
Ignatoski, Joseph, Pres.--ISK BioSciences, Memphis, TN; Int'l, pg. 689
Ihamuotila, Jaakko, Chm. Bd. & Chief Exec. Officer--Neste Oy, Espoo, Finland; Int'l, pg. 912
Iida, Yozo, Pres. & Chief Exec. Officer--Descente Ltd., Osaka, Japan; Int'l, pg. 395
Iijima, Nobuhiro, Pres.--Yamazaki Baking Co., Ltd., Tokyo, Japan; Int'l, pg. 1519
Iiori, John, Pres.--American National Can Canada Inc., Brampton, Canada; Int'l, pg. 1029
Iitsuka, Nobuo, Pres.--Dai Nippon Shoji Co., Ltd., Tokyo, Japan; Int'l, pg. 363
Iizima, M., Pres.--Minebea Credit Co., Ltd., Tokyo, Japan; Int'l, pg. 868
Iizuka, Kohji, Pres.--Dow Corning Toray Silicon Co., Ltd., Tokyo, Japan; Int'l, pg. 1400
Iizuka, Mitsuo, Chm. Bd.--Toshoku Ltd., Tokyo, Japan; Int'l, pg. 1407
Ijuin, M., Pres.--Nissho Iwai Steel Leasing Co. Ltd., Tokyo, Japan; Int'l, pg. 947
Ikebata, Katsuhiko, Pres.--DNP Denmark A/S, Karlslunde, Denmark; Int'l, pg. 363
Ikeda, Mitsuaki, Pres.--Kawasaki Precision Machinery (UK) Ltd., Plymouth, United Kingdom; Int'l, pg. 726
Ikeda, Satoru, Pres.--Capy U.S.A. Inc., Culver City, CA; Int'l, pg. 253
Ikuno, Takayoshi, Pres.--Nikkei Home Publishing, Inc., Tokyo, Japan; Int'l, pg. 929
Ikuta, Masaki, Pres.--Mikuni Corporation, Tokyo, Japan; Int'l, pg. 867
Ilardo, Rosario, Pres.--Mamma Ilardo's Corp., Baltimore, MD; U.S. Private, pg. 699
Ilaria, Peter V., Chm. Bd. & Pres.--Tropar Mfg. Co., Inc., Florham Park, NJ; U.S. Private, pg. 1105
Iles, D.A., Pres. & Chief Oper. Officer--Western Union Insurance Co., Calgary, Canada; Int'l, pg. 651
Ilitch, Michael, Chm. Bd. & Pres.--Little Caesar Enterprises, Inc., Detroit, MI; U.S. Private, pg. 671
Ill, Richard C., Pres. & Chief Exec. Officer--Triumph Group, Inc., Wayne, PA; U.S. Public, pg. 1640
Illig, Clifford W., Pres. & Chief Oper. Officer--Cerner Corporation, Kansas City, MO; U.S. Public, pg. 331
Imai, Kiyosuke, Pres.--Matsushita Electric Works, Ltd., Osaka, Japan; Int'l, pg. 847
Imai, Takashi, Pres.--Nippon Steel Corporation, Tokyo, Japan; Int'l, pg. 939
Imamura, Harusuke, Pres.--Shimizu Corporation, Tokyo, Japan; Int'l, pg. 1233
Imanse, Andy, Pres.--El Dorado National, Chino, CA; U.S. Public, pg. 1602
Imanse, Andy, Pres.--El Dorado National, Salina, KS; U.S. Public, pg. 1602
Imazato, Eisaku, Deputy Pres.--Nikko Bank (Switzerland) Ltd., Zurich, Switzerland; Int'l, pg. 930
Imazoto, Eisaku, Deputy Pres.--Nikko Bank (Switzerland) Ltd., Zurich, Switzerland; Int'l, pg. 930
Imbimbo, Victor, Jr., Pres. & Chief Exec. Officer--Cohn & Wells, New York, NY; Int'l, pg. 601
Imbler, Martin R., Pres. & Chief Exec. Officer--Berry Plastics Corporation, Evansville, IN; U.S. Private, pg. 137
Imhoff, Herbert F., Jr., Pres., Chief Oper. Officer & Gen. Counsel--General Employment Enterprises, Inc., Oak Brook Terrace, IL; U.S. Public, pg. 714
Imle, John F., Jr., Pres.--Unocal Corporation, El Segundo, CA; U.S. Public, pg. 1698
Imperia, Enio, Pres.--Imperia Bros., Inc., Pelham Manor, NY; U.S. Private, pg. 558
Imperiale, Mark F., Pres., Chief Oper. Officer & Chief Fin. Officer--Data Broadcasting Corporation, Jackson, WY; U.S. Public, pg. 484
Imura, Akiya, Pres.--Pitney Bowes Japan, Tokyo, Japan; U.S. Public, pg. 1304
Inaba, H., Pres.--Fanuc USA Corp., Elk Grove Village, IL; Int'l, pg. 477
Inada, Shigetoshi, Pres.--The Haokkaido Takushoku Securities Co. (Sapporo), Sapporo, Japan; Int'l, pg. 626
Inaganti, Prasad, Chm. Bd. & Pres.--Howes Leather Corporation, Curwensville, PA; U.S. Private, pg. 543
Incrocci, C. Joseph, Pres.--Alkco Lighting Company, Franklin Park, IL; Int'l, pg. 821
Indelicato, Vincent, Chm. Bd. & Pres.--Delicato Vineyards, Manteca, CA; U.S. Private, pg. 322
Indursky, Harry, Chm. Bd. & Pres.--Cambridge Street Metal Co., Allston, MA; U.S. Private, pg. 203
Inerney, Michael M., Pres. & Chief Exec. Officer--Gibson Electric Co., Oak Brook, IL; U.S. Public, pg. 572
Infantino, Bob, Pres.--Bostonian Shoe Co., Newton, MA; Int'l, pg. 297
Infantino, Ray, Pres.--Hilb, Rogal and Hamilton Insurance Services of Orange County, Inc., Placentia, CA; U.S. Public, pg. 827
Ingalls, Rob, Mng. Partner & Creative Dir.--Ingalls Moranville Advertising, San Francisco, CA; U.S. Private, pg. 316
Ingersoll, Ted, Principal--The Ingersoll Group, Dallas, TX; U.S. Private, pg. 651
Ingman, Tom, Pres. & Chief Oper. Officer--Condor D.C. Power Supplies Inc., Oxnard, CA; U.S. Public, pg. 1419
Ingram, E.W., III, Chm. Bd., Pres. & Chief Exec. Officer--White Castle System, Inc., Columbus, OH; U.S. Private, pg. 1171
Ingram, Jack R., Chm. Bd. & Pres.--XETA Corporation, Tulsa, OK; U.S. Public, pg. 1783
Ingram, Robert A., Pres. & Chief Exec. Officer--Glaxo Wellcome Inc., Research Triangle Park, NC; Int'l, pg. 552
Ingram, Robert A., Mng. Dir.--Media Incorporated, New York, NY; U.S. Private, pg. 726
Ingram, Tony, Pres.--B & B Homes Corporation, Casper, WY; U.S. Private, pg. 105
Ingrando, Leonard, Pres.--Tuscan/Lehigh Dairies LP, Union, NJ; U.S. Private, pg. 1110
Ingrassia, Lawrence, London Bureau Chief--The Wall Street Journal Europe, London, United Kingdom; U.S. Public, pg. 525
Ings, D.M., Pres.--Solar Turbines Incorporated, San Diego, CA; U.S. Public, pg. 316
Inkpen, Ross, Pres. & Chief Exec. Officer--Richard De Boo Publishers, Scarborough, Canada; U.S. Public, pg. 1601
Inman, Darrel F., Pres.--Blount, Inc. Sporting Equipment Group, Lewiston, ID; U.S. Public, pg. 238
Inman, William J., Pres.--NVR Mortgage, Mc Lean, VA; U.S. Public, pg. 1148
Inmon, Ernest, Pres.--Chickasha Cotton Oil Co., Chandler, AZ; Int'l, pg. 1395
Innes, Jeanine, Pres.--Cable Spinning Equipment Inc., New London, MN; U.S. Private, pg. 197
Inoue, Chushichi, Pres.--Seiko Corporation, Tokyo, Japan; Int'l, pg. 1218
Inoue, Hiroshi, Pres.--Koyo Seiko Company, Ltd., Osaka, Japan; Int'l, pg. 760
Inoue, M., Pres.--Nissho Iwai General Merchandise Corp., Tokyo, Japan; Int'l, pg. 946
Inoue, Noriyuki, Pres.--Daikin Industries, Ltd., Osaka, Japan, ; Int'l, pg. 365
Inoue, Osamu, Pres.--Fuji Photo Film U.S.A., Inc., Elmsford, NY; Int'l, pg. 524
Inoue, Tadayuki, Pres. & Chief Oper. Officer--Panasonic Consumer Electric Co., Secaucus, NJ; Int'l, pg. 847
Inoue, Tsuyohito, Pres.--Rohm Fuji Co., Ltd., Yamanashi, Japan; Int'l, pg. 1125
Inserra, Lawrence, Jr., Pres.--Inserra Shoprite, Mahwah, NJ; U.S. Private, pg. 565
Insetta, Victor, Pres. & Chief Exec. Officer--American Technical Ceramics Corp., Huntington Station, NY; U.S. Public, pg. 93
Insetta, Victor, Pres.--ATC International Technical Ceramics, Inc., Huntington Station, NY; U.S. Public, pg. 93
Inwalle, Dennis, Pres.--Reliance Medical Products, Inc., Mason, OH; U.S. Private, pg. 921
Inzantino, Robert J., Pres.--Clarks Cos. N.A., Newton, MA; Int'l, pg. 297
Iochpe, Ivoncuy, Pres.--Iochpe-Maxion S.A., Sao Paulo, Brazil; Int'l, pg. 688
Iordanou, C., Pres. & Chief Exec. Officer--Zurich American Insurance Company of Illinois, Schaumburg, IL; Int'l, pg. 1530
Iorio, Frank, Pres.--Dani Michaels, Inc., New York, NY; U.S. Private, pg. 309
Iott, Richard B., Pres. & Chief Exec. Officer--Seaway Food Town, Inc., Maumee, OH; U.S. Public, pg. 1452
Ira, Steven D., Pres.--Property Asset Management, Denver, CO; U.S. Private, pg. 891
Iraola, Manuel J., Pres.--Phelps Dodge Industries, Phoenix, AZ; U.S. Public, pg. 1286
Iraola, Manuel J., Pres.--Phelps Dodge & Alcoa Fios e Cabos Electricos S.A., Sao Paulo, Brazil; U.S. Public, pg. 1286
Ireland, Rob J., Pres. & Chief Exec. Officer--Roquette America Inc., Keokuk, IA; U.S. Private, pg. 944
Irie, Hiroshi, Pres.--Asatsu Hong Kong Ltd., Causeway Bay, Hong Kong; Int'l, pg. 86
Iriyama, Yosuke, Exec. V.P.--Sanken Electric U.S.A. Corp., Worcester, MA; Int'l, pg. 1188
Irvin, Stanton L., Pres. & Gen. Mgr.--Tri-State Wholesale Associated Grocers, Inc., El Paso, TX; U.S. Private, pg. 1101
Irvine, George A., Pres. & Chief Oper. Officer--Airtite Contractors Inc., Chicago, IL; U.S. Private, pg. 29
Irvine, George A., Pres.--Steel Ceilings Inc., Coshocton, OH; U.S. Private, pg. 29
Irvine, Richard H., Pres. & Chief Oper. Officer--Mikohn Gaming Corporation, Las Vegas, NV; U.S. Public, pg. 1111
Irwin, C.C., Mng. Dir.--Guinness Publishing Ltd., London, United Kingdom; Int'l, pg. 412
Irwin, David K., Pres.--Cadbury Beverages Canada Inc., Mississauga, Canada; Int'l, pg. 248
Irwin, George M., Pres. & Chief Exec. Officer--Irwin Toy Ltd., Toronto, Canada; Int'l, pg. 688
Irwin, John N., III, Pres.--Hillside Capital Incorporated, New York, NY; U.S. Private, pg. 530
Irwin, John R., Pres. & Chief Exec. Officer--Atwood Oceanics, Inc., Houston, TX; U.S. Public, pg. 146
Irwin, John R., Pres.--Eagle Oceanics, Inc., Houston, TX; U.S. Public, pg. 146
Irwin, John R., Pres.--Swiftdrill, Inc., Houston, TX; U.S. Public, pg. 146
Irwin, John R., Pres.--Atwood Oceanics Australia Pty. Ltd., O'Connor, Australia; U.S. Public, pg. 146
Irwin, John R., Pres.--Clearways Drilling (M) SDN BHD, Kuala Lumpur, Malaysia; U.S. Public, pg. 146
Irwin, Michael L., Pres. & Chief Exec. Officer--Cadmus Direct Marketing, Inc., Charlotte, NC; U.S. Public, pg. 290
Irwin, Will, Pres. & Chief Oper. Officer--Labelon Corporation, Canandaigua, NY; U.S. Private, pg. 641
Isaac, Gregory, Pres.--Foam Pro Manufacturing, Irvine, CA; U.S. Private, pg. 415
Isaacs, Robert C., Pres. & Chief Oper. Officer--CPAC, Inc., Leicester, NY; U.S. Public, pg. 282
Isaak, Russell, Pres.--CPI Corp., Saint Louis, MO; U.S. Public, pg. 283
Isahikawa, Mr., Chm. Bd. & Pres.--Nissei Sangyo Co., Ltd., Tokyo, Japan; Int'l, pg. 945
Isaka, Satoru, Chief Rep.--The Hokkaido Takushoku Bank, Ltd. (Beijing), Beijing, China; Int'l, pg. 627
Isakson, Michael, Pres.--ServiceMaster Residential/Commercial Services Co., Memphis, TN; U.S. Public, pg. 1461
Isbell, A.B., Pres. & Chief Oper. Officer--Outdoor Communications, Inc., Corinth, MS; U.S. Private, pg. 822
Isemoto, Leslie, Pres. & Treas.--Isemoto Contracting Co. Ltd., Hilo, HI; U.S. Private, pg. 575
Isenberg, Howard, Pres. & Chief Exec. Officer--CCL Custom Manufacturing, Niles, IL; Int'l, pg. 238
Isham, Lance, Pres. & Chief Oper. Officer--Polo/Ralph Lauren Corporation, New York, NY; U.S. Private, pg. 874
Ishbia, Earl D., Partnership Mgr.--Sherwood Food Distributors, Detroit, MI; U.S. Private, pg. 993
Ishee, Robert R., Pres.--MACtac North America, Brampton, Canada; U.S. Public, pg. 210
Ishibashi, Katsuhiko, Pres.--Flender Ishibashi Co. Ltd., Fukuoka, Japan; Int'l, pg. 400
Ishigaki, Yukichi, Pres.--Chinon Industries Inc., Tokyo, Japan; Int'l, pg. 286
Ishihara, K., Pres.--NI Tubulars, Inc., Houston, TX; Int'l, pg. 947
Ishihara, Soichi, Pres.--Kanebo, Ltd., Tokyo, Japan; Int'l, pg. 722
Ishii, Hugo, Pres.--Mizuno (UK) Ltd., Wokingham, United Kingdom; Int'l, pg. 885
Ishii, Kikwichiro, Pres. & Chief Oper. Officer--Mikimoto (America) Co. Ltd., New York, NY; Int'l, pg. 866
Ishii, Seiichiro, Pres.--The Pilot Corporation, Tokyo, Japan; Int'l, pg. 1057
Ishii, Takafumi, Pres. & Chief Exec. Officer--Nippon Credit Trust Company, New York, NY; Int'l, pg. 933
Ishikawa, S., Pres.--Q & B Foods, Inc., Irwindale, CA; Int'l, pg. 1074
Ishikawa, Tetsuro, Pres.--Snow Brand Milk Products Co. Ltd., Tokyo, Japan; Int'l, pg. 1271
Ishikura, S., Pres.--Sharp Technology (Taiwan) Corporation, Taipei, Taiwan; Int'l, pg. 1230
Ishimaru, Tsuneo, Pres. & Chief Exec. Officer--Nippondenso Co., Ltd., Kariya, Japan; Int'l, pg. 1412
Ishimatsu, Takao, Pres.--Rohm Amagi Co., Ltd., Fukuoka, Japan; Int'l, pg. 1125
Ishimoto, Kiyoo, Pres.--Nikkei Custom Publishing Services, Inc., Tokyo, Japan; Int'l, pg. 929
Ishimura, Kazukiyo, Pres.--Yamaha Corporation, Hamamatsu, Japan; Int'l, pg. 1515
Ishitani, Akira, Pres.--Toray Research Center, Inc., Tokyo, Japan; Int'l, pg. 1399

Ishitsubo, Ichizo, Pres.--Clarion Co., Ltd., Tokyo, Japan; *Int'l*, pg. 296
Ishizaka, Akira, Pres.--John Crane (Japan) Inc., Shiga, Japan; *Int'l*, pg. 1339
Ishizaka, Yoshio, Pres. & Chief Exec. Officer--Toyota Motor Sales, U.S.A., Inc., Torrance, CA; *Int'l*, pg. 1412
Ishizuka, Hisai, Pres.--Foster Wheeler k.k., Tokyo, Japan; *U.S. Public*, pg. 677
Ishizumi, Tad, Pres.--Reed Exhibition Companies-Asia North, Tokyo, Japan; *Int'l*, pg. 1096
Ismail, Yusca, Pres., Gen. Mgr. & Dir.--Perwanal/D'Arcy Masius Benton & Bowles, Jakarta, Indonesia; *U.S. Private*, pg. 305
Isotalo, Jukka, Pres.--Valmet Chile Ltda., Santiago, Chile; *Int'l*, pg. 1448
Israel, Charles, Pres.--Pitkin County Bank & Trust Company, Aspen, CO; *U.S. Public*, pg. 1793
Israel, David, Pres.--SuperValu, Inc.-Greenville Div., Greenville, KY; *U.S. Public*, pg. 1540
Israel, Larry, Chm. Bd., Pres. & Chief Exec. Officer--Telesensory Corporation, Sunnyvale, CA; *U.S. Private*, pg. 1074
Israel, Robert L., Pres. & Chief Oper. Officer--Empire National Bank, Traverse City, MI; *U.S. Private*, pg. 374
Israelson, Erik, Pres.--The Dorris Lumber & Moulding Co., Sacramento, CA; *U.S. Private*, pg. 341
Issac, Bill, Pres.--Texas Apparel, El Paso, TX; *U.S. Public*, pg. 1429
Isshiki, Toru, Pres.--Taiwan Toto Co., Ltd., Taipei, Taiwan; *Int'l*, pg. 1410
Issleib, Lutz, Chm. Bd. & Pres.--S & P Company, Mill Valley, CA; *U.S. Private*, pg. 954
Issler, James E., Pres. & Chief Oper. Officer--H.H. Brown Shoe Company, Inc., Greenwich, CT; *U.S. Public*, pg. 217
Istock, Verne G., Chm. Bd., Pres. & Chief Exec. Officer--First Chicago NBD Corporation, Chicago, IL; *U.S. Public*, *pg. 627*
Itin, Thomas W., Pres. & Chief Exec. Officer--Ajay Sports Inc., Delavan, WI; *U.S. Public*, pg. 34
Itin, Thomas W., Chm. Bd., Pres. & Chief Exec. Officer--Williams Controls, Inc., Portland, OR; *U.S. Public*, pg. 1769
Ito, Hironobu, Pres.--Dai-Ichi Kikaku Co. Ltd., Tokyo, Japan; *Int'l*, pg. 357
Ito, J., Pres.--Sambow Plastics Co., Ltd., Osaka, Japan; *Int'l*, pg. 947
Ito, Kaneo, Pres.--Pioneer Electronic Corporation, Tokyo, Japan; *Int'l*, pg. 1057
Ito, Ken, Pres.--Shinto Paint Co., Ltd., Amagasaki, Japan; *Int'l*, pg. 1311
Ito, Kengi, Pres.--Japan Travel Bureau International, Inc., New York, NY; *U.S. Private*, pg. 582
Ito, Kenichi, Pres.--Shanghai Office, Shanghai, China; *Int'l*, pg. 578
Ito, Kinichi, Pres.--Itoham Foods Inc., Tokyo, Japan; *Int'l*, pg. 695
Ito, M., Pres. & Chief Exec. Officer--Sankosha Corporation, Tokyo, Japan; *Int'l*, pg. 1189
Ito, Masatoshi, Chm. Bd.--The Southland Corporation, Dallas, TX; *Int'l*, pg. 693
Ito, Shinichi, Pres.--Sumitomo Bank of New York Trust Company, New York, NY; *Int'l*, pg. 1309
Itoh, Kensuke, Pres.--Kyocera Corporation, Kyoto, Japan; *Int'l*, pg. 775
Itoh, Kiyoshi, Pres. & Chief Exec. Officer--Seiko Instruments Inc., Chiba, Japan; *Int'l*, pg. 1219
Itoh, Tomomi, Pres.--Hitachi Home Electronics, Norcross, GA; *Int'l*, pg. 621
Ittner, George, Pres.--Newport News, Inc., New York, NY; *U.S. Public*, pg. 1499
Ivanier, Paul, Pres. & Chief Exec. Officer--The Ivaco Group, Montreal, Canada; *Int'l*, pg. 695
Ivans, Paul, Mng. Partner & Exec. V.P.--Dugan Valva Contess Inc., Morristown, NJ; *U.S. Private*, pg. 345
Ivansson, Kenneth, Pres.--NCC Uddevalla, Uddevalla, Sweden; *Int'l*, pg. 899
Iversen, Arve, Pres.--Kvaerner Professional Services Ltd., Aberdeen, United Kingdom; *Int'l*, pg. 768
Ivester, M. Douglas, Pres.--The Coca-Cola Export Corporation, Atlanta, GA; *U.S. Public*, pg. 392
Ivester, M. Douglas, Pres.--Coca-Cola Interamerican Corp., Atlanta, GA; *U.S. Public*, pg. 392
Ivins, Robert, Pres.--Silver Furniture Co., Inc., Knoxville, TN; *U.S. Public*, pg. 352
Ivory, Brian, Grp. Chief Exec.--The Highland Distilleries Company plc, Glasgow, United Kingdom; *Int'l*, pg. 619
Ivy, Jim, Pres. & Chief Exec. Officer--Savin Corporation, Stamford, CT; *Int'l*, pg. 1114
Ivy, Jim, Pres. & Chief Exec. Officer--Gestetner Corporation, Greenwich, CT; *Int'l*, pg. 1115
Iwagaki, Kenji, Pres.--Scripto-Tokai Corp., Fontana, CA; *U.S. Private*, pg. 977
Iwai, M., Pres.--Nissho Iwai Aerospace Corp., Tokyo, Japan; *Int'l*, pg. 946
Iwai, Toshiyuki, Pres.--Nomura Land & Building Co. Ltd., Tokyo, Japan; *Int'l*, pg. 956
Iwai, Yasushi, Pres.--ORIX Baseball Club, Kobe, Japan; *Int'l*, pg. 1008
Iwaki, Koichiro, Pres.--Asahi Breweries U.S.A., Inc., Los Angeles, CA; *Int'l*, pg. 83
Iwakura, Joe, Pres.--Wako Bank (Schweiz) AG, Zurich, Switzerland; *Int'l*, pg. 1485
Iwano, Shunpei, Pres.--Konica Photo Service U.S.A., Inc., East Hartford, CT; *Int'l*, pg. 748
Iwasaki, T., Pres.--Noritake Co., Inc., Secaucus, NJ; *Int'l*, pg. 959
Izak, S. Wilzig, Chm. Bd.--Wilshire Oil Co. of Texas, Jersey City, NJ; *U.S. Public*, pg. 1770
Izuel, Cesareo Alierta, Chm. Bd., Pres. & Chief Exec. Officer--Tabacalera, S.A., Madrid, Spain; *Int'l*, pg. 1345
Izumi, Masaharu, Pres.--United Asset Management (Japan), Inc., Tokyo, Japan; *U.S. Public*, pg. 1674
Jabbour, Michael, Pres.--Lewis Gace Bozell Healthcare Worldwide, Fort Lee, NJ; *U.S. Public*, pg. 1642
Jackman, Brian J., Pres.-Tellabs Opers.--Tellabs Operations, Inc., Lisle, IL; *U.S. Public*, pg. 1572
Jackman, Joseph R., Chm. Bd., Pres. & Chief Exec. Officer--Reactive Metals & Alloys Corporation (REMACOR), West Pittsburg, PA; *U.S. Private*, pg. 913
Jackson, Bruce, Pres.--Coast Steel Fabricators Ltd., Port Coquitlam, Canada; *Int'l*, pg. 31
Jackson, Christopher, Pres. & Chief Exec. Officer--DynetCom, Guyancourt, France; *Int'l*, pg. 425
Jackson, David N., Pres. & Gen. Mgr.--Williams Detroit Diesel-Allison Midwest, Inc., Brunswick, OH; *U.S. Private*, *pg. 1179*
Jackson, Dick, Pres.--Pedus Services, Inc., Los Angeles, CA; *U.S. Private*, pg. 846
Jackson, Dick, Pres.--Pedus Building Services, Los Angeles, CA; *U.S. Private*, pg. 846
Jackson, Dick, Pres.--Pedus Security Services, Los Angeles, CA; *U.S. Private*, pg. 846
Jackson, Dick, Pres.--Pedus Office Services, Los Angeles, CA; *U.S. Private*, pg. 846
Jackson, Dick, Pres.--Pedus Food Services, Los Angeles, CA; *U.S. Private*, pg. 846
Jackson, Eddie L., Pres.-Lil' Champs--Lil'Champ/Food Stores Inc., Jacksonville, FL; *U.S. Private*, pg. 837
Jackson, Eric, Pres.--Shieldalloy Metallurgical Corportation, Newfield, NJ; *U.S. Private*, pg. 735
Jackson, Fred A., Pres.--American & Efird, Inc., Mount Holly, NC; *U.S. Public*, pg. 1412
Jackson, J. Andrew, Pres.--Optiroc Ltd., Manchester, United Kingdom; *Int'l*, pg. 1200
Jackson, J.L., Chm. Bd., Pres. & Chief Exec. Officer--Global Industrial Technologies, Dallas, TX; *U.S. Public*, pg. 747
Jackson, Jim, Pres.--DeSoto Inc., Joliet, IL; *U.S. Public*, pg. 956
Jackson, Joe, Pres.--Spartan Automatic Retailers, Memphis, TN; *U.S. Private*, pg. 1020
Jackson, Margaret A., Pres.--Western Pacific Data Systems, La Jolla, CA; *U.S. Private*, pg. 1168
Jackson, Mary Anne, Chm. Bd., Pres., Chief Oper. & Chief Exec. Officer--My Own Meals, Inc., Deerfield, IL; *U.S. Private*, pg. 770
Jackson, Mary Anne, Pres.--J&M Company, Deerfield, IL; *U.S. Private*, pg. 770
Jackson, Meryl, Pres.--Almega Corporation, Bensenville, IL; *U.S. Public*, pg. 546
Jackson, Michael, Pres.--Mercedes-Benz of North America, Inc., Montvale, NJ; *Int'l*, pg. 368
Jackson, Michael L., Pres.--SuperValu, Inc.-Tacoma Div., Tacoma, WA; *U.S. Public*, pg. 1541
Jackson, Penny, Pres.--Nevada Landing, Jean, NV; *U.S. Public*, pg. 375
Jackson, Quintin, Pres. & Chief Exec. Officer--Alfa Laval Inc., Kenosha, WI; *Int'l*, pg. 1378
Jackson, R.A., Chm. Bd., Pres. & Chief Exec. Officer--Nuburn Capital, Calgary, Canada; *Int'l*, pg. 990
Jackson, Richard L., Chm. Bd., Pres. & Chief Exec. Officer--Allegiant Physician Services, Atlanta, GA; *U.S. Public*, pg. 45
Jackson, Richard L., Pres.--Quest Staffing, Atlanta, GA; *U.S. Public*, pg. 45
Jackson, Richard L., Pres.--Surgical Information Systems, Atlanta, GA; *U.S. Public*, pg. 45
Jackson, Robert, Interim Pres. & Chief Exec. Officer--The Bombay Company, Inc., Fort Worth, TX; *U.S. Public*, pg. 244
Jackson, Robert, Interim Pres. & Chief Exec. Officer--The Bombay Company, Fort Worth, TX; *U.S. Public*, pg. 244
Jackson, T.A., Pres.--The Trust Company of Bank of Montreal, Toronto, Canada; *Int'l*, pg. 153
Jackson, W. Ronald, Chm. Bd. & Pres.--Jackson Furniture Industries, Cleveland, TN; *U.S. Private*, pg. 579
Jackson, Wendy, Pres.-Direct Mktg.--EvansGroup, Salt Lake City, UT; *U.S. Private*, pg. 385
Jackson, William, Pres.--Hardaway Concrete Co., Inc., Columbia, SC; *U.S. Private*, pg. 501
Jackson, William L., Chm. Bd. & Pres.--Parrish Tire Company, Inc., Winston Salem, NC; *U.S. Private*, pg. 840
Jacob, James A., Pres.--Ajax Paving Industries Inc., Madison Heights, MI; *U.S. Private*, pg. 29
Jacobi, C.M., Pres. & Chief Exec. Officer--Timex Corporation, Middlebury, CT; *U.S. Private*, pg. 1088
Jacobi, Pete, Pres. & Chief Oper. Officer--Levi Strauss & Co., San Francisco, CA; *U.S. Private*, pg. 662
Jacobs, Bruce, Pres.--Grede Transport, Inc., Milwaukee, WI; *U.S. Private*, pg. 476
Jacobs, Bruce, Pres. & Chief Exec. Officer--Grede-Pryor, Inc., Pryor, OK; *U.S. Private*, pg. 476
Jacobs, Bruce E., Pres. & Chief Exec. Officer--Grede Foundries, Inc., Milwaukee, WI; *U.S. Private*, pg. 476
Jacobs, Daniel L., Pres.--Jacobs Asset Management, Fort Lauderdale, FL; *U.S. Public*, pg. 1673
Jacobs, Francis B., Pres.--EA Financial, Inc., Wilmington, DE; *U.S. Public*, pg. 541
Jacobs, Herman, Pres. & Chief Oper. Officer--Allou Health & Beauty Care, Inc., Brentwood, NY; *U.S. Public*, pg. 55
Jacobs, Herman, Pres.--Allou Distributors Inc., Brentwood, NY; *U.S. Public*, pg. 55
Jacobs, Howard, Pres.--R & R Marketing, West Caldwell, NJ; *U.S. Private*, pg. 902
Jacobs, Howard, Pres.--Royal Division, West Caldwell, NJ; *U.S. Private*, pg. 902
Jacobs, Howard, Pres.--Reitman Division, West Caldwell, NJ; *U.S. Private*, pg. 902
Jacobs, Howard, Pres.--Spectrum Division, West Caldwell, NJ; *U.S. Private*, pg. 902
Jacobs, Howard, Pres.--Raritan Display Division, West Caldwell, NJ; *U.S. Private*, pg. 902
Jacobs, Jeffrey D., Pres. & Chief Oper. Officer--Harpo Entertainment Group, Chicago, IL; *U.S. Private*, pg. 504
Jacobs, Jerry, Pres. & Chief Exec. Officer--First National Bank, Nashville, Nashville, AR; *U.S. Public*, pg. 630
Jacobs, Leonard J., Chm. Bd., Pres. & Chief Exec. Officer--Jet Spray Corp., Norwood, MA; *U.S. Private*, pg. 586
Jacobs, Mark L., Pres. & Chief Exec. Officer--Watkins Incorporated, Winona, MN; *U.S. Private*, pg. 1153
Jacobs, Norman, Chm. Bd. & Pres.--Century Publishing Company, Evanston, IL; *U.S. Private*, pg. 226
Jacobs, P. Anthony, CFA, Pres. & Chief Oper. Officer--Seafield Capital Corporation, Kansas City, MO; *U.S. Public*, pg. 1449
Jacobs, Paul, Pres. & Chief Exec. Officer--IsoQuest, Inc., Fairfax, VA; *U.S. Private*, pg. 958
Jacobs, Peter H., Chm. Bd. & Pres.--Fone America, Inc., Portland, OR; *U.S. Public*, pg. 661
Jacobs, Sharon, Asst. Pres.--Bomaine Corporation, Santa Monica, CA; *U.S. Private*, pg. 155
Jacobsen, Aage, Pres.--Chr. Hansen Argentina S.A.I.C., Quilmes, Argentina; *Int'l*, pg. 289
Jacobsen, Earl D., Pres. & Chief Oper. Officer--Central Data Corporation, Champaign, IL; *U.S. Private*, pg. 223
Jacobsen, I., Chm. Bd. & Pres.--Fuller Company, Bethlehem, PA; *Int'l*, pg. 475
Jacobsen, Thomas H., Chm. Bd., Pres. & Chief Exec. Officer--Mercantile Bancorporation Inc., Saint Louis, MO; *U.S. Public*, pg. 1087
Jacobsen, Uwe, Pres.--Saarbrucker Zeitung Verlag und Druckerei GmbH, Saarbruecken, Germany; *Int'l*, pg. 1478
Jacobsen, William R., Pres.--Jacobsen Manufacturing, Inc., Safety Harbor, FL; *U.S. Private*, pg. 580
Jacobson, Arnold E., Pres.--Goddess Bra Company, East Boston, MA; *U.S. Private*, pg. 458
Jacobson, Edwin, Pres. & Chief Exec. Officer--Avatar Holdings Inc., Coral Gables, FL; *U.S. Public*, pg. 151
Jacobson, Fred, Pres.--Money Point Diamond Co., Chesapeake, VA; *U.S. Private*, pg. 757
Jacobson, Harvey, Pres., Chief Exec. Officer & Sec.--Glencraft Lingerie, Inc., New York, NY; *U.S. Private*, pg. 456
Jacobson, Max M., Pres.--Harris Building Services Corporation, Chicago, IL; *Int'l*, pg. 154
Jacobson, Mitchell, Pres. & Chief Exec. Officer--Sid Tool Co. Inc., Plainview, NY; *U.S. Private*, pg. 998
Jacobson, Mitchell, Pres. & Chief Exec. Officer--MSC Industrial Supply Co., Plainview, NY; *U.S. Private*, pg. 998
Jacobson, Rick, Pres. & Chief Exec. Officer--Norpac Foods, Inc., Stayton, OR; *U.S. Private*, pg. 802
Jacobus, Martin K., Pres.-Publications & Directory Sls.--World Color Press, Inc., Greenwich, CT; *U.S. Public*, pg. 1778
Jacobus, Phillip R., Pres.--Hartger & Willard Mortgage Associates, Inc., Grand Rapids, MI; *U.S. Public*, pg. 1216
Jacoby, Thomas, Pres.--Harman Consumer Group, Woodbury, NY; *U.S. Public*, pg. 787
Jacoby, Thomas, Pres.--JBL Consumer, Woodbury, NY; *U.S. Public*, pg. 787
Jacoff, Sydney, Pres.--Great Neck Saw Manufacturers, Inc., Mineola, NY; *U.S. Private*, pg. 475
Jacquillat, Thierry, Pres.--Groupe Pernod Ricard, Paris, France; *Int'l*, pg. 566
Jadow, Henry C., Exec. V.P.--Krazy Glue Inc., New York, NY; *U.S. Private*, pg. 158
Jae, Park Byung, Pres.--Hyundai Motor Company, Seoul, Korea; *Int'l*, pg. 641
Jaeger, Joseph A., Chm. Bd. & Pres.--MCC Group, L.L.C., Metairie, LA; *U.S. Private*, pg. 686
Jaen, Juan Pedro Gomez, Pres.--Suria K, S.A., Madrid, Spain; *Int'l*, pg. 1225
Jaffe, Arthur M., Pres.--American Mathematical Society, Inc., Providence, RI; *U.S. Private*, pg. 59
Jaffe, Ira, Pres.-Famous Music--Paramount Pictures Corporation, Los Angeles, CA; *U.S. Private*, pg. 776
Jaffe, Richard B., Chm. Bd., Pres. & Chief Exec. Officer--Safeskin Corporation, San Diego, CA; *U.S. Public*, pg. 1425
Jaffee, Daniel S., Pres. & Chief Exec. Officer--Oil-Dri Corporation of America, Chicago, IL; *U.S. Public*, pg. 1214
Jaffee, Keith, Pres.--Amco Corporation, Chicago, IL; *U.S. Public*, pg. 985
Jaffre, Philippe, Chm. Bd., Pres. & Chief Exec. Officer--Elf Aquitane, Paris, France; *Int'l*, pg. 444
Jager, Durk I., Pres. & Chief Oper. Officer--The Procter & Gamble Company, Cincinnati, OH; *U.S. Public*, pg. 1330
Jager, Durk I., Pres. & Chief Oper. Officer--Richardson-Vicks, Inc., Health Care Products, Cincinnati, OH; *U.S. Public*, pg. 1331
Jagraeus, Anders, Pres.--AB Carl Munters, Sollentuna, Sweden; *Int'l*, pg. 669
Jahnke, William, Pres.--Vernon Computer Leasing Inc., Stamford, CT; *Int'l*, pg. 559
Jakowsky, Richard H., Pres., Chief Exec. Officer & Chief Oper. Officer--Anderson Electric, Inc., Springfield, IL; *U.S. Private*, pg. 72
Jalichandra, Kirkkiat, Pres.--Bangkok Bank of Commerce Ltd., Bangkok, Thailand; *Int'l*, pg. 146
Jamar, John P., Pres. & Chief Exec. Officer--Cable Constructors, Inc., Iron Mountain, MI; *U.S. Private*, pg. 197
James, Artis E., Jr., Pres. & Chief Exec. Officer--Purcell Co., Inc., Diamondhead, MS; *U.S. Private*, pg. 895
James, Betty M., Pres. & Dir.-Mktg. & Pub. Rels.--James Industries Inc., Hollidaysburg, PA; *U.S. Private*, pg. 580
James, Carl, Pres.--Riverchase Homes, Haleyville, AL; *U.S. Public*, pg. 319
James, Donald M., Pres. & Chief Exec. Officer--Vulcan Materials Company, Birmingham, AL; *U.S. Public*, pg. 1725
James, Jerry S., Pres.--James Building Corporation, Northbrook, IL; *U.S. Private*, pg. 580
James, Juanita, Pres.--Newbridge Communications, Inc., New York, NY; *Int'l*, pg. 191
James, Larry M., Chm. Bd., Pres. & Chief Exec. Officer--USLD Communications Corp., San Antonio, TX; *U.S. Public*, pg. 969

James, Lawrence E., Pres.--ReliaStar Mortgage Company, West Des Moines, IA; *U.S. Public*, pg. 1376
James, Matt, Pres. & Gen. Mgr.--KTVE, Inc., Channel 10, Monroe, LA; *U.S. Public*, pg. 759
James, P.G., Pres.--Hydro Conduit Corp., Houston, TX; *Int'l*, *pg. 245*
James, Patrick M., Pres. & Chief Exec. Officer--Rio Algom Limited, Toronto, Canada; *Int'l*, pg. 1118
James, Rick, Pres.--JTC LLC, Fort Wayne, IN; *U.S. Private*, pg. 579
James, Ronald, Pres.--Ceridian Employer Services, Bloomington, MN; *U.S. Public*, pg. 331
James, Sean, Pres. & Chief Exec. Officer--Wagner Spray Tech Corp., Plymouth, MN; *U.S. Private*, pg. 1146
James, William, Pres. & Chief Exec. Officer--Inmet Mining Corporation, Toronto, Canada; *Int'l*, pg. 678
James, William J., Pres.--Northrop Grumman International, Inc., Arlington, VA; *U.S. Public*, pg. 1198
Jameson, B.W., Pres.--TGM Detectors Inc., Waltham, MA; *Int'l*, pg. 892
Janaczek, Stephen J., Pres.--Power Piping Company, Pittsburgh, PA; *U.S. Public*, pg. 1029
Janes, Michael A., Pres.--Hilb, Rogal and Hamilton Company of Arizona, Phoenix, AZ; *U.S. Public*, pg. 827
Janes, Tim, Pres.--Olson Rug Company, Chicago, IL; *U.S. Private*, pg. 815
Janeway, Dean, Pres.--Wakefern Food Corporation, Elizabeth, NJ; *U.S. Private*, pg. 1146
Jang, Chull-Hoon, Chm. Bd. & Pres.--Cho Hung Bank, Seoul, Korea; *Int'l*, pg. 287
Janik, Richard A., Pres. & Chief Exec. Officer--Janik & Associates, Inc., Los Angeles, CA; *U.S. Private*, pg. 582
Janikies, Nicholas, Pres.--Jan-Co., Inc., Cranston, RI; *U.S. Private*, pg. 581
Janitz, John, Pres.--Randall Textron, Troy, MI; *U.S. Public*, pg. 1590
Janitz, John A., Chm. Bd., Pres. & Chief Exec. Officer--Textron Automotive Company, Troy, MI; *U.S. Public*, pg. 1590
Janjak, Vinko, Pres.--Jotul a.s., Fredrikstad, Norway; *Int'l*, pg. 42
Jankovic, Paul, Pres., Chief Exec. & Chief Oper. Officer--GHM Industries, Inc., Worcester, MA; *U.S. Private*, pg. 435
Janning, James C., Pres. & Chief Oper. Officer--Harbour Group Ltd., Saint Louis, MO; *U.S. Private*, pg. 500
Jannotta, Lou, Chm. Bd. & Pres.--L&J Technologies, Hillside, IL; *U.S. Private*, pg. 638
Jans, Thomas, Pres.--Recognition Division, Memphis, TN; *U.S. Public*, pg. 934
Jansen Kraemer, Harry M., Jr., Pres., Chief Fin. Officer & Sr. V.P.--Baxter International Inc., Deerfield, IL; *U.S. Public*, pg. 196
Jansen, James H., Pres., Chief Exec. & Oper. Officer--Lynden Incorporated, Seattle, WA; *U.S. Private*, pg. 683
Jansen, Piet, Pres.--Rust-Oleum Nederland B.V., Roosendaal, Netherlands; *U.S. Public*, pg. 1358
Jansen, Raymond A., Pres., Chief Exec. Officer & Publr.--Newsday, Melville, NY; *U.S. Public*, pg. 1616
Jansen, W. David, Pres.& Chief Exec. Officer--WJW Constructors, LLC, Mesa, AZ; *U.S. Private*, pg. 1187
Janson, Peter S., Pres.--ABB Inc., Norwalk, CT; *Int'l*, pg. 3
Janssens, Chester G., Pres.--Crusader Marine Engines, Sterling Heights, MI; *U.S. Public*, pg. 1591
Jansson, Christian W., Pres.--Ellos AB, Boras, Sweden; *Int'l*, *pg. 643*
Jantz, Cort, Pres.--TV Host Inc., Harrisburg, PA; *U.S. Private*, pg. 1066
Janzem, Glen N., Pres. & Chief Exec. Officer--Ranchers Cotton Oil, Fresno, CA; *U.S. Private*, pg. 908
Jaques, Frederick M., Pres.--Kellogg Canada Inc., Rexdale, Canada; *U.S. Public*, pg. 947
Jarc, Lyn, Partner & Sr. V.P.--Media That Works, Cincinnati, OH; *U.S. Private*, pg. 727
Jarmain, Eric, Pres.--Farmatic Research, Inc., London, Canada; *Int'l*, pg. 478
Jarman, David W., Pres.--Dresser Drilling & Production Services, Aberdeen, United Kingdom; *U.S. Public*, pg. 529
Jarosz, William D., Pres. & Chief Exec. Officer--Fansteel, Inc., North Chicago, IL; *U.S. Public*, pg. 612
Jarvis, J. Andrew, Pres. & Chief Oper. Officer--Ewing Cole Cherry Brott, Philadelphia, PA; *U.S. Private*, pg. 387
Jarvis, Ron, Pres. & Chief Oper. Officer--Technicolor, Inc., North Hollywood, CA; *Int'l*, pg. 272
Jas, Dick, Chm. Bd.--Possehl Electronic Nederland bv, s Hertogenbosch, Netherlands; *Int'l*, pg. 1064
Jasick, Thomas A., Pres.--Berkley Information Services, Luverne, MN; *U.S. Public*, pg. 216
Jaskol, Leonard R., Chm. Bd., Pres. & Chief Exec. Officer--Lydall, Inc., Manchester, CT; *U.S. Public*, pg. 1020
Jasmann, Dwight E., Pres. & Gen. Mgr.--COMSAT International Ventures, Bethesda, MD; *U.S. Public*, pg. 425
Jason, Floyd, Pres.--Best Provision Co., Inc., Newark, NJ; *U.S. Private*, pg. 140
Jasper, Charles, Pres. & Chief Exec. Officer--Espey Huston Associates, Inc., Austin, TX; *U.S. Private*, pg. 826
Jastrow, Kenneth M., II, Pres. & Chief Exec. Officer--Guaranty F.S.B., Dallas, TX; *U.S. Public*, pg. 1575
Jasurda, Bruce, Pres. & Chief Oper. Officer--David Cravit & Associates Advertising, Chicago, IL; *U.S. Private*, pg. 287
Jatusipitak, Som, Dr., Pres. & Chief Exec. Officer--Siam City Bank Public Company Limited, Bangkok, Thailand; *Int'l*, pg. 1239
Jaume, Feliciano Fuster, Chm. Bd. & Pres.--ENDESA - Empresa Nacional de Electricidad, S.A., Madrid, Spain; *Int'l*, pg. 1224
Jaunzemis, Earl, Pres.--Can Corporation of America, Blandon, PA; *U.S. Private*, pg. 204
Javitch, Gary, Pres.--American Fence & Security Company, Phoenix, AZ; *U.S. Private*, pg. 54
Jaworski, Kenneth, Pres.--Miken Companies, Inc., Cheektowaga, NY; *U.S. Private*, pg. 745
Jay, Dan, Pres., Chief Exec. Officer & Chief Fin. Officer--Campmor Inc., Upper Saddle River, NJ; *U.S. Private*, pg. 204
Jayson, Joseph M., Chm. Bd., Pres. & Chief Exec. Officer--J.M. Jayson & Co., Inc., Getzville, NY; *U.S. Private*, pg. 584
Jean, Emilio Azcarraga, Pres. & Chief Exec. Officer--Grupo Televisa, S.A. de C.V., Mexico, Mexico; *Int'l*, pg. 576
Jean, Raymond A., Pres. & Chief Oper. Officer--Varlen Corporation, Naperville, IL; *U.S. Public*, pg. 1710
Jeans, Michael D., Pres.--Nashua Photo Products Div., Nashua, NH; *U.S. Public*, pg. 1152
Jedlinski, Ronald T., Pres. & Chief Exec. Officer--Roman, Inc., Roselle, IL; *U.S. Private*, pg. 942
Jefferson, E. Jeff, Pres. & Chief Exec. Officer--Fresh Choice, Inc., Santa Clara, CA; *U.S. Public*, pg. 682
Jefferson, William H., Pres.--General Latex & Chemical Corporation, Cambridge, MA; *U.S. Private*, pg. 444
Jeffery, Kim, Pres. & Chief Exec. Officer--The Perrier Group of America, Greenwich, CT; *Int'l*, pg. 919
Jeffery, Kim, Pres. & Chief Exec. Officer--Great Bear Spring Company, Greenwich, CT; *Int'l*, pg. 919
Jeffery, Peter, Pres., Chief Exec. Officer & New Bus. Contact--Gee, Jeffery & Partners Advertising Inc., Toronto, Canada; *Int'l*, pg. 542
Jeffrey, Bob, Pres. & New Bus. Contact--Goldsmith/Jeffrey Inc., New York, NY; *U.S. Private*, pg. 462
Jeffrey, Kim, Pres.--Poland Spring Corporation, Greenwich, CT; *Int'l*, pg. 919
Jeffs, Thomas H. II, Pres. & Chief Oper. Officer--NBD Bank (Michigan), Troy, MI; *U.S. Public*, pg. 628
Jelenic, Robert M., Chm. Bd., Pres. & Chief Exec. Officer--Journal Register Company, Trenton, NJ; *U.S. Public*, pg. 934
Jemal, Lawrence, Pres.--Nobody Beats the Wiz, Carteret, NJ; *U.S. Private*, pg. 800
Jencks, David C., Pres.--Detroit Coil Company, Ferndale, MI; *U.S. Private*, pg. 328
Jendahl, Staffan, Pres.--Gyproc Balsta Plant, Balsta, Sweden; *Int'l*, pg. 1200
Jenkins, Benjamin P., III, Pres. & Chief Oper. Officer--First Union National Bank of Virginia, Roanoke, VA; *U.S. Public*, pg. 640
Jenkins, Christopher D., Pres.--Todd-AO Studios, Hollywood, CA; *U.S. Public*, pg. 1619
Jenkins, Christopher D., Pres.--Todd-AO Preservation Services, Hollywood, CA; *U.S. Public*, pg. 1619
Jenkins, D. Wayne, Pres.--Quik Print Inc., Wichita, KS; *U.S. Private*, pg. 421
Jenkins, David A., Chm. Bd. & Pres.--Arrhythmia Research Technology, Inc., Austin, TX; *U.S. Public*, pg. 133
Jenkins, Don, Jr., Pres. & Treas.--Athens Paper Co. Inc., Nashville, TN; *U.S. Private*, pg. 94
Jenkins, J. Michael, Pres. & Chief Exec. Officer--Vicorp Restaurants, Inc., Denver, CO; *U.S. Public*, pg. 1719
Jenkins, J.S.B., Pres. & Chief Exec. Officer--Tandy Brands Accessories, Inc., Arlington, TX; *U.S. Public*, pg. 1560
Jenkins, Joseph, M.D., Pres. & Chief Exec. Officer--Prime Medical Services, Inc., Austin, TX; *U.S. Public*, pg. 1327
Jenkins, P., Pres.--Thruway Fasteners Inc., North Tonawanda, NY; *U.S. Private*, pg. 1084
Jenkins, Robert H., Chm. Bd., Pres. & Chief Exec. Officer--Sundstrand Corporation, Rockford, IL; *U.S. Public*, pg. 1533
Jenkins, Robert M., Pres. & Chief Fin. Officer--Specialty Industries, Inc., Red Lion, PA; *U.S. Private*, pg. 1022
Jenkins, S. Clark, Pres.--Royster-Clark, Inc., Tarboro, NC; *U.S. Private*, pg. 949
Jenkins, Samuel P., Jr., Pres.--The Boeing Travel Company, Irvine, CA; *U.S. Public*, pg. 241
Jenkins, Stephen, Pres.--KLT Power Inc., Kansas City, MO; *U.S. Public*, pg. 943
Jenkinson, D.J., Pres.--Early Learning Centre, Swindon, United Kingdom; *Int'l*, pg. 707
Jennier, Walt, Pres.--Quality Toyota, Longwood, FL; *U.S. Private*, pg. 899
Jennings, A. Drue, Chm. Bd., Pres. & Chief Exec. Officer--Kansas City Power & Light Company, Kansas City, MO; *U.S. Public*, pg. 943
Jennings, David J., Pres.--Newbold's Asset Management Inc., Bryn Mawr, PA; *U.S. Public*, pg. 1673
Jennings, Eugene, Chm. Bd., Pres. & Chief Exec. Officer--Universal Standard Healthcare, Inc., Southfield, MI; *U.S. Public*, pg. 1697
Jennings, Glenn R., Pres. & Chief Exec. Officer--Delta Natural Gas Company, Inc., Winchester, KY; *U.S. Public*, *pg. 497*
Jenny, Charles W., Pres. & Chief Exec. Officer-N.A. Div.--Schneider Electric S.A., Boulogne-Billancourt, France; *Int'l*, pg. 1207
Jensen, A.C., Pres.--International Pipe Machinery Corp., Sioux City, IA; *U.S. Private*, pg. 571
Jensen, Alfred F., Pres.--Central Steel & Wire Company, Chicago, IL; *U.S. Public*, pg. 327
Jensen, Bjarne Skov, Pres.--Danisco Seed, Holeby, Denmark; *Int'l*, pg. 378
Jensen, Colin C., Pres.--Irving F. Jensen Co., Inc., Sioux City, IA; *U.S. Private*, pg. 586
Jensen, Hans-Jurgen, Pres.--Bayer A/S, Skytta, Norway; *Int'l*, pg. 174
Jensen, Jim, Pres.--Northland Furniture Co., LLC, Bend, OR; *U.S. Private*, pg. 77
Jensen, Robert K., Pres.--Fleischli Oil Company, Inc., Cheyenne, WY; *U.S. Private*, pg. 410
Jensen, Roy A., Pres.--Simrad Optronics A/S, Oslo, Norway; *Int'l*, pg. 770
Jensen, Steven R., Pres. & Chief Exec. Officer--Norbest, Inc., Midvale, UT; *U.S. Private*, pg. 801
Jensik, Charles, Pres.--Piezo Crystal Co., Carlisle, PA; *U.S. Private*, pg. 865
Jenson, Robert M., Pres.--Sysco Food Services of Seattle, Inc., Kent, WA; *U.S. Public*, pg. 1552
Jeon, Byung-Soo, Pres.--Bum-A Petroleum Co., Ltd., Seoul, Korea; *Int'l*, pg. 1292
Jeon, Yong Sang, Pres.--Kolon-Met Life Insurance Company Limited, Seoul, Korea; *U.S. Private*, pg. 738
Jepson, Mark, Pres. & Chief Exec. Officer--First National Bank, McCook, NE; *U.S. Public*, pg. 629
Jerge, Pat, Pres. Chief Exec. Officer--First Commerce Technologies, Lincoln, NE; *U.S. Public*, pg. 629
Jerney, Adam, Pres. & Chief Oper. Officer--ICN Pharmaceuticals, Inc., Costa Mesa, CA; *U.S. Public*, pg. 853
Jerome, Jerry K., Pres. & Chief Exec. Officer--Jerome Foods Inc., Barron, WI; *U.S. Private*, pg. 586
Jeska, Philip K., Pres.--Allsteel, Inc., Aurora, IL; *U.S. Public*, pg. 772
Jespersen, C.K., Pres.--Nova Gas International Ltd., Calgary, Canada; *Int'l*, pg. 971
Jespersen, Keith, Pres.--Russ Reid Company, Inc., Pasadena, CA; *U.S. Private*, pg. 952
Jesperson, Daryl, Pres.--RE/MAX International, Inc., Englewood, CO; *U.S. Private*, pg. 912
Jesse, W.C., Pres. & Chief Exec. Officer--Tangram Enterprise Solutions, Inc., Cary, NC; *U.S. Public*, pg. 1424
Jessen, Erhardt, Pres.--Graham, Milwaukee, WI; *Int'l*, pg. 377
Jester, John R., Pres. & Chief Exec. Officer--Muzak Limited Partnership, Seattle, WA; *U.S. Private*, pg. 222
Jester, L.T., III, Pres.--Plantation Pipe Line Co., Atlanta, GA; *U.S. Public*, pg. 348
Jett, Dan, Pres.--Hunter Marine Corporation, Alachua, FL; *U.S. Private*, pg. 549
Jett, Dennis D., Pres. & Chief Exec. Officer--Oklahoma National Bank of Duncan, Duncan, OK; *U.S. Public*, pg. 630
Jett, Donald W., Pres.--CDI Marine Company, Jacksonville, FL; *U.S. Public*, pg. 277
Jewel, Maxwell, Pres.--Fike Corporation, Blue Springs, MO; *U.S. Private*, pg. 404
Jewell, Everett G., Chm. Bd., Pres., Chief Exec. Officer & Treas.--Jewell Building Systems, Dallas, NC; *U.S. Private*, pg. 587
Jewell, John B., III, Pres.--The Parman Corporation, Nashville, TN; *U.S. Private*, pg. 840
Jewett, Steven R., Pres.--First American Co. of Alaska, Anchorage, AK; *U.S. Public*, pg. 625
Jezuit, L., Pres.--Robertshaw Controls Company, Richmond, VA; *Int'l*, pg. 1243
Jezuit, Leslie J., Pres. & Chief Oper. Officer--Quixote Corporation, Chicago, IL; *U.S. Public*, pg. 1353
Jii, Tsu, Pres.--TDK Electronics, New York, Port Washington, NY; *Int'l*, pg. 1336
Jilek, John P., Pres. & Chief Oper. Officer--Lawter International, Inc., Kenosha, WI; *U.S. Public*, pg. 980
Jilk, Lawrence T., Jr., Pres. & Chief Exec. Officer--National Penn Bancshares, Inc., Boyertown, PA; *U.S. Public*, pg. 1158
Jilot, Dennis L., Pres. & Chief Exec. Officer--Springborn Testing & Research, Inc., Enfield, CT; *U.S. Private*, pg. 1027
Jimenez, Joe, Pres.-Wesson/Peter Pan Foods Co.--Hunt-Wesson, Inc., Fullerton, CA; *U.S. Public*, pg. 428
Jiminez, Joe, Pres.--Wesson/Peter Pan Foods Co., Fullerton, CA; *U.S. Public*, pg. 428
Jinghall, Kent, Pres. & Chief Exec. Officer--Fermenta AB, Stockholm, Sweden; *Int'l*, pg. 480
Joa, Martha F., Pres.--Curt G. Joa, Inc., Sheboygan Falls, WI; *U.S. Private*, pg. 588
Joaansson, Gora K., Pres.--Kvaerner Ships Equipment AB, Goteborg, Sweden; *Int'l*, pg. 771
Joachim, Michael, Pres.--Pocahontas Foods, USA, Richmond, VA; *U.S. Public*, pg. 1278
Joannou, Carine, Pres.--G. Joannou Cycle Co. Inc., Northvale, NJ; *U.S. Private*, pg. 588
Jobe, Jan, Pres.--Principal International, Inc., Des Moines, IA; *U.S. Private*, pg. 886
Joblon, Kenneth, Pres.--Brittany Dyeing & Printing Corporation, New Bedford, MA; *U.S. Private*, pg. 170
Jochum, George T., Chm. Bd., Pres. & Chief Exec. Officer--Mid Atlantic Medical Services, Inc., Rockville, MD; *U.S. Public*, pg. 1109
Joffe, Seymour, Pres. & Chief Oper. Officer--Porta Systems Corp., Syosset, NY; *U.S. Public*, pg. 1317
Joffrin, Alain, Pres. & Dir. Gen.--Kodak Pathe S.A., Paris, France; *U.S. Public*, pg. 554
Joffrion, A.A., Pres.--Joffko International, Houston, TX; *U.S. Private*, pg. 589
Johanneson, Gerald B., Pres. & Chief Exec. Officer--Haworth, Inc., Holland, MI; *U.S. Private*, pg. 511
Johannessen, Keith N., Pres.--Capital Senior Living, Inc., Dallas, TX; *U.S. Public*, pg. 302
Johannesson, Nils-Erik, Pres.--Bengtssons Maskin AB, Arlov, Sweden; *Int'l*, pg. 678
Johannsen, Stephen D., Pres.--RMT, Inc., Madison, WI; *U.S. Public*, pg. 1728
Johannsen, Tony, Pres.--James Burn Intl., Poughkeepsie, NY; *U.S. Public*, pg. 1506
Johannsen, Tony, Pres.--James Burn International Limited, Esher, United Kingdom; *U.S. Public*, pg. 1507
Johannsson, Fridrik, Pres.--Vatryggingarfelagid Skandia HF, Reykjavik, Iceland; *Int'l*, pg. 1258
Johansen, Richard W., Pres. & Chief Exec. Officer--Hudson, RCI, Temecula, CA; *U.S. Private*, pg. 546
Johanson, Nancy, Pres. & Chief Exec. Officer--Johanson Manufacturing Corporation, Boonton, NJ; *U.S. Private*, pg. 589
Johansson, Bengt, Pres.--Stora Purchasing & Transport, Falun, Sweden; *Int'l*, pg. 1303
Johansson, Hans, Pres.--ASSA AB, Eskilstuna, Sweden; *Int'l*, pg. 17
Johansson, Hans, Pres.--ASSA Industrie AB, Eskilstuna, Sweden; *Int'l*, pg. 17
Johansson, Henry, Pres.--Kvaerner Ships Equipment Inc., New Orleans, LA; *Int'l*, pg. 770
Johansson, Kjell, Pres.--Astra Pharmaceutical Production AB, Sodertalje, Sweden; *Int'l*, pg. 93

Johansson, Kurt S., Pres.--Mark IV Automotive, Solvesborg, Sweden; *U.S. Public*, pg. 1045

Johansson, Nils-Erik, Pres.--J S Hemkopskedjan AB, Falun, Sweden; *Int'l*, pg. 708

Johansson, Ulf, Pres.--NCC Building, Linkoping, Sweden; *Int'l*, pg. 898

Johansson, Ulf, Pres. & Chief Exec. Officer--Spectra-Physics AB, Stockholm, Sweden; *Int'l*, pg. 1288

John, Edward F., Pres. & Chief Exec. Officer--Gudebrod, Inc., Pottstown, PA; *U.S. Private*, pg. 486

John, Francis D., Pres., Chief Exec. Officer & Chief Fin. Officer--Key Energy Group Inc., East Brunswick, NJ; *U.S.* Public, pg. 953

Johns, John D., Pres. & Chief Oper. Officer--Protective Life Corporation, Birmingham, AL; *U.S. Public*, pg. 1336

Johns, Richard G., Pres.--Wright Plastic Products, Inc., Sheridan, MI; *U.S. Public*, pg. 1061

Johnsen, Erik F., Pres.--International Shipholding Corporation, New Orleans, LA; *U.S. Public*, pg. 907

Johnsen, Walter C., Pres. & Chief Exec. Officer--Acme United Corporation, Fairfield, CT; *U.S. Public*, pg. 17

Johnsey, Walter F., Pres. & Chief Exec. Officer--Jasper Corp., Birmingham, AL; *U.S. Private*, pg. 583

Johnson, Al, Sr., Pres.--Dobson & Johnson, Inc., Nashville, TN; *U.S. Private*, pg. 337

Johnson, Allan R., Pres.--Farm Progress Publications, Carol Stream, IL; *U.S. Public*, pg. 513

Johnson, Allen, Pres.--Great West Casualty Company, South Sioux City, NE; *U.S. Public*, pg. 1218

Johnson, Art, Pres.--Lockheed Martin Air Traffic Management, Rockville, MD; *U.S. Public*, pg. 1008

Johnson, Berton, Pres.--Gay Johnson's Inc., Grand Junction, CO; *U.S. Private*, pg. 595

Johnson, Brad, Partner & Sr. V.P.--Media That Works, Cincinnati, OH; *U.S. Private*, pg. 727

Johnson, Bruce, Pres. & Chief Oper. Officer--Richardson Electronics, Ltd., Lafox, IL; *U.S. Public*, pg. 1387

Johnson, Carl, Pres. & Chief Exec. Officer--Simon & Associates, New Providence, NJ; *U.S. Private*, pg. 1001

Johnson, Carl A., Pres., Chief Exec. & Chief Oper. Officer--The Berlin Steel Construction Company, Berlin, CT; *U.S. Private*, pg. 136

Johnson, Carl P., Pres.--Diamond Energy Operating Co., Dallas, TX; *U.S. Public*, pg. 584

Johnson, Charles B., Pres. & Chief Exec. Officer--Franklin Resources, Inc., San Mateo, CA; *U.S. Public*, pg. 679

Johnson, Charles Brook, Chm. Bd., Pres. & Chief Exec. Officer--CS Brooks Canada Inc., Greenwich, CT; *U.S. Private*, pg. 197

Johnson, Charles S., Pres. & Chief Exec. Officer--Pioneer Hi-Bred International, Inc., Des Moines, IA; *U.S. Public*, pg. 1298

Johnson, Claude, Pres, Chief Exec. Officer & Chief Fin. Officer--Research, Incorporated, Eden Prairie, MN; *U.S. Public*, pg. 1382

Johnson, Clif A., Pres.--Hytek Finishes Co., Kent, WA; *U.S. Public*, pg. 594

Johnson, Craig T., Pres. & Chief Exec. Officer--Crabar Business Systems, Dayton, OH; *U.S. Private*, pg. 283

Johnson, D., Pres. & Chief Exec. Officer--Blandin Paper Company, Grand Rapids, MN; *Int'l*, pg. 495

Johnson, Dave, Pres.--Cenex/Land O'Lakes, Inc., Inver Grove Heights, MN; *U.S. Private*, pg. 222

Johnson, David, Pres.--Atlas Copco AFS Inc., Sterling Heights, MI; *Int'l*, pg. 96

Johnson, David, Chm. Bd., Pres. & Chief Exec. Officer--Swanson, Camden, NJ; *U.S. Public*, pg. 299

Johnson, David J., Chm. Bd., Pres. & Chief Exec. Officer--KinderCare Learning Centers, Inc., Portland, OR; *U.S. Public*, pg. 961

Johnson, David W., Pres. & Chief Exec. Officer--Campbell Sales Company, Camden, NJ; *U.S. Public*, pg. 299

Johnson, Dennis R., Pres. & Chief Exec. Officer--XATA Corporation, Burnsville, MN; *U.S. Public*, pg. 1783

Johnson, Dick, Pres. & Representative Dir.--Amway (Japan) Limited, Tokyo, Japan; *U.S. Private*, pg. 70

Johnson, Don, Pres.--Georgia Woodlands Railroad Co., Washington, GA; *U.S. Private*, pg. 171

Johnson, Donald R., Pres. & Chief Oper. Officer--Modine Manufacturing Company, Racine, WI; *U.S. Public*, pg. 1121

Johnson, Donald R., Pres.--Airfoil Technologies International LLC, Cincinnati, OH; *U.S. Public*, pg. 1569

Johnson, Douglas, Pres.--Precision Carbide Tool Company, Inc., Niles, IL; *U.S. Private*, pg. 879

Johnson, Dudley, Pres.--Young & Franklin, Inc., Liverpool, NY; *U.S. Private*, pg. 1196

Johnson, E. Marvin, Pres.--House of Raeford Farms, Inc., Raeford, NC; *U.S. Private*, pg. 542

Johnson, Edward C., III, Chm. Bd. & Chief Exec. Officer--Fidelity Investments (FMR Corp.), Boston, MA; *U.S. Private*, pg. 402

Johnson, Eldon, Pres. & Chief Exec. Officer--Dakota Electric Association, Farmington, MN; *U.S. Private*, pg. 308

Johnson, Gary, Mgr.-Bus.--EIS, Inc., Salt Lake City, UT; *U.S. Private*, pg. 368

Johnson, Gary S., Pres. & Chief Exec. Officer--Superior Oil Co. Inc., Indianapolis, IN; *U.S. Private*, pg. 1055

Johnson, George Dean, Jr., Pres.-Domestic Consumer Div.--Blockbuster Entertainment Group, Dallas, TX; *U.S. Private*, pg. 775

Johnson, Gilbert F., Pres.--California Microwave, Inc.-Government Grp., Sunnyvale, CA; *U.S. Public*, pg. 293

Johnson, Glendon E., Chm. Bd., Pres. & Chief Exec. Officer--John Alden Financial Corporation, Miami, FL; *U.S. Public*, pg. 39

Johnson, Gregory, Pres. & Chief Exec. Officer--Waccamaw Corporation, Myrtle Beach, SC; *U.S. Private*, pg. 1145

Johnson, J. Harold, Pres.--STS Services Inc., Nashville, TN; *U.S. Public*, pg. 277

Johnson, J.A., Pres.--Treadwell Corporation, Thomaston, CT; *U.S. Private*, pg. 1098

Johnson, J.C.H., Pres. & Chief Exec. Officer--American International Co. Ltd., Pembroke, Bermuda; *U.S. Public*, pg. 85

Johnson, Jack, Mng. Partner-IT--TN Services Inc., Omaha, NE; *U.S. Public*, pg. 1642

Johnson, James, Pres.--Micron Separations, Inc., Westborough, MA; *U.S. Private*, pg. 742

Johnson, James Gibb, Dr., Pres.--State Volunteer Mutual Insurance Co., Brentwood, TN; *U.S. Private*, pg. 1037

Johnson, James M., Pres.--G.E. Johnson Construction Co., Inc., Colorado Springs, CO; *U.S. Private*, pg. 591

Johnson, James T., Pres.--General Electric Capital Aviation Services, San Francisco, CA; *U.S. Public*, pg. 712

Johnson, Jim, Pres. & Chief Oper. Officer--The Apogee Companies, Inc., Lake Oswego, OR; *U.S. Private*, pg. 77

Johnson, Jim, Pres. & Gen. Mgr.--KFXX/KGON, Inc., Portland, OR; *U.S. Private*, pg. 378

Johnson, Jim, Pres.--Lusk, Irvine, CA; *U.S. Private*, pg. 681

Johnson, Jim, Pres. & Chief Exec. Officer--Anspach Grossman Enterprise, New York, NY; *Int'l*, pg. 1483

Johnson, John, Pres.--Cooper Smith, Inc., Mobile, AL; *U.S. Public*, pg. 547

Johnson, John, Pres.--David Weekley Homes, Houston, TX; *U.S. Private*, pg. 1158

Johnson, John B., Pres., Treas. & Editor--Johnson Newspaper Corporation, Watertown, NY; *U.S. Private*, pg. 591

Johnson, John D., Pres. & Chief Exec. Officer--Harvest States Cooperatives, Saint Paul, MN; *U.S. Private*, pg. 508

Johnson, John K., Pres.--Seoul-Heinz Ltd., Inchon, Korea; *U.S. Public*, pg. 807

Johnson, Jon L., Pres. & Gen. Mgr.--Industrial Construction, Inc., Idaho Falls, ID; *U.S. Private*, pg. 560

Johnson, Joseph, Pres. & Gen. Mgr.--CPC/AJI (Taiwan) Ltd., Taipei, Taiwan; *U.S. Public*, pg. 225

Johnson, Kevin, Pres. & Chief Exec. Officer--Dianon Systems, Inc., Stratford, CT; *U.S. Public*, pg. 506

Johnson, Larry, Plant Mgr.--Air Control Products, Roxboro, NC; *U.S. Public*, pg. 556

Johnson, Lawrence, Chm. Bd., Pres., Chief Exec. Officer & Gen. Counsel--Kelley Company, Inc., Milwaukee, WI; *U.S. Private*, pg. 612

Johnson, Lawrence, Chm. Bd., Pres., Chief Exec. Officer & Gen Counsel--Kelley Dock Systems, Milwaukee, WI; *U.S.* Private, pg. 612

Johnson, Linda E., Pres. & Chief Exec. Officer--JCI Data Processing, Inc., Cinnaminson, NJ; *U.S. Private*, pg. 577

Johnson, Lloyd, Pres.--Roberts & Schaefer Co., Chicago, IL; *U.S. Private*, pg. 371

Johnson, Lloyd, Pres.--Thompson-Starrett Construction Company, Inc., Chicago, IL; *U.S. Private*, pg. 371

Johnson, Mark, Pres.--Comdisco Integrated Services, Minnetonka, MN; *U.S. Public*, pg. 408

Johnson, Mark, Chm. Bd., Pres. & Chief Exec. Officer--ITEQ, Inc., Houston, TX; *U.S. Public*, pg. 914

Johnson, Mark K., Pres.--Security Van Lines, Kenner, LA; *U.S. Private*, pg. 594

Johnson, Mark K., Pres.--Denver Moving & Storage Co., Denver, CO; *U.S. Private*, pg. 594

Johnson, Mark O., Pres.--Rice Lake Weighing Systems, Rice Lake, WI; *U.S. Private*, pg. 927

Johnson, Marvin L., Pres.--Associated Power, Inc., Wilmington, CA; *U.S. Private*, pg. 92

Johnson, Maury, Pres.--Precision Products Corporation, Rockford, IL; *U.S. Private*, pg. 879

Johnson, Michael A., Pres.--Continental Machines, Inc., Savage, MN; *U.S. Private*, pg. 268

Johnson, Norman E., Pres. & Chief Oper. Officer--CLARCOR, Inc., Rockford, IL; *U.S. Public*, pg. 381

Johnson, O.B., III, Pres.--White Star Steel, Houston, TX; *U.S. Private*, pg. 775

Johnson, Okey B., Jr., Chm. Bd. & Pres.--Nashville Steel Corp., Nashville, TN; *U.S. Private*, pg. 775

Johnson, Pamela, Pres.-Pub. Rels. Div.--Serino Coyne Public Relations, New York, NY; *U.S. Private*, pg. 985

Johnson, Patrick L., Pres. & Chief Oper. Officer--ServiCenter USA, Deerfield Beach, FL; *U.S. Public*, pg. 1201

Johnson, Paul E., Jr., Pres.-Marriott Senior Living--Marriott International, Inc., Washington, DC; *U.S. Public*, pg. 1047

Johnson, Peter, Pres. & Chief Exec. Officer--Agouron Pharmaceuticals, Inc., La Jolla, CA; *U.S. Public*, pg. 28

Johnson, Phil, Pres.--Colle & McVoy, Inc., Minneapolis, MN; *U.S. Private*, pg. 252

Johnson, Phil, Pres.--Colle & McVoy Marketing Communications, Minneapolis, MN; *U.S. Private*, pg. 252

Johnson, R. Larry, Pres.--Oxford Slacks Division, New York, NY; *U.S. Public*, pg. 1239

Johnson, R.K. Peter, Pres. & Chief Exec. Officer--Faribault Woolen Mill Co., Faribault, MN; *U.S. Private*, pg. 394

Johnson, Ralph, Chm. Bd. & Pres.--Lake County Press, Waukegan, IL; *U.S. Private*, pg. 643

Johnson, Ralph W., Pres.--Turner International Industries, Inc., New York, NY; *U.S. Public*, pg. 1646

Johnson, Randy D., Pres.--E Z Loader Corporate, Airway Heights, WA; *U.S. Private*, pg. 352

Johnson, Richard, Pres.--Banta Merchandising Products, Milwaukee, WI; *U.S. Public*, pg. 188

Johnson, Richard E., Pres. & Chief Exec. Officer--The Stratevest Group, N.A., Burlington, VT; *U.S. Public*, pg. 187

Johnson, Robert J., Pres.--BET West Coast Media/Affiliate Sales & BET Action Pay Per View, Santa Monica, CA; *U.S. Public*, pg. 235

Johnson, Robert L., Pres.--BET Cable Network Operations, Washington, DC; *U.S. Public*, pg. 235

Johnson, Robert L., Pres.--BET West Coast Operations, Burbank, CA; *U.S. Public*, pg. 235

Johnson, Robert L., Pres.--BET New York Media Sales, New York, NY; *U.S. Public*, pg. 235

Johnson, Robert L., Pres.--BET Midwest Media/Affiliate Sales, Chicago, IL; *U.S. Public*, pg. 235

Johnson, Robert L., Pres.--BET Media Sales, Southfield, MI; *U.S. Public*, pg. 235

Johnson, Roger, Pres.--Pyramid Mountain Lumber, Seeley Lake, MT; *U.S. Private*, pg. 896

Johnson, Ronald, Pres. & Chief Oper. Officer--Hoogovens Aluminium Corp., Secaucus, NJ; *Int'l*, pg. 755

Johnson, Sandy, Mng. Dir.--Black & Edgington Ltd., London, United Kingdom; *Int'l*, pg. 197

Johnson, Shelba D., Pres.--Shelba D. Johnson Trucking, Thomasville, NC; *U.S. Private*, pg. 594

Johnson, Stephen C., Pres. & Chief Exec. Officer--Komag, Incorporated, San Jose, CA; *U.S. Public*, pg. 966

Johnson, Steve, Chief Exec. Officer & Pres.--Komag Incorporated, Milpitas, CA; *Int'l*, pg. 84

Johnson, Terry, Pres.--Cotton Electric Co-Op, Walters, OK; *U.S. Private*, pg. 278

Johnson, Terry L., Pres.--Holt Hosiery Mills, Inc., Burlington, NC; *U.S. Private*, pg. 536

Johnson, Thomas, Pres. & Chief Exec. Officer--Chesapeake Corporation, Richmond, VA; *U.S. Public*, pg. 346

Johnson, Thomas E., Pres.--Tom Johnson Investment Management, Inc., Oklahoma City, OK; *U.S. Public*, pg. 1673

Johnson, Thomas L., Co-Chm. Bd., Pres. & Chief Exec. Officer--Objective Systems Integrators, Inc., Folsom, CA; *U.S. Public*, pg. 1209

Johnson, Van, Pres. & Chief Exec. Officer--First Citizens Bank of Hohenwald, Hohenwald, TN; *U.S. Public*, pg. 1669

Johnson, Van R., Pres. & Chief Exec. Officer--Sutter Health, Sacramento, CA; *U.S. Private*, pg. 1057

Johnson, Virland, Pres.--Unitech Industries, Inc., Tempe, AZ; *U.S. Public*, pg. 1672

Johnson, Virland, Pres. & Chief Exec. Officer--Solidex, Scottsdale, AZ; *U.S. Public*, pg. 1672

Johnson, W. Thomas Jr., Pres.--CNN (Cable News Network), Atlanta, GA; *U.S. Public*, pg. 1614

Johnson, Walter D., Pres. & Chief Exec. Officer--Johnson Bros. Corporation, Litchfield, MN; *U.S. Private*, pg. 590

Johnson, Walter F., III, Pres.--Johnson & Towers, Inc., Mount Laurel, NJ; *U.S. Private*, pg. 590

Johnson, Wesley, Jr., Pres.--Blue Boar Cafeteria Co., Louisville, KY; *U.S. Private*, pg. 151

Johnson, William L., Pres. & Chief Exec. Officer--Southeastern Michigan Gas Enterprises, Inc., Port Huron, MI; *U.S. Public*, pg. 1489

Johnson, William R., Pres. & Chief Exec. Officer--H.J. Heinz Company, Pittsburgh, PA; *U.S. Public*, pg. 805

Johnston, Chap, Pres. & Chief Exec. Officer--Tanner Co., Rutherfordton, NC; *U.S. Private*, pg. 1068

Johnston, Charles, Pres.--Philip Laser Magnetic Storage, Colorado Springs, CO; *Int'l*, pg. 1054

Johnston, Dare P., Pres.--TII-Ditel, Hickory, NC; *U.S. Public*, *pg. 1556*

Johnston, David, Pres.--Highland Valley Copper, Logan Lake, Canada; *Int'l*, pg. 308

Johnston, Dennis N., Pres.--Norwest Financial Business Credit, Inc., Des Moines, IA; *U.S. Public*, pg. 1202

Johnston, Dixon R., Pres.--Consumer Products Div., Valdese, NC; *U.S. Public*, pg. 36

Johnston, Duane, Gen. Mgr.--Rugby Farmers Union Elevator Company, Rugby, ND; *U.S. Private*, pg. 950

Johnston, Eric, Pres.--Retirement Community Specialists, Inc., Phoenix, AZ; *U.S. Private*, pg. 925

Johnston, Gary E., Pres.--Wilhold Inc., Cleveland, OH; *U.S. Public*, pg. 78

Johnston, Gayle, Pres.--Thin Film Technology Division, Rochester, NY; *U.S. Public*, pg. 194

Johnston, John C., Pres. & Chief Oper. Officer--Farr Company, El Segundo, CA; *U.S. Public*, pg. 613

Johnston, Paul, Pres. & Gen. Mgr--Agri-Mark, Inc., Lawrence, MA; *U.S. Private*, pg. 26

Johnston, Robert, Pres.--Hauenstein & Burmeister, Inc., Minneapolis, MN; *U.S. Private*, pg. 510

Johnston, Skeeter, Pres.-East Grp.--The Coca-Cola Bottling Co. of New York, Inc., Hawthorne, NY; *U.S. Public*, pg. 393

Johnston, Thomas G., Pres. & Chief Oper. Officer--Alumax Inc., Atlanta, GA; *U.S. Public*, pg. 59

Johnston, William, Pres.--Morton Salt, Chicago, IL; *U.S. Public*, pg. 1135

Johnston, William E., Jr., Pres. & Chief Oper. Officer--Morton International Inc., Chicago, IL; *U.S. Public*, pg. 1134

Johnstone, Michael B., Pres. & Chief Exec. Officer--TCF Bank Illinois, Oak Brook, IL; *U.S. Public*, pg. 1554

Joiner, Eric J., Pres.--AJC International, Inc., Atlanta, GA; *U.S. Private*, pg. 6

Jokiel, Peter E., Pres.--CNA Financial Corp., Chicago, IL; *U.S. Public*, pg. 1010

Joll, D.J., Mng. Dir.--Bernard Matthews PLC, Norwich, United Kingdom; *Int'l*, pg. 189

Jolosky, Richard, Pres.--Payless ShoeSource, Inc., Topeka, KS; *U.S. Public*, pg. 1268

Jonas, Hilton, Pres. & Chief Exec. Officer--A.P. Wyott, Dallas, TX; *U.S. Private*, pg. 1193

Jones, Barry, Pres.-DMB&B Asia/Pacific North--DMB&B/ Hong Kong, Quarry Bay, Hong Kong; *U.S. Private*, pg. 303

Jones, Barry, Pres.-DmB&B Asisa/Pacific Nroth--DMB&B/ Hong Kong, Quarry Bay, Hong Kong; *U.S. Private*, pg. 303

Jones, Boisfeuillet, Pres.--The Washington Post, Washington, DC; *U.S. Public*, pg. 1743

Jones, Brian R., Pres.--AirTouch Cellular, Walnut Creek, CA; *U.S. Public*, pg. 34

Jones, Carl E., Jr., Pres. & Chief Oper. Officer--Regions Financial Corporation, Birmingham, AL; *U.S. Public*, pg. 1371

Jones, Chester, Pres. & Chief Exec. Officer--Hunter Corp., Portage, IN; *U.S. Private*, pg. 549

Jones, D.H., Pres.--Morganite Inc., Dunn, NC; *Int'l*, pg. 893

Jones, Dan, Pres.--Hayssen, Duncan, SC; *U.S. Private*, pg. 118

Jones, Dan F., Pres.--Automatic Castings Division, Green Forest, AR; *U.S. Public*, pg. 986
Jones, David A., Chm. Bd., Pres. & Chief Exec. Officer--RAYOVAC Corporation, Madison, WI; *U.S. Private*, pg. 912
Jones, David D., Pres.--Mercury Marine, Fond Du Lac, WI; *U.S. Public*, pg. 265
Jones, David R., Pres. & Chief Exec. Officer--AGL Resources, Atlanta, GA; *U.S. Public*, pg. 6
Jones, Dennis M., Chm., Pres. & Chief Exec. Officer--Jones Medical Industries Inc., Saint Louis, MO; *U.S. Public*, pg. 933
Jones, Don, Pres.--Luhrs Corporation, Saint Augustine, FL; *U.S. Private*, pg. 680
Jones, Don, Pres.--Mainship Corporation, Saint Augustine, FL; *U.S. Private*, pg. 697
Jones, Don, Pres.--Silverton Marine Corporation, Millville, NJ; *U.S. Private*, pg. 1000
Jones, Dudle, Pres.--Walla Walla Grain Growers, Inc., Walla Walla, WA; *U.S. Private*, pg. 1148
Jones, Edward C., Pres. & Chief Oper. Officer--Jones Dairy Farm, Fort Atkinson, WI; *U.S. Private*, pg. 596
Jones, F. Clark, Pres.--First Commercial Bank, Huntsville, AL; *U.S. Public*, pg. 1549
Jones, Fletcher, Jr., Pres. & Chief Exec. Officer--Fletcher Jones Management Group, Las Vegas, NV; *U.S. Private*, pg. 597
Jones, George, Pres.--Warner Bros. Consumer Products, Burbank, CA; *U.S. Public*, pg. 1610
Jones, Glenn, Pres.--GREFCO, Inc., Torrance, CA; *U.S. Private*, pg. 903
Jones, Glenn R., Chm. Bd., Pres. & Chief Exec. Officer--Jones International, Ltd., Englewood, CO; *U.S. Private*, pg. 597
Jones, Gordon, Pres. & Chief Exec. Officer--Arcade Inc., Chattanooga, TN; *U.S. Private*, pg. 79
Jones, Harrison P., Pres.--Vincent Metals Division, Minneapolis, MN; *Int'l*, pg. 1118
Jones, J. Kevin, Pres.--Rev-A-Shelf, Louisville, KY; *U.S. Private*, pg. 925
Jones, James C., Pres.--Airco Mechanical Inc., Sacramento, CA; *U.S. Private*, pg. 29
Jones, James L., Jr., Pres.--Jones & Jones, Inc., McAllen, TX; *U.S. Private*, pg. 596
Jones, James M., Jr., Chm., Pres. & Chief Exec. Officer--Peoples & Union Bank, Lewisburg, TN; *U.S. Public*, pg. 639
Jones, James R., Pres. & Chief Oper. Officer--Dodson Group, Kansas City, MO; *U.S. Private*, pg. 338
Jones, James R., Pres.--Warnaco Inc.-International Div., New York, NY; *U.S. Public*, pg. 1738
Jones, Jeffrey, Pres.--Jones Chemicals, Inc., Le Roy, NY; *U.S. Private*, pg. 596
Jones, John W., Pres. & Chief Exec. Officer--Modern Welding Co., Inc., Owensboro, KY; *U.S. Private*, pg. 755
Jones, Joseph L., III, Pres.--Stanley Tools Div., New Britain, CT; *U.S. Public*, pg. 1509
Jones, L. Hollis, Pres. & Chief Oper. Officer--The Morning Star Group, Dallas, TX; *U.S. Public*, pg. 1527
Jones, Lincoln, III, Pres.--Enron Operations Corp., Houston, TX; *U.S. Public*, pg. 584
Jones, Lloyd T., Pres. & Chief Exec. Officer--The Bank of North Arkansas, Melbourne, AR; *U.S. Public*, pg. 641
Jones, Lloyd W., Pres.--International Container Systems, Tampa, FL; *Int'l*, pg. 685
Jones, M. David, Pres.--Fleetguard Inc., Nashville, TN; *U.S. Public*, pg. 468
Jones, M. David, Pres.--Fleetguard Inc., Lake Mills, IA; *U.S. Public*, pg. 468
Jones, Martin, Pres.--Domecq Importers Inc., Old Greenwich, CT; *Int'l*, pg. 63
Jones, Millard H., Pres.--HMT Inc., Houston, TX; *U.S. Public*, pg. 914
Jones, Paul, Pres. & Chief Exec. Officer--Rule Industries, Inc., Gloucester, MA; *U.S. Public*, pg. 950
Jones, Pete, Pres.-BMG Distr.--Bertelsmann Music Group, Wilmington, DE; *Int'l*, pg. 191
Jones, R.N., Mng. Dir.--Cussons (U.K.) LTD., Cheadle, United Kingdom; *Int'l*, pg. 1024
Jones, Randy B., Jr., Pres.--Sumter Bank and Trust Company, Americus, GA; *U.S. Public*, pg. 1549
Jones, Rex, Pres.--Schilling Companies, Inc., Germantown, TN; *U.S. Private*, pg. 970
Jones, Richard D., Pres. & Chief Oper. Officer--Centex Construction Products, Inc., Dallas, TX; *U.S. Public*, pg. 322
Jones, Richard H., Pres.--Coventry Health & Life Insurance, Fort Worth, TX; *U.S. Public*, pg. 454
Jones, Richard H., Pres. & Chief Exec. Officer--Group Health Plan, Inc., Saint Louis, MO; *U.S. Public*, pg. 454
Jones, Robert, Pres. & Chief Oper. Officer--Entex, Houston, TX; *U.S. Public*, pg. 843
Jones, Robert L., Pres. & Chief Exec. Officer--First National Bank of Magnolia, Magnolia, AR; *U.S. Public*, pg. 641
Jones, Robert L., Pres. & Chief Exec. Officer--Southeast Power Corporation, Titusville, FL; *U.S. Public*, pg. 750
Jones, Roger, Pres.--Magic Valley Foods, Inc., Rupert, ID; *U.S. Private*, pg. 695
Jones, Ronald, Pres. & Chief Exec. Officer--Sealy Corporation, Cleveland, OH; *U.S. Private*, pg. 978
Jones, Ronald, Pres. & Chief Exec. Officer--Royal Doulton USA Inc., Somerset, NJ; *Int'l*, pg. 1135
Jones, Ronald L., Chm. Bd., Pres. & Chief Exec. Officer--Dawn Food Products, Inc., Jackson, MI; *U.S. Private*, pg. 316
Jones, Stanley, Pres., Chief Exec. Officer & Gen. Mgr.--Buhrman-Pharr Hardware Company, Texarkana, AR; *U.S. Private*, pg. 179
Jones, Steve, Pres.--Princor Management Corporation, Des Moines, IA; *U.S. Private*, pg. 886
Jones, Steve, Pres.--Princor Financial Services Corporation, Des Moines, IA; *U.S. Private*, pg. 886
Jones, Sydney T., III, Pres. & Treas.--Hudson Valley Paper Company, Albany, NY; *U.S. Private*, pg. 546
Jones, W.C., Pres.--Eastman Gelatine Corp., Peabody, MA; *U.S. Public*, pg. 551
Jones, Wallace A., Pres. & Chief Exec. Officer--El Chico Restaurants, Inc., Dallas, TX; *U.S. Private*, pg. 283
Jones, Warren, Pres.--NSO Co., Oil City, PA; *Int'l*, pg. 1110
Jones, Wilbur S., Jr., Pres. & Chief Exec. Officer--Stone & Thomas, Wheeling, WV; *U.S. Private*, pg. 1044
Jones, Will, Pres.--Lau Div., Dayton, OH; *Int'l*, pg. 1398
Jones, William F., Pres.--Coppus Murray Group, Tuthill Corporation, Millbury, MA; *U.S. Private*, pg. 1110
Jones, William W., Jr., Pres. & Chief Exec. Officer--Baltimore Stationery Co./Total Office, Baltimore, MD; *U.S. Private*, pg. 113
Jongebloed, James T., Chm. Bd., Pres. & Chief Exec. Officer--Pool Energy Services Co., Houston, TX; *U.S. Public*, pg. 1316
Jongeling, George B., Pres.--Pace Power Constructors, Inc., Worcester, MA; *Int'l*, pg. 401
Jongstra, Robert, Pres.-Health & Beauty Div.--Procter & Gamble France, Neuilly-sur-Seine, France; *U.S. Public*, pg. 1332
Jonson, Jim, Pres. & Chief Oper. Officer--Gulfstream Aerospace Corporation, Savannah, GA; *U.S. Private*, pg. 419
Jonsson, Bo, Pres.--Uddeholm Kraft AB, Karlstad, Sweden; *Int'l*, pg. 1471
Jonsson, Kent, Pres.--Skanska Fastigheter Goteborg AB, Goteborg, Sweden; *Int'l*, pg. 1260
Jonsson, Peter, Pres.--Stabilator AB, Danderyd, Sweden; *Int'l*, pg. 1261
Jordal, Anders, Pres.--Kvaerner Fjellstrand A/S, Omastrand, Norway; *Int'l*, pg. 768
Jordan, Andrew, Pres.--Club Med Sales, Inc., New York, NY; *Int'l*, pg. 298
Jordan, Ennis, Pres.--CSR West, Las Vegas, NV; *Int'l*, pg. 245
Jordan, J. Gary, Pres.--Cordis, a Johnson & Johnson Company, Miami, FL; *U.S. Public*, pg. 928
Jordan, J. Gary, Pres.--Cordis, a Johnson & Johnson Company, Warren, NJ; *U.S. Public*, pg. 928
Jordan, J. Luther, Jr., Chm. Bd.--Baton Rouge Water Works Company, Baton Rouge, LA; *U.S. Private*, pg. 122
Jordan, James R., Pres.--Merchant & Planters Bank N.A. of Camden, Camden, AR; *U.S. Public*, pg. 641
Jordan, John W., II, Mng. Partner--The Jordan Company, New York, NY; *U.S. Private*, pg. 597
Jordan, Ken, Pres.--Robert Skeels & Co., Compton, CA; *U.S. Public*, pg. 1782
Jordan, Mary B., Pres.--Candian Regional Airlines, Etobicoke, Canada; *Int'l*, pg. 256
Jordan, Michael L., Pres. & Chief Exec. Officer--SI/Baker, Inc., Easton, PA; *U.S. Public*, pg. 1418
Jordan, William M., Pres. & Chief Oper. Officer--Flowserve Corporation, Dayton, OH; *U.S. Public*, pg. 658
Jordan, William M., Pres. & Chief Oper. Officer--Flowserve Corporation, Long Beach, CA; *U.S. Public*, pg. 658
Jorden, Edwin W., Pres. & Chief Exec. Officer--Barclay White Incorporated, Berwyn, PA; *U.S. Private*, pg. 115
Jordon, Fred, Publr.--Pantheon Books, Inc., New York, NY; *U.S. Private*, pg. 21
Jordon, Melton, Jr., Pres.--Rural Electric Co-op, Lindsay, OK; *U.S. Private*, pg. 952
Jordon, Roger, Pres.--Eon Labs, Jamaica, NY; *U.S. Private*, pg. 379
Jorgenson, Don, Pres. & Chief Exec. Officer--Hypro Corporation, New Brighton, MN; *U.S. Public*, pg. 1767
Jorndt, L. Daniel, Pres. & Chief Oper. Officer--Walgreen Co., Deerfield, IL; *U.S. Public*, pg. 1733
Jose, David, Pres.--Autoswage Products, Inc., Shelton, CT; *U.S. Private*, pg. 101
Joselow, Linda, Exec. Principal & Grp. Mngmt. Supvr.--Publicis/Bloom, New York, NY; *Int'l*, pg. 470
Joseph, Alex A., Acting Pres.--Qualitrol Corp., Fairport, NY; *U.S. Public*, pg. 482
Joseph, Alex A., Pres.--Namco Controls Corporation, Highland Heights, OH; *U.S. Public*, pg. 482
Joseph, Daniel S., Pres.--Donnelly Optics Corporation, Tucson, AZ; *U.S. Public*, pg. 519
Joseph, Gary, Pres.--Heraeus Precious Metals Management Inc., New York, NY; *Int'l*, pg. 616
Joseph, Gerald, Pres.--Gerber International Inc., New York, NY; *U.S. Private*, pg. 448
Joseph, James, Pres.--Bandini Fertilizer Company, Los Angeles, CA; *U.S. Private*, pg. 113
Joseph, Jeffrey F., Pres.--Presidential Realty Corporation, White Plains, NY; *U.S. Public*, pg. 1323
Joseph, Jeffrey F., Pres.--Presidential Continental Gardens Corp., White Plains, NY; *U.S. Public*, pg. 1323
Joseph, Jeffrey F., Pres.--Presidential Realty of Iowa, Inc., White Plains, NY; *U.S. Public*, pg. 1324
Joseph, John, Pres.-USA--Ketchum Directory Advertising/Chicago, Chicago, IL; *U.S. Private*, pg. 616
Joseph, John B., Chm. Bd., Pres. & Chief Exec. Officer--West Coast Bancorp, Newport Beach, CA; *U.S. Public*, pg. 1755
Joseph, Marcel P., Pres. & Chief Oper. Officer--Augat, Inc., Mansfield, MA; *U.S. Public*, pg. 1597
Josephson, John E., Pres. & Chief Exec. Officer--Big Bear Stores Company, Columbus, OH; *U.S. Public*, pg. 1270
Joshi, Krishan K., Pres. & Chief Exec. Officer--UES, Inc., Dayton, OH; *U.S. Private*, pg. 1112
Joslin, Donald E., Pres. & Chief Exec. Officer--Monitor Life Insurance Company of New York, Utica, NY; *U.S. Private*, pg. 258
Joubert, Charles, Pres.--Newpark Environmental Services, Inc., Lafayette, LA; *U.S. Public*, pg. 1179
Jovanovich, Peter, Pres.--Educational & Professional Publishing Group, New York, NY; *U.S. Public*, pg. 1070
Joy, Frank R., Jr., Pres. & Chief Exec. Officer--The Bradford National Bank of Greenville, Greenville, IL; *U.S. Private*, pg. 164
Joyce, Burton M., Pres. & Chief Exec. Officer--Terra Industries, Inc., Sioux City, IA; *U.S. Public*, pg. 1581
Joyce, James R., Pres. & Chief Exec., Fin. & Acctg. Officer--Magellan Petroleum Corporation, Madison, CT; *U.S. Public*, pg. 1036
Joyce, K.R., Pres. & Chief Exec. Officer--Texas-New Mexico Power Co., Fort Worth, TX; *U.S. Public*, pg. 1557
Joyce, Kevern R., Chm. Bd., Pres., Chief Exec. Officer & Dir.--TNP Enterprises, Inc., Fort Worth, TX; *U.S. Public*, pg. 1557
Joyce, Michael H., Pres. & Chief Oper. Officer--Twin Disc, Incorporated, Racine, WI; *U.S. Public*, pg. 1646
Joyce, Richard F., Pres.--Dixon Ticonderoga Company, Heathrow, FL; *U.S. Public*, pg. 514
Joyce, Thomas P., Jr., Pres.--Delta Consolidated Industries, Inc., Raleigh, NC; *U.S. Public*, pg. 481
Joyce, William H., Chm. Bd., Pres. & Chief Exec. Officer--Union Carbide Corporation, Danbury, CT; *U.S. Public*, pg. 1666
Joyner, F. Belton, III, Pres.--Williamsburg Foods, Inc., Toano, VA; *U.S. Public*, pg. 1479
Jozoff, Malcolm, Chm., Pres. & Chief Exec. Officer--The Dial Corporation, Phoenix, AZ; *U.S. Public*, pg. 505
Jreidini, Ramzi T., Pres.--Ikon Office Solutions, Orlando, FL; *U.S. Public*, pg. 863
Juanarena, Douglas B., Pres. & Chief Exec. Officer--Pressure Systems, Inc., Hampton, VA; *Int'l*, pg. 1130
Juanet, J.A., Pres.--Esso Standard Oil S.A. Limited, Nassau, Bahamas; *U.S. Public*, pg. 602
Jubelirer, Mark B., Pres.--John Reyer Company, Sharon, PA; *U.S. Private*, pg. 926
Judge, Fred, Pres. & Chief Exec. Officer--Titan Information Systems, San Diego, CA; *U.S. Public*, pg. 1618
Juelich, Richard J., Pres.--AmClyde Engineered Products Co., Inc., Saint Paul, MN; *U.S. Public*, pg. 778
Juett, J. Lee, Chm. Bd., Pres. & Chief Exec. Officer--J. Lee Hackett Co., Farmington, MI; *U.S. Private*, pg. 492
Juhn, Jun-Yong, Pres.--Shinryu Cement Corp., Osaka, Japan; *Int'l*, pg. 1291
Juhos, Les, Pres.--Capitol Metals Company, Torrance, CA; *U.S. Private*, pg. 206
Juilfs, George, Pres. & Chief Exec. Officer--SENCORP, Newport, KY; *U.S. Private*, pg. 983
Julian, Paul, Pres. & Chief Oper. Officer--General Medical Corp., Richmond, VA; *U.S. Public*, pg. 1073
Juliano, Mark, Pres. & Chief Oper. Officer--Boardwalk Regency Corporation, Atlantic City, NJ; *U.S. Public*, pg. 1512
Julius, George P., Jr., Pres. & Chief Oper. Officer--Beverage America, Inc., Holland, MI; *U.S. Private*, pg. 141
Julius, Robert P., Chm. Bd., Pres. & Chief Exec. Officer--Nice-Pak Products, Inc., Orangeburg, NY; *U.S. Private*, pg. 798
Jumbe, F.A., Chm. Bd. & Pres.--National Bank of Malawi, Blantyre, Malawi; *Int'l*, pg. 1296
Jumonville, Dan, Chm. Bd. & Pres.--Group Insurance Inc. of Louisiana, Baton Rouge, LA; *U.S. Private*, pg. 484
Junck, Roland, Pres.--TrefilARBED Bissen S.a.r.l, Bissen, Luxembourg; *Int'l*, pg. 80
Juneau, Paul, Pres.--Acces Capital, Montreal, Canada; *Int'l*, pg. 249
Juneau, Paul, Pres.--Acces Capital Quebec, Montreal, Canada; *Int'l*, pg. 249
Jung, Jerrold M., Pres.--Michigan Cat, Novi, MI; *U.S. Private*, pg. 740
Jung, Patrick, Pres.--Huber & Suhner AG, Pfaffikon, Switzerland; *Int'l*, pg. 637
Jung, S.N., Pres.--Han Ryuk Electronics Co., LTD., Seoul, Korea; *Int'l*, pg. 628
Jung, Seon-Ki, Pres.--Ssangyong Paper Co., Ltd., Seoul, Korea; *Int'l*, pg. 1292
Jungers, Blaine C., Pres.--WWW Retail, Inc., Rockford, MI; *U.S. Public*, pg. 1775
Junkin, J.S., Pres.--California Products Corp., Cambridge, MA; *U.S. Private*, pg. 201
Jurado Baena, D. Jose Luis, Pres.--Asociacion Telefonica Para Asistencia A Minusvalidos (A.T.A.M.), Madrid, Spain; *Int'l*, pg. 1371
Jurgensen, James P., Pres.--Valley Asphalt Corporation, Cincinnati, OH; *U.S. Private*, pg. 1131
Jurick, Geoffrey, Chm. Bd & Pres.--Emerson Radio Corp., Parsippany, NJ; *U.S. Public*, pg. 578
Jusseaume, Rich, Chm. Bd., Pres. & Chief Exec. Officer--Graphic Enterprises of Ohio, Inc., Canton, OH; *U.S. Private*, pg. 471
Justice, R. D., Pres.--United Producers & Consumers Co-Op, Phoenix, AZ; *U.S. Private*, pg. 1123
Justiss, James F., Jr., Chm. Bd., Pres. & Chief Exec. Officer--Justiss Oil Co., Inc., Jena, LA; *U.S. Private*, pg. 602
Juusela, Jyrki, Chm. Bd., Pres. & Chief Exec. Officer--Outokumpu Oyj, Espoo, Finland; *Int'l*, pg. 1015
Kabel, Steve, Pres.--Richmond American Homes, Inc., Phoenix, AZ; *U.S. Public*, pg. 1025
Kachapis, Paul, Pres. & Chief Exec. Officer--Alden Auto Parts Warehouse, Inc., Somerset, MA; *U.S. Private*, pg. 33
Kacin, William L., Pres. & Chief Exec. Officer--Met-Pro Corporation, Harleysville, PA; *U.S. Public*, pg. 1100
Kadanoff, Marcia, Partner & Exec. V.P.--Miller/Kadanoff/Huber Direct & Interactive, San Francisco, CA; *U.S. Private*, pg. 747
Kadiri, Hamid, Chief Exec. Officer--Klem EURO RSCG, Casablanca, Morocco; *Int'l*, pg. 603
Kadlec, Rudy, Pres.--Geophysical Survey Systems, Inc., Salem, NH; *Int'l*, pg. 1019
Kady, Tom, Pres.--Handex of New Jersey, Inc., Morganville, NJ; *U.S. Private*, pg. 499
Kady, William, Pres.--Anamet Inc., Waterbury, CT; *U.S. Private*, pg. 70
Kaempfer, J.W., Jr., Pres.--BAA Mc Arthur-Glen Europe, Washington, DC; *U.S. Private*, pg. 604
Kaenzig, J. Gary, Pres.--Grace Packaging, Duncan, SC; *U.S. Public*, pg. 755
Kaercher, Dan, Editor--Midwest Living Magazine, Des Moines, IA; *U.S. Public*, pg. 1094

Kaess, Ken, Pres.-DDB Needham U.S.--DDB Needham Worldwide Inc., New York, NY; *Int'l*, pg. 357
Kaess, Ken, Pres.-DDB Needham U.S.--DDB Needham Worldwide Inc., New York, NY; *U.S. Public*, pg. 1223
Kafadar, C.B., Dr., Pres. & Chief Oper. Officer--OEA, Inc., Aurora, CO; *U.S. Public*, pg. 1206
Kafafian, Lori, Partner-Global H.R.--Ketchum Public Relations Worldwide, New York, NY; *U.S. Private*, pg. 617
Kafka, Rick, Pres.--Pointe Group Ltd., Phoenix, AZ; *U.S. Private*, pg. 873
Kafka, Rick, Pres. & Dir.-Mktg.--Gosnell Builders, Phoenix, AZ; *U.S. Private*, pg. 873
Kafoure, Michael D., Pres. & Chief Oper. Officer--Interstate Bakeries Corporation, Kansas City, MO; *U.S. Public*, pg. 909
Kafoure, Michael D., Pres. & Chief Oper. Officer--Interstate Brands Corporation, Kansas City, MO; *U.S. Public*, pg. 909
Kagan, Jonathan M., Pres.--Novel Biomedical, Plymouth, MN; *U.S. Public*, pg. 401
Kagawa, Kozaburo, Pres.--Hebron S.A., Barcelona, Spain; *Int'l*, pg. 1014
Kagaya, Tetsuo, Pres.--Summit Specialty Chemicals Corporation, Fort Lee, NJ; *Int'l*, pg. 1312
Kageyama, Koichiro, Pres.--Nissho Iwai Australia Ltd., Sydney, Australia; *Int'l*, pg. 948
Kageyama, Yoshio, Pres.--Toray Plastics (America), Inc., North Kingstown, RI; *Int'l*, pg. 1400
Kahan, Max, Pres.--Max Kahan Inc., New York, NY; *U.S. Private*, pg. 604
Kahana, Aron, Chm. Bd. & Pres.--Israel Discount Bank of New York, New York, NY; *Int'l*, pg. 645
Kahl, James, Pres. & Chief Exec. Officer--La Petite Academy Inc., Overland Park, KS; *U.S. Private*, pg. 640
Kahler, John S., Pres. & Chief Exec. Officer--Cincinnati Incorporated, Harrison, OH; *U.S. Private*, pg. 240
Kahlig, Clarence J., Pres.--North Park Lincoln Mercury Inc., San Antonio, TX; *U.S. Private*, pg. 805
Kahn, David, Pres.--Croscill, Inc., New York, NY; *U.S. Private*, pg. 290
Kahn, Douglas, Pres.-Royal Home Fashions--Croscill, Inc., New York, NY; *U.S. Private*, pg. 290
Kahn, Harold D., Chm. Bd. & Chief Exec. Officer--Macy's East, New York, NY; *U.S. Public*, pg. 618
Kahn, Jan, Pres., Sls. & Mktg.--Caron International, De Kalb, IL; *U.S. Private*, pg. 786
Kahn, Jeffrey L., Pres.--Whiting Corporation, Harvey, IL; *U.S. Private*, pg. 1173
Kahn, Jenette, Pres. & Editor-In-Chief--DC Comics, Inc., New York, NY; *U.S. Public*, pg. 1614
Kahn, Mark, Pres.--Production Tool Supply Co., Warren, MI; *U.S. Private*, pg. 889
Kahn, Richie, Partner, Exec. V.P. & Co-Creative Dir.--Harris Drury Cohen, Fort Lauderdale, FL; *U.S. Private*, pg. 505
Kairys, L.N., Pres.--Lustine Oldsmobile & Buick, Inc., Hyattsville, MD; *U.S. Private*, pg. 681
Kaiser, A.E., Pres.--Acme Refrigeration Of Baton Rouge Inc., Baton Rouge, LA; *U.S. Private*, pg. 13
Kaiser, John R., Sr., Pres.--Kaiser Wholesale, Inc., New Albany, IN; *U.S. Private*, pg. 605
Kaiser, Marshall J., Pres. & Chief Exec. Officer--Safe Harbor Water Power Corp., Conestoga, PA; *U.S. Public*, pg. 172
Kaiser, Marshall J., Pres. & Chief Exec. Officer--Pennsylvania Power & Light Company-Northeast Div., Wilkes-Barre, PA; *U.S. Public*, pg. 1244
Kaiser, Marshall J., Pres. & Chief Exec. Officer--Safe Harbor Water Power Corp., Conestoga, PA; *U.S. Public*, pg. 1244
Kaiser, R.S., Pres.--Gallagher-Kaiser Corp., Detroit, MI; *U.S. Private*, pg. 438
Kaiser, Steven, Pres. & Chief Exec. Officer--Baume Mercier, Inc., New York, NY; *U.S. Private*, pg. 124
Kaitz, Ben B., Pres. & Chief Exec. Officer--Palm Beach Beauty Products Co., Minneapolis, MN; *U.S. Private*, pg. 834
Kaizaki, Yoichiro, Pres.--Bridgestone Corporation, Tokyo, Japan; *Int'l*, pg. 213
Kajinski, Shogo, Pres.--ORIX Computer Systems Corporation, Tokyo, Japan; *Int'l*, pg. 1008
Kajita, Mike, Pres.--Kabuto International Phoenix Inc., San Francisco, CA; *Int'l*, pg. 721
Kakiage, Masatoshi, Pres. & Chief Exec. Officer--Mitsui Fudosan (USA), Inc., New York, NY; *Int'l*, pg. 882
Kakudoh, Kenichi, Pres.--The Norinchukin Bank, Tokyo, Japan; *Int'l*, pg. 958
Kakures, Dennis C., Pres. & Chief Oper. Officer--McGrath RentCorp, Livermore, CA; *U.S. Public*, pg. 1069
Kalahar, T.L., Chief Exec. Officer--Camelot Communications, Inc., Dallas, TX; *U.S. Private*, pg. 203
Kalangis, Ike, Chm. Bd., Pres. & Chief Exec. Officer--NationsBank Sunwest, Inc., Albuquerque, NM; *U.S. Public*, pg. 1165
Kalb, Jeffrey C., Pres. & Chief Exec. Officer--California Micro Devices, Milpitas, CA; *U.S. Public*, pg. 293
Kalb, Kermit, Pres.--Farmer's Cooperative Association, Lawrence, KS; *U.S. Private*, pg. 395
Kaldellis, Emanuel, Chm. Bd., Pres. & Chief Exec. Officer--Copais Food & Beverage Company S.A., Athens, Greece; *U.S. Public*, pg. 806
Kalin, Edward L., Pres.--Kalin Enterprises, Inc., Sarasota, FL; *U.S. Private*, pg. 606
Kalin, Edward L., Pres.--Kalin Financial Division, Sarasota, FL; *U.S. Private*, pg. 606
Kalinske, Thomas, Pres. & Chief Exec. Officer--Sega of America Inc., Redwood City, CA; *Int'l*, pg. 1218
Kalish, William B., Pres.--IPD Printing & Distributing, Inc., Chamblee, GA; *U.S. Public*, pg. 1735
Kalitta, Conrad, Pres. & Chief Exec. Officer--American International Airways, Ypsilanti, MI; *U.S. Private*, pg. 57
Kalkhoven, Kevin, Pres. & Chief Exec. Officer--Uniphase Corporation, San Jose, CA; *U.S. Public*, pg. 1670
Kall, Terry, Pres.--General Felt Industries, Inc., Linwood, PA; *U.S. Private*, pg. 1094
Kallet, Peter J., Pres. & Chief Oper. Officer--Oneida Ltd., Oneida, NY; *U.S. Public*, pg. 1225
Kallman, Irwin, Pres.--Bookazine Company, Inc., Bayonne, NJ; *U.S. Private*, pg. 156
Kalmbach, Lisa, Pres.--Kaufman and Broad of Northern California, Inc., San Ramon, CA; *U.S. Public*, pg. 945
Kalmet, J. John, Pres. & Chief Oper. Officer--Wheaton River Minerals Ltd., Toronto, Canada; *Int'l*, pg. 1498
Kaloyanides, James M., Pres. & Chief Oper. Officer--New England Coffee Company, Malden, MA; *U.S. Private*, pg. 792
Kalpala, Asmo, Chief Exec. Officer--Tapiola-Yhtiot, Espoo, Finland; *Int'l*, pg. 1354
Kaltz, Kenneth, Pres.--Tranter, Inc., Augusta, GA; *U.S. Public*, pg. 521
Kamada, Toshio, Pres.--Settsu Corporation, Amagasaki, Japan; *Int'l*, pg. 1225
Kaman, Charles H., Chm. Bd., Pres. & Chief Exec. Officer--Kaman Corporation, Bloomfield, CT; *U.S. Public*, pg. 941
Kamat, Ulas N., Pres.--Republic Container Corp., Jersey City, NJ; *U.S. Private*, pg. 923
Kambayashi, Akio, Pres. & Chief Exec. Officer--Kasumi Co., Ltd., Tsuchiura, Japan; *Int'l*, pg. 724
Kamberos, Chris, Chm. Bd., Pres. & Chief Oper. Officer--Treasure Island Foodmarts Inc., Chicago, IL; *U.S. Private*, pg. 1098
Kamborian, Jacob S., Pres.--International Shoe Machine Corp., Nashua, NH; *U.S. Private*, pg. 572
Kamei, Toshio, Pres.--Kawasaki Heavy Industries, Ltd., Kobe, Japan; *Int'l*, pg. 725
Kamenstein, Peter, Chm., Pres. & Chief Exec. Officer--M. Kamenstein, Inc., Elmsford, NY; *U.S. Private*, pg. 606
Kamiel, Jerald, Pres.--Garan, Incorporated, New York, NY; *U.S. Public*, pg. 703
Kaminow, Edward S., Pres. & Chief Exec. Officer--West Mill Clothes, Inc., Woodside, NY; *U.S. Private*, pg. 1163
Kamins, Philip E., Chm. Bd. & Pres.--PMC, Inc., Sun Valley, CA; *U.S. Private*, pg. 827
Kaminski, Jerold, Pres. & Chief Oper. Officer--Northland Cranberries, Inc., Wisconsin Rapids, WI; *U.S. Public*, pg. 1197
Kaminski, Mark, Pres.--Commonwealth Aluminum-Lewisport, Lewisport, KY; *U.S. Public*, pg. 415
Kaminski, Mark V., Pres. & Chief Exec. Officer--Commonwealth Industries, Inc., Louisville, KY; *U.S. Public*, pg. 415
Kaminski, Mark V., Pres. & Chief Exec. Officer--Alflex, Long Beach, CA; *U.S. Public*, pg. 415
Kaminsky, Larry E., Chm. Bd., Pres. & Chief Exec. Officer--H. R. Kaminsky & Sons, Inc., Fitzgerald, GA; *U.S. Private*, pg. 606
Kamishima, M., Pres.--Ebara UK Ltd., Hounslow, United Kingdom; *Int'l*, pg. 432
Kamitaki, Tadami, Pres.--Maui Varieties, Ltd., Honolulu, HI; *U.S. Private*, pg. 715
Kamiya, K., Pres.--Asahi Glass America, Inc., New York, NY; *Int'l*, pg. 84
Kamiya, Soichiro, Chm. Bd. & Pres.--Shizuoka Bank, Ltd., Shizuoka, Japan; *Int'l*, pg. 1236
Kamm, Jacob O., II, Chm. Bd., Pres. & Chief Exec. & Fin. Officer--Electric Furnace Co., Salem, OH; *U.S. Private*, pg. 367
Kampouris, Emmanuel A., Chm. Bd., Pres. & Chief Exec. Officer--American Standard Inc., Piscataway, NJ; *U.S. Public*, pg. 91
Kamstra, Garrett A., Pres.--Hutch Sports USA, Inc., Hebron, KY; *U.S. Public*, pg. 1354
Kanagawa, Chihiro, Pres. & Chief Exec. Officer--Shin-Etsu Chemical Co. ltd., Tokyo, Japan; *Int'l*, pg. 1234
Kanai, Hisao, Pres.--Japan Aviation Electronics Industry, Ltd., Tokyo, Japan; *Int'l*, pg. 701
Kanai, Noritoshi, Pres.--Mutual Trading Co., Inc., Los Angeles, CA; *U.S. Private*, pg. 770
Kanai, Tsutomu, Pres.--Hitachi, Ltd., Tokyo, Japan; *Int'l*, pg. 621
Kanamori, K., Pres.--NYK Line (North America) Inc., Secaucus, NJ; *Int'l*, pg. 941
Kanas, John Adam, Chm. Bd., Pres. & Chief Exec. Officer--North Fork Bancorporation, Inc., Melville, NY; *U.S. Public*, pg. 1194
Kanaya, Osamu, Pres.--Minolta Co., Ltd., Osaka, Japan; *Int'l*, pg. 869
Kanayama, Yoshiharu, Pres.--Nishimatsu Construction Co., Ltd., Tokyo, Japan; *Int'l*, pg. 942
Kanda, Takafumi, Pres.--ORIX Hotels International Private Limited, Hong Kong, Hong Kong; *Int'l*, pg. 1009
Kandel, Jerry, Pres.--Life-Like Products, Inc., Baltimore, MD; *U.S. Private*, pg. 666
Kane, Dennis B., Pres. & Chief Exec. Officer--ABC/Kane Productions International, Inc., Washington, DC; *U.S. Public*, pg. 511
Kane, Gary A., Pres. & Chief Oper. Officer--J.G. Hook, Inc., New York, NY; *U.S. Private*, pg. 538
Kane, Jerry, Pres.--Sam Kane Beef Processors, Inc., Corpus Christi, TX; *U.S. Private*, pg. 607
Kane, John C., Pres. & Chief Oper. Officer--Cardinal Health Inc., Dublin, OH; *U.S. Public*, pg. 304
Kane, Joseph R., Jr., Pres. & Chief Exec. Officer--Days Inns of America, Inc., Parsippany, NJ; *U.S. Public*, pg. 321
Kane, Robert J., Pres.--Cement Transit Co., Cleveland, OH; *U.S. Public*, pg. 1084
Kane, Robert J., Pres.--Canadian Cement Ltd., Owen Sound, Canada; *U.S. Public*, pg. 1084
Kaneb, Gary, Pres.--Gulf Oil Limited Partnership, Chelsea, MA; *U.S. Private*, pg. 487
Kaneb, John, Mng. Partner--Catamount Petroleum, Chelsea, MA; *U.S. Private*, pg. 220
Kaneda, Hiroo, Pres.--Sunstar Inc., Takatsuki, Japan; *Int'l*, pg. 1320
Kaneff, Howard T., Pres.--Arkay Packaging Corporation, Hauppauge, NY; *U.S. Private*, pg. 82
Kaneko, Hisashi, Pres.--NEC Corporation, Tokyo, Japan; *Int'l*, pg. 899
Kaneko, Zenichiro, Pres.--Sakata Seed Corporation, Yokohama, Japan; *Int'l*, pg. 1178
Kanfer, Joseph, Pres. & Chief Exec. Officer--Go Jo Industries, Cuyahoga Falls, OH; *U.S. Private*, pg. 458
Kang, John H., Pres.--Medical Manager Corporation, Tampa, FL; *U.S. Public*, pg. 1080
Kangas, Markku, Pres.--Valmet Automation Inc., Helsinki, Finland; *Int'l*, pg. 1449
Kanies, David, Pres.--The Ramsey Company, Marlborough, MA; *U.S. Private*, pg. 189
Kanner, Robert H., Chm. Bd., Pres., Chief Exec./Fin. Officer & Treas.--Pubco Corporation, Cleveland, OH; *U.S. Public*, pg. 1339
Kanno, Yukihiro, Pres.--P.T. Nikko Securities Indonesia, Jakarta, Indonesia; *Int'l*, pg. 931
Kanode, Robert L., Pres. & Gen. Mgr.--VARTA Batteries Inc., Elmsford, NY; *Int'l*, pg. 1452
Kantor, Nathan, Pres. & Chief Oper. Officer--Winstar Communications, New York, NY; *U.S. Public*, pg. 1772
Kantz, Phil, Pres. & Chief Exec. Officer--Tab Products Co., Palo Alto, CA; *U.S. Public*, pg. 1559
Kapash, Richard, Pres.--Symbol Technologies, Portable Systems Division, Costa Mesa, CA; *U.S. Public*, pg. 1546
Kapcsandy, Lou, Chm. Bd. & Pres.--Baugh Construction Company, Seattle, WA; *U.S. Private*, pg. 123
Kapella, Roger R., Pres. & Chief Oper. Officer--Patrick Cudahy Inc., Cudahy, WI; *U.S. Public*, pg. 1479
Kaplan, Arnold H., Pres.--APCI (U.K.), Inc., Allentown, PA; *U.S. Public*, pg. 30
Kaplan, Bernard H., Pres.--BSA Advertising, Inc., New York, NY; *U.S. Private*, pg. 107
Kaplan, Edward, Chm., Pres. & Chief Exec. Officer--Zebra Technologies Corporation, Vernon Hills, IL; *U.S. Public*, pg. 1790
Kaplan, Harley B., Pres.--Koehler Manufacturing Company, Marlborough, MA; *U.S. Private*, pg. 706
Kaplan, Herbert M., Pres.--Warren Equities Inc., Providence, RI; *U.S. Private*, pg. 1151
Kaplan, James, Pres.--Kaplan Electronics, Wayne, NJ; *U.S. Private*, pg. 607
Kaplan, James A., Pres.--Capital Management Sciences, Los Angeles, CA; *U.S. Public*, pg. 484
Kaplan, Leslie, Sr. V.P. & Mng. Partner-Direct--Hill, Holliday, Connors, Cosmopulos, Inc., Boston, MA; *U.S. Private*, pg. 529
Kaplan, Nancy Korda, Mng. Partner & Client Services Dir.--Compton Partners, New York, NY; *U.S. Public*, pg. 1422
Kaplan, Philip, Pres. & Chief Oper. Officer--Loehmann's, Inc., Bronx, NY; *U.S. Public*, pg. 1010
Kaplan, Ronald W., Pres.--Taylor-Wharton Gas Equipment, Camp Hill, PA; *U.S. Public*, pg. 793
Kaplanek, Charles, Jr., Chm. Bd., Pres. & Chief Exec. Officer--Floral Glass & Mirror, Inc., Hauppauge, NY; *U.S.* Private, pg. 414
Kapp, Michael, Pres.--Warner Special Products, Burbank, CA; *U.S. Public*, pg. 1612
Kappauf, Donald W., Pres.--Digital Staff ConnXions, Somerset, NJ; *U.S. Public*, pg. 508
Kappler, George, Chm. Bd., Pres. & Chief Exec. Officer--Kappler Safety Group, Inc., Guntersville, AL; *U.S. Private*, pg. 607
Kappler, George, Chm. Bd. & Pres.--Kappler USA, Guntersville, AL; *U.S. Private*, pg. 607
Kappus, Gerd, Pres.--Filterwerk Mann & Hummel GmbH, Speyer, Germany; *Int'l*, pg. 484
Kapson, Craig, Pres.--Jordan Motors, Inc., Mishawaka, IN; *U.S. Private*, pg. 599
Kapusta, George, Pres.--Commerce Bank, College Park, MD; *U.S. Public*, pg. 1038
Karabots, Nick G., Chm. Bd.--S L C Graphics, LP, Pittston, PA; *U.S. Private*, pg. 955
Karaffa, Corwin J., Pres.--Preferred Public Storage Co., Los Angeles, CA; *U.S. Private*, pg. 227
Karakas, Steve, Principal & Adv.--Karakas, VanSickle, Ouellette Advertising & Public Relations, Portland, OR; *U.S. Private*, pg. 607
Karam, Thomas, Pres. & Chief Exec. Officer--PG Energy, Inc., Wilkes-Barre, PA; *U.S. Public*, pg. 1271
Karam, Thomas F., Pres. & Chief Exec. Officer--Pennsylvania Enterprises Inc., Wilkes-Barre, PA; *U.S. Public*, pg. 1271
Karapetian, Vahe, Pres.--A A Cater Truck Manufacturing Company, Inc., Los Angeles, CA; *U.S. Private*, pg. 1
Karasawa, Shuji, Pres.--Universal Securities Co., Ltd., Tokyo, Japan; *Int'l*, pg. 1444
Karass, Larry T., Pres., Chief Exec. Officer & Chief Oper. Officer--Caristrap International Inc., Laval, Canada; *Int'l*, pg. 271
Karatz, Bruce, Chm. Bd., Pres. & Chief Exec. Officer--Kaufman and Broad Home Corporation, Los Angeles, CA; *U.S. Public*, pg. 944
Karchon, James, Pres.--Engineering Service, Inc., Southfield, MI; *U.S. Private*, pg. 376
Kardos, Andy, Pres.--Publicis BCP Direct Inc., Toronto, Canada; *Int'l*, pg. 116
Kardos, Paul J., Pres., Chief Exec. Officer & Chief Oper. Officer--Horace Mann Educators Corporation, Springfield, IL; *U.S. Public*, pg. 835
Karger, Lynn, Mng. Partner & Creative Dir.--Dugan/Farley Communications, Upper Saddle River, NJ; *U.S. Public*, pg. 1642
Karges, Edwin, Chm. Bd. & Pres.--The Karges Furniture Company Inc., Evansville, IN; *U.S. Private*, pg. 607
Karis, William G., Pres. & Chief Exec. Officer--Consol, Pittsburgh, PA; *U.S. Public*, pg. 531
Karis, William G., Pres. & Chief Exec. Officer--Consol, Pittsburgh, PA; *Int'l*, pg. 1081
KarKinkead, Karl, V.P. & Gen. Mgr.--Ansul Incorporated, Marinette, WI; *U.S. Public*, pg. 1648
Karl, Susan Gamson, Pres. & Chief Exec. Officer--Annabelle Candy Company, Inc., Hayward, CA; *U.S. Private*, pg. 75

Karlan, Mark S., Pres. & Chief Exec. Officer--Imperial Credit Commercial Mortgage Investment Corp., Los Angeles, CA; U.S. Public, pg. 872
Karlin, Robert, Pres.--Santa Monica Ford Company, Santa Monica, CA; U.S. Private, pg. 965
Karlsen, Terje, Pres.--Lysaker Reisebyra a.s., Lysaker, Norway; Int'l, pg. 769
Karlson, Gert, Pres.--Jarnia AB, Ulricehammn, Sweden; Int'l, pg. 188
Karlsson, Conny, Pres.--Duni AB, Stockholm, Sweden; Int'l, pg. 421
Karlsson, Tommy H., Pres.--Crown Cork & Seal, European Division, Paris, France; U.S. Public, pg. 464
Karlyn, William M., Pres.--Autoroll Machine Co., LLC, Middleton, MA; U.S. Private, pg. 101
Karman, James A., Pres.--RPM, Inc., Medina, OH; U.S. Public, pg. 1356
Karman, James B., Pres. & Chief Exec. Officer--Spaulding & Slye, Boston, MA; U.S. Private, pg. 1021
Karnes, Gary A., Pres.--Appleton Electric Co., Chicago, IL; U.S. Public, pg. 572
Karns, Randy, V.P. & Gen. Mgr.--BKI, Simpsonville, SC; U.S. Public, pg. 1506
Karol, Steven E., Pres. & Chief Exec. Officer--H M K Enterprises, Inc., Waltham, MA; U.S. Private, pg. 489
Karp, Allen, Pres. & Chief Exec. Officer--Cineplex Odeon Corporation, Toronto, Canada; Int'l, pg. 292
Karp, Franklin, Pres.--Harvey Electronics, Inc., Lyndhurst, NJ; U.S. Public, pg. 796
Karp, Jack L., Pres.--L. Karp & Sons, Inc., Elk Grove Village, IL; U.S. Private, pg. 607
Karp, Mark E., Pres. & Chief Exec. Officer--Moore Medical Corp., New Britain, CT; U.S. Public, pg. 1128
Karpenski, Martin, Pres. & Chief Oper. Officer--Foster Wheeler Power Systems, Inc., Clinton, NJ; U.S. Public, pg. 677
Karpik, Michael, Pres.--Bigsby & Kruthers Companies, Chicago, IL; U.S. Private, pg. 143
Karrick, Robert, Pres. & Chief Exec. Officer--Gelco Information Network, Inc., Eden Prairie, MN; U.S. Private, pg. 442
Karter, E.M., Pres.--Forest Kraft Company, Dayton, OH; U.S. Public, pg. 1076
Karter, Jerome, Pres. & Chief Exec. Officer--SCOR U.S. Corporation, New York, NY; Int'l, pg. 1152
Kartsotis, Kosta, Pres.--Fossil Inc., Richardson, TX; U.S. Private, pg. 420
Karvois, Paul J., Pres. & Chief Oper. Officer--Jevic Transportation, Inc., Delanco, NJ; U.S. Public, pg. 927
Kasai, Yoshiyuki, Pres.--Central Japan Railway Company, Nagoya, Japan; Int'l, pg. 279
Kasai, Yutaka, Pres.--Kawasaki Heavy Industries (Europe) B.V., Amsterdam, Netherlands; Int'l, pg. 726
Kasch, Jeffrey C., Pres.--M.W. Kasch Company, Mequon, WI; U.S. Private, pg. 608
Kasden, Allen J., Pres.--William L. Crow Construction Co., New York, NY; Int'l, pg. 633
Kash, J., Pres.--Dresser-Rand Co. (Wellsville), Wellsville, NY; U.S. Public, pg. 529
Kashgegian, Glen, Pres. & Chief Oper. Officer--Printed Circuit Corporation, Woburn, MA; U.S. Private, pg. 886
Kashima, Toshiyuki, Pres.--Sumitomo Bank Capital Markets, Inc., New York, NY; Int'l, pg. 1308
Kashio, Kazuo, Pres.--Casio Computer Co., Ltd., Tokyo, Japan; Int'l, pg. 274
Kashiwa, Junro, Pres.--Okuma Corporation, Niwa, Japan; Int'l, pg. 1000
Kashnow, Richard A., Pres.--Schuller International, Inc., Denver, CO; U.S. Public, pg. 927
Kashnow, Richard A., Dr., Chm. Bd., Pres. & Chief Exec. Officer--Raychem Corporation, Menlo Park, CA; U.S. Public, pg. 1362
Kaske, Wolfgang, Dr., Pres. & Chief Exec. Officer--AMB Aachener und Muenchener Beteiligungs-AG, Aachen, Germany; Int'l, pg. 15
Kaskel, Roy R., Pres.--Enron Liquids Services Corp., Houston, TX; U.S. Public, pg. 584
Kasle, Don, Pres. & Chief Exec. Officer--Western Financial Bank, Irvine, CA; U.S. Public, pg. 1757
Kaspar, Don, Pres.--Bassick by Kaspar, Shiner, TX; U.S. Private, pg. 122
Kaspar, Don G., Chm. Bd. & Pres.--Kaspar Wire Works, Inc., Shiner, TX; U.S. Private, pg. 608
Kaspar, Franz, Pres.--Parker Hannifin Corporation, Hemel Hempstead, United Kingdom; U.S. Public, pg. 1261
Kaspar, Lewis P., Pres.--Linde Hydraulics Corporation, Canfield, OH; Int'l, pg. 810
Kasparek, Joe E., Pres.--Fugro Group Companies, Houston, TX; U.S. Private, pg. 430
Kasputys, Joseph E., Chm. Bd., Pres. & Chief Exec. Officer--Primark Corporation, Waltham, MA; U.S. Public, pg. 1325
Kassab, Charles S., Chm. Bd., Pres., Chief Exec. Officer & Treas.--Huntington Bancshares Michigan, Inc., Troy, MI; U.S. Public, pg. 850
Kassab, Robert L., Pres.--Stainless Incorporated, Deerfield Beach, FL; U.S. Private, pg. 1029
Kassab, Robert L., Pres.--Charter House Incorporated, Holland, MI; U.S. Private, pg. 1029
Kassad, Gabe, Pres.--Elias Brothers Restaurants, Inc., Warren, MI; U.S. Private, pg. 371
Kassan, Michael E., Pres. & Chief Oper. Officer--Western International Media Corporation, Los Angeles, CA; U.S. Private, pg. 1165
Kassel, Robert L., Chm. Bd., Pres., Chief Exec. Officer & Treas.--U.S. Home & Garden Inc., San Francisco, CA; U.S. Public, pg. 1682
Kassouf, James, Pres., Chief Exec. Officer & Treas.--Metropolitan Properties Systems, Cleveland, OH; U.S. Private, pg. 739
Kasten, Stan, Pres.--Atlanta Hawks, Inc., Atlanta, GA; U.S. Public, pg. 1614
Kasten, Stan, Pres.--Atlanta Braves, Inc., Atlanta, GA; U.S. Public, pg. 1614
Katagiri, T., Pres.--Achilles USA, Inc., Everett, WA; Int'l, pg. 22
Kataoka, Masataka, Pres. & Chief Exec. Officer--Alps Electric Co., Ltd., Tokyo, Japan; Int'l, pg. 65
Katawczik, Dennis M., Pres.--Framesi USA, Inc./Roffler Industries, Inc./Casa di Colore, Inc., Coraopolis, PA; U.S. Private, pg. 419
Katayama, Shozo, Pres. & Chief Exec. Officer--Toyo Tire & Rubber Co., Ltd., Osaka, Japan; Int'l, pg. 1411
Katayama, Wayne, Pres.--Kilauea Agronomics, Inc., Kilauea, HI; U.S. Private, pg. 190
Katayana, Akira, Pres.--Kyotaru Co., Ltd., Tokyo, Japan; Int'l, pg. 777
Katerman, Mike, Pres.--The Magee Carpet Company, Bloomsburg, PA; U.S. Private, pg. 694
Kathwari, M. Farooq, Chm. Bd., Pres. & Chief Exec. Officer--Ethan Allen Interiors Inc., Danbury, CT; U.S. Public, pg. 595
Kathwari, M. Farooq, Chm., Pres. & Chief Exec. Officer--Ethan Allen, Inc., Danbury, CT; U.S. Public, pg. 595
Kato, Akira, Pres.--Kumagai Properties Inc., Honolulu, HI; Int'l, pg. 764
Kato, Akua, Pres.--Asahi Industries Co. Ltd., Tokyo, Japan; Int'l, pg. 1178
Kato, Motonobu, Pres.--Gunze Sangyo, Inc., Tokyo, Japan; Int'l, pg. 578
Kato, Shinji, Pres.--DKB Financial Futures Corp., Chicago, IL; Int'l, pg. 360
Kato, Shuzo, Pres.--Uniden Corporation, Tokyo, Japan; Int'l, pg. 1433
Katoh, Motoaki, Pres.--Colonial Beef Co., Philadelphia, PA; U.S. Private, pg. 253
Katopodis, Louis, Pres. & Chief Exec. Officer--Fiesta Mart Inc., Houston, TX; U.S. Private, pg. 403
Katri, David E., Pres. & Chief Oper. Officer--Fluke Corporation, Everett, WA; U.S. Public, pg. 659
Katsu, Yasuhiko, Pres.--Gougler Industries, Inc., Kent, OH; U.S. Private, pg. 466
Katsumata, Mark, Pres.--Indo-Pacific Energy Ltd., Vancouver, Canada; Int'l, pg. 422
Katsuzagi, M., Pres.--Minolta Marketing (M) SDN BHD, Petaling Jaya, Malaysia; Int'l, pg. 869
Katz, Alvin, Pres.--Manhattan Store Interiors, Inc., Brooklyn, NY; U.S. Private, pg. 699
Katz, Donald L., Pres.--Capitol Manufacturing Co., Westerville, OH; U.S. Public, pg. 793
Katz, J.G., Pres.--SABRE Travel Information Network, Fort Worth, TX; U.S. Public, pg. 10
Katz, Jeanette Nostra, Pres.--G-III Apparel Group, Ltd., New York, NY; U.S. Public, pg. 690
Katz, Nathan, Pres.--Dana Lighting, Inc., Easton, MA; U.S. Public, pg. 314
Katz, Neil J., Pres.--Liz Claiborne Cosmetics, Inc., New York, NY; U.S. Public, pg. 1006
Katz, Stewart, Pres. & Chief Oper. Officer--Noodle Kidoodle Inc., Syosset, NY; U.S. Public, pg. 1188
Katz, Warren, Pres.-Stores Div.--Salant Corporation, New York, NY; U.S. Public, pg. 1429
Katzen, Cyrus, Dr., Pres. & Chief Exec. Officer--Mozel Development Corp., Baileys Crossroads, VA; U.S. Private, pg. 765
Katzenberg, Jeffrey, Partner--DreamWorks SKG, Universal City, CA; U.S. Private, pg. 342
Katzenberger, George, Pres.--Upright, Saint Louis, MO; U.S. Private, pg. 1128
Katzman, Fred, Pres.--Nielsen & Bainbridge, Cranbury, NJ; Int'l, pg. 460
Katzman, Michael, Pres.--Mastercraft Furniture Corp., Omaha, NE; U.S. Private, pg. 714
Katzman, Richard, Pres.--Kaz, Inc., New York, NY; U.S. Private, pg. 610
Kauffman, James B., Jr., Chm. Bd., Pres. & Chief Exec. Officer--Keystone Bank, Horsham, PA; U.S. Public, pg. 956
Kauffman, Michael L., Pres.--Nobel/Sysco Food Services Company-Denver, Denver, CO; U.S. Public, pg. 1551
Kauffman, Reese, Pres.--Kauffman Products, Inc., Carmel, IN; U.S. Private, pg. 609
Kauffman, Will, Chief Oper. Officer & Sr. V.P.--Komag, Incorporated, San Jose, CA; U.S. Public, pg. 966
Kaufman, Bruce J., Pres. & Chief Exec. Officer--Kaufel Group Ltd., Dorval, Canada; Int'l, pg. 724
Kaufman, Greg, Pres.--Amstore Corporation, Muskegon, MI; U.S. Private, pg. 68
Kaufman, Herbert W., Pres. & Chief Exec. Officer--H.W. Kaufman Financial Group, Inc., Farmington, MI; U.S. Private, pg. 609
Kaufman, Jerry, Pres. & Chief Exec. Officer--Nationwide Credit Inc., Marietta, GA; U.S. Private, pg. 788
Kaufman, Jerry M., Pres.--Nationwide Credit, Marietta, GA; U.S. Public, pg. 631
Kaufman, Michael, Pres.--Kaufel America Inc., Baldwin, NY; Int'l, pg. 725
Kaufman, Michael, Pres. & Chief Exec. Officer--Ponderosa Steakhouse, Dallas, TX; U.S. Private, pg. 736
Kaufman, Michael, Pres.--RCM Design, New York, NY; U.S. Private, pg. 947
Kaufman, Robert, Pres.--Care Matrix Corp., Needham, MA; U.S. Public, pg. 305
Kaufman, Thomas H., Pres.--Kaufman Footwear, Kitchener, Canada; Int'l, pg. 725
Kaufmann, David, Pres.--The Vacation Store, Virginia Beach, VA; U.S. Private, pg. 649
Kaufmann, Luiz, Pres. & Chief Exec. Officer--Aracruz Celulose S.A., Rio de Janeiro, Brazil; Int'l, pg. 78
Kaul, David, Gen. Mgr.-North America--Cab-o-Sil Div. Cabot Corp., Tuscola, IL; U.S. Public, pg. 289
Kaul, Rakesh K., Pres. & Chief Exec. Officer--Hanover Direct, Inc., Weehawken, NJ; U.S. Public, pg. 782
Kauppila, Jarmo, Pres.--Sensodec Oy, Kajaani, Finland; Int'l, pg. 1449
Kausman, Carl, Pres.--Kenneth Gordon IAG, Inc., New Orleans, LA; U.S. Private, pg. 581
Kautz, Robert F., Pres. & Chief Fin. Officer--Koo Koo Roo, Inc., Los Angeles, CA; U.S. Public, pg. 966
Kavanagh, J.P., Pres. & Chief Exec. Officer--Schieffelin & Somerset Co., New York, NY; Int'l, pg. 412
Kavanah, John, Chm. Bd., Pres. & Chief Exec. Officer--Marketing Corp. of America, Westport, CT; U.S. Private, pg. 704
Kavanaugh, Penn, Pres. & Chief Exec. Officer--Shieffelin Somerset Co., New York, NY; Int'l, pg. 412
Kawai, Hirotaka, Pres.--Kawai Musical Instruments Mfg. Co., Ltd., Hamamatsu, Japan; Int'l, pg. 725
Kawai, Kazuyoshi, Pres.--Western Alaska Fisheries Inc., Seattle, WA; Int'l, pg. 845
Kawai, Kazuyoshi, Pres.--Trans Ocean Products, Inc., Bellingham, WA; Int'l, pg. 845
Kawamoto, Nobuhiko, Pres. & Chief Exec. Officer--Honda Motor Co., Ltd., Tokyo, Japan; Int'l, pg. 634
Kawamura, Hajime, Pres.--Tomen America Inc., New York, NY; Int'l, pg. 1395
Kawamura, Kentaro, Pres.--Nippon Yusen K.K., Tokyo, Japan; Int'l, pg. 941
Kawamura, Masaharu, Pres.--Nambokusha Inc., Tokyo, Japan; Int'l, pg. 904
Kawamura, Takeo, Pres.--Taisei America Corp., Long Beach, CA; Int'l, pg. 1347
Kawamura, Yoshibumi, Pres.--Sankyo Company Limited, Tokyo, Japan; Int'l, pg. 1189
Kawamura, Yoshinori, Pres.--ARS Chemical (Thailand) Co., Ltd., Bangkok, Thailand; Int'l, pg. 1014
Kawanaka, Katsuo, Pres.--Y.O. Machinery Leasing Co., Ltd., Tokyo, Japan; Int'l, pg. 1009
Kawata, Itsuo, Pres.--AG Ajikawa Corporation, Osaka, Japan; Int'l, pg. 39
Kawatani, Sadamasa, Pres.--The Hokkaido Takushoku Bank, Ltd., Sapporo, Japan; Int'l, pg. 626
Kawer, Sheldon, Partner--Media First International, Inc., New York, NY; U.S. Private, pg. 726
Kay, Brian, Pres. & Chief Exec. Officer--Connecting Point Computer Services, Canton, OH; U.S. Private, pg. 471
Kay, Jack, Pres. & Chief Exec. Officer--Phoenix Technologies Ltd., San Jose, CA; U.S. Public, pg. 1292
Kay, Jay, Pres.--Phoenix Technologies Ltd., Norwood, MA; U.S. Public, pg. 1292
Kay, John W., Pres.--The Kay Company, Inc., Frankfort, IN; U.S. Private, pg. 610
Kay, R., Pres.--Filtertek Inc., Hebron, IL; U.S. Public, pg. 546
Kaye, Alan, Chm. & Chief Exec. Officer--Dobson Park Industries Plc, Wigan, United Kingdom; U.S. Public, pg. 789
Kaye, Michael S., Pres.--Secomerica, Inc., Newport Beach, CA; Int'l, pg. 1217
Kaye, Steve, Pres.--GTCO Corporation, Columbia, MD; U.S. Private, pg. 436
Kayho, Kimmo, Pres.--Esselte Oy, Helsinki, Finland; Int'l, pg. 461
Kayotaka, Hiroshi, Pres.--Nozaki & Company Ltd., Tokyo, Japan; Int'l, pg. 990
Kaysen, Richard L., Pres.--Cheyenne Light, Fuel & Power Co., Cheyenne, WY; U.S. Public, pg. 1170
Kayser, Kraig H., Pres. & Chief Exec. Officer--Seneca Foods Corporation, Pittsford, NY; U.S. Public, pg. 1456
Kaywork, E. Lee, Pres. & Gen. Mgr.--AT&T Wireless Services, Paramus, NJ; U.S. Public, pg. 11
Kazama, Hachizaemon, Pres.--Tsumura & Co., Tokyo, Japan; Int'l, pg. 1425
Kazemi, Shah, Pres.--Monterey Mushrooms, Inc., Watsonville, CA; U.S. Private, pg. 758
Kealey, Darwin, Pres.--GPC Communications (Ontario), Toronto, Canada; U.S. Public, pg. 1225
Kealy, Joseph P., Chm. Bd., Pres. & Chief Exec. Officer--International FiberCom, Phoenix, AZ; U.S. Public, pg. 898
Kean, D. Bruce, Pres.--Multifoods Specialty Distribution Inc., Denver, CO; U.S. Public, pg. 901
Kean, John, Jr., Pres. & Chief Exec. Officer--NUI Corporation, Bedminster, NJ; U.S. Public, pg. 1147
Keane, Kevin T., Pres. & Chief Exec. Officer--Astronics Corporation, Buffalo, NY; U.S. Public, pg. 142
Kearney, Joseph P., Pres. & Chief Exec. Officer--U.S. Generating Company, Bethesda, MD; U.S. Public, pg. 1241
Kearney, Joseph P., Pres. & Chief Exec. Officer--PG&E Gas Transmission, San Francisco, CA; U.S. Public, pg. 1241
Kearney, Joseph S., Jr., Pres.--Northwestern Industrial Piping, Niles, IL; U.S. Private, pg. 806
Kearns, John P., Pres.--TECO Manufacturing, Inc., Alvin, TX; U.S. Public, pg. 1562
Kearns, Robert F., Pres.--B.H. Aircraft Co., Inc., Farmingdale, NY; U.S. Private, pg. 107
Keating, Brendan, Pres.--Bowne Business Communications, Inc., New York, NY; U.S. Public, pg. 248
Keating, Daniel J., III, Pres.--Keating Building Corp., Bala Cynwyd, PA; U.S. Private, pg. 610
Keating, J. Edmund, Mng. Partner--Griffin Bacal Inc., New York, NY; U.S. Private, pg. 480
Keating, John J., Pres. & Asst. Treas.--P.J. Keating Company, Lunenburg, MA; U.S. Private, pg. 610
Keating, Phillip J., Pres.--Rieke Corporation, Auburn, IN; U.S. Public, pg. 1054
Keating, Pierce J., Pres. & Chief Exec. Officer--Daniel J. Keating Co., Ardmore, PA; U.S. Private, pg. 610
Keating, Susan, Pres. & Chief Exec. Officer--Dauphin Deposit Bank and Trust Company, Harrisburg, PA; Int'l, pg. 64
Keating, Susan C., Pres.--First Maryland Credit Corp., Baltimore, MD; Int'l, pg. 64
Keating, Susan C., Pres.--The York Bank and Trust Company, York, PA; Int'l, pg. 65
Keaton, Bill, Pres.--Carolina Shoe Company, Morganton, NC; U.S. Public, pg. 217
Keaveny, Denis J., Pres.--Cains Foods, L.P., Ayer, MA; U.S. Private, pg. 199

Keay, Jim, Pres.--Morflex, Inc., Greensboro, NC; *U.S. Private*, pg. 919
Kebrdle, Dave, Pres.-Sls. & Mktg.--Domore Corporation, Elkhart, IN; *U.S. Private*, pg. 339
Kebrdle, David, Pres.--Sican Corp., Elkhart, IN; *U.S. Private*, *pg. 997*
Kec, Robert F., Pres.--Western States Petroleum Inc., Phoenix, AZ; *U.S. Private*, pg. 1169
Keddy, Patrick, Pres.--PB Leasing Ltd., London, United Kingdom; *U.S. Public*, pg. 1304
Kedrowski, Leonard, Pres.--North Coast Mortgage, Inc., Roseville, MN; *U.S. Public*, pg. 1406
Keefe, Gary, Pres.--Consolidated Device Inc., City of Industry, CA; *U.S. Public*, pg. 1481
Keefe, Mark, Pres.--PrimeNet Marketing Services, Saint Paul, MN; *U.S. Private*, pg. 602
Keefe, Tom, Pres.--GH Hensley Industries, Inc., Dallas, TX; *U.S. Private*, pg. 439
Keegan, Joseph, Pres.--Becton Dickinson Labware, Franklin Lakes, NJ; *U.S. Public*, pg. 199
Keeler, Alexander, Pres. & Treas.--Keeler Motor Car Company, Inc., Latham, NY; *U.S. Private*, pg. 611
Keeler, D.J., Pres.--Keeler Instruments Inc., Broomall, PA; *Int'l*, pg. 590
Keeler, James L., Pres. & Chief Exec. Officer--WLR Foods, Inc., Timberville, VA; *U.S. Public*, pg. 1727
Keelor, James M., Pres.--Cosmos Broadcasting Corp., Greenville, SC; *U.S. Public*, pg. 992
Keen, Gerald S., Pres.--MGS Storage Services, Inc., Mobile, AL; *U.S. Public*, pg. 1120
Keen, J. Merrill, Pres.--Keen Compressed Gas Co., Wilmington, DE; *U.S. Private*, pg. 611
Keen, Jack W., Pres.--Lynch Telephone Corporation, Greenwich, CT; *U.S. Public*, pg. 1022
Keenan, Michael, Pres.--Tampa Bay Ship Building & Repair Co., Tampa, FL; *U.S. Private*, pg. 1067
Keenan, Thomas, Pres.--NIDEC, Canton, MA; *Int'l*, pg. 933
Keenan, Thomas, Pres.--NIDEC Power General, Canton, MA; *Int'l*, pg. 933
Keene, David L., Pres.--Fiduciary Trust International of California, Los Angeles, CA; *U.S. Public*, pg. 621
Keene, Howard, Chm. Bd., Pres.,Chief Exec. & Oper. Officer--Rawlings Sporting Goods Company, Fenton, MO; *U.S. Public*, pg. 1361
Keene, Michael R., Pres.--John Roberts Company, Minneapolis, MN; *U.S. Private*, pg. 935
Keene, Richard A., Pres.--Holstein Association USA, Inc., Brattleboro, VT; *U.S. Private*, pg. 536
Keener, J.W., Jr., Chm. Bd., Pres., Chief Exec. Officer--The Chardon Rubber Co., Chardon, OH; *U.S. Private*, pg. 229
Keener, Larry, Pres.--Palm Harbor Homes, Inc., Dallas, TX; *U.S. Public*, pg. 1254
Keener, Wayne, Pres. & Chief Exec. Officer--Keeners, Inc., Renton, WA; *U.S. Private*, pg. 611
Keener, Wayne, Pres. & Chief Exec. Officer--Beef Distributors, Inc., Renton, WA; *U.S. Private*, pg. 611
Keeney, Michael D., Pres. & Chief Oper. Officer--Walle Corporation, Harahan, LA; *U.S. Private*, pg. 1148
Keersmaeker, Charles A., Pres.--The John Johnson Co., Detroit, MI; *U.S. Private*, pg. 591
Keeter, Daren, Pres.--Royal Oak Enterprises, Inc., Atlanta, GA; *U.S. Private*, pg. 948
Kefalas, Paul T., Pres. & Chief Exec. Officer--ABB in Canada, Saint-Laurent, Canada; *Int'l*, pg. 7
Kehoe, John M., Pres. & Chief Exec. Officer--Wheelabrator Technologies Inc., Hampton, NH; *U.S. Public*, pg. 1745
Keiser, Donald M., Pres. & Chief Exec. Officer--SunTrust Bank, Northwest Georgia, N.A., Rome, GA; *U.S. Public*, pg. 1538
Keiser, Jack, Pres.--Bird Products Corporation, Palm Springs, CA; *U.S. Public*, pg. 1591
Keiser, Robert L., Chm. Bd., Pres. & Chief Exec. Officer--Oryx Energy, Dallas, TX; *U.S. Public*, pg. 1232
Keisling, Gary, Pres.--International Correspondence Schools, Inc., Scranton, PA; *U.S. Public*, pg. 783
Keisling, Gary, Pres.--National Learning Systems, Inc., Scranton, PA; *U.S. Public*, pg. 783
Keisling, Gary, Pres.--NBD Incorporated, Scranton, PA; *U.S. Public*, pg. 783
Keisling, Gary M., Pres.--ICS Learning Systems, Inc., Scranton, PA; *U.S. Public*, pg. 783
Keitel, Hans-Peter, Dr., Pres.--Hochtief AG, Essen, Germany; *Int'l*, pg. 623
Keith, Carter, Sr. Principal & Grp. Acct. Dir.--Publicis/Bloom, Dallas, TX; *Int'l*, pg. 469
Keith, Lee, Pres.--C.D. Smith Drug Company, Saint Joseph, MO; *U.S. Private*, pg. 1007
Keith, R. Drake, Pres.--Entergy Arkansas, Inc., Little Rock, AR; *U.S. Public*, pg. 586
Keith, Robert, Pres. & Chief Exec. Officer--ServiceMaster Management Services Corporation, Downers Grove, IL; *U.S. Public*, pg. 1462
Keith, Robert E., Pres. & Chief Exec. Officer--TL Ventures, Wayne, PA; *U.S. Public*, pg. 1424
Keithley, Joseph P., Chm. Bd., Pres. & Chief Exec. Officer--Keithley Instruments, Inc., Cleveland, OH; *U.S. Public*, pg. 946
Kelb, Karl, Pres.--High Point Oil Co., Indianapolis, IN; *U.S. Private*, pg. 528
Kelbel, Craig, Pres.--US Benefits Insurance Services, Inc., Costa Mesa, CA; *U.S. Public*, pg. 328
Kelleher, Daniel L., Pres.--New Jersey-American Resources Company, Haddon Heights, NJ; *U.S. Public*, pg. 95
Kelleher, Herbert D., Chm. Bd., Pres. & Chief Exec. Officer--Southwest Airlines Co., Dallas, TX; *U.S. Public*, pg. 1493
Kelleher, Richard M., Pres. & Chief Exec. Officer--Doubletree Corporation, Memphis, TN; *U.S. Public*, pg. 1335
Keller, David, Pres. & Chief Exec. Officer--UPB of Mid-Missouri, Columbia, MO; *U.S. Public*, pg. 1669
Keller, Ed, Pres.--Roper Starch Worldwide, Mamaroneck, NY; *U.S. Private*, pg. 944
Keller, Fritz, Chm. Bd. & Pres.--Brauerei Eichhof, Lucerne, Switzerland; *Int'l*, pg. 213
Keller, Gary H., Chm. Bd. & Pres.--Hotel Corporation of America, Maple Hill, KS; *U.S. Private*, pg. 541
Keller, Richard D., Pres. & Chief Exec. Officer--Electric Fuel Corp., Saint Petersburg, FL; *U.S. Public*, pg. 655
Keller, Robert L., Pres. & Chief Exec. Officer--J.J. Keller & Associates, Inc., Neenah, WI; *U.S. Private*, pg. 612
Keller, Thomas, Pres. & Gen. Mgr.--Thermoplastics, Inc., Mishawaka, IN; *U.S. Public*, pg. 1590
Keller, Thomas M., Pres.--Time Insurance, Milwaukee, WI; *Int'l*, pg. 499
Keller, Thomas M., Pres.--Fortis Life, Milwaukee, WI; *Int'l*, pg. 499
Keller, W. Richard, Pres.--Radiometer America Inc., Westlake, OH; *Int'l*, pg. 1083
Keller, William L., III, Pres.--Keymark Corporation, Fonda, NY; *U.S. Private*, pg. 618
Kellermeyer, Donald V., Pres., Chief Exec. Officer & Treas.--Kellermeyer Co., Toledo, OH; *U.S. Private*, pg. 612
Kelley, Brian J., Pres. & Chief Exec. Officer--Cognitronics Corporation, Danbury, CT; *U.S. Public*, pg. 394
Kelley, Bruce G., Pres., Chief Exec. Officer & Treas.--EMC Insurance Group, Inc., Des Moines, IA; *U.S. Public*, pg. 545
Kelley, Gary L., Chm. Bd., Pres. & Chief Exec. Officer--Kelley Bean Co., Inc., Morrill, NE; *U.S. Private*, pg. 612
Kelley, James E., Pres.--Warm Brothers Construction Company, Cincinnati, OH; *U.S. Private*, pg. 1150
Kelley, James M., Pres.--Dixie Crystals Brands, Inc., Savannah, GA; *U.S. Public*, pg. 872
Kelley, James M., Pres.--Savannah Investment Company, Wilmington, DE; *U.S. Public*, pg. 873
Kelley, James V., Chm. Bd., Pres. & Chief Exec. Officer--First United Bancshares, Inc., El Dorado, AR; *U.S. Public*, pg. 641
Kelley, Joe, Pres. & Chief Exec. Officer--AGC Life Insurance Co., Nashville, TN; *U.S. Public*, pg. 76
Kelley, Joe, Pres. & Chief Exec. Officer--American General Life & Accident Insurance Co., Nashville, TN; *U.S. Public*, pg. 76
Kelley, Larry I., Pres. & Chief Exec. Officer--One Price Clothing Stores, Inc., Duncan, SC; *U.S. Public*, pg. 1225
Kelley, Mike, Pres.--Richards Industries Valve Group, Cincinnati, OH; *U.S. Private*, pg. 929
Kelley, Peter H., Pres. & Chief Oper. Officer--Southern Union Company, Austin, TX; *U.S. Public*, pg. 1491
Kelley, Robert, Chm. Bd., Pres. & Chief Exec. Officer--Noble Affiliates, Inc., Ardmore, OK; *U.S. Public*, pg. 1186
Kelley, Scott, Pres.--Natvar Company, Clayton, NC; *U.S. Private*, pg. 528
Kelley, Thomas, Pres.--Kelley Automotive Group, Fort Wayne, IN; *U.S. Private*, pg. 612
Kelley, Thomas M., Pres.--First American Title Co. of Los Angeles, Glendale, CA; *U.S. Public*, pg. 625
Kelley, William, Pres. & Mgr.-Opers.--Fiber-Resin Corporation, Chatsworth, CA; *U.S. Public*, pg. 686
Kellman, Mildred, Chm. Bd. & Pres.--Globe-Amerada Glass Company, Elk Grove Village, IL; *U.S. Private*, pg. 458
Kellogg, C.G., Pres.--Chateau Communities, Inc., Englewood, CO; *U.S. Public*, pg. 341
Kellogg, Charles T., Pres., Chief Exec. Officer & Treas.--Hubbard Hall Inc., Waterbury, CT; *U.S. Private*, pg. 544
Kellogg, Martin N., Pres. & Chief Exec. Officer--UFE Incorporated, Stillwater, MN; *U.S. Private*, pg. 1112
Kellogg, Tom N., Pres. & Chief Oper. Officer--General Reinsurance Corp., Stamford, CT; *U.S. Public*, pg. 725
Kells, Geoffrey, Pres. & Mng. Dir.--CSR Limited, Sydney, Australia; *Int'l*, pg. 245
Kelly, Andrew W., Pres.--The Crystal Tissue Co., Middletown, OH; *U.S. Private*, pg. 294
Kelly, Anthony O., Pres. & Chief Exec. Officer--Mannington Mills, Inc., Salem, NJ; *U.S. Private*, pg. 700
Kelly, Brian, Pres., Chief. Oper. Officer & Sec.--Activision, Santa Monica, CA; *U.S. Public*, pg. 17
Kelly, David M., Chm. Bd., Pres. & Chief Exec. Officer--Matthews International Corp., Pittsburgh, PA; *U.S. Public*, *pg. 1059*
Kelly, Dennis, Pres.--Baxter Tube Company, Warrensville Heights, OH; *U.S. Public*, pg. 1632
Kelly, Don, Pres.--North Central Division, Norcross, GA; *U.S. Public*, pg. 1255
Kelly, Edmund F., Pres. & Chief Oper. Officer--Liberty Mutual Insurance Co., Boston, MA; *U.S. Private*, pg. 666
Kelly, Francis J., III, Mng. Partner & Chief Mktg. Officer--Arnold Communications, Inc., Boston, MA; *U.S. Private*, pg. 83
Kelly, Fred W., Jr., Pres. & Chief Exec. Officer--Sun Bancorp, Inc., Selinsgrove, PA; *U.S. Public*, pg. 1529
Kelly, J. Fredrick, Jr., Pres. & Chief Exec. Officer--Aeroglide Corporation, Cary, NC; *U.S. Private*, pg. 24
Kelly, J. Peter, Pres. & Chief Oper. Officer--The LTV Corporation, Cleveland, OH; *U.S. Public*, pg. 971
Kelly, John, Pres. & Chief Exec. Officer--Biederman, Kelly & Shaffer, Inc., New York, NY; *U.S. Private*, pg. 142
Kelly, John D., Pres. & Chief Exec. Officer--Na-Churs Plant Food Company, Marion, OH; *U.S. Private*, pg. 1096
Kelly, John F., Chm. Bd., Pres, Chief Exec. & Oper. Officer--Alaska Air Group, Inc., Seattle, WA; *U.S. Public*, pg. 35
Kelly, John J., Pres. & Chief Exec. Officer--Willis Corroon Corp. of New York, New York, NY; *Int'l*, pg. 1506
Kelly, John L., Pres.--CWC Textron Company, Muskegon, MI; *U.S. Public*, pg. 1590
Kelly, John L., Pres.--CWC Castings Textron, Muskegon, MI; *U.S. Public*, pg. 1590
Kelly, John M., Pres.--Midvale Plaza, Madison, WI; *U.S. Private*, pg. 784
Kelly, Linda, Pres.--Astra Pharmaceuticals Ltd., Kings Langley, United Kingdom; *Int'l*, pg. 94
Kelly, Michael N., Pres.--Tera Pharmaceuticals, Buena Park, CA; *U.S. Public*, pg. 196
Kelly, Pat, Pres.--PSS, Cincinnati, OH; *U.S. Public*, pg. 1294
Kelly, Patrick, Pres. & Chief Exec. Officer--Physician Sales and Services Inc., Jacksonville, FL; *U.S. Public*, pg. 1293
Kelly, Richard C., Pres.--E Prime, Inc., Denver, CO; *U.S. Public*, pg. 1170
Kelly, Richard E., Pres.--Clipper Belt Lacer Company, Grand Rapids, MI; *U.S. Private*, pg. 413
Kelly, Robert, Pres. & Chief Exec. Officer--Eagle Food Centers, Inc., Milan, IL; *U.S. Public*, pg. 547
Kelly, Robert, Pres. & Chief Exec. Officer--Nicklaus Golf Company, L.C., West Palm Beach, FL; *U.S. Private*, pg. 799
Kelly, Robert J., Pres.--Bull HN Information Systems Inc., Billerica, MA; *Int'l*, pg. 316
Kelly, Robert, Jr., Pres.--MacSteel Div., Jackson, MI; *U.S. Public*, pg. 1349
Kelly, Robert, Jr., Pres.--MacSteel Div., Fort Smith, AR; *U.S.* Public, pg. 1349
Kelly, Stephen J., Chm. Bd., Pres. & Chief Exec. Officer--SouthCo. Inc., Concordville, PA; *U.S. Private*, pg. 1014
Kelly, Terry, Pres.--Baker Distributing Company, Jacksonville, FL; *U.S. Public*, pg. 1746
Kelly, Thomas J., Chm Bd., Pres., & Chief Exec. Officer--Somerset Savings Bank, Somerville, MA; *U.S. Public*, pg. 1484
Kelly, Timothy, Pres.--Mercury Adjustment Bureau, Inc., Lynbrook, NY; *U.S. Private*, pg. 406
Kelly, Tom, Publr. & Chief Exec. Officer--Catholic Digest, Saint Paul, MN; *U.S. Private*, pg. 220
Kelly, Tony, Pres. & Chief Exec. Officer, Mannington Mills--Mannington Resilient Floors, Salem, NJ; *U.S. Private*, pg. 700
Kelsey, Rich, Pres.--Encore Shoe Corporation, Rochester, NH; *U.S. Private*, pg. 375
Kelsey, Robert E., Pres.--Kelsey Construction, Inc., Orlando, FL; *U.S. Private*, pg. 613
Kelso, Richard W., Pres. & Chief Exec. Officer--PQ Corporation, Berwyn, PA; *U.S. Private*, pg. 827
Kemeny, Robert A., Pres. & Chief Exec. Officer--This End Up Furniture, Richmond, VA; *U.S. Private*, pg. 1081
Kemmish, Kirk C., Pres.--Phelps Dodge Magnet Wire Co., Fort Wayne, IN; *U.S. Public*, pg. 1286
Kemp, K. Thomas, Pres. & Chief Exec. Officer--Fund American Enterprises Holdings, Inc., Hanover, NH; *U.S. Public*, pg. 688
Kemp, Melvin T., Pres. & Chief Exec. Officer--B & K Steel & Supply, Inc., Ogden, UT; *U.S. Private*, pg. 105
Kemp, Melvin T., Pres.--Bowman & Kemp Rebar, Ogden, UT; *U.S. Private*, pg. 105
Kemp, Steven E., Pres. & Chief Exec. Officer--Regions Bank/Rome, Rome, GA; *U.S. Public*, pg. 1372
Kemper, Alexander, Pres.--UMB Financial Corporation, Kansas City, MO; *U.S. Public*, pg. 1653
Kemper, David W., Chm. Bd., Pres. & Chief Exec. Officer--Commerce Bancshares, Inc., Kansas City, MO; *U.S. Public*, pg. 409
Kemper, Jonathan M., Chm. Bd., Pres. & Chief Exec. Officer--Commerce Bank N.A., Kansas City, MO; *U.S. Public*, pg. 409
Kemper, Michael J., Pres. & Chief Exec. Officer--Northern Pipeline Construction Co., Phoenix, AZ; *U.S. Public*, pg. 1493
Kempinski, Chester F., Pres.--McCoy Electronics Co., Mount Holly Springs, PA; *U.S. Public*, pg. 1209
Kempner, James C., Pres. & Chief Exec. Officer--Imperial Holly Corporation, Sugar Land, TX; *U.S. Public*, pg. 872
Kendal, N.P., Mng. Dir.--Alcan Ekco, Chesham, United Kingdom; *Int'l*, pg. 51
Kendall, Donald S., III, Chm. Bd. & Pres.--Mack Molding Company Inc., Arlington, VT; *U.S. Private*, pg. 691
Kendall, Stephen F., Pres. & Chief Exec. Officer--Aluminum Shapes, LLC, Delair, NJ; *U.S. Private*, pg. 47
Kendall, Steve, Pres. & Chief Exec. Officer--Electrical Insulation Suppliers, Atlanta, GA; *U.S. Private*, pg. 368
Kendell, Ross E., Pres. & Chief Exec. Officer--Key Bank of Utah, Salt Lake City, UT; *U.S. Public*, pg. 954
Kendrick, Jack, Sr. Principal & Creative Dir.--Publicis/Bloom, Dallas, TX; *Int'l*, pg. 469
Kenerleber, A.J., Pres. & Chief Oper. Officer--Video Display Corporation, Tucker, GA; *U.S. Public*, pg. 1720
Kenkel, Jeff, Pres.--KHR, Omaha, NE; *U.S. Private*, pg. 603
Kenlon, John, Pres. & Chief Oper. Officer--Scott's Miracle-Gro Products, Inc., Port Washington, NY; *U.S. Public*, pg. 1447
Kenneally, J.T., Pres.--International Systems & Controls Corp., Houston, TX; *U.S. Private*, pg. 572
Kenneally, Thomas F., Sr., Pres. & Chief Exec. Officer--Town Pump, Inc., Butte, MT; *U.S. Private*, pg. 1093
Kennedy, Bernard D., Pres. & Chief Oper. Officer--King Kullen Grocery Co., Inc., Westbury, NY; *U.S. Private*, pg. 621
Kennedy, Bernard J., Chm. Bd., Pres. & Chief Exec. Officer--National Fuel Gas Company, Buffalo, NY; *U.S. Public*, pg. 1156
Kennedy, James A., Pres. & Chief Exec. Officer--National Starch and Chemical Company, Bridgewater, NJ; *Int'l*, pg. 1435
Kennedy, James C., Chm. Bd. & Chief Exec. Officer--Cox Enterprises, Inc., Atlanta, GA; *U.S. Private*, pg. 281
Kennedy, John, Pres. & Chief Oper. Officer--Budget Group, Inc., Daytona Beach, FL; *U.S. Private*, pg. 178
Kennedy, John, Pres. & Chief Oper. Officer--Budget Rent A Car Corporation, Lisle, IL; *U.S. Private*, pg. 178
Kennedy, John C., Chm. Bd., Pres. & Chief Exec. Officer--Autocam Corporation, Grand Rapids, MI; *U.S. Public*, pg. 148
Kennedy, John C., Pres.--Autocam Acquisition, Inc., Hayward, CA; *U.S. Public*, pg. 148
Kennedy, John C., Pres.--Autocam Laser Technologies, Inc., Hayward, CA; *U.S. Public*, pg. 148
Kennedy, John C., Pres.--Autocam-Pax, Inc., Dowagiac, MI; *U.S. Public*, pg. 148
Kennedy, John C., Pres.--Autocam South Carolina, Inc., Gaffney, SC; *U.S. Public*, pg. 148

Kennedy, John M., Chm. Bd., Pres. & Gen. Mgr.--T.H. Rogers Lumber Co., Edmond, OK; *U.S. Private,* pg. 940

Kennedy, John R., Pres. & Chief Exec. Officer--Federal Paper Board Company, Inc., Montvale, NJ; *U.S. Public,* pg. 903

Kennedy, Michael, Pres.--WinCup, Phoenix, AZ; *U.S. Private,* pg. 1182

Kennedy, Parker S., Pres.--The First American Financial Corporation, Santa Ana, CA; *U.S. Public,* pg. 624

Kennedy, Patrick W., Pres.--Kennedy Tank & Manufacturing Co., Inc., Indianapolis, IN; *U.S. Private,* pg. 614

Kennedy, Paul L., Pres.--Dominick & Dominick, Incorporated, New York, NY; *U.S. Private,* pg. 338

Kennedy, Vincent, Pres.--Applied Industrial Materials Corporation, Stamford, CT; *U.S. Public,* pg. 1736

Kennedy, W. Keith, Jr., Dr., Pres. & Chief Exec. Officer--Watkins-Johnson Company, Palo Alto, CA; *U.S. Public,* pg. 1745

Kenney, Martin E., Jr, Pres.--Simon & Schuster Education Technology Group, New York, NY; *U.S. Private,* pg. 778

Kenney, Thomas, Pres.--The Summit Media Group, New York, NY; *U.S. Private,* pg. 1050

Kenney, Tricia, Pres. & Exec. V.P.--Ayer Public Relations, New York, NY; *U.S. Private,* pg. 104

Kenny, David, Partner--Bronner Slosberg Humphrey/ Strategic Interactive Group, Boston, MA; *U.S. Private,* pg. 171

Kenny, Greg, Pres.--Carol Cable Company, Highland Heights, KY; *Int'l,* pg. 1487

Kenny, James R., Pres., Chief Exec. Officer & Sec.--SJNB Financial Corp., San Jose, CA; *U.S. Public,* pg. 1418

Kenny, Michael J., Pres.--Laporte Inc., Princeton, NJ; *Int'l,* pg. 802

Kent, Gage A., Pres.--Grain Processing Corp., Muscatine, IA; *U.S. Private,* pg. 1134

Kent, J.H., Pres.--Varied Investments, Inc., Muscatine, IA; *U.S. Private,* pg. 1134

Kent, Jerald, Pres.--Charter Communications, Inc., Saint Louis, MO; *U.S. Private,* pg. 230

Kent, Mark B., Pres. & Chief Oper. Officer--The Kent Manufacturing Co., Pickens, SC; *U.S. Private,* pg. 615

Kent, Marsha, Co-Pres. & Chief Exec. Officer--Kent & Spiegel Direct, Culver City, CA; *U.S. Private,* pg. 615

Kentner, Pat, Gen. Mgr. & Dir.--Railway Educational Bureau, Omaha, NE; *U.S. Private,* pg. 1000

Kenton, James, Pres.--Futuro Inc., Milford, OH; *Int'l,* pg. 182

Kenton, James A., Pres.--Beiersdorf, Inc., Norwalk, CT; *Int'l, pg. 182*

Kenyon, E. Niles, Pres. & Chief Oper. Officer--The Conair Group, Inc., Pittsburgh, PA; *U.S. Private,* pg. 261

Keogh, C.J., Pres.--Niedner Limited, Coaticook, Canada; *Int'l,* pg. 1485

Keohane, Sean, Pres.--Banta Global Turnkey Group, Cork, Ireland; *U.S. Public,* pg. 189

Keon, William T., III, Pres. & Chief Exec. Officer--Pueblo Xtra International, Inc., Pompano Beach, FL; *U.S. Private,* pg. 894

Keosayian, Raymond, Pres.--Holmes Protection of Long Island, Inc., Islandia, NY; *U.S. Public,* pg. 1649

Kerbs, Charles F., Jr., Pres.--Federal Chicago Corporation, North Chicago, IL; *U.S. Private,* pg. 398

Kerckhoff, Richard D., Jr., Gen. Mgr.--Pevely Dairy Company, Saint Louis, MO; *U.S. Private,* pg. 879

Keret, M., Pres. & Chief Exec. Officer--Israel Aircraft Industries Ltd., Israel; *Int'l,* pg. 689

Kerins, Donald J., Pres.--Government Electronics Div., Woodland Hills, CA; *U.S. Public,* pg. 293

Kerkorian, Kirk, Chm. Bd., Pres. & Chief Exec. Officer--Tracinda Corporation, Las Vegas, NV; *U.S. Private,* pg. 1095

Kerley, Gary, Pres.--SMI Rail, Seguin, TX; *U.S. Public,* pg. 413

Kerman, Harold M., Pres.--Steiner Electric Company, Chicago, IL; *U.S. Private,* pg. 1039

Kerman, Richard, Pres. & Chief Oper. Officer--Steiner Electric Company, Elk Grove Village, IL; *U.S. Private,* pg. 1039

Kern, Frank, III, Pres.--Maxitrol Co., Southfield, MI; *U.S. Private,* pg. 716

Kern, Lawrence A., Pres.--Dole Fresh Vegetables, Salinas, CA; *U.S. Public,* pg. 515

Kernan, Margaret B., Pres.--Sampler Publications Inc., Saint Charles, IL; *U.S. Private,* pg. 963

Kerns, Michael, Pres.--Jani King of California, Inc., Huntington Beach, CA; *U.S. Private,* pg. 581

Kerr, Bill, Pres. & Chief Exec. Officer--Country Home Magazine, Des Moines, IA; *U.S. Public,* pg. 1094

Kerr, Charles, Pres.--Trans-American Steamship Agency, San Pedro, CA; *Int'l,* pg. 1418

Kerr, Donald J., Pres. & Chief Exec. Officer--Crestar Food Products, Inc., Brentwood, TN; *U.S. Public,* pg. 805

Kerr, Howard J., Chm. Bd., Pres. & Chief Exec. Officer--Consolidated Pipe & Supply Company, Birmingham, AL; *U.S. Private,* pg. 266

Kerr, Richard L., Pres. & Chief Exec. Officer--IMCO Recycling Inc., Irving, TX; *U.S. Public,* pg. 870

Kerr, William, Pres.--Subaru Canada Inc., Mississauga, Canada; *Int'l,* pg. 523

Kerr, William, Pres.--Professional Loss Control, Kingston, TN; *U.S. Public,* pg. 795

Kerry, Alan E., Pres.--American Trading Real Estate Properties, Inc., Baltimore, MD; *U.S. Private,* pg. 64

Kerry, F.R., Pres.--Fine Art Developments plc, Bradford, United Kingdom; *Int'l,* pg. 485

Kers, F.M., Pres.--TFA - Trans-maritime Freight Agencies B.V., Rotterdam, Netherlands; *Int'l,* pg. 682

Kerschen, Richard, Chm. Bd., Pres. & Chief Exec. Officer--The Law Company, Inc., Wichita, KS; *U.S. Private,* pg. 653

Kershaw, Michael P., Pres. & Chief Oper. Officer--Shirmax Retail Ltd., Montreal, Canada; *Int'l,* pg. 1235

Kerstetter, Bert, Pres.--Everfast Inc., Kennett Square, PA; *U.S. Private,* pg. 386

Kerstetter, Bert, Pres.--Calico Corners, Kennett Square, PA; *U.S. Private,* pg. 386

Kersulis, Bernard J., Pres., Chief Exec. Officer & Chief Oper. Officer--Standun, Inc., Inglewood, CA; *U.S. Private, pg. 1032*

Kertzman, Mitchell, Pres.--Sybase Professional Services, Burlington, MA; *U.S. Public,* pg. 1544

Kertzman, Mitchell, Pres.--Sybase Inc., Concord, MA; *U.S. Public,* pg. 1544

Kervick, Robert B., Pres.--Kervick Enterprises, Inc., Worcester, MA; *U.S. Private,* pg. 616

Kerwin, Barry, Pres.--Waukesha Foundry Inc., Waukesha, WI; *U.S. Private,* pg. 1154

Kerwin, J.P., M.D., Pres.--Krug Life Sciences Inc., Houston, TX; *U.S. Public,* pg. 968

Kerz, Paul J., Chm. Bd., Pres. & Chief Exec. Officer--Health Management Systems, Inc., New York, NY; *U.S. Public,* pg. 802

Kerzner, Howard B., Pres.--Sun International Hotels Limited, Fort Lauderdale, FL; *U.S. Public,* pg. 1531

Kesl, James R., Pres. & Chief Exec. Officer--Willis Corroon Corp. of Seattle, Seattle, WA; *Int'l,* pg. 1507

Kesler, Phillip, Pres.--Warner Candy Company, Inc., Schiller Park, IL; *U.S. Private,* pg. 1150

Kessler, Betsy, Partner--Houston Herstek Favat, Boston, MA; *U.S. Private,* pg. 542

Kesteloot, Thomas M., Pres.--Sysco Intermountain Food Services, Inc., Salt Lake City, UT; *U.S. Public,* pg. 1552

Kesterson, Tommy, Chm. Bd. & Pres.--Kesterson Food Company, Inc., Paris, TN; *U.S. Private,* pg. 616

Keston, Michael I., Pres.--Larwin Company, Encino, CA; *U.S. Private,* pg. 652

Ketcham, Henry, III, Pres. & Chief Exec. Officer--West Fraser Timber Co. Ltd., Vancouver, Canada; *Int'l,* pg. 1490

Ketesledger, Roger, Pres. & Chief Exec. Officer--Yale/ Chase Materials Handling, Inc., City of Industry, CA; *U.S.* Private, pg. 1195

Ketner, William O., Jr., Pres. & Sec.--Exclusive Healthcare, Inc., Omaha, NE; *U.S. Private,* pg. 770

Kettelhut, Willis, Pres.--Reinke Manufacturing Co., Inc., Deshler, NE; *U.S. Private,* pg. 920

Kettell, Russell W., Pres. & Treas.--Golden West Financial Corporation, Oakland, CA; *U.S. Public,* pg. 750

Kettler, James M., Pres., Exec. V.P. & Gen Mgr.--Kettler Brothers, Inc., Montgomery Village, MD; *U.S. Private,* pg. 617

Keup, Rick E., Pres. & Chief Oper. Officer--Ames Company, Parkersburg, WV; *U.S. Public,* pg. 1683

Kever, Jim, Pres. & Co-Chief Exec. Officer--Envoy Corporation, Nashville, TN; *U.S. Public,* pg. 587

Kevtko, Colleen, Pres. & Chief Exec. Officer--Fifth-Third Trust Co. & Savings Bank, FSB, Naples, FL; *U.S. Public, pg. 622*

Kewer, David B., Pres. & Chief Oper. Officer--Eskimo Pie Corporation, Richmond, VA; *U.S. Public,* pg. 592

Key, Derrick N., Chm. Bd., Pres. & Chief Exec. Officer--Roper Industries, Inc., Bogart, GA; *U.S. Public,* pg. 1405

Key, J. Douglas, Pres. & Chief Oper. Officer--Cabre Exploration Ltd., Calgary, Canada; *Int'l,* pg. 247

Key, James Richard, Pres. & Chief Exec. Officer--Regions Bank/Chilton County, Thorsby, AL; *U.S. Public,* pg. 1372

Key, John, Pres. & Chief Exec. Officer--Clinton State Bank, Clinton, IN; *U.S. Public,* pg. 1217

Keymer, Ken, Pres.--Sonic Industries, Inc., Oklahoma City, OK; *U.S. Public,* pg. 1485

Keys, Howard, Pres.--Keyes Motors, Inc., Van Nuys, CA; *U.S. Private,* pg. 618

Keyser, Richard L., Pres. & Chief Exec. Officer--W.W. Grainger, Inc., Lincolnshire, IL; *U.S. Public,* pg. 758

Keyser, Richard L., Pres.--Grainger, Lincolnshire, IL; *U.S. Public,* pg. 758

Keyte, Roger, Pres.--Hart Graphics Inc., Austin, TX; *U.S. Private,* pg. 507

Kezuka, Tomio, Pres.--Nomura Satellite Communications Co., Ltd., Tokyo, Japan; *Int'l,* pg. 956

Khalifeh, Julie, Pres.--Business Equipment Center, Washington, DC; *U.S. Private,* pg. 189

Khan, Saeed U., Pres.--Kvaerner R J Brown Pte. Ltd., Singapore, Singapore; *Int'l,* pg. 767

Khan, Sultan W., Pres. & Chief Exec. Officer--Newcom, Inc., Westlake Village, CA; *U.S. Public,* pg. 147

Kheng, Gwee Lian, Pres. & Chief Exec. Officer--United Overseas Land Limited, Singapore, Singapore; *Int'l,* pg. 1443

Khim, Jay W., Dr., Chm. Bd., Pres. & Chief Exec. Officer--JWK International Corp., Annandale, VA; *U.S. Private,* pg. 579

Khouri, R., Dr., Pres.--L-Zos Optics, Ltd., Detroit, MI; *U.S. Private,* pg. 639

Khumalo, M.G., Chm. Bd & Pres.--JCI Limited, Johannesburg, South Africa; *Int'l,* pg. 696

Ki-Bum, Yoo, Pres.-General Trading Div.--Daewoo Corporation, Seoul, Korea; *Int'l,* pg. 357

Ki, Lee Yun, Pres.--Daewoo Corporation, Seoul, Korea; *Int'l, pg. 357*

Kibler, Michael E., Pres.--Blue & Gray Brokerage, Gary, IN; *U.S. Public,* pg. 1687

Kibler, Micheal E., Pres.--US 1 Industries Inc., Gary, IN; *U.S. Public,* pg. 1687

Kiburz, William, Partner & Business-to-Business Client Services--Kupper Parker Communications Inc., Saint Louis, MO; *U.S. Private,* pg. 637

Kidd, Kenneth, Chm. Bd. & Pres.--Superior Label Systems, Inc., Mason, OH; *U.S. Private,* pg. 1055

Kidd, Wilmot H., Pres.--Central Securities Corporation, New York, NY; *U.S. Public,* pg. 326

Kidder, Norman, Pres. & Chief Exec. Officer--Rauland-Borg Corporation, Skokie, IL; *U.S. Private,* pg. 911

Kidner, Raymond L., Pres.--Tosoh SMD Korea Ltd., Kyongki, Korea; *Int'l,* pg. 1408

Kidon, Modi, Pres.--Gitam/BBDO, Ramat Gan, Israel; *Int'l,* pg. 552

Kieckhafer, Thomas W., Pres.--The West Bend Co., West Bend, WI; *U.S. Public,* pg. 1322

Kiefer, Charles F., III, Partner & Chief Fin. Officer--Arnold Communications, Inc., Boston, MA; *U.S. Private,* pg. 83

Kiefer, William C., Chm. Bd. & Pres.--Bel-Ray Company, Inc., Farmingdale, NJ; *U.S. Private,* pg. 130

Kieffer, Dominique, Pres.--Polarcup France S.A., Auneau, France; *Int'l,* pg. 638

Kieffer, William, Pres.--Komori Canada Ltd., Milton, Canada; *Int'l,* pg. 745

Kiefus, Jerry, Pres.--Big Joe Manufacturing Co., Lincolnwood, IL; *U.S. Private,* pg. 143

Kiehm, John, Pres.--PAR Vision Systems Corporation, New Hartford, NY; *U.S. Public,* pg. 1256

Kiel, Douglas G., Pres.--Journal Broadcast Group, Inc., Milwaukee, WI; *U.S. Private,* pg. 601

Kielholz, Walter B., Pres. & Chief Exec. Officer--Swiss Reinsurance Company, Zurich, Switzerland; *Int'l,* pg. 1332

Kiely, W. Leo, III, Pres. & Chief Oper. Officer--Coors Brewing Company, Golden, CO; *U.S. Public,* pg. 445

Kiepper, Alan F., Pres.--New York City Transit Authority, Brooklyn, NY; *U.S. Private,* pg. 739

Kierlin, Robert A., Chm. Bd., Pres. & Chief Exec. Officer--Fastenal Company, Winona, MN; *U.S. Public,* pg. 614

Kies, A.M., Pres. & Chief Exec. Officer--Erico International, Solon, OH; *U.S. Private,* pg. 381

Kieseman, Joseph, Pres. & Chief Exec. Officer--Allied Mercantile Company, Philadelphia, PA; *U.S. Private,* pg. 39

Kiesling, Richard, Pres.--Belmont Telephone Company, Madison, WI; *U.S. Public,* pg. 1022

Kieta, D.L., Pres.--Century Contractors West Inc., Kingwood, TX; *U.S. Public,* pg. 950

Kihara, Ken, Pres.--TDK Electronics Corporation, Port Washington, NY; *Int'l,* pg. 1336

Kihara, Terutaka, Pres.--Descente America Inc., Englewood, CO; *Int'l,* pg. 395

Kikkawa, Akikazu, Pres. & Chief Exec. Officer--Ajinomoto U.S.A., Inc., Teaneck, NJ; *Int'l,* pg. 40

Kikuchi, Kyo, Chm. & Pres.--Yasuda Bank and Trust Company (U.S.A.), New York, NY; *Int'l,* pg. 1520

Kikuchi, Yukio, Pres.--Brighton Corporation, Chiba, Japan; *Int'l,* pg. 600

Kilbane, J. Kevin, Pres.--Lowara S.p.A, Montecchio Maggiore, Italy; *U.S. Public,* pg. 861

Kilbride, William, Pres.--American Rug Craftsmen, Sugar Valley, GA; *U.S. Public,* pg. 1121

Kilby, Leonard, Pres.--SASIB Bakery North America Inc., Plano, TX; *Int'l,* pg. 1194

Kilchman, Patrick, Pres.--Frigorex AG fur Kaltetechnik, Lucerne, Switzerland; *Int'l,* pg. 1306

Kilcollin, T. Eric, Pres. & Chief Exec. Officer--Chicago Mercantile Exchange, Chicago, IL; *U.S. Private,* pg. 235

Kilduff, Jack, Pres. & Chief Oper. Officer--Dr. Pepper Co., Dallas, TX; *Int'l,* pg. 248

Kiley, James, Chief Exec. Officer & Gen. Mgr.--Sioux Valley Southwestern Electric Association, Colman, SD; *U.S. Private,* pg. 1004

Kiley, Michael T., Partner, Chief Fin. Officer, & Exec. V.P.--Media That Works, Cincinnati, OH; *U.S. Private,* pg. 727

Kilfeather, Terry D., Pres.--Fibo ExClay Ltd., Tilbury, United Kingdom; *Int'l,* pg. 1200

Kilgore, Gregory M., Pres. & Chief Oper. Officer--Track 'n Trail, El Dorado Hills, CA; *U.S. Public,* pg. 1626

Kilgore, Tom D., Pres. & Chief Exec. Officer--Georgia Transmission Corporation, Tucker, GA; *U.S. Private,* pg. 448

Kilgore, Tom D., Pres. & Chief Exec. Officer--Oglethorpe Power Corp., Tucker, GA; *U.S. Private,* pg. 812

Kilguss, Howard M., Pres.--Excell Manufacturing Company, Providence, RI; *U.S. Private,* pg. 387

Kilian, Fredrick P., Pres.--National Grape Co-Op Association, Inc., Westfield, NY; *U.S. Private,* pg. 784

Kilissanly, Peter E., Pres. & Chief Oper. Officer--Physician Corporation of America, Miami, FL; *U.S. Public,* pg. 1293

Kilkenny, J., Pres.--Monsanto Enviro-Chem. Systems, Inc., Saint Louis, MO; *U.S. Public,* pg. 1125

Kill, Robert H., Chm. Bd., Pres. & Chief Exec. Officer--Ciprico, Inc., Plymouth, MN; *U.S. Public,* pg. 370

Killgallon, Martin L., II, Pres. & Chief Oper. Officer--The Ohio Art Company, Inc., Bryan, OH; *U.S. Public,* pg. 1214

Killinger, Kerry K., Chm. Bd., Pres. & Chief Exec. Officer--Washington Mutual Inc., Seattle, WA; *U.S. Public,* pg. 1741

Killoran, F.J., Pres. & Chief Exec. Officer--Taro Industries Limited, Calgary, Canada; *Int'l,* pg. 1424

Kilpatrick, Chris, Pres.--Interplay Productions, Inc., Irvine, CA; *U.S. Private,* pg. 572

Kilpatrick, Kenneth R., Pres.--Elgar Corporation, San Diego, CA; *U.S. Public,* pg. 789

Kilts, James M., Chm. Bd., Pres. & Chief Exec. Officer--Nabisco Inc., Parsippany, NJ; *U.S. Public,* pg. 1355

Kim, Chang Hee, Pres. & Chief Exec. Officer--Daewoo Securities Co., Ltd., Seoul, Korea; *Int'l,* pg. 358

Kim, Chong-Chin, Pres.--Pohang Iron & Steel Co., Ltd., Kyongbuk, Korea; *Int'l,* pg. 1061

Kim, Dae-Young, Pres.--Ssangyong Finance Inc., Seoul, Korea; *Int'l,* pg. 1292

Kim, Duck-Hwan Hyung, Pres.-Plng. & Devel. Office--Ssangyong Business Group, Seoul, Korea; *Int'l,* pg. 1291

Kim, Edward, Pres., Chief Oper. & Chief Exec. Officer--Pantech Construction Co., Lanham, MD; *U.S. Private,* pg. 837

Kim, Jae Koo, Pres. & Chief Exec. Officer--Cho Hung Bank of Canada, Toronto, Canada; *Int'l,* pg. 288

Kim, Jeong-Hwan, Pres.--Ssangyong Investment & Finance Co., Ltd., Inchon, Korea; *Int'l,* pg. 1292

Kim, Keith, Owner & Pres.--Granny Goose Foods, Inc., Oakland, CA; *U.S. Private,* pg. 469

Kim, Kenneth H., Chm., Pres., Chief Exec. Officer, Corp. Sec. & Treas.--Medieval Times Dinner & Tournament, Inc., Buena Park, CA; *U.S. Private,* pg. 728

Kim, S.T., Pres. & Chief Oper. Officer--AST Research Inc., Irvine, CA; *Int'l*, pg. 1181

Kim, S.W., Pres.--Korea Bundy Corporation, Kyongki, Korea; *Int'l*, pg. 1341

Kim, Se-Yung, Pres.--TrefilARBED Korea Co. Ltd., Yangsan, Korea; *Int'l*, pg. 80

Kim, Suk-Dong, Pres.--Ssangyong Investment & Securities Co., Ltd., Seoul, Korea; *Int'l*, pg. 1292

Kim, Sun-Dong, Pres.--Ssangyong Oil Refining Co. Ltd., Seoul, Korea; *Int'l*, pg. 1292

Kim, Syng Jeung, Pres.--Sunkyong Industries Co., Kyonggi-do, Korea; *Int'l*, pg. 1320

Kim, T.H., Pres.--IPC Corporation (Korea) Ltd., Seoul, Korea; *Int'l*, pg. 651

Kim, Taek-ki, Pres.--Dong Bu Insurance Co., Seoul, Korea; *Int'l*, pg. 416

Kim, Tai Hwan, Pres.--Dong-A Otsuka Co., Ltd., Anyang, Korea; *Int'l*, pg. 1014

Kim, W.K., Pres. & Chief Exec. Officer--Kia Motors America, Inc., Irvine, CA; *Int'l*, pg. 733

Kim, Y.H., Pres. & Chief Exec. Officer--Hyundai Electronics America, San Jose, CA; *Int'l*, pg. 641

Kim, Yong-Un, Pres.--Dong-Suh Foods Corporation, Inchon, Korea; *Int'l*, pg. 416

Kim, Yoo-suk, Pres.--International Aero-Sea Forwarders, Ltd., Seoul, Korea; *Int'l*, pg. 682

Kim, Young Han, Pres. & Chief Oper. Officer--Daewoo Securities (America) Inc., New York, NY; *Int'l*, pg. 359

Kimball, David J., Pres.--Market Entry Omega, Bothell, WA; *U.S. Public*, pg. 1222

Kimball, John G., Pres.--Old Kent Bank-Southwest, Kalamazoo, MI; *U.S. Public*, pg. 1217

Kimball, R. Jeffrey, Pres. & Chief Oper. Officer--L. Robert Kimball & Associates, Ebensburg, PA; *U.S. Private*, pg. 619

Kimball, Richard, Pres.--Granite Prods. Div., Barre, VT; *U.S. Public*, pg. 1396

Kimball, Richard, Pres.--Rock of Ages Canada, Inc., Beebe, Canada; *U.S. Public*, pg. 1396

Kimbell, David A., Chm. Bd. & Pres.--Burk Royalty Co., Wichita Falls, TX; *U.S. Private*, pg. 182

Kimbell, John S., Pres. & Chief Exec. Officer--Vermont Gas Systems, Inc., South Burlington, VT; *Int'l*, pg. 542

Kimbrell, James R., Pres. & Chief Exec. Officer--La Mesa R V Center, Inc., San Diego, CA; *U.S. Private*, pg. 640

Kimbrough, James H., Pres. & Chief Exec. Officer--SunTrust Bank, Nature Coast, Brooksville, FL; *U.S. Public*, pg. 1537

Kimbrough, Lawrence M., Pres. & Chief Exec. Officer--First Charter Corporation, Concord, NC; *U.S. Public*, pg. 627

Kime, Jeff, Pres.--Four Wind International Corp., Elkhart, IN; *U.S. Public*, pg. 1602

Kimker, Klay, Pres.--Liberty Property Management Co., Oklahoma City, OK; *U.S. Public*, pg. 174

Kimmel, J. Stephen, Pres.--Akzo Nobel Chemicals Inc., Chicago, IL; *Int'l*, pg. 47

Kimmel, Jerry E., Chm. Bd., Pres. & Chief Exec. Officer--Kevco, Inc., Fort Worth, TX; *U.S. Public*, pg. 952

Kimmell, Garman O., Pres.--Kimray, Inc., Oklahoma City, OK; *U.S. Private*, pg. 620

Kimoto, Yasuyuki, Pres.--Sumitomo Bank Financial Services, Inc., New York, NY; *Int'l*, pg. 1308

Kimsey, Gary, Pres.--Gemtron Corporation, Sweetwater, TN; *Int'l*, pg. 1523

Kimura, Seishi "Woody", Pres.--Sanden International (U.S.A.), Inc., Wylie, TX; *Int'l*, pg. 1184

Kimura, Takemune, Pres.--Mitsubishi Motors Corporation, Tokyo, Japan; *Int'l*, pg. 875

Kimura, Ted, Pres. & Chief Exec. Officer--Yamaha Motor Corp., U.S.A., Cypress, CA; *Int'l*, pg. 1516

Kinard, David, Pres.--Pacificare of Nevada, Las Vegas, NV; *U.S. Public*, pg. 1251

Kincaid, Brent B., Pres. & Chief Exec. Officer--Broyhill Furniture Industries, Inc., Saint Louis, MO; *U.S. Public*, pg. 688

Kincaid, John, Pres. & Chief Exec. Officer--Schaake Corporation, Ellensburg, WA; *U.S. Private*, pg. 969

Kincer, Jim A., Pres.--Ikon Office Solutions-Kentucky, Louisville, KY; *U.S. Public*, pg. 863

Kindig, Karl K., Pres. & Chief Exec. Officer--Pittston Minerals Group, Inc., Lebanon, VA; *U.S. Public*, pg. 1305

Kindlund, Newton C., Chm. Bd., Pres., Chief Exec. & Chief Oper. Officer--Holiday RV Superstores, Inc., Orlando, FL; *U.S. Public*, pg. 829

Kindt, Robert J., Pres.--Monarch Cortland Div., Cortland, NY; *U.S. Public*, pg. 1124

Kindt, Robert J., Pres.--Monarch Wetkzengmaschinen GmbH, Duren, Germany; *U.S. Public*, pg. 1124

Kindt, Robert J., Pres.--Stamco (U.K.) Ltd., Walsall, United Kingdom; *U.S. Public*, pg. 1124

Kindt, Robert J., Pres.--Stamco-Depiereux GMBH, Dueren, Germany; *U.S. Public*, pg. 1124

Kindt, Robert J., Pres.--Busch Gmbh, Duren, Germany; *U.S.* Public, pg. 1124

Kindt, Robert J., Pres.--Busch U.S., Sidney, OH; *U.S. Public, pg. 1124*

King, Alan, Gen. Mgr.--Analog Devices, Santa Clara, CA; *U.S. Public*, pg. 108

King, Allen B., Pres. & Chief Oper. Officer--Universal Corporation, Richmond, VA; *U.S. Public*, pg. 1694

King, Burt, Pres. & Chief Exec. Officer--Gibson County Bank, Princeton, IN; *U.S. Public*, pg. 1217

King, Carolyn, Pres.--Provident National Assurance Co., Chattanooga, TN; *U.S. Public*, pg. 1338

King, Charles, Pres.--NationsBank Securities, Inc., Charlotte, NC; *U.S. Public*, pg. 1165

King, Chris, Partner & Brdcst. Production Dir.--Eric Mower and Associates/Buffalo, Inc., Buffalo, NY; *U.S. Private*, pg. 765

King, David C., Chm. Bd., Pres. & Chief Exec. Officer--Proxim, Inc., Mountain View, CA; *U.S. Public*, pg. 1338

King, Dennis E., Pres. & Treas.--Dunlap & Co. Inc., Columbus, IN; *U.S. Private*, pg. 346

King, Dennis, M., Pres. & Chief Exec. Officer--Harley Ellington Design, Southfield, MI; *U.S. Private*, pg. 503

King, Douglas, Pres.--Gunther Mele Packaging, Inc., Buffalo, NY; *Int'l*, pg. 578

King, Douglas M., Pres.--Gunther Mele Limited, Brantford, Canada; *Int'l*, pg. 578

King, Edwin D., Pres.--King Fuels Inc., Troy, NY; *U.S. Private*, pg. 620

King, George, Pres.--Real Time Solutions, Napa, CA; *U.S. Private*, pg. 866

King, Gilman, Pres.--GCI Holdings Corporation, Chicago, IL; *U.S. Private*, pg. 434

King, Gilman R., Pres. & Chief Exec. Officer--AEC/Application Automation, Inc., Wood Dale, IL; *U.S. Private*, pg. 1041

King, Harvey C., Pres.--PENCO-Hawaii, Honolulu, HI; *Int'l*, pg. 1508

King, Jack H., Pres. & Chief Exec. Officer--Zitel Corporation, Fremont, CA; *U.S. Public*, pg. 1793

King, John H., Pres. & Chief Oper. Officer--HDS Services, Farmington Hills, MI; *U.S. Private*, pg. 490

King, Kelly, Pres.--BB&T Corporation, Winston Salem, NC; *U.S. Public*, pg. 159

King, Leroy A. Jr., Chm. Bd., Pres. & Chief Exec. Officer--Tighe Industries, Inc., York, PA; *U.S. Private*, pg. 1086

King, Maclellan E., Jr., Pres. & Chief Exec. Officer--Nevada Bell, Reno, NV; *U.S. Public*, pg. 1416

King, Michael, Pres. & Chief Exec. Officer--King World Productions, Los Angeles, CA; *U.S. Public*, pg. 961

King, Mike, Pres.--Mid-Continent Screw Products Co., Lincolnwood, IL; *U.S. Private*, pg. 743

King, Mike, Pres.--Victory Packaging, Plymouth, MI; *U.S. Private*, pg. 1139

King, Nuala M., Pres.--Coca-Cola Financial Corporation, Atlanta, GA; *U.S. Public*, pg. 392

King, R.L., Jr., Pres.--Mount Vernon Dryer Fabrics, Greenville, SC; *U.S. Private*, pg. 835

King, Richard L., Pres. & Chief Oper. Officer--Albertson's, Inc., Boise, ID; *U.S. Public*, pg. 38

King, Richard S., Chm. Bd. & Pres.--King Industries, Inc., Norwalk, CT; *U.S. Private*, pg. 620

King, Robert, Pres. & Chief Oper. Officer--Corporate Express, Inc., Broomfield, CO; *U.S. Public*, pg. 449

King, Robert C., Sr., Pres.--Richmond Motor Company, Richmond, VA; *U.S. Private*, pg. 929

King, Robert J., Pres.--The Fifth Third Bank of Northwestern Ohio, National Association, Toledo, OH; *U.S. Public*, pg. 622

King, Ron, Pres. & Chief Exec. Officer--Member Service Life Insurance Co., Tulsa, OK; *U.S. Private*, pg. 152

King, Ronald F., Pres. & Chief Exec. Officer--Blue Cross and Blue Shield of Oklahoma, Tulsa, OK; *U.S. Private*, pg. 151

King, T.S., Pres. & Gen. Mgr.--Sherwin-Williams Consumer Brands Division, Cleveland, OH; *U.S. Public*, pg. 1466

Kingsbury, Robert J., Pres.--Los Alamos Technical Associates, Inc., Los Alamos, NM; *U.S. Private*, pg. 676

Kingsley, Alfred D., Sr. Mng. Dir.--Greenway Partners, L.P., New York, NY; *U.S. Private*, pg. 478

Kingston, Ellery, Pres.--Standard Industries, Inc., Salt Lake City, UT; *U.S. Private*, pg. 1031

Kinlein, David, Pres. & Chief Exec. Officer--Optic Graphics, Inc., Glen Burnie, MD; *U.S. Private*, pg. 818

Kinney, Michael J., Pres.--Philip Morris Capital Corporation, Rye Brook, NY; *U.S. Public*, pg. 1289

Kinney, Steven, Pres. & Chief Exec. Officer--Weslock National, Inc., Los Angeles, CA; *U.S. Private*, pg. 1163

Kinnie, R.H., Chm. Bd. & Pres.--Canada Safeway Limited, Calgary, Canada; *U.S. Public*, pg. 1426

Kinning, Rick L., Pres. & Treas.--RK Mechanical, Inc., Denver, CO; *U.S. Private*, pg. 904

Kinsch, J., Pres.--Circuit Foil Luxembourg S.A., Wiltz, Luxembourg; *Int'l*, pg. 80

Kinsch, Joseph, Chm. Bd., Pres. & Chief Exec. Officer--Arbed S.A., Luxembourg, Luxembourg; *Int'l*, pg. 78

Kinsel, Curt, Pres. & Chief Oper. Officer--Apple South, Inc., Madison, GA; *U.S. Public*, pg. 121

Kinsella, John J., Pres. & Chief Exec. Officer--Admiral Insurance Company, Cherry Hill, NJ; *U.S. Public*, pg. 216

Kinsey, Gary S., Pres. & Chief Oper. Officer--Great Oaks Insurance Company, Dublin, OH; *U.S. Public*, pg. 786

Kinzel, Richard L., Pres. & Chief Exec. Officer--Cedar Fair, L.P., Sandusky, OH; *U.S. Public*, pg. 319

Kinzler, Morton H., Chm. Bd., Pres. & Chief Exec. Officer--Barnwell Industries, Inc., Honolulu, HI; *U.S. Public*, pg. 190

Kiousis, Martin J., Pres.--M-Tron Industries, Inc., Yankton, SD; *U.S. Public*, pg. 1022

Kipec, Anita, Pres. & Chief Exec. Officer--Steck-Vaughn Publishing Corporation, Austin, TX; *U.S. Public*, pg. 784

Kiplinger, Knight A., Pres.--The Kiplinger Washington Editors, Inc., Washington, DC; *U.S. Private*, pg. 623

Kipnis, Harvey, Partner--Bronner Slosberg Humphrey/Strategic Interactive Group, Boston, MA; *U.S. Private*, pg. 171

Kipp, Louis D., Pres.--Quipp Systems, Inc., Hialeah, FL; *U.S.* Public, pg. 1353

Kipping, Arthur, Chm. Bd. & Pres.--Ray-Carroll County Grain Co-op, Richmond, MO; *U.S. Private*, pg. 911

Kirby, Carroll R., Pres.--Hydro/Kirby Agri Service, Inc., Lancaster, PA; *U.S. Private*, pg. 552

Kirby, Jerry L., Chm. Bd., Pres., & Chief Exec. Officer--CitFed Bancorp, Inc., Dayton, OH; *U.S. Public*, pg. 376

Kirby, Robert, Pres.--Westmoreland Energy, Inc., Charlottesville, VA; *U.S. Public*, pg. 1761

Kirby, Robert P., Chm. Bd., Pres. & Chief Exec. Officer--Castleberry/Snow's Brands Inc., Augusta, GA; *U.S. Private*, pg. 219

Kirch, Robert J., Pres.--Aspen Pet Products, Inc., Denver, CO; *U.S. Public*, pg. 566

Kirchman, Donna, Sr. Partner & Deputy Media Opers. Dir.--EURO RSCG Tatham, Chicago, IL; *Int'l*, pg. 601

Kirchner, Vinson E., Pres. & Chief Oper. Officer--Owens Country Sausage, Inc., Richardson, TX; *U.S. Public*, pg. 596

Kirdar, Nemir A., Pres. & Chief Exec. Officer--Investcorp International, Manama, Bahrain; *Int'l*, pg. 686

Kirk, James L., Chm. Bd., Pres. & Chief Exec. Officer--OHM Corporation, Findlay, OH; *U.S. Public*, pg. 1207

Kirk, Mark, Pres., Chief Oper. Officer & Chief Fin. Officer--HMI Industries, Cleveland, OH; *U.S. Public*, pg. 771

Kirk, Spencer F., Pres. & Chief Exec. Officer--Megahertz Holding Inc., Salt Lake City, UT; *U.S. Public*, pg. 1604

Kirk, Tony, Pres.--Genesee A & B, Inc., Old Hickory, TN; *U.S. Private*, pg. 446

Kirkland, Gerry P., Pres.--CTR Manufacturing, Inc., Union Grove, NC; *U.S. Public*, pg. 238

Kirkland, Stanford L., Pres.--Countrywide Asset Management Corporation, Pasadena, CA; *U.S. Public*, pg. 452

Kirkpatrick, Don O., Chm. Bd. & Pres.--Quality Foods Inc., Little Rock, AR; *U.S. Private*, pg. 898

Kirkpatrick, Elwood, Pres.--Michigan Milk Producers Association, Novi, MI; *U.S. Private*, pg. 741

Kirpalani, Andrew, Pres. & Chief Exec. Officer--Andrew Sports Club Inc., Secaucus, NJ; *U.S. Private*, pg. 73

Kirschman, Arnold, Pres.--Morris Kirschman & Company, Inc., New Orleans, LA; *U.S. Private*, pg. 623

Kirschner, Gerold, Pres.--Glamorise Foundations, Inc., New York, NY; *U.S. Private*, pg. 455

Kirschner, Ron, Pres.--Allied Foods, Inc., Atlanta, GA; *U.S. Private*, pg. 39

Kirshner, Hal, Pres., Chief Oper. Officer, V.P. & Acting Dir.-Mktg.--LORAD Corporation, Danbury, CT; *U.S. Public*, pg. 1595

Kirshner, Hal, Pres. & Chief Exec. Officer--Trex Medical Corporation, Danbury, CT; *U.S. Public*, pg. 1595

Kirstien, Ronald D., Chm. Bd., Pres. & Chief Exec. Officer--Davco Restaurants Inc., Crofton, MD; *U.S. Public*, pg. 488

Kirtley, John F., Chm., Pres. & Chief Exec. Officer--Florida Capital Partners, Tampa, FL; *U.S. Private*, pg. 414

Kirwan, M. Lee, Pres.--Bright Star Industries, Inc., Wilkes-Barre, PA; *U.S. Public*, pg. 1341

Kisanuki, Yutaka, Pres.--Nippon Novellus KK, Tokyo, Japan; *U.S. Public*, pg. 1204

Kishi, Fusao, Pres.--Hughes-JVC Technology Corp., Carlsbad, CA; *U.S. Public*, pg. 721

Kishi, Fusao, Pres.--Hughes-JVC Technology Corp., Carlsbad, CA; *Int'l*, pg. 846

Kishimoto, Kiyokazu, Pres.--Toray Italia S.r.l., Milan, Italy; *Int'l*, pg. 1400

Kishimoto, Masatoshi, Pres.--Olympus Optical Co., Ltd., Tokyo, Japan; *Int'l*, pg. 1004

Kisiel, Boguslaw, Pres.--Bosta Beton Sp.z.o o., Warsaw, Poland; *Int'l*, pg. 1200

Kislak, Jay I., Chm. Bd., Pres. & Chief Exec. Officer--J.I. Kislak Inc., Hialeah, FL; *U.S. Private*, pg. 624

Kislevitz, Joshua, Mng. Dir.--Colorforms, Ramsey, NJ; *U.S. Public*, pg. 1625

Kissling, Richard W., Jr., Pres.--A.C. Kissling, Inc., Philadelphia, PA; *U.S. Private*, pg. 624

Kissling, Walter, Pres. & Chief Exec. Officer--H.B. Fuller Company, Saint Paul, MN; *U.S. Public*, pg. 686

Kissling, Walter, Pres.--F.A.I. Trading Company, Pompano Beach, FL; *U.S. Public*, pg. 686

Kissling, Walter, Pres.--H.B. Fuller International Inc., Saint Paul, MN; *U.S. Public*, pg. 687

Kissling, Willy Dr., Pres.--Landis & Staefa AG, Zug, Switzerland; *Int'l*, pg. 800

Kissner, Charles, Chm. Bd., Pres. & Chief Exec. Officer--Digital Microwave Corporation, San Jose, CA; *U.S. Public*, pg. 508

Kissner, Matthew, Pres.--Pitney Bowes Financial Services, Norwalk, CT; *U.S. Public*, pg. 1303

Kissner, Matthew, Pres. & Chief Exec. Officer--Pitney Bowes Real Estate Financing Corporation, Norwalk, CT; *U.S. Public*, pg. 1303

Kistner, Charles, Pres.--Buffalo Pumps, Inc., North Tonawanda, NY; *U.S. Public*, pg. 103

Kita, Shuji, Pres.--Hanwa Co., Ltd., Tokyo, Japan; *Int'l*, pg. 595

Kitahara, Kunio, Pres.--Kawasaki do Brazil Industria E Comercio Ltda., Sao Paulo, Brazil; *Int'l*, pg. 726

Kitahara, Yoshitaka, Pres.--Nanjing Toto Co., Ltd., Nanjing, China; *Int'l*, pg. 1410

Kitajima, Yoshitoshi, Pres. & Chief Exec. Officer--Dai Nippon Printing Co., Ltd., Tokyo, Japan; *Int'l*, pg. 363

Kitajima, Yoshitoshi, Pres.--Hokkaido Coca-Cola Bottling Co., Ltd., Sapporo, Japan; *Int'l*, pg. 363

Kitamura, Masato, Pres.--Toto Dalian Co., Ltd., Dalian, China; *Int'l*, pg. 1410

Kitanaka, Makoto, Pres.--Odakyu Electric Railway Co., Ltd., Tokyo, Japan; *Int'l*, pg. 996

Kitanishi, Yasuhiko, Pres.--The Kyoei Life Insurance Co., Ltd.-New York Office, New York, NY; *Int'l*, pg. 776

Kitano, Toshio, Pres.--Toto USA, Inc., Morrow, GA; *Int'l*, pg. 1410

Kitano, Toshio, Pres.--Toto Kiki USA, Inc., Morrow, GA; *Int'l, pg. 1410*

Kitaoka, Takashi, Pres.--Mitsubishi Electric Corporation, Tokyo, Japan; *Int'l*, pg. 872

Kitasato, Ichiro, Pres.--Meiji Seika Kaisha, Ltd., Tokyo, Japan; *Int'l*, pg. 855

Kitashiro, Kakutaroh, Pres. & Chief Exec. Officer--IBM Japan, Ltd., Tokyo, Japan; *U.S. Public*, pg. 897

Kitazo, Hiroyki, Pres. & Chief Oper. Officer--JRC Canida, Inc., Fort Worth, TX; *U.S. Private*, pg. 578

Kitchen, D., Pres.--Labatt Breweries of Canada, Toronto, Canada; *Int'l*, pg. 679

Kitchen, Michael B., Pres. & Chief Exec. Officer--CUNA Mutual Insurance Society, Madison, WI; *U.S. Private*, pg. 296

Kitchen, Willis M., Pres.--Gulf Coast Recycling, Tampa, FL; *U.S. Private*, pg. 487

Kitsuda, Yoshikazu, Pres.--Nomura Finance Co., Ltd., Tokyo, Japan; *Int'l*, pg. 955
Kitteridge, David, Pres.--Fields Stores, Richmond, Canada; *Int'l*, pg. 637
Kittoe, Larry, Pres.--DeBruce Grain Inc., Kansas City, MO; *U.S. Private*, pg. 319
Kittscher, Gerhard, Pres.--Bankenunion Aktiengesellschaft, Frankfurt, Germany; *Int'l*, pg. 504
Kitzmiller, Mike, Pres.--Crest Cadillac Company, Nashville, TN; *U.S. Private*, pg. 289
Kivenko, Ken, Pres. & Chief Exec. Officer--NBS Technologies, Inc., Mississauga, Canada; *Int'l*, pg. 898
Kivenko, Ken, Pres. & Chief Exec. Officer--NBS Technologies Inc., Mississauga, Canada; *Int'l*, pg. 898
Kivimaki, Mikko, Chm. Bd., Pres. & Chief Exec. Officer--Rautaruukki Oy, Helsinki, Finland; *Int'l*, pg. 1088
Kiwak, Bernd, Mng. Dir.-Europe & Exec. V.P.--Simon Marketing International GmbH - Frankfurt, Dreieich, Germany; *U.S. Private*, pg. 1001
Kiyokawa, Akira, Pres.--The Nomura Trust and Banking Co., Ltd., Tokyo, Japan; *Int'l*, pg. 956
Kiyokawa, Mitsuo, Pres.--P.T. Daiwa Indonesia Securities, Jakarta, Indonesia; *Int'l*, pg. 375
Kizer, Robert, Pres. & Chief Exec. Officer--Arkansas Lime Co., Batesville, AR; *U.S. Public*, pg. 1685
Kizer, Robert, Pres.--Corson Lime Company, Plymouth Meeting, PA; *U.S. Public*, pg. 1685
Kizer, Robert, Pres. & Chief Exec. Officer--Texas Lime Co., Cleburne, TX; *U.S. Public*, pg. 1685
Kjellgren, Hans, Pres.--NCC Industry, Solna, Sweden; *Int'l*, pg. 899
Kjellman, Jan, Pres.--Ikea North America, Inc., Plymouth Meeting, PA; *Int'l*, pg. 660
Klages, Weley W., Pres.--Camtronics Ltd., Hartland, WI; *U.S. Public*, pg. 109
Klanderud, Barry, Pres.--Valmont Industries, Inc., Springville, UT; *U.S. Public*, pg. 1707
Klapheke, Harry, Pres.--Lee's Famous Recipe Restaurant, Nashville, TN; *U.S. Private*, pg. 906
Klas, Robert C., Jr., Pres.--Tapemark, Saint Paul, MN; *U.S. Private*, pg. 1068
Klasener, Ralf, Pres.--Koralle Verlag GmbH, Berlin, Germany; *Int'l*, pg. 102
Klatsky, Bruce J., Chm. Bd., Pres. & Chief Exec. Officer--Phillips-Van Heusen Corporation, New York, NY; *U.S. Public*, pg. 1291
Klaus, Frank A., Pres.--Bristol Industries, Brea, CA; *U.S. Private*, pg. 169
Klaus, Robert, Pres. & Chief Exec. Officer--Klaus Radio Inc., Peoria, IL; *U.S. Private*, pg. 625
Klausing, Ronald, Pres.--I & K Distributors, Inc., Delphos, OH; *U.S. Private*, pg. 552
Klebba, Robert H., Pres.--Fillauer, Inc., Chattanooga, TN; *U.S. Public*, pg. 214
Klee, Rainer, Pres. & Chief Exec. Officer--Deutsche Babcock Technologies, Inc., Duluth, GA; *Int'l*, pg. 401
Kleiger, Edward J., Pres.--Welcome Home, Inc., Wilmington, NC; *U.S. Private*, pg. 598
Klein, Calvin, Pres. & Chief Exec. Officer--Calvin Klein, Inc., New York, NY; *U.S. Private*, pg. 202
Klein, E.L., Pres.--Williams-Rolls, Inc., Walled Lake, MI; *U.S.* Private, pg. 1178
Klein, Frank, Pres.--Carnival Creations, Linden, NJ; *U.S. Private*, pg. 213
Klein, Frank J., Pres.--PEC Israel Economic Corporation, New York, NY; *Int'l*, pg. 644
Klein, James B., Pres.--Eastland Shoe Manufacturing Corporation, Freeport, ME; *U.S. Private*, pg. 357
Klein, Jonathan, Pres.--CBS Television Stations Div., New York, NY; *U.S. Public*, pg. 275
Klein, Joseph M., Pres.--CCI Corporation, Tulsa, OK; *U.S. Private*, pg. 193
Klein, Michael S., Pres.--Sentinel Consumer Products, Inc., Mentor, OH; *U.S. Private*, pg. 984
Klein, Raphael, Chm. Bd. & Pres.--Xicor, Inc., Milpitas, CA; *U.S. Public*, pg. 1785
Klein, Richard, Principal--Fogarty Klein & Partners, Houston, TX; *U.S. Private*, pg. 415
Klein, Richard M., Dr., Chm. Bd., Pres. & Chief Exec. Officer--Sybron Chemicals Inc., Birmingham, NJ; *U.S. Public*, pg. 1544
Klein, Richard T. Jr., Pres. & Chief Oper. Officer--Klein Tools Inc., Skokie, IL; *U.S. Private*, pg. 625
Klein, Stephen, Pres. & Gen. Counsel--Encore Marketing International, Inc., Lanham, MD; *U.S. Public*, pg. 580
Klein, Stephen, Pres. & Gen. Counsel--Encore Clubs, Inc., Lanham, MD; *U.S. Public*, pg. 580
Klein, Stephen, Pres. & Gen. Counsel--E.M.I. Travel Center, Inc., Lanham, MD; *U.S. Public*, pg. 580
Klein, Stephen, Pres. & Gen. Counsel--Encore Group, Inc., Lanham, MD; *U.S. Public*, pg. 580
Klein, Stephen, Pres. & Gen. Counsel--Quality Services International, Inc., Lanham, MD; *U.S. Public*, pg. 580
Klein, William, Chm. Bd., Pres. & Chief Exec. Officer--The Cerplex Group, Inc., Tustin, CA; *U.S. Public*, pg. 332
Kleinlein, Bruce, Pres.--Illinois Fruit & Produce Corp., Streator, IL; *U.S. Public*, pg. 918
Kleinman, Ira, Gen. Partner--Harvest Partners Inc., New York, NY; *U.S. Private*, pg. 508
Kleinman, Richard D., Pres. & Chief Oper. Officer--AFA Protective Systems, Inc., Syosset, NY; *U.S. Public*, pg. 5
Kleisner, Ted, Pres. & Mng. Dir.--The Greenbrier, White Sulphur Springs, WV; *U.S. Public*, pg. 284
Kleist, Robert A., Chm. Bd., Pres. & Chief Exec. Officer--Printronix, Inc., Irvine, CA; *U.S. Public*, pg. 1329
Klenz, Walter T., Pres.--Wine World Estates Company, Saint Helena, CA; *Int'l*, pg. 917
Klesse, Richard C., Pres.--Beneficial Credit Services, Inc., Wilmington, DE; *U.S. Public*, pg. 211
Klessen, Rainer, Pres.--Carl Zeiss, Oberkochen, Germany; *Int'l*, pg. 1522
Klett, Hans Jurgen, Pres.--Nestle Japan Ltd., Kobe, Japan; *Int'l*, pg. 921
Klevay, Walter S., Sr., Chm., Pres. & Chief Exec. Officer--Kleco Corp., Valley View, OH; *U.S. Private*, pg. 625
Klibert, Jeffery M., Pres. & Chief Exec. Officer--Lift-All Co., Inc., Manheim, PA; *U.S. Private*, pg. 667
Klieen, Mr., Pres.-Americas & Germany--Storck International GmbH, Halle, Germany; *Int'l*, pg. 1304
Kline, J. Peter, Pres. & Chief Exec. Officer--Bristol Hotels & Resorts, Dallas, TX; *U.S. Public*, pg. 253
Kline, Jerome C., Pres. & Chief Exec. Officer--Kline Iron & Steel Co., Inc., Columbia, SC; *U.S. Private*, pg. 626
Kline, Richard D., Vice Chm., Pres. & Chief Oper. Officer.--Lehigh Portland Cement Company, Allentown, PA; *Int'l*, pg. 605
Kline, Richard G., Pres. & Publr.--Gardner Publications, Inc., Cincinnati, OH; *U.S. Private*, pg. 440
Klingaman, Richard, Pres.--Stinson Seafood Company, Prospect Harbor, ME; *U.S. Private*, pg. 1043
Klingele, Michael, Pres.--Hollytex Carpet Mills, Inc., Ontario, CA; *U.S. Private*, pg. 535
Klingensmith, Michael J., Pres.--Entertainment Weekly Inc., New York, NY; *U.S. Public*, pg. 1613
Klinger, Kathryn, Pres.--Georgette Klinger, Inc., New York, NY; *U.S. Private*, pg. 626
Klink, Patricia de Blank, Pres. & Chief Exec. Officer--Advisers Capital Management Inc., New York, NY; *U.S. Private*, pg. 23
Klinkenberg, Peter, Owner & Pres.--Harrington's of Vermont, Inc., Richmond, VT; *U.S. Private*, pg. 504
Klippa, Edmund, Pres.--Details, New York, NY; *U.S. Private*, *pg. 1038*
Klitzky, David, Pres.--The Great Frame Up Systems, Inc., Franklin Park, IL; *U.S. Private*, pg. 473
Kloiber, Dr. Herbert, Mng. Dir.--Tele-Munchen Fernseh GmbH & Co., Munich, Germany; *Int'l*, pg. 1362
Klong, Lawrence A., Pres.--K & R Express Systems Inc., Hinsdale, IL; *U.S. Private*, pg. 602
Kloss, Hans, Pres.--Bally Gaming Inc., Las Vegas, NV; *U.S. Public*, pg. 47
Kloss, Robert W., Pres. & Chief Exec. Officer--Provident Mutual Life Insurance Co., Berwyn, PA; *U.S. Private*, pg. 891
Kloster, Carol G., Pres. & Chief Exec. Officer--The Chas. Levy Company, Chicago, IL; *U.S. Private*, pg. 664
Klosterman, Brian, Pres.--StarSight Telecast, Inc., Fremont, CA; *U.S. Public*, pg. 705
Klosterman, Edward, Pres.--Shield Security, Inc., Los Angeles, CA; *U.S. Private*, pg. 994
Klosterman, Ken Jr., Pres.--Klosterman Baking Company, Inc., Cincinnati, OH; *U.S. Private*, pg. 626
Klotsche, Allan J., Pres. & Chief Exec. Officer--Willis Corroon Corp. of Minnesota, Minneapolis, MN; *Int'l*, pg. 1506
Klovstad, Oystein, Pres. & Mng. Dir.--Toyota Norge A/S, Drammen, Norway; *Int'l*, pg. 1414
Klowden, Michael L., Pres. & Chief Oper. Officer--Jefferies Group, Inc., Los Angeles, CA; *U.S. Public*, pg. 924
Klowden, Michael L., Pres. & Chief Oper. Officer--Jefferies & Company, Inc., Los Angeles, CA; *U.S. Public*, pg. 925
Klug, Mark, Pres.--Palomar Systems, Inc., Escondido, CA; *U.S. Public*, pg. 569
Kluge, John W., Chm. & Pres.--Metromedia Company, East Rutherford, NJ; *U.S. Private*, pg. 736
Kluge, John W., Chm. Bd. & Pres.--Metromedia International Group, Inc., East Rutherford, NJ; *U.S. Public*, pg. 1102
Kluzer, Silvio, Chm. & Pres.--Cerestar Holding B.V., Sas-van-Gent, Netherlands; *Int'l*, pg. 324
Klym, Richard W., Pres. & Chief Exec. Officer--Kirkwood Industries, Inc., Cleveland, OH; *U.S. Private*, pg. 623
Kmet, W.A., Pres.--ATCO Structures Inc., Calgary, Canada; *Int'l*, pg. 95
Knaebel, Joseph I., Pres.--Mid-Am Building Supply, Inc., Moberly, MO; *U.S. Private*, pg. 743
Knaebel, Stephen P., Pres.--Cummins de Mexico S.A., Mexico, Mexico; *U.S. Public*, pg. 468
Knape, Susan, Pres.--The Knape Group, Dallas, TX; *U.S. Private*, pg. 651
Knapheide, H.W., III, Pres.--The Knapheide Mfg. Co., Quincy, IL; *U.S. Private*, pg. 626
Knapp, Maurice P., Pres.--Mettler-Toledo, Inc., Hightstown, NJ; *U.S. Private*, pg. 4
Knapp, Seaman A., III, Pres.--Riverside Book & Bible House, Inc., Iowa Falls, IA; *U.S. Private*, pg. 598
Knepper, Barry, Pres. & Chief Exec. Officer--Unitel Video, Inc., New York, NY; *U.S. Public*, pg. 1692
Knetzger, Edwin L., III, Pres. & Chief Exec. Officer--Greenwich Capital Markets, Inc., Greenwich, CT; *Int'l*, pg. 911
Kniberg, Alfred A., Pres. & Chief Oper. Officer--The Strouse, Adler Company, New Haven, CT; *U.S. Private*, pg. 1047
Knigen, Melvin, Div. Pres.--Cinema Etoile Division, New York, NY; *U.S. Public*, pg. 1141
Knight, Dennis, Pres.--Medusa Aggregate Co., Cleveland, OH; *U.S. Public*, pg. 1084
Knight, J.A., Chm. Bd., Pres. & Chief Exec. Officer--Heat Controller, Inc., Jackson, MI; *U.S. Private*, pg. 518
Knight, John W., Chm. Bd., Pres. & Chief Exec. Officer--The Fabri-Form Company, Byesville, OH; *U.S. Private*, pg. 390
Knight, Richard, Chm. Bd., Pres. & Chief Exec. Officer--Greate Bay Casino Corporation, Atlantic City, NJ; *U.S. Public*, pg. 760
Knigiu, Neil, Pres. & Chief Oper. Officer--Movie Star, Inc., New York, NY; *U.S. Public*, pg. 1140
Knitt, Peter W., Pres.--M & I Merchants Bank, Rhinelander, WI; *U.S. Public*, pg. 1050
Knobloch, Peter, Pres.--R.J. Palmer, Inc., New York, NY; *U.S. Private*, pg. 835
Knodel, William C., Pres.--Condea Vista Company, Houston, TX; *Int'l*, pg. 325
Knollenberg, Norma Jean, Pres.--Top Brands, Inc., Oshkosh, WI; *U.S. Private*, pg. 1091
Knopf, Chris, Pres.--Mintz & Hoke Inc., Avon, CT; *U.S. Private*, pg. 751
Knopke, Richard J., Pres.--Contractors Supply Company, Inc., Kansas City, MO; *U.S. Private*, pg. 270
Knoss, Kenneth, Pres.--School Apparel, Inc., San Bruno, CA; *U.S. Private*, pg. 972
Knostman, Rick, Pres.--Gesco International, San Antonio, TX; *U.S. Public*, pg. 189
Knott, Joseph, Pres.--Fisons Corporation Limited, Pickering, Canada; *Int'l*, pg. 1111
Knowles, C. Harry, Chm. Bd., Pres. & Chief Exec. Officer--Metrologic Instruments, Inc., Blackwood, NJ; *U.S. Public*, *pg. 1102*
Knowles, David, Pres.--M.A. Hanna Resin Distribution, Kent, WA; *U.S. Public*, pg. 781
Knowles, David, Pres.--M.A. Hanna Resin Distribution, Ayer, MA; *U.S. Public*, pg. 781
Knowles, Robert, Pres.--Ruska Instrument Corporation, Houston, TX; *U.S. Private*, pg. 952
Knowles, Roger E., Pres. & Chief Exec. Officer--Willis Corroon Corp. of Texas, Dallas, TX; *Int'l*, pg. 1507
Knowlton, Thomas A., Pres.--Kellogg North America Division, Battle Creek, MI; *U.S. Public*, pg. 947
Knowlton, Thomas A., Pres.--Kellogg USA Inc., Battle Creek, MI; *U.S. Public*, pg. 947
Knowlton, Warren D., Pres.--Owens-Corning Building Products UK Ltd., Saint Helens, United Kingdom; *U.S. Public*, pg. 1237
Knox, Fred, Pres.--Varon, Hialeah, FL; *U.S. Public*, pg. 233
Knox, James, Pres.--Billiards Div. of Brunswick, Bristol, WI; *U.S. Public*, pg. 265
Knox, John, Jr., Pres.--Universal Surety of America, Houston, TX; *U.S. Public*, pg. 303
Knox, Richard, Pres., Treas. & Sec.--Knox Oil of Texas Inc., Dallas, TX; *U.S. Private*, pg. 627
Knudsen, William, Pres.--Knudsen & Sons, Inc., Chico, CA; *U.S. Public*, pg. 1480
Knueppel, Henry W., Pres.--Marathon Electric Manufacturing Corp., Wausau, WI; *U.S. Public*, pg. 1371
Knurr, Hans, Chm.-Bd. of Mgmnt.--Knurr AG, Munich, Germany; *Int'l*, pg. 739
Knuths, Leroy R., Chm. Bd., Pres. & Chief Exec. Officer--Rosco Manufacturing Co., Madison, SD; *U.S. Private*, pg. 944
Knutsen, Anders, Pres. & Chief Exec. Officer--Bang & Olufsen A/S, Struer, Denmark; *Int'l*, pg. 145
Kobacker, Edward J., Pres.--IP Timberlands, Ltd., Purchase, NY; *U.S. Public*, pg. 904
Kobayashi, Hideo, Pres.--Rohm Logistec Co., Ltd., Okayama, Japan; *Int'l*, pg. 1125
Kobayashi, Hiroji, Pres.--Minebea Electronics & Hi-Tech Components (Shanghai) Ltd., Shanghai, China; *Int'l*, pg. 868
Kobayashi, Katsuhiko, Pres.--Oyo Corporation U.S.A., Houston, TX; *Int'l*, pg. 1019
Kobayashi, Kazamasa, Pres. & Chief Exec. Officer--Kobayashi Pharmaceutical Co., Ltd., Osaka, Japan; *Int'l*, pg. 740
Kobayashi, Kinmio, Pres.--Calpis Food Industry Co. Ltd., Tokyo, Japan; *Int'l*, pg. 252
Kobayashi, Setsuo, Pres.--Nippon Piston Ring Co., Ltd., Tokyo, Japan; *Int'l*, pg. 938
Kobayashi, Shigeru, Chm. Bd. & Pres.--Shuwa Corporation, Tokyo, Japan; *Int'l*, pg. 1237
Kobayashi, T., Pres.--Hamamatsu Kohan Kako Co., Ltd., Shizuoka, Japan; *Int'l*, pg. 946
Kobayashi, Takashi, Chief Mgr.--The Bank of Tokyo-Mitsubishi, Ltd. (Frankfurt Branch), Frankfurt/Main, Germany; *Int'l*, pg. 158
Kobayashi, Takashi, Pres.--Fukoku Mutual Life Insurance Company, Tokyo, Japan; *Int'l*, pg. 529
Kobayashi, Takuya, Pres.--Sanyo Fisher Company, Chatsworth, CA; *Int'l*, pg. 1191
Kobayashi, Takuya, Pres.--Sanyo Office Automation, Chatsworth, CA; *Int'l*, pg. 1191
Kobayashi, Toshiaki, Pres.--Sakura Capital India, Limited, Mumbai, India; *Int'l*, pg. 1180
Kobayashi, Toshihiro, Pres.--Paloma Industries Limited, Nagoya, Japan; *Int'l*, pg. 1022
Kobayashi, Toshimine, Pres. & Representative Dir.--Mycal, Corp., Osaka, Japan; *Int'l*, pg. 897
Kobayashi, Yotaro, Pres.--Fuji Xerox Company Ltd., Tokyo, Japan; *U.S. Public*, pg. 1785
Kobylarek, Thomas, Pres. & Chief Exec. Officer--IMI Cash Valve, Inc., Cullman, AL; *Int'l*, pg. 646
Koch, Anthony H., Chm. Bd., Pres. & Chief Exec. Officer--Alamo Industrial Group, San Antonio, TX; *U.S. Private*, pg. 31
Koch, Charles John, Chm. Bd., Pres. & Chief Exec. Officer--Charter One Financial, Inc., Cleveland, OH; *U.S. Public*, pg. 336
Koch, Charles John, Pres.--Charter One Bank, Cleveland, OH; *U.S. Public*, pg. 336
Koch, Christopher, Pres.--New Era Cap. Co., Derby, NY; *U.S. Private*, pg. 793
Koch, Craig, Pres.--Hertz Equipment Rental Corp., Park Ridge, NJ; *U.S. Public*, pg. 664
Koch, Craig, Pres.--Hertz Corporation, Newark, NJ; *U.S. Public*, pg. 664
Koch, H., Pres.--Sharp Electronics (Schweiz) AG, Dallikon, Switzerland; *Int'l*, pg. 1230
Koch, Hans-Wolfgang, Pres. & Chief Exec. Officer--BDAG Balcke-Durr AG, Ratingen, Germany; *Int'l*, pg. 399
Koch, Jim, Pres.--Boston Beer Company, Boston, MA; *U.S. Public*, pg. 246
Koch, John E., Pres. & Chief Exec. Officer--M & I Citizens American Bank, Merrill, WI; *U.S. Public*, pg. 1050
Koch, Peter, Pres. & Chief Oper. Officer--Plywood Plastics Inc., Buffalo, NY; *U.S. Private*, pg. 873
Koch, Robert L. II, Pres. & Chief Exec. Officer--George Koch Sons, Inc., Evansville, IN; *U.S. Private*, pg. 628
Koch, Robert M., Pres. & Chief Exec. Officer--First Stuttgart Bank & Trust, Stuttgart, AR; *U.S. Public*, pg. 641

Koch, Walter, Pres. & Gen. Mgr.--Nestle Del Uruguay S.A., Montevideo, Uruguay; *Int'l*, pg. 921
Koch, William I., Pres. & Chief Exec. Officer--Oxbow Corporation, West Palm Beach, FL; *U.S. Private*, pg. 825
Kochi, M., Pres.--Ebara America Corporation, Foster City, CA; *Int'l*, pg. 431
Kochman, Michael, Pres.--Sharplan Lasers, Inc., Allendale, NJ; *Int'l*, pg. 429
Kochy, Tom, Pres.--Western Division, Norcross, GA; *U.S. Public*, pg. 1255
Kodama, Tadahiro, Pres.--Bridgestone Cycle (U.S.A.), Inc., San Leandro, CA; *Int'l*, pg. 213
Kodama, Yukiharu, Pres.--Shoko Chukin Bank, Tokyo, Japan; *Int'l*, pg. 1236
Koechlein, Gregg, Pres. & Chief Exec. Officer--Mallory, Inc., Carson City, NV; *U.S. Private*, pg. 698
Koehn, George W., Chm. Bd., Pres. & Chief Exec. Officer--SunTrust, Orlando, FL; *U.S. Public*, pg. 1537
Koehn, Michael, Pres. & Chief Exec. Officer--Analytic TSA Global Asset Management Inc., Los Angeles, CA; *U.S. Public*, pg. 1672
Koehrer, Ralph, Pres. & Chief Oper. Officer--Anacomp, Inc., Indianapolis, IN; *U.S. Public*, pg. 106
Koeller, Gerald, Pres.--Dairyland Power Cooperative, La Crosse, WI; *U.S. Private*, pg. 307
Koenemund, Frank "Doc", Pres.--Mister Cookie Face, Inc., Lakewood, NJ; *U.S. Private*, pg. 753
Koenig, Douglas B., Pres.--Wenco Inc., Hamburg, PA; *U.S. Public*, pg. 1754
Koenig, Howard, Pres.--American White Cross, Dayville, CT; *U.S. Public*, pg. 694
Koenitzer, Jeff D., Pres.--Helwig Carbon Products, Inc., Milwaukee, WI; *U.S. Private*, pg. 521
Koertner, William A., Pres. & Chief Exec. Officer--CIPSCO Investment Company, Springfield, IL; *U.S. Public*, pg. 66
Koester, Alexis, Pres.--Smith Brothers Farms, Inc., Kent, WA; *U.S. Private*, pg. 1007
Koether, Robert E., Pres.--Infincom, Tempe, AZ; *U.S. Public*, pg. 864
Koffel, Martin M., Chm. Bd., Pres. & Chief Exec. Officer--URS Corporation, San Francisco, CA; *U.S. Public*, pg. 1655
Koffman, Burton, Pres. & Treas.--Ben Arnold Co., Inc., Vestal, NY; *U.S. Private*, pg. 83
Koffman, Burton I., Chm. Bd.--Apparel America, Inc., New Haven, CT; *U.S. Public*, pg. 120
Koffman, Burton I., Chm. Bd. & Pres.--Great American Industries, Inc., Vestal, NY; *U.S. Private*, pg. 473
Koffman, Jeffrey, Pres.--Apparel America, Inc., New Haven, CT; *U.S. Public*, pg. 120
Koffman, Robert G., Pres. & Chief Exec. Officer--United Properties, Bay City, MI; *U.S. Private*, pg. 1123
Kogan, Richard J., Pres. & Chief Exec. Officer--Schering-Plough Corporation, Madison, NJ; *U.S. Public*, pg. 1438
Kogod, Mark, Pres.--Maurice Electric Supply Company, Washington, DC; *U.S. Private*, pg. 715
Kogumazaka, M., Pres.--Shin-Meito Co., Ltd., Chiba, Japan; *Int'l*, pg. 947
Koh, Katsuo, Pres. & Chief Exec. Officer--Marubeni America Corporation, New York, NY; *Int'l*, pg. 844
Kohan, Raul E., Pres.--Schering-Plough Animal Health, Union, NJ; *U.S. Public*, pg. 1438
Kohl, Herb, Pres.--Milwaukee Bucks, Inc., Milwaukee, WI; *U.S. Private*, pg. 749
Kohlberg, James A., Mng. Dir.--Kohlberg & Company, LLC, Mount Kisco, NY; *U.S. Private*, pg. 629
Kohler, Burt, Pres.--Hubert Company, Harrison, OH; *U.S. Private*, pg. 545
Kohler, Herbert V., Jr., Chm. Bd & Pres.--Kohler Company, Kohler, WI; *U.S. Private*, pg. 630
Kohler, John T., Pres. & Chief Exec. Officer--Technology Solutions Company (TSC), Chicago, IL; *U.S. Public*, pg. 1564
Kohler, Kim, Partner & Media Dir.--TLPartnership, Dallas, TX; *U.S. Public*, pg. 1224
Kohler, Michael, Pres.--Facemate Corporation, Chicopee, MA; *U.S. Private*, pg. 391
Kohlhaussen, Martin, Pres.--Commerzbank AG, Frankfurt, Germany; *Int'l*, pg. 308
Kohn, Jacques, Pres.--Baltek Corporation, Northvale, NJ; *U.S. Public*, pg. 171
Kohn, Thomas W., Pres.--Chemical Bank Montcalm, Stanton, MI; *U.S. Public*, pg. 345
Kohut, Hershal, Pres.--ARCO Marine, Incorporated, Long Beach, CA; *U.S. Public*, pg. 144
Koiso-Kanttila, Kimmo, Pres.--Oy Saab-Auto Ab, Helsinki, Finland; *Int'l*, pg. 1449
Koivunen, Kari, Pres.--Lohja Abetoni Oy AB, Perttila, Finland; *Int'l*, pg. 1199
Koizumi, Takashi, Pres.--ORIX Aircraft Corporation, Tokyo, Japan; *Int'l*, pg. 1008
Koizumi, Takashi, Pres.--ORIX Maritime Corporation, Tokyo, Japan; *Int'l*, pg. 1009
Kojabashian, C., Pres. & Chief Exec. Officer--Foster-Miller, Inc., Waltham, MA; *U.S. Private*, pg. 421
Kojima, Junichiro, Deputy Pres.--The Sanwa Bank Limited, Osaka, Japan; *Int'l*, pg. 1189
Kojima, Matao, Pres.--Sumitomo Metal Industries, Ltd., Tokyo, Japan; *Int'l*, pg. 1315
Kojima, Okinari, Pres.--Amano Deutschland GmbH, Erkrath, Germany; *Int'l*, pg. 71
Kojima, Okinari, Pres.--Amano Electronics Europe, N.V., Genk, Belgium; *Int'l*, pg. 71
Kokkinen, Heikki, Pres.--Nokia Multimedia Network Terminals, Helsinki, Finland; *Int'l*, pg. 952
Kokuno, S., Pres.--K. Mikimoto & Co., Ltd., Tokyo, Japan; *Int'l*, pg. 866
Kolasinski, Edward M., Pres.--Pryon Corporation, Menomonee Falls, WI; *U.S. Public*, pg. 1336
Kolen, Joel, Pres. & Chief Exec. Officer--Empress International Ltd., Port Washington, NY; *U.S. Private*, pg. 375
Kolikof, Robert A., Pres., Chief Exec. Officer & Treas.--Prudential Metal Supply Corp., East Dedham, MA; *U.S. Private*, pg. 893
Kolinski, James C., Pres.-Grove Manlift--Grove WorldWide, Shady Grove, PA; *Int'l*, pg. 593
Kolker, Stephen D., Pres.--Posnick & Kolker, Inc., New York, NY; *U.S. Private*, pg. 876
Koller, Alois J., Jr., Pres.--Koller Enterprises, Inc., Fenton, MO; *U.S. Private*, pg. 631
Kollisch, Richard, Pres.--Sopur Medizintechnik GmbH, Maisach, Germany; *U.S. Public*, pg. 1536
Kolloff, Jean, Pres.--Burberrys Shirts, New York, NY; *Int'l*, pg. 194
Kolody, Phil, Pres.--Lummi Fisheries Supply, Bellingham, WA; *U.S. Public*, pg. 429
Koloski, Richard F., Pres.--Petroleum & Resources Corp., Baltimore, MD; *U.S. Public*, pg. 1280
Kolp, Casey J., Pres.--M & I First National Leasing Corp., Milwaukee, WI; *U.S. Public*, pg. 1051
Kolpin, Marc, Pres.--Physics International Co., San Leandro, CA; *U.S. Public*, pg. 1219
Komansky, David H., Pres. & Chief Exec. Officer--Merrill Lynch, Pierce, Fenner & Smith, Inc., New York, NY; *U.S. Public*, pg. 1098
Komar, Charles E., Pres. & Chief Exec. Officer--Charles Komar & Sons, Inc., New York, NY; *U.S. Private*, pg. 631
Komatsu, Kyoichi, Pres.--Otsuka Packaging Industries Ltd., Tokushima, Japan; *Int'l*, pg. 1013
Komatsubara, Hiroyuki, Pres.--Sumitomo Dow Ltd., Osaka, Japan; *Int'l*, pg. 1311
Kominami, I., Pres. & Chief Exec. Officer--Toyo Aluminium K.K., Osaka, Japan; *Int'l*, pg. 52
Komline, Russell M., Pres.--Komline-Sanderson Engineering Corp., Peapack, NJ; *U.S. Private*, pg. 631
Kommerstad, Robert, Chm. Bd. & Pres.--Provident Investment Counsel, Inc., Pasadena, CA; *U.S. Public*, pg. 1674
Komori, Yoshiharu, Pres.--Komori Corporation, Tokyo, Japan; *Int'l*, pg. 745
Komoto, Takahisa, Pres. & Chief Oper. Officer--Diamond Star Motors, Normal, IL; *Int'l*, pg. 875
Komoto, Yasuyoshi, Pres.--Amano Corporation, Kanagawa, Japan; *Int'l*, pg. 70
Komura, Kazuro, Pres.--The Meijiseimei Asset Management of America, Ltd., New York, NY; *Int'l*, pg. 854
Komura, Kazuro, Pres.--The Meijiseimei Realty of America, Inc., New York, NY; *Int'l*, pg. 854
Konaga, Keiichi, Pres.--Arabian Oil Company, Ltd., Tokyo, Japan; *Int'l*, pg. 78
Koncelik, David G., Pres. & Chief Exec. Officer--California & Hawaiian Sugar Company Inc., Crockett, CA; *U.S. Public*, pg. 39
Konczal, Dennis R., Pres.--The Sierra Capital Companies, San Francisco, CA; *U.S. Private*, pg. 998
Kondo, Akira, Pres.--Japan Airlines Company, Ltd., Tokyo, Japan; *Int'l*, pg. 699
Kondo, Katsuhiko, Deputy Pres.--The Dai-Ichi Kangyo Bank, Limited, Tokyo, Japan; *Int'l*, pg. 359
Kondo, Yoshikazu, Pres.--Ferro Enamels (Japan) Ltd., Osaka, Japan; *U.S. Public*, pg. 619
Kondoh, Y., Pres.--Sharp Thebnakorn Manufacturing (Thailand), Nakornpathom, Thailand; *Int'l*, pg. 1230
Kong, Cheong Choong, Dr., Mng. Dir.--Singapore Airlines Ltd., Singapore, Singapore; *Int'l*, pg. 1374
Kongsiri, Aswin, Pres.--The Industrial Finance Corporation of Thailand, Bangkok, Thailand; *Int'l*, pg. 677
Konig, Gerhard, Pres. & Chief Exec. Officer--Quanterra Environmental Services, Englewood, CO; *U.S. Private*, pg. 899
Konig, Thomas, Pres. & Chief Exec. Officer--Meritcare, Inc., Sewickley, PA; *U.S. Private*, pg. 733
Konigsberg, Max, Chm., Pres. & Chief Exec. Officer--Shirmax Leasing Ltd., Montreal, Canada; *Int'l*, pg. 1235
Kono, Keizo, Pres.--Fuji Bank (Mexico) S.A., Mexico, Mexico; *Int'l*, pg. 521
Kono, Tetsuyuki, Pres.--Long-Term Credit Bank of Japan (Schweiz) AG, Zurich, Switzerland; *Int'l*, pg. 816
Konopik, M. Gene, Pres.--Federal Systems Group, Mc Lean, VA; *U.S. Public*, pg. 1516
Kontogouris, Venetia, Pres.--Cognizant Enterprises, Inc., Westport, CT; *U.S. Public*, pg. 395
Kontos, Arthur, Pres. & Chief Exec. Officer--The Sherwood Group, Inc., Jersey City, NJ; *U.S. Public*, pg. 1466
Konuntakiet, Phornpun, Pres. & Chief Exec. Officer--Unicord Public Co. LTD., Bangkok, Thailand; *Int'l*, pg. 1432
Koo, John, Pres.--LG Group Inc., Englewood Cliffs, NJ; *Int'l*, pg. 779
Koo, Kitty, Pres.--Names for Dames, Inc., Carlstadt, NJ; *U.S. Private*, pg. 773
Koob, Mark, Pres.--Bumble Bee Seafoods Inc., San Diego, CA; *U.S. Private*, pg. 526
Koogle, Tim, Pres. & Chief Exec. Officer--Yahoo!, Inc., Santa Clara, CA; *U.S. Public*, pg. 1787
Kookootsedes, John, Pres. & Chief Exec. Officer--Willis Corroon Corp. of Orange County, Santa Ana, CA; *Int'l*, pg. 1506
Koon, Dan, Pres.--Pacificare of Guam, Tamuning, GU; *U.S. Public*, pg. 1251
Koon, Ivan, Pres.--S.Two Systems Corporation, Dallas, TX; *U.S. Public*, pg. 1524
Koon, Richard D., Pres. & Chief Exec. Officer--Cubic Worldwide Technical Services, Inc., San Diego, CA; *U.S. Public*, pg. 466
Koons, John L., Pres.--Landstar T.L.C., Inc., Saint Clair, MO; *U.S. Public*, pg. 978
Koontz, James L., Pres. & Chief Exec. Officer--Kingsbury Corporation, Keene, NH; *U.S. Private*, pg. 621
Koop, Robin, Pres.--AMI Metals, Inc., Fontana, CA; *U.S. Public*, pg. 1375
Koos, Tom, Pres.--BernzOmatic, Medina, NY; *U.S. Public*, pg. 1177
Kopec, Anita, Pres.--Steck-Vaughn Company, Austin, TX; *U.S. Public*, pg. 784
Kopec, Anita, Pres.--Steck-Vaughn Distribution Company, Austin, TX; *U.S. Public*, pg. 784
Koper, R.M., V.P. & Gen. Mgr.--Svedala Bulk Materials Handling Engineered Products, Pittsburgh, PA; *Int'l*, pg. 1326
Kopew, Mell, Pres.--Faulkner Cadillac Inc., Trevose, PA; *U.S. Private*, pg. 397
Kopko, Edward M., Chm. Bd., Pres., Chief Exec. & Chief Oper. Officer--Butler International, Inc., Montvale, NJ; *U.S. Public*, pg. 270
Koplik, Michael, Pres. & Chief Exec. Officer--Perry H. Koplik & Sons, New York, NY; *U.S. Private*, pg. 632
Koplovitz, Kay, Pres. & Chief Exec. Officer--USA Networks, New York, NY; *U.S. Public*, pg. 1686
Kopnisky, Jack L., Pres.--Key Investments, Inc., Cleveland, OH; *U.S. Public*, pg. 954
Koppelman, Jeff, Pres.--Gans Ink & Supply Company, Inc., Los Angeles, CA; *U.S. Private*, pg. 440
Koppelman, Joel M., Pres.--Primavera Systems, Inc., Bala Cynwyd, PA; *U.S. Private*, pg. 884
Koppensteiner, Walter, Pres. & Mng. Dir.--AGA Ges.m.b.H., Vienna, Austria; *Int'l*, pg. 13
Kopperud, Dean C., Pres.--Fortis Financial Group, Woodbury, MN; *Int'l*, pg. 499
Kops, Paul F., Jr., Pres.--Pemko Manufacturing Company, Ventura, CA; *U.S. Private*, pg. 848
Korach, Kenneth W., Pres.--The Euclid Chemical Company, Cleveland, OH; *U.S. Public*, pg. 1358
Korallus, Horst, Pres.--Volvo and Honda Sales & Service, Lisle, IL; *U.S. Private*, pg. 1143
Korba, Robert W., Pres.--Sammons Enterprises, Inc., Dallas, TX; *U.S. Private*, pg. 963
Korbell, Charles, Pres.--Clarke American Corp., San Antonio, TX; *Int'l*, pg. 267
Korducki, Stephen A., Pres.--E.W. Blanch Capital Risk Solutions, Inc., Minneapolis, MN; *U.S. Public*, pg. 236
Koreeda, Atsushi, Pres.--Nikkei Newspaper Marketing, Inc., Tokyo, Japan; *Int'l*, pg. 929
Korell, Brad, Pres.--National Bank of Commerce, Lincoln, NE; *U.S. Public*, pg. 629
Korman, Berton E., Partner--Korman Services, L.P., Trevose, PA; *U.S. Private*, pg. 632
Korman, Leonard I., Partner--Korman Services, L.P., Trevose, PA; *U.S. Private*, pg. 632
Korman, Scott, Pres. & Chief Exec. Officer--Welsh Farms, Inc., Long Valley, NJ; *U.S. Private*, pg. 1162
Korman, Steven H., Partner--Korman Services, L.P., Trevose, PA; *U.S. Private*, pg. 632
Korn, Bernard, Chm. Bd. & Pres.--Colonial Commercial Corp., Levittown, NY; *U.S. Public*, pg. 400
Korn, Michael, Mng. Partner & Exec. V.P.--Ryan Drossman & Partners, New York, NY; *U.S. Private*, pg. 953
Kornafel, Peter, Pres.--Carquest Corporation, Lakewood, CO; *U.S. Private*, pg. 215
Kornberg, Fred, Chm. Bd., Pres. & Chief Exec. Officer--Comtech Telecommunications Corp., Melville, NY; *U.S. Public*, pg. 425
Kornblum, Eugene, Pres.--St. Louis Music, Inc., Saint Louis, MO; *U.S. Private*, pg. 960
Kornbrekke, Henning, Pres. & Gen. Mgr.--Stanley Hardware Div., New Britain, CT; *U.S. Public*, pg. 1509
Kornstein, Don R., Pres. & Chief Exec. Officer--Jackpot Enterprises, Inc., Las Vegas, NV; *U.S. Public*, pg. 920
Kornswiet, Neil, Pres. & Chief Exec. Officer--One Stop Mortgage, Inc., Costa Mesa, CA; *U.S. Public*, pg. 12
Kornswiet, Neil B., Vice Chm. & Pres.--Aames Financial Corporation, Los Angeles, CA; *U.S. Public*, pg. 12
Korpan, Richard, Pres. & Chief Exec. Officer--Florida Progress Corporation, Saint Petersburg, FL; *U.S. Public*, pg. 655
Korpan, Richard, Pres. & Chief Exec. Officer--Progress Capital Holdings, Inc., Saint Petersburg, FL; *U.S. Public*, pg. 655
Korte, Steven, Pres.--Rigby Education, Crystal Lake, IL; *Int'l*, pg. 1094
Kosai, Akio, Pres.--Sumitomo Chemical Company, Ltd., Tokyo, Japan; *Int'l*, pg. 1310
Kosaka, Kenji, Deputy Pres. Dir.--P.T. Indonesia Dai-Ichi Kangyo Bank, Jakarta, Indonesia; *Int'l*, pg. 362
Kosann, Sindey, Pres.--Shelby Yarn Company, Shelby, NC; *U.S. Private*, pg. 991
Koschel, Peter Jurgen, Pres.--Babcock Rohrleitungsbau GmbH, Oberhausen, Germany; *Int'l*, pg. 399
Koseki, Keinosuke, Mgr.-Mktg. Div.--Nippon Polaroid K.K., Tokyo, Japan; *U.S. Public*, pg. 1314
Koshima, D., Pres.--Sharp Manufacturing Company of U.K., Wrexham, United Kingdom; *Int'l*, pg. 1230
Koshino, Hidemasa, Pres.--Josephine Cosmetics, Inc., Osaka, Japan; *Int'l*, pg. 1126
Koshy, Varghese T., Pres.--AKAY Flavours & Aromatics Ltd., Kerala, India; *Int'l*, pg. 288
Kosloff, Theodore L., Pres.--Roosevelt Paper Co., Philadelphia, PA; *U.S. Private*, pg. 943
Kosmick, Edward, Pres.--Berwind Corporation, Philadelphia, PA; *U.S. Private*, pg. 138
Koss, Michael J., Pres., Chief Exec., Oper. & Fin. Officer--Koss Corporation, Milwaukee, WI; *U.S. Public*, pg. 966
Koss, Michael J., Pres., Chief Exec. Officer & Chief Fin. Officer--Koss Classics Ltd., Milwaukee, WI; *U.S. Public*, pg. 966
Koss, Michael J., Pres.--Koss Europe, Stabio, Switzerland; *U.S. Public*, pg. 966
Kost, J., Pres.--Makhteshim Agan of North America Inc., New York, NY; *Int'l*, pg. 830
Kosta, John, Pres.--Advance Business Graphics, Mira Loma, CA; *U.S. Private*, pg. 18
Kostek, Joe, Pres.--Reynolds Machine Tool Corp., Melrose Park, IL; *U.S. Private*, pg. 926
Kostelni, James C., Chm. Bd., Pres. & Chief Exec. Officer--Georgia-Bonded Fibers, Inc., Newark, NJ; *U.S. Public*, pg. 734
Kostrzewa, Siegfried, Pres.--Deutsche Babcock Energie-und Umwelttechnik AG, Oberhausen, Germany; *Int'l*, pg. 398

Kostrzewa, Siegfried, Pres.--Babcock Lentjes Kraftwerkstechnik, Oberhausen, Germany; *Int'l*, pg. 398
Kostusiak, Karl, Pres. & Chief Exec. Officer--Detection Systems, Inc., Fairport, NY; *U.S. Public*, pg. 501
Kostyra, Richard J., Pres.--Media First International, Inc., New York, NY; *U.S. Private*, pg. 726
Kosugi, Kazuo, Pres.--Kosugi Sangyo Co., Ltd., Tokyo, Japan; *Int'l*, pg. 759
Kotani, Koichi, Pres.--Sanken Electric Co., Ltd., Niiza, Japan; *Int'l*, pg. 1188
Kotani, Y., Pres., Chief Exec. & Oper. Officer--Waterville TG Inc., Waterville, Canada; *Int'l*, pg. 1487
Kotcher, Raymond L., Sr. Partner & Pres.--Ketchum Public Relations Worldwide, New York, NY; *U.S. Private*, pg. 617
Kote, Chris, Opers. Mgr.--Ammco Tools, Inc., La Vergne, TN; *U.S. Public*, pg. 480
Kotek, William, Pres. & Chief Exec. Officer--Raffi & Swanson, Inc., Wilmington, MA; *U.S. Private*, pg. 907
Koth, Robert J., Pres.--API Group Inc., Saint Paul, MN; *U.S. Private*, pg. 7
Kothoda, Toyoaki, Pres. & Gen. Mgr.--ITW Nifco, Inc., Hilliard, OH; *U.S. Public*, pg. 867
Kothoda, Toyoaki, Pres. & Gen. Mgr.--ITW Nifco, Inc., Hilliard, OH; *Int'l*, pg. 929
Kotkamp, Ruediger, Dr., Pres. & Chief Oper. Officer--Rheinische Olefinwerke GmbH, Wesseling, Germany; *Int'l*, pg. 105
Kotkins, Henry L., Jr., Pres.--Skyway Luggage Co., Seattle, WA; *U.S. Private*, pg. 1005
Kotler, Steven, Pres.--Schroder & Co. Inc., New York, NY; *Int'l*, pg. 1210
Kotlikoff, Barbara, Pres.--Accecones Ricci U.S.A., Inc., New York, NY; *Int'l*, pg. 445
Kott, Gary L., Pres. & Chief Oper. Officer--Global Marine Drilling Co., Houston, TX; *U.S. Public*, pg. 748
Kouck, Alain, Pres.--Diffulivre, Saint Sulpice, Switzerland; *Int'l*, pg. 795
Koul, M.K., Dr., Pres. & Chief Oper. Officer--Atlantic Metals Corporation, Philadelphia, PA; *U.S. Private*, pg. 95
Kouleyan, Aram, Owner--Knar Gold & Silver Exchange, Los Angeles, CA; *U.S. Private*, pg. 626
Kourkoumelis, Dan, Pres.--Hughes Family Markets, Inc., Irwindale, CA; *U.S. Public*, pg. 1349
Kouzuma, Makoto, Pres. & Chief Exec. Officer--SpeedFan International, Inc., Chandler, AZ; *U.S. Public*, pg. 1497
Kovac, Gary W., Pres.--MariTrend, Inc., New Orleans, LA; *U.S. Private*, pg. 1135
Kovacevich, Richard M., Chm. Bd., Pres. & Chief Exec. Officer--Norwest Corporation, Minneapolis, MN; *U.S. Public*, pg. 1201
Kovach, Albert F., Pres.--Stamping & Frame Div., Rochester, MI; *Int'l*, pg. 1388
Kovacs, George, Pres.--George Kovacs Lighting, Inc., Glendale, NY; *U.S. Private*, pg. 634
Kovacs, Peter, Pres.--The NutraSweet Kelco Company, San Diego, CA; *U.S. Public*, pg. 1125
Kovaleski, Charles J., Pres.--Attorneys' Title Insurance Fund, Orlando, FL; *U.S. Private*, pg. 98
Kovithvathanaphong, Pakhawat, Pres.--Securities One Limited, Bangkok, Thailand; *Int'l*, pg. 485
Kowal, W., Pres.--Senior Flexonics Inc., Bartlett, IL; *Int'l*, pg. 1222
Kowalski, Jeff, Pres.--SVG Thermco Systems, Orange, CA; *U.S. Public*, pg. 1474
Kowalski, Michael, Pres. & Chief Exec. Officer--Kowalski Sausage Co., Inc., Hamtramck, MI; *U.S. Private*, pg. 634
Kowalski, Michael J., Pres. & Chief Oper. Officer--Tiffany & Co., New York, NY; *U.S. Public*, pg. 1608
Kowalski, Wojciech, Pres.--Foster Wheeler Energy Fakop, Ltd., Sosnowiec, Poland; *U.S. Public*, pg. 677
Koyama, H., Pres.--Koyo International Inc. of America, Hauppauge, NY; *Int'l*, pg. 760
Koyama, K., Sr. V.P.--American Honda Motor Co., Inc. Motorcycle Division, Torrance, CA; *Int'l*, pg. 634
Koza, Gerald, Pres.--Associated Equipment Co., Inc., Pearland, TX; *U.S. Private*, pg. 90
Kozacki, J., Pres.--Total Plastic Inc., Kalamazoo, MI; *U.S. Public*, pg. 313
Kozak, Allan J., Pres. & Chief Oper. Officer--Digital Courier International Inc., Burnaby, Canada; *Int'l*, pg. 413
Kozlowski, L. Dennis, Chm. Bd., Pres. & Chief Exec. Officer--Tyco International Ltd., Exeter, NH; *U.S. Public*, pg. 1647
Kozlowski, Ronald, Pres.--Worcester Controls Corp., Marlborough, MA; *Int'l*, pg. 128
Kozub, Michael J., Pres.--Janlynn Corporation, Indian Orchard, MA; *U.S. Private*, pg. 582
Kozy, William A., Pres.--Becton Dickinson Division, Franklin Lakes, NJ; *U.S. Public*, pg. 199
Kracum, Richard, Mng. Dir.--Windpoint Partners, Southfield, MI; *U.S. Private*, pg. 1182
Kraemer, Robert P., Pres.--Gilroy Energy Company, Gilroy, CA; *U.S. Public*, pg. 296
Kraeutler, John A., Pres. & Chief Oper. Officer--Meridian Diagnostics, Inc., Cincinnati, OH; *U.S. Public*, pg. 1094
Krafcik, Robert J., Pres.--Durel Corporation, Chandler, AZ; *U.S. Public*, pg. 1403
Kraft, Bernie, Pres.--Demeter, Inc., Folwer, IN; *U.S. Public*, pg. 127
Kraft, Harold E., Chm. Bd. & Chief Exec. Officer--Ward Kraft, Inc., Fort Scott, KS; *U.S. Private*, pg. 634
Kraft, Marvin E., Pres.--Lario Oil & Gas Company, Wichita, KS; *U.S. Private*, pg. 651
Kraft, Roger, Pres.--Ward Kraft, Inc., Fort Scott, KS; *U.S. Private*, pg. 634
Kraftsow, Stanley A., Chm. Bd. & Pres.--Craftmatic Industries, Inc., Trevose, PA; *U.S. Private*, pg. 284
Kraftsow, Stanley A., Chm. Bd. & Pres.--Craftmatic Organization, Inc., Trevose, PA; *U.S. Private*, pg. 284
Kragsterman, Cecilia, Pres.--Skandialink Livforsakrings AB, Stockholm, Sweden; *Int'l*, pg. 1258
Krakaver, Leonard, Pres.--Pall Rai, Inc., Hauppauge, NY; *U.S. Public*, pg. 1254
Krakow, Howie, Partner--Messner Vetere Berger McNamee Schmetterer/EURO RSCG, New York, NY; *Int'l*, pg. 602
Krakowsky, Robert, Pres.--Kropp Forge Co., Cicero, IL; *U.S. Private*, pg. 1064
Krall, George F., Pres. & Chief Exec. Officer--Mebane Packaging Group, Mebane, NC; *U.S. Private*, pg. 726
Krall, George F., Pres. & Chief Exec. Officer--Mebane Packaging Group., Kearny, NJ; *U.S. Private*, pg. 726
Kramer, Arnold A., Pres. & Chief Exec. Officer--Trimfit, Inc., Bristol, PA; *U.S. Private*, pg. 1103
Kramer, Dale, Pres. & Chief Exec. Officer--ShopKo Stores, Inc., Green Bay, WI; *U.S. Public*, pg. 1467
Kramer, Earl, Pres., Chief Exec. & Chief Oper. Officer--Concord Fabrics Inc., New York, NY; *U.S. Public*, pg. 429
Kramer, Francis J., Pres. & Chief Oper. Officer--II-VI Incorporated, Saxonburg, PA; *U.S. Public*, pg. 1647
Kramer, Gordon M., Chm. Bd., Pres. & Chief Exec. Officer--Continental Plastic Card Co., Coral Springs, FL; *U.S. Private*, pg. 269
Kramer, Joel, Pres. & Publisher--Star Tribune, Minneapolis-St. Paul, Minneapolis, MN; *U.S. Private*, pg. 281
Kramer, Jon, Pres.--J. Brown/LMC Group, Stamford, CT; *U.S. Public*, pg. 764
Kramer, Joseph J., Pres.--Busch Creative Services Corporation, Saint Louis, MO; *U.S. Public*, pg. 114
Kramer, L.D., Pres.--Kester Solder, Des Plaines, IL; *U.S. Public*, pg. 1003
Kramer, Nancy, Pres.--Resource Marketing, Inc., Columbus, OH; *U.S. Private*, pg. 924
Kramer, Richard, Pres.--Fulmer Supermarkets, Inc., Springfield, OH; *U.S. Private*, pg. 431
Kramer, Richard, Pres.--Leslie Fay Sportswear, New York, NY; *U.S. Public*, pg. 989
Kramm, Michael, Pres.--Moulinex Appliances, Inc., Closter, NJ; *Int'l*, pg. 896
Kramme, Paul E., Jr., Pres.--Ace Glass Incorporated, Vineland, NJ; *U.S. Private*, pg. 12
Kramp, Kerry A., Pres.--Buffets, Inc., Eden Prairie, MN; *U.S. Public*, pg. 267
Kran, Kjell O., Pres. & Chief Exec. Officer--Union Bank of Norway, Oslo, Norway; *Int'l*, pg. 1439
Krangel, Stan E., Pres.--Lenox Collections, Langhorne, PA; *U.S. Public*, pg. 261
Krantz, Andrew, Chm. Bd., Pres. & Chief Oper. Officer--Eagle Iron Works, Des Moines, IA; *U.S. Private*, pg. 354
Krantz, Bryan, Pres. & Gen. Mgr.--Fair Grounds Corporation, New Orleans, LA; *U.S. Public*, pg. 609
Krantz, John M., Pres.--Adventure Lands of America, Inc., Des Moines, IA; *U.S. Private*, pg. 22
Krantz, K. Theodor, Pres.--Velcro Industries N.V., Willemstad, Netherlands Antilles; *Int'l*, pg. 1462
Krantz, K. Theodor, Pres.--Velcro Group Corporation, Manchester, NH; *Int'l*, pg. 1462
Krantz, K. Theodore, Pres.--Velcro USA Inc., Manchester, NH; *Int'l*, pg. 1462
Krapek, Karl J., Pres.--Pratt & Whitney Operations, East Hartford, CT; *U.S. Public*, pg. 1690
Krasne, Charles A., Chm. Bd., Pres. & Chief Exec. Officer--Krasdale Foods Inc., White Plains, NY; *U.S. Private*, pg. 635
Krasnicki, Edward, Pres.--Enidine Incorporated, Orchard Park, NY; *U.S. Private*, pg. 377
Krattenmaker, Kelly, Pres.--Young Gas Storage Company, Denver, CO; *U.S. Public*, pg. 1170
Kraus, Margery, Pres. & Chief Exec. Officer-APCO Associates--GCI Group Inc., New York, NY; *U.S. Public*, pg. 764
Kraus, William, Grp. Pres.--Aviation & Performance Chemicals Division, Philadelphia, PA; *Int'l*, pg. 446
Krause, Barry, Pres.--Hal Riney & Partners Heartland, Chicago, IL; *U.S. Private*, pg. 931
Krause, Gary W., Pres.--Kasser/Laird Distilling Co., Horsham, PA; *U.S. Private*, pg. 643
Krause, Steven, Pres.--Krause Plow Corp., Hutchinson, KS; *U.S. Private*, pg. 635
Krause, Thelma, Pres.--Oakland Tool & Manufacturing Company, Fraser, MI; *U.S. Private*, pg. 809
Krauss, Axel, Pres.--Best Foods, Englewood Cliffs, NJ; *U.S. Public*, pg. 224
Krauss, Brant A., Pres.--Spartan International Inc., Holt, MI; *U.S. Private*, pg. 1020
Krauss, Carl R., Pres.--Lakewood Engineering & Manufacturing Co., Chicago, IL; *U.S. Private*, pg. 644
Krauter, Hal J., Chm. Bd., Pres. & Chief Exec. Officer--Leasing Solutions, Inc., San Jose, CA; *U.S. Public*, pg. 982
Kravec, Rafael, Pres. & Chief Exec. Officer--French Fragrances Inc., Miami, FL; *U.S. Public*, pg. 681
Kravitz, Edward N., Pres. & Chief Oper. Officer--The Flxible Corp., Delaware, OH; *U.S. Private*, pg. 444
Kravitz, Harry, Pres.--Shannock Quebec Audio and Video Inc., Montreal, Canada; *Int'l*, pg. 1343
Kravitz, Ralph, Pres.--ORIX Polska S.A., Warsaw, Poland; *Int'l*, pg. 1010
Kravscik, J.W., Pres.--Electrodynamics, Inc., Rolling Meadows, IL; *U.S. Public*, pg. 308
Kravtin, Karen, Sr. Partner & Acct. Mngmt.--EURO RSCG Tatham, Chicago, IL; *Int'l*, pg. 601
Krawczyk, David T., Pres.--Wickes Inc., Vernon Hills, IL; *U.S. Public*, pg. 1391
Krbec, Jerry, Pres.--Dahlberg, Inc., Golden Valley, MN; *U.S. Public*, pg. 194
Krebel, Albert D., Pres. & Chief Exec. Officer--Reed & Barton Corporation, Taunton, MA; *U.S. Private*, pg. 916
Krebs, Robert D., Chm. Bd., Pres. & Chief Exec. Officer--Burlington Northern Santa Fe Corporation, Fort Worth, TX; *U.S. Public*, pg. 268
Kreh, Gordon W., Pres. & Chief Exec. Officer--The Hartford Steam Boiler Inspection & Insurance Co., Hartford, CT; *U.S. Public*, pg. 795
Kreh, Kent Q., Pres. & Chief Exec. Officer--Weight Watchers International, Inc., Woodbury, NY; *U.S. Public*, pg. 806
Krehbiel, John H., Jr., Pres. & Chief Oper. Officer--Molex Incorporated, Lisle, IL; *U.S. Public*, pg. 1121
Kreher, Thomas W., Pres.--Kreher Steel Co., Inc., Melrose Park, IL; *U.S. Private*, pg. 635
Kreick, Dr. John R., Pres.--Sanders, A Lockheed Martin Company, Nashua, NH; *U.S. Public*, pg. 1008
Kreidel, Richard S., Pres. & Chief Oper. Officer--Adams Rite Manufacturing Co., City of Industry, CA; *U.S. Private*, pg. 17
Kreilick, Thomas K., Pres.--Candle Corporation of America, Des Plaines, IL; *U.S. Public*, pg. 239
Krein, Fred, Pres.--Williams Healthcare Systems, Elgin, IL; *U.S. Public*, pg. 1507
Kreisler, Jerold A., Pres.--MCC Behavioral Care of California, Inc., Glendale, CA; *U.S. Public*, pg. 362
Kreiss, Olivier, Pres.--Degremont Inc., Rueil-Malmaison, France; *Int'l*, pg. 822
Kreiter, Harry, Chm. Bd. & Pres.--Castcraft Industries, Inc., Skokie, IL; *U.S. Private*, pg. 219
Kremer, Gilbert, Pres.--TrefilARBED Bettembourg S.a.r.l, Bettembourg, Luxembourg; *Int'l*, pg. 80
Krempa, Frank S., Pres. & Chief Exec. Officer--Lenape Forge, Inc., West Chester, PA; *U.S. Private*, pg. 659
Kremsdorf, Joel, Pres.--Gussco Manufacturing, Inc., Brooklyn, NY; *U.S. Private*, pg. 488
Krenz, Keith, Pres.--Technology Systems Corporation, Bethlehem, PA; *U.S. Public*, pg. 1425
Kreppel, Robert J., Pres.--National Fuel Resources, Buffalo, NY; *U.S. Public*, pg. 1156
Kresa, Kent, Chm. Bd., Pres. & Chief Exec. Officer--Northrop Grumman Corporation, Los Angeles, CA; *U.S. Public*, pg. 1197
Kress, Edward C., Pres.--Great Lakes Power Inc., Toronto, Canada; *Int'l*, pg. 433
Kress, William F., Pres.--Green Bay Packaging Inc., Green Bay, WI; *U.S. Private*, pg. 476
Kretzer, William T., Pres. & Chief Exec. Officer--Unifi Inc., Greensboro, NC; *U.S. Public*, pg. 1665
Kretzmer, Anthony, Pres. & Chief Exec. Officer--Angeles Housing Concepts, Canoga Park, CA; *U.S. Private*, pg. 71
Kreusch, Leonard P., III, Pres.--Leonard Kreusch, Inc., Northvale, NJ; *U.S. Private*, pg. 635
Kreuscher, Eugene, Pres.--Yoo Hoo Chocolate Beverage Corp., Carlstadt, NJ; *Int'l*, pg. 567
Kricfalusi, Michael C., Pres. & Chief Exec. Officer--Key Clearing Corp., Brooklyn, OH; *U.S. Public*, pg. 955
Krick, Mike, Pres.--Mrs. Smith's Bakery of Pennsylvania, Pottstown, PA; *U.S. Public*, pg. 658
Kriebel, Barry F., Pres.--Sun-Maid Growers of California, Kingsburg, CA; *U.S. Private*, pg. 1051
Krieg, Wolfgang, Pres.--Pipetronix Ltd., Concord, Canada; *Int'l*, pg. 1071
Kriegel, David L., Chm. Bd., Pres. & Chief Exec. Officer--Drug Emporium, Inc., Powell, OH; *U.S. Public*, pg. 530
Kriegel, William, Chm. Bd., Pres. & Chief Exec. Officer--Sithe Energies, Inc., New York, NY; *U.S. Private*, pg. 1004
Krieger, Joseph Halby, Pres.--Canadian Art Prints, Richmond, Canada; *U.S. Public*, pg. 503
Krier, B. Bruce, Chm. Bd. & Pres.--Krier Foods, Inc., Brown Deer, WI; *U.S. Private*, pg. 636
Kries, Harold, Pres. & Dir.-MKtg.--Humphrey, Inc., San Diego, CA; *U.S. Public*, pg. 1376
Krieser, Kurt, Pres.--Evy Of California, Inc., Los Angeles, CA; *U.S. Private*, pg. 387
Krihak, Peter P., Pres.--Holbrook Lumber Company, Albany, NY; *U.S. Private*, pg. 533
Krippaehne, William W., Jr., Pres. & Chief Exec. Officer--Fisher Companies Inc., Seattle, WA; *U.S. Public*, pg. 647
Krishnan, N., Pres.--State Bank of India (Canada), Toronto, Canada; *Int'l*, pg. 1297
Kristiansen, Kjeld Kirk, Pres.--Lego System A/S, Billund, Denmark; *Int'l*, pg. 805
Kristiansen, Knut, Pres.--Aker Subsea a.s., Stord, Norway; *Int'l*, pg. 42
Kristiansen, Thor, Pres.--Fine Chemicals, Oslo, Norway; *U.S. Public*, pg. 58
Krivetsky, David, Pres.--Native Textiles, New York, NY; *U.S. Public*, pg. 1684
Krivkovich, Peter G., Pres. & Chief Oper. Officer--Cramer-Krasselt, Milwaukee, WI; *U.S. Private*, pg. 285
Krivkovich, Peter G., Pres.--Cramer-Krasselt, Chicago, IL; *U.S. Private*, pg. 285
Krivkovich, Peter G., Pres.--Cramer-Krasselt Public Relations, Milwaukee, WI; *U.S. Private*, pg. 286
Kroeger, Barney, Pres.--A & A Associates, Santa Fe Springs, CA; *U.S. Private*, pg. 1206
Kroeger, Dan, Pres.--Gold Medal Products Co., Cincinnati, OH; *U.S. Private*, pg. 459
Kroese, Chris, Pres.--Gaffney-Kroese Electrical Supply Corp., Rahway, NJ; *U.S. Private*, pg. 437
Kroetch, Arthur A., Chm. Bd. & Pres.--Krofam Inc., Philip, SD; *U.S. Private*, pg. 636
Krogsgaard, Povl, Pres.--Mejeriernes Produktionsselskab A.m.b.a., Viby, Denmark; *Int'l*, pg. 826
Kroll, Robert D., Pres. & Chief Exec. Officer--The B. Manischewitz Company, Jersey City, NJ; *U.S. Private*, pg. 699
Kronberg, Ake, Pres.--Fagersta Stainless AB, Fagersta, Sweden; *Int'l*, pg. 476
Kronen, Terry, Pres.--PPG Inc., Seattle, WA; *U.S. Private*, pg. 827
Kronen, Terry, Pres. & Mgr.-Natl. Sls.--Graphic Jackets, Seattle, WA; *U.S. Private*, pg. 827
Kronenberger, Robert, Pres. & Chief Exec. Officer--Petty Company, Inc., Effingham, IL; *U.S. Private*, pg. 860
Kronick, Barry L., Pres. & Chief Exec. Officer--Furman Lumber Company, Inc., Billerica, MA; *U.S. Private*, pg. 431
Kronk, Claude F., Pres. & Chief Exec. Officer--J & L Specialty Products Corp., Pittsburgh, PA; *Int'l*, pg. 572
Kroot, Brian, Pres.--Northeastern Graphic Supply, Inc., Portland, ME; *U.S. Private*, pg. 805

Kropf, James L., Pres.--Financiere Equipment S.A., Valente, France; *Int'l*, pg. 485
Kropf, Omer G., Pres. & Chief Exec. Officer--Supreme Corporation, Goshen, IN; *U.S. Public*, pg. 1542
Krueger, Robert A., Pres., Chief Exec. Officer & Treas.--Tri-Mark Metal Corp., Shelby, MI; *U.S. Private*, pg. 1100
Kruela, Seppo, Pres.--Outokumpu Copper Products Oy, Espoo, Finland; *Int'l*, pg. 1016
Krul, J.A., Pres. & Chief Oper. Officer--Hardings, Inc., Elmira, NY; *U.S. Private*, pg. 502
Krumm, Peter, Pres.--EnviroTech PumpSystems, Salt Lake City, UT; *Int'l*, pg. 1489
Krumscheid, R.W. Jr., Pres.--Minor Rubber Co., Inc., Bloomfield, NJ; *U.S. Private*, pg. 751
Krumwiede, James, Chm. Bd., Pres. & Chief Oper. Officer--C-Line Products, Inc., Des Plaines, IL; *U.S. Private*, pg. 192
Krupa, Calvin, Chm. Bd., Pres. & Chief Exec. Officer--Ultra Pac, Inc., Rogers, MN; *U.S. Public*, pg. 1662
Kruse, Howard W., Pres. & Chief Exec. Officer--Blue Bell Creameries, L.P., Brenham, TX; *U.S. Private*, pg. 150
Kruse, Kenneth, Pres.--COMSAT RSI, Richardson, TX; *U.S. Public*, pg. 424
Kruse, Mitchell, Pres., Chief Exec. Officer & Auctioneer--Kruse International, Auburn, IN; *U.S. Private*, pg. 636
Kruy, Joseph F., Chm. Bd., Pres., Chief Exec. & Chief Oper. Officer--Cambex Corporation, Waltham, MA; *U.S. Public*, pg. 296
Kruyer, Peter J., Pres.--Sandhills Inc., Wilmington, DE; *U.S. Private*, pg. 837
Kruyer, Peter J., Pres.--TC Capital Management Inc., Wilmington, DE; *U.S. Private*, pg. 837
Kruzel, Gerry, Pres.--Shelter Products Group, Elkhart, IN; *Int'l*, pg. 1396
Krysiak, Bruce, Pres.--Dollar General Corporation, Nashville, TN; *U.S. Public*, pg. 515
Kuban, William G., Pres., Chief Exec. Officer & Treas.--Kurt Manufacturing Co. Inc., Fridley, MN; *U.S. Private*, pg. 637
Kubicek, R.T., Pres. & Chief Exec. Officer--AppleTree Markets, Houston, TX; *U.S. Private*, pg. 78
Kubicki, Charles, Pres.--Cincinnati United Contractors, Loveland, OH; *U.S. Private*, pg. 240
Kubik, Robert, Pres.--Cody Energy, Inc., Denver, CO; *U.S. Private*, pg. 249
Kubisch, John, Pres.--Becton Dickinson Pharmaceutical Systems, Franklin Lakes, NJ; *U.S. Public*, pg. 199
Kubit, Dennis M., Pres.--Trans-General Life Insurance Company, Pittsburgh, PA; *U.S. Private*, pg. 529
Kubo, Noboru, Pres.--Ikegami Tsushinki Co., Ltd., Tokyo, Japan; *Int'l*, pg. 660
Kubota, S., Pres.--Fuji Seito Co., Ltd., Shimizu, Japan; *Int'l*, pg. 947
Kucharik, John, Pres.--Aurora Pump, North Aurora, IL; *U.S. Public*, pg. 726
Kucharik, John, Pres. & Chief Oper. Officer--Minnesota Valley Engineering/Cryogenic Association, Bloomington, MN; *U.S. Private*, pg. 751
Kuck, Duane, Pres. & Chief Exec. Officer--Regal Marine Industries Inc., Orlando, FL; *U.S. Private*, pg. 917
Kuebler, Clarke, Pres.--Kold Draft, Erie, PA; *U.S. Private*, pg. 1117
Kuebler, J. Clarke, Pres. & Chief Exec. Officer--Uniflow Manufacturing Co., Erie, PA; *U.S. Private*, pg. 1117
Kuehne, Carl W., Pres. & Chief Exec. Officer--American Foods Group, Inc., Green Bay, WI; *U.S. Private*, pg. 54
Kuester, D.J., Pres.--Marshall & Ilsley Corporation, Milwaukee, WI; *U.S. Public*, pg. 1049
Kufeldt, James, Pres. & Chief Oper. Officer--Winn-Dixie Stores, Inc., Jacksonville, FL; *U.S. Public*, pg. 1771
Kugler, Seymour, Chm. Bd., Pres. & Chief Exec. Officer--Winston Resources, Inc., New York, NY; *U.S. Public*, pg. 1772
Kuhl, Claus, Pres.--ZymoGenetics, Inc., Seattle, WA; *Int'l*, pg. 987
Kuhlman, J.T., Pres.--Inter-Continental Hotels & Resorts Corporation, New York, NY; *Int'l*, pg. 1178
Kuhlman, Lyle S., Pres.--Agriland Company, Byron, MN; *U.S. Private*, pg. 26
Kuhlman, Ronald, Pres.--Kuhlman, Inc., Menomonee Falls, WI; *U.S. Private*, pg. 636
Kuhlmann, William, Pres., Chief Oper. & Exec. Officer--General Physics Corporation, Columbia, MD; *U.S. Public*, *pg. 694*
Kuhn, Paul J., Sr., Pres.--Park Motor Sales Company, Detroit, MI; *U.S. Private*, pg. 840
Kuhn, R.J., Pres.--Reliable Castings Corporation, Cincinnati, OH; *U.S. Private*, pg. 920
Kuhne, K.M., Pres.--Kuehne & Nagel (AG & Co.), Bremen, Germany; *Int'l*, pg. 763
Kuhne, K.M., Pres.--Kuehne & Nagel GmbH, Vienna, Austria; *Int'l*, pg. 763
Kuhnt, Dietmar, Dr., Chm. Bd., Pres. & Chief Exec. Officer--RWE AG, Essen, Germany; *Int'l*, pg. 1081
Kuiper, Karl D., Pres.--Grindmaster Corporation, Louisville, KY; *U.S. Private*, pg. 482
Kuivkaev, Harri, Pres.--Rae Betoon AS, Maakond, Estonia; *Int'l*, pg. 1201
Kujan, Mirsad, Pres.--Lukenheimer Energo Valves Inc., New York, NY; *U.S. Private*, pg. 680
Kujovich, Larry, Pres. & Chief Exec. Officer--Dietzgen Corporation, Palatine, IL; *U.S. Private*, pg. 332
Kuk, Kenneth U., Pres. & Chief Exec. Officer--Washington Square Advisors, Inc., Minneapolis, MN; *U.S. Public*, pg. 1376
Kukk, Toomas J., Pres. & Chief Exec. Officer--Chempower, Inc., Akron, OH; *Int'l*, pg. 74
Kuks, Martin, Pres.--Rapid Engineering Inc., Comstock Park, MI; *U.S. Private*, pg. 910
Kulek, Maurice, Pres. & Chief Exec. Officer--DeMert & Dougherty, Inc., Coal City, IL; *U.S. Private*, pg. 323
Kulenkampf, Arnfred, Pres. & Chief Exec. Officer--TLT-Babcock, Inc., Akron, OH; *Int'l*, pg. 401
Kulick, Cliff, Pres. & Chief Oper. Officer--Driv-Lok, Inc., Sycamore, IL; *U.S. Private*, pg. 343
Kulicke, C. Scott, Chm. Bd. & Chief Exec. Officer--Kulicke & Soffa Industries, Inc., Willow Grove, PA; *U.S. Public*, pg. 968
Kulkarni, Deepak, Chm. Bd. & Pres.--Wolverine Massachusetts Corporation, Merrimac, MA; *U.S. Private*, pg. 1186
Kull, Laurie, V.P. & Chief Oper. Officer--Land O'Lakes, Inc., Kiel, WI; *U.S. Private*, pg. 646
Kulle, Richard J., Pres. & Chief Exec. Officer--Siliconix, Inc., Santa Clara, CA; *Int'l*, pg. 367
Kulow, Fred, Pres.--Bioriginal Food & Science Corp., Saskatoon, Canada; *Int'l*, pg. 1195
Kulp, Frank E., III, Pres. & Chief Exec. Officer--Younkers, Inc., Des Moines, IA; *U.S. Public*, pg. 1334
Kumabe, Yasumasa, Pres.--Pasco Corporation, Tokyo, Japan; *Int'l*, pg. 1024
Kumagai, Taichiro, Pres.--Kumagai Gumi Co., Ltd., Tokyo, Japan; *Int'l*, pg. 763
Kumamoto, Masahiro, Pres. & Chief Exec. Officer--Kobe Steel, Ltd., Kobe, Japan; *Int'l*, pg. 740
Kuman, Peg, Ms., Pres.--The Power Line, Port Washington, NY; *U.S. Private*, pg. 893
Kumar, Sanjay, Pres. & Chief Oper. Officer--Computer Associates International, Inc., Islandia, NY; *U.S. Public*, pg. 420
Kumar, Sanjay, Pres. & Chief Oper. Officer--Cheyenne, Roslyn Heights, NY; *U.S. Public*, pg. 420
Kumar, Sanjay, Pres. & Chief Oper. Officer--ACCPAC International, Santa Clara, CA; *U.S. Public*, pg. 420
Kumar, Sanjay, Pres. & Chief Oper. Officer--Acacia Technologies, Lisle, IL; *U.S. Public*, pg. 420
Kumar, Sanjay, Pres. & Chief Oper. Officer--NetHaven, Islandia, NY; *U.S. Public*, pg. 420
Kumar, Sanjay, Pres. & Chief Oper. Officer--Computer Associates International, Inc., Islandia, NY; *U.S. Public*, pg. 420
Kumar, Sanjay, Pres. & Chief Oper. Officer--MK Group, Islandia, NY; *U.S. Public*, pg. 420
Kummant, Alex, Pres.--Sweco, Florence, KY; *U.S. Public*, pg. 574
Kummer, Fred S., Chm., Pres., Chief Exec. Officer, Treas. & Founder--HBE Corporation/Design Build Divisions, Saint Louis, MO; *U.S. Private*, pg. 489
Kumoda, Yasuo, Pres.--Morinaga Nutritional Foods, Inc., Torrance, CA; *Int'l*, pg. 895
Kumokawa, Toshio, Pres.--Kintetsu World Express, Inc., Tokyo, Japan; *Int'l*, pg. 734
Kumonjo, Masashige, Pres.--House of Lloyd Japan, Inc., Osaka, Japan; *Int'l*, pg. 422
Kunii, Yasuo, Pres.--Nippon Suisan Kaisha, Ltd., Tokyo, Japan; *Int'l*, pg. 940
Kunimoto, Lloyd, Pres.--Calgene LLC, Davis, CA; *U.S. Public*, pg. 1124
Kunitzsh, Eberhard, Pres.--Knurr-Lommatec Beteiligungs-u. Verw Gmbh, Munich, Germany; *Int'l*, pg. 739
Kunk, Stephen E., Pres. & Chief Exec. Officer--Provident Bank of Florida, Sarasota, FL; *U.S. Public*, pg. 1338
Kunkel, Edward T., Pres. & Chief Exec. Officer--Foster's Brewing Group Limited, Southbank, Australia; *Int'l*, pg. 500
Kunkle, Gerald K., Pres. & Chief Oper. Officer--Dentsply International Inc., York, PA; *U.S. Public*, pg. 498
Kunnen, F.R., Pres.--Sharp Electronics Benelux B.V., Houten, Netherlands; *Int'l*, pg. 1229
Kuntz, Lawrence G., Pres.--Dielectric Polymers, Inc., Holyoke, MA; *U.S. Public*, pg. 1258
Kunzig, Dick, Pres.--Morven Partners LP, Edenton, NC; *U.S. Private*, pg. 763
Kunzler, Christian C., Jr., Chm. Bd. & Pres.--Kunzler & Company, Inc., Lancaster, PA; *U.S. Private*, pg. 636
Kunzler, James, Pres.--TrustCorp Mortgage Company, South Bend, IN; *U.S. Public*, pg. 638
Kuo, J.H., Pres.--Taiwan Power Company, Taipei, Taiwan; *Int'l*, pg. 1348
Kupcis, Allan, Pres.--Ontario Hydro, Toronto, Canada; *Int'l*, pg. 1007
Kupfer, Peter, Pres.--The Private Bank Group, Zurich, Switzerland; *Int'l*, pg. 345
Kupferman, Ronald J., Chm. Bd., Chief Exec. Officer & Pres.--Global Software, Inc., Raleigh, NC; *U.S. Private*, pg. 457
Kupiec, Russel, Pres. & Chief Exec. Officer--Wells Aluminum Corp., Baltimore, MD; *U.S. Private*, pg. 1161
Kupietzky, Arlene, Pres.--Gilda Marx Inc., Los Angeles, CA; *U.S. Private*, pg. 710
Kupper, Bruce D., Mng. Partner--Kupper Parker Communications Inc., Saint Louis, MO; *U.S. Private*, pg. 637
Kupperman, Melvin, Pres. & Chief Exec. Officer--A. Epstein and Sons, Intl., Inc., Chicago, IL; *U.S. Private*, pg. 379
Kurahashi, Yoshihito, Pres.--Rohm LSI Systems Inc., San Jose, CA; *Int'l*, pg. 1125
Kurauchi, Noritaka, Pres.--Sumitomo Electric Industries, Ltd., Osaka, Japan; *Int'l*, pg. 1313
Kurita, Shoji, Pres.--P.T. Fuji Bank International Indonesia, Jakarta, Indonesia; *Int'l*, pg. 521
Kurlak, Ray, Pres.--Hamilton Standard, Windsor Locks, CT; *U.S. Public*, pg. 1690
Kurland, Marc E., Pres.--Handy Store Fixtures, Inc., Newark, NJ; *U.S. Private*, pg. 499
Kurland, Stanford L., Pres. & Chief Oper. Officer--Countrywide Home Loans Inc., Pasadena, CA; *U.S. Public*, pg. 452
Kurniawan, Tanto, Pres.--P.T. Jaya Fuji Leasing Pratama, Jakarta, Indonesia; *Int'l*, pg. 521
Kurnit, Paul, Pres. & Chief Oper. Officer--Griffin Bacal Inc., New York, NY; *U.S. Private*, pg. 480
Kurose, Sugayoshi, Pres.--ORIX COMMODITIES Corporation, Tokyo, Japan; *Int'l*, pg. 1008
Kursman, Peter J., Pres.--Jetronic Industries, Inc., Philadelphia, PA; *U.S. Public*, pg. 926
Kurstein-Jensen, Peter, Pres.--Radiometer Medical A/S, Bronshoj, Denmark; *Int'l*, pg. 1083
Kurtenbach, Aelred J., Chm. Bd., Pres., Chief Exec. & Oper. Officer--Daktronics, Inc., Brookings, SD; *U.S. Public*, pg. 478
Kurtz, Grant W., Pres.--The Advest Group, Inc., Hartford, CT; *U.S. Public*, pg. 23
Kurtz, Grant W., Pres.--Advest, Inc., Hartford, CT; *U.S. Public*, pg. 23
Kurtz, Robert M., Jr., Pres.--Kurtz Bros., Inc., Clearfield, PA; *U.S. Private*, pg. 637
Kurtzhalts, Jody, Pres.--Robicon, New Kensington, PA; *U.S. Private*, pg. 528
Kurtzman, Zvi, Pres. & Chief Exec. Officer--Aura Systems, Inc., El Segundo, CA; *U.S. Public*, pg. 147
Kurumizawa, H., Pres.--Epson Portland Inc., Hillsboro, OR; *Int'l*, pg. 1219
Kurz, Andreas, Pres.--Hugo Boss USA, Inc., New York, NY; *Int'l*, pg. 637
Kurz, Herbert, Chm. Bd., Pres. & Chief Exec. Officer--Presidential Life Corporation, Nyack, NY; *U.S. Public*, pg. 1323
Kurz, Mitch, Pres. & Chief Oper. Officer--Young & Rubicam Inc., New York, NY; *U.S. Private*, pg. 1196
Kusakai, Hiroyuki, Pres.--Nissho Iwai Hong Kong Corporation Limited, Hong Kong, Hong Kong; *Int'l*, pg. 948
Kuschewski, Gus, Pres.--National Controls Corporation, West Chicago, IL; *U.S. Private*, pg. 277
Kuse, James, Pres.--Davidson Printing Company, Duluth, MN; *U.S. Private*, pg. 314
Kushell, Charles J., IV, Pres. & New Bus. Contact--Hill, Holliday/Altschiller, New York, NY; *U.S. Private*, pg. 529
Kushins, Joel, Mng. Partner-N. America--Bozell Worldwide, Inc., New York, NY; *U.S. Public*, pg. 1642
Kushlick, W.J., Pres. & Chief Exec. Officer--Weiser Inc., Burnaby, Canada; *U.S. Public*, pg. 1055
Kussell, Paul D., Pres.--Shepard Clothing Company, New Bedford, MA; *U.S. Private*, pg. 992
Kusumi, Gary, Pres. & Chief Exec. Officer--Leader National Insurance Company, Dallas, TX; *U.S. Public*, pg. 75
Kutas, David, Pres.--Mennen Medical Inc., Clarence, NY; *Int'l*, pg. 858
Kutella, Ronald J., Pres.--Sedgwick, Inc., Memphis, TN; *Int'l*, *pg. 1218*
Kutner, Jack P., Pres. & Chief Exec. Officer--Investors Services Group, Boston, MA; *U.S. Public*, pg. 631
Kutsche, Ron A., Pres.--BetzDearborn Paper Process Group, Jacksonville, FL; *U.S. Public*, pg. 226
Kuttner, Ludwig, Chm. Bd., Pres. & Chief Exec. Officer--Hampshire Group, Ltd., Anderson, SC; *U.S. Public*, pg. 778
Kuzeppa, Michael S., Pres.--Dial Bank, Sioux Falls, SD; *U.S. Public*, pg. 1202
Kuzmich, Richard, Pres. & Chief Exec. Officer--Associated Merchandising Corp. (AMC), New York, NY; *U.S. Private*, *pg. 91*
Kvamme, Mark D., Pres. & Chief Exec. Officer--CKS Group, Cupertino, CA; *U.S. Private*, pg. 195
Kvarnstrom, Ann-Christin, Pres.--Astra Production Liquid AB, Sodertalje, Sweden; *Int'l*, pg. 93
Kvist, Anders, Pres.--Skandia Life Insurance Company Ltd., Stockholm, Sweden; *Int'l*, pg. 1257
Kwader, Alex, Pres. & Chief Exec. Officer--FiberMark Inc., Brattleboro, VT; *U.S. Public*, pg. 620
Kwan, Yule, Pres.--Advanced Remediation Inc. (ARM), Kenner, LA; *U.S. Private*, pg. 22
Kwanchaithanya, Suraphol, Pres.--Siam City Syndicate Finance & Securities Co., Ltd., Bangkok, Thailand; *Int'l*, pg. 1239
Kwasek, Matthew J., Jr., Pres. & Chief Exec. Officer--Freezer Queen Foods Inc., Buffalo, NY; *Int'l*, pg. 340
Kwee Chong, John Moo, Grp. Mng. Dir.--CSA Holdings Ltd., Singapore, Singapore; *Int'l*, pg. 242
Kwon, H.S., Pres.--Doosan Crown Can Mfg. Co. Ltd., Seoul, Korea; *U.S. Public*, pg. 465
Kwon, Hugh, Pres. & Mng. Dir.--Leo Burnett Sonyon Inc., Seoul, Korea; *U.S. Private*, pg. 185
Kyle, David L., Pres. & Chief Oper. Officer--ONEOK Inc., Tulsa, OK; *U.S. Public*, pg. 1226
Kyle, David L., Pres.--Oklahoma Natural Gas Company, Tulsa, OK; *U.S. Public*, pg. 1226
Kyman, Larry, Pres. & Chief Exec. Officer--Ultimo Ltd., Chicago, IL; *U.S. Private*, pg. 1116
Kyne, J.F., Pres.--Hauck Manufacturing Company Inc., Lebanon, PA; *Int'l*, pg. 1149
Kyu, Park Shin, Pres.--Royal Toto Metal Co., Ltd., Inchon, Korea; *Int'l*, pg. 1410
L'Esperance, Thomas F., Pres.-Commercial Laundry Div.--Raytheon Appliances, Ripon, WI; *U.S. Public*, pg. 1366
La Maina, Francis C., Pres. & Chief Oper. Officer--Dick Clark Productions, Inc., Burbank, CA; *U.S. Public*, pg. 382
La Rosa, Michael, Pres. & Chief Oper. Officer--La Rosa's, Inc., Cincinnati, OH; *U.S. Private*, pg. 640
La Trace, Richard W., Pres.--Delchamps, Inc., Mobile, AL; *U.S. Private*, pg. 588
Laanemets, Allan, Pres.--Rexcan Circuits Inc., Belleville, Canada; *Int'l*, pg. 628
LaBant, Robert, Pres. & Chief Oper. Officer--Candle Corporation, Santa Monica, CA; *U.S. Private*, pg. 204
LaBarge, Craig E., Pres. & Chief Exec. Officer--LaBarge, Inc., Saint Louis, MO; *U.S. Public*, pg. 973
LaBarge, Pierre, III, Chm. Bd. & Pres.--LaBarge Pipe & Steel Company, Saint Louis, MO; *U.S. Private*, pg. 641
Labarre, Michel, Pres.--Weber Aircraft, Inc., Fullerton, CA; *Int'l*, pg. 572
Labatt, Blair P., Jr., Pres. & Chief Exec. Officer--Labatt Food Service, San Antonio, TX; *U.S. Private*, pg. 641
Laboon, Jr., James L., Chm. Bd. & Chief Exec. Officer--Athens First Bank & Trust Co., Athens, GA; *U.S. Public*, pg. 1549
LaBorde, Ronald A., Pres. & Chief Exec. Officer--Piccadilly Cafeterias, Inc., Baton Rouge, LA; *U.S. Public*, pg. 1294

Labordore, Raphael, Pres.--Eastern Canvas Products, Inc., Ward Hill, MA; *U.S. Private*, pg. 357
Laborerio, Stephen, Pres.--Koch Otto H. York Co., Inc., Parsippany, NJ; *U.S. Private*, pg. 628
Labowsky, Andrew, Pres.--Diamond Productions, Inc., Wayne, NJ; *U.S. Private*, pg. 330
Labrecque, Richard J., Pres. & Chief Exec. Officer--ITT Fluid Technology Corporation, Midland Park, NJ; *U.S. Public*, pg. 860
Labrecque, Richard J., Pres. & Chief Exec. Officer--ITT Fluid Handling, Morton Grove, IL; *U.S. Public*, pg. 860
Labrecque, Thomas G., Pres. & Chief Oper. Officer--The Chase Manhattan Corporation, New York, NY; *U.S. Public*, pg. 337
Labreque, Richard J., Pres. & Chief Exec. Officer--Goulds Pumps, Incorporated, Fairport, NY; *U.S. Public*, pg. 860
Labry, Edward, Pres.--Concord EFS, Inc., Memphis, TN; *U.S. Public*, pg. 429
LaBuick, Ed, Pres.--Quality Special Products, Scarborough, Canada; *Int'l*, pg. 1075
LaCava, Domenic J., Pres. & Chief Oper. Officer--PictureTel, Andover, MA; *U.S. Public*, pg. 1294
Lacey, Dennis J., Pres. & Chief Exec. Officer--Capital Associates, Inc., Lakewood, CO; *U.S. Public*, pg. 302
Lacey, John S., Pres. & Chief Exec. Officer--WIC Western International Communications Ltd., Vancouver, Canada; *Int'l*, pg. 1481
Lachaume, Philippe, Pres.--Damart S.A., Robaix, France; *Int'l*, pg. 376
Lachenmayer, Greg, Pres. & Chief Exec. Officer--Collegeville Flag & Mfg. Company, Collegeville, PA; *U.S.* Private, pg. 252
Lackman, Thomas F., Chm. Bd. & Pres.--Lackman Food Service, Woodbury, NY; *U.S. Private*, pg. 642
Lacombe, Anne, Sr. Principal & Mngmt. Supvr.--Carlson & Partners, Inc., New York, NY; *U.S. Private*, pg. 211
Lacourciere, Paul A., Pres. & Chief Oper. Officer--Jameco Industries, Inc., Spindale, NC; *U.S. Public*, pg. 1746
Lacourciere, Paul A., Pres.--Watts Regulator Co., Andover, MA; *U.S. Public*, pg. 1747
Lacourciere, William J., Chm. Bd., Pres. & Chief Exec. Officer--Novametrix Medical Systems Inc., Wallingford, CT; *U.S. Public*, pg. 1203
Lacy, Andre B., Chm. Bd., Pres. & Chief Exec. Officer--LDI, Ltd., Indianapolis, IN; *U.S. Private*, pg. 639
Lacy, Linwood A., Pres. & Chief Exec. Officer--Micro Warehouse, Inc., Norwalk, CT; *U.S. Public*, pg. 1104
Lacy, William H., Pres. & Chief Exec. Officer--MGIC Investment Corporation, Milwaukee, WI; *U.S. Public*, pg. 1026
Ladd, Alan, Jr., Chm. Bd., Pres., Chief Exec. & Chief Oper. Officer--MGM Entertainment Company, Culver City, CA; *U.S. Public*, pg. 1614
Ladds, H.P., Jr., Pres. & Chief Exec. Officer--Columbus McKinnon Corp., Amherst, NY; *U.S. Public*, pg. 405
Ladet, Jean, Pres.--Sefcal S.A., Saint Julien de Peyrolas, France; *Int'l*, pg. 289
LaDue, Jack W., Pres. & Treas.--Gas Equipment Company, Inc., Dallas, TX; *U.S. Private*, pg. 440
Laehy, Timothy P., Pres.--Leasing Solutions Receivables, Inc., San Jose, CA; *U.S. Public*, pg. 983
Laemgrich, Norbert, Pres. & Chief Exec. Officer--Embedded Performance, Inc., Milpitas, CA; *U.S. Private*, pg. 373
Laengrich, Arthur R., Pres.--OEL, Ltd., Midland, TX; *U.S. Public*, pg. 568
Laesch, Will, Plant Mgr.--Ridg's Finer Foods, Garland, TX; *U.S. Public*, pg. 1288
Laethem, Ray, Pres.--Ray Laethem Pontiac-Buick-GMC-Truck, Inc., Detroit, MI; *U.S. Private*, pg. 642
Lafarge, Christophe, Co-Pres.--EURO RSCG Scher, Lefarge, Levallois-Perret, France; *Int'l*, pg. 601
Laferriere, Pierre, Pres. & Chief Oper. Officer--Teleglobe International Inc., Montreal, Canada; *Int'l*, pg. 1373
Laferriere, Richard, Pres. & Chief Oper. Officer--Coscient Group Inc., Montreal, Canada; *Int'l*, pg. 335
LaFetra, A.W., Pres.--Rain Bird Sprinklers Manufacturing Corp., Glendora, CA; *U.S. Private*, pg. 907
Laffler, Howard A., Pres.--LNR Communications, Hauppauge, NY; *U.S. Private*, pg. 639
Laffoon, Glen A., Pres.--Western Reserve Administrative Services, Inc., Strongsville, OH; *U.S. Public*, pg. 326
LaFleur, Kevin, Pres.--Monfort, Inc., Greeley, CO; *U.S. Public*, pg. 427
LaFlotte, Roberta, Partner-Creative--Lewis Gace Bozell Healthcare Worldwide, Fort Lee, NJ; *U.S. Public*, pg. 1642
LaFrance, Stephen, Chm. Bd. & Pres.--Stephen LaFrance Holdings, Inc., Pine Bluff, AR; *U.S. Private*, pg. 642
LaFrance, Stephen L., Chm. Bd. & Pres.--Super D Drugs Acquisition Co., Pine Bluff, AR; *U.S. Private*, pg. 642
Laftwein, Engelbert, Pres.--Krantz America, Inc., Charlotte, NC; *Int'l*, pg. 401
Lagno, Robert A., Pres.--Airtron, Morris Plains, NJ; *U.S. Public*, pg. 1003
LaGrega, Angelo, Pres.--Mass Market Division, Greensboro, NC; *U.S. Public*, pg. 1702
Lagstaff, David H., Pres. & Chief Exec. Officer--Calspan SRL Corporation, Washington, DC; *U.S. Private*, pg. 1136
Lahar, David, Pres.--Aurora Electronics, San Diego, CA; *U.S. Public*, pg. 147
Lahar, David, Pres.--Aurora Electronics, Marina Del Rey, CA; *U.S. Public*, pg. 147
Lahdesmaki, Tuomo, Pres. & Chief Exec. Officer--Leiras Oy, Turku, Finland; *Int'l*, pg. 639
Lahey, Joseph P., Pres.--Furmanite Worldwide, Inc., Richardson, TX; *U.S. Public*, pg. 942
LaHowchic, Nicholas J., Pres. & Chief Exec. Officer--Limited Distribution Services, Columbus, OH; *U.S. Public*, pg. 995
Lahti, Peter H., Chm. Bd., Pres. & Chief Exec. Officer--Kirkpatrick Pettis Smith Polian, Inc., Omaha, NE; *U.S. Private*, pg. 770
Lai, Peter, Pres.--Rohm Electronics (H.K.) Co., Ltd., Kowloon, Hong Kong; *Int'l*, pg. 1125
Lai, S.Y., Pres.--China Steel Structure Co., Ltd., Kao-hsiung, Taiwan; *Int'l*, pg. 286
Laidlaw, W.S.H., Pres. & Chief Oper. Officer--Amerada Hess Corporation, New York, NY; *U.S. Public*, pg. 65
Laidley, Ron, Pres.--Yale E Key, Inc., Midland, TX; *U.S. Public*, pg. 953
Laing, Bert, Pres.--LINC Quantum Analytics, Foster City, CA; *U.S. Public*, pg. 996
Laing, Robert E., Pres.--LINC Capital Group, Chicago, IL; *U.S. Public*, pg. 996
Laing, Sir Maurice, Pres.--John Laing PLC, London, United Kingdom; *Int'l*, pg. 796
Laird, Larrie W., Pres. & Chief Exec. Officer--Laird & Company, Eatontown, NJ; *U.S. Private*, pg. 642
Laird, Tom, Pres.--Wood Equipment Company, Oregon, IL; *U.S. Private*, pg. 1186
Lake, David, Pres.--Quebecor Printing MIL Inc., Don Mills, Canada; *Int'l*, pg. 1077
Lake, John H., Pres.--Nelson Photo Supplies, San Diego, CA; *U.S. Private*, pg. 791
Lake, Matt, Partner & Grp. Acct. Dir.--Hampel/Stefanides, New York, NY; *U.S. Private*, pg. 498
Lake, Munro, Pres.--TIE Systems, Inc. Illinois, Arlington Heights, IL; *U.S. Private*, pg. 1085
Lake, Munro, Pres.--TIE Systems-Kalamazoo, Kalamazoo, MI; *U.S. Private*, pg. 1085
Lake, Munro, Pres.--TIE Systems, Inc. New England, Needham, MA; *U.S. Private*, pg. 1085
Lake, Munro, Pres.--TIE Systems, Inc. New York, Rye, NY; *U.S. Private*, pg. 1085
Lake, Munro, Pres.--TIE Systems Ohio, Worthington, OH; *U.S. Private*, pg. 1085
Lake, R.D., Pres.--NFC International Holdings (U.S.A.) Inc., Dover, DE; *Int'l*, pg. 901
Lakin, Edwin A., Pres.--Boscov's Department Store, Inc., Reading, PA; *U.S. Private*, pg. 160
Lakin, Ken, Pres.--Lakin General Corporation, Chicago, IL; *U.S. Private*, pg. 644
Lam Lo, Yuk, Pres.--Bio-Rad Pacific, Hong Kong, Hong Kong; *U.S. Public*, pg. 230
LaMacchia, John T., Pres. & Chief Exec. Officer--Cincinnati Bell Telephone, Cincinnati, OH; *U.S. Public*, pg. 367
LaMantia, Charles R., Pres. & Chief Exec. Officer--Arthur D. Little, Inc., Cambridge, MA; *U.S. Private*, pg. 670
LaMantia, Santo, Pres.--Shure Brothers Incorporated, Evanston, IL; *U.S. Private*, pg. 997
Lamarre, Jacques, Pres. & Chief Exec. Officer--SNC-Lavalin Group Inc., Montreal, Canada; *Int'l*, pg. 1161
Lamattina, Larry, Pres. & Chief Exec. Officer--All American Television, Inc., New York, NY; *U.S. Public*, pg. 41
Lamb, Isabelle S., Chm. Bd., Pres. & Treas.--Enterprises International Inc., Hoquiam, WA; *U.S. Private*, pg. 377
Lamb, Isabelle S., Pres.--Meridian Machine Works, Inc., Meridian, MS; *U.S. Private*, pg. 378
Lamb, Michael R., Pres.--Lamb Engineering & Construction Co., Salt Lake City, UT; *U.S. Private*, pg. 644
Lamb, Ronald M., Pres. & Chief Oper. Officer--Casey's General Stores, Inc., Ankeny, IA; *U.S. Public*, pg. 312
Lambert, James L., Pres. & Chief Exec. Officer--Artecon, Inc., Carlsbad, CA; *U.S. Private*, pg. 409
Lambert, John P., Pres.--Matrix Aviation, Inc., Wichita, KS; *U.S. Public*, pg. 187
Lambert, Robert, Chm. Bd.--Aviall, Inc., Dallas, TX; *U.S. Public*, pg. 154
Lambert, Timothy, Pres.--VF International, Wyomissing, PA; *U.S. Public*, pg. 1702
Lambesis, Nicholas, Chm. Emeritus & Founder--Lambesis, Del Mar, CA; *U.S. Private*, pg. 644
Lambright, Bernard, Pres.--Jayco Inc., Middlebury, IN; *U.S. Private*, pg. 583
Lamby, Dr. Werner, Chm. Supervisory Bd.--Saarbergwerke Aktiengesellschaft, Saarbruecken, Germany; *Int'l*, pg. 1166
Lamer, Gerald P., Pres., Chief Exec. & Chief Oper. Officer--Marine Travelift, Inc., Sturgeon Bay, WI; *U.S. Private*, pg. 703
Lamers, Wilf, Pres. & Client Services Mgr.--M.L.&S. Werbeagentur GmbH, Dusseldorf, Germany; *Int'l*, pg. 827
Lamesch, Fred, Pres.--TrefilARBED Inc., New York, NY; *Int'l*, pg. 79
Lamm, Donald S., Chm. Bd. & Pres.--W.W. Norton & Company, Inc., New York, NY; *U.S. Private*, pg. 807
Lamm, Peter, Pres.--Fenway Partners Inc., New York, NY; *U.S. Private*, pg. 401
Lammert, Marilyn, Pres.--FFG Investments, Inc., Springfield, IL; *U.S. Public*, pg. 644
Lammle, Guy M., Chm. Bd., Pres. & Chief Exec. Officer--NxTrend Technology, Inc., Colorado Springs, CO; *U.S. Private*, pg. 809
Lamoreux, F. Holmes, Chm. Bd., Pres. & Chief Exec. Officer--Sabreliner Corporation, Saint Louis, MO; *U.S. Private*, pg. 959
Lamothe, Jean, Pres.--Capital International CDPQ, Montreal, Canada; *Int'l*, pg. 249
Lamoure, Jean-Pierre, Chm. Bd. & Pres.--Forasol S.A., Velizy-Villacoublay, France; *Int'l*, pg. 496
Lampe, John, Pres.--Bridgestone/Firestone Tire Sales Company, Nashville, TN; *Int'l*, pg. 213
Lampe, Peter, Pres.--Thyssen Immobilien GmbH, Oberhausen, Germany; *Int'l*, pg. 1388
Lampert, Albert, Pres.--Aspen Systems Corp., Rockville, MD; *Int'l*, pg. 1513
Lampert, David, Jr., Pres.--Swix Sport USA Inc., Wilmington, MA; *Int'l*, pg. 1390
Lampi, Steve, Pres. & Chief Oper. Officer--Bridgeman's Restaurants Inc., Minnetonka, MN; *U.S. Private*, pg. 167
Lamping, Mark, Pres. & Chief Exec. Officer--St. Louis National Baseball Club L.P., Saint Louis, MO; *U.S. Private*, pg. 961
Lampropoulos, Fred P., Chm. Bd., Pres. & Chief Exec. Officer--Merit Medical Systems, Inc., South Jordan, UT; *U.S. Public*, pg. 1096
Lampton, Leslie B., Sr., Chm. Bd. & Pres.--Ergon, Inc., Jackson, MS; *U.S. Private*, pg. 380
Lampton, Mason H., Pres.--The Hardaway Company, Columbus, GA; *U.S. Private*, pg. 501
Lan Ma, Sue, Chm. Bd., Pres. & Chief Exec. Officer--Elwell-Parker Limited, Cleveland, OH; *U.S. Private*, pg. 373
Lancaster, B. Allen, Pres. & Chief Exec. Officer--Regions Bank/Raybun County, Clayton, GA; *U.S. Public*, pg. 1372
Lancaster, James J., Pres. & Chief Exec. Officer--Lantech Inc., Louisville, KY; *U.S. Private*, pg. 650
Land, Kris, Pres.--CM Partners, Inc., Rolling Meadows, IL; *U.S. Private*, pg. 195
Land, Raymond J., Pres.--Citation Plastics, Co., Pleasantville, NJ; *U.S. Public*, pg. 1755
Land, Raymond J., Pres.--The West Company of Delaware, Inc., Wilmington, DE; *U.S. Public*, pg. 1755
Land, Raymond J., Pres.--West International Sales Corporation, Charlotte Amalie, VI; *U.S. Public*, pg. 1755
Landan, Amnon, Pres. & Chief Exec. Officer--Mercury Interactive Corp., Sunnyvale, CA; *U.S. Public*, pg. 1093
Landau, Thomas A., Pres.--Landau Building Co., Wexford, PA; *U.S. Private*, pg. 646
Landegger, Carl M., Pres.--The Black Clawson Company, New York, NY; *U.S. Private*, pg. 147
Landel, Michael, Pres. & Chief Exec. Officer--Sodexho USA, Waltham, MA; *Int'l*, pg. 1274
Lander, Greg, Pres.--TransCapacity, L.P., Peabody, MA; *U.S. Public*, pg. 550
Lander, Howard, Publisher & Pres.--Billboard Magazine, New York, NY; *Int'l*, pg. 1446
Landers, John W., Pres.--Harold Moore & Associates, Inc., Fayetteville, TN; *U.S. Private*, pg. 759
Landfiedel, Peter, Pres.--Amerford International Corporation, Atlanta, GA; *Int'l*, pg. 1388
Landgraf, Kurt, Pres. & Chief Exec. Officer--The Du Pont Merck Pharmaceutical Company, Wilmington, DE; *U.S. Public*, pg. 531
Landis, Leonard R., Pres.--United Credit Corp. & Patroit Funding, New York, NY; *U.S. Private*, pg. 1121
Landon, Richard, Pres. & Chief Oper. Officer--The Marley Cooling Tower Co., Overland Park, KS; *U.S. Public*, pg. 1676
Landrum, J. Terrell, Pres.--Ceco Building Systems, Columbus, MS; *U.S. Private*, pg. 221
Landry, Bryan, Pres.--SECO Industries, Inc., Metairie, LA; *U.S. Public*, pg. 1460
Landry, Donald J., Pres.--Manor Healthcare Corp., Gaithersburg, MD; *U.S. Public*, pg. 1041
Landry, Richard, Pres. & Chief Exec. Officer--Hypermedia Communications, Inc., San Mateo, CA; *U.S. Public*, pg. 851
Landry, Thomas H., Pres.--Alex J. Etkin, Inc., Farmington, MI; *U.S. Private*, pg. 384
Landuyt, William M., Pres.--Hanson PLC, London, United Kingdom; *Int'l*, pg. 592
Landy, Thomas M., Pres. & Chief Exec. Officer--Convair Cooler Corp., Phoenix, AZ; *U.S. Private*, pg. 271
Lane, Alan, Pres.--Pacific Pride Bakeries, Escondido, CA; *Int'l*, pg. 575
Lane, Albert, Jr., Pres.--Rome Research Corporation, New Hartford, NY; *U.S. Public*, pg. 1256
Lane, Clifford, Chm. Bd., Pres. & Chief Exec. & Chief Oper. Officer--ILC Industries, Inc., Bohemia, NY; *U.S. Private*, pg. 555
Lane, Davina C., Pres. & Chief Exec. Officer--HealthCare USA, Jacksonville, FL; *U.S. Public*, pg. 454
Lane, James G., Jr., Chm. Bd., Pres. & Chief Exec. Officer--Synalloy Corporation, Spartanburg, SC; *U.S. Public*, pg. 1547
Lane, Jim A., Pres.--Customer Development Corporation, Peoria, IL; *U.S. Private*, pg. 298
Lane, John M., Jr., Pres.--Potomac Graphic Industries, Inc., New York, NY; *Int'l*, pg. 699
Lane, Joseph C., Pres. & Chief Exec. Officer--GATX Capital Corporation, San Francisco, CA; *U.S. Public*, pg. 690
Lane, R. D., Pres.-Waylight--EnviroSource-International Mill Service, Inc., Horsham, PA; *U.S. Public*, pg. 587
Lane, Raymond, Pres. & Chief Oper. Officer--Oracle Corporation, Redwood City, CA; *U.S. Public*, pg. 1227
Lane, Richard, Pres.--International Petroleum Corporation of Lafayette, Lafayette, LA; *U.S. Public*, pg. 906
Lane, Robert A., Pres. & Chief Oper. Officer--Sonat Exploration Company, Houston, TX; *U.S. Public*, pg. 1485
Lane, Robert B., Pres.--NationsBank of Texas, N.A., Dallas, TX; *U.S. Public*, pg. 1163
Lane, Russell S., Pres.--Atlas Weathering DSET Laboratories, Phoenix, AZ; *U.S. Private*, pg. 96
Lane, Timothy, Pres. & Chief Exec. Officer--Bass PLC, London, United Kingdom; *Int'l*, pg. 169
Lane, William N., III, Chm. Bd., Pres. & Chief Exec. Officer--Lane Industries, Inc., Northbrook, IL; *U.S. Private*, pg. 649
Laner, Jerry, Pres.--Jimmy Dean Foods, Cordova, TN; *U.S. Public*, pg. 1433
Laney, Herb, Pres.-Catalogs & Exec. V.P.--Playboy Enterprises, Inc., Chicago, IL; *U.S. Public*, pg. 1309
Laney, Herbert, Pres.-Catalogs--Playboy Preferred, Inc., Itasca, IL; *U.S. Public*, pg. 1310
Lanford, Nathan Adrian, Pres.--Lufthansa Systems GmbH, Kelsterbach, Germany; *Int'l*, pg. 407
Lang, Daniel, Pres. & Chief Exec. Officer--American Decal & Mfg. Co., Chicago, IL; *U.S. Private*, pg. 53
Lang, Donald G., Pres.--CCL Custom Manufacturing, Rosemont, IL; *Int'l*, pg. 238
Lang, Everett, Pres. & Chief Exec. Officer--National Discount Brokers, New York, NY; *U.S. Public*, pg. 1467
Lang, G. Thomas, Pres.--Dad's Products Co., Inc., Meadville, PA; *U.S. Private*, pg. 306

Lang, Robert H., Jr., Pres. & Chief Exec. Officer--Horn Packaging Corporation, Ayer, MA; *U.S. Private*, pg. 539

Langan, Kevin, Pres.--Northway Motorcar Corporation, Latham, NY; *U.S. Private*, pg. 806

Langballe, Hakon, Pres.--Petrokjemi/Petrochemicals, Oslo, Norway; *Int'l*, pg. 960

Langbein, Thomas K., Chm. Bd., Pres. & Chief Exec. Officer--Medicore Inc., Hialeah, FL; *U.S. Public*, pg. 1080

Langdal, Ole, Pres.--Kvaerner Kincaid Ltd., Greenock, United Kingdom; *Int'l*, pg. 772

Langdale, Mark, Pres.--Posadas USA Inc., Dallas, TX; *Int'l*, pg. 576

Langdon, Daniel R., Pres.--East Penn Mfg. Co., Lyon Station, PA; *U.S. Private*, pg. 357

Langdon, John, Pres. & Chief Exec. Officer--CPC Baking Business, Bay Shore, NY; *U.S. Public*, pg. 224

Lange, Chadwick S., Pres.--Owatonna Canning Company, Owatonna, MN; *U.S. Public*, pg. 349

Lange, George W., Jr., Pres.--Marshall & Ilsley Trust Company of Florida, Naples, FL; *U.S. Public*, pg. 1051

Lange, Paul L., Chm. Bd., Pres. & Chief Exec. Officer--Dynamic Materials Corporation, Lafayette, CO; *U.S. Public*, pg. 539

Lange, Roger, Pres.--Sterling, Inc., Milwaukee, WI; *U.S. Private*, pg. 1041

Langeheine, Jurgen, Dr., Pres. & Chief Exec. Officer--EMTEC Magnetics GmbH, Ludwigshafen, Germany; *Int'l*, *pg. 743*

Langer, Ralph, Pres.--Blumenthal/Lansing Company, Lansing, IA; *U.S. Public*, pg. 1187

Langford, Dean, Pres. & Chief Exec. Officer--Osram Sylvania Inc., Malvern, PA; *Int'l*, pg. 1245

Langgartner, Claus, Pres.--Buss (America) Inc., Bloomingdale, IL; *Int'l*, pg. 490

Langhammer, Fred H., Pres. & Chief Oper. Officer--Estee Lauder Companies Inc., New York, NY; *U.S. Public*, pg. 594

Langhan, Terri, Pres. & Chief Oper. Officer--First Strategic Group, Whittier, CA; *U.S. Public*, pg. 1157

Langille, John G., Pres.--Canadian Natural Resources Limited, Calgary, Canada; *Int'l*, pg. 258

Langley, Edward, Gen. Mgr.--The Weetabix Company, Inc., Clinton, MA; *Int'l*, pg. 1488

Langmoen, Jou, Pres.--Jordan A/S, Oslo, Norway; *Int'l*, pg. 714

Langone, Vincent P., Pres.--Formica Corporation, Wayne, NJ; *Int'l*, pg. 129

Langston, John, Pres.--Regency Insurance Company, Charlotte, NC; *U.S. Public*, pg. 685

Langston, Robert E., Pres.--Langston Companies, Memphis, TN; *U.S. Private*, pg. 650

Langteau, Joseph E., Pres.--Scott's Food Services Inc., Markham, Canada; *Int'l*, pg. 1213

Langton, Bryan D., Chm. Bd. & Chief Exec. Officer--Holiday Inn Worldwide, Atlanta, GA; *Int'l*, pg. 170

Lanham, Edgar S., II, Pres.--NationsBank Investment Corporation, Richmond, VA; *U.S. Public*, pg. 1163

Lanham, Joel, Pres. & Chief Oper. Officer--Rhodes, Inc., Atlanta, GA; *U.S. Public*, pg. 805

Lanier, D., Gen. Mgr.--Sanford Facility, Sanford, NC; *Int'l*, pg. 535

Lanigan, John J., Jr., Pres. & Chief Exec. Officer Lanco Intl.--MI-Jack Products, Inc., Hazel Crest, IL; *U.S. Private*, *pg. 740*

Lanigan, Michael, Pres.-Mi-Jack & Exec. V.P.--MI-Jack Products, Inc., Hazel Crest, IL; *U.S. Private*, pg. 740

Lanigan, Robert J., Pres.--Daniel F. Young, Inc., New York, NY; *U.S. Private*, pg. 1200

Lankford, C. Frederick, Pres.--Lankford-Sysco Food Services, Inc., Pocomoke City, MD; *U.S. Public*, pg. 1551

Lankford, James E., Pres.--Sysco Food Services Company, Harrisburg, PA; *U.S. Public*, pg. 1551

Lankford, James E., Pres.--Sysco Food Services of Philadelphia, Inc., Philadelphia, PA; *U.S. Public*, pg. 1552

Lankford, Ronald B., Pres.--Old National Bancorp, Evansville, IN; *U.S. Public*, pg. 1217

Lanktree, Charles T., Pres., Chief Exec. Officer & Chief Oper. Officer--Eggland's Best, Inc., King of Prussia, PA; *U.S. Private*, pg. 366

Lannebo, Anders, Pres.--Robur, Stockholm, Sweden; *Int'l*, pg. 1328

Lansche, Wayne, Pres. & Gen. Mgr.--Westwind Communications, Bakersfield, CA; *U.S. Private*, pg. 1170

Lansing, Andrew, Pres.-Opers. & Gen. Counsel--The Levy Organization, Chicago, IL; *U.S. Private*, pg. 664

Lanthorne, Rodney, Pres.--Kyocera International, Inc., San Diego, CA; *Int'l*, pg. 775

Lantis, B.T., Pres. & Chief Exec. Officer--Mooney Aircraft Corporation, Kerrville, TX; *U.S. Private*, pg. 759

Lantto, Reijo, Pres.--Nokia Display Products Inc., Salo, Finland; *Int'l*, pg. 951

Lanzagorta, Javier, Pres. & Chief Exec. Officer--The Walworth Company USA, Houston, TX; *U.S. Private*, pg. 1149

Lapaglia, Louis T., Pres.--Craddock-Terry Inc., Lynchburg, VA; *U.S. Private*, pg. 284

LaPan, Karl, Pres.--NBS Imaging Systems, Inc., Fort Wayne, IN; *Int'l*, pg. 898

Lapelle, Brian, Pres.--Dutch Housing, Inc., White Pigeon, MI; *U.S. Public*, pg. 333

LaPenta, Robert, Pres. & Chief Fin. Officer--L3 Communications, New York, NY; *U.S. Private*, pg. 638

Lapeyre, Jay, Jr., Chm. & Pres.--The Laitram Corporation, Harahan, LA; *U.S. Private*, pg. 643

Laphen, James A., Pres. & Chief Oper. Officer--Commercial Federal Corporation, Omaha, NE; *U.S. Public*, pg. 411

Laphen, Michael W., Pres.--Integrated Systems Division, Moorestown, NJ; *U.S. Public*, pg. 423

Lapides, John S., Pres.--United Aluminum Corporation, North Haven, CT; *U.S. Private*, pg. 1120

Lapin, Byron, Pres.--Clayton Metals Corp., Fenton, MO; *U.S. Private*, pg. 244

Lapin, Byron, Pres.--Clayton Plastics Corp., Fenton, MO; *U.S. Private*, pg. 244

Lapin, Byron, Pres.--Convenience Products, Inc., Fenton, MO; *U.S. Private*, pg. 244

Lapin, Byron R., Pres. & Chief Exec. Officer--Clayton Corporation, Fenton, MO; *U.S. Private*, pg. 244

Lapin, Phil, Pres.--Falcon Safety Products Inc., Somerville, NJ; *U.S. Private*, pg. 392

Lapin, Steven B., Pres.--Geneve Corporation, Stamford, CT; *U.S. Private*, pg. 446

Lapin, Steven B., Pres. & Chief Oper. Officer--Independence Holding Company, Stamford, CT; *U.S. Private*, pg. 446

Lapointe, Paul, V.P. & Gen. Mgr.--Roehlen Engraving, Rochester, NY; *U.S. Public*, pg. 1506

LaPointe, William J., Pres. & Chief Exec. Officer--Andover Controls, Andover, MA; *U.S. Private*, pg. 73

Laporta, Michael, Pres.--Automotive Rentals, Inc. (ARI), Mount Laurel, NJ; *U.S. Private*, pg. 535

LaPorte, Thomas B., Pres.--Reliance Elevator Company, Chicago, IL; *U.S. Private*, pg. 921

Lappes, Constantine T., Pres. & Chief Exec. Officer--NYLIFE Administration Corp., Austin, TX; *U.S. Private*, pg. 795

Laprade, Ed, Pres.--Sullair Corporation, Michigan City, IN; *U.S. Public*, pg. 1534

Laptewicz, Joseph E., Jr., Pres. & Chief Exec. Officer--EMPI, Inc., Saint Paul, MN; *U.S. Public*, pg. 545

Laracy, Mark A., Pres.--Parfums De Coeur Ltd., Darien, CT; *U.S. Private*, pg. 839

Laraway, Steven D., Pres. & Chief Exec. Officer--First American Trust Company of Minnesota, Saint Cloud, MN; *U.S. Private*, pg. 167

Laraya, R.G., Pres.--Benguet Ebara Real Estate Corporation, Manila, Philippines; *Int'l*, pg. 432

Lardner, Peter, Chm. Bd., Pres. & Chief Exec. Officer--Bituminous Casualty Corp., Rock Island, IL; *U.S. Public*, pg. 1218

Largen, Joseph, Pres. & Chief Oper. Officer--Brodart Company, Williamsport, PA; *U.S. Private*, pg. 170

Largent, Michael T., Pres.--Roper Bros. Lumber Co., Inc., Petersburg, VA; *U.S. Private*, pg. 944

LaRiche, Louis, Pres.--Lou LaRiche Chevrolet Inc., Plymouth, MI; *U.S. Private*, pg. 651

Larison, H.H., Pres. & Chief Exec. Officer--Columbia Paint & Coatings, Spokane, WA; *U.S. Private*, pg. 256

Larkin, Carl, Pres. & Chief Exec. Officer--Larkin Meeder & Schweidel, Dallas, TX; *U.S. Private*, pg. 651

Larkin, Frank, Pres.--North Shore Movers, Northbrook, IL; *U.S. Private*, pg. 805

Larkin, J.P., Pres.--Spectra Marketing Systems, Chicago, IL; *Int'l*, pg. 1447

Larkin, James J., Pres.--Romac Industries, Inc., Seattle, WA; *U.S. Private*, pg. 942

Larkins, Mary L., Pres.--CitFed Mortgage Corporation of America, Dayton, OH; *U.S. Public*, pg. 376

LaRoche, Calvin, Pres. & Chief Exec. Officer-Mtel. International--MTel International, Washington, DC; *U.S. Public*, pg. 1120

Larochelle, Richard, Pres. & Chief Exec. Officer--Irving Tanning Co., Hartland, ME; *U.S. Private*, pg. 575

Larock, Duane, Pres.--R.A. Mueller, Inc., Cincinnati, OH; *U.S. Private*, pg. 766

LaRosa, Charles, Pres. & Chief Exec. Officer--Pharmaceutical Formulations, Inc., Edison, NJ; *U.S. Public*, pg. 1284

Larrain, Nicolas, Pres.--ADN/ADD, Santiago, Chile; *U.S. Private*, pg. 1200

Larrainzar, D. Miguel Canalejo, Pres.--Alcatel Standard Electrica, S.A, Madrid, Spain; *Int'l*, pg. 56

Larrimore, Randall W., Pres. & Chief Exec. Officer--United Stationers Inc., Des Plaines, IL; *U.S. Public*, pg. 1689

Larsen, Asbjorn, Pres. & Chief Exec. Officer--Saga Petroleum ASA, Sandvika, Norway; *Int'l*, pg. 1169

Larsen, Marshall O., Pres.--B.F. Goodrich Aerospace, Akron, OH; *U.S. Public*, pg. 751

Larsen, Ole-Johannes, Pres.--Kvaerner Rosenberg Newfoundland Ltd., Saint Johns, Canada; *Int'l*, pg. 768

Larsen, Ralph S., Chm. Bd., Pres. & Chief Exec. Officer--Johnson & Johnson, New Brunswick, NJ; *U.S. Public*, pg. 927

Larsen, Terrence A., Chm. Bd., Pres. & Chief Exec. Officer--CoreStates Financial Corp., Philadelphia, PA; *U.S. Public*, pg. 446

Larsen, Warren, Chief Exec.--New Zealand Dairy Board, Wellington, New Zealand; *Int'l*, pg. 923

Larson, Clay, Pres.--First National Bank of Central California, Salinas, CA; *U.S. Public*, pg. 1248

Larson, Clayton C., Pres. & Chief Fin. Officer--Pacific Capital Bancorp, Salinas, CA; *U.S. Public*, pg. 1247

Larson, Dale, Pres.--Larson Manufacturing Company, Brookings, SD; *U.S. Private*, pg. 652

Larson, Dave, Pres.--Cargill Animal Nutrition Div., Minneapolis, MN; *U.S. Private*, pg. 210

Larson, Greg, Pres. & Chief Exec. Officer--Demco Inc., Madison, WI; *U.S. Private*, pg. 323

Larson, Jack, Pres. & Chief Exec. Officer--Career Education Corporation, Hoffman Estates, IL; *U.S. Private*, pg. 209

Larson, Johan H., Pres.--SkandiaBanken Fonder AB, Stockholm, Sweden; *Int'l*, pg. 1257

Larson, John D., Pres. & Chief Exec. Officer--National Guardian Life Insurance Company, Madison, WI; *U.S. Private*, pg. 784

Larson, John D., Pres.--NGL Holdings Inc., Madison, WI; *U.S. Private*, pg. 784

Larson, John D., Pres.--NGL Financial Services Inc., Madison, WI; *U.S. Private*, pg. 784

Larson, John D., Pres.--NGL Investment Services Inc., Madison, WI; *U.S. Private*, pg. 784

Larson, Ken, Pres. & Chief Oper. Officer--Polaris Industries, Inc., Minneapolis, MN; *U.S. Public*, pg. 1313

Larson, LeRoy, Pres.--Saskatchewan Wheat Pool, Regina, Canada; *Int'l*, pg. 1195

Larson, Linden, Pres.--Alliance Management, Inc., Seattle, WA; *U.S. Private*, pg. 38

Larson, Steve, Pres. & Chief Exec. Officer--Repap Enterprises Inc., Montreal, Canada; *Int'l*, pg. 1104

Larson, Steve, Pres. & Chief Exec. Officer--Repap New Brunswick Inc., Montreal, Canada; *Int'l*, pg. 1104

Larsson, Lars Olov, Pres.--Perstorp Components, Lambrecht, Germany; *Int'l*, pg. 1040

Larsson, Per, Pres.--Astra Export & Trading AB, Sodertalje, Sweden; *Int'l*, pg. 93

LaRuffa, Richard A., Pres.--Value Engineering & Management, Inc., Morristown, NJ; *U.S. Private*, pg. 365

Lashkajani, Hadi B., Pres.--SunPure Ltd., Avon Park, FL; *U.S. Private*, pg. 1053

Laskey, Bill, V.P. & Gen. Mgr.--Wix Div., Gastonia, NC; *U.S.* Public, pg. 479

Lasko, John C., Chm. Bd., Pres. & Treas.--Republic Die & Tool Company, Belleville, MI; *U.S. Private*, pg. 923

Lasko, Oscar, Pres.--Lasko Metal Products, Inc., West Chester, PA; *U.S. Private*, pg. 652

Lasky, David, Chm. Bd. & Pres.--Curtiss-Wright Corp., Lyndhurst, NJ; *U.S. Public*, pg. 469

Lass, Mark, Pres.--Press Communications, LLC, Wall, NJ; *U.S. Private*, pg. 882

Lassiter, Phillip B., Chm. Bd., Pres. & Chief Exec. Officer--AMBAC Financial Group, Inc., New York, NY; *U.S. Public*, pg. 62

Laster, Ralph W., Jr., Pres. & Chief Exec. Officer--Amvestors Financial Corporation, Topeka, KS; *U.S. Private*, pg. 59

Latham, Colin, Pres.--Maritime Telegraph & Telephone Company, Ltd., Halifax, Canada; *Int'l*, pg. 116

Latham, John, Pres. & Chief Exec. Officer--Colony Insurance Company, Richmond, VA; *U.S. Private*, pg. 430

Lathrop, Peter, Pres.--Hartmann Luggage & Leather Goods Group, Lebanon, TN; *U.S. Public*, pg. 261

Lathrop, Thomas C., Pres. & Chief Exec. Officer--M & I Thunderbird Bank, Phoenix, AZ; *U.S. Public*, pg. 1050

Latimer, E.J., Pres.--Monarch Development Corporation, Willowdale, Canada; *Int'l*, pg. 1359

Latimer, E.J., Pres.--The Monarch Group, Willowdale, Canada; *Int'l*, pg. 1359

Latimer, John A., III, Pres. & Chief Exec. Officer--Jamison Door Company, Hagerstown, MD; *U.S. Private*, pg. 581

Latiolais, Rene L., Pres. & Chief Exec. Officer--Freeport-McMoRan Inc., New Orleans, LA; *U.S. Public*, pg. 680

LaTorre, L. Donald, Pres. & Chief Oper. Officer--Engelhard Corporation, Iselin, NJ; *U.S. Public*, pg. 582

Latrous, T., Pres.--Industries Mecaniques Maghrebines, Tunis, Tunisia; *Int'l*, pg. 693

Latthanan, Pornlert, Pres.--SCF Finance & Securities Co., Ltd., Bangkok, Thailand; *Int'l*, pg. 1239

Latumahina, F.P., Pres.--ING Insurance Indonesia, Jakarta, Indonesia; *Int'l*, pg. 650

Lau, Chris, Pres.--Towne Development Of Hawaii, Inc., Honolulu, HI; *U.S. Private*, pg. 1206

Lau, Richard, Pres.--Go-Gro Industries, Ltd., Kowloon Bay, Hong Kong; *U.S. Public*, pg. 314

Lau, Winston, Div. Pres.--The Palnut Company, Mountainside, NJ; *U.S. Public*, pg. 1632

Lau, Winston, Pres.--Industrial Retaining Ring Company, Irvington, NJ; *U.S. Public*, pg. 1632

Lau, Winston, Pres.--Waldes Truarc/Industrial Retaining Ring, Somerset, NJ; *U.S. Public*, pg. 1632

Laubich, Arnold, Pres. & Chief Oper. Officer--New Plan Realty Trust, New York, NY; *U.S. Public*, pg. 1172

Lauchert, F.N., Pres.--Elf Atochem North America, Fluorochemical Div., Philadelphia, PA; *Int'l*, pg. 446

Lauchert, F.N., Grp. Pres.-Industrial Chemicals--Elf Atochem North America, Basic Chemicals Div., Philadelphia, PA; *Int'l*, pg. 446

Laucirica, Louis, Pres., Chief Exec. Officer & Chief Oper. Officer--Norton Performance Plastics, Wayne, NJ; *Int'l*, pg. 1174

Lauder, Arthur W., Pres.--Bettis Canada Limited, Edmonton, Canada; *U.S. Public*, pg. 483

Lauer, Brian, Gen Mgr.- MIS Div.--Ajax Services Inc., Warren, OH; *Int'l*, pg. 113

Lauer, Timothy C., Pres. & Gen. Mgr.--Unocal Indonesia, Ltd., Jakarta, Indonesia; *U.S. Public*, pg. 1698

Laufer, Hans K., Pres.--Superior Machine Company Of South Carolina, Inc., Florence, SC; *U.S. Private*, pg. 1055

Laufer, Harry, Pres.--Associated Food Stores, Inc., Jamaica, NY; *U.S. Private*, pg. 90

Laughlin, Philip M., Sr. V.P. & Pres.-Cardiac Surgery Bus.--Medtronic, Inc., Minneapolis, MN; *U.S. Public*, pg. 1082

Laughlin, Steven L., Partner & Creative Dir.--Laughlin/Constable, Inc., Milwaukee, WI; *U.S. Private*, pg. 653

Laughton, A.W., Chm. Bd., Pres. & Mng. Dir.--British Trimmings Ltd., Stockport, United Kingdom; *U.S. Public*, pg. 434

Lauletta, John F., Pres. & Chief Exec. Officer--Tuboscope Incorporated, Houston, TX; *U.S. Public*, pg. 1643

Laulhere, M., Pres.--Lombardi Holdings Inc., Whittier, CA; *U.S. Private*, pg. 673

Laurance, Dale R., Dr., Pres. & Sr. Oper. Officer--Occidental Petroleum Corporation, Los Angeles, CA; *U.S. Public*, pg. 1210

Lauren, Hakan, Pres.--Cultor Food Science Inc., New York, NY; *Int'l*, pg. 349

Lauridsen, Jorgen, Pres.--Colgate-Palmolive France, Courbevoie, France; *U.S. Public*, pg. 398

Lauritsen, K. Bruce, Pres. & Chief Exec. Officer--Flexsteel Industries, Inc., Dubuque, IA; *U.S. Public*, pg. 653

Lauritzen, Peter, Pres.--MD Foods Ingriedients amba, Viby, Denmark; *Int'l*, pg. 826

Laursen, Allan, Pres.--A/S Fibo, Risskov, Denmark; *Int'l*, pg. 1200

Lautenschlager, Jack L., Pres.--Peabody Development Company, Saint Louis, MO; *Int'l*, pg. 594

Lauzier, Marijean, Pres.--The Weber Group, Cambridge, MA; *U.S. Private*, pg. 1157

Lauzon, D.A., Pres. & Chief Exec. Officer--Dow Chemical Canada, Inc., Sarnia, Canada; *U.S. Public*, pg. 523

Lavau, Alain, Pres. & Gen. Dir.--Ecom et Partenaire, Neuilly-sur-Seine, France; *Int'l*, pg. 433
Lavender, Fred C., Pres.--F.E. Myers, Ashland, OH; *U.S. Public*, pg. 1273
Laver, Ken, Pres.--Messier-Dowty Inc., Toronto, Ajax, Canada; *Int'l*, pg. 1340
Laverty, Roger M., III, Pres. & Chief Exec. Officer--Smart & Final, Vernon, CA; *Int'l*, pg. 563
Lavin, Jesus Redondo, Pres.--I.C.S.A. - Internacional de Composites, S.A., Madrid, Spain; *Int'l*, pg. 1224
Lavington, Mike, Pres. & Chief Exec. Officer--Resorts USA Inc., Bushkill, PA; *Int'l*, pg. 1087
Lavoie, James R., Pres.--Integrated Performance Decisions, North Stonington, CT; *U.S. Public*, pg. 110
Lavruhin, G., Chief Mktg. Officer--AutotractorExport, Moscow, Russia; *Int'l*, pg. 101
Law-Smith, David J., Chm. Bd., Pres. & Chief Exec. Officer--Caltex Petroleum Corporation, Irving, TX; *U.S. Public*, pg. 348
Law, D. Brian, Pres.--Magline, Inc., Pinconning, MI; *U.S. Private*, pg. 695
Law, Jordan, Chm. Bd., Pres. & Chief Exec. Officer--KTI, Orange, CA; *U.S. Public*, pg. 939
Lawernce, W. Larry Jr., Pres. & Chief Exec. Officer--Sunline Coach Co., Inc., Denver, PA; *U.S. Private*, pg. 1053
Lawing, Tim, Pres.--Walker & Associates, Inc., Welcome, NC; *U.S. Private*, pg. 1147
Lawler, Patrick A., Pres.--Frederick Manufacturing Corporation, Kansas City, MO; *U.S. Public*, pg. 238
Lawless, Robert J., Pres. & Chief Exec. Officer--McCormick & Company, Incorporated, Sparks, MD; *U.S. Public*, pg. 1066
Lawrence, A.L. John, Pres.--Phelps Dodge Exploration Corporation, Phoenix, AZ; *U.S. Public*, pg. 1287
Lawrence, Frederick D., Chm. Bd., Pres. & Chief Exec. Officer--California Microwave, Inc., Sunnyvale, CA; *U.S. Public*, pg. 293
Lawrence, G. Barry, Pres.--Gear Research Incorporated, Grand Rapids, MI; *U.S. Private*, pg. 598
Lawrence, Ralph, Pres. & Chief Oper. Officer--Hyde Manufacturing Co., Southbridge, MA; *U.S. Private*, pg. 551
Lawrence, Richard, V.P.--New Zealand Lamb Co., Inc., White Plains, NY; *U.S. Private*, pg. 796
Lawrence, Robert L., Pres.--Jacor Communications, Inc., Covington, KY; *U.S. Public*, pg. 922
Lawrence, Stephen, Pres.--Lawrence Metal Products, Inc., Bay Shore, NY; *U.S. Private*, pg. 654
Lawrence, Steve, Pres.--California Custom Foods, Lodi, CA; *U.S. Private*, pg. 831
Lawrence, Steve, Pres.--Pepsico de Mexico, S.A. de C.V., Mexico, Mexico; *U.S. Public*, pg. 1277
Lawson, Adrian, Pres.--Allied Colloids (Australia) Pty. Ltd., Wyong, Australia; *Int'l*, pg. 62
Lawson, Charles E., Pres. & Chief Exec. Officer--The Lion Brewery, Inc., Wilkes-Barre, PA; *U.S. Public*, pg. 1000
Lawson, James, Pres.--Pneumatic Scale Corporation, Cuyahoga Falls, OH; *U.S. Private*, pg. 118
Lawson, Lowell, A., Chm. Bd. & Chief Exec. Officer--Raytheon E-Systems, Greenville, TX; *U.S. Public*, pg. 1365
Lawson, Rodney, Pres., Chief Oper. Officer & Chief Exec. Officer--Lawson Mechanical Contractors, Sacramento, CA; *U.S. Private*, pg. 654
Lawson, William, Pres. & Chief Exec. Officer--Lawson Software, Minneapolis, MN; *U.S. Private*, pg. 654
Lawson, William H., Chm. Bd. & Chief Exec. Officer--Franklin Electric Co., Inc., Bluffton, IN; *U.S. Public*, pg. 679
Lawson, William J., Pres. & Chief Oper. Officer--American States Insurance Companies, Indianapolis, IN; *U.S. Public*, pg. 997
Lawyer, Joseph C., Pres. & Chief Exec. Officer--Chatwins Group, Inc., Pittsburgh, PA; *U.S. Private*, pg. 231
Lax, Bobby A., Pres. & Gen. Mgr.--Distributors Oil Company, Inc., Baton Rouge, LA; *U.S. Private*, pg. 336
Lay, Charles, Pres. & Chief Exec. Officer--Geneva Pharmaceuticals, Inc., Broomfield, CO; *Int'l*, pg. 973
Lay, Joe L., Jr., Chm. Bd., Pres. & Chief Exec. Officer--Lay's Fine Foods, Knoxville, TN; *U.S. Private*, pg. 655
Layman, Harold E., Pres.--Blount Development Corp., Montgomery, AL; *U.S. Public*, pg. 239
Layne, Audrey, Pres. & Chief Fin. Officer--The Great Atlantic Management Company, Hampton, VA; *U.S. Private*, pg. 473
Layne, Gregory W., Pres.--Intesys Technologies, Gilbert, AZ; *U.S. Private*, pg. 574
Layton, Mark C., Pres., Chief Exec. & Oper. Officer--Daisytek International Corporation, Plano, TX; *U.S. Public*, pg. 477
Layton, Mark C., Pres., Chief Exec. & Oper. Officer--Daisytek (Canada) Inc., Toronto, Canada; *U.S. Public*, pg. 477
Layton, Mark C., Pres., Chief Exec. & Oper. Officer--Daisytek Latin America, Miami, FL; *U.S. Public*, pg. 477
Layton, Mark C., Pres., Chief Exec. & Oper. Officer--Daisytek De Mexico S.A. de C.V., Mexico, Mexico; *U.S. Public*, pg. 477
Layton, Mark C., Pres., Chief Exec. & Oper. Officer--Priority Fulfillment Services, Inc., Plano, TX; *U.S. Public*, pg. 477
Layton, Mark C., Pres., Chief Exec. & Oper. Officer--Daisytek Australia Pty. Ltd., Alexandria, Australia; *U.S. Public*, pg. 477
Layton, Tim W., Pres. & Chief Exec. Officer--Medeco Security Locks, Inc., Salem, VA; *U.S. Public*, pg. 828
Lazarchick, Robert, Pres. & Chief Exec. Officer--Terre Hill Concrete Products, Inc., Terre Hill, PA; *U.S. Private*, pg. 1077
Lazarus, James J., Pres.--L&R Manufacturing Co., Kearny, NJ; *U.S. Private*, pg. 638
Lazarus, John, Mng. Partner & Natl. Brdcst. Opers. Dir.--BJK&E Media Group, New York, NY; *U.S. Public*, pg. 1642
Le Blanc, Richard, Pres.--Microlite Corporation, West Chicago, IL; *U.S. Public*, pg. 1306
Le Boutiellier, John, Pres.--Iron-Ore Company of Canada, Montreal, Canada; *Int'l*, pg. 967
Le Marquand, Phillip, Pres.--ALstrip East, Exton, PA; *U.S. Public*, pg. 43
Le Mener, Georges, Pres. & Chief Exec. Officer--Motel 6 Operating L.P., Dallas, TX; *Int'l*, pg. 21
Lea, George A. Jr., Chm. Bd., Pres. & Chief Exec. Officer--The Mad Butcher, Inc., Pine Bluff, AR; *U.S. Private*, pg. 693
Leach, Brock, Pres. & Chief Fin. Officer--Frito-Lay Company, Plano, TX; *U.S. Public*, pg. 1277
Leach, Edwin, F., II, Pres.--Leach & Garner Company, North Attleboro, MA; *U.S. Private*, pg. 655
Leadbeater, Seth, Pres.--Commerce Bank, N.A., Clayton, MO; *U.S. Public*, pg. 409
Leadbetter, Bruce, Pres. & Chief Exec. Officer--Dalfort Aerospace, Dallas, TX; *Int'l*, pg. 1253
Leahey, Lynn, Editor-in-Chief--Soap Opera Digest, New York, NY; *U.S. Public*, pg. 1328
Leahy, Terry, Pres. & Chief Exec. Officer--Stream International Holdings Inc., Canton, MA; *U.S. Public*, pg. 518
Leaman, Stephen, Pres.--Maryland Casualty Co., Baltimore, MD; *Int'l*, pg. 1530
Leary, John, Pres.--The Motorlease Corp., Farmington, CT; *U.S. Private*, pg. 764
Leary, Mikel J., Pres.--Dairy Queen of Georgia, Inc., Decatur, GA; *U.S. Public*, pg. 220
Leary, Richard, Pres.--Red Wing Products, Inc., Plainview, NY; *Int'l*, pg. 480
Leasher, Randy S., Pres. & Chief Oper. Officer--Cassano's Inc., Dayton, OH; *U.S. Private*, pg. 218
Leasure, George, Pres., Chief Exec. Officer, Chief Fin. Officer & Treas.--Ghent Manufacturing, Inc., Lebanon, OH; *U.S. Private*, pg. 450
Leasure, George, Pres.--Waddell Display Cases Div. of Ghent Mfg. Co., Greenfield, OH; *U.S. Private*, pg. 450
Leasure, Lukoki W., Pres.--L3 Communications Hycor Div., Woburn, MA; *U.S. Private*, pg. 638
Leatherby, Russell E., Pres. & Chief Exec. Officer--UniCARE Financial Corp., Irvine, CA; *U.S. Private*, pg. 152
Leatherdale, D.W., Chm. Bd., Pres. & Chief Exec. Officer--The St. Paul Companies, Inc., Saint Paul, MN; *U.S. Public*, pg. 1429
Leavitt, H. Huntington, Pres.--Spontex, Inc., Columbia, TN; *Int'l*, pg. 1409
Lebel, Andre, Pres. & Chief Exec. Officer--Teleglobe Canada Inc., Montreal, Canada; *Int'l*, pg. 1373
Lebensfeld, Steven A., Pres.--Toymax International Inc., Plainview, NY; *U.S. Public*, pg. 1626
Leberz, Kent A., Pres.--Indiana Bell Telephone Company, Inc., Indianapolis, IN; *U.S. Public*, pg. 98
Leblanc, Jean-Yves, Pres. & Chief Oper. Officer--Transportation Equipment Group-North America, Saint-Bruno, Canada; *Int'l*, pg. 200
Leblanc, Jean-Yves, Pres. & Chief Oper. Officer--Transportation Equipment Group, Saint-Bruno, Canada; *Int'l*, pg. 200
LeBlanc, Robert D., Pres. & Chief Oper. Officer--Handy & Harman, New York, NY; *U.S. Public*, pg. 780
Lebovitz, Charles B., Chm. Bd., Pres. & Chief Exec. Officer--CBL & Associates Properties, Inc., Chattanooga, TN; *U.S. Public*, pg. 273
LeBow, Bennett S., Chm. Bd., Pres. & Chief Exec. Officer--Brooke Group Ltd., Miami, FL; *U.S. Public*, pg. 259
LeBow, Bennett S., Chm. Bd., Pres. & Chief Exec. Officer--BGLS Inc., Miami, FL; *U.S. Public*, pg. 259
Lebowitz, Glenn, Pres.--Optima Direct, Inc., Vienna, VA; *U.S. Public*, pg. 1224
Leclabart, Vincent, Chm. & Pres.--Australie, Levallois-Perret, France; *Int'l*, pg. 600
LeClair, Darryl A., Chm. Bd., Pres. & Chief Exec. Officer--Echelon International Corporation, Saint Petersburg, FL; *U.S. Public*, pg. 560
Leclerc, Michel-Edouard, Vice Chm. & Pres.--Leclerc, Issy-les-Moulineaux, France; *Int'l*, pg. 805
Leclere, Yves, Pres.--Messier-Bugatti S.A., Velizy-Villacoublay, France; *Int'l*, pg. 1165
Leclere, Yves, Pres.--Messier Services Inc., Sterling, VA; *Int'l*, pg. 1165
LeCompte, Jerry, Pres.--MMLJ, Inc., Houston, TX; *U.S. Private*, pg. 687
Ledbetter, Dale, Pres.--Shelter Distribution, Elkhart, IN; *U.S. Public*, pg. 953
Ledbetter, Rick, Pres.--Guarantee Electrical Company, Saint Louis, MO; *U.S. Private*, pg. 485
Lederer, Bertroui, Pres.--Teknor Color Company, Pawtucket, RI; *U.S. Private*, pg. 1073
Lederer, Paul R., Co-Pres.--Fel-Pro Incorporated, Skokie, IL; *U.S. Private*, pg. 399
Lee, Alan, Pres.--Unity Sewing Supply Div., Carteret, NJ; *U.S. Private*, pg. 1177
Lee, Andrew, Chm. Bd., Pres. & Chief Oper. Officer--Daniel Caron Sportswear, New York, NY; *U.S. Private*, pg. 309
Lee, Bobbie, Pres.--Superior Reprographics, Seattle, WA; *U.S. Private*, pg. 418
Lee, C.T., Pres.--Formosa Plastics Corp., U.S.A., Livingston, NJ; *Int'l*, pg. 498
Lee, Candy, Pres. & V.P.--Silhouette Books, New York, NY; *Int'l*, pg. 1402
Lee, Charles R., Chm. Bd., Chief Exec. Officer & Chief Oper. Officer--GTE Corporation, Stamford, CT; *U.S. Public*, pg. 696
Lee, Dan K., Pres. & Chief Exec. Officer--Willis Corroon Property & Casualty Programs Div., Nashville, TN; *Int'l*, pg. 1508
Lee, David B., Pres. & Chief Exec. Officer--Omega Bank, N.A., State College, PA; *U.S. Public*, pg. 1222
Lee, David B., Pres. & Chief Exec. Officer--Montour Bank, Danville, PA; *U.S. Public*, pg. 1222
Lee, Debra L., Pres. & Chief Oper. Officer--Black Entertainment Television Holdings Inc., Washington, DC; *U.S. Public*, pg. 235
Lee, Doo-Hwan, Pres.--Ssangyong Uni-Charm Co., Ltd., Kumi, Korea; *Int'l*, pg. 1291
Lee, Doyle, Pres. & Chief Exec. Officer--Weatherford National Bank, Weatherford, TX; *U.S. Public*, pg. 633
Lee, Gary D., Pres.--Lee-Rowan Company, Saint Louis, MO; *U.S. Public*, pg. 1177
Lee, H. Clark, Pres.--Valley Detroit Diesel Allison, City of Industry, CA; *U.S. Private*, pg. 1132
Lee, J. Tyler, Pres.--Royal Financial Services Inc., Southfield, MI; *Int'l*, pg. 1130
Lee, James C., III, Pres.--Buffalo Rock Company, Birmingham, AL; *U.S. Private*, pg. 179
Lee, Jerry D., Pres.--Macpherson Meistergram, Inc., Greensboro, NC; *U.S. Private*, pg. 1177
Lee, Jim, Pres. & Chief Oper. Officer--Furst-McNess Company, Freeport, IL; *U.S. Private*, pg. 432
Lee, John, Pres.--Harris Enterprises Inc., Hutchinson, KS; *U.S. Private*, pg. 505
Lee, John E., Pres. & Chief Exec. Officer--Carver, Inc., Savannah, GA; *U.S. Private*, pg. 217
Lee, Jong-Kyu, Pres.--Ssangyong Precision Industry Co., Ltd., Inchon, Korea; *Int'l*, pg. 1292
Lee, K.H., Pres.--Sharp Korea Corporation (Inchon), Inchon, Korea; *Int'l*, pg. 1230
Lee, Kenneth, Pres.--Lawrence Division, Lawrence, MA; *U.S. Public*, pg. 27
Lee, Leighton, III, Pres.--Lee Company, Westbrook, CT; *U.S. Private*, pg. 657
Lee, Michael, Partner--Messner Vetere Berger McNamee Schmetterer/EURO RSCG, New York, NY; *Int'l*, pg. 602
Lee, Mike, Chm., Pres. & Chief Exec. Officer--Famous Restaurants Inc., Scottsdale, AZ; *U.S. Private*, pg. 393
Lee, Mike, Pres.--Fiesta Restaurants, Inc., Oklahoma City, OK; *U.S. Public*, pg. 555
Lee, Ramon G., Pres.--Illinois-American Water Co., Belleville, IL; *U.S. Public*, pg. 95
Lee, Robert, Pres.--Vulcan Inc., Foley, AL; *U.S. Private*, pg. 1144
Lee, Robert E., Pres. & Chief Exec. Officer--Millennium Inorganic Chemicals, Hunt Valley, MD; *Int'l*, pg. 593
Lee, Ronald G., Chm. Bd. & Pres.--Lee Pharmaceuticals, South El Monte, CA; *U.S. Public*, pg. 984
Lee, S., Pres.--Semiconductor Div., Mountain View, CA; *U.S. Public*, pg. 1365
Lee, Sang-On, Pres.--Ssangyong Fire & Marine Insurance Co., Ltd., Seoul, Korea; *Int'l*, pg. 1292
Lee, Sang-Won, Pres.--Ssangyong Shipping Co. Ltd., Seoul, Korea; *Int'l*, pg. 1292
Lee, Seung-Hyum, Pres.--Ssangyong (Hong Kong) Co., Ltd., Central, Hong Kong; *Int'l*, pg. 1291
Lee, T.T., Pres.--King Car Otsuka Co., Ltd., Taipei, Taiwan; *Int'l*, pg. 1014
Lee, Thomas Chua Boon, Grp. Chief Exec. Officer--Cycle & Carriage Industries (1986) Pte. Limited, Singapore, Singapore; *Int'l*, pg. 350
Lee, Thomas H., Pres.--Thomas H. Lee Co., Boston, MA; *U.S. Private*, pg. 658
Lee, Tim, Pres.--Lakeside Industries, Issaquah, WA; *U.S. Private*, pg. 644
Lee, Warren H.W., Pres.--Hawaii Electric Light Co., Inc., Hilo, HI; *U.S. Public*, pg. 800
Lee, Y.I., Pres. & Chief Exec. Officer--Hyundai Motor America, Fountain Valley, CA; *Int'l*, pg. 641
Lee, Youn-Jae, Chm. Bd. & Chief Exec. Officer--Jinwoong Inc., Seoul, Korea; *Int'l*, pg. 706
Lee, Young Ho, Pres.--NMB Korea Co., Ltd., Seoul, Korea; *Int'l*, pg. 868
Leebern, Donald, III, Pres.--Georgia Crown Distributing, Columbus, GA; *U.S. Private*, pg. 448
Leebow, Steven, Chm. Bd., Pres. & Chief Exec. Officer--Pacesetter Steel Service, Inc., Kennesaw, GA; *U.S. Private*, pg. 830
Leech, James W., Pres. & Chief Exec. Officer--Union Energy Inc., Toronto, Canada; *Int'l*, pg. 1492
Leeds, Jeffrey, Pres. & Chief Oper. Officer--Elsinore Corporation, Las Vegas, NV; *U.S. Public*, pg. 570
Leeds, Michael S., Pres. & Chief Exec. Officer--CMP Media, Inc., Manhasset, NY; *U.S. Public*, pg. 279
Leeds, Robert K., Chm. Bd. & Pres.--Jewelmont Corporation, Minneapolis, MN; *U.S. Private*, pg. 587
Leef, James M., Pres.--Industrial Towel & Uniform, New Berlin, WI; *U.S. Private*, pg. 561
Leegfe, W., Pres.--Ambac B.V., Breda, Netherlands; *Int'l*, pg. 71
Leemans, Michel F., Chm. Bd., Pres. & Chief Exec. Officer--IL International Inc., Stratford, CT; *U.S. Public*, pg. 855
Leeolou, Stephen R., Pres.--Vanguard Cellular Systems, Inc., Greensboro, NC; *U.S. Public*, pg. 1707
Leer, Steven F., Pres. & Chief Exec. Officer--Arch Coal, Inc., Saint Louis, MO; *U.S. Public*, pg. 139
Leever, Daniel H., Pres. & Chief Exec. Officer--MacDermid Incorporated, Waterbury, CT; *U.S. Public*, pg. 1029
Lefebure, Monique, Pres.--Quebecor Multimedia Inc., Montreal, Canada; *Int'l*, pg. 1076
Leff, Martin J., Chm. Bd., Pres. & Chief Fin. Officer--Carole Wren, Inc., New York, NY; *U.S. Private*, pg. 1192
Lefkof, Alan B., Pres. & Chief Exec. Officer--Netopia, Inc., Alameda, CA; *U.S. Public*, pg. 1168
Lefkovits, Samuel, Pres.--Roselle Paper Co., Inc., Roselle, NJ; *U.S. Private*, pg. 945
LeFrak, Richard S., Pres.--Lefrak Organization Inc., Rego Park, NY; *U.S. Private*, pg. 658
Lefton, Al Paul, Jr., Pres. & Chief Exec. Officer--Al Paul Lefton Co., Inc., Philadelphia, PA; *U.S. Private*, pg. 658
Legatti, Raymond H., Pres.--Technology Research Corporation, Clearwater, FL; *U.S. Public*, pg. 1564
Legaz, Alfredo Llorente, Pres.--ENUSA - E.N. del Uranio, S.A., Madrid, Spain; *Int'l*, pg. 1224
Leger, Bernard, Pres.--Lodal, Inc., Kingsford, MI; *U.S. Private*, pg. 672

Leger, Buster, Pres.--Woolcan, Lachine, Canada; *U.S. Private*, pg. 1188
Leger, J.C., Pres. & Chief Exec. Officer--CGTX Inc., Mississauga, Canada; *Int'l*, pg. 604
Leggetter, Barry, Pres., Sr. Partner, Mng. Dir. & Exec. V.P.--Fleishman-Hillard U.K. Limited, London, United Kingdom; *U.S. Private*, pg. 411
LeGrand, David J., Pres.--Nordyne Inc., Saint Louis, MO; *U.S. Public*, pg. 1193
Legum, Jeffrey A., Pres. & Chief Exec. Officer--The Park Circle Motor Co., Baltimore, MD; *U.S. Private*, pg. 839
Lehman, Chris, Chm. Bd., Pres. & Chief Exec. Officer--SRDS, Des Plaines, IL; *U.S. Private*, pg. 958
Lehman, Paul, Co-Pres.--Fel-Pro Incorporated, Skokie, IL; *U.S. Private*, pg. 399
Lehmann, Richard J., Pres. & Chief Oper. Officer--Banc One Corporation, Columbus, OH; *U.S. Public*, pg. 172
Lehmuskoski, Pekka, Pres.--Fiskars Power Systems, Espoo, Finland; *Int'l*, pg. 127
Lehnen, Gerhard, Pres.--Komatsu Hanomag AG, Hannover, Germany; *Int'l*, pg. 744
Lehrer, P.M., Pres.--Bovis Inc., New York, NY; *Int'l*, pg. 1033
Lehrer, Peter, Chm. Bd. & Chief Exec. Officer--Lehrer McGovern Bovis Inc., New York, NY; *Int'l*, pg. 1035
Lehtinen, Veikko, Deputy Pres.-Legal Affairs, Human Resources & Corp. Communication--Outokumpu Oyj, Espoo, Finland; *Int'l*, pg. 1015
Leibovitz, Mitchell G., Chm. Bd., Pres. & Chief Exec. Officer--The Pep Boys-Manny, Moe & Jack, Philadelphia, PA; *U.S. Public*, pg. 1276
Leicht, Richard F., Jr., Pres. & Chief Exec. Officer--Eclipse Manufacturing Company, Sheboygan, WI; *U.S. Private*, pg. 361
Leifeld, Ellen, Publr.--Ithaca Journal, Ithaca, NY; *U.S. Public*, *pg. 700*
Leiff, Ann Spector, Pres. & Chief Exec. Officer--Spec's Music, Inc., Miami, FL; *U.S. Public*, pg. 1497
Leighty, D.A., Pres.--Perma Pure Inc., Toms River, NJ; *Int'l*, pg. 590
Leinenkugel, Jake, Pres.--Jacob Leinenkugel Brewing Co., Chippewa Falls, WI; *U.S. Public*, pg. 1289
Leinweber, John L., Pres. & Chief Exec. Officer--Danka Business Systems, La Grange, IL; *Int'l*, pg. 379
Leistner, Ralph, Pres. & Chief Exec. Officer--McAlear Associates, Inc., Grand Rapids, MI; *Int'l*, pg. 1508
Leith, William T., Pres.--Quality Park Products, Saint Paul, MN; *U.S. Public*, pg. 1038
Leiting, Denis E., Chm. Bd. & Pres.--Ag Processing Inc., A Cooperative, Omaha, NE; *U.S. Private*, pg. 26
Leiweke, Tim, Pres.--Denver Nuggets Limited Partnership, Denver, CO; *U.S. Public*, pg. 138
Lekach, Zalman, Pres. & Chief Oper. Officer--Parlux Fragrances Inc., Fort Lauderdale, FL; *U.S. Public*, pg. 1264
Lekowitz, Joel, Pres.--Hoboken Wood Flooring Corporation, Wayne, NJ; *U.S. Private*, pg. 532
Lelakis, Anthony, Pres.--Regency Cruises Inc., New York, NY; *U.S. Private*, pg. 918
Lemaire, Laurent, Pres. & Chief Exec. Officer--The Cascades Group, Kingsey Falls, Canada; *Int'l*, pg. 273
Lemaire, Laurent, Pres. & Chief Exec. Offficer--Cascades, Inc., Kingsey Falls, Canada; *Int'l*, pg. 273
Lemarchand, Patrick, Pres.--Atlas Editions, Paris, France; *Int'l*, pg. 96
LeMarquand, Philip J., Pres.--ALstrip, Inc., Skokie, IL; *U.S. Public*, pg. 43
LeMay, Jennifer, Sr. Partner & Exec. Creative Dir.--EURO RSCG Tatham, Chicago, IL; *Int'l*, pg. 601
Lemay, Raymond, Pres.--Quebecor Communications, Inc., Montreal, Canada; *Int'l*, pg. 1076
Lemay, Ronald T., Pres. & Chief Oper. Officer--Sprint Corporation, Westwood, KS; *U.S. Public*, pg. 1500
Lembo, Anthony, Pres.--Dataflex Corporation, Clearwater, FL; *U.S. Private*, pg. 313
Lembre, Hakan, Pres.--TAC Control AB, Malmo, Sweden; *Int'l*, pg. 670
Lemeunier, Anny-Claude, Pres. & Chief Creative Officer-BL/LB Group--Bordelais, Lemeunier-Leo Burnett Paris, Levallois-Perret, France; *U.S. Private*, pg. 184
LeMire, Arthur J., Pres.--Kasper Machine Company, Madison Heights, MI; *U.S. Private*, pg. 608
Lemley, Jack, Chm. Bd., Pres. & Chief Exec. Officer--American Ecology Corporation, Boise, ID; *U.S. Public*, pg. 71
Lemman, Peter R., Pres.--North Coast Electric Company, Bellevue, WA; *U.S. Private*, pg. 804
Lemmenes, Larry, Pres.--Alto Dairy Cooperative, Waupun, WI; *U.S. Private*, pg. 47
Lemmon, David, Pres. & Chief Exec. Officer--Colonial Pipeline Company, Atlanta, GA; *U.S. Private*, pg. 254
Lemmon, George B., Jr., Pres. & Chief Exec. Officer--Owosso Corporation, King of Prussia, PA; *U.S. Public*, pg. 1238
Lenart, Deb, Pres.--Ameritech New Media, Chicago, IL; *U.S.* Public, pg. 98
Leng, James W., Chief Exec. Officer & Mng. Dir.--Laporte plc, Luton, United Kingdom; *Int'l*, pg. 801
Lengnick, G.F., Pres.--Wacker Silicones Corporation, Adrian, MI; *Int'l*, pg. 625
Lengyel, David S., Pres.--The Pfaltzgraff Co., York, PA; *U.S.* Private, pg. 860
Lengyel, Peter, Pres.--BT Commercial Corporation, New York, NY; *U.S. Public*, pg. 185
Lenhart, Ronald G., Pres.-Mount Morris Facility--AMCORE Bank, Rock River Valley, Mount Morris, IL; *U.S. Public*, pg. 64
Lenig, Larry, Pres. & Chief Exec. Officer--Grant Geophysical Inc., Houston, TX; *U.S. Private*, pg. 470
Lenkel, Goran, Pres.--SkandiaBanken AB, Stockholm, Sweden; *Int'l*, pg. 1257
Lenker, Max V., Pres.--Racetrac Petroleum, Inc., Smyrna, GA; *U.S. Private*, pg. 906
Lenkin, Harvey, Pres.--Public Storage, Inc., Glendale, CA; *U.S. Public*, pg. 1340
Lennar, Leonard, Pres.--Lennar Homes Inc., Miami, FL; *U.S.* Public, pg. 988
Lennox, Gregory P., Pres. & Chief Exec. Officer--P.L. Porter Co., Woodland Hills, CA; *U.S. Private*, pg. 876
Lenoci, V. William, Pres. & Chief Exec. Officer--Industrial Coated Fabrics Group, Spartanburg, SC; *U.S. Private*, pg. 507
Lenoir, Phillip, Pres.--Precismeca S.A., Saverne, France; *Int'l*, pg. 399
Lenox, John W., Pres. & Chief Exec. Officer--Shelter Mutual Insurance Company, Columbia, MO; *U.S. Private*, pg. 992
Lentzsch, Craig, Pres. & Chief Exec. Officer--Greyhound Lines, Inc., Dallas, TX; *U.S. Public*, pg. 765
Lenway, Fred, Pres.--Aramark Uniform Services, Burbank, CA; *U.S. Private*, pg. 79
Lenz, Sidney, Pres.--LandSafe Title Agency, Inc., Pasadena, CA; *U.S. Public*, pg. 453
Lenzie, Charles A., Chm. Bd., Pres. & Chief Exec. Officer--Nevada Power Company, Las Vegas, NV; *U.S. Public*, pg. 1169
Lenzner, Dale, Principal--Center Partners Management LLC, New York, NY; *U.S. Private*, pg. 222
Leon, Gilberto, Pres.--UCAR Polimeros y Quimicos C.A., Guayaquil, Ecuador; *U.S. Public*, pg. 1667
Leon, Juan, Pres.--Leather Center, Inc., Carrollton, TX; *U.S.* Private, pg. 656
Leonard, J.B., Pres.--Bath Fashions Division, Fort Mill, SC; *U.S. Public*, pg. 1500
Leonard, James E., Pres.--ConAgra Poultry Foodservice Co., Omaha, NE; *U.S. Public*, pg. 427
Leonard, K.E., Pres. & Chief Exec. Officer--Leonard & Harral Packing Co., San Antonio, TX; *U.S. Private*, pg. 660
Leonard, Michael, Pres.--Harman Automotive, Farmington Hills, MI; *U.S. Public*, pg. 796
Leonard, Richard, Pres.--Sunstates Realty Group Inc., Raleigh, NC; *U.S. Public*, pg. 1536
Leonard, Thomas, Pres.-North America--Samsonite Corporation, Denver, CO; *U.S. Public*, pg. 1430
Leonard, Thomas C., Pres. & Chief Exec. Officer--Alpha Industries, Inc., Woburn, MA; *U.S. Public*, pg. 57
Leonard, Tom, Pres.--Lark Luggage Company, Inc., Denver, CO; *U.S. Public*, pg. 1430
Leonard, William, Pres. & Chief Oper. Officer--Aramark Corp., Philadelphia, PA; *U.S. Private*, pg. 78
Leone, John A., Pres. & Chief Exec. Officer--Bonney Forge Corporation, Allentown, PA; *U.S. Private*, pg. 156
Leone, Lucas G., Pres.--Ethical Nutriment, Inc., King of Prussia, PA; *U.S. Private*, pg. 366
Leong, Bo, Pres.--Machinery North, Umea, Sweden; *Int'l*, pg. 899
Leong, Wong Chee, Pres. & Chief Exec. Officer--Bangkok Bank Berhad, Kuala Lumpur, Malaysia; *Int'l*, pg. 146
Leonhard, R.W., Chm. Bd., Pres. & Chief Exec. Officer--Southwestern Industries, Inc., Rancho Dominguez, CA; *U.S. Private*, pg. 1019
Leonhardt, Thomas C., Pres. & Chief Exec. Officer--Rust Environment & Infrastructure, Inc., Greenville, SC; *U.S. Public*, pg. 1745
Leoni, Rino, Pres.--EUROIPEX, S.p.A., Milan, Italy; *U.S. Public*, pg. 593
Leonsis, Ted, Chm. Bd., Chief Exec. Officer, Pres. & New Bus. Contact--Redgate Communications Corp., Vero Beach, FL; *U.S. Public*, pg. 66
Leopando, Oddie, Pres.--Datcon Instrument Co., East Petersburg, PA; *U.S. Private*, pg. 528
Leopold, Ernest S., Chm. Bd., Pres. & Chief Exec. Officer--Crown Vantage Inc., Oakland, CA; *U.S. Public*, pg. 465
Lepofsky, Robert J., Pres. & Chief Exec. Officer--Helix Technology Corp., Mansfield, MA; *U.S. Public*, pg. 808
Lepore, Donald, Pres. & Chief Exec. Officer--NutraMax Products, Inc., Gloucester, MA; *U.S. Public*, pg. 1206
LePore, Patrick G., Chm. Bd., Pres. & Chief Exec. Officer--Boron LePore Group, Fair Lawn, NJ; *U.S. Public*, pg. 246
Lepp, H.J., Pres. & Chief Exec. Officer--AltaSteel Ltd., Edmonton, Canada; *Int'l*, pg. 1299
Leppo, Harold, Interim Pres.--Casual Male, Inc., Hyde Park, MA; *U.S. Public*, pg. 168
Lerch, Allan, Pres.--Porcelain Metals Corp., Louisville, KY; *U.S. Private*, pg. 876
Lerch, Robert J., Pres.--Mazo Lerch Company, Inc., Alexandria, VA; *U.S. Public*, pg. 918
Lerenius, Bo, Pres. & Chief Exec. Officer--Stena Line AB, Goteborg, Sweden; *Int'l*, pg. 1300
Lerner, Michael H., Chm. Bd., Pres. & Chief Exec. Officer--Marisa Christina Inc., New Hyde Park, NY; *U.S. Public*, pg. 1044
Lerner, Robert C., Pres.--Wang Canada Limited, Scarborough, Canada; *U.S. Public*, pg. 1737
LeRoux, Kevin, Pres. & Gen. Mgr.--WGGB-TV, Springfield, MA; *U.S. Private*, pg. 439
Leroux, Marc, Pres. & Chief Oper. Officer--Teleglobe World Mobility, Montreal, Canada; *Int'l*, pg. 1373
Leroy, J.M., Pres.--N.V. Johnson Wax Belgium S.A., Groot-Bijgaarden, Belgium; *U.S. Private*, pg. 593
LeRoy, Pierre, Pres.--John Deere Industrial Equipment Company, Moline, IL; *U.S. Public*, pg. 492
Lervick, Rodger O., Pres.--Twin City Foods, Inc., Stanwood, WA; *U.S. Private*, pg. 1111
LeSaffre, Peter, Chm. Bd. & Pres.--Real World, Andover, MA; *U.S. Private*, pg. 913
LeSaffre, Tony, Pres.--Plastimo S.A., Lorient, France; *U.S. Public*, pg. 933
Lesage, Yves, Chm. Bd., Pres. & Chief Exec. Officer--Compagnie Generale de Geophysique, Massy, France; *Int'l*, pg. 241
Lesar, David J., Pres. & Chief Oper. Officer--Halliburton Company, Dallas, TX; *U.S. Public*, pg. 775
Lesar, Nicholas, Pres.--Weiler & Company, Inc., Whitewater, WI; *U.S. Private*, pg. 1160
Leseigneur, Urita, Pres.--Electricite de France, Mexico, Mexico; *Int'l*, pg. 437
Leskinen, Eero, Pres.--IKON Cully S.A., Cully, Switzerland; *Int'l*, pg. 18
Leslie, Charles J., Pres.--Fuji Medical Systems USA, Inc., Stamford, CT; *Int'l*, pg. 524
Leslie, Jack, Pres. & Partner--BSMG Worldwide, New York, NY; *U.S. Public*, pg. 1642
Leslie, James K., Pres. & Chief Exec. Officer--Pharmakinetics Laboratories, Inc., Baltimore, MD; *U.S. Public*, pg. 1285
Lesok, Eddie, Pres. & Chief Exec. Officer--Sun Coast Industries, Inc, Dallas, TX; *U.S. Public*, pg. 1529
Lessard, Claude, Pres. & Chief Exec. Officer--Cossette Communication Marketing, Quebec, Canada; *Int'l*, pg. 335
Lesser, Richard, Pres.--T.J. Maxx, Framingham, MA; *U.S. Public*, pg. 1557
Lesser, Richard, Pres.--The Marmax Group, Framingham, MA; *U.S. Public*, pg. 1557
Lesser, Stanford J., Pres.--Alba Forwarding Co., Inc., Jersey City, NJ; *U.S. Private*, pg. 32
Lestardo, Eugene, Pres.--Holmes Protection of New York, Incorporated, New York, NY; *U.S. Public*, pg. 1649
Lester, James L., III, Pres.--J.L. Lester & Son, Inc., Rockmart, GA; *U.S. Private*, pg. 660
Lester, L.J., Pres. & Chief Oper. Officer--Man-Gill Chemical Company, Cleveland, OH; *U.S. Private*, pg. 699
Lester, Raymond R., Pres.--J.L. Lester & Son, Inc., Rockmart, GA; *U.S. Private*, pg. 660
Lester, W. Bernard, Pres. & Chief Oper. Officer--Alico, Inc., La Belle, FL; *U.S. Public*, pg. 41
Lestina, Jerry, Pres. & Chief Oper. Officer--Roundy's, Inc., Pewaukee, WI; *U.S. Private*, pg. 948
LeStrange, Dennis P., Pres.--Ikon Office Solutions-New England, Glastonbury, CT; *U.S. Public*, pg. 863
Letaw, Harry, Jr., Chm. Bd., Pres. & Chief Exec. Officer--Essex Corporation, Columbia, MD; *U.S. Public*, pg. 593
Letbetter, S., Pres. & Chief Oper. Officer--Houston Industries Incorporated, Houston, TX; *U.S. Public*, pg. 842
Letbetter, S., Pres. & Chief Oper. Officer--NorAm Energy Corp., Houston, TX; *U.S. Public*, pg. 843
Letica, Illija, Pres. & Chief Exec. Officer--Letica Corporation, Rochester, MI; *U.S. Private*, pg. 661
Letke, Dave, Pres.--Preston Trucking Company, Inc., Preston, MD; *U.S. Public*, pg. 1788
Letmithe, Peter Bribeck, Pres.--Nestle S.A., Vevey, Switzerland; *Int'l*, pg. 915
Letters, Jerry, Pres. & Chief Exec. Officer--Farmers Union Marketing & Processing Association, Redwood Falls, MN; *U.S. Private*, pg. 395
Lettmann, John W., Pres.--Malt-O-Meal Company, Minneapolis, MN; *U.S. Private*, pg. 699
Letts, Charles E., Jr., Pres. & Chief Exec. Officer--Letts Industries, Inc., Detroit, MI; *U.S. Private*, pg. 661
Letwin, Stephen J.J., Pres.--TransCanada Energy USA Inc., Houston, TX; *Int'l*, pg. 1417
Letzler, John, Pres.-Hanes Printables--Sara Lee Knit Products, Winston Salem, NC; *U.S. Public*, pg. 1434
Leuliette, Timothy D., Pres. & Chief Oper. Officer--Penske Corporation, Detroit, MI; *U.S. Private*, pg. 850
Leum, Leonard L., Pres.--Pioneer Foods, Inc., Los Angeles, CA; *U.S. Private*, pg. 866
Leung, Johnson C., Pres. & Mng. Dir., Far East--Anheuser-Busch Asia, Inc., Tokyo, Japan; *U.S. Public*, pg. 115
Levan, Alan B., Chm. Bd., Pres. & Chief Exec. Officer--BankAtlantic Bancorp, Inc., Fort Lauderdale, FL; *U.S. Public*, pg. 183
LeVan, David M., Chm. Bd., Pres. & Chief Exec. Officer--Conrail, Inc., Philadelphia, PA; *U.S. Public*, pg. 431
Levan, David M., Chm. Bd., Pres. & Chief Exec. Officer--CRR Industries, Inc., Philadelphia, PA; *U.S. Public*, pg. 432
Levene, David A., Chm. Bd., Pres. & Chief Exec. Officer--Metropolitan Insurance & Annuity Co., New York, NY; *U.S. Private*, pg. 737
Levene, David A., Chm. Bd., Pres. & Chief Exec. Officer--Metropolitan Tower Life Insurance Co., New York, NY; *U.S. Private*, pg. 737
Levenhagan, David, Pres.--The Loan Store, Inc., Michigan City, IN; *U.S. Private*, pg. 539
Levenick, Mark, Pres. & Chief Exec. Officer--Tidel Engineering, Inc., Carrollton, TX; *U.S. Public*, pg. 1608
Levenson, Barbara L., Pres. & Chief Exec. Officer--Levenson & Hill, Inc., Dallas, TX; *U.S. Private*, pg. 662
Levenson, Ted, Pres.--Medical Management Associates, Inc., Thousand Oaks, CA; *U.S. Public*, pg. 839
Leveque, Timothy J., Pres.--Alcoa Closure Systems, International, Richmond, IN; *U.S. Public*, pg. 60
Levesque, Joseph, Chm. Bd., Pres. & Chief Exec. Officer--Aetrium Inc., Saint Paul, MN; *U.S. Public*, pg. 27
Levi, Malcolm, Jr., Pres.--Mayer Myers Paper Company, Memphis, TN; *U.S. Private*, pg. 718
Levin, Gilbert V., Dr., Chm., Pres., Chief Exec. Officer & Treas.--Biospherics Incorporated, Beltsville, MD; *U.S. Public*, pg. 232
Levin, Jo, Sr. Principal & Mngmt. Supvr.--Carlson & Partners, Inc., New York, NY; *U.S. Private*, pg. 211
Levin, Michael S., Pres. & Chief Exec. Officer--The Titan Industrial Corp., New York, NY; *U.S. Private*, pg. 1089
Levin, Moshe, Pres.--Orbotech Inc., Billerica, MA; *Int'l*, pg. 1007
Levin, Ralph, Chm. Bd. & Pres.--Sturgis Iron & Metal Company, Inc., Sturgis, MI; *U.S. Private*, pg. 1048
Levin, Ralph, Pres.--Elkhart Metals Division, Elkhart, IN; *U.S. Private*, pg. 1048
Levine, David, Pres.--Fashion Shop of Kentucky Inc., Louisville, KY; *U.S. Private*, pg. 397
Levine, Elliot, Pres. & Chief Oper. Officer--Softmart, Inc., Downingtown, PA; *U.S. Private*, pg. 1012
Levine, George, Pres.--Cantex Inc., Mineral Wells, TX; *Int'l*, pg. 1312

Levine, Howard R., Pres. & Chief Oper. Officer--Family Dollar Stores, Inc., Matthews, NC; *U.S. Public*, pg. 612
Levine, Irving M., Pres.--MultiQuip, Inc., Carson, CA; *Int'l*, pg. 695
Levine, Jesse, Pres. & Chief Exec. Officer--Los Angeles Times Syndicate, Los Angeles, CA; *U.S. Public*, pg. 1616
Levine, Jules B., Pres. & Chief Exec. Officer--Pick Quick Foods, Jamaica, NY; *U.S. Private*, pg. 864
Levine, Larry, Pres.--Larry Levine, New York, NY; *U.S. Private*, pg. 947
Levine, Martin, Pres. & Chief Exec. Officer--MarketSource Corporation, Cranbury, NJ; *U.S. Private*, pg. 705
Levine, Ralph, Pres. & Chief Oper. Officer--Carter-Wallace, Inc., New York, NY; *U.S. Public*, pg. 309
Levinson, Arthur D., Ph.D., Pres. & Chief Exec. Officer--Genentech, Inc., South San Francisco, CA; *Int'l*, pg. 1120
Levinson, Sara, Pres.--National Football League Properties, Inc., New York, NY; *U.S. Private*, pg. 783
Levit, Max, Pres.--Grocers Supply Co. Inc., Houston, TX; *U.S. Private*, pg. 483
Leviton, Howard, Pres. & Chief Exec. Officer--Leviton Mfg. Co., Inc., Little Neck, NY; *U.S. Private*, pg. 663
Levitt, Brian, Pres. & Chief Exec. Officer--Imasco Limited, Montreal, Canada; *Int'l*, pg. 112
Levitt, Richard, Pres. & Chief Exec. Officer--Lillie Rubin Fashions Inc., Miami, FL; *U.S. Private*, pg. 667
Levy-Ganz, Ellen, Pres.--Esprit Accessories, San Francisco, CA; *U.S. Private*, pg. 383
Levy, Bennett S., Pres.--M. Block & Sons, Inc., Chicago, IL; *U.S. Private*, pg. 150
Levy, Brian, Pres.--Levitz Furniture Incorporated, Boca Raton, FL; *U.S. Public*, pg. 990
Levy, Bruce L., Pres.--Energy Initiatives, Inc., Parsippany, NJ; *U.S. Public*, pg. 695
Levy, Bruce L., Pres.--El Energy, Inc., Parsippany, NJ; *U.S. Public*, pg. 695
Levy, Bruce L., Pres.--El Power, Inc., Parsippany, NJ; *U.S. Public*, pg. 695
Levy, Edward C., Jr., Pres. & Treas.--Edward C. Levy Co., Dearborn, MI; *U.S. Private*, pg. 664
Levy, Elio, Pres. & Chief Exec. Officer--Tech Data Canada, Inc., Mississauga, Canada; *U.S. Public*, pg. 1562
Levy, Enrique, Pres. & Chief Oper. Officer--Caprius, Inc., Wilmington, MA; *U.S. Public*, pg. 303
Levy, Frank L., Pres. & Chief Exec. Officer--L & L Oil Company, Inc., Metairie, LA; *U.S. Private*, pg. 638
Levy, Frank L., Pres. & Chief Exec. Officer--L & L Environmental Services, Metairie, LA; *U.S. Private*, pg. 638
Levy, Irvin L., Pres.--NCH Corporation, Irving, TX; *U.S. Public*, pg. 1145
Levy, Jack, Pres.--Jack Levy Associates, Chicago, IL; *U.S. Private*, pg. 664
Levy, Jeffrey M., Pres. & Chief Oper. Officer--EMCOR Group, Inc., Norwalk, CT; *U.S. Public*, pg. 571
Levy, Jerry, Chm. Bd. & Pres.--JL Media, Inc., Union, NJ; *U.S. Private*, pg. 577
Levy, Joe, Pres.--CIO Publishing Corp., Framingham, MA; *U.S. Private*, pg. 569
Levy, Joel M., Pres.--Rice Food Markets Inc., Houston, TX; *U.S. Private*, pg. 927
Levy, Leslie W., Pres. & Chief Oper. Officer--Heritage Sportswear, Marion, SC; *U.S. Public*, pg. 1472
Levy, Mark A., Pres. & Chief Oper. Officer--Oriole Homes Corp., Delray Beach, FL; *U.S. Public*, pg. 1230
Levy, Mark S., Chm. Bd. & Pres.--Fire Lite Alarms, Inc./Notifier Co., Northford, CT; *U.S. Public*, pg. 1306
Levy, Moshey, Pres.--Safeguards Technology, Inc., Hackensack, NJ; *Int'l*, pg. 1286
Levy, Myron, Pres.--Herley Industries, Inc., Lancaster, PA; *U.S. Public*, pg. 811
Levy, Myron, Pres.--Herley Vega Industry, Lancaster, PA; *U.S. Public*, pg. 811
Levy, Paul, Partner & Pres.--Joseph, Littlejohn & Levy, New York, NY; *U.S. Private*, pg. 601
Levy, Robert, Pres., Chief Exec. Officer & Chief Oper. Officer--Norman Levy Associates, Inc., Southfield, MI; *U.S. Private*, pg. 664
Levy, Robert I., M.D., Pres.--Wyeth-Ayerst Laboratories-Research & Development, Radnor, PA; *U.S. Public*, pg. 80
Levy, Sam, Pres.--Mactavish Machine Manufacturing Company, Richmond, VA; *U.S. Private*, pg. 693
Levy, Steve, Pres. & Chief Exec. Officer--Jacob Levy & Bros., Inc., Louisville, KY; *U.S. Private*, pg. 664
Lewin, Joseph, Chm. Bd., Pres. & Chief Exec. Officer--Health Products Corporation, Yonkers, NY; *U.S. Private*, pg. 514
Lewis-Gordon, Danna, Pres. & Chief Exec. Officer--Surfer Publications, Inc., Dana Point, CA; *U.S. Private*, pg. 417
Lewis, Bryan L., Pres.--Teledyne Continental Motors, Mobile, AL; *U.S. Public*, pg. 43
Lewis, Byron E., Chm. Bd. & Chief Exec. Officer--Uniworld Group, Inc., New York, NY; *U.S. Private*, pg. 1128
Lewis, Carlyn, Pres.--Insurance Brokers & Managers, Inc., New Orleans, LA; *U.S. Public*, pg. 1677
Lewis, Charles, Chm, Pres, & Chief Exec. Officer--The Check Store, Lakewood, CO; *U.S. Public*, pg. 785
Lewis, Christopher H., Pres.--Foreign Trade Division, Glendale, CA; *Int'l*, pg. 917
Lewis, Delbert R., Pres.--MAC America Communications, Inc., Phoenix, AZ; *U.S. Private*, pg. 685
Lewis, Dennis J., Pres.--Ultimate Technology Corporation, Victor, NY; *U.S. Public*, pg. 1637
Lewis, J. Gary, Pres.--Bowman Distribution, Cleveland, OH; *U.S. Public*, pg. 190
Lewis, Jack S., Pres.--MBS Holding, Inc., Arlington, TX; *U.S. Private*, pg. 685
Lewis, Jeff, Sr. V.P.-Sls. & Opers.--Lafarge Construction Materials, Canfield, OH; *Int'l*, pg. 788
Lewis, Jerald P., Pres. & Chief Exec. Officer--First American Trust Co., Santa Ana, CA; *U.S. Public*, pg. 626
Lewis, Jerry, Pres. & Chief Oper. Officer--Sterling Vision, Inc., East Meadow, NY; *U.S. Public*, pg. 1516
Lewis, Kenneth D., Pres.--NationsBank Corporation, Charlotte, NC; *U.S. Public*, pg. 1162
Lewis, Lemuel E., Pres. & Gen. Mgr.--WTVF, Nashville, TN; *U.S. Private*, pg. 647
Lewis, Leslie B., Chm. Bd., Pres. & Chief Exec. Officer--Asahi/America, Inc., Malden, MA; *U.S. Public*, pg. 137
Lewis, Merle D., Chm. Bd., Pres. & Chief Exec. Officer--Northwestern Public Service, Huron, SD; *U.S. Public*, pg. 1200
Lewis, Michael, Pres. & Chief Exec. Officer--ILD Communications, Inc., Carrollton, TX; *U.S. Public*, pg. 887
Lewis, Michael D., Pres.--Kvaerner National Division of Kvaerner Singapore Pte. Ltd., Singapore, Singapore; *Int'l*, pg. 768
Lewis, Michael J., Pres.--S.C. Food Services (Canada) Inc., Markham, Canada; *Int'l*, pg. 1213
Lewis, Parnell, Jr., Pres.--Anderson-Tully Co., Memphis, TN; *U.S. Private*, pg. 73
Lewis, Peter B., Chm. Bd., Pres. & Chief Exec. Officer--The Progressive Corporation, Cleveland, OH; *U.S. Public*, pg. 1334
Lewis, Price, Pres.--Roll Source, Inc., Minneapolis, MN; *U.S. Public*, pg. 1671
Lewis, R. Jack, Jr., Pres. & Chief Exec. Officer--Lewis Brothers Bakeries, Inc., Evansville, IN; *U.S. Private*, pg. 665
Lewis, R. Jack, Jr., Pres., Chief Oper. & Exec. Officer--Hartford Bakery, Inc., Evansville, IN; *U.S. Private*, pg. 665
Lewis, Richard A., Pres. & Reg. Mgr.--Lewis Homes Management Corp., Upland, CA; *U.S. Private*, pg. 665
Lewis, Richard H., Chm. Bd., Pres., Chief Exec. & Fin. Officer & Treas.--Prima Energy Corporation, Denver, CO; *U.S. Public*, pg. 1325
Lewis, Richard S., Pres. & Chief Exec. Officer--Countrywide Partnership Investments, Inc., Pasadena, CA; *U.S. Public*, pg. 453
Lewis, Robert, Pres.--enterWorks.com, inc., Ashburn, VA; *U.S. Public*, pg. 1573
Lewis, Russell T., Pres. & Chief Oper. Officer--The New York Times Company, New York, NY; *U.S. Public*, pg. 1173
Lewis, Simon, Pres.--Royal Mutual Funds Inc., Toronto, Canada; *Int'l*, pg. 1131
Lewis, Simon, Pres.-Asia/Pacific--Diversified Agency Services, New York, NY; *U.S. Public*, pg. 1223
Lewis, Timothy, Pres.--Bethlehem Steel-Structural Products Division, Bethlehem, PA; *U.S. Public*, pg. 226
Lewis, William, Chm. Bd., Pres. & Chief Exec. Officer--Career Blazers Inc., New York, NY; *U.S. Private*, pg. 209
Lewitt, Bert, Pres.--Morley Construction Co., Inc., Santa Monica, CA; *U.S. Private*, pg. 762
Lewtan, Douglas, Pres.--Lewtan Industries Corp., Hartford, CT; *U.S. Private*, pg. 666
Lewton, Larry L., Pres. & Chief Exec. Officer--Boulevard Bancorp, Inc., Chicago, IL; *U.S. Public*, pg. 1680
Ley, Anthony J., Chm. Bd., Pres. & Chief Exec. Officer--Harmonic Lightwaves, Sunnyvale, CA; *U.S. Public*, pg. 788
Ley, James A., Pres. & Chief Exec. Officer--First Vantage-Tennessee, Knoxville, TN; *U.S. Public*, pg. 641
Leyendecker, R.F., Pres. & Chief Oper. Officer--Northwestern Energy Corp., Huron, SD; *U.S. Public*, pg. 1201
Leyendecker, R.F., Pres. & Chief Oper. Officer--Nekota Resources Inc., Huron, SD; *U.S. Public*, pg. 1201
Lezin, Jeremy, Pres. & Chief Exec. Officer--Salz Leathers, Inc., Santa Cruz, CA; *U.S. Private*, pg. 963
Lhota, William J., Pres. & Chief Oper. Officer--Kentucky Power Co., Ashland, KY; *U.S. Public*, pg. 72
Lhota, William J., Pres. & Chief Oper. Officer--Wheeling Power Company, Wheeling, WV; *U.S. Public*, pg. 73
Li, Stephanie, Partner & Sr. V.P.--Scotchbrook Communications Ltd., Wan Chai, Hong Kong; *U.S. Private*, pg. 411
Liang, Christine, Pres.--ASI Corp., Fremont, CA; *U.S. Private*, pg. 8
Liang, Y.G., Pres.--Qingdao Rolled Glass Co., Ltd., Qingdao, China; *Int'l*, pg. 1348
Liao, Duke, Pres.--DTK Computer Inc., City of Industry, CA; *U.S. Private*, pg. 306
Liao, Duke, Chm. Bd., Pres. & Chief Exec. Officer--Liuski International, Inc., Norcross, GA; *U.S. Public*, pg. 1005
Libbe, Kent, Pres.--Rudolph/Libbe, Inc., Walbridge, OH; *U.S. Private*, pg. 950
Liberman, Z., Pres.--Talk-A-Phone Co., Chicago, IL; *U.S. Private*, pg. 1067
Libertiny, Attila G., Chm. Bd., Pres. & Chief Exec. Officer--Seneca Falls Technology Group, Seneca Falls, NY; *U.S. Private*, pg. 984
Licavoli, Sam, Pres.--Textron Automotive Interiors Company, Troy, MI; *U.S. Public*, pg. 1590
Licht, J.M., Pres. & Chief Exec. Officer--Duraco Products, Inc., Streamwood, IL; *U.S. Private*, pg. 348
Lichtenberger, Rudi, Pres. & Chief Exec. Officer--EDS Fides, Zurich, Switzerland; *U.S. Public*, pg. 570
Lichtendahl, Kenneth, Pres.--Hudepohl-Schoenling Brewing Company, Cincinnati, OH; *U.S. Private*, pg. 545
Lichter, Mark, Pres.--Baltic Linen Company, Inc., Valley Stream, NY; *U.S. Private*, pg. 113
Lick, Fred, Jr., Chm. Bd., Pres. & Chief Exec. Officer--Central Reserve Life Corporation, Strongsville, OH; *U.S. Public*, pg. 326
Liddell, W.K., Pres., Chief Exec. & Chief Oper. Officer--Irex Corporation, Lancaster, PA; *U.S. Public*, pg. 913
Liddy, Edward M., Pres. & Chief Oper. Officer--The Allstate Corporation, Northbrook, IL; *U.S. Public*, pg. 55
Liddy, Lucien, Pres.--Intergen Center for Diagnostic Products, Milford, MA; *U.S. Private*, pg. 567
Liddy, Richard A., Chm. Bd., Pres. & Chief Exec. Officer--General American Life Insurance Co., Saint Louis, MO; *U.S. Private*, pg. 443
Lidow, Eric, Chm. Bd., Pres. & Chief Oper. Officer--International Rectifier Corporation, El Segundo, CA; *U.S. Public*, pg. 906
Lieb, Mark A., Pres.--Spectrum Asset Management, Inc., Stamford, CT; *U.S. Public*, pg. 1674
Liebau, F. Jack, Pres. & Chief Exec. Officer--Patriot American Hospitality Operating Company, San Mateo, CA; *U.S. Public*, pg. 1265
Liebenow, Larry, Pres. & Chief Exec. Officer--Quaker Fabric Corporation, Fall River, MA; *U.S. Public*, pg. 1347
Lieberg, Eric N., Pres., Chief Fin. Officer & Exec. V.P.--Rundel Products, Inc., Portland, OR; *U.S. Private*, pg. 951
Liebergesell, Rolf K., Chm. Bd., Pres. & Chief Exec. Officer & Chief Oper. Officer--Farrel Corporation, Ansonia, CT; *U.S. Public*, pg. 614
Lieberman, Daniel, Pres.--A&W Restaurants, Inc.-Carousel Div., Minneapolis, MN; *U.S. Private*, pg. 2
Lieberman, Drew, Pres.--Oak Grigsby, Sugar Grove, IL; *U.S. Public*, pg. 1209
Lieberman, Harvey, Chm. Bd. & Pres.--Esquire Radio & Electronics Inc., Brooklyn, NY; *U.S. Private*, pg. 383
Lieberman, Paul J., Pres.--Superior Drapery Company, Hackensack, NJ; *U.S. Private*, pg. 1054
Liebetrau, Bernd, Chm.--Schleicher & Schuell GmbH, Einbeck, Germany; *Int'l*, pg. 1206
Liebman, Tom, Pres.--Coilcraft, Inc., Cary, IL; *U.S. Private*, pg. 250
Liederbach, Denis J., Pres. & Gen. Mgr.--Tocco, Inc., Boaz, AL; *U.S. Public*, pg. 1259
Lienau, Robert, Jr., Pres.--Trend Offset Printing Services, Los Alamitos, CA; *U.S. Private*, pg. 1099
Lienhard, Fredy A., Chm. Bd. & Pres.--Lista Holding AG, Erlen, Switzerland; *Int'l*, pg. 812
Lientz, James R., Jr., Pres.--NationsBank Georgia Corporation, Atlanta, GA; *U.S. Public*, pg. 1162
Lieppe, Charles, Pres. & Chief Exec. Officer--DBT Online, Inc., Las Vegas, NV; *U.S. Public*, pg. 472
Lieppe, Charles, Pres. & Chief Exec. Officer--Berol Corporation, Brentwood, TN; *U.S. Public*, pg. 1178
Liess, Paul J., Pres.--National Rural Utilities Cooperative Finance Corporation, Herndon, VA; *U.S. Private*, pg. 786
Lietz, Andrew E., Pres. & Chief Exec. Officer--Hadco Corporation, Salem, NH; *U.S. Public*, pg. 773
Lievense, Richard, Pres.--Old Kent Bank of Holland, Holland, MI; *U.S. Public*, pg. 1217
Lievense, Robert J., Pres. & Chief Oper. Officer--A.C. Nielsen, Stamford, CT; *U.S. Public*, pg. 1183
Liew, Ken, Pres.--Mal Pacific Technology Sdn. Bhd., Kuala Lumpur, Malaysia; *Int'l*, pg. 1293
Liff, Michael A., Pres.--Media General Broadcasting, Inc. (WJWB-TV), Jacksonville, FL; *U.S. Public*, pg. 1078
Liggett, Gary, Pres.--Justin Boot Company, Fort Worth, TX; *U.S. Public*, pg. 937
Liggins, Alfred, Pres. & Gen. Mgr.--Radio One Inc., Lanham, MD; *U.S. Private*, pg. 906
Light, L.L., Pres. & Chief Oper. Officer--L.B. Smith, Inc., Camp Hill, PA; *U.S. Private*, pg. 1009
Light, Nathan, Chm. Bd., Pres. & Chief Exec. Officer--Sterling Inc., Akron, OH; *Int'l*, pg. 1248
Ligon, W. Austin, Pres.--Car Max, Glen Allen, VA; *U.S. Public*, pg. 374
Liguori, James J., Pres. & Chief Oper. Officer--Morgan's Foods, Inc., Beachwood, OH; *U.S. Public*, pg. 1133
Liimatainen, B.C., Pres.--A. Finkl & Sons Co., Chicago, IL; *U.S. Private*, pg. 405
Liles, Dean, Pres.--Electronic Tax Systems, Inc., Carrollton, TX; *U.S. Public*, pg. 421
Liles, Dean, Pres.--Fast-Tax, Carrollton, TX; *U.S. Public*, pg. 421
Liles, Jack D., Pres. & Treas.--TVESCO, Inc., Memphis, TN; *U.S. Private*, pg. 1066
Lilius, Mikael, Pres. & Chief Exec. Officer--Incentive AB, Stockholm, Sweden; *Int'l*, pg. 666
Lill, John W., Pres.--Barrick Chile Ltda., Santiago, Chile; *Int'l*, pg. 169
Lilley, David, Pres. & Chief Oper. Officer--Cytec Industries Inc., West Paterson, NJ; *U.S. Public*, pg. 471
Lillis, Charles, Pres. & Chief Exec. Officer--U S West Media Group, Englewood, CO; *U.S. Public*, pg. 1689
Lilly, Ed, Pres. & Chief Exec. Officer--Serta, Inc., Itasca, IL; *U.S. Private*, pg. 985
Lilly, Peter B., Pres. & Chief Oper. Officer--Peabody Holding Company, Inc., Saint Louis, MO; *Int'l*, pg. 594
Lim, David, Pres.--Petrosul International Ltd., Vancouver, Canada; *Int'l*, pg. 1046
Lim, H.P., Pres. & Chief Exec. Officer--Baker Engineering, NY, Inc., Elmsford, NY; *U.S. Public*, pg. 168
Lim, Yeap Tang, Pres. & Chief Exec. Officer--Spider/DMB&B, Petaling Jaya, Malaysia; *U.S. Private*, pg. 305
Lima, Helio, Pres. & Chief Oper. Officer--Citibank (Florida) N.A., Dania, FL; *U.S. Public*, pg. 377
Lima, Marcos, Pres. & Chief Exec. Officer--CODELCO Chile (Corporacion Nacional Del Cobre De Chile), Santiago, Chile; *Int'l*, pg. 302
Limato, John, Pres. & Chief Oper. Officer--J.T. Slocomb Company, South Glastonbury, CT; *U.S. Private*, pg. 1006
Limaye, Prakash V., Pres.--Harding Lawson Associates, Infrastructure, Inc., Bellevue, WA; *U.S. Public*, pg. 785
Limbrick, Alfred, Grp. Pres.--Kohl's Food Stores, Wauwatosa, WI; *Int'l*, pg. 1375
Limerick, The Earl of, The Rt Hon, Chm. Bd.--De La Rue plc, London, United Kingdom; *Int'l*, pg. 386
Limongelli, Anthony, Pres.--Atlas Copco Compressors, Inc., Holyoke, MA; *Int'l*, pg. 96
Lin, Feng-Liang, Chm. Bd., Pres. & Chief Exec. Officer--Payless Car Rental System, Inc., Saint Petersburg, FL; *U.S. Private*, pg. 844
Lin, Frank C., Chm. Bd., Pres. & Chief Exec. Officer--Trident Microsystems, Inc., Mountain View, CA; *U.S. Public*, pg. 1637

Lin, Jack, Pres. & Chief Exec. Officer--National Technical Systems, Inc., Calabasas, CA; *U.S. Public*, pg. 1161
Lin, P.C., Pres.--Qingdao Float Glass Co., Ltd., Qingdao, China; *Int'l*, pg. 1348
Lin, P.F., Pres.--Chang Jiang Float Glass Co., Ltd., Jiangsu, China; *Int'l*, pg. 1348
Lin, P.S., Pres.--Taiwan Glass Industry Corp., Taipei, Taiwan; *Int'l*, pg. 1348
Lin, Raymond C., Chief Exec. Officer--Premisys Communications, Inc., Fremont, CA; *U.S. Public*, pg. 1323
Lin, Tsangsheng, Pres.--President Enterprises Corp., Tainan, Taiwan; *Int'l*, pg. 1068
Linard, Jay M., Pres.--Alumax Extrusions, Inc., Cressona, PA; *U.S. Public*, pg. 60
Linard, Jay M., Pres.--Alumax Engineered Metal Processes, Inc., Saint Louis, MO; *U.S. Public*, pg. 60
Lincoln, John, Pres.--Revenue Collection Group, San Diego, CA; *U.S. Public*, pg. 466
Lincoln, John, Pres. & Chief Exec. Officer--Revenue Collection Group World Headquarters, San Diego, CA; *U.S. Public*, pg. 466
Lincoln, Larry W., Pres. & Chief Exec. Officer--Mark III Industries, Ocala, FL; *U.S. Private*, pg. 704
Lind, Steven R., Pres. & Chief Exec. Officer--Top Air Manufacturing, Inc., Cedar Falls, IA; *U.S. Public*, pg. 1621
Lindahl, Goran, Pres. & Chief Exec. Officer--ABB Asea Brown Boveri (Holding) Ltd., Zurich, Switzerland; *Int'l*, pg. 1
Lindahl, Herbert W., Pres. & Chief Oper. Officer--State Industries Inc., Ashland City, TN; *U.S. Private*, pg. 1036
Lindal, Douglas F., Pres. & Chief Oper. Officer--Lindal Cedar Homes, Inc., Seattle, WA; *U.S. Public*, pg. 998
Lindbloom, Paul M., Pres. & Chief Oper. Officer--Acrometal Companies, Inc., Plymouth, MN; *U.S. Private*, pg. 14
Lindborg, Ed, Pres.--Fritz Co. Inc., Newport, MN; *U.S. Private*, pg. 429
Linde, K., Pres. & Chief Exec. Officer--Principal Health Care, Inc., Rockville, MD; *U.S. Private*, pg. 885
Linde, Ken, Pres.--Principal Behavioral Health Care, Inc., Rockville, MD; *U.S. Private*, pg. 885
Lindegaard, Jorgen, Pres. & Chief Exec. Officer--GN Great Nordic Ltd., Copenhagen, Denmark; *Int'l*, pg. 536
Lindekens, Jean-Louis, V.P.-North America--Sabena Belgian World Airlines, Manhasset, NY; *Int'l*, pg. 1168
Lindemann, D.L., Pres. & Chief Exec. Officer--Citizens Gas & Coke Utility, Indianapolis, IN; *U.S. Private*, pg. 241
Lindemann, Glen W., Pres. & Chief Exec. Officer--Figgie International Inc., Cleveland, OH; *U.S. Public*, pg. 622
Linden, Gurun, Pres.--Swedish Match S.A., Stockholm, Sweden; *Int'l*, pg. 1328
Lindan, Jan H., Pres.--Spintab, Stockholm, Sweden; *Int'l*, pg. 1328
Linder, Douglas, Pres.--Cargill Citro-America, Inc., Minneapolis, MN; *U.S. Private*, pg. 210
Linder, H. Willard, Pres.--Minnesota Electric Supply Company, Willmar, MN; *U.S. Private*, pg. 750
Lindgren, Lennard, Pres.--Sandvik Coromant Skandinavien AB, Stockholm, Sweden; *Int'l*, pg. 1185
Lindgren, T.J., Pres.--Fruit Growers Supply Co., Sherman Oaks, CA; *U.S. Private*, pg. 430
Lindhe, Bo, Pres.--Ahlens AB, Stockholm, Sweden; *Int'l*, pg. 708
Lindig, Bill M., Pres. & Chief Exec. Officer--Sysco Corporation, Houston, TX; *U.S. Public*, pg. 1550
Lindkvist, Mats, Pres.--SINSER Holding AB, Stockholm, Sweden; *Int'l*, pg. 1256
Lindner, Carl H., III, Co-Pres.--American Financial Group, Cincinnati, OH; *U.S. Public*, pg. 74
Lindner, Carl H., III, Pres. & Chief Oper. Officer--American Financial Group, Cincinnati, OH; *U.S. Public*, pg. 75
Lindner, Keith, Co-Pres.--American Financial Group, Cincinnati, OH; *U.S. Public*, pg. 74
Lindner, Robert D., Jr., Pres.--United Dairy Farmers, Inc., Cincinnati, OH; *U.S. Private*, pg. 1121
Lindner, S. Craig, Co-Pres.--American Financial Group, Cincinnati, OH; *U.S. Public*, pg. 74
Lindquist, Berthold, Pres. & Chief Exec. Officer--Gambro AB, Lund, Sweden; *Int'l*, pg. 666
Lindquist, Roy W., Pres.--J.W. Aluminum Company, Mount Holly, SC; *U.S. Public*, pg. 1736
Lindsay, Edward W., Jr., Pres.--Lindsay Manufacturing Inc., Ponca City, OK; *U.S. Private*, pg. 668
Lindsay, John B., Pres.--Franklin Electric Co., Inc., Bluffton, IN; *U.S. Public*, pg. 679
Lindsay, JoLynnn, Partner & Acct. Supvr.--Lewis Gace Bozell Healthcare Worldwide, Fort Lee, NJ; *U.S. Public*, pg. 1642
Lindsey, Bobby, Pres.--Dixie Oil Company, Tifton, GA; *U.S. Private*, pg. 337
Lindsey, George, Pres.--Nelson Publications, Port Chester, NY; *U.S. Public*, pg. 1328
Lindstorm, Steve, Pres.--Pacificare of Arizona, Phoenix, AZ; *U.S. Public*, pg. 1251
Lindstrom, Bjorn, Pres.--Oy Novatool AB, Vantaa, Finland; *Int'l*, pg. 678
Linen, Worth, Pres.-BMG Direct--Bertelsmann Music Group, Wilmington, DE; *Int'l*, pg. 191
Linford, James C., Pres.--Testronics, Freeport, TX; *U.S. Private*, pg. 487
Linford, James C., Pres.--GSI of California, Pittsburg, CA; *U.S. Private*, pg. 487
Linford, Jim, Pres. & Chief Exec. Officer--Gulf States, Inc., Freeport, TX; *U.S. Private*, pg. 487
Ling, John, Pres. & Chief Exec. Officer--Bettcher Manufacturing Corp., Cleveland, OH; *U.S. Private*, pg. 169
Lingnau, Lutz, Pres. & Chief Exec. Officer--Schering Berlin Inc., Cedar Knolls, NJ; *Int'l*, pg. 1204
Linier, J. Hicks, Chm. Bd. & Pres.--Oxford Industries, Inc., Atlanta, GA; *U.S. Public*, pg. 1239
Link, James, Pres.-BACI--Beech Acceptance Corp., Inc., Wichita, KS; *U.S. Public*, pg. 1365
Link, Perry, Pres.--O.P. Link Handle Company, Salem, IN; *U.S. Private*, pg. 668
Linkous, R.E., Pres. & Chief Exec. Officer--Linkous Construction Company, Inc., Memphis, TN; *U.S. Private*, pg. 669
Linn, Randy, Pres.--Linn Products, Inc., Charlotte, MI; *U.S. Private*, pg. 669
Linser, Herbert, Pres.--Ameri-Forge Corporation, Houston, TX; *U.S. Public*, pg. 748
Linsmayer, J. Nicholas, Pres.--Villaume Industries, Inc., Saint Paul, MN; *U.S. Private*, pg. 1140
Linsmayer, Robert M., Pres.--Valley Forest Resources Co., Marcell, MN; *U.S. Private*, pg. 1140
Linster, John, Pres. & Chief Exec. Officer--Pentech International, Inc., Edison, NJ; *U.S. Public*, pg. 1274
Linstrom, Bjorn, Pres.--Oy Colly Company AB, Vantaa, Finland; *Int'l*, pg. 678
Lintecum, Randall, Pres.--International Billing Services, El Dorado Hills, CA; *U.S. Public*, pg. 1659
Lintz, Richard P., Chm. Bd. & Pres.--Busch Properties, Inc., Saint Louis, MO; *U.S. Public*, pg. 114
Linver, Sid, Pres.--Logicon Technical Services Inc., Leavenworth, KS; *U.S. Public*, pg. 1199
Lionheart, Ely, Pres.--QST Industries, Inc., Chicago, IL; *U.S.* Private, pg. 897
Lipari, Rachel, Pres. & Chief Oper. Officer--Standard Security Life Insurance Company of New York, New York, NY; *U.S. Private*, pg. 446
Lipes, Edward B., Pres.--Osteonics Corp., Allendale, NJ; *U.S. Public*, pg. 1526
Lipinski, Jack, Pres.--Coastal Refining & Marketing, Wichita, KS; *U.S. Public*, pg. 390
Lipke, Brian J., Chm. Bd., Pres. & Chief Exec. Officer--Gibraltar Steel Corp., Buffalo, NY; *U.S. Public*, pg. 742
Lipkin, Gerald H., Chm. Bd., Pres. & Chief Exec. Officer--Valley National Bancorp, Wayne, NJ; *U.S. Public*, pg. 1705
Lipman, Allan M., Jr., Pres. & Chief Exec. Officer--The Amalgamated Sugar Company LLC, Ogden, UT; *U.S. Private*, pg. 48
Lipman, Ira A., Chm. Bd. & Pres.--Guardsmark, Inc., Memphis, TN; *U.S. Private*, pg. 486
Lipner, William E., Chm. Bd, Pres. & Chief Exec. Officer--NFO Research, Inc., Greenwich, CT; *U.S. Public*, pg. 1146
Lipoff, Steven, Pres., Chief Fin. Officer & Treas.--Butler Foods, Inc., Philadelphia, PA; *U.S. Private*, pg. 190
Lipovsky, Ronald P., Pres.--Maritz Marketing Research, Inc., Fenton, MO; *U.S. Private*, pg. 704
Lippe, George, Pres. & Chief Exec. Officer--Trammell Crow Company, Dallas, TX; *U.S. Public*, pg. 1628
Lippert, Douglas, Pres.--Lippert Components, Inc., Alma, MI; *U.S. Public*, pg. 529
Lippincott, Walter H., Dir.--Princeton University Press, Princeton, NJ; *U.S. Private*, pg. 885
Lipscomb, Michael, Pres.--J.C. Carter Company, Inc., Costa Mesa, CA; *U.S. Private*, pg. 81
Lipscomb, Michael S., Pres. & Chief Exec. Officer--Argo-Tech Corporation, Cleveland, OH; *U.S. Private*, pg. 81
Lipsky, Mark, Pres.--Radio Direct Response, Broomall, PA; *U.S. Private*, pg. 906
Lipson, David S., Pres. & Chief Exec. Officer--Integrated Systems Consulting Group, Wayne, PA; *U.S. Public*, pg. 1425
Lipson, Robert, Pres.--Sherwood Foods, Maple Heights, OH; *U.S. Private*, pg. 994
Liptak, Gregory J., Pres.--Jones Spacelink, Ltd., Englewood, CO; *U.S. Private*, pg. 597
Liptak, Robert G., Jr., Pres.--Shenango Valley Water Co., Sharon, PA; *U.S. Public*, pg. 439
Lipton, Ivan, Pres. & Chief Exec. Officer--Strawberries Inc., Milford, MA; *U.S. Private*, pg. 1046
Lipton, Ivan, Pres.--Waxie Maxie Quality Music Co., Milford, MA; *U.S. Private*, pg. 1047
Lipton, Jeffrey M., Pres.--Nova Corporation, Calgary, Canada; *Int'l*, pg. 971
LiPuma, Tommy, Pres.--GRP Records, New York, NY; *Int'l*, pg. 1215
Lisanke, Vincent P., Pres. & Chief Exec. Officer--American Express Credit Corporation, Wilmington, DE; *U.S. Public, pg. 74*
Lischer, Larry, Pres.--Medicalodges, Inc., Coffeyville, KS; *U.S. Private*, pg. 728
Liscomb, Clark N., Pres.--Corning International K.K., Tokyo, Japan; *U.S. Public*, pg. 449
Lisherness, Harley, Chm. Bd. & Pres.--Roofing Wholesale Co., Inc., Phoenix, AZ; *U.S. Private*, pg. 943
Lisker, Lisker, Pres.--Antwerp Diamond Distributors Inc., New York, NY; *U.S. Private*, pg. 76
Liskowski, Fred J., Pres. & Chief Exec. Officer--First Western Trust Services Co., New Castle, PA; *U.S. Public*, pg. 642
Lisowski, Dave, Pres. & Dir.--Denver Wholesale Florists Company, Denver, CO; *U.S. Private*, pg. 326
Liss, Robert, Pres.--Neptune Trucking, Inc., Memphis, TN; *U.S. Public*, pg. 1046
Liss, Victor, Vice Chm., Pres. & Chief Exec. Officer--Trans-Lux Corporation, Norwalk, CT; *U.S. Public*, pg. 1628
List, Donald A., Pres.--Alatec Products, Inc., Chatsworth, CA; *U.S. Private*, pg. 31
List, Herbert A., Jr., Pres.--List Industries, Inc., Deerfield Beach, FL; *U.S. Private*, pg. 669
Lister, Richard L., Pres. & Chief Exec. Officer--Zemex Corporation, Toronto, Canada; *Int'l*, pg. 1523
Listi, Frank J., Jr., Pres.--Universal Flavors Corp., Indianapolis, IN; *U.S. Public*, pg. 1695
Liston, Alan A., Pres.--Domgroup Ltd., Toronto, Canada; *Int'l*, pg. 631
Liston, Edward, Pres.--EUA Cogenex Corporation, Lowell, MA; *U.S. Public*, pg. 549
Liston, Edward T., Pres.--Rendva, Smithfield, RI; *U.S. Public*, pg. 549
Liston, Edward T., Pres.--Northeast Energy Management, Lowell, MA; *U.S. Public*, pg. 549
Lites, James, Pres.--Dallas Stars, Irving, TX; *U.S. Private*, pg. 309
Litman, Arthur, Pres.--Castelazo & Associates, Los Angeles, CA; *U.S. Public*, pg. 1071
Littfin, John A., Pres.--Littfin Lumber Company, Winsted, MN; *U.S. Private*, pg. 670
Little, C.A., Chief Exec. Officer & Mng. Dir.--British Mohair Spinners Limited, Bradford, United Kingdom; *Int'l*, pg. 219
Little, Christopher, Pres.-Magazine Grp.--Meredith Publishing Group, Des Moines, IA; *U.S. Public*, pg. 1094
Little, J. Lanier, Pres.--Norwest Bank of Wisconsin, Milwaukee, WI; *U.S. Public*, pg. 1202
Little, James, Pres.--Casualty Insurance Co., Chicago, IL; *U.S. Public*, pg. 681
Little, Lewis R., Pres. & Chief Oper. Officer--Smithfield Foods, Inc., Norfolk, VA; *U.S. Public*, pg. 1479
Little, Roger G., Chm. Bd., Pres. & Chief Exec. Officer--Spire Corporation, Bedford, MA; *U.S. Public*, pg. 1499
Little, Roger G., Pres.--Spire International Sales Corporation, Bedford, MA; *U.S. Public*, pg. 1499
Little, S. Martin, Pres.--Horizon Distribution Inc., Summerville, SC; *U.S. Private*, pg. 539
Little, W. Norris, Pres. & Chief Oper. Officer--Shaw Industries, Inc., Dalton, GA; *U.S. Public*, pg. 1464
Little, William G., Chm. Bd., Pres. & Chief Exec. Officer--The West Company, Incorporated, Lionville, PA; *U.S. Public*, pg. 1755
Littleton, David B., Pres.--American Plastic Toys Inc., Walled Lake, MI; *U.S. Private*, pg. 60
Littman, Irv, Pres.--Clearfield Insurance, Ltd., Boise, ID; *U.S.* Public, pg. 243
Litton, Richard, Pres.--Erieview Cartage, Inc., Warren, OH; *Int'l*, pg. 50
Litwin, Nicholas E., Pres.--Ellison Graphics, Jupiter, FL; *U.S.* Private, pg. 524
Litwinski, Jan, Pres. & Chief Exec. Officer--Polskie Linie Lotnicze LOT S.A., Warsaw, Poland; *Int'l*, pg. 1062
Liu, Lee, Pres.--IES Investments Inc., Cedar Rapids, IA; *U.S. Public*, pg. 855
Liu, S.C., Pres., Chief Exec. & Chief Oper. Officer--Tatung Company of America, Long Beach, CA; *Int'l*, pg. 1357
Liu, Steve, Pres. & Chief Exec. Officer--Esprit Systems, Inc., San Jose, CA; *U.S. Private*, pg. 383
Liuzzi, R.C., Pres. & Chief Exec. Officer--CF Industries, Inc., Long Grove, IL; *U.S. Private*, pg. 193
Lively, Larry G., Pres.--Federal Compress & Warehouse Company, Inc., Memphis, TN; *U.S. Private*, pg. 398
Lively, R. Luke, Pres. & Chief Admin. Officer--First Virginia Bank-Mountain Empire, Abingdon, VA; *U.S. Public*, pg. 642
Livet, R.G., Pres.--P.T. Agra Monenco, Jakarta, Indonesia; *Int'l*, pg. 31
Livingston, Doug, Pres.--Western Interactive Media, Los Angeles, CA; *U.S. Private*, pg. 1166
Livingston, Robert W., Chm. Bd., Pres. & Chief Exec. Officer--GB Holdings, Jurong, Singapore; *Int'l*, pg. 531
Livingston, Robert W., Pres. & Mng. Dir.--American Marine Pte. Ltd., Jurong, Singapore; *Int'l*, pg. 531
Livingston, W. Curtis, III, Pres., Chief Exec. Officer--Pacific American Income Shares, Inc., Pasadena, CA; *U.S. Public*, pg. 1247
Lizza, Joseph R., Pres. & Chief Exec. Officer--Fairfax Savings Bank, Baltimore, MD; *U.S. Public*, pg. 1543
Ljungberg, Robert, Chm. Bd., Pres., Chief Exec. & Chief Oper. Officer--Ultra Tool & Plastics, Inc., Amherst, NY; *U.S. Private*, pg. 1116
Llaneza, Frank, Pres.--Villazon Company Inc., Upper Saddle River, NJ; *U.S. Private*, pg. 1140
Llobet, Eduardo I., Pres.--La Union Gremial Compania Argentina de Seguros S.A., Rosario, Argentina; *U.S. Public*, pg. 216
Lloyd, Carmen L., Pres. & Chief Exec. Officer--Canadian Marconi Company, Montreal, Canada; *Int'l*, pg. 545
Lloyd, G.E.D., Pres. & Gen. Mgr.--Bulk Systems Management Ltd., Burnaby, Canada; *Int'l*, pg. 1424
Lloyd, Harold S., Pres.--Lloyd Controls, Inc., Mountlake Terrace, WA; *U.S. Private*, pg. 672
Lloyd, Jack, Pres.--Blackeyed Pea Restaurants Inc., Scottsdale, AZ; *U.S. Public*, pg. 498
Lloyd, Jack M., Chm. Bd., Pres. & Chief Exec. Officer--DenAmerica Corp., Scottsdale, AZ; *U.S. Public*, pg. 498
Lloyd, Larry, Pres.-Southern Golf--Putt Putt Golf Courses of America, Inc., Fayetteville, NC; *U.S. Private*, pg. 896
Lo Alker, Pauline, Pres. & Chief Exec. Officer--Network Peripherals Inc., Milpitas, CA; *U.S. Public*, pg. 1169
Lo, Dobbin, Pres. & Chief Fin. Officer--Robeson Appliance, Inc., Chino, CA; *U.S. Public*, pg. 1394
Loader, Helen, Pres.--Sally Fourmy & Associates, Toronto, Canada; *U.S. Public*, pg. 113
Loban, George B., Co-Chm. Bd. & Pres.--FSF Financial Corp., Hutchinson, MN; *U.S. Public*, pg. 608
Loban, George B., Co-Chm. & Pres.--First Federal FSB, Hutchinson, MN; *U.S. Public*, pg. 608
Lobanoff, Mark, Pres. & Chief Exec. Officer--NSK-Autoliv, Inc., Bloomfield Hills, MI; *Int'l*, pg. 439
Lobao, Luiz, Pres.--Coca-Cola Industrias Ltda., Rio de Janeiro, Brazil; *U.S. Public*, pg. 392
Lobbestail, Mike, Pres.--Steelcase Canada Ltd., Markham, Canada; *U.S. Private*, pg. 1038
Lochmann, Lee, Pres. & Chief Oper. Officer--Armour Swift Eckrich, Downers Grove, IL; *U.S. Public*, pg. 426
Lochmondy, Rich, Pres.--Arrow Pneumatics Co. Inc., Lake Zurich, IL; *U.S. Private*, pg. 85
Lock, Terry R., Pres.--Boise Cascade Asia Ltd., Boise, ID; *U.S. Public*, pg. 243
Locke, Joseph J., Pres.--USLIFE Financial Institution Marketing Group, Inc., Chicago, IL; *U.S. Public*, pg. 77
Lockett, F. Walker, Jr., Pres.--Bank One, Louisiana, Baton Rouge, LA; *U.S. Public*, pg. 173
Lockhardt, Ralph, Pres.--Biamp Systems Corp., Portland, OR; *U.S. Private*, pg. 911
Lockhart, Dennis P., Pres.--Heller International Group, Inc., Chicago, IL; *Int'l*, pg. 519

Lockhart, Freda L., Pres. & Chief Exec. Officer--Lockhart Cadillac Inc., Indianapolis, IN; *U.S. Private*, pg. 672
Lockwood, Earl F., Chm. Bd., Pres. & Chief Exec. Officer--Betac International Corporation, Alexandria, VA; *U.S. Private*, pg. 140
Lockwood, Robert, Pres. & Chief Exec. Officer--Our Sunday Visitor, Inc., Huntington, IN; *U.S. Private*, pg. 821
Lockyer, Katie, Pres.--Handar, Inc., Sunnyvale, CA; *U.S. Public*, pg. 1559
Locurto, Wayne W., Pres. & Chief Exec. Officer--News America Marketing, Norwalk, CT; *Int'l*, pg. 925
Loden, D. John, Pres. & Chief Exec. Officer--FCB HealthCare, San Francisco, CA; *U.S. Public*, pg. 1641
Lodge, Michael L., Pres.--Castle Cement Limited, Birmingham, United Kingdom; *Int'l*, pg. 1201
Lodge, Thomas R., Sr., Pres.--Delaware Ribbon Manufacturers, Inc., Philadelphia, PA; *U.S. Private*, pg. 322
Lodrini, Ronald J., Pres.--Integrated Marketing Group, Harrison, NY; *U.S. Private*, pg. 566
Loducca, Celso, Pres.--Lowe Loducca & Partners, Sao Paulo, Brazil; *U.S. Private*, pg. 678
Loeb, H. Richard, Pres.--Piknik Products Company, Inc., Montgomery, AL; *U.S. Private*, pg. 865
Loeb, Jerome T., Pres.--The May Department Stores Company, Saint Louis, MO; *U.S. Public*, pg. 1063
Loebach, D.C., Pres.--P.T. Natra Raya, Jakarta, Indonesia; *U.S. Public*, pg. 317
Loeber, George, Pres.--Loeber Motors, Inc., Chicago, IL; *U.S. Private*, pg. 672
Loeber, George, Pres.--Loeber Motors, Inc., Lincolnwood, IL; *U.S. Private*, pg. 672
Loeffler, Martin H., Chm. Bd., Pres. & Chief Exec. Officer--Amphenol Corporation, Wallingford, CT; *U.S. Private*, pg. 629
Loescher, Robert W., Pres.--Sealaska Corporation, Juneau, AK; *U.S. Private*, pg. 978
Loewenberg, William Ira, Pres.--Southern Leather Co., Inc., Memphis, TN; *U.S. Private*, pg. 1016
Lofgren, Carlton R., Pres.--McAnally Enterprises, Inc., Yucaipa, CA; *U.S. Private*, pg. 718
Lofquist, Peter A., Pres.--Mellon Leasing Corporation, Chicago, IL; *U.S. Public*, pg. 1085
Loftin, William L., Pres.--Sysco Food Services-Syracuse, Warners, NY; *U.S. Public*, pg. 1552
Loftus, Donald, Pres. & Chief Exec. Officer--Sanofi Beaute, Inc., New York, NY; *Int'l*, pg. 445
Lofy, Jack, Pres.--CommAir Mechanical Services, Oakland, CA; *U.S. Public*, pg. 2
Logan, Don, Pres. & Chief Exec. Officer--People, New York, NY; *U.S. Public*, pg. 1613
Logan, Frank G., III, Chm. Bd. & Pres.--Nematron Corp., Ann Arbor, MI; *U.S. Private*, pg. 791
Logan, Oran, Pres. & Chief Oper. Officer--Alamo Group, Inc., Seguin, TX; *U.S. Public*, pg. 34
Logan, Robert, Pres.--CF Group, Southern Pines, NC; *U.S. Private*, pg. 193
Logghe, Eugene A., Pres.--Logghe Stamping Company, Fraser, MI; *U.S. Private*, pg. 672
Loghry, Richard M., Pres. & Chief Exec. Officer--Mason & Hanger Corporation, Inc., Lexington, KY; *U.S. Private*, pg. 711
Loghry, Richard M., Pres.--Mason & Hanger Corporation, Inc., Lexington, KY; *U.S. Private*, pg. 711
Logston, R.W., Pres.--Timken do Brasil S.A. Comercio e Industria Limitada, Sao Paulo, Brazil; *U.S. Public*, pg. 1618
Logue, Gerry, Pres.--Grey Entertainment Inc., New York, NY; *U.S. Public*, pg. 764
Loh, Greg, Partner & Mngmt. Supvr.--Eric Mower and Associates, Inc., Syracuse, NY; *U.S. Private*, pg. 765
Loh, Greg, Partner & Mngmt. Supvr.--EMA Public Relations Services, Inc., Syracuse, NY; *U.S. Private*, pg. 765
Lohaus, Peter, Pres. & Chief Exec. Officer--Tetko, Inc., Briarcliff Manor, NY; *U.S. Private*, pg. 1078
Lohia, Mohanlal, Pres. & Dir.--Indo Rama Synthetics P.T., Jakarta, Indonesia; *Int'l*, pg. 673
Lohmann, Tom, Pres.--Taurus Energy Co., Dallas, TX; *U.S. Public*, pg. 584
Lohse, Herb, Pres.--Midwest Auto Parts Distributors, Inc., Saint Paul, MN; *U.S. Private*, pg. 744
Loizzo, Mary, Pres.--Lab Safety Supply Inc., Janesville, WI; *U.S. Public*, pg. 758
Lokey, James, Pres. & Chief Exec. Officer--Downey Financial Corp., Newport Beach, CA; *U.S. Public*, pg. 525
Lokey, James W., Pres. & Chief Exec. Officer--Downey Savings & Loan Association, F.A., Newport Beach, CA; *U.S. Public*, pg. 526
Lombard, George, Pres.--Lockheed Martin Information Display Systems, Atlanta, GA; *U.S. Public*, pg. 1008
Lombard, George E., Pres. & Chief Exec. Officer--Lombard Company, Alsip, IL; *U.S. Private*, pg. 673
Lombard, George E., Pres. & Chief Exec. Officer--Lombard Architectural Precast Prod. Co, Alsip, IL; *U.S. Private*, pg. 673
Lombardi, Paul V., Pres. & Chief Exec. Officer--DynCorp, Reston, VA; *U.S. Private*, pg. 351
Lombardo, Peter, Pres.--Robertet, Inc., Oakland, NJ; *Int'l*, pg. 1119
Lomelin Guillen, Jaime, Pres. & Chief Exec. Officer--Industrias Penoles S.A. de C.V., Cuauhtemoc, Mexico; *Int'l*, pg. 677
Loncharich, Tim, Pres. & Chief Exec. Officer--Snelling Personnel Services, Dallas, TX; *U.S. Private*, pg. 1010
Londchal, Marc, Pres. & Chief Exec. Officer--Tredi, Paris, France; *Int'l*, pg. 459
London, Eric, Pres.--London Litho Aluminum Co., Inc., Lincolnwood, IL; *U.S. Private*, pg. 673
London, J.P., Dr., Chm. Bd., Pres. & Chief Exec. Officer--CACI International Inc, Arlington, VA; *U.S. Public*, pg. 272
London, Terry E., Pres. & Chief Exec. Officer--Gaylord Entertainment Co., Nashville, TN; *U.S. Public*, pg. 704
Long, Bo, Gen. Mgr.-The Americas--FINNAIR, New York, NY; *Int'l*, pg. 485
Long, Bob, Pres.--Tektronix NewStar, Inc., Madison, WI; *U.S. Public*, pg. 1567
Long, D.L., Pres.--PDM Strocal, Inc., Stockton, CA; *U.S. Public*, pg. 1305
Long, David, Publisher--Sports Illustrated, New York, NY; *U.S. Public*, pg. 1613
Long, David R., Pres. & Chief Exec. Officer--Snokist Growers, Yakima, WA; *U.S. Private*, pg. 1011
Long, G.L., Pres.--Turbine Engine Components Textron, Thomasville, GA; *U.S. Public*, pg. 1588
Long, J.R., Pres. & Chief Oper. Officer--Ladbroke Racing Corporation, Pittsburgh, PA; *Int'l*, pg. 788
Long, James N., Pres.--Long's Electronics, Inc., Birmingham, AL; *U.S. Private*, pg. 675
Long, John W., Pres.--First American Real Estate Information Services, Inc., Saint Petersburg, FL; *U.S. Public*, pg. 625
Long, Jonathan R., Pres., Chief Exec. Officer & Chief Fin. Officer--J.E. Higgins Lumber Co., Concord, CA; *U.S. Private*, pg. 527
Long, Noah H., Jr., Pres.--Rosser International, Inc., Atlanta, GA; *U.S. Private*, pg. 946
Long, Phil, Pres. & Chief Oper. Officer--Biggs Gilmore Communications, Kalamazoo, MI; *U.S. Private*, pg. 143
Long, R. Dean, Pres.--Evanston Bank, Evanston, IL; *U.S. Public*, pg. 760
Long, Richard, Pres.--Iowa Mold Tooling Co., Inc., Garner, IA; *U.S. Public*, pg. 894
Long, Robert F., Pres.--Daily Express, Inc., Carlisle, PA; *U.S. Private*, pg. 307
Long, Ronald C., Pres. & Chief Exec. Officer--Independent Bank-East Michigan, Caro, MI; *U.S. Public*, pg. 874
Long, William D., Chm. Bd. & Pres.--Waremart Inc., Boise, ID; *U.S. Private*, pg. 1150
Long, William E., Pres.--Technologies Division, Joplin, MO; *U.S. Private*, pg. 355
Long, William J., Pres. & Chief Exec. Officer--Sprayroq, Inc., Birmingham, AL; *U.S. Public*, pg. 882
Long, Zelma, Chm. Bd., Pres. & Chief Exec. Officer--Simi Winery, Healdsburg, CA; *Int'l*, pg. 781
Longaberger, Tami, Pres.--The Longaberger Company, Dresden, OH; *U.S. Private*, pg. 675
Longfield, Craig N., Chm. Bd., Pres. & Chief Exec. Officer--PacifiCorp Financial Services, Inc., Portland, OR; *U.S. Public*, pg. 1252
Longfield, Craig N., Pres.--PacifiCorp Aviation (Holdings), Inc., Portland, OR; *U.S. Public*, pg. 1252
Longinotti, Ron, Pres. & Gen. Mgr.--KOTV Inc., Tulsa, OK; *U.S. Public*, pg. 209
Longo, A., Pres.--Van Leer Embalagens Industriais do Brazil Ltda., Rio de Janeiro, Brazil; *Int'l*, pg. 1146
Longstaff, G. Geoffrey, Pres. & Chief Exec. Officer--Regions Bank/Orlando, Longwood, FL; *U.S. Public*, pg. 1372
Longstreet, Dennis, Pres.--Johnson & Johnson Health Care Systems Inc., Piscataway, NJ; *U.S. Public*, pg. 928
Longtin, Joel, Pres.--LDB Corporation, Kerrville, TX; *U.S. Private*, pg. 639
Longtin, Joel C., Pres.--Mr. Gatti's, Inc., Kerrville, TX; *U.S. Private*, pg. 639
Loomis, Charles E., Jr., Pres.--Loomis Brothers, Inc., Cedar Rapids, IA; *U.S. Private*, pg. 675
Loos, A.W., Chm. Bd. & Pres.--Loos & Co., Inc., Pomfret, CT; *U.S. Private*, pg. 675
Lopatin, Jeffrey A., Pres.--Kleinert's Inc. of Florida, Largo, FL; *U.S. Private*, pg. 625
Loper, David, Pres.--Intermat, Biddeford, ME; *U.S. Private*, pg. 402
Lopez, Alvaro Munoz, Pres.--Musini, Sociedad Mutua de Seguros y Reaseguros a Prima Fija, Madrid, Spain; *Int'l*, pg. 1225
Lopez, Emilio Gonzalez, Pres.--Mead Johnson de Mexico, S.A. de C.V., Mexico, Mexico; *U.S. Public*, pg. 256
Lopez, Isidro, Pres.--Grupo Industrial Saltillo, Saltillo, Mexico; *Int'l*, pg. 1469
Lopina, Thomas J., Pres. & Chief Exec. Officer--Ingersoll Equipment Co., Inc., Winneconne, WI; *Int'l*, pg. 1129
Lopker, Pamela Meyer, Chm. Bd. & Pres.--QAD Inc, Carpinteria, CA; *U.S. Public*, pg. 1345
Lora, Jose Manuel, Chm. Bd. & Pres.--Editorial Planeta - DeAgostini, S.A., Barcelona, Spain; *Int'l*, pg. 433
Loran, Haim, Pres.--Valcor Engineering Corp., Springfield, NJ; *U.S. Private*, pg. 1131
Loran, Mike, Pres.--Associated Plastics, Inc., Riverside, CA; *U.S. Private*, pg. 417
Lorber, Arnold, Pres.--Lorber Industries Of California, Gardena, CA; *U.S. Private*, pg. 675
Lorber, Howard M., Pres. & Chief Oper. Officer--New Valley Corporation, Miami, FL; *U.S. Public*, pg. 1173
Lorberbaum, Jeffery, Pres. & Chief Oper. Officer--Mohawk Industries, Inc., Calhoun, GA; *U.S. Public*, pg. 1121
Lorberbaum, Jeffery, Pres. & Chief Exec. Officer--Aladdin Mills, Dalton, GA; *U.S. Public*, pg. 1121
Lorch, George A., Chm. Bd. & Chief Exec. Officer--Armstrong World Industries, Inc., Lancaster, PA; *U.S. Public*, pg. 131
Lord, John, Pres.--Carrier Corporation, Indianapolis, IN; *U.S.* Public, pg. 1689
Lord, John, Pres.--Carrier Corp., Indianapolis, IN; *U.S. Public*, pg. 1690
Lord, Suzanne, Sr. Partner & Acct. Mngmt.--EURO RSCG Tatham, Chicago, IL; *Int'l*, pg. 601
LoRe, Linda, Pres. & Chief Exec. Officer--Giorgio Beverly Hills, Santa Monica, CA; *U.S. Public*, pg. 1331
Lorentzen, Oivind, Pres.--Northern Navigation International Inc., Greenwich, CT; *U.S. Private*, pg. 805
Lorenz, Jon, Pres.--Colorado Business Bankshares, Inc., Denver, CO; *U.S. Private*, pg. 255
Lorenzini, Paul G., Pres.--Bunzl USA Inc., Saint Louis, MO; *Int'l*, pg. 233
Loreto, Jesus, Pres.--Laboratorios Pharmacia & Upjohn, C.A., Caracas, Venezuela; *Int'l*, pg. 1049
Loring, Scott R., Chm. Bd., Pres. & Chief Exec. Officer--Heald Colleges, San Francisco, CA; *U.S. Private*, pg. 514
Lortie, Pierre, Pres.--Bombardier Regional Aircraft Division, Downsview, Canada; *U.S. Public*, pg. 242
Lorton, Donald, Pres.--Maytag Cleveland Cooking Products, Cleveland, TN; *U.S. Public*, pg. 1064
Los, Hendrik J.M., Pres.--Walker Magnetics Group, Inc., Worcester, MA; *U.S. Private*, pg. 1147
Losurdo, Michael, Pres.--Losurdo Foods, Inc., Hackensack, NJ; *U.S. Private*, pg. 677
Lotan, Noam, Pres. & Chief Exec. Officer--MRV Communications, Inc., Chatsworth, CA; *U.S. Public*, pg. 1027
Lothongkam, Poe, Pres.--Multichip Technology, San Jose, CA; *U.S. Public*, pg. 470
Loudemilk, Billy R., Pres. & Chief Exec. Officer--Regions Bank/Gilmer County, Ellijay, GA; *U.S. Public*, pg. 1372
Lougee, Alan T., Pres.--The Chicago Faucet Co., Des Plaines, IL; *U.S. Private*, pg. 234
Lough, D.K., Pres. & Chief Oper. Officer--The Halifax Insurance Company, Toronto, Canada; *Int'l*, pg. 648
Loughlin, Pat, Plant Mgr.--Air Products, Langley, SC; *U.S. Public*, pg. 30
Loughran, Joseph E., Pres.--Airline Hydraulics Corporation, Bensalem, PA; *U.S. Private*, pg. 29
Louinslai, El Ross, Pres.--Davis Wire Corp., Irwindale, CA; *U.S. Private*, pg. 859
Louis, Kenneth C., Pres. & Chief Oper. Officer--Ameritas Life Insurance Corp., Lincoln, NE; *U.S. Private*, pg. 65
Loury, George C., Pres.--Norgren Co., Littleton, CO; *Int'l*, pg. 647
Lovaas, John, Pres., Treas. & Gen. Mgr.--Harrington & King, Chicago, IL; *U.S. Private*, pg. 504
Love, Dennis, Pres.--Printpack Inc., Atlanta, GA; *U.S. Private*, pg. 886
Love, Donald, Pres.--Clover Financial Corporation, Merchantville, NJ; *U.S. Private*, pg. 247
Love, Mike, Pres.--Vecta, Grand Prairie, TX; *U.S. Private*, pg. 1038
Love, Randolph D., Sr., Pres.--Love Packaging Group, Wichita, KS; *U.S. Private*, pg. 677
Lovejoy, William J., Gen. Mgr.--Service Parts Operations, Flint, MI; *U.S. Public*, pg. 720
Lovelady, Ernest, Pres.--In-Sink-Erator, Racine, WI; *U.S. Public*, pg. 573
Loveland, Peter G., Pres. & Treas.--Maze Nails, Peru, IL; *U.S. Private*, pg. 718
Lovell, Gerald, Pres.--Fargo Glass & Paint Company, Fargo, ND; *U.S. Private*, pg. 393
Lovell, P.J., Pres.--Bantrel Inc., Calgary, Canada; *Int'l*, pg. 118
Lovell, William, Pres.--Sandvik/Milford Corporation, Branford, CT; *Int'l*, pg. 1185
Lovell, William H., III, Pres.--First Commercial Bank, N.A. of Memphis, Memphis, TN; *U.S. Public*, pg. 630
Lovett, Donald R., Chm. Bd., Pres. & Chief Exec. Officer--AMCORE Bank, Rock River Valley, Dixon, IL; *U.S. Public*, pg. 64
Lovgren, Hans, Pres.--Colly Company AB, Kista, Sweden; *Int'l*, pg. 678
Lovin, Charles R., Pres. & CHief Exec. Officer--PacAero, Burbank, CA; *U.S. Public*, pg. 187
Lovro, Elton O., Gen. Mgr.--Finley Farmers Grain & Elevator Company, Finley, ND; *U.S. Private*, pg. 405
Low, Charles, Dir.--DB U.K. Finance p.l.c., London, United Kingdom; *Int'l*, pg. 404
Low, K. Prescott, Chm. Bd., Pres. & Publr.--George W. Prescott Publishing Co., Quincy, MA; *U.S. Private*, pg. 882
Lowd, Harvey, Pres.--High Point Chemical Corporation, High Point, NC; *Int'l*, pg. 717
Lowden, Paul W., Pres.--Resort Marketing International, Las Vegas, NV; *U.S. Public*, pg. 1432
Lowden, Paul W., Pres.--Hacienda Hotel Inc., Las Vegas, NV; *U.S. Public*, pg. 1432
Lowden, Paul W., Pres.--Hacienda Hawaiian Properties, Inc., Las Vegas, NV; *U.S. Public*, pg. 1432
Lowden, Paul W., Pres.--Sahara Resorts, Las Vegas, NV; *U.S. Public*, pg. 1432
Lowden, Paul W., Pres.--Sahara Illinois Corp., Las Vegas, NV; *U.S. Public*, pg. 1432
Lowden, Paul W., Pres.--Sahara Nevada Corp., Las Vegas, NV; *U.S. Public*, pg. 1432
Lowden, Paul W., Pres.--Santa Fe Coffee Company, Las Vegas, NV; *U.S. Public*, pg. 1432
Lowden, Paul W., Pres.--Santa Fe Hotel Inc., Las Vegas, NV; *U.S. Public*, pg. 1432
Lowden, Paul W., Pres.--Pioneer Finance Corp., Las Vegas, NV; *U.S. Public*, pg. 1432
Lowden, Paul W., Pres.--Sahara Mississippi Management Company, Inc., Las Vegas, NV; *U.S. Public*, pg. 1432
Lowden, Paul W., Pres.--Sahara Parkville, Inc., Las Vegas, NV; *U.S. Public*, pg. 1432
Lowden, Paul W., Pres.--Santa Fe Valley, Inc., Las Vegas, NV; *U.S. Public*, pg. 1432
Lowe, Alan S., Pres. & Chief oper. Officer--Read-Rite Corporation, Milpitas, CA; *U.S. Public*, pg. 1366
Lowe, J. Millar, Pres.--Kvaerner Boving (ANZ) Pty Ltd, Hawthorn, Australia; *Int'l*, pg. 772
Lowe, J.B., Jr., Chm. Bd., Pres. & Chief Exec. Officer--TD Industries Inc., Dallas, TX; *U.S. Private*, pg. 1063
Lowe, John, Pres.--American Granby, Inc., Liverpool, NY; *U.S. Private*, pg. 55
Lowe, Ken, Pres.--Home & Garden Television, Knoxville, TN; *U.S. Public*, pg. 1447
Lowe, Vernon, Pres.--National Seating Co., Vonore, TN; *U.S. Private*, pg. 786
Lowe, Vernon, Pres.--Judd-Olin (U.K.) Limited, Coventry, United Kingdom; *U.S. Public*, pg. 1219
Lowell, David, Pres. & Chief Exec. Officer--Diversified Communications, Portland, ME; *U.S. Private*, pg. 336
Lower, James, Pres. & Chief Exec. Officer--Vision One, Norwich, CT; *U.S. Private*, pg. 1141

Lower, Martin A., Pres. & Treas.--Ludlow Textiles Co., Inc., Ludlow, MA; *U.S. Private*, pg. 680
Lowhagen, Lars, Pres.--Skanska Vast, Goteborg, Sweden; *Int'l*, pg. 1261
Lowrance, Darrell J., Chm. Bd., Pres. & Chief Exec. Officer--Lowrance Electronics, Inc., Tulsa, OK; *U.S. Public*, pg. 1015
Lowrance, Darrell J., Pres.--Lowrance Avionics, Tulsa, OK; *U.S. Public*, pg. 1016
Lowrie, William D., Pres.--Amoco Corporation, Chicago, IL; *U.S. Public*, pg. 101
Lowrie, William G., Pres.--Amoco Production Company, Chicago, IL; *U.S. Public*, pg. 102
Lozyniak, Andrew, Chm. Bd. & Pres.--Dynamics Corporation of America, Greenwich, CT; *U.S. Public*, pg. 286
Lubbert, Mario, Pres. & Creative Dir.--Prolam/Young & Rubicam S.A., Santiago, Chile; *U.S. Private*, pg. 1200
Lubetkin, Alvin N., Pres. & Chief Oper. Officer--Oshman's Sporting Goods, Inc., Houston, TX; *U.S. Public*, pg. 1233
Lubetkin, Roy, Pres.--Churny Company Inc., Northbrook, IL; *U.S. Public*, pg. 1288
Luborsky, Brian, Pres. & Chief Exec. Officer--Premier Salons International, Edina, MN; *U.S. Private*, pg. 881
Lubrano, Al, Pres.--Technical Materials, Inc., Lincoln, RI; *U.S. Public*, pg. 266
Lubs, John, Pres. & Chief Oper. Officer--Mason Shoe Mfg. Co., Chippewa Falls, WI; *U.S. Private*, pg. 712
Lubs, John, Pres. & Chief Oper. Officer--B.A. Mason, Chippewa Falls, WI; *U.S. Private*, pg. 712
Lubs, John A., Pres. & Chief Exec. Officer--Wissota Trader Ltd., Chippewa Falls, WI; *U.S. Private*, pg. 712
Luby, Dallas W., Chm. Bd. & Pres.--Herbert Clough, Inc., New York, NY; *U.S. Public*, pg. 726
Luby, Harvey, Pres.--Premium Tank Line Inc., Jackson, MS; *U.S. Private*, pg. 329
Luca, Raymond J., Pres. & Chief Exec. Officer--LogEtronics Corporation, Springfield, VA; *U.S. Public*, pg. 6
Lucas, Dave, Pres.--Budgetel Inns, Inc., Milwaukee, WI; *U.S. Public*, pg. 1044
Lucas, Don, Pres.--Century Fence Company, Pewaukee, WI; *U.S. Private*, pg. 226
Lucas, P.N., Pres.--Glaxo Wellcome Inc., Mississauga, Canada; *Int'l*, pg. 553
Lucas, Rafael Tapia, Pres.--PUCARSA - Puerto de Carboneras, S.A., Madrid, Spain; *Int'l*, pg. 1224
Lucchesi, Donald A., Pres.--Landstar Gemini, Inc., Jacksonville, FL; *U.S. Public*, pg. 978
Lucchetti, David J., Pres. & Chief Exec. Officer--Pacific Coast Building Products Inc., Sacramento, CA; *U.S. Private*, pg. 830
Lucchini, Luigi C., Chm. Bd. & Pres.--Compart SpA, Milan, Italy; *Int'l*, pg. 324
Lucci, Mike, Pres. & Chief Oper. Officer--Bally Total Fitness Corporation, Chicago, IL; *U.S. Public*, pg. 171
Lucero, John A., Pres.--ILC Technology, Inc., Sunnyvale, CA; *U.S. Public*, pg. 856
Lucet, Catherine, Pres. Dir. Gen.--Editions Scientifiques et Medicales Elsevier, Paris, France; *Int'l*, pg. 1099
Lucey, Richard E., Pres.--Bell Atlantic Credit Company, New York, NY; *U.S. Public*, pg. 202
Luchesi, Scott, Pres.--Garden State Life Insurance Company, League City, TX; *U.S. Public*, pg. 88
Lucien, Kent T., Pres.--Mauna Loa Macadamia Partners, L.P., Honolulu, HI; *U.S. Public*, pg. 1060
Luck, Dave, Pres.--American Tire & Service Company, Rolling Meadows, IL; *Int'l*, pg. 213
Lucki, Anthony, Pres.--Harcourt General, Inc., Chestnut Hill, MA; *U.S. Public*, pg. 782
Luczaj, Kenneth J., V.P. & G.M.--Lewis Engineering Company, Naugatuck, CT; *U.S. Public*, pg. 402
Luczo, Stephen J., Chm. Bd., Pres. & Chief Oper. Officer--Seagate Technology Inc., Scotts Valley, CA; *U.S. Public*, *pg. 1449*
Ludchak, Ron, Pres.--Furnival/State Machinery Co., Hatfield, PA; *Int'l*, pg. 744
Luddy, Robert, Pres. & Chief Exec. Officer--Captive-Aire Systems, Inc., Youngsville, NC; *U.S. Private*, pg. 207
Ludes, John T., Pres. & Chief Oper. Officer--Fortune Brands, Inc., Old Greenwich, CT; *U.S. Public*, pg. 674
Ludes, John T., Chm. Bd. & Chief Exec. Officer--ABCO, Inc., Old Greenwich, CT; *U.S. Public*, pg. 674
Ludington, David, Pres. & Chief Oper. Officer--Ludington News Co. Inc., Detroit, MI; *U.S. Private*, pg. 679
Ludlow, Robert B., Pres.--Bedford Industries, Inc., Worthington, MN; *U.S. Private*, pg. 129
Ludlow, Stephen J., Pres. & Chief Oper. Officer--Veritas DGC Inc., Houston, TX; *U.S. Private*, pg. 1136
Ludlow, Stephen J., Pres. & Chief Exec. Officer--Veritas DGC Inc, Houston, TX; *U.S. Private*, pg. 1136
Ludt, Steve G., Pres., Chief Exec. Officer & Treas.--Columbian Rope Company, Guntown, MS; *U.S. Private*, pg. 256
Ludwick, Edward, Pres.--Fairmont Homes, Inc., Nappanee, IN; *U.S. Private*, pg. 391
Ludwig, Charles, Pres.--Glasteel Industrial Laminates, Collierville, TN; *U.S. Private*, pg. 45
Ludwig, William, Pres. & Chief Exec. Officer--Rice Growers Association of California, West Sacramento, CA; *U.S. Private*, pg. 927
Luecke, David A., Pres. & Chief Exec. Officer--Riemeier Lumber Company, Inc., Cincinnati, OH; *U.S. Private*, pg. 930
Luedtke, Lou, Pres.--Tuchenhagen North America, Inc., Columbia, MD; *Int'l*, pg. 1426
Luft, R.v.d., Pres.-Europe--Du Pont de Nemours International S.A., Geneva, Switzerland; *U.S. Public*, pg. 532
Lugar, Thomas R., Pres.--Thomas L. Green & Co., Inc., Indianapolis, IN; *U.S. Private*, pg. 477
Luger, Donald R., Chm., Pres. & Chief Exec. Officer--Lockwood Greene Engineers, Inc., Spartanburg, SC; *Int'l*, pg. 633
Lujambio, Ricardo, Pres--Herramientas Klein S.A. de C.V., Mexico, Mexico; *U.S. Private*, pg. 625
Lukas, Stanley S., Pres.--Bank of Matteson, Matteson, IL; *U.S. Private*, pg. 474
Lukash, Seth M., Chm. Bd., Pres. & Chief Exec. Officer--Tridex Corporation, Westport, CT; *U.S. Public*, pg. 1637
Luke, Donald L., Pres. & Chief Oper. Officer--Group Maintenance America Corp., Houston, TX; *U.S. Public*, pg. 766
Luke, R.P., Pres.--Rio Algom Mining Corp., Oklahoma City, OK; *Int'l*, pg. 1118
Lukens, Joseph C., II, Pres.--Insurance Management Associates, Wichita, KS; *U.S. Private*, pg. 565
Lukens, Max L., Chm. Bd., Pres. & Chief Exec. Officer--Baker Hughes Incorporated, Houston, TX; *U.S. Public*, pg. 165
Luksa, Robert A., Pres. & Chief Oper. Officer--Philadelphia Suburban Water Company, Bryn Mawr, PA; *U.S. Public*, pg. 1287
Luksch, James A., Chm. Bd., Pres. & Chief Exec. Officer--Blonder-Tongue Laboratories, Inc., Old Bridge, NJ; *U.S. Public*, pg. 237
Lumbroso, Claude, Pres.--Bio-Rad S.A., Paris, France; *U.S. Public*, pg. 230
Lumme, Larry, Pres. & Chief Exec. Officer--Republic Automotive-AEA Division, Charlotte, NC; *U.S. Public*, pg. 1377
Lund, James E., Pres. & Chief Exec. Officer--BHA Group Holdings Inc., Kansas City, MO; *U.S. Public*, pg. 161
Lund, Jon, Pres.--Aker Stord a.s., Stord, Norway; *Int'l*, pg. 42
Lund, Olof, Pres. & Chief Exec. Officer--Celsius AB, Stockholm, Sweden; *Int'l*, pg. 276
Lund, Peter A., Pres. & Chief Exec. Officer--CBS Broadcast Group, New York, NY; *U.S. Public*, pg. 274
Lund, Peter A., Pres. & Chief Exec. Officer-CBS Television & Cable Grp.--CBS Television Network, New York, NY; *U.S. Public*, pg. 274
Lund, Richard, Pres. & Chief Exec. Officer--Farmington National Bank, Farmington, NH; *U.S. Public*, pg. 187
Lund, Richard A., Pres. & Chief Oper. Officer--Cade Industries, Inc., Lansing, MI; *U.S. Public*, pg. 289
Lund, Russell T., III, Chm. Bd., Pres. & Chief Exec. Officer--Lund Food Holdings, Inc., Edina, MN; *U.S. Private*, pg. 680
Lund, Russell T., III, Pres. & Chief Exec. Officer--Lund's Inc., Edina, MN; *U.S. Private*, pg. 680
Lundberg, Fredrik, Pres. & Chief Exec. Officer--L E Lundbergforetagen AB, Stockholm, Sweden; *Int'l*, pg. 820
Lundberg, Lance, Pres.--Icon International, Stamford, CT; *U.S. Private*, pg. 556
Lunde, H., Chm. Bd.--Tine-Vestlandsmeieriet, Minde,, Norway; *Int'l*, pg. 1390
Lundeen, David, Pres.-Tech. Div. Of Blockburster & Pres.-Newleaf Corp.--Blockbuster Entertainment Group, Dallas, TX; *U.S. Private*, pg. 775
Lundeen, Kenneth C., Pres. & Chief Exec. Officer--C.J. Langenfelder & Son, Inc., Baltimore, MD; *U.S. Private*, pg. 650
Lundell, Ulf, Pres.--Alimak Elevator Company, Bridgeport, CT; *U.S. Private*, pg. 34
Lunder, Peter, Pres., Chief Oper. Officer & Sec.--Dexter Shoe Company, Dexter, ME; *U.S. Public*, pg. 217
Lunderstadt, Carl, Pres. & Chief Oper. Officer--Florida Crushed Stone Company, Leesburg, FL; *U.S. Private*, pg. 414
Lundgren, Terry, Pres. & Chief Exec. Officer-The Neiman-Marcus Grp.--The Neiman-Marcus Group, Inc., Chestnut Hill, MA; *U.S. Public*, pg. 784
Lundgren, Terry J., Pres.--Federated Department Stores, Inc., Cincinnati, OH; *U.S. Public*, pg. 617
Lundholm, Lars-Arne, Pres. & Chief Exec. Officer--Modernfold, Inc., New Castle, IN; *U.S. Private*, pg. 755
Lundin, Richard, Pres. & Chief Exec. Officer--Da-Lite Screen Company, Inc., Warsaw, IN; *U.S. Private*, pg. 306
Lundquist, Bo, Pres. & Chief Exec. Officer--Esselte AB, Solna, Sweden; *Int'l*, pg. 459
Lundregan, Stephen, Pres.--Colonial Insurance Company of California, Anaheim, CA; *U.S. Private*, pg. 788
Lundstedt, David, Pres. & Chief Exec. Officer--Prestone Products Corporation, Danbury, CT; *U.S. Public*, pg. 51
Lundy, Francis E., Pres.--Technical Instrument Company, Sunnyvale, CA; *U.S. Public*, pg. 1795
Lundy, Larry E., Pres. & Chief Exec. Officer--Lundy Enterprises, Inc., New Orleans, LA; *U.S. Private*, pg. 681
Lundy, Richard, Jr., Pres.--Lundy Construction Co., Inc., Williamsport, PA; *U.S. Private*, pg. 681
Luneburg, Karsten, Pres.--Scanstone GmbH, Hamburg, Germany; *Int'l*, pg. 1199
Lung, David D., Pres. & Chief Oper. Officer--Patrick Industries Inc., Elkhart, IN; *U.S. Public*, pg. 1264
Lunger, Gary, Pres.--Erie Press Systems, Erie, PA; *U.S. Private*, pg. 353
Lunsford, W. Bruce, Chm. Bd., Pres. & Chief Exec. Officer--Vencor, Inc., Louisville, KY; *U.S. Public*, pg. 1711
Lunsford, William, Pres. & Creative Dir.--The Weightman Group, Philadelphia, PA; *U.S. Private*, pg. 1159
Lunt, James H., Pres.--Rogers, Lunt & Bowlen Co., Greenfield, MA; *U.S. Private*, pg. 939
Luntz, Andrew, Pres. & Chief Oper. Officer--Luntz Corporation, Canton, OH; *U.S. Private*, pg. 681
Lupberger, Ed, Chm. Bd., Pres. & Chief Exec. Officer--Entergy Corporation, New Orleans, LA; *U.S. Public*, pg. 585
Lupient, James W., Pres. & Treas.--Jim Lupient Enterprises, Golden Valley, MN; *U.S. Private*, pg. 681
Lupinetti, Alexander, Pres.--Visions Systems, Billerica, MA; *U.S. Public*, pg. 283
Lupinetti, Alexander R., Chm., Pres. & Chief Exec. Officer--CSP Inc., Billerica, MA; *U.S. Public*, pg. 283
Luppert, Charles W., Pres. & Cashier--Williamsport National Bank, Williamsport, PA; *U.S. Public*, pg. 1543
Luppinacci, Vince, Pres.--Six Flags Great Adventure Theme Park & Wild Safari Animal Park, Jackson, NJ; *U.S. Public*, pg. 1611
Lurcott, Robert A., Pres. & Chief Exec. Officer--Henkel Corporation, King of Prussia, PA; *Int'l*, pg. 610
Lurio, Lee H., Pres. & Treas.--Elbeco Incorporated, Reading, PA; *U.S. Private*, pg. 367
Lury, Adam, Mng. Partner--Howell Henry Chaldecott Lury & Partners, London, United Kingdom; *Int'l*, pg. 637
Lusic, Ronald, Pres. & Chief Exec. Officer--Fleming Company, Waukesha, WI; *U.S. Public*, pg. 653
Luskey, Alvin, Pres.--Ryon's Saddle & Ranch Supply, Fort Worth, TX; *U.S. Private*, pg. 681
Luskey, Alvin (Butch), Pres.--Luskeys Western Stores, Inc., Fort Worth, TX; *U.S. Private*, pg. 681
Luskin, Cary, Pres.--Luskin's, Inc., Columbia, MD; *U.S. Private*, pg. 681
Luskin, Meyer, Chm. Bd., Pres. & Chief Exec. Officer--Scope Industries, Santa Monica, CA; *U.S. Public*, pg. 1444
Lussier, Gaetan, Pres. & Chief Exec. Officer--Culinar Inc., Montreal, Canada; *Int'l*, pg. 348
Lustbader, Edward E., Chm. Bd., Pres., Chief Exec. Officer & Treas.--The P.J. Carlin Construction Company, New Rochelle, NY; *U.S. Private*, pg. 211
Luszcz, Franz R., Pres.--Fenn Manufacturing Co., Newington, CT; *U.S. Public*, pg. 1676
Luther, Jon, Pres.--Popeye's Chicken & Biscuits, Atlanta, GA; *U.S. Private*, pg. 5
Luttmann, J.C., Co-Pres.--Sphere SA, Courcouronnes, France; *Int'l*, pg. 21
Lutz, Christian F., Pres.--Allianz Fire and Marine Insurance Japan Ltd., Tokyo, Japan; *Int'l*, pg. 59
Lutz, David, Pres. & Treas.--Wellco Enterprises, Inc., Waynesville, NC; *U.S. Public*, pg. 1752
Lutz, Gunther, Pres.--AGRA CI Power Limited, Oakville, Canada; *Int'l*, pg. 30
Lutz, John C., Pres., Chief Exec. Officer & Chief Oper. Officer--Elco Textron, Rockford, IL; *U.S. Public*, pg. 1590
Lutz, Steve, Pres.--Washington State Apple Commission, Wenatchee, WA; *U.S. Private*, pg. 1152
Luxion, W.T., Pres.--Wil-Freds Inc., Aurora, IL; *U.S. Private*, pg. 1176
Lybarger, Stanley A., Pres. & Chief Exec. Officer--BOK Financial Corp., Tulsa, OK; *U.S. Public*, pg. 163
Lydick, J. Lee, Pres., Chief Oper. Officer & Treas.--Grant-Lydick Beverage Co., San Antonio, TX; *U.S. Private*, pg. 470
Lydick, Larry, Pres.--Sterner Lighting Systems Incorporated, Eden Prairie, MN; *U.S. Private*, pg. 1042
Lyman, James M., Chm. Bd., Pres. & Chief Exec. Officer--G.I. Plastek, Elyria, OH; *U.S. Private*, pg. 435
Lyman, Roger B., Pres.--HMO Oregon, Salem, OR; *U.S. Private*, pg. 918
Lyman, Russ C., Pres.--Peerless Confection Company, Chicago, IL; *U.S. Private*, pg. 847
Lynch, Alexander P., Co. Pres. & Co-Chief Exec. Officer--The Bridgeford Group, New York, NY; *Int'l*, pg. 674
Lynch, John, Chm. Bd. & Chief Exec. Officer--Towers Perrin, New York, NY; *U.S. Private*, pg. 1093
Lynch, John H., Pres. & Chief Exec. Officer--Knoll, Inc., Greenville, PA; *U.S. Private*, pg. 627
Lynch, John J., Jr., Pres.--CCH Legal Information Services, Inc., New York, NY; *Int'l*, pg. 1513
Lynch, Michael J., Mgr.-Volkswagen L.A. Zone--Volkswagen of America Administration Center West, Westlake Village, CA; *Int'l*, pg. 1474
Lynch, Michael P., Pres.--Kmart (Canada) Ltd., Brampton, Canada; *U.S. Public*, pg. 963
Lynch, Patrick J., Pres.--Texaco International Financial Corp., White Plains, NY; *U.S. Public*, pg. 1583
Lynch, Richard, Pres. & Chief Oper. Officer--The Sports Authority Inc., Fort Lauderdale, FL; *U.S. Public*, pg. 1499
Lynch, Robin M., Pres.--Sea Containers U.S. Gulf Inc., Deer Park, TX; *Int'l*, pg. 1214
Lynkowski, Garry, Pres. & Chief Fin. Officer--Highwood Resources Ltd., Calgary, Canada; *U.S. Public*, pg. 1411
Lynn, Anthony J., Pres.--Alta Loma Productions, Inc., Beverly Hills, CA; *U.S. Public*, pg. 1310
Lynn, Anthony J., Pres.--After Dark Video, Inc., Beverly Hills, CA; *U.S. Public*, pg. 1310
Lynn, Jeffrey G., Pres. & Chief Exec. Officer--Dunham's Athleisure Corporation, Waterford, MI; *U.S. Private*, pg. 346
Lynn, Robert G., Pres. & Chief Mdsg. Officer--Bradlees Inc., Braintree, MA; *U.S. Public*, pg. 249
Lynne, Michael, Pres. & Chief Oper. Officer--New Line Cinema Corporation, New York, NY; *U.S. Public*, pg. 1614
Lyon, David L., Pres.--Pacific Communication Sciences, Inc., San Diego, CA; *U.S. Public*, pg. 375
Lyon, Gary, Pres.--Wetmore & Company, Houston, TX; *U.S. Public*, pg. 1736
Lyon, L. Max, Pres.--Bard Diagnostic Sciences, Redmond, WA; *U.S. Public*, pg. 189
Lyon, Russel T., Pres.-Carpet Div.--Buchanan Industries, Inc., Dalton, GA; *U.S. Public*, pg. 1052
Lyon, Stephen, Pres.--Halm Industries Company, Incorporated, Glen Head, NY; *U.S. Private*, pg. 496
Lyon, Wayne B., Chm. Bd., Pres. & Chief Exec. Officer--Furnishings International, Inc., Thomasville, NC; *U.S. Private*, pg. 431
Lyon, Wayne B., Chm. Bd., Pres. & Chief Exec. Officer--LifeStyle Furnishings International, Ltd., Thomasville, NC; *U.S. Private*, pg. 431
Lyon, Wayne M., Pres. & Chief Oper. Officer--Masco Corporation, Taylor, MI; *U.S. Public*, pg. 1052
Lyon, William, Chm. Bd. & Pres.--William Lyon Company, Newport Beach, CA; *U.S. Private*, pg. 684
Lyons, Chuck, Pres.--The Gazette Newspapers, Inc., Gaithersburg, MD; *U.S. Public*, pg. 1743
Lyons, Edward M., Pres. & Chief Exec. Officer--Conley Frog/Switch & Forge Co., Memphis, TN; *U.S. Private*, pg. 263
Lyons, James E., Pres.--University Press of America, Inc., Lanham, MD; *U.S. Private*, pg. 1127

Lyons, James F., Pres. & Chief Exec. Officer--GenRad, Inc., Westford, MA; *U.S. Public*, pg. 731
Lyons, James F., Pres. & Chief Exec. Officer--GenRad Electronic Manufacturing Tests Systems, Westford, MA; *U.S. Public*, pg. 731
Lyons, R.J., Pres. & Chief Oper. Officer--HBD Industries, Inc., Bellefontaine, OH; *U.S. Private*, pg. 489
Lyons, Richard M., Pres.--Gap Stores Division, San Bruno, CA; *U.S. Public*, pg. 702
Lyons, Stuart, Pres. & Chief Exec. Officer--Royal Doulton Plc., Stoke on Trent, United Kingdom; *Int'l*, pg. 1135
Lyons, W. David, Pres.--Ocelot International Ltd., Saint Helier, United Kingdom; *Int'l*, pg. 996
Lyons, W. David, Pres.--Ocelot International U.K. Ltd., Guildford, United Kingdom; *Int'l*, pg. 996
Lyons, Wayne, Pres.--Lafarge Canada, Calgary, Canada; *Int'l*, pg. 788
Lyons, Wayne, Pres. & Chief Exec. Officer--Lafarge Construction Materials, Canfield, OH; *Int'l*, pg. 788
Lyons, William M., Pres.--American Century Companies, Inc., Kansas City, MO; *U.S. Private*, pg. 52
Lytle, L. Ben, Pres. & Chief Exec. Officer--Anthem, Inc., Indianapolis, IN; *U.S. Private*, pg. 76
Lytle, R.D., Chm. Bd., Pres. & Chief Exec. Officer--Star Bronze Company, Alliance, OH; *U.S. Private*, pg. 1034
Ma, Walter K. W., Chm. Bd.--The Sincere Co. Ltd., Hong Kong, Hong Kong; *Int'l*, pg. 1252
Maaloe, Jens, Pres. & Chief Exec. Officer--GN Nettest, Telecom Division, Brondby, Denmark; *Int'l*, pg. 536
Maanan, Tim, Co-Pres.--The Hibbert Company, Trenton, NJ; *U.S. Private*, pg. 525
Maas, C., Pres.--Hartwell Corporation, Placentia, CA; *U.S. Private*, pg. 1168
Mabe, James G., Pres.--Columbia Farms Inc., Leesville, SC; *U.S. Private*, pg. 255
Mabuchi, Tom, Pres.--Yamaha Motor Canada Ltd., North York, Canada; *Int'l*, pg. 1516
Mac Mahon, Thomas P., Chm. Bd., Pres. & Chief Exec. Office--Laboratory Corp. of America Holdings, Burlington, NC; *U.S. Public*, pg. 973
MacArthur, Earl W., Chm. Bd.--Community Bank N.A., De Witt, NY; *U.S. Public*, pg. 416
Macaskill, Bridget, Pres. & Chief Exec. Officer--Oppenheimer Funds, Inc., New York, NY; *U.S. Private*, pg. 712
Macaskill, Bridget A., Pres. & Chief Exec. Officer--OppenheimerFunds Distributor, Inc., New York, NY; *U.S.* Private, pg. 818
Macatee, John C., Pres. & Chief Oper. Officer--Office Depot Inc., Delray Beach, FL; *U.S. Public*, pg. 1212
Maccarone, Roque, Chm. Bd., Pres. & Chief Exec. Officer--Banco de la Nacion Argentina, Buenos Aires, Argentina; *Int'l*, pg. 140
MacConnell, Christopher J., Pres.--Thomson MacConnell Cadillac, Inc., Cincinnati, OH; *U.S. Private*, pg. 1084
MacCurdy, Jean, Pres.--Hanna-Barbera Productions, Inc., Hollywood, CA; *U.S. Public*, pg. 1614
Macdaid, D.J.A., Pres.--Taylor Woodrow Construction Corp., New York, NY; *Int'l*, pg. 1359
MacDevette, William, Pres.--Elof Hansson Paper & Board, Inc., Elmsford, NY; *Int'l*, pg. 595
Macdonald, Dave, Pres. & Chief Exec. Officer--New Haven Mfg. Corp., New Haven, CT; *U.S. Private*, pg. 793
MacDonald, Erin E., Pres. & Chief Oper. Officer--Sierra Health Services, Inc., Las Vegas, NV; *U.S. Public*, pg. 1469
MacDonald, Grant, Partner & Exec. V.P.--North Castle Partners Advertising, Inc., Stamford, CT; *U.S. Private*, pg. 804
MacDonald, James B., Pres. & Chief Exec. Officer--WIC Television Ltd., Vancouver, Canada; *Int'l*, pg. 1482
Macdonald, James B., Pres. & Chief Exec. Officer--WIC Entertainment Ltd., Vancouver, Canada; *Int'l*, pg. 1482
MacDonald, Jay C., Pres. & Chief Exec. Officer--MacDonald Communications, New York, NY; *U.S. Private*, pg. 691
MacDonald, John, Pres.--Northern Telecom Finance Corporation, Nashville, TN; *Int'l*, pg. 969
MacDonald, John E., Pres.--Martin Marietta Canada Ltd., Ottawa, Canada; *U.S. Public*, pg. 1009
MacDonald, K. Lin, Pres. & Chief Oper. Officer--Noranda Forest Inc., Toronto, Canada; *Int'l*, pg. 434
MacDonald, Michael, Pres. & Chief Oper. Officer--Carson Pirie Scott & Co., Milwaukee, WI; *U.S. Public*, pg. 309
MacDonald, Peter, Pres.--James Hardie USA, Mission Viejo, CA; *Int'l*, pg. 597
MacDonald, Reid V., Pres. & Chief Exec. Officer--Faribault Foods Inc., Minneapolis, MN; *U.S. Private*, pg. 393
MacDonald, Wayne, Pres. & Publisher--The Record, Kitchener, Canada; *Int'l*, pg. 631
MacDonald, William F., Jr., Chm. Bd., Pres., Chief Exec. & Chief Oper. Officer--Houghton International Inc., Valley Forge, PA; *U.S. Private*, pg. 541
MacDougald, James E., Chm. Bd., Chief Exec. Officer & Pres.--ABR Information Services, Inc., Palm Harbor, FL; *U.S. Public*, pg. 2
Mace, Eugene, Pres.--Central Valley Publishing, Festus, MO; *U.S. Private*, pg. 225
MacEachran, Angus, Pres. & Editor--The Commercial Appeal, Memphis, TN; *U.S. Public*, pg. 1447
Maceikonis, Vytas, Pres.--Gilette Food Flavorings, Inc., Union, NJ; *U.S. Private*, pg. 453
MacFadyen, C.R., Pres.--Moore & Taber Grouting Services, Anaheim, CA; *Int'l*, pg. 31
MacFarland, Peter, Pres.--Magikitch'n, Inc., Quakertown, PA; *U.S. Public*, pg. 1065
Macfarlane, Don B., Mng. Dir.--Amcor Limited, Melbourne, Australia; *Int'l*, pg. 71
MacFarlane, John C., Chm. Bd., Pres. & Chief Exec. Officer--Otter Tail Power Company, Fergus Falls, MN; *U.S. Public*, pg. 1234
MacFarlane, Phil, Pres. & Chief Exec. Officer--OmniTRAX Inc., Chicago, IL; *U.S. Private*, pg. 171
MacFarlane, Phil, Pres.--Chicago Rail Link, Chicago, IL; *U.S. Private*, pg. 171
MacFarlane, Phil, Pres.--Chicago West Pullman & Southern Railroad, Chicago, IL; *U.S. Private*, pg. 171
Macfarlane, W.E., Pres.--Morganite Canada Corporation, Mississauga, Canada; *Int'l*, pg. 895
MacGregor, Bruce, Pres. & Chief Oper. Officer--L.A. Gear, Inc., Santa Monica, CA; *U.S. Public*, pg. 969
MacGregor, Ian, Pres.--Instron Schenck Testing Systems Limited, High Wycombe, United Kingdom; *U.S. Public*, pg. 883
MacGregor, Jack, Pres.--Chi-Chi's Inc., Louisville, KY; *U.S. Private*, pg. 393
Macgregor, Robert, Pres.--Reed Exhibition Companies-Canada, Scarborough, Canada; *Int'l*, pg. 1096
Machado, Gus, Pres. & Chief Exec. Officer--Gus Machado Enterprises, Hialeah, FL; *U.S. Private*, pg. 691
Macher, Frank E., Pres.--ITT Automotive, Inc., Auburn Hills, MI; *U.S. Public*, pg. 859
Machida, Katsuhiko, Pres.--Yamaichi Italia S.p.A. Societa di Intermediazione Mobiliare, Milan, Italy; *Int'l*, pg. 1518
Machida, Tetsuo, Pres. & Chief Exec. Officer--DCA Advertising, Inc., New York, NY; *Int'l*, pg. 393
Machidori, Keizo, Pres.--The Taiyo Mutual Life Insurance Co., Tokyo, Japan; *Int'l*, pg. 1348
Machii, A., Pres.--Loctite (Japan) Corp., Yokohama, Japan; *Int'l*, pg. 611
Machulak, Edward L., Chm. Bd., Pres., Chief Exec. Officer & Chief Oper. Officer--Commerce Group Corp., Milwaukee, WI; *U.S. Public*, pg. 410
MacIntyre, R. Douglas, Chm. Bd., Pres. & Chief Exec. Officer--Brock International Inc., Atlanta, GA; *U.S. Public*, *pg. 258*
MacIntyre, R. Douglas, Pres. & Chief Exec. Officer--Dun & Bradstreet Software Services, Atlanta, GA; *Int'l*, pg. 532
Mack, James A., Pres. & Chief Exec. Officer--Cambrex Corporation, East Rutherford, NJ; *U.S. Public*, pg. 297
Mack, Jim, Pres.--Frankel & Company, Chicago, IL; *U.S. Private*, pg. 424
Mack, John, Pres. & Chief Exec. Officer--Morgan Stanley Group Inc., New York, NY; *U.S. Public*, pg. 1132
Mack, John J., Pres. & Chief Oper. Officer--Morgan Stanley Dean Witter & Co., New York, NY; *U.S. Public*, pg. 1132
Mack, Stephan J., Pres.--Holm Industries, Inc., Scottsburg, IN; *U.S. Public*, pg. 1504
Mack, Thomas, Pres.--EMS-Togo, Taylor, MI; *Int'l*, pg. 981
Mackay, David J., Pres.--John Menzies (UK) Limited, Edinburgh, United Kingdom; *Int'l*, pg. 707
MacKenzie, Brian S., Pres. & Chief Exec. Officer--Builder Marts of America, Inc., Greenville, SC; *U.S. Private*, pg. 179
MacKenzie, G. Allan, Pres. & Chief Oper. Officer--Gendis Inc., Winnipeg, Canada; *Int'l*, pg. 542
MacKenzie, J. Gregory, Pres.--Hilb, Rogal and Hamilton Company of Orlando, Orlando, FL; *U.S. Public*, pg. 827
MacKenzie, Norman, Pres. & Chief Exec. Officer--Agripac Inc., Salem, OR; *U.S. Private*, pg. 26
MacKenzie, Thomas D., Pres. & Chief Exec. Officer--Everest Insurance Company of Canada, Toronto, Canada; *U.S. Public*, pg. 597
Mackey, Paul N., Pres. & Chief Exec. Officer--Prym-Dritz Corporation, Spartanburg, SC; *Int'l*, pg. 1499
Mackey, Richard Jr., Pres.--Oliver Oil Company, Inc., Chambersburg, PA; *U.S. Private*, pg. 815
Mackey, William K., Chm. Bd., Pres., Chief Exec. Officer & Treas.--Aqua Care Systems Inc., Coral Springs, FL; *U.S. Public*, pg. 126
Mackie, D.B., Pres. & Chief Exec. Officer--Great Lakes Dredge & Dock Co., Oak Brook, IL; *U.S. Private*, pg. 474
Mackie, Greg C., Chm. Bd., Pres. & Chief Exec. Officer--Mackie Designs, Inc., Woodinville, WA; *U.S. Public*, pg. 1030
Mackie, Tom, Grp. Pres.--Instrumentation Group, Cleveland, OH; *U.S. Public*, pg. 1261
Mackin, Gary, Pres.--Manville Canada Inc., Etobicoke, Canada; *U.S. Public*, pg. 927
Mackin, John H., Pres. & Chief Exec. Officer--SouthTrust Bank, Gadsden, Gadsden, AL; *U.S. Public*, pg. 1491
Mackler, Paul, Pres.--Reed Exhibition Companies-North America, Norwalk, CT; *Int'l*, pg. 1096
Macksey, David, Pres.--The Wine Group, San Francisco, CA; *U.S. Private*, pg. 1182
Maclachlan, Tim, Pres.--EMTEC Magnetics Australia Pty. Ltd., Mulgrave, Australia; *Int'l*, pg. 743
MacLaurin, Anthony, Pres.--Rexam DSI, South Hadley, MA; *Int'l*, pg. 1106
Maclay, G.G., Jr., Pres. & Chief Exec. Officer--Ziegler Asset Management, Inc., West Bend, WI; *U.S. Public*, pg. 1792
MacLean, Barry L., Chm. Bd., Pres., Chief Exec. & Chief Oper. Officer--Maclean-Fogg Co., Mundelein, IL; *U.S. Private*, pg. 692
MacLean, John S., Pres.--Therakos, Inc., Exton, PA; *U.S. Public*, pg. 929
MacLeay, Thomas, Pres. & Chief Oper. Officer--National Life Insurance Company, Montpelier, VT; *U.S. Private*, pg. 785
Macleod, Bruce, Pres.--Nance's Food Products, Inc., Macedon, NY; *U.S. Public*, pg. 1347
MacLeod, Malcolm W., Pres. & Chief Exec. Officer--Moran Transporation Company, Greenwich, CT; *U.S. Private*, pg. 760
MacLeod, Malcolm W., Pres. & Chief Exec. Officer--Moran Towing Corporation, Greenwich, CT; *U.S. Private*, pg. 760
Macleod, Malcolm W., Pres.--Moran Bulk Corporation, Greenwich, CT; *U.S. Private*, pg. 760
Macleod, Malcolm W., Pres.--Moran Towing Of Delaware, Inc, Greenwich, CT; *U.S. Private*, pg. 760
Macleod, Malcolm W., Chm. Bd., Pres. & Chief Exec. Officer--Jakobson Shipyard, Inc, Greenwich, CT; *U.S. Private*, pg. 760
Macleod, Malcolm W., Pres.--Moran Barge Corporation, Greenwich, CT; *U.S. Private*, pg. 760
Macleod, Malcolm W., Pres.--Moran Towing Of Texas Corporation, Greenwich, CT; *U.S. Private*, pg. 761
Macleod, Malcolm W., Pres.--Moran Shipyard Corporation, Greenwich, CT; *U.S. Private*, pg. 761
MacLeod, Richard, Pres. & Chief Oper. Officer--Tapco International Corporation, Plymouth, MI; *U.S. Private*, pg. 1068
MacLeod, Tom, Pres. & Chief Oper. Officer--Iams Company, Dayton, OH; *U.S. Private*, pg. 556
MacMahon, James, Pres.--Acme Tube Inc., Somerset, NJ; *U.S. Private*, pg. 14
MacManamon, Owen P., Pres.--Quaker State Inc., Burlington, Canada; *U.S. Public*, pg. 1348
MacMorran, Henry G., Pres. & Chief Oper. Officer--LaSalle Cragin Bank, Chicago, IL; *Int'l*, pg. 10
MacNamara, Frank, Pres.--MacNamara, Stewart & Saperstein, New York, NY; *U.S. Private*, pg. 692
MacNeil, Bruce M., Pres.--Ark-Les Corporation, Stoughton, MA; *U.S. Private*, pg. 82
MacNeill, Brian F., Pres. & Chief Exec. Officer--IPL Energy Inc., Calgary, Canada; *Int'l*, pg. 651
MacNeill, Brian F., Pres. & Chief Exec. Officer--Interprovincial Pipe Line Inc., Edmonton, Canada; *Int'l*, pg. 652
MacPhail, Donald E.A., Pres.--Ocelot International Tanzania Ltd., Dar es Salaam, Tanzania; *Int'l*, pg. 996
MacPherson, Donald R., Pres. & Chief Exec. Officer--Red Devil Inc., Union, NJ; *U.S. Private*, pg. 915
MacVittie, Paula R., Pres. & Chief Exec. Officer--Caldwell VanRiper, Inc., Indianapolis, IN; *U.S. Private*, pg. 200
Maczuzak, John A., Pres. & Chief Oper. Officer--National Steel Corporation, Mishawaka, IN; *Int'l*, pg. 902
Madanes, Miguel, Chm. Bd. & Pres.--Y.P.F., S.A., Buenos Aires, Argentina; *Int'l*, pg. 1515
Madavi, Syrus P., Pres. & Chief Exec. Officer--Burr-Brown Corporation, Tucson, AZ; *U.S. Public*, pg. 270
Madden, J., Pres.--Mohawk Marketing, Virginia Beach, VA; *Int'l*, pg. 869
Madden, John, Pres.--Crystal Flash Petroleum Corp., Indianapolis, IN; *U.S. Private*, pg. 294
Madden, Will, Pres.--CABVAL, Houston, TX; *U.S. Public*, pg. 801
Maddock, Thomas S., Pres.--Boyle Engineering Corp., Newport Beach, CA; *U.S. Private*, pg. 163
Maddox, D.N., Pres.--NIPA Hardwicke, Inc., Wilmington, DE; *U.S. Private*, pg. 771
Maddox, Gary, Pres. & Chief Exec. Officer--A. Pomerantz & Company, Philadelphia, PA; *U.S. Private*, pg. 875
Maddox, James A., Pres.--Ermco, Inc., Indianapolis, IN; *U.S.* Private, pg. 381
Maddox, James D., Pres.--Tri-State Mack Inc, Memphis, TN; *U.S. Private*, pg. 1101
Maddox, L.E., Pres. & Chief Exec. Officer--PG&E Energy Trading, Houston, TX; *U.S. Public*, pg. 1241
Maddrey, E.E., II, Pres. & Chief Exec. Officer--Delta Woodside Industries, Inc., Greenville, SC; *U.S. Public*, pg. 497
Madia, Dan, Sr. Partner & Global Chief Admin.Officer--Ketchum Public Relations Worldwide, New York, NY; *U.S. Private*, pg. 617
Madigan, John W., Chm. Bd., Pres. & Chief Exec. Officer--Tribune Company, Chicago, IL; *U.S. Public*, pg. 1635
Madison, Chris, Pres.--Madison Graham Colorgraphics, Inc., Los Angeles, CA; *U.S. Private*, pg. 694
Madison, D. Raymond, Chm. Bd. & Chief Exec. Officer--Dynamic Homes, Inc., Detroit Lakes, MN; *U.S. Public*, pg. 538
Madni, Asad M., Dr., Pres.--BEI Sensors and Systems Company, Sylmar, CA; *U.S. Public*, pg. 160
Madsen, Per, Pres.--Aker Elementbygg a.s., Moss, Norway; *Int'l*, pg. 41
Madsen, Richard H., Chm. Bd., Pres. & Chief Exec. Officer--Zions Co-operative Mercantile Institution, Salt Lake City, UT; *U.S. Public*, pg. 1793
Madson, Paul C., Pres. & Chief Exec. Officer--Border States Industries, Inc., Fargo, ND; *U.S. Private*, pg. 160
Maeda, Isamu, Pres.--Valmet Japan Co., Ltd., Tokyo, Japan; *Int'l*, pg. 1448
Maeda, Noburo, Pres. & Chief Exec. Officer--Fujisawa U.S.A., Deerfield, IL; *Int'l*, pg. 525
Maeda, Noburu, Pres. & Chief Exec. Officer--Fujisawa U.S.A. Inc., Deerfield, IL; *Int'l*, pg. 525
Maeda, S., Pres.--Sharp Electronic Components (Taiwan) Corporation, Taipei, Taiwan; *Int'l*, pg. 1229
Maeda, Shigeru, Pres.--Ebara Corporation, Tokyo, Japan; *Int'l*, pg. 431
Maeda, Tsuguhiro, Pres.--NHK Spring Co., Ltd., Yokohama, Japan; *Int'l*, pg. 901
Maeda, Y., Pres.--Nissho Iwai Real Estate Corp., Tokyo, Japan; *Int'l*, pg. 947
Maehlmann, Peter, Pres.--Hamburger Sparkasse, Hamburg, Germany; *Int'l*, pg. 590
Maekawa, Tetsurou, Deputy Pres.--The Tokai Bank, Limited, Nagoya, Japan; *Int'l*, pg. 1391
Maender, Charles R., Pres. & Chief Oper. Officer--Central States Diversified, Inc., Saint Louis, MO; *U.S. Private*, pg. 224
Maeyama, Yoshito, Pres.--Komatsu Huanan Ltd., Hong Kong, Hong Kong; *Int'l*, pg. 744
Maeyama, Yoshito, Pres.--Komatsu (Shanghai) Ltd., Shanghai, China; *Int'l*, pg. 744
Maffic, Michael O., Pres. & Chief Exec. Officer--Carson Water Co., Las Vegas, NV; *U.S. Public*, pg. 1493
Maffie, Michael O., Pres. & Chief Exec. Officer--Southwest Gas Corporation, Las Vegas, NV; *U.S. Public*, pg. 1493
Maffie, Michael O., Pres. & Chief Exec. Officer--LNG Energy, Inc., Phoenix, AZ; *U.S. Public*, pg. 1493
Magaro, James E., Pres.--Aycock, Inc., Hummelstown, PA; *U.S. Private*, pg. 103
Magee, Brian, Pres.--Canac Kitchens Ltd, Thornhill, Canada; *U.S. Private*, pg. 630
Magee, Michael M., Jr., Pres. & Chief Exec. Officer--Independent Bank, Ionia, MI; *U.S. Public*, pg. 874
Magee, Robert P., Pres.--Totem Ocean Trailer Express, Seattle, WA; *U.S. Private*, pg. 1092

Magendans, Wim, Pres.--Thomassen International Holding B.V., Rheden, Netherlands; *Int'l*, pg. 401

Magerman, Michael, Pres.--Tommy Armour Golf, Morton Grove, IL; *U.S. Public*, pg. 1683

Maggio, Claudio, Pres.--MAF S.p.A., Nembro, Italy; *Int'l*, pg. 1449

Maghielse, Craig, Chm. Bd., Pres. & Chief Exec. Officer--Maghielse Tool Corporation, Grand Rapids, MI; *U.S. Private*, pg. 694

Magid, Alfred, Pres.--JM Company, Hasbrouck Heights, NJ; *U.S. Private*, pg. 577

Maglia, Lou, Pres.-Zoo Entertainment--Bertelsmann Music Group, Wilmington, DE; *Int'l*, pg. 191

Maglio, Louis A., Pres.--Walpole Woodworkers, Inc., Walpole, MA; *U.S. Private*, pg. 1148

Magliocca, Sam, Pres.--Keller Building Products of Charlotte, Inc., Charlotte, NC; *U.S. Private*, pg. 612

Magliocco, Antonio, Jr., Pres.--Peerless Importers, Inc., Brooklyn, NY; *U.S. Private*, pg. 847

Magliochetti, Joseph M., Pres.--Dana Corporation, Toledo, OH; *U.S. Public*, pg. 479

Magnan, Larry, Pres. & Chief Exec. Officer--Cruise Holdings Ltd., Miami, FL; *U.S. Private*, pg. 293

Magnan, Larry, Pres.--Premier Cruises, Miami, FL; *U.S. Private*, pg. 293

Magnano, Louis A., Pres. & Chief Exec. Officer--Blue Bird Coach Lines Inc., Olean, NY; *U.S. Private*, pg. 150

Magnell, Steffen I., Pres.--Coleman Powermate Compressors, Springfield, MN; *U.S. Private*, pg. 691

Magner, Marjorie, Pres. & Chief Oper. Officer--Commercial Credit Company, Baltimore, MD; *U.S. Public*, pg. 1633

Magnussen, Jonn-Borger, Pres.--Aker Singel & Grus a.s., Sandnes, Norway; *Int'l*, pg. 42

Magnusson, Jonn-Borger, Pres.--NorStone a.s, Sandnes, Norway; *Int'l*, pg. 1199

Magoon, Robert, Pres.--Amelco, Inc., Honolulu, HI; *U.S. Public*, pg. 65

Magowan, Peter, Pres.--San Francisco Giants Baseball Club, San Francisco, CA; *U.S. Private*, pg. 964

Magrath, Jr., George N., Pres.--Peoples Federal Savings & Loan Association, Conway, SC; *U.S. Public*, pg. 634

Magruder, Ronald N., Pres. & Chief Oper. Officer--Cracker Barrel Old Country Store, Inc., Lebanon, TN; *U.S. Public*, *pg. 455*

Maguire, Carter, Pres.--Turner Network Sales, Atlanta, GA; *U.S. Public*, pg. 1615

Maguire, Cary M., Chm. Bd., Pres. & Chief Exec. Officer--Maguire Oil Co., Dallas, TX; *U.S. Private*, pg. 696

Maguire, D.E., Chm. Bd., Pres. & Chief Exec. Officer--Kemet Corporation, Simpsonville, SC; *U.S. Public*, pg. 949

Maguire, Robert F., III, Mng. Partner--Maguire Partners, Los Angeles, CA; *U.S. Private*, pg. 696

Maguisak, Michael H., Pres.--ShowBiz Pizza Time, Inc., Irving, TX; *U.S. Public*, pg. 1468

Mahaffey, Paul F., Pres. & Chief Exec. Officer--PLUM, Eden Prairie, MN; *Int'l*, pg. 1504

Mahaffy, Patrick J., Pres. & Chief Exec. Officer--Nexstar Pharmaceuticals, Inc., Boulder, CO; *U.S. Public*, pg. 1180

Maharam, Donald, Pres.--Maharam, Hauppauge, NY; *U.S. Private*, pg. 696

Maharry, Anne, Pres. & Chief Fin. Officer--Bull, Inc., San Diego, CA; *U.S. Private*, pg. 976

Mahendroo, Vikeesh, Pres.--William M. Mercer Companies, Inc., New York, NY; *U.S. Public*, pg. 1049

Maher, David L., Pres. & Chief Oper. Officer--American Stores Company, Salt Lake City, UT; *U.S. Public*, pg. 92

Maheu, Jean, Chm. Bd.--Radio France, Paris, France; *Int'l*, pg. 1083

Mahler, Darrell, Pres., Gen. Mgr. & Mgr.-Adv./Sls. Promo.--Blue Cross Laboratories, Saugus, CA; *U.S. Private*, pg. 152

Mahler, James, Pres.--Americoal Services Company, Fairview Heights, IL; *U.S. Public*, pg. 1790

Mahlik, Michael B., Pres. & Chief Exec. Officer--Associated Trust Company, Inc., Milwaukee, WI; *U.S. Public*, pg. 140

Mahon Egen, Maureen, Pres.--Warner Books, Inc., New York, NY; *U.S. Public*, pg. 1614

Mahoney, John T., Pres. & Chief Exec. Officer--TransLogic Corp., Denver, CO; *Int'l*, pg. 1387

Mahoney, Michael J., Pres. & Chief Oper. Officer--RCN Corporation, Princeton, NJ; *U.S. Public*, pg. 1354

Mahoney, P. Michael, Pres.--Bankmanagers Corp., Milwaukee, WI; *U.S. Private*, pg. 114

Mahoney, Thomas E., Pres. & Gen. Mgr.--Stanley Customer Support Div., New Britain, CT; *U.S. Public*, pg. 1509

Mahoney, William, Pres.--SCT Utilities Systems, Inc., Columbia, SC; *U.S. Public*, pg. 1552

Mahr, Rene, Pres. & Chief Exec. Officer--Paul Wurth S.A., Luxembourg, Luxembourg; *Int'l*, pg. 80

Mahrlig, George, Partner--Media First International, Inc., New York, NY; *U.S. Private*, pg. 726

Mai, Vincent, Pres. & Chief Exec. Officer--AEA Investors Inc., New York, NY; *U.S. Private*, pg. 4

Maibach, Benjamin C., III, Pres.--Barton Malow Enterprises, Inc., Southfield, MI; *U.S. Private*, pg. 120

Maibach, Benjamin C., III, Pres.--Barton Malow Co., Southfield, MI; *U.S. Private*, pg. 120

Maier, Craig F., Pres. & Chief Exec. Officer--Frisch's Restaurants, Inc., Cincinnati, OH; *U.S. Public*, pg. 682

Maier, Craig F., Pres.--Frisch Florida, Inc., Cincinnati, OH; *U.S. Public*, pg. 682

Maier, Craig F., Pres.--Frisch Germantown Road, Inc., Cincinnati, OH; *U.S. Public*, pg. 682

Maier, Craig F., Pres.--Frisch Kentucky, Inc., Cincinnati, OH; *U.S. Public*, pg. 682

Maier, Craig F., Pres.--Kip's of Oklahoma, Inc., Cincinnati, OH; *U.S. Public*, pg. 682

Maier, Craig F., Pres.--Frisch Ohio, Inc., Cincinnati, OH; *U.S. Public*, pg. 682

Maier, Craig F., Pres.--Frisch Indiana, Inc., Cincinnati, OH; *U.S. Public*, pg. 682

Maier, Walter, Pres.--Sandvik Sorting Systems, Louisville, KY; *Int'l*, pg. 1186

Mailind, Jesper, Pres. & Chief Oper. Officer--GN Danavox A/S, Taastrup, Denmark; *Int'l*, pg. 537

Maillot, Jacques, Pres.--Nouvelles Frontieres, Paris, France; *Int'l*, pg. 971

Mains, Donald A., Pres.--Tradehome Shoe Stores, Inc., Saint Paul, MN; *U.S. Private*, pg. 1095

Mainthia, Nik, Pres.--The Media Investment Group, Atlanta, GA; *U.S. Private*, pg. 726

Maire, Jacques, Pres. & Chief Exec. Officer--Gaz de France, Paris, France; *Int'l*, pg. 541

Maitland, John B., Pres.--Business Information Technology, Media, PA; *U.S. Public*, pg. 356

Maitrepierre, Philippe, Chief Exec. Officer--Techalloy Co., Inc., Mahwah, NJ; *Int'l*, pg. 572

Maiuccoro, John M., Pres. & Treas.--Imperial Pools, Inc., Latham, NY; *U.S. Private*, pg. 558

Majerczak, Edward, Pres.--Berlin Industries, Inc., Carol Stream, IL; *U.S. Private*, pg. 136

Majerczak, Edward, Pres.--Berlin Industries, Inc., Elk Grove Village, IL; *U.S. Private*, pg. 136

Majeski, David L., Pres.--Consolidated Lumber Co., Stillwater, MN; *U.S. Private*, pg. 265

Major, Robert A., Pres. & Chief Oper. Officer--ContiMortgage Corporation, Horsham, PA; *U.S. Public*, pg. 439

Makarewicz, David C., Pres. & Chief Oper. Officer--J2, Inc., Deerfield, IL; *U.S. Private*, pg. 598

Makarewicz, Stephen E., Pres. & Chief Oper. Officer--J.M. Tull Metals Co., Inc., Norcross, GA; *U.S. Public*, pg. 879

Makhani, Madan P., Chm. Bd., Pres., Chief Oper. & Chief Fin. Officer--American Foundry Group, Inc., Bixby, OK; *U.S. Private*, pg. 54

Maki, Glen, Pres.--Maki Corporation, Lunenburg, MA; *U.S. Private*, pg. 697

Maki, Koichi, Pres.--ORIX Insurance Services Corporation, Tokyo, Japan; *Int'l*, pg. 1008

Makihara, Minoru, Pres.--Mitsubishi Corporation, Tokyo, Japan; *Int'l*, pg. 871

Makinen, Eero, Pres.--Kvaerner Masa Marine Inc., Vancouver, Canada; *Int'l*, pg. 771

Makinen, Heimo, Pres. & Chief Exec. Officer--Montgomery KONE Inc., Moline, IL; *Int'l*, pg. 746

Makinen, Heimo, Pres.--Montgomery Elevator International Company, Moline, IL; *Int'l*, pg. 746

Makino, Arata, Pres.--Japan Polychem Corp., Tokyo, Japan; *Int'l*, pg. 871

Makino, Jiro, Pres.--Makino Milling Machine Co. Ltd., Tokyo, Japan; *Int'l*, pg. 831

Makita, Shinichiro, Pres.--GAEART Kumagai Co., Ltd., Tokyo, Japan; *Int'l*, pg. 763

Makkonen, G., Pres.--Skanska Oy, Helsinki, Finland; *Int'l*, pg. 1261

Makowski, Karen, Pres. & Chief Exec. Officer--Key Bank of Vermont, Burlington, VT; *U.S. Public*, pg. 954

Malach, Ken, Pres.--Stephen Gould of Arizona, Inc., Tempe, AZ; *U.S. Private*, pg. 467

Malafronte, Thomas J., Pres.--Amerchol Corporation, Edison, NJ; *U.S. Public*, pg. 1667

Malara, Anthony C., Pres.--CBS Affiliate Relations Division, New York, NY; *U.S. Public*, pg. 274

Malchow, Dennis, Pres.--The Martin-Brower Company, Lombard, IL; *Int'l*, pg. 376

Malcolm, Bruce, Pres.--Electro Optical Ind., Santa Barbara, CA; *U.S. Private*, pg. 228

Maldonado Elizondo, Carlos, Co-Pres.--Copamex Industrias S.A. de C.V., Garza Garcia, Mexico; *Int'l*, pg. 330

Maldonado Elizondo, Carlos, Pres.--Industrial Papelera Mexicana S.A. de C.V., Uruapan, Mexico; *Int'l*, pg. 330

Maldonado Elizondo, Carlos, Pres.--Papelera de Chihuahua S.A. de C.V., Chihuahua, Mexico; *Int'l*, pg. 330

Maldonado Quiroga, Juan Bosco, Co-Pres.--Copamex Industrias S.A. de C.V., Garza Garcia, Mexico; *Int'l*, pg. 330

Malecha, Kenneth, Pres.--Best Brands, Saint Paul, MN; *Int'l*, *pg. 617*

Malenick, Donal H., Pres. & Chief Oper. Officer--Worthington Industries, Inc., Columbus, OH; *U.S. Public*, pg. 1780

Malerba, James J., Pres. & Chief Oper. Officer--Key Bank of Washington, Tacoma, WA; *U.S. Public*, pg. 954

Malette, Gaston, Chm. Bd., Pres. & Chief Exec. Officer--Malette Quebec, Inc., Montreal, Canada; *Int'l*, pg. 833

Malette, Gaston, Chm. Bd., Pres. & Chief Exec. Officer--Panneaux Malette-OSB Inc., Saint-Georges, Canada; *Int'l*, pg. 833

Malixi, Conrado R., Pres. & Chief Exec. Officer--La Tondena Distillers, Inc., Manila, Philippines; *Int'l*, pg. 785

Malkani, Roma, Pres. & Chief Exec. Officer--Information Systems & Network Corporation, Bethesda, MD; *U.S. Private*, pg. 561

Malkiewicz, Bob, Co-Pres. & Chief Oper. Officer--Helm, Inc., Detroit, MI; *U.S. Private*, pg. 520

Mallet, Robert I., Pres.--Mallet & Co., Carnegie, PA; *U.S. Private*, pg. 698

Mallet, Thierry, Pres. & Chief Exec. Officer--Air & Water Technologies Corporation, Branchburg, NJ; *U.S. Public*, pg. 29

Mallin, Ed, Pres.--Compilers Plus Inc., Montvale, NJ; *U.S. Public*, pg. 70

Mallinckrodt, George, Pres.--Schroders PLC, London, United Kingdom; *Int'l*, pg. 1210

Malloy, Fred P., Pres. & Corp. Travel Planner--Consolidated Coatings Corp., Brunswick, OH; *U.S. Public*, pg. 1357

Malm, Goran S., Pres. & Chief Exec. Officer--GE Medical Systems Asia Ltd., Tokyo, Japan; *U.S. Public*, pg. 713

Malm, Timothy O., Pres.--Fleischmann Malting Company, Inc., Minneapolis, MN; *U.S. Public*, pg. 128

Malmgren, J., Pres.--SBC Arbitech AB, Stockholm, Sweden; *Int'l*, pg. 1330

Malms, Christoph, Pres. & Chief Exec. Officer--ISL Marketing A.G., Lucerne, Switzerland; *Int'l*, pg. 394

Malone, Robert A., Pres., Chief Exec. & Oper. Officer--Alyeska Pipeline Service Company, Anchorage, AK; *U.S. Private*, pg. 47

Malone, Tom, Pres. & Chief Oper. Officer--Milliken & Company, Spartanburg, SC; *U.S. Private*, pg. 748

Malone, Wallace D., Jr., Pres. & Chief Exec. Officer--SouthTrust Corporation, Birmingham, AL; *U.S. Public*, pg. 1491

Maloney, Irvin W., Pres. & Chief Exec. Officer--Dataproducts Corporation, Simi Valley, CA; *Int'l*, pg. 620

Maloney, Raymond, Pres. & Chief Exec. Officer--Intertec Publishing, Atlanta, GA; *U.S. Public*, pg. 1328

Maloney, Raymond E., Pres. & Chief Exec. Officer--Intertec Publishing, Overland Park, KS; *U.S. Public*, pg. 1327

Maloney, Raymond E., Pres. & Chief Oper. Officer--Farm Press, Clarksdale, MS; *U.S. Public*, pg. 1328

Maloney, Richard A., Pres. & Chief Exec. Officer--Meier & Frank, Portland, OR; *U.S. Public*, pg. 1064

Maloof, Richard C., Pres. & Chief Oper. Officer--Bird Incorporated, Norwood, MA; *Int'l*, pg. 1170

Malott, T.J, Pres. & Chief Exec. Officer--Siemens Energy & Automation Inc., Alpharetta, GA; *Int'l*, pg. 1245

Malpas, Robert, Non-Exec. Co.-Chm. & Co-Pres.--The Eurotunnel Group, London, United Kingdom; *Int'l*, pg. 466

Malpass, Frederick, Chm. Bd. & Pres.--East Jordan Iron Works, East Jordan, MI; *U.S. Private*, pg. 356

Malvaso, James J., Pres. & Chief Oper. Officer--The Raymond Corporation, Greene, NY; *Int'l*, pg. 123

Malys, G.J., Pres.--Amax Energy, Inc., Englewood, CO; *U.S. Public*, pg. 470

Malzahn, Edwin, Chm. Bd. & Pres.--Charles Machine Works, Inc., Perry, OK; *U.S. Private*, pg. 230

Manaker, Ralph, Pres.--BTI Americas, Inc., Northbrook, IL; *U.S. Private*, pg. 108

Manassah, Edward E., Pres. & Publisher--The Courier-Journal Louisville Times Co., Louisville, KY; *U.S. Public*, pg. 700

Manby, Joel, Pres. & Chief Exec. Officer--Saab Cars USA, Inc., Norcross, GA; *Int'l*, pg. 687

Manceron, Jacques, Pres.--Georges Renoult S.A., Saint Sebastien, France; *Int'l*, pg. 96

Manchester, David E., Pres. & Chief Exec. Officer--J.E. Baker Co., York, PA; *U.S. Private*, pg. 112

Manchester, Eli, Pres. & Chief Exec. Officer--Kewaunee Scientific Corporation, Statesville, NC; *U.S. Public*, pg. 953

Mancinelli, Victor A., Pres.--Mustang Manufacturing Company, Inc., Owatonna, MN; *U.S. Public*, pg. 704

Mancini, Brooks T., Pres. & Treas.--B.T. Mancini Co., Inc., Milpitas, CA; *U.S. Private*, pg. 699

Mancke, Kimball, Pres.--Bomarko, Inc., Plymouth, IN; *U.S. Private*, pg. 156

Mancuso, Paul A., Pres.--Calvin Klein Cosmetics Company, New York, NY; *Int'l*, pg. 1435

Mandabach, Caryn, Pres.--Carsey-Werner Company, LLC, Studio City, CA; *U.S. Private*, pg. 216

Mandala, Muchtar, Pres. Commissioner--P.T. IBJ Indonesia Bank, Jakarta, Indonesia; *Int'l*, pg. 676

Mandarich, David D., Pres.--Richmond Homes, Inc. I, Denver, CO; *U.S. Public*, pg. 1025

Mandelbaum, Lawrence, Pres. & Chief Exec. Officer--Big M, Inc., Totowa, NJ; *U.S. Private*, pg. 143

Mandelbaum, Mervyn, Chm. Bd., Pres., Chief Exec. & Chief Oper. Officer--Superba, Inc., Los Angeles, CA; *U.S. Private*, pg. 1054

Mandell, Lawrence, Pres.--Key Food Stores Co-operative, Inc., Brooklyn, NY; *U.S. Private*, pg. 617

Mandell, Robert A., Pres.--Greater Construction Corp., Altamonte Springs, FL; *U.S. Private*, pg. 476

Mandor, Robert, Pres.--Concord Assets Group, Boca Raton, FL; *U.S. Private*, pg. 261

Mandorf, Kaj, Pres.--AB Kaj Mandorf, Molnlycke, Sweden; *Int'l*, pg. 678

Maness, John D., Pres.--Dick Bruhn Incorporated, Salinas, CA; *U.S. Private*, pg. 175

Maness, Kenneth P., Sr., Pres.--Maness Industries, Inc., Long Beach, CA; *U.S. Private*, pg. 699

Maney, Steven R., Pres. & Chief Exec. Officer--Regions Bank/Barrow County, Winder, GA; *U.S. Public*, pg. 1371

Mang, W.P.E., Pres. & Chief Exec. Officer--Fedmet International Inc., Mississauga, Canada; *Int'l*, pg. 1150

Mangan, Daniel A., Pres.--Valex Corp., Ventura, CA; *U.S. Public*, pg. 1375

Mangin, Joseph A., Pres. & Chief Exec. Officer--Barr Brothers & Co., Inc., New York, NY; *U.S. Private*, pg. 117

Maniatty, George, Pres.--Precision Roll Grinders, Inc., Allentown, PA; *U.S. Private*, pg. 880

Maniglier, Bernard, Pres.--Compaq Computer S.A.R.L., Les Ulis, France; *U.S. Public*, pg. 418

Maniscalco, Rosemary, Pres.--Uniforce Information Services, Woodbury, NY; *U.S. Public*, pg. 409

Manke, Charles, Pres.--Manke Lumber Company, Inc., Tacoma, WA; *U.S. Private*, pg. 699

Mann, Andrew, Pres.--The Cook Bates Division, Venice, FL; *Int'l*, pg. 815

Mann, David, Pres. & Chief Exec. Officer--Nova Scotia Power Inc., Halifax, Canada; *Int'l*, pg. 971

Mann, George S., Chm. Bd. & Pres.--Unicorp American Corporation, New York, NY; *Int'l*, pg. 1433

Mann, Howard, Pres. & Chief Exec. Officer--McCain Foods Limited, Florenceville, Canada; *Int'l*, pg. 850

Mann, James L., Chm. Bd., Pres. & Chief Exec. Officer--SunGard Data Systems Inc., Wayne, PA; *U.S. Public*, pg. 1534

Mann, John K., Pres. & Chief Exec. Officer--Chelsea State Bank, Chelsea, MI; *U.S. Private*, pg. 231

Mann, John, Jr., Pres.--Moline Accessories Company, Moline, IL; *Int'l*, pg. 746

Mann, M. J., Pres.--Alternative Remedial Technologies, Inc., Tampa, FL; *Int'l*, pg. 607

Mann, Marvin L., Chm. Bd. & Chief Exec. Officer--Lexmark International Group, Inc., Lexington, KY; *U.S. Public*, pg. 991
Mann, Richard, Pres.--Lance Industries, Sylmar, CA; *U.S. Private*, pg. 645
Mann, Robert, Pres.--Hardman Division of Harcros Chemicals, Inc., Belleville, NJ; *Int'l*, pg. 598
Mann, Samuel J., Chm. Bd., Pres. & Chief Exec. Officer--Inverness Corp., Fair Lawn, NJ; *U.S. Private*, pg. 574
Mann, Samuel J., Pres.--Inverness France, Paris, France; *U.S. Private*, pg. 574
Mann, Samuel J., Pres.--Inverness UK LTD., Slough, United Kingdom; *U.S. Private*, pg. 574
Mann, Samuel J., Pres.--ERI Laboratories, Fair Lawn, NJ; *U.S. Private*, pg. 574
Mann, Timothy, Pres.--Swisher International Group, Inc., Darien, CT; *U.S. Public*, pg. 1543
Mann, William J., Pres.--Southam Magazine and Information Group, North York, Canada; *Int'l*, pg. 631
Manna, Daniel C., Pres. & Chief Exec. Officer--Paul Mueller Company, Springfield, MO; *U.S. Public*, pg. 1141
Manne, Stan, Chm. Bd. & Pres.--Brawney Plastics, Inc., Chicago, IL; *U.S. Private*, pg. 166
Mannesson, Magnus, Pres.--NCC Real Estate, Solna, Sweden; *Int'l*, pg. 899
Manning, Frank, Pres.--Dunbarton Corporation, Dothan, AL; *U.S. Private*, pg. 194
Manning, Frank B., Pres. & Chief Exec. Officer--Zoom Telephonics, Inc., Boston, MA; *U.S. Public*, pg. 1794
Manning, J. William, Sr., Chm. Bd. & Chief Exec. Officer--Manning Equipment, Inc., Louisville, KY; *U.S. Private*, pg. 700
Manning, James, Chm. Bd. & Pres.--Auburn Hosiery Mills, Inc., Auburn, KY; *U.S. Private*, pg. 98
Manning, James, Pres.--Synetic, Inc., Elmwood Park, NJ; *U.S. Public*, pg. 1548
Manning, Kenneth P., Chm. Bd., Pres. & Chief Exec. Officer--Universal Foods Corporation, Milwaukee, WI; *U.S. Public*, pg. 1695
Manning, Laurence R., Pres. & Gen. Counsel--The Racal Corporation, Sunrise, FL; *Int'l*, pg. 1082
Manning, Wayne, Pres. & Chief Oper. Officer--Bashas, Chandler, AZ; *U.S. Private*, pg. 120
Manning, William R., Pres. & Chief Exec. Officer--Statewide Mortgage Company, Birmingham, AL; *U.S. Public*, pg. 1202
Mannix, P.C., Pres.--Eveready Battery Co., Saint Louis, MO; *U.S. Public*, pg. 1360
Mannos, James, Pres.--Sony Microelectronics, San Jose, CA; *Int'l*, pg. 1284
Manos, John, Pres., Chief Exec. Officer & New Bus. Contact--DKB & Partners, Inc., Morristown, NJ; *U.S. Private*, pg. 302
Manos, Pete L., Chm. Bd., Pres. & Chief Exec. Officer--Giant Food Inc., Landover, MD; *U.S. Public*, pg. 741
Manos, Pete L., Pres. & Chief Exec. Officer--Leco Inc., Hyattsville, MD; *U.S. Public*, pg. 741
Manos, Pete L., Pres.--Cole Engineering, Inc., Hyattsville, MD; *U.S. Public*, pg. 741
Manrique, Javier, Pres.--AJL Park, Caracas, Venezuela; *U.S. Private*, pg. 389
Mansell, Bill, Mgr.-Opers.--Furon Co., Bristol, RI; *U.S. Public*, pg. 689
Mansfield, Barry C., Pres.--BASF Ireland Limited, Blackrock, Ireland; *Int'l*, pg. 106
Mansfield, Michael F., Chm. Bd. & Pres.--Mansfield Oil Company, Gainesville, GA; *U.S. Private*, pg. 700
Mansion, Yves, Dep. Chm. & Pres.--AGF Assurances, Paris, France; *Int'l*, pg. 14
Mansson, Ola, Pres.--Skanska Teknik AB, Malmo, Sweden; *Int'l*, pg. 1261
Manston, Harlan, Pres.--Square Butte Electric Cooperative, Grand Forks, ND; *U.S. Private*, pg. 751
Mantegazza, Paolo, Pres. & Chief Exec. Officer--Globus & Cosmos, Littleton, CO; *U.S. Private*, pg. 458
Mantor, Tom, Pres.--BWC Financial Corp., Walnut Creek, CA; *U.S. Private*, pg. 108
Mantoulides, Christina, Mng. Partner-Reg. Brdcst. Opers.--BJK&E Media Group, New York, NY; *U.S. Public*, pg. 1642
Manuel, Jackie, Pres.--Travis County Title Company, Austin, TX; *U.S. Public*, pg. 441
Manuel, Patti S., Pres.--Sprint Business, Dallas, TX; *U.S. Public*, pg. 1501
Manuel, Thomas L., Pres. & Chief Oper. Officer--ConAgra Trading Companies (CTC), Omaha, NE; *U.S. Public*, pg. 428
Manuel, Tom, Pres.--ConAgra Trading & Processing Companies, Omaha, NE; *U.S. Public*, pg. 428
Manz, George, Pres. & Chief Oper. Officer--Data Control Systems, Gaithersburg, MD; *U.S. Public*, pg. 420
Maples, Gary D., Pres. & Chief Exec. Officer--M & I Bank, Superior, WI; *U.S. Public*, pg. 1050
Maragall i Mira, Excmo. Sr. D., Pres.--Promocio De Ciutat Vella, Barcelona, Spain; *Int'l*, pg. 1372
Maraia, A.O., Pres. & Chief Exec. Officer--National Gypsum Company, Charlotte, NC; *Int'l*, pg. 790
Marasca, Al, Pres. & Chief Oper. Officer--Ralphs Grocery Company, Compton, CA; *U.S. Private*, pg. 1202
Marashlian, Zohrab B., Pres.--Perini-Metropolitan New York Div., Hawthorne, NY; *U.S. Public*, pg. 1278
Marberg, Edwin, Owner, Pres. & Chief Exec. Officer--MCM Enterprises, Inc., Crawfordsville, IN; *U.S. Private*, pg. 686
Marberg, William, Pres. & Chief Exec. Officer--Wilcox Electric, Inc., Kansas City, MO; *Int'l*, pg. 1384
Marblestone, Arthur, Partner-Entertainment--Media First International, Inc., New York, NY; *U.S. Private*, pg. 726
Marcalus, Nicholas R., Pres. & Chief Exec. Officer--Marcal Paper Mills, Inc., Elmwood Park, NJ; *U.S. Private*, pg. 701
Marcegaglia, Antonio, Dr., Pres. & Chief Exec. Officer--Damascus Bishop Tube Co., Greenville, PA; *Int'l*, pg. 842
March, Ronald E., Pres.--Cliggott Publishing, Greenwich, CT; *U.S. Private*, pg. 246
Marchand, Jim, Pres.--Carter Chambers Supply, Inc., Baton Rouge, LA; *U.S. Private*, pg. 216
Marchesano, Michael, Pres. & Chief Exec. Officer--BPA International, New York, NY; *U.S. Private*, pg. 107
Marchesi, G.A., Chm. Bd., Pres. & Chief Exec. Officer--Steiner Co., Inc., Chicago, IL; *U.S. Private*, pg. 1039
Marchesi, Guy, Pres.--Change-O-Matic/Wesco, Aurora, IL; *U.S. Private*, pg. 1039
Marchi, David, Pres. & Chief Oper. Officer--TLP East, Wilton, CT; *U.S. Public*, pg. 1224
Marchi, Marc, Pres.--Sodetair, Roissy, France; *Int'l*, pg. 560
Marchio, Angelo, Pres.--Riunione Adriatica di Sicurta S.p.A., Milan, Italy; *Int'l*, pg. 61
Marchioli, Nelson J., Pres. & Sr. V.P.--El Pollo Loco, Irvine, CA; *U.S. Public*, pg. 23
Marchioni, Allen, Chm. Bd., Pres. & Chief Exec. Officer--William Morrow & Co., Inc., New York, NY; *U.S. Private*, pg. 515
Marchitto, Al, Chm. Bd. & Chief Exec. Officer--Simmons Juvenile Products, Rutherford, NJ; *U.S. Private*, pg. 1001
Marciano, Paul, Pres. & Chief Oper. Officer--Guess ?, Inc., Los Angeles, CA; *U.S. Public*, pg. 768
Marcil, William C., Pres., Chief Exec. Officer, & Publr. of The Forum--Forum Communications Company, Fargo, ND; *U.S. Private*, pg. 420
Marconi, Robert C., Pres.--AAllied Die Casting Mfg., Inc., Franklin Park, IL; *U.S. Private*, pg. 903
Marcotte, Brian W.G., Pres.--Unocal Thailand, Bangkok, Thailand; *U.S. Public*, pg. 1698
Marcoux, Remi, Chm. Bd., Pres. & Chief Exec. Officer--G.T.C. Transcontinental Group Ltd., Montreal, Canada; *Int'l*, pg. 538
Marcucilli, Stephen J., Pres.--FHL Lease Holding Company, Inc., Honolulu, HI; *U.S. Public*, pg. 634
Marcus, Barbara A., Pres.--Trumpet Book Clubs, New York, NY; *U.S. Public*, pg. 1440
Marcus, Carl, Pres.--Harold Leonard & Company, Inc., Union, NJ; *U.S. Private*, pg. 660
Marcus, Martin, Pres.--Marcus Brothers Textiles, Inc., New York, NY; *U.S. Private*, pg. 702
Marcus, Richard G., Pres. & Chief Oper. Officer--American Biltrite Inc., Wellesley Hills, MA; *U.S. Public*, pg. 68
Marcus, Roger S., Pres. & Chief Exec. Officer--Congoleum Corporation, Mercerville, NJ; *U.S. Public*, pg. 69
Marcus, Stephen, Pres.--SelectRehab, Mechanicsburg, PA; *U.S. Public*, pg. 839
Marcus, Stephen, Chm. Bd., Pres. & Chief Exec. Officer--The Marcus Corporation, Milwaukee, WI; *U.S. Public*, pg. 1044
Marcy, Charles F., Pres. & Chief Exec. Officer--Sealright Company, Inc., De Soto, KS; *U.S. Public*, pg. 1451
Marcy, Ray, Pres. & Chief Exec. Officer--Interim Services Inc., Fort Lauderdale, FL; *U.S. Public*, pg. 892
Marcyes, Alan D., Pres.--First American Bank N.A., Saint Cloud, MN; *U.S. Private*, pg. 167
Marden, James L., Pres.--D.P. Fitness, Opelika, AL; *U.S. Public*, pg. 1354
Marek, Larry T., Pres.--Allen-Lewis Manufacturing Co., Inc., Denver, CO; *U.S. Public*, pg. 1554
Marenzi, Gary, Pres.--MGM/UA Telecommunications Group, Santa Monica, CA; *U.S. Public*, pg. 1102
Mares, Nick, Pres.--Cummings-Moore Graphite Co., Detroit, MI; *U.S. Private*, pg. 87
Maresco, Richard, Pres.--Reico, Inc., Springfield, VA; *U.S. Private*, pg. 919
Marge, Guy, Pres. & Chief Exec. Officer--Millhouse Group, Glendora, CA; *U.S. Private*, pg. 748
Margerison, Rick, Pres.--Vinson Supply Company, Dallas, TX; *U.S. Private*, pg. 963
Margerison, Rick, Pres.--Briggs Weaver Vinson, Dallas, TX; *U.S. Private*, pg. 963
Margeuson, R. W., Pres.--Composite Thread Protectors, Inc., Houston, TX; *U.S. Private*, pg. 963
Margherio, Martin J., Pres. & Chief Exec. Officer--Crowley Foods, Inc., Binghamton, NY; *Int'l*, pg. 752
Margolis, Michael L., Pres. & Chief Exec. Officer--Tekelec, Calabasas, CA; *U.S. Public*, pg. 1566
Margulies, Fred, Pres.--Leather Warehouse, Inc., Rutherford, NJ; *U.S. Private*, pg. 656
Margus, Brad, Pres.--Kitchens Of The Oceans, Inc., Deerfield Beach, FL; *U.S. Private*, pg. 625
Maria, Joseph, Pres.--Wall Colmonoy Corp., Madison Heights, MI; *U.S. Private*, pg. 1148
Marianacci, Louis, Pres.--Davox Corp., Westford, MA; *U.S. Public*, pg. 488
Mariani, Gary, Pres.--The Winn Art Group, Ltd., Seattle, WA; *U.S. Public*, pg. 503
Mariani, Harry, Pres. & Chief Oper. Officer--Castello Banfi Srl., Siena, Italy; *U.S. Private*, pg. 113
Mariani, Harry, Pres.--Banfi Product Corp, Old Brookville, NY; *U.S. Private*, pg. 113
Mariani, Harry, Pres.--Villadco Inc., Old Brookville, NY; *U.S. Private*, pg. 113
Mariano, Robert J., Pres. & Chief Exec. Officer--Branford Savings Bank, Branford, CT; *U.S. Public*, pg. 250
Marien, Katherine C., Pres. & Chief Oper. Officer--Allied Capital Lending Corporation, Washington, DC; *U.S. Public*, pg. 48
Marier, Guy, Pres.--Telebec Ltee, Anjou, Canada; *Int'l*, pg. 116
Marin, Richard, Pres.--BT Private Clients Group, New York, NY; *U.S. Public*, pg. 185
Marineau, Philip A., Pres. & Chief Exec. Officer/Pepsi-Cola N. America--Pepsi-Cola Company, Somers, NY; *U.S. Public*, pg. 1277
Marini, Alex P., Pres.--Hydromechanics Div., Erie, PA; *U.S. Public*, pg. 1794
Marini, Alex P., Pres.--Zurn Plumbing Products Group, Erie, PA; *U.S. Public*, pg. 1794
Marino, David J., Pres.--Penright!, Fremont, CA; *U.S. Public*, pg. 1573
Marino, John T., Pres.--United Metering Inc., Long Island City, NY; *U.S. Public*, pg. 1692
Marino, Kenneth, Pres.--Orbel Corporation, Phillipsburg, NJ; *U.S. Private*, pg. 819
Marino, Michael, Pres.--Wyse Advertising/Cleveland, Cleveland, OH; *U.S. Private*, pg. 1194
Marino, Raymond V., Pres. & Chief Exec. Officer--Pacific Gateway Properties, San Francisco, CA; *U.S. Public*, pg. 1250
Marino, Robert J., Pres. & Chief Exec. Officer--Cincinnati Bell Information Systems Inc., Cincinnati, OH; *U.S. Public*, pg. 367
Marino, Thomas, Pres.--Exotic Rubber & Plastics Corp., Farmington Hills, MI; *U.S. Private*, pg. 388
Mario, Ronald J., Pres.--COMSAT Mobile Communications, Clarksburg, MD; *U.S. Public*, pg. 424
Marion, James P., III, Pres. & Chief Exec. Officer--Bloomsburg Mills Inc., New York, NY; *U.S. Private*, pg. 150
Mariotte, Olivier, Pres.--EURO RSCG Audience, Levallois-Perret, France; *Int'l*, pg. 600
Marischen, Robert J., Pres.--HSI Aviation, Inc., Springfield, MO; *U.S. Public*, pg. 849
Maritz, Steve, Pres.--Maritz Inc., Fenton, MO; *U.S. Private*, pg. 703
Mark, Thomas E., Pres. & Chief Oper. Officer--Detrex Corporation, Southfield, MI; *U.S. Public*, pg. 501
Markee, Richard L., Pres.--Kids "R" Us, Paramus, NJ; *U.S. Public*, pg. 1626
Markee, Richard L., Pres.--Babies "R" Us, Paramus, NJ; *U.S. Public*, pg. 1626
Markel, Anthony F., Pres. & Chief Oper. Officer--Markel Corporation, Glen Allen, VA; *U.S. Public*, pg. 1046
Markell, Rick, Chm. Bd. & Pres.--Southern Bag Corporation, Madison, MS; *U.S. Private*, pg. 1015
Markey, Jonathan H., Pres. & Chief Oper. Officer--Bergen Record Corp., Hackensack, NJ; *U.S. Private*, pg. 693
Markfield, Roger, Pres.--American Eagles Outfitters Inc., Warrendale, PA; *U.S. Private*, pg. 53
Markley, J. Thomas, Pres.--XEL Corporation, Aurora, CO; *U.S. Public*, pg. 1430
Marko, Neil, Pres.--Universal Industrial Products Co., Pioneer, OH; *U.S. Public*, pg. 1677
Markoff, Steven, Pres. & Chief Exec. Officer--A-Mark Financial, Santa Monica, CA; *U.S. Private*, pg. 2
Markowitz, Steven, Pres.--Allen Organ Company, Macungie, PA; *U.S. Public*, pg. 45
Markowitz, Steven, Pres.--VIR, Inc., Southampton, PA; *U.S. Public*, pg. 45
Markowitz, Steven, Pres.--Eastern Research, Inc., Moorestown, NJ; *U.S. Public*, pg. 45
Markowitz, Steven, Pres.--Linear Switch Corporation, Moorestown, NJ; *U.S. Public*, pg. 45
Markowitz, William, Pres.--Brown Jordan Company, El Monte, CA; *U.S. Private*, pg. 174
Marks, David, Pres.--Allianz of America, Inc., Westport, CT; *Int'l*, pg. 58
Marks, E. Matthew, Pres. & Chief Exec. Officer--Intermodal Transportation Services, Inc., Parsippany, NJ; *Int'l*, pg. 1153
Marks, Francis A., Pres.--Chem Free Corporation, Norcross, GA; *U.S. Public*, pg. 888
Marks, Frank, Pres.--Intelligent Enclosures Corp., Norcross, GA; *U.S. Public*, pg. 888
Marks, Julius, Jr., Pres.--Libertyville Lincoln-Mercury Sales, Inc., Libertyville, IL; *U.S. Private*, pg. 666
Marks, Michael, Co-Pres.--Allied Sporting Goods Inc., Louisville, KY; *U.S. Private*, pg. 41
Marks, P.J., Pres.--Gomar Manufacturing Co., Inc., Linden, NJ; *U.S. Public*, pg. 51
Marks, Richard, Pres.--Motorcar Parts & Accessories, Torrance, CA; *U.S. Public*, pg. 1136
Marks, Robert, Pres.--Imediate Pharmaceutical Services Inc., Medina, OH; *U.S. Private*, pg. 334
Marks, Steven L., Pres. & Chief Exec. Officer--Advertising Display Co., Englewood Cliffs, NJ; *U.S. Private*, pg. 23
Markson, Peter, Pres.--Paris Accessories, New York, NY; *U.S. Private*, pg. 839
Markson, Peter, Pres.--Baar & Beards, New York, NY; *U.S. Private*, pg. 839
Markus, Dennis W., Pres.--Transamerica HomeFirst, Inc., San Francisco, CA; *U.S. Public*, pg. 1630
Markwick, James C., Pres.--Manchester Guardian, New York, NY; *Int'l*, pg. 577
Markwort, Helmut, Editor-in-Chief--Focus Magazin Verlag, Munich, Germany; *Int'l*, pg. 233
Marlantes, Lorian L., Pres. & Chief Exec. Officer--Rockefeller Group, Inc., New York, NY; *Int'l*, pg. 873
Marlatt, James, Pres.--Titeflex Corporation, Springfield, MA; *Int'l*, pg. 1340
Marlatt, James W., Pres.--Titeflex Industrial Americas, Springfield, MA; *Int'l*, pg. 1340
Marlatt, James W., Pres.--VARI-FORM, Warren, MI; *Int'l*, pg. 1340
Marlatt, Terry L., Pres.--Carbomedics, Inc., Austin, TX; *Int'l*, pg. 1307
Marlborough, Donald J., Pres.--La Grange Foundry Inc., La Grange, MO; *U.S. Public*, pg. 142
Marlen, James S., Chm. Bd., Pres. & Chief Exec. Officer--Ameron International Corporation, Pasadena, CA; *U.S. Public*, pg. 99
Marling, Mark E., Chm. Bd & Pres.--Ed Marling Stores, Inc., Topeka, KS; *U.S. Private*, pg. 705
Marlow, Alan, Pres. & Chief Oper. Officer--Harvey Industries, Inc., Waltham, MA; *U.S. Private*, pg. 508
Marlow, C. Guy, Pres.--Amersham Corporation, Arlington Heights, IL; *Int'l*, pg. 992
Marlow, C.Guy, Pres.--Amersham Life Science, Inc., Arlington Heights, IL; *Int'l*, pg. 992
Marlow, Raymond, Pres.--Marlow Industries, Dallas, TX; *U.S. Private*, pg. 705
Marlow, Ted, Pres.--Henri Bendel, New York, NY; *U.S. Public*, pg. 995

Marold, Ronald, Pres. & Chief Exec. Officer--Maxcor Manufacturing, Inc., Colorado Springs, CO; *U.S. Private*, pg. 716

Marone, Joseph, Pres.--Sysco Food Services of Eastern Wisconsin, Jackson, WI; *U.S. Public*, pg. 1551

Maroone, Michael E., Pres.-Car Div.--Maroone Automotive Group, Pembroke Pines, FL; *U.S. Public*, pg. 1379

Maroteaux, Patrick, Pres.--Societe Eurosucre S.N.C., Paris, France; *Int'l*, pg. 549

Marotta, Thomas S., Chm. Bd., Pres. & Chief Exec. Officer--Marotta Scientific Controls, Inc., Montville, NJ; *U.S. Private*, pg. 706

Marozsan, John R., Pres.--Aspen Publishers, Inc., Gaithersburg, MD; *Int'l*, pg. 1513

Marquardt, Arthur C., Pres. & Chief Oper. Officer--CTG Resources, Inc., Hartford, CT; *U.S. Public*, pg. 285

Marquardt, Arthur C., Pres. & Chief Oper. Officer--Connecticut Natural Gas Corporation, Hartford, CT; *U.S. Public*, pg. 285

Marquardt, Arthur C., Pres. & Chief Oper. Officer--Energy Networks, Inc. (ENI), Hartford, CT; *U.S. Public*, pg. 285

Marquis, Dale M., Pres.--Invest West Financial Corporation, Santa Barbara, CA; *U.S. Private*, pg. 832

Marquis, Doug, Pres. & Chief Exec. Officer--Handgards Inc., Northbrook, IL; *U.S. Private*, pg. 499

Marr, Malcolm, Pres. & Chief Exec. Officer--Imperial Litho & Dryography, Inc., Phoenix, AZ; *U.S. Private*, pg. 558

Marra, Ed, Pres.--Nestle Beverage Company, Glendale, CA; *Int'l*, pg. 917

Marram, Edward P., Dr., Chm. Bd., Pres., Chief Exec. Officer & Treas.--Geo-Centers, Inc., Newton, MA; *U.S. Private*, pg. 447

Marriott, John, Pres.--K & M Electronics, Inc., West Springfield, MA; *Int'l*, pg. 395

Marriott, R., Pres.--Banister Majestic, Edmonton, Canada; *Int'l*, pg. 118

Marrus, Allan J., Pres.--The Arlen Corporation, New York, NY; *U.S. Public*, pg. 131

Mars, Forrest E., Jr., Chm. Bd. & Co-Pres.--Mars, Incorporated, Mc Lean, VA; *U.S. Private*, pg. 707

Marsal, Bryan, Pres. & Chief Exec. Officer--Arrow Shirt Company, New York, NY; *Int'l*, pg. 194

Marsalo, Hannu, Pres.--MTV-palvelukiinteistot, Helsinki, Finland; *Int'l*, pg. 828

Marsan, Andre, Chm. Bd., Pres. & Chief Exec. Officer--Montrusco Associates, Inc., Montreal, Canada; *Int'l*, pg. 888

Marsh, Daniel C., Pres.--Premarc Corporation, Durand, MI; *U.S. Private*, pg. 881

Marsh, Don E., Chm. Bd., Pres. & Chief Exec. Officer--Marsh Supermarkets, Inc., Indianapolis, IN; *U.S. Public*, pg. 1049

Marsh, Jeffrey, Pres.--Westwood-Squibb Pharmaceuticals Inc., Buffalo, NY; *U.S. Public*, pg. 255

Marshall, Charles R., Pres. & Gen. Mgr.--Westlie Motor Company, Minot, ND; *U.S. Private*, pg. 1169

Marshall, David, Pres. & Chief Exec. Officer--Berkshire Realty Company, Inc., Boston, MA; *U.S. Public*, pg. 221

Marshall, Griffith M., Pres., Chief Exec. Officer & Chief Oper. Officer--Herbert Malarkey Roofing Company, Portland, OR; *U.S. Private*, pg. 698

Marshall, Harold D., Pres. & Chief Oper. Officer--Associates First Capital Corporation, Dallas, TX; *U.S. Public*, pg. 662

Marshall, J.J.S., Chief Exec.--De La Rue plc, London, United Kingdom; *Int'l*, pg. 386

Marshall, Janice, Pres.--USAA Buying Service, San Antonio, TX; *U.S. Private*, pg. 1114

Marshall, Jeffrey, Pres. & Chief Exec. Officer--Aluma Systems Corp., Toronto, Canada; *Int'l*, pg. 1423

Marshall, R.J., Pres.--The R.J. Marshall Co., Southfield, MI; *U.S. Private*, pg. 708

Marshall, Richard A., Pres.--International Imaging Materials, Inc., Amherst, NY; *U.S. Public*, pg. 1266

Marshall, Robert, Pres.--Raytheon Constructors, Inc.-Ebasco Construction, Lyndhurst, NJ; *U.S. Public*, pg. 1366

Marshall, Robin L., Pres. & Chief Exec. Officer--Great Lakes Technologies Corp., Kalamazoo, MI; *U.S. Private*, pg. 475

Marshall, Scott, Pres.--Hal Riney & Partners, Inc., San Francisco, CA; *U.S. Private*, pg. 931

Marshman, John C., Pres.--Sioux Falls Construction Company, Sioux Falls, SD; *U.S. Private*, pg. 1003

Marsiello, Lawrence A., Pres. & Chief Exec. Officer--The CIT Group/Commercial Services, New York, NY; *Int'l*, pg. 360

Marsilius, Newman M., III, Pres. & Chief Exec. Officer--The Producto Machine Co., Bridgeport, CT; *U.S. Private*, pg. 889

Marsilius, Newman M., III, Pres. & Chief Exec. Officer--Producto Machine Co. Ring Division, Jamestown, NY; *U.S. Private*, pg. 889

Marsilius, Newman M., III, Pres. & Chief Exec. Officer--Moore Tool Company, Inc., Bridgeport, CT; *U.S. Private*, pg. 889

Marsinek, George E., Grp. Pres.--Lamb Electric Div., Kent, OH; *U.S. Public*, pg. 100

Marston, Theodore U., Dr., Pres. & Chief Exec. Officer--P and G Specialty Insurance Services, Newport Beach, CA; *U.S. Private*, pg. 354

Mart, Marcel, Pres.--Banque Generale du Luxembourg SA, Luxembourg, Luxembourg; *Int'l*, pg. 548

Martel, Bob, Pres. & Chief Exec. Officer--Cerdec Corporation, Washington, PA; *Int'l*, pg. 292

Martel, Curtis W., Pres. & Chief Exec. Officer--United Farm Tools, Inc., Glasgow, KY; *U.S. Private*, pg. 1122

Martello, Richard, Pres.--Rockwell Clutch Company, Troy, MI; *U.S. Public*, pg. 1096

Marten, Randolph L., Chm. Bd., Chief Oper. Officer & Pres.--Marten Transport, Ltd., Mondovi, WI; *U.S. Public*, pg. 1052

Martens, James A., Pres.--Peers & Co., New York, NY; *Int'l*, *pg. 816*

Martensson, Arne, Pres. & Chief Exec. Officer--Svenska Handelsbanken, Stockholm, Sweden; *Int'l*, pg. 1327

Marti, Wayne, Pres.--Ott Food Products, Carthage, MO; *U.S. Private*, pg. 821

Martimco, James, Grp. V.P.--Tecumseh Products Co. Engine & Transmission Group, Grafton, WI; *U.S. Public*, pg. 1566

Martin Bringas, Francisco Javier, Pres.--Tiendas de Descuento Sultana S.A. de C.V., Monterrey, Mexico; *Int'l*, pg. 1008

Martin-Lof, Sverker, Pres. & Chief Exec. Officer--Svenska Cellulosa Aktiebolaget (SCA), Stockholm, Sweden; *Int'l*, pg. 1326

Martin, Andrew P., Pres. & Chief Oper. Officer--Premium Budget Plan, Inc., Winston Salem, NC; *U.S. Public*, pg. 1453

Martin, Andrew P., Pres. & Chief Oper. Officer--The Innovative Company, Winston Salem, NC; *U.S. Public*, pg. 1454

Martin, Andrew P., Pres. & Chief Oper. Officer--Universal Insurance Co., Winston Salem, NC; *U.S. Public*, pg. 1454

Martin, B.J., Pres.--Prime Option Services, Sandy, UT; *U.S. Public*, pg. 1132

Martin, Bernard, Pres.--The Carpenter Group, San Francisco, CA; *U.S. Private*, pg. 215

Martin, Brian, Pres.--Refrigeration Supplies Distributors, Monterey Park, CA; *U.S. Private*, pg. 917

Martin, Frederick J., Pres. & Chief Exec. Officer--Dobbs International Services, Inc., Memphis, TN; *U.S. Public*, pg. 1718

Martin, Gary C., Pres.--Martin Sprocket & Gear, Inc., Arlington, TX; *U.S. Private*, pg. 709

Martin, Gerry L., Pres. & Chief Oper. Officer--Horizon Paper Co., Inc., New York, NY; *U.S. Private*, pg. 539

Martin, Harry, Pres.--Waycrosse Inc., Minneapolis, MN; *U.S. Private*, pg. 1155

Martin, J. Edward, Partner--AC Martin Partners, Los Angeles, CA; *U.S. Private*, pg. 708

Martin, J. Landis, Chm. Bd., Pres. & Chief Exec. Officer--Tremont Corporation, Denver, CO; *U.S. Private*, pg. 270

Martin, J. Landis, Pres. & Chief Exec. Officer--Titanium Metals Corporation, Denver, CO; *U.S. Private*, pg. 270

Martin, J.P., Gen. Mgr.--Engineered Fasteners Div., Massillon, OH; *U.S. Public*, pg. 557

Martin, James R., Pres.--Meadville Forging Co., Meadville, PA; *U.S. Private*, pg. 726

Martin, Jay, Pres.--National Safety Associates, Memphis, TN; *U.S. Private*, pg. 786

Martin, Jim, Pres. & Chief Exec. Officer--UPB of the Cumberlands, Cookeville, TN; *U.S. Public*, pg. 1669

Martin, Joshua W., III, Pres.--Bell Atlantic-DE, Wilmington, DE; *U.S. Public*, pg. 202

Martin, Ken, Chm. & Chief Exec. Officer--Sedgwick Noble Lowndes, Memphis, TN; *Int'l*, pg. 1218

Martin, Kenneth D., Pres.--Martin Door Mfg., Inc., Salt Lake City, UT; *U.S. Private*, pg. 708

Martin, Kenneth J., Pres.--Whitehall-Robins Healthcare, Madison, NJ; *U.S. Public*, pg. 80

Martin, L.C., Chm. Bd., Pres. & Chief Exec. Officer--Aztec Manufacturing Co., Crowley, TX; *U.S. Public*, pg. 159

Martin, Larry W., Chm. Bd. & Pres.--Data Dimensions, Inc., Culver City, CA; *U.S. Public*, pg. 485

Martin, Lewis N., Div. Pres.--Spang Power Control, Sandy Lake, PA; *U.S. Private*, pg. 1020

Martin, Lloyd, Pres.--Martin's Famous Pastry Shoppes, Chambersburg, PA; *U.S. Private*, pg. 710

Martin, Ralph, Pres.--Mattson Technology, Inc., Fremont, CA; *U.S. Public*, pg. 1060

Martin, Ralph J., Pres. & Chief Exec. Officer--Community Newspaper Holdings Inc., Lexington, KY; *U.S. Private*, pg. 259

Martin, Rex, Chm. Bd., Pres. & Chief Exec. Officer--NIBCO, Inc., Elkhart, IN; *U.S. Private*, pg. 798

Martin, Richard O., Pres. & Chief Exec. Officer--Physio-Control Corporation, Redmond, WA; *U.S. Public*, pg. 1294

Martin, Robert M., Pres. & Chief Exec. Officer--Deutsche Financial Services Corporation, Saint Louis, MO; *Int'l*, pg. 403

Martin, Rodney O., Pres. & Chief Exec. Officer--American General Life Insurance Company of New York, Syracuse, NY; *U.S. Public*, pg. 76

Martin, Ron, Gen. Mgr.--Lectrodryer Div., Ajax Magnethermic Corp., Richmond, KY; *Int'l*, pg. 113

Martin, Roy C., Jr., Pres.--Triangle Electric Company, Madison Heights, MI; *U.S. Private*, pg. 1102

Martin, Ruben S., III, Pres. & Chief Exec. Officer--Martin Gas Corporation, Kilgore, TX; *U.S. Private*, pg. 709

Martin, Scott, Pres.--Quality Chemicals, Inc., Tyrone, PA; *U.S. Public*, pg. 344

Martin, Scott, Pres.--Quality Chemicals, Inc., Dayton, OH; *U.S. Public*, pg. 345

Martin, Steve, Pres.--ServiceMaster Diversified Health Services, Inc., Memphis, TN; *U.S. Public*, pg. 1462

Martin, Theodore E., Pres. & Chief Exec. Officer--Barnes Group Inc., Bristol, CT; *U.S. Public*, pg. 189

Martin, Theodore E., Pres.--Barnes Group Aerospace Components, Windsor, CT; *U.S. Public*, pg. 190

Martin, Thomas W., Pres.--Pacific Valves, Long Beach, CA; *U.S. Public*, pg. 457

Martin, W.G., Pres.--Burgess Manning, Inc., Orchard Park, NY; *U.S. Private*, pg. 799

Martin, Wayne, Pres. & Chief Exec. Officer--Plains Co-op Oil Mill, Lubbock, TX; *U.S. Private*, pg. 868

Martineau, James, Pres. & Chief Exec. Officer--Viracon, Inc., Owatonna, MN; *U.S. Public*, pg. 120

Martinez Boudes, D. Diego, Pres.--Telefonica Investigacion Y Desarrollo, S.A. (Tidsa), Madrid, Spain; *Int'l*, pg. 1372

Martinez, Angel, Pres.--The Rockport Company, Marlborough, MA; *U.S. Public*, pg. 1370

Martinez, Claude, Pres.--Elida Faberge, Paris, France; *Int'l*, pg. 1437

Martinez, D. Francisco, Pres.--Servicios Teledistribucion, S.A. (St-Hilo), Madrid, Spain; *Int'l*, pg. 1371

Martinez, Frederico, Pres.--La Hacienda S.A. de C.V., Mexico, Mexico; *U.S. Public*, pg. 901

Martinez, Gene, Pres.--Avanti Press Inc., Miami, FL; *U.S. Private*, pg. 101

Martinez, H., Pres.--International Columbia Resources Corporation, Bogota, Colombia; *U.S. Public*, pg. 602

Martinez, Joaquin Marinez, Pres.--Binter Canarias, S.A., Las Palmas, Spain; *Int'l*, pg. 1224

Martinez, Julio, Chm. Bd. & Pres.--Chemtex International, Inc., New York, NY; *Int'l*, pg. 872

Martinez, Norma, Pres. & Chief Exec. Officer--Southwestern Bell Messaging Services, San Antonio, TX; *U.S. Public*, pg. 1416

Martinez, Tom, Pres.--Plateau Electric Construction Inc., Redmond, WA; *U.S. Public*, pg. 65

Martino, Mark A., Pres. & Chief Oper. Officer--Maaco Enterprises Inc., King of Prussia, PA; *U.S. Private*, pg. 689

Martino, Raymond, Pres.--Stanley Door Systems, Troy, MI; *U.S. Public*, pg. 1509

Martino, Raymond J., Pres. & Gen. Mgr.--Stanley Home Decor Div., New Britain, CT; *U.S. Public*, pg. 1509

Martins, Jose Carlos, Pres.--Acos Villares S.A., Sao Paulo, Brazil; *Int'l*, pg. 23

Martinstein, Eddy, Pres.--DirecTV Inc., El Segundo, CA; *U.S. Public*, pg. 720

Martling, Len, Pres.--The Weitz Company, Inc., Omaha, NE; *U.S. Private*, pg. 1161

Marto, Robert, Pres. & Chief Exec. Officer--White River Corporation, White Plains, NY; *U.S. Public*, pg. 1765

Martocci, James, Pres.--Special Program Management, Inc., Jersey City, NJ; *Int'l*, pg. 1504

Martorell, Fernando Abril, Pres.--Union Naval de Levante, S.A., Madrid, Spain; *Int'l*, pg. 1442

Martorell, Jaime, Pres.--Motorola Espana S.A., Madrid, Spain; *U.S. Public*, pg. 1139

Marttinen, Heikki, Chm. Bd., Pres. & Chief Exec. Officer--Imatran Voima Oy, Helsinki, Finland; *Int'l*, pg. 660

Martyny, Milton D., Pres.--U.S. Axle, Inc., Pottstown, PA; *U.S. Private*, pg. 1124

Martz, D. Stephen, Pres. & Chief Oper. Officer--Omega Financial Corporation, State College, PA; *U.S. Public*, pg. 1222

Martz, D. Stephen, Chm. Bd., Pres. & Chief Exec. Officer--Hollidaysburg Trust Company, Hollidaysburg, PA; *U.S. Public*, pg. 1222

Maruccilli, Stephen J., Pres.--First Hawaiian Leasing, Inc., Honolulu, HI; *U.S. Public*, pg. 635

Maruyama, Hiroshi, Pres.--ORIX Credit Corporation, Tokyo, Japan; *Int'l*, pg. 1008

Maruyama, M., Pres.--CBM America Corp., Fort Lee, NJ; *U.S. Private*, pg. 192

Maruyama, Takashi, Pres.--Otsuka Electronics Co., Ltd., Osaka, Japan; *Int'l*, pg. 1013

Marvin, John W., Pres. & Chief Oper. Officer--Marvin Lumber & Cedar Company, Warroad, MN; *U.S. Private*, pg. 710

Marwil, William, Pres.--Marwil Products Company, Fort Loramie, OH; *U.S. Public*, pg. 137

Marz, John F., Pres.--Dunn Reber Glenn Marz, Reno, NV; *U.S. Private*, pg. 347

Marz, John F., Pres.--Dunn Reber Glenn Marz/Las Vegas, Las Vegas, NV; *U.S. Private*, pg. 347

Mas, Jorge, Pres. & Chief Exec. Officer--MasTec, Inc., Miami, FL; *U.S. Public*, pg. 1055

Masatomo, Hiromu, Pres.--Sakata INX Corporation, Osaka, Japan; *Int'l*, pg. 1311

Mascali, Rosemary, Pres.--Quantum Plus, New York, NY; *U.S. Public*, pg. 1224

Mascia, Frank R., Chm., Pres. & Chief Exec. Officer--United HealthCare of North Carolina, Inc., Greensboro, NC; *U.S. Public*, pg. 1678

Masco, John R., Pres. & Chief Exec. Officer--First National Bank of Ohio, Akron, OH; *U.S. Public*, pg. 646

Masefield, C.B.G., Pres.--British Aerospace Regional Aircraft Limited, Middleton, United Kingdom; *Int'l*, pg. 218

Masefield, Charles B., Pres.--British Aerospace Regional Aircraft, Avro Intl. Aerospace Div., Woodford, United Kingdom; *Int'l*, pg. 218

Masefield, John, Chm. Bd., Pres. & Chief Exec. Officer--Isomedix Inc., Whippany, NJ; *U.S. Public*, pg. 1515

Masek, Joseph P., Pres.--Masek Distributing Inc., Gering, NE; *U.S. Private*, pg. 711

Masek, Timothy A., Pres.--Bostrom Seating, Inc., Piedmont, AL; *U.S. Public*, pg. 933

Mash, Patricia A., Pres.--Mileage Plus Marketing, Inc., Elk Grove Village, IL; *U.S. Public*, pg. 1653

Mashall, Stephen, Pres.--Meggitt Avionics Inc., Manchester, NH; *Int'l*, pg. 853

Mashburn, Harry L., Pres. & Treas.--Mashburn Construction Company, Columbia, SC; *U.S. Private*, pg. 711

Masiero, Ronald J., Pres.--Gerber Life Insurance Co., White Plains, NY; *Int'l*, pg. 973

Maslow, Lester, Chm. Bd. & Pres.--Best Manufacturing, Inc., New York, NY; *U.S. Private*, pg. 139

Mason, David D. S., Pres., Chief Exec. & Chief Fin. Officer & Treas.--Toms Sierra Company, Ione, CA; *U.S. Private*, pg. 1090

Mason, Douglas L., Pres. & Chief Exec. Officer--Clearly Canadian Beverage Corp., Vancouver, Canada; *Int'l*, pg. 297

Mason, James F., Pres.--Wagner Castings Company, Decatur, IL; *U.S. Public*, pg. 894

Mason, James L., Pres. & Chief Exec. Officer--Wampler Foods, Timberville, VA; *U.S. Public*, pg. 1727

Mason, Kenneth H., Pres.--Integra Resort Management, Inc., Dallas, TX; *U.S. Public*, pg. 778

Mason, Kenneth H., Pres.--Condo, Hotel & Resort Management, Dallas, TX; *U.S. Public*, pg. 778

Mason, L. Mike, Pres. & Chief Exec. Officer--Telsco Industries, Garland, TX; *U.S. Private*, pg. 1074

Mason, Peter I., Pres. & Chief Exec. Officer--May & Speh, Inc., Downers Grove, IL; *U.S. Public*, pg. 1063

Mason, Raymond A., Chm. Bd., Pres. & Chief Exec. Officer--Legg Mason, Inc., Baltimore, MD; *U.S. Public*, pg. 984
Mason, Ronald V., Pres.--Federal Cartridge Co., Anoka, MN; *U.S. Public*, pg. 239
Mason, Scott P., Pres. & Chief Exec. Officer--Investment Technology Group, Inc., New York, NY; *U.S. Public*, pg. 924
Mason, Thomas R., Pres. & Chief Oper. Officer--CalEnergy Co., Omaha, NE; *U.S. Public*, pg. 292
Mason, Tom, Pres. & Chief Exec. Officer--Schwinn Holdings, Boulder, CO; *U.S. Private*, pg. 975
Masotti, David, Pres.--Spar Space Systems, Brampton, Canada; *Int'l*, pg. 1288
Massa, Joseph, Pres. & Gen. Mgr.--House of Bianchi, Inc., Medford, MA; *U.S. Private*, pg. 541
Massa, Ronald E., Pres.--A.O. Smith Water Products Company, Irving, TX; *U.S. Public*, pg. 1477
Massarasky, Steven J., Pres. & Publr.--Acclaim Comics, New York, NY; *U.S. Public*, pg. 15
Massaro, Anthony A., Chm. Bd., Pres. & Chief Exec. Officer--The Lincoln Electric Company, Cleveland, OH; *U.S. Public*, pg. 996
Massaro, Carl, Pres.--Ajax Manufacturing Company, Inc., Hillsborough, NJ; *U.S. Private*, pg. 1030
Massaro, Karl, Pres.--Standard Automotive Corporation, Hillsborough, NJ; *U.S. Private*, pg. 1030
Massengale, Jim E., Pres.--West Coast Life Insurance Co., San Francisco, CA; *U.S. Public*, pg. 1336
Masseu, Jeff, Chm. Bd., Pres. & Chief Exec. Officer--United Design Corporation, Noble, OK; *U.S. Private*, pg. 1121
Massey, Donald E., Pres. & Chief Exec. Officer--Don Massey Cadillac Inc., Plymouth, MI; *U.S. Private*, pg. 712
Massey, John, Pres.--Hilb, Rogal & Hamilton Company of Amarillo, Amarillo, TX; *U.S. Public*, pg. 827
Massey, Stewart R., Pres. & Chief Exec. Officer--Robert Fleming, Inc., New York, NY; *Int'l*, pg. 493
Massey, William J., III, Pres.--Neumaticos Goodyear SA, Buenos Aires, Argentina; *U.S. Public*, pg. 753
Massicotte, Paul, Pres.--Cooperative Federee de Quebec, Montreal, Canada; *Int'l*, pg. 330
Massing, Gunnar, Pres.--Nordiska Kompaniet (NK) AB, Stockholm, Sweden; *Int'l*, pg. 899
Massman, Henry J., IV, Pres.--Massman Construction Company, Kansas City, MO; *U.S. Private*, pg. 713
Masson, H., Pres.--SBS Gestion S.A., Paris, France; *Int'l*, pg. 1331
Mastandrea, James C., Chm. Bd., Pres. & Chief Exec. Officer--First Union Real Estate Investments, Cleveland, OH; *U.S. Public*, pg. 640
Masters, Derek, Pres.--Asia Pacific Division, Frenchs Forest, Australia; *U.S. Public*, pg. 1516
Masters, Larry W., Pres.--South Florida Test Service, Miami, FL; *U.S. Private*, pg. 96
Masters, Melvin L., Chm. Bd., Pres. & Chief Exec. Officer--LaserMaster Technologies, Inc., Eden Prairie, MN; *U.S. Public*, pg. 979
Masterson, Michael M., Pres.--Midland National Life Insurance Co., Sioux Falls, SD; *U.S. Private*, pg. 963
Masterson, Patrick F., Pres.--Topflight Corp., York, PA; *U.S. Private*, pg. 1091
Mastroianni, Martin J., Pres. & Chief Oper. Officer--Mechanical Technology Inc., Latham, NY; *U.S. Public*, pg. 1077
Masuda, Kazuyuki, Pres. Dir.--P.T. Bumi Daya-IBJ Leasing, Jakarta, Indonesia; *Int'l*, pg. 676
Masuda, Kunitoshi, Pres.--ORIX Alpha Corporation, Tokyo, Japan; *Int'l*, pg. 1008
Masuda, Nobuyuki, Pres.--Mitsubishi Heavy Industries Ltd., Tokyo, Japan; *Int'l*, pg. 873
Masuno, Hiroyasu, Pres.--P.T. Multicor Securities, Jakarta, Indonesia; *Int'l*, pg. 817
Matchett, Chris, Pres.--Hutchinson Wil-Rich Manufacturing Co., Dallas, TX; *U.S. Private*, pg. 1063
Mateer, Mike, Pres.--Mount Vernon Neon, Mount Vernon, IL; *U.S. Private*, pg. 386
Mathews, Cannon, Pres.--Rogerson Kratos, Pasadena, CA; *U.S. Private*, pg. 940
Mathewson, John, Pres. & Chief Exec. Officer--AGA Catalog Marketing & Design, New York, NY; *U.S. Private*, pg. 5
Mathewson, John, Pres.--AGA Catalog Marketing & Design, New York, NY; *U.S. Private*, pg. 295
Mathias, James P., Pres. & Chief Oper. Officer--The JPM Company, Lewisburg, PA; *U.S. Public*, pg. 919
Mathot, Jean-Claude, Pres. & Chief Oper. Officer--BFX Hospitality Group, Inc., Fort Worth, TX; *U.S. Public*, pg. 160
Mathur, Pracheesh, Pres.--Aerospace Operations Asia Pacific, Singapore, Singapore; *Int'l*, pg. 1337
Matlock, Dave, Pres.--Continental Homes of San Antonio, L.P., San Antonio, TX; *U.S. Public*, pg. 441
Matney, R.C., Chm. Bd., Pres. & Chief Exec. Officer--Mark VII, Inc., Memphis, TN; *U.S. Public*, pg. 1046
Matoba, Takemasa, Pres.--Nanto DC Card Co., Ltd., Nara, Japan; *Int'l*, pg. 905
Matons, J., Pres.--Amersham Corporation (Amersham QSA), Arlington Heights, IL; *Int'l*, pg. 992
Matorell, Fernando Abril, Pres.--Union Naval De Levante, S.A. (Madrid), Valencia, Spain; *Int'l*, pg. 1442
Matricaria, Ronald A., Chm. Bd., Pres. & Chief Exec. Officer--St. Jude Medical, Inc., Saint Paul, MN; *U.S. Public*, pg. 1427
Matsuba, Kiyoshi, Pres.--Daiwa Singapore Limited, Singapore, Singapore; *Int'l*, pg. 376
Matsuda, Masatake, Pres.--East Japan Railway Company, Tokyo, Japan; *Int'l*, pg. 431
Matsue, Shigeki, Pres. & Chief Exec. Officer--NEC Electronics Inc., Santa Clara, CA; *Int'l*, pg. 900
Matsueda, Masahiko, Pres.--Nisshin Steel USA, Inc., New York, NY; *Int'l*, pg. 946
Matsumoto, Noboru, Pres.--Kobelco Stewart Bolling, Inc., Hudson, OH; *Int'l*, pg. 740
Matsumoto, Y., Pres.--P.T. Ebara Prima Indonesia, Serang, Indonesia; *Int'l*, pg. 432
Matsunaga, Jiro, Pres.--Rohm Mechatech Philippines, Inc., Cavite, Philippines; *Int'l*, pg. 1125
Matsuno, John, Pres.--U.N.A. Corporation, Elk Grove Village, IL; *Int'l*, pg. 1001
Matsuo, Hiroto, Pres.--Kuraray Co., Ltd., Osaka, Japan; *Int'l*, pg. 764
Matsuo, Y., Pres.--Silmax, Inc., Albuquerque, NM; *Int'l*, pg. 1317
Matsuoka, Iwao, Pres.--Laura Ashley Japan Co., Ltd., Tokyo, Japan; *Int'l*, pg. 28
Matsushita, Toshiharu, Pres.--PT Katsushiro Indonesia, Bekasi, Indonesia; *Int'l*, pg. 745
Matsuzaki, Toshiyuki, Pres.--P.T. Mesin Isuzu Indonesia, Tangerang, Indonesia; *Int'l*, pg. 693
Matsuzaki, Toshiyuki, Pres.--P.T. Mesin Isuzu Indonesia, Tangerang, Indonesia; *U.S. Public*, pg. 724
Matsuzawa, H., Pres.--Kasei Verbatim Corporation, Odawara, Japan; *U.S. Public*, pg. 552
Matsuzawa, Katsumi, Pres.--Sakura Trust Company, New York, NY; *Int'l*, pg. 1179
Matsuzawa, Katsumi, Pres.--Sakura Securities, New York, NY; *Int'l*, pg. 1179
Matsuzawa, Mitsuo, Pres.--INX Corporation, Elk Grove Village, IL; *Int'l*, pg. 1311
Matt, Nicholas O., Pres. & Treas.--The F.X. Matt Brewing Co., Utica, NY; *U.S. Private*, pg. 714
Matteson, Hollis, Pres.--Burns & Roe Construction Group Inc., Oradell, NJ; *U.S. Private*, pg. 187
Mattews, James F., Pres.--Lear Siegler Diversified Holdings Corp., Summit, NJ; *U.S. Private*, pg. 655
Matthaei, William L., Pres. & Chief Exec. Officer--Roman Meal Company, Tacoma, WA; *U.S. Private*, pg. 942
Matthews, Clark J. II, Pres., Chief Exec. Officer & Sec.--The Southland Corporation, Dallas, TX; *Int'l*, pg. 693
Matthews, Craig G., Pres. & Chief Oper. Officer--Brooklyn Union, Brooklyn, NY; *U.S. Public*, pg. 259
Matthews, Gary, Pres. & Chief Exec. Officer--Guinness Import Company, Stamford, CT; *Int'l*, pg. 412
Matthews, J., Pres.--Dundridge College Limited, Totnes, United Kingdom; *Int'l*, pg. 544
Matthews, Jack, Pres. & Chief Exec. Officer--Environetx, Itasca, IL; *U.S. Private*, pg. 378
Matthews, Leo L., Pres. & Chief Oper. Officer--Allied Construction Products, Inc., Cleveland, OH; *U.S. Public*, pg. 1339
Matthews, Robert, Pres.--Red Kap Industries, Nashville, TN; *U.S. Public*, pg. 1702
Matthews, Scott, Pres.--American Nutrition, Inc., Ogden, UT; *U.S. Private*, pg. 60
Matthewson, Edwin, Pres. & Chief Exec. Officer--Pullman Industries, Inc., Pullman, MI; *U.S. Private*, pg. 894
Matthias, Donald, Pres.--Little Falls Color Print, Little Falls, NY; *U.S. Private*, pg. 1050
Matthys, Paul, Vice Chm., Pres. & Mng. Dir.--Sidmar N.V., Gent, Belgium; *Int'l*, pg. 79
Mattia, Arthur, Chm. Bd. & Pres.--Action Manufacturing Co., Philadelphia, PA; *U.S. Private*, pg. 15
Mattie, Richard J., Pres.--A-G Safety Sales, Inc., Baton Rouge, LA; *U.S. Public*, pg. 1650
Mattingly, John, Pres.--COMSAT World Systems, Bethesda, MD; *U.S. Public*, pg. 424
Mattingly, Thomas J., Pres. & Chief Exec. Officer--Metro Foods, Inc., Olive Branch, MS; *U.S. Private*, pg. 736
Mattis, David S., Pres. & Chief Exec. Officer--Ausco Products, Inc., Benton Harbor, MI; *U.S. Private*, pg. 299
Mattly, James, Pres.--Loomis-Fargo & Co., Houston, TX; *U.S. Public*, pg. 245
Mattola, Guy A., Pres.--Ikon Office Solutions-Pittsburgh, Pittsburgh, PA; *U.S. Public*, pg. 864
Mattson, Bradford C., Pres.--Bay Mills (Delaware), Inc., Wilmington, DE; *Int'l*, pg. 1170
Mattson, Bradford C., Pres.--Perma Glas-Mesh, Inc., Dover, OH; *Int'l*, pg. 1171
Mattson, Bradford C., Pres. & Chief Oper. Officer--Vetrotex CertainTeed Corporation, Wichita Falls, TX; *Int'l*, pg. 1171
Mattsson, Bjorn, Pres. & Chief Exec. Officer--Cultor Ltd., Helsinki, Finland; *Int'l*, pg. 349
Matuja, Robert D., Pres.--Groesbeck Lumber & Supply, Inc., Warren, MI; *U.S. Private*, pg. 483
Matveld, H. Edward, Pres. & Chief Exec. Officer--Alpha Therapeutic Corp., Los Angeles, CA; *Int'l*, pg. 558
Matyjek, Adam, Pres.--Chr. Hansen Poland Sp. z.o.o., Warsaw, Poland; *Int'l*, pg. 289
Matz, Monte, Pres.--Progress West Corporation, Omaha, NE; *U.S. Private*, pg. 890
Matz, Robert, Pres.--Trahan, Burden & Charles, Inc., Baltimore, MD; *U.S. Private*, pg. 1095
Matz, Roland, Pres.--Saba Trading AB, Arsta, Sweden; *Int'l*, pg. 709
Matz, V., Pres.--Kirk & Matz Ltd., Danbury, CT; *U.S. Private*, pg. 623
Maubert, Philippe, Pres. & Dir.--Robertet S.A., Grasse, France; *Int'l*, pg. 1119
Maughan, Rex, Chm. Bd., Pres. & Chief Exec. Officer--Forever Living Products International, Inc., Scottsdale, AZ; *U.S. Private*, pg. 418
Maught, Adrien, Jr., Pres.--Datametrics Corporation, Calabasas, CA; *U.S. Public*, pg. 487
Maul, Peter, Pres.--Nanocor, Inc., Arlington Heights, IL; *U.S. Public*, pg. 64
Mauldin, Earle, Pres. & Chief Exec. Officer--BellSouth Enterprises, Inc., Atlanta, GA; *U.S. Public*, pg. 208
Mauldin, Larry D., Chm., Pres. & Chief Exec. Officer--SunTrust Bank, East Tennessee, N.A., Knoxville, TN; *U.S. Public*, pg. 1538
Maunder, Andrew, Pres. & Chief Exec. Officer--Axiom Inc., Moorestown, NJ; *U.S. Public*, pg. 157
Mauney, William K., III, Pres.--Mauney Hosiery Mills, Inc., Kings Mountain, NC; *U.S. Private*, pg. 715
Maupay, Walter R., Jr., Pres.--Calgon Vestal Laboratories, Saint Louis, MO; *U.S. Public*, pg. 1515
Maurer, Don, Pres. & Chief Exec. Officer--McKinney & Silver, Raleigh, NC; *U.S. Private*, pg. 723
Maurer, Jeffrey, Pres. & Chief Oper. Officer--U.S. Trust Corporation, New York, NY; *U.S. Public*, pg. 1688
Maurer, Kurt, Pres.--Knurr-Heinzinger Electronic GmbH, Rosenheim, Germany; *Int'l*, pg. 739
Maurer, Terrence, V.P. & Gen. Mgr.--Stroehmann Bakeries, Harrisburg, PA; *Int'l*, pg. 1495
Maurer, Theodore A., Pres. & Chief Oper. Officer--CommonHealth USA, Parsippany, NJ; *Int'l*, pg. 1483
Maurerer, Antone, Pres.--Karl Kauerman Nassauische Sparkasse, Wiesbaden, Germany; *Int'l*, pg. 724
Maurey, Joseph E., Chm. Bd. & Pres.--Maurey Manufacturing Corp., Chicago, IL; *U.S. Private*, pg. 715
Mauritz, F., Pres. & Gen. Mgr.--Bank Mendes Gans NV, Amsterdam, Netherlands; *Int'l*, pg. 647
Mauro, Thomas, Pres.--Homestead House Inc., Westminster, CO; *U.S. Private*, pg. 537
Maus, Manfred, Pres. & Chief Exec. Officer--OBI Bau-und Heimwerkermaerkte GmbH & Co. KG, Wermelskirchen, Germany; *Int'l*, pg. 993
Maussner, Richard A., Pres.--Rama Group of Companies, Cheektowaga, NY; *U.S. Private*, pg. 908
Mautz, Bernhard F., Jr., Chm. Bd. & Pres.--Mautz Paint Co., Madison, WI; *U.S. Private*, pg. 715
Mauzey, James J., Pres.--Bristol-Myers Squibb Pharmaceutical Division, Evansville, IN; *U.S. Public*, pg. 254
Mavel, James C., Chm. Bd., Pres. & Chief Exec. Officer--Scan-Optics, Inc., Manchester, CT; *U.S. Public*, pg. 1436
Mavrikis, Costas, Dir.-Germany--Olympic Airways, New York, NY; *Int'l*, pg. 1004
Max, Yves, Pres.--Credit Foncier de Monaco, Monaco, Monaco; *Int'l*, pg. 314
Maxheim, John H., Chm. Bd., Pres. & Chief Exec. Officer--Piedmont Natural Gas Co., Inc., Charlotte, NC; *U.S. Public*, pg. 1295
Maxheim, John H., Pres.--Piedmont Energy Company, Charlotte, NC; *U.S. Public*, pg. 1295
Maxheim, John H., Pres.--Piedmont Intrastate Pipeline Company, Charlotte, NC; *U.S. Public*, pg. 1295
Maxheim, John H., Pres.--Piedmont Interstate Pipeline Company, Charlotte, NC; *U.S. Public*, pg. 1295
Maxwell, Carlyle, Jr., Pres.--SMI-Owen Steel Company, Columbia, SC; *U.S. Public*, pg. 413
Maxwell, H.G., III, Pres.--Goldsboro Milling Company, Goldsboro, NC; *U.S. Private*, pg. 462
Maxwell, James, Partner & Chief Exec. Officer-Scope Ketchum--Scope Ketchum Communications Ltd., London, United Kingdom; *U.S. Private*, pg. 617
Maxwell, R.L., Pres. & Chief Exec. Officer--The Lathrop Company, Toledo, OH; *U.S. Public*, pg. 1645
Maxwell, Robert O., Pres. & Chief Exec. Officer--Security American Financial Enterprises, Inc., Minnetonka, MN; *U.S. Private*, pg. 980
Maxwell, Robert O., Pres.--Security Life Insurance Company of America, Minnetonka, MN; *U.S. Private*, pg. 980
Maxwell, Robert O., Pres.--Congress Life Insurance Company, Minnetonka, MN; *U.S. Private*, pg. 980
May, Andrew, Pres. & Chief Exec. Officer--Paradyne, Largo, FL; *U.S. Private*, pg. 838
May, Jim, Pres.--Heatec, Inc., Chattanooga, TN; *U.S. Public*, pg. 141
May, John, Pres.--Kent Feeds Inc., Muscatine, IA; *U.S. Private*, pg. 1134
May, Peter W., Pres. & Chief Oper. Officer--Triarc Companies, Inc., New York, NY; *U.S. Public*, pg. 1634
May, T. Michael, Pres. & Chief Exec. Officer--Hawaiian Electric Company, Inc., Honolulu, HI; *U.S. Public*, pg. 800
May, Thomas J., Chm. Bd., Pres. & Chief Exec. Officer--Boston Edison Company, Boston, MA; *U.S. Public*, pg. 247
May, Thomas O., Pres.--Weil-McLain, Michigan City, IN; *U.S. Public*, pg. 1676
May, Van, Pres. & Chief Exec. Officer--Plains Cotton Co-op Association, Lubbock, TX; *U.S. Private*, pg. 868
Mayben, William R., Pres. & Chief Exec. Officer--Nebraska Public Power District, Columbus, NE; *U.S. Private*, pg. 789
Mayberry, John T., Pres. & Chief Exec. Officer--DoFasco, Inc., Hamilton, Canada; *Int'l*, pg. 414
Maydan, Dan, Dr., Pres.--Applied Materials, Inc., Santa Clara, CA; *U.S. Public*, pg. 123
Mayell, Michael J., Pres. & Chief Oper. Officer--The Meridian Resource Corporation, Houston, TX; *U.S. Public*, pg. 1095
Mayer, Cyrus, Chm. Bd & Pres.--Mayer/Berkshire Corporation, Wayne, NJ; *U.S. Private*, pg. 717
Mayer, Girard H., Pres. & Chief Exec. Officer--Benefit Plans Administrative Services, Inc., Utica, NY; *U.S. Public*, pg. 416
Mayer, Len, Pres.--Mayer & Schweitzer, Inc., Jersey City, NJ; *U.S. Public*, pg. 1443
Mayer, Robert H., Pres. & Chief Exec Officer--Danisco Ingredients USA, Inc., New Century, KS; *Int'l*, pg. 378
Mayer, Robert L., Pres.--Cole Hersee Company, Boston, MA; *U.S. Private*, pg. 251
Mayhall, David, Pres.--Tri-State Armature & Electric Works, Memphis, TN; *U.S. Private*, pg. 1100
Mayhew, Adelaide K., Pres.--Prism-Dae, Inc., Mc Lean, VA; *U.S. Public*, pg. 110
Maynard, James H., Chm. Bd., Pres., Chief Exec. Officer & Treas.--Investors Management Corp., Raleigh, NC; *U.S. Private*, pg. 574
Maynard, Otto, Pres. & Chief Exec. Officer--Wolf Creek Nuclear Operating Corp., Burlington, KS; *U.S. Public*, pg. 1759
Maynard, Philip C., Pres. & Sec.--ICS Intangibles Holding Company, Irvine, CA; *U.S. Public*, pg. 783
Maynard, Robert E., Pres. & Chief Exec. Officer--Allianz Canada, Toronto, Canada; *Int'l*, pg. 59
Mayne, Robert, Pres.--Holy Cross Electric Association, Inc., Glenwood Springs, CO; *U.S. Private*, pg. 536
Maynell, Colin, Mng. Dir.--Arena Lighting Ltd., West Bromwich, United Kingdom; *Int'l*, pg. 80

Mayo, Larry S., Pres.--Ikon Office Solutions New York, New York, NY; *U.S. Public,* pg. 863
Mayoral, Carmelo, Pres.--Repsol Distribucion, S.A., Madrid, Spain; *Int'l,* pg. 1104
Mays, William, Pres.--Mays Chemical Company, Indianapolis, IN; *U.S. Private,* pg. 718
Maza, Xavier Autrey, Chm. Bd. & Pres.--Altos Hornos de Mexico, S.A., Monclova, Mexico; *Int'l,* pg. 66
Maziarka, Donald, Pres., Chief Exec. & Chief Oper. Officer--George Sollitt Construction, Wood Dale, IL; *U.S. Private,* pg. 1013
Mazur, Jack M., Pres. & Chief Exec. Officer--PHP Healthcare Corporation, Reston, VA; *U.S. Public,* pg. 1241
Mazza, Giorgio, Pres.--Standex International S.r.L., Gorgonzola, Italy; *U.S. Public,* pg. 1507
Mazza, Giorgio, Pres.--Standex International S.r.L. (Procon Division), Gorgonzola, Italy; *U.S. Public,* pg. 1508
Mazza, Giorgio, Pres.--Standex International S.r.L. (Mold-Tech Division), Gorgonzola, Italy; *U.S. Public,* pg. 1508
Mazzantini, Mr., Pres.--Pirelli U.K. Tyres Limited, Burton on Trent, United Kingdom; *Int'l,* pg. 1059
Mazzella, David G., Pres. & Chief Exec. Officer--Moscom Corporation, Pittsford, NY; *U.S. Public,* pg. 1136
Mazzotta, Dorothy, Pres. & Chief Exec. Officer--Friendly Holidays Inc., Lake Success, NY; *U.S. Private,* pg. 428
McAdam, John, Pres. & Chief Oper. Officer--Sequent Computer Systems, Inc., Beaverton, OR; *U.S. Public,* pg. 1459
McAfee, Dwayne L., Pres. & Chief Exec. Officer--First Image Management Co., Atlanta, GA; *U.S. Public,* pg. 631
McAfee, Robert, Pres. & Chief Exec. Officer--Lincoln Foodservice Products, Inc., Fort Wayne, IN; *Int'l,* pg. 188
McAlaine, Robert, Pres.--Namico, Inc., Philadelphia, PA; *U.S. Private,* pg. 773
McAliley, Kevin, Pres. & Chief Exec. Officer--Films for the Humanities & Sciences, Inc., Monmouth Junction, NJ; *U.S. Public,* pg. 1327
McAllen, David D., Pres.--Geupel DeMars, Inc., Indianapolis, IN; *U.S. Private,* pg. 449
McAllister, Dan, Pres. & Chief Exec. Officer--Kilovac Corporation, Carpinteria, CA; *U.S. Private,* pg. 259
McAllister, Larry N., Pres.--Metal Masters Foodservice Equipment, Clayton, DE; *U.S. Private,* pg. 734
McAlpine, Ross, Pres.--Inter-Tel Leasing, Inc., Phoenix, AZ; *U.S. Public,* pg. 888
McAlpine, Ross E., Pres.--Inter-Tel Net Solutions, Phoenix, AZ; *U.S. Public,* pg. 888
McAndrew, Mark S., Pres.--Globe Life And Accident Insurance Co., Oklahoma City, OK; *U.S. Public,* pg. 1622
McAndrews, J.J., Pres. & Chief Exec. Officer--Mona Industries, Inc., Paterson, NJ; *U.S. Private,* pg. 756
McArthur, J.C., Pres. & Chief Exec. Officer--Hartford Insurance Group of Canada, Willowdale, Canada; *U.S. Public,* pg. 794
McAtee, James C., Pres.--Electric Power Equipment Co., Columbus, OH; *U.S. Private,* pg. 368
McAulay, Jeffrey J., Chm. Bd. & Pres.--Moran Insurance Company Limited, Greenwich, CT; *U.S. Private,* pg. 760
McAuley, Thomas H., Pres. & Chief Exec. Officer--IRT Property Company, Atlanta, GA; *U.S. Public,* pg. 858
McAuliff, Timothy M., Pres. & Chief Exec. Officer--Blair Television, New York, NY; *U.S. Private,* pg. 148
McAuliffe, John, Chm. Bd. & Pres.--Compendium Systems Corporation, Greenwich, CT; *U.S. Private,* pg. 259
McBeth, Robert D., Chm. Bd., Pres. & Chief Exec. Officer--Associated Industrial Supply, Inc., Columbia, SC; *U.S. Private,* pg. 91
McBride, T. Eugene, Chm. Bd., Pres. & Chief Exec. Officer--Dyersburg Corporation, Dyersburg, TN; *U.S. Public,* pg. 538
McBride, T. Eugene, Pres. & Chief Exec. Officer--Dyersburg Fabric, Dyersburg, TN; *U.S. Public,* pg. 538
McBride, Teresa N., Pres. & Chief Exec. Officer--McBride and Associates, Inc., Albuquerque, NM; *U.S. Private,* pg. 719
McCabe, Robert A., Jr., Vice Chm. & Pres.-First American Enterprises--First American Corporation, Nashville, TN; *U.S. Public,* pg. 624
McCabe, Robert L., Pres. & Chief Exec. Officer--Narragansett Energy Resources Company, Providence, RI; *U.S. Public,* pg. 1171
McCabe, Roger, Pres.--All Pro Bumper to Bumper Inc., Florence, KY; *U.S. Private,* pg. 35
McCafferty, George, Pres.--Holmes Protection of Philadelphia, Inc., Philadelphia, PA; *U.S. Public,* pg. 1649
McCafferty, Michael, Pres. & Chief Exec. Officer--TTC Illinois Inc., Kankakee, IL; *U.S. Private,* pg. 1066
McCaffray, S.J., Chm. Bd. & Pres.--National Frozen Foods Corp., Seattle, WA; *U.S. Private,* pg. 783
McCaffrey, Gary, Pres.--National Service Cleaning Corporation, South Windsor, CT; *U.S. Public,* pg. 1208
McCague, Beth, Chm. Bd., Pres. & Chief Exec. Officer--First Union National Bank of Tennessee, Nashville, TN; *U.S. Public,* pg. 640
McCaig, Jeffrey J., Pres. & Chief Exec. Officer--Trimac Corporation, Calgary, Canada; *Int'l,* pg. 1423
McCaleb, Draydean, Pres.--The Florists Assn. of Greater Cleveland, Inc., Cleveland, OH; *U.S. Private,* pg. 415
McCall, John, Gen. Mgr.--Frank Paxton Lumber Company, Denver, CO; *U.S. Private,* pg. 585
McCall, R.H., Pres.--McCall Properties, Inc., Portland, OR; *U.S. Private,* pg. 719
McCall, R.H., Pres.--GWC Properties, Inc., Portland, OR; *U.S. Private,* pg. 719
McCall, R.H., Pres. & Chief Exec. Officer--McCall Oil Real Estate Corporation, Portland, OR; *U.S. Private,* pg. 719
McCall, Robert H., Chm. Bd., Pres. & Chief Exec. Officer--McCall Oil & Chemical Corp., Portland, OR; *U.S. Private,* pg. 719
McCall, Thomas, Partner & Mngmt. Supvr.--Eric Mower & Associates, Atlanta, GA; *U.S. Private,* pg. 765
McCall, Tom, Partner & Mngmt. Supvr.--Eric Mower and Associates, Rochester, NY; *U.S. Private,* pg. 765
McCallin, Daniel J., Pres.--Steel, Inc., Commerce City, CO; *U.S. Private,* pg. 1037
McCallum, Craig L., Pres. & Chief Exec. Officer--Mission Viejo Company, Mission Viejo, CA; *U.S. Public,* pg. 1289
McCallum, Dan, Pres.--Woodward & Dickerson, Portland, OR; *U.S. Private,* pg. 1188
McCallum, Elkin, Pres. & Chief Exec. Officer--Joan Fabrics Corp., Tyngsboro, MA; *U.S. Private,* pg. 588
McCallum, John D., Pres.--Potomac Capital Investment Corporation, Washington, DC; *U.S. Public,* pg. 1319
McCamy, Charles, Pres.--Burke Mills, Inc., Valdese, NC; *U.S. Public,* pg. 267
McCann, Bill, Pres.--Choctaw Electric Co-Op, Hugo, OK; *U.S. Private,* pg. 238
McCann, Dave, Pres.--Toronto Dominion Securities (U.S.A.) Inc., New York, NY; *Int'l,* pg. 1401
McCann, James, Pres.--800-FLOWERS, Inc., Westbury, NY; *U.S. Private,* pg. 366
McCann, John P., Pres. & Chief Exec. Officer--United Dominion Realty Trust, Inc., Richmond, VA; *U.S. Public,* pg. 1677
McCann, L.D., Chm. Bd., Pres. & Chief Exec. Officer--Standco Industries, Inc., Houston, TX; *U.S. Private,* pg. 1032
McCanna, William, Pres.--Meadowcraft, Inc., Birmingham, AL; *U.S. Private,* pg. 725
McCarles, Angus, Pres.-Natl. Sls.--Ralston Purina Canada Inc., Mississauga, Canada; *U.S. Public,* pg. 1360
McCarley, Thomas D., Pres.--CommLink, Houston, TX; *U.S. Public,* pg. 809
McCarron, T. Robert, Pres.--Insurance Management Incorporated, New Haven, CT; *U.S. Public,* pg. 827
McCartan, Patrick F., Mng. Partner--Jones, Day, Reavis & Pogue, Cleveland, OH; *U.S. Private,* pg. 596
McCarten, William, Pres. & Chief Exec. Officer--Host Marriott Services Corporation, Bethesda, MD; *U.S. Public,* pg. 841
McCarter, James P., Pres.--Ikon Office Solutions-Atlanta, Norcross, GA; *U.S. Public,* pg. 863
McCarter, William J., Pres. & Chief Exec. Officer--WTTW (Channel 11), Chicago, IL; *U.S. Private,* pg. 1145
McCarthy, C. James, Pres.--Reily Foods Company, New Orleans, LA; *U.S. Private,* pg. 919
McCarthy, Daniel J., Pres. & Chief Exec. Officer--American Crystal Sugar Company, Moorhead, MN; *U.S. Private,* pg. 52
McCarthy, Denis, Pres.-Fidelity Trust--Fidelity Investments (FMR Corp.), Boston, MA; *U.S. Private,* pg. 402
McCarthy, Dennis, Pres.--Joern's Sunrise Medical, Stevens Point, WI; *U.S. Public,* pg. 1536
McCarthy, Jack, Pres.--Kamax-G.B. DuPont L.P., Troy, MI; *U.S. Private,* pg. 606
McCarthy, James E., Pres.--Woodward-Clyde Federal Services, Denver, CO; *U.S. Public,* pg. 1657
McCarthy, James R., Pres.--The Buschman Co., Cincinnati, OH; *U.S. Private,* pg. 188
McCarthy, Kevin P., Pres.--UNUM Japan Accident Insurance Company Limited, Tokyo, Japan; *U.S. Public,* pg. 1700
McCarthy, Tim, Pres.--Avon Workshop Ficks Reed, Cincinnati, OH; *U.S. Private,* pg. 102
McCartney, William G., Pres. & Chief Exec. Officer--TSC Shannock Corporation, Burnaby, Canada; *Int'l,* pg. 1343
McCarty, D.L., Pres.--Aquionics Inc., Erlanger, KY; *Int'l,* pg. 590
McCaskey, Raymond F., Pres. & Chief Exec. Officer--Blue Cross & Blue Shield of Illinois, Chicago, IL; *U.S. Private,* pg. 151
McCaul, Daniel, Pres.--Callaway Chemical Company, Columbus, GA; *U.S. Public,* pg. 1726
McCauley, Arthur, Chm. Bd. & Pres.--Norwalk Co., Inc., Norwalk, CT; *U.S. Private,* pg. 807
McCauley, Robert, Pres.--Devoe Paint, Cleveland, OH; *Int'l,* pg. 663
McCausland, Peter, Chm. Bd., Pres. & Chief Exec. Officer--Airgas, Inc., Radnor, PA; *U.S. Public,* pg. 33
McCausland, Thomas, Pres. & Chief Exec. Officer--Siemens Medical Systems, Inc., Iselin, NJ; *Int'l,* pg. 1246
McChord, M. Jackson, Pres. & Chief Oper. Officer--Peco Mfg. Co., Inc., Portland, OR; *U.S. Private,* pg. 846
McClain, Dennis, Pres.--Temerlin McClain, Irving, TX; *U.S. Public,* pg. 1642
McClain, John D., Pres.--Brillion Iron Works, Inc., Brillion, WI; *U.S. Public,* pg. 933
McClain, John R., Pres.--Owen Pacific, Los Angeles, CA; *U.S. Private,* pg. 824
McClain, Kenneth D., Chm. Bd., Pres. & Chief Exec. Officer--McClain Industries, Inc., Sterling Heights, MI; *U.S. Public,* pg. 1065
McClain, Kenneth D., Pres.--McClain of Georgia, Inc., Macon, GA; *U.S. Public,* pg. 1065
McClain, Kenneth D., Pres.--Shelby Steel Processing Co., River Rouge, MI; *U.S. Public,* pg. 1065
McClanahan, D., Pres. & Chief Oper. Officer--Houston Lighting & Power Company, Houston, TX; *U.S. Public,* pg. 843
McClane, Robert S., Pres.--Cullen/Frost Bankers, Inc., San Antonio, TX; *U.S. Public,* pg. 467
McClatchy, James B., Publisher--McClatchy Newspapers Inc., Sacramento, CA; *U.S. Public,* pg. 1065
McCleary, James W., Pres.--Facultative Resources, Inc., Stamford, CT; *U.S. Public,* pg. 215
McClellan, John, Pres. & Chief Exec. Officer--ASCG, Inc., Anchorage, AK; *U.S. Private,* pg. 80
McClellan, Richard P., Pres. & Chief Exec. Officer--Pro-Log Corporation, Monterey, CA; *U.S. Private,* pg. 887
McClelland, Kent, Pres.--Shamrock Foods Company, Phoenix, AZ; *U.S. Private,* pg. 989
McClelland, Mike, Pres. & Chief Exec. Officer--Hardware Wholesalers, Inc., Fort Wayne, IN; *U.S. Private,* pg. 502
McClelland, Norman P., Chief Exec. Officer--Shamrock Foods Company, Phoenix, AZ; *U.S. Private,* pg. 989
McClellen, Robert E., Jr., Pres. & Chief Exec. Officer--Florists' Mutual Insurance Co., Edwardsville, IL; *U.S. Private,* pg. 415
McClenagan, Robert, Pres.--Ruby Tuesday, Inc., Mobile, AL; *U.S. Public,* pg. 1411
McClenagan, Robert, Pres.--Ruby Tuesday Restaurants, Mobile, AL; *U.S. Public,* pg. 1412
McClintock, Jessica G., Pres.--Jessica McClintock Inc., San Francisco, CA; *U.S. Private,* pg. 719
McCloskey, John A., Pres. & Chief Exec. Officer--The Barden Corporation, Danbury, CT; *Int'l,* pg. 468
McClung, Gary N., Pres. & Gen. Mgr.--Midway Ford Truck Center Inc., Kansas City, MO; *U.S. Private,* pg. 744
McClung, Perry, Pres.--Universal Standard HealthCare of Michigan, Inc., Southfield, MI; *U.S. Public,* pg. 1698
McClung, Perry, Pres.--Universal Standard HealthCare of Ohio Inc., Southfield, MI; *U.S. Public,* pg. 1698
McClung, Perry, Pres.--Universal Standard HealthCare of Delaware, Inc., Southfield, MI; *U.S. Public,* pg. 1698
McClure, Alan, Pres.--Perfecseal, Inc., Mankato, MN; *U.S. Public,* pg. 210
McClure, Alan, Pres.--Perfecseal Company, Philadelphia, PA; *U.S. Public,* pg. 210
McClure, Allan, Pres. & Chief Exec. Officer--First National Bank, West Point, NE; *U.S. Public,* pg. 629
McClure, Charles G., Pres.--Detroit Diesel Corp., Detroit, MI; *U.S. Private,* pg. 850
McClure, Frank L., Pres.--Holmes Tuttle Ford, Inc., Tucson, AZ; *U.S. Private,* pg. 535
McClure, Rex A., III, Pres.--Copperweld Miami Industries, Piqua, OH; *Int'l,* pg. 662
McClurg, Douglas G., Pres. & Chief Exec. Officer--Mossberg Industries, Inc., Cumberland, RI; *U.S. Private,* pg. 763
McCluskey, Richard T., Chm. Bd., Pres. & Chief Exec. Officer--Fiske Brothers Refining Company, Newark, NJ; *U.S. Private,* pg. 408
McCoin, O.B., Pres. & Chief Exec. Officer--Hospital Affiliates Development Corporation, Nashville, TN; *U.S. Private,* pg. 540
McCollem, James, Pres.--Grumman Olson Division, Sturgis, MI; *U.S. Public,* pg. 1198
McCollough, W. Alan, Pres. & Chief Oper. Officer--Circuit City Stores, Inc., Richmond, VA; *U.S. Public,* pg. 374
McCollum, Jr., L. Gwaltney, Pres. & Chief Exec. Officer--First National Bank, Jasper, AL; *U.S. Public,* pg. 1549
McCollum, Robert, Pres.--Comtech Communications Corp., Tempe, AZ; *U.S. Public,* pg. 425
McCollum, Robert, Pres. & Chief Exec. Officer--R.S. Hughes Co., Inc., Sunnyvale, CA; *U.S. Private,* pg. 547
McComas, David, Pres.--Circuit City Western Div., Walnut, CA; *U.S. Public,* pg. 374
McComas, Murray K., Chm. Bd. & Pres.--Blair Corporation, Warren, PA; *U.S. Public,* pg. 236
McCombs, Richard, Pres.--The Beverage Source, Inc., Los Angeles, CA; *U.S. Public,* pg. 591
McCombs, Rick, Pres.--Flowers Baking Co. of Norfolk, Inc., Norfolk, VA; *U.S. Public,* pg. 657
McConahey, Stephen G., Pres. & Chief Oper. Officer--EVEREN Securities, Inc., Chicago, IL; *U.S. Public,* pg. 597
McConnell, Edwin, Pres.--McConnell Automotive, Mobile, AL; *U.S. Private,* pg. 720
McConnell, Gerald, Pres.--A.B. Dick Company, Niles, IL; *U.S. Private,* pg. 791
McConnell, J. Steven, Pres.--AAR Aircraft Turbine Center, Elk Grove Village, IL; *U.S. Public,* pg. 1
McConnell, James, Pres. & Chief Exec.Officer--Wilson/Shore Instruments, Canton, MA; *U.S. Public,* pg. 883
McConnell, James A., Pres.--Northrop Grumman Allied Industries, Inc., Sturgis, MI; *U.S. Public,* pg. 1198
McConnell, James M., Pres. & Chief Exec. Officer--Instron Corporation, Canton, MA; *U.S. Public,* pg. 882
McConnell, John, Pres. & Chief Exec. Officer--Medic Computer Systems, Inc., Raleigh, NC; *Int'l,* pg. 870
McConnell, John W., Pres. & Chief Exec. Officer--Fairfield Communities, Inc., Little Rock, AR; *U.S. Public,* pg. 610
McConnell, Michael A., Chm. Bd. & Pres.--Visioneer, Inc., Fremont, CA; *U.S. Public,* pg. 1722
McConnell, Paul R., Chm., Pres. & Chief Exec. Officer--Fleet Bank of Maine, Portland, ME; *U.S. Public,* pg. 649
McConnell, Sam, Pres.--HATCO, Inc., Garland, TX; *U.S. Private,* pg. 510
McConnell, William R., Chm. Bd. & Pres.--McConnell Cabinets, Inc., El Monte, CA; *U.S. Private,* pg. 720
McConville, Rick, Country Mgr.--IMSA S.A., Montevideo, Uruguay; *U.S. Public,* pg. 447
McCoole, Robert F., Pres.--J.S. Alberici Construction Co., Inc., Saint Louis, MO; *U.S. Private,* pg. 32
McCord, Herbert W., Chm. Bd., Pres. & Chief Exec. Officer--Granum Communications, Red Bank, NJ; *U.S. Private,* pg. 470
McCord, Jim, Pres.--Oacis Healthcare Systems, Inc., Greenbrae, CA; *U.S. Public,* pg. 1208
McCord, Patrick J., Pres.--Yale Security, Inc., Charlotte, NC; *Int'l,* pg. 1499
McCorkindale, Douglas H., Vice Chm. & Pres.--Gannett Company, Inc., Arlington, VA; *U.S. Public,* pg. 698
McCormack, Justin, Pres.-Petersen Enterprises--Petersen Publishing Company, L.L.C., Los Angeles, CA; *U.S. Private,* pg. 856
McCormack, Mark H., Chm. Bd., Pres. & Chief Exec. Officer--IMG, Cleveland, OH; *U.S. Private,* pg. 555
McCormack, Maryanne, Pres.--Visible Changes, Houston, TX; *U.S. Private,* pg. 1141
McCormick, Brendan K., Pres.--Thompson Steel Co., Inc., Canton, MA; *U.S. Private,* pg. 1083
McCormick, Daniel J., Pres. & Chief Exec. Officer--NWNL Health Management Corp., Minneapolis, MN; *U.S. Public,* pg. 1375
McCormick, G. Roger, Pres. & Chief Exec. Officer--People's Bank & Trust Co., Mount Vernon, IN; *U.S. Public,* pg. 1217
McCormick, Gerard F., Pres.--The Savogran Company, Norwood, MA; *U.S. Private,* pg. 968

McCormick, Mike, Pres.--J.H. McCormick, Inc., Burbank, CA; *U.S. Private*, pg. 720

McCormick, R., III, Pres. & Chief Oper. Officer--American Sweetners, inc., Frazer, PA; *U.S. Private*, pg. 63

McCormick, Richard D., Chm. Bd., Pres. & Chief Exec. Officer--U S West Inc., Englewood, CO; *U.S. Public*, pg. 1688

McCormick, Robert A., Pres. & Chief Exec. Officer--TrustCo Bank Corp., NY, Schenectady, NY; *U.S. Public*, pg. 1643

McCormick, Robert L., Pres.--Rieth-Riley Construction Co. Inc., Goshen, IN; *U.S. Private*, pg. 930

McCormick, Robert V., Pres. & Chief Exec. Officer--Laserscope Inc., San Jose, CA; *Int'l*, pg. 616

McCormick, Robert V., Pres. & Chief Exec. Officer--Laserscope Surgical Systems, San Jose, CA; *U.S. Public*, pg. 979

McCormick, T.P., Pres.--McCormick Paint Works Company, Rockville, MD; *U.S. Private*, pg. 720

McCormick, Thomas, Pres.--Carolina Mailing Service, Charlotte, NC; *U.S. Public*, pg. 1735

McCormick, Thomas P., Pres. & Chief Exec. Officer--Horizon Bancorp, Michigan City, IN; *U.S. Private*, pg. 538

McCormick, William, Pres. & Chief Exec. Officer--Riverside Cement Co., Diamond Bar, CA; *Int'l*, pg. 1293

McCourt, Kenneth W., Pres. & Chief Exec. Officer--Buffalo Color Corporation, Parsippany, NJ; *U.S. Private*, pg. 178

McCoy, Brian, Co-Pres.--McCoy's Building Supply Centers, San Marcos, TX; *U.S. Private*, pg. 720

McCoy, James T., Pres. & Chief Oper. Officer--The John C. Groub Company Inc., Seymour, IN; *U.S. Private*, pg. 484

McCoy, Michael A., Pres.--Associated Process Controls, Pleasanton, CA; *U.S. Private*, pg. 92

McCoy, Mike, Co-Pres.--McCoy's Building Supply Centers, San Marcos, TX; *U.S. Private*, pg. 720

McCoy, R. Michael, Chm. Bd. & Pres.--McCoy Group Inc., Shullsburg, WI; *U.S. Private*, pg. 720

McCoy, V. Glenn, Pres.--Fleetwood Aluminum Products, Corona, CA; *U.S. Private*, pg. 410

McCrary, Dennie L., Pres. & Chief Exec. Officer--Sea Island Company, Sea Island, GA; *U.S. Private*, pg. 977

McCraw, Joan, Pres. & Publr.--Los Angeles Magazine, Inc., Los Angeles, CA; *U.S. Public*, pg. 513

McCrea, Bill, Pres.--VJ Growers, Inc., Apopka, FL; *U.S. Private*, pg. 1130

McCready, James P., Pres. & Chief Oper. Officer--The Cypress Companies, Akron, OH; *U.S. Private*, pg. 299

McCree, Donald H., Jr., Pres. & Chief Exec. Officer--IBJ Schroder Bank & Trust Company, New York, NY; *Int'l*, pg. 674

McCrone, Kevin E., Pres.-The Delfield Company--Delfield Company, Mount Pleasant, MI; *U.S. Public*, pg. 1445

McCroskey, M.W., Pres.--American National Triflex Fund, Inc., Galveston, TX; *U.S. Public*, pg. 87

McCroskey, V.D., Pres. & Chief Exec. Officer--WGM Safety Corporation, Reading, PA; *Int'l*, pg. 462

McCrossan, Thomas, Pres.--Investors Fiduciary Trust Company, Kansas City, MO; *U.S. Public*, pg. 944

McCue, Michael, Pres.--Skyland Scientific Services, Inc., Bozeman, MT; *U.S. Public*, pg. 1515

McCue, Peter, Partner & Sr. V.P.--Fleishman-Hillard, Inc., New York, NY; *U.S. Private*, pg. 411

McCulla, Gary W., Pres. & Dir.-Sls. & Mktg.--Tel-Save Holdings, Inc., New Hope, PA; *U.S. Public*, pg. 1568

McCulloch, Dave, Pres. & Chief Exec. Officer--Garland Commercial Ranges, Ltd., Mississauga, Canada; *Int'l*, pg. 189

McCullogh, S. Donald, Pres. & Chief Oper. Officer--Signature Brands USA, Inc., Solon, OH; *U.S. Public*, pg. 1472

McCullough, Eugene R., Pres.--Fidelity National Title Insurance Company of Tennessee, Knoxville, TN; *U.S. Public*, pg. 621

McCullough, J.E., Pres. & Chief Exec. Officer--South Jersey Energy Co., Folsom, NJ; *U.S. Public*, pg. 1488

McCullough, K.P., Pres.--Havens Steel Co., Kansas City, MO; *U.S. Private*, pg. 510

McCullough, Margaret, Dr., Pres.--Christian Children's Fund, Inc., Richmond, VA; *U.S. Private*, pg. 238

McCune, Thomas, Pres.--M.A. Mortenson Company, Minneapolis, MN; *U.S. Private*, pg. 763

McCurdy, Charles G., Pres.--Primedia Inc., New York, NY; *U.S. Public*, pg. 1327

McCurdy, D.W., Pres.--Marathon Monitors Incorporated, Cincinnati, OH; *Int'l*, pg. 590

McCurdy, Larry W., Chm., Pres. & Chief Exec. Officer--Echlin Inc., Branford, CT; *U.S. Public*, pg. 560

McCurley, F. Cedric, Pres.--LINSCO Reinsurance Company, Indianapolis, IN; *U.S. Private*, pg. 998

McCutchen, Joan, Pres.--Yuba Heat Transfer Division, Tulsa, OK; *U.S. Private*, pg. 264

McDaniel, Gary, Chm. Bd. & Pres.--MAC Equipment Inc., Houston, TX; *U.S. Private*, pg. 685

McDaniel, John, Chief Oper. Officer--Farmers Telephone Co-Op, Kingstree, SC; *U.S. Private*, pg. 395

McDaniel, R. Leon, Pres. & Chief Oper. Officer--Pioneer Oil Company Inc., Fort Worth, TX; *U.S. Private*, pg. 866

McDaniel, Ray, Pres. & Chief Oper. Officer--Flowers Baking Co. of Jacksonville, Inc., Jacksonville, FL; *U.S. Public*, pg. 657

McDavid, David, Sr., Pres.--David McDavid Auto Dealership, Irving, TX; *U.S. Private*, pg. 721

McDavid, G.E., Pres.--Houston Chronicle, Houston, TX; *U.S. Private*, pg. 517

McDavid, R.S., Pres.--Concorp, Inc., Nitro, WV; *U.S. Private*, *pg. 262*

McDavid, Tim, Pres.--Graver Tank & Mfg. Co., Inc., Pasadena, TX; *U.S. Public*, pg. 914

McDermitt, Edward A., Jr., Chm., Pres. & Chief Exec. Officer--National Bulk Carriers, Inc., New York, NY; *U.S. Private*, pg. 780

McDermott, Jim, Pres.--J.M. Process Systems Inc., Orland Park, IL; *U.S. Private*, pg. 577

McDoffie, Woodie, Pres.--Miller Intermodal Logistics Services Inc., Jackson, MS; *U.S. Private*, pg. 329

McDonagh, William M., Pres. & Chief Oper. Officer--Broderbund Software, Inc., Novato, CA; *U.S. Public*, pg. 258

McDonald, D.E., Pres.--Caterpillar Americas Co., Peoria, IL; *U.S. Public*, pg. 315

McDonald, Daniel W., Pres.--Baker Support Services, Inc., Dallas, TX; *U.S. Public*, pg. 168

McDonald, Fred A., Pres. & Chief Exec. Officer--Cadmus Marketing Services, Atlanta, GA; *U.S. Public*, pg. 291

McDonald, J.M., III, Chm. Bd., Pres. & Chief Exec. Officer--A.Y. McDonald Industries Inc., Dubuque, IA; *U.S. Private*, pg. 721

McDonald, Jack, Pres.--LASCO Fluid Distribution Products, Brownsville, TN; *Int'l*, pg. 1398

McDonald, James F., Pres. & Chief Exec. Officer--Scientific-Atlanta, Inc., Norcross, GA; *U.S. Public*, pg. 1443

McDonald, John J., Pres. & Chief Exec. Officer--Casio, Inc., Dover, NJ; *Int'l*, pg. 274

McDonald, Kelli, Pres.--EvansGroup, Denver, CO; *U.S. Private*, pg. 385

McDonald, Mackey J., Pres., Chief Exec. Officer & Chief Oper. Officer--VF Corporation, Wyomissing, PA; *U.S. Public*, pg. 1702

McDonald, Peter J., Pres.--Ameritech Advertising Services, Troy, MI; *U.S. Public*, pg. 97

McDonald, Robert B., Pres. & Chief Exec. Officer--Great Lakes Chemical Corporation, West Lafayette, IN; *U.S. Public*, pg. 760

McDonald, Roy K., Pres. & Chief Exec. Officer--Connectix Corporation, San Mateo, CA; *U.S. Private*, pg. 264

McDonald, Scott, Pres. & Chief Exec. Officer--McDonald Equipment Co., Willoughby, OH; *U.S. Private*, pg. 721

McDonald, Stuart R., Pres., Chief Exec. Officer & Treas.--Marshall & Williams Co., Greenville, SC; *U.S. Private*, pg. 708

McDonald, Tom, Pres. & Chief Exec. Officer--Keller Kitchen Cabinets, De Land, FL; *U.S. Private*, pg. 612

McDonald, William E., Pres. & Chief Exec. Officer--National City Bank, Cleveland, OH; *U.S. Public*, pg. 1154

McDonnell, Dennis, Pres. & Chief Exec. Officer--Trace Mountain Products, San Jose, CA; *U.S. Private*, pg. 1095

McDonnell, Kevin R., Pres. & Chief Exec. Officer--Skyline Chili, Inc., Fairfield, OH; *U.S. Public*, pg. 1475

McDonnell, Michael, Pres.--West Union Corporation, Memphis, TN; *U.S. Private*, pg. 1163

McDonnell, Terry, Editor--Men's Journal, New York, NY; *U.S. Private*, pg. 1162

McDonough, Neil, Pres.--Flexcon Co., Inc., Spencer, MA; *U.S. Private*, pg. 412

McDonough, Victoria R., Pres.--Rollins Hudig Hall of Indiana, Inc., Indianapolis, IN; *U.S. Public*, pg. 117

McDougall, Ronald A., Pres. & Chief Exec. Officer--Brinker International, Inc., Dallas, TX; *U.S. Public*, pg. 253

McDow, Tom, Pres.-Great American Opportunities, Inc.--Southwestern/Great American Inc., Nashville, TN; *U.S. Private*, pg. 1018

McDowell, Frank, Pres. & Chief Exec. Officer--BRE Properties, Inc., San Francisco, CA; *U.S. Public*, pg. 163

McDowell, J. Walter, Pres. & Chief Exec. Officer--Wachovia Bank of North Carolina, N.A., Winston Salem, NC; *U.S. Public*, pg. 1730

McDowell, Robert, Pres. & Chief Exec. Officer--Olan Mills, Inc., Chattanooga, TN; *U.S. Private*, pg. 749

McDowell, Thomas W., Jr., Pres.--Rice, Hall, James & Associates, San Diego, CA; *U.S. Public*, pg. 1674

McEachern, Ron, Pres. & Chief Exec. Officer--Pepsi-Cola Canada, Ltd., Toronto, Canada; *U.S. Public*, pg. 1277

McEachran, Angus, Editor & Pres.--Memphis Publishing Co., Memphis, TN; *U.S. Public*, pg. 1448

McEldowney, Roger, Pres.--Clark Gum Company, Buffalo, NY; *U.S. Private*, pg. 243

McElhaney, George M., Pres.--Polaris Packaging Inc., Robbinsville, NJ; *U.S. Public*, pg. 1486

McElhaney, Jack B., Pres. & Chief Exec. Officer--Ministers Life Resources, Saint Paul, MN; *U.S. Private*, pg. 750

McElnea, Jeffrey K., Pres. & Chief Exec. Officer--Einson Freeman Inc., Paramus, NJ; *Int'l*, pg. 1483

McEniry, Robert G., Pres.--nexAir, LLC, Memphis, TN; *U.S. Private*, pg. 797

McEniry, Robert G., Pres.--nexAir, Memphis, TN; *U.S. Private*, pg. 797

McEvoy, A.P., Jr., Pres.--Western Extrusions, Carrollton, TX; *U.S. Private*, pg. 1165

McEwen, James, Sr. V.P. & Publisher--The Family Circle, Inc., New York, NY; *Int'l*, pg. 190

McEwen, Joseph, Pres.--Moreco Inc., Bristol, PA; *U.S. Private*, pg. 755

McEwen, Neal, Pres.--Public Health Software Systems, Norcross, GA; *U.S. Public*, pg. 888

McEwen, Robert R., Chm. & Chief Exec. Officer--CSA Management Inc., Toronto, Canada; *Int'l*, pg. 243

McFadden, Gordon, Pres.--Helly-Hansen (US), Inc., Redmond, WA; *Int'l*, pg. 1010

McFadden, Joel, Pres.--Stokes Vacuum Inc., Philadelphia, PA; *Int'l*, pg. 426

McFall, Tom, Chm. Bd., Pres. & Chief Exec. Officer--Weatherly Private Capital, Inc., New York, NY; *U.S. Private*, pg. 1156

McFarland, Bill, Pres.--Comet American Marketing, Houston, TX; *U.S. Public*, pg. 591

McFarland, James D., Pres. & Chief Oper. Officer--Husky Oil Ltd., Calgary, Canada; *Int'l*, pg. 640

McFarland, John A., Pres.--Baldor Electric Company, Fort Smith, AR; *U.S. Public*, pg. 168

McFarland, Mike, Pres. & Chief Exec. Officer--Citizens First Bank, Arkadelphia, AR; *U.S. Public*, pg. 630

McFarling, Donald P., Pres. & Chief Exec. Officer--McFarling Foods, Inc., Indianapolis, IN; *U.S. Private*, pg. 721

McFeely, Clifton, Pres. & Partner--North Castle Partners Advertising, Inc., Stamford, CT; *U.S. Private*, pg. 804

McGagin, Tim A., Pres. & Chief Oper. Officer--Coastal Lumber Company, Weldon, NC; *U.S. Private*, pg. 248

McGarland, William H., Pres. & Chief Exec. Officer--Irvine Apartment Communities Incorporated, Newport Beach, CA; *U.S. Private*, pg. 575

McGarry, Christopher, Pres.--Barouh Eaton Allen Corporation, Brooklyn, NY; *U.S. Private*, pg. 117

McGarry, John P., Jr., Pres.-Young & Rubicam Inc.--Young & Rubicam Inc., New York, NY; *U.S. Private*, pg. 1196

McGarry, Rich, Pres.--Sugarbush, Warren, VT; *U.S. Private*, pg. 62

McGarry, Ron, Pres.--Elgin Sweeper Company, Elgin, IL; *U.S. Public*, pg. 617

McGee, Julie, Pres.--McDougal/Littell, Evanston, IL; *U.S. Public*, pg. 841

McGeehan, Robert L., Pres. & Chief Exec. Officer--Kennametal Inc., Latrobe, PA; *U.S. Public*, pg. 950

McGehee, Frank S., Co-Chm. Bd. & Co-Chief Exec. Officer--Mac Papers, Inc., Jacksonville, FL; *U.S. Private*, pg. 689

Mcgehee, Frank S., Jr., Pres.--Mac Papers, Inc., Jacksonville, FL; *U.S. Private*, pg. 689

McGehee, Scott, Pres. & Chief Exec. Officer--Fort Wayne Newspapers, Inc., Fort Wayne, IN; *U.S. Public*, pg. 964

McGhan, Jim J., Pres.--Inamed Corporation, Las Vegas, NV; *U.S. Public*, pg. 873

McGhie, Austin, Pres. & Chief Exec. Officer--Young & Rubicam San Francisco, San Francisco, CA; *U.S. Private*, pg. 1198

McGill, James D., Pres. & Treas.--United McGill Corp., Groveport, OH; *U.S. Private*, pg. 1122

McGill, Joanne, Pres.--VSM, Inc., New York, NY; *U.S. Private*, pg. 1130

McGill, S.R., Pres.--Esso N.V./S.A., Maasmechelen, Belgium; *U.S. Public*, pg. 602

McGill, Terrance L., Pres.--Columbia Gulf Transmission Co., Charleston, WV; *U.S. Public*, pg. 403

McGinn, Richard A., Pres. & Chief Exec. Officer--Lucent Technologies Inc., Murray Hill, NJ; *U.S. Public*, pg. 1017

McGinnis, Arthur J., Jr., Pres.--Simmons-Boardman Publishing Corp., New York, NY; *U.S. Private*, pg. 1000

McGinnis, Michael E., Chm. Bd., Pres. & Chief Exec. Officer--American Eco Corporation, Toronto, Canada; *Int'l*, pg. 73

McGinnis, Patrick W., Co-Pres. & Co-Chief Exec. Officer--Ralston Purina Company, Saint Louis, MO; *U.S. Public*, pg. 1359

McGinty, Fredaerick W., Chief Exec. Officer--Hilb, Rogal and Hamilton Company of Savannah, Inc., Savannah, GA; *U.S. Public*, pg. 827

McGirr, David, Pres.--GAB Robins North America, Inc., Parsippany, NJ; *Int'l*, pg. 1153

McGlothlin, James E., Chm. Bd & Pres.--Quintron Systems, Inc., Santa Maria, CA; *U.S. Private*, pg. 901

McGlothlin, James W., Chm. Bd. & Chief Exec. Officer--The United Company, Bristol, VA; *U.S. Private*, pg. 1121

McGonagle, Patrick J., Pres. & Chief Exec. Officer--National Gas & Oil Company, Newark, OH; *U.S. Public*, pg. 1156

McGougan, Joe, Pres.--AMCORE Mortgage, Inc., Rockford, IL; *U.S. Public*, pg. 64

McGough, George, Chm., Pres. & Chief Exec. Officer--Principal Financial Securities, Dallas, TX; *U.S. Private*, pg. 885

McGoun, Sam H., Pres. & Chief Exec. Officer--Willis Corroon Corp. of Michigan, Livonia, MI; *Int'l*, pg. 1506

McGovern, Terrence J., Pres. & Chief Exec. Officer--Liggett-Stashower, Inc., Cleveland, OH; *U.S. Private*, pg. 667

McGowan, Donald J., Pres.--Flagship Bank & Trust Company, Worcester, MA; *U.S. Public*, pg. 351

McGowan, James, Pres. & Chief Exec. Officere--EIS International Inc., Herndon, VA; *U.S. Public*, pg. 544

McGrail, Michael, Pres. & Gen. Mgr.-Cable Data--USCS International, Inc., Rancho Cordova, CA; *U.S. Public*, pg. 1659

McGrail, Michael, Pres. & Gen. Mgr.--Cabledata, Inc., Rancho Cordova, CA; *U.S. Public*, pg. 1659

McGrain, Joe, Pres.--Gaggenau USA Corporation, Norwood, MA; *U.S. Private*, pg. 437

McGrath, Don J., Pres. & Chief Exec. Officer--Bank of the West, Walnut Creek, CA; *Int'l*, pg. 163

McGrath, Eugene R., Chm. Bd., Pres. & Chief Exec. Officer--Consolidated Edison Company of New York, Inc., New York, NY; *U.S. Public*, pg. 434

McGrath, G.J., Chm. Bd. & Pres.--Mico Inc., North Mankato, MN; *U.S. Private*, pg. 741

McGrath, John, Pres., Chief Oper. Officer & Chief Credit Officer--The San Francisco Co., San Francisco, CA; *U.S. Public*, pg. 1430

McGrath, John P., Pres. & Chief Exec. Officer--Hilb, Rogal and Hamilton Company of Pittsburgh, Inc., Pittsburgh, PA; *U.S. Public*, pg. 827

McGrath, Judith, Pres.--MTV: Music Television, New York, NY; *U.S. Private*, pg. 779

McGrath, Margaret H., Pres. & Chief Oper. Officer--PPG Canada Inc., Mississauga, Canada; *U.S. Public*, pg. 1245

McGrath, Patrick J., Pres. & Chief Exec. Officer--Jordan, McGrath, Case & Taylor Inc., New York, NY; *U.S. Private*, pg. 598

McGraw, Harold W. III, Pres. & Chief Oper. Officer--The McGraw-Hill Companies, New York, NY; *U.S. Public*, pg. 1069

McGraw, Richard D., Pres. & Chief Exec. Officer--Vitran Corporation Inc., Toronto, Canada; *Int'l*, pg. 1469

McGraw, Robert P., Exec. V.P.--McGraw-Hill Professional Publishing Group, New York, NY; *U.S. Public*, pg. 1070

McGraw, Steve, Pres.--Planet Products Corp., Cincinnati, OH; *U.S. Private*, pg. 869

McGraw, Tim, Pres.--Horizon Aerospace LLC, Victor, NY; *U.S. Private*, pg. 538

McGregor, Robert, Pres.--Eighty Four Coal Co., Indiana, PA; *U.S. Public*, pg. 1395

McGrenery, John, Pres.--Howden Fluid Systems, Santa Barbara, CA; *U.S. Public*, pg. 1045

McGrevin, Gene R., Chm. Bd. & Pres.--Isolyser Company, Inc., Norcross, GA; *U.S. Public*, pg. 914

McGrory, Jack, Pres. & Chief Exec. Officer--Price Enterprises, Inc., San Diego, CA; *U.S. Public*, pg. 1324

McGuire, Henry, Pres.--Outlander, New York, NY; *U.S. Public*, pg. 989

McGuire, Michael, Pres. & Chief Exec. Officer--Astrex, Inc., Plainview, NY; *U.S. Public*, pg. 141

McGuire, Michael, Pres.--T.F. Cushing, Inc., West Springfield, MA; *U.S. Public*, pg. 141

McGuire, Michael, Pres. & Chief Exec. Officer--Progress International Limited, Plainview, NY; *U.S. Public*, pg. 141

McGuire, Michael, Pres.--Avest, Inc., Plainview, NY; *U.S. Public*, pg. 141

McGuire, Michael, Pres.--MBIA Assurance S.A., Armonk, NY; *U.S. Public*, pg. 1023

McGuire, Paul A., Pres.--Electro-Voice, Inc., Buchanan, MI; *U.S. Private*, pg. 479

McGuire, Richard J., Jr., Pres.--TRC Mariah Associates, Inc., Laramie, WY; *U.S. Public*, pg. 1558

McGuire, William W., M.D., Chm. Bd., Pres. & Chief Exec. Officer--United HealthCare Corporation, Minnetonka, MN; *U.S. Public*, pg. 1677

McGuire, William W., M.D., Chm. Bd., Pres. & Chief Exec. Officer--United HealthCare Services, Inc., Minnetonka, MN; *U.S. Public*, pg. 1678

McGuirk, P.W., Pres. & Chief Exec. Officer--Kao Infosystems Company (MA), Plymouth, MA; *Int'l*, pg. 717

McHale, Brian, Partner, V.P. & Natl. Media Dir.--Media That Works, Cincinnati, OH; *U.S. Private*, pg. 727

McHale, Hank, Pres.--GO/DAN Industries, New Haven, CT; *U.S. Public*, pg. 1631

McHale, Hank, Pres.--The G & O Manufacturing Co., New Haven, CT; *U.S. Public*, pg. 1631

McHale, Hank P., Pres. & Chief Exec. Officer--TransPro, Inc., New Haven, CT; *U.S. Public*, pg. 1631

McHale, John W., Pres.--Texaco International Trader Inc., White Plains, NY; *U.S. Public*, pg. 1583

McHale, Judith, Pres. & Chief Oper. Officer--Discovery Communications, Inc., Bethesda, MD; *U.S. Private*, pg. 334

McHenry, Daniel, Pres.--Oasis Outsourcing, Inc., Palm Beach Gardens, FL; *U.S. Public*, pg. 1731

McHugh, J. Carey, Pres.--Texaco Bahamas Ltd., Nassau, Bahamas; *U.S. Public*, pg. 1584

McHugh, James P., Pres. & Chief Exec. Officer--James McHugh Construction Co., Chicago, IL; *U.S. Private*, pg. 721

McHugh, M. Joseph, Pres. & Chief Oper. Officer--Triangle Pacific Corporation, Dallas, TX; *U.S. Public*, pg. 1634

McHugh, M. Joseph, Pres. & Chief Oper. Officer--Bruce Hardwood Floors, Dallas, TX; *U.S. Public*, pg. 1634

McHugh, Peter, Pres. & Chief Oper. Officer--Holland America Line Westours, Seattle, WA; *U.S. Public*, pg. 306

McIlnay, Donald, Pres. & Chief Exec. Officer--The Gibson-Homans Company, Twinsburg, OH; *U.S. Private*, pg. 451

McIlnay, Donald R., Pres.--Newell Window Furnishings Co., Freeport, IL; *U.S. Public*, pg. 1177

McIlnay, Donald R., Pres.--Levolor, Greensboro, NC; *U.S. Public*, pg. 1177

McIlnay, Donald R., Pres.--Levolor Home Fashions, Westminster, CA; *U.S. Public*, pg. 1177

McIlrath, James A., Pres.--DSC Logistics, Inc., Des Plaines, IL; *U.S. Private*, pg. 306

McIlvain, J. Gibson, III, Pres.--J. Gibson McIlvain Co., White Marsh, MD; *U.S. Private*, pg. 722

McIlwaine, Steve, Pres.--Metcraft, Inc., Grandview, MO; *Int'l*, pg. 453

McInerney, James S., Pres.--Hydrocorp, Inc., Bridgeport, CT; *U.S. Public*, pg. 126

McInerney, James S., Pres. & Chief Exec. Officer--Aquarion Management Services, Bridgeport, CT; *U.S. Public*, pg. 126

McInerney, Martin J., Pres.--McInerney Inc., Oak Park, MI; *U.S. Private*, pg. 722

McInerney, Tom, Gen. Partner--Welsh Carson Anderson & Stowe, New York, NY; *U.S. Private*, pg. 1162

McIngvale, James, Pres.--Gallery Furniture, Houston, TX; *U.S. Private*, pg. 438

McInnes, Allen, Pres. & Chief Exec. Officer--Tetra Technologies, Woodlands, TX; *U.S. Public*, pg. 1582

McInnes, Ross, Pres.--Cereol S.A., Neuilly-sur-Seine, France; *Int'l*, pg. 324

McIntosh, J. David, V.P.-Strategic Bus.--Lawn-Boy Inc., Bloomington, MN; *U.S. Public*, pg. 1624

McIntyre, Burt, Pres.--Claremont Flock Corporation, Claremont, NH; *U.S. Private*, pg. 241

McIntyre, Melissa E., RN, OCN, Pres. & Chief Oper. Officer--I.V. One, Altamonte Springs, FL; *U.S. Public*, pg. 229

McIntyre, Scott, Jr., Pres.--Crabtree Premium Finance, Lombard, IL; *U.S. Public*, pg. 1677

McIntyre, William D., Pres. & Chief Exec. Officer--American Speedy Printing Centers, Inc., Troy, MI; *U.S. Private*, pg. 62

McIsaac, Larry, Pres.--Zebco, Tulsa, OK; *U.S. Public*, pg. 265

McIsaac, Larry, Pres.--Martin Reels, A Division of Zebco, Tulsa, OK; *U.S. Public*, pg. 265

McIvor, William, Pres.--Oxford Health Plans (FL), Inc., Sarasota, FL; *U.S. Public*, pg. 1239

McKane, Tom, Pres. & Chief Exec. Officer--S-B Power Tool Company, Chicago, IL; *Int'l*, pg. 205

McKay, Carl, Pres. & Chief Exec. Officer--Sioux Manufacturing Corp., Fort Totten, ND; *U.S. Private*, pg. 1003

McKay, David, Pres.--Puritan-Bennett Australia Pty. Ltd., Thomastown, Australia; *U.S. Public*, pg. 1040

McKay, Robert C., Pres. & Chief Exec. Officer--Tenera, Inc., San Francisco, CA; *U.S. Public*, pg. 1576

McKean, Brad, Pres.--McKean Oldsmobile Company, Pittsburgh, PA; *U.S. Private*, pg. 722

McKean, Gilbert R., Pres.--Breckenridge Material Company, Saint Louis, MO; *U.S. Private*, pg. 166

McKean, M.H., Pres.--Wrigley Canada Inc., Don Mills, Canada; *U.S. Public*, pg. 1781

McKee, Ernest H., Pres. & Chief Exec. Officer--Westwood Corporation, Tulsa, OK; *U.S. Public*, pg. 1763

McKee, Gregg, Pres.--Energy Products, San Diego, CA; *U.S. Public*, pg. 1061

McKee, Jack C., Pres. & Chief Exec. Officer--McKee Foods Corporation, Collegedale, TN; *U.S. Private*, pg. 723

McKee, Ken, Pres.--Interstate Producers Livestock Association, Peoria, IL; *U.S. Private*, pg. 573

McKee, W.W., Pres., Chief Exec. & Chief Oper. Officer--Pitt-Des Moines, Inc., Pittsburgh, PA; *U.S. Public*, pg. 1304

McKenna, John A., Jr., Pres. & Chief Exec. Officer--Entex Information Services, Rye Brook, NY; *U.S. Private*, pg. 378

McKenna, Matthew J., Pres.--Baltimore Aircoil Company, Jessup, MD; *U.S. Private*, pg. 68

McKenna, Michael J., Pres. & Chief Oper. Officer--Crown Cork & Seal Company, Inc., Philadelphia, PA; *U.S. Public*, pg. 462

McKenna, Michael J., Pres.--Crown Cork de Puerto Rico, Inc., Carolina, PR; *U.S. Public*, pg. 463

McKenna, P.W., Chm. Bd., Pres. & Chief Exec. Officer--Plasti-Kote Company Inc., Medina, OH; *U.S. Private*, pg. 870

McKenna, Robert J., Chm. Bd., Pres. & Chief Exec. Officer--Acme Electric Corporation, East Aurora, NY; *U.S. Public*, pg. 16

McKenney, J.K., Pres.--The Figaro Company, Inc., Mesquite, TX; *U.S. Private*, pg. 404

McKenney, S.S., III, Chm. Bd. & Pres.--W & B Refrigeration Service Co., Dallas, TX; *U.S. Public*, pg. 685

McKenney, S.S., III, Pres.--Air Pro, Dallas, TX; *U.S. Public*, pg. 685

McKenzie, Bob, Pres. & Publisher--The Prince George Citizen, Prince George, Canada; *Int'l*, pg. 631

McKenzie, Christopher C., Pres.--General DataComm Ltd., Willowdale, Canada; *U.S. Public*, pg. 708

McKenzie, Gary, Pres.--TIC, Steamboat Springs, CO; *U.S. Private*, pg. 1064

McKenzie, James, Pres. & Chief Exec. Officer--Leo Burnett Company Ltd., Toronto, Canada; *U.S. Private*, pg. 185

McKenzie, Mary Alice, Pres.--McKenzies of Vermont, Inc., Burlington, VT; *U.S. Private*, pg. 723

McKenzie, Michael K., Chm. Bd., Pres. & Chief Exec. Officer--GSC Enterprises, Inc., Sulphur Springs, TX; *U.S. Private*, pg. 436

McKeon, John S., Pres. & Chief Exec. Officer--Golden Valley Microwave Foods, Inc., Edina, MN; *U.S. Public*, pg. 427

McKernan, R.T., Pres.--Packard Instrument Co., Inc., Meriden, CT; *U.S. Private*, pg. 833

McKim, Alan S., Chm. Bd., Pres. & Chief Exec. Officer--Clean Harbors, Inc., Braintree, MA; *U.S. Public*, pg. 383

McKinley, Martin J., Pres.--Norwest Business Credit, Inc., Minneapolis, MN; *U.S. Public*, pg. 1202

McKinnerney, Floyd, Pres & Chief Oper. Officer--ConAgra Agri-Products Co., Greeley, CO; *U.S. Public*, pg. 426

McKinnery, Jim, Pres.--Brim, Inc., Portland, OR; *U.S. Private*, pg. 168

McKinney, James A., Pres.--Federal Express Logistics, Inc., Memphis, TN; *U.S. Public*, pg. 604

McKinney, John B., Pres. & Chief Exec. Officer--Laclede Steel Company, Saint Louis, MO; *U.S. Public*, pg. 974

McKinney, Marni, Pres. & Chief Exec. Officer--The Somerset Group, Inc., Indianapolis, IN; *U.S. Public*, pg. 1484

McKinney, Myron W., Chm. Bd., Pres. & Chief Exec. Officer--The Empire District Electric Company, Joplin, MO; *U.S. Public*, pg. 579

McKinney, Reynold, Chm. Bd. & Pres.--McKinney & McKinney Advertising, Redondo Beach, CA; *U.S. Private*, pg. 723

McKinney, William H., Pres. & Chief Exec. Officer--The Royal China & Porcelain Companies Inc., Moorestown, NJ; *U.S. Private*, pg. 948

McKinnin, Michael, J., Pres.--McKinnon Bridge Co., Franklin, TN; *U.S. Private*, pg. 723

McKinnish, Richmond D., Pres. & Gen. Mgr.--Carlisle Tire & Wheel Company, Aiken, SC; *U.S. Public*, pg. 305

McKinniss, Sherman L., Chm. Bd., Pres. & Chief Exec. Officer--Rotonics Manufacturing Inc., Gardena, CA; *U.S. Public*, pg. 1406

McKinnon, Bob E., Pres. & Chief Exec. Officer--Century Furniture Industries, Hickory, NC; *U.S. Private*, pg. 226

McKinnon, Tony, Pres.--American Classic Voyagers Company, New Orleans, LA; *U.S. Private*, pg. 380

McKinstry, Reginald, Pres.--Tech-Tran Corporation, Rancocas, NJ; *U.S. Private*, pg. 560

McKissick, A. Foster, III, Pres.--Fairway Ford, Inc., Greenville, SC; *U.S. Private*, pg. 392

McKissick, Foster, III, Pres.--Fairway Ford of Anderson, Anderson, SC; *U.S. Private*, pg. 392

McKitrick, James T., Pres. & Chief Exec. Officer--Central Tractor Farm & Country, Inc., Des Moines, IA; *U.S. Private*, pg. 237

McKitrick, Jim, Pres.--Country General Stores, Grand Island, NE; *U.S. Private*, pg. 237

McKnight, Andrew D., Chm. Bd., Pres. & Chief Exec. Officer--Tri-Chem, Inc., Harrison, NJ; *U.S. Private*, pg. 1100

McKnight, Rick, Pres.--Paravant Computer Systems, Inc., Melbourne, FL; *U.S. Public*, pg. 1257

McKnight, Susan, Pres.--William O'Neil & Co., Inc., Los Angeles, CA; *U.S. Private*, pg. 817

McKnight, William B., Jr., Pres. & Chief Exec. Officer--Wise Foods, Inc., Parsippany, NJ; *U.S. Private*, pg. 157

McKone, F.L., Pres. & Chief Exec. Officer--Albany International Corp., Albany, NY; *U.S. Public*, pg. 36

McLagan, Donald L., Chm. Bd., Pres. & Chief Exec. Officer--NewsEdge Corporation, Burlington, MA; *U.S. Public*, pg. 1180

McLain, Jim, Pres.--Volt VIEWtech, Inc., Orange, CA; *U.S. Public*, pg. 1724

McLain, Mike A., Pres. & Chief Exec. Officer--DowBrands, L.P., Indianapolis, IN; *U.S. Public*, pg. 523

McLaine, John J., Pres. & Chief Oper. Officer--Excel Communications, Inc., Dallas, TX; *U.S. Public*, pg. 598

McLane, James W., Pres. & Chief Oper. Officer--NovaCare Inc., King of Prussia, PA; *U.S. Public*, pg. 1203

McLane, Tim, Pres. & Chief Exec. Officer--Skinner Corp., Lanett, AL; *U.S. Private*, pg. 1005

McLaughlin, Brian D., Chm. Bd., Pres. & Cbief Exec. Officer--Hurco Companies, Inc., Indianapolis, IN; *U.S. Public*, pg. 850

McLaughlin, Dennis, Pres.--Veterinary Medicine Publishing Co., Inc., Lenexa, KS; *U.S. Public*, pg. 1600

McLaughlin, Harry Y., Pres.--McLaughlin Industrial Distributors, Inc., Pico Rivera, CA; *U.S. Private*, pg. 724

McLaughlin, J.J., Pres. & Chief Exec. Officer--DAP Inc., Tipp City, OH; *Int'l*, pg. 1486

McLaughlin, John T., Pres.--Royal Oak Ford Inc., Royal Oak, MI; *U.S. Private*, pg. 948

McLaughlin, Paul, Pres. & Chief Exec. Officer--The Butcher Company, Marlborough, MA; *U.S. Private*, pg. 189

McLaughlin, Philip L., Pres. & Chief Oper. Officer--Horizon Bancorp, Inc., Beckley, WV; *U.S. Public*, pg. 836

McLaughlin, Philip L., Pres. & Chief Exec. Officer--Greenbrier Valley National Bank, Lewisburg, WV; *U.S. Public*, pg. 836

McLaughlin, Rich, Pres.--Aliant Systems Inc., Lincoln, NE; *U.S. Public*, pg. 41

McLaughlin, William F., Pres. & Chief Exec. Officer--Sweetheart Cup Company Inc., Owings Mills, MD; *U.S. Private*, pg. 1058

McLay, William S., Pres.--Ryobi America Corp., Anderson, SC; *Int'l*, pg. 1151

McLean, Donald A., Pres.--British Columbia Packers Limited, Vancouver, Canada; *Int'l*, pg. 1495

McLean, Edward L., Pres.--Connors Bros. Limited, Blacks Harbour, Canada; *Int'l*, pg. 1495

McLean, Gary R., Chm. Bd. & Pres.--Interstate Distributor Company, Tacoma, WA; *U.S. Private*, pg. 573

McLean, James A., Jr., Pres.--McLean-Thomas Inc., Buffalo, NY; *U.S. Private*, pg. 724

McLean, William L., III, Chm. Bd. & Pres.--Independent Publications, Inc., Bryn Mawr, PA; *U.S. Private*, pg. 559

McLellan, Robert S., Pres.--Bixby International Corp., Newburyport, MA; *U.S. Private*, pg. 146

McLennan, Lawrence, Pres.--DZIC, Schenectady, NY; *U.S. Private*, pg. 317

McLeod, D.A., Pres. & Chief Exec. Officer--Newhawk Gold Mines LTD., Vancouver, Canada; *U.S. Public*, pg. 833

Mcleod, John S, Jr., Pres.--Mar-Mac Manufacturing Company, Inc., McBee, SC; *U.S. Private*, pg. 701

McLeod, P.L. "Mac", Jr., Pres.--The Colonial BancGroup, Inc., Montgomery, AL; *U.S. Public*, pg. 400

McLeod, S.D., Pres.--CIMCO Refrigeration, Toronto, Canada; *Int'l*, pg. 1400

McLeod, Wayne M.E., Pres. & Chief Exec. Officer--CCL Industries, Inc., Willowdale, Canada; *Int'l*, pg. 238

McLevish, Timothy R., Pres.--Mead Specialty Paper, South Lee, MA; *U.S. Public*, pg. 1074

McLoughlin, Michael J., Pres.--Sysco Food Services of Portland, Inc., Wilsonville, OR; *U.S. Public*, pg. 1552

McLoughlin, Robert, Pres.--Blodgett Combi, Burlington, VT; *U.S. Public*, pg. 1064

McLuckey, John A., Pres.--Boeing North American, Seal Beach, CA; *U.S. Public*, pg. 241

McMahon, Don, Pres.-Strapping Div.--A.J. Gerrard and Company, Des Plaines, IL; *U.S. Private*, pg. 449

McMahon, Kevin J., Pres.--Edwards and Kelcey, Inc., Boston, MA; *U.S. Private*, pg. 364

McMahon, Kevin J., Pres.--Edwards & Kelcey Wireless, Morristown, NJ; *U.S. Private*, pg. 364

McMahon, Patrick, Pres. & Chief Exec. Officer--Virginia Tourism Corp., Richmond, VA; *U.S. Private*, pg. 1141

McMahon, Raymond D., Pres.--Baldwin InLine Finishing, Willowbrook, IL; *U.S. Public*, pg. 170

McMahon, Richard A., Pres. & Chief Exec. Officer--Minnesota Brewing Company, Saint Paul, MN; *U.S. Public*, pg. 1115

McMahon, William J., Pres. & Chief Exec. Officer--Lund International Holdings, Inc., Anoka, MN; *U.S. Public*, pg. 1020

McMahon, William J., Pres.--Lund Industries Inc., Anoka, MN; *U.S. Public*, pg. 1020

McManimon, Thomas, Mng. Partner & Creative Dir.--Gillespie, Lawrenceville, NJ; *U.S. Private*, pg. 453

McManus, James A., Pres. & Chief Exec. Officer--Radio City Productions, New York, NY; *Int'l*, pg. 873

McManus, James T., Pres. & Chief Oper. Officer--Taurus Exploration, Inc., Birmingham, AL; *U.S. Public*, pg. 581

McManus, Michael F., Chm. Bd., Pres. & Chief Exec. Officer--Header Products Inc., Romulus, MI; *U.S. Private*, pg. 514

McMeekin, H. Thomas, Pres.--Lincoln Investment Management Inc., Fort Wayne, IN; *U.S. Public*, pg. 998

McMeekin, H. Thomas, Pres.--Lincoln National Realty Corporation, Fort Wayne, IN; *U.S. Public*, pg. 998

McMeekin, H. Thomas, Pres.--Lincoln National Income Fund, Inc., Baltimore, MD; *U.S. Public*, pg. 998

McMeekin, William D., Pres. & Chief Exec. Officer--Granite Savings Bank & Trust Company, Barre, VT; *U.S. Public*, pg. 187

McMichael, John, Pres.--Performance Chevrolet & GEO, Sacramento, CA; *U.S. Private*, pg. 853

McMillan, C. Steven, Pres.--Sara Lee Corporation, Chicago, IL; *U.S. Public*, pg. 1432

McMillan, Howard L., Jr., Pres. & Chief Oper. Officer--Deposit Guaranty Corp., Jackson, MS; *U.S. Public*, pg. 500

McMillan, Peter B., Pres. & Chief Oper. Officer--The Mills Corporation, Arlington, VA; *U.S. Public*, pg. 1113

McMillen, John, Pres. & Chief Exec. Officer--The Garber Company, Ashland, OH; *U.S. Public*, pg. 303

McMillen, Karl, Pres.--Todd Pipe & Supply Hawthorne, Hawthorne, CA; *U.S. Private*, pg. 1090

McMillen, Karl, Pres.--Todd Pipe & Supply-West L.A., Los Angeles, CA; *U.S. Private*, pg. 1090

McMorris, Jerry, Pres. & Chief Exec. Officer--NW Transport Service, Inc., Denver, CO; *U.S. Private*, pg. 772

McMullen, Bob, Pres.--I.P.C., Tucker, GA; *U.S. Public*, pg. 484
McMullen, Kevin, Pres.--GenCorp Wallcovering Div., Salem, NH; *U.S. Public*, pg. 706
McMullen, Kevin, Pres.--GenCorp Decorative & Building Products Div., Maumee, OH; *U.S. Public*, pg. 706
McMullen, Kevin, Pres.--GenCorp Designed Product Div., Columbus, MS; *U.S. Public*, pg. 706
McMullen, Kevin, Pres.--GenCorp Designed Product Mfg. Div., Jeannette, PA; *U.S. Public*, pg. 706
McMullen, Kevin, Pres.--GenCorp Decorative Product Manufacturing Div., Auburn, PA; *U.S. Public*, pg. 706
McMullen, Tom, Pres.--Varlen Instruments, Inc., Bellwood, IL; *U.S. Public*, pg. 1711
McMullin, Dan, Pres.--Mini Mart, Inc., Casper, WY; *U.S. Public*, pg. 967
McMunn, William H., Pres.--Indigo Development Inc., Daytona Beach, FL; *U.S. Public*, pg. 437
McMurray, Darin, Pres.--Lee/Collier, Fort Myers, FL; *U.S. Public*, pg. 1683
McMurray, John, Pres.--Viking Pump, Inc., Cedar Falls, IA; *U.S. Public*, pg. 862
McMurry, W.N., Pres.--Rissler & McMurry Company, Casper, WY; *U.S. Private*, pg. 933
McNable, John, Pres. & Chief Exec. Officer--NVF Company, Yorklyn, DE; *U.S. Private*, pg. 772
McNair, Carl H., Pres.--Enterprise Management, Reston, VA; *U.S. Private*, pg. 351
McNair, Joe, Pres. & Chief Exec. Officer--Whitfield Foods, Inc., Montgomery, AL; *U.S. Private*, pg. 1173
McNally, Robert, Pres.--Bridgestone/Firestone Off Road Tire Company, Nashville, TN; *Int'l*, pg. 213
McNally, Thomas M., Pres.--Abbott Chemical & Agricultural Products Division, Abbott Park, IL; *U.S. Public*, pg. 13
McNamara, Austin T., Pres. & Chief Exec. Officer--General Cigar Company, Inc., Bloomfield, CT; *U.S. Public*, pg. 708
McNamara, David, Pres.--RMT Technology, Bellwood, IL; *U.S. Private*, pg. 927
McNamara, Dennis C., Sr., Pres.--McNamara Pontiac Isuzu Inc., Orlando, FL; *U.S. Private*, pg. 724
McNamara, James, Pres. & Chief Exec. Officer--New World Entertainment, Inc., Los Angeles, CA; *Int'l*, pg. 926
McNamara, Jim, Pres.-Worldwide T.V. Distr.--Universal Studios TV, Universal City, CA; *Int'l*, pg. 1215
McNamara, John D., Pres.--ADM Processing Div., Decatur, IL; *U.S. Public*, pg. 127
McNamara, Kevin J., Pres.--Chemed Corporation, Cincinnati, OH; *U.S. Public*, pg. 343
McNamara, Michael, Exec. V.P. & Gen. Mgr.-Global Mktg. & U.S. Bus.--Neutrogena Corporation, Los Angeles, CA; *U.S. Public*, pg. 928
McNamara, Robert, Pres.--Bank of Dwight, Dwight, IL; *U.S. Public*, pg. 1316
McNamara, William P., III, Pres. & Chief Exec. Officer--Famous-Barr, Saint Louis, MO; *U.S. Public*, pg. 1063
McNamee, James M., Chm. Bd., Pres. & Chief Exec. Officer--Hooper Holmes Corporation, Basking Ridge, NJ; *U.S. Public*, pg. 835
McNamee, Rick, Chm. Bd., Pres. & Chief Exec. Officer--Continental Circuits Corp., Phoenix, AZ; *U.S. Public*, pg. 440
McNaughton, Robert L., Chm. Bd. & Pres.--McNaughton & Gunn, Inc., Saline, MI; *U.S. Private*, pg. 724
McNealy, Scott G., Chm. Bd., Pres. & Chief Exec. Officer--Sun Microsystems, Inc., Palo Alto, CA; *U.S. Public*, pg. 1531
McNeel, Clayton W., Pres. & Chief Oper. Officer--McNeel International Corp., Tampa, FL; *U.S. Private*, pg. 724
McNeel, R.L., Pres.--Amoco Performance Products, Inc., Alpharetta, GA; *U.S. Public*, pg. 102
McNeeley, Bob, Pres.--Reilly Industries Inc., Indianapolis, IN; *U.S. Private*, pg. 919
McNeeley, Donald R., Pres. & Chief Oper. Officer--Chicago Tube & Iron Co., Chicago, IL; *U.S. Private*, pg. 235
McNeeley, Robert D., Pres.--Reilly Industries, Inc., Indianapolis, IN; *U.S. Private*, pg. 919
McNeil, D., Pres.--Great Northern Paper, Inc., Millinocket, ME; *U.S. Public*, pg. 248
McNeil, Gordon H., Pres.--Magnetic Technologies Corporation, Rochester, NY; *U.S. Public*, pg. 1420
McNeil, Robert D., Pres.--Penguin Industries, Inc., Coatesville, PA; *U.S. Private*, pg. 849
McNeill, Corbin A., Jr., Chm. Bd., Pres. & Chief Exec. Officer--PECO Energy Company, Philadelphia, PA; *U.S. Public*, pg. 1268
McNeill, Michael, Pres. & Chief Exec. Officer--Gifford-Hill Company, Dallas, TX; *Int'l*, pg. 593
McNeilly, Robert E., III, Chm., Pres. & Chief Exec. Officer--SunTrust Bank, Alabama, N.A., Florence, AL; *U.S. Public*, pg. 1538
McNeilus, Denzil, Pres.--McNeilus Companies, Dodge Center, MN; *U.S. Private*, pg. 725
McNelis, Michael F., Pres. & Chief Exec. Officer--Equitable Financial Consultants, Inc., New York, NY; *U.S. Public*, pg. 589
McNerney, W. James, Pres.--G.E. Aircraft Engines, Cincinnati, OH; *U.S. Public*, pg. 710
McNiel, Bruce, Pres.--Dayco Products Inc., Miamisburg, OH; *U.S. Public*, pg. 1045
McNiel, Bruce A., Pres.--Dayco Swan Corporation, Worthington, OH; *U.S. Public*, pg. 1045
McNiel, Bruce A., Pres.--Mark IV Industrial, Dayton, OH; *U.S. Public*, pg. 1045
McNulty, James F., Pres. & Chief Exec. Officer--Parsons Corporation, Pasadena, CA; *U.S. Private*, pg. 841
McNulty, James F., III, Pres.--Total Security Solutions, Chicago, IL; *U.S. Public*, pg. 245
McNulty, R.W. Roy, Pres.--Shorts Brothers PLC, Belfast, United Kingdom; *Int'l*, pg. 200
McNutt, Don, Pres.--Midwest Petroleum Co., Saint Louis, MO; *U.S. Private*, pg. 745
McNutt, Robert P., Pres. & Chief Oper. Officer--Collin Street Bakery, Corsicana, TX; *U.S. Private*, pg. 252
McPhail, Douglas J., Pres., Chief Exec. & Fin. Officer & Treas.--Indiana Records Managers, Fishers, IN; *U.S. Private*, pg. 560
McPhail, Gary, Pres.--AmerUS Life, Des Moines, IA; *U.S. Private*, pg. 59
McPhail, Robert L., Gen. Mgr.--Basin Electric Power Cooperative, Bismarck, ND; *U.S. Private*, pg. 121
McPhearson, J.R., Jr., Pres.--Strachan Shipping Co., Garden City, GA; *U.S. Private*, pg. 1045
McPhedrain, Willard M., Pres.--Mary Maxim, Inc., Port Huron, MI; *U.S. Private*, pg. 716
McPhee, Jim, Pres.--FS Concepts, Inc., Anaheim, CA; *U.S. Private*, pg. 818
McPheters, Rebecca, Pres. & Chief Exec. Officer--Simmons, New York, NY; *Int'l*, pg. 1483
McPike, Rod A., Pres.--Propak Systems Ltd., Airdrie, Canada; *Int'l*, pg. 1071
McQueary, C.E., Pres.--Lucent Technologies Advanced Technology Systems, Greensboro, NC; *U.S. Public*, pg. 1017
McQueen, Trina, Pres.--The Discovery Channel, Willowdale, Canada; *Int'l*, pg. 1343
McQueen, William L., Pres. & Treas.--Bergstrom Capital Corporation, Seattle, WA; *U.S. Public*, pg. 215
McQuern, Marcia, Pres., Editor & Publr.--Press Enterprise Company, Riverside, CA; *U.S. Public*, pg. 209
McQuinn, A.E., Pres.--Lor Al Products Inc, Benson, MN; *U.S. Public*, pg. 6
McRae, D. Gary, Chm. Bd., Pres. & Chief Exec. Officer--McRae Industries, Inc., Mount Gilead, NC; *U.S. Public*, pg. 1073
McRae, D. Gary, Pres.--Compsee, Inc., Mount Gilead, NC; *U.S. Public*, pg. 1073
McRae, D. Gary, Pres.--McRae Graphics, Inc., Mount Gilead, NC; *U.S. Public*, pg. 1074
McRoberts, T. Michael, Pres.--McGuire Manufacturing, Cheshire, CT; *U.S. Private*, pg. 126
McShane, Brian, Pres. & Chief Exec. Officer--Advertising Checking Bureau Incorporated, New York, NY; *U.S. Private*, pg. 23
McSwain, Ronald, Pres.--McSwain Carpets Inc., Cincinnati, OH; *U.S. Private*, pg. 725
McTeer, Robert D., Jr., Pres. & Chief Exec. Officer--Federal Reserve Bank of Dallas, Dallas, TX; *U.S. Private*, pg. 399
McVay, Jesse, Pres.--Bryan Steam Corporation, Peru, IN; *U.S. Private*, pg. 176
McWane, Phillip, Pres.--McWane, Inc., Birmingham, AL; *U.S. Private*, pg. 725
McWhinnie, Craig, Pres.--Summit-Canada, Toronto, Canada; *U.S. Public*, pg. 78
McWilliams, Alexander M., Pres.--McWilliams Forge Co., Rockaway, NJ; *U.S. Private*, pg. 725
Mead, Dana G., Chm. Bd., Pres. & Chief Exec. Officer--Tenneco Inc., Greenwich, CT; *U.S. Public*, pg. 1577
Mead, Gary L., Pres. & Chief Exec. Officer--La Quinta Inns, Inc., San Antonio, TX; *U.S. Public*, pg. 972
Meade, John, Pres. & Chief Exec. Officer--Hanover Bank, Mechanicsville, VA; *U.S. Public*, pg. 1039
Meade, Kenneth, Pres.--Meade Group, Inc., Utica, MI; *U.S. Private*, pg. 725
Meade, William C., Pres.--The Journal, Williamston, SC; *U.S. Private*, pg. 601
Meader, Peggy, Pres. & Chief Exec. Officer--Inland Associates, Olathe, KS; *U.S. Private*, pg. 563
Meader, Scott, Pres. & Chief Exec. Officer--The Milnot Company, Saint Louis, MO; *U.S. Private*, pg. 749
Meadlock, James W., Chm. Bd., Pres. & Chief Exec. Officer--Intergraph Corporation, Huntsville, AL; *U.S. Public*, pg. 890
Meador, Thomas E., Pres. & Chief Oper. Officer--The Balcor Company, Bannockburn, IL; *U.S. Public*, pg. 74
Meadows, Arthur, Pres.--Erdle Perforating of Carolina, Charlotte, NC; *U.S. Private*, pg. 380
Meagher, Joseph B., Pres. & Chief Exec. Officer--Yankee Publishing Incorporated, Dublin, NH; *U.S. Private*, pg. 1195
Meakem, John J., Jr., Chm. Bd., Pres. & Chief Exec. Officer--Advanced Polymer Systems, Redwood City, CA; *U.S. Public*, pg. 22
Mealey, Don, Pres.--Royal Jeep Eagle Chrysler Plymouth, Inc., Casselberry, FL; *U.S. Private*, pg. 948
Mealey, Donald, Pres.--Don Mealey Chevrolet Inc., Orlando, FL; *U.S. Private*, pg. 726
Mealey, George A., Pres. & Chief Oper. Officer--Freeport-McMoRan Copper & Gold, Inc., New Orleans, LA; *U.S. Public*, pg. 680
Meanti, Luigi, Chm. & Pres.--ENI S.p.A., Rome, Italy; *Int'l*, pg. 428
Meany, William F., Pres.--SAFECO Credit Company, Inc., Seattle, WA; *U.S. Public*, pg. 1423
Mears, William A., Pres.--Lan-O-Sheen, Inc., Saint Paul, MN; *U.S. Private*, pg. 645
Mebane, David C., Chm. Bd., Pres., Chief Exec. & Oper. Officer--Madison Gas and Electric Company, Madison, WI; *U.S. Public*, pg. 1032
Mebus, Philip K., Jr., Pres. & Treas.--Arrow Metal Products Corporation, Detroit, MI; *U.S. Private*, pg. 85
Mechanic, William M., Pres.--Twentieth Century Fox Film Corp., Los Angeles, CA; *Int'l*, pg. 926
Mechigian, Robert, Sr., Pres.--Farmington Hills Holding Company, Farmington, MI; *U.S. Private*, pg. 395
Mechlin, David, Sr. Partner & Worldwide Client Service Dir.-Kimberly-Clark NY--Ogilvy & Mather Worldwide, Inc., New York, NY; *Int'l*, pg. 1483
Mechura, Frank, Pres. & Chief Exec. Officer--Crown Cork of Canada Ltd., Concord, Canada; *U.S. Public*, pg. 464
Mechura, Frank J., Pres. & Chief Exec. Officer--Crown Cork & Seal Canada, Inc., Concord, Canada; *U.S. Public*, pg. 464
Medary, William, Pres. & Chief Exec. Officer--Bass Enterprises Production Company, Fort Worth, TX; *U.S. Private*, pg. 122
Medavoy, Michael, Chm. Bd.--Tri-Star Pictures, Inc., Culver City, CA; *Int'l*, pg. 1282
Medhurst, Tom, Pres.--L & L Nursery Supply, Inc., Chino, CA; *U.S. Private*, pg. 638
Medico, Thomas, Pres.--Medico Industries, Inc., Wilkes-Barre, PA; *U.S. Private*, pg. 728
Medina, Agustin, Chm., Pres. & Creative Dir.--La Banda de Agustin Medina S.A., Madrid, Spain; *Int'l*, pg. 783
Medina, Armando M., Pres. & Chief Exec. Officer--Rizal Commercial Banking Corporation, Makati, Philippines; *Int'l*, pg. 1190
Medina, Dionisio Garza, Chm. Bd., Pres. & Chief Exec. Officer--Alfa, S.A. de C.V., Garza Garcia, Mexico; *Int'l*, pg. 56
Medley, Ben, Pres.--Tracor Flight Systems, Inc., Mojave, CA; *U.S. Public*, pg. 1627
Medlin, Tom, Pres.--Marine Midland Mortgage Servicing Corporation, Charlotte, NC; *Int'l*, pg. 581
Medved, Jon, Pres.--Walter Drake, Inc., Colorado Springs, CO; *U.S. Private*, pg. 421
Mee, George, Chm. & Pres.--Mallery Lumber Corp., Emporium, PA; *U.S. Private*, pg. 698
Meecham, Bob, Pres.--Mohawk Plastics, Inc., Riviera Beach, FL; *U.S. Private*, pg. 755
Meeker, Thomas H., Pres. & Chief Exec. Officer--Churchill Downs, Inc., Louisville, KY; *U.S. Public*, pg. 356
Meelia, Richard D., Pres. & Chief Exec. Officer--The Kendall Company, Mansfield, MA; *U.S. Public*, pg. 1647
Meelia, Richard D., Pres.--Kendall Healthcare Products Company, Mansfield, MA; *U.S. Public*, pg. 1647
Meerstadt, Bert, Pres. & Chief Exec. Officer--PMSVW/Young & Rubicam B.V., Amsterdam, Netherlands; *U.S. Private*, pg. 1199
Meese, Gerhard, Pres.--Universal Instruments Corporation, Binghamton, NY; *U.S. Public*, pg. 522
Meeuwsen, Michael D., Pres. & Chief Exec. Officer--First Northern Capital Corp., Green Bay, WI; *U.S. Public*, pg. 636
Mefford, Dean A., Pres. & Chief Exec. Officer--Viskase Corporation, Chicago, IL; *U.S. Public*, pg. 586
Mega, John, Pres.--L3 Communications Narda-Microwave Div., Hauppauge, NY; *U.S. Private*, pg. 638
Mehiel, Dennis, Chm. Bd. & Pres.--Four M Corporation, Inc., Valhalla, NY; *U.S. Private*, pg. 421
Mehlis, David L., Chm. Bd., Pres. & Chief Exec. Officer--Cook Communication Ministries, Colorado Springs, CO; *U.S. Private*, pg. 272
Mehta, Shailesh J., Chm. Bd., Pres. & Chief Exec. Officer--Providian Financial Corporation, San Francisco, CA; *U.S. Public*, pg. 1338
Meider, Elmer, Jr., Pres.--Highlights for Children, Inc., Columbus, OH; *U.S. Private*, pg. 528
Meier, Norman M., Pres. & Chief Exec. Officer--Columbia Laboratories, Inc., Miami, FL; *U.S. Public*, pg. 405
Meier, Paul, Pres.--Credit Suisse, Zurich, Switzerland; *Int'l*, pg. 345
Meier, Robert C., Pres.--Taylor - Morley Management Company, Saint Louis, MO; *U.S. Private*, pg. 1071
Meiners, Donald E., Pres.--Entergy Mississippi, Inc., Jackson, MS; *U.S. Public*, pg. 586
Meinert, K.J., Pres. & Chief Exec. Officer--CGC Inc., Mississauga, Canada; *U.S. Public*, pg. 1660
Meinig, Peter, Pres. & Chief Exec. Officer--HM International, Tulsa, OK; *U.S. Private*, pg. 491
Meirelles, Henrique de Campos, Pres. & Chief Oper. Officer--BankBoston Corporation, Boston, MA; *U.S. Public*, pg. 183
Meissner, Art, Pres.--600 Racing Inc., Harrisburg, NC; *U.S. Public*, pg. 1498
Meith, Mateland L., Jr., Pres.--GTE California Incorporated, Irving, TX; *U.S. Public*, pg. 697
Mektrakarn, Wicha, Pres.--Burgmann Thailand Co. Ltd., Rayong, Thailand; *Int'l*, pg. 234
Melancon, Barry C., Pres. & Chief Exec. Officer--American Institute of C.P.A.'s Inc., New York, NY; *U.S. Private*, pg. 57
Melchiorre, Donald, Pres.--Pennsylvania Crusher Corp., Broomall, PA; *U.S. Private*, pg. 850
Melchor, Joseph, Pres.--Gunther Nash Mining Construction, Saint Louis, MO; *U.S. Private*, pg. 32
Meldahl, Michael J., Pres. & Chief Oper. Officer--Tetragenics, Inc., Butte, MT; *U.S. Public*, pg. 1127
Meldahl, Michael J., Pres. & Chief Oper. Officer--TRI Touch America, Butte, MT; *U.S. Public*, pg. 1127
Meldrum, Stephen T., Pres.--Lincoln National (China) Inc., Fort Wayne, IN; *U.S. Public*, pg. 998
Mele, Dennis A., Pres.--Cleaners Hanger Co., Palm Harbor, FL; *U.S. Private*, pg. 245
Melgaard, John, Pres.--Chr. Hansen G.m.b.H., Lubeck, Germany; *Int'l*, pg. 289
Melgar, Ismael, Pres.--Spicer Driveshaft Div., Toledo, OH; *U.S. Public*, pg. 479
Melia, Kevin, Pres. & Chief Exec. Officer--Manufacturers' Services Ltd., Concord, MA; *U.S. Private*, pg. 701
Mellema, Andries, Pres.--A.G. Simpson Co. Limited, Scarborough, Canada; *Int'l*, pg. 1252
Mellen, Harold J., Jr., Pres. & Chief Exec. Officer--MDU Resources Group, Inc., Bismarck, ND; *U.S. Public*, pg. 1025
Mellen, Timothy J., Pres.--Edwards Systems Tech, Cheshire, CT; *U.S. Public*, pg. 726
Mellick, William L., Pres. & Chief Exec. Officer--20th Century Industries, Woodland Hills, CA; *U.S. Public*, pg. 1646
Melling, A. Frederick, Pres. & Chief Exec. Officer--Willis Corroon Melling Inc., Montreal, Canada; *Int'l*, pg. 1509
Mellis, Warren, Pres.--Golden Sun Feeds, Inc., Estherville, IA; *U.S. Private*, pg. 895
Mellott, Paul C., Jr., Pres.--H.B. Mellott Estate, Inc., Warfordsburg, PA; *U.S. Private*, pg. 730
Mellow, James, Pres.--Draw-Tite, Inc., Canton, MI; *U.S. Public*, pg. 1054
Melloy, Robert E., Pres.--Melloy Bros. Enterprises, Albuquerque, NM; *U.S. Private*, pg. 730

Melnuk, Paul D., Chm. Bd., Pres. & Chief Oper. Officer--Clark Refining & Marketing Inc., Saint Louis, MO; U.S. Private, pg. 243
Meloni, Stefano, Chm. Bd., Pres. & Chief Exec. Officer--Eridania Beghin-Say Group, Neuilly-sur-Seine, France; Int'l, pg. 324
Meloon, Walter N., Pres. & Chief Exec. Officer--Correct Craft, Inc., Orlando, FL; U.S. Private, pg. 276
Melsop, J. William, Pres. & Chief Exec. Officer--The Austin Company, Cleveland, OH; U.S. Private, pg. 99
Melton, Owen B., Jr., Pres. & Chief Oper. Officer--First Indiana Corporation, Indianapolis, IN; U.S. Public, pg. 1484
Meltzer, Howard C., Pres. & Chief Oper. Officer--PC Quote, Inc., Chicago, IL; U.S. Public, pg. 1240
Meltzer, Robert K., Pres. & Chief Exec. Officer--Evans, Inc., Chicago, IL; U.S. Public, pg. 596
Melucci, Thomas, Pres. & Chief Exec. Officer--Priority Finishing Corp., Fall River, MA; U.S. Private, pg. 887
Melville, James, Pres.--First Commonwealth Corporation, Springfield, IL; U.S. Private, pg. 406
Melville, James, Pres. & Chief Oper. Officer--Abraham Lincoln Insurance Co., Springfield, IL; U.S. Private, pg. 406
Melville, James, Pres. & Chief Oper. Officer--Universal Guarantee Life Insurance, Springfield, IL; U.S. Private, pg. 406
Melvin, John G., Pres.--Cone Drive Textron, Traverse City, MI; U.S. Public, pg. 1589
Melvin, Joseph, Pres. & Chief Oper. Officer--Finlay Fine Jewelry Corporation, New York, NY; U.S. Public, pg. 624
Melvin, T. Stephen, Pres.--Datron Incorporated, Windsor, CT; U.S. Private, pg. 313
Melzer, Robert M., Pres. & Chief Exec. Officer--Property Capital Trust, Boston, MA; U.S. Public, pg. 1335
Memelstein, Joseph, Pres.--Elgin Watch Company, Long Island City, NY; U.S. Private, pg. 371
Menapace, J. Howard, Pres.--Rico Motor Company, Gallup, NM; U.S. Private, pg. 930
Menard, Alain, Pres.--LeaRonal France, Lyon, France; U.S. Public, pg. 982
Menard, John, Pres.--Menards, Inc., Eau Claire, WI; U.S. Private, pg. 731
Menchace, Anthony L., Pres.--Comp-U-Card Division, Stamford, CT; U.S. Public, pg. 320
Mende, Toshio, Pres.--Chiba Kogyo Bank, Chiba, Japan; Int'l, pg. 283
Mendell, Mark R., Pres.--Cannon, Grand Island, NY; U.S. Private, pg. 205
Mendello, William L., Pres. & Chief Oper. Officer--Fender Musical Instruments, Scottsdale, AZ; U.S. Private, pg. 400
Mendelsohn, Robert V., Chm. Bd., Pres. & Chief Exec. Officer--Royal Insurance, Charlotte, NC; Int'l, pg. 1130
Mendelson, Ira, Pres. & Chief Exec. Officer--Murry's, Inc., Upper Marlboro, MD; U.S. Private, pg. 768
Mendelson, Laurans, Chm. Bd., Pres. & Chief Exec. Officer--HEICO Corporation, Hollywood, FL; U.S. Public, pg. 804
Mendez, Dr. Elena Salgado, Pres.--Hispasat, S.A., Madrid, Spain; Int'l, pg. 1372
Mendez, Ivan A., Pres. & Chief Oper. Officer--Scotiabank de Puerto Rico, Hato Rey, PR; Int'l, pg. 156
Mendez, Martin, Pres.--H.H. Robertson, Inc., Burlington, Canada; U.S. Public, pg. 1394
Mendik, Bernard H., Chm. Bd.--MENDIK Management Co., Inc., New York, NY; U.S. Private, pg. 731
Mendius, T., Pres.--Silbrico Corporation, Hodgkins, IL; U.S. Private, pg. 1000
Mendoza, Lope M., Pres.--Corporacion Grupo Quimico, S.A.C.A., Caracas, Venezuela; Int'l, pg. 331
Menechian, A., Pres.--AGRA Spectrocan Limited, Ottawa, Canada; Int'l, pg. 30
Menegazzi, Carmen, Mng. Dir.--Columbia Tri-Star Films (UK), London, United Kingdom; Int'l, pg. 1281
Menezes, Lenny, Pres.--Taj International Hotels, Washington, DC; U.S. Private, pg. 1067
Meng, Tan Siak, Pres.--Torita Corporation Ltd., Zhuhai, China; Int'l, pg. 651
Mengedoth, Donald R., Chm. Bd., Pres., & Chief Exec. Officer--Community First Bankshares, Inc., Fargo, ND; U.S. Public, pg. 416
Mengel, Richard R., Chief Exec. Officer--Glen-Gery Corporation, Wyomissing, PA; Int'l, pg. 658
Menger, Joe L., Pres.--The Machine Tool Group, Cleveland, OH; U.S. Public, pg. 503
Menholt, Dennis, Pres.--Denny Menholt Frontier Chevrolet, Billings, MT; U.S. Private, pg. 324
Menniti, Joseph, Pres.--DNE Systems, Inc., Wallingford, CT; U.S. Public, pg. 58
Menten, Jurgen, Chief Oper. Officer & Chief Fin. Officer--Boehringer Mannheim GmbH, Mannheim, Germany; Int'l, pg. 331
Mentzer, Carl F., Chm. Bd., Pres. & Chief Exec. Officer--SunTrust Bank, Tampa Bay, Tampa, FL; U.S. Public, pg. 1538
Menzer, Donald, Pres.--Marathon Cheese Corp., Marathon, WI; U.S. Private, pg. 701
Menzies, Evan, Pres.--Warren Gorham Lamont, New York, NY; U.S. Public, pg. 1602
Menzies, Jack, Pres.--E.R. Probyn Ltd., New Westminster, Canada; Int'l, pg. 1071
Menzies, Jack, Pres.--Allmac Lumber Ltd., New Westminster, Canada; Int'l, pg. 1071
Menzies, Jack, Pres.--Probyn Log, Ltd., New Westminster, Canada; Int'l, pg. 1071
Menzies, James P., Pres. & Chief Exec. Officer--Key Bank of New York, Albany, NY; U.S. Public, pg. 954
Menzilcoiglu, Onat, Pres.--FORE Systems, Inc., Warrendale, PA; U.S. Public, pg. 667
Menzler, Jurgen, Dr., Chief Exec. Officer--Pittler Maschinenfabrik AG, Langen, Germany; Int'l, pg. 1128
Mer, Francis, Chm. Bd. & Chief Exec. Officer--Groupe Usinor, Paris, France; Int'l, pg. 570
Merber, Gene, Pres.--U.S. Lock, Brentwood, NY; U.S. Public, pg. 1748
Mercer, James, Pres.--GeoTrans, Inc., Sterling, VA; U.S. Public, pg. 1582
Mercer, William J., Pres. & Chief Exec. Officer--ALARIS Medical, Inc., San Diego, CA; U.S. Public, pg. 35
Merceron-Vicat, Jacques, Pres.--Vicat S.A., Paris, France; Int'l, pg. 606
Mercier, Douglas, Pres.--Carlton Manufacturing, Inc., Goshen, IN; U.S. Private, pg. 212
Mercier, Gustavo, Pres.--Sealy Mattress Company of Puerto Rico, Rio Piedras, PR; U.S. Private, pg. 979
Merck, J. Wayne, Pres.--Shakespeare Composites & Electronics, Newberry, SC; U.S. Public, pg. 940
Meredith, George, Pres. & Creative Dir.--Gianettino & Meredith Advertising, Short Hills, NJ; U.S. Private, pg. 450
Merelli, F.H., Chm. Bd., Pres. & Chief Exec. Officer--Key Production Company, Inc., Denver, CO; U.S. Public, pg. 953
Merenyi, Eva, Mgr.--GGK Budapest, Budapest, Hungary; Int'l, pg. 1335
Merillat, Richard, Chief Oper. Officer--Merillat Industries Inc., Adrian, MI; U.S. Public, pg. 1053
Meringola, Paul D., Chm. Bd., Pres., Chief Exec. Officer & Chief Oper. Officer--Medical Action Industries Inc., Hauppauge, NY; U.S. Public, pg. 1079
Merinoff, Charles, Pres.--Charmer Industries, Astoria, NY; U.S. Private, pg. 230
Merkel, P. Peter, Pres.--Band-It-Idex, Inc., Denver, CO; U.S. Public, pg. 862
Merkel, Steve, Pres.--Loctite Corp. North American Group, Rocky Hill, CT; Int'l, pg. 611
Merkhofer, James, Pres.--Mexican Industries in Michigan, Detroit, MI; U.S. Private, pg. 739
Merkley, Parry, Pres.--Merkley Newman Harty, New York, NY; U.S. Public, pg. 1224
Merksamer, Gerald M., Pres.--De Vons Jewelers, Sacramento, CA; U.S. Private, pg. 318
Merksamer, Samuel J., Pres. & Chief Exec. Officer--Barry's Jewelers, Inc., Monrovia, CA; U.S. Public, pg. 192
Merloni, Vittorio, Dtre., Chm. Bd., Pres. & Chief Exec. Officer--Merloni Elettrodomestici S.P.A., Fabriano, Italy; Int'l, pg. 860
Mermelstein, David, Pres.--Croton Watch Company & Nationwide Time, New York, NY; U.S. Private, pg. 291
Merodio Lopez, Juan Carlos, Pres.--Transportacion Maritima Mexicana S.A. de C.V., Mexico, Mexico; Int'l, pg. 1418
Merrell, F.Max, Pres.--Mobil Mining & Minerals Company, Ashland, VA; U.S. Public, pg. 1118
Merrell, John K., Pres., Chief Exec. Officer & Chief Oper. Officer--Industrial Dielectrics, Inc., Noblesville, IN; U.S. Private, pg. 560
Merrell, W.M., Pres. & Chief Exec. Officer--Howard, Merrell & Partners, Inc., Raleigh, NC; U.S. Private, pg. 542
Merrick, Jim, Pres.--Roth Corporation, Minnetonka, MN; U.S. Private, pg. 1099
Merrifield, Ann, Pres.--Genzyme Genetics Div., Santa Fe, NM; U.S. Public, pg. 733
Merrill, Keniston P., Chm. Bd., Pres. & Chief Exec. Officer--Sentinel Advisors, Inc., Montpelier, VT; U.S. Private, pg. 785
Merrill, Keniston P., Chm., Pres. & Chief Exec. Officer--National Life Investment Management Co., Inc., Montpelier, VT; U.S. Private, pg. 785
Merrill, Philip, Pres. & Publr.--Capital-Gazette Communications, Inc., Annapolis, MD; U.S. Private, pg. 649
Merrill, Terry M., Pres.--Mar-Hyde Corporation, Cincinnati, OH; U.S. Public, pg. 1357
Merrill, Terry M., Pres.--Bondo/Mar-Hyde Corporation, Atlanta, GA; U.S. Public, pg. 1357
Merriman, Mike, Chm. Bd., Pres. & Chief Exec. Officer--Royal Appliance Mfg. Co., Cleveland, OH; U.S. Public, pg. 1410
Merritt, Robert J., Pres.--CIT Group/Industrial Financing, Livingston, NJ; Int'l, pg. 360
Merritt, S., Pres.--Van Leer (U.K.) Ltd., Cobham, United Kingdom; Int'l, pg. 1147
Merritts, Glenn, Pres. & Chief Exec. Officer--Mednet, MPC Corporation, Las Vegas, NV; U.S. Public, pg. 1082
Merry, Bob, Pres. & Chief Exec. Officer--USDATA Corporation, Richardson, TX; U.S. Public, pg. 1425
Mershad, Fred, Pres. & Chief Oper. Oficer--The Elder-Beerman Stores Corp., Dayton, OH; U.S. Private, pg. 367
Mershad, Frederick J., Pres.--Proffitt's of Tri-Cities, Inc., Alcoa, TN; U.S. Public, pg. 1334
Mersky, Robert B., Pres.--Peregrine Capital Management, Inc., Minneapolis, MN; U.S. Public, pg. 1202
Merson, Robert, Pres. & Chief Exec. Officer--Southern Electric Supply Co., Inc., Meridian, MS; Int'l, pg. 1107
Mertens, Lynne, Pres. & Chief Exec. Officer--Warrens Waller Press, Inc., South San Francisco, CA; U.S. Private, pg. 1151
Mertes, Wayne M., Pres. & Chief Exec. Officer--National R.V., Inc., Perris, CA; U.S. Public, pg. 1159
Mesel, Bob, Pres.--BP Chemicals, Inc., Cleveland, OH; Int'l, pg. 220
Meske, Donald E., Pres.--Deluxe Homes Of PA., Inc., Berwick, PA; U.S. Private, pg. 323
Meslow, John A., Sr. V.P. & Pres.-Neurological Bus.--Medtronic, Inc., Minneapolis, MN; U.S. Public, pg. 1082
Messenger, George L., Pres. & Chief Oper. Officer--Kemper Reinsurance Co., Long Grove, IL; U.S. Private, pg. 614
Messer, James, Pres.--E & D Grain Marketing Co, Covington, KY; U.S. Private, pg. 353
Messer, John R., Pres. & Chief Exec. Officer--SaskPower, Regina, Canada; Int'l, pg. 1195
Messier, Jean-Marie, Chm. Bd. & Pres.--Compagnie Generale Des Eaux, Paris, France; Int'l, pg. 321
Messier, John R., Pres.--GTE Government Systems Corporation, Needham, MA; U.S. Public, pg. 696
Messina, Dana, Pres. & Chief Exec. Officer--Utilimaster Corp., Wakarusa, IN; U.S. Private, pg. 1130
Messina, George, Pres. & Chief Exec. Officer--Burdick, Inc., Milton, WI; U.S. Private, pg. 181
Messino, Frank, Pres. & Chief Exec. Officer--Carme' Cosmeceutical Sciences, Inc., Napa, CA; U.S. Private, pg. 213
Messmer, Daniel A., Pres.--Harvard Sports, Inc., Compton, CA; U.S. Public, pg. 591
Messmer, Harold M., Jr., Chm. Bd., Pres. & Chief Exec. Officer--Robert Half International Inc., Menlo Park, CA; U.S. Public, pg. 774
Messner, Thomas, Partner--Messner Vetere Berger McNamee Schmetterer/EURO RSCG, New York, NY; Int'l, pg. 602
Metcalfe, Jeremy W., Pres. & Chief Exec. Officer--Millicom International Cellular SA, Bertrange, Luxembourg; Int'l, pg. 867
Metcalfe, Randolph, Pres.--U.S. Pipeline, Inc., Houston, TX; Int'l, pg. 31
Metelski, John, Pres.--Front Royal Insurance Company, Richmond, VA; U.S. Private, pg. 430
Meteny, Dennis S., Pres. & Chief Exec. Officer--Respironics, Inc., Pittsburgh, PA; U.S. Public, pg. 1383
Metros, Pete, Pres.--Rapistan Demag Corp., Grand Rapids, MI; Int'l, pg. 837
Mettler, Jack, Pres. & Sec.--Circuit-Wise, Inc., North Haven, CT; U.S. Private, pg. 240
Metz, Bob, Pres.--Haas Publishing Companies, Inc., Norcross, GA; U.S. Public, pg. 1327
Metz, J. A., Pres.--Consumer Products Company, Muncie, IN; U.S. Public, pg. 56
Metz, Tom, Pres.--Model Glass Company, Anaheim, CA; U.S. Private, pg. 754
Metzger, Michael, Pres. & Chief Exec. Officer--Willis Corroon Corp. of Arizona, Phoenix, AZ; Int'l, pg. 1505
Metzger, Richard, Pres.--Verson Division, Chicago, IL; U.S. Public, pg. 48
Metzger, Samuel, Pres. & Chief Oper. Officer--Chipwich Inc., Ridgewood, NJ; U.S. Private, pg. 237
Metzler, Andrea, Pres.--Highway One Communications, Integrated Marketing Services, San Francisco, CA; U.S. Private, pg. 303
Meuleman, Robert J., Pres. & Chief Exec. Officer--Amcore Financial, Inc., Rockford, IL; U.S. Public, pg. 64
Meulnart, Alain, Pres. & Dir. Gen.--Generale Sucriere SNC, Paris, France; Int'l, pg. 548
Meuser, Scott, Pres. & Chief Exec. Officer--Pride Health Care, Inc., Exeter, PA; U.S. Private, pg. 883
Meyer, Bernard, Pres. & Chief Oper. Officer--Allright Corporation, Houston, TX; U.S. Private, pg. 42
Meyer, Douglas, Pres.-North America--Benckiser Consumer Products Inc., Greenwich, CT; Int'l, pg. 185
Meyer, Edward H., Chm., Chief Exec. Officer & Pres.-Grey Worldwide--Grey Advertising Inc., New York, NY; U.S. Public, pg. 764
Meyer, Edward J., Pres.--ERI Services, Pittsburgh, PA; U.S. Public, pg. 589
Meyer, J.J., Pres.--Holmatro Industrial & Rescue Equipment, Raamsdonksveer, Netherlands; Int'l, pg. 632
Meyer, James B., Pres. & Chief Fin. Officer--Spartan Stores Inc., Grand Rapids, MI; U.S. Private, pg. 1021
Meyer, Jerome J., Chm. Bd., Pres. & Chief Exec. Officer--Tektronix, Inc., Wilsonville, OR; U.S. Public, pg. 1567
Meyer, Jerry C., Pres.--SunBridge Assisted Living, Albuquerque, NM; U.S. Public, pg. 1531
Meyer, Lisa, Sr. Partner & Chief Oper. Officer--Carmichael Lynch, Inc., Minneapolis, MN; U.S. Private, pg. 213
Meyer, Mary Ann, Pres.--Sperry Owens, Inc., New York, NY; U.S. Private, pg. 1025
Meyer, Mary Ann, Pres.--National Dynamics, New York, NY; U.S. Private, pg. 1025
Meyer, Maurice, Jr., Chm. of the Trustees--Texas Pacific Land Trust, New York, NY; U.S. Public, pg. 1586
Meyer, Mike, Pres. & Chief Exec. Officer--CAP Gemini America, New York, NY; Int'l, pg. 263
Meyer, Paul, Pres.--Knurr AG, Fallanden, Switzerland; Int'l, pg. 739
Meyer, Paula R., Pres. & Dir.-Mktg.--Piper Capital Management, Incorporated, Minneapolis, MN; U.S. Public, pg. 1303
Meyer, Peter, Pres.--Brunner Engineering & Manufacturing, Inc., Bedford, IN; U.S. Private, pg. 176
Meyer, Raymond, Pres.--Deltec Corporation, San Diego, CA; Int'l, pg. 492
Meyer, Raymond E., Pres.--Deltec, San Diego, CA; Int'l, pg. 126
Meyer, Richard, Pres.--Soligar GmbH, Stuttgart, Germany; U.S. Private, pg. 6
Meyer, Rockford G., Pres. & Chief Exec. Officer--Citrus Corp., Houston, TX; U.S. Public, pg. 585
Meyer, Ron, Pres. & Chief Oper. Officer--Universal Studios, Inc., Universal City, CA; Int'l, pg. 1215
Meyer, Scott C., Pres.--Summit Tool Company, Akron, OH; U.S. Private, pg. 1050
Meyer, Stuart F., Pres. & Chief Exec. Officer--Civic Center Corporation, Saint Louis, MO; U.S. Public, pg. 114
Meyer, Tim, Pres.--Winters Welding Works, Inc., Winters, TX; U.S. Private, pg. 1183
Meyer, W. Darrell, Chm. Bd., Pres. & Chief Exec. Officer--Arkansas Bank & Trust, Hot Springs Village, AR; U.S. Public, pg. 630
Meyer, William J., Pres.--Central Sprinkler Corporation, Lansdale, PA; U.S. Public, pg. 327
Meyer, Wolfgang, Pres.--Battenfeld of America, West Warwick, RI; Int'l, pg. 825
Meyers, A.J., Pres.--Bio-Chem Valve Inc., Boonton, NJ; Int'l, pg. 590
Meyers, Bernard M., Pres.--Robern, Inc., Bristol, PA; U.S. Private, pg. 630
Meyers, Gerald A., Pres. & Chief Oper. Officer--Century Aluminum Company, Monterey, CA; U.S. Public, pg. 328

Meyers, Gerald A., Pres. & Chief Oper. Officer--Ravenswood Aluminum Corp., Ravenswood, WV; *U.S. Public*, pg. 328
Meyers, Howard M., Chm. Bd., Pres. & Chief Exec. Officer--Quexco Incorporated, Dallas, TX; *U.S. Private*, pg. 900
Meyers, Jerome E. Jr., Pres. & Chief Oper Officer--Dugan & Meyers Interests, Inc., Cincinnati, OH; *U.S. Private*, pg. 345
Meyers, John R., Pres. & Chief Exec. Officer--Treadco, Inc., Fort Smith, AR; *U.S. Public*, pg. 131
Meyers, Raymond N., Pres.--Halliburton Energy Services, Huntington, IN; *U.S. Public*, pg. 776
Meyers, Richard W., Pres.--Hershey Canada Inc., Mississauga, Canada; *U.S. Public*, pg. 812
Meyerson, Andrew S., Pres. & Chief Oper. Officer--Metanetics Corp., Bothell, WA; *U.S. Public*, pg. 1573
Meyocks, Terry, Pres.--New York Racing Association, Jamaica, NY; *U.S. Private*, pg. 795
Mezger, Dieter J., Pres.--Compass Design Automation Inc., San Jose, CA; *U.S. Public*, pg. 1703
Mezzano, Dario, Pres.--EURO RSCG Mezzano Costantini Mignani, Milan, Italy; *Int'l*, pg. 603
Mica, Daniel, Pres.--Credit Union National Association, Madison, WI; *U.S. Private*, pg. 288
Micali, James, Chm. Bd. & Pres.--Michelin North America, Greenville, SC; *Int'l*, pg. 322
Micciche, Romano, Pres.--Advanced Instruments, Inc., Norwood, MA; *U.S. Private*, pg. 22
Micek, Ernest S., Pres. & Chief Oper. Officer--Cargill, Wayzata, MN; *U.S. Private*, pg. 210
Michael, David, Pres.--Professional Apartment Management, Inc., Lodi, CA; *U.S. Private*, pg. 889
Michael, Dennis, Pres.--Banner Associates Inc., Laramie, WY; *U.S. Private*, pg. 114
Michael, Edward A., Pres. & Chief Exec. Officer--Diamond Brands, Inc., Cloquet, MN; *U.S. Private*, pg. 330
Michael, H. Martin, Pres.--Chromcraft Corporation, Senatobia, MS; *U.S. Public*, pg. 352
Michael, J. Christopher, Pres.--Associated Wholesalers Inc., Robesonia, PA; *U.S. Private*, pg. 93
Michael, Jeffrey J., Pres. & Chief Exec. Officer--ENStar, Inc., Eden Prairie, MN; *U.S. Public*, pg. 585
Michael, Jonathan E., Pres. & Chief Exec. Officer--RLI Insurance Company, Peoria, IL; *U.S. Public*, pg. 1356
Michael, Jonathan E., Pres. & Chief Exec. Officer--Mt. Hawley Insurance Company, Peoria, IL; *U.S. Public*, pg. 1356
Michael, Robert W., Pres. & Chief Oper. Officer--Jim Walter Homes, Inc., Tampa, FL; *U.S. Public*, pg. 1737
Michaels, Eugene H., Pres.--American Health Assistance Foundation, Rockville, MD; *U.S. Private*, pg. 56
Michaels, Jack D., Chm. Bd., Pres. & Chief Exec. Officer--HON Industries Inc., Muscatine, IA; *U.S. Public*, pg. 772
Michaels, John H., Pres.--Michaels Development Group, Inc., Clifton Park, NY; *U.S. Private*, pg. 740
Michaels, R.H., Pres.--Halma Asia Pte. Limited, Singapore, Singapore; *Int'l*, pg. 590
Michaels, Robert A., Pres. & Chief Oper. Officer--General Growth Properties Inc., Chicago, IL; *U.S. Public*, pg. 715
Michalko, M. Mark, Pres. & Chief Exec. Officer--International Lottery & Totalizator Systems, Inc., Carlsbad, CA; *U.S. Public*, pg. 900
Michel, Peter A., Pres. & Chief Exec. Officer--Brink's Home Security, Inc., Irving, TX; *U.S. Public*, pg. 1305
Michel, Philippe, Pres. & Chief Exec. Officer--Bobst Group Inc., Roseland, NJ; *Int'l*, pg. 198
Michel, Werner, Sr. Partner & Natl. Programming Dir.--BJK&E Media Group, New York, NY; *U.S. Public*, pg. 1642
Micheletto, Joe R., Pres. & Chief Exec. Officer--Ralcorp Holdings Inc., Saint Louis, MO; *U.S. Public*, pg. 1359
Michelin, Francois, Mng. Dir.--Compagnie Generale des Etablissements Michelin, Clermont, France; *Int'l*, pg. 322
Michell, S., Pres. & Chief Exec. Officer--Jardine Davies Inc., Manila, Philippines; *Int'l*, pg. 705
Michelsen, Finn, Pres.--OYO Geosciences Corporation, Houston, TX; *Int'l*, pg. 1019
Michelson, Larry D., Pres. & Treas.--Sate-Lite Manufacturing Company, Niles, IL; *U.S. Private*, pg. 598
Michner, Karl, Pres.--J. Riggings, Saint Louis, MO; *U.S. Public*, pg. 564
Micik, Alan T., Pres.--AMCORE Investment Services, Inc., Rockford, IL; *U.S. Public*, pg. 64
Mickelson, Timothy C., Pres. & Chief Oper. Officer--Marquette Medical Systems, Inc., Milwaukee, WI; *U.S. Public*, pg. 1047
Micsky, William A., Pres.--BetzDearborn Metals Process Group, Horsham, PA; *U.S. Public*, pg. 226
Middaugh, John F., Pres.--Electronic Devices and Materials, San Carlos, CA; *U.S. Public*, pg. 1003
Middleton, Charles S., Chm. Bd., Pres. & Chief Exec. Officer--Cal-Air Inc., Whittier, CA; *U.S. Private*, pg. 199
Middleton, Dale, Pres.--General Spring, Inc., Hartsville, TN; *U.S. Private*, pg. 445
Midgley, Graham, Pres. & Chief Exec. Officer--Heath Consultants Incorporated, Houston, TX; *U.S. Private*, pg. 518
Midlam, Gary R., Pres.--ACG Componentes, S.A., Agoncillo, Spain; *U.S. Public*, pg. 724
Miele, Rudolph, Co.-Pres.--Miele & Cie, GmbH, Gutersloh, Germany; *Int'l*, pg. 865
Miercort, Clifford R., Pres. & Chief Exec. Officer--The North American Coal Corporation, Dallas, TX; *U.S. Public*, pg. 1149
Might, Thomas O., Pres. & Chief Exec. Officer--Post-Newsweek Cable Division, Phoenix, AZ; *U.S. Public*, pg. 1743
Miglin, Marilyn, Pres.--Marilyn Miglin, L.P., Chicago, IL; *U.S. Private*, pg. 745
Miglio, Daniel J., Chm. Bd., Pres. & Chief Exec. Officer--The Southern New England Telephone Company, New Haven, CT; *U.S. Public*, pg. 1491
Migliori, Richard J., M.D., Pres. & Chief Exec. Officer--United HealthCare Plans of New England, Inc., Warwick, RI; *U.S. Public*, pg. 1678
Mignacco, Dominique, Pres. Chief Oper. Officer--Farr Incorporated, Chomedey, Canada; *U.S. Public*, pg. 614
Mignault, Pierre L., Pres. & Chief Exec. Officer--Provigo Inc., Montreal, Canada; *Int'l*, pg. 1072
Mignault, Pierre L., Pres. & Chief Exec. Officer--Loeb Inc., Ottawa, Canada; *Int'l*, pg. 1073
Miguel, Ricardo Mario, Pres. & Chief Fin. Officer--SmithKline Beecham Laboratorios Ltda., Rio de Janeiro, Brazil; *Int'l*, pg. 1266
Miguelucci, Edwin, Pres.--Progress Casting Group, Inc., Plymouth, MN; *U.S. Private*, pg. 890
Mihaichuk, Garry P., Pres. & Chief Exec. Officer--TransCanada International Ltd., Calgary, Canada; *Int'l*, pg. 1417
Mihailovic, Mike, Pres.--Mince Master, Chicago, IL; *U.S. Private*, pg. 749
Mihaly, Gabe, Pres. & Chief Exec. Officer--Acorn Products, Inc., Columbus, OH; *U.S. Public*, pg. 17
Mihaly, Gabe, Pres. & Chief Exec. Officer--UnionTools, Inc., Columbus, OH; *U.S. Public*, pg. 17
Mihaylo, Steve, Pres.--Inter-Tel, Incorporated-New Jersey, Phoenix, AZ; *U.S. Public*, pg. 888
Mihaylo, Steven G., Pres.--Inter-Tel Japan, Inc., Tokyo, Japan; *U.S. Public*, pg. 888
Mihos, Christy, Pres.--Christy's Markets, Inc., Brockton, MA; *U.S. Private*, pg. 238
Miisho, K., Gen. Mgr.--BancTec Japan Inc., Tokyo, Japan; *U.S. Public*, pg. 177
Mikailli, Riza, Pres.--Unify Corporation, San Jose, CA; *U.S. Public*, pg. 1665
Mikalsen, Kjell, Pres.--Kvaerner Govan Ltd., Glasgow, United Kingdom; *Int'l*, pg. 772
Mikalunas, Ed, Pres.--Laidlaw Transit, Inc., Chicago, IL; *Int'l*, *pg. 259*
Mikawa, Eiji, Pres.--Yokogawa Electric Corporation, Tokyo, Japan; *Int'l*, pg. 1520
Mikawa, Naoyoshi, Pres.--NYK Bulkship (USA) Inc., New York, NY; *Int'l*, pg. 941
Mikel, Steven, Pres.--Amerac Energy Corp., Houston, TX; *U.S. Public*, pg. 1490
Miki, Atsuo, Pres.--Yamaichi Securities Co., Ltd., Tokyo, Japan; *Int'l*, pg. 1516
Miki, Clemis, Pres.--AGA del Ecuador C.A., Quito, Ecuador; *Int'l*, pg. 13
Miki, Harakazu, Pres.--Miki Pulley Co., Ltd., Kawasaki, Japan; *Int'l*, pg. 866
Miki, Hirofumi, Pres.--Toyo Seikan Kaisha, Ltd., Tokyo, Japan; *Int'l*, pg. 1411
Miki, S., Pres.--Nissho Iwai Building Materials Corp., Tokyo, Japan; *Int'l*, pg. 946
Miki, Yuzaburo, Pres.--Kikkoman International, Inc., San Francisco, CA; *Int'l*, pg. 733
Miklas, Robert, Pres. & Chief Exec. Officer--National Fiberstock Corporation, Norristown, PA; *U.S. Private*, pg. 782
Mikon, Arnold, Chm., Pres. & Chief Exec. Officer--SmithGroup, Inc., Detroit, MI; *U.S. Private*, pg. 1010
Mikos, Paul W., Pres. & Chief Exec. Officer--RemedyTemp, Inc., San Juan Capistrano, CA; *U.S. Public*, pg. 1376
Mikulak, John, Pres.--Wolverine Vinyl Siding, Valley Forge, PA; *Int'l*, pg. 1171
Mikulak, John P., Pres.--CertainTeed Ventures, Inc., Valley Forge, PA; *Int'l*, pg. 1171
Mikulsky, Philip M., Pres. & Chief Exec. Officer--WPS Energy Services, Inc., Green Bay, WI; *U.S. Public*, pg. 1728
Mikuni, S., Pres.--Sharp Electronics (Europe) GmbH, Hamburg, Germany; *Int'l*, pg. 1230
Milane, John A., Pres.--Tinius Olsen Testing Machine Co., Inc., Willow Grove, PA; *U.S. Private*, pg. 1088
Milawer, Teresa, Pres.--Lectorum Publications, New York, NY; *U.S. Public*, pg. 1440
Milazzo, E.J., Pres.--Ward Products Corporation, North Brunswick, NJ; *U.S. Private*, pg. 1149
Milch, Neal, Pres.--Bermil Industries Corp., Inwood, NY; *U.S. Private*, pg. 136
Miles, David, Pres.--Schlegel North American Automotive Operations, Madison Heights, MI; *Int'l*, pg. 128
Miles, John F., Div. Pres.--Hamilton Specialty Bar, Hamilton, Canada; *Int'l*, pg. 1262
Miles, John Greg, Pres.--Dorfile Company, Memphis, TN; *U.S. Public*, pg. 1177
Miles, Perry, Pres.--Spirit Cruises, Inc., Norfolk, VA; *Int'l*, pg. 1274
Miles, Richard F., Chm. Bd. & Pres.--CogniSeis Development, Inc., Houston, TX; *U.S. Public*, pg. 1563
Miles, Richard J., Pres.--Hilb, Rogal & Hamilton Company of the Quad Cities, Moline, IL; *U.S. Public*, pg. 827
Miles, Ronald William Gordon, Pres. & Gen. Mgr.--Ceras Johnson Ltda., Rio de Janeiro, Brazil; *U.S. Private*, pg. 593
Miles, Walter, Pres.--Miles Sand & Gravel Company, Auburn, WA; *U.S. Private*, pg. 745
Mileski, Alan S., Pres. & Chief Oper. Officer--Nelson Westerberg, Inc., Elk Grove Village, IL; *U.S. Private*, pg. 1163
Mileski, Alan S., Pres. & Chief Oper. Officer--Nelson Westerberg, Somerville, NJ; *U.S. Private*, pg. 1164
Mileski, Alan S., Pres. & Chief Oper. Officer--Nelson Westerberg Atlas, Mableton, GA; *U.S. Private*, pg. 1164
Mill, Victor J., III, Pres. & Chief Exec. Officer--Lawrence Pumps, Inc., Lawrence, MA; *U.S. Private*, pg. 654
Millar, I.W., Pres.--Mead Packaging, Atlanta, GA; *U.S. Public*, pg. 1074
Millar, James F., Grp. Pres.--Cardinal Distribution, Dublin, OH; *U.S. Public*, pg. 304
Millard, Dan, Chm. Bd., Pres., Chief Exec. & Chief Oper. Officer--Central Illinois Steel Company, Carlinville, IL; *U.S. Private*, pg. 223
Millard, Donald R., Pres., Chief Exec. Officer & Chief Fin. Officer--Matria Healthcare, Inc., Marietta, GA; *U.S. Public*, pg. 1057
Millard, J.B., Dr., Pres. & Chief Exec. Officer-Mitel Corp.--Mitel, Inc., Herndon, VA; *Int'l*, pg. 870
Millard, John B., Dr., Pres. & Chief Exec. Officer--Mitel Corporation, Kanata, Canada; *Int'l*, pg. 870
Millard, Ken C., Pres.--Artistcare Pty. Ltd., Brookvale, Australia; *Int'l*, pg. 460
Millard, Suzanne T., Chm. Bd., Pres. & Chief Exec. Officer--Turtle & Hughes, Inc., Linden, NJ; *U.S. Private*, pg. 1110
Millen, Lewis, Pres. & Chief Exec. Officer--Industrial Ceramics, Inc., Lima, NY; *U.S. Private*, pg. 560
Miller-Smith, Susan J., Pres.--Merisel Canada, Concord, Canada; *U.S. Public*, pg. 1096
Miller, Alan, Chm. Bd., Pres. & Chief Exec. Officer--Edison Brothers Stores, Inc., Saint Louis, MO; *U.S. Public*, pg. 563
Miller, Alan B., Chm. Bd., Pres. & Chief Exec. Officer--Universal Health Services, Inc., King of Prussia, PA; *U.S.* Public, pg. 1696
Miller, Augustus C., Chm. Bd., Pres., & Chief Exec. Officer--Miller Oil Co., Inc., Norfolk, VA; *U.S. Private*, pg. 747
Miller, Barry, Pres.--Firestone Tire & Rubber Company of New Zealand Limited, Auckland, New Zealand; *Int'l*, pg. 214
Miller, Ben, Pres.--Acme Boot Co., Inc., El Paso, TX; *U.S. Private*, pg. 394
Miller, Bernard J., III, Pres.--Columbian Advertising Inc., Chicago, IL; *U.S. Private*, pg. 256
Miller, Bill, Pres., Chief Exec. & Chief Oper. Officer--Contico International, Inc., Saint Louis, MO; *U.S. Private*, pg. 267
Miller, Brian, Pres. & Chief Exec. Officer--Willis Corroon Corp. of Wash. D.C., Bethesda, MD; *Int'l*, pg. 1507
Miller, Bruce, Pres. & New Bus. Contact--Suissa Miller Advertising, Inc., Los Angeles, CA; *U.S. Private*, pg. 1049
Miller, C. Douglas, Chm. Bd., Pres. & Chief Oper. Officer--Norrell Corporation, Atlanta, GA; *U.S. Public*, pg. 1192
Miller, C. Doyle, Sr. V.P. & Pres.-Hercules Chemical Specialties Co.--Hercules Incorporated, Wilmington, DE; *U.S. Public*, pg. 809
Miller, C.Q., Chm. Bd. & Chief Exec. Officer--Raytheon Engineers & Constructors, Inc., Englewood, CO; *U.S. Public*, pg. 1366
Miller, Calvin J., Pres.--Associated Grocers of Florida, Inc., Miami, FL; *U.S. Private*, pg. 91
Miller, Charles C., III, Pres.--BellSouth International, Inc., Atlanta, GA; *U.S. Public*, pg. 208
Miller, Charles R., Chm. Bd., Pres. & Chief Exec. Officer--Champion HealthCare Corporation, Houston, TX; *U.S. Public*, pg. 333
Miller, Chris, Pres.--Planet Earth Products, Carlsbad, CA; *U.S. Public*, pg. 940
Miller, Chuck, Pres.--Garrett Airline Services Division, Phoenix, AZ; *U.S. Public*, pg. 50
Miller, Chuck, Pres.--AlliedSignal Commercial Avionics Systems, Redmond, WA; *U.S. Public*, pg. 50
Miller, Craig, Pres. & Chief Exec. Officer--Uno Restaurant Corporation, West Roxbury, MA; *U.S. Public*, pg. 1698
Miller, D.K., Pres.--CNL Financial Corp., Macon, GA; *U.S. Public*, pg. 281
Miller, D.K., Pres.--CNL/Resource Marketing Corp., Macon, GA; *U.S. Public*, pg. 282
Miller, Dale A., Pres. & Chief Exec. Officer--Sandoz Agro, Inc., Des Plaines, IL; *Int'l*, pg. 974
Miller, Dane A., Ph.D., Pres. & Chief Exec. Officer--Biomet, Inc., Warsaw, IN; *U.S. Public*, pg. 231
Miller, Daniel, Pres.-Mktg.--Dexter Shoe Company, Dexter, ME; *U.S. Public*, pg. 217
Miller, Dave, Pres. & Chief Exec. Officer--Consumers Markets Inc., Springfield, MO; *U.S. Public*, pg. 653
Miller, David, Pres. & Chief Exec. Officer--H.L. Bouton Company Inc., Buzzards Bay, MA; *U.S. Private*, pg. 162
Miller, David, Pres. & Chief Exec. Officer--Lensclean, Inc., Buzzards Bay, MA; *U.S. Private*, pg. 162
Miller, David, Pres.--Brenton Engineering Company, Alexandria, MN; *Int'l*, pg. 395
Miller, David, Pres. & Chief Oper. Officer--Holder Corporation, Atlanta, GA; *U.S. Private*, pg. 533
Miller, David, Pres.--McInerney-Miller Brothers Inc., Detroit, MI; *U.S. Private*, pg. 722
Miller, David J., Pres.--The Testor Corporation, Rockford, IL; *U.S. Public*, pg. 1358
Miller, David P., Pres. & Chief Exec. Officer--Columbia National Group, Inc., Cleveland, OH; *U.S. Private*, pg. 255
Miller, Donald E., Chm. Bd., Pres. & Chief Exec. Officer--Ederer Inc., Seattle, WA; *U.S. Private*, pg. 363
Miller, Donald P., Chm. Bd. & Pres.--Roppe Corp., Fostoria, OH; *U.S. Private*, pg. 944
Miller, Doug, Pres.--Norrell Services Inc., Atlanta, GA; *U.S. Public*, pg. 1192
Miller, Ed, Pres.--Crescent Manufacturing Company, Fremont, OH; *U.S. Private*, pg. 289
Miller, Elwood M., Pres. & Chief Exec. Officer--Blessings Corporation, Newport News, VA; *U.S. Private*, pg. 1179
Miller, Eric, Pres.--Brooklyn Bottling Co. of Milton, NY, Milton, NY; *U.S. Private*, pg. 171
Miller, Floyd, Pres. & Partner--Miller/Kadanoff/Huber Direct & Interactive, San Francisco, CA; *U.S. Private*, pg. 747
Miller, Fred, Pres.--121 S.W. Salmon St. Corp., Portland, OR; *U.S. Public*, pg. 585
Miller, Fred, Pres.--Trout-Blue Cheliau, Inc., Chelan, WA; *U.S. Private*, pg. 1105
Miller, Gary W., Pres.--Baldwin & Lyons, Inc., Indianapolis, IN; *U.S. Public*, pg. 169
Miller, Gaylen D., Pres. & Chief Exec. Officer--Ag Services of America, Inc., Cedar Falls, IA; *U.S. Public*, pg. 6
Miller, George, Chm. Bd. & Pres.--Peace River Electric Cooperative, Inc., Wauchula, FL; *U.S. Private*, pg. 845
Miller, George D., Pres. & Chief Exec. Officer--National Fire Protection Association, Quincy, MA; *U.S. Private*, pg. 782

Miller, George E., Pres. & Chief Exec. Officer--Peter Piper, Inc., Phoenix, AZ; *Int'l*, pg. 157

Miller, Gerd, Chm. Bd., Pres. & Treas.--Miller Curtain Co., Inc., San Antonio, TX; *U.S. Private*, pg. 746

Miller, Henry E., III, Pres.--Miller Building Corp., Wilmington, NC; *U.S. Private*, pg. 746

Miller, J., Pres.--Sharp Corporation of New Zealand Ltd., Mangere, New Zealand; *Int'l*, pg. 1229

Miller, J.A., Pres.--G.E.-Hitachi HVB Inc., Norcross, GA; *Int'l, pg. 622*

Miller, J.H., Pres. & Chief Exec. Officer--Howard Miller, Zeeland, MI; *U.S. Private*, pg. 747

Miller, Jack, Pres. & Chief Exec. Officer--Industrial Indemnity Company, San Francisco, CA; *U.S. Public*, pg. 681

Miller, Jack, Pres.--Quill Corp., Lincolnshire, IL; *U.S. Private, pg. 901*

Miller, James, Pres.--Bartlett & Co., Cincinnati, OH; *U.S. Public*, pg. 985

Miller, James A., Pres. & Chief Exec. Officer--Alliant Foodservice, Inc., Deerfield, IL; *U.S. Private*, pg. 244

Miller, James A., Pres.--Dewey Corporation, Jackson, MS; *U.S. Private*, pg. 329

Miller, James D., Pres.--Magnetics, Butler, PA; *U.S. Private*, pg. 1020

Miller, James H., Chm. Bd., Pres. & Chief Exec. Officer--Meridian Medical Technology, Inc., Columbia, MD; *U.S. Public*, pg. 1095

Miller, James L., Pres. & Chief Exec. Officer--JP Foodservice Distributors, Inc., Columbia, MD; *U.S. Public*, pg. 918

Miller, Jay, Pres. & Chief Exec. Officer--TargetCom, Inc., Chicago, IL; *U.S. Private*, pg. 1069

Miller, Jeff, Pres. & Chief Exec. Officer--Aqua-Chem Inc., Milwaukee, WI; *Int'l*, pg. 824

Miller, Jerry K., Pres.--Sunwest Bank of Rio Arriba, N.A., Espanola, NM; *U.S. Public*, pg. 1165

Miller, Jim, Pres.--The Howden Fan Co., Buffalo, NY; *U.S. Private*, pg. 543

Miller, John, Pres.--Master Graphic, Inc., Memphis, TN; *U.S.* Private, pg. 713

Miller, John C., Pres. & Chief Exec. Officer--Miller-St. Nazianz, Inc., Saint Nazianz, WI; *U.S. Private*, pg. 748

Miller, John S., Pres. & Chief Exec. Officer--Tencarva Machinery Co., Inc., Greensboro, NC; *U.S. Private*, pg. 1075

Miller, John T., Pres. & Chief Exec. Officer--Pacific Generation Company, Portland, OR; *U.S. Public*, pg. 1252

Miller, Karen G., Pres.--Larry H. Miller Group, Murray, UT; *U.S. Private*, pg. 747

Miller, Keith R., Pres.-Mechanical Packing Div.--Garlock Sealing Technologies, Palmyra, NY; *U.S. Public*, pg. 402

Miller, Ken, Pres.--Young Stuff Apparel Group, Inc., New York, NY; *U.S. Private*, pg. 1202

Miller, Larry, Pres.--Corinthian Media, Inc., New York, NY; *U.S. Private*, pg. 275

Miller, Leonard, Chm. Bd. & Pres.--Lennar Corporation, Miami, FL; *U.S. Public*, pg. 987

Miller, Leonard, Chm. Bd., Pres. & Chief Exec. Officer--Development Corporation of America, Miami, FL; *U.S. Public*, pg. 987

Miller, Lloyd, Pres.--American Laubscher Corp., Farmingdale, NY; *U.S. Private*, pg. 58

Miller, Mark, Pres. & Chief Oper. Officer--Cogentrix Incorporated, Charlotte, NC; *U.S. Private*, pg. 249

Miller, Mark, Pres.--Ocean Showboat, Inc., Atlantic City, NJ; *U.S. Public*, pg. 1469

Miller, Marlin J., Jr., Pres. & Chief Exec. Officer--Arrow International, Inc., Reading, PA; *U.S. Public*, pg. 135

Miller, Michael A., Pres. & Chief Exec. Officer--Firestone Financial, Newton, MA; *U.S. Public*, pg. 1660

Miller, Michael J., Pres.--Wm. H. McGee & Co., Inc., New York, NY; *U.S. Public*, pg. 1231

Miller, Mickey, Pres.--Flowers Baking Co. of Thomasville, Inc., Thomasville, GA; *U.S. Public*, pg. 657

Miller, Mont, Pres.--Club Car, Inc., Martinez, GA; *U.S. Public*, pg. 877

Miller, Nicole, Pres.--Kobra International Ltd, New York, NY; *U.S. Private*, pg. 628

Miller, P. Dan, Pres.--Whirlpool do Brazil S.A., Sao Paulo, Brazil; *U.S. Public*, pg. 1765

Miller, Paul A., Pres. & Chief Exec. Officer--Lawrence Savings Bank, North Andover, MA; *U.S. Public*, pg. 980

Miller, Ralph, Pres.--APX International, Auburn Hills, MI; *U.S. Private*, pg. 7

Miller, Richard A., Pres. & Treas.--Prentiss Incorporated, Floral Park, NY; *U.S. Private*, pg. 882

Miller, Richard C., Pres. & Chief Oper. Officer--GoodMark Foods, Inc., Raleigh, NC; *U.S. Public*, pg. 751

Miller, Richard J., Pres.--Old Reliable Casualty Co., Webster Groves, MO; *U.S. Public*, pg. 1374

Miller, Robert, Pres.--Northeast Environmental Services, Inc., Canastota, NY; *U.S. Public*, pg. 546

Miller, Robert, Pres.--Miller Advertising Agency Inc., New York, NY; *U.S. Private*, pg. 746

Miller, Robert A., Pres.-Marriott Leisure--Marriott International, Inc., Washington, DC; *U.S. Public*, pg. 1047

Miller, Robert G., Pres. & Chief Exec. Officer--Fred Meyer Incorporated, Portland, OR; *U.S. Public*, pg. 1103

Miller, Robert G., Pres. & Chief Exec. Officer--Smith's Food & Drug Centers, Inc., Salt Lake City, UT; *U.S. Public*, pg. 1103

Miller, Robert G., Pres.--Fred Meyer Stores, Portland, OR; *U.S. Public*, pg. 1103

Miller, Robert S., Chm. Bd., Pres. & Chief Exec. Officer--Waste Management, Inc., Oak Brook, IL; *U.S. Public*, pg. 1744

Miller, Rod, Pres.--American Consolidation Services Ltd., Oakland, CA; *Int'l*, pg. 912

Miller, Russell W., Pres.--Zions Insurance Agency, Inc., Salt Lake City, UT; *U.S. Public*, pg. 1793

Miller, Scott F., Pres.--Miller Transporters, Inc., Jackson, MS; *U.S. Private*, pg. 329

Miller, Stanford, Pres.--Rosco Laboratories, Inc., Stamford, CT; *U.S. Private*, pg. 944

Miller, Steven, Chm. Bd., Pres. & Chief Exec. Officer--Miller Resources International, Inc., North Brunswick, NJ; *U.S. Private*, pg. 748

Miller, Ted, Pres.--E.A. Miller Company, Hyrum, UT; *U.S. Public*, pg. 428

Miller, Thomas, Pres. & Chief Exec. Officer--Carl Zeiss, Inc., Thornwood, NY; *Int'l*, pg. 1523

Miller, Thomas B., Chm. Bd., Pres. & Chief Exec. & Oper. Officer--Berry Bearing Company, Lyons, IL; *U.S. Public*, pg. 732

Miller, Victor J., Pres. & Chief Exec. Officer--Mill-Rose Company, Mentor, OH; *U.S. Private*, pg. 746

Miller, Virgil, Pres.--Sauder Manufacturing Corporation, Archbold, OH; *U.S. Private*, pg. 967

Miller, Wayne, Pres.--Century Supply Corp., Madison Heights, MI; *U.S. Public*, pg. 1389

Miller, William F., Pres.--McKellar Companies, San Diego, CA; *U.S. Private*, pg. 723

Milley, Alexander M., Chm. Bd., Pres. & Chief Exec. Officer--ELXSI Corporation, Orlando, FL; *U.S. Public*, pg. 545

Millgard, V. Dennis, Pres. & Chief Exec. Officer--The Millgard Corp., Livonia, MI; *U.S. Private*, pg. 748

Millick, Mark, Pres.--John M. Olson Company, Saint Clair Shores, MI; *U.S. Private*, pg. 815

Milligan, Bruce, Pres. & Chief Exec. Officer--Republic Financial Services, Inc., Dallas, TX; *Int'l*, pg. 346

Milligan, Bruce R., Pres.--Republic Underwriters Insurance Co., Dallas, TX; *Int'l*, pg. 346

Milligan, Bruce R., Pres.--Republic-Vanguard Life Insurance Co., Dallas, TX; *Int'l*, pg. 346

Milligan, Bruce R., Pres. & Chief Exec. Officer--Republic Diversified Services, Inc., Dallas, TX; *Int'l*, pg. 346

Milligan, Bruce R., Chm. Bd. & Pres.--Southern County Mutual Insurance Company, Dallas, TX; *Int'l*, pg. 346

Milligan, Bruce R., Pres.--Southern Insurance Co., Dallas, TX; *Int'l*, pg. 346

Milligan, Bruce R., Pres.--Republic Financial Services, Inc., Dallas, TX; *Int'l*, pg. 346

Milligan, Bruce R., Pres.--Southern Underwriters Insurance Company, Dallas, TX; *Int'l*, pg. 346

Milligan, Bruce R., Pres.--Republic Fire & Casualty Insurance Company, Dallas, TX; *Int'l*, pg. 346

Milligan, Bruce R., Pres.--Republic Group No. Two, Dallas, TX; *Int'l*, pg. 346

Milligan, Bruce R., Pres.--Eagle General Agency, Dallas, TX; *Int'l*, pg. 346

Milligan, Bruce R., Pres.--Allied Premium Finance, Dallas, TX; *Int'l*, pg. 346

Milligan, George, Pres.--Graham Group, Inc., Des Moines, IA; *U.S. Private*, pg. 468

Milligan, Patrick M., Pres. & Chief Exec. Officer--Willis Corroon Corp. of Northern Ohio, Dublin, OH; *Int'l*, pg. 1506

Milling, R. King, Pres.--Whitney Holding Corporation, New Orleans, LA; *U.S. Public*, pg. 1766

Millman, Richard J., Pres.--Textron Systems, Wilmington, MA; *U.S. Public*, pg. 1589

Millner, Thomas, Chm. Bd., Pres. & Chief Oper. Officer--Remington Arms Company, Inc., Madison, NC; *U.S. Private*, pg. 921

Mills, Andrew, Pres.--Medline Industries, Inc., Mundelein, IL; *U.S. Private*, pg. 728

Mills, Gerald J., Chm. Bd. & Pres.--Mills & Clement Inc., Bakersfield, CA; *U.S. Private*, pg. 749

Mills, Howard C., Pres. & Chief Exec. Officer--Halifax Corporation, Alexandria, VA; *U.S. Public*, pg. 775

Mills, Howard C., Pres. & Chief Exec. Officer--Halifax Engineering, Inc., Alexandria, VA; *U.S. Public*, pg. 775

Mills, Howard C., Pres. & Chief Exec. Officer--Halifax Technical Services, Alexandria, VA; *U.S. Public*, pg. 775

Mills, Melvin, Pres.--Anderson Electrical Sales, Salt Lake City, UT; *Int'l*, pg. 736

Mills, P. Gerald, Chm. Bd., Pres & Chief Exec. Officer--Jacobson Stores Inc., Jackson, MI; *U.S. Public*, pg. 922

Mills, P. Gerald, Pres.--Jacobson Stores Realty Company, Jackson, MI; *U.S. Public*, pg. 922

Mills, P. Gerald, Pres.--Jacobson Credit Corporation, Jackson, MI; *U.S. Public*, pg. 922

Mills, R.D., Pres.--Amax Research & Development Inc., Englewood, CO; *U.S. Public*, pg. 470

Mills, Russell, Pres. & Publisher--The Ottawa Citizen, Ottawa, Canada; *Int'l*, pg. 631

Mills, Walter C., Pres.--Sysco Food Services of Indianapolis, Inc., Indianapolis, IN; *U.S. Public*, pg. 1551

Millstein, Jack H., Jr., Pres.--Millstein Industries, Youngwood, PA; *U.S. Private*, pg. 749

Millstein, Jack H., Jr., Pres.--Lightcraft, Jeannette, PA; *U.S. Private*, pg. 749

Millstein, Jack, Jr., Pres.--Cherry Creek Golf, Youngwood, PA; *U.S. Private*, pg. 749

Millstein, Steven A., Pres.--Westar Security, Topeka, KS; *U.S. Public*, pg. 1760

Millweard, Tom, Pres.--Ackerman McQueen, Inc., Oklahoma City, OK; *U.S. Private*, pg. 12

Millwee, Robert, Pres. & Chief Exec. Officer--Garney Holding Company, Inc., Kansas City, MO; *U.S. Private*, pg. 440

Milmo, Emilio Azcarraga, Chm. Bd. & Grp. Pres.--Grupo Televisa, S.A. de C.V., Mexico, Mexico; *Int'l*, pg. 576

Milne, David S., Jr., Pres. & Chief Exec. Officer--Gas Energy Inc., Brooklyn, NY; *U.S. Public*, pg. 296

Milne, Philip, Pres. & Chief Exec. Officer--Travelers Express Company, Inc., Saint Louis Park, MN; *U.S. Public*, pg. 1718

Milne, Stephen A., Pres., Chief Exec. Officer--Erie Family Life Insurance Company, Erie, PA; *U.S. Public*, pg. 590

Milne, Stephen A., Pres.--Erie Insurance Group, Erie, PA; *U.S. Public*, pg. 591

Milne, Stephen A., Pres.--Erie Indemnity Company, Erie, PA; *U.S. Public*, pg. 591

Milne, Stephen A., Pres.--Erie Insurance Exchange, Erie, PA; *U.S. Public*, pg. 591

Milne, Stephen A., Pres.--Flagship City Insurance Company, Erie, PA; *U.S. Public*, pg. 591

Milner, Bruce D., Pres. & Chief Oper. Officer--Carat ICG, Los Angeles, CA; *U.S. Private*, pg. 207

Milner, Duncan, Sr. Partner & Exec. Creative Dir.--TBWA Chiat/Day St. Louis, Saint Louis, MO; *U.S. Private*, pg. 1062

Milner, S.A., Pres.--Chieftain Development Co. Ltd., Edmonton, Canada; *Int'l*, pg. 49

Milner, Stanley A., Pres. & Chief Exec. Officer--Chieftain International, Inc., Edmonton, Canada; *Int'l*, pg. 284

Milnor, George S., Chm. Bd., Pres. & Chief Exec. Officer--Millers Mutual Insurance Assn., Alton, IL; *U.S. Private*, pg. 748

Milnor, George S., Pres.--Millers Classified Insurance Company, Alton, IL; *U.S. Private*, pg. 748

Milosavljevic, Milos, Pres.--Jugobanka Banking Group, Belgrade, Serbia; *Int'l*, pg. 716

Milovich, Mitch, Pres.--Baker Material Handling Corp., Summerville, SC; *Int'l*, pg. 810

Milowitz, Billy, Pres.--Balson-Hercules Ltd., New York, NY; *Int'l*, pg. 326

Milstein, Howard P., Chm. Bd. & Pres.--Douglas Elliman, New York, NY; *U.S. Private*, pg. 341

Milstein, Monroe G., Chm. Bd., Pres. & Chief Exec. Officer--Burlington Coat Factory Warehouse Corporation, Burlington, NJ; *U.S. Public*, pg. 268

Milstein, Philip, Pres. & Chief Exec. Officer--Emigrant Savings Bank, New York, NY; *U.S. Private*, pg. 373

Milton, James W., Pres.--Milton Can Co., Inc., Elizabeth, NJ; *U.S. Private*, pg. 749

Mimran, Joseph, Pres.--Club Monaco Inc., Toronto, Canada; *Int'l*, pg. 298

Min, Pyungsoo, Pres.--Oricom Inc., Seoul, Korea; *Int'l*, pg. 1008

Minami, Isoh, Pres.--Hitachi Zosen Corporation, Osaka, Japan; *Int'l*, pg. 622

Minchk, Frederick, Pres. & Chief Oper. Officer--National Loss Control Service Corp., Long Grove, IL; *U.S. Private, pg. 614*

Mindell, David A., Pres.--Western Corporate Enterprises Inc., Vancouver, Canada; *Int'l*, pg. 1494

Miner, Brian, Pres.--Anchor Lamina Inc., Windsor, Canada; *Int'l*, pg. 75

Miner, Brian, Pres.--Reliance Steel Fabricators Limited, Tilbury, Canada; *Int'l*, pg. 75

Miner, Brian, Pres.--Superior Steel Acquisition Corporation, Cheshire, CT; *Int'l*, pg. 75

Minerva, Daniel O., Co-Pres. & Co-Chief Exec. Officer--Eastbridge Capital Inc., New York, NY; *Int'l*, pg. 933

Mingchen, Zhou, Pres.--China National Cereals, Oils & Foodstuffs Corporation (COFCO), Beijing, China; *Int'l*, pg. 285

Miniat, Ronald, Chm., Pres. & Chief Exec. Officer--Ed Miniat, Inc., Chicago, IL; *U.S. Private*, pg. 750

Minick, L. Scott, Pres. & Chief Oper. Officer--Sequus Pharmaceuticals, Inc., Menlo Park, CA; *U.S. Public*, pg. 1460

Minigh, Howard L., Ph.D., Pres.--Cyanamid Agricultural Products Division, Parsippany, NJ; *U.S. Public*, pg. 79

Minihan, John M., Pres. & Chief Exec. Officer--Louisville Bedding Company, Louisville, KY; *U.S. Private*, pg. 677

Minkhorst, Robert, Pres. & Chief Exec. Officer--Philips Consumer Electronics, Knoxville, TN; *Int'l*, pg. 1054

Minkhorst, Robert, Pres.--Philips Lighting, Somerset, NJ; *Int'l*, pg. 1055

Minkoff, Michael R., Pres.--WF Corroon Canada Inc., Montreal, Canada; *Int'l*, pg. 1502

Minor, G. Gilmer III, Chm. Bd., Pres. & Chief Exec. Officer--Owens & Minor Inc., Glen Allen, VA; *U.S. Public*, pg. 1236

Minor, Henry H., III, Pres.--P.W. Minor & Son, Inc., Batavia, NY; *U.S. Private*, pg. 751

Minor, Jesse, Pres.--Sage Energy Company, San Antonio, TX; *U.S. Public*, pg. 1426

Minor, Michael L., Pres.--First Insurance Agency, Inc., Mount Vernon, WA; *U.S. Public*, pg. 1740

Minotto, Gene J., Pres. & Chief Exec. Officer--Basic American Medical Products, Inc., Atlanta, GA; *U.S. Public*, pg. 758

Mintz, Gerry, Pres.--American Banker Bond Buyer, New York, NY; *U.S. Public*, pg. 1600

Mintz, Robert, Pres.--Kvaerner FSSL Inc., Sugar Land, TX; *Int'l*, pg. 770

Mira, Sal E., Pres. & Chief Exec. Officer--KDI Precision Products, Inc., Cincinnati, OH; *U.S. Private*, pg. 603

Miranda, Guillermo, Jr., Chm., Chief Exec. Officer & Pres.--Gator Industries Inc., Hialeah, FL; *U.S. Private*, pg. 441

Mirante, Arthur J., II, Pres. & Chief Exec. Officer--Cushman & Wakefield, Inc., New York, NY; *Int'l*, pg. 873

Mirner, Kevin, Pres.--Harcros Chemicals Inc., Kansas City, KS; *Int'l*, pg. 598

Mirsky, B.S., Pres.--Bard Urological Div., Covington, GA; *U.S. Public*, pg. 189

Misasi, Enrico, Pres.--Olivetti do Brasil S.A., Sao Paulo, Brazil; *Int'l*, pg. 1003

Misch, Donald L., Chief Exec. Officer & Gen. Mgr.--Jasper County Farm Bureau Co-op Association, Inc., Rensselaer, IN; *U.S. Private*, pg. 583

Mischinski, Paul, Pres. & Chief Exec. Officer-Bali Brand--Bali Company, Winston Salem, NC; *U.S. Public*, pg. 1433

Mise, Yoshinari, Pres.--CPC Japan, Ltd., Tokyo, Japan; *U.S.* Public, pg. 447

Misiak, Greg, Pres.-Laser Systems--Laser Systems, Apopka, FL; *U.S. Public*, pg. 1002

Misiak, Tom, Pres.--The Falk Corporation, Milwaukee, WI; *U.S. Public*, pg. 1534

Misitano, Anthony, Pres. & Chief Exec. Officer--Continental Medical Systems, Inc., Mechanicsburg, PA; *U.S. Public*, pg. 839

Misra, Mohan, Dr., Pres.--Global Solar Energy, Tucson, AZ; *U.S. Public*, pg. 1670

Misra, Rajendra, Pres.--Tekelec-India Pvt. Ltd., Bangalore, India; *U.S. Public*, pg. 1566

Misrasi, John, Pres. & Chief Exec. Officer--Commtek Communications, Corp., Vienna, VA; *U.S. Private*, pg. 258
Missett, Judi, Chm. Bd., Pres. & Chief Exec. Officer--Jazzercise, Inc., Carlsbad, CA; *U.S. Private*, pg. 584
Misumi, Yoshio, Pres. & Chief Exec. Officer--Pioneer/Eclipse Corp., Sparta, NC; *Int'l*, pg. 71
Mita, Yoshihiro, Pres.--Mita Industrial Company, Ltd., Osaka, Japan; *Int'l*, pg. 870
Mitarai, Fujiro, Pres.--Canon Inc., Tokyo, Japan; *Int'l*, pg. 261
Mitchel, Bud, Pres.--HomeAdd Financial Corporation, Greenville, SC; *U.S. Public*, pg. 1358
Mitchel, Thomas L., Chm. Bd. & Pres.--Mitchel & Scott Machine Co., Inc., Indianapolis, IN; *U.S. Private*, pg. 753
Mitchell, Alan, Pres. & Owner--Service Web Offset Corporation, Chicago, IL; *U.S. Private*, pg. 987
Mitchell, Bo, Pres. & Chief Exec. Officer--Marshall Jaccoma Mitchell Advertising, New York, NY; *U.S. Private*, pg. 708
Mitchell, Brian J., Pres.--MIC Technology Corporation, North Andover, MA; *U.S. Public*, pg. 24
Mitchell, Bruce, Pres.--Risser Oil Corp., Clearwater, FL; *U.S. Private*, pg. 932
Mitchell, Dick, Pres.--Gorges/Quik-To-Fix Foods, Dallas, TX; *U.S. Private*, pg. 465
Mitchell, Doug, Chm. Bd. & Pres.--Perryton Equity, Perryton, TX; *U.S. Private*, pg. 855
Mitchell, Harvey G., Pres.--Mitchell Coach Manufacturing, Pryor, OK; *U.S. Private*, pg. 753
Mitchell, James A., Pres.--IDS Life Insurance Co. of New York, Albany, NY; *U.S. Public*, pg. 73
Mitchell, James J., Pres.--NN Ball & Roller, Inc., Erwin, TN; *U.S. Public*, pg. 1146
Mitchell, James P., Pres.--Patent Construction Systems, Paramus, NJ; *U.S. Public*, pg. 793
Mitchell, John M., Pres., Chief Exec. & Chief Oper. Officer--Pluess-Staufer Industries, Inc., Proctor, VT; *Int'l*, pg. 1061
Mitchell, Lydell, Owner--Parks LLC, Baltimore, MD; *U.S. Private*, pg. 840
Mitchell, Michael A., Pres.--Textron Automotive Company, Troy, MI; *U.S. Public*, pg. 1590
Mitchell, Mike, Pres.--Aunt Fanny's Bakery, Atlanta, GA; *U.S. Public*, pg. 657
Mitchell, Patrick, Pres. & Chief Oper. Officer--Cold Spring Granite Company, Cold Spring, MN; *U.S. Private*, pg. 250
Mitchell, Paul D., Pres.--McNeil Consumer Products Company, Guelph, Canada; *U.S. Public*, pg. 931
Mitchell, Robert, Pres.--Teledyne Ryan Aeronautical, San Diego, CA; *U.S. Public*, pg. 43
Mitchell, Stephen C., Pres. & Chief Oper. Officer--Lester B. Knight & Associates, Inc., Chicago, IL; *U.S. Private*, pg. 626
Mitchell, Thomas, Pres. & Chief Exec. Officer--Davenport Insulation, Inc, Upper Marlboro, MD; *U.S. Private*, pg. 314
Mitchell, W. F., Pres.--Benzonia Manufacturing, Benzonia, MI; *U.S. Private*, pg. 753
Mitchell, W. F., Pres.--Mitchell Corporation, Clare Div., Clare, MI; *U.S. Private*, pg. 753
Mitchell, Warren I., Pres.--Southern California Gas Co., Los Angeles, CA; *U.S. Public*, pg. 1249
Mitchell, Warren I., Pres.--EcoTrans OEM Transportation, Los Angeles, CA; *U.S. Public*, pg. 1249
Mitchell, William A., Jr., Pres. & Chief Exec. Officer--Carter & Associates, Atlanta, GA; *U.S. Private*, pg. 216
Mitchell, William F., Chm. Bd., Pres. & Chief Exec. Officer--Environmental Tectonics Corporation (ETC), Southampton, PA; *U.S. Public*, pg. 587
Mitchell, William F., Chm. Bd., Pres. & Chief Exec. Officer--Mitchell Corporation of Owosso, Owosso, MI; *U.S. Private*, pg. 753
Mitchum, John, Pres. & Chief Exec. Officer--Tricord Systems, Inc., Plymouth, MN; *U.S. Public*, pg. 1637
Mitieus, Rene, Chm. Bd., Pres. & Chief Exec. Officer--Imetal, Paris, France; *Int'l*, pg. 661
Mitsui, Kouhei, Pres. & Chief Exec. Officer--Kubota Corp., Osaka, Japan; *Int'l*, pg. 762
Mitte, Roy, Chm. Bd., Pres. & Chief Exec. Officer--Financial Industries Corp., Austin, TX; *U.S. Public*, pg. 622
Mittelstadt, Eric, Pres. & Chief Exec. Officer--FANUC Robotics North America, Inc., Rochester Hills, MI; *Int'l*, pg. 477
Mittnacht, John, Partner & Grp. Dir.--Deutsch, Inc., New York, NY; *U.S. Private*, pg. 328
Miura, Akira, Pres.--Mitsubishi Chemical Corporation, Tokyo, Japan; *Int'l*, pg. 870
Miura, N. Brian, Pres.--Pentax Canada Inc., Mississauga, Canada; *Int'l*, pg. 85
Miura, Shozo, Pres.--Yamaichi France S.A., Paris, France; *Int'l*, pg. 1517
Miyagawa, Masahiro, Pres.--Dun & Bradstreet Japan Ltd., Tokyo, Japan; *U.S. Public*, pg. 536
Miyagoshi, Takeshi, Pres.--Kawasaki Heavy Industries (U.S.A.), Inc., New York, NY; *Int'l*, pg. 725
Miyakawa, Y., Pres.--Datastream International (Japan) KK, Tokyo, Japan; *U.S. Public*, pg. 1326
Miyamoto, Masanori, Pres.--NMB Electro Precision Inc., Miyagi, Japan; *Int'l*, pg. 868
Miyamoto, Susumu, Pres.--Mitsui & Co. (Canada) Ltd., Toronto, Canada; *Int'l*, pg. 880
Miyamoto, Yasutaka, Pres.--The Zenshinren Bank, Tokyo, Japan; *Int'l*, pg. 1527
Miyano, Toshiharu, Pres.--Miyano Machinery, Inc., Wood Dale, IL; *U.S. Private*, pg. 754
Miyaoka, Hideki, Pres.--Toto Kiki (H.K.) Ltd., Wan Chai, Hong Kong; *Int'l*, pg. 1410
Miyasaka, Katsuro, Pres.--Shin-Etsu Polymer Co. Ltd., Tokyo, Japan; *Int'l*, pg. 1234
Miyashita, Takeshiro, Pres.--Nippon Paper Industries Company Limited, Tokyo, Japan; *Int'l*, pg. 937
Miyauchi, Koji, Pres.--Yamato Transport Co., Ltd., Tokyo, Japan; *Int'l*, pg. 1519
Miyauchi, Yoshihiko, Pres. & Grp. Chief Exec. Officer--Orix Corporation, Tokyo, Japan; *Int'l*, pg. 1008
Miyazaki, Morio, Pres.--P.T. Sanwa Indonesia Bank, Jakarta, Indonesia; *Int'l*, pg. 1190
Miyazaki, Tsuyoshi, Pres.--Mitsubishi Logistics Corp., Tokyo, Japan; *Int'l*, pg. 874
Miyazu, Jun-ichiro, Pres.--Nippon Telegraph and Telephone Corporation, Tokyo, Japan; *Int'l*, pg. 940
Miyoshi, Ryuhei, Pres.--Thai Sakura Finance & Securities Co., Ltd., Bangkok, Thailand; *Int'l*, pg. 677
Miyoshi, Shunkichi, Pres.--NKK Corporation, Tokyo, Japan; *Int'l*, pg. 902
Miyoshi, Yasuya, Pres.--Hitachi Sales Corp., Tokyo, Japan; *Int'l*, pg. 621
Mize, John A., Pres.--Regions Bank/Tuscaloosa, Tuscaloosa, AL; *U.S. Public*, pg. 1373
Mizel, Larry A., Chm. Bd., Pres. & Chief Exec. Officer--M.D.C. Holdings, Inc., Denver, CO; *U.S. Public*, pg. 1025
Mizell, James H., Pres.--Willis Corroon Corp. of Sacramento, Sacramento, CA; *Int'l*, pg. 1507
Mizoguchi, Isao, Pres. & Chief Exec. Officer--The Nikkan Kogyo Shimbun, Ltd., Tokyo, Japan; *Int'l*, pg. 930
Mizoguchi, Shiro, Pres.--Beijing Descente Co., Ltd., Beijing, China; *Int'l*, pg. 396
Mizomoto, Mark, Pres.--Universal Fasteners Inc., Lawrenceburg, KY; *Int'l*, pg. 1515
Mizuno, Masato, Pres.--Mizuno Corporation, Osaka, Japan; *Int'l*, pg. 884
Mizusawa, Masatake, Pres.--Komatsu Asia & Pacific Pte. Ltd., Jurong, Singapore; *Int'l*, pg. 744
Mizushima, Shigeru, Pres. & Chief Oper. Officer--Daido Hoxan Inc., Tokyo, Japan; *Int'l*, pg. 363
Mizushima, Shigeru, Pres.--Hoxan America Incorporated, Piscataway, NJ; *Int'l*, pg. 363
Mnaymneh, Sami, Partner--HIG Capital Management, Miami, FL; *U.S. Private*, pg. 490
Mo, Kwoen Soon, Pres.--Ssangyong Australia Pty., Ltd., Sydney, Australia; *Int'l*, pg. 1291
Moakley, Michael, Pres. & Chief Exec. Officer--Philips Electronics North America Corporation, New York, NY; *Int'l*, pg. 1053
Moakley, Thomas J., Pres.--Graphic Instruments, East Greenwich, RI; *U.S. Public*, pg. 481
Moberg, Anders, Pres.--Ikea Holdings AB, Amsterdam, Netherlands; *Int'l*, pg. 659
Mobley, Paul W., Chm. Bd., Pres. & Chief Exec. Officer--Noble Roman's Inc., Indianapolis, IN; *U.S. Public*, pg. 1187
Mochel, John, Pres.--5 Rubber Corporation, Kittanning, PA; *U.S. Public*, pg. 1504
Mochizuki, Yoshito, Pres.--American Isuzu Motors Inc., Whittier, CA; *Int'l*, pg. 692
Mockley, B.A., Chm. Bd. & Pres.--Anchor Gasoline Corporation, Tulsa, OK; *U.S. Private*, pg. 70
Mockley, B.A., Pres.--Canal Refining Co., Tulsa, OK; *U.S. Private*, pg. 71
Mockley, B.A., Pres.--Cove Petroleum, Tulsa, OK; *U.S. Private*, pg. 71
Moda, Frank, Jr., Pres.--Palmer Manufacturing Company, Malden, MA; *U.S. Private*, pg. 835
Moddelmog, Hala, Pres.--Church's Chicken, Inc., Atlanta, GA; *U.S. Private*, pg. 5
Modena, Goffred O., Pres.--Forem S.p.A., Milan, Italy; *U.S. Public*, pg. 46
Modzelewski, John F., Sr. Partner, Exec. V.P. & Gen. Mgr.--Fleishman-Hillard, Inc., Chicago, IL; *U.S. Private*, pg. 411
Moe, Henrik, Pres., Chief Oper. & Exec. Officer--DEC International, Inc., Madison, WI; *U.S. Private*, pg. 301
Moehring, Hartmut, Dr., Pres. & Chief Oper. Officer--BASF Australia Ltd., Melbourne, Australia; *Int'l*, pg. 105
Moeller, John, Pres.--Simmons Juvenile Products Co., Inc., New London, WI; *U.S. Private*, pg. 1001
Moeller, Paul R., Pres.--Hercon Environmental Corporation, York, PA; *U.S. Public*, pg. 802
Moeller, Sverker, Pres.--Kvaerner Korea Ltd., Choryang, Korea; *Int'l*, pg. 767
Moeller, Sverker, Pres.--Kvaerner Korea Ltd., Pusan, Korea; *Int'l*, pg. 772
Moeller, William E., Pres.--Sanwa Business Credit Corporation, Chicago, IL; *Int'l*, pg. 1189
Moenkhaus, James E., Pres. & Chief Exec. Officer--Willis Corroon Corp. of Northern Ohio, Cleveland, OH; *Int'l*, pg. 1506
Moersch, Kevin P., Pres. & Chief Exec. Officer--MFS Network Technologies, Inc., Omaha, NE; *U.S. Public*, pg. 1779
Moersdorf, Gerard B., Jr., Pres., Chief Exec. Officer & Treas.--Applied Innovation Inc., Dublin, OH; *U.S. Public*, pg. 123
Moessner, Reynold, Chm. Bd. & Pres.--Amana Society, Inc., Amana, IA; *U.S. Private*, pg. 48
Moffett, James R., Chm. Bd. & Pres.--Freeport-McMoRan Inc., New Orleans, LA; *U.S. Public*, pg. 680
Mogan, Jim, Pres.--Olga Div., Bridgeport, CT; *U.S. Public*, pg. 1738
Mogas, V. Louis, Pres. & Chief Exec. Officer--Mogas Industries, Inc., Houston, TX; *U.S. Private*, pg. 755
Mogi, Takashi, Pres.--Bandai Co., Ltd., Tokyo, Japan; *Int'l*, pg. 145
Mogi, Yoshifumi, Pres.--TOHO America International Inc., New York, NY; *Int'l*, pg. 1390
Mogi, Yuzaburo, Pres.--Kikkoman Corporation, Chiba, Japan; *Int'l*, pg. 733
Mogren, Hakan, Pres. & Chief Exec. Officer--Astra AB, Sodertalje, Sweden; *Int'l*, pg. 93
Mohn, Blair, Pres.--Cloister Pure Spring Water Co., Inc., Lancaster, PA; *U.S. Private*, pg. 247
Mohn, Blair, Pres.--Chester Springs Distribution Point, Chester Springs, PA; *U.S. Private*, pg. 247
Mohn, Blair, Pres.--Beltsville Distribution Point, Baltimore, MD; *U.S. Private*, pg. 247
Mohn, Reinhard, Chm.-Supervisory Bd.--Gruner + Jahr AG & Co., Hamburg, Germany; *Int'l*, pg. 190
Mohrman, LeRoy, Chm. Bd., Pres. & Chief Exec. Officer--Handling Systems Engineering, Jacksonville, FL; *U.S. Private*, pg. 499
Moilanen, Thomas A., Pres. & Chief Exec. Officer--Cloverdale Equipment Co., Oak Park, MI; *U.S. Private*, pg. 247
Mojden, Andrew W., Pres.--Fleetwood Systems, Inc., Romeoville, IL; *U.S. Private*, pg. 410
Mojo, Jean, Sr. Partner--Einson Freeman Inc., Paramus, NJ; *Int'l*, pg. 1483
Mokhtari, Shawn, Pres.--National Educational International Corp., Irvine, CA; *U.S. Public*, pg. 784
Moksnes, Jan, Pres.--Norwegian Contractors A/S, Stabekk, Norway; *Int'l*, pg. 42
Moksnes, Knut, Pres.--Aquatic Animal Health, Oslo, Norway; *U.S. Public*, pg. 58
Molari, Russell E., Pres.--Scientific Systems Division, Redwood City, CA; *U.S. Public*, pg. 1516
Molenaar, Kelly, Pres.--Concept Manufacturing Company, Inc., Plainwell, MI; *U.S. Private*, pg. 548
Moles, Robert T., Pres. & Chief Exec. Officer--Century 21 Real Estate Corp., Parsippany, NJ; *U.S. Public*, pg. 321
Molin, Kim E., Pres.--Molin Auto Parts Inc., Buffalo, NY; *U.S. Private*, pg. 756
Molin, Per, Pres. & Chief Exec. Officer--Avesta Sheffield AB, Stockholm, Sweden; *Int'l*, pg. 221
Molina, Antonio Castro, Pres.--Grupo Carpenter S.A. de C.V., Tlalnepantla, Mexico; *U.S. Public*, pg. 308
Molinari, John, Pres. & Chief Exec. Officer--Media 100, Inc., Marlborough, MA; *U.S. Public*, pg. 1079
Molinari, Philip, Pres.--The Arrow Shirt Company, New York, NY; *Int'l*, pg. 194
Moll, Klaus, Pres.--Babcock-BSH AG, Bad Hersfeld, Germany; *Int'l*, pg. 399
Moll, Ted, Pres.--Aircap Industries Corp., Verona, MS; *U.S. Private*, pg. 688
Mollard, Peter, Pres.--Lafarge Materials, Toronto, Canada; *Int'l*, pg. 789
Moller-Racke, Marcus, Pres. & Chm. Bd.--A. Racke GmbH, Bingen, Germany; *Int'l*, pg. 1083
Molloy, Fintan, Pres.--Boehringer Ingelheim Animal Health Inc., Saint Joseph, MO; *Int'l*, pg. 199
Molloy, Patrick, Chief Exec. Officer--Bank of Ireland, Dublin, Ireland; *Int'l*, pg. 152
Molloy, Peter, Pres.--MJB Rice Company, Union City, CA; *Int'l*, pg. 917
Molman, D., Pres.--Admedia bv, Amstelveen, Netherlands; *Int'l*, pg. 1445
Moloney, Earl, Chm. Bd. & Chief Exec. Officer--Molon Motor & Coil Corp., Rolling Meadows, IL; *U.S. Private*, pg. 756
Moloney, William K., Pres.--Molon Motor & Coil Corp., Rolling Meadows, IL; *U.S. Private*, pg. 756
Molotsky, Barbara, Partner--BSMG Worldwide, New York, NY; *U.S. Public*, pg. 1642
Momose, Nobuo, Chm. & Pres.--Dentsu USA Inc.-New York, New York, NY; *Int'l*, pg. 393
Monahan, Michael T., Pres.-Comerica Inc. & Comerica Bank--Comerica Incorporated, Detroit, MI; *U.S. Public*, pg. 408
Monahan, Michael T., Pres. & Chief Oper. Officer--Comerica Bank Michigan, Detroit, MI; *U.S. Public*, pg. 409
Monahan, Pierre, Pres. & Chief Exec. Officer--Alliance Forest Products Inc., Montreal, Canada; *Int'l*, pg. 57
Monahan, William D., Pres. & Chief Exec. Officer--The Monahan Company, Eastpointe, MI; *U.S. Private*, pg. 756
Monark, Ronald, Pres. & Chief Exec. Officer--Mitchell International, San Diego, CA; *U.S. Public*, pg. 1601
Monchein, Robert F., Pres.--Forest City Land Group, Cleveland, OH; *U.S. Public*, pg. 668
Monckton, Rosamond, Pres.--Tiffany & Co., London, United Kingdom; *U.S. Public*, pg. 1609
Moncrief, Lee E., Chm. Bd., Pres. & Chief Exec. Officer--SouthTrust Bank, Shoals, Florence, AL; *U.S. Public*, pg. 1492
Mondavi, R. Michael, Pres. & Chief Exec. Officer--Robert Mondavi Winery, Inc., Oakville, CA; *U.S. Public*, pg. 1393
Monday, John, Pres. & Gen. Mgr.--Multi Metals Div., Louisville, KY; *U.S. Public*, pg. 575
Monderer, Benjamin, Chm. Bd., Pres. & Chief Tech. Officer--Box Hill Systems Corporation, New York, NY; *U.S. Public*, pg. 249
Monerris, Antonio, Partner & Mgr.--Vinizius/Young & Rubicam, S.A., Barcelona, Spain; *U.S. Private*, pg. 1199
Monette, Edward A., Chm. Bd., Pres., Chief Exec. Officer & Chief Oper. Officer--St. Croix Press, Inc., New Richmond, WI; *U.S. Private*, pg. 960
Money, Kent, Pres.--Zion's Securities Corp., Salt Lake City, UT; *U.S. Private*, pg. 327
Mongan, Thomas, Pres.--Guarantee Title & Trust Co., Cincinnati, OH; *U.S. Private*, pg. 485
Monge, Dimitri, Pres. & Chief Oper. Officer--Airtex Products, Fairfield, IL; *U.S. Private*, pg. 1113
Monikan, John, Pres.--Liberty House, Inc., Honolulu, HI; *U.S. Private*, pg. 578
Monikan, John, Pres.--Liberty House, Honolulu, HI; *U.S. Private*, pg. 578
Monk, Albert C., III, Pres.--DIMON, Incorporated, Danville, VA; *U.S. Public*, pg. 509
Monk, Albert C., III, Pres. & Chief Exec. Officer--DIMON, International, Inc., Farmville, NC; *U.S. Public*, pg. 510
Monk, Richard H., Jr., Pres.--Avondale Foreign Sales Corporation, Sylacauga, AL; *U.S. Private*, pg. 103
Monkiewicz, Ray, Pres. & Chief Exec. Officer--Kayem Foods, Inc., Chelsea, MA; *U.S. Private*, pg. 610
Monnier, Nicolas, Pres. & Mng. Dir.--Alice, Paris, France; *U.S. Private*, pg. 678
Monnoyeur, Baudouin, Chm. Bd. & Pres.--Monnoyeur SCA, Saint Denis, France; *Int'l*, pg. 888
Monoley, Ed, Pres. & Chief Exec. Officer--Ridley Canada Limited, Winnipeg, Canada; *Int'l*, pg. 1116
Monroe, Bruce B., Pres. & Chief Exec. Officer--The Johnson Corporation, Three Rivers, MI; *U.S. Private*, pg. 591

Monroe, Mark E., Pres. & Chief Exec. Officer--Louis Dreyfus Natural Gas Corp., Oklahoma City, OK; *U.S. Private*, pg. 342
Monroe, Tom, Pres. & Chief Creative Officer--Fogarty Klein & Partners, Houston, TX; *U.S. Private*, pg. 415
Monroe, William, Pres. & Chief Exec. Officer--Bertolli USA, Inc., Secaucus, NJ; *Int'l*, pg. 655
Monson, Robert, Chm. Bd., Pres. & Treas.--Monson Trucking, Inc., Duluth, MN; *U.S. Private*, pg. 758
Monsour, Michael, Pres.--Market Place Print, Inc., Pittsburgh, PA; *U.S. Private*, pg. 701
Montador, Paul, Pres.--Johnson & Johnson Medical Products Inc., Peterborough, Canada; *U.S. Public*, pg. 931
Montague, William P., Pres. & Chief Oper. Officer--Mark IV Industries Inc., Amherst, NY; *U.S. Public*, pg. 1044
Montalvo, Paco, Pres.--Lowe MBAC, Barcelona, Spain; *U.S. Private*, pg. 678
Montani, Anthony A., Pres. & Chief Oper. Officer--McInnes Steel Company, Corry, PA; *U.S. Private*, pg. 722
Montano, Frank M., Pres. & Chief Oper. Officer--Moto Photo, Inc., Dayton, OH; *U.S. Public*, pg. 1136
Montanus, Phil, Partner & Pres.-Devel.--Towne Properties, Cincinnati, OH; *U.S. Private*, pg. 1093
Montero, Eduardo, Pres.--Industrias Pacocha S.A. (Unilever), Lima, Peru; *Int'l*, pg. 1437
Montfort, Richard L., Pres. & Chief Oper. Officer--ConAgra Red Meat Companies, Greeley, CO; *U.S. Public*, pg. 427
Montgomery, David, Pres.--The Phillies-A Limited Partnership, Philadelphia, PA; *U.S. Private*, pg. 861
Montgomery, George, Pres. & Chief Exec. Officer--Taylor Made Golf Co. Inc., Carlsbad, CA; *Int'l*, pg. 1181
Montgomery, Joseph S., Chm. Bd., Pres. & Chief Exec. Officer--Cannondale Corporation, Bethel, CT; *U.S. Public, pg. 301*
Montgomery, Robert, Pres.--Bob Montgomery Chevrolet/Honda, Louisville, KY; *U.S. Private*, pg. 758
Montgomery, Ron, Pres.-N.W. Arkansas Div.--Nabholz Construction Corp., Conway, AR; *U.S. Private*, pg. 772
Monti, Carmel, Pres.--The Hilsinger Co. L.P., Plainville, MA; *U.S. Private*, pg. 530
Monto, Edward A., Pres. & Chief Oper. Officer--Houston Industries Energy, Inc., Houston, TX; *U.S. Public*, pg. 843
Montoya, Benjamin F., Pres. & Chief Exec. Officer--Public Service Company of New Mexico, Albuquerque, NM; *U.S. Public*, pg. 1339
Montrone, Paul M., Chm. Bd., Pres. & Chief Exec. Officer--Fisher Scientific International, Hampton, NH; *U.S. Private*, pg. 658
Montross, Albert E., Pres. & Chief Exec. Officer--Mylex Corporation, Fremont, CA; *U.S. Public*, pg. 1143
Monty, Jean C., Pres. & Chief Exec. & Oper. Officer--BCE Inc., Montreal, Canada; *Int'l*, pg. 114
Monzel, Carl, Mng. Principal--Baxter Hodell Donnelly Preston Inc., Cincinnati, OH; *U.S. Private*, pg. 124
Monzino, Antonio Jr., Pres.--Monzino S.p.A., Milan, Italy; *Int'l*, pg. 888
Mooar, William E., Pres.--Coast Manufacturing Company, Yonkers, NY; *U.S. Private*, pg. 248
Moody, Bill, Pres.--Coast Fed Services, Chatsworth, CA; *U.S. Public*, pg. 389
Moody, Dan T., Pres.--Eddins-Walcher Company, Midland, TX; *U.S. Private*, pg. 362
Moody, Dwight, Pres.--First Union Brokerage Services, Inc., Charlotte, NC; *U.S. Public*, pg. 640
Moody, Jeffrey A., Pres. & Chief Concept Officer--Kentucky Fried Chicken Corporation (KFC), Louisville, KY; *U.S. Public*, pg. 1636
Moody, Maxey D., III, Pres.--M.D. Moody & Sons Inc., Jacksonville, FL; *U.S. Private*, pg. 759
Moody, Raymond L., Jr., Pres.--Batson-Cook Company, West Point, GA; *U.S. Private*, pg. 123
Moody, Ross R., Pres. & Chief Oper. Officer--National Western Life Insurance Company, Austin, TX; *U.S. Public*, pg. 1161
Moon, Alan C., Pres.--TransAlta Enterprises Corporation, Calgary, Canada; *Int'l*, pg. 1416
Moon, Don, Pres.--Tandy Leather Co., Fort Worth, TX; *U.S. Public*, pg. 1561
Moon, Hangup, Pres.--Electronics Stamping Corp., Rancho Dominguez, CA; *U.S. Private*, pg. 370
Moon, Heon Sang, Chm. Bd. & Pres.--The Export-Import Bank of Korea, Seoul, Korea; *Int'l*, pg. 467
Moon, J.S., Pres.--Patterson Laboratories, Inc., Detroit, MI; *U.S. Private*, pg. 843
Moon, James B., Chm. Bd., Pres. & Chief Exec. Officer--Protocol Systems, Inc., Beaverton, OR; *U.S. Public*, pg. 1336
Moonan, Tom, Co-Pres.--The Hibbert Company, Trenton, NJ; *U.S. Private*, pg. 525
Moone, Michael J., Pres. & Chief Exec. Officer--Faroudja, Inc., Sunnyvale, CA; *U.S. Public*, pg. 613
Moone, Robert H., Pres. & Chief Oper. Officer--State Automobile Mutual Insurance Co., Columbus, OH; *U.S. Private*, pg. 1036
Mooney, Eugene C., Pres. & Chief Oper. Officer--Orange-Co., Inc., Bartow, FL; *U.S. Public*, pg. 1229
Mooney, J., Pres. & Chief Exec. Officer--A&W Food Services of Canada Inc., North Vancouver, Canada; *Int'l, pg. 1*
Mooney, Joseph T., Jr., Pres.--Monsey-Bakor, Kimberton, PA; *U.S. Private*, pg. 757
Mooney, Michael M., Pres. & Chief Exec. Officer--Key Bank of Idaho, Boise, ID; *U.S. Public*, pg. 954
Mooney, Stuart A., Pres. & Chief Oper. Officer--Vernon Rentals & Leasing Inc., Toronto, Canada; *Int'l*, pg. 559
Moonves, Leslie, Pres. & Exec. V.P.-CBS--CBS Entertainment, Los Angeles, CA; *U.S. Public*, pg. 274
Moore, Ann S., Pres.--People, New York, NY; *U.S. Public*, pg. 1613
Moore, B.L., Pres. & Chief Exec. Officer--Chep USA, Orlando, FL; *Int'l*, pg. 211
Moore, Bradley G., Pres. & Chief Exec. Officer--Sparks State Bank, Sparks, MD; *U.S. Public*, pg. 1089
Moore, Charles, Pres. & Mng. Partner--The Bank Funds Company LLC, Chicago, IL; *U.S. Private*, pg. 113
Moore, Charles V., Pres.--Trainer Wortham & Company Incorporated, New York, NY; *U.S. Private*, pg. 1095
Moore, Clyde R., Pres. & Chief Oper. Officer--Thomas & Betts Corporation, Memphis, TN; *U.S. Public*, pg. 1597
Moore, David, Pres.--Kelley Atlantic, LTD, Ajax, Canada; *U.S. Private*, pg. 613
Moore, Glenn R., Pres. & Chief Oper. Officer--Maynard Oil Co., Dallas, TX; *U.S. Public*, pg. 1064
Moore, Herbert B., Pres.--Blackman Uhler Chemical Co., Augusta, GA; *U.S. Public*, pg. 1548
Moore, Herbert B., Jr., Pres.--Blackman Uhler Chemical Co., Spartanburg, SC; *U.S. Public*, pg. 1548
Moore, Ivan R., Jr., Pres.--Sysco Food Services-San Antonio, Inc., San Antonio, TX; *U.S. Public*, pg. 1552
Moore, Jack, Pres.--Union Underwear Co., Inc., Bowling Green, KY; *U.S. Public*, pg. 686
Moore, Jack R., Pres. & Chief Exec. Officer--Stahl Specialty Company, Kingsville, MO; *U.S. Private*, pg. 1029
Moore, Jackson W., Pres. & Chief Oper. Officer--Union Planters Corporation, Cordova, TN; *U.S. Public*, pg. 1668
Moore, James E., Pres. & Chief Exec. Officer--ContiFinancial Corporation, New York, NY; *U.S. Public*, pg. 439
Moore, James E., Pres. & Mng. Dir.--ContiFinancial Services Corporation, New York, NY; *U.S. Public*, pg. 439
Moore, James L., Pres.--Case Advertising, Inc., Charlotte, NC; *U.S. Public*, pg. 391
Moore, James L., Pres. & Chief Oper. Officer--Coca-Cola Consolidated, Charlotte, NC; *U.S. Public*, pg. 392
Moore, James L., Jr., Pres. & Chief Oper. Officer--Coca-Cola Bottling Co. Consolidated, Charlotte, NC; *U.S. Public*, pg. 391
Moore, John, Pres.--Dallas Peterbilt, Inc., Irving, TX; *U.S. Private*, pg. 309
Moore, John, Pres.--Moore Electric Supply, Inc., Charlotte, NC; *U.S. Public*, pg. 847
Moore, John, Pres., Chief Exec. & Oper. Officer--Mindscape, Inc., Novato, CA; *Int'l*, pg. 1026
Moore, John A., Pres.--Sun Alliance USA, Inc., New York, NY; *Int'l*, pg. 1131
Moore, John R., Pres. & Chief Exec. Officer--Midas-International Corp., Chicago, IL; *U.S. Public*, pg. 1766
Moore, Keith F., Pres. & Chief Exec. Officer--Hawker Siddeley Canada Inc., Mississauga, Canada; *Int'l*, pg. 604
Moore, Kenneth O., Pres.--American West Trading Co., Dresden, TN; *U.S. Public*, pg. 1073
Moore, Leon, Chm. Bd., Pres. & Chief Exec. Officer--Sholodge, Inc., Hendersonville, TN; *U.S. Public*, pg. 1467
Moore, Malcolm, Pres.--Ipsen International, Inc., Cherry Valley, IL; *Int'l*, pg. 1149
Moore, Marilyn A., Pres.--Team Rehab, Inc., Saint Louis, MO; *U.S. Public*, pg. 1373
Moore, Michael, Pres.--Sun Process Converting Company, Elk Grove Village, IL; *U.S. Private*, pg. 1051
Moore, Michael J., Chm. Bd. & Pres.--Southland Industries, Long Beach, CA; *U.S. Private*, pg. 1018
Moore, Peter, Pres. & Chief Exec. Officer--Adidas International, Portland, OR; *Int'l*, pg. 24
Moore, Randolph G., Pres.--Molokai Ranch Ltd., Honolulu, HI; *Int'l*, pg. 216
Moore, Richard L., Pres. & Chief Exec. Officer--Grant Marketing Communications, Ardmore, PA; *U.S. Private*, pg. 470
Moore, Richard L., Pres. & Chief Exec. Officer--Kingswood Advertising, Inc., Ardmore, PA; *U.S. Private*, pg. 622
Moore, Richard L., Pres. & Chief Exec. Officer--Kingswood Interactive, Ardmore, PA; *U.S. Private*, pg. 622
Moore, Robert, Pres.--Gensym Corporation, Cambridge, MA; *U.S. Public*, pg. 731
Moore, Robert, II, Pres.--Apartment Service Co., Los Angeles, CA; *U.S. Private*, pg. 77
Moore, Sam, Chm. Bd., Pres. & Chief Exec. Officer--Thomas Nelson Inc., Nashville, TN; *U.S. Public*, pg. 1167
Moore, Stanley A., Pres.--Overton Moore & Associates, Gardena, CA; *U.S. Private*, pg. 823
Moore, Steven E., Chm. Bd., Pres. & Chief Exec. Officer--OGE Energy Corp., Oklahoma City, OK; *U.S. Public*, pg. 1207
Moore, Steven R., Pres.--Rex Moore Electrical Contractors & Engineers, West Sacramento, CA; *U.S. Private*, pg. 760
Moore, Thomas, Pres.--WICO, Niles, IL; *U.S. Private*, pg. 1144
Moore, Thomas R., Pres. & Chief Exec. Officer--Remmele Engineering, Inc., New Brighton, MN; *U.S. Private*, pg. 921
Moore, Thomas W., Pres.--Sunniland Corporation, Sanford, FL; *U.S. Private*, pg. 1053
Moore, William M., Jr., Chm. Bd. & Pres.--Trident Financial Corporation, Raleigh, NC; *U.S. Private*, pg. 1103
Moore, William P., Pres.--Steelcraft Manufacturing Company, Cincinnati, OH; *U.S. Public*, pg. 877
Moorman, Dr. Gunter, Mng. Dir.--Uniferm GmbH & Co., Werne, Germany; *Int'l*, pg. 1143
Moorman, Michael F., Pres.--Peebles, Inc., South Hill, VA; *U.S. Private*, pg. 846
Moorstein, Brian, Pres.--Forstmann & Company, Inc., New York, NY; *U.S. Public*, pg. 670
Moos, Frank, Pres.--Collegeville Advertising, Norristown, PA; *U.S. Public*, pg. 1422
Moos, J. Clifford, Chm. Bd., Pres. & Chief Exec. Officer--Economy Folding Box Corp., Chicago, IL; *U.S. Private*, pg. 362
Mooslin, Michael D., Pres.--Color Me Mine, Inc., Van Nuys, CA; *U.S. Public*, pg. 966
Moothart, William H., Pres.--Chatsworth Data Corporation, Chatsworth, CA; *U.S. Private*, pg. 231
Moquist, Ronald M., Pres.--Beta Raven Inc., Bridgeton, MO; *U.S. Public*, pg. 1361
Mora, Manuel Medina, Pres.--Grupo Financiero Banamex/Accival, S.A. de C.V., Mexico, Mexico; *Int'l*, pg. 574
Mora, Richard, Pres. & Chief Exec. Officer--Coastcast Corporation, Gardena, CA; *U.S. Public*, pg. 391
Moraes, Eduardo, Pres.--Bundy Latin America, Sao Paulo, Brazil; *Int'l*, pg. 1342
Morais, Douglas H., Dr., Pres.--California Microwave, Inc.-Wireless Products Grp., Sunnyvale, CA; *U.S. Public*, pg. 293
Moralez, Abelardo, Pres. & Chief Exec. Officer--Banca Serfin, S.A., New York Agency, New York, NY; *Int'l*, pg. 137
Moran, Arthur, Pres.--Art Moran Pontiac-GMC Inc., Southfield, MI; *U.S. Private*, pg. 760
Moran, Bill, Pres.--Save-A-Lot, Inc., Saint Louis, MO; *U.S. Public*, pg. 1541
Moran, Charles E., Pres.--National Education Training Group, Naperville, IL; *U.S. Public*, pg. 784
Moran, Chuck, Pres.--NETG Holding, Inc., Irvine, CA; *U.S. Public*, pg. 784
Moran, E.A., Pres.--Public Service Resources Corporation, Newark, NJ; *U.S. Public*, pg. 1340
Moran, E.A., Pres.--Enterprise Group Development Corporation, Newark, NJ; *U.S. Public*, pg. 1340
Moran, Edmond J., Jr., Pres.--Hampton Roads Land Co., Ltd, Greenwich, CT; *U.S. Private*, pg. 760
Moran, Edmund J., Jr., Pres.-Mid-Atlantic Grp.--Moran Towing of Maryland, Baltimore, MD; *U.S. Private*, pg. 761
Moran, John J., Pres.--Kevlin Corporation, Wilmington, MA; *U.S. Public*, pg. 953
Moran, Keenan, Pres. & Chief Exec. Officer--Tuffy Associates Corp., Toledo, OH; *U.S. Private*, pg. 1109
Moran, M. Marcus, Jr., Pres.--W.E. Aubuchon Co., Inc., Westminster, MA; *U.S. Private*, pg. 98
Moran, Manuel, Pres.--Aerolineas Argentinas, Miami, FL; *Int'l*, pg. 575
Moran, Mike, Pres. & Chief Oper. Officer--The Care Group, Inc., New York, NY; *U.S. Public*, pg. 305
Moran, Mike, Pres. & Gen. Mgr.--KGAN-TV, Cedar Rapids, IA; *U.S. Private*, pg. 439
Moran, Patricia, Pres. & Chief Exec. Officer--JM Family Enterprises Inc., Deerfield Beach, FL; *U.S. Private*, pg. 577
Moran, Robert J., Pres. & Chief Exec. Officer--Ludlow Composites Corporation, Fremont, OH; *U.S. Private*, pg. 680
Moran, Thomas J., Pres. & Chief Exec. Officer--Mutual of America Life Insurance Company, New York, NY; *U.S. Private*, pg. 769
Moran, Thomas J., Pres. & Chief Exec. Officer--American Life Insurance Company of New York, New York, NY; *U.S. Private*, pg. 769
Moran, W. Dennis, Pres.--Weston International, Inc., West Chester, PA; *U.S. Public*, pg. 1761
Moran, William M., Jr., Pres. & Chief Exec. Officer--Moran Foods, Inc./Save-A-Lot Ltd., Saint Louis, MO; *U.S. Public*, pg. 1541
Moranville, David, Mng. Partner & Creative Dir.--Ingalls Moranville Advertising, San Francisco, CA; *U.S. Private*, pg. 316
Moravec, Frank, Pres. & Chief Exec. Officer--INX International, Milwaukee, WI; *Int'l*, pg. 1311
Morcillo, D. Francisco Mochon, Pres.--Telefonia y Finanzas, S.A. (Telfisa), Madrid, Spain; *Int'l*, pg. 1372
Morden, Reid, Pres. & Chief Exec. Officer--Atomic Energy of Canada Ltd., Mississauga, Canada; *Int'l*, pg. 97
Morean, William, Chm. Bd. & Chief Exec. Officer--Jabil Circuit, Inc., Saint Petersburg, FL; *U.S. Public*, pg. 919
Moreau, C.P., Pres.--Texaco Puerto Rico, Inc., San Juan, PR; *U.S. Public*, pg. 1583
Moreau, P., Sr. V.P. & Gen. Mgr. Quebec--Publicite McKim Ltee., Montreal, Canada; *U.S. Private*, pg. 104
Morehead, C. Richard, Pres. & Chief Oper. Officer--American Heritage Life Investment Corp., Jacksonville, FL; *U.S. Public*, pg. 78
Morelli, Joseph, Chm. Bd., Pres. & Chief Exec. Officer--M.H. Rhodes, Inc., Avon, CT; *U.S. Private*, pg. 927
Moren, John G., Pres.--Parsons Construction Services, Inc., Houston, TX; *U.S. Private*, pg. 842
Moreno, Arthur R., Pres. & Chief Exec. Officer--Outdoor Systems, Inc., Phoenix, AZ; *U.S. Public*, pg. 1235
Moreno, Frutos, Mng. Dir.-Madrid--TBWA Madrid, S.A., Madrid, Spain; *U.S. Private*, pg. 1063
Moreno, R., Pres.--Wometco de Puerto Rico Inc., Santurce, PR; *U.S. Private*, pg. 1186
Morgami, M., Pres.--Minolta Singapore (Pte.) Ltd., Singapore, Singapore; *Int'l*, pg. 869
Morgan, Alfred Y., Jr., Pres.--White Rock Products Corp., Whitestone, NY; *U.S. Private*, pg. 1173
Morgan, Braxton, Pres.--PEPCON Systems, Inc., Las Vegas, NV; *U.S. Public*, pg. 88
Morgan, Charles D., Jr., Chm. Bd., Pres. & Chief Exec. Officer--Acxiom Corporation, Conway, AR; *U.S. Public*, pg. 18
Morgan, Colin J., Pres.--Helene Curtis International, Chicago, IL; *Int'l*, pg. 1434
Morgan, Frank R., Pres. & Chief Exec. Officer--Star Fine Foods, Inc., Fresno, CA; *U.S. Private*, pg. 1034
Morgan, George D., Pres.--McQuick's Oilube, Inc., Muncie, IN; *U.S. Public*, pg. 1348
Morgan, Gwyn, Pres. & Chief Exec. Officer--Alberta Energy Company, Ltd., Calgary, Canada; *Int'l*, pg. 48
Morgan, J.M., Pres.-Shell Oil Prods.--Shell Oil Company, Houston, TX; *Int'l*, pg. 1136
Morgan, James H., Pres. & Chief Exec. Officer--Interstate/Johnson Lane, Inc., Charlotte, NC; *U.S. Public*, pg. 909
Morgan, James H., Pres. & Chief Exec. Officer--Interstate/Johnson Lane Corporation, Charlotte, NC; *U.S. Public*, pg. 910
Morgan, Jerry, Pres. & Chief Oper. Officer--Sargent & Greenleaf, Inc., Nicholasville, KY; *U.S. Private*, pg. 965
Morgan, Jerry, Pres.--Sargent and Greenleaf, Nicholasville, KY; *U.S. Private*, pg. 981

Morgan, Jim, Pres.--Hood Lumber Co., Mill City, OR; *U.S. Private*, pg. 538
Morgan, Jim, Pres.--Hanel Lumber Co., Inc., Hood River, OR; *U.S. Private*, pg. 538
Morgan, Joseph, Pres.--Pasta Central, Atlanta, GA; *U.S. Public*, pg. 236
Morgan, Phillip R., Pres. & Chief Exec. Officer--Morgan Construction Co., Worcester, MA; *U.S. Private*, pg. 761
Morgan, Robert B., Pres. & Chief Exec. Officer--Cincinnati Financial Corp., Fairfield, OH; *U.S. Public*, pg. 368
Morgan, Robert W., Pres.--Environmental Health Strategies, Menlo Park, CA; *U.S. Public*, pg. 609
Morgan, Stephen, Pres.--EUA Citizens Conservation Services, Inc., Lowell, MA; *U.S. Public*, pg. 549
Morgan, Thomas I., Pres. & Chief Exec. Officer--U.S. Office Products Company, Washington, DC; *U.S. Public*, pg. 1686
Morgan, Thomas J., Pres.--Sysco Food Services of Idaho, Inc., Boise, ID; *U.S. Public*, pg. 1551
Morgan, V. Harley, Pres.--Pac Paper Inc., Vancouver, WA; *U.S. Private*, pg. 828
Morganthall, Fred J., II, Pres.--Harris Teeter, Inc., Charlotte, NC; *U.S. Public*, pg. 1412
Morgensen, Jerry L., Pres.--Hensel Phelps Construction Co., Greeley, CO; *U.S. Private*, pg. 523
Morgenstern, William E., Pres. & Chief Exec. Officer--Rent-Way, Inc., Erie, PA; *U.S. Public*, pg. 1377
Mori, Katsuhisa, Pres.--Nichifu Company Ltd., Osaka, Japan; *Int'l*, pg. 927
Mori, Katsuo, Pres.--Asahi Optical Co., Ltd., Tokyo, Japan; *Int'l*, pg. 85
Mori, Kazid Kazitaka, Pres.--SPS/Unbrako K.K., Tokyo, Japan; *U.S. Public*, pg. 1420
Mori, Reijiro, Pres. & Chief Exec. Officer--Sumitomo Sitix Corporation, Amagasaki, Japan; *Int'l*, pg. 1317
Mori, Susumu, Chm. Bd. & Pres.--Miyata Industry Co., Ltd., Chigasaki, Japan; *Int'l*, pg. 884
Mori, Takashi, Pres.--Unikis Japan Co. Ltd., Osaka, Japan; *Int'l*, pg. 1432
Moribe, Kazuo, Pres.--Mitsumi Electric Co., Ltd., Tokyo, Japan; *Int'l*, pg. 884
Morikawa, Derek, Pres. & Chief Oper. Officer--Wavetek Corporation, San Diego, CA; *U.S. Private*, pg. 1154
Morin, Curtis L., Pres., Treas. & Sec.--Bennington Iron Works, Inc., Bennington, VT; *U.S. Private*, pg. 133
Morin, L., Pres.--La Brasserie Labatt Limitee, La Salle, Canada; *Int'l*, pg. 679
Morin, Michael K., Pres.--Comsearch, Inc., Reston, VA; *U.S. Public*, pg. 46
Morin, Patrick, Pres.--Halterm Container Terminal, Halifax, Canada; *Int'l*, pg. 924
Morin, Robert E., Pres.--Keystone Morin, Inc., Pelham, AL; *U.S. Public*, pg. 1650
Morini, Angelo S., Chm. Bd., Pres. & Chief Exec. Officer--Galaxy Food Company, Orlando, FL; *U.S. Public*, pg. 697
Morishita, Yoichi, Pres.--Matsushita Electric Industrial Co., Ltd., Kadoma, Japan; *Int'l*, pg. 846
Morison, John H., III, Pres. & Chief Exec. Officer--Hitchiner Manufacturing Company, Inc., Milford, NH; *U.S. Private*, pg. 531
Morison, Stephen G., Vice Chm., Pres. & Chief Exec. Officer--Chancellor Corporation, Boston, MA; *U.S. Public*, *pg. 335*
Morita, Keikichi, Pres.--Shikishima Baking Co., Ltd., Nagoya, Japan; *Int'l*, pg. 1231
Moritz, Donald I., Pres. & Interim Chief Exec. Officer--Equitable Resources, Inc., Pittsburgh, PA; *U.S. Public*, pg. 589
Moritz, John D., Pres.--Moritz Cadillac-BMW Inc., Arlington, TX; *U.S. Private*, pg. 761
Mork, Bjorn, Pres.--Gyproc Gipsplatefabrikk A/S, Fredrikstad, Norway; *Int'l*, pg. 1200
Mork, John, Chief Exec. Officer--Eastern American Energy Corporation, Charleston, WV; *U.S. Private*, pg. 357
Mork, Richard G., Pres., Chief Exec. Officer & Chief Oper. Officer--A.M. Castle & Co., Franklin Park, IL; *U.S. Public*, *pg. 312*
Morley, Michael, Deputy Chm. & Pres.-New York--Edelman Worldwide, Inc., New York, NY; *U.S. Private*, pg. 362
Morley, Philip, Mng. Dir.--Landor Cartons, Birmingham, United Kingdom; *Int'l*, pg. 801
Morley, Walter J., Pres.--Cantrock Realty Corp., Hicksville, NY; *U.S. Private*, pg. 509
Mormarco, Jon, Pres.--Callaway Vineyard & Winery, Temecula, CA; *Int'l*, pg. 63
Moroney, Pat, Pres.--Continental Homes of Miami, Miami, FL; *U.S. Public*, pg. 441
Morooka, Yasukazu, Pres.--Sumitomo Metal U.S.A. Corp., Chicago, IL; *Int'l*, pg. 1316
Moros, N.P., Pres.--Cyprus Amax Coal Sales Corporation, Milford, OH; *U.S. Public*, pg. 471
Morr, Hector Perez, Pres.--Mead Johnson de Venezuela, S.A., Caracas, Venezuela; *U.S. Public*, pg. 256
Morrell, N.J., Deputy Mng. Dir.--Lonrho plc, London, United Kingdom; *Int'l*, pg. 817
Morreo, Phillip A., Pres. & Chief Exec. Officer--Emergi-Lite, Inc., Westbrook, CT; *Int'l*, pg. 725
Morrill, Robert J., Pres.--Microwave Radio Communications, Chelmsford, MA; *U.S. Public*, pg. 294
Morris, Brian, Pres.--Dailey & Associates, West Hollywood, CA; *U.S. Public*, pg. 909
Morris, Charles H., Pres.--Morris Newspaper Corporation, Savannah, GA; *U.S. Private*, pg. 762
Morris, Donald E., Pres. & Chief Exec. Officer--Acorn Engineering Company, City of Industry, CA; *U.S. Private*, pg. 14
Morris, Edna K., Pres.--Quincy Family Steak House, Spartanburg, SC; *U.S. Public*, pg. 23
Morris, G. Ronald, Pres. & Chief Exec. Officer--Western Industries, Inc., Milwaukee, WI; *U.S. Private*, pg. 1165
Morris, George C., Pres.--Niagara Blower Company, Buffalo, NY; *U.S. Private*, pg. 798
Morris, Gil, Pres.--Hilti Inc., Tulsa, OK; *Int'l*, pg. 620
Morris, Herman, Pres. & Chief Exec. Officer--Memphis Light, Gas & Water, Memphis, TN; *U.S. Private*, pg. 731
Morris, John L., Pres.--Bass Pro Shops, Inc., Springfield, MO; *U.S. Private*, pg. 122
Morris, John R., Pres. & Chief Oper. Officer--Builders Transport, Incorporated, Camden, SC; *U.S. Public*, pg. 267
Morris, John R., Pres.--CCG Corp., Camden, SC; *U.S. Public*, pg. 267
Morris, Leslie M., Jr., Pres.--Sands Investments, Inc., Myrtle Beach, SC; *U.S. Private*, pg. 964
Morris, Lou, Pres.--Simplicity Holdings Inc., New York, NY; *U.S. Private*, pg. 1002
Morris, Mark L., Pres. & Chief Exec. Officer--First National Bank of Fort Myers, Fort Myers, FL; *U.S. Public*, pg. 608
Morris, Michael, Pres. & Chief Exec. Officer--Consumers Energy, Jackson, MI; *U.S. Public*, pg. 280
Morris, Michael G., Chm. Bd., Pres. & Chief Exec. Officer--Northeast Utilities, Berlin, CT; *U.S. Public*, pg. 1194
Morris, Nigel W., Pres. & Chief Oper. Officer--Capital One Financial Corporation, Falls Church, VA; *U.S. Public*, pg. 302
Morris, Richard, Pres.-Sigma Aldrich Research Div.--Sigma-Aldrich Corporation, Saint Louis, MO; *U.S. Public*, pg. 1471
Morris, Richard G., Div. V.P.--Construction & Home Improvement Markets Division, Saint Paul, MN; *U.S. Public*, pg. 1605
Morris, Robert, Pres. & Chief Exec. Officer--City National Bank, Hastings, NE; *U.S. Public*, pg. 629
Morris, Stephen B., Pres.--The Arbitron Company, New York, NY; *U.S. Public*, pg. 331
Morris, Stewart, Pres. & Co.-Chief Exec. Officer--Stewart Information Services Corporation, Houston, TX; *U.S. Public*, pg. 1518
Morris, T.N., Jr., Chm., Pres. & Chief Exec. Officer--Calcasieu Lumber Company, Austin, TX; *U.S. Private*, pg. 200
Morris, Thomas E., Pres. & Chief Exec. Officer--Scotty's, Inc., Winter Haven, FL; *Int'l*, pg. 533
Morris, Tom, Pres.--Interlock Industries, Inc., Sellersburg, IN; *U.S. Private*, pg. 567
Morris, V. T., Pres.--Metal Sales Manufacturing Corporation, Sellersburg, IN; *U.S. Private*, pg. 567
Morris, W. S., 111, Pres.--Athens Newspapers, Inc., Augusta, GA; *U.S. Private*, pg. 996
Morris, William C., Chm. Bd. & Pres.--J. & W. Seligman & Co., New York, NY; *U.S. Private*, pg. 982
Morris, William S., IV, Pres.--Shivers Trading & Operating Co., Augusta, GA; *U.S. Private*, pg. 994
Morris, William, IV, Pres.--Morris Communications Corporation, Augusta, GA; *U.S. Private*, pg. 995
Morrison, Albert, III, Pres. & Chief Exec. Officer--Burnham, Lancaster, PA; *U.S. Public*, pg. 270
Morrison, Bill, Pres.--Supermarket Insurance Agency, Inc., Shawnee Mission, KS; *U.S. Private*, pg. 93
Morrison, Bill, Pres.--Benchmark Insurance Company, Shawnee Mission, KS; *U.S. Private*, pg. 93
Morrison, Bob, Pres.--AGRA Foundations Limited, Edmonton, Canada; *Int'l*, pg. 30
Morrison, Charles E., Partner, Exec. V.P., Strategic Plng. Dir. & New Bus. Contact--Don Coleman Advertising, Inc., Southfield, MI; *U.S. Private*, pg. 251
Morrison, Craig, Pres.--Van Leer Containers, Inc., Alsip, IL; *Int'l*, pg. 1146
Morrison, Dale, Pres.--Campbell Sales, Dallas, TX; *U.S. Public*, pg. 299
Morrison, Dale F., Pres. & Chief Exec. Officer--Campbell Soup Company, Camden, NJ; *U.S. Public*, pg. 298
Morrison, Dennis R., Pres. & Chief Exec. Officer--Norwest Bank Illinois, N.A., Galesburg, IL; *U.S. Public*, pg. 1202
Morrison, Dolphus, Pres.--SMI Steel, Inc., Birmingham, AL; *U.S. Public*, pg. 412
Morrison, J.M., Chm. Bd., Pres. & Sec.--Morrison, Inc., Hammond, IN; *U.S. Private*, pg. 762
Morrison, Jerry L., Pres. & Chief Oper. Officer--BRC Holdings, Dallas, TX; *U.S. Public*, pg. 163
Morrison, Keith, Pres. & Chief Exec. Officer--Western Broadcast Sales Ltd., Toronto, Canada; *Int'l*, pg. 1482
Morrison, Richard S., Pres. & Chief Exec. Officer--Molded Fiber Glass Companies, Ashtabula, OH; *U.S. Private*, pg. 755
Morrison, Robert S., Chm. & Chief Exec. Officer--Kraft Foods, Inc., Northfield, IL; *U.S. Public*, pg. 1287
Morrison, Robert S., Chm. Bd., Pres. & Chief Exec. Officer--The Quaker Oats Company, Chicago, IL; *U.S. Public*, pg. 1347
Morrison, Ronald C., Pres. & Gen. Mgr.--Kodak Canada Inc., Toronto, Canada; *U.S. Public*, pg. 553
Morrison, Scott, Pres. & Chief Exec. Officer--Commercial Testing & Engineering Co., Lombard, IL; *Int'l*, pg. 1153
Morrison, William, Chm. Bd., Pres. & Chief Exec. Officer--Northern Trust Bank of Florida, N.A., Miami, FL; *U.S. Public*, pg. 1196
Morrisroe, Frank, Pres.--Lodgistix, Inc., Phoenix, AZ; *U.S. Public*, pg. 1527
Morrissette, Arthur, Jr., Pres.--Interstate Van Lines, Inc., Springfield, VA; *U.S. Private*, pg. 573
Morrissey, Tim, Pres.--KFSM-TV, Fort Smith, AR; *U.S. Public*, pg. 1174
Morrod, James, Pres. & Chief Exec. Officer--ITK International, Inc., Chelmsford, MA; *U.S. Private*, pg. 556
Morrow, Andre, Pres.--Groupe Morrow Inc., Montreal, Canada; *Int'l*, pg. 566
Morrow, Charles B., Pres.--Fannie May Candy Shops, Inc., Chicago, IL; *U.S. Private*, pg. 598
Morrow, Clark, Pres.--Sunwest Bank of Las Cruces, N.A., Las Cruces, NM; *U.S. Public*, pg. 1165
Morse, Alan, Pres.--Research Institute of America, New York, NY; *U.S. Public*, pg. 1602
Morse, Edward J., Jr., Pres.--Ed Morse Automotive Group, Fort Lauderdale, FL; *U.S. Private*, pg. 763
Morse, Howard L., Pres. & Chief Oper. Officer--Acurex Environmental Corp., Mountain View, CA; *Int'l*, pg. 607
Morse, Robert, Pres.--Morse Hardware Company, Bellingham, WA; *U.S. Private*, pg. 763
Mortensen, Christian, Pres.--Mejeriernes Maelkedisponeringsselskab A.m.b.a, Viby, Denmark; *Int'l*, *pg. 826*
Mortensen, Peter, Chm. Bd., Pres. & Chief Exec. Officer--F.N.B. Corporation, Hermitage, PA; *U.S. Public*, pg. 607
Mortenson, G. Russell, Chm. Bd., Pres. & Chief Exec. Officer--Amtech Corporation, Dallas, TX; *U.S. Public*, pg. 105
Mortenson, Lee N., Pres. & Chief Exec. Officer--Alba-Waldensian, Inc., Valdese, NC; *U.S. Public*, pg. 35
Mortenson, Lee N., Pres. & Chief Exec. Officer--Pilot Research Corp., Valdese, NC; *U.S. Public*, pg. 36
Mortenson, Lee N., Pres. & Chief Exec. Officer--Sunstates Corporation, Raleigh, NC; *U.S. Public*, pg. 1536
Mortimer, Jim, Pres.& Gen. Mgr.--Deseret News, Salt Lake City, UT; *U.S. Private*, pg. 327
Morton, B. Carole, Pres.--Information Management Division, Woodland Hills, CA; *U.S. Public*, pg. 1516
Morton, David L., Pres. & Chief Exec. Officer--The Quaker Oats Co. of Canada Ltd., Peterborough, Canada; *U.S. Public*, pg. 1348
Morton, Grant, Pres.--Hughes Group, Clarksville, IN; *U.S. Private*, pg. 546
Morton, Jay W., Pres. & Chief Exec. Officer--United Engines, Inc., Oklahoma City, OK; *U.S. Private*, pg. 1122
Morton, Larry T., Pres. & Chief Oper. Officer--Stocker Resources, Inc., Los Angeles, CA; *U.S. Public*, pg. 1308
Morton, Mark, Pres.--Bowmar Technologies, Fort Wayne, IN; *U.S. Public*, pg. 248
Morton, Robert H., Pres. & Rep. Dir.--Janssen-Cilag K.K., Tokyo, Japan; *U.S. Public*, pg. 929
Mosack, Carl L., Pres. & Chief Exec. Officer--Conbraco Industries Inc., Matthews, NC; *U.S. Private*, pg. 261
Mosco, Robert M., Pres. & Chief Exec. Officer-Mdsg.--Proffitt's, Inc., Alcoa, TN; *U.S. Public*, pg. 1333
Moscowitz, Gene, Pres.--Peerless Umbrella Co., Inc., Harrison, NJ; *U.S. Private*, pg. 847
Moser, Harry, Pres.--Charmilles Technologies Corp., Lincolnshire, IL; *Int'l*, pg. 489
Moser, Rainer, Pres.--Pfaff American Sales Corp., Paramus, NJ; *Int'l*, pg. 1046
Moses, Willy, Pres.--AlliedSignal Air Transport Avionics, Fort Lauderdale, FL; *U.S. Public*, pg. 50
Mosesian, Harry, Pres.--EMS Eastern Regional Office, Foxboro, MA; *U.S. Public*, pg. 565
Mosgrove, Harry, Pres.--Copper Mountain Resort, Frisco, CO; *Int'l*, pg. 685
Moshe, Celes, Pres.--Netwiz Ltd., Haifa, Israel; *Int'l*, pg. 645
Mosher, James, Pres.--Scotia Trawler Equipment Limited, Lunenburg, Canada; *Int'l*, pg. 909
Mosher, Walter W., Jr., Ph.D., Chm. Bd. & Pres.--Precision Dynamics Corporation, San Fernando, CA; *U.S. Private*, pg. 879
Moskowitz, Joel P., Chm. Bd., Pres. & Chief Exec. Officer--Ceradyne, Inc, Costa Mesa, CA; *U.S. Public*, pg. 330
Moss, M. G., Pres.--Moss Bros Group PLC, London, United Kingdom; *Int'l*, pg. 895
Moss, Michael C., Pres. & Chief Oper. Officer--Atlas Automotive, Inc., Albany, GA; *U.S. Private*, pg. 444
Moss, Victor, Pres. & Chief Exec. Officer--Tomco Auto Products, Inc., Los Angeles, CA; *U.S. Private*, pg. 1090
Moss, William, Pres.--Unichem, Houston, TX; *U.S. Public*, pg. 161
Mossberg, Alan I., Pres., Chief Exec. & Chief Oper. Officer & Treas.--O.F. Mossberg & Sons, Inc., North Haven, CT; *U.S. Private*, pg. 764
Mosser, Jakob, Pres.--North American Refractories Company, Cleveland, OH; *U.S. Private*, pg. 803
Mosser, Thomas W., Pres.--Avatar Vacation Resorts, Inc., Coral Gables, FL; *U.S. Public*, pg. 151
Mostrom, Joel, Pres.--Delmarva Properties, Inc., West Point, VA; *U.S. Public*, pg. 347
Mota-Velasco, German Larrea, Chm. & Pres.--Grupo Mexico S.A. de C.V., Mexico, Mexico; *U.S. Public*, pg. 138
Motherway, Thomas J., Pres. & Chief Fin. Officer--Boeing Realty Corporation, Long Beach, CA; *U.S. Public*, pg. 241
Motley, Lyle, Pres. & Chief Exec. Officer--Miami Div., Hialeah, FL; *U.S. Public*, pg. 1148
Motoi, Takashi, Deputy Pres.--The Tokai Bank, Limited, Nagoya, Japan; *Int'l*, pg. 1391
Motoshige, Eiichi, Pres.--Kajima Development Corp., Monterey Park, CA; *Int'l*, pg. 722
Motraghi, Mahyar, Pres.--Nokia Display Products Inc., Sausalito, CA; *Int'l*, pg. 954
Mott, David M., Pres. & Chief Oper. Officer--MedImmune, Inc., Gaithersburg, MD; *U.S. Public*, pg. 1081
Mott, Frederick B., Jr., Pres. & Publr.--The State-Record Company, Columbia, SC; *U.S. Public*, pg. 964
Mottola, Thomas D., Pres. & Chief Oper. Officer-SMEI--Sony Music Entertainment, Inc., New York, NY; *Int'l*, pg. 1281
Mougeot, Robert F., Chm. Bd. & Pres.--HEI Investment Corp., Honolulu, HI; *U.S. Public*, pg. 800
Moulchly-Weiss, Harriet, Mng. Partner--Strategy XXI, New York, NY; *U.S. Public*, pg. 1642
Moult, William, Pres. & Chief Exec. Officer--ASI Market Research, Inc., Stamford, CT; *U.S. Private*, pg. 554
Moulter, Larry, Pres. & Chief Exec. Officer--Woolf Associates, Boston, MA; *U.S. Private*, pg. 84
Mount, John M., Pres. & Chief Exec. Officer--Service America Systems, Inc., Deerfield Beach, FL; *U.S. Public*, *pg. 344*
Mountcastle, Thomas L., Pres.--Halifax Technology Services Company, Richmond, VA; *U.S. Public*, pg. 775
Mouser, Les, Pres.--Campbell Mithun Esty, Minneapolis, MN; *U.S. Private*, pg. 204
Moussu, Gerard, Pres.--Bensons, Paris, France; *Int'l*, pg. 460
Mowatt, George, Pres.--Kvaerner H&G Offshore Ltd, Croydon, United Kingdom; *Int'l*, pg. 771

Mowatt, Thomas, Pres. & Chief Oper. Officer--Champion Laboratories, Inc., Albion, IL; *U.S. Private*, pg. 1113
Mowder, John P., Pres.--Dixon Industries, Inc., Coffeyville, KS; *U.S. Public*, pg. 238
Mower, Barry, Pres.--Lifetime Products Inc., Clearfield, UT; *U.S. Private*, pg. 667
Mower, Clark M., Pres.--Bonneville Pacific Corporation, Salt Lake City, UT; *U.S. Public*, pg. 244
Mower, Don, Pres. & Chief Oper. Officer--Edwards Baking Co., Norcross, GA; *U.S. Private*, pg. 365
Mowitz, Hakan, Pres.--ICA Meny Foretagen AB, Bromma, Sweden; *Int'l*, pg. 643
Moyan, Francois, Pres. & Chief Exec. Officer--Companhia Siderurgica Belgo-Mineira, Belo Horizonte, Brazil; *Int'l*, pg. 79
Moyano, Angel, Pres.--Marco del Pont S.A., Buenos Aires, Argentina; *Int'l*, pg. 842
Moyer, Greg, Pres. & Chief Editorial Officer--Discovery Networks, Inc., Bethesda, MD; *U.S. Private*, pg. 334
Moyer, Gregory B., Pres. & Chief Editorial & Creative Officer--Discovery Communications, Inc., Bethesda, MD; *U.S. Private*, pg. 334
Moyer, Kevin, Pres.-Capital Markets Group--Dana Commercial Credit Corp. (Ohio), Toledo, OH; *U.S. Public*, pg. 479
Moyer, William C., Dr., Chm. Bd., Pres. & Chief Exec. Officer--SFA, Inc., Hyattsville, MD; *U.S. Private*, pg. 956
Moyes, Jerry, Pres.--Swift Leasing Co., Phoenix, AZ; *U.S. Public*, pg. 1543
Moyes, Jerry C., Chm. Bd., Pres. & Chief Exec. Officer--Swift Transportation Co., Sparks, NV; *U.S. Public*, pg. 1543
Moynahan, Stephen R., Pres. & Chief Exec. Officer--Dolphin & Bradbury, Inc., Philadelphia, PA; *U.S. Private*, pg. 338
Moynan, John, Pres.--Financial Collection Agencies, Inc., Phoenix, AZ; *Int'l*, pg. 471
Moynan, John, Pres.--Financial Collection Agencies, Hato Rey, PR; *Int'l*, pg. 471
Moynan, John, Pres.--Financial Collection Agencies of Pennsylvania Inc, Wayne, PA; *Int'l*, pg. 471
Moynan, John H., Pres. & Chief Exec. Officer--FCA International Ltd., Westmount, Canada; *Int'l*, pg. 470
Moynan, John H., Pres.--Financial Collection Agencies (UK) Limited, London, United Kingdom; *Int'l*, pg. 471
Moynan, John H., Pres.--FCA Holdings, Inc., Wayne, PA; *Int'l*, pg. 471
Moynan, John H., Pres.--Financial Collection Agencies (1990) Inc., Mobile, AL; *Int'l*, pg. 471
Moynan, John H., Pres.--Financial Collection Agencies (1990) Inc., Cohoes, NY; *Int'l*, pg. 471
Moynan, John H., Pres.--Financial Collection Agencies (1990) Inc., Scotch Plains, NJ; *Int'l*, pg. 471
Moynan, John H., Pres.--Financial Collection Agencies (1990) Inc., Boston, MA; *Int'l*, pg. 471
Moynan, John H., Pres.--Financial Collection Agencies (1990) Inc., Lombard, IL; *Int'l*, pg. 471
Moynan, John H., Pres.--Financial Collection Agencies (1990) Inc., Houston, TX; *Int'l*, pg. 471
Moynan, John H., Pres.--Financial Collection Agencies (1990) Inc., Milwaukee, WI; *Int'l*, pg. 471
Moynan, John H., Pres.--Financial Collection Agencies (1990) Inc., Richmond, VA; *Int'l*, pg. 471
Moynan, John H., Pres.--Financial Collection Agencies (1990) Inc., San Diego, CA; *Int'l*, pg. 471
Moynan, John H., Pres.--Financial Collection Agencies, Manchester, United Kingdom; *Int'l*, pg. 471
Moynan, John H., Pres.--Structured Financial Capital Inc., Wayne, PA; *Int'l*, pg. 471
Moynan, John H., Pres.--Recon Consultants, Inc., Wayne, PA; *Int'l*, pg. 471
Moynihan, James J., AIA, Pres. & Chief Exec. Officer--Heery International, Inc., Atlanta, GA; *U.S. Private*, pg. 519
Moyse, Herman, III, Chm. Bd.--City National Bank of Baton Rouge, Baton Rouge, LA; *U.S. Public*, pg. 629
Mruz, Michael J., Pres. & Chief Exec. & Oper. Officer--Nichols Research Corporation, Huntsville, AL; *U.S. Public*, pg. 1182
Mucha, Horst, Pres.--Hohner/HSS Inc., Ashland, VA; *U.S. Private*, pg. 533
Muck, Philip F., Pres., Chief Exec. Officer & Treas.--Munroe, Inc., Pittsburgh, PA; *U.S. Private*, pg. 767
Mudrak, Ota, Pres.--Mann Filtr Jipap s.r.o., Okrisky, Czech Republic; *Int'l*, pg. 484
Mueller, Alfred K., Div. Mgr.--Interstate Brick Company, West Jordan, UT; *U.S. Private*, pg. 830
Mueller, Charles W., Chm. Bd., Pres. & Chief Exec. Officer--Ameren Corporation, Saint Louis, MO; *U.S. Public*, pg. 65
Mueller, Charles W., Pres. & Chief Exec. Officer--AmerenUE, Saint Louis, MO; *U.S. Public*, pg. 66
Mueller, Curt, R.Ph., Pres.--Mueller Sports Medicine, Inc., Prairie Du Sac, WI; *U.S. Private*, pg. 766
Mueller, Ed, Pres. & Chief Exec. Officer--Pacific Bell, San Ramon, CA; *U.S. Public*, pg. 1416
Mueller, Ed, Pres. & Chief Exec. Officer--Pacific Bell, San Francisco, CA; *U.S. Public*, pg. 1416
Mueller, Fred, Pres.--Card Technology Corp., Paramus, NJ; *Int'l*, pg. 898
Mueller, Guenther, Chief Exec. Officer--B/W Werbeagentur GWA, Dusseldorf, Germany; *Int'l*, pg. 130
Mueller, Jack J., Pres. & Chief Exec. Officer--Cincinnati Bell Directory Inc., Cincinnati, OH; *U.S. Public*, pg. 367
Mueller, John H., Pres.--G & W Electric Co., Blue Island, IL; *U.S. Private*, pg. 433
Mueller, Kurt, Dr., Pres.--Kvaerner Pulping AG, Zurich, Switzerland; *Int'l*, pg. 768
Mueller, Larry, Pres.--ABB Process Analytics, Lewisburg, WV; *Int'l*, pg. 5
Mueller, Martin R., Pres.--Information Technology Division, Bellevue, NE; *U.S. Public*, pg. 1516
Mueller, Paul, Chm. Bd.--Paul Mueller Company, Springfield, MO; *U.S. Public*, pg. 1141
Mueller, Rand, Pres.--Tessco Group, Inc., Georgetown, TX; *U.S. Public*, pg. 394
Mueller, Rand, Pres.--Code Alarm Security Systems, Madison Heights, MI; *U.S. Public*, pg. 394
Mueller, Rand W., Chm. Bd., Pres. & Chief Exec. Officer--Code-Alarm, Inc., Madison Heights, MI; *U.S. Public*, pg. 393
Mueller, Richard G., Mng. Dir.--Toro-Wheel Horse, South Bend, IN; *U.S. Public*, pg. 1624
Mueller, Robert, Pres.--Lockheed Martin Electro-Optical Systems, Pasadena, CA; *U.S. Public*, pg. 1008
Mueller, Robert W., Pres. & Chief Exec. Officer--Victoria Financial Corporation, Cleveland, OH; *U.S. Public*, pg. 1660
Mueller, Robert W., Pres. & Chief Exec. Officer--Victoria Fire & Casualty, Cleveland, OH; *U.S. Public*, pg. 1660
Muellner, Steven L., Pres.--Applause Inc., Woodland Hills, CA; *U.S. Private*, pg. 78
Muffler, Thomas, Pres.--Allo Pro GmbH, Gelsenkirchen, Germany; *Int'l*, pg. 1307
Mukunda, Ram, Pres., Chief Exec. Officer & Treas.--Startec Global Communications Corporation, Bethesda, MD; *U.S. Public*, pg. 1511
Mulally, Alan R., Pres.--Boeing Defense & Space Group, Kent, WA; *U.S. Public*, pg. 240
Mulcahy, J. Patrick, Co-Pres. & Co-Chief Exec. Officer--Ralston Purina Company, Saint Louis, MO; *U.S. Public*, pg. 1359
Mulcahy, Richard T., V.P. & Div. Mgr.--Ragnar Benson, Inc., Monroeville, PA; *U.S. Private*, pg. 99
Mulder, Lawrence, Chm. Bd. & Pres.--ODL Incorporated, Zeeland, MI; *U.S. Private*, pg. 809
Muldrow, Ken, Pres. & Chief Exec. Officer--Goodpasture, Inc., Brownfield, TX; *U.S. Private*, pg. 464
Mulford, Mark C., Pres. & Chief Oper. Officer--Ameriquest Technologies, Santa Ana, CA; *U.S. Public*, pg. 96
Mulhaupt, F., Pres.--NFPA Research Foundation, Quincy, MA; *U.S. Private*, pg. 783
Mulhern, Patrick M., Pres.--Mulhern Belting, Inc., Oakland, NJ; *U.S. Private*, pg. 766
Mulholland, C. Bradley, Pres. & Chief Exec. Officer--Matson Navigation Company, Inc., San Francisco, CA; *U.S. Public*, pg. 39
Mulkey, Terry, Pres.--Sunrise Mobility Products Division, Longmont, CO; *U.S. Public*, pg. 1536
Mullagh, Michael, Pres. & Chief Exec. Officer--Whisper Communications, Sunnyvale, CA; *U.S. Public*, pg. 1425
Mullan, James F., Pres. & Chief Exec. Officer--PrimeSource Corporation, Pennsauken, NJ; *U.S. Public*, pg. 1329
Mullen, David P., Pres. & Chief Exec. Officer--Robinsons-May, North Hollywood, CA; *U.S. Public*, pg. 1064
Mullen, Dennis M., Pres. & Chief Exec. Officer--Curtice Burns Foods, Rochester, NY; *U.S. Private*, pg. 887
Mullen, J.J., Pres.--Apple Vacations West Inc., Elk Grove Village, IL; *U.S. Private*, pg. 78
Mullen, James X., Principal & Chief Exec. Officer--Mullen Advertising, Inc., Wenham, MA; *U.S. Private*, pg. 766
Mullen, John, Pres.--Financial Indemnity, Burbank, CA; *U.S. Public*, pg. 1694
Mullen, Paul B., Pres. & Chief Exec. Officer--GES Exposition Services, Inc., Las Vegas, NV; *U.S. Public*, pg. 1718
Muller, D.B., Pres.--Morganite Inc., Dunn, NC; *Int'l*, pg. 891
Muller, Daniel, Pres.--Ohio Alloy Steels Corporation, Youngstown, OH; *U.S. Public*, pg. 1617
Muller, Dennis M., Pres. & Chief Exec. Officer--Southern Frozen Foods, Montezuma, GA; *U.S. Private*, pg. 887
Muller, George T., Pres.--Subaru of America, Inc., Cherry Hill, NJ; *Int'l*, pg. 523
Muller, H., Pres. & Chief Exec. Officer--Voith Sulzer Papiertechnik GmbH, Heidenheim, Germany; *Int'l*, pg. 1307
Muller, Kurt, Pres.--Parker Hannifin GmbH/Pradifa Packing Division, Bietigheim-Bissingen, Germany; *U.S. Public*, pg. 1262
Muller, P.B., Pres.--Peabody Engineering Corp., Stamford, CT; *Int'l*, pg. 1065
Muller, William P., Pres.--Moran Services Corporation, Greenwich, CT; *U.S. Private*, pg. 760
Muller, William P., Pres.--Seaboard Barge Corporation, Greenwich, CT; *U.S. Private*, pg. 761
Muller, William P., Pres.--Petroleum Transportation Corporation, Greenwich, CT; *U.S. Private*, pg. 761
Mullet, Paul, Pres.--Excel Industries, Inc., Hesston, KS; *U.S. Private*, pg. 387
Mullican, Mark, Pres.--First Maryland Brokerage Corporation, Baltimore, MD; *Int'l*, pg. 64
Mullican, Mark, Pres.--First Maryland Annuities Agency Corporation, Baltimore, MD; *Int'l*, pg. 64
Mulliez, Gerard, Pres.--Auchan S.A., Croix, France; *Int'l*, pg. 98
Mulligan, Gerald T., Pres. & Chief Exec. Officer--Andover Bancorp, Inc., Andover, MA; *U.S. Public*, pg. 111
Mullin, L., Pres.--Cliffside Utility Contractors, Scarborough, Canada; *Int'l*, pg. 118
Mullin, Leo F., Pres. & Chief Exec. Officer--Delta Air Lines, Inc., Atlanta, GA; *U.S. Public*, pg. 497
Mullinax, Larry, Pres.--Ed Mullinax Ford, Inc., Amherst, OH; *U.S. Public*, pg. 1379
Mullins, Roy L., Jr., Pres. & Chief Exec. Officer--Beacon Sales Corporation, Jacksonville, FL; *U.S. Private*, pg. 126
Mulloy, Gary M., Pres. & Chief Oper. Officer--ADVO, Inc., Windsor, CT; *U.S. Public*, pg. 23
Mullvaney, Kevin, Pres.--DRI/McGraw-Hill, Lexington, MA; *U.S. Public*, pg. 1071
Mulroney, John P., Pres. & Chief Oper. Officer--Rohm and Haas Company, Philadelphia, PA; *U.S. Public*, pg. 1403
Mulva, J.J., Pres. & Chief Oper. Officer--Phillips Petroleum Company, Bartlesville, OK; *U.S. Public*, pg. 1290
Muma, Leslie M., Vice Chm., Pres. & Chief Oper. Officer--Fiserv, Inc., Brookfield, WI; *U.S. Public*, pg. 647
Munaf, Triawan, Pres., Chief Exec. Officer & Creative Dir.--Adwork! EURO RSCG Partnership, Jakarta, Indonesia; *Int'l*, pg. 602
Munafo, Samuel J., Pres. & Chief Exec. Officer--Clyde Savings Bank Company, Clyde, OH; *U.S. Public*, pg. 632
Mundinger, William D., Pres.--YSD Industries, Youngstown, OH; *U.S. Private*, pg. 1194
Mundschau, Walter J., Pres.--Kalmbach Publishing Co., Waukesha, WI; *U.S. Private*, pg. 606
Mundt, G. Henry, III, Pres. & Chief Exec. Officer--MasterCard International-Cirrus Brand, Purchase, NY; *U.S. Private*, pg. 714
Mundy, John F., Chm. Bd., Pres. & Chief Exec. Officer--Lava World International/Haggerty Enterprises, Inc., Chicago, IL; *U.S. Private*, pg. 653
Mundy, Roy W., II, Pres.--Kentucky-American Water Co., Lexington, KY; *U.S. Public*, pg. 95
Muneyuki, Masayuki, Pres.--Fuji Photo Film Co., Ltd., Tokyo, Japan; *Int'l*, pg. 523
Mungo, Stewart, Pres.--Michael J. Mungo Company, Inc., Irmo, SC; *U.S. Private*, pg. 767
Munkley, Ronald, Pres. & Chief Exec. Officer--The Consumers' Gas Company Ltd., Scarborough, Canada; *Int'l*, pg. 652
Munnich, Walter, Pres.--A. Friedrich Flender AG, Bocholt, Germany; *Int'l*, pg. 400
Munoz, Angel, Chm. Bd., Pres. & Chief Exec. Officer--Tropic Communications Inc., Columbus, OH; *U.S. Public*, pg. 1641
Munro, Donald, Pres.--RYCO-Alberici, Ltd., Hamilton, Canada; *U.S. Private*, pg. 32
Munro, R. Daniel, Pres.--TIE Systems New Mexico, Albuquerque, NM; *U.S. Private*, pg. 1085
Munro, Scott, Pres. & Chief Exec. Officer--Western Micro Technology, Inc., Campbell, CA; *U.S. Public*, pg. 1759
Munshani, Shanker, Pres. & Chief Exec. Officer--Micronics Computers, Inc., Fremont, CA; *U.S. Public*, pg. 1106
Muoio, Michael, Pres.--Miles Kimball Company, Oshkosh, WI; *U.S. Private*, pg. 745
Murakami, Koji, Pres.--Kyodo TDI Limited Company, Tokyo, Japan; *U.S. Public*, pg. 1219
Murakami, Tomio, Pres.--Laboratorios Miquel, S.A., Barcelona, Spain; *Int'l*, pg. 1014
Muramatsu, Isao, Pres.--SmithKline Beecham Pharmaceuticals, Tokyo, Japan; *Int'l*, pg. 1266
Murase, Haruo, Pres. & Chief Exec. Officer--Canon U.S.A., Inc., Lake Success, NY; *Int'l*, pg. 262
Murata, Junichi, Pres. & Chief Exec. Officer--Murata Machinery, Ltd., Kyoto, Japan; *Int'l*, pg. 897
Murata, Makoto, Pres.--Showa Denko K.K., Tokyo, Japan; *Int'l*, pg. 1236
Murata, Taketo, Pres.--ConAgra Grocery Products Packaging Company, Omaha, NE; *U.S. Public*, pg. 428
Murata, Yasutaka, Pres.--Murata Manufacturing Co., Ltd., Kyoto, Japan; *Int'l*, pg. 897
Muratore, Robert, Pres. & Chief Exec. Officer--KPR, New York, NY; *U.S. Public*, pg. 1224
Muratori, Walter J., Pres.--Cameron Ashley Building Products, Inc, Dallas, TX; *U.S. Public*, pg. 298
Murayama, Takayoshi, Pres. & Chief Exec. Officer--Asahi Advertising Inc., Tokyo, Japan; *Int'l*, pg. 81
Murdoch, Keith Rupert, Chm. Bd. & Chief Exec. Officer--The News Corporation Limited, Sydney, Australia; *Int'l*, pg. 925
Murdock, Bill, Pres. & Gen. Mgr.--KSL-TV, Salt Lake City, UT; *U.S. Private*, pg. 327
Murdock, David H., Pres. & Chief Exec. Officer--Pacific Holding Corporation, Los Angeles, CA; *U.S. Private*, pg. 831
Murdock, Richard D., Pres. & Chief Exec. Officer--CellPro, Incorporated, Bothell, WA; *U.S. Public*, pg. 320
Murga, Rogelio M., Pres. & Chief Oper. Officer--EEI Corporation, Manila, Philippines; *Int'l*, pg. 425
Murgolo, Joseph, Pres.--Friendship Dairies, Inc., Jericho, NY; *U.S. Private*, pg. 429
Murgolo, Joseph, Pres., Chief Exec. Officer & Chief Oper. Officer--Friendship Dairies, Inc., Friendship, NY; *U.S. Private*, pg. 429
Murillo, Jose I., Dr., Pres.--Filtros Mann S.A., Zaragoza, Spain; *Int'l*, pg. 484
Murnin, Stephen, Pres. & Chief Oper. Officer--Network Real Estate Inc., Capitola, CA; *U.S. Private*, pg. 791
Murofushi, Minoru, Chm. Bd., Pres. & Chief Exec. Officer--Itochu Corporation, Tokyo, Japan; *Int'l*, pg. 694
Murphey, Britt, Pres.--B&B Molders, Mishawaka, IN; *U.S. Private*, pg. 105
Murphy, Andrea, Mng. Partner & Exec. Creative Dir.--Grant/Jacoby, Inc., Chicago, IL; *U.S. Private*, pg. 470
Murphy, Charles O., Chm. Bd., Pres. & Chief Exec. Officer--SouthTrust Bank, Suncoast, Sarasota, FL; *U.S. Public*, pg. 1492
Murphy, Christopher J., III, Pres. & Chief Exec. Officer--1st Source Corporation, South Bend, IN; *U.S. Public*, pg. 638
Murphy, Christopher J., III, Pres & Chief Exec. Officer--1st Source Bank Consolidated, South Bend, IN; *U.S. Public*, pg. 638
Murphy, D.A., Pres.--Erly Industries, Inc., Los Angeles, CA; *U.S. Public*, pg. 591
Murphy, Daniel T., Pres. & Chief Investment Officer--Northern Capital Management, Inc., Madison, WI; *U.S. Public*, pg. 1673
Murphy, Donald, Pres.--IAC Industries, Brea, CA; *U.S. Private*, pg. 553
Murphy, Douglas A., Pres. & Chief Exec. Officer--American Rice Inc., Houston, TX; *U.S. Public*, pg. 591
Murphy, Edward, Pres.--PWS-Kent Publishing Co., Boston, MA; *U.S. Public*, pg. 1600
Murphy, Fred, Pres. & Chief Oper. Officer--Fisher Gauge Limited, Peterborough, Canada; *Int'l*, pg. 491
Murphy, Fred, Pres. & Chief Oper. Officer--Fishercast, Peterborough, Canada; *Int'l*, pg. 491
Murphy, Fred, Pres. & Chief Oper. Officer--Fishertech, Peterborough, Canada; *Int'l*, pg. 491

Murphy, George E., Pres.--Jupiter Industries, Inc., Northbrook, IL; *U.S. Private*, pg. 602
Murphy, George E., Pres.--Jupiter Energy Corp., Chicago, IL; *U.S. Private*, pg. 602
Murphy, Gregory E., Pres. & Chief Oper. Officer--Selective Insurance Group, Inc, Branchville, NJ; *U.S. Public*, pg. 1455
Murphy, James, Pres. & Mng. Dir.--Provident Securities & Investment Company, Cincinnati, OH; *U.S. Public*, pg. 1338
Murphy, James, Pres. & Chief Exec. Officer--Willis Corroon Corp. of Los Angeles, Glendale, CA; *Int'l*, pg. 1506
Murphy, James J., Pres. & Chief Oper. Officer--Entech, Inc., Butte, MT; *U.S. Public*, pg. 1127
Murphy, James R., Chm. Bd., Pres. & Chief Exec. Officer--Bentley Pharmaceuticals, Inc., Tampa, FL; *U.S. Public*, pg. 212
Murphy, James Timmerman, Pres.--Dun & Bradstreet Poland SP. Z.O.O., Warsaw, Poland; *U.S. Public*, pg. 536
Murphy, Joseph M., Pres. & Sec.--838 Investment Group, Inc., Wilmington, DE; *U.S. Public*, pg. 1729
Murphy, Kenneth T., Chm. Bd., Pres. & Chief Exec. Officer--First Financial Bankshares, Inc., Abilene, TX; *U.S. Public*, *pg. 633*
Murphy, Michael, Pres.--Hilb, Rogal and Hamilton Company of Baltimore, Baltimore, MD; *U.S. Public*, pg. 827
Murphy, Noel, Pres. & Chief Exec. Officer--True Life, Dublin, Ireland; *Int'l*, pg. 1425
Murphy, Noel, Pres.--Camp Healthcare, Jackson, MI; *Int'l*, pg. 1425
Murphy, Patrick F., Pres. & Chief Exec. Officer--AGA Gas, Inc., Independence, OH; *Int'l*, pg. 13
Murphy, Peter F., Pres.--Bard Vascular Systems Div., Billerica, MA; *U.S. Public*, pg. 189
Murphy, Peter J., Pres. & Chief Exec. Officer--Parlex Corporation, Methuen, MA; *U.S. Public*, pg. 1264
Murphy, Peter, Jr., Chm. Bd., Pres. & Chief Exec. Officer--Murphy Company, Eugene, OR; *U.S. Private*, pg. 768
Murphy, Robert E., Pres.--Japs-Olson Company, Minneapolis, MN; *U.S. Private*, pg. 582
Murphy, Steve, Chm. Bd. & Pres.--Producers Co-op Association, Inc., Girard, KS; *U.S. Private*, pg. 888
Murphy, Tim, Pres.--Southland Ford Sterling Truck, Memphis, TN; *U.S. Private*, pg. 1018
Murray, Allen E., Chm. Bd., Pres. & Chief Exec. Officer--Mobil Oil Corporation, Fairfax, VA; *U.S. Public*, pg. 1118
Murray, Graeme, Pres.--Colgate-Palmolive Canada Inc., Toronto, Canada; *U.S. Public*, pg. 398
Murray, James C., Pres. & Chief Exec. Officer--Utilities Construction Co., Inc. Of South Carolina, Charleston, SC; *U.S. Private*, pg. 1130
Murray, John J., Pres.--RB&W Corporation, Cleveland, OH; *U.S. Public*, pg. 1259
Murray, Michael, Chm. Bd. & Pres.--NT Dor-omatic, Harwood Heights, IL; *U.S. Private*, pg. 771
Murray, N. Leight, Pres. & Chief Exec. Officer--The Airolite Company, Marietta, OH; *U.S. Private*, pg. 29
Murray, Richard C., Pres.--Wacoal America Inc., New York, NY; *Int'l*, pg. 1484
Murray, Robert J., Chm. Bd., Pres. & Chief Exec. Officer--New England Business Service, Inc., Groton, MA; *U.S. Public*, pg. 1170
Murray, Robert W., Pres., Chief Exec. Officer & Chief Fin. Officer--Mercantile Bank of Iowa, Des Moines, IA; *U.S. Public*, pg. 1087
Murray, Sadra, Pres.--Philip Morris/Cash & Carry Ltd., London, United Kingdom; *U.S. Public*, pg. 1290
Murray, T., Pres.--Tyton Hellermann Canada Incorporated, Markham, Canada; *Int'l*, pg. 209
Murray, Terrence, Chm. Bd., Pres. & Chief Exec. Officer--Fleet Financial Group, Inc., Boston, MA; *U.S. Public*, pg. 648
Murrell, Mike, Partner, Exec. V.P. & Dir.-Integrated Svcs.--Miller Meester Advertising Inc., Minneapolis, MN; *U.S. Private*, pg. 747
Murrell, R., Pres. & Chief Exec. Officer--Birdsall, Inc., Riviera Beach, FL; *U.S. Public*, pg. 1182
Murrer, Thomas, Pres.--Renold, Inc., Westfield, NY; *Int'l*, pg. 1104
Murschel, William H., Pres. & Chief Oper. Officer--Skyline Corporation, Elkhart, IN; *U.S. Public*, pg. 1476
Muse, Albert C., Pres. & Chief Exec. Officer--Crown Coal & Coke Co. Inc., Pittsburgh, PA; *U.S. Private*, pg. 292
Muse, Scott, Pres.--Progress Lighting, Spartanburg, SC; *U.S. Public*, pg. 1684
Muselman, Arthur, Pres.--House of White Birches, Inc., Berne, IN; *U.S. Private*, pg. 542
Muselman, Arthur K., Pres.--E.P. Graphics, Inc., Berne, IN; *U.S. Private*, pg. 354
Mushkin, Albert S., Pres. & Chief Oper. Officer--Master Industries Corp., New York, NY; *U.S. Private*, pg. 713
Mushler, Clifford, Pres.--Krause Publications, Inc., Iola, WI; *U.S. Private*, pg. 635
Musil, Ronald J., Pres.--Banta Book Group, Menasha, WI; *U.S. Public*, pg. 188
Musilli, Charles A., Pres.--Selective Technical Administrative Services, Inc., Branchville, NJ; *U.S. Public*, pg. 1456
Muskat, Irwin, Chm. Bd., Pres. & Chief Exec. Officer--Jac Pac Foods, Ltd., Manchester, NH; *U.S. Private*, pg. 579
Must, Alan, Pres.--Detroit City Dairy, Inc., Detroit, MI; *U.S. Private*, pg. 328
Mustain, William G., Chm. Bd., Pres. & Chief Exec. Officer--Comdial Corporation, Charlottesville, VA; *U.S. Public*, pg. 407
Musto, Michael L., Chm. Bd., Pres. & Chief Exec. Officer--Reptron Electronics, Inc., Tampa, FL; *U.S. Public*, pg. 1377
Muston, Michael J., Pres.--Mycogen Seeds, Saint Paul, MN; *U.S. Public*, pg. 1142
Musu, Rumengan, Pres. & Chief Exec. Officer--P.T. International Nickel Indonesia, Jakarta, Indonesia; *Int'l*, pg. 947
Muta, Koichi, Pres.--ORIX Securities Co., Ltd., Tokyo, Japan; *Int'l*, pg. 1009
Mutchler, Patrick D., Pres.--Personal Products Co., Skillman, NJ; *U.S. Public*, pg. 929
Muth, Richard, Pres.--Orco Block Company, Stanton, CA; *U.S. Private*, pg. 819
Muti, Arthur M., Pres.--Penco Products, Oaks, PA; *U.S. Private*, pg. 848
Muto, Hiroshi, Pres.--Mutoh Industries Ltd., Tokyo, Japan; *Int'l*, pg. 897
Mutz, John M., Pres.--Cinergy, Plainfield, IN; *U.S. Public*, pg. 369
Mutz, O.U., Pres.--Security Group Inc., Indianapolis, IN; *U.S. Private*, pg. 981
Muzzio, Carlos, Gen. Mgr.--Varig Brazilian Airlines, New York, NY; *Int'l*, pg. 1451
Myers, A. Maurice, Chm. Bd., Pres. & Chief Exec. Officer--Yellow Corporation, Overland Park, KS; *U.S. Public*, pg. 1788
Myers, Al, Pres.--Media Recovery, Inc., Graham, TX; *U.S. Private*, pg. 726
Myers, C.C., Pres. & Chief Exec. Officer--C.C. Myers, Inc., Rancho Cordova, CA; *U.S. Private*, pg. 770
Myers, Charles, Pres.--Bellamy Brothers, Inc., Ellenwood, GA; *U.S. Private*, pg. 132
Myers, Charles C., Pres.--Superior Industries of Nebraska, Inc., Omaha, NE; *U.S. Private*, pg. 1055
Myers, Chuck, Chm. Bd., Pres. & Chief Exec. Officer--Kitchen Investment Group, Madison, WI; *U.S. Private*, pg. 624
Myers, Chuck, Pres. & Chief Exec. Officer--Country Kitchen International, Inc., Madison, WI; *U.S. Private*, pg. 624
Myers, D. Fredric, Pres. & Chief Exec. Officer--Fournier Furniture, Saint Paul, VA; *U.S. Private*, pg. 422
Myers, David L., Pres.--Corrections Corporation of America, Nashville, TN; *U.S. Public*, pg. 450
Myers, Douglas G., Exec. Dir.-Zoological Society--Zoological Society of San Diego, San Diego, CA; *U.S. Private*, pg. 1207
Myers, Frank E., Pres.--WestEx, Inc., Phoenix, AZ; *U.S. Public*, pg. 1788
Myers, Gary F., Pres. & Chief Oper. Officer--Kocolene Oil Corp., Seymour, IN; *U.S. Private*, pg. 629
Myers, Jay, Pres. & Chief Exec. Officer--Andiamo, Inc., Fountain Valley, CA; *U.S. Private*, pg. 73
Myers, John, Pres.--Chicago Machine Tool Company, Elk Grove Village, IL; *U.S. Private*, pg. 235
Myers, Joseph E., Chm. Bd. & Pres.--Collins Oldsmobile Inc., Indianapolis, IN; *U.S. Private*, pg. 253
Myers, Kurt J., Pres. & Chief Exec. Officer & Treas.--Amalgamated Automotive Industries, Inc., Enola, PA; *U.S. Private*, pg. 48
Myers, L.G., Pres. & Chief Exec. Officer--LubeCon Systems, Inc., White Cloud, MI; *U.S. Private*, pg. 679
Myers, Norman S., Pres., Chief Exec. & Fin. Officers & Treas.--IDM Controls, Houston, TX; *U.S. Private*, pg. 554
Myers, R., Pres.--United Sciences Inc., Gibsonia, PA; *Int'l*, pg. 208
Myers, Stephen E., Pres. & Chief Exec. Officer--Myers Industries, Inc., Akron, OH; *U.S. Public*, pg. 1143
Myers, Stuart, Pres. & Mng. Dir.--Otsuka Pharmaceutical Australia Pty. Ltd., Pymble, Australia; *Int'l*, pg. 1014
Myers, Wayne, Pres.--Spicer Axle Div., Fort Wayne, IN; *U.S. Public*, pg. 479
Myerson, James Parker, Pres.--Ben Myerson Candy Company, Inc., Los Angeles, CA; *U.S. Private*, pg. 771
Mygind, Hans Ole, Pres.--MD Foods Italia S.r.l., Lomazzo, Italy; *Int'l*, pg. 826
Myhre, Larry E., Pres.--Hallidie Machinery Company, Inc., Seattle, WA; *U.S. Private*, pg. 495
Myhre, Oyvind, Pres.--Kvaerner Thune A/S, Hamar, Norway; *Int'l*, pg. 769
Myklebust, Egil, Pres. & Chief Exec. Officer--Norsk Hydro a.s, Oslo, Norway; *Int'l*, pg. 959
Mynster, Harold, Pres.--Exsil, Inc., San Jose, CA; *Int'l*, pg. 802
Myra, Harold, Pres. & Chief Exec. Officer--Christianity Today, Inc., Carol Stream, IL; *U.S. Private*, pg. 238
Myrick, B. Harold, Jr., Pres.--Myrick Construction Inc., Biscoe, NC; *U.S. Private*, pg. 771
Myrick, Goodwin L., Chm. Bd. & Pres.--Alfa Corporation, Montgomery, AL; *U.S. Public*, pg. 40
Myrick, Goodwin L., Chm. Bd. & Pres.--Alfa Realty, Inc., Montgomery, AL; *U.S. Public*, pg. 40
Myslenski, Jack, Pres.--Fluid Connectors Group, Cleveland, OH; *U.S. Public*, pg. 1260
Myslinski, Thomas, Pres.--Keystone Pipeline Services, Inc., South Windsor, CT; *U.S. Public*, pg. 1271
Naber, S.S., Pres.--Lucas Aerospace Power Transmission, Utica, NY; *Int'l*, pg. 820
Nabetani, N., Pres.--Nissho Propane Sekiyu Corp., Sapporo, Japan; *Int'l*, pg. 947
Nabors, J. Mervyn, Chm. Bd., Pres. & Chief Exec. Officer--Aerosonic Corporation, Clearwater, FL; *U.S. Public*, pg. 25
Naccarati, David C., Pres.--Phelps Dodge Tyrone, Tyrone, NM; *U.S. Public*, pg. 1287
Naccarato, Vincent A., Chm. Bd., Pres. & Chief Exec. Officer--Wilton Industries, Inc., Woodridge, IL; *U.S. Private*, pg. 1181
Nachman, G., Pres.--Metal Improvement Co., Paramus, NJ; *U.S. Public*, pg. 469
Nacht, Stephen, Pres.--Shonac Corporation, Columbus, OH; *U.S. Private*, pg. 996
Nada, S., Pres.--Shimadzu Oceania Pty. Ltd., Rydalmere, Australia; *Int'l*, pg. 1232
Nadata, Arthur, Pres. & Chief Exec. Officer--Nu Horizons Electronics Corp., Melville, NY; *U.S. Public*, pg. 1205
Nadata, Arthur, Pres.--Nu Visions Manufacturing Corp., Springfield, MA; *U.S. Public*, pg. 1205
Nadel, Herbert, Pres. & Chief Exec. Officer--Nadel Architects, Inc., Los Angeles, CA; *U.S. Private*, pg. 773
Nadel, Herbert, Pres. & Chief Exec. Officer--Nadel Architects, PC Nevada, Las Vegas, NV; *U.S. Private*, pg. 773
Nadel, Martin, Pres.--Jack Nadel, Inc., Culver City, CA; *U.S. Private*, pg. 773
Nadel, Paul, Pres. & Chief Oper. Officer--Ferolie Group, Montvale, NJ; *U.S. Private*, pg. 401
Nadig, Gerald G., Chm. Bd., Pres. & Chief Exec. Officer--Material Sciences Corporation, Elk Grove Village, IL; *U.S. Public*, pg. 1056
Nadolski, Keith, Pres.--Beech Holdings, Inc., Wichita, KS; *U.S. Public*, pg. 1365
Nadorf, Ben J., Pres.--Everlast World Boxing Corp., Bronx, NY; *U.S. Private*, pg. 386
Nadorf, Ben J., Pres.--Everlast Sports Manufacturing Corp., Bronx, NY; *U.S. Private*, pg. 386
Nady, John, Pres. & Chief Exec. Officer--Nady Systems, Inc., Emeryville, CA; *U.S. Private*, pg. 773
Nafilyan, Guy, Pres. & Chief Exec. Officer--Kaufman and Broad, France, Paris, France; *U.S. Public*, pg. 945
Nagahiro, Maomi, Pres.--UBE Industries Ltd., Tokyo, Japan; *Int'l*, pg. 1426
Nagai, Kazuo, Pres.--Toyo Tire (U.S.A.) Corporation, Cypress, CA; *Int'l*, pg. 1411
Nagai, S., Pres.--Sharp Electronics (Taiwan) Co., Ltd., Kaohsiung, Taiwan; *Int'l*, pg. 1230
Nagai, Tatsuo, Mng. Dir.--Suzuki Marina, Hamanako, Co., Ltd., Shizuoka, Japan; *Int'l*, pg. 1323
Nagai, Yasushi, Pres.--NLI International Canada Inc., Toronto, Canada; *Int'l*, pg. 936
Nagal, Toshizasu, Pres.--Union Carbide Japan K.K., Tokyo, Japan; *U.S. Public*, pg. 1667
Nagami, Tohru, Pres.--Toho Kagaku Kenkyusho Co., Ltd., Tokyo, Japan; *U.S. Public*, pg. 540
Nagamine, Mitsuru, Pres.--Civil Engineering Instrument Center, Kanagawa, Japan; *Int'l*, pg. 868
Nagamori, Shigendou, Chm. Bd. & Pres.--Nippon Densan (NIDEC), Kyoto, Japan; *Int'l*, pg. 933
Nagamura, Yoshiro, Pres.--Koito Manufacturing Co., Tokyo, Japan; *Int'l*, pg. 743
Naganoma, Kazuhiko, Pres.--ORIX Capital Corporation, Tokyo, Japan; *Int'l*, pg. 1008
Nagao, Katsuyoshi, Pres.--Tekken Corporation, Tokyo, Japan; *Int'l*, pg. 1362
Nagaoka, Hiroshi, Pres.--LEC, Inc., Tokyo, Japan; *Int'l*, pg. 929
Nagashima, Kazushige, Pres. & Representative Director--Japan Energy Corporation, Tokyo, Japan; *Int'l*, pg. 702
Nagayama, Osamu, Pres.--Chugai Pharmaceutical Co., Ltd., Tokyo, Japan; *Int'l*, pg. 290
Nagayama, Toru, Pres.--Haseko (Hawaii) Inc., Honolulu, HI; *Int'l*, pg. 600
Nagayama, Toru, Pres.--Haseko Realty Inc., Honolulu, HI; *Int'l*, pg. 600
Nagel, Bruce, Pres.--Cole-Layer-Trumble Company (CLT), Dayton, OH; *U.S. Private*, pg. 317
Nagel, Daryl D., Pres. & Chief Exec. Officer--Lanoga Corporation, Redmond, WA; *U.S. Private*, pg. 650
Nagel, Joseph J., Pres. & Chief Oper. Officer--American Ecology Corporation, Boise, ID; *U.S. Public*, pg. 71
Nagel, Richard, Pres.--Sax Arts & Crafts, Inc., New Berlin, WI; *U.S. Public*, pg. 1687
Nagorske, Lynn A., Pres. & Chief Oper. Officer--TCF Financial Corp., Minneapolis, MN; *U.S. Public*, pg. 1554
Nagura, Masao, Pres.--American Suzuki Motor Corporation, Brea, CA; *Int'l*, pg. 1323
Nahal, Gary, Pres.--Fedders International, Inc., Liberty Corner, NJ; *U.S. Public*, pg. 614
Nahey, Brian L., Pres. & Chief Exec. Officer--Venturedyne, Ltd., Milwaukee, WI; *U.S. Private*, pg. 1136
Nahm, Sang-Jo, Pres. & Chief Exec. Officer--Daehong Advertising Inc., Seoul, Korea; *Int'l*, pg. 357
Nahmad, Albert H., Chm. Bd., Pres. & Chief Exec. Officer--Watsco, Inc., Coconut Grove, FL; *U.S. Public*, pg. 1745
Naito, Haruo, Pres. & Chief Exec. Officer--Eisai Co., Ltd., Tokyo, Japan; *Int'l*, pg. 435
Naito, Mitsuaki, Deputy Pres.--The Sanwa Bank Limited, Osaka, Japan; *Int'l*, pg. 1189
Naito, Susumu, Pres.--Rinnai Corp., Nagoya, Japan; *Int'l*, pg. 1118
Najjar, Edward, Pres. & Chief Exec. Officer--Hampshire Chemical Corp., Lexington, MA; *U.S. Private*, pg. 498
Nakabe, Keijiro, Pres.--Maruha Corporation, Tokyo, Japan; *Int'l*, pg. 845
Nakada, Sotowo, Pres.--Nissho Iwai Panama International S.A., Panama, Panama; *Int'l*, pg. 948
Nakagaki, T., Pres.--Hokuriku (Singapore) PTE., LTD., Singapore, Singapore; *Int'l*, pg. 628
Nakagaki, T., Pres.--Hokuriku (Malaysia), Sdn. Bhd., Shah Alam, Malaysia; *Int'l*, pg. 628
Nakagawa, Itaru, Pres.--Tabuchi Electric Company of America, Cordova, TN; *Int'l*, pg. 1346
Nakagawa, Kenzo, Chm. Bd. & Mng. Dir.--Showpla Asia Limited, Singapore, Singapore; *Int'l*, pg. 1237
Nakajima, Shigeo, Pres.--Sumikin Bussan International (HK) Ltd., Kowloon, Hong Kong; *Int'l*, pg. 1308
Nakajima, Yoji, Pres.--Yoshitomi-Astra Ltd., Osaka, Japan; *Int'l*, pg. 94
Nakamura, Hisao, Pres.--Chori Co., Ltd., Osaka, Japan; *Int'l*, *pg. 288*
Nakamura, Katsumi, Pres.--NLI Properties Central, Inc., Chicago, IL; *Int'l*, pg. 935
Nakamura, Masaharie, Chm. & Pres.--Tokio Marine Management Inc., New York, NY; *Int'l*, pg. 1392
Nakamura, Masaru, Pres.--Mitsubishi Electric Industrial Control, Mount Prospect, IL; *Int'l*, pg. 872
Nakamura, Minoru, Pres.--Nanto Card Services Co., Ltd., Nara, Japan; *Int'l*, pg. 905
Nakamura, Minoru, Pres. & Chief Exec. Officer--Nissan Motor Corporation in U.S.A., Gardena, CA; *Int'l*, pg. 945
Nakamura, Nobuhiko, Pres.--Kawasaki Motoren GmbH, Friedrichsdorf, Germany; *Int'l*, pg. 726
Nakamura, Tadashi, Pres.--Nanto Estate Co., Ltd., Osaka, Japan; *Int'l*, pg. 905
Nakamura, Toshiya, Mng. Dir.--NLI International France S.A., Paris, France; *Int'l*, pg. 936

Nakane, Tsuyoshi, Pres.--United-Asatsu International Ltd., Taipei, Taiwan; *Int'l*, pg. 86
Nakano, H., Pres.--Nakano Foods, Burlingame, CA; *Int'l*, pg. 883
Nakano, Haduhida, Pres.--Mitsukan & Nakano Vinegar Company Ltd., Handa, Japan; *Int'l*, pg. 883
Nakano, Hiroshi, Pres.--Cosmo Securities Co., Ltd., Osaka, Japan; *Int'l*, pg. 335
Nakano, Junichi, Pres.--Nomura Real Estate Development Co., Ltd., Tokyo, Japan; *Int'l*, pg. 956
Nakano, Matazaemon, Pres.--Nakano Vinegar Co., Ltd., Handa, Japan; *Int'l*, pg. 904
Nakano, Shogo, Pres.--Daishowa Paper Mfg. Co., Ltd., Fuji, Japan; *Int'l*, pg. 373
Nakano, T., Pres.--Sharp (Philippines) Corporation, Manila, Philippines; *Int'l*, pg. 1230
Nakano, Toyoshi, Deputy Pres.--The Mitsubishi Trust and Banking Corporation, Tokyo, Japan; *Int'l*, pg. 876
Nakao, Kanehiro, Pres.--MMC Electronics America Inc., Rolling Meadows, IL; *Int'l*, pg. 875
Nakash, Joseph, Chm. Bd. & Pres.--Jordache Enterprises, Inc., New York, NY; *U.S. Private*, pg. 597
Nakashige, Steve L., Pres. & Chief Oper. Officer--Hologic, Inc., Waltham, MA; *U.S. Public*, pg. 831
Nakasone, Robert C., Pres. & Chief Oper. Officer--Toys "R" Us, Inc., Paramus, NJ; *U.S. Public*, pg. 1626
Nakasuji, Shunsuke, Pres.--DKB Data Services (USA) Inc., Jersey City, NJ; *Int'l*, pg. 360
Nakata, H., Pres.--NIK Metal Corp., Osaka, Japan; *Int'l*, pg. 946
Nakatani, Kanetake, Pres.--Komatsu Shantui Construction Machinery Co., Ltd., Shandong, China; *Int'l*, pg. 744
Nakatsugawa, Naoaki, Pres. & Chief Exec. Officer--The Industrial Bank of Japan Trust Company, New York, NY; *Int'l*, pg. 675
Nakauchi, Isao, Chm. Bd., Pres. & Chief Exec. Officer--The Daiei, Inc., Kobe, Japan; *Int'l*, pg. 364
Nakayama, Hayao, Pres. & Chief Exec. Officer--Sega Enterprises Ltd., Tokyo, Japan; *Int'l*, pg. 1218
Nakayama, Hisashi, Pres.--Meiji Milk Products Co., Ltd., Tokyo, Japan; *Int'l*, pg. 855
Nakayama, I., Dir.--Marantz Japan Inc., Sagamihara, Japan; *Int'l*, pg. 841
Nakazato, Junya, Pres.--Taiyo Life International (H.K.), Ltd., Central, Hong Kong; *Int'l*, pg. 1349
Nakazato, Yoshihiko, Pres.--Fuji Electric Co., Ltd., Tokyo, Japan; *Int'l*, pg. 522
Nakazawa, Teruo, Chm. Bd. & Pres.--Konica Business Machines USA, Inc., Windsor, CT; *Int'l*, pg. 748
NaLamlieng, Chumpol, Pres.--The Siam Cement Public Company Limited, Bangkok, Thailand; *Int'l*, pg. 1237
Nallathambi, Anand, Pres.--First American Appraisal Services, San Diego, CA; *U.S. Public*, pg. 625
Nalle, Alan, Pres. & Chief Exec. Officer--Nalle Plastics Inc., Austin, TX; *U.S. Private*, pg. 773
Nalls, Billy E., Pres.--The Citizens Bank of Cochran, Cochran, GA; *U.S. Public*, pg. 1549
Nally, Michael J., Pres. & Chief Oper. Officer--Sportcraft Ltd., Mount Olive, NJ; *U.S. Private*, pg. 1026
Nam, Sohn Choong, Pres.--Ssangyong International Ltd., Monrovia, Liberia; *Int'l*, pg. 1292
Nan-ya, Shojiro, Pres.--West Japan Railway Company, Osaka, Japan; *Int'l*, pg. 1490
Nance, Deborah, Pres.--Therapy Management Associates, LLC, Collierville, TN; *U.S. Public*, pg. 1642
Nanot, Yves Rene, Chm. Bd., Pres. & Chief Exec. Officer--Ciments Francais, Paris, France; *Int'l*, pg. 292
Nantel, Gilles, Pres.--CAE ScreenPlates Inc., Lennoxville, Canada; *Int'l*, pg. 237
Nantell, William, Pres.--ASI Technology, Colorado Springs, CO; *U.S. Public*, pg. 110
Naples, Ronald J., Chm. Bd., Pres. & Chief Exec. Officer--Quaker Chemical Corporation, Conshohocken, PA; *U.S. Public*, pg. 1346
Naqvi, Saiyid T., Pres. & Chief Exec. Officer--PNC Mortgage Corporation of America, Vernon Hills, IL; *U.S. Public*, pg. 1243
Nardelli, Robert L., Pres. & Chief Exec. Officer--G.E. Power Systems, Schenectady, NY; *U.S. Public*, pg. 711
Nardi, Ronald G., Pres.--General Motors Egypt S.A.E., Cairo, Egypt; *Int'l*, pg. 692
Nardi, Ronald G., Pres.--General Motors Egypt S.A.E., Cairo, Egypt; *U.S. Public*, pg. 724
Nardoni, Dennis, Pres. & Chief Exec. Officer--Chicago Steel Tape, Bradley, IL; *U.S. Private*, pg. 235
Nardulli, Ettore, Pres. & Chief Oper. Officer--Black Dot Graphics, Inc., Crystal Lake, IL; *U.S. Public*, pg. 503
Nardulli, Ettore G., Pres.--Typo-Graphics, Inc., Orlando, FL; *U.S. Public*, pg. 503
Nardulli, Ettore G., Pres.--Taproot Interactive, Inc., Chicago, IL; *U.S. Public*, pg. 503
Narita, Akhito, Pres.--Symantec K.K., Tokyo, Japan; *U.S. Public*, pg. 1545
Narita, Fujiaki, Pres.--Narita Giken Co., Ltd., Amagasaki, Japan; *Int'l*, pg. 1125
Narita, Yosuke, Pres.--Kawasaki Heavy Industries (H.K.) Ltd., Central, Hong Kong; *Int'l*, pg. 726
Narita, Yutaka, Pres.--Dentsu Inc., Tokyo, Japan; *Int'l*, pg. 392
Narlinger, Dennis, Chm. Bd., Pres. & Chief Exec. Officer--Shugart Corporation, Mission Viejo, CA; *U.S. Private*, pg. 997
Narmon, Francois, Pres.--Credit Communal De Belgique SA, Brussels, Belgium; *Int'l*, pg. 343
Nasella, Henry, Pres. & Chief Exec. Officer--Star Markets Company, Inc., Cambridge, MA; *U.S. Private*, pg. 1035
Nash, Merrill L., Pres.--Symons Corporation, Pasadena, CA; *U.S. Private*, pg. 932
Nash, Richard A., Pres.--SunTrust Insurance Company, Atlanta, GA; *U.S. Public*, pg. 1538
Nason, Charles T., Chm. Bd., Pres. & Chief Exec. Officer--The Acacia Group - Acacia Life Insurance Co., Bethesda, MD; *U.S. Private*, pg. 10
Nason, Charles T., Pres. & Chief Exec. Officer--Acacia Financial Corporation, Bethesda, MD; *U.S. Private*, pg. 11
Nason, Charles T., Pres. & Chief Exec. Officer--Acacia National Life Ins. Co., Bethesda, MD; *U.S. Private*, pg. 11
Nason, Charles W., Chm. Bd. & Pres.--Worzalla Publishing Co., Inc., Stevens Point, WI; *U.S. Private*, pg. 1191
Nason, James, Pres.--Empress Foods Ltd., Vancouver, Canada; *U.S. Public*, pg. 1426
Nason, Tucker, Pres. & Chief Exec. Officer--Burbank Aircraft Supply Inc., Sun Valley, CA; *U.S. Public*, pg. 187
Nast, Christian, Pres. & Chief Exec. Officer--Rexall Sundown Inc., Boca Raton, FL; *U.S. Public*, pg. 1384
Nasu, A., Pres.--Mita Copystar America Inc., Fairfield, NJ; *Int'l*, pg. 870
Natale, James L., Pres.-Corp. Mktg. & Sls.--C.R. Bard, Inc., Murray Hill, NJ; *U.S. Public*, pg. 189
Natale, Jim L., Pres.--Corporate Marketing and Services, Murray Hill, NJ; *U.S. Public*, pg. 189
Nathan, Joseph A., Pres. & Chief Oper. Officer--Compuware Corporation, Farmington Hills, MI; *U.S. Public*, pg. 423
Nathe, Gerald A., Chm. Bd., Pres. & Chief Exec. Officer--Baldwin Technology Company, Inc., Norwalk, CT; *U.S. Public*, pg. 169
Nation, Jim, Pres. & Chief Exec. Officer--The Spring Air Company, Des Plaines, IL; *U.S. Private*, pg. 1027
Natoli, Joseph, Pres.--The Miami Herald, Miami, FL; *U.S. Public*, pg. 964
Natori, Tadaaki, Pres.--Japan Securities Agents, Ltd., Tokyo, Japan; *Int'l*, pg. 702
Naughton, James, Gen. Mgr.--The Walworth Company USA, Houston, TX; *U.S. Private*, pg. 1149
Nauleau, Heidi, Pres.--The Aarque Companies, Jamestown, NY; *U.S. Private*, pg. 9
Nauleau, Heidi, Pres.--Aarque Steel Corporation, Jamestown, NY; *U.S. Private*, pg. 9
Nauleau, Heidi, Pres.--Aarque Management Corp., Jamestown, NY; *U.S. Private*, pg. 9
Nauman, Ralph, Pres.--Wah Chang, Albany, OR; *U.S. Public*, pg. 44
Naumann, Michael, Pres.--Henry Holt & Co. Publishing, New York, NY; *Int'l*, pg. 1479
Nausler, R. Terry, Pres.--Coors Distributing Co., Golden, CO; *U.S. Public*, pg. 445
Navarian, Andre, Pres. & Owner--Waterbury Farrel Technologies, Cheshire, CT; *U.S. Private*, pg. 461
Nave, Michael, Pres.--Mercury Distributing Co., Inc., Chatsworth, CA; *U.S. Private*, pg. 732
Navolio, Margaret, Pres., Chief Exec. Officer & New Bus. Contact--CPM, Inc., Chicago, IL; *U.S. Private*, pg. 196
Nawrocki, Christopher, Pres.--Benchmark Electronics, Inc.- Winona Division, Winona, MN; *U.S. Public*, pg. 211
Nawrocki, Richard A., Pres. & Chief Exec. Officer--CMI International Inc., Southfield, MI; *U.S. Private*, pg. 195
Nazarian, Robert G., Pres.--Levonian Brothers Inc., Troy, NY; *U.S. Private*, pg. 663
Nazario, Miguel A., Pres. & Chief Exec. Officer--Puerto Rican Cement Co., Inc., Guaynabo, PR; *U.S. Public*, pg. 1341
Neal, Gary M., Pres. & Chief Exec. Officer--Watlow Electric Manufacturing Company, Saint Louis, MO; *U.S. Private*, pg. 1153
Neal, Henry, Pres. & Gen. Mgr.--BHP Hawaii, Inc., Honolulu, HI; *Int'l*, pg. 225
Neal, John R., Chm. Bd & Pres.--JRN, Inc., Columbia, TN; *U.S. Private*, pg. 578
Neal, Loyd, Pres.--Hilb, Rogal and Hamilton Company of Corpus Christi, Corpus Christi, TX; *U.S. Public*, pg. 827
Neal, Michael, Pres.--Alenite L.P., Chicago, IL; *U.S. Private*, pg. 33
Neal, Philip M., Pres. & Chief Oper. Officer--Avery Dennison Corporation, Pasadena, CA; *U.S. Public*, pg. 152
Neal, Robert E., Pres.--Datacor/ISM (Information Systems Management Atlantic Corp.), Moncton, Canada; *Int'l*, pg. 230
Neale, Gary L., Chm. Bd., Pres. & Chief Exec. Officer--NIPSCO Industries, Inc., Hammond, IN; *U.S. Public*, pg. 1185
Neally, Phillip, Chm. Bd., Pres. & Chief Exec. Officer--Aldi Food Inc., Batavia, IL; *U.S. Private*, pg. 33
Necker, Tyll, Pres.--Hako-Werke GmbH & Co., Bad Oldesloe, Germany; *Int'l*, pg. 587
Nedley, Robert E., Pres. & Chief Oper. Officer--St. Joe Corp., Jacksonville, FL; *U.S. Public*, pg. 1426
Neeb, Robert, Pres.--Neeb Corporation, Bad Axe, MI; *U.S. Private*, pg. 790
Needham, Rick, Pres.--Circle Seal Controls, Inc., Corona, CA; *U.S. Public*, pg. 1746
Needham, Tim, Pres. & Chief Oper. Officer--Williamhouse-Regency, Inc., New York, NY; *U.S. Public*, pg. 89
Needle, Edward G., Pres.--Atlantic Plumbing Supply Company, Washington, DC; *U.S. Private*, pg. 95
Needleman, Elliot, Pres.--American Systems Corporation, Chantilly, VA; *U.S. Private*, pg. 63
Neel, M.L., Pres.--Bellsouth China, Inc., Beijing, China; *U.S. Public*, pg. 208
Neel, Thomas H., Pres.--ADS Environmental Services Inc., Huntsville, AL; *Int'l*, pg. 709
Neely, Bill, Pres. & Chief Oper. Officer--M.B. Kahn Construction Co., Inc., Columbia, SC; *U.S. Private*, pg. 604
Neely, Juanita L., Pres.--Layman Candy Company, Inc., Salem, VA; *U.S. Private*, pg. 655
Neff, Deborah J., Pres.--Becton Dickinson Immunocytometry Systems, San Jose, CA; *U.S. Public*, pg. 199
Neff, Phillip R., Pres. & Chief Exec. Officer--Willis Corroon Corp. of Kansas, Wichita, KS; *Int'l*, pg. 1506
Negishi, Yoshiya, Pres. & Chief Oper. Officer--Tokyo Senko International Inc., Tokyo, Japan; *Int'l*, pg. 1394
Negre, Jean-Luc, Pres.--Baccarat (Cie des Cristalleries), Paris, France; *Int'l*, pg. 132
Negre, Jean-Luc, Pres.--Baccarat, Inc., Edison, NJ; *Int'l*, pg. 132
Neighbors, Thomas H., Pres. & Chief Oper. Officer--SAIC, Mc Lean, VA; *U.S. Private*, pg. 976
Neil, John, Pres.--J-Star Industries, Inc., Fort Atkinson, WI; *U.S. Private*, pg. 576
Neill, Donald M., Pres. & Chief Exec. Officer--Lufkin National Bank, Lufkin, TX; *U.S. Public*, pg. 630
Neill, R.A., Pres. & Chief Oper. Officer--Orenda Aerospace Corporation, Mississauga, Canada; *Int'l*, pg. 829
Neill, Richard, Pres. & Chief Oper. Officer--Magellan Aerospace Corporation, Mississauga, Canada; *Int'l*, pg. 829
Neill, Richard A., Pres.--Orenda (Canada), Mississauga, Canada; *Int'l*, pg. 604
Neilson, Kenneth T., Chm. Bd., Pres. & Chief Exec. Officer--Hubco, Inc., Mahwah, NJ; *U.S. Public*, pg. 845
Neis, Arnold Hayward, Pres.--E.T. Browne Drug Co., Inc., Englewood Cliffs, NJ; *U.S. Private*, pg. 175
Neisel, Peter, Chief Exec. Officer--Schwab Corp., Lafayette, IN; *U.S. Private*, pg. 974
Neisewander, Ray H., Jr., Pres.--Raynor Garage Doors, Dixon, IL; *U.S. Private*, pg. 912
Nekman, Donald, Chm., Partner & Chief Fin. Officer--EURO RSCG, Copenhagen, Copenhagen, Denmark; *Int'l*, pg. 602
Neller, Blair, Pres.--Globe Furniture Rentals, Cincinnati, OH; *U.S. Private*, pg. 458
Nelsen, C. Davis, II, Chm. Bd., Pres. & Chief Exec. Officer--Nelsen Steel & Wire Co., Franklin Park, IL; *U.S. Private*, pg. 790
Nelson, Allen F., Pres.--Allen Nelson & Co., Seattle, WA; *U.S. Private*, pg. 790
Nelson, Barry E., Pres. & Chief Exec. Officer--Cincinnati Bell Long Distance Inc., Cincinnati, OH; *U.S. Public*, pg. 367
Nelson, Bruce, Pres.--BT-U.S.A., Inc., Buffalo Grove, IL; *Int'l*, pg. 756
Nelson, Bruce H., Pres.--Syntron, Inc., Houston, TX; *U.S. Public*, pg. 1563
Nelson, Charles E., Chm. Bd., Pres. & Chief Exec. Officer--Liberty Bank & Trust Company of Oklahoma City, Oklahoma City, OK; *U.S. Public*, pg. 174
Nelson, Curt, Pres.--Continental Homes of Denver, Englewood, CO; *U.S. Public*, pg. 441
Nelson, Dennis H., Pres. & Chief Exec. Officer--The Buckle, Inc., Kearney, NE; *U.S. Public*, pg. 267
Nelson, Dwight, Pres.--Barton Nelson Inc., Kansas City, MO; *U.S. Private*, pg. 120
Nelson, Eric B., Pres.--Energy Pacific, Los Angeles, CA; *U.S. Public*, pg. 584
Nelson, Eric B., Pres.--Pacific Interstate Company, Los Angeles, CA; *U.S. Public*, pg. 1249
Nelson, Eric B., Pres.--Pacific Lighting Gas Development Co., Los Angeles, CA; *U.S. Public*, pg. 1249
Nelson, Eric B., Pres.--Pacific Western Resources Co., Los Angeles, CA; *U.S. Public*, pg. 1249
Nelson, Eric B., Pres.--Pacific Synthetic Fuel Company, Los Angeles, CA; *U.S. Public*, pg. 1249
Nelson, Eric B., Pres.--Pacific Interstate Offshore Company, Los Angeles, CA; *U.S. Public*, pg. 1249
Nelson, Eric B., Pres.--Pacific Interstate Transmission Company, Los Angeles, CA; *U.S. Public*, pg. 1249
Nelson, Eric B., Pres.--Pacific Interstate Mojave Company, Los Angeles, CA; *U.S. Public*, pg. 1249
Nelson, Eric B., Pres.--Pacific Interstate Transmission Company (Arctic), Los Angeles, CA; *U.S. Public*, pg. 1249
Nelson, Eric B., Pres.--Energy Pacific, Los Angeles, CA; *U.S. Public*, pg. 1249
Nelson, Frederick, Pres.--Kaiser Cement Corporation, Pleasanton, CA; *Int'l*, pg. 593
Nelson, Gregory N., Pres.--Seadrift Pipeline Corp., Danbury, CT; *U.S. Public*, pg. 1667
Nelson, Gregory N., Pres.--Ucar Pipeline, Inc., Danbury, CT; *U.S. Public*, pg. 1667
Nelson, H. Donald, Pres. & Chief Exec. Officer--United States Cellular Corporation, Chicago, IL; *U.S. Public*, pg. 1572
Nelson, J.F., Jr., Pres. & Gen. Mgr.--Golden Gem Growers Inc., Umatilla, FL; *U.S. Private*, pg. 460
Nelson, John, Pres.--Signet Scientific Co., El Monte, CA; *Int'l*, pg. 489
Nelson, John P., Pres. & Chief Oper. Officer--Acceptance Insurance Co., Inc., Omaha, NE; *U.S. Public*, pg. 14
Nelson, Ken, Pres.--Barrel O'Fun Snack Foods Co., Perham, MN; *U.S. Private*, pg. 118
Nelson, Kenneth M., Pres.--Nelson & Small Inc., Portland, ME; *U.S. Private*, pg. 790
Nelson, Kirk N., Pres. & Chief Exec. Officer--Federated Mutual Insurance Company, Owatonna, MN; *U.S. Private*, pg. 399
Nelson, Kurt, Chm. Bd, Pres. & Chief Exec. Officer--Manning & Lewis Engineering Co., Union, NJ; *U.S. Private*, pg. 700
Nelson, M. Bruce, Pres.--BT Office Products International, Inc, Buffalo Grove, IL; *Int'l*, pg. 756
Nelson, M. Bruce, Pres. & Chief Oper. Officer--Viking Office Products, Torrance, CA; *U.S. Public*, pg. 1720
Nelson, M.C., Pres. & Chief Exec. Officer--Radisson Hotel Corporation, Minneapolis, MN; *U.S. Private*, pg. 212
Nelson, Maurice F., Pres. & Chief Exec. Officer--Earle M. Jorgensen Company, Brea, CA; *U.S. Private*, pg. 600
Nelson, Peter C., Pres. & Chief Exec. Officer--California Water Service Co., San Jose, CA; *U.S. Public*, pg. 294
Nelson, Robert, Pres. & V.P.--Avondale Mills Yarn Div., Sylacauga, AL; *U.S. Private*, pg. 103
Nelson, Roy C., Pres. & Chief Oper. Officer--Bank of Utah, Ogden, UT; *U.S. Private*, pg. 114
Nelson, Steve, Pres.--Taylor Rental, East Butler, PA; *U.S. Private*, pg. 1108
Nelson, Todd S., Pres.--Apollo Group, Inc., Phoenix, AZ; *U.S. Public*, pg. 120

Nemerov, Jackwyn, Pres.--Jones Apparel Group, Inc., Bristol, PA; *U.S. Public*, pg. 933
Nemirow, Arnold M., Chm. Bd., Pres. & Chief Exec. Officer--Bowater Incorporated, Greenville, SC; *U.S. Public*, pg. 247
Nemschoff, Mark, Pres., Chief Exec. Officer & Treas.--Nemschoff Chairs, Inc., Sheboygan, WI; *U.S. Private*, pg. 791
Nener, R.M., Pres.--Reynolds Extrusion Company, Richmond Hill, Canada; *U.S. Public*, pg. 1387
Nennecker, Werner G., Pres. & Chief Exec. Officer--Pegasus Gold Corporation, Spokane, WA; *U.S. Public*, pg. 1269
Nerad, Jerry, Pres.--TimeMed Labeling Systems, Inc., Burr Ridge, IL; *U.S. Private*, pg. 1087
Nerbonne, Robert A., Pres.--Pitco Frialator Inc., Bow, NH; *U.S. Public*, pg. 1065
Neri, Ronald G., Pres.--Union Carbide Asia Pacific Inc., Singapore, Singapore; *U.S. Public*, pg. 1667
Nero, Robert A., Pres. & Chief Exec. Officer--Interface Systems, Inc., Ann Arbor, MI; *U.S. Public*, pg. 889
Nesbitt, Allen J., Pres.--Lason, Inc., Troy, MI; *U.S. Public*, pg. 979
Nesbitt, Arthur, Pres. & Chief Exec. Officer--Nasco International, Inc., Fort Atkinson, WI; *U.S. Private*, pg. 446
Nesbitt, Gregory L., Chm. Bd., Pres. & Chief Exec. Officer--Central Louisiana Electric Company, Inc., Pineville, LA; *U.S. Public*, pg. 325
Ness, Duane, Pres.--Tower Electronics, Inc., Fridley, MN; *U.S. Public*, pg. 20
Ness, Steven, Pres. & Chief Exec. Officer--Ness Holding Co., Portland, OR; *U.S. Private*, pg. 791
Ness, Tee K., Pres.--Hawthorne Machinery Company, San Diego, CA; *U.S. Private*, pg. 512
Nesta, Vincenzo, Pres.--Pittway Tecnologica S.p.A., Trieste, Italy; *U.S. Public*, pg. 1307
Nester, Dallas G., Pres. & Chief Exec. Officer--Brown Wooten Mills, Inc., Burlington, NC; *U.S. Private*, pg. 174
Nestrick, Dwight L., Pres. & Chief Exec. Officer--Citizens Bank of Kentucky, Henderson, KY; *U.S. Public*, pg. 280
Neto, Jose Ferreira, Pres.--Banco Internacional de Credito S.A., Lisbon, Portugal; *Int'l*, pg. 142
Netter, Alfred E., Pres. & Chief Exec. Officer--GAF Premium Products, Inc., Wayne, NJ; *U.S. Private*, pg. 433
Neubauer, Joseph, Chm. Bd., Pres. & Chief Exec. Officer--Aramark Corp., Philadelphia, PA; *U.S. Private*, pg. 78
Neubayer, Joseph, Pres.--Aramark Correctional Services, Oak Brook, IL; *U.S. Private*, pg. 79
Neuchterlien, Dave, Pres.--ENPAC, Eastlake, OH; *U.S. Public*, pg. 592
Neuenschwander, Paul A., Pres. & Chief Exec. Officer--Zions Mortgage Company, Salt Lake City, UT; *U.S. Public*, pg. 1793
Neukirchen, Kajo, Chm.-Exec. Bd.--Metallgesellschaft AG, Frankfurt, Germany; *Int'l*, pg. 860
Neumaier, Gerhard J., Chm. Bd. & Pres.--Ecology and Environment, Inc., Lancaster, NY; *U.S. Public*, pg. 562
Neuman, David A., Pres.--Walt Disney Network Television, Burbank, CA; *U.S. Public*, pg. 511
Neuman, Werner E., Pres.--Corcom, Inc., Libertyville, IL; *U.S. Public*, pg. 446
Neumann, Frank G., Pres.--Valu Discount, Incorporated, Louisville, KY; *U.S. Private*, pg. 1132
Neumann, Klas, Pres.--Kvaerner Ships Equipment GmbH After Sales Service, Hamburg, Germany; *Int'l*, pg. 768
Neuvile, Patrick Martin, Pres. & Chief Exec. Officer--Calberson Overseas, Roissy, France; *Int'l*, pg. 549
Neuwirth, Frank, Chm. Bd. & Pres.--Unex Conveying Systems, Inc., Jackson, NJ; *U.S. Private*, pg. 1117
Neuwirth, Frank, Pres.--Span-Track, Jackson, NJ; *U.S. Private*, pg. 1117
Nevelle, Tim, Pres.--Creation Windows of Indiana, Inc., Elkhart, IN; *U.S. Private*, pg. 287
Nevers, Ronald, Pres.--D'Agostino Supermarkets Inc., Larchmont, NY; *U.S. Private*, pg. 306
Neveu, Jean, Pres. & Chief Exec. Officer--Quebecor Inc., Montreal, Canada; *Int'l*, pg. 1075
Neville, N.J., Pres.--Schlumberger Oilfield Services, Houston, TX; *U.S. Public*, pg. 1439
Neville, Robert J., Chm. Bd., Pres. & Chief Exec. Officer--The North American Manufacturing Co., Cleveland, OH; *U.S. Private*, pg. 803
Nevin, Bob, Pres.--Wilmer Service Line, Dayton, OH; *U.S. Public*, pg. 1385
Nevin, Robert C., Pres.--Reynolds and Reynolds-Business Forms Division, Oklahoma City, OK; *U.S. Public*, pg. 1385
New, James C., Pres. & Chief Exec. Officer--AmeriPath, Inc., Riviera Beach, FL; *U.S. Public*, pg. 96
Newberry, Richard A., Pres. & Chief Oper. Officer--Crown International, Inc., Elkhart, IN; *U.S. Private*, pg. 293
Newberry, William E., Pres.--Channel Industries, Inc., Santa Barbara, CA; *U.S. Private*, pg. 228
Newcomb, Jonathan, Pres. & Chief Exec. Officer--Simon & Schuster, New York, NY; *U.S. Private*, pg. 777
Newcomer, Frank III, Pres.--D.W. Newcomer's Sons, Inc., Kansas City, MO; *U.S. Private*, pg. 796
Newell, James, Pres.--Cummins Komatsu Engine Company, Seymour, IN; *U.S. Public*, pg. 468
Newell, James, Pres.--Cummins Komatsu Engine Company, Seymour, IN; *Int'l*, pg. 744
Newell, Liz, Pres., Chief Exec. Officer & New Bus. Contact--Kragie/Newell, Des Moines, IA; *U.S. Private*, pg. 634
Newell, William, Pres. & Chief Fin. Officer--Noll Printing Corporation, Huntington, IN; *U.S. Private*, pg. 821
Newham, D.H., Mng. Dir.--A.C. Labs (Pty.) Ltd., Sebenza, South Africa; *U.S. Public*, pg. 38
Newkirk, Gerry, Pres. & Chief Oper. Officer--Tractor Supply Co., Nashville, TN; *U.S. Public*, pg. 1627
Newland, Richard, Pres. & Chief Exec. Officer--Anoka Electric Cooperative, Ramsey, MN; *U.S. Private*, pg. 75
Newland, Tom D., Pres.--The East Ohio Gas Co., Cleveland, OH; *U.S. Public*, pg. 435
Newlin, Steven, Pres.--Nalco Europe, Leiden, Netherlands; *U.S. Public*, pg. 1151
Newman, Frank, Chm. Bd., Pres. & Chief Exec. Officer--Eckerd Corporation, Largo, FL; *U.S. Public*, pg. 917
Newman, Frank N., Chm. Bd., Pres. & Chief Exec. Officer--Bankers Trust New York Corporation, New York, NY; *U.S. Public*, pg. 185
Newman, G. Robert, Pres.--Fairmont Tamper, West Columbia, SC; *U.S. Public*, pg. 793
Newman, Gordon, Pres.--Rotorex Company, Inc., Walkersville, MD; *U.S. Public*, pg. 615
Newman, Mark S., Chm. Bd., Pres. & Chief Exec. Officer--DRS Technologies, Inc., Parsippany, NJ; *U.S. Public*, pg. 474
Newman, Michael H., Pres.--Golub & Co., Chicago, IL; *U.S. Private*, pg. 463
Newman, Mike, Pres.--Polo/Ralph Lauren, Lyndhurst, NJ; *U.S. Private*, pg. 875
Newman, Paul, Pres.--Newman's Own, Inc., Westport, CT; *U.S. Private*, pg. 797
Newman, R., Pres.--UTLAS International, Overland Park, KS; *U.S. Public*, pg. 1600
Newman, R. Stephen, Pres. & Chief Exec. Officer--Bacon's Information, Inc., Chicago, IL; *U.S. Public*, pg. 1327
Newman, Roland H., Pres.--Universal Shoe Mfg. Co., Lynchburg, VA; *U.S. Private*, pg. 284
Newman, William, Chm. Bd. & Chief Exec. Officer--New Plan Realty Trust, New York, NY; *U.S. Public*, pg. 1172
Newnham, Dennis, Pres. & Chief Exec. Officer--Tsumura International, Secaucus, NJ; *Int'l*, pg. 1426
Newsome, Ken, Pres.--AMF Bakery Systems, Richmond, VA; *U.S. Private*, pg. 6
Newton, Paul E., Pres. & Chief Exec. Officer--Boole & Babbage, Inc., San Jose, CA; *U.S. Public*, pg. 244
Newton, Steven T., Pres. & Gen. Mgr.--Occidental De Colombia, Inc., Bogota, Colombia; *U.S. Public*, pg. 1210
Newton, Thomas Alex, Pres. & Chief Oper. Officer--Daniel Industries, Inc., Houston, TX; *U.S. Public*, pg. 482
Ney, Joe, Pres.-Insurance--Certified Grocers of California, Los Angeles, CA; *U.S. Private*, pg. 226
Ney, Joseph, Pres.--Grocers and Merchants Insurance, Inc., Covina, CA; *U.S. Private*, pg. 227
Ney, Joseph, Pres.--Grocers & Merchants Management Co., Covina, CA; *U.S. Private*, pg. 227
Ney, Joseph A., Pres.--Springfield Insurance Company, Covina, CA; *U.S. Private*, pg. 227
Neyer, Thomas, Sr., Chm. Bd. & Pres.--Al Neyer, Inc., Cincinnati, OH; *U.S. Private*, pg. 797
Neyts, Freddy, Pres.--Radio Contact, Brussels, Belgium; *Int'l*, pg. 561
Nicandros, Constantine S., Pres. & Chief Exec. Officer--Conoco Inc., Houston, TX; *U.S. Public*, pg. 531
Nicastro, Neil D., Pres. & Chief Exec. Officer--WMS Industries Inc., Chicago, IL; *U.S. Public*, pg. 1727
Nicely, Olza M., Pres. & Chief Exec. Officer-Insurance Opers.--GEICO Corporation, Washington, DC; *U.S. Public*, pg. 219
Nichol, David A., Chm., Pres & Chief Exec. Officer--Destination Products International, Inc., Toronto, Canada; *Int'l*, pg. 338
Nichol, Thomas J., Pres.--Rolled Alloys, Inc., Temperance, MI; *U.S. Private*, pg. 941
Nicholas, Derick, Pres.--Spafas, Inc., Preston, CT; *U.S. Public*, pg. 195
Nicholas, Donna H., Chm. Bd. & Pres.--The Orr Felt Company, Piqua, OH; *U.S. Private*, pg. 820
Nicholas, Peter M., Chm. Bd., Pres. & Chief Exec. Officer--Boston Scientific Corp., Natick, MA; *U.S. Public*, pg. 247
Nichols, Francis T., Mng. Partner-EMA Mngmt. Services Group, Inc.--Eric Mower and Associates, Inc., Syracuse, NY; *U.S. Private*, pg. 765
Nichols, Fred R., Chm. Bd., Pres. & Chief Exec. Officer--TCA Cable TV, Inc., Tyler, TX; *U.S. Public*, pg. 1553
Nichols, Fred R., Chm. Bd., Pres. & Chief Exec. Officer--TCA Management Company, Tyler, TX; *U.S. Public*, pg. 1553
Nichols, Grace, Pres. & Chief Exec. Officer--Victoria's Secret Stores, Reynoldsburg, OH; *U.S. Public*, pg. 995
Nichols, J. Larry, Pres. & Chief Exec. Officer--Devon Energy Corporation, Oklahoma City, OK; *U.S. Public*, pg. 503
Nichols, James T., Pres. & Chief Exec. Officer--InterTAN Inc., Fort Worth, TX; *U.S. Public*, pg. 910
Nichols, Jim, Pres.--Walker-Pioneer Graphics, New York, NY; *U.S. Private*, pg. 1147
Nichols, Mack G., Pres. & Chief Oper. Officer--Mallinckrodt Inc., Saint Louis, MO; *U.S. Public*, pg. 1039
Nichols, Peter, Pres.--Allied Colloids Inc., Suffolk, VA; *Int'l*, pg. 62
Nichols, Steven, Chm. Bd. & Pres.--K-Swiss Inc., Chatsworth, CA; *U.S. Public*, pg. 937
Nichols, W.C., Chm. Bd., Pres. & Chief Exec. Officer--Renfro Corp., Mount Airy, NC; *U.S. Private*, pg. 922
Nicholson, David L., Pres.--Allen & Hoshall, Inc., Memphis, TN; *U.S. Private*, pg. 36
Nicholson, Gary D., Chm. Bd., Pres. & Chief Exec. Officer--Camco International Inc., Houston, TX; *U.S. Public*, pg. 297
Nicholson, Gary D., Pres. & Chief Exec. Officer--Camco International Inc., Houston, TX; *U.S. Public*, pg. 298
Nicholson, James B., Pres. & Chief Exec. Officer--PVS Chemicals, Inc., Detroit, MI; *U.S. Private*, pg. 828
Nicholson, Will F., Jr., Chm. Bd. & Pres.--Colorado National Bankshares, Inc., Denver, CO; *U.S. Public*, pg. 1680
Nichter, Mark S., Pres.--ProSoft International Co., Inc., Colorado Springs, CO; *U.S. Public*, pg. 441
Nick, John W., Pres.--Dresdner-NY Inc., New York, NY; *Int'l*, pg. 418
Nickel, Albert G., Pres. & Chief Oper. Officer--Lyons Lavey Nickel Swift, Inc., New York, NY; *U.S. Public*, pg. 1224
Nickel, David, Pres.--AC Corporation, Greensboro, NC; *U.S. Private*, pg. 3
Nickel, Delton D., Pres.--Hoffman Engineering Company, Anoka, MN; *U.S. Public*, pg. 1273
Nickel, Dieter H., Chm. Bd. & Pres.--Church Mutual Insurance Co., Merrill, WI; *U.S. Private*, pg. 239
Nickele, Greg, Pres.--Alliant Foodservice, Bensenville, IL; *U.S. Private*, pg. 244
Nickell, Bob, Pres.--Tucker-Rocky Distributing, Irving, TX; *U.S. Private*, pg. 639
Nickels, William F., Pres. & Chief Exec. Officer--Replogle Globes, Inc., Broadview, IL; *U.S. Private*, pg. 923
Nickerson, Joshua A., Jr., Chm. Bd. & Pres.--Nickerson Lumber Company, Orleans, MA; *U.S. Private*, pg. 798
Nicklasson, Martin, Pres.--Astra Hassle AB, Molndal, Sweden; *Int'l*, pg. 93
Nickly, John, Pres. & Chief Exec. Officer--Regence Life & Health Insurance Co., Portland, OR; *U.S. Private*, pg. 918
Nicolette, Thomas A., Pres. & Chief Exec. Officer--Sentry Technology Corp., Hauppauge, NY; *U.S. Public*, pg. 1458
Nicoletti, Arthur A., Pres.--Texaco Trading & Transportation Inc., Denver, CO; *U.S. Public*, pg. 1583
Nicolosi, Richard R., Pres. & Chief Exec. Officer--Samsonite Corporation, Denver, CO; *U.S. Public*, pg. 1430
Nidiffer, Douglas A., Pres. & Chief Exec. Officer--C & K Market, Inc., Brookings, OR; *U.S. Private*, pg. 191
Niedergang, Claude, Pres.--SCPA, Mulhouse, France; *Int'l*, pg. 459
Nield, David A., Pres. & Chief Exec. Officer--The Canada Life Assurance Company, Toronto, Canada; *Int'l*, pg. 254
Nielsen, B.L., Pres.--American Refractories & Crucible Corporation, North Haven, CT; *Int'l*, pg. 893
Nielsen, Carsten D., Mng. Dir.--The East Asiatic Company Ltd. A/S, Copenhagen, Denmark; *Int'l*, pg. 430
Nielsen, Claude B., Pres. & Chief Exec. Officer--Coca-Cola Bottling Co. United, Inc., Birmingham, AL; *U.S. Private*, pg. 248
Nielsen, Gary R., Pres. & Gen. Mgr.--WOKR-TV, Rochester, NY; *U.S. Private*, pg. 439
Nielsen, Lars Poppelgaard, Pres.--Danisco Flexible, Horsens, Denmark; *Int'l*, pg. 378
Nielsen, Mogens, Pres.--Gyproc A/S, Kalundborg, Denmark; *Int'l*, pg. 1200
Nielsen, Ole, Pres.--M.H. Greenebaum, Inc., Parsippany, NJ; *U.S. Private*, pg. 477
Nielsen, S. Christian, III, Pres.--The Nielsen Company, Florence, KY; *U.S. Private*, pg. 799
Nielsen, Steven E., Pres. & Chief Oper. Officer--Dycom Industries, Inc., Palm Beach Gardens, FL; *U.S. Public*, pg. 538
Niemela, Juha, Pres. & Chief Exec. Officer--UPM-Kymmene Corporation, Helsinki, Finland; *Int'l*, pg. 1427
Niemi, Steve, Pres.--TSI Mason Laboratories, Worcester, MA; *U.S. Public*, pg. 733
Niemi, Timo J., Pres.--PT. Valmet Indonesia, Pondok Gede, Indonesia; *Int'l*, pg. 1448
Niemiec, Leo P., Pres. & Chief Exec. Officer--Lawnware Products, Inc., Morton Grove, IL; *U.S. Private*, pg. 653
Nierenberg, Nico, Pres. & Chief Exec. Officer--Actuate Software Corporation, San Mateo, CA; *U.S. Private*, pg. 16
Nierenberg, Roy A., Pres.--Experience In Software, Inc., Berkeley, CA; *U.S. Private*, pg. 388
Niermeyer, David A., Pres.--Stakmore Inc., Owego, NY; *U.S.* Private, pg. 1029
Nies, Thomas M., Chm. Bd., Pres. & Chief Exec. Officer--Cincom Systems, Inc., Cincinnati, OH; *U.S. Private*, pg. 240
Nieto, Enrique, Pres.--Asesores Publicitarios, S.A., San Jose, Costa Rica; *U.S. Private*, pg. 1200
Nigbor, Donald E., Pres. & Chief Exec. Officer--Benchmark Electronics Inc., Angleton, TX; *U.S. Public*, pg. 210
Nigbor, Robert, Pres.--Agbabian Associates, Inc., Pasadena, CA; *Int'l*, pg. 1019
Nightingale, John A., Pres.--Rio Algom Limited, Elliot Lake, Canada; *Int'l*, pg. 1118
Nihei, S., Pres.-USA Leader--Leader Instruments Corporation, Hauppauge, NY; *U.S. Private*, pg. 655
Niira, Atsushi, Pres.--The Sumitomo Trust & Banking Co., Ltd., Osaka, Japan; *Int'l*, pg. 1317
Niisato, Yoshimasa, Pres.--Kintetsu World Express (France) S.A., Roissy, France; *Int'l*, pg. 735
Nikkel, John G., Pres. & Chief Oper. Officer--Unit Corporation, Tulsa, OK; *U.S. Public*, pg. 1672
Nikkila, Kalevi, Pres.--Outokumpu Technology Oy, Espoo, Finland; *Int'l*, pg. 1017
Nikolaev, Richard D., Pres. & Chief Exec. Officer--Wright Medical Technology, Arlington, TN; *U.S. Private*, pg. 1192
Nikopoulos, Nikos, Pres.--Producta-TBWA, Athens, Greece; *U.S. Private*, pg. 1062
Nileansson, Olle, Pres.--NCC Building - Karlstad, Karlstad, Sweden; *Int'l*, pg. 898
Niles, Lou, Pres. & Chief Exec. Officer--Benson Industries, Inc., Portland, OR; *U.S. Private*, pg. 133
Niles, Nicholas H., Pres. & Chief Exec. Officer--The Sporting News Publishing Company, Saint Louis, MO; *U.S. Public*, pg. 1616
Niles, Terry, Pres.--Gage Adistra Corp., Plymouth, MI; *U.S. Private*, pg. 437
Nilsen, Leif, Mng. Dir.--Kaldnes Heavy Lift Trucks, Tonsberg, Norway; *Int'l*, pg. 965
Nilsen, Leone A., Chm. & Pres.--Inter-Community Telephone Company, Nome, ND; *U.S. Public*, pg. 1022
Nilson, Marianne, Pres. & Mng. Dir.--Atlet AB, Molnlycke, Sweden; *Int'l*, pg. 97
Nilsson, Bengt, Pres.--MRC Bearings, Jamestown, NY; *Int'l*, pg. 1157
Nilsson, Kjell, Pres. & Chief Exec. Officer--Trelleborg AB, Trelleborg, Sweden; *Int'l*, pg. 1419
Nilsson, Tommy, Pres.--NCC Invest, Solna, Sweden; *Int'l*, pg. 899
Nilsson, Torbjorn, Pres.--Precon AB, Falkenberg, Sweden; *Int'l*, pg. 1199
Nilstoft, Clas, Pres.--Rexam Closures, Evansville, IN; *Int'l*, pg. 1106

Nimrodi, Jackob, Chm. Bd. & Pres.--The Israel Land Development Co., Ltd., Tel Aviv, Israel; *Int'l*, pg. 691
Nims, Charles W., Pres.--Branson Ultrasonics Corp. - Precision Cleaning Div., Danbury, CT; *U.S. Public*, pg. 574
Nisbit, Michael M., Pres. & Chief Exec. Officer--AFCO Credit Corp., New York, NY; *U.S. Public*, pg. 1085
Nishida, Keiu, Pres.--The Mitsui Trust and Banking Company, Limited, Tokyo, Japan; *Int'l*, pg. 882
Nishigaki, Satoru, Pres.--The Tokai Bank, Limited, Nagoya, Japan; *Int'l*, pg. 1391
Nishiguchi, Hiromune, Pres.--The Nanto Bank, Ltd., Nara, Japan; *Int'l*, pg. 905
Nishikata, M.N., Pres.-Emerson Japan--Aichi-Emerson Electric Co., Nagoya, Japan; *U.S. Public*, pg. 578
Nishikawa, Katsuhiro, Pres.--Thai Toray Textile Mills Public Company Limited, Bangkok, Thailand; *Int'l*, pg. 1400
Nishikawa, Yoshifumi, Pres.--The Sumitomo Bank, Limited, Osaka, Japan; *Int'l*, pg. 1308
Nishikawa, Yoshifumi, Pres.--The Sumitomo Bank, LTD.-Tokyo, Tokyo, Japan; *Int'l*, pg. 1308
Nishiki, Hiroshi, Deputy Pres.--The Mitsui Trust and Banking Company, Limited, Tokyo, Japan; *Int'l*, pg. 882
Nishimura, Kanji, Pres.--Wuxi Sanwa Garment Materials Co., Ltd., Wuxi, China; *Int'l*, pg. 579
Nishimura, Koichi, Ph.D., Chm. Bd., Pres. & Chief Exec. Officer--Solectron Corporation, Milpitas, CA; *U.S. Public*, pg. 1483
Nishimura, Masao, Pres.--The Industrial Bank of Japan, Limited, Tokyo, Japan; *Int'l*, pg. 674
Nishimuro, Atsushi, Pres.--Futaba Corporation, Mobara, Japan; *Int'l*, pg. 531
Nishimuro, Taizo, Pres. & Chief Exec. Officer--Toshiba Corporation, Tokyo, Japan; *Int'l*, pg. 1402
Nishina, Hiroaki, Pres.--ORIX Auto Leasing Corporation, Tokyo, Japan; *Int'l*, pg. 1008
Nishino, Shinichi, Pres.--Asahi Bank (Deutschland) GmbH, Frankfurt/Main, Germany; *Int'l*, pg. 83
Nishio, Akira, Pres.--Nissho Iwai Corporation, Tokyo, Japan; *Int'l*, pg. 946
Nishio, Masaharu, Pres. & Chief Exec. Officer--Muratech America, Inc., Plano, TX; *Int'l*, pg. 897
Nishio, Shojiro, Chm.--Daiko Advertising, Inc., Tokyo, Japan; *Int'l*, pg. 365
Nishiyama, Isao, Pres.--BTM Leasing & Finance, Inc., New York, NY; *Int'l*, pg. 157
Nishiyama, Masaharu, Pres.--Nippon Dome Structures Co., Ltd., Tokyo, Japan; *Int'l*, pg. 763
Nishizawa, Susumu, Pres.--Sekisui Chemical Co., Ltd., Osaka, Japan; *Int'l*, pg. 1219
Nissen, Dietmar, Dr., Pres. & Chief Oper. Officer--BASF Japan Ltd., Tokyo, Japan; *Int'l*, pg. 106
Nissen, William, Chm. Bd. & Pres.--Apache Hose & Belting Company, Inc., Cedar Rapids, IA; *U.S. Private*, pg. 76
Nitta, Koji, Pres.--Tomen (U.K.) Plc., London, United Kingdom; *Int'l*, pg. 1395
Nitta, Toyoharu, Pres.--Quaker State Japan Co., Ltd., Tokyo, Japan; *U.S. Public*, pg. 1348
Niwa, Nobukazu, Pres.--Nikkei Advertising Co., Tokyo, Japan; *Int'l*, pg. 930
Niwa, Norio, Pres. & Chief Exec. Officer--Epson America Inc., Torrance, CA; *Int'l*, pg. 1219
Nix, W.S., Pres.--Lumonics Inc., Kanata, Canada; *Int'l*, pg. 1314
Nixon, Geoffrey R., Pres. & Chief Oper. Officer--Austin Kelley Advertising, Inc., Atlanta, GA; *U.S. Private*, pg. 100
Nixon, P. Andrews, Pres. & Chief Exec. Officer--Dead River Company, Portland, ME; *U.S. Private*, pg. 318
Nizam, I., Chm. Bd., Pres. & Chief Exec. Officer--Master International Corp., Santa Monica, CA; *U.S. Private*, pg. 713
Noble, David, Pres.--American Life Holding Corp., Des Moines, IA; *U.S. Public*, pg. 432
Noble, Jerry F., Pres.--Institute for Professional Development, Phoenix, AZ; *U.S. Public*, pg. 120
Noble, Ray, Pres.--Storm Products Company, Inc., Santa Monica, CA; *U.S. Private*, pg. 1045
Noble, Robert B., Pres. & Chief Exec. Officer--Noble & Associates Promotion Group, Springfield, MO; *U.S. Private*, pg. 800
Nobles, Bruce R., Chm. Bd., Pres. & Chief Exec. Officer--Hawaiian Airlines, Inc., Honolulu, HI; *U.S. Public*, pg. 799
Nodland, J.M., Pres. & Chief Oper. Officer--McWhorter Technologies, Inc., Carpentersville, IL; *U.S. Public*, pg. 1074
Noe, Greg, Pres. & Chief Exec. Officer--Pilliod Furniture, Greensboro, NC; *U.S. Public*, pg. 974
Noel, Gerard, Acting Pres.--Great Lakes Confectionery, Cleveland, OH; *Int'l*, pg. 865
Noel, J-C, Chm. Bd., Pres. & Chief Exec. Officer--Hilton Canada Inc., Montreal, Canada; *Int'l*, pg. 788
Noel, John, Chm. Bd. & Pres.--Noel Olson Group, Stevens Point, WI; *U.S. Private*, pg. 800
Noel, Rob, Pres.--Practice Patterns Science, Maryland Heights, MO; *U.S. Public*, pg. 601
Noel, Rodger, Pres.--Noel Canning Corporation, Yakima, WA; *U.S. Private*, pg. 800
Noel, Ronald R., Pres.--Newport Steel Corporation, Newport, KY; *U.S. Public*, pg. 1147
Noel, T. Howard, Pres. & Chief Exec. Officer--Hayes, Seay, Mattern & Mattern, Inc., Roanoke, VA; *U.S. Private*, pg. 513
Noels, Jacques, Pres., Chief Exec. Officer & Chief Oper. Officer--Zenith Data Systems, Deerfield, IL; *Int'l*, pg. 317
Noelting, Jean, Pres. & Chief Exec. Officer--Parmalat Canada Ltd., Etobicoke, Canada; *Int'l*, pg. 1023
Noer, John A., Chm., Pres. & Chief Exec. Officer--Northern States Power Co. (Wis.), Eau Claire, WI; *U.S. Public*, pg. 1195
Noergaard, Leif, Pres.--Chr. Hansen, Inc., Milwaukee, WI; *Int'l*, pg. 288
Noesen, Thierry, Pres.--EMTEC Magnetics Benelux N.V., Brussels, Belgium; *Int'l*, pg. 743
Noetzli, Hans C., Chm. Bd. & Pres.--Lonza Inc., Fair Lawn, NJ; *Int'l*, pg. 67
Noguchi, K., Pres.--Sharp Electronics France S.A., Roissy, France; *Int'l*, pg. 1230
Nogueira de Brito, Jose Luis, Co.-Pres.--FIMA-Productos Alimentares, Lda, Lisbon, Portugal; *Int'l*, pg. 471
Noia, Alan J., Pres. & Chief Exec. Officer--Allegheny Power System, Inc., Hagerstown, MD; *U.S. Public*, pg. 42
Nojima, Paul, Pres.--Bandai America, Inc., Cypress, CA; *Int'l*, pg. 145
Nolan, Cary J., Pres. & Chief Exec. Officer--Picker International, Inc., Cleveland, OH; *Int'l*, pg. 545
Nolan, David, Pres.--Comdisco Continuity Services, Rosemont, IL; *U.S. Public*, pg. 408
Nolan, John G., Pres.--National School Bus Service, Barrington, IL; *Int'l*, pg. 1213
Nolan, Peter, Pres.--Dole Packaged Food Company, Westlake Village, CA; *U.S. Public*, pg. 515
Noland, Lloyd U., III, Chm. Bd. & Pres.--Noland Company, Newport News, VA; *U.S. Public*, pg. 1187
Nolen, Robert B., Jr., Pres.--Pinnacle Bank, Jasper, AL; *U.S. Public*, pg. 1297
Noll, Gregory P., Pres. & Chief Exec. Officer--The Provident Bank of Kentucky, Cincinnati, OH; *U.S. Public*, pg. 1338
Noma, Sawako, Pres.--Kodansha Ltd., Tokyo, Japan; *Int'l*, pg. 742
Nomiyama, Hiroshi, Pres.--Asatsu (Deutschland) GmbH, Trebur, Germany; *Int'l*, pg. 86
Nomura, Hiromasa, Pres.--Taiyo Kogyo Corporation, Osaka, Japan; *Int'l*, pg. 1348
Nomura, Masanari, Pres.--Hokuriku Electric Industry Co., Ltd., Toyama, Japan; *Int'l*, pg. 627
Noonan, Bill, Pres.--Noonan Machine Co., Franklin Park, IL; *U.S. Private*, pg. 801
Noonan, Bill, Pres.--L.A.B. Equipment, Skaneateles, NY; *U.S. Private*, pg. 801
Noonan, Edward J., Pres. & Chief Exec. Officer--American Re Corporation, Princeton, NJ; *Int'l*, pg. 897
Noonan, Frank R., Pres.--The Reuben H. Donnelley Corporation, Purchase, NY; *U.S. Public*, pg. 535
Noonan, Jack, Pres. & Chief Exec. Officer--SPSS Inc., Chicago, IL; *U.S. Public*, pg. 1420
Noonan, Pat, Pres.--Whittenberg Construction Co., Louisville, KY; *U.S. Private*, pg. 1174
Noonan, Terrence A., Pres. & Chief Oper. Officer--Furon Company, Laguna Niguel, CA; *U.S. Public*, pg. 688
Noonan, Timothy J., Pres. & Chief Oper. Officer--Rite Aid Corporation, Camp Hill, PA; *U.S. Public*, pg. 1390
Noorduyn, A., Pres.--Erven Lucas Bols S.A., Buenos Aires, Argentina; *Int'l*, pg. 751
Noordwijk, John, Pres.--Atlas Copco Comptec Inc., Voorheesville, NY; *Int'l*, pg. 96
Nooteboom, Gijs, Pres. & Gen. Mgr.--Polarcup Benelux B.V., Groenlo, Netherlands; *Int'l*, pg. 638
Norbitz, Wayne, Pres. & Chief Oper. Officer--Nathan's Famous Inc., Westbury, NY; *U.S. Public*, pg. 1152
Norden, Roger C., Pres.--Standard Medical Imaging, Inc., Columbia, MD; *U.S. Private*, pg. 1032
Nordin, Roger, Pres.--Green Spot Packaging Inc., Claremont, CA; *U.S. Private*, pg. 477
Nordin, Stig, Mng. Dir.--Korsnas AB, Gavle, Sweden; *Int'l*, pg. 759
Nordloh, Gary L., Pres. & Chief Exec. Officer--Wexpro Company, Salt Lake City, UT; *U.S. Public*, pg. 1352
Nordmann, Philippe, Pres.--Maus Freres S.A., Geneva, Switzerland; *Int'l*, pg. 849
Nordstrom, Blake, Co-Pres.--Nordstrom, Inc., Seattle, WA; *U.S. Public*, pg. 1190
Nordstrom, Erik, Co-Pres.--Nordstrom, Inc., Seattle, WA; *U.S. Public*, pg. 1190
Nordstrom, J. Daniel, Co-Pres.--Nordstrom, Inc., Seattle, WA; *U.S. Public*, pg. 1190
Nordstrom, James A., Co-Pres.--Nordstrom, Inc., Seattle, WA; *U.S. Public*, pg. 1190
Nordstrom, Lars, Pres.--AB Novum, Helsingborg, Sweden; *Int'l*, pg. 678
Nordstrom, Peter E., Co-Pres.--Nordstrom, Inc., Seattle, WA; *U.S. Public*, pg. 1190
Nordstrom, William E., Co-Pres.--Nordstrom, Inc., Seattle, WA; *U.S. Public*, pg. 1190
Norheim, Oddvar, Chm. Bd. & Pres.--American Crane & Equipment Corp., Douglassville, PA; *U.S. Private*, pg. 52
Norman, Lewis G., III, Pres.--Bernhardt Furniture Co., Lenoir, NC; *U.S. Private*, pg. 137
Norman, Reeve, Pres.--Electrical Wholesale Supply Company, Inc., Idaho Falls, ID; *U.S. Private*, pg. 368
Norman, T.A., Pres.--Ziegler Medical Equipment Group, Inc., Omaha, NE; *U.S. Public*, pg. 1792
Norman, William, Pres.-Norman Enterprises, Inc.--Photo Control Corporation, Minneapolis, MN; *U.S. Public*, pg. 1292
Normandin, James, Publr.--The Haverhill Gazette, Haverhill, MA; *U.S. Public*, pg. 1343
Norris, Brad, Pres.--Deerfield Manufacturing Co., Inc., Mason, OH; *U.S. Private*, pg. 1044
Norris, Charles H., Jr., Pres.--Resolite, Zelienople, PA; *U.S. Public*, pg. 1676
Norris, David W., Pres. & Chief Exec. Officer--PCC Flow Technologies, Inc., Houston, TX; *U.S. Public*, pg. 1320
Norris, Frank W., Jr., Pres.--Badger Equipment Co., Winona, MN; *U.S. Private*, pg. 102
Norris, John, Pres.--New Hermes Incorporated, Duluth, GA; *U.S. Private*, pg. 793
Norris, John F., Jr., Pres.--Duke Engineering & Services, Inc., Charlotte, NC; *U.S. Public*, pg. 534
Norris, Roy H., III, Pres.--Raytheon Aircraft Company, Wichita, KS; *U.S. Public*, pg. 1365
Norris, Thomas C., Chm., Pres. & Chief Exec. Officer--P.H. Glatfelter Company, Spring Grove, PA; *U.S. Public*, pg. 746
Norrman, Ulf, Pres.--Skanska Capital AB, Danderyd, Sweden; *Int'l*, pg. 1260
North, D., Exec. V.P. & Gen. Mgr.--United Technologies, Chemical Systems Div., San Jose, CA; *U.S. Public*, pg. 1690
Nortink, Rich, Pres.--Jones Interactive, Inc., Englewood, CO; *U.S. Private*, pg. 597
Norton, Gerald R., Pres.--DeVlieg-Bullard Tooling Systems Division, Frankenmuth, MI; *U.S. Public*, pg. 502
Norton, J. Patrick, Chm. Bd., Pres. & Chief Exec. Officer--Fabreeka International, Inc., Stoughton, MA; *U.S. Private*, pg. 390
Norton, James, Pres.--Muralo Co., Inc., Bayonne, NJ; *U.S. Private*, pg. 767
Norton, James J., Pres.--Washington Specialty Metals, Buffalo Grove, IL; *U.S. Public*, pg. 1020
Norton, Lawrence J., Pres.--Modern Equipment Rentals Inc., Wilmington, DE; *U.S. Private*, pg. 754
Norton, Richard, Pres.--Aero Manufacturing, Inc., Syracuse, IN; *U.S. Public*, pg. 1602
Norton, Richard, Pres.--Dutchmen Fold Down Camper Division, Syracuse, IN; *U.S. Public*, pg. 1602
Norton, Robert, Pres. & Chief Exec. Officer--FTD, Inc./ Florists Transworld Delivery, Inc., Downers Grove, IL; *U.S. Private*, pg. 389
Norton, Robert R., Chm. Bd., Pres. & Chief Exec. Officer--BeefAmerica Operating Co., Inc., Omaha, NE; *U.S. Private*, pg. 130
Norvik, Harald, Pres. & Chief Exec. Officer--Statoil, Stavanger, Norway; *Int'l*, pg. 1297
Norwood, Mike, Pres. & Chief Oper. Officer--Electron Corp., Littleton, CO; *U.S. Private*, pg. 370
Nose, Kensaku, Pres.--Beijing Office, Beijing, China; *Int'l*, pg. 578
Noskin, Arthur, Pres.--Polymer Plastics Corporation, Hauppauge, NY; *U.S. Private*, pg. 875
Nosler, John S., Pres.--Pacific Metal Company, Portland, OR; *U.S. Private*, pg. 832
Notebaert, Edmond F., Pres. & Chief Exec. Officer--The Children's Hospital of Philadelphia, Philadelphia, PA; *U.S. Private*, pg. 236
Notebaert, Richard C., Chm. Bd., Pres. & Chief Exec. Officer--Ameritech Corporation, Chicago, IL; *U.S. Public*, pg. 97
Noteware, James D., Pres. & Chief Exec. Officer--MAXXAM Property Company, Houston, TX; *U.S. Public*, pg. 1062
Nothburft, Arthur, Chm. Bd. & Pres.--Alno AG, Pfullendorf, Germany; *Int'l*, pg. 65
Nothstine, David E., Pres.--Boeing Services, Inc., Khamis Mushayt, Saudi Arabia; *U.S. Public*, pg. 242
Noto, Lucio A., Chm. Bd., Pres., Chief Exec. & Chief Oper. Officer--Mobil Oil Corporation, Fairfax, VA; *U.S. Public*, pg. 1118
Noto, Pete, Mng. Partner-Creative Art--Lewis Gace Bozell Healthcare Worldwide, Fort Lee, NJ; *U.S. Public*, pg. 1642
Nova, Gianluigi, Pres., Chief Exec. Officer & Controller--Itam Tech Italimplianti, Inc., Coraopolis, PA; *Int'l*, pg. 655
Novak, David C., Vice Chm. & Pres.--Tricon Global Restaurants, Inc., Louisville, KY; *U.S. Public*, pg. 1636
Novak, John S., Jr., Pres.--Sokol & Company, Countryside, IL; *U.S. Private*, pg. 1012
Novak, Mark, Pres. & Chief Exec. Officer--Arrowhead Mills, Inc., Hereford, TX; *U.S. Private*, pg. 86
Novela, Frederick Melville, Chm. Bd. & Pres.--Aviateca, Guatemala, Guatemala; *Int'l*, pg. 102
Novo, C.R., Pres.--John Wyeth Laboratories S.A., Buenos Aires, Argentina; *U.S. Public*, pg. 82
Nowicki, John, Pres.--Advance Mechanical Systems, Inc., Mount Prospect, IL; *U.S. Private*, pg. 18
Noyes, Ken, Pres. & Chief Oper. Officer--Schwan's Sales Enterprises, Marshall, MN; *U.S. Private*, pg. 974
Nozawa, Ryoichiro, Pres. & Chief Oper. Officer--Fanuc Ltd., Yamanashi, Japan; *Int'l*, pg. 477
Nozko, Henry W., Sr., Chm. Bd., Pres. & Chief Exec. Officer--ACMAT Corporation, New Britain, CT; *U.S. Public*, pg. 16
Nuckols, William M., Pres. & Chief Exec. Officer--Pass & Seymour/Legrand, Syracuse, NY; *Int'l*, pg. 806
Nudson, Steve, Pres.--Sweet Life Foods, Inc., Suffield, CT; *U.S. Public*, pg. 1541
Nugent, Jeffrey, Pres.-Worldwide--Neutrogena Corporation, Los Angeles, CA; *U.S. Public*, pg. 928
Nugent, John O.C., Sr. V.P.-Consumer Products Grp.--Chesebrough-Pond's, Trumbull, CT; *Int'l*, pg. 1436
Nugent, Robert, Chm. Bd., Pres. & Chief Exec. Officer--Foodmaker, Inc., San Diego, CA; *U.S. Public*, pg. 661
Nulman, Richard, Pres.--Pace Advertising, New York, NY; *Int'l*, pg. 1483
Nulton, Karl E., Pres.--Johnson Acoustical & Supply Co., Portland, OR; *U.S. Private*, pg. 590
Numauchi, Motohiko, Pres. & Chief Exec. Officer--Mitsubishi International Corporation, New York, NY; *Int'l*, pg. 871
Nune, David, Pres.--Alpine American, Natick, MA; *Int'l*, pg. 635
Nunes, Jawad G., Pres. & Chief Oper. Officer--American Tool Companies, Inc., Hoffman Estates, IL; *U.S. Private*, pg. 63
Nunez, Elpidio, Chm. Bd. & Pres.--Northwestern Meats Inc., Miami, FL; *U.S. Private*, pg. 807
Nunez, Jaine, Chm. Bd. & Pres.--Bagley S.A., Buenos Aires, Argentina; *Int'l*, pg. 379
Nunez, Juan Luis Ruiz, Pres.--Santa Barbara Empresa Nacional de Industrias Militares, S.A., Madrid, Spain; *Int'l*, pg. 1224
Nunez, Ramon A., Pres. & Chief Exec. Officer--IKOS Systems, Inc., Cupertino, CA; *U.S. Public*, pg. 864
Nunley, John, Pres.--Better Living Inc., Charlottesville, VA; *U.S. Private*, pg. 141
Nunley, Richard L., Chm. Bd., Pres. & Treas.--Better Living Inc., Charlottesville, VA; *U.S. Private*, pg. 141
Nunnery, Dale, Pres.--Shenandoah Mills, Inc., Lebanon, TN; *U.S. Private*, pg. 992
Nusbaum, W., Pres. & Chief Exec. Officer--Long Manufacturing, Ltd., Oakville, Canada; *Int'l*, pg. 815

Nussbaum, R. Michael, Pres.--Southern Foods, Inc., Greensboro, NC; *U.S. Private*, pg. 1016
Nussbaum, V.M., Pres.--Home Division, Greensboro, NC; *U.S. Private*, pg. 1016
Nussbaum, V.M., Pres.--Institutional Division, Greensboro, NC; *U.S. Private*, pg. 1016
Nussdorf, Bernard, Pres.--Quality King Distributors Inc., Ronkonkoma, NY; *U.S. Private*, pg. 899
Nussrallahi, Steve, Pres.--Syntellect, Inc., Phoenix, AZ; *U.S.* Public, pg. 1550
Nutter, W. Lee, Pres. & Chief Oper. Officer--Rayonier Inc., Stamford, CT; *U.S. Public*, pg. 1363
Nutting, G. Ogden, Pres.--Ogden Newspapers, Inc., Wheeling, WV; *U.S. Private*, pg. 812
Nuzum, Mike, Pres.--Dupey Management Corp., Coppell, TX; *U.S. Private*, pg. 348
Nuzzaci, Edward, Pres.--Sandvik Steel Co., Scranton, PA; *Int'l*, pg. 1185
Nyberg, D.A., Pres.--Tesoro Marine Services, Houston, TX; *U.S. Public*, pg. 1582
Nybo, Howard J., Pres.--Will & Baumer Incorporated, Liverpool, NY; *U.S. Private*, pg. 1176
Nybo, Svein G., Pres. & Chief Exec. Officer--Frionor A/S, Lysaker, Norway; *Int'l*, pg. 516
Nye, Erle, Pres. & Chief Exec. Officer--Texas Utilities Company, Dallas, TX; *U.S. Public*, pg. 1586
Nye, Gordie, Pres.--Voit Sports, Inc., Carlsbad, CA; *U.S. Private*, pg. 1143
Nygren, Magne, Pres.--Munck Automation Technology, Newport News, VA; *U.S. Private*, pg. 767
Nyland, Bob, Pres.--Outdoor Services, New York, NY; *U.S. Private*, pg. 1166
Nyland, Robert, Pres.--Outdoor Services, Chicago, IL; *U.S. Private*, pg. 1166
Nyland, Robert M., Pres. & Chief Exec. Officer--Outdoor Services, San Francisco, CA; *U.S. Private*, pg. 1166
Nyquist, Carl-Erik, Pres. & Chief Exec. Officer--Vattenfall AB, Stockholm, Sweden; *Int'l*, pg. 1452
Nystrom, Lars-Erik, Pres.--Aseri Tellis AS, Aseri, Estonia; *Int'l*, pg. 1200
Nystrom, Lars-Erik, Pres.--Optimix AS, Aravete, Estonia; *Int'l*, pg. 1200
O' Mahony, Jack, Pres.--Howmedica, Inc., Rutherford, NJ; *U.S. Public*, pg. 1282
O'Brien, Charles, Pres.--Frozfruit Corporation, Gardena, CA; *U.S. Private*, pg. 430
O'Brien, Charles J., Pres. & Chief Exec. Officer--MTL Inc., Plant City, FL; *U.S. Public*, pg. 1028
O'Brien, Charles P., Pres. & Chief Exec. Officer--Reliance Standard Life Insurance Company, Philadelphia, PA; *U.S.* Public, pg. 496
O'Brien, Charles R., Pres.--Ring Screw Works, Madison Heights, MI; *U.S. Private*, pg. 931
O'Brien, Coby, Pres. & Chief Exec. Officer--Darwin Digital, New York, NY; *U.S. Public*, pg. 1422
O'Brien, Daniel R., Pres. & Chief Exec. Officer--Beneficial Insurance Group, Inc., Peapack, NJ; *U.S. Public*, pg. 211
O'Brien, Daniel W., Pres.--F.H. Stoltze Land & Lumber Company, Saint Paul, MN; *U.S. Private*, pg. 1044
O'Brien, David P., Chm. Bd., Pres. & Chief Exec. Officer--Canadian Pacific Limited, Calgary, Canada; *Int'l*, pg. 258
O'Brien, G.R., Pres.--Connecticut General Corporation, Bloomfield, CT; *U.S. Public*, pg. 358
O'Brien, James, Pres.--Valvoline Company, Lexington, KY; *U.S. Public*, pg. 139
O'Brien, James, Pres.--The Valvoline Company, Lexington, KY; *U.S. Public*, pg. 139
O'Brien, John D., Pres.--Borg-Warner Protective Services Corporation, Parsippany, NJ; *U.S. Public*, pg. 245
O'Brien, John F., Pres. & Chief Exec. Officer--Allmerica Financial Corporation, Worcester, MA; *U.S. Public*, pg. 54
O'Brien, Ken, Pres. & Chief Exec. Officer--R.W. Beck, Inc., Seattle, WA; *U.S. Private*, pg. 128
O'Brien, Mark E., Pres.--Roy O'Brien Inc., Saint Clair Shores, MI; *U.S. Private*, pg. 810
O'Brien, Patrick J., Pres.--A & M Products, Danbury, CT; *U.S. Public*, pg. 627
O'Brien, R. Michael, Pres.--GMAC Mortgage Corporation, Horsham, PA; *U.S. Public*, pg. 720
O'Brien, Richard T., Pres.--PacifiCorp Group Holdings Company, Portland, OR; *U.S. Public*, pg. 1251
O'Brien, William, Pres.--Converter Power, Inc., Ipswich, MA; *U.S. Public*, pg. 856
O'Bryan, Michael L., Pres.--O'Bryan Brothers Inc., Chicago, IL; *U.S. Private*, pg. 810
O'Bryan, P. Jack, Pres. & Chief Oper. Officer--USG Corporation, Chicago, IL; *U.S. Public*, pg. 1660
O'Callaghan, Kevin, Pres.--Universal Builders Supply, Inc., Mount Vernon, NY; *U.S. Private*, pg. 1126
O'Colmaine, Peter, Gen. Mgr.--Four Seasons Resorts, Kihei, HI; *Int'l*, pg. 502
O'Connell, Frank J., Chm. Bd., Pres. & Chief Exec. Officer--Gibson Greetings, Inc., Cincinnati, OH; *U.S. Public*, pg. 742
O'Connell, G.M., Pres. & Chief Oper. Officer--TN Technologies Inc., Westport, CT; *U.S. Public*, pg. 1641
O'Connell, Terry, Pres.--Warner Cable Communications, Inc., Columbus, OH; *U.S. Public*, pg. 1611
O'Conner, Joe, Pres. & Controller--American Metal & Plastics Inc., Grand Rapids, MI; *U.S. Private*, pg. 59
O'Connor-Vos, Lynn, Pres. & Chief Exec. Officer-GHG--Grey Healthcare Group, New York, NY; *U.S. Public*, pg. 765
O'Connor, David, Pres.--Merle Norman Cosmetics, Inc., Los Angeles, CA; *U.S. Private*, pg. 733
O'Connor, John, Pres.--Day & Zimmerman Infrastructure, Inc., Philadelphia, PA; *U.S. Private*, pg. 317
O'Connor, Laurence P., Chm. Bd., Pres. & Chief Exec. Officer--Unigard Insurance Co., Bellevue, WA; *Int'l*, pg. 345
O'Connor, Laurence P., Chm. Bd., Pres. & Chief Exec. Officer--Unigard Indemnity Co., Bellevue, WA; *Int'l*, pg. 345
O'Connor, Neal, Pres.--George T. Schmidt, Niles, IL; *U.S. Private*, pg. 970
O'Connor, Patrick, Pres.--Modern Medical Modalities Corp., Morristown, NJ; *U.S. Public*, pg. 1121
O'Connor, Thomas D., Chm. Bd. & Pres.--Mohawk Paper Mills, Inc., Cohoes, NY; *U.S. Private*, pg. 755
O'Connor, William E., Pres.--Waukesha Engine Division, Waukesha, WI; *U.S. Public*, pg. 528
O'Connor, William Y., Pres. & Chief Exec. Officer--GTECH Corporation, West Greenwich, RI; *U.S. Public*, pg. 767
O'Conor, Raymond F., Pres.--Sartoga National Bank & Trust Company, Saratoga Springs, NY; *U.S. Public*, pg. 135
O'Day, Sean, Pres.--SIGAL CONSTRUCTION CORP., Washington, DC; *U.S. Private*, pg. 999
O'Dea, Patrick, Pres. & Chief Oper. Officer--Mother's Cake & Cookie Co., Oakland, CA; *U.S. Private*, pg. 1022
O'Dell, James J., Chm. Bd., Pres. & Chief Exec. Officer--Valley Bank & Trust, Brighton, CO; *U.S. Private*, pg. 1132
O'Dell, Jane, Pres. & Treas.--Westfall GMC Truck Inc., Kansas City, MO; *U.S. Private*, pg. 1169
O'Dell, W.W., Pres.--Liebert Corp.--Liebert Corporation, Columbus, OH; *U.S. Public*, pg. 573
O'Donnell, Dwight, Pres.--SierraPine Limited, Roseville, CA; *U.S. Private*, pg. 999
O'Donnell, James, Pres.--Color Arts, Inc., Racine, WI; *U.S. Private*, pg. 254
O'Donnell, Joseph, Co-Chm. Bd., Pres. & Chief Exec. Officer--Computer Products, Inc., Boca Raton, FL; *U.S. Public*, pg. 422
O'Donnell, Michael, Pres.--Wechsler Coffee Corp., Moonachie, NJ; *U.S. Private*, pg. 1158
O'Donnell, P.A., Pres.--Strand Lighting Inc., Rancho Dominguez, CA; *Int'l*, pg. 1087
O'Donnell, Thomas H., Pres.--Sunrise Medical Mobility Products, Fresno, CA; *U.S. Public*, pg. 1536
O'Donnell, Tim, Pres.--Keltatim Publishing Company, Olathe, KS; *U.S. Private*, pg. 613
O'Donnell, Tim, Pres.--Olathe Daily News, Olathe, KS; *U.S. Private*, pg. 613
O'Donovan, Timothy J., Pres. & Chief Oper. Officer--Wolverine World Wide, Inc., Rockford, MI; *U.S. Public*, pg. 1775
O'Gorman, Thomas, Pres.--Glenoit Mills, Inc., Tarboro, NC; *U.S. Private*, pg. 456
O'Hagan, Malcolm E., Pres.--National Electrical Manufacturers Association, Arlington, VA; *U.S. Private*, pg. 782
O'Hagan, William D., Pres.--Mueller Industries, Inc., Memphis, TN; *U.S. Public*, pg. 1141
O'Halloran, Martin, Pres.--ISS Cleaning Services Group, Inc., New York, NY; *Int'l*, pg. 656
O'Halloran, Martin, Pres. & Chief Exec. Officer--ISS International Service System, Inc., Atlanta, GA; *Int'l*, pg. 656
O'Halloran, Terry, Pres.--Titus Products Div., Richardson, TX; *Int'l*, pg. 1398
O'Hanlon, Michael, Chm. Bd., Pres. & Chief Exec. & Oper. Officer--DVI Financial Services Inc., Newport Beach, CA; *U.S. Public*, pg. 476
O'Hanlon, Michael A., Pres. & Chief Oper. Officer--DVI, Inc., Doylestown, PA; *U.S. Public*, pg. 476
O'Hanlon, Michael A., Pres. & Chief Oper. Officer--DVI Business Credit, Inc., Newport Beach, CA; *U.S. Public*, pg. 476
O'Hara, Robert P., Pres.--First National Mortgage Corporation, Glen Burnie, MD; *Int'l*, pg. 64
O'Hare, Richard, Pres.--Todd-AO Video Services, Hollywood, CA; *U.S. Public*, pg. 1619
O'Hare, Thomas, Pres.--Subaru Distributor Corp., Orangeburg, NY; *Int'l*, pg. 523
O'Kane, Colleen, Sr. Principal & Media Dir.--Publicis/Bloom, Dallas, TX; *Int'l*, pg. 469
O'Keefe, Daniel, Pres. & Chief Exec. Officer--Thermotron Industries, Holland, MI; *U.S. Private*, pg. 1136
O'Keeffe, K.J., Pres.--Regent-Sheffield Ltd., New Hyde Park, NY; *Int'l*, pg. 852
O'Keeffe, William F., Pres.--O'Keeffe's, Inc., San Francisco, CA; *U.S. Private*, pg. 813
O'Leary, Dennis P., Chm. Bd. & Pres.--The F.D. Lawrence Electric Co., Cincinnati, OH; *U.S. Private*, pg. 654
O'Leary, Edward T., Pres. & Chief Exec. Officer--First Security Bank of New Mexico, Albuquerque, NM; *U.S. Public*, pg. 637
O'Leary, John, Pres.--Forwest Inc., Houston, TX; *Int'l*, pg. 496
O'Leary, John P., Jr., Chm. Bd., Pres. & Chief Exec. Officer--Tuscarora Incorporated, New Brighton, PA; *U.S. Public*, pg. 1646
O'Leary, Kevin, Pres.--The Learning Co., Inc., Cambridge, MA; *U.S. Public*, pg. 982
O'Leary, Patrick B., Pres.--Landau & Heyman Inc., Chicago, IL; *U.S. Private*, pg. 646
O'Malia, Daniel J., Pres. & Chief Exec. Officer--O'Malia Food Markets Inc., Carmel, IN; *U.S. Private*, pg. 816
O'Malley, Robert, Pres.--MicroAge, Inc., Tempe, AZ; *U.S. Public*, pg. 1104
O'Malley, William, Chm. Bd., Pres. & Chief Oper. Officer--Tidewater Inc., New Orleans, LA; *U.S. Public*, pg. 1608
O'Meara, John, Pres.--Telegenix Inc., Cherry Hill, NJ; *U.S. Private*, pg. 1073
O'Meara, Robert P., Pres. & Chief Exec. Officer--First Midwest Bancorp, Inc., Itasca, IL; *U.S. Public*, pg. 636
O'Neal, Bob H., Pres.--Stewart & Stevenson Services, Inc., Houston, TX; *U.S. Public*, pg. 1517
O'Neil, James P., Pres. & Chief Oper. Officer--Bowne & Co., Inc., New York, NY; *U.S. Public*, pg. 248
O'Neil, R.S., Pres.--DeLeuw, Cather & Company, Memphis, TN; *U.S. Private*, pg. 841
O'Neil, R.S., Pres.--DeLeuw, Cather & Company, San Francisco, CA; *U.S. Private*, pg. 841
O'Neil, R.S., Pres.--DeLeuw Cather & Co., Fairfax, VA; *U.S. Private*, pg. 841
O'Neil, R.S., Pres.--DeLeuw, Cather International Ltd., Abu Dhabi, United Arab Emirates; *U.S. Private*, pg. 842
O'Neil, Robert, Pres.--DeLeuw, Cather & Company, Washington, DC; *U.S. Private*, pg. 841
O'Neil, Robert L., II, Pres.--Ashley International & Paschen, Chicago, IL; *U.S. Private*, pg. 88
O'Neil, W.E., Chm. Bd.--O'Neil Industries Inc., Chicago, IL; *U.S. Private*, pg. 817
O'Neill, Dan, Pres.--Star-Kist Foods Inc., Newport, KY; *U.S. Public*, pg. 805
O'Neill, Dan, Pres.--Star-Kist Foods, Inc., Newport, KY; *U.S.* Public, pg. 806
O'Neill, John, Pres.--Berwick Bay Oil Co. Inc., Morgan City, LA; *U.S. Private*, pg. 138
O'Neill, Joseph, Partner--Messner Vetere Berger McNamee Schmetterer/EURO RSCG, New York, NY; *Int'l*, pg. 602
O'Neill, Kevin B., Pres. & Chief Creative Officer--Warwick Baker O'Neill, New York, NY; *U.S. Private*, pg. 1152
O'Neill, Leo C., Pres. & Chief Ratings Officer--Standard & Poor's Ratings Services, New York, NY; *U.S. Public*, pg. 1071
O'Neill, Stephen, Pres. & Chief Exec. Officer--Alvey Systems, Inc, Saint Louis, MO; *U.S. Private*, pg. 47
O'Neill, Steve, Pres. & Chief Exec. Officer--Pinnacle Automation Inc., Saint Louis, MO; *U.S. Private*, pg. 866
O'Neill, Thomas J., Pres. & Chief Exec. Officer--Parsons Brinckerhoff Inc., New York, NY; *U.S. Private*, pg. 841
O'Rahilly, Patrick J., Pres. & Chief Exec. Officer--Creative Marketing International Corp., West Chicago, IL; *U.S. Private*, pg. 287
O'Reilly, David, Pres. & Chief Exec. Officer--O'Reilly Automotive Inc., Springfield, MO; *U.S. Public*, pg. 1230
O'Reilly, David, Pres.--Hi/LO Automotive, Inc., Houston, TX; *U.S. Public*, pg. 1230
O'Reilly, Jim M., Pres.--Capital Data Systems, Inc., Cary, NC; *U.S. Public*, pg. 347
O'Reilly, Knowlton J., Pres.--Oxford Separates, New York, NY; *U.S. Public*, pg. 1239
O'Reilly, Patricia, Partner--Messner Vetere Berger McNamee Schmetterer/EURO RSCG, New York, NY; *Int'l*, pg. 602
O'Rourke, Bill, Gen. Mgr.--Sani-Mist, Inc., Bala Cynwyd, PA; *U.S. Private*, pg. 965
O'Rourke, Chuck, Pres.--First American Title Insurance Co. of Oregon, Portland, OR; *U.S. Public*, pg. 626
O'Rourke, Gerald J., Pres.--A&A Manufacturing Co., New Berlin, WI; *U.S. Private*, pg. 1
O'Rourke, William F., Pres.--Coca-Cola Bottling Co. of Chicago, Niles, IL; *U.S. Private*, pg. 248
O'Shane, Thomas J., Chm. Bd., Pres. & Chief Exec. Officer--First Western Bancorp, Inc., New Castle, PA; *U.S. Public*, pg. 642
O'Shea, Bill, Pres.--Lucent Technologies, Business Communications Systems Div., Basking Ridge, NJ; *U.S. Public*, pg. 1017
O'Shea, Michael, Pres.--New Century Media, Seattle, WA; *U.S. Private*, pg. 792
O'Shea, Mortimer J., Chm. Bd., Pres. & Chief Exec. Officer--Ramapo Financial Corporation, Wayne, NJ; *U.S. Public*, pg. 1360
O'Sullivan, A.P., Pres.--Morgan Refractories Inc., Canon City, CO; *Int'l*, pg. 893
O'Tool, Michael, Pres. & Chief Exec. Officer--Templeton, Kenly & Co., Inc., Broadview, IL; *U.S. Private*, pg. 1075
O'Toole, M., Pres.--Simon Aerials Inc., Milwaukee, WI; *Int'l*, pg. 1252
O'Toole, Robert J., Chm. Bd., Pres. & Chief Exec. Officer--A.O. Smith Corporation, Milwaukee, WI; *U.S. Public*, pg. 1476
O'Toole, Timothy T., Pres.--The St. Lawrence & Adirondack Railway Co., Philadelphia, PA; *U.S. Public*, pg. 432
Oakerson, William, Pres. & Chief Oper. Officer--Boat America Corp., Alexandria, VA; *U.S. Private*, pg. 153
Oakes, Eric J., Pres. & Chief Oper. Officer--Foster Wheeler Energy International, Inc., Clinton, NJ; *U.S. Public*, pg. 676
Oakes, Gary E., Pres., Chief Exec. & Oper. Officer--American Precast Concrete, Inc., Indianapolis, IN; *U.S. Private*, pg. 60
Oakley, Dennis, Pres. & Gen. Mgr.--Bruce Oakley, Inc., North Little Rock, AR; *U.S. Private*, pg. 809
Oaks, J.G., Pres.--CRC Properties, Inc., Philadelphia, PA; *U.S. Public*, pg. 432
Oates, James G., Pres.--Leo Burnett Company, Inc., Chicago, IL; *U.S. Private*, pg. 183
Oatway, Francis C., Pres. & Chief Exec. Officer--Hargro Enterprises, Inc., Stamford, CT; *U.S. Private*, pg. 502
Obara, Hiroshi, Pres.--SpeedFam Co Ltd., Ayase, Japan; *U.S. Public*, pg. 1498
Oben, Walter J., Jr., Chm. Bd., Pres., Treas. & Sec.--Southgate Ford Inc., Southgate, MI; *U.S. Private*, pg. 1018
Oberly, K.E., Pres.--Fluid Conservation Systems Inc., Milford, OH; *Int'l*, pg. 590
Obermayer, William G., Pres.--Sprint North Supply, New Century, KS; *U.S. Public*, pg. 1501
Obermeyer, James R., Pres.--Geo-Con, Inc., Voorhees, NJ; *U.S. Public*, pg. 1657
Obermeyer, James R., Pres.--Geo-Con, Inc., Rancho Cordova, CA; *U.S. Public*, pg. 1657
Obermeyer, James R., Pres.--Geo-Con, Inc., Denver, CO; *U.S. Public*, pg. 1657
Obermeyer, Klaus, Pres.--Sport Obermeyer Ltd., USA, Aspen, CO; *U.S. Private*, pg. 1026
Obert, Mark J., Pres.--General Automotive Corporation, Ann Arbor, MI; *U.S. Private*, pg. 443
Obert, Mark J., Pres. & Chief Oper. Officer--ASIA flxible Automotive Tech. Corp., Ann Arbor, MI; *U.S. Private*, pg. 444
Oberting, V.A., Jr., Pres.--Interstate Commodities Inc., Troy, NY; *U.S. Private*, pg. 573
Obokata, H., Pres.--Cosmo Oil of U.S.A. Inc., New York, NY; *Int'l*, pg. 335

Ochiltree, Jock, Pres. & Chief Oper. Officer--Information Storage Devices, San Jose, CA; *U.S. Public*, pg. 876

Ochylski, Daniel, Pres.--The Iowa Packing Co., Des Moines, IA; *U.S. Private*, pg. 575

Ockels, Theodore S., Pres., Chief Exec. Officer, Chief Fin. Officer & Treas.--Up-Right Work Platforms Division, Selma, CA; *U.S. Private*, pg. 1128

Odawara, Yoshiki, Pres.--Fuji Bank (Schweiz) AG, Zurich, Switzerland; *Int'l*, pg. 521

Oddaker, Oddbjorn, Pres.--J.L. Tiedemanns Tobaksfabrik, Oslo, Norway; *Int'l*, pg. 1390

Oddis, Alvo M., Pres. & Chief Exec. Officer--Clayton Group, Inc., Tampa, FL; *U.S. Private*, pg. 244

Odell, Stephen, Pres.--Sugar Foods Corp, New York, NY; *U.S. Private*, pg. 1049

Oden, Clyde W., Dr., Pres. & Chief Exec. Officer--UHP Healthcare, Inglewood, CA; *U.S. Private*, pg. 1113

Oden, D. Keith, Pres. & Chief Oper. Officer--Camden Property Trust, Houston, TX; *U.S. Public*, pg. 298

Odio, Carlos E., Pres.--Gumaco Industria E Comercio Ltda., Sao Paulo, Brazil; *U.S. Public*, pg. 705

Odiotti, Massie, V.P. & Gen. Mgr.--Sun Chemical General Printing Inc., Northlake, IL; *Int'l*, pg. 370

Odom, F.A., Pres. & Chief Exec. Officer--United States National Bank, Galveston, TX; *U.S. Public*, pg. 467

Odom, Howard, Pres. & Chief Exec. Officer--Ortronics, Inc., Pawcatuck, CT; *Int'l*, pg. 806

Odom, John P., Co-Chm. Bd., Pres. & Chief Exec. Officer--The Odom Corporation, Seattle, WA; *U.S. Private*, pg. 811

Odum, John, Pres.--Six Flags St. Louis, Eureka, MO; *U.S. Public*, pg. 1612

Odum, Kathleen O'Neil, Pres.--GTE Northwest Incorporated, Irving, TX; *U.S. Public*, pg. 697

Oean, Kirk, Pres.--Norwest Bank Minnesota Southwest, N.A., Marshall, MN; *U.S. Public*, pg. 1202

Oechsle, Vernon E., Pres. & Chief Exec. Officer--Quanex Corporation, Houston, TX; *U.S. Public*, pg. 1349

Oehlke, Jack W., Pres. & Chief Exec. Officer--Key Tronic Corporation, Spokane, WA; *U.S. Public*, pg. 953

Oelbaum, Harold, Pres.--Kane-Miller Corp., Tarrytown, NY; *U.S. Private*, pg. 607

Oeltjen, Ed. J., Pres.--Consolidated Metco, Inc., Portland, OR; *U.S. Public*, pg. 1710

Oess, George, Pres.--Cadaco, Chicago, IL; *U.S. Private*, pg. 910

Off, George W., Pres. & Chief Exec. Officer--Catalina Marketing Corporation, Saint Petersburg, FL; *U.S. Public*, *pg. 314*

Offergeld, Egon, Pres.--VITS Maschinenbau GmbH, Lagenfeld, Germany; *Int'l*, pg. 399

Officer, J. David, Pres.--Boston Safe Deposit & Trust Co., Boston, MA; *U.S. Public*, pg. 1085

Officer, Ronald, Pres.--Creative Group Inc., Appleton, WI; *U.S. Private*, pg. 287

Offit, Ronald D., Pres.--R.D. Offit Company, Fargo, ND; *U.S. Private*, pg. 812

Offray, Claude, Jr., Pres. & Chief Exec. Officer--C.M. Offray & Son Inc., Chester, NJ; *U.S. Private*, pg. 812

Ogasawara, Hideo, Deputy Pres.--The Tokai Bank, Limited, Nagoya, Japan; *Int'l*, pg. 1391

Ogasawara, Toshiaki, Chm. Bd. & Pres.--Nifco Inc., Yokohama, Japan; *Int'l*, pg. 928

Ogasawara, Toshiaki, Chm. Bd. & Pres.--Simmons Co. Ltd., Zama, Japan; *Int'l*, pg. 929

Ogata, Keith, Pres., Chief Exec. Officer & Treas.--National Education Credit Corporation, Irvine, CA; *U.S. Public*, pg. 784

Ogawara, Akihiro, Pres.--Earth Environmental Sanitary Service Co., Ltd., Osaka, Japan; *Int'l*, pg. 1013

Ogden, Brad, Jr., Pres.--Bargain Supply Company, Louisville, KY; *U.S. Private*, pg. 116

Ogden, J.H., Jr., Chm. Bd., Pres. & Chief Exec. Officer--Conestoga Corporation, Stamford, CT; *U.S. Private*, pg. 262

Ogden, John C., Pres. & Chief Exec. Officer--Suncor Development Company, Phoenix, AZ; *U.S. Public*, pg. 1298

Oggs, Larry, Pres.--Crown Buick, Inc., Metairie, LA; *U.S. Private*, pg. 292

Ogier, Michael O., Pres. & Chief Exec. Officer--Pioneer Concrete of America, Houston, TX; *Int'l*, pg. 1058

Ogilvie, G., Pres.--Midwesco Filter Resources Inc., Winchester, VA; *U.S. Public*, pg. 1026

Ogilvie, R. M., Pres.--Toromont CAT, Concord, Canada; *Int'l*, pg. 1400

Ogilvie, Robert M., Chm. Bd., Pres. & Chief Exec. Officer--Toromont Industries Ltd., Concord, Canada; *Int'l*, pg. 1400

Ogino, Goro, Pres. & Rep. Dir.--Minebea Co., Ltd., Tokyo, Japan; *Int'l*, pg. 867

Ogiwara, Tatsuro, Pres.--Nikko International Capital Management Co., Ltd., Tokyo, Japan; *Int'l*, pg. 930

Ogiwara, Tsutomu, Pres.--SIA Co., Ltd., Tokyo, Japan; *Int'l*, pg. 1189

Ogren, D. John, Pres.--Production Operators Inc., Houston, TX; *U.S. Public*, pg. 298

Ogren, D. John, Pres.--Production Operators, Inc., Houston, TX; *U.S. Public*, pg. 298

Oh, Dong-Hwee, Pres.--Ssangyong Research Institute, Seoul, Korea; *Int'l*, pg. 1292

Ohama, Fumio, Pres.--Unitika America Corp., New York, NY; *Int'l*, pg. 1444

Ohashi, Atsuo, Pres.--Tokyo Printing Ink Manufacturing Co., Ltd., Tokyo, Japan; *Int'l*, pg. 1394

Ohashi, Susumu, Pres.--Uniden America Corporation, Fort Worth, TX; *Int'l*, pg. 1433

Ohayon, Michel, Pres. & Chief Exec. Officer--VKO, Inc., Taunton, MA; *U.S. Private*, pg. 1130

Ohgusu, Hironobu, Pres.--Cognex K.K., Tokyo, Japan; *U.S. Public*, pg. 394

Ohishi, Masaaki, Pres.--Aichi Steel Works, Ltd., Arao, Japan; *Int'l*, pg. 35

Ohiwa, Toshiaki, Pres.--Falconbridge (Japan) Ltd., Tokyo, Japan; *Int'l*, pg. 434

Ohkuni, Masahiko, Pres.--Oji Paper Co., Ltd., Tokyo, Japan; *Int'l*, pg. 998

Ohlemeyer, K.A., Pres.--Sporlan Valve Company, Washington, MO; *U.S. Private*, pg. 1026

Ohlhues, Robert D., Pres. & Chief Oper. Officer--Associated Commercial Mortgage, Inc., Green Bay, WI; *U.S. Public*, pg. 140

Ohlson, Karl Olof, Pres.--Stora Financial Services, Stockholm, Sweden; *Int'l*, pg. 1303

Ohlsson, Sven, Pres. & Chief Exec. Officer--Scancem AB, Malmo, Sweden; *Int'l*, pg. 1198

Ohmura, K., Pres.--Mitsubishi Fuso Truck of America, Inc., Bridgeport, NJ; *Int'l*, pg. 875

Ohmura, Nobuaki, Pres. & Chief Oper. Officer--Daiwa Securities America Inc., New York, NY; *Int'l*, pg. 375

Ohmura, Nobuaki, Pres.--Daiwa Securities Canada Limited, Toronto, Canada; *Int'l*, pg. 376

Ohnishi, Kenichi, Pres.--Nissho Iwai Korea Corporation, Seoul, Korea; *Int'l*, pg. 948

Ohno, Akira, Chm. Bd. & Pres.--Morinaga Milk Industry Co., Ltd., Tokyo, Japan; *Int'l*, pg. 895

Ohno, Haruo, Pres.--Calsonic Corp., Tokyo, Japan; *Int'l*, pg. 944

Ohno, Shigeru, Pres.--Kyushu Electric Power Co., Inc., Fukuoka, Japan; *Int'l*, pg. 778

Ohsawa, Hidejiro, Pres.--Nippon Oil Company, Limited (NiSSEKI), Tokyo, Japan; *Int'l*, pg. 936

Ohsawa, Shigeru, Pres.--Chuo Senko Advertising Co., Ltd., Tokyo, Japan; *Int'l*, pg. 291

Ohshima, Yasuhiro, Pres.--Plaza Create, Tokyo, Japan; *Int'l*, *pg. 1060*

Ohtsu, Kiyokazu, Pres.--Shizuki Electric Corporation, Nishinomiya, Japan; *Int'l*, pg. 1236

Ohya, Satoru, Pres.--OYO Corporation, Tokyo, Japan; *Int'l*, pg. 1019

Ojanpaa, Paave, Pres.--Schauman Wood Oy, Lahti, Finland; *Int'l*, pg. 1430

Oka, Koji, Pres.--Nomura Tourist Bureau, Inc., Tokyo, Japan; *Int'l*, pg. 956

Oka, Makoto, Pres.--Kenwood Corporation, Tokyo, Japan; *Int'l*, pg. 730

Okabe, Keiichiro, Pres.--Cosmo Oil Co., Ltd., Tokyo, Japan; *Int'l*, pg. 335

Okada, Akishige, Pres.--The Sakura Bank, Limited, Tokyo, Japan; *Int'l*, pg. 1178

Okada, Kazuhiro, Pres.--P.T. Asian Development Securities, Jakarta, Indonesia; *Int'l*, pg. 1517

Okada, Toru, Pres.--Sony Corporation of Panama, Panama, Panama; *Int'l*, pg. 1284

Okado, Hiroshi, Pres.--P.T. Komatsu Indonesia Tbk, Jakarta, Indonesia; *Int'l*, pg. 744

Okagaki, Sam, Pres. & Chief Exec. Officer--Amano Cincinnati, Inc., Roseland, NJ; *Int'l*, pg. 70

Okagawa, Hideki, Pres.--Shanghai Yin Tong Trust Co., Ltd., Shanghai, China; *Int'l*, pg. 1010

Okahashi, Osamu, Pres. & Chief Exec. Officer--The Sumitomo Bank of Canada, Toronto, Canada; *Int'l*, pg. 1310

Okai, M., Pres.--General Sekiyu K.K., Tokyo, Japan; *U.S. Public*, pg. 602

Okamoto, Masahiro, Pres.--Asatsu Europe B.V., Hoofddorp, Netherlands; *Int'l*, pg. 86

Okashige, Tadayoshi, Deputy Pres.--Wako Securities Co., Ltd., Tokyo, Japan; *Int'l*, pg. 1485

Okaya, Tokuichi, Pres.--Okaya & Co. Ltd., Nagoya, Japan; *Int'l*, pg. 999

Okayama, Morio, Pres.--Sumitomo Life America, Inc., New York, NY; *Int'l*, pg. 1315

Okazaki, Mitsuo, Pres.--Sumikin Bussan International Corp. - Los Angeles Branch, Los Angeles, CA; *Int'l*, pg. 1308

Okazaki, Y., Pres. & Chief Exec. Officer--ITOCHU International Inc., New York, NY; *Int'l*, pg. 694

Oken, Brian, Pres.--Holga Inc., Van Nuys, CA; *U.S. Public*, pg. 772

Okoso, Yoshinori, Chm. Bd. & Pres.--Nippon Meat Packers, Inc., Osaka, Japan; *Int'l*, pg. 936

Okubo, T., Sr. Mng. Dir.-Gen. Affairs--The Kyoei Life Insurance Co., Ltd., Tokyo, Japan; *Int'l*, pg. 776

Okuda, Hiroshi, Pres.--Toyota Motor Corporation, Tokyo, Japan; *Int'l*, pg. 1411

Okuda, K., Pres.--Sharp International Finance (U.K.) PLC., Watford, United Kingdom; *Int'l*, pg. 1230

Okuda, Minoru, Pres.--Otsuka Ohmi Ceramics Co., Ltd., Osaka, Japan; *Int'l*, pg. 1013

Okuda, Tadashi, Pres.--The Dai-Ichi Kangyo Bank, Limited, Tokyo, Japan; *Int'l*, pg. 359

Okuda, Takehiko, Pres.--Wuxi Okuda Garment Co. Ltd., Wuxi, China; *Int'l*, pg. 579

Okuda, Yoshinori, Pres.--Nihon Keizai Shimbun America, Inc., New York, NY; *Int'l*, pg. 929

Okudaira, Takamochi, Pres.--Tokai Credit Corporation, Pasadena, CA; *Int'l*, pg. 1391

Okui, Isao, Pres. & Representative Dir.--Sekisui House, Ltd., Osaka, Japan; *Int'l*, pg. 1219

Okumura, Ariyoshi, Pres. & Chief Exec. Officer--IBJ NW Asset Management Co., Ltd., Tokyo, Japan; *Int'l*, pg. 1485

Okumura, Masaya, Pres.--Toshiba International Corporation, Utility Division, San Francisco, CA; *Int'l*, pg. 1405

Okumura, Nelson, Pres.--Valley Isle Produce, V.I.P. Food Service, Kahului, HI; *U.S. Private*, pg. 1132

Okuyama, Carl, Pres. & Chief Exec. Officer--Sure Save Super Market Ltd., Keaau, HI; *U.S. Private*, pg. 1056

Oland, Thomas E., Chm. Bd., Pres., Chief Exec. Officer & Treas.--Techne Corporation, Minneapolis, MN; *U.S. Public*, pg. 1563

Olave, Roberto, Pres. & Gen. Mgr.--Baccardi-Martini Uruguay S.A., Montevideo, Uruguay; *U.S. Private*, pg. 109

Olbers, Klaus, Pres.--Intervet America, Inc., Millsboro, DE; *Int'l*, pg. 48

Olcott, Emery G., Pres. & Chief Exec. Officer--Packard BioScience Company, Meriden, CT; *U.S. Private*, pg. 833

Oldenburg, Wayne C., Pres. & Chief Exec. Officer--The Oldenburg Group Companies, Milwaukee, WI; *U.S. Private*, pg. 814

Oldenburg, Wayne C., Owner--Lake Shore, Inc., Kingsford, MI; *U.S. Private*, pg. 814

Older, Thomas, Pres. & Chief Exec. Officer--Svedala Industri AB, Malmo, Sweden; *Int'l*, pg. 1323

Oldfather, Grayson W., Pres. & Chief Fin. Officer--Tristate Electrical Supply Co., Inc., Hagerstown, MD; *U.S. Private*, pg. 1104

Oldsey, William, Pres.--Prentice Hall Business Publishing, Upper Saddle River, NJ; *U.S. Private*, pg. 778

Olen, Gary, Pres., Chief Exec. Officer--The Sportsman's Guide, Inc., Saint Paul, MN; *U.S. Public*, pg. 1499

Oleson, Douglas E., Dr., Pres. & Chief Exec. Officer--Battelle Memorial Institute, Columbus, OH; *U.S. Private*, pg. 123

Oliana, P.L., Pres.--Orion SpA., Colfosco di Susegana, Italy; *Int'l*, pg. 1432

Olida, Carmine T., Pres. & Chief Exec. Officer--Microtel International Inc., Ontario, CA; *U.S. Public*, pg. 1108

Oliel, Claude, Pres.--Colrado, Boulogne, France; *Int'l*, pg. 601

Olinde, J. Beauregard, Pres.--Olinde Hardware & Supply Co., Baton Rouge, LA; *U.S. Private*, pg. 814

Oliva, Jean-Pierre, Pres.--Nordlys SA, Bailleul, France; *Int'l*, pg. 415

Oliver, Aloysius J., Pres. & Chief Exec. Officer--Chemical Financial Corporation, Midland, MI; *U.S. Public*, pg. 345

Oliver, Aloysius J., Pres. & Treas.--CFC Data Corp., Midland, MI; *U.S. Public*, pg. 345

Oliver, David R., Pres.--F-P Electronics, Mississauga, Canada; *U.S. Public*, pg. 1045

Oliver, Gene, Pres. & Chief Exec. Officer--SouthTrust Bank, West Florida, Saint Petersburg, FL; *U.S. Public*, pg. 1492

Oliver, Heath, Pres.--Bardons & Oliver, Inc., Solon, OH; *U.S. Private*, pg. 116

Oliver, Juan Tesoro, Pres.--AHM ALTOS HORNOS DEL MEDITERRANEO, S.A., Sagunto, Spain; *Int'l*, pg. 1223

Oliver, Luis Puig, Pres. & Dir.--Vicente Puig Oliver S.A., Crevillente, Spain; *Int'l*, pg. 1001

Oliver, Robert W., Pres.--Tesoro Exploration & Production Co., San Antonio, TX; *U.S. Public*, pg. 1582

Oliveras, Ramon Pinto, Pres.--CESA - Compania Espanola de Sistemas Aeronauticos, S.A., Getafe, Spain; *Int'l*, pg. 1224

Oliveres, Michel, Pres.--Dumez-Jaya Sdn Bhd, Kuala Lumpur, Malaysia; *Int'l*, pg. 823

Oliveri, Joseph F., Pres.--Interface Electronics Corporation, Hopkinton, MA; *U.S. Private*, pg. 567

Olivieri, Ian, Pres.--NS Komatsu Pty., Ltd., Fairfield, Australia; *Int'l*, pg. 745

Olivieri, Peter, Pres.--Olivieri Foods, Vancouver, Canada; *Int'l*, pg. 841

Olivieri, Rene, Mng. Dir.--Blackwell Publishers Ltd., Oxford, United Kingdom; *Int'l*, pg. 197

Ollila, Jorma, Pres., Chief Exec. Officer & Chm.-Grp. Exec. Bd.--Oy Nokia Ab/Nokia Group, Helsinki, Finland; *Int'l*, pg. 951

Ollinger, R.J., Pres.--Harris Ford, Inc., Lynnwood, WA; *U.S. Private*, pg. 506

Olofsson, Bengt, Pres.--NCC Sundsvall, Sundsvall, Sweden; *Int'l*, pg. 899

Olofsson, Gunnar, Pres.--Strabruken AB, Sollentuna, Sweden; *Int'l*, pg. 899

Olsea, Lawrence T., Pres.--Cowles Syndicate, Inc., New York, NY; *U.S. Private*, pg. 518

Olsen, Donald, Pres. & Chief Exec. Officer--United States Ceramic Tile Co., East Sparta, OH; *U.S. Private*, pg. 1124

Olsen, Richard, Pres.--Custom Pak, Inc., Clinton, IA; *U.S. Private*, pg. 298

Olsen, Richard J., Pres.--Candela Skin Care Centers, Inc., Boston, MA; *U.S. Public*, pg. 300

Olsen, Rick, Pres.--C & J Clark America, Inc., Kennett Square, PA; *Int'l*, pg. 297

Olsen, Torben, Pres.--MD Foods Deutschland GmbH, Dusseldorf, Germany; *Int'l*, pg. 826

Olsman, Robert C., Pres. & Chief Oper. Officer--Reliance Insurance Company, Philadelphia, PA; *U.S. Public*, pg. 1374

Olson, Archie, Pres.--Juno, Inc., Plymouth, MN; *U.S. Private*, *pg. 290*

Olson, Arthur L., Pres. & Chief Oper. Officer--R.L. Polk & Co., Southfield, MI; *U.S. Private*, pg. 874

Olson, B.L., Pres.--Salem Furnace Co., Carnegie, PA; *U.S. Private*, pg. 961

Olson, B.L., Pres.--Salem Erectors, Carnegie, PA; *U.S. Private*, pg. 961

Olson, Barclay, Pres.--Greenlee Textron, Rockford, IL; *U.S. Public*, pg. 1589

Olson, Bruce J., Pres.--Marcus Theatres Corp., Milwaukee, WI; *U.S. Public*, pg. 1044

Olson, Dale E., Pres.--Citizens Insurance of Evansville, Evansville, IN; *U.S. Public*, pg. 280

Olson, Eric, Pres.--VASA Brougher, Inc., Indianapolis, IN; *Int'l*, pg. 464

Olson, James N., Pres.--Rockford Acromatic Product Co., Rockford, IL; *U.S. Private*, pg. 938

Olson, Kenneth E., Chm. Bd., Pres. & Chief Exec. Officer--Proxima Corporation, San Diego, CA; *U.S. Public*, pg. 1339

Olson, Mary, Pres.--ABP Interactive LLC, New York, NY; *U.S. Private*, pg. 17

Olson, Matt, Product Mgr.--Faultless Nutting, Watertown, SD; *Int'l*, pg. 473

Olson, Paul M., Pres. & Chief Exec. Officer--Cable Design Technologies Corporation, Pittsburgh, PA; *U.S. Public*, pg. 287

Olson, Ralph J., Chm. Bd., Pres. & Chief Exec. Officer--R.A. Jones & Co. Inc., Covington, KY; *U.S. Private*, pg. 597

Olson, Ronald G., Pres. & Chief Exec. Officer--Grow Biz International, Inc., Minneapolis, MN; *U.S. Public*, pg. 767
Olson, Ronald G., Pres. & Chief Exec. Officer--Grow Biz Games, Inc., Minneapolis, MN; *U.S. Public*, pg. 767
Olson, Sherman V., Pres. & Treas.--Danafilms, Inc., Westborough, MA; *U.S. Private*, pg. 309
Olson, Tom, Pres. & Chief Exec. Officer--Katz Media Group, Inc., New York, NY; *U.S. Public*, pg. 335
Olsrud, Sherman, Pres.--Sherms Thunderbird Market, Medford, OR; *U.S. Private*, pg. 993
Olsson, Bjorn E., Pres. & Chief Exec. Officer--Harmon Industries, Inc., Blue Springs, MO; *U.S. Public*, pg. 788
Olsson, Hans-Olof, Pres.--Stockholm Regional Office, Kista, Sweden; *Int'l*, pg. 899
Olsson, Sven-Erik, Pres.--Kvaerner Pulping Pte. Ltd., San Centre, Singapore; *Int'l*, pg. 768
Olsten, Stuart, Vice Chm. & Pres.--Olsten Corporation, Melville, NY; *U.S. Public*, pg. 1220
Oltmans, Joseph O., II, Pres. & Chief Fin. Officer--Oltmans Construction Company, Whittier, CA; *U.S. Private*, pg. 815
Olvey, Daniel R., Pres. & Chief Exec. Officer--Wausau-Mosinee Paper Corporation, Mosinee, WI; *U.S. Public*, pg. 1747
Oman, Larry, V.P.-Opers.--Eaton Corporation, Engine Components Division, Marshall, MI; *U.S. Public*, pg. 556
Oman, Norma J., Pres. & Chief Exec. Officer--Meridian Insurance Group, Inc., Indianapolis, IN; *U.S. Public*, pg. 1095
Oman, Norma J., Pres. & Cheif Exec. Officer--Meridian Security Insurance Company, Indianapolis, IN; *U.S. Public*, pg. 1095
Omano, Julio Gavito, Pres.--Barreras Hijos De J. Barreras, S.A., Vigo, Spain; *Int'l*, pg. 1223
Omreng, Bjorn H., Pres.--Kvaerner Hydro Power, Inc., Stamford, CT; *Int'l*, pg. 770
Omreng, Bjorn H., Pres.--Kvaerner Energy Development, Inc., Stamford, CT; *Int'l*, pg. 770
Omreng, Bjorn H., Pres.--Kvaerner Inc., New York, NY; *Int'l*, *pg. 770*
Onaran, Ohran, Pres.--EROL'S Internet, Springfield, VA; *U.S. Private*, pg. 382
Onda, Tsuneo, Pres. & Chief Exec. Officer--Sumitomo Bank of California, San Francisco, CA; *Int'l*, pg. 1309
Onderick, Michael, Pres.--John Zink Co., Tulsa, OK; *U.S. Private*, pg. 628
Onishi, Susumu, Pres.--Excerpta Medica Limited-Japan, Tokyo, Japan; *Int'l*, pg. 1099
Onn, D., Pres.--Israel Aircraft Industries International Inc., New York, NY; *Int'l*, pg. 690
Ono, Keiichiro, Pres.--Yokogawa-Kitz-Valtek Corp. (Y-K-V), Tokyo, Japan; *U.S. Public*, pg. 659
Onoda, Masayoshi, Pres. & Chief Oper. Officer--Yamanouchi Pharmaceutical Co. Ltd., Tokyo, Japan; *Int'l*, pg. 1518
Onodera, J., Pres.--Toko America, Inc., Mount Prospect, IL; *Int'l*, pg. 1393
Onoe, Hisao, Pres.--Glory Ltd., Himeji, Japan; *Int'l*, pg. 554
Onogi, Katsunobu, Pres.--The Long-Term Credit Bank of Japan, Limited, Tokyo, Japan; *Int'l*, pg. 815
Onopa, Ronald F., Pres.--Port City Electrical Supply, Inc., Orlando, FL; *U.S. Public*, pg. 847
Onose, Tadashi, Pres.--Hitachi Koki Co., Ltd., Tokyo, Japan; *Int'l*, pg. 620
Onstead, R. Randall, Jr., Pres. & Chief Exec. Officer--Randalls Food Markets, Inc., Houston, TX; *U.S. Private*, pg. 909
Onzik, John, Pres. & Chief Exec. Officer--Dickten & Masch Manufacturing Co., Nashotah, WI; *U.S. Private*, pg. 331
Ooka, Tadahisa, Pres.--Sumitomo Chemical Agro Europe S.A., Saint Dizier, France; *Int'l*, pg. 1311
Ophey, Lothar, Dr. Ing., Pres.--Traub Drehmaschinen GmbH, Reichenbach, Germany; *Int'l*, pg. 1419
Opler, Edmond, Jr., Chm. Bd., Pres. & Chief Exec. Officer--World's Finest Chocolate, Inc., Chicago, IL; *U.S. Private*, *pg. 1191*
Oppegaard, Grant E., Pres. & Chief Exec. Officer--Genmar Holdings, Inc., Minneapolis, MN; *U.S. Private*, pg. 447
Oppegard, Mark, Pres.--Nebraska Book Co., Inc., Lincoln, NE; *U.S. Private*, pg. 789
Oppliger, Gerald T., Pres.--Lockheed Space Operations Co., Titusville, FL; *U.S. Public*, pg. 1009
Oram, John, Pres.--ICC Industries, Inc., New York, NY; *U.S. Private*, pg. 553
Orban, J., Pres.--Distribution Control Systems, Inc. (DCS), Hazelwood, MO; *U.S. Public*, pg. 546
Orden, Ted, Chm. Bd. & Pres.--Thrifty Oil Co., Santa Fe Springs, CA; *U.S. Private*, pg. 1084
Ordre, Michael, Pres. & Gen. Mgr.--New York Revenue Automation, New York, NY; *U.S. Public*, pg. 466
Ordway, Peter S., Chm. Bd., Pres. & Chief Exec. Officer--Union Pump Company, Battle Creek, MI; *U.S. Private*, pg. 1119
Orem, Nick, Pres.--Logic Associates, Inc., White River Junction, VT; *U.S. Private*, pg. 673
Oren, Doandl G., Pres.--Dart Transit Company, Eagan, MN; *U.S. Private*, pg. 311
Orenstein, Robert S., Pres.--International Wine Accessories, Inc., Dallas, TX; *U.S. Private*, pg. 572
Orfao, David, Pres. & Chief Exec. Officer--Allaire Corporation, Cambridge, MA; *U.S. Private*, pg. 36
Orfinik, Michael H., Pres.--Melnor Inc., Winchester, VA; *U.S. Public*, pg. 1234
Orgera, George, Pres.--Diamond P Sports, Saint Petersburg, FL; *U.S. Private*, pg. 544
Orito, Yusuke, Pres.--Toray Deutschland GmbH, Frankfurt/Main, Germany; *Int'l*, pg. 1400
Orlandini, Andrea, Pres.--Nikko Italia Societa Di Intermediazione Mobilare S.p.A., Milan, Italy; *Int'l*, pg. 931
Orlich, Robert F., Pres. & Chief Exec. Officer--Transatlantic Holdings Inc., New York, NY; *U.S. Public*, pg. 84
Orlick, Arnie, Pres.--Rich's/Lazarus/Goldsmith's, Atlanta, GA; *U.S. Public*, pg. 618
Orlowski, Henry, Pres. & Chief Exec. Officer--Emtec Products Corporation, Coldwater, MI; *U.S. Public*, pg. 968
Orlowsky, Marty, Pres.--Lorillard Tobacco Company, Greensboro, NC; *U.S. Public*, pg. 1011
Ormond, Paul A., Chm. Bd., Pres. & Chief Exec. Officer--Health Care & Retirement Corporation, Toledo, OH; *U.S. Public*, pg. 801
Orn, Gerald S., Pres., Chief Oper. Officer & Treas.--Central Allied Enterprises, Canton, OH; *U.S. Private*, pg. 222
Oropeza, Frank, Pres.--Transpo Electronics, Inc., Orlando, FL; *U.S. Private*, pg. 1097
Oros, Mike, Pres.--Alford Refrigerated Warehouse, Inc., Dallas, TX; *U.S. Private*, pg. 33
Orr, Brad, Pres.--John Burnham & Co., San Diego, CA; *U.S. Private*, pg. 186
Orr, Bruce, Pres. & Chief Exec. Officer--TLPartnership, Dallas, TX; *U.S. Public*, pg. 1224
Orr, Charles L., Pres. & Chief Exec. Officer--Shaklee Corporation, San Francisco, CA; *Int'l*, pg. 1518
Orr, Clark, Jr., Pres. & Chief Exec. Officer--Orr Safety Company, Louisville, KY; *U.S. Private*, pg. 820
Orr, David, Pres. & Chief Exec. Officer--Alcatel Telecom, Richardson, TX; *Int'l*, pg. 55
Orr, Donald C., Chm. Bd., Pres. & Chief Exec. Officer--Nashville Machine Co. Inc., Nashville, TN; *U.S. Private*, pg. 774
Orr, James F., III, Chm. Bd., Pres. & Chief Exec. Officer--UNUM Corporation, Portland, ME; *U.S. Public*, pg. 1699
Orr, Michael P., Pres.--Farm Plan Corporation, Madison, WI; *U.S. Public*, pg. 492
Orr, W. Gregory, Pres.--Campbell Wells Corporation, Lafayette, LA; *U.S. Public*, pg. 1686
Orrall, Roy E., Chm. Bd. & Pres.--Winthrop Printing Company, Inc., Boston, MA; *U.S. Private*, pg. 1184
Orrgren, Kenneth, Pres.--NCC Building, Goteborg, Sweden; *Int'l*, pg. 898
Orrgren, Kenneth, Pres.--NCC HUS, Goteborg, Sweden; *Int'l*, pg. 899
Orsino, Philip, Pres. & Chief Exec. Officer--Premdor Inc., Mississauga, Canada; *Int'l*, pg. 1066
Orten, Arnfinn, Pres.--Kvaerner Oil & Gas Services, Aberdeen, United Kingdom; *Int'l*, pg. 768
Ortino, Hector R., Pres. & Chief Oper. Officer--Ferro Corporation, Cleveland, OH; *U.S. Public*, pg. 618
Ortiz Salinas, Jorge Eugenio, Pres.--Grupo SYR, S.A. de C.V., Mexico, Mexico; *Int'l*, pg. 576
Ortiz, Edgar, Pres.--Halliburton Energy Services, Houston, TX; *U.S. Public*, pg. 776
Ortiz, Edgar, Pres.--Halliburton Energy Services, Inc., Dallas, TX; *U.S. Public*, pg. 776
Ortiz, Juan Hilario, Pres.--Chr. Hansen de Mexico, S.A. de CV, Mexico, Mexico; *Int'l*, pg. 289
Ortiz, Ramiro, Pres.--SunTrust Bank, Miami, N.A., Miami, FL; *U.S. Public*, pg. 1537
Ortman, Raymond L., Pres.--Kokomo Grain Co., Inc., Kokomo, IN; *U.S. Private*, pg. 631
Ortolani, Timothy S., Chm. Bd., Pres. & Chief Exec. Officer--Carton-Craft Corporation, Buffalo, NY; *U.S. Private*, pg. 217
Ortwein, Hank, Pres.--Allegheny Rail Products, Pittsburgh, PA; *U.S. Public*, pg. 676
Orza, Vincent F., Jr., Chm. Bd., Pres. & Chief Exec. Officer--Eateries, Inc., Oklahoma City, OK; *U.S. Public*, pg. 555
Orza, Vincent F., Jr., Chm. Bd., Pres. & Chief Exec. Officer--Pepperoni Grill, Oklahoma City, OK; *U.S. Public*, pg. 555
Osabe, Bunjiro, Chm. Bd., Pres. & Chief Exec. Officer--Ozeki Corporation, Nishinomiya, Japan; *Int'l*, pg. 1019
Osawa, Mikio, Pres.--Nikkei News Bulletin, Inc., Tokyo, Japan; *Int'l*, pg. 929
Osawa, Tamatsu, Pres.--Daio Paper Corporation, Tokyo, Japan; *Int'l*, pg. 372
Osborn, Michael J., Pres.--Burdines, Miami, FL; *U.S. Public*, pg. 618
Osborne, Burl, Pres.-Publ. Division--A.H. Belo Corporation, Dallas, TX; *U.S. Public*, pg. 209
Osborne, Burl, Publisher & Editor--The Dallas Morning News, Inc., Dallas, TX; *U.S. Public*, pg. 209
Osborne, Charles M., Pres. & Chief Oper. Officer--Graco Inc., Golden Valley, MN; *U.S. Public*, pg. 756
Osborne, Edward, Pres.--AMI Industries, Inc., Colorado Springs, CO; *U.S. Public*, pg. 401
Osborne, Richard C., Chm. Bd., Pres. & Chief Exec. Officer--Scotsman Industries, Inc., Vernon Hills, IL; *U.S. Public*, pg. 1444
Osborne, Richard de J., Chm. Bd., Pres. & Chief Exec. Officer--Asarco Incorporated, New York, NY; *U.S. Public*, *pg. 137*
Osborne, Roger, Pres.--Work 'n Gear, Hyde Park, MA; *U.S. Public*, pg. 168
Osborne, Ronald, Pres. & Chief Exec. Officer--Bell Canada, Montreal, Canada; *Int'l*, pg. 115
Osborne, Tom, Pres.--Grow Group, Inc., Cleveland, OH; *Int'l*, pg. 663
Osbourne, James, Pres. & Chief Exec. Officer--Selectone, Inc., Hayward, CA; *U.S. Private*, pg. 982
Oshima, Terry, Pres.--Kyotaru USA, Hawthorne, CA; *Int'l*, pg. 778
Oshima, Yuji, Pres. & Chief Exec. Officer--Yasuda Mutual Life Insurance Co., Tokyo, Japan; *Int'l*, pg. 1519
Oshio, Mark S., Pres.--Schuman Carriage Company, Honolulu, HI; *Int'l*, pg. 523
Oshio, Takashi, Pres.--Rock of Ages Asia Corp., Osaka, Japan; *U.S. Public*, pg. 1396
Osiek, Ross G., Pres. & Chief Oper. Officer--Nooter Corporation, Saint Louis, MO; *U.S. Private*, pg. 801
Osler, Randy W., Pres.--Carrier Markets, Overland Park, KS; *U.S. Public*, pg. 1500
Osman, Borhanuddin, Mng. Partner & Mng. Dir.--Paragon Communications Sdn. Bhd. (Kuala Lumpur), Kuala Lumpur, Malaysia; *U.S. Private*, pg. 325
Osment, Jim L., Pres. & Chief Exec. Officer--Arrow Automotive Industries, Inc., Framingham, MA; *U.S. Public*, pg. 133
Osmer, Robert H., Pres.--Devoe Coatings Co., Louisville, KY; *Int'l*, pg. 663
Oson, Tom, Pres.-Scherer Financial--Scherer Bros. Lumber Company, Minneapolis, MN; *U.S. Private*, pg. 970
Osorio, Atillo E., Pres.--Carbozulia, S.A., Maracaibo, Venezuela; *Int'l*, pg. 1045
Osouf, Serge, Pres. & Chief Oper. Officer--SCOR, Paris, France; *Int'l*, pg. 1152
Osowski, Tom, Pres. & Chief Oper. Officer--Harrison Paint Corp., Canton, OH; *U.S. Private*, pg. 506
Ostby, Kevin C., Pres.--Davis Paint Company, Kansas City, MO; *U.S. Private*, pg. 315
Osteicher, Victor, Pres.--Mother's Food Products, Newark, NJ; *U.S. Private*, pg. 941
Ostendorf, R.E., Pres.--TRI-GLAS, Daleville, AL; *U.S. Private*, pg. 848
Ostenson, Gunnar, Pres.--Skanska Oresund AB, Malmo, Sweden; *Int'l*, pg. 1261
Oster, Flemming, Pres.--EMTEC Magnetics Nordic A/S, Copenhagen, Denmark; *Int'l*, pg. 743
Ostergard, Tonn, Pres. & Chief Exec. Officer--Crete Carrier Corp., Lincoln, NE; *U.S. Private*, pg. 289
Ostergren, Greg V., Pres. & Chief Exec. Officer--American National General Insurance Company, Springfield, MO; *U.S. Public*, pg. 88
Osterlund, Kaj, Pres.--Oy Lining AB, Vantaa, Finland; *Int'l*, pg. 678
Osterlund, Kaj, Pres.--YTM Industrial Oy, Vantaa, Finland; *Int'l*, pg. 678
Osterman, James S., Pres.--Blount, Inc. Oregon Cutting Systems Division, Portland, OR; *U.S. Public*, pg. 238
Osterman, James S., Pres.--Blount Europe, S.A., Nivelles, Belgium; *U.S. Public*, pg. 238
Osterman, James S., Pres.--Blount Japan Inc., Tokyo, Japan; *U.S. Public*, pg. 239
Osterman, James S., Pres.--Blount Holdings Ltd., Guelph, Canada; *U.S. Public*, pg. 239
Osterman, James S., Pres.--Blount Canada Ltd., Guelph, Canada; *U.S. Public*, pg. 239
Osterman, John C., Pres., Chief Oper. Officer & Treas.--Chicago Rivet & Machine Company, Naperville, IL; *U.S. Public*, pg. 348
Osterneck, Myles, Chm. Bd., Pres. & Treas.--The Osterneck Co. Inc., Lumberton, NC; *U.S. Private*, pg. 821
Ostertag, Bob, Pres.--Michigan Bulb Company, Grand Rapids, MI; *U.S. Private*, pg. 421
Ostertag, Robert A., Jr., Pres. & Chief Exec. Officer--Foster & Gallagher, Inc., Peoria, IL; *U.S. Private*, pg. 420
Ostertag, Ronald A., Pres. & Chief Exec. Officer--General Semiconductor, Inc., Melville, NY; *U.S. Public*, pg. 726
Ostiguy, Michel, Pres.--BOS (Beauchesne Ostiguy & Simard), Montreal, Canada; *U.S. Private*, pg. 1062
Ostin, Gunnar, Pres.--Silja Line AB, Stockholm, Sweden; *Int'l*, pg. 899
Ostlund, Kurt, Pres.--Procordia Food AB, Malmo, Sweden; *Int'l*, pg. 1011
Ostlund, Sture, Pres.--NCC Building - Helsingborg, Helsingborg, Sweden; *Int'l*, pg. 898
Ostrander, Charles, Co-Pres. & Chief Oper. Officer-Slipper Div.--R.G. Barry Corporation, Pickerington, OH; *U.S. Public*, pg. 192
Ostrander, Gregg A., Pres. & Chief Exec. Officer--Michael Foods, Inc., Minneapolis, MN; *U.S. Public*, pg. 1103
Ostroff, Michael I., Dr., Pres. & Chief Exec. Officer--GraphLine Inc., Tamarac, FL; *U.S. Private*, pg. 471
Ostrover, Mitchell, Pres.--American Fabrics Company, New York, NY; *U.S. Private*, pg. 53
Ostrow, Barnet D., Chm. Bd.--LeaRonal, Inc., Freeport, NY; *U.S. Public*, pg. 982
Ostrow, Joel, Pres.--Plej's Linen Supermarket, Rock Hill, SC; *U.S. Private*, pg. 821
Ostrow, Joel J., Pres.--Ostrow Textile Co., Inc., Rock Hill, SC; *U.S. Private*, pg. 821
Ostrow, Ronald F., Pres. & Chief Exec. Officer--LeaRonal, Inc., Freeport, NY; *U.S. Public*, pg. 982
Oswald, John H., Pres.--The Riverside Publishing Co., Chicago, IL; *U.S. Public*, pg. 841
Oswald, Robert, Pres.--Apex Precision Technology Inc., Indianapolis, IN; *U.S. Private*, pg. 77
Oswald, Robert, Chm., Pres. & Chief Exec. Officer--Robert Bosch Corporation, Broadview, IL; *Int'l*, pg. 204
Oswald, Robert, Pres.--Bosch Braking Systems-North America, South Bend, IN; *Int'l*, pg. 204
Oswaldson, Rolf, Pres.--Kvaerner Pulp Equipment AB, Gavle, Sweden; *Int'l*, pg. 768
Osweiler, Stan, Pres.--Yorktown Tool & Die Corporation, Yorktown, IN; *U.S. Private*, pg. 1196
Ota, Hiroji, Pres.--Chubu Electric Power Company, Inc., Nagoya, Japan; *Int'l*, pg. 290
Ota, Tetsuo, Pres.--Quick Corp., Tokyo, Japan; *Int'l*, pg. 929
Ota, Yutaka, Pres.--Zexel Corporation, Tokyo, Japan; *Int'l*, pg. 1528
Otaki, Katsuhiko, Pres. & Chief Oper. Officer--The Industrial Bank of Japan, Limited (Canada), Toronto, Canada; *Int'l*, *pg. 675*
Otaki, Katsuhiko, Pres. & Chief Exec. Officer--The Industrial Bank of Japan (Canada), Toronto, Canada; *Int'l*, pg. 676
Otakie, Daniel A., Chm. Bd., Pres., Chief Exec. Officer & Treas.--Futures Personnel Services, Baltimore, MD; *U.S. Private*, pg. 433
Otero, Richard J., Chm. Bd., Pres. & Chief Exec. Officer--RJO Enterprises, Inc., Lanham, MD; *U.S. Private*, pg. 904
Otin, Rodolfo, Gen. Mgr.--CIBA-GEIGY S.A., Barcelona, Spain; *Int'l*, pg. 979
Ots, Tony, Pres.--Raypak, Inc., Westlake Village, CA; *Int'l*, pg. 1022
Otsuka, Akihiko, Pres.--Otsuka Pharmaceutical Co., Ltd., Tokyo, Japan; *Int'l*, pg. 1013
Otsuka, Akihiko, Pres.--Otsuka Foods Co., Ltd., Osaka, Japan; *Int'l*, pg. 1013
Otsuka, Isao, Pres.--Otsuka Science Co., Ltd., Aichi, Japan; *Int'l*, pg. 1013

Otsuka, Koki, Pres.--Narumi China Corporation, Nagoya, Japan; *Int'l*, pg. 906
Otsuka, Masatomi, Pres.--Earth Chemical Co., Ltd., Tokyo, Japan; *Int'l*, pg. 1013
Otsuka, Masatomi, Pres.--Earth Biochemical Co., Ltd., Tokyo, Japan; *Int'l*, pg. 1013
Otsuka, Soichi, Pres.--The Kyoei Life Insurance Co., Ltd., Tokyo, Japan; *Int'l*, pg. 776
Otsuka, Yuya, Pres.--Otsuka Beverage Co., Ltd., Tokyo, Japan; *Int'l*, pg. 1013
Ott, Robert B., Jr., Pres.--The Hennegan Company, Florence, KY; *U.S. Private*, pg. 522
Ott, Thomas L., Pres.--Palisades Energy Services, Pearl River, NY; *U.S. Public*, pg. 1229
Ott, William, Pres.--Brookhurst, Inc., Compton, CA; *U.S. Private*, pg. 171
Ottaway, James H., Jr., Chm., Pres. & Chief Exec. Officer--Ottaway Newspapers, Inc., Campbell Hall, NY; *U.S. Public*, pg. 525
Otten, Leslie B., Owner & Chief Exec. Officer--Killington Limited, Killington, VT; *U.S. Private*, pg. 61
Otterbeck, Lars, Pres.--Dagab Snabbgross AB, Solna, Sweden; *Int'l*, pg. 708
Ottesen, Gunvald, Pres.--Aker Elektro a.s., Sagvag, Norway; *Int'l*, pg. 41
Ottie, Timothy W., Pres. & Gen. Mgr.--Thermal Transfer Corp., Monroeville, PA; *U.S. Public*, pg. 29
Ottmann, Steve, Pres.--Lettuce Entertain You Enterprises, Inc., Chicago, IL; *U.S. Private*, pg. 661
Otto, Doug, Pres. & Chief Exec. Officer--Deckers Outdoor Corporation, Goleta, CA; *U.S. Public*, pg. 491
Otto, Dr. Michael, Chm.-Exec. Bd. & Pres.--Otto Versand (GmbH & Co.), Hamburg, Germany; *Int'l*, pg. 1014
Otto, Joachim, Pres.--AB Carlsson & Moller, Helsingborg, Sweden; *Int'l*, pg. 678
Otto, Joachim, Pres.--Linatex A/S, Vallensbaek, Denmark; *Int'l*, pg. 678
Otto, Tim, Pres. & Chief Exec. Officer--Sid Harvey Industries, Valley Stream, NY; *U.S. Private*, pg. 998
Oudshoorn, R.H., Pres. & Mng. Dir.--Fredestein Banden, Enschede, Netherlands; *Int'l*, pg. 504
Ouedraogo, Gaspart, Pres.--Banque Internationale du Burkina (BIB), Ouagadougou, Burkina Faso; *Int'l*, pg. 548
Ouellette, Pierre, Principal & Creative Dir.--Karakas, VanSickle, Ouellette Advertising & Public Relations, Portland, OR; *U.S. Private*, pg. 607
Ouf, Hazem, Pres., Chief Exec. Officer & Sr. V.P.--Lyon's Restaurants, Inc., Foster City, CA; *U.S. Private*, pg. 684
Ouimet, Gilles P., Pres. & Chief Oper. Officer--Pratt & Whitney Canada Inc., Longueuil, Canada; *U.S. Public*, pg. 1690
Ouimet, Pierre-Andre, Pres.--E-Z-EM Canada Inc., Anjou, Canada; *U.S. Public*, pg. 540
Ounjian, George E., Pres.--Careers USA Inc., Philadelphia, PA; *U.S. Private*, pg. 209
Oura, Hiroshi, Pres.--Advantest Corporation, Tokyo, Japan; *Int'l*, pg. 25
Ousley, James E., Pres. & Chief Exec. Officer--Control Data Systems, Inc., Arden Hills, MN; *U.S. Public*, pg. 441
Ousseime, Khaled, Chm.--Gefinor S.A. Luxembourg, Luxembourg, Luxembourg; *Int'l*, pg. 542
Oustalet, A.J.M. Butch, Pres.--Butch Oustalet Ford Saab, Inc., Gulfport, MS; *U.S. Private*, pg. 821
Outcalt, Jon H., Pres.--Federal Process Corp., Cleveland, OH; *U.S. Private*, pg. 399
Outlaw, Lanny F., Pres. & Chief Oper. Officer--Western Gas Resources, Inc., Denver, CO; *U.S. Public*, pg. 1758
Overlie, Ola, Pres.--Moxy Trucks AS, Elnesvagen, Norway; *Int'l*, pg. 745
Overstreet, Thomas E, Jr., Sr. Pres.--Overstreet Paving Company, Largo, FL; *U.S. Private*, pg. 823
Overton, David, Chm. Bd., Pres. & Chief Exec. Officer--Cheesecake Factory Incorporated, Calabasas Hills, CA; *U.S. Public*, pg. 343
Ovlisen, Mads, Pres. & Chief Exec. Officer--Novo Nordisk A/S, Bagsvaerd, Denmark; *Int'l*, pg. 987
Ovshinsky, Stanford R., Pres. & Chief Exec. Officer--Energy Conversion Devices, Inc., Troy, MI; *U.S. Public*, pg. 581
Ovshinsky, Stanford R., Pres. & Chief Exec. Officer--United Solar Systems Corp., Troy, MI; *U.S. Public*, pg. 581
Owen-Jones, Lindsay, Chm. Bd. & Chief Exec. Officer--L'Oreal S.A., Clichy, France; *Int'l*, pg. 818
Owen, E.H., Pres.--Baton Rouge Water Works Company, Baton Rouge, LA; *U.S. Private*, pg. 122
Owen, E.H., Pres.--Ascension Water Co., Baton Rouge, LA; *U.S. Private*, pg. 123
Owen, H. Lee, Pres.--Farmers Bank & Trust Co., Madisonville, KY; *U.S. Public*, pg. 1217
Owen, Joe, Pres.--General Parts, Inc., Raleigh, NC; *U.S. Private*, pg. 445
Owen, Mark, Pres., Chief Exec. Officer & Gen. Mgr.--Aero Corporation, Lake City, FL; *U.S. Public*, pg. 1766
Owen, Richard F., Pres.--Central Plains Steel Co., Kansas City, KS; *U.S. Private*, pg. 824
Owen, Richard S., Pres.--Lamons Metal Gasket Co., Houston, TX; *U.S. Public*, pg. 1054
Owen, Robert E., Chm. Bd. & Pres.--Owen Industries, Inc., Carter Lake, IA; *U.S. Private*, pg. 824
Owen, Robert E., Pres. & Mng. Dir.--Paxton & Vierling, Omaha, NE; *U.S. Private*, pg. 824
Owens, Bobby, Pres.-Putt-Putt Golf & Chief Exec. Officer--Putt Putt Golf Courses of America, Inc., Fayetteville, NC; *U.S. Private*, pg. 896
Owens, John, Pres.--The Clarinda Company, Clarinda, IA; *U.S. Private*, pg. 206
Owens, Phil, Pres. & Chief Oper. Officer--Top-Seal Corp., Phoenix, AZ; *U.S. Private*, pg. 1071
Owens, R. Harold, Pres. & Chief Oper. Officer--World Acceptance Corporation, Greenville, SC; *U.S. Public*, pg. 1778
Owens, Stewart K., Pres. & Chief Oper. Officer--Bob Evans Farms, Inc., Columbus, OH; *U.S. Public*, pg. 596
Owens, William, Pres. & Chief Exec. Officer--Recon/Optical, Inc., Barrington, IL; *U.S. Private*, pg. 914
Owens, William A., Vice Chm., Pres. & Chief Oper. Officer--Science Applications International Corp., San Diego, CA; *U.S. Private*, pg. 975
Ownes, David, Pres.--Asia Minerals Corp., Vancouver, Canada; *U.S. Public*, pg. 1411
Owsley, T. Reed, Pres.--Owsley & Sons, Inc., Fort Mill, SC; *U.S. Private*, pg. 824
Oxenberg, Harvey, Pres.--Purity Products Inc., Miami, FL; *U.S. Private*, pg. 896
Oxman, Jeff, Pres.--Career Blazers of Washington, DC, Washington, DC; *U.S. Private*, pg. 209
Oyler, James R., Pres. & Chief Exec. Officer--Evans & Sutherland Computer Corporation, Salt Lake City, UT; *U.S. Public*, pg. 595
Oyster, William, Pres., Chief Oper. Officer & Mgr.-Adv., Sls. & Mktg.--Dallas Gold & Silver Exchange, Inc., Dallas, TX; *U.S. Public*, pg. 478
Ozaki, K., Pres.--Man Nen Sha Inc., Osaka, Japan; *Int'l*, pg. 834
Ozawa, Mitoshi, Pres. & Chief Exec. Officer--Sumitomo Heavy Industries, Ltd., Tokyo, Japan; *Int'l*, pg. 1314
Ozawa, Mitsuru, Pres.--Grand Hyatt Seoul, Seoul, Korea; *U.S. Private*, pg. 551
Ozbirn, W.P., Pres.--Hobbs Corporation, Springfield, IL; *Int'l*, pg. 127
Ozbun, David, Pres.--Citizens Banc Leasing, Louisville, KY; *U.S. Public*, pg. 280
Ozcelik, Vejdi, Pres.--Akcansa, Istanbul, Turkey; *Int'l*, pg. 605
Ozeki, Hiroshi, Pres.--Mazda Research & Development of North America, Inc., Irvine, CA; *Int'l*, pg. 849
Ozeki, Shiro, Co-Pres.--Sanwa Securities (USA) Co., L.P., New York, NY; *Int'l*, pg. 1189
Ozuna, Robert, Pres.--New Bedford Panoramex Corporation, Upland, CA; *U.S. Private*, pg. 792
Ozur, Mark, Pres.--Digital Sound Corporation, Carpinteria, CA; *U.S. Public*, pg. 508
Paananen, Leena, Mng. Dir.--Oy Dagmar Ab, Helsinki, Finland; *Int'l*, pg. 359
Paass, K., Pres.--BIAO Togo, Lome, Togo; *Int'l*, pg. 547
Pace, John, Creative Partner--Bull Calvert Pace, Cape Town, South Africa; *U.S. Private*, pg. 678
Pace, Robert, Owner--Maritime Broadcasting System Ltd., Halifax, Canada; *Int'l*, pg. 842
Pacer, Thomas H., Chm. Bd., Pres. & Chief Exec. Officer--First Union National Bank of Georgia, Atlanta, GA; *U.S. Public*, pg. 640
Pachl, Rudy, Pres.--Barry Callebaut, Saint Albans, VT; *Int'l*, pg. 252
Pacholder, Sylvia A., Pres. & Chief Exec. Officer--ICO, Inc., Houston, TX; *U.S. Public*, pg. 853
Pacholder, Sylvia A., Pres.--Wedco Technology, Bloomsbury, NJ; *U.S. Public*, pg. 854
Pachulski, Phil, Pres.--Prime Technology Imports, Ltd., Grand Rapids, MI; *U.S. Private*, pg. 884
Pacifico, Joe David, Pres.--Pacifico Auto Group, Philadelphia, PA; *U.S. Private*, pg. 832
Packard Thomas M., Pres. & Chief Exec. Officer--Land O'Lakes Fluid Dairy Division, Arden Hills, MN; *U.S. Private*, pg. 646
Packard, James, Chm. Bd., Pres. & Chief Exec. Officer--National Twist Drill Div., South Beloit, IL; *U.S. Public*, pg. 1370
Packard, James L., Chm. Bd., Pres. & Chief Exec. Officer--Regal-Beloit Corporation, Beloit, WI; *U.S. Public*, pg. 1370
Packard, John T., Pres.--Montgomery St. Income Securities, Inc., San Francisco, CA; *U.S. Public*, pg. 1127
Packer, Clyde, Pres.--USA Vacuum Ind. Inc. LLC, Saint James, MO; *U.S. Private*, pg. 1067
Packer, Daniel F., Pres.--Entergy New Orleans, Inc., New Orleans, LA; *U.S. Public*, pg. 586
Packer, Richard A., Pres.--Zoll Medical Corporation, Burlington, MA; *U.S. Private*, pg. 1207
Packham, William D., Pres.--Midland Walwyn Capital Inc., Toronto, Canada; *Int'l*, pg. 865
Padden, Preston, Pres.--ABC Television Network Group, New York, NY; *U.S. Public*, pg. 511
Paddock, James S., Pres. & Chief Exec. Officer--Titanium Industries, Inc., Morristown, NJ; *U.S. Public*, pg. 43
Paddock, M. David, Chm. Bd., Pres., Chief Exec. & Oper. Officer--Peoples National Bank, Lawrenceville, IL; *U.S. Public*, pg. 1217
Paddon, Patrick E., Chm. Bd., Pres. & Chief Exec. Officer--Amplicon, Inc., Santa Ana, CA; *U.S. Public*, pg. 104
Padewer, Harvey, Pres.--Aquila Energy Corp., Omaha, NE; *U.S. Public*, pg. 1701
Padnos, Jeffrey S., Pres. & Chief Oper. Officer--Louis Padnos Iron & Metal Co., Holland, MI; *U.S. Private*, pg. 834
Paetzold, David, Pres. & Chief Exec. Officer--SouthTrust Bank, Southwest Florida, Fort Myers, FL; *U.S. Public*, pg. 1492
Paffenholz, Heinz-Peter, Pres.--CEAG Sicherheitstechnik GmbH, Soest, Germany; *U.S. Public*, pg. 444
Pagan, Efren, Pres. & Gen. Mgr.--Leo Burnett Inc., Hato Rey, PR; *U.S. Private*, pg. 185
Pagano, Philip A., Exec. Dir.--Metra Commuter Rail, Chicago, IL; *U.S. Private*, pg. 919
Pagano, Vince, Pres.--Hygrade Metal Moulding Mfg. Corp., Bethlehem, PA; *U.S. Private*, pg. 552
Page, Fred, Pres.--ConAgra Grain Companies, Minneapolis, MN; *U.S. Public*, pg. 426
Page, Richard, Pres. & Chief Exec. Officer--Grand Holdings, Inc., Edina, MN; *U.S. Private*, pg. 468
Page, Robert B., Pres. & Chief Exec. Officer--Romacorp, Inc., Dallas, TX; *U.S. Public*, pg. 1147
Page, Robert L., Pres. & Chief Exec. Officer--Replacements, Ltd., Mc Leansville, NC; *U.S. Private*, pg. 923
Page, Roger B., Chm. Bd., Pres., Chief Exec. Officer & Fin. Officer--Pace Oil Co., Inc., Winston Salem, NC; *U.S. Private*, pg. 829
Page, Steve, Pres.--Sears Point Raceway, Sonoma, CA; *U.S. Public*, pg. 1498
Pagels, George, Pres.--Baumgarten Stamp Co., Baltimore, MD; *U.S. Private*, pg. 58
Paherson, Henry F., Pres.--E'town Properties Inc., Westfield, NJ; *U.S. Public*, pg. 540
Pahidis, Peter, Pres. & Chief Exec. Officer--Cedar Farms Company, Inc., Philadelphia, PA; *U.S. Private*, pg. 221
Pahl, Greg, Pres.--J.H. Larson Electrical Company, Golden Valley, MN; *U.S. Private*, pg. 652
Pahwa, Lalit K., Pres.--Webb India Ltd., Bangalore, India; *U.S. Private*, pg. 1157
Paicu, G.N., Pres.--Frontec Corporation, Edmonton, Canada; *Int'l*, pg. 95
Paidas, George P., Pres. & Chief Exec. Officer--The Old Phoenix National Bank of Medina, Medina, OH; *U.S. Public*, pg. 646
Paige, Richard, Pres.--PRO Group, Inc., Englewood, CO; *U.S. Private*, pg. 887
Paisley, Wes, Pres.--Mid-West Conveyor Co., Inc., Kansas City, KS; *Int'l*, pg. 1398
Paisner, Bruce L., Pres.--Hearst Entertainment, New York, NY; *U.S. Private*, pg. 516
Pajak, Andrew P., Pres. & Chief Oper. Officer--GZA GeoEnvironmental, Inc., Newton, MA; *U.S. Public*, pg. 697
Pajak, Andrewd P., Pres. & Chief Exec. Officer--GZA GeoEnvironmental Technologies, Inc., Newton, MA; *U.S. Public*, pg. 697
Pajak, John J., Pres. & Chief Oper. Officer--Massachusetts Mutual Life Insurance Co., Springfield, MA; *U.S. Private*, pg. 712
Pajak, Stanislaw, Pres.--Pol Krusz S.A., Warsaw, Poland; *Int'l*, pg. 1200
Pajk, Anthony, Pres.--Branson Ultrasonics Corp.-Plastics Joining Div., Danbury, CT; *U.S. Public*, pg. 574
Pajoharju, Tapio, Pres.--Leaf Poland Sp.z.o.o, Legionowo, Poland; *Int'l*, pg. 638
Pak, Kua Hong, Pres. & Chief Exec. Officer--Times Publishing Limited, Singapore, Singapore; *Int'l*, pg. 1390
Palacio, Enrique, Pres.--Juan Minetti S.A., Cordoba, Argentina; *Int'l*, pg. 869
Palagonia, Joseph P., Pres.--J.M.P. Bakery Co., Inc., Brooklyn, NY; *U.S. Private*, pg. 578
Palan, Robert, Pres.--King Louie International, Grandview, MO; *U.S. Private*, pg. 621
Palavidis, Manos, Vice Chm., Mng. Dir., Creative Dir. & New Bus. Contact--EURO RSCG, Maroussi, Greece; *Int'l*, pg. 602
Palazzo, Phil, Pres.-Intl. Opers.--Ammirati Puris Lintas Worldwide, New York, NY; *U.S. Public*, pg. 908
Palazzo, Richard, Pres.--Con-Way Central Express, Inc., Ann Arbor, MI; *U.S. Public*, pg. 281
Paleologos, Nicholas G., Pres.--Miller & Long Co. Inc., Bethesda, MD; *U.S. Private*, pg. 746
Palermo, John P., Pres. & Chief Exec. Officer--Victor Corporation, West Warwick, RI; *U.S. Private*, pg. 1138
Paley, Douglas, Pres.--The Texwipe Co., Inc., Upper Saddle River, NJ; *U.S. Private*, pg. 1079
Palhares, Antonio Joaquim P.C., Pres.--Apolo Produtos de Aco S.A., Rio de Janeiro, Brazil; *Int'l*, pg. 78
Palieri, Raffaele, Pres.--ANIE-Associazione Nazionale Industrie Elettrotecniche ed Elettroniche, Milan, Italy; *Int'l*, pg. 16
Palk, Eun Hak, Pres. & Chief Exec. Officer--California Cho Hung Bank, Los Angeles, CA; *Int'l*, pg. 287
Palk, Roy, Pres. & Chief Exec. Officer--East Kentucky Power Co-op, Winchester, KY; *U.S. Private*, pg. 356
Palko, George, Pres.--Great Lakes Construction Co., Independence, OH; *U.S. Private*, pg. 474
Palko, Lorri, Pres.--Dorsey Trailers, Inc., Elba, AL; *U.S. Public*, pg. 520
Palko, Lorri M., Pres. & Chief Oper. Officer--Dorsey Trailers, Inc., Atlanta, GA; *U.S. Public*, pg. 520
Pallak, Hal, Pres.--Harte Hanks Shoppers, Redwood City, CA; *U.S. Public*, pg. 794
Palm, John, Pres.--Gannett New Media, Arlington, VA; *U.S. Public*, pg. 699
Palm, Lars, Pres.--NCC Building, Sundsvall, Sweden; *Int'l*, pg. 898
Palmblad, Ulf, Pres.--Skanska Data AB, Danderyd, Sweden; *Int'l*, pg. 1260
Palmer, A. Robert, Chm. Bd., Pres. & Chief Exec. Officer--Eastern Color Printing Company, Avon, CT; *U.S. Private*, pg. 357
Palmer, C. Robert, Chm. Bd., Pres. & Chief Exec. Officer--Rowan Companies, Inc., Houston, TX; *U.S. Public*, pg. 1409
Palmer, C.R., Pres.--RDC Marine, Inc., Houston, TX; *U.S. Public*, pg. 1410
Palmer, David, Pres.--F.T. Publications Inc., New York, NY; *Int'l*, pg. 1026
Palmer, Douglas E., Pres. & Chief Fin. Officer--Terminal Grain Corp., Sioux City, IA; *U.S. Private*, pg. 1077
Palmer, Eldon D., Pres. & Chief Exec. Officer--Kenworth of Indianapolis Inc., Indianapolis, IN; *U.S. Private*, pg. 615
Palmer, Frank, Pres. & Chief Exec. Officer--Palmer Jarvis Communications, Vancouver, Canada; *Int'l*, pg. 1022
Palmer, George R., Pres.--Photon Systems Ltd., Calgary, Canada; *U.S. Public*, pg. 1563
Palmer, Jeffrey W., Pres.--Palmer Moving & Storage Co., Troy, MI; *U.S. Private*, pg. 835
Palmer, R. Jay, Pres.--Old Kent Financial Life Insurance Company, Grand Rapids, MI; *U.S. Public*, pg. 1217
Palmer, Richard M., Jr., Chm. Bd. & Pres.--R.M. Palmer Company, Reading, PA; *U.S. Private*, pg. 835
Palmer, Robert B., Chm. Bd., Pres. & Chief Exec. Officer--Digital Equipment Corporation, Maynard, MA; *U.S. Public*, pg. 507
Palmer, Roger, Pres.--Colloid Environmental Technologies Company (CETCO), Arlington Heights, IL; *U.S. Public*, pg. 64
Palmer, Ron, Pres. & Chief Exec. Officer--Business Air, Grosse Ile, MI; *U.S. Private*, pg. 539

Palmer, Steven L., Pres. & Chief Exec. Officer--Intermountain Farmers Association, Salt Lake City, UT; *U.S. Private*, pg. 568
Palmer, Wayne L., Pres.--Palmer International, Inc., Worcester, PA; *U.S. Private*, pg. 834
Palmieri, Frank, Pres.--The Media & Marketing Group, Cherry Hill, NJ; *U.S. Private*, pg. 902
Palmiero, Robert, Pres.--Southern Apparel Corporation, Largo, FL; *U.S. Private*, pg. 1015
Palmon, Dan, Dr., Pres.--FOCUS2020, Inc., Tenafly, NJ; *U.S. Private*, pg. 415
Palonen, Gary L., Pres. & Chief Oper. Officer--Veridian, Alexandria, VA; *U.S. Private*, pg. 1136
Palonen, Gary L., Pres. & Chief Oper. Officer--Veda International, Inc., Alexandria, VA; *U.S. Private*, pg. 1136
Palovaara, Pekka, Pres.--Valmet Vertrieb Gmbh, Pfungstadt, Germany; *Int'l*, pg. 1448
Palovaara, Pekka, Pres.--Valmet Service GmbH, Pfungstadt, Germany; *Int'l*, pg. 1449
Palsho, Dorothea Coccoli, Pres.--Dow Jones Interactive, Princeton, NJ; *U.S. Public*, pg. 524
Palsho, Dorothea Coccoli, Pres.--Dow Jones Interactive Publishing, Princeton, NJ; *U.S. Public*, pg. 524
Paluch, Brian, Pres. & Gen. Mgr.--Mrs. Alison's Cookie Company, Saint Louis, MO; *U.S. Private*, pg. 765
Pamplin, R.B., Jr., Dr., Pres. & Chief Exec. Officer--K.F. Jacobson Co., Portland, OR; *U.S. Private*, pg. 836
Pamplin, Robert B., Jr., Dr., Pres., Chief Oper. Officer & Sec.--R.B. Pamplin Corp., Portland, OR; *U.S. Private*, pg. 835
Pan, Michael J., Pres. & Chief Oper. Officer--Snyder's Drug Stores, Inc., Minnetonka, MN; *U.S. Private*, pg. 1011
Pan, Peter, Dr., Pres.--Thiele Engineering, Minneapolis, MN; *U.S. Private*, pg. 118
Panagopulos, D., Pres.--Theo Davies Marine Agencies, Inc., Honolulu, HI; *Int'l*, pg. 704
Panas, Louis, Pres.--Ottawa River Steel Co., Toledo, OH; *U.S. Public*, pg. 1095
Panayi, Andreas, Sr. Partner & Intl. Dir.--Poppe Tyson, New York, NY; *U.S. Public*, pg. 1642
Pancio, Alfonso Gomez, Pres. & Chief Exec. Officer--Anchor Glass Container Corporation, Tampa, FL; *Int'l*, pg. 327
Pando, Robert T., Chm. Bd. & Pres.--Lynch Machinery, Inc., Bainbridge, GA; *U.S. Public*, pg. 1022
Pando, Robert T., Pres.--Tri-Can International, Ltd., Alsip, IL; *U.S. Public*, pg. 1022
Panettiere, John M., Pres. & Chief Exec. Officer--Blount International, Inc., Montgomery, AL; *U.S. Public*, pg. 237
Panettiere, John M., Pres. & Chief Exec. Officer--Blount, Inc., Montgomery, AL; *U.S. Public*, pg. 238
Panettiere, John M., Pres.--4520 Corp., Inc., Montgomery, AL; *U.S. Public*, pg. 239
Pangilinan, Manuel V., Chief Exec. Officer & Mng. Dir.--First Pacific Company Limited, Hong Kong, Hong Kong; *Int'l*, pg. 487
Pannell, Derek, Pres. & Chief Exec. Officer--Brunswick Mining & Smelting Corp. Ltd., Bathurst, Canada; *Int'l*, pg. 434
Pantano, Bruce, Pres. & Chief Oper. Officer--Publishers Clearing House, Port Washington, NY; *U.S. Private*, pg. 893
Pantel, Richard, V.P.--Gefinor U.S.A., Inc., New York, NY; *Int'l*, pg. 542
Pantoja, Francisco Botia, Pres.--Central Termica Litoral de Almeria A.I.E., Carboneras, Spain; *Int'l*, pg. 1224
Panton, Keith S., Dr., Pres.--Alcan Jamaica Co., Manchester, Jamaica; *Int'l*, pg. 51
Panzica, Ignatius J., Chm. Bd., Pres. & Chief Exec. Officer--Global Motor Sport Group, Inc., Morgan Hill, CA; *U.S. Public*, pg. 748
Pao, Henry C., Dr., Chm. Bd., Pres. Chief Exec. Officer & Chief Oper. Officer--Supertex, Inc., Sunnyvale, CA; *U.S. Public*, pg. 1539
Paolo, Foraen, Pres.--Arnoldo Mondadori Editore S.p.A., Segrate, Italy; *Int'l*, pg. 887
Papa, Mark G., Pres.-N.A. Opers.--Enron Corp., Houston, TX; *U.S. Public*, pg. 584
Papa, Mark G., Pres.--Enron Oil & Gas Co., Houston, TX; *U.S. Public*, pg. 584
Papadia, Enzo, Pres.--Gedy Iberica, Barcelona, Spain; *Int'l*, pg. 542
Papalia, Anthony C., Pres.--Chefs International, Inc., Point Pleasant Beach, NJ; *U.S. Public*, pg. 343
Papasan, Larry, Pres.--Smith & Nephew Orthopedics, Memphis, TN; *Int'l*, pg. 1263
Pape, John J., Pres.--NorLease, Inc., Chicago, IL; *U.S. Public*, pg. 1196
Papera, Joseph R., Pres.--Allstate Can Corporation, Parsippany, NJ; *U.S. Private*, pg. 44
Papesh, Ron, Pres.--Meco USA Inc., Rock Hill, SC; *Int'l*, pg. 1064
Papesh, Ronald, Pres.--Meco Metal Finishing USA Inc., Rock Hill, SC; *Int'l*, pg. 1064
Papit, Ted J., Pres. & Chief Exec. Officer--Furr's/Bishops, Inc., Lubbock, TX; *U.S. Public*, pg. 689
Papows, Jeffrey, Pres. & Chief Oper. Officer--Lotus Development Corporation, Cambridge, MA; *U.S. Public*, pg. 896
Pappalardo, Frank S., Pres.--TRI-S Incorporated, Ellington, CT; *U.S. Public*, pg. 546
Pappas, M.M., Pres.--Blazer Financial Services, Cordova, TN; *U.S. Public*, pg. 1741
Pappas, Michael, Pres.--The Keyes Company Realtors, Miami, FL; *U.S. Private*, pg. 618
Pappas, Michael M., Pres.--Consumer Finance Group, Tampa, FL; *U.S. Public*, pg. 1741
Pappenthenasi, Arthur J., Pres. & Chief Exec. Officer--Scangas Brothers Holdings, Inc., Lynn, MA; *U.S. Private*, pg. 969
Papson, Hardy, Pres.--PT BHP Steel Indonesia, Cilegon, Indonesia; *Int'l*, pg. 227
Paquette, Dick, Pres.--Air Midwest, Inc., Wichita, KS; *U.S. Public*, pg. 1099
Paquette, M.W., Pres. & Reg. Dir.-Americas--Devro-Teepak, Inc., Westchester, IL; *Int'l*, pg. 408
Para, Dan, Pres.--U.S.S. Seko Worldwide, Elk Grove Village, IL; *U.S. Private*, pg. 1115
Paracchini, Dan, Pres.--Gilmore Envelope Corp., Los Angeles, CA; *U.S. Private*, pg. 454
Pardon, Barry, Pres.--Techdyne, Inc., Hialeah, FL; *U.S. Public*, pg. 1080
Pare, Jean, Pres.--Magazines Maclean Hunter Quebec, Montreal, Canada; *Int'l*, pg. 1123
Paredes, Lombardo, Pres.--CIED Centro Internacional de Educacion y Desarrollo, Caracas, Venezuela; *Int'l*, pg. 1045
Parell, Jeff J., Pres. & Chief Oper. Officer--National Car Rental System, Inc., Minneapolis, MN; *U.S. Public*, pg. 1379
Parent, Calvin L., Pres.--Ross Roy Communications Canada, Limited, Windsor, Canada; *U.S. Private*, pg. 946
Parfet, Martha, Chm. Bd.--Gilmore Bros., Inc., Kalamazoo, MI; *U.S. Private*, pg. 454
Paridy, David, Chm. Bd., Pres. & Chief Exec. Officer--Plews/Edelmann, Buffalo Grove, IL; *Int'l*, pg. 1396
Parise, Andrew J., Pres. & Chief Oper. Officer--Texfi Industries, Inc., Raleigh, NC; *U.S. Public*, pg. 1588
Parise, Thomas, Pres. & Chief Oper. Officer--Inter-Tel, Incorporated, Phoenix, AZ; *U.S. Public*, pg. 888
Parise, Thomas C., Pres.--Inter-Tel Integrated Systems, Inc., Chandler, AZ; *U.S. Public*, pg. 888
Parise, Thomas C., Pres.--Inter-Tel Equipment UK, Ltd., Wellingborough, United Kingdom; *U.S. Public*, pg. 888
Parisi, Joseph, Jr., Pres.--Parisi Inc./Royal Store Fixture, Philadelphia, PA; *U.S. Private*, pg. 839
Park, Byung Jae, Pres.--Hyundai Motor Company, Seoul, Korea; *Int'l*, pg. 641
Park, C.S., Dr., Pres. & Chief Exec. Officer--Maxtor Corporation, Milpitas, CA; *Int'l*, pg. 641
Park, Chung-Il, Pres.--Bum-A Petroleum Co., Ltd., Seoul, Korea; *Int'l*, pg. 1292
Park, J. Leonard, Chm. Bd., Pres., Chief Exec. Officer & Treas.--George W. Park Seed Co., Inc., Greenwood, SC; *U.S. Private*, pg. 839
Park, James C., Pres. & Chief Exec. Officer--Besser Company, Alpena, MI; *U.S. Private*, pg. 139
Park, Je Hyuk, Pres.--KIA Motors Corp., Seoul, Korea; *Int'l*, pg. 732
Park, Raymond, Chm. Bd. & Pres.--Park Corp., Cleveland, OH; *U.S. Private*, pg. 839
Park, S.H., Pres.--Karahm Company Limited, Kyongki, Korea; *Int'l*, pg. 891
Park, Sam Koo, Pres. & Chief Exec. Officer--Asiana Airlines, Los Angeles, CA; *U.S. Private*, pg. 89
Park, Seung-Ki, Pres.--Dongseong Express Tourists Co., Ltd., Busan, Korea; *Int'l*, pg. 1292
Park, Steven, Partner--Dimeling, Schreiber & Park, Philadelphia, PA; *U.S. Private*, pg. 333
Park, Sung-Hoon, Chm. Bd. & Pres.--Jaeneung Education Co., Ltd., Seoul, Korea; *Int'l*, pg. 697
Parker, Barry J.C., Pres. & Chief Exec. Officer--Luby's Cafeterias, Inc., San Antonio, TX; *U.S. Public*, pg. 1017
Parker, Bruce, Pres.--Smith & Nephew Casting, Inc., Charlotte, NC; *Int'l*, pg. 1263
Parker, Daniel, Pres.--Surface Technology Business, East Windsor, CT; *U.S. Public*, pg. 582
Parker, David H., Chm. Bd., Pres. & Chief Exec. Officer--Pelican Products, Torrance, CA; *U.S. Private*, pg. 848
Parker, Don, Pres. & Chief Oper. Officer--Farr Filtration, Ltd., Birmingham, United Kingdom; *U.S. Public*, pg. 614
Parker, Gary D., Chm. Bd. Pres. & Chief Exec. Officier--Lindsay Manufacturing Company, Lindsay, NE; *U.S. Public*, pg. 999
Parker, Melvin C., Chm. Bd., Pres., Chief Exec. Officer, Chief Fin. Officer & Treas.--Investors Insurance Group, Inc., Boca Raton, FL; *U.S. Public*, pg. 911
Parker, Michael D., Pres.--Dow Chemical North America, Midland, MI; *U.S. Public*, pg. 522
Parker, Nancy, Pres.--Winchell's Donut Houses, L.P., Santa Ana, CA; *Int'l*, pg. 1230
Parker, Richard, Pres. & Chief Exec. Officer--Artco-Bell Corporation, Temple, TX; *U.S. Private*, pg. 86
Parker, Richard E., Jr., Pres.--XLM Company, Mount Pleasant, IA; *U.S. Public*, pg. 772
Parker, Robert A., Pres. & Chief Exec. Officer--Regions Bank/Stephens County, Toccoa, GA; *U.S. Public*, pg. 1373
Parker, Robert S., Pres.--Berol Inc., Bellwood, IL; *U.S. Public*, pg. 1177
Parker, Robert S., Pres.--Sanford Corporation, Bellwood, IL; *U.S. Public*, pg. 1178
Parker, Robert S., Pres.--Sanford Beroc Corp., Brentwood, TN; *U.S. Public*, pg. 1178
Parker, Ron, Pres. & Chief Exec. Officer--Hampton Resources Inc., Portland, OR; *U.S. Private*, pg. 498
Parker, Ron, Pres.--MGM Brakes Div., Charlotte, NC; *U.S. Private*, pg. 560
Parker, Ronald I., Chm. Bd., Pres. & Chief Exec. Officer--Indian Head Industries Inc., Charlotte, NC; *U.S. Private*, pg. 559
Parker, Samuel J., Chm. Bd., Pres. & Chief Exec. Officer--PETsMART, Inc., Phoenix, AZ; *U.S. Public*, pg. 1281
Parker, Scott S., Pres. & Chief Exec. Officer--Intermountain Health Care Inc., Salt Lake City, UT; *U.S. Private*, pg. 568
Parker, Todd, Owner--Continental Coin Corporation, Van Nuys, CA; *U.S. Private*, pg. 267
Parkhill, J.S., Pres.--Stackpole Ltd., Newton, MA; *U.S. Private*, pg. 1028
Parkinson, Kirk, Publr.--The Daily Herald, Provo, UT; *U.S. Public*, pg. 1343
Parkinson, Nigel, Pres.--Kvaerner de Mexico, S.A. de C.V., Mexico, Mexico; *Int'l*, pg. 767
Parkinson, Richard, Pres., Chief Exec. Officer & Gen Mgr.--Associated Food Stores Inc., Salt Lake City, UT; *U.S. Private*, pg. 90
Parks, Delton C., Pres. & Chief Exec. Officer--Country Fresh, Inc., Grand Rapids, MI; *U.S. Public*, pg. 1526
Parks, John R., Pres. & Chief Exec. Officer--Parks Products, Inc., Hollywood, CA; *U.S. Private*, pg. 840
Parks, Raymond F., Pres. & Chief Oper. Officer--J.H. Fletcher & Co., Huntington, WV; *U.S. Private*, pg. 412
Parlog, John, III, Pres.--Valmark Industries, Inc., Fremont, CA; *U.S. Private*, pg. 598
Parmelee, H.J., Pres. & Chief Oper. Officer--The Turner Corporation, New York, NY; *U.S. Public*, pg. 1645
Parmelee, Harold J., Pres.--Turner Development Corporation, New York, NY; *U.S. Public*, pg. 1646
Parod, Richard W., Pres.--Irritol System, Riverside, CA; *U.S. Public*, pg. 1624
Parodi, Donald, Pres.--Setco, Inc., Anaheim, CA; *U.S. Public*, pg. 1066
Parque, Ronald D., Pres.--Mrs. Cubbison's Foods, Inc., Montebello, CA; *U.S. Public*, pg. 909
Parr, Paul, Pres.--Quebecor Litho Plus, Willowdale, Canada; *Int'l*, pg. 1076
Parra, Luis Guillermo, Pres. & Chief Oper. Officer--BASF Quimica Colombiana S.A., Bogota, Colombia; *Int'l*, pg. 107
Parra, Tim, Pres.--F.P.A., Inc., Irving, TX; *U.S. Private*, pg. 389
Parrales, Juan Bosco, Pres. & Creative Dir.--JB/Young & Rubicam, Managua, Nicaragua; *U.S. Private*, pg. 1200
Parrette, William, Pres. & Chief Exec. Officer--Solitec Wafer Processing, Inc., San Jose, CA; *U.S. Private*, pg. 1013
Parrillo, Gillian M., Pres.--Systems Management Group, Plano, TX; *U.S. Public*, pg. 1516
Parrish, Henry N., Pres.--Chicago West Pullman Heavy Industries, Cincinnati, OH; *U.S. Private*, pg. 236
Parrish, John W., Jr., Pres. & Chief Exec. Officer--Loxcreen Company, West Columbia, SC; *U.S. Private*, pg. 679
Parrish, Ronald K., Pres.--Elastomer Seals - North America, Morton Grove, IL; *Int'l*, pg. 1338
Parrish, Stanton C., Pres.--Harbor Financial Services, Spokane, WA; *U.S. Public*, pg. 1516
Parrott, Roy E., Chm. Bd., Pres. & Chief Exec. Officer--Simpson Industries, Inc., Plymouth, MI; *U.S. Public*, pg. 1474
Parsley, Harry, Pres. & Chief Exec. Officer--Racke USA, Sonoma, CA; *Int'l*, pg. 1083
Parsley, Harry, Pres. & Chief Exec. Officer--Buena Vista Winery, Sonoma, CA; *Int'l*, pg. 1083
Parsons, Larry E., Pres.--Ken-Mac Metals, Inc., Cleveland, OH; *Int'l*, pg. 1388
Parsons, Richard, Pres.--Time Warner Inc., New York, NY; *U.S. Public*, pg. 1610
Partain, C. Raymond, Pres.--Metric Constructors, Inc., Charlotte, NC; *Int'l*, pg. 633
Parten, Steve, Pres. & Chief Exec. Officer--Bromar Inc., Newport Beach, CA; *U.S. Private*, pg. 171
Partridge, James E., Chm. Bd. & Pres.--Smith-Emery Company, Los Angeles, CA; *U.S. Private*, pg. 1007
Pascal, Amy, Pres.--Columbia Pictures, Culver City, CA; *Int'l*, pg. 1281
Pascal, Edward, Partner--Kombi, Ltd., Essex Junction, VT; *U.S. Private*, pg. 631
Pascarella, Carl, Pres.--Visa U.S.A. Inc., San Francisco, CA; *U.S. Private*, pg. 1141
Paschall, Charles C., Pres. & Chief Admin. Officer--First Virginia Bank-Clinch Valley, Richlands, VA; *U.S. Public*, pg. 641
Paschall, John, Pres.--Williams Advanced Materials, Inc., Buffalo, NY; *U.S. Public*, pg. 266
Pascucci, Leon, Pres.--G. Leblanc Corporation, Kenosha, WI; *U.S. Private*, pg. 656
Paskal, Joseph, Pres.--J & R Film / Moviola Digital Co., Hollywood, CA; *U.S. Private*, pg. 576
Pasquale, Michael F., Pres.--Hershey Chocolate U.S.A., Hershey, PA; *U.S. Public*, pg. 812
Pasquale, Vincent J., Pres.--Intercraft Company, Taylor, TX; *U.S. Public*, pg. 1177
Pasquale, Vincent J., Pres.--Decorel Incorporated, Taylor, TX; *U.S. Public*, pg. 1177
Pasquarello, Theodore, Pres. & Chief Exec. Officer--Chiswick Trading Inc., Sudbury, MA; *U.S. Private*, pg. 237
Pasquelale, Doug, Pres. & Chief Exec. Officer--Richfield Hospitality Services, Englewood, CO; *U.S. Private*, pg. 929
Pasquerilla, Frank J., Chm. Bd & Chief Exec. Officer--Crown American Realty Trust, Johnstown, PA; *U.S. Public*, pg. 461
Pasquerilla, Mark E., Pres. & Head-Asset Mngmnt.--Crown American Realty Trust, Johnstown, PA; *U.S. Public*, pg. 461
Passow, Harry D., Pres.--St. Louis Division, Saint Louis, MO; *U.S. Public*, pg. 509
Passy, David S., Pres.--American Guarantee Insurance Company, Raleigh, NC; *U.S. Public*, pg. 629
Passy, David S., Pres.--Triangle Life Insurance, Raleigh, NC; *U.S. Public*, pg. 629
Pastena, Jim, Pres.--EBI Medical Systems, Inc., Parsippany, NJ; *U.S. Public*, pg. 231
Pataky, Nicolas, Pres.--P.T. Bristol-Myers Indonesia, Jakarta, Indonesia; *U.S. Public*, pg. 255
Patch, Ed, Pres.--Benchmark Industries, Brookville, OH; *U.S. Private*, pg. 132
Patch, Lauren N., Pres. & Chief Exec. Officer--Ohio Casualty Corporation, Hamilton, OH; *U.S. Public*, pg. 1214
Pate, James L., Pres.--Pennzoil Products Co., Houston, TX; *U.S. Public*, pg. 1272
Pate, Mike, Pres. & Publr.--Tallahassee Democrat, Inc., Tallahassee, FL; *U.S. Public*, pg. 964
Pate, R. Carter, Pres.--Plastics Manufacturing Company, Dallas, TX; *U.S. Public*, pg. 1530
Pate, Stephen T., Pres. & Chief Oper. Officer--Western Surety Company, Sioux Falls, SD; *U.S. Public*, pg. 303
Patel, D.S., Chm. Bd., Pres. & Chief Exec. Officer--Circuit Systems, Inc., Elk Grove Village, IL; *U.S. Public*, pg. 374

Patel, Homi B., Pres. & Chief Oper. Officer--Hartmarx Corporation, Chicago, IL; *U.S. Public*, pg. 795

Patel, Ken N., Pres. & Chief Exec. Officer--Carrier Vibrating Equipment, Inc., Louisville, KY; *U.S. Private*, pg. 215

Patel, Mahendra, Pres., Chief Exec. Officer & Gen. Mgr.--Philway Products, Inc., Ashland, OH; *U.S. Private*, pg. 862

Patel, Ray, Pres.--Harmony Engineering Corporation, Minneapolis, MN; *U.S. Private*, pg. 503

Patenge, Kenneth E., Chm. Bd., Pres. & Chief Exec. Officer--Wohlert Corp., Lansing, MI; *U.S. Private*, pg. 1185

Paterna, Salvatore A., Chm. Bd., Pres., Chief Exec. Officer & Chief Oper. Officer--John Solomon, Inc., Somerville, MA; *U.S. Private*, pg. 1013

Patient, William F., Chm. Bd., Pres. & Chief Exec. Officer--The Geon Company, Avon Lake, OH; *U.S. Public*, pg. 733

Patin, Gabriel, Pres.--Sakata Seed America, Inc., Morgan Hill, CA; *Int'l*, pg. 1178

Patinella, John, Pres. & Chief Exec. Officer--Homestead Publishing, Bel Air, MD; *U.S. Public*, pg. 1616

Patout, William S., III, Pres. & Chief Fin. Officer--M.A. Patout & Son, Jeanerette, LA; *U.S. Private*, pg. 843

Patrician, Robert A., Pres.--Rockwell Heavy Vehicle Suspension Systems Company, Inc., Troy, MI; *U.S. Public*, pg. 1096

Patrick, Dave, Pres.--Arrow Industries, Inc., Carrollton, TX; *U.S. Public*, pg. 426

Patrick, Michael W., Pres. & Chief Exec. Officer--Carmike Cinemas, Inc., Columbus, GA; *U.S. Public*, pg. 305

Patrick, Stuart K., Pres. & Chief Exec. Officer--Baird, Patrick & Co., Inc., New York, NY; *U.S. Private*, pg. 111

Patron, Ann, Pres.--Frank Smythson Inc., New York, NY; *Int'l*, pg. 707

Patsley, Pamela H., Pres. & Chief Exec. Officer--First USA Paymentech, Inc., Salem, NH; *U.S. Public*, pg. 174

Pattberg, Herbert K., Pres.-Hercules Europe--Hercules Incorporated, Wilmington, DE; *U.S. Public*, pg. 809

Patten, Charles R., Chm. Bd. & Pres.--Colfax Envelope Corporation, Buffalo Grove, IL; *U.S. Private*, pg. 252

Patten, John W., Pres.--Business Week, New York, NY; *U.S. Public*, pg. 1069

Patten, Joseph P., Pres.--LeFebure Corp., Cedar Rapids, IA; *Int'l*, pg. 387

Patterson, A. Glenn, Pres. & Chief Oper. Officer--Patterson Energy, Inc., Snyder, TX; *U.S. Public*, pg. 1265

Patterson, Brian, Chief Exec. Officer--Waterford Wedgwood UK Plc, Stoke on Trent, United Kingdom; *Int'l*, pg. 1487

Patterson, Charles, Pres., Chief Exec. Officer & Chief Oper. Officer--Walman Optical Company, Minneapolis, MN; *U.S. Private*, pg. 1148

Patterson, Donald A.W., Pres. & Chief Exec. Officer--Home Federal Bank, Hamilton, OH; *U.S. Public*, pg. 633

Patterson, James E., Pres. & Chief Oper. Officer--Fred B. Johnston Company, Inc., Chapin, SC; *U.S. Private*, pg. 595

Patterson, Jeff, Pres. & Chief Exec. Officer--F.W. Myers & Co., Inc., Rouses Point, NY; *U.S. Private*, pg. 770

Patterson, John R., Pres.--TLC Group, Inc., Zeeland, MI; *U.S. Public*, pg. 352

Patterson, Kent E., Pres.--ERM-EnviroClean, Exton, PA; *U.S. Private*, pg. 379

Patterson, L., Pres.--Menardi-Criswell, Trenton, SC; *Int'l*, pg. 636

Patterson, Ray, Pres.--Bell & Howell Ltd., Woodbridge, Canada; *U.S. Public*, pg. 201

Patterson, Richard, Pres. & Chief Oper. Officer--Rosenthal Automotive Organization, Arlington, VA; *U.S. Private*, pg. 946

Patterson, Richard L., Pres.--Interkal, Inc., Kalamazoo, MI; *Int'l*, pg. 759

Patterson, Terry, Pres. & Chief Exec. Officer--Strauss Discount Auto, South River, NJ; *U.S. Private*, pg. 1046

Patterson, Terry W., Pres. & Chief Exec. Officer--Frederick's of Hollywood, Inc., Hollywood, CA; *U.S. Private*, pg. 424

Patterson, Tom, Pres.--TXEN, Birmingham, AL; *U.S. Public*, pg. 1182

Pattillo, Bob, Pres. & Chief Exec. Officer--Shop 'n Save Warehouse Foods, Inc., Kirkwood, MO; *U.S. Public*, pg. 1541

Pattinson, Michael, Pres.--Teca Corporation, Pleasantville, NY; *Int'l*, pg. 1468

Pattison, James A., Chm. Bd., Pres., Chief Exec. Officer & Mng. Dir.--Great Pacific Enterprises Inc., Vancouver, Canada; *Int'l*, pg. 557

Patton, Charles A., Pres.--Virginia First Financial Corp., Petersburg, VA; *U.S. Public*, pg. 1721

Patton, Charles A., Pres. & Chief Oper. Officer--Virginia First Savings Bank, F.S.B., Petersburg, VA; *U.S. Public*, pg. 1721

Patton, Frank, Pres.--Pompeiian, Inc., Baltimore, MD; *U.S. Private*, pg. 875

Patton, George, Chm. Bd., Pres. & Chief Exec. Officer--Leblanc Communications, Inc., Richardson, TX; *U.S. Private*, pg. 656

Patton, James, Pres.--Triton Manufacturing, Inc., Atlanta, GA; *U.S. Private*, pg. 1104

Patton, T.V., Chm. Bd. & Pres.--Triton Manufacturing, Inc., Atlanta, GA; *U.S. Private*, pg. 1104

Patz, Lawrence C., Pres. & Chief Exec. Officer--Concord General Life Insurance Company, Concord, NH; *U.S. Public*, pg. 79

Pauek, Tommy, Pres., Chief Exec. & Oper. Officer--Alabama Farmers Co-op, Decatur, AL; *U.S. Private*, pg. 30

Paukstis, John, Pres.--McBee Systems, Inc., Parsippany, NJ; *U.S. Private*, pg. 718

Paul, A.S., Pres.--Bard Access Systems, Salt Lake City, UT; *U.S. Public*, pg. 189

Paul, Ben E., Pres.--OEA Aerospace, Inc., Fairfield, CA; *U.S. Public*, pg. 1207

Paul, John, Pres.--Best Power, Necedah, WI; *U.S. Private*, pg. 140

Paul, John D., Pres.--Old Kent Bank-Grand Traverse, Traverse City, MI; *U.S. Public*, pg. 1216

Paul, M., Joint Chief Exec.--Caparo Industries Plc., Birchills, United Kingdom; *Int'l*, pg. 265

Paul, Robert A., Pres. & Chief Exec. Officer--Ampco-Pittsburgh Corporation, Pittsburgh, PA; *U.S. Public*, pg. 103

Paul, Robert G., Pres. & Chief Exec. Officer--Allen Telecom, Inc., Beachwood, OH; *U.S. Public*, pg. 45

Paul, Roger, Pres.--VSK Group, Harelbeke, Belgium; *U.S. Public*, pg. 49

Paul, Thomas A., Pres. & Chief Exec. Officer--International Thomson Publishing Limited, London, United Kingdom; *U.S. Public*, pg. 1600

Pauli, Charles G., Pres.--Alox Corporation, Niagara Falls, NY; *U.S. Public*, pg. 1357

Pauli, Charles G., Pres.--Day-Glo Color Corp., Cleveland, OH; *U.S. Public*, pg. 1357

Pauli, Charles G., Pres.--Kop-Coat, Pittsburgh, PA; *U.S. Public*, pg. 1357

Paulk, Wayne, Plant Mgr.--Cooper Tools, Statesboro, GA; *U.S. Public*, pg. 444

Paulsen, Christian, Pres.--Diatom Verktoj A/S, Hvidovre, Denmark; *Int'l*, pg. 678

Paulson, Bruce, Pres.--King Company, Owatonna, MN; *U.S. Public*, pg. 1676

Paulson, Henry, Jr., Pres. & Chief Oper. Officer--Goldman, Sachs & Co., New York, NY; *U.S. Private*, pg. 462

Paulson, Randall, Pres.--Transcontinental Realty Investors, Inc., Dallas, TX; *U.S. Public*, pg. 1630

Paulson, Randall M., Pres.--Continental Mortgage and Equity Trust, Dallas, TX; *U.S. Public*, pg. 441

Pausch, J., Pres.--Marshall Labs Inc., Hopkins, MN; *U.S. Public*, pg. 531

Pauza, Frank, Pres. & Chief Oper. Officer--Universal Folding Box Company, Inc., Hoboken, NJ; *U.S. Private*, pg. 1127

Pavao, James S., Pres.--Whaling Industries, Inc., Fall River, MA; *U.S. Private*, pg. 1170

Paxton, G. Ward, Chm. Bd. & Pres.--ODS Networks, Inc., Richardson, TX; *U.S. Public*, pg. 1206

Paxton, Gary, Pres. & Chief Exec. Officer--Dollar Rent A Car, Tulsa, OK; *U.S. Public*, pg. 354

Paxton, Michael J., Pres. & Chief Exec. Officer--The Haagen-Dazs Company Inc., Minneapolis, MN; *Int'l*, pg. 411

Payne, David L., Chm. Bd., Pres. & Chief Exec. Officer--Westamerica Bancorporation, Fairfield, CA; *U.S. Public*, pg. 1756

Payne, H.P., Pres. & Gen. Mgr.--Baylor Company, Sugar Land, TX; *Int'l*, pg. 1134

Payne, James L., Chm. Bd., Pres. & Chief Exec. Officer--Santa Fe Energy Resources, Inc., Houston, TX; *U.S. Public*, pg. 1431

Payne, Thomas H., Pres. & Chief Exec. Officer--Market Facts, Inc., Arlington Heights, IL; *U.S. Public*, pg. 1046

Payne, Walter F., Pres. & Chief Exec. Officer--Blue Diamond Growers, Sacramento, CA; *U.S. Private*, pg. 152

Payson, Brian, Acting Pres.--AI/FOCS, Inc., Franklin, MA; *U.S. Public*, pg. 1776

Payton, Earl E., Pres., Chief Exec. Officer & Chief Fin. Officer--Cowden Metal-San Jose, San Jose, CA; *U.S. Private*, pg. 280

Payton, Roger, Pres. & Chief Exec. Officer--International Logistics Limited, Hillside, IL; *U.S. Private*, pg. 571

Payton, Roger E., Pres. & Chief Exec. Officer--Merchants Home Delivery Service Inc., Oxnard, CA; *Int'l*, pg. 901

Pazos, Guillermo, Pres.--Bridgestone/Firestone do Brasil Industria e Commercio Ltda, Sao Paulo, Brazil; *Int'l*, pg. 214

Peabody, C. Matthew, Pres. & Chief Oper. Officer--X-Rite, Incorporated, Grandville, MI; *U.S. Public*, pg. 1783

Peabody, Jonathan C., Pres. & Treas.--Peabody Office Furniture Corporation, Boston, MA; *U.S. Private*, pg. 844

Peach, A.D., Pres.--AGRA Shawmont Limited, Saint John, Canada; *Int'l*, pg. 30

Peacock, Robert A., Pres.--BB&T Leasing Corp., Charlotte, NC; *U.S. Public*, pg. 160

Pearce, Earl R., Pres.--Weston Resources, Toronto, Canada; *Int'l*, pg. 1495

Pearce, Gary M., Vice Chm. & Pres.--Pearce Industries Inc., Houston, TX; *U.S. Private*, pg. 845

Pearce, Ron L., Pres. & Chief Exec. Officer--Deltic Timber Corporation, El Dorado, AR; *U.S. Public*, pg. 498

Pearce, W. McFall, Pres. & Chief Exec. Officer--PYA/Monarch, Inc., Greenville, SC; *U.S. Public*, pg. 1433

Pearce, Walter, Pres. & Chief Fin. Officer--KCI Communications, Inc, Mc Lean, VA; *U.S. Private*, pg. 784

Peardon, Thomas, Pres. & Chief Exec. Officer--Brunschwig & Fils, Inc., White Plains, NY; *U.S. Private*, pg. 176

Pearlman, Earl, Pres. & Chief Exec. Officer--MTI Technology Corporation, Anaheim, CA; *U.S. Public*, pg. 1028

Pearlman, Herbert M., Chm. Bd., Pres. & Chief Exec. Officer--Helm Resources Inc., Greenwich, CT; *U.S. Public*, pg. 808

Pearlman, Jack, Pres.--Atlite Lighting Equip, Inc., Maspeth, NY; *U.S. Public*, pg. 443

Pearlstine, Edwin, Jr., Pres.--Pearlstine Distributors Inc., Charleston, SC; *U.S. Private*, pg. 845

Pears, D.G., Pres.--Midwest Pipeline Contractors Ltd., Edmonton, Canada; *Int'l*, pg. 31

Pears, D.G., Pres.--Midwest Management (1987) Limited, Edmonton, Canada; *Int'l*, pg. 31

Pearson, Brian, Pres.--Allied Colloids (Asia) Ltd., Wan Chai, Hong Kong; *Int'l*, pg. 62

Pearson, C., Pres. & Chief Exec. Officer--PNC Bank, Camp Hill, PA; *U.S. Public*, pg. 1243

Pearson, Donna Sutherland, Pres. & Partner--Sutherland Lumber Co., Kansas City, MO; *U.S. Private*, pg. 1057

Pearson, Harry, Chm. Bd. & Pres.--United Farm Family Life Insurance Co., Indianapolis, IN; *U.S. Private*, pg. 1122

Pearson, John, Pres.--Ervin Industries, Inc., Ann Arbor, MI; *U.S. Private*, pg. 382

Pearson, Joseph, Chm. Bd. & Chief Exec. Officer--National Real Estate Services, Inc., Vancouver, Canada; *Int'l*, pg. 909

Pearson, Martin J., Pres.--Reader's Digest European Systems Group, Limited, Swindon, United Kingdom; *U.S. Public*, pg. 1368

Pearson, Ronald, Chm. Bd., Pres. & Chief Exec. Officer--Hy-Vee Food Stores Incorporated, West Des Moines, IA; *U.S. Private*, pg. 550

Pearson, Ronald A., Pres.--New Mech Companies, Inc., Saint Paul, MN; *U.S. Private*, pg. 794

Peavey, Melia, Pres. & Chief Oper. Officer--Peavey Electronics Corp., Meridian, MS; *U.S. Private*, pg. 845

Pecci, Alberto, Chm. Bd. & Pres.--Fondiaria S.P.A., Florence, Italy; *Int'l*, pg. 496

Pechota, Gary, Chm. Bd., Pres., & Chief Exec. Officer--Giant Cement Holding Inc., Summerville, SC; *U.S. Public*, pg. 741

Peck, Douglas E., Pres. & Gen. Counsel--Renosol Corp., Saline, MI; *U.S. Private*, pg. 922

Pecker, David J., Pres. & Chief Exec. Officer--Hachette Filipacchi Magazines Inc., New York, NY; *Int'l*, pg. 794

Peckham, John R., Pres.--Peckham Industries, Inc., White Plains, NY; *U.S. Private*, pg. 846

Pedersen, Calvin J., Pres. & Chief Exec. Officer--Duff & Phelps Utilities Income Inc., Chicago, IL; *U.S. Public*, pg. 534

Pedersen, Jens Bang, Pres.--MD Foods USA Inc., Springfield, NJ; *Int'l*, pg. 826

Pedersen, Jetre W., Pres.--MD Foods Espana, Gava, Spain; *Int'l*, pg. 826

Pedersen, Niels Ulrich, Pres.--MD Foods Caltsoyias Hellas S.A., Athens, Greece; *Int'l*, pg. 826

Pedone, Antonio, Pres.--Crediop-Credito Per Le Imprese e le Opere Pubbliche SpA, Rome, Italy; *Int'l*, pg. 341

Pedone, Michael F., Pres. & Chief Exec. Officer--Pedone & Partners Adv., Inc., New York, NY; *U.S. Private*, pg. 846

Pedoussant, Bernard, Pres.--Logo of the Americas, Fort Lauderdale, FL; *Int'l*, pg. 462

Peebler, Charles D., Jr., Pres.-True North & Chm. & Chief Exec. Officer-TN Div. Cos.--True North Communications Inc., Chicago, IL; *U.S. Public*, pg. 1641

Peeler, Bobby J., Pres.--Peelers Rug Company, Inc., Gaffney, SC; *U.S. Private*, pg. 846

Peeler, John R., Pres. & Chief Exec. Officer--Telecommunications Techniques Corp., Germantown, MD; *U.S. Public*, pg. 539

Peery, Tom A., Pres. & Chief Oper. Officer--Heilig Meyers Furniture Co., Richmond, VA; *U.S. Public*, pg. 804

Peery, Troy A., Jr., Pres. & Chief Oper. Officer--Heilig-Meyers Company, Richmond, VA; *U.S. Public*, pg. 804

Pefanis, Harry N., Pres.--Plains Marketing & Transportation, Houston, TX; *U.S. Public*, pg. 1308

Pegler, Donald H., III, Pres.--Pegler-Sysco Food Services Co., Lincoln, NE; *U.S. Public*, pg. 1550

Pei, Tian Wen, Pres.--Guangdong Otsuka Pharmaceutical Co., Ltd., Guangdong, China; *Int'l*, pg. 1014

Peifer, Charles, Pres. & Chief Exec. Officer--Prince Sports Group Inc., Bordentown, NJ; *U.S. Private*, pg. 884

Peister, Alan, Pres.--David L. Peister Co., Inc., New York, NY; *U.S. Private*, pg. 848

Peladeau, Pierre, Chm. Bd., Pres. & Chief Exec. Officer--Quebecor Inc., Montreal, Canada; *Int'l*, pg. 1075

Peled, Rafi, Pres. & Chief Exec. Officer--The Israel Electric Corporation Ltd., Haifa, Israel; *Int'l*, pg. 690

Peled, Zvi, Pres. & Chief Exec. Officer--Bogen Communications, Inc., Ramsey, NJ; *U.S. Public*, pg. 739

Peline, Val P., Jr., Pres. & Chief Exec. Officer--Stanford Telecommunications, Sunnyvale, CA; *U.S. Public*, pg. 1508

Pelino, Dennis, Pres. & Chief Oper. Officer--Fritz Companies, Inc., San Francisco, CA; *U.S. Public*, pg. 683

Pelisson, Gerard, Co.-Chm. & Co-Pres.--Accor S.A., Evry, France; *Int'l*, pg. 20

Pellegrino, John B., Pres. & Chief Exec. Offcier--Ridg-U-Rak, Inc., North East, PA; *U.S. Private*, pg. 930

Pellenberg, Charles, Pres.--American Down & Textile Company, La Crosse, WI; *U.S. Public*, pg. 782

Pellenberg, Charles, Pres.--Company Store Holdings, Inc., La Crosse, WI; *U.S. Public*, pg. 782

Peller, John E., Pres. & Chief Exec. Officer--Andres Wines Ltd., Winona, Canada; *Int'l*, pg. 75

Pelletier, Peter, Pres. & Chief Exec. Officer--Robertson Factories, Inc., Taunton, MA; *U.S. Private*, pg. 936

Peltier, Robert L., Pres.--U.S. Manufacturing Corp., Fraser, MI; *U.S. Private*, pg. 1125

Peltola, Timo, Chm. Bd., Pres. & Chief Exec. Officer--Huhtamaki Oy, Espoo, Finland; *Int'l*, pg. 638

Pemberton, Brian, Pres. & Chief Exec. Officer--ROHN Industries, Inc., Peoria, IL; *U.S. Public*, pg. 1404

Pemberton, Brian B., Pres.--UNR-Rohn Div., Peoria, IL; *U.S. Public*, pg. 1404

Pena, Luis X., Pres., Chief Exec. Officer & Chief Fin. Officer--Gulf States Asphalt Company, Inc., South Houston, TX; *U.S. Private*, pg. 487

Penafiel, Jesus, Pres.--Serpo Onena S.A., Munguia, Spain; *Int'l*, pg. 1200

Penaloza Sandoval, David, Chm. Bd. & Pres.--Grupo Tribasa S.A. de C.V., Mexico, Mexico; *Int'l*, pg. 577

Pence, Dennis, Vice Chm., Pres. & Chief Exec. Officer--Coldwater Creek, Sandpoint, ID; *U.S. Public*, pg. 396

Pencer, Gerald N., Chm. Bd., Pres. & Chief Exec. Officer--Cott Corporation, Pointe-Claire, Canada; *Int'l*, pg. 337

Penedo, Dilio Sergio, Pres.--Embratel-Empresa Brasileira de Telecomunicagoes S.A., Rio de Janeiro, Brazil; *Int'l*, pg. 1362

Penfold, Richard, Pres. & Chief Exec. Officer--Buffalo Truck Center, Buffalo, NY; *U.S. Private*, pg. 179

Penhoet, Edward E., Ph.D., Pres. & Chief Exec. Officer--Chiron Corporation, Emeryville, CA; *U.S. Public*, pg. 349

Penido, Jose Luciano, Pres.--Samarco Mineracao SA, Belo Horizonte, Brazil; *Int'l*, pg. 224

Penland, James J., Pres. & Chief Exec. Officer--Regions Bank/Winchester, Winchester, TN; *U.S. Public*, pg. 1373

Penman, James A., Pres. & Chief Exec. Officer--Stephenson Equipment, Inc., Harrisburg, PA; *U.S. Private*, pg. 1040

Penn, Daniel A., Pres. & Chief Exec. Officer--Peck Jones Construction, Los Angeles, CA; *U.S. Private*, pg. 846

Penn, Les, Pres.--Flowers Specialty Foods of Montgomery, Inc., Montgomery, AL; *U.S. Public*, pg. 657

Penn, Richard L., Pres.--Cummins Mid-South, Inc., Memphis, TN; *U.S. Private*, pg. 295

Penn, Tony, Pres.--Western American Manufacturing, Inc., San Diego, CA; *U.S. Public*, pg. 1749

Penner, Donald, Pres.--Dynalectric Company, Mc Lean, VA; *U.S. Public*, pg. 571

Pennesse, Michael, Pres.--Infu-Tech, Englewood Cliffs, NJ; *U.S. Public*, pg. 440

Penney, C. Bradford, Pres. & Chief Exec. Officer--Streamlight Inc., Norristown, PA; *U.S. Private*, pg. 1047

Pennings, J.V.H., Dr., Pres. & Chief Exec. Officer--Oce-van der Grinten N.V., Venlo, Netherlands; *Int'l*, pg. 993

Penny, Philip L., Pres.--Cowles Enthusiast Media, Inc., Stamford, CT; *U.S. Private*, pg. 281

Penny, Roger P., Pres. & Chief Oper. Officer--Bethlehem Steel Corporation, Bethlehem, PA; *U.S. Public*, pg. 226

Penrod, Allen, Pres.--Maryland Plastics, Inc., Federalsburg, MD; *U.S. Private*, pg. 641

Penta, David Della, Pres.--Sani-Tech Inc., Lafayette, NJ; *U.S. Public*, pg. 1545

Pentecost, Jim, Pres.--Power & Telephone Supply Company, Memphis, TN; *U.S. Private*, pg. 877

Pentz, Paul E., Pres. & Chief Oper. Officer--TruServ Corporation, Chicago, IL; *U.S. Private*, pg. 1108

Pepe, Michael, Grp. Publisher--Money, New York, NY; *U.S. Public*, pg. 1613

Pepin, Marcel, Pres.--The Imperial Life Assurance Co., Toronto, Canada; *Int'l*, pg. 396

Pepper, David, Pres.--Harry Pepper & Associates, Jacksonville, FL; *U.S. Private*, pg. 851

Pepper, J. Stanley, Pres. & Chief Exec. Officer--The Pepper Companies, Inc., Chicago, IL; *U.S. Private*, pg. 851

Pepper, Joe, Pres. & Chief Exec. Officer--OEC Medical Systems, Inc., Salt Lake City, UT; *U.S. Public*, pg. 1207

Peppercorn, J.E., Pres.--Chevron Chemical Co., San Ramon, CA; *U.S. Public*, pg. 348

Pepys, Shirley, Pres. & Chief Exec. Officer--Noel Joanna, Inc., Rancho Santa Margarita, CA; *U.S. Public*, pg. 465

Perakis, James A., Chm. Bd., Pres. & Chief Exec. Officer--Hyperion Software, Stamford, CT; *U.S. Public*, pg. 851

Percelay, David, Pres. & Chief Exec. Officer--Scripps Howard Productions, Santa Monica, CA; *U.S. Public*, pg. 1448

Percival, Robert, Chm. & Pres.--Intelligent Controls Inc., Lynnwood, WA; *U.S. Private*, pg. 566

Perconti, Paul J., Pres. & Chief Exec. Officer--Thornton Oil Corp., Louisville, KY; *U.S. Private*, pg. 1084

Percy, K.E., Chief Exec. Officer--Morgan Grenfell Asset Management Limited, London, United Kingdom; *Int'l*, pg. 405

Percy, Steven, Chief Exec. Officer & Pres.--BP Oil Co., Cleveland, OH; *Int'l*, pg. 220

Perdigao, Mark A., Pres.--BNY Brokerage, Inc., New York, NY; *U.S. Public*, pg. 178

Perdue, Jim, Pres.--Perdue Farms, Inc., Showell, MD; *U.S. Private*, pg. 852

Peredo, Edsonr, Pres.--Buckman Laboratories Inc., Memphis, TN; *U.S. Private*, pg. 180

Pereira, J.F., Bus. Unit Mgr.--Van Leer Elpack A.E.B.E., Mandra-Attikis, Greece; *Int'l*, pg. 1146

Pereira, Richard, Pres.--Univex Corporation, Salem, NH; *U.S. Private*, pg. 1128

Perel, Jonathan S., Pres.--General Services Corporation, Richmond, VA; *U.S. Private*, pg. 445

Pereles, Richard S., Pres.--Cato Oil & Grease Co., Oklahoma City, OK; *Int'l*, pg. 1045

Perez, Alana S., Pres. & Chief Exec. Officer--OFC/DMB&B Bucharest, Bucharest, Romania; *U.S. Private*, pg. 305

Perez, Angel Alvarez, Pres. & Chief Exec. Officer--First Federal Finance Corporation, Santurce, PR; *U.S. Public*, pg. 644

Perez, Angel Alvarez, Pres. & Chief Exec. Officer--First Leasing & Rental Corporation, Toa Baja, PR; *U.S. Public*, pg. 644

Perez, J. Peter, Chm. Bd., Pres., & Chief Exec. Officer--InterBio Inc., Woodlands, TX; *U.S. Private*, pg. 566

Perez, Jean-Yves, Pres.--Woodward-Clyde Group, Inc., Denver, CO; *U.S. Public*, pg. 1655

Perez, Jean-Yves, Pres.--Woodward-Constructors, Denver, CO; *U.S. Public*, pg. 1657

Perez, John D., Pres. & Chief Exec. Officer--Perez Trading Co. Inc., Miami, FL; *U.S. Private*, pg. 852

Perez, Lombardo, Chm. Bd., Pres. & Chief Oper. Officer--Metro Ford Inc., Miami, FL; *U.S. Private*, pg. 736

Perez, Ricardo, Chm. Bd. & Pres.--Ricardo Perez Asociados, Madrid, Spain; *Int'l*, pg. 1036

Perez, Samuel, Pres.--Lowe RZR, Madrid, Spain; *U.S. Private*, pg. 678

Perez, William D., Pres. & Chief Exec. Officer--S.C. Johnson & Son, Inc., Racine, WI; *U.S. Private*, pg. 592

Perfect, S., Pres.--BFC Civil, Scarborough, Canada; *Int'l*, pg. 118

Perfect, S., Pres.--The Foundation Company, Scarborough, Canada; *Int'l*, pg. 118

Perham, Leonard C., Pres. & Chief Exec. Officer--Integrated Device Technology, Inc., Santa Clara, CA; *U.S. Public*, pg. 884

Periard, Ronal W., Pres., Chief Exec. Officer & Sec. of the Bd.--Central National Bank of Mattoon, Mattoon, IL; *U.S.* Public, pg. 643

Peribanez, Jimmie, Pres.--Majorica Jewelry Ltd., New York, NY; *U.S. Private*, pg. 697

Perini, Albert, Pres.--Newberg Perini, Chicago, IL; *U.S. Public*, pg. 1278

Perkett, Charles R., Pres.--CSC Logic, Inc., Dallas, TX; *U.S.* Public, pg. 422

Perkins, Bill, Pres.--Wells BDDP, Inc., New York, NY; *Int'l*, pg. 117

Perkins, Brian D., Pres.--McNeil Consumer Products Company, Fort Washington, PA; *U.S. Public*, pg. 928

Perkins, Charles, Pres.--Cole Papers Inc., Fargo, ND; *U.S. Private*, pg. 251

Perkins, Hap A., Pres.--Connecticut Container Corporation, North Haven, CT; *U.S. Private*, pg. 263

Perkins, J.O., Pres. & Corp. Exec. Officer--Equifax Insurance Services Inc., Atlanta, GA; *U.S. Public*, pg. 588

Perkins, Jeff, Pres.--First American Title Insurance Agency of Yavapai, Inc., Prescott, AZ; *U.S. Public*, pg. 626

Perkins, Jim, Pres. & Chief Exec. Officer--Hendrick Automotive Group, Charlotte, NC; *U.S. Private*, pg. 522

Perkins, John J., Pres.--Western Environmental Contracting, Inc., Los Angeles, CA; *U.S. Public*, pg. 296

Perkins, John J., Pres.--Western Thermal Soils Co., Los Angeles, CA; *U.S. Public*, pg. 296

Perkins, Kevin, Pres. & Chief Exec. Officer--Sizzler International, Inc., Los Angeles, CA; *U.S. Public*, pg. 1475

Perkins, Kevin, Pres. & Chief Exec. Officer--CFI Pty., Ltd., Los Angeles, CA; *U.S. Public*, pg. 1475

Perkins, Leigh H., Jr., Pres. & Chief Exec. Officer--The Orvis Company, Inc., Manchester, VT; *U.S. Private*, pg. 820

Perkins, Polly, Pres.-Sport--Petersen Publishing Company, L.L.C., Los Angeles, CA; *U.S. Private*, pg. 856

Perkins, Richard, Pres.--Algonquin Gas Transmission Corporation, Boston, MA; *U.S. Public*, pg. 534

Perkins, William C., Pres.--Discount Auto Parts, Inc., Lakeland, FL; *U.S. Public*, pg. 510

Perko, Stephen, Pres.--Blockhouse Co., Inc., York, PA; *U.S.* Private, pg. 150

Perks, Douglas,, Pres. & Chief Exec. Officer--Eclipse Inc., Rockford, IL; *U.S. Private*, pg. 360

Perlberg, Mark, Sr. V.P., Pres., Fin. Sls. Mktg. Division--The Check Store, Lakewood, CO; *U.S. Public*, pg. 785

Perlegos, George, Chm. Bd., Pres. & Chief Exec. Officer--Atmel Corporation, San Jose, CA; *U.S. Public*, pg. 145

Perlis, Morris, Pres.--Counsel Corporation, Toronto, Canada; *Int'l*, pg. 338

Perlis, Morris, Pres. & Chief Exec. Officer--Stadtlander Drug Company, Inc., Pittsburgh, PA; *Int'l*, pg. 338

Perlis, Morris, Pres. & Chief Exec. Officer--Health Management, Inc., Ronkonkoma, NY; *Int'l*, pg. 338

Perlman, Lawrence, Chm. Bd., Pres. & Chief Exec. Officer--Ceridian Corporation, Bloomington, MN; *U.S. Public*, pg. 330

Perlman, Lee, Pres.--Eastern Air Devices, Inc., Dover, NH; *U.S. Private*, pg. 357

Perlman, Willa, Pres. & Publisher--Golden Books Family Entertainment Inc., New York, NY; *U.S. Public*, pg. 749

Pernell, Robert, Pres.--Sacramento Municipal Utility District, Sacramento, CA; *U.S. Private*, pg. 959

Peroni, Roger, Pres.--Parmalat USA Corporation, Teaneck, NJ; *Int'l*, pg. 1023

Perot, Ross, Interim Pres. & Chief Exec. Officer--Perot Systems Corporation, Dallas, TX; *U.S. Private*, pg. 854

Perott, Edward J., Pres. & Chief Exec. Officer--Chip Supply Inc., Orlando, FL; *U.S. Private*, pg. 237

Perozzi, Donald J., Pres.--BellSouth Advertising & Publishing Corp., Atlanta, GA; *U.S. Public*, pg. 208

Perrault, Paul, Pres.--Chittenden Bank, Burlington, VT; *U.S. Public*, pg. 351

Perrault, Paul A., Pres. & Chief Exec. Officer--Chittenden Corporation, Burlington, VT; *U.S. Public*, pg. 350

Perre, Len, Pres.--Hanovia Colight, Union, NJ; *Int'l*, pg. 17

Perreault, Fernand, Pres.--Cadev, Montreal, Canada; *Int'l*, pg. 249

Perreault, Fernand, Pres. & Chief Oper. Officer--SITQ Immobilier, Montreal, Canada; *Int'l*, pg. 249

Perrella, James E., Chm. Bd., Pres. & Chief Exec. Officer--Ingersoll-Rand Company, Woodcliff Lake, NJ; *U.S. Public*, pg. 876

Perrett, T. Robert, Pres.--Aesculap, Inc., South San Francisco, CA; *Int'l*, pg. 29

Perriello, Alex, Pres. & Chief Exec. Officer--Coldwell Banker Real Estate Corporation, Parsippany, NJ; *U.S. Public*, pg. 321

Perrin, Hubert, Pres.--Usines Dehousse SA, Pau, France; *Int'l*, pg. 1166

Perrino, S. Ronald, Chm. Bd., Pres. & Chief Exec. Officer--S.T. Research, Newington, VA; *U.S. Private*, pg. 958

Perron, Allen A., Pres. & Treas.--Tellus, Inc., Bellevue, WA; *U.S. Public*, pg. 1342

Perrone, Michael M., Pres. & Chief Oper. Officer--Fields Financial Services, Inc., Bryan, TX; *U.S. Public*, pg. 942

Perrot, Gerard, Pres.--Valois of America, Inc., Greenwich, CT; *U.S. Public*, pg. 125

Perrotto, Larry J., Pres. & Chief Exec. Officer--American Publishing Management Services Inc., West Frankfort, IL; *Int'l*, pg. 632

Perry, Allan E., Pres. & Chief Exec. Officer--Knape & Vogt Mfg. Co., Grand Rapids, MI; *U.S. Public*, pg. 963

Perry, Arlin R., Pres.--Gear Products Inc., Tulsa, OK; *U.S. Public*, pg. 238

Perry, Christopher J., Pres.--Continental Illinois Venture Corp., Chicago, IL; *U.S. Public*, pg. 181

Perry, David, Pres.--Shiny Entertainment Inc., Laguna Beach, CA; *U.S. Private*, pg. 573

Perry, David H., Pres.--Cardinal Scale Manufacturing Company, Webb City, MO; *U.S. Private*, pg. 209

Perry, David H., Pres.--Detecto Scale Company, Webb City, MO; *U.S. Private*, pg. 209

Perry, James M., Pres.--Massachusetts Capital Resources Company, Hingham, MA; *U.S. Public*, pg. 95

Perry, Laine, Pres.--Perry Equipment Corporation, Mineral Wells, TX; *U.S. Private*, pg. 855

Perry, M. Dunham, Jr., Pres.--Flo-Line Filters, Inc., Amarillo, TX; *U.S. Private*, pg. 855

Perry, M. Dunham, Jr., Pres.--United Filters, Inc., Amarillo, TX; *U.S. Private*, pg. 855

Perry, M. Dunman, Jr., Chm. Bd., Pres. & Chief Exec. Officer--Perry Equipment Corporation, Mineral Wells, TX; *U.S. Private*, pg. 855

Perry, Michael W., Pres. & Chief Oper. Officer--INMC Mortgage Holdings, Inc., Pasadena, CA; *U.S. Public*, pg. 857

Perry, Michael W., Pres. & Chief Exec. Officer--Indimac, Inc., Pasadena, CA; *U.S. Public*, pg. 857

Perry, Michael W., Pres.--Indimac Mortgage Obligations, Inc., Pasadena, CA; *U.S. Public*, pg. 858

Perry, Michael W., Pres.--Indimac Mortgage Obligations, II, Inc., Pasadena, CA; *U.S. Public*, pg. 858

Perry, Richard, Pres.-Intl. Division--Waverly International, Baltimore, MD; *U.S. Public*, pg. 1748

Perry, Robert, Pres.--Hydro-Mill Co., Chatsworth, CA; *U.S. Public*, pg. 1640

Perry, Stephen C., Pres.--Leucadia Inc. Manufacturing Division, Lincolnton, NC; *U.S. Public*, pg. 990

Perry, Wes, Pres.--BF Goodrich Avionic Systems, Inc., Grand Rapids, MI; *U.S. Public*, pg. 751

Persson, Per-Ingemar, Pres.--Skanska Syd, Malmo, Sweden; *Int'l*, pg. 1260

Persson, Unger, Pres.--NCC Building - Vaxjo, Vaxjo, Sweden; *Int'l*, pg. 899

Perticaroli, Francesco, Pres.--Metropolitana Milanese S.P.A., Milan, Italy; *Int'l*, pg. 863

Pertz, Douglas A., Pres. & Chief Exec. Officer--Culligan International Company, Northbrook, IL; *U.S. Public*, pg. 467

Perugino, Joseph F., Pres.--PG Energy Services, Wilkes-Barre, PA; *U.S. Public*, pg. 1272

Pesce, James A., Pres.--US ServVis, West Orange, NJ; *U.S. Public*, pg. 1687

Pesch, Alan J., Chm. Bd., Pres. & Chief Exec. Officer--Ship Analytics, Inc., North Stonington, CT; *U.S. Private*, pg. 994

Pesch, Robert C., Pres.--Houston Foods Company, Franklin Park, IL; *U.S. Private*, pg. 542

Pesci, Jose, Pres.--Lemo SA, Ecublens, Switzerland; *Int'l*, pg. 806

Peshkin, J.R., Pres.--Taylor Woodrow Homes Florida Inc., Sarasota, FL; *Int'l*, pg. 1359

Peslar, Norman, Pres.--Automotive Moulding Company, Warren, MI; *U.S. Private*, pg. 485

Pessolano, Joseph, Jr., Partner & Chief Fin. Officer--Houston Herstek Favat, Boston, MA; *U.S. Private*, pg. 542

Pesut, Gerald A., Pres. & Gen. Mgr.--StorageTek Canada, Inc., Toronto, Canada; *U.S. Public*, pg. 1523

Pesut, Gerry, Pres. & Chief Exec. Officer--Distributed Systems Division, Lisle, IL; *U.S. Public*, pg. 1522

Petch, Ronald S., Pres. & Chief Oper. Officer--Calprop Corporation, Marina Del Rey, CA; *U.S. Public*, pg. 296

Peter, Alfred, Pres.--Elma Electronic Ltd., Wetzikon, Switzerland; *Int'l*, pg. 1305

Peter, Hugh M., Jr., Pres.--Peter Lumber Company, Pleasantville, NJ; *U.S. Private*, pg. 856

Peter, Jean D., Pres.--Union Carbide do Brasil S/A, Sao Paulo, Brazil; *U.S. Public*, pg. 1667

Peter, N.R., Pres.--The Bay, Toronto, Canada; *Int'l*, pg. 637

Peterfy, Joe, Pres. & Gen. Mgr.--Publicitas C.A., Guayaquil, Ecuador; *U.S. Public*, pg. 1422

Peters, Daniel L., Pres.--Nycomed Amersham, Princeton, NJ; *Int'l*, pg. 993

Peters, David, Pres.--Peters Construction Corp., Waterloo, IA; *U.S. Private*, pg. 856

Peters, David, Pres.--Sellstrom Manufacturing Co., Palatine, IL; *U.S. Private*, pg. 983

Peters, Donald J., Pres. & Chief Oper. Officer--American Stone-Mix, Inc., Towson, MD; *U.S. Private*, pg. 62

Peters, Earl W., Pres. & Chief Exec. Officer--Farmers Bank & Trust Co., Henderson, KY; *U.S. Public*, pg. 1217

Peters, Frederick C., III, Pres.--1st Main Line Bank, Saint Davids, PA; *U.S. Public*, pg. 1159

Peters, Gerret M., Pres.--Conap Inc., Olean, NY; *U.S. Private*, pg. 261

Peters, J.E., Pres.--Delmar Photographic and Printing Company, Charlotte, NC; *U.S. Private*, pg. 268

Peters, J.E., Pres.--Delmar Studios, Charlotte, NC; *U.S. Private*, pg. 268

Peters, James D., Pres. & Chief Oper. Officer--E & B Marine Incorporated, Edison, NJ; *U.S. Public*, pg. 1756

Peters, Jay, Pres.--Horizon International, Etobicoke, Canada; *Int'l*, pg. 1012

Peters, Jon, Co-Chief Exec. Officer--The Guber Peters Entertainment Company, Los Angeles, CA; *Int'l*, pg. 1283

Peters, Joseph M., Pres.--Weeks And Leo Co., Inc., Des Moines, IA; *U.S. Private*, pg. 1158

Peters, Lawrence W., Pres. & Chief Oper. Officer--Long Island Bancorp, Inc., Melville, NY; *U.S. Public*, pg. 1013

Peters, Robert L., Chm. Bd., Pres. & Chief Exec. Officer--Holmquist Grain & Lumber Co., Oakland, NE; *U.S. Private*, pg. 535

Peters, Samuel L., Pres.--Miami Systems Corporation, Cincinnati, OH; *U.S. Private*, pg. 740

Peters, Samuel L., Pres.--Specialty Envelope, Cincinnati, OH; *U.S. Private*, pg. 740

Petersen, Bruce, Pres.--American Reliable Insurance Company, Scottsdale, AZ; *U.S. Public*, pg. 67

Petersen, C., Pres.--Minebea Electronics Mexico S.A. de C.V., Nogales, Mexico; *Int'l*, pg. 868

Petersen, Fred M., Pres. & Chief Exec. Officer--Omaha Public Power District, Omaha, NE; *U.S. Private*, pg. 815

Petersen, Gary N., Pres. & Chief Oper. Officer--Minnegasco, Minneapolis, MN; *U.S. Public*, pg. 843

Petersen, K.C., Pres. & Chief Oper. Officer--Schenectady International, Inc., Schenectady, NY; *U.S. Private*, pg. 969

Petersen, March, Pres. & Sec.--Petersen Graphics Group, South Bend, IN; *U.S. Private*, pg. 856

Petersen, Mike, Pres. & Chief Oper. Officer--Baker's Supermarkets, Inc., Omaha, NE; *U.S. Public*, pg. 652

Petersen, Mike, Pres.--Petersen Aluminum Corporation, Elk Grove Village, IL; *U.S. Private*, pg. 856

Petersmeyer, Gary S., Pres. & Chief Oper. Officer--Collagen Corporation, Palo Alto, CA; *U.S. Public*, pg. 399

Peterson, Arthur M., Pres.--Kampgrounds of America, Inc., Billings, MT; *U.S. Private*, pg. 603

Peterson, Bob, Pres.--ENSR, Acton, MA; *U.S. Private*, pg. 354

Peterson, Borje, Pres.--ETP Transmission AB, Linkoping, Sweden; *Int'l*, pg. 678

Peterson, Carl, Pres., Chief Exec. Officer & Gen. Mgr.--Kansas City Chiefs Football Club, Inc., Kansas City, MO; *U.S. Private*, pg. 607

Peterson, Charles, Pres.--Hoffco/Comet Industries, Inc., Richmond, IN; *U.S. Private*, pg. 532

Peterson, David, Pres.--First District Association, Litchfield, MN; *U.S. Private*, pg. 406

Peterson, David H., Chm. Bd., Pres. & Chief Exec. Officer--NRG Energy, Inc., Minneapolis, MN; *U.S. Public*, pg. 1195

Peterson, Dean, Pres.--Harmon City, Inc., Salt Lake City, UT; *U.S. Private*, pg. 503

Peterson, Diane, Pres.--First Deposit National Bank, Tilton, NH; *U.S. Public*, pg. 1338

Peterson, Eric C., Pres.--Peterson American Corp., Southfield, MI; *U.S. Private*, pg. 857

Peterson, H.A., Pres.--Minn-Dak Growers, Ltd., Grand Forks, ND; *U.S. Private*, pg. 750

Peterson, Howard, Pres.--MNX Trucking, Inc., Saint Joseph, MO; *U.S. Public*, pg. 1046

Peterson, Jack, Pres.--Entertainment Partners, Burbank, CA; *U.S. Private*, pg. 554

Peterson, Jim, Pres. & Chief Exec. Officer--Bojangles' Restaraunts, Inc., Charlotte, NC; *U.S. Private*, pg. 154

Peterson, Kent D., Pres.--Bituminous Roadways, Inc., Inver Grove Heights, MN; *U.S. Private*, pg. 146

Peterson, Mark A., Pres.--Fidelity Investments (FMR Corp.), Boston, MA; *U.S. Private*, pg. 402

Peterson, Marvin, Pres.--Peterson Motor Company, Boise, ID; *U.S. Private*, pg. 857

Peterson, Michael, Pres.--Adolfson & Peterson, Inc., Minneapolis, MN; *U.S. Private*, pg. 17

Peterson, Norman A., Pres. & Chief Exec. Officer--Willis Corroon Corp. of Wisconsin, Milwaukee, WI; *Int'l*, pg. 1507

Peterson, Preben, Pres.--Danfoss Fluid Power, Racine, WI; *Int'l*, pg. 377

Peterson, Ralph R., Pres. & Chief Exec. Officer--CH2M Hill, Inc., Greenwood Village, CO; *U.S. Private*, pg. 195

Peterson, Randall J., Pres. & Chief Oper. Officer--Associated Bank Green Bay, Green Bay, WI; *U.S. Public*, *pg. 141*

Peterson, Raymond, Pres.--Eastern Fine Paper, Brewer, ME; *U.S. Private*, pg. 357

Peterson, Robert L., Chm. Bd., Pres. & Chief Exec. Officer--IBP, Inc., Dakota City, NE; *U.S. Public*, pg. 852

Peterson, Ron, Pres.--The Peterson Group, New York, NY; *U.S. Public*, pg. 1642

Peterson, William P., Pres. & Chief Exec. Officer--Clarin, Lake Bluff, IL; *U.S. Private*, pg. 242

Petersson, Conny, Pres.--Ventim AB, Kalmar, Sweden; *Int'l*, pg. 678

Petersson, Lars-Eric, Pres. & Chief Exec. Officer--Skandia Insurance Company Limited, Stockholm, Sweden; *Int'l*, pg. 1256

Petit de Mirbeck, Gilbert, Pres.--Sodetif, Ivry-sur-Seine, France; *Int'l*, pg. 560

Petit, Francesc, Mng. Partner--DPZ-Duailibi, Petit, Zaragoza, Propaganda S.A., Sao Paulo, Brazil; *Int'l*, pg. 352

Petitt, Richard G., Pres.--Conseco Life of New York, Orangeburg, NY; *U.S. Public*, pg. 433

Petitt, Richard G., Chm. Bd. & Pres.--Empire Insurance Group, New York, NY; *U.S. Public*, pg. 990

Petitt, Richard G., Chm. Bd., Pres. & Chief Exec. Officer--Allcity Insurance Co., New York, NY; *U.S. Public*, pg. 990

Petner, Edward J., Pres.--Lynch & Mayer, Inc, New York, NY; *U.S. Public*, pg. 998

Petot, Philippe, Pres.--Dickson Elberton Mills Inc., Elberton, GA; *U.S. Private*, pg. 331

Petrarca, Anthony A., Pres.--The Cedarwood Construction Company, Akron, OH; *U.S. Private*, pg. 221

Petras, Gregory J., Pres. & Chief Exec. Officer--National Health Enhancement Systems, Inc., Phoenix, AZ; *U.S. Public*, pg. 1157

Petrello, Anthony G., Pres. & Chief Oper. Officer--Nabors Industries, Inc., Houston, TX; *U.S. Public*, pg. 1148

Petricca, Robert W., Pres.--Petricca Industries, Inc., Pittsfield, MA; *U.S. Private*, pg. 858

Petricoff, Mark, Pres.--Leshner Mills. Inc., Hamilton, OH; *U.S. Private*, pg. 660

Petrie, Ed, Pres.--Ackerley Airport Advertising, New York, NY; *U.S. Public*, pg. 15

Petrie, William, Pres.--Hendrickson International, Woodridge, IL; *U.S. Private*, pg. 155

Petrilli, Frank, Pres., Chief Exec. Officer & Chief Oper. Officer--Waterhouse Investor Services, New York, NY; *Int'l*, pg. 1401

Petrocelli, A.F., Chm. Bd., Pres. & Chief Exec. Officer--United Capital Corp., Great Neck, NY; *U.S. Public*, pg. 1674

Petrou, David, Pres. & Chief Oper. Officer-Eisner Petrou & Assoc. Pub. Rels.--Eisner & Associates, Inc., Baltimore, MD; *U.S. Private*, pg. 366

Petrou, David, Pres. & Chief Oper. Officer--Eisner, Petrou & Associates, Inc., Baltimore, MD; *U.S. Private*, pg. 366

Petrowski, J. H., Pres.--CNG Power Services Corporation, Pittsburgh, PA; *U.S. Public*, pg. 435

Petrowski, Joseph H., Pres.--CNG Energy Services Corporation, Pittsburgh, PA; *U.S. Public*, pg. 435

Petruccio, Joseph, Mng. Partner & Chief Creative Officer--Compton Partners, New York, NY; *U.S. Public*, pg. 1422

Petry, Paul E., Pres. & Chief Oper. Officer--Boston Mutual Life Insurance Co., Canton, MA; *U.S. Private*, pg. 161

Petshler, Jan, Pres.--NCC Building - Umea, Umea, Sweden; *Int'l*, pg. 898

Pettapiece, Jay, CLU, Pres. & Chief Exec. Officer--Vision Financial Corporation, Keene, NH; *U.S. Private*, pg. 1141

Petterson, Bengt, Pres. & Chief Exec. Officer--Mo och Domsjo AB, Stockholm, Sweden; *Int'l*, pg. 885

Petterson, John S., Pres.--Tiffany & Co. ICT, Inc., New York, NY; *U.S. Public*, pg. 1609

Petterson, Thomas, Pres.--Elof Hansson AB, Goteborg, Sweden; *Int'l*, pg. 595

Pettersson, Torbjorn, Pres.--Stora Billerud AB, Skoghall, Sweden; *Int'l*, pg. 1302

Pettesson, Leif, Pres.--NCC Vaxjo, Vaxjo, Sweden; *Int'l*, pg. 899

Pettine, William, Pres.--Dutchmen Manufacturing, Inc., Goshen, IN; *U.S. Public*, pg. 1602

Pettine, William, Pres.--Thor Indiana, Inc., Bristol, IN; *U.S. Public*, pg. 1602

Pettit, Wallace, Pres.--Polka Dot Dairy/Tom Thumb, Inc., Hastings, MN; *U.S. Private*, pg. 874

Petty, Gary, Pres.--Johnson Storage Moving Co, Denver, CO; *U.S. Private*, pg. 594

Petty, George K., Pres. & Chief Exec. Officer--Telus Corporation, Edmonton, Canada; *Int'l*, pg. 1374

Petty, J.W., Pres. & Chief Exec. Officer--Orval Kent Food Co., Wheeling, IL; *U.S. Private*, pg. 820

Petty, John L., Pres. & Chief Exec. Officer--Mid-South Milling Company, Inc., Memphis, TN; *U.S. Private*, pg. 744

Petty, Mark, Pres.--Industrial Drives Div., Radford, VA; *U.S. Public*, pg. 965

Petty, R.B., Chm. Bd., Pres. & Chief Exec. Officer--SouthTrust Bank, Montgomery, Montgomery, AL; *U.S. Public*, pg. 1491

Peugeot, MM. Bertrand, Pres.--Cycles Europe, Romilly-sur-Seine, France; *Int'l*, pg. 350

Peveler, James J., Pres.--Western Electrochemical Company, Cedar City, UT; *U.S. Public*, pg. 88

Pevey, Scott, Principal & Mngmt. Supvr.--Publicis/Bloom, Dallas, TX; *Int'l*, pg. 469

Pewter, Graham, Pres.--Commercial Risk Partners Ltd., Hamilton, Bermuda; *Int'l*, pg. 1152

Peyrelevade, Jean, Chm. Bd., Pres. & Chief Exec. Officer--Credit Lyonnais S.A., Paris, France; *Int'l*, pg. 343

Peyrelongue, Guy, Pres. & Chief Exec. Officer--Cosmair, Inc., New York, NY; *Int'l*, pg. 818

Peyser, Paul, Pres.--David Peyser Sportswear Inc., Bay Shore, NY; *U.S. Private*, pg. 860

Peyton, Herbert H., Chm. Bd. & Pres.--Gate Petroleum Company, Jacksonville, FL; *U.S. Private*, pg. 441

Peyton, Robert G., Pres.--The W.W. Williams Company, Columbus, OH; *U.S. Private*, pg. 1178

Pfaff, Fred, Pres.--Anchor Metal Processing, Cleveland, OH; *U.S. Private*, pg. 71

Pfaff, Frederick A., Pres. & Chief Exec. Officer--Anchor Tool & Die Company, Cleveland, OH; *U.S. Private*, pg. 71

Pfaff, Jeff, Pres. & Gen. Mgr.--Condor Tool & Die, Inc., Cleveland, OH; *U.S. Private*, pg. 71

Pfeffer, Philip M., Pres. & Chief Oper. Officer--Random House, Inc., New York, NY; *U.S. Private*, pg. 20

Pfeifer, David, Pres.--Gamma One, Inc., North Haven, CT; *U.S. Public*, pg. 228

Pfeiffer, Didier, Vice Chm. & Mng. Dir.--Compagnie UAP, Paris, France; *Int'l*, pg. 323

Pfeiffer, Eckhard, Pres. & Chief Exec. Officer--COMPAQ Computer Corporation, Houston, TX; *U.S. Public*, pg. 417

Pfeiffer, Michael, Pres. & Chief Exec. Officer--Aircraft of Canada Ltd., Calgary, Canada; *U.S. Public*, pg. 1365

Pfeiffer, Richard N., Pres.--Neill-LaVielle Supply Co., Louisville, KY; *U.S. Private*, pg. 790

Pfennig, Richard, Pres.--PSA Airlines, Inc., Vandalia, OH; *U.S. Public*, pg. 1680

Pfister, Jacques, Pres. & Chief Exec. Officer--Orangina France, Aix-en-Provence, France; *Int'l*, pg. 566

Pfister, Karl A., Pres.--MPI International, Inc., Rochester Hills, MI; *Int'l*, pg. 737

Pflaster, Felix, Pres.--Arnold Steel Company, Inc., Lakewood, NJ; *U.S. Private*, pg. 84

Phares, Elwood W., II, Chm. Bd. & Pres.--Wechco, Inc., Princeton, NJ; *U.S. Private*, pg. 1158

Pharris, Walter, Pres. & Chief Exec. Officer--Fairfield Industries, Inc., Houston, TX; *U.S. Private*, pg. 391

Phelps, Ashton, Jr., Pres. & Publr.--The Times-Picayune Publishing Corp., New Orleans, LA; *U.S. Private*, pg. 1087

Phelps, Isaac E., II, Pres. & Chief Exec. Officer--World Aerospace Corporation, Maple Grove, MN; *U.S. Private*, pg. 1188

Phelps, Richard J., Pres.--Superior Brands, Inc., Quincy, MA; *Int'l*, pg. 917

Phelps, William, Pres.--Buffalo Air Handling, Amherst, VA; *U.S. Public*, pg. 103

Pherigo, William L., Pres., Chief Oper. Officer & Treas.--NBSC Corporation, Columbia, SC; *U.S. Public*, pg. 1549

Pherigo, William L., Pres. & Chief Exec. Officer--The National Bank of South Carolina, Sumter, SC; *U.S. Public*, pg. 1549

Phikas, Aristomenis D., Pres.--Hansen Hellas Abee, Thessaloniki, Greece; *Int'l*, pg. 289

Philbin, Thomas W., Pres.--HEC, Inc., Natick, MA; *U.S. Public*, pg. 1194

Philip, Robert W., Pres.--Schnitzer Steel Industries, Inc., Portland, OR; *U.S. Public*, pg. 1439

Philip, Robert W., Pres.--Proler International Corp., Portland, OR; *U.S. Public*, pg. 1440

Philipon, Jean, Pres.--Flender-Graffenstaden S.A., Illkirch-Graffenstaden, France; *Int'l*, pg. 400

Phillips, Cody H., Pres.--Delta Life Corporation, Memphis, TN; *U.S. Private*, pg. 59

Phillips, Daniel J., Gen. Mgr.--Partridge Meats, Inc., Cincinnati, OH; *U.S. Public*, pg. 75

Phillips, Donald C., Pres. & Chief Exec. Officer--Bank of Coweta, Newnan, GA; *U.S. Public*, pg. 1549

Phillips, Donald J.M., Principal--Vox Medica Corporation, Philadelphia, PA; *U.S. Private*, pg. 1143

Phillips, Ira H., Pres. & Chief Oper. Officer--Quoizel Inc., Goose Creek, SC; *U.S. Private*, pg. 901

Phillips, J. Russell, Pres. & Chief Exec. Officer--Shurflo Pump Manufacturing Co., Santa Ana, CA; *U.S. Public*, pg. 1767

Phillips, John H., Acting Pres. & Chief Exec. Officer--Cadmus, Sandston, VA; *U.S. Public*, pg. 290

Phillips, Michael, Pres.--Young-Phillips Sales Co., Clemmons, NC; *U.S. Private*, pg. 1201

Phillips, Michael J., Pres. & Chief Exec. Officer--Frank Russell Company, Tacoma, WA; *U.S. Private*, pg. 952

Phillips, R.J., Jr., Pres.--Pangburn Candy Company, Fort Worth, TX; *U.S. Private*, pg. 836

Phillips, Raymond A., Pres. & Chief Exec. Officer--Cives Corporation, Roswell, GA; *U.S. Private*, pg. 241

Phillips, Richard, Pres. & Chief Exec. Officer--Pilot Air Freight Corp., Lima, PA; *U.S. Private*, pg. 865

Phillips, Steven, Pres.--Gilmore Bros., Inc., Kalamazoo, MI; *U.S. Private*, pg. 454

Phillips, Thomas, Pres.--Groen, A Dover Industries Co., Elk Grove Village, IL; *U.S. Public*, pg. 521

Phillips, Thomas L., Chm. Bd., Pres. & Chief Exec. Officer--Phillips Publishing International, Inc., Potomac, MD; *U.S. Private*, pg. 862

Phillips, William, Pres.--World Book, Inc., Columbus, OH; *U.S. Public*, pg. 218

Phillips, William, Pres.--Phillips Service Industries, Inc., Livonia, MI; *U.S. Private*, pg. 862

Philosophe, Isidore, Pres. & Chief Exec. Officer--Cinram Ltd., Scarborough, Canada; *Int'l*, pg. 293

Philpot, Gerald, Pres.--Lagerquist Corporation, Minneapolis, MN; *U.S. Public*, pg. 521

Phippen, Michael, Pres. & Chief Oper. Officer--Western Staff Services, Walnut Creek, CA; *U.S. Public*, pg. 1760

Phippen, Michael K., Pres.--Western Light Industrial Services, Walnut Creek, CA; *U.S. Public*, pg. 1760

Phippen, Peter, Mng. Dir.--BBC Magazines, London, United Kingdom; *Int'l*, pg. 114

Phipps, Allen, Pres. & Chief Exec. Officer--SRI Consulting, Menlo Park, CA; *U.S. Private*, pg. 958

Phornprapha, Phornpong, Pres.--Siam Kabaya Co., Ltd., Samutprakan, Thailand; *Int'l*, pg. 727

Phornprapha, Phornthep, Pres.--Bangkok Komatsu Co., Ltd., Chon Buri, Thailand; *Int'l*, pg. 745

Piana, Michael R., Gen. Mgr.--Wolf's Head Oil Company, Houston, TX; *U.S. Public*, pg. 1273

Piatt, Lou, Pres.--The Prudential - Jon Douglas Company, Los Angeles, CA; *U.S. Private*, pg. 892

Piazza, John, Chief Exec. Officer--Sara Lee Hosiery, Winston Salem, NC; *U.S. Public*, pg. 1434

Piccinini, Robert M., Chm. Bd., Chief Exec. Officer & Pres.--Save Mart Supermarkets, Modesto, CA; *U.S. Private*, pg. 968

Piccirilli, Joseph, Vice Chm., Pres. & Chief Exec. Officer--Keystone Brewers, Inc., Pittsburgh, PA; *U.S. Private*, pg. 618

Piccirilli, Joseph, Pres. & Chief Oper. Officer--Pittsburgh Brewing Company, Pittsburgh, PA; *U.S. Private*, pg. 619

Pichan, William W., Pres.--T & N Industries, Inc., Ann Arbor, MI; *Int'l*, pg. 1334

Pichotta, Nicholas, Pres.--CooperSurgical Inc., Shelton, CT; *U.S. Public*, pg. 442

Pickens, Steve A., Pres.--Nocona Boot Co., Nocona, TX; *U.S. Public*, pg. 937

Pickering, Allen, Pres.--Pickering Inc., Tacoma, WA; *U.S. Private*, pg. 864

Pickering, Ken, Pres.--Minera Escondida Limitada, Santiago, Chile; *Int'l*, pg. 227

Pickett, Lenord, Pres.--Crosman Corp., East Bloomfield, NY; *U.S. Private*, pg. 291

Pickett, Leonard, Pres.--Crosman Airguns, East Bloomfield, NY; *U.S. Private*, pg. 291

Pickett, Martin, Pres.--Griswold Industries, Inc., Costa Mesa, CA; *U.S. Private*, pg. 482

Pickett, Martin, Pres.--Cla-Val Div., Newport Beach, CA; *U.S. Private*, pg. 482

Pickett, Michael H., Pres. & Publisher--Harcourt Brace & Company Farm Publications Inc., Orlando, FL; *U.S. Public*, pg. 783

Pickle, Kirby, Pres.--MFS Intelenet Companies, San Ramon, CA; *U.S. Public*, pg. 1779

Pickle, Kirby G., Pres. & Chief Exec. Officer--MFS Intelenet Companies, Jersey City, NJ; *U.S. Public*, pg. 1779

Picknelly, Peter A., Jr., Pres. & Chief Exec. Officer--Peter Pan Bus Lines, Inc., Springfield, MA; *U.S. Private*, pg. 856

Piecuch, J.M., Pres. & Chief Exec. Officer--Lafarge Canada Inc., Montreal, Canada; *Int'l*, pg. 789

Pien, Howard, Pres.-Pharmaceuticals/North America--SmithKline Beecham Pharmaceuticals, International Division, Brentford, United Kingdom; *Int'l*, pg. 1264

Pieper, Roel, Pres. & Chief Exec. Officer--UB Networks, Santa Clara, CA; *Int'l*, pg. 924

pier, Arne, Pres.--Malmo Regional Office, Malmo, Sweden; *Int'l*, pg. 899

Pieranunzi, Richard, Pres.-U.S. Opers.--SGS-Thomson Microelectronics, Inc., Carrollton, TX; *Int'l*, pg. 1153

Pierard, Morin, Pres.--ETEX, Vernouillet, France; *Int'l*, pg. 430

Pierce, Brian, Pres. & Chief Exec. Officer--Peirce-Phelps, Inc., Philadelphia, PA; *U.S. Private*, pg. 847

Pierce, Cecil, Pres.--Rogers Bridge Company, Inc., Atlanta, GA; *U.S. Private*, pg. 993

Pierce, Garrett E., Pres. & Chief Exec. Officer--Materials Research Corporation, Gilbert, AZ; *Int'l*, pg. 1283

Pierce, Harvey, Pres. & Chief Oper. Officer--American Family Mutual Insurance Co., Madison, WI; *U.S. Private*, pg. 53

Pierce, J.L., Pres. & Chief Exec. Officer--Mid-Continent Casualty Company, Tulsa, OK; *U.S. Public*, pg. 75
Pierce, Pamela, Pres.--Austin Productions, Inc., Holbrook, NY; *U.S. Private*, pg. 100
Pierce, Roger, Pres.--First Data Corporation, Hackensack, NJ; *U.S. Public*, pg. 630
Pierce, Vince, Pres. & Chief Oper. Officer--McIlhenny Company, Avery Island, LA; *U.S. Private*, pg. 722
Piergallini, Alfred A., Pres.--Gerber Products Company, Fremont, MI; *Int'l*, pg. 973
Pieros, Larry, Pres. & Chief Exec. Officer--Armor All Products Group, Oakland, CA; *U.S. Public*, pg. 387
Pierringer, Dean E., Pres.--Research Products Corporation, Madison, WI; *U.S. Private*, pg. 924
Pietramala, Anthony, Pres. & Chief Oper. Officer--Pro-Pastries Inc., Mississauga, Canada; *U.S. Public*, pg. 806
Pietramala, Anthony, Pres. & Chief Oper. Officer--Heinz Bakery Products, Mississauga, Canada; *U.S. Public*, pg. 806
Pietrini, Andrew, Chm. Bd., Pres. & Chief Exec. Officer--UIS, Inc., Jersey City, NJ; *U.S. Private*, pg. 1113
Pifer, Jay S., Pres.--Monongahela Power Co., Fairmont, WV; *U.S. Public*, pg. 42
Pifer, Jay S., Pres.--The Potomac Edison Co., Hagerstown, MD; *U.S. Public*, pg. 42
Pike, Bruce, Pres.-Howell Exports--Howell Instruments Inc., Fort Worth, TX; *U.S. Private*, pg. 543
Pike, Gregory, Pres. & Chief Exec. Officer--First County Bank, Chardon, OH; *U.S. Public*, pg. 607
Pike, Larry R., Chm., Pres. & Chief Exec. Officer--The Union Central Life Insurance Co., Cincinnati, OH; *U.S. Private*, pg. 1118
Pike, Matthew Lee, III, Pres.--Elite Lamp, Inc., West Memphis, AR; *U.S. Private*, pg. 371
Pikus, Stanton M., Chm. Bd., Pres. & Chief Exec. Officer--Canterbury Corporate Services, Inc., Medford, NJ; *U.S. Public*, pg. 301
Piletti, Dominic, Pres.--Thomas & Betts Electronics Division, Memphis, TN; *U.S. Public*, pg. 1597
Pilgrim, Lindy M., Pres. & Chief Oper. Officer--Pilgrim's Pride Corporation, Pittsburg, TX; *U.S. Public*, pg. 1296
Pilkama, Eero, Pres.--MTV Finland, Helsinki, Finland; *Int'l*, pg. 827
Pillard, L.G., Pres.--A.E. Staley Manufacturing Co., Decatur, IL; *Int'l*, pg. 1356
Pilliter, Charles J., Pres. & Sr. V.P.-Northern California--Certified Grocers of California, Los Angeles, CA; *U.S. Private*, pg. 226
Pillow, George, Pres.--NAFCO National Floor Company, Florence, AL; *Int'l*, pg. 415
Pim, Ken, Pres.--Channel Products, Inc., Chesterland, OH; *U.S. Private*, pg. 228
Pinard, Jean C., Pres. & Chief Oper. Officer--Hypotheques CDPQ, Montreal, Canada; *Int'l*, pg. 249
Pinault, G., Pres. & Dir. General--Brossette BTI SA, Lyon, France; *Int'l*, pg. 1511
Pindyck, Bruce E., Chm. Bd. & Chief Exec. Officer--Meridian Industries, Inc., Milwaukee, WI; *U.S. Private*, pg. 732
Pineau-Valencienne, Didier, Chm. Bd. & Chief Exec. Officer--Schneider S.A., Boulogne-Billancourt, France; *Int'l*, pg. 1207
Pingel, Paul, Chm. Bd. & Pres.--New Cooperative Inc., Fort Dodge, IA; *U.S. Private*, pg. 792
Pink, Ronald A., Pres. & Chief Oper. Officer--Distribution America, Des Plaines, IL; *U.S. Private*, pg. 335
Pinker, Lamont T., Pres. & Chief Oper. Officer--Gateway Communications, Johnson City, NY; *U.S. Private*, pg. 693
Pinkert, Michael, Pres. & Chief Exec. Officer--MHM Services Inc., Vienna, VA; *U.S. Public*, pg. 1027
Pinkerton, Guy C., Chm. Bd., Pres. & Chief Exec. Officer--Washington Federal Savings, Seattle, WA; *U.S. Public*, pg. 1740
Pinkerton, John H., Pres. & Chief Exec. Officer--Lomak Petroleum Inc., Fort Worth, TX; *U.S. Public*, pg. 1012
Pinkerton, John H., Pres.--Lomak Production Company, Hartville, OH; *U.S. Public*, pg. 1012
Pinkerton, John H., Pres. & Chief Exec. Officer--Lomak Operating Company, Hartville, OH; *U.S. Public*, pg. 1012
Pinkham, Mike, Pres. & Chief Exec. Officer--Columbia Universal Life Insurance Company, Austin, TX; *U.S. Public*, pg. 79
Pinkin, James E., Pres.--The Corporate Communications Group, Whippany, NJ; *U.S. Private*, pg. 276
Pinner, Douglas K., Chm. Bd., Pres. & Chief Exec. Officer--Tokheim Corporation, Fort Wayne, IN; *U.S. Public*, pg. 1620
Pinnow, Werner, Pres.--Hapag-Lloyd (America), Inc., Piscataway, NJ; *Int'l*, pg. 596
Pino, John A., Pres. & Chief Exec. Officer--ACT Manufacturing, Hudson, MA; *U.S. Public*, pg. 3
Pinon, Christian, Pres.--Alcatel Telspace, Nanterre, France; *Int'l*, pg. 56
Pinsley, Sol, Chm. Bd., Pres., Chief Exec. & Chief Oper. Officer--Espey Mfg. & Electronics Corp., Saratoga Springs, NY; *U.S. Public*, pg. 592
Pinto, Fernando, Pres. & Chief Exec. Officer--Varig Brazilian Airlines S.A., Rio de Janeiro, Brazil; *Int'l*, pg. 1451
Pinto, James J., Pres. & Chief Exec. Officer--Action Instruments, Inc., San Diego, CA; *U.S. Private*, pg. 15
Pinzino, Thomas F., Pres. & Chief Exec. Officer--Sunnyland Refining Co., Inc., Birmingham, AL; *U.S. Private*, pg. 607
Piper, Addison L., Chm. Bd., Pres. & Chief Exec. Officer--Piper Jaffray Companies, Inc., Minneapolis, MN; *U.S. Public*, pg. 1300
Pipitone, Guy L., Div. Mgr.--Ohio Edison Co.-Akron Div., Akron, OH; *U.S. Public*, pg. 645
Pippin, M. Lenny, Pres. & Chief Exec. Officer--Lykes Brothers Inc., Tampa, FL; *U.S. Private*, pg. 682
Pirella, Emanuele, Pres. & Mng. Dir.--Pirella Gottsche Lowe, Milan, Italy; *U.S. Private*, pg. 678
Pires, Ernani, Pres. & Chief Exec. Officer--SGS International Certification Services, Inc., Rutherford, NJ; *Int'l*, pg. 1153
Pirtle, Ronald M., Gen. Mgr.--Delphi Harrison Thermal Systems, Lockport, NY; *U.S. Public*, pg. 719
Pisa, Michael A., Jr., Pres.--Continental Paper & Supply Co., Detroit, MI; *U.S. Private*, pg. 269
Pisani, Anthony, Pres.--APG Security, Inc., Denver, CO; *U.S. Private*, pg. 7
Pisani, Gerald V., Pres.--Pollak Division, Boston, MA; *U.S. Private*, pg. 1045
Pishkur, Walter J., Pres.--Consumers Ohio Water Company, Boardman, OH; *U.S. Public*, pg. 438
Piske, Richard A., III, Pres.--Olsten Staffing Services, Melville, NY; *U.S. Public*, pg. 1221
Pistilli, Frederick M., Pres.--Westclox, Norcross, GA; *U.S. Private*, pg. 445
Pistilli, Frederick M., Chm. & Chief Exec. Officer--Seth Thomas, Norcross, GA; *U.S. Private*, pg. 445
Pistulka, Louis, Gen. Mgr.--Big Horn Co-Op Marketing Association, Greybull, WY; *U.S. Private*, pg. 143
Pitkowsky, Murray, Pres.--Bioplex Medical B.V., Vaals, Netherlands; *U.S. Public*, pg. 487
Pitkowsky, Murray, Pres.--Datascope FSC, Ltd., Paramus, NJ; *U.S. Public*, pg. 487
Pitkowsky, Murray, Pres.--Datascope Holding Corp., Paramus, NJ; *U.S. Public*, pg. 487
Pitkowsky, Murray, Pres.--Datascope B.V., Hoevelaken, Netherlands; *U.S. Public*, pg. 488
Pitou, Augustus, III, Pres.--K2 Bike, Woonsocket, RI; *U.S. Public*, pg. 940
Pitt, David, Pres.--Art's-Way Manufacturing Co., Inc., Armstrong, IA; *U.S. Public*, pg. 136
Pitt, David, Pres.--Kvaerner AM Ltd., United Kingdom; *Int'l*, pg. 767
Pitt, Murray C., Pres.--Murray's Discount Auto Stores, Belleville, MI; *U.S. Private*, pg. 768
Pittelkow, Charles R., Chm. Bd. & Pres.--Equitable Savings & Loan Association, Wauwatosa, WI; *U.S. Private*, pg. 380
Pitterich, Michael P., Chm. Bd. & Pres.--Moltrup Steel Products Company, Beaver Falls, PA; *U.S. Private*, pg. 756
Pittman, Gary, Chm. Bd., Pres., Chief Exec., Chief Oper. & Chief Fin. Officer--PCI, Austin, TX; *U.S. Private*, pg. 826
Pitts, Jerry M., Pres. & Chief Oper. Officer--Bayou Steel Corporation, La Place, LA; *U.S. Public*, pg. 197
Pitts, Keith B., Chm. Bd., Pres. & Chief Exec. Officer--Paragon Health Network, Inc., Atlanta, GA; *U.S. Public*, pg. 1256
Pitts, Preston, Pres. & Chief Oper. Officer--Legacy Marketing Group, Petaluma, CA; *U.S. Private*, pg. 658
Pitz, Peter E., Pres. & Publr.--The Wichita Eagle and Beacon Publishing Co., Inc., Wichita, KS; *U.S. Public*, pg. 964
Pizzagalli, Angelo P., Pres.--Pizzagalli Construction Co., South Burlington, VT; *U.S. Private*, pg. 868
Pizzini, Jose, Pres.--Direct Press Modern Litho Corporation, Huntington Station, NY; *U.S. Private*, pg. 334
Pizzuti, Everett V., Pres. & Chief Oper. Officer--Astro-Med, Inc., West Warwick, RI; *U.S. Public*, pg. 141
Pla, Carlos, Chm. Bd., Pres. & Dir.-Opers.--Noblex Argentina S.A.C. e I., Buenos Aires, Argentina; *Int'l*, pg. 951
Placek, Robert A., Chm. Bd., Pres. & Chief Exec. Officer--Wegener Corporation, Duluth, GA; *U.S. Public*, pg. 1751
Plais, Marie Helene, Pres.--Sofamor, S.N.C., Rang-du-Fliers, France; *U.S. Public*, pg. 1482
Plamann, Alfred A., Pres. & Chief Exec. Officer--Certified Grocers of California, Los Angeles, CA; *U.S. Private*, pg. 226
Plana, Eduardo, Chm. Bd. & Chief Exec. Officer--EURO RSCG, Madrid, Spain; *Int'l*, pg. 602
Planes, John, Pres., Chief Exec. Officer & Sec.--Planes Moving And Storage, Inc., Cincinnati, OH; *U.S. Private*, pg. 869
Plant, George E., Pres.--Bardon (England) Ltd., Leicester, United Kingdom; *Int'l*, pg. 166
Plante, N.R., Div. Pres.--Sorel Forge Inc., Sorel, Canada; *Int'l*, pg. 1262
Plasman, Christian G., Pres.--Baker Knapp & Tubbs Inc., Grand Rapids, MI; *U.S. Private*, pg. 630
Platania, Andrew, Pres.--The Finals, Inc., Port Jervis, NY; *U.S. Private*, pg. 404
Plate, Dick, Pres.--Atlas Copco Compressor Canada, Dorval, Canada; *Int'l*, pg. 96
Platek, Henry J., Jr., Pres.--Krantor Corporation, Syosset, NY; *U.S. Public*, pg. 966
Plato, James N., Pres.--United Presidential Life Insurance Co., Carmel, IN; *U.S. Public*, pg. 434
Platt, George, Pres. & Chief Exec. Officer--InteCom, Dallas, TX; *Int'l*, pg. 794
Platt, Lewis E., Chm. Bd., Pres. & Chief Exec. Officer--Hewlett-Packard Company, Palo Alto, CA; *U.S. Public*, pg. 813
Platt, Marc, Pres.--Tri-Star Pictures, Inc., Culver City, CA; *Int'l*, pg. 1282
Platt, Stuart, Pres.--DRS Precision Echo, Inc., Santa Clara, CA; *U.S. Public*, pg. 474
Platt, Stuart F., Pres.--Data Systems Group, Santa Clara, CA; *U.S. Public*, pg. 474
Pleshette Murphy, Ann, Editor-in-Chief--Parents Magazine, New York, NY; *Int'l*, pg. 191
Plimpton, T.E., Gen. Mgr.--Peterbilt Motors Co., Denton, TX; *U.S. Public*, pg. 1247
Plocinik, Tom, Pres.--Trico Products Corporation, Buffalo, NY; *Int'l*, pg. 1397
Plouffe, Dan, Pres.--Firstcom Marketing Inc., Toronto, Canada; *U.S. Private*, pg. 1200
Plummer, Terry, Pres.--The Zippertubing Co., Los Angeles, CA; *U.S. Private*, pg. 1207
Poage, Roy L., Pres.--DeKalb Swine Breeders, Inc., De Kalb, IL; *U.S. Public*, pg. 493
Pocapalia, Dan, Chm. Bd., Pres. & Chief Exec. Officer--Kit Manufacturing Company, Long Beach, CA; *U.S. Public*, pg. 962
Pochick, Daniel T., Pres. & Chief Exec. Officer--Rish Equipment Company, Bluefield, WV; *U.S. Private*, pg. 932
Pocklington, Terry, Pres.--Hansberger Precision Golf Inc., Pontotoc, MS; *U.S. Private*, pg. 499
Pode, John S., Sr. V.P. & Pres.- Comet Rice Div.--American Rice Inc., Houston, TX; *U.S. Public*, pg. 591
Podowski, Charles, Pres.--Advanta Insurance Companies, Horsham, PA; *U.S. Public*, pg. 22
Podowski, Charles H., Pres.--Advanta Business Services, Voorhees, NJ; *U.S. Public*, pg. 22
Poe, John D., Pres. & Chief Exec. Officer--Semtech Corporation, Newbury Park, CA; *U.S. Public*, pg. 1456
Poe, Keith, Pres.--Prime Manufacturing Company, Oak Creek, WI; *U.S. Public*, pg. 1711
Poe, Thomas R., Pres. & Chief Exec. Officer--National City Commercial Finance, Inc., Cleveland, OH; *U.S. Public*, pg. 1154
Poehlmann, Karl M., Pres. & Chief Exec. Officer--George Uhe Co., Inc., Paramus, NJ; *U.S. Private*, pg. 1115
Poehner, Michael, Pres. & Chief Exec. Officer--DMR Group, Inc., Montreal, Canada; *Int'l*, pg. 527
Pogge, Horst, Pres.--Grassland Equipment & Irrigation Corp., Latham, NY; *U.S. Private*, pg. 471
Pogge, Horst, Pres.--Grassland Equipment & Irrigation Corp., Blasdell, NY; *U.S. Private*, pg. 471
Poggi, Michael J., Pres. & Chief Exec. Officer--Willis Corroon Corp. of Western Michigan, Grand Rapids, MI; *Int'l*, pg. 1507
Pogmore, James W., Pres. & Chief Exec. Officer--Cramer Company, Old Saybrook, CT; *U.S. Public*, pg. 1238
Pogran, Jed, Pres.--Gump's, San Francisco, CA; *U.S. Public*, pg. 782
Pohan, Armand, Pres.--A-P-A Transport Corp., North Bergen, NJ; *U.S. Private*, pg. 2
Pohlad, Carl R., Pres.--Marquette Bancshares Inc., Minneapolis, MN; *U.S. Private*, pg. 706
Pohlad, Carl R., Chm. Bd.--Mesaba Holdings, Inc., Minneapolis, MN; *U.S. Public*, pg. 1099
Pohlman, Bert, Pres.--Richco Inc., Chicago, IL; *U.S. Private*, pg. 929
Pohs, Arnold C., Pres. & Chief Exec. Officer--CommNet Cellular Inc., Englewood, CO; *U.S. Public*, pg. 414
Poindexter, John, Owner--Gem Top Mfg., Inc., Clackamas, OR; *U.S. Private*, pg. 443
Poindexter, John E., Pres.--Basic Construction Company, Newport News, VA; *U.S. Private*, pg. 121
Poinssot, Alain, Chm. Bd., Pres. & Chief Exec. Officer--GEODIS, Paris, France; *Int'l*, pg. 549
Poirier, Robert J., Chm. Bd., Pres. & Chief Exec. Officer--USA Floral Products, Inc., Washington, DC; *U.S. Public*, pg. 1685
Poirier, Victor L., Pres., Chief Exec. & Oper. Officer--Thermo Cardiosystems Inc., Woburn, MA; *U.S. Public*, pg. 1592
Poiry, James R., Pres.--Harris-Kayot, Inc., Fort Wayne, IN; *U.S. Private*, pg. 506
Poist, William G., Pres. & Chief Exec. Officer--Commonwealth Energy System, Cambridge, MA; *U.S. Public*, pg. 414
Poitevint, A.L., Chm. Bd. & Pres.--Flint River Mills, Bainbridge, GA; *U.S. Private*, pg. 413
Pojani, Gregory, Pres.--Wasco Products, Inc., Sanford, ME; *U.S. Private*, pg. 1152
Pokelwaldt, Robert N., Chm. Bd., Pres. & Chief Exec. Officer--York International Corporation, York, PA; *U.S. Public*, pg. 1788
Pol, Steve W., Chm. Bd. & Pres.--Airtrol, Inc., Baton Rouge, LA; *U.S. Private*, pg. 29
Polacheck, Isabelle, Pres.--Reliable Knitting Works, Milwaukee, WI; *U.S. Private*, pg. 920
Polack, Jack, Pres.--Acme Poultry Company, Inc., Renton, WA; *U.S. Private*, pg. 13
Polan, Jesse N., Pres.--Federal APD, Inc., Farmington, MI; *U.S. Public*, pg. 616
Poland, William F., Pres. & Chief Exec. Officer--Willis Corroon Corp. of California, San Francisco, CA; *Int'l*, pg. 1505
Polensky, W., Chief Exec. Officer--William Prym GmbH & Co. KG, Stolberg, Germany; *Int'l*, pg. 1499
Poling, Brock, Pres.--MC2 Cyberspace, Columbus, OH; *U.S. Private*, pg. 955
Politis, Donald A., Pres.--Global Special Risks Insurance Services California, San Francisco, CA; *Int'l*, pg. 1503
Polivka, Sherri A., Pres. & Chief Oper. Officer--Ivy, Vernon, CA; *U.S. Public*, pg. 948
Polivka, Sherri A., Pres. & Chief Oper. Officer--A.J. Brandon, Vernon, CA; *U.S. Public*, pg. 948
Pollack, Aileen C., Pres. & Chief Oper. Officer--Key Industries, Inc., Fort Scott, KS; *U.S. Private*, pg. 618
Pollack, Dan, Pres. & Chief Oper. Officer--Stock Yards Packing Co., Inc., Chicago, IL; *U.S. Private*, pg. 1043
Pollack, Gerald M., Pres.--Pollack Corporation, Scarborough, ME; *U.S. Private*, pg. 874
Pollack, Larry, Pres. & Chief Fin. Officer--Heublein Inc., Hartford, CT; *Int'l*, pg. 410
Pollaert, Ted, Pres.--Lurgi Corporation, Paramus, NJ; *Int'l*, pg. 861
Pollak, Henry M., Pres.--American Machine & Tool Company, Inc., Royersford, PA; *U.S. Private*, pg. 58
Pollak, Louis M., Pres.--Injectron Corporation, Plainfield, NJ; *U.S. Private*, pg. 563
Pollara, John, Pres.--Zieman Manufacturing Company, Whittier, CA; *U.S. Private*, pg. 1205
Polley, Dale, Pres.--First American National Bank, Bowling Green, KY; *U.S. Public*, pg. 624
Polley, David, Pres. & Chief Oper. Officer--World Carpets, Inc., Dalton, GA; *U.S. Private*, pg. 1190
Polley, R. Stephen, Chm. Bd., Pres. & Chief Exec. Officer--Interphase Corporation, Dallas, TX; *U.S. Public*, pg. 908
Pollick, Richard R., Pres.--Toro Probiotic Products, Inc., Bloomington, MN; *U.S. Public*, pg. 1624
Pollinger, Richard, Pres.--Stapo Hollander Industries, Lakewood, NJ; *U.S. Private*, pg. 1033

Pollock, John, Pres. & Chief Exec. Officer--General Casualty Company of Illinois, Freeport, IL; Int'l, pg. 346
Pollock, John G., Pres.--ServiceMaster Business & Industry Group, Downers Grove, IL; U.S. Public, pg. 1462
Pollock, John R., Pres. & Chief Exec. Officer--General Casualty Company of Wisconsin, Sun Prairie, WI; Int'l, pg. 345
Pollock, Larry M., Pres. & Chief Exec. Officer--Canadian Western Bank, Edmonton, Canada; Int'l, pg. 259
Pollock, Mayer, II, Pres., Chief Exec. Officer & Chief Oper. Officer--The Pollock Corp., Pottstown, PA; U.S. Private, pg. 874
Pollock, Robert B., Pres. & Chief Exec. Officer--Fortis Benefits Insurance Company, Kansas City, MO; Int'l, pg. 499
Pollock, William I., Pres.--Atlas Alloys, Etobicoke, Canada; Int'l, pg. 1118
Polman, Ron, Pres.--Furness BV, Rotterdam, Netherlands; Int'l, pg. 530
Polo, Paul S., Pres.--Gunver Manufacturing Co., Manchester, CT; U.S. Private, pg. 488
Pomerantz, Howard K., Pres.--Franklin-Burlington Plastics, Conshohocken, PA; U.S. Public, pg. 1496
Pomeranz, Edward, Pres.--Stanley Roberts, Inc., Lodi, NJ; U.S. Private, pg. 936
Pomeroy, Cynthia, Pres.--First American Title Guaranty Agency of Cheyenne, Cheyenne, WY; U.S. Public, pg. 625
Pomeroy, David B., Chm. Bd., Pres. & Chief Exec. Officer--Pomeroy Computer Resources, Hebron, KY; U.S. Public, pg. 1315
Pomeroy, Jeffrey C., Pres.--HNTB Design & Build, Irvine, CA; U.S. Private, pg. 492
Pompea, Charles E., Pres.--Primac Corp., Middletown, CT; U.S. Private, pg. 883
Pond-Heide, Debbie, Pres.--Adecco S.A., Lausanne, Switzerland; Int'l, pg. 23
Pond, Debbie, Pres.--Adecco Employment Services, Redwood City, CA; Int'l, pg. 24
Pond, Gerry, Pres. & Chief Exec. Officer--Bruncor, Inc., Saint John, Canada; Int'l, pg. 230
Pond, Gerry, Pres. & Chief Exec. Officer--The New Brunswick Telephone Company, Limited (NBTel), Saint John, Canada; Int'l, pg. 230
Pond, P. Michael, Pres.--Caterpillar Investment Management Ltd., Peoria, IL; U.S. Public, pg. 316
Ponsolle, Patrick, Exec. Chm. & Co.-Pres.--The Eurotunnel Group, London, United Kingdom; Int'l, pg. 466
Pontano, Benjamin A., Dr., Pres.--COMSAT Laboratories, Clarksburg, MD; U.S. Public, pg. 424
Pontarelli, Thomas, Pres.--Washington National Insurance Co., Carmel, IN; U.S. Public, pg. 434
Pontet, Philippe, Chm., Pres. & Chief Exec. Officer--Compagnie Generale Maritime et Financiere, Suresnes, France; Int'l, pg. 322
Pontillo, Charles, Pres.--MTI/The Image Group, Inc., New York, NY; U.S. Private, pg. 688
Pontius, Stanley N., Pres. & Chief Exec. Officer--First Financial Bancorp, Hamilton, OH; U.S. Public, pg. 632
Pool, Daniel F., Pres.--Cosco Fire Protection Inc., Gardena, CA; U.S. Public, pg. 1795
Poole, A. Mitchell, Pres. & Chief Oper. Officer--Allied Holdings, Inc., Decatur, GA; U.S. Public, pg. 48
Poole, Chris, Pres.--Elite Information Systems, Inc., Los Angeles, CA; U.S. Public, pg. 258
Poore, Jeffrey, Dr., Pres.--CompHealth, Inc., Salt Lake City, UT; U.S. Public, pg. 839
Pope, Carter D., Pres.--Atlanta Blueprint Company, Atlanta, GA; U.S. Public, pg. 1735
Pope, Graham, Pres.--BGF Industries Inc., Greensboro, NC; U.S. Private, pg. 106
Pope, Jim, Pres.--Atlantic States Bank, Norcross, GA; U.S. Public, pg. 629
Pope, John R., Pres.--Williams Printing Company, Atlanta, GA; U.S. Public, pg. 1736
Pope, John W., Pres.--Variety Wholesalers, Incorporated, Raleigh, NC; U.S. Private, pg. 1134
Pope, Lawrence D.J., Pres.--Brown & Root Petroleum and Chemicals, Houston, TX; U.S. Public, pg. 775
Pope, Michael, Pres.--Control Dynamics Division, Huntsville, AL; U.S. Private, pg. 106
Pope, Robert M., Pres.--Minot Builders Supply Association, Minot, ND; U.S. Private, pg. 751
Pope, W.A., Pres.--NZU, Inc., Albuquerque, NM; U.S. Public, pg. 1172
Pope, William A., Pres. & Chief Exec. Officer--New Mexico & Arizona Land Co., Phoenix, AZ; U.S. Public, pg. 1172
Pope, William A., Pres.--NZ Development Corporation, Phoenix, AZ; U.S. Public, pg. 1172
Pope, William A., Pres.--NZ Properties, Inc., Phoenix, AZ; U.S. Public, pg. 1172
Popeil, Ron, Pres.--Ronco, Inventions. LLC, Chatsworth, CA; U.S. Private, pg. 943
Popik, Carlos, Pres.--Monsanto Argentina S.A.I.C., Buenos Aires, Argentina; U.S. Public, pg. 1125
Popp, John F., Chm. Bd. & Pres.--Perfection Bakeries Inc., Fort Wayne, IN; U.S. Private, pg. 852
Poppe, Rick, Pres.--Weitz-Cohen Construction Co., Denver, CO; U.S. Private, pg. 1161
Poppe, William G., Jr., Pres.--Primepak Company, Teaneck, NJ; U.S. Private, pg. 884
Popwell, Lynda W., Pres.--Carolina Eastman Co., Columbia, SC; U.S. Public, pg. 550
Poran, Rafi, Pres.--Adanet Communications, Or Yehud, Israel; Int'l, pg. 645
Porco, Dominick, Pres.--News America Publishing Inc., New York, NY; Int'l, pg. 925
Port, Nancy, Pres. & Chief Oper. Officer--Equity Services, Inc., Montpelier, VT; U.S. Private, pg. 785
Porta, Earnest, Pres.--DCV Inc., Wilmington, DE; U.S. Private, pg. 301
Portelance, M., Pres.--Labatt Breweries of Canada - Prairie Region, Edmonton, Canada; Int'l, pg. 679
Porter, Charles, Chm. & Partner--Crispin Porter & Bogusky, Miami, FL; U.S. Private, pg. 290
Porter, Donald E., Pres., Chief Exec. Officer & Treas.--The Woodbury Telephone Company, Woodbury, CT; U.S. Public, pg. 1491
Porter, George, Pres.--Levi's Brand, San Francisco, CA; U.S. Private, pg. 663
Porter, Jamie D., Gen. Mgr.--Missouri Auction Services Corp., Springfield, MO; U.S. Private, pg. 282
Porter, Jim, Pres. & Chief Exec. Officer--Higginbotham-Bartlett Co., Lubbock, TX; U.S. Private, pg. 527
Porter, M. McNeil, Pres. & Chief Exec. Officer--CSX Intermodal, Inc., Hunt Valley, MD; U.S. Public, pg. 284
Porter, Michael, Pres. & Chief Exec. Officer--Acheson Industries, Inc., Port Huron, MI; U.S. Private, pg. 12
Porter, Michael A., Pres. & Chief Oper. Officer--Belcan Corporation, Cincinnati, OH; U.S. Private, pg. 131
Porter, Mike, Pres.--First American Bank Valley, Grand Forks, ND; U.S. Private, pg. 167
Porter, Robert L., Pres. & Chief Oper. Officer--Oliver Products Company, Grand Rapids, MI; U.S. Private, pg. 815
Porter, William, Pres.--McMullen/Argus Publishers, Placentia, CA; U.S. Public, pg. 1328
Porter, William, Pres.--Argus Publishers, Placentia, CA; U.S. Public, pg. 1328
Portman, Robert G., Pres.--Carlton Cards Division, Cleveland, OH; U.S. Public, pg. 78
Porzio, D.K., Pres.--Marley Electric Heating Company, Bennettsville, SC; U.S. Public, pg. 1676
Posen, L.M., Pres. & Chief Exec. Officer--Beltone Electronics Corporation, Chicago, IL; U.S. Private, pg. 132
Posencheg, Alan N., Pres. & Chief Exec. Officer--UJB Discount Brokerage, Ridgefield Park, NJ; U.S. Public, pg. 1528
Posey, Billy, Pres. & Chief Exec. Officer--Univest Financial Services, LLC, Atlanta, GA; U.S. Private, pg. 1128
Posey, Richard E., Pres. & Chief Exec. Officer--Hamilton Beach/Proctor-Silex, Inc., Glen Allen, VA; U.S. Public, pg. 1149
Posinski, Frank J., Pres. & Chief Oper. Officer--Cincinnati Gear Company, Cincinnati, OH; U.S. Private, pg. 240
Posner, Gerald D., Pres.--Electronic Measurements, Inc., Neptune, NJ; U.S. Private, pg. 138
Posner, Victor, Pres.--APL Corporation, Miami Beach, FL; U.S. Private, pg. 7
Posso, Patrick, Chm. Bd. & Pres.--Posso S.A., Paris, France; Int'l, pg. 1064
Post, Dan, Pres.--Charter Group, Inc., Dallas, TX; Int'l, pg. 1257
Post, Gary, Pres. & Chief Oper. Officer--Muskegon Construction Company, Muskegon, MI; U.S. Private, pg. 824
Post, Glen F., III, Vice Chm., Pres. & Chief Exec. Officer--Century Telephone Enterprises, Inc., Monroe, LA; U.S. Public, pg. 329
Post, Gregory, Pres.--MeritCare Health System, Fargo, ND; U.S. Private, pg. 733
Post, William J., Pres.--Pinnacle West Capital Corporation, Phoenix, AZ; U.S. Public, pg. 1297
Post, William J., Pres. & Chief Exec. Officer--APS, Phoenix, AZ; U.S. Public, pg. 1297
Postewait, Jerry, Pres.--Mercantile Insurance Services, Inc., Saint Louis, MO; U.S. Public, pg. 1088
Postl, James, Pres.--Hostess Frito-Lay Co., Mississauga, Canada; U.S. Public, pg. 1277
Poston, Henry, Pres. & Chief Oper. Officer--Martin Color-Fi, Edgefield, SC; U.S. Public, pg. 1052
Postwaite, Jerry, Pres.--Mississippi Valley Life Insurance Company, Saint Louis, MO; U.S. Public, pg. 1087
Potack, Michael R., Pres.--A & P Coat, Apron & Linen Supply, Bronx, NY; U.S. Private, pg. 1
Potamkin, Alan, Pres.--Potamkin Toyota, Inc., Miami, FL; U.S. Private, pg. 877
Potashner, Kenneth F., Chm. Bd., Pres., Chief Exec. & Chief Oper. Officer--Maxwell Technologies, Inc., San Diego, CA; U.S. Public, pg. 1061
Pote, Hal, Partner--The Beacon Group, New York, NY; U.S. Private, pg. 125
Pote, Hal, Chm. Bd., Pres., Chief Exec. Officer & Sec.--Ambar, Inc., Lafayette, LA; U.S. Private, pg. 126
Poth, R.E., Pres.--Pendleton Woolen Mills, Inc., Portland, OR; U.S. Private, pg. 848
Potila, Antti, Chm.-Bd.of Mgmnt., Pres. & Chief Exec. Officer--FinnAir Oy, Helsinki, Finland; Int'l, pg. 485
Potkin, Harvey, Pres. & Chief Oper. Officer--National Foods Inc., Bronx, NY; U.S. Public, pg. 429
Potter, Keith, Pres.--Leaver Mushrooms Co. Limited, Campbellville, Canada; U.S. Public, pg. 428
Potter, Nelson W., Pres. & Chief Oper. Officer--Fleetwood Enterprises, Inc., Riverside, CA; U.S. Public, pg. 650
Potter, Robert J., Pres. & Chief Exec. Officer--Construction Equip. Div., Lubbock, TX; U.S. Private, pg. 355
Potthoff, G.A., Pres.--Systems & Electronics Inc., Saint Louis, MO; U.S. Public, pg. 547
Pottinger, Don, Pres.--Ag-Chem Equipment Co., Inc., Minnetonka, MN; U.S. Public, pg. 6
Pottow, Geoffrey W.J., Pres. & Chief Exec. Officer--Becker Milk Co. Ltd., Scarborough, Canada; Int'l, pg. 182
Pottruck, David S., Pres. & Chief Oper. Officer--The Charles Schwab Corporation, San Francisco, CA; U.S. Public, pg. 1442
Potts, Richard W., Pres.--Peerless Tube Company, Bloomfield, NJ; U.S. Public, pg. 1269
Potts, Thomas H., Pres.--Resource Mortgage Capital, Inc., Glen Allen, VA; U.S. Public, pg. 1382
Potts, William, Pres.--Precor, Inc., Bothell, WA; U.S. Public, pg. 1322
Pouliot, Adrien D., Pres. & Chief Exec. Officer--CFCF Inc., Montreal, Canada; Int'l, pg. 240
Poulsen, Jans Peter, Pres.--MD Foods Norge A/S, Oslo, Norway; Int'l, pg. 826
Poulson, Larry, Pres.--Haartz-Mason, Inc., Watertown, MA; U.S. Public, pg. 1358
Poulter, Donald, Pres.--ConferTech Canada Inc., Etobicoke, Canada; U.S. Public, pg. 683
Poulton, Ted, Pres.--Old Kent Bank of Grand Haven, Grand Haven, MI; U.S. Public, pg. 1217
Pountain, Eric, Sir, Chm. Bd.--IMI Plc, Witton, United Kingdom; Int'l, pg. 646
Poure, James A., Chm. Bd., Pres. & Chief Exec. Officer--General Alum & Chemical, Holland, OH; U.S. Private, pg. 443
Poure, Timothy, Pres. & Chief Oper. Officer--General Alum & Chemical, Holland, OH; U.S. Private, pg. 443
Poussot, Bernard, Pres.--Whitehall-Robins International, Inc., Madison, NJ; U.S. Public, pg. 80
Poussot, Bernard, Pres.--Wyeth-Ayerst International, Inc., Radnor, PA; U.S. Public, pg. 80
Poutanen, Heikki, Pres.--Millar Elevator Industries, Inc., Holland, OH; Int'l, pg. 1205
Povah, Trevor H., Pres.--Hamilton Stores, Inc., Bozeman, MT; U.S. Private, pg. 497
Pow, Albert, Pres.--Kaufman and Broad Inland Empire, Anaheim, CA; U.S. Public, pg. 945
Powch, George, Pres. & Chief Exec. Officer--Champlain Cable Corp., Colchester, VT; Int'l, pg. 637
Powell, Alan, Pres.--Danisco Pack Ltd., Altrincham, United Kingdom; Int'l, pg. 378
Powell, David L., Pres. & Chief Oper. Officer--Coherent Communications Systems Corp., Ashburn, VA; U.S. Public, pg. 1424
Powell, Hugo, Pres. & Chief Exec. Officer--Labatt Brewing Company Limited, Toronto, Canada; Int'l, pg. 679
Powell, Joanne, Partner & Grp. Acct. Dir.--TLPartnership, Dallas, TX; U.S. Public, pg. 1224
Powell, John A., Pres. & Chief Exec. Officer--Wajax Limited, Delta, Canada; Int'l, pg. 1484
Powell, Kendall, Pres.--Big 'G' Div., Minneapolis, MN; U.S. Public, pg. 718
Powell, Kent D., Pres.--Ames Co., Inc., Woodland, CA; U.S. Public, pg. 1746
Powell, M. Lee, III, Pres.--APAC/Ballenger Paving Company, Inc., Taylors, SC; U.S. Public, pg. 139
Powell, R. Edward, Pres. & Chief Exec. Officer--CAIRE, Inc., Burnsville, MN; U.S. Private, pg. 751
Powell, Richard M., Pres. & Chief Exec. Officer--L. Powell Co., Inc., Culver City, CA; U.S. Private, pg. 877
Powell, Thomas W., Chm. Bd., Pres. & Chief Exec. Officer--Powell Industries, Inc., Houston, TX; U.S. Public, pg. 1319
Powell, Tom, Pres.--Directional Furniture, High Point, NC; U.S. Private, pg. 193
Powell, Tom, Pres.--Thor West, Ontario, CA; U.S. Public, pg. 1602
Powell, Tom, Pres.--Thor California, Inc., Moreno Valley, CA; U.S. Public, pg. 1602
Powell, William, Pres. & Chief Exec. Officer--Union Planters Bank of Alabama, Decatur, AL; U.S. Public, pg. 1669
Powell, William K., Pres.--Fred Weber, Inc., Maryland Heights, MO; U.S. Private, pg. 424
Power, Alan, Pres.--Decoma International Inc., Concord, Canada; Int'l, pg. 829
Power, William, Chm. Bd., Pres. & Chief Exec. Officer--Canada--Young & Rubicam Ltd., Toronto, Canada; U.S. Private, pg. 1200
Powers, Frederic B., Jr., Chm. Bd. & Pres.--Powers Fastening, Inc., New Rochelle, NY; U.S. Private, pg. 878
Powers, Harry, Pres.--Outlook Eyewear Company, Denver, CO; U.S. Public, pg. 195
Powers, Larry, Pres. & Chief Exec. Officer--The Genlyte Group Incorporated, Union, NJ; U.S. Public, pg. 729
Powers, Paul J., Chm. Bd., Pres. & Chief Exec. Officer--Commercial Intertech Corp., Youngstown, OH; U.S. Public, pg. 411
Poythress, James H., Pres.--Foster Mortgage Corporation, Fort Worth, TX; U.S. Public, pg. 1675
Pozza, Duane C., Pres., Chief Exec. Officer & Treas.--Bartlett Cocke, Inc., San Antonio, TX; U.S. Private, pg. 249
Pozzo, Jim Dal, Pres. & Chief Fin. Officer--Jacmar Companies, Inc., Alhambra, CA; U.S. Private, pg. 580
Pradas, Francisco, Pres.--Intevep, S.A., Los Taques, Venezuela; Int'l, pg. 1045
Prairie, Duane, Pres. & Chief Exec. Officer--Park Construction Company, Minneapolis, MN; U.S. Private, pg. 839
Pranckun, John, Pres.--World Tableware, Inc., Dallas, TX; Int'l, pg. 1056
Pranka, Tom, Pres.--Spartan Tool, Mendota, IL; U.S. Private, pg. 860
Prann, John R., Jr., Pres. & Chief Exec. Officer--Katy Industries, Inc., Englewood, CO; U.S. Public, pg. 944
Pras, Robert T., Pres.-Marriott Distribution Services--Marriott International, Inc., Washington, DC; U.S. Public, pg. 1047
Prasad, Suresh, Pres.--Ellesmere Britannia Ltd., Georgetown, Cayman Islands; Int'l, pg. 31
Prasser, Gary P., Pres.--Joslyn Manufacturing Co., Chicago, IL; U.S. Public, pg. 481
Prather, Rick, Pres.--JII/Sales Promotion Associates, Inc., Coshocton, OH; U.S. Private, pg. 598
Prather, Robert S., Pres. & Chief Exec. Officer--Bull Run Corporation, Atlanta, GA; U.S. Public, pg. 267
Pratt, Brian, Chm. Bd., Pres. & Chief Exec. Officer--ARB Inc., Lake Forest, CA; U.S. Private, pg. 7
Pratt, Brian, Pres.--ARB, Inc.-Building Division, Lake Forest, CA; U.S. Private, pg. 7
Pratt, Cliff W., Pres. & Treas.--Anaheim Extrusion Co., Anaheim, CA; U.S. Private, pg. 1127
Pratt, Courtney, Pres.--Noranda Inc., Toronto, Canada; Int'l, pg. 433
Pratt, Donald H., Pres.--Butler Manufacturing Company, Kansas City, MO; U.S. Public, pg. 271
Pratt, Edward T., III, Pres.--Hollywood Casino Corp, Atlantic City, NJ; U.S. Public, pg. 830

Pratt, Michael G., Pres. & Chief Exec. Officer--Coats & Clark Inc., Greenville, SC; *Int'l*, pg. 300
Pratt, R. George, Jr., Pres. & Treas.--Bradford Oil Company, Inc., Bradford, VT; *U.S. Private*, pg. 164
Pratt, Robert N., Chm. Bd., Pres. & Chief Oper. & Chief Exec. Officer--Alta Gold Co., Henderson, NV; *U.S. Public*, pg. 58
Pratt, Steven D., Pres. & Chief Exec. Officer--Esco Corporation, Portland, OR; *U.S. Private*, pg. 382
Pratt, Tomn, Pres. & Chief Exec. Officer--Florida Tile Industries, Inc., Lakeland, FL; *U.S. Public*, pg. 1322
Praw, Albert Z., Pres.--Kaufman and Broad-Antelope Valley Regional Office, Palmdale, CA; *U.S. Public*, pg. 945
Prawer, Tod, Pres.--S.P.C. Transport, Auburn, ME; *U.S. Private*, pg. 957
Pray, Bill, Pres.--Barnett Inc., Jacksonville, FL; *U.S. Public*, pg. 1749
Preble, C. G., Pres.--Southern Peru Copper Corp., New York, NY; *U.S. Public*, pg. 138
Precious, Ernest, Pres.--Seal Products Incorporated, Naugatuck, CT; *U.S. Public*, pg. 849
Precourt, Jay A., Vice Chm., Pres. & Chief Exec. Officer--Tejas Gas Corporation, Houston, TX; *Int'l*, pg. 1136
Pregulman, John, Pres.--Sisken Steel, Chattanooga, TN; *U.S. Public*, pg. 1375
Preis, Herwig, Co-Owner & Chm.--Select Communications, L.P., New York, NY; *U.S. Private*, pg. 982
Preis, Herwig, Pres.--Select Communications, GmbH, Koblenz, Koblenz, Germany; *U.S. Private*, pg. 982
Prendergast, Thomas, Pres.-LIRR--MTA Long Island Rail Road, Jamaica, NY; *U.S. Private*, pg. 739
Prendergast, Vic, Pres.--Shaklee Canada Inc., Burlington, Canada; *Int'l*, pg. 1518
Prescott, Gerald, Pres.--King Group, Inc., Ann Arbor, MI; *U.S. Private*, pg. 620
Prescott, J.B., Mng. Dir. & Chief Exec. Officer--The Broken Hill Proprietary Company Limited, Melbourne, Australia; *Int'l*, pg. 223
Prescott, James, Pres.--Alumax Mill Products, Inc., Morris, IL; *U.S. Public*, pg. 59
Prescott, Roger, Pres. & Gen. Mgr.--Akzo Nobel Fortafil Fibers Inc., Rockwood, TN; *Int'l*, pg. 48
Present, Randy, Chm. Bd. & Pres.--CH Mortgage Company, Scottsdale, AZ; *U.S. Public*, pg. 441
Press, Barbara, Partner--Messner Vetere Berger McNamee Schmetterer/EURO RSCG, New York, NY; *Int'l*, pg. 602
Press, Clifford, Pres.--High Voltage Engineering Corporation, Wakefield, MA; *U.S. Private*, pg. 528
Pressler, Paul, Pres.-Disneyland Resort--Disneyland, Anaheim, CA; *U.S. Public*, pg. 511
Pressley, George, Pres. & Chief Oper. Officer--Lapp Insulator Company, Le Roy, NY; *U.S. Private*, pg. 473
Pressman, James R., Chm. Bd., Pres. & Chief Oper. Officer--Pressman Toy Corp., New York, NY; *U.S. Private*, pg. 882
Pressman, Thane, Pres.--Labatt U.S.A., Darien, CT; *Int'l*, pg. 679
Prestenburg, H., Jr., Pres.--Intrepid Enterprises, Inc., Harvey, LA; *U.S. Private*, pg. 574
Prestidge, D. Mark, Pres.--Tom Thumb Food & Pharmacy, Dallas, TX; *U.S. Private*, pg. 909
Pretak, Thomas, Pres.--The Turner & Seymour Mfg. Company, Torrington, CT; *U.S. Private*, pg. 1109
Previte, Richard, Pres. & Chief Oper. Officer--Advanced Micro Devices, Inc., Sunnyvale, CA; *U.S. Public*, pg. 21
Previti, James, Chm. Bd, Pres. & Chief Exec. Officer--Forecast Group, Rancho Cucamonga, CA; *U.S. Private*, pg. 418
Prible, Larry L., Pres. & Chief Exec. Officer--Indianapolis Life Insurance Co., Indianapolis, IN; *U.S. Private*, pg. 560
Price, Derek, Pres.--Fisher & Ludlow, Burlington, Canada; *Int'l*, pg. 598
Price, Donald, Pres.--Shawver Price, Inc., Kansas City, MO; *U.S. Private*, pg. 511
Price, E.P., Pres.--Chevron Shale Oil Co., Englewood, CO; *U.S. Public*, pg. 348
Price, Francis, Pres. & Chief Exec. Officer--Q3 Stamped Metal, Columbus, OH; *U.S. Private*, pg. 897
Price, Francis, Chm. & Pres.--Q3 Industries, Urbana, OH; *U.S. Private*, pg. 897
Price, Fredric D., Pres., Chief Exec. Officer & Acting Chief Fin. Officer--AMBI Inc., Tarrytown, NY; *U.S. Public*, pg. 7
Price, Gayle B., Jr., Pres. & Chief Exec. Officer--Price Brothers Co., Dayton, OH; *U.S. Private*, pg. 883
Price, Hank, Pres. & Gen. Mgr.--KARE-TV, Minneapolis, MN; *U.S. Public*, pg. 702
Price, J.F., Pres.--Princess Hotels International Inc., New York, NY; *Int'l*, pg. 818
Price, Jeffrey D., Pres.--Price Woods, Inc., Mesa, AZ; *U.S. Private*, pg. 1187
Price, Jerry D., Pres.--Rutt Custom Cabinetry, Goodville, PA; *U.S. Private*, pg. 507
Price, Mary Beth, Founder--Media That Works, Cincinnati, OH; *U.S. Private*, pg. 727
Price, Michael, Pres.--Esix, Atlanta, GA; *U.S. Private*, pg. 565
Price, Robert, Chm. Bd. & Pres.--Price Communications Corporation, New York, NY; *U.S. Public*, pg. 1324
Price, Robert E., Chm. Bd., Pres. & Chief Exec. Officer--PriceSmart Inc., San Diego, CA; *U.S. Public*, pg. 1324
Price, Robin, Mng. Partner & Fin.--Howell Henry Chaldecott Lury & Partners, London, United Kingdom; *Int'l*, pg. 637
Price, Steven S., Pres.--AlliedSignal, Automotive Aftermarket, Rumford, RI; *U.S. Public*, pg. 51
Price, Thomas P., Jr., Pres. & Chief Exec. Officer--Sabin Robbins Paper Co., Cincinnati, OH; *U.S. Private*, pg. 959
Price, Thomas W., Pres.--T&W Financial Corporation, Tacoma, WA; *U.S. Public*, pg. 1552
Price, Timothy F., Pres. & Chief Oper. Officer--MCI Communications Corp., Atlanta, GA; *U.S. Public*, pg. 1023
Price, Timothy F., Pres.-MCI Bus. Markets--MCI Telecommunications Corp., Washington, DC; *U.S. Public*, pg. 1024
Price, Trevor, Pres.--EMTEC Magnetics U.K. Limited, Branbury, United Kingdom; *Int'l*, pg. 743
Price, Westcott W., III, Pres. & Chief Exec. Officer--Pacificare Health Systems, Santa Ana, CA; *U.S. Public*, pg. 1251
Price, William, Pres. & Mgr.-Adv. & Mktg.--Your Man Tours, Inc., Inglewood, CA; *U.S. Private*, pg. 1202
Pridemore, Stephen, Pres.--Bright of America, Inc., Summersville, WV; *U.S. Public*, pg. 223
Priem, Ted, Chm., Pres. & Chief Exec. Officer--Nobles Mfg. Inc., Saint Croix Falls, WI; *U.S. Private*, pg. 800
Priem, Ted, Pres.--NV-Mannor, Saint Croix Falls, WI; *U.S. Private*, pg. 800
Priester, Lonnie, Pres. & Chief Fin. Officer--Fosters Freeze International, Inc., San Luis Obispo, CA; *U.S. Public*, pg. 677
Prijatel, John, Pres.--Farmland MissChem, Ltd., Port of Spain, Trinidad & Tobago; *U.S. Public*, pg. 1117
Prillaman, Albert L., Chm. Bd., Pres. & Chief Exec. Officer--Stanley Furniture Co. Inc., Stanleytown, VA; *U.S. Public*, pg. 1508
Primrose, Mike, Pres. & Chief Exec. Officer--Henry Lee Company, Miami, FL; *U.S. Private*, pg. 657
Prince, Gary J., Pres.--Stroehmann Bakeries, L.C., Horsham, PA; *Int'l*, pg. 1495
Prince, Robert, Chm. Bd. & Pres.--Printing House, Inc., Quincy, FL; *U.S. Private*, pg. 886
Pringle, W.J., Pres. & Chief Exec. Oper.--Brookfield Homes, Del Mar, CA; *Int'l*, pg. 228
Pringle, William J., Pres. & Chief Exec. Officer--Brookfield Homes Ltd., Toronto, Canada; *Int'l*, pg. 228
Prinsen, W., Pres.--ING Baring (U.S.) Holdings, New York, NY; *Int'l*, pg. 647
Prinsen, W., Pres.--ING (U.S.) Financial Services kk, New York, NY; *Int'l*, pg. 648
Prior, David, Pres.--Codar Technology Inc., Longmont, CO; *U.S. Public*, pg. 1144
Prischak, Joseph J., Chm. Bd. & Pres.--Plastek Group, Erie, PA; *U.S. Private*, pg. 870
Pritchard, Beth, Pres.--Bath & Body Works, Reynoldsburg, OH; *U.S. Public*, pg. 995
Pritchard, Marc S., Pres.--Procter & Gamble Cosmetics Co., Hunt Valley, MD; *U.S. Public*, pg. 1330
Pritchard, Phillip L., Pres. & Chief Oper. Officer--Cooker Restaurant Corporation, West Palm Beach, FL; *U.S. Public*, pg. 442
Pritts, G. Robert, Pres.--Carmun International, San Antonio, TX; *Int'l*, pg. 646
Pritzker, Robert A., Pres. & Chief Exec. Officer--The Marmon Group, Inc., Chicago, IL; *U.S. Private*, pg. 706
Pritzker, Thomas, Pres.--Northridge Industries, Inc., Chicago, IL; *U.S. Private*, pg. 551
Probert, Colin, Partner & Pres.--Goodby, Silverstein & Partners, San Francisco, CA; *U.S. Public*, pg. 1224
Probert, Timothy J., Pres.--Baker Hughes INTEQ, Houston, TX; *U.S. Public*, pg. 166
Prochaska, Joe, Pres.--Willmar Manufacturing, Willmar, MN; *U.S. Private*, pg. 210
Proctor, Richard, Pres.--Cruising Equipment Company, Seattle, WA; *U.S. Public*, pg. 1705
Proctor, Thomas E., Chm. Bd. & Pres.--American Technical Publishers, Inc., Homewood, IL; *U.S. Private*, pg. 63
Profaci, John J., Pres.--Colivita USA, Inc., Linden, NJ; *U.S. Private*, pg. 252
Prostor, Jeffrey J., Pres.--Brookfield Homes-Orange County, Santa Ana, CA; *Int'l*, pg. 228
Prostrollo, Pat, Pres.--Prostrollo Motor Company, Madison, SD; *U.S. Private*, pg. 891
Prot, Baudouin, Pres. & Chief Oper. Officer--Banque Nationale de Paris, Paris, France; *Int'l*, pg. 163
Proteau, Jocelyn, Pres. & Chief Exec. Officer--Federation des caisses populaires Desjardins, Montreal, Canada; *Int'l*, pg. 479
Prothro, C.V., Chm. Bd., Pres. & Chief Exec. Officer--Dallas Semiconductor Corporation, Dallas, TX; *U.S. Public*, pg. 478
Proto, Rodney R., Pres. & Chief Oper. Officer--USA Waste Services, Inc., Houston, TX; *U.S. Public*, pg. 1686
Proto, Rodney R., Pres. & Chief Oper. Officer--Sanifill, Inc., Houston, TX; *U.S. Public*, pg. 1686
Protze, Gerhard, Chm. Bd., Chief Exec. Officer, Chief Fin. Officer & Mng. Dir.--Traub AG, Reichenbach, Germany; *Int'l*, pg. 1419
Prou, Michael, Pres.--Roussel Corporation, Montvale, NJ; *Int'l*, pg. 625
Prough, Jeffrey, Pres.--Guardian Alarm Co., Southfield, MI; *U.S. Private*, pg. 485
Prout, Stephen, Pres. & Chief Exec. Officer--Alpha Q, Inc., Colchester, CT; *U.S. Private*, pg. 45
Prout, Steven, L., Pres.--Southern Gage Inc., Erin, TN; *U.S. Private*, pg. 45
Provo Kluit, Piet, Pres.--Akzo Nobel Inc., Chicago, IL; *Int'l*, pg. 47
Provost, Normand, Pres.--Capital d'Amerique CDPQ, Montreal, Canada; *Int'l*, pg. 249
Prueter, Williams R., Pres. & Chief Exec. Officer--Metropolitan Life Insurance Company Of Canada, Ottawa, Canada; *U.S. Private*, pg. 738
Pruim, E.G., Chm. Bd., Pres. & Chief Exec. Officer--Wrought Washer Mfg., Inc., Milwaukee, WI; *U.S. Private*, pg. 1192
Pruitt, Gary B., Pres. & Chief Exec. Officer--McClatchy Newspapers Inc., Sacramento, CA; *U.S. Public*, pg. 1065
Pruitt, J. Doug, Pres. & Chief Oper. Officer--Sundt Corp., Tucson, AZ; *U.S. Private*, pg. 1051
Prusiewicz, Richard, Pres.--Kearney Company, Tucker, GA; *U.S. Public*, pg. 444
Prutzman, P. Edward, Pres., Chief Oper. Officer & V.P.--Sunbank Joslyn, Inc., Paso Robles, CA; *U.S. Public*, pg. 482
Pry, Jim, Pres.--Standard Products (Canada) Ltd., Stratford, Canada; *U.S. Public*, pg. 1505
Pryde, John, Pres.--General Coach, Hensall, Canada; *U.S. Public*, pg. 1602
Prym, Michael, Pres.--William Prym GmbH & Co. KG, Stolberg, Germany; *Int'l*, pg. 1499
Pryne, P.D., Pres.--NI Industries, Inc., Seal Beach, CA; *U.S. Public*, pg. 1054
Pryne, Wilson H., Pres. & Chief Oper. Officer--American Felt & Filter, Newburgh, NY; *U.S. Private*, pg. 54
Pryor, Robert, Pres.--Poe & Brown of Texas, Houston, TX; *U.S. Public*, pg. 1312
Psarouthakis, John, Chm. Bd., Pres. & Chief Exec. Officer--JPE, Inc., Ann Arbor, MI; *U.S. Public*, pg. 919
Psomas, Tim, Pres.--Psomas & Associates, Santa Monica, CA; *U.S. Private*, pg. 893
Psomas, Tim, Pres.--Psomas Associates, Salt Lake City, UT; *U.S. Private*, pg. 893
Pucci, Mark, Pres. & Chief Exec. Officer--Walker Group/CNI Inc., New York, NY; *Int'l*, pg. 1483
Puccini, Robert, Pres.--Mizuno USA, Inc., Norcross, GA; *Int'l*, pg. 885
Pudil, Michael J., Pres. & Chief Exec. Officer--Washington Scientific Industries, Inc., Long Lake, MN; *U.S. Public*, pg. 1744
Pudles, Stephen, Pres.--Tanon Express, West Long Branch, NJ; *U.S. Public*, pg. 541
Puente, E. A., Pres. & Chief Exec. Officer--Tree of Life, Inc., Saint Augustine, FL; *Int'l*, pg. 752
Puette, Bob, Pres. & Chief Exec. Officer--Centigram Communications Corporation, San Jose, CA; *U.S. Public*, pg. 323
Puetz, J.D., Pres.--Great Lakes Biochemical Co., Inc., Milwaukee, WI; *Int'l*, pg. 802
Puget, Lionel, Pres.--Axson S.A., Paris, France; *Int'l*, pg. 102
Pugh, Loren, Pres.--Cummins Intermountain Diesel, Salt Lake City, UT; *U.S. Private*, pg. 295
Pugh, William, Jr., Chm. Bd., Pres. & Treas.--Pugh Oil Company, Racine, WI; *U.S. Private*, pg. 894
Puglisi, John, Pres. & Chief Oper. Officer--Lowe McAdams Healthcare, New York, NY; *U.S. Private*, pg. 678
Puig, Mariano, Pres.--Paco Rabanne Parfums, Neuilly-sur-Seine, France; *Int'l*, pg. 1073
Pulgar, Juan J., Pres. & Chief Exec. Officer--BITOR America Corp., Boca Raton, FL; *Int'l*, pg. 1045
Pulido, Mark A., Pres. & Chief Exec. Officer--McKesson Corporation, San Francisco, CA; *U.S. Public*, pg. 1072
Pulido, Mike, Pres. & Chief Exec. Officer--McKesson U.S. Health Care, San Francisco, CA; *U.S. Public*, pg. 1073
Pulitzer, Michael E., Chm. Bd., Pres. & Chief Exec. Officer--Pulitzer Publishing Company, Saint Louis, MO; *U.S. Public*, pg. 1343
Pulliam, Larry, Pres.--AGCO Inc., Norcross, GA; *U.S. Private*, pg. 26
Pulliam, Robert F., Chm. Bd. & Pres.--Pulliam Motor Company, Columbia, SC; *U.S. Private*, pg. 894
Puls, Michael G., Pres. & Chief Exec. Officer--InnoServ Technologies, Inc., Arlington, TX; *U.S. Public*, pg. 879
Pumpelly, R. Glenn, Pres.--Pumpelly Oil, Inc., Westlake, LA; *U.S. Private*, pg. 895
Pundt, Jeffrey L., Pres.--Landstar Inway, Inc., Rockford, IL; *U.S. Public*, pg. 978
Puno, Jimmy, Pres., Chief Exec. Officer & Chief Oper. Officer--Dentsu Young & Rubicam-Alcantara Inc. (Manila), Manila, Philippines; *U.S. Private*, pg. 325
Puntil, Ronald M., Pres. & Chief Oper. Officer--Grubb & Ellis Management Services, Inc., Northbrook, IL; *U.S. Public*, pg. 767
Puorro, Gerard E., Chm. Bd., Pres. & Chief Exec. Officer--Candela Corporation, Wayland, MA; *U.S. Public*, pg. 300
Purcell, Pat, Publisher & Pres.--The Boston Herald, Boston, MA; *Int'l*, pg. 926
Purdin, James S., Pres.--Sterling Plastics Co., Madison, WI; *U.S. Public*, pg. 1178
Purdue, Shawn W., Pres.--New North Media Inc., Saint John, Canada; *Int'l*, pg. 230
Purdy, Kenneth, Pres.--Prime Tanning Co., Inc., Rochester, NH; *U.S. Private*, pg. 884
Puricelli, Enrique, Exec. Pres.--Sudamtex de Uruguay, S.A., Montevideo, Uruguay; *Int'l*, pg. 1304
Puris, Martin, Pres. & Chief Exec. Officer--Ammirati, Puris & Lintas, Inc., New York, NY; *U.S. Private*, pg. 66
Purl, Doug, Pres.--Hygeia Dairy Co., Inc., Harlingen, TX; *U.S. Private*, pg. 552
Purlow, Ari, Pres.--Armin Plastics Division, Jersey City, NJ; *U.S. Public*, pg. 1647
Purmort, F. W., III, Chm. Bd. & Pres.--Central Mutual Insurance Co., Van Wert, OH; *U.S. Private*, pg. 223
Purmort, F.W., Jr., Pres.--All America Insurance Company, Van Wert, OH; *U.S. Private*, pg. 224
Purpura, Vicnent M., Pres. & Chief Oper. Officer--D.A. Davidson & Co., Great Falls, MT; *U.S. Private*, pg. 314
Pursell, Tate, Pres.--American Metal Products, Olive Branch, MS; *U.S. Public*, pg. 1053
Pursell, Taylor, Pres. & Chief Exec. Officer--Pursell Industries, Sylacauga, AL; *U.S. Private*, pg. 896
Purser, Lat W., III, Pres. & Chief Exec. Officer--Lat Purser & Associates, Charlotte, NC; *U.S. Private*, pg. 896
Purtch, John, Pres.--Signal Apparel Company, Inc., Chattanooga, TN; *U.S. Public*, pg. 1472
Purvis, J.E., Pres. & Treas.--A.C. Legg Packing Company, Inc., Birmingham, AL; *U.S. Private*, pg. 658
Puschel, Gerald W., Pres. & Chief Oper. Officer--F. Schumacher & Co., New York, NY; *U.S. Private*, pg. 973
Puskar, Milan, Chm. Bd., Pres. & Chief Exec. Officer--Mylan Laboratories, Inc., Pittsburgh, PA; *U.S. Public*, pg. 1143
Putnam, Carl E., Pres. & Chief Oper. Officer--Anicom, Inc., Rosemont, IL; *U.S. Public*, pg. 115
Putnam, David C., Pres.--TBV, Inc., Westborough, MA; *U.S. Private*, pg. 1138
Putnam, Frederic L., III, Pres. & Chief Exec. Officer--Colonial Gas Company, Lowell, MA; *U.S. Public*, pg. 400
Putnam, James, Pres.--Markem Corporation, Keene, NH; *U.S. Private*, pg. 704
Putnam, Katherine E., Pres.--Package Machinery Co., Springfield, MA; *U.S. Private*, pg. 832

Puton, Roland, Pres.--Rolex Industries, Inc., New York, NY; *Int'l*, pg. 1126
Pyatt, Alan, Chm. Bd., Pres. & Chief Exec. Officer--Sandwell Inc., Vancouver, Canada; *Int'l*, pg. 1188
Pyle, Jerry H., Pres.--Gulf States Toyota, Inc., Houston, TX; *U.S. Private*, pg. 488
Pyne, J.H., Pres. & Chief Exec. Officer--Kirby Corporation, Houston, TX; *U.S. Public*, pg. 961
Pyott, David, Pres. & Chief Exec. Officer--Novartis Nutrition Corporation, Saint Louis Park, MN; *Int'l*, pg. 974
Pyson, R.S., Pres.--Penn Central Communications Corp., Philadelphia, PA; *U.S. Public*, pg. 432
Quackenbush, David S., Pres.--Quackenbush Co. Inc., Buffalo, NY; *U.S. Private*, pg. 897
Quadracci, H.V., Pres. & Chief Exec. Officer--Quad/Graphics, Inc., Pewaukee, WI; *U.S. Private*, pg. 897
Quagliata, John, Pres.--Select Restaurants, Inc., Cleveland, OH; *U.S. Private*, pg. 982
Quain, Robert C., Pres.--MacNaughton Einson Graphics, Fair Lawn, NJ; *U.S. Private*, pg. 692
Qualters, Irene M., Pres.--Cray Research, Eagan, MN; *U.S. Public*, pg. 1473
Quam, Norm, Pres.--Bettis Corporation, Waller, TX; *U.S. Public*, pg. 482
Quarles, John M., Chm. Bd., Pres. & Chief Exec. Officer--Wolverine Tube Inc., Huntsville, AL; *U.S. Public*, pg. 1774
Quartararo, Phil, Pres.--Warner Bros. Records, Inc., Burbank, CA; *U.S. Public*, pg. 1611
Quebedeaus, Thomas, Pres.--Quebedeaux Pontiac, Inc., Tucson, AZ; *U.S. Private*, pg. 900
Queen, Richard K., Pres. & Chief Oper. Officer--C S Crable Sportswear, Inc., Batavia, OH; *U.S. Public*, pg. 1111
Queenan, J.P., Pres.--Blackhawk Collision Repair Inc., Waukesha, WI; *U.S. Public*, pg. 805
Quell, Ron, Pres.--The Bentley-Harris Manufacturing Co., Lionville, PA; *Int'l*, pg. 1334
Quere, Jean Pierre, Pres.--Polive/Tricosteril, Courbevoie, France; *U.S. Public*, pg. 673
Quesnel, Gregory L., Pres. & Chief Oper. Officer--CNF Transportation Inc., Palo Alto, CA; *U.S. Public*, pg. 281
Quest, Robert W., Pres.--Advanced Controls, Inc., Irvine, CA; *U.S. Private*, pg. 21
Queste, Yves, Pres. & Chief Oper. Officer--Ferry-Morse Seed Company, Modesto, CA; *Int'l*, pg. 566
Quevedo, Benito Cantalapiedra, Pres.--Banco Santander Puerto Rico, Hato Rey, PR; *Int'l*, pg. 143
Quick, J. Douglas, Pres. & Chief Exec. Officer--Lakeside Foods, Inc., Manitowoc, WI; *U.S. Private*, pg. 643
Quick, Leslie C., III, Pres. & Chief Oper. Officer--U.S. Clearing Corp., New York, NY; *U.S. Public*, pg. 650
Quick, Peter, Pres.--Quick & Reilly, Inc., New York, NY; *U.S. Public*, pg. 650
Quick, Thomas C., Pres. & Chief Oper. Officer--The Quick & Reilly Group Inc., Palm Beach, FL; *U.S. Public*, pg. 650
Quicke, John J., Pres. & Chief Oper. Officer--Sequa Corporation, New York, NY; *U.S. Public*, pg. 1458
Quigley, G. L., Pres.-European Opers.--Moore Products Co. B.V., Ridderkerk, Netherlands; *U.S. Public*, pg. 1129
Quigley, Robert J., Pres.--International Thoroughbred Breeders, Inc., Cherry Hill, NJ; *U.S. Public*, pg. 908
Quillen, James R., Pres.--Thunderbird Steel Corporation, Albuquerque, NM; *U.S. Public*, pg. 298
Quillen, Joan, Pres.--JC Penney National Bank, Harrington, DE; *U.S. Public*, pg. 917
Quinlan, Mary Lou, Pres. & Chief Exec. Officer--N.W. Ayer & Partners, New York, NY; *U.S. Private*, pg. 103
Quinlan, Michael R., Chm. & Chief Exec. Officer--McDonald's Corporation, Oak Brook, IL; *U.S. Public*, pg. 1068
Quinlan, William, Pres. & Chief Exec. Officer--Processed Products Division, Cincinnati, OH; *U.S. Private*, pg. 1191
Quinlen, W.L., III, Pres.--Choctaw, Inc., Memphis, TN; *U.S. Private*, pg. 238
Quinn, Dan, Pres.--CCC Conveyors, Inc., Dallas, TX; *U.S. Private*, pg. 351
Quinn, James E., Pres.--Tiffany & Co. Mexico, S.A. de C.V., Mexico, Mexico; *U.S. Public*, pg. 1609
Quinn, Jay, Mng. Partner--Eric Mower and Associates, Rochester, NY; *U.S. Private*, pg. 765
Quinn, Larry, Pres. & Chief Exec. Officer--Niagara Frontier Hockey, L.P., Buffalo, NY; *U.S. Private*, pg. 798
Quinn, M.F., Pres.--National Silicates Ltd., Etobicoke, Canada; *U.S. Private*, pg. 827
Quinn, Robert E., Pres.--Starmet Corporation, Concord, MA; *U.S. Public*, pg. 1511
Quinn, Thomas, Pres.--Continental Cement Co. Inc., Margate, FL; *Int'l*, pg. 1201
Quinn, Thomas H., Pres. & Chief Oper. Officer--Jordan Industries, Inc., Deerfield, IL; *U.S. Private*, pg. 598
Quinn, Thomas L., Pres.--J.W. Messner, Inc., Grand Rapids, MI; *U.S. Private*, pg. 734
Quinn, William F., Pres.--AMR Investment Services, Inc., Dallas-Fort Worth Airport, TX; *U.S. Public*, pg. 9
Quinnell, Bruce, Pres.--Walden Book Company, Ann Arbor, MI; *U.S. Public*, pg. 245
Quint, Manfred, Pres.--Mann & Hummel Hydromation GmbH, Ludwigsburg, Germany; *Int'l*, pg. 484
Quintana Isaac, Bernardo, Pres.--Empresas ICA Sociedad Controladora S.A.C.V., Mexico, Mexico; *Int'l*, pg. 454
Quintero, Ramon Mantellini, Pres.--Deltaven S.A., Caracas, Venezuela; *Int'l*, pg. 1045
Quirch, Guillermo, Sr., Pres.--E & G Foods, Miami, FL; *U.S. Private*, pg. 352
Quirk, John E., Pres. & Chief Exec. Officer--Village Car Company, Bangor, ME; *U.S. Private*, pg. 1140
Quirk, William M., Pres.--Horsehead Resource Development Co., Inc., New York, NY; *Int'l*, pg. 860
Quist, Chad, Pres.--Information Products, Inc., Holland, MI; *U.S. Public*, pg. 519
Quist, Steve, Pres.-Rosemount Measurement Div.--Rosemount Measurement Division, Eden Prairie, MN; *U.S. Public*, pg. 574
Raab, Simon, Ph.D., Chm. Bd., Pres. & Chief Exec. Officer--FARO Technologies, Inc., Lake Mary, FL; *U.S. Public*, pg. 613
Raaf, David, Pres.--Atlas Systems, Independence, MO; *U.S. Private*, pg. 511
Raasch, Kenneth E., Chm. Bd., Pres. & Chief Exec. Officer--Media Arts Group, Inc., San Jose, CA; *U.S. Public*, pg. 1077
Raaths, William, Pres.--Wisconsin Tissue Mills, Inc., Menasha, WI; *U.S. Public*, pg. 347
Rabbi, Luigi, Mng. Dir.--Olivetti Supplies, Inc., Middletown, PA; *Int'l*, pg. 1002
Rabil, Richard J., Pres. & Exec. V.P.--The Van Metres Companies, Burke, VA; *U.S. Private*, pg. 1132
Rabin, Stanley A., Chm. Bd., Pres. & Chief Exec. Officer--Commercial Metals Company, Dallas, TX; *U.S. Public*, pg. 411
Rabinovitch, Donald, Pres.--AFP Imaging Corporation, Elmsford, NY; *U.S. Public*, pg. 6
Rabinowitz, Martin J., Chm. Bd., Pres. & Chief Exec. Officer--Thackeray Corporation, New York, NY; *U.S. Public*, pg. 1590
Rabinowitz, Stephen, Pres. & Chief Exec. Officer--General Cable Corporation, Highland Heights, KY; *Int'l*, pg. 1486
Rabold, Robert E.H., Chm. Bd., Pres. & Chief Exec. Officer--Motorists Mutual Insurance Co., Columbus, OH; *U.S. Private*, pg. 764
Rabold, Robert E.H., Chm. Bd., Pres. & Chief Exec. Officer--American Hardware Mutual Insurance Co., Columbus, OH; *U.S. Private*, pg. 764
Raboy, Doug, Mng. Partner--Hanft Byrne Raboy Abrams & Partners, Inc., New York, NY; *U.S. Private*, pg. 499
Rabuck, Robert, Pres.--Pathway Bellows, Inc., Oak Ridge, TN; *U.S. Public*, pg. 521
Rabun, John T. Jr., Pres.--Powers Construction Co., Inc., Florence, SC; *U.S. Private*, pg. 878
Rackoff, J. M., V.P. & Gen. Mgr.--Asko, Inc, Homestead, PA; *U.S. Private*, pg. 89
Rackoff, W.H., Pres.--Asko, Inc, Homestead, PA; *U.S. Private*, pg. 89
Radaelli, Leonardo, Pres. & Mng. Dir.--BRB, Milan, Italy; *U.S. Public*, pg. 765
Radau, Gene, Dir.-Corp. Communications--Ford, Bacon & Davis Companies Inc., Duluth, GA; *Int'l*, pg. 401
Radek, Edward A., Jr., Pres.--Ready Metal Manufacturing Company, Chicago, IL; *U.S. Private*, pg. 913
Radiguet, Michel Naquet, Pres.--Interbrew Italia S.p.A., Comun Nuovo, Italy; *Int'l*, pg. 679
Radler, F. David, Pres. & Chief Oper. Officer--Hollinger Inc., Vancouver, Canada; *Int'l*, pg. 630
Radler, Jeffrey, Pres. & Chief Fin. Officer--Chessco Industries, Inc., Westport, CT; *U.S. Private*, pg. 234
Radley, Gordon, Pres.--Lucasfilm Ltd., San Rafael, CA; *U.S. Private*, pg. 679
Rados, Alexander, Pres.--The Rados Companies, Santa Ana, CA; *U.S. Private*, pg. 907
Radtke, H. Helmut, Pres. & Chief Exec. Officer--Melitta U.S.A., Inc., Clearwater, FL; *Int'l*, pg. 857
Radtke, Linda, Pres.--Intech Technology Corporation, Broadview, IL; *Int'l*, pg. 490
Radus, Philip, Pres. & Chief Exec. Officer--Ribbon Narrow Fabric Company, Secaucus, NJ; *U.S. Private*, pg. 927
Radwill, Scott, Pres., Chief Exec., Oper. & Fin. Officer--Master Appliance Corp., Racine, WI; *U.S. Private*, pg. 713
Rady, Ernest S., Chm. Bd., Pres. & Chief Exec. Officer--Westcorp, Irvine, CA; *U.S. Public*, pg. 1756
Rady, Paul M., Pres. & Chief Exec. Officer--Barrett Resources Corporation, Denver, CO; *U.S. Public*, pg. 191
Radzievsky, Yuri, Pres. & Chief Exec. Officer--YAR Communications, New York, NY; *U.S. Private*, pg. 1195
Raemer, Steven I., Pres. & Chief Oper. Officer--Radix Corporation, Salt Lake City, UT; *U.S. Private*, pg. 906
Rafael Henao, Juan, Pres.-Central Latin America--Procter & Gamble Venezuela, C.A., Caracas, Venezuela; *U.S. Public*, pg. 1332
Rafferty, Don, Pres.--Time Warner Cable Liberty Division, Ferndale, NY; *U.S. Public*, pg. 1611
Rafferty, James J., Jr., Pres.--AMI Gibson, Inc., Luquillo, PR; *U.S. Public*, pg. 1564
Raffo, A.J., Pres.--CMI Industries, Inc., Elkin, NC; *U.S. Private*, pg. 195
Ragland, Bob, Pres.--Zoeller Co., Louisville, KY; *U.S. Private*, pg. 1207
Ragland, David, Pres. & Chief Exec. Officer--Duncan Equipment Company, Oklahoma City, OK; *U.S. Private*, pg. 346
Ragland, Ron, Chm. Bd. & Chief Exec. Officer--Remec, Inc., San Diego, CA; *U.S. Public*, pg. 1376
Ragsdale, T. Smith, III, Pres. & Chief Exec. Officer--Embers Charcoal Company, Inc., Conway, SC; *U.S. Private*, pg. 373
Rahal, Robert, Pres.--Financial Trust Corp, Carlisle, PA; *U.S. Public*, pg. 956
Rahe, Maribeth S., Pres.--Bank of Montreal Global, Inc., Chicago, IL; *Int'l*, pg. 154
Rahr, Stewart, Pres., Chief Exec. Officer & Chief Fin. Officer--Kinray Inc., Whitestone, NY; *U.S. Private*, pg. 622
Rahunen, Jukka, Chief Oper. Officer--Foodie Oy, Toijala, Finland; *Int'l*, pg. 1085
Raibley, David, Reg. Pres.--Citizens Bank, Posey County Region, Mount Vernon, IN; *U.S. Public*, pg. 281
Raimann, Ginny, Partner-H.R. Mgr. & Admin. Svcs.--Dugan/Farley Communications, Upper Saddle River, NJ; *U.S. Public*, pg. 1642
Raimondo, A.F., Pres. & Chief Exec. Officer--Behlen Mfg. Co., Columbus, NE; *U.S. Private*, pg. 130
Raimondo, Orlando, Pres. & Chief Exec. Officer--Pirelli Cable Corporation, Florham Park, NJ; *Int'l*, pg. 1059
Raines, Johnny, Pres.--Simpson County Bank, Franklin, KY; *U.S. Public*, pg. 1669
Rainville, Donald, Pres. & Chief Oper. Officer--Universal Dynamics, Inc., Woodbridge, VA; *Int'l*, pg. 484
Rainville, William, Pres.--Thermo Fibertek, Inc., Waltham, MA; *U.S. Public*, pg. 1593
Raisbeck, Peter, Pres. & Chief Exec. Officer--Institutional Financing Services, Benicia, CA; *U.S. Public*, pg. 1652
Raiskin, James, Pres.--Winston Steel Products Co., Detroit, MI; *U.S. Private*, pg. 1183
Rakestraw, John, Sr. V.P. & Gen. Mgr.--Cattle Feeding Div., Boulder, CO; *U.S. Private*, pg. 268
Rakocy, Terry J., Pres.--Consumers Illinois Water Co., Kankakee, IL; *U.S. Public*, pg. 438
Rakow, Thomas S., Pres., Chief Exec. Officer & Treas.--IHC Group, Inc., South Elgin, IL; *U.S. Private*, pg. 555
Rakstang, Robert, Pres.--Hanna Corporation, Chicago, IL; *U.S. Private*, pg. 231
Raleigh, W.J., Pres.--CMI Industries, Inc., New York, NY; *U.S. Private*, pg. 195
Ramaekers, Larry, Pres. & Chief Oper. Officer--Color Tile, Inc., Fort Worth, TX; *Int'l*, pg. 686
Ramaker, David B., Pres. & Chief Exec. Officer--Chemical Bank & Trust Company, Midland, MI; *U.S. Public*, pg. 345
Ramat, Charles, Chm. Bd., Pres., Chief Exec. Officer & Asst. Sec.--Aris Industries, Inc., New York, NY; *U.S. Public*, pg. 129
Ramat, Charles S., Pres.--Members Only By Europe Craft, New York, NY; *U.S. Public*, pg. 129
Rambo, Larry, Pres. & Chief Exec. Officer--PrimeCare Health Plan, Inc., Milwaukee, WI; *U.S. Public*, pg. 1678
Ramella, Daniel J., Pres. & Chief Oper. Officer--Penton Publishing, Inc., Cleveland, OH; *U.S. Public*, pg. 1306
Ramer, Douglas, Pres. & Chief Oper. Officer--Bruning Paint Company, Baltimore, MD; *U.S. Private*, pg. 176
Ramierz, Mario, Pres.--Circuit City Southern Div., Atlanta, GA; *U.S. Public*, pg. 374
Ramirez-Isava, Daniel, Pres. & Chief Exec. Officer--BITOR Europe, Brentford, United Kingdom; *Int'l*, pg. 1046
Ramirez, Eddie, Pres.--Palmaven, S.A., Caracas, Venezuela; *Int'l*, pg. 1045
Ramiro, Angel Juan Simon, Pres.--ENSA - Equipos Nucleares, S.A., Madrid, Spain; *Int'l*, pg. 1224
Ramlow, Don, Pres.--Matheson Gas Products, Inc., Secaucus, NJ; *Int'l*, pg. 938
Ramm, Robert, Pres.--Topsy's International Inc., Kansas City, MO; *U.S. Private*, pg. 1092
Ramos, Antonio C., Pres. & Treas.--New England Stone Industries, Inc., Esmond, RI; *U.S. Private*, pg. 793
Ramos, Antonio C., Pres.--Georgia Stone Industries, Inc., Elberton, GA; *U.S. Private*, pg. 793
Ramos, Gary, Chm. Bd., Pres. & Chief Exec. Officer--Advanced Manufacturing & Development, Willits, CA; *U.S. Private*, pg. 22
Rampey, Charles A., Jr., Pres.--SCANA Energy Marketing Inc., Columbia, SC; *U.S. Public*, pg. 1436
Rampino, Louis J., Pres. & Chief Oper. Officer--Fremont General Corporation, Santa Monica, CA; *U.S. Public*, pg. 681
Rampone, David F., Pres.--Hart Engineering Corporation, Greenville, RI; *U.S. Private*, pg. 507
Ramqvist, Lars, Pres.--Telefonaktiebolaget LM Ericsson, Stockholm, Sweden; *Int'l*, pg. 1363
Ramsay, Dennis A., Pres.--Bristol Laboratories (Philippines), Inc., Manila, Philippines; *U.S. Public*, pg. 255
Ramsey, Chuck, Pres.--Dayton Tire Company-Oklahoma City, Oklahoma City, OK; *Int'l*, pg. 214
Ramsey, Chuck, Pres.--Firestone Agricultural Tire Company, Des Moines, IA; *Int'l*, pg. 214
Ramsey, Dave, Pres.--Morgan Keegan Mortgage Company, Inc., Memphis, TN; *U.S. Public*, pg. 1131
Ramsey, Greg, Pres.--Royle Systems Group, Pompton Lakes, NJ; *U.S. Private*, pg. 949
Ramsey, John, Pres.--Darlington Veneer Company, Darlington, SC; *U.S. Private*, pg. 311
Ramsey, John C., Pres. & Gen. Mgr.--Diamond Hill Plywood Company, Darlington, SC; *U.S. Private*, pg. 311
Ramsey, K.C., Pres.--United States Bronze Powders, Inc., Flemington, NJ; *U.S. Private*, pg. 1124
Ramsey, P.M., Pres.--Flexible Steel Lacing Company, Downers Grove, IL; *U.S. Private*, pg. 413
Ranck, Bruce E., Pres. & Chief Exec. Officer--Browning-Ferris Industries, Inc., Houston, TX; *U.S. Public*, pg. 262
Rand, Albert, Pres. & Chief Exec. Officer--Dynamics Research Corporation, Andover, MA; *U.S. Public*, pg. 539
Rand, David, Pres. & Chief Oper. Officer--Tingley Rubber Corporation, South Plainfield, NJ; *U.S. Private*, pg. 1088
Randall, James H., Pres.--Allfast Fastening Systems, Inc., City of Industry, CA; *U.S. Private*, pg. 37
Randall, Roger D., Pres.--Farm Journal Inc., Philadelphia, PA; *U.S. Private*, pg. 394
Randall, Ronald F., Chm. Bd., Pres. & Chief Exec. Officer--Randall Stores, Inc., Mitchell, SD; *U.S. Private*, pg. 909
Randall, Thomas K., Pres.--MassWest Insurance Company, West Springfield, MA; *Int'l*, pg. 345
Randell, Joe, Pres. & Chief Oper. Officer--Air Nova, Bedford, Canada; *Int'l*, pg. 36
Randolph, Jackson H., Chm. Bd., Pres. & Chief Exec. Officer--Lawrenceburg Gas Co., Cincinnati, OH; *U.S. Public*, pg. 369
Randolph, Ron, Pres. & Chief Exec. Officer--Associated Grocers of the South, Inc., Birmingham, AL; *U.S. Private*, pg. 91
Randolph, Tony, Pres.--Integral Corp., Dallas, TX; *U.S. Private*, pg. 1019
Rands, Tara, Pres. & Chief Exec. Officer--Brush Research Manufacturing Company, Los Angeles, CA; *U.S. Private*, pg. 176
Rangarajan, Murralia, Pres.--Logistix, Fremont, CA; *U.S. Private*, pg. 673
Rankin, Alfred M. Jr., Chm. Bd., Pres. & Chief Exec. Officer--NACCO Industries, Inc., Cleveland, OH; *U.S. Public*, pg. 1149

Rankin, Bonnie L., Pres. & Chief Oper. Officer--New York Casualty Insurance Co., Watertown, NY; *U.S. Public*, pg. 787
Rankin, Sheldon, Pres.--J&H Marsh & McLennan Ltd., Toronto, Canada; *U.S. Public*, pg. 1049
Rankine, Peter F., Pres.--Honeywell Limited, North York, Canada; *U.S. Public*, pg. 835
Ransdell, Thomas R., Pres.--Vulcan Materials Company-Southwest Div., San Antonio, TX; *U.S. Public*, pg. 1726
Ransmayr, Michael, Pres.--Hali-Buromobel Vertriebs GesmbH, Eferding, Austria; *Int'l*, pg. 589
Ransmayr, Winsfried, Chief Oper. Officer--Hali-Buromobel Vertriebs GesmbH, Eferding, Austria; *Int'l*, pg. 589
Ranson, Richard C., Pres.--Crescent Resources, Inc., Charlotte, NC; *U.S. Public*, pg. 534
Ranzau, Dennis R., Pres.--Equity Fund Advisors Inc., Houston, TX; *U.S. Private*, pg. 380
Rao, Chintamani, Pres.-MAA Bozell--MAA Communications Bozell, Bangalore, India; *U.S. Public*, pg. 1642
Rao, Dan, Pres.--Chadwick's of Boston, West Bridgewater, MA; *U.S. Public*, pg. 996
Raos, John G., Pres. & Chief Oper. Officer--U.S. Industries, Inc., Iselin, NJ; *U.S. Public*, pg. 1683
Rapelje, Ronald D., Pres. & Chief Exec. Officer--Ebeling & Reuss Company, Allentown, PA; *U.S. Private*, pg. 358
Rapoport, M., Pres. & Chief Exec. Officer--Mosler Inc., Hamilton, OH; *U.S. Private*, pg. 763
Rapp, C., Pres.--Carborundum Abrasives North America, High Point, NC; *Int'l*, pg. 1174
Rapp, C.J., Pres. & Chief Exec. Officer--Global Beverage Co., Rochester, NY; *U.S. Private*, pg. 457
Rapp, Kenneth M., Pres. & Chief Oper. Officer--DynaMark, Inc., Saint Paul, MN; *U.S. Public*, pg. 610
Rapp, William M., Pres. & Chief Exec. Officer--Vance Industries, Inc., Chicago, IL; *U.S. Private*, pg. 1133
Rappaport, Claude, Pres.--L & S Bearing Co., Oklahoma City, OK; *U.S. Public*, pg. 970
Rappaport, Edward, Pres.--W. Braun Company, Chicago, IL; *U.S. Private*, pg. 166
Rappaport, Nort, Pres.--IMPAXX, Inc., Schaumburg, IL; *U.S. Private*, pg. 558
Rappeport, G., Pres.--Donlen Corp., Northbrook, IL; *U.S. Private*, pg. 340
Rapton, Mallon, Pres.--Mel Rapton Honda, Sacramento, CA; *U.S. Private*, pg. 911
Rashkow, Ronald, Pres.--A-OK Delaware Inc., Schaumburg, IL; *Int'l*, pg. 533
Rask, Jan, Pres. & Chief Exec. Officer--Marine Drilling Companies, Inc., Sugar Land, TX; *U.S. Public*, pg. 1044
Rasmusen, Poul Steen, Pres.--Leca Portugal Argilas Expandidas S.A., Avelar, Portugal; *Int'l*, pg. 1200
Rasp, Bob, Pres.--Teledyne Laars, Moorpark, CA; *U.S. Public*, pg. 43
Raspino, Mr., Pres.--Fiat Auto Belgio SA, Brussels, Belgium; *Int'l*, pg. 481
Ratchford, Bob, Pres.-Mfg.--Shurfine International, Inc., Northlake, IL; *U.S. Private*, pg. 997
Ratcliff, Keith, Pres.--AGRA Plastics Inc., Mississauga, Canada; *Int'l*, pg. 30
Ratcliffe, G.J., Jr., Chm. Bd., Pres. & Chief Exec. Officer--Hubbell Incorporated, Orange, CT; *U.S. Public*, pg. 844
Ratcliffe, Kenneth, Pres. & Chief Oper. Officer--PC Connection, Inc., Milford, MA; *U.S. Private*, pg. 826
Rath, Frank E., Jr., Chm. Bd. & Pres.--Spang & Company, Butler, PA; *U.S. Private*, pg. 1020
Rath, John, Pres.--Insurance Administration Center., Inc., Tampa, FL; *U.S. Public*, pg. 1312
Rathemacher, Carl P., Pres.--Modern Handling Equipment of N.J., Inc., Edison, NJ; *U.S. Private*, pg. 755
Rathke, Dieter B., Pres.--Philipp Holzmann USA, Ltd., Charlotte, NC; *Int'l*, pg. 633
Ratia, Lauri, Pres.--Lohja Rudus Oy AG, Helsinki, Finland; *Int'l*, pg. 1200
Ratican, Peter J., Chm. Bd., Pres. & Chief Exec. Officer--Maxicare Health Plans, Inc., Los Angeles, CA; *U.S. Public*, pg. 1061
Ratke, J., Pres.--Vandemoortele N.V., Izegem, Belgium; *Int'l*, pg. 1451
Ratliff, D. Mark, Pres.--The Virtual Group, Allen Park, MI; *U.S. Private*, pg. 1141
Ratliff, Robert J., Chm. Bd., Pres. & Chief Exec. Officer--AGCO Corporation, Duluth, GA; *U.S. Public*, pg. 28
Ratner, Charles A., Pres. & Chief Exec. Officer--Forest City Enterprises, Inc., Cleveland, OH; *U.S. Public*, pg. 667
Ratner, James A., Pres. & Chief Exec. Officer--Forest City Commercial Construction Company, Inc., Cleveland, OH; *U.S. Public*, pg. 668
Ratner, James A., Pres. & Chief Exec. Officer--Forest City Rental Properties Corporation, Cleveland, OH; *U.S. Public*, pg. 668
Ratner, Michael H., Pres.--Richter & Ratner Contracting Corporation, Maspeth, NY; *U.S. Private*, pg. 930
Ratner, Phillip, Chm. Bd., Pres. & Chief Exec. Officer--Spaghetti Warehouse, Inc., Garland, TX; *U.S. Public*, pg. 1495
Ratner, Ronald A., Pres. & Chief Exec. Officer--Forest City Residential Development Inc., Cleveland, OH; *U.S. Public*, pg. 669
Rattee, David, Pres.--CIGL Holdings Ltd., Toronto, Canada; *Int'l*, pg. 241
Rattmann, Thomas, Pres. & Chief Oper. Officer--Columbian Mutual Life Insurance Co., Binghamton, NY; *U.S. Private*, *pg. 256*
Rattner, Selma, Pres.--Paragon Paint & Varnish Corp., Long Island City, NY; *U.S. Private*, pg. 838
Rau, Jerome E., Pres. & Chief Exec. Officer--Minuteman International, Inc., Addison, IL; *Int'l*, pg. 587
Rau, John, Pres. & Chief Exec. Officer--Chicago Title & Trust Co., Chicago, IL; *U.S. Public*, pg. 42
Rau, John, Pres. & Chief Exec. Officer--Chicago Title Insurance Co., Chicago, IL; *U.S. Public*, pg. 42
Rau, Lou, Pres.--NRCTSC, Atlanta, GA; *U.S. Public*, pg. 1182
Rau, Ralph E., Jr., Pres.--Edwin B. Stimpson Company, Inc., Bayport, NY; *U.S. Private*, pg. 1043
Rau, Robert H., Pres. & Chief Exec. Officer--Rohr, Inc., Chula Vista, CA; *U.S. Public*, pg. 751
Rauber, Hans, Pres.--Corona Engineering Corporation, Lithonia, GA; *U.S. Public*, pg. 1761
Rauch, Donald, Pres. & Chief Exec. Officer--M & C Specialties Company, Southampton, PA; *U.S. Private*, pg. 684
Rauch, Peter, Pres. & Chief Exec. Officer--Rauch Industries, Inc., Gastonia, NC; *U.S. Private*, pg. 1061
Rauchle, Craig, Pres.--Inter-Tel DataComm, Inc., Phoenix, AZ; *U.S. Public*, pg. 888
Rauchle, Craig W., Pres.--Inter-Tel Technologies, Inc., Phoenix, AZ; *U.S. Public*, pg. 888
Rauchle, Craig W., Pres.--Southwest Telephone Systems, Inc., Phoenix, AZ; *U.S. Public*, pg. 888
Rauenhorst, Mark, Pres. & Chief Exec. Officer--OPUS Corp., Minnetonka, MN; *U.S. Private*, pg. 818
Rauenhorst, Neil, Pres. & Chief Exec. Officer--Opus South Corporation, Tampa, FL; *U.S. Private*, pg. 818
Raugust, T., Pres.--Autocon Industries Inc., Saint Paul, MN; *Int'l*, pg. 1026
Rauh, Markus, Dr., Chief Exec. Officer--Leica A.G., Saint Gallen, Switzerland; *Int'l*, pg. 806
Raunchle, Craig W., Pres.--Inter-Tel Midwest, Inc., Phoenix, AZ; *U.S. Public*, pg. 888
Rav, David, Pres.--Standard Examiner, Ogden, UT; *U.S. Private*, pg. 1031
Raven, Charles H., Pres.--Hanson Investment Management Company, San Rafael, CA; *U.S. Public*, pg. 1673
Raven, Gregory, Pres. & Chief Exec. Officer--Hills Stores Co., Canton, MA; *U.S. Public*, pg. 828
Raven, Gregory, Pres.--Hills Department Store Company, Canton, MA; *U.S. Public*, pg. 828
Ravi, D., Ph.D, Pres.--IA Corporation, Emeryville, CA; *U.S. Private*, pg. 553
Ravin, Richard M., Chm. Bd., Pres. & Chief Exec. Officer--Combined Insurance Company of America, Chicago, IL; *U.S. Public*, pg. 118
Raviv, Gabriel, Ph.D., Pres. & Chief Exec. Officer--Bio-Logic Systems Corp., Mundelein, IL; *U.S. Public*, pg. 230
Ravizza, Eugene A., Chm. Bd. & Pres.--Synergism, Inc., Sunnyvale, CA; *U.S. Private*, pg. 1060
Rawlings, Dolores, Pres.--Crown Central Petroleum Foundation, Baltimore, MD; *U.S. Public*, pg. 462
Rawlings, Michael S., Pres. & Chief Concept Officer--Pizza Hut, Inc., Dallas, TX; *U.S. Public*, pg. 1636
Rawlinson, C.F.M., Pres.--Morgan Grenfell Asia Limited (Singapore), Singapore, Singapore; *Int'l*, pg. 406
Rawls, Benjamin M., Chm. Bd., Pres. & Chief Exec. Officer--Versar Inc., Springfield, VA; *U.S. Public*, pg. 1717
Rawls, Benjamin M., Pres.--Versar Risk Management, Inc., Springfield, VA; *U.S. Public*, pg. 1717
Rawson, Catherine A., Pres.--Rawson-Koenig, Inc., Houston, TX; *U.S. Public*, pg. 1362
Ray, Bingham, Co-Pres.--October Films, Inc., New York, NY; *Int'l*, pg. 1216
Ray, Bradford T., Pres. & Chief Oper. Officer--Steel Technologies Inc., Louisville, KY; *U.S. Public*, pg. 1513
Ray, Clarence L., Jr., Pres.--Duke/Fluor Daniel, Charlotte, NC; *U.S. Public*, pg. 535
Ray, Gene W., Pres. & Chief Exec. Officer--The Titan Corporation, San Diego, CA; *U.S. Public*, pg. 1618
Ray, John, Pres. & Gen. Mgr.--WJHG-TV, Inc., Channel 7, Panama City, FL; *U.S. Public*, pg. 759
Ray, Russell L., Jr., Pres. & Chief Exec. Officer--World Airways, Inc., Herndon, VA; *U.S. Public*, pg. 1780
Ray, Terry, Pres.--American Color, Phoenix, AZ; *U.S. Public*, *pg. 1133*
Ray, William D., Jr., Pres. & Owner--Bill Ray Nissan, Inc., Longwood, FL; *U.S. Private*, pg. 911
Ray, William S., Pres. & Chief Exec. Officer--Ray Communications, Inc., Kill Devil Hills, NC; *U.S. Private*, pg. 911
Rayden, Michael, Pres.--Limited, Too, Columbus, OH; *U.S. Public*, pg. 996
Rayman, Evan, Pres.--Executive Capital Corp., Big Rock, IL; *U.S. Private*, pg. 388
Raymond, Walter, Pres.--Heinkel Filtering Systems Inc., Bridgeport, NJ; *Int'l*, pg. 609
Rayner, Robert, Pres.--Essroc Cement, Corp., Speed, IN; *U.S. Private*, pg. 384
Rayve, Robert G., Chm. Bd., Pres. & Chief Exec. Officer--The Spencer Turbine Co., Windsor, CT; *U.S. Private*, pg. 1025
Razek, Edward, Pres.--The Limited, Inc., Columbus, OH; *U.S. Public*, pg. 995
Razmilovic, Tomo, Pres. & Chief Oper. Officer--Symbol Technologies, Inc., Holtsville, NY; *U.S. Public*, pg. 1546
Read, Bill, Pres.--Bank One, Wisconsin, Milwaukee, WI; *U.S. Public*, pg. 174
Read, Rosalie, Country Mgr.--Berlitz Schools of Languages Ltd., London, United Kingdom; *U.S. Public*, pg. 222
Reading, Andrew, Pres.--Micro Processor Systems, Inc., Sterling Heights, MI; *U.S. Public*, pg. 558
Reading, Anthony, Chm. Bd.--Smith & Wesson Corp., Springfield, MA; *Int'l*, pg. 1397
Ready, Robert J., Chm. Bd., Pres. & Chief Exec. Officer--LSI Industries, Inc., Cincinnati, OH; *U.S. Public*, pg. 971
Reagan, Charles, Pres.--Patterson-Kelley Company, Tulsa, OK; *U.S. Public*, pg. 793
Reagan, Thomas N., Pres.--Reagan Equipment Company, Inc., Gretna, LA; *U.S. Private*, pg. 913
Reamer, Norton H., Pres. & Chief Exec. Officer--United Asset Management Corporation, Boston, MA; *U.S. Public*, pg. 1672
Reardon, Daniel R., Pres.--G.H. Bass & Co., South Portland, ME; *U.S. Public*, pg. 1291
Reardon, Philip H., Pres. & Chief Exec. Officer--Essex County Gas Company, Amesbury, MA; *U.S. Public*, pg. 593
Reardon, Philip H., Pres. & Chief Exec. Officer--LNG Storage Inc., Amesbury, MA; *U.S. Public*, pg. 593
Reardon, Thomas J., Pres. & Chief Oper. Officer--C.H. Patrick & Co., Inc., Greenville, SC; *U.S. Public*, pg. 751
Reardon, Warren J., III, Pres.--Daniel Green Co., Dolgeville, NY; *U.S. Private*, pg. 477
Reasor, Robert A., Pres. & Chief Exec. Officer--Security Bank & Trust Co., Mount Carmel, IL; *U.S. Public*, pg. 1217
Rebello, Anthony J., Pres. & Chief Exec. Officer--Park Foods L.P., Barrington, IL; *U.S. Private*, pg. 839
Reber, Stephen A., Pres.--Macbeth Div., New Windsor, NY; *U.S. Public*, pg. 965
Rebolledo, Ernesto Martens, Pres.--Corporacion Internacional de Aviacion (CINTRA), Mexico, Mexico; *Int'l*, pg. 332
Recanati, Leon, Joint Mng. Dir.--IDB Holding Corporation, Tel Aviv, Israel; *Int'l*, pg. 643
Recanati, Raphael, Chm. Bd. & Mng. Dir.--IDB Holding Corporation, Tel Aviv, Israel; *Int'l*, pg. 643
Rechler, Scott, Pres. & Chief Oper. Officer--Reckson Associates Realty Corp., Melville, NY; *U.S. Public*, pg. 1368
Reckmann, Christian, Mng. Dir.--Deutsche Bank AG (Sao Paulo), Sao Paulo, Brazil; *Int'l*, pg. 404
Recordati, Giovanni, Pres. & Chief Oper. Officer--Recordati Industria Chimica e Farmaceutica S.p.A., Milan, Italy; *Int'l*, pg. 1090
Reddekopp, Joe, Gen. Mgr.--Nashua Photo Limited, Saskatoon, Canada; *U.S. Public*, pg. 1152
Redding, Peter S., Pres. & Chief Exec. Officer--The Standard Register Company, Dayton, OH; *U.S. Public*, pg. 1505
Reddrop, Colin, Pres.--Astra Charnwood, Leicester, United Kingdom; *Int'l*, pg. 93
Reddy, Govi C., Pres. & Chief Oper. Officer--General Binding Corporation, Northbrook, IL; *U.S. Public*, pg. 707
Reddy, James M., Pres.--Pluess-Staufer (California), Inc., Lucerne Valley, CA; *Int'l*, pg. 1061
Reddy, N. Damodar, Chm. Bd., Pres. & Chief Exec. Officer--Alliance Semiconductor Corp., San Jose, CA; *U.S. Public*, pg. 47
Redento, Jose, Pres.--Air Cruisers Co., Belmar, NJ; *Int'l*, pg. 572
Redman, Peter, Pres.--Cessna Finance Corp., Wichita, KS; *U.S. Public*, pg. 1589
Redman, Richard C., Chm. Bd., Pres. & Chief Exec. Officer--Sellen Construction Company, Seattle, WA; *U.S. Private*, pg. 982
Redmon, John W., Pres.--Brown & Root Power & Mfg., Houston, TX; *U.S. Public*, pg. 775
Redmond, Donald P., Pres. & Chief Exec. Officer--Integon Corporation, Winston Salem, NC; *U.S. Public*, pg. 719
Redmond, Donald P., Pres. & Chief Exec. Officer--Integon National Insurance Co., Winston Salem, NC; *U.S. Public*, *pg. 720*
Redmond, Donald P., Pres. & Chief Exec. Officer--Integon Indemnity Corporation, Winston Salem, NC; *U.S. Public*, pg. 720
Redmond, Donald P., Pres. & Chief exec. Officer--Integon General Insurance Corporation, Winston Salem, NC; *U.S. Public*, pg. 720
Redmond, Donald P., Pres. & Chief Exec. Officer--New South Insurance Company, Winston Salem, NC; *U.S. Public*, pg. 720
Redmond, Donald P., Pres. & Chief Exec. Officer--Integon Specialty Insurance Company, Winston Salem, NC; *U.S. Public*, pg. 720
Redmond, Donald P., Pres. & Chief Exec. Officer--Integon Preferred Insurance Company, Winston Salem, NC; *U.S. Public*, pg. 720
Redmond, Donald P., Pres. & Chief Exec. Officer--Integon Casualty Insurance Company, Winston Salem, NC; *U.S. Public*, pg. 720
Redmond, Donald P., Pres.--National General Insurance Co., Earth City, MO; *U.S. Public*, pg. 721
Redmond, John, Pres. & Chief Exec. Officer--Hoover Group, Inc., Alpharetta, GA; *U.S. Private*, pg. 538
Redmond, Paul A., Chm. Bd. & Chief Exec. Officer--The Washington Water Power Company, Spokane, WA; *U.S. Public*, pg. 1744
Redmond, William, Pres. & Chief Exec. Officer--Garden Way, Inc., Troy, NY; *U.S. Private*, pg. 440
Redner, Robert R., Pres. & Controller--General Filters, Inc., Novi, MI; *U.S. Private*, pg. 444
Reeb, H.B., Pres.--NRI Schools, Washington, DC; *U.S. Public*, pg. 1071
Reece, Paris G., III, Pres.--Financial Asset Management Corporation, Denver, CO; *U.S. Public*, pg. 1025
Reece, Thomas, Pres. & Chief Exec. Officer--Dover Corporation, New York, NY; *U.S. Public*, pg. 520
Reed, Andrew M., Ph.D., Pres.--PolyMedica Wound Care Company, Golden, CO; *U.S. Public*, pg. 1315
Reed, C.W., Pres. & Chief Oper. Officer--Escalade Sports, Evansville, IN; *U.S. Public*, pg. 591
Reed, Charles L., Jr., Pres. & V.P.-Mktg.--Integra Technologies Corp., Waltham, MA; *U.S. Private*, pg. 565
Reed, Don, Pres. & Chief Exec. Officer--SA-SO Company, Dallas, TX; *U.S. Private*, pg. 955
Reed, Donald B., Pres. & Chief Exec. Officer--Cabletron Systems, Inc., Rochester, NH; *U.S. Public*, pg. 288
Reed, E.C., Chm. Bd., Pres. & Sec.--Utica Boilers Inc., Utica, NY; *U.S. Private*, pg. 1129
Reed, Earl, Chm. Bd. & Pres.--Reed Grain & Bean Company, Buhl, ID; *U.S. Private*, pg. 916
Reed, G. Thomas, Pres. & Chief Oper. Officer--Ethika Corporation, Hilton Head Island, SC; *U.S. Public*, pg. 595
Reed, Grant O., Pres. & Chief Exec. Officer--LaRoche Industries Inc., Atlanta, GA; *U.S. Private*, pg. 651
Reed, Jackie L., Pres. & Chief Exec. Officer--Regions Bank/Heard County, Franklin, GA; *U.S. Public*, pg. 1372
Reed, James R., Pres.--SeaquistPerfect Dispensing, Cary, IL; *U.S. Public*, pg. 125
Reed, John E., Chm. Bd., Pres. & Chief Exec. Officer--Mestek, Inc., Westfield, MA; *U.S. Public*, pg. 1099

Reed, John L., Sr., Pres.--Reed Motors, Inc., Orlando, FL; *U.S. Private*, pg. 916
Reed, Mark, Pres.--In Focus Services, Inc., Wilsonville, OR; *U.S. Public*, pg. 873
Reed, Richard C., Chm. Bd. & Pres.--Kova Fertilizer Inc., Greensburg, IN; *U.S. Private*, pg. 634
Reed, Robert A., Pres. & Chief Exec. Officer--Physicians Mutual Insurance Co., Omaha, NE; *U.S. Private*, pg. 864
Reed, Sam, Pres. & Chief Exec. Officer--Keebler Company, Elmhurst, IL; *U.S. Public*, pg. 657
Reed, W., Pres.--North Safety Products, Safety Equipment Division, Cranston, RI; *Int'l*, pg. 1243
Reed, W.L., Pres.--North Safety Products, Hand Protection Division, Charleston, SC; *Int'l*, pg. 1243
Reed, W.L., Pres.--North Safety Products, Health Care Division, Rockford, IL; *Int'l*, pg. 1243
Reed, William R., Jr., Chm. Bd., Pres. & Chief Exec. Officer--NBC Bank, FSB (Belzoni), Belzoni, MS; *U.S. Public*, pg. 1155
Reese, J. Sandy, Pres.--Zentox Corp., Ocala, FL; *U.S. Private*, pg. 1204
Reese, R. Allan, Ph.D., Chm. Bd. & Pres.--Ace Tank & Equipment Co., Seattle, WA; *U.S. Private*, pg. 12
Reese, Richard B., Pres. & Chief Exec. Officer--JBB Worldwide, Inc., Deerfield, IL; *U.S. Public*, pg. 675
Reese, Richard B., Pres.--Bourbon Warehouse Receipts, Inc., Deerfield, IL; *U.S. Public*, pg. 675
Reese, Stuart E., Pres.--Massmutual Corporate Investors, Springfield, MA; *U.S. Public*, pg. 1055
Reese, Ulf, Pres.--Handelsbanken Finans, Stockholm, Sweden; *Int'l*, pg. 1327
Reeves, Alvin, Pres.--Thermal Technology Industries, North Kansas City, MO; *U.S. Private*, pg. 1080
Reeves, Donna, Pres. & Chief Oper. Officer--Frontier Cellular, Rochester, NY; *U.S. Public*, pg. 683
Reeves, Scott, Pres.--Jinwoong Inc., San Jose, CA; *Int'l*, pg. 707
Reeves, Thomas, Pres.--Russell Sigler Inc., Phoenix, AZ; *U.S. Private*, pg. 999
Refioglu, Ilhan, Pres.--International Microcircuits, Inc., Milpitas, CA; *U.S. Private*, pg. 571
Regal, Robert J., Pres. & Chief Exec. Officer--Universal-Rundle Corp., New Castle, PA; *U.S. Public*, pg. 1193
Regan, Bob, Pres.--Air Systems Ltd., Brampton, Canada; *Int'l*, pg. 1398
Regan, Harold, Pres. & Chief Exec. Officer--The H.W. Wilson Co., Bronx, NY; *U.S. Private*, pg. 1180
Regan, Maureen, Pres.--Lally, McFarland & Pantello Inc., New York, NY; *Int'l*, pg. 601
Regelin, Eric G., Pres. & Chief Exec. Officer--Atlantic Builders Group Inc., Baltimore, MD; *U.S. Private*, pg. 95
Regulinski, Stephan G., Pres.--United Cogen, Inc., San Francisco, CA; *U.S. Public*, pg. 1653
Reheman, R.G., Pres.--Southern Indiana Properties, Inc., Evansville, IN; *U.S. Public*, pg. 1471
Reheman, R.G., Chm. Bd., Pres. & Chief Exec. Officer--ComSource, Inc., Evansville, IN; *U.S. Public*, pg. 1471
Reheman, Ronald G., Chm. Bd., Pres. & Chief Exec. Officer--SIGCORP, Inc., Evansville, IN; *U.S. Public*, pg. 1471
Reheman, Ronald G., Chm. Bd., Pres. & Chief Exec. Officer--Southern Indiana Gas & Electric Co., Evansville, IN; *U.S. Public*, pg. 1471
Rehnman, Lars, Pres.--NCC Building - Jonkoping, Jonkoping, Sweden; *Int'l*, pg. 898
Rehulka, Mario, Co-Pres.--Austrian Airlines, Vienna, Austria; *Int'l*, pg. 101
Reichborn, P.K., Pres.--Goodway Technologies Corporation, Stamford, CT; *U.S. Private*, pg. 464
Reichel, Manfred, Pres.--Hermann Berstorff Maschinenbau GmbH, Hannover, Germany; *Int'l*, pg. 617
Reichelt, Ferdinand H., Pres.--Fireside Thrift, Newark, CA; *U.S. Public*, pg. 1694
Reicher, Michael, Pres.--UDL Laboratories, Inc., Rockford, IL; *U.S. Public*, pg. 1143
Reichert, Charles M., Pres. & Gen. Mgr.--BNI Coal, Ltd., Bismarck, ND; *U.S. Public*, pg. 1116
Reichert, Donald G., Pres.--ABC Packaging Machine Corp., Tarpon Springs, FL; *U.S. Private*, pg. 3
Reichert, Robert C., Pres.--Kings Toyota Suzuki, Cincinnati, OH; *U.S. Private*, pg. 621
Reichman, Joel H., Pres. & Chief Exec. Officer--Designs, Inc., Needham, MA; *U.S. Public*, pg. 501
Reichmann, Charles, Chief Exec. Officer--Dri Mark Products, Inc., Port Washington, NY; *U.S. Private*, pg. 342
Reichmann, Louis, Pres.--Dri Mark Products, Inc., Port Washington, NY; *U.S. Private*, pg. 342
Reichmann, Philip, Pres.--Olympia & York Developments Ltd., Toronto, Canada; *Int'l*, pg. 1004
Reichwein, John H., Jr., Pres.--Revcor, Inc., Carpentersville, IL; *U.S. Private*, pg. 925
Reid, Andrew, Pres.--Andy Johns Fashions, Inc., New York, NY; *U.S. Public*, pg. 233
Reid, David, Pres.--Medscreen Limited, London, United Kingdom; *U.S. Public*, pg. 1286
Reid, Frederik, Pres.--Deutsche Lufthansa AG, Cologne, Germany; *Int'l*, pg. 407
Reid, Hugh J., Pres. & Gen. Mgr.--Hazelwood Farms Bakeries, Inc., Atlanta, GA; *U.S. Public*, pg. 1541
Reid, J., Pres.--Ranco Inc., Plain City, OH; *Int'l*, pg. 1243
Reid, J. Marshall, Pres.--Mercantile-Safe Deposit & Trust Co., Baltimore, MD; *U.S. Public*, pg. 1089
Reid, John W., Exec. V.P. & Chief Fin. Officer--Ranco North America, Plain City, OH; *Int'l*, pg. 1243
Reid, M. Bagley, Pres. & Chief Exec. Officer--Scott & Stringfellow Capital Management, Inc., Richmond, VA; *U.S. Public*, pg. 1445
Reid, Mike, Mng. Partner-Creative Copy--Lewis Gace Bozell Healthcare Worldwide, Fort Lee, NJ; *U.S. Public*, pg. 1642
Reid, Peter, Pres.--Titan Steel Corp., Baltimore, MD; *U.S. Private*, pg. 1089
Reid, Richard A., Pres.--AMS Operations Corporation, Inc., Lakewood, CO; *U.S. Public*, pg. 86
Reid, Travis, Pres.--Loews Theatre Management Corp., New York, NY; *Int'l*, pg. 1282
Reid, William P., Pres. & Chief Exec. Officer--Gundle/SLT Environmental, Inc., Houston, TX; *U.S. Public*, pg. 769
Reid, William P., Pres. & Chief Exec. Officer--GSE Living Technology, Inc., Houston, TX; *U.S. Public*, pg. 770
Reid, William T., Pres.--G.I. Trucking Co., La Mirada, CA; *U.S. Public*, pg. 131
Reidy, Carolyn K., Pres. & Publisher--Simon & Schuster Trade Division, New York, NY; *U.S. Private*, pg. 777
Reidy, Martin, Pres. & Chief Oper. Officer--R/GA Interactive, New York, NY; *U.S. Public*, pg. 1641
Reiff, Doug, Pres. & Chief Exec. Officer--Otsuka America Pharmaceutical, Inc., Rockville, MD; *Int'l*, pg. 1013
Reifschneider, Darrel, Chm. Bd. & Chief Exec. Officer--Manchester Tank & Equipment Company, Brentwood, TN; *U.S. Private*, pg. 699
Reigle, Jeffrey A., Pres. & Chief Exec. Officer--Regal Ware, Inc., Kewaskum, WI; *U.S. Private*, pg. 917
Reijula, Peter, Pres.--McCain Citrus Inc., Oak Brook, IL; *Int'l*, pg. 850
Reike, Paul, Pres.--Outboard Marine Corp. of Canada Ltd., Peterborough, Canada; *U.S. Private*, pg. 478
Reilly, Albert, Pres.--Rough Brothers, Inc., Cincinnati, OH; *U.S. Private*, pg. 947
Reilly, David, Pres.--CamEra, Inc., Saint Petersburg, FL; *U.S. Public*, pg. 1457
Reilly, Donald C., Pres.--Superior Tube Company, Collegeville, PA; *U.S. Private*, pg. 1056
Reilly, Edward T., Pres. & Chief Exec. Officer--Big Flower Press Holdings, Inc., New York, NY; *U.S. Public*, pg. 228
Reilly, Emmett, Pres.--John W. Danforth Co., Buffalo, NY; *U.S. Private*, pg. 309
Reilly, James P., Pres. & Chief Exec. Officer--Cantel Industries, Inc., Clifton, NJ; *U.S. Public*, pg. 301
Reilly, James W., Pres.--Sherman & Reilly, Inc., Chattanooga, TN; *U.S. Private*, pg. 993
Reilly, John, Pres. & Chief Exec. Officer--Stant Corporation, Denver, CO; *Int'l*, pg. 1396
Reilly, Kevin, Jr., Pres. & Chief Exec. Officer--Lamar Corporation, Baton Rouge, LA; *U.S. Private*, pg. 644
Reilly, Lawrence J., Pres.--Granite State Electric Co., Lebanon, NH; *U.S. Public*, pg. 1171
Reilly, Lawrence J., Pres.--Massachusetts Electric Co., Westborough, MA; *U.S. Public*, pg. 1171
Reilly, Lawrence J., Pres. & Chief Exec. Officer--Narragansett Electric Co., Providence, RI; *U.S. Public*, pg. 1171
Reilly, Paul V., Pres. & Chief Oper. & Fin. Officer--Mail-Well Inc., Englewood, CO; *U.S. Public*, pg. 1037
Reilly, Paul V., Pres.--American Mail-Well Envelope, Englewood, CO; *U.S. Public*, pg. 1038
Reilly, Richard M., Pres.--Allmerica Securities Trust, Worcester, MA; *U.S. Public*, pg. 54
Reily, W.B. III, Pres.--William B. Reily & Co., Inc., New Orleans, LA; *U.S. Private*, pg. 919
Reiman, Stephen W., Pres., Chief Exec. Officer & Mgr.-Sls.--W.A. Roosevelt Co., La Crosse, WI; *U.S. Private*, pg. 943
Reimerdes, Carl, Pres.--Fenton Hill American Limited, Valley Stream, NY; *Int'l*, pg. 103
Reimerdes, Carl, Pres.--The Sports Section Inc., Chicago, IL; *Int'l*, pg. 103
Reimers, Larry, Pres.--The Segerdahl Corp., Wheeling, IL; *U.S. Private*, pg. 981
Reinas, Jan, Pres. & Chief Exec. Officer--Norske Skogindustrier A.S, Skogn, Norway; *Int'l*, pg. 965
Reiner, Arthur E., Vice Chm., Pres. & Chief Exec. Officer--Finlay Enterprises, Inc., New York, NY; *U.S. Public*, pg. 623
Reinert, Jerry, Pres.--First National Bank of Springdale, Springdale, AZ; *U.S. Public*, pg. 639
Reining, Robert R., Pres.--Dutchess Quarry & Supply Co. Inc., Pleasant Valley, NY; *U.S. Private*, pg. 350
Reinke, Jerome, Pres. & Chief Exec. Officer--Armada Corporation, Detroit, MI; *U.S. Private*, pg. 82
Reinke, Jerome, Pres. & Chief Exec. Officer--Hoskins Mfg. Co., Detroit, MI; *U.S. Private*, pg. 83
Reinking, C. William, Pres. & Chief Exec. Officer--Exchange Bank, Santa Rosa, CA; *U.S. Public*, pg. 599
Reinstetle, Dwight, Pres.--Morgan Lumber Sales Co., Columbus, OH; *U.S. Private*, pg. 761
Reis, Tony R., Mng. Dir.--IBM Switzerland, Zurich, Switzerland; *U.S. Public*, pg. 897
Reisner, John A., Pres.--Chemical Bank West, Cadillac, MI; *U.S. Public*, pg. 345
Reiss, Jacques, Pres.--Sanofi Canada, Mississauga, Canada; *Int'l*, pg. 445
Reiss, Richard T., Pres. & Treas.--R.C.A. Rubber Company, Akron, OH; *U.S. Private*, pg. 902
Reist, M.V., Pres.--Howe Monenco Inc., Thunder Bay, Canada; *Int'l*, pg. 31
Reist, Walter, Chm. Bd. & Pres.--WRH Walter Reist Holding AG, Zurich, Switzerland; *Int'l*, pg. 1484
Reiter, William M., M.D., Chm. Bd., Pres. & Chief Exec. Officer--Health Professionals, Inc., Fort Lauderdale, FL; *U.S. Public*, pg. 802
Reith, James N., Pres. & Chief Exec. Officer--Jennie-O Foods, Inc., Willmar, MN; *U.S. Public*, pg. 840
Reitman, Jeremy H., Pres.--Reitmans (Canada) Limited, Montreal, Canada; *Int'l*, pg. 1102
Reitman, Jeremy H., Pres.--Reitmans Inc., Montreal, Canada; *Int'l*, pg. 1102
Reitman, Robert S., Chm. Bd., Pres. & Exec. Officer--The Tranzonic Companies, Pepper Pike, OH; *U.S. Public*, pg. 1632
Reitz, William, Pres. & Chief Exec. Officer--Scott's Food Stores Inc., Fort Wayne, IN; *U.S. Public*, pg. 1541
Reives, Louis, Pres.--Versatech Engineering, Lexington, KY; *U.S. Private*, pg. 712
Relf, Daniel H., Pres.--California Reconveyance Co., Chatsworth, CA; *U.S. Public*, pg. 1741
Rella, William, Chm. Bd., Pres., Chief Exec. & Oper. Officer--LCS Industries, Inc., Clifton, NJ; *U.S. Public*, pg. 970
Rello Vega, Enrique, Pres.--Embotelladores del Valle de Anahuac S.A. de C.V., Mexico, Mexico; *Int'l*, pg. 452
Relyea, K.S., Pres. & Chief Exec. Officer--Family Restaurants, Inc., Irvine, CA; *U.S. Private*, pg. 393
Remack, Bob, Pres.--revolution, inc., Kansas City, MO; *U.S. Private*, pg. 1131
Rembutsu, Katsuhari, Chm. & Pres.--Daiwa Securities Trust Company, Jersey City, NJ; *Int'l*, pg. 375
Remensperger, Thomas, Pres. & Chief Oper. Officer--Ninteman Construction Company, Inc., San Diego, CA; *U.S. Private*, pg. 1052
Remington, H. Joseph, Pres.--Better Baked Foods, Inc., North East, PA; *U.S. Private*, pg. 141
Remley, William L., Vice Chm., Pres. & Chief Exec. Officer--Weldotron Corporation, Piscataway, NJ; *U.S. Public*, pg. 1752
Ren, Q.J., Pres.--Shanghai Ebara Engineering and Services Co., Ltd., Shanghai, China; *Int'l*, pg. 432
Renard, Antoine, Pres.--Freinrail S.A., Reims, France; *Int'l*, pg. 738
Renaud, Ronald, Pres.--Flashmedia Advertising Inc., Outremont, Canada; *Int'l*, pg. 1076
Renbarger, Larry D., Pres. & Chief Exec. Officer--Shelter Components Corporation, Elkhart, IN; *U.S. Public*, pg. 952
Renker, Greg, Co-Pres.--Guthy-Renker Corp., Palm Desert, CA; *U.S. Private*, pg. 488
Renner, Reinhard, Chief Exec. Officer & Bus. Devel/Information--MHI Partners Werbeagentur GMBH, Starnberg, Germany; *U.S. Public*, pg. 1422
Rennert, Ira Leon, Pres. & Chief Exec. Officer--Renco Group, New York, NY; *U.S. Private*, pg. 922
Renno, Joel Mendes, Chm. Bd. & Pres.--Petrobras - Petroleo Brasileiro S.A., Rio de Janeiro, Brazil; *Int'l*, pg. 1041
Reno, John F., Chm. Bd., Pres. & Chief Exec. Officer--Dynatech Corporation, Burlington, MA; *U.S. Public*, pg. 539
Renollet, Lewis R., Pres. & Chief Exec. Officer--The Citizens Savings Bank Company, Pemberville, OH; *U.S. Public*, pg. 1412
Renschler, C. Arnold, M.D., Pres. & Chief Exec. Officer--PharMerica, Inc., Tampa, FL; *U.S. Public*, pg. 1286
Renshaw, Maurice, Pres.-Parke-Davis U.S. & Mexico--Parke-Davis Group, Morris Plains, NJ; *U.S. Public*, pg. 1739
Rensing, Victor, Pres.--Quest International, Naarden, Netherlands; *Int'l*, pg. 1438
Rentenbach, T.M., Pres. & Chief Exec. Officer--Rentenbach Engineering Company, Knoxville, TN; *U.S. Private*, pg. 923
Renwick, Ken, Pres. & Chief Exec. Officer--All-Phase Electric Supply Co., Benton Harbor, MI; *U.S. Private*, pg. 35
Reny, L. Guy, Chm. Bd. & Pres.--Standard Duplicating Machines Corp., Andover, MA; *U.S. Private*, pg. 1031
Renyi, Thomas A., Pres.--The Bank of New York Company, Inc., New York, NY; *U.S. Public*, pg. 178
Repeta, Richard J., Pres.--Maguire Group Inc., Foxboro, MA; *U.S. Private*, pg. 696
Repman, Jim, Pres.--Onoda Northwest, Inc., Seattle, WA; *Int'l*, pg. 284
Requien, Jean-Marc, Pres.--EURO RSCG Quartet, Ecueille, France; *Int'l*, pg. 601
Requien, Jean-Marc, Pres.--EURO RSCG Quartet, Annecy, France; *Int'l*, pg. 601
Resch, George, Pres.--Resource, Inc., Tampa, FL; *U.S. Public*, pg. 896
Reseigh, Christopher, Pres.--Parsons Brinckerhoff Construction Services, Inc., Herndon, VA; *U.S. Private*, pg. 841
Resende, Itamar, Pres.--Metallurg do Brazil Ltda., Sao Paulo, Brazil; *U.S. Private*, pg. 735
Resnick, Stewart, Chm. Bd & Pres.--Roll International Corporation, Los Angeles, CA; *U.S. Private*, pg. 941
Resnick, Stewart, Pres.--The Franklin Mint, Franklin Center, PA; *U.S. Private*, pg. 941
Ressler, Barry, Chm. & Pres., Chief Exec. Officer--Universal Voltronics Corporation, Mount Kisco, NY; *U.S. Public*, pg. 1596
Resweber, Louis J., Pres. & Chief Exec. Officer--Network Acquisition Corp., Baton Rouge, LA; *U.S. Public*, pg. 1169
Retelle, John P., Pres.--PAR Government Systems Corporation, New Hartford, NY; *U.S. Public*, pg. 1256
Retzlaff, Robert Z., Pres. & Chief Fin. Officer--Retzlaff Incorporated, San Rafael, CA; *U.S. Private*, pg. 925
Reuben, George, Pres. & Chief Oper. Officer--Reuben Organization, Philadelphia, PA; *U.S. Private*, pg. 925
Reuflinger, Paul, Pres.--Sobelair S.A., Brussels, Belgium; *Int'l*, pg. 1168
Reuhl, Douglas G., Pres.--American TV & Appliance of Madison, Inc., Madison, WI; *U.S. Private*, pg. 64
Reuland, Noel, Pres. & Chief Exec. Officer--Reuland Electric Company, City of Industry, CA; *U.S. Private*, pg. 925
Reum, James L., Pres.--Aircraft Technology, Inc., Hollywood, FL; *U.S. Public*, pg. 804
Reum, W. Robert, Chm. Bd., Pres. & Chief Exec. Officer--The Interlake Corporation, Lisle, IL; *U.S. Public*, pg. 892
Reuter, Bernard, Pres.--Villeroy & Boch Tableware, Ltd., Princeton, NJ; *Int'l*, pg. 1468
Reuter, William J., Chm. Bd., Pres. & Chief Exec. Officer--Farmers and Merchants Bank and Trust, Hagerstown, MD; *U.S. Public*, pg. 1542
Reuter, William J., Pres.--Susquehanna Bancshares South, Inc., Lititz, PA; *U.S. Public*, pg. 1543
Reuterskiold, Clas, Pres. & Chief Exec. Officer--AB Industrivarden, Stockholm, Sweden; *Int'l*, pg. 678
Reutlinger, Paul, Pres. & Chief Exec. Officer--Sabena, Zaventem, Belgium; *Int'l*, pg. 1168

Revely, Thomas, III, Pres. & Chief Exec. Officer--Cincinnati Bell Supply Company, Cincinnati, OH; *U.S. Public*, pg. 367
Revey, Jim, Pres.--Tri-State Motor Transit Co., Joplin, MO; *U.S. Private*, pg. 1101
Rex, William J., Chm. Bd., Pres. & Chief Exec. Officer--Rexhall Industries, Inc., Lancaster, CA; *U.S. Public*, pg. 1384
Reyenger, Rick, Pres.--Carl A. Lowe Industries, Inc., Lebanon, MO; *U.S. Private*, pg. 478
Reyenger, Rick, Pres.--Sea Nymph Inc., Lebanon, MO; *U.S. Private*, pg. 478
Reyes, Cesar G., Pres.--Mabuhay Philippines Satellite Corp., Makati, Philippines; *Int'l*, pg. 1051
Reyman, Meryl Fischman, Pres. & Chief Oper. Officer--Harrison & Star, Inc., New York, NY; *U.S. Private*, pg. 506
Reynolds, Brian T., Pres.--Correctional Foodservices Management, Palm Beach Gardens, FL; *U.S. Public*, pg. 1731
Reynolds, Edgar L., Pres.--Bellsouth Wireless, Inc., Atlanta, GA; *U.S. Public*, pg. 208
Reynolds, Eugene, Pres.--Vile-Goller, Fine Art Printing & Lithography, Kansas City, KS; *U.S. Private*, pg. 1140
Reynolds, James G., Chm. Bd. & Pres.--Portland Food Products Company, Forest Grove, OR; *U.S. Private*, pg. 876
Reynolds, Jerry, Mng. Partner--Prestige Ford, Garland, TX; *U.S. Private*, pg. 882
Reynolds, John J., Pres. & Gen. Mgr.--Spicer Clark-Hurth, Statesville, NC; *U.S. Public*, pg. 479
Reynolds, John K., Pres.--F.T. Reynolds Company, Glendive, MT; *U.S. Private*, pg. 926
Reynolds, Joseph C., Pres.--Carolina First Mortgage Company, Columbia, SC; *U.S. Public*, pg. 306
Reynolds, Marshall T., Chm. Bd., Pres. & Chief Exec. Officer--Champion Industries, Huntington, WV; *U.S. Public*, pg. 333
Reynolds, Michael J., Pres.--Godwins Booke & Dickenson, Inc., Briarcliff Manor, NY; *U.S. Public*, pg. 118
Reynolds, R.J., Pres.--Jaguar Canada Inc., Bramalea, Canada; *U.S. Public*, pg. 667
Reynolds, Randolph N., Pres.--Aroaima Bauxite Company Ltd., Bridgetown, Barbados; *U.S. Public*, pg. 1386
Reynolds, Ron, Gen. Mgr.--INCA Presswood Pallets, Ltd., Sardis, MS; *Int'l*, pg. 678
Reynolds, S.L., Pres.--Porth Plastic Co., Des Plaines, IL; *Int'l*, pg. 233
Reznik, Maurice, Pres.--Warner's, Bridgeport, CT; *U.S. Public*, pg. 1738
Rezzo, Kathleen, Pres. & Chief Exec. Officer--Construction Lending Corporation of America-Builder Division, Pasadena, CA; *U.S. Public*, pg. 857
Rhea, Stephen L., Pres., New Bus. Contact & Acct. Services Mgr.--Rhea & Kaiser Marketing Communications, Naperville, IL; *U.S. Private*, pg. 927
Rhein, Arthur, Pres. & Chief Oper. Officer--Pioneer-Standard Electronics, Inc., Cleveland, OH; *U.S. Public*, pg. 1300
Rhein, Timothy J., Pres. & Chief Exec. Officer--APL Limited, Oakland, CA; *Int'l*, pg. 912
Rhene, Sylvia, Pres.-Atco East West--Atco/East-West Records, New York, NY; *U.S. Public*, pg. 1611
Rhines, Wally, Pres. & Chief Exec. Officer--Mentor Graphics Corporation, Wilsonville, OR; *U.S. Public*, pg. 1086
Rhoades, Jeffrey P., Pres.--Rhoades Development, Santa Ana, CA; *U.S. Private*, pg. 927
Rhoads, Mitchel, Chm. Bd., Pres. & Chief Exec. Officer--Le Peep's Grill Inc., Littleton, CO; *U.S. Private*, pg. 655
Rhodenbaugh, Jeffrey P., Pres.--Beverage-Air Co., Spartanburg, SC; *U.S. Public*, pg. 1496
Rhodes, Calvin, Pres.--Flowers Baking Co. of Opelika, Inc., Opelika, AL; *U.S. Public*, pg. 657
Rhodes, Richard G., Pres. & Chief Exec. Officer--Regions Bank/Dalton/Cartersville/Chattanooga, Dalton, GA; *U.S. Public*, pg. 1372
Rhodes, Rick, Pres.--First National Bank of Sweetwater, Sweetwater, TX; *U.S. Public*, pg. 633
Rhodes, Russell, Pres.--Tubular Services, Inc., Houston, TX; *U.S. Private*, pg. 1108
Rhulen, Harry W., Pres.--Frontier Pacific Insurance Company, La Jolla, CA; *U.S. Public*, pg. 685
Rhulen, Walter A., Chm. Bd. & Pres.--Frontier Insurance Group, Inc., Rock Hill, NY; *U.S. Public*, pg. 684
Riahi, Brahim Ben, Pres. Dir. Gen.--Societe Tunisienne d'Assurances et de Reassurances, Tunis, Tunisia; *Int'l*, pg. 61
Ribas, Iraja B., Pres.--Kvaerner Pulping Ltda., Curitiba, Brazil; *Int'l*, pg. 768
Ribas, Iraja B., Pres.--Gotaverken Energy do Brasil, Rio de Janeiro, Brazil; *Int'l*, pg. 771
Ribohn, L.U., Pres.--Electrolux San Jose, Pordenone, Italy; *Int'l*, pg. 442
Ribolde, Nestor, Gen. Mgr.--Sancor Cooperativas Unidas Limitadas, Buenos Aires, Argentina; *Int'l*, pg. 1183
Ribolla, Luigi, Pres.--Heinz Plasmon Dietetici Alimentari S.p.A., Milan, Italy; *U.S. Public*, pg. 806
Ricard, John R., Bishop, Chm. Bd. & Pres.--Catholic Relief Services, Baltimore, MD; *U.S. Private*, pg. 220
Ricart, Rhett, Pres.--Ricart Ford Inc., Groveport, OH; *U.S. Private*, pg. 927
Riccardi, Anthony, Pres., Treas. & Sec.--William A. Randolph, Inc., Morton Grove, IL; *U.S. Private*, pg. 909
Riccardi, Robert, Partner & Gen. Mgr.--Goodby, Silverstein & Partners, San Francisco, CA; *U.S. Public*, pg. 1224
Ricciardi, Salvatore, Pres. & Chief Exec. Officer--Purity Wholesale Grocers, Boca Raton, FL; *U.S. Private*, pg. 896
Riccitiello, John S., Pres. & Chief Oper. Officer--Electronic Arts, San Mateo, CA; *U.S. Public*, pg. 569
Ricco, Gary, Pres.--Farley Candy Company, Chicago, IL; *U.S. Private*, pg. 397
Ricco, William, Pres.--Oxford Health Centers, Norwalk, CT; *U.S. Public*, pg. 1239
Riccobon, Paul J., Pres.--Riccobon & Company, Inc., Santa Fe Springs, CA; *U.S. Private*, pg. 927
Rice, Bruce C., Pres. & Chief Exec. Officer--Buster Brown Apparel, Inc., Chattanooga, TN; *U.S. Private*, pg. 189
Rice, Charles A., Pres. & Chief Exec. Officer--Dey Laboratories Inc., Napa, CA; *Int'l*, pg. 812
Rice, J. Craig, Pres.--Quality Bearing Service of Nevada, Inc., Sparks, NV; *U.S. Public*, pg. 1711
Rice, John D., Pres.--ADM Food Oils, Decatur, IL; *U.S. Public*, pg. 128
Rice, Linda Johnson, Pres. & Chief Oper. Officer--Johnson Publishing Company, Inc., Chicago, IL; *U.S. Private*, pg. 591
Rice, Ronald J., Pres.--Tanning Research Labs., Inc., Ormond Beach, FL; *U.S. Private*, pg. 1068
Rice, Steve, Pres.--NAI Systems Division, Columbia, MD; *U.S. Public*, pg. 1144
Rice, Tandy, Jr., Chm. Bd. & Chief Exec. Officer--Top Billing Inc., Nashville, TN; *U.S. Private*, pg. 1091
Rice, Thomas, Pres. & Publr.--Alton Telegraph, Alton, IL; *U.S. Public*, pg. 934
Rice, Thomas E., Pres. & Chief Exec. Officer--Suburban Newspapers of Greater St. Louis, Saint Louis, MO; *U.S. Public*, pg. 935
Rich, Bob, Mng. Principal--Baxter Hodell Donnelly Preston Inc., Cincinnati, OH; *U.S. Private*, pg. 124
Rich, Francis P., Pres.--Action Tire, Candia, NH; *U.S. Private*, pg. 15
Rich, Francis P., Jr., Chm. Bd. & Pres.--Action Equipment, Candia, NH; *U.S. Private*, pg. 14
Rich, Francis P., Jr., Pres.--AC Leasing Corporation, Candia, NH; *U.S. Private*, pg. 15
Rich, Francis P., Jr., Pres.--Action Supply, Candia, NH; *U.S. Private*, pg. 15
Rich, Francis P., Jr., Pres.--JJJ Realty Trust, Candia, NH; *U.S. Private*, pg. 15
Rich, Jeffrey A., Pres. & Chief Oper. Officer--Affiliated Computer Services, Inc., Dallas, TX; *U.S. Public*, pg. 27
Rich, John W., Jr., Chm. Bd. & Pres.--Reading Anthracite Co., Pottsville, PA; *U.S. Private*, pg. 913
Rich, Melvin L., Chm. Bd., Pres. & Treas.--Evergood Products Corporation, Hicksville, NY; *U.S. Private*, pg. 386
Rich, Michael, Pres.--Tenax Corporation, Danbury, CT; *Int'l*, pg. 193
Rich, Norman, Pres.--Weis Markets, Inc., Sunbury, PA; *U.S. Public*, pg. 1751
Rich, Robert E., Jr., Pres.--Rich Products Corp., Buffalo, NY; *U.S. Private*, pg. 928
Richard, David, Pres. & Chief Exec. Officer--Norstan, Inc., Plymouth, MN; *U.S. Public*, pg. 1192
Richard, Gary, Pres. & Chief Exec. Officer--P.C. Richard & Son, Farmingdale, NY; *U.S. Private*, pg. 928
Richard, Oliver G., III, Chm. Bd., Pres. & Chief Exec. Officer--Columbia Energy Group, Reston, VA; *U.S. Public*, pg. 402
Richard, Oliver G., III, Chm. Bd., Pres. & Chief Exec. Officer--Columbia Gas System Service Corp., Wilmington, DE; *U.S. Public*, pg. 403
Richard, Russell R., Pres. & Chief Oper. Officer--Monticello Management Co., San Diego, CA; *U.S. Private*, pg. 759
Richardi, Ralph, Pres. & Chief Oper. Officer--Simmons American Eagle Airlines, Dallas-Fort Worth Airport, TX; *U.S. Public*, pg. 10
Richardi, Ralph L., Pres.--Simmons Airlines, Chicago, IL; *U.S. Public*, pg. 9
Richards, Jack E., Pres. & Chief Oper. Officer--Adventure Tours USA, Inc., Dallas, TX; *U.S. Private*, pg. 22
Richards, John D., Acting. Chm. Bd., Pres. & Chief Exec. & Oper. Officer--Granite Furniture Co., Salt Lake City, UT; *U.S. Private*, pg. 469
Richards, Stan, Principal & Creative Dir.--The Richards Group, Inc., Dallas, TX; *U.S. Private*, pg. 929
Richards, Stan, Principal--Jackhammer, Dallas, TX; *U.S. Private*, pg. 929
Richards, Thomas P., Pres. & Chief Exec. Officer--Grey Wolf, Inc., Houston, TX; *U.S. Public*, pg. 765
Richards, Thomas S., Chm. Bd., Pres. & Chief Exec. Officer--Rochester Gas And Electric Corporation, Rochester, NY; *U.S. Public*, pg. 1395
Richards, Wells E., Pres. & Chief Oper. Officer--Richards Brothers of Mountain Grove, Mountain Grove, MO; *U.S. Private*, pg. 928
Richardson, C. Vance, Pres.--Clayson Knitting Co. Inc., Star, NC; *U.S. Private*, pg. 244
Richardson, Chris, Pres.--Square D Company, Palatine, IL; *Int'l*, pg. 1208
Richardson, John, Pres.--Branch Group Inc., Upper Marlboro, MD; *U.S. Private*, pg. 165
Richardson, John G., Pres., Chief Exec. & Chief Fin. Officer--Sugar Creek Packing Co., Washington Court House, OH; *U.S. Private*, pg. 1049
Richardson, Joseph E., III, Pres.--Richardson Industries, Inc., Sheboygan Falls, WI; *U.S. Private*, pg. 929
Richardson, Joseph H., Pres. & Chief Exec. Officer--Florida Power Corporation, Saint Petersburg, FL; *U.S. Public*, pg. 655
Richardson, Kenneth, Pres.--Foster Wheeler Zack, Inc., Clinton, NJ; *U.S. Public*, pg. 677
Richardson, Mark, Pres. & Publisher--The Daily News, Dartmouth, Canada; *Int'l*, pg. 924
Richardson, Maurice M., Pres.--Sonoco Engraph, Inc., Atlanta, GA; *U.S. Public*, pg. 1486
Richardson, Michael A., Chm. Bd., Pres., Chief Exec. Officer & Chief Oper. Officer--American Consumers, Inc., Fort Oglethorpe, GA; *U.S. Public*, pg. 70
Richardson, Michael C., Pres.--Air Land Forwarders, Inc., Jacksonville, FL; *U.S. Private*, pg. 1049
Richardson, Mike, Pres.--Dark Horse Comics, Inc., Milwaukie, OR; *U.S. Private*, pg. 311
Richardson, R. Fred, Pres.--Crown Life Investment Management Company (CLIMCO), Toronto, Canada; *Int'l*, pg. 468
Richardson, Robert, Pres. & Publisher--The Sault Star Ltd., Sault Sainte Marie, Canada; *Int'l*, pg. 631
Richardson, Tony, Pres.--Networks and Peripherals Ltd., Huntingdon, United Kingdom; *Int'l*, pg. 645
Richardson, Tony, Pres.--Decision Data U.K. Ltd., Huntingdon, United Kingdom; *Int'l*, pg. 645
Richardson, William S., Pres. & Chief Exec. Officer--Dow Hickam Pharmaceuticals Inc., Sugar Land, TX; *U.S. Public*, pg. 1143
Richer, Alvin, Chm., Pres. & Chief Exec. Officer--Arnold Machinery Company, Salt Lake City, UT; *U.S. Private*, pg. 84
Richer, Jurgen, Dr., Pres.--Ullstein GmbH, Berlin, Germany; *Int'l*, pg. 102
Richey, Don, Pres. & Chief Exec. Officer--House of Fabrics, Inc., Sherman Oaks, CA; *U.S. Public*, pg. 842
Richey, Steve, Chm. Bd. & Pres.--Precision Parts Corp., Morristown, TN; *U.S. Private*, pg. 879
Richey, Van L., Pres. & Chief Exec. Officer--American Cast Iron Pipe Co., Birmingham, AL; *U.S. Private*, pg. 51
Richings, Michael, Pres. & Chief Exec. Officer--Granges, Inc., Denver, CO; *U.S. Public*, pg. 1723
Richings, Michael B., Pres. & Chief Exec. Officer--Vista Gold Corp., Denver, CO; *U.S. Public*, pg. 1723
Richings, Mike, Pres.--Sociedad Industrial Minera Yamin Ltda., Denver, CO; *U.S. Public*, pg. 1723
Richman, David, Pres.--S.D. Richman Sons, Inc., Philadelphia, PA; *U.S. Private*, pg. 929
Richman, Joshua V., Pres. & Chief Exec. Officer--Straw Hat Cooperative Corp., Dublin, CA; *U.S. Private*, pg. 1046
Richmond, A. Vernon, Pres.--W.M. Barr & Co., Inc., Memphis, TN; *U.S. Private*, pg. 117
Richmond, George R., Pres. & Chief Oper. Officer--Jim Walter Resources, Inc., Brookwood, AL; *U.S. Public*, pg. 1737
Richmond, Mark, Gen. Mgr. & Publr.--The Advocate, Newark, OH; *U.S. Private*, pg. 23
Richmond, Rick, Pres.--Young Dental Manufacturing, Earth City, MO; *U.S. Private*, pg. 1201
Richmond, Wayne, Pres.--Balanced Foods, Inc., North Bergen, NJ; *Int'l*, pg. 752
Richomme, Yannick, Pres.--Alfa Laval Separation Inc., Warminster, PA; *Int'l*, pg. 1378
Richter, Garrett S., Pres. & Chief Exec. Officer--First National Bank of Naples, Naples, FL; *U.S. Public*, pg. 607
Richter, Joe, Pres.--Kenwood USA, Long Beach, CA; *Int'l*, pg. 730
Richter, Rick, Pres. & Publisher--Simon & Schuster Children's Publishing, New York, NY; *U.S. Private*, pg. 777
Richter, Yochai, Pres. & Chief Exec. Officer--Orbotech Ltd., Yavne, Israel; *Int'l*, pg. 1007
Rickard, Keith G., Pres.--Storage Management Division, Rancho Cordova, CA; *U.S. Public*, pg. 1516
Rickert, Lynn, Pres. & Chief Exec. Officer--Union Trust Bank, Union City, IN; *U.S. Public*, pg. 633
Ricknoland, L.F., Pres.--Whitmire Micro-gen Research Laboratories Inc., Saint Louis, MO; *U.S. Private*, pg. 592
Ricks, R. Roydon, Pres. & Chief Oper. Officer--Trans-Apparel Group, Michigan City, IN; *U.S. Public*, pg. 796
Ricoy, Luis Dans, Pres.--CACESA - Compania Auxiliar Al Cargo Expres, S.A., Coslada, Spain; *Int'l*, pg. 1224
Ricoy, Martin, Pres. & Chief Exec. Officer--Grupo Synkro, S.A. de C.V., Mexico, Mexico; *Int'l*, pg. 576
Riddell, A.J., Pres.--Canadian Timken Ltd., Saint Thomas, Canada; *U.S. Public*, pg. 1617
Riddell, Glenn, Pres.--Laurel Steel, Burlington, Canada; *Int'l*, pg. 598
Ridderstrale, Carl-Erik, Pres. & Chief Exec. Officer--BT Industries AB, Mjolby, Sweden; *Int'l*, pg. 123
Riddle, Stephen, Pres.--Asbury Carbons, Inc., Asbury, NJ; *U.S. Private*, pg. 87
Riddle, Stephen, Pres.--Asbury Louisiana, Inc., De Quincy, LA; *U.S. Private*, pg. 87
Riddleberger, James E., Pres.--Riddleberger Bros.. Inc., Mount Crawford, VA; *U.S. Private*, pg. 930
Rideau, Charles, Pres. & Gen. Mgr.--First American Title Insurance Agency of Pinal, Casa Grande, AZ; *U.S. Public*, pg. 626
Rideout, Roy P., Pres. & Chief Oper. Officer--Newfoundland Capital Corporation Limited, Dartmouth, Canada; *Int'l*, pg. 924
Rider, Robert F., Jr., Pres.--O.A. Newton & Son Co., Bridgeville, DE; *U.S. Private*, pg. 797
Ridge, Garry O., Pres. & Chief Exec. Officer--WD-40 Company, San Diego, CA; *U.S. Public*, pg. 1726
Ridgley, Robert L., Pres. & Chief Exec. Officer--Northwest Natural Gas Company, Portland, OR; *U.S. Public*, pg. 1200
Ridings, Louis, Pres. & Chief Exec. Officer--Quixx Corporation, Amarillo, TX; *U.S. Public*, pg. 1170
Ridling, Jim L., Pres. & Chief Exec. Officer--Southern Guaranty Insurance Companies, Montgomery, AL; *Int'l*, pg. 346
Ridout, Derek M., Pres. & Chief Exec. Officer--Silcorp Limited, Scarborough, Canada; *Int'l*, pg. 1249
Rieben, W. P., Pres.--GE Fanuc Automation Europe S.A., Echternach, Luxembourg; *Int'l*, pg. 478
Rieber, John, Grp. Pres.--Lee's Famous Recipe Restaurant, Nashville, TN; *U.S. Private*, pg. 906
Rieck, Tim, Pres.--Pies, Inc., Chaska, MN; *U.S. Public*, pg. 658
Riedel, Steven C., Pres. & Chief Oper. Officer--Precision Castparts Corp., Portland, OR; *U.S. Public*, pg. 1320
Riedel, Steven C., Acting Pres.--PCC Specialty Products, Inc., Worcester, MA; *U.S. Public*, pg. 1321
Riederer, Richard K., Pres. & Chief Exec. Officer--Weirton Steel Corporation, Weirton, WV; *U.S. Public*, pg. 1751
Riefler, Grover, Pres.--T.L. Smith Machine, Springville, NY; *U.S. Private*, pg. 1009
Riegel, J. Kent, Pres. & Gen. Counsel--ICI Americas, Inc., Wilmington, DE; *Int'l*, pg. 663

Rieger, Robert, Pres. & Chief Exec. Officer--Exolon-Esk Company, Tonawanda, NY; *U.S. Public*, pg. 600
Rieh, Chong Hun, Pres.--Korea Electric Power Corporation (KEPCO), Seoul, Korea; *Int'l*, pg. 758
Riehl, James E., Sr., Pres.--Roseville Chrysler Plymouth Jeep Inc., Roseville, MI; *U.S. Private*, pg. 946
Riener, John, Pres.--Nurses Inc., Houston, TX; *Int'l*, pg. 1285
Riepenhausen, Peter, Pres. & Chief Exec. Officer--Resound Corporation, Redwood City, CA; *U.S. Public*, pg. 1382
Riese, Dennis, Pres.--National Restaurant Management, Inc., New York, NY; *U.S. Private*, pg. 786
Rieson, Dean A., Pres. & Chief Exec. Officer--Carlson Real Estate Company, Minnetonka, MN; *U.S. Private*, pg. 212
Riess, John M., Pres. & Chief Oper. Officer--The Gates Rubber Company, Denver, CO; *Int'l*, pg. 1396
Rietberg, C.C. Th., Pres.--Van Leeuwen Pipe and Tube Group B.V., Zwijndrecht, Netherlands; *Int'l*, pg. 1449
Rieth, Robert, Pres. & Chief Exec. Officer--Wyle Laboratories, Inc., El Segundo, CA; *U.S. Private*, pg. 1193
Riethman, Ron, Pres.--Norcold, Sidney, OH; *U.S. Private*, pg. 352
Rife, John A., Pres.--United Fire & Casualty Company, Cedar Rapids, IA; *U.S. Public*, pg. 1677
Rife, John A., Pres. & Chief Oper. Officer--United Life Insurance Company, Cedar Rapids, IA; *U.S. Public*, pg. 1677
Rifkin, Daniel M., Pres. & Chief Oper. Officer--Omnisource Corporation, Fort Wayne, IN; *U.S. Private*, pg. 817
Rigby, Jay, Pres.--P & E, Inc., Orlando, FL; *U.S. Private*, pg. 825
Riggins, Jim, Pres.--UPB of Southwest Missouri, Springfield, MO; *U.S. Public*, pg. 1669
Riggio, Joseph, Pres.--Holmes Protection of New Jersey, Inc., Edison, NJ; *U.S. Public*, pg. 1649
Riggio, Leonard, Chm. Bd., Pres. & Chief Exec. Officer--Barnes & Noble Inc., New York, NY; *U.S. Public*, pg. 189
Riggs, C. Daniel, Pres.--Riggs Industries, Inc., Stoystown, PA; *U.S. Private*, pg. 930
Riggs, Daniel, Pres.--Somerset Steel, Stoystown, PA; *U.S. Private*, pg. 930
Riggs, Dave, Pres.--California Strawberry Commission, Watsonville, CA; *U.S. Private*, pg. 201
Riggs, John A., IV, Pres.--J.A. Riggs Tractor Co., Little Rock, AR; *U.S. Private*, pg. 930
Riggs, Louis V., Pres. & Chief Exec. Officer--A. Teichert & Son, Inc., Sacramento, CA; *U.S. Private*, pg. 1072
Rigney, R. Lee, Pres.--Capstar Partners, Inc., New York, NY; *Int'l*, pg. 816
Rigsby, James H., Jr., Pres. & Chief Exec. Officer--Allied Bank of Georgia, Thomson, GA; *U.S. Public*, pg. 1373
Riha, Raymond R., Pres.--Office Equipment Company Of Chicago, Elmhurst, IL; *U.S. Private*, pg. 812
Rihm, John W., Pres.--Rihm Motor Company, Saint Paul, MN; *U.S. Private*, pg. 931
Riisager, Birger, Pres. & Chief Exec. Officer--FLS Industries A/S, Valby, Denmark; *Int'l*, pg. 474
Rijos, John, Pres.--Lane Hospitality, Inc., Northbrook, IL; *U.S. Private*, pg. 650
Riley, Ann A., Pres.--Clayton Reinsurance, Ltd., Webster Groves, MO; *U.S. Public*, pg. 1374
Riley, David P., Pres. & Chief Exec. Officer--The Middleby Corporation, Rolling Meadows, IL; *U.S. Public*, pg. 1109
Riley, H. John, Jr., Chm. Bd., Pres. & Chief Exec. Officer--Cooper Industries, Inc., Houston, TX; *U.S. Public*, pg. 442
Riley, H. Patrick, Pres.--CNG Producing Co., New Orleans, LA; *U.S. Public*, pg. 435
Riley, Richard W., Pres.--Label-Aire Inc., Fullerton, CA; *U.S. Private*, pg. 641
Riley, T. J., Pres.--Aero Tech Manufacturing Inc., North Salt Lake, UT; *Int'l*, pg. 1400
Riley, Tom, Pres.--Riley Natural Gas, Bridgeport, WV; *U.S. Public*, pg. 1281
Riley, William W., Pres.--ABC Transportation Co., Eufaula, AL; *U.S. Public*, pg. 69
Rimbey, Robert A., Pres. & Chief Exec. Officer--Reeves Bank, Beaver Falls, PA; *U.S. Public*, pg. 607
Rimel III, William P., Pres. & Chief Exec. Officer--American Inks & Coatings Corp., Phoenixville, PA; *U.S. Private*, pg. 56
Rimer, Harlan L., Pres. & Chief Exec. Officer--Four-S Baking Company, Los Angeles, CA; *U.S. Private*, pg. 422
Rinaldi, Richard A., Pres. & Chief Exec. Officer--CCX, Inc., Charlotte, NC; *U.S. Private*, pg. 193
Rinaldi, Rodolfo, Deputy Chm. Bd.--Banca Nazionale del Lavoro Sj.A., Rome, Italy; *Int'l*, pg. 136
Rinaldi, Vincent, Pres.--Information Leasing Corporation, Cincinnati, OH; *U.S. Public*, pg. 1338
Rinck, Jacobus Johannes, Pres.--Singapore Petroleum Company Ltd., Singapore, Singapore; *U.S. Public*, pg. 102
Rincon, Antonio Fernandez, Pres.--Mead Johnson Ecuador, S.A., Guayaquil, Ecuador; *U.S. Public*, pg. 256
Rincon, Jose A., Pres. & Chief Oper. Officer--Grupo Industrial Durango S.A. de C.V., Durango, Mexico; *Int'l*, pg. 575
Rinerson, Darrell D., Chm. Bd., Pres. & Sec.--Micron Quantum Devices, Inc., Santa Clara, CA; *U.S. Public*, pg. 1105
Ring, William, Pres.--Long Island Water Corporation, Lynbrook, NY; *U.S. Private*, pg. 674
Ringler, James M., Chm. Bd., Pres. & Chief Exec. Officer--Premark International, Inc., Deerfield, IL; *U.S. Public*, pg. 1321
Rini, Charles A. Sr., Pres.--Rini-Rego Supermarkets, Inc., Cleveland, OH; *U.S. Private*, pg. 451
Rini, Charles A., Sr., Pres. & Chief Oper. Officer--Riser Foods, Inc., Bedford, OH; *U.S. Private*, pg. 450
Rinker, Thomas L., Pres.--Kvaerner EnviroPower Inc., Owings Mills, MD; *Int'l*, pg. 770
Rinsch, Charles E., Pres. & Chief Exec. Officer--Argonaut Group, Inc., Los Angeles, CA; *U.S. Public*, pg. 129
Rinsch, Charles E., Chm. Bd. & Pres.--Argonaut Co., Menlo Park, CA; *U.S. Public*, pg. 129
Riordan, James J., Pres.--Mann & Hummel Filter Technology Inc., Greensboro, NC; *Int'l*, pg. 484
Riordan, John F., Chm. Bd., Pres. & Chief Exec. Officer--MidCon Texas Pipeline Operator, Inc., Houston, TX; *U.S. Public*, pg. 1210
Riordan, Michael T., Pres. & Chief Oper. Officer--Fort James Corporation, Richmond, VA; *U.S. Public*, pg. 670
Riordan, Steven, Pres.--Communications Supply Corporation, Stamford, CT; *U.S. Private*, pg. 259
Riordan, Steven, Pres.--GNWC Wire, Cable & Network Products, Downers Grove, IL; *U.S. Private*, pg. 259
Riordan, Thomas, Pres.--Service Solution, Warren, MI; *U.S. Public*, pg. 1421
Rios, Francisco Emilio, Dr., Pres.--Filtros Mann S.A., Buenos Aires, Argentina; *Int'l*, pg. 484
Rios, Victor N., Pres. & Gen. Mgr.--ITT Gilfillan, Van Nuys, CA; *U.S. Public*, pg. 859
Ripich, Terry, Pres.--American Tank & Fabricating Co., Cleveland, OH; *U.S. Private*, pg. 63
Ripley, Barrett F., Chm.Bd., Pres. & Chief exec. Officer--Troy Mills, Inc., Troy, NH; *U.S. Private*, pg. 1106
Ripley, John A., Pres. & Chief Exec. Officer--Precision Tune Autocare Inc., Leesburg, VA; *U.S. Public*, pg. 1321
Ripley, Richard L., Pres.--South Trust Bank of Georgia, Atlanta, GA; *U.S. Public*, pg. 1492
Ripps, Harold A., Pres. & Chief Exec. Officer--Dairyland Greyhound Park, Inc., Kenosha, WI; *U.S. Private*, pg. 307
Risdall, Charles A., Pres. & Chief Exec. Officer--Smith System Manufacturing Company, Plano, TX; *U.S. Private*, pg. 1009
Riseman, Milton, Pres.--Advanta Mortgage Corp. USA, Fort Washington, PA; *U.S. Public*, pg. 22
Rishel, C.A., Pres.--Linder & Associates, Inc., Wichita, KS; *U.S. Private*, pg. 668
Rising, Nelson C., Pres. & Chief Exec. Officer--Catellus Development Corporation, San Francisco, CA; *U.S. Public*, pg. 314
Risinger, James A., Pres. & Chief Exec. Officer--Old National Bank, Evansville, IN; *U.S. Public*, pg. 1217
Risk, Richard R., Pres. & Chief Exec. Officer--Advocate Health Care, Oak Brook, IL; *U.S. Private*, pg. 23
Riskedal, Steve, Pres.--La Salle County Farm Supply, Ottawa, IL; *U.S. Private*, pg. 640
Riskind, Kenneth J., Pres. & Chief Exec. Officer--Fullerton Metals Co., Northbrook, IL; *U.S. Private*, pg. 431
Rislakki, Jaakko, Pres.--UPM Pack, Valkeakoski, Finland; *Int'l*, pg. 1430
Risley, Christopher A., Pres.--On Technology Corporation, Cambridge, MA; *U.S. Public*, pg. 1225
Risley, Gary, Pres.--Mesa Airlines Pilot Development, Inc., Farmington, NM; *U.S. Public*, pg. 1099
Risley, John, Pres.--Clearwater Fine Foods Inc., Bedford, Canada; *Int'l*, pg. 297
Risley, Phil, Pres.--Sunrise Nissan of Orange Park, Orange Park, FL; *U.S. Private*, pg. 1053
Rislov, Gerald, Pres.--Dakota Case Inc., Philip, SD; *U.S. Private*, pg. 636
Risner, Ray D., Pres. & Chief Oper. Officer--Southern Electronics Corporation, Tucker, GA; *U.S. Public*, pg. 1490
Risse, K. H., Ph.D., Pres. & Chief Exec. Officer--Bayer Corporation/Diagnostics Division, Tarrytown, NY; *Int'l*, pg. 173
Rissi, M.W., Pres.--Highway Equipment Company, Cedar Rapids, IA; *U.S. Private*, pg. 529
Rissman, Randy, Pres.--Tiger Electronics, Inc., Vernon Hills, IL; *U.S. Private*, pg. 1086
Risso, M.A., Pres.--Jannock Vinyl Group, Pittsburgh, PA; *Int'l*, pg. 699
Ristau, Harry, Gen. Mgr.--General Slicing/Red Goat Disposers, Murfreesboro, TN; *U.S. Public*, pg. 1506
Riswick, Erik, Pres.--Ready Bake Foods Inc., Mississauga, Canada; *Int'l*, pg. 1495
Ritchey, Steve, Pres.--Seattle Pacific Industries, Inc., Seattle, WA; *U.S. Private*, pg. 980
Ritchie, Alan, Chm. Bd & Pres.--Marson/Creative Fastener, Inc., Stoughton, MA; *U.S. Private*, pg. 708
Ritchie, Arthur, Pres.--Sand Technology Systems Inc., Iselin, NJ; *Int'l*, pg. 1183
Ritchie, Arthur G., Chm. Bd., Pres. & Chief Exec. Officer--Sand Technology Systems, Westmount, Canada; *Int'l*, pg. 1183
Ritchie, Clark, Pres. & Chief Exec. Officier--B & J Operations Company, Inc., Fairmont, WV; *U.S. Public*, pg. 850
Ritchie, David R., Chm. Bd., Pres. & Chief Exec. Officer--Farmers Bank of Maryland, Annapolis, MD; *U.S. Public*, pg. 641
Ritchie, H.T., Pres. & Chief Oper. Officer--Ritchie Corporation, Wichita, KS; *U.S. Private*, pg. 933
Ritchie, R., Pres. & Chief Exec. Officer--Canadian Pacific Railway, Calgary, Canada; *Int'l*, pg. 258
Ritchie, Rex, Pres.--Ashworth Bros., Inc., Fall River, MA; *U.S. Private*, pg. 89
Ritchie, Robert D., Pres. & Chief Exec. Officer--Vox Medica Corporation, Philadelphia, PA; *U.S. Private*, pg. 1143
Ritsema, Larry J., Pres. & Chief Exec. Officer--The Challenge Machinery Co., Grand Haven, MI; *U.S. Private*, pg. 227
Ritter, C. Dowd, Pres. & Chief Exec. Officer--AmSouth Bancorporation, Birmingham, AL; *U.S. Public*, pg. 105
Ritter, Christopher, Partner & Mngmt. Supvr.--Eric Mower and Associates, Inc., Syracuse, NY; *U.S. Private*, pg. 765
Ritter, Don, Gen. Mgr.--Mexia Fabricators, Inc., Wortham, TX; *U.S. Public*, pg. 424
Ritter, Martin L., Pres.--Ritter Sysco Food Service, Inc., Jersey City, NJ; *U.S. Public*, pg. 1550
Ritter, R.A., Pres.--The Pipelines of Puerto Rico, Inc., San Juan, PR; *U.S. Public*, pg. 1584
Ritter, Richard, Pres.--Refineria Texaco de Honduras, S.A., San Pedro Sula, Honduras; *U.S. Public*, pg. 1584
Rittinghaus, Erhard, Pres.--AGFA Division of Bayer Corporation, Ridgefield Park, NJ; *Int'l*, pg. 172
Rittwage, William R., Chm. Bd., Pres. & Chief Exec. Officer--COP Communications, Glendale, CA; *U.S. Private*, pg. 196
Ritvala, Kai, Pres.--Valmet (SEA) Pte Ltd. Paper Machinery Division, Singapore, Singapore; *Int'l*, pg. 1448
Rivard, Dick, Publr.--The Newport Daily Express, Newport, VT; *U.S. Public*, pg. 1343
Rivera, Jose, Pres.--Staff/DMB&B, Santo Domingo, Dominican Republic; *U.S. Private*, pg. 305
Rivera, Raul, Pres. & Chief Oper. Officer--National Benefit Life Insurance Co., New York, NY; *U.S. Public*, pg. 1633
Rivera, Richard, Pres. & Chief Exec. Officer--TGI Friday's, Inc., Addison, TX; *U.S. Private*, pg. 212
Rivers, Ronald D., Pres.--Vigoro Industries, Inc., Washington Court House, OH; *U.S. Public*, pg. 856
Rivkin, Elliott R., Pres.--Amram's Distributing, Ltd., Etobicoke, Canada; *U.S. Public*, pg. 223
Rizzo, Michael, Pres.--United Distillers USA, Inc., Stamford, CT; *Int'l*, pg. 412
Rizzuto, Leandro P., Chm. Bd. & Pres.--Conair Corporation, Stamford, CT; *U.S. Private*, pg. 261
Roach, Howard, Pres.--Howards TV & Appliances, Inc., La Habra, CA; *U.S. Private*, pg. 543
Roach, John V., Acting Pres.--Computer City, Fort Worth, TX; *U.S. Public*, pg. 1560
Roach, Timothy J., Vice Chm., Pres. & Chief Exec. Officer--TII Industries, Inc., Copiague, NY; *U.S. Public*, pg. 1556
Roark, M., Pres.--Ferag Inc., Bristol, PA; *Int'l*, pg. 1484
Roath, Kenneth B., Chm. Bd., Pres. & Chief Exec. Officer--Health Care Property Investors, Inc., Newport Beach, CA; *U.S. Public*, pg. 801
Roath, Stephen D., Pres.--Longs Drug Stores Corporation, Walnut Creek, CA; *U.S. Public*, pg. 1013
Robbins, Donald M., Pres.-Racing Opers. Div.--Hollywood Park, Inc., Inglewood, CA; *U.S. Public*, pg. 830
Robbins, James O., Chm. Bd., Pres. & Chief Exec. Officer--Cox Communications, Inc., Atlanta, GA; *U.S. Public*, pg. 454
Robbins, James O., Pres. & Chief Exec. Officer-Cox Communications--Arizona Sports Programming Network, Phoenix, AZ; *U.S. Public*, pg. 455
Robbins, L.C., Pres. & Chief Exec. Officer--Star Food Processing, Inc., San Antonio, TX; *U.S. Private*, pg. 1034
Robbins, Marty, Pres.--Valtek Controls, Ltd., Edmonton, Canada; *U.S. Public*, pg. 659
Robbins, Robert, Pres.--Yellow Book of New Jersey, Paramus, NJ; *U.S. Private*, pg. 767
Roberson, David A., Pres. & Chief Exec. Officer--Cavalier Homes, Inc., Wichita Falls, TX; *U.S. Public*, pg. 318
Robert, Dean E., Jr., Chm. Bd. & Pres.--Roberts Foods, Inc., Springfield, IL; *U.S. Private*, pg. 935
Robert, Donald A., Pres.--First American CREDCO, San Diego, CA; *U.S. Public*, pg. 625
Robert, George, Pres.--Benjamin Sheridan Co., East Bloomfield, NY; *U.S. Private*, pg. 291
Robert, Ralph, Pres.--Stuart Anderson's Black Angus/Cattle Company Restaurants, Los Altos, CA; *U.S. Private*, pg. 61
Roberts, Alex, Pres.--Pressure Systems, Inc., City of Commerce, CA; *U.S. Private*, pg. 882
Roberts, Alex, Pres.--Programmed Composites, Inc., Anaheim, CA; *U.S. Private*, pg. 882
Roberts, Brian L., Pres.--Comcast Corporation, Philadelphia, PA; *U.S. Public*, pg. 406
Roberts, David A., Pres.--International Div., AM International, Mount Prospect, IL; *U.S. Public*, pg. 1141
Roberts, David J., Chm. Bd., Pres. & Chief Exec. Officer--Foster Wheeler Real Estate Development Corp., Clinton, NJ; *U.S. Public*, pg. 677
Roberts, David J., Chm. & Pres.--Foster Wheeler Trading Co., Ltd., Hamilton, Bermuda; *U.S. Public*, pg. 677
Roberts, E.K., Pres. & Treas.--Fahnestock Viner Holdings Inc., Toronto, Canada; *Int'l*, pg. 476
Roberts, Gary, Pres. & Chief Oper. Officer--Greenstone Roberts Advertising, Melville, NY; *U.S. Public*, pg. 763
Roberts, Gary, Pres. & Chief Oper. Officer--Greenstone Roberts Public Relations, Coconut Creek, FL; *U.S. Public*, pg. 763
Roberts, Gary, Pres. & Chief Oper. Officer--Greenstone Roberts/Florida, Orlando, FL; *U.S. Public*, pg. 763
Roberts, Gary J., Pres. & Chief Exec. Officer--The Metropolitan Savings Bank of Ohio, Youngstown, OH; *U.S. Public*, pg. 608
Roberts, John, Chm. Bd. & Pres.--Busch Entertainment Corp., Clayton, MO; *U.S. Public*, pg. 114
Roberts, John K., Jr., Pres. & Chief Exec. Officer--Pan-American Life Insurance Company, New Orleans, LA; *U.S. Private*, pg. 836
Roberts, Ken, Chm. Bd. & Pres.--Lippincott & Margulies, Inc., New York, NY; *U.S. Public*, pg. 1048
Roberts, Kenny, Pres.--SouthTrust Bank, Russell County, Phenix City, AL; *U.S. Public*, pg. 1492
Roberts, Lee, Pres. & Chief Oper. Officer--FileNet Corporation, Costa Mesa, CA; *U.S. Public*, pg. 622
Roberts, Leonard H., Pres.--Tandy Corporation, Fort Worth, TX; *U.S. Public*, pg. 1560
Roberts, Leonard H., Pres.--RadioShack, Fort Worth, TX; *U.S. Public*, pg. 1560
Roberts, M. Gary, Pres.--Vanguard Bank & Trust Company, Valparaiso, FL; *U.S. Public*, pg. 1549
Roberts, Ralph L., Chm. Bd. & Pres.--Gator Freightways, Inc., Wilmington, OH; *U.S. Private*, pg. 441
Roberts, Ralph L., Owner & Pres.--R & L Carriers, Wilmington, OH; *U.S. Private*, pg. 441
Roberts, Richard S., Pres.-Fibers & Sr. V.P.--Guilford Mills, Inc., Greensboro, NC; *U.S. Public*, pg. 768
Roberts, Stephen M., Pres., Chief Exec. Officer & Treas.--F.L. Roberts & Co. Inc., Springfield, MA; *U.S. Private*, pg. 935
Roberts, Steven D., Co-Pres.--The Echo Design Group, Inc., New York, NY; *U.S. Private*, pg. 359

Roberts, Thomas B., Pres. & Treas.--C.F. Haglin & Sons, Edina, MN; *U.S. Private*, pg. 493
Roberts, Wade, Pres.--Hale Products Inc., Conshohocken, PA; *U.S. Public*, pg. 862
Roberts, William, Pres.--Brooks/Cole Publishing Co., Pacific Grove, CA; *U.S. Public*, pg. 1600
Roberts, William Ted, Pres. & Chief Exec. Officer--SouthTrust Bank of Elba, Elba, AL; *U.S. Public*, pg. 1492
Robertshaw, Robert, Pres.--General Tools Mfg., Co. Inc., New York, NY; *U.S. Private*, pg. 445
Robertson, D. Page, Pres.--Monaco Coach Corporation, Coburg, OR; *U.S. Public*, pg. 1123
Robertson, Dan M., Pres.--Berkley Risk Managers, Somerset, NJ; *U.S. Public*, pg. 215
Robertson, G. Bruce, Pres. & Chief Exec. Officer--Robertson Marketing Inc., Charlotte, NC; *U.S. Private*, pg. 936
Robertson, G. Bruce, Pres. & Chief Exec. Officer--RMI Educational Services, Charlotte, NC; *U.S. Private*, pg. 936
Robertson, James C., Chm. Bd., Pres. & Chief Exec. Officer--Consumers Financial Corporation, Camp Hill, PA; *U.S. Public*, pg. 437
Robertson, Joseph E., Jr., Pres.--The Ore & Chemical Corp., New York, NY; *Int'l*, pg. 862
Robertson, Peter, Pres.--Chevron U.S.A. Inc., San Francisco, CA; *U.S. Public*, pg. 348
Robertson, Philip L., Pres.--Specification Rubber Products Inc., Alabaster, AL; *U.S. Private*, pg. 52
Robertson, Robert G., Pres. & Chief Exec. Officer--White Hen Pantry, Inc., Elmhurst, IL; *U.S. Private*, pg. 1172
Robertson, Scott V., Pres. & Chief Exec. Officer--Robertson's Auto Salvage, Wareham, MA; *U.S. Private*, pg. 936
Robertson, Walt, Pres.--Maxwell Federal Division, San Diego, CA; *U.S. Public*, pg. 1062
Robertson, Walter, Pres.--Maxwell Technologies-Federal Division, San Diego, CA; *U.S. Public*, pg. 1062
Robertson, William L., Pres. & Chief Exec. Officer--Roy F. Weston, Inc., West Chester, PA; *U.S. Public*, pg. 1761
Robin, Arnold M., Pres.--Syndicated Office Systems, Inc., Orange, CA; *U.S. Public*, pg. 1577
Robinette, Gary, Pres.--Erb Lumber, Inc., Birmingham, MI; *Int'l*, pg. 1512
Robinette, Larry R., Pres. & Chief Exec. Officer--Morgan Products Ltd., Williamsburg, VA; *U.S. Public*, pg. 1132
Robins, John, Pres. & Gen. Mgr.--SMI Joist Florida, Starke, FL; *U.S. Public*, pg. 412
Robins, John, Pres.--SMI Joist South Carolina, West Columbia, SC; *U.S. Public*, pg. 412
Robins, John, Pres. & Gen. Mgr.--SMI Joist Company, Hope, AR; *U.S. Public*, pg. 413
Robins, John, Pres.--SMI Joist Nevada, Fallon, NV; *U.S. Public*, pg. 413
Robinson, Bill, Pres. & Chief Exec. Officer--Pacific Mutual Distributors, Newport Beach, CA; *U.S. Private*, pg. 831
Robinson, Bob, Pres. & Chief Exec. Officer--Doane Products Co., Joplin, MO; *U.S. Private*, pg. 337
Robinson, Bruce, Pres.--The Foxboro Company, Foxboro, MA; *Int'l*, pg. 1243
Robinson, Charles K., Jr., Pres. & Treas.--Swayne Robinson & Company, Richmond, IN; *U.S. Private*, pg. 936
Robinson, Claude D., Pres. & Chief Exec. Officer--Sivyer Steel Corporation, Bettendorf, IA; *U.S. Private*, pg. 1008
Robinson, David G., Pres.--CSC Index, Inc., Cambridge, MA; *U.S. Public*, pg. 422
Robinson, Douglas F., Pres. & Chief Exec. Officer--Computalog Ltd., Calgary, Canada; *Int'l*, pg. 325
Robinson, E. Montogmery, Pres. & Treas.--Top Flight, Inc., Chattanooga, TN; *U.S. Private*, pg. 1091
Robinson, Edward J., Pres.--Avon Products, Inc., New York, NY; *U.S. Public*, pg. 155
Robinson, Floyd, Pres.--NationsCredit Commercial Corporation, Cleveland, OH; *U.S. Public*, pg. 1165
Robinson, Frank, Pres.--Robinson Helicopter Company, Torrance, CA; *U.S. Private*, pg. 936
Robinson, Gary J., Pres. & Chief Oper. Officer-Columbia Gas of PA & MD--Columbia Gas Distribution Companies, Columbus, OH; *U.S. Public*, pg. 402
Robinson, Gary J., Pres. & Chief Exec. Officer--Columbia Gas of Maryland, Inc., Columbus, OH; *U.S. Public*, pg. 403
Robinson, Gary J., Pres. & Chief Exec. Officer--Columbia Gas of Pennsylvania, Inc., Columbus, OH; *U.S. Public*, pg. 403
Robinson, H. Ivens, Pres. & Chief Fin. Officer--Robinson Lumber & Export Company, New Orleans, LA; *U.S. Private*, pg. 936
Robinson, Hugh C. III, Pres., Chief Exec. Officer & Chief Oper. Officer--Presto Food Stores, Inc., Plant City, FL; *U.S. Private*, pg. 882
Robinson, J. Douglas, Pres. & Chief Oper. Officer--Utica Mutual Insurance Company, New Hartford, NY; *U.S. Private*, pg. 1129
Robinson, J. Douglas, Pres.--Utica National Life Insurance Company, Utica, NY; *U.S. Private*, pg. 1130
Robinson, J.M., Chm. Bd., Pres. & Chief Exec. Officer--Footstar Inc., Mahwah, NJ; *U.S. Public*, pg. 661
Robinson, James A., Pres.--Fairchild Dornier USA, San Antonio, TX; *U.S. Private*, pg. 391
Robinson, James M., Pres. & Gen. Mgr.-WRQX-FM--WMAL, Inc., Washington, DC; *U.S. Public*, pg. 512
Robinson, Jim, Pres.--Fairchild Aerospace Corporation, San Antonio, TX; *U.S. Private*, pg. 391
Robinson, John H., Grp. Chief Exec. Officer--Smith & Nephew PLC, London, United Kingdom; *Int'l*, pg. 1263
Robinson, Leon, Jr., Pres.--Robinson Bus Service, Evanston, IL; *U.S. Private*, pg. 936
Robinson, Murray, Pres. & Chief Oper. Officer--Delta & Pine Land Company, Scott, MS; *U.S. Public*, pg. 497
Robinson, Otto P., Jr., Pres. & Gen. Counsel--Penn Security Bank and Trust Co., Scranton, PA; *U.S. Public*, pg. 1270
Robinson, Patricia, Pres.--Mead School & Office Products, Dayton, OH; *U.S. Public*, pg. 1074
Robinson, Ralph A., Pres.--Weston Bakeries Limited, Etobicoke, Canada; *Int'l*, pg. 1495
Robinson, Richard, Chm. Bd., Pres. & Chief Exec. Officer--Scholastic Corporation, New York, NY; *U.S. Public*, pg. 1440
Robinson, Roby, Jr., Pres. & Dir.--The Robinson-Humphrey Company, Inc., Atlanta, GA; *U.S. Public*, pg. 1633
Robinson, Ron, Pres.--Svedala Industries Inc., Waukesha, WI; *Int'l*, pg. 1326
Robinson, Ronald, Pres.--Carbolon Division, Sterling, MA; *U.S. Private*, pg. 528
Robinson, Scott S., Pres. & Chief Exec. Officer--The Berkshire Gas Company, Pittsfield, MA; *U.S. Public*, pg. 216
Robinson, Thomas C., Grp. Pres.--Technology Management Group, Falls Church, VA; *U.S. Public*, pg. 423
Robinson, Thomas C., Acting Pres.--Integrated Business Services, Falls Church, VA; *U.S. Public*, pg. 423
Robinson, Thomas E., Pres. & Chief Oper. Officer--The Entwistle Company, Hudson, MA; *U.S. Private*, pg. 378
Robinson, William B., Pres.--Fortis Long Term Care, Milwaukee, WI; *Int'l*, pg. 499
Robinson, William B., Jr., Pres. & Chief Exec. Officer--George & Lynch, Inc., New Castle, DE; *U.S. Private*, pg. 448
Robison, Kevin, Pres. & Chief Oper. Officer--Quanta SecurSystems, Inc., Hanover, MD; *U.S. Public*, pg. 420
Robison, Lyle Douglas, Pres.--Cloud Corporation, Des Plaines, IL; *U.S. Private*, pg. 247
Robles, Ricardo, Pres. & Chief Fin. Officer--La Reina, Inc., Los Angeles, CA; *U.S. Private*, pg. 640
Robson, Steve, Pres.--Robson Communities, Sun Lakes, AZ; *U.S. Private*, pg. 937
Roby, Joe L., Pres. & Chief Oper. Officer--Donaldson, Lufkin, & Jenrette, Inc., New York, NY; *U.S. Public*, pg. 589
Rocco, Anthony, V.P. & Plant Mgr.--Grist Mill Company, Danville, IL; *U.S. Public*, pg. 766
Roch, Ronald, Pres.--Morgan Matroc Inc.-Electro Ceramics Division, Bedford, OH; *Int'l*, pg. 893
Roche, David H., Pres. & Chief Oper. Officer--Michigan Sugar Company, Saginaw, MI; *U.S. Public*, pg. 873
Roche, David H., Pres.--Savannah Foods Industrial, Inc., Savannah, GA; *U.S. Public*, pg. 873
Roche, Geoffrey B., Pres. & Creative Dir.--Roche Macaulay & Partners, Toronto, Canada; *U.S. Private*, pg. 678
Roche, George A., Chm. Bd., Pres. & Mng. Dir.--T. Rowe Price Associates, Inc., Baltimore, MD; *U.S. Public*, pg. 1324
Roche, John F., Chm. Bd., Pres. & Chief Exec. Officer--PMC Industries Inc., Wickliffe, OH; *U.S. Private*, pg. 827
Roche, Joyce, Pres.--Carson Products Company, Savannah, GA; *U.S. Public*, pg. 309
Roche, P.C. "Hoop", Pres. & Chief Exec. Officer--Erie Plastics, Corry, PA; *U.S. Private*, pg. 381
Roche, Thomas J., Pres.--Roche Constructors, Inc., Greeley, CO; *U.S. Private*, pg. 937
Rochon, John P., Pres. & Chief Exec. Officer--Mary Kay Corporation, Dallas, TX; *U.S. Private*, pg. 710
Rock, Bradley E., Chm. Bd., Pres. & Chief Exec. Officer--Bank of Smithtown, Smithtown, NY; *U.S. Private*, pg. 114
Rock, Bradley E., Chm. Bd., Pres. & Chief Exec. Officer--Smithtown Bancorp, Inc., Smithtown, NY; *U.S. Public*, pg. 1479
Rock, Douglas L., Chm. Bd., Pres., Chief Exec. & Oper. Officer--Smith International, Inc., Houston, TX; *U.S. Public*, pg. 1478
Rock, John D., V.P. & Gen. Mgr.--Oldsmobile Div. General Motors Corp., Lansing, MI; *U.S. Public*, pg. 720
Rock, Merle, Pres.--Bee Line Company, Bettendorf, IA; *U.S. Private*, pg. 129
Rocker, Kirk B., Pres. & Chief Exec. Officer--Bank of Millen, Millen, GA; *U.S. Public*, pg. 1371
Rod, Raymond, Pres.--Bensons International Systems Inc., Clifton, NJ; *Int'l*, pg. 460
Rodbell, Sidney P., Pres.--Apex Supply Co., Inc., Atlanta, GA; *U.S. Private*, pg. 77
Rodde, Anton, PhD, Pres. & Chief Exec. Officer--Western Data Systems, Calabasas, CA; *U.S. Private*, pg. 1165
Roddey, Sidney, Pres.--The State Printing Company, Inc., Columbia, SC; *U.S. Public*, pg. 1736
Roddy, R. Tom, Pres.--Benson Motors Corporation, Metairie, LA; *U.S. Private*, pg. 134
Roddy, Tom, Pres.--Benson Automotive World, San Antonio, TX; *U.S. Private*, pg. 133
Rodefeld, Gary H., Pres.--Rodefeld Co., Inc., Richmond, IN; *U.S. Private*, pg. 939
Roden, Donald R., Pres., Chief Exec. Officer & Chief Oper. Officer--Bergen Brunswig Corporation, Orange, CA; *U.S. Public*, pg. 213
Roden, Steve, Pres.--ITC Learning Corp., Herndon, VA; *U.S. Public*, pg. 859
Rodenstock, Randolf, Pres.--Optische Werke G. Rodenstock, Munich, Germany; *Int'l*, pg. 1007
Roderer, Jaime, Principal & Brdcst. Production Dir.--Publicis/Bloom, Dallas, TX; *Int'l*, pg. 469
Rodgers, Bow, Pres.--PowerTV, Inc., Cupertino, CA; *U.S. Public*, pg. 1443
Rodgers, Patricia, Pres.--Rodgers Builders, Inc., Charlotte, NC; *U.S. Private*, pg. 939
Rodgers, Ronald, Chm. Bd. & Pres.--J.B. Rodgers Mechanical Contractors, Phoenix, AZ; *U.S. Private*, pg. 939
Rodgers, Ronald W., Pres. & Chief Oper. Officer--Tri Tech Laboratories, Inc., Lynchburg, VA; *U.S. Private*, pg. 1101
Rodgers, T.J., Pres. & Chief Exec. Officer--Cypress Semiconductor Corporation, San Jose, CA; *U.S. Public*, pg. 470
Rodhouse, Thomas, Pres.--J.H. Roberts Industries Inc., Des Plaines, IL; *U.S. Private*, pg. 935
Rodia, Robert, Pres.--People's Securities Incorporated, Bridgeport, CT; *U.S. Public*, pg. 1274
Rodin, Robert, Pres. & Chief Exec. Officer--Marshall Industries, El Monte, CA; *U.S. Public*, pg. 1051
Rodkn, Gary, Pres.--Tropicana Dole Beverages North America, Bradenton, FL; *Int'l*, pg. 1217
Rodman, Stuart, Pres.--Alliance Automated, Rochester, NY; *U.S. Private*, pg. 38
Rodrigue, Myron, Pres.--Aker Gulf Marine, Ingleside, TX; *Int'l*, pg. 42
Rodriguez, Carlos J., Pres.--Mason Distributors, Inc., Hialeah, FL; *U.S. Private*, pg. 712
Rodriguez, Francisco Gonzalez, Pres.--Argentaria Corporacion Bancaria de Espana, S.A., Madrid, Spain; *Int'l*, pg. 80
Rodriguez, Godofredo R., Pres. & Mng. Dir.--Johnson & Johnson Medical (Philippines), Inc., Manila, Philippines; *U.S. Public*, pg. 931
Rodriguez, Godofredo R., Pres. & Gen. Mgr.--Johnson & Johnson (Philippines) Inc., Manila, Philippines; *U.S. Public*, pg. 931
Rodriguez, Jessica, Pres.--Travel Channel-Latin America, Miami, FL; *U.S. Private*, pg. 647
Rodriguez, Juan, Pres.--OTRASA, Buenos Aires, Argentina; *Int'l*, pg. 1515
Rodriguez, Juan, Pres.--Petroleos Transandinos YPF S.A., Santiago, Chile; *Int'l*, pg. 1515
Rodriguez, Ruben O., Pres.--Boston Overseas Financial Corporation S.A., Buenos Aires, Argentina; *U.S. Public*, pg. 185
Rodstein, Barbara I., Pres.--Harden Industries, Inc., Los Angeles, CA; *U.S. Private*, pg. 501
Rodstein, Richard M., Pres. & Chief Exec. Officer--K2 Inc., Los Angeles, CA; *U.S. Public*, pg. 940
Roe, David H., Pres. & Chief Exec. Officer--Bankers Security Life Insurance Society, Woodbury, NY; *U.S. Public*, pg. 1375
Roe, K. Keith, Chm. Bd., Pres. & Chief Exec. Officer--Burns & Roe Enterprises, Inc., Oradell, NJ; *U.S. Private*, pg. 187
Roe, Tony, Pres.--Salon & Fitness Systems, Brooklyn, NY; *U.S. Private*, pg. 962
Roebuck, Tim, Pres.--Britrail Travel International Inc., New York, NY; *Int'l*, pg. 1165
Roeder, Howard, Pres.--Sleepy's The Mattress Professionals, Bethpage, NY; *U.S. Private*, pg. 1005
Roehm, MacDonell, Jr., Chm. Bd., Pres. & Chief Exec. Officer--Bill's Dollar Stores, Inc., Ridgeland, MS; *U.S. Private*, pg. 144
Roelandts, Willem P., Pres. & Chief Exec. Officer--Xilinx, Inc., San Jose, CA; *U.S. Public*, pg. 1786
Roell, R., Pres. & Chief Exec. Officer--Ceramtec North America Applications, Inc., Mansfield, MA; *Int'l*, pg. 860
Roemer, James, Pres. & Chief Exec. Officer--Bell & Howell Holdings, Skokie, IL; *U.S. Public*, pg. 201
Roenigk, Martin A., Chm. Bd., Pres. & Chief Exec. Officer--CompuDyne Corporation, Willimantic, CT; *U.S. Public*, pg. 419
Roesener, Prof. Dr. Karlheinz, Dep. Pres.--Thyssen Stahl AG, Duisburg, Germany; *Int'l*, pg. 1388
Roesing, Jim, Pres. & Chief Exec. Officer--Super Sky Products, Inc., Mequon, WI; *U.S. Private*, pg. 1054
Roessler, E.C., Pres. & Chief Exec. Officer--CCB Financial Corporation, Durham, NC; *U.S. Public*, pg. 276
Roessner, John K., III, Chm. Bd. & Pres.--E.J. Brooks Company, Newark, NJ; *U.S. Private*, pg. 172
Rog, Joseph W., Chm. Bd., Pres. & Chief Exec. Officer--Corrpro Companies, Inc., Medina, OH; *U.S. Public*, pg. 451
Rogal, Andrew L., Pres. & Chief Exec. Officer--Hilb, Rogal and Hamilton Company, Glen Allen, VA; *U.S. Public*, pg. 826
Rogan, Owen F., Pres.--Ikon Office Solutions (British Columbia), Vancouver, Canada; *U.S. Public*, pg. 864
Rogel, Steven R., Pres. & Chief Exec. Officer--Willamette Industries, Inc., Portland, OR; *U.S. Public*, pg. 1768
Roger, Serge, Chm. Bd. & Pres.--Elscint France S.A., Bagnolet, France; *Int'l*, pg. 450
Rogers, Bill, Pres. & Chief Exec. Officer--Weather Tec Corporation, Fresno, CA; *U.S. Private*, pg. 1155
Rogers, C. Jeffrey, Pres. & Chief Exec. Officer--Pizza Inn, Inc., Dallas, TX; *U.S. Public*, pg. 1307
Rogers, Charles G., Pres.--BellSouth Products, Inc., Roanoke, VA; *U.S. Public*, pg. 209
Rogers, Dale, Pres. & Chief Oper. Officer--Drug Emporium of Arizona, Scottsdale, AZ; *U.S. Private*, pg. 343
Rogers, Gary L., Pres. & Chief Exec. Officer--G.E. Plastics, Pittsfield, MA; *U.S. Public*, pg. 710
Rogers, James E., Vice Chm., Pres. & Chief Exec. Officer--Cinergy Corp., Cincinnati, OH; *U.S. Public*, pg. 368
Rogers, James E., Vice Chm., Pres. & Chief Exec. Officer--CINergy Services, Inc., Cincinnati, OH; *U.S. Public*, pg. 369
Rogers, Joe W., Jr., Pres. & Chief Exec. Officer--Waffle House, Incorporated, Norcross, GA; *U.S. Private*, pg. 1146
Rogers, John, Pres. & Chief Exec. Officer--MDS Inc., Etobicoke, Canada; *Int'l*, pg. 826
Rogers, M. M., Pres.--Lippincott-Raven Publishing, New York, NY; *Int'l*, pg. 1513
Rogers, M. Weldon, III, Chm. Bd., Pres. & Chief Exec. Officer--EAC Corporation, Saint Louis, MO; *U.S. Private*, pg. 353
Rogers, Mike, Pres.--Computerworld, Inc., Framingham, MA; *U.S. Private*, pg. 569
Rogers, P.G., Pres. & Chief Exec. Officer--Cashco, Inc., Ellsworth, KS; *U.S. Private*, pg. 218
Rogers, Ray, Pres.--Innovative Membrane Systems, Inc., Norwood, MA; *U.S. Public*, pg. 1320
Rogers, Robert D., Pres. & Chief Exec. Officer--Texas Industries, Inc., Dallas, TX; *U.S. Public*, pg. 1585
Rogers, Samuel H., Jr., Chm. Bd. & Pres.--Wilkins-Rogers Incorporated, Ellicott City, MD; *U.S. Private*, pg. 1176
Rogers, Stephen, Pres. & Creative Dir.--Black Rogers Sullivan Goodnight, Inc., Houston, TX; *U.S. Private*, pg. 147
Rogers, Ted, Pres. & Chief Exec. Officer--Rogers Communications, Inc., Toronto, Canada; *Int'l*, pg. 1122

Rogers, Thomas W., Pres. & Chief Exec. Officer--Apollo Colors Inc., Northbrook, IL; *U.S. Private*, pg. 77
Rogers, William H., Pres.--Rogers Markets Inc., Fort Wayne, IN; *U.S. Private*, pg. 940
Rogers, Yandell, Jr., Pres.--Wilco Reprographic, Inc., Las Vegas, NV; *U.S. Private*, pg. 1176
Rogers, Yandell, Jr., Pres., Chief Exec. Officer & Gen. Counsel--YRJ Corporation, Houston, TX; *U.S. Private*, pg. 1176
Rogers, Yandell, Jr., Pres.--Ridgway's, Inc., Houston, TX; *U.S. Private*, pg. 1176
Rogers, Yandell, Jr., Pres.--US Reprographics, Inc., Philadelphia, PA; *U.S. Private*, pg. 1176
Rogerson, Michael, Chm. Bd., Pres. & Chief Exec. Officer--Rogerson Aircraft Corporation, Irvine, CA; *U.S. Private*, pg. 940
Rogerson, William D., Pres.--De-Sta-Co, A Dover Resources Co., Troy, MI; *U.S. Public*, pg. 521
Rogersson, Leif, Pres.--Alfa Laval AB, Lund, Sweden; *Int'l*, pg. 1378
Rohde, Bruce, Vice Chm., Pres., & Chief Exec. Officer--ConAgra, Inc., Omaha, NE; *U.S. Public*, pg. 425
Rohde, Ellen, Pres.--Vanity Fair, New York, NY; *U.S. Public*, *pg. 1702*
Roher, Charles, Pres. Chief Exec. & Fin. Officer--C. Roher Inc., Fleetwood, PA; *U.S. Private*, pg. 940
Rohkamm, Eckhard, Dr., Pres.--Thyssen Industrie Aktiengesellschaft, Bad-Wuertt, Germany; *Int'l*, pg. 1387
Rohleder, Michael J., Pres. & Chief Exec. Officer--Wyle Electronics, Irvine, CA; *Int'l*, pg. 1457
Rohr, James E., Pres.--PNC Bank Corp., Pittsburgh, PA; *U.S. Public*, pg. 1242
Rohrer, John P., Pres.--Rohrer Corporation, Wadsworth, OH; *U.S. Private*, pg. 940
Rohrman, Bob, Pres.--Bob Rohrman Auto Group, Lafayette, IN; *U.S. Private*, pg. 940
Rohrmann, Guenter, Pres. & Chief Exec. Officer--Air Express International Corporation, Darien, CT; *U.S. Public*, pg. 30
Rohs, Thomas W., Chm. Bd. & Chief Exec. Officer--American Modern Home Insurance Group, Amelia, OH; *U.S. Public*, pg. 1110
Rohtbart, David S., Pres. & Chief Exec. Officer--Cattleman's, Inc., Detroit, MI; *U.S. Public*, pg. 318
Rojas, Vince, Pres.--Maxine of Hollywood, Inc., Los Angeles, CA; *U.S. Private*, pg. 716
Rokhvarg, Alex, Pres.--Advanced Conversion Products, Cedar Knolls, NJ; *U.S. Private*, pg. 1097
Rokin, Michael, Pres. & Chief Oper. Officer--Bell Mobility Radio Inc., Saint-Laurent, Canada; *Int'l*, pg. 115
Rokop, Joseph, Jr., Pres.--Rokop Corporation, Bridgeville, PA; *U.S. Private*, pg. 941
Roland, Donald E., Pres. & Chief Exec. Officer--Treasure Chest Advertising Co., Inc., Glendora, CA; *U.S. Public*, pg. 228
Roland, Frank, Pres., Chief Exec. Officer & Chief Oper. Officer--Rubatex Corporation, Roanoke, VA; *U.S. Private*, *pg. 56*
Roland, William F., Pres.--Megapulse, Inc., Bedford, MA; *U.S. Private*, pg. 729
Rolano, Luciano, Chm. & Pres.--Iveco Trucks Of North America Inc., Bensalem, PA; *Int'l*, pg. 484
Rolf, Randolph K., Chm. Bd., Pres. & Chief Exec. Officer--Unitog Company, Kansas City, MO; *U.S. Public*, pg. 1693
Rolla, M.F., Pres. & Chief Oper. Officer--Gem Industries Finance Corporation, Toccoa, GA; *U.S. Private*, pg. 442
Rolla, Stephen J., Pres.--3kon Office Solutions-Upstate New York, Rochester, NY; *U.S. Public*, pg. 864
Rolland, Alain, Pres.--Jelmoli AG, Zurich, Switzerland; *Int'l*, pg. 705
Rolland, Frank, Pres. & Chief Oper. Officer--RBX Corporation, Roanoke, VA; *U.S. Private*, pg. 56
Rolland, Ian M., Chm. Bd., Pres. & Chief Exec. Officer--Lincoln National Corporation, Fort Wayne, IN; *U.S. Public*, pg. 997
Rollen, Ola, Pres.--Kanthal AB, Hallstahammar, Sweden; *Int'l*, pg. 723
Rollin, Daniel J., Pres.--Heights Heating & Cooling, Auburn Hills, MI; *U.S. Private*, pg. 519
Rollins, David, Pres. & Chief Exec. Officer--Nashville Wire Product Co., Nashville, TN; *U.S. Private*, pg. 775
Rollins, Gary W., Pres. & Chief Oper. Officer--Rollins, Inc., Atlanta, GA; *U.S. Public*, pg. 1404
Rollins, John W., Jr., Pres. & Chief Oper. Officer--Rollins Truck Leasing Corp., Wilmington, DE; *U.S. Public*, pg. 1405
Rollins, Kenneth J., Pres.--Quincy Compressor Division Coltec Industries, Quincy, IL; *U.S. Public*, pg. 402
Rollo, Leonardo, Pres.--Metalac S.A. Industria e Comercio, Sorocaba, Brazil; *U.S. Public*, pg. 1420
Roloff, Marvin, Pres.--Augsburg Fortress, Publishers, Minneapolis, MN; *U.S. Private*, pg. 98
Rolston, David W., Dr., Pres. & Chief Exec. Officer--Multigen Inc., San Jose, CA; *U.S. Public*, pg. 1425
Roman, G.R., Pres.--Northeast Texas Farmers Co-Op, Sulphur Springs, TX; *U.S. Private*, pg. 805
Roman, Paul, Pres.--Rollins Protective Services, Atlanta, GA; *U.S. Public*, pg. 1404
Roman, Stanley R., Pres.--Air Products of Puerto Rico, Inc., Allentown, PA; *U.S. Public*, pg. 31
Roman, William S., Pres.--Parsons Brinckerhoff Energy Services Inc., New York, NY; *U.S. Private*, pg. 841
Romandetti, John A., Pres.--Denny's, Inc., Spartanburg, SC; *U.S. Public*, pg. 23
Romaniuk, Don, Pres.--TELUS Advertising Services, Calgary, Canada; *Int'l*, pg. 1374
Romann, Gad, Pres. & Creative Dir.--Romann & Tannenholz Advertising, Inc., New York, NY; *U.S. Private*, pg. 942
Romano, James R., Pres.--Bel-Air Patrol, Santa Monica, CA; *U.S. Public*, pg. 245
Romano, Joe, Pres. & Chief Exec. Officer--Advantage Life Products, Inc., Tampa, FL; *U.S. Public*, pg. 22
Romanowski, Thomas S., Pres. & Chief Exec. Officer--CILCORP Investment Management Inc., Peoria, IL; *U.S. Public*, pg. 367
Romanowski, Thomas S., Pres. & Chief Exec. Officer--CILCORP Ventures Inc., Peoria, IL; *U.S. Public*, pg. 367
Romeo, Delores, Pres.--Worldwide Food Products Inc., Jamaica, NY; *U.S. Private*, pg. 1191
Romer, Gordon, Pres.--Solion, Westwood, MA; *U.S. Public*, pg. 1293
Romeu, Mike E., Pres.--Automax Finance, Santurce, PR; *U.S. Public*, pg. 644
Rominiecki, Ronald R., Pres. & Chief Oper. Officer--National Propane Corp., Cedar Rapids, IA; *U.S. Public*, pg. 1635
Romita, Mauro C., Pres.--Castle Oil Corporation, Harrison, NY; *U.S. Private*, pg. 219
Rompala, Richard, Pres.--The Valspar Corp. Protective Coatings Div., Baltimore, MD; *U.S. Public*, pg. 1707
Rompala, Richard M., Pres. & Chief Exec. Officer--Valspar Paints, Minneapolis, MN; *U.S. Public*, pg. 1707
Ronald, Mark, Pres.--GEC-Marconi Hazeltine Corporation, Greenlawn, NY; *Int'l*, pg. 544
Ronca, M.V., Pres.--Domain Energy Ventures Corporation, Houston, TX; *U.S. Public*, pg. 516
Ronca, M.V., Pres.--Domain Energy Production Corporation, Houston, TX; *U.S. Public*, pg. 516
Ronca, M.V., Pres.--Domain Energy International Corporation, Houston, TX; *U.S. Public*, pg. 516
Ronca, M.V., Pres.--Domain Energy Finance Corporation, Houston, TX; *U.S. Public*, pg. 516
Ronca, Michael, Pres. & Chief Exec. Officer--Domain Energy Corporation, Houston, TX; *U.S. Public*, pg. 515
Ronchetti, Sal, Pres.--Interpoint, Redmond, WA; *U.S. Public*, *pg. 457*
Ronchey, Alberto, Pres.--R.C.S. Editori S.p.A., Milan, Italy; *Int'l*, pg. 1078
Rondou, Stephan, Pres.--Martin Mathys, NV, Zelem, Belgium; *U.S. Public*, pg. 1358
Rones, Richard, Pres.--Americo Manufacturing Co., Inc., Acworth, GA; *U.S. Private*, pg. 64
Roney, Blake M., Pres.--Nu Skin International, Provo, UT; *U.S. Private*, pg. 808
Roney, Patrick E., Chm. Bd., Pres. & Chief Exec. Officer--Electro Mechanical Design Services, Inc., Gaithersburg, MD; *U.S. Private*, pg. 369
Roney, Walter E., Pres. & Chief Exec. Officer--Willis Corroon Corp. of Mobile, Mobile, AL; *Int'l*, pg. 1506
Ronner, Oskar K., Pres. & Chief Exec. Officer--Electrowatt Ltd., Zurich, Switzerland; *Int'l*, pg. 1246
Roof, R. Phil, Pres. & Chief Exec. Officer--RPR & Associates, Inc., Columbia, SC; *U.S. Private*, pg. 905
Rooke, Kevin C., Pres. & Gen. Mgr.--Pathfinder Div., Canon City, CO; *U.S. Public*, pg. 1318
Rooks, W. Howard, Pres.--Weichert Realty, Inc., Alexandria, VA; *U.S. Private*, pg. 1159
Rooney, David R., Mgr.-Natl. Adv.-Jeep/Eagle--Jeep, Auburn Hills, MI; *U.S. Public*, pg. 353
Rooney, John E., Pres.--Ameritech Consumer Services, Hoffman Estates, IL; *U.S. Public*, pg. 98
Rooney, L.F., III, Chm. Bd. & Pres.--Rooney Brothers Company, Tulsa, OK; *U.S. Private*, pg. 943
Rooney, Patrick W., Chm. Bd., Pres. & Chief Exec. Officer--Cooper Tire & Rubber Company, Findlay, OH; *U.S. Public*, pg. 445
Rooney, Thomas D., Chm. Bd., Pres. & Chief Exec. Officer--Multigraphics Inc., Mount Prospect, IL; *U.S. Public*, pg. 1141
Rooney, Timothy P., Pres.--Manhattan Construction Company, Tulsa, OK; *U.S. Private*, pg. 943
Root, Greg, Pres.--Thompson Bankwatch, Inc., New York, NY; *U.S. Public*, pg. 1600
Root, John A., Chm. Bd. & Pres.--A.I. Root Company, Medina, OH; *U.S. Private*, pg. 944
Root, Larry D., Pres. & Chief Oper. Officer--IES Industries Inc., Cedar Rapids, IA; *U.S. Public*, pg. 855
Root, Larry D., Pres. & Chief Oper. Officer--IES Utilities Inc., Cedar Rapids, IA; *U.S. Public*, pg. 855
Roper, Helen, Pres. & Gen. Mgr.--American International Management Co. (Barbados) Ltd., Bridgetown, Barbados; *U.S. Public*, pg. 85
Roper, John L. III, Pres. & Chief Exec. Officer--Norfolk Shipbuilding & Drydock Corporation, Norfolk, VA; *U.S. Private*, pg. 802
Roper, Robert E., Pres. & Gen Mgr.--Ropak Corporation, Fullerton, CA; *Int'l*, pg. 811
Rorke, Kevin C., Pres. & Gen. Mgr.--Flomaster Div., Canon City, CO; *U.S. Public*, pg. 1318
Rosa, Jack, Pres.--Electroid Co., Springfield, NJ; *U.S. Private*, pg. 369
Rosane, Edwin L., Pres. & Chief Exec. Officer--USAA Life Insurance Co., San Antonio, TX; *U.S. Private*, pg. 1115
Rosania, W. Stanley, Pres.--Structural Foam Plastics, Inc., Somerville, NJ; *U.S. Private*, pg. 1047
Rosanio, Linda, Chm. Bd. & Pres.--RBT/Strum, Cherry Hill, NJ; *U.S. Private*, pg. 902
Rosanvallon, John G., Pres.--Dassault Falcon Jet Corp., South Hackensack, NJ; *Int'l*, pg. 383
Rosasco, Nat G., Pres.--Northwestern Golf Company, Elmhurst, IL; *U.S. Private*, pg. 806
Rosati, Robert S., Pres. & Chief Exec. Officer--Transtar Holdings, L.P., Monroeville, PA; *U.S. Private*, pg. 1097
Roscoe, Michael R., Pres. & Chief Exec. Officer--Distribution Services, Inc., Lantana, FL; *U.S. Public*, pg. 87
Rose, D.N., Pres. & Chief Exec. Officer--Mountain Fuel Supply Company, Salt Lake City, UT; *U.S. Public*, pg. 1352
Rose, D.N., Pres. & Chief Exec. Officer--Questar Pipeline Company, Salt Lake City, UT; *U.S. Public*, pg. 1352
Rose, Dan, Pres.--DuCoa L.P., Highland, IL; *U.S. Private*, pg. 301
Rose, Gervase R., Pres.--Roman Electric Company, Inc., Milwaukee, WI; *U.S. Private*, pg. 942
Rose, Kenneth L., Pres. & Chief Exec. Officer--Henkels & McCoy, Inc., Blue Bell, PA; *U.S. Private*, pg. 522
Rose, Lynn, Pres.--Siga, Inc., Atlanta, GA; *U.S. Private*, pg. 999
Rose, Paul E., Pres.--Promotion Information Management (PIM), Chicago, IL; *U.S. Private*, pg. 649
Rose, Porter B., Chm. Bd. & Pres.--Liberty Investment Group, Inc., Greenville, SC; *U.S. Public*, pg. 992
Rose, Richard J., Pres.--Sysco Food Services of Cleveland, Inc., Bedford, OH; *U.S. Public*, pg. 1551
Rose, Robert E., Pres. & Chief Exec. Officer--Diamond Offshore Drilling, Inc., Houston, TX; *U.S. Public*, pg. 1011
Rose, William R., Chm. Bd., Pres. & Chief Exec. Officer--Rose Packing Company, Barrington, IL; *U.S. Private*, pg. 945
Rose, William T., Jr., Chm. Bd., Pres. & Chief Exec. Officer--Uncle B's Bakery, Inc., Ellsworth, IA; *U.S. Public*, pg. 1664
Roseberry, Thomas D., Pres. & Chief Exec. Officer--Willis Corroon Corp. of Utah, Salt Lake City, UT; *Int'l*, pg. 1507
Rosedale, Miles, Chm. Bd., Pres. & Chief Exec. Officer--Monrovia Nursery Co., Azusa, CA; *U.S. Private*, pg. 757
Rosemore, Lance B., Pres., Chief Exec. Officer & Sec.--PMC Capital Inc., Dallas, TX; *U.S. Public*, pg. 1242
Rosen, Arthur, Pres.--The Pace Collection, Long Island City, NY; *U.S. Private*, pg. 829
Rosen, Benedict P., Chm. Bd., Pres. & Chief Exec. Officer--AVX Corporation, Myrtle Beach, SC; *Int'l*, pg. 775
Rosen, David, Pres. & Chief Exec. Officer--CB North America, Inc., Saratoga Springs, NY; *U.S. Private*, pg. 192
Rosen, Edward, Pres.--Star Children's Dress Company, Inc., New York, NY; *U.S. Private*, pg. 1034
Rosen, Elaine D., Pres.--First UNUM Life Insurance Company, Tarrytown, NY; *U.S. Public*, pg. 1699
Rosen, Elaine D., Pres.--UNUM Life Insurance Company of America, Portland, ME; *U.S. Public*, pg. 1699
Rosen, Elaine D., Pres.--Continental National Life Insurance Co., Piscataway, NJ; *U.S. Public*, pg. 1700
Rosen, Elaine D., Pres.--Continental International Life Insurance Co., Piscataway, NJ; *U.S. Public*, pg. 1700
Rosen, Fred K., Pres.--Grayline Housewares, Carol Stream, IL; *U.S. Private*, pg. 472
Rosen, Frederick D., Pres. & Chief Exec. Officer--Ticketmaster Corporation, West Hollywood, CA; *U.S. Private*, pg. 1084
Rosen, Jack, Chm. Bd., Pres. & Chief Exec. Officer--Continental Health Affiliates, Inc., Englewood Cliffs, NJ; *U.S. Public*, pg. 440
Rosen, Jack, Pres.--CompreMedx, Inc., Englewood Cliffs, NJ; *U.S. Public*, pg. 440
Rosen, Jack, Chm. Bd. & Pres.--Hazel Bishop International, Englewood Cliffs, NJ; *U.S. Private*, pg. 514
Rosen, Kermit, Jr., Pres.--Alaskan Copper Companies, Seattle, WA; *U.S. Private*, pg. 31
Rosen, Lawrence, Pres. & Chief Exec. Officer--Rose Art Industries, Livingston, NJ; *U.S. Private*, pg. 945
Rosen, Morris, Pres.--Pearl-Pressman-Liberty Communications Group, Philadelphia, PA; *U.S. Private*, pg. 845
Rosen, Robert A., Pres.--Rosen Associates Management Corp., Jericho, NY; *U.S. Private*, pg. 945
Rosen, Thomas, Pres.--Rosens Diversified, Inc., Fairmont, MN; *U.S. Private*, pg. 945
Rosenauer, James, Pres.--Paradata Financial Systems, Chesterfield, MO; *U.S. Public*, pg. 1778
Rosenband, Phillip, Pres.--Morgan Marshall Industries, Inc., Chicago Heights, IL; *U.S. Private*, pg. 904
Rosenbaum, Eli, Pres.--Bruckner Machine & Tool Corp., Port Washington, NY; *U.S. Private*, pg. 175
Rosenberg, Alan, Pres. & Chief Exec. Officer--Seaman Furniture Company, Inc., Woodbury, NY; *U.S. Public*, pg. 1452
Rosenberg, Charles, Pres.--Rose Printing Company, Inc., Tallahassee, FL; *U.S. Private*, pg. 945
Rosenberg, Gary, Pres. & Chief Oper. Officer--The Homestead L.C., Hot Springs, VA; *U.S. Private*, pg. 247
Rosenberg, Henry A., Jr., Chm. Bd., Pres., Chief Exec. & Oper. Officer--Crown Central Petroleum Corporation, Baltimore, MD; *U.S. Public*, pg. 462
Rosenberg, Kenneth, Pres. & Treas.--Napco Security Systems, Inc., Amityville, NY; *U.S. Public*, pg. 1151
Rosenberg, Kenneth B., Pres., Chief Exec. Officer & Sec.--Eastern Smelting & Refining Corporation, Lynn, MA; *U.S. Private*, pg. 357
Rosenberg, Kurt, Chm. Bd. & Pres.--The Promotion in Motion Companies, Closter, NJ; *U.S. Private*, pg. 890
Rosenberg, Marvin, Partner--Towne Properties, Cincinnati, OH; *U.S. Private*, pg. 1093
Rosenberg, Michael A., Pres.--Diodes Incorporated, Westlake Village, CA; *U.S. Public*, pg. 510
Rosenberg, Robert, Pres. & Chief Exec. Officer--Baskin-Robbins Incorporated, Glendale, CA; *Int'l*, pg. 63
Rosenberg, Shelly, Pres. & Chief Exec. Officer--Equity Group Investments, Chicago, IL; *U.S. Private*, pg. 380
Rosenberg, Steven, Pres.--Home Box Office International, Inc., New York, NY; *U.S. Public*, pg. 1612
Rosenberger, Larry E., Pres. & Chief Exec. Officer--Fair, Isaac and Company, Inc., San Rafael, CA; *U.S. Public*, pg. 609
Rosenberger, Philip E., Pres.--Jepson-Murray Advertising, Lansing, MI; *U.S. Private*, pg. 586
Rosenberger, William L., Pres.--Rosenbergers Dairies, Inc., Hatfield, PA; *U.S. Private*, pg. 945
Rosenblum, Barry, Pres.--Time Warner Cable of New York City, New York, NY; *U.S. Public*, pg. 1611
Rosenblum, Michael, Pres.--NYT Video News International, Philadelphia, PA; *U.S. Public*, pg. 1174
Rosendahl, David E., Pres. & Chief Oper. Officer--The Medical Protective Company, Fort Wayne, IN; *U.S. Private*, pg. 728
Rosenfeld, Irene, Pres.--Kraft Canada Inc., Don Mills, Canada; *U.S. Public*, pg. 1288
Rosenfeld, Laurence, Pres.--Stackig Advertising and Public Relations, Mc Lean, VA; *U.S. Private*, pg. 1028

Rosenfield, Richard, Pres.--California Pizza Kitchen Inc., Los Angeles, CA; *U.S. Public*, pg. 1277
Rosengren, U., Pres.--Rubsteel AB, Perstorp, Sweden; *Int'l*, pg. 1146
Rosenkrantz, Howard M., Pres. & Chief Oper. Officer--U.S. Surgical Corp., Norwalk, CT; *U.S. Public*, pg. 1687
Rosenkranz, Robert, Chm. Bd., Pres. & Chief Exec. Officer--Delphi Financial Group, Inc., Wilmington, DE; *U.S. Public*, pg. 496
Rosenshein, Bernard J., Pres.--Rosenshein Associates, Mamaroneck, NY; *U.S. Private*, pg. 945
Rosensteel, John W., Pres. & Chief Exec. Officer--Keyport Life Insurance Company, Boston, MA; *U.S. Private*, pg. 666
Rosenthal, George I., Chm. Bd. & Pres.--Raleigh Enterprises, Inc., Santa Monica, CA; *U.S. Private*, pg. 907
Rosenthal, James, Pres.--National Lumber Co., Warren, MI; *U.S. Private*, pg. 785
Rosenthal, Mark, Pres. & Chief Oper. Officer--MTV Networks, New York, NY; *U.S. Private*, pg. 779
Rosenthal, Richard H., Chm. Bd. & Pres.--F & W Publications, Inc., Cincinnati, OH; *U.S. Private*, pg. 388
Rosenthal, Robert M., Chm. Bd.--Rosenthal Automotive Organization, Arlington, VA; *U.S. Private*, pg. 946
Rosenthal, Robert, Ph.D, Pres., Chief Exec. Officer & Chief Oper. Officer--Thermo Jarrell Ash Corporation, Franklin, MA; *U.S. Public*, pg. 1594
Rosenzweig, Mark, Pres.--Edwards High Vacuum International, Wilmington, MA; *Int'l*, pg. 121
Rosenzweig, Richard S., Pres. & Asst. Treas.--Playboy Shows, Inc., Beverly Hills, CA; *U.S. Public*, pg. 1310
Rosetti, Richard, Pres.--Impulse Productions, Inc., Beverly Hills, CA; *U.S. Public*, pg. 1310
Rosevear, Kenneth A., Pres. & Chief Oper. Officer--MGM Grand Development, Inc., Las Vegas, NV; *U.S. Public*, pg. 1027
Rosewall, Ray, Pres.--Harmon Industries-Riverside, Riverside, CA; *U.S. Public*, pg. 788
Rosewall, Ray, Pres.--Harmon Industries-Grain Valley, Grain Valley, MO; *U.S. Public*, pg. 788
Rosey, R., Pres.--Ebara Solar, Inc., Large, PA; *Int'l*, pg. 432
Roshak, Arthur J., Pres.--Colonial Dodge, Inc., Eastpointe, MI; *U.S. Private*, pg. 253
Rosholm, Peter, Pres.--Kvaerner Ships Equipment AB, Goteborg, Sweden; *Int'l*, pg. 768
Rosica, Gabriel, Chief Oper. Officer--Bailey Controls Company, Wickliffe, OH; *Int'l*, pg. 654
Rosilier, Glenn D., Pres.--CSW Leasing, Inc., Dallas, TX; *U.S. Public*, pg. 324
Roskovensky, E. A., Pres. & Chief Oper. Officer--Robertson-Ceco Corporation, San Ramon, CA; *U.S. Public*, pg. 1394
Rosner, Carl H., Pres.--Intercool Energy Corporation, Latham, NY; *U.S. Public*, pg. 894
Rosoff, Alan, Pres.--Green Seed Co., Baltimore, MD; *U.S. Private*, pg. 477
Rosoff, Alan, Pres.--Seed Corporation of America, Baltimore, MD; *U.S. Private*, pg. 981
Ross, Barry J., Pres.--Robinhood Homes, Inc., Solana Beach, CA; *U.S. Private*, pg. 936
Ross, Cameron M., Pres.--Westminster Homes of North Carolina, Inc., Greensboro, NC; *U.S. Public*, pg. 1741
Ross, Charles M., Pres.--Charles Curtain Company, Inc., Dallas, TX; *U.S. Private*, pg. 229
Ross, Fred C., Pres. & Chief Exec. Officer--Allied Old English, Inc., Port Reading, NJ; *U.S. Private*, pg. 39
Ross, Gary, Pres.--On Cue, Inc., Minnetonka, MN; *U.S. Public*, pg. 1142
Ross, Gary L., Pres.--Sysco Food Services of Austin, Inc., Round Rock, TX; *U.S. Public*, pg. 1551
Ross, Gerald, Pres., Chief Exec. & Chief Fin. Officer--MGR Equipment Corp., Inwood, NY; *U.S. Private*, pg. 687
Ross, Jack, Pres.--Jack Ross Motors Inc., Tempe, AZ; *U.S. Private*, pg. 946
Ross, Joseph J., Chm. Bd., Pres. & Chief Exec. Officer--Federal Signal Corporation, Oak Brook, IL; *U.S. Public*, pg. 616
Ross, Mike, Pres.--UPB of Missouri, Saint Louis, MO; *U.S. Public*, pg. 1669
Ross, Morton M., Chm. Bd. & Pres.--International Plastics Company, New York, NY; *U.S. Private*, pg. 571
Ross, Patrick, Pres.--GPC Government Policy Consultants (Federal), Ottawa, Canada; *U.S. Public*, pg. 1225
Ross, Phillip, President--Sun Micro Stamping Inc., Clearwater, FL, *U.S. Public*, pg. 1531
Ross, Raymond E., Pres. & Chief Oper. Officer--Cincinnati Milacron Inc., Cincinnati, OH; *U.S. Public*, pg. 368
Ross, Richard, Pres.--DRS Photronics, Inc., Oakland, NJ; *U.S. Public*, pg. 474
Ross, Richard, Pres.--Volvo Truck North America Inc., Milton, Canada; *Int'l*, pg. 1477
Ross, Ronald R., Pres. & Chief Oper. Officer--CACI International Inc, Arlington, VA; *U.S. Public*, pg. 272
Ross, Ronald R., Pres.--Systems Engineering Div., Falls Church, VA; *U.S. Public*, pg. 423
Ross, Scott B., Pres.--MCI Systemhouse, Atlanta, GA; *U.S. Public*, pg. 1024
Ross, Tammy, Pres.-Opers. & Chief Fin. Officer--Hampton Print Works, Inc., Johnson City, TN; *U.S. Private*, pg. 498
Rosser, Darryl, Pres. & Chief Oper. Officer--Falcon Products, Inc., Saint Louis, MO; *U.S. Public*, pg. 611
Rossi, Carlo, Pres. & Gen. Mgr.--Carlo Rossi Vineyards, Modesto, CA; *U.S. Private*, pg. 438
Rossi, Massimo, Pres.--Swedish Match S.A., Nyon, Switzerland; *Int'l*, pg. 1328
Rossiter, Robert, Pres. & Chief Oper. Officer--Lear Corporation, Southfield, MI; *U.S. Public*, pg. 981
Rosskam, Skip, III, Pres. & Chief Oper. Officer--David Michael & Co. Inc., Philadelphia, PA; *U.S. Private*, pg. 740
Rosskamm, Alan, Chm. Bd., Pres. & Chief Exec. Officer--Fabri-Centers of America, Inc., Hudson, OH; *U.S. Public*, pg. 609
Rossman, Ray, Pres.--World Fuel Services of FL, Miami Springs, FL; *U.S. Public*, pg. 906
Rotando, Lynn, Mng. Partner--Arnold Communications, Inc., Boston, MA; *U.S. Private*, pg. 83
Roten, Robert W., Pres. & Chief Exec. Officer--Sterling Chemicals Holdings, Inc., Houston, TX; *U.S. Public*, pg. 1515
Roten, Robert W., Pres. & Chief Exec. Officer--Sterling Chemicals, Inc., Houston, TX; *U.S. Public*, pg. 1515
Roth, Francis H., Pres. & Chief Oper. Officer--HarCor Energy, Inc., Houston, TX; *U.S. Public*, pg. 782
Roth, Jim, Pres. & Chief Exec. Officer--GRC International, Inc., Vienna, VA; *U.S. Public*, pg. 695
Roth, John A., Pres. & Chief Exec. Officer--MICOM Communications Corp., Simi Valley, CA; *Int'l*, pg. 969
Roth, Larry, Co-Pres.--Marchon Eyewear, Melville, NY; *U.S. Private*, pg. 702
Roth, Michael JC, Pres. & Chief Exec. Officer--USAA Investment Management Co., San Antonio, TX; *U.S. Private*, pg. 1114
Roth, Myron, Pres.--Scotti Brothers Entertainment Industries, Santa Monica, CA; *U.S. Public*, pg. 41
Roth, Myron I., Pres. & Chief Oper. Officer--All American Communications, Inc., Santa Monica, CA; *U.S. Public*, pg. 41
Roth, Richard, Partner--Messner Vetere Berger McNamee Schmetterer/EURO RSCG, New York, NY; *Int'l*, pg. 602
Roth, Robert, Pres.--Chicago Reader, Inc., Chicago, IL; *U.S.* Private, pg. 235
Roth, Robert S., Pres.--World Oil Corp., South Gate, CA; *U.S. Private*, pg. 1190
Roth, Steven I., Pres.--ADI (Ademco Distribution, Inc.), Syosset, NY; *U.S. Public*, pg. 1306
Roth, W.R., Pres.--SJW Corp., San Jose, CA; *U.S. Public*, pg. 1418
Roth, W.R., Chief Oper. Officer--San Jose Water Company, San Jose, CA; *U.S. Public*, pg. 1418
Rothbaum, Michael, Pres. & Chief Exec. Officer--The Harwood Companies, Inc., Fort Lauderdale, FL; *U.S. Public*, pg. 1433
Rothbloom, Steven R., Pres.--Bank of Montreal Trust Company (C.I.) Ltd., Saint Helier, United Kingdom; *Int'l*, pg. 155
Rothenberger, E.C., Pres.--Vari Tronics Company, Inc., Duarte, CA; *U.S. Private*, pg. 1134
Rothenberger, Helmut, Chm.-Mngmt. Bd. & Chief Exec. Officer--Rothenberger Group GmbH, Kelheim, Germany; *Int'l*, pg. 1127
Rothschild, Diane, Pres.--Grace & Rothschild, New York, NY; *U.S. Private*, pg. 468
Rothschild, Stanford Z., Jr., Pres.--Rothschild/Pell, Rudman & Co., Inc., Baltimore, MD; *U.S. Public*, pg. 1674
Rothstein, Fred, Pres.-Licensing--Salant Corporation, New York, NY; *U.S. Public*, pg. 1429
Rothstein, Marty, Pres.-Toronto--Bozell Retail, Toronto, Canada; *Int'l*, pg. 209
Rothwell, Brian G., Pres. & Chief Exec. Officer--Bay State Milling Co., Quincy, MA; *U.S. Private*, pg. 124
Rott, Herbert F., Jr., Pres.--Des Moines Tire, Des Moines, IA; *U.S. Private*, pg. 947
Rotter, David H., Pres., Chief Exec. Officer & Sec.--The Rottlund Company, Inc., Roseville, MN; *U.S. Public*, pg. 1406
Rouleau, Mark, Pres. & Chief Exec. Officer--Associated Hosts, Inc., Indianapolis, IN; *Int'l*, pg. 215
Round Turner, Sheena, Chief Exec. Officer--MCL, Nairobi, Kenya; *U.S. Public*, pg. 1422
Rounick, Marvin, Pres., Chief Exec. Officer & Chief Oper. Officer--Deb Shops, Inc., Philadelphia, PA; *U.S. Public*, pg. 491
Roush, J. Kenneth, Pres.--Calumet Carton Company, South Holland, IL; *U.S. Private*, pg. 201
Roush, Richard K., Pres. & Gen. Mgr.--Georgie Boy Manufacturing, Inc., Edwardsburg, MI; *U.S. Public*, pg. 388
Rousseau, Henri-Paul, Pres. & Chief Exec. Officer--Laurentian Bank of Canada, Montreal, Canada; *Int'l*, pg. 396
Roussel, Bernard, Pres.--SK Hand Tool Corp., Chicago, IL; *Int'l*, pg. 570
Roussel, Louis J., Jr., Chm. Bd., Pres. & Chief Exec. Officer--Victory Financial Group, Inc., Metairie, LA; *U.S. Private*, pg. 1139
Roussis, Theo, Pres.--Mazzucchelli Polimeri Srl, Castiglione, Italy; *Int'l*, pg. 850
Roussis, Theo, Pres.--C & C Coloring & Compounding SRL, Castiglione Olona, Italy; *Int'l*, pg. 850
Rousso, Dominic, Chm. Bd., Pres. & Chief Exec. Officer--F.H. Chase, Inc., Mansfield, MA; *U.S. Private*, pg. 230
Routh, Thomas M., Chm. Bd., Pres. & Chief Exec. Officer--J.H. Routh Packing Co., Sandusky, OH; *U.S. Private*, pg. 948
Roux, Michel, Pres. & Chief Exec. Officer--Carillon Importers, Ltd., Fort Lee, NJ; *Int'l*, pg. 409
Rowan, Frederick J., Pres. & Chief Exec. Officer--The William Carter Company, Morrow, GA; *U.S. Private*, pg. 217
Rowan, Henry M., Jr., Chm. Bd., Pres. & Chief Exec. Officer--Inductotherm Industries, Inc., Rancocas, NJ; *U.S. Private*, pg. 560
Rowan, Roddy, Regional Pres.--BB&T of South Carolina, Greenville, SC; *U.S. Public*, pg. 160
Rowberry, Jon H., Pres. & Chief Oper. Officer--Franklin Covey, Salt Lake City, UT; *U.S. Public*, pg. 679
Rowcliffe, Simon, Chm.--Geers Gross Advertising Limited, London, United Kingdom; *Int'l*, pg. 542
Rowe, Clifford R., Pres.--Trumbull Corporation/P.J. Dick, Inc., West Mifflin, PA; *U.S. Private*, pg. 1107
Rowe, John W., Pres. & Chief Exec. Officer--New England Electric System, Westborough, MA; *U.S. Public*, pg. 1171
Rowe, Josiah P., III, Chm. Bd., Pres., Chief Exec. Officer & Gen. Mgr.--The Free Lance-Star Publishing Co., Fredericksburg, VA; *U.S. Private*, pg. 424
Rowe, Murray A., Pres.--Bidwell Div., Canton, SD; *U.S. Public*, pg. 279
Rowe, William E., Pres. & Chief Oper. Officer--Stewart Enterprises, Inc., Metairie, LA; *U.S. Public*, pg. 1518
Rowe, William J., Pres., Chief Exec. Officer & Publr.--Greenwich Times, Greenwich, CT; *U.S. Public*, pg. 1616
Rowell, Lester John, Jr., Pres.--Provident Mutual Life & Annuity Company of America, Berwyn, PA; *U.S. Private*, pg. 892
Rowen, Harold C., Pres. & Chief Exec. Officer--Kinney Shoe Corporation, New York, NY; *U.S. Public*, pg. 1777
Rowland, Dennie, Pres.--First American Title Insurance Co. of Texas, Inc., Houston, TX; *U.S. Public*, pg. 626
Rowland, Lawrence, Chm., Pres. & Chief Exec. Officer--Lincoln National Administrative Services Corp., Fort Wayne, IN; *U.S. Public*, pg. 998
Rowland, Mark E., Interim Pres.--The Peoples Banking Company, Findlay, OH; *U.S. Public*, pg. 1413
Rowland, Michael D., Pres.--Metal Trades, Inc., Hollywood, SC; *U.S. Private*, pg. 734
Rowland, Pleasant T., Pres.--Pleasant Company, Middleton, WI; *U.S. Private*, pg. 872
Rowley, Clayton, Pres.--Bead Industries Inc., Bridgeport, CT; *U.S. Private*, pg. 126
Rowley, Don G., Publr.--The Arizona Daily Sun, Flagstaff, AZ; *U.S. Public*, pg. 1343
Rowley, G.R., Chm. Bd.--Greenham Construction Materials Limited, Isleworth, United Kingdom; *Int'l*, pg. 1358
Rowley, Ivan R., Pres. & Chief Exec. Officer--Astra USA, Inc., Westborough, MA; *Int'l*, pg. 93
Rowley, Ronald L., Pres. & Chief Exec. Officer--BCP Technical Service, Inc., Gretna, LA; *U.S. Private*, pg. 106
Rowse, Sam B., Pres.--Veryfine Products, Inc., Westford, MA; *U.S. Private*, pg. 1137
Rowsey, Paul, III, Pres. & Gen. Counsel--Rosewood Property Company, Dallas, TX; *U.S. Private*, pg. 946
Roy, Louise, Pres. & Chief Exec. Officer--Telemedia Inc., Montreal, Canada; *Int'l*, pg. 1373
Roy, Peter, Pres.--Whole Foods Market, Inc., Austin, TX; *U.S. Public*, pg. 1767
Roy, Pierre-Andre, Pres. & Chief Oper. Officer--Bombardier Capital Group, Colchester, VT; *Int'l*, pg. 200
Royan, John, Pres.--Silicon Power Cube Corporation, San Pedro, CA; *U.S. Private*, pg. 1000
Rozar, Rick L., Pres. & Chief Exec. Officer--CDB Infotec Inc., Santa Ana, CA; *U.S. Private*, pg. 193
Rozman, Robert, Pres.--Diehl Machines, Wabash, IN; *U.S. Public*, pg. 944
Rubel, Matt, Pres.--The Princess Marcella Borghese, Inc., New York, NY; *U.S. Private*, pg. 690
Rubel, Matt, Pres.--Popular Club Plan, Garfield, NJ; *U.S. Private*, pg. 1078
Rubeli, Paul E., Chm. Bd., Pres. & Chief Exec. Officer--Aztar Corporation, Phoenix, AZ; *U.S. Public*, pg. 158
Rubenstein, Stephen, Pres. & Chief Exec. Officer--JB Oxford Holdings Inc., Beverly Hills, CA; *U.S. Public*, pg. 916
Rubertone, Donna, Pres.--AmVestors Acquisition Subsidiary, Inc., Topeka, KS; *U.S. Private*, pg. 59
Rubin, Bill, Pres.--Phototype Color Graphics, Inc., Pennsauken, NJ; *U.S. Private*, pg. 864
Rubin, Donald, Chm. Bd. & Pres.--M. Rubin & Sons Inc., Long Island City, NY; *U.S. Private*, pg. 949
Rubin, Gerrold R., Pres. & Chief Exec. Officer--Rubin Postaer & Associates, Santa Monica, CA; *U.S. Private*, pg. 949
Rubin, Joseph H., Pres. & Chief Exec. Officer--Abrams Industries, Inc., Atlanta, GA; *U.S. Public*, pg. 14
Rubin, Lewis, Pres. & Chief Exec. Officer--Xtra Corporation, Boston, MA; *U.S. Public*, pg. 1786
Rubin, Mark A., Pres.--Shogyo International Corporation, Plainview, NY; *U.S. Private*, pg. 996
Rubin, Michael, Pres. & Chief Fin. Officer--Hudson General Corporation, Great Neck, NY; *U.S. Public*, pg. 845
Rubin, Michael B., Pres.--Shokai Far East Ltd., Peekskill, NY; *U.S. Private*, pg. 996
Rubin, Robert Stephen, Chm. Bd. & Mng. Dir.--Pentland Group PLC, London, United Kingdom; *Int'l*, pg. 1035
Rubin, Stephen, Pres. & Publisher--Doubleday Publishing Company, New York, NY; *Int'l*, pg. 191
Rubin, Stephen, Pres.--Vita Food Products, Inc., Chicago, IL; *U.S. Private*, pg. 1142
Rubin, Stuart A., Pres.--Stevens-Lee Company, Minneapolis, MN; *U.S. Private*, pg. 1042
Rubino, Bill, Pres.--Jofco Inc., Jasper, IN; *U.S. Private*, pg. 588
Rubinstein, Dan, Pres.--Ervaco Gruppen AB, Stockholm, Sweden; *Int'l*, pg. 459
Rubner, David, Pres. & Chief Exec. Officer--ECI Telecom Ltd., Petah Tiqwa, Israel; *Int'l*, pg. 643
Rubow, Steven, Pres. & Chief Exec. Officer--Topco Associates, Inc., Skokie, IL; *U.S. Private*, pg. 1091
Rubright, James A., Pres.--Southern Natural Gas Company, Birmingham, AL; *U.S. Public*, pg. 1485
Ruby, Ronald, Pres.--Ram Graphics, Inc., Alexandria, IN; *U.S. Private*, pg. 908
Ruchjaibun, Parames, Pres.--Dentsu Young & Rubicam Ltd. (Bangkok), Bangkok, Thailand; *U.S. Private*, pg. 325
Ruckriegel, Robert, Pres.--BR Associates, Inc., Jasper, IN; *U.S. Private*, pg. 107
Ruda, Kevin, Pres. & Chief Exec. Officer--Beatrice Cheese Co., Waukesha, WI; *U.S. Public*, pg. 426
Rudderow, Sam, Pres.--Paris Foods Corp., Camden, NJ; *U.S. Private*, pg. 839
Ruddy, Thomas, Pres. & Gen. Mgr.--Circle A.W. Products, Co., Portland, OR; *U.S. Public*, pg. 1471
Rudin, Steven, Pres.--Koret of California, Inc., San Francisco, CA; *U.S. Private*, pg. 632
Rudis, Jim, Pres. & Chief Exec. Officer--Overhill Farms, Inc., Culver City, CA; *U.S. Public*, pg. 1315
Rudnicki, E.H., Pres.--First Church Financing Corporation, West Bend, WI; *U.S. Public*, pg. 1792
Rudolph, James E., Pres. & Chief Exec. Officer--Rudolph Foods Company, Lima, OH; *U.S. Private*, pg. 950

Rudolph, John, Pres.--Rudolph and Sletten, Inc., Foster City, CA; *U.S. Private*, pg. 950
Rudolph, Scott, Chm. Bd., Pres., Chief Exec. Officer & Chief Oper. Officer--Nature's Bounty Inc., Bohemia, NY; *U.S. Public*, pg. 1166
Rudolph, Scott, Pres.--The Hudson Corporation, Bohemia, NY; *U.S. Public*, pg. 1166
Rudolph, Scott, Pres.--Vitamin World, Bohemia, NY; *U.S. Public*, pg. 1166
Rudrum, Malcolm, Pres.--Benelux Division, Brussels, Belgium; *U.S. Public*, pg. 423
Rue, Rolf, Pres.--Airbus Industrie Beijing, Beijing, China; *Int'l*, pg. 39
Ruegg, Fred, Pres.--ELMA Electronic Inc., Fremont, CA; *Int'l*, pg. 1305
Ruegg, Hans R., Pres. & Chief Exec. Officer--Baumann Federn AG, Ruti, Switzerland; *Int'l*, pg. 171
Ruelle, Mark A., Chm. Bd. & Pres.--Westar Energy, Topeka, KS; *U.S. Public*, pg. 1759
Ruettgers, Michael C., Pres. & Chief Exec. Officer--EMC Corporation, Hopkinton, MA; *U.S. Public*, pg. 545
Ruffin, Shelton, Pres.--Ruffin Building Systems, Inc., Oak Grove, LA; *U.S. Private*, pg. 950
Rugaber, D.A., Pres.--AGR International, Inc., Butler, PA; *U.S. Private*, pg. 5
Rugaber, Walter, Pres. & Publr.--The Roanoke Times, Roanoke, VA; *U.S. Private*, pg. 649
Ruggeberg, Jan, Vice Chm.--Pferd/August Rueggeberg, Marienheide, Germany; *Int'l*, pg. 1046
Ruggeberg, Tom, Vice Chm.--Pferd/August Rueggeberg, Marienheide, Germany; *Int'l*, pg. 1046
Ruggeri, Salvatore, Pres.--Energy Valve Division, Houston, TX; *U.S. Public*, pg. 528
Ruggiero, Lou, Pres.--The Food Emporium, Bronx, NY; *Int'l, pg. 1375*
Ruggirello, John R., Pres.--AES Enterprise, Arlington, VA; *U.S. Public*, pg. 5
Ruhle, Frank S., Chm. Bd., Pres. & Chief Exec. Officer--Ruhle Companies, Inc., Valhalla, NY; *U.S. Private*, pg. 950
Ruhlman, Robert G., Pres. & Chief Oper. Officer--Preformed Line Products, Cleveland, OH; *U.S. Public*, pg. 1321
Ruhno, R., Pres.--PQ Australia Pty., Ltd., Dandenong, Australia; *U.S. Private*, pg. 827
Rui, Luis, Chm. Bd & Pres.--RIU International Pan American Ocean Resort Hotel, Miami Beach, FL; *U.S. Private*, pg. 904
Ruijssenaars, Andries, Pres. & Chief Oper. Officer--Eagle-Picher Industries, Inc., Cincinnati, OH; *U.S. Private*, pg. 355
Ruisi, Christopher S., Pres. & Chief Oper. Officer--USLIFE Corporation, New York, NY; *U.S. Public*, pg. 77
Ruiz, Filho, Antonio, Pres.--AHP do Brasil, Sao Paulo, Brazil; *U.S. Public*, pg. 80
Rukajarvi, Mauri, Pres.--Oulun Kumitehdas Oy, Oulu, Finland; *Int'l*, pg. 1449
Rule, Ronald C., Chm. Bd., Pres. & Chief Exec. Officer--The United States Playing Card Company, Cincinnati, OH; *U.S. Private*, pg. 1125
Rumack, B.H., M.D., Pres.--Micromedex, Inc., Denver, CO; *U.S. Public*, pg. 1601
Rumble, R.M., Pres. & Chief Exec. Officer--MediVators, Inc., Eagan, MN; *U.S. Public*, pg. 301
Rummage, Paula, Pres.--Stratos Boat Company, Ltd., Old Hickory, TN; *U.S. Private*, pg. 478
Rummage, Paula, Pres.--Hydra-Sports Corporation, Nashville, TN; *U.S. Private*, pg. 478
Rummel, Eric F., Pres.--Laurel Bank, Johnstown, PA; *U.S. Public*, pg. 164
Rummell, Grant D., Pres. & Chief Exec. Officer--Linear Corporation, Carlsbad, CA; *U.S. Public*, pg. 1193
Rummurthy, Gitch, Pres. & Chief Oper. Officer--InfoVest, Inc., Chicago, IL; *U.S. Private*, pg. 562
Rummurthy, Gitch, Pres. & Chief Oper. Officer--CCC Information Services, Chicago, IL; *U.S. Private*, pg. 562
Rumy, Zsolt, Chm. Bd., Pres. & Chief Exec. Officer--Zoltek Companies, Inc., Saint Louis, MO; *U.S. Public*, pg. 1794
Rundell, C.A., Jr., Pres. & Chief Exec. Officer--Tyler Corporation, Dallas, TX; *U.S. Public*, pg. 1651
Rune, Gunnar, Pres.--NVS Nordiska Varme Sana AB, Malmo, Sweden; *Int'l*, pg. 899
Runk, John W., Chm. Bd. & Pres.--Directory Distributing Associates, Inc., Saint Louis, MO; *U.S. Private*, pg. 334
Rupard, Hay, Pres.--Peake Printers, Inc., Cheverly, MD; *U.S.* Private, pg. 845
Rupel, Robert A., Pres.--Bank of Pennsylvania, Reading, PA; *Int'l*, pg. 64
Rupert, David J., Pres.--Pitney Bowes Business Supplies & Services, Stamford, CT; *U.S. Public*, pg. 1303
Rupkey, Kevin P., Pres.--Warrantech Consumer Product Services, Inc., Euless, TX; *U.S. Public*, pg. 1740
Rupp, Glenn R., Chm. Bd., Pres. & Chief Exec. Officer--Converse Inc., North Reading, MA; *U.S. Public*, pg. 441
Rus, Arlyn D., Chm. Bd., Pres. & Chief Exec. Officer--Raritan Bancorp Inc., Bridgewater, NJ; *U.S. Public*, pg. 1361
Rusch, Bruce R., Pres. & Chief Oper. Officer--Analogic Corporation, Peabody, MA; *U.S. Public*, pg. 109
Rusch, Bruce R., Pres.--SKY Computers, Inc., Chelmsford, MA; *U.S. Public*, pg. 109
Rush, Carl V., Jr., Pres. & Chief Exec. Officer--The GNI Group, Inc., Deer Park, TX; *U.S. Public*, pg. 693
Rush, Gerald L., Chm. Bd. & Pres.--NBD Mortgage Corporation, Indianapolis, IN; *U.S. Public*, pg. 628
Rush, Richard, Interm Pres.--Pacificare of Ohio, Cincinnati, OH; *U.S. Public*, pg. 1251
Rushen, Frank J., Pres.--Instrument Specialties Company, Delaware Water Gap, PA; *U.S. Private*, pg. 565
Ruskoski, Eric, Pres.--Seaquist Closures, Mukwonago, WI; *U.S. Public*, pg. 125
Rusling, Con, Pres.--Sheshunoff Information Services, Inc., Austin, TX; *U.S. Public*, pg. 1601
Russ, Jim, Pres.--Rockville Crushed Stone, Inc., Rockville, MD; *Int'l*, pg. 166
Russ, Jim, Pres.--Millville Quarry Inc., Millville, WV; *Int'l*, pg. 166
Russ, Robert, Pres. & Co-Chief Exec. Officer--Diablo Research Corporation, Sunnyvale, CA; *U.S. Public*, pg. 1424
Russano, Richard, Pres. & Chief Oper. Officer--Winstar Global Products, Inc., Fairfield, NJ; *U.S. Public*, pg. 1772
Russeil, Jacques, Pres.--Lafarge Refractaires Monolithiques, Montrouge, France; *Int'l*, pg. 789
Russel, Terence A., Pres. & Chief Exec. Officer--Morgan Drive Away, Inc., Elkhart, IN; *U.S. Public*, pg. 1022
Russell, Bob, Pres.--Russell Chevrolet Company, Sherwood, AR; *U.S. Private*, pg. 952
Russell, Brian P., Pres.--CoMed Communications, Inc., Philadelphia, PA; *U.S. Private*, pg. 1083
Russell, Brian P., Principal--Vox Medica Corporation, Philadelphia, PA; *U.S. Private*, pg. 1143
Russell, Chester D., Jr., Pres.--Associated of Los Angeles, Los Angeles, CA; *U.S. Private*, pg. 92
Russell, E. Wayne, Jr., Pres.--Russell Petroleum Corporation, Montgomery, AL; *U.S. Private*, pg. 953
Russell, Ed, Chm. Bd., Pres. & Chief Exec. Officer--Minnesota Power, Duluth, MN; *U.S. Public*, pg. 1116
Russell, John R., Pres. & Chief Exec. Officer--Western Atlas Inc., Houston, TX; *U.S. Public*, pg. 1757
Russell, John R., Pres. & Chief Exec. Officer--Western Atlas International, Inc., Houston, TX; *U.S. Public*, pg. 1757
Russell, John, Jr., Chm., Pres. & Chief Exec. Officer-Hospitality Div.--HFS, Incorporated, Parsippany, NJ; *U.S. Public*, pg. 321
Russell, Marv, Owner--Maritime Broadcasting System Ltd., Halifax, Canada; *Int'l*, pg. 842
Russell, Nancy H., Pres.--Food & Gas, Inc., Norcross, GA; *U.S. Private*, pg. 417
Russell, Richard C., Pres. & Chief Exec. Officer--The Danis Companies, Dayton, OH; *U.S. Private*, pg. 310
Russell, Richard F., Pres. & Chief Exec. Officer--Amerisure Companies, Farmington Hills, MI; *U.S. Private*, pg. 65
Russell, Richard G., Chm. Bd., Pres. & Chief Exec. Officer--Tech Spray, Inc., Amarillo, TX; *U.S. Private*, pg. 1071
Russell, Richard R., Pres., Chief Exec. Officer & Mng. Dir.--The General Chemical Group, Inc., Hampton, NH; *U.S. Public*, pg. 707
Russell, Robert B., Jr., Pres.--Ruscon Corp., Charleston, SC; *U.S. Private*, pg. 952
Russell, William H., Pres.--MainStreet Trust Company, N.A., Martinsville, VA; *U.S. Public*, pg. 1039
Russillo, Thomas R., Pres. & Chief Oper. Officer--Ben Venue Laboratories, Inc., Bedford, OH; *U.S. Private*, pg. 1136
Russo, Anthony J., Chm. Bd & Pres.--E.C.D., Inc., Hillside, NJ; *U.S. Private*, pg. 353
Russo, Barbara Gans, Exec. Principal & Exec. Dir.-Brdcst. Prod./Creative Admin.--Publicis/Bloom, New York, NY; *Int'l*, pg. 470
Russo, Peter R., Pres.--Data Instruments, Inc., Acton, MA; *U.S. Private*, pg. 312
Russo, Richard A., Pres.--Tidewater Utilities, Inc., Odessa, DE; *U.S. Public*, pg. 1110
Russo, Richard A., Pres.--White Marsh Environmental Systems, Inc., Odessa, DE; *U.S. Public*, pg. 1110
Russo, Richard A., Pres.--Pinelands Water & Wastewater Co., Broadway, NJ; *U.S. Public*, pg. 1110
Russo, Richard A., Pres.--Public Water Supply Company, Millsboro, DE; *U.S. Public*, pg. 1110
Russo, Robert S., Pres.--American Technical Services Group, Inc., Norcross, GA; *U.S. Public*, pg. 1523
Russo, Thomas J., Pres.--Miami Subs USA, Inc., Fort Lauderdale, FL; *U.S. Public*, pg. 1103
Rust, Edward B., Jr., Chm. Bd., Pres. & Chief Exec. Officer--State Farm Mutual Automobile Insurance Company, Bloomington, IL; *U.S. Private*, pg. 1036
Rust, Lois, Pres. & Chief Exec. Officer--Rose Acre Farms, Seymour, IN; *U.S. Private*, pg. 944
Rutan, Elbert L., Pres.--Scaled Composites, Inc., Mojave, CA; *U.S. Public*, pg. 1782
Ruth, George, Pres.--Sunwest Bank of Roswell, N.A., Roswell, NM; *U.S. Public*, pg. 1165
Rutherford, Clyde E., Chm. Bd. & Pres.--Dairylea Cooperative Inc., East Syracuse, NY; *U.S. Private*, pg. 307
Rutherford, J. Larry, Pres. & Chief Exec. Officer--Atlantic Gulf Communities Corporation, Miami, FL; *U.S. Public*, pg. 144
Rutherfurd, John, Pres.--Moody's Investors Service, Inc., New York, NY; *U.S. Public*, pg. 536
Ruthman, T.R., Pres., Gen. Mgr. & Adv. Dir.--Gusher Pumps, Inc., Dry Ridge, KY; *U.S. Private*, pg. 488
Rutkin, Michael J., Pres.--Stratus Services Group, Inc., Manalapan, NJ; *U.S. Private*, pg. 1046
Rutledge, A. Bradley, Pres. & Chief Exec. Officer--Regions Bank/Pickens County, Jasper, GA; *U.S. Public*, pg. 1372
Rutledge, William A., Pres. & Chief Exec. Officer--Farmers Mutual Hail Insurance Co. of Iowa, Des Moines, IA; *U.S. Private*, pg. 395
Ruttenberg, Harold, Chm. Bd. & Pres.--Just For Feet, Inc., Pelham, AL; *U.S. Public*, pg. 935
Rutter, H. Richard, Pres.--The GMR Group, Fort Washington, PA; *U.S. Public*, pg. 1224
Ruud, Tom, Pres. & Chief Exec. Officer--Aker Raj Asa, Oslo, Norway; *Int'l*, pg. 41
Ruud, Tom, Pres. & Chief Exec. Officer--Christiania Bank og Kreditkasse ASA, Oslo, Norway; *Int'l*, pg. 289
Ruusunen, Kari, Pres.--Kvaerner Masa-Yards Inc., Piikkio Works, Piikkio, Finland; *Int'l*, pg. 771
Ruzicka, Jerry, Pres.--Starkey Laboratories, Inc., Eden Prairie, MN; *U.S. Private*, pg. 1035
Ryan, Arthur F., Chm. Bd., Pres. & Chief Exec. Officer--The Prudential Investment Corp., Newark, NJ; *U.S. Private*, pg. 892
Ryan, Ashton J., Jr., Pres. & Chief Exec. Officer--First National Bank of Commerce, New Orleans, LA; *U.S. Public*, pg. 629
Ryan, Bill, Pres.--Price/Palmer Wireless Corp., Fort Myers, FL; *U.S. Public*, pg. 1324
Ryan, Bruce E., Pres.--FMC-Crosby Valve, Inc., Wrentham, MA; *U.S. Public*, pg. 605
Ryan, Charles P., Jr., Chm. Bd. & Pres.--Charan Industries, Inc., Garden City, NY; *U.S. Private*, pg. 229
Ryan, Colleen, Pres.--Ryan Oldsmobile, Billings, MT; *U.S. Private*, pg. 953
Ryan, Conall E., Pres.--Houghton Mifflin Interactive Corp., Somerville, MA; *U.S. Public*, pg. 841
Ryan, Edward R., Pres. & Chief Exec. Officer--Sandusky International Inc., Sandusky, OH; *U.S. Private*, pg. 964
Ryan, Edward T., Jr., Pres. & Gen. Mgr.--Talley Defense Systems, Inc., Mesa, AZ; *U.S. Public*, pg. 308
Ryan, Frank, Pres.--Ethicon, Inc., Somerville, NJ; *U.S. Public*, pg. 928
Ryan, G. William, Pres.--Post-Newsweek Stations, Inc., Hartford, CT; *U.S. Public*, pg. 1743
Ryan, Joe, Pres.--EMTEC Magnetics Pro Media Inc., Valencia, CA; *Int'l*, pg. 743
Ryan, John D., Pres. & Chief Exec. Officer--Worldvision Enterprises, New York, NY; *U.S. Private*, pg. 776
Ryan, John G., Pres. & Chief Oper. Officer--Global Marine Inc., Houston, TX; *U.S. Public*, pg. 748
Ryan, John M., Pres.--AMC, Inc., Atlanta, GA; *U.S. Private*, pg. 6
Ryan, Kevin, Pres. & Chief Exec. Officer--Wesley-Jessen, Des Plaines, IL; *U.S. Private*, pg. 111
Ryan, Kevin, Pres. & Chief Exec. Officer--Pilkington Barnes Hind (PBH), San Diego, CA; *U.S. Private*, pg. 111
Ryan, Mark, Pres.--Pub/Data, Inc., Cicero, IL; *Int'l*, pg. 1076
Ryan, Matthew, Pres. & Chief Exec. Officer--Ryan Drossman & Partners, New York, NY; *U.S. Private*, pg. 953
Ryan, Pat, Pres.--Ryan Construction Company of Minnesota, Inc., Minneapolis, MN; *U.S. Private*, pg. 953
Ryan, Patrick G., Chm. Bd., Pres. & Chief Exec. Officer--AON Corporation, Chicago, IL; *U.S. Public*, pg. 117
Ryan, Richard, Pres.--Computer Corporation of America, Framingham, MA; *U.S. Private*, pg. 260
Ryan, Richard, Pres.--MarketPulse, Framingham, MA; *U.S. Private*, pg. 260
Ryan, Richard O., Pres. & Chief Oper. Officer--Dekalb Genetics Corporation, De Kalb, IL; *U.S. Public*, pg. 493
Ryan, Robert W., Pres.--Wally Findlay Galleries International, Chicago, IL; *U.S. Private*, pg. 405
Ryan, Robert W., Pres.--Wally Findlay Galleries, Inc., Palm Beach, FL; *U.S. Private*, pg. 405
Ryan, Robert W., Pres.--Wally Findlay Galleries, Inc., New York, NY; *U.S. Private*, pg. 405
Ryan, Rosemarie, Pres.--Kirshenbaum, Bond & Partners, New York, NY; *U.S. Private*, pg. 624
Ryan, Stephen F., Pres. & Chief Exec. Officer--Selas Corporation of America, Dresher, PA; *U.S. Public*, pg. 1454
Ryan, Thomas F., Jr., Pres. & Chief Oper. Officer--The American Stock Exchange, New York, NY; *U.S. Private*, pg. 62
Ryan, Thomas M., Vice Chm., Pres., Chief Exec. Officer & Chief Oper. Officer-CVS--CVS Corp., Woonsocket, RI; *U.S. Public*, pg. 287
Ryan, Tom, Pres.-Design Services Grp.--SuperValu, Inc., Eden Prairie, MN; *U.S. Public*, pg. 1540
Ryan, Wayne, Gen. Mgr.--Tristar Industries Ltd., Delta, Canada; *Int'l*, pg. 1473
Ryan, William A., Chm. Bd., Pres. & Chief Exec. Officer--Team, Inc., Alvin, TX; *U.S. Public*, pg. 1562
Ryan, William J., Chm. Bd., Pres. & Chief Exec. Officer--Peoples Heritage Financial Group, Inc., Portland, ME; *U.S. Public*, pg. 1275
Rychel, William M., Co-Pres.-Graphics Div.--Tekgraf, Inc., Norcross, GA; *U.S. Private*, pg. 1073
Ryden, D. Ray, Pres.-Located in Boise, ID--Minnesota, Dakota & Western Railway Co., International Falls, MN; *U.S. Public*, pg. 243
Ryden, John G., Dir.--Yale University Press, New Haven, CT; *U.S. Private*, pg. 1195
Ryder, John, Pres. & Chief Oper. Officer-Retail--Metro/Basics, Baltimore, MD; *U.S. Public*, pg. 1388
Ryder, Kenneth, Pres.--All Pro Window Supply, Inc., Ocala, FL; *U.S. Private*, pg. 35
Ryder, Robert G., Pres. & Chief Exec. Officer--The First National Bank of Lake Charles, Lake Charles, LA; *U.S. Public*, pg. 630
Ryder, Thomas O., Pres.--American Express Travel Related Services Co., Inc., New York, NY; *U.S. Public*, pg. 73
Rydin, Craig, Pres.--Godiva Chocolatier, Inc., New York, NY; *U.S. Public*, pg. 299
Rygiel, Edward K., Pres.--MDS Health Ventures Capital Corp., Etobicoke, Canada; *Int'l*, pg. 827
Ryker, Gary E., Pres. & Chief Exec. Officer--Union Switch & Signal Inc., Pittsburgh, PA; *Int'l*, pg. 77
Rylander, Goran, Pres.--Swedbank (Luxembourg) S.A., Luxembourg, Luxembourg; *Int'l*, pg. 1328
Ryno, Ronald P., Pres.--Cuplex, Inc., Garland, TX; *U.S. Private*, pg. 297
Rynone, Richard T., Pres.--Rynone Manufacturing Corporation, Sayre, PA; *U.S. Private*, pg. 953
Ryoki, Shin-ichiro, Pres.--Osaka Gas Co., Ltd., Osaka, Japan; *Int'l*, pg. 1011
Ryon, Rich, Pres.--The Georgia Marble Company, Kennesaw, GA; *U.S. Private*, pg. 448
Rypien, John M., Pres.--O.J. Pipelines Corp., Nisku, Canada; *Int'l*, pg. 996
Ryzman, Zvi, Pres. & Chief Exec. Officer--American International Industries, City of Commerce, CA; *U.S. Private*, pg. 57
Ryzman, Zvi, Pres. & Chief Exec. Officer--Andrea International, City of Commerce, CA; *U.S. Private*, pg. 57
Ryzman, Zvi, Pres. & Chief Exec. Officer--All Clubman, City of Commerce, CA; *U.S. Private*, pg. 57
Ryzman, Zvi, Pres. & Chief Exec. Officer--Delore, City of Commerce, CA; *U.S. Private*, pg. 57

Ryzman, Zvi, Pres. & Chief Exec. Officer--GiGi, City of Commerce, CA; *U.S. Private*, pg. 57
Ryzman, Zvi, Pres. & Chief Exec. Officer--SuperNail, City of Commerce, CA; *U.S. Private*, pg. 57
Saarikangas, Martin, Pres.--Kvaerner Masa-Yards Inc., Helsinki New Shipyard, Helsinki, Finland; *Int'l*, pg. 771
Sabatino, Victor, Chm. Bd., Pres. & Chief Exec. Officer--Family Smacks, Inc., Liberty, MO; *U.S. Private*, pg. 393
Sabbag, Allen, Pres.--Better Homes and Gardens Real Estate Service, Des Moines, IA; *U.S. Public*, pg. 1094
Sabbeth, Stephen J., Chm. Bd. & Pres.--Sabbeth Industries Ltd, Carle Place, NY; *U.S. Private*, pg. 959
Sabin, Dan, Pres.--Iowa Northern Railroad, Greene, IA; *U.S.* Private, pg. 575
Sabol, Thomas A., Pres.--Englekirk & Sabol, Inc., Los Angeles, CA; *U.S. Private*, pg. 377
Sabounchi, Farid, Pres.--Aetrium-FSA, Grand Prairie, TX; *U.S. Public*, pg. 27
Saca, David, Pres.--Filco, Inc., Sacramento, CA; *U.S. Private*, pg. 404
Sacco, Donald, Pres. & Chief Exec. Officer--Regence BlueCross BlueShield of Oregon, Portland, OR; *U.S. Private*, pg. 917
Sacco, Thomas, Pres.--Triangle Food Services Co., Dallas, TX; *U.S. Private*, pg. 1102
Sachs, Bruce I., Pres. & Chief Exec. Officer--Stratus Computer, Inc., Marlborough, MA; *U.S. Public*, pg. 1524
Sachs, Philip E., Pres. & Chief Exec. Officer--Legg Mason Capital Management Inc., Baltimore, MD; *U.S. Public*, pg. 985
Sachse, Rich, Pres. & Chief Exec. Officer--Woodcraft Industries, Inc., Saint Cloud, MN; *U.S. Private*, pg. 1187
Sack, Han, Pres. & Chief Exec. Officer--Latrobe Steel Company, Latrobe, PA; *U.S. Public*, pg. 1617
Sack, Han, Pres.--Latrobe Special Products Div., Latrobe, PA; *U.S. Public*, pg. 1617
Sack, Thomas F., Pres., Chief Exec. Officer & Chief Oper. Officer--Haddon Craftsmen, Inc., Scranton, PA; *U.S. Public*, pg. 518
Sackett, Janice J., Pres.--LeGrand Johnson Construction Co., Logan, UT; *U.S. Private*, pg. 591
Sackett, Neil, Pres.--Carter-Jones Lumber Co., Kent, OH; *U.S. Private*, pg. 217
Sackmann, Thomas F., Pres.--Action Mortgage Company, Spokane, WA; *U.S. Public*, pg. 1516
Sacks, Ann, Pres.--Ann Sacks Tile & Stone, Inc., Portland, OR; *U.S. Private*, pg. 630
Sada, Armando Garza, Pres.--Sigma Alimentos, S.A. de C.V., Garza Garcia, Mexico; *Int'l*, pg. 56
Sada, Francisco, Pres.--Wisdom Imports Sales Co. Inc., Irvine, CA; *Int'l*, pg. 679
Sadanowicz, Andrew, Pres.--The Purdy Corporation, Manchester, CT; *U.S. Private*, pg. 895
Sadler, David, Pres.--RI Holdings, Grand Rapids, MI; *U.S. Private*, pg. 904
Sadler, David G., Pres.--Rowe International, Inc., Grand Rapids, MI; *U.S. Private*, pg. 904
Sadler, Mike, Pres. & Chief Exec. Officer--SF Services, North Little Rock, AR; *U.S. Private*, pg. 956
Sadler, Robert E., Jr., Pres.--First Empire State Corporation, Buffalo, NY; *U.S. Public*, pg. 631
Sadler, Robert E., Jr., Pres.--Manufacturers & Traders Trust Company, Buffalo, NY; *U.S. Public*, pg. 631
Sadler, Robert L., Pres. & Chief Exec. Officer--Old Kent Bank, Grand Rapids, MI; *U.S. Public*, pg. 1216
Sadler, Stephen J., Pres.--Geac Computer Corporation Limited, Markham, Canada; *Int'l*, pg. 532
Sadler, William S., Pres. & Treas.--Dotronix, Inc., New Brighton, MN; *U.S. Public*, pg. 520
Sadove, Stephen I., Pres.--Clairol, Inc., Stamford, CT; *U.S. Public*, pg. 254
Sadowski, James, Pres. & Chief Oper. Officer--Chart Industries, Inc., Cleveland, OH; *U.S. Public*, pg. 336
Sadowski, James, Pres. & Chief Oper. Officer--PSI-Process Systems International, Inc., Cleveland, OH; *U.S. Public*, pg. 336
Sadowski, Rick, Pres. & Publr.--Saint Paul Pioneer Press Division, Saint Paul, MN; *U.S. Public*, pg. 964
Sadrossasatzadeh, S.M., Pres.--Monenco Iran, Tehran, Iran; *Int'l*, pg. 31
Saegusa, Masato, Pres.--Actus Corporation, Tokyo, Japan; *Int'l*, pg. 868
Saeki, Naotaka, Pres.--The Sanwa Bank Limited, Osaka, Japan; *Int'l*, pg. 1189
Saeki, Takehiko, Pres.--Kawasaki Motors Manufacturing Corp., U.S.A., Lincoln, NE; *Int'l*, pg. 725
Saenc, Alfredo, Pres.--Banco Espanol de Credito SA, Madrid, Spain; *Int'l*, pg. 143
Saeranie, Shan, Pres.--Harper-Wyman Co., Aurora, IL; *U.S. Public*, pg. 1209
Sagansky, Jeffrey, Co-Pres.--Sony Pictures Entertainment, Culver City, CA; *Int'l*, pg. 1281
Sagar, Ravi, Mgr.--Arms Communications P. Ltd., Mumbai, India; *U.S. Public*, pg. 1642
Sagawa, Nobuo, Pres.--The Meijiseimei Insurance Agency of New York, Inc., New York, NY; *Int'l*, pg. 854
Sage, George, Pres.--Bonanza Bus Lines, Inc., Providence, RI; *U.S. Private*, pg. 156
Sager, Robert, Pres.--Gordon Brothers Partners Inc., Boston, MA; *U.S. Private*, pg. 465
Saginaw, David, Pres. & Chief Oper. Officer--Roytex, Inc., New York, NY; *U.S. Private*, pg. 949
Sagol, Sami, Pres.--Keter Plastic Ltd., Herzliyya, Israel; *Int'l, pg. 732*
Sahlsten, Carl, Pres.--Carrabba's Italian Grill, Inc., Tampa, FL; *U.S. Public*, pg. 1235
Sahora, Karl, Pres.--Philips Speech Processing, Atlanta, GA; *Int'l*, pg. 1055
Saillant, J., Pres.--Stihl Eastern Canada Ltd., Vanier, Canada; *Int'l*, pg. 1301
Sainsbury, Alan John, Baron of Drury Lane, Joint Pres.--J. Sainsbury plc, London, United Kingdom; *Int'l*, pg. 1169
Sainsbury, Sir Robert, Joint Pres.--J. Sainsbury plc, London, United Kingdom; *Int'l*, pg. 1169
Saint-Pierre, Guy, Pres. & Chief Exec. Officer--SNC-Lavalin Inc., Montreal, Canada; *Int'l*, pg. 1162
Saiontz, Steven J., Pres.--Lennar Financial Services, Inc., Miami, FL; *U.S. Public*, pg. 988
Saito, Atsushi, Pres.--Nomura Human Resources Development Co., Ltd., Tokyo, Japan; *Int'l*, pg. 955
Saito, Keishiro, Pres.--Toray Europe Ltd., London, United Kingdom; *Int'l*, pg. 1400
Saito, Naotake, Pres.--Eastern Harbour Crossing Co., Ltd., Hong Kong, Hong Kong; *Int'l*, pg. 764
Saito, Naotake, Pres.--New Hong Kong Tunnel Co., Ltd., Hong Kong, Hong Kong; *Int'l*, pg. 764
Saito, Naoto, Pres.--Sumitomo Rubber Industries Ltd., Kobe, Japan; *Int'l*, pg. 1316
Saito, Shichiro, Pres. & Chief Exec. Officer--Mitsui & Co. (Canada), Montreal, Canada; *Int'l*, pg. 880
Saito, Takeshi, Pres.--NLI Properties West, Inc., Los Angeles, CA; *Int'l*, pg. 935
Saito, Toshio, Pres.--ZEXEL Illinois Inc., Decatur, IL; *Int'l*, pg. 1528
Sakai, H., Pres.--Sunrack Oyodo Co., Ltd., Izumi-Otsu, Japan; *Int'l*, pg. 947
Sakai, Hideki, Pres. & Chief Exec. Officer--Hirose Electric Co., Ltd., Tokyo, Japan; *Int'l*, pg. 620
Sakai, Hiroto, Pres.--Sumitomo Bank (Deutschland) GmbH, Frankfurt/Main, Germany; *Int'l*, pg. 1310
Sakai, Tadamasa, Pres.--Seoul Office, Seoul, Korea; *Int'l*, pg. 578
Sakamoto, Hiroshi, Pres.--Toko Inc., Tokyo, Japan; *Int'l*, pg. 1393
Sakane, Masahiro, Pres.--Komatsu America Corp., Lincolnshire, IL; *Int'l*, pg. 744
Sakata, Haruo, Pres.--Gunsan Exportadora e Importadora Ltda., Sao Paulo, Brazil; *Int'l*, pg. 579
Sakayama, Larry K., Pres.--TEC Cellular, Melbourne, FL; *U.S. Public*, pg. 1430
Saker, Joseph J., Chm. Bd. & Pres.--Foodarama Supermarkets, Inc., Freehold, NJ; *U.S. Public*, pg. 661
Sakiz, Alex, Pres.-Prism Montreal--Bozell Retail, Toronto, Canada; *Int'l*, pg. 209
Sakogawa, Ridai, Pres. & Chief Exec. Officer--TOHO Mutual Life Insurance Company, Tokyo, Japan; *Int'l*, pg. 1390
Sakonju, T., Pres.--Nissho Iwai Nonferrous Metals Corp., Tokyo, Japan; *Int'l*, pg. 947
Sakuma, K., Chm. & Pres.--Otto Sumisho Inc., Tokyo, Japan; *Int'l*, pg. 1015
Sakuma, Toshi, Gen. Mgr.--Yamaha Corp. of America, Sporting Goods Div., Buena Park, CA; *Int'l*, pg. 1516
Sakumah, Hajime, Pres.--Shin Caterpillar Mitsubishi Ltd., Yokohama, Japan; *U.S. Public*, pg. 317
Sakumah, Hajime, Pres.--Shin Caterpillar Mitsubishi Ltd., Yokohama, Japan; *Int'l*, pg. 873
Sakurai, Masamitsu, Pres.--Ricoh Company, Ltd., Tokyo, Japan; *Int'l*, pg. 1114
Sakurai, Shoji, Pres.--Daiwa Securities Bank (Switzerland) Head Office, Zurich, Switzerland; *Int'l*, pg. 376
Sakurai, Takahide, Pres.--Dai-ichi Mutual Life Insurance Company, Tokyo, Japan; *Int'l*, pg. 362
Sala, Lawrence, Pres.--Anaren Microwave Inc., East Syracuse, NY; *U.S. Public*, pg. 110
Salameh, Samer, Pres. & Chief Exec. Officer--Prodigy Inc., White Plains, NY; *U.S. Private*, pg. 888
Salamon, Robert, Pres.--Pic N'Pay Supermarkets, Inc., Dania, FL; *U.S. Private*, pg. 864
Salamone, Anthony, Pres.--Sunroc Corporation, Dover, DE; *U.S. Private*, pg. 1053
Salanski, Charles W., Pres. & Chief Oper. Officer--Wire Rope Corporation of America, Inc., Saint Joseph, MO; *U.S. Private*, pg. 1184
Salazar, Rogelio C., Pres. & Chief Exec. Officer--Atlas Consolidated Mining & Development Corporation, Manila, Philippines; *Int'l*, pg. 95
Salegard, Jarl, Pres.--Ballast Vast AB, Goteborg, Sweden; *Int'l*, pg. 899
Salerno, Robert, Pres. & Chief Oper. Officer--Avis Car Leasing, Garden City, NY; *U.S. Public*, pg. 321
Salerno, Robert, Pres. & Chief Oper. Officer--Avis Rent A Car System, Inc., Garden City, NY; *U.S. Public*, pg. 321
Salhany, Lucie, Pres.--Fox Broadcasting Company (FBC), Beverly Hills, CA; *Int'l*, pg. 926
Salicetti, Arturo Casado, Pres.--Leo Burnett Venezuela, C.A., Caracas, Venezuela; *U.S. Private*, pg. 186
Salina Amorini, Elizabeth, Chm. Bd. & Pres.--SGS Societe Generale de Surveillance Holding S.A., Geneva, Switzerland; *Int'l*, pg. 1153
Salinas Pliego, Ricardo B., Chm. Bd. & Pres.--Grupo Elektra S.A. de C.V., Mexico, Mexico; *Int'l*, pg. 573
Salinger, John J., Pres.-Trade & Political Risk Div. & Special Services Div.--American International Underwriters Corp., New York, NY; *U.S. Public*, pg. 85
Salizzoni, Frank L., Pres. & Chief Exec. Officer--H & R Block, Inc., Kansas City, MO; *U.S. Public*, pg. 770
Salles, Lywal, Pres.--Chase Bank of Maryland, Baltimore, MD; *U.S. Public*, pg. 338
Salles, Paulo, Pres. & Chief Exec. Officer--Salles/DMB&B Publicidade S.A., Sao Paulo, Brazil; *U.S. Private*, pg. 305
Salley, J. Ronald, Pres.--Shannon & Wilson, Inc., Seattle, WA; *U.S. Private*, pg. 989
Sallin, Lars-Erik, Pres.--Machinery East, Linkoping, Sweden; *Int'l*, pg. 899
Sallis, Richard, Pres.--Playmates Toys Inc., Costa Mesa, CA; *Int'l*, pg. 1060
Salman, Steven L., Pres. & Chief Exec. Officer--Kentucky Medical Insurance Company (KMIC), Louisville, KY; *U.S. Private*, pg. 741
Salmon, John, Pres.--CDP, London, United Kingdom; *Int'l*, pg. 239
Salo, J., Pres.--Nokia Telecommunications Inc., Roanoke, TX; *Int'l*, pg. 953
Salpeter, Michael, Pres.--Warrantech Corporation, Stamford, CT; *U.S. Public*, pg. 1740
Salsbury, Phillip J., Dr., Pres. & Chief Exec. Officer--SEEQ Technology Inc., Fremont, CA; *U.S. Public*, pg. 1417
Saltoun, M., Pres. & Dir.-Opers.--A.S. Management Corporation, Stamford, CT; *U.S. Private*, pg. 7
Saltzman, Robert, Pres. & Chief Exec. Officer--Jackson National Life Insurance Company, Lansing, MI; *Int'l*, pg. 1073
Salucci, Anthony, Pres.-Military--Hughes-Treitler Manufacturing Corporation, Garden City, NY; *U.S. Private*, pg. 547
Salvadori, Fabrizio, Pres.--Rimoldi Necchi S.R.L., Milan, Italy; *Int'l*, pg. 1117
Salvati, Sandro, Dr., Pres.--Lloyd Adriatico S.p.A, Trieste, Italy; *Int'l*, pg. 60
Salvatori, Romano, Pres.--Nations Energy Corporation, Tucson, AZ; *U.S. Public*, pg. 1670
Salwasser, Dennis, Pres.--Salwasser Manufacturing Company, Inc., Reedley, CA; *U.S. Private*, pg. 963
Salzano, Joe, Pres.--Amerex Men's, New York, NY; *U.S. Private*, pg. 49
Salzberger, Lee R., Pres. & Gen. Mgr.--WVEC-TV, Inc., Norfolk, VA; *U.S. Public*, pg. 209
Samans, Robert A., Chm. Bd. & Pres.--Scanforms, Inc., Bristol, PA; *U.S. Public*, pg. 228
Samatas, Sam, Pres.--Atlas Electric Devices Co., Chicago, IL; *U.S. Private*, pg. 96
Sambol, David, Pres. & Chief Exec. Officer--Countrywide Capital Markets, Inc., Pasadena, CA; *U.S. Public*, pg. 453
Sambrowsky, Joe, Pres.--Seltec Selective Technology Inc., Dallas, TX; *Int'l*, pg. 1528
Sambur, Marvin R., Pres. & Gen. Mgr.--ITT Aerospace/Communications Div., Fort Wayne, IN; *U.S. Public*, pg. 859
Samburg, A. Gene, Chm. Bd., Pres. & Chief Exec. Officer--Kastle Systems LLC, Arlington, VA; *U.S. Private*, pg. 608
Samide, Michael R., Pres.--Titan Wheel Corporation, Walcott, IA; *U.S. Public*, pg. 1618
Samis, Michael S., Pres. & Chief Exec. Officer--Macklanburg-Duncan Co., Oklahoma City, OK; *U.S. Private*, pg. 692
Sammaranett, Juan Antonio, Pres.--La Caixa, Barcelona, Spain; *Int'l*, pg. 784
Sammon, Dr. John W., Jr., Chm. Bd., Pres. & Chief Exec. Officer--PAR Technology Corporation, New Hartford, NY; *U.S. Public*, pg. 1256
Sammons, Bob, Pres.--Piper Impact, Inc., New Albany, MS; *U.S. Public*, pg. 1349
Sammons, Vic, Pres.--Taylor Made, Indiana, Kendallville, IN; *U.S. Private*, pg. 1071
Sammons, Victor, Pres.--Taylor Made-New York, Gloversville, NY; *U.S. Private*, pg. 1070
Samper, J. Phillip, Pres.--Sun Microsystems Computer Corporation, Mountain View, CA; *U.S. Public*, pg. 1531
Sampietro, Giorgio, Pres.--Unil-It S.p.A., Milan, Italy; *Int'l*, pg. 1438
Sample, David, Chm. Bd., Pres. & Chief Exec. Officer--PSDI, Bedford, MA; *U.S. Private*, pg. 828
Samplik, Jaroslav, Mng. Dir.--Cokoladovny, Prague, Czech Republic; *Int'l*, pg. 381
Sampson, Curtis A., Chm. Bd., Pres. & Chief Exec. Officer--Communications Systems, Inc., Hector, MN; *U.S. Public*, pg. 415
Sampson, Curtis A., Chm., Pres. & Chief Exec. Officer--Suttle Caribe, Inc., Humacao, PR; *U.S. Public*, pg. 415
Sampson, Gerald A., Pres. & Chief Oper. Officer--Neiman Marcus Co., Dallas, TX; *U.S. Public*, pg. 785
Sampson, Scott B., Pres.--Coast Business Credit, Los Angeles, CA; *U.S. Public*, pg. 872
Sams, Kenneth D., Pres.--Cherokee Brick & Tile Co., Macon, GA; *U.S. Private*, pg. 233
Samson, Bernice, Chm. & Pres.--Sterling Supply Company, Inc., Lisle, IL; *U.S. Private*, pg. 1041
Samuels, Allen, Pres.--Allen Samuels Chevrolet GEO, Waco, TX; *U.S. Private*, pg. 964
Samuels, Bill, Jr., Pres.--Maker's Mark Distillery, Inc., Louisville, KY; *Int'l*, pg. 63
Samuels, William, Pres.-Sls.--Mathews & Boucher, Rochester, NY; *U.S. Private*, pg. 714
San, Lim Hock, Pres. & Chief Exec. Officer--Singapore Land Limited, Singapore, Singapore; *Int'l*, pg. 1252
Sanada, Takashi, Pres. & Chief Oper. Officer--KYB Corporation of America, Lombard, IL; *Int'l*, pg. 727
Sananvatananont, Preecha, Pres.--Reed Exhibition Companies-Thailand, Nonthaburi, Thailand; *Int'l*, pg. 1097
Sanborn, Bruce, Chm. Bd. & Chief Exec. Officer--Financial Life Companies, Inc., Saint Paul, MN; *U.S. Private*, pg. 404
Sanchez Lugo, Manuel, Pres.--Avantel, S.A., Mexico, Mexico; *Int'l*, pg. 574
Sanchez-Llaca, Juan, Pres.--Imperial Hotels, El Segundo, CA; *U.S. Private*, pg. 558
Sanchez, Frank, Pres.--Sanchez Computer Associates, Malvern, PA; *U.S. Public*, pg. 1425
Sanchez, Gregorio Gonzalez-Irun, Pres.--CARBOEX - Sociedad Espanola de Carbon Exterior, S.A., Madrid, Spain; *Int'l*, pg. 1224
Sandberg, Bob, Pres.-Automotive/Industrial--Sackner Products, Grand Rapids, MI; *U.S. Public*, pg. 924
Sandberg, Roger, Pres.--Trencor, Inc., Grand Prairie, TX; *U.S. Public*, pg. 141
Sanderford, Robin E., Pres.--Gayfers, Montgomery, AL; *U.S.* Public, pg. 1090
Sanders, Dean L., Pres. & Chief Exec. Officer--Sam's Clubs Div., Bentonville, AR; *U.S. Public*, pg. 1733
Sanders, E. Craig, Chm. Bd., Pres. & Chief Exec. Officer--Peoples Telephone Company, Inc., Miami, FL; *U.S. Public*, pg. 1275
Sanders, Harvey, Chm. Bd., Pres. & Chief Exec. Officer--Nautica Enterprises, Inc., New York, NY; *U.S. Public*, pg. 1167
Sanders, James N., Mng. Dir. & Chief Exec. Officer--Ansaldo Signal N.V., Amsterdam, Netherlands; *Int'l*, pg. 77

Sanders, Mark, Pres. & Chief Exec. Officer--Pinnacle Systems, Inc., Mountain View, CA; *U.S. Public*, pg. 1297
Sanders, Max, Pres.--Pico-Matic Inc., Evanston, IL; *U.S. Private*, pg. 813
Sanders, O'Neil, Chm. Bd., Pres., Chief Exec. & Chief Oper. Officer--Associated Petroleum Carriers, Spartanburg, SC; *U.S. Private*, pg. 92
Sanders, R.G., Pres. & Gen. Mgr.--Black Warrior Transmission Corp., Brookwood, AL; *U.S. Public*, pg. 1485
Sanders, R.G., Pres. & Gen. Mgr.--Black Warrior Methane Corp., Brookwood, AL; *U.S. Public*, pg. 1737
Sanders, R.G., Pres. & Gen. Mgr.--Black Warrior Transmission Corp., Brookwood, AL; *U.S. Public*, pg. 1737
Sanders, Steve, Chm. Bd. & Pres.--MMC Corp., Leawood, KS; *U.S. Private*, pg. 687
Sanders, V. William, Pres.--Sirach Capital Management, Inc., Seattle, WA; *U.S. Public*, pg. 1674
Sanders, Wayne R., Chm. Bd. & Chief Exec. Officer--Kimberly-Clark Corporation, Dallas, TX; *U.S. Public*, pg. 958
Sanders, William D., Chm. Bd., Pres. & Chief Exec. Officer--Security Capital Group Incorporated, Santa Fe, NM; *U.S.* Private, pg. 980
Sanderson, Joe F., Jr., Pres. & Chief Exec. Officer--Sanderson Farms, Inc., Laurel, MS; *U.S. Public*, pg. 1430
Sanderson, Michael, Pres. & Chief Exec. Officer--Instinet Corporation, New York, NY; *Int'l*, pg. 1106
Sanderson, Mike, Pres. & Chief Exec. Officer--Chronos Richardson, Fairfield, NJ; *Int'l*, pg. 1299
Sanderson, Sandra, Pres.--Sani-Med, Columbus, MS; *U.S. Private*, pg. 964
Sanderson, Sandra, Pres.--Manufactured Home, Columbus, MS; *U.S. Private*, pg. 964
Sanderson, Sandra B., Pres. & Chief Exec. Officer--Sanderson Plumbing Products Inc., Columbus, MS; *U.S. Private*, pg. 964
Sandhagen, Ray, Pres.--SunTrust Bank, Gulf Coast, Sarasota, FL; *U.S. Public*, pg. 1537
Sandhu, Chain, Pres.--Atrex Incorporated, Warren, MI; *U.S. Private*, pg. 97
Sandhu, M.S., Chm. Bd., Pres. & Chief Exec. Officer--SRS Technologies, Newport Beach, CA; *U.S. Private*, pg. 958
Sandifer, Michael, Pres.--Cain & Bultman, Jacksonville, FL; *U.S. Private*, pg. 199
Sandifur, C. Paul, Jr., Pres. & Chief Exec. Officer--Metropolitan Mortgage & Securities Co., Inc., Spokane, WA; *U.S. Private*, pg. 738
Sandison, G., Pres.--Saudi Arabian Texaco Inc., White Plains, NY; *U.S. Public*, pg. 1583
Sandker, Tim, Pres.--Rotary Lift, Madison, IN; *U.S. Public*, pg. 521
Sandler, Steven, Pres.--L.M. Sandler & Sons, Virginia Beach, VA; *U.S. Private*, pg. 964
Sandlin, David, Pres.--Flight International Aviation, Inc., Newport News, VA; *U.S. Public*, pg. 654
Sandlin, David E., Chm. Bd. & Pres.--The Flight International Group, Inc., Newport News, VA; *U.S. Public*, pg. 654
Sandman, Edward L., Pres.--Northwest Alloys, Inc., Addy, WA; *U.S. Public*, pg. 61
Sando, Barry M., Pres.--First American Flood Data Services, Austin, TX; *U.S. Public*, pg. 625
Sandor, Thomas L., Pres. & Chief Exec. Officer--Superior Group, Inc., Radnor, PA; *U.S. Private*, pg. 1055
Sandoval Granados, Alberto, Pres.--Internacional de Ceramica S.A. de C.V., Chihuahua, Mexico; *Int'l*, pg. 680
Sands, Louis, IV, Pres.--Sands Motor Company, Inc., Glendale, AZ; *U.S. Private*, pg. 964
Sands, Richard, Pres. & Chief Exec. Officer--Canandaigua Wine Company, Inc., Canandaigua, NY; *U.S. Public*, pg. 300
Sandstrom, Anton, Pres.--AB Svensk Leca, Linkoping, Sweden; *Int'l*, pg. 1200
Sandstrom, Anton, Pres.--Fibo ExClay Eesti AS, Parnu, Estonia; *Int'l*, pg. 1200
Sandusky, James, Pres.--NicSand, Inc., Cleveland, OH; *U.S.* Private, pg. 799
Sandvoss, Ernst-Otto, Chm. Bd.--Deutsche Girozentrale-Deutsche Kommunalbank, Frankfurt/Main, Germany; *Int'l*, pg. 406
Sanford, Bill R., Chm. Bd., Pres. & Treas.--Steris Corporation, Mentor, OH; *U.S. Public*, pg. 1515
Sanford, J., Pres. & Chief Oper. Officer--Rolls-Royce Inc., Reston, VA; *Int'l*, pg. 1127
Sanford, Joseph P., Pres.--Mellon First Business Bank, Los Angeles, CA; *U.S. Public*, pg. 1085
Sanford, Robert P., Pres.--Sanford & Hawley, Inc., Unionville, CT; *U.S. Private*, pg. 965
Sanghi, Steve, Chm. Bd., Pres. & Chief Exec. Officer--Microchip Technology, Inc., Chandler, AZ; *U.S. Public*, pg. 1105
Sangiacomo, Michael J., Pres. & Chief Exec. Officer--Norcal Waste Systems, San Francisco, CA; *U.S. Public*, pg. 1188
Sangster, Brian, Pres. & Chief Oper. Officer--Lakehead Pipe Line Co., Inc., Superior, WI; *Int'l*, pg. 652
Sanguinetti, P.A., Pres.--Consolidated Publishing Company, Anniston, AL; *U.S. Private*, pg. 266
Sani, Ashok, Pres.--CGS Industries, Inc., Long Island City, NY; *U.S. Private*, pg. 194
Sankes, Gary, Chm. Bd. & Pres.--Scrufari Construction Co. Inc., Niagara Falls, NY; *U.S. Private*, pg. 977
Sankpill, L. Alan, Pres. & Chief Exec. Officer--U.S. Safety, Lenexa, KS; *U.S. Private*, pg. 1125
Sanna, Gavino, Pres.--BGS DMB&B Milan, Milan, Italy; *U.S.* Private, pg. 303
Sanna, Gavino, Pres.--Gavino Sanna Associati, Milan, Italy; *U.S. Private*, pg. 304
Sano, Shoji, Pres.--GSI (Beijing) Hosiery Co., Ltd., Beijing, China; *Int'l*, pg. 579
Sanoshy, Robert, Pres.--Crown Moving & Storage Inc., of Illinois, Gurnee, IL; *U.S. Private*, pg. 1171
Sansone, Paul, Pres. & Chief Exec. Officer--Sansone Auto Mall, Avenel, NJ; *U.S. Private*, pg. 965
Sansone, Thomas A., Pres.--Jabil Circuit, Inc., Saint Petersburg, FL; *U.S. Public*, pg. 919
Sant, Stephen R., Pres. & Chief Exec. Officer--First Western Bank, National Association, New Castle, PA; *U.S. Public*, pg. 642
Santacrose, Mark F., Pres.--Bagcraft Corporation of America, Chicago, IL; *U.S. Public*, pg. 136
Santanlaria, Kevin, Pres.--Vantage Companies, Dallas, TX; *U.S. Private*, pg. 1134
Santo Domingo, Julio Mario, Pres.--Central de Cervejas, S.A., Lisbon, Portugal; *Int'l*, pg. 279
Santorelli, Vincent, Pres.--Victor O. Schinnerer & Co., Ltd., Chevy Chase, MD; *U.S. Public*, pg. 1049
Santos, Francisco, Pres.--Jeronimo Martins, Lisbon, Portugal; *Int'l*, pg. 705
Santos, Joseph M., Pres.--MBC Leasing, Baltimore, MD; *U.S. Public*, pg. 1089
Santowski, Jerome G., Pres.--Broan Mfg. Co., Inc., Hartford, WI; *U.S. Public*, pg. 1193
Santry, Michael G., Chm. Bd., Pres. & Chief Exec. Officer--ATC Communications Group, Inc., Dallas, TX; *U.S. Public*, pg. 11
Santulli, Richard T., Chm. Bd., Pres. & Chief Exec. Officer--Executive Jet Aviation, Inc., Columbus, OH; *U.S. Private*, *pg. 388*
Sanz, Juan, Pres.--Opel Espana, Zaragoza, Spain; *U.S. Public*, pg. 724
Sanzone, Vincent P., Pres.--Tecot Electric Supply Company, New Castle, DE; *U.S. Private*, pg. 951
Saolona, Bemba, Pres.--SARL GB Zaire, Kinshasa, Congo; *Int'l*, pg. 534
Saper, Lawrence, Chm. Bd., Pres. & Chief Exec. Officer--Datascope Corp., Montvale, NJ; *U.S. Public*, pg. 487
Saperstein, Carol, Pres.--Kraft Hardware, Inc., New York, NY; *U.S. Private*, pg. 634
Saponaro, Joseph A., Pres.--Intermetrics, Inc., Burlington, MA; *U.S. Private*, pg. 567
Saponja, Walter, Pres. & Chief Oper. Officer--TransAlta Utilities, Calgary, Canada; *Int'l*, pg. 1416
Sapos, Mary Ann, Pres. & Chief Exec. Officer--Hutchins/Young & Rubicam, Rochester, NY; *U.S. Private*, pg. 1197
Sapp, A. Eugene, Jr., Pres. & Chief Oper. Officer--SCI Systems, Inc., Huntsville, AL; *U.S. Public*, pg. 1416
Sappenfield, Richard W., Pres.--DeVlieg-Bullard Services Group, Rockford, IL; *U.S. Public*, pg. 502
Sappington, Donald, Pres. & Chief Exec. Officer--C.F. Hathaway, Waterville, ME; *U.S. Private*, pg. 510
Saquier, Julio, Dr., Pres.--La Nacion S.A., Buenos Aires, Argentina; *Int'l*, pg. 785
Sarcinelli, Mario, Chm. Bd.--Banca Nazionale del Lavoro Sj.A., Rome, Italy; *Int'l*, pg. 136
Sardina, Eduardo M., Pres.--Bacardi Service Corp., (North America), Coral Gables, FL; *Int'l*, pg. 131
Sardina, Eduardo M., Pres. & Chief Exec. Officer--Bacardi-Martini U.S.A., Inc., Miami, FL; *Int'l*, pg. 131
Sardina, Edvardo, Pres. & Chief Exec. Officer--Bacardi-Martini, USA, Inc., Miami, FL; *U.S. Private*, pg. 109
Sargent, Charles, Pres. & Chief Oper. Officer--Evans Industries, Inc., Detroit, MI; *U.S. Private*, pg. 385
Sargent, David K., Pres.--Up-Right, Inc., Selma, CA; *U.S. Private*, pg. 1128
Sargent, Henry B., Pres. & Chief Exec. Officer--El Dorado Investment Company, Phoenix, AZ; *U.S. Public*, pg. 1298
Sargent, John, Pres. & Chief Exec. Officer--DK Publishing, New York, NY; *Int'l*, pg. 417
Sargent, Joseph D., Pres. & Chief Exec. Officer--The Guardian Life Insurance Company of America, New York, NY; *U.S. Private*, pg. 486
Sargent, Joseph D., Pres.--The Guardian Insurance & Annuity Co. (GIAC), New York, NY; *U.S. Private*, pg. 486
Sargent, Lee M., Pres. & Chief Exec. Officer--Todd & Sargent, Inc., Ames, IA; *U.S. Private*, pg. 1089
Sargent, Stewart, Pres.--Monterey's Acquisition Corp., Houston, TX; *U.S. Private*, pg. 758
Sargent, Stuart, Pres.--Monterey's Acquisition Corporation, Houston, TX; *U.S. Private*, pg. 758
Sarin, Arun, Pres. & Chief Oper. Officer--AirTouch Communications, Inc., San Francisco, CA; *U.S. Public*, pg. 34
Sarkie, Robert M., Pres.--Entertainment Publications, Inc., Troy, MI; *U.S. Public*, pg. 320
Sarkisian, Norman,, Owner, Pres. & Chief Exec. Officer--Beacon Group, Bloomfield, CT; *U.S. Private*, pg. 126
Sarkisian, Robert, Chm. Bd., Pres. & Chief Exec. Officer--Marketing Displays International, Farmington Hills, MI; *U.S. Private*, pg. 705
Sarmiento, Antonio A., Chm. Bd., Pres. & Sec.--Lumas Realty, Inc., Miami, FL; *U.S. Private*, pg. 680
Sarner, Gary, Pres.--TLC, Milwaukee, WI; *U.S. Public*, pg. 352
Sarner, Gary R., Pres.--Martinique Holdings, San Diego, CA; *U.S. Public*, pg. 352
Sarno, Russell J., Pres.--Flo Control, Inc., Burbank, CA; *U.S. Private*, pg. 414
Sarnow, Greg, Pres.--American Television Time, Inc., Austin, TX; *U.S. Private*, pg. 63
Sarrat, Fernand B., Pres. & Chief Exec. Officer--Cylink Corp., Sunnyvale, CA; *U.S. Public*, pg. 1306
Sartain, James T., Pres. & Chief Oper. Officer--FirstCity Financial Corporation, Waco, TX; *U.S. Public*, pg. 644
Sasabe, Shogo, Pres.--Bando Chemical Industries, Ltd., Kobe, Japan; *Int'l*, pg. 145
Sasaki, Masaaki, Pres.--Kokusai Electric Co., Ltd. America, San Jose, CA; *Int'l*, pg. 743
Sasaki, Shunji, Pres.--ORIX Rentec Corporation, Tokyo, Japan; *Int'l*, pg. 1009
Sasaki, T., Pres.--Ebara (Thailand) Limited, Bangkok, Thailand; *Int'l*, pg. 432
Sasaki, T., Pres.--Nissho Iwai Delica Corp., Kawasaki, Japan; *Int'l*, pg. 946
Sasaki, Yoshio, Pres.--Kansai Paint Co., Ltd., Osaka, Japan; *Int'l*, pg. 723
Sasser, Stephen A., Pres. & Chief Oper. Officer--Symix Systems, Inc., Columbus, OH; *U.S. Public*, pg. 1546
Sastri, M.S., Pres.--Aluma Shield Industries, Inc., Daytona Beach, FL; *U.S. Private*, pg. 47
Satcher, James R., Pres. & Chief Exec. Officer--Southland Oil Company, Jackson, MS; *U.S. Private*, pg. 1018
Sato, Akinari, Pres.--Amano Korea Corporation, Seoul, Korea; *Int'l*, pg. 71
Sato, Hiroshi, Pres.--TDK Corporation, Tokyo, Japan; *Int'l*, pg. 1336
Sato, Isao, Pres. & Chief Exec. Officer--Hosokawa Micron International Inc., New York, NY; *Int'l*, pg. 635
Sato, Jun, Pres.--Showa Products Co., Ltd., Osaka, Japan; *U.S. Public*, pg. 1487
Sato, Ken, Pres.--Rohm Co., Ltd., Kyoto, Japan; *Int'l*, pg. 1124
Sato, Kozo, Pres.--Rohm Corporation, San Jose, CA; *Int'l*, pg. 1125
Sato, Kozo, Pres.--Rohm U.S.A., Inc., San Jose, CA; *Int'l*, pg. 1125
Sato, M., Pres.--Kobe Steel U.S.A. Inc. (New York), New York, NY; *Int'l*, pg. 740
Sato, Mitsuo, Chm. Bd. & Pres.--Asian Development Bank, Manila, Philippines; *Int'l*, pg. 88
Sato, Shigenori, Pres.--Nissho Iwai del Ecuador S.A., Quito, Ecuador; *Int'l*, pg. 948
Sato, Shigeruo, Pres.--Kabuto Decom Inc., Sapporo, Japan; *Int'l*, pg. 721
Sato, Takahisa, Pres.--ORIX Taiwan Corporation, Taipei, Taiwan; *Int'l*, pg. 1010
Sato, Takayoshi, Pres.--San-Jirushi, Kuwana, Japan; *Int'l*, pg. 1183
Sato, Takayoshi, Pres.--San-J Intl. Inc., Richmond, VA; *Int'l*, *pg. 1183*
Sato, Tsuguo, Pres.--Tokyu Agency International/DMB&B Japan, Tokyo, Japan; *U.S. Private*, pg. 305
Sato, Yasuhiko, Pres.--Heraeus Shin-Etsu America Inc., Camas, WA; *Int'l*, pg. 616
Sato, Yukio, Pres.--Yamaichi Bank (Switzerland), Zurich, Switzerland; *Int'l*, pg. 1517
Satoh, H., Pres.--Morganite Carbon Kabushiki Kaisha, Osaka, Japan; *Int'l*, pg. 892
Satoh, Hiroshi, Pres.--Tri Petch Isuzu Sales Co., Ltd., Bangkok, Thailand; *Int'l*, pg. 693
Satoh, Yasuhiro, Pres.--Kirin Brewery Co., Ltd., Tokyo, Japan; *Int'l*, pg. 735
Satre, Philip G., Chm. Bd., Pres. & Chief Exec. Officer--Harrah's Entertainment, Inc., Memphis, TN; *U.S. Public*, pg. 790
Satterfield, James, Pres.--United Capitol Insurance Company, Atlanta, GA; *U.S. Public*, pg. 685
Satterthwaite, Chris, Mng. Partner--Howell Henry Chaldecott Lury & Partners, London, United Kingdom; *Int'l*, pg. 637
Saubert, Walter E., Pres.--Red Ball Forwarders, Inc., Indianapolis, IN; *U.S. Private*, pg. 97
Saucer, Willie, Chm. Bd., Pres. & Chief Exec. Officer--Farmers Co-op Market Inc., Frisco City, AL; *U.S. Private*, *pg. 395*
Sauder, Maynard, Pres. & Chief Exec. Officer--Sauder Woodworking Co., Archbold, OH; *U.S. Private*, pg. 967
Sauer, Mark, Pres.--Pittsburgh Pirates, Pittsburgh, PA; *U.S. Private*, pg. 867
Sauey, Craig L., Pres. & Chief Exec. Officer--Flambeau Corporation, Baraboo, WI; *U.S. Private*, pg. 409
Sauey, Eric W., Pres. & Chief Oper. Officer--Seats Incorporated, Reedsburg, WI; *U.S. Private*, pg. 410
Sauey, Jason, Pres.--Duncan Toys Company, Middlefield, OH; *U.S. Private*, pg. 409
Sauey, Jason C., Pres. & Chief Oper. Officer--Flambeau Products Corp., Middlefield, OH; *U.S. Private*, pg. 409
Sauey, W.R., Chm. Bd., Pres. & Treas.--Flambeau Corporation, Baraboo, WI; *U.S. Private*, pg. 409
Saul, Bill, Pres.--Beach City Chevrolet Co., Long Beach, CA; *U.S. Private*, pg. 125
Saul, John, Pres.--Emcee Cellular, Inc., Wilmington, DE; *U.S. Public*, pg. 571
Saul, Julian, Pres.--Queen Carpet Corporation, Dalton, GA; *U.S. Private*, pg. 900
Saul, Neil, Pres.--Empire Industries, Inc., Tarboro, NC; *U.S. Public*, pg. 579
Saunders, Chip, Pres. & Dir.-Dell Computer K.K.--Dell Computer Japan, Kanagawa, Japan; *U.S. Public*, pg. 496
Saunders, Don, Pres. & V.P.--Epson Canada Limited, Willowdale, Canada; *Int'l*, pg. 1219
Saunders, Donald E., Pres.--DuBois Chemicals, Cincinnati, OH; *Int'l*, pg. 1437
Saunders, Neil, Pres.--Container Graphics Corporation, Cary, NC; *U.S. Private*, pg. 267
Saunders, Perry, Pres.--Harrington Hoists, Inc., Manheim, PA; *U.S. Private*, pg. 504
Saunders, Richard D., Pres. & Chief Exec. Officer--Kenetech Corp., San Francisco, CA; *U.S. Public*, pg. 950
Saunders, Robert F., Pres.--Amleco Leasing Limited, Stellarton, Canada; *Int'l*, pg. 454
Sautter, Remy, Pres. & Chief Exec. Officer--CLT-UFA, Luxembourg, Luxembourg; *Int'l*, pg. 561
Saux, Juan, Pres.--Park Advertising & Direct Marketing, Lima, Peru; *U.S. Private*, pg. 389
Savage, John E., Pres., Chief Oper. Officer, Co-Chief Exec. Officer & Sec.--Amwest Insurance Group, Inc., Calabasas, CA; *U.S. Public*, pg. 106
Savage, Peter P., Pres. & Chief Exec. Officer--Applied Digital Access, San Diego, CA; *U.S. Public*, pg. 122
Savaiano, N.J., Chm. Bd. & Pres.--United Laboratories, Inc., Saint Charles, IL; *U.S. Private*, pg. 1122
Savarese, Dr. Edward, Chm. Bd., Pres. & Chief Exec. Officer--Imaging Technologies Corp., San Diego, CA; *U.S. Public*, pg. 870
Savel, Bill, Pres. & Chief Exec. Officer--Alta-Dena Certified Dairy, City of Industry, CA; *Int'l*, pg. 201

Saviano, James P., Pres.--CSC Consulting Group, Waltham, MA; *U.S. Public*, pg. 422

Saviano, James P., Acting Pres.--Consulting & Systems Integration, Waltham, MA; *U.S. Public*, pg. 422

Saviers, F. Grant, Chm. Bd., Pres. & Chief Exec. Officer--Adaptec, Inc., Milpitas, CA; *U.S. Public*, pg. 19

Savistsky, Steven, Pres.--ATC Healthcare Services Inc., Atlanta, GA; *U.S. Private*, pg. 8

Savitske, Michael B., Pres. & Chief Exec. Officer--National-Standard Co., Niles, MI; *U.S. Public*, pg. 1160

Savitsky, Stephen, Chm. Bd., Pres. & Chief Exec. Officer--Staff Builders Inc., Lake Success, NY; *U.S. Public*, pg. 1501

Savitz, S. Alan, M.D., Pres.--PacifiCare Behavioral Health, Laguna Hills, CA; *U.S. Public*, pg. 1251

Savoie, Michael P., Sr., Pres.--Mike Savoie Chevrolet Inc., Troy, MI; *U.S. Private*, pg. 968

Savonen, Lasse, Pres.--Suomen Astra Oy, Masaby, Finland; *Int'l*, pg. 94

Sawa, Yasuhiro, Pres.--Dentsu Hokkaido, Sapporo, Japan; *Int'l*, pg. 393

Sawada, Hiroyki, Pres.--Tigers Polymer Corporation, Toyonaka, Japan; *Int'l*, pg. 1390

Sawamura, Shiko, Pres. & Chief Exec. Officer--Oki Electric Industry Company, Ltd., Tokyo, Japan; *Int'l*, pg. 999

Sawchuk, Arthur R., Chm. Bd., Pres. & Chief Exec. Officer--Du Pont Canada Inc., Mississauga, Canada; *U.S. Public*, pg. 532

Sawin, Craiges B., Chm. & Chief Exec. Officer--Drake Beam Morin, Inc., New York, NY; *U.S. Public*, pg. 783

Sawyer, David, Pres.--Tony Downs Foods Company, Saint James, MN; *U.S. Private*, pg. 342

Sawyer, Hugh, Pres.--National Linen & Uniform Service, Atlanta, GA; *U.S. Public*, pg. 1160

Sawyer, James E., Pres.--Boeing Canada Technology Ltd., Arnprior Division, Arnprior, Canada; *U.S. Public*, pg. 242

Sawyer, John, Pres.--Penhall International, Anaheim, CA; *U.S. Private*, pg. 849

Sawyer, Kenneth I., Chm. Bd., Pres. & Chief Exec. Officer--Pharmaceutical Resources, Spring Valley, NY; *U.S. Public*, pg. 1285

Sawyer, Linda, Mng. Partner & Gen. Mgr.--Deutsch, Inc., New York, NY; *U.S. Private*, pg. 328

Saxon, Ronald, Pres.--Ron Saxon Ford, Inc., Saint Paul, MN; *U.S. Private*, pg. 969

Saxton, Paul A., Chm. Bd., Pres. & Chief Exec. Officer--General Housewares Corp., Terre Haute, IN; *U.S. Public*, *pg. 715*

Saxton, Robert L., Pres.--APT Coin Machines, Inc., Las Vegas, NV; *U.S. Public*, pg. 47

Saydah, Richard, Pres.--Cecil Saydah Company, Los Angeles, CA; *U.S. Private*, pg. 969

Sayle, John G., Pres., Chief Exec. Officer & Treas.--The Hall China Company, East Liverpool, OH; *U.S. Private*, pg. 494

Sbarro, Mario, Chm. Bd. & Pres.--Sbarro, Inc., Commack, NY; *U.S. Public*, pg. 1435

Scalisi, Sam A., Jr., Pres. & Chief Exec. Officer--Regions Bank/Blount County, Oneonta, AL; *U.S. Public*, pg. 1372

Scalise, Joseph, Pres.--Smith-Edwards-Dunlap Company, Philadelphia, PA; *U.S. Private*, pg. 1007

Scanlan, John D., Vice Chm. & Exec. Pres.--Eatelcorp Inc., Gonzales, LA; *U.S. Private*, pg. 358

Scanlan, Thomas M., Jr., Pres.--The Ward Machinery Company, Hunt Valley, MD; *U.S. Private*, pg. 1149

Scannel, Herb, Pres.--Nickelodeon/Nick At Nite, New York, NY; *U.S. Private*, pg. 779

Scansaroli, John M., Pres.--Electrocatalytic, Inc., Union, NJ; *U.S. Private*, pg. 369

Scarbough, Steven, Pres.--Standard Pacific Corp., Costa Mesa, CA; *U.S. Public*, pg. 1503

Scarfe, Harry Jr., Pres.--North Electric Supply, Inc., Auburn Hills, MI; *U.S. Private*, pg. 805

Scariot, Terry G., Sr., Pres. & Chief Oper. Officer--Desa International, Bowling Green, KY; *U.S. Private*, pg. 326

Schachenmann, Max Andre, Chm. Bd. & Mng. Dir.--Pluess-Staufer AG, Oftringen, Switzerland; *Int'l*, pg. 1061

Schachter, William, Pres. & Chief Exec. Officer--CSI International Corporation, New York, NY; *U.S. Private*, pg. 197

Schack, Preben, Pres--Dagbladet Boersen A/S, Copenhagen, Denmark; *Int'l*, pg. 359

Schaedler, James D., Pres.--Schaedler Brothers, Inc., Harrisburg, PA; *U.S. Private*, pg. 969

Schaefer, George A., Jr., Chm. Bd., Pres. & Chief Exec. Offficer--Fifth Third Bancorp, Cincinnati, OH; *U.S. Public*, *pg. 621*

Schaefer, Gerard J., Pres.--Moss Telecommunications Services, Grand Rapids, MI; *U.S. Private*, pg. 763

Schaefer, Joy, Pres.--WFS Financial, Inc., Irvine, CA; *U.S. Public*, pg. 1757

Schaefer, Richard H., Pres.--Diebel Manufacturing Co., Morton Grove, IL; *U.S. Private*, pg. 331

Schaefer, Rowland, Chm. Bd., Pres. & Chief Exec. Officer-Claire's Stores--Claire's Stores Inc., Pembroke Pines, FL; *U.S. Public*, pg. 381

Schaeffer, Glenn, Pres. & Chief Fin. Officer--Circus Circus - Las Vegas, Las Vegas, NV; *U.S. Public*, pg. 374

Schaeffer, Leonard, Chm. Bd. & Chief Exec. Officer--Blue Cross of California, Woodland Hills, CA; *U.S. Private*, pg. 152

Schaeffer, Milo, Pres.--The BOC Group Inc. (Delaware), Murray Hill, NJ; *Int'l*, pg. 121

Schaeffer, Scott, Pres.--Plibrico Co., Chicago, IL; *U.S. Private*, pg. 872

Schaeffer, Scott F., Sr. V.P.-Real Estate & Pres.-Resource Properties, Inc.--Resource America, Inc., Philadelphia, PA; *U.S. Public*, pg. 1382

Schafer, C.J., Pres.--Lockheed Martin Tactical Defense Systems (Akron), Akron, OH; *U.S. Public*, pg. 1009

Schafer, Glenn S., Pres.--Pacific Life Insurance Company, Newport Beach, CA; *U.S. Private*, pg. 831

Schaffer, Ian, Pres.--Gordon & Ferguson of Delaware, Inc., Plymouth, MN; *U.S. Private*, pg. 465

Schaffer, Peter, Pres.--Case Paper Co., Inc., Long Island City, NY; *U.S. Private*, pg. 218

Schaffner, Roger A., Pres.--Palisades Media Group, Inc., Santa Monica, CA; *U.S. Private*, pg. 834

Schank, John W., Pres.--Spirit Energy 76, Sugar Land, TX; *U.S. Public*, pg. 1698

Schar, Dwight, Chm. Bd. & Chief Exec. Officer--NVR, Inc., Mc Lean, VA; *U.S. Public*, pg. 1148

Schara, Charles G., Pres.--Criterion Life Insurance Co., Washington, DC; *U.S. Public*, pg. 219

Schardt, Ronald, Chm. Bd., Chief Exec. Officer & Chief Oper. Officer--Reinke Manufacturing Co., Inc., Deshler, NE; *U.S. Private*, pg. 920

Scharf, Michael J., Chm. Bd., Pres. & Chief Exec. Officer--Niagara Corporation, New York, NY; *U.S. Public*, pg. 1181

Scharlau, Charles E., Chm. Bd. & Pres.--Southwestern Energy Production Co., Houston, TX; *U.S. Public*, pg. 1494

Scharlau, Charles E., Chm. Bd & Pres.--Arkansas Western Pipeline Company, Fayetteville, AR; *U.S. Public*, pg. 1494

Schasers, Walter, Pres.--PKL Verpackungssysteme GmbH, Linnich, Germany; *Int'l*, pg. 1020

Schatteman, S., Pres. & Chief Exec. Officer--PNC Bank, Ohio National Assoc., Fort Mitchell, KY; *U.S. Public*, pg. 1243

Schatteman, S., Pres. & Chief Exec. Officer--PNC Bank, Northern Kentucky, Union, KY; *U.S. Public*, pg. 1243

Schatz, Douglas S., Pres. & Chief Exec. Officer--Advanced Energy Industry, Fort Collins, CO; *U.S. Public*, pg. 20

Schauer, Ronald L., Chm. Bd., Pres. & Chief Exec. Officer--HMT Technology Corporation, Fremont, CA; *U.S. Public*, pg. 771

Schauerman, Chris L., Pres. & Chief Exec. Officer--Capital Lending Services, Inc., Roswell, GA; *U.S. Private*, pg. 206

Schaufeld, Fred, Chm. Bd., Pres. & Chief Exec. Officer--National Electronics Warranty Corporation, Sterling, VA; *U.S. Private*, pg. 782

Schawk, David A., Pres. & Chief Exec. Officer--Schawk, Inc., Des Plaines, IL; *U.S. Public*, pg. 1437

Scheafer, David, Pres. & Chief Exec. Officer--Lynx Golf, Inc., City of Industry, CA; *U.S. Private*, pg. 684

Schear, Mitchell, Pres.--The Kaempfer Company, Investment Builders, Washington, DC; *U.S. Private*, pg. 604

Scheerer, William J., Pres.--Harmon Industries-Jacksonville, Jacksonville, FL; *U.S. Public*, pg. 788

Scheessele, John R., Pres.--WHX Corporation, New York, NY; *U.S. Public*, pg. 1726

Scheffer, Jeffrey R., Pres.--American Drew, Greensboro, NC; *U.S. Public*, pg. 974

Scheiber, Patrice, Pres. & Chief Oper. Officer--I.C. System, Inc., Vadnais Heights, MN; *U.S. Private*, pg. 553

Scheid, Dr. Erich Mittelsten, Pres.-Advisory Bd.--Vorwerk & Co., Wuppertal, Germany; *Int'l*, pg. 1480

Scheideler, Albert, Chm. Bd., Pres. & Chief Exec. Officer--McNally Industries, Inc., Grantsburg, WI; *U.S. Private*, pg. 724

Scheinkman, Steven W., Co-Pres.--Ferro Union, Inc., Torrance, CA; *U.S. Private*, pg. 402

Scheinkman, Steven W., Pres., Chief Fin. Officer & Mng. Dir.--Samsteel, Inc., Torrance, CA; *U.S. Private*, pg. 402

Scheinman, Tom, Pres.--New York Water Service Corp., Merrick, NY; *U.S. Private*, pg. 993

Scheinman, Tom, Pres. & Chief Exec. Officer--The Unimax Corporation, New York, NY; *U.S. Private*, pg. 1118

Schelfhaudt, Peter, Partner & Chief Fin. Officer--Earle Palmer Brown Public Relations, New York, NY; *U.S. Private*, pg. 174

Schelle, Rolf, Pres.--Filterwerk Mann & Hummel GmbH, Marklkofen, Germany; *Int'l*, pg. 484

Schemmer, Neil, Pres. & Chief Exec. Officer--Security National Bank & Trust Co. of Norman, Norman, OK; *U.S. Public*, pg. 630

Schengili, Josef, Pres. & Chief Exec. Officer--Numetrix Ltd., Toronto, Canada; *Int'l*, pg. 990

Schenian, Dale, Pres.--McClain Easy Pack, Galion, OH; *U.S. Public*, pg. 1065

Schenk, Douglas, Pres. & Chief Exec. Officer--Maui Pineapple Co., Ltd., Kahului, HI; *U.S. Public*, pg. 1060

Schenk, Greg F., Chm. Bd. & Pres.--Cookie Tree Inc., Salt Lake City, UT; *U.S. Private*, pg. 273

Schenk, James M., Pres.--BellSouth Financial Services Corporation, Atlanta, GA; *U.S. Public*, pg. 209

Schenk, P. Edward, Chm. Bd., Pres. & Chief Exec. Officer--Rymer Foods Inc., Chicago, IL; *U.S. Public*, pg. 1414

Schenk, P.E., Jr., Pres.--Rymer Meat Inc., Chicago, IL; *U.S. Public*, pg. 1414

Scher, Gilbert, Co-Pres. & Creative Dir.--EURO RSCG Scher, Lefarge, Levallois-Perret, France; *Int'l*, pg. 601

Scherer, Gilbert, Pres.--American Passage Media Corporation, Seattle, WA; *U.S. Private*, pg. 60

Scherer, John, Pres. & Owner--Berlin Glove Company Ltd., Berlin, WI; *U.S. Private*, pg. 136

Scherer, John, Pres. & Owner--Mid-Western, Berlin, WI; *U.S. Private*, pg. 136

Scherer, Karl, Pres.--Intrafin S.A., Zug, Switzerland; *U.S. Public*, pg. 256

Scherer, Michael J., Pres.--Starcraft Automotive Group, Inc., Goshen, IN; *U.S. Public*, pg. 1511

Scherer, Peter, Pres. & Chief Exec. Officer--Scherer Bros. Lumber Company, Minneapolis, MN; *U.S. Private*, pg. 970

Scherer, Robert P., Jr., Chm. Bd. & Chief Exec. Officer--Vital Signs, Englewood, CO; *U.S. Public*, pg. 1723

Scherr, Ted, Pres. & Gen. Mgr.--Dakota Drug, Inc., Minot, ND; *U.S. Private*, pg. 308

Scherzer, D. J., Pres. & Chief Exec. Officer--NMI Corporation, Dallas, TX; *Int'l*, pg. 900

Scheuing, Eckart, Pres.--Robert Bosch Inc., Mississauga, Canada; *Int'l*, pg. 205

Scheurer, John M., Pres. & Chief Oper. Officer--Allied Capital Commercial Corporation, Washington, DC; *U.S. Public*, pg. 47

Scheuring, G.J., Pres. & Chief Exec. Officer--Midlantic Bank, N.A., Edison, NJ; *U.S. Public*, pg. 1242

Scheuring, Garry, Chm. Bd., Pres. & Chief Exec. Officer--Midlantic Bank, N.A., Philadelphia, PA; *U.S. Public*, pg. 1242

Schiano, Tony, Pres. & Chief Oper. Officer--Edwards Super Food Stores, Carlisle, PA; *Int'l*, pg. 749

Schiavone, Phillip, Pres. & Chief Exec. Officer--E.W. Howell Company, Inc., Port Washington, NY; *Int'l*, pg. 995

Schiavoni, Vince, Pres.--Duraloy Technologies, Scottdale, PA; *U.S. Private*, pg. 839

Schiavoni, Vince, Pres.--Electro Alloys, Elyria, OH; *U.S. Private*, pg. 839

Schibuola, Dino, Pres. & Chief Exec. Officer--Costa Cruise Lines, N.V., Miami, FL; *U.S. Private*, pg. 278

Schichtel, Gerald F., Pres. & Chief Oper. Officer--Hilliard Corporation, Elmira, NY; *U.S. Private*, pg. 530

Schiciano, Jason C., Pres.--The Coon-De Visser Co., Royal Oak, MI; *U.S. Private*, pg. 273

Schieman, L. Richard, Chm. Bd., Pres., Chief Exec. Officer & Chief Oper. Officer--Hughes-Peters, Inc., Cincinnati, OH; *U.S. Private*, pg. 546

Schiera, Richard, Sr. Principal & Grp. Creative Dir.--Publicis/Bloom, Dallas, TX; *Int'l*, pg. 469

Schiever, David, Pres.--Wyse Direct, Cleveland, OH; *U.S. Private*, pg. 1194

Schiewetz, Richard F., Pres.--Primus Inc., Dayton, OH; *U.S. Private*, pg. 884

Schifter, Craig R., Pres.--Squire-Cogswell Company, Gurnee, IL; *U.S. Private*, pg. 1027

Schikorra, G.E., P.E., Pres. & Chief Exec. Officer--Jagenberg, Inc., Enfield, CT; *Int'l*, pg. 1108

Schild, Harold, Pres. & Chief Exec. Officer--Tillamook County Creamery Assn., Tillamook, OR; *U.S. Private*, pg. 1086

Schiller, Harvey W., Pres.--Turner Sports, Inc., Atlanta, GA; *U.S. Public*, pg. 1615

Schiller, Jo Anne, Pres.--Everyday Learning/Creative Publications Group, Chicago, IL; *U.S. Public*, pg. 1635

Schiller, Leonard M., Owner & Dir.-Acq.--The Dearborn Group, Chicago, IL; *U.S. Private*, pg. 319

Schilling, Ernie, Pres. & Chief Exec. Officer--Powell Electronics Inc., Philadelphia, PA; *U.S. Private*, pg. 877

Schilling, Theodor, Pres.--Knurr-Interplast GmbH, Bremen, Germany; *Int'l*, pg. 739

Schilt, Chris, Pres. & Publr.--The Albany Herald Publishing Co., Inc., Albany, GA; *U.S. Public*, pg. 759

Schimberg, Henry A., Pres. & Chief Oper. Officer--Coca-Cola Enterprises Inc., Atlanta, GA; *U.S. Public*, pg. 393

Schimkaitis, John R., Pres. & Chief Oper. Officer--Chesapeake Utilities Corporation, Dover, DE; *U.S. Public*, *pg. 347*

Schimmelbusch, Heinz, Ph.D., Pres. & Chief Exec. Officer--Safeguard International Group, Wayne, PA; *U.S. Public*, pg. 1424

Schindler, Andrew J., Pres. & Chief Exec. Officer-RJR Nabisco--R.J. Reynolds Tobacco Company, Winston Salem, NC; *U.S. Public*, pg. 1355

Schindler, Jeorg, Mng. Dir.--Ragolds Susswaren GmbH & Co., Karlsruhe, Germany; *Int'l*, pg. 1084

Schindler, Ralph, Pres.--Chicago Fire Brick Co., Chicago, IL; *U.S. Private*, pg. 194

Schini, Thomas W., Chm. Bd., Pres. & Chief Exec. Officer--First Federal Capital Corp., La Crosse, WI; *U.S. Public*, pg. 632

Schinler, Richard J., Pres. & Chief Exec. Officer--Integrity Mutual Insurance Company, Appleton, WI; *U.S. Private*, pg. 566

Schirmang, William A., Pres. & Treas.--Skokie Valley Beverage Co., Wheeling, IL; *U.S. Private*, pg. 1005

Schlackman, Neil, M.D., Pres.--U.S. Quality Algorithms, Inc., Blue Bell, PA; *U.S. Public*, pg. 27

Schlagenhauf, Paul, Pres.--Badger Truck Center, Inc., Milwaukee, WI; *U.S. Private*, pg. 110

Schlanger, Richard, Co-Pres. & Sec.--West Shore Envelope Company, Inc., New York, NY; *U.S. Private*, pg. 1163

Schlatter, Donald A., Pres., Chief Exec. Officer & Gen. Counsel--Art Iron, Inc., Toledo, OH; *U.S. Private*, pg. 86

Schlatter, Hans R., Chm. Bd. & Pres.--H.A. Schlatter AG, Schlieren, Switzerland; *Int'l*, pg. 1205

Schlegel, David M., Pres.--Envirco Corporation, Albuquerque, NM; *U.S. Public*, pg. 1639

Schlesinger, Alan, Chm. Bd., Pres. & Chief Exec. Officer--Lamonts Apparel, Inc., Kirkland, WA; *U.S. Public*, pg. 975

Schlesinger, Peter, Mng. Dir.--ABG Allgemeine Baumaschinen-Gesellschaft mbH, Hameln, Germany; *U.S. Public*, pg. 877

Schlesinger, Vicki, Sr. Partner & Exec. V.P.--Fleishman-Hillard Inc., Saint Louis, MO; *U.S. Private*, pg. 411

Schlessman, Gary, Pres.--Greeley Gas Co., Denver, CO; *U.S. Public*, pg. 145

Schleyer, Robert J., Pres.--United Casualty Insurance Company of America, Chicago, IL; *U.S. Public*, pg. 1694

Schleyer, Robert J., Pres.--United Insurance Company of America, Schiller Park, IL; *U.S. Public*, pg. 1694

Schlichfting, H., Reg. Pres.--Melitta Hong Kong Ltd., Hong Kong, Hong Kong; *Int'l*, pg. 857

Schlicht, Robert A., Pres. & Chief Oper. Officer--M & I Madison Bank, Madison, WI; *U.S. Public*, pg. 1050

Schllig, Christian, Publisher--Coward-McCann, Inc., New York, NY; *Int'l*, pg. 1027

Schlosser, Carl, Pres.--Salant Childrens Apparel Group, New York, NY; *U.S. Public*, pg. 1429

Schlotfeldt, Walter, Pres. & Chief Exec. Officer--Badger Air Brush Company, Franklin Park, IL; *U.S. Private*, pg. 110

Schlott, Jack, Pres.--Warren Distribution, Inc., Omaha, NE; *U.S. Private*, pg. 1151

Schlotterbeck, David L., Pres. & Chief Oper. Officer--Pacific Scientific Company, Newport Beach, CA; *U.S. Public*, pg. 1250

Schlussel, Edward, Pres.--Apex Mills Corporation, Inwood, NY; *U.S. Private*, pg. 77
Schluter, Andreas S., Pres.--Deutsche Babcock Industrie und Systemtechnik AG, Oberhausen, Germany; *Int'l*, pg. 399
Schmedding, Gary N., Pres.--New Mexico Broadcasting Co., Albuquerque, NM; *U.S. Public*, pg. 984
Schmeider, Luke R., Pres., Treas. & Chief Exec. Officer--Mesa Laboratories, Inc., Wheat Ridge, CO; *U.S. Public*, pg. 1099
Schmelzer, Jim, Pres.-Distribution--Coolidge Glass Co., Inc., Waukesha, WI; *U.S. Private*, pg. 273
Schmermund, William H., Pres.--The Sawtooth Group, Woodbridge, NJ; *U.S. Private*, pg. 969
Schmid, Hans, Mng. Dir.--GGK Wien Werbeagentur GmbH, Vienna, Austria; *Int'l*, pg. 1336
Schmid, Howard G., Pres.--Nodak Mutual Insurance Company, Fargo, ND; *U.S. Private*, pg. 800
Schmidheiny, Thomas, Chm. Bd. & Pres.--Holderbank Financiere Glaris Ltd., Glaris, Switzerland; *Int'l*, pg. 628
Schmidt-Menschner, K., Pres.--Bayer B.V., Mijdrecht, Netherlands; *Int'l*, pg. 175
Schmidt, Arnold, Pres.--Bay Industries Inc., Green Bay, WI; *U.S. Private*, pg. 124
Schmidt, Bjarne Th., Pres.--a.s. Norsk Leca, Oslo, Norway; *Int'l*, pg. 1200
Schmidt, G. Gerry, Chm. Bd. & Pres.--Pacific Handy Cutter, Inc., Costa Mesa, CA; *U.S. Private*, pg. 831
Schmidt, G. Gerry, Chm. Bd. & Pres.--Spectrum Razor Tools, Costa Mesa, CA; *U.S. Private*, pg. 831
Schmidt, J. Stephen, Pres.--American Commonwealth Management Services Company, Inc., Hershey, PA; *U.S. Public*, pg. 95
Schmidt, John, Co-Pres.--October Films, Inc., New York, NY; *Int'l*, pg. 1216
Schmidt, Ken, Pres.--Xerox Imaging Systems, Inc., Palo Alto, CA; *U.S. Public*, pg. 1785
Schmidt, Larry, Pres. & Chief Oper. Officer--Coca-Cola Bottling Co. of Elizabethtown, Elizabethtown, KY; *U.S. Private*, pg. 248
Schmidt, Marcus, Pres. & Chief Exec. Officer--Atlas Tool Inc., Roseville, MI; *U.S. Private*, pg. 97
Schmidt, Martin, Partner--Media First International, Inc., New York, NY; *U.S. Private*, pg. 726
Schmidt, Oscar, Dir. General--Metropolitan Life Seguros de Vida, S.A., Buenos Aires, Argentina; *U.S. Private*, pg. 738
Schmidt, Peter, Pres.--Klockner Stadler Hurter, Ltd., Montreal, Canada; *Int'l*, pg. 1081
Schmidt, Peter G., Pres. & Chief Exec. Officer--Marine Construction & Design Co., Seattle, WA; *U.S. Private*, pg. 703
Schmidt, Pierre, Pres.--Bongard, Holtzheim, France; *Int'l*, pg. 570
Schmidt, Richard K., Ph.D., Pres. & Chief Exec. Officer--Aquarion Company, Bridgeport, CT; *U.S. Public*, pg. 126
Schmidt, Rob T., Pres.--Canadian American Railroad Company, Bangor, ME; *U.S. Private*, pg. 575
Schmidt, Robert, Pres. & Chief Exec. Officer--M & I Mid-State Bank, Stevens Point, WI; *U.S. Public*, pg. 1050
Schmidt, Robert H., Pres.--Dreyfus Service Corp., New York, NY; *U.S. Public*, pg. 1085
Schmidt, Robert T., Pres. & Chief Exec. Officer--Iron Road Railways Inc., Washington, DC; *U.S. Private*, pg. 575
Schmidt, Ronald, Pres. & Chief Exec. Officer--I.B. Diffusion, LP, Chicago, IL; *U.S. Private*, pg. 553
Schmidt, Uwe, Pres. & Chief Exec. Officer--Olympic Continental Resources, LLC, Pepper Pike, OH; *U.S. Public*, pg. 1221
Schmidt, Waldemar, Pres. & Chief Exec. Officer--ISS-International Service System A/S, Holte, Denmark; *Int'l*, pg. 656
Schmidt, Wayne L., Pres. & Gen. Mgr.--Rubbermaid Healthcare Products, Newark, NJ; *U.S. Public*, pg. 1411
Schmidtgall, William H., Chm. Bd., Pres., Chief Exec. Officer & Chief Oper. Officer--DMI, Inc., Goodfield, IL; *U.S. Private*, pg. 305
Schmieding, Lawrence H., Pres.--Schmieding Enterprises Inc., Springdale, AR; *U.S. Private*, pg. 971
Schmitt, Andrew, Pres. & Chief Exec. Officer--Layne Christenson Co., Mission Woods, KS; *U.S. Public*, pg. 981
Schmitt, Andrew, Pres.--Christensen Products, Salt Lake City, UT; *U.S. Public*, pg. 981
Schmitt, Edward A., Pres. & Chief Oper. Officer--Georgia Gulf Corporation, Atlanta, GA; *U.S. Public*, pg. 734
Schmitt, F., Pres.--Filter Media, Lyon, France; *Int'l*, pg. 636
Schmitt, Mike, Pres.--Richards Industries Metalworking Group, Cincinnati, OH; *U.S. Private*, pg. 929
Schmitt, Thomas M., Pres. & Chief Exec. Officer--Paul A. Schmitt Music Company, Minneapolis, MN; *U.S. Private*, pg. 971
Schmitz, Hank, Pres.--Victory Refrigeration Co. LC, Cherry Hill, NJ; *U.S. Private*, pg. 1139
Schmitz, Werner, Pres.--Deutz Corporation, Norcross, GA; *Int'l*, pg. 408
Schnabel, Brian T., Pres. & Chief Exec. Officer--Elmer's Products, Inc., Columbus, OH; *U.S. Private*, pg. 158
Schnabel, James, Chm. Bd., Pres. & Chief Exec. Officer--Sun Electric, Lincolnshire, IL; *U.S. Public*, pg. 1480
Schnackel, Jay, Pres.--Greer Steel Co., Dover, OH; *U.S. Private*, pg. 479
Schneeberger, Donald G., Pres. & Chief Oper. Officer--H.C. Miller Company, Milwaukee, WI; *U.S. Private*, pg. 747
Schneider, Albert, Pres.--Schneider Mills, Inc., New York, NY; *U.S. Private*, pg. 971
Schneider, Bruce, Pres. & Chief Exec. Officer--Future Foam, Inc., Council Bluffs, IA; *U.S. Private*, pg. 433
Schneider, Charles R., Pres. & Chief Exec. Officer--U.S. Security Associates, Inc., Roswell, GA; *U.S. Private*, pg. 1126
Schneider, Donald J., Pres.--Schneider National, Inc., Green Bay, WI; *U.S. Private*, pg. 971
Schneider, Francis, Pres.--GTL Truck Lines, Inc., Norfolk, NE; *U.S. Public*, pg. 1152
Schneider, Frank, Pres.--Plastag Corporation, Elk Grove Village, IL; *U.S. Private*, pg. 870
Schneider, Joseph, Pres.--Madison Electric Co., Warren, MI; *U.S. Private*, pg. 694
Schneider, Lee, Pres.--Commonwealth Toy & Novelty Company, New York, NY; *U.S. Private*, pg. 258
Schneider, Milton, Pres. & Chief Exec. Officer--I. Appel Corporation, New York, NY; *U.S. Private*, pg. 78
Schneider, Norbert, Pres.--The Fuller Brush Company, Great Bend, KS; *U.S. Public*, pg. 282
Schneider, Norbert J., Pres.--The Fuller Brush Company, Great Bend, KS; *U.S. Public*, pg. 282
Schneider, Ronald E., Chm. Bd., Pres. & Chief Exec. Officer--First National Bank in Cleburne, Cleburne, TX; *U.S. Public*, pg. 633
Schneider, Steven L., Pres. & Chief Exec. Officer--Trion, Inc., Sanford, NC; *U.S. Public*, pg. 1639
Schneider, William, Pres.--Schneider's Dairy, Inc., Pittsburgh, PA; *U.S. Private*, pg. 971
Schneiderman, David, Pres. & Publr.--VV Publishing Corp., New York, NY; *U.S. Private*, pg. 1131
Schneier, Lance W., Pres.--Enron Acess, Dublin, OH; *U.S. Public*, pg. 584
Schnell, Lloyd J., Pres.--Imasco Finance L.L.C., Wilmington, DE; *Int'l*, pg. 112
Schneuwly, Peter, Pres. & Chief Exec. Officer--UMS Swiss Metalworks Holding Ltd, Dornach, Switzerland; *Int'l*, pg. 1427
Schnitzer, Kenneth L., Jr., Pres.--Park Place Motorcars, Ltd., Dallas, TX; *U.S. Private*, pg. 840
Schnoppe, J. Thomas, Pres.--Foster Wheeler Facilities Management, Inc., Clinton, NJ; *U.S. Public*, pg. 677
Schnuck, Scott, Pres. & Chief Oper. Officer--Schnuck Markets, Inc., Saint Louis, MO; *U.S. Private*, pg. 971
Schockemoehl, Gene F., Pres.--Braden Manufacturing Co., Tulsa, OK; *U.S. Public*, pg. 924
Schoeck, Clyde C., Pres.--Modern Woodmen of America, Rock Island, IL; *U.S. Private*, pg. 755
Schoeffler, Michael H., Pres. & Chief Oper. Officer--Starcraft Corporation, Goshen, IN; *U.S. Public*, pg. 1510
Schoeller, Monika, Pres.--S. Fischer Verlag GmbH, Frankfurt/Main, Germany; *Int'l*, pg. 1478
Schoenecker, Guy, Pres. & Chief Exec. Officer--Schoeneckers, Inc., Minneapolis, MN; *U.S. Private*, pg. 971
Schoeneman, Herbert M., Pres.--Schoeneman Brothers Company, Sioux Falls, SD; *U.S. Private*, pg. 972
Schoenfeld, Jeffry A., Partner-Institutional--Brown Brothers Harriman & Co., New York, NY; *U.S. Private*, pg. 173
Schoenhals, Marvin N., Chm. Bd., Pres. & Chief Exec. Officer--WSFS Financial Corporation, Wilmington, DE; *U.S. Public*, pg. 1728
Schoeniger, Terrence, Pres., Gen. Counsel & Asst. Treas.--Safety National Casualty Corp., Saint Louis, MO; *U.S. Public*, pg. 496
Schoenwitz, Frank, Pres. & Chief Exec. Officer--Weldun International, Inc., Bridgman, MI; *Int'l*, pg. 205
Schoettert, J., Pres.--J & F Steel Corporation, Chicago, IL; *Int'l*, pg. 79
Schofield, Philip W., Gen. Mgr.--Fiber Optic Products Division, Chicago, IL; *U.S. Public*, pg. 1101
Scholl, Hermann, Chm.-Mgmnt. Bd. & Pres.--Robert Bosch GmbH, Gerlingen, Germany; *Int'l*, pg. 203
Scholl, Thomas, Pres. & Chief Exec. Officer--Scholls Inc., Arden Hills, MN; *U.S. Private*, pg. 972
Scholler, Ray, Pres. & Chief Exec. Officer--Times Printing Company, Inc., Random Lake, WI; *U.S. Private*, pg. 1087
Schollmaier, Edgar H., Chm. Bd., Pres. & Chief Exec. Officer--Alcon Laboratories, Inc., Fort Worth, TX; *Int'l*, pg. 916
Scholobhm, Roy, Pres.--National Corset Supply House, Los Angeles, CA; *U.S. Private*, pg. 781
Scholtz, Ed, Pres. & Chief Exec. Officer--The Murray Ohio Mfg. Co., Brentwood, TN; *Int'l*, pg. 1397
Schomaker, Hans-Peter, Pres.--Reckitt & Colman S.A., Massy, France; *Int'l*, pg. 1090
Schomer, William P., Pres.--Allied Chucker & Engineering Company, Jackson, MI; *U.S. Private*, pg. 38
Schonmeier, Manfred, Pres. & Chief Exec. Officer--F.W. Woolworth GmbH Co. (Germany), Frankfurt/Main, Germany; *U.S. Public*, pg. 1778
Schoonyoung, Frank, Pres. & Gen. Mgr.-Industrial Yeast North America--Fleischmann's Yeast, Fenton, MO; *Int'l*, pg. 237
Schoonyoung, Frank, Pres.--Crompton & Knowles Ingredient Technology Corp., Mahwah, NJ; *U.S. Public*, pg. 459
Schori, Ueli, Pres.--EMTEC Magnetics (Schweiz) GmbH, Waedenswil, Switzerland; *Int'l*, pg. 743
Schorling, Thomas, Pres.--EG & G Astrophysics, Long Beach, CA; *U.S. Public*, pg. 543
Schornack, Paul, Pres.--Snappy Air Distribution Products, Detroit Lakes, MN; *U.S. Public*, pg. 1506
Schorr, Howell S., Pres.--First Choice, Deer Park, NY; *U.S. Public*, pg. 978
Schorr, Marc D., Pres.--Treasure Island, Corp., Las Vegas, NV; *U.S. Public*, pg. 1117
Schott, Michael, Pres.--Schott Brothers, Inc., Perth Amboy, NJ; *U.S. Private*, pg. 972
Schott, Owen W., Pres. & Chief Exec. Officer--Schott Corporation, Wayzata, MN; *U.S. Private*, pg. 972
Schottenstein, Saul, Pres.--Schottenstein Stores Corporation, Columbus, OH; *U.S. Private*, pg. 972
Schottland, Peter, Pres.--American Packaging Corporation, Rochester, NY; *U.S. Private*, pg. 60
Schottland, Steve B., Chm. Bd. & Pres.--American Packaging Corporation, Philadelphia, PA; *U.S. Private*, pg. 60
Schottler, Hans-Peter, Joint Pres.--Kohler Interconsult GmbH, Elmshorn, Germany; *Int'l*, pg. 1420
Schowe, Carlton P., Pres.--IMI Systems Inc., Melville, NY; *U.S. Public*, pg. 1221
Schrader, Bob, Pres.--TACTech, Inc., Yorba Linda, CA; *U.S. Public*, pg. 1792
Schrader, Robert E., Chm. Bd., Pres. & Chief Exec. Officer--Zing Technologies, Inc., Valhalla, NY; *U.S. Public*, pg. 1792
Schrader, Thomas F., Pres. & Chief Oper. Officer--WICOR, Inc., Milwaukee, WI; *U.S. Public*, pg. 1767
Schrader, Thomas F., Pres. & Chief Exec. Officer--Wisconsin Gas Company, Milwaukee, WI; *U.S. Public*, pg. 1767
Schrader, William, Pres.--Salt River Project Agricultural Improvement and Power District, Tempe, AZ; *U.S. Private*, pg. 962
Schraeder, Robert, Pres.--WFI International, Inc., Houston, TX; *U.S. Private*, pg. 1144
Schrag, W. Fred, Pres.--Olander & Brophy, Inc., Monroeville, PA; *U.S. Public*, pg. 847
Schrage, D. C., Pres. & Partner--Brown Marketing Communications, Chicago, IL; *U.S. Private*, pg. 174
Schrager, Harley, Pres. & Chief Oper. Officer--Pacesetter Corporation, Omaha, NE; *U.S. Private*, pg. 830
Schram, John, Pres.--Silver Burdett Ginn, Parsippany, NJ; *U.S. Private*, pg. 778
Schramm, Howard M., Jr., Chm. Bd. & Pres.--Turner Supply Company, Mobile, AL; *U.S. Private*, pg. 1110
Schrank, Mike, Pres.--Walser Automotive Group, Bloomington, MN; *U.S. Private*, pg. 1148
Schraufnagel, Harland, Pres.--Abbyland Foods, Inc., Abbotsford, WI; *U.S. Private*, pg. 10
Schreck, Richard H., Pres. & Chief Oper. Officer--Hofmann Industries, Inc., Sinking Spring, PA; *U.S. Private*, pg. 533
Schreiber, Michael, Pres.--Royal Farms Inc., Brooklyn, NY; *U.S. Private*, pg. 948
Schreiber, Raymond G., Pres.--H & D Steel Service, Inc., Cleveland, OH; *U.S. Private*, pg. 489
Schreiber, Richard, Partner--Dimeling, Schreiber & Park, Philadelphia, PA; *U.S. Private*, pg. 333
Schreier, Bradley, Pres. & Chief Oper. Officer--Taylor Corporation, Mankato, MN; *U.S. Private*, pg. 1070
Schreiner, Dan, Pres.--Kaufman and Broad Mortgage Co., Woodland Hills, CA; *U.S. Public*, pg. 945
Schreiner, Richard, Pres.--Fluid Regulators Co., Painesville, OH; *U.S. Public*, pg. 594
Schremp, John, Pres.--Firestone Synthetic Rubber & Latex Co., Akron, OH; *Int'l*, pg. 214
Schreuder, Donald L., Pres. & Chief Exec. Officer--Harding Lawson Associates Group, Inc., Novato, CA; *U.S. Public*, pg. 785
Schriber, Thomas L., Pres.--Donahue Schriber, Newport Beach, CA; *Int'l*, pg. 253
Schrickel, Patrick D., Pres. & Chief Oper. Officer--Wisconsin Public Service Corporation, Green Bay, WI; *U.S. Public*, pg. 1728
Schrier, Eric, Pres.--Time Inc. Health, New York, NY; *U.S. Public*, pg. 1613
Schrier, Eric, Pres. & Chief Exec. Officer--Time Inc. Health, San Francisco, CA; *U.S. Public*, pg. 1613
Schrimpf, Bill, Pres. & Controller--Piasa Motor Fuels Inc., Hartford, IL; *U.S. Private*, pg. 864
Schroder, Johan, Pres. & Chief Exec. Officer--Radiometer A/S, Bronshoj, Denmark; *Int'l*, pg. 1083
Schroeder, Christian, Co-Owner & Pres.--Select Communications, L.P., New York, NY; *U.S. Private*, pg. 982
Schroeder, Frank C., Pres.--First Maryland Intl. Banking Corp., York, PA; *Int'l*, pg. 64
Schroeder, Haus-Ulrich, Pres. & Chief Exec. Officer--Ascom Holding AG, Bern, Switzerland; *Int'l*, pg. 86
Schroeder, Kenneth L., Pres. & Chief Oper. Officer--KLA Tencor Corporation, San Jose, CA; *U.S. Public*, pg. 939
Schroeder, Manfred F., Pres. & Chief Exec. Officer--VAW of America, Inc., Ellenville, NY; *Int'l*, pg. 1466
Schroeder, Poul, Pres.--Finagrain, Cie Commerciale Agricole et Financiere S.A., Geneva, Switzerland; *U.S. Private*, pg. 268
Schroeder, Richard, Pres.--Cresline Plastic Pipe Co. Inc., Evansville, IN; *U.S. Private*, pg. 289
Schroeder, Richard H., Pres. & Chief Oper. Officer--Harken Energy Corporation, Irving, TX; *U.S. Public*, pg. 785
Schroeder, Steven B., Pres.--Atlas Refinery, Newark, NJ; *U.S. Private*, pg. 96
Schroeder, William, Pres.--Excel Co-Op Inc., Monticello, IN; *U.S. Private*, pg. 387
Schroeder, William J., Pres. & Chief Exec. Officer--Diamond Multimedia Systems, Inc., San Jose, CA; *U.S. Public*, pg. 505
Schroepfer, Mark T., Pres.--Lincoln Industrial, Saint Louis, MO; *U.S. Public*, pg. 1273
Schron, Jack H., Jr., Pres.--Jergens Inc., Cleveland, OH; *U.S. Private*, pg. 586
Schropshire, Lewis, Pres.--Holiday Inn, Athens, GA; *U.S. Private*, pg. 134
Schrum, E.P., Pres., Chief Exec. Officer & Treas.--Carolina Mills, Inc., Maiden, NC; *U.S. Private*, pg. 214
Schrushy, Richard, Pres. & Chief Exec. Officer--Healthsouth Corporation, Sunnyvale, CA; *U.S. Public*, pg. 803
Schryber, Mark, Pres.--Star Furniture Company, Houston, TX; *U.S. Public*, pg. 221
Schub, Barry A., Pres.--UAM Retirement Plan Services, Inc., New York, NY; *U.S. Public*, pg. 1674
Schube, Frank W., Chm. Bd., Pres. & Chief Exec. Officer--Dualite Inc., Williamsburg, OH; *U.S. Private*, pg. 344
Schube, Greg, Pres. & Chief Exec. Officer--Dualite Sales & Service, Inc., Williamsburg, OH; *U.S. Private*, pg. 344
Schubert, Clayton, Pres.--Clarklift Of Minnesota, Inc., Bloomington, MN; *U.S. Private*, pg. 243
Schubert, J.R., Pres.--Schubert Industries Inc., Akron, OH; *U.S. Private*, pg. 973
Schubert, J.R., Pres.--The Springwall Mattress Co., Akron, OH; *U.S. Private*, pg. 973
Schubert, William C., Pres., Chief Exec. Officer & Treas.--Kitchell Corporation, Phoenix, AZ; *U.S. Private*, pg. 624
Schuck, Jackye, Pres.--Schuck & Sons Construction Co., Glendale, AZ; *U.S. Private*, pg. 973

Schudmak, Mel E., Pres.--Cora Texas Manufacturing Co., Inc., White Castle, LA; *U.S. Private*, pg. 275

Schue, G.K., Pres.--Great Lakes Chemical (Europe) Ltd., Frauenfeld, Switzerland; *U.S. Public*, pg. 760

Schuermann, Fred L., Jr., Pres. & Chief Exec. Officer--Ladd Furniture, Inc., Greensboro, NC; *U.S. Public*, pg. 974

Schuette, John A., Pres.--Invincible Office Furniture, Manitowoc, WI; *U.S. Private*, pg. 575

Schuette, Marvin, Chm. Bd., Pres., Chief Exec. Officer & Chief Oper. Officer--Wausau Homes, Inc., Rothschild, WI; *U.S. Private*, pg. 1154

Schuette, Marvin, Chm. Bd., Pres., Chief Exec. Officer & Chief Oper. Officer--Sterling Building Systems, Inc., Rothschild, WI; *U.S. Private*, pg. 1154

Schuff, Scott, Pres. & Chief Exec. Officer--Schuff Steel Co., Phoenix, AZ; *U.S. Private*, pg. 973

Schuh, Dale R., Pres. & Chief Exec. Officer--Sentry Insurance, A Mutual Company, Stevens Point, WI; *U.S. Private*, pg. 984

Schuhmacher, Jurgen A., Pres.--NORD/LB Norddeutsche Securities, London, United Kingdom; *Int'l*, pg. 958

Schuit, Bram, Pres.--ALK Benelux BV, Groningen, Netherlands; *Int'l*, pg. 288

Schuldt, David A., Chm. Bd., Pres. & Chief Exec. Officer--CASI-RUSCO Inc., Boca Raton, FL; *U.S. Private*, pg. 218

Schuler, Michael, Pres. & Chief Exec. Officer--Zippo Manufacturing Company, Bradford, PA; *U.S. Private*, pg. 1207

Schull, Lee, Pres.--Building Products Inc., Watertown, SD; *U.S. Private*, pg. 180

Schulman, Marc S., Pres.--Eli's Cheese Cake Company, Chicago, IL; *U.S. Private*, pg. 371

Schulman, Paul M., Pres.--Paul Schulman Co., New York, NY; *Int'l*, pg. 117

Schulman, Sharon E., Pres.--Consumers New Jersey Water Company, Hamilton, NJ; *U.S. Public*, pg. 438

Schulman, Sharon E., Pres.--Consumers New Hampshire Water Co., Londonderry, NH; *U.S. Public*, pg. 438

Schult, Alex, Pres. & Chief Exec. Officer--The Chinet Co., Norwalk, CT; *Int'l*, pg. 1146

Schult, Robert W., Pres. & Chief Oper. Officer--Nestle USA, Glendale, CA; *Int'l*, pg. 916

Schulte, Alison I., Partner--Chicago Creative Partnership, Chicago, IL; *U.S. Private*, pg. 234

Schulte, Fritz, Pres. & Chief Oper. Officer--Hampshire Hosiery, Inc., Spruce Pine, NC; *U.S. Public*, pg. 778

Schulte, Johnie, Pres. & Chief Exec. Officer--NCI Building Systems, Inc., Houston, TX; *U.S. Public*, pg. 1145

Schultz, Howard, Pres. & Chief Exec. Officer--Starbucks Coffee Company, Seattle, WA; *U.S. Public*, pg. 1510

Schultz, James R., Pres. & Chief Exec. Officer--Great Lakes Lithograph Co., Cleveland, OH; *U.S. Private*, pg. 474

Schultz, James R., Pres.--GL Direct, Avon Lake, OH; *U.S. Private*, pg. 475

Schultz, Michael, Pres.--Urban Outfitters, Inc., New York, NY; *U.S. Public*, pg. 1700

Schultz, Ray, Pres. & Chief Exec. Officer--Promus Hotel Corporation, Memphis, TN; *U.S. Public*, pg. 1335

Schultz, Robert A., Pres.--Illinova Energy Partners, Inc., Oak Brook, IL; *U.S. Public*, pg. 870

Schultz, Robert B., Pres. & Chief Exec. Officer--Midland Walwyn Inc., Toronto, Canada; *Int'l*, pg. 865

Schulweis, Melvin, Pres.--Judel Products Corp., Elmsford, NY; *U.S. Public*, pg. 1609

Schulz, Ekkehard, Dr., Pres.--Thyssen Stahl AG, Duisburg, Germany; *Int'l*, pg. 1388

Schulz, John, Pres.--Rogerson Aircraft Systems, Irvine, CA; *U.S. Private*, pg. 940

Schulze-Oberlaender, C.R., Chm. Bd. & Pres.--American Barmag Co., Charlotte, NC; *U.S. Private*, pg. 51

Schulze, Fred, Pres., Chief Oper. Officer & Gen. Mgr.--Basler Electric Company, Highland, IL; *U.S. Private*, pg. 121

Schulze, Horst, Pres. & Chief Oper. Officer--The Ritz-Carlton Hotel Company LLC, Atlanta, GA; *U.S. Private*, pg. 594

Schulze, Horst H., Pres. & Chief Oper. Officer-The Ritz-Carlton Hotel Company--Marriott International, Inc., Washington, DC; *U.S. Public*, pg. 1047

Schulze, John B., Chm. Bd., Pres. & Chief Exec. Officer--The Lamson & Sessions Co., Cleveland, OH; *U.S. Public*, pg. 976

Schulze, Kent, Pres. & Chief Oper. Officer--AgriBioTech, Inc., Las Vegas, NV; *U.S. Public*, pg. 28

Schulze, Robert E., Pres.--Bridgford Foods Corporation, Anaheim, CA; *U.S. Public*, pg. 252

Schumacher, Donald, Chm. Bd. & Pres.--Schumacher Electric Corporation, Mount Prospect, IL; *U.S. Private*, pg. 973

Schumacher, Hans H., Pres. & Chief Exec. Officer--Voest-Alpine International Corporation, New York, NY; *Int'l*, pg. 1470

Schumacher, Juergen, Pres.--Dole Latin America, San Jose, Costa Rica; *U.S. Public*, pg. 515

Schumacher, Larry, Pres.--Schumacher-Dugan Construction, West Chester, OH; *U.S. Private*, pg. 973

Schumacher, Yves, Pres.--Publik AG, Kusnacht, Switzerland; *Int'l*, pg. 666

Schumaker, Tom, Publr.--Keynoter Publishing Company, Inc., Marathon, FL; *U.S. Public*, pg. 964

Schuman, Allan L., Pres. & Chief Exec. Officer--Ecolab Inc., Saint Paul, MN; *U.S. Public*, pg. 562

Schumann, Malcolm E., Jr., Pres.--Sanitary-Dash Manufacturing Co., Inc., North Grosvenordale, CT; *U.S. Public*, pg. 1795

Schupp, Rudy E., Chm. Bd., Pres. & Chief Exec. Officer--Republic Security Financial Corporation, West Palm Beach, FL; *U.S. Public*, pg. 1381

Schupphaus, Herbert, Pres.--Eickhoff Corporation, Pittsburgh, PA; *Int'l*, pg. 542

Schurr, Karl, Pres.--Minco Products, Inc., Minneapolis, MN; *U.S. Private*, pg. 749

Schurz, Franklin D., Jr., Pres.--Schurz Communications, Inc., South Bend, IN; *U.S. Private*, pg. 973

Schuster, Loes, Pres., Treas. & Production Dir.--Schuster & Partner, Neuss, Germany; *Int'l*, pg. 1210

Schuster, R.W., Pres. & Chief Exec. Officer--Global Environmental Corp., Hagerstown, MD; *U.S. Public*, pg. 747

Schuster, Ronald W., Pres.--Ceco Concrete Construction LLC, Gladstone, MO; *U.S. Private*, pg. 859

Schuster, Werner, Pres.--Schuster & Partner, Neuss, Germany; *Int'l*, pg. 394

Schutz, Bob, Pres.--Litton Systems, Inc. Advanced Circuitry Div., Springfield, MO; *U.S. Public*, pg. 1003

Schutz, Hans-Josef, Pres.--Pfeiffer of America, Inc., Princeton, NJ; *U.S. Public*, pg. 125

Schwab, Anthony, Pres. & Chief Exec. Officer--Claire Manufacturing Co., Addison, IL; *U.S. Private*, pg. 462

Schwab, Anthony, Pres. & Chief Exec. Officer--Sprayway, Inc., Addison, IL; *U.S. Private*, pg. 462

Schwab, Frederick J., Pres. & Chief Exec. Officer--Porsche Cars North America, Inc., Reno, NV; *Int'l*, pg. 1063

Schwab, Israel, Pres.--D&H Distributing Company, Harrisburg, PA; *U.S. Private*, pg. 300

Schwab, James E., Pres. & Chief Oper. Officer--Xtek, Inc., Cincinnati, OH; *U.S. Private*, pg. 1194

Schwab, Jim, Pres. & Chief Exec. Officer--Gramex Corporation, Bridgeton, MO; *U.S. Private*, pg. 468

Schwab, Samuel C., Pres. & Chief Exec. Officer--S. Schwab Company, Cumberland, MD; *U.S. Private*, pg. 974

Schwab, Shelly, Pres.--Universal Studios TV, Universal City, CA; *Int'l*, pg. 1215

Schwach, Gary, Pres. & Gen. Mgr.--AAR Cadillac Manufacturing Div., Cadillac, MI; *U.S. Public*, pg. 1

Schwade, Hans, Pres. & Chief Exec. Officer--Bergemann USA, Inc., Atlanta, GA; *Int'l*, pg. 401

Schwager, John L., Pres. & Chief Exec. Officer--Alamco, Inc., Charleston, WV; *U.S. Public*, pg. 403

Schwager, John L., Pres.--Alamco-Delaware, Inc., Wilmington, DE; *U.S. Public*, pg. 403

Schwaller, Jim, Pres.--Guzzler Manufacturing, Inc., Birmingham, AL; *U.S. Public*, pg. 616

Schwallie, Ambrose, Pres.--Westinghouse Savannah River Co., Aiken, SC; *U.S. Public*, pg. 273

Schwamberger, Kurt R., Pres. & Chief Oper. Officer--American Modern Home Insurance Group, Amelia, OH; *U.S. Public*, pg. 1110

Schwan, Charles A., Pres. & Chief Exec. Officer--Cohu, Inc., San Diego, CA; *U.S. Public*, pg. 396

Schwan, Geoffrey E., Pres.--Double AA Builders, Ltd., Scottsdale, AZ; *U.S. Private*, pg. 341

Schwanter, Jim, Pres. & Chief Mktg. Officer--Wickersham Hunt Schwantner, Boston, MA; *U.S. Private*, pg. 84

Schwanz, Don, Pres.--Space & Aviation Control, Phoenix, AZ; *U.S. Public*, pg. 834

Schwartz, Alan D., Co-Pres.--Superior Surgical Mfg. Co., Inc., Seminole, FL; *U.S. Public*, pg. 1539

Schwartz, Arthur L., Pres.--Parsons & Whittemore, Inc., Rye Brook, NY; *U.S. Private*, pg. 840

Schwartz, Bruce J., Pres.--Sysco Food Services of Los Angeles, Inc., Walnut, CA; *U.S. Public*, pg. 1551

Schwartz, Craig, Pres.--American Steel LLC, Portland, OR; *U.S. Public*, pg. 1375

Schwartz, Curtis, Pres.--Hartz Group, New York, NY; *U.S. Private*, pg. 508

Schwartz, Daniel L., Pres., Treas. & Sec.--Schwartz & Benjamin, Inc., New York, NY; *U.S. Private*, pg. 974

Schwartz, David, Pres. & Chief Exec. Officer--Bio-Rad Laboratories, Inc., Hercules, CA; *U.S. Public*, pg. 230

Schwartz, David, Pres.--Phar-Mor, Inc., Youngstown, OH; *U.S. Public*, pg. 1284

Schwartz, Dennis, Pres. & Chief Exec. Officer--Valley American Bank, South Bend, IN; *U.S. Public*, pg. 674

Schwartz, Fred W., Pres.--Leviton Mfg. Co., Inc., Little Neck, NY; *U.S. Private*, pg. 663

Schwartz, Gerald W., Chm. Bd., Pres. & Chief Exec. Officer--Onex Corporation, Toronto, Canada; *Int'l*, pg. 1006

Schwartz, H.G., Jr., Chm. Bd. & Pres.--Sverdrup Environmental Inc., Maryland Heights, MO; *U.S. Private*, pg. 1057

Schwartz, Jack, Pres.--Jack Schwartz Shoes, Inc., New York, NY; *U.S. Private*, pg. 974

Schwartz, Jeanne M., Pres.--The Remembrance Institute, Atlanta, GA; *Int'l*, pg. 499

Schwartz, Joel A., Pres.--Benihana, Inc., Miami, FL; *U.S. Public*, pg. 211

Schwartz, Joel A., Pres.--Benihana International, Inc., Miami, FL; *U.S. Public*, pg. 212

Schwartz, Joel P., Pres.--Ben Schwartz Market, Inc., Peoria, IL; *U.S. Private*, pg. 974

Schwartz, Leanord, Pres.--VGF Corporation, Lake Success, NY; *U.S. Public*, pg. 15

Schwartz, Leonard, Chm. Bd., Pres. & Chief Exec. Officer--Aceto Corporation, Lake Success, NY; *U.S. Public*, pg. 15

Schwartz, M.G., Chm. Bd., Pres. & Chief Exec. Officer--Quaker City Motor Parts Company, Middletown, DE; *U.S. Private*, pg. 898

Schwartz, Mike, Pres. & Chief Oper. Officer--Armstrong Air Conditioning Inc., Bellevue, OH; *U.S. Private*, pg. 659

Schwartz, Paul N., Pres. & Chief Oper. & Fin. Officer--Maxxam Inc., Houston, TX; *U.S. Public*, pg. 1062

Schwartz, Randy S., Pres.--Process & Industrial Division-S.E., Charlotte, NC; *U.S. Private*, pg. 317

Schwartz, Richard, Chm. Bd., Pres. & Chief Exec. Officer--Alliant Techsystems, Hopkins, MN; *U.S. Public*, pg. 47

Schwartz, Richard, Pres.--North American Enclosures, Inc., Central Islip, NY; *U.S. Private*, pg. 803

Schwartz, Russell, Pres.--Gramercy Pictures, Beverly Hills, CA; *U.S. Private*, pg. 468

Schwartz, Sanford M., Dr., Pres.--Market Facts-New York, Inc., New York, NY; *U.S. Public*, pg. 1047

Schwartz, Saul P., Pres.--Kinney System, Inc., New York, NY; *U.S. Private*, pg. 622

Schwartz, Thomas A., Pres.--Simpson Gumpertz & Heger Inc., Arlington, MA; *U.S. Private*, pg. 1002

Schwartzbeck, Tom, Pres., Chief Oper. Officer & Exec. V.P.--Duron, Inc., Beltsville, MD; *U.S. Private*, pg. 349

Schwarz, Guenther, Pres. & Chief Exec. Officer--Agrolinz Melamin GmbH, Lienz, Austria; *Int'l*, pg. 356

Schwarz, Hainz, Pres.--Karl M. Reich Maschinenfabrik GmbH, Nurtingen, Germany; *Int'l*, pg. 1101

Schwarzer, Fred, Pres. & Chief Exec. Officer--Heska Corporation, Fort Collins, CO; *U.S. Public*, pg. 812

Schwarzman, Stephen A., Pres. & Chief Exec. & Oper. Officer--The Blackstone Group, New York, NY; *U.S. Private*, pg. 147

Schwarzwalder, Daniel, Pres. & Chief Exec. Officer--Chernin's Shoes, Inc., Chicago, IL; *U.S. Private*, pg. 233

Schwecke, Fred, Pres.--Relm Communications, Inc., Indianapolis, IN; *U.S. Public*, pg. 1376

Schwedel, Alan R., Pres.--Amerbelle Corporation, Rockville, CT; *U.S. Private*, pg. 48

Schwegmann, John, Chm. Bd., Pres. & Chief Exec. Officer--Schwegmann Giant Super Markets, New Orleans, LA; *U.S. Private*, pg. 629

Schweitzer, Louis, Grp. Chm. Bd. & Chief Exec. Officer--Renault, Boulogne-Billancourt, France; *Int'l*, pg. 1102

Schweitzer, Peter, Pres.-J. Walter Thompson, JWT/ Americas & Global Bus. Dir.-Ford--J. Walter Thompson Company, New York, NY; *Int'l*, pg. 1483

Schweizer, Melvin, Chm. Bd. & Pres.--Prairie Farms Dairy, Inc., Carlinville, IL; *U.S. Private*, pg. 878

Schweizer, Rolf Walter, Dr., Chm. Bd. & Pres.--Clariant International Ltd., Muttenz, Switzerland; *Int'l*, pg. 624

Schweizer, W. Stuart, Pres.--Schweizer Aircraft Corporation, Big Flats, NY; *U.S. Private*, pg. 975

Schwelm, Frederick C., Pres. & Gen. Mgr.--Rockbestos-Suprenant Cable Corp., Clinton, MA; *U.S. Private*, pg. 938

Schwenger, Bruce, Pres.--Bank of Montreal Investor Services Limited, Toronto, Canada; *Int'l*, pg. 153

Schwenk, Harold S., Jr., Dr., Chm. Bd., Pres., & Chief Exec. Officer--BGS Systems, Inc., Waltham, MA; *U.S. Public*, pg. 161

Schwerin, Clayton A., Chm. Bd., Pres. & Chief Exec. Officer--Alliance Construction Solutions, Inc., Fort Collins, CO; *U.S. Private*, pg. 38

Schwesig, Norman L., Pres.--Maritz Performance Improvement Company, Fenton, MO; *U.S. Private*, pg. 704

Schwiezer, Tim, Pres.--Broadcast Supply Worldwide, Inc., Tacoma, WA; *U.S. Private*, pg. 170

Schwing, Gerhard, Pres.--Schwing Gmbh, Herne, Germany; *Int'l*, pg. 1211

Schwinger, Eugene A., Pres.--River Oaks Trust Company, Houston, TX; *U.S. Public*, pg. 419

Schyler, Jerry, Pres.--ARCO Dubai, Incorporated, Dubai, United Arab Emirates; *U.S. Public*, pg. 144

Sciame, Frank, Pres., Treas., Chief Exec. & Chief Fin. Officer--F.J. Sciame Construction Co. Inc., New York, NY; *U.S. Private*, pg. 975

Scibelli, R. M., Pres. & Chief Exec. Officer--Ener-Tek International Corporation, Pawcatuck, CT; *U.S. Private*, pg. 376

Scibelli, R.M., Pres. & Chief Exec. Officer--Yardney Technical Products, Inc., Pawcatuck, CT; *U.S. Private*, pg. 376

Scidenberger, Phil, Pres. & Gen. Mgr.--Southern Post South Carolina, West Columbia, SC; *U.S. Public*, pg. 413

Sciuto, John J., Chm. Bd., Pres. & Chief Exec. Officer--Comptek Research, Inc., Buffalo, NY; *U.S. Public*, pg. 419

Scodari, Joseph C., Pres. & Chief Oper. Officer--Centocor, Inc., Malvern, PA; *U.S. Public*, pg. 323

Scofeld, Rick, Pres.--Emson, Inc., Bridgeport, CT; *U.S. Private*, pg. 375

Scoggins, Don W., Pres.--Texas Eastman Co., Longview, TX; *U.S. Public*, pg. 550

Scohier, Pierre, Chm. Bd. & Pres.--GIB Group, Brussels, Belgium; *Int'l*, pg. 532

Scordato, Richard E., Pres.--Medical Laboratory Automation, Inc., Pleasantville, NY; *U.S. Private*, pg. 727

Scorsone, L.V., Pres.--Engineered Construction Division, Woodlands, TX; *U.S. Public*, pg. 1304

Scott, Allan, Pres. & Chief Oper. Officer--TELUS Marketing Communications, Edmonton, Canada; *Int'l*, pg. 1374

Scott, Charles R., Pres.--Computrol, Inc., Boise, ID; *U.S. Private*, pg. 83

Scott, Dave, Pres. & Chief Exec. Officer--Dimco-Gray Company, Centerville, OH; *U.S. Private*, pg. 333

Scott, David, Pres.--Huval Bakery, Inc., Lafayette, LA; *U.S. Public*, pg. 657

Scott, Derek, Pres.--Fosbel, Inc., Berea, OH; *Int'l*, pg. 234

Scott, E. Lynn, Pres. & Chief Exec. Officer--Brass Eagle Inc., Rogers, AR; *U.S. Public*, pg. 250

Scott, E.Michael D., Principal & Exec. V.P.--Vox Medica Corporation, Philadelphia, PA; *U.S. Private*, pg. 1143

Scott, Ed, Pres. & Chief Oper. Officer--Restonic Mattress Corporation, Rosemont, IL; *U.S. Private*, pg. 925

Scott, Harry, Pres. & Chief Exec. Oper.--Corporate Travel Services, San Francisco, CA; *U.S. Private*, pg. 276

Scott, Jack, Pres.--AGRA Vadeko Inc., Oakville, Canada; *Int'l*, pg. 30

Scott, James S., Pres.--Mercantile Bank, Brownsville, TX; *U.S. Private*, pg. 731

Scott, Jim, Pres.--Atlas Supply Company, Atlanta, GA; *U.S. Private*, pg. 96

Scott, John B., Pres.--IIT Research Institute, Chicago, IL; *U.S. Private*, pg. 555

Scott, Mark, Pres.--Sport Mart, Inc., Wheeling, IL; *U.S. Public*, pg. 1499

Scott, Patrick, Pres. & Chief Exec. Officer--Fisher Broadcasting Inc., Seattle, WA; *U.S. Public*, pg. 648

Scott, Randall, Pres.--Meadowlark, Inc., Englewood, CO; *U.S. Public*, pg. 471

Scott, Randall J., Pres.--Amax Coal Company, Keensburg, IL; *U.S. Public*, pg. 470

Scott, Randall J., Pres.--Ayrshire Land Company, Sullivan, IN; *U.S. Public*, pg. 471

Scott, Randall J., Pres.--Beech Coal Company, Bicknell, IN; *U.S. Public*, pg. 471
Scott, Robert, Pres. & Chief Exec. Officer--NewBold Corporation, Rocky Mount, VA; *U.S. Private*, pg. 796
Scott, Robert M., Pres.--Integrated Marketing Services, Omaha, NE; *U.S. Public*, pg. 631
Scott, Roger, Pres.--Amerimark Inc., Raleigh, NC; *U.S. Public*, pg. 1237
Scott, Roland, Pres. & Chief Exec. Officer--Whitney Blake Company of Vermont, Inc., Bellows Falls, VT; *U.S. Private*, pg. 148
Scott, Roland E., Pres. & Treas.--Burtco, Inc., Westminster Station, VT; *U.S. Private*, pg. 188
Scott, Ronald H., Pres.--Midwest Carbide Corporation, Keokuk, IA; *U.S. Public*, pg. 33
Scott, Samuel C., Pres. & Chief Oper. Officer--Corn Products International, Inc., Bedford Park, IL; *U.S. Public*, pg. 447
Scott, Steven, Dr., Chm. Bd., Pres. & Chief Exec. Officer--Coastal Physician Group, Inc., Durham, NC; *U.S. Public*, pg. 391
Scott, Walter, Jr., Pres.--Scott Printing Corporation, New Providence, NJ; *U.S. Private*, pg. 977
Scott, William J., Sr., Pres.--Joy Environmental Technologies, Inc., Houston, TX; *U.S. Public*, pg. 789
Scotten, Tom, Pres.--Bechtel Power Corporation, Gaithersburg, MD; *U.S. Private*, pg. 128
Scotton, William P., Pres.--Custom Decor, Inc., Smyrna, DE; *U.S. Private*, pg. 298
Scovic, Peter, Pres.--Ronningen-Petter Div., Portage, MI; *U.S. Public*, pg. 521
Scozzie, James A., Dr., Pres.--Ricera Inc., Painesville, OH; *Int'l*, pg. 689
Scribner, Robert K., Pres.--Esselte Corporation, Garden City, NY; *Int'l*, pg. 459
Scriven, J., Pres.--Teshmont Consultants Inc., Winnipeg, Canada; *Int'l*, pg. 31
Scrofano, Robert, Pres.--AlliedSignal Ocean Systems, Sylmar, CA; *U.S. Public*, pg. 50
Scuderi, Frank, Pres.-Manhattan Sportswear--Salant Corporation, New York, NY; *U.S. Public*, pg. 1429
Scully, Dennis, Pres.--Cordley Temprite, Oak Brook, IL; *U.S. Private*, pg. 372
Seaberg, Ladd M., Pres. & Chief Exec. Officer--Midwest Grain Products, Inc., Atchison, KS; *U.S. Public*, pg. 1111
Seabolt, Stephen J., Pres. & Chief Exec. Officer--Sunset Publishing Corporation, Menlo Park, CA; *U.S. Public*, pg. 1613
Seabrook, James H., Jr., Pres. & Chief Exec. Officer--Seabrook Wallcoverings, Inc., Memphis, TN; *U.S. Private*, pg. 978
Seabrook, James M., Jr., Pres.--Seabrook Brothers & Sons, Inc., Seabrook, NJ; *U.S. Private*, pg. 978
Seagraves, Harold E., Pres.--H.E.S. International, Inc., Kansas City, KS; *U.S. Public*, pg. 1209
Seal, Thomas F., Pres. & Chief Exec. Officer--Alpnet Inc., Salt Lake City, UT; *U.S. Public*, pg. 58
Seaman, Irwin, Pres.--AIM Electronics Corporation, Sunrise, FL; *U.S. Private*, pg. 598
Seaman, James D., Pres. & Chief Exec. Officer--Seaman Timber Company, Inc., Montevallo, AL; *U.S. Private*, pg. 979
Seaman, James D., Pres.--King Fisher, Inc., Montevallo, AL; *U.S. Private*, pg. 979
Seaman, Jeffrey, Chm. Bd. & Pres.--RTG Furniture Corp., Seffner, FL; *U.S. Private*, pg. 905
Seaman, John F., Pres.--Sulzer Plasma Technik, Inc., Troy, MI; *Int'l*, pg. 1307
Seaman, Wayne, Chief Exec. Officer & Gen. Mgr.--West Central Cooperative, Ralston, IA; *U.S. Private*, pg. 1163
Seamans, Thomas J., Pres.--Beemak Plastics, Gardena, CA; *U.S. Private*, pg. 598
Searle, Gregg A., Pres.--Diebold, Incorporated, Canton, OH; *U.S. Public*, pg. 506
Searles, Mark A., Pres. & Chief Oper. Officer--Eastex Energy Inc., Houston, TX; *U.S. Public*, pg. 567
Sears, Mike, Pres.--McDonnell Aircraft & Missile Systems Div., Berkeley, MO; *U.S. Public*, pg. 241
Seaton, Charles E., Pres.--IMC Agribusiness, Collinsville, IL; *U.S. Public*, pg. 856
Seaton, Kenneth M., Chm. Bd., Pres. & Chief Exec. Officer--Family Inns of America, Inc., Pigeon Forge, TN; *U.S. Private*, pg. 392
Seaton, Reed, Pres.--Southwest Recreational Industries Inc., Leander, TX; *U.S. Private*, pg. 1018
Seats, Harlan, Pres.--West Building Materials, Atlanta, GA; *U.S. Private*, pg. 1163
Seaver, Christopher T., Pres. & Chief Exec. Officer--Hydril Company, Houston, TX; *U.S. Private*, pg. 551
Seavitt, James, Pres.--Village Ford Inc., Dearborn, MI; *U.S. Private*, pg. 1140
Sebring, Joseph B., Pres. & Chief Oper. Officer--John Morrell & Co., Cincinnati, OH; *U.S. Public*, pg. 1479
Seccombe, Col, Pres.--Garst Seed Company, Slater, IA; *Int'l*, pg. 1524
Sechler, Scott I., Chm. Bd. & Pres.--Farmer's Pride, Inc., Fredericksburg, PA; *U.S. Private*, pg. 395
Secrest, John, Pres.--Barber Industries Inc., Calgary, Canada; *Int'l*, pg. 164
Secrist, Richard, Chm. Bd., Pres. & Chief Exec. Officer--Blue Tee Corporation, New York, NY; *U.S. Private*, pg. 153
Sedler, Herbert L., Pres. & Chief Exec. Officer--Paper Enterprises, Inc., Bronx, NY; *U.S. Private*, pg. 837
Sedlmeier, M.E., Pres. & Chief Exec. Officer--Ziegler Leasing Corp., West Bend, WI; *U.S. Public*, pg. 1792
Seegal, Denise, Pres.--Liz Claiborne, Inc., New York, NY; *U.S. Public*, pg. 1005
Seeger, John, Jr., Pres.--Dayton Rogers Mfg. Co., Blaine, MN; *U.S. Private*, pg. 318
Seegmiller, Ray R., Pres. & Chief Oper. Officer--Cabot Oil & Gas Corporation, Houston, TX; *U.S. Public*, pg. 289
Seeley, Raynor M. Jr., Chm. Bd., Pres. & Chief Exec. Officer--PTA Corporation, Oxford, CT; *U.S. Private*, pg. 828
Seeley, Raynor M., Jr., Pres.--PTA Corporation, Oxford, CT; *U.S. Private*, pg. 828
Seely, Timothy A., Pres. & Chief Oper. Officer--Gwaltney of Smithfield, Ltd., Smithfield, VA; *U.S. Public*, pg. 1479
Seevers, Tim, Pres.--HCC Inc., Mendota, IL; *U.S. Private*, pg. 490
Sefiani, Robyn, Pres.-Asia Pacific--Daniel J. Edelman Pty. Ltd., Melbourne, Australia; *U.S. Private*, pg. 363
Segal, George, Pres.--Automotive Supply Associates, Inc., Concord, NH; *U.S. Private*, pg. 101
Segal, George, Pres.--Sanel Auto Parts Co., Concord, NH; *U.S. Private*, pg. 101
Segal, John, Pres.--North American Products Corp., Jasper, IN; *U.S. Private*, pg. 803
Segal, Myron, Chm. Bd., Pres. & Chief Exec. Officer--Premier Mill Corp., Reading, PA; *U.S. Private*, pg. 881
Segal, Myron, Chm. Bd., Pres. & Chief Exec. Officer--Integrated Press Systems, Reading, PA; *U.S. Private*, pg. 881
Segawa, Shuichi, Pres.--NLI Properties, New York, NY; *Int'l*, pg. 935
Segel, Richard M., Pres. & Chief Exec. Officer--Dunmore Corporation, Newtown, PA; *U.S. Private*, pg. 346
Segerdahl, Anders, Pres.--Albert Trostel & Sons Co., Milwaukee, WI; *U.S. Private*, pg. 1105
Segerdahl, Anders, Pres.--Eagle-Ottawa Leather Co., Grand Haven, MI; *U.S. Private*, pg. 1105
Seglem, Christopher K., Chm. Bd., Pres. & Chief Exec. Officer--Westmoreland Coal Co., Colorado Springs, CO; *U.S. Public*, pg. 1761
Segonds, Daniel, Pres.--SocKalb G.I.E. France, Rodez, France; *U.S. Public*, pg. 493
Segsworth, Walter T., Pres.--Westim Resources Ltd., Vancouver, Canada; *Int'l*, pg. 435
Sehring, Louis J., Pres.--Harris Bank Batavia, N.A., Batavia, IL; *Int'l*, pg. 154
Seibel, Yvette, Pres.--Seibel & Stern Corp., New York, NY; *U.S. Private*, pg. 981
Seid, Lynne, Pres.--Partners & Shevack, Inc., New York, NY; *U.S. Private*, pg. 842
Seidel, Emil, Dr., Pres.--Klockner-Moeller GmbH, Bonn, Germany; *Int'l*, pg. 736
Seidenberg, Ivan G., Pres. & Chief Oper. Officer--Bell Atlantic Corporation, New York, NY; *U.S. Public*, pg. 201
Seidenberg, Phil, Pres. & Gen. Mgr.--SMI Steel-Arkansas, Magnolia, AR; *U.S. Public*, pg. 413
Seidenberger, Phil, Pres.--Southern Post Company, Magnolia, AR; *U.S. Public*, pg. 412
Seigel, Dan, Pres. & Chief Exec. Officer--Earl Scheib, Inc., Beverly Hills, CA; *U.S. Public*, pg. 1437
Seimer, Arnold B., Pres.--Automatic Timing & Controls, Lancaster, PA; *U.S. Private*, pg. 327
Seinsheimer, J. Fellman, III, Pres. & Chief Exec. Officer--American Indemnity Financial Corp., Galveston, TX; *U.S.* Public, pg. 83
Seipp, Philip J., Pres.--Sysco Food Services of Minnesota, Inc., Saint Paul, MN; *U.S. Public*, pg. 1551
Seitz, Edgar c., III, Pres.--Service Supply Co. Inc. of Indiana, Indianapolis, IN; *U.S. Private*, pg. 987
Sejpal, David A., Chm. Bd., Pres., Chief Exec. & Oper. Officer & Sec.--Clothestime Stores, Inc., Anaheim, CA; *U.S. Public*, pg. 387
Sekeres, Charles E., Pres. & Chief Exec. Officer--Physicians Weight Loss Centers, Inc., Akron, OH; *U.S. Private*, pg. 864
Sekeres, Charles E., Pres. & Chief Exec. Officer--Diet Center Worldwide, Inc., Akron, OH; *U.S. Private*, pg. 864
Sekeres, Chuck, Pres.--Form-You-3 International, Inc., Akron, OH; *U.S. Private*, pg. 418
Seki, Akiyoshi, Pres.--P.T. Surya Toto Indonesia, Jakarta, Indonesia; *Int'l*, pg. 1410
Seki, Akiyoshi, Pres.--Totokiki (Malaysia) Sdn.Bhd., Seremban, Malaysia; *Int'l*, pg. 1410
Seki, Kazuhira, Pres.--Isuzu Motors Limited, Tokyo, Japan; *Int'l*, pg. 692
Seki, T., Pres. & Gen. Mgr.--Wyeth (Japan) Corporation, Tokyo, Japan; *U.S. Public*, pg. 82
Sekiguchi, Kinya, Pres.--Nihon Shortwave Broadcasting Co., Ltd., Tokyo, Japan; *Int'l*, pg. 929
Sekine, Hideo, Pres.--Anritsu Elektronik GmbH, Dusseldorf, Germany; *Int'l*, pg. 77
Sekiya, Kenichi, Pres.--Disco Corporation, Tokyo, Japan; *Int'l*, pg. 413
Sekiya, Tetsuo, Pres.--NSK Ltd., Tokyo, Japan; *Int'l*, pg. 903
Sekizawa, Tadashi, Pres. & Rep. Dir.--Fujitsu Limited, Tokyo, Japan; *Int'l*, pg. 525
Seko, Akira, Pres. & Chief Exec. Officer--ORIX USA Corporation-New York, New York, NY; *Int'l*, pg. 1009
Seko, Akira, Pres. & Chief Exec. Officer--ORIX USA Corporation-San Francisco, San Francisco, CA; *Int'l*, pg. 1009
Selander, Lennart, Pres. & Chief Exec. Officer--AGA AB, Lidingo, Sweden; *Int'l*, pg. 12
Selander, Robert, Pres. & Chief Exec. Officer--Mastercard International, Inc., Purchase, NY; *U.S. Private*, pg. 714
Selders, Wim, H.J., Pres. & Chief Exec. Officer--Ortel Corporation, Alhambra, CA; *U.S. Public*, pg. 1232
Seldin, James, Pres.--Miss Elaine Inc., Saint Louis, MO; *U.S. Private*, pg. 752
Selecman, Charles E., Chm. Bd., Pres. & Chief Exec. Officer--Input/Output, Inc., Stafford, TX; *U.S. Public*, pg. 880
Seley, Peter S., Pres.--Advanco Constructors, Inc., Upland, CA; *U.S. Public*, pg. 1795
Selig, Clyde, Pres. & Chief Oper. Officer-CMC Steel Grp.--Structural Metals, Inc., Seguin, TX; *U.S. Public*, pg. 412
Selig, Jeff, Pres.--Capitol City Steel Co., Buda, TX; *U.S. Public*, pg. 413
Seligman, Scott J., Pres.--Seligman & Associates, Inc., Southfield, MI; *U.S. Private*, pg. 982
Selky, John L., Pres.--I/N Kote, New Carlisle, IN; *U.S. Public*, pg. 879
Selland, Howard M., Pres.--Aeroquip Corporation, Maumee, OH; *U.S. Public*, pg. 24
Sellers, Robert B., Pres.--Bob Sellers Pontiac GMC Truck Inc., Farmington, MI; *U.S. Private*, pg. 983
Sellers, Thomas D., Pres.--Dean Sellers Ford Inc., Troy, MI; *U.S. Private*, pg. 983
Sellman, Michael B., Pres. & Chief Exec. Officer--Maine Yankee, Brunswick, ME; *U.S. Public*, pg. 325
Sells, James, Pres. & Chief Oper. Officer--Matson Intermodal System, Inc., San Francisco, CA; *U.S. Public*, *pg. 40*
Selover, George H., Pres.--Selover Buick, Inc., Billings, MT; *U.S. Private*, pg. 983
Seltzer, Bernard, Chm. Bd. & Pres.--Hi-Tech Pharmacal Co., Inc., Amityville, NY; *U.S. Public*, pg. 825
Seltzer, Edwin C., Chm. Bd. & Pres.--Roller Derby Skate Corp., Litchfield, IL; *U.S. Private*, pg. 941
Seltzer, Samuel M., Chm. Bd. & Pres.--Allison Corporation, Livingston, NJ; *U.S. Private*, pg. 41
Selvey, Anthony R., Pres. & Chief Exec. Officer--Taylor & Francis Group Ltd., London, United Kingdom; *Int'l*, pg. 1357
Selvey, Anthony R., Pres.--Taylor & Francis Philadelphia, Bristol, PA; *Int'l*, pg. 1358
Selvey, Anthony R., Pres.--Taylor & Francis, Washington, DC; *Int'l*, pg. 1358
Selvin, Neil, Pres.--Global Village Communication, Sunnyvale, CA; *U.S. Public*, pg. 748
Selzer, Steve, Pres.--NTS, Fort Worth, TX; *U.S. Public*, pg. 631
Semel, Robert K., Pres., Chief Oper. Officer & Sec.--Uniflex, Inc., Hicksville, NY; *U.S. Public*, pg. 1665
Semel, Terry S., Co-Chm. Bd., Pres. & Chief Oper. Officer--Warner Bros. Studios, Inc., Burbank, CA; *U.S. Public*, pg. 1611
Semelsberger, Kenneth J., Pres. & Chief Oper. Officer--The Scott Fetzer Company, Westlake, OH; *U.S. Public*, pg. 217
Semler, Jerry D., Chm. Bd., Pres. & Chief Exec. Officer--American United Life Insurance Company, Indianapolis, IN; *U.S. Private*, pg. 64
Semmelhack, Henry P., Chm. Bd., Pres. & Chief Exec. Officer--Barrister Information Systems Corporation, Buffalo, NY; *U.S. Public*, pg. 192
Semmler, Steve, Pres.--Corken, Inc., Oklahoma City, OK; *U.S. Public*, pg. 862
Semon, Joseph R., Pres.--Casket Shells, Inc., Eynon, PA; *U.S. Private*, pg. 218
Semprevio, Phil, Pres.--Justrite Manufacturing Company, Des Plaines, IL; *U.S. Public*, pg. 617
Semrod, T. Joseph, Chm. Bd., Pres. & Chief Exec. Officer--United Jersey Bank, Hackensack, NJ; *U.S. Public*, pg. 1528
Senft, Paul, Publr.--The Daily Chronicle, De Kalb, IL; *U.S. Public*, pg. 1343
Senie, Kevin, Pres. & Chief Exec. Officer--The Travel Channel, Atlanta, GA; *U.S. Private*, pg. 647
Senior, Robert, Pres.--Richard E. Thibaut, Inc., Newark, NJ; *U.S. Public*, pg. 1358
Senior, Robert, Pres.--Wm. Zinsser & Co., Inc., Somerset, NJ; *U.S. Public*, pg. 1358
Senior, Robert, Pres.--Bradshaw-Praeger Co., Chicago, IL; *U.S. Public*, pg. 1358
Senior, Robert, Pres.--Mantrose Bradshaw Zinsser Group, Westport, CT; *U.S. Public*, pg. 1358
Senk, Glen, Pres.--Anthropologie, Philadelphia, PA; *U.S. Public*, pg. 1700
Senoh, Hirobumi, Pres.--Sogei Inc., Tokyo, Japan; *Int'l*, pg. 1277
Senty, James A., Chm. Bd. & Pres.--Consolidated Midwest, Inc., La Crosse, WI; *U.S. Private*, pg. 265
Seo, Kim Yong, Pres.--Ssangyong Information & Communication Corporation, Seoul, Korea; *Int'l*, pg. 1292
Serada, Syuji, Pres.--Nissho Iwai New Zealand Limited, Auckland, New Zealand; *Int'l*, pg. 948
Seragnoli, Isabella, Pres.--G.D. S.p.A., Bologna, Italy; *Int'l*, pg. 531
Seramur, John C., Pres., Chief Exec. Officer & Chief Oper. Officer--First Financial Corporation, Stevens Point, WI; *U.S. Public*, pg. 140
Sereci, Mark, Pres.--Kinemetrics, Inc., Pasadena, CA; *Int'l*, pg. 1019
Sergey, John M., Pres. & Chief Exec. Officer--Strategic Distribution Inc., Bensalem, PA; *U.S. Public*, pg. 1523
Sergi, Martin, Vice Chm., Pres. & Chief Fin. Officer--KTI, Inc., Guttenberg, NJ; *U.S. Public*, pg. 939
Serin, Bernard, Pres.--Edgcomb Metals, Bensalem, PA; *Int'l*, *pg. 572*
Serino, John, Pres.--ADAP Inc., Brockton, MA; *U.S. Private*, pg. 4
Serino, Matthew, Pres. & Chief Oper. Officer--Serino Coyne Inc., New York, NY; *U.S. Private*, pg. 985
Serino, Matthew, Pres.--Serino Coyne Public Relations, New York, NY; *U.S. Private*, pg. 985
Serls, Phillip, Pres. & Chief Oper. Officer--Colonial Metals Co., Columbia, PA; *U.S. Private*, pg. 253
Serna, Ricardo, Pres.--Janssen Farmaceutica, S.A. de C.V., Mexico, Mexico; *U.S. Public*, pg. 929
Serogham, Joe, Jr., Pres. & Gen. Mgr.--Broadway Chevrolet, Louisville, KY; *U.S. Private*, pg. 170
Serra Ramoneda, Antoni, Chm. Bd. & Pres.--Caixa d'Estalvis de Catalunya, Barcelona, Spain; *Int'l*, pg. 249
Serralta, Pierre, Pres.--The Athlete's Foot Group, Inc., Kennesaw, GA; *U.S. Private*, pg. 94
Serrano, Isidoro, Pres. & Regional Dir.--Leo Burnett Comunica S.A., Guatemala, Guatemala; *U.S. Private*, pg. 185
Serrianne, Mark, Pres.--Northlich Stolley LaWarre Public Relations, Cincinnati, OH; *U.S. Private*, pg. 806
Serrianne, Mark A., Pres. & Chief Oper. Officer--Northlich Stolley LaWarre, Cincinnati, OH; *U.S. Private*, pg. 806

Serruya, Michael, Pres. & Chief Exec. Officer--Yogen Fruz Worldwide Inc., Markham, Canada; *Int'l*, pg. 1520
Servaas, Beurt, Chm. Bd. & Pres.--Servaas, Inc., Indianapolis, IN; *U.S. Private*, pg. 986
SerVaas, Cory, M.D., Chm. Bd., Pres. & Chief Exec. Officer--Benjamin Franklin Literary & Medical Society, Inc., Indianapolis, IN; *U.S. Private*, pg. 133
Servedio, Dominick M., Pres. & Chief Oper. Officer--STV Group, Inc., Douglassville, PA; *U.S. Public*, pg. 1421
Servedro, D., Pres.--STV International, New York, NY; *U.S. Public*, pg. 1421
Servedro, D.M., Pres.--STV Construction Services, Douglassville, PA; *U.S. Public*, pg. 1421
Seta, Y., Pres.--Japan Marine Technologies Ltd., Tokyo, Japan; *Int'l*, pg. 1339
Setiawan, Putu, Pres. & Dir.--P.T. Asuransi Allianz Aken Life, Jakarta, Indonesia; *Int'l*, pg. 60
Seto, Yuzo, Pres.--Asahi Breweries Ltd., Tokyo, Japan; *Int'l, pg. 83*
Settepassi, Cesare, Pres.--Tiffany-Faraone, S.p.A. (Milan), Milan, Italy; *U.S. Public*, pg. 1609
Settles, Tom, Pres.--Power Contracting & Engineering Corp., Schaumburg, IL; *U.S. Private*, pg. 877
Setubal, Roberto Egydio, Pres. & Chief Exec. Officer--Banco Itau S.A., Sao Paulo, Brazil; *Int'l*, pg. 142
Setzer, Jeff, Co.-Pres.--Setzer Forest Products, Sacramento, CA; *U.S. Private*, pg. 987
Setzer, Scott, Co.-Pres.--Setzer Forest Products, Sacramento, CA; *U.S. Private*, pg. 987
Sevenstern, Ferdinand, Pres.--Netherlands Car B.V., Born, Netherlands; *Int'l*, pg. 876
Severe, John, Pres. & Gen. Mgr.--Western Grain, Inc., Wichita, KS; *U.S. Private*, pg. 1165
Severin, Eric, Pres.--Poggenpohl Mobelwerke GmbH, Herford, Germany,; *Int'l*, pg. 1261
Severson, Allan W., Chm. Bd., Pres. & Chief Exec. Officer--Grossmont Bank, San Diego, CA; *U.S. Public*, pg. 1793
Sevier, Helen, Chm. Bd., Pres., Chief Exec. & Chief Oper. Officer--B.A.S.S., Inc., Montgomery, AL; *U.S. Private*, pg. 105
Sevin, Irik, Chm. Bd., Pres. & Chief Exec. Officer--Petroleum Heat & Power Co., Stamford, CT; *U.S. Public, pg. 1281*
Seward, John E., Jr., Pres. & Chief Exec. Officer--The Paty Company, Piney Flats, TN; *U.S. Private*, pg. 844
Sewell, Chris, Pres.--Lithotype Company, Inc., South San Francisco, CA; *U.S. Private*, pg. 670
Sewell, D.J., Chief Exec. Officer--Clayhithe P.L.C., Aylesbury, United Kingdom; *Int'l*, pg. 297
Sewell, George, Pres.--Quaker Oats Limited, Southall, United Kingdom; *U.S. Public*, pg. 1348
Sewell, William E., Pres.--Cupples Products, Inc., Saint Louis, MO; *U.S. Private*, pg. 297
Sexton, G. Len, Pres.--Synovus Securities, Inc., Columbus, GA; *U.S. Public*, pg. 1550
Sexton, Marvin E., Pres.--Montgomery Tank Lines, Inc., Plant City, FL; *U.S. Public*, pg. 1028
Sexton, Michael, Pres.--Central Maine Newspapers, Augusta, ME; *U.S. Private*, pg. 439
Seya, Hiromichi, Pres. & Chief Exec. Officer--Asahi Glass Co., Ltd., Tokyo, Japan; *Int'l*, pg. 84
Seydi, Idris, Pres.--Societe Generale de Banques Au Senegal, Dakar, Senegal; *Int'l*, pg. 548
Seymour Heatley, Nancy, Chm. Bd. & Pres.--Seymour of Sycamore, Inc., Sycamore, IL; *U.S. Private*, pg. 988
Seymour, W.J., Joint Pres.--Janus Elevator Products Inc., Hauppauge, NY; *Int'l*, pg. 590
Shackelford, Mark, Pres.--Kettle Restaurants, Houston, TX; *U.S. Private*, pg. 617
Shackouls, Bobby S., Pres. & Chief Exec. Officer--Burlington Resources Inc., Houston, TX; *U.S. Public*, pg. 269
Shackouls, Bobby S., Pres. & Chief Exec. Officer--Meridian Oil Holding Inc., Houston, TX; *U.S. Public*, pg. 269
Shade, Robert, Jr., Pres.--Sierra Coating Technologies, De Pere, WI; *U.S. Private*, pg. 998
Shaefer, W.N., Pres.--LASMO America Inc., Houston, TX; *Int'l*, pg. 804
Shaeffer, James, Chief Exec. Officer--McKenzie Tank Lines, Inc., Tallahassee, FL; *U.S. Private*, pg. 723
Shafer, Byron A., Pres. & Chief Exec. Officer--Shafer Commercial Seating Inc., Denver, CO; *U.S. Private*, pg. 988
Shafer, Dennis, Pres.--Rollerblade, Inc., Minnetonka, MN; *U.S. Private*, pg. 941
Shaff, Gerald, Pres.--Custom Products Corporation, North Haven, CT; *U.S. Public*, pg. 244
Shaffer, David, Pres. & Chief Oper. Officer--Arrow Tru-Line, Inc., Archbold, OH; *U.S. Private*, pg. 85
Shaffer, David N., Co-Pres.--Just Born, Inc., Bethlehem, PA; *U.S. Private*, pg. 602
Shaffer, James B., Pres. & Chief Exec. Officer--Guy Gannett Communications, Portland, ME; *U.S. Private*, pg. 439
Shaffer, Lee P., Pres. & Chief Exec. Officer--Kenan Transport Company, Chapel Hill, NC; *U.S. Public*, pg. 949
Shaffer, Martin M., Pres.--Tru-Weld Grating, Inc., Wexford, PA; *U.S. Private*, pg. 1107
Shaffer, Michael L., Pres.-U.S. Van Lines Transportation Group--Atlas Van Lines, Inc., Evansville, IN; *U.S. Private, pg. 97*
Shafler, R. Scott, Pres.--Cortec Group, New York, NY; *U.S. Private*, pg. 277
Shaftman, Frederick K., Pres.--BellSouth Network Solutions, Inc., Atlanta, GA; *U.S. Public*, pg. 209
Shah, Ajay B., Chm. Bd., Pres. & Chief Exec. Officer--Smart Modular Technologies, Fremont, CA; *U.S. Public*, pg. 1476
Shah, Harry, Pres.--National Food Stores, Inc., Edison, NJ; *U.S. Private*, pg. 783
Shah, Satish, Pres. & Chief Exec. Officer--Accra Pac Group, Elkhart, IN; *U.S. Private*, pg. 11
Shaheen, Gabriel L., Pres.--Lincoln National Health & Casualty Insurance Co., Fort Wayne, IN; *U.S. Public*, pg. 998
Shaheen, Gabriel L., Pres. & Chief Exec. Officer--Lincoln National Reinsurance Company (Barbados) Limited, Fort Wayne, IN; *U.S. Public*, pg. 998
Shain, Joseph, Pres.--SCP Direct Inc., New York, NY; *U.S. Public*, pg. 1224
Shake, Ed, Pres. & Chief Exec. Officer--Roadmaster/Brunswick, Olney, IL; *U.S. Public*, pg. 265
Shaker, Anthony I., Pres.--Energy Systems Industries, Inc., Boston, MA; *U.S. Private*, pg. 376
Shaker, Anthony I., Pres.--Balco, Inc., Boston, MA; *U.S. Private*, pg. 376
Shaker, Joseph G., Pres.--Shaker Advertising Agency, Oak Park, IL; *U.S. Private*, pg. 988
Shalam, John J., Pres. & Chief Exec. Officer--Audiovox Corporation, Hauppauge, NY; *U.S. Public*, pg. 147
Shallcross, Charles, Mng. Partner--EURO RSCG Healthcare, London, United Kingdom; *Int'l*, pg. 603
Shanahan, William S., Pres. & Chief Oper. Officer--Colgate-Palmolive Company, New York, NY; *U.S. Public*, pg. 397
Shaneour, Dwight C., Jr., Chm. Bd., Pres. & Chief Exec. Officer--The Shane Group Inc., Hillsdale, MI; *U.S. Private*, pg. 989
Shaner, William, Pres. & Chief Oper. Officer--Laneco, Inc., Easton, PA; *U.S. Public*, pg. 1541
Shaner, William, Jr., Pres.--SuperValu, Inc.-Maryland Div., Williamsport, MD; *U.S. Public*, pg. 1540
Shank, David, Pres.--G.P. Putnam Sons, New York, NY; *Int'l*, pg. 1215
Shank, Glen L., Pres. & Chief Exec. Officer--Duckwall-Alco Stores, Inc., Abilene, KS; *U.S. Public*, pg. 533
Shankar, R. Sam, Pres., Chief Oper. Officer & Co-Chief Exec. Officer--Tork, Inc., Mount Vernon, NY; *U.S. Private*, pg. 1092
Shanklin, Jerry C., Chm. Bd., Pres. & Chief Exec. Officer--Sundowner Offshore Services, Inc., Houston, TX; *U.S. Public*, pg. 1149
Shanks, L.E., Pres.--Double-Cola Co.-USA, Chattanooga, TN; *U.S. Private*, pg. 341
Shannahan, Tim, Chm. Bd., Pres. & Chief Exec. Officer--Video Products Distributors, Inc., Sacramento, CA; *U.S. Private*, pg. 1139
Shannon, Michael G., Pres.--Gayfers, Mobile, AL; *U.S. Public*, pg. 1090
Shannon, Michael G., Pres.--Maison Blanche, Inc., Baton Rouge, LA; *U.S. Public*, pg. 1090
Shannon, O John C., Chm., Pres.-Grey Intl. & Chief Exec. Officer-Eur., Mid. E., Afr.--Grey Europe/London, London, United Kingdom; *U.S. Public*, pg. 765
Shannon, Tim, Pres.--Bradner Central Company, Chicago, IL; *U.S. Private*, pg. 164
Shapell, Nathan, Chm. Bd., Pres. & Chief Exec. Officer--Shapell Industries, Inc., Beverly Hills, CA; *U.S. Private*, pg. 990
Shapiro, Albert, Pres.--Commander Oil Corporation, Oyster Bay, NY; *U.S. Private*, pg. 257
Shapiro, David, Pres.--Familian Corp., Van Nuys, CA; *Int'l*, pg. 1512
Shapiro, Harry, Pres.--Strick Lease, Inc., Fairless Hills, PA; *U.S. Public*, pg. 1787
Shapiro, Harvey A., Pres. & Chief Oper. Officer--Dynacare, Inc., Toronto, Canada; *Int'l*, pg. 425
Shapiro, Leonard, Pres.--Shapco, Inc., Santa Monica, CA; *U.S. Private*, pg. 989
Shapiro, Mark, Pres. & New Bus. Contact--Louis London Advertising & Sales Promotion, Saint Louis, MO; *U.S. Private*, pg. 674
Shapiro, Mark R., Pres.--Golden Grain Company, Pleasanton, CA; *U.S. Public*, pg. 1348
Shapiro, Richard B., Chm. Bd., Pres. & Chief Exec. Officer--Charles River Data Systems, Inc., Framingham, MA; *U.S.* Private, pg. 230
Shapiro, Thomas J., Pres.--Wayne Steel, Inc., Wooster, OH; *U.S. Public*, pg. 1101
Sharbaugh, Thomas, Pres.--The Leap Partnership, Chicago, IL; *U.S. Private*, pg. 655
Sharer, Kevin W., Pres. & Chief Oper. Officer--Amgen Inc., Thousand Oaks, CA; *U.S. Public*, pg. 100
Sharira, Eli, Pres.--IIS Intelligent Information Systems Ltd., Yokneam, Israel; *Int'l*, pg. 645
Sharma, Arun, Pres.--Precision Fasteners Ltd., Thane, India; *U.S. Public*, pg. 1420
Sharma, D. Verne, Pres.--Summit Technology, Inc., Waltham, MA; *U.S. Public*, pg. 1528
Sharoky, Melvin, Pres.--Somerset Pharmaceuticals Inc., Tampa, FL; *U.S. Public*, pg. 1143
Sharoky, Melvin, Pres. & Chief Exec. Officer--Circa Pharmaceuticals, Inc., Copiague, NY; *U.S. Public*, pg. 1746
Sharon, Thomas E., Dr., Pres. & Chief Exec. Officer--Electromagnetic Sciences, Inc., Norcross, GA; *U.S. Public*, pg. 569
Sharp, Bill, Pres.--Katin, Costa Mesa, CA; *U.S. Public*, pg. 940
Sharp, Charles, Chm. Bd., Pres. & Chief Exec. Officer--Clinton State Bank, Clinton, AR; *U.S. Public*, pg. 630
Sharp, Dabney L., Pres.--Suburban Propane Group, Inc., Sumter, SC; *U.S. Public*, pg. 1436
Sharp, David L., Pres.--Wedgestone Financial Inc., Irwindale, CA; *U.S. Public*, pg. 1751
Sharp, David L., Pres.--Wedgestone Automotive Corp., Irwindale, CA; *U.S. Public*, pg. 1751
Sharp, Jack B., Pres.--Sharp Oil Company, Anthony, NM; *U.S. Private*, pg. 990
Sharp, Joe, Pres.--Fairfield Electric Cooperative, Winnsboro, SC; *U.S. Private*, pg. 391
Sharp, Lemuel, III, Pres.--W.G. Mills, Inc., Sarasota, FL; *U.S. Private*, pg. 749
Sharp, Michael, Pres.--Unbrako Div., Jenkintown, PA; *U.S. Public*, pg. 1420
Sharpe, Gary, Pres.--Delphax Systems, Randolph, MA; *U.S.* Public, pg. 153
Sharpe, John L., Pres. & Chief Oper. Officer--Four Seasons Hotels Inc., Don Mills, Canada; *Int'l*, pg. 502
Sharpe, John M., Pres.--Buntin Out of Home Media, Nashville, TN; *U.S. Private*, pg. 181
Sharpe, Louis K., Chm. Bd. & Pres.--Sharpe Dry Goods Co., Inc., Checotah, OK; *U.S. Private*, pg. 990
Sharpe, Ray, Pres.--Alpha Metals, Inc., Jersey City, NJ; *Int'l, pg. 328*
Shatner, Jerome, Pres.--Hitachi Data Systems Inc., Montreal, Canada; *Int'l*, pg. 622
Shattuck, Mayo A., III, Pres. & Chief Oper. Officer--BT Alex. Brown Inc., Baltimore, MD; *U.S. Public*, pg. 185
Shaughnessy, Jack, Pres.--Boston Security Counsellors, Inc., Boston, MA; *U.S. Public*, pg. 23
Shaughnessy, Jack, Pres.--Dilks Stamp Co., Philadelphia, PA; *U.S. Private*, pg. 58
Shaughnessy, Jack, Pres.--Quaker City Stamp Co., Philadelphia, PA; *U.S. Private*, pg. 59
Shaughnessy, Keith C., Pres. & Chief Exec. Officer--Metapoint Partners, Peabody, MA; *U.S. Private*, pg. 735
Shaughnessy, Kevin, Pres.--CCW Stamp Co., Cherry Hill, NJ; *U.S. Private*, pg. 58
Shaughnessy, Michael W,, Pres.--Lario Oil & Gas Company, Calgary, Canada; *U.S. Private*, pg. 651
Shaughnessy, William J., Pres. & Chief Exec. Officer--Wilbur Chocolate Co., Inc., Lititz, PA; *U.S. Private*, pg. 210
Shaver, William G., Pres.--Airborne Systems Integration Division, Baltimore, MD; *U.S. Public*, pg. 293
Shaver, William G., Pres.--Airborne Systems Integration Division, Belcamp, MD; *U.S. Public*, pg. 293
Shaw Jr,., William D, Pres. & Chief Exec. Officer--Aubrey G. Lanston & Co. Inc., New York, NY; *Int'l*, pg. 675
Shaw, Bill, Chief Exec. Officer--Earl May Seed & Nursery L.c., Shenandoah, IA; *U.S. Private*, pg. 356
Shaw, Craig W., Pres.--Perini Building Co., Inc. Western U.S. Division, Phoenix, AZ; *U.S. Public*, pg. 1278
Shaw, David, Pres.--Standard Arrow Ltd., Winnipeg, Canada; *Int'l*, pg. 127
Shaw, David, Pres.--Delta V Technologies, Inc., Tucson, AZ; *U.S. Public*, pg. 1324
Shaw, Greg, Pres.--Orbit Valve International, Inc., Little Rock, AR; *U.S. Private*, pg. 819
Shaw, James C., Pres.--Spirol International Corp., Danielson, CT; *U.S. Private*, pg. 1026
Shaw, James C., Pres.--Spirol International Corp., Cuyahoga Falls, OH; *U.S. Private*, pg. 1026
Shaw, James R., Jr., Pres. & Chief Exec. Officer--Regions Bank/Jackson County, Jefferson, GA; *U.S. Public*, pg. 1372
Shaw, M.M., Pres.--Atco Gas Services Ltd., Calgary, Canada; *Int'l*, pg. 95
Shaw, Morris, Pres. & Gen. Mgr.--Shaw Creations, Inc., Edison, NJ; *U.S. Private*, pg. 990
Shaw, Ray, Chm. Bd., Pres., Chief Exec. Officer & Chief Oper. Officer--American City Business Journals, Inc., Charlotte, NC; *U.S. Private*, pg. 19
Shaw, Robert, Chm Bd., Pres., & Chief Exec. Officer--Recoton Auto Corporation, Lincolnshire, IL; *U.S. Public*, pg. 1369
Shaw, Robert, Pres. & Chief Exec. Officer--NHT, Benicia, CA; *U.S. Public*, pg. 1369
Shaw, Robert A., Chm. Bd. & Pres.--Allied Plywood Corp., Alexandria, VA; *U.S. Private*, pg. 40
Shaw, Ronald G., Pres. & Chief Oper. Officer--The Pilot Pen Corp. of America, Trumbull, CT; *Int'l*, pg. 1057
Shaw, Tony, Pres.--Technology Transfer Institute, Santa Monica, CA; *U.S. Private*, pg. 1072
Shaw, Wayne E., Chm. Bd., Pres. & Chief Exec. Officer--Industra Service Corporation, New Westminster, Canada; *Int'l*, pg. 74
Shaw, William, Pres.--National American Corporation, Gautier, MS; *U.S. Public*, pg. 1688
Shaw, William, Chm. Bd. & Pres.--Volt Information Sciences, Inc., New York, NY; *U.S. Public*, pg. 1724
Shaw, William J., Pres. & Chief Oper. Officer--Marriott International, Inc., Washington, DC; *U.S. Public*, pg. 1047
Shaw, William J., Chm. Bd., Pres. & Chief Exec. Officer--U.S. Trails, Dallas, TX; *U.S. Public*, pg. 1688
Shawley, W.C., Pres.--Tate & Lyle Inc., Wilmington, DE; *Int'l*, pg. 1357
Shay, Donald E., Pres.--The Natkin Service Co., Englewood, CO; *U.S. Public*, pg. 84
Shaykin, Leonard, Mng. Partner--Shaykin & Company, New York, NY; *U.S. Private*, pg. 990
Shea, Andrew J., Pres.--Sico Incorporated, Edina, MN; *U.S. Private*, pg. 997
Shea, Christina L., Pres.--Betty Crocker Products, Minneapolis, MN; *U.S. Public*, pg. 718
Shea, Dan, Pres.--S.A.S.I. Corporation, Collinsville, IL; *U.S. Private*, pg. 955
Shea, James P., Pres. & Chief Exec. Officer--Renex Corp., Coral Gables, FL; *U.S. Public*, pg. 1377
Shea, Michael D., Pres. & Chief Oper. Officer--Defiance Precision Products, Inc., Defiance, OH; *U.S. Public*, pg. 493
Shea, Michael D., Pres.--Shea Communications Co., Smyrna, GA; *U.S. Private*, pg. 990
Shea, William E., Pres.--Ames Safety Envelope Company, Inc., Somerville, MA; *U.S. Private*, pg. 66
Shealy, T.W., Pres.--Springs Industries, Bedding Division, Charlotte, NC; *U.S. Public*, pg. 1500
Sheard, C.K., Pres.--Northwestern Utilities Limited, Edmonton, Canada; *Int'l*, pg. 95
Shearer, Jonathan, Pres.--Paine Furniture Co., Natick, MA; *U.S. Private*, pg. 834
Shearer, Martin P., Pres. & Chief Exec. Officer--Southern Belle Dairy Company, Somerset, KY; *U.S. Private*, pg. 1015
Shearman, Thomas B., III, Pres.--Shearman Corporation, Lake Charles, LA; *U.S. Private*, pg. 991
Sheavaleau, Dennis, Pres.--Ameda AG, Hunenberg, Switzerland; *U.S. Private*, pg. 535
Sheckell, Frank N., Jr., Pres.--Chivas Products Ltd., Sterling Heights, MI; *U.S. Private*, pg. 238

Shee, Darrell, Creative Partner--Bryant, Fulton & Shee, Vancouver, Canada; *U.S. Private,* pg. 678
Sheehan, Dan, Pres.--Ferguson Manufacturing & Equipment Company, Inc., Dallas, TX; *U.S. Private,* pg. 401
Sheehan, Dennis W., Chm. Bd., Pres. & Chief Exec. Officer--AXIA Incorporated, Lombard, IL; *U.S. Private,* pg. 103
Sheehan, Edward T., Pres. & Chief Oper. Officer--United Waste Systems, Inc., Houston, TX; *U.S. Public,* pg. 1691
Sheehan, Jeremiah J., Pres.--Reynolds Metals Co., Consumer Products Div., Richmond, VA; *U.S. Public,* pg. 1386
Sheehy, Robert J., Pres. & Chief Exec. Officer--United HealthCare of Ohio, Inc., Columbus, OH; *U.S. Public,* pg. 1678
Sheets, Mary J., Pres. & Chief Exec. Officer--Rapid Industries, Inc., Louisville, KY; *U.S. Private,* pg. 910
Sheetz, Stanton R., Pres. & Chief Exec. Officer--Sheetz, Inc., Altoona, PA; *U.S. Private,* pg. 991
Sheffield, John W., Jr., Pres.--Sheffield Hardware Company, Americus, GA; *U.S. Private,* pg. 335
Sheffield, Scott, Pres. & Chief Exec. Officer--Pioneer Natural Resources Co., Irving, TX; *U.S. Public,* pg. 1299
Sheffler, Dudley P., Pres. & Chief Exec. Officer--RELTEC Corporation, Cleveland, OH; *U.S. Private,* pg. 921
Sheffler, Tom, Pres.--L3 Communications Conic Div., San Diego, CA; *U.S. Private,* pg. 638
Shehata, R., Pres.--Krupp Robins, Inc., Englewood, CO; *Int'l,* pg. 511
Shei, Kurt, Dir.-Mfg.--Essex Specialty Products, Auburn Hills, MI; *U.S. Public,* pg. 523
Sheldon, Danley K., Pres.--Ferrellgas Partners, L.P., Liberty, MO; *U.S. Public,* pg. 618
Sheldon, J.M., Chm. Bd., Pres., Chief Exec. Officer & Chief Oper. Officer--Sheldons' Inc., Antigo, WI; *U.S. Private,* pg. 992
Shelk, S.J., Jr., Pres.--Ochoco Lumber Company, Prineville, OR; *U.S. Private,* pg. 811
Shell, Owen G., Jr., Pres.--NationsBank of Tennessee, Nashville, TN; *U.S. Public,* pg. 1163
Shell, Owen G., Jr., Pres. & Chief Exec. Officer--Nationsbank/Tennessee, Nashville, TN; *U.S. Public,* pg. 1163
Shellenbarger, David, Pres. & Chief Exec. Officer--Macro Computer Products Inc., Rochester Hills, MI; *U.S. Private,* pg. 693
Shelly, Ronald, Pres.--Solectron Texas, Austin, TX; *U.S. Public,* pg. 1483
Shelton, Darold E., Pres. & Chief Exec. Officer--United Missouri Bank of Cass County, Peculiar, MO; *U.S. Public,* pg. 1655
Shelton, E. Kirk, Pres. & Chief Oper. Officer--CUC International, Inc., Stamford, CT; *U.S. Public,* pg. 320
Shelton, James D., Chm., Pres. & Chief Exec. Officer--First Federal Savings, East Hartford, CT; *U.S. Public,* pg. 632
Shelton, Paul, Pres.--Ameri-Co Carriers, Inc., Scottsbluff, NE; *U.S. Public,* pg. 63
Shelton, Paul, Pres.--Nationwide Freight Services, Inc., Scottsbluff, NE; *U.S. Public,* pg. 64
Shelton, Tad, Pres.--The Reliable Life Insurance Company, Webster Groves, MO; *U.S. Public,* pg. 1374
Shelton, Thomas R., Pres.--Case Foods, Inc., Salisbury, MD; *U.S. Private,* pg. 217
Shenkenburg, W.J., Pres. & Chief Exec. Officer--M & I Bank of Racine, Racine, WI; *U.S. Public,* pg. 1050
Shepard, Donald J., Chm. Bd., Pres. & Chief Exec. Officer--AEGON USA, Inc., Baltimore, MD; *Int'l,* pg. 26
Shepard, Jeffrey A., Pres. & Chief Exec. Officer--Meldisco, Mahwah, NJ; *U.S. Public,* pg. 661
Shepard, Terry, Pres.--St. Jude Medical Division, Saint Paul, MN; *U.S. Public,* pg. 1428
Shepard, Victor, Pres.--Computer Design Inc., Grand Rapids, MI; *U.S. Private,* pg. 465
Shephard, K. Craig, Pres. & Chief Oper. Officer--QST Energy, Inc., Peoria, IL; *U.S. Public,* pg. 367
Shepherd, Donald R., Chm. Bd.--Loomis, Sayles & Co., Boston, MA; *U.S. Private,* pg. 737
Shepherd, J. Harold, Chief Exec. Officer--Shepherd Construction Co., Inc., Atlanta, GA; *U.S. Private,* pg. 993
Shepherd, Jim, Pres. & Chief Oper. Officer--Crestbrook Forest Industries Ltd., Cranbrook, Canada; *Int'l,* pg. 348
Shepherd, Stephen B., Pres.--Shepherd Construction Co., Inc., Atlanta, GA; *U.S. Private,* pg. 993
Shepherd, Ted, Pres.--Archibald Candy Company, Chicago, IL; *U.S. Private,* pg. 597
Shepherd, William C., Chm. Bd., Pres. & Chief Exec. Officer--Allergan, Inc., Irvine, CA; *U.S. Public,* pg. 46
Sherbon, David, Chief Exec. Officer--SSB Advertising Sydney, Sydney, Australia; *Int'l,* pg. 394
Sheridan, Gregory C., Pres. & Chief Exec. Officer--Huntington Bancshares Indiana, Inc., Indianapolis, IN; *U.S. Public,* pg. 850
Sheridan, R. Champlin, Chm. Bd.--The Sheridan Group, Hanover, PA; *U.S. Private,* pg. 993
Sheridan, Richard, Pres.--Printing Service Incorporated, Madison Heights, MI; *U.S. Public,* pg. 1736
Sheridan, Stan, Pres.--Faygo Beverages, Inc., Detroit, MI; *U.S. Public,* pg. 1153
Sheridan, Terrance, V.P..--Keithley Instruments Inc.-Radiation Measurements Div., Cleveland, OH; *U.S. Public,* pg. 946
Sheridan, Wayne M., Pres.--Fischbach & Moore, Inc., New York, NY; *U.S. Public,* pg. 84
Sherling, George L., Pres. & Chief Exec. Officer--Compass Bank Dallas, Richardson, TX; *U.S. Public,* pg. 419
Sherman, Brooks F., Pres.--Selkirk HVAC, Dallas, TX; *U.S. Public,* pg. 1795
Sherman, Christopher R., Pres.--Pacific Enterprises International, Los Angeles, CA; *U.S. Public,* pg. 1249
Sherman, George M., Pres. & Chief Exec. Officer--Danaher Corporation, Washington, DC; *U.S. Public,* pg. 480
Sherman, Jeffrey, Pres.--Bloomingdale's, New York, NY; *U.S. Public,* pg. 617
Sherman, John, Jr., Pres. & Chief Exec. Officer--Scott & Stringfellow Financial, Inc., Richmond, VA; *U.S. Public,* pg. 1445
Sherman, John, Jr., Pres. & Chief Exec. Officer--Scott & Stringfellow, Inc., Richmond, VA; *U.S. Public,* pg. 1445
Sherman, L.J., Pres. & Chief Oper. Officer--A.Y. McDonald Mfg. Co., Dubuque, IA; *U.S. Private,* pg. 721
Sherman, Larry, Pres.--Lombard Lincoln-Mercury & Leasing, Inc., Lombard, IL; *U.S. Private,* pg. 673
Sherman, Malcolm L., Pres.--Ekco Cleaning, Inc., Franklin Park, IL; *U.S. Public,* pg. 566
Sherman, Peter M., Chm. Bd., Pres. & Chief Exec. Officer--Independence Capital Management, Inc., Horsham, PA; *U.S. Private,* pg. 849
Sherman, R. Keith, Pres.--Caterpillar Risk Management Services Ltd., Peoria, IL; *U.S. Public,* pg. 316
Sherman, Robert, Pres.--Nitram Energy Inc., Orchard Park, NY; *U.S. Private,* pg. 799
Sherman, Robert L., Pres.--National Bedding Co., Beloit, WI; *U.S. Private,* pg. 780
Sherman, Thomas W., Pres.--Bay State Energy Development, Inc., Westborough, MA; *U.S. Public,* pg. 197
Shernit, Bill, Pres.--Quality Systems Inc., Mc Lean, VA; *U.S. Public,* pg. 1627
Sherrer, Robert, Pres.--Tom James Company, Franklin, TN; *U.S. Private,* pg. 580
Sherry, James, Pres.--News Holdings Corp., Vienna, VA; *U.S. Private,* pg. 797
Sherwin, Gerry, Sr. Partner-Career Devel.--Bozell Worldwide, Inc., New York, NY; *U.S. Public,* pg. 1642
Sherwin, Mark, Pres.--CENTRIA, Moon Township, PA; *U.S. Private,* pg. 225
Sherwin, Richard, Co-Pres.--Metromedia International Telecommunications, Inc., Stamford, CT; *U.S. Public,* pg. 1103
Sherwood, James B., Pres.--Sea Containers Ltd., Hamilton, Bermuda; *Int'l,* pg. 1213
Sherwood, Steven, Co-Chm. Bd. & Pres.--Clayton, Williams & Sherwood, Inc., Newport Beach, CA; *U.S. Private,* pg. 245
Shesmesh, Yoram, Pres.--World Class Film Corporation, Yonkers, NY; *U.S. Private,* pg. 1190
Sheth, Hasu, Pres.--TLT-Engineering India Pvt. Ltd., Ahmedabad, India; *Int'l,* pg. 401
Sheth, Viren, Pres. & Chief Exec. Officer--Tristar Corp., San Antonio, TX; *U.S. Public,* pg. 1640
Shetter, Thaine, Publr.--Ravalli Republic, Hamilton, MT; *U.S. Public,* pg. 1343
Shettle, John F., Jr., Pres. & Chief Exec. Officer--Avemco Corporation, Frederick, MD; *U.S. Public,* pg. 151
Shewmake, C.B., Jr., Pres.--Algernon Blair International, Montgomery, AL; *U.S. Private,* pg. 33
Shibata, Minoru, Pres.--Toyobo Co., Ltd., Osaka, Japan; *Int'l,* pg. 1411
Shibatoa, Shotaro, Pres. & Representative Dir.--Kokusai Electric Co., Ltd., Tokyo, Japan; *Int'l,* pg. 743
Shibuya, Kameo, Pres.--Nippon Express U.S.A. Inc., New York, NY; *Int'l,* pg. 934
Shibuya, Naoaki, Pres.--CPB Inc., Honolulu, HI; *U.S. Public,* pg. 282
Shibuya, Naoaki, Pres. & Chief Oper. Officer--Central Pacific Bank, Honolulu, HI; *U.S. Public,* pg. 283
Shibuya, Naoaki, Pres.--CPB Properties, Inc., Honolulu, HI; *U.S. Public,* pg. 283
Shidler, Jay, Pres. & Mng. Partner--The Shidler Group, Honolulu, HI; *U.S. Private,* pg. 994
Shiel, James G., Pres.--Berkley Dean & Company, Inc., Greenwich, CT; *U.S. Public,* pg. 216
Shields, Gerald N., Chm. Bd., Pres. & Chief Exec. Officer--Graymills Corp., Chicago, IL; *U.S. Private,* pg. 473
Shields, Jeffrey, Dir.-Fin.--Dreyer's Grand Ice Cream, Inc., Oakland, CA; *U.S. Public,* pg. 529
Shields, John, Publr.--Santa Maria Times, Santa Maria, CA; *U.S. Public,* pg. 1343
Shiely, John S., Pres. & Chief Oper. Officer--Briggs & Stratton Corporation, Wauwatosa, WI; *U.S. Public,* pg. 252
Shifo, Tom, Pres.--The Ingersoll Milling Machine Co., Rockford, IL; *U.S. Private,* pg. 562
Shigehisa, Yoshihiro, Pres.--JGC Corporation, Tokyo, Japan; *Int'l,* pg. 697
Shigemitsu, Hirouyuki, V.P. & Gen. Mgr.--Lotte U.S.A., Inc., Battle Creek, MI; *Int'l,* pg. 819
Shigeta, Hiroaki, Pres.--Nippon Roche K.K., Tokyo, Japan; *Int'l,* pg. 1121
Shigeta, Toyohiko, Pres.--Nova Promotion Group Inc., Hackensack, NJ; *Int'l,* pg. 393
Shigimitsu, T., Pres.--Lotte Company Ltd., Tokyo, Japan; *Int'l,* pg. 819
Shillima, Don, Pres.--Kalitta Flying Service, Ypsilanti, MI; *U.S. Private,* pg. 57
Shillman, Robert J., Chm. Bd., Pres. & Chief Exec. Officer--Cognex Corporation, Natick, MA; *U.S. Public,* pg. 394
Shilvock, Ray J., Chm. Bd.--Graham Paint and Varnish Company, Chicago, IL; *U.S. Private,* pg. 468
Shim, Jae Hyung, Pres.--Rohm Electronics (Tianjin) Co., Ltd., Tianjin, China; *Int'l,* pg. 1125
Shim, Jae Jin, Pres.--Rohm Electronics Korea Corporation, Seoul, Korea; *Int'l,* pg. 1125
Shim, Jang Sop, Pres.--Rohm Korea Corporation, Seoul, Korea; *Int'l,* pg. 1125
Shim, Young-Cheol, Pres.--Ssangyong Resources Development Co., Ltd., Tonghae, Korea; *Int'l,* pg. 1291
Shima, Koshi, Pres.--Shima Trading Co. Ltd., Osaka, Japan; *Int'l,* pg. 1231
Shimacu, Takeshi, Pres.--Kirin USA, Inc., New York, NY; *Int'l,* pg. 736
Shimada, Kunio, Pres.--Komatsu Changlin Construction Machinery Corp., Jiangsu, China; *Int'l,* pg. 745
Shimamoto, Toshihiko, Terminal Mgr.--Kintetsu World Express Inc., Miami, FL; *Int'l,* pg. 735
Shimano, Keizo, Pres.--Shimano Inc., Osaka, Japan; *Int'l,* pg. 1232
Shimazoe, Kazuhiro, Pres.--Sumitomo Life Insurance Agency America, Inc., New York, NY; *Int'l,* pg. 1315
Shimazu, Toshio, Gen. Mgr.--Yamaha Motor do Brasil Ltda., Convica, Brazil; *Int'l,* pg. 1516
Shimizu, Hironori, Pres.--Kyokuyo Co. Ltd., Tokyo, Japan; *Int'l,* pg. 777
Shimizu, Makoto, Pres.--Sanwa Bank (Deutschland) AG, Frankfurt/Main, Germany; *Int'l,* pg. 1190
Shimizu, Shinobu, Chm. Bd. & Pres.--Tokyu Corporation, Tokyo, Japan; *Int'l,* pg. 1394
Shimizu, Takuji, Pres., Chief Exec. Officer & Chief Oper. Officer--Meitsu Inc., Tokyo, Japan; *Int'l,* pg. 856
Shimizu, Yusuke, Pres.--Ismac, Inc., Calhoun, GA; *Int'l,* pg. 744
Shimoda, Kouichi, Pres.--GSI Europe-Import & Export GmbH, Dusseldorf, Germany; *Int'l,* pg. 579
Shimokawa, Tokiji, Pres.--Kintetsu Intermodal (U.S.A.), Inc., Carson, CA; *Int'l,* pg. 735
Shimokawa, Tomohiro, Pres.--Sanyo Energy (U.S.A.) Corporation, San Diego, CA; *Int'l,* pg. 1191
Shin, Isao, Pres.--Sumitomo Pharmaceuticals Co., Ltd., Osaka, Japan; *Int'l,* pg. 1311
Shine, Jack, Pres.--First Financial Group, Inc., Encino, CA; *U.S. Private,* pg. 407
Shine, John B., Pres.--Samtec Inc., New Albany, IN; *U.S. Private,* pg. 963
Shine, T.K., Pres. & Chief Exec. Officer--Logo 7, Inc., Indianapolis, IN; *U.S. Public,* pg. 1644
Shingyoji, Shintaro, Pres.--Hitachi Koki U.S.A. Ltd., Norcross, GA; *Int'l,* pg. 620
Shinn, Lyle B., Jr., Pres.--Chicago Lock Company, Pleasant Prairie, WI; *U.S. Private,* pg. 235
Shinohara, Hiroaki, Pres.--Foster Electric Co., Ltd., Tokyo, Japan; *Int'l,* pg. 500
Shinohara, Hisao, Pres.--Heartland Lysine Inc., Chicago, IL; *Int'l,* pg. 40
Shinohara, M., Pres.--MSP Steel Works Ltd., Singapore, Singapore; *Int'l,* pg. 948
Shintani, Isao, Pres.--"K" Line (Kawasaki Kisen Kaisha, Ltd.), Tokyo, Japan; *Int'l,* pg. 717
Shintani, Isao, Pres.--Kawasaki Kisen Kaisha, Ltd., Tokyo, Japan; *Int'l,* pg. 726
Shiokawa, Mitsuru, Pres.--Kawasho Corporation, Tokyo, Japan; *Int'l,* pg. 726
Shiono, Yoshihiko, Pres. & Representative Dir.--Shionogi & Co., Ltd., Osaka, Japan; *Int'l,* pg. 1234
Shipley, Richard C., Pres.--Shipley Co., LLC, Marlborough, MA; *U.S. Public,* pg. 1403
Shipley, William S., III, Pres.--Shipley Companies, York, PA; *U.S. Private,* pg. 994
Shipman, Jack H., Pres. & Chief Oper. Officer--Great Financial Bank FSB, Louisville, KY; *U.S. Private,* pg. 473
Shipman, Mark L., Pres.--Coco's & Carrows Restaurants, Irvine, CA; *U.S. Public,* pg. 23
Shipmon, Frederick S., III, Pres.--Drake Construction Company, Portland, OR; *U.S. Private,* pg. 347
Shipp, Barry, Pres.--Parman Lubricants, Nashville, TN; *U.S. Private,* pg. 840
Shipp, Donald L., Pres.--Hawkins Chemical, Inc., Minneapolis, MN; *U.S. Public,* pg. 800
Shipp, Robbie, Pres.--Rembrandt Photo Services, City of Commerce, CA; *U.S. Private,* pg. 222
Shirai, Tadahiro, Pres.--Nissan Europe N.V., Amsterdam, Netherlands; *Int'l,* pg. 945
Shiraishi, Shinobu, Pres.--ORIX Life Insurance Corporation, Tokyo, Japan; *Int'l,* pg. 1009
Shiraishi, Shozo, Pres. & Chief Exec. Officer--Miura Co., Ltd., Matsuyama, Japan; *Int'l,* pg. 884
Shiraishi, Yutaka, Pres.--ORIX Estate Corporation, Osaka, Japan; *Int'l,* pg. 1008
Shiraishi, Yutaka, Pres.--ORIX Interior Corporation, Osaka, Japan; *Int'l,* pg. 1008
Shirk, James A., Pres.--Beer Nuts, Inc., Bloomington, IL; *U.S. Private,* pg. 130
Shirvanian, Kosti, Chm. Bd., Pres. & Chief Exec. Officer--Western Waste Industries, Torrance, CA; *U.S. Public,* pg. 1686
Shivery, Charles W., Pres.--Constellation Power, Inc., Baltimore, MD; *U.S. Public,* pg. 172
Shlomm, Boris, Pres. & Chief Exec. Officer--Amicale Industries, Inc., New York, NY; *U.S. Private,* pg. 66
Shockley, Thomas V., III, Pres. & Chief Oper. Officer--Central and South West Corporation, Dallas, TX; *U.S. Public,* pg. 324
Shoemate, C.R., Chm. Bd., Pres. & Chief Exec. Officer--Bestfoods, Englewood Cliffs, NJ; *U.S. Public,* pg. 223
Shoen, E.J., Chm. Bd. & Pres.--Amerco, Reno, NV; *U.S. Private,* pg. 48
Shoen, E.J. "Joe", Pres.--U-Haul International, Inc., Phoenix, AZ; *U.S. Private,* pg. 49
Shoffner, John P., Pres.--Dura-Line Corp., Middlesboro, KY; *U.S. Private,* pg. 598
Shogan, Edward N., Pres.--Springfield Division, New York, NY; *U.S. Public,* pg. 1500
Shoham, Y., Pres. & Chief Exec. Officer--Onyx Technologies Ltd., Tel Aviv, Israel; *Int'l,* pg. 1007
Shoham, Y., Pres. & Chief Exec. Officer--Onyx Interactive Multimedia Ltd., Tel Aviv, Israel; *Int'l,* pg. 1007
Shoji, Takashi, Pres. & Chief Exec. Officer--Hakuhodo Incorporated, Tokyo, Japan; *Int'l,* pg. 587
Shoji, Tsuyoshi, Pres.--Yamaichi International (Canada) Limited/Limitee, Montreal, Canada; *Int'l,* pg. 1517
Shokrgozar, Hamid, Pres. & Chief Exec. Officer--Bowmar Instrument Corporation, Phoenix, AZ; *U.S. Public,* pg. 248
Shokrgozar, Hamid, Pres.--White Microelectronics, Phoenix, AZ; *U.S. Public,* pg. 248
Sholder, Jason, Pres.--Datascope Cardiac Assist Division, Fairfield, NJ; *U.S. Public,* pg. 487
Shon, M., Pres.--Bohlin Instruments Inc., Cranbury, NJ; *Int'l,* pg. 208
Shon, Mark S., Pres. & Chief Exec. Officer--E-C Apparatus Corp., Saint Petersburg, FL; *U.S. Public,* pg. 1595

Shondel, Joe, Pres.--Selecto-Flash, Inc., West Orange, NJ; *U.S. Private*, pg. 982
Shonsey, Ed, Pres. & Chief Exec. Officer--Northrup King Co., Golden Valley, MN; *Int'l*, pg. 974
Shor, Charles, Pres.--Duro Bag Manufacturing Co., Ludlow, KY; *U.S. Private*, pg. 348
Shore, Brian, Pres.--Park Electrochemical Corporation, Lake Success, NY; *U.S. Public*, pg. 1258
Shore, Marc P., Chm. Bd., Pres. & Chief Exec. Officer--Shorewood Packaging Corporation, New York, NY; *U.S. Public*, pg. 1468
Shorenstein, Douglas W., Pres. & Chief Exec. Officer--Shorenstein Company, San Francisco, CA; *U.S. Private*, pg. 996
Shorin, Arthur T., Chm. Bd., Pres. & Chief Exec. Officer--The Topps Company, Inc., New York, NY; *U.S. Public*, pg. 1621
Short, Alan L., Pres. & Chief Exec. Officer--Peoples Bank & Trust Company, Sunman, IN; *U.S. Public*, pg. 633
Shostack, G. Lynn, Chm. Bd. & Pres.--Joyce International, Inc., New York, NY; *U.S. Private*, pg. 602
Shotts, David A., Pres.--Frisby P.M.C. Incorporated, Elk Grove Village, IL; *U.S. Public*, pg. 894
Shoulders, Barry W., Pres. & Chief Exec. Officer--BWI Kartridg Pak, Davenport, IA; *Int'l*, pg. 130
Shoup, Allen C., Pres. & Chief Exec. Officer--Stimson Lane Ltd., Woodinville, WA; *U.S. Public*, pg. 1661
Shoup, Andrew J., Jr., Pres. & Chief Exec. Officer--The Wiser Oil Company, Dallas, TX; *U.S. Public*, pg. 1773
Shouse, H.T., Chm., Pres. & Chief Exec. Officer--Morganfield National Bank, Morganfield, KY; *U.S. Public*, *pg. 1217*
Showalter, Neil D., Pres.--Cassco Ice & Cold Storage, Inc., Harrisonburg, VA; *U.S. Public*, pg. 1727
Showalter, Robert, Pres. & Chief Exec. Officer--National City Processing, Inc., Louisville, KY; *U.S. Public*, pg. 1154
Shreiber, Gerald B., Chm. Bd., Pres. & Chief Exec. Officer--J & J Snack Foods Corporation, Pennsauken, NJ; *U.S. Public*, pg. 916
Shrode, Dick, Pres.--Baldwin Filters, Kearney, NE; *U.S. Public*, pg. 381
Shroyer, J., Pres.--Sharp Digital Information Products, Inc., Irvine, CA; *Int'l*, pg. 1229
Shroyer, J., Pres.--Sharp Flat Display Manufacturing Company, Camas, WA; *Int'l*, pg. 1229
Shroyer, Jon A., Pres.--Sharp Microelectronics Technology, Inc., Camas, WA; *Int'l*, pg. 1229
Shubert, Jack, Partner & Corp. Media Dir.--Earle Palmer Brown, New York, NY; *U.S. Private*, pg. 173
Shubin, Lewis, Pres.--Sope Creek, Marietta, GA; *U.S. Public*, pg. 1539
Shucet, Phillip, Pres.--Baker Environmental, Inc., Coraopolis, PA; *U.S. Public*, pg. 168
Shuck, Michael, Pres.--Overholtzer Church Furniture, Inc., Modesto, CA; *U.S. Private*, pg. 823
Shuey, John H., Chm. Bd., Pres., Chief Exec. & Oper. Officer--Amcast Industrial Corporation, Dayton, OH; *U.S. Public*, pg. 63
Shuey, John H., Pres.--Amcast Industrial Ltd., Burlington, Canada; *U.S. Public*, pg. 63
Shuford, Jim, Pres.--Bowen Brothers Fruit Co., Inc., Winter Haven, FL; *U.S. Private*, pg. 162
Shuldiner, Arthur, Pres.--Durlacher & Co., Inc., Long Island City, NY; *U.S. Private*, pg. 348
Shull, Thomas C., Pres. & Chief Oper. Officer--Barneys Inc., New York, NY; *U.S. Private*, pg. 116
Shulman, Martin L., Pres. & Chief Oper. Officer--Customedix Corporation, Wallingford, CT; *U.S. Private*, pg. 298
Shultz, David C., Acting Pres.--Warner Press, Inc., Anderson, IN; *U.S. Private*, pg. 1150
Shultz, Ed, Pres.--Diamond Financial Holdings, Inc., Toledo, OH; *U.S. Public*, pg. 480
Shultz, Gerald, Chm. Bd., Pres. & Chief Exec. Officer--Micro-Met L Corp., Indianapolis, IN; *U.S. Private*, pg. 742
Shultz, Gordon W., Pres.--Schultz Steel Company, South Gate, CA; *U.S. Private*, pg. 973
Shultz, K., Pres. & Chief Oper. Officer--Swepco Tube Corporation, Clifton, NJ; *U.S. Private*, pg. 1058
Shultz, L.E., Pres. & Chief Exec. Officer--Smith & Wesson Corp., Springfield, MA; *Int'l*, pg. 1397
Shum, Martin, Chm. Bd., Pres. & Chief Exec. Officer--ACT Networks, Inc., Camarillo, CA; *U.S. Public*, pg. 3
Shundman, Bart C., Pres. & Chief Exec. Officer--Transact Technologies Incorporated, Wallingford, CT; *U.S. Public*, pg. 1629
Shupe, John, Pres.--TWC of Florida, Incorporated, Saint Petersburg, FL; *U.S. Public*, pg. 1755
Shura, Richard, Pres.--Central States Enterprises, Inc., Heathrow, FL; *U.S. Private*, pg. 225
Shure, Daniel B., Pres. & Chief Exec. Officer--Strombecker Corporation, Chicago, IL; *U.S. Private*, pg. 1047
Shurman, John, Pres.--Naturalle Springs, Inc., Greeneville, TN; *U.S. Private*, pg. 106
Shuster, George, Pres. & Chief Exec. Officer--Cranston Print Works Company, Cranston, RI; *U.S. Private*, pg. 286
Shuster, Jay, Pres. & Chief Oper. Officer--Rock-Tenn Company, Norcross, GA; *U.S. Public*, pg. 1396
Shusterman, Alan, Pres.--CMG Health, Owings Mills, MD; *U.S. Public*, pg. 1036
Shwed, Gil, Pres., Chief Exec. Officer & Co-Founder--Check Point Software Technologies Ltd., Redwood City, CA; *U.S. Public*, pg. 342
Shweky, Jack, Pres.--Regent International, New York, NY; *U.S. Private*, pg. 918
Shydlowski, L. Michael, Pres. & Chief Exec. Officer--Master Builders Inc., Cleveland, OH; *Int'l*, pg. 1465
Siciliano, Arthur A., Ph.D., Pres.--PolyMedica Industries, Inc., Woburn, MA; *U.S. Public*, pg. 1315
Siciliano, Arthur A., Ph.D., Pres.--PolyMedica Pharmaceuticals (U.S.A.), Inc., Woburn, MA; *U.S. Public*, pg. 1315
Sicina, Robert V., Pres.--American Express Bank Ltd., New York, NY; *U.S. Public*, pg. 73
Sicola, Tom, Pres. & Chief Exec. Officer--SicolaMartin Inc., Austin, TX; *U.S. Private*, pg. 998
Sicouri, Daniel, Pres.-O&M Paris--Ogilvy & Mather Worldwide, Inc., New York, NY; *Int'l*, pg. 1483
Siddens, Ernest G., Pres.--Union Electric Steel N.V., Tessenderlo, Belgium; *U.S. Public*, pg. 104
Siddens, Larry, Pres.--Reeves Brothers Inc., New York, NY; *U.S. Private*, pg. 507
Sidersky, Jean Pierre, Pres.--Mead Johnson S.A., Paris, France; *U.S. Public*, pg. 256
Sides, Harold L., Pres.--Engineers & Fabricators Co., Houston, TX; *U.S. Private*, pg. 377
Sidhu, Jay S., Pres. & Chief Exec. Officer--Sovereign Bancorp, Inc., Wyomissing, PA; *U.S. Public*, pg. 1494
Sidman, Ronald J., Chm. Bd., Pres. & Chief Exec. Officer--The First Years Inc., Avon, MA; *U.S. Public*, pg. 642
Sidor, Marek, Pres.--LOT Polish Airlines SA, New York, NY; *Int'l*, pg. 1062
Siebel, Carl, Pres. & Chief Exec. Officer--AptarGroup, Inc., Crystal Lake, IL; *U.S. Public*, pg. 125
Siebenburgen, David A., Pres. & Chief Oper. Officer--Comair Holdings, Inc., Erlanger, KY; *U.S. Public*, pg. 406
Siegal, Michael D., Chm. Bd., Pres. & Chief Exec. Officer--Olympic Steel Inc., Cleveland, OH; *U.S. Public*, pg. 1221
Siegel, Brad, Pres.--Turner Network Television, Inc., Atlanta, GA; *U.S. Public*, pg. 1615
Siegel, David, Pres.--Anglo Fabrics Company, Inc., New York, NY; *U.S. Private*, pg. 74
Siegel, David N., Pres.--Continental Express, Houston, TX; *U.S. Public*, pg. 439
Siegel, E. Courtney, Pres. & Chief Exec. Officer--Concurrent Computer Corporation, Fort Lauderdale, FL; *U.S. Public*, pg. 430
Siegel, Edward M., Jr., Pres. & Chief Exec. Officer--Russel Metals Inc., Mississauga, Canada; *Int'l*, pg. 1149
Siegel, Fred, Pres.--Secretly Yours Inc., Harrison, NJ; *U.S. Private*, pg. 565
Siegel, Herbert J., Chm. Bd. & Pres.--Chris-Craft Industries, Inc., New York, NY; *U.S. Public*, pg. 351
Siegel, Herbert J., Chm. Bd. & Pres.--BHC Communications, Inc., New York, NY; *U.S. Public*, pg. 352
Siegel, Jeffrey, Pres.--Blue Ridge Farms, Inc., Brooklyn, NY; *U.S. Private*, pg. 153
Siegel, L. Pendleton, Pres. & Chief Oper. Officer--Potlatch Corporation, Spokane, WA; *U.S. Public*, pg. 1318
Siegel, Randy, Partner, Exec. V.P. & Gen. Mgr.--Fleishman-Hillard, Inc., Atlanta, GA; *U.S. Private*, pg. 411
Siegel, Robert, Chm. Bd., Pres. & Chief Exec. Officer--The Stride Rite Corporation, Lexington, MA; *U.S. Public*, pg. 1524
Siegel, Scott, Pres.--R.S. Owens, Chicago, IL; *U.S. Private*, pg. 824
Siegel, Stuart N., Pres. & Mng. Dir.--Sotheby's International Realty, New York, NY; *U.S. Public*, pg. 1487
Siegel, Terry, Pres.--Butler Ventamatic Corp., Mineral Wells, TX; *U.S. Private*, pg. 190
Siegel, William D., Pres. & Chief Oper. Officer--BHC Communications, Inc., New York, NY; *U.S. Public*, pg. 352
Siegele, Stephen, Pres.--ADCS, Inc., Austin, TX; *U.S. Public*, pg. 12
Siegrist, Terrence, Pres.--Maxwell Technologies-Information Systems Division, San Diego, CA; *U.S. Public*, pg. 1062
Siegrist, Terry, Pres.--Information Systems Division, San Diego, CA; *U.S. Public*, pg. 1062
Sielck, Rainer, Dr., Pres.--AdvoCard Rechtsschutzversichereng AG, Hamburg, Germany; *Int'l*, pg. 15
Siemer, Arnold B., Chm. Bd. & Pres.--Desco Corporation, Columbus, OH; *U.S. Private*, pg. 326
Siemer, Richard C., Pres. & Chief Exec. Officer--Siemer Milling Company, Teutopolis, IL; *U.S. Private*, pg. 998
Siemers, Frank, Pres. & Gen. Counsel--Norddeutsche Landesbank (NORD/LB), Hannover, Germany; *Int'l*, pg. 957
Sierk, James, Acting Pres. & Chief Exec. Officer--Iomega Corporation, Roy, UT; *U.S. Public*, pg. 912
Sierra, Anthony, Pres.--Business Mens Insurance Corporation, Coral Gables, FL; *U.S. Private*, pg. 189
Siess, Robert D., P.E., Pres. & Chief Oper. Officer--Tarlton Corporation, Saint Louis, MO; *U.S. Private*, pg. 1069
Siewert, Reinhart, Chm. Bd. & Pres.--Koenig & Bauer-Albert AG, Wurzburg, Germany; *Int'l*, pg. 742
Sigal, Gerald R., Chm. Bd. & Pres.--SIGAL CONSTRUCTION CORP., Washington, DC; *U.S. Private*, pg. 999
Sigel, Arthur R., Chm. Bd., Pres. & Chief Exec. Officer--Velsicol Chemical Corporation, Rosemont, IL; *U.S. Private*, pg. 1135
Sigley, Timothy D., Pres.--Plastic Packaging Company, Muncie, IN; *U.S. Public*, pg. 57
Sigman, Stan, Pres. & Chief Exec. Officer--Southwestern Bell Mobile Systems, Inc., Dallas, TX; *U.S. Public*, pg. 1415
Sigmund, Tom, Pres.--Sportsman Supply, Saint Clair, MO; *U.S. Private*, pg. 1026
Signeski, Leonard L., Chm. Bd., Pres. & Chief Exec. Officer--Syndicate Systems, Inc., Middlebury, IN; *U.S. Private*, pg. 1060
Signorelli, Ivan, Pres.--American Flange & Manufacturing Co. Inc., Carol Stream, IL; *Int'l*, pg. 1146
Sik, Eom Dae, Pres.--Korea Otsuka Pharmaceutical Co., Ltd., Seoul, Korea; *Int'l*, pg. 1014
Sikes, Alfred C., Pres.--Hearst New Media & Technology, New York, NY; *U.S. Private*, pg. 517
Silavanich, Thanarak, Pres.--Siam Mariwasa Toto, Inc., Manila, Philippines; *Int'l*, pg. 1410
Silbermayr, Franz, Dr., Gen. Mgr.--J.M. Voith AG, Saint Polten, Austria; *Int'l*, pg. 1473
Silberstein, Bruce Jay, Pres.--Columbus Pipe & Equipment Company, Columbus, OH; *U.S. Private*, pg. 257
Siler, Ron, Pres.--West Kentucky Division, Sturgis, KY; *Int'l*, pg. 337
Silk, Bert, Pres. & Div. Mgr.--Bisceglia Brothers Wine Co., Madera, CA; *U.S. Public*, pg. 300
Sill, Michael, II, Pres.--Road Machinery & Supplies Co., Savage, MN; *U.S. Private*, pg. 934
Sills, Lawrence I., Pres. & Chief Exec. & Oper. Officer--Standard Motor Products Inc., Long Island City, NY; *U.S.* Public, pg. 1503
Sills, Stephen J., Pres. & Chief Exec. Officer--Executive Risk, Inc., Simsbury, CT; *U.S. Public*, pg. 599
Silva Salgado, Ricardo Espirito Santo, Vice Chm., Pres. & Chief Exec. Officer--Banco Espirito Santo e Comercial de Lisboa SA, Lisbon, Portugal; *Int'l*, pg. 142
Silva, Antonio Britoda, Pres.--Portuguese Railways (CP), Lisbon, Portugal; *Int'l*, pg. 1063
Silva, Gil, Pres.--J.A. Sexauer, Inc., Scarsdale, NY; *U.S. Private*, pg. 352
Silver, Abby, Pres.--Wolf Manufacturing Company, Waco, TX; *U.S. Private*, pg. 1186
Silver, Bertram R., Pres.--Jenkins Spirits Corp. Ltd., Londonderry, NH; *U.S. Private*, pg. 585
Silver, Martin, Chm. Bd., Pres. & Chief Exec. Officer--Star Industries Inc., Syosset, NY; *U.S. Private*, pg. 1034
Silver, Stan, Pres. & Chief Oper. Officer--The Children's Place Retail Stores, Inc., West Caldwell, NJ; *U.S. Private*, pg. 237
Silver, Walton A., Pres. & Chief Exec. Officer--Akrochem Corporation, Akron, OH; *U.S. Private*, pg. 30
Silverman, Bruce, Pres. & New Bus. Contact--Asher/Gould Advertising, Inc., Los Angeles, CA; *U.S. Private*, pg. 88
Silverman, Gene, Pres.--Hawthorne Communications, Inc., Fairfield, IA; *U.S. Private*, pg. 512
Silverman, Henry R., Pres. & Chief Exec. Officer--Cendant Corporation, Stamford, CT; *U.S. Public*, pg. 320
Silverman, Mark, Publr. & Editor--The Detroit News, Detroit, MI; *U.S. Public*, pg. 700
Silverman, Michael D., Pres.--The Jaydor Corporation, Millburn, NJ; *U.S. Private*, pg. 584
Silverman, Paul, Principal & Chief Creative Officer--Mullen Advertising, Inc., Wenham, MA; *U.S. Private*, pg. 766
Silvers, Brett N., Chm. Bd. & Pres.--First International Bancorp, Inc., Hartford, CT; *U.S. Public*, pg. 635
Silverstein, Allan, Pres. & Chief Oper. Officer--The Bethlehem Corporation, Easton, PA; *U.S. Public*, pg. 225
Silverstein, Robert, Pres. & Chief Exec. Officer--Arch Aluminium & Glass L.C., Tamarac, FL; *U.S. Private*, pg. 79
Silvertooth, Jerry, Pres.--Hausted, Medina, OH; *U.S. Private*, *pg. 1001*
Silvestri, Phil, Partner--Messner Vetere Berger McNamee Schmetterer/EURO RSCG, New York, NY; *Int'l*, pg. 602
Simard, Jean Francois, Pres. & Gen. Mgr.--Lumec, Inc., Boisbriand, Canada; *U.S. Public*, pg. 1599
Simard, Ronald F.E., Pres. & Chief Oper. Officer--Nowsco Well Service Ltd., Calgary, Canada; *Int'l*, pg. 989
Simeons, P.C.C., Pres.--Koninklijke Bunge B.V., Rotterdam, Netherlands; *Int'l*, pg. 753
Simkins, L.J., Chm. Bd., Pres., Chief Exec. & Chief Oper. Officer--Simkins Industries, Inc., New Haven, CT; *U.S. Private*, pg. 1000
Simko, John S., Pres.--Minera Sunshine Del Peru, S.A., Lima, Peru; *U.S. Public*, pg. 1536
Simm, David, Pres. & Chief Oper. Officer--Doncasters plc, Melbourn, United Kingdom; *Int'l*, pg. 416
Simmers, Terry, Pres.--Silver Springs Citrus Co-op, Howey in the Hills, FL; *U.S. Private*, pg. 1000
Simmons, A.R., Pres.--Pipe Fabricating & Supply Company, Santa Fe Springs, CA; *U.S. Private*, pg. 867
Simmons, Christopher J., Pres.--U.S. Filter, Lowell, MA; *U.S.* Public, pg. 1682
Simmons, D. Ramsay, Jr., Pres. & Chief Exec. Officer--Elberta Crate & Box Company, Bainbridge, GA; *U.S. Private*, pg. 367
Simmons, Gary F., Pres.--Healthtex, Greensboro, NC; *U.S. Public*, pg. 1702
Simmons, Gaylan, Pres. & Chief Exec. Officer--Pacific Northern Inc., Seattle, WA; *U.S. Private*, pg. 832
Simmons, George M., Pres.--First Chemical Corp., Pascagoula, MS; *U.S. Public*, pg. 344
Simmons, Hardwick, Pres. & Chief Exec. Officer--Prudential Securities Inc., New York, NY; *U.S. Private*, pg. 892
Simmons, Harold C., Chm. Bd., Pres. & Chief Exec. Officer--Contran Corporation, Dallas, TX; *U.S. Private*, pg. 270
Simmons, Harris H., Pres. & Chief Exec. Officer--Zions Bancorporation, Salt Lake City, UT; *U.S. Public*, pg. 1792
Simmons, James P., Pres.--The Weitz Company, Inc., Des Moines, IA; *U.S. Private*, pg. 1161
Simmons, John, Pres.--Hoosier Insurance Company, Indianapolis, IN; *Int'l*, pg. 346
Simmons, Paul, Chm. Bd. & Pres.--Simons Palmer Denton Clemmow & Johnson Ltd., London, United Kingdom; *Int'l*, pg. 1252
Simmons, Richard E., III, Pres. & Chief Exec. Officer--Hilb, Rogal and Hamilton Company of Alabama, Inc., Birmingham, AL; *U.S. Public*, pg. 827
Simmons, Richard P., Chm. Bd., Pres. & Chief Exec. Officer--Allegheny Teledyne Incorporated, Pittsburgh, PA; *U.S. Public*, pg. 43
Simms, Richard, Pres.--Media Partnership Corporation, Norwalk, CT; *U.S. Private*, pg. 1168
Simms, Stephen, Pres.--Danaher Tool Group, Chicago, IL; *U.S. Public*, pg. 481
Simms, Steven E., Pres.-Professional Tools Div.--Danaher Tool Group, Lancaster, PA; *U.S. Public*, pg. 480
Simms, Steven E., Acting Pres.--Hennessy Industries, Inc., La Vergne, TN; *U.S. Public*, pg. 481
Simo, Zoltan, Pres. & Chief Oper. Officer--TecSyn International, Inc., Saint Catharines, Canada; *Int'l*, pg. 1361
Simoes, Joao, Pres.--Kvaerner do Brasil Ltda, Rio de Janeiro, Brazil; *Int'l*, pg. 767
Simoes, Joao, Pres.--Kvaerner Ships Equipment Ltda., Rio de Janeiro, Brazil; *Int'l*, pg. 768

Simon, Abdallah H., Chm.--Seagram Chateau & Estate Wines Co., New York, NY; *Int'l*, pg. 1215

Simon, Alan, Co-Pres.--Allied Sporting Goods Inc., Louisville, KY; *U.S. Private*, pg. 41

Simon, Bruce, Pres.--Omaha Steaks, Omaha, NE; *U.S. Private*, pg. 815

Simon, David A., Chm. Bd., Pres. & Chief Exec. Officer--Prime Hospitality Corp., Fairfield, NJ; *U.S. Public*, pg. 1326

Simon, Donald R., Chm. Bd., Pres. & Treas.--Contractors Steel Company, Livonia, MI; *U.S. Private*, pg. 270

Simon, Donald S., Jr., Pres.--Serta Mattress Company, Vacaville, CA; *U.S. Private*, pg. 985

Simon, Edward, Pres.--Eagle Button Co., Inc., Carlstadt, NJ; *U.S. Private*, pg. 354

Simon, Edward, Pres.--Tho-Ro Products, Inc., Carlstadt, NJ; *U.S. Private*, pg. 354

Simon, Georg, Pres.--Rosenthal U.S.A. Limited, Carlstadt, NJ; *Int'l*, pg. 1127

Simon, Irwin D., Pres. & Chief Exec. Officer--The Hain Food Group Inc., Uniondale, NY; *U.S. Public*, pg. 774

Simon, Juan Antonio Per, Pres.--Telefonos de Mexico S.A. de C.V., Mexico, Mexico; *Int'l*, pg. 1373

Simon, Loretta L., Pres.--Nason and Cullen Inc., King of Prussia, PA; *U.S. Private*, pg. 775

Simon, Martin, Pres.--Triangle Brass Manufacturing, Los Angeles, CA; *U.S. Private*, pg. 1101

Simon, Phillip, Pres.--Joseph Simon & Sons, Inc., Tacoma, WA; *U.S. Private*, pg. 1001

Simon, Ralph, Dr., Pres. & Chief Exec. Officer--QT Optoelectronics, Sunnyvale, CA; *U.S. Private*, pg. 897

Simon, Raymond, Pres.--Giant Industries, Toledo, OH; *U.S. Private*, pg. 451

Simonds, Christopher E., Pres. & Chief Exec. Officer--Genelco, Inc., Saint Louis, MO; *U.S. Private*, pg. 443

Simone, James, Jr., Pres.--Ideal Forging Corporation, Southington, CT; *U.S. Private*, pg. 557

Simone, John J., Pres.--LTCB Trust Company, New York, NY; *Int'l*, pg. 816

Simonin, Dominique, Mng. Partner-Europe--Conquest Europe, Turin, Italy; *Int'l*, pg. 1484

Simons, Carl, Pres.--Gateway Apparel, Inc., Saint Louis, MO; *U.S. Private*, pg. 441

Simonson, Karl D., Pres.--Ontario Foods, Inc., Albion, NY; *U.S. Public*, pg. 728

Simonson, Robert, Pres.--MARC Promotion, Indianapolis, IN; *U.S. Private*, pg. 701

Simourian, John, II, Pres. & Chief Oper. Officer--Lily Transportation Corp., Needham, MA; *U.S. Private*, pg. 667

Simpson, Barrie, Pres.--Warren Industries, Inc., Lafayette, IN; *U.S. Private*, pg. 945

Simpson, Bruce D., Pres. & Chief Exec. Officer--Lucent Netcare Messaging Services, Dallas, TX; *U.S. Public*, pg. 1018

Simpson, Bruce W., Pres. & Chief Oper. Officer--Nova Gas Transmission Ltd., Calgary, Canada; *Int'l*, pg. 971

Simpson, David W., Pres.--Westmoreland Resources, Inc., Billings, MT; *U.S. Public*, pg. 1761

Simpson, Jim, Pres.-Periscope Communication Alternatives--Periscope Marketing Communications, Minneapolis, MN; *U.S. Private*, pg. 853

Simpson, John, Pres. & Chief Exec. Officer--H.E. Sargent, Inc., Stillwater, ME; *U.S. Private*, pg. 966

Simpson, Louis A., Pres. & Chief Exec. Officer-Capital Opers.--GEICO Corporation, Washington, DC; *U.S. Public*, pg. 219

Simpson, Mark E., Pres.--Portsmouth Savings Bank, Portsmouth, NH; *U.S. Public*, pg. 278

Simpson, Murray S., Jr., V.P.--Super Concrete Corp., Washington, DC; *Int'l*, pg. 166

Simpson, Phil, Chm. Bd., Pres. & Chief Exec. Officer--Republic Group Incorporated, Hutchinson, KS; *U.S. Public*, pg. 1378

Simpson, Sam, Pres. & Chief Exec. Officer--Cable Car Beverage Corporation, Denver, CO; *U.S. Public*, pg. 1635

Sims-Brown, Priscilla, Pres.--Lincoln Financial Advisors, Fort Wayne, IN; *U.S. Public*, pg. 998

Sims, James K., Pres. & Chief Exec. Officer--Cambridge Technology Partners, Cambridge, MA; *U.S. Public*, pg. 1424

Sims, Jerry L., Pres. & Treas.--Hilb, Rogal and Hamilton Company of Houston, Houston, TX; *U.S. Public*, pg. 827

Sims, Larry D., Pres. & Chief Exec. Officer--Marley Floors (USA) Inc., Tuscumbia, AL; *Int'l*, pg. 843

Sims, Paul, Pres.--Houston Division, Houston, TX; *U.S. Public*, pg. 1683

Sims, Richard, Pres.--Tranzonic Industrial Textiles Division, Highland Heights, OH; *U.S. Public*, pg. 1632

Sims, Robert, Mng. Dir.--The Media Shop Limited, London, United Kingdom; *Int'l*, pg. 853

Sims, William J., Pres.--Zenith Sales Co. Div., Glenview, IL; *U.S. Public*, pg. 1790

Sims, Willis D., Pres. & Chief Exec. Officer--SunTrust Bank, South Georgia, N.A., Albany, GA; *U.S. Public*, pg. 1538

Simunek, Tom, Pres. & Chief Exec. Officer--Bradley Printing Company, Des Plaines, IL; *U.S. Public*, pg. 1776

Simunovich, Joseph, Pres.--United Water Management & Services, Harrington Park, NJ; *U.S. Public*, pg. 1692

Sin, Lau Chan, Deputy Pres. & Deputy Chief Oper. Officer--DBS Bank Ltd., Singapore, Singapore; *Int'l*, pg. 350

Sinclair, Bruce, Pres.--Dell Computer Corporation, North York, Canada; *U.S. Public*, pg. 496

Sinclair, Christopher A., Pres. & Chief Exec. Officer--Quality Food Centers, Inc., Bellevue, WA; *U.S. Public*, pg. 1349

Sinclair, Christopher D., Pres. & Chief Exec. Officer--QFC Holding Company, Stamford, CT; *U.S. Public*, pg. 1349

Sinclair, D., Pres.--Noma-International, Inc., Itasca, IL; *Int'l*, pg. 955

Sinclair, David, Pres. & Chief Fin. Officer--Pasotex Corporation, El Paso, TX; *U.S. Private*, pg. 842

Sinclair, Desmond, Chm. Bd. & Pres.--DEECO Industries, Hillside, NJ; *U.S. Private*, pg. 320

Sinclair, Desmond W., Pres.--Siltin Industries, Inc., Hillside, NJ; *U.S. Private*, pg. 320

Sinclair, Robert J., Pres.--Sinclair Printing & Litho, Inc., Los Angeles, CA; *U.S. Private*, pg. 1003

Sincoff, Jerome J., Pres.--Hellmuth, Obata & Kassabaum, Inc., Saint Louis, MO; *U.S. Private*, pg. 520

Sindelka, Ing. Dr. Josef, Gen. Dir.--Austrian Postal & Telegraph Administration, Vienna, Austria; *Int'l*, pg. 101

Sinden, Roy, Pres.--Ready-Lite Mfg. Ltd., Victoria, Canada; *Int'l*, pg. 725

Sinegal, James D., Pres. & Chief Exec. Officer--Costco Wholesale, Issaquah, WA; *U.S. Public*, pg. 451

Sines, James V., Pres.--United Aviation Fuels Corp., Elk Grove Village, IL; *U.S. Public*, pg. 1653

Singer, Elliott, Pres.--Fox-Knapp, Bay Shore, NY; *U.S. Private*, pg. 860

Singer, Garold G., Pres. & Chief Exec. Officer--Alpine Packing Company, Stockton, CA; *U.S. Private*, pg. 45

Singer, H.L., Pres.--Powers Process Controls, Skokie, IL; *U.S. Public*, pg. 457

Singer, James O., Pres. & Chief Oper. Officer--International Total Services, Independence, OH; *U.S. Public*, pg. 908

Singer, Joel L., Pres. & Chief Oper. Officer--Bay State Gas Company, Westborough, MA; *U.S. Public*, pg. 196

Singer, Karl, Pres.--Karl Singer Companies, Inc., Chicago, IL; *U.S. Public*, pg. 118

Singer, Marty, Pres.--Safco Technologies, Inc., Chicago, IL; *U.S. Public*, pg. 1430

Singer, Robert W., Pres., Chief Exec. Officer & Chief Oper. Officer--Keystone Consolidated Industries, Inc., Dallas, TX; *U.S. Public*, pg. 955

Singer, Stephen H., Pres.--Merchants Rent A Car, Inc., Hooksett, NH; *U.S. Private*, pg. 732

Singh, Jeet, Pres. & Chief Exec. Officer--Art Technology Group, Boston, MA; *U.S. Private*, pg. 86

Singh, Ranjit, Pres.--Ranjit Corporation, Cedar Knolls, NJ; *U.S. Private*, pg. 909

Singleton, R.L., Pres. & Chief Exec. Officer--Russell-Stanley Corporation, Red Bank, NJ; *U.S. Private*, pg. 953

Singleton, William Dean, Pres. & Chief Exec. Officer--MediaNews Group Inc., Denver, CO; *U.S. Private*, pg. 727

Sinton, Thomas H., Chm. Bd., Pres. & Chief Exec. Officer--ProBusiness Services, Inc., Pleasanton, CA; *U.S. Public*, pg. 1330

Sipf, Eric, Pres.--Pacificare of Colorado, Englewood, CO; *U.S. Public*, pg. 1251

Sipos, Donald J., Pres.--SL Surface Technology, Inc., Camden, NJ; *U.S. Public*, pg. 1419

Siraci, Serdar, Pres.--Danko Gida Ticaret A.S., Istanbul, Turkey; *Int'l*, pg. 288

Sirotek, H. Bruce, Pres.--Illinois Auto Electric Co., Elmhurst, IL; *U.S. Private*, pg. 557

Sirotkin, Paul, Pres.--Rapid Industrial Plastics Company, Jersey City, NJ; *U.S. Private*, pg. 910

Sison III, Leopoldo S., Pres.--BMC Forestry Corporation, Baguio, Philippines; *Int'l*, pg. 186

Sissel, George A., Chm. Bd., Pres. & Chief Exec. Officer--Ball Corporation, Muncie, IN; *U.S. Public*, pg. 170

Sisson, Thomas W., Pres. & Chief Oper. Officer--Citibank, Federal Savings Bank (Illinois), Chicago, IL; *U.S. Public*, pg. 378

Sitarz, Richard, Pres. & Chief Oper. Officer--Prospect Foundry, Inc., Minneapolis, MN; *U.S. Public*, pg. 142

Siteman, Alvin, Pres.--Site Oil Company of Missouri, Clayton, MO; *U.S. Private*, pg. 1004

Sitt, Eddie, Pres.--Baby Togs, Inc., New York, NY; *U.S. Private*, pg. 108

Sitver, Leonard A., Pres.--Dexter Chemical Corp., Bronx, NY; *U.S. Private*, pg. 329

Sivalls, C. Richard, Pres. & Chief Exec. Officer--Sivalls, Inc., Odessa, TX; *U.S. Private*, pg. 1004

Sivitz, William, Pres.--Wallpapers-To-Go, Houston, TX; *U.S. Private*, pg. 1175

Sivoolt, Gelt, Pres.--Falkema AB, Falkenberg, Sweden; *Int'l, pg. 477*

Sizemore, Mason, Pres. & Chief Oper. Officer--Seattle Times Company, Seattle, WA; *U.S. Private*, pg. 980

Sjoberg, Alf, Pres.--Industriventilation Produkt AB, Vaxjo, Sweden; *Int'l*, pg. 1260

Sjogren, Hans, Pres.--Esselte Europe, London, United Kingdom; *Int'l*, pg. 460

Sjogren, Wade R., Pres.--Whibco, Inc., Bridgeton, NJ; *U.S. Private*, pg. 1171

Sjokvist, Goran, Pres.--LBI Luftbehandling AB, Karlstad, Sweden; *Int'l*, pg. 1261

Sjoqvist, Jan, Pres. & Chief Exec. Officer--NCC AB, Solna, Sweden; *Int'l*, pg. 898

Skaggs, James B., Chm. Bd., Pres. & Chief Exec. Officer--Tracor, Inc., Austin, TX; *U.S. Public*, pg. 1627

Skaggs, Robert C., Jr., Pres. & Chief Exec. Officer--Columbia Gas of Kentucky, Inc., Columbus, OH; *U.S. Public*, pg. 403

Skaggs, Robert C., Jr., Pres. & Chief Exec. Officer--Columbia Gas of Ohio, Inc., Columbus, OH; *U.S. Public*, pg. 403

Skandalaris, Robert J., Pres. & Chief Exec. Officer--Noble International Ltd., Bloomfield Hills, MI; *U.S. Public*, pg. 1187

Skates, Ronald L., Pres. & Chief Exec. Officer--Data General Corporation, Westborough, MA; *U.S. Public*, pg. 485

Skawski, Robert, Pres.--Motek Engineering & Manufacturing Company, Cambridge, MN; *U.S. Private*, pg. 764

Skeates, William B., Pres.--Naylor Pipe Company, Chicago, IL; *U.S. Private*, pg. 789

Skelley, John, Pres.--Arizona Grains Inc., Casa Grande, AZ; *U.S. Private*, pg. 81

Skerl, Damir, Pres.--Western Atlas Logging Services, Houston, TX; *U.S. Public*, pg. 1757

Skibitsky, William S., Pres. & Chief Oper. Officer--MYR Group Inc., Rolling Meadows, IL; *U.S. Public*, pg. 1029

Skidmore, A. Allan, Vice Chm., Pres. & Chief Exec. Officer-Automotive Grp.--TCG International Inc., Burnaby, Canada; *Int'l*, pg. 1336

Skidmore, Doug, Pres.--Hobie Cat Company, Oceanside, CA; *U.S. Private*, pg. 531

Skidmore, James A., Jr., Chm. Bd., Pres. & Chief Exec. Officer--Science Management Corporation, Bridgewater, NJ; *U.S. Public*, pg. 1717

Skidmore, Thomas E., Chm. Bd., Pres. & Chief Exec. Officer--Glentel Inc., Burnaby, Canada; *Int'l*, pg. 1336

Skiff, Tom, Pres.--Amex Life Assurance Co., San Rafael, CA; *U.S. Public*, pg. 712

Skiles, ALlan, Pres.--Tolk, Inc., Fairfax, VA; *U.S. Private*, pg. 329

Skilling, Jeffrey K., Pres. & Chief Oper. Officer--Enron Corp., Houston, TX; *U.S. Public*, pg. 584

Skilton, Harry I., Pres. & Chief Exec. Officer--American Meter Company, Horsham, PA; *Int'l*, pg. 1149

Skinner, John, Pres.--Jeweler's Financial Service, Inc., Irving, TX; *U.S. Public*, pg. 1789

Skinner, Samuel K., Pres.--Unicom Corporation, Chicago, IL; *U.S. Public*, pg. 1664

Skinner, Samuel K., Pres.--ComEd, Chicago, IL; *U.S. Public, pg. 1664*

Skipper, John, V.P. of Magazines--Discover, New York, NY; *U.S. Public*, pg. 513

Skirka, Kenneth John, Pres., Chief Exec. & Oper. Officer, Mng. Dir.--Australian Oil & Gas Corporation Limited, Sydney, Australia; *Int'l*, pg. 101

Skjelbred, Gunnar, Pres.--Kvaerner Gibralter Ltd., Gibraltar, Gibraltar; *Int'l*, pg. 772

Skoda, Dan, Pres.--Marshall Field, Chicago, IL; *U.S. Public*, pg. 489

Skoda, Mark, Pres.--TNT Logistics North America, Linthicum Heights, MD; *Int'l*, pg. 1343

Skoghall, Daniel, Pres.--Drott AB, Goteborg, Sweden; *Int'l*, pg. 1260

Skogsberg, Lennart, Pres.--NCC Goteburg, Goteborg, Sweden; *Int'l*, pg. 899

Skolds, John L., Pres.--SCANA Resources, Inc., Columbia, SC; *U.S. Public*, pg. 1436

Skornicki, Eli, Pres.--Cometals, New York, NY; *U.S. Public*, pg. 412

Skough, Jan, Pres. & Chief Oper. Officer--Skandia U.S. Holding Corporation, New York, NY; *Int'l*, pg. 1257

Skov, Per, Pres.--RT Reklamebureau A/S, Albertslund, Denmark; *Int'l*, pg. 1081

Skraning, Gyrd, Pres. & Chief Exec. Officer--Helly-Hansen A/S, Moss, Norway; *Int'l*, pg. 1010

Skrenes, Larry D., Pres.--TDS Computing Services, Inc., Madison, WI; *U.S. Public*, pg. 1572

Skrypek, John, Pres.--Sequa Can Machinery, East Rutherford, NJ; *U.S. Public*, pg. 1458

Skuba, William C., Chm. Bd., Pres., Chief Exec. Officer & Sec.--Eastern Environmental Services, Inc., Drums, PA; *U.S. Public*, pg. 549

Skweres, Mark, Pres.--Evans Environmental & Geological Science and Management Inc., Miami, FL; *U.S. Public*, pg. 563

Skyes, Joe W., Pres.--Key Risk Management Services, Inc., Greensboro, NC; *U.S. Public*, pg. 216

Slack, John L., Chm. Bd., Pres., Chief Exec. Officer & Acting Treas.--DBA Systems, Inc., Melbourne, FL; *U.S. Public*, pg. 472

Slade, Len, Pres.--SuperValu, Inc.-Hazelwood Div., Hazelwood, MO; *U.S. Public*, pg. 1540

Slade, Leonard J., Pres.--SuperValu, Inc.-St. Louis Div., Hazelwood, MO; *U.S. Public*, pg. 1541

Slade, Thomas H., Pres.--TCI, Inc., Ellaville, GA; *U.S. Public*, pg. 1358

Sladek, Keith, Pres.--Lyon Metal Products, Inc., Montgomery, IL; *U.S. Private*, pg. 638

Slaine, Mason P., Pres. & Chief Exec. Officer--Thomson Financial Services, Stamford, CT; *U.S. Public*, pg. 1601

Slama, Thomas G., Pres. & Chief Exec. Officer--National Infusion Services, Inc., Indianapolis, IN; *U.S. Public*, pg. 229

Slane, John C., Pres.--Slane Hosiery Mills, Inc., High Point, NC; *U.S. Private*, pg. 1005

Slate, Johnny, Chm. Bd. & Pres.--Affiliated Publishers, Inc., Nashville, TN; *U.S. Private*, pg. 26

Slate, William K., II, Pres. & Chief Exec. Officer--American Arbitration Association, New York, NY; *U.S. Private*, pg. 50

Slater, John, Pres.--ARCO Coal Company, Denver, CO; *U.S. Public*, pg. 144

Slater, John, Chm. Bd. & Pres.--Orange Grove Co-operative, Orange Grove, TX; *U.S. Private*, pg. 818

Slater, John E., Jr., Pres. & Chief Exec. Officer--Haverty Furniture Companies, Inc., Atlanta, GA; *U.S. Public*, pg. 799

Slater, Thomas F., Chm. Bd., Pres. & Chief Exec. Officer--Actron Manufacturing Company, Cleveland, OH; *U.S. Private*, pg. 16

Slattery, James F., Pres. & Chief Oper. Officer--Correctional Services Corporation, Sarasota, FL; *U.S. Public*, pg. 450

Slattery, Nora Jane, Sr. Partner & Corp. Communications Dir.--Ogilvy & Mather Worldwide, Inc., New York, NY; *Int'l*, pg. 1483

Slaughter, C. Lane, Pres.--Glenroy Construction Co. Inc., Indianapolis, IN; *U.S. Private*, pg. 456

Slavin, Roy H., Chm. Bd., Pres. & Chief Exec. Officer--Wonderware Corporation, Irvine, CA; *U.S. Public*, pg. 1775

Slaybaugh, Jon, Pres.--Namco Controls GmbH, Herzhorn, Germany; *U.S. Public*, pg. 482

Slayton, Maurice, Pres.--Conning, Hartford, CT; *U.S. Private, pg. 443*

Sleepeck, Michael, Pres.--Sleepeck Printing Company, Bellwood, IL; *U.S. Private*, pg. 1005

Sleewuwenhoek, Hans, Pres. & Chief Exec. Officer--Tactyl Technologies, Inc., Vista, CA; *U.S. Public*, pg. 1425

Slehofer, Gerald, Pres.--Aydin Molded Devices Div., Rancho Dominguez, CA; *U.S. Public*, pg. 158

Sleigh, Ron, Pres. & Chief Exec. Officer--UPB of North Central Tennessee, Erin, TN; *U.S. Public*, pg. 1669
Slevin, Jack, Chm. Bd., Pres. & Chief Exec. Officer--Comdisco, Inc., Rosemont, IL; *U.S. Public*, pg. 407
Slifka, Alfred A., Pres. & Chief Exec. Officer--Global Petroleum Corp., Waltham, MA; *U.S. Private*, pg. 457
Slingerlend, Mac J., Pres. & Chief Oper. Officer--Ciber, Inc., Englewood, CO; *U.S. Public*, pg. 356
Sloan, Craig, Pres.--The GSI Group, Inc., Assumption, IL; *U.S. Private*, pg. 436
Sloan, Janet N., Pres.--Willis Corroon Corp. of South Carolina, Greenville, SC; *Int'l*, pg. 1507
Sloan, Morton, Chm. Bd. & Pres.--Inner Secrets, Inc., Harrison, NJ; *U.S. Private*, pg. 564
Sloan, Temple, III, Pres.--Carquest Corp., Lakewood, CO; *U.S. Private*, pg. 445
Sloan, William P., Pres.--George Lithograph, Brisbane, CA; *U.S. Private*, pg. 448
Sloane, Larry, Pres.--Questron Div., Los Angeles, CA; *Int'l*, pg. 1215
Sloane, Thomas G., Pres.--Hamlin, Inc., Lake Mills, WI; *U.S. Public*, pg. 251
Slobig, R.J., Gen. Mgr.--Emerson Motor Company, Sturgeon Bay, WI; *U.S. Public*, pg. 573
Slocum, Christopher B., Pres.--Cornell Storefront Systems, Inc., Mountain Top, PA; *U.S. Private*, pg. 276
Slocum, Frank H., Pres.--Raybestos Aftermarket Products Co., Crawfordsville, IN; *U.S. Public*, pg. 1363
Slocum, G.F., Pres.--Detector Electronics Corporation, Minneapolis, MN; *Int'l*, pg. 1500
Slocum, Ronald A., Chm. & Pres.--Bank of America Idaho, Boise, ID; *U.S. Public*, pg. 180
Slogrove, Richard, Pres.--Memorex Telex Canada Inc., Markham, Canada; *Int'l*, pg. 857
Sloma, Greg, Pres. & Chief Oper. Officer--Data Transmission Network Corporation, Omaha, NE; *U.S. Public*, pg. 486
Slosberg, Lee R., Pres.--Crown America Life Insurance Company, Alexandria, VA; *Int'l*, pg. 468
Sloss, Lynes, Pres. & Chief Exec. Officer--Bellwether Technology Corporation, New Orleans, LA; *U.S. Private*, pg. 132
Slott, David M., Pres.--TruGreen-ChemLawn, Memphis, TN; *U.S. Public*, pg. 1461
Sloup, Frank B., Pres.--Pet Life Foods, Inc., Willowbrook, IL; *U.S. Private*, pg. 856
Slovin, Bruce, Pres.--MacAndrews & Forbes Holdings Inc., New York, NY; *U.S. Private*, pg. 689
Slovin, Bruce, Pres.--Andrews Group, Incorporated, New York, NY; *U.S. Private*, pg. 689
Slowik, Lawrence, Pres. & Chief Exec. Officer--AR Accessories Group, Inc., Milwaukee, WI; *U.S. Private*, pg. 7
Slusarchuk, William A., Pres. & Chief Exec. Officer--AGRA Earth & Environmental Limited, Calgary, Canada; *Int'l*, pg. 30
Sluszka, Peter, Pres.--Steinman, Boynton, Gronquist & Birdsall Inc., New York, NY; *U.S. Private*, pg. 842
Sly, P.J., Pres.--Ridge Tool Co., Elyria, OH; *U.S. Public*, pg. 574
Slyman, Peter J., Pres.--Wagnerware Corporation, Sidney, OH; *U.S. Private*, pg. 1146
Small, George M., Pres.--Offshore Logistics, Inc., Lafayette, LA; *U.S. Public*, pg. 1212
Small, Lawrence M., Pres. & Chief Oper. Officer--Federal National Mortgage Association (Fannie Mae), Washington, DC; *U.S. Public*, pg. 615
Small, Robert, Pres. & Chief Exec. Officer--The Fairmont Hotels, San Francisco, CA; *U.S. Private*, pg. 391
Smalley, Gary, Pres.--Dayton Parts, Inc., Harrisburg, PA; *U.S. Public*, pg. 919
Smalley, Randall S., Pres. & Chief Exec. Officer--Cruise America, Inc., Mesa, AZ; *U.S. Private*, pg. 178
Smallwood, Robert, Pres.--Allied Colloids Chemicals (Far East) Pte. Ltd., Singapore, Singapore; *Int'l*, pg. 62
Smead, L.H., Pres.--Sasco Group, Cerritos, CA; *U.S. Private*, pg. 967
Smeller, Carl J., Pres. & Chief Exec. Officer--Buckeye Corrugated Inc., Wooster, OH; *U.S. Private*, pg. 177
Smets, Raymond J., II, Pres.--BellSouth Applied Technologies, Inc., Atlanta, GA; *U.S. Public*, pg. 209
Smialek, Robert L., Pres. & Chief Exec. Officer--Insilco Corporation, Dublin, OH; *U.S. Public*, pg. 881
Smillie, Greg, Pres.--Hennells, Inc., Ferndale, MI; *U.S. Private*, pg. 522
Smit, Jack, Pres.--Miracle Feeds Inc., London, Canada; *U.S. Private*, pg. 432
Smit, James H., Pres. & Chief Exec. Officer--Spartan Oil Corp., Lansing, MI; *U.S. Private*, pg. 1021
Smith, A.W., Jr., Pres. & Chief Exec. Officer--Watson Wyatt Worldwide, Bethesda, MD; *U.S. Private*, pg. 1154
Smith, Al, Pres.--Computer Sales International Inc., Saint Louis, MO; *U.S. Private*, pg. 260
Smith, Al, Pres.--JbQ Sport LLC, New York, NY; *U.S. Private*, pg. 577
Smith, Al, Pres.--Quantum Sport, New York, NY; *U.S. Private*, pg. 900
Smith, Albert A., Pres. & Chief Exec. Officer--Utility Engineering Corporation, Amarillo, TX; *U.S. Public*, pg. 1170
Smith, Albert E., Pres.--Piedmont Mechanical, Inc., Spartanburg, SC; *U.S. Private*, pg. 865
Smith, Allen D., Pres.--First Citizens Investor Services, Inc., Raleigh, NC; *U.S. Public*, pg. 629
Smith, Allen J., Pres. & Chief Exec. Officer--Oriel Instruments Corporation, Stratford, CT; *U.S. Private*, pg. 819
Smith, Barry Cooper, Pres.--CPS Chemical Company Inc., Woodbridge, NJ; *U.S. Private*, pg. 196
Smith, Benson F., Pres. & Chief Oper. Officer--C.R. Bard, Inc., Murray Hill, NJ; *U.S. Public*, pg. 189
Smith, Bill, Pres.--George Fischer Sloane, Inc., Little Rock, AR; *Int'l*, pg. 430
Smith, Bill, Pres. & Owner--Keller Smith Supply, Inc., Mobile, AL; *U.S. Private*, pg. 1008
Smith, Bill, Gen. Mgr.--Metz Baking Co., Chicago, IL; *U.S. Private*, pg. 1022
Smith, Brad, Pres.--South Valley National Bank, Gilroy, CA; *U.S. Public*, pg. 1248
Smith, Bradley C., Pres. & Gen. Mgr.--Universal Composites-U.S.C., Manheim, PA; *U.S. Private*, pg. 1126
Smith, Brian, Pres. & Chief Oper. Officer--Cole National Corporation, Cleveland, OH; *U.S. Public*, pg. 396
Smith, Brian, Pres.--Cole Gift Centers, Inc., Cleveland, OH; *U.S. Public*, pg. 396
Smith, Brian B., Pres.--Things Remembered, Inc., Highland Heights, OH; *U.S. Public*, pg. 397
Smith, Bruce A., Chm. Bd., Pres. & Chief Exec. Officer--Tesoro Petroleum Corporation, San Antonio, TX; *U.S. Public*, pg. 1581
Smith, Bruton, Pres.--Texas Motor Speedway, Fort Worth, TX; *U.S. Public*, pg. 1498
Smith, Bryan Scott, Pres. & Chief Oper. Officer--Sonic Automotive, Inc., Charlotte, NC; *U.S. Public*, pg. 1485
Smith, C. Michael, Pres., Chief Oper. Officer & Sec.--Orders Distributing Co., Greenville, SC; *U.S. Private*, pg. 819
Smith, C. Peter, Pres.--Schmidt Baking Co., Inc., Baltimore, MD; *U.S. Private*, pg. 970
Smith, Carl W., Pres.--Smith Farms, Inc., Flatonia, TX; *U.S. Private*, pg. 1008
Smith, Carlos W., Pres.--Florida Favorite Fertilizer, Lakeland, FL; *Int'l*, pg. 1064
Smith, Christopher, Pres.--H.J. Baker & Bro., Inc., Stamford, CT; *U.S. Private*, pg. 112
Smith, Clarence, Pres.--Essence Communications Inc., New York, NY; *U.S. Private*, pg. 383
Smith, Clifton L., Pres. & Chief Exec. Officer--Corning Asahi Video Products Company, Corning, NY; *Int'l*, pg. 84
Smith, Clifton L., Pres. & Chief Exec. Officer--Corning Asahi Video Products Company, Corning, NY; *U.S. Public*, pg. 449
Smith, Craig, Chm. Bd., Pres. & Chief Exec. Officer--Hereford State Bank, Hereford, TX; *U.S. Public*, pg. 633
Smith, Craig R., Pres. & Chief Exec. Officer--Raytech Corporation, Shelton, CT; *U.S. Public*, pg. 1363
Smith, Cullen F., Pres. & Chief Exec. Officer--Bergen Brunswig Medical Corporation, Orange, CA; *U.S. Public*, pg. 214
Smith, D. L., Pres.--Kimmel Motz Refrigeration Corp., Los Angeles, CA; *Int'l*, pg. 1400
Smith, Dan F., Pres. & Chief Exec. Officer--Lyondell Petrochemical Company, Houston, TX; *U.S. Public*, pg. 1022
Smith, Dan L., Chm. Bd., Pres. & Chief Exec. Officer--Shoreline Financial Corp., Benton Harbor, MI; *U.S. Public*, pg. 1467
Smith, Darrell, Pres. & Chief Exec. Officer--Hickory Printing Group, Inc., Conover, NC; *U.S. Private*, pg. 525
Smith, Daryl D., Pres. & Chief Exec. Officer--Troy Corporation, Florham Park, NJ; *U.S. Private*, pg. 1105
Smith, David, Pres. & Chief Exec. Officer--American Eurocopter Corp., Grand Prairie, TX; *Int'l*, pg. 29
Smith, David, Pres. & Chief Exec. Officer--Quad Systems Corporation, Willow Grove, PA; *U.S. Private*, pg. 898
Smith, David M., Pres. & Chief Exec. Officer--Chemical Exchange Industries, Houston, TX; *U.S. Private*, pg. 232
Smith, David M., Pres.--Fortis Sales, Milwaukee, WI; *Int'l*, pg. 499
Smith, Dennis A., Chm. Bd., Pres. & Chief Exec. Officer--Crawford & Company, Atlanta, GA; *U.S. Public*, pg. 458
Smith, Derrick A. M., Pres.--Damsmith Corp., Sanford, NC; *U.S. Private*, pg. 309
Smith, Donald E., Pres. & Chief Exec. Officer--First Financial Corporation, Terre Haute, IN; *U.S. Public*, pg. 633
Smith, Donald E., Pres. & Chief Exec. Officer--Terre Haute First National Bank, Terre Haute, IN; *U.S. Public*, pg. 634
Smith, Donald G., Chm. Bd., Pres., Chief Exec. Officer & Treas.--Roanoke Electric Steel Corporation, Roanoke, VA; *U.S. Public*, pg. 1392
Smith, Donald L., Jr., Chm. Bd., Pres. & Chief Exec. Officer--Devcon International Corp., Deerfield Beach, FL; *U.S. Public*, pg. 502
Smith, Donald N., Chm. Bd. & Pres.--Friendly Ice Cream Corp., Wilbraham, MA; *U.S. Public*, pg. 682
Smith, Doug C., Pres.--MD Foods Canada Inc., Brampton, Canada; *Int'l*, pg. 826
Smith, Douglas V., Chm. Bd., Pres. & Chief Exec. Officer--Lufkin Industries, Inc., Lufkin, TX; *U.S. Public*, pg. 1019
Smith, Douglass C., Pres. & Chief Oper. Officer--Industrial Distribution Group, Tucker, GA; *U.S. Public*, pg. 875
Smith, E. Brian, Chm., Pres. & Chief Exec. Officer--Smith Environmental Technologies Corp., Plymouth Meeting, PA; *U.S. Public*, pg. 1477
Smith, E. Warren, Jr., Pres. & Chief Exec. Officer--Regions Bank/Middle Tennessee, Nashville, TN; *U.S. Public*, pg. 1372
Smith, Eric, Pres. & Chief Oper. Officer--Howe Furniture Corporation, Trumbull, CT; *U.S. Private*, pg. 543
Smith, Eric, Pres.--Panel Processing, Inc., Alpena, MI; *U.S. Private*, pg. 836
Smith, Ernie, Pres.--Condor Pacific Industries, Inc., Westlake Village, CA; *U.S. Private*, pg. 262
Smith, Everett G., Chm. Bd. & Pres.--Everett Smith Group, Ltd., Milwaukee, WI; *U.S. Private*, pg. 1007
Smith, Francis C., Chm. Bd.--Burgess & Niple, Limited, Columbus, OH; *U.S. Private*, pg. 182
Smith, Frederick W., Chm. Bd., Pres. & Chief Exec. Officer--FDX Corporation, Memphis, TN; *U.S. Public*, pg. 603
Smith, G. Edward, Pres.--Gai-Tronics Corporation, Mohnton, PA; *U.S. Public*, pg. 1430
Smith, G. Edward, Pres.--Instrument Associates, Inc., Memphis, TN; *U.S. Public*, pg. 1430
Smith, Gary B., Pres. & Chief Exec. Officer--Glenayre Technologies, Inc., Charlotte, NC; *U.S. Public*, pg. 746
Smith, Gary K., Pres.--American Uniform Co., Cleveland, TN; *U.S. Private*, pg. 1039
Smith, Gary W., Chm. Bd., Pres. & Chief Exec. Officer--Proto Systems of Atlanta, Alpharetta, GA; *U.S. Private*, pg. 891
Smith, Ge. E., Pres.--BHP Coated Steel Corp., Rancho Cucamonga, CA; *Int'l*, pg. 226
Smith, George, Pres.--Dixie Synthetic Yarn Group, Gastonia, NC; *U.S. Public*, pg. 514
Smith, George, Pres.--Drumheller Bag & Supply, Valdosta, GA; *U.S. Private*, pg. 802
Smith, George E., Pres. & Chief Exec. Officer--Alco Industries, Inc., Valley Forge, PA; *U.S. Private*, pg. 32
Smith, George J., Pres. & Chief Exec. Officer--Arrow Group Industries, Inc., Wayne, NJ; *U.S. Private*, pg. 477
Smith, Gilbert P., Pres.--Helene Curtis North America, Chicago, IL; *Int'l*, pg. 1434
Smith, Gordon H., Chm. Bd., Pres. & Chief Exec. Officer--Sargent-Fletcher Inc., El Monte, CA; *Int'l*, pg. 301
Smith, Gordon R., Pres. & Chief Exec. Officer--Pacific Gas & Electric Company, San Francisco, CA; *U.S. Public*, pg. 1241
Smith, Gregory H., Chm. Bd. & Pres.--Maine Potato Growers, Inc., Presque Isle, ME; *U.S. Private*, pg. 697
Smith, Gregory W., Pres. & Chief Oper. Officer--Jay Advertising, Inc., Rochester, NY; *U.S. Private*, pg. 583
Smith, H. Kemer, Chm. Bd., Pres. & Chief Exec. Officer--Stone & Webster Engineering & Constructors Corp., Boston, MA; *U.S. Public*, pg. 1519
Smith, H. Kerner, Chm. Bd., Pres. & Chief Exec. Officer--Stone & Webster, Incorporated, Boston, MA; *U.S. Public*, *pg. 1519*
Smith, H.B., II, Pres.--Leica Inc., Deerfield, IL; *Int'l*, pg. 806
Smith, Harrison, Pres.--Smith Management Co., Inc., Shreveport, LA; *U.S. Private*, pg. 1009
Smith, Henry B., Pres. & Chief Exec. Officer--The Bank of Bermuda Limited, Hamilton, Bermuda; *Int'l*, pg. 150
Smith, Henry Dale, Jr., Vice Chm. & Pres.--J.M. Smith Corp., Spartanburg, SC; *U.S. Private*, pg. 1008
Smith, J. Edward, Pres. & Chief Exec. Officer--WIC Radio Ltd., Vancouver, Canada; *Int'l*, pg. 1482
Smith, J. K., Pres.--NGE Enterprises, Inc., Binghamton, NY; *U.S. Public*, pg. 1173
Smith, J.J., Pres.--Dominion Stores, Inc., Martinsville, VA; *U.S. Public*, pg. 1644
Smith, J.L., Pres. & Chief Exec. Officer--J.R. Smith Manufacturing Company, Montgomery, AL; *U.S. Private*, pg. 1008
Smith, Jack, Pres. & Chief Exec. Officer--Pharmacists Public Relations Bureau, Wichita, KS; *U.S. Private*, pg. 295
Smith, Jack, Pres. & Chief Exec. Officer--Pharmacists Public Relations Bureau, New York, NY; *U.S. Private*, pg. 295
Smith, Jack, Pres.--Neway Anchorlok International Inc., Muskegon, MI; *U.S. Private*, pg. 796
Smith, Jake, Pres.--Smith Enterprises, Rock Hill, SC; *U.S. Private*, pg. 1007
Smith, James, Pres. & Chief Oper. Officer--ConAgra Prepared Food Companies, Omaha, NE; *U.S. Public*, pg. 427
Smith, James A. III, Pres.--Smith & Sons Foods, Inc., Macon, GA; *U.S. Private*, pg. 1006
Smith, James C., Pres. & Chief Exec. Officer--First Health Group Corp., Downers Grove, IL; *U.S. Public*, pg. 635
Smith, James Keith, II, Pres. & Chief Exec. Officer--Keith Smith Company, Hot Springs National Park, AR; *U.S. Private*, pg. 1008
Smith, James M., Pres. & Chief Exec. Officer--AIL Systems Inc., Deer Park, NY; *U.S. Public*, pg. 556
Smith, James T., Pres.--ConAgra Frozen Food Company, Omaha, NE; *U.S. Public*, pg. 427
Smith, Jay L., Pres. & Chief Exec. Officer--Smith Industries, Inc., Montgomery, AL; *U.S. Private*, pg. 1008
Smith, Jeffrey M., Pres.--Churchill Downs Management Co., Louisville, KY; *U.S. Public*, pg. 356
Smith, Jerry M., Pres. & Chief Oper. Officer--Tuesday Morning Corporation, Dallas, TX; *U.S. Public*, pg. 1644
Smith, Joel A., III, Pres.--NationsBank South Carolina Corporation, Columbia, SC; *U.S. Public*, pg. 1163
Smith, John, Pres.--Material Handling Equipment Co., Bristol, PA; *U.S. Private*, pg. 754
Smith, John F., Jr., Chm. Bd., Pres. & Chief Exec. Officer--General Motors Corporation, Detroit, MI; *U.S. Public*, pg. 718
Smith, Joseph, Pres.--Air Products Group, York, PA; *U.S. Public*, pg. 1789
Smith, Joseph H., Pres.--40 Fort Eye Associates, Forty Fort, PA; *U.S. Private*, pg. 420
Smith, Joseph T., Pres. & Chief Oper. Officer--Right Management Consultants, Inc., Philadelphia, PA; *U.S. Public*, pg. 1390
Smith, Kevin J., Pres.--Container Care International, Galena Park, TX; *U.S. Private*, pg. 266
Smith, Larry, Pres.--BPMC, Inc., Minneapolis, MN; *U.S. Private*, pg. 118
Smith, Lee, Pres.--Items International/Airwalk, Inc., Altoona, PA; *U.S. Private*, pg. 576
Smith, Llewellyn, Pres.--E.D. Smith, Winona, Canada; *Int'l*, pg. 1263
Smith, Lowndes A., Pres. & Chief Oper. Officer--Hartford Life Insurance Co., Hartford, CT; *U.S. Public*, pg. 795
Smith, Maclin F., III, Pres.--Regions Bank/Birmingham, Birmingham, AL; *U.S. Public*, pg. 1371
Smith, Malcolm, Pres.--W.R. Grace (Hong Kong) Ltd., Quarry Bay, Hong Kong; *U.S. Public*, pg. 756
Smith, Mark, Pres. & Chief Exec.Officer--Stewart Smith East, Inc., New York, NY; *Int'l*, pg. 1508
Smith, Michael J., Pres. & Chief Exec. Officer--Lands' End, Inc., Dodgeville, WI; *U.S. Public*, pg. 977
Smith, Murray, Pres. & Chief Exec. Officer--CSS USA, New York, NY; *U.S. Public*, pg. 1642
Smith, Murray T., Pres.--Midwest Coast Transport L.P., Sioux Falls, SD; *U.S. Private*, pg. 744

Smith, Ned A., Pres. & Chief Exec. Officer--American Steamship Company, Williamsville, NY; *U.S. Public*, pg. 690
Smith, Neil, Pres. & Gen. Mgr.--New York Rangers Hockey Club, New York, NY; *U.S. Public*, pg. 288
Smith, P.S., Pres.--AMI, Crawley, United Kingdom; *Int'l*, pg. 707
Smith, P.S., Pres.--Concorde Express, Bedford, United Kingdom; *Int'l*, pg. 707
Smith, Patrick, F., Chm. Bd. & Pres.--Tekni-Plex, Inc., Somerville, NJ; *U.S. Private*, pg. 1073
Smith, Peter G., Pres. & Chief Oper. Officer--Lawson Products, Inc., Des Plaines, IL; *U.S. Public*, pg. 980
Smith, R.A., Pres.--BSL Engineering Limited, Manchester, United Kingdom; *Int'l*, pg. 212
Smith, R.L., Pres.--Eastman Kodak (Japan) Ltd., Tokyo, Japan; *U.S. Public*, pg. 552
Smith, Randy P., Pres.--Automatic Switch Co., Florham Park, NJ; *U.S. Public*, pg. 573
Smith, Raymond, Pres.--Andover Bank NH, Salem, NH; *U.S. Public*, pg. 112
Smith, Raymond, Grp. V.P.--Shasta Beverages, Inc., Hayward, CA; *U.S. Public*, pg. 1153
Smith, Raymond J., Chm. Bd. & Pres.--Lakeland Industries, Inc., Ronkonkoma, NY; *U.S. Public*, pg. 975
Smith, Richard, Pres.--All Nation Insurance Company, Southfield, MI; *U.S. Private*, pg. 35
Smith, Richard, Pres. & Chief Exec. Officer--Stern-Leach Company, Attleboro, MA; *Int'l*, pg. 329
Smith, Richard, Pres. & Chief Exec. Officer--Namanco LLC, Tulsa, OK; *U.S. Private*, pg. 773
Smith, Richard A., Chm., Pres. & Chief Exec. Officer-Real Estate Div.--HFS, Incorporated, Parsippany, NJ; *U.S. Public*, pg. 321
Smith, Richard D., Pres.--Hathaway Corporation, Littleton, CO; *U.S. Public*, pg. 798
Smith, Richard L., Pres.--The Fremont Co., Fremont, OH; *U.S. Private*, pg. 426
Smith, Richard M., Pres. & Chief Fin. Officer--Coram Healthcare Corporation, Denver, CO; *U.S. Public*, pg. 446
Smith, Richard M., Pres. & Editor-in-Chief--Newsweek, Inc., New York, NY; *U.S. Public*, pg. 1743
Smith, Rick, Pres.--Millennium Technology Services, Inc., White City, OR; *U.S. Private*, pg. 746
Smith, Rick, Pres.--Meridian Inc., Spring Lake, MI; *U.S. Public*, pg. 1112
Smith, Robert, V.P. & Gen. Mgr.--Avery Dennison Corporation Label Group, Ontario, CA; *U.S. Public*, pg. 153
Smith, Robert A., Pres. & Chief Oper. Officer--GC Companies, Inc., Chestnut Hill, MA; *U.S. Public*, pg. 693
Smith, Robert E., Pres.--Rudel Machinery Company, Inc., Shelton, CT; *U.S. Private*, pg. 950
Smith, Robert J., Pres.--Hunt Foreign Investment Corp., West Paterson, NJ; *U.S. Public*, pg. 1219
Smith, Robert M., Pres.--Barrick Gold Corporation, Toronto, Canada; *Int'l*, pg. 168
Smith, Rodney, Chm. Bd., Pres. & Chief Exec. Officer--Altera Corporation, San Jose, CA; *U.S. Public*, pg. 59
Smith, Roger F., Pres.--Citizens First Bank, Rome, GA; *U.S. Public*, pg. 1549
Smith, Roger W., Pres.--Pawling Corporation, Pawling, NY; *U.S. Private*, pg. 844
Smith, Roland C., Pres.--Triarc Restaurant Group, Fort Lauderdale, FL; *U.S. Public*, pg. 1635
Smith, S.A., Pres.--Intertec Presentations, Englewood, CO; *U.S. Public*, pg. 1328
Smith, S.B., Pres. & Chief Exec. Officer--Ph. Orth Co., Oak Creek, WI; *Int'l*, pg. 244
Smith, Scott, Pres. & Publr.--Chicago Tribune Co., Chicago, IL; *U.S. Public*, pg. 1635
Smith, Sharon L., Pres.--Smith Frozen Foods, Inc., Weston, OR; *U.S. Private*, pg. 1008
Smith, Sheldon E., Chm. Bd., Pres. & Chief Exec. Officer--Old Fashion Foods, Inc., Austell, GA; *U.S. Private*, pg. 814
Smith, Stephen E., Chm. Bd. & Pres.--LSJ Sportswear Inc., Deerfield, WI; *U.S. Private*, pg. 732
Smith, Stephen F., Pres.--Sysco Food Services of Central Florida, Inc., Ocoee, FL; *U.S. Public*, pg. 1551
Smith, Steve, Pres. & Chief Exec. Officer--UPB of Central Arkansas NA, Clinton, AR; *U.S. Public*, pg. 1669
Smith, Steve, Pres.--Bank of Commerce, Woodbury, TN; *U.S. Public*, pg. 1669
Smith, Steve C., Pres.--K-VA-T, Abingdon, VA; *U.S. Private*, pg. 603
Smith, Steven, Pres.--Fresh Juice Company, Great Neck, NY; *U.S. Private*, pg. 427
Smith, Steven B., Chm. Bd., Pres. & Chief Exec. Officer--SBS Enterprises Inc., Waco, TX; *U.S. Private*, pg. 955
Smith, Steven B., Chm. Bd., Pres. & Chief Exec. Officer--Spenco Medical Corporation, Waco, TX; *U.S. Private*, pg. 955
Smith, Steven J., Pres.--Journal Communications Inc., Milwaukee, WI; *U.S. Private*, pg. 601
Smith, Steven P., Pres.--Universal Construction Company, Inc., Kansas City, KS; *U.S. Private*, pg. 1127
Smith, T.W., Pres.--Calcot, Ltd., Bakersfield, CA; *U.S. Private*, pg. 200
Smith, Ted, Pres.--Honeywell Asia Pacific Inc., Wan Chai, Hong Kong; *U.S. Public*, pg. 834
Smith, Terry, Pres.--Putzmeister, Inc., Sturtevant, WI; *U.S. Private*, pg. 896
Smith, Thad, III, Pres.--Brown & Root Civil, Houston, TX; *U.S. Public*, pg. 775
Smith, Thad, III, Pres.--Brown & Root Environmental, Houston, TX; *U.S. Public*, pg. 775
Smith, Theodore B., Chm. Bd. & Pres.--HITCO, Westbury, NY; *U.S. Private*, pg. 509
Smith, Theodore B. III, Pres. & Chief Oper. Officer--John Hassall, Inc., Westbury, NY; *U.S. Private*, pg. 509
Smith, Theodore B., Jr., Chm. Bd. & Chief Exec. Officer--John Hassall, Inc., Westbury, NY; *U.S. Private*, pg. 509
Smith, Thomas J., Pres. & Chief Exec. Officer--Coats North America, Charlotte, NC; *Int'l*, pg. 300
Smith, Thomas J., Pres. & Chief Exec. Officer--Norwesco, Inc., Saint Bonifacius, MN; *U.S. Private*, pg. 808
Smith, Thomas L., Pres.--Yellow Services, Inc., Overland Park, KS; *U.S. Public*, pg. 1788
Smith, Tom E., Chm. Bd., Pres. & Chief Exec. Officer--Food Lion, Inc., Salisbury, NC; *Int'l*, pg. 463
Smith, W. Heard, Pres.--Caro Knit (Jefferson Plant), Jefferson, SC; *U.S. Public*, pg. 514
Smith, W. Norman, Pres.--Astec, Inc., Chattanooga, TN; *U.S. Public*, pg. 141
Smith, W.T., Pres. & Gen. Mgr.--Tidelands Oil Production Co., Long Beach, CA; *U.S. Private*, pg. 1084
Smith, W.T., Pres.--Flexible Technologies Inc., Abbeville, SC; *Int'l*, pg. 1267
Smith, Wally, Pres. & Chief Exec. Officer--Recreational Equipment, Inc., Kent, WA; *U.S. Private*, pg. 914
Smith, Wayne, Chm. Bd., Pres. & Chief Exec./Fin. Officer--Bekins Distribution Services Co., Saint Louis, MO; *U.S. Public*, pg. 841
Smith, Wayne A., Pres.--GenCorp Vehicle Sealing Div., Evansville, IN; *U.S. Public*, pg. 706
Smith, Wayne A., Pres.--GenCorp Vehicle Sealing Div., Fort Smith, AR; *U.S. Public*, pg. 706
Smith, Wilburn, Pres.--Pre-Paid Legal Services, Inc., Ada, OK; *U.S. Public*, pg. 1320
Smith, William B., Ph.D., Pres. & Chief Exec. Officer--Telco Systems, Inc., Norwood, MA; *U.S. Public*, pg. 1568
Smith, William D., Pres. & Chief Exec. Officer--Brown & Bigelow, Inc., Saint Paul, MN; *U.S. Private*, pg. 172
Smith, William D., Pres.--Kemper Insurance Companies, Long Grove, IL; *U.S. Private*, pg. 614
Smith, William J., Pres. & Chief Exec. Officer--Scotia Investment Management Ltd., Toronto, Canada; *Int'l*, pg. 155
Smith, William J., Chm. Bd., Pres. & Chief Exec. Officer--U.S. Can Company, Oak Brook, IL; *U.S. Public*, pg. 1681
Smith, William S., Pres.--Leo Burnett Kyodo Co. Ltd., Tokyo, Japan; *U.S. Private*, pg. 185
Smith, William T., Pres.--Flexible Technologies Inc., La Mirada, CA; *Int'l*, pg. 1267
Smithies, David, Pres.--Waldbaum's Supermarkets, Inc., Central Islip, NY; *Int'l*, pg. 1375
Smithson, John W., Pres. & Chief Exec. Officer--Pennsylvania Manufacturers Corp., Blue Bell, PA; *U.S. Public*, pg. 1272
Smola, Steve, Pres. & Chief Exec. Officer--Wheeler Brothers Grain Co., Watonga, OK; *U.S. Private*, pg. 1171
Smolinski, Bob, Pres.--Modular Power Systems, Hackettstown, NJ; *U.S. Private*, pg. 1097
Smollar, Marvin, Pres. & Chief Oper. Officer--CLR Corporation, Tarboro, NC; *U.S. Public*, pg. 579
Smoot, Richard L., Pres.--PNC Bank, Philadelphia, PA; *U.S. Public*, pg. 1243
Smucker, Richard K., Pres.--J.M. Smucker Company, Orrville, OH; *U.S. Public*, pg. 1480
Smythe, Hugh, Pres.--Blackcomb Skiing Enterprises Ltd., Whistler, Canada; *Int'l*, pg. 685
Smythe, Thomas M., Chm. Bd. & Pres.--Keller Crescent Co., Evansville, IN; *U.S. Private*, pg. 612
Snapp, James A., Pres. & Chief Exec. Officer--Certified Alloy Products, Inc., Long Beach, CA; *Int'l*, pg. 1467
Snavely, Stephen V., Pres.--Snavely Forest Products, Inc., Pittsburgh, PA; *U.S. Private*, pg. 1010
Snavely, Wayne H., Chm. Bd., Pres. & Chief Exec. Officer--Imperial Credit Industries, Inc., Torrance, CA; *U.S. Public*, pg. 872
Sndler, Inn, Pres.--Shenango Industries, Terre Haute, IN; *U.S. Private*, pg. 992
Snead, Michael J., Pres. & Chief Exec. Officer--Carolina Casualty Insurance Company, Jacksonville, FL; *U.S. Public*, pg. 216
Snead, Tom, Pres. & Chief Oper. Officer--Trigon Blue Cross & Blue Shield, Richmond, VA; *U.S. Public*, pg. 1637
Sneddon, Paul, Pres. & Chief Exec. Officer--H.J. Heinz Co. of Canada Ltd., North York, Canada; *U.S. Public*, pg. 806
Sneddon, Paul, Pres. & Chief Exec. Officer--Omstead Foods Limited, Wheatley, Canada; *U.S. Public*, pg. 806
Snediker, James M., Pres., Chief Exec. Officer & Chief Oper. Officer--Chicago Show Printing Co., Morton Grove, IL; *U.S. Private*, pg. 235
Snell, E.A., Pres. & Chief Oper. Officer--Hunt-Wesson, Inc., Fullerton, CA; *U.S. Public*, pg. 428
Snell, James, Pres. & Chief Oper. Officer--Shield Healthcare Centers, Valencia, CA; *Int'l*, pg. 740
Snell, Richard A., Chm. Bd., Pres. & Chief Exec. Officer--Federal-Mogul Corporation, Southfield, MI; *U.S. Public*, pg. 615
Snell, Robert, Pres.--United Supermarkets Inc., Lubbock, TX; *U.S. Private*, pg. 1126
Snelling, Mark H., Pres.--The Shelburne Corporation, Shelburne, VT; *U.S. Private*, pg. 991
Snider, Jeffrey A., Chm. Bd., Pres. & Chief Exec. Officer--PAULA Financial, Pasadena, CA; *U.S. Public*, pg. 1266
Sniegowski, Bob, Pres. & Gen. Mgr.--Jesco Company, Bloomington, MN; *U.S. Private*, pg. 590
Snodgrass, Rick H., Pres.--Richmond American Homes, Inc., Tucson, AZ; *U.S. Public*, pg. 1025
Snow, David P., Jr., Pres.--Oxford Health Plans (PA), Inc., Philadelphia, PA; *U.S. Public*, pg. 1239
Snow, John, Pres.--Strippit, Inc., Akron, NY; *U.S. Public*, pg. 862
Snow, John J., Pres. & Chief Exec. Officer--First NH Investment Services Corporation, Manchester, NH; *Int'l*, pg. 153
Snow, John T., Pres.--Hilb, Rogal and Hamilton Company of Tampa Bay, Inc., Tampa, FL; *U.S. Public*, pg. 827
Snow, John W., Chm. Bd., Pres. & Chief Exec. Officer--CSX Corporation, Richmond, VA; *U.S. Public*, pg. 284
Snowball, Michael, Pres.--Mead Containerboard, Atlanta, GA; *U.S. Public*, pg. 1074
Snowball, Michael, Pres.--Mead Coated Board, Atlanta, GA; *U.S. Public*, pg. 1074
Snowden, David, Pres. & Chief Exec. Officer--Tarco, North Little Rock, AR; *U.S. Private*, pg. 1068
Snowden, Gerald W., Pres.--McCormick Canada, Ltd., London, Canada; *U.S. Public*, pg. 1067
Snowden, William F., Chm. Bd., Pres. & Chief Exec. Officer--Topline Imports, Inc., Bellevue, WA; *U.S. Private*, pg. 1091
Snyder, Arthur, Chm. Bd. & Pres.--A.M. Best Company, Oldwick, NJ; *U.S. Private*, pg. 139
Snyder, Bill, Pres.--CSR Florida, West Palm Beach, FL; *Int'l*, pg. 245
Snyder, Charles H., Pres.--American Equipment Company, Inc., Greenville, NC; *U.S. Public*, pg. 660
Snyder, Christopher, Pres. & Gen. Mgr.--Huffy Bicycle Company, Celina, OH; *U.S. Public*, pg. 846
Snyder, Daniel M., Chm. Bd., Pres. & Chief Exec. Officer--Snyder Communications, Inc., Bethesda, MD; *U.S. Public*, pg. 1481
Snyder, Donald D., Pres. & Chief Admin. Officer--Boyd Gaming Corporation, Las Vegas, NV; *U.S. Public*, pg. 249
Snyder, John, Pres.--The Ajax Manufacturing Company, Cleveland, OH; *U.S. Public*, pg. 1258
Snyder, John C., Chm. Bd. & Acting Pres.--Snyder Oil Corporation, Fort Worth, TX; *U.S. Public*, pg. 1481
Snyder, Kenneth E., Pres.--Colgate-Palmolive Co., Institutional Products Div., Tenafly, NJ; *U.S. Public*, pg. 397
Snyder, Lynn E., Pres. & Chief Exec. Officer--Churubusco State Bank, Churubusco, IN; *U.S. Public*, pg. 674
Snyder, Peter, Pres.--Miller Shandwick Technologies, Boston, MA; *Int'l*, pg. 1227
Snyder, Richard G., Pres. & Chief Exec. Officer--Reflectone, Inc., Tampa, FL; *Int'l*, pg. 218
Snyder, Robert, Pres.--On Command Video, Santa Clara, CA; *U.S. Public*, pg. 138
Snyder, Ron, Pres.--H.E. Williams, Inc., Carthage, MO; *U.S. Private*, pg. 1178
Snyder, Ross, Pres.--Group Life & Health Insurance Company, Richardson, TX; *U.S. Private*, pg. 152
Snyder, Stephen G., Pres. & Chief Exec. Officer--Transalta Corporation, Calgary, Canada; *Int'l*, pg. 1416
Snyder, Stuart, Pres. Chief Oper. Officer--Feld Productions, Vienna, VA; *U.S. Private*, pg. 399
Snyder, Thomas, Pres.--Delco Remy International, Inc., Anderson, IN; *U.S. Public*, pg. 495
Soares da Fonseca, Jose Manuel Capelo, Pres.--UNICER-Uniao Cervejeira, S.A., Mamede de Infesta, Portugal; *Int'l*, pg. 1432
Soares, Ciro, Pres.-Bundy Mercosur--TI Brazil Industria E Comerico Ltda., Sao Jose dos Campos, Brazil; *Int'l*, pg. 1342
Soares, Ciro, Pres.-Mercosur--Bundy Argentina SA, Victoria, Argentina; *Int'l*, pg. 1342
Sobel, Robert, Co-Pres.--Land N Sea, Inc., New York, NY; *U.S. Private*, pg. 645
Sobey, Paul D., Pres.--Atlantic Shopping Centres Limited, Stellarton, Canada; *Int'l*, pg. 454
Sobin, Stephen A., Pres.--Superior Bank, Chicago, IL; *U.S. Private*, pg. 1054
Soble, David S., Pres. & Chief Exec. Officer--Interstate Steel Co. Inc., Des Plaines, IL; *Int'l*, pg. 572
Sobol, Yehiel, Pres. & Chief Exec. Officer--Kao Infosystems Canada, Inc., Arnprior, Canada; *Int'l*, pg. 717
Socol, Jerry M., Pres. & Chief Exec. Officer--Morse Shoe, Inc., Canton, MA; *U.S. Public*, pg. 168
Sodaro, Don, Pres.--The Accor Group, Inc., Corona Del Mar, CA; *Int'l*, pg. 21
Sodeberg, Per-Olaf, Pres. & Chief Exec. Officer--Dahl International AB, Stockholm, Sweden; *Int'l*, pg. 359
Soderberg, Dick, Pres.--Hassle Lakemedel AB, Molndal, Sweden; *Int'l*, pg. 93
Soderlund, Tony, Pres.--Kvaerner Generator AB, Partille, Sweden; *Int'l*, pg. 767
Soderquist, Craig, Pres.--Artel Utah Scientific, Inc., Salt Lake City, UT; *U.S. Private*, pg. 86
Sodeyama, Humitaka, Pres.--Toray Industries (H.K.) Ltd., Kowloon, Hong Kong; *Int'l*, pg. 1400
Sodhi, Ajit, Pres. & Chief Oper. Officer--Securiplex Inc., Dorval, Canada; *Int'l*, pg. 1162
Sodini, Peter J., Pres. & Chief Exec. Officer--The Pantry, Inc., Sanford, NC; *U.S. Private*, pg. 837
Sodupe Roure, D. Jaime, Pres.--Eritel, S.A., Madrid, Spain; *Int'l*, pg. 1372
Soehnlen, Daniel P., Pres.--Superior Dairy, Inc., Canton, OH; *U.S. Private*, pg. 1054
Soejima, Naoki, Pres.--Taiyo Life International (U.K.), Ltd., London, United Kingdom; *Int'l*, pg. 1349
Soennichsen, Svend, Mng. Dir.--Vestjyske Slagterier, Struer, Denmark; *Int'l*, pg. 1464
Sofia, Zuheir, Pres., Chief Oper. Officer & Treas.--Huntington Bancshares Inc., Columbus, OH; *U.S. Public*, pg. 849
Sohl, Brandon A., Pres.--Auto Driveaway Co., Chicago, IL; *U.S. Private*, pg. 100
Sohm, Woo-Heon, Pres.--Ssangyong Investment Management Co., Ltd., Seoul, Korea; *Int'l*, pg. 1292
Sohmer, Paul, Dr., Pres.--Nellcor Puritan Bennett Incorporated, Pleasanton, CA; *U.S. Public*, pg. 1039
Soila, Anssi, Pres. & Chief Oper. Officer--Kone Corporation, Helsinki, Finland; *Int'l*, pg. 746
Sokol, Si, Chm. Bd., Pres. & Chief Exec. Officer--Bancinsurance Corp., Columbus, OH; *U.S. Public*, pg. 175
Sokolov, Richard, Pres. & Chief Oper. Officer--Simon DeBartolo Group, Inc., Indianapolis, IN; *U.S. Public*, pg. 1474
Sola, Enrico, Pres.--Del Monte Royal Corporation, Rivonia, South Africa; *Int'l*, pg. 388
Sola, Enrico, Pres. & Chief Oper. Officer--Del Monte Foods International Limited, Staines, United Kingdom; *Int'l*, pg. 388

Solan, George D., Pres.--S & S Graphics, Inc., Laurel, MD; *U.S. Private*, pg. 955
Solberg, Elizabeth T., Sr. Partner, Exec. V.P. & Gen. Mgr.--Fleishman-Hillard, Inc., Kansas City, MO; *U.S. Private*, pg. 411
Solberg, James L., Pres., Chief Exec. & Oper. Officer--AutoAlliance International Inc., Flat Rock, MI; *Int'l*, pg. 849
Solda, Marc, Pres. & Treas.--Jamison Plastic Corporation, Allentown, PA; *U.S. Private*, pg. 581
Soldano, Steve, Partner & Exec. Media Dir.--Deutsch, Inc., New York, NY; *U.S. Private*, pg. 328
Soldateli, Ilarioo, Pres.--Fiat Automisveis S.A., Sao Paulo, Brazil; *Int'l*, pg. 483
Solender, Michael, Chm. Bd. & Chief Oper. Officer--The Solender Group, Inc., Los Angeles, CA; *U.S. Private*, pg. 1012
Solender, Stephen L., Esq., Pres. & Chief Exec. Officer--The Solender Group, Inc., Los Angeles, CA; *U.S. Private*, pg. 1012
Soler, Arthur, Pres.--Cadbury Chocolate Canada, Inc., Toronto, Canada; *Int'l*, pg. 248
Solheim, John, Pres.--Karsten Manufacturing Corporation, Phoenix, AZ; *U.S. Private*, pg. 608
Solheim, Karsten, Owner--Karsten Manufacturing Corporation, Phoenix, AZ; *U.S. Private*, pg. 608
Solheim, Ola, Pres.--Igloo Pool, Oslo, Norway; *Int'l*, pg. 766
Soliman, Anwar, Chm. Bd. & Chief Exec. Officer--American Restaurant Group, Inc., Newport Beach, CA; *U.S. Private*, pg. 61
Solla, Jose Luis, Pres.--Hispano Olivetti Office, Barcelona, Spain; *Int'l*, pg. 1003
Solombrino, Scott, Chm. Bd., Pres. & Chief Exec. Officer--Dav-El Worldwide, Chelsea, MA; *U.S. Private*, pg. 314
Solombrino, Scott, Pres.--Dav-El West, Hawthorne, CA; *U.S. Private*, pg. 314
Solombrino, Scott, Pres.--Dav-El Washington DC Inc., Long Island City, NY; *U.S. Private*, pg. 314
Solomon, H. Bryce, Pres.--Blue Ridge Finance Co., Inc., Greenville, SC; *U.S. Public*, pg. 306
Solomon, Harvey, Pres.--Sag Harbor, New York, NY; *U.S. Public*, pg. 948
Solomon, Howard, Pres.--Forest Laboratories, Inc., New York, NY; *U.S. Public*, pg. 670
Solomon, Russell S., Pres. & Chief Exec. Officer--MTS, Inc., West Sacramento, CA; *U.S. Private*, pg. 688
Solomon, William R., Pres.--American Fluorescent Corporation, Waukegan, IL; *U.S. Private*, pg. 54
Solon, Richard A., Pres. & Chief Exec. Officer--Snorkel, Saint Joseph, MO; *U.S. Private*, pg. 500
Solso, Theodore M., Pres. & Chief Oper. Officer--Cummins Engine Company, Inc., Columbus, IN; *U.S. Public*, pg. 467
Solsvig, Curtis G., Pres. & Chief Exec. Officer--Gilbert & Bennett Manufacturing Company, Georgetown, CT; *U.S. Private*, pg. 453
Soltis, Bruce L., Pres.--Arrow-Sysco Food Services, Inc., Harahan, LA; *U.S. Public*, pg. 1551
Soma, Jack, Pres.--Otari Corporation, Foster City, CA; *Int'l*, pg. 1013
Somerville, Ervin W., Pres. & Chief Exec. Officer--M & I Central Bank & Trust, Marshfield, WI; *U.S. Public*, pg. 1050
Somerville, Leo, Pres.--Renishaw Inc., Schaumburg, IL; *Int'l*, pg. 1103
Somerville, Mary, Pres.--American Library Association, Chicago, IL; *U.S. Private*, pg. 58
Somerville, Robert, Pres.--American Bureau of Shipping, New York, NY; *U.S. Private*, pg. 51
Somm, Mr., Pres.--Asea Brown Boveri AG, Baden, Switzerland; *Int'l*, pg. 1
Sommer, Frederick F., Pres. & Chief Oper. Officer--Citation Corporation, Birmingham, AL; *U.S. Public*, pg. 376
Sommer, James, Pres., Chief Oper. & Fin. Officer & Treas.--Service Motor Company, Dale, WI; *U.S. Private*, pg. 986
Sommer, John, Pres.--Mid Continent Market Center, Topeka, KS; *U.S. Public*, pg. 1759
Sommer, Jon W., Chm. Bd. & Pres.--Sommer Metalcraft Corporation, Crawfordsville, IN; *U.S. Private*, pg. 1013
Sommer, Ron, Pres. & Chief Oper. Officer--Sony Electronics, Park Ridge, NJ; *Int'l*, pg. 1281
Sommerer, Peter, Pres. & Chief Oper. Officer--Newbridge Networks Corporation, Kanata, Canada; *Int'l*, pg. 924
Sommers, James B., Pres.--NationsBank Trust, Atlanta, GA; *U.S. Public*, pg. 1165
Sommers, John G., Pres.--Allied Printing Services, Inc., Manchester, CT; *U.S. Private*, pg. 40
Sommers, Patrick C., Chm. Bd., Pres. & Chief Exec. Officer--Medicus Systems Corporation, Evanston, IL; *U.S. Public*, pg. 1080
Sommers, William, Pres. & Chief Exec. Officer--SRI International, Menlo Park, CA; *U.S. Private*, pg. 958
Son, Masayoshi, Pres. & Chief Exec. Officer--Softbank Corporation, Tokyo, Japan; *Int'l*, pg. 1276
Sondhi, Vir K., Chm. Bd. & Pres.--Nasco Industries Inc., Medina, OH; *U.S. Private*, pg. 774
Sondhi, Vir K., Pres. & Chief Exec. Officer--Overseas Capital Corporation, Medina, OH; *U.S. Private*, pg. 774
Sondker, Edward H., Pres. & Chief Exec. Officer--Bay View Capital Corporation, San Mateo, CA; *U.S. Public*, pg. 197
Song, K.R., Pres.--Samsung Electronics America, Inc., Ridgefield Park, NJ; *Int'l*, pg. 1183
Songy, Gerald E., Pres.--Maurin-Ogden Properties, New Orleans, LA; *U.S. Private*, pg. 715
Sonis, Larry, Pres.-Pub. Rels.--The William Cook Agency, Inc., Jacksonville, FL; *U.S. Private*, pg. 273
Sonis, Larry, Pres.--William Cook Public Relations, Inc., Jacksonville, FL; *U.S. Private*, pg. 273
Sonju, David A., Pres.--August West Systems, Worcester, MA; *U.S. Private*, pg. 98
Sonnabend, Stephanie, Pres.--Sonesta International Hotels Corporation, Boston, MA; *U.S. Public*, pg. 1485
Sonnenberg, Ralph, Pres. & Chief Exec. Officer--Hunter Douglas N.V., Rotterdam, Netherlands; *Int'l*, pg. 639
Sonnenberg, Willie B., Chm. Bd. & Exec. Creative Dir.--Sonnenberg Murphy Leo Burnett, Sunninghill, South Africa; *U.S. Private*, pg. 186
Sonner, Harvey, Pres.--Lightalarms Electronics Corporation, Baldwin, NY; *Int'l*, pg. 725
Sonobe, Takashi, Pres. & Chief Exec. Officer--Mitsubishi Motor Sales of America, Inc., Cypress, CA; *Int'l*, pg. 875
Sontag, Frederick B., Pres.--Unison Industries, Jacksonville, FL; *U.S. Private*, pg. 1120
Soobuym, Young, Pres. & Chief Exec. Officer--Inkel USA Corporation, La Mirada, CA; *U.S. Private*, pg. 563
Soon, Deborah M., Pres.--Larscom Inc., Santa Clara, CA; *Int'l*, pg. 710
Soon, Lee Meng, Pres.--PT Bank DBS Buana, Jakarta, Indonesia; *Int'l*, pg. 350
Soong, Leo, Pres.--Crystal Geyser, Calistoga, CA; *U.S. Private*, pg. 294
Soong, Leo, Pres.--Crystal Geyser Water Company, Calistoga, CA; *Int'l*, pg. 1013
Soper, Willard B., II, Pres. & Chief Exec. Officer--MidCoast Mortgage Corporation, Lake Worth, FL; *U.S. Private*, pg. 744
Sophonpanich, Chartsiri, Pres.--Bangkok Bank Public Company Limited, Bangkok, Thailand; *Int'l*, pg. 146
Sopko, W.E., Pres. & Owner--Stamco Industries Inc., Euclid, OH; *U.S. Private*, pg. 1029
Soran, Robert L., Pres. & Chief Oper. Officer--Uniroyal Technology Corporation, Sarasota, FL; *U.S. Public*, pg. 1670
Sorba, Olivier, Pres. & Chief Exec. Officer--Lagardere Groupe North America, New York, NY; *Int'l*, pg. 794
Sorensen, Erik, Pres. & Chief Exec. Officer--Chr. Hansen Holding A/S, Horsholm, Denmark; *Int'l*, pg. 288
Sorensen, Robert C., Chm. Bd. & Pres.--Duro-Lite International, Fairfield, NJ; *U.S. Private*, pg. 349
Sorensen, Robert C., Pres.--Duro-Test Corporation, Fairfield, NJ; *U.S. Private*, pg. 349
Sorensen, Robert C., Pres.--Duro-Test Intl. Corp., Fairfield, NJ; *U.S. Private*, pg. 349
Sorensen, Tor Magne, Pres.--Aker Base a.s., Tananger, Norway; *Int'l*, pg. 41
Sorenson, John, Pres. & Chief Exec. Officer--Rogers N.K. Seed Co., Boise, ID; *Int'l*, pg. 974
Sorenson, Peter P., Pres.--Georg Fischer Disa, Inc., Holly, MI; *Int'l*, pg. 490
Sorley, Tom, Pres. & Chief Oper. Officer--Rosendin Electric, Inc., San Jose, CA; *U.S. Private*, pg. 945
Sormani, Charles R., Pres.--ULICO Indemnity, Washington, DC; *U.S. Private*, pg. 1116
Sormani, Charles R., Pres.--ULICO Casualty Company, Washington, DC; *U.S. Private*, pg. 1116
Sormani, Charles R., Pres.--Union Standard of America Life Insurance Co., Washington, DC; *U.S. Private*, pg. 1116
Sorokwasz, Michael, Pres. & Chief Exec. Officer--TST/Impreso, Inc., Coppell, TX; *U.S. Private*, pg. 1066
Sorrell, C.S., Pres. & Chief Exec. Officer--Calvert Group, Ltd., Bethesda, MD; *U.S. Private*, pg. 11
Sorrentino, Chuck, Pres. & Chief Oper. Officer--Pameco Corp., Norcross, GA; *U.S. Public*, pg. 1255
Sorrentino, Ralph, Pres. & Chief Oper. Officer--Quantum Media International, Inc., New York, NY; *U.S. Private*, pg. 899
Sorsa, Pekka, Pres.--Xyrofin (UK) Ltd., Redhill, United Kingdom; *Int'l*, pg. 350
Sortino, Mike, Pres.--Schnieber Fine Foods, Inc., Lincoln, NE; *U.S. Private*, pg. 971
Sosrosukarto, Budiardjo, Pres.--PT Hokuriku United Forging Industries, Bekasi, Indonesia; *Int'l*, pg. 745
Sossong, A.T., Pres.--Reitz Coal Company, Windber, PA; *U.S. Private*, pg. 139
Soto, D. Gernam Ancochea, Pres.--Telefonica Internacional De Espana S.A., Madrid, Spain; *Int'l*, pg. 1372
Soto, Raymond M., Pres., Chief Exec. & Fin. Officer & Treas.--Bolt Technology Corporation, Norwalk, CT; *U.S. Public*, pg. 244
Sottile, John H., Pres. & Chief Exec. Officer--The Goldfield Corporation, Melbourne, FL; *U.S. Public*, pg. 750
Souden, Dean, Pres.--Sterling Color Process, Kentwood, MI; *U.S. Private*, pg. 387
Soukup, Mark A., Pres. & Chief Exec. Officer--The State Bank and Trust Company, Defiance, OH; *U.S. Public*, pg. 1413
Soulas, Alain, Chief Exec. Officer--Arjo Wiggins Appleton plc, Basingstoke, United Kingdom; *Int'l*, pg. 567
Soultanian, Sarkis, Chm. Bd. & Pres.--National Utility Service, Inc., Park Ridge, NJ; *U.S. Private*, pg. 787
South, John R., Pres. & Chief Exec. Officer--Staodyn Inc., Longmont, CO; *U.S. Public*, pg. 1509
Southard, Donald, Pres.--Datascope Patient Monitoring Division, Paramus, NJ; *U.S. Public*, pg. 487
Southerland, S. Duane, Jr., Pres. & Chief Exec. Officer--Conso Products Company, Union, SC; *U.S. Public*, pg. 434
Southern, William, Pres.--Mason Electric Co., San Fernando, CA; *U.S. Public*, pg. 594
Southworth, Paul, Pres.--Meadox Medicals, Inc., Oakland, NJ; *U.S. Public*, pg. 247
Southworth, Richard A., Pres. & Chief Exec. Officer--Spectrum Control, Inc., Erie, PA; *U.S. Public*, pg. 1497
Sovey, William P., Pres.--Newell Operating Company, Freeport, IL; *U.S. Public*, pg. 1177
Sowles, Daniel, Pres.--L.H. Sowles Company, Inc., Minneapolis, MN; *U.S. Private*, pg. 1019
Spadone, John C., Pres. & Treas.--Spadone Inc., Norwalk, CT; *U.S. Private*, pg. 1019
Spahr, Bradley W., Pres.--HR Textron, Valencia, CA; *U.S. Public*, pg. 1589
Spalding, Daniel L., Pres.--Powercor Australia Limited, Southbank, Australia; *U.S. Public*, pg. 1252
Spalla, Frank, Pres. & Chief Exec. Officer--Ajax Magnethermic Corp., Warren, OH; *Int'l*, pg. 113
Spandet, Terry L., Pres.--Central Rubber Company, Belvidere, IL; *U.S. Public*, pg. 1776
Spandet, Terry L., Pres.--Daniel Woodhead Company, Northbrook, IL; *U.S. Public*, pg. 1776
Spangler, C. Gregory, Chm. Bd., Pres. & Chief Exec. Officer--Spangler Candy Company, Bryan, OH; *U.S. Private*, pg. 1020
Spangler, Dave, Pres.--Hooker Industries, Ontario, CA; *U.S. Private*, pg. 538
Spangler, David B., Pres. & Chief Exec. Officer--Jefferson Mills, Inc., Pulaski, VA; *U.S. Private*, pg. 584
Spangler, David L., Chm. Bd., Pres. & Chief Exec. Officer--First National Bank of Huntington, Huntington, IN; *U.S. Public*, pg. 674
Spangler, John, Pres. & Chief Exec. Officer--Milestone Contractors Inc., Indianapolis, IN; *U.S. Private*, pg. 745
Spanos, Alex G., Chm. Bd. & Pres.--San Diego Chargers, San Diego, CA; *U.S. Private*, pg. 964
Spanos, Dean A., Pres.--The Spanos Companies, Stockton, CA; *U.S. Private*, pg. 1020
Sparby, Neal R., Pres. & Chief Exec. Officer--Payco American Corporation, Brookfield, WI; *U.S. Public*, pg. 1267
Sparks, Jack B., Jr., Pres.--Lamb Grays Harbor Co, Hoquiam, WA; *U.S. Private*, pg. 378
Sparks, William B., Pres. & Chief Oper. Officer--Greif Brothers Corporation, Delaware, OH; *U.S. Public*, pg. 763
Spatz, D. Dean, Chm. Bd., Pres. & Chief Exec. Officer--Osmonics, Inc., Minnetonka, MN; *U.S. Public*, pg. 1233
Spatz, William, Pres. & Dir.--Spatz Centers Inc., Northbrook, IL; *U.S. Private*, pg. 1021
Spatz, William, Pres.--Spatz & Co. Development, Northbrook, IL; *U.S. Private*, pg. 1021
Spatz, William, Pres.--Spatz Centers, Inc., Northbrook, IL; *U.S. Private*, pg. 1021
Spatz, William, Pres.--S & C Maintenance Corp., Northbrook, IL; *U.S. Private*, pg. 1021
Spaulding, Peter C., Pres.--Wilton Tool Div., Palatine, IL; *U.S. Private*, pg. 1181
Speakman, W.A. III, Pres. & Chief Exec. Officer--Speakman Company, Wilmington, DE; *U.S. Private*, pg. 1021
Spearing, John R., Pres.--ITT Federal Services Corporation, Colorado Springs, CO; *U.S. Public*, pg. 859
Spearing, Robert, Pres.--Telos Information Systems, Pasadena, CA; *U.S. Public*, pg. 1573
Spears, Richard F., Pres.--Landmark Specialty Publications, Inc., Norfolk, VA; *U.S. Private*, pg. 649
Spears, Tom, Pres.--Rosemount Analytical, Uniloc Div., Irvine, CA; *U.S. Public*, pg. 574
Spears, William E., Pres.--Tupperware U.S., Inc., Orlando, FL; *U.S. Public*, pg. 1644
Specht, Bill, Pres.--Cousins Submarines, Menomonee Falls, WI; *U.S. Private*, pg. 280
Speed, Malcom, Partner--Bronner Slosberg Humphrey/Strategic Interactive Group, Boston, MA; *U.S. Private*, pg. 171
Speers, Douglas E., Pres. & Chief Exec. & Oper. Officer--Emco Limited, London, Canada; *Int'l*, pg. 452
Speetzen, Robert W., Pres.--General Electric Capital Railcar Services, Chicago, IL; *U.S. Public*, pg. 712
Speice, Byron, Pres.--Diamond Chain Company, Indianapolis, IN; *U.S. Private*, pg. 68
Speicher, Donald E., Pres.--Ross Technology Corp., Leola, PA; *U.S. Private*, pg. 946
Speiser, Marvin M., Chm. Bd. & Pres.--Health-Chem Corporation, New York, NY; *U.S. Public*, pg. 802
Speiser, Robert D., Pres.--Hercon Laboratories Corp., New York, NY; *U.S. Public*, pg. 802
Speiser, Robert D., Pres.--Transderm Laboratories Corporation, New York, NY; *U.S. Public*, pg. 802
Speizman, Robert S., Chm. Bd. & Pres.--Speizman Industries, Inc., Charlotte, NC; *U.S. Public*, pg. 1498
Spelde, M.E., Chm. Bd., Pres. & Chief Exec. Officer--Empire Airlines, Coeur D'Alene, ID; *U.S. Private*, pg. 374
Spellings, George E., Pres.-Gen. Precision Tool & Die Division--General Precision Tool & Die Division, Muscle Shoals, AL; *U.S. Public*, pg. 986
Speltz, Steve, Pres.--MPH Industries, Riverside, MI; *U.S. Public*, pg. 726
Spence, Bill, Pres.--Ameripol Synpol Corp., Port Neches, TX; *U.S. Private*, pg. 65
Spence, David, Pres.--OzEmail Limited, Sydney, Australia; *Int'l*, pg. 1019
Spence, Jeffrey E., Chm. Bd., Pres., Controller & Chief Exec. & Fin. Officer--Controlled Systems of Wisconsin, Inc., Nashotah, WI; *U.S. Private*, pg. 271
Spence, John C., Pres.--Avco Insurance Services/Balboa Life & Casualty, Irvine, CA; *U.S. Public*, pg. 1589
Spence, Robert L., Chm. Bd. & Pres.--Pacific Lumber & Shipping Co., Seattle, WA; *U.S. Private*, pg. 832
Spence, Roy, Pres.--GSD&M, Austin, TX; *U.S. Private*, pg. 436
Spence, Wesley, Pres.--Southside Ford Truck Sales Inc., Chicago, IL; *U.S. Private*, pg. 1018
Spence, Will B., Pres. & Chief Exec. Officer--South Carolina National Corporation, Columbia, SC; *U.S. Public*, pg. 1730
Spence, Will B., Pres. & Chief Exec. Officer--Wachovia Bank of South Carolina, N.A., Columbia, SC; *U.S. Public*, pg. 1730
Spencer, G.W., Pres.--The Spencer Group Inc., Princeton, NJ; *U.S. Private*, pg. 1025
Spencer, Guy J., Jr., Chm. Bd., Pres. & Chief Exec. Officer--Spencer Companies Inc., Huntsville, AL; *U.S. Private*, pg. 1024
Spencer, R.E., Pres.--Svedala Industries-Universal Engineering, Cedar Rapids, IA; *Int'l*, pg. 1326
Spencer, Ronald E., Pres.--Faber Enterprises, Inc., Canoga Park, CA; *U.S. Private*, pg. 390
Spendiff, James A., Pres. & Chief Oper. Officer--Freedom Forge Corporation, Burnham, PA; *U.S. Private*, pg. 425
Spengler, James R., Jr., Pres. & Chief Exec. Officer--Osmose Wood Preserving, Inc., Buffalo, NY; *U.S. Private*, pg. 821

Spenlinhauer, Stephen, Pres.--Spencer Press, Inc., Wells, ME; *U.S. Private*, pg. 1025
Sperber, Burton S., Chm. Bd., Pres. & Chief Exec. Officer--Environmental Industries, Inc., Calabasas, CA; *U.S. Private*, pg. 378
Sperber, Perry, Chm. Bd. & Pres.--Metal Fab Corporation, Ormond Beach, FL; *U.S. Public*, pg. 658
Sperry, Tom, Mng. Partner--CF2GS, Seattle, WA; *U.S. Private*, pg. 194
Spertell, Alayne, Pres.--Smith's Personnel Service, Inc., New York, NY; *U.S. Private*, pg. 1010
Speyer, Stuart W., Pres.--Tennsco Corporation, Dickson, TN; *U.S. Private*, pg. 1077
Speyer, W. Kip, Pres.--Leisegang Medical, Inc., Boca Raton, FL; *U.S. Public*, pg. 698
Spidalette, Lou, Pres.--LINC Medical Imaging, Newport Beach, CA; *U.S. Public*, pg. 996
Spiegel, Arthur H., III, Pres.--CSC Healthcare Group, New York, NY; *U.S. Public*, pg. 423
Spiegel, Jeffery, Pres. & Chief Exec. Officer--Randa Corp., Kinston, NC; *U.S. Private*, pg. 909
Spiegel, Larry, Principal & Media Dir.--The Richards Group, Inc., Dallas, TX; *U.S. Private*, pg. 929
Spiegel, Peter, Co-Pres. & Chm. Bd.--Kent & Spiegel Direct, Culver City, CA; *U.S. Private*, pg. 615
Spiegel, William D., Pres.--Southwark Metal Manufacturing Company, Philadelphia, PA; *U.S. Private*, pg. 1018
Spielberg, Steven, Partner--DreamWorks SKG, Universal City, CA; *U.S. Private*, pg. 342
Spielman, Jeff, Pres.--SIMS Portex Inc., Keene, NH; *Int'l*, pg. 1268
Spielvogel, Andrew, Pres.--SuperValu, Inc.-Maine Div., Portland, ME; *U.S. Public*, pg. 1540
Spiewak, Roy, Pres., Chief Oper. Officer & Chief Fin. Officer--I. Spiewak & Sons, Inc., New York, NY; *U.S. Private*, pg. 1025
Spiker, T. Scott, Pres.--IFG Asset Management Services, Inc., Minneapolis, MN; *U.S. Public*, pg. 476
Spiller, Ben M., Pres. & Chief Oper. Officer--Southern Pilot Insurance Company, Greensboro, NC; *Int'l*, pg. 346
Spillers, R.C., Pres.--Arkansas Eastman Co., Batesville, AR; *U.S. Public*, pg. 550
Spilman, Robert H., Jr., Pres. & Chief Oper. Officer--Bassett Furniture Industries, Incorporated, Bassett, VA; *U.S. Public*, pg. 193
Spina, David A., Pres. & Chief Oper. Officer--State Street Corporation, Boston, MA; *U.S. Public*, pg. 1513
Spina, David A., Pres. & Chief Oper. Officer--State Street Bank & Trust Co., Boston, MA; *U.S. Public*, pg. 1513
Spindler, G.R., Pres.--Cyprus Amax Coal Co., Englewood, CO; *U.S. Public*, pg. 470
Spires, Hank, Pres.--Cross Creek Apparel, Inc., Mount Airy, NC; *U.S. Public*, pg. 1413
Spitalnick, Dennis, Pres.--Wellmade Industries, Incorporated, New York, NY; *U.S. Private*, pg. 1161
Spitler, Kenneth F., Pres.--Sysco Food Services of Houston, Inc., Houston, TX; *U.S. Public*, pg. 1551
Spitzer, Joseph, Pres.--Perfect Pearl Company, Inc., New York, NY; *U.S. Private*, pg. 852
Spitzer, T. Quinn, Pres. & Chief Exec. Officer--Kepner-Tregoe, Inc., Skillman, NJ; *U.S. Public*, pg. 1659
Spitznagel, John T., Pres. & Chief Exec. Officer--Roberts Pharmaceutical Corporation, Eatontown, NJ; *U.S. Public*, *pg. 1393*
Spitznagel, John T., Pres. & Chief Exec. Officer--VRG International, Inc., Eatontown, NJ; *U.S. Public*, pg. 1393
Spitznagel, John T., Pres. & Chief Oper. Officer--Roberts Laboratories, Inc., Eatontown, NJ; *U.S. Public*, pg. 1393
Spitznagel, John T., Pres. & Chief Exec. Officer--Monmouth Pharmaceutical, Ltd., Guildford, United Kingdom; *U.S. Public*, pg. 1394
Spitznagel, John T., Pres. & Chief Exec. Officer--Roberts Pharmaceutical of Canada, Oakville, Canada; *U.S. Public*, pg. 1394
Splain, Francis J., Jr., Pres. & Treas.--Resolute Management Corp., Stamford, CT; *U.S. Public*, pg. 220
Splude, John, Chm. Bd., Pres. & Chief Exec. Officer--HK Systems, Inc., New Berlin, WI; *U.S. Private*, pg. 491
Spoerri, Robert C., Pres.--LaSalle Partners, Chicago, IL; *U.S. Public*, pg. 978
Sponseller, Gene B., Pres.--Warsaw Orthopedic Inc., Winona Lake, IN; *U.S. Public*, pg. 1482
Spoon, Alan G., Pres. & Chief Oper. Officer--The Washington Post Company, Washington, DC; *U.S. Public*, pg. 1742
Spooner, R. Kenneth, Pres.--Georgia Tent & Awning Inc., Atlanta, GA; *U.S. Private*, pg. 448
Spoor, John, Pres.--State Electric Supply Co., Huntington, WV; *U.S. Private*, pg. 1036
Spore, Keith, Pres.--Milwaukee Journal Sentinel, Milwaukee, WI; *U.S. Private*, pg. 601
Sport, Michael C., Chm. Bd., Pres. & Chief Exec. Officer--Production Management Companies, Inc., Harvey, LA; *U.S. Private*, pg. 888
Spradley, James W., Jr., Pres. & Chief Exec. Officer--Standard Candy Co., Inc., Nashville, TN; *U.S. Private*, pg. 1030
Spradlin, Robert, Pres. & Chief Exec. Officer--Contract Interiors Inc., Taylor, MI; *U.S. Private*, pg. 270
Spraetz, Kenneth, Pres.--Performance Contracting Group, Lenexa, KS; *U.S. Private*, pg. 853
Sprague, Doug, Pres. & Chief Exec. Officer--Computerized Medical Systems, Inc., Saint Louis, MO; *U.S. Private*, pg. 260
Sprague, William W., III, Pres. & Chief Exec. Officer--Savannah Foods & Industries, Inc., Savannah, GA; *U.S. Public*, pg. 872
Spranger, Hanno W., Pres. & Chief Exec. Officer--Netzsch Incorporated, Exton, PA; *U.S. Private*, pg. 792
Spring, Ueli, Pres. & Chief Exec. Officer--Aetna Industries, Inc., Center Line, MI; *U.S. Private*, pg. 25
Springer, Andrew, Pres. & Chief Exec. Officer--Lee Grocery Company, Everett, WA; *U.S. Private*, pg. 657
Springer, J. Darryl, Pres.--Major Smith Inc., New Holland, PA; *Int'l*, pg. 201
Sprole, Robert R., III, Pres.--Therm, Inc., Ithaca, NY; *U.S. Private*, pg. 1079
Sprott, H.B., Jr., Pres. & Chief Exec. Officer--Sprott Oil Co., Inc., Manning, SC; *U.S. Private*, pg. 1027
Spurck, Fredric C., Pres. & Chief Exec. Officer--Webster Industries Inc., Tiffin, OH; *U.S. Private*, pg. 1157
Spurlock, Feth, Pres.--Vinings Industries Inc., Atlanta, GA; *U.S. Private*, pg. 1141
Spurrier, Hal, Pres. & Chief Oper. Officer--Snyder Industries, Inc., Lincoln, NE; *U.S. Private*, pg. 1011
Squeri, John, Pres.--Squeri Foodservice, Cincinnati, OH; *U.S. Public*, pg. 918
Squier-Dow, Mae H., Pres.--ACC TeleCom, Rochester, NY; *U.S. Public*, pg. 3
Squier, Robert C., Pres.--Curtis Screw Co., Inc., Buffalo, NY; *U.S. Private*, pg. 298
Srednicki, Richard, Pres. & Chief Exec. Officer-Universal Card Services--AT&T Corporation, Basking Ridge, NJ; *U.S. Public*, pg. 10
Srednicki, Richard, Pres. & Chief Exec. Officer--AT&T Universal Card Services Corp., Jacksonville, FL; *U.S. Public*, pg. 11
Sret, Albert, Pres.--Mueller's Muehle GmbH, Gelsenkirchen, Germany; *Int'l*, pg. 896
Sroka, Terry F., Pres.--Jarke Corporation, Niles, IL; *U.S. Private*, pg. 583
St. Amour, Andre, Pres. & Chief Oper. Officer--National Reinsurance Company of Canada, Toronto, Canada; *U.S. Private*, pg. 443
St. Charles, David P., Pres. & Chief Oper. Officer--Integrated Systems, Inc., Sunnyvale, CA; *U.S. Public*, pg. 885
St. George, Nicholas J., Chm. Bd., Pres. & Chief Exec. Officer--Oakwood Homes Corporation, Greensboro, NC; *U.S. Public*, pg. 1209
St. John, John, Pres.--Baldwin Stobb San Bernardino, San Bernardino, CA; *U.S. Public*, pg. 170
St. Laurent, David E., Chm. Bd. & Pres.--Electric Insurance Co., Beverly, MA; *U.S. Private*, pg. 368
St. Louis, Paul, Pres.--BPCO, Dorval, Canada; *Int'l*, pg. 453
St-Pierre, Ghislain, Pres. & Gen. Mgr.--Champlain Productions Inc., Montreal, Canada; *Int'l*, pg. 241
Staab, Gary, Pres.--Spangler Inc., Kansas City, KS; *U.S. Private*, pg. 1020
Staab, Robert J., Pres.--Candle-Lite, A Lancaster Colony Co., Cincinnati, OH; *U.S. Public*, pg. 976
Staab, Walter, Chm. Bd.--SFM Media Corporation, New York, NY; *U.S. Private*, pg. 956
Staaterman, Robyn, Pres.--CT Corporation System, New York, NY; *Int'l*, pg. 1513
Staats, Glen E., Pres. & Chief Exec. Officer--CCI/Triad Corporation, Austin, TX; *U.S. Private*, pg. 193
Stabile, Jeffrey, Pres. & Chief Exec. Officer--Aero Systems Aviation Corp., Miami, FL; *U.S. Private*, pg. 24
Stabler, Donald B., Chm. Bd.--Stabler Companies, Inc., Harrisburg, PA; *U.S. Private*, pg. 1028
Stabler, Donald B., Chm. Bd. & Pres.--Eastern Industries, Harrisburg, PA; *U.S. Private*, pg. 1028
Stabler, Donald B., Chm. Bd. & Pres.--Protection Services, Harrisburg, PA; *U.S. Private*, pg. 1028
Stabler, Donald B., Chm. Bd. & Pres.--Precision Solar Controls, Harrisburg, PA; *U.S. Private*, pg. 1028
Stabler, Donald B., Chm. Bd. & Pres.--Work Area Protection, Harrisburg, PA; *U.S. Private*, pg. 1028
Stacho, Robert, Pres. & Chief Oper. Officer--Midco International Inc., Chicago, IL; *U.S. Private*, pg. 744
Stachura, Robert D., V.P. & Exec. Mgr.--Douglas & Lomason Company, Troy, MO; *Int'l*, pg. 830
Stade, Yngve, Pres.--Kamyr AB, Karlstad, Sweden; *Int'l*, pg. 771
Stade, Yngve, Pres.--Stora Corporate Research, Falun, Sweden; *Int'l*, pg. 1303
Staecker, Detlev, Exec. V.P. & Gen. Mgr.--Deutsche Bank AG (New York Branch), New York, NY; *Int'l*, pg. 403
Staehelin, Gaudenz, Dr., Pres.--Basel Trading Company Ltd., Basel, Switzerland; *Int'l*, pg. 169
Staes, Charles W., Pres.--Sysco Food Services Chicago, Inc., Des Plaines, IL; *U.S. Public*, pg. 1551
Staff, Christopher, Pres. & Chief Oper. Officer--Authentic Fitness Corp., Los Angeles, CA; *U.S. Public*, pg. 147
Staff, Joel, Chm. Bd., Pres. & Chief Exec. Officer--National-Oilwell Inc., Houston, TX; *U.S. Public*, pg. 1158
Staffa, Donald J., Chm. Bd. & Pres.--Quality Medical Adjudication, Inc., Rancho Cordova, CA; *U.S. Public*, pg. 802
Stafford, Gerry S., Pres. & Chief Exec. Officer--Commercial Union of Canada Holdings Ltd, Toronto, Canada; *Int'l*, pg. 308
Stafford, Gerry S., Pres. & Chief Exec. Officer--Commercial Union Assurance Company of Canada, Toronto, Canada; *Int'l*, pg. 308
Stafford, James F., Pres. & Chief Exec. Officer--Chips and Technologies, Inc., San Jose, CA; *U.S. Public*, pg. 349
Stafford, John R., Chm. Bd., Pres. & Chief Exec. Officer--American Home Products Corporation, Madison, NJ; *U.S. Public*, pg. 79
Stafford, Randy, Pres. & Chief Exec. Officer--The Court Company, Memphis, TN; *U.S. Private*, pg. 279
Stafford, Robert G., Pres.--Telsmith, Inc., Mequon, WI; *U.S. Public*, pg. 141
Stafford, Rodney, Pres.--American Radio Relay League, Newington, CT; *U.S. Private*, pg. 60
Stager, D., Pres.--Tri-Mark Inc., Piqua, OH; *U.S. Public*, pg. 866
Stagliano, Adam, Pres. & Acct. Plng. Dir.--Weiss, Whitten, Stagliano Inc., New York, NY; *U.S. Private*, pg. 1160
Stahl, Dale E., Pres. & Chief Oper. Officer--Gaylord Container Corporation, Deerfield, IL; *U.S. Public*, pg. 704
Stahl, Jack, Pres.--Coca-Cola USA, Atlanta, GA; *U.S. Public*, pg. 392
Stahlman, G.M., Pres.--Hydro Group, Inc., Bridgewater, NJ; *U.S. Private*, pg. 552
Stahura, John, Pres.--Vanner, Inc., Hilliard, OH; *Int'l*, pg. 449
Stalberg, Carl-Eric, Pres.--JM Byggnads och Fastighets AB, Stockholm, Sweden; *Int'l*, pg. 1260
Staley, George R., Pres.--Toys "R" Us International, Paramus, NJ; *U.S. Public*, pg. 1626
Stallkamp, Thomas T., Pres.--Chrysler Corporation, Auburn Hills, MI; *U.S. Public*, pg. 352
Stallman, Keith, Pres.--SAIC, Sacramento, CA; *U.S. Private*, pg. 976
Stalvey, Rupert A., Pres.--First Southeast Insurance Agency, Conway, SC; *U.S. Public*, pg. 634
Stamm, James A., Pres.-Specialized Transportation Group--Atlas Van Lines, Inc., Evansville, IN; *U.S. Private*, pg. 97
Stammers, Frank, Acting Pres.--Graphics Arts Center, Pasadena, CA; *U.S. Public*, pg. 1038
Stanard, Douglas, Pres.--AMF Bowling Worldwide, Richmond, VA; *U.S. Private*, pg. 6
Standberg, Robert C., Pres. & Chief Exec. Officer--PSC Inc., Webster, NY; *U.S. Public*, pg. 1245
Standen, Michael, Chm. Bd., Pres. & Chief Exec. Officer--Metallurg, Inc., New York, NY; *U.S. Private*, pg. 735
Standish, Victor J., Chm. Bd., Pres. & Chief Exec. Officer--York Barbell Co., Inc., York, PA; *U.S. Private*, pg. 1196
Stanford, James M., Pres. & Chief Exec. Officer--Petro-Canada, Calgary, Canada; *Int'l*, pg. 1041
Stang, Olav, Pres.--Nokia Mobile Phones Japan K.K., Tokyo, Japan; *Int'l*, pg. 952
Stanke, Mary, Pres.--JS&A Group, Inc., Las Vegas, NV; *U.S. Private*, pg. 578
Stanley, Bruce, Pres.--Berkel Incorporated, La Porte, IN; *Int'l*, pg. 545
Stanley, Clifford W., Pres. & Chief Exec. Officer--Guest Supply, Inc., Monmouth Junction, NJ; *U.S. Public*, pg. 768
Stanley, John R., Chm. Bd., Pres. & Chief Exec. Officer--Transamerican Natural Gas Corporation, Houston, TX; *U.S. Private*, pg. 1096
Stanley, Kyle, Pres.--West Coast Entertainment Inc., Langhorne, PA; *U.S. Public*, pg. 1755
Stanley, Lowell, Pres.--Brown Wood Preserving Company, Louisville, KY; *U.S. Private*, pg. 174
Stanley, Paul, Pres. & Creative Dir.--PS Promotions, Inc., Chicago, IL; *U.S. Private*, pg. 828
Stanley, Ronald G., Pres.--Landstar Express America, Inc., Charlotte, NC; *U.S. Public*, pg. 978
Stanley, Theodore R., Pres.--MBI Inc., Norwalk, CT; *U.S. Private*, pg. 685
Stanley, Theodore R., Pres.--Danbury Mint, Norwalk, CT; *U.S. Private*, pg. 685
Stansberry, Warren H., III, Pres. & Treas.--Stanco Metal Products, Inc., Grand Haven, MI; *U.S. Private*, pg. 1030
Stansfield, Elaine, Pres. & Chief Oper. Officer--The Sunflower Group, Overland Park, KS; *U.S. Private*, pg. 1052
Stanton, David T., Pres.--Beverly National Bank, Wilmington, IL; *U.S. Public*, pg. 227
Stanton, Peter M., Pres.--Intercomp Resource Development & Engineering (Canada) Ltd., Calgary, Canada; *U.S. Public*, pg. 1444
Stanton, Susan M., Pres. & Chief Oper. Officer--Payless Cashways, Inc., Kansas City, MO; *U.S. Public*, pg. 1267
Stanzak, Adam, Pres.--Key Cadillac, Inc., Edina, MN; *U.S. Private*, pg. 617
Stanzione, Dan, Pres.--Lucent Technologies, Network Systems Div., Warren, NJ; *U.S. Public*, pg. 1017
Staple, Edmund W., Pres.--Cherry Textron, Santa Ana, CA; *U.S. Public*, pg. 1589
Stapleton, Nigel, Chm. & Pres.--Reed Elsevier Inc., New York, NY; *Int'l*, pg. 1095
Stara, Friedrich, Pres. & Chief Exec. Officer--Henkel Austria Group, Vienna, Austria; *Int'l*, pg. 611
Staribacher, Josef, Dr., Pres.--Osterreichische Industrieholding AG, Vienna, Austria; *Int'l*, pg. 1012
Stark, Peter, Pres.--Deutz AG, Cologne, Germany; *Int'l*, pg. 407
Stark, Peter, Pres.--Motoren-Werke Mannheim AG, Mannheim, Germany; *Int'l*, pg. 408
Stark, Udo, Pres.--AGIV Group, Frankfurt, Germany; *Int'l*, pg. 14
Starkweather, Larry D., Pres. & Chief Exec. Officer--Fiberesin Industries Inc., Oconomowoc, WI; *U.S. Private*, *pg. 402*
Starling, H. Ray, Pres.--HEI Power Corp., Honolulu, HI; *U.S. Public*, pg. 800
Starnes, Michael S., Chm. Bd., Pres. & Chief Exec. Officer--M.S. Carriers, Inc., Memphis, TN; *U.S. Public*, pg. 1027
Starr, F. B., Pres.--Thomasville Furniture Industries, Inc., Thomasville, NC; *U.S. Public*, pg. 688
Starr, Lawrence D., Pres.--Koch Supplies Inc., Kansas City, MO; *U.S. Private*, pg. 628
Starrett, Douglas A., Pres.--The L.S. Starrett Company, Athol, MA; *U.S. Public*, pg. 1511
Starrett, Douglas R., Chm. Bd. & Chief Exec. Officer--The L.S. Starrett Company, Athol, MA; *U.S. Public*, pg. 1511
Starrett, Frederick D., III, Pres. & Treas.--Penobscot Frozen Foods, Inc., Belfast, ME; *U.S. Private*, pg. 850
Startjes, Gerardes, Pres.--HCl Chemtech, Chesterfield, MO; *U.S. Private*, pg. 490
Stastny, Wayne, Gen. Mgr.--Harig Products, Elgin, IL; *U.S. Public*, pg. 252
Statler, Gerard, Pres.--Cleveland City Forge, Cleveland, OH; *U.S. Public*, pg. 1258
Staton, B. Gene, Pres. & Chief Exec. Officer--Morrilton Security Bank, N.A., Morrilton, AR; *U.S. Public*, pg. 630
Stauber, Daniel A., Pres. & Chief Exec. Officer--Med/Waste, Inc., Hialeah, FL; *U.S. Public*, pg. 1077
Staudt, James, Pres.--Vance Publishing Corporation, Lincolnshire, IL; *U.S. Private*, pg. 1133
Staudt, John, Pres. & Chief Exec. Officer--Frontier Foundry, Inc., Titusville, PA; *U.S. Private*, pg. 430
Stauffer, Tom, Pres.--Renaissance International Hotels, Cleveland, OH; *U.S. Public*, pg. 1048

Stauffer, Tom, Pres.--Ramada International Hotels & Resorts, Cleveland, OH; *U.S. Public*, pg. 1048

Stavinoha, Rayburn F., Pres.--Sentry Polymers, Inc., Freeport, TX; *U.S. Public*, pg. 1357

Stavis, Frank, Pres.--Blue Bell/King Koil, Inc., Windsor, CT; *U.S. Private*, pg. 150

Stavropoulos, William S., Pres. & Chief Exec. Officer--The Dow Chemical Company, Midland, MI; *U.S. Public*, pg. 522

Stawasz, Cherie, Pres. & Partner--Stawasz & Partners/ Health Care Communications, New York, NY; *U.S. Private*, pg. 599

Stawicki, James, Pres.--Peterson Builders, Inc., Sturgeon Bay, WI; *U.S. Private*, pg. 857

Stayer, Ralph C., Pres. & Chief Exec. Officer--Johnsonville Foods, Inc., Kohler, WI; *U.S. Private*, pg. 595

Stead, James, Chm. Bd. & Pres.--GMS Corporation, Woonsocket, RI; *U.S. Private*, pg. 435

Steadman, Gil, Pres.--Southchem, Durham, NC; *U.S. Private*, pg. 1014

Steadman, John H., Pres.--Norandal U.S.A., Newport, AR; *Int'l*, pg. 434

Steakley, John W., Pres.--Steakley Chevrolet GEO Subaru Inc., Dallas, TX; *U.S. Private*, pg. 1037

Stearns, Richard E., Pres. & Chief Exec. Officer--Lenox, Incorporated, Lawrenceville, NJ; *U.S. Public*, pg. 261

Stearns, Robert P., Pres.--SCS Engineers, Long Beach, CA; *U.S. Private*, pg. 955

Stearrett, William, Pres. & Chief Oper. Officer--Seradyn, Inc., Indianapolis, IN; *Int'l*, pg. 871

Stecher, Harry, Pres.--Sears Portrait Studios, Saint Louis, MO; *U.S. Public*, pg. 283

Steckart, James G., Pres. & Chief Oper. Officer--Advantage Companies, Inc., Wichita, KS; *U.S. Private*, pg. 22

Stecko, Paul T., Pres. & Chief Exec. Officer--Tenneco Packaging, Evanston, IL; *U.S. Public*, pg. 1579

Steed, Frank, Pres.--American Tourister, Inc., Warren, RI; *U.S. Public*, pg. 1430

Steed, Michael R., Pres.--Trust Fund Advisors, Inc., Washington, DC; *U.S. Private*, pg. 1116

Steed, Michael R., Pres.--MRCO, Washington, DC; *U.S. Private*, pg. 1116

Steedman, Donald L., Pres. & Chief Exec. Officer--Littleford Day Inc., Florence, KY; *U.S. Private*, pg. 671

Steedman, Ralph B., Pres.--Moore Business Forms & Systems Ltd., Mississauga, Canada; *Int'l*, pg. 889

Steel, George, Pres. & Chief Oper. Officer--Scientific Software-Intercomp, Inc., Denver, CO; *U.S. Public*, pg. 1443

Steele, Denny, Pres.--Inteplex, Orange, CA; *U.S. Public*, pg. 215

Steele, Harold, Pres.--H S Die & Engineering, Inc., Grand Rapids, MI; *U.S. Private*, pg. 489

Steele, William W., Pres. & Chief Exec. Officer--ABM Industries, San Francisco, CA; *U.S. Public*, pg. 2

Steen, Donald E., Pres. & Chief Exec. Officer--Columbia/ H.C.A., Dallas, TX; *U.S. Public*, pg. 404

Steenberg, W.D., Chm. Bd. & Pres.--Steenberg Homes, Inc., Fond Du Lac, WI; *U.S. Private*, pg. 1039

Steenkist, Piet, Pres.--CCMP N.V., Antwerp, Belgium; *Int'l*, pg. 678

Steenkist, Piet, Pres.--Hitma BV, Uithoorn, Netherlands; *Int'l*, pg. 678

Steer, Brian L., Pres.--Zimmer International, S.A., Brussels, Belgium; *U.S. Public*, pg. 257

Stefan, Joseph P., Pres.--Rent Roll, Inc, Carrollton, TX; *U.S. Public*, pg. 421

Stefanelli, Joseph, Pres.--Amex Commodities Corporation, New York, NY; *U.S. Private*, pg. 62

Stefanides, Dean, Partner & Creative Dir.--Hampel/ Stefanides, New York, NY; *U.S. Private*, pg. 498

Stefano, Ross, Pres.--Jos. J. Pietrafesa Co., Liverpool, NY; *U.S. Private*, pg. 865

Stefanutti, Oscar, Pres. & Chief Exec. Officer--AFM, Sterling Heights, MI; *U.S. Public*, pg. 1363

Steffensen, Dwight, Pres.--Dr. T.C. Smith Co. Inc., Asheville, NC; *U.S. Public*, pg. 214

Steffey, Rex, Pres. & Chief Exec. Officer--Jay Jacobs, Inc., Seattle, WA; *U.S. Public*, pg. 922

Stegemiller, David C., Pres.--Cast Products, Jackson, MI; *U.S. Public*, pg. 796

Stegner, Edward J., Chm. Bd. & Chief Exec. Officer--Stegner Food Products Co., Cincinnati, OH; *U.S. Private*, *pg. 1039*

Steib, J. Nicholas, Mng. Dir.--GGK Barcelona, Barcelona, Spain; *Int'l*, pg. 1335

Stein, Bill, Pres., Chief Exec. Officer & New Bus. Contact--McConnaughy Stein Schmidt Brown, Chicago, IL; *U.S. Private*, pg. 720

Stein, Gerald, Pres.--Zilber, Ltd., Milwaukee, WI; *U.S. Private*, pg. 1206

Stein, James C., Pres. & Chief Oper. Officer--Fluor Daniel Inc., Irvine, CA; *U.S. Public*, pg. 660

Stein, Jay, Pres. & Chief Exec. Officer--Butterick Company, Inc., New York, NY; *U.S. Private*, pg. 190

Stein, John S., Pres. & Chief Exec. Officer--Golden Enterprises Inc., Birmingham, AL; *U.S. Public*, pg. 749

Stein, Larry, Pres.--Crown Foods Inc., Saint Louis, MO; *U.S.* Private, pg. 292

Stein, Lester, Pres.--Charles River Foods, Inc., Boston, MA; *U.S. Private*, pg. 230

Stein, Martin, Pres. & Chief Exec. Officer--Dawn Joy Fashions, Inc., New York, NY; *U.S. Private*, pg. 316

Stein, Martin, Pres. & Treas.--Sterling Paper Co., Philadelphia, PA; *U.S. Private*, pg. 1041

Stein, Michael Alan, Pres. & Chief Oper. Officer--Electro-Science Laboratories, Inc., King of Prussia, PA; *U.S. Private*, pg. 369

Stein, Robert, Pres. & Chief Exec. Officer--Dairy Mart Convenience Stores, Inc., Cuyahoga Falls, OH; *U.S. Public*, pg. 476

Stein, Robert, Pres. & Chief Exec. Officer--Tejon Ranch Company, Lebec, CA; *U.S. Public*, pg. 1566

Stein, Steven B., Pres. & Chief Oper. Officer--Allied Security, Inc., Pittsburgh, PA; *U.S. Private*, pg. 40

Steinbach, James, Pres.--Magnacraft, Struthers, Dunn, Inc., Northfield, IL; *U.S. Private*, pg. 695

Steinbacher, Horst, Pres.--HALI-Buromobel Vertriebs GesmbH, Vienna, Austria; *Int'l*, pg. 589

Steinback, Michael, Pres.--Communications Instruments Inc., Fairview, NC; *U.S. Private*, pg. 259

Steinbarth, Richard, Pres.--La Preferida, Inc., Chicago, IL; *U.S. Private*, pg. 640

Steinbecker, Terry F., Pres. & Chief Exec. Officer--St. Joseph Light & Power Co., Saint Joseph, MO; *U.S. Public*, pg. 1427

Steinbecker, Terry F., Pres.--SJLP Inc., Saint Joseph, MO; *U.S. Public*, pg. 1427

Steinberg, Barry, Pres. & Chief Exec. Officer--Manchester Equipment Co., Hauppauge, NY; *U.S. Private*, pg. 699

Steinberg, Burt, Pres.--The Dress Barn, Inc., Suffern, NY; *U.S. Public*, pg. 528

Steinberg, Dennis P., Pres.--TPC Corporation, Houston, TX; *U.S. Public*, pg. 1252

Steinberg, Joseph S., Pres.--Leucadia National Corporation, New York, NY; *U.S. Public*, pg. 989

Steinberg, Lawrence, Pres. & Chief Exec. Officer--Unisystems, Inc., New York, NY; *U.S. Private*, pg. 1120

Steinberg, Robert M., Pres. & Chief Oper. Officer--Reliance Group Holdings, Inc., New York, NY; *U.S. Public*, pg. 1374

Steinberg, S.L., Pres.--Carboline Co., Saint Louis, MO; *U.S. Public*, pg. 1357

Steinberger, David, Pres.--Basic Books, Inc., New York, NY; *Int'l*, pg. 927

Steinbrueck, Charles, Pres. & Chief Exec. Officer--Grease Monkey International Inc., Denver, CO; *U.S. Public*, pg. 759

Steinbuch, E., Pres.--Zim-American Israeli Shipping Co., New York, NY; *U.S. Private*, pg. 1206

Steiner, Bob, IV, Pres. & Chief Exec. Officer--Regions Bank/Lee County, Auburn, AL; *U.S. Public*, pg. 1372

Steiner, Edward S., Pres.--Clover Yarns Inc., Milford, DE; *U.S. Private*, pg. 247

Steiner, Jeffrey, Pres.--Fairchild Aerospace Fasteners Division, Chantilly, VA; *U.S. Public*, pg. 610

Steiner, Jeffrey J., Chm. Bd., Pres. & Chief Exec. Officer--The Fairchild Corporation, Chantilly, VA; *U.S. Public*, pg. 610

Steiner, John E., Pres.--MagneTek Lighting Products Group, Nashville, TN; *U.S. Public*, pg. 1037

Steiner, Richard R., Pres. & Chief Exec. Officer--Steiner Corporation, Salt Lake City, UT; *U.S. Private*, pg. 1039

Steiner, Ron, Pres.--International Electronic Research Corp., Burbank, CA; *U.S. Public*, pg. 286

Steiness, Harald, Pres.--NorBetong a.s, Oslo, Norway; *Int'l*, pg. 1199

Steinhart, Ronald G., Pres.--Bank One, Texas Corp., Dallas, TX; *U.S. Public*, pg. 173

Steinhauer, Frederick C., Chm. Bd. & Pres.--Madison Dairy Produce Company, Madison, WI; *U.S. Private*, pg. 694

Steinhaus, A. E., Vice Chm., Pres. & Chief Exec. Officer--AFG, Inc., Westmont, IL; *U.S. Public*, pg. 955

Steinitz, Paul S., Pres.-Asia/Pacific--Moore Products Co. (S) Pte. Ltd., Singapore, Singapore; *U.S. Public*, pg. 1129

Steinmetz, Mark S., Pres. & Gen. Mgr.--KQRS, Inc., Minneapolis, MN; *U.S. Public*, pg. 512

Steinnes, Harald, Pres.--Aker Betong a.s., Oslo, Norway; *Int'l*, pg. 42

Steinwert, Kent A., Pres. & Chief Exec. Officer--Farmers & Merchants Bank of Central California, Lodi, CA; *U.S. Private*, pg. 394

Steiny, Susan, Pres.--Steiny & Company, Inc., Baldwin Park, CA; *U.S. Private*, pg. 1039

Steitz, William N., Pres.--Sauer Industries, Inc., Pittsburgh, PA; *U.S. Private*, pg. 967

Stell, Louis E., Pres. & Chief Exec. Officer--First National Bank of Conway, Conway, AR; *U.S. Public*, pg. 630

Steltenkamp, R. Stephen, Pres.--Matrix Building Co., Inc., Covington, KY; *U.S. Private*, pg. 694

Stemen, Milton, Pres. & Chief Oper. Officer--R & B Machine Tool Co., Saline, MI; *U.S. Private*, pg. 901

Stemmler, Robert M., Pres. & Chief Exec. Officer--AirSensors, Inc., Seattle, WA; *U.S. Public*, pg. 33

Stemmler, Robert M., Pres. & Chief Exec. Officer--IMPCO AirSensors Technologies, Cerritos, CA; *U.S. Public*, pg. 34

Stenberg, Jan, Pres., Chief Exec. Officer & Chief Oper. Officer--Scandinavian Airlines System (SAS), Solna, Sweden; *Int'l*, pg. 1201

Stendahl, Stig, Pres. & Chief Exec. Officer--Fiskars Oy AB, Helsinki, Finland; *Int'l*, pg. 492

Stenius, Robert, Pres.--Kvaerner Masa-Yards Inc., Turku New Shipyard, Turku, Finland; *Int'l*, pg. 771

Stensrud, Patricia, Pres. & Chief Exec. Officer--Victoria Creations, Inc., Warwick, RI; *U.S. Private*, pg. 1139

Stenzel, James, Pres.--Adra Systems, Inc., Chelmsford, MA; *U.S. Private*, pg. 18

Stepan, F. Quinn, Chm. Bd., Pres. & Chief Exec. Officer--Stepan Company, Northfield, IL; *U.S. Public*, pg. 1514

Stepan, Walter, Pres. & Chief Exec. Officer--Uvex Safety, Inc., Smithfield, RI; *Int'l*, pg. 132

Stephan, Joseph, Pres. & Chief Exec. Officer--Vertel, Woodland Hills, CA; *U.S. Public*, pg. 1717

Stephen, James, Pres.--Weber-Stephen Products Co., Palatine, IL; *U.S. Private*, pg. 1157

Stephen, Philip, Chm. Bd., Pres., Chief Oper. & Chief Exec. Officer--Aid Auto Stores, Inc., Westbury, NY; *U.S. Public*, *pg. 29*

Stephen, Randall, Pres.--Circuit City Northeast Division, Richmond, VA; *U.S. Public*, pg. 374

Stephens, Arthur E., Pres.--Brown & Root Services Corporation, Houston, TX; *U.S. Public*, pg. 775

Stephens, Frank, Pres.--Specialty Brands, San Francisco, CA; *Int'l*, pg. 237

Stephens, Gerald D., Pres. & Chief Exec. Officer--RLI Corp., Peoria, IL; *U.S. Public*, pg. 1356

Stephens, J.M., Pres. & Chief Oper. Officer--Davis Electrical Constructors, Inc., Greenville, SC; *U.S. Private*, pg. 315

Stephens, J.T., Pres. & Chief Exec. Officer--EBSCO Industries, Inc., Birmingham, AL; *U.S. Private*, pg. 358

Stephens, James H., Pres.--Tribble & Stephens Co., Houston, TX; *U.S. Private*, pg. 1102

Stephens, John J., Pres. & Chief Exec. Officer--U.S. Timberlands Company, L.P., Klamath Falls, OR; *U.S. Public*, pg. 1688

Stephens, Richard T., Pres. & Chief Oper. Officer--Delaware North Companies, Inc., Buffalo, NY; *U.S. Private*, pg. 321

Stephens, W. Lackey, Pres.--R.L. Zeigler Co. Inc., Tuscaloosa, AL; *U.S. Private*, pg. 1204

Stephens, W. Thomas, Pres. & Chief Exec. Officer--MacMillan Bloedel Limited, Vancouver, Canada; *Int'l*, pg. 828

Stephenson, Bryan, Pres. & Chief Exec. Officer--Independent Bankshares, Inc., Abilene, TX; *U.S. Public*, pg. 874

Stephenson, David, Pres.--Rohde & Schwarz, Inc., Lanham, MD; *Int'l*, pg. 1124

Stephenson, G.W., Jr., Pres. & Treas.--Stephenson, Inc., Alexandria, VA; *U.S. Private*, pg. 1040

Stephenson, James, Pres. & Chief Oper. Officer--KineticSystems Corporation, Lockport, IL; *U.S. Private*, pg. 620

Stephenson, William V., Chm. Bd., Pres. & Chief Exec. Officer--First Brands Corporation, Danbury, CT; *U.S. Public*, pg. 626

Ster, Brian, Pres.--Zimmer Spain S.A., Barcelona, Spain; *U.S. Public*, pg. 257

Sterchak, Joseph M., Pres.--Robert E. Lamb, Inc., Valley Forge, PA; *U.S. Private*, pg. 644

Sterlin, Larry O., Pres.--Asia-Pacific Operations, Singapore, Singapore; *U.S. Public*, pg. 1795

Sterling, John R., Pres.--John Sterling Corporation, Richmond, IL; *U.S. Private*, pg. 1041

Stern, Arlene H., Pres. & Chief Exec. Officer--Gantos Inc., Stamford, CT; *U.S. Public*, pg. 702

Stern, Arnold, Pres.--Jarchem Industries, Inc., Newark, NJ; *U.S. Private*, pg. 582

Stern, Charles J., Chm. Bd. & Pres.--The Bionetics Corporation, Newport News, VA; *U.S. Private*, pg. 145

Stern, David J., Commissioner--National Basketball Association, New York, NY; *U.S. Private*, pg. 780

Stern, Doug, Pres. & Chief Exec. Officer--United Media, New York, NY; *U.S. Public*, pg. 1448

Stern, M.L., Pres.--M.L. Stern & Company, Inc., Beverly Hills, CA; *U.S. Private*, pg. 1041

Stern, Michael, Pres. & Chief Exec. Officer--HC Holdings, Columbus, OH; *U.S. Private*, pg. 489

Stern, Michael, Pres.--Custom Shop Shirtmakers Inc., New York, NY; *U.S. Private*, pg. 490

Stern, Mitchell, Pres. & Chief Oper. Officer--Fox Television Stations Inc., Los Angeles, CA; *Int'l*, pg. 926

Stern, Rodolfo, Pres.--Landstar Development Company, Orlando, FL; *U.S. Private*, pg. 649

Stern, William J., Pres.--Stern Advertising, Inc., Cleveland, OH; *U.S. Private*, pg. 1041

Sternbach, Stephen, Chm. Bd., Pres. & Chief Exec. Officer--Star Multi Care Services Inc., Hicksville, NY; *U.S. Public*, *pg. 1510*

Sternberg, Seymour, Chm. Bd., Pres., Chief Exec. Officer & Chief Oper. Officer--New York Life Insurance Company, New York, NY; *U.S. Private*, pg. 794

Sterner, Dr. Frank, Pres.--Wagner Casters and Wheels, Hustisford, WI; *U.S. Private*, pg. 1146

Sterner, Frank M., Dr., Pres. & Chief Exec. Officer--E.R. Wagner Manufacturing, Milwaukee, WI; *U.S. Private*, pg. 1146

Sternheimer, Mark A., Chm. Bd. & Pres.--Sternheimer Brothers Inc., Sandston, VA; *U.S. Private*, pg. 1042

Sternlicht, Barry, Pres. & Chief Exec. Officer--Starwood Capital Group LLC, Greenwich, CT; *U.S. Private*, pg. 1036

Sterrett, W.E., Pres., Chief Fin. Officer & Sec.--Wheaton Van Lines, Inc., Indianapolis, IN; *U.S. Private*, pg. 1171

Stetler, Daniel, Chm. Bd. & Pres.--Louis Allis Company, Milwaukee, WI; *U.S. Private*, pg. 677

Steuart, David L., Pres.-Pulp Grp.--Avenor, Inc., Montreal, Canada; *Int'l*, pg. 101

Steuart, Guy T., II, Pres.--Steuart Investment Company, Chevy Chase, MD; *U.S. Private*, pg. 1042

Steuck, Gary R., Pres.--Lands' End Japan, K.K., Yokohama, Japan; *U.S. Public*, pg. 978

Stevens, Andrew E., Chm. Bd., Pres. & Dir.-Mktg. & Pub. Rels.--GWP, Inc., Los Angeles, CA; *U.S. Private*, pg. 437

Stevens, Bruce A., Pres.--Steinway Musical Instruments, Inc., Waltham, MA; *U.S. Public*, pg. 1514

Stevens, Clark, Pres.--Mesa Airlines, Inc., Farmington, NM; *U.S. Public*, pg. 1099

Stevens, Derek, Pres. & Chief Exec. Officer--Cold Heading Co., Warren, MI; *U.S. Private*, pg. 250

Stevens, Derek, Pres. & Chief Exec. Officer--Ajax Metal Processing, Detroit, MI; *U.S. Private*, pg. 250

Stevens, Gary, Pres. & Treas.--Integrated Brands Inc., Ronkonkoma, NY; *U.S. Public*, pg. 883

Stevens, Greg, Publr.--The World, Coos Bay, OR; *U.S. Public*, pg. 1343

Stevens, Gus, Pres., Chief Oper. Officer & Treas.--Cyberex, Inc., Mentor, OH; *U.S. Public*, pg. 481

Stevens, J. Clark, Pres. & Chief Oper. Officer--Mesa Air Group, Las Vegas, NV; *U.S. Public*, pg. 1098

Stevens, Jim J., Pres.--Lincoln Provision, Inc., Chicago, IL; *U.S. Private*, pg. 668

Stevens, John M., Pres.--The Gunlocke Company, Wayland, NY; *U.S. Public*, pg. 772

Stevens, John R., Pres. & Chief Oper. Officer--Eastern Utilities Associates, Boston, MA; *U.S. Public*, pg. 549

Stevens, John R., Pres.--EUA Bioten, Inc., Boston, MA; *U.S. Public*, pg. 549

Stevens, June, Mng. Partner-Press--Mediapolis, London, United Kingdom; *Int'l*, pg. 853

Stevens, Richard I., Pres. & Chief Oper. Officer--Stevens International, Inc., Fort Worth, TX; *U.S. Public*, pg. 1517

Stevens, T. Randy, Pres. & Chief Oper. Officer--First Farmers & Merchants National Bank, Columbia, TN; *U.S. Private*, pg. 407

Stevens, William D., Pres. & Chief Oper. Officer--Mitchell Energy & Development Corp., Spring, TX; *U.S. Public*, pg. 1117

Stevens, William J., Chm. Bd. & Pres.--Motion Industries, Inc., Irondale, AL; *U.S. Public*, pg. 732

Stevenson, Charles E., Jr., Chm., Pres. & Chief Exec. Officer--CEBCOR (Consolidated Employment Benefits Corp.), Chicago, IL; *U.S. Private*, pg. 220

Stevenson, Craig H., Jr., Pres., Chief Exec. & Oper. Officer--OMI Corp., New York, NY; *U.S. Public*, pg. 1208

Stevenson, Elaine S., Pres.--MetLife Securities, Inc., New York, NY; *U.S. Private*, pg. 738

Stevenson, Gary, Pres.--Icon Health & Fitness, Inc., Logan, UT; *U.S. Private*, pg. 556

Stevenson, Greg, Pres.--Magnet Properties, Seattle, WA; *U.S. Private*, pg. 38

Stevenson, Judy G., Pres., Chief Exec. Officer & Treas.--Magnetrol International, Downers Grove, IL; *U.S. Private*, pg. 696

Stevenson, Larry, Pres. & Chief Exec. Officer--Chapters Inc., Etobicoke, Canada; *Int'l*, pg. 280

Stevenson, Robert L., Pres. & Chief Exec. Officer--Eastman Worldwide, Buffalo, NY; *U.S. Private*, pg. 358

Steves, Sam Bel, II, Pres. & Chief Oper. Officer--Steves & Sons, Inc., San Antonio, TX; *U.S. Private*, pg. 1042

Steward, H.L., Chm. Bd. & Pres.--Inexco Oil Company, New Orleans, LA; *U.S. Public*, pg. 269

Stewart, Andrew K., Chm. Bd., Pres. & Chief Exec. Officer--Computer Methods Corporation, Livonia, MI; *U.S. Private*, pg. 260

Stewart, B.D., Pres.--The Thompson's Company, Memphis, TN; *U.S. Public*, pg. 1466

Stewart, Barry L., Pres., Chief Exec. Officer, Chief Fin. Officer & Treas.--Eneco Tech Group, Denver, CO; *U.S. Private*, pg. 376

Stewart, Craig W., Pres. & Chief Exec. Officer--Poco Petroleums Ltd., Calgary, Canada; *Int'l*, pg. 1061

Stewart, David, Gen. Mgr.--Creditanstalt Export Finance Ltd., London, United Kingdom; *Int'l*, pg. 348

Stewart, David B., Pres. & Chief Exec. Officer--The UCS Group, Toronto, Canada; *Int'l*, pg. 792

Stewart, Doug, Pres. & Chief Exec. Officer--Sobey Inc., Stellarton, Canada; *Int'l*, pg. 454

Stewart, Eric W., Pres.--Kvaerner Computing & Consultancy Ltd., Gateshead, United Kingdom; *Int'l*, pg. 767

Stewart, Gordon W., Pres.--HHH, Inc., Wilmington, DE; *U.S. Public*, pg. 847

Stewart, Gordon W., Pres.--HSI Corp., Wilmington, DE; *U.S. Public*, pg. 847

Stewart, J. Michael, Pres. & Chief Exec. Officer--Texas Micro, Inc., Houston, TX; *U.S. Public*, pg. 1586

Stewart, J. Michael, Pres.--Texas Microsystems Inc., Houston, TX; *U.S. Public*, pg. 1586

Stewart, J.W., Chm. Bd., Pres. & Chief Exec. Officer--BJ Services Company, Houston, TX; *U.S. Public*, pg. 161

Stewart, James W., Pres.--Southern Mortgage Associates, Inc., Levittown, NY; *U.S. Public*, pg. 400

Stewart, Joe J., Pres.-Govt. Grp.--Babcock & Wilcox Co., Barberton, OH; *U.S. Public*, pg. 1068

Stewart, John, Pres.--Duff-Norton, Charlotte, NC; *U.S. Public*, pg. 406

Stewart, Lawrence, Pres.--Weatherby Health Care, Norwalk, CT; *U.S. Private*, pg. 1155

Stewart, Peter, Gen. Mgr.--EG & G Rotron, Woodstock, NY; *U.S. Public*, pg. 543

Stewart, Richard R., Pres.--Cypress Acquisition, Inc., Houston, TX; *U.S. Public*, pg. 1517

Stewart, Robert H., Jr., Pres.--York Building Products Co., Inc., York, PA; *U.S. Private*, pg. 1196

Stewart, Robert N., Pres.--Portsmouth Navigation Corporation, Greenwich, CT; *U.S. Private*, pg. 761

Stewart, Ronald L., Pres.--Doehler-Jarvis, Inc., Toledo, OH; *U.S. Public*, pg. 796

Stewart, Wayne, Pres.--Steelworks, Incorporated, Des Moines, IA; *U.S. Private*, pg. 1039

Stich, Andrew C., Pres. & Chief Exec. Officer--Robert Scott/David Brooks, Dedham, MA; *U.S. Public*, pg. 948

Stich, Mike, Pres.--Manning Equipment, Inc., Louisville, KY; *U.S. Private*, pg. 700

Stich, Mike, Pres.--Manning Truck Modification, Louisville, KY; *U.S. Private*, pg. 700

Stickles, David, Pres.--G2 Advertising, Huntington Beach, CA; *U.S. Public*, pg. 764

Stief, Dennis, Pres.--Ammirati & Puris Ltd./Toronto, Toronto, Canada; *U.S. Private*, pg. 67

Stiefel, C. W., Pres.--Stiefel Laboratories, Inc., Coral Gables, FL; *U.S. Private*, pg. 1043

Stiefel, W. K., Chm. Bd. & Chief Exec. Officer--Stiefel Laboratories, Inc., Coral Gables, FL; *U.S. Private*, pg. 1043

Stiefler, Jeff, Pres.--American Express Europe Limited, London, United Kingdom; *U.S. Public*, pg. 74

Stiegelmeyer, Jim, Pres.-Oliver Trucking Co.-Indianapolis, In.--Queens Group, Inc., Long Island City, NY; *U.S. Private*, pg. 900

Stieler, Eric, Pres.--Danske Landmaend K/S, Copenhagen, Denmark; *Int'l*, pg. 826

Stien, Gaston, Pres. & Gen. Mgr.--Henkel Hellas, Moschato, Greece; *Int'l*, pg. 612

Stiff, P. Enoch, Pres. & Chief Exec. Officer--OmniQuip International, Inc., Port Washington, WI; *U.S. Private*, pg. 500

Stihl, Hans Peter, Pres.--Andreas Stihl, Waiblingen, Germany; *Int'l*, pg. 1301

Stiles, Mark W., Pres.--Trinity Construction Products, Dallas, TX; *U.S. Public*, pg. 1639

Stiles, Robert F., Pres.--Production Oil Tools, Irving, TX; *U.S. Public*, pg. 547

Stilitano, Carl P., Pres.--Babcock Lumber Company, Pittsburgh, PA; *U.S. Private*, pg. 108

Still, Willard J., Pres. & Chief Exec. Officer--Dealers Electrical Supply Co., Waco, TX; *U.S. Private*, pg. 318

Stiller, Robert P., Pres.--Green Mountain Coffee Roasters, Inc., Waterbury, VT; *U.S. Public*, pg. 761

Stillman, Larry, Pres. & Chief Exec. Officer--Ingram Paper Company, City of Industry, CA; *U.S. Public*, pg. 904

Stillman, Walter R., Chm. Bd. & Pres.--Stillman & Hoag, Inc., Englewood, NJ; *U.S. Private*, pg. 1043

Stimpson, Fred T., Pres. & Chief Exec. Officer--Gulf Lumber Company, Inc., Mobile, AL; *U.S. Private*, pg. 487

Stinnette, Joe L., Jr., Pres. & Chief Exec. Officer--Fireman's Fund Insurance Company, Novato, CA; *Int'l*, pg. 58

Stinson, Frank, Pres.--Roundtree Automotive Group, Shreveport, LA; *U.S. Private*, pg. 947

Stinson, Mark, Pres.--Hamilton Communications Group, Inc., Chicago, IL; *U.S. Private*, pg. 497

Stinson, Mark, Pres.--The Hamilton Communications Group, Chicago, IL; *U.S. Private*, pg. 497

Stinson, Terry D., Pres. & Chief Exec. & Oper. Officer--Bell Helicopter Textron, Hurst, TX; *U.S. Public*, pg. 1588

Stipanovich, James, Pres.--Midland Title Security, Inc., Cleveland, OH; *U.S. Public*, pg. 626

Stipes, Frank C., Esq., Chm. Bd., Pres. & Chief Exec. Officer--Westernbank of Puerto Rico, Mayaguez, PR; *U.S. Public*, pg. 1760

Stipp, Scott L., Pres. & Chief Exec. Officer--District Petroleum Products, Inc., Sandusky, OH; *U.S. Private*, pg. 336

Stirrup, John T., Pres. & Chief Oper. Officer--BWAY Corp., Atlanta, GA; *U.S. Public*, pg. 164

Stitzer, Todd, Pres. & Chief Exec. Officer--Dr Pepper/Seven Up No. America, Dallas, TX; *Int'l*, pg. 248

Stock, Alan, Pres.--Cinemark USA, Inc., Dallas, TX; *U.S. Private*, pg. 240

Stockbridge, Karl M., Pres.--For Better Living, Inc., Auburn, CA; *U.S. Private*, pg. 417

Stocker, Michael A., Pres. & Chief Exec. Officer--Empire Blue Cross & Blue Shield, New York, NY; *U.S. Private*, pg. 374

Stockton, Frederic P., Pres. & Chief Exec. Officer--TRM Copy Centers Corporation, Portland, OR; *U.S. Public*, pg. 1558

Stoddard, Brandon, Pres.--Empty Chair Productions, Inc., Los Angeles, CA; *U.S. Public*, pg. 511

Stoddard, Brandon, Pres. & Chief Oper. Officer--JBS Productions Holding Company, Inc., New York, NY; *U.S. Public*, pg. 511

Stoddard, Randy, Pres.--First National Insurance Co. of America, Seattle, WA; *U.S. Public*, pg. 1423

Stoddard, Randy, Pres.--SAFECO Insurance Co. of America, Seattle, WA; *U.S. Public*, pg. 1423

Stoddard, Randy, Pres.--SAFECO Lloyds Insurance Co., Richardson, TX; *U.S. Public*, pg. 1423

Stoddard, Richard C., Pres.--Healthcare Staffing Solutions, Inc., Lowell, MA; *U.S. Public*, pg. 1373

Stoddard, W. Randall, Pres.--SAFECO Property & Casualty Insurance Companies, Seattle, WA; *U.S. Public*, pg. 1423

Stoehr, James H., III, Pres. & Chief Exec. Officer--Robbins, Inc., Cincinnati, OH; *U.S. Private*, pg. 934

Stokely, John E., Pres. & Chief Exec. Officer--Richfood Holdings, Inc., Glen Allen, VA; *U.S. Public*, pg. 1388

Stokes, Curt, Pres.--Dean Operations Inc., Kansas City, MO; *U.S. Private*, pg. 318

Stokes, James, Pres.--Quorum Health Resources, Inc., Brentwood, TN; *U.S. Public*, pg. 1354

Stokes, Patrick T., Pres.--Anheuser-Busch, Inc., Saint Louis, MO; *U.S. Public*, pg. 114

Stokes, Thomas P., Pres.-CPG Div.--Tree Top, Inc., Selah, WA; *U.S. Private*, pg. 1098

Stokes, W.J., Jr., Pres.--LEXIS Document Services, Springfield, IL; *Int'l*, pg. 1096

Stokol, John E., Pres. & Mng. Dir.--Union Carbide (Europe) S.A., Meyrin, Switzerland; *U.S. Public*, pg. 1667

Stoll, John, Pres.--Lepel Corporation, Edgewood, NY; *U.S. Private*, pg. 560

Stoll, Kurt, Dr. I, Pres. & Mng. Dir.--Festo AG & Co., Esslingen am Neckar, Germany; *Int'l*, pg. 480

Stollenwerk, John J., Pres. & Chief Exec. Officer--Allen-Edmonds Shoe Corp., Port Washington, WI; *U.S. Private*, pg. 36

Stollery, A. Gordon, Chm. Bd., Pres. & Chief Exec. Officer--Morrison Petroleums Ltd., Calgary, Canada; *Int'l*, pg. 895

Stolmeier, Robert C., Chm. Bd. & Pres.--KCL Corporation, Shelbyville, IN; *U.S. Private*, pg. 603

Stolte, Sandra L., Pres., Chief Exec. Officer & Sec.--Central Bank, Fairview Heights, IL; *U.S. Public*, pg. 643

Stoltz, Bob, Chm. Bd. & Pres.--Tiernay Metals, Redondo Beach, CA; *U.S. Private*, pg. 1085

Stoltz, Mitch, Pres.--NWS Inc., Chicago, IL; *U.S. Private*, pg. 772

Stoltz, Ove, Pres.--Asea Brown Boveri Industrie B.V., Apeldoorn, Netherlands; *Int'l*, pg. 8

Stoltz, Volker, Pres.--Shandwick Deutschland GmbH, Bonn, Germany; *Int'l*, pg. 1227

Stone, Brian Stuart, Pres.--Magnetics Data Inc., Goleta, CA; *U.S. Private*, pg. 695

Stone, Charles Rivers, Pres.--Umbro International, Inc., Greenville, SC; *U.S. Private*, pg. 1116

Stone, Craig, Chm. Bd., Pres. & Chief Exec. Officer--K-D Lamp Company, Cincinnati, OH; *U.S. Private*, pg. 603

Stone, David, Pres.--Southwestern Financial Corporation, New York, NY; *U.S. Private*, pg. 1018

Stone, David, Pres. & Chief Oper. Officer--Sterilite Corporation, Townsend, MA; *U.S. Private*, pg. 1040

Stone, David J., Pres.--La Franco Penn Life Compania De Segures De Vida S.A., Buenos Aires, Argentina; *U.S. Public*, pg. 1271

Stone, Elliot, Pres.--Sorbee International Ltd., Philadelphia, PA; *U.S. Private*, pg. 1014

Stone, Gary V., Pres.--Milprint Inc., Oshkosh, WI; *U.S. Public*, pg. 210

Stone, Howard S., Pres. & Sec.--Bake-Line Products, Inc., Des Plaines, IL; *U.S. Public*, pg. 657

Stone, James L., Pres.--Mercer Transportation Co., Louisville, KY; *U.S. Private*, pg. 732

Stone, John McWilliams, Jr., Chm. Bd., Pres., Chief Exec. Officer & Chief Oper. Officer--Dukane Corporation, Saint Charles, IL; *U.S. Private*, pg. 345

Stone, Patrick F., Pres.--Fidelity National Title Insurance Company, Irvine, CA; *U.S. Public*, pg. 620

Stone, Patrick F., Pres.--Fidelity National Title Insurance Company of Pennsylvania, Hialeah, FL; *U.S. Public*, pg. 621

Stone, Robert M., Chm. Bd. & Pres.--J. A. Jones Applied Research Co., Charlotte, NC; *Int'l*, pg. 633

Stone, Roger W., Chm. Bd., Pres. & Chief Exec. Officer--Stone Container Corporation, Chicago, IL; *U.S. Public*, pg. 1520

Stone, Sherrill, Chm. Bd.,Pres. & Chief Exec. Officer--Peerless Mfg. Co., Dallas, TX; *U.S. Public*, pg. 1268

Stoneback, W. Keith, Pres. & Chief Exec. Officer--Surgical Laser Technologies, Inc., Montgomeryville, PA; *U.S. Public*, pg. 1542

Stonecipher, David A., Pres. & Chief Exec. Officer--Jefferson-Pilot Corporation, Greensboro, NC; *U.S. Public*, pg. 925

Stonehouse, Glenn A., Pres.--Grafton Fraser Inc., Willowdale, Canada; *Int'l*, pg. 556

Stoner, John M., Pres.--True Temper Hardware Company, Camp Hill, PA; *U.S. Public*, pg. 846

Stoner, W.C., Pres.--Bulova Watch Company Limited, Toronto, Canada; *U.S. Public*, pg. 1011

Stoops, John C., Pres.--Wiegand Industrial-Chromalox, Pittsburgh, PA; *U.S. Public*, pg. 573

Storch, David P., Pres., Chief Exec. & Oper. Officer--AAR Corp., Wood Dale, IL; *U.S. Public*, pg. 1

Storen, Robert S., Pres.--Perini Building Company-Central U.S. Division, Southfield, MI; *U.S. Public*, pg. 1278

Storey, Kenneth, Pres.--Dixieland Food Stores Inc., Geneva, AL; *U.S. Private*, pg. 337

Storhoff, Donald, Pres.--Foremost Farms USA Cooperative, Baraboo, WI; *U.S. Private*, pg. 418

Stork, Donald A., Pres.--Advanswers Media/Programming, Saint Louis, MO; *Int'l*, pg. 117

Stork, Jeffrey M., Pres.--Stonhard, Inc., Maple Shade, NJ; *U.S. Public*, pg. 1358

Stormes, Ben F., II, Pres. & Chief Exec. Officer--The Wickman Corp., Oak Park, MI; *U.S. Private*, pg. 1175

Storms, Charles D., Pres. & Chief Exec. Officer--Red Spot Paint & Varnish Co., Evansville, IN; *U.S. Private*, pg. 915

Storozum, Ted, Pres.--Dominion Industrial Fabrics Company, Montreal, Canada; *Int'l*, pg. 415

Storrie, Karl F., Pres. & Chief Exec. Officer--Dura Automotive Systems, Inc., Minneapolis, MN; *U.S. Public*, pg. 537

Story, Edward T., Pres. & Chief Exec. Officer--SOCO International, Inc., Houston, TX; *U.S. Public*, pg. 1482

Story, Gary, Pres.--Premier Parks Inc., Oklahoma City, OK; *U.S. Public*, pg. 1323

Stoudt, M., Pres.--Edicon Systems, Rochester, NY; *U.S. Public*, pg. 551

Stouffer, Ronald D., Pres. & Chief Exec. Officer--Bowles Fluidics Corporation, Columbia, MD; *U.S. Public*, pg. 248

Stouffer, Spencer R., Pres.-Miller & Smith Homes--Miller & Smith, Inc., Mc Lean, VA; *U.S. Private*, pg. 746

Stough, Bill, Pres. & Gen. Mgr.--WGME-TV, Portland, ME; *U.S. Private*, pg. 439

Stoughton, Richard H., Pres.--Charleston Financial Services, Inc., Charleston, SC; *U.S. Public*, pg. 634

Stoughton, W. Vickery, Pres.--SmithKline Beecham Clinical Laboratories, Nashville, TN; *Int'l*, pg. 1265

Stout, Everett E., Pres., Chief Exec. Officer, Chief Fin. Officer & Controller--Metaltech, Inc., Kirkwood, MO; *U.S. Private*, pg. 735

Stout, Gary, Pres. & Chief Exec. Officer--Gannett Offset, Springfield, VA; *U.S. Public*, pg. 699

Stout, Harry Lee, Pres.--KCS Energy Marketing Inc., Edison, NJ; *U.S. Public*, pg. 938

Stout, Harry Lee, Pres.--Enercop Gas Marketing, Houston, TX; *U.S. Public*, pg. 938

Stout, Harry Lee, Pres.--KCS Energy Marketing, Inc., Houston, TX; *U.S. Public*, pg. 939

Stout, Harry Lee, Pres.--KCS Pipeline Systems, Inc., Houston, TX; *U.S. Public*, pg. 939

Stout, Harry Lee, Pres.--KCS Michigan Resources, Inc., Houston, TX; *U.S. Public*, pg. 939

Stout, Harry Lee, Pres.--KCS Energy Services, Inc., Houston, TX; *U.S. Public*, pg. 939

Stout, Lonnie J., II, Chm. Bd., Pres. & Chief Exec. Officer--J. Alexanders Corporation, Nashville, TN; *U.S. Public*, pg. 40

Stout, Mike, Pres.--Thor America, Middleburg, PA; *U.S. Public*, pg. 1602

Stout, Raymond M., Pres. & Chief Exec. Officer--Fabwel Inc., Elkhart, IN; *U.S. Private*, pg. 390

Stover, Matthew J., Pres. & Chief Exec. Officer--Bell Atlantic Yellow Pages, Middleton, MA; *U.S. Public*, pg. 203

Straat, H.C., Pres.--Uitgeversmaatschappij De Limburger bv, Maastricht, Netherlands; *Int'l*, pg. 1445

Stradling, Pap G., Pres. & Mng. Dir.--Coutts & Co Trust Holdings Limited, Nassau, Bahamas; *Int'l*, pg. 911

Straeter, Terry A., Dr., Pres.--GDE Systems, Inc., San Diego, CA; *U.S. Public*, pg. 1627

Strahman, Richard D., Chm. Bd. & Pres.--Strahman Valves, Inc., Florham Park, NJ; *U.S. Private*, pg. 1046

Strahmmer, Peter, Chm. & Pres.--Voest-Alpine Stahl AG, Lienz, Austria; *Int'l*, pg. 1470

Straitz, John F., III, Pres.--NAO, Inc., Philadelphia, PA; *U.S. Private*, pg. 771

Straka, Mark, Pres.--Southern California Air Gas, Gardena, CA; *U.S. Public*, pg. 33

Straka, Mark, Pres.--Southern California Air Gas, Lakewood, CA; *U.S. Public*, pg. 33

Stranaland, David, Pres.--Dan-Co Bakery, Inc., Forest Park, GA; *U.S. Public*, pg. 657
Strand, James W., Pres.-Diversified Opers.--Aliant Communications Inc., Lincoln, NE; *U.S. Public*, pg. 40
Strand, Lars, Pres.--Optiroc A.S., Varde, Denmark; *Int'l*, pg. 1200
Strange, Bob, Pres.--Commercial Cold Storage, Inc., Atlanta, GA; *U.S. Public*, pg. 1519
Strange, J. Leland, Pres. & Chief Exec. Officer--Intelligent Systems Corp., Norcross, GA; *U.S. Public*, pg. 888
Strange, Peter S., Pres. & Chief Exec. Officer--Frank Messer & Sons Construction Co., Cincinnati, OH; *U.S. Private*, pg. 734
Strano, Paul V., Pres.--Strano Syscco Foodservice Limited, Peterborough, Canada; *U.S. Public*, pg. 1552
Straschnoy, Dario, Pres.--Young & Rubicam de Buenos Aires, Buenos Aires, Argentina; *U.S. Private*, pg. 1200
Strassberg, Gerson, Pres.--Anglers Roslyn Group Ltd., Flushing, NY; *U.S. Private*, pg. 74
Strassburger, Chris, V.P.-Printing (Intermountain Area)--Zellerbach Division, Denver, CO; *U.S. Public*, pg. 1075
Strassler, Hans Rudolf, Pres. & Chief Oper. Officer--Forbo Holding SA, Eglisau, Switzerland; *Int'l*, pg. 496
Strassler, Hans-Rudolf, Pres. & Chief Oper. Officer--Forbo International SA, Eglisau, Switzerland; *Int'l*, pg. 497
Stratakos, John, Pres.--ENI, Rochester, NY; *U.S. Private*, pg. 354
Stratton, Harold M., II, Pres. & Chief Exec. Officer--Strattec Securities Corporation, Milwaukee, WI; *U.S. Public*, pg. 1523
Stratton, Richard A., Pres. & Chief Exec. Officer--Litchfield Financial Corporation, Williamstown, MA; *U.S. Public*, pg. 1001
Stratton, Terry A., Pres.--Aviation Constructors, Inc., Atlanta, GA; *U.S. Private*, pg. 246
Straub, Kenneth, Pres.--Par Enterprises, Inc., Wheeling, WV; *U.S. Private*, pg. 838
Straub, Walter W., Chm. Bd., Pres. & Chief Exec. Officer--Rainbow Technologies, Inc., Irvine, CA; *U.S. Public*, pg. 1359
Straus, Roger W., Jr., Pres. & Chief Exec. Officer--Farrar, Straus & Giroux, Inc., New York, NY; *Int'l*, pg. 1479
Strausbaugh, Robert L., Vice Chm., Pres. & Chief Exec. Officer--Spring Grove National Bank, Spring Grove, PA; *U.S. Public*, pg. 1542
Strauss, Charles B., Pres. & Chief Exec. Officer--Lever Brothers Co., New York, NY; *Int'l*, pg. 1435
Strauss, Christianne L., Pres.--General Mills Canada Inc., Etobicoke, Canada; *U.S. Public*, pg. 718
Strauss, David, Pres. & Chief Exec. Officer--Key Container Corporation, Pawtucket, RI; *U.S. Private*, pg. 617
Strauss, Gary J., Pres.--Ikon Office Solutions-St. Louis, Saint Louis, MO; *U.S. Public*, pg. 864
Strauss, Phil, Pres.--Multiplex Technology, Inc., Brea, CA; *U.S. Public*, pg. 1705
Strauss, Richard H., Pres. & Chief Exec. Officer--Advance Packaging Corporation, Grand Rapids, MI; *U.S. Private*, pg. 18
Straut, Charles, Mng. Dir.--Hillside Capital Incorporated, New York, NY; *U.S. Private*, pg. 530
Straw, Erwin T., Chm. Bd., Pres. & Chief Exec. Officer--Prime Bancorp, Inc., Fort Washington, PA; *U.S. Public*, pg. 1326
Straw, Martyn, Pres.-Interbrand Schechter--Interbrand Schechter, New York, NY; *U.S. Public*, pg. 1224
Streatfield, D.A., Pres.--Christies International plc, London, United Kingdom; *Int'l*, pg. 289
Street, Chriss W., Chm. Bd., Pres. & Chief Exec. & Oper. Officer--Comprehensive Care Corporation, Corona Del Mar, CA; *U.S. Public*, pg. 419
Street, E. Gene, Partner--Cracken, Harkey, Street & Co., LLC, Dallas, TX; *U.S. Private*, pg. 283
Street, Gordon P., Jr., Chm. Bd., Pres., Chief Exec. & Chief Oper. Officer--North American Royalties, Inc., Chattanooga, TN; *U.S. Private*, pg. 803
Street, W. Garland, Chm. Bd., Pres. & Chief Exec. Officer--Andy's Restaurants Inc., Little Rock, AR; *U.S. Private*, pg. 74
Street, William M., Pres. & Chief Exec. Officer--Brown-Forman Beverages Worldwide, Louisville, KY; *U.S. Public*, pg. 261
Streeter, Bruce A., Pres.--Gulf Offshore Marine, Lafayette, LA; *U.S. Public*, pg. 769
Streff, Darrell, Pres.--Feterl Mfg. Co., Salem, SD; *U.S. Public*, pg. 1676
Stremme, Steffen, Dr., Chm. Bd., Pres. & Chief Exec. Officer--Quelle Group, Furth, Germany; *Int'l*, pg. 1078
Strickland, D. Gordon, Pres. & Chief Exec. Officer--Kerr Group, Inc., Lancaster, PA; *U.S. Public*, pg. 952
Strickland, David, Mng. Dir.--Chapter One Group Limited, Tewkesbury, United Kingdom; *Int'l*, pg. 280
Strickland, Ed, Pres. & Chief Exec. Officer--Valley Systems, Inc., Canal Fulton, OH; *U.S. Public*, pg. 1706
Strickler, Charles O., Pres.--Rocco Inc., Harrisonburg, VA; *U.S. Private*, pg. 937
Strickler, Mark, Pres.--Rocco Building Supplies Inc., Harrisonburg, VA; *U.S. Private*, pg. 937
Stried, Richard, Pres.--Medical Surgical Specialties, Ltd., Kalamazoo, MI; *U.S. Private*, pg. 728
Striegler, Kenneth, Pres.--Chr. Hansen Industria e Comercio Ltda., Sao Paulo, Brazil; *Int'l*, pg. 289
Strigl, Dennis F., Pres. & Chief Exec. Officer--Bell Atlantic Mobile, Bedminster, NJ; *U.S. Public*, pg. 202
Stringer, J. Kenneth, III, Pres.--Flir Systems, Inc., Portland, OR; *U.S. Public*, pg. 654
Strite, L. Gerald, Pres. & Chief Exec. Officer--Shenandoah Mfg. Co. Inc., Harrisonburg, VA; *U.S. Private*, pg. 992
Strittmatter, Hermann, Pres.--TBWA/GGK, Zurich, Switzerland; *U.S. Private*, pg. 1063
Strittmatter, Hermann, Chm. & Pres.--TBWA GGK Zurick, Zurich, Switzerland; *Int'l*, pg. 1335
Stroble, Michael, Pres. & Gen. Mgr.--North Dakota Mill & Elevator Association, Grand Forks, ND; *U.S. Private*, pg. 804
Stroburg, Jeff, Pres. & Chief Exec. Officer--Countrymark Cooperative, Inc., Indianapolis, IN; *U.S. Private*, pg. 279
Stroh, B. Gregory, Pres.-Package--Packaging Business, Milford, OH; *U.S. Public*, pg. 671
Stroh, B. Gregory, Pres.--Folding Carton Group, Milford, OH; *U.S. Public*, pg. 671
Strom, C., Pres.--Draka Kabel B.V., Amsterdam, Netherlands; *Int'l*, pg. 417
Strom, Richard, Pres.--Pulte Houston Division, Houston, TX; *U.S. Public*, pg. 1344
Strom, Robert B., Pres.--Foulds Inc., Libertyville, IL; *U.S. Private*, pg. 421
Strombos, Nick, Pres.--Alpha Coatings, Livonia, MI; *U.S. Private*, pg. 1152
Strome, Stephen, Pres. & Chief Exec. Officer--Handleman Company, Troy, MI; *U.S. Public*, pg. 779
Stromsoe, Erik, Pres.--Kvaerner Chile S.A., Santiago, Chile; *Int'l*, pg. 767
Strong, Donald, Pres.--Elwell-Parker, Inc., Farmington, MI; *U.S. Private*, pg. 373
Strong, Peter, Pres.--Krautkramer-Branson, Inc., Lewistown, PA; *U.S. Public*, pg. 574
Strong, Robert F., II, Pres. & Chief Oper. Officer--Longview National Bank, Longview, TX; *U.S. Public*, pg. 630
Stroot, Michael, Pres.--InnerVision Studios Inc., Saint Louis, MO; *U.S. Public*, pg. 114
Stroud, R., Pres.--Ain Plastics, Inc., Mount Vernon, NY; *Int'l, pg. 1388*
Stroud, Steve, Pres.--Mercantile Investment & Trust Services, Des Moines, IA; *U.S. Public*, pg. 1088
Stroud, Wilfred C., Chm. Bd. & Pres.--Strouds, Inc., City of Industry, CA; *U.S. Public*, pg. 1525
Stroup, Paul A., III, Pres. & Chief Exec. Officer--Lance, Inc., Charlotte, NC; *U.S. Public*, pg. 977
Strub, Peter, Co-Owner & Chief Fin. Officer--Eurad RSCG, Zurich, Switzerland; *Int'l*, pg. 602
Struder, Robert, Pres.--Union Bank of Switzerland, Zurich, Switzerland; *Int'l*, pg. 1439
Strumbos, Nick, Pres.--Washers, Incorporated, Livonia, MI; *U.S. Private*, pg. 1152
Strumwasser, Barry, Pres.--Baker Norton Pharmaceuticals, Inc., Miami, FL; *U.S. Public*, pg. 914
Strutz, George A., Pres.--Clopay Corporation, Cincinnati, OH; *U.S. Public*, pg. 766
Strutz, Richard, Pres.--National Bancorp of Alaska, Inc., Anchorage, AK; *U.S. Public*, pg. 1153
Stuart, Arthur, Pres.--Bridgestone/Firestone Original Equipment Tire Sales Company, Southfield, MI; *Int'l*, pg. 213
Stuart, Ian, Pres.--Mead Johnson Nutritionals, Evansville, IN; *U.S. Public*, pg. 255
Stuart, Timothy R., Pres. & Chief Oper. Officer--Stuart Entertainment Inc., Council Bluffs, IA; *U.S. Public*, pg. 1526
Stubblefield, David E., Pres. & Chief Exec. Officer--ABF Freight System, Inc., Fort Smith, AR; *U.S. Public*, pg. 130
Stubbs, Stoney M., Jr., Chm. Bd., Pres. & Chief Exec. Officer--Frozen Food Express Industries, Inc., Dallas, TX; *U.S. Public*, pg. 685
Stubbs, Stoney M., Jr., Pres.--AM Can, Dallas, TX; *U.S. Public*, pg. 685
Stubler, Daniel J., Pres. & Chief Oper. Officer--Toastmaster, Inc., Columbia, MO; *U.S. Public*, pg. 1619
Stuckey, Charles R., Jr., Chm. Bd., Pres. & Chief Exec. Officer--Security Dynamics Technologies, Bedford, MA; *U.S. Public*, pg. 1453
Stucki, A., Dr., Pres.--Cruspi S.A., Dallikon, Switzerland; *Int'l*, pg. 348
Stucki, Wayne, Pres. & Chief Fin. Officer--Rocky Mountain Company, Saint George, UT; *U.S. Private*, pg. 938
Stucky, Darrel, Pres.--Benmar Marine Electronics, Inc., Santa Ana, CA; *U.S. Private*, pg. 133
Stuelpe, G. Walter, Jr., Pres. & Chief Exec. Officer--Apcoa, Inc., Cleveland, OH; *U.S. Private*, pg. 533
Stuenkel, Wayne E., Pres.--American Foundation Life Insurance Company, Birmingham, AL; *U.S. Public*, pg. 1336
Stueve, Juergen, Pres.--Frankfurter Sparkasse, Frankfurt, Germany; *Int'l*, pg. 504
Stultz, B.M., Pres.--FPC, Inc., Hollywood, CA; *U.S. Public*, pg. 551
Stumpo, James H., Pres. & Chief Exec. Officer--Athey Products Corporation, Wake Forest, NC; *U.S. Public*, pg. 142
Stuntz, William, Pres.--WPT, Inc., Edison, NJ; *U.S. Private*, pg. 1144
Stupka, John T., Pres. & Chief Exec. Officer--Mobile Telecommunications Technologies Corp., Jackson, MS; *U.S. Public*, pg. 1120
Stupp, Robert P., Pres.--Stupp Bros, Inc., Saint Louis, MO; *U.S. Private*, pg. 1048
Sturgeon, John A., Pres.--Mutual of Omaha Insurance Company, Omaha, NE; *U.S. Private*, pg. 769
Sturgeon, John A., Pres.--Companion Life Insurance Co., Rye, NY; *U.S. Private*, pg. 770
Sturgeon, John A., Pres.--United World Life Insurance Company, Omaha, NE; *U.S. Private*, pg. 770
Sturgeon, John A., Pres.--United of Omaha Life Insurance Company, Omaha, NE; *U.S. Private*, pg. 770
Sturiale, Thomas, Pres. & Chief Exec. Officer--Neles-Jamesbury Corp., Worcester, MA; *Int'l*, pg. 1428
Sturman, Peter, Pres. & Gen. Mgr.--Mail Media Companies, Phoenix, AZ; *U.S. Public*, pg. 1509
Sturrock, Wilma, Pres.--Ridge Vineyards Inc., Cupertino, CA; *Int'l*, pg. 1013
Stuzin, Charles B., Chm. Bd., Chief Exec. Officer & Pres.--NationsBank/Miami, Miami, FL; *U.S. Public*, pg. 1162
Styrlund, Kenneth A., Pres.--Witcher Construction Co., Minneapolis, MN; *U.S. Private*, pg. 1185
Styrvold, Knut, Pres.--Erling Sande A/S, Oslo, Norway; *Int'l, pg. 1390*
Styslinger, Lee J., III, Pres. & Chief Exec. Officer--Altec Industries, Inc., Birmingham, AL; *U.S. Private*, pg. 47
Suarez, Alfonso Fuertes, Pres.--Iber-Swiss Catering, S.A., Madrid, Spain; *Int'l*, pg. 1225
Suarez, Benjamin D., Pres.--Suarez Corporation Industries, Canton, OH; *U.S. Private*, pg. 1048
Suarez, Gonzalez, Pres.--Suarez & Clavera/DMB&B, Montevideo, Uruguay; *U.S. Private*, pg. 305
Subia, Robert, Chm., Pres. & Chief Exec. Officer--Micron Custom Manufacturing Services, Inc., Nampa, ID; *U.S. Public*, pg. 1105
Subijana, Pedro Sagues, Pres.--Infoleasing SAF, S.A., Madrid, Spain; *Int'l*, pg. 1225
Subilia, Maurice H., Pres.--Fiber Materials, Inc., Biddeford, ME; *U.S. Private*, pg. 402
Subramaniam, Shivan S., Chm. Bd., Pres. & Chief Exec. Officer--Allendale Mutual Insurance Co., Johnston, RI; *U.S. Private*, pg. 37
Suchor, Lawrence F., Pres.--Larrys, Inc., Gillette, WY; *U.S. Private*, pg. 652
Sudderth, John, Pres.--Dowell Schlumberger Canada Inc., Calgary, Canada; *U.S. Public*, pg. 1439
Suehiro, S., Pres.--Taiyo Chemical Industry Co., Ltd., Osaka, Japan; *Int'l*, pg. 947
Suenaga, Teiji, Pres.--Janome Sewing Machine Co., Ltd., Tokyo, Japan; *Int'l*, pg. 699
Suerth, Hank, Pres.--Infinity Systems, Inc., Chatsworth, CA; *U.S. Public*, pg. 787
Suetsugu, Hiroshi, Pres. & Chief Exec. Officer--Nippon Steel U.S.A., Inc., New York, NY; *Int'l*, pg. 939
Suey, David, Pres.--Dempster Industries Inc., Beatrice, NE; *U.S. Private*, pg. 324
Sugahara, Kaytaro G., Pres.--Fairfield Maxwell Ltd., New York, NY; *U.S. Private*, pg. 391
Sugar, Lawrence, Pres.--South Central Florida Express, Inc., Clewiston, FL; *U.S. Private*, pg. 1126
Suggitt, N.W.S., Chm. Bd. & Pres.--Olin Far East, Limited, Stamford, CT; *U.S. Public*, pg. 1219
Suggs, Carroll W., Chm. Bd., Pres. & Chief Exec. Officer--Petroleum Helicopters, Inc., Metairie, LA; *U.S. Public*, pg. 1281
Sugimachi, Toshitaka, Pres. & Chief Oper. Officer--Secom Co., Ltd., Tokyo, Japan; *Int'l*, pg. 1217
Sugino, Naomichi, Pres.--Television Tokyo Channel 12 Ltd., Tokyo, Japan; *Int'l*, pg. 929
Sugishita, Masaaki, Pres.--Wako Securities Co., Ltd., Tokyo, Japan; *Int'l*, pg. 1485
Sugita, Takashi, Pres.--Kyodo Advertising Co., Ltd., Tokyo, Japan; *Int'l*, pg. 776
Sugiyama, Mineo, Pres.--NEC Industries, Inc., New York, NY; *Int'l*, pg. 900
Sugiyama, Mineo, Pres. & Chief Exec. Officer--NEC America, Inc., Melville, NY; *Int'l*, pg. 900
Sugiyama, Mineo, Pres.--NEC USA, Inc., Melville, NY; *Int'l*, pg. 900
Sugo, Kazuo, Pres.--Sakura Bank (Schweiz) AG, Zurich, Switzerland; *Int'l*, pg. 1180
Suh, Chan, Pres. & Chief Exec. Officer--Agency.Com, New York, NY; *U.S. Public*, pg. 1223
Suhowatsky, Stephen J., Pres. & Chief Exec. Officer--Syracuse Supply Company, Syracuse, NY; *U.S. Private*, pg. 1060
Suhre, Richard, Pres.--Cassens Transport Company, Edwardsville, IL; *U.S. Private*, pg. 219
Suila, Keijo, Pres. & Chief Exec. Officer--Leaf Group B.V., Espoo, Finland,; *Int'l*, pg. 638
Suisman, Gary, Pres. & Publr.--Lansing State Journal, Lansing, MI; *U.S. Public*, pg. 701
Suk, S.K., Pres.--Varian Korea Ltd., Kyonggi-do, Korea; *U.S.* Public, pg. 1710
Sukarna, Agus, Pres. & Dir.--P.T. Bank Merincorp, Jakarta, Indonesia; *Int'l*, pg. 1310
Suknow, Irving, Pres.--Reading Body Works, Inc., Reading, PA; *U.S. Private*, pg. 913
Sul, Yong U., Pres.--H.K. International, Inc., Northbrook, IL; *U.S. Private*, pg. 491
Sulentic, Thomas, Pres.-Special Mkts. Div.--Danaher Tool Group, Lancaster, PA; *U.S. Public*, pg. 480
Sullam, Ronaldo, Pres.--Air Products Europe, Inc., Allentown, PA; *U.S. Public*, pg. 30
Sullivan, Brian W., Pres.-Comml. Div.--World Color Press, Inc., Greenwich, CT; *U.S. Public*, pg. 1778
Sullivan, Charles, Pres.--Cargill Salt, Newark, CA; *U.S. Private*, pg. 210
Sullivan, Dan J., Jr., Pres.--Sullivan & Cozart Inc., Louisville, KY; *U.S. Private*, pg. 1049
Sullivan, Daniel J., Chm. Bd., Pres. & Chief Exec. Officer--Caliber System, Inc., Akron, OH; *U.S. Public*, pg. 604
Sullivan, Diane, Pres.-Children's Grp.--The Stride Rite Corporation, Lexington, MA; *U.S. Public*, pg. 1524
Sullivan, Don, Pres. & Chief Exec. Officer--Osicom Technologies Inc., Annapolis Junction, MD; *U.S. Public*, pg. 1233
Sullivan, Donald M., Chm. Bd., Pres. & Chief Exec. Officer--MTS Systems Corporation, Eden Prairie, MN; *U.S. Public*, pg. 1028
Sullivan, Douglas B., Pres. & Chief Oper. Officer--Michaels Stores, Inc., Irving, TX; *U.S. Public*, pg. 1104
Sullivan, Fred R., Chm. Bd. & Pres.--Richton International Corporation, Madison, NJ; *U.S. Public*, pg. 1389
Sullivan, G. Craig, Chm. Bd., Pres. & Chief Exec. Officer--The Clorox Company, Oakland, CA; *U.S. Public*, pg. 386
Sullivan, Gregory B., Pres.--Ugly Duckling Corp., Phoenix, AZ; *U.S. Public*, pg. 1662
Sullivan, Harold, III, Pres.--Payson Casters, Inc., Gurnee, IL; *U.S. Private*, pg. 844
Sullivan, J., Pres.--Columbia Scientific Industries Corporation, Austin, TX; *Int'l*, pg. 1500
Sullivan, James R., Pres.--Commodore Holdings, Hollywood, FL; *U.S. Public*, pg. 414
Sullivan, Jeremiah J., Pres.--Macy's West, San Francisco, CA; *U.S. Public*, pg. 618
Sullivan, John B., Pres. & Chief Exec. Officer--Willis Corroon Corp. of Illinois, Chicago, IL; *Int'l*, pg. 1506

Sullivan, John Fox, Chm., Pres., Chief Exec. Officer & Publr.--National Journal Group, Washington, DC; *U.S. Private*, pg. 785
Sullivan, John J., Pres.--Carlton Cards, Ltd., Toronto, Canada; *U.S. Public*, pg. 78
Sullivan, Kenneth R., Pres. & Chief Exec. Officer--Sullivan Oil Company, Baton Rouge, LA; *U.S. Private*, pg. 1050
Sullivan, Michael P., Pres. & Chief Exec. Officer--International Dairy Queen, Inc., Minneapolis, MN; *U.S. Public*, pg. 220
Sullivan, Mike, Partner, V.P. & Client Services Dir.--Hadeler Sullivan Ewing, Dallas, TX; *U.S. Private*, pg. 493
Sullivan, Rhonda L., Pres.--Lavelle Industries Inc., Burlington, WI; *U.S. Private*, pg. 653
Sullivan, Richard, Pres.--Cargill Detroit Corp., Clawson, MI; *U.S. Private*, pg. 210
Sullivan, Richard, Sr. Partner, Exec. V.P. & Gen. Mgr.--Fleishman-Hillard, Inc., Washington, DC; *U.S. Private*, pg. 411
Sullivan, Stephen, Pres. & Chief Oper. Officer--Ling Electronics Inc., Anaheim, CA; *U.S. Public*, pg. 1077
Sullivan, T., Pres.--Switching Systems International, Placentia, CA; *Int'l*, pg. 208
Sullivan, Terrence T., Pres. & Chief Exec. Officer--American Paging, Inc., Minneapolis, MN; *U.S. Public*, pg. 1570
Sullivan, Thomas C., Pres. & Chief Fin. Officer--Sullivan Paper Company, West Springfield, MA; *U.S. Private*, pg. 1050
Sullivan, Tim, Partner & Sr. V.P.--Media That Works, Cincinnati, OH; *U.S. Private*, pg. 727
Sullivan, Vincent P., Pres.--Serco Company, Dallas, TX; *U.S. Public*, pg. 1676
Sullivan, William M., Pres. & Chief Exec. Officer--Oxford Health Plans Inc., Norwalk, CT; *U.S. Public*, pg. 1238
Sulprizio, Ray R., Pres.--United Engine & Machine Company, Carson City, NV; *U.S. Private*, pg. 1121
Sult, Erroll, Pres.--National Welders Supply Co. Inc., Charlotte, NC; *U.S. Private*, pg. 788
Suma, Charles M., Pres. & Chief Exec. Officer--The New Piper Aircraft, Inc., Vero Beach, FL; *U.S. Private*, pg. 794
Sumas, Perry, Pres. & Chief Exec. Officer--Village Super Market Inc., Springfield, NJ; *U.S. Public*, pg. 1721
Sumino, Jack, Pres.--CIE America, Inc., Irvine, CA; *Int'l*, pg. 694
Sumiya, Takashi, Pres.--Sumikin Bussan International (Korea) Co., Ltd., Seoul, Korea; *Int'l*, pg. 1308
Summa, Timo, Pres. & Chief Exec. Officer--Tamrock Corp., Tampere, Finland; *Int'l*, pg. 1352
Summe, Greg, Pres.--AlliedSignal Commercial Avionic Systems, Olathe, KS; *U.S. Public*, pg. 50
Summe, Gregory L., Pres. & Chief Oper. Officer--EG & G, Inc., Wellesley, MA; *U.S. Public*, pg. 542
Summerford, Allen, Pres.--United Piece Dye Works, LP, New York, NY; *U.S. Private*, pg. 1123
Summers, Cary, Pres. & Chief Exec. Officer--Silver Dollar City, Inc., Branson, MO; *U.S. Private*, pg. 1000
Summers, Toby, Pres. & Chief Oper. Officer--Coca-Cola Bottling Co. of the Southwest, San Antonio, TX; *U.S. Private*, pg. 248
Summers, William B. Jr., Pres. & Chief Exec. Officer--McDonald & Company Investments, Inc., Cleveland, OH; *U.S. Public*, pg. 1068
Sumpter, Jerry, Pres.--The Akro Corporation, Canton, OH; *U.S. Public*, pg. 399
Sun, Lee Young, Pres.--Namkwang Engineering & Construction Co., Ltd., Seoul, Korea; *Int'l*, pg. 1291
Sunayama, Hiroyasu, Pres.--World Fashion Hosiery Inc., Kowloon, Hong Kong; *Int'l*, pg. 579
Sund, Ake, Pres.--VingCard Systems Inc., Dallas, TX; *Int'l*, pg. 18
Sundberg, David, Pres.--Paktronics Controls, Inc., Fort Worth, TX; *U.S. Private*, pg. 716
Sundberg, Matti, Chm. Bd., Pres. & Chief Exec. Officer--Valmet Corporation, Helsinki, Finland; *Int'l*, pg. 1447
Sunderland, Lee, Pres. & Chief Exec. Officer--Cliftex, New Bedford, MA; *U.S. Public*, pg. 1777
Sundman, David M., Pres.--Littleton Coin Co., Inc., Littleton, NH; *U.S. Private*, pg. 671
Sung, Ha-Bong, Pres.--Xiamen Jinwoong Enterprise Co., Ltd., Xiamen, China; *Int'l*, pg. 707
Sunley, Robert J., Pres.--NETG Limited, London, United Kingdom; *U.S. Public*, pg. 784
Sunley, Roy, Pres.--NETG Applied Learning GmbH, Dusseldorf, Germany; *U.S. Public*, pg. 784
Sunley, Roy, Pres.--NETG Applied Learning GmbH, Vienna, Austria; *U.S. Public*, pg. 784
Sunley, Roy, Pres.--A.S.I. (Computer Training) Netherlands B.V., Amsterdam, Netherlands; *U.S. Public*, pg. 784
Suntayodom, Thanan, Pres.--Thai Otsuka Pharmaceutical Co., Ltd., Bangkok, Thailand; *Int'l*, pg. 1014
Suokas, Matti, Pres.--Finnsugar Ltd., Kantvik, Finland; *Int'l*, pg. 349
Suominen, Hanna, Pres.--Nokia Industrial Electronics, Salo, Finland; *Int'l*, pg. 951
Suominen, Jukka, Pres.--SILJA OY Ab, Helsinki, Finland; *Int'l*, pg. 899
Supple, Jack, Pres., Mng. Partner & Chief Creative Officer--Carmichael Lynch, Inc., Minneapolis, MN; *U.S. Private*, pg. 213
Surber, Donald E., Pres.--ATF, Inc., Lincolnwood, IL; *U.S. Private*, pg. 8
Surdell, Daniel, Pres.--Orent GraphicArts, Inc., Omaha, NE; *U.S. Public*, pg. 503
Surdell, Daniel L., Pres.--Meridian Retail, Inc., Troy, MI; *U.S. Public*, pg. 503
Surgenor, Keith S., Pres. & Chief Oper. Officer--Tampa Electric Co., Tampa, FL; *U.S. Public*, pg. 1565
Suriyakumar, K., Pres.--Ford Graphics, South Pasadena, CA; *U.S. Private*, pg. 418
Suronegoro, Subijanto, Pres. Commissioner--P.T. Bumi Daya-IBJ Leasing, Jakarta, Indonesia; *Int'l*, pg. 676
Surpin, Jo, Pres.--MEDIQ Management Services, Inc., Pennsauken, NJ; *U.S. Public*, pg. 1081
Surpin, Jo, Pres.--MEDIQ Diagnostic Centers, Pennsauken, NJ; *U.S. Public*, pg. 1081
Surville, Hubert D., Pres. & Dir.-Opers.--Marie Brizard Wines & Spirits USA, North Miami, FL; *U.S. Private*, pg. 702
Suscavage, Michael G., Pres. & Chief Exec. Officer--Global Marketing Resources (GMR), New York, NY; *U.S. Private*, pg. 457
Susukida, Katsuyuki, Pres.--P.T. Mazda Indonesia Manufacturing, Bekasi, Indonesia; *Int'l*, pg. 849
Suter, Ulrich H., Exec. V.P.--Alusuisse-Lonza America Inc., New York, NY; *Int'l*, pg. 67
Sutherland, Allan, Pres.--Roberts Systems, Inc., Charlotte, NC; *Int'l*, pg. 395
Sutherland, Herman, Pres. & Partner--Sutherland Lumber Co., Kansas City, MO; *U.S. Private*, pg. 1057
Sutherland, Michael, Pres. & Chief Exec. Officer--Spinnerin Inc., South Hackensack, NJ; *U.S. Private*, pg. 1025
Sutherlin, James, Pres.--HSB Reliability Technologies, Hartford, CT; *U.S. Public*, pg. 795
Suthern, Paul C., Pres. & Chief Oper. Officer--MEDCO Containment Services, Inc., Montvale, NJ; *U.S. Public*, pg. 1091
Sutika, James M., Pres.--Service Steel Division, Detroit, MI; *U.S. Private*, pg. 1133
Sutter, Carl F., Jr., Pres.--Fisheries Supply Company, Seattle, WA; *U.S. Private*, pg. 408
Sutton, Howard G., Pres. & Gen. Mgr.--Providence Journal-Bulletin, Providence, RI; *U.S. Public*, pg. 209
Sutton, James, Pres.--Sky Bros. Inc., Altoona, PA; *U.S. Public*, pg. 918
Sutton, Yacha, Pres. & Chief Oper. Officer--Laser Industries Ltd., Tel Aviv, Israel; *Int'l*, pg. 429
Suwa, M., Pres.--Funai Corporation, Teterboro, NJ; *Int'l*, pg. 530
Suwak, Lawrence M., Pres.--H.L. Yoh Group LLC, Philadelphia, PA; *U.S. Private*, pg. 317
Suwalsky, Salomon, Pres.--Royal Consumer Business Products, Bridgewater, NJ; *Int'l*, pg. 1002
Suzuki, H., Pres.--Nihon Seiko Co. Ltd., Tokyo, Japan; *Int'l*, pg. 947
Suzuki, Hidehiko, Pres.--Kawasaki Motors N.V., Vianen, Netherlands; *Int'l*, pg. 726
Suzuki, Hideji, Pres.--The Kyoei Mutual Fire & Marine Insurance Company, Tokyo, Japan; *Int'l*, pg. 777
Suzuki, Hideo, Pres.--Makita Canada Inc., Whitby, Canada; *Int'l*, pg. 832
Suzuki, Hitoshi, Pres.--Meijiseimei International France S.A., Paris, France; *Int'l*, pg. 854
Suzuki, Jisuke, Pres.--The Daishi Bank, Ltd., Niigata, Japan; *Int'l*, pg. 372
Suzuki, Junichi, Pres.--Komatsu America Industries Corp., Wood Dale, IL; *Int'l*, pg. 744
Suzuki, Keita, Pres. & Chief Oper. Officer--Nissho Iwai (Chile) LTDA, Santiago, Chile; *Int'l*, pg. 948
Suzuki, Mutsuji, Deputy Pres.--Shizuoka Bank, Ltd., Shizuoka, Japan; *Int'l*, pg. 1236
Suzuki, Nobuo, Pres.--Maruzen Company Limited, Tokyo, Japan; *Int'l*, pg. 845
Suzuki, Osamu, Pres. & Chief Exec. Officer--Suzuki Motor Corporation, Shizuoka, Japan; *Int'l*, pg. 1322
Suzuki, Shigero, Pres. & V.P.-Japan Opers.--Tekelec, Ltd., Tokyo, Japan; *U.S. Public*, pg. 1566
Suzuki, Tadao, Pres.--Mercian Corporation, Tokyo, Japan; *Int'l*, pg. 858
Suzuki, Takashi, Pres.--Nikkei Business Publications Inc., Tokyo, Japan; *Int'l*, pg. 929
Suzuki, Takashi, Pres.--Nikkei International Ltd., Tokyo, Japan; *Int'l*, pg. 929
Suzumaru, H., Pres.--Minolta (UK) Ltd., Milton Keynes, United Kingdom; *Int'l*, pg. 869
Suzumasa, Hirokazu, Pres.--Rohm Electronics Taiwan Co., Ltd., Taipei, Taiwan; *Int'l*, pg. 1125
Svanberg, Carl-Henric, Pres. & Chief Exec. Officer--Assa Abloy AB, Stockholm, Sweden; *Int'l*, pg. 17
Svanberg, Torben, Pres.--Sonofon, Horsholm, Denmark; *Int'l*, pg. 537
Svatek, Dennis, Pres.--Discovery Plastic--RHC/Spacemaster Corporation, Melrose Park, IL; *U.S. Private*, pg. 904
Svatek, Dennis, Pres.--Discovery Plastics, Inc., Albany, OR; *U.S. Private*, pg. 904
Svellentrop, Steve, Pres.--ARCO British Limited, Guildford, United Kingdom; *U.S. Public*, pg. 144
Svendsen, David I., Pres.--Rollins Hudig Hall of Northern California, Inc., Palo Alto, CA; *Int'l*, pg. 117
Svendsen, Erik, Pres.--Bohler-Uddeholm Corp., Rolling Meadows, IL; *Int'l*, pg. 1471
Svenson, Eric, Pres.--Bohler, Houston, TX; *Int'l*, pg. 1471
Svensson, Dag, Pres.--NCC Building, Malmo, Sweden; *Int'l*, pg. 898
Svensson, Gouran, Pres.--NCC Anlaggring, Stockholm, Sweden; *Int'l*, pg. 899
Svensson, H. Kjell, Pres. & Chief Exec. Officer--Cardo AB, Malmo, Sweden; *Int'l*, pg. 268
Svinky, Eddie A., Gen. Mgr.--DMD Dresser Measurement Operation, Houston, TX; *U.S. Public*, pg. 528
Swaback, Ray, Pres.-Sls.--Medline Industries, Inc., Mundelein, IL; *U.S. Private*, pg. 728
Swaffar, Billy J., Pres.--First Electric Cooperative, Corp., Jacksonville, AR; *U.S. Private*, pg. 407
Swafford, Tom, Exec. V.P.--Nasco Modesto, Modesto, CA; *U.S. Private*, pg. 446
Swagerty, James, Pres.--Orchids Paper Products Co., Pryor, OK; *U.S. Private*, pg. 819
Swahn, Hans, Pres.--Esselte Meto International GmbH, Heppenheim, Germany; *Int'l*, pg. 461
Swain, E.P., Jr., Pres.--Port Townsend Paper Corporation, Bainbridge Island, WA; *Int'l*, pg. 586
Swain, G. Joseph, Pres.--Chemical Bank North, Grayling, MI; *U.S. Public*, pg. 345
Swain, Jeff, Pres. & Chief Oper. Officer--Townsends, Inc., Wilmington, DE; *U.S. Private*, pg. 1094
Swain, Randy, Pres.--Ackerley Communications of the Northwest-Seattle, Seattle, WA; *U.S. Public*, pg. 15
Swain, Terrence P., Pres.--Derlan Inc./Phoenix Facility, Phoenix, AZ; *Int'l*, pg. 395
Swan, Alex, Gen. Mgr.--ITOCHU Building Products Co., Inc., Miami, FL; *Int'l*, pg. 694
Swan, Alfred, Jr., Pres.--AmSouth Bank, Tampa, FL; *U.S. Public*, pg. 105
Swan, Frank, Pres.--Nationwide Beef, Inc., Chicago, IL; *U.S. Private*, pg. 788
Swan, Frank J., Pres.--Cadbury Beverages North America, Stamford, CT; *Int'l*, pg. 248
Swan, Paul H., Pres.--NBD Insurance Agency, Inc., Troy, MI; *U.S. Public*, pg. 628
Swanberg, Art, Pres.--Delcar Digital, New York, NY; *U.S. Public*, pg. 1642
Swaner, Gary, Pres.--Swaner Hardwood Company, Inc., Burbank, CA; *U.S. Private*, pg. 1057
Swank, Andrew, Partner & Grp. Acct. Dir.--Hampel/Stefanides, New York, NY; *U.S. Private*, pg. 498
Swank, Charles, Pres.--Florida Pneumatic Mfg. Corp., Jupiter, FL; *U.S. Public*, pg. 1240
Swanson, Armour F., Acting Pres. & Chief Exec. Officer--Carolina Steel Corporation, Greensboro, NC; *U.S. Private*, pg. 214
Swanson, Dennis D., Pres. & Chief Oper. Officer--ABC Sports Holding Company, Inc., New York, NY; *U.S. Public*, pg. 511
Swanson, Douglas E., Chm. Bd., Pres. & Chief Exec. Officer--Cliffs Drilling Company, Houston, TX; *U.S. Public*, pg. 386
Swanson, Robert, Pres. & Chief Exec. Officer--Fulton Industries Inc., Wauseon, OH; *U.S. Private*, pg. 431
Swanson, Robert, Pres.--R & R Plastics, Swanton, OH; *U.S. Private*, pg. 431
Swanson, Robert H., Jr., Pres. & Chief Exec. Officer--Linear Technology Corp., Milpitas, CA; *U.S. Public*, pg. 1000
Swanson, Roger W., Pres.--Champion Business Forms, Glendale Heights, IL; *U.S. Private*, pg. 228
Swanson, S. Keith, Pres.--Joslyn Electronic Systems Corporation, Goleta, CA; *U.S. Public*, pg. 481
Swanstrom, Kenneth A., Chm. Bd., Pres. & Chief Exec. Officer--Penn Engineering & Manufacturing Corp., Danboro, PA; *U.S. Public*, pg. 1269
Swanstrom, Steiner, Pres. & Chief Exec. Officer--Luxo A/S, Oslo, Norway; *Int'l*, pg. 821
Swart, Wayne R., Pres.--Roundy's, Evansville, IN; *U.S. Private*, pg. 948
Swartout, Hank B., Chm. Bd., Pres. & Chief Exec. Officer--Precision Drilling Corporation, Calgary, Canada; *Int'l*, pg. 1066
Swartwout, James R., Chm. Bd., Pres. & Chief Fin. Officer--Summa Industries, Torrance, CA; *U.S. Public*, pg. 1527
Swartz, James K., Pres. & Chief Oper. Officer--NPC International, Inc., Pittsburg, KS; *U.S. Public*, pg. 1146
Swartz, Sidney W., Chm. Bd., Pres. & Chief Exec. Officer--The Timberland Company, Stratham, NH; *U.S. Public*, pg. 1609
Swayne, Keith, Pres. & Chief Exec. Officer--Case-Swayne Co. Inc., Corona, CA; *U.S. Private*, pg. 218
Swayne, William, Pres.--Holmatro, Inc., Glen Burnie, MD; *Int'l*, pg. 632
Sweatman, Sharon, Pres.--United Missouri Brokerage Services, Kansas City, MO; *U.S. Public*, pg. 1655
Sweatt, Blaine, II, Pres.--Bahama Breeze, Orlando, FL; *U.S. Public*, pg. 484
Sweatt, Safford, Pres.--Fitz & Floyd, Dallas, TX; *U.S. Private*, pg. 409
Sweebe, Richard C., Pres.--Mid America International Trucks, Inc., Memphis, TN; *U.S. Private*, pg. 743
Sweeney, Anne, Pres.--The Disney Channel, Burbank, CA; *U.S. Public*, pg. 513
Sweeney, Jacob B., Jr., Pres.--Jake Sweeney Automotive Inc., Cincinnati, OH; *U.S. Private*, pg. 1058
Sweeney, Joan M., Pres. & Chief Oper. Officer--Allied Capital Advisors, Inc., Washington, DC; *U.S. Public*, pg. 47
Sweeney, Mary S., Pres. & Dir.-Adv.--Jake Sweeney Auto Leasing, Inc., Cincinnati, OH; *U.S. Private*, pg. 1058
Sweeney, Sean, Pres.--Elkay Products, Inc., Shrewsbury, MA; *U.S. Private*, pg. 372
Sweet, Stedman G., Pres. & Chief Exec. Officer--The Eastern Company, Naugatuck, CT; *U.S. Public*, pg. 548
Sweetland, Mark R., Pres. & Chief Exec. Officer--SofTECH, Inc., Grand Rapids, MI; *U.S. Public*, pg. 1482
Sweetnam, James M., Pres.--Holset Engineering Company Ltd., Madison, IN; *U.S. Public*, pg. 468
Sweitzer, Brandon W., Pres. & Chief Exec. Officer--Guy Carpenter & Co., Inc, New York, NY; *U.S. Public*, pg. 1048
Sweney, Liz, Pres.--Cricket Lane, West Bridgewater, MA; *U.S. Public*, pg. 948
Swenson, Kurt M., Chm. Bd., Pres. & Chief Exec. Officer--Rock of Ages Corporation, Graniteville, VT; *U.S. Public*, pg. 1396
Swenson, Robert L., Pres.--Frankel Metal Company, Detroit, MI; *U.S. Private*, pg. 735
Swerlkolte, Steve, Pres. & Chief Oper. Officer--Full Service Beverage Company, Wichita, KS; *U.S. Private*, pg. 34
Swetnam, Paul, Pres.--Aeroflex Lintek Corp., Powell, OH; *U.S. Public*, pg. 24
Swett, Ralph J., Chm. Bd., Pres. & Chief Exec. Officer--IXC Communications, Inc., Austin, TX; *U.S. Private*, pg. 556
Swiackey, Steve, Pres.--The American Group, Ferndale, WA; *U.S. Private*, pg. 56
Swider, Ronald, Pres.--Scott Lumber Company, Bridgeport, OH; *U.S. Private*, pg. 977
Swift, A. Earl, Pres. & Chief Exec. Officer--Swift Energy Company, Houston, TX; *U.S. Public*, pg. 1543
Swift, Charles O., Chm. Bd. & Pres.--Chuck Swift Sales & Leasing, Davis, CA; *U.S. Private*, pg. 1058
Swift, Humphrey H., Pres., Chief Exec. Officer & Mgr.-Adv. & Sls. Promo.--Swift Instruments, Inc., Dorchester, MA; *U.S. Private*, pg. 1058
Swift, M. Allen, Chm. Bd., Pres. & Treas.--M. Swift & Sons Inc., Hartford, CT; *U.S. Private*, pg. 1059

Swift, Richard J., Chm. Bd., Pres. & Chief Exec. Officer--Foster Wheeler Corporation, Clinton, NJ; *U.S. Public*, pg. 676
Swiggett, Jeff, Pres.--Helikon Furniture Co., Inc., Taftville, CT; *U.S. Private*, pg. 520
Swinehart, Keith, II, Pres.--Vanguard Plastics, Inc., Mc Pherson, KS; *U.S. Private*, pg. 1134
Swink, Gary, Pres. & Gen. Mgr.--Simco, Hatfield, PA; *U.S. Public*, pg. 865
Swink, James W., Pres., Chief Exec. Officer & Chief Oper. Officer--Young Pecan Company (A Partnership), Florence, SC; *U.S. Private*, pg. 1201
Swinsky, Morton, Pres. & Chief Exec. Officer--Fuji Securities Inc.-New York, New York, NY; *Int'l*, pg. 519
Swirsky, Benjamin, Pres. & Chief Exec. Officer--Slater Industries Inc., North York, Canada; *Int'l*, pg. 1262
Swisher, John B., Pres. & Chief Exec. Officer--United Feeds, Inc., Sheridan, IN; *U.S. Private*, pg. 1122
Switzer, David A., Pres. & Chief Oper. Officer--Battle Creek Gas Company, Battle Creek, MI; *U.S. Public*, pg. 1489
Switzer, Mel, Jr., Pres. & Chief Exec. Officer--Sonoma Valley Bank, Sonoma, CA; *U.S. Public*, pg. 1487
Swope, Richard S., Pres.--Sam Swope Auto Group, Inc., Louisville, KY; *U.S. Private*, pg. 1059
Sy, Jane, Pres. & Treas.--Christian Mutual Life Insurance Co., Houston, TX; *U.S. Private*, pg. 225
Sy, Victor K., Pres.--McCormick Thailand, Inc., Bangkok, Thailand; *U.S. Public*, pg. 1067
Syar, James M., Pres. & Chief Oper. Officer--Syar Industries, Inc., Napa, CA; *U.S. Private*, pg. 1059
Sydnor, Dale, Chm. Bd., Pres. & Chief Exec. Officer--Wireless Telecom Group, Inc., Paramus, NJ; *U.S. Public*, *pg. 1772*
Sykes, Greg, Pres. & Chief Exec. Officer--Hygrade Food Products Corporation, Southfield, MI; *U.S. Public*, pg. 1433
Sykes, Greg, Pres.--Seitz Foods Inc., Saint Joseph, MO; *U.S. Public*, pg. 1434
Sykes, Guy R., Vice Chm., Pres. & Chief Exec. Officer--Camellia Food Stores, Inc., Norfolk, VA; *U.S. Private*, pg. 203
Sykes, Jolene, Publisher--Fortune, New York, NY; *U.S. Public*, pg. 1613
Sylva, Eugene R., Chm. Bd. & Pres.--Dimensional Merchandising, Inc., Wharton, NJ; *U.S. Private*, pg. 333
Sylvester, Paul R., Pres. & Chief Exec. Officer--Manatron, Inc., Kalamazoo, MI; *U.S. Public*, pg. 1040
Symes, John, Pres.--MGM Worldwide Television, Group., Santa Monica, CA; *U.S. Public*, pg. 1102
Syms, Marcy, Pres.--Syms Corporation, Secaucus, NJ; *U.S. Public*, pg. 1547
Synott, Lee, Chm. Bd., Pres. & Chief Exec. Officer--Ingram Book Company, La Vergne, TN; *U.S. Private*, pg. 563
Syphard, David W., Pres.--CRSS International, Inc., Houston, TX; *U.S. Public*, pg. 922
Syverson, David B., Pres.--Dave Syverson Lincoln Mercury, Albert Lea, MN; *U.S. Private*, pg. 1061
Syvertsen, Edwin T., Jr., Pres.--Rolero Omega Operations, Cleveland, OH; *U.S. Public*, pg. 443
Syz, Dieter M., Pres.--Swisscom, Bern, Switzerland; *Int'l*, pg. 1334
Sze, Andy, Pres. & Chief Exec. Officer--Clipper Exxpress, Lemont, IL; *U.S. Public*, pg. 130
Sze, Andy, Pres.--Caro Trans Intl., Lemont, IL; *U.S. Public*, pg. 130
Szescila, Andy, Pres.--Hughes Christensen, Houston, TX; *U.S. Public*, pg. 166
Szomjassy, Michael A., Pres.--OHM International, Inc., Findlay, OH; *U.S. Public*, pg. 1208
Sztykiel, John E., Pres. & Chief Oper. Officer--Spartan Motors, Inc., Charlotte, MI; *U.S. Public*, pg. 1495
Szymanski, Conrad, Pres.--Beall's Dept. Stores, Bradenton, FL; *U.S. Private*, pg. 126
Szymaszek, P.G., Chm. Bd. & Pres.--Vilter Manufacturing Corporation, Cudahy, WI; *U.S. Private*, pg. 1140
Tabachneck, Avrum, Pres.--Trading Port, Inc., Albany, NY; *U.S. Private*, pg. 1095
Tabata, Hideki, Pres.--Sumitomo Life Realty (N.Y.), Inc., New York, NY; *Int'l*, pg. 1315
Tabata, Nobuyuki, Pres.--Amano Cleantech Malaysia Sdn. Bhd., Petaling Jaya, Malaysia; *Int'l*, pg. 71
Tablak, Jeff, Pres., Chief Exec. Officer & Co-Founder--Nextron, San Jose, CA; *U.S. Public*, pg. 1424
Tabor, Jon K., Chm. Bd., Pres. & Chief Exec. Officer--Allied Mineral Products, Inc., Columbus, OH; *U.S. Private*, pg. 39
Tabor, Maury, Chm. Bd & Pres.--Condere Corporation, Natchez, MS; *U.S. Private*, pg. 262
Tabuchi, Teruhisa, Chm. Bd. & Pres.--Tabuchi Electric Co., Ltd., Sanda, Japan; *Int'l*, pg. 1346
Tachikawa, Achira, Pres.--Tetsudo Sharyo Kogyo Co., Ltd., Tokyo, Japan; *Int'l*, pg. 764
Tachikawa, Masami, Pres. & Chief Exec. Officer--The Yasuda Trust and Banking Co., Ltd., Tokyo, Japan; *Int'l*, pg. 1520
Tacony, Kenneth, Pres.--Tacony Corporation, Fenton, MO; *U.S. Private*, pg. 1066
Tadlock, W. L., Pres.--NationsBank Credit Corporation, Elizabeth City, NC; *U.S. Public*, pg. 1163
Taffer, Mike, Pres.--Stilwell Foods, Inc., Stilwell, OK; *U.S. Public*, pg. 658
Taggart, R., Pres.--Pringle of Scotland, New York, NY; *Int'l*, pg. 386
Taggart, Rick, Pres.--Swiss Army Brands, Inc., Shelton, CT; *U.S. Public*, pg. 1544
Taguchi, Eiichi, Pres.--Mitsubishi Rayon Co., Ltd., Tokyo, Japan; *Int'l*, pg. 876
Taguchi, Keita, Pres.--Unitika Ltd., Osaka, Japan; *Int'l*, pg. 1444
Tague, John, Pres. & Chief Exec. Officer--American Trans Air, Inc., Indianapolis, IN; *U.S. Public*, pg. 106
Tague, John P., Pres. & Chief Exec. Officer--Amtran, Inc., Indianapolis, IN; *U.S. Public*, pg. 106
Tahtinen, Kari, Pres.--Imatra Steel Oy Ab, Helsinki, Finland; *Int'l*, pg. 863
Tait, David C., Pres.--MBC Realty, Inc., Baltimore, MD; *U.S. Public*, pg. 1089
Tait, Stewart R., Pres.--Narrow Fabric Industries, Inc., Reading, PA; *U.S. Private*, pg. 774
Taittinger, Claude, Chm. Bd. & Pres.--Taittinger, Reims, France; *Int'l*, pg. 1348
Taitz, Andrew, Chm. Bd.--Union City Body Company, L.P., Union City, IN; *U.S. Private*, pg. 1118
Takada, Hironaka, Pres. & Chief Exec. Officer--DBP - Daiwa Securities (Philippines), Inc., Manila, Philippines; *Int'l*, pg. 375
Takada, O, Pres.--Kobe Alumina Associates (Australia) Pty. Ltd., Perth, Australia; *Int'l*, pg. 741
Takafuku, M., Pres.--Sharp Electronics (Svenska) AB, Skarholmen, Sweden; *Int'l*, pg. 1230
Takagaki, Katsusuke, Pres.--Tong Shing Inc., Taipei, Taiwan; *Int'l*, pg. 1400
Takagaki, Tasuku, Pres.--The Bank of Tokyo-Mitsubishi, Ltd., Tokyo, Japan; *Int'l*, pg. 157
Takagi, Shigeru, Pres.--MEC USA, Inc., Wilmington, DE; *Int'l*, pg. 873
Takagi, Tamakazu, Chm. Bd. & Pres.--Takagi Chokoku Co., Ltd., Wakayama, Japan; *Int'l*, pg. 1349
Takahashi, Hiderion, Pres.--Aero Asahi Corporation, Tokyo, Japan; *Int'l*, pg. 1178
Takahashi, Ikuo, Pres.--IDD Co., LTD., Tokyo, Japan; *Int'l*, pg. 1125
Takahashi, Jay, Pres.--YKK (U.S.A.), Marietta, GA; *Int'l*, pg. 1515
Takahashi, Osamu, Pres.--Dainichiseika Colour & Chemicals Mfg. Co., Ltd., Tokyo, Japan; *Int'l*, pg. 369
Takahashi, Takemitsu, Chm. Bd. & Pres.--Dainippon Ink & Chemicals, Inc., Tokyo, Japan; *Int'l*, pg. 369
Takahashi, Yoshiyuki, Pres.--ASICS Tiger Corporation, Fountain Valley, CA; *U.S. Private*, pg. 89
Takai, Keiji, Pres.--Kawasaki Rail Car, Inc., Yonkers, NY; *Int'l*, pg. 725
Takakura, Hisashi, Pres. & Chief Oper. Officer--Clarins KK, Tokyo, Japan; *Int'l*, pg. 295
Takakura, Ken, Pres.--U.S. Tsubaki, Inc., Wheeling, IL; *Int'l*, pg. 1425
Takakura, Tom, Pres. & Chief Exec. Officer--Sanwa Bank California, Los Angeles, CA; *Int'l*, pg. 1189
Takamori, Kotaro, Pres.--China Orient Leasing Co., Ltd., Beijing, China; *Int'l*, pg. 1009
Takao, Kichiro, Pres.--The Nikko Securities Co., Ltd., Tokyo, Japan; *Int'l*, pg. 930
Takasu, Shitomi, Pres.--The Chugoku Electric Power Co., Inc., Hiroshima, Japan; *Int'l*, pg. 291
Takavitz, F.J., Pres.--Exel Logistics North America, Westerville, OH; *Int'l*, pg. 901
Takayoshi, Okamota, Pres.--Aderans Co., Ltd., Tokyo, Japan; *Int'l*, pg. 24
Takechi, Sueharu, Pres.--O.S. Engines Mfg. Co., Ltd., Osaka, Japan; *Int'l*, pg. 531
Takeda, Kazuhiko, Pres.--Nippon Kayaku Co. Ltd., Tokyo, Japan; *Int'l*, pg. 934
Takeda, Kunio, Pres.--Takeda Chemical Industries, Ltd., Osaka, Japan; *Int'l*, pg. 1350
Takeda, Shozo, Pres.--Hosho America Inc., Seattle, WA; *Int'l*, pg. 733
Takeda, T., Pres.--Nalco Japan Co., Ltd., Tokyo, Japan; *U.S. Public*, pg. 1151
Takeda, Tamotsu, Pres.--Sun Wave Industrial Co., Tokyo, Japan; *Int'l*, pg. 1320
Takeda, Tsutomu, Pres. & Chief Oper. Officer--Asatsu Inc., Tokyo, Japan; *Int'l*, pg. 85
Takehana, Hiroshi, Pres. & Chief Exec. Officer--G-Net Corporation, Osaka, Japan; *Int'l*, pg. 531
Takehisa, T., Pres.--Nissho Electronics Corp., Tokyo, Japan; *Int'l*, pg. 946
Takei, M., Pres.--Nissho Iwai Petroleum Corp., Osaka, Japan; *Int'l*, pg. 947
Takei, Toshifumi, Pres. & Chief Exec. Officer--Ishikawajima-Harima Heavy Industries Co., Ltd., Tokyo, Japan; *Int'l*, pg. 689
Takekawa, Neil M., Pres.--Island Air, Honolulu, HI; *U.S. Private*, pg. 44
Takenaka, Shuichi, Pres.--P.T. Bank LTCB Central Asia, Jakarta, Indonesia; *Int'l*, pg. 816
Takenaka, Toichi, Pres. & Chief Exec. Officer--Takenaka Corporation, Osaka, Japan; *Int'l*, pg. 1351
Takeuchi, Masakazu, Pres. & Chief Exec. Officer--Gradco (Japan), Ltd., Tokyo, Japan; *U.S. Public*, pg. 757
Takeuchi, Nobuyoshi, Pres.--The Toyo Trust and Banking Company, Limited, Tokyo, Japan; *Int'l*, pg. 1411
Takeuchi, Toshio, Pres.--Credit Saison Co., Ltd., Tokyo, Japan; *Int'l*, pg. 1178
Takimoto, Shingo, Pres.--Shimadzu Scientific Instruments, Inc., Columbia, MD; *Int'l*, pg. 1232
Takishima, Yoshimitsu, Deputy Pres.--Shoko Chukin Bank, Tokyo, Japan; *Int'l*, pg. 1236
Tako, Anthony, Chm. Bd. & Pres.--A.J. Gerrard and Company, Des Plaines, IL; *U.S. Private*, pg. 449
Tako, Tony, Pres.--Pabco Metals Corporation, Houston, TX; *U.S. Private*, pg. 449
Talbert, J. Michael, Pres. & Chief Oper. Officer--Lone Star Energy Co., Dallas, TX; *U.S. Public*, pg. 1587
Talbert, John B., Jr., Pres.--Hanes Companies, Inc., Winston Salem, NC; *U.S. Public*, pg. 986
Talbot, Dave, Pres.--Bata Shoe Co., Inc., Belcamp, MD; *U.S. Private*, pg. 195
Talbot, John, Pres.--Epstein Civil Engineering, Inc., Chicago, IL; *U.S. Private*, pg. 379
Talbot, Randall H., Pres.--Talbot Financial Corporation, Albuquerque, NM; *U.S. Public*, pg. 1423
Talbot, Todd, Pres.--Alsons Corporation, Hillsdale, MI; *U.S. Public*, pg. 1053
Talen, Edward J., Pres.--Clover Insurance Agency, Inc., Ontario, CA; *U.S. Public*, pg. 826
Talermo, Roger, Pres. & Chief Exec. Officer--Amer Group Ltd., Helsinki, Finland; *Int'l*, pg. 72
Taljaard, D.L.M., Pres. & Chief Exec. Officer--London & Leeds (USA) Corporation, New York, NY; *Int'l*, pg. 788
Tallackson, Harvey, Pres.--Minnkota Power Cooperative, Inc., Grand Forks, ND; *U.S. Private*, pg. 751
Tallarigo, Lorenzo, Pres.--Lilly France S.A., Saint Cloud, France; *U.S. Public*, pg. 994
Talley, W.F., Pres.--Smiths Industries Aerospace & Defense Systems Inc.-Florham Park Operation, Florham Park, NJ; *Int'l*, pg. 1268
Tallichet, David C., Jr., Chm. Bd., Pres. & Chief Exec. Officer--Specialty Restaurants Corporation, Anaheim, CA; *U.S. Private*, pg. 1022
Tallman, Steven C., Pres.--Quinton Instrument Company, Bothell, WA; *U.S. Public*, pg. 80
Talovich, Michael, Sr. V.P. & Brand Mktg. Partner--DMB&B Detroit, Troy, MI; *U.S. Private*, pg. 302
Tamahori, Tamehiko, Pres.--Tonen Corporation, Tokyo, Japan; *Int'l*, pg. 1398
Tamaki, Takashi, Pres.--The Chiba Bank, Ltd., Chiba, Japan; *Int'l*, pg. 283
Tamarites, John, Pres. & Chief Exec. Officer--Michigan Wheel Corporation, Grand Rapids, MI; *U.S. Private*, pg. 741
Tamaroff, Jeffrey L., Pres.--Jeffrey Buick-Nissan Inc., Roseville, MI; *U.S. Private*, pg. 585
Tamaroff, Marvin, Pres.--Tamaroff Buick Inc., Southfield, MI; *U.S. Private*, pg. 1067
Tambakeras, Marcos, Pres.--Honeywell, Inc., Fort Washington, PA; *U.S. Public*, pg. 834
Tamberlane, John, Pres.--Republic Bank for Savings, New York, NY; *U.S. Public*, pg. 1380
Tamer, Anthony, Partner--HIG Capital Management, Miami, FL; *U.S. Private*, pg. 490
Tamke, G.W., Pres. & Chief Oper. Officer--Emerson Electric Co., Saint Louis, MO; *U.S. Public*, pg. 572
Tamminen, Markku, Pres.--Auto-Bon Oy, Vantaa, Finland; *Int'l*, pg. 72
Tamura, Norio, Pres. & Chief Exec. Officer--Teac Corporation, Tokyo, Japan; *Int'l*, pg. 1360
Tamura, Y., Pres.--Daihatsu Diesel Mfg. Co., Ltd., Osaka, Japan; *Int'l*, pg. 364
Tanabe, K., Pres.--Hit Union Company Ltd., Osaka, Japan; *Int'l*, pg. 620
Tanabe, Kuninori, Pres. & Chief Exec. Officer--Fuji Bank Canada, Toronto, Canada; *Int'l*, pg. 521
Tanahashi, K., Pres.--Alloy Tool Steel Inc., Santa Fe Springs, CA; *Int'l*, pg. 947
Tanaka, Chiaki, Pres.--Japan Storage Battery Co., Ltd., Tokyo, Japan; *Int'l*, pg. 702
Tanaka, Haruhiko, Pres.--Japan Information Processing Service Co. Ltd., Tokyo, Japan; *Int'l*, pg. 702
Tanaka, Hideo, Pres.--Kawasaki Motors Netherlands N.V., Hoofddorp, Netherlands; *Int'l*, pg. 726
Tanaka, Hiroshi, Chm. Bd. & Chief Exec. Officer--Kyotaru Co., Ltd., Tokyo, Japan; *Int'l*, pg. 777
Tanaka, I., Pres.--Nissho Iwai (Shanghai) Corporation, Shanghai, China; *Int'l*, pg. 948
Tanaka, Jun-Ichiro, Pres. & Chief Exec. Officer--Mitsui Fudosan Co., Ltd., Tokyo, Japan; *Int'l*, pg. 882
Tanaka, Kenji, Pres.--Asahi Bank of California, Los Angeles, CA; *Int'l*, pg. 82
Tanaka, Koji, Pres.--Nikko Espana Sociedad de Valores, S.A., Madrid, Spain; *Int'l*, pg. 930
Tanaka, Masuo, Pres.--Fujitsu Computer Products of America, Inc., San Jose, CA; *Int'l*, pg. 526
Tanaka, Nobuo, Pres.--GSI Trading Hong Kong Limited, Kowloon, Hong Kong; *Int'l*, pg. 579
Tanaka, P.H., Pres.--GKN Japan Ltd., Osaka, Japan; *Int'l*, pg. 536
Tanaka, Shigenobu, Pres.--Fujikura Ltd., Tokyo, Japan; *Int'l*, *pg. 525*
Tanaka, Shinichiro, Pres. & Chief Exec. Officer--Fuji Capital Markets Corporation, New York, NY; *Int'l*, pg. 519
Tanaka, Stuart, Pres.--Hokuriku U.S.A. Co., Ltd., Huntsville, AL; *Int'l*, pg. 628
Tanaka, Takeshi, Pres.--Fuji Heavy Industries, Ltd., Tokyo, Japan; *Int'l*, pg. 522
Tanaka, Tatsuro, Pres.--Takashimaya Company, Limited, Osaka, Japan; *Int'l*, pg. 1349
Tanaka, Tsunehisa, Deputy Pres.--The Norinchukin Bank, Tokyo, Japan; *Int'l*, pg. 958
Tanaka, Tsuneo, Pres.--Hitachi America, Ltd., Tarrytown, NY; *Int'l*, pg. 622
Tanaka, Yasuo, Office Mgr.--Kintetsu World Express Inc., Minneapolis, MN; *Int'l*, pg. 734
Tananbaum, Andrew, Pres. & Chief Fin. Officer--Century Business Credit Corporation, New York, NY; *U.S. Private*, pg. 225
Tancred, Grace M., Pres.--Northwest Tobacco & Candy Co., Fayetteville, AR; *U.S. Private*, pg. 806
Tandler, Bob, Pres.--Fritzi of California Manufacturing Corp., San Francisco, CA; *U.S. Private*, pg. 429
Tang, Cyrus, Chm. Bd., Pres., & Chief Exec. Officer--Tang Industries Inc., Las Vegas, NV; *U.S. Private*, pg. 1068
Tang, Oscar, Pres.--Reich & Tang, New York, NY; *U.S. Private*, pg. 737
Tang, Oscar L., Chm. Bd. & Pres.--KOA Holdings, New York, NY; *U.S. Private*, pg. 603
Tang, Patrick, Pres.--ADC L.P., Wheeling, IL; *U.S. Private*, pg. 4
Tangel, Frank, Chief Oper. Officer & Facilities Mgr.--Contadina Dalla Casa Buitoni, Glendale, CA; *Int'l*, pg. 916
Taniguchi, Barry, Pres.--Puna Plantation Hawaii Ltd., Hilo, HI; *U.S. Private*, pg. 895
Tanimoto, Douglas, Dr., Pres. & Chief Oper. Officer--Laser Power Corporation, San Diego, CA; *U.S. Private*, pg. 652
Tanimoto, Michiharu, Pres.--Kawasaki Robotics (U.S.A.), Inc., Farmington, MI; *Int'l*, pg. 725
Tanishima, H., Pres.--Ebara - Elliott Service (Taiwan) Co., Ltd., Tai-chung, Taiwan; *Int'l*, pg. 432
Taniyama, Yasuro, Pres. & Chief Oper. Officer--Suntory International Corp., New York, NY; *Int'l*, pg. 1321

Tannen, L.P., Pres.--Fairmont Snack Group, Inc., Independence, OH; U.S. Private, pg. 392
Tannenbaum, Eric, Pres.--Columbia TriStar Television, Culver City, CA; Int'l, pg. 1282
Tannenberg, Dieter E.A., Pres. & Chief Exec. Officer--Bell & Howell Document Management Products Company, Chicago, IL; U.S. Public, pg. 201
Tanner, Alexandra, Sr. Principal & Strategic Plng. & Res. Dir.--Publicis/Bloom, New York, NY; Int'l, pg. 470
Tanner, Arthur A., Pres.--Standard-Knapp, Inc., Portland, CT; U.S. Private, pg. 1031
Tanner, Paul A., Chm. Bd., Pres. & Chief Exec. Officer--Polyphase Corporation, Dallas, TX; U.S. Public, pg. 1315
Tanner, Ronald F., Pres.--Great Vacations International, Sedona, AZ; U.S. Public, pg. 1172
Tanner, Roy, Pres.--Control Laser Corporation, Orlando, FL; U.S. Public, pg. 599
Tanner, Travis, Pres.-Carlson Travel Grp.; Co-Pres. & Chief Exec. Officer CWT--Carlson Wagonlit Travel, Minneapolis, MN; U.S. Private, pg. 212
Tanner, Van G., Pres.--HRH Insurance Services of the Coachella Valley, Inc., Palm Desert, CA; U.S. Public, pg. 826
Tannnehill, Mr., Pres.--Master-Halco, Inc., La Habra, CA; Int'l, pg. 695
Tansey, Mark C., Pres. & Chief Oper. Officer--Berkley Risk Services, Inc., Minneapolis, MN; U.S. Public, pg. 215
Tanuma, Hidehisa, Pres.--Nomura Business Services Co., Ltd., Tokyo, Japan; Int'l, pg. 956
Tanuma, Takeshi, Pres.--Nippo Corporation, Tokyo, Japan; Int'l, pg. 932
Tanzer, David, Pres.--Channel One Communications, New York, NY; U.S. Public, pg. 1328
Tanzi, Calisto, Pres.--Parmalat S.p.A., Parma, Italy; Int'l, pg. 1023
Tao, Harold L., Pres. & Chief Exec. Officer--International Commercial Bank of Cathay, Toronto, Canada; Int'l, pg. 684
Tapella, Gary I., Pres. & Chief Exec. Officer--Rheem Manufacturing Co., New York, NY; Int'l, pg. 1022
Taradash, Elliott, Pres.--M. Grossman & Son, Inc., Passaic, NJ; U.S. Private, pg. 483
Tarajano, Rick, Pres.--Pala Group, Inc., Baton Rouge, LA; U.S. Private, pg. 834
Tarantino, Robert V., Pres. & Chief Exec. Officer--Dataram Corporation, Princeton, NJ; U.S. Public, pg. 487
Tarantino, Ronald M., Pres.--Diamond Crystal Specialty Foods, Inc., Wilmington, MA; U.S. Private, pg. 330
Tarasevich, D.J., Pres.--Tuscaloosa Steel Corp., Tuscaloosa, AL; Int'l, pg. 221
Taratoot, James M., Pres.--Taracorp, Inc., Atlanta, GA; U.S. Private, pg. 1068
Tarello, John A., Pres.--Analogic Foreign Sales Corp., Saint Thomas, VI; U.S. Public, pg. 109
Targoff, Michael B., Pres. & Chief Oper. Officer--Loral Space & Communications, New York, NY; U.S. Public, pg. 1014
Tarica, Laurence, Pres.--Jimlar Corporation, Great Neck, NY; U.S. Private, pg. 587
Tarica, Lawrence, Pres.--The Frye Company, Great Neck, NY; U.S. Private, pg. 430
Tarlow, Arthur S., Jr., Pres.--Alden Shoe Co., Inc., Middleboro, MA; U.S. Private, pg. 33
Tarlton, Peter W., Pres.--Wheelock Inc., Long Branch, NJ; U.S. Private, pg. 1171
Tarng, Karen, Mng. Dir./Partner--EURO RSCG Partnership, Taipei, Taiwan; Int'l, pg. 602
Tarnon, Michael M., Pres.--Merck Frosst Canada Inc., Kirkland, Canada; U.S. Public, pg. 1092
Tarongi, Jose Ignacio Gracia, Pres.--SODIAR - Sociedad Para el Desarrollo Industrial de Aragon, S.A., Zaragoza, Spain; Int'l, pg. 1225
Taronick, Felix, Pres.--Kay Home Products, Inc., Cleveland, OH; U.S. Public, pg. 1258
Tarorick, Felix, Pres.--Marshallan Industries, Cleveland, OH; U.S. Public, pg. 1259
Tarpey, James W., Pres.--Clove Development Corp., Pearl River, NY; U.S. Public, pg. 1229
Tarpey, James W., Pres.--O & R Development, Inc., Pearl River, NY; U.S. Public, pg. 1229
Tarrant, R. Lane, Chm. Bd., Pres. & Chief Exec. Officer--Tarrant Service, Inc., Louisville, KY; U.S. Private, pg. 1069
Tarrant, Richard, Pres. & Chief Exec. Officer--IDX Systems Corporation, Burlington, VT; U.S. Public, pg. 854
Tarrant, Ronald W., Chm. Bd., Pres. & Chief Exec. Officer--Flow International Corporation, Kent, WA; U.S. Public, pg. 656
Tarses, Jamie, Pres.--ABC Inc., Los Angeles, CA; U.S. Public, pg. 511
Tartaglione, Nicholas L., Pres.--Akemi Plastics Inc., Eaton Rapids, MI; U.S. Public, pg. 1061
Tarui, Shiroo, Pres.--Q.P. Corporation, Tokyo, Japan; Int'l, pg. 1074
Tarver, David, Pres.--Telecom Analysis Systems, Eatontown, NJ; Int'l, pg. 208
Tarzian, Thomas, Chm. Bd.--Sarkes Tarzian, Bloomington, IN; U.S. Private, pg. 966
Taschner, Terry, Pres.--BIEC International Inc., Bethlehem, PA; Int'l, pg. 226
Tase, D., Pres.--Wienerschnitzel, Newport Beach, CA; U.S. Private, pg. 437
Tase, Dennis, Pres.--Galardi Group, Inc., Newport Beach, CA; U.S. Private, pg. 437
Tash, Martin E., Chm. Bd., Pres. & Chief Exec. Officer--Gradco Systems, Inc., Las Vegas, NV; U.S. Public, pg. 757
Tash, Martin E., Chm. Bd., Pres. & Chief Exec. Officer--Plenum Publishing Corporation, New York, NY; U.S. Public, pg. 1311
Tashie, Joe, Pres. & Chief Oper. Officer--Hardin's Bakery, Inc., Tuscaloosa, AL; U.S. Public, pg. 657
Tashiro, Madoka, Pres. & Chief Exec. Officer--Tosoh Corporation, Tokyo, Japan; Int'l, pg. 1407
Tashiro, Masaaki, Pres. & Chief Exec. Officer--ORIX Real Estate Equities, Inc., Chicago, IL; Int'l, pg. 1009
Tashiro, Shigeo, Pres.--Applied Materials Japan, Inc., Chiba, Japan; U.S. Public, pg. 123
Tashiro, Shunji, Pres. & Chief Exec. Officer--NEC Systems Laboratory, Inc., San Jose, CA; Int'l, pg. 900
Tashiro, Takao, Pres.--Tokai Securities, Inc., New York, NY; Int'l, pg. 1391
Tassell, Don, Pres.--Leslie Metal Arts Co., Inc., Grand Rapids, MI; U.S. Private, pg. 660
Tassin, Ed, Pres. & Chief Exec. Officer--Capital Imaging, Summerville, SC; U.S. Private, pg. 206
Tasuchiya, Hiroo, Pres.--Nippon Sanso Corporation, Tokyo, Japan; Int'l, pg. 938
Tatar, Jerome F., Chm. Bd., Pres. & Chief Exec. Officer--The Mead Corporation, Dayton, OH; U.S. Public, pg. 1074
Tate, Carey K., Pres.--Rea Construction Co., Charlotte, NC; Int'l, pg. 633
Tate, Charles W., Pres.--Hicks, Muse, Tate & Furst Inc., Dallas, TX; U.S. Private, pg. 526
Tate, Mark A., Pres.--Equitable Pipeline Company, Pittsburgh, PA; U.S. Public, pg. 590
Tate, Mark K., Pres.--Louisiana Intrastate Gas Corporation, Houston, TX; U.S. Public, pg. 590
Tateisi, Yoshio, Pres. & Dir.--Omron Corporation, Kyoto, Japan; Int'l, pg. 1005
Tateiwa, Kazuyoshi, Pres.--P.T. Tokai Lippo Bank, Jakarta, Indonesia; Int'l, pg. 1391
Tatesi, Fumio, Pres.--Omron Canada, Inc., Scarborough, Canada; Int'l, pg. 1005
Tatlock, Anne M., Pres.--Fiduciary Trust Company International, New York, NY; U.S. Public, pg. 621
Tatro, Deborah A., Pres.--United Insurance Corporation of America, Milwaukee, WI; U.S. Public, pg. 1694
Tatsch, Michael G., Pres. & Chief Exec. Officer--Chromium Corp., Dallas, TX; U.S. Public, pg. 568
Tattersall, Keith, Chm. Bd., Pres. & Chief Exec. Officer--Amperif Corporation, Chatsworth, CA; U.S. Public, pg. 1523
Tatum, W.L., Pres.--Tatum Farms Int., Inc., Dawsonville, GA; U.S. Private, pg. 1069
Taube, George S., Pres. & Creative Dir.--Taube/Violante, Inc., Norwalk, CT; U.S. Private, pg. 1069
Tauber, Orner J., Jr., Pres. & Chief Exec. Officer--Tauber Oil Company, Houston, TX; U.S. Private, pg. 1069
Taubman, Robert S., Pres. & Chief Exec. Officer--Taubman Centers, Inc., Bloomfield Hills, MI; U.S. Public, pg. 1561
Taucher, P.H., Pres. & Chief Exec. Officer--Young & Rubicam Finland, Helsinki, Finland; U.S. Private, pg. 1199
Taule, Egil, Pres.--Titech-Autosort, Oslo, Norway; Int'l, pg. 1390
Taunton-Rigby, Alison, Ph.D, Pres. & Chief Exec. Officer--Aquila Biopharmaceuticals, Inc., Worcester, MA; U.S. Public, pg. 126
Taurel, Sidney, Pres. & Chief Oper. Officer--Eli Lilly and Company, Indianapolis, IN; U.S. Public, pg. 992
Tavares, Tony, Pres.--The Mighty Ducks of Anaheim, Anaheim, CA; U.S. Public, pg. 513
Tavel, Mark K., Pres. & Chief Investment Officer--Rothchild Asset Management Inc., New York, NY; U.S. Private, pg. 947
Tavenas, Gerard, Pres. & Gen. Dir.--Lalique S.A., Paris, France; Int'l, pg. 797
Tawil, Morris E., Pres.--Tawil Associates Inc., Carteret, NJ; U.S. Private, pg. 1070
Taxe, Howard, Pres.--RS Electronics, Livonia, MI; U.S. Private, pg. 905
Taxell, Christoffer, Pres. & Chief Exec. Officer--Partek Corporation, Helsinki, Finland; Int'l, pg. 1024
Taylor-Morrell, Brett, Pres.--Todays Temporary, Inc., Dallas, TX; U.S. Public, pg. 277
Taylor, A., Pres.--AGRA Inc., Calgary, Canada; Int'l, pg. 30
Taylor, A., Pres.--Maxum Engineering Enterprises Ltd., Calgary, Canada; Int'l, pg. 31
Taylor, A. Edward, Pres.--Scotia Mortgage Corporation, Scarborough, Canada; Int'l, pg. 156
Taylor, Alec, Pres. & Chief Oper. Officer--Chattem, Inc., Chattanooga, TN; U.S. Public, pg. 341
Taylor, Alex, Pres.--AGRA Inc., Oakville, Canada; Int'l, pg. 30
Taylor, Alexander, Pres. & Chief Exec. Officer--Agra Inc., Calgary, Canada; Int'l, pg. 30
Taylor, Alexander, Pres.--Ellesmere Developments Ltd., Calgary, Canada; Int'l, pg. 31
Taylor, Anderson, Pres.--Taylor Oil Co. Inc., Winston Salem, NC; U.S. Private, pg. 1071
Taylor, Andrew C., Pres. & Chief Exec. Officer--Enterprise Rent-A-Car Company, Saint Louis, MO; U.S. Private, pg. 377
Taylor, Benjamin B., Pres.--Globe Newspaper Company, Boston, MA; U.S. Public, pg. 1175
Taylor, Benjamin B., Pres.--The Boston Globe, Boston, MA; U.S. Public, pg. 1175
Taylor, Bill, Pres.--Sunstrand Fluid Handling, Arvada, CO; U.S. Public, pg. 1534
Taylor, Bradley E., Pres.--AmericanAnglian Environmental Technologies, Inc., Voorhees, NJ; U.S. Public, pg. 95
Taylor, Bruce W., Pres.--Taylor Capital Group, Wheeling, IL; U.S. Private, pg. 1070
Taylor, Bruce W., Pres. & Chief Exec. Officer--Cole Taylor Bank, Wheeling, IL; U.S. Private, pg. 1070
Taylor, Cathy, Pres.--Cole-Haan, Yarmouth, ME; U.S. Public, pg. 1184
Taylor, Dale, Pres. & Chief Exec. Officer--Abelson-Taylor, Inc., Chicago, IL; U.S. Private, pg. 10
Taylor, Daniel J., Chm. Bd. & Pres.--Advantage Companies, Inc., Wichita, KS; U.S. Private, pg. 22
Taylor, David, Pres.--Donnelly Electronics, Holly, MI; U.S. Public, pg. 519
Taylor, David, Pres.--Velcon Filters, Inc., Colorado Springs, CO; U.S. Private, pg. 1135
Taylor, David P., Pres. & Chief Exec. Officer--ICI Explosives USA Inc., Dallas, TX; Int'l, pg. 663
Taylor, David R., Pres. & Chief Exec. Officer--Centex Forcum-Lannom, Inc., Dyersburg, TN; U.S. Public, pg. 322
Taylor, Dian C., Chm. Bd., Pres. & Chief Exec. Officer--Artesian Resources Corporation, Newark, DE; U.S. Public, pg. 135
Taylor, Diane C., Pres.--Artesian Wastewater Management Inc., Newark, DE; U.S. Public, pg. 135
Taylor, Dick, Pres.--Plantation Foods Inc., Waco, TX; U.S. Private, pg. 869
Taylor, Donald, Dr., Pres.--Aydin Displays (East), Horsham, PA; U.S. Public, pg. 158
Taylor, Ford, Pres. & Chief Exec. Officer--Brazos Sportswear Inc., Cincinnati, OH; U.S. Public, pg. 251
Taylor, George, Pres.--CFB Industries, Inc., Chicago, IL; U.S. Private, pg. 194
Taylor, Gerald H., Pres. & Chief Oper. Officer--MCI Telecommunications Corp., Washington, DC; U.S. Public, pg. 1024
Taylor, Glenn D., Pres. & Chief Exec. Officer--Medical Graphics Corp., Saint Paul, MN; U.S. Public, pg. 1080
Taylor, Gregory F., Pres. & Chief Exec. Officer--Stifel Financial Corp., Saint Louis, MO; U.S. Public, pg. 1518
Taylor, Gus, Pres.--Firstar Capital Markets Group, Las Vegas, NV; U.S. Public, pg. 643
Taylor, H. Wayne, Pres. & Chief Exec. Officer--Pontiac Bancorp, Inc., Pontiac, IL; U.S. Public, pg. 1316
Taylor, Hollis, Pres. & Chief Exec. Officer--Pancho's Mexican Buffet, Inc., Fort Worth, TX; U.S. Public, pg. 1255
Taylor, Jack, Pres.--Star Building Systems, Oklahoma City, OK; U.S. Public, pg. 1394
Taylor, James, Pres. & Chief Exec. Officer--Andros Incorporated, Berkeley, CA; U.S. Private, pg. 74
Taylor, James, Pres. & Chief Exec. Officer--Andros Service Inc., Hoenheim, France; U.S. Private, pg. 74
Taylor, James, Pres. & Chief Exec. Officer--Scitec Corporation, Kennewick, WA; U.S. Private, pg. 74
Taylor, James, Pres. & Chief Exec. & Fin. Officers--Reuter Manufacturing Inc., Hopkins, MN; U.S. Public, pg. 1383
Taylor, James I., Pres. & Chief Exec. Officer--Penn National Insurance, Harrisburg, PA; U.S. Private, pg. 850
Taylor, Jeff, Pres. & Exec. V.P.-Interactive, TMPW--TMP Worldwide/Interactive Division, Framingham, MA; U.S. Private, pg. 1065
Taylor, Jim, Pres.--QDI, Inc., Denver, CO; U.S. Private, pg. 82
Taylor, John, Pres.-Gaming & Entertainment--Dreamport, Inc., Boca Raton, FL; U.S. Public, pg. 767
Taylor, Kenneth, Pres.--Ohio Machinery Co., Cleveland, OH; U.S. Private, pg. 812
Taylor, Kenneth, Dr., Pres.--Syntex, Palo Alto, CA; Int'l, pg. 1120
Taylor, Mark D., Pres. & Chief Exec. Officer--Tyndale House Publishers, Inc., Carol Stream, IL; U.S. Private, pg. 1112
Taylor, Matthew A., Pres.--Cyro Industries, Rockaway, NJ; Int'l, pg. 1454
Taylor, Maurice M., Jr., Pres. & Chief Exec. Officer--Titan International, Inc., Quincy, IL; U.S. Public, pg. 1618
Taylor, Norman J., Pres. & Chief Oper. Officer--Adience Inc., Carnegie, PA; U.S. Public, pg. 58
Taylor, Paul, Pres.--Southeastern Freight Lines, Inc., Lexington, SC; U.S. Private, pg. 1015
Taylor, Peter, Pres.--Y.P.F. Gas S.A., Buenos Aires, Argentina; Int'l, pg. 1515
Taylor, R. Eugene, Pres.--NationsBank Florida, Tampa, FL; U.S. Public, pg. 1162
Taylor, Robert M., Pres.--Maui Divers of Hawaii, Honolulu, HI; U.S. Private, pg. 715
Taylor, Ronald L., Pres. & Chief Oper. Officer--DeVry Institutes, Oak Brook Terrace, IL; U.S. Public, pg. 503
Taylor, Ronald L., Pres.--Becker CPA Review, Encino, CA; U.S. Public, pg. 504
Taylor, Ronald S., Pres.--Capital Industries, Inc., Seattle, WA; U.S. Private, pg. 206
Taylor, Thomas A., Pres. & Chief Exec. Officer--Amica Mutual Insurance Co., Lincoln, RI; U.S. Private, pg. 66
Taylor, Volney, Chm. Bd.--Dun & Bradstreet, Murray Hill, NJ; U.S. Public, pg. 535
Taylor, W.A., III, Pres.--Taylor Machine Works, Inc., Louisville, MS; U.S. Private, pg. 1070
Taylor, William, Pres. & Chief Exec. Officer--Fidelity Mutual Life Insurance Co., Radnor, PA; U.S. Private, pg. 403
Taylor, William, Pres. & Chief Oper. Officer--Taylor-Morley, Inc., Saint Louis, MO; U.S. Private, pg. 1071
Taylor, William W., Chm. Bd. & Chief Exec. Officer--D.C. Taylor Co., Cedar Rapids, IA; U.S. Private, pg. 1070
Tazaki, Kazuaki, Pres.--Brother (Schweiz) A.G., Baden, Switzerland; Int'l, pg. 230
Tazaki, Kazuaki, Pres.--Brother Macchine Industriali S.R.L., Bologna, Italy; Int'l, pg. 230
Tchang, K.T. Thomas, Pres.--Red Star Yeast & Products Div., Milwaukee, WI; U.S. Public, pg. 1695
Teagle, James C., Pres. & Chief Oper. Officer--Koger Equity Inc., Jacksonville, FL; U.S. Public, pg. 965
Teague, Robert M., Pres. & Chief Oper. Officer--Thermo Industries Inc., Charlotte, NC; U.S. Private, pg. 1080
Teague, Thomas L., Pres. & Chief Exec. Officer--Salem National Corporation, Winston Salem, NC; U.S. Private, pg. 962
Teasley, Larkin, Pres. & Chief Exec. Officer--Golden State Mutual Life Insurance Company, Los Angeles, CA; U.S. Private, pg. 461
Tebbutt, Anthony, Pres.--Whitby, Inc., Richmond, VA; Int'l, pg. 1427
Tedeschi, Ed, Partner--Messner Vetere Berger McNamee Schmetterer/EURO RSCG, New York, NY; Int'l, pg. 602
Teel, E. Gerald, Pres., Chief Exec. Officer & Chief Oper. Officer--Vitamilk Dairy, Inc., Seattle, WA; U.S. Private, pg. 1142
Teel, Michael J., Pres.--Raley's & Bel Air, West Sacramento, CA; U.S. Private, pg. 907

Teela, Jack E., Pres.--Amerock Corporation, Rockford, IL; *U.S. Public,* pg. 1177
Tees, Jim, Pres. & Chief Exec. Officer--Pioneer Plastics Corporation, Auburn, ME; *U.S. Private,* pg. 867
Teets, Peter B., Pres. & Chief Oper. Officer--Lockheed Martin Corporation, Bethesda, MD; *U.S. Public,* pg. 1006
Tegarden, William H., Chm. Bd., Pres. & Chief Exec. Officer--Citizens Bank of Central Indiana-Orleans Region, Orleans, IN; *U.S. Public,* pg. 280
Teich, Irwin, Pres.--Fleet Capital Corporation, Glastonbury, CT; *U.S. Public,* pg. 649
Teigen, Charles, Pres.--Rugby Farmers Union Elevator Company, Rugby, ND; *U.S. Private,* pg. 950
Teilborg, Ray, Pres.--WMF/USA, Farmingdale, NY; *U.S. Private,* pg. 1144
Teixeira, Joseph, Partner, Fin. Dir. & Reg. Opers. Dir.--Arnold Communications, Inc., Boston, MA; *U.S. Private,* pg. 83
Tejuca Suarez, Luis Manuel, Chm. Bd. & Pres.--Hulleras Del Norte, S.A. (HUNOSA), Asturias, Spain; *Int'l,* pg. 639
Telechea, Julio, Pres.--Servired YPF S.A., Buenos Aires, Argentina; *Int'l,* pg. 1515
Telfer, George, Pres.--Nodeco, Ltd., Aberdeen, United Kingdom; *U.S. Public,* pg. 1750
Tellechea, Julio, Pres.--O.P.E.S.S.A., Buenos Aires, Argentina; *Int'l,* pg. 1515
Tellier, P.M., Chm. Bd.--Grand Trunk Corporation (GTC), Detroit, MI; *Int'l,* pg. 258
Tellier, Paul, Pres. & Chief Exec. Officer--Canadian National Railway Company, Montreal, Canada; *Int'l,* pg. 258
Tellor, Michael D., Pres.--Rust-Oleum Corporation, Vernon Hills, IL; *U.S. Public,* pg. 1358
Temkin, Steven, Pres. & Acct. Exec.--Temkin & Temkin, Northbrook, IL; *U.S. Private,* pg. 1074
Tempelsman, Leon, Vice Chm. & Pres.--Lazare Kaplan Intl., Inc., New York, NY; *U.S. Public,* pg. 981
Tempest, Brian, Pres.--Medeva Pharmaceuticals, Rochester, NY; *Int'l,* pg. 852
Temple, David J., Pres. & Chief Exec. Officer--Canplas Industries Ltd., Barrie, Canada; *Int'l,* pg. 430
Temple, John, Pres. & Chief Exec. Officer--Guideposts Associates, Inc., Carmel, NY; *U.S. Private,* pg. 487
Temple, Steve, Pres.--CAE Ransohoff Inc., Cincinnati, OH; *Int'l,* pg. 237
Temple, Thomas C., Pres.--U.S. Oil & Refining Co., Tacoma, WA; *U.S. Private,* pg. 1086
Templeton, Robert, Pres.--NewCap Broadcasting, Bedford, Canada; *Int'l,* pg. 924
TenBroek, James, Mng. Dir.--Windpoint Partners, Southfield, MI; *U.S. Private,* pg. 1182
Tendler, Lance, Pres., Chief Exec. Officer& Treas.--Kennington Ltd., Inc., Van Nuys, CA; *U.S. Private,* pg. 615
Tendler, Lance, Pres.--Com Corp Factors, Inc., Van Nuys, CA; *U.S. Private,* pg. 615
Tendler, Lance, Pres.--Stanleigh International, Inc., Van Nuys, CA; *U.S. Private,* pg. 615
Tenenbaum, Harold, Pres.--A. Tenenbaum Co. Inc., North Little Rock, AR; *U.S. Private,* pg. 1076
Tenney, Arnold S., Pres. & Chief Exec. Officer--ARC International Corporation, Downsview, Canada; *Int'l,* pg. 17
Tenney, Robert N., Pres. & Chief Exec. Officer--Fremont Financial Corporation, Santa Monica, CA; *U.S. Public,* pg. 681
Tennison, R., Pres.--Simpson Investment Co., Seattle, WA; *U.S. Private,* pg. 1003
Tenny, Morton, Pres. & Chief Exec. Officer--Union Pen Company, Greenwich, CT; *U.S. Private,* pg. 1119
Tenoso, Harold J., Ph.D., Pres. & Chief Exec. Officer--Serologicals Corporation, Clarkston, GA; *U.S. Public,* pg. 1460
Teo, Alfred, Pres.--Alpha Industries, Lyndhurst, NJ; *U.S. Private,* pg. 45
Teo, Alfred, Pres.--Beta Plastics, Carlstadt, NJ; *U.S. Private, pg. 45*
Teo, Alfred, Pres.--Omega Plastics, Lyndhurst, NJ; *U.S. Private,* pg. 45
Tepas, Gary L., Pres. & Chief Exec. Officer--Emkay, Inc., Itasca, IL; *U.S. Private,* pg. 374
Tepas, Thomas G., Pres. & Chief Oper. Officer--ChemFirst Inc., Jackson, MS; *U.S. Public,* pg. 344
Terada, Tokio, Pres.--Tsudakoma Corp., Kanazawa, Japan; *Int'l,* pg. 1425
Terao, Koichi, Pres.--NEC Technologies Philippines, Inc., Cebu, Philippines; *Int'l,* pg. 900
Terao, Koichi, Pres.--NEC Technologies (Thailand) Co., Ltd., Pathum Thani, Thailand; *Int'l,* pg. 900
Terao, Munekazu, Pres.--Wako Securities (America), Inc., New York, NY; *Int'l,* pg. 1485
Terasawa, Tsuyoshi, Pres.--Kawasho International (U.S.A.) Inc., Fort Lee, NJ; *Int'l,* pg. 726
Terashima, Ikuo, Pres.--Tokai Bank Canada, Toronto, Canada; *Int'l,* pg. 1391
Terborgh, Eliot, Pres. & Chief Exec. Officer--SmarTrunk Systems, Inc., Hayward, CA; *U.S. Private,* pg. 1006
Terek, Ted S., Pres.--SuperValu, Inc.-Milton Div., Milton, WV; *U.S. Public,* pg. 1540
Terhar, Bill, Pres. & Chief Oper. Officer--Ocean Beauty Seafoods, Inc., Seattle, WA; *U.S. Private,* pg. 810
Terhar, Louis F., Pres.--David Joseph Co., Cincinnati, OH; *U.S. Private,* pg. 601
Terhune, Michael, Pres.--Wells Fargo Alarm Services, Inc., King of Prussia, PA; *U.S. Public,* pg. 246
Terlato, William A., Pres. & Chief Oper. Officer--Paterno Imports Limited, Lake Bluff, IL; *U.S. Private,* pg. 843
Termeer, Henri A., Chm. Bd., Pres. & Chief Exec. Officer--Genzyme Corporation, Cambridge, MA; *U.S. Public,* pg. 733
Ternus, Gary S., Pres.--Dunn Nutratech, Dunn, NC; *U.S. Public,* pg. 128
Ternus, Gary S., Pres.--Nutratech Animal Health, Douglas, GA; *U.S. Public,* pg. 128
Terracciano, Anthony P., Pres.--First Union Corporation, Charlotte, NC; *U.S. Public,* pg. 639
Terradas, Rosendo, Pres.--Bridgestone/Firestone Venezolana, C.A., Valencia, Venezuela; *Int'l,* pg. 214
Terral, Thomas F., Pres. & Chief Exec. Officer--Terral Seed Co., Inc., Lake Providence, LA; *U.S. Private,* pg. 1077
Terrell, Charles L., Pres., Chief Exec. Officer & Treas.--New Haven Savings Bank, New Haven, CT; *U.S. Private,* pg. 793
Terrell, James R., Pres. & Chief Oper. Officer-TV Stations--Gaylord Broadcasting Co., Nashville, TN; *U.S. Public,* pg. 704
Terrell, William P., Pres. & Gen. Mgr.--Cadmus Financial, Charlotte, NC; *U.S. Public,* pg. 291
Terrien, Jean Francois, Pres. & Chief Exec. Officer--Neyrpic Framatome Mecanique (NFM), Paris, France; *Int'l,* pg. 503
Terrill, J.E., Pres. & Chief Exec. Officer--Jefferson Smurfit Corporation, Saint Louis, MO; *Int'l,* pg. 1271
Terry, Glen C., Pres. & Chief Exec. Officer--Napa Valley Bank, Napa, CA; *U.S. Public,* pg. 1756
Terry, James W., Jr., Pres.--Carolina First Bank, Greenville, SC; *U.S. Public,* pg. 306
Terry, Mark, Pres.--JBL Professional, Northridge, CA; *U.S. Public,* pg. 787
Teruya, Mark, Pres.--Armstrong Produce Ltd., Honolulu, HI; *U.S. Private,* pg. 83
Teruya, Raymond, Chm. Bd., Pres. & Chief Exec. Officer--Teruya Bros., Limited, Honolulu, HI; *U.S. Private,* pg. 1077
Teruzzi, Orlando, Chm. Bd. & Pres.--Precision Resource Inc., Shelton, CT; *U.S. Private,* pg. 880
Tervel, Javier, Pres. & Gen. Mgr.--Colgate-Palmolive, S.A. De C.V., Mexico, Mexico; *U.S. Public,* pg. 399
Terzic, Branco, Chm. Bd., Pres. & Chief Exec. Officer--Yankee Energy System, Inc., Meriden, CT; *U.S. Public,* pg. 1787
Tesch, Mike, Partner, Exec. V.P. & Co-Creative Dir.--Harris Drury Cohen, Fort Lauderdale, FL; *U.S. Private,* pg. 505
Teshima, Tadashi, Pres.--Nichirei Corporation, Tokyo, Japan; *Int'l,* pg. 928
Teshinsky, Fred, Pres.--Tulip Corporation, City of Industry, CA; *U.S. Private,* pg. 1109
Teshoian, Nishan, Pres.--Keystone International Holdings Corp., Houston, TX; *U.S. Public,* pg. 1650
Tesone, Antonio, Chm. Bd. & Pres.--Olivetti SpA, Turin, Italy; *Int'l,* pg. 1002
Tessier, Edward J., Chm., Pres. & Chief Exec. Officer--Amerifoods Inc., Lancaster, PA; *U.S. Private,* pg. 65
Tessier, Robert, Pres. & Chief Exec. Officer--Gaz Metropolitain & Company, Montreal, Canada; *Int'l,* pg. 541
Tessmer, Raymond R., Pres.--Jefferson Chevrolet Co., Detroit, MI; *U.S. Private,* pg. 584
Tesstore, Roberto, Mng. Dir.--Fiat Auto SpA, Turin, Italy; *Int'l,* pg. 480
Testen, Christer, Pres.--Astra Pharmaceuticals Pty. Ltd., Sydney, Australia; *Int'l,* pg. 94
Testut, Michel, Pres.--EURO RSCG D 10, Perigueux, France; *Int'l,* pg. 600
Testwuide, Thomas R., Pres. & Chief Exec. Officer--Schreier Malting Co., Sheboygan, WI; *U.S. Private,* pg. 972
Teter, Gordon F., Chm. Bd., Pres. & Chief Oper. Officer--Wendy's International Inc., Dublin, OH; *U.S. Public,* pg. 1754
Teti, Joseph A., Jr., Chm. Bd. & Pres.--La France Corporation, Philadelphia, PA; *U.S. Private,* pg. 640
Teufel, Robert J., Pres. & Chief Oper. Officer--Rodale Press, Inc., Emmaus, PA; *U.S. Private,* pg. 939
Tews, Herb, Pres.--Precision Plastics Inc., Columbia City, IN; *U.S. Private,* pg. 879
Thabault, Laurent, Pres.--SCOR Canada Reinsurance Company, Toronto, Canada; *Int'l,* pg. 1152
Thacker, William L., Jr., Chm. Bd., Pres. & Chief Exec. Officer--TEPPCO Partners L.P., Houston, TX; *U.S. Public, pg. 534*
Thacker, William L., Jr., Pres. & Chief Exec. Officer--Texas Eastern Products Pipeline Company, L.P., Houston, TX; *U.S. Public,* pg. 535
Thampi, P.M., Pres. & Chief Oper. Officer--BASF India Ltd., Mumbai, India; *Int'l,* pg. 106
Thanarugchok, C., Pres.--Asia Shinwa Engineering Co., Ltd., Bangkok, Thailand; *Int'l,* pg. 432
Tharp, James T., Chm. Bd. & Pres.--McCrory Construction Co., Inc., Columbia, SC; *U.S. Private,* pg. 720
Thayer, James N., Chm. Bd., Pres. & Chief Exec. Officer--Gibraltar Savings, Simi Valley, CA; *U.S. Public,* pg. 181
Thayer, Lester R., Chm. Bd. & Pres.--Multiple Allied Services, Inc., Hayward, CA; *U.S. Private,* pg. 767
Thede, Merv, Pres.--Alcoa Steamship Co., Inc., Pittsburgh, PA; *U.S. Public,* pg. 61
Theel, Mark, Pres.--Sterling Software Application Development Division, Plano, TX; *U.S. Public,* pg. 1516
Theeranartsin, Nibhondh, Pres.--Siam Sanitary Ware Co., Ltd., Bangkok, Thailand; *Int'l,* pg. 1410
Theis, Stephen, Pres.--Simonds-Shields-Theis Grain Co., Kansas City, MO; *U.S. Private,* pg. 1001
Theisen, Claude I., Pres. & Chief Exec. Officer--T & S Brass & Bronze Works, Inc., Travelers Rest, SC; *U.S. Private,* pg. 1061
Theobald, Stephen W., Pres. & Chief Exec. Officer--Stokely USA, Inc., Oconomowoc, WI; *U.S. Public,* pg. 1518
Theofilos, John S., Pres.--Theochem Labs., Inc., Tampa, FL; *U.S. Private,* pg. 1079
Theriault, Roger, Pres. & Chief Exec. Officer--Brigham's, Inc., Arlington, MA; *U.S. Private,* pg. 483
Therien, Michel, Pres.--Desjardins-Laurentian Financial Corporation, Montreal, Canada; *Int'l,* pg. 396
Therien, Michel, Pres. & Chief Exec. Officer--Assurance vie Desjardins-Laurentienne, Levis, Canada; *Int'l,* pg. 396
Theumim, Moshe, Chm. Bd. & Pres.--Gitam/BBDO, Ramat Gan, Israel; *Int'l,* pg. 552
Theurauf, Ingo, Pres. & Chief Exec. Officer--Preussag North America, Greenwich, CT; *Int'l,* pg. 1070
Thiagarajan, Arun, Pres.--ASEA Limited, Bangalore, India; *Int'l,* pg. 8
Thiel, Stephen, Chm. Bd., Pres. & Chief Exec. Officer--Thiel Cheese Co., Hilbert, WI; *U.S. Private,* pg. 1081
Thiel, Wilbert, Pres.--ABN AMRO Chicago Corporation, Chicago, IL; *Int'l,* pg. 10
Thiel, Wilbert, Pres.--ABN AMRO Chicago Corp., Chicago, IL; *Int'l,* pg. 10
Thiele, P.A., Pres. & Chief Exec. Officer--St. Paul Fire and Marine Insurance Co., Saint Paul, MN; *U.S. Public,* pg. 1429
Thielemans, Leo, Pres.--Synerfi SA, Brussels, Belgium; *Int'l, pg. 547*
Thierstein, Hans, Chm. Bd. & Pres.--Ares-Serono S.A., Geneva, Switzerland; *Int'l,* pg. 80
Thigpen, John C., Pres. & Chief Oper. Officer--Westgate Inc., Port Allen, LA; *U.S. Private,* pg. 1169
Thijs, Johnny, Chief Exec. Officer--Interbrew S.A., Leuven, Belgium; *Int'l,* pg. 679
Thiry, Kent J., Pres. & Chief Exec. Officer--Vivra Incorporated, San Mateo, CA; *U.S. Public,* pg. 1723
Thiry, Kent J., Pres.--Viva Specialty Partners, San Mateo, CA; *U.S. Public,* pg. 1724
Tholan, Kenneth M., Pres.--Team Industrial Services, Inc., Alvin, TX; *U.S. Public,* pg. 1562
Tholan, Kenneth M., Pres.--Pipe Repairs, Inc., Alvin, TX; *U.S. Public,* pg. 1562
Thom, William C., Pres.--Harmony House Records & Tapes, Troy, MI; *U.S. Private,* pg. 503
Thoma, Ronald R., Pres.--Crown Cork & Seal Company, Inc.-Subsidiaries Division, Philadelphia, PA; *U.S. Public,* pg. 463
Thoman, Richard, Pres. & Chief Oper. Officer--Xerox Corporation, Stamford, CT; *U.S. Public,* pg. 1783
Thomann, Michael, Pres. & Chief Exec. Officer--Brad Ragan, Inc., Charlotte, NC; *U.S. Public,* pg. 753
Thomas, Barbara, Partner-Product Services--Eric Mower and Associates, Rochester, NY; *U.S. Private,* pg. 765
Thomas, Berl M., Pres. & Chief Exec. Officer--Speedling Incorporated, Sun City, FL; *U.S. Private,* pg. 1024
Thomas, C.W., III, Pres.--Simcoe Leaf Tobacco Company, Ltd., Simcoe, Canada; *U.S. Public,* pg. 1695
Thomas, Charles, Pres.--Pepsi-Cola Bottling Co. of Long Island City, Long Island City, NY; *U.S. Public,* pg. 1276
Thomas, Christopher R., Pres.--Sizzler USA, Inc., Los Angeles, CA; *U.S. Public,* pg. 1475
Thomas, Dave, Pres.--Alphabet Design Center, Cortland, OH; *U.S. Private,* pg. 1044
Thomas, David G., Pres.--EvansGroup, Salt Lake City, UT; *U.S. Private,* pg. 385
Thomas, David L., Pres.--Alphabet Division, Warren, OH; *U.S. Private,* pg. 1044
Thomas, Edmond, Pres. & Chief Oper. Officer--The Wet Seal, Inc., Irvine, CA; *U.S. Public,* pg. 1763
Thomas, Frank, Pres.--Cummins Southwest Inc., Phoenix, AZ; *U.S. Private,* pg. 296
Thomas, Frank L., Pres. & Chief Exec. Officer--Genstar Development Company, San Diego, CA; *Int'l,* pg. 112
Thomas, G. Andes, Chm. Bd., Pres. & Chief Exec. Officer--Magna Group, Inc., Saint Louis, MO; *U.S. Public,* pg. 1037
Thomas, G.N., Chm. Bd., Pres., & Chief Exec. Officer--A. Levy & J. Zentner Co., Sacramento, CA; *U.S. Private,* pg. 663
Thomas, J. Grover, Jr., Pres. & Chief Exec. Officer--United Family Life Insurance Co., Atlanta, GA; *Int'l,* pg. 499
Thomas, Jack, Publr.--Herald Voice, Hazard, KY; *U.S. Public,* pg. 1343
Thomas, James A., Mng. Partner--Maguire Partners, Los Angeles, CA; *U.S. Private,* pg. 696
Thomas, Jim, Pres.--Dacor Corporation, Northfield, IL; *U.S. Private,* pg. 306
Thomas, Jim, Owner & Mng. Partner--Sacramento Kings, Sacramento, CA; *U.S. Private,* pg. 959
Thomas, John E., Pres. & Chief Exec. Officer--Tippins Incorporated, Pittsburgh, PA; *U.S. Private,* pg. 1088
Thomas, John W., III, Pres. & Chief Exec. Officer--Thomas Built Buses, Inc., High Point, NC; *U.S. Private,* pg. 1082
Thomas, Karl, Mng. Dir.--Integral Hydraulik & Co., Meerbusch, Germany; *Int'l,* pg. 679
Thomas, Larry, Pres.--Triton Engineering Services Company, Houston, TX; *U.S. Public,* pg. 1186
Thomas, Larry R., Pres.--MK Centennial, Arvada, CO; *U.S. Public,* pg. 1134
Thomas, Lisa, Pres.--Card Pak, Inc., Cleveland, OH; *U.S. Private,* pg. 208
Thomas, Michael E., Pres. & Chief Exec. Officer--Chromcraft Revington, Inc., Delphi, IN; *U.S. Public,* pg. 352
Thomas, Michael S., Pres.--Vara Internatonal, Vero Beach, FL; *U.S. Public,* pg. 293
Thomas, Newton B., Chm. Bd. & Pres.--The Newtron Group Inc., Baton Rouge, LA; *U.S. Private,* pg. 797
Thomas, Peter G., Pres. & Mng. Dir.--Holden's Engine Products Overseas Corporation, Melbourne, Australia; *U.S. Public,* pg. 723
Thomas, R., Mng. Dir.--Scholl (UK) Ltd., London, United Kingdom; *U.S. Public,* pg. 1439
Thomas, Raymond L., Pres.--Frederick Trading Company, Frederick, MD; *U.S. Private,* pg. 335
Thomas, Richard E., Pres.--COMSAT RSI, Inc., Sterling, VA; *U.S. Public,* pg. 424
Thomas, Robert L., Pres. & Treas.--Saul Bros. & Company, Inc., Norcross, GA; *U.S. Private,* pg. 968
Thomas, Rowland H., Jr., Pres. & Chief Oper. Officer--Encore Computer Corporation, Fort Lauderdale, FL; *U.S. Public,* pg. 580
Thomas, Stephen S., Pres.--Datapro Information Services Grp., Delran, NJ; *U.S. Public,* pg. 1070
Thomas, Steve, Pres.--REPP Ltd. Big and Tall, Saint Louis, MO; *U.S. Public,* pg. 564

Thomas, Steven C., Pres. & Chief Exec. Officer--MPS Corporation, Pittsburgh, PA; *U.S. Private*, pg. 687
Thomas, Steven C., Vice Chm. & Pres.--Mulach Steel Corporation, Leetsdale, PA; *U.S. Private*, pg. 766
Thomas, T. Paul, Pres. & Chief Oper. Officer--Artisoft, Inc., Tucson, AZ; *U.S. Public*, pg. 136
Thomas, Terence W., Chm. Bd. & Pres.--Arizona Wholesale Supply Company, Phoenix, AZ; *U.S. Private*, pg. 82
Thomas, William O., Pres. & Chief Exec. Officer--DeVlieg-Bullard Inc., Westport, CT; *U.S. Public*, pg. 502
Thomason, Scott L., Pres. & Chief Exec. Officer--Thomason Auto Group, Gladstone, OR; *U.S. Private*, pg. 1083
Thomlinson, G.A., Pres.--National Mutual Holdings Limited, Melbourne, Australia; *Int'l*, pg. 908
Thomlinson, G.A., Pres.--The National Mutual Life Association of Australia Limited, Melbourne, Australia; *Int'l*, pg. 909
Thomopulos, Greg G., Pres.--The Stanley Consultants Group, Muscatine, IA; *U.S. Private*, pg. 1032
Thomopulos, Greg G., Pres.--Stanley Consultants, Inc., Muscatine, IA; *U.S. Private*, pg. 1033
Thomopulos, Gregs G., Chm. Bd. & Pres.--Stanley Design-Build, Inc., Muscatine, IA; *U.S. Private*, pg. 1033
Thompson, Andy M., Pres.--Self-Insurance Administrators, Inc., Stone Mountain, GA; *U.S. Public*, pg. 144
Thompson, C.H., Jr., Pres.--Burlington Basket Co., Burlington, IA; *U.S. Private*, pg. 183
Thompson, C.M., Chief Exec. Officer--Rentokil Initial plc, East Grinstead, United Kingdom; *Int'l*, pg. 1285
Thompson, D. Gary, Pres. & Chief Exec. Officer--Wachovia Bank of Georgia, N.A., Atlanta, GA; *U.S. Public*, pg. 1730
Thompson, Dan, Pres.--Border States Paving, Inc., Fargo, ND; *U.S. Private*, pg. 160
Thompson, Dan, Pres. & Chief Exec. Officer--ElectroCom Automation L.P., Arlington, TX; *Int'l*, pg. 1244
Thompson, David, Pres. & Chief Exec. Officer--Datamarine International, Inc., Mountlake Terrace, WA; *U.S. Public*, pg. 486
Thompson, David A., Pres., Chief Exec. Officer, Chief Fin. Officer--Cominco, Ltd., Vancouver, Canada; *Int'l*, pg. 307
Thompson, David R., Pres. & Chief Exec. Officer--Kennedy Manufacturing Company, Van Wert, OH; *U.S. Private*, pg. 614
Thompson, David W., Chm. Bd., Pres. & Chief Exec. Officer--Orbital Sciences Corporation, Dulles, VA; *U.S. Public*, pg. 1229
Thompson, Donald L., Chm. Bd., Pres. & Chief Exec. Officer--Hunt Corporation, Philadelphia, PA; *U.S. Public*, pg. 848
Thompson, Fred, Mng. Partner--Kerry Kelly Thompson, Greenwich, CT; *U.S. Private*, pg. 174
Thompson, G.W., Pres. & Chief Exec. Officer--Getchell Gold Corp., Englewood, CO; *U.S. Public*, pg. 740
Thompson, J. Kenneth, Pres.--ARCO Alaska Inc., Anchorage, AK; *U.S. Public*, pg. 144
Thompson, J. Mace, Pres.--Lyman Products Corporation, Middletown, CT; *U.S. Private*, pg. 683
Thompson, J.D., Pres.--Southland Life Insurance Company, Atlanta, GA; *Int'l*, pg. 648
Thompson, Jack, Pres.--Penda Corporation, Portage, WI; *U.S. Private*, pg. 848
Thompson, Jack E., Pres. & Chief Exec. Officer--Homestake Mining Company, San Francisco, CA; *U.S. Public*, pg. 832
Thompson, Jack L., Pres.--Monroe Auto Equipment Co., Monroe, MI; *U.S. Public*, pg. 1577
Thompson, James R., Pres.--Ikon Office Solutions (Atlantic), Halifax, Canada; *U.S. Public*, pg. 864
Thompson, James R., Pres.--T & R Electric Supply Company, Inc., Colman, SD; *U.S. Private*, pg. 1061
Thompson, James W., Pres. & Chief Exec. Officer--Vallen Corporation, Houston, TX; *U.S. Public*, pg. 1705
Thompson, James W., Pres. & Chief Exec. Officer--Vallen Safety Supply Company, Houston, TX; *U.S. Public*, pg. 1705
Thompson, James W., Pres. & Chief Exec. Officer--Vallen Safety Supply Company, Ltd., Markham, Canada; *U.S. Public*, pg. 1705
Thompson, Jim, Pres. & Gen. Mgr.--The Sports Network (TSN), Willowdale, Canada; *Int'l*, pg. 1343
Thompson, John, Pres. & Chief Exec. Officer--Montreal Trustco, Montreal, Canada; *Int'l*, pg. 155
Thompson, John B., Pres.--AC Rochester Overseas Corporation, Southampton, United Kingdom; *U.S. Public*, pg. 722
Thompson, John F., Pres. & Chief Oper. Officer--Aurora Electronics, Inc., Irvine, CA; *U.S. Public*, pg. 147
Thompson, John S., Pres. & Chief Exec.--BTR, Inc., Stamford, CT; *Int'l*, pg. 127
Thompson, Keith, Pres.--Measurement Systems, Inc., Fairfield, CT; *Int'l*, pg. 1431
Thompson, Keith M., Pres. & Chief Exec. Officer--Republic Automotive Parts, Inc., Brentwood, TN; *U.S. Public*, pg. 1377
Thompson, Kevin, Partner & Sr. Grp. Art Dir.--Lewis Gace Bozell Healthcare Worldwide, Fort Lee, NJ; *U.S. Public*, pg. 1642
Thompson, Kirk, Pres. & Chief Exec. Officer--J.B. Hunt Transport Services, Inc., Lowell, AR; *U.S. Public*, pg. 849
Thompson, L. Dan, Pres. & Chief Exec. Officer--Lou Ana Foods, Inc., Opelousas, LA; *Int'l*, pg. 879
Thompson, Leo G., Pres. & Chief Exec. Officer--Lindberg Corporation, Rosemont, IL; *U.S. Public*, pg. 999
Thompson, Michael D., Pres. & Chief Exec. Officer--Thompson Tractor Company, Birmingham, AL; *U.S. Private*, pg. 1083
Thompson, Norman J., Sr. V.P.--Air New Zealand Ltd. (U.S.A.), El Segundo, CA; *Int'l*, pg. 38
Thompson, Paul, Pres.--Bou-Matic, Madison, WI; *U.S. Private*, pg. 301
Thompson, Peter, Pres. & Chief Exec. Officer--Snack Ventures Europe, Zaventem, Belgium; *U.S. Public*, pg. 718
Thompson, R.K., Pres.--Xebec Corporation, Kansas City, MO; *U.S. Private*, pg. 1194
Thompson, Randall, Pres.--Freedom Investment, Omaha, NE; *Int'l*, pg. 476
Thompson, Raymon F., Chm. Bd., Pres. & Chief Exec. Officer--Semitool, Inc., Kalispell, MT; *U.S. Public*, pg. 1456
Thompson, Richard, Pres. & Chief Exec. Officer--Microlog Corporation, Germantown, MD; *U.S. Public*, pg. 1105
Thompson, Richard K., Pres.--DIT-MCO Intl., Kansas City, MO; *U.S. Private*, pg. 1194
Thompson, Robert E., Pres.--Old Kent Bank of St. Johns, Saint Johns, MI; *U.S. Public*, pg. 1217
Thompson, Robert M., Pres. & Chief Exec. Officer--Thompson-McCully Co., Belleville, MI; *U.S. Private*, pg. 1083
Thompson, Ronald H., Dr., Pres--Polar Material Inc., Pennsville, NJ; *Int'l*, pg. 68
Thompson, Terry W., Chm. Bd., Pres. & Chief Exec. Officer--State Bank of Standish, Standish, MI; *U.S. Public*, pg. 379
Thompson, Tom, Pres. & Chief Oper. Officer--CKE Restaurants Inc., Anaheim, CA; *U.S. Public*, pg. 278
Thompson, Tom, Pres.--Circuit Works, Mundelein, IL; *U.S. Private*, pg. 669
Thompson, W.H., Jr., Pres.--Liberty Bancorp, Inc., Oklahoma City, OK; *U.S. Public*, pg. 174
Thompson, Wade F.B., Chm. Bd., Pres. & Chief Exec. Officer--Thor Industries, Inc., Jackson Center, OH; *U.S. Public*, pg. 1602
Thompson, Wayne, Pres. & Treas.--Tank Service, Inc., Knoxville, TN; *U.S. Public*, pg. 521
Thompson, Wes, Pres.--W.G. Thompson & Sons Ltd., Blenheim, Canada; *Int'l*, pg. 1381
Thompson, William J., Pres.--Scherer Healthcare, Inc., Atlanta, GA; *U.S. Public*, pg. 1437
Thompson, William J., Pres. & Chief Oper. Officer--Vital Signs, Englewood, CO; *U.S. Public*, pg. 1723
Thompson, William R., Chm., Pres. & Chief Exec. Officer--SunTrust Bank, Augusta, N.A., Augusta, GA; *U.S. Public*, pg. 1538
Thoms, Allen S., Pres.--Canadian Shipbuilding & Engineering Ltd., Saint Catharines, Canada; *Int'l*, pg. 259
Thoms, Carl, Pres.--Fortifiber Corporation, Incline Village, NV; *U.S. Private*, pg. 419
Thomsen, Paul A., Pres.--Schoep's Ice Cream, Inc., Madison, WI; *U.S. Private*, pg. 972
Thomson, Donald, Pres.--Precision Arc Co., Bridgeport, CT; *U.S. Private*, pg. 1008
Thomson, James A., Pres. & Chief Exec. Officer--RAND, Santa Monica, CA; *U.S. Private*, pg. 908
Thomson, James S., Pres.--CNG International Corp., Reston, VA; *U.S. Public*, pg. 435
Thomson, Michael J., Pres. & Chief Exec. Officer--Community Energy Alternatives Incorporated, Ridgewood, NJ; *U.S. Public*, pg. 1340
Thorburn, Bill, Sr. Partner-Carmichael Lynch Thorburn Design--Carmichael Lynch, Inc., Minneapolis, MN; *U.S. Private*, pg. 213
Thorell, Algot F., Jr., Pres.--Chestnut Hill National Bank, Philadelphia, PA; *U.S. Public*, pg. 1159
Thoresen, Guttorm, Pres.--GPA Plast A/S, Ski, Norway; *Int'l*, pg. 678
Thorlakson, Al, Pres. & Chief Exec. Officer--Tolko Industries Ltd., Vernon, Canada; *Int'l*, pg. 1395
Thornburgh, Jeff, Pres.--Dekko Heating Technologies, Inc., Cromwell, IN; *U.S. Private*, pg. 484
Thornburgh, Jeff, Pres.--Dekko Heating Technologies, Inc., Afton, IA; *U.S. Private*, pg. 484
Thornburgh, Jeff, Pres.--Dekko Heating Technologies, Inc., North Webster, IN; *U.S. Private*, pg. 484
Thornburn, Roger, Pres.--Anritsu Wiltron, Morgan Hill, CA; *Int'l*, pg. 77
Thorne, Carl F., Chm. Bd., Pres. & Chief Exec. Officer--Ensco International Incorporated (ENSCO), Dallas, TX; *U.S. Public*, pg. 585
Thorne, Mike, Exec. Dir.--Port of Portland, Portland, OR; *U.S. Private*, pg. 876
Thornhill, Amie, Pres. & Asst. Treas.--Thornhill Oil Company, Inc., Fort Wayne, IN; *U.S. Private*, pg. 1084
Thornhill, Glenn, Pres.--Sea Cliff Water Company, Sea Cliff, NY; *U.S. Public*, pg. 126
Thornhill, Joe, Pres.--Taylor Impression, Inc., Nashville, TN; *U.S. Private*, pg. 1070
Thornton, Dan, Pres.--Scoville Press, Inc., Minneapolis, MN; *U.S. Private*, pg. 977
Thornton, Monte, Pres.-Residential Bus.--Karastan, Calhoun, GA; *U.S. Public*, pg. 1121
Thornton, Peter B., Pres.--Stern & Stern Industries Inc., New York, NY; *U.S. Private*, pg. 1041
Thornton, Robert M., Jr., Pres.--Krug International Corp., Houston, TX; *U.S. Public*, pg. 967
Thornton, T.D., II, Pres. & Treas.--Progress Printing Company, Lynchburg, VA; *U.S. Private*, pg. 890
Thorp, Albert, III, Pres.--Technitrol Investments, Inc., Wilmington, DE; *U.S. Public*, pg. 1564
Thorpe, Albert, III, Pres.--Technitrol International, Inc., Wilmington, DE; *U.S. Public*, pg. 1564
Thorpe, Donald E., Pres.--Hy Vee Weitz Construction, L.C., West Des Moines, IA; *U.S. Private*, pg. 1161
Thorstensson, Robert, Pres.--Skanska Fastigheter Riks AB, Danderyd, Sweden; *Int'l*, pg. 1260
Thrailkill, Howard A., Pres. & Chief Oper. Officer--ADTRAN, Inc., Huntsville, AL; *U.S. Public*, pg. 20
Thrall, Jerome Jeffrey, Pres. & Chief Oper. Officer--Thrall Enterprises, Inc., Chicago, IL; *U.S. Private*, pg. 1084
Thrash, James E., Pres.--Gilbert/Commonwealth International, Inc., Louisville, TN; *U.S. Private*, pg. 841
Thrash, James E., Pres.--Parsons Main, Inc., Boston, MA; *U.S. Private*, pg. 842
Threshie, R. David, Publisher--The Orange County Register, Santa Ana, CA; *U.S. Private*, pg. 425
Throgmartin, Jerry, Pres.--Gregg Appliances Inc., Indianapolis, IN; *U.S. Private*, pg. 479
Thron, John E., Pres.--Programart Corporation, Cambridge, MA; *U.S. Private*, pg. 890
Thron, John E., Pres.--Programart France Incorporated, Clichy, France; *U.S. Private*, pg. 890
Thunell, Lars, Pres. & Chief Exec. Officer--Trygg-Hansa, Stockholm, Sweden; *Int'l*, pg. 1425
Thunell, Lars, Pres.--Trygg-Hansa Insurance Co. Ltd., Stockholm, Sweden; *Int'l*, pg. 1425
Thurman, Ken, Pres.--Thurman Industries, Inc., Bothell, WA; *U.S. Private*, pg. 1084
Thurman, R.H., Exec. V.P. & Grp. Pres.--Rhone-Poulenc Rorer - U.S., Collegeville, PA; *Int'l*, pg. 1110
Thurman, Ron, Vice Adm., Pres.--CAE Electronics Inc.-New York, Leesburg, VA; *Int'l*, pg. 237
Thurston, Jerry L., Pres.--DSM Engineering Plastic Products, Reading, PA; *Int'l*, pg. 354
Thurston, Ray, Pres. & Chief Oper. Officer--Sonic Couriers of Arizona, Inc., Scottsdale, AZ; *U.S. Private*, pg. 1123
Thybony, James D., Pres.--Thybony Wall Coverings Co., Chicago, IL; *U.S. Private*, pg. 1084
Thyen, James C., Pres.--Kimball International, Inc., Jasper, IN; *U.S. Public*, pg. 956
Thygesen, Clifford C., Pres. & Chief Exec. Officer--American Educational Products, Boulder, CO; *U.S. Public*, pg. 71
Tibus, Karen, Pres.--Saturn of Plymouth, Plymouth, MI; *U.S. Private*, pg. 713
Tibus, Karen M., Pres.--Saturn of Okemos, Okemos, MI; *U.S. Private*, pg. 713
Tidball, Robert N., Pres. & Chief Exec. Officer--PLM International, Inc., San Francisco, CA; *U.S. Public*, pg. 1241
Tidball, Robert N., Pres.--Transportation Equipment Corporation, San Francisco, CA; *U.S. Public*, pg. 1241
Tideman, Philip, Chm. Bd. & Pres.--United Power Association, Elk River, MN; *U.S. Private*, pg. 1123
Tidik, Steve, Pres.--Dunbar Sales Inc., City of Commerce, CA; *U.S. Public*, pg. 1720
Tidwell, Jim, Pres.--Heritage Press, Inc., Dallas, TX; *U.S. Public*, pg. 1735
Tierney, Brian P., Pres. & Chief Exec. Officer--Tierney & Partners, Philadelphia, PA; *U.S. Public*, pg. 1641
Tierney, Kathy, Pres.--Smith & Hawken, Mill Valley, CA; *U.S. Public*, pg. 279
Tierney, Richard E., Pres.--Interstate Electronics Corp., Anaheim, CA; *U.S. Public*, pg. 622
Tierney, Thomas T., Pres.--Vitatech International, Inc., Tustin, CA; *U.S. Private*, pg. 1142
Tiffany, James J., Pres.--Stuart Hall Co., Inc., Kansas City, MO; *U.S. Public*, pg. 1178
Tiffin, Robert A., Jr., Pres.--Tiffin Motor Homes, Inc., Red Bay, AL; *U.S. Private*, pg. 1086
Tiger, Francois, Pres. & Chief Exec. Officer-France--DMB&B Paris, Asnieres-sur-Seine, France; *U.S. Private*, pg. 304
Tighe Gaye, Kathleen, Partner-Direct Mktg. Services--Eric Mower and Associates, Inc., Syracuse, NY; *U.S. Private*, pg. 765
Tighe Gaye, Kathleen, Partner-Direct Mktg. Services--Eric Mower and Associates/Buffalo, Inc., Buffalo, NY; *U.S. Private*, pg. 765
Tighe Gaye, Kathleen, Partner-Direct Mktg. Services--Eric Mower and Associates, Rochester, NY; *U.S. Private*, pg. 765
Tighe Gaye, Kathleen, Partner-Direct Mktg. Services--Eric Mower & Associates, Albany, NY; *U.S. Private*, pg. 765
Tighe Gaye, Kathleen, Partner-Direct Mktg. Services--Eric Mower & Associates, Atlanta, GA; *U.S. Private*, pg. 765
Tight, Thomas N., Pres.--First Virginia Insurance Services, Inc., Falls Church, VA; *U.S. Public*, pg. 642
Tikkakoski, Matti, Pres. & Chief Exec. Officer--Polarcup Group Headquarters, Espoo, Finland; *Int'l*, pg. 638
Tilford, Todd, Principal--Jackhammer, Dallas, TX; *U.S. Private*, pg. 929
Tilive, Joanne, Partner--Messner Vetere Berger McNamee Schmetterer/EURO RSCG, New York, NY; *Int'l*, pg. 602
Tillander, Thomas, Pres.--Koret Pierre Cardin, New York, NY; *U.S. Private*, pg. 632
Tilley, Ralph W., Chm. Bd., Pres. & Chief Exec. Officer--Vevay Deposit Bank, Vevay, IN; *U.S. Public*, pg. 633
Tillisch, Christian F., Pres.--GN Netcom A/S, Copenhagen, Denmark; *Int'l*, pg. 537
Tillman, Robert L., Chm. Bd., Pres. & Chief Exec. Officer--Lowe's Companies, Inc., North Wilkesboro, NC; *U.S. Public*, pg. 1015
Tilmant, Michel, Pres. & Chief Exec. Officer--Bank Brussels Lambert, Brussels, Belgium; *Int'l*, pg. 146
Tilton, Glenn F., Chm. & Pres.--TRMI Holdings Inc., Houston, TX; *U.S. Public*, pg. 1583
Timble, James N., Pres. & Chief Exec. Officer--Bearing Headquarters Co., Broadview, IL; *U.S. Private*, pg. 127
Timken, W.R., Jr., Chm. Bd., Pres. & Chief Exec. Officer--The Timken Company, Canton, OH; *U.S. Public*, pg. 1617
Timm, Christopher, Pres.--Environmental & Commercial Insurance, Columbus, OH; *U.S. Public*, pg. 684
Timmerman, William B., Chm. Bd., Pres., Chief Exec. & Oper. Officer--SCANA Corporation, Columbia, SC; *U.S. Public*, pg. 1436
Timmins, Kelley, Pres.--Nautilus International, Independence, VA; *U.S. Public*, pg. 498
Timmons, Dick, Publr.--The Daily News, Rhinelander, WI; *U.S. Public*, pg. 1343
Timms, Peter, Pres.--Dialight Corporation, Manasquan, NJ; *Int'l*, pg. 1130
Timpe, R.E., Pres. & Chief Exec. Officer--Standard Insurance Co., Portland, OR; *U.S. Private*, pg. 1031
Tinberg, Richard W., Pres. & Chief Exec. Officer--Bradford Exchange Ltd., Niles, IL; *U.S. Private*, pg. 163
Tindberg, Gunnar, Pres.--GA Lindberg AB, Kista, Sweden; *Int'l*, pg. 678
Tinder, Richard, Pres.--The American Companies, Inc., Topeka, KS; *U.S. Private*, pg. 52
Ting, James H., Chm., Pres. & Chief Exec. Officer--Semi-Tech Corporation, Markham, Canada; *Int'l*, pg. 1220

Ting, Kenneth, Pres.--Bachmann Industries, Inc., Philadelphia, PA; *U.S. Private*, pg. 109
Tinggren, Jurgen, Pres.--Sika Corporation, Lyndhurst, NJ; *Int'l*, pg. 1249
Tingley, Charles E., Pres. & Chief Exec. Officer--Transamerica Leasing Inc., Purchase, NY; *U.S. Public*, pg. 1630
Tinley, J. Patrick, Pres. & Chief Oper. Officer--Ross Systems, Inc., Atlanta, GA; *U.S. Public*, pg. 1406
Tino, J. Robert, Pres. & Chief Exec. Officer--Sandusky Plastics, Inc., Sandusky, OH; *U.S. Public*, pg. 586
Tinstman, Robert A., Pres. & Chief Exec. Officer--Morrison Knudsen Corporation, Boise, ID; *U.S. Public*, pg. 1133
Tintle, Myles, Pres.--Wilcom Products, Inc., Laconia, NH; *U.S. Public*, pg. 1144
Tipermas, Marc, Pres. & Chief Oper. Officer--ICF Kaiser International Inc., Fairfax, VA; *U.S. Public*, pg. 852
Tisch, James S., Pres. & Chief Oper. Officer--Loews Corporation, New York, NY; *U.S. Public*, pg. 1010
Tisch, Jonathan M., Pres. & Chief Exec. Officer--Loews Hotels, New York, NY; *U.S. Public*, pg. 1011
Tiseo, Benedict, Pres.--NTH Consultants, Ltd., Farmington, MI; *U.S. Private*, pg. 772
Tishman, John L., Chm. Bd. & Pres.--Tishman Realty & Construction Co., Inc., New York, NY; *U.S. Private*, pg. 1089
Tittle, David E., Pres. & Chief Oper. Officer--Cosco Industries, Spring Valley, NY; *U.S. Private*, pg. 277
Titus, Don, Pres.--Kewanee Boiler Manufacturing Company, Inc., Kewanee, IL; *U.S. Public*, pg. 270
Titus, Robert, Pres.--Minuteman Press International, Farmingdale, NY; *U.S. Private*, pg. 752
Tjerandsen, Tom, Pres. & Gen. Mgr.--California Fresh Apricot Council, San Francisco, CA; *U.S. Private*, pg. 200
Toake, Yoshikazu, Pres.--Amano International Trading (Shanghai) Co. Ltd., Shanghai, China; *Int'l*, pg. 71
Toal, Lawrence J., Chm. Bd., Pres. & Chief Exec. Officer--The Dime Savings Bank of New York, New York, NY; *U.S. Public*, pg. 509
Toal, Mike, Pres.--CompPair LeRoi, Sidney, OH; *Int'l*, pg. 1242
Toan, Barrett A., Pres. & Chief Exec. Officer--Express Scripts, Inc., Maryland Heights, MO; *U.S. Public*, pg. 600
Tober, Irwin E., Pres.--Tober Industries, Inc., Saint Louis, MO; *U.S. Private*, pg. 1089
Tober, Lester V., Chm. Bd. & Chief Exec. Officer--Tober Industries, Inc., Saint Louis, MO; *U.S. Private*, pg. 1089
Tober, Lester V., Pres.--World Import Co., Saint Louis, MO; *U.S. Private*, pg. 1089
Toberman, Allen, Pres.--Toberman, Clayton, MO; *U.S. Private*, pg. 1089
Tobey, Gary, Pres. & Chief Exec. Officer--Haworth Group Inc., Minneapolis, MN; *U.S. Private*, pg. 511
Tobey, Gary, Pres. & Chief Exec. Officer--The Haworth Group, Inc., Los Angeles, CA; *U.S. Private*, pg. 511
Tobiason, Allan, Pres.--Fenton Press, Inc., Addison, IL; *U.S. Private*, pg. 400
Tobin, James R., Pres. & Chief Exec. Officer--Biogen, Inc., Cambridge, MA; *U.S. Public*, pg. 230
Tockarshewsky, Joseph B., Chm. Bd., Pres. & Chief Exec. Officer--Poughkeepsie Financial Corp., Poughkeepsie, NY; *U.S. Public*, pg. 1319
Tod, G. Robert, Pres. & Chief Oper. Officer--CML Group, Inc., Acton, MA; *U.S. Public*, pg. 279
Tod, G. Robert, Pres. & Chief Exec. Officer--NordicTrack, Inc., Chaska, MN; *U.S. Public*, pg. 279
Todaro, Ralph, Pres.--Pacific Library Tower, Los Angeles, CA; *U.S. Public*, pg. 1249
Todd, A.J., III, Pres.--A.M. Todd Company, Kalamazoo, MI; *U.S. Private*, pg. 1089
Todd, J.L., Chm. Bd. & Pres.--J.L. Todd Auction Co., Rome, GA; *U.S. Private*, pg. 1090
Todd, Paul, Jr., Pres.--Kalamazoo Holdings, Inc., Kalamazoo, MI; *U.S. Private*, pg. 606
Todd, S., Pres.--Rolls-Royce Industries Canada Inc., Lachine, Canada; *Int'l*, pg. 1127
Toellner, Fritz, Pres.--Cardinal EG Saws Corp., Elk Grove Village, IL; *Int'l*, pg. 228
Toffolo, Dennis, Pres.--Hudson's, Southfield, MI; *U.S. Public*, pg. 489
Tognietti, Terry, Co-Chief Exec. Officer--Dryper's Corp., Vancouver, WA; *U.S. Private*, pg. 344
Togo, Shigeoki, Pres.--The Nippon Credit Bank, Ltd., Tokyo, Japan; *Int'l*, pg. 932
Tointon, Robert G., Pres.--Phelps Tointon Inc., Greeley, CO; *U.S. Private*, pg. 860
Tojek, Gile, Pres.--Iochpe-Maxion Ohio, Inc., Cleveland, OH; *Int'l*, pg. 688
Tokiwa, Fumikatsu, Pres.--Kao Corporation, Tokyo, Japan; *Int'l*, pg. 717
Tokumaru, Kohsuki, Dep. Pres.--Daishowa Paper Mfg. Co., Ltd., Fuji, Japan; *Int'l*, pg. 373
Tokuzumi, Mario Masayoshi, Pres.--Rohm Electronics Brasil Ltda., Sao Paulo, Brazil; *Int'l*, pg. 1125
Toland, R.F., Pres.--Temperature Equipment Corporation, Lansing, IL; *U.S. Private*, pg. 1075
Toland, Richard E., Pres.--KPL, Topeka, KS; *U.S. Public*, pg. 1759
Tolaney, Murli, Chm. Bd., Pres. & Chief Exec. Officer--Montgomery Watson, Pasadena, CA; *U.S. Private*, pg. 759
Toledo, Gabriel, Dir. Gen.--Praxair Espania S.A., Madrid, Spain; *U.S. Public*, pg. 1320
Toler, John, Pres. & Chief Exec. Officer--Little Switzerland, Inc., Charlotte Amalie, VI; *U.S. Public*, pg. 1001
Toll, Bruce E., Pres., Chief Oper. Officer & Sec.--Toll Brothers, Inc., Huntingdon Valley, PA; *U.S. Public*, pg. 1620
Tolliver, Ron, Pres. & Chief Exec. Officer--Interactive Telecard Services, Inc. (ITS), Miami, FL; *U.S. Private*, pg. 566
Tollman, Brett G., Pres.--Tollman/Hundley Hotels, Hopewell Junction, NY; *U.S. Private*, pg. 1090
Tolone, Thomas A., Pres. & Chief Oper. Officer--Paoli, Inc., Orleans, IN; *U.S. Private*, pg. 837
Tolson, Ray H., Chm. Bd., Pres. & Chief Exec. Officer--Pride International, Inc., Houston, TX; *U.S. Public*, pg. 1324
Tomasetta, Louis R., Pres. & Chief Exec. Officer--Vitesse Semiconductor Corporation, Camarillo, CA; *U.S. Public*, pg. 1723
Tomasetti, Thomas, Pres. & Chief Exec. Officer--Consilium, Inc., Mountain View, CA; *U.S. Public*, pg. 434
Tomasso, Donald C., Pres.--Manor Care, Inc., Gaithersburg, MD; *U.S. Public*, pg. 1041
Tombros, Peter, Pres. & Chief Exec. Officer--Enzon, Inc., Piscataway, NJ; *U.S. Public*, pg. 587
Tomchin, Lawrence, Pres. & Chief Oper. Officer--Rex Stores Corp., Dayton, OH; *U.S. Public*, pg. 1384
Tomeu, Enrique A., Pres. & Chief Exec. Officer--ECOS Group, Inc., West Palm Beach, FL; *U.S. Public*, pg. 563
Tomislav Antoni Zinner, Tomas, Pres.--Uniao de Bancos Brasileiros S.A. (Unibanco), Sao Paulo, Brazil; *Int'l*, pg. 1431
Tomita, Hiroshi, Pres.--Citic Golden Tiger Group Co., Ltd., Beijing, China; *Int'l*, pg. 579
Tomita, Kanji, Pres.--Daido Steel Co., Ltd., Nagoya, Japan; *Int'l*, pg. 364
Tomita, Ushio, Pres.--Sampo Techno Construction Co., Ltd., Toyokawa, Japan; *Int'l*, pg. 764
Tomito, Kazuhiro, Pres.--Otsuka Tokyo Assay Laboratories Inc., Tokyo, Japan; *Int'l*, pg. 1013
Tomiyama, Tsuguo, Pres. & Chief Exec. Officer--DIC Trading (USA) Inc., Fort Lee, NJ; *Int'l*, pg. 369
Tomjack, Thomas J., Chm Bd. & Pres.--North Pacific Lumber Company, Portland, OR; *U.S. Private*, pg. 805
Tomkins, Trevor, Dr., Pres. & Chief Oper. Officer--Milk Specialties Company, Dundee, IL; *U.S. Private*, pg. 746
Tomlin, Eugene B., Pres. & Chief Exec. Officer--I.H. French & Co. Inc., Champaign, IL; *U.S. Private*, pg. 427
Tomlinson, John W., Pres.--Monumental Millwork, Inc., Westminster, MD; *U.S. Private*, pg. 759
Tomlinson, Philip W., Pres.--Total System Services, Inc., Columbus, GA; *U.S. Public*, pg. 1550
Tomlinson, Vince, Co-Pres.--Schroff, Straubenhardt, Germany; *U.S. Public*, pg. 1274
Tomono, Norio, Pres.--Chiyoda Life Realty France S.A., Courbevoie, France; *Int'l*, pg. 287
Tompkins, J. Richard, Chm. Bd. & Pres.--Middlesex Water Company, Iselin, NJ; *U.S. Public*, pg. 1110
Tompkins, J. Richard, Pres.--Utility Service Affiliates, Inc., Iselin, NJ; *U.S. Public*, pg. 1110
Tompkins, Richard, Pres.--Diamond Electronics, Inc., Carroll, OH; *U.S. Public*, pg. 1663
Tompkins, S. Craig, Pres.--Craig Corporation, Los Angeles, CA; *U.S. Public*, pg. 456
Toms, Nick, Pres.--Edwardstone & Company, Inc., New York, NY; *U.S. Private*, pg. 365
Toms, Nick, Pres.--Toms Sierra Company, Colfax, CA; *U.S. Private*, pg. 1090
Tomsich, Robert J., Chm. Bd.--NESCO, Inc., Cleveland, OH; *U.S. Private*, pg. 791
Tonaka, Kiichiro, Pres.--NCR-Japan Ltd., Toyko, Japan; *U.S. Public*, pg. 1146
Tondulykul, Boonsong, Pres.--Bangkok Rubber Public Co., Ltd., Bangkok, Thailand; *Int'l*, pg. 146
Tonge, Charles R., Pres.--Harris Bank Barrington, N.A., Barrington, IL; *Int'l*, pg. 154
Tongson, Mario M., Pres.--Union Carbide Philippines (Far East) Inc., Manila, Philippines; *U.S. Public*, pg. 1667
Tonkon, Ed, Pres. & Gen. Mgr.--Huffy Service First, Inc., Miamisburg, OH; *U.S. Public*, pg. 846
Tonn, Jorg, Pres.--Dachser GmbH & Co., Kempten, Germany; *Int'l*, pg. 356
Tonseth, Erik, Grp. Pres. & Chief Exec. Officer-Kvaerner a.s.--Kvaerner a.s.a., Lysaker, Norway; *Int'l*, pg. 766
Tonseth, Erik, Pres. & Chief Exec. Officer--Kvaerner a.s, Oslo, Norway; *Int'l*, pg. 766
Toohey, Patrick A., Pres.--Associated Administrators, Inc., Portland, OR; *U.S. Private*, pg. 918
Tooker, Carl, Pres., Chief Exec. Officer--Stage Stores, Inc., Houston, TX; *U.S. Private*, pg. 1028
Toole, David J., Pres. & Chief Exec. Officer--GaSonics International, San Jose, CA; *U.S. Public*, pg. 703
Tooley, Roger, Pres.--Flowers Baking Co. of Jamestown, Inc., Jamestown, NC; *U.S. Public*, pg. 657
Toolson, Kay L., Chm. Bd., Pres. & Chief Exec. Officer--Monaco Coach Corporation, Coburg, OR; *U.S. Public*, pg. 1123
Toombs, Eugene M., Pres. & Chief Exec. Officer--MiTek, Inc., Chesterfield, MO; *Int'l*, pg. 1106
Toran, Daniel J., Pres. & Chief Oper. Officer--The Penn Mutual Life Insurance Company, Philadelphia, PA; *U.S. Private*, pg. 849
Torcasio, Anthony J., Pres. & Chief Exec. Officer & Vice Chm.-TMDSC--May Merchandising Company, Saint Louis, MO; *U.S. Public*, pg. 1064
Torcolini, Robert J., Pres.--Dynamet Inc., Washington, PA; *U.S. Public*, pg. 307
Toresco, Donald, Pres.--Ocean Chevrolet, Inc., Toms River, NJ; *U.S. Private*, pg. 810
Toresco, Donald, Pres.--Toresco Enterprises, Springfield, NJ; *U.S. Private*, pg. 1092
Torgersen, Helge, Pres.--Chr. Hansen AS, Oslo, Norway; *Int'l*, pg. 289
Torian, Henry, Owner--Tasha, Fremont, CA; *U.S. Private*, pg. 1069
Torii, Shinichiro, Pres.--Suntory Ltd., Osaka, Japan; *Int'l*, pg. 1321
Torinus, John B., Jr., Chm. Bd. & Chief Exec. Officer--Serigraph, Inc., West Bend, WI; *U.S. Private*, pg. 985
Toriumi, Iwao, Pres.--Marubeni Corporation, Osaka, Japan; *Int'l*, pg. 844
Torke, Michael J., Pres.--Fleet Mortgage Group, Inc., Columbia, SC; *U.S. Public*, pg. 650
Torke, Ward J., Pres.--Torke Coffee Roasting Company, Sheboygan, WI; *U.S. Private*, pg. 1092
Tornich, F., Chm.--Italimpianti S.p.A., Genoa, Italy; *Int'l*, pg. 654
Tornquist, Ulf, Pres.--NCC Building, Orebro, Sweden; *Int'l*, pg. 898
Torrens, Frank J., Pres. & Chief Exec. Officer--Elopak, Inc., New Hudson, MI; *Int'l*, pg. 1390
Torrington, Timothy F., Chm. Bd. & Pres.--Atlapac Trading Company, Inc., Los Angeles, CA; *U.S. Private*, pg. 96
Torris, Jean-Paul, Gen. Mgr.--BG SAS, Le Tholy, France; *Int'l*, pg. 201
Torstenson, Robert H., Chm. Bd. & Pres.--Duo-Fast Corporation, Huntley, IL; *U.S. Private*, pg. 347
Tortellot, Peter L., Pres. & Chief Oper. Officer--Carolina Biological Supply Co., Burlington, NC; *U.S. Private*, pg. 213
Torton, Shay, Pres.--American Fine Wire Corp., Selma, AL; *U.S. Public*, pg. 969
Tortoriello, Anthony M., Chm. Bd. & Pres.--Torco Oil Co., Chicago, IL; *U.S. Private*, pg. 1092
Torum, Alf Richard, Pres.--Kvaerner Ships Equipment a.s Dubai Branch, Dubai, United Arab Emirates; *Int'l*, pg. 768
Tory, John H., Q.C., Pres. & Chief Exec. Officer--Maclean Hunter Publishing Ltd., Toronto, Canada; *Int'l*, pg. 1123
Tosi, Mark, Pres.--The Pastene Companies Ltd., Canton, MA; *U.S. Private*, pg. 842
Tosto, Leo R., Pres.--Trerice Tosto Colliers International, Bingham Farms, MI; *U.S. Private*, pg. 1099
Toth, Michael C., Chm. Bd., Pres. & New Bus. Contact--Toth Design, Concord, MA; *U.S. Private*, pg. 1093
Toth, Richard, Pres.--New England Dairies, Inc., Hartford, CT; *U.S. Private*, pg. 793
Toth, Steve, Jr., Chm. Bd., Pres. & Exec. V.P.--VSI Holdings, Inc., Bloomfield Hills, MI; *U.S. Public*, pg. 1703
Tott, Carl, Pres.--The Tog Shop, Americus, GA; *U.S. Private*, pg. 1090
Totten, David, Pres.--Totten Tubes, Inc., Los Angeles, CA; *U.S. Private*, pg. 1093
Tough, Doug, Pres.-Europe, Africa, Middle East--Schweppes Europe Limited, Watford, United Kingdom; *Int'l*, pg. 248
Touhey, Carl E., Pres. & Treas.--Orange Motor Company Inc., Albany, NY; *U.S. Private*, pg. 818
Toups, Roland, Pres.--Turner Industries, Baton Rouge, LA; *U.S. Private*, pg. 1109
Tous, Francese, Pres.--Leaf Iberia S.A., Barcelona, Spain; *Int'l*, pg. 638
Towatari, H., Pres.--Sharp Corporation of Australia Pty. Ltd., Blacktown, Australia; *Int'l*, pg. 1229
Tower, H.L., III, Chm. Bd., Pres. & Chief Exec. Officer--Stanhome Inc., Westfield, MA; *U.S. Public*, pg. 1508
Town, Joe, Pres.--The Blodgett Oven Co., Inc., Burlington, VT; *U.S. Public*, pg. 1064
Townes, Stephen, Pres.--SabreTech, Inc., Phoenix, AZ; *U.S. Private*, pg. 959
Townsend, D., Pres., Chief Exec. Officer & Gen. Mgr.--Simpson Dura-Vent Co., Inc., Vacaville, CA; *U.S. Public*, pg. 1474
Townsend, Donald W., Pres.--Simula, Inc., Phoenix, AZ; *U.S. Public*, pg. 1475
Townsend, Ernest W., Pres. & Chief Oper. Officer--Frank's Nursery & Crafts, Inc., Detroit, MI; *U.S. Public*, pg. 715
Townsend, Ted, Pres.--Townsend Engineering Co., Des Moines, IA; *U.S. Private*, pg. 1094
Townsend, Thomas, Pres.--Kentucky Hydrocarbon Division, Langley, KY; *U.S. Public*, pg. 589
Toyama, Noriyuki, Pres.--Banyu Pharmaceutical Co. Ltd., Tokyo, Japan; *U.S. Public*, pg. 1091
Toyama, Yoji, Pres.--Mazda Motor of America, Inc., Irvine, CA; *Int'l*, pg. 849
Toyama, Yoji, Pres.--Mazda (North America), Inc., Irvine, CA; *Int'l*, pg. 849
Toyoda, Kanshiro, Pres.--Aisin Seiki Co. Ltd., Kariya, Japan; *Int'l*, pg. 39
Toyoda, Kuni, Pres. & Chief Exec. Officer--Seed Restaurant Group, Inc., Lexington, KY; *U.S. Private*, pg. 981
Toyokawa, Hiroshi, Pres.--Okura & Co., Tokyo, Japan; *Int'l*, pg. 1001
Toyomaru, Koichi, Pres. & Chief Exec. Officer--Nippon Life Insurance Company of America, New York, NY; *Int'l*, pg. 935
Trachtenberg, Joseph M., Chm. Bd. & Chief Exec. Officer--Victaulic Company of America, Easton, PA; *U.S. Private*, pg. 1138
Tracy, Lawrence R., Pres.--Radionics, Inc., Salinas, CA; *U.S. Public*, pg. 501
Tracy, William A., Acting Pres.--Cleveland Thermal Energy Corporation, Cleveland, OH; *U.S. Public*, pg. 913
Tracy, William A., Acting Pres.--Cleveland District Cooling Corp., Cleveland, OH; *U.S. Public*, pg. 913
Traeger, Peter, Pres. & Chief Exec. Officer--Artistic Carton Company, Elgin, IL; *U.S. Private*, pg. 87
Trafton, Stephen J., Chm. Bd., Pres., Chief Exec. Officer & Chief Oper. Officer--Glendale Federal Bank, F.S.B., Glendale, CA; *U.S. Public*, pg. 747
Trahan, Guy, Pres.--Imprimerie Quebecor Montreal, Montreal, Canada; *Int'l*, pg. 1077
Train, Mark, Pres. & Sec.--Jason Incorporated, Milwaukee, WI; *U.S. Public*, pg. 923
Trainor, Edward J., Pres. & Chief Exec. Officer--Standex International Corporation, Salem, NH; *U.S. Public*, pg. 1505
Trainor, James J., Pres.--Federal Business Products, Inc., Clifton, NJ; *U.S. Public*, pg. 398
Trallo, Ralph A., Pres. & Chief Exec. Officer--Canisco Resources, Inc., Wilmington, DE; *U.S. Public*, pg. 301
Tran, Henri, Pres.--PTDBS Securities Indonesia, Jakarta, Indonesia; *Int'l*, pg. 351
Tran, Thinh Q., Chm. Bd. & Chief Exec. Officer--Sigma Designs, Inc., Fremont, CA; *U.S. Public*, pg. 1472
Trani, John M., Pres. & Chief Exec. Officer--G.E. Medical Systems, Milwaukee, WI; *U.S. Public*, pg. 710
Trapani, Kevin A., Pres.--The Redwoods Group, Morrisville, NC; *U.S. Private*, pg. 430
Trapp, Donald, Pres.--Leson Chevrolet Company, Inc., Harvey, LA; *U.S. Private*, pg. 660

Traut, Joseph, Pres.--AT Information Products, Mahwah, NJ; *U.S. Private*, pg. 8
Trauth, David E., Chm. Bd., Pres. & Chief Exec. Officer--Trauth Dairy Inc., Newport, KY; *U.S. Private*, pg. 1098
Travis, Timothy J., Pres. & Chief Exec. Officer--Eaton Metal Products Company, Denver, CO; *U.S. Private*, pg. 358
Trawick, Jack D., Pres.--STRAFCO, Inc., San Antonio, TX; *U.S. Private*, pg. 1046
Traylor, Alan, Pres.--Alnor Instrument Company, Skokie, IL; *U.S. Public*, pg. 1559
Traylor, Steve, Pres. & Chief Exec. Officer--Regions Bank/Santa Rosa County, Pensacola, FL; *U.S. Public*, pg. 1372
Traylor, Thomas W., Pres.--Traylor Brothers, Inc., Evansville, IN; *U.S. Private*, pg. 1098
Traynor, Michael, Pres.--Haws Drinking Faucet Co., Berkeley, CA; *U.S. Private*, pg. 512
Trbovich, Dr. Nicholas D., Chm. Bd. & Pres.--Servotronics, Inc., Elma, NY; *U.S. Public*, pg. 1462
Treace, James T., Chm. Bd., Pres. & Cheif Exec. Officer--Xomed Surgical Products, Jacksonville, FL; *U.S. Public*, pg. 253
Treadaway, Randy, Pres.--Marco Color Labs, Inc., Hawthorne, CA; *U.S. Private*, pg. 702
Trebel, John, Pres. & Chief Exec. Officer--Waterloo Industries, Inc., Waterloo, IA; *U.S. Public*, pg. 675
Trebilcock, William, Pres.--Mid Continent Bottlers, Inc, West Des Moines, IA; *U.S. Private*, pg. 142
Tredennick, Curtis, Pres. & Chief Exec. Officer--Resco Products, Inc., Conshohocken, PA; *U.S. Private*, pg. 924
Tredinnick, Richard, Pres. & Chief Exec. Officer--Old America Stores, Howe, TX; *U.S. Public*, pg. 1215
Treffiletti, Joseph A., Pres.--J. Treffiletti & Sons, Inc., Albany, NY; *U.S. Private*, pg. 1099
Tregurtha, Paul R., Chm. Bd. & Pres.--Mormac Marine Transport, Inc., Stamford, CT; *U.S. Private*, pg. 762
Treiber, Walter G., Jr., Pres. & Chief Oper. Officer--Chicago White Metal Casting, Inc., Bensenville, IL; *U.S. Private*, pg. 236
Treinin, Thomas F., Chm. Bd. & Pres.--Special Devices, Incorporated, Newhall, CA; *U.S. Public*, pg. 1496
Treis, Donald J., Pres. & Chief Oper. Officer--Arandell Corporation, Menomonee Falls, WI; *U.S. Private*, pg. 79
Treis, Donald J., Pres. & Chief Oper. Officer--Arandell-Schmidt, Menomonee Falls, WI; *U.S. Private*, pg. 79
Tremaine, B.G., III, Pres.--The Miller Company, Meriden, CT; *U.S. Private*, pg. 746
Tremaine, B.G., Jr., Chm. Bd.--The Miller Company, Meriden, CT; *U.S. Private*, pg. 746
Tremblay, Marcel J., Pres. & Chief Exec. Officer--EnerMark Income Fund, Calgary, Canada; *Int'l*, pg. 454
Tremblay, Rene, Pres. & Chief Oper. Officer--Ivanhoe, Montreal, Canada; *Int'l*, pg. 249
Tremont, Dr. Edmund, Pres.--Novavax Inc., Rockville, MD; *U.S. Public*, pg. 855
Trenkamp, Robert, Pres. & Chief Exec. Officer--Prepress Solutions, Inc., Billerica, MA; *U.S. Private*, pg. 882
Treonis, Norm, Pres.-Inland Property Management Group, Inc.--The Inland Group, Inc., Oak Brook, IL; *U.S. Private*, *pg. 564*
Trepicchio, Michael J., Pres. & Chief Oper. Officer--Klemtner Advertising Inc., New York, NY; *U.S. Public*, pg. 1422
Trevino, Alex, Jr., Chm. Bd., Pres. & Chief Exec. Officer--ACR Group, Houston, TX; *U.S. Public*, pg. 3
Trevino, Carlos, Pres.--Aerolitoral, Nuevo Leon, Mexico; *Int'l*, pg. 332
Trevino, Jose, Pres.--Mark Net World, Mequon, WI; *U.S. Private*, pg. 108
Trevvett, Herbert E., Pres. & Chief Exec. Officer--Commercial Travelers Mutual Insurance Company, Utica, NY; *U.S. Private*, pg. 258
Trewhella, Raymond M., Pres. & Chief Oper. Officer--Glassmaster Company, Lexington, SC; *U.S. Public*, pg. 745
Trexler, Terry E., Chm. Bd. & Pres.--Nobility Homes, Inc., Ocala, FL; *U.S. Public*, pg. 1186
Treyllys, Jean-Noel, Pres.--Lipha Chemicals S.A., Lyon, France; *Int'l*, pg. 812
Triant, Deborah, Pres. & Chief Exec. Officer--Check Point Software Technologies Inc., Redwood City, CA; *U.S. Public*, pg. 342
Tribel, Philip, Pres.--Tipper Tie, Inc., Apex, NC; *U.S. Public*, pg. 520
Tribone, Thomas A., Pres.--AES Americas, Arlington, VA; *U.S. Public*, pg. 5
Tribull, Christoph, Chm. Bd., Pres., Chief Exec. Officer & Chief Oper. Officer--Sierracin Corporation, Sylmar, CA; *U.S. Private*, pg. 999
Trice, Robert H., Pres.--The Boeing Company, London, United Kingdom; *U.S. Public*, pg. 242
Triggs, Donald, Pres. & Chief Exec. Officer--Vincor International, Niagara Falls, Canada; *Int'l*, pg. 1468
Trimble, Charles R., Chm. Bd., Pres. & Chief Exec. Officer--Trimble Navigation Limited, Sunnyvale, CA; *U.S. Public*, pg. 1638
Trimble, William S., Jr., Pres.--Wm. S. Trimble Company, Inc., Knoxville, TN; *U.S. Private*, pg. 1103
Trinchero, Roger J., Pres.--Sutter Home Winery, Inc., Saint Helena, CA; *U.S. Private*, pg. 1057
Trinkle, Robert C., Pres.--Trinkle Sales, Inc., Cherry Hill, NJ; *U.S. Private*, pg. 1103
Trinkunas, Julius, Pres.--Lagoven, S.A., Caracas, Venezuela; *Int'l*, pg. 1045
Tripp, Doug, Pres.--Pulte Tampa Division, Tampa, FL; *U.S. Public*, pg. 1345
Tripp, Maxwell L., Pres.--Willcox & Gibbs, Inc., Carteret, NJ; *U.S. Private*, pg. 1177
Trippitelli, Gerard J., Pres. & Chief Exec. Officer--Matlack Systems, Inc., Wilmington, DE; *U.S. Public*, pg. 1057
Trisler, James, Pres.--Paramount Fitness Corp., Los Angeles, CA; *U.S. Private*, pg. 838
Tritt, John R., Pres.--QA Products, Inc., Elk Grove Village, IL; *Int'l*, pg. 244
Trofholz, LeRoy, Pres. & Chief Exec. Officer--Wagner Mills Inc., Schuyler, NE; *U.S. Private*, pg. 1146
Troger, Jay R., Pres. & Chief Exec. Officer--Transportation Technologies, Inc., Washington, NC; *U.S. Private*, pg. 1097
Troger, Jay R., Pres. & Chief Exec. Officer--Hackney and Sons, Inc., Washington, NC; *U.S. Private*, pg. 1097
Troncalli, Charles D., Pres.--Troncalli Motors, Inc., Decatur, GA; *U.S. Private*, pg. 1104
Tropeano, Anthony, Dr., Pres.--Hunter Engineering Co., Inc., Riverside, CA; *Int'l*, pg. 474
Troschow, Michael, Pres. & Chief Exec. Officer--White Consolidated Industries, Inc., Cleveland, OH; *Int'l*, pg. 439
Trotman, Alexander J., Chm. Bd., Pres. & Chief Exec. Officer--Ford Motor Company, Dearborn, MI; *U.S. Public*, *pg. 661*
Trotman, William, Pres. & Gen. Mgr.--Gould Electronics Inc., Shawmut Circuit Protection Division, Newburyport, MA; *U.S. Public*, pg. 1592
Trott, Ralph, Pres. & Chief Exec. Officer--Beaver Lumber Company Limited, Markham, Canada; *Int'l*, pg. 887
Trotter, Lloyd G., Pres. & Chief Exec. Officer--G.E. Electric Distribution & Control Manufacturing, Plainville, CT; *U.S. Public*, pg. 710
Trotter, Phillip, Pres. & Chief Exec. Officer--Vanguard Energy Corp., Houston, TX; *U.S. Private*, pg. 1133
Trotter, Thomas R., Pres. & Chief Exec. Officer--Orthologic Corporation, Tempe, AZ; *U.S. Public*, pg. 1232
Troup, Brian M., Pres. & Chief Oper. Officer--The Hallwood Group Incorporated, Dallas, TX; *U.S. Public*, pg. 777
Troupe, Terry L., Pres.--MBC Agency, Inc., Baltimore, MD; *U.S. Public*, pg. 1089
Trouse, Wayne, Pres.--Hermes Electronics, Inc., Dartmouth, Canada; *Int'l*, pg. 1431
Troutman, F. Gil Jr., Pres. & Chief Exec. Officer--DSP Technology Inc., Fremont, CA; *U.S. Public*, pg. 475
Troutman, William M., Pres. & Chief Exec. Officer--Lone Star Industries, Inc., Stamford, CT; *U.S. Public*, pg. 1012
Troyer, Cliff, Pres.--Troyer Potato Products, Inc., Waterford, PA; *U.S. Private*, pg. 1106
Troyer, Kermit, Pres. & Chief Oper. Officer--Troyer Foods, Inc., Goshen, IN; *Int'l*, pg. 619
Trubatsch, Gustav, Pres.--Castrol Austria GmbH, Wiener Neustadt, Austria; *Int'l*, pg. 235
Trubisz, Anthony, Jr., Pres.--Columbia Energy Services Corporation, Pittsburgh, PA; *U.S. Public*, pg. 402
Truchard, James J., Chm. Bd., Pres. & Chief Exec. Officer--National Instruments Corp., Austin, TX; *U.S. Public*, pg. 1157
Truchi, David, Pres. & Chief Exec. Officer--Trucchis Markets, Raynham, MA; *U.S. Private*, pg. 1107
Trucksess, William, Pres.--Philadelphia Sign Company, Palmyra, NJ; *U.S. Private*, pg. 861
Trudel, Michel, Pres. & Chief Exec. Officer--Inglis Limited, Mississauga, Canada; *U.S. Public*, pg. 1765
True, Harry S., Pres.--Graham Paint and Varnish Company, Chicago, IL; *U.S. Private*, pg. 468
Truesdell, J.E., Jr., Pres. & Sec.--Austin Group, Flint, MI; *U.S. Private*, pg. 99
Trugman, Leonard A., Chm. Bd., Pres. & Chief Exec. Officer--Del Global Technologies, Valhalla, NY; *U.S. Public*, pg. 493
Truitt, Roger E., Pres.--ARCO Products Co., Los Angeles, CA; *U.S. Public*, pg. 144
Trullinger, Fred L., Pres.--The Chas. H. Lilly Co., Portland, OR; *U.S. Private*, pg. 667
Trump, Donald J., Pres.--Trump Organization, New York, NY; *U.S. Private*, pg. 1108
Trump, Eddie, Pres.--The Trump Group, Miami, FL; *U.S. Private*, pg. 1107
Trussler, Gary J., Pres.--ACCO Europe Plc, Peterborough, United Kingdom; *U.S. Public*, pg. 674
Tryon, Michael, Pres.--Harris Waste Mgmt. Group, Inc., Peachtree City, GA; *Int'l*, pg. 473
Tsaggaris, Lex, Pres.--DQE Energy Services, Pittsburgh, PA; *U.S. Public*, pg. 474
Tsai, Mar-Ling, Pres.--China Hi-Ment Corp., Kao-hsiung, Taiwan; *Int'l*, pg. 285
Tsampalieros, Gabriel, Pres. & Chief Oper. Officer--Cara Operations Limited, Toronto, Canada; *Int'l*, pg. 266
Tschudin, Jean-Charles, Pres.--R.P. Scherer (Europe) AG, Zug, Switzerland; *U.S. Public*, pg. 1438
Tskukimura, Ray R., Pres.--Aerotest Operations, Inc., San Ramon, CA; *U.S. Public*, pg. 1207
Tsuboi, Takayori, Pres.--Mitsubishi Chemical America, Inc., White Plains, NY; *Int'l*, pg. 871
Tsubokawa, Norio, Pres. & Chief Exec. Officer--YKK Corporation of America, Lyndhurst, NJ; *Int'l*, pg. 1515
Tsuchida, Toru, Pres.--Nomura Asset Management Co., Ltd., Tokyo, Japan; *Int'l*, pg. 955
Tsuda, Kosuke, Pres.--Sumitomo Chemical (U.K.) plc, London, United Kingdom; *Int'l*, pg. 1312
Tsuda, Shoji, Pres. & Chief Exec. Officer--Mitsukoshi, Ltd., Tokyo, Japan; *Int'l*, pg. 883
Tsue, Kakuichi, Pres.--Kvaerner Pulping KK, Tokyo, Japan; *Int'l*, pg. 768
Tsui, Cyrus Y., Chm. Bd., Pres. & Chief Exec. Officer--Lattice Semiconductor Corporation, Hillsboro, OR; *U.S. Public*, pg. 979
Tsui, John K, Pres. & Chief Oper. Officer--First Hawaiian Bank, Honolulu, HI; *U.S. Public*, pg. 634
Tsui, John K., Pres.--First Hawaiian, Inc., Honolulu, HI; *U.S. Public*, pg. 634
Tsui, John K., Pres.--FHB Properties, Inc., Honolulu, HI; *U.S. Public*, pg. 635
Tsui, John K., Pres.--Real Estate Delivery, Inc., Honolulu, HI; *U.S. Public*, pg. 635
Tsui, John K., Pres.--American Security Properties, Inc., Honolulu, HI; *U.S. Public*, pg. 635
Tsuji, Akihiro, Pres.--Tomen Corporation, Osaka, Japan; *Int'l*, pg. 1395
Tsuji, Haruo, Pres.--Sharp Corporation, Osaka, Japan; *Int'l*, pg. 1228
Tsuji, Kaoru, Pres.--Tokuyama Corporation, Tokyo, Japan; *Int'l*, pg. 1393
Tsuji, Nobuo, Pres.--Nissho Iwai France S.A., Paris, France; *Int'l*, pg. 948
Tsujimoto, Y., Pres.--Sharp Manufacturing France S.A., Soultz, France; *Int'l*, pg. 1230
Tsuka, Masayoshi, Pres.--Koei Chemical Company, Ltd., Osaka, Japan; *Int'l*, pg. 1311
Tsukada, E., Pres.--Nissho Iwai Apparel Co., Ltd., Osaka, Japan; *Int'l*, pg. 946
Tsukada, E., Pres.--Nissho Iwai Fiber & Yarn Ltd., Osaka, Japan; *Int'l*, pg. 946
Tsukahara, Kazuhiro, Pres.--Kirin USA, Inc., Los Angeles, CA; *Int'l*, pg. 736
Tsukamoto, Yoshikata, Pres.--Wacoal Corporation, Kyoto, Japan; *Int'l*, pg. 1484
Tsukiji, Yoshinori, Pres. Dir.--P.T. ORIX Indonesia Finance, Jakarta, Indonesia; *Int'l*, pg. 1009
Tsukuda, Ryoji, Pres.--The Bank of Fukuoka, Ltd., Fukuoka, Japan; *Int'l*, pg. 152
Tsumuro, Takao, Pres.--Obayashi Corporation, Tokyo, Japan; *Int'l*, pg. 995
Tsunemi, Hideo, Pres.--Ashikaga Bank, Tochigi, Japan; *Int'l*, *pg. 88*
Tsunoda, Ichiro, Pres.--Nomura Babcock & Brown Co., Ltd., Tokyo, Japan; *Int'l*, pg. 955
Tsuru, T., Pres.--Eagle Industry, Ltd., Tokyo, Japan; *U.S. Public*, pg. 544
Tsuruta, Takuhiko, Pres. & Chief Exec. Officer--Nihon Keizai Shimbun, Inc., Tokyo, Japan; *Int'l*, pg. 929
Tsurutani, Masatoshi, Pres.--Kawasaki Motors Corp., U.S.A., Irvine, CA; *Int'l*, pg. 725
Tsutsui, Yasuo, Pres.--Otsuka Techno Co., Ltd., Tokushima, Japan; *Int'l*, pg. 1013
Tu, John, Pres.--Kingston Technology Corporation, Fountain Valley, CA; *U.S. Private*, pg. 622
Tu, Way, Pres.--Lam Research Corporation, Fremont, CA; *U.S. Public*, pg. 975
Tu, Wen-Hu, Chm. Bd., Pres. & Chief Exec. Officer--Transico Incorporated, Santa Ana, CA; *U.S. Public*, pg. 1630
Tuchel, Charles, Pres.--Universal Flavors-U.S.A., Indianapolis, IN; *U.S. Public*, pg. 1696
Tuck, William M., Pres.--Crouse-Hinds, Syracuse, NY; *U.S. Public*, pg. 444
Tucker, Dale, Pres.--Eagle Window & Door, Inc., Dubuque, IA; *U.S. Public*, pg. 67
Tucker, F. Louis, Jr., Pres.--Mustang Tractor & Equip. Co., Houston, TX; *U.S. Private*, pg. 768
Tucker, Garland, Pres. & Chief Exec. Officer--First Travelcorp Inc., Raleigh, NC; *U.S. Private*, pg. 408
Tucker, Gary F., Pres. & Chief Exec. Officer--Pope Resources, Poulsbo, WA; *U.S. Public*, pg. 1317
Tucker, N.E., Jr., Chm. Bd. & Pres.--Nantahala Power and Light Company, Bryson City, NC; *U.S. Public*, pg. 534
Tucker, Richard B.C., Sr., Sr. Chm. Bd. & Pres.--Wm. T. Burnett & Co., Inc., Baltimore, MD; *U.S. Private*, pg. 186
Tucker, Robert B., Pres.--The Shoe Show of Rocky Mt., Inc., Concord, NC; *U.S. Private*, pg. 996
Tucker, Terry L., Pres.--Gulfmark Energy Inc., Houston, TX; *U.S. Public*, pg. 19
Tucker, Thomas S., Jr., Pres. & Chief Oper. Officer--Associated Mortgage, Inc., De Pere, WI; *U.S. Public*, pg. 140
Tuckerman, Rodger, Pres.--Brown, Harris, Stevens, Inc., New York, NY; *U.S. Private*, pg. 174
Tuckman, Mitchell, Pres. & Chief Exec. Officer--General Microwave Corporation, Amityville, NY; *U.S. Public*, pg. 717
Tuckman, Mitchell, Pres.--Math Associates, Amityville, NY; *U.S. Public*, pg. 717
Tuerk-Ward, Doris L., Pres.--Standard Brokerage Services, Inc., Troy, MI; *Int'l*, pg. 11
Tuggle, Thomas M., Pres.--Regency Finance Company, Hermitage, PA; *U.S. Public*, pg. 607
Tuite, James E., Pres. & Chief Oper. Officer--TCF Bank Minnesota FSB, Minneapolis, MN; *U.S. Public*, pg. 1554
Tuley, B.B., Pres. & Chief Exec. Officer--Pic'n Pay Stores, Inc., Matthews, NC; *U.S. Private*, pg. 864
Tulin, John, Pres. & Chief Exec. Officer--Swank, Inc., Attleboro, MA; *U.S. Public*, pg. 1543
Tulin, John, Pres.--Crestline Div., Norwalk, CT; *U.S. Public*, pg. 1543
Tullio, Douglas J., Pres. & Chief Exec. Officer--Alpha Microsystems, Santa Ana, CA; *U.S. Public*, pg. 57
Tullis, David A., Pres. & Chief Exec. Officer--Customer Service Center of F.N.B., L.L.C., Naples, FL; *U.S. Public*, *pg. 607*
Tullmann, Sig, Pres.--EMTEC Magnetics DataSource Media Inc., Bedford, MA; *Int'l*, pg. 743
Tuner, Wesley, Pres. & Publisher--Star-Telegram Newspaper, Inc., Fort Worth, TX; *U.S. Public*, pg. 964
Tunmire, Robert, Pres. & Chief Exec. Officer--The Dwyer Group, Inc., Waco, TX; *U.S. Public*, pg. 537
Tunmire, Robert, Pres.--Mr. Appliance Corp., Waco, TX; *U.S. Public*, pg. 538
Tunmore, E. Roger, Pres. & Sec.--Tunmore Oldsmobile Inc., Buffalo, NY; *U.S. Private*, pg. 1109
Tunnicliffe, Paul, V.P. & Gen. Mgr.--Redland Ohio Inc., Woodville, OH; *Int'l*, pg. 1091
Tunnicliffe, Peter, Pres.--CDM Engineers & Constructors Inc., Cambridge, MA; *U.S. Private*, pg. 204
Tuominen, Matti, Pres.--Rammer Oy, Lahti, Finland; *Int'l*, pg. 1352
Tupper, Wallace L., Pres.--Old Kent Bank of Hillsdale, Hillsdale, MI; *U.S. Public*, pg. 1217
Turano, Joseph A., III, Pres.--Co-Counsel, Inc., Houston, TX; *U.S. Public*, pg. 1221
Turco, Lou, Pres.--Freeman Manufacturing & Supply Company, Avon, OH; *U.S. Private*, pg. 426
Turcotte, Norman J., Pres. & Chief Exec. Officer--Associated Grocers of New England, Inc., Manchester, NH; *U.S. Private*, pg. 91

Turesky, Jack A., Pres. & Chief Oper. Officer--National Health Care Affiliates, Inc., Buffalo, NY; *U.S. Private*, pg. 784
Turf, Barbara, Pres.--Euromarket Designs, Inc., Northbrook, IL; *U.S. Private*, pg. 384
Turfitt, Myron, Pres.--United Refining Company, Warren, PA; *U.S. Private*, pg. 915
Turgeon, Robert, Pres.--TQM Pipeline Partnership, Montreal, Canada; *Int'l*, pg. 541
Turiaux, Josef, Pres.--Stadtsparkasse Munchen, Munich, Germany; *Int'l*, pg. 1293
Turley, Robert, Pres. & Chief Oper. Officer--Perdue Farms Incorporated, Salisbury, MD; *U.S. Private*, pg. 852
Turner, Andrew, Chm. Bd., Pres. & Chief Exec. Officer--Sun Healthcare Group Inc., Albuquerque, NM; *U.S. Public*, pg. 1530
Turner, Barry, Chm. Bd., Pres. & Chief Exec. Officer--KTI Fish, Houston, TX; *U.S. Private*, pg. 604
Turner, C.O., III, Chm. Bd. & Pres.--Manufacturers Consolidation Service, Inc., Memphis, TN; *U.S. Private*, pg. 700
Turner, Carlton E., Pres. & Chief Exec. Officer--Carrington Laboratories, Inc., Irving, TX; *U.S. Public*, pg. 309
Turner, Don, Pres.--ELE International, Inc./Soiltest, Lake Bluff, IL; *Int'l*, pg. 1287
Turner, James E., Jr., Pres. & Chief Oper. Officer--General Dynamics Corporation, Falls Church, VA; *U.S. Public*, pg. 708
Turner, Jeffrey F., Pres. & Chief Exec. Officer--Peninsula Bank, Princess Anne, MD; *U.S. Public*, pg. 1089
Turner, Jerry, Pres.--American Sporting Goods Corporation, Irvine, CA; *U.S. Private*, pg. 62
Turner, Joe Ben, Chm. Bd., Pres. & Chief Exec. Officer--Willis Corroon Corp. of Knoxville, Knoxville, TN; *Int'l*, pg. 1506
Turner, John D., Pres.--Copperweld Bimetallics Products Co., Fayetteville, TN; *Int'l*, pg. 662
Turner, John D., Pres.--Copperweld Tubing, Pittsburgh, PA; *Int'l*, pg. 662
Turner, John M., Pres.--RELA, Inc., Boulder, CO; *U.S. Public*, pg. 401
Turner, L.J., Pres.--Fuller, Smith & Turner Plc, London, United Kingdom; *Int'l*, pg. 529
Turner, Richard W., Pres. & Chief Exec. Officer--BEI Medical Systems Company, Hackensack, NJ; *U.S. Private*, pg. 106
Turner, Ronald L., Pres. & Chief Exec. Officer--Computing Devices International, Bloomington, MN; *U.S. Public*, pg. 331
Turner, Thomas E., Pres.--Datamax International Corporation, Orlando, FL; *U.S. Private*, pg. 313
Turner, W.B., Jr., Pres. & Chief Oper. Officer--W.C. Bradley Co., Columbus, GA; *U.S. Private*, pg. 164
Turney, Duane, Pres.--Scope Beauty Ent., Inc., Whittier, CA; *U.S. Public*, pg. 1444
Turri, William, Pres.--The Case-Hoyt Corporation, Rochester, NY; *U.S. Private*, pg. 101
Turri, William, Pres.--Monroe Litho Inc., Rochester, NY; *U.S. Public*, pg. 1736
Turtletaub, Marc, Pres. & Chief Exec. Officer--The Money Store, Sacramento, CA; *U.S. Public*, pg. 1124
Turturro, August B., Pres. & Chief Exec. Officer--Fischbach Corporation, Englewood, CO; *U.S. Public*, pg. 84
Tushman, Earl, Pres.--Orleans International, Inc., Bloomfield Hills, MI; *U.S. Private*, pg. 820
Tushman, Larry, Partnership Mgr.--Sherwood Food Distributors, Detroit, MI; *U.S. Private*, pg. 993
Tutcher, Dan, Pres. & Chief Exec. Officer--Midcoast Energy Resources, Inc., Houston, TX; *U.S. Public*, pg. 1109
Tuten, Henderson G., Pres. & Chief Exec. Officer--Rothschild North America Inc., New York, NY; *U.S. Private*, pg. 947
Tuthill, James G., Jr., Pres. & Chief Exec. Officer--Tuthill Corporation, Hinsdale, IL; *U.S. Private*, pg. 1110
Tutor, Ronald N., Pres. & Chief Exec. Officer--Tutor-Saliba Corporation, Sylmar, CA; *U.S. Private*, pg. 1111
Tuttle, Daniel J., Pres.--Keck Instruments, Inc., Williamston, MI; *U.S. Public*, pg. 367
Tuttle, J.L., Pres. & Chief Exec. Officer--Ohio Gas Company, Bryan, OH; *U.S. Private*, pg. 812
Tuttle, John R., Chm. Bd., Pres. & Treas.--Micron Communications, Inc., Boise, ID; *U.S. Public*, pg. 1105
Twa, C.O., Pres. & Chief Oper. Officer--ATCO Group Co., Calgary, Canada; *Int'l*, pg. 95
Twa, C.O., Pres. & Chief Oper. Officer--Canadian Utilities Limited, Calgary, Canada; *Int'l*, pg. 95
Twa, Warren L., Pres.--Loffland Brothers de Venezuela, C.A., Caracas, Venezuela; *U.S. Public*, pg. 1149
Twaalfhoven, B.W.M., Pres.--Indivers B.V., Hilversum, Netherlands; *Int'l*, pg. 673
Tweddle, Michael E., Chm. Bd. & Pres.--Tweddle Litho Company, Clinton Township, MI; *U.S. Private*, pg. 1111
Twedell, Wayne C., Pres.--The JCM Group, Los Angeles, CA; *U.S. Private*, pg. 846
Tweedle, Michael, Dr., Pres.--Bracco Research, Inc., Princeton, NJ; *Int'l*, pg. 210
Tweten, James, Pres.--Magnolia Hi-Fi, Inc., Kent, WA; *U.S. Private*, pg. 696
Twiner, Don, Pres.-Consumer Foods--Robin Hood Multifoods Inc., Markham, Canada; *U.S. Public*, pg. 901
Twomey, Christopher A., Pres. & Chief Exec. Officer--Arctic Cat Inc., Thief River Falls, MN; *U.S. Public*, pg. 128
Twomley, Dale E., Pres. & Chief Exec. Officer--Worthington Foods Inc., Worthington, OH; *U.S. Public*, pg. 1780
Tyabji, Hatim A., Chm. Bd., Pres. & Chief Exec. Officer--VeriFone, Inc., Redwood City, CA; *U.S. Public*, pg. 815
Tychsen, Ulf C., Pres. & Chief Fin. Officer--The West Company Deutschland, Eschweiler, Germany; *U.S. Public*, pg. 1756
Tyler, David, Pres.--Christie's Inc., New York, NY; *Int'l*, pg. 290
Tyler, H.H., Pres. & Chief Exec. Officer--The Northern Trust Company, Lake Forest, IL; *U.S. Public*, pg. 1197
Tyler, H.H., Pres. & Chief Exec. Officer--The Northern Trust Company, Lake Bluff, IL; *U.S. Public*, pg. 1197
Tyler, James, Pres.--El Dorado Tire Co., Troy, MI; *Int'l*, pg. 1312
Tyler, K. Scott, Pres. & Chief Exec. Officer--The Lane Company, Inc., Altavista, VA; *U.S. Public*, pg. 688
Tyrone, J.C., Pres.--Fine Paper Div., Chillicothe, OH; *U.S. Public*, pg. 1074
Tyson, Ted H., Pres., Chief Exec. & Chief Oper. Officer--The Dickerson Group, Inc., Monroe, NC; *U.S. Private*, pg. 331
Tyson, Thomas J., Dr., Chm. Bd., Pres. & Chief Exec. Officer--Energy & Environmental Research Corp., Irvine, CA; *U.S. Private*, pg. 376
Uchida, Hisashi, Pres. & Chief Exec. Officer--Mitsubishi Silicon America, Salem, OR; *Int'l*, pg. 875
Uchida, Hisashi, Pres. & Chief Exec. Officer--Mitsubishi Silicon America, Palo Alto, CA; *Int'l*, pg. 875
Uchida, Shun, Pres. & Chief Oper. Officer--Otsuka America, Inc., San Francisco, CA; *Int'l*, pg. 1013
Uchida, Tsuneo, Deputy Pres.--The Dai-Ichi Kangyo Bank, Limited, Tokyo, Japan; *Int'l*, pg. 359
Uchida, Y., Pres.--Sharp Precision Manufacturing (U.K.) Ltd., Wrexham, United Kingdom; *Int'l*, pg. 1230
Uchigasaki, Morikuni, Pres.--Sumitomo Bank (Schweiz) AG, Zurich, Switzerland; *Int'l*, pg. 1310
Uchino, Yoshio, Pres.--P.T. Bank Sakura Swadharma, Jakarta, Indonesia; *Int'l*, pg. 1180
Uda, Makoto, Pres.--The Hiroshima Bank, Ltd., Tokyo, Japan; *Int'l*, pg. 620
Uda, Ryuzo, Pres.--Sumitomo Chemical Engineering Co., Ltd., Chiba, Japan; *Int'l*, pg. 1311
Udagawa, Yonezo, Pres. & Chief Exec. Officer--I&S Corp., Tokyo, Japan; *Int'l*, pg. 642
Uding, George E., Jr., Pres. & Chief Oper. Officer--Medusa Corporation, Cleveland, OH; *U.S. Public*, pg. 1084
Ueda, Nobuyuki, Pres.--Amada Co., Ltd., Kanagawa, Japan; *Int'l*, pg. 70
Ueda, T., Pres.--Nippla Kasei Co., Ltd., Tokyo, Japan; *Int'l*, pg. 946
Uehara, Akira, Pres.--Taisho Pharmaceutical Co., Ltd., Tokyo, Japan; *Int'l*, pg. 1348
Uehlinger, Robert E., Pres.--Johnson Supply & Equipment Corp., Houston, TX; *U.S. Private*, pg. 594
Ueltschi, Albert L., Chm. Bd. & Pres.--FlightSafety International Inc., Flushing, NY; *U.S. Public*, pg. 218
Ueltschi, H.P., Chm. Bd., Pres. & Chief Exec. Officer--Bernina Holding AG, Steckborn, Switzerland; *Int'l*, pg. 189
Uematsu, Tomiji, Pres. & Chief Exec. Officer--Konica Corporation, Tokyo, Japan; *Int'l*, pg. 748
Uemura, Keiichi, Pres.--Daiwa House Industry Co., Ltd., Osaka, Japan; *Int'l*, pg. 374
Ueno, Makoto, Pres.--Katsushiro Rome Corporation, Rome, GA; *Int'l*, pg. 744
Ueno, Shinzo, Pres. & Chief Exec. Officer--Dentsu, Sudler & Hennessey Inc., Tokyo, Japan; *U.S. Private*, pg. 325
Ueno, Takashi, Pres. & Chief Exec. Officer--Sakura Global Capital, Inc., New York, NY; *Int'l*, pg. 1179
Uesato, S., Pres.--Bleim Steel Company, Toledo, OH; *Int'l*, pg. 845
Ueshima, Shigeji, Pres. & Chief Exec. Officer--Mitsui & Co., Ltd., Tokyo, Japan; *Int'l*, pg. 877
Uhl, R.W., Pres.--Bar-S Foods Co., Phoenix, AZ; *U.S. Private*, pg. 114
Uhl, Richard J., Pres. & Chief Exec. Officer--Chicago Holdings, Inc., Pittsburgh, PA; *U.S. Private*, pg. 234
Uhlmann, Steve, Pres.--The Tech Group, Scottsdale, AZ; *U.S. Private*, pg. 1071
Uhrig, John A., Chm. Bd.--Australian Guarantee Corporation Limited, Sydney, Australia; *Int'l*, pg. 1496
Uihlein, Walter R., Pres. & Chief Exec. Officer--Acushnet Company, Fairhaven, MA; *U.S. Public*, pg. 675
Uihlein, Walter R., Pres.--Acushnet International Inc., Fairhaven, MA; *U.S. Public*, pg. 675
Uihlein, Walter R., Chm. Bd.--Cobra Golf Incorporated, Carlsbad, CA; *U.S. Public*, pg. 675
Ujiie, Junichi, Pres. & Chief Exec. Officer--The Nomura Securities Co., Ltd., Tokyo, Japan; *Int'l*, pg. 955
Ulbrich, Frederick C., Jr., Chm. Bd., Pres. & Chief Exec. Officer--Ulbrich Stainless Steels & Special Metals, Inc., North Haven, CT; *U.S. Private*, pg. 1115
Ulery, Byron, Pres., Chief Exec. Officer & Gen. Mgr.--Farmway Co-Op Inc., Beloit, KS; *U.S. Private*, pg. 396
Ulewicz, William, Pres.--Casablanca Fan Company, Pomona, CA; *U.S. Private*, pg. 549
Ullenberg, Ronald T., Pres.--World Pacific Ullenberg Corp., Chattanooga, TN; *U.S. Public*, pg. 861
Ullman, S. Peter, Pres., Chief Exec. & Oper. Officer--Harris Calorific Co., Gainesville, GA; *U.S. Public*, pg. 996
Ullmark, Hans, Pres. & Chief Exec. Officer--Anderson & Lembke Inc., New York, NY; *U.S. Private*, pg. 72
Ullmark, Hans, Pres.--Anderson & Lembke Inc., San Francisco, CA; *U.S. Private*, pg. 72
Ullring, Sven, Pres. & Chief Exec. Officer--Det Norske Veritas, Hovik, Norway; *Int'l*, pg. 396
Ulmanen, Tomi, Pres.--Valmet Korea Inc., Seoul, Korea; *Int'l*, pg. 1448
Ulrich, Dean, Pres.--Ventura Coastal Corporation, Ventura, CA; *U.S. Private*, pg. 1136
Ulrich, Jerry, Pres.--Netwave Technologies, Inc., Pleasanton, CA; *U.S. Public*, pg. 1564
Ulrich, Keith, Sr. V.P. & Brand Mktg. Partner--DMB&B Detroit, Troy, MI; *U.S. Private*, pg. 302
Ulsh, Gordon, Pres. & Chief Exec. Officer--Wagner Lighting Products, Chesterfield, MO; *U.S. Public*, pg. 442
Ulsh, Gordon, Pres.--Champion Ignition Products, Chesterfield, MO; *U.S. Public*, pg. 442
Umbach, Joseph, Pres.--Joseph Victori Wines, Inc., New Rochelle, NY; *U.S. Private*, pg. 1139
Umeda, Sadao, Pres.--Kajima Corporation, Tokyo, Japan; *Int'l*, pg. 721
Umeno, Masaya, Pres.--KCK Co., Ltd., Tokyo, Japan; *Int'l*, pg. 875
Umphenour, Russell, Jr., Chm. Bd., Pres. & Chief Exec. Officer--R.T.M. Winners, Atlanta, GA; *U.S. Private*, pg. 906
Umphrey, Kirk A., Pres.--Quaker State Q-Lube, Inc., Salt Lake City, UT; *U.S. Public*, pg. 1348
Unanue, Joseph, Pres.--Goya Foods, Inc., Secaucus, NJ; *U.S. Private*, pg. 468
Underwood, Marsha, Pres.--Shepard Niles, Inc., Montour Falls, NY; *U.S. Private*, pg. 992
Underwood, Vernon, Chm. Bd., Pres. & Chief Exec. Officer--Young's Holdings Inc., Orange, CA; *U.S. Private*, pg. 1202
Unfried, Charles, Pres.--Mercantile Credit Corp., Baton Rouge, LA; *U.S. Public*, pg. 1090
Unger, David, Pres.--MFRI Inc., Niles, IL; *U.S. Public*, pg. 1026
Unger, Les, Pres. & Chief Exec. Officer--Bufkor, Inc., Clearwater, FL; *U.S. Private*, pg. 179
Unger, Michael, Pres.--CAM Manufacturing, Inc., Cokato, MN; *U.S. Private*, pg. 293
Unger, Robert F., Pres.--Raytheon Marine, Manchester, NH; *U.S. Public*, pg. 1366
Ungerer, S.B., Pres.--ATE Investment, Inc., Pleasantville, NJ; *U.S. Public*, pg. 430
Unhjem, Michael, Pres.--Pioneer Mutual Life Insurance Company, Fargo, ND; *U.S. Private*, pg. 866
Uno, Ikuo, Pres.--Nippon Life Insurance Co., Osaka, Japan; *Int'l*, pg. 934
Uno, Sadao, Pres.--Rohm Mechatech Co., Ltd., Kyoto, Japan; *Int'l*, pg. 1125
Unschuld, Doran J., Pres. & Chief Exec. Officer--Binks Sames Corporation, Franklin Park, IL; *U.S. Public*, pg. 229
Unsworth, Lisa, Partner & Pres.--Houston Herstek Favat, Boston, MA; *U.S. Private*, pg. 542
Unum, Arnfinn, Pres.--Kvaerner Process Systems a.s, Billingstad, Norway; *Int'l*, pg. 769
Unwin, Brian, Sir, Chm. Bd. & Pres.--European Investment Bank, Luxembourg, Luxembourg; *Int'l*, pg. 465
Upbin, Hal J., Pres. & Chief Exec. Officer--Kellwood Company, Chesterfield, MO; *U.S. Public*, pg. 948
Upchurch, M., Pres.--Burns, Philp Inc., San Francisco, CA; *Int'l*, pg. 236
Upton, Herbert H., Jr., Pres.--Malloy Lithographing Inc., Ann Arbor, MI; *U.S. Private*, pg. 698
Urakami, Akio, Dr., Chm. Bd. & Pres.--Ryobi Motor Products, Anderson, SC; *Int'l*, pg. 1151
Urakami, Hiroshi, Pres.--Ryobi Ltd., Tokyo, Japan; *Int'l*, pg. 1151
Uratsuji, Toshihiko, Pres.--Mitsubishi Caterpillar Forklift America Inc. (MCFA), Houston, TX; *U.S. Public*, pg. 316
Uratsuji, Toshihiko, Pres.--Mitsubishi Caterpillar Forklift America Inc. (MCFA), Houston, TX; *Int'l*, pg. 874
Urban, Phil, Pres. & Chief Exec. Officer--Guarantee National Insurance Company, Englewood, CO; *U.S. Public*, pg. 1231
Urbanowski, Richard, Chm. Bd. & Pres.--ISK Biotech, Mentor, OH; *Int'l*, pg. 689
Urdaneta, Luis, Pres.--Interven, S.A., Caracas, Venezuela; *Int'l*, pg. 1045
Urek, Robert M., Pres. & Chief Exec. Officer--Heublein, Inc., Hartford, CT; *Int'l*, pg. 410
Urgoiti, Juan Manuel, Pres.--Banco 21, Madrid, Spain; *Int'l*, pg. 145
Urip, Sri, Pres.--Unilever Financierings Maatschappij B.V., Rotterdam, Netherlands; *Int'l*, pg. 1439
Urland, Robert S., Pres. & Chief Exec. Officer--Griffin Technology Incorporated, Farmington, NY; *U.S. Public*, pg. 506
Urquahrt, Richard A., III, Pres. & Treas.--Golden Corral Corporation, Raleigh, NC; *U.S. Private*, pg. 575
Urquhart, Margaret, Pres.--Lowe's Food Stores, Inc., Winston Salem, NC; *U.S. Private*, pg. 657
Urquiza, Fernando Correa, Pres.--The Boston Investment Group S.A., Buenos Aires, Argentina; *U.S. Public*, pg. 185
Urquiza, Fernando Correa, Pres.--Berkley International, S.A., Buenos Aires, Argentina; *U.S. Public*, pg. 216
Urrutia, Mike, Chm. Bd. & Pres.--Producers Livestock, North Salt Lake, UT; *U.S. Private*, pg. 888
Urschel, Robert R., Pres.--Urschel Labs Incorporated, Valparaiso, IN; *U.S. Private*, pg. 1129
Urushisako, T., Chm. & Pres.--Sharp Electronics Corporation, Mahwah, NJ; *Int'l*, pg. 1228
Urwin, T., Mng. Dir.--GEC Plessey Semiconductors, Swindon, United Kingdom; *Int'l*, pg. 544
Ury, Claude, Pres.--Orlane Institut de Beaute, Paris, France; *Int'l*, pg. 1011
Usami, Moriaki, Pres.--BlueWave Inn Corporation, Tokyo, Japan; *Int'l*, pg. 1008
Usami, Toru, Pres.--Okayama Taiho Pharmaceutical Co., Ltd., Okayama, Japan; *Int'l*, pg. 1013
Usdan, James M., Pres. & Chief Exec. Officer--RehabCare Group, Inc., Saint Louis, MO; *U.S. Public*, pg. 1373
Uselton, J.C., Pres.--Sverdrup Corporation, Maryland Heights, MO; *U.S. Private*, pg. 1057
Uselton, J.C., Chm. Bd. & Pres.--Sverdrup Investments, Inc., Maryland Heights, MO; *U.S. Private*, pg. 1057
Usher, George, Pres. & Chief Exec. Officer--Polydex Pharmaceuticals Limited, Scarborough, Canada; *Int'l*, pg. 1062
Ushigome, Susumu, Chm. Bd. & Pres.--TYK Corporation, Tokyo, Japan; *Int'l*, pg. 1345
Ushikubo, Masayoshi, Pres.--Sanden Corporation, Tokyo, Japan; *Int'l*, pg. 1184
Ushio, Eiji, Pres.--Kintetsu World Express (Deutschland) GmbH, Ratingen, Germany; *Int'l*, pg. 735
Ushioda, Kenjiro, Pres. & Chief Exec. Officer--Tostem Corporation, Tokyo, Japan; *Int'l*, pg. 1408
Usibelli, Joseph E., Jr., Pres.--Usibelli Coal Mine, Inc., Healy, AK; *U.S. Private*, pg. 1129
Usinger, Fritz, Pres.--Fred Usinger, Inc., Milwaukee, WI; *U.S. Private*, pg. 1129

Usrey, W. Bruce, Vice Chm. & Pres.--Monrovia Nursery Co., Azusa, CA; *U.S. Private*, pg. 757
Ussery, Dave, Pres. & Representative Dir.--Amway Korea, Ltd., Seoul, Korea; *U.S. Private*, pg. 70
Usui, Yutaro, Pres.--Usui Bundy Tubing Co. Ltd., Shizuoka, Japan; *Int'l*, pg. 1341
Utaski, James R., Pres.--Johnson & Johnson Development Corporation, New Brunswick, NJ; *U.S. Public*, pg. 928
Utick, David, Pres. & Chief Exec.. Officer--Hehr International Inc., Los Angeles, CA; *U.S. Private*, pg. 519
Utley, Steven, Pres.--First Worthing Company, Dallas, TX; *U.S. Private*, pg. 408
Utray, Jorge Fabra, Pres.--Red Electrica de Espana, S.A., Madrid, Spain; *Int'l*, pg. 1224
Utsumi, Jun, Pres. & Chief Exec. Officer--OMRON Systems, Inc., Schaumburg, IL; *Int'l*, pg. 1005
Utt, Bill, Pres.--CRSS Inc., Houston, TX; *Int'l*, pg. 1415
Uusitale, Tuure, Pres.--Finbow Oy, Nokia, Finland; *Int'l*, pg. 1449
Uyeda, Allen B., Pres. & Chief Exec. Officer--First Insurance Co. of Hawaii, Ltd., Honolulu, HI; *U.S. Public*, pg. 1011
Uyeda, Allen B., Pres. & Chief Exec. Officer--First Insurance Co. of Hawaii, Ltd., Honolulu, HI; *Int'l*, pg. 1392
Uytengsu, Michael R.B., Pres.--GF Industries, Inc., San Mateo, CA; *U.S. Private*, pg. 434
Vaajoki, Jorma, Pres. & Chief Exec. Officer--Metsa-Serla Corporation, Espoo, Finland; *Int'l*, pg. 863
Vainola, Toomas, Pres.--Rudus Eesti AS, Tallinn, Estonia; *Int'l*, pg. 1201
Vaira, Dale, V.P. & Gen. Mgr.--Winter Volvo & Lincoln Mercury, Sacramento, CA; *U.S. Private*, pg. 1183
Vaiya, Farid, Pres.--Raleigh Industries of Canada Ltd., Oakville, Canada; *Int'l*, pg. 394
Vakil, Usman U., Chm. Bd., Pres. & Treas.--Lights Of America, Inc., Walnut, CA; *U.S. Private*, pg. 667
Vakoutis, John, Pres. & Chief Exec. Officer--Curative Health Services, East Setauket, NY; *U.S. Public*, pg. 469
Valade, Mark, Pres.--Carhartt, Inc., Dearborn, MI; *U.S. Private*, pg. 210
Valaoras, George, Pres. & Chief Oper. Officer--Tempel Steel Company, Skokie, IL; *U.S. Private*, pg. 1075
Valbona, Bruno M., Pres.--Waring Products, New Hartford, CT; *U.S. Public*, pg. 286
Valdes, R.J., V.P. & Gen. Mgr.--G.E. Harris Energy Control Systems, LLC, Melbourne, FL; *U.S. Public*, pg. 712
Valebrokk, Kare, Mng. Dir. & Editor-in-Chief--The A/S Norges Handels og Sjoefartstidende Group, Oslo, Norway; *Int'l*, pg. 958
Valente, Dan, Chm. Bd., Pres. & Chief Exec. Officer--Palomar Medical Technologies, Lexington, MA; *U.S. Public*, pg. 1255
Valenti, Lewis, Pres.-Ladies Div.--Swank, Inc., Attleboro, MA; *U.S. Public*, pg. 1543
Valenti, Nick, Pres. & Chief Exec. Officer--Restaurant Associates Corporation, New York, NY; *U.S. Private*, pg. 924
Valenti, Robert M., Pres.--Quantic Industries, Inc., San Carlos, CA; *U.S. Private*, pg. 899
Valentine, Dean, Pres. & Chief Exec. Officer--UPN-United Paramount Network, Los Angeles, CA; *U.S. Public*, pg. 352
Valentine, Dean, Pres. & Chief Exec. Officer--UPN-United Paramount Network, Los Angeles, CA; *U.S. Private*, pg. 777
Valentine, Joseph C., Chm. Bd., Pres. & Chief Exec. Officer--Lubrication Engineers, Inc., Fort Worth, TX; *U.S. Private*, pg. 679
Valentine, Joseph P., Pres.--Consolidated Industries, Inc., Cheshire, CT; *U.S. Private*, pg. 265
Valentine, Mathias, Pres.--John B. Sanfilippo & Son, Inc., Elk Grove Village, IL; *U.S. Public*, pg. 1431
Valentine, Michael, Pres.--Mele Manufacturing Co., Inc., Utica, NY; *U.S. Private*, pg. 730
Valentine, Robert J., Jr., Pres. & Gen. Mgr.--Kysor/ Medallion, Spring Lake, MI; *U.S. Public*, pg. 968
Valentine, Victor V., Pres.--Triple S Plastics, Inc., Vicksburg, MI; *U.S. Public*, pg. 1639
Valentino, Harry, Pres. & Chief Oper. Officer--Fresh Mark, Inc., Canton, OH; *U.S. Private*, pg. 427
Valk, Ted P., Pres.--Valk Manufacturing Company, New Kingstown, PA; *U.S. Private*, pg. 1131
Vallan, Ronald L., Pres.--Young Supply Company, Detroit, MI; *U.S. Private*, pg. 1202
Vallee, Louis-Eric, Pres. & Chief Exec. Officer--Saint Jacques Vallee Young & Rubicam, Inc., Montreal, Canada; *U.S. Private*, pg. 1200
Vallee, Roy, Chm. Bd., Pres. & Chief Exec. & Oper. Officer--Avnet, Inc., Great Neck, NY; *U.S. Public*, pg. 155
Vallely, Mark J., Pres.--A.T. Clayton & Company, Inc., Greenwich, CT; *U.S. Private*, pg. 244
Vallerie, Donald E., Sr., Pres.--Vallerie's Transport Service, Inc., Norwalk, CT; *U.S. Private*, pg. 1131
Valles, Gene, Pres.--Arts & Crafts Press, San Diego, CA; *U.S. Private*, pg. 268
Valley, R. Bruce, Chm. Bd., Pres. & Chief Exec. Officer--Piedmont Trust Bank, Martinsville, VA; *U.S. Public*, pg. 1039
Valluzzo, John V., Chm. Bd. & Pres.--DCG Precision Manufacturing Corporation, Bethel, CT; *U.S. Private*, pg. 301
Valmaseda, Martin Eyries, Chm. Bd. & Chief Exec. Officer--Vallehermoso, S.A., Madrid, Spain; *Int'l*, pg. 1447
Valotaire, J., Pres. & Chief Oper. Officer--Belair Insurance Company, Montreal, Canada; *Int'l*, pg. 648
Valva, George, Pres.--Dugan Valva Contess Inc., Morristown, NJ; *U.S. Private*, pg. 345
Vamos, Istvan, Pres.--Advanced Forming Technology, Inc., Longmont, CO; *U.S. Public*, pg. 1320
Van Adel, Robert, Pres.--AGRA Monenco, Oakville, Canada; *Int'l*, pg. 30
Van Alsberg, Cecil, Pres.--Applied Films Corp., Boulder, CO; *U.S. Public*, pg. 519
Van Anken, Richard A., Pres. & Chief Exec. Officer--Jennings & Churella Construction Company, Wellington, OH; *U.S. Private*, pg. 586
Van Baren, Gise, Pres. & Gen. Mgr.--Hy-Alloy Steels Co., Chicago, IL; *U.S. Public*, pg. 313
Van Beek, Keith, Pres.--Toys "R" US (Canada) Ltd., Concord, Canada; *U.S. Public*, pg. 1626
Van Bell, Richard J., Pres.--John Deere Health Care, Inc., Moline, IL; *U.S. Public*, pg. 492
Van Bogan, R., Chm. Bd., Pres. & Chief Exec. Officer--SouthTrust Bank, Orlando, Orlando, FL; *U.S. Public*, pg. 1492
Van Brunt, John, Pres. & Chief Exec. Officer--Agrium Inc., Calgary, Canada; *Int'l*, pg. 31
Van Buren, David, Pres. & Chief Exec. Officer--Tecstar Inc., City of Industry, CA; *U.S. Private*, pg. 1072
Van Buren, Robert W., Pres. & Chief Exec. Officer--Domco Inc., Farnham, Canada; *Int'l*, pg. 415
Van Cleave, Robert C., Pres. & Chief Exec. Officer--Centex Construction Company, Dallas, TX; *U.S. Public*, pg. 322
van Dam, B., Pres. & Chief Exec. Officer--Van Leeuwen Pipe and Tube Group B.V., Zwijndrecht, Netherlands; *Int'l*, pg. 1449
Van Dawark, Tom, Pres. & Chief Exec. Officer--Foss Maritime Co., Seattle, WA; *U.S. Private*, pg. 1092
van de Geijn, P., Chm. Bd., Pres. & Chief Exec. Officer--AEGON Nederland N.V., Hague, Netherlands; *Int'l*, pg. 26
van de Pas, K.H., Pres.--Uitgeversmaatschappij De Gelderlander bv, Nijmegen, Netherlands; *Int'l*, pg. 1445
van der Driest, C.J., Chm. Bd. of Mngmt.--Koninklijke Van Ommeren NV, Rotterdam, Netherlands; *Int'l*, pg. 758
van der Hoeven, Lees, Pres.--Koninklijke Ahold NV, Zaandam, Netherlands; *Int'l*, pg. 749
van der Kaay, Erik, Pres.--Allen Telecom Inc., Solon, OH; *U.S. Public*, pg. 45
Van der Pas, John, Pres.--Lips USA Inc., Ocean Springs, MS; *Int'l*, pg. 812
van der Wansem, Paul J., Chm. Bd., Pres. & Chief Exec. Officer--BTU International, Inc., North Billerica, MA; *U.S. Public*, pg. 164
van der Wielen, J.C.T., Pres.--Nutricia BV, Zoetermeer, Netherlands; *Int'l*, pg. 991
Van Doorn, Dean, Pres.--Sobel NV, Aason, Netherlands; *Int'l*, pg. 1272
Van Doorselaere, I., Pres.--Interbrew Netherlands, Breda, Netherlands; *Int'l*, pg. 679
van Duinen, Dan, Pres.--Jacuzzi Bros., Jacuzzi, Inc., Little Rock, AR; *U.S. Public*, pg. 1684
van Dyk, T., Pres. & Treas.--Gist-Brocades, Inc., Wilmington, DE; *Int'l*, pg. 1143
Van Dyke, R. Scott, Pres. & Chief Exec. Officer--Explorer Pipeline Co., Tulsa, OK; *U.S. Public*, pg. 1584
Van Dyke, William G., Chm. Bd., Pres. & Chief Exec. Officer--Donaldson Company, Inc., Minneapolis, MN; *U.S. Public*, pg. 517
van Etten, R., Pres.--Kvaerner Ships Equipment b.v., Ridderkerk, Netherlands; *Int'l*, pg. 768
Van Faasen, William, Pres. & Chief Exec. Officer--Blue Cross and Blue Shield of Massachusetts, Boston, MA; *U.S. Private*, pg. 151
Van Fossan, Janet, Sr. Partner & Human Resources Dir.--Carmichael Lynch, Inc., Minneapolis, MN; *U.S. Private*, pg. 213
van Gils, Rafael, Pres.--CPAC Europe N.V., Herentals, Belgium; *U.S. Public*, pg. 282
Van Hefty, Claude L., Pres. & Chief Exec. Officer--Badger Paper Mills, Inc., Peshtigo, WI; *U.S. Public*, pg. 165
Van Hoose, David, Pres.-Mexican Opers.--Alimentos Balanceados Pilgrim's Pride, Queretaro, Mexico; *U.S. Public*, pg. 1296
Van Horn, John E., Pres.-Catalog Sls.--World Color Press, Inc., Greenwich, CT; *U.S. Public*, pg. 1778
Van Horn, L.R., Pres.--Ziegler Collateralized Securities, Inc., West Bend, WI; *U.S. Public*, pg. 1792
Van Houten, Hans-Peter, Pres.--Firmenich Incorporated, Plainsboro, NJ; *Int'l*, pg. 486
Van Houten, James F., Pres. & Chief Exec. Officer--MSI Insurance Companies, Arden Hills, MN; *U.S. Private*, pg. 688
Van Hulle, John V., Pres.--Cosan Chemical Corp., Carlstadt, NJ; *U.S. Public*, pg. 297
Van Hulle, John V., Pres.--CasChem Inc., Bayonne, NJ; *U.S. Public*, pg. 297
Van Kanegan, Roy W., Jr., Pres.--Target Stamped Products Corp., Kinsman, OH; *U.S. Private*, pg. 1069
Van Kleeck, Peter, Pres. & Chief Exec. Officer--Progressive Bank, Inc., Fishkill, NY; *U.S. Public*, pg. 1334
Van Kleeck, Peter, Pres. & Chief Exec. Officer--Pawling Savings Bank, Pawling, NY; *U.S. Public*, pg. 1334
Van Lede, Cga, Pres. & Chief Exec. Officer--Akzo Nobel N.V., Arnhem, Netherlands; *Int'l*, pg. 42
Van Leeuwen, John E., Pres.--Trans Canada Credit Corporation, Etobicoke, Canada; *U.S. Public*, pg. 1202
van Lijnden, A.F. Baron, Mng. Dir.--H. Albert de Bary & Co. N.V. (Amsterdam), Amsterdam, Netherlands; *Int'l*, pg. 404
Van Loan, Charles C., Pres. & Chief Exec. Officer--Independent Bank Corporation, Ionia, MI; *U.S. Public*, pg. 874
Van Loan, Dave, Pres. & Chief Exec. Officer--Everett Charles Technologies, Pomona, CA; *U.S. Private*, pg. 386
Van Loan, Dave, Pres.--Ostby & Barton Co., Warwick, RI; *U.S. Private*, pg. 386
Van Melis, Charles, Pres.--Key Handling Systems, Inc., Moonachie, NJ; *U.S. Private*, pg. 618
Van Melle, I.L.G., Chm. Bd.-Mngmt. & Pres.--Van Melle N.V., Breda, Netherlands; *Int'l*, pg. 1450
van Melle, Marius, Pres. & Gen. Mgr.--Van Melle USA, Inc., Erlanger, KY; *Int'l*, pg. 1451
Van Meter, John D., Pres.--Ashland Oil Intl. Ltd., London, United Kingdom; *U.S. Public*, pg. 139
Van Mollenberg, H., Chm. Bd., Pres. & Chief Exec. Officer--Mollenberg-Betz Inc., Buffalo, NY; *U.S. Private*, pg. 756
Van Ness, Kathy, Pres.-Swimwear/Taren--Cole of California, Los Angeles, CA; *U.S. Public*, pg. 148
Van Nort, Peter, Pres.--H.B. Zachry, San Antonio, TX; *U.S. Private*, pg. 1203
Van Nort, Peter S., Pres.--ABB Combustion Engineering Nuclear Power, Windsor, CT; *Int'l*, pg. 3
Van Oijen, J.G.M., Chm. Bd.-Mngmt.--Gamma Holding N.V., Helmond, Netherlands; *Int'l*, pg. 539
van Oordt, R.W.F., Chm. Bd.--N.V. Koninklijke KNP BT, Amsterdam, Netherlands; *Int'l*, pg. 756
Van Ort, Dale, Pres. & Chief Oper. Officer--Freeman Decorating Co., Dallas, TX; *U.S. Private*, pg. 426
van Osnabrugge, Jan, Pres. & Chief Exec. Officer--Peerless Industrial Group, Inc., Winona, MN; *U.S. Public*, pg. 1268
van Osnabrugge, Jan, Pres. & Chief Exec. Officer--Peerless Chain Company, Winona, MN; *U.S. Public*, pg. 1268
Van Ouytnel, Bart, Pres.--Structural Europe, Herentals, Belgium; *U.S. Public*, pg. 593
van Parys, Frederick, Pres. & Chief Exec. Officer--Pitney Bowes of Canada Ltd., Toronto, Canada; *U.S. Public*, pg. 1304
van Patter, R. Allen, Pres.-Weston Bakeries West--Weston Bakeries Limited, Etobicoke, Canada; *Int'l*, pg. 1495
Van Pelt, Donald C., Jr., Pres. & Chief Exec. Officer--Plymouth Tube Company, Warrenville, IL; *U.S. Private*, pg. 873
Van Remmen, Thomas, Pres. & Chief Oper. Officer--Andersen 2000 Inc., Peachtree City, GA; *U.S. Public*, pg. 462
Van Rooy, Jean-Pierre, Pres.--Otis Elevator Company, Farmington, CT; *U.S. Public*, pg. 1690
van Rysdam, Casey, Div. Pres.--American Natural Snacks, Saint Augustine, FL; *Int'l*, pg. 752
Van Sant, R.W., Pres.--Sponsor's Plan Asset Management, Inc., New Castle, DE; *U.S. Public*, pg. 1020
Van Steenkiste, Dwight P., Pres.--Genova Products, Inc., Davison, MI; *U.S. Private*, pg. 447
Van Tiem, Donald C., Chm. Bd., Pres. & Treas.--Hoban Foods, Inc., Detroit, MI; *U.S. Private*, pg. 531
Van Tiflin, James, Pres. & Chief Exec. Officer--Second National Bank of Saginaw, Saginaw, MI; *U.S. Public*, pg. 379
Van Tuyl, Cecil L., Chm. Bd., Pres. & Chief Exec. Officer--V.T. Inc., Merriam, KS; *U.S. Private*, pg. 1131
Van Tyle, Cecil, Pres.--Reliable Chevrolet, Richardson, TX; *U.S. Private*, pg. 920
Van Velkinburgh, Stephen, Pres.--Penguin's Industries, Granada Hills, CA; *Int'l*, pg. 201
van Vlissingen, F.H. Fentener, Chm.-Supervisory Bd.--CSM N.V., Diemen, Netherlands; *Int'l*, pg. 243
van Voorden, H., Pres.--Enraf B.V., Delft, Netherlands; *Int'l*, pg. 389
Van Wagenen, Paul G., Chm. Bd., Pres. & Chief Exec. Officer--Pogo Producing Company, Houston, TX; *U.S. Public*, pg. 1312
Van Weelden, Thomas H., Pres. & Chief Exec. Officer--Allied Waste Industries, Scottsdale, AZ; *U.S. Public*, pg. 49
Van Winkle, John D., Pres. & Chief Exec. Officer--Beverly Bancorporation Inc., Chicago, IL; *U.S. Public*, pg. 227
Van Zandt, Russell, Pres.--Intervascular, S.A., La Ciotat, France; *U.S. Public*, pg. 488
Van Zant, David, Pres.--Sureco Inc., Fort Valley, GA; *U.S. Public*, pg. 1390
Van Zliet, Peter, Pres.--Furness North America Inc., Houston, TX; *Int'l*, pg. 530
van't Hooft, E., Pres.--Delft Instruments Defense BV, Delft, Netherlands; *Int'l*, pg. 388
Vana-Paxhia, Steven R., Pres & Chief Exec. Officer--INSO Corporation, Boston, MA; *U.S. Public*, pg. 882
Vanco, David, Pres.--Management Data Service, Elmhurst, IL; *U.S. Public*, pg. 1687
Vande Steeg, Nickolas W., Pres.--Seal Group, Irvine, CA; *U.S. Public*, pg. 1262
Vanden Eynden, Jerry, Pres.--Indiana Glass Company, Cincinnati, OH; *U.S. Public*, pg. 976
Vandenberg, Peter, Jr., Pres. & Chief Fin. Officer--Biscayne Apparel Inc., Clifton, NJ; *U.S. Public*, pg. 232
Vander Bie, Thomas J., Pres.--Castex Incorporated, Holland, MI; *U.S. Public*, pg. 1577
Vander Heyden, William, Pres.--Badger Meter Industrial Div., Milwaukee, WI; *U.S. Public*, pg. 165
Vander Leegf, W., Pres.--Steelweld BV, Breda, Netherlands; *Int'l*, pg. 71
Vander Leegh, W., Pres.--Vimarc, Breda, Netherlands; *Int'l*, pg. 71
Vanderbilt, H.B., Jr., Pres. & Chief Exec. Officer--R.T. Vanderbilt Company, Inc., Norwalk, CT; *U.S. Private*, pg. 1133
Vanderboom, Steve, Pres. & Chief Exec. Officer--Pace Analytical Services, Minneapolis, MN; *U.S. Private*, pg. 829
Vandermeulen, E.S.J.B.M., Pres.--Nucletron BV, Veenendaal, Netherlands; *Int'l*, pg. 389
Vanderminden, Henry J.W., III, Pres.--Telescope Casual Furniture, Inc., Granville, NY; *U.S. Private*, pg. 1074
Vanderslice, John, Pres. & Chief Oper. Officer--Aydin Corporation, Horsham, PA; *U.S. Public*, pg. 158
VanHorn, John E., Pres.--World Color-Chicago Div., Elk Grove Village, IL; *U.S. Public*, pg. 1778
Vanlandingham, Donald W., Pres.--Ball Aerospace & Technologies Corp., Broomfield, CO; *U.S. Public*, pg. 171
VanLuvanee, Donald R., Pres. & Chief Exec. Officer--Electro Scientific Industries, Inc., Portland, OR; *U.S. Public*, pg. 568
Vann, James A., Jr., Pres. & Chief Exec. Officer--Alabama Electric Cooperative, Inc., Andalusia, AL; *U.S. Private*, pg. 30
Vannoy, Jack, Pres. & Chief Exec. Officer--Megas Beauty Care, Inc., Cleveland, OH; *U.S. Private*, pg. 729

Vanourek, Robert A., Pres. & Chief Exec. Officer--Sensormatic Electronics Corporation, Boca Raton, FL; *U.S. Public*, pg. 1457

VanSickle, Sharon, Principal & Pub. Rels.--Karakas, VanSickle, Ouellette Advertising & Public Relations, Portland, OR; *U.S. Private*, pg. 607

Vara, Francisco Javier Alvarez, Pres.--CASA - Construcciones Aeronauticas, S.A., Madrid, Spain; *Int'l*, pg. 1224

Varacchi, John, Pres.--Furniture Consultants, New York, NY; *U.S. Public*, pg. 1686

Varakian, Robert, Pres.--B.Via International Housewares, Inc., Franklin Park, IL; *U.S. Public*, pg. 566

Vardeman, J. Rex, Chm. Bd., Pres. & Chief Exec. Officer--Vertex Communications Corporation, Kilgore, TX; *U.S. Public*, pg. 1717

Varel, Daniel W., Chm. Bd., Pres., Chief Exec. Officer & Gen. Mgr.--Varel Manufacturing Co., Dallas, TX; *U.S. Private*, pg. 1134

Varga, C., Pres.--Freios Varga S/A, Limeira, Brazil; *Int'l*, pg. 820

Vargas, Adrian Lajous, Pres. & Dir. Gen.--Petroleos Mexicanos, Mexico, Mexico; *Int'l*, pg. 1046

Vargas, Arnulfo, Pres., Chief Exec. Officer & Investor Rels. Dir.--Cash & Carry Grocer Inc., Chicago, IL; *U.S. Private, pg. 218*

Vargo, Timothy D., Pres. & Chief Oper. Officer--AutoZone, Inc., Memphis, TN; *U.S. Public*, pg. 150

Varholick, Joe, Pres.--Microdot/Recoil, Placentia, CA; *U.S. Public*, pg. 940

Varjabedian, H., Pres.--La Compagnie Foundation Limitee, Laval, Canada; *Int'l*, pg. 118

Varlet, Didier, Pres. & Chief Exec. Officer--Carr Asset Management Inc., Chicago, IL; *Int'l*, pg. 313

Varn, Rex E., Pres.--Sonoco Ltd., Brantford, Canada; *U.S. Public*, pg. 1487

Varner, Larary, Pres.--Tyco, Spencer, NC; *U.S. Public*, pg. 1058

Varner, Ted, Pres. & Chief Oper. Officer--Convenience Stores Distributors, Richmond, IN; *U.S. Public*, pg. 1049

Vasami, Ralph J., Pres.--Fiberlux, Inc., Purchase, NY; *U.S. Public*, pg. 1634

Vascocu, Jerome, Pres.--Central Bank, N.A., Oxford, AL; *U.S. Public*, pg. 418

Vasella, Daniel, Dr., Pres.--Novartis AG, Basel, Switzerland; *Int'l*, pg. 971

Vass, David T., Pres.--Bondex Intl., Inc., Saint Louis, MO; *U.S. Public*, pg. 1357

Vassiliadis, William, Pres. & Chief Exec. Officer--R&R Advertising, Las Vegas, NV; *U.S. Private*, pg. 902

Vaszily, Joseph, Pres.--Brooks Instrument, Hatfield, PA; *U.S. Public*, pg. 574

Vaughan-Johnson, Charles, Pres.--Bermuda Trust (Guernsey) Limited, Saint Peter Port, United Kingdom; *Int'l*, pg. 151

Vaughan, Curtis T., III, Pres. & Chief Exec. Officer--Vaughan & Sons, Inc., San Antonio, TX; *U.S. Private*, pg. 1134

Vaughan, I., Pres.--Van Leer Australia Pty. Ltd., Epping, Australia; *Int'l*, pg. 1146

Vaughn, Donald C., Pres. & Chief Oper. Officer--Dresser Industries, Inc., Dallas, TX; *U.S. Public*, pg. 528

Vaughn, Ronald H., Pres.--Neapco, Inc., Pottstown, PA; *U.S. Private*, pg. 1113

Vauthier, T., Pres.--Labatt Breweries British Columbia, New Westminster, Canada; *Int'l*, pg. 679

Vayrila, Juha, Pres.--Betomix AO, Saint Petersburg, Russia; *Int'l*, pg. 1200

Vazzano, Thomas, Pres.--Welcome Wagon-Intl., Inc., Trumbull, CT; *U.S. Public*, pg. 321

Veale, Keith, Gen. Mgr.--Peyton Meats, El Paso, TX; *U.S. Public*, pg. 75

Vecchia, George S., Pres.--New England Wholesale Drug Company, Brockton, MA; *U.S. Public*, pg. 229

Vedoy, Arne W., Pres.--Kvaerner Singapore Pte Ltd, Singapore, Singapore; *Int'l*, pg. 768

Veerman, Andre, Pres.--Leaf Germany, Hagen, Germany; *Int'l*, pg. 638

Vega, Frank, Pres. & Chief Exec. Officer--Detroit Newspapers, Detroit, MI; *U.S. Public*, pg. 965

Veil, Lynne C., Partner & Exec. V.P.--Media That Works, Cincinnati, OH; *U.S. Private*, pg. 727

Veit, David M., Pres.--Pearson, Inc., New York, NY; *Int'l*, pg. 1026

Velaheezan, Jap, Pres.-Laundry & Detergents--Procter & Gamble France, Neuilly-sur-Seine, France; *U.S. Public*, pg. 1332

Velasquez, Arthur R., Chm. Bd., Pres. & Chief Exec. Officer--Azteca Foods, Incorporated, Chicago, IL; *U.S. Private*, pg. 104

Vella, William J., Pres. & Chief Oper. Officer--Carsen Group Inc., Markham, Canada; *U.S. Public*, pg. 301

Vellano, Vittorio, Chief Exec. Officer--Fiat USA Inc., New York, NY; *Int'l*, pg. 483

Venberg, Walter W., Pres.--Homes By Dave Brown, Tempe, AZ; *U.S. Private*, pg. 537

Vengroff, Joel, Pres.-New York--Vengroff Williams & Associates, Inc., Commack, NY; *U.S. Private*, pg. 1135

Vengroff, Mark, Pres.-California--Vengroff Williams & Associates, Inc., Commack, NY; *U.S. Private*, pg. 1135

Venowa, Masahiro, Pres. & Mng. Dir.--Isuzu-General Motors Australia Ltd., Melbourne, Australia; *Int'l*, pg. 693

Venowa, Masahiro, Pres. & Mng. Dir.--Isuzu-General Motors Australia Ltd., Melbourne, Australia; *U.S. Public*, pg. 725

Vensel, John, Chm. Bd., Pres. & Chief Exec. Officer--Crucible Materials Corp., Solvay, NY; *U.S. Private*, pg. 293

Vent, Richard H., Pres. & Chief Oper. Officer--Caribiner International, Inc., New York, NY; *U.S. Public*, pg. 305

Vento, Richard G., Co-Chm. Bd., Pres. & Chief Exec. Officer--Objective Systems Integrators, Inc., Folsom, CA; *U.S. Public*, pg. 1209

Ventre, Marc, Pres. & Chief Exec. Officer--Fan Blade Associates, Inc., Wilmington, DE; *Int'l*, pg. 1166

Ventre, Martin, Pres.--Ventre Packing Company, Inc., Syracuse, NY; *U.S. Private*, pg. 1135

Venuti, Steve, Pres. & Chief Exec. Officer--LVL Interactive, Palo Alto, CA; *U.S. Private*, pg. 640

Veratti, Robert N., Pres. & Chief Exec. Officer--National Media Corporation, Philadelphia, PA; *U.S. Public*, pg. 1158

Verbicky, John W., Pres. & Chief Exec. Officer--Chemfab Corporation, Merrimack, NH; *U.S. Public*, pg. 344

Verble, C. Michael, Pres. & Chief Exec. Officer--North American Roofing Systems, Inc., Arden, NC; *U.S. Private*, pg. 803

Verdon, Raymond J., Pres.--Nabisco Biscuit Company, East Hanover, NJ; *U.S. Public*, pg. 1355

Verdoorn, Sid, Pres., Chief Exec. & Chief Oper. Officer--C.H. Robinson Co., Eden Prairie, MN; *U.S. Public*, pg. 1394

Verebay, Leonard J., Pres.--Queens Group, Inc., Long Island City, NY; *U.S. Private*, pg. 900

Vereen, W.J., Pres., Chief Exec. Officer & Treas.--Riverside Manufacturing Co., Moultrie, GA; *U.S. Private*, pg. 934

Verfaillie, Hendrik A., Pres.--Monsanto Company, Saint Louis, MO; *U.S. Public*, pg. 1124

Vergakis, Ron, Pres.--Mannington Wood Floors, High Point, NC; *U.S. Private*, pg. 700

Vergani, Alberto, Pres.--Opticos S.r.l., Brembate di Sopra, Italy; *Int'l*, pg. 1007

Verges, Henri, Pres.--Auxitrol S.A., Saint Cloud, France; *U.S. Public*, pg. 594

Vergnes, Bernard P., Pres.--Microsoft Europe, Paris, France; *U.S. Public*, pg. 1108

Vergon, James F., Pres. & Chief Oper. Officer--Central Illinois Light Company, Peoria, IL; *U.S. Public*, pg. 367

Vergona, A.B., Pres. & Gen. Mgr.--LVT, Rochester, NY; *U.S. Public*, pg. 551

Verhaeghe de Naeyer, Thierry, Chm. Bd. & Pres.--N.V. Bekaert S.A., Kortrijk, Belgium; *Int'l*, pg. 183

Verhagen, J.K., Pres. & Chief Oper. Officer--Compaction America, Kewanee, IL; *U.S. Public*, pg. 1676

Verkamp, Gilbert, Pres. & Chief Exec. Officer--Aristokraft, Inc., Jasper, IN; *U.S. Public*, pg. 675

Verkuyten, A.A.A.J.M., Pres.--Blydenstein-Willink N.V., Hengelo, Netherlands; *Int'l*, pg. 198

Verkyk, Robert, Chm. Bd. & Pres.--Misener Marine Construction, Tampa, FL; *U.S. Private*, pg. 752

Vermaut, Pierre, Mng. Dir.--Barry Callebaut N.V., Lebbeke, Belgium; *Int'l*, pg. 252

Vermeer, Gary J., Founder--Vermeer Manufacturing Company, Pella, IA; *U.S. Private*, pg. 1137

VerMerris, R.C., Chm. Bd. & Pres. & Chief Exec. Officer--Radix Wire Company, Cleveland, OH; *U.S. Private*, pg. 907

Vermylen, John B., Pres.--A. Zeregas Sons, Inc., Fair Lawn, NJ; *U.S. Private*, pg. 1204

Vermylen, Paul A., Jr., Pres., Treas. & Sec.--Meenan Oil Co. L.P., Syosset, NY; *U.S. Private*, pg. 729

Verner, James R., Pres. & Chief Oper. Officer--Acousti Engineering Co. of Florida, Orlando, FL; *U.S. Private*, pg. 14

Verni, Ralph F., Chm. Bd., Pres. & Chief Exec. Officer--State Street Research & Management Company, Boston, MA; *U.S. Private*, pg. 738

Vernick, Mitchell F., Pres. & Chief Exec. Officer--Transamerica Commercial Finance Corp., Inc., Chicago, IL; *U.S. Public*, pg. 1630

Vernon, W. Anthony, Pres.--Johnson & Johnson/Merck Consumer Pharmaceuticals Co., Whitehouse Station, NJ; *U.S. Public*, pg. 929

Vernon, W.F., Chm. Bd. & Pres.--The Vernon Company, Newton, IA; *U.S. Private*, pg. 1137

Veron, Marc, Pres.--Groupe Air France, Roissy, France; *Int'l*, pg. 559

Verona, Dominic J., Pres.--National Marine, Inc., New Orleans, LA; *U.S. Private*, pg. 1135

Veroni, Clive, Pres. & Chief Exec. Officer--Stringer Veroni Ketchum Advertising, Toronto, Canada; *U.S. Private*, pg. 617

Verrando, R., Pres. & Chief Oper. Officer--Presstek, Inc., Hudson, NH; *U.S. Public*, pg. 1324

Verresa, A., Pres.--Brabants Nieuwsblad BV, Roosendaal, Netherlands; *Int'l*, pg. 1445

Verrette, William C., Pres.--Champion, Inc., Iron Mountain, MI; *U.S. Private*, pg. 228

Verryk, J.F., Mng. Dir.--De Bussy Harms N.V., Diemen, Netherlands; *Int'l*, pg. 386

Verschelde, Patrick, Pres. & Chief Exec. Officer--Air Liquide America Corporation, Houston, TX; *Int'l*, pg. 37

Versluys, F., Pres.--Delft Instruments Electro-Optics B.V., Delft, Netherlands; *Int'l*, pg. 389

Versluys, F., Pres.--OIP N.V., Oudenaarde, Belgium; *Int'l*, pg. 389

Versock, Gottfried, Pres.--Flender Corporation, Elgin, IL; *Int'l*, pg. 400

Verstraete, Roy M., Pres.--Velcro Canada Inc., Brampton, Canada; *Int'l*, pg. 1462

Verwelct, Herman, Pres.--ASLK-CGER, Antwerp, Belgium; *Int'l*, pg. 17

Vesstan, Kevin, Pres.--Indeck Energy Services, Inc., Buffalo Grove, IL; *U.S. Private*, pg. 559

Vest, Herb D., Chm. Bd., Pres. & Chief Exec. Officer--HD Vest Financial Services, Irving, TX; *U.S. Public*, pg. 770

Vesta, Rich, Pres.--Packerland Packing Co., Green Bay, WI; *U.S. Private*, pg. 833

Vetere, Barry, Partner--Messner Vetere Berger McNamee Schmetterer/EURO RSCG, New York, NY; *Int'l*, pg. 602

Vetterli, John E., Pres.--The Flecto Co., Inc., Oakland, CA; *U.S. Private*, pg. 410

Vezza, Richard J., Pres.--Gremac Inc., Hackensack, NJ; *U.S. Private*, pg. 693

Viars, E. Leon, Pres.--Maremont Exhaust Systems Product Division, Loudon, TN; *U.S. Public*, pg. 137

Viars, Leon, Pres.--Maremont Exhaust System Division, Loudon, TN; *U.S. Public*, pg. 137

Viboolmeth, Nipon, Pres.--Siam City Credit Finance & Securities Co., Ltd., Bangkok, Thailand; *Int'l*, pg. 1239

Vicic, Joseph J., Pres.--Parker Hannifin Hong Kong Ltd., Fluid Handling Headquarters, Kwai Chung, Hong Kong; *U.S. Public*, pg. 1263

Vick, R. John, Pres. & Chief Oper. Officer--Perini Land and Development Co., Framingham, MA; *U.S. Public*, pg. 1278

Vie, Richard C., Pres. & Chief Exec. Officer--Unitrin, Inc., Chicago, IL; *U.S. Public*, pg. 1693

Vierling, Ed, Pres.--Jerell, Inc., Dallas, TX; *U.S. Private*, pg. 586

Viesbuchen, Ditmar, Pres.--Braun Canada Ltd., Mississauga, Canada; *U.S. Public*, pg. 744

Vietor, Sandy, Pres. & Chief Exec. Officer--Willis Corroon Marine & Energy, New York, NY; *Int'l*, pg. 1508

Viets, Robert O., Pres. & Chief Exec. Officer--CILCORP Inc., Peoria, IL; *U.S. Public*, pg. 367

Vignon, Dominique, Chm. Bd. & Pres.--Framatome SA, Paris, France; *Int'l*, pg. 502

Viinanen, Jukka, Vice Chm., Pres. & Chief Oper. Officer--Neste Oy, Espoo, Finland; *Int'l*, pg. 912

Vilaitanarak, Vivat, Mng. Dir.--Synergie Tokyu DMB&B Ltd., Bangkok, Thailand; *U.S. Private*, pg. 305

Vilas, Jose Maria, Pres.--CPC Spain, S.A., Barcelona, Spain; *U.S. Public*, pg. 225

Vilett, J.M., Jr., Pres.--Northland Electric Supply Company, Minneapolis, MN; *U.S. Private*, pg. 806

Vilgrain, Jean-Louis, Pres.--Grands Moulins de Paris S.A., Paris, France; *Int'l*, pg. 556

Vilgrain, Stanislas, Pres. & Chief Oper. Officer--Cuisine Solutions, Inc., Alexandria, VA; *U.S. Public*, pg. 466

Villa-Massone, Gilbert, Chm. Bd. & Pres.--Gachot S.A., Montmorency, France; *U.S. Public*, pg. 1650

Villa, Rodolfo Martin, Pres.--Central Nuclear Vandellos II A.I.E., Barcelona, Spain; *Int'l*, pg. 1224

Villani, Edmond D., Pres. & Chief Exec. Officer--Scudder Kemper Investments, Inc., New York, NY; *Int'l*, pg. 1530

Villanueva, Roberto G., Jr., Pres.--AGP Industrial Corporation, Manila, Philippines; *Int'l*, pg. 14

Villar, Salvador, Pres. & Chief Exec. Officer--California Commerce Bank, Los Angeles, CA; *Int'l*, pg. 574

Villarejo, Juan Temboury, Pres.--ELECBRO - Termoelectrica del Ebro, S.A., Escatron, Spain; *Int'l*, pg. 1224

Villneff, Larry T., Pres.--Ikon Office Solutions, Edmonton, Canada; *U.S. Public*, pg. 864

Vincent, D. Glenn, Pres.--Hilb, Rogal and Hamilton Company of Daytona Beach, Inc., Daytona Beach, FL; *U.S. Public*, pg. 827

Vincent, G.A., Chm. Bd., Pres., Chief Exec. Officer & Chief Oper. Officer--The C.P. Hall Company, Chicago, IL; *U.S. Private*, pg. 495

Vincent, Philip S., Pres. & Chief Oper. Officer--Southern Mills, Inc., Union City, GA; *U.S. Private*, pg. 1016

Vincent, Robert A., Pres.--David Clark Company Incorporated, Worcester, MA; *U.S. Private*, pg. 242

Vincent, Thomas, Pres.--American Electric Co., Ltd., Honolulu, HI; *U.S. Public*, pg. 65

Vinciarelli, Patrizio, Chm. Bd. & Pres.--Vicor Corporation, Andover, MA; *U.S. Public*, pg. 1719

Vinciarelli, Patrizio, Pres.--VLT Corporation, Andover, MA; *U.S. Public*, pg. 1719

Vinciarelli, Patrizio, Pres.--Vicor International, Andover, MA; *U.S. Public*, pg. 1719

Vinciguerra, Salvatore J., Pres. & Chief Exec. Officer--Ferrofluidics Corporation, Nashua, NH; *U.S. Public*, pg. 620

Vinciquerra, Richard E., Pres.--Tyler Elevator Products, Inc., Valley View, OH; *U.S. Private*, pg. 1112

Vinson, Stan W., Pres.--Uniblend Spinners, Inc., Conway, SC; *U.S. Private*, pg. 1117

Vinyard, Lee E., Chief Oper. Officer--Intermatic Inc., Spring Grove, IL; *U.S. Private*, pg. 567

Viola, F., Pres.--Sharp Electronics (Italia) S.p.A., Milan, Italy; *Int'l*, pg. 1230

Viola, Robert, Pres.--Zotos International, Darien, CT; *Int'l*, pg. 1236

Viola, Ronald J., Pres. & Chief Exec. Officer--Rapid Power Technologies, Inc., Brookfield, CT; *U.S. Private*, pg. 910

Vipond, Mike, Pres.--USSI, Carter Lake, IA; *U.S. Public*, pg. 1629

Virgilio, Abramo, Pres.--Bristol Europe S.p.A., Latina, Italy; *U.S. Public*, pg. 255

Virrankoski, Risto, Deputy Pres.--Outokumpu Oyj, Espoo, Finland; *Int'l*, pg. 1015

Virtue, Robert A., Chm. Bd., Pres. & Chief Exec. Officer--Virco Mfg. Corporation, Torrance, CA; *U.S. Public*, pg. 1721

Visconti, Joseph, Pres.--Nantucket Industries, Inc., Melville, NY; *U.S. Public*, pg. 1151

Visich, Charles, Pres.--Klipsch, Inc., Hope, AR; *U.S. Private, pg. 626*

Vita, Giuseppe, Pres.--Schering AG, Berlin, Germany; *Int'l*, pg. 1203

Vitale, Jody, Chm. Bd & Pres.--Perfect Fit Industries, Inc., Monroe, NC; *U.S. Private*, pg. 852

Vitale, Kenneth, Pres.--Rotary Multiforms, Inc., Warren, MI; *U.S. Private*, pg. 947

Vitale, Neal, Pres. & Chief Oper. Officer--Petersen Publishing Company, L.L.C., Los Angeles, CA; *U.S. Private*, pg. 856

Vitale, Pietro, Pres.--Oh Boy Corporation, San Fernando, CA; *U.S. Private*, pg. 812

Vitito, Robert J., Pres. & Chief Exec. Officer--Citizens Banking Corporation, Flint, MI; *U.S. Public*, pg. 379

Vitito, Robert J., Chm. Bd.--Second National Bank of Saginaw, Saginaw, MI; *U.S. Public*, pg. 379

Vitner, William A., Pres.--C.J. Vitner Co., Chicago, IL; *U.S. Private*, pg. 1142

Vito, Dennis, Pres.--Day & Zimmermann Information Solutions, Wayne, PA; *U.S. Private*, pg. 317

Vittore, Ross F., Pres.--Great Northern Mortgage Company, Rolling Meadows, IL; *U.S. Public*, pg. 141

Vivian, Harry M., Pres.--Vivian Millworks, Forty Fort, PA; *U.S. Private*, pg. 1143
Viviano, Anthony J., Pres.--Sterling Heights Dodge, Inc., Sterling Heights, MI; *U.S. Private*, pg. 1041
Viviano, Joseph P., Pres. & Chief Oper. Officer--Hershey Foods Corporation, Hershey, PA; *U.S. Public*, pg. 811
Vivieros, Michael, Pres.--Rainbow Rentals, Inc., Canfield, OH; *U.S. Private*, pg. 907
Vivona, Bill, Pres.--Harrisburg Stamp Co., Harrisburg, PA; *U.S. Private*, pg. 59
Vizcaino, Carlos, Pres. & Mng. Dir.--Young & Rubicam, S.A. de C.V., Mexico, Mexico; *U.S. Private*, pg. 1200
Vizzi, C.J., Pres.--York Wallcoverings Inc., York, PA; *U.S. Private*, pg. 1196
Vlahakis, Bernard, Pres. & Chief Exec. Officer--Trailer Wheel & Frame Company, Houston, TX; *U.S. Private*, pg. 1095
Vlamis, Ted A., Pres.--Continental American Corp., Wichita, KS; *U.S. Private*, pg. 267
Vlasic, Richard, Chm. Bd. & Pres.--O/E Automation, Inc., Troy, MI; *U.S. Private*, pg. 809
Vlasich, Bill, Pres.--Power Conversion, Inc., Elmwood Park, NJ; *Int'l*, pg. 127
Vlcek, Don, Pres.--Domino's Pizza Distribution Corp., Ann Arbor, MI; *U.S. Private*, pg. 339
Vlewiez, William, Pres.--Casablanca Fan Co., Inc., Memphis, TN; *U.S. Private*, pg. 549
Voelker, James F., Pres.--Nextlink Communications Inc., Bellevue, WA; *U.S. Public*, pg. 1181
Vogel, A., Pres.--Alpine Aktiengesellschaft, Augsburg, Germany; *Int'l*, pg. 636
Vogel, Dieter H ., Dr., Pres.--Thyssen Handelsunion AG, Dusseldorf, Germany; *Int'l*, pg. 1388
Vogel, George N., Pres.--McLean Engineering, Princeton Junction, NJ; *U.S. Public*, pg. 1791
Vogel, Michael J., Pres. & Gen. Mgr.--Day-Timers, Inc., East Texas, PA; *U.S. Public*, pg. 674
Vogel, Michael J., Pres. & Chief Exec. Officer--Day-Timers of Canada, Limited, Niagara Falls, Canada; *U.S. Public*, pg. 674
Vogel, Peter H., Pres.--Zellerbach Division, Miamisburg, OH; *U.S. Public*, pg. 1074
Vogel, Robert, Pres.--Hardwoods Of Michigan, Inc., Clinton, MI; *U.S. Private*, pg. 502
Vogel, Ronald B., Pres.--Great Western Malting Co., Vancouver, WA; *U.S. Public*, pg. 428
Vogel, Stanley N., Pres.--Zero-Max, Inc., Minneapolis, MN; *Int'l*, pg. 866
Vogl, Charles J., Pres. & Chief Oper. Officer--Wilton Corporation, Palatine, IL; *U.S. Private*, pg. 1181
Vogt, Errol, Div. Pres.--Northwest Dietetic Supply, Inc., Kent, WA; *Int'l*, pg. 752
Vogt, Valentin, Pres.--Sulzer Metco AG, Wohlen, Switzerland; *Int'l*, pg. 1307
Vogt, William, Pres. & Chief Exec. Officer--Springfield Precision Instruments, Inc., Wood Ridge, NJ; *U.S. Private*, pg. 1027
Vogtlander, Peter, Pres. & Chief Exec. Officer--Montell Polyolefins, Hoofddorp, Netherlands; *Int'l*, pg. 1136
Voigt, Gary, Pres. & Chief Exec. Officer--Arkansas Electric Cooperatives Inc., Little Rock, AR; *U.S. Private*, pg. 82
Vokos, T., Pres. & Chief Exec. Officer--Miller Freeman Asia Ltd, Wan Chai, Hong Kong; *Int'l*, pg. 1443
Volanakis, George, Pres.--The Ertl Company, Inc, Dyersville, IA; *U.S. Public*, pg. 1684
Vold, Raymond, Pres.--Timesavers Inc., Crystal, MN; *U.S. Private*, pg. 1088
Volgenau, Ernst, Dr., Pres. & Chief Exec. Officer--SRA International Inc., Arlington, VA; *U.S. Private*, pg. 957
Volkenborn, Arnold, Pres.--Pequiven, S.A., Caracas, Venezuela; *Int'l*, pg. 1045
Volker, Cathy, Pres.--Hanes Hosiery, Inc., Winston Salem, NC; *U.S. Public*, pg. 1434
Vollaro, John D., Pres. & Chief Oper. Officer--W.R. Berkley Corporation, Greenwich, CT; *U.S. Public*, pg. 215
Vollaro, John D., Pres. & Chief Exec. Officer--Signet Star Reinsurance Company, Florham Park, NJ; *U.S. Public*, pg. 216
Vollaro, John D., Pres. & Chief Exec. Officer--Signet Star Holdings, Inc., Stamford, CT; *U.S. Public*, pg. 216
Vollbracht, David E., Pres. & Chief Exec. Officer--Fleischer Manufacturing, Inc., Columbus, NE; *U.S. Private*, pg. 410
Vollert, Hans, Chief Oper. Officer (Agro)--Quimica Schering Colombiana S. A., Bogota, Colombia; *Int'l*, pg. 1204
Vollmer, Richard, Office Mgr.--Kintetsu World Express Inc., Erlanger, KY; *Int'l*, pg. 734
Vollrath, Walter III, Pres. & Chief Exec. Officer--Polar Ware Company, Sheboygan, WI; *U.S. Private*, pg. 873
Volny, Peter I., Pres., Chief Exec. Officer & New Bus. Contact--Griffin Bacal Volny, Toronto, Canada; *U.S. Private*, pg. 480
Volpi, G., Pres.--Habisat Svergie AB, Reinich, Switzerland; *Int'l*, pg. 585
Volstad, Conrad, Pres.--Merrill Lynch Derivative Products, Inc., New York, NY; *U.S. Public*, pg. 1097
von der Porten, Bob, Pres.--Speedy Muffler King, Inc., Toronto, Canada; *U.S. Public*, pg. 1578
Von der Ruhr, Gerhard J., Chm. Bd., Pres. & Treas.--Criticare Systems, Inc., Waukesha, WI; *U.S. Public*, pg. 459
Von Hall, Birger, Pres.--Goteborg Regional Office, Goteborg, Sweden; *Int'l*, pg. 899
von Heeder, Paul, Principal & Creative Dir.--Latitude, Dallas, TX; *U.S. Private*, pg. 929
von Holtzbrinck, Dieter, Chm. Bd. & Pres.--Georg von Holtzbrinck GmbH, Stuttgart, Germany; *Int'l*, pg. 1478
von Holtzbrinck, Dieter, Pres.--Zeitverlag Gerd Bucerius GmbH, Hamburg, Germany; *Int'l*, pg. 1479
von Kalm, Dr., Gen. Mgr.--Voith S.A. Maquinas e Equipamentos, Sao Paulo, Brazil; *Int'l*, pg. 1473
von Kantzow, Lars, Pres.--Perstorp Flooring, Raleigh, NC; *Int'l*, pg. 1039
Von Le Fort, Baron, Pres.--Maxi-Papier Market GmbH, Hamburg, Germany; *U.S. Public*, pg. 1510
Von Liebermann, Don, Pres.--Cutco Industries, Inc., Syosset, NY; *U.S. Public*, pg. 470
Von Pichler, Cletus, Pres.--Demag Delaval Turbine, Trenton, NJ; *Int'l*, pg. 837
von Pierer, Heinrich, Dr., Pres. & Chief Exec. Officer--Siemens AG, Munich, Germany; *Int'l*, pg. 1244
von Rickenbach, Josef, Chm. Bd., Pres. & Chief Exec. Officer--PAREXEL International Corporation, Waltham, MA; *U.S. Public*, pg. 1257
von Rosenberg, Joseph L., Pres. & Chief Exec. Officer-Marine Gen. Corp--Zapata Corporation, Houston, TX; *U.S. Public*, pg. 1789
von Schack, Wesley W., Chm. Bd., Pres. & Chief Exec. Officer--New York State Electric & Gas Corporation, Binghamton, NY; *U.S. Public*, pg. 1173
von Simson, D., Pres.--Societe de Banque Suisse S.A., Paris, France; *Int'l*, pg. 1331
von Spreckelsen, John, Pres.--Rhenania Schiffahrts-und Speditions-Gesellschaft mbH, Mannheim, Germany; *Int'l*, *pg. 1033*
von Trapp, Johannes, Pres.--Trapp Family Lodge, Inc., Stowe, VT; *U.S. Private*, pg. 1098
von Walcke-Wulffen, Dirk-Joachim, Dr., Dir.--Deutsche Bank AG (Antwerp), Antwerp, Belgium; *Int'l*, pg. 403
von Wyss, Marc R., Pres. & Chief Exec. Officer--Holnam Inc. (West Division), Lakewood, CO; *Int'l*, pg. 628
Von Zuben, Fred G., Pres. & Chief Exec. Officer--The Newark Group, Inc., Cranford, NJ; *U.S. Private*, pg. 796
vonder Porten, Bob, Pres.--Speedy Car-X, Inc., Chicago, IL; *U.S. Public*, pg. 1578
Vongas, Greg, Pres.--Metex Corporation, Edison, NJ; *U.S. Public*, pg. 1674
Vonk, Gary, Pres. & Chief Oper. Officer--Snappy Car Rental, Inc., Tulsa, OK; *U.S. Private*, pg. 1010
Vornadoe, Susan C., Pres.--Applied Science Associates, Inc., Mc Lean, VA; *U.S. Public*, pg. 109
Vornanen, Sakari, Pres.--Sahkolahteenmaki Oy, Paimio, Finland; *Int'l*, pg. 8
Vortmann, R.H., Pres. & Chief Exec. Officer--National Steel & Shipbuilding Company, San Diego, CA; *U.S. Private*, pg. 787
Vos, Arend W.D., Pres.--PPG Industries Asia/Pacific Ltd., Tokyo, Japan; *U.S. Public*, pg. 1245
Vosburg, N.E., Pres. & Chief Exec. Officer--Pacific Hide & Fur Depot, Great Falls, MT; *U.S. Private*, pg. 831
Voscherau, Eggert, Pres. & Chief Exec. Officer--BASF Corporation, Mount Olive, NJ; *Int'l*, pg. 105
Voss, Marianne, Pres.--Voss Industries, Inc., Cleveland, OH; *U.S. Private*, pg. 1143
Voss, Michael, Pres. & Chief Exec. Officer--BVK/McDonald, Milwaukee, WI; *U.S. Private*, pg. 108
Voss, Peter S., Pres. & Chief Exec. Officer--New England Investment Companies, Inc., Boston, MA; *U.S. Private*, pg. 737
Voss, Timothy, Pres.--Flexible Flyer Toys, West Point, MS; *U.S. Private*, pg. 412
Voss, William H., Pres.--Crown Cork & Seal, Asia-Pacific Division, Singapore, Singapore; *U.S. Public*, pg. 464
Vosseller, Jim, Pres.--Everpure Inc., Westmont, IL; *U.S. Public*, pg. 467
Voutilainen, Pertti, Pres.--Merita Ltd., Helsinki, Finland; *Int'l*, pg. 858
Voves, Joseph, Pres. & Mgr.-Mktg.--Metric & Multistandard Components, Hawthorne, NY; *U.S. Private*, pg. 736
Vowell, J. Larry, Pres. & Chief Exec. Officer--Hussmann Corp., Bridgeton, MO; *U.S. Public*, pg. 1766
Voyer, Nil, Chm. Bd. & Pres.--Purdel, Cooperative Agro-Alimentaire, Bic, Canada; *Int'l*, pg. 1073
Vraciu, Bob, Pres.--Vivra Health Advantage, Inc., Brentwood, TN; *U.S. Public*, pg. 1724
Vrancart, Al, Pres.--NBS Card Services, Inc., South Plainfield, NJ; *Int'l*, pg. 898
Vriesenga, Jerry, Pres.--Dole Hawaii, Wahiawa, HI; *U.S. Public*, pg. 515
Vucins, Viesturs, Pres. & Chief Exec. Officer--Global One, Reston, VA; *U.S. Public*, pg. 1501
Vukadinovic, Borivoje, Pres. & Chief Exec. Officer--Retrospettiva, Inc., Beverly Hills, CA; *U.S. Public*, pg. 1383
Vullings, Jaque T.H., Pres. & Chief Exec. Officer--TA Triumph-Adler Vertriebs GmbH, Nuremberg, Germany; *Int'l*, pg. 1004
Vumbacco, Joseph V., Pres. & Chief Oper. Officer--Health Management Associates, Inc., Naples, FL; *U.S. Public*, pg. 802
Vyas, C.B., Pres. & Chief Exec. Officer--Zeigler Coal Holding Company, Fairview Heights, IL; *U.S. Public*, pg. 1790
Wabiszewski, Edmund E., Pres.--Maynard Steel Casting Company, Milwaukee, WI; *U.S. Private*, pg. 718
Wachi, Takashi, Pres. & Chief Exec. Officer--Terumo Corporation, Tokyo, Japan; *Int'l*, pg. 1375
Wachner, Brian Gary, Chm. Bd. & Pres.--BGW Systems, Inc., Hawthorne, CA; *U.S. Private*, pg. 107
Wachner, Linda, Pres.--Authentic Fitness Corp. East Coast Region, New York, NY; *U.S. Public*, pg. 148
Wachner, Linda J., Chm. Bd., Pres. & Chief Exec. Officer--Warnaco Inc., New York, NY; *U.S. Public*, pg. 1738
Wachstein, Barbara, Pres. & Chief Exec. Officer--Great Lakes Realty Corp., Livonia, MI; *U.S. Private*, pg. 475
Wackenhut, Richard R., Pres. & Chief Oper. Officer--The Wackenhut Corporation, Palm Beach Gardens, FL; *U.S. Public*, pg. 1731
Wacker, Fred G., III, Pres.--Liquid Controls LLC, Lake Bluff, IL; *U.S. Private*, pg. 669
Wada, Horoyoshi, Pres. & Dir.--Tokio Marine Delaware Corporation, Dover, DE; *Int'l*, pg. 1392
Wada, Tadashi, Pres.--Shin-Etsu Handotai Co. Ltd., Tokyo, Japan; *Int'l*, pg. 1234
Waddell, R. Scott, Pres.--Standard Locknut, Inc., Westfield, IN; *U.S. Private*, pg. 1031
Waddell, William R., Pres.--Capital Resources of Virginia, Inc., Richmond, VA; *U.S. Private*, pg. 657
Wade, Bill, Pres.--CR Services, Elgin, IL; *Int'l*, pg. 1157
Wade, Daniel M., Pres. & Chief Oper. Officer--MGM Grand Hotel, Inc., Las Vegas, NV; *U.S. Public*, pg. 1027
Wade, William S., Jr., Pres. & Chief Exec. Officer--FAG Bearings Corporation, Danbury, CT; *Int'l*, pg. 469
Wadensten, Ted S., Pres. & Adv. Mgr.--Vibco Inc., Wyoming, RI; *U.S. Private*, pg. 1138
Wadensten, Ted S., Pres.--Vibco Vibration Products, Mississauga, Canada; *U.S. Private*, pg. 1138
Wadsten, Gary, V.P.-Sls.--Fairfield Myrtle Beach, Inc., North Myrtle Beach, SC; *U.S. Public*, pg. 611
Wadsworth, John S., Jr., Pres.--Morgan Stanley Japan Ltd., Tokyo, Japan; *U.S. Public*, pg. 1133
Wadsworth, Samuel T., Pres.--United Parking, Inc., Atlanta, GA; *U.S. Private*, pg. 1123
Wadsworth, Stanley, Pres. & Chief Exec. Officer--Golf Hosts, Inc., Palm Harbor, FL; *U.S. Private*, pg. 1036
Wagar, Mark L., Pres. & Chief Oper. Officer--Medpartners Inc., Birmingham, AL; *U.S. Public*, pg. 1082
Wagenhals, Fred W., Chm. Bd., Pres. & Chief Exec. Officer--Action Performance Companies, Inc., Phoenix, AZ; *U.S. Public*, pg. 17
Wagman, Lee H., Pres.--TrizecHahn Centers Inc., San Diego, CA; *Int'l*, pg. 1425
Wagner, Arthur, Pres.--Active International, Pearl River, NY; *U.S. Private*, pg. 15
Wagner, David, Pres.--Accessory Design Group, Ltd., Arlington, TX; *U.S. Public*, pg. 1560
Wagner, David J., Chm. Bd., Pres. & Chief Exec. Officer--Old Kent Financial Corporation, Grand Rapids, MI; *U.S. Public*, pg. 1216
Wagner, Harold A., Chm. Bd., Pres. & Chief Exec. Officer--Air Products and Chemicals, Inc., Allentown, PA; *U.S. Public*, pg. 30
Wagner, John R., Pres.--City Machine Tool & Die Company, Inc., Muncie, IN; *U.S. Private*, pg. 241
Wagner, Lawrence M., Pres. & Chief Oper. Officer--The Hillman Company, Pittsburgh, PA; *U.S. Private*, pg. 530
Wagner, Matthew P., Pres. & Chief Exec. Officer--Western Bancorp, Newport Beach, CA; *U.S. Public*, pg. 1757
Wagner, Peter, Chief Exec. Officer--Danzas Holding Ltd., Basel, Switzerland; *Int'l*, pg. 382
Wagner, Rodger, Pres.--Big Horn Redi-Mix, Powell, WY; *U.S. Public*, pg. 1124
Wagner, Roger P., Pres. & Chief Oper. Officer--Trump's Marina Casino Resort, Atlantic City, NJ; *U.S. Private*, pg. 1108
Wagner, Tom, Pres. & Chief Exec. Officer--Jones Blair Company, Dallas, TX; *U.S. Private*, pg. 596
Wagner, Wayne E., Pres. & Gen. Mgr.--Horne & Pitfield, Edmonton, Canada; *Int'l*, pg. 1012
Wagniere, Daniel C., Pres.-Exec. Bd. & Chief Oper. Officer--Sandoz (Hellas) S.A.C.I., Athens, Greece; *Int'l*, pg. 984
Wagstaff, David, 111, 2res. & Chief Exec. Officer--Vectura Group, Inc., New Orleans, LA; *U.S. Private*, pg. 1135
Wagstaff, Robert, Pres.--Wagstaff Inc., Spokane, WA; *U.S. Private*, pg. 1146
Wahl, C. Richard, Pres. & Chief Oper. Officer--Wheatland Tube Company, Collingswood, NJ; *U.S. Private*, pg. 1170
Wahl, Ed, Pres.--Apex Oil Company, Inc., Saint Louis, MO; *U.S. Private*, pg. 77
Wahl, Eugene R., Pres.--Vibra Screw Inc., Totowa, NJ; *U.S.* Private, pg. 1138
Wahl, Lothar, Pres. & Chief Oper. Officer--BOMAG, Boppard, Germany; *U.S. Public*, pg. 1677
Wahle, Elliott, Pres. & Chief Exec. Officer--Dylex Limited, Toronto, Canada; *Int'l*, pg. 425
Wahle, Elliott, Pres.--Braemar Apparel Inc., Toronto, Canada; *Int'l*, pg. 425
Wahle, James L., Pres. & Chief Oper. Officer--Accu-Sort Systems, Inc., Telford, PA; *U.S. Private*, pg. 11
Wahlin, Olof, Pres. & Mng. Dir.--Foga System International AB, Vastra Frolunda, Sweden; *Int'l*, pg. 496
Wahlke, Bob, Pres.-Towne Properties Asset Management Co.--Towne Properties, Cincinnati, OH; *U.S. Private*, pg. 1093
Wahlstrom, Mats, Pres.--COBE Laboratories, Inc., Lakewood, CO; *Int'l*, pg. 667
Waite, Peter G., Pres.--PCC Airfoils, Inc., Beachwood, OH; *U.S. Public*, pg. 1320
Wakabayashi, Shohachiro, Pres.--Oriental Motor Co., Ltd., Tokyo, Japan; *Int'l*, pg. 1008
Wakasa, K., Pres.--Shimadzu Precision Instruments, Inc., Torrance, CA; *Int'l*, pg. 1232
Wake, John, Pres. & Chief Exec. Officer--Western States Machine Company, Hamilton, OH; *U.S. Private*, pg. 1168
Wake, Richard, Co-Pres.--Eby-Brown Co., Naperville, IL; *U.S. Private*, pg. 359
Wake, Tom, Co-Pres.--Eby-Brown Co., Naperville, IL; *U.S. Private*, pg. 359
Wakehurst, Christopher L., Rt. Hon. Lord, Chm. Bd.--Philadelphia National Limited, London, United Kingdom; *U.S. Public*, pg. 447
Wakelin, Alan, Pres.--N.V. Allied Colloids Belgium S.A., Nivelles, Belgium; *Int'l*, pg. 62
Wakley, James T., Pres.--Colonial Millwork, Inc., Beverly, WV; *U.S. Private*, pg. 706
Wakuyama, T., Pres.--SEIKO Canada Inc., Markham, Canada; *Int'l*, pg. 1218
Wakuyama, Takashi, Pres.--SEIKO Corporation of America, Mahwah, NJ; *Int'l*, pg. 1218
Walburn, H. Fred, Pres. & Chief Exec. Officer--Regions Bank/Sumter County, Livingston, AL; *U.S. Public*, pg. 1373
Wald, Ann, Editor-in-Chief--Princeton University Press, Princeton, NJ; *U.S. Private*, pg. 885
Walden, L.T. Jr., Pres.--E-Z-GO Textron, Augusta, GA; *U.S. Public*, pg. 1589
Walden, Philip, Pres.--Imperial Business Credit, San Diego, CA; *U.S. Public*, pg. 872
Waldheger, R.A., Pres.--Carbon Technology Inc., Slocum, RI; *Int'l*, pg. 891
Waldhof, Jens, Pres.--Rhodia A.G., Freiburg, Germany; *Int'l*, *pg. 1112*

Waldin, Thomas B., Pres. & Chief Exec. Officer--Essef Corporation, Chardon, OH; *U.S. Public*, pg. 592
Waldorf, Robert, Chm. Bd. & Pres.--Idea Man, Inc., Los Angeles, CA; *U.S. Private*, pg. 557
Waldron, W. Daniel, Pres.--Elyria Savings & Trust National Bank, Elyria, OH; *U.S. Public*, pg. 646
Waldrop, Richard E., Pres., Chief Oper. Officer & V.P.-Sls.--Edwards Engineering Corporation, Pompton Plains, NJ; *U.S. Private*, pg. 365
Waldrop, Thomas E., Chm. Bd. & Pres.--Media General Cable of Fairfax County Inc., Chantilly, VA; *U.S. Public*, pg. 1078
Waldschurz, Gerhard, Chm. Bd., Pres. & Chief Exec. Officer--Optimaxx International, Rockleigh, NJ; *U.S. Private*, pg. 818
Waldthausen, Kurt, Pres.--Holz-Her U.S. Inc., Charlotte, NC; *Int'l*, pg. 1101
Walicki, Robert R., Pres. & Chief Oper. Officer--Village Pantries, Inc., Indianapolis, IN; *U.S. Public*, pg. 1049
Walker, C. Denny, Pres. & Chief Exec. Officer--Draper Texmaco, Inc., Spartanburg, SC; *U.S. Private*, pg. 342
Walker, Chris L., Pres. & Chief Oper. Officer--E.W. Blanch Holdings, Inc., Minneapolis, MN; *U.S. Public*, pg. 236
Walker, D.T., V.P. & Gen. Mgr.--Acheson Colloids Company, Port Huron, MI; *U.S. Private*, pg. 12
Walker, Donald, Pres.& Chief Exec. Officer--Magna International Inc., Markham, Canada; *Int'l*, pg. 829
Walker, Doug, Pres. & Chief Exec. Officer--WRQ, Inc., Seattle, WA; *U.S. Private*, pg. 1145
Walker, Harry M., Pres. & Chief Oper. Officer--Trustmark National Bank, Jackson, MS; *U.S. Public*, pg. 1643
Walker, Jack A., Pres.--Cubic Applications, Inc., Lacey, WA; *U.S. Public*, pg. 466
Walker, James, Pres.--Zemenick & Walker, Inc., Saint Louis, MO; *U.S. Public*, pg. 644
Walker, James A., Jr., Pres.--Jones Company, Inc., Waycross, GA; *U.S. Private*, pg. 596
Walker, Jimmy, Pres.--Fuel South, Inc., Hazlehurst, GA; *U.S.* Private, pg. 596
Walker, John R., Pres.--Walker Die Casting, Inc., Lewisburg, TN; *U.S. Private*, pg. 1147
Walker, John T., Chm. Bd., Pres. & Chief Exec. Officer--St. Paul Metalcraft, Inc., Saint Paul, MN; *U.S. Private*, pg. 961
Walker, Joseph P., Chm. Bd., Pres. & Chief Exec. Officer--CTS Corporation, Elkhart, IN; *U.S. Public*, pg. 285
Walker, K.D., Pres. & Chief Exec. Officer--Meineke Discount Muffler Shops, Inc., Charlotte, NC; *Int'l*, pg. 535
Walker, Robert, Pres.--Fairfield Group, Horsham, PA; *U.S. Public*, pg. 985
Walker, Ron, Pres.--Captain D's Restaurant, Nashville, TN; *U.S. Public*, pg. 1467
Walker, Steven C., Pres. & Chief Exec. Officer--Cand Investments Inc., Shreveport, LA; *U.S. Public*, pg. 501
Walker, T.J., Pres. & Gen. Mgr.--Electrical Equipment Company, Raleigh, NC; *U.S. Private*, pg. 368
Walker, Thomas K., Pres.--Amcast Automotive, Southfield, MI; *U.S. Public*, pg. 63
Walker, W.T., Pres.--Somerset Refinery Inc., Somerset, KY; *U.S. Private*, pg. 1013
Walker, William W., Pres.--Minera Hispaniola, S.A., Santo Domingo, Dominican Republic; *U.S. Public*, pg. 302
Wall, Jack, Pres.--Al Larson Boat Shop, Inc., Terminal Island, CA; *U.S. Private*, pg. 652
Wall, James, Pres.--AMREP Southwest, Inc., Rio Rancho, NM; *U.S. Public*, pg. 104
Wall, John Lyndon, Pres.--Bryant Electric Company, Inc., High Point, NC; *U.S. Private*, pg. 176
Wall, John R., Pres. & Chief Exec. Officer--Wall Data Incorporated, Kirkland, WA; *U.S. Public*, pg. 1734
Wall, Kent, Pres.--Dockers Footwear, Nashville, TN; *U.S. Public*, pg. 728
Wall, Michael, Pres.--Premier Industries, Inc., Tacoma, WA; *U.S. Private*, pg. 881
Wall, Steven E., Pres. & Chief Oper. Officer--Society National Bank, Cleveland, OH; *U.S. Public*, pg. 954
Wall, Terrence D., Chm. Bd., Pres. & Chief Exec. Officer--Vital Signs, Inc., Totowa, NJ; *U.S. Public*, pg. 1723
Wallace, Alan, Pres.--J.G. Hook Enterprises, Inc., Burlington, NJ; *U.S. Private*, pg. 538
Wallace, Bryan, Pres.--SCANLAB Sdn. Bhd., Kuala Lumpur, Malaysia; *Int'l*, pg. 1390
Wallace, Carol P., Pres. & Chief Exec. Officer--Cooper Instrument Corp., Middlefield, CT; *U.S. Private*, pg. 274
Wallace, Donald W., Pres.--Lazy Days R V Center, Inc., Seffner, FL; *U.S. Private*, pg. 655
Wallace, Douglas A., Pres.--Stanley Enviromental, Inc., Coralville, IA; *U.S. Private*, pg. 1033
Wallace, Henry D.G., Pres.--Mazda Motor Corporation, Hiroshima, Japan; *Int'l*, pg. 849
Wallace, James D., Pres. & Chief Exec. Officer--National Travelers Life Co., West Des Moines, IA; *U.S. Private*, pg. 787
Wallace, James E., Pres. & Chief Exec. Officer--Hamilton, Allen & Associates, Inc., Atlanta, GA; *U.S. Public*, pg. 1673
Wallace, Kevin, Pres. & Chief Exec. Officer--Thermo Separation Products, San Jose, CA; *U.S. Public*, pg. 1594
Wallace, Michael R., Pres. & Chief Oper. Officer--Jack Henry & Associates, Inc., Monett, MO; *U.S. Public*, pg. 808
Wallace, Ray, Pres.--Abbott Laboratories, Mountain View, CA; *U.S. Public*, pg. 13
Wallace, Reg, Pres.--Crane Carrier Company, Tulsa, OK; *U.S. Private*, pg. 286
Wallace, Terry, Pres.--AmeriTruck Refrigerated Transport, Inc., Waupaca, WI; *U.S. Private*, pg. 66
Wallace, Thomas T., Pres.--Johnston, Lemon & Co. Inc., Washington, DC; *U.S. Private*, pg. 595
Wallace, W. Ray, Chm. Bd., Pres. & Chief Exec. Officer--Trinity Industries Inc., Dallas, TX; *U.S. Public*, pg. 1638
Wallace, W. Ray, Pres.--Trinity Difco, Findlay, OH; *U.S. Public*, pg. 1639
Wallace, Walker J., V.P.-Olestra--Olestra Div., Cincinnati, OH; *U.S. Public*, pg. 1330
Wallace, William F., Pres. & Chief Oper. Officer--Plains Petroleum Operating Co., Lakewood, CO; *U.S. Public*, pg. 191
Wallach, James, Pres. & Chief Exec. Officer--Central National-Gottesman Inc., Purchase, NY; *U.S. Private*, pg. 224
Wallack, Al, Pres. & Chief Exec. Officer--Royal Olympic Cruises, New York, NY; *U.S. Public*, pg. 1411
Wallbridge, Van, Chm. Bd., Pres. & Chief Exec. Officer--Mobil Tool International, Westminster, CO; *Int'l*, pg. 1486
Wallen, Ernest, Pres.--Heat Bath Park Metallurgical Corp., Indian Orchard, MA; *U.S. Private*, pg. 518
Wallenfelsz, James D., Pres.--Interplastic Corp., Saint Paul, MN; *U.S. Private*, pg. 572
Waller, David, Pres.--W.L. Hailey & Company, Inc., Nashville, TN; *U.S. Private*, pg. 494
Waller, K. Nick, Pres.--Datasouth Computer Corporation, Charlotte, NC; *U.S. Public*, pg. 267
Waller, Peter C., Pres. & Chief Concept Officer--Taco Bell Corp., Irvine, CA; *U.S. Public*, pg. 1637
Wallis, Graham, Pres.--Javelin Systems, Syosset, NY; *U.S. Public*, pg. 1306
Wallis, Lloyd, Pres.--Associated Concrete Products, Inc., Santa Ana, CA; *U.S. Private*, pg. 417
Wallis, Lloyd, Pres.--Center Line, Tulsa, OK; *U.S. Public*, pg. 457
Walliser, Carl J., Pres.--Print-O-Tape, Inc., Mundelein, IL; *U.S. Private*, pg. 886
Wallner, Edgar, Pres. & Chief Exec. Officer--Orthofix International N.V., Curacao, Netherlands Antilles; *Int'l*, pg. 1011
Wallrabe, Horst, Pres.--Bayer Corporation/Pharmaceutical Division, West Haven, CT; *Int'l*, pg. 173
Wallwork, William W., III, Pres.--W.W. Wallwork, Inc., Fargo, ND; *U.S. Private*, pg. 1148
Walmsley, Gregory H., Pres.--Oxarc Inc., Spokane, WA; *U.S. Private*, pg. 825
Walnes, Jack R., Pres.--Varity Zecal, Churchville, NY; *Int'l*, pg. 820
Walpole, R.H., Pres. & Chief Oper. Officer--Walbro Engine Management Corporation, Cass City, MI; *U.S. Public*, pg. 1733
Walrack, Rich, Pres.--Santee Dairies, Los Angeles, CA; *U.S.* Public, pg. 1349
Walsh, Chuck, Mng. Partner & Chief Fin. Officer--Earle Palmer Brown, New York, NY; *U.S. Private*, pg. 173
Walsh, Daniel J., Pres.--Walsh Group, Chicago, IL; *U.S. Private*, pg. 1148
Walsh, Donald L., Pres.--Magnetic Metals Corp., Camden, NJ; *U.S. Private*, pg. 560
Walsh, Eric, Pres.--Good Humor/Breyers Ice Cream, Green Bay, WI; *Int'l*, pg. 1435
Walsh, G., Pres. & Chief Exec. Officer--Pratt & Whitney, Grand Prairie, TX; *U.S. Public*, pg. 1690
Walsh, John, Pres.--La Marche Mfg. Co., Des Plaines, IL; *U.S. Private*, pg. 640
Walsh, John, Pres. & Exec. V.P.-Shaving Prods. Grp.--Warner-Lambert Shaving Products Group, Milford, CT; *U.S. Public*, pg. 1739
Walsh, John T., Pres.--Columbian Chemicals Company, Atlanta, GA; *U.S. Public*, pg. 1286
Walsh, Joseph A., Pres., Chief Exec. Officer & Sls. Dir.--Multi-Local Media Corporation, Rockville Centre, NY; *U.S. Private*, pg. 767
Walsh, Karen C., Pres.--Milage Plus, Inc., Rolling Meadows, IL; *U.S. Public*, pg. 1653
Walsh, Kevin M., Pres. & Chief Oper. Officer--Expeditors International of Washington, Inc., Seattle, WA; *U.S. Public*, pg. 600
Walsh, Michael, Pres.--Ocean Properties, Ltd., Delray Beach, FL; *U.S. Private*, pg. 811
Walsh, Michael J., Pres. & Chief Exec. Officer--Tandycrafts, Inc., Fort Worth, TX; *U.S. Public*, pg. 1561
Walsh, Paul, Pres.--Wright Express Corporation, South Portland, ME; *U.S. Public*, pg. 321
Walsh, Robert J., Pres.--Sprint Publishing & Advertising, Overland Park, KS; *U.S. Public*, pg. 1501
Walsh, Thomas J., III, Pres. & Gen. Mgr.--Walsh Construction Company, Trumbull, CT; *U.S. Public*, pg. 143
Walsh, Thomas L., Pres.--Energy Dynamics Division, Chandler, AZ; *U.S. Public*, pg. 1250
Walsmith, Joe, Pres.--Willitts Design, Petaluma, CA; *U.S. Private*, pg. 1180
Walsworth, Don O., Pres. & Chief Exec. Officer--Walsworth Publishing Company, Inc., Marceline, MO; *U.S. Private*, pg. 1148
Walter, Curtis, Pres.--Bongards Creameries Inc., Norwood, MN; *U.S. Private*, pg. 156
Walter, John A., Pres. & Chief Exec. Officer--The Gorman-Rupp Company, Mansfield, OH; *U.S. Public*, pg. 754
Walter, Mike, Pres.-ConAgra Specialty Grain Products Company--ConAgra Fruen Milling Co., Omaha, NE; *U.S. Public*, pg. 428
Walter, Paul F., Chm. Bd., Pres. & Chief Exec. Officer--Thermo Electric Co., Inc., Saddle Brook, NJ; *U.S. Private*, pg. 1080
Walters, Alan H., Pres.--G & W Life Insurance Co., Jackson, MS; *U.S. Public*, pg. 501
Walters, Bruce, Pres.--AVM Inc., Marion, SC; *U.S. Public*, pg. 137
Walters, Robert P., Pres.--Thomasville Upholstery, Inc., Hickory, NC; *U.S. Public*, pg. 688
Walters, Thomas J., Pres.--Morton's of Chicago, Inc., Chicago, IL; *U.S. Public*, pg. 1136
Walters, Tom, Pres.--Carder Concrete Products Co., Littleton, CO; *U.S. Private*, pg. 208
Walther, Norbert H.H., Pres.--Demag Komatsu GmbH, Dusseldorf, Germany; *Int'l*, pg. 745
Walzman, Mark, Pres.--Mark Fabricks, Inc., Los Angeles, CA; *U.S. Private*, pg. 704
Wamhoff, Richard H., Pres. & Chief Exec. Officer--Ore-Ida Foods, Inc., Boise, ID; *U.S. Public*, pg. 805
Wampler, John G., Pres.--Pulaski Furniture Corporation, Pulaski, VA; *U.S. Public*, pg. 1342
Wandel, Albrecht, Pres. & Chief Exec. Officer--Wandel & Goltermann GmbH & Co., Elektronische Messtechnik, Eningen, Germany; *Int'l*, pg. 1485
Wanderon, Anton, Pres.--ERJ Insurance Group, Miami Springs, FL; *U.S. Public*, pg. 79
Wang, David, Pres.--Tech Industries, Inc., Woonsocket, RI; *U.S. Private*, pg. 1071
Wang, Robert, Pres.--Wang's International, Inc., Memphis, TN; *U.S. Private*, pg. 1149
Wang, W.N., Pres.--China Steel Global Trading Corporation, Kao-hsiung, Taiwan; *Int'l*, pg. 285
Wang, William, Pres.--MAG Innovision Co., Inc., Santa Ana, CA; *U.S. Private*, pg. 694
Wang, Xuebing, Chm. Bd. & Pres.--Bank of China, Beijing, China; *Int'l*, pg. 152
Wang, Yungtsai, Pres.--Formosa Plastics Corporation, Kao-hsiung, Taiwan; *Int'l*, pg. 498
Wanglee, Thamnoon, Pres.--Thai Airways International Ltd., Bangkok, Thailand; *Int'l*, pg. 1381
Wanglee, Thamnu, Pres.--Nakornthon Bank Public Company Limited, Bangkok, Thailand; *Int'l*, pg. 904
Wann, Robert F.S., Pres.--Parker Brothers, Beverly, MA; *U.S. Public*, pg. 797
Wanninger, Charles T., Pres. & Publr.--Press-Citizen Company, Inc., Iowa City, IA; *U.S. Public*, pg. 701
Wannop, Guy, Pres.--Walter Kidde Portable Equipment Inc., Mebane, NC; *Int'l*, pg. 1500
Wapp, Jeffery, Pres.--Hollywood Entertainment Corp., Wilsonville, OR; *U.S. Private*, pg. 535
Ward, Brian P., Pres., Chief Exec. Officer & Treas.--Cortland Line Co., Inc., Cortland, NY; *U.S. Private*, pg. 277
Ward, D. Les, Pres. & Chief Exec. Officer--Source Services Corporation, Dallas, TX; *U.S. Public*, pg. 1488
Ward, David K., Pres.--Ward Trucking Corp., Altoona, PA; *U.S. Private*, pg. 1149
Ward, Don, Pres. & Gen. Mgr.--AAR Oklahoma, Oklahoma City, OK; *U.S. Public*, pg. 1
Ward, Doug, Pres. & Dir.-Mktg.--Amcor, Inc., Bountiful, UT; *Int'l*, pg. 242
Ward, Jerry L., Pres.--Dresser Valve & Controls Div., Woodlands, TX; *U.S. Public*, pg. 528
Ward, John, Pres.--The Leslie Fay Companies, Inc., New York, NY; *U.S. Public*, pg. 989
Ward, John, Pres.--Leslie Fay Dress, New York, NY; *U.S. Public*, pg. 989
Ward, John A., Pres.--Chroma Corporation, McHenry, IL; *U.S. Private*, pg. 238
Ward, John B., Pres.--First American Field Services, Lakewood, NJ; *U.S. Public*, pg. 625
Ward, Lloyd, Exec. V.P. & Pres.-N.A. Appliance--Maytag Corporation, Newton, IA; *U.S. Public*, pg. 1064
Ward, Milton H., Chm. Bd., Pres. & Chief Exec. Officer--Cyprus Amax Minerals Company, Englewood, CO; *U.S. Public*, pg. 470
Ward, Nelson, Pres. & Chief Oper. Officer--Ennis Business Forms, Inc., Ennis, TX; *U.S. Public*, pg. 583
Ward, Richard, Pres.--Guaranty Asset Protection Services, Inc., West Hills, CA; *U.S. Public*, pg. 857
Ward, Rick, Pres.--Standard Chlorine Cloroben Chemical Corporation, Kearny, NJ; *U.S. Private*, pg. 1031
Ward, Scott H., Pres. & Chief Fin. Officer--Russell Stover Candies, Inc., Kansas City, MO; *U.S. Private*, pg. 953
Ward, Thomas J., Pres. & Chief Oper. Officer--WestPoint Stevens Inc., West Point, GA; *U.S. Public*, pg. 1762
Ward, Thomas S., Pres. & Oper. Exec. Officer--Russell Stover Candies, Inc., Kansas City, MO; *U.S. Private*, pg. 953
Ward, William, Chm. Bd. & Pres.--Ashley F. Ward, Inc., Mason, OH; *U.S. Private*, pg. 1149
Wardrop, Richard, Chm. Bd., Pres. & Chief Exec. Officer--AK Steel Corporation, Middletown, OH; *U.S. Public*, pg. 7
Ware, Carl, Pres.--Coca-Cola Southern Africa (Pty) Ltd., Johannesburg, South Africa; *U.S. Public*, pg. 392
Ware, Dennert O., Pres. & Chief Exec. Officer--Corange U.S. Holdings, Inc, Indianapolis, IN; *Int'l*, pg. 331
Ware, James, Pres.--Durametallic Corp., Kalamazoo, MI; *U.S. Public*, pg. 658
Wareham, John P., Pres. & Chief Oper. Officer--Beckman Instruments, Inc., Fullerton, CA; *U.S. Public*, pg. 199
Warehime, John A., Chm. Bd., Pres. & Chief Exec. Officer--Hanover Foods Corporation, Hanover, PA; *U.S. Private*, pg. 499
Warfield, Ronald, Pres.--Country Life Insurance Company, Bloomington, IL; *U.S. Private*, pg. 278
Wargo, Cindy, Pres.--North Coast Behavioral Research Group, Cleveland, OH; *U.S. Private*, pg. 1194
Warhover, Stephen, Pres.--The Gorton Group, Gloucester, MA; *Int'l*, pg. 1434
Warik, Olle, Pres.--NCC Building - Uppsala, Uppsala, Sweden; *Int'l*, pg. 899
Waring, Saul, Pres. & Co-Chief Exec. Officer--Waring & LaRosa, Inc., New York, NY; *U.S. Private*, pg. 1150
Warkentin, Donald, Pres.--APT, Chicago, IL; *U.S. Public*, pg. 1570
Warlick, Anderson, Pres. & Chief Oper. Officer--Parkdale Mills, Gastonia, NC; *U.S. Private*, pg. 840
Warn, Michael T., Pres. & Chief Exec. Officer--Warn Industries, Inc., Clackamas, OR; *U.S. Private*, pg. 1150
Warner, Charles N., Pres.--The U.S. Baird Corporation, Stratford, CT; *U.S. Private*, pg. 1124
Warner, Douglas A., Pres.--Morgan Guaranty Trust Company of New York, New York, NY; *U.S. Public*, pg. 1129
Warner, Fred, Pres.--Laubeck Corporation/Cross, Carbondale, PA; *U.S. Private*, pg. 652
Warner, James, Pres.-CBS Enterprises Div.--CBS Broadcast Group, New York, NY; *U.S. Public*, pg. 274

Warner, James J., Pres.--Warner Vineyards, Paw Paw, MI; *U.S. Private*, pg. 1151
Warner, John D., Pres.--Boeing Computer Services, Bellevue, WA; *U.S. Public*, pg. 240
Warner, John D., Pres.--Boeing Information & Support Services, Bellevue, WA; *U.S. Public*, pg. 241
Warp, Harold G., Pres.--Flex-O-Glass, Inc., Chicago, IL; *U.S. Private*, pg. 412
Warren, Donald G., Pres.--Suitt Construction Company, Inc., Greenville, SC; *U.S. Private*, pg. 106
Warren, Everett, Chm. Bd. & Pres.--American Manufacturing Company, Chattanooga, TN; *U.S. Private*, pg. 58
Warren, Frank M., Jr., Pres. & Chief Exec. Officer--Rogers Group Inc., Nashville, TN; *U.S. Private*, pg. 939
Warren, Frank Raymond, Pres.--Warren Properties, Escondido, CA; *U.S. Private*, pg. 1151
Warren, James R., Pres. & Chief Exec. Officer--Cameron & Barkley Company, Charleston, SC; *U.S. Private*, pg. 203
Warren, John C., Chm. Bd., Pres. & Chief Exec. Officer--Washington Trust Bancorp, Inc., Westerly, RI; *U.S. Public*, pg. 1744
Warren, John C., Pres. & Chief Exec. Officer--The Washington Trust Company, Westerly, RI; *U.S. Public*, pg. 1744
Warren, Jorden, Partner & Gen. Mgr.--CKS Partners/San Francisco, San Francisco, CA; *U.S. Private*, pg. 195
Warren, Patricia, Pres.--Cherokee Inc., Van Nuys, CA; *U.S. Public*, pg. 345
Warren, Paul B., Chm. Bd. & Pres.--UVP, Inc., Upland, CA; *U.S. Private*, pg. 1115
Warren, Robert C., Jr., Pres. & Chief Exec. Officer--Cascade Corporation, Troutdale, OR; *U.S. Public*, pg. 310
Warren, Robert, III, Pres.--Warren Distributing Corp., Raleigh, NC; *U.S. Private*, pg. 1151
Warren, Terry W., Pres. & Chief Exec. Officer--MedTrac, Inc., Nashville, TN; *Int'l*, pg. 1504
Warren, Will H., Pres. & Chief Fin. Officer--NES Holdings, Inc., Raleigh, NC; *U.S. Private*, pg. 771
Warren, Wm. Michael, Jr., Pres. & Chief Exec. Officer--Energen Corporation, Birmingham, AL; *U.S. Public*, pg. 581
Warrilow, C.B., Pres.--Volkswagen Canada, Inc., Ajax, Canada; *Int'l*, pg. 1475
Warrilow, Clive B., Pres. & Chief Exec. Officer--Volkswagen of America, Inc., Auburn Hills, MI; *Int'l*, pg. 1474
Warrington, Clayton L., Pres. & Chief Exec. Officer--Dugan/Farley Communications, Upper Saddle River, NJ; *U.S. Public*, pg. 1642
Warrington, Gary L., Pres.--United Companies Life Insurance Co., Baton Rouge, LA; *U.S. Public*, pg. 1271
Warrington, George, Acting Chm. Bd., Pres. & Chief Exec. Officer--Amtrak-National Railroad Passenger Corp., Washington, DC; *U.S. Private*, pg. 68
Warrington, Robert H., Pres.--Old Kent Mortgage Company, Grand Rapids, MI; *U.S. Public*, pg. 1216
Warsaw, Eugene, Pres.--Hampshire Designers Inc., Anderson, SC; *U.S. Public*, pg. 778
Warshaw, Steven G., Pres., Chief Oper. & Fin. Officer--Chiquita Brands International, Inc., Cincinnati, OH; *U.S. Public*, pg. 349
Warshawsky, Stanford S., Co-Pres.--Arnhold and S. Bleichroeder, Inc., New York, NY; *U.S. Private*, pg. 83
Wartnaby, Lord King of, Pres.--British Airways PLC, London, United Kingdom; *Int'l*, pg. 218
Wasek, Matt K., Pres. & Chief Oper. Officer--Valley Fresh, Inc., Turlock, CA; *U.S. Private*, pg. 1132
Washbrook, E.H., Pres.--Ascolectric Limited, Brantford, Canada; *U.S. Public*, pg. 575
Washlesky, Mike, Sr. Principal & Creative Dir.--Publicis/Bloom, Dallas, TX; *Int'l*, pg. 469
Waskiewicz, David F., Pres.--Rodney Hunt Company, Orange, MA; *U.S. Private*, pg. 549
Wasp, Tricia, Chm. Bd. & Pres.--Ronco Communications & Electronics Inc., Tonawanda, NY; *U.S. Private*, pg. 943
Wass, S.J., Pres.--Thomas De La Rue Inc., Chantilly, VA; *Int'l*, pg. 387
Wassarman, Elliot, Pres. & Chief Exec. Officer--Mitek Systems, Inc., San Diego, CA; *U.S. Public*, pg. 1117
Wasserlein, John, Pres.--Fraser Papers, Inc., Stamford, CT; *Int'l*, pg. 434
Wasserman, A., Sr. V.P., Branch Mgr. & Dir., Creative Services-BC/AL--McKim Advertising Ltd., Vancouver, Canada; *U.S. Private*, pg. 104
Wasserman, Stephen, Pres. & Chief Exec. Officer--National Bank of Hastings, Hastings, MI; *U.S. Public*, pg. 633
Wasserspring, Fredric R., Pres. & Chief Oper. Officer--Michael Anthony Jewelers, Inc., Mount Vernon, NY; *U.S.* Public, pg. 1103
Wasserstrom, Rodney, Pres. & Chief Exec. Officer--Wasserstrom Company, Columbus, OH; *U.S. Private*, pg. 1152
Wassman, Ernest, Pres.--Tecmar Technologies International, Inc., Concord, Canada; *Int'l*, pg. 1361
Wassmann, Ernest H., Pres.--Legacy Storage Systems Corp., Markham, Canada; *Int'l*, pg. 805
Wassner, Leonard, Pres.--Arnav Industries, Inc., New York, NY; *U.S. Private*, pg. 83
Wasson, Ron, Pres.--KLT Telecom Inc., Kansas City, MO; *U.S. Public*, pg. 943
Wasson, Ronald, Pres.--KLT Inc., Kansas City, MO; *U.S. Public*, pg. 943
Wassong, D.K., Chm. Bd., Pres. & Chief Exec. Officer--Sally Hansen, Farmingdale, NY; *U.S. Public*, pg. 494
Wassong, Dan K., Chm. Bd., Pres. & Chief Exec. Officer--Del Laboratories, Inc., Farmingdale, NY; *U.S. Public*, pg. 494
Watabe, Tsayoshi, Pres.--Penfabric Sdn. Berhad, Penang, Malaysia; *Int'l*, pg. 1400
Watanabe, Hiromi, Pres.--Komatsu Changlin Foundry Corporation, Jiangsu, China; *Int'l*, pg. 745
Watanabe, Hiroshi, Pres.--Hitachi Maxell, Ltd., Osaka, Japan; *Int'l*, pg. 621
Watanabe, Sizuo, Pres.--Toray Composites (America), Inc., Tacoma, WA; *Int'l*, pg. 1400
Watanabe, Susumu, Pres.--Nichiyu Koki Co., Ltd., Nagoya, Japan; *Int'l*, pg. 763
Watanabe, Tadashi, Pres.--Dentsu Espana S.A., Barcelona, Spain; *Int'l*, pg. 393
Watanabe, Takao, Pres.--Murata of America, Inc., Charlotte, NC; *Int'l*, pg. 897
Watanabe, Takashi, Pres.--Banque IBJ (France) S.A., Paris, France; *Int'l*, pg. 676
Watanabe, Takashi, Pres.--Rohm Electronics, Eastern Sales Div., Antioch, TN; *Int'l*, pg. 1125
Watari, Akira, Pres.--Nichimen Corporation, Tokyo, Japan; *Int'l*, pg. 927
Watase, Lincoln, Pres.--Yum Yum Donut Shop, Inc., City of Industry, CA; *U.S. Private*, pg. 1203
Watchorn, W.E., Pres.--Ensis Corporation Inc., Winnipeg, Canada; *Int'l*, pg. 455
Waterfield, Harry Lee II, Chm. Bd., Pres. & Chief Exec. Officer--Kentucky Investors, Inc., Frankfort, KY; *U.S. Public*, pg. 951
Waterfield, Patrick, Pres. & Chief Exec. Officer--Guerlain, Inc., New York, NY; *Int'l*, pg. 780
Waters, Martin C., Pres. & Chief Exec. Officer--Platinum Solutions, Inglewood, CA; *U.S. Public*, pg. 1309
Waters, Paul, Reg. Pres.--Citizens Bank, Gibson County Region, Princeton, IN; *U.S. Public*, pg. 281
Waters, Ron, Pres.--Rocco Farms, Harrisonburg, VA; *U.S. Private*, pg. 937
Waters, Ron, Pres.--Rocco Farm Foods, Inc., Edinburg, VA; *U.S. Private*, pg. 937
Waters, Scott, V.P.& Div. Mgr.--Bernard Johnson Young Inc., Bethesda, MD; *U.S. Private*, pg. 136
Waters, Warner S., Jr., Chm., Pres. & Chief Exec. Officer--Mellon Bank (DE) National Association, Wilmington, DE; *U.S. Public*, pg. 1085
Wathusing, Larry, Pres.--Dealers Truck Equipment, Louisville, KY; *U.S. Private*, pg. 700
Watkins, Benjamin L., III, Pres.--Specialty Fabrics Segment, Fort Mill, SC; *U.S. Public*, pg. 1500
Watkins, Benjamin L., III, Pres.--Retail & Specialty Fabrics, Rock Hill, SC; *U.S. Public*, pg. 1500
Watkins, D.H., Pres.--Amax Exploration, Inc., Englewood, CO; *U.S. Public*, pg. 470
Watkins, D.H., Pres.--Cyprus Exploration & Development Corporation, Englewood, CO; *U.S. Public*, pg. 471
Watkins, Edward G., Chm. Bd., Pres. & Chief Exec. Officer--Simplex Time Recorder Co., Gardner, MA; *U.S. Private*, pg. 1002
Watkins, Gary, Pres. & Chief Oper. Officer--Allison-Erwin Co. Inc., Charlotte, NC; *U.S. Private*, pg. 41
Watkins, Greg, Pres.--Watkins Contracting, Inc., San Diego, CA; *U.S. Public*, pg. 1384
Watkins, James D., Pres. & Chief Oper. Officer--ConAgra Diversified Products Companies, Omaha, NE; *U.S. Public*, pg. 426
Watkins, Jeff, Pres.--Watkins Manufacturing Corp./Hot Spring Portable Spas, Vista, CA; *U.S. Public*, pg. 1054
Watkins, Leo, Pres.--Servitex, Inc., Raleigh, NC; *U.S. Private*, pg. 781
Watkins, Neil, Pres.--Gulf States Manufacturers, Inc., Starkville, MS; *Int'l*, pg. 699
Watkins, Scott D., Pres. & Chief Exec. Officer--Access Corporation, Cincinnati, OH; *Int'l*, pg. 994
Watson, Albert O., Pres.--Watson's Quality Turkey Products, Inc., Turnersville, NJ; *U.S. Private*, pg. 1154
Watson, Charles E., Pres.--First Citizens Bank of Virginia Corporation, Roanoke, VA; *U.S. Public*, pg. 629
Watson, Colin D., Pres. & Chief Exec. Officer--Spar Aerospace Limited, Toronto, Canada; *Int'l*, pg. 1287
Watson, David N., Pres.--Comcast Cellular Communications, Inc., Wayne, PA; *U.S. Public*, pg. 407
Watson, Donald K., Pres. & Chief Exec. Officer--Griffin Envelope, Inc., Seattle, WA; *U.S. Public*, pg. 1038
Watson, Donald K., Pres. & Chief Exec. Officer--Emerald Warehouse & Distribution Services, Seattle, WA; *U.S. Public*, pg. 1038
Watson, George W., Pres. & Chief Exec. Officer--Transcanada Pipelines Limited, Calgary, Canada; *Int'l*, pg. 1416
Watson, Harold, Pres. & Gen. Mgr.--Williams Detroit Diesel-Allison S.E., Inc., Atlanta, GA; *U.S. Private*, pg. 1179
Watson, J.H., Chm., Pres. & Chief Exec. Officer--Confed Investment Counselling Limited, Toronto, Canada; *Int'l*, pg. 325
Watson, J.S., Pres.--Chevron Canada Limited, Vancouver, Canada; *U.S. Public*, pg. 348
Watson, Jack O., Pres. & Chief Exec. Officer--Stanback Company, Salisbury, NC; *U.S. Private*, pg. 1030
Watson, James F., Jr., Pres.--Thermo King Corporation, Minneapolis, MN; *U.S. Public*, pg. 877
Watson, John C., Chm. Bd., Pres. & Chief Exec. Officer--NACOLAH Holding Corp. Inc., Chicago, IL; *U.S. Private*, pg. 963
Watson, Larry, Pres.--Union Planters Bank of Northwest Tennessee, Paris, TN; *U.S. Public*, pg. 1669
Watson, Malcolm Lee, Pres.--Watson Electric, Dallas, TX; *U.S. Private*, pg. 1151
Watson, Max P., Jr., Chm. Bd., Pres. & Chief Exec. Officer--BMC Software, Inc., Houston, TX; *U.S. Public*, pg. 162
Watson, Noel G., Pres. & Chief Exec. Officer--Jacobs Engineering Group Inc., Pasadena, CA; *U.S. Public*, pg. 921
Watson, Peter D., Pres. & Chief Oper. Officer--Willis Corroon Melling Ltd., Edmonton, Canada; *Int'l*, pg. 1509
Watson, W. James, Pres.--General Motors Acceptance Corporation of Canada Limited, Toronto, Canada; *U.S. Public*, pg. 720
Watson, William B., Pres. & Chief Exec. Officer--SouthTrust Bank, Hartselle, Decatur, AL; *U.S. Public*, pg. 1491
Watt, James W., Pres.--Watt Publishing Co., Mount Morris, IL; *U.S. Private*, pg. 1154
Watters, Joseph, Pres.--Crystal Cruises, Inc., Los Angeles, CA; *Int'l*, pg. 941
Wattman, Kenneth E., Pres.--Kao Corporation of America (DE), Wilmington, DE; *Int'l*, pg. 717
Watts, Carl S., Pres. & Chief Exec. Officer--Tasty Baking Company, Philadelphia, PA; *U.S. Public*, pg. 1561
Watts, David H., Pres. & Chief Exec. Officer--Granite Construction Incorporated, Watsonville, CA; *U.S. Public*, pg. 759
Watts, Harry K., Chief Exec. Officer & Mng. Dir.--Woolworths Limited, Yennora, Australia; *Int'l*, pg. 676
Watts, Michael, Pres.--Harman Interactive Group, San Jose, CA; *U.S. Public*, pg. 787
Watts, William E., Pres. & Chief Exec. Officer--General Nutrition, Inc., Pittsburgh, PA; *U.S. Public*, pg. 725
Wattz, Carl S., Pres. & Chief Exec. Officer--TBC Financial Services, Philadelphia, PA; *U.S. Public*, pg. 1561
Waxman, Armond, Pres., Co-Chief Exec. Officer & Treas.--Waxman Industries, Inc., Bedford, OH; *U.S. Public*, pg. 1748
Waxman, Jerry, Pres.--Alan Lithograph, Inc., Inglewood, CA; *U.S. Private*, pg. 31
Waxman, Laurence, Pres.--Waxman Consumer Products Group, Bedford, OH; *U.S. Public*, pg. 1749
Way, Charles D., Chm. Bd., Pres. & Chief Exec. Officer--Ryan's Family Steak Houses, Inc., Greer, SC; *U.S. Public*, pg. 1413
Way, Richard D., Pres. & Chief Oper. Officer--Northwestern Steel & Wire Co., Sterling, IL; *U.S. Public*, pg. 1201
Way, Ron W., Pres.--Rentway Truck Leasing, Perrysburg, OH; *Int'l*, pg. 1424
Waycaster, Bill, Pres.--Texas Petro Chemicals, Houston, TX; *U.S. Private*, pg. 1078
Waye, Ron W., Pres.--Rentway Inc., Etobicoke, Canada; *Int'l*, pg. 1424
Weaber, Galen G., Pres.--Weaber, Inc, Lebanon, PA; *U.S. Private*, pg. 1155
Weatherby, Ed, Chm. Bd. & Pres.--Weatherby, Inc., Atascadero, CA; *U.S. Private*, pg. 1155
Weathersby, Joe, Pres.--Texas Valley Div., McAllen, TX; *U.S. Public*, pg. 1683
Weathersby, Joe, Pres.--San Antonio Div., San Antonio, TX; *U.S. Public*, pg. 1683
Weathersby, William C., Pres. & Chief Oper. Officer--American Safety Razor Company, Verona, VA; *U.S. Private*, pg. 597
Weatherston, Bob, Pres.--Hastings, Inc., Barrie, Canada; *U.S. Public*, pg. 798
Weaver, Amy, Pres.--Emons Finance Corp., York, PA; *U.S. Public*, pg. 578
Weaver, Amy S., Pres., Treas. & Sec.--Emons Finance Corporation, Wilmington, DE; *U.S. Public*, pg. 578
Weaver, Arnold L., Pres. & Chief Oper. Officer--Pinnacle Financial Services Inc., Saint Joseph, MI; *U.S. Public*, pg. 1297
Weaver, Charles S., Pres. & Chief Exec. Officer--Peerless Pottery, Inc., Rockport, IN; *U.S. Private*, pg. 847
Weaver, Dennis, V.P. & Gen. Mgr.--Aro Fluid Products Division, Bryan, OH; *U.S. Public*, pg. 877
Weaver, Michael E., Pres., Chief Exec. Officer & Chief Oper. Officer--Weaver Popcorn Company, Inc., Van Buren, IN; *U.S. Private*, pg. 1156
Weaver, Phil, Pres.--Eck Miller Transportation Corporation, Rockport, IN; *U.S. Public*, pg. 911
Weaver, Robert, Pres. & Chief Exec. Officer--P.A.M. Transport, Inc., Tontitown, AR; *U.S. Private*, pg. 825
Weaver, W. Ross, Pres.--Pan-Alberta Gas Ltd., Calgary, Canada; *Int'l*, pg. 971
Weaver, W.S., Pres.--Puget Sound Energy Co., Bellevue, WA; *U.S. Public*, pg. 1342
Weaver, W.S., Pres.--Puget Energy Inc., Bothell, WA; *U.S. Public*, pg. 1342
Weaver, William C., Pres.--Halliburton Energy Services, Carmel, IN; *U.S. Public*, pg. 776
Weaver, William S., Pres.--Puget Sound Energy, Inc., Bellevue, WA; *U.S. Public*, pg. 1342
Weaving, Rick, Pres.--Thomas Equipment Limited, Centreville, Canada; *Int'l*, pg. 850
Web, Tony A., Pres. & Chief Exec. Officer--Trust Corporation of Canada, Toronto, Canada; *Int'l*, pg. 1131
Webb, Carol A., Pres.--Ortho Biotech Inc., Raritan, NJ; *U.S.* Public, pg. 929
Webb, George H., Chm. Bd., Pres. & Chief Exec. Officer--Jervis B. Webb Company, Farmington Hills, MI; *U.S. Private*, pg. 1156
Webb, Harley D., Chm. Bd. & Pres.--Webb Builders Hardware, Arlington, TX; *U.S. Private*, pg. 1156
Webb, Henry E., Jr., Pres.--Whiting Metals, Inc., Camden, SC; *U.S. Public*, pg. 1548
Webb, J.J., Pres. & Chief Exec. Officer--Atlantic Steel Industries, Inc., Atlanta, GA; *Int'l*, pg. 696
Webb, Jeffrey G., Pres.--Varsity Intropa, Memphis, TN; *U.S. Public*, pg. 1389
Webb, Jeffrey G., Pres.--Varsity USA, Memphis, TN; *U.S. Public*, pg. 1389
Webb, Lewis, Pres.--Webb Automotive Group, Cerritos, CA; *U.S. Private*, pg. 1156
Webb, O. Glenn, Chm. Bd. & Pres.--Growmark, Inc., Bloomington, IL; *U.S. Private*, pg. 484
Webb, R.M., Pres. & Chief Exec. Officer--Webb, Murray & Associates, Houston, TX; *U.S. Private*, pg. 1157
Webb, Rollie, Pres. & Chief Oper. Officer--Todd Pacific Shipyards Corp., Seattle, WA; *U.S. Public*, pg. 1619
Webb, William H., Pres. & Chief Exec. Officer--Philip Morris International Inc., Rye Brook, NY; *U.S. Public*, pg. 1289
Webber, Roy A., Gen. Mgr.--Saint-Gobain Advanced Materials Corporation, Louisville, KY; *Int'l*, pg. 1173
Webber, Ruby, Pres. & Chief Exec. Officer--Contempo Colors, Kalamazoo, MI; *U.S. Private*, pg. 267
Weber, Alfred, Chm. Bd., Pres. & Chief Exec. Officer--C&D Charter Power Systems, Blue Bell, PA; *U.S. Public*, pg. 271
Weber, Alfred, Chm. Bd., Pres. & Chief Exec. Officer--C & D Technologies, Inc., Blue Bell, PA; *U.S. Public*, pg. 272

Weber, Andrew J., Pres. & Chief Exec. Officer--McKnight Medical Communications Company, Northfield, IL; *U.S. Public*, pg. 1601
Weber, Brad, Pres.--Weber Marking Systems, Inc., Arlington Heights, IL; *U.S. Private*, pg. 1157
Weber, Gerry, Pres.--Blockbuster Music, Marietta, GA; *U.S. Private*, pg. 776
Weber, John, Pres.--Vickers, Incorporated, Maumee, OH; *U.S. Public*, pg. 24
Weber, Mark E., Pres.--LaFehr Chan Technologies, Houston, TX; *U.S. Private*, pg. 642
Weber, O.G., Pres.--Foundation Nuclear Managers, Mississauga, Canada; *Int'l*, pg. 118
Weber, Phil, Pres.--Abex Friction Products, Winchester, VA; *U.S. Public*, pg. 443
Weber, Richard, Pres. & Gen. Mgr.--TENERA Energy, LLC, San Francisco, CA; *U.S. Public*, pg. 1576
Weber, Robin, Pres.--Elastomeric Technologies, Inc., Hatboro, PA; *U.S. Public*, pg. 1598
Webster, Dan, Pres.--Nodak Electric Co-op, Grand Forks, ND; *U.S. Private*, pg. 800
Webster, David L., Pres.--Shoals Supply, Inc., Arlington, TX; *U.S. Public*, pg. 529
Webster, Geoffrey, Pres.--Givaudan-Roure, Corporation-Fragrances Div., Teaneck, NJ; *Int'l*, pg. 1120
Webster, George K., Pres. & Chief Exec. Officer--Miltope Group, Inc., Hope Hull, AL; *U.S. Public*, pg. 1114
Webster, Steven A., Pres. & Chief Exec. Officer--R&B Falcon Corporation, Houston, TX; *U.S. Public*, pg. 1354
Webster, Timothy S., Pres. & Chief Exec. Officer--American Italian Pasta Company, Excelsior Springs, MO; *U.S. Public*, pg. 85
Wechsberg, Orin, Pres.--GREAT! Communications, New York, NY; *U.S. Public*, pg. 764
Wedaman, David, Pres.--MNX Carriers, Inc., Saint Joseph, MO; *U.S. Public*, pg. 1046
Wedaman, David H., Pres.--Mark VII Transportation Company, Inc., Greenwood, IN; *U.S. Public*, pg. 1046
Wedding, I. J., Pres. Dir.--PT AMP Panin Life, Jakarta, Indonesia; *Int'l*, pg. 100
Weddle, J.R., Jr., Pres.--Gold Medal Insurance Co., Minneapolis, MN; *U.S. Public*, pg. 718
Wedemeyer, Lyle, Partner & Creative Dir.--Martin/Williams Advertising Inc., Minneapolis, MN; *U.S. Private*, pg. 710
Wedgworth, George H., Pres.--Sugar Cane Growers Cooperative of Florida, Belle Glade, FL; *U.S. Private*, pg. 1049
Weed, Mark A., Pres. & Chief Exec. Officer--Fisher Properties Inc., Seattle, WA; *U.S. Public*, pg. 648
Weeder, Charles E., Chm. Bd., Pres. & Chief Exec. Officer--Homes of Merit Inc., Bartow, FL; *U.S. Private*, pg. 537
Weeks, James C., Pres. & Chief Oper. Officer--The New York Times Company Regional Newspaper Group, Atlanta, GA; *U.S. Public*, pg. 1174
Weeks, Ralph W., Pres. & Chief Exec. Officer--Quality Petroleum Corp., Lakeland, FL; *U.S. Private*, pg. 899
Weeks, Roland, Publisher--Sun Herald, Gulfport, MS; *U.S. Public*, pg. 964
Weg, Kenneth, Pres.-Bristol-Myers Squibb--Bristol-Myers Squibb U.S. Pharmaceutical Group, Plainsboro, NJ; *U.S. Public*, pg. 255
Weg, Kenneth E., Pres.--Bristol-Myers Squibb International, Princeton, NJ; *U.S. Public*, pg. 254
Wegener, William S., Pres.--ARCO Coal Australia, Inc., Brisbane, Australia; *U.S. Public*, pg. 144
Wegman, Daniel R., Pres.--Wegmans Food Markets, Inc., Rochester, NY; *U.S. Private*, pg. 1158
Wegner, David A., Pres.--Seitel Gas & Energy Corp., Houston, TX; *U.S. Public*, pg. 1454
Wegner, Hellmut, Pres. & Chief Exec. Officer--GIW Industries, Inc., Grovetown, GA; *Int'l*, pg. 721
Wegner, Pamela J., Pres.--REAC, Inc., Madison, WI; *U.S. Public*, pg. 1728
Wehberg, Joyce, Pres.--Shillcraft, Inc., Baltimore, MD; *U.S. Private*, pg. 994
Wehle, Charles S., Pres.--Genesee Corporation, Rochester, NY; *U.S. Public*, pg. 728
Wehle, Charles S., Pres.--The Genesee Brewing Company, Inc., Rochester, NY; *U.S. Public*, pg. 728
Wehmeier, Heige H., Pres. & Chief Exec. Officer--Bayer Corporation, Pittsburgh, PA; *Int'l*, pg. 172
Wehmeier, Heige H., Pres. & Chief Exec. Officer--Bayer Corporation, Parsippany, NJ; *Int'l*, pg. 172
Wehmeier, Helge H., Pres. & Chief Exec. Officer--Bayer Corporation, Pittsburgh, PA; *Int'l*, pg. 172
Wehr, Gerhard H., Pres.--Dresdner Securities (Asia) Ltd., Tokyo, Japan; *Int'l*, pg. 420
Wehrle, Gary, Chm. Bd. & Chief Exec. Officer--Pacific Crest Capital, Inc., Agoura Hills, CA; *U.S. Public*, pg. 1248
Wehrle, Henry B., III, Pres. & Chief Exec. Officer--McJunkin Corporation, Charleston, WV; *U.S. Private*, pg. 722
Wehrung, Vernon, Pres.--Modern Concrete Septic Tank Company, Ottsville, PA; *U.S. Private*, pg. 754
Wei, Chong Eng, Acting Pres.--IPC Peripherals, Inc., Fremont, CA; *Int'l*, pg. 651
Wei, T.H., Pres.--Taiwan Otsuka Pharmaceutical Co., Ltd., Taipei, Taiwan; *Int'l*, pg. 1014
Weibel, Benedikt, Pres.--Schweizerische Bundesbahnen - SBB AG, Bern, Switzerland; *Int'l*, pg. 1211
Weibel, Fred E., Jr., Chm. Bd., Pres. & Chief Exec. Officer--Weibel Winery, Lodi, CA; *U.S. Private*, pg. 1159
Weichel, Timothy J., Pres.-Retail--Carlton Cards, Ltd., Toronto, Canada; *U.S. Public*, pg. 78
Weichert, James M., Pres.--Weichert Company, Morris Plains, NJ; *U.S. Private*, pg. 1159
Weida, G.R., Pres.--Penn Racquet Sports, Phoenix, AZ; *U.S. Public*, pg. 706
Weida, G.R., Pres.--Penn Racquet Sports, Mullingar, Ireland; *U.S. Public*, pg. 706
Weil, Adolph, III, Pres.--Weil Brothers Cotton Inc., Montgomery, AL; *U.S. Private*, pg. 1159
Weil, David S., Pres., Chief Exec. Officer & Chief Oper. Officer--Ampacet Corporation, Tarrytown, NY; *U.S. Private*, pg. 67
Weil, Louis A., III, Pres. & Chief Exec. Officer--Central Newspapers, Inc., Indianapolis, IN; *U.S. Public*, pg. 326
Weiler, Gerhard, Pres. & Chief Exec. Officer--Automatic Liquid Packaging, Inc., Woodstock, IL; *U.S. Private*, pg. 101
Weiler, Michael, Pres. & Chief Exec. Officer--Preferred Risk Life Insurance Co., West Des Moines, IA; *U.S. Private*, pg. 880
Weill, Fred, Pres.--Central Lewmar International, New York, NY; *U.S. Private*, pg. 223
Weill, Richard L., Pres.--MBIA Inc., Armonk, NY; *U.S. Public*, pg. 1023
Weimer, Garry, Pres. & Chief Exec. Officer--Westinghouse Canada Inc., Hamilton, Canada; *U.S. Public*, pg. 275
Wein, Bernard J., Chm. Bd., Pres. & Chief Exec. Officer--Catherines Stores Corporation, Memphis, TN; *U.S. Public*, pg. 317
Weinbach, Arthur F., Pres. & Chief Exec. Officer--Automatic Data Processing, Inc., Roseland, NJ; *U.S. Public*, pg. 150
Weinberg, Rhona, Pres. & Gen. Mgr.--Coast Grain Company, Inc., Ontario, CA; *U.S. Private*, pg. 248
Weinberg, Steven J., Pres. & Chief Oper. Officer--Cyborg Systems, Inc., Chicago, IL; *U.S. Private*, pg. 299
Weinbrum, Brad, Pres.--Office Connection, Inc., Fort Lauderdale, FL; *U.S. Public*, pg. 1687
Weiner, David, Pres.--K-Tel International, Inc., Minneapolis, MN; *U.S. Public*, pg. 937
Weiner, Jeffrey R., Pres.--Design/Craft Fabric Corp., Niles, IL; *U.S. Public*, pg. 1357
Weiner, Louis, Pres. & Chief Exec. Officer--City Postal, Inc., New York, NY; *U.S. Private*, pg. 241
Weiner, Steven J., Pres. & Chief Oper. Officer--Hickey-Freeman/Bobby Jones, Rochester, NY; *U.S. Public*, pg. 795
Weinhardt, W. John, Pres.--Fayette Tubular Products, Troy, MI; *U.S. Public*, pg. 481
Weinhart, James J., Pres.--Master Molded Products Corporation, Elgin, IL; *U.S. Private*, pg. 714
Weinkam, Joseph, Pres.--Wyant Coporation, Somerville, NJ; *U.S. Public*, pg. 1781
Weins, Robert, Pres.--FACS Records Centre Inc., Vancouver, Canada; *Int'l*, pg. 1494
Weinseis, John, Pres.--Bowdens Media Monitoring Limited, Scarborough, Canada; *Int'l*, pg. 1124
Weinstein, Alan I., Pres. & Chief Exec. Officer--J. Baker, Inc., Canton, MA; *U.S. Public*, pg. 167
Weinstein, Howard J., Chm. Bd., Pres. & Chief Exec. Officer--Adams Wine Co., Atlanta, GA; *U.S. Private*, pg. 17
Weinstein, Jeffrey A., Pres. & Mng. Dir.--Ekco Group, Inc., Nashua, NH; *U.S. Public*, pg. 566
Weinstein, Jeffrey A., Pres. & Mng. Dir.--Ekco International, Inc., Nashua, NH; *U.S. Public*, pg. 566
Weinstein, Jerry L., Pres.--Owens Corning/Foamular, Parsippany, NJ; *U.S. Public*, pg. 1237
Weinstein, John, Pres.--Torre Lazur/Weber Healthcare Public Relations, Parsippany, NJ; *U.S. Private*, pg. 1157
Weinstein, Leo, Pres.--Levlad, Inc., Chatsworth, CA; *U.S. Private*, pg. 663
Weinstein, Michael, Pres. & Chief Exec. Officer--Ark Restaurants Corp., New York, NY; *U.S. Public*, pg. 129
Weinstock, Lord, Mng. Dir.--The General Electric Company, p.l.c., London, United Kingdom; *Int'l*, pg. 543
Weir, David, Pres., Chief Exec. Officer & Chief Fin. Officer--Denison Hydraulics, Inc., Marysville, OH; *U.S. Private*, pg. 324
Weir, David A., Pres.--Pepsi-Cola Albany Bottling Co., Inc., Latham, NY; *U.S. Private*, pg. 852
Weir, R. Brian, Pres. & Chief Oper. Officer--Supershuttle Inc., Phoenix, AZ; *U.S. Private*, pg. 1056
Weirsoe, Steen, Pres.--Danisco Ingredients, Brabrand, Denmark; *Int'l*, pg. 378
Weis, Arthur M., Pres. & Chief Exec. Officer--Capintec Inc., Ramsey, NJ; *U.S. Private*, pg. 205
Weis, Bernd, Principal--Conquest Europe, Frankfurt/Main, Germany; *Int'l*, pg. 1484
Weis, Dick, Pres. & Chief Exec. Officer--Food Services of America, Seattle, WA; *U.S. Private*, pg. 987
Weis, Jim, Pres. & Chief Exec. Officer--Publicker Industries Inc., Fairfield, CT; *U.S. Public*, pg. 1341
Weisbach, Lou, Chm. Bd., Pres. & Chief Exec. Officer--Ha-Lo Industries, Inc., Niles, IL; *U.S. Public*, pg. 773
Weisbecker, Lutz, Pres.--Battenfeld GmbH, Meinerzhagen, Germany; *Int'l*, pg. 825
Weisberg, R.A., Pres.--Senior Engineering, Lyman, SC; *Int'l*, pg. 1222
Weisenborn, W., Pres.--ING Futures & Options, Chicago, IL; *Int'l*, pg. 647
Weisend, C. Frederick, Chm. Bd., Pres. & Chief Exec. Officer--Fritz Industries Inc., Mesquite, TX; *U.S. Private*, pg. 429
Weiser, Irving, Chm. Bd., Pres. & Chief Exec. Officer--Dain Rauscher Corporation, Minneapolis, MN; *U.S. Public*, pg. 476
Weisiger, Ed, Jr., Pres.--Carolina Tractor & Equipment Co., Charlotte, NC; *U.S. Private*, pg. 214
Weiskircher, Ron, Pres.--Acco Chain & Lifting Products, York, PA; *Int'l*, pg. 473
Weisman, Ezra, Pres. & Chief Exec. Officer--New Brunswick Scientific Co., Inc., Edison, NJ; *U.S. Public*, pg. 1169
Weisman, Robert, Pres.--Bessin Corporation, Chicago, IL; *U.S. Public*, pg. 1433
Weisman, Robert, Pres. & Chief Exec. Officer--Shofar Kosher Foods, Linden, NJ; *U.S. Public*, pg. 1433
Weisman, Stephen, Pres.--Plainville Stock Company, Inc., Plainville, MA; *U.S. Private*, pg. 868
Weismantel, Lyle, Pres.--First American Bank Southwest, Marshall, MN; *U.S. Private*, pg. 167
Weisner, Bob, Pres.--Robbins Auto Parts, Inc., Dover, NH; *U.S. Private*, pg. 934
Weiss, Arnold, Pres.--Cosmos Communications, Inc., Long Island City, NY; *U.S. Private*, pg. 278
Weiss, David E., Chm. Bd., Pres. & Chief Exec. Officer--Storage Technology Corporation, Louisville, CO; *U.S. Public*, pg. 1522
Weiss, Donald, Pres.--White Systems, Incorporated, Kenilworth, NJ; *U.S. Private*, pg. 866
Weiss, Larry, Chm. Bd., Pres., Chief Exec. Officer & Sec.--Fresh Food, Inc., Hobart, IN; *U.S. Private*, pg. 427
Weiss, Martin, Pres.--Weiss Group., Palm Beach Gardens, FL; *U.S. Private*, pg. 1160
Weiss, Martin, Pres.--Weiss Rating, Inc., Palm Beach Gardens, FL; *U.S. Private*, pg. 1160
Weiss, Martin, Pres.--Weiss Research, Inc., Palm Beach Gardens, FL; *U.S. Private*, pg. 1160
Weiss, Michael, Pres.--Express, Columbus, OH; *U.S. Public*, pg. 995
Weiss, Peter, Pres.--Bradford Industries, Inc., Lowell, MA; *U.S. Private*, pg. 163
Weiss, Ronald, Pres. & Chief Oper. Officer--Bell Mobility Paging Inc., Downsview, Canada; *Int'l*, pg. 115
Weiss, Sam, Chm. Bd., Pres. & Chief Exec. Officer--United Receptical, Inc., Pottsville, PA; *U.S. Private*, pg. 1123
Weiss, Wolfgang, Pres., Mgr. & Dir.--Mazda Austria GmbH, Klagenfurt, Austria; *Int'l*, pg. 849
Weissglass, Allan, Pres.--Magruder Color Company, Inc., Elizabeth, NJ; *U.S. Private*, pg. 696
Weisshaar, Kenneth R., Pres.--Becton Dickinson Consumer Prods., Franklin Lakes, NJ; *U.S. Public*, pg. 199
Weissman, Jerrold, Pres. & Chief Exec. Officer--Carl Weissman & Sons, Inc., Great Falls, MT; *U.S. Private*, pg. 1160
Weisz, Stephen P., Exec. V.P.-Marriott Lodging & Pres.-Marriott Vacation Club Intl.--Marriott International, Inc., Washington, DC; *U.S. Public*, pg. 1047
Weitz, Eric, Pres. & Chief Oper. Officer--Apparal America, Inc., New York, NY; *U.S. Public*, pg. 120
Weitz, Eric T., Pres. & Chief Exec. Officer--Robby Len Fashions, New York, NY; *U.S. Public*, pg. 121
Weitz, Robert, Pres.--Samuel Meisel & Company, Inc., Glen Burnie, MD; *Int'l*, pg. 103
Weitz, Robert, Pres.--Lipschutz Brothers Inc, Philadelphia, PA; *Int'l*, pg. 103
Weitzman, William, Pres. & Chief Oper. Officer--Electro Rent Corporation, Van Nuys, CA; *U.S. Public*, pg. 568
Welch, Jerry, Pres.--Right Start, Inc., Westlake Village, CA; *U.S. Private*, pg. 930
Welch, Joseph F., Chm. Bd., Pres. & Chief Exec. Officer--Bachman Company, Reading, PA; *U.S. Private*, pg. 109
Welch, Norman H., Jr., Pres.--Eva-Tone Inc., Clearwater, FL; *U.S. Private*, pg. 384
Welch, Patrick, Pres.--GNA Corp., Seattle, WA; *U.S. Public*, pg. 712
Welch, Patrick, Pres.--G.E. Capital Assurance, Seattle, WA; *U.S. Public*, pg. 712
Weldon, N., Pres.--Adtech Inc., Honolulu, HI; *Int'l*, pg. 208
Welge, Donald E., Pres. & Gen. Mgr.--Gilster Mary Lee Corp., Chester, IL; *U.S. Private*, pg. 455
Welk, Donald, Pres. & Chief Exec. Officer--Patch Communications, Titusville, FL; *U.S. Private*, pg. 842
Wellauer, Thomas, Dr., Pres.-Corp. Exec. Bd. & Chief Exec. Officer--Winterthur Schweizerische Versicherungs Gesellschaft, Winterthur, Switzerland; *Int'l*, pg. 345
Wellehan, Daniel, Jr., Pres.--Sebago, Inc., Gorham, ME; *U.S. Private*, pg. 980
Wellens, Leroy, Chm. Bd., Pres., Chief Exec. & Chief Fin. Officer & Treas.--Wellens & Co., Inc., Minneapolis, MN; *U.S. Private*, pg. 1161
Weller, Johnathan B., Pres. & Chief Oper. Officer--Pennsylvania Real Estate Investment Trust, Fort Washington, PA; *U.S. Public*, pg. 1272
Welles, D.K., Jr., Chm. Bd. & Chief Exec. Officer--Therma-Tru Corp., Maumee, OH; *U.S. Private*, pg. 1079
Wellman, Jon, Pres.--American Business Advertising, Omaha, NE; *U.S. Private*, pg. 51
Wellman, Jon, Pres. & Chief Oper. Officer--American Business Information, Inc., Omaha, NE; *U.S. Public*, pg. 69
Wells, Bradley H., Pres. & Chief Exec. Officer--Cohn & Wells, San Francisco, CA; *Int'l*, pg. 601
Wells, Calvin B., Chm. Bd., Pres. & Chief Exec. Officer--North Carolina Natural Gas Corporation, Fayetteville, NC; *U.S. Public*, pg. 1194
Wells, George M., Pres.--Ash Grove Cement Company, Shawnee Mission, KS; *U.S. Private*, pg. 87
Wells, James M., III, Pres. & Chief Oper. Officer--Crestar Financial Corporation, Richmond, VA; *U.S. Public*, pg. 458
Wells, John R., Pres. & Chief Exec. Officer--Interface Flooring Systems Inc., La Grange, GA; *U.S. Public*, pg. 889
Wells, Kenneth R., Pres. & Chief Exec. Officer--Briggs Industries, Inc., Tampa, FL; *U.S. Private*, pg. 168
Wells, Mark, Chm. Bd. & Pres.--Case France S.A., Paris, France; *U.S. Public*, pg. 1579
Wells, Norman E., Jr., Pres. & Chief Exec. Officer--Easco Inc., Girard, OH; *U.S. Public*, pg. 548
Wells, Ron, Pres.--Furniture Brook Industries, Fridley, MN; *U.S. Private*, pg. 432
Wells, W.C., Pres.--FieldBrook Farms, Inc., Dunkirk, NY; *U.S. Private*, pg. 403
Wells, Wallace J., Pres.--International Chemical Company, Tulsa, OK; *U.S. Private*, pg. 568
Wells, William, Pres.--Delaware Electric Co-Op, Greenwood, DE; *U.S. Private*, pg. 321
Welsey, Norman H., Pres. & Chief Exec. Officer--ACCO Canada Inc., Willowdale, Canada; *U.S. Public*, pg. 674
Welty, John, Chm. Bd., Pres. & Dir.-Mktg. & Adv.--Swensen's Ice Cream Co., Ronkonkoma, NY; *U.S. Public*, pg. 883
Welty, Stanley R., Jr., Pres.--The Wooster Brush Company, Wooster, OH; *U.S. Private*, pg. 1188
Weltz, Skip, Pres. & Chief Exec. Officer--Lafayette Precast, Fremont, CA; *U.S. Private*, pg. 1149
Wenaas, Eric P., Pres. & Chief Exec. Officer--Jacor, Inc., San Diego, CA; *U.S. Private*, pg. 584

Wenaas, Eric P., Ph.D., Chm. Bd., Pres. & Chief Exec. Officer--Jaymark, Inc., San Diego, CA; U.S. Private, pg. 584

Wendel, Thomas, Pres. & Chief Exec. Officer--Bridge, New York, NY; U.S. Private, pg. 1162

Wendell, E.W., Pres. & Chief Exec. Officer--Gaylord Entertainment/Opryland USA, Nashville, TN; U.S. Public, pg. 704

Wendle, Kevin, Pres. & Chief Oper. Officer--Quincy Jones Entertainment, Los Angeles, CA; U.S. Public, pg. 1611

Wendt, Gary C., Chm., Pres. & Chief Exec. Officer--General Electric Capital Services, Inc., Stamford, CT; U.S. Public, pg. 711

Wendt, John, Pres.--Maybelline, Inc., New York, NY; Int'l, pg. 819

Wendt, John, Owner--Rudel Machinery Company, Inc., Shelton, CT; U.S. Private, pg. 950

Wendt, Roderick, Pres.--Jeld-Wen, Inc., Klamath Falls, OR; U.S. Private, pg. 585

Wenerowicz, Bill, Pres. & Chief Exec. Officer--Instrumentarium Imaging, Inc., Milwaukee, WI; U.S. Private, pg. 565

Wenk-Woff, Kai, Pres.--NAPP Systems, San Marcos, CA; U.S. Private, pg. 875

Wenk-Wolff, Kai, Pres. & Chief Oper. Officer--NAPP Systems Inc, San Marcos, CA; U.S. Public, pg. 984

Wenner, David, Pres.--B&G Foods, Inc., Roseland, NJ; U.S. Private, pg. 105

Wenner, Jann S., Chm. Bd.--Wenner Media, New York, NY; U.S. Private, pg. 1162

Wenrich, Robert, Pres. & Chief Exec. Officer--Germantown (USA) Co., Broomall, PA; Int'l, pg. 555

Wenrick, Nelson, Pres.--Wenco Inc., New Carlisle, OH; U.S. Public, pg. 1754

Wenstrand, Thomas W., Pres.--Hawkeye Steel Products, Inc., Houghton, IA; U.S. Private, pg. 511

Wenstrup, H.D., Pres. & Chief Exec. Officer--CHEMCENTRAL Corporation, Bedford Park, IL; U.S. Private, pg. 231

Wentworth, Robert, Pres., Chief Exec. Officer, V.P.-Fin., Admin. & Treas.--Alden Electronics, Inc., Westborough, MA; U.S. Private, pg. 872

Wenz, Richard E., Pres. & Chief Oper. Officer--Safety 1st, Inc., Chestnut Hill, MA; U.S. Public, pg. 1425

Werble, Cole, Pres.--FDC Reports Inc., Chevy Chase, MD; Int'l, pg. 1100

Werdelin, Hans, Pres. & Chief Exec. Officer--Sophus Berendsen A/S, Soeborg, Denmark; Int'l, pg. 1284

Werderman, John, Pres.--I-Bus Division, San Diego, CA; U.S. Public, pg. 1062

Werkendam, Simon, Mng. Partner--Bercum Boender Cardozo & Werkendam B.V., Amsterdam, Netherlands; U.S. Private, pg. 1198

Werkowski, Andrzej, Pres.--Optiroc Group Sp.z.o.o., Warsaw, Poland; Int'l, pg. 1200

Werner, Greg, Pres.--Gra-Gar Inc., Omaha, NE; U.S. Public, pg. 1755

Werner, Gregory L., Pres.--Werner Enterprises, Inc., Omaha, NE; U.S. Public, pg. 1754

Werner, Helmut, Pres. & Chief Exec. Officer--Mercedes-Benz AG, Stuttgart, Germany; Int'l, pg. 368

Werner, Rupert W., Pres. & Sec.--Perry Engineering Company, Inc., Winchester, VA; U.S. Private, pg. 854

Werner, Thomas C., Pres.--ADT Security Systems, Inc., Carmel, IN; U.S. Public, pg. 1649

Wernette, Beverly F., Pres.--Ted Thomas Associates Inc. Advertising, Philadelphia, PA; U.S. Private, pg. 1083

Wernette, Beverly F., Principal--Vox Medica Corporation, Philadelphia, PA; U.S. Private, pg. 1143

Wernz, Logan F., Pres. & Gen. Mge.--Kysor/Warren, Conyers, GA; U.S. Public, pg. 1445

Werra, John, Pres.--Univesco Inc., Dallas, TX; U.S. Private, pg. 1128

Wertch, Bryce, Pres.--First National Bank in Chicago Heights, Chicago Heights, IL; U.S. Public, pg. 760

Werthan, Bernard, Jr., Pres. & Chief Exec. Officer--Werthan Packaging, Inc., Nashville, TN; U.S. Private, pg. 1162

Wertman, Howard, Pres. & Chief Exec. Officer--Anthony and Sylvan Pools Corporation, Doylestown, PA; U.S. Public, pg. 593

Wertz, Richard L., Chm. Bd. & Pres.--Amos-Hill Associates, Inc., Edinburgh, IN; U.S. Private, pg. 67

Wessel, Onno, Partner--KKBR/Conquest, Amsterdam, Netherlands; Int'l, pg. 1484

Wessell, Dave, Pres. & Chief Exec. Officer--Towne Square Furniture, Inc., Hillsboro, TX; U.S. Private, pg. 1093

Wessling, Roger, Pres.--West Central Cooperative, Ralston, IA; U.S. Private, pg. 1163

Wesson, Steve, Pres. & Chief Exec. Officer--Citadel Holdings Corp., Los Angeles, CA; U.S. Public, pg. 456

West, B. Kenneth, Pres.--Bankmont Financial Corp., New York, NY; Int'l, pg. 154

West, Benjamin B., Pres.--WestWayne, Inc., Atlanta, GA; U.S. Private, pg. 1170

West, Charles, Pres.--MasterCraft Boat Company, Maryville, TN; U.S. Private, pg. 689

West, Charles H., Pres.--Delagra Corporation, Bridgeville, DE; U.S. Private, pg. 321

West, Donald, Pres. & Chief Exec. Officer--Total Petroleum Canada Ltd., Calgary, Canada; Int'l, pg. 1409

West, Donald T., Pres. & Chief Exec. Officer--Rigel Energy Corporation, Calgary, Canada; Int'l, pg. 1117

West, Donald T., Pres. & Chief Exec. Officer--Rigel Oil & Gas Ltd., Calgary, Canada; Int'l, pg. 1117

West, Donald T., Pres. & Chief Exec. Officer--Rigel Petroleum, Inc., Calgary, Canada; Int'l, pg. 1117

West, Donald T., Pres. & Chief Exec. Officer--Rigel Petroleum (NI) Limited, Calgary, Canada; Int'l, pg. 1117

West, Donald T., Pres. & Chief Exec. Officer--Rigel Petroleum UK Limited, Calgary, Canada; Int'l, pg. 1117

West, Doyle D., Chm. Bd., Pres. & Chief Exec. Officer--Matrix Service Company, Tulsa, OK; U.S. Public, pg. 1057

West, Eileen, Pres.--Lanz, Inc., San Francisco, CA; U.S. Private, pg. 650

West, Jim, Pres.--Florafax International, Inc., Vero Beach, FL; U.S. Public, pg. 654

West, John H., Pres.--Cimlinc Incorporated, Itasca, IL; U.S. Private, pg. 239

West, Mark, Pres.--Aerostar International, Sioux Falls, SD; U.S. Public, pg. 1361

West, Peter, Pres.--Dieffenbacher North America, Windsor, Canada; Int'l, pg. 413

West, Randall E., Pres.--Automotive Carrier Div., Troy, MI; U.S. Public, pg. 1414

West, Steve, Pres.--West Jewel Inc., Tuscaloosa, AL; U.S. Private, pg. 1163

West, Thomas L., Jr., Pres. & Chief Exec. Officer--The Variable Annuity Life Insurance Co., Houston, TX; U.S. Public, pg. 76

West, Wayne, Pres.--Heritage Cutlery, Inc., Bolivar, NY; U.S. Private, pg. 940

West, William G., Chm. Bd. & Pres.--Stanchem Inc., East Berlin, CT; U.S. Private, pg. 1030

Wester, Anders, Pres., Creative Dir. & Art Dir.--Hall & Cederquist/Young & Rubicam, Stockholm, Sweden; U.S. Private, pg. 1198

Wester, Bob, Pres.--WEN Products, Inc., Bensenville, IL; U.S. Private, pg. 1144

Westerbeke, John H., Jr., Chm. Bd. & Pres.--Westerbeke Corporation, Avon, MA; U.S. Public, pg. 1757

Westerberg, Lars, Pres. & Chief Exec. Officer--Granges AB, Stockholm, Sweden; Int'l, pg. 439

Westerdahl, Bernt, Pres.--Ballast Syd AB, Malmo, Sweden; Int'l, pg. 899

Westerdahl, Bertil, Pres.--Machinery South, Malmo, Sweden; Int'l, pg. 899

Westerfeld, William A., Chm. Bd., Pres., Chief Exec. Officer & Treas.--The Westerfelds, Inc., Pittsford, NY; U.S. Private, pg. 1164

Westerink, Jan, Pres.--Perstorp Analytical B.V, Oud-Beijerland, Netherlands; Int'l, pg. 1039

Westerman, William, Pres. & Chief Oper. Officer--Cogsdill Tool Products, Inc., Lugoff, SC; U.S. Private, pg. 250

Western, James, Pres.--Macro Soft, Rochester Hills, MI; U.S. Private, pg. 693

Westfall, Don, Pres., Chief Exec. & Chief Fin. Officer--Newsprint South, Inc., Jackson, MS; U.S. Private, pg. 797

Westhousing, Larry, Pres.--Manning Light Truck Equipment, Louisville, KY; U.S. Private, pg. 700

Westin, David, Pres.-Prod., ABC Television Network Grp. & Sr. V.P.--ABC, Inc, New York, NY; U.S. Public, pg. 511

Westin, David, Pres.--ABC News, Inc., New York, NY; U.S. Public, pg. 511

Westin, David, Pres.--American Broadcasting Companies, Inc., New York, NY; U.S. Public, pg. 511

Westin, Richard, Co-Pres.--Schnieber Fine Foods, Inc., Lincoln, NE; U.S. Private, pg. 971

Westlake, W. James, Pres. & Chief Exec. Officer--RBC Insurance Holdings Inc., Mississauga, Canada; Int'l, pg. 1131

Westmoreland, J., Pres.--Chevron Land & Development Company, San Francisco, CA; U.S. Public, pg. 348

Westmoreland, J., Pres.--Huntington Beach Co., San Francisco, CA; U.S. Public, pg. 348

Westoff, Gregory J., Pres. & Chief Oper. Officer--Alarmguard Holdings, Inc., Orange, CT; U.S. Public, pg. 35

Weston, Christopher J., Chm. Bd. & Pres.--Phillips Fine Art Auctioneers, New York, NY; U.S. Private, pg. 861

Weston, J., Pres.--Mellon Corporation, New York, NY; U.S. Private, pg. 730

Weston, Magaret, Pres.--The Portland Newspapers, Portland, ME; U.S. Private, pg. 439

Weston, Mike, Pres.--Manchester Plastics, Troy, MI; U.S. Public, pg. 399

Weston, Patrick H., Pres. & Chief Exec. Officer--Golden Eagle Group, Inc., Humble, TX; U.S. Public, pg. 749

Weston, Roger, Pres.--GreatBanc Trust Company, Aurora, IL; U.S. Public, pg. 760

Westover, Tim, Pres.--Litton Systems Canada Ltd., Etobicoke, Canada; U.S. Public, pg. 1005

Westphal, Gordon E., Pres. & Chief Oper. Officer--Western States Envelope Co., Milwaukee, WI; U.S. Private, pg. 1168

Westphal, Hans, Pres.--Deutsche Babcock Borsig AG, Berlin, Germany; Int'l, pg. 399

Westrick, Thomas G., Pres. & Chief Exec. Officer--Sangamon Industries, Taylorville, IL; U.S. Private, pg. 965

Wetmore, Byron, Pres.--The Lane Construction Corp., Meriden, CT; U.S. Private, pg. 649

Wetmore, Vernon E., Jr., Pres.--Sysco Food Services-Jamestown, Falconer, NY; U.S. Public, pg. 1551

Wetsel, Cecil, Jr., Pres. & Treas.--Wetsel-Oviatt Lumber Company, El Dorado Hills, CA; U.S. Private, pg. 1170

Wetsit, Mary, Pres.--A & S Tribal Industries, Poplar, MT; U.S. Private, pg. 1

Wevers, Pierre, Pres.--Bigg's Hyper Shoppes, Inc., Milford, OH; U.S. Public, pg. 1541

Wevers, Pierre Albert, Pres. & Chief Exec. Officer--Bigg's Hyper Shoppes Ohio, Inc., Milford, OH; U.S. Public, pg. 1541

Wexler, Lewis P., Chm. Bd., Pres., Chief Exec. Officer & Chief Oper. Officer--Free Service Tire Company, Inc., Johnson City, TN; U.S. Private, pg. 425

Wexler, Robert, Pres.--Tourneau Inc., New York, NY; U.S. Private, pg. 1093

Wexner, Leslie H., Pres. & Chief Exec. Officer--Intimate Brands, Inc., Columbus, OH; U.S. Public, pg. 995

Weyand, William, Pres. & Chief Exec. Officer--Structural Dynamics Research Corp., Milford, OH; U.S. Public, pg. 1525

Weyerhaeuser, George, Jr, Pres. & Chief Exec. Officer--Weyerhaeuser Canada Ltd., Vancouver, Canada; U.S. Public, pg. 1764

Weyers, Larry L., Chm. Bd., Pres. & Chief Exec. Officer--WPS Resources Corp., Green Bay, WI; U.S. Public, pg. 1728

Weyers, Larry L., Pres. & Chief Exec. Officer--WPS Power Development, Inc., Green Bay, WI; U.S. Public, pg. 1728

Weyers, Larry L., Pres. & Chief Exec. Officer--WPS Leasing, Inc., Green Bay, WI; U.S. Public, pg. 1728

Weyforth, Frank G., Jr., Chm. Bd., Pres. & Chief Exec. Officer--MRA, An Integrated Marketing Communications Agency, Overland Park, KS; U.S. Private, pg. 687

Weyl, Tom, Pres. & Chief Creative Officer--Martin/Williams Advertising Inc., Minneapolis, MN; U.S. Private, pg. 710

Weymuller, Bruno, Chm. Bd. & Pres.--Elf Aquitaine, Inc., New York, NY; Int'l, pg. 445

Whalen, Kevin H., Pres.--Sterling McCall Toyota Group, Houston, TX; U.S. Private, pg. 719

Whalen, Mark W., Pres.--Sterling Capital Management Company, Charlotte, NC; U.S. Public, pg. 1674

Whalen, Michael J., Pres. & Chief Exec. Officer--Old Kent Bank-Illinois, Elmhurst, IL; U.S. Public, pg. 1216

Whaley, Harry E., Pres.--Woodstream Corporation, Lititz, PA; U.S. Public, pg. 566

Whatley, Steve, Pres.--ALLTEL Alabama, Leeds, AL; U.S. Public, pg. 55

Wheat, Allen D., Chm. Bd., Pres. & Chief Exec. Officer--Credit Suisse First Boston, Inc., New York, NY; Int'l, pg. 345

Wheat, Douglas, Pres.--Haas, Wheat & Partners, Dallas, TX; U.S. Private, pg. 492

Wheat, James M., Pres.--Jiffy Lube International, Inc., Houston, TX; U.S. Public, pg. 1272

Wheat, James M., Pres.--Heritage Merchandising Co., Inc., Colonial Heights, VA; U.S. Public, pg. 1272

Wheat, James M., Pres.--Jiffy Lube International of Maryland, Inc., Houston, TX; U.S. Public, pg. 1272

Wheatcroft, K.M., Pres.--CRR Investments, Inc., Philadelphia, PA; U.S. Public, pg. 432

Wheatley, Charles N., Pres. & Chief Exec. Officer--Sahara Enterprises Inc., Chicago, IL; U.S. Private, pg. 960

Wheatley, John, Pres. & Chief Exec. Officer--Willis Corroon Corp. of Anchorage, Anchorage, AK; Int'l, pg. 1505

Wheaton, Robert E., Pres. & Chief Exec. Officer--Star Buffet, Inc., Salt Lake City, UT; U.S. Public, pg. 278

Wheeler, Dennis E., Chm., Pres. & Chief Exec. Officer--Coeur D'Alene Mines Corporation, Coeur D'Alene, ID; U.S. Public, pg. 394

Wheeler, H.A., Pres. & Chief Oper. Officer--Speedway Motorsports, Inc., Concord, NC; U.S. Public, pg. 1498

Wheeler, H.A., Pres.--Charlotte Motor Speedway, Concord, NC; U.S. Public, pg. 1498

Wheeler, Jack, Pres.--Norel Paper Corporation, Little Ferry, NJ; U.S. Public, pg. 1671

Wheeler, Larry G., Pres. & Chief Exec. Officer--Mrs. Baird's Bakeries, Inc., Fort Worth, TX; U.S. Private, pg. 765

Wheeler, Larry G., Pres.--Alpo Pet Foods, Inc., Allentown, PA; Int'l, pg. 917

Wheeler, Nigel, Pres. & Chief Oper. Officer--Trikon Technologies Inc., Chatsworth, CA; U.S. Public, pg. 1638

Wheeler, Richard, Pres.--Wyoming Machinery Company, Casper, WY; U.S. Private, pg. 1193

Wheeler, Robert C., Pres. & Chief Exec. Officer--Hill's Pet Nutrition, Topeka, KS; U.S. Public, pg. 397

Wheeler, Robert R., Pres. & Chief Oper. Officer--AFC Cable Systems, Inc., Providence, RI; U.S. Public, pg. 6

Wheeler, Thomas M., Pres. & Chief Oper. Officer--Biltwell Company, Inc., Saint Louis, MO; U.S. Public, pg. 795

Wheeler, Wendell, Pres.--Electronic Form Systems, Carrollton, TX; U.S. Public, pg. 1385

Wheeling, James R., Pres. & Chief Admin. Officer--First Virginia Bank-Southwest, Roanoke, VA; U.S. Public, pg. 642

Whelan, J. Douglas, Pres.--Wyman-Gordon Forgings, North Grafton, MA; U.S. Public, pg. 1782

Whelan, J. Douglas, Pres.--Wyman-Gordon Forgings Inc, Houston, TX; U.S. Public, pg. 1782

Whelan, Robert, Pres.--Buff Whelan Chevrolet & GEO, Inc., Sterling Heights, MI; U.S. Private, pg. 1171

Whelen, J. Douglas, Pres.--Wyman-Gordon Forgings, Inc., Houston, TX; U.S. Public, pg. 1782

Whipple, Dennis L., Pres.--ALLTEL Mobile Communications, Inc., Little Rock, AR; U.S. Public, pg. 56

Whipple, Donald E., Pres.--LSI Industries, Inc., Cincinnati, OH; U.S. Public, pg. 971

Whipple, Harry M., Pres. & Publr.--The Cincinnati Enquirer, Inc., Cincinnati, OH; U.S. Public, pg. 700

Whipps, George, Pres. & Chief Fin. Officer--Whipps, Athol, MA; U.S. Private, pg. 1171

Whisenhunt, Andrew, Pres.--Arkansas Farm Bureau Federation, Little Rock, AR; U.S. Private, pg. 82

Whisler, J. Steven, Pres. & Chief Oper. Officer--Phelps Dodge Corporation, Phoenix, AZ; U.S. Public, pg. 1286

Whitaker, C., Pres. & Chief Exec. Officer--Johnson Worldwide Associates, Inc., Sturtevant, WI; U.S. Public, pg. 932

Whitaker, Sheila, Pres.--EDS of Canada Ltd., Whitby, Canada; U.S. Public, pg. 570

Whitaker, Terence M., Pres.--Teton Land Title Company, Jackson, WY; U.S. Public, pg. 626

Whitaker, Wharton P., Pres.--Eaton Vance Distributors, Inc., Boston, MA; U.S. Public, pg. 559

Whitcome, Philip J., Pres. & Chief Exec. Officer--Neurogen Corporation, Branford, CT; U.S. Public, pg. 1169

White-Thomson, I. L., Pres.--U.S. Borax Inc., Valencia, CA; Int'l, pg. 1119

White, A. Thomas, Pres.--Dowty Aerospace Aviation Services, Sterling, VA; Int'l, pg. 1337

White, Barney, Pres.--Varity Dayton Walther, Dayton, OH; Int'l, pg. 820

White, Charles, Pres. & Chief Oper. Officer--Unisource Worldwide, Inc., Berwyn, PA; U.S. Public, pg. 1670

White, Craig, Pres.--Flowers Baking Co. of Miami, Inc., Miami, FL; U.S. Public, pg. 657

White, Don W., Pres.--Sunwest Bank of Grant County, Silver City, NM; U.S. Public, pg. 1165

White, Ed, Pres.--Vallet Food Serv Inc., Dubuque, IA; *U.S. Private*, pg. 1131
White, Eliot C., Pres., Treas. & Publr.--The Record-Journal Publishing Company, Meriden, CT; *U.S. Private*, pg. 914
White, Fred, Pres.--Upright, Lutz, FL; *U.S. Private*, pg. 1128
White, George, Pres. & Chief Oper. Officer--Cape Breton Development Corporation, Glace Bay, Canada; *Int'l*, pg. 265
White, George, Pres. & Chief Exec. Officer--Gymboree Corporation, Burlingame, CA; *U.S. Public*, pg. 770
White, Harvey P., Pres.--QUALCOMM, San Diego, CA; *U.S. Public*, pg. 1348
White, Jack, Pres.--Ovalstrapping Inc., Hoquiam, WA; *U.S. Private*, pg. 378
White, Jack E., Pres.--Plastex Extruders Inc., USA, Fort Payne, AL; *U.S. Private*, pg. 378
White, James, Pres.--360 Degrees Long Distance, Cary, NC; *U.S. Public*, pg. 1607
White, James E., Pres.--Bronto Skylift Oy AB, Tampere, Finland; *U.S. Public*, pg. 617
White, James E., Pres.--Sysco Food Services of Beaumont, Inc., Beaumont, TX; *U.S. Public*, pg. 1551
White, James S., Pres.--Morrison Berkshire Inc., North Adams, MA; *U.S. Private*, pg. 762
White, Jeff, Co-Pres.--Marchon Eyewear, Melville, NY; *U.S. Private*, pg. 702
White, John, Pres.-Columbia Div.--Thomas & Howard Co., Columbia, SC; *U.S. Private*, pg. 1081
White, John F., Chm. Bd., Pres. & Chief Exec. Officer--Haemonetics Corporation, Braintree, MA; *U.S. Public*, pg. 773
White, John H., Jr., Pres.--Taco Incorporated, Cranston, RI; *U.S. Private*, pg. 1066
White, John Morrison, Pres.--Morrison Textile Machinery Co., Fort Lawn, SC; *U.S. Private*, pg. 762
White, Kenneth, Pres.--Mrs. Smith's Bakeries of Pennsylvania, Inc., London, KY; *U.S. Public*, pg. 658
White, Lawrence D., Chm. Bd., Pres., & Chief Exec. Officer--Menley & James Laboratories, Inc., Horsham, PA; *U.S. Public*, pg. 1086
White, Loy, Pres.--Austin Jet Ltd., Austin, TX; *U.S. Private*, pg. 100
White, Michael H., Pres. & Chief Exec. Officer--Rite-Hite Corporation, Milwaukee, WI; *U.S. Private*, pg. 933
White, Michael J., Pres. & Chief Oper. Officer--National Trust Company, Stratford, Canada; *Int'l*, pg. 910
White, R.J., Pres.--Chevron TCI Inc., Houston, TX; *U.S. Public*, pg. 348
White, Randall W., Chm. Bd., Pres. & Treas.--Educational Development Corporation, Tulsa, OK; *U.S. Public*, pg. 564
White, Richard C., Pres. & Chief Exec. Officer--Community Bancorp, Derby, VT; *U.S. Public*, pg. 416
White, Richard D., Pres. & Chief Exec. Officer--Regions Bank, Gainesville, GA; *U.S. Public*, pg. 1371
White, Rivhard L., Pres.--Bayer Corporation/Fibers, Organics & Rubber Division, Pittsburgh, PA; *Int'l*, pg. 172
White, Robert, Pres.--Breeze Eastern, Union, NJ; *U.S. Public*, pg. 1632
White, Robert E., Pres. & Chief Exec. Officer--Bankers Systems Incorporated, Saint Cloud, MN; *U.S. Private*, pg. 114
White, Russell, Pres.--Elsevier Science Inc., New York, NY; *Int'l*, pg. 1100
White, Scott, Pres.-Hadeler White Public Relations--Hadeler Sullivan Ewing, Dallas, TX; *U.S. Private*, pg. 493
White, Thomas S., Pres. & Chief Exec. Officer--Monarch Tile, Inc., Florence, AL; *U.S. Private*, pg. 287
White, Tony L., Chm. Bd., Pres. & Chief Exec. Officer--The Perkin-Elmer Corporation, Norwalk, CT; *U.S. Public*, pg. 1279
White, Tony L., Chm. Bd., Pres. & Chief Exec. Officer--Applied Biosystems, Foster City, CA; *U.S. Public*, pg. 1279
White, William, Pres.--Shoppers Food Warehouse, Lanham, MD; *U.S. Public*, pg. 484
Whiteford, Russell E., Pres. & Chief Exec. Officer--DHP Limited Partnership, Chicopee, MA; *U.S. Private*, pg. 302
Whitehead, Doug W.G., Pres. & Chief Exec. Officer-Canadian Opers.--Fletcher Challenge Canada Limited, Vancouver, Canada; *Int'l*, pg. 495
Whiteman, John O., Pres.--EMPIRE Machinery, Mesa, AZ; *U.S. Private*, pg. 374
Whiteman, Jon, Pres. & Chief Oper. Officer--Morris Coupling Co., Erie, PA; *U.S. Private*, pg. 762
Whitener, Tim, Pres.--Luwa Bahnson, Inc., Winston Salem, NC; *U.S. Private*, pg. 682
Whiteside, W.G., Pres.--Block Drug Co. (Canada) Ltd., Toronto, Canada; *U.S. Public*, pg. 237
Whitford, Peter D., Pres. & Chief Exec. Officer--Structure, Columbus, OH; *U.S. Public*, pg. 996
Whiting, R. Bruce, Pres. & Chief Oper. Officer--Kaibab Industries, Phoenix, AZ; *U.S. Private*, pg. 605
Whiting, Richard M., Pres.--Peabody COALSALES Company, Saint Louis, MO; *Int'l*, pg. 594
Whiting, Richard T., Pres. & Chief Exec. Officer--Whiting Manufacturing Co., Inc., Cincinnati, OH; *U.S. Private*, pg. 1174
Whitley, Douglas L., Pres.--Ameritech, Chicago, IL; *U.S. Public*, pg. 97
Whitley, Edward A., Pres. & Chief Exec. Officer--Centex-Rodgers Construction Company, Nashville, TN; *U.S. Public*, pg. 322
Whitley, Michael R., Chm. Bd., Pres. & Chief Exec. & Oper. Officer--KU Energy, Lexington, KY; *U.S. Public*, pg. 940
Whitley, Michael R., Chm. Bd., Pres. & Chief Exec. Officer--Kentucky Utilities Company, Lexington, KY; *U.S. Public*, pg. 941
Whitley, Michael R., Pres. & Chief Oper. Officer--KU Capital Corporation, Lexington, KY; *U.S. Public*, pg. 941
Whitlock, C. William, Jr., Pres.--Old Kent Bank-Central, Owosso, MI; *U.S. Public*, pg. 1216
Whitlow, Don, Pres. & Chief Oper. Officer--Barbour Thread, Inc., Blue Mountain, AL; *Int'l*, pg. 618
Whitlow, Maurice, Pres. & Chief Exec. Officer--General Processors, Inc., Oxford, NC; *U.S. Public*, pg. 1502
Whitman, Bob, Pres. & Chief Exec. Officer--Malibu Entertainment Worldwide, Dallas, TX; *U.S. Public*, pg. 1039
Whitman, Christine, Chm. Bd., Pres. & Chief Exec. Officer--CVC Products, Inc., Rochester, NY; *U.S. Private*, pg. 197
Whitmarsh, Robert M., Pres. & Chief Exec. Officer--Willis Corroon Corp. of Portland, Portland, OR; *Int'l*, pg. 1507
Whitmer, Jack E., Pres.--McGraw-Hill Professional Publishing Group, New York, NY; *U.S. Public*, pg. 1070
Whitmer, Richard E., Pres. & Chief Exec. Officer--Blue Cross & Blue Shield of Michigan, Detroit, MI; *U.S. Private*, pg. 151
Whitmire, J.L., Pres.--Phillips Alaska Natural Gas Corporation, Bellaire, TX; *U.S. Public*, pg. 1291
Whitmore, David, Pres.--Tecknit Incorporated, Cranford, NJ; *U.S. Private*, pg. 1072
Whitmore, John R., Pres. & Chief Exec. Officer--Bessemer Group, Inc., New York, NY; *U.S. Private*, pg. 139
Whitney, Brad P., Pres. & Chief Oper. Officer--Linfinity Microelectronics Inc., Garden Grove, CA; *U.S. Public*, pg. 1547
Whitney, Dickson L., Jr., Pres. & Chief Exec. Officer--McGean-Rohco, Inc., Cleveland, OH; *U.S. Private*, pg. 721
Whitney, Haynes, Jr., Pres.--Democrat Printing & Lithograph Company, Little Rock, AR; *U.S. Private*, pg. 323
Whitney, Jerry, Pres.--J. Korber & Company, Albuquerque, NM; *U.S. Private*, pg. 632
Whitney, Michael C., Jr., Chm. Bd., Pres. & Chief Exec. Officer--Fleet Bank NH, Manchester, NH; *U.S. Public*, pg. 649
Whitsell, William A., Pres.--Copeland Lumber Yard, Inc., Portland, OR; *U.S. Private*, pg. 274
Whitt, David, Pres. & Chief Oper. Officer--Elixir Industries, Gardena, CA; *U.S. Private*, pg. 371
Whittle, Danny, Pres.--Heckethorn Mfg. Company, Inc., Dyersburg, TN; *U.S. Private*, pg. 519
Whittle, John J., Chm. Bd., Pres. & Chief Exec. Officer--Farmers and Traders Life Insurance Co., Syracuse, NY; *U.S. Private*, pg. 394
Whittle, Mack I., Jr., Pres. & Chief Exec. Officer--Carolina First Corporation, Greenville, SC; *U.S. Public*, pg. 306
Whyte, Fred, Pres.--Stihl Inc., Virginia Beach, VA; *Int'l*, pg. 1301
Whyte, George C., Jr., Chm. Bd., Pres. & Chief Exec. Officer--Dakotah, Inc., Webster, SD; *U.S. Public*, pg. 477
Wiaderek, Slawomir, Pres.--EMTEC Magnetics Polska Sp. z.o.o., Warsaw, Poland; *Int'l*, pg. 743
Wiatt, James, Pres.--International Creative Management, Inc., Los Angeles, CA; *U.S. Private*, pg. 554
Wichlenski, John J., Sr., Pres. & Chief Exec. Officer-Air Systems--Engineered Support Systems Inc., Saint Louis, MO; *U.S. Public*, pg. 583
Wichman, John, Pres.--Wenco Inc., San Dimas, CA; *U.S. Private*, pg. 1754
Wichtrich, John, Pres.--Rhone-Poulenc Specialty Chemicals Division, Cranbury, NJ; *Int'l*, pg. 1110
Wick, Jeff, Pres. & Chief Exec. Officer--Wick Building Systems, Mazomanie, WI; *U.S. Private*, pg. 1174
Wick, Michael A., Pres.--Warner-Jenkinson Co., Saint Louis, MO; *U.S. Public*, pg. 1696
Wick, Philip, Pres.--Les Schwab Tire Centers, Prineville, OR; *U.S. Private*, pg. 974
Wicken, Michael J., Pres. & Chief Exec. Officer--Motch Corporation, Cleveland, OH; *Int'l*, pg. 1128
Wicker, Alain, Pres.--Fimagest, Paris, France; *Int'l*, pg. 548
Wickersham, John, Pres. & Chief Exec. Officer--Bill Communications, Inc., New York, NY; *Int'l*, pg. 1446
Wickett, John, Pres.--Seaman-Patrick Paper Company, Detroit, MI; *U.S. Private*, pg. 979
Wickham, Michael W., Pres. & Chief Exec. Officer--Roadway Express, Inc., Akron, OH; *U.S. Public*, pg. 1392
Wickins, David, Chm. Bd.--British Car Auction Group, Hindhead, United Kingdom; *U.S. Public*, pg. 1649
Wickland, Roy, Pres.--Wickland Corporation, Sacramento, CA; *U.S. Private*, pg. 1174
Wickline, Ronald, Pres.--Danfoss Fluid Power, a division of Danfoss, Inc., Racine, WI; *Int'l*, pg. 377
Wickre, Gary L., Pres.--First American Bank West, Minot, ND; *U.S. Private*, pg. 167
Wicks, Clyde, Pres. & Publisher--The Sun Times, Owen Sound, Canada; *Int'l*, pg. 631
Wicks, Floyd E., Pres. & Chief Exec. Officer--Southern California Water Company, San Dimas, CA; *U.S. Public*, pg. 1489
Widdicombe, Elizabeth, Pres.--W.H. Freeman & Co., New York, NY; *Int'l*, pg. 1479
Widham, Susan, Pres.--Beech-Nut Nutrition Corporation, Saint Louis, MO; *U.S. Public*, pg. 1359
Widmer, Hans, Dr., Chm. Bd., Pres., Chief Exec. & Oper. Officer--Oerlikon-Buhrle Holding AG, Zurich, Switzerland; *Int'l*, pg. 996
Wiecek, Barbara H., Sr. Partner & Exec. Creative Dir.--EURO RSCG Tatham, Chicago, IL; *Int'l*, pg. 601
Wiedeking, Wendelin, Dr., Pres. & Chief Exec. Officer--Porsche AG, Stuttgart, Germany; *Int'l*, pg. 1063
Wiedemer, Richard A. Jr., Pres.--Hinkley Lighting Inc., Cleveland, OH; *U.S. Private*, pg. 530
Wieden, Dan G., Pres.--Wieden & Kennedy, Inc., Portland, OR; *U.S. Private*, pg. 1175
Wiedenhaupt, Kurt, Chm. Bd. & Pres.--American Precision Industries Inc., Buffalo, NY; *U.S. Public*, pg. 90
Wiegand, Phillips, Pres. & Chief Exec. Officer--T.W. Phillips Gas and Oil Co., Butler, PA; *U.S. Private*, pg. 862
Wiegandt, Woodrow, Pres.--Binkley Company, Warrenton, MO; *U.S. Private*, pg. 534
Wieland, Bernard, Pres.--Unarco Material, Springfield, TN; *U.S. Private*, pg. 922
Wieland, John F., Chm. Bd., Pres. & Chief Exec. Officer--John Wieland Homes Inc., Atlanta, GA; *U.S. Private*, pg. 1175
Wieman, Beverly J., Pres.--Survey Sampling, Inc., Fairfield, CT; *U.S. Private*, pg. 1056
Wiener, Daniel E., Pres. & Chief Exec. Officer--Lone Star Equities Inc., Lynbrook, NY; *U.S. Private*, pg. 674
Wienick, Mitch, Pres. & Chief Exec. Officer--CDI Corp., Philadelphia, PA; *U.S. Public*, pg. 276
Wienstein, David, Pres.--Concord House Division, New York, NY; *U.S. Public*, pg. 430
Wiersbe, Dale E., Jr., Pres. & Chief Oper. Officer--Inland Steel Products Company, East Chicago, IN; *U.S. Public*, pg. 879
Wiersum, T., Pres.--BV Delft Electronic Products, Roden, Netherlands; *Int'l*, pg. 388
Wiesemes, Rhoda, Pres. & Treas.--Quality Packaging Products, Inc., Benton Harbor, MI; *U.S. Private*, pg. 899
Wieseneck, Robert L., Pres.--SPS Payment Systems, Inc., Riverwoods, IL; *U.S. Public*, pg. 1132
Wiesner, Richard, Pres.--LifeScan, Inc., Milpitas, CA; *U.S. Public*, pg. 928
Wigand, Art F., Pres. & Chief Exec. Officer--Cubic Communications, San Diego, CA; *U.S. Public*, pg. 466
Wigand, Emeric, Jr., Pres.--Wigand Corporation, Colorado Springs, CO; *U.S. Private*, pg. 1038
Wiggel, Theo, Pres.--Marine Power Australia, Pty. Ltd., Dandenong, Australia; *U.S. Public*, pg. 266
Wiggins, David, Pres.--Empire Kosher Poultry, Inc., Mifflintown, PA; *U.S. Private*, pg. 374
Wiggins, Jerome M., Pres.-Opers.--Dyersburg Corporation, Dyersburg, TN; *U.S. Public*, pg. 538
Wiggins, William H., Pres. & Chief Oper. Officer--Thiele Kaolin Co., Sandersville, GA; *U.S. Private*, pg. 1081
Wigginton, Eugene H., Pres.--Standard Publishing, Cincinnati, OH; *U.S. Public*, pg. 1506
Wightman, David, Pres.--Electro Kinetics Div., Santa Barbara, CA; *U.S. Public*, pg. 1250
Wigley, Michael R., Pres., Chief Exec. Officer & Treas.--Great Plains Companies, Inc., Roseville, MN; *U.S. Private*, pg. 475
Wiik, Ingrid, Pres.--International Pharmaceuticals, Oslo, Norway; *U.S. Public*, pg. 58
Wijkander, Evert, Pres.--Morgardshammar AB, Smedjebacken, Sweden; *Int'l*, pg. 378
Wikman, Bruno, Pres.--NCC Umea, Umea, Sweden; *Int'l*, pg. 899
Wilansky, Heywood, Pres. & Chief Exec. Officer--The Bon Ton Stores, Inc., York, PA; *U.S. Public*, pg. 244
Wilbraham, David, Dr., Chief Exec. Officer--Hickson International Plc, Castleford, United Kingdom; *Int'l*, pg. 618
Wilbrett, Robert, Pres. & Chief Exec. Officer--Hilb, Rogal and Hamilton Company of Port Huron, Port Huron, MI; *U.S. Public*, pg. 827
Wilbur, Brayton, Jr., Pres. & Chief Exec. Officer--Wilbur-Ellis Company & Connell Brothers Company, San Francisco, CA; *U.S. Private*, pg. 1175
Wilburn, Robert, Pres. & Chief Exec. Officer--Colonial Williamsburg Foundation, Williamsburg, VA; *U.S. Private*, pg. 254
Wilby, Bruce, Pres.--JPS Elastomerics Corp., Holyoke, MA; *U.S. Private*, pg. 578
Wilcott, Scott J., Pres.--CalMat Land Co., Los Angeles, CA; *U.S. Public*, pg. 295
Wilcott, Scott J., Pres.--Reliance Land Co., Los Angeles, CA; *U.S. Public*, pg. 296
Wilcox, Janet, Pres.--Mountain States Pipe & Supply Company, Colorado Springs, CO; *U.S. Private*, pg. 764
Wilcox, Jay, Pres.--Woodlore, Port Washington, WI; *U.S. Private*, pg. 37
Wilcox, Richard W. Jr., Pres.--Hilb, Rogal and Hamilton Company of Fort Lauderdale, Fort Lauderdale, FL; *U.S. Public*, pg. 827
Wilcox, William H., Pres. & Chief Oper. Officer-M.C.I.I.--Columbia/H.C.A., Dallas, TX; *U.S. Public*, pg. 404
Wilcoxson, Bill, Pres.--Morgan Trailer Manufacturing Co., Morgantown, PA; *U.S. Private*, pg. 761
Wild, Floyd, Chm. Bd. & Pres.--Lyon County Co-op Oil Co., Marshall, MN; *U.S. Private*, pg. 684
Wildauer, Werner K., Chm. Bd. & Pres.--Leupold & Stevens, Inc., Beaverton, OR; *U.S. Private*, pg. 662
Wilder, Duane, Chm. Bd., Pres. & Treas.--Wilder Deem, Inc., New York, NY; *U.S. Private*, pg. 1176
Wilding, Ernest L., Chm. Bd., Pres. & Chief Exec. Officer--Spray-Tech, Inc., Longwood, FL; *U.S. Private*, pg. 1026
Wildman, John, Pres.--Cardio-Fitness Corporation, New York, NY; *U.S. Public*, pg. 806
Wildman, John A., Pres.--The Fitness Institute, Willowdale, Canada; *U.S. Public*, pg. 806
Wildrick, Robert N., Chm. Bd., Pres. & Chief Exec. Officer--Venture Stores, Inc., O Fallon, MO; *U.S. Public*, pg. 1716
Wilen, Joseph, Pres.--Wilen Manufacturing Company, Inc., Atlanta, GA; *U.S. Private*, pg. 1176
Wiley, D. Linn, Pres. & Chief Exec. Officer--CVB Financial Corp., Ontario, CA; *U.S. Public*, pg. 286
Wilhelm, James M., Pres. & Chief Exec. Officer--F.A. Wilhelm Construction Co., Inc., Indianapolis, IN; *U.S. Private*, pg. 1176
Wilhelmsson, Ola, Pres.--AB Gustaf Kahr, Nybro, Sweden; *Int'l*, pg. 1260
Wilhoit, Joseph W., Pres.--Phoenix Fuel Company, Inc., Phoenix, AZ; *U.S. Private*, pg. 863
Wilk, Cornelius, Pres.--Epipharm GmbH, Lienz, Austria; *Int'l*, pg. 288
Wilk, Steven J., Pres.--TransNet Corporation, Somerville, NJ; *U.S. Public*, pg. 1631
Wilke, William P., IV, Pres.--Hammond Group Inc., Hammond, IN; *U.S. Private*, pg. 498
Wilken, Richard, Pres.--Grand Prairie Co-op, Inc., Tolono, IL; *U.S. Private*, pg. 468
Wilkens, Ian G., Pres. & Gen. Mgr.--Fischbein Co., Statesville, NC; *U.S. Private*, pg. 103
Wilkens, Roy A., Pres. & Chief Exec. Officer-WilTel--WorldCom, Inc., Jackson, MS; *U.S. Public*, pg. 1779
Wilkens, Roy A., Pres. & Chief Exec. Officer--LDDS WorldCom, Tulsa, OK; *U.S. Public*, pg. 1779

Wilkes, James E., Pres.--Ameritech, Detroit, MI; *U.S. Public*, pg. 97
Wilkes, John, Pres. & Chief Exec. Officer--John Dusenbery Co., Inc., Randolph, NJ; *U.S. Private*, pg. 349
Wilkes, Robert E., Pres.--First Valley Corporation, Bethlehem, PA; *U.S. Public*, pg. 1528
Wilkie, Michael L., Chm. Bd., Pres., Chief Exec. & Chief Oper. Officer--DOALL Company, Des Plaines, IL; *U.S. Private*, pg. 337
Wilkins, Amy, Pres.-'Teen, All About You--Petersen Publishing Company, L.L.C., Los Angeles, CA; *U.S. Private*, pg. 856
Wilkins, Gregory C., Pres. & Chief Oper. Officer--TrizecHahn Corporation, Toronto, Canada; *Int'l*, pg. 1424
Wilkins, P.D., Pres.--Morganite Environmental Services Inc., Dunn, NC; *Int'l*, pg. 894
Wilkinson, B. Andrew, Pres. & Chief Exec. Officer--Statex Petroleum, Inc., Dallas, TX; *U.S. Public*, pg. 1245
Wilkinson, C., Div. Mgr.--Pneumatic Div., Cannock, United Kingdom; *U.S. Public*, pg. 1264
Wilkinson, Dave, Pres. & Gen. Mgr.--St. Clair Paint and Wallpaper Corporation, Toronto, Canada; *Int'l*, pg. 1170
Wilkinson, Eugene R., Chm. Bd., Pres., & Chief Exec. Officer--Hanson Engineers Inc., Springfield, IL; *U.S. Private*, pg. 500
Wilkinson, Jay, Pres.--Public Employees Benefit Services Corp., Columbus, OH; *U.S. Private*, pg. 789
Wilkinson, Michael, Chm. Bd. & Pres.--DSC Ltd., Trenton, MI; *U.S. Private*, pg. 305
Wilkinson, Trevor S., Chm. Bd.--Butler Lutos Sutton Wilkinson, London, United Kingdom; *Int'l*, pg. 237
Wilkinson, William, Pres.--Dover Corp. (Canada) Ltd., Mississauga, Canada; *U.S. Public*, pg. 522
Wilks, David M., Pres. & Chief Oper. Officer--Southwestern Public Service Company, Amarillo, TX; *U.S. Public*, pg. 1170
Wilkus, Richard, Pres.--ISI Insortex, Schaumburg, IL; *U.S. Private*, pg. 428
Will, James F., Chm. Bd., Pres. & Chief Exec. Officer--Armco Inc., Pittsburgh, PA; *U.S. Public*, pg. 131
Willard, Bruce, Pres.--The Territory Ahead, Santa Barbara, CA; *U.S. Private*, pg. 1077
Willard, Greg, Pres.--Quality Control Corporation, Chicago, IL; *U.S. Private*, pg. 898
Willard, Jane, Pres.--Willard Grain & Feed, Inc., Celina, TX; *U.S. Private*, pg. 1177
Willard, Larry, Chm. & Pres.--Norwest Bank New Mexico, N.A., Albuquerque, NM; *U.S. Public*, pg. 1202
Willard, Wynn, Pres.--Planters Company, East Hanover, NJ; *U.S. Public*, pg. 1355
Willardsen, Steve, Pres.--Shady Brook Farms, Dayton, VA; *U.S. Private*, pg. 937
Willardson, Craig, Pres.--Nulaid Foods, Ripon, CA; *U.S. Private*, pg. 809
Willcock, Clarence, Mng. Dir.--Frialator International, Warrington, United Kingdom; *U.S. Public*, pg. 1065
Willcox, James, Pres., Chief Exec. & Chief Oper. Officer--American Marketing Industries, Inc., Kansas City, MO; *U.S. Private*, pg. 58
Willems, Bert, Pres.--Knurr NV Belgie, Kontich, Belgium; *Int'l*, pg. 739
Willems, Bert, Pres.--Knurr Nederland B.V., Breda, Netherlands; *Int'l*, pg. 739
Willert, William D., Pres.--Willert Home Products, Inc., Saint Louis, MO; *U.S. Private*, pg. 1177
Willes, Mark, Chm. Bd., Pres. & Chief Exec. Officer--The Times Mirror Company, Los Angeles, CA; *U.S. Public*, pg. 1615
Willet, Richard H., Chm. Bd., Pres. & Chief Exec. Officer--Consoltex Group Inc., Ville Saint Laurent, Canada; *Int'l*, pg. 326
Willett, Bill, Pres.--Colorado Prime Corporation, Farmingdale, NY; *U.S. Private*, pg. 255
Willey, Frank P., Pres.--Fidelity National Financial, Inc., Irvine, CA; *U.S. Public*, pg. 620
Williams, Andrew, Pres.--Cadmus Interactive, Tucker, GA; *U.S. Public*, pg. 291
Williams, B.B., Pres. & Gen. Mgr.--P.T. Stanvac Indonesia, Jakarta, Indonesia; *U.S. Public*, pg. 603
Williams, Bruce E., Pres. & Treas.--Williams Company Of Orlando, Inc., Orlando, FL; *U.S. Private*, pg. 1177
Williams, Charles, Pres.--Addwest Minerals, Inc., Arvada, CO; *U.S. Private*, pg. 17
Williams, Charles T., Co-Pres.--The Echo Design Group, Inc., New York, NY; *U.S. Private*, pg. 359
Williams, Christopher J., Pres.--Reinsurance Alternatives, Inc., Minneapolis, MN; *Int'l*, pg. 1503
Williams, Chuck, Pres. & Chief Exec. Officer--Brightware, Inc., Novato, CA; *U.S. Private*, pg. 168
Williams, Clint O., Pres. & Chief Exec. Officer--Union Planters Bank of West Tennessee, Humboldt, TN; *U.S. Public*, pg. 1669
Williams, Colin V.K., Pres. & Chief Exec. Officer--MFS International, Inc., Vienna, VA; *U.S. Public*, pg. 1779
Williams, D. Wayne, Pres. & Chief Exec. Officer--Century Data Systems, Incorporated, Raleigh, NC; *U.S. Private*, pg. 226
Williams, D.K., Pres. & Chief Exec. Officer--Nuovo Pignone S.p.a., Florence, Italy; *Int'l*, pg. 990
Williams, David A., Pres.--Linpac Mouldings Limited, Birmingham, United Kingdom; *Int'l*, pg. 811
Williams, David A., Pres., Chief Oper. Officer & Gen. Mgr.--Regency Lincoln Mercury, Inc., Dallas, TX; *U.S. Private*, pg. 918
Williams, David J., Chm. Bd., Pres. & Chief Exec. Officer--Power Process Piping, Inc., Plymouth, MI; *U.S. Private*, pg. 878
Williams, David J., Pres. & Chief Oper. Officer--Connaught Laboratories, Inc., Swiftwater, PA; *Int'l*, pg. 1109
Williams, David P., Pres. & Chief Oper. Officer--The Budd Company, Troy, MI; *Int'l*, pg. 1388
Williams, Edward D., Pres.--Strategic Outsourcing Services Inc., Parsippany, NJ; *U.S. Public*, pg. 421
Williams, Eldridge M., Pres.--Universal Financial Services, Memphis, TN; *U.S. Private*, pg. 1127
Williams, Francis M., Chm. Bd., Pres. & Chief Exec. Officer--Kimmins Corp., Tampa, FL; *U.S. Public*, pg. 960
Williams, Frank E., III, Chm. Bd., Pres. & Chief Exec. Officer--Williams Industries, Inc., Falls Church, VA; *U.S. Public*, pg. 1769
Williams, Fred A., Pres.--JC Penney Reinsurance Company, Plano, TX; *U.S. Public*, pg. 917
Williams, Glenn, Chm. Bd. & Pres.--Heritage Co-op, Rushville, IN; *U.S. Private*, pg. 524
Williams, Gregg G., Pres. & Chief Oper. Officer--Williams International, Walled Lake, MI; *U.S. Private*, pg. 1178
Williams, H. Edward, Pres. & Chief Exec. Officer--Security Bank & Trust Co., Vincennes, IN; *U.S. Public*, pg. 1217
Williams, J.L., Pres.--Minyard Food Stores, Inc., Coppell, TX; *U.S. Private*, pg. 752
Williams, Jack, Pres.--Royal Caribbean Cruises Ltd., Miami, FL; *U.S. Public*, pg. 1410
Williams, James, Pres.--BC-USA, New Holland, PA; *Int'l*, pg. 201
Williams, James B., Pres. & Chief Oper. Officer--Acklands Limited, Toronto, Canada; *Int'l*, pg. 23
Williams, James C., Pres.--Williams Distributing Company, Grand Rapids, MI; *U.S. Private*, pg. 1177
Williams, Jay, Pres.-Firstar, Illinois--Firstar Corporation, Milwaukee, WI; *U.S. Public*, pg. 642
Williams, Jay, Pres.-Firstar, Illinois--Firstar Milwaukee Bank, N.A., Milwaukee, WI; *U.S. Public*, pg. 643
Williams, Jeffrey W., Pres. & Chief Exec. Officer--American Security Group, Atlanta, GA; *Int'l*, pg. 499
Williams, John, Pres. & Chief Exec. Officer--Gray Communications Systems, Inc., Albany, GA; *U.S. Public*, pg. 759
Williams, John A., Pres. & Dir.--LL&E Algeria, Ltd., Hamilton, Bermuda; *U.S. Public*, pg. 269
Williams, John A., Pres.--LL&E Indonesia, Ltd., Road Town, Virgin Islands (British); *U.S. Public*, pg. 269
Williams, John A., Pres.--LL&E Tunisia, Ltd., Hamilton, Bermuda; *U.S. Public*, pg. 269
Williams, John A., Pres.--Memphis Group, Inc., Memphis, TN; *U.S. Private*, pg. 730
Williams, John D., Jr., Pres.--Williams International Industries, Inc., Richmond, VA; *U.S. Private*, pg. 1178
Williams, John H., Jr., Pres. & Chief Oper. Officer--Stein Mart, Inc., Jacksonville, FL; *U.S. Public*, pg. 1514
Williams, Jon M., Pres. & Chief Oper. Officer--Integrated Waste Services, Inc., Buffalo, NY; *U.S. Public*, pg. 886
Williams, Kent, Pres.--Walter Lorenz Surgical, Inc., Jacksonville, FL; *U.S. Public*, pg. 231
Williams, Lewis T., M.D., Ph.D, Pres.--Chiron Technologies, Emeryville, CA; *U.S. Public*, pg. 350
Williams, Mel, Pres.--Danzer Industries Inc., Hagerstown, MD; *U.S. Public*, pg. 747
Williams, Mike, Pres. & Chief Exec. Officer--Texas Electric Cooperatives, Inc., Austin, TX; *U.S. Private*, pg. 1078
Williams, Neil, Publr.--The Coalinga Record, Coalinga, CA; *U.S. Public*, pg. 1343
Williams, Neil, Publr.--The Avenal Progress, Avenal, CA; *U.S. Public*, pg. 1343
Williams, Neil, Publr.--The Twin Cities Times/Riverdale Free Press, Fresno, CA; *U.S. Public*, pg. 1343
Williams, Neil, Publr.--The Lemoore Advance, Lemoore, CA; *U.S. Public*, pg. 1343
Williams, Neil D., Publr.--The Hanford Sentinel, Hanford, CA; *U.S. Public*, pg. 1343
Williams, Nicholas, Pres.--Premisys Communications, Inc., Fremont, CA; *U.S. Public*, pg. 1323
Williams, Peggy M., Pres. & Chief Exec. Officer--First State Bank, Greenville, KY; *U.S. Public*, pg. 1217
Williams, Philip A., Pres., Trust Officer & Sec. of the Bd.--Farmers and Merchants Bank of Carlinville, Carlinville, IL; *U.S. Public*, pg. 644
Williams, R.L., Pres. & Chief Oper. Officer--Dan River Inc., Danville, VA; *U.S. Public*, pg. 478
Williams, Robert, Pres.--ITW Switches, Chicago, IL; *U.S. Public*, pg. 867
Williams, Robert, Chief Exec. Officer--Vengroff Williams & Associates, Inc., Commack, NY; *U.S. Private*, pg. 1135
Williams, Robert J., Sr., Chm. Bd. & Chief Exec. Officer--Cadillac Products, Inc., Troy, MI; *U.S. Private*, pg. 198
Williams, Robert M., Jr., Pres. & Treas.--Williams Patent Crusher and Pulverizer Co., Saint Louis, MO; *U.S. Private*, pg. 1178
Williams, Ron, Pres.--Blue Cross of California, Woodland Hills, CA; *U.S. Private*, pg. 152
Williams, Ronald, Pres. & Chief Exec. Officer--Gary-Williams Energy Corporation, Denver, CO; *U.S. Private*, pg. 440
Williams, Roy, Pres.--Keystone (Canada) Ltd., Burlington, Canada; *U.S. Public*, pg. 1650
Williams, Shari, Pres.--Arnold Direct, Boston, MA; *U.S. Private*, pg. 84
Williams, Sonny, Pres.--Fasco Industries, Inc., Southfield, MI; *Int'l*, pg. 125
Williams, Stephen, Pres. & Chief Exec. Officer--Carver Corporation, Lynnwood, WA; *U.S. Public*, pg. 310
Williams, Sterling L., Pres. & Chief Exec. Officer--Sterling Software, Inc., Dallas, TX; *U.S. Public*, pg. 1516
Williams, Steven R., Pres.--Petroleum Development Corporation, Bridgeport, WV; *U.S. Public*, pg. 1280
Williams, Thomas, Pres.--Horizon Initiatives, Wilmington, DE; *U.S. Public*, pg. 423
Williams, Thomas A., Pres.--Brown Shoe Company, Saint Louis, MO; *U.S. Public*, pg. 262
Williams, Thomas C., Pres. & Chief Exec. Officer--Rurban Financial Corp., Defiance, OH; *U.S. Public*, pg. 1412
Williams, Thomas E., Pres. & Chief Exec. Officer--Applied Extrusion Technologies, Inc., Peabody, MA; *U.S. Public*, pg. 122
Williams, William D., Pres.--Phyxis Corporation, San Diego, CA; *U.S. Public*, pg. 305
Williamson, Hugh H., III, Pres. & Chief Exec. Officer--KTM Holdings Corp., Denver, CO; *U.S. Private*, pg. 604
Williamson, Hugh H., III, Pres. & Chief Exec. Officer--Ketema, Inc., Denver, CO; *U.S. Private*, pg. 604
Williamson, John B., III, Pres. & Chief Exec. Officer--Roanoke Gas Company, Roanoke, VA; *U.S. Public*, pg. 1392
Williamson, John W., Pres.--Southwestern Bell Technology Resources, Saint Louis, MO; *U.S. Public*, pg. 1416
Williamson, Max, Pres.--Scottsdale Insurance Company, Scottsdale, AZ; *U.S. Private*, pg. 789
Williamson, Philip C., Chm. Bd., Pres. & Chief Exec. Officer--Williamson-Dickie Mfg. Co., Fort Worth, TX; *U.S. Private*, pg. 1179
Williamson, Ralph, Pres.--Airline Manufacturing Company, Inc., Columbus, MS; *U.S. Private*, pg. 29
Williamson, Richard B., Chm. Bd., Pres. & Chief Exec. Officer--T.D. Williamson, Inc., Tulsa, OK; *U.S. Private*, pg. 1179
Williamson, Richard C., Pres. & Chief Exec. Officer--Pacific One Bank, Portland, OR; *U.S. Public*, pg. 635
Williard, Danny, Pres.--The Arundel Corporation, Sparks, MD; *U.S. Public*, pg. 656
Willies, Douglas, Pres.--The At-A-Glance Group, Sidney, NY; *U.S. Private*, pg. 295
Williford, Robert, Pres.--American Health Consultants, Atlanta, GA; *U.S. Public*, pg. 1601
Willingham, Thomas K., Pres.--Kex Products, Inc., La Vergne, TN; *U.S. Private*, pg. 138
Williome, Jack H., Pres. & Chief Exec. Officer--Kaufman and Broad of Texas, Ltd., San Antonio, TX; *U.S. Public*, pg. 945
Willis, David F., Pres. & Co-Creative Dir.--JMCT/Direct, New York, NY; *U.S. Private*, pg. 599
Willis, Gary K., Pres. & Chief Exec. Officer--Zygo Corporation, Middlefield, CT; *U.S. Public*, pg. 1795
Willis, Larry, Pres. & Chief Oper. Officer--IGA, Inc. (Independent Grocers Alliance), Chicago, IL; *U.S. Private*, pg. 555
Willis, Robert E., Pres. & Chief Exec. Officer--EPX, Portland, ME; *U.S. Private*, pg. 354
Willis, Thomas N., Pres.--Matco Tools, Stow, OH; *U.S. Public*, pg. 482
Willoch, Ray, Pres.--Georgia Duck & Cordage Mills, Scottdale, GA; *U.S. Private*, pg. 448
Willott, Michael, Pres.--Adhesive Films, Santa Ana, CA; *U.S. Public*, pg. 165
Willoughby, H. William, Pres. & Sec.--CRIIMI MAE, Rockville, MD; *U.S. Public*, pg. 459
Willoughby, H. William, Pres.--CRI Liquidating REIT, Inc., Rockville, MD; *U.S. Public*, pg. 459
Wills, J. Blacklock, Jr., Pres. & Chief Exec. Officer--Wills Group, Inc., La Plata, MD; *U.S. Private*, pg. 1180
Wills, Sir John, Pres.--Bristol & West Building Society, Bristol, United Kingdom; *Int'l*, pg. 216
Wills, Travers H., Pres. & Chief Exec. Officer--HealthWise of America, Nashville, TN; *U.S. Public*, pg. 1678
Wills, Travers H., Pres.--United HealthCare of Nevada, Inc., Las Vegas, NV; *U.S. Public*, pg. 1678
Willson, John M., Pres. & Chief Exec. Officer--Placer Dome Inc., Vancouver, Canada; *Int'l*, pg. 1060
Wilmers, John P., Pres. & Chief Exec. Officer--Ballantyne of Omaha, Inc., Omaha, NE; *Int'l*, pg. 17
Wilmore, Melvin A., Pres. & Chief Oper. Officer--Ross Stores, Inc., Newark, CA; *U.S. Public*, pg. 1405
Wilmot, Thomas C., Pres. & Chief Exec. Officer--Wilmorite, Inc., Rochester, NY; *U.S. Private*, pg. 1180
Wilsey, Michael W., Chm. Bd. & Pres.--Wilsey Bennett Co., San Francisco, CA; *U.S. Private*, pg. 1180
Wilska, Kari-Pekka, Pres.--Nokia Inc., Irving, TX; *Int'l*, pg. 952
Wilskey, Richard, Pres.--D.W. Close Company, Seattle, WA; *U.S. Public*, pg. 1029
Wilson, B., Pres.--Albany Port Railroad Co., Albany, NY; *U.S. Public*, pg. 432
Wilson, C. Richard, Pres. & Chief Oper. Officer--Buckeye Partners, L.P., Allentown, PA; *U.S. Public*, pg. 266
Wilson, Carl W., Jr., Pres.--BS & B Process Systems, Inc., Houston, TX; *U.S. Private*, pg. 572
Wilson, Charles A., Pres. & Chief Exec. Officer--Connor Corporation, Fort Wayne, IN; *U.S. Private*, pg. 264
Wilson, Claude, Pres. & Gen. Mgr.--Wilson & Lafleur, Limitee, Montreal, Canada; *Int'l*, pg. 1076
Wilson, Clifford D., Pres. & Chief Exec. Officer--Ritchie Industries, Inc., Conrad, IA; *U.S. Private*, pg. 933
Wilson, Darrell D., Pres. & Chief Oper. Officer--American Waste Services, Inc., Warren, OH; *U.S. Public*, pg. 94
Wilson, David, Pres.--Rapid Mounting & Finishing, Union City, CA; *U.S. Private*, pg. 910
Wilson, David W., Chm. Bd. & Pres.--Wilson Products Co., Salt Lake City, UT; *U.S. Private*, pg. 1181
Wilson, Diane M., Chm. Bd., Pres. & Chief Exec. Officer--Trend Laboratories Inc., Atlanta, GA; *U.S. Public*, pg. 1634
Wilson, Douglas, Pres.--Hawk Corp., Cleveland, OH; *U.S. Private*, pg. 511
Wilson, Douglas, Pres.--The S.K. Wellman Friction Products Co., Brook Park, OH; *U.S. Private*, pg. 511
Wilson, Duncan Baldwin, Deputy Chm. & Joint Mng. Dir.--VG Instruments plc, Crawley, United Kingdom; *U.S. Public*, pg. 1595
Wilson, Ed, Pres.-CBS Enterprises & Eyemark Entertainment--CBS Enterprises Division, New York, NY; *U.S. Public*, pg. 274
Wilson, G., Pres.--Rantec Microwave and Electronics, Inc., Calabasas, CA; *U.S. Public*, pg. 546
Wilson, G. Larry, Chm. Bd., Pres. & Chief Exec. Officer--Policy Management Systems Corporation, Blythewood, SC; *U.S. Public*, pg. 1314
Wilson, Gary E., Pres.--Springs Canada, Ltd., Mississauga, Canada; *U.S. Public*, pg. 1500
Wilson, George P., Pres. & Chief Exec. Officer--Equitrac Corporation, Coral Gables, FL; *U.S. Public*, pg. 590
Wilson, Glen W., Pres. & Chief Exec. Officer--AMCORE Trust Company, Rockford, IL; *U.S. Public*, pg. 65

Wilson, Gregory L., Chm. Bd., Pres. & Chief Exec. Officer--Mity-Lite, Inc., Orem, UT; *U.S. Public*, pg. 1118
Wilson, Ian R., Chm. Bd., Pres., & Chief Exec. Officer--Dartford Partnership, San Francisco, CA; *U.S. Private*, pg. 312
Wilson, J., Pres. & Dir.--Hilton International (Switzerland) AG, Basel, Switzerland; *Int'l*, pg. 788
Wilson, J. Steven, Chm. Bd., Pres. & Chief Exec. Officer--Riverside Group, Inc., Jacksonville, FL; *U.S. Public*, pg. 1391
Wilson, J.S., Jr., Pres. & Chief Exec. Officer--Conwood Company L.P., Memphis, TN; *U.S. Private*, pg. 272
Wilson, James D., Pres. & Chief Exec. Officer--Martin Industries, Inc. (AL), Florence, AL; *U.S. Private*, pg. 709
Wilson, James R., Chm. Bd., Pres. & Chief Exec. Officer--Thiokol Corporation, Ogden, UT; *U.S. Public*, pg. 1596
Wilson, James W., III, Pres.--Mason & Hanger Engineering Inc., Lexington, KY; *U.S. Private*, pg. 711
Wilson, James W., Jr., Pres.--Jim Wilson & Associates, Inc., Montgomery, AL; *U.S. Private*, pg. 1181
Wilson, Jay, Pres.e Mgr.--Cavalier Acceptance Corporation, Hamilton, AL; *U.S. Public*, pg. 318
Wilson, Jay, Pres.--Cavalier Insurance Agency, Inc., Hamilton, AL; *U.S. Public*, pg. 318
Wilson, John, Pres.--Amtech Systems Corporation, Dallas, TX; *U.S. Public*, pg. 105
Wilson, John H., Pres. & Chief Exec. Officer--Hilb, Rogal and Hamilton Company of the District of Columbia, Rockville, MD; *U.S. Public*, pg. 827
Wilson, John, III, Pres.--Whitehall Corporation, Dallas, TX; *U.S. Public*, pg. 1765
Wilson, Lawrence A., Pres. & Chief Exec. Officer--HCBeck, Dallas, TX; *U.S. Private*, pg. 490
Wilson, Marc, Pres. & Chief Exec. Officer--Safway Steel Products Inc., Waukesha, WI; *Int'l*, pg. 1389
Wilson, Mark, Pres.--Peace Industries Inc., Rolling Meadows, IL; *U.S. Private*, pg. 845
Wilson, Mark, Pres.--Spotnails, Rolling Meadows, IL; *U.S. Private*, pg. 845
Wilson, Martin D., Pres., Chief Oper. Officer & Sec.--D & K Healthcare Resources, Inc., Saint Louis, MO; *U.S. Public*, pg. 471
Wilson, Penny, Pres.--Alias Wavefront, Toronto, Canada; *U.S. Public*, pg. 1474
Wilson, R.M., Pres.--Simon United States Holdings Inc., Cincinnati, OH; *Int'l*, pg. 1252
Wilson, R.P., Chief Exec. Officer--The RTZ Corporation PLC, London, United Kingdom; *Int'l*, pg. 1118
Wilson, Ralph C., Jr., Chm. Bd. & Pres.--Ralph C. Wilson Enterprises, Detroit, MI; *U.S. Private*, pg. 1181
Wilson, Rich, Jr., Chm. Bd., Pres. & Chief Exec. Officer--Heavy Machines, Inc., Memphis, TN; *U.S. Private*, pg. 518
Wilson, Robert, Pres.--CSI Services, Knoxville, TN; *U.S. Public*, pg. 573
Wilson, Robert, Pres. & Chief Exec. Officer--Curtin & Pease/Peneco, Inc, Dunedin, FL; *U.S. Public*, pg. 1306
Wilson, Robert, Pres.--Feather Fine Services, Tampa, FL; *U.S. Public*, pg. 1306
Wilson, Ron, Pres. & Chief Oper. Officer--Harrison Wilson & Associates, Parsippany, NJ; *U.S. Public*, pg. 1224
Wilson, Ronald D., Pres.--Philadelphia Coca-Cola Bottling Co., Philadelphia, PA; *U.S. Private*, pg. 861
Wilson, Spence, Pres.--Kemmons Wilson, Inc., Memphis, TN; *U.S. Private*, pg. 613
Wilson, Steven A., Pres. & Chief Oper. Officer--BASES Worldwide, Covington, KY; *U.S. Private*, pg. 120
Wilson, Thomas A., Pres. & Chief Exec. Officer--Seer Technologies, Inc., Cary, NC; *U.S. Public*, pg. 1453
Wilson, Tim, Pres.--Ernest Paper Products, Inc., Los Angeles, CA; *U.S. Private*, pg. 381
Wilson, Tim, Pres. & Chief Exec. Officer--Marmac Corporation, Vienna, WV; *U.S. Private*, pg. 705
Wilson, Tony H., Pres.--Premier Metal Products Co., Carrollton, TX; *U.S. Private*, pg. 881
Wilson, Veronica, Pres. & Chief Exec. Officer--Aladdin Hotel & Casino, Las Vegas, NV; *U.S. Private*, pg. 30
Wilson, Wallace S., Chm. Bd., Pres. & Chief Exec. Officer--Wilson Industries Inc., Houston, TX; *U.S. Private*, pg. 1181
Wiltshire, R.W., Jr., Pres. & Chief Exec. Officer--Home Beneficial Corporation, Richmond, VA; *U.S. Public*, pg. 76
Wiltz, James W., Pres.--Patterson Dental Supply, Inc., Saint Paul, MN; *U.S. Public*, pg. 1265
Wimberly, Joseph J., IV, Pres.--I.C. Thomasson Associates, Inc., Nashville, TN; *U.S. Private*, pg. 1083
Win, Paul, Pres.--Enterprise Service Solutions, Carrollton, TX; *U.S. Public*, pg. 729
Winch, John J., Pres.--The Minster Machine Company, Minster, OH; *U.S. Private*, pg. 751
Winchell, W. Blake, Pres. & Chief Exec. Officer--Kleer-Vu Plastics, Inc., Compton, CA; *U.S. Public*, pg. 962
Windemuller, Michael, Pres.--Windemuller Electric Inc., Wayland, MI; *U.S. Private*, pg. 1182
Windham, Robert T., Sr., Chm. Bd., Pres. & Chief Exec. Officer--The Windham Company, Pensacola, FL; *U.S. Private*, pg. 1182
Windmuller, David T., Pres.--Fluid Management, Inc., Wheeling, IL; *U.S. Public*, pg. 862
Windsor, R., Mgr.-Mktg.--Eaton Corporation, Engineered Fasteners Division, Brunswick, OH; *U.S. Public*, pg. 556
Windus, J. Preston, Pres. & Chief Fin. Officer--Comtech PST Corp., Melville, NY; *U.S. Public*, pg. 425
Winer, Jonathan H., Pres.--Mountain Energy, Inc., South Burlington, VT; *U.S. Public*, pg. 761
Winfield, Michael D., Pres. & Chief Exec. Officer--UOP, Des Plaines, IL; *U.S. Public*, pg. 52
Wing, David, Partner--Joseph, Littlejohn & Levy, New York, NY; *U.S. Private*, pg. 601
Wing, Sam A., Jr., Chm. Bd., Pres. & Chief Exec. Officer--Wing Industries, Inc., Greenville, TX; *U.S. Private*, pg. 1183
Wing, Sonnie, Pres.--SKF Mfg. Singapore (Pte.) Ltd., Singapore, Singapore; *Int'l*, pg. 1159
Wingate, David A., Chm. Bd., Pres. & Chief Exec. Officer--Hi-Shear Industries Inc., New Hyde Park, NY; *U.S. Public*, pg. 824
Winger, Kenneth W., Pres. & Chief Exec. Officer--Laidlaw Environmental Services, Inc., Columbia, SC; *U.S. Public*, pg. 975
Wingrove, Dennis, Pres.--Taisil Electronic Materials Corporation, Hsin-chu, Taiwan; *Int'l*, pg. 286
Wink, William J., III, Pres.--Bill Wink Chevrolet, Dearborn, MI; *U.S. Private*, pg. 144
Winkhaus, Hans-Dietrich, Pres. & Chief Exec. Officer--Henkel KGaA, Dusseldorf, Germany; *Int'l*, pg. 609
Winkler, Agnieszka, Pres. & Chief Exec. Officer--Winkler Advertising, San Francisco, CA; *U.S. Private*, pg. 1183
Winkler, Paul, Pres.--Winkler Forming, Santa Fe Springs, CA; *U.S. Private*, pg. 827
Winkofske, Thomas, Pres.--LiphaTech, Inc., Milwaukee, WI; *Int'l*, pg. 812
Winn, Bruce, Pres.--CSC United States, Wilmington, DE; *U.S. Private*, pg. 197
Winn, Elwood, Pres. & Chief Exec. Officer--Certified Grocers Midwest, Inc., Hodgkins, IL; *U.S. Private*, pg. 226
Winn, Paul T., Pres. & Chief Exec. Officer--Genicom Corporation, Chantilly, VA; *U.S. Public*, pg. 729
Winn, Stephen T., Pres. & Chief Exec. Officer--Computer Language Research, Inc., Carrollton, TX; *U.S. Public*, pg. 421
Winney, Brad, Pres.--Poppe Tyson, New York, NY; *U.S. Public*, pg. 1642
Winninghoff, Albert C.M., Chm. & Chief Exec. Officer--Noordervliet & Winninghoff/Leo Burnett B.V., Amsterdam, Netherlands; *U.S. Private*, pg. 186
Winnowski, T.R., Chm. Bd., Pres. & Chief Exec. Officer--Key Bank of Oregon, Portland, OR; *U.S. Public*, pg. 954
Winship, Blanton C., Pres. & Chief Exec. Officer--Transus Intermodal L.L.C., Atlanta, GA; *U.S. Private*, pg. 1097
Winslow, Barry, Pres. & Chief Oper. Officer--Great Lakes Bancorp, Ann Arbor, MI; *U.S. Public*, pg. 1554
Winslow, Dr. Robert, Pres.--Blood Cells, Inc., La Jolla, CA; *U.S. Public*, pg. 855
Winspear, William W., Pres.--Associated Materials Incorporated, Dallas, TX; *U.S. Private*, pg. 91
Winstead, Dwight, Pres.--Owen Health Care, Inc., Houston, TX; *U.S. Public*, pg. 304
Winston, Ronald, Pres.--Harry Winston, Inc., New York, NY; *U.S. Private*, pg. 1183
Wint, Dennis, Pres. & Chief Exec. Officer--The Franklin Institute, Philadelphia, PA; *U.S. Private*, pg. 424
Winter, Frank D., Pres.--FirstMiss Steel, Inc., Hollsopple, PA; *U.S. Public*, pg. 344
Winter, J. Burgess, Pres. & Chief Exec. Officer--BHP Copper North America, Tucson, AZ; *Int'l*, pg. 224
Winter, Raymond F., Pres. & Chief Oper. Officer--BIC Corporation, Milford, CT; *Int'l*, pg. 1273
Winter, William R., Jr., Pres. & Chief Oper. Officer--Williams Steel & Hardware Company, Minneapolis, MN; *U.S. Private*, pg. 1178
Wintermans, Jos, Pres. & Chief Exec. Officer--Canadian Tire Acceptance Ltd., Welland, Canada; *Int'l*, pg. 259
Wintermute, Eric G., Pres. & Chief Exec. Officer--American Vanguard Corporation, Newport Beach, CA; *U.S. Public*, pg. 94
Winters, Henry, Pres.--British Steel, Inc., Schaumburg, IL; *Int'l*, pg. 221
Winters, Henry, Pres.--Slater Steels Corporation, Fort Wayne, IN; *Int'l*, pg. 1263
Winters, Steve D., Chm. Bd. & Pres.--Bepco, Inc., Winston Salem, NC; *U.S. Private*, pg. 134
Wintrode, Jim, Pres.--Six Flags Great America, Inc., Gurnee, IL; *U.S. Public*, pg. 1611
Wirdenius, Fredrik, Pres.--Skanska Fastigheter Stockholm AB, Danderyd, Sweden; *Int'l*, pg. 1260
Wirt, John, Pres.--Brown-Minneapolis Tank & Fabricating Co., Eagan, MN; *U.S. Public*, pg. 914
Wirta, Ray, Pres. & Chief Oper. Officer--Koll Co., Newport Beach, CA; *U.S. Private*, pg. 631
Wirth, Peter, Dr., Pres. & Chief Exec. Officer--Mikron Holding AG, Biel, Switzerland; *Int'l*, pg. 866
Wirtz, William W., Pres. & Chief Exec. Officer--Wirtz Corporation, Chicago, IL; *U.S. Private*, pg. 1184
Wise, Allen F., Pres. & Chief Exec. Officer--Coventry Corporation, Nashville, TN; *U.S. Public*, pg. 454
Wise, H.J., Pres.--Chemtronics Inc., Kennesaw, GA; *Int'l*, pg. 892
Wise, John, Pres.--South Charleston Stamping & Manufacturing, South Charleston, WV; *U.S. Private*, pg. 1030
Wise, Robert L., Pres.--GPU Generation Corporation, Johnstown, PA; *U.S. Public*, pg. 695
Wise, Sam, Pres.--Fischer Packing Co., Louisville, KY; *Int'l*, pg. 201
Wise, Sam, Pres.--Field Packing Company, Owensboro, KY; *U.S. Private*, pg. 403
Wise, William A., Chm. Bd., Pres. & Chief Exec. Officer--El Paso Natural Gas Co., Houston, TX; *U.S. Public*, pg. 567
Wishart, James, Pres. & General Mgr.--Spectra-Tech, Shelton, CT; *U.S. Public*, pg. 1593
Wishart, Steven W., Pres. & Chief Exec. Officer--ReliaStar Investment Research, Inc., Minneapolis, MN; *U.S. Public*, pg. 1376
Wislon, Alan, Pres.--Tubed Products, Inc., Easthampton, MA; *U.S. Public*, pg. 1066
Wismer, E.E., Pres.--Harvel Plastics, Inc., Easton, PA; *U.S. Public*, pg. 502
Wisne, Lawrence A., Pres. & Chief Exec. Officer--Progressive Tool & Industries Co., Southfield, MI; *U.S. Private*, pg. 890
Wisner, J.D., Pres.--The Gerstenslager Company, Wooster, OH; *U.S. Public*, pg. 1780
Wisneski, Joseph J., Pres. & Chief Oper. Officer--ERD Waste Corp., Commack, NY; *U.S. Public*, pg. 546
Wisnewski, Steve, Pres.--Hickson Corporation, Smyrna, GA; *Int'l*, pg. 619
Wissehr, Kurt, Pres. & Chief Oper. Officer--Bunker Hill Foods Inc., Bedford, VA; *U.S. Private*, pg. 219
Wissel, P.M., Pres.--Texaco Capital Inc., White Plains, NY; *U.S. Public*, pg. 1583
Wissler, Robert C., Pres. & Chief Oper. Officer--Comprehensive Business Services Inc., Mission Viejo, CA; *U.S. Private*, pg. 423
Wistisen, Martin, Pres. & Chief Exec. Officer--AgriNorthwest, Inc., Pasco, WA; *U.S. Private*, pg. 26
Wiswall, John P., Sr. V.P. & Gen Mgr.--Cosmair, Inc., Ralph Lauren Fragrance Division, New York, NY; *Int'l*, pg. 818
Withall, David W., Pres.--Miner Enterprises Inc., Geneva, IL; *U.S. Private*, pg. 749
Withers, Dan, Pres.--First Citizens Bank & Trust Company-White Sulphur Springs, White Sulphur Springs, WV; *U.S. Public*, pg. 629
Withers, Dan, Pres.--First Citizens Bank & Trust Company-West Virginia, Marlinton, WV; *U.S. Public*, pg. 629
Witherwax, Jeffrey T., Pres. & Treas.--Naugatuck Glass Company, Naugatuck, CT; *U.S. Private*, pg. 789
Withka, Thomas F., Pres.--KCS Power Marketing, Inc., Edison, NJ; *U.S. Public*, pg. 939
Withun, Frank, Pres. & Chief Exec. Officer--Acordia, Inc., Indianapolis, IN; *U.S. Private*, pg. 14
Witkin, Gary M., Pres. & Chief Exec. Officer--Service Merchandise Company, Inc., Brentwood, TN; *U.S. Public*, pg. 1461
Witkowski, Johannes, Pres.--Leobersdorfer Maschinenfabuk AG, Leobersdorf, Austria; *Int'l*, pg. 399
Witmer, Thomas H., Pres. & Chief Exec. Officer--Medrad, Inc., Indianola, PA; *Int'l*, pg. 1204
Witowski, John, Pres.--Home Curtain Corporation, New York, NY; *U.S. Private*, pg. 536
Witt, Barry, Pres. & Chief Exec. Officer--Westgate Fabrics, Inc., Grand Prairie, TX; *U.S. Private*, pg. 1169
Witt, Howard B., Chm. Bd., Pres. & Chief Exec. Officer--Littelfuse, Inc., Des Plaines, IL; *U.S. Public*, pg. 1001
Wittau, Manfred, Pres. Dir.--P.T. Asuransi Allianz Utama Indonesia, Jakarta, Indonesia; *Int'l*, pg. 60
Wittekindt, Widu, Pres.--SIHI GmbH & Co. KG, Itzehoe, Germany; *Int'l*, pg. 1156
Witten, Jack, Pres.--Edmonson Wheat Growers, Inc., Edmonson, TX; *U.S. Private*, pg. 364
Wittersheim, James, Pres.--Semblex Corporation, Elmhurst, IL; *U.S. Private*, pg. 983
Witteveen, Raoul J., Pres., Chief Oper. Officer & Chief Fin. Officer--Interpool, Inc., Princeton, NJ; *U.S. Public*, pg. 908
Wittig, David C., Pres.--Western Resources, Inc., Topeka, KS; *U.S. Public*, pg. 1759
Wittman, T. Scott, Pres., Sec. & Treas.--Vantage Global Advisors, Inc., New York, NY; *U.S. Public*, pg. 998
Witwer, Richard P., Pres.--Kalas Manufacturing, Inc., Denver, PA; *U.S. Private*, pg. 606
Wlaker, Nancy, Pres. & Chief Exec. Officer--Krames Communications, San Bruno, CA; *U.S. Public*, pg. 1616
Wlos, Paul M., Pres.--Electron Beam Technologies, Kankakee, IL; *U.S. Private*, pg. 370
Wnuk, Wade, Pres.--Norriseal Controls, Houston, TX; *U.S. Public*, pg. 521
Woerner, Klaus, Pres.--ATS Automation Tooling Systems, Inc., Cambridge, Canada; *Int'l*, pg. 18
Woerner, Valerie, Pres.--Artichoke Industries, Inc., Castroville, CA; *U.S. Private*, pg. 86
Woertz, P.A., Pres.--Chevron International Trading Company-West Africa, Abidjan, Cote d'Ivoire; *U.S. Public*, pg. 348
Woessner, Mark, Dr., Pres. & Chief Exec. Officer--Bertelsmann AG, Gutersloh, Germany; *Int'l*, pg. 189
Woeste, Bill F., Jr., Pres.--Beechmont Investments Inc., Cincinnati, OH; *U.S. Private*, pg. 129
Wohland, Helmut, Dr., Chm. Bd. & Pres.--Suspa Compart AG, Altdorf, Germany; *Int'l*, pg. 1322
Woitas, Clayton H., Pres. & Chief Exec. Officer--Renaissance Energy Ltd., Calgary, Canada; *Int'l*, pg. 1102
Wojcik, Frederick R., Pres.--Cheyenne Outfitters, Inc., Cheyenne, WY; *U.S. Private*, pg. 234
Wojcik, Paul N., Pres. & Chief Exec. Officer--The Bureau of National Affairs, Inc., Washington, DC; *U.S. Private*, pg. 181
Wojcik, Paul N., Pres. & Chief Exec. Officer--BNA Books Div., Washington, DC; *U.S. Private*, pg. 181
Wojnowich, Saul, Pres. & Chief Exec. Officer--Highland Mills Inc., Charlotte, NC; *U.S. Private*, pg. 528
Wolande, Charles, Pres.--Comark, Bloomingdale, IL; *U.S. Private*, pg. 257
Wolcott, Andrew, Pres. & Treas.--Heraeus Investment Corporation, Florham Park, NJ; *Int'l*, pg. 616
Wolcott, James D., Jr., Chm. Bd. & Pres.--Weldon, Williams & Lick, Inc., Fort Smith, AR; *U.S. Private*, pg. 1161
Wold, Casey R., Pres.--TrizecHahn Properties Inc., Chicago, IL; *Int'l*, pg. 1425
Wolf, Dennis C., Pres.--Composite Structures International, Inc., Dallas, TX; *U.S. Public*, pg. 1357
Wolf, Gregory H., Pres. & Chief Exec. Officer--Humana Inc., Louisville, KY; *U.S. Public*, pg. 847
Wolf, Gregory H., Pres. & Chief Oper. Officer--Humana Health Chicago, Inc., Chicago, IL; *U.S. Public*, pg. 847
Wolf, Gregory H., Pres. & Chief Oper. Officer--Employers Health Insurance Company, Green Bay, WI; *U.S. Public*, pg. 847
Wolf, Gregory H., Pres. & Chief Oper. Officer--Humana Health Plan of Texas, Inc., San Antonio, TX; *U.S. Public*, pg. 848
Wolf, Gregory H., Pres. & Chief Oper. Officer--Humana Health Plan of Alabama, Inc., Montgomery, AL; *U.S. Public*, pg. 848
Wolf, Gregory H., Pres. & Chief Oper. Officer--Humana Wisconsin Health Organization Insurance Corporation, Milwaukee, WI; *U.S. Public*, pg. 848

Wolf, Gregory H., Pres. & Chief Oper. Officer--Network EPO, Inc., Milwaukee, WI; *U.S. Public*, pg. 848
Wolf, Gregory H., Pres.--Humana Wisconsin Health Organization Insurance Corporation, Milwaukee, WI; *U.S. Public*, pg. 848
Wolf, Jack D., Pres.--Targetbase Marketing, Irving, TX; *U.S. Public*, pg. 1023
Wolf, Lawrence, Pres., Chief Exec. Officer, Treas. & Sec.--Leonard Wholesale, Inc., Springfield, NJ; *U.S. Private*, pg. 660
Wolf, Randy A., Pres.--Walters & Wolf, Fremont, CA; *U.S. Private*, pg. 1149
Wolf, Robert D., Pres. & Chief Exec. Officer--Howard B. Wolf, Inc., Dallas, TX; *U.S. Public*, pg. 1774
Wolf, Tom, Chm. Bd., Pres. & Chief Exec. Officer--STS Consultants, Inc., Deerfield, IL; *U.S. Private*, pg. 959
Wolfe, F.C., Pres. & Chief Exec. Officer--NN Financial, Don Mills, Canada; *Int'l*, pg. 650
Wolfe, H.G., Pres. & Chief Exec. Officer--Ney Dental International, Bloomfield, CT; *Int'l*, pg. 388
Wolfe, Herb, Pres. & Chief Exec. Officer--Atlantic City Showboat, Atlantic City, NJ; *U.S. Public*, pg. 1469
Wolfe, Jack, Pres.--AMCORE Bank, South Beloit, IL; *U.S. Public*, pg. 64
Wolfe, Jack A., Pres.--AMCORE Financial Life Insurance Company, Rockford, IL; *U.S. Public*, pg. 64
Wolfe, John F., Pres., Chief Exec. Officer & Publisher--The Dispatch Printing Company, Columbus, OH; *U.S. Private*, pg. 334
Wolfe, Jonathan, Pres. & Chief Oper. Officer--Oshawa Foods, Mississauga, Canada; *Int'l*, pg. 1012
Wolfe, Jonathan A., Pres. & Chief Oper. Officer--The Oshawa Group Limited, Etobicoke, Canada; *Int'l*, pg. 1012
Wolfe, Robert, Pres.--Aerojet, Sacramento, CA; *U.S. Public*, pg. 706
Wolfe, Robert, Pres.--Aerojet Azusa Operations, Azusa, CA; *U.S. Public*, pg. 706
Wolfe, Robert, Pres.--Aerojet, Rancho Cordova, CA; *U.S. Public*, pg. 706
Wolfe, Robert A., Pres.--Pratt & Whitney Commercial Engine Business, East Hartford, CT; *U.S. Public*, pg. 1690
Wolfe, Ronald J., Pres. & Chief Exec. Officer--Restaurant Developers Corp., Independence, OH; *U.S. Private*, pg. 925
Wolfe, Thomas E., Chm. Bd, Pres. & Chief Exec. Officer--Ziebart International Corporation, Troy, MI; *U.S. Private*, pg. 1205
Wolfe, Tom, Pres. & Chief Exec. Officer--Persoft, Inc., Madison, WI; *U.S. Private*, pg. 856
Wolfensohn, James D., Pres.--The World Bank, Washington, DC; *U.S. Private*, pg. 1188
Wolfer, Rudy, Pres.--Dreis & Krump Manufacturing Company, Chicago, IL; *U.S. Private*, pg. 342
Wolfert, Frederick E., Pres. & Chief Exec. Officer--KeyCorp Leasing Ltd., Albany, NY; *U.S. Public*, pg. 954
Wolff, Derish M., Pres.--Louis Berger International Inc., East Orange, NJ; *U.S. Private*, pg. 135
Wolff, Hans-Joachim, Dr. Ing., Chm. Bd. & Pres.--Dyckerhoff & Widmann AG, Munich, Germany; *Int'l*, pg. 423
Wolfington, Richard I., Pres.--Wolfington Body Company, Exton, PA; *U.S. Private*, pg. 1186
Wolfkeil, Bob, Pres.--Southwest Vacuum Devices, Inc., Stone Mountain, GA; *U.S. Public*, pg. 1720
Wolfson, Richard A., Pres.--U.S. Healthcare Dental Plan, Inc. (New Jersey), Blue Bell, PA; *U.S. Public*, pg. 26
Wolfson, Richard A., Pres.--U.S. Healthcare Dental Plan, Inc. (Delaware), Blue Bell, PA; *U.S. Public*, pg. 26
Wolfson, Richard A., Pres.--U.S. Healthcare Dental Plan, Inc. (Pennsylvania), Blue Bell, PA; *U.S. Public*, pg. 26
Wolken, Hal, Pres. & Chief Exec. Officer--A.W. Mendenhall Co., Inc., Elk Grove Village, IL; *U.S. Private*, pg. 731
Wollenberg, R.P., Pres.--Longfibre Ltd., Longview, WA; *U.S. Public*, pg. 1014
Wollenberg, Richard P., Chm. Bd., Pres. & Chief Exec. Officer--Longview Fibre Company, Longview, WA; *U.S. Public*, pg. 1013
Wollenzien, Dennis H., Pres.--M & I Lake Country Bank, Hartland, WI; *U.S. Public*, pg. 1050
Wollschlager, Burkhard, Pres. & Chief Exec. Officer--Krauss-Maffei AG, Munich, Germany; *Int'l*, pg. 836
Wolohan, James L., Chm. Bd., Pres. & Chief Exec. Officer--Wolohan Lumber Co., Saginaw, MI; *U.S. Public*, pg. 1774
Wolpert, Arthur, Pres.--AMI Leasing Corporation, Worcester, MA; *U.S. Private*, pg. 7
Wolpert, Mike, Pres.--Cardkey Systems, Inc., Simi Valley, CA; *U.S. Public*, pg. 105
Wolstein, Scott A., Chm. Bd., Pres. & Chief Exec. Officer--Developers Diversified Realty Corporation, Moreland Hills, OH; *U.S. Public*, pg. 502
Wolters, Kornel, Pres.--J.L. de Ball-Girmes of America, Inc., Montreal, Canada; *Int'l*, pg. 552
Woltz, H.O., III, Pres. & Chief Exec. Officer--Insteel Industries, Inc., Mount Airy, NC; *U.S. Public*, pg. 882
Woltz, William, Jr., Pres. & Chief Exec. Officer--Page Holdings, Inc., Mount Airy, NC; *U.S. Private*, pg. 834
Womack, Craig, Pres. & Chief Admin. Officer--The Sharper Image, San Francisco, CA; *U.S. Public*, pg. 1464
Womelsdorf, L. Kenneth, Pres.--Custom Hoists, Inc., Hayesville, OH; *U.S. Public*, pg. 1506
Won, Moon Sang, Pres. & Gen. Mgr--Cho Hung Bank of New York, New York, NY; *Int'l*, pg. 287
Won, Sohn Myung, Pres.--Ssangyong Motor Company, Seoul, Korea; *Int'l*, pg. 1292
Wong, James, Pres.--AIC International, Inc., New York, NY; *U.S. Private*, pg. 6
Wong, James, Pres.--Allied Impex Corp., New York, NY; *U.S. Private*, pg. 6
Wong, James, Pres.--Interstate Photo Supply Corp., New York, NY; *U.S. Private*, pg. 6
Wong, John E., Pres.--Duray/J.F. Duncan Industries, Inc., Downey, CA; *U.S. Private*, pg. 348
Wong, Kenneth P., Pres.--Walt Disney Imagineering, Glendale, CA; *U.S. Public*, pg. 513
Wong, Louis, Pres. & Exec. Creative Dir.--FCB/MegacoM, Guangzhou, China; *U.S. Private*, pg. 389
Woo, Duck-Chang, Pres.--Ssangyong Cement Industrial Co., Ltd., Seoul, Korea; *Int'l*, pg. 1291
Woo, Peter, Pres.--Wharf Hotel Investments Ltd., Kowloon, Hong Kong; *Int'l*, pg. 1497
Wood, Brian, Pres.--Paisano Publications, Inc., Agoura, CA; *U.S. Private*, pg. 834
Wood, Bruce, Chm. Bd., Pres. & Chief Exec. Officer--Agromac International, Inc., Gering, NE; *U.S. Private*, pg. 27
Wood, Charles L., Pres.--United Insurance Company of America, Woodland Hills, CA; *U.S. Public*, pg. 1694
Wood, David E., Vice Chm. & Chief Oper. Officer--Harris Farms, Inc., Coalinga, CA; *U.S. Private*, pg. 505
Wood, Diane, Pres.--John Wiley & Sons, Canada, Ltd., Etobicoke, Canada; *U.S. Public*, pg. 1768
Wood, J.J., Pres.--BMY-Wheeled Vehicles, Marysville, OH; *U.S. Public*, pg. 793
Wood, James, Pres.--J.R. Wood Inc., Atwater, CA; *U.S. Private*, pg. 1186
Wood, James F., Pres.-Power Generation Grp.--Babcock & Wilcox Co., Barberton, OH; *U.S. Public*, pg. 1068
Wood, John B., Pres. & Chief Exec. Officer--Telos Corporation, Ashburn, VA; *U.S. Public*, pg. 1573
Wood, Patricia A., Pres.--Leucadia Financial Corporation, Salt Lake City, UT; *U.S. Public*, pg. 990
Wood, R. Ray, Chm. Bd., Pres., Chief Exec. & Oper. Officer--Rockford Products Corp., Rockford, IL; *U.S. Private*, pg. 938
Wood, Richard D., Jr., Pres. & Chief Exec. Officer--Wawa, Inc., Media, PA; *U.S. Private*, pg. 1155
Wood, Robert C., Pres. & Chief Exec. Officer--Winterthur Reinsurance Corporation of America, New York, NY; *Int'l*, pg. 346
Wood, Robert J., Pres.--RisComp Industries, Inc., Minneapolis, MN; *U.S. Private*, pg. 932
Wood, Robert J., Pres.--RJ Associates, Plymouth, MN; *U.S. Private*, pg. 932
Wood, Roger, Pres.--Soap Opera Magazine, Lantana, FL; *U.S. Public*, pg. 87
Wood, Roger, Pres.--Star Editorial, Inc., Lantana, FL; *U.S. Public*, pg. 87
Wood, Roger, Pres.--Bentley & Bentley, Fremont, CA; *U.S. Private*, pg. 1186
Wood, Roger, Pres.--Big Valley Marketing Corp., Fremont, CA; *U.S. Private*, pg. 1186
Wood, Ron, Pres.--Dieffenbacher Toronto, Willowdale, Canada; *Int'l*, pg. 413
Wood, Stephen F., Pres. & Chief Exec. Officer--Constellation Energy Projects & Services, Inc., Baltimore, MD; *U.S. Public*, pg. 172
Wood, T.G., Pres.--SmithKline Beecham Laboratories, Bristol, TN; *Int'l*, pg. 1264
Wood, Ted G., Pres.--Boehringer Mannheim Pharmaceuticals Corp., Rockville, MD; *Int'l*, pg. 331
Wood, W. Barton III, Pres.--The W.B. Wood Company, New Providence, NJ; *U.S. Private*, pg. 1186
Wood, W.G., Pres.--Tolleson Lumber Company, Inc., Perry, GA; *U.S. Private*, pg. 1090
Wood, Warren G., Pres.--Cabot Medical Corporation, Langhorne, PA; *U.S. Public*, pg. 373
Woodall, Bill, Pres.--Chicago Consolidated, Lemont, IL; *U.S. Private*, pg. 533
Woodard, Geoffrey, Pres.--Millipore Analytical Div., Bedford, MA; *U.S. Public*, pg. 1112
Woodbeck, Milford E., Jr., Pres.--Overhead Conveyor Co., Ferndale, MI; *U.S. Private*, pg. 822
Woodbury, Dan, Partner & Mktg. Services Dir.--Martin/Williams Advertising Inc., Minneapolis, MN; *U.S. Private*, pg. 710
Woodhull, John R., Pres. & Chief Exec. Officer--Logicon, Inc., Torrance, CA; *U.S. Public*, pg. 1198
Woodland, Fred, Pres. & Chief Exec. Officer--Hydroscience, Inc., Dallas, TX; *U.S. Private*, pg. 552
Woodring, Greig, Pres. & Chief Exec. Officer--Reinsurance Group Of America, Saint Louis, MO; *U.S. Private*, pg. 443
Woodroofe, Rob, Pres.--Interwood Marketing Group, Concord, Canada; *Int'l*, pg. 685
Woodrow, Ken, Pres.--Target Stores, Minneapolis, MN; *U.S. Public*, pg. 489
Woods, Charles H., Pres. & Gen. Mgr.--First American Title Co. of New Mexico, Albuquerque, NM; *U.S. Public*, pg. 625
Woods, Doug, Pres.--DPR Construction, Inc., Redwood City, CA; *U.S. Private*, pg. 305
Woods, Douglas, Pres. & Chief Exec. Officer--Liberty Precision Industries, Rochester, NY; *U.S. Private*, pg. 666
Woods, Gary V., Pres.--McCombs Automotive, San Antonio, TX; *U.S. Private*, pg. 720
Woods, Herb, Pres.--GMSI, Inc., Kanata, Canada; *U.S. Public*, pg. 740
Woods, James R., Pres. Chief Oper. Officer--SunBank Capital Management, N.A., Orlando, FL; *U.S. Public*, pg. 1537
Woods, Joe E., Chm. Bd., Pres. & Chief Exec. Officer--Joe E. Woods, Inc., Mesa, AZ; *U.S. Private*, pg. 1187
Woods, John, Pres. & Chief Exec. Officer--Western Multiplex Corporation, Sunnyvale, CA; *U.S. Public*, pg. 747
Woodson, Glen, II, Pres. & Chief Oper. Officer--Crouch Supply Company, Inc., Fort Worth, TX; *U.S. Private*, pg. 291
Woodson, Melinda, Pres.--Wholesale Electronic Supply, Dallas, TX; *U.S. Private*, pg. 1174
Woodward, Bruce M., Pres.--Medalist Industries, Elk Grove Village, IL; *U.S. Public*, pg. 867
Woodworth, Pat, Chm. Bd., Pres. & Chief Exec. Officer--Winona Knits, Winona, MN; *U.S. Private*, pg. 1183
Woodworth, Peter, Pres.--Winona Knitting Mills, Inc., Winona, MN; *U.S. Public*, pg. 779
Wook, Kim Dai, Pres.--Ssangyong Japan Corporation, Tokyo, Japan; *Int'l*, pg. 1291
Wool, Martin R., Pres.--First American Home Buyers Protection Corp., Van Nuys, CA; *U.S. Public*, pg. 625
Wooldridge, Ray W., Pres.--Space Master International, Atlanta, GA; *U.S. Private*, pg. 1019
Wooley, John C., Chm. Bd. & Pres.--Schlotzsky's, Inc., Austin, TX; *U.S. Public*, pg. 1439
Woolf, Robert W., Pres. & Chief Oper. Officer--Chemi-Trol Chemical Co., Gibsonburg, OH; *U.S. Public*, pg. 345
Woolf, Sheldon M., Pres.--NHD Hardware, Stoughton, MA; *U.S. Private*, pg. 3
Woolley, June C., Pres.--Old Home Foods, Inc., Saint Paul, MN; *U.S. Private*, pg. 814
Woolverton, Fred T., Jr., Pres.--Woolverton Oldsmobile-G.M.C. Truck, Inc., Jacksonville, FL; *U.S. Private*, pg. 1188
Wooten, F. Thomas, Pres.--Research Triangle Institute, Research Triangle Park, NC; *U.S. Private*, pg. 924
Wordsworth, Jerry, Chm. Bd. & Pres.--MBM, Rocky Mount, NC; *U.S. Private*, pg. 685
Work, Harold K., Chm. Bd., Pres. & Chief Exec. Officer--Elcor Corporation, Dallas, TX; *U.S. Public*, pg. 567
Work, Harold K., Pres. & Chief Exec. Officer--Elk Corporation of Dallas, Dallas, TX; *U.S. Public*, pg. 568
Workman, Dave, Pres.--Audio King Corporation, Thornton, CO; *U.S. Public*, pg. 1662
Workman, David J., Pres. & Chief Oper. Officer--Ultimate Electronics, Thornton, CO; *U.S. Public*, pg. 1662
Workman, R.E., Pres.--Tru-Fit Products Corp., Medina, OH; *U.S. Private*, pg. 1107
Wormington, S.L., Pres.--Tesoro Alaska Petroleum Company, Kenai, AK; *U.S. Public*, pg. 1582
Wormington, S.L., Pres.--Tesoro Alaska Pipeline Company, Anchorage, AK; *U.S. Public*, pg. 1582
Wormington, Steven, Pres.--Tesoro Alaska Petroleum Co., Anchorage, AK; *U.S. Public*, pg. 1582
Wornick, Ronald C., Pres. & Chief Exec. Officer--The Wornick Company, Burlingame, CA; *U.S. Private*, pg. 1191
Worrell, Ken, Pres.--Southland Mower Corp., Selma, AL; *U.S. Private*, pg. 1144
Worsley, W. Cecil, III, Pres.--Entrepreneur, Inc., Wilmington, NC; *U.S. Private*, pg. 1191
Worsley, Walter C., III, Pres.--Worsley Companies Inc., Wilmington, NC; *U.S. Private*, pg. 1191
Wortberg, Ernst J., Chm. Bd. & Pres.--L. Possehl & Co. mbH, Lubeck, Germany; *Int'l*, pg. 1063
Wortell, Brent, Pres.--Triton Industries, Inc., Chicago, IL; *U.S. Private*, pg. 1104
Worthington, Norman, Pres. & Chief Tech. Officer--Infresco Corporation, Sarasota, FL; *U.S. Public*, pg. 420
Worthington, Samuel A., Pres. & Natl. Exec. Dir.--Plan International USA, Inc., Warwick, RI; *U.S. Private*, pg. 869
Wozniak, Donald R., Pres.--Carpenter Special Products Corp., El Cajon, CA; *U.S. Public*, pg. 307
Wozniak, Edward F., Pres. & Chief Exec. Officer--Wozniak Industries, Inc., Oak Brook Terrace, IL; *U.S. Private*, pg. 1192
Wraith, W., Co-Pres.--Nomura Securities International, Inc., New York, NY; *Int'l*, pg. 956
Wraith, William, IV, Co-Pres.--Nomura Holding America, Inc., New York, NY; *Int'l*, pg. 956
Wratten, Thomas, Pres.--Principal Commercial Advisors, Inc., Overland Park, KS; *U.S. Private*, pg. 885
Wray, Donald E., Pres. & Chief Oper. Officer--Tyson Foods, Inc., Springdale, AR; *U.S. Public*, pg. 1652
Wray, Fred H., Pres.--TN Media Inc., Chicago, IL; *U.S. Public*, pg. 1641
Wray, Tom, Pres. & Chief Exec. Officer--Farmers & Merchants Bank, Rogers, AR; *U.S. Public*, pg. 630
Wrede, Bernd, Chief Exec.--Hapag-Lloyd AG, Hamburg, Germany; *Int'l*, pg. 596
Wrede, Harold, Pres.--Battenfeld Gloucester Engineering Co. Inc., Gloucester, MA; *U.S. Private*, pg. 123
Wrede, Harold F., Pres.--Battenfeld Gloucester Engineering Co., Inc., Gloucester, MA; *Int'l*, pg. 825
Wreede, Paul G., Pres. & Chief Exec. Officer--The Commercial Bank, Delphos, OH; *U.S. Public*, pg. 410
Wren, John, Pres. & Chief Exec. Officer--Omnicom Group Inc., New York, NY; *U.S. Public*, pg. 1223
Wren, Karl, Pres.--Rauland-Borg (Canada) Inc., Mississauga, Canada; *U.S. Private*, pg. 911
Wrench, W. David, Pres.--Fleck Manufacturing Inc., Tillsonburg, Canada; *Int'l*, pg. 955
Wright, Christopher, Pres.--Stolt-Nielsen S.A., London, United Kingdom; *Int'l*, pg. 1301
Wright, Dan, Pres.--Professional Sound Group--Telex Communications, Inc., Minneapolis, MN; *U.S. Private*, pg. 1074
Wright, David, Pres. & Chief Exec. Officer--Durakon Industries, Inc., Lapeer, MI; *U.S. Public*, pg. 537
Wright, Donald F., Pres. & Chief Exec. Officer--Los Angeles Times, Los Angeles, CA; *U.S. Public*, pg. 1616
Wright, Felix E., Pres. & Chief Oper. Officer--Leggett & Platt, Incorporated, Carthage, MO; *U.S. Public*, pg. 985
Wright, Frank, Pres.--American Colloid Company, Arlington Heights, IL; *U.S. Public*, pg. 63
Wright, Gordon L., Pres.--CMS Nomeco, Jackson, MI; *U.S. Public*, pg. 280
Wright, Jack, Pres.--Pace Die Cast Products, Inc., Gardena, CA; *U.S. Private*, pg. 986
Wright, Jeff, Pres.-Periscope Advertising Communications--Periscope Marketing Communications, Minneapolis, MN; *U.S. Private*, pg. 853
Wright, John, Pres.--Discount Drug Mart Inc., Medina, OH; *U.S. Private*, pg. 334
Wright, John, Pres.-Int'l Div.--Wendy's International Inc., Dublin, OH; *U.S. Public*, pg. 1754
Wright, John P., Pres.--Ariel Corporation, Mount Vernon, OH; *U.S. Private*, pg. 81

Wright, Larry M., Pres. & Chief Oper. Officer--Panaco, Inc., Kansas City, MO; *U.S. Public,* pg. 1255
Wright, Mark H., Acting Pres. & Chief Exec. Officer--USAA Federal Savings Bank, San Antonio, TX; *U.S. Private,* pg. 1114
Wright, Michael W., Chm. Bd., Pres. & Chief Exec. Officer--SuperValu, Inc., Eden Prairie, MN; *U.S. Public,* pg. 1540
Wright, Norman, Mng. Dir.--EMAP Apex, Peterborough, United Kingdom; *Int'l,* pg. 451
Wright, P.J., Pres. & Chief Oper. Officer--Jefferson Smurfit Group p.l.c., Dublin, Ireland; *Int'l,* pg. 1269
Wright, Patrick E., Pres.--Owensboro Grain Co., Inc., Owensboro, KY; *U.S. Private,* pg. 824
Wright, Peter W., Pres.--Dowty Aerospace Turbine Engine Components Group, Mountain Top, PA; *Int'l,* pg. 1337
Wright, Robert A., Pres. & Chief Oper. Officer--Amcor Capital Corporation, Coachella, CA; *U.S. Public,* pg. 64
Wright, Robert C., Pres. & Chief Exec. Officer--National Broadcasting Co., Inc., New York, NY; *U.S. Public,* pg. 712
Wright, Robert S., Pres.--North America Foods, Minnetonka, MN; *U.S. Public,* pg. 901
Wright, Russell D., Pres. & Chief Oper. Officer-Electric & Gas Division--Commonwealth Energy System, Cambridge, MA; *U.S. Public,* pg. 414
Wright, Russell D., Pres. & Chief Oper. Officer--Cambridge Electric Light Co., Cambridge, MA; *U.S. Public,* pg. 414
Wright, Russell D., Pres. & Chief Oper. Officer--Commonwealth Energy System, Electric Division, Cambridge, MA; *U.S. Public,* pg. 414
Wright, Russell D., Pres. & Chief Oper. Officer--Canal Electric Co., Cambridge, MA; *U.S. Public,* pg. 415
Wright, Russell D., Pres. & Chief Oper. Officer--Commonwealth Electric Co., Cambridge, MA; *U.S. Public,* pg. 415
Wright, Thomas C., Pres.--BMO Financial, Inc., Chicago, IL; *Int'l,* pg. 154
Wright, Thomas C., Chm. Bd. & Chief Exec. Officer--Wright Group Publishing, Inc., Bothell, WA; *U.S. Public,* pg. 1636
Wright, Thomas J., Pres.--PCS Phosphate - Raleigh, Raleigh, NC; *Int'l,* pg. 1064
Wright, Tim, Pres.--Mr. Wright's Amazing Coffee Factory, San Jose, CA; *U.S. Private,* pg. 765
Wright, W. Dan, Pres. & Chief Exec. Officer--Wright Brand Foods, Inc., Vernon, TX; *U.S. Private,* pg. 1192
Wright, Wayne, Pres.--East River Electric Cooperative, Madison, SD; *U.S. Private,* pg. 357
Wright, William, Pres.--Barrier Films Corp., Sparks, NV; *U.S. Private,* pg. 1190
Wright, William M., Pres.--Hearst Book Group, New York, NY; *U.S. Private,* pg. 515
Wright, William S., Pres.--John R. Lyman Company, Chicopee, MA; *U.S. Private,* pg. 683
Wrigley, William, Chm. Bd., Pres. & Chief Oper. Officer--Wm. Wrigley Jr. Company, Chicago, IL; *U.S. Public,* pg. 1781
Wruble, Brian F., Pres. & Chief Oper. Officer--Delaware Management Holdings, Inc., Philadelphia, PA; *U.S. Public,* pg. 997
Wsebolojskoy, Nicolas, Pres.--General Motors Chile S.A., Industria Automotriz, Santiago, Chile; *U.S. Public,* pg. 721
Wu, T., Pres.--China Synthetic Rubber Corporation, Taipei, Taiwan; *Int'l,* pg. 286
Wulf, Walter H., Jr., Pres., Chief Exec. Officer & Vice Chm.--Monarch Cement Co., Humboldt, KS; *U.S. Public,* pg. 1123
Wurm, Robert J., Chm. Bd., Pres. & Chief Exec. Officer--Quest Technologies, Inc., Oconomowoc, WI; *U.S. Private,* pg. 900
Wurzburger, Jan, Partner--Media First International, Inc., New York, NY; *U.S. Private,* pg. 726
Wurzel, Tom, Pres. & Chief Exec. Officer--AAI/ACL Technologies, Santa Ana, CA; *U.S. Public,* pg. 1679
Wyandt, Steven P., Pres. & Chief Exec. & Fin. Officer--Niches, Inc., San Diego, CA; *U.S. Public,* pg. 1181
Wyandt, Steven P., Chm., Pres. & Chief Exec. Officer--Body Drama, Inc., Culver City, CA; *U.S. Public,* pg. 1182
Wyant, Corbin A., Pres. & Publisher--Naples Daily News, Naples, FL; *U.S. Public,* pg. 1448
Wyatt, Gene, Pres.--Firstbank, Texarkana, TX; *U.S. Public,* pg. 641
Wyatt, John W., Pres.--Venchurs Packaging, Inc., Adrian, MI; *U.S. Private,* pg. 1135
Wyatt, Peter F., Pres. & Controller--N E D Corp., Worcester, MA; *U.S. Private,* pg. 771
Wyatt, W. Whitlow, Chm. Bd., Pres. & Chief Exec. Officer--Altama Delta Corporation, Atlanta, GA; *U.S. Private,* pg. 47
Wyckaert, Luke, Chm. Bd., Pres. & Chief Exec. Officer--Intertrade Industries, Huntington Beach, CA; *U.S. Private,* pg. 573
Wykoff, Richard L., Pres.--Imperial Nurseries Inc., Granby, CT; *U.S. Public,* pg. 707
Wyler, Jeff, Pres.--Jeff Wyler Dealer Group, Inc., Cincinnati, OH; *U.S. Private,* pg. 1193
Wylie, Rick, Pres.--Beutler Heating & Air Conditioning Inc., Sacramento, CA; *U.S. Private,* pg. 141
Wyne, Robert L., Pres. & Chief Exec. Officer--Citizens First State Bank, Hartford City, IN; *U.S. Public,* pg. 632
Wynkoop, Roger D., Pres.--ACF Industries, Inc., Saint Charles, MO; *U.S. Private,* pg. 556
Wynn, Ronnie, Pres.--Colonial Mortgage Company, Montgomery, AL; *U.S. Public,* pg. 400
Wynn, Stephen A., Chm. Bd., Pres. & Chief Exec. Officer--Mirage Resorts Incorporated, Las Vegas, NV; *U.S. Public,* pg. 1116
Wynne, George C., Pres.--Presque Isle Insurance Div., Erie, PA; *U.S. Public,* pg. 215
Wynne, John O., Pres. & Chief Exec. Officer--Landmark Communications, Inc., Norfolk, VA; *U.S. Private,* pg. 647
Wynne, Robert, Co-Pres.--Sony Pictures Entertainment, Culver City, CA; *Int'l,* pg. 1281
Wyse, D.L., Pres.--Projects Unlimited, Inc., Dayton, OH; *U.S. Private,* pg. 890
Wyse, Lois, Pres.--Wyse Advertising, Cleveland, OH; *U.S. Private,* pg. 1193
Wyvill, R.D., Pres.--The Elco Corp., Cleveland, OH; *U.S. Public,* pg. 502
Ximenes Alves Ferreira, Paulo Cesar, Chm. Bd. & Pres.--Banco do Brasil, Brasilia, Brazil; *Int'l,* pg. 141
Yabe, Shigeo, Pres.--Wako Computer System Co., Ltd., Tokyo, Japan; *Int'l,* pg. 1485
Yacenda, Richard, Pres.--Yesawich, Moss & Brown, New York, NY; *U.S. Private,* pg. 1196
Yadama, Kaz, Pres.--Nissan Forklift Corporation, North America, Marengo, IL; *Int'l,* pg. 944
Yaeger, Douglas H., Pres. & Chief Oper. Officer--Laclede Gas Company, Saint Louis, MO; *U.S. Public,* pg. 973
Yaffe, Fred, Chm. Bd. & Chief Exec. Officer--Yaffe & Company, Southfield, MI; *U.S. Private,* pg. 1195
Yager, William L., Pres. & Chief Oper. Officer--The Rival Company, Kansas City, MO; *U.S. Public,* pg. 1391
Yago, N., Pres.--Ebara Technologies Inc., Sacramento, CA; *Int'l,* pg. 432
Yahn, C.H., Pres.--Leisure Life, Inc., Baxter, TN; *U.S. Public,* pg. 34
Yahn, Chuck, Pres. & Chief Exec. Officer--Ajay Leisure Products, Inc., Delavan, WI; *U.S. Public,* pg. 34
Yajima, Hisashi, Pres. & Chief Exec. Officer--Prap Japan, Inc., Tokyo, Japan; *U.S. Private,* pg. 617
Yakir, David, Pres. & Exec. V.P.--Blue Marble Advanced Communications Group, New York, NY; *U.S. Private,* pg. 104
Yalen, Gary, Pres.--Fortis Advisers, Inc., New York, NY; *Int'l,* pg. 499
Yalof, Herbert, Pres.--Hit or Miss, Inc., Stoughton, MA; *U.S. Private,* pg. 531
Yamada, Masuyosha, Pres.--PARCO Co. Ltd., Tokyo, Japan; *Int'l,* pg. 1178
Yamada, Mr., Pres.--ITOCHU Aviation, Inc., El Segundo, CA; *Int'l,* pg. 694
Yamada, Shuichi, Pres.--Farrell Wako Global Investment Management, Inc., New York, NY; *Int'l,* pg. 1485
Yamada, Yasukuni, Pres. & Chief Exec. Officer--Rohto Pharmaceutical Co., Osaka, Japan; *Int'l,* pg. 1126
Yamada, Yoji, Pres. & Chief Exec. Officer--Nippon Shinpan Co., Ltd., Tokyo, Japan; *Int'l,* pg. 939
Yamagata, E., Pres. & Chief Exec. Officer--Yokohama Tire Corporation, Fullerton, CA; *Int'l,* pg. 1521
Yamagishi, Takayuki, Pres.--Minebea Electronics Co., Ltd., Shizuoka, Japan; *Int'l,* pg. 868
Yamaguchi, Hajime, Chm. Bd. & Pres.--Teac America, Inc., Montebello, CA; *Int'l,* pg. 1360
Yamaguchi, Haruki, Pres.--Yasuda Life America Capital Management, Ltd., New York, NY; *Int'l,* pg. 1520
Yamaguchi, Hiroshi, Pres.--Maxell Corp. Of America, Fair Lawn, NJ; *Int'l,* pg. 621
Yamaguchi, Hisakichi, Pres.--Shin Nippon Koki Co. Ltd., Osaka, Japan; *Int'l,* pg. 1234
Yamaguchi, Jinichi, Pres.--Nippon Credit Bank AG, Frankfurt/Main, Germany; *Int'l,* pg. 933
Yamaguchi, Koju, Pres.--Herman Miller Japan, Tokyo, Japan; *U.S. Public,* pg. 1112
Yamaguchi, Satoshi, Pres.--Wako Finance Co., Ltd., Tokyo, Japan; *Int'l,* pg. 1485
Yamaguchi, Seiji, Pres.--Nanto Staff Service Co., Ltd., Nara, Japan; *Int'l,* pg. 906
Yamaguchi, Takashi, Pres. & Chief Exec. Officer--Shiseido Cosmetics (America) Ltd., New York, NY; *Int'l,* pg. 1235
Yamaguchi, Yuzuru, Pres.--Kawasho International (Australia) Pty., Ltd., Sydney, Australia; *Int'l,* pg. 727
Yamakawa, Nobuyoshi, Pres.--Rohm Electronics Dalian Co., LTD., Dalian, China; *Int'l,* pg. 1125
Yamakawa, Yoji, Pres.--DNP (AMERICA), Inc., New York, NY; *Int'l,* pg. 363
Yamakoshi, Warren, Pres.--Nobart, Inc., Chicago, IL; *U.S. Public,* pg. 503
Yamakoshi, Warren, Pres.--Nobart, Inc., Chicago, IL; *U.S. Private,* pg. 800
Yamamota, H., Pres.--Kratos Group Plc/Kratos Analytical ltd., Manchester, United Kingdom; *Int'l,* pg. 1232
Yamamoto, Hideki, Pres.--Nitto Denko Corporation, Osaka, Japan; *Int'l,* pg. 950
Yamamoto, Hyozo, Pres.--Taisei Corporation, Tokyo, Japan; *Int'l,* pg. 1347
Yamamoto, Kayunori, Pres. & Chief Exec. Officer--Pioneer Electronics (USA) Inc., Long Beach, CA; *Int'l,* pg. 1058
Yamamoto, Kazumoto, Pres.--Asahi Chemical Industry Co., Ltd., Tokyo, Japan; *Int'l,* pg. 83
Yamamoto, Kohei, Pres.--Rohm Apollo Electronics (Thailand) Co., Ltd., Pathum Thani, Thailand; *Int'l,* pg. 1125
Yamamoto, Masakazu, Pres.--KHI (Dalian) Computer Technology Co., Ltd., Dalian, China; *Int'l,* pg. 726
Yamamoto, Minoru, Pres.--Nikko France S.A., Paris, France; *Int'l,* pg. 930
Yamamoto, Mitsuyoshi, Pres.--P.T. Easterntex, Jakarta, Indonesia; *Int'l,* pg. 1400
Yamamoto, Phil, Pres.--Aromat Corporation, New Providence, NJ; *Int'l,* pg. 847
Yamamoto, Phil, Pres.--Aromat Mid Atlantic Sales, New Providence, NJ; *Int'l,* pg. 848
Yamamoto, Toshio, Pres.--Namba Press Works Co., Ltd., Kurashiki, Japan; *Int'l,* pg. 904
Yamamoto, Yoshihide, Chm. Bd., Pres. & Chief Exec. Officer--Sumikin Bussan Corporation, Osaka, Japan; *Int'l,* pg. 1308
Yamamoto, Yoshihito, Pres.--Sumigin Metro Investment Corp., Manila, Philippines; *Int'l,* pg. 1310
Yamamoto, Yoshiro, Pres. & Chief Exec. Officer--The Fuji Bank, Limited, Tokyo, Japan; *Int'l,* pg. 519
Yamamoto, Yukio, Pres. & Chief Exec. Officer--Aiwa America, Inc., Mahwah, NJ; *Int'l,* pg. 1280
Yamanaka, Masayoshi, Pres.--NMB (USA) Inc., Chatsworth, CA; *Int'l,* pg. 868
Yamanoto, Kohei, Pres.--Apollo Electronics Co., Ltd., Fukuoka, Japan; *Int'l,* pg. 1125
Yamaoka, Takeo, Pres. & Chief Exec. Officer--Juki Corporation, Tokyo, Japan; *Int'l,* pg. 716
Yamasaghi, Mr., Pres.--Leader Instruments Corporation, Hauppauge, NY; *U.S. Private,* pg. 655
Yamauchi, Hiroshi, Pres.--Nintendo Company, Ltd., Kyoto, Japan; *Int'l,* pg. 932
Yamazaki, Katsuhiko, Pres.--Nikkei Visual Images, Inc., Tokyo, Japan; *Int'l,* pg. 929
Yamazaki, Mitsuo, Pres.--Seibu Department Stores, Ltd., Tokyo, Japan; *Int'l,* pg. 1178
Yamazawa, Tadahide, Pres.--Kyowa Takken Kaihatsu Co., Ltd., Tokyo, Japan; *Int'l,* pg. 763
Yanagida, Tokio, Pres.--Mitsubishi Shindoh Co., Ltd., Tokyo, Japan; *Int'l,* pg. 875
Yanagihara, Takahika, Pres.-U.S.--Takara Belmont U.S.A., Inc., New York, NY; *Int'l,* pg. 1349
Yanagihara, Takahiko, Pres.-U.S.--Koken Mfg. Co. Inc., Saint Louis, MO; *Int'l,* pg. 1349
Yanai, N., Pres.--Metalart Corporation, Kusatsu, Japan; *Int'l, pg. 946*
Yancey, George F.T., Jr., Pres.--Perry's Ice Cream Co., Inc., Akron, NY; *U.S. Private,* pg. 855
Yanke, Ron, Pres. & Owner--Nashua Homes of Idaho Inc., Boise, ID; *U.S. Private,* pg. 774
Yano, Makoto, Pres.--Kawasaki Loaders Manufacturing Corp., (U.S.A.), Newnan, GA; *Int'l,* pg. 725
Yano, Tamotsu, Pres.--Toray Industries (Singapore) Pte. Ltd., Singapore, Singapore; *Int'l,* pg. 1400
Yano, Yoichiro, Pres.--Aoki Corporation, Tokyo, Japan; *Int'l, pg. 78*
Yantis, Thomas G., Pres. & Chief Exec. Officer--Yantis Corporation, San Antonio, TX; *U.S. Private,* pg. 1195
Yaquimenko, Walter, Pres.--Kvaerner Eureka Espanola S.A., Madrid, Spain; *Int'l,* pg. 767
Yaquimenko, Walter, Pres.--Kvaerner Eureka Espanola S A, Villagarcia de Arosa, Spain; *Int'l,* pg. 767
Yared, Paul, Pres. & Chief Exec. Officer--McNeil & NRM., Inc., Akron, OH; *U.S. Private,* pg. 725
Yarenda, Richard, Pres.--Yesawich, Pepperdine & Moss, Phoenix, AZ; *U.S. Private,* pg. 1196
Yarmark, Murray B., Pres.--Triboro Electric Co., Doylestown, PA; *U.S. Private,* pg. 1102
Yarsin, A.B., Pres.--Miller Products Company, Inc., North Bergen, NJ; *U.S. Private,* pg. 747
Yarussi, E.A., Pres.--Emerson Power Transmission Corporation, Ithaca, NY; *U.S. Public,* pg. 573
Yashima, Kenso, Pres.--The Hokuriku Bank, Ltd., Toyama, Japan; *Int'l,* pg. 627
Yashima, Toshiaki, Pres.--Tohoku Electric Power Co., Ltd., Sendai, Japan; *Int'l,* pg. 1390
Yasinsky, John B., Chm. Bd., Pres. & Chief Exec. Officer--GenCorp Inc., Fairlawn, OH; *U.S. Public,* pg. 705
Yasuda, Isao, Pres.--Asahi Chemical Industry America, Inc., New York, NY; *Int'l,* pg. 84
Yasue, N., Pres.--Nissho Iwai Gas Co., Ltd., Tokyo, Japan; *Int'l,* pg. 946
Yasui, Shosaku, Pres. & Chief Oper. Officer--Teijin Limited, Osaka, Japan; *Int'l,* pg. 1362
Yasui, Yoshihiro, Pres.--Brother Industries, Ltd., Nagoya, Japan; *Int'l,* pg. 229
Yasukawa, Hideaki, Pres.--Seiko Epson Corporation, Nagano, Japan; *Int'l,* pg. 1219
Yasuno, Shiro, Pres.--Princeville Corporation, Princeville, HI; *U.S. Private,* pg. 885
Yates, Cleon R., Pres.--Cryco Quartz, Inc., Austin, TX; *Int'l,* pg. 1408
Yates, Cleon R., Pres.--Cryco Twenty Two, Inc., Austin, TX; *Int'l,* pg. 1408
Yates, John, Pres.--Butterworths Canada, Markham, Canada; *Int'l,* pg. 1095
Yau, Sam, Chm. Bd. & Pres.--National Education Payroll Corp., Irvine, CA; *U.S. Public,* pg. 784
Yavorsky, David, Pres.--First American Real Estate Tax Service, Inc., Irving, TX; *U.S. Public,* pg. 625
Yazaki, Yasuhiko, Pres.--Yazaki Corporation, Tokyo, Japan; *Int'l,* pg. 1520
Yazawa, Masahiko, Pres.--Sapporo U.S.A., Inc., New York, New York, NY; *Int'l,* pg. 1193
Ybarra y Churruca, Emilio, Pres.--Banco Bilbao Vizcaya, S.A., Bilbao, Spain; *Int'l,* pg. 138
Yeargan, Edmund L., Jr., Pres.--Battey Machinery Company, Rome, GA; *U.S. Private,* pg. 123
Yeates, Douglas T., Pres. & Chief Exec. Officer--Regions Bank/Habersham County, Cornelia, GA; *U.S. Public,* pg. 1372
Yelsey, Arthur R., Pres.--Mediaspot, Inc., Corona Del Mar, CA; *U.S. Private,* pg. 727
Yemenidjian, Alex, Pres. & Chief Oper. & Fin. Officer--MGM Grand, Inc., Las Vegas, NV; *U.S. Public,* pg. 1026
Yen, Anthony, Pres.--Adec International Automation Corp., Cleveland, OH; *U.S. Private,* pg. 17
Yeovil, Lord Peiton of, Pres.--British Alcan Aluminium plc, Gerrards Cross, United Kingdom; *Int'l,* pg. 51
Yerant, Gene S., Chm. Bd. & Pres.--Transport Insurance Co., Dallas, TX; *U.S. Public,* pg. 75
Yesawich, Peter C., Ph.D., Pres. & Chief Exec. Officer--Yesawich, Pepperdine & Brown, Orlando, FL; *U.S. Private,* pg. 1195
Yeshoua, Jack, Pres.--Lucky Winner, Inc., New York, NY; *U.S. Private,* pg. 679
Yoba, Gerald, Pres.--Great Lakes-Eglinton, Bridgeport, MI; *U.S. Public,* pg. 1676
Yocum, Dr. Ronald H., Pres. & Chief Exec. Officer--Millennium Petrochemicals, Inc., Cincinnati, OH; *Int'l,* pg. 594
Yoda, Masahiro, Pres.--Sanwa Bank Trust Company of New York, New York, NY; *Int'l,* pg. 1189
Yoder, Edward L., Pres. & Chief Exec. Officer--Rurban Life Insurance Company, Defiance, OH; *U.S. Public,* pg. 1413
Yoder, Kent, Pres. & Chief Exec. Officer--Yoder Oil Company Inc., Elkhart, IN; *U.S. Private,* pg. 1196

Yoder, Steve, Pres.--American Systems Technologies, Verona, WI; *U.S. Public*, pg. 2
Yoe, Robert H., III, Pres.--DeSoto Mills, Inc., Fort Payne, AL; *U.S. Public*, pg. 1413
Yoh, Hal, III, Pres.--Day & Zimmermann, Inc., Philadelphia, PA; *U.S. Private*, pg. 316
Yoh, Michael H., Pres.--Munitions Technology Division, Nash, TX; *U.S. Private*, pg. 317
Yohalem, Alan, Pres.--The Economics Press, Inc., Fairfield, NJ; *U.S. Private*, pg. 362
Yokana, Andre, Pres.--Sterling Davis Standard, South Plainfield, NJ; *Int'l*, pg. 1240
Yokoi, Hiromasa, Vice Chm., Pres. & Chief Exec. Officer--Berlitz International, Inc., Princeton, NJ; *U.S. Public*, pg. 221
Yokotachi, Katsushige, Pres.--Dentsu Tohoku Inc., Sendai, Japan; *Int'l*, pg. 393
Yokouchi, Akira, Pres.--Nissho Iwai Canada Ltd., Toronto, Canada; *Int'l*, pg. 948
Yokoyama, Kazuo, Pres.--ORIX Rent-A-Car, Tokyo, Japan; *Int'l*, pg. 1009
Yokoyama, Masayuki, Pres.--KHI Europe Finance B.V., Amsterdam, Netherlands; *Int'l*, pg. 726
Yokoyama, Toshio, Co-Pres. & Co-Chief Exec. Officer--The Nikko Securities Co. International Inc., New York, NY; *Int'l*, pg. 930
Yomantas, Gary C., Pres. & Chief Exec. Officer--New Hampshire Ball Bearings, Inc., Peterborough, NH; *Int'l*, pg. 868
Yomazzo, Michael J., Pres. & Chief Exec. Officer--Photronics, Inc., Brookfield, CT; *U.S. Public*, pg. 1293
Yonemoto, Hiroshi, Pres. & Chief Exec. Officer--Nissan Mutual Life Insurance Company, Tokyo, Japan; *Int'l*, pg. 945
Yoneyama, Kohtaro, Pres.--Tottori Sanyo Electric Co., Ltd., Tottori, Japan; *Int'l*, pg. 1191
Yoneyama, Minoru, Chief Exec. Officer--Yonex Co., Ltd., Tokyo, Japan; *Int'l*, pg. 1522
Yoneyama, Minoru, Pres.--Yonex Corporation, Torrance, CA; *Int'l*, pg. 1522
Yoneyama, Reiji, Pres.--Chiyoda Mutual Life Insurance Company, Tokyo, Japan; *Int'l*, pg. 286
Yong, Yun Jong, Pres. & Chief Exec. Officer--Samsung Group, Seoul, Korea; *Int'l*, pg. 1181
Yonker, Michael T., Pres. & Chief Exec. Officer--Portec, Inc., Lake Forest, IL; *U.S. Public*, pg. 1317
Yontz, Kenneth F., Chm. Bd., Pres., & Chief Exec. Officer--Sybron International Corporation, Milwaukee, WI; *U.S. Public*, pg. 1544
Yoon, Young J., Pres.--Crown Confectionery Co., Ltd., Seoul, Korea; *Int'l*, pg. 348
York, John C., III, Pres.--Louisiana Downs, Bossier City, LA; *U.S. Private*, pg. 319
Yoshida, Haruki, Pres.--The Wako Research Institute of Economics, Inc. (WRI), Tokyo, Japan; *Int'l*, pg. 1485
Yoshida, Hiromi, Pres.--SEIKO France S.A., Paris, France; *Int'l*, pg. 1218
Yoshida, Hiroshi, Pres.--Sato Kogyo Co., Ltd., Tokyo, Japan; *Int'l*, pg. 1197
Yoshida, K., Pres.--Nissho Iwai Industrial Machinery Inc., Osaka, Japan; *Int'l*, pg. 946
Yoshida, Kanetaka, Pres. & Chief Exec. Officer--Union Bank of California, San Francisco, CA; *Int'l*, pg. 157
Yoshida, Katsumi, Pres.--Ricoh Electronics, Inc., Tustin, CA; *Int'l*, pg. 1114
Yoshida, Koichi, Pres.--Sumitomo Life Insurance Company, Osaka, Japan; *Int'l*, pg. 1315
Yoshida, Kyosuke, Pres.--The Japan Bond Research Institute, Tokyo, Japan; *Int'l*, pg. 929
Yoshida, Masaki, Pres.--Japan Associated Finance Co., Ltd., Tokyo, Japan; *Int'l*, pg. 955
Yoshida, Nobuyuki, Pres.--Kawasaki Heavy Industries GmbH, Dusseldorf, Germany; *Int'l*, pg. 726
Yoshida, Nobuyuki, Pres.--Xentek, Inc., San Marcos, CA; *Int'l*, pg. 1349
Yoshida, Shoichiro, Pres.--Nikon Corporation, Tokyo, Japan; *Int'l*, pg. 931
Yoshida, Tadahiro, Pres.--YKK Corporation, Tokyo, Japan; *Int'l*, pg. 1514
Yoshida, Yoichi, Pres.--Chiba International Ltd., London, United Kingdom; *Int'l*, pg. 283
Yoshikawa, Atsushi, Co-Pres.--Nomura Holding America, Inc., New York, NY; *Int'l*, pg. 956
Yoshikawa, Hidetaka, Pres.--Takara Belmont Co., Ltd., Osaka, Japan; *Int'l*, pg. 1349
Yoshino, Shigehiko, Pres.--The Asahi Bank, Ltd., Tokyo, Japan; *Int'l*, pg. 81
Yoshioka, Jim, Pres.--California Hospital Medical Center, Los Angeles, CA; *U.S. Private*, pg. 1118
Yoshitome, Yasuo, Pres., Mng. Dir.--Dentsu (Thailand) Ltd., Bangkok, Thailand; *Int'l*, pg. 394
Yosomiya, Masao, Pres.--Kanematsu Corporation, Tokyo, Japan; *Int'l*, pg. 722
Yost, Carl, Pres.--Day & Zimmerman Construction Inc., Greenville, SC; *U.S. Private*, pg. 317
Yost, Jan, Pres., Treas. & Sec.--D.S.U.-Peterbilt & GMC, Inc., Portland, OR; *U.S. Private*, pg. 306
Yost, Jeff, Pres.--Kingfisher Co-Op Elevator Association, Kingfisher, OK; *U.S. Private*, pg. 621
Yost, R. David, Pres. & Chief Exec. Officer--AmeriSource Health Corp., Malvern, PA; *U.S. Public*, pg. 96
Yotsumoto, Osamu, Pres.--Kawasaki Heavy Industries (Singapore) Pte. Ltd., Singapore, Singapore; *Int'l*, pg. 726
Young, Bruce J., Pres.--Mesirow Financial, Chicago, IL; *U.S. Private*, pg. 733
Young, C. Steve, Pres. & Chief Exec. Officer--MicroBilt Corporation, Atlanta, GA; *U.S. Public*, pg. 631
Young, Clifford, Jr., Pres.--Florida Heat Pump, Fort Lauderdale, FL; *U.S. Private*, pg. 506
Young, Daniel, Pres. & Chief Exec. Officer--Federal Data Corporation, Bethesda, MD; *U.S. Private*, pg. 398
Young, Donald A., Pres. & Chief Exec. Officer--Kapalua Land Co., Ltd., Lahaina, HI; *U.S. Public*, pg. 1060
Young, F. Gaylon, Pres.--Rodney D. Young Insurance, Dallas, TX; *U.S. Private*, pg. 1202
Young, F.M., Jr., Pres.--Young Radiator Company, Racine, WI; *U.S. Private*, pg. 1201
Young, Fred C., Pres., Chief Oper. Officer, Treas. & Sec.--Black Box Corporation of PA, Lawrence, PA; *U.S. Public*, pg. 235
Young, Jack, Chm. Bd., Pres., Chief Exec. & Chief Fin. Officer--Jack Young Associates, Hazleton, PA; *U.S. Private*, pg. 1201
Young, Jayne, Pres. & Publr.--The Atlantic Advertising Sales, New York, NY; *U.S. Private*, pg. 95
Young, Jeff, Pres.--Lexington Furniture Industries, Lexington, NC; *U.S. Private*, pg. 432
Young, Jerry D., Pres.--Borden Foods Canada, Etobicoke, Canada; *U.S. Private*, pg. 159
Young, John A., III, Pres.--Burd & Fletcher Company, Kansas City, MO; *U.S. Private*, pg. 181
Young, Lawrence J., Pres.--Angelica Image Apparel, Saint Louis, MO; *U.S. Public*, pg. 113
Young, Lawrence J., Pres.--Life Uniform & Shoe Shops, Saint Louis, MO; *U.S. Public*, pg. 113
Young, Lee In, Pres.--Top Mix Concrete, Singapore, Singapore; *Int'l*, pg. 1293
Young, Lee In, Pres.--Aeracom Technologies Pte. Ltd., Jurong, Singapore; *Int'l*, pg. 1293
Young, Michael T., Pres.--Young Electric Sign Company, Salt Lake City, UT; *U.S. Private*, pg. 1201
Young, Patricia, Pres.--Canadian Ad-Check Services Inc., Markham, Canada; *Int'l*, pg. 1124
Young, Richard F., Chm. Bd., Pres. & Chief Exec. Officer--Sues, Young & Brown Inc., Baldwin Park, CA; *U.S. Private*, pg. 1049
Young, Robert A., III, Pres. & Chief Exec. Officer--Arkansas Best Corporation, Fort Smith, AR; *U.S. Public*, pg. 130
Young, Robert F., Publisher--Good Food Magazine, New York, NY; *Int'l*, pg. 925
Young, Robert H., Pres. & Chief Exec. Officer--Central Vermont Public Service Corporation, Rutland, VT; *U.S. Public*, pg. 327
Young, Robert H., Pres.--C.V. Realty, Inc., Rutland, VT; *U.S. Public*, pg. 328
Young, Robert H., Pres. & Chief Exec. Officer--Smart Energy Services, Inc., Rutland, VT; *U.S. Public*, pg. 328
Young, Robert H., Pres.--Catamount Investment Corporation, Rutland, VT; *U.S. Public*, pg. 328
Young, Robert S., Pres.--R.S. Young Excavating, Inc., Flint, MI; *U.S. Private*, pg. 1202
Young, Stewart B., Sr. Partner & Grp. Brand Res. Dir.--EURO RSCG Tatham, Chicago, IL; *Int'l*, pg. 601
Young, Tom, Pres.--Busse Brothers Inc., Randolph, WI; *U.S. Private*, pg. 866
Young, Walter R., Jr., Chm. Bd., Pres. & Chief Exec. Officer--Champion Enterprises, Inc., Auburn Hills, MI; *U.S. Public*, pg. 332
Young, William B., Pres. & Chief Exec. Officer--The National Bank of Fredericksburg, Fredericksburg, VA; *U.S. Public*, pg. 1089
Young, William C., Pres.--Plastipak Packaging Inc., Plymouth, MI; *U.S. Private*, pg. 872
Young, William D., Sr., Pres. & Chief Exec. Officer--General Wholesale Company, Inc., Atlanta, GA; *U.S. Private*, pg. 445
Young, William J., Chm. Bd., Pres. & Chief Exec. Officer--Advanced Machine Vision Corp., Medford, OR; *U.S. Public*, pg. 20
Young, William J., Pres.--Volkswagen of America, Inc., Orangeburg, NY; *Int'l*, pg. 1474
Youngblood, Gary C., Pres. & Chief Oper. Officer--Alabama Gas Corporation, Birmingham, AL; *U.S. Public*, pg. 581
Youngblood, Henri, Pres.--World Trade Transport of Virginia, Sterling, VA; *U.S. Public*, pg. 749
Youngblood, Wilfred E., Pres., Treas. & Sec.--Louisiana Gaming Management, Inc., Metairie, LA; *U.S. Private*, pg. 677
Younger, Gordon M., Pres.--Seattle Packaging Corporation, Seattle, WA; *U.S. Private*, pg. 980
Yount, Bradley A., Pres.--APEX Specialty Materials, Inc., New Castle, DE; *U.S. Private*, pg. 77
Youssefzadeh, Emil, Pres.--Satellite Technical Management, Costa Mesa, CA; *Int'l*, pg. 1154
Youssefzadeh, Emil, Pres., Chief Exec. Officer & Sec.--STM Wireless, Inc., Irvine, CA; *U.S. Public*, pg. 1421
Yu, Quincy, Pres. & Chief Oper. Officer--Red Sky Interactive, San Francisco, CA; *U.S. Public*, pg. 1224
Yuasa, Teruhisa, Pres. & Chief Exec. Officer--Yuasa Corporation, Tokyo, Japan; *Int'l*, pg. 1522
Yuen, Henry C., Pres.--Gemstar International Group Limited, Pasadena, CA; *U.S. Public*, pg. 705
Yuen, Tim, Pres. & Mng. Dir.--GrandeTel Technologies Inc., Richmond, Canada; *Int'l*, pg. 556
Yui, Akira, Pres., Chief Oper. Officer--Dentsu Burson Marsteller, Inc., New York, NY; *Int'l*, pg. 393
Yull, Melbourn, Pres.--Intertape Polymer Group, Green Bay, WI; *Int'l*, pg. 685
Yun, David, Pres.--Scholastic Book Fairs, Inc., Lake Mary, FL; *U.S. Public*, pg. 1440
Yun, Lee Jae, Pres.--Kelim Toto Co., Ltd., Kyung Buk, Korea; *Int'l*, pg. 1410
Yung, M. S., Deputy Gen. Mgr.--Asia Pacific Breweries Ltd., Singapore, Singapore; *Int'l*, pg. 608
Yung, Richard, Pres. & Chief Exec. Officer--MCRB Service Bureau, Inc., Chatsworth, CA; *U.S. Private*, pg. 686
Yurkovic, Leonard S., Pres. & Chief Exec. Officer--SI Handling Systems, Inc., Easton, PA; *U.S. Public*, pg. 1418
Yusa, Shigeyuki, Pres.--The Meijiseimei Insurance Services of California, Inc., San Francisco, CA; *Int'l*, pg. 854
Zabel, Ron, Pres. & Chief Exec. Officer--Worldwide Sports & Recreation, Inc., Tulsa, OK; *U.S. Private*, pg. 1191
Zablatnik, Gabe, Pres.--Little Giant Pump Company, Oklahoma City, OK; *U.S. Public*, pg. 1566
Zable, Walter J., Chm. Bd., Pres. & Chief Exec. Officer--Cubic Corporation, San Diego, CA; *U.S. Public*, pg. 466
Zabriskie, John L., Ph.D., Pres. & Chief Exec. Officer--Pharmacia & Upjohn, Kalamazoo, MI; *Int'l*, pg. 1048
Zaccaria, Adrian, Pres. & Chief Oper. Officer--Bechtel Group, Inc., San Francisco, CA; *U.S. Private*, pg. 128
Zaccone, Judith, Pres.--Energy Brokers Guild, Bloomfield, NJ; *U.S. Private*, pg. 376
Zachary, C. Ross, Jr., Pres.--Rigesa, Ltda., Sao Paulo, Brazil; *U.S. Public*, pg. 1762
Zacks, Gordon, Chm. Bd., Pres. & Chief Exec. Officer--R.G. Barry Corporation, Pickerington, OH; *U.S. Public*, pg. 192
Zacky, Albert, Pres.--Zacky Farms, Inc., South El Monte, CA; *U.S. Private*, pg. 1203
Zadel, C. William, Chm. Bd., Pres. & Chief Exec. Officer--Millipore Corporation, Bedford, MA; *U.S. Public*, pg. 1112
Zaengerle, Rudolf, Pres.--Von Roll, Inc., Duluth, GA; *Int'l*, pg. 1480
Zafir, George, Pres.--Clark Door Co., Inc., Maryland Heights, MO; *U.S. Private*, pg. 242
Zafiropoulo, Arthur W., Chm. Bd., Pres. & Chief Exec. Officer--Ultratech Stepper, Inc., San Jose, CA; *U.S. Public*, pg. 1663
Zagar, Constance L., Pres.--Litton Precision Products International, Munich, Germany; *U.S. Public*, pg. 1004
Zahn, Randall, Pres.--Uniseal, Inc., Evansville, IN; *U.S. Private*, pg. 628
Zahn, Richard W., Pres.--Schering Laboratories, Kenilworth, NJ; *U.S. Public*, pg. 1438
Zaks, Rodnay, Pres. & Chief Exec. Officer--Sybex, Inc., Alameda, CA; *U.S. Private*, pg. 1059
Zalaznick, David W., Mng. Partner--The Jordan Company, New York, NY; *U.S. Private*, pg. 597
Zalenski, Anthony F., Pres. & Chief Exec. Officer--Boca Research Inc., Boca Raton, FL; *U.S. Public*, pg. 239
Zaleschuk, Victor J., Pres., Chief Exec. & Fin. Officer--Canadian Occidental Petroleum Ltd., Calgary, Canada; *U.S. Public*, pg. 1210
Zaleski, Stephen C., Pres.--New York Systems Exchange Corp., Melville, NY; *U.S. Private*, pg. 1060
Zall, Lawrence, Pres.--Paris Presents, Gurnee, IL; *U.S. Private*, pg. 839
Zambonini, Renato, Pres. & Chief Exec. Officer--Cognos Inc., Ottawa, Canada; *Int'l*, pg. 305
Zambonini, Ron, Pres. & Chief Oper. Officer--Cognos Corp., Burlington, MA; *Int'l*, pg. 306
Zamoiski, Calman, Chm. Bd. & Pres.--The Zamoiski Co., Baltimore, MD; *U.S. Private*, pg. 1203
Zampella, Arthur, Pres.--Graber-Rogg, Inc., Cranford, NJ; *U.S. Private*, pg. 468
Zampetis, Theodore K., Pres. & Chief Oper. Officer--The Standard Products Company, Dearborn, MI; *U.S. Public*, pg. 1504
Zamrzla, Pam, Owner--Western Pacific Roofing, Palmdale, CA; *U.S. Private*, pg. 1168
Zanchuk, Walter, Pres.--Tafa Incorporated, Concord, NH; *U.S. Public*, pg. 866
Zanck, Charie A., Pres., Chief Exec. Officer & Dir.--AMCORE Bank N.A., Northwest, Woodstock, IL; *U.S. Public*, pg. 64
Zander, Glenn R., Pres. & Chief Exec. Officer--Aloha Airgroup, Inc., Honolulu, HI; *U.S. Private*, pg. 44
Zander, Jeffrey, Pres. & Controller--Zander's Creamery Inc., Cross Plains, WI; *U.S. Private*, pg. 1203
Zandman, Felix, Dr., Chm. Bd., Pres. & Chief Exec. Officer--Vishay Intertechnology, Inc., Malvern, PA; *U.S. Public*, pg. 1721
Zane, Ken, Pres. & Chief Exec. Officer--Idea Engineering & Fabricating, Detroit, MI; *U.S. Private*, pg. 557
Zantop, James M., Pres. & Chief Oper. Officer--Zantop International Airlines, Inc., Ypsilanti, MI; *U.S. Private*, pg. 1204
Zanville, Joel, Pres.--Advance Steel Co., Detroit, MI; *U.S. Private*, pg. 21
Zapico, Antonio Rodriguez, Pres.--Ini Medioambiente, S.A., Madrid, Spain; *Int'l*, pg. 1225
Zappa, R., Chief Exec. Officer--Zappa Plastics, Phillipsburg, NJ; *U.S. Private*, pg. 172
Zappa, Robert J., Pres.--PolyMedica Healthcare, Inc., Golden, CO; *U.S. Public*, pg. 1315
Zaragoza, Jose, Mng. Partner--DPZ-Dualibi, Petit, Zaragoza, Propaganda S.A., Sao Paulo, Brazil; *Int'l*, pg. 352
Zaremba, Walter, Pres. & Chief Exec. Officer--Zaremba Group, Inc., Lakewood, OH; *U.S. Private*, pg. 1204
Zarges, Thomas H., Pres. & Chief Exec. Officer--Morrison Knudsen Corp.-Engineering & Construction, Cleveland, OH; *U.S. Public*, pg. 1134
Zargo, James, Pres.--McCormick Distilling Co., Weston, MO; *U.S. Private*, pg. 720
Zarin, Larry, Pres.--Express Scripts Vision, Earth City, MO; *U.S. Public*, pg. 601
Zarker, Gary, Superintendent--Seattle City Light, Seattle, WA; *U.S. Private*, pg. 979
Zarrow, Henry, Pres. & Chief Exec. Officer--Sooner Pipe & Supply Corp., Tulsa, OK; *U.S. Private*, pg. 1014
Zax, Stanley R., Chm. Bd. & Pres.--Zenith National Insurance Corp., Woodland Hills, CA; *U.S. Public*, pg. 1790
Zazulia, Irwin, Pres. & Chief Exec. Officer--Hecht's, Arlington, VA; *U.S. Public*, pg. 1063
Zbinden, Peter, Chief Oper. Officer--Schindler Holding AG, Hergiswil, Switzerland; *Int'l*, pg. 1204
Zebrack, Herbert, Pres.--Lithographix, Inc., Los Angeles, CA; *U.S. Private*, pg. 670
Zeck, Fritz, Pres.--Cooper Lighting Division, Elk Grove Village, IL; *U.S. Public*, pg. 443
Zee, Tien P., Pres.--Intex Corp., Long Beach, CA; *U.S. Private*, pg. 574
Zeglis, John D., Pres.--AT&T Corporation, Basking Ridge, NJ; *U.S. Public*, pg. 10
Zeher, Mike, Pres. & Chief Oper. Officer--Lander Co., Inc., Englewood, NJ; *U.S. Private*, pg. 647
Zeigler, Charles E., Jr., Chm. Bd., Pres. & Chief Exec. Officer--Public Service Company of North Carolina, Inc., Gastonia, NC; *U.S. Public*, pg. 1340

Zeiler, Jeffrey, V.P. & Mng. Partner-Acct.--Wells BDDP, Inc., New York, NY; *Int'l*, pg. 117
Zeilinger, Alan F., Pres.--Magic American Corporation, Cleveland, OH; *U.S. Private*, pg. 695
Zeillmann, L., Pres.--Gaylord Chemical Corporation, Slidell, LA; *U.S. Public*, pg. 704
Zeitler, Klaus M., Pres. & Chief Exec. Officer--Metall Mining Corporation, Toronto, Canada; *Int'l*, pg. 862
Zeitlin, Mark, Pres.--Insurance Automation Systems, Cleveland, OH; *U.S. Public*, pg. 1660
Zekaria, Maurice, Pres.--Windsor Fashions, Los Angeles, CA; *U.S. Private*, pg. 1182
Zelazo, R.E., Dr., Pres.--Astronautics Corporation of America, Milwaukee, WI; *U.S. Private*, pg. 93
Zelcer, Ami, Pres.--AAR Technical Service Center, Garden City, NY; *U.S. Public*, pg. 1
Zeller, Herve, Pres.--Remy Amerique Inc., New York, NY; *Int'l*, pg. 1102
Zeller, M.C., Pres. & Chief Exec. Officer--Zeller Corp., Defiance, OH; *U.S. Private*, pg. 1204
Zelms, Jeffrey L., Chief Exec. Officer--The Doe Run Company, Saint Louis, MO; *U.S. Private*, pg. 922
Zelnak, Stephen P., Jr., Vice Chm., Pres. & Chief Exec. Officer--Martin Marietta Materials, Inc., Raleigh, NC; *U.S. Public*, pg. 1007
Zeloski, Richard P., Pres. & Chief Exec. Officer--First Signature Bank & Trust Co., Portsmouth, NH; *U.S. Private*, pg. 589
Zeman, A.L., Pres.--The Wyco Tool Co., Racine, WI; *U.S. Private*, pg. 906
Zeman, Gregory C., Pres.--CDW Computer Centers, Inc., Vernon Hills, IL; *U.S. Public*, pg. 277
Zemanek, Bob, Pres. & Chief Exec. Officer--Public Service Company of Oklahoma, Tulsa, OK; *U.S. Public*, pg. 324
Zemenick, Carl A., Pres., Chief Exec. Officer & Chief Oper. Officer--GF Office Furniture Ltd., Gallatin, TN; *U.S. Private*, pg. 434
Zemsky, Howard, Pres.--Zemco Industries, Inc., Buffalo, NY; *U.S. Private*, pg. 1204
Zenk, Saul, Pres. & Treas.--Monico Alloys, Inc., Los Angeles, CA; *U.S. Private*, pg. 757
Zenner, Michael E., Pres.--DG Bank (Switzerland) Ltd., Zurich, Switzerland; *Int'l*, pg. 352
Zenner, Patrick J., Pres. & Chief Exec. Officer--Hoffmann-La Roche Inc., Nutley, NJ; *Int'l*, pg. 1120
Zensen, Dennis C., Chm. Bd., Pres. & Chief Exec. Officer--Sylvan Inc., Saxonburg, PA; *U.S. Public*, pg. 1545
Zenz, Barbara E., Chm. Bd., Pres. & New Bus. Contact--The Stephenz Group, Inc., San Jose, CA; *U.S. Private*, pg. 1040
Zept, Frank, Pres.--Zept Technologies, Clearwater, FL; *U.S. Private*, pg. 118
Zeratsky, J.G., Pres.--National Rivet & Manufacturing Company, Waupun, WI; *U.S. Private*, pg. 786
Zercher, Edward, Pres.--Sensenich Propeller Manufacturing Co., Inc., Lancaster, PA; *U.S. Private*, pg. 861
Zerfoss, David R., Pres.--Husqvarna Forest & Garden Products, Charlotte, NC; *Int'l*, pg. 440
Zermeno, Jorge Farrel, Pres.--Tokio Marine Compania de Seguros, S.A. de C.V., Mexico, Mexico; *Int'l*, pg. 1393
Zetcher, Arnold B., Pres. & Chief Exec. Officer--Talbots, Inc., Hingham, MA; *Int'l*, pg. 28
Zetterstrom, Lars, Pres.--NCC Malmo, Malmo, Sweden; *Int'l*, pg. 899
Zeus, William, Jr., Pres. & Chief Exec. Officer--National Tool & Manufacturing Company, Kenilworth, NJ; *U.S. Private*, pg. 787
Zewiske, D., Pres.--Phillips & Jacobs/South, Norcross, GA; *U.S. Public*, pg. 1329
Ziccardi, Donald P., Pres. & Chief Exec. Officer--Ziccardi & Partners, Inc., New York, NY; *U.S. Private*, pg. 1205
Ziegenbein, Klaus, Chm. Bd., Pres. & Chief Exec. Officer--Koh-I-Noor, Inc., Bloomsbury, NJ; *U.S. Private*, pg. 629
Zieger, Claus D., Chm. Bd., Pres., Chief Exec. Officer & Treas.--Interbath, Inc., City of Industry, CA; *U.S. Private*, pg. 566
Ziegler, Gordon S., Jr., Pres. & Chief Oper. Officer--Ziegler Chemical & Mineral Corp., Jericho, NY; *U.S. Private*, pg. 1205
Ziegler, Harold, Pres.--Harold Ziegler Ford-Elkhart, Elkhart, IN; *U.S. Private*, pg. 1205
Ziegler, Harold, Jr., Pres.--Ziegler Tire & Supply Company, Inc., Canton, OH; *U.S. Private*, pg. 1205
Ziegler, John B., Pres.-N.A.--SmithKline Beecham Consumer Healthcare, U.S., Pittsburgh, PA; *Int'l*, pg. 1264
Ziegler, P.D., Pres. & Chief Exec. Officer--The Ziegler Companies, Inc., West Bend, WI; *U.S. Public*, pg. 1791
Ziegler, Vince, Pres.--AGRA Land Surveys Ltd., Sherwood Park, Canada; *Int'l*, pg. 30
Ziehm, Richard, Pres., Chief Exec. Officer & Treas.--Precision Extrusions, Bensenville, IL; *U.S. Private*, pg. 879
Zien, Richard, Pres.--Mendelsohn/Zien Advertising, Inc., Los Angeles, CA; *U.S. Private*, pg. 731
Zierdt, John V., Pres. & Chief Exec. Officer--Transcorp, Nashville, TN; *U.S. Public*, pg. 451
Ziering, Michael, Pres. & Chief Oper. Officer--Diagnostic Products Corporation, Los Angeles, CA; *U.S. Public*, pg. 505
Zifferer, Morton F., Jr., Pres. & Chief Exec. Officer--New Standard Corporation, Mount Joy, PA; *U.S. Private*, pg. 794
Zigel, James M., Pres.--Lucas Industries Inc., Buffalo, NY; *Int'l*, pg. 820
Zildjian, Armand, Chm. Bd. & Pres.--Avedis Zildjian Company, Norwell, MA; *U.S. Private*, pg. 1206
Zilinski, James W., Pres.--Berkshire Life Insurance Company, Pittsfield, MA; *U.S. Private*, pg. 136
Zils, Joseph C., Pres. & Chief Fin. Officer--Flex Products, Inc., Santa Rosa, CA; *U.S. Public*, pg. 1227
Zimdar, Dorothy L., Pres.--Zimdar Enterprises/Frames Unlimited, Wyoming, MI; *U.S. Private*, pg. 1206
Zimlich, Albert L., Jr., Pres.--Jack Daniels Distillery, Lynchburg, TN; *U.S. Public*, pg. 261
Zimlich, Albert L., Jr., Pres.--Early Times Distillers Co., Louisville, KY; *U.S. Public*, pg. 261
Zimmer, Alan M., Pres. & Chief Exec. Officer--Reeds Jewelers, Inc., Wilmington, NC; *U.S. Public*, pg. 1370
Zimmerli, Kurt, Chm. Bd., Pres., & Chief Exec. Officer--Zima Corporation, Spartanburg, SC; *U.S. Private*, pg. 637
Zimmerman, Alan K., Pres.--Marval Industries, Inc., Mamaroneck, NY; *U.S. Private*, pg. 710
Zimmerman, Dennis A., Pres. & Chief Exec. Officer--ComSonics, Inc., Harrisonburg, VA; *U.S. Private*, pg. 260
Zimmerman, James, Pres.--Media General Broadcast Group, Inc., Tampa, FL; *U.S. Public*, pg. 1078
Zimmerman, Jordan, Chm. Bd., Pres. & New Bus. Contact--Zimmerman & Partners Advertising, Inc., Fort Lauderdale, FL; *U.S. Private*, pg. 1206
Zimmerman, Ronald C., Pres. & Chief Exec. Officer--Hornor, Townsend & Kent, Philadelphia, PA; *U.S. Private*, pg. 849
Zimmerman, William R., Chm. Bd., Pres. & Chief Exec. Officer--Zimmerman Holdings, Inc., San Marino, CA; *U.S. Private*, pg. 1206
Zimmermann, F.N., Chm. Bd. & Pres.--March Manufacturing Inc., Glenview, IL; *U.S. Private*, pg. 702
Zimpleman, Larry, Pres.--Principal Financial Advisors, Inc., Des Moines, IA; *U.S. Private*, pg. 885
Zinbarg, Benson, Pres., Chief Exec. Officer, Chief Fin. Officer & Treas.--Sun Hill Industries, Inc., Stamford, CT; *U.S. Private*, pg. 1051
Zingale, Anthony, Pres. & Chief Exec. Officer--Clarify Inc., San Jose, CA; *U.S. Public*, pg. 382
Zingle, Roger, Pres.--C.A. Muer Corp., Detroit, MI; *U.S. Private*, pg. 766
Zingraff, Rene, Mng. Dir.--Compagnie Generale des Etablissements Michelin, Clermont, France; *Int'l*, pg. 322
Zinkann, Peter, Dr., Co.-Pres.--Miele & Cie, GmbH, Gutersloh, Germany; *Int'l*, pg. 865
Zinn, Thomas R., Pres. & Sec.--Stearns Enterprises, Inc., Lexington, KY; *U.S. Private*, pg. 1037
Ziraldo, Donald, Pres.--InnisKillin Wines, Inc., Niagara on the Lake, Canada; *Int'l*, pg. 1468
Ziskin, Barry, Pres.--Z-Seven Fund, Inc., Mesa, AZ; *U.S. Public*, pg. 1789
Zito, Dan, Pres.--Gannett Media Technologies International, Cincinnati, OH; *U.S. Public*, pg. 699
Zito, Paul M., Pres. & Chief Exec. Officer--Bacharach Inc., Pittsburgh, PA; *U.S. Private*, pg. 109
Zitting, Gordon, Pres. & Chief Exec. Officer--Macrotech Plyseal, Inc., Salt Lake City, UT; *U.S. Private*, pg. 693
Zitz, Jay T., Pres. & Chief Exec. Officer--Fort Wayne Newspaper Agency, Fort Wayne, IN; *U.S. Public*, pg. 964
Zitz, Jay T., Pres. & Chief Exec. Officer--Newspapers First, New York, NY; *U.S. Public*, pg. 964
Zizza, Salvatore J., Chm. Bd., Pres. & Chief Exec. Officer--First Medical Group Inc., Stamford, CT; *U.S. Public*, pg. 636
Zlotnik, Arnold, Pres.--Surco Products, Inc., Pittsburgh, PA; *U.S. Private*, pg. 1056
Zmijewski, Robert, Pres.--First Maryland Life Insurance Company, Baltimore, MD; *Int'l*, pg. 64
Zobl, Manfred, Pres. & Chief Exec. Officer--The Swiss Life/Rentenanstalt Group, Zurich, Switzerland; *Int'l*, pg. 1332
Zobrist, Phil, Pres. & Chief Exec. Officer--Valley Food Distributors of Nevada, Las Vegas, NV; *U.S. Public*, pg. 919
Zoffinger, George, Pres., Chief Exec. Officer--Value Property Trust, New Brunswick, NJ; *U.S. Public*, pg. 1707
Zoffinger, George, Pres.--Value Property Trust, Woodland Hills, CA; *U.S. Public*, pg. 1707
Zoll, Steven, Pres.--Zoll Food Corp., South Holland, IL; *U.S. Public*, pg. 426
Zoltak, John, Pres.--Support Systems Associates, Inc., Hauppauge, NY; *U.S. Private*, pg. 1056
Zoota, Murray, Pres. & Chief Exec. Officer--Fremont Investment & Loan, Anaheim, CA; *U.S. Public*, pg. 681
Zorich, Bruce M., Pres.--Huck International, Inc., Tucson, AZ; *U.S. Public*, pg. 1597
Zorrilla, Juan Carlos, Pres.--Banco Provincial S.A. Banco Universal, Caracas, Venezuela; *Int'l*, pg. 142
Zriny, Robert, Pres.--Clairson International Corp., Ocala, FL; *U.S. Public*, pg. 575
Zucaro, Aldo C., Chm. Bd., Pres. & Chief Exec. Officer--Old Republic International Corporation, Chicago, IL; *U.S. Public*, pg. 1218
Zucker, Fredrick, Pres. & Chief Exec. Officer--Advanced Input Devices, Inc., Coeur D'Alene, ID; *U.S. Private*, pg. 21
Zucker, Jerry, Chm. & Pres.--The Intertech Group Inc., Charleston, SC; *Int'l*, pg. 113
Zuckerman, Benjamin R., Pres.& Chief Exec. Officer--Zuckerman-Honickman Inc., King of Prussia, PA; *U.S. Private*, pg. 1207
Zuege, David A., Pres. & Chief Exec. Officer--The Oilgear Company, Milwaukee, WI; *U.S. Public*, pg. 1215
Zuendt, William, Pres.--Wells Fargo Bank, National Assn., San Francisco, CA; *U.S. Public*, pg. 1753
Zuendt, William, Pres.- Wells Fargo--First Interstate Bank of California, Los Angeles, CA; *U.S. Public*, pg. 1753
Zuern, David, Pres.--PNC Bank, Erie, PA; *U.S. Public*, pg. 1243
Zugel, F.J., Pres.--Wyman-Gordon Investment Castings, Inc., Groton, CT; *U.S. Public*, pg. 1782
Zuji, Tao, Chief Exec. Officer--Shanghai Industrial Consultants, Shanghai, China; *Int'l*, pg. 1228
Zuk, Ben, Chm. Bd. & Pres.--Plastic Reel Corp. of America, Lyndhurst, NJ; *U.S. Private*, pg. 871
Zulauf, Dale, Pres.--Sunrise Healthcare Corporation, Newton, MA; *U.S. Public*, pg. 1531
Zulli, John, Jr., Pres.--Southwestern Reprographics Inc., Las Vegas, NV; *U.S. Private*, pg. 1176
Zultowsky, Dennis, Mng. Partner-Creative Art--Lewis Gace Bozell Healthcare Worldwide, Fort Lee, NJ; *U.S. Public*, pg. 1642
Zumbiel, Robert W., Pres.--C.W. Zumbiel Company, Norwood, OH; *U.S. Private*, pg. 1207
Zuppe, William W., Pres. & Chief Oper. Officer--Sterling Financial Corporation, Spokane, WA; *U.S. Public*, pg. 1516
Zurcher, Steve, Pres.--Ammex Tax & Duty Free Shops, Ridgefield, CT; *Int'l*, pg. 103
Zurcher, Steve, Pres.--Ammex Tax & Duty Free Shops West, Inc., Ridgefield, CT; *Int'l*, pg. 103
Zurcher, Steven, Pres.--Ammex Warehouse Company, Inc., Ridgefield, CT; *Int'l*, pg. 103
Zureich, Herbert H., Pres.--Ameritech Audiotex Services Inc., Chicago, IL; *U.S. Public*, pg. 98
Zurilla, Tom, Pres. & Chief Exec. Officer--G B Stores, Columbus, OH; *U.S. Private*, pg. 972
Zurlage, Greg, Pres.--American Health Packaging, Columbus, OH; *U.S. Public*, pg. 96
ZurSchmiede, Thomas, Pres. & Chief Oper. Officer--Federal Screw Works, Detroit, MI; *U.S. Public*, pg. 616
Zvolensky, John, Pres. & Chief Exec. Officer--Kuhlman Electric Corporation, Versailles, KY; *U.S. Public*, pg. 968
Zweig, Bob, Pres.--Charlie Thomas Dealerships, Houston, TX; *U.S. Private*, pg. 1082
Zybrycki, George, Pres.--Milwaukee Seasonings, Inc., Germantown, WI; *U.S. Public*, pg. 224
Zychick, Joel D., Pres. & Chief Exec. Officer--Getko Group Inc., Westbury, NY; *U.S. Public*, pg. 320
Zylstra, Russell, Pres. & Chief Exec. Officer--Rena-Ware Distributors Inc., Redmond, WA; *U.S. Private*, pg. 922

PRESIDENT WITHIN OFFICE

Abbott, Herschell L., Jr., State Pres.-Louisiana--BellSouth Telecommunications, Inc., Atlanta, GA; *U.S. Public*, pg. 209
Abel, Greg, Chief Acctg. Officer & Pres. & COO-CalEnergy Europe--CalEnergy Co., Omaha, NE; *U.S. Public*, pg. 292
Abruzzese, Joseph, Pres.-Sls. CBS Television Network--CBS Broadcast Group, New York, NY; *U.S. Public*, pg. 274
Abudawood, J.E. Hussein H., Pres.--National Cleaning Products Ltd., Dammam, Saudi Arabia; *U.S. Public*, pg. 387
Ackley, Robert W., V.P. & Pres.- Davis Standard--Crompton & Knowles Corporation, Stamford, CT; *U.S. Public*, pg. 459
Adams, Rick L., V.P. & Pres.-Parts Company of America--W.W. Grainger, Inc., Lincolnshire, IL; *U.S. Public*, pg. 758
Adams, Rodney K., Grp. Pres.-Canadian Grp.--Beneficial Corporation, Wilmington, DE; *U.S. Public*, pg. 211
Adams, Steve, Grp. Pres. & Creative Dir.--Keyes Martin, East Hanover, NJ; *U.S. Private*, pg. 618
Adams, Trish, Pres.-Home Mortgage--Robson Communities, Sun Lakes, AZ; *U.S. Private*, pg. 937
Adams, Wayne K., Pres.-Latin America--Moore Corporation Limited, Toronto, Canada; *Int'l*, pg. 888
Agin, Joerg D., Pres.-Motion Picture & Television Imaging, Entertainment Imaging--Eastman Kodak Company, Rochester, NY; *U.S. Public*, pg. 550
Ahearn, Brian, Pres.-Galion Div.--Komatsu America International Company, Vernon Hills, IL; *Int'l*, pg. 744
Ahsmuhs, C. Richard, Pres.-City Banking Region--United Missouri Bank N.A., Kansas City, MO; *U.S. Public*, pg. 1654
Aiken, John, Pres.-Intl Construction--Suitt Construction Company, Inc., Greenville, SC; *U.S. Private*, pg. 106
Akchin, Brian, Pres.-Fraenkel Bedding Co.--Fraenkel Company, Baton Rouge, LA; *U.S. Private*, pg. 423
Akimoto, Keizo, Pres.-Vari-Lite Asia--Vari-Lite International, Dallas, TX; *U.S. Public*, pg. 1709
Akin, Paul N., Grp. Pres. & Chief Oper. Officer--Inman Construction Corporation, Memphis, TN; *U.S. Private*, pg. 564
Akir, Steven, Pres.-Fidelity Sys. Company--Fidelity Investments (FMR Corp.), Boston, MA; *U.S. Private*, pg. 402
Akizuki, Teiken, Pres.--NS Finance, Inc., New York, NY; *Int'l*, pg. 940
Ala-Pietila, Pekka, Pres.-Nokia Mobile Phones Business Grp.--Oy Nokia Ab/Nokia Group, Helsinki, Finland; *Int'l*, pg. 951
Alahuhta, Matti, Pres.-Nokia Telecommunications Bus. Grp.--Oy Nokia Ab/Nokia Group, Helsinki, Finland; *Int'l*, pg. 951
Albertini, Stephen, Partner & Gen. Mgr.--Earle Palmer Brown/Philadelphia, Philadelphia, PA; *U.S. Private*, pg. 174
Albus, Robert E., Sr. V.P. & Pres.-OTC & Specialty--Advanced Polymer Systems, Redwood City, CA; *U.S. Public*, pg. 22
Alesio, Steven W., Pres.-Small Bus. Services, Consumer Travel & Govt. Card--American Express Company, New York, NY; *U.S. Public*, pg. 73
Alexander, Gerard C., Exec. V.P. & Pres.-Central Div.--Stewart Enterprises, Inc., Metairie, LA; *U.S. Public*, pg. 1518
Alfson, Donald G., V.P. & Pres.-Vishay Electonic Components, U.S.--Vishay Intertechnology, Inc., Malvern, PA; *U.S. Public*, pg. 1721
Alibrio, Anthony F., Pres.-Health Care Services/Marriott Management--Marriott International, Inc., Washington, DC; *U.S. Public*, pg. 1047
Alibrio, Anthony F., Pres.-Health Care Services--Marriott Management Services (MMS), Washington, DC; *U.S. Public*, pg. 1048
Alic, James M., Pres.-Advanstar Expositions--Advanstar Communications, Cleveland, OH; *U.S. Private*, pg. 22
Allen, Gerald, Pres.-Avatar Utilities Inc.--Avatar Holdings Inc., Coral Gables, FL; *U.S. Public*, pg. 151
Allen, J. Norman, Pres.-New Prod. Tech.--Duracell International Inc., Bethel, CT; *U.S. Public*, pg. 743

Allen, Kenneth L., Pres.-Atlantic Homes Div.--The Great Atlantic Management Company, Hampton, VA; *U.S. Private*, pg. 473

Allen, Sam, Pres.-Intl.--The Sports Authority Inc., Fort Lauderdale, FL; *U.S. Public*, pg. 1499

Alles, J.A., Pres.-ICI Films Grp.--ICI Americas, Inc., Wilmington, DE; *Int'l*, pg. 663

Allgood, J. Kelly, State Pres.-Mississippi--BellSouth Telecommunications, Inc., Atlanta, GA; *U.S. Public*, pg. 209

Alter, Amos, Pres.-Madacy Entertainment Grp.--Handleman Company, Troy, MI; *U.S. Public*, pg. 779

Altinok, Tevfik, Pres.-Fin. Grp.--Koc Holding A.S., Istanbul, Turkey; *Int'l*, pg. 741

Altmann, Rainer, Area Pres.--NVR Homes, Inc., Gaithersburg, MD; *U.S. Public*, pg. 1148

Altrudo, Mike, Pres.-Sls.--Zeigler Coal Holding Company, Fairview Heights, IL; *U.S. Public*, pg. 1790

Ambroseo, John, Dr., Exec. V.P. & Pres.-GM Coherent Laser Grp.--Coherent, Inc., Santa Clara, CA; *U.S. Public*, pg. 395

Ambrosino, Allan, Pres.--Database America Companies, Montvale, NJ; *U.S. Public*, pg. 70

Amen, Robert M., Pres.-Intl. Paper Europe--International Paper Company, Purchase, NY; *U.S. Public*, pg. 901

Ames, A. Gary, Pres. & Chief Exec. Officer-Intl.--U S West Inc., Englewood, CO; *U.S. Public*, pg. 1688

Ames, Roger, Pres.-Polygram Music Grp.--Polygram N.V., Baarn, Netherlands; *Int'l*, pg. 1051

Amin, Ramesh G., Pres.-Consumer Electronics--Zenith Electronics Corp., Glenview, IL; *U.S. Public*, pg. 1790

Ammons, Larry B., V.P. & Pres.-Riverside Div.--The Penn Traffic Company, Syracuse, NY; *U.S. Public*, pg. 1270

Ampulski, Gary W., Pres.-Business Communication Services--Moore Corporation Limited, Toronto, Canada; *Int'l*, pg. 888

Anderson, Chris, Pres.-Bus. Devel. Group--The Andersons Incorporated, Maumee, OH; *U.S. Public*, pg. 111

Anderson, Dan, Pres.-Retail Group--The Andersons Incorporated, Maumee, OH; *U.S. Public*, pg. 111

Anderson, Douglas E., Exec. V.P. & Sec.--Boddie-Noell Enterprises Inc., Rocky Mount, NC; *U.S. Private*, pg. 154

Anderson, Glenn, Pres.-Commercial Lines--USF&G Corporation, Baltimore, MD; *U.S. Public*, pg. 1659

Anderson, Joe M., Jr., State Pres.-South Carolina--BellSouth Telecommunications, Inc., Atlanta, GA; *U.S. Public*, pg. 209

Anderson, Richard A., Grp. Pres.-Complex Bus. Svcs.--BellSouth Corporation, Atlanta, GA; *U.S. Public*, pg. 207

Anderson, Richard A., Pres.-BellSouth Business Systems--BellSouth Telecommunications, Inc., Atlanta, GA; *U.S. Public*, pg. 209

Andersson, Yngve, Pres.-Trygg Banken--Trygg-Hansa, Stockholm, Sweden; *Int'l*, pg. 1425

Andrews, Steve, Pres.-MediaOne--U S West Inc., Englewood, CO; *U.S. Public*, pg. 1688

Andrusko, Frank G., Pres.-Amoco Fabrics & Fibers--Amoco Corporation, Chicago, IL; *U.S. Public*, pg. 101

Anfield, Frank, Pres. & Chief Exec. Officer-Special Communications Group--Young & Rubicam Inc., New York, NY; *U.S. Private*, pg. 1196

Angel, Eugene J., V.P. & Pres.-USRB--General Binding Corporation, Northbrook, IL; *U.S. Public*, pg. 707

Ankerson, Perry, Pres.-Point of Pur. Div.--Everbrite, Inc., Greenfield, WI; *U.S. Private*, pg. 386

Anthony, Polly, Pres.--Sony Music Entertainment, Inc., New York, NY; *Int'l*, pg. 1281

Anthony, Polly, Pres.-Epic Records & 550 Music--Sony Music Entertainment, New York, NY; *Int'l*, pg. 1284

Antoun, S.D., Pres.-Worldwide Sls.--Dresser-Rand Sales, Houston, TX; *U.S. Public*, pg. 529

Anziano, Leon B., V.P. & Pres.-Chlor-Alkali Prods.--Olin Corporation, Norwalk, CT; *U.S. Public*, pg. 1218

Aono, Keiji, Dep. Pres.--Daido Hoxan Inc., Tokyo, Japan; *Int'l*, pg. 363

Applebaum, Bruce S., Pres.-Exploration--Texaco Worldwide Exploration & Production, Scroggins, TX; *U.S. Public*, pg. 1583

Applegate, Malcolm W., Pres. & Gen. Mgr.-Indianapolis Newspapers, Inc.--Central Newspapers, Inc., Indianapolis, IN; *U.S. Public*, pg. 326

Arai, Hiroji, Pres.-Japan Pharmaceutical Grp.--Bristol-Myers Squibb Company, New York, NY; *U.S. Public*, pg. 253

Arena, A.A., Pres.-Logistics--RB&W Corporation, Cleveland, OH; *U.S. Public*, pg. 1259

Argyris, Marcia, Pres.-McKesson Foundation--McKesson Corporation, San Francisco, CA; *U.S. Public*, pg. 1072

Arikan, Necati, Pres.-Corp. Plng. Grp.--Koc Holding A.S., Istanbul, Turkey; *Int'l*, pg. 741

Armstrong, Brendan, Pres.-Paging Network-Atlantic Region, Inc.--Paging Network, Inc., Plano, TX; *U.S. Public*, pg. 1252

Armstrong, Frank, Pres. & Mng. Dir.-Alamo Europe--Alamo Rent-A-Car Inc., Fort Lauderdale, FL; *U.S. Public*, pg. 1379

Armstrong, M. Reid, Pres.--Mission Supply Co., Overland Park, KS; *U.S. Public*, pg. 1788

Arnold, David, Dir.-Corp. Mktg. & Pres.-Tulsa Div.--Nabholz Construction Corp., Conway, AR; *U.S. Private*, pg. 772

Arnold, George L., Pres.-Dallas & Dir.--EvansGroup, Salt Lake City, UT; *U.S. Private*, pg. 385

Arsel, Celik, Pres.-Energy & Mining Grp.--Koc Holding A.S., Istanbul, Turkey; *Int'l*, pg. 741

Artigas, Ricardo, Pres. & Chief Exec. Officer-G.E. Power Controls--G.E. Electric Distribution & Control Manufacturing, Plainville, CT; *U.S. Public*, pg. 710

Arvela, Pentti, Pres.-Newsprint--UPM-Kymmene Corporation, Helsinki, Finland; *Int'l*, pg. 1427

Asaro, Vincent J., Pres.-SunAmerica Securities--SunAmerica Inc., Los Angeles, CA; *U.S. Public*, pg. 1532

Asbury, O. Neal, Pres.-Asbury--The Middleby Corporation, Rolling Meadows, IL; *U.S. Public*, pg. 1109

Aschenbroich, Jacques, Pres.-Flat Glass Div.--Saint-Gobain, Courbevoie, France; *Int'l*, pg. 1170

Aschkenes, Elayne Fleischman, Pres.-Dress Div.--Liz Claiborne, Inc., New York, NY; *U.S. Public*, pg. 1005

Ash, Robert L., Pres.-AIG Asset Management Services, Inc.--American International Group, Inc., New York, NY; *U.S. Public*, pg. 83

Ashbaugh, Don, Area Pres.--NVR Homes, Inc., Gaithersburg, MD; *U.S. Public*, pg. 1148

Ashkin, Stephen P., V.P.-Institutional Div.--Rochester Midland Corporation, Rochester, NY; *U.S. Private*, pg. 937

Ashmore, Thomas B., Pres.-Ten Market Reg.--JC Penney Company, Inc., Plano, TX; *U.S. Public*, pg. 916

Asinari, Matthew, Pres & Chief Exec. Officer-Singapore--Dentsu Young & Rubicam Partnerships, New York, NY; *U.S. Private*, pg. 325

Atay, Temel, Pres.-Tofas Grp.--Koc Holding A.S., Istanbul, Turkey; *Int'l*, pg. 741

Atherton, James D., Pres.-Publishing Grp.--Penton Publishing, Inc., Cleveland, OH; *U.S. Public*, pg. 1306

Atkinson, Richard, Grp. Pres.-Network Mgmnt.--Bowthorpe plc, Crawley, United Kingdom; *Int'l*, pg. 207

Attenborough, T. Neale, Exec. V.P.-Opers. & Pres.-Wholesale Opers.--Genesco Inc., Nashville, TN; *U.S. Public*, pg. 728

Atwood, Mark W., Pres.-Res.--Cyanamid Agricultural Products Division, Parsippany, NJ; *U.S. Public*, pg. 79

Auld, Jeffrey M., Pres.-Magna Investments--Magna Group, Inc., Saint Louis, MO; *U.S. Public*, pg. 1037

Aumueller, Juergen, Pres.-Europe--American Express Travel Related Services Co., Inc., New York, NY; *U.S. Public*, pg. 73

Autolitano, Astrid, Pres.-Mattel Intl.--Mattel, Inc., El Segundo, CA; *U.S. Public*, pg. 1057

Autterson, Matthew E., Pres.-Resources Trust Company--SunAmerica Inc., Los Angeles, CA; *U.S. Public*, pg. 1532

Aversa, Eric, Co-Pres.--Friendly Holidays Inc., Lake Success, NY; *U.S. Private*, pg. 428

Avery, David, Pres.-European Opers.--Novellus Systems, Inc., San Jose, CA; *U.S. Public*, pg. 1204

Aylsworth, John S., Chief Oper. Officer & Exec. Pres.--President Casinos, Inc., Saint Louis, MO; *U.S. Public*, pg. 1323

Azumi, Masahiro, Pres.--Kanebo Spinning Corporation, Osaka, Japan; *Int'l*, pg. 722

Babbio, Lawrence T., Jr., Pres. & Chief Exec. Officer-Network Group--Bell Atlantic Corporation, New York, NY; *U.S. Public*, pg. 201

Babineau, Jay, Pres.-Creative & Admin.--Simon Marketing, Inc., Oak Brook Terrace, IL; *U.S. Private*, pg. 1001

Baccei, Louis J., Dr., Pres.-Res. & Devel.--Loctite Corporation, Rocky Hill, CT; *Int'l*, pg. 611

Bacharach, Dov, V.P. & Pres.-Wyle/Ginsburg--Wyle Electronics, Irvine, CA; *Int'l*, pg. 1457

Back, George, Pres.-Syndication Sls.--All American Television, Inc., New York, NY; *U.S. Public*, pg. 41

Bader, Jamie B., Pres.-Frequency Control Grp.--Oak Industries Inc., Waltham, MA; *U.S. Public*, pg. 1209

Baez, Manuel A., Sr. V.P. & Pres.-Analytical Instruments--The Perkin-Elmer Corporation, Norwalk, CT; *U.S. Public*, pg. 1279

Baffico, Paul A., Pres.-Automotive Grp. & Tire Grp.--Sears, Roebuck and Co., Hoffman Estates, IL; *U.S. Public*, pg. 1452

Baggove, Selim, Pres.-Southbend--The Middleby Corporation, Rolling Meadows, IL; *U.S. Public*, pg. 1109

Bagriacik, Alpay, Pres.-Auditing Grp.--Koc Holding A.S., Istanbul, Turkey; *Int'l*, pg. 741

Bailey, David A., Pres.-Intl. Paper/Poland--International Paper Company, Purchase, NY; *U.S. Public*, pg. 901

Bailliart, Christian, V.P. & Chm. Bd.-Selas S.A.--Selas Corporation of America, Dresher, PA; *U.S. Public*, pg. 1454

Baish, Richard Owen, Pres.-El Paso Natural Gas--El Paso Natural Gas Co., Houston, TX; *U.S. Public*, pg. 567

Baker, Christopher N., Pres.-Pillowtex Div.--Pillowtex Corporation, Dallas, TX; *U.S. Public*, pg. 1296

Baker, E. Pat, Pres.-Distr. Grp.--Airgas, Inc., Radnor, PA; *U.S. Public*, pg. 33

Baker, James D., Pres.-Midwest Industrial Contractors, Inc.--Matrix Service Company, Tulsa, OK; *U.S. Public*, pg. 1057

Baker, John M., Sr. V.P. & Pres.-ADC Wireless Sys. Grp.--ADC Telecommunications, Inc., Minnetonka, MN; *U.S. Public*, pg. 4

Baksha, Joseph, V.P. & Pres.-Packaging Group--Outlook Group Corporation, Neenah, WI; *U.S. Public*, pg. 1235

Baksha, Joseph, Pres.--Outlook Label Systems, Inc., Neenah, WI; *U.S. Public*, pg. 1235

Baksha, Joseph, Pres.--Outlook Packaging, Inc., Oak Creek, WI; *U.S. Public*, pg. 1236

Baldi, Anthony, Div. Pres.--Aceto Corporation, Lake Success, NY; *U.S. Public*, pg. 15

Baldwin, Richard O., Jr., Exec. V.P. & Pres.-Corp. Devel. Div.--Stewart Enterprises, Inc., Metairie, LA; *U.S. Public*, pg. 1518

Balkema, Gary S., Pres.-Consumer Care Div. & Exec. V.P.--Bayer Corporation, Pittsburgh, PA; *Int'l*, pg. 172

Balkema, Gary S., Exec. V.P. & Pres.-Consumer Care Div.--Bayer Corporation, Parsippany, NJ; *Int'l*, pg. 172

Ball, David A., Pres.-Public Carrier Networks & Sr. V.P.--Northern Telecom Limited, Brampton, Canada; *Int'l*, pg. 968

Balleyquier, Claude, Pres.-European Opers.--Tektronix, Inc., Wilsonville, OR; *U.S. Public*, pg. 1567

Ballou, Roger H., Pres.-Travel Services Grp.--American Express Travel Related Services Co., Inc., New York, NY; *U.S. Public*, pg. 73

Bane, Keith J., Pres.-Americas Reg.--Motorola, Inc., Schaumburg, IL; *U.S. Public*, pg. 1136

Banig, L.C., Pres.-Consumer Products--Actron Manufacturing Company, Cleveland, OH; *U.S. Private*, pg. 16

Banner, William C., V.P. & Pres.-Security Services Division--ABM Industries, San Francisco, CA; *U.S. Public*, pg. 2

Bannister, Denise, Grp. Pres.-Gulf Coast Newspaper Grp.--Gannett Company, Inc., Arlington, VA; *U.S. Public*, pg. 698

Bannon, Robert N., V.P.-Opers. & Pres.-Petrochemicals Div.--Sterling Chemicals Holdings, Inc., Houston, TX; *U.S. Public*, pg. 1515

Bannon, Robert N., V.P.-Opers. & Pres.-Petrochemical--Sterling Chemicals, Inc., Houston, TX; *U.S. Public*, pg. 1515

Bantoft, Chris, Pres. & Mng. Dir.-ACC Europe--ACC Corp., Rochester, NY; *U.S. Public*, pg. 2

Baratz, Alan E., Pres.-JavaSoft--Sun Microsystems, Inc., Palo Alto, CA; *U.S. Public*, pg. 1531

Barber, Kathryn, Pres.-Outbound Telemarketing Svcs.--LCS Industries, Inc., Clifton, NJ; *U.S. Public*, pg. 970

Barber, Norman V., Chm.-Aerospace Grp.--Smiths Industries plc, London, United Kingdom; *Int'l*, pg. 1266

Barlucchi, Claudio, Pres--EMTEC Magnetics Italia Spa, Cesano Maderno, Italy; *Int'l*, pg. 743

Barnard, Brian, Pres.-Florida Reg.--FPA Medical Management, Inc., San Diego, CA; *U.S. Public*, pg. 608

Barnes, Galen, Pres.-Nationwide Insurance Enterprise--Nationwide Mutual Insurance Co., Columbus, OH; *U.S. Private*, pg. 789

Barnes, James A., Pres.-Asia/Pacific Region--R.J. Reynolds Tobacco Intl., Inc., Geneva, Switzerland; *U.S. Public*, pg. 1355

Barnes, Peter L., Pres.-Philip Morris Asia--Philip Morris International Inc., Rye Brook, NY; *U.S. Public*, pg. 1289

Barnett, Robert, Pres.-Land Mobile Products--Motorola, Inc., Schaumburg, IL; *U.S. Public*, pg. 1136

Barnhouse, Bob, V.P.-FoodService--Big Valley Marketing Corp., Fremont, CA; *U.S. Private*, pg. 1186

Baron, Donald, Pres.-Goodman Grp. E.--Goodman Knitting Company, Brockton, MA; *U.S. Public*, pg. 948

Barr, John, Pres.-N. American Opers.--Haemonetics Corporation, Braintree, MA; *U.S. Public*, pg. 773

Barrett, Brian W., V.P. & Pres.-Animal Health Grp.--Pfizer Inc., New York, NY; *U.S. Public*, pg. 1281

Barrett, Carolyn, Pres.-Brdcstg. Div.--Diversified Communications, Portland, ME; *U.S. Private*, pg. 336

Barrett, H. Scott, Pres.-Video Div.--Blockbuster Entertainment Group, Dallas, TX; *U.S. Private*, pg. 775

Barringer, Victor, Pres.-CLI--Coastal Lumber Company, Weldon, NC; *U.S. Private*, pg. 248

Barron, Patricia C., V.P. & Pres.-Xerox Engineering Systems Div.--Xerox Corporation, Stamford, CT; *U.S. Public*, pg. 1783

Barry, David P., Pres.-VRC--Vivra Incorporated, San Mateo, CA; *U.S. Public*, pg. 1723

Barry, Steve, Pres.-January & Assoc.--Creative Alliance, Inc., Louisville, KY; *U.S. Private*, pg. 287

Bars, Joe, Pres.-Horizon Properties--Horizon Enterprises Group LLC, Taylor, MI; *U.S. Private*, pg. 539

Barter, John W., Exec. V.P. & Pres.-AlliedSignal Automotive--AlliedSignal Inc., Morristown, NJ; *U.S. Public*, pg. 49

Barthelme, J.P., V.P. & Pres.-European Opers.--Hein-Werner Corporation, Waukesha, WI; *U.S. Public*, pg. 805

Bartlett, Thomas A., Pres. & Chief Exec. Officer-Intl. Wireless Unit--Bell Atlantic Corporation, New York, NY; *U.S. Public*, pg. 201

Barton, Glen A., Grp. Pres.--Caterpillar Inc., Peoria, IL; *U.S. Public*, pg. 315

Basore, J. Neff, Jr., Pres.-Bella Vista Village--Cooper Communities, Inc., Bella Vista, AR; *U.S. Private*, pg. 273

Bastis, T.E., Grp. Pres.--HC&D Div., Honolulu, HI; *U.S. Public*, pg. 99

Battaglia, Anthony, Pres.-Processing-Chiquita Brands, Inc.--Chiquita Brands International, Inc., Cincinnati, OH; *U.S. Public*, pg. 349

Battaglia, Anthony D., Pres.-Chiquita Diversified Foods--Chiquita Banana North America, Cincinnati, OH; *U.S. Public*, pg. 349

Battersby, Jack, Pres.-Summit Food Distributors--Cara Operations Limited, Toronto, Canada; *Int'l*, pg. 266

Bauer, P.A., Pres.-HSN Credit Corp.--Home Shopping Network, Inc., Saint Petersburg, FL; *U.S. Public*, pg. 1685

Baughman, Gary, Pres.-Fischer Price, Inc.--Mattel, Inc., El Segundo, CA; *U.S. Public*, pg. 1057

Baumgardt, James R., Pres.-Western Hemishpere Sls.--Guidant Corporation, Indianapolis, IN; *U.S. Public*, pg. 768

Baumgardt, Jim, Pres.-Western Hemisphere Sls.--Guidant Corporation-Cardiac Rhythm Management Group, Saint Paul, MN; *U.S. Public*, pg. 768

Baumgartner, Steven M., Exec. V.P. & Sector Pres.-Global Printing--R.R. Donnelley & Sons Company, Chicago, IL; *U.S. Public*, pg. 517

Baxter, Donald, Pres.-Mining Div.--Drummond Company, Inc., Jasper, AL; *U.S. Private*, pg. 343

Baxter, Greg, Pres.-ORC Electronic Prods.--BEC Group, Inc., Rye, NY; *U.S. Public*, pg. 160

Baxter, James G., Chief Fin. Officer & Pres.-Consumer Prods. Grp.--CSS Industries, Inc., Philadelphia, PA; *U.S. Public*, pg. 283

Bayindir, Gokce, Pres.-Otosan Grp.--Koc Holding A.S., Istanbul, Turkey; *Int'l*, pg. 741

Bayman, Scott R., Pres. & Chief Exec. Officer-G.E. India--General Electric International Operations, London, United Kingdom; *U.S. Public*, pg. 713

Bear, Stephen E., Pres.-Worldwide Consumer Medicines--Bristol-Myers Squibb Company, New York, NY; *U.S. Public*, pg. 253

Beaubien, Francois De Gaspe, Pres.-Telemedia Publishing--Telemedia Inc., Montreal, Canada; *Int'l*, pg. 1373

Beauchamp, Guy R., Pres. & Chief Oper. Officer-Cable TV--CFCF Inc., Montreal, Canada; *Int'l*, pg. 240

Beauchamp, Lee, Pres.-Ada Crude Oil Company--Adams Resources & Energy, Inc., Houston, TX; *U.S. Public*, pg. 18

Beaudoin, Claude, Pres.-Telemedia Broadcasting--Telemedia Inc., Montreal, Canada; *Int'l*, pg. 1373

Bebe, Ronald W., Pres.-Michigan Airgas--Airgas, Inc., Radnor, PA; *U.S. Public*, pg. 33
Becker, Folke, Exec. V.P. & Pres.-BT Products AB--BT Industries AB, Mjolby, Sweden; *Int'l*, pg. 123
Beckstrom, Jan, Pres.-Commercial Sls.--Preferred Risk Mutual Insurance, West Des Moines, IA; *U.S. Private*, pg. 880
Beckwith, Gerald L., Sr. V.P. & Pres.-Commun. Sys. Division--QUALCOMM, San Diego, CA; *U.S. Public*, pg. 1348
Beece, Deborah, Pres.-Nick Features--Viacom Entertainment, New York, NY; *U.S. Private*, pg. 779
Beghini, Victor G., Vice Chm. & Pres.-Marathon Grp.--USX Corporation, Pittsburgh, PA; *U.S. Public*, pg. 1661
Behar, Howard, Pres.-Starbucks Intl.--Starbucks Coffee Company, Seattle, WA; *U.S. Public*, pg. 1510
Beirise, John H., Grp. Pres.-Capital Markets--Mercantile Bancorporation Inc., Saint Louis, MO; *U.S. Public*, pg. 1087
Belan, Robert D., Pres.-Utility Div.--Badger Meter, Inc., Milwaukee, WI; *U.S. Public*, pg. 164
Belanger, Charles, Pres. & Chief Exec. Officer-Brdcst. Group--CFCF Inc., Montreal, Canada; *Int'l*, pg. 240
Belanger, Jean, Pres.-Premier Tech Ltee--Premier CDN Enterprises Ltd., Dorval, Canada; *Int'l*, pg. 1067
Belgin, Ural, Pres.-Automotive Supplies Grp.--Koc Holding A.S., Istanbul, Turkey; *Int'l*, pg. 741
Belill, Leo T., Pres.-Cleaning Div.--Church & Dwight Co., Inc., Princeton, NJ; *U.S. Public*, pg. 355
Belill, Leo T., Pres.-Cleaning Div.--Church & Dwight Specialty Products Division, Princeton, NJ; *U.S. Public*, pg. 356
Bell, Alan J., Pres.-Broadcast Div. & Exec. V.P.--Freedom Communication Inc., Irvine, CA; *U.S. Private*, pg. 425
Bell, Tom, Pres. & Chief Exec. Officer-Burson-Marsteller--Young & Rubicam Inc., New York, NY; *U.S. Private*, pg. 1196
Belle, Gerald, Pres.-Hoechst Marion Roussel Canada--Hoechst Marion Roussel North America, Kansas City, MO; *Int'l*, pg. 625
Bellin, Jim, Pres.-American Trucker--Southam Magazine and Information Group, North York, Canada; *Int'l*, pg. 631
Belton, Y. Marc, V.P. & Pres.-New Ventures--General Mills, Inc., Minneapolis, MN; *U.S. Public*, pg. 717
Bemis, Peter, Pres.-Frankfurt Balkind West--Frankfurt Balkind Partners, New York, NY; *U.S. Private*, pg. 424
Bendush, William E., Pres.-Fin.--Silicon Systems, Inc., Tustin, CA; *U.S. Public*, pg. 1585
Bengtsson, Stig, Pres.-Scancem Reinsurance--Scancem AB, Malmo, Sweden; *Int'l*, pg. 1198
Benham, Ronald C., V.P. & Sr. Div. Pres.-Dexter Electronics--The Dexter Corporation, Windsor Locks, CT; *U.S. Public*, pg. 504
Benjamin, Floyd, Exec. V.P. & Pres.-Injectable Div.--Akorn, Inc., Lincolnshire, IL; *U.S. Public*, pg. 34
Benjamin, Nash, Deputy Pres. & Chief Oper. Officer--F. J. Benjamin Holdings Ltd., Singapore, Singapore; *Int'l*, pg. 187
Bennett, Tim, Pres.-Harpo Productions--Harpo Entertainment Group, Chicago, IL; *U.S. Private*, pg. 504
Bennice, Dennis, Pres.-Dana Risk Management--Dana Corporation, Toledo, OH; *U.S. Public*, pg. 479
Bennington, Richard M., Pres.-Bus. Svcs. Division--Office Depot Inc., Delray Beach, FL; *U.S. Public*, pg. 1212
Benson, Keith, Pres.-Mall Stores--Musicland Group Inc., Minnetonka, MN; *U.S. Public*, pg. 1142
Benson, T. Craig, V.P. & Pres.-Investment Capital Corp.--Service Corporation International, Houston, TX; *U.S. Public*, pg. 1460
Bentley, Sara, Grp. Pres.-Northwest Newspaper Grp.--Gannett Company, Inc., Arlington, VA; *U.S. Public*, pg. 698
Berenson, Robert L., Pres.-Grey U.S.--Grey Advertising Inc., New York, NY; *U.S. Public*, pg. 764
Bergeman, Carl T., Pres.-Computer Knowledge--Computer Horizons Corp., Mountain Lakes, NJ; *U.S. Public*, pg. 421
Berger, Jeffrey, Pres.-Food Service Division--Heinz U.S.A. Div., Pittsburgh, PA; *U.S. Public*, pg. 805
Berger, Steve, Pres.-Promotional Brdcst. Services--Western International Media Corporation, Los Angeles, CA; *U.S. Private*, pg. 1165
Bergeron, Albert A., V.P. & Pres.-PartyLite Gifts, Inc.--Blyth Industries, Greenwich, CT; *U.S. Public*, pg. 239
Bergeron, George E., V.P. & Pres.-Alcoa Rigid Pkgng.--Aluminum Company of America, Pittsburgh, PA; *U.S. Public*, pg. 60
Bergeson, Rolly, Pres.-United Express Div.--Mesa Air Group, Las Vegas, NV; *U.S. Public*, pg. 1098
Berglund, Bo, Pres.--ICA Handlarna Norr AB, Umea, Sweden; *Int'l*, pg. 642
Bergstrom, Stig-Erik, Dep. Pres.-Fin., Treas., Information Mngmt. & Real Estate--OY Stockmann AB, Helsinki, Finland; *Int'l*, pg. 1301
Berman, Joel, Pres.-TV Distr.--Paramount Pictures Corporation, Los Angeles, CA; *U.S. Private*, pg. 776
Bermea, Javier, Grp. Pres.--Grupo Industrial Durango S.A. de C.V., Durango, Mexico; *Int'l*, pg. 575
Bernau, Tom, Pres.-Amerus Leasing Co.--American Mutual Life Holding Co., Des Moines, IA; *U.S. Private*, pg. 59
Berndt, Wolfgang C., Exec. V.P. & Pres.-N. America--The Procter & Gamble Company, Cincinnati, OH; *U.S. Public*, pg. 1330
Bernholz, Martin, Pres.-Domestic Oper. Company--Kenny Rogers Roasters, Fort Lauderdale, FL; *U.S. Private*, pg. 939
Bernstein, Alan B., Exec. V.P. & Pres.-N. American Opers. Grp.--The Wackenhut Corporation, Palm Beach Gardens, FL; *U.S. Public*, pg. 1731
Bernstock, Robert F., Pres.-U.S. Grocery & Exec. V.P.--Campbell Soup Company, Camden, NJ; *U.S. Public*, pg. 298
Beronja, Branko, Pres.-N. American Opers.--Snap-On Tools Corporation, Kenosha, WI; *U.S. Public*, pg. 1480
Berrios, Filiberto, Sr. V.P. & Pres.-Blockbuster Div.--Pueblo Xtra International, Inc., Pompano Beach, FL; *U.S. Private*, pg. 894
Berube, Jacques B., Pres.-Nortel Europe & Sr. V.P.-Special Projects--Northern Telecom Limited, Brampton, Canada; *Int'l*, pg. 968
Bethke, William, Pres.-Capital Mngmt.--The Prudential Insurance Company of America, Newark, NJ; *U.S. Private*, pg. 892
Bettacchi, Robert J., V.P. & Pres.-Grace Construction Products--W.R. Grace & Co., Boca Raton, FL; *U.S. Public*, pg. 754
Bettcher, Tom, Pres.-AC--Copeland Corporation, Sidney, OH; *U.S. Public*, pg. 573
Bibring, Yoram, Pres. & Chief Exec. Officer-Geotek Intl. Networks--Geotek Communications, Montvale, NJ; *U.S. Public*, pg. 739
Bilotta, Peter, Pres.-Interplay Europe--Interplay Productions, Inc., Irvine, CA; *U.S. Private*, pg. 572
Biltz, Timothy G., Pres.-U.S. Wireless Opers.--Vanguard Cellular Systems, Inc., Greensboro, NC; *U.S. Public*, pg. 1707
Bilyea, M.E., Pres.-Maple Leaf Foods Intl.--Maple Leaf Foods Inc., Toronto, Canada; *Int'l*, pg. 841
Bingleman, Jack, Pres.-Staples Intl.--Staples, Inc., Westborough, MA; *U.S. Public*, pg. 1509
Binkley, Chris, Pres.-Southeast Division & Sr. V.P.--Kaiser Permanente, Oakland, CA; *U.S. Private*, pg. 605
Binswanger, Frank G., III, Pres.-Binswanger Intl.--Binswanger, Philadelphia, PA; *U.S. Private*, pg. 144
Birch, Murray P., Pres.-West Coast Energy Australia--Westcoast Energy Inc., Vancouver, Canada; *Int'l*, pg. 1492
Birck, Michael J., Pres. & Chief Exec. Officer-Tellabs, Inc.--Tellabs Operations, Inc., Lisle, IL; *U.S. Public*, pg. 1572
Bishop, Robert M., Pres.-Godwins Overseas, Inc.--Godwins Booke & Dickenson, Inc., Briarcliff Manor, NY; *U.S. Public*, pg. 118
Bissell, Matthew R., Pres.-Graphics Div.--Bissell Inc., Grand Rapids, MI; *U.S. Private*, pg. 145
Bjorn, Erland, Pres.--ICA Handlarna Sydost AB, Vaxjo, Sweden; *Int'l*, pg. 643
Black, Cathleen, Pres.-Hearst Magazines--The Hearst Corporation, New York, NY; *U.S. Private*, pg. 515
Black, Cathleen, Pres.-Magazine Div.--Cosmopolitan, New York, NY; *U.S. Private*, pg. 517
Black, David, Pres.-MacIntosh Div.--Clarion Corporation of America, Gardena, CA; *Int'l*, pg. 296
Black, Thomas B., Reg. Chm., Pres. & Chief Exec. Officer--Mellon Bank, N.A.-Northern Region, Erie, PA; *U.S. Public*, pg. 1085
Blackwell, James A., Pres.-Aeronautics Sector--Lockheed Martin Corporation, Bethesda, MD; *U.S. Public*, pg. 1006
Blackwood, Jason T., Pres.-Physiotherapy Associates--Stryker Corporation, Kalamazoo, MI; *U.S. Public*, pg. 1525
Blaha, Bill, Pres.-Sls.--Pacesetter Corporation, Omaha, NE; *U.S. Private*, pg. 830
Blanchard, Norman H., Pres.-Animal Health--SmithKline Beecham Corporation, Philadelphia, PA; *Int'l*, pg. 1264
Blanchard, Robert T., Grp. V.P. & Pres.-Beauty Care Prods./North America--The Procter & Gamble Company, Cincinnati, OH; *U.S. Public*, pg. 1330
Blattner, Robert, Pres.-MCA Home Video, Inc. & V.P.--Universal Studios, Inc., Universal City, CA; *Int'l*, pg. 1215
Blaugrund, Clifford, Pres.-American Business Interiors & V.P.--American Furniture Company, Albuquerque, NM; *U.S. Private*, pg. 55
Blazin, Bernard, Pres.-Intl. Div.--Clarins, Neuilly-sur-Seine, France; *Int'l*, pg. 295
Block, Peter, Pres.-European Div.--Block Drug Company, Inc., Jersey City, NJ; *U.S. Public*, pg. 236
Blok, Thorleif, Pres.-Ahlstrom Paper--A. Ahlstrom Corporation, Helsinki, Finland; *Int'l*, pg. 32
Bluestein, David, Sr. V.P. & Pres.-IFF Flavors--International Flavors & Fragrances, Inc., New York, NY; *U.S. Public*, pg. 898
Blum, Bradley D., Pres.-The Olive Garden--Darden Restaurants, Inc., Orlando, FL; *U.S. Public*, pg. 483
Blumberg, Jerald, Pres.-DuPont Europe Div.--Du Pont (E.I. Du Pont De Nemours & Co.), Wilmington, DE; *U.S. Public*, pg. 530
Boardman, Donald, Pres.-Oxford Securities Corp.--Oxford Realty Financial Group, Bethesda, MD; *U.S. Private*, pg. 825
Bobis, Arthur H., Pres.-Metal Div.--RHC/Spacemaster Corporation, Melrose Park, IL; *U.S. Private*, pg. 904
Boddie, Michael W., Exec. V.P.-Hardee's Opers. Grp.--Boddie-Noell Enterprises Inc., Rocky Mount, NC; *U.S. Private*, pg. 154
Boden, A., Exec. V.P., Natl. Media Dir. & Pres.-McKim Media Grp.--BBDO Canada, Toronto, Canada; *U.S. Private*, pg. 104
Bodensteiner, Carol A., Pres.-CMF&Z Pub. Rels.--Creswell, Munsell, Fultz & Zirbel, L.P., Cedar Rapids, IA; *U.S. Private*, pg. 1197
Boderck, Steve, Pres.-Installation Equipment Div.--Huck International, Inc., Tucson, AZ; *U.S. Public*, pg. 1597
Bodin, Fred, Pres.-Volvo Aero--AB Volvo, Goteborg, Sweden; *Int'l*, pg. 1476
Boeckmann, Alan L., Grp. Pres.-Energy & Chemicals--Fluor Daniel Inc., Irvine, CA; *U.S. Public*, pg. 660
Boggess, Jerry, Pres.-Fire Protection--Grinnell Corporation, Exeter, NH; *U.S. Public*, pg. 1651
Boggess, Jerry R., Pres.-Tyco Fire & Security & V.P.--Tyco International Ltd., Exeter, NH; *U.S. Public*, pg. 1647
Bognanno, Paul, Pres.-Res. Mortgages--The Principal Financial Group, Des Moines, IA; *U.S. Private*, pg. 885
Bognanno, Paul, Pres.-Residential Mortgages--Principal Mutual Life Insurance Co., Des Moines, IA; *U.S. Private*, pg. 886
Boies, Jeffrey E., Pres.-VSA--International Multifoods Corporation, Minneapolis, MN; *U.S. Public*, pg. 900
Bokser, Stephen R., Pres.-White Rose Div.--Di Giorgio Corporation, Carteret, NJ; *U.S. Private*, pg. 330
Bolohan, Gary, Pres.-Distr. Div.--Reptron Electronics, Inc., Tampa, FL; *U.S. Public*, pg. 1377
Bolster, William, Pres.-CNBC--National Broadcasting Co., Inc., New York, NY; *U.S. Public*, pg. 712
Bonadio, Edward, Pres.-Rocky Mtn.--TAD Resources International, Inc., Cambridge, MA; *U.S. Private*, pg. 1062
Bond, Bruce, Pres. & Chief Exec. Officer-ANS Communications--America Online Incorporated, Dulles, VA; *U.S. Public*, pg. 66
Bond, Richard L., Pres.-Fresh Meats--IBP, Inc., Dakota City, NE; *U.S. Public*, pg. 852
Bondurant, William, Pres.-Alasys Inc.--Alamo Rent-A-Car Inc., Fort Lauderdale, FL; *U.S. Public*, pg. 1379
Bonilla, Pedro P., Pres.-CPAC Imaging Group--CPAC, Inc., Leicester, NY; *U.S. Public*, pg. 282
Bonner, Pauline, Pres.-Rocky Mountain Area Opers.--Paragon Health Network, Inc., Atlanta, GA; *U.S. Public*, pg. 1256
Bonnie, Richard J., V.P. & Pres.-AM Graphics--Multigraphics Inc., Mount Prospect, IL; *U.S. Public*, pg. 1141
Bonpun, Henri, Pres.-Africa--Unilever Plc, London, United Kingdom; *Int'l*, pg. 1433
Bonta, Patricio, Exec. V.P., Pres. & CEO JWT/Argentina--J. Walter Thompson Company, New York, NY; *Int'l*, pg. 1483
Boone-Isaacs, Cheryl, Pres.-Theatrical Mktg.--New Line Cinema Corporation, New York, NY; *U.S. Public*, pg. 1614
Boone, Kenneth T., Pres.-Unitrive--Superior Consultant Holdings Corp., Southfield, MI; *U.S. Public*, pg. 1538
Boorin, Robert S., Pres.-Mass Markets--Frontier Corporation, Rochester, NY; *U.S. Public*, pg. 683
Booth, Melvin, Pres.-Syntex Pharmaceuticals-Pacific & V.P.--Syntex, Palo Alto, CA; *Int'l*, pg. 1120
Borden, Glenn A., Pres.-Reg.--1st Source Bank Consolidated, South Bend, IN; *U.S. Public*, pg. 638
Borkey, Lin, Pres.-Martin Interactive--The Martin Agency, Richmond, VA; *U.S. Private*, pg. 678
Borst, Dennis, Pres.-Motivational Incentives Grp.--Western International Media Corporation, Los Angeles, CA; *U.S. Private*, pg. 1165
Bosshart, Walter, Pres.-Schweizerischen Volksbank--Providentia, Nyon, Switzerland; *Int'l*, pg. 1072
Boucher, Jean-Pierre, Pres.-Stryker Europe--Stryker Corporation, Kalamazoo, MI; *U.S. Public*, pg. 1525
Boudreau, R.J., Pres.-Maple Leaf Mills Intl.--Maple Leaf Foods Inc., Toronto, Canada; *Int'l*, pg. 841
Boulan, Thierry, Pres. & Dir. General--Societe de Banque de l'Orleanais, Orleans, France; *Int'l*, pg. 548
Bourgoin, John, Sr. V.P. & Pres.-MIPS Grp.--Silicon Graphics, Inc., Mountain View, CA; *U.S. Public*, pg. 1473
Bourne, Randall, Pres.-Exposures--Miles Kimball Company, Oshkosh, WI; *U.S. Private*, pg. 745
Bourque, Normand R., Exec. V.P. & Pres.-NORDX/CDT--Cable Design Technologies Corporation, Pittsburgh, PA; *U.S. Public*, pg. 287
Bouts, Larry, Pres. & Chief Exec. Officer-Six Flags Theme Parks Inc.--Six Flags Magic Mountain & Six Flags Hurricane Harbor, Valencia, CA; *U.S. Public*, pg. 1611
Bovaird, John R., Pres.-Bovaird Intl.--Bovaird Supply Co., Tulsa, OK; *U.S. Private*, pg. 162
Bowen, Peter L., Pres.-Retail Prods. Grp.--Heinz U.S.A. Div., Pittsburgh, PA; *U.S. Public*, pg. 805
Bowen, Terrell L., V.P. & Pres.-Consumer Prods.--Leggett & Platt, Incorporated, Carthage, MO; *U.S. Public*, pg. 985
Bower, Haywood, Pres.--Porcelain Products, Carey, OH; *U.S. Public*, pg. 308
Bowling, Bill J., Exec. V.P. & Pres.-Steel--The Timken Company, Canton, OH; *U.S. Public*, pg. 1617
Boxer, Scott J., V.P. & Pres.-Unitary Products Grp.--York International Corporation, York, PA; *U.S. Public*, pg. 1788
Boyd, Stephen D., Pres. & Chief Exec. Officer-Mktg. Resources Grp.--U S West Inc., Englewood, CO; *U.S. Public*, pg. 1688
Boyd, Steve, Pres. & Chief Exec. Officer--U S West DEX, Denver, CO; *U.S. Public*, pg. 1689
Boyle, Chris, Pres.-Gage Europe--Gage Marketing Group, Minneapolis, MN; *U.S. Private*, pg. 437
Boyle, Coulter R., III, Pres.-AEP Indiana & Michigan--American Electric Power Company, Inc., Columbus, OH; *U.S. Public*, pg. 71
Boyle, Jim, Pres.-Fin. Div.--Komatsu America International Company, Vernon Hills, IL; *Int'l*, pg. 744
Boynton, Peter G., Sr. V.P.-Gaming & Pres. & CEO-Caesars World, Inc.--ITT Corporation, New York, NY; *U.S. Public*, pg. 1512
Bracken, Richard, Pres.-West Grp.--Columbia/HCA Healthcare Corporation, Nashville, TN; *U.S. Public*, pg. 403
Bradley, Glen, Pres.-CIBA Vision--Novartis AG, Basel, Switzerland; *Int'l*, pg. 971
Brady, Joseph F., V.P. & Pres.-Centrilift--Baker Hughes Incorporated, Houston, TX; *U.S. Public*, pg. 165
Brady, Philip T., Pres. & Chief Exec. Officer-Thomas Ferguson Associates--CommonHealth USA, Parsippany, NJ; *Int'l*, pg. 1483
Braker, Joseph, Pres.-Agriculture Group--The Andersons Incorporated, Maumee, OH; *U.S. Public*, pg. 111
Brandenberg, Frank G., V.P. & Pres.-Client/Server Systems--Unisys Corporation, Blue Bell, PA; *U.S. Public*, pg. 1671
Brander, Doug, Pres. & Gen. Mgr.--Knowles Electronics, Inc., Itasca, IL; *U.S. Private*, pg. 627
Brandt, Jan, Pres.-Mktg.--America Online Incorporated, Dulles, VA; *U.S. Public*, pg. 66
Brannon, George M., Grp. V.P. & Pres.-Nalco Pacific--Nalco Chemical Company, Naperville, IL; *U.S. Public*, pg. 1150
Brashears, Melvin R., Pres. & Chief Oper. Officer-Space & Strategic Missiles--Lockheed Martin Corporation, Bethesda, MD; *U.S. Public*, pg. 1006

Bratcher, Richard W., Jr., Pres.-Showco--Vari-Lite International, Dallas, TX; *U.S. Public*, pg. 1709

Bratton, Todd, Pres.-Daniel Measurement & Control, Western Hemisphere--Daniel Industries, Inc., Houston, TX; *U.S. Public*, pg. 482

Braun, Neil, Pres.-Television Network--National Broadcasting Co., Inc., New York, NY; *U.S. Public*, pg. 712

Brauninger, Andrew W., Pres.-Seabulk Offshore, Ltd.--Hvide Marine Incorporated, Fort Lauderdale, FL; *U.S. Public*, pg. 851

Bray, Jack, Pres.-Bath Division--Home Innovations, Inc., New York, NY; *U.S. Private*, pg. 536

Bray, John J., Chm.-Forum Europe Ltd.--The Forum Corporation, Boston, MA; *U.S. Private*, pg. 420

Breech, Stephen V., Sr. V.P. & Pres.-Big Bear Div.--The Penn Traffic Company, Syracuse, NY; *U.S. Public*, pg. 1270

Breen, Roger, Pres.-Spicers Paper Inc.--Spicers Paper Limited, Preston, Australia; *Int'l*, pg. 72

Brennan, Bob, Pres.-STARCOM Media Services--Leo Burnett Company, Inc., Chicago, IL; *U.S. Private*, pg. 183

Brennan, Edward J., Pres.-Southeast--TAD Resources International, Inc., Cambridge, MA; *U.S. Private*, pg. 1062

Brewer, John C., Pres.--The New York Times Syndication Sales Corporation, New York, NY; *U.S. Public*, pg. 1174

Brewster, Dan, Pres.-Amex Publ.--American Express Publishing Corporation, New York, NY; *U.S. Public*, pg. 74

Bricker, Marvin, Co-Pres. & Treas.--Hawkeye Steel Products, Inc., Houghton, IA; *U.S. Private*, pg. 511

Bridger, Mac, Pres.--Collins & Aikman Floorcoverings, Inc., Dalton, GA; *U.S. Private*, pg. 192

Bridgman, Larry W., Pres.-Simmons Outdoor Corp.--Blount International, Inc., Montgomery, AL; *U.S. Public*, pg. 237

Briggs, J. Scott, Pres.-Consumer Media Grp.--Ziff-Davis Publishing Company, New York, NY; *Int'l*, pg. 1276

Broad, Robert C., Pres.-CCL Label & V.P.--CCL Industries, Inc., Willowdale, Canada; *Int'l*, pg. 238

Brochand, Bernard, Pres.-Intl. Div.--DDB Needham Worldwide Inc., New York, NY; *Int'l*, pg. 357

Brochand, Bernard, Pres.-Intl. Div.--DDB Needham Worldwide Inc., New York, NY; *U.S. Public*, pg. 1223

Brock, John F., Pres.-CBI--Cadbury Beverages North America, Stamford, CT; *Int'l*, pg. 248

Brody, Eric, Pres.-Branding Place--The Sawtooth Group, Woodbridge, NJ; *U.S. Private*, pg. 969

Bromley, Peter, Grp. Pres.-Agrichemicals--Elf Atochem North America, Inc., Philadelphia, PA; *Int'l*, pg. 445

Brooke, Jennifer, Partner & Creative Dir.--Earle Palmer Brown/New York, New York, NY; *U.S. Private*, pg. 174

Brookes, George A., V.P.-Admin.--Aero Service Corp., Houston, TX; *U.S. Public*, pg. 1003

Brookes, George S., Pres.-Northern Ohio Region--Huntington National Bank, Columbus, OH; *U.S. Public*, pg. 850

Brooks, David R., V.P. & Pres.-American Airlines Cargo Div.--American Airlines, Inc., Fort Worth, TX; *U.S. Public*, *pg. 9*

Brooks, Rhonda, V.P. & Pres.-Roofing Sys. Bus.--Owens Corning, Toledo, OH; *U.S. Public*, pg. 1236

Brophy, Daniel R., Pres.-Pacific Opers.--Tektronix, Inc., Wilsonville, OR; *U.S. Public*, pg. 1567

Brown, Bill, Pres.-Wolverine Intl.--Wolverine World Wide, Inc., Rockford, MI; *U.S. Public*, pg. 1775

Brown, David, V.P. & Pres.-Insulation Sys.--Owens Corning, Toledo, OH; *U.S. Public*, pg. 1236

Brown, Duncan W., Ph.D., Pres.-Epitronics--ATMI, Inc., Danbury, CT; *U.S. Public*, pg. 12

Brown, Gerry, Pres.--Coleman Powermate, Inc., Omaha, NE; *U.S. Private*, pg. 691

Brown, Jeremy, Partner & Exec. V.P.--Yesawich, Pepperdine & Brown, Orlando, FL; *U.S. Private*, pg. 1195

Brown, Kenneth C., Pres.-G.E. Southeast Asia--General Electric (USA) Asia Co., Singapore, Singapore; *U.S. Public*, pg. 713

Brown, Mark A., Pres.-Brown Steel Contractors, Inc.--Matrix Service Company, Tulsa, OK; *U.S. Public*, pg. 1057

Brown, Max, Sr. V.P. & Pres.-Diamond Park Div.--Zale Corporation, Irving, TX; *U.S. Public*, pg. 1789

Brown, Roger A., Pres.-Smith Diamond Technology--Smith International, Inc., Houston, TX; *U.S. Public*, pg. 1478

Brown, Roy, Pres.-Food & Beverages Grp./Europe--Unilever Plc, London, United Kingdom; *Int'l*, pg. 1433

Brown, Roy, Pres.-Tyson Seafood Division--Tyson Foods, Inc., Springdale, AR; *U.S. Public*, pg. 1652

Brown, William R., Pres.-Latin American Opers.--Carrier Corporation, Indianapolis, IN; *U.S. Public*, pg. 1689

Broyles, Joseph R., Pres.-IWC Industries--IWC Resources Corporation, Indianapolis, IN; *U.S. Public*, pg. 1185

Brucker, L. Randy, Pres.-Hot Springs Village--Cooper Communities, Inc., Bella Vista, AR; *U.S. Private*, pg. 273

Brunow, Berndt, Pres.-Special Products--UPM-Kymmene Corporation, Helsinki, Finland; *Int'l*, pg. 1427

Bryja, Frank J., Pres. & Chief Oper. Officer-Supermarket Div.--Marsh Supermarkets, Inc., Indianapolis, IN; *U.S. Public*, pg. 1049

Buchanan, Bruce T., Grp. Pres.--Menasha Corporation, Neenah, WI; *U.S. Private*, pg. 731

Buchanan, Danne L., Pres.--Zions Data Service Co., Salt Lake City, UT; *U.S. Public*, pg. 1793

Buchheit, Charles E., Pres.-Graphic Services--Moore Corporation Limited, Toronto, Canada; *Int'l*, pg. 888

Buchter, Ted, Sr. V.P. & Chief Oper. Officer-KCI Therapeutic Services--Kinetic Concepts, Inc., San Antonio, TX; *U.S. Private*, pg. 620

Buckelew, Larry, Pres.-Medical Group--Teleflex Incorporated, Plymouth Meeting, PA; *U.S. Public*, pg. 1569

Buckley, Peter, Pres.-Old Spaghetti Factory Canada, Ltd.--Spaghetti Warehouse, Inc., Garland, TX; *U.S. Public*, pg. 1495

Budkey, Barry, Pres.-Southern Div.--Centimark Corporation, Canonsburg, PA; *U.S. Private*, pg. 222

Buechne, Lynn, Pres.-Nautica--Bernard Chaus, Inc., New York, NY; *U.S. Public*, pg. 342

Buescher, Tom, Area Pres.--NVR Homes, Inc., Gaithersburg, MD; *U.S. Public*, pg. 1148

Bull, Heinz W., Pres.-Pharmaceuticals Div.--Altana AG, Bad Homburg, Germany; *Int'l*, pg. 65

Bumgarner, John C., Jr., Sr. V.P.-Corp. Devel. & Plng. & Pres.-Williams Intl. Co.--The Williams Companies, Inc., Tulsa, OK; *U.S. Public*, pg. 1769

Bunnell, John, Pres.-Inacom Prof. Svcs.--Inacom Corp., Omaha, NE; *U.S. Public*, pg. 873

Bunnell, John W., Pres.-Latin America--SHL Systemhouse - Latin America Operations, Arlington, VA; *Int'l*, pg. 1154

Burgmans, Antony, Pres.-Ice Cream & Frozen Foods/Europe--Unilever Plc, London, United Kingdom; *Int'l*, pg. 1433

Burke, Stephen R., Reg. Chm., Pres. & Chief Exec. Officer--Mellon Bank, N.A.-Commonwealth Region, Harrisburg, PA; *U.S. Public*, pg. 1085

Burnham, Daniel P., Exec. V.P. & Pres.-AlliedSignal Aerospace Co.--AlliedSignal Inc., Morristown, NJ; *U.S. Public*, pg. 49

Burns, Bob, Pres.-APS--Kaynar/K-Fast/APS, Fullerton, CA; *U.S. Public*, pg. 940

Burns, Robin, Pres.-Estee Lauder USA & Canada--Estee Lauder Companies Inc., New York, NY; *U.S. Public*, pg. 594

Burns, Ronald S., Exec V.P., Pres. Global Bus. & Global Bus Dir.-Kraft--J. Walter Thompson Company, New York, NY; *Int'l*, pg. 1483

Burns, Samuel D., Area Pres.--New Fortis Corp., King, NC; *U.S. Public*, pg. 843

Burnside, Elliott, Pres.-Crowley American Transport--Crowley Maritime Corporation, Oakland, CA; *U.S. Private*, pg. 292

Burrus, Michael C., Pres.-Multimedia Cablevision & Multimedia Security--Gannett Company, Inc., Arlington, VA; *U.S. Public*, pg. 698

Bursma, Albert, Jr., Exec. V.P. & Pres.-Great Source Education Group--Houghton Mifflin Company, Boston, MA; *U.S. Public*, pg. 841

Busby, Dan, Pres.-Industrial Div.--Huck International, Inc., Tucson, AZ; *U.S. Public*, pg. 1597

Bushey, Craig S., Sr. V.P. & Pres.-Hardee's--Advantica Restaurant Group, Inc., Spartanburg, SC; *U.S. Public*, pg. 22

Busquet, Anne M., Pres.-American Express Relationship Services--American Express Company, New York, NY; *U.S. Public*, pg. 73

Bussieres, Rene, Pres.-Levy Transport--MTL Inc., Plant City, FL; *U.S. Public*, pg. 1028

Butler, Gary C., Pres.-Employer Services--Automatic Data Processing, Inc., Roseland, NJ; *U.S. Public*, pg. 150

Butler, William J., Pres.-Gulton Graphic Instruments--Danaher Corporation, Washington, DC; *U.S. Public*, pg. 480

Butler, William K., II, Pres.-Eastern Region--Crestar Financial Corporation, Richmond, VA; *U.S. Public*, pg. 458

Butler, William K., III, Pres.-Eastern Reg.--Crestar Bank, Richmond, VA; *U.S. Public*, pg. 458

Butters, Gerald J., Pres.-Network Systems (N. America)--Lucent Technologies Inc., Murray Hill, NJ; *U.S. Public*, pg. 1017

Byers, John, Div. Pres.-CA Steel & Tube--Ferro Union, Inc., Torrance, CA; *U.S. Private*, pg. 402

Byrnes, Bruce L., Grp. V.P. & Pres.-Health Care Prods./North America--The Procter & Gamble Company, Cincinnati, OH; *U.S. Public*, pg. 1330

CaFarelli, John, Sector Pres.--Burnham, Atlanta, GA; *Int'l*, pg. 686

Cahill, Douglas J., V.P. & Pres.-Winchester--Olin Corporation, Norwalk, CT; *U.S. Public*, pg. 1218

Caine, Robert, Sr. V.P. & Pres.-Bath & Floor Fashions--Peerless Carpet Corporation, Acton Vale, Canada; *Int'l*, pg. 1032

Calder, Robert A., Pres.-Light Vehicle Systems--Rockwell International Corporation, Costa Mesa, CA; *U.S. Public*, pg. 1397

Caldwell, Robert J., Pres.-Drilling Grp.--Camco International Inc., Houston, TX; *U.S. Public*, pg. 297

Caldwell, Royce S., Pres.-Southwestern Bell Opers.--SBC Communications Inc., San Antonio, TX; *U.S. Public*, pg. 1415

Caliari, Roberto, Pres.-Reinforcements Div.--Saint-Gobain, Courbevoie, France; *Int'l*, pg. 1170

Caliari, Roberto, Pres.-Reinforcement Div.--Vetrotex France, Chambery, France; *Int'l*, pg. 1177

Call, Charlie, Pres.-Trim Company--JPE, Inc., Ann Arbor, MI; *U.S. Public*, pg. 919

Callaghan, James M., Pres.-Transmedia Restaurant Co. & V.P.--Transmedia Network Inc., Miami, FL; *U.S. Public*, pg. 1631

Callahan, Michael, Pres.-Intl.--Doremus & Company, New York, NY; *U.S. Public*, pg. 1223

Callanan, John, Pres.-Shoe Div.--The Biltrite Corporation, Waltham, MA; *U.S. Private*, pg. 144

Callaway, James R., Pres.-Microflect Div.--Valmont Industries, Inc., Valley, NE; *U.S. Public*, pg. 1706

Cameron, Allan C., V.P. & Pres.-Bath Iron Works--General Dynamics Corporation, Falls Church, VA; *U.S. Public*, pg. 708

Camp, Edward P., V.P. & Pres.-Hobby Div.--The Topps Company, Inc., New York, NY; *U.S. Public*, pg. 1621

Camp, Kevin, Pres.-Copy Club & V.P.-Franchise Devel.--International Center for Entrepreneurial Development, Inc., Cypress, TX; *U.S. Private*, pg. 568

Camp, Michael, Pres. & Chief Exec. Officer--Olicom, Inc., Marlborough, MA; *Int'l*, pg. 1001

Campbell, Darrell, Pres.-VPI Comml., Inc.--TCA Cable TV, Inc., Tyler, TX; *U.S. Public*, pg. 1553

Campbell, David, Pres.-BBN Systems & Technologies Div.--GTE Internetworking, Cambridge, MA; *U.S. Public*, pg. 696

Campbell, Howard F., Pres.-Emco Distribution--Emco Limited, London, Canada; *Int'l*, pg. 452

Campbell, J. Michael, Grp. Pres.--Masco Corporation, Taylor, MI; *U.S. Public*, pg. 1052

Camus, Philippe, Pres.-Matra Hachette & Chm.-Fin. Committee--Lagardere Groupe, Paris, France; *Int'l*, pg. 791

Cannady, A. Dale, Pres.-Capital Region--Crestar Financial Corporation, Richmond, VA; *U.S. Public*, pg. 458

Cannady, A. Dale, Pres.-Capital Region--Crestar Bank, Richmond, VA; *U.S. Public*, pg. 458

Cantrell, Donnie K., Pres.-Narrow Fabrics Div.--Texfi Industries, Inc., Raleigh, NC; *U.S. Public*, pg. 1588

Cantrell, Wesley E., Pres.-Lanier Worldwide, Inc--Harris Corporation, Melbourne, FL; *U.S. Public*, pg. 791

Capell, Peter S., Pres.-Snacks Unlimited--General Mills, Inc., Minneapolis, MN; *U.S. Public*, pg. 717

Capell, Robert L., III, Pres.-Small Bus. Services--BellSouth Telecommunications, Inc., Atlanta, GA; *U.S. Public*, pg. 209

Carder, David L., Pres.-Vulcan Lands, Inc.--Vulcan Materials Company, Birmingham, AL; *U.S. Public*, pg. 1725

Cardoro, John J., Pres.-Louisiana--Entergy Gulf States, Inc., Beaumont, TX; *U.S. Public*, pg. 586

Cargill, William B., Pres.-Actmedia Intl.--News America Marketing, Norwalk, CT; *Int'l*, pg. 925

Carleton, Dale L., Vice Chm. & Pres.-Fin. Markets--State Street Corporation, Boston, MA; *U.S. Public*, pg. 1513

Carlile, James C., Pres.-Medical Imaging--Mallinckrodt Inc., Saint Louis, MO; *U.S. Public*, pg. 1039

Carlino, John, Grp. Pres.--Keyes Martin, East Hanover, NJ; *U.S. Private*, pg. 618

Carlson, Kay, Pres.-The Equitable Foundation, V.P., & Corp. Grants Contact--The Equitable Companies Incorporated, New York, NY; *U.S. Public*, pg. 588

Carmitchel, Harry E., Pres.-Stryker Medical--Stryker Corporation, Kalamazoo, MI; *U.S. Public*, pg. 1525

Carmody, James M., Pres.-Opers. & Maintenance--Morrison Knudsen Corp.-Engineering & Construction, Cleveland, OH; *U.S. Public*, pg. 1134

Carneal, Jeffrey J., Pres.-Eagle Publ.--Phillips Publishing International, Inc., Potomac, MD; *U.S. Private*, pg. 862

Carpenter, Farris E., Pres.-Disneyland Intl. & Chief Fin. Officer--Walt Disney Attractions Division, Anaheim, CA; *U.S. Public*, pg. 511

Carr, Cassandra C., Pres.-TX--Southwestern Bell Telephone Co., Saint Louis, MO; *U.S. Public*, pg. 1416

Carr, Watts, Pres.-Cone Denim North America--Cone Apparel Products, Greensboro, NC; *U.S. Public*, pg. 430

Carriker, Roy C., Pres. & Chief Oper. Officer-TFX Aerospace--Teleflex Incorporated, Plymouth Meeting, PA; *U.S. Public*, pg. 1569

Carroll, Peter J., Grp. Pres.-United Kingdom--Beneficial Corporation, Wilmington, DE; *U.S. Public*, pg. 211

Carroll, William J., Pres.-Automotive Components--Dana Corporation, Toledo, OH; *U.S. Public*, pg. 479

Carson, John C., Sr. V.P.--Cadbury Beverages North America, Stamford, CT; *Int'l*, pg. 248

Carson, R. Daniel, Jr., Pres.-AEP Virginia & Tennessee--American Electric Power Company, Inc., Columbus, OH; *U.S. Public*, pg. 71

Carter, Paul R., Exec. V.P. & Pres.-Wal-Mart Realty--Wal-Mart Stores, Inc., Bentonville, AR; *U.S. Public*, pg. 1732

Carty, Donald J., Pres.--American Airlines, Inc., Fort Worth, TX; *U.S. Public*, pg. 9

Case, Dan, Pres. & Gen. Mgr.-Voice Systems Div.--Glenayre Technologies, Inc., Charlotte, NC; *U.S. Public*, pg. 746

Casey, James P., V.P. & Pres.-Fibers Grp.--Wellman, Inc., Shrewsbury, NJ; *U.S. Public*, pg. 1752

Cassady, Ken, Pres.-Monarch U.S.A.--PAXAR Corporation, White Plains, NY; *U.S. Public*, pg. 1266

Cassara, Anthony, Pres.-Paramount Stations--Paramount Pictures Corporation, Los Angeles, CA; *U.S. Private*, pg. 776

Cassara, Tony, Pres.-Carrier Services & Strategic Accts.--Frontier Communications Services, Bingham Farms, MI; *U.S. Public*, pg. 684

Cassel, William M., Pres.-Kaibab Petroleum Co.--Kaibab Industries, Phoenix, AZ; *U.S. Private*, pg. 605

Cassidy, John F., Pres.-Wireless--Cincinnati Bell Telephone Company, Cincinnati, OH; *U.S. Public*, pg. 367

Cassidy, Paul J., Pres.-Cordillera Communications--Evening Post Publishing Co., Charleston, SC; *U.S. Private*, pg. 385

Cassin, James A., Pres.-Asia/Pacific Region--Mastercard International, Inc., Purchase, NY; *U.S. Private*, pg. 714

Castleberry, John K., Pres.--Williston Basin Interstate Pipeline Company, Bismarck, ND; *U.S. Public*, pg. 1026

Cathy, Dan T., Pres.-Intl. & Exec. V.P.--Chick-fil-A, Inc., Atlanta, GA; *U.S. Private*, pg. 236

Catlow, Walter S., Pres.-Intl. & Exec. V.P.--Ameritech Corporation, Chicago, IL; *U.S. Public*, pg. 97

Caughran, Carl, Pres.-Nalleys Fine Foods Div. & Exec. V.P.--Curtice Burns Foods, Rochester, NY; *U.S. Private*, pg. 887

Caulo, Ralph D., Exec. V.P. & Pres.-Educational Publishing--Simon & Schuster, New York, NY; *U.S. Private*, pg. 777

Cavey, Gary L., Grp. Pres. & Chief Oper. Officer-Indus. Prods. Grp.--Valmont Industries, Inc., Valley, NE; *U.S. Public*, pg. 1706

Cazalot, Clarence P., Jr., Pres.-Intl. Production & V.P.--Texaco Inc., White Plains, NY; *U.S. Public*, pg. 1582

Cedraschi, T., Pres. & Chief Exec. Officer-CN Investment Div.--Canadian National Railway Company, Montreal, Canada; *Int'l*, pg. 258

Cerny, Mark, Pres.-Universal Interactive Studios--Universal Studios, Inc., Universal City, CA; *Int'l*, pg. 1215

Chadbourne, Brian D., Sr. V.P. & Pres.-IFF Fragrances--International Flavors & Fragrances, Inc., New York, NY; *U.S. Public*, pg. 898

Chamberlain, Michael D., Sr. V.P. & Pres.-SCT Software Group--Systems & Computer Technology Corporation, Malvern, PA; *U.S. Public*, pg. 1552

Chambers, James R., Pres.-U.S. Comml. Bus.--Information Resources, Inc., Chicago, IL; *U.S. Public*, pg. 875

Chambrello, Michael R., Exec. V.P. & Pres.-GTECH Lottery--GTECH Corporation, West Greenwich, RI; *U.S. Public*, pg. 767

Chan, Francis, V.P. & Pres.-Intl. Div.--Mentholatum Company, Buffalo, NY; *Int'l*, pg. 1126

Chan, Kwok C., Pres. & Chief Exec. Officer-LaFehr Chan Technologies--Logicon Geodynamic, Torrance, CA; *U.S. Public*, pg. 1199

Chan, Matthew, Pres.-Asia Opers.--Novellus Systems, Inc., San Jose, CA; *U.S. Public*, pg. 1204

Chandler, T., Pres. & Chief Exec. Officer-The Western Sugar Company--Tate & Lyle PLC, London, United Kingdom; *Int'l*, pg. 1356

Chandran, Clarence J., Pres.-Northern Telecom CALA & Sr. V.P.--Northern Telecom Limited, Brampton, Canada; *Int'l, pg. 968*

Chapel, John, Grp. Pres.--Waterhouse Investor Services, New York, NY; *Int'l*, pg. 1401

Chapla, Richard E., Div. Pres.--Heckett MultiServ, Butler, PA; *U.S. Public*, pg. 793

Chappell, Sarah S., Pres.-Motor Fuels Div.--Spencer Companies Inc., Huntsville, AL; *U.S. Private*, pg. 1024

Charlesworth, John S., Pres.-Div.--McDonald's Corporation, Oak Brook, IL; *U.S. Public*, pg. 1068

Chastain, Jim D., Pres.-Commodity Mktg. Division--The Scoular Company, Omaha, NE; *U.S. Private*, pg. 977

Cheek, Michael V., Pres.-North American Grp.--Brown-Forman Beverages Worldwide, Louisville, KY; *U.S. Public*, pg. 261

Cheng, Mei-Wei, Pres. & Chief Exec. Officer-G.E. China--General Electric (USA) China Company, Ltd., Hong Kong, Hong Kong; *U.S. Public*, pg. 713

Chernin, Peter, Pres.--News America Holdings Inc., New York, NY; *Int'l*, pg. 925

Chester, Reed, Pres.-Adv. Promo. Inc.--Scott's Liquid Gold-Inc., Denver, CO; *U.S. Public*, pg. 1447

Cheung, Alex, Mng. Dir.--Getinge Hong Kong Ltd., Wan Chai, Hong Kong,; *Int'l*, pg. 551

Chivukula, Kamesh V., Pres.-Algonquin Division--Rea Magnet Wire Company, Inc., Fort Wayne, IN; *U.S. Private*, pg. 913

Chlebek, Robert W., Pres.-Electronic Instruments Grp.--AMETEK, Inc., Paoli, PA; *U.S. Public*, pg. 99

Choonavala, Bobby A.F., V.P. & Pres.-Asia/Pacific--Digital Equipment Corporation, Maynard, MA; *U.S. Public*, pg. 507

Choquette, Roger, Pres.-Furniture Grp.--U.S. Office Products Company, Washington, DC; *U.S. Public*, pg. 1686

Choufoer, F. R., Pres.-Plastic Products & Energy--DSM N.V., Heerlen, Netherlands; *Int'l*, pg. 352

Christiansen, Robert, Pres.-Magna France--Magna Group, Inc., Saint Louis, MO; *U.S. Public*, pg. 1037

Christofferson, Randy, Pres.-American Express Relationship Services--American Express Travel Related Services Co., Inc., New York, NY; *U.S. Public*, pg. 73

Christopher, Socrates S., Pres.-CRS Sirrine Engineers, Inc.--CRSS Inc., Houston, TX; *Int'l*, pg. 1415

Chung, Nak-Kyung, Pres.-Korea Opers.--Novellus Systems, Inc., San Jose, CA; *U.S. Public*, pg. 1204

Church, Kenneth E., Exec. V.P. & Pres.-Upholstery Group--Ladd Furniture, Inc., Greensboro, NC; *U.S. Public*, pg. 974

Cicio, Joseph, Pres.-Retail Devel.--Donna Karan, New York, NY; *U.S. Public*, pg. 517

Cirar, James E., Pres.-Johnstown America Corp.--Johnstown America Industries, Chicago, IL; *U.S. Public*, pg. 933

Cirello, John, Exec. V.P. & Pres. & Chief Exec. Officer-Florida Water Services--Minnesota Power, Duluth, MN; *U.S. Public*, pg. 1116

Cirino, Jenny, Pres.-Health Care Products--Picker International, Inc., Cleveland, OH; *Int'l*, pg. 545

Ciszewski, Jerome J., Pres.-Lenox Opers.--Lenox, Incorporated, Lawrenceville, NJ; *U.S. Public*, pg. 261

Clark-Jackson, Susan, Sr. Grp. Pres.-Pacific Newspaper Grp.--Gannett Company, Inc., Arlington, VA; *U.S. Public*, pg. 698

Clark, Alan S., Pres.-U.S. Opers.--Eli Lilly and Company, Indianapolis, IN; *U.S. Public*, pg. 992

Clark, Duncan, Pres.-Columbia TriStar Film Distr.--Columbia Pictures, Culver City, CA; *Int'l*, pg. 1281

Clark, R. Kerry, Grp. V.P. & Pres.-Laundry & Cleaning Prods./North America--The Procter & Gamble Company, Cincinnati, OH; *U.S. Public*, pg. 1330

Clark, T. Daniel, V.P.-Opers. Devel. & Sr. Div. Pres.--The Dexter Corporation, Windsor Locks, CT; *U.S. Public*, pg. 504

Clark, Ted, Pres.-PRC Aerospace--Courtaulds Aerospace, Glendale, CA; *Int'l*, pg. 339

Clark, Thomas H., Pres.-Guaranty Income Life Insurance Co.--Guaranty Corporation, Baton Rouge, LA; *U.S. Private*, pg. 485

Clasen, Robert B., Sr. V.P. & Pres.-Comcast International--Comcast Corporation, Philadelphia, PA; *U.S. Public*, pg. 406

Classon, Rolf A., Pres.-Diagnostics Div. & Exec. V.P.--Bayer Corporation, Pittsburgh, PA; *Int'l*, pg. 172

Clements, Roy S., Pres.-Asia Pacific--Moore Corporation Limited, Toronto, Canada; *Int'l*, pg. 888

Cleveland, Cynthia C., Pres.-Mdsg. & Licensing--Spencer Gifts, Inc., Egg Harbor Township, NJ; *Int'l*, pg. 1216

Cleveland, James, Pres.-North American Opers.--Telxon Corporation, Akron, OH; *U.S. Public*, pg. 1573

Clifton, Gregg, Pres.-Sports & Entertainment Mgmnt.--Woolf Associates, Boston, MA; *U.S. Private*, pg. 84

Clouser, Richard L., Pres.-Mobile Div.--Unitel Video, Inc., New York, NY; *U.S. Public*, pg. 1692

Cloutier, Harris, Pres.-Independent Dealer Div.--ICI Paints, Cleveland, OH; *Int'l*, pg. 664

Coates, Michael B., Pres. & Chief Exec. Officer-Canada--Hill and Knowlton, Inc., New York, NY; *Int'l*, pg. 1483

Coats, Douglas J., Pres.-Acceleration Nat. Insurance Co. & Exec. V.P.--ACCEL International Corporation, Dublin, OH; *U.S. Public*, pg. 14

Cobbe, Brian, Pres.-Karacters Graphic Services--Palmer Jarvis Communications, Vancouver, Canada; *Int'l*, pg. 1022

Coe, Charles B., Grp. Pres.-Customer Opers.--BellSouth Telecommunications, Inc., Atlanta, GA; *U.S. Public*, pg. 209

Coe, Dennis R., Pres.--Lois/EJL Los Angeles, Los Angeles, CA; *U.S. Private*, pg. 673

Coffey, Larry R., Pres.-Landmark Community Newspapers, Inc.--Landmark Communications, Inc., Norfolk, VA; *U.S. Private*, pg. 647

Coffey, Steve, Pres.-Fragrances--Fragrance Resources, Inc., Clifton, NJ; *U.S. Private*, pg. 423

Cofod, Robert, Pres.-Fraudetect--Betac International Corporation, Alexandria, VA; *U.S. Private*, pg. 140

Cogan, James, Pres.-WCO--EA Industries, West Long Branch, NJ; *U.S. Public*, pg. 541

Cohen, Brent, Pres.-Intl. Opers.--Packard Bell NEC, Sacramento, CA; *U.S. Private*, pg. 833

Cohen, Ed, Dr., Pres.--Land of AHHS, Oklahoma City, OK; *U.S. Public*, pg. 384

Cohen, Fred, Pres.-King World International--King World Productions, Inc., New York, NY; *U.S. Public*, pg. 961

Cohen, Hy, Pres.-Royal Alliance Associates--SunAmerica Inc., Los Angeles, CA; *U.S. Public*, pg. 1532

Cohen, Meryl, Pres.-Mktg.--Paramount Pictures Corporation, Los Angeles, CA; *U.S. Private*, pg. 776

Cohen, Peter, Divisional Pres.--Sylvan Learning Systems Inc., Baltimore, MD; *U.S. Public*, pg. 1545

Cohen, Rona, Pres.-PHP Travel--PHP Healthcare Corporation, Reston, VA; *U.S. Public*, pg. 1241

Cohen, Sid, Pres.-Domestic TV Distr.--MGM Worldwide Television, Group., Santa Monica, CA; *U.S. Public*, pg. 1102

Cole, Bernard N., Pres.-Off-Highway Components--Dana Corporation, Toledo, OH; *U.S. Public*, pg. 479

Cole, Charles, Pres.--Burlington Sportswear Div., Greensboro, NC; *U.S. Public*, pg. 268

Cole, David D., Pres.-Mobile Communications Grp.--Century Telephone Enterprises, Inc., Monroe, LA; *U.S. Public*, pg. 329

Cole, Herbert M., V.P. & Pres.-AMP Asia/Pacific--AMP Incorporated, Harrisburg, PA; *U.S. Public*, pg. 7

Cole, Kenneth R., Pres.-Telephone Grp.--Century Telephone Enterprises, Inc., Monroe, LA; *U.S. Public*, pg. 329

Colebatch, Phillip M., Pres.-Credit Suisse Asset Management--Credit Suisse Group, Zurich, Switzerland; *Int'l*, pg. 345

Coleman, Michael J., Sr. Grp. Pres.-South Newspaper Grp.--Gannett Company, Inc., Arlington, VA; *U.S. Public*, pg. 698

Collier, Joseph W., Pres.--Allied Automotive Group, Decatur, GA; *U.S. Public*, pg. 48

Collingwood, J.A., Pres. & Chief Exec. Officer-Tioxide Americas--ICI Americas, Inc., Wilmington, DE; *Int'l*, pg. 663

Collins, Michelle, V.P.-Retail--Big Valley Marketing Corp., Fremont, CA; *U.S. Private*, pg. 1186

Colson, Joe S., Jr., Pres.-Network Systems--Lucent Technologies Inc., Murray Hill, NJ; *U.S. Public*, pg. 1017

Coltart, Michael, Pres. & Chief Exec. Officer--Andes Candies Inc., Delavan, WI; *U.S. Private*, pg. 163

Compton, Robert A., Grp. Pres.-Opers.--Sofamor Danek Group, Inc., Memphis, TN; *U.S. Public*, pg. 1482

Conant, Douglas R., Pres.-Sales & Integrated Logistics Company & Grp. Exec. V.P.--Nabisco Inc., Parsippany, NJ; *U.S. Public*, pg. 1355

Connavino, Nicholas A., Pres.-Northeastern Region--Sweet Life Foods, Inc., Suffield, CT; *U.S. Public*, pg. 1541

Connell, Daniel J., Pres.-CQI--McGraw-Hill Financial Information Services Group, New York, NY; *U.S. Public*, pg. 1071

Connelly, Michael F., Pres.-Engineered Wire Division--Rea Magnet Wire Company, Inc., Fort Wayne, IN; *U.S. Private*, pg. 913

Conner, E. David, Pres.-West--TAD Resources International, Inc., Cambridge, MA; *U.S. Private*, pg. 1062

Connors, Kevin P., Exec. V.P. & Pres.-GM Coherent Medical--Coherent, Inc., Santa Clara, CA; *U.S. Public*, pg. 395

Conrad, James A., Pres.-Source One Mortgage Services Corp.--Fund American Enterprises Holdings, Inc., Hanover, NH; *U.S. Public*, pg. 688

Contadino, Joseph, Exec. V.P. & Pres.-Coventry Homes--Del Webb Corporation, Phoenix, AZ; *U.S. Public*, pg. 494

Cook, Ian, Pres.-Colgate U.S.--Colgate-Palmolive Company, New York, NY; *U.S. Public*, pg. 397

Cook, John, Pres.-Consumer Foods--Burns, Philp & Company Limited, Sydney, Australia; *Int'l*, pg. 236

Cooke, John W., Pres.-Suburbanite Div.--Easy Day Manufacturing Company, Holliston, MA; *U.S. Private*, pg. 358

Cooke, Peter H., Pres.-Eastern Cement Region & Sr. V.P.--Lafarge Corporation, Reston, VA; *Int'l*, pg. 788

Cooke, William J., Pres.-Advanstar Mktg. Svcs. & Exec. V.P.--Advanstar Communications, Cleveland, OH; *U.S. Private*, pg. 22

Cooney, Wilson C., Pres.-P&C Insurance--Property & Casualty Insurance, San Antonio, TX; *U.S. Private*, pg. 1114

Cooper, Daniel W., Pres.-Tellico Village--Cooper Communities, Inc., Bella Vista, AR; *U.S. Private*, pg. 273

Cooper, Gareth, Pres.-Stena Line Ltd.--Stena Line AB, Goteborg, Sweden; *Int'l*, pg. 1300

Cooper, Robert N., Pres.-Ameritech-Michigan--Ameritech Corporation, Chicago, IL; *U.S. Public*, pg. 97

Cooper, Ronald B., V.P. & Pres.-Price Pfister--The Black & Decker Corporation, Towson, MD; *U.S. Public*, pg. 233

Coopersmith, Jeffrey, Pres.-HMS Direct--HMS Partners, Columbus, OH; *U.S. Private*, pg. 491

Copeland, Frederick L., Chm.-Home Furnishings Products--Masco Corporation, Taylor, MI; *U.S. Public*, pg. 1052

Corcoran, Thomas A., Pres.-Electronics Sector--Lockheed Martin Corporation, Bethesda, MD; *U.S. Public*, pg. 1006

Cornwall, J. Michael, Pres.-Retail Bank--Guaranty F.S.B., Dallas, TX; *U.S. Public*, pg. 1575

Corpora, Placido, Pres.-Book Div.--Rodale Press, Inc., Emmaus, PA; *U.S. Private*, pg. 939

Corporron, Randy J., Pres.--K-Tec Electronics, Sugar Land, TX; *U.S. Public*, pg. 951

Correa, Flavio, Pres.-Latin America/Sao Paulo--Ogilvy & Mather Worldwide, Inc., New York, NY; *Int'l*, pg. 1483

Corso, Vincent T., Grp. Pres. & Chief Oper. Officer-Irrigation & Coatings Grp.--Valmont Industries, Inc., Valley, NE; *U.S. Public*, pg. 1706

Corvin, Joe E., Pres. & Chief Oper. Officer--Oregon Steel Mills Inc., Portland, OR; *U.S. Public*, pg. 1230

Cosman, James H., Pres.-Solid Waste Svcs. Div.--Republic Industries, Inc., Fort Lauderdale, FL; *U.S. Public*, pg. 1378

Costello, Richard N., Pres.-Universal Strategic Mktg. Grp.--Universal Studios, Inc., Universal City, CA; *Int'l*, pg. 1215

Coughlin, Christopher J., Pres. & Chief Exec. Officer--Nabisco Inc., Parsippany, NJ; *U.S. Public*, pg. 1355

Coughlin, Karen A., Pres.-Div. II--Humana Inc., Louisville, KY; *U.S. Public*, pg. 847

Cowan, J.A., Pres.--Cable Tech Company Limited, Stouffville, Canada; *Int'l*, pg. 955

Coyne, Martin M., II, V.P. & Pres.-Health Sciences Div.--Eastman Kodak Company, Rochester, NY; *U.S. Public*, pg. 550

Crabtree, Richard, Pres.-Casualty & Property--Nationwide Mutual Insurance Co., Columbus, OH; *U.S. Private*, pg. 789

Crabtree, Richard D., Pres. & Chief Oper. Officer-P/C Company--Nationwide Insurance Enterprise, Columbus, OH; *U.S. Private*, pg. 788

Craig, George, Pres.-Book Opers.--News America Publishing Inc., New York, NY; *Int'l*, pg. 925

Craig, Ian A., Pres.-Broadband Network & Sr. V.P.--Northern Telecom Limited, Brampton, Canada; *Int'l*, pg. 968

Craig, James W., Pres.-PPG Europe & V.P.-Coatings & Resins/Europe--PPG Industries, Inc., Pittsburgh, PA; *U.S. Public*, pg. 1245

Craig, John, Pres. & V.P.-Adams U.S.A.--Adams U.S.A., Morris Plains, NJ; *U.S. Public*, pg. 1739

Crandell, Donnie, Sr. V.P.-Corp. Devel. & Pres.-MP/Real Estate Holdings--Minnesota Power, Duluth, MN; *U.S. Public*, pg. 1116

Crawford, Curtis J., Pres.-Microelectronics--Lucent Technologies Inc., Murray Hill, NJ; *U.S. Public*, pg. 1017

Crawford, Donald, V.P.-Private Labels--Tanner Co., Rutherfordton, NC; *U.S. Private*, pg. 1068

Crawford, Kathy, Pres.-Dir. Response--Western International Media Corporation, Los Angeles, CA; *U.S. Private*, pg. 1165

Crawford, Kathy, Pres.-Western Direct--Western International Media Corporation, Los Angeles, CA; *U.S. Private*, pg. 1165

Crawford, William P., Pres. & Chief Exec. Officer-Steelcase Design Partnership--Steelcase Inc., Grand Rapids, MI; *U.S. Private*, pg. 1038

Creasman, Kevin L., Pres. & Chief Oper. Officer-SC Johnson Comml. Markets--S.C. Johnson & Son, Inc., Racine, WI; *U.S. Private*, pg. 592

Crecelis, Rein W., Pres.--Sun Life Trust Company, Toronto, Canada; *Int'l*, pg. 1319

Creighton, Christopher B., Pres.-Spicers Paper--Spicers Paper Limited, Preston, Australia; *Int'l*, pg. 72

Creydt, Martin, Pres.-European Opers.--United Technologies Automotive, Dearborn, MI; *U.S. Public*, pg. 1691

Crichton, Alfred, Pres.-Western Div.--Airgas, Inc., Radnor, PA; *U.S. Public*, pg. 33

Crimaldi, Sam, Pres.-S. Florida Opers.--U.S. Home Corporation, Houston, TX; *U.S. Public*, pg. 1682

Crippen, Robert, Pres.-Thiokol Aerospace Grp.--Thiokol Corporation, Ogden, UT; *U.S. Public*, pg. 1596

Crittenden, Gary L., Pres.-Hardware Stores--Sears, Roebuck and Co., Hoffman Estates, IL; *U.S. Public*, pg. 1452

Cron, Kenneth, Pres.-Publ. U.S.A.--CMP Media, Inc., Manhasset, NY; *U.S. Public*, pg. 279

Crosby, Mike, Pres.-Automotive Components Div.--Freudenberg-NOK, Plymouth, MI; *U.S. Private*, pg. 427

Crosby, Robert C., Sr. V.P. & Pres. ATH--Beverly Enterprises, Inc., Fort Smith, AR; *U.S. Public*, pg. 227

Cross, Michael, Pres.--CCMCS, Inc., San Antonio, TX; *U.S. Public*, pg. 383

Crotty, Gerald C., Sr. V.P. & Pres.-ITT Information Services, Inc.--ITT Corporation, New York, NY; *U.S. Public*, pg. 1512

Crouzet, Philippe, Pres.-Industrial Ceramics Div.--Saint-Gobain, Courbevoie, France; *Int'l*, pg. 1170

Crowl, David H., Pres.-Radio Div.--Jacor Communications, Inc., Covington, KY; *U.S. Public*, pg. 922

Crown, John, Pres.-Devel.--Performance Food Group Company, Richmond, VA; *U.S. Public*, pg. 1278

Crumley, Robert L., Pres.-Interior Systems Grp.--Peregrine Incorporated, Southfield, MI; *U.S. Private*, pg. 852

Crumling, R.T., III, Pres.-Macco Adhesives & V.P.-Human Resources--ICI Paints, Cleveland, OH; *Int'l*, pg. 664

Crusa, Jack D., V.P. & Pres.-Automotive Components--Leggett & Platt, Incorporated, Carthage, MO; *U.S. Public, pg. 985*

Csokasy, Louis R., V.P. & Pres.-Automotive Window & Door Sys.--Excel Industries, Inc., Elkhart, IN; *U.S. Public*, pg. 598

Cuatrecassas, Pedro M., M.D., Pres.-Parke-Davis Res. & V.P.--Warner-Lambert Company, Morris Plains, NJ; *U.S. Public*, pg. 1738

Cuello, Alfredo, Exec. V.P. & Pres.-Opers./Europe--Avon Products, Inc., New York, NY; *U.S. Public*, pg. 155
Cueto, Ben, Pres.-Synadyne--Outsource International, Deerfield Beach, FL; *U.S. Public*, pg. 1236
Cullen, Nicholas T., Exec. V.P. & Pres.-Performance Prods. Div.--Bayer Corporation, Pittsburgh, PA; *Int'l*, pg. 172
Culleton, James E., Corp. Sec. & Pres.-First Commercial Bank--First Banks, Inc., Sacramento, CA; *U.S. Public*, pg. 626
Cumming, Douglas G., Pres.-Acklands-Grainger Inc.--W.W. Grainger, Inc., Lincolnshire, IL; *U.S. Public*, pg. 758
Cumming, Marilee, Pres.-Women's Apparel--JC Penney Company, Inc., Plano, TX; *U.S. Public*, pg. 916
Cummings, James C., Pres.-Value-Added Svcs. Div./ Americas--Molex Incorporated, Lisle, IL; *U.S. Public*, pg. 1121
Cundiff, Rich, Pres.-Southern California Region--Whole Foods Market, Inc., Austin, TX; *U.S. Public*, pg. 1767
Cuneo, F. Peter, Pres.-Personal Care Division--Clairol, Inc., Stamford, CT; *U.S. Public*, pg. 254
Cunliffe, Stephen J., Pres.-Nestle Refrigerated Food Co.--Nestle Frozen, Refrigerated, and Ice Cream Companies, Solon, OH; *Int'l*, pg. 918
Cunningham, Philip F., Exec. V.P.-Mktg. & Pres.-Mackenzie Financial Services Inc.--Mackenzie Financial Corporation, Toronto, Canada; *Int'l*, pg. 828
Cuny, Jean-Pierre, Pres.-Leisure Services--Sodexho S.A., Montigny-le-Bretonneux, France; *Int'l*, pg. 1274
Curley, Dwight G., Leader-Major Prods. & Pres.-Granite State Gas Transmission, Inc.--Bay State Gas Company, Westborough, MA; *U.S. Public*, pg. 196
Curley, Thomas, Pres. & Publr.-USA Today--Gannett Company, Inc., Arlington, VA; *U.S. Public*, pg. 698
Curran, Paul, Pres.-Art & Design Group & Sr. V.P.--BPI Communications Inc., New York, NY; *Int'l*, pg. 1446
Current, Jim, Jr., Pres.-NCG Global Energy Svcs. & Sr. V.P.--NGC Corporation, Houston, TX; *U.S. Public*, pg. 1146
Currer, William R., Grp. Pres.-Commun. Prods.--Andrew Corporation, Orland Park, IL; *U.S. Public*, pg. 112
Cushing-Jones, Nancy, Pres.-MCA Publishing Rights--Spencer Gifts, Inc., Egg Harbor Township, NJ; *Int'l*, pg. 1216
Cuthbert, John, Pres.-Automotive Div.--Special Devices, Incorporated, Newhall, CA; *U.S. Public*, pg. 1496
Cygan, Thomas S., Pres.-West--Joseph T. Ryerson & Son, Inc., Chicago, IL; *U.S. Public*, pg. 879
Czerny, Walter J., Pres.-ABS Pacific--American Bureau of Shipping, New York, NY; *U.S. Private*, pg. 51
Dabringhausen, Peter, Grp. V.P. & Pres.-Process Chemicals Div.--Nalco Chemical Company, Naperville, IL; *U.S. Public*, pg. 1150
Dacey, Mark A., Pres.-Adweek Magazines--BPI Communications Inc., New York, NY; *Int'l*, pg. 1446
Dachowski, Peter, Pres.-Insulation Div.--Saint-Gobain, Courbevoie, France; *Int'l*, pg. 1170
Daft, Douglas N., Pres.-Middle & Far East Grp.--The Coca-Cola Company, Atlanta, GA; *U.S. Public*, pg. 392
Dailey, Allan J., Pres.-Western Territory--World Book Educational Products, Elk Grove Village, IL; *U.S. Public*, pg. 218
Damiani, Vincenzo, V.P. & Pres.-Digital Europe--Digital Equipment Corporation, Maynard, MA; *U.S. Public*, pg. 507
Dangelo, Charles, Pres.-Primary Casualty/Risk Management--American International Group, Inc., New York, NY; *U.S. Public*, pg. 83
Daniel, John E., Pres.-Kaiser Primary Prods.--Kaiser Aluminum & Chemical Corporation, Pleasanton, CA; *U.S.* Public, pg. 1062
Daniel, Patrick D., Pres. & Chief Oper. Officer-IPL Pipe Line--Interprovincial Pipe Line Inc., Edmonton, Canada; *Int'l*, pg. 652
Dare, Larry G., Grp. V.P. & Pres.-Paper & Beverage Prods./ Europe--The Procter & Gamble Company, Cincinnati, OH; *U.S. Public*, pg. 1330
Darnis, Geraud, Pres.-European & Transcontinental Opers.--Carrier Corporation, Indianapolis, IN; *U.S. Public*, pg. 1689
Davidson, Paul E., Grp. Pres.-Refrigeration--Toromont Industries Ltd., Concord, Canada; *Int'l*, pg. 1400
Davies, John L., Pres.-AOL Intl.--America Online Incorporated, Dulles, VA; *U.S. Public*, pg. 66
Daviron, Pierre, Pres.-OPCAP International--OppenheimerFunds Distributor, Inc., New York, NY; *U.S.* Private, pg. 818
Davis, Donn M., Pres.-Tribune Ventures--Tribune Company, Chicago, IL; *U.S. Public*, pg. 1635
Davis, Jack W., Jr., Pres. & Publisher--The Daily Press, Incorporated, Newport News, VA; *U.S. Public*, pg. 1635
Davis, James W., Pres.-Midwest--TAD Resources International, Inc., Cambridge, MA; *U.S. Private*, pg. 1062
Davis, Lynn J., Sr. V.P. & Pres.-Broadband Connectivity Grp.--ADC Telecommunications, Inc., Minnetonka, MN; *U.S. Public*, pg. 4
Davis, Margaret, Pres. & Chief Oper. Officer--Selective Insurance Company of South Carolina, Charlotte, NC; *U.S. Public*, pg. 1455
Davis, Margaret, Pres. & Chief Oper. Officer--Selective Insurance Company of the Southeast, Charlotte, NC; *U.S. Public*, pg. 1456
Davis, Tom, Pres.-Inpatient Svcs.--RehabCare Group, Inc., Saint Louis, MO; *U.S. Public*, pg. 1373
Davison, Bill, V.P. & Pres.-Ag Daily--Data Transmission Network Corporation, Omaha, NE; *U.S. Public*, pg. 486
Dawes, Terry, Pres.-Nelson/Word Ltd.(Canada)--Thomas Nelson Inc., Nashville, TN; *U.S. Public*, pg. 1167
de Bakker, Ferry, Pres. & Chief Exec. Officer-Europe (London)--Burson-Marsteller, New York, NY; *U.S. Private*, *pg. 1197*
de Cailleux, Patrice, Pres.-Bldg. Matls.--Saint-Gobain, Courbevoie, France; *Int'l*, pg. 1170
de Chalendar, Pierre Andre, Pres.-Abrasives Div.--Saint-Gobain, Courbevoie, France; *Int'l*, pg. 1170
De Cuniac, Herve, Pres.-Food & Mngmt. Services/Asian Opers.--Sodexho S.A., Montigny-le-Bretonneux, France; *Int'l*, pg. 1274
de Lange, Pim, Pres.-Stena Line Holland BV--Stena Line AB, Goteborg, Sweden; *Int'l*, pg. 1300
de Roquemaurel, Gerald, Pres.-Hachette Filipacchi Presse--Lagardere Groupe, Paris, France; *Int'l*, pg. 791
De Sola, George, Pres.-Inacom Communications--Inacom Corp., Omaha, NE; *U.S. Public*, pg. 873
de Visser, R.J.L., Pres.-Elastomers--DSM N.V., Heerlen, Netherlands; *Int'l*, pg. 352
Deal, James A., Exec. V.P. & Pres.-DTCA--American Healthcorp Inc., Nashville, TN; *U.S. Public*, pg. 78
Dean, John, Div. Pres.--Solar Communications, Inc., Naperville, IL; *U.S. Private*, pg. 1012
Dean, Warren M., Pres.-CRSS Constructors International, Inc.--CRSS Inc., Houston, TX; *Int'l*, pg. 1415
Dearborn, Steve, Pres.-ICI Paints, Puerto Rico, Inc.--ICI Paints, Cleveland, OH; *Int'l*, pg. 664
Dearnley, Steve, Pres.-Intl.--BAX Global, Irvine, CA; *U.S. Public*, pg. 1305
Deas, James C., Pres.-Nortel Asia South Pacific--Northern Telecom Limited, Brampton, Canada; *Int'l*, pg. 968
Debin-Cohen, Jill, Pres.-NY Post Production--Unitel Video, Inc., New York, NY; *U.S. Public*, pg. 1692
DeCamp, Richard, Pres.-Value Brand Sls.--R.G. Barry Corporation, Pickerington, OH; *U.S. Public*, pg. 192
DeCarlo, David J., Pres.-Bronze Division--Matthews International Corp., Pittsburgh, PA; *U.S. Public*, pg. 1059
DeChellis, Al, Pres.-Fragrances--Dana Perfumes Corp., New York, NY; *U.S. Private*, pg. 922
Decker, Dwight W., Pres.-Rockwell Semiconductor Systems--Rockwell International Corporation, Costa Mesa, CA; *U.S. Public*, pg. 1397
Decker, Glenn J., Pres.-Phelps Dodge High Performance Conductors--Phelps Dodge Intl. Corp., Coral Gables, FL; *U.S. Public*, pg. 1286
Deckman, Joseph T., Pres.-Bldg. Prods. & Svcs.--Apogee Enterprises, Inc., Minneapolis, MN; *U.S. Public*, pg. 120
Deedy, Justin, Pres.--Superior Telecommunications, Atlanta, GA; *U.S. Public*, pg. 58
Deering, Joseph W., Grp. V.P. & Pres.-Food Equipment Grp.--Premark International, Inc., Deerfield, IL; *U.S. Public*, pg. 1321
Deese, George, Pres. & Chief Oper. Officer-Flowers Bakeries, Inc.--Flowers Industries, Inc., Thomasville, GA; *U.S. Public*, pg. 656
DeFeo, Dave, Pres.-DyeCasters--Tanner Co., Rutherfordton, NC; *U.S. Private*, pg. 1068
DeForest, Walter E., Sr. V.P. & Pres.-Leidy Hub, Inc.--National Fuel Gas Company, Buffalo, NY; *U.S. Public*, pg. 1156
DeFranco, Joe, Pres.-Separation & Recovery Sys.--American Eco Corporation, Toronto, Canada; *Int'l*, pg. 73
DeGennaro, Michael A., Pres.-Professional Products Division--Clairol, Inc., Stamford, CT; *U.S. Public*, pg. 254
deGraffenreid, James T., Pres.-Hart Publications--Phillips Publishing International, Inc., Potomac, MD; *U.S. Private*, *pg. 862*
Delaney, George W., V.P. & Pres.-Powermatic--DeVlieg-Bullard Inc., Westport, CT; *U.S. Public*, pg. 502
Dell, Richard C., Grp. Pres.--Newell Co., Freeport, IL; *U.S. Public*, pg. 1176
DeLora, C.A., Pres.-Real Estate--Service Supply Co. Inc. of Indiana, Indianapolis, IN; *U.S. Private*, pg. 987
DeLuccia, Robert, Pres.-Sanofi Winthrop Pharmaceuticals--Sanofi Pharmaceuticals, Inc., New York, NY; *Int'l*, pg. 445
Demers, Richard P., V.P.-Mktg., Sls. & Adv.--EnergyNorth, Inc., Manchester, NH; *U.S. Public*, pg. 581
Denne, Donald R., Sr. V.P. & Pres.-Healthcare--Alba-Waldensian, Inc., Valdese, NC; *U.S. Public*, pg. 35
Denney, Christopher, Pres.-Kolmar Laboratories, Inc. & V.P.--CCL Industries, Inc., Willowdale, Canada; *Int'l*, pg. 238
Denny, Charles W., Pres. & Chief Exec. Officer-N. American Division/Schneider Elec.--Schneider S.A., Boulogne-Billancourt, France; *Int'l*, pg. 1207
Denton, William J., Grp. Pres.--Newell Co., Freeport, IL; *U.S. Public*, pg. 1176
Depaul, John R., Pres.-Components Grp.--The Lehigh Press, Inc., Cherry Hill, NJ; *U.S. Private*, pg. 658
Derderian, Kevork M., Pres.-Office Div.--Prime Group Realty Trust, Chicago, IL; *U.S. Public*, pg. 1326
Deromedi, Roger, Pres.-W. Europe & Exec. V.P.--Kraft Jacobs Suchard AG, Zurich, Switzerland; *U.S. Public*, pg. 1288
DeStefanis, John, Pres. & Chief Exec. Officer-Charter--Magellan Health Services, Inc., Atlanta, GA; *U.S. Public*, pg. 1033
Deters, Tom, Assoc. Publr.-Mens Group--Weider Publications, Inc., Woodland Hills, CA; *U.S. Private*, pg. 1159
Deuer, James C., V.P. & Pres.-Deuer Manufacturing, Inc.--Selas Corporation of America, Dresher, PA; *U.S. Public*, pg. 1454
Deulofeu, Julio, Pres.-San Francisco & Dir.--EvansGroup, Salt Lake City, UT; *U.S. Private*, pg. 385
Deutschman, Ira, Pres.-Fine Line Features--New Line Cinema Corporation, New York, NY; *U.S. Public*, pg. 1614
Devanny, Trace, Chief Oper. Officer & Pres.-ADAC Healthcare Info. Sys.--ADAC Laboratories Inc., Milpitas, CA; *U.S. Public*, pg. 3
Devereux, Anne, Pres.-CHW--Harrison & Star, Inc., New York, NY; *U.S. Private*, pg. 506
Devine, C.R., Pres.-Oil & Gas Exploration--KCS Energy Inc., Edison, NJ; *U.S. Public*, pg. 938
Devitre, Dinyar S., Chm. & Chief Exec. Officer-PMKK Japan--Philip Morris International Inc., Rye Brook, NY; *U.S. Public*, pg. 1289
Dewey, R. Gene, V.P. & Pres.-Molycorp, Inc.--Unocal Carbon & Minerals, Brea, CA; *U.S. Public*, pg. 1698
Dhenain, Jean-Michel, Pres.-Food & Mngmt. Services/ French Opers.--Sodexho S.A., Montigny-le-Bretonneux, France; *Int'l*, pg. 1274
Di Cristine, Rene, Pres.-Ready Mix Concrete--Puerto Rican Cement Co., Inc., Guaynabo, PR; *U.S. Public*, pg. 1341
DiBartolo, Angela, Pres.-Direct--Earle Palmer Brown/ Philadelphia, Philadelphia, PA; *U.S. Private*, pg. 174
Dick, Matthew G., V.P. & Pres.-Baker Hughes Process Equipment Co.--Baker Hughes Incorporated, Houston, TX; *U.S. Public*, pg. 165
Dickey, Brian N., Pres.-Worldwide Commercial Bus.--Booz, Allen & Hamilton Inc., New York, NY; *U.S. Private*, pg. 157
Dickinson, Robert H., Pres. & Chief Oper. Officer - Carnival Cruise Lines--Carnival Corporation, Miami, FL; *U.S. Public*, pg. 306
DiDonato, Ronald J., Pres.-HSN Fulfillment, Inc.--Home Shopping Network, Inc., Saint Petersburg, FL; *U.S. Public*, pg. 1685
DiGeso, Amy, Pres. & Chief Exec. Officer-MaryKay, Inc.--Mary Kay Corporation, Dallas, TX; *U.S. Private*, pg. 710
Dillon, Donald F., Vice Chm. & Pres.-Information Tech.--Fiserv, Inc., Brookfield, WI; *U.S. Public*, pg. 647
Dilschneider, Ray, Pres.-Ing. Div.--Tree Top, Inc., Selah, WA; *U.S. Private*, pg. 1098
DiMinno, Frank D., Pres.-Industrial Div.--Edmund Scientific Company, Barrington, NJ; *U.S. Private*, pg. 364
Dimma, William A., Chm. Bd.-Fleet Aerospace--Aeronca, Inc., Middletown, OH; *Int'l*, pg. 829
Dinsdale, Chris, Pres.-Tillamook Food Sls.--Tillamook County Creamery Assn., Tillamook, OR; *U.S. Private*, pg. 1086
Diodati, Frank, Pres.-RMSI Canada--PLM Railcar Management Services, Inc., Chicago, IL; *U.S. Public*, pg. 1241
DiPasquale, Richard, V.P. & Pres.-Latin America--Owens Corning, Toledo, OH; *U.S. Public*, pg. 1236
DiPentima, Renato A., Pres.-SRA Federal Systems--SRA International Inc., Arlington, VA; *U.S. Private*, pg. 957
DiPietro, Robert M., Pres.-Marine Grp.--Teleflex Incorporated, Plymouth Meeting, PA; *U.S. Public*, pg. 1569
Ditmore, Dana C., Pres.-North Amer. Bus. Opers.--Applied Materials, Inc., Santa Clara, CA; *U.S. Public*, pg. 123
Dixon, Daryl A., Pres. & Gen. Mgr.-Contract Rehabilitation Div.--NovaCare Inc., King of Prussia, PA; *U.S. Public*, pg. 1203
Dixon, Edward J., Pres.-Northbrook Property & Casualty--The Allstate Corporation, Northbrook, IL; *U.S. Public*, pg. 55
Doan, D.T., Pres.-Insurance Opers.--American Mutual Life Holding Co., Des Moines, IA; *U.S. Private*, pg. 59
Doctorow, Eric, Pres.-Worldwide Video--Paramount Pictures Corporation, Los Angeles, CA; *U.S. Private*, pg. 776
Dohring, Edward A., Pres.-SVG Lithography Systems Div. & V.P.--Silicon Valley Group, Inc., San Jose, CA; *U.S. Public*, pg. 1474
Dolan, Peter R., Pres.-Nutritionals & Medical Devices Grp.--Bristol-Myers Squibb Company, New York, NY; *U.S. Public*, pg. 253
Domene, Jose, Pres.-Cemex International--Cemex, S.A. de C.V., Monterrey, Mexico; *Int'l*, pg. 278
Donaghy, Patl, Pres.-School Publishing Grp.--Scott Foresman/Addison Wesley, Glenview, IL; *Int'l*, pg. 927
Donahee, Gary Richard, Pres.-Nortel CALA & Sr. V.P.--Northern Telecom Limited, Brampton, Canada; *Int'l*, pg. 968
Donahue-Dalton, Ellen I., Sr. V.P.-Mktg. & Pres.-GameScape, Inc.--GTECH Corporation, West Greenwich, RI; *U.S. Public*, pg. 767
Donatsch, Andreas, Co-Pres.-Fin.--The Swiss Life/ Rentenanstalt Group, Zurich, Switzerland; *Int'l*, pg. 1332
Donchak, Andrew, Pres.-Consumer Div.--Konami Corporation of America Inc., Buffalo Grove, IL; *Int'l*, pg. 746
Donnell, Michael D., Pres.-Paging Network-Northwestern Region, Inc.--Paging Network, Inc., Plano, TX; *U.S. Public*, pg. 1252
Donnell, Thomas, V.P. & Pres. & Chief Exec. Officer-Cain's Coffee Co.--Chock Full O' Nuts Corporation, New York, NY; *U.S. Public*, pg. 351
Donohoe, Michael J., Corp. V.P. & Pres.-Europe--Allergan, Inc., Irvine, CA; *U.S. Public*, pg. 46
Donovan, Stephen P., Jr., Grp. V.P. & Pres.-Food & Beverage Prods./North America--The Procter & Gamble Company, Cincinnati, OH; *U.S. Public*, pg. 1330
Doornink, R., Pres.-Orville Redenbacher/Swiss Miss Foods Co.--Hunt-Wesson, Inc., Fullerton, CA; *U.S. Public*, pg. 428
Dopper, J. G., Pres.-Resins--DSM N.V., Heerlen, Netherlands; *Int'l*, pg. 352
Doran, Robert J., Jr., V.P.--Ace Doran Hauling & Rigging Company, Cincinnati, OH; *U.S. Private*, pg. 340
Doran, Vincent F., Pres.-Job Corps Opers.--Res-Care Incorporated, Louisville, KY; *U.S. Public*, pg. 1382
Doria, Joseph D., V.P. & Pres.-Lincoln Electric Co. of Canada--The Lincoln Electric Company, Cleveland, OH; *U.S. Public*, pg. 996
Dorr, John H., Pres.-Ryder Public Transportation Svcs.--Ryder System, Inc., Miami, FL; *U.S. Public*, pg. 1413
Dorr, John H., Pres.-Ryder Public Transportation Services--Vehicle Leasing & Services Div., Miami, FL; *U.S. Public*, pg. 1414
Dotson, George S., Pres.-Intl.--Helmerich & Payne, Inc., Tulsa, OK; *U.S. Public*, pg. 808
Douay, Michel, Pres.-Clestra--Groupe Strafor Facom, Morangis, France; *Int'l*, pg. 569
Douazer, Pierre, Pres.-Pharmaceuticals--Novartis AG, Basel, Switzerland; *Int'l*, pg. 971
Dowling, Peter, Pres.-Worldwide Mfg.--Loctite Corporation, Rocky Hill, CT; *Int'l*, pg. 611

Dowling, Robert, Pres. & Exec. V.P.-The Hollywood Reporter--BPI Communications Inc., New York, NY; *Int'l*, pg. 1446

Doyle, Dennis M., Exec. V.P. & Pres.-Far & Middle East, Austral/Asia--Chiquita Banana North America, Cincinnati, OH; *U.S. Public*, pg. 349

Doyle, Kevin J., Pres.-Wassall USA--Wassall Plc, London, United Kingdom; *Int'l*, pg. 1486

Doyle, William J., Pres.-Sls.--Potash Corporation of Saskatchewan Inc., Saskatoon, Canada; *Int'l*, pg. 1064

Dozier, Alan P., Pres.-Pharmaceuticals Div. & V.P.--Bausch & Lomb Incorporated, Rochester, NY; *U.S. Public*, pg. 194

Drews, Jurgen, Sr. V.P.-Hoffmann LaRoche Inc. & Pres.-Intl. Research--Hoffmann-La Roche Inc., Nutley, NJ; *Int'l*, pg. 1120

Driessens, Jan, Pres.-Valmont Europe--Valmont Industries, Inc., Valley, NE; *U.S. Public*, pg. 1706

Driscoll, Brian J., Pres.-Sls. & Integrated Logistics Co.--Nabisco Inc., Parsippany, NJ; *U.S. Public*, pg. 1355

Droz, Henry, Pres.-Universal Music & Video Distribution--Universal Studios, Inc., Universal City, CA; *Int'l*, pg. 1215

Drummond, Jere, Pres. & Chief Exec. Officer-BellSouth Communications Grp.--BellSouth Corporation, Atlanta, GA; *U.S. Public*, pg. 207

Dubnik, Steve M., Pres. & Chief Oper. Officer-ACC North America--ACC Corp., Rochester, NY; *U.S. Public*, pg. 2

Duda, Joseph A., Pres.-Duda land--A. Duda & Sons Inc., Oviedo, FL; *U.S. Private*, pg. 344

Duda, Walter, Pres.- Duda Farms--A. Duda & Sons Inc., Oviedo, FL; *U.S. Private*, pg. 344

Dudley, Michael A., Exec. V.P. & Pres.-CDT Intl.--Cable Design Technologies Corporation, Pittsburgh, PA; *U.S. Public*, pg. 287

Duff-Bloom, Gale, Pres.-Mktg. & Co. Communications--JC Penney Company, Inc., Plano, TX; *U.S. Public*, pg. 916

Duffy, E. Patrick, Sr. V.P. & Pres.-Coated Paper & Pulp Div.--Bowater Incorporated, Greenville, SC; *U.S. Public*, pg. 247

Duffy, Rick, Pres. & Chief Oper. Officer--Creative Alliance, Inc., Louisville, KY; *U.S. Private*, pg. 287

Dufour, Pierre, V.P.-Intl.--SNC-Lavalin Inc., Montreal, Canada; *Int'l*, pg. 1162

Dugan, D.R., Pres.-AFG--PLM International, Inc., San Francisco, CA; *U.S. Public*, pg. 1241

Duloc, Michael, Pres.-Kable Distr. Services--AMREP Corporation, New York, NY; *U.S. Public*, pg. 104

Dulski, Anton, Pres.-Minteq Intl. Inc.--Minerals Technologies, Inc., New York, NY; *U.S. Public*, pg. 1115

Dumas, Cleive C., Pres.-Industrial Pump Group--Ingersoll-Dresser Pump Company, Liberty Corner, NJ; *U.S. Public*, *pg. 529*

Dunavant, Leslie D., Pres. & Chief Oper. Officer-Claire's Boutiques--Claire's Stores Inc., Pembroke Pines, FL; *U.S. Public*, pg. 381

Duncan, D.F., Pres.-Toromont Process Systems Canada--Toromont Industries Ltd., Concord, Canada; *Int'l*, pg. 1400

Dunn, Kevin, Pres.-Div.--McDonald's Corporation, Oak Brook, IL; *U.S. Public*, pg. 1068

Dunn, Nancy M., Pres.-Tangram Consulting Solutions--Tangram Enterprise Solutions, Inc., Cary, NC; *U.S. Public*, pg. 1424

Dunn, Raymond, Pres.-Sunflower Carriers--Crete Carrier Corp., Lincoln, NE; *U.S. Private*, pg. 289

Dunn, Raymond, Pres.--Sunflower Carriers, York, NE; *U.S. Private*, pg. 289

Dunton, Gary, Pres.-Family & Bus. Insurance Grp.--USF&G Corporation, Baltimore, MD; *U.S. Public*, pg. 1659

duPont, Jill G., Pres.-Berkshire--Mayer/Berkshire Corporation, Wayne, NJ; *U.S. Private*, pg. 717

DuPree, Don, Pres.-ORC Electroformed Prods.--BEC Group, Inc., Rye, NY; *U.S. Public*, pg. 160

Durand-Adams, Michelle, Pres.-Magna Student Loan Co.--Magna Group, Inc., Saint Louis, MO; *U.S. Public*, pg. 1037

Dusa, Jerry, Pres.-Eagle Technology--Anthem Electronics Inc., San Jose, CA; *U.S. Public*, pg. 134

Dusenberry, Thomas, Pres.-Hasbro Interactive Worldwide--Hasbro, Inc., Pawtucket, RI; *U.S. Public*, pg. 797

Dutta, Sanat, Pres.-U.S.--Ingram Micro Inc., Santa Ana, CA; *U.S. Public*, pg. 878

Dynan, Bob, Pres.-US Airways Express Div.--Mesa Air Group, Las Vegas, NV; *U.S. Public*, pg. 1098

Each, Thomas C., Pres.-Chemitax Div.--Namico, Inc., Philadelphia, PA; *U.S. Private*, pg. 773

Earles, Barney, Pres.-Harbert Realty Svcs.--Harbert Corporation, Birmingham, AL; *U.S. Private*, pg. 500

Easley, William K., Sr. V.P. & Pres.-Textile Mfg.--Home Furnishings Segment, Fort Mill, SC; *U.S. Public*, pg. 1500

Ebbers, Bernard J., Pres. & Chief Exec. Officer--LDDS/WorldCom Communications, Revere, MA; *U.S. Public*, pg. 1779

Ebeid, Russell J., Pres.-Glass Grp.--Guardian Industries Corp., Auburn Hills, MI; *U.S. Private*, pg. 485

Ebersol, Dick, Pres.-NBC Sports--National Broadcasting Co., Inc., New York, NY; *U.S. Public*, pg. 712

Ebsworth, David R., Exec. V.P. & Pres.-Pharmaceutical Division--Bayer Corporation, Pittsburgh, PA; *Int'l*, pg. 172

Ebsworth, David, Ph.D., Pres.-Pharmaceutical Div. & Exec. V.P.--Bayer Corporation, Pittsburgh, PA; *Int'l*, pg. 172

Ebsworth, David, Ph.D., Exec. V.P. & Pres.-Pharmaceutical Div.--Bayer Corporation, Parsippany, NJ; *Int'l*, pg. 172

Eckels, Steve, Pres.-Europe--Wunderman Worldwide Limited, London, United Kingdom; *U.S. Private*, pg. 1199

Eckert, David D., Pres.--Rhone-Poulenc Basic Chemicals Co., Shelton, CT; *Int'l*, pg. 1110

Edgeworth, Allan L., Pres.-Pipeline Div.--Westcoast Energy Inc., Vancouver, Canada; *Int'l*, pg. 1492

Edmund, Gwynne, Pres.-Consumer Div.--Edmund Scientific Company, Barrington, NJ; *U.S. Private*, pg. 364

Edmunds, Geoffrey H., Pres.-Edmunds Toll, LP--Toll Brothers, Inc., Huntingdon Valley, PA; *U.S. Public*, pg. 1620

Edwards, Jeffrey B., Pres. & Chief Exec. Officer-MICROS-Fidelio Software GmbH & Co. KG--Micros Systems Inc., Beltsville, MD; *U.S. Public*, pg. 1106

Edwards, Robert D., Pres.-M.P. Electric & Exec. V.P.--Minnesota Power, Duluth, MN; *U.S. Public*, pg. 1116

Egan, John, Pres.-Antec Ltd.--Anixter International, Chicago, IL; *U.S. Public*, pg. 115

Egan, John F., V.P. & Pres.-Janitorial Services Division--ABM Industries, San Francisco, CA; *U.S. Public*, pg. 2

Eggers, Thomas F., Pres.-Broker/Dealer Div.--The Dreyfus Corporation, New York, NY; *U.S. Public*, pg. 1085

Eichenholz, Joseph, Pres.-HLS Management Systems--CommonHealth USA, Parsippany, NJ; *Int'l*, pg. 1483

Eilers, Daniel L., Pres. & Chief Exec. Officer--Claris Corporation, Santa Clara, CA; *U.S. Public*, pg. 121

Einhorn, Stephen, Pres.-New Line Home Video, Inc.--New Line Cinema Corporation, New York, NY; *U.S. Public*, pg. 1614

Eino, Moni, Dr., Pres.-Ingredients Div. & Sr. V.P.-Opers.--Parmalat Canada Ltd., Etobicoke, Canada; *Int'l*, pg. 1023

Einsmann, Harald, Exec. V.P. & Pres.-Europe, Middle East & Africa--The Procter & Gamble Company, Cincinnati, OH; *U.S. Public*, pg. 1330

Eisen, Juan Carlos, Pres.-Latin American Grp.--Griffith Colombia S.A., Medellin, Colombia; *U.S. Private*, pg. 481

Eisenberg, Howard, Pres.-Dearfoams Sls.--R.G. Barry Corporation, Pickerington, OH; *U.S. Public*, pg. 192

Eittreim, Dennis, Pres.-Americas--BAX Global, Irvine, CA; *U.S. Public*, pg. 1305

Elenbaas, Ronald A., V.P. & Pres.-Surgical Grp.--Stryker Corporation, Kalamazoo, MI; *U.S. Public*, pg. 1525

Elias, Craig, Pres.--Pan Canadian Energy Services, Houston, TX; *Int'l*, pg. 259

Eliason, L.R., Chief Nuclear Officer & Pres.-Nuclear Bus. Unit--Public Service Electric & Gas Co., Newark, NJ; *U.S. Public*, pg. 1340

Ellevold, Brad, Pres.-Intl.--Bollinger Industries Inc., Grand Prairie, TX; *U.S. Public*, pg. 243

Elliott, Bill, Pres.-BBMC--Bergen Brunswig Corporation, Orange, CA; *U.S. Public*, pg. 213

Elliott, Dale F., Pres.-Industrial--Snap-On Tools Corporation, Kenosha, WI; *U.S. Public*, pg. 1480

Elliott, Pam, Pres.-Haleyville Reg.--Pinnacle Bank, Jasper, AL; *U.S. Public*, pg. 1297

Ellis, Barry, Pres. & Mng. Dir.--Essex House Limited Partnership, Bella Vista, AR; *U.S. Private*, pg. 274

Ellis, Barry, Pres. of Gen. Partner & Mngng. Dir.--Blair Tower Limited Partnership, Bella Vista, AR; *U.S. Private*, pg. 274

Ellis, J.K., Exec. Gen. Mgr. & Chief Exec. Officer-BHP Minerals--The Broken Hill Proprietary Company Limited, Melbourne, Australia; *Int'l*, pg. 223

Ellis, John, Pres.-European Opers.--Novellus Systems, Inc., San Jose, CA; *U.S. Public*, pg. 1204

Elmquist, Ronald E., Pres.-Global Food Service--Campbell Soup Company, Camden, NJ; *U.S. Public*, pg. 298

Emerson, Nedwin, Pres.-Family Adv. Agency--The Troy Savings Bank, Troy, NY; *U.S. Private*, pg. 1106

Empey, Gene, Pres.-Western Div.--International Total Services, Independence, OH; *U.S. Public*, pg. 908

Emura, Ryuzo, Deputy Pres.--The Daishi Bank, Ltd., Niigata, Japan; *Int'l*, pg. 372

Ena, Teruhiko, Pres.-Space Communications Corp.--Mitsubishi Corporation, Tokyo, Japan; *Int'l*, pg. 871

Engle, Charles A., Pres.-Cabinet Division--Triangle Pacific Corporation, Dallas, TX; *U.S. Public*, pg. 1634

Engle, Roger, Pres.-Superior Water Light & Power--Minnesota Power, Duluth, MN; *U.S. Public*, pg. 1116

English, Michela, Pres.-Discovery Enterprises Worldwide--Discovery Communications, Inc., Bethesda, MD; *U.S. Private*, pg. 334

Epperson, Dale, Pres.-Western Div.--Centimark Corporation, Canonsburg, PA; *U.S. Private*, pg. 222

Epstein, Robert, Pres.-Lace Fabric Div.--Liberty Fabrics, Inc., New York, NY; *Int'l*, pg. 340

Ericson, Nils, Pres.-Syscon Corp.--Logicon, Inc., Torrance, CA; *U.S. Public*, pg. 1198

Espegard, Duaine C., Exec. V.P. & Grp. Pres.--Bremer Financial Corporation, Saint Paul, MN; *U.S. Private*, pg. 167

Estenfelder, L.G., Pres.-European Opers.--The Gates Rubber Company, Denver, CO; *Int'l*, pg. 1396

Estes, Dean, Pres.-Wolverine Work & Outdoor Footwear--Wolverine World Wide, Inc., Rockford, MI; *U.S. Public*, pg. 1775

Esty, Brad, Pres.-Eastern Opers.--Alcone Marketing Group, Irvine, CA; *U.S. Public*, pg. 1223

Eterovic, Cedomir, Pres.-Dana South America--Dana Corporation, Toledo, OH; *U.S. Public*, pg. 479

Evans, Dave, Pres.-TRS--Betac International Corporation, Alexandria, VA; *U.S. Private*, pg. 140

Evans, Philip, Sr. V.P. & Pres.-Betterware Company--Avon Products, Inc., New York, NY; *U.S. Public*, pg. 155

Evans, Stuart M., Grp. Pres.-Electronic Security Grp.--Amtech Corporation, Dallas, TX; *U.S. Public*, pg. 105

Everhart, Rod, Pres.-SCT Education Sys.--Systems & Computer Technology Corporation, Malvern, PA; *U.S. Public*, pg. 1552

Ezell, DeWitt, Jr., State Pres.-Tennessee--BellSouth Telecommunications, Inc., Atlanta, GA; *U.S. Public*, pg. 209

Fahl, Douglas R., Mng. Principal-Land Design & Survey Div.--Dewberry & Davis, Fairfax, VA; *U.S. Private*, pg. 329

Fahl, John, Pres.-Tire Opers. & V.P.--Cooper Tire & Rubber Company, Findlay, OH; *U.S. Public*, pg. 445

Fairey, Laurence Y., Pres.-Americas, Asia & Pacific Div.--Sofamor Danek Group, Inc., Memphis, TN; *U.S. Public*, pg. 1482

Fairnington, Alan, Exec. V.P., Pres.-JWT/Asia Pacific--J. Walter Thompson Company, New York, NY; *Int'l*, pg. 1483

Falco, Randy, Pres.-B & NO--National Broadcasting Co., Inc., New York, NY; *U.S. Public*, pg. 712

Faletti, Richard P., Pres.-Multimedia Communication Systems & Sr. V.P.--Northern Telecom Limited, Brampton, Canada; *Int'l*, pg. 968

Fallon, Ken, III, Pres.-Surgical Opers.--Haemonetics Corporation, Braintree, MA; *U.S. Public*, pg. 773

Fanning, Richard P., V.P. & Pres.-Western Grp.--Leggett & Platt, Incorporated, Carthage, MO; *U.S. Public*, pg. 985

Farley, Claire S., Pres.-N. America Production & V.P.--Texaco Inc., White Plains, NY; *U.S. Public*, pg. 1582

Farley, Claire S., Pres.-N. America Production--Texaco Worldwide Exploration & Production, Scroggins, TX; *U.S. Public*, pg. 1583

Farrell, John, Pres.-DMB&B North America--DMB&B Communications, New York, NY; *U.S. Private*, pg. 302

Fashek, Chris, Pres.-KCI Therapeutic Svcs.--Kinetic Concepts, Inc., San Antonio, TX; *U.S. Private*, pg. 620

Faucett, Sam P., Pres.-Southwestern Reg.--Regions Financial Corporation, Birmingham, AL; *U.S. Public*, pg. 1371

Fauconneau, Guy, Pres.-N. American Opers.--Carrier Corporation, Indianapolis, IN; *U.S. Public*, pg. 1689

Faust, James L., Exec. V.P. & Pres.-Antec International--The Antec Corporation, Rolling Meadows, IL; *U.S. Public*, pg. 116

Feely, Martin, Chm.-Mktg. Info. Services--BPI Communications Inc., New York, NY; *Int'l*, pg. 1446

Fehlandt, Ricardo, Exec. Pres.--Bayer de Chile S.A., Santiago, Chile; *Int'l*, pg. 175

Feidler, Mark L., Pres.-Interconnection Services--BellSouth Telecommunications, Inc., Atlanta, GA; *U.S. Public*, pg. 209

Feighner, Mark S., Pres.-Wireless--GTE Corporation, Stamford, CT; *U.S. Public*, pg. 696

Feldman, Alan, Pres.-Div.--McDonald's Corporation, Oak Brook, IL; *U.S. Public*, pg. 1068

Feola, Louis A., Pres.-Universal Studios Home Video--Universal Pictures, Universal City, CA; *Int'l*, pg. 1216

Feraco, Frank J., Pres. & Sector Exec.-P&SP Intl./Sterling Plumbing Grp.--Kohler Company, Kohler, WI; *U.S. Private*, pg. 630

Fergus, Jeff, Grp. Pres.-Europe/Middle East/Africa & Asia Pacific--Leo Burnett Company, Inc., Chicago, IL; *U.S. Private*, pg. 183

Fergus, Jeff, Grp. Pres.-Europe, Middle East, Africa & Asia/Pacific--Leo Burnett Greater China, Quarry Bay, Hong Kong; *U.S. Private*, pg. 185

Fergus, Jeff, Grp. Pres.-Europe, Middle EAst, Africa & Asia-Pacific--Leo Burnett Worldwide Asia/Pacific Hdqtrs., Hong Kong, Hong Kong; *U.S. Private*, pg. 186

Fern, Nicholas, Ph.D., Pres.-Dyes & Chemicals/Asia--Crompton & Knowles Corporation, Stamford, CT; *U.S. Public*, pg. 459

Fernandez, Greg, Pres.-Labor & Mngmt. Partnerships--Kaiser Permanente, Oakland, CA; *U.S. Private*, pg. 605

Fernandez, Miguel A., Pres.-Latin America & Caribbean--American Express Travel Related Services Co., Inc., New York, NY; *U.S. Public*, pg. 73

Fernandez, Ralph, V.P. & Pres.-Lincoln Electric Latin America--The Lincoln Electric Company, Cleveland, OH; *U.S. Public*, pg. 996

Ferreira, Jose, Jr., Exec. V.P. & Pres.-Asia Pacific--Avon Products, Inc., New York, NY; *U.S. Public*, pg. 155

Ferries, John C., Pres.-Americas--D'Arcy Masius Benton & Bowles, New York, NY; *U.S. Private*, pg. 303

Ferris, Michael J., Pres.--Vulcan Chemicals, Birmingham, AL; *U.S. Public*, pg. 1725

Ferry, William L., Sr. V.P. & Pres.-North America--Wang Laboratories, Inc., Billerica, MA; *U.S. Public*, pg. 1737

Fettig, Jeff M., Pres.-Whirlpool Europe B.V. & Exec. V.P.--Whirlpool Corporation, Benton Harbor, MI; *U.S. Public*, pg. 1764

Fichtner, Franz, Pres.-Diamond Europe--Diamond Multimedia Systems, Inc., San Jose, CA; *U.S. Public*, pg. 505

Fichtner, Werner W., V.P. & Reg. Pres.-Europe--Molex Incorporated, Lisle, IL; *U.S. Public*, pg. 1121

Fickenscher, Gerald H., Ph.D., Pres.-Dyes & Chemicals/Europe--Crompton & Knowles Corporation, Stamford, CT; *U.S. Public*, pg. 459

Fiebig, Phil, Pres.-Leo Burnett-Kyodo/Tokyo--Leo Burnett Company, Inc., Chicago, IL; *U.S. Private*, pg. 183

Fiedler, Lee N., V.P. & Pres.-Kelly-Springfield Div.--The Goodyear Tire & Rubber Company, Akron, OH; *U.S. Public*, pg. 752

Fields, William R., Pres. & Chief Exec. Officer-Wal Mart Stores Div.--Wal-Mart Stores, Inc., Bentonville, AR; *U.S. Public*, pg. 1732

Fifield, James G., Pres. & Chief Exec. Officer-EMI Music--EMI Group plc, London, United Kingdom; *Int'l*, pg. 426

Finley, J.H., Pres.--Craft-Co Enterprises Inc., Morton, MS; *Int'l*, pg. 955

Finn, Matthew W., Pres.-Magna Trust Co.--Magna Group, Inc., Saint Louis, MO; *U.S. Public*, pg. 1037

Finnigan, G. Michael, Chief Fin. Officer, Exec. V.P., Treas. & Pres.-Gaming Div.--Hollywood Park, Inc., Inglewood, CA; *U.S. Public*, pg. 830

Fiorina, Carleton S., Pres.-Consumer Products--Lucent Technologies Inc., Murray Hill, NJ; *U.S. Public*, pg. 1017

Fischer, Robert A., Pres.--Agway Agricultural Products (AAP), Syracuse, NY; *U.S. Private*, pg. 27

Fisher, Barbara, Pres.-Universal Television Entertainment--Universal Studios TV, Universal City, CA; *Int'l*, pg. 1215

Fisher, Roger K., Grp. Pres.-Bus. Devel.--Andrew Corporation, Orland Park, IL; *U.S. Public*, pg. 112

Fisher, William M., Pres.-PPC Industries--Advance Ross Corporation, Chicago, IL; *U.S. Public*, pg. 320

Fitzgerald, Garry R., Pres.-Paging Network of Canada Inc.--Paging Network, Inc., Plano, TX; *U.S. Public*, pg. 1252

Fitzgibbons, Jack, Pres.-Cable Div.--C & M Corporation, Wauregan, CT; *U.S. Private*, pg. 191

Fitzpatrick, Thomas J., Pres.--Spring Financial Services, Mount Laurel, NJ; *U.S. Public*, pg. 176

Fitzsimmons, T. Christopher, V.P. & Pres.-Commercial & Govt. Systems--Eastman Kodak Company, Rochester, NY; *U.S. Public*, pg. 550

Flaherty, Gerald S., Grp. Pres.--Caterpillar Inc., Peoria, IL; *U.S. Public*, pg. 315

Flanagan, Richard L., Pres. & Chief Oper. Officer-Borders--Borders Group, Inc., Ann Arbor, MI; *U.S. Public*, pg. 245

Flanagan, Theresa, Pres.-Quality Mngmt.--Total Research Corporation, Princeton, NJ; *U.S. Public*, pg. 1625

Fleetwood, James M., Jr., Pres.-Atlantic Grp.--Columbia/HCA Healthcare Corporation, Nashville, TN; *U.S. Public*, pg. 403

Fleischhacker, James E., V.P. & Pres.-Data/Comm Div./Americas--Molex Incorporated, Lisle, IL; *U.S. Public*, pg. 1121

Fleming, David D., Sr. V.P. & Pres.-Diagnostic Prods.--Genzyme Corporation, Cambridge, MA; *U.S. Public*, pg. 733

Fleming, George, Pres.-United Resources--United Grocers Inc., Portland, OR; *U.S. Private*, pg. 1122

Fletcher, William A., Pres.-Lemmon Company & V.P.-North American Sls.--Teva Pharmaceutical Industries Ltd., Petah Tiqwa, Israel; *Int'l*, pg. 1380

Floathe, Maury, Pres.-Technology & Dir.--EvansGroup, Salt Lake City, UT; *U.S. Private*, pg. 385

Flock, Michael, Pres.-Asia/Pacific, Canada & Latin America--Dun & Bradstreet, Murray Hill, NJ; *U.S. Public*, pg. 535

Flohr, Thomas, Pres.-Europe--Comdisco, Inc., Rosemont, IL; *U.S. Public*, pg. 407

Flood, Gregory, Pres.-Mngmt. Liability Div.--National Union Fire Ins. Co. of Pittsburgh, Pa., New York, NY; *U.S. Public*, pg. 84

Flood, Roy M., Sr. V.P. & Pres.-P&C Div.--The Penn Traffic Company, Syracuse, NY; *U.S. Public*, pg. 1270

Flynn, John V., Pres.-Intl. Paper CIS--International Paper Company, Purchase, NY; *U.S. Public*, pg. 901

Flynn, Michael E., Pres.-Computer Renaissance--Grow Biz International, Inc., Minneapolis, MN; *U.S. Public*, pg. 767

Flynn, Michael T., Pres.-AK--Southwestern Bell Telephone Co., Saint Louis, MO; *U.S. Public*, pg. 1416

Flynn, Pat, Pres.-K-Byte Div.--Reptron Electronics, Inc., Tampa, FL; *U.S. Public*, pg. 1377

Fogelman, P., Pres.-Publisher, Dial--Penguin Putnam Inc., New York, NY; *Int'l*, pg. 1027

Foote, E.L., Exec. V.P. & Pres.-Indus. Chemicals Division--Bayer Corporation, Pittsburgh, PA; *Int'l*, pg. 172

Footer, Harris, Pres.-Easy Day Div.--Easy Day Manufacturing Company, Holliston, MA; *U.S. Private*, pg. 358

Fording, Edmund H., Jr., V.P. & Pres.- Dyes & Chemicals/Americas--Crompton & Knowles Corporation, Stamford, CT; *U.S. Public*, pg. 459

Forgeard, Noel, Pres.-Matra Hachette--Lagardere Groupe, Paris, France; *Int'l*, pg. 791

Forgie, James L., Pres.-Emco Custom Prods.--Emco Limited, London, Canada; *Int'l*, pg. 452

Forsell, A. Arne, Pres.--Pharmacia & Upjohn Biotech AB, Uppsala, Sweden; *Int'l*, pg. 1047

Forses, James J., Pres.-Intl. Opers. & Exec. V.P.--Ikon Office Solutions, Inc., Malvern, PA; *U.S. Public*, pg. 862

Forsyth, G. Fred, Pres.-Prof. Prods. Div.--Iomega Corporation, Roy, UT; *U.S. Public*, pg. 912

Forte, Mary, Sr. V.P. & Pres.-Gordon's Div.--Zale Corporation, Irving, TX; *U.S. Public*, pg. 1789

Fortems, Court, Pres.-Scientific Software-Intercomp (Canada) Ltd.--Scientific Software-Intercomp, Inc., Denver, CO; *U.S. Public*, pg. 1443

Fortier, H. Lee, Pres.-Western Region--EMCON, San Mateo, CA; *U.S. Public*, pg. 571

Foscante, Robert E., Dr., Grp. Pres.--Ameron B.V., Protective Coatings Division-Europe, Geldermalsen, Netherlands; *U.S. Public*, pg. 99

Fossati-Bellani, Vittorio, Dr., Exec. V.P. & Pres.-GM Semiconductor Grp.--Coherent, Inc., Santa Clara, CA; *U.S. Public*, pg. 395

Foster, Charles, Pres.-SBC Opers.--SBC Communications Inc., San Antonio, TX; *U.S. Public*, pg. 1415

Fostkiewicz, Victor A., Pres.-Northern Div.--NUI Corporation, Bedminster, NJ; *U.S. Public*, pg. 1147

Fourteau, Patrick P., Pres.-Intl.--St. Jude Medical, Inc., Saint Paul, MN; *U.S. Public*, pg. 1427

Fowler, John P., II, Mng. Principal-Transportation/Structures--Dewberry & Davis, Fairfax, VA; *U.S. Private*, pg. 329

Fowlstone, G., Pres.-Corp. Affairs--Burns, Philp & Company Limited, Sydney, Australia; *Int'l*, pg. 236

Fox, David M., Pres. & Chief Exec. Officer--Unapix Entertainment Inc., New York, NY; *U.S. Public*, pg. 1664

Fox, Greg, Grp. Pres.--Harbour Group Ltd., Saint Louis, MO; *U.S. Private*, pg. 500

Fox, Jeff, Grp. Pres.--Harbour Group Ltd., Saint Louis, MO; *U.S. Private*, pg. 500

Fox, Susan B., Pres.-KS--Southwestern Bell Telephone Co., Saint Louis, MO; *U.S. Public*, pg. 1416

Foy, Dwight D., Pres.-Speciality Prods.--North Pacific Lumber Company, Portland, OR; *U.S. Private*, pg. 805

Frain, William T., Jr., Pres. & Chief Oper. Officer--Public Service Company of New Hampshire, Manchester, NH; *U.S. Public*, pg. 1195

Franceschetti, C., Pres.-Publisher, Dutton Childrens--Penguin Putnam Inc., New York, NY; *Int'l*, pg. 1027

Frandsen, Lau, Grp. Pres.-Europe--Masco Corporation, Taylor, MI; *U.S. Public*, pg. 1052

Frank, Richard H., Pres.-Speciality Vehicle/Commercial Truck Division--Cambridge Industries Inc., Madison Heights, MI; *U.S. Private*, pg. 202

Frank, Robert, Pres.-Media Services Div.--SFM Media Corporation, New York, NY; *U.S. Private*, pg. 956

Frank, Thomas, Pres.-Intl. Office Prods. Opers.--Corporate Express, Inc., Broomfield, CO; *U.S. Public*, pg. 449

Frank, William Douglas, Corp. V.P. & Pres.-West Hudson--Allegiance Healthcare Corp., McGaw Park, IL; *U.S. Public*, pg. 44

Franklin, Marvin A., Pres.-Dana Intl.--Dana Corporation, Toledo, OH; *U.S. Public*, pg. 479

Frankovic, Richard R., Pres.-Rugby Laboratories--Hoechst Marion Roussel North America, Kansas City, MO; *Int'l*, pg. 625

Frankovich, Jim, Pres.-PCA, Far East & Pacific--Philip Crosby Associates, Inc., Winter Park, FL; *Int'l*, pg. 1072

Fraser, Jeff, Pres.-Central Asia & Middle East--Unilever Plc, London, United Kingdom; *Int'l*, pg. 1433

Frattaroli, Jonathan, Partner & Gen. Mgr.--Earle Palmer Brown/New York, New York, NY; *U.S. Private*, pg. 174

Fredrick, William A., Pres.-Special Mkts. Div.--Thomas & Betts Reznor Division, Memphis, TN; *U.S. Public*, pg. 1598

Freeman, Bruce, Pres.-Castle & Cooke Development--Castle & Cooke Inc., Los Angeles, CA; *U.S. Public*, pg. 313

Freiwald, Cris, Pres.-Intl. Div.--Inacom Corp., Omaha, NE; *U.S. Public*, pg. 873

Frick, Raymond A., Pres. & Chief Oper. Officer-Comml. Book & New Markets Grp.--Quebecor Printing (USA) Corp., Boston, MA; *Int'l*, pg. 1076

Fridette, Pamela, Pres.-Horizons Consulting Inc.--Computer Horizons Corp., Mountain Lakes, NJ; *U.S. Public*, pg. 421

Friedberg, Alan G., Pres.-Renovation Div.--Hospitality Worldwide Services, Inc., New York, NY; *U.S. Public*, pg. 841

Friedman, David, Pres.-Resources Grp.--Catellus Development Corporation, San Francisco, CA; *U.S. Public*, pg. 314

Friedman, Gary G., Chief Mdsg. Officer & Pres.-Retail Div.--Williams-Sonoma, Inc., San Francisco, CA; *U.S. Public*, pg. 1770

Friedman, Robert, Pres.-New Line Television--New Line Cinema Corporation, New York, NY; *U.S. Public*, pg. 1614

Friedman, Stephen, Pres.-Japan/Pacific/Asia/Australia--American Express Travel Related Services Co., Inc., New York, NY; *U.S. Public*, pg. 73

Friedson-Garrett, Barbara, Pres.-Windmere U.S. Sls. & Mktg.--Windmere-Durable Holdings, Hialeah, FL; *U.S. Public*, pg. 1771

Fritz, Donald G., Exec. V.P. & Pres.-Kellogg Europe--Kellogg Company, Battle Creek, MI; *U.S. Public*, pg. 947

Fritz, Fred, Pres. & Chief Oper. Officer--The Coleman Company, Inc., Golden, CO; *U.S. Private*, pg. 690

Froelich, R. Kelly, Pres.-Coastal Electric Services--The Coastal Corporation, Houston, TX; *U.S. Public*, pg. 389

Frolich, Bruce D., Pres.--Chevron Research and Technology Company, Richmond, CA; *U.S. Public*, pg. 348

Froman, John, V.P. & Pres.-Central Div.--Circuit City Stores, Inc., Richmond, VA; *U.S. Public*, pg. 374

Frye, Douglas P., Pres.-Institutional Svcs. Grp.--Grubb & Ellis Company, Northbrook, IL; *U.S. Public*, pg. 767

Fuchtenkort, Hans-Gerd, Pres.-Europe, Middle East & Africa--A.C. Nielsen, Stamford, CT; *U.S. Public*, pg. 1183

Fuhrmann, Curt, Pres.-Fortis Sls.--Time Insurance, Milwaukee, WI; *Int'l*, pg. 499

Fukuda, Takeji, Pres.-Kashima Oil Grp.--Japan Energy Corporation, Tokyo, Japan; *Int'l*, pg. 702

Fukui, Kikuo, V.P.-Intl./Japan Reg. & Pres.-Tiffany & Co. Japan Inc.--Tiffany & Co., New York, NY; *U.S. Public*, pg. 1608

Fuller, Arthur D., Sr. V.P. & Pres.-Newsprint Div.--Bowater Incorporated, Greenville, SC; *U.S. Public*, pg. 247

Fuller, John, Pres. & Chief Exec. Officer-Automotive Fin. Corp.--Minnesota Power, Duluth, MN; *U.S. Public*, pg. 1116

Fulton, Robert, Pres.-Eastern Div.--Centimark Corporation, Canonsburg, PA; *U.S. Private*, pg. 222

Fumizono, Yoshiro, Pres.--NSK-RHP France S.A., Voisins-le-Bretonneux, France; *Int'l*, pg. 904

Funes, Carlos Oliva, Pres.-Swift Armour Argentina--Campbell Soup Company, Camden, NJ; *U.S. Public*, pg. 298

Funk, Charles N., Chief Investment Officer, Corp. Sr. V.P. & Pres.-Des Moines--Brenton Banks, Inc., Des Moines, IA; *U.S. Public*, pg. 251

Furlong, Steward S., Pres.-WWF Book Publishing--WWF Paper Corporation, Bala Cynwyd, PA; *U.S. Private*, pg. 1145

Gadsby, R.E., Pres.-ICI Chemicals & Polymers--ICI Americas, Inc., Wilmington, DE; *Int'l*, pg. 663

Gaffney, D. Bruce, Pres.-Ervin Leasing Co.--Ervin Industries, Inc., Ann Arbor, MI; *U.S. Private*, pg. 382

Gagliardi, Gerald, Exec. V.P. & Pres.-Global Customer Services--Unisys Corporation, Blue Bell, PA; *U.S. Public*, pg. 1671

Galanski, Stan, Pres.-New Hampshire Insurance Co.--American International Group, Inc., New York, NY; *U.S. Public*, pg. 83

Gallagher, B.P., Mng. Dir.-Consumer & Commercial Holdings--Reunert Ltd., Sandton, South Africa; *Int'l*, pg. 1105

Galli, Joseph, Exec. V.P. & Pres.-Power Tools--The Black & Decker Corporation, Towson, MD; *U.S. Public*, pg. 233

Gallo, A.C., Pres.-Northeast Region--Whole Foods Market, Inc., Austin, TX; *U.S. Public*, pg. 1767

Galvis, Christian, Co-Pres. & Chief Oper. Officer-Slipper Div.--R.G. Barry Corporation, Pickerington, OH; *U.S. Public*, pg. 192

Gambler, Andreas, Pres.-Philip Morris EFTA/E. Europe, Middle East & Africa--Philip Morris International Inc., Rye Brook, NY; *U.S. Public*, pg. 1289

Gandolfo, Joseph C., Pres.-Mattel Opers.--Mattel, Inc., El Segundo, CA; *U.S. Public*, pg. 1057

Gannon, John J., Pres.-Physician Practice Mngmt. Division--Medpartners Inc., Birmingham, AL; *U.S. Public*, pg. 1082

Gannon, William, Jr., Pres.-Sentry Research Services--Sentry Technology Group, Westborough, MA; *U.S. Public*, pg. 1425

Ganot, Harvey, Pres.-Adv. & Promo. Sls.--MTV Networks, New York, NY; *U.S. Private*, pg. 779

Ganz, Axel, Pres.-Internal Mktg. Div.--Parents Magazine, New York, NY; *Int'l*, pg. 191

Garcia, Carlos G. Segovia, Pres.-Capital Goods Div.--Vitro, Sociedad Anonima, Garza Garcia, Mexico; *Int'l*, pg. 1469

Gardner, David, Pres.-Indus. Div.--Freudenberg-NOK, Plymouth, MI; *U.S. Private*, pg. 427

Garger, Liz, Pres.-Special Events Mngmt.--J. Brown/LMC Group, Stamford, CT; *U.S. Public*, pg. 764

Garil, Bernard, Pres.-OPCAP Advisors--OppenheimerFunds Distributor, Inc., New York, NY; *U.S. Private*, pg. 818

Garofalo, Richard, Pres.-Health Acquisitin Corp.--National Home Health Care Corp., Scarsdale, NY; *U.S. Public*, pg. 1157

Garrett, James, Sr. V.P. & Pres.-Fin. Markets Div.--John H. Harland Company, Decatur, GA; *U.S. Public*, pg. 785

Garrett, James K., Pres.-Paging Network-Southeastern Region, Inc.--Paging Network, Inc., Plano, TX; *U.S. Public*, pg. 1252

Garrity, John, Pres.-South--The Ryland Group, Inc., Columbia, MD; *U.S. Public*, pg. 1414

Garrity, Norman E., Pres.-Corning Technologies--Corning Incorporated, Corning, NY; *U.S. Public*, pg. 448

Garro, Dennis, Pres.-Retail Div. Stride Rite Children's Group, Inc.--The Stride Rite Corporation, Lexington, MA; *U.S. Public*, pg. 1524

Gartner, Michael, Pres.-NBC News--National Broadcasting Co., Inc., New York, NY; *U.S. Public*, pg. 712

Garvey, Richard A., Pres.-Corp. Plng. & New Bus. Devel.--The Reader's Digest Association, Inc., Pleasantville, NY; *U.S. Public*, pg. 1367

Gary, Robert W., Pres.-Allstate Personal Lines--The Allstate Corporation, Northbrook, IL; *U.S. Public*, pg. 55

Garza, Francisco, Pres.-Cemex Mexico--Cemex, S.A. de C.V., Monterrey, Mexico; *Int'l*, pg. 278

Gasper, Joseph G., Pres. & Chief Oper. Officer-Life Companies--Nationwide Insurance Enterprise, Columbus, OH; *U.S. Private*, pg. 788

Gasper, Joseph J., Pres.-Life Co.--Nationwide Mutual Insurance Co., Columbus, OH; *U.S. Private*, pg. 789

Gattuso, Joseph, Pres. & Chief Exec. Officer-Ferguson 2000--CommonHealth USA, Parsippany, NJ; *Int'l*, pg. 1483

Gausz, Beeler, Pres.-Quality College--Philip Crosby Associates, Inc., Winter Park, FL; *Int'l*, pg. 1072

Gaynor, Philip, Pres.-Missy & Special Sizes--Fritzi of California Manufacturing Corp., San Francisco, CA; *U.S. Private*, pg. 429

Gazerwitz, George, Exec. V.P. & Pres.-Computer Systems Prods. Grp.--Unisys Corporation, Blue Bell, PA; *U.S. Public*, pg. 1671

Gburek, John L., V.P. & Pres.-Pep. & Peptech.--BMC Industries, Inc., Minneapolis, MN; *U.S. Public*, pg. 162

Gearhart, Lloyd E., Pres.-Western Div. Services--John Alden Financial Corporation, Miami, FL; *U.S. Public*, pg. 39

Geer, Carlton L., Pres. & Chief Exec. Officer-Las Vegas Showboat--Showboat, Incorporated, Las Vegas, NV; *U.S. Public*, pg. 1469

Geiger, William, Pres.-Carole Fabrics--Hunter Douglas, Inc., Upper Saddle River, NJ; *Int'l*, pg. 639

Geisler, Rosemary P., Pres.-Fin. Mngmt. Div.--Comdisco, Inc., Rosemont, IL; *U.S. Public*, pg. 407

Gelber, Robert M., Exec. V.P. & Pres.-GM Coherent Auburn Grp.--Coherent, Inc., Santa Clara, CA; *U.S. Public*, pg. 395

Gentine, Lawrence J., Pres.-Food Service Div.--Sargento Foods Inc., Plymouth, WI; *U.S. Private*, pg. 966

George, Albert, Pres.-Service Vouchers--Sodexho S.A., Montigny-le-Bretonneux, France; *Int'l*, pg. 1274

George, Dennis, Pres.-BFS Information Services--Bridgestone/Firestone, Inc., Nashville, TN; *Int'l*, pg. 213

George, Mary J., Pres. & Chief Oper. Officer--Bell Sports Corp., San Jose, CA; *U.S. Public*, pg. 207

George, Thomas D., Exec. V.P. & Pres. & Gen. Mgr.-Semiconductor Prods.--Motorola, Inc., Schaumburg, IL; *U.S. Public*, pg. 1136

Gerber, Michael H., Pres.-First-Run, International Distr. & Acquisitions--Viacom Enterprises, New York, NY; *U.S. Private*, pg. 779

Gerber, William G., M.D., V.P.--Chiron Corporation, Emeryville, CA; *U.S. Public*, pg. 349

Gerken, William R., Pres.-Retail--Norwalk Furniture Corporation, Norwalk, OH; *U.S. Private*, pg. 807

Gernert, William R., Pres.-Providian Capital Management--AEGON USA, Inc., Louisville, KY; *Int'l*, pg. 26

Gershaw, Gerald, Pres.-Intl. Div.--Therapedic Associates, Inc., Middlesex, NJ; *U.S. Private*, pg. 1079

Gershberg, Jay, Sr. V.P. & Pres.-Travel Nurse Grp.--Hospital Staffing Services, Inc., Fort Lauderdale, FL; *U.S. Public*, pg. 840

Ghormley, Hugh, Pres.-Fab Plants/CMC Steel Grp.--Structural Metals, Inc., Seguin, TX; *U.S. Public*, pg. 412

Gianelli, S.P., Pres.-Toromont Process Systems--Toromont Industries Ltd., Concord, Canada; *Int'l*, pg. 1400

Giangiordano, Rich, Pres.-Commercial Products Grp.--Courtaulds Aerospace, Glendale, CA; *Int'l*, pg. 339

Giese, T.P., Grp. Pres.--Ameron Concrete & Steel Pipe (Northern Div.), Tracy, CA; *U.S. Public*, pg. 99

Giese, T.P., Grp. Pres.--Concrete & Steel Pipe Group (Southern Div.), Rancho Cucamonga, CA; *U.S. Public*, pg. 99

Giese, Thomas P., Grp. Pres.-Concrete & Steel--Ameron International Corporation, Pasadena, CA; *U.S. Public*, pg. 98

Gilbert, John, V.P. & Pres.-Collagen Prods. Div.--Datascope Corp., Montvale, NJ; *U.S. Public*, pg. 487

Gilbertson, Roger, MD, Corp. Pres.--MeritCare Health System, Fargo, ND; *U.S. Private*, pg. 733

Gill, Eric W., Exec. V.P. & Central Reg. Pres.--Marine Midland Bank, Buffalo, NY; *Int'l*, pg. 581

Gillespie, Dennis G., Pres.-Worldwide Mktg. & Domestic Sls.--Viacom Enterprises, New York, NY; *U.S. Private*, pg. 779
Gillespie, William A., MD, Pres.-Southwest Division & Sr. V.P.--Kaiser Permanente, Oakland, CA; *U.S. Private*, pg. 605
Gilligan, Edward P., Pres.-Corp. Services--American Express Company, New York, NY; *U.S. Public*, pg. 73
Gilligan, Kevin, Pres.-Solutions & Svcs.--Home and Building Control, Minneapolis, MN; *U.S. Public*, pg. 833
Gilligan, Patrick J., Pres.-Nord Photo Engineering--Photo Control Corporation, Minneapolis, MN; *U.S. Public*, pg. 1292
Gillis, Lawrence J., Pres.-Roto-Rooter Services--Roto-Rooter, Cincinnati, OH; *U.S. Public*, pg. 344
Gilmore, George H., Jr., Pres.-Business Systems--Moore Corporation Limited, Toronto, Canada; *Int'l*, pg. 888
Gilmore, Merle L., Exec. V.P. & Pres.-Europe, Middle East & Africa--Motorola, Inc., Schaumburg, IL; *U.S. Public*, pg. 1136
Giordano, Salvatore, III, Pres.-Melcor Corp. & V.P.--Fedders Corp., Liberty Corner, NJ; *U.S. Public*, pg. 614
Giorgio, Robert, Pres.-Day & Zimmermann International, Inc.--Day & Zimmermann, Inc., Philadelphia, PA; *U.S. Private*, pg. 316
Giovannini, Alberto, Pres. -Latin America--Tupperware Corporation, Orlando, FL; *U.S. Public*, pg. 1644
Girotto, John R., Pres.-Intelligent Transportation Systems--Rockwell International Corporation, Costa Mesa, CA; *U.S. Public*, pg. 1397
Giuliani, Alan V., Pres.-Rykoff-Sexton Mfg. Div.--Rykoff-Sexton, Inc., Wilkes-Barre, PA; *U.S. Public*, pg. 918
Gladden, Roger D., Sr. V.P. & Pres.-Commercial Fixtures & Displays Group--Leggett & Platt, Incorporated, Carthage, MO; *U.S. Public*, pg. 985
Glascock, William L., Leader-Energy Prods. & Services & Pres.-Energy USA--Bay State Gas Company, Westborough, MA; *U.S. Public*, pg. 196
Glass, J. Kenneth, Pres.-Tennessee Banking Grp.--First Tennessee National Corporation, Memphis, TN; *U.S. Public*, pg. 638
Glass, J. Kenneth, Exec. V.P. & Pres.-Tennessee Banking Grp.--First Tennessee Bank National Association, Memphis, TN; *U.S. Public*, pg. 639
Glass, William, Pres.-Recognition Resource Grp.--Adair Greene Advertising, Atlanta, GA; *U.S. Private*, pg. 16
Glassman, Karl G., V.P. & Pres.-Bedding Components--Leggett & Platt, Incorporated, Carthage, MO; *U.S. Public*, pg. 985
Gleason, Larry, Pres.-Worldwide Theatrical Distr.--Metro-Goldwyn-Mayer Inc., Santa Monica, CA; *U.S. Public*, pg. 1101
Gleason, Larry, Pres.-Worldwide Theater, Dist.--MGM/UA Distribution Co., Santa Monica, CA; *U.S. Public*, pg. 1102
Glick, Barry, V.P. & Pres.-Alro Metals Service Center--Alro Group, Jackson, MI; *U.S. Private*, pg. 45
Glore, Jodie K., Sr. V.P. & Pres.-Rockwell Automation--Rockwell International Corporation, Costa Mesa, CA; *U.S. Public*, pg. 1397
Glynn, Gary A., Pres.-United States Steel & Carnegie Pension Fund--USX Corporation, Pittsburgh, PA; *U.S. Public*, pg. 1661
Godard, Alain, Pres.-Agro--Rhone-Poulenc S.A., Courbevoie, France; *Int'l*, pg. 1108
Godbersen, Bruce, Pres.-Byron Originals--Midwest Industries, Inc., Ida Grove, IA; *U.S. Private*, pg. 744
Goecke, Joseph M., Pres. & Chief Oper. Officer-Valmont Irrigation--Valmont Industries, Inc., Valley, NE; *U.S. Public*, pg. 1706
Goer, Alan, Pres.-Goer Mfg. Co.--RHC/Spacemaster Corporation, Melrose Park, IL; *U.S. Private*, pg. 904
Gold, Christina A., Exec. V.P.-Global Direct-Selling Devel. & Pres.-North America--Avon Products, Inc., New York, NY; *U.S. Public*, pg. 155
Gold, Daniel E., Sr. V.P. & Pres.-Century Cable Division--Century Communications Corp., New Canaan, CT; *U.S. Public*, pg. 329
Goldberg, Arthur M., Exec. V.P. & Pres.-Gambling Opers.--Hilton Hotels Corporation, Beverly Hills, CA; *U.S. Public*, pg. 828
Golden, Jerome, Pres.-Income Mgr. Grp.--The Equitable Companies Incorporated, New York, NY; *U.S. Public*, pg. 588
Goldman, Mitchell, Pres.-New Line Marketing & Distribution--New Line Cinema Corporation, New York, NY; *U.S. Public*, pg. 1614
Goldman, Steven, Pres.-Domestic TV & Exec. V.P.-TV Grp.--Paramount Pictures Corporation, Los Angeles, CA; *U.S. Private*, pg. 776
Goldsmith, Marvin, Pres.-Sls. & Mktg.-TV Network--ABC, Inc, New York, NY; *U.S. Public*, pg. 511
Goldstein, Richard, Pres.-Foods/N. America--Unilever Plc, London, United Kingdom; *Int'l*, pg. 1433
Goldstein, Stewart, Pres.-Credit--Sears, Roebuck and Co., Hoffman Estates, IL; *U.S. Public*, pg. 1452
Goldwyn, John, Pres.-Motion Picture Grp. Production--Paramount Pictures Corporation, Los Angeles, CA; *U.S. Private*, pg. 776
Goluskin, Norman, Partner--Earle Palmer Brown/New York, New York, NY; *U.S. Private*, pg. 174
Gomes, Dennis C., Pres.-Resort Opers.--Aztar Corporation, Phoenix, AZ; *U.S. Public*, pg. 158
Gommel, Richard, Pres.-North America--Safeguard Business Systems, Inc., Fort Washington, PA; *U.S. Private*, pg. 960
Gonome, Akira, Pres.--Synergy Computer Graphics Corporation, Santa Clara, CA; *Int'l*, pg. 940
Gonzalez, Antonio Felix, Pres.-Carlton Mexico S.A. de C.V.--American Greetings Corporation, Cleveland, OH; *U.S. Public*, pg. 77
Gonzalez, Federico Sada, Pres.-Containers N. America Div.--Vitro, Sociedad Anonima, Garza Garcia, Mexico; *Int'l*, pg. 1469
Gonzalez, Jesus E., V.P.-North American On-Site Gases & Pres.-Praxair Mexico--Praxair Inc., Danbury, CT; *U.S. Public*, pg. 1319
Goode, Denny P., Pres.-Kawneer North America--Kawneer Company, Norcross, GA; *U.S. Public*, pg. 60
Goodman, Larry, Pres.-CNN Sls. & Mktg.--CNN (Cable News Network), Atlanta, GA; *U.S. Public*, pg. 1614
Goodman, Robert L., M.D., Pres.-Oncology Ctrs. Div.--Universal Health Services, Inc., King of Prussia, PA; *U.S. Public*, pg. 1696
Goodwin, James K., Pres.-Consumer Prods.--Fort James Corporation, Richmond, VA; *U.S. Public*, pg. 670
Goraleski, Michael, Pres.--GLENFED Brokerage Services, Glendale, CA; *U.S. Public*, pg. 747
Gorda, Ronald B., Sr. V.P. & Pres.-Linkabit--The Titan Corporation, San Diego, CA; *U.S. Public*, pg. 1618
Gorder, Mark S., V.P., Pres.& Chief Exec. Officer-Resistance Technology, Inc.--Selas Corporation of America, Dresher, PA; *U.S. Public*, pg. 1454
Gordon, Bruce, Pres.-Intl. TV--Paramount Pictures Corporation, Los Angeles, CA; *U.S. Private*, pg. 776
Gordon, Bruce S., Pres.-Consumer & Small Bus. Services--Bell Atlantic Corporation, New York, NY; *U.S. Public*, pg. 201
Gordon, Bruce S., Grp. Pres.-Consumer & Small Bus. Serices--Bell Atlantic Network Services, Inc., Arlington, VA; *U.S. Public*, pg. 202
Gordon, David G., V.P. & Sr. Div. Pres.--The Dexter Corporation, Windsor Locks, CT; *U.S. Public*, pg. 504
Gore, James L., V.P. & Pres. & Chief Exec. Officer-Coventry HealthCare Mngmt.--Coventry Corporation, Nashville, TN; *U.S. Public*, pg. 454
Gorog, Chris, Pres.-New Bus. & Devel.--Universal Studios Recreation Services Group, Universal City, CA; *Int'l*, pg. 1216
Goryance, F. Kim, Pres.-Antenna Specialists Div.--Allen Telecom Inc., Solon, OH; *U.S. Public*, pg. 45
Goudard, Jean-Michel, Pres.-Intl. & Dir.--BBDO Worldwide Inc., New York, NY; *U.S. Public*, pg. 1223
Gouwens, Bob, Pres.-Worldwide Foods Div.--La Preferida, Inc., Chicago, IL; *U.S. Private*, pg. 640
Gracie, J.S., V.P. & Pres.-First Brands Intl.--First Brands Corporation, Danbury, CT; *U.S. Public*, pg. 626
Graeber, George C., Exec. V.P. & Pres.-Montrose/CDT--Cable Design Technologies Corporation, Pittsburgh, PA; *U.S. Public*, pg. 287
Graff, Mike, Pres.-Bombardier Business Aircraft--Bombardier Aerospace, Dorval, Canada; *Int'l*, pg. 200
Grafton, Daniel A., Pres.-Raytheon Aerospace--Raytheon Aircraft Company, Wichita, KS; *U.S. Public*, pg. 1365
Grams, J.I., V.P. & Pres.-Potters Industries, Inc.--PQ Corporation, Berwyn, PA; *U.S. Private*, pg. 827
Granath, Herbert A., Pres.-ABC Cable & Intl. Broadcast Grp. & Sr. V.P.--ABC, Inc, New York, NY; *U.S. Public*, pg. 511
Granger, Daniel D., Exec. V.P. & Pres.-Catalina Mktg. Services--Catalina Marketing Corporation, Saint Petersburg, FL; *U.S. Public*, pg. 314
Gratlan, Pete, Pres.-Construction Co.--The Donohoe Companies, Inc., Washington, DC; *U.S. Private*, pg. 340
Grava, Alfred H., Grp. V.P.--MascoTech, Inc., Taylor, MI; *U.S. Public*, pg. 1055
Gray, Josef E., Pres.--Seafirst Corporation, Seattle, WA; *U.S. Public*, pg. 181
Gray, Joseph M., Pres.-Exterior Systems Grp.--Peregrine Incorporated, Southfield, MI; *U.S. Private*, pg. 852
Gray, P. Nigel, V.P. & Pres.-Medical Technology Grp.--Pfizer Inc., New York, NY; *U.S. Public*, pg. 1281
Grazier, George, Pres.-Farmland Foods, Inc.--Farmland Industries, Inc., Kansas City, MO; *U.S. Private*, pg. 395
Greaves, R. Malcolm, Chief Exec. Officer & Pres.-Haskel Intl.--Haskel International, Inc., Burbank, CA; *U.S. Public*, pg. 798
Greco, Edward, Pres.-Bd. of Dirs.--EA Engineering, Science & Technology de Mexico, S.A. de C.V., Colonia, Mexico; *U.S. Public*, pg. 541
Greco, Edward M., Sr. V.P. & Pres.-EA International, Inc.--EA Engineering, Science & Technology, Inc., Hunt Valley, MD; *U.S. Public*, pg. 540
Green, Howard B., Pres.-Office Prods.--General Binding Corporation, Northbrook, IL; *U.S. Public*, pg. 707
Green, Judson, Pres.-Walt Disney Attraction--Disneyland, Anaheim, CA; *U.S. Public*, pg. 511
Green, Terence Anthony, Chief Exec.-Debenhams--The Burton Group PLC, London, United Kingdom; *Int'l*, pg. 237
Greenberg, Eugene R., V.P. & Pres.-Alumax Materials Management--Alumax Inc., Atlanta, GA; *U.S. Public*, pg. 59
Greene, Donald R., Pres.-The Coca-Cola Foundation--The Coca-Cola Company, Atlanta, GA; *U.S. Public*, pg. 392
Greenwood, Lawrence D., Pres.-Solutions Consulting Grp.--Ciber, Inc., Englewood, CO; *U.S. Public*, pg. 356
Gregorich, Thomas M., Pres.-Data Management Systems--Moore Corporation Limited, Toronto, Canada; *Int'l*, pg. 888
Gregory, Jon M., Pres.-Quarry Div.--Rock of Ages Corporation, Graniteville, VT; *U.S. Public*, pg. 1396
Greisinger, James R., Grp. V.P. & Pres.-Dean Pickle & Specialty Products Co.--Dean Foods Company, Franklin Park, IL; *U.S. Public*, pg. 489
Gresham, Mike, Pres. & Gen. Mgr.-Wireless Interconnect Grp.--Glenayre Technologies, Inc., Charlotte, NC; *U.S. Public*, pg. 746
Grey, Michael G., Pres.-BioChem Therapeutic Inc.--BioChem Pharma Inc., Laval, Canada; *Int'l*, pg. 196
Griffin, James, Pres.-Ryder Transportation Svcs.--Ryder System, Inc., Miami, FL; *U.S. Public*, pg. 1413
Griffin, James B., Pres.-Ryder Transportation Services--Vehicle Leasing & Services Div., Miami, FL; *U.S. Public*, pg. 1414
Griffin, John, Pres.-Magazine Div.--Rodale Press, Inc., Emmaus, PA; *U.S. Private*, pg. 939
Griffin, Randall M., Pres.-Constellation Real Estate Grp.--Constellation Holdings, Inc., Baltimore, MD; *U.S. Public*, pg. 172
Griffith, Edward L., Jr., Pres.-Southeast Region--EMCON, San Mateo, CA; *U.S. Public*, pg. 571
Griffiths, Gordon A., Pres.-Quebecor Printing Canada--Quebecor Printing, Inc., Montreal, Canada; *Int'l*, pg. 1076
Griffiths, Gordon A., Pres.-Quebecor Printing Canada--Imprimerie Quebecor Inc., Montreal, Canada; *Int'l*, pg. 1077
Griffiths, Richard, Pres.-Epic Records--Sony Music Entertainment, Inc., New York, NY; *Int'l*, pg. 1281
Grigelevich, Joseph, Jr., Pres.-American Modular Technologies--American Buildings Co., Eufaula, AL; *U.S. Public*, pg. 69
Grigg, Ted, Pres.-William Cook Direct--The William Cook Agency, Inc., Jacksonville, FL; *U.S. Private*, pg. 273
Grinney, Jay, Pres.-Eastern Grp.--Columbia/HCA Healthcare Corporation, Nashville, TN; *U.S. Public*, pg. 403
Groban, Mark D., M.D., Pres.-Alliance PPO, Inc. & Mid Atlantic Psychiatric--Mid Atlantic Medical Services, Inc., Rockville, MD; *U.S. Public*, pg. 1109
Groome, Harry C., III, Pres.-Clinical Laboratories--SmithKline Beecham Corporation, Philadelphia, PA; *Int'l*, pg. 1264
Groot, Jacobus, Grp. V.P. & Pres.-Asia/North--The Procter & Gamble Company, Cincinnati, OH; *U.S. Public*, pg. 1330
Groot, Steven L., Pres.-Allstate Indemnity--The Allstate Corporation, Northbrook, IL; *U.S. Public*, pg. 55
Gros, Didier, Co-Pres.-Sphere Intl.--Accor S.A., Evry, France; *Int'l*, pg. 20
Gross, Arnold, Sr. V.P.-Intl. & Pres.-Handleman Intl.--Handleman Company, Troy, MI; *U.S. Public*, pg. 779
Groveunder, Dave, Sector Pres.--Burnham, Atlanta, GA; *Int'l*, pg. 686
Grubbs, Robert W., Pres.-Anixter, Inc.--Anixter International, Chicago, IL; *U.S. Public*, pg. 115
Grumbly, Thomas P., Grp. Pres.-Environ. & Facilities Mngmt. Grp. & V.P.--ICF Kaiser International Inc., Fairfax, VA; *U.S. Public*, pg. 852
Grymes, John, Pres.-Williamhouse Div.--American Pad and Paper Company, Dallas, TX; *U.S. Public*, pg. 88
Guccione, Nina, Exec. V.P. & Pres.-New Media--General Media International Inc., New York, NY; *U.S. Private*, pg. 444
Guensch, Susan, Pres.-Speedo Div.--Authentic Fitness Corp., Los Angeles, CA; *U.S. Public*, pg. 147
Guequierre, John P., Pres.-Manufactured Housing--Schult Homes Corporation, Middlebury, IN; *U.S. Public*, pg. 1442
Guerin, Robert A., Pres.-Security Svcs.--Republic Industries, Inc., Fort Lauderdale, FL; *U.S. Public*, pg. 1378
Guglielmi, Peter A., Chief Fin. Officer & Pres.-Tellabs Intl--Tellabs Operations, Inc., Lisle, IL; *U.S. Public*, pg. 1572
Guinot, Francois, Pres.-Chemical--Rhone-Poulenc S.A., Courbevoie, France; *Int'l*, pg. 1108
Gulden, Frank, Pres.-Textron Fastening Sys.--Textron Inc., Providence, RI; *U.S. Public*, pg. 1588
Gurski, John E., V.P. & Pres.-AMP Global Opers.--AMP Incorporated, Harrisburg, PA; *U.S. Public*, pg. 7
Gurtler, Hans-Beat, Dr., Pres.-Animal Health--Novartis AG, Basel, Switzerland; *Int'l*, pg. 971
Gustafson, Paul A., Exec. V.P. & Pres.-Fastening Sys.--The Black & Decker Corporation, Towson, MD; *U.S. Public*, pg. 233
Gustavsson, Sven-Gote, Pres.--ICA Handlarna Vast AB, Kungalv, Sweden; *Int'l*, pg. 643
Gustin, Joseph A., Pres.--Mid-America Energy Resources, Indianapolis, IN; *U.S. Public*, pg. 913
Gutierrez, Carlos M., Exec. V.P. & Pres.-Kellogg Asia-Pacific--Kellogg Company, Battle Creek, MI; *U.S. Public*, pg. 947
Guttman, James, Pres.-Mon River Towing, Inc.--The Guttman Group, Belle Vernon, PA; *U.S. Private*, pg. 488
Gutzler, Lowell E., Pres.-Corp. Services--Marriott Management Services (MMS), Washington, DC; *U.S. Public*, pg. 1048
Haas, Lisa B., Pres.-Alaska Region--EMCON, San Mateo, CA; *U.S. Public*, pg. 571
Haas, Timothy J., Pres.-Latin America Group & V.P.--The Coca-Cola Company, Atlanta, GA; *U.S. Public*, pg. 392
Haase, Bronson J., Pres.-Ameritech Wisconsin--Ameritech Corporation, Chicago, IL; *U.S. Public*, pg. 97
Habib, S. Amjad, Pres. & Creative Dir.-East-West Design--The Buntin Group, Nashville, TN; *U.S. Private*, pg. 181
Hadesman, Edward S., Pres.-Indus. Div.--Prime Group Realty Trust, Chicago, IL; *U.S. Public*, pg. 1326
Haefele, Raymond J., Sr. V.P. & Pres.-Continental Deli Foods--Foodbrands America, Inc., Oklahoma City, OK; *U.S. Public*, pg. 852
Haggerty, LeRoy F., Pres.-Ajilon--Adecco Employment Services, Redwood City, CA; *Int'l*, pg. 24
Haglund, Mark, V.P. & Pres.-STP Products--First Brands Corporation, Danbury, CT; *U.S. Public*, pg. 626
Haglund, Mark, Pres.-Automotive--STP Corporation, Danbury, CT; *U.S. Public*, pg. 627
Hahs, Dwain L., Pres.-Eyewear Div.--Bausch & Lomb Incorporated, Rochester, NY; *U.S. Public*, pg. 194
Haishimoto, Takashi, Pres.--Mitsui T & B Options Inc., New York, NY; *Int'l*, pg. 883
Hajek, Anna Marie, Exec. V.P. & Pres.-MMI Healthcare Svcs. Grp.--MMI Companies, Inc., Deerfield, IL; *U.S. Public*, pg. 1027
Hakansson, Bengt, Pres.-Stena Line Scandinavia AB--Stena Line AB, Goteborg, Sweden; *Int'l*, pg. 1300
Halaska, Robert H., V.P. & Pres.-WHP Health Initiatives--Walgreen Co., Deerfield, IL; *U.S. Public*, pg. 1733
Hale, Leonard C., Grp. Pres.-Sporting Equipment--Blount International, Inc., Montgomery, AL; *U.S. Public*, pg. 237
Halef, Besim, Pres.-MM Industra--American Eco Corporation, Toronto, Canada; *Int'l*, pg. 73
Haley, Michael P., Exec. V.P. & Pres.-Contract Sls. Grp.--Ladd Furniture, Inc., Greensboro, NC; *U.S. Public*, pg. 974

Hall, David, Pres.-Communications Grp.--Gaylord Entertainment Co., Nashville, TN; *U.S. Public*, pg. 704
Hall, Edward R., Pres.-Hydraulics--Parker Hannifin Corporation, Hemel Hempstead, United Kingdom; *U.S. Public*, pg. 1263
Hall, James O., Pres.-Medical Publishing Grp.--Maclean Hunter Publishing Ltd., Toronto, Canada; *Int'l*, pg. 1123
Hall, Kurt C., Chief Fin. Officer & Exec. V.P.--United Artists Theatre Circuits Incorporated, Englewood, CO; *U.S. Private*, pg. 1120
Hall, Les, Pres.-The Turner Grp.--American Eco Corporation, Toronto, Canada; *Int'l*, pg. 73
Hall, Robert D., Pres.-Whirlpool Asia, Inc. & Exec. V.P.--Whirlpool Corporation, Benton Harbor, MI; *U.S. Public*, pg. 1764
Hall, William, Pres.-Hall Family Foundations--Hallmark Cards, Inc., Kansas City, MO; *U.S. Private*, pg. 495
Hallet, Bruce, Pres.-Time--Time Inc., New York, NY; *U.S. Public*, pg. 1612
Hallett, James P., Pres. & Chief Exec. Officer-ADESA--Minnesota Power, Duluth, MN; *U.S. Public*, pg. 1116
Haltom, John D., Div. Pres.-Pictsweet Mushroom Farms--United Foods, Inc., Bells, TN; *U.S. Public*, pg. 1677
Halverson, Kenneth A., Sr. V.P.-Mktg.--Comdisco, Inc., Rosemont, IL; *U.S. Public*, pg. 407
Ham, Fred, Pres.-Interior Systems & Components--United Technologies Automotive, Dearborn, MI; *U.S. Public*, pg. 1691
Ham, Marc, Pres.-Flapdoodles--Marisa Christina Inc., New Hyde Park, NY; *U.S. Public*, pg. 1044
Hamad, Samuel A., Pres.-Europe, Worldwide Pharmaceuticals Grp.--Bristol-Myers Squibb Company, New York, NY; *U.S. Public*, pg. 253
Hamaya, Mike, Pres.-BFS Technology--Bridgestone/Firestone, Inc., Nashville, TN; *Int'l*, pg. 213
Hambly, Lawrence W., Pres.-SunService--Sun Microsystems, Inc., Palo Alto, CA; *U.S. Public*, pg. 1531
Hamilton, Jean, Pres.-Diversified Opers.--The Prudential Insurance Company of America, Newark, NJ; *U.S. Private*, pg. 892
Hamilton, K. Bruce, V.P. & Pres.-Tracor Sys. Tech.--Tracor, Inc., Austin, TX; *U.S. Public*, pg. 1627
Hamm, Charles S., Grp. Pres.-Mobile Systems--BellSouth Enterprises, Inc., Atlanta, GA; *U.S. Public*, pg. 208
Hamman, William W., Pres.-Education Services/Marriott Management--Marriott International, Inc., Washington, DC; *U.S. Public*, pg. 1047
Hamman, William W., Pres.-Education Services--Marriott Management Services (MMS), Washington, DC; *U.S. Public*, pg. 1048
Hammarskjold, Alexis, Pres.-Stena Line IT Services AB--Stena Line AB, Goteborg, Sweden; *Int'l*, pg. 1300
Hammergren, John H., Pres.-McKesson Health Systems--McKesson Corporation, San Francisco, CA; *U.S. Public*, pg. 1072
Hanauer, James D., Pres.-Brown-Forman Distillery Co.--Brown-Forman Beverages Worldwide, Louisville, KY; *U.S. Public*, pg. 261
Haney, Jerry L., Pres.-Clinidata Medical Solutions--Hoechst Marion Roussel North America, Kansas City, MO; *Int'l*, pg. 625
Hanks, W. Bruce, Pres.-Telecommunications Svcs.--Century Telephone Enterprises, Inc., Monroe, LA; *U.S. Public*, pg. 329
Hannes, Peter J., Pres.-Special Mkts.--Jockey International, Inc., Kenosha, WI; *U.S. Private*, pg. 588
Hanninen, Juhani, Pres. & Chief Exec. Officer-Ahlstrom Pumps--A. Ahlstrom Corporation, Helsinki, Finland; *Int'l*, pg. 32
Hanson, Michael E., Pres.-Internal Medicine Business Unit--Eli Lilly and Company, Indianapolis, IN; *U.S. Public*, pg. 992
Hanway, H. Edward, Pres.-CIGNA Healthcare--Cigna Corp., Philadelphia, PA; *U.S. Public*, pg. 356
Hara, Susumu, Exec. Deputy Pres.--The Nikko Securities Co., Ltd., Tokyo, Japan; *Int'l*, pg. 930
Harbert, Philip M., Pres.-Reg.--1st Source Bank Consolidated, South Bend, IN; *U.S. Public*, pg. 638
Harcourt, David, Pres.-North America--Timesavers Inc., Crystal, MN; *U.S. Private*, pg. 1088
Harden, David R., Sr. V.P. & Pres.-West Penn/CDT--Cable Design Technologies Corporation, Pittsburgh, PA; *U.S. Public*, pg. 287
Hardiek, Bernard L., Pres.-Worldwide Agricultural Equipment Div.--Deere & Company, Moline, IL; *U.S. Public*, pg. 491
Hardin, Joseph S., Jr., Exec. V.P. & Pres.-Sam's--Wal-Mart Stores, Inc., Bentonville, AR; *U.S. Public*, pg. 1732
Hardin, Lonnie, Pres.-USHT--Avatex Corporation, Dallas, TX; *U.S. Public*, pg. 151
Harding, Larry G., Pres.-Maple Leaf Meats--Maple Leaf Foods Inc., Toronto, Canada; *Int'l*, pg. 841
Hardy, David L., Pres.-Custom Weave & Wunda Weave Sls. Div.--World Carpets, Inc., Dalton, GA; *U.S. Private*, pg. 1190
Hardy, Dr. Lester B., Pres., Gillette Medical Evaluation Laboratories--Corporate Product Integrity, Boston, MA; *U.S. Public*, pg. 744
Harper, James A., Pres.-Endocrine Business Unit--Eli Lilly and Company, Indianapolis, IN; *U.S. Public*, pg. 992
Harper, Robert, Pres.-Mktg.--Twentieth Century Fox Film Corp., Los Angeles, CA; *Int'l*, pg. 926
Harris, Alan F., Exec. V.P. & Pres.-Kellogg Latin America--Kellogg Company, Battle Creek, MI; *U.S. Public*, pg. 947
Harris, Barbara, Editor-in-Chief, Shape--Weider Publications, Inc., Woodland Hills, CA; *U.S. Private*, pg. 1159
Harris, Darryl, Pres.-H.H. Brown Canada--H.H. Brown Shoe Company, Inc., Greenwich, CT; *U.S. Public*, pg. 217
Harris, F. Edward, Pres.-Western Reg.--Crestar Financial Corporation, Richmond, VA; *U.S. Public*, pg. 458
Harris, F. Edward, Pres.-Western Reg.--Crestar Bank, Richmond, VA; *U.S. Public*, pg. 458
Harris, Gerald G., V.P. & Pres.-GM Div.--Lear Corporation, Southfield, MI; *U.S. Public*, pg. 981
Harris, Hugh R., Pres.--Homeside Lending Company, Jacksonville, FL; *Int'l*, pg. 906
Harrison, Stephen G., Pres.-Lee Hecht Harrison--Adecco Employment Services, Redwood City, CA; *Int'l*, pg. 24
Harrison, Thomas L., Pres.-Diversified Agency Services--Harrison & Star, New York, NY; *U.S. Private*, pg. 506
Harruff, Robert, Pres.-Identity Sys. Div.--Everbrite, Inc., Greenfield, WI; *U.S. Private*, pg. 386
Harshbarger, H. William, Pres.-AES Deepwater, Inc.--AES Corporation, Arlington, VA; *U.S. Public*, pg. 5
Hart, Garrett S., Pres.-Network TV--Paramount Pictures Corporation, Los Angeles, CA; *U.S. Private*, pg. 776
Hart, Philip, Pres.-Professional Group--Harman International Industries, Inc., Woodbury, NY; *U.S. Public*, pg. 787
Hart, Robert C., Pres.-Coastal Power Co.--The Coastal Corporation, Houston, TX; *U.S. Public*, pg. 389
Hartnett, Robert B., Pres.-Bus. Sls. & Services--MCI Communications Corp., Atlanta, GA; *U.S. Public*, pg. 1023
Harvey, F.L. Mike, Sr. V.P. & Grp. Pres.--Sterling Software, Inc., Dallas, TX; *U.S. Public*, pg. 1516
Hassan, Javad K., V.P. & Pres.-AMP Global Interconnect Systems Business--AMP Incorporated, Harrisburg, PA; *U.S. Public*, pg. 7
Hassey, L. Patrick, V.P. & Pres.-Aerospace/Commercial Rolled Prods.--Aluminum Company of America, Pittsburgh, PA; *U.S. Public*, pg. 60
Hatch, Rebecca A., Pres.-Bed & Bath Div. & Exec. V.P.--CHF Industries, Inc., New York, NY; *U.S. Private*, pg. 1094
Haten, P., Pres.-Melamine--DSM N.V., Heerlen, Netherlands; *Int'l*, pg. 352
Hattori, Hidehiko, Dep. Pres.--The Sumitomo Trust & Banking Co., Ltd., Osaka, Japan; *Int'l*, pg. 1317
Hautanen, Osmo, Pres.-Consumer Communications--Philips Electronics North America Corporation, New York, NY; *Int'l*, pg. 1053
Havers, Charles M., Pres.-Supply Div.--The Genlyte Group Incorporated, Union, NJ; *U.S. Public*, pg. 729
Haviland, E. Bernard, Pres.-Haviland Products--Haviland Enterprises, Grand Rapids, MI; *U.S. Private*, pg. 511
Haviland, R. Michael, Pres.-Haviland Engrng.--Haviland Enterprises, Grand Rapids, MI; *U.S. Private*, pg. 511
Hawkins, Frank, Pres.-Hawk Associates--KTI, Inc., Guttenberg, NJ; *U.S. Public*, pg. 939
Hawkins, Lawrence, Sr. V.P. & Pres.-Investors Trust, Inc.--Stewart Enterprises, Inc., Metairie, LA; *U.S. Public*, pg. 1518
Haws, Richard, Pres.-Residential Construction Div.--American Buildings Co., Eufaula, AL; *U.S. Public*, pg. 69
Hayden, Steve, Pres.-Worldwide Brand Services, IBM (NY)--Ogilvy & Mather Worldwide, Inc., New York, NY; *Int'l*, pg. 1483
Hayes, Edward J., Pres.--Equitable Holding Corporation, Secaucus, NJ; *U.S. Public*, pg. 589
Hayes, Kenneth G., Pres.-Image Guided Surgery Div.--Sofamor Danek Group, Inc., Memphis, TN; *U.S. Public*, pg. 1482
Hayes, R., Pres.-Publisher, Viking Childrens--Penguin Putnam Inc., New York, NY; *Int'l*, pg. 1027
Hayes, Stephen L., V.P. & Pres.-Parker Bertes Aerospace Group--Parker Hannifin Corporation, Cleveland, OH; *U.S.* Public, pg. 1259
Hays, Russell, Exec. V.P. & Pres.-Hospital Bus.--Nellcor Puritan Bennett Incorporated, Pleasanton, CA; *U.S. Public*, pg. 1039
Hazen, Thomas L., Pres.-New Bus. Devel.--Texaco Worldwide Exploration & Production, Scroggins, TX; *U.S.* Public, pg. 1583
Head, J. Michael, Pres.-Mark VII Risk Management Div.--Mark VII, Inc., Memphis, TN; *U.S. Public*, pg. 1046
Heasley, Philip G., Vice Chm. & Pres.-Retail Prod. Grp.--U.S. Bancorp, Minneapolis, MN; *U.S. Public*, pg. 1680
Hector, Roger, Pres.-Universal Studios Digital Arts--Universal Studios, Inc., Universal City, CA; *Int'l*, pg. 1215
Hedlen, Rodney, Pres.-Bus. Forms Div.--The Reynolds and Reynolds Company, Dayton, OH; *U.S. Public*, pg. 1384
Hedlund, Carl B., V.P. & Pres.-Asia Pacific--Owens Corning, Toledo, OH; *U.S. Public*, pg. 1236
Heffron, Brent F., Sr. V.P. & Pres.-Southern Div.--Stewart Enterprises, Inc., Metairie, LA; *U.S. Public*, pg. 1518
Heikonen, Pekka, Pres.--Detec International Oy, Lahti, Finland; *Int'l*, pg. 1352
Hein, Andrea, Pres.-Viacom Consumer Prods.--Paramount Pictures Corporation, Los Angeles, CA; *U.S. Private*, pg. 776
Heiner, Dennis G., Exec. V.P. & Pres.-Security Hardware Grp.--The Black & Decker Corporation, Towson, MD; *U.S. Public*, pg. 233
Helfrich, Carl P., Pres.-Turner Properties--Turner Broadcasting System Inc., Atlanta, GA; *U.S. Public*, pg. 1614
Hellman, Anders, Pres.-Volvo Penta--AB Volvo, Goteborg, Sweden; *Int'l*, pg. 1476
Henderson, Gary, Pres.-In-Store Mktg. Grp.--Muzak Limited Partnership, Seattle, WA; *U.S. Private*, pg. 222
Hendrickson, Julie, Pres.-Mktg.--Equity Services, Inc., Montpelier, VT; *U.S. Private*, pg. 785
Hengst, Wolf, Pres.-Regent International--Four Seasons Hotels Inc., Don Mills, Canada; *Int'l*, pg. 502
Henkel, Herbert L., Pres.-Textron Industrial Prods.--Textron Inc., Providence, RI; *U.S. Public*, pg. 1588
Hennessy, Scott C., V.P. & Pres.-True Temper Sports--The Black & Decker Corporation, Towson, MD; *U.S. Public*, pg. 233
Henry, Ragan A., Pres.--Mediacomm National, Inc., Haddonfield, NJ; *U.S. Public*, pg. 384
Henry, Roger P., Pres.-Swingster Div.--American Marketing Industries, Inc., Kansas City, MO; *U.S. Private*, pg. 58
Hensel, C.L., Sr. V.P. & Pres.-Titan Systems--The Titan Corporation, San Diego, CA; *U.S. Public*, pg. 1618
Hensel, J.E., Pres.-Shur-Gain--Maple Leaf Foods Inc., Toronto, Canada; *Int'l*, pg. 841
Henwood, Derek, Pres.--Great Lakes Gas Transmission Co., Detroit, MI; *Int'l*, pg. 1417
Heppener, Jan, Mng. Dir.-Stena Line BV--Stena Line AB, Goteborg, Sweden; *Int'l*, pg. 1300
Heppenstall, D. Barry, Pres.-Smith Tool--Smith International, Inc., Houston, TX; *U.S. Public*, pg. 1478
Herman, Michael F., Pres.-Diversified Tech. Grp.--Comdisco, Inc., Rosemont, IL; *U.S. Public*, pg. 407
Heron, William J., Pres.-American Express Financial Services Direct--American Express Company, New York, NY; *U.S. Public*, pg. 73
Herrera, Alain, Ph.D., V.P. & Pres.-Chiron Therapeutics/Europe--Chiron Corporation, Emeryville, CA; *U.S. Public*, pg. 349
Herring, James E., Pres.-IQUE--Dyersburg Corporation, Dyersburg, TN; *U.S. Public*, pg. 538
Hesse, Daniel, Pres.-AT&T Wireless Services & Exec. V.P.--AT&T Corporation, Basking Ridge, NJ; *U.S. Public*, pg. 10
Hester, Ronald M., Pres.-Alamar Knits Div.--WestPoint Stevens Inc., West Point, GA; *U.S. Public*, pg. 1762
Heuer, Alan J., Pres.-U.S. Region--Mastercard International, Inc., Purchase, NY; *U.S. Private*, pg. 714
Heydt, Steven, Pres.-Active Travel--Active International, Pearl River, NY; *U.S. Private*, pg. 15
Heyer, Steven J., Pres.-Worldwide Sls., Mktg., Distr. & Intl. Networks Group--Turner Broadcasting System Inc., Atlanta, GA; *U.S. Public*, pg. 1614
Hibbett, Chuck, Pres.-Sls.--McGill Manufacturing Company, Inc., Valparaiso, IN; *U.S. Public*, pg. 573
Hickingbotham, F. Todd, Pres.-Riverport Equip. & Distr.--TCBY Enterprises Inc., Little Rock, AR; *U.S. Public*, pg. 1553
Higgins, David, Pres.-Wine Grp.--Brown-Forman Beverages Worldwide, Louisville, KY; *U.S. Public*, pg. 261
Higley, Stephen S., Pres.-Cold Finished Bar Div.--Republic Engineered Steels, Inc., Massillon, OH; *U.S. Public*, pg. 1378
Hilder, Paul B., Pres.-Maintenance Mngmt.--Donlen Corp., Northbrook, IL; *U.S. Private*, pg. 340
Hill, Andrew W., Pres.-Progamming, Channel One Network--Primedia Inc., New York, NY; *U.S. Public*, pg. 1327
Hill, David C., Pres.-Fibers--AlliedSignal Inc., Engineered Materials, Morristown, NJ; *U.S. Public*, pg. 51
Hill, J.C., Pres.-Petroleum Prods. Div.--Phillips Petroleum Co. Europe-Africa, Woking, United Kingdom; *U.S. Public*, *pg. 1291*
Hill, Jake, Pres.-Endura Sls. Div.--The Biltrite Corporation, Waltham, MA; *U.S. Private*, pg. 144
Hillback, Elliott, Jr., Sr. V.P. & Pres. & Chief Exec. Officer-IG Laboratories--Genzyme Corporation, Cambridge, MA; *U.S. Public*, pg. 733
Hillege, J. W., Pres.-Engrng. Plastic Prods.--DSM N.V., Heerlen, Netherlands; *Int'l*, pg. 352
Hilyard, James E., V.P.--CertainTeed Corporation, Valley Forge, PA; *Int'l*, pg. 1170
Hinds, Joe M., Jr., Pres.-Northern Reg.--Regions Financial Corporation, Birmingham, AL; *U.S. Public*, pg. 1371
Hinds, Thomas M., Chm. Bd., Pres. & Chief Exec. Officer--Regions Bank/Mobile, Mobile, AL; *U.S. Public*, pg. 1372
Hinkaty, Charles, V.P. & Pres.-DelPharm--Del Laboratories, Inc., Farmingdale, NY; *U.S. Public*, pg. 494
Hiraishi, Yumio, Exec. Deputy Pres.--The Nikko Securities Co., Ltd., Tokyo, Japan; *Int'l*, pg. 930
Hirsch, Bradley, Pres.-Bonnie/Shane Div.--Jaclyn, Inc., West New York, NJ; *U.S. Public*, pg. 920
Hirsch, Steven, Pres.-Camelot Entertainment Sls., Inc.--King World Productions, Inc., New York, NY; *U.S. Public*, pg. 961
Hirschauer, Tom, Pres.-Indianapolis & Dir.--EvansGroup, Salt Lake City, UT; *U.S. Private*, pg. 385
Hirschhorn, Charles, Pres.-Walt Disney Television--Walt Disney Network Television, Burbank, CA; *U.S. Public*, pg. 511
Hiscock, Ronald G., Pres. & Gen. Mgr.-Outpatient Div.--NovaCare Inc., King of Prussia, PA; *U.S. Public*, pg. 1203
Hitt, Chris, Pres.-Mid-Atlantic Reg.--Whole Foods Market, Inc., Austin, TX; *U.S. Public*, pg. 1767
Hobson, Tony, Pres.-AG Mktg. & Commun.--Adair Greene Advertising, Atlanta, GA; *U.S. Private*, pg. 16
Hockema, Jack, Pres.-Kaiser Extruded Prods.--Kaiser Aluminum & Chemical Corporation, Pleasanton, CA; *U.S.* Public, pg. 1062
Hodges, Jim, Pres.-Asia/Pacific & Latin American Opers.--The Gates Rubber Company, Denver, CO; *Int'l*, pg. 1396
Hodgkins, R.J.J., Grp. Pres.-Asia Pacific--Keystone Pacific Pty. Ltd., Nowra, Australia; *U.S. Public*, pg. 1650
Hodgson, Richard N., V.P. & Pres.-Components Div.--Lear Corporation, Southfield, MI; *U.S. Public*, pg. 981
Hodnett, Robert, Pres.-Junior Sportswear--Fritzi of California Manufacturing Corp., San Francisco, CA; *U.S. Private*, pg. 429
Hoerig, Jerry, Pres.-Syntex Chemicals Inc. & V.P.-Chemical Opers.& Engrng. Serv.--Syntex, Palo Alto, CA; *Int'l*, pg. 1120
Hoff, George H., Pres.-Consumer Prod. Div.--Sargento Foods Inc., Plymouth, WI; *U.S. Private*, pg. 966
Hoffman, Hans, Pres.-Textile Dyes Div.--Ciba Specialty Chemicals, Tarrytown, NY; *Int'l*, pg. 291
Hoffman, Mark, Pres.-N. American Office Prods. Opers.--Corporate Express, Inc., Broomfield, CO; *U.S. Public*, pg. 449
Hoffman, Patti, Pres.-U.S. Reg. Offices & H.R.--Total Research Corporation, Princeton, NJ; *U.S. Public*, pg. 1625
Hoffmann, Kenneth O., V.P. & Pres.-Office Imaging--Eastman Kodak Company, Rochester, NY; *U.S. Public*, pg. 550
Hoffner, Larry, Pres.-Sls.--National Broadcasting Co., Inc., New York, NY; *U.S. Public*, pg. 712
Hofman, George, Pres.-Auto Grp.--Teleflex Incorporated, Plymouth Meeting, PA; *U.S. Public*, pg. 1569

Hofmann, George B., II, Pres. & Chief Exec. Officer--Nevada State Bank, Las Vegas, NV; *U.S. Public*, pg. 1793
Hofstra, Johan, Pres.-DMB&B Europe, Middle East, Africa, India & Pakistan--DMB&B Communications, New York, NY; *U.S. Private*, pg. 302
Hohage, Frederick, Exec. V.P. & Pres.-Sls. Grp.--Robert Bosch Corporation, Broadview, IL; *Int'l*, pg. 204
Hohorst, Wolfgang, Grp. Pres.-Interconnection--Bowthorpe plc, Crawley, United Kingdom; *Int'l*, pg. 207
Holburg, Terry, Pres.-ZD Brand--Ziff-Davis Publishing Company, New York, NY; *Int'l*, pg. 1276
Holden, Betsy, Pres.-Cheese Div.--Kraft Foods, Inc., Northfield, IL; *U.S. Public*, pg. 1287
Holder, George H., Pres.-Syntex Agribus.,Inc. & V.P.--Syntex, Palo Alto, CA; *Int'l*, pg. 1120
Holder, Patrick M., Pres.-Lexford Properties, Inc.--Lexford Residential Trust, Columbus, OH; *U.S. Public*, pg. 991
Holguin R., Juan Manuel, Pres.-Glassware Div.--Vitro, Sociedad Anonima, Garza Garcia, Mexico; *Int'l*, pg. 1469
Holland, Mike, Pres.-Southern Steel Company--Phelps Tointon Inc., Greeley, CO; *U.S. Private*, pg. 860
Hollander, Ted, Pres.-Presray Corp.--Pawling Corporation, Pawling, NY; *U.S. Private*, pg. 844
Hollars, James A., Sr. V.P. & Pres.-BMW Div.--Lear Corporation, Southfield, MI; *U.S. Public*, pg. 981
Holman-Rao, Marie, Pres.-Limited Design Services--The Limited, Inc., Columbus, OH; *U.S. Public*, pg. 995
Holmes, John B., Jr., Pres.-Sonat Exploration--Sonat Exploration Company, Houston, TX; *U.S. Public*, pg. 1485
Holmes, John E., Exec. V.P. & Pres.-JWT/Latin America & Caribbean--J. Walter Thompson Company, New York, NY; *Int'l*, pg. 1483
Hooley, John H., V.P. & Pres. & Chief Exec. Officer-Cub Foods--SuperValu, Inc., Eden Prairie, MN; *U.S. Public*, pg. 1540
Hoopes, Franky, Mgr.-Monomers--ICI Acrylics Inc., Cordova, TN; *Int'l*, pg. 663
Hoopis, Michael P., Exec. V.P. & Pres.-Household Prods.--The Black & Decker Corporation, Towson, MD; *U.S. Public*, pg. 233
Hoose, David Van, Pres.-Mexican Opers.--Pilgrim's Pride Corporation, Pittsburg, TX; *U.S. Public*, pg. 1296
Hoover, Charles E., Pres.--Capsugel, Morris Plains, NJ; *U.S. Public*, pg. 1739
Hopcraft, Lawrence J., V.P. & Pres.-Automotive Refrigeration Group--Parker Hannifin Corporation, Cleveland, OH; *U.S. Public*, pg. 1259
Hopkins, M.B., Pres. & Chief Exec. Officer-North America--Hunter Douglas N.V., Rotterdam, Netherlands; *Int'l*, pg. 639
Hoppel, Ronald W., Pres.-Pump Div.--Flowserve Corporation, Long Beach, CA; *U.S. Public*, pg. 658
Hopson, Andy, Pres.-Pub. Rels. & Dir.--EvansGroup, Salt Lake City, UT; *U.S. Private*, pg. 385
Horan, Peter, Pres.-IMS--International Data Group, Boston, MA; *U.S. Private*, pg. 569
Horne, Hugh W., Pres.-Real Estate Acquisitions--Public Storage, Inc., Glendale, CA; *U.S. Public*, pg. 1340
Horowitz, Dennis J., V.P. & Pres.-Americas--AMP Incorporated, Harrisburg, PA; *U.S. Public*, pg. 7
Horvath, Francis A., Pres.-Goodman Mfg. Co. of Canada, Ltd.--Goodman Equipment Corp., Bedford Park, IL; *U.S. Private*, pg. 464
Hoskins, Ken, Pres.-Pub. Rels. & Pub. Affairs--Creative Alliance, Inc., Louisville, KY; *U.S. Private*, pg. 287
Hotta, Kensuke, Deputy Pres.--The Sumitomo Bank, Limited, Osaka, Japan; *Int'l*, pg. 1308
Hourselt, Gary L., Pres.-Aerospace Div.--Huck International, Inc., Tucson, AZ; *U.S. Public*, pg. 1597
Houry, Jean Michel, Sr. V.P. & Pres.-Sensormatic Europe Retail Opers.--Sensormatic Electronics Corporation, Boca Raton, FL; *U.S. Public*, pg. 1457
House, David, Pres.-Establishment Services Worldwide--American Express Company, New York, NY; *U.S. Public*, *pg. 73*
House, Karen Elliott, Pres.-Intl.--Dow Jones & Company, Inc., New York, NY; *U.S. Public*, pg. 524
Howard, Al, Pres. & Gen. Mgr.--WFAA-TV, Dallas, TX; *U.S. Public*, pg. 209
Howard, Ed, Pres.-West--JC Penney Company, Inc., Plano, TX; *U.S. Public*, pg. 916
Howard, Mary Jayne, Pres.-Pub. Storage Commercial Properties Grp.,Inc.--Public Storage, Inc., Glendale, CA; *U.S. Public*, pg. 1340
Howell, Edwin C., V.P. & Pres.-Baker Oil Tools--Baker Hughes Incorporated, Houston, TX; *U.S. Public*, pg. 165
Hrieik, John, Jr., Pres.-WSFS Credit Corp.--WSFS Financial Corporation, Wilmington, DE; *U.S. Public*, pg. 1728
Hubbard, Robert W., Pres.-TV Grp. & V.P.--Hubbard Broadcasting, Inc., Saint Paul, MN; *U.S. Private*, pg. 543
Huber, Bruce, Pres.-Telemarketing Div.--Ruppman Marketing Technologies, Inc., Peoria, IL; *U.S. Private*, pg. 951
Hubert, Roger, Pres.-Manoir Industries--Groupe Strafor Facom, Morangis, France; *Int'l*, pg. 569
Huckesrein, Dieter H., Exec. V.P.-Opers. & Pres.-Hotel Opers.--Hilton Hotels Corporation, Beverly Hills, CA; *U.S.* Public, pg. 828
Hudetz, Mike, Div. Pres.--Solar Communications, Inc., Naperville, IL; *U.S. Private*, pg. 1012
Hudetz, Peter, Div. Pres.--Solar Communications, Inc., Naperville, IL; *U.S. Private*, pg. 1012
Hudkins, Jerry H., V.P. & Pres.-Wire Grp.--Leggett & Platt, Incorporated, Carthage, MO; *U.S. Public*, pg. 985
Huey, Ward L., Jr., Vice Chm. & Pres.-Broadcasting Div.--A.H. Belo Corporation, Dallas, TX; *U.S. Public*, pg. 209
Hufham, Wilbur B., Pres.-Southern Reg.--Regions Financial Corporation, Birmingham, AL; *U.S. Public*, pg. 1371
Hughes, Christopher D., V.P. & Pres.-Booth/Crystal Tips--Scotsman Industries, Inc., Vernon Hills, IL; *U.S. Public*, pg. 1444
Hughes, Ivan, Pres.-Plastic Div.--Duro Bag Manufacturing Co., Ludlow, KY; *U.S. Private*, pg. 348
Hughes, J.H., Pres.-U.K.--GKN North America Services Inc., Memphis, TN; *Int'l*, pg. 535
Hughes, Louis R., Exec. V.P., Pres. & Gen. Mgr.-Intl. Opers.--General Motors Corporation, Detroit, MI; *U.S. Public*, pg. 718
Hughes, Nora O., Pres.--Sumitomo Bank Securities, Inc., New York, NY; *Int'l*, pg. 1309
Hunkin, John, Pres.-Wood Grundy--Canadian Imperial Bank of Commerce, Toronto, Canada; *Int'l*, pg. 256
Hunter, John C., Pres.-Westcoast Energy (Asia) Inc.--Westcoast Energy Inc., Vancouver, Canada; *Int'l*, pg. 1492
Hunter, Michael T., Pres.--Lone Star Pipeline Company, Dallas, TX; *U.S. Public*, pg. 1587
Hunter, Robert D., Pres.-Fin. Info. Services Group--McGraw-Hill Financial Information Services Group, New York, NY; *U.S. Public*, pg. 1071
Hur, Jong Wook, Deputy Pres. & Dir.--Cho Hung Bank, Seoul, Korea; *Int'l*, pg. 287
Hurrelbrink, Dick, Pres.-Cash Plus--Campbell Mithun Esty, Minneapolis, MN; *U.S. Private*, pg. 204
Huschle, Ralph, Pres.-F.O.L. Intl. Div.--Union Underwear Co., Inc., Bowling Green, KY; *U.S. Public*, pg. 686
Huser, Fred, Pres.-Consumer Div.--Sandoz Pharmaceuticals Corp., East Hanover, NJ; *Int'l*, pg. 974
Hushdon, John D., Pres.-El Paso Energy Intl. Co.--El Paso Natural Gas Co., Houston, TX; *U.S. Public*, pg. 567
Huskey, Art, Pres.-Scoular Properties, Inc.--The Scoular Company, Omaha, NE; *U.S. Private*, pg. 977
Huston, James M., V.P. & Pres.-First Recovery--Valvoline Company, Lexington, KY; *U.S. Public*, pg. 139
Huttenburg, Debra Buck, Grp. Pres.-Antenna Sys.--Andrew Corporation, Orland Park, IL; *U.S. Public*, pg. 112
Huyard, Wayne E., Pres.-Mass Markets--MCI Communications Corp., Atlanta, GA; *U.S. Public*, pg. 1023
Hyde, Gerald, Pres.-Athletic Div.--Dexter Shoe Company, Dexter, ME; *U.S. Public*, pg. 217
Hyde, James R., Sr. V.P. & Pres.-Grace Div.--W.R. Grace & Co., Boca Raton, FL; *U.S. Public*, pg. 754
Ibanez, James, Pres.-Window Div.--CHF Industries, Inc., New York, NY; *U.S. Private*, pg. 1094
Idell, Cheryl, Pres.-Res. & Strategic Plng.--Western International Media Corporation, Los Angeles, CA; *U.S. Private*, pg. 1165
Ikematsu, Masayoshi, Exec. Dir. & Pres. of Dentsu Actis Inc.--Dentsu Inc., Tokyo, Japan; *Int'l*, pg. 392
Ilkhani-Pour, Mehdi, Pres.-Automotive Vibration Div.--Freudenberg-NOK, Plymouth, MI; *U.S. Private*, pg. 427
Illingworth, David, Exec. V.P. & Pres.-Alternatecare Bus.--Nellcor Puritan Bennett Incorporated, Pleasanton, CA; *U.S. Public*, pg. 1039
Imhof, Heinz T., Pres.-Agriculture, Seeds--Novartis AG, Basel, Switzerland; *Int'l*, pg. 971
Ingham, Clive, Pres.-Europe--Moore Corporation Limited, Toronto, Canada; *Int'l*, pg. 888
Inglesino, Bert J., Pres.-Northeast Region--BNY Holdings (New Jersey) Corp., West Paterson, NJ; *U.S. Public*, pg. 178
Inman, Darrel F., Pres.-Sporting Equipment Div.--Blount International, Inc., Montgomery, AL; *U.S. Public*, pg. 237
Inman, Sam I., Pres.-North America--IBM Personal Computer Company, Somers, NY; *U.S. Public*, pg. 896
Inoue, T., Dir.-Intl. Opers.--Bando Chemical Industries, Ltd., Kobe, Japan; *Int'l*, pg. 145
Irvin, John W., Pres.-Catalog Div.--Spiegel, Inc., Downers Grove, IL; *U.S. Public*, pg. 1498
Irwin, Joseph P., Pres.-Knit Apparel Div.--Russell Corporation, Alexander City, AL; *U.S. Public*, pg. 1413
Isdell, E. Neville, Pres.-Greater Europe Grp.--The Coca-Cola Company, Atlanta, GA; *U.S. Public*, pg. 392
Iselin, John W., Jr., Pres.-U.S. Bakery Prods.--The Earthgrains Company, Clayton, MO; *U.S. Public*, pg. 547
Ishak, H.B., Pres.--EMTEC Magnetics China Ltd., Kowloon, Hong Kong; *Int'l*, pg. 743
Ishee, R., Pres.-Mactac N. America--MACtac Morgan Adhesive Company, Stow, OH; *U.S. Public*, pg. 210
Ishihara, Tatsuo, Pres.-N.S. Japan--National Semiconductor Corporation, Santa Clara, CA; *U.S. Public*, pg. 1159
Isom, Gerald A., Pres.-CIGNA Property & Casualty/Domestic--Cigna Corp., Philadelphia, PA; *U.S. Public*, pg. 356
Ito, Takashi, Dep. Pres.--Daido Hoxan Inc., Tokyo, Japan; *Int'l*, pg. 363
Ivester, Ann M., Pres.-Cornerstone Title Company--Ryland Mortgage Co., Columbia, MD; *U.S. Public*, pg. 1414
Iwasaki, Tetsuo, Pres.-Applied Komatsu Technology, Inc.--Applied Materials, Inc., Santa Clara, CA; *U.S. Public*, pg. 123
Iwashita, Kenneth M., Pres. & Chief Oper. Officer-Lubrizol Foundation--The Lubrizol Corporation, Wickliffe, OH; *U.S.* Public, pg. 1016
Jackson, Mark, Pres.-Recording Heads Grp.--Quantum Corporation, Milpitas, CA; *U.S. Public*, pg. 1350
Jacobs, Phil S., Sr. V.P.-Managed Network Solutions & Pres.-BellSouth BSE, Inc.--BellSouth Corporation, Atlanta, GA; *U.S. Public*, pg. 207
Jacobson, Andrew, Pres.--Little Bear Organic Foods, Inc., Carson, CA; *U.S. Public*, pg. 774
Jacuzzi, Paul V., Pres.-Watts Indust.--Watts Industries, Inc., North Andover, MA; *U.S. Public*, pg. 1746
Jacuzzi, Roy A., Pres.--Jacuzzi, Inc., Walnut Creek, CA; *U.S. Public*, pg. 1684
James, Donald M., Pres.--Vulcan Materials Company-Southern Div., Birmingham, AL; *U.S. Public*, pg. 1726
James, Elizabeth R., Pres.-Synovus Administrative Services Corp.--Synovus Financial Corp., Columbus, GA; *U.S. Public*, pg. 1548
James, Elizabeth R., Pres.-Synovus Service Corp.--Total System Services, Inc., Columbus, GA; *U.S. Public*, pg. 1550
James, Graham S., Mng. Dir.-Amcor Europe--Amcor Limited, Melbourne, Australia; *Int'l*, pg. 71
Janas, Steven L., Pres.-Time-Life Music--Time-Life, Inc., Alexandria, VA; *U.S. Public*, pg. 1613
Jantzen, Robert J., Jr., Pres.-Marriott Corporate Services & Marriott Management--Marriott International, Inc., Washington, DC; *U.S. Public*, pg. 1047
Jarrett, Mike, Branch Pres.--First State Bank N.A., Abilene, Abilene, TX; *U.S. Public*, pg. 874
Jasperson, Roger, Pres.-Englander Sleep Products--Schottenstein Stores Corporation, Columbus, OH; *U.S. Private*, pg. 972
Jeannet, Roland, Dr., Pres.-Consumer Health--Novartis AG, Basel, Switzerland; *Int'l*, pg. 971
Jeans, Michael D., Corp. V.P. & Pres.-Nashua Photo Inc.--Nashua Corporation, Nashua, NH; *U.S. Public*, pg. 1152
Jeffcoat, James W., Pres.-Constellation Health Services--Constellation Holdings, Inc., Baltimore, MD; *U.S. Public*, pg. 172
Jeffs, Thomas H., II, Vice Chm. & Pres.-NBD Bank (Michigan)--First Chicago NBD Corporation, Chicago, IL; *U.S. Public*, pg. 627
Jenkin, Tom, Pres.-Ahlstrom Machinery--A. Ahlstrom Corporation, Helsinki, Finland; *Int'l*, pg. 32
Jensen, Irv, Pres.-CMF&Z Des Moines--Creswell, Munsell, Fultz & Zirbel, L.P., Cedar Rapids, IA; *U.S. Private*, pg. 1197
Jerritts, Stephen G., Pres.-Latin America--Wang Laboratories, Inc., Billerica, MA; *U.S. Public*, pg. 1737
Jobe, Jan, Pres.-Principal Interntional, Inc.--Principal Mutual Life Insurance Co., Des Moines, IA; *U.S. Private*, pg. 886
Joffrin, Alain, Pres.-Europe, Africa & Middle East--Eastman Kodak Company, Rochester, NY; *U.S. Public*, pg. 550
Johannesson, Tuve, Pres.-Flagship Car Div.--AB Volvo, Goteborg, Sweden; *Int'l*, pg. 1476
Johansson, Bjorn, Pres.-Lion Ferry AB--Stena Line AB, Goteborg, Sweden; *Int'l*, pg. 1300
Johns, Benjamin I., Jr., Pres.-The Bacova Guild, Ltd.--Burlington Industries, Inc., Greensboro, NC; *U.S. Public*, pg. 268
Johnson, Andrew F., Co-Chief Exec. Officer & Pres.-Opers.--Hastings Manufacturing Company, Hastings, MI; *U.S. Public*, pg. 798
Johnson, B. Kristine, Sr. V.P. & Pres.-Vascular Business--Medtronic, Inc., Minneapolis, MN; *U.S. Public*, pg. 1082
Johnson, Ben, Pres.--Eneron Co., San Marcos, TX; *U.S. Private*, pg. 1080
Johnson, Chris, V.P. & Gen. Mgr.-PWB Products)--Dexter Electronic Materials Division, City of Industry, CA; *U.S. Public*, pg. 504
Johnson, Dixon R., V.P. & Pres.-Consumer Prods.--Alba-Waldensian, Inc., Valdese, NC; *U.S. Public*, pg. 35
Johnson, H. Fisk, Ph.D., Pres.-Consumer Prods., Americas, India, Asia-Pacific--S.C. Johnson & Son, Inc., Racine, WI; *U.S. Private*, pg. 592
Johnson, Harold O., Sr. V.P.-Contact Lens Div.--Bausch & Lomb Incorporated, Rochester, NY; *U.S. Public*, pg. 194
Johnson, Jennie M., Pres.--Pierce National Life Insurance Co., Greenville, SC; *U.S. Public*, pg. 992
Johnson, Karen R., Pres.-Texas--Entergy Gulf States, Inc., Beaumont, TX; *U.S. Public*, pg. 586
Johnson, Mark R.S., Co-Chief Exec. Officer & Pres.-Mktg.--Hastings Manufacturing Company, Hastings, MI; *U.S. Public*, pg. 798
Johnson, Peter, Pres.-Oil Div.--Sinclair Oil Corp., Salt Lake City, UT; *U.S. Private*, pg. 1003
Johnson, Robert, Pres. & Chief Exec. Officer-Dry Bulk Services--Chemical Leaman Tank Lines, Inc., Exton, PA; *U.S. Private*, pg. 233
Johnson, Ron, Pres.-Principal Casualty & V.P.-Grp. Opers.--The Principal Financial Group, Des Moines, IA; *U.S. Private*, pg. 885
Johnson, Stuart C., Grp. Pres.-Large Bus. & Information Services--Bell Atlantic Network Services, Inc., Arlington, VA; *U.S. Public*, pg. 202
Johnson, Thomas H., Pres.-Riverhead Industrial Inc.--Johns Manville Corporation, Denver, CO; *U.S. Public*, pg. 927
Johnson, Tom, Pres.-CNN--CNN Headline News, Atlanta, GA; *U.S. Public*, pg. 1614
Johnson, W. Thomas, Pres.-CNN--Turner Broadcasting System Inc., Atlanta, GA; *U.S. Public*, pg. 1614
Johnson, William, Area Pres.--New Fortis Corp., King, NC; *U.S. Public*, pg. 843
Johnston, Robert L., Pres.-AES Placerita, Inc.--AES Corporation, Arlington, VA; *U.S. Public*, pg. 5
Johnston, Summerfield K., III, Sr. V.P. & Pres.-Eastern Grp.--Coca-Cola Enterprises Inc., Atlanta, GA; *U.S. Public*, pg. 393
Jones, Barry, Pres.-DMB&B Asia/Pacific, North--DMB&B Communications, New York, NY; *U.S. Private*, pg. 302
Jones, David, Pres.-UK Grp.--DMB&B/London, London, United Kingdom; *U.S. Private*, pg. 304
Jones, Jeffrey D., Grp. V.P. & Pres.-Latin America/South--The Procter & Gamble Company, Cincinnati, OH; *U.S. Public*, pg. 1330
Jones, P.F., Pres.-Rendering Operations--Maple Leaf Foods Inc., Toronto, Canada; *Int'l*, pg. 841
Jones, Ron, Pres.-Home Furnishings Prods.--Masco Corporation, Taylor, MI; *U.S. Public*, pg. 1052
Jones, Russell H., Mng. Dir.-Amcor Fibre Packaging--Amcor Limited, Melbourne, Australia; *Int'l*, pg. 71
Jones, Steve, Pres.-Princor & V.P.-Principal Financial Group--Principal Mutual Life Insurance Co., Des Moines, IA; *U.S. Private*, pg. 886
Jones, William H., Chm. Bd. & Pres.--Foster Wheeler Energy Corporation, Clinton, NJ; *U.S. Public*, pg. 676
Jordan, Denny, Pres.-Home Fashion Div.--F. Schumacher & Co., New York, NY; *U.S. Private*, pg. 973
Jordan, Guy J., Grp. Pres.--C.R. Bard, Inc., Murray Hill, NJ; *U.S. Public*, pg. 189
Jordan, William E., Pres.-Central Reg.--Regions Financial Corporation, Birmingham, AL; *U.S. Public*, pg. 1371
Josefsen, Turi, Exec. V.P. & Pres.-Intl. Opers.--U.S. Surgical Corp., Norwalk, CT; *U.S. Public*, pg. 1687

Josendale, John D., Grp. Pres.-Wire Rope Prods.--Wire Rope Corporation of America, Inc., Saint Joseph, MO; *U.S. Private*, pg. 1184

Josephson, Barry, Pres.-Production--Columbia Pictures, Culver City, CA; *Int'l*, pg. 1281

Joslyn, Vern, Pres.-Northeast Div.--The Home Depot, Inc., Atlanta, GA; *U.S. Public*, pg. 831

Judge, Frederick L., Sr. V.P. & Pres.-Titan Information Systems--The Titan Corporation, San Diego, CA; *U.S. Public*, pg. 1618

Junck, Mary E., Pres.-Eastern newspapers--Times Mirror Magazines, Inc., New York, NY; *U.S. Public*, pg. 1616

Jund, Daniel E., Pres.-Transamerica Assurance Co. & Sr. V.P.--Transamerica Life Companies, Los Angeles, CA; *U.S. Public*, pg. 1630

Jung, Andrea, Exec. V.P. & Pres.-Global Mktg. & New Bus.--Avon Products, Inc., New York, NY; *U.S. Public*, pg. 155

Juranville, Benoit, Pres.-Invacare Europe--Invacare Corporation, Elyria, OH; *U.S. Public*, pg. 911

Kaenzig, J. Gary, Jr., Sr. V.P. & Pres.-Grace Packaging--W.R. Grace & Co., Boca Raton, FL; *U.S. Public*, pg. 754

Kaesbeck, Norbert, Dr., Mng. Dir.-Org. & Construction Mngmt.--Commerzbank AG, Frankfurt, Germany; *Int'l*, pg. 308

Kagawa, Cliff, Pres. & Chief Exec. Officer-Asia Pacific--Hill and Knowlton, Inc., New York, NY; *Int'l*, pg. 1483

Kalagher, Steven, Exec. V.P. & Pres.-Spirits & Wine Grp.--The Seagram Company Ltd., Montreal, Canada; *Int'l*, pg. 1214

Kalosis, Stephen, Pres.-Bldg. Prods. Div.--Libbey Owens Ford Co., Toledo, OH; *Int'l*, pg. 1056

Kaman, C. William, II, Exec. V.P. & Pres.-Kaman Music--Kaman Corporation, Bloomfield, CT; *U.S. Public*, pg. 941

Kamdar, Taroon, Pres.-Asia Pacific Div. & Exec. V.P.--Micropolis Corporation, Chatsworth, CA; *U.S. Private*, pg. 742

Kammerer, Michael J., Sr. V.P. & Pres.-Engineered Equipment & Systems Group--Dresser Industries, Inc., Dallas, TX; *U.S. Public*, pg. 528

Kanan, Charles V., Pres.-Play It Again Sports--Grow Biz International, Inc., Minneapolis, MN; *U.S. Public*, pg. 767

Kangas, Markku, Pres.-Valmet Automation Inc.--Valmet Corporation, Helsinki, Finland; *Int'l*, pg. 1447

Kaplan, Barry S., Pres.-Transmedia ServiceCo. & V.P.--Transmedia Network Inc., Miami, FL; *U.S. Public*, pg. 1631

Kaplan, Jay G., Pres.-Plastics--AlliedSignal Inc., Engineered Materials, Morristown, NJ; *U.S. Public*, pg. 51

Kaplan, Martin A., Pres.-Network Services Grp.--Pacific Bell, San Ramon, CA; *U.S. Public*, pg. 1416

Karszes, Arthur J., V.P. & Pres.-Applied Physical Sciences Div.--Springborn Testing & Research, Inc., Enfield, CT; *U.S. Private*, pg. 1027

Katen, Karen L., V.P., Exec. V.P.-Pfizer Pharmaceuticals Grp. & Pres.-U.S. Pharm.--Pfizer Inc., New York, NY; *U.S. Public*, pg. 1281

Kates, Thomas, Pres.-Realty--Stiles Corporation, Fort Lauderdale, FL; *U.S. Private*, pg. 1043

Katoh, Shigeyoshi, Deputy Pres.--The Sumitomo Bank, Limited, Osaka, Japan; *Int'l*, pg. 1308

Kauffman, James H., Pres.-Div.--Keystone Steel & Wire Co., Peoria, IL; *U.S. Public*, pg. 955

Kaufman, Donald L., Pres.-Alside Div.--Associated Materials Incorporated, Dallas, TX; *U.S. Private*, pg. 91

Kaufman, John S., Pres.-Koo Koo Roo USA--Koo Koo Roo, Inc., Los Angeles, CA; *U.S. Public*, pg. 966

Kawalek, Polly B., Pres.-Hot Breakfasts--U.S. & Canadian Food Products, Chicago, IL; *U.S. Public*, pg. 1347

Kazzaz, Amos, Pres.-Shuttle by United--United Air Lines, Inc., Elk Grove Village, IL; *U.S. Public*, pg. 1653

Kearney, Matthew B., Pres.--Resorts International Hotel Financing, Inc., Atlantic City, NJ; *U.S. Private*, pg. 480

Keating, Brian A., Exec. V.P. & Western Reg. Pres.--Marine Midland Bank, Buffalo, NY; *Int'l*, pg. 581

Keating, Susan, Exec. V.P. & Pres.-Dauphin Deposit Bank--First Maryland Bancorp, Baltimore, MD; *Int'l*, pg. 64

Keegan, Robert J., Pres.-Consumer Imaging & Sr. V.P.--Eastman Kodak Company, Rochester, NY; *U.S. Public*, pg. 550

Keeley, Kenneth, Pres.-North Division--Airgas, Inc., Radnor, PA; *U.S. Public*, pg. 33

Kehela, Karen, Pres.-Production--Imagine Entertainment, Los Angeles, CA; *U.S. Private*, pg. 558

Keighley, David B., V.P. & Pres.-David Keighley Productions--Imax Corporation, Mississauga, Canada; *Int'l*, pg. 661

Keirle, Stuart O., Pres.-Circle Trade Services--Circle International Group, Inc., San Francisco, CA; *U.S. Public*, pg. 370

Keith, John E., Pres.-Retail Div.--Rock of Ages Corporation, Graniteville, VT; *U.S. Public*, pg. 1396

Keith, Robert F., Pres.-ServiceMaster Mngmt. Svcs.--The ServiceMaster Company, Downers Grove, IL; *U.S. Public*, pg. 1461

Keller, Larry J., Mng. Principal-Architecture--Dewberry & Davis, Fairfax, VA; *U.S. Private*, pg. 329

Kelley, Bernard J., Pres.-Merck Mfg. Div.--Merck & Co., Inc., Whitehouse Station, NJ; *U.S. Public*, pg. 1090

Kelley, Edward B., Pres.-USAA Real Estate Co.--USAA (United Services Automobile Association), San Antonio, TX; *U.S. Private*, pg. 1114

Kelley, John C., Jr., Pres.-Memphis Banking Grp.--First Tennessee National Corporation, Memphis, TN; *U.S. Public*, pg. 638

Kelley, John C., Jr., Exec. V.P. & Pres.-Memphis Banking Grp.--First Tennessee Bank National Association, Memphis, TN; *U.S. Public*, pg. 639

Kelley, Kendall D., Grp. Pres.-Northwest Grp.--Beneficial Corporation, Wilmington, DE; *U.S. Public*, pg. 211

Kelly, Frank, Pres.-Creative Affairs--Paramount Pictures Corporation, Los Angeles, CA; *U.S. Private*, pg. 776

Kelly, Karri, Pres.-Robson Cable--Robson Communities, Sun Lakes, AZ; *U.S. Private*, pg. 937

Kelly, Kevin O., Pres.-Michael Sales Group--Michael Foods, Inc., Minneapolis, MN; *U.S. Public*, pg. 1103

Kelman, J. Brent, Pres.-Truscan Realty Ltd. & Sr. V.P.--CT Financial Services, Inc., Toronto, Canada; *Int'l*, pg. 112

Kendall, Jerry T., Pres.-North American Retail Opers.--Sensormatic Electronics Corporation, Boca Raton, FL; *U.S. Public*, pg. 1457

Kennedy, George M., Chm.-Medical Systems Grp.--Smiths Industries plc, London, United Kingdom; *Int'l*, pg. 1266

Kennedy, James, Pres.-National Starch & Crosfield--Unilever Plc, London, United Kingdom; *Int'l*, pg. 1433

Kennedy, Jerry W., Pres.-Cone Sportswear Fabrics Div.--Cone Apparel Products, Greensboro, NC; *U.S. Public*, pg. 430

Kent, Ginger, Pres.-Brands & Prod. Devel. Grp.--Hasbro, Inc., Pawtucket, RI; *U.S. Public*, pg. 797

Kenyon, Alfred, Pres. & Chief Oper. Officer--Lumbermen's Mutual Casualty Company, Long Grove, IL; *U.S. Private*, pg. 614

Kenyon, Alfred, Pres. & Chief Oper. Officer--American Manufacturers Mutual Insurance Company, Long Grove, IL; *U.S. Private*, pg. 614

Kenyon, Bruce D., Pres. & Chief Exec. Officer-Nuclear--Northeast Utilities, Berlin, CT; *U.S. Public*, pg. 1194

Keohane, Jeffrey P., Pres.-Integrated Tech. Svcs.--Comdisco, Inc., Rosemont, IL; *U.S. Public*, pg. 407

Kerr, James L., V.P.-Distributor Div.--Rochester Midland Corporation, Rochester, NY; *U.S. Private*, pg. 937

Kerwin, Joseph P., M.D., Pres.-Krug Life Sciences, Inc.--Krug International Corp., Houston, TX; *U.S. Public*, pg. 967

Kesler, Steven D., Pres.-Constellation Investments--Constellation Holdings, Inc., Baltimore, MD; *U.S. Public*, pg. 172

Kessavan, Sudakar, Grp. Pres. & Exec. V.P.--ICF Kaiser International Inc., Fairfax, VA; *U.S. Public*, pg. 852

Kessell, Frederick C., Pres. & Chief Investment Officer-Providian Capital Mngmt.--AEGON USA, Inc., Louisville, KY; *Int'l*, pg. 26

Kessler, Richard L., Grp. Pres.-Wire Prods.--Wire Rope Corporation of America, Inc., Saint Joseph, MO; *U.S. Private*, pg. 1184

Ketchum, Mark D., Grp. V.P. & Pres.-Paper Prods./North America--The Procter & Gamble Company, Cincinnati, OH; *U.S. Public*, pg. 1330

Kevorkian, Aram T., Pres.-RMC Distributor--Rochester Midland Corporation, Rochester, NY; *U.S. Private*, pg. 937

Kidokoro, Takashi, Exec. Deputy Pres.--The Nikko Securities Co., Ltd., Tokyo, Japan; *Int'l*, pg. 930

Kieckhafer, Thomas W., Corp. V.P. & Pres.-The West Bend Company--Premark International, Inc., Deerfield, IL; *U.S. Public*, pg. 1321

Kiesau, Kenneth A., Grp. Pres.-Promotional & Informational Graphics--Menasha Corporation, Neenah, WI; *U.S. Private*, pg. 731

Kilduff, John M., Pres.-Dr. Pepper USA--Dr. Pepper Co., Dallas, TX; *Int'l*, pg. 248

Killduff, John A., Pres.-Comml. & Indus. Div.--Howard Hughes Corporation, Las Vegas, NV; *U.S. Public*, pg. 1407

Killingsworth, Cleve L., Jr., Pres.-Central East Division & Sr. V.P.--Kaiser Permanente, Oakland, CA; *U.S. Private*, pg. 605

Kilpatrick, Kevin, Pres.-Birmingham Reg.--Pinnacle Bank, Jasper, AL; *U.S. Public*, pg. 1297

Kilroy, Bruce G., Exec. V.P. & Pres.-Lehigh Valley Div.--National Penn Bank, Boyertown, PA; *U.S. Public*, pg. 1159

Kimball, Richard C., Vice Chm. & Pres.-Memorials Div.--Rock of Ages Corporation, Graniteville, VT; *U.S. Public*, pg. 1396

Kindela, Jerry, Editor-in-Chief, Flex--Weider Publications, Inc., Woodland Hills, CA; *U.S. Private*, pg. 1159

King, Elton R., Grp. Pres.-Network & Tech.--BellSouth Telecommunications, Inc., Atlanta, GA; *U.S. Public*, pg. 209

King, Gerry, Pres.-Catalog Fullfillment Svcs. & Chief Oper. Officer--LCS Industries, Inc., Clifton, NJ; *U.S. Public*, pg. 970

King, James S., Pres.-Kraft Foods/Asia Pacific--Kraft Foods International, Rye Brook, NY; *U.S. Public*, pg. 1288

King, Jim, Pres.-Sls.--Things Remembered, Inc., Highland Heights, OH; *U.S. Public*, pg. 397

King, Ken, Pres.-Land Pride Division--Great Plains Manufacturing, Inc., Salina, KS; *U.S. Private*, pg. 475

King, Richard C., Chm., Pres. & Chief Exec. Officer-MBK & MBKC--Mercantile Bancorporation Inc., Saint Louis, MO; *U.S. Public*, pg. 1087

King, Robert S., Pres.-Phillps Publ.--Phillips Publishing International, Inc., Potomac, MD; *U.S. Private*, pg. 862

Kingsbury, Peter, Pres. & Chief Exec. Officer-Asia/Pacific (Singapore)--Burson-Marsteller, New York, NY; *U.S. Private*, pg. 1197

Kinne, Harold, Pres.-Additives Div.--Ciba Specialty Chemicals, Tarrytown, NY; *Int'l*, pg. 291

Kinney, Dale F., Pres.-Govt. Systems Grp.--Day & Zimmermann, Inc., Philadelphia, PA; *U.S. Private*, pg. 316

Kinsey, William C., Pres.--Bird Vinyl, Bardstown, KY; *Int'l*, pg. 699

Kipperman, Robert P., Pres.-CBS Radio Networks--Westwood One, Inc., New York, NY; *U.S. Public*, pg. 1763

Kippur, Stephen, Exec. V.P. & Grp. Pres.--Professional Reference & Trade Group, New York, NY; *U.S. Public*, pg. 1768

Kippur, Stephen A., Exec. V.P. & Grp. Pres., PRT--John Wiley & Sons, Inc., New York, NY; *U.S. Public*, pg. 1768

Kirk, J. Philip Jr., V.P. & Pres.-DST Realty, Inc.--DST Systems, Inc., Kansas City, MO; *U.S. Public*, pg. 943

Kirk, James R., Sr. V.P. & Pres.-Res. & Devel.--Campbell Soup Company, Camden, NJ; *U.S. Public*, pg. 298

Kirk, Robert L., Chm. Bd., Pres. & Chief Exec. Officer--British Aerospace Holdings Inc., Chantilly, VA; *Int'l*, pg. 218

Kirkland, Gerry P., Pres.-CTR Manufacturing, Inc.--Blount International, Inc., Montgomery, AL; *U.S. Public*, pg. 237

Kisanuki, Yutaka, Pres.-Japan Opers.--Novellus Systems, Inc., San Jose, CA; *U.S. Public*, pg. 1204

Kiselick, William, Area Pres.--New Fortis Corp., King, NC; *U.S. Public*, pg. 843

Kistinger, Robert F., Pres.-Chiquita Banana Grp.--Chiquita Brands International, Inc., Cincinnati, OH; *U.S. Public*, pg. 349

Kistinger, Robert F., Pres.-Chiquita Banana Grp.--Chiquita Banana North America, Cincinnati, OH; *U.S. Public*, pg. 349

Kitch, Gerald C., Exec. V.P. & Pres.-Intl. Bus. Devel.--Pentair, Inc., Saint Paul, MN; *U.S. Public*, pg. 1273

Kitchen, Robert, Pres.--Freedom Textiles Chemicals Co., Charlotte, NC; *U.S. Private*, pg. 425

Kittredge, George, Pres.-RMC East Div.--Rochester Midland Corporation, Rochester, NY; *U.S. Private*, pg. 937

Klasky, Jack, Pres.-Leadtec Sys., Inc. & V.P.--Willcox & Gibbs, Inc., Carteret, NJ; *U.S. Private*, pg. 1177

Klausman, Michael, Pres.-Studio Center--CBS, New York, NY; *U.S. Public*, pg. 273

Klein, Howard, Pres.-Reprise Records--Warner Bros. Records, Inc., Burbank, CA; *U.S. Public*, pg. 1611

Klein, James J., Pres.-Consumer Prods. Grp.--Spencer Gifts, Inc., Egg Harbor Township, NJ; *Int'l*, pg. 1216

Klein, Jonathan, Pres.-TV Stations Grp.--CBS Broadcast Group, New York, NY; *U.S. Public*, pg. 274

Kleisner, Fred, Pres. & Chief Oper. Officer-Westin Hotel Co.--Westin Hotels & Resorts, Seattle, WA; *U.S. Public*, pg. 1512

Kline, Richard D., Pres.-North American Opers.--S.A. Cimenteries CBR, Brussels, Belgium; *Int'l*, pg. 605

Klinger, Douglas E., Pres.-Cigna Dental Health--Cigna Corp., Philadelphia, PA; *U.S. Public*, pg. 356

Klipfell, John M., Pres.-CreataCard--American Greetings Corporation, Cleveland, OH; *U.S. Public*, pg. 77

Kluge, Holger, Pres.-Personal & Commercial Bank--Canadian Imperial Bank of Commerce, Toronto, Canada; *Int'l*, pg. 256

Knapp, Mike, Pres.-Iowa Realty--American Mutual Life Holding Co., Des Moines, IA; *U.S. Private*, pg. 59

Knez, Brian J., Grp. V.P. & Pres.-Harcourt Brace & Company--Harcourt General, Inc., Chestnut Hill, MA; *U.S. Public*, pg. 782

Knoblock, Richard G., V.P. & Div. Pres.--Electro Kinetics Div., Santa Barbara, CA; *U.S. Public*, pg. 1250

Knopke, Raymond C., Jr., Sr. V.P. & Pres.-Western Div.--Stewart Enterprises, Inc., Metairie, LA; *U.S. Public*, pg. 1518

Knowles, G. Michael, Pres.-Kiwi Brands--Kiwi Brands, Douglassville, PA; *U.S. Public*, pg. 1433

Knowlton, Thomas A., Exec. V.P. & Pres.-Kellogg Europe--Kellogg Company, Battle Creek, MI; *U.S. Public*, pg. 947

Knudsen, A. Don, Pres.-Paging Network-Southern Region, Inc.--Paging Network, Inc., Plano, TX; *U.S. Public*, pg. 1252

Knudsen, Brent R., Pres.-Mass & Sporting Goods Div.--Bell Sports Corp., San Jose, CA; *U.S. Public*, pg. 207

Knudsen, Doug, Pres.-Grocery Prods.--Hunt-Wesson, Inc., Fullerton, CA; *U.S. Public*, pg. 428

Kobacker, Edward J., Pres.-IP Forest Resources Co.--International Paper Company, Purchase, NY; *U.S. Public*, pg. 901

Koenig, Debra A., Pres.-Div.--McDonald's Corporation, Oak Brook, IL; *U.S. Public*, pg. 1068

Kohle, Peter, Pres.-Svedala Intl.--Svedala Industri AB, Malmo, Sweden; *Int'l*, pg. 1323

Kolowich, David, Vice Chm.--NewsEdge Corporation, Burlington, MA; *U.S. Public*, pg. 1180

Kolpin, Marc A., V.P. & Pres.-Physics Intl.--Olin Corporation, Norwalk, CT; *U.S. Public*, pg. 1218

Komisarjevsky, Chris, Pres. & Chief Exec. Officer-U.S. (New York)--Burson-Marsteller, New York, NY; *U.S. Private*, pg. 1197

Konishi, Atsuo, Pres.--SBCM Limited, London, United Kingdom; *Int'l*, pg. 1310

Konopik, M. Gene, Exec. V.P. & Grp. Pres.--Sterling Software, Inc., Dallas, TX; *U.S. Public*, pg. 1516

Koo, Timothy T.M., Pres.-Specialty Insurance Div.--Fireman's Fund Insurance Company, Novato, CA; *Int'l*, pg. 58

Kopf, Robert, Pres.-Hunter Douglas Independent Fabricator Group--Hunter Douglas, Inc., Upper Saddle River, NJ; *Int'l*, pg. 639

Korndorf, Ferdinand F., Pres.-Worldwide Commercial & Consumer Equipment Div.--Deere & Company, Moline, IL; *U.S. Public*, pg. 491

Kosick, Howard A., Pres.-U.S. Group--Bell Sports Corp., San Jose, CA; *U.S. Public*, pg. 207

Koskinen, Meikki, Pres.-Nokia Multimedia Network Terminals--Oy Nokia Ab/Nokia Group, Helsinki, Finland; *Int'l*, pg. 951

Koster, Steven, Pres.-Menswear Div.--Burlington Coat Factory Warehouse Corporation, Burlington, NJ; *U.S. Public*, pg. 268

Kotan, Kaya, Pres.-Tourism & Services Grp.--Koc Holding A.S., Istanbul, Turkey; *Int'l*, pg. 741

Kotowski, Andreas F., Pres.-U.S. Opers./Rapiscan U.S.A.--OSI Systems, Inc., Hawthorne, CA; *U.S. Public*, pg. 1208

Kovach, A., Pres.-Stamping & Frame Div.--The Budd Company, Troy, MI; *Int'l*, pg. 1388

Kowalski, Jeffrey M., Pres.-Thermco Systems Div. & V.P.--Silicon Valley Group, Inc., San Jose, CA; *U.S. Public*, pg. 1474

Kral, Theodore P., Reg. V.P.--American Mail-Well Envelope, Englewood, CO; *U.S. Public*, pg. 1038

Krangel, Stanley E., Pres.-Lenox Collections--Lenox, Incorporated, Lawrenceville, NJ; *U.S. Public*, pg. 261

Krantz, Barry, Pres.-Mexican Div.--El Torito Restaurants Inc., Irvine, CA; *U.S. Private*, pg. 393

Kraus, Harry, Partner--Earle Palmer Brown/New York, New York, NY; *U.S. Private*, pg. 174

Krauss, Alan J., Sr. Grp. Pres.--Masco Corporation, Taylor, MI; *U.S. Public*, pg. 1052

Krauss, Axel, Sr. V.P. & Pres.-Best Food Div.--Bestfoods, Englewood Cliffs, NJ; *U.S. Public*, pg. 223

Krawczyk, David T., Exec. V.P. & Pres.-Contractor's Warehouse Div.--Grossman's, Inc., Stoughton, MA; *U.S. Private*, pg. 585

Krbec, Jerry R., Pres.-Miracle-Ear--Bausch & Lomb Incorporated, Rochester, NY; *U.S. Public*, pg. 194

Krebser, Juerg, Grp. Pres.-Piping Systems Grp.--Georg Fischer Ltd., Schaffhausen, Switzerland; *Int'l*, pg. 488

Kreilick, Thomas K., V.P. & Pres.-Candle Co.--Blyth Industries, Greenwich, CT; *U.S. Public*, pg. 239

Kreppel, Robert J., Pres.-National Fuel Resources, Inc.--National Fuel Gas Company, Buffalo, NY; *U.S. Public*, pg. 1156

Kreuscher, Gene, Pres.-Soft Drink--Austin Nichols & Co. Inc., New York, NY; *Int'l*, pg. 566

Kropf, Susan J., Exec. V.P. & Pres.-U.S. Opers.--Avon Products, Inc., New York, NY; *U.S. Public*, pg. 155

Kruger, Hans, Pres.-Saab Aircraft AB--Saab AB, Linkoping, Sweden; *Int'l*, pg. 686

Kruit, J. H., Pres.-Hydrocarbons--DSM N.V., Heerlen, Netherlands; *Int'l*, pg. 352

Krzyzewski, James M., V.P. & Pres.-Plastic Prods.--Excel Industries, Inc., Elkhart, IN; *U.S. Public*, pg. 598

Kuckuck, William, Pres.-Intl. Div.--Tyson Foods, Inc., Springdale, AR; *U.S. Public*, pg. 1652

Kulig, James S., Pres.-Diamond Power Specialty Co.--McDermott International, Inc., New Orleans, LA; *U.S. Public*, pg. 1067

Kuman, Peg, Pres.-The Power Line--Publishers Clearing House, Port Washington, NY; *U.S. Private*, pg. 893

Kumar, Alex, Pres.-Intl. Consumer-Prods. Div.--Revlon International Corporation, New York, NY; *U.S. Private*, pg. 690

Kun, Andrew Wong Kwok, Pres.-Asia/Pacific--Renaissance Hotel Group N.V., Central, Hong Kong; *U.S. Public*, pg. 1048

Kuperman, Bob, Pres., Chief Exec. Officer-West--TBWA Chiat/Day Los Angeles, Venice, CA; *U.S. Private*, pg. 1062

Kuperman, Robert, Pres. & Chief Exec. Officer-West--TBWA Chiat/Day, New York, NY; *U.S. Private*, pg. 1062

Kupper, Josef, Deputy Co-Pres. & Chief Actuary--The Swiss Life/Rentenanstalt Group, Zurich, Switzerland; *Int'l*, pg. 1332

Kuraytim, Fuad O., Grp. V.P. & Pres.-Middle East, Africa & Gen. Export--The Procter & Gamble Company, Cincinnati, OH; *U.S. Public*, pg. 1330

Kurylowicz, Stanley R., Pres.--SHL Systemhouse - Canada/Asia, Ottawa, Canada; *Int'l*, pg. 1154

Kurz, Kelli McDonald, Pres. & Chief Oper. Officer-Denver & Dir.--EvansGroup, Salt Lake City, UT; *U.S. Private*, pg. 385

Kurz, Mitch, Pres. & Chief Oper. Officer-Y&R Wunderman Partnership--Young & Rubicam Inc., New York, NY; *U.S. Private*, pg. 1196

Kurz, Mitch, Pres. & Chief Oper. Officer--Young & Rubicam Inc., New York, NY; *U.S. Private*, pg. 1196

Kushlick, Bill, Pres.-Weiser Canada--Weiser Lock, Tucson, AZ; *U.S. Public*, pg. 1053

Kutas, David, Pres.-Mennen U.S.A.--Mennen Medical Ltd., Rehovot, Israel; *Int'l*, pg. 858

Kutchinsky, Chas, Pres.- Creative Comm. Production--The McClure Group, Wayne, PA; *U.S. Private*, pg. 719

Kvist, Lars-Erik, Chief Credit & Legal Affairs Officer--Swedbank, Stockholm, Sweden; *Int'l*, pg. 1328

Kyle, Frederick W., Pres.-Worldwide Pharmaceuticals--SmithKline Beecham Corporation, Philadelphia, PA; *Int'l*, pg. 1264

Kynaston, David, V.P. & Pres.-Solectron Europe--Solectron Corporation, Milpitas, CA; *U.S. Public*, pg. 1483

Labe, James P., Pres.-Comdisco Venture Lease Div.--Comdisco, Inc., Rosemont, IL; *U.S. Public*, pg. 407

Labergere, Alain, Exec. V.P. & Pres.-CPC Europe--Bestfoods, Englewood Cliffs, NJ; *U.S. Public*, pg. 223

Lacher, Joseph P., State Pres.-Florida--BellSouth Telecommunications, Inc., Atlanta, GA; *U.S. Public*, pg. 209

Lachman, L.M., Pres.-North American Aircraft Div.--Boeing North American, Seal Beach, CA; *U.S. Public*, pg. 241

Lack, Andrew, Pres.-NBC News--National Broadcasting Co., Inc., New York, NY; *U.S. Public*, pg. 712

Lacombe, Michel, Sr. V.P. & Pres.-Microsoft Europe--Microsoft Corporation, Redmond, WA; *U.S. Public*, pg. 1107

LaCour, Blair P., Pres. & Gen. Mgr.-Mid-Western Div., Paint Stores Grp.--The Sherwin-Williams Company, Cleveland, OH; *U.S. Public*, pg. 1465

Lafaye, Jean-Paul, Pres.-Worldwide (Paris HQ)--Wunderman Cato Johnson, New York, NY; *U.S. Private*, pg. 1197

Lafever, Dan, Pres.-Midwest Div.--Thriftway, Inc., Louisville, KY; *U.S. Public*, pg. 1771

Lafferty, John, Pres.-FJIR--Farm Journal Inc., Philadelphia, PA; *U.S. Private*, pg. 394

Lafley, Alan G., Exec. V.P. & Pres.-Asia--The Procter & Gamble Company, Cincinnati, OH; *U.S. Public*, pg. 1330

LaFollette, Larry, Pres.-Rocky Mountain Prestress--Phelps Tointon Inc., Greeley, CO; *U.S. Private*, pg. 860

LaForge, Elwood L., Jr., V.P. & Pres.-Worldwide Affiliate Grp.--Blyth Industries, Greenwich, CT; *U.S. Public*, pg. 239

Laidlaw, Vic, Pres.-Construction Services Grp.--Koll Co., Newport Beach, CA; *U.S. Private*, pg. 631

Lamb, Tom, V.P. & Pres.-Imaging Solutions Divisions--Lexmark International Group, Inc., Lexington, KY; *U.S. Public*, pg. 991

Lamb, Tom, V.P. & Pres.-Imaging Solutions--Lexmark International, Inc., Lexington, KY; *U.S. Public*, pg. 991

Lambert, Ken, Pres.-DMB&B Asia/Pacific, South--DMB&B Communications, New York, NY; *U.S. Private*, pg. 302

Lambeth, Timothy A., V.P. & Pres.-Europe and Asian Opers.--VF Corporation, Wyomissing, PA; *U.S. Public*, pg. 1702

Lambo, Joseph, Reg. Pres.--First National Bank of Pennsylvania, Hermitage, PA; *U.S. Public*, pg. 607

Lambroussis, Harry G., Pres.-Intl. Paper Latin/S. America--International Paper Company, Purchase, NY; *U.S. Public*, pg. 901

Lamendola, Robert J., Pres.-Surety Grp.--USF&G Corporation, Baltimore, MD; *U.S. Public*, pg. 1659

LaMontagna, Dennis, Pres.-Great Lakes Div.--Leslie Paper, Minneapolis, MN; *U.S. Public*, pg. 903

Lancey, Chris, Pres.-Syndication--Western International Media Corporation, Los Angeles, CA; *U.S. Private*, pg. 1165

Landau, Henry V., V.P. & Pres.-Measurements Grp.--Vishay Intertechnology, Inc., Malvern, PA; *U.S. Public*, pg. 1721

Landau, Igor, Pres.-Health--Rhone-Poulenc S.A., Courbevoie, France; *Int'l*, pg. 1108

Landau, Michael, Pres.-Wallcoverings Div.--F. Schumacher & Co., New York, NY; *U.S. Private*, pg. 973

Landel, Michel, Pres.-Food & Mngmt. Services/North American Opers.--Sodexho S.A., Montigny-le-Bretonneux, France; *Int'l*, pg. 1274

Lander, Howard, Pres.-Music Group & Exec. V.P.--BPI Communications Inc., New York, NY; *Int'l*, pg. 1446

Landry, Michael G., Exec. V.P. & Pres.-Mackenzie Investment Management Inc.--Mackenzie Financial Corporation, Toronto, Canada; *Int'l*, pg. 828

Landy, Sheldon, V.P. & Pres.-Railpool Div.--Interpool, Inc., Princeton, NJ; *U.S. Public*, pg. 908

Lane, Bill, Pres.-Systems Grp. & Sr. V.P.--Stackig Advertising and Public Relations, Mc Lean, VA; *U.S. Private*, pg. 1028

Lang, Donald G., Pres.-CCL Manufacturing & V.P.--CCL Industries, Inc., Willowdale, Canada; *Int'l*, pg. 238

Lange, Ann, Pres.-Worldwide Traffic Svcs.--Western International Media Corporation, Los Angeles, CA; *U.S. Private*, pg. 1165

Lange, Ann, Pres.-Worldwide Traffic Services--Western International Media Corporation, Los Angeles, CA; *U.S. Private*, pg. 1165

Langenskiold, Bertel, Pres.--Tampella Power Inc., Tampere, Finland; *Int'l*, pg. 1353

Langman, Rich, V.P. & Pres.-Trans Tech, Inc.--Alpha Industries, Inc., Woburn, MA; *U.S. Public*, pg. 57

Langner, Klaus D., Pres.-Western Europe/Americas Region--R.J. Reynolds Tobacco Intl., Inc., Geneva, Switzerland; *U.S. Public*, pg. 1355

Langston, Gregory M., Pres.-Utility Div.--Thomas & Betts Corporation, Memphis, TN; *U.S. Public*, pg. 1597

Langteau, Joseph E., Pres.-KFC Division--Scott's Restaurants Inc., Markham, Canada; *Int'l*, pg. 1213

Lanigan, John, Pres.-Transportation Grp.--Schneider National, Inc., Green Bay, WI; *U.S. Private*, pg. 971

Lanning, Dennis, Pres.-Bakery & Deli Div.--Rich Products Corp., Buffalo, NY; *U.S. Private*, pg. 928

Lansing, William A., Grp. Pres.-Forest Products--Menasha Corporation, Neenah, WI; *U.S. Private*, pg. 731

Lansu, Emil, Exec. V.P. & Pres.-Agriculture Division--Bayer Corporation, Pittsburgh, PA; *Int'l*, pg. 172

Lansue, Emil, Pres.-Agricultural Div. & Exec. V.P.--Bayer Corporation, Pittsburgh, PA; *Int'l*, pg. 172

Lantow, Richard, Pres.-K-Fast--Kaynar/K-Fast/APS, Fullerton, CA; *U.S. Public*, pg. 940

Lantto, Reijo, Pres.-Nokia Display Products--Oy Nokia Ab/Nokia Group, Helsinki, Finland; *Int'l*, pg. 951

LaPerre, Timothy L., Pres.-Ryerson Coil Processing--Joseph T. Ryerson & Son, Inc., Chicago, IL; *U.S. Public*, pg. 879

Lapidus, Michael, Pres.-Retail Opers.--Jockey International, Inc., Kenosha, WI; *U.S. Private*, pg. 588

Lapin, Jay F., Pres. & Chief Exec. Officer-Japan--General Electric International Operations, London, United Kingdom; *U.S. Public*, pg. 713

Lapinsky, Joseph F., Pres.-Hot Rolled Bar Div.--Republic Engineered Steels, Inc., Massillon, OH; *U.S. Public*, pg. 1378

Larsen, Charles W., Pres.-MTM Worldwide Distribution--International Family Entertainment, Inc., Virginia Beach, VA; *Int'l*, pg. 927

Larsen, Chuck, Pres.-Worldwide Distribution--MTM Enterprises, Inc., Studio City, CA; *Int'l*, pg. 927

Larson, Paul E., Pres.--Equitable Life Insurance Company of Iowa, Des Moines, IA; *Int'l*, pg. 647

Larsson, Bjorn, Pres.-Volvo Busses--AB Volvo, Goteborg, Sweden; *Int'l*, pg. 1476

Lascurain, Miguel, Pres.--Merisel Mexico, Cuauhtemoc, Mexico; *U.S. Public*, pg. 1096

Lassally, Stacey, Pres.-Production--TriStar Pictures, Culver City, CA; *Int'l*, pg. 1283

Latham, Paul, Pres. & Chief Oper. Officer-SportsNation--Costco Wholesale, Issaquah, WA; *U.S. Public*, pg. 451

Lathan, Barry R., Pres. & Chief Exec. Officer--Xerox Colorgraphics, San Jose, CA; *U.S. Public*, pg. 1784

Laube, William T., III, V.P. & Pres.-Stryker Pacific--Stryker Corporation, Kalamazoo, MI; *U.S. Public*, pg. 1525

Laupert, Aldert, V.P. & Pres.-St. Gallen--Providentia, Nyon, Switzerland; *Int'l*, pg. 1072

Lavely, Tony, Pres.-Consumer Mktg.--Creative Alliance, Inc., Louisville, KY; *U.S. Private*, pg. 287

Lavinia, Robert J., Exec. V.P. & Pres.-The Circle K Company & Tosco Mktg. Company--Tosco Corporation, Stamford, CT; *U.S. Public*, pg. 1624

Lawler, Patrick A., Pres.-Frederick Manufacturing Corp. & Orbex, Inc.--Blount International, Inc., Montgomery, AL; *U.S. Public*, pg. 237

Lawrence, A.L. John, Pres.-PD Exploration Corp.--Phelps Dodge Corporation, Phoenix, AZ; *U.S. Public*, pg. 1286

Lawson, Paul E., Pres.-Pepper Lawson Const. Inc.--The Pepper Companies, Inc., Chicago, IL; *U.S. Private*, pg. 851

Lawton, Mike, Pres.-U.S. Baby Care--Gerber Products Company, Fremont, MI; *Int'l*, pg. 973

Layfield, Allen W., V.P. & Pres.-Communication Works--Cadmus Marketing Services, Atlanta, GA; *U.S. Public*, pg. 291

Layhee, David C., Pres.-Consumer Prods.--IBP, Inc., Dakota City, NE; *U.S. Public*, pg. 852

Lazaras, Herb, Pres.-Carsey-Werner Intl.--Carsey-Werner Company, LLC, Studio City, CA; *U.S. Private*, pg. 216

Lazo, J. Frank, Pres.-Confectionary Sector & V.P.--Warner-Lambert Company, Morris Plains, NJ; *U.S. Public*, pg. 1738

Leal, Roberto, Exec. V.P., Pres. & CEO-JWT/Brazil--J. Walter Thompson Company, New York, NY; *Int'l*, pg. 1483

Lebherz, Kent A., Pres.-Ameritech Indiana--Ameritech Corporation, Chicago, IL; *U.S. Public*, pg. 97

LeBlanc, Jim, V.P. & Pres.-Whirlpool Fin. Corp.--Whirlpool Corporation, Benton Harbor, MI; *U.S. Public*, pg. 1764

Lebow, Gerald M., Pres.-Sage Alerting Systems, Inc.--AmeriData Technologies, Inc., Stamford, CT; *U.S. Public*, pg. 711

Lecher, Theodore M., V.P. & Pres.-GB Electrical Inc.--Applied Power Inc., Butler, WI; *U.S. Public*, pg. 124

Leduc, Gilles, Pres.-Bowne de Montreal, Inc.--Bowne & Co., Inc., New York, NY; *U.S. Public*, pg. 248

Lee, Alan B., Pres.-Unity Sewing Supply & V.P.--Willcox & Gibbs, Inc., Carteret, NJ; *U.S. Private*, pg. 1177

Lee, Dale G., Pres.-U.S. Sls.--Nature's Sunshine Products, Inc., Provo, UT; *U.S. Public*, pg. 1166

Lee, James, Exec. V.P. & Pres.-Licensed Discount Div.--J. Baker, Inc., Canton, MA; *U.S. Public*, pg. 167

Lee, John D., III, Pres.-Southeast Area Opers.--Paragon Health Network, Inc., Atlanta, GA; *U.S. Public*, pg. 1256

Lee, Kai-Fu, Dr., Pres.-Cosmo Software--Silicon Graphics, Inc., Mountain View, CA; *U.S. Public*, pg. 1473

Lee, Kenneth, Pres.-Workstations & Sys. Storage Grp. & Chief Tech. Officer--Quantum Corporation, Milpitas, CA; *U.S. Public*, pg. 1350

Lee, Ray, Pres.-Prentic Hall Ginn Canada--Prentice Hall Canada, Inc., Scarborough, Canada; *U.S. Private*, pg. 778

Lee, Robert, Pres.-Bus. Communications Services--Pacific Bell, San Ramon, CA; *U.S. Public*, pg. 1416

Lee, Shi-Chuan, Pres.-Semiconductor--Raytheon Company, Lexington, MA; *U.S. Public*, pg. 1364

Lee, Y.B., Pres.-Far East Opers.--Russ Berrie and Company, Inc., Oakland, NJ; *U.S. Public*, pg. 222

Leeds, Bruce, Vice Chm. & Pres.-Intl. Opers.--Global Direct Mail Corp, Port Washington, NY; *U.S. Public*, pg. 747

Leeds, Daniel H., Pres.-Intl.--CMP Media, Inc., Manhasset, NY; *U.S. Public*, pg. 279

Leeds, Robert, Vice Chm. & Pres.-Domestic Opers.--Global Direct Mail Corp, Port Washington, NY; *U.S. Public*, pg. 747

Leeman, Omar T., Pres.-Bus. Opers.--MCI Communications Corp., Atlanta, GA; *U.S. Public*, pg. 1023

Leemon, Daniel J., Pres.--Vulcan Materials Company-Midsouth Div., Knoxville, TN; *U.S. Public*, pg. 1726

Leenstra, Kenneth J., V.P. & Pres.-Armament Systems--General Dynamics Corporation, Falls Church, VA; *U.S. Public*, pg. 708

Lefkowitz, Marcia M., Pres.-Readers's Digest, USA--The Reader's Digest Association, Inc., Pleasantville, NY; *U.S. Public*, pg. 1367

Lehman, Carl B., Pres.-Traveler's Cheque Grp./USA--American Express Travel Related Services Co., Inc., New York, NY; *U.S. Public*, pg. 73

Lehmann, Carl B., Pres.-Stored Value Grp./American Express Travel Related Services--American Express Company, New York, NY; *U.S. Public*, pg. 73

Lehn, Jacques, Pres.--Lagardere Groupe, Paris, France; *Int'l*, pg. 791

Leibensperger, Robert L., Exec. V.P. & Pres.-Bearings--The Timken Company, Canton, OH; *U.S. Public*, pg. 1617

Leliakor, Paul, Pres.-Investment Corp.--The Money Store, Sacramento, CA; *U.S. Public*, pg. 1124

Leman, Jane, Pres.-Allied Grp.--IBP, Inc., Dakota City, NE; *U.S. Public*, pg. 852

LeMesurier, Tony, Dir.-Customer Svcs.--Air UK Ltd., Stansted, United Kingdom; *Int'l*, pg. 38

Lenny, Richard H., Pres.-Pillsbury Specialty Brands--The Pillsbury Company, Minneapolis, MN; *Int'l*, pg. 411

Lentz, Stephen D., Pres.-FiT TV--International Family Entertainment, Inc., Virginia Beach, VA; *Int'l*, pg. 927

Lenz, Joseph, Pres.-CACI Products Co.--CACI International Inc, Arlington, VA; *U.S. Public*, pg. 272

Leonard, John K., Pres.-CIGNA Group Insurance: Life, Accident, Disability--Cigna Corp., Philadelphia, PA; *U.S. Public*, pg. 356

Leonard, Mason A., Div. Pres.-Pictsweet Frozen Foods--United Foods, Inc., Bells, TN; *U.S. Public*, pg. 1677

Leonard, Paul, Sr. V.P. & Pres.-Guild Div.--Zale Corporation, Irving, TX; *U.S. Public*, pg. 1789

Leonsis, Theodore, Pres. & Chief Exec. Officer-AOL Studios--America Online Incorporated, Dulles, VA; *U.S. Public*, pg. 66

Lepola, Ismo, Pres.-Magazine papers--UPM-Kymmene Corporation, Helsinki, Finland; *Int'l*, pg. 1427

Leppo, Harold, Interim Pres.-The Casual Male, Inc.--J. Baker, Inc., Canton, MA; *U.S. Public*, pg. 167

Lerner, Robert C., Pres.-Canada--Wang Laboratories, Inc., Billerica, MA; *U.S. Public*, pg. 1737

Leroy, Pierre E., Pres.-Worldwide Commercial Wquipment Div.--Deere & Company, Moline, IL; *U.S. Public*, pg. 491

Lesher, Cynthia L., Pres.-NSP Gas--Northern States Power Company, Minneapolis, MN; *U.S. Public*, pg. 1195

LeSieur, Donald H., Exec. V.P. & Pres. Intl. Div.--Block Drug Company, Inc., Jersey City, NJ; *U.S. Public*, pg. 236

Lesko, James H., V.P. & Pres.-Desktop Products Group--Xerox Corporation, Stamford, CT; *U.S. Public*, pg. 1783

Lester, Donald R., Pres.-Forest Prods.--North Pacific Lumber Company, Portland, OR; *U.S. Private*, pg. 805

Lesters, Frank, Pres.-Indiana Group--Edward C. Levy Co., Dearborn, MI; *U.S. Private*, pg. 664

Lestz, Earl, Pres.-Studio Grp.--Paramount Pictures Corporation, Los Angeles, CA; *U.S. Private*, pg. 776
Letwin, Stephen J., Pres.-TransCanada Energy USA Inc.--Transcanada Pipelines Limited, Calgary, Canada; *Int'l*, pg. 1416
Letwin, Stephen J.J., Pres.-Petroleum Group--TransCanada Energy Ltd., Calgary, Canada; *Int'l*, pg. 1417
Leung, Brenda, Pres.--Maxon Industries, Inc., Huntington Park, CA; *U.S. Private*, pg. 717
Leven, M.A., Pres.-Franchise Hotel Div.--Holiday Inn Worldwide, Atlanta, GA; *Int'l*, pg. 170
Levenick, Mark K., Pres.-Operating Subsidiaries--Tidel Technologies, Inc., Houston, TX; *U.S. Public*, pg. 1608
Levin, Robert, Pres.-Worldwide Mktg., Sony Pictures--Columbia Pictures, Culver City, CA; *Int'l*, pg. 1281
Levin, Robert, Pres.-Worldwide Mktg.--Sony Pictures Entertainment, Culver City, CA; *Int'l*, pg. 1281
Levin, Samuel, Pres.-Scotdue--Special Devices, Incorporated, Newhall, CA; *U.S. Public*, pg. 1496
Levine, Ed, Pres.-Studios--Unitel Video, Inc., New York, NY; *U.S. Public*, pg. 1692
Levins, Ilyssa, Vice Chm. & Pres.-GHG & Pub. Rels.--Grey Healthcare Group, New York, NY; *U.S. Public*, pg. 765
Levinson, Sara, Pres.-MTV--MTV Networks, New York, NY; *U.S. Private*, pg. 779
Levy, Harold, Div. Pres.--TMP Worldwide/Recruitment Division, New York, NY; *U.S. Private*, pg. 1065
Levy, James P., Pres.-Harcourt Brace Education Grp.--Harcourt General, Inc., Chestnut Hill, MA; *U.S. Public*, pg. 782
Levy, Neil, Pres.-Hearing Instruments Grp.--Telex Communications, Inc., Minneapolis, MN; *U.S. Private*, pg. 1074
Levy, Rich, Pres.-Health Care--Adair Greene Advertising, Atlanta, GA; *U.S. Private*, pg. 16
Lewellen, Wayne, Pres.-Distr.--Paramount Pictures Corporation, Los Angeles, CA; *U.S. Private*, pg. 776
Lewis, Claude H., Pres.-Service Transport Company--Adams Resources & Energy, Inc., Houston, TX; *U.S. Public*, pg. 18
Lewis, David J., Vice Chm.--Cogentrix Incorporated, Charlotte, NC; *U.S. Private*, pg. 249
Lewis, Mike, Pres.-America West Express Div.--Mesa Air Group, Las Vegas, NV; *U.S. Public*, pg. 1098
Lewis, Robert A., Dr., Pres.-Syntex Discovery Res. & Sr. V.P.--Syntex, Palo Alto, CA; *Int'l*, pg. 1120
Lewis, Robert E., Pres.-NV Opers. & Exec. V.P.--Lewis Homes Management Corp., Upland, CA; *U.S. Private*, pg. 665
Lewkowjcz, Martin, Pres.-Intl.--Ranir Corporation/DCP, Grand Rapids, MI; *U.S. Private*, pg. 909
Lezama, Fernando, Exec. V.P. & Pres.-Mexico, Central & South America--Avon Products, Inc., New York, NY; *U.S. Public*, pg. 155
Li, Jun-Sheng, Pres.-Logistics--J.B. Hunt Transport Services, Inc., Lowell, AR; *U.S. Public*, pg. 849
Libes, Stewart C., Pres.-Accountants on Call--Adecco Employment Services, Redwood City, CA; *Int'l*, pg. 24
Librizzi, Osvaldo, Pres.-Latin American Div.--ITT Sheraton Corporation, Boston, MA; *U.S. Public*, pg. 1512
Liebman, Martin, Exec. V.P. & New York/Long Island Reg. Pres.--Marine Midland Bank, Buffalo, NY; *Int'l*, pg. 581
Lierman, Bruce, Pres.-Colt Construction Co., Inc.--Matrix Service Company, Tulsa, OK; *U.S. Public*, pg. 1057
Liles, William J., III, Pres.-Rail Services--KLLM Transport Services, Inc., Jackson, MS; *U.S. Public*, pg. 939
Lill, John W., Pres.-Chilean Opers.--Barrick Gold Corporation, Toronto, Canada; *Int'l*, pg. 168
Lin, M. S., Pres.-Wyse Tech. (Taiwan), Ltd.--Wyse Technology Inc., San Jose, CA; *U.S. Private*, pg. 1194
Lin, Simon, Pres.-Information Prods. Grp.--Acer Incorporated, Taipei, Taiwan; *Int'l*, pg. 22
Lindberg, Terrance L., V.P. & Pres.-MT & Heavy Truck Window & Door Sys.--Excel Industries, Inc., Elkhart, IN; *U.S. Public*, pg. 598
Linder, Gert, Mng. Dir.--Getinge Skarhamm AB, Skarhamn, Sweden; *Int'l*, pg. 551
Linder, Richard A., Grp. Pres.--CBS Corporation, Pittsburgh, PA; *U.S. Public*, pg. 273
Lindh, Einar, Chm.-Indus. Grp.--Smiths Industries plc, London, United Kingdom; *Int'l*, pg. 1266
Lindley, Joe, Pres.-SPD Div.--C & M Corporation, Wauregan, CT; *U.S. Private*, pg. 191
Lindsay, Steve, Pres.-Applied Matls. Europe--Applied Materials, Inc., Santa Clara, CA; *U.S. Public*, pg. 123
Link, William J., Ph.D., V.P., Chm. & Chief Exec. Officer-Chiron Vision--Chiron Corporation, Emeryville, CA; *U.S. Public*, pg. 349
Link, William P., Pres. & Chief Exec. Officer-Prudential HealthCare Grp.--The Prudential Insurance Company of America, Newark, NJ; *U.S. Private*, pg. 892
Lino Costa, Antonio C., Pres.-ABS Americas--American Bureau of Shipping, New York, NY; *U.S. Private*, pg. 51
Linville, Randal L., Pres.-Grain Mktg. Division--The Scoular Company, Omaha, NE; *U.S. Private*, pg. 977
Lipes, Edward B., V.P. & Pres.-Osteonics Corp.--Stryker Corporation, Kalamazoo, MI; *U.S. Public*, pg. 1525
Lipke, Eric, Pres.-Distr. & Svcs Grp.--Gibraltar Steel Corp., Buffalo, NY; *U.S. Public*, pg. 742
Lipkin, Boris, Pres.-Track Sys. Div.--Silicon Valley Group, Inc., San Jose, CA; *U.S. Public*, pg. 1474
Liss, Robert E., Pres.-Mark VII Special Services Div.--Mark VII, Inc., Memphis, TN; *U.S. Public*, pg. 1046
Lister, Steve, Pres.-Far East--Colgate-Palmolive Company, New York, NY; *U.S. Public*, pg. 397
Little, Christopher, Pres.-Publishing Grp.--Country Home Magazine, Des Moines, IA; *U.S. Public*, pg. 1094
Little, Jack E., Pres.-Shell Exploration & Prod. Co.--Shell Oil Company, Houston, TX; *Int'l*, pg. 1136
Littlefield, Warren, Pres.-NBC Entertainment--National Broadcasting Co., Inc., New York, NY; *U.S. Public*, pg. 712
Liubinski, E., Pres.-H/O ATEX--Belarus Machinery, Inc., Milwaukee, WI; *Int'l*, pg. 101
Livingston, Doug, Pres.-Interactive Media--Western International Media Corporation, Los Angeles, CA; *U.S. Private*, pg. 1165
Lloyd, George, Pres. & Gen. Mgr.--Trimac Transportation System, Calgary, Canada; *Int'l*, pg. 1424
Lmbert, Ken, Pres.-DMB&B Asia/Pacific South--DMB&B/Hong Kong, Quarry Bay, Hong Kong; *U.S. Private*, pg. 303
Locicero, Joseph A., Exec. V.P. & Pres./Chief Exec. Officer-Bulk Consultants, Inc.--Mellon Bank Corporation, Pittsburgh, PA; *U.S. Public*, pg. 1084
Lockhart, H. Eugene, Pres.-Global Retail Bank--BankAmerica Corporation, San Francisco, CA; *U.S. Public*, pg. 179
Lockhart, Kirk W., V.P.-Intl. & Pres.-Elekom Corp.--Egghead, Inc., Liberty Lake, WA; *U.S. Public*, pg. 566
Lockwood, James, Pres.-Lancaster Colony Automotive Group--Lancaster Colony Automotive Group, Dublin, OH; *U.S. Public*, pg. 977
Lofberg, Per G.H., Pres.-MEDCO Managed Care--MEDCO Containment Services, Inc., Montvale, NJ; *U.S. Public*, pg. 1091
Lohr, D.G., Pres.-Trade Sls.--California Products Corp., Cambridge, MA; *U.S. Private*, pg. 201
Loizzo, Larry J., V.P. & Pres.-Lab Safety Supply, Inc.--W.W. Grainger, Inc., Lincolnshire, IL; *U.S. Public*, pg. 758
Lomangino, Nicholas, Pres.-Floorcovering Div.--F. Schumacher & Co., New York, NY; *U.S. Private*, pg. 973
Lombardi, Louis B., Pres.-Northwest Region--BNY Holdings (New Jersey) Corp., West Paterson, NJ; *U.S. Public*, pg. 178
Lomelino, Susan, Pres.-Publicis Pub. Rels.--Publicis/Bloom Inc., New York, NY; *Int'l*, pg. 470
Lonergan, Robert C., V.P. & Pres.-Bldg. Matls./Europe/Africa--Owens Corning, Toledo, OH; *U.S. Public*, pg. 1236
Long, James R., Pres. & Chief Oper. Officer-Nortel World Trade--Northern Telecom Limited, Brampton, Canada; *Int'l*, pg. 968
Lookabough, Tom, Pres.-DiviCom Inc.--C-Cube Microsystems, Milpitas, CA; *U.S. Public*, pg. 272
Loose, John W., Pres.-Corning Communications--Corning Incorporated, Corning, NY; *U.S. Public*, pg. 448
Lopardo, Nicholas A., Vice Chm. & Pres.-Investment Mngmt. Activities--State Street Corporation, Boston, MA; *U.S. Public*, pg. 1513
Lopiano, John A., Sr. V.P. & Pres.-Production Systems Group--Xerox Corporation, Stamford, CT; *U.S. Public*, pg. 1783
Lortie, Pierre, Pres.-Bombardier Reg. Aircraft Div.--Bombardier Aerospace, Dorval, Canada; *Int'l*, pg. 200
Lotz, Marvin, Pres.-Pub. Storage Mngmt.--Public Storage, Inc., Glendale, CA; *U.S. Public*, pg. 1340
Loughlin, John, Pres.-Broadcast Grp.--Meredith Corporation, Des Moines, IA; *U.S. Public*, pg. 1094
Lounsbury, Charles, Grp. V.P. & Pres.--The Toro Company, Bloomington, MN; *U.S. Public*, pg. 1623
LoVecchio, Joseph, Pres.-Schumacher Div.--F. Schumacher & Co., New York, NY; *U.S. Private*, pg. 973
Loveless, Mary-Ellen, Pres.-Entertainment--Adair Greene Advertising, Atlanta, GA; *U.S. Private*, pg. 16
Lowater, David B., Pres. & Chief Oper. Officer-Visual Communications Group--Electrohome Ltd., Kitchener, Canada; *Int'l*, pg. 438
Lower, Louis G., II, Pres.-Allstate Life Insurance Company--The Allstate Corporation, Northbrook, IL; *U.S. Public*, pg. 55
Lubrano, Louis, Pres.-Middle Market Div.--National Union Fire Ins. Co. of Pittsburgh, Pa., New York, NY; *U.S. Public*, pg. 84
Lucas, Walter, Mng. Dir.--Egon Lucas Medizin Technik GmbH, Munster, Germany; *Int'l*, pg. 551
Luehrs, Robert, Pres.-Sls. Div.--Henry I. Siegel Company, Inc., New York, NY; *U.S. Private*, pg. 998
Luehrs, William G., Pres.-Network Systems--Zenith Electronics Corp., Glenview, IL; *U.S. Public*, pg. 1790
Luffman, Peter J., Pres.-Newsweek Intl. & Exec. V.P.--Newsweek, Inc., New York, NY; *U.S. Public*, pg. 1743
Lukes, Edward F., Pres. & Mng. Dir.--SHL Systemhouse Europe Ltd., London, United Kingdom; *Int'l*, pg. 1154
Lundgren, John F., Pres.-European Consumer Prods.--Fort James Corporation, Richmond, VA; *U.S. Public*, pg. 670
Lundy, Roland, Pres.-Records & Music--Word, Incorporated, Dallas, TX; *U.S. Public*, pg. 704
Lupton, Brent K., Pres.-GulfMark Energy, Inc.--Adams Resources & Energy, Inc., Houston, TX; *U.S. Public*, pg. 18
Lusted, Carl G., Pres.-Central--Joseph T. Ryerson & Son, Inc., Chicago, IL; *U.S. Public*, pg. 879
Luttio, Ken, Pres.-ORC Lighting Prods.--BEC Group, Inc., Rye, NY; *U.S. Public*, pg. 160
Luttmann, J.C., Co-Pres.-Sphere Intl.--Accor S.A., Evry, France; *Int'l*, pg. 20
Lynch, J.P., Pres.-ICI Explosives Grp.--ICI Americas, Inc., Wilmington, DE; *Int'l*, pg. 663
Lynn, Anthony J., Exec. V.P. & Pres. Entertainment Grp.--Playboy Enterprises, Inc., Chicago, IL; *U.S. Public*, pg. 1309
Lyon, Geoffrey D., Pres.-Inventory Finance Grp.--Deutsche Financial Services Corporation, Saint Louis, MO; *Int'l*, pg. 403
Macalister, Kim, Exec. V.P., Pres. & Gen. Mgr.-JWT/Singapore--J. Walter Thompson Company, New York, NY; *Int'l*, pg. 1483
Macdonald, G.F., Pres.-Country Style Donuts--Maple Leaf Foods Inc., Toronto, Canada; *Int'l*, pg. 841
MacDonald, John, Pres.-Union Carbide Foundation--Union Carbide Corporation, Danbury, CT; *U.S. Public*, pg. 1666
MacDonnell, Kathleen, Pres.-Frozen Foods & Specialty Foods--Campbell Soup Company, Camden, NJ; *U.S. Public*, pg. 298
MacDonnell, Kathleen, Pres.-FFG--Swanson, Camden, NJ; *U.S. Public*, pg. 299
MacDonnell, Kathleen, Pres.-Frozen Food & Specialty Foods--Campbell USA, Camden, NJ; *U.S. Public*, pg. 299
Mackenzie, Hugh C., Pres.-Retail Business Grp.--Northeast Utilities, Berlin, CT; *U.S. Public*, pg. 1194
Mackie, Tom, V.P. & Pres.-Instrumentation Grp.--Parker Hannifin Corporation, Cleveland, OH; *U.S. Public*, pg. 1259
MacLeod, Malcolm W., Pres. & Chief Exec. Officer, CT--Moran Towing of Maryland, Baltimore, MD; *U.S. Private*, pg. 761
MacLeod, S.D., Pres.-CIMCO Refrigeration--Toromont Industries Ltd., Concord, Canada; *Int'l*, pg. 1400
MacMachon, Thomas E., V.P.-Hoffmann LaRoche Inc. & Pres.-Diagnostics Div.--Hoffmann-La Roche Inc., Nutley, NJ; *Int'l*, pg. 1120
MacPhail, Andrew B., Pres. & Chief Exec. Officer--Chicago National League Ball Club, Inc. (Chicago Cubs), Chicago, IL; *U.S. Public*, pg. 1635
MacQueen, Rhonda S., Grp. Pres.-Fin. Printing Svcs. Grp.--R.R. Donnelley & Sons Company, Chicago, IL; *U.S. Public*, pg. 517
Madden, Michael J., Pres.-U.S. Toy Store Opers.--Toys "R" Us, Inc., Paramus, NJ; *U.S. Public*, pg. 1626
Madel, Michael, Exec. V.P., Chm., Pres. & Chief Exec. Officer-JWT/Europe--J. Walter Thompson Company, New York, NY; *Int'l*, pg. 1483
Mahady, Joseph M., Pres.-U.S. Pharmaceutical Business Div.--American Home Products Corporation, Madison, NJ; *U.S. Public*, pg. 79
Mahle, Stephen H., Pres.-Bradycardia Pacing Bus.--Medtronic, Inc., Minneapolis, MN; *U.S. Public*, pg. 1082
Mahoney, David, Pres.-Pharmaceutical & Retail Sls.--McKesson U.S. Health Care, San Francisco, CA; *U.S. Public*, pg. 1073
Mahoney, David L., V.P. & Pres.-Pharmaceutical Services Group--McKesson Corporation, San Francisco, CA; *U.S. Public*, pg. 1072
Mahoney, Tom, Pres.-Consumer Sls. Americas--The Stanley Works, New Britain, CT; *U.S. Public*, pg. 1508
Majeske, Mark T., Pres.-McKesson Customer Opers.--McKesson Corporation, San Francisco, CA; *U.S. Public*, pg. 1072
Majewski, Rich, Pres.-Labels & Label Systems--Moore Corporation Limited, Toronto, Canada; *Int'l*, pg. 888
Majkowski, E. Jon, V.P. & Pres.-URI, PPI & TEI--United Illuminating Company, New Haven, CT; *U.S. Public*, pg. 1678
Major, John E., Exec. V.P. & Pres.-Infrastructure Prods. Division--QUALCOMM, San Diego, CA; *U.S. Public*, pg. 1348
Makkonen, Kari, Pres.-Sawmilling--UPM-Kymmene Corporation, Helsinki, Finland; *Int'l*, pg. 1427
Malchoff, Kevin, Pres.-Food Svcs. Div.--Rich Products Corp., Buffalo, NY; *U.S. Private*, pg. 928
Mallardi, Michael P., Pres.-Broadcast Grp. & Sr. V.P.--ABC, Inc, New York, NY; *U.S. Public*, pg. 511
Mallmann, Jeanene M., V.P. & Pres.-McCamly Square Div.--Kellogg Company, Battle Creek, MI; *U.S. Public*, pg. 947
Mallof, Joseph T., Pres.-North American Consumer Prods.--S.C. Johnson & Son, Inc., Racine, WI; *U.S. Private*, pg. 592
Malmos, Karsten, Pres.-Intl.--Tyco Toys, Inc., Mount Laurel, NJ; *U.S. Public*, pg. 1058
Maloof, Richard C., Pres.--Bird Roofing Products, Inc., Norwood, MA; *Int'l*, pg. 1171
Malyan, Richard H., Pres.-Intl.--Bristol-Myers Squibb Consumer Products Group, New York, NY; *U.S. Public*, pg. 254
Mancini, Louis, Pres.-GNC--General Nutrition, Inc., Pittsburgh, PA; *U.S. Public*, pg. 725
Mandel, Lon, Pres. & Chief Oper. Officer-List Marketing Services--LCS Industries, Inc., Clifton, NJ; *U.S. Public*, pg. 970
Mandes, Bob, Div. Pres.-Steak & Ale--Bennigan's, Dallas, TX; *U.S. Private*, pg. 736
Manley, Ted R., Exec. V.P.-Opers. & Pres.-Once Upon A Child--Grow Biz International, Inc., Minneapolis, MN; *U.S. Public*, pg. 767
Mann, Peter C., Pres.-U.S. Div.--Block Drug Company, Inc., Jersey City, NJ; *U.S. Public*, pg. 236
Mann, William J., Pres.-Southam Magazine & Information Grp.--Southam Inc., Don Mills, Canada; *Int'l*, pg. 631
Mansfield, J. Patrick, Pres.-U.S. Systems & Svcs. Opers.--Bull HN Information Systems Inc., Billerica, MA; *Int'l*, pg. 316
Mansour, Ned, Pres.-Mattel USA & Sec.--Mattel, Inc., El Segundo, CA; *U.S. Public*, pg. 1057
Marasco, Fran, Pres.-Pharmacy Benefit Mngmt. & Mail Service Pharmacy & Sr. V.P.--Eckerd Corporation, Largo, FL; *U.S. Public*, pg. 917
Marciano, Jay, Pres.-Universal Concerts--Universal Studios, Inc., Universal City, CA; *Int'l*, pg. 1215
Marcott, Dennis, Pres.-Environmental Prods.--AAF-International, Louisville, KY; *U.S. Private*, pg. 3
Margolis, David, Pres.-Winners--The TJX Companies, Inc., Framingham, MA; *U.S. Public*, pg. 1556
Marineau, Rene, Pres.-Lightolier Canada--The Genlyte Group Incorporated, Union, NJ; *U.S. Public*, pg. 729
Marino, Michael C., Pres.-Wyse Cleveland--Wyse Advertising, Cleveland, OH; *U.S. Private*, pg. 1193
Marion, Jim, Pres. & Gen. Mgr.-Wireless Messaging Grp.--Glenayre Technologies, Inc., Charlotte, NC; *U.S. Public*, pg. 746
Mariucci, Anne L., Sr. V.P. & Pres. & Gen. Mgr.-Terravita Corp.--Del Webb Corporation, Phoenix, AZ; *U.S. Public*, pg. 494
Markham, Rudy, Pres.-North East Asia--Unilever Plc, London, United Kingdom; *Int'l*, pg. 1433
Marks, Stephen S., Pres.-Silhouettes--Hanover Direct, Inc., Weehawken, NJ; *U.S. Public*, pg. 782
Markwood, Ronald, Pres.-Load King Div.--CMI Corporation, Oklahoma City, OK; *U.S. Public*, pg. 278
Marlowe, Brian, Exec. V.P. & Pres.-Eastern Div.--Stewart Enterprises, Inc., Metairie, LA; *U.S. Public*, pg. 1518

Maroone, Michael E., Pres.-AutoNation New Vehicle Div.--Republic Industries, Inc., Fort Lauderdale, FL; *U.S. Public*, pg. 1378
Marple, Allen C., Pres.--Spectrum Mutual Fund Services Inc., Toronto, Canada; *Int'l*, pg. 1319
Marquiss, James J., Sr. V.P. & Co-Pres.-Ag. Svcs.--Data Transmission Network Corporation, Omaha, NE; *U.S. Public*, pg. 486
Marsan, Marc, Pres.-Invention Company--The Sawtooth Group, Woodbridge, NJ; *U.S. Private*, pg. 969
Marshall, Richard A., Pres.-IIMAK--PAXAR Corporation, White Plains, NY; *U.S. Public*, pg. 1266
Marterer, Gerald C., Pres.-Intl. Paper Asia--International Paper Company, Purchase, NY; *U.S. Public*, pg. 901
Martin-Busutil, Ramon, Pres.-CBE--Cadbury Beverages North America, Stamford, CT; *Int'l*, pg. 248
Martin, Bob L., Exec. V.P. & Pres.-Intl.--Wal-Mart Stores, Inc., Bentonville, AR; *U.S. Public*, pg. 1732
Martin, Craig, Pres.-In-Store Mktg.--Gage Marketing Group, Minneapolis, MN; *U.S. Private*, pg. 437
Martin, Craig, Pres.-CRSS Architects Inc. & Sr. V.P.-Opers.--CRSS Inc., Houston, TX; *Int'l*, pg. 1415
Martin, David W., M.D., Pres.--Chiron Therapeutics, Emeryville, CA; *U.S. Public*, pg. 350
Martin, Jean, Pres.-Central & Eastern Europe--Unilever Plc, London, United Kingdom; *Int'l*, pg. 1433
Martin, John C., Pres.-Retail Stores--OfficeMax, Shaker Heights, OH; *U.S. Public*, pg. 1212
Martin, Patrick J., V.P. & Pres.-Americas Customer Opers.--Xerox Corporation, Stamford, CT; *U.S. Public*, pg. 1783
Martin, Richard A., Pres.-Fin. & Admin.--Calvin Klein, Inc., New York, NY; *U.S. Private*, pg. 202
Martin, Steve, Pres.-Diversified Health Services--The ServiceMaster Company, Downers Grove, IL; *U.S. Public*, pg. 1461
Martin, T.L., Pres.-Halsey Div.--Post Glover Resistors Inc., Erlanger, KY; *Int'l*, pg. 590
Martin, Wayne, Pres. & Gen. Mgr.--WKYT-TV, Lexington, KY; *U.S. Public*, pg. 759
Martin, William L., III, Sr. V.P. & Pres.-Bus. Broadband Grp.--ADC Telecommunications, Inc., Minnetonka, MN; *U.S. Public*, pg. 4
Martineau, Lynn, Pres.-Western Div.--The Home Depot, Inc., Atlanta, GA; *U.S. Public*, pg. 831
Martini, Brent, Pres.-BBDC--Bergen Brunswig Corporation, Orange, CA; *U.S. Public*, pg. 213
Martner, David, Design Partner--AC Martin Partners, Los Angeles, CA; *U.S. Private*, pg. 708
Martone, Gene L., V.P. & Pres.-Riedal Waste Systems Inc.--Smith Technologies Corp., Portland, OR; *U.S. Public*, pg. 1478
Masi, Edward A., V.P. & Pres.-Supercomputer Systems Div.--Intel Corporation, Santa Clara, CA; *U.S. Public*, pg. 886
Masin, Michael T., Vice Chm. & Pres.-Intl. Div.--GTE Corporation, Stamford, CT; *U.S. Public*, pg. 696
Mason, Dan, Pres.-CBS Radio Station Grp.--CBS Broadcast Group, New York, NY; *U.S. Public*, pg. 274
Mason, Ronald V., Pres.-Federal Cartridge Co.--Blount International, Inc., Montgomery, AL; *U.S. Public*, pg. 237
Masotti, David F., Pres.-Spar Space Systems--Spar Aerospace Limited, Toronto, Canada; *Int'l*, pg. 1287
Massingale, H. Lynn, M.D., Pres.-Team Health--Medpartners Inc., Birmingham, AL; *U.S. Public*, pg. 1082
Masson, Bernard, V.P. & Pres.-Consumer Printer Division--Lexmark International Group, Inc., Lexington, KY; *U.S. Public*, pg. 991
Masson, Bernard, V.P. & Pres.-Consumer Printer--Lexmark International, Inc., Lexington, KY; *U.S. Public*, pg. 991
Masters, Jerry W., Pres.-Retail Markets Grp.--TDS Telecommunications Corporation, Madison, WI; *U.S. Public*, pg. 1570
Mathews, Cannon, Pres.-Rogerson Kratos--Rogerson Aircraft Corporation, Irvine, CA; *U.S. Private*, pg. 940
Mathies, William A., Exec. V.P. & Pres.-Beverly Health & Rehab.--Beverly Enterprises, Inc., Fort Smith, AR; *U.S. Public*, pg. 227
Matsushita, Sheila, Pres.--A-Mold Corp., Mason, OH; *Int'l*, pg. 1427
Matthies, Helmut, Pres. & Chief Exec. Officer-WCJ Europe (Frankfurt HQ)--Wunderman Cato Johnson, New York, NY; *U.S. Private*, pg. 1197
Mauch, Danna, Ph.D., Pres. & Chief Oper. Officer-Magellan Public Solutions--Magellan Health Services, Inc., Atlanta, GA; *U.S. Public*, pg. 1033
Maul, Peter, V.P. & Pres.-Nanocor--AMCOL International Corp., Arlington Heights, IL; *U.S. Public*, pg. 63
Mayer, Susan, Pres.-SkyMCI--MCI Communications Corp., Atlanta, GA; *U.S. Public*, pg. 1023
Mayr, Gerhard N., Pres.-Intercontinental Opers.--Eli Lilly and Company, Indianapolis, IN; *U.S. Public*, pg. 992
Mays, Mark Pitman, Pres. & Chief Oper. Officer--Clear Channel Communications, Inc., San Antonio, TX; *U.S. Public*, pg. 383
Mazurk, John, Pres.-Play Programs--Gymboree Corporation, Burlingame, CA; *U.S. Public*, pg. 770
Mazzotta-Green, Joanne, Co-Pres. & Chief Exec. Officer--Friendly Holidays Inc., Lake Success, NY; *U.S. Private*, pg. 428
McAllister, Stuart, Chief Exec. Officer-HMV--EMI Group plc, London, United Kingdom; *Int'l*, pg. 426
McCallister, Michael B., Pres.-Division I--Humana Inc., Louisville, KY; *U.S. Public*, pg. 847
McCallum, William T., Pres. & Chief Exec. Officer-U.S.--The Great-West Life Assurance Company, Winnipeg, Canada; *Int'l*, pg. 557
McCann, Thomas, Div. Pres.--Kirby Building Systems, Inc., Portland, TN; *Int'l*, pg. 699
McCarley, Thomas G., Sr. V.P. & Pres.-Food Service Div.--Foodbrands America, Inc., Oklahoma City, OK; *U.S. Public*, pg. 852
McCarter, John T., Pres.-G.E. South America--General Electric International Operations, London, United Kingdom; *U.S. Public*, pg. 713
McCarthy, Dennis J., Pres.-Continuing Care Grp.--Sunrise Medical, Inc., Carlsbad, CA; *U.S. Public*, pg. 1535
McCarthy, William E., Pres.-Catalog Div.--JC Penney Company, Inc., Plano, TX; *U.S. Public*, pg. 916
McCarthy, William J., Pres.-Pepper Const. of IN, LLC--The Pepper Companies, Inc., Chicago, IL; *U.S. Private*, pg. 851
McCartney, John, Pres.-Client Access--3Com Corporation, Santa Clara, CA; *U.S. Public*, pg. 1603
McCaughen, Robert Alan, Pres.-Canada--Bell Sports Corp., San Jose, CA; *U.S. Public*, pg. 207
McCauley, Douglas A., V.P. & Gen. Mgr.-Tech. Div.--Mechanical Technology Inc., Latham, NY; *U.S. Public*, pg. 1077
McCauley, R. W., Pres.-Paint Store Div.--ICI Paints, Cleveland, OH; *Int'l*, pg. 664
McClean, Murray R., Pres.-Intl. Div.--Commercial Metals Company, Dallas, TX; *U.S. Public*, pg. 411
McClorey, Michael T., Pres.-Health Resource Publishing Company--Catalina Marketing Corporation, Saint Petersburg, FL; *U.S. Public*, pg. 314
McClung, Perry, Pres.-Managed Care Corp.--Universal Standard Healthcare, Inc., Southfield, MI; *U.S. Public*, pg. 1697
McClure, John W., Grp. Pres.-Community Banking--Mercantile Bancorporation Inc., Saint Louis, MO; *U.S. Public*, pg. 1087
McComas, David, V.P. & Pres.-Western Div.--Circuit City Stores, Inc., Richmond, VA; *U.S. Public*, pg. 374
McCourt, Mark, Pres.-Sentry Bus. Commun.--Sentry Technology Group, Westborough, MA; *U.S. Public*, pg. 1425
McCoy, Fred, Pres.-Pacific Rim Sls.--Guidant Corporation, Indianapolis, IN; *U.S. Public*, pg. 768
McCoy, Michael R., Pres. & Chief Exec. Officer-Geotek USA--Geotek Communications, Montvale, NJ; *U.S. Public*, pg. 739
McCullough, Dick R., Pres.-Mechanical Prods. Div.--Thomas & Betts Corporation, Memphis, TN; *U.S. Public*, pg. 1597
McCurdy, Michelle, Pres-Kaizen Media--Palmer Jarvis Communications, Vancouver, Canada; *Int'l*, pg. 1022
McDaniel, Thomas R., Pres. & Chief Exec. Officer--Mission Land Company, Irvine, CA; *U.S. Public*, pg. 564
McFaland, Paul, Exec. V.P.-Opers.--Long John Silver's, Inc., Lexington, KY; *U.S. Private*, pg. 674
McFeetors, Raymond L., Pres. & Chief Exec. Officer-Canada--The Great-West Life Assurance Company, Winnipeg, Canada; *Int'l*, pg. 557
McGee, Jim, Pres.-Hospital Div., Chief Oper. Officer & Exec. V.P.--Schein Pharmaceutical, Inc., Florham Park, NJ; *U.S. Private*, pg. 969
McGoldrick, John, Pres.-Asia Pacific--Gandalf Technologies Inc., Nepean, Canada; *Int'l*, pg. 540
McGrath, J. Brian, Pres.-Intl.--Universal Studios Recreation Services Group, Universal City, CA; *Int'l*, pg. 1216
McGrath, Margaret H., Pres.-PPG Canada & V.P.-Coatings/Canada--PPG Industries, Inc., Pittsburgh, PA; *U.S. Public*, *pg. 1245*
McGrath, Ted, Pres.-Imaging Prods.--Fuji Photo Film U.S.A., Inc., Elmsford, NY; *Int'l*, pg. 524
McGregor, G.W., Exec. Gen. Mgr. & Chief Exec. Officer-BHP Service Companies Grp.--The Broken Hill Proprietary Company Limited, Melbourne, Australia; *Int'l*, pg. 223
McGuire, Gerald A., Corp. V.P., Pres. & Chief Exec. Officer-Pepsi Cola Gen. Bottlers--Whitman Corporation, Rolling Meadows, IL; *U.S. Public*, pg. 1766
McGuirk, James F., II, V.P. & Pres.-Federal Systems Div.--Unisys Corporation, Blue Bell, PA; *U.S. Public*, pg. 1671
McInerney, Robert J., Pres.-Comml. Systems Grp., MTI Systems Corp.--MTI Systems Corp., Melville, NY; *U.S. Public*, pg. 134
McIntire, Harold, Pres.-Food 4 Less Div.--Ralphs Grocery Company, Compton, CA; *U.S. Private*, pg. 1202
McIntosh, David, Grp. V.P. & Pres.--The Toro Company, Bloomington, MN; *U.S. Public*, pg. 1623
McIntyre, Timothy J., Exec. V.P. & Pres.-Promo. Conferencing Svcs. Div.--Boron LePore Group, Fair Lawn, NJ; *U.S. Public*, pg. 246
McKay, Eugene, III, Pres.-Opers. & Fin.--Archway Cookies, Inc., Battle Creek, MI; *U.S. Private*, pg. 80
McKenna, Andrew, W., Pres.-Midwest Div.--The Home Depot, Inc., Atlanta, GA; *U.S. Public*, pg. 831
McKenzie, James, Pres. & Chief Exec. Officer-Canada--Leo Burnett Company, Inc., Chicago, IL; *U.S. Private*, pg. 183
McKenzie, Naomi, Pres.-School Services/Marriott Management--Marriott International, Inc., Washington, DC; *U.S. Public*, pg. 1047
McKenzie, Naomi, Pres.-School Services--Marriott Management Services (MMS), Washington, DC; *U.S. Public*, pg. 1048
McKiernan, Michael P., Pres.-Transaction Svcs./Central Reg.--Grubb & Ellis Company, Northbrook, IL; *U.S. Public*, pg. 767
McKinnell, Henry A., Ph.D., Exec. V.P. & Pres.-Pfizer Pharmaceuticals Grp.--Pfizer Inc., New York, NY; *U.S. Public*, pg. 1281
McLaughlin, Susan A., Pres. & Gen. Mgr.-Kodak Imagiang Services, Inc.--Eastman Kodak Company, Rochester, NY; *U.S. Public*, pg. 550
McLean, Graham J., Pres. & Chief Oper. Officer-Magazine, Catalog & Retail Grp.--Quebecor Printing (USA) Corp., Boston, MA; *Int'l*, pg. 1076
McManis, Gerald L., Pres.-MMI Strategic Mngmt. Consulting Grp.--MMI Companies, Inc., Deerfield, IL; *U.S. Public*, pg. 1027
McManus, Sean, Pres.--CBS Sports Div., New York, NY; *U.S. Public*, pg. 274
McMillan, R.H., Pres.-ICI Acrylics--ICI Americas, Inc., Wilmington, DE; *Int'l*, pg. 663
McMillan, Ross, Pres.-Americas Reg.--ICI Acrylics Inc., Cordova, TN; *Int'l*, pg. 663
McMillen, David G., V.P. & Pres.-AES Shady Point, Inc.--AES Corporation, Arlington, VA; *U.S. Public*, pg. 5
McMullen, Kevin, V.P. & Pres.-Decorative Prods. Grp.--GenCorp Inc., Fairlawn, OH; *U.S. Public*, pg. 705
McMullen, Michael W.D., Pres.-HSN Intl. Div.--Home Shopping Network, Inc., Saint Petersburg, FL; *U.S. Public*, pg. 1685
McNamara, Charles J., Pres.-Engine Components--Dana Corporation, Toledo, OH; *U.S. Public*, pg. 479
McNamara, Joseph P., Pres. & Gen. Mgr.-Seiscor--Raytheon Company, Lexington, MA; *U.S. Public*, pg. 1364
McNeil, Donald G., Sr. V.P. & Pres.-Great Northern Paper, Inc.--Bowater Incorporated, Greenville, SC; *U.S. Public*, pg. 247
McNeilly, R.J., Exec. Gen. Mgr. & Chief Exec. Officer-BHP Steel--The Broken Hill Proprietary Company Limited, Melbourne, Australia; *Int'l*, pg. 223
Mead, Robert P., Pres.-Tyco Flow Control & V.P.--Tyco International Ltd., Exeter, NH; *U.S. Public*, pg. 1647
Mead, Robert P., Pres.--Grinnell Flow Control, Exeter, NH; *U.S. Public*, pg. 1650
Meaney, E. Robert, Pres. & Chief Oper. Officer-Intl. Div.--Valmont Industries, Inc., Valley, NE; *U.S. Public*, pg. 1706
Medlin, K.A., Pres.-North American Aircraft Modification Div.--Boeing North American, Seal Beach, CA; *U.S. Public*, pg. 241
Meek, Phillip J., Pres.-Publishing Grp. & Sr. V.P.--ABC, Inc, New York, NY; *U.S. Public*, pg. 511
Meers, Bob, Pres.-Reebok Brands--Reebok International Ltd., Stoughton, MA; *U.S. Public*, pg. 1369
Megarbane, Teddy, Pres.-Food & Mngmt. Services/European Opers.--Sodexho S.A., Montigny-le-Bretonneux, France; *Int'l*, pg. 1274
Meier, K. H., Pres.--Noma (Hong Kong) Limited, Kowloon, Hong Kong; *Int'l*, pg. 955
Meier, Robert C., Pres.-Mngmt. Co.--Taylor-Morley, Inc., Saint Louis, MO; *U.S. Private*, pg. 1071
Melani, Kenneth R., M.D., Exec. V.P.-Health Svcs.--Highmark Inc., Pittsburgh, PA; *U.S. Private*, pg. 528
Melton, George, Pres.-Tracor Aerospace, Inc.--Tracor Aerospace Electronics Systems, Inc., Lansdale, PA; *U.S.* Public, pg. 1627
Melton, George R., V.P. & Pres.-Tracor Aerospace, Inc.--Tracor, Inc., Austin, TX; *U.S. Public*, pg. 1627
Melton, James P., Pres.-Chemical Res. & Tech. & V.P.-Press Opers.--Quad/Graphics, Inc., Pewaukee, WI; *U.S. Private*, pg. 897
Menerey, Robert J., Sr. V.P. & Pres.-Drilling & Production Group--Dresser Industries, Inc.; Dallas, TX; *U.S. Public*, pg. 528
Menger, Joe L., V.P. & Pres.-Machine Tool Grp.--DeVlieg-Bullard Inc., Westport, CT; *U.S. Public*, pg. 502
Mentzer, Russell S., V.P. & Pres.-North American Pasta Prods.--Borden, Inc., Columbus, OH; *U.S. Private*, pg. 157
Merbler, Ken, Pres.-PCA, Europe--Philip Crosby Associates, Inc., Winter Park, FL; *Int'l*, pg. 1072
Merkel, Stephen, Pres.-North American Grp.--Loctite Corporation, Rocky Hill, CT; *Int'l*, pg. 611
Merz, Louis R., Grp. V.P.--MascoTech, Inc., Taylor, MI; *U.S.* Public, pg. 1055
Mette, Virgil L., Pres.-Mosby Health & Safety--Mosby-Year Book, Inc., Saint Louis, MO; *U.S. Public*, pg. 1616
Mettler, Robert L., Pres.-Mdsg.--Sears, Roebuck and Co., Hoffman Estates, IL; *U.S. Public*, pg. 1452
Metzler, Stephen, Pres.-Central Div.--International Total Services, Independence, OH; *U.S. Public*, pg. 908
Meyer, Claude L., Grp. V.P. & Pres.-Laundry & Cleaning Prods./Europe--The Procter & Gamble Company, Cincinnati, OH; *U.S. Public*, pg. 1330
Meyers, A.L., Pres.-Claims Mngmt. Svcs.--Crawford & Company, Atlanta, GA; *U.S. Public*, pg. 458
Mezger, Dieter J., Sr. V.P.-VLSI Tech. Inc., Pres.-COMPASS Design Automation, Inc.--VLSI Technology, Inc., San Jose, CA; *U.S. Public*, pg. 1703
Micati, Victor P., V.P., Exec. V.P.-Pfizer Pharmaceuticals & Area Pres.-Europe--Pfizer Inc., New York, NY; *U.S. Public*, pg. 1281
Michalou, Brian, Div. Pres.-So. East--Ferro Union, Inc., Torrance, CA; *U.S. Private*, pg. 402
Michot, Yves, Pres.-Helicopter Div. & Chief Oper. Officer--Aerospatiale, Paris, France; *Int'l*, pg. 28
Midgett, Leon A., Pres.-Metal Bev. Container Grp.--Ball Metal Beverage Container Corp., Westminster, CO; *U.S. Public*, pg. 171
Miele, Arthur R., V.P.-Mktg. & Pres.-PD Sales Co.--Phelps Dodge Corporation, Phoenix, AZ; *U.S. Public*, pg. 1286
Migeon, Nicole, Mgr.-Paintings & Prints--Phillips Fine Art Auctioneers, New York, NY; *U.S. Private*, pg. 861
Milam, Tom, Pres.-Heritage House--Southwestern/Great American Inc., Nashville, TN; *U.S. Private*, pg. 1018
Milchovich, Raymond J., Pres.-Kaiser Flat Rolled Prods. & Micromills--Kaiser Aluminum & Chemical Corporation, Pleasanton, CA; *U.S. Public*, pg. 1062
Miller, Charles C., III, Pres.-Intl.--BellSouth Corporation, Atlanta, GA; *U.S. Public*, pg. 207
Miller, Charles C., III, Pres.-Intl.--BellSouth Enterprises, Inc., Atlanta, GA; *U.S. Public*, pg. 208
Miller, Dennis K., Pres.-Seattle & Dir.--EvansGroup, Salt Lake City, UT; *U.S. Private*, pg. 385
Miller, George, Pres.-Distr.--Anixter Inc., Skokie, IL; *U.S. Public*, pg. 115
Miller, Grant, Pres.-Brand Svcs.--Baskin-Robbins Incorporated, Glendale, CA; *Int'l*, pg. 63
Miller, John D., Pres.-Rothschild Ventures--Rothschild North America Inc., New York, NY; *U.S. Private*, pg. 947
Miller, Jon, Pres. & Chief Exec. Officer-USA Broadcasting--USA Networks, Inc., Saint Petersburg, FL; *U.S. Public*, pg. 1685
Miller, Martin J., Pres.-PAREXEL/S&FA--PAREXEL International Corporation, Waltham, MA; *U.S. Public*, pg. 1257
Miller, Michael A., Pres.-Apparel Div.--Texfi Industries, Inc., Raleigh, NC; *U.S. Public*, pg. 1588

Miller, Mike, Pres.-Sager Bell--Creative Alliance, Inc., Louisville, KY; *U.S. Private*, pg. 287

Miller, Peter D., Pres.-Northeastern Reg.--Regions Financial Corporation, Birmingham, AL; *U.S. Public*, pg. 1371

Miller, Richard G., Pres.-Speedy Auto Glass--TCG International Inc., Burnaby, Canada; *Int'l*, pg. 1336

Miller, Robert, Pres.-Sentry Consulting Services--Sentry Technology Group, Westborough, MA; *U.S. Public*, pg. 1425

Miller, Robert L., Pres.-Time Inc. Ventures--Time Inc., New York, NY; *U.S. Public*, pg. 1612

Miller, Russell W., Pres.--Zions Life Insurance Co., Salt Lake City, UT; *U.S. Public*, pg. 1793

Miller, William T., Jr., Pres.-North American Opers.--Otis Elevator Company, Farmington, CT; *U.S. Public*, pg. 1690

Miller, Woody, Pres.-Plastics Div.--Edison Plastics Co., McAlester, OK; *U.S. Private*, pg. 1179

Mills, Don, Pres.-Corp. Research Assoc.--Maritime Telegraph & Telephone Company, Ltd., Halifax, Canada; *Int'l*, pg. 116

Milne, George M., Jr. Ph.D., V.P. & Pres.-Central Research--Pfizer Inc., New York, NY; *U.S. Public*, pg. 1281

Minor, R.G., Pres.-Space Systems Div.--Boeing North American, Seal Beach, CA; *U.S. Public*, pg. 241

Miranda, Gustavo, Pres.-Hispanic Div.--Russ Reid Company, Inc., Pasadena, CA; *U.S. Private*, pg. 952

Mirosh, Walentin, Pres.-Alberta Natural Gas Co. Ltd.--Transcanada Pipelines Limited, Calgary, Canada; *Int'l*, pg. 1416

Mitchell, Bruce W., Pres.-North Central Div.--Leslie Paper, Minneapolis, MN; *U.S. Public*, pg. 903

Mitchell, Donald L., Exec. V.P. & Pres.-Ladd Casegoods Grp.--Ladd Furniture, Inc., Greensboro, NC; *U.S. Public*, pg. 974

Mitchell, Hurley, Pres.-Hunter Douglas Manufacturing Group--Hunter Douglas, Inc., Upper Saddle River, NJ; *Int'l*, pg. 639

Mitchell, John, V.P. & Pres.-Bus. Printer Division--Lexmark International Group, Inc., Lexington, KY; *U.S. Public*, pg. 991

Mitchell, John, V.P. & Pres.-Bus. Printer Division--Lexmark International, Inc., Lexington, KY; *U.S. Public*, pg. 991

Mitchell, John C., Pres.-Planters/Lifesavers Company--Nabisco Inc., Parsippany, NJ; *U.S. Public*, pg. 1355

Mitchell, Robert, Pres.-Office Ours--Outsource International, Deerfield Beach, FL; *U.S. Public*, pg. 1236

Mittweg, Rolf, Pres.-New Line International Releasing--New Line Cinema Corporation, New York, NY; *U.S. Public*, pg. 1614

Mitzner, Donald, Pres.-CBS Cable--CBS, New York, NY; *U.S. Public*, pg. 273

Mixon, John R., Pres.-Paging Network-Northeastern Region, Inc.--Paging Network, Inc., Plano, TX; *U.S. Public*, pg. 1252

Miyahira, Wallace S., Pres.-N. American Residential & Hawaii Commercial Opers.--Castle & Cooke Inc., Los Angeles, CA; *U.S. Public*, pg. 313

Miyazaki, Kiyosada, Deputy Pres.--Sumitomo Life Insurance Company, Osaka, Japan; *Int'l*, pg. 1315

Mizrachi, David, Pres.-Institutional Sls.--Leshner Mills. Inc., Hamilton, OH; *U.S. Private*, pg. 660

Modell, Michael S., Co-Pres.--Henry Modell & Company, Inc., New York, NY; *U.S. Private*, pg. 754

Modell, Mitchell B., Co-Pres. & Chief Exec. Officer--Henry Modell & Company, Inc., New York, NY; *U.S. Private*, pg. 754

Moffitt, Don, Pres.-Southeast Region--Whole Foods Market, Inc., Austin, TX; *U.S. Public*, pg. 1767

Moger, Stanley, Pres.-SFM Entertainment Div.--SFM Media Corporation, New York, NY; *U.S. Private*, pg. 956

Mohr, Charles J., Pres.-SunAmerica Asset Mngmt.--SunAmerica Inc., Los Angeles, CA; *U.S. Public*, pg. 1532

Mohr, John R., Pres.-Regional Sports Services--Rainbow Programming Holdings, Inc., Woodbury, NY; *U.S. Public*, pg. 288

Monaghan, Terrence E., Pres.-Fin. & Admin.--World Book Educational Products, Elk Grove Village, IL; *U.S. Public*, pg. 218

Money, Jim, Pres.-Tandem--Outsource International, Deerfield Beach, FL; *U.S. Public*, pg. 1236

Monk, Douglas R., V.P.& Pres.-Aluminum Extrusions--Tredegar Industries Inc., Richmond, VA; *U.S. Public*, pg. 1633

Montoya, Jorge P., Exec. V.P. & Pres.-Latin America--The Procter & Gamble Company, Cincinnati, OH; *U.S. Public*, *pg. 1330*

Moody, Jack, Pres.-Construction--Robson Communities, Sun Lakes, AZ; *U.S. Private*, pg. 937

Moody, John N.D., Pres.-Mailing Systems--Pitney Bowes Inc., Stamford, CT; *U.S. Public*, pg. 1303

Moon, Allen C., Pres. & Chief Oper. Officer-Energy--Transalta Corporation, Calgary, Canada; *Int'l*, pg. 1416

Moon, J.L., Pres.--American Chrome & Chemicals, Inc., Corpus Christi, TX; *Int'l*, pg. 598

Moor, Kristian P., Pres.-National Union--American International Group, Inc., New York, NY; *U.S. Public*, pg. 83

Moore, Alfred Paynter, Pres.-Central Resource Grp.--American Mutual Life Holding Co., Des Moines, IA; *U.S. Private*, pg. 59

Moore, Garth W., Pres.-Potash--Potash Corporation of Saskatchewan Inc., Saskatoon, Canada; *Int'l*, pg. 1064

Moore, James R., Chief Fin. Officer, Exec. V.P. & Sec.--Urstadt Biddle Properties, Inc., Greenwich, CT; *U.S. Public*, pg. 1700

Moore, John R., Corp. V.P., Pres. & Chief Exec. Officer-Midas Intl. Corp.--Whitman Corporation, Rolling Meadows, IL; *U.S. Public*, pg. 1766

Moore, Robert B., Jr., Pres.-Sperry Top-Sider, Inc.--The Stride Rite Corporation, Lexington, MA; *U.S. Public*, pg. 1524

Moore, Sam Joseph, Exec. V.P. & Pres.-Thomas Nelson Gifts--Thomas Nelson Inc., Nashville, TN; *U.S. Public*, pg. 1167

Moose, John, Pres.--Collins & Aikman Products Co., Roxboro, NC; *U.S. Public*, pg. 399

Moraes, Eduardo N.P., Pres.-Bundy Latin America--Bundy International, Warren, MI; *Int'l*, pg. 1340

Morehouse, Sherry R., Sr. V.P.-Network Engrng.--MCI Communications Corp., Atlanta, GA; *U.S. Public*, pg. 1023

Moreno, Karen, Pres.-Gannett Supply Corp.--Gannett Company, Inc., Arlington, VA; *U.S. Public*, pg. 698

Morgan, Joseph, Grp. Pres.-BLIMPIE Subs & Salads & Pasta Central--Blimpie International, Inc., Atlanta, GA; *U.S. Public*, pg. 236

Morgan, Ken, Pres.-Texas Area Opers.--Paragon Health Network, Inc., Atlanta, GA; *U.S. Public*, pg. 1256

Morgan, Nathan J., Pres.--Zions Investment Securities, Inc., Salt Lake City, UT; *U.S. Public*, pg. 1793

Morgenthal, Steven, Pres.-Unified Systems Solutions Inc.--Computer Horizons Corp., Mountain Lakes, NJ; *U.S. Public*, pg. 421

Morisugi, Norio, Pres.--Helene Curtis Japan Inc., Tokyo, Japan; *Int'l*, pg. 1434

Morita, Tomijiro, Deputy Pres.--Dai-ichi Mutual Life Insurance Company, Tokyo, Japan; *Int'l*, pg. 362

Morrell, Andres F., Pres.--Velco, Caparra Heights, PR; *U.S. Public*, pg. 176

Morris, Ginny, Pres.-Radio Grp. & V.P.--Hubbard Broadcasting, Inc., Saint Paul, MN; *U.S. Private*, pg. 543

Morrison, Dale F., Pres.-Pepperidge Farm--Bakery & Confectionary Division, Camden, NJ; *U.S. Public*, pg. 299

Morrisson, J. Norman, Pres.-Premier Distr.--Premier CDN Enterprises Ltd., Dorval, Canada; *Int'l*, pg. 1067

Morrow, Donald P., Pres.-Transaction Svcs./Western Reg.--Grubb & Ellis Company, Northbrook, IL; *U.S. Public*, pg. 767

Morse, Robert, Pres.-Franchise--ITT Sheraton Corporation, Boston, MA; *U.S. Public*, pg. 1512

Morton, B. Carole, Sr. V.P. & Pres.-Info. Mngmt. Div.--Sterling Software, Inc., Dallas, TX; *U.S. Public*, pg. 1516

Morton, David L., Pres. & Chief Exec. Officer--U.S. & Canadian Food Products, Chicago, IL; *U.S. Public*, pg. 1347

Morton, S. Morgan, Pres.-Warner Lambert Consumer Healthcare U.S.A. & V.P.--Warner-Lambert Company, Morris Plains, NJ; *U.S. Public*, pg. 1738

Morton, S. Morgan, Pres. & V.P.-Consumer Healthcare--Warner-Lambert Consumer Healthcare, Morris Plains, NJ; *U.S. Public*, pg. 1739

Moscheni, Claude, Pres.-Sofitel--Accor S.A., Evry, France; *Int'l*, pg. 20

Mosher, Timothy C., Pres.-AEP Kentucky--American Electric Power Company, Inc., Columbus, OH; *U.S. Public*, pg. 71

Mosher, William, Sr. Pres.-Sls.--Circle Plastics Products, Inc., Circleville, OH; *U.S. Private*, pg. 240

Mosier, Dale, Grp. Pres.-Poly Hi Solidur--Menasha Corporation, Neenah, WI; *U.S. Private*, pg. 731

Mosser, Thomas W., Pres.-Avatar Vacation Resorts, Inc.--Avatar Holdings Inc., Coral Gables, FL; *U.S. Public*, pg. 151

Mostrom, Joel, Pres.-Land Devel. Opers.--Chesapeake Corporation, Richmond, VA; *U.S. Public*, pg. 346

Motley, Lyle C., Jr., Pres.-Southern Div.--NUI Corporation, Bedminster, NJ; *U.S. Public*, pg. 1147

Moule, James C., Pres.-Nichols Federal--Nichols Research Corporation, Huntsville, AL; *U.S. Public*, pg. 1182

Mowder, John P., Pres.-Dixon Industries, Inc.--Blount International, Inc., Montgomery, AL; *U.S. Public*, pg. 237

Moylan, James E., Jr., Chief Fin. Officer & Sr. V.P. & Pres.-Sonat Services Inc.--Sonat Inc., Birmingham, AL; *U.S. Public*, pg. 1484

Mrozek, Ernest J., Pres.-ServiceMaster Svcs.--The ServiceMaster Company, Downers Grove, IL; *U.S. Public*, pg. 1461

Muchnick, H.F., Pres.-CN Tower Ltd.--Canadian National Railway Company, Montreal, Canada; *Int'l*, pg. 258

Muckleroy, Merle C., Pres.-Prods. & Svcs. Grp.--Camco International Inc., Houston, TX; *U.S. Public*, pg. 297

Muckleroy, Merle C., Pres.-Prod. & Svcs.--Camco International Inc., Houston, TX; *U.S. Public*, pg. 298

Mudford, Anthony, Pres.-Detex International--Detex Corporation, New Braunfels, TX; *U.S. Private*, pg. 327

Mueller, Brett, Pres.-Magnum Div. & V.P.-Sls. & Mktg.--Mueller Sports Medicine, Inc., Prairie Du Sac, WI; *U.S. Private*, pg. 766

Muhlebach, Karl, Deputy Co-Pres.-Intl. Div.--The Swiss Life/Rentenanstalt Group, Zurich, Switzerland; *Int'l*, pg. 1332

Mulally, Alan R., Sr. V.P. & Pres.-Boeing Defense & Space Grp.--The Boeing Company, Seattle, WA; *U.S. Public*, pg. 239

Mullis, B. B., Pres.-Fibre Intermediates--DSM N.V., Heerlen, Netherlands; *Int'l*, pg. 352

Munechika, Hirokuni, Deputy Pres.-Investment Service--Daiwa Securities Co. Ltd., Tokyo, Japan; *Int'l*, pg. 374

Munn, William H., Pres.-BGE Home Prods. & Svcs., Inc.--Baltimore Gas and Electric Company, Baltimore, MD; *U.S. Public*, pg. 172

Munro, Juan Pedro, Pres.-Philip Morris/Latin America--Philip Morris International Inc., Rye Brook, NY; *U.S. Public*, pg. 1289

Muratore, Peter, Pres.-OPCAP Distributors--OppenheimerFunds Distributor, Inc., New York, NY; *U.S.* Private, pg. 818

Muratore, Robert P., Pres. & Chief Exec. Officer-Ferguson Direct--CommonHealth USA, Parsippany, NJ; *Int'l*, pg. 1483

Murphy, David D., Sr. V.P. & Pres.-Intl. Foods--General Mills, Inc., Minneapolis, MN; *U.S. Public*, pg. 717

Murphy, Susan, Pres.-Oppenheimer Capital Trust Co.--OppenheimerFunds Distributor, Inc., New York, NY; *U.S.* Private, pg. 818

Murray, Michael J., Pres.-Global Wholesale Bank--BankAmerica Corporation, San Francisco, CA; *U.S. Public*, pg. 179

Murray, Patrick M., Sr. V.P. & Pres.-Strategic Intiative Technology--Dresser Industries, Inc., Dallas, TX; *U.S. Public*, pg. 528

Musacchio, Michael J., Pres.-Mark VII Logistics Services Div.--Mark VII, Inc., Memphis, TN; *U.S. Public*, pg. 1046

Musselman, John, Pres.-Eastern Division--Airgas, Inc., Radnor, PA; *U.S. Public*, pg. 33

Mut, Stephen R., Sr. V.P. & Pres.-ARCO Global Energy Ventures--Atlantic Richfield Company, Los Angeles, CA; *U.S. Public*, pg. 144

Mutzenbecher, Gerhard von, Dr., Pres.-Syntex Pharmaceuticals-Europe & V.P.--Syntex, Palo Alto, CA; *Int'l*, pg. 1120

Myers, David L., Grp. Pres.-Indus.--Fluor Daniel Inc., Irvine, CA; *U.S. Public*, pg. 660

Myers, Wayne, Pres.-Axle Prods.--Dana Corporation, Toledo, OH; *U.S. Public*, pg. 479

Myslenski, Jack, V.P. & Pres.-Fluid Connectors Group--Parker Hannifin Corporation, Cleveland, OH; *U.S. Public*, pg. 1259

Nadelberg, Stephen, Sr. V.P. & Pres.-North Coast Entertainment--Handleman Company, Troy, MI; *U.S. Public*, pg. 779

Nadler, Lothar, Pres.-Adv. Sls.--Burda Holding GmbH & Co., KG, Munich, Germany; *Int'l*, pg. 233

Nagai, Hisamoto, Deputy Pres.--Dai-ichi Mutual Life Insurance Company, Tokyo, Japan; *Int'l*, pg. 362

Nagel, David, Pres.-AT&T Labs--AT&T Corporation, Basking Ridge, NJ; *U.S. Public*, pg. 10

Nahai, Gary J., Pres.-Fedders International & V.P.--Fedders Corp., Liberty Corner, NJ; *U.S. Public*, pg. 614

Nakai, Minoru, Pres.-AFLAC Intl.--AFLAC Incorporated, Columbus, GA; *U.S. Public*, pg. 28

Nakamura, Pres.--UBE Machinery, Inc., Ann Arbor, MI; *Int'l*, pg. 1427

Narhi, Antti, Pres.--Outokumpu Steel Oy, Tornio, Finland; *Int'l*, pg. 1018

Narita, Akihiko, Mng. Dir. & Pres.-Japan--Symantec Corporation, Cupertino, CA; *U.S. Public*, pg. 1545

Nassau, Richard J., Pres.-Real Estate--CC Industries, Inc., Chicago, IL; *U.S. Private*, pg. 192

Nastri, Wayne H., Pres.-Environ. Mediation, Inc.--American Vanguard Corporation, Newport Beach, CA; *U.S. Public*, pg. 94

Natale, James L., V.P. & Pres.-Corp. Healthcare Services--C.R. Bard, Inc., Murray Hill, NJ; *U.S. Public*, pg. 189

Nathanson, Michael, Pres.-MGM Pictures--Metro-Goldwyn-Mayer Pictures, Inc., Santa Monica, CA; *U.S. Public*, pg. 1102

Nderstedt, Sven, Pres.--ICA Handlarna Syd AB, Arlov, Sweden; *Int'l*, pg. 643

Nechiporchik, John D., Pres.--ASC Incorporated, Southgate, MI; *U.S. Private*, pg. 8

Necovetich, John, Pres.-Tokheim North America--Tokheim Corporation, Fort Wayne, IN; *U.S. Public*, pg. 1620

Needleman, Stuart M., Sr. V.P. & Pres.-CompUSA Direct--CompUSA, Dallas, TX; *U.S. Public*, pg. 420

Neely, Alexander, Pres.--Burlington Menswear, New York, NY; *U.S. Public*, pg. 268

Neff, Jerome C., Pres.-Custom Communications Grp.--Penton Publishing, Inc., Cleveland, OH; *U.S. Public*, pg. 1306

Neil, Joe R., Pres.-Communications Papers--Fort James Corporation, Richmond, VA; *U.S. Public*, pg. 670

Neirotti, Mario, Mng. Dir.--Getinge AB Italia, Udine, Italy; *Int'l*, pg. 551

Nelly, Henry M., III, Pres.-Provident Services, Inc.--Service Corporation International, Houston, TX; *U.S. Public*, pg. 1460

Nelson, Chuck, Pres.-Sls. Promo. Div.--Barton Nelson Inc., Kansas City, MO; *U.S. Private*, pg. 120

Nelson, David, Pres.-Casablanca Prods.--Western International Media Corporation, Los Angeles, CA; *U.S. Private*, pg. 1165

Nelson, David, Pres.-Sierra Military Health Svcs.--Sierra Health Services, Inc., Las Vegas, NV; *U.S. Public*, pg. 1469

Nelson, Eric B., Pres.-Energy Pacific--Pacific Enterprises, Los Angeles, CA; *U.S. Public*, pg. 1249

Nelson, Jim, Pres. & Chief Exec. Officer-Southern Progress Corp.--Time Inc., New York, NY; *U.S. Public*, pg. 1612

Nelson, Kenneth P., Exec. V.P. & Grp. Pres.--Bremer Financial Corporation, Saint Paul, MN; *U.S. Private*, pg. 167

Nelson, Mary Jo, Pres.-Yellow Pages Div.--Ruppman Marketing Technologies, Inc., Peoria, IL; *U.S. Private*, pg. 951

Nelson, Wayne B., Pres.-Harbert Power--Harbert Corporation, Birmingham, AL; *U.S. Private*, pg. 500

Nemecek, John, Pres.-Property Mngmt. Grp.--Duke Realty Investments, Inc., Indianapolis, IN; *U.S. Public*, pg. 535

Nesvig, Jon, Pres.-Sls.--Fox Broadcasting Company (FBC), Beverly Hills, CA; *Int'l*, pg. 926

Neuman, David A., Pres.-Television Div.--The Walt Disney Company, Burbank, CA; *U.S. Public*, pg. 511

Neupaver, Albert J., Pres.-Electromechanical Grp.--AMETEK, Inc., Paoli, PA; *U.S. Public*, pg. 99

Nevin, Robert C., Pres.-Automotive Div.--The Reynolds and Reynolds Company, Dayton, OH; *U.S. Public*, pg. 1384

Newcomb, Jonathan, Pres. & Chief Exec. Officer-Simon & Schuster--National Amusements, Inc., Dedham, MA; *U.S.* Private, pg. 775

Newell, Gregory J., Pres.-Asia Pacific--BeautiControl Cosmetics, Inc., Carrollton, TX; *U.S. Public*, pg. 198

Newell, James C., Pres.-Global Svcs.--I.M.S. International, Inc., Totowa, NJ; *U.S. Public*, pg. 395

Newlin, Stephen D., Grp. V.P. & Pres.-Nalco Pacific--Nalco Chemical Company, Naperville, IL; *U.S. Public*, pg. 1150

Newton, Peter C., Pres.-Professional Mkts. Grp.--Van den Bergh Foods Company, Lisle, IL; *Int'l*, pg. 1436

Nichols, Max T., Pres.--Zions Credit Corporation, Salt Lake City, UT; *U.S. Public*, pg. 1793
Nick, Jeffrey J., Pres. & Chief Exec. Officer-Lincoln National Investment Companies--Lincoln National Corporation, Fort Wayne, IN; *U.S. Public*, pg. 997
Nicohls, George Q., V.P. & Pres.-Natl. Publ. Co.--Courier Corporation, North Chelmsford, MA; *U.S. Public*, pg. 453
Nicoletti, Anthony C., V.P. & Pres.-Asia Pacific--Data General Corporation, Westborough, MA; *U.S. Public*, pg. 485
Niederkorn, Mike, Div. Pres.-So. West--Ferro Union, Inc., Torrance, CA; *U.S. Private*, pg. 402
Niederpruem, Gary J., Pres.-East--Joseph T. Ryerson & Son, Inc., Chicago, IL; *U.S. Public*, pg. 879
Nielsen, Wendy, Pres.-HLS Corp.--CommonHealth USA, Parsippany, NJ; *Int'l*, pg. 1483
Niemy, Roman P., Pres.-Corp. Brands--Shoppers Drug Mart, Ltd., Toronto, Canada; *Int'l*, pg. 112
Niermeyer, Donald L., Pres.-Paging Network/Central Region, Inc.--Paging Network, Inc., Plano, TX; *U.S. Public*, pg. 1252
Niles, Terry, Pres.-Trade Support Services--Gage Marketing Group, Minneapolis, MN; *U.S. Private*, pg. 437
Nilsson, Svante, Pres.--ICA Handlarna Ost AB, Arsta, Sweden; *Int'l*, pg. 642
Nimtz, Richard H., Pres.-Kappa Properties--Giant Eagle, Inc., Pittsburgh, PA; *U.S. Private*, pg. 450
Nishimura, Leslie T., Sr. V.P. & Pres.-Solectron Washington, Inc.--Solectron Corporation, Milpitas, CA; *U.S. Public*, pg. 1483
Nissenfeld, Mark, Pres.-Global Health Care & PHT--Total Research Corporation, Princeton, NJ; *U.S. Public*, pg. 1625
Nixon, A.M., Pres.--The Torrington Co., Torrington, CT; *U.S.* Public, pg. 877
Noble, H. Lee, Exec. V.P. & Pres.-Polymers Division--Bayer Corporation, Pittsburgh, PA; *Int'l*, pg. 172
Noble, H. Lee, Pres.-Polymers Div. & Exec. V.P.--Bayer Corporation, Pittsburgh, PA; *Int'l*, pg. 172
Noble, H. Lee, Exec. V.P. & Pres.-Polymers Div.--Bayer Corporation, Parsippany, NJ; *Int'l*, pg. 172
Noddle, Jeffrey, Exec. V.P., Pres. & Chief Oper. Officer-Wholesale Food Companies--SuperValu, Inc., Eden Prairie, MN; *U.S. Public*, pg. 1540
Noel, Dennis, Pres.--NASTECH Corp., Bennington, VT; *Int'l*, *pg. 903*
Nolan, David, Pres.-Comdisco Continuity Svcs.--Comdisco, Inc., Rosemont, IL; *U.S. Public*, pg. 407
Nolan, Frankie, V.P.-Social Responsibility & Pres.-Borden Foundation--Borden, Inc., Columbus, OH; *U.S. Private*, pg. 157
Nolan, J. Timothy, Pres.-Consumer Prods. Div.--Rich Products Corp., Buffalo, NY; *U.S. Private*, pg. 928
Norling, James A., Exec. V.P. & Pres.-Messaging, Info. & Media--Motorola, Inc., Schaumburg, IL; *U.S. Public*, pg. 1136
Norman, William, Pres.-Norman Enterprises, Inc.--Photo Control Corporation, Minneapolis, MN; *U.S. Public*, pg. 1292
Norris, Michael L., Pres.-Trans Financial Mortgage Co.--Trans Financial, Inc., Bowling Green, KY; *U.S. Public*, pg. 1628
Norris, Paul J., Pres.-Chemicals & Catalysts--AlliedSignal Inc., Engineered Materials, Morristown, NJ; *U.S. Public*, pg. 51
North, Julia B., Pres.-Consumer Services--BellSouth Telecommunications, Inc., Atlanta, GA; *U.S. Public*, pg. 209
Northrup, Vic, Pres.-Telephony Div.--Executone Information Systems, Inc., Milford, CT; *U.S. Public*, pg. 599
Norton, James J., Pres.-Washington Specialty Metals--Lukens Inc., Coatesville, PA; *U.S. Public*, pg. 1019
Nostrand, Peter F., Pres.-Greater Washington Region--Crestar Financial Corporation, Richmond, VA; *U.S. Public*, pg. 458
Noteborn, F.H.M.A., Pres.-Polymers--DSM N.V., Heerlen, Netherlands; *Int'l*, pg. 352
Novack, Kenneth M., Pres.-Schnitzer Investment Corp. & Exec. V.P.-Schnitzer Steel--Schnitzer Steel Industries, Inc., Portland, OR; *U.S. Public*, pg. 1439
Novik, Richard D., Pres.--Clear Channel Communications International, Ancramdale, NY; *U.S. Public*, pg. 383
Nudelman, Phillip A., Pres.-Northwest Division & Sr. V.P.--Kaiser Permanente, Oakland, CA; *U.S. Private*, pg. 605
Nuechtern, Martin J., Grp. V.P. & Pres.-ASEAN & Australasia--The Procter & Gamble Company, Cincinnati, OH; *U.S. Public*, pg. 1330
Numaguchi, Motohiko, Pres. & Mng. Dir.-Mitsubishi Intl. Corp.--Mitsubishi Corporation, Tokyo, Japan; *Int'l*, pg. 871
Nunez, Armando, Jr., Pres.-Intl. Distr.--New World Entertainment, Inc., Los Angeles, CA; *Int'l*, pg. 926
Nunez, Armando, Jr., Pres.--Universal Studios TV, Universal City, CA; *Int'l*, pg. 1215
Nunn, Kent G., Pres. & Chief Exec. Officer-One Sys. Grp. LLC--Farmland Industries, Inc., Kansas City, MO; *U.S. Private*, pg. 395
Nutting, Ronald G., V.P. & Pres.-Riedel OMNI Rubber Prods. Inc.--Smith Technologies Corp., Portland, OR; *U.S. Public*, pg. 1478
Nuzzo, Mark, Pres.-Property Mngmt.--Fairfield Communities, Inc., Little Rock, AR; *U.S. Public*, pg. 610
Nuzzo, Silvio, Pres. & Chief Exec. Officer-BioChem ImmunoSystems--BioChem Pharma Inc., Laval, Canada; *Int'l*, pg. 196
O'Brien, Patrick J., V.P. & Pres.-A & M Prods.--First Brands Corporation, Danbury, CT; *U.S. Public*, pg. 626
O'Connor, John J., Pres.-Worldwide Exploration & Exec. V.P.--Texaco Inc., White Plains, NY; *U.S. Public*, pg. 1582
O'Dell, Charles, Pres.-Marriott Mngmt.--Marriott International, Inc., Washington, DC; *U.S. Public*, pg. 1047
O'Donnell, Thomas H., Pres.-Homehealth Care Grp.--Sunrise Medical, Inc., Carlsbad, CA; *U.S. Public*, pg. 1535
O'Farrell, John, Pres.-Interactive Svcs.--U S West Inc., Englewood, CO; *U.S. Public*, pg. 1688
O'Hara, Kevin J., Pres.-MFS Devel.--MFS WorldCom, Inc., Omaha, NE; *U.S. Public*, pg. 1779
O'Keefe, James, Grp. V.P. & Pres.-Health & Beauty Care Prods./Europe--The Procter & Gamble Company, Cincinnati, OH; *U.S. Public*, pg. 1330
O'Malley, Wiliam, Pres.--Point Marine, Inc., New Orleans, LA; *U.S. Public*, pg. 1608
O'Malley, William, Pres.--Pental Insurance Co., Ltd., New Orleans, LA; *U.S. Public*, pg. 1608
O'Malley, William, Pres.--Tidewater Marine, Inc., Amelia, LA; *U.S. Public*, pg. 1608
O'Malley, William, Pres.--Tidewater Marine International, Inc., New Orleans, LA; *U.S. Public*, pg. 1608
O'Malley, William, Pres.--Tidewater Marine Western, Inc., New Orleans, LA; *U.S. Public*, pg. 1608
O'Malley, William, Pres.--Tidewater Offshore Services, Inc., New Orleans, LA; *U.S. Public*, pg. 1608
O'Malley, William, Pres.--Seafarer Boat Corporation, New Orleans, LA; *U.S. Public*, pg. 1608
O'Malley, William C., Pres. & Chief Oper. Officer--Tidewater Marine Service, Inc., New Orleans, LA; *U.S. Public*, pg. 1608
O'Malley, William M., Pres.--Twenty Grand Offshore, New Orleans, LA; *U.S. Public*, pg. 1608
O'Neal, James, Pres. & Chief Exec. Officer-Intl. Bus.--Frito-Lay Company, Plano, TX; *U.S. Public*, pg. 1277
O'Neill, Daniel J., Pres.-U.S. Soup--Campbell Soup Company, Camden, NJ; *U.S. Public*, pg. 298
O'Neill, Daniel J.rtin, Pres.-U.S. Soup--Campbell USA, Camden, NJ; *U.S. Public*, pg. 299
O'Neill, William J., Jr., Pres.-Bus. Devel. & Exec. V.P.--Polaroid Corporation, Cambridge, MA; *U.S. Public*, pg. 1313
O'Ray, Patrick, Sr. V.P. & Pres.-Specialty Brands Div.--Foodbrands America, Inc., Oklahoma City, OK; *U.S. Public*, pg. 852
O'Reilly, David, Corp. V.P. & Pres.-Chevron Prods.--Chevron Corporation, San Francisco, CA; *U.S. Public*, pg. 347
O'Reilly, Kelley, Pres.-Impact Adv. Inc. & V.P.-Mktg.--Big O Tires Incorporated, Englewood, CO; *U.S. Public*, pg. 1553
O'Riordan, Dan, Sr. Grp. V.P. & Pres.-Intl. Foods--Borden, Inc., Columbus, OH; *U.S. Private*, pg. 157
O'Rourke, James, Pres.-Nameplate Div.--Fred B. Johnston Company, Inc., Chapin, SC; *U.S. Private*, pg. 595
O'Rourke, Terrence E., V.P. & Pres.-Ford Div.--Lear Corporation, Southfield, MI; *U.S. Public*, pg. 981
O'Shea, William T., Pres.-Network Systems--Lucent Technologies Inc., Murray Hill, NJ; *U.S. Public*, pg. 1017
O'Shei, Donald M., Jr., Pres. & Chief Oper. Officer-CalEnergy Asia--CalEnergy Co., Omaha, NE; *U.S. Public*, *pg. 292*
Oberfeld, Steven J., Pres. & Gen. Mgr.-South-Western Div., Paint Stores Grp.--The Sherwin-Williams Company, Cleveland, OH; *U.S. Public*, pg. 1465
Oberhill, John S., Sr. V.P.-Corp. Mfg. Services--R.R. Donnelley & Sons Company, Chicago, IL; *U.S. Public*, pg. 517
Obourn, Candy M., V.P. & Pres.-Bus. Imaging Systems--Eastman Kodak Company, Rochester, NY; *U.S. Public*, pg. 550
Odell, Thomas, Pres.-Standard Prods. Div.--National Semiconductor Corporation, Santa Clara, CA; *U.S. Public*, pg. 1159
Odom, Roderick D., Jr., Pres.-BellSouth Bus. Systems--BellSouth Telecommunications, Inc., Atlanta, GA; *U.S. Public*, pg. 209
Oebel, Klaus D., V.P. & Pres.-AYDIN Communications Systems Grp.--Aydin Corporation, Horsham, PA; *U.S. Public*, pg. 158
Oehmichen, Klaus, Dr., Pres.-Chemicals Div.--Altana AG, Bad Homburg, Germany; *Int'l*, pg. 65
Offsay, Jerry R., Pres.-Programming--Showtime Networks Inc., New York, NY; *U.S. Private*, pg. 779
Ogiens, Michael, Pres.-MTM Television--International Family Entertainment, Inc., Virginia Beach, VA; *Int'l*, pg. 927
Ogiens, Michael, Pres.-T.V.--MTM Enterprises, Inc., Studio City, CA; *Int'l*, pg. 927
Oglesby, G. Thomas, Jr., Pres.-Keystone Div.--Rock of Ages Corporation, Graniteville, VT; *U.S. Public*, pg. 1396
Ohashi, Hiroshi, Dep. Pres.--The Sumitomo Trust & Banking Co., Ltd., Osaka, Japan; *Int'l*, pg. 1317
Ohlmeyer, Donald W., Jr., Pres.-NBC/West Coast--National Broadcasting Co., Inc., New York, NY; *U.S. Public*, pg. 712
Ojanpaa, Paavo, Pres.-Plywood--UPM-Kymmene Corporation, Helsinki, Finland; *Int'l*, pg. 1427
Oleson, Donald L., Pres.-Natl. Sls. Div.--Allied Digital Technologies, Hauppauge, NY; *U.S. Public*, pg. 48
Olin, Thomas F. Jr., Pres.-Sls. & Mktg.--Archway Cookies, Inc., Battle Creek, MI; *U.S. Private*, pg. 80
Olinger, Lawrence W., Mng. Principal-Mngmt. Engrng. & Tech. Services--Dewberry & Davis, Fairfax, VA; *U.S. Private*, pg. 329
Oliver, Byron D., Pres.-CIGNA Retirement & Investment Services--Cigna Corp., Philadelphia, PA; *U.S. Public*, pg. 356
Oliver, Charlie, Grp. Pres.-Sls., Reg. Coord. & Strategic Plng.--Fluor Daniel Inc., Irvine, CA; *U.S. Public*, pg. 660
Oliver, Paul, Pres.-Pillsbury Bakeries & Foodservice Inc.--The Pillsbury Company, Minneapolis, MN; *Int'l*, pg. 411
Olivie, Marc R., Pres.-Worldwide Bldg. Prods. Opers.--Armstrong World Industries, Inc., Lancaster, PA; *U.S. Public*, pg. 131
Olivier, Louison, Exec. V.P. & Pres.-Groundwood Opers. & Sls.--Abitibi-Consolidated Inc., Montreal, Canada; *Int'l*, pg. 19
Olson, Larry D., Exec. V.P. & Pres.-Kent Components--Kent Electronics Corp., Houston, TX; *U.S. Public*, pg. 951
Omahne, Robert, Pres.-Fin. Institutions Div.--National Union Fire Ins. Co. of Pittsburgh, Pa., New York, NY; *U.S. Public*, pg. 84
Ono, Masataka, Pres.--Air Products Japan, Inc., Tokyo, Japan; *U.S. Public*, pg. 31
Ono, Toshihiko, Pres.--NS Invest, Inc., New York, NY; *Int'l*, pg. 940
Opdyke, William H., Pres.-U.S. Refrigerated Dough Prods.--The Earthgrains Company, Clayton, MO; *U.S. Public*, pg. 547
Opet, Bill, Pres.-Geotek Data Co.--Geotek Communications, Montvale, NJ; *U.S. Public*, pg. 739
Opferman, Joseph, Pres.-RV/Transport Div.--Morgan Drive Away, Inc., Elkhart, IN; *U.S. Public*, pg. 1022
Oppenheimer, Jim, Pres.-Florida Reg.--Whole Foods Market, Inc., Austin, TX; *U.S. Public*, pg. 1767
Ordonez, Kathy, V.P.-Hoffmann LaRoche Inc. & Pres.-Roche Molecular Systems--Hoffmann-La Roche Inc., Nutley, NJ; *Int'l*, pg. 1120
Orleans, Stephen, Pres.-Safety 1st-Canada--Safety 1st, Inc., Chestnut Hill, MA; *U.S. Public*, pg. 1425
Ornest, Harry, Vice Chm. & Pres.-Hollywood Park, Inc.--Hollywood Park, Inc., Inglewood, CA; *U.S. Public*, pg. 830
Orr, Michael P., Pres.-Fin. Services Div.--Deere & Company, Moline, IL; *U.S. Public*, pg. 491
Orrico, John G., Pres.-Transaction Svcs./Eastern Reg.--Grubb & Ellis Company, Northbrook, IL; *U.S. Public*, pg. 767
Ortwein, Dick, Pres.-Koll Real Estate Grp.--Koll Co., Newport Beach, CA; *U.S. Private*, pg. 631
Osborne, Roger, Pres.-Work 'n Gear Stores & Exec. V.P.--J. Baker, Inc., Canton, MA; *U.S. Public*, pg. 167
Ostendorf, Robert, Pres.--ASC Incorporated, Southgate, MI; *U.S. Private*, pg. 8
Osterman, James S., Grp. Pres.-Outdoor Products Grp.--Blount International, Inc., Montgomery, AL; *U.S. Public*, pg. 237
Ota, Pres.--Nintendo of Europe GmbH, Germany; *Int'l*, pg. 932
Otradovec, Peter, Pres.-Mesa Div.--Mesa Air Group, Las Vegas, NV; *U.S. Public*, pg. 1098
Otto, Heinz-J., V.P. & Pres.-Composites--Owens Corning, Toledo, OH; *U.S. Public*, pg. 1236
Ovlinger, Bengt, Pres.-Construction Equipment--AB Volvo, Goteborg, Sweden; *Int'l*, pg. 1476
Owen, Dan, Pres.-Hasbro Toy Grp.--Tonka Corporation, Pawtucket, RI; *U.S. Public*, pg. 797
Owen, Richard F., Pres.-Southern Divisions & Exec. V.P.--Owen Industries, Inc., Carter Lake, IA; *U.S. Private*, pg. 824
Owens, James W., Grp. Pres.--Caterpillar Inc., Peoria, IL; *U.S. Public*, pg. 315
Owens, Kenneth C., Pres.-AdviNet--Beverly Enterprises, Inc., Fort Smith, AR; *U.S. Public*, pg. 227
Packham, William D., Pres.-Midland Walwyn Capital Inc.--Midland Walwyn Inc., Toronto, Canada; *Int'l*, pg. 865
Paddy, Pattie, Pres.-Kwik Kopy Corp.--International Center for Entrepreneurial Development, Inc., Cypress, TX; *U.S.* Private, pg. 568
Pages, Mauricio, Pres.-Americas--A.C. Nielsen, Stamford, CT; *U.S. Public*, pg. 1183
Paine, Andrew J., Jr., Exec. V.P. & Pres.-NBD Indiana--First Chicago NBD Corporation, Chicago, IL; *U.S. Public*, pg. 627
Painter, Richard O., Pres.-Prudential Insurance & Fin. Svcs.--The Prudential Insurance Company of America, Newark, NJ; *U.S. Private*, pg. 892
Paisley, Thomas N., Pres.-Structural/Functional Division--Cambridge Industries Inc., Madison Heights, MI; *U.S. Private*, pg. 202
Pajot, Gilles, Vice Chm. & Pres.-IMS Europe Reg.--I.M.S. International, Inc., Totowa, NJ; *U.S. Public*, pg. 395
Palmblad, Ulf, Pres.-Skanska Data AB--Skanska AB, Danderyd, Sweden; *Int'l*, pg. 1260
Palmer, Roger, Sr. V.P. & Pres.-CETCO--AMCOL International Corp., Arlington Heights, IL; *U.S. Public*, pg. 63
Palsho, Dorothea Coccoli, Pres.-Bus. Info. Svcs.--Dow Jones & Company, Inc., New York, NY; *U.S. Public*, pg. 524
Paluszek, John L., Pres.-Pub. Affairs--Ketchum Public Relations Worldwide, New York, NY; *U.S. Private*, pg. 617
Panayotopoulos, Dimitri, Grp. V.P. & Pres.-China/Proctor & Gamble Asia--The Procter & Gamble Company, Cincinnati, OH; *U.S. Public*, pg. 1330
Pardum, Thomas E., Pres. & Chief Exec. Officer-Multimedia Communications--U S West Inc., Englewood, CO; *U.S. Public*, pg. 1688
Pare, Jean, Pres.-Magzines -Maclean Hunter Quebec--Maclean Hunter Publishing Ltd., Toronto, Canada; *Int'l*, pg. 1123
Parent, Christophe, Pres.-Remote Site Services--Sodexho S.A., Montigny-le-Bretonneux, France; *Int'l*, pg. 1274
Park, Arnold, Pres. & Chief Exec. Officer-McCain Foods (Canada)--McCain Foods Limited, Florenceville, Canada; *Int'l*, pg. 850
Park, Dennis S., V.P. & Pres.-Home Furniture Components--Leggett & Platt, Incorporated, Carthage, MO; *U.S. Public*, *pg. 985*
Parker, Jimmy, Branch Pres.--First State Bank N.A., Abilene, Abilene, TX; *U.S. Public*, pg. 874
Parker, W. Neil, Pres.-Electrical Components Div.--Thomas & Betts Corporation, Memphis, TN; *U.S. Public*, pg. 1597
Parker, William C., Pres.-Clearwater Opers.--Aerosonic Corporation, Clearwater, FL; *U.S. Public*, pg. 25
Parkinson-Marcoux, Edythe A., Pres.-Heavy Oil Div.--Gulf Canada Resources Ltd., Calgary, Canada; *Int'l*, pg. 577
Parks, Aterling, Pres.-Transporation Grp.--Park Drop Forge Div., Cleveland, OH; *U.S. Public*, pg. 1258
Parra, Ignacio, Grp. Pres.--Grupo Industrial Durango S.A. de C.V., Durango, Mexico; *Int'l*, pg. 575

Parrillo, Gillian M., Sr. V.P. & Grp. Pres.--Sterling Software, Inc., Dallas, TX; *U.S. Public*, pg. 1516
Parrish, J.P., Pres.-Shell Services Co.--Shell Oil Company, Houston, TX; *Int'l*, pg. 1136
Parrish, O.H., Pres.-Virginia Banking--Crestar Bank, Richmond, VA; *U.S. Public*, pg. 458
Parrish, O.H., Jr., Pres.-Reg. Banking--Crestar Financial Corporation, Richmond, VA; *U.S. Public*, pg. 458
Parrish, Stephen, Mng. Dir.--Getinge Sterilizing Equipment Inc., Cambridge, Canada; *Int'l*, pg. 552
Paschal, Bruce, Pres.-Duda Sls. Division--A. Duda & Sons Inc., Oviedo, FL; *U.S. Private*, pg. 344
Pascual, Carlos, V.P. & Pres.-U.S. Customer Opers.--Xerox Corporation, Stamford, CT; *U.S. Public*, pg. 1783
Paster, R.D., Pres.-Autonetics & Missile Systems Div.--Boeing North American, Seal Beach, CA; *U.S. Public*, pg. 241
Patek, Paul, Pres.-Fisher Scientific Company/Res. Div.--Fisher Scientific Company, Pittsburgh, PA; *U.S. Private*, pg. 658
Patron, Ronald H., Chief Fin. Officer, Pres.-Corp. Div. & Exec. V.P.--Stewart Enterprises, Inc., Metairie, LA; *U.S. Public*, pg. 1518
Patt, Pehr-Eric, Pres.-Fine Papers--UPM-Kymmene Corporation, Helsinki, Finland; *Int'l*, pg. 1427
Patterson, Dave, Pres. & Chief Oper. Officer--Kemper National Services, Plantation, FL; *U.S. Private*, pg. 614
Patterson, Donald H. Jr., Pres.-Landmark Broadcasting & Exec. V.P.--Landmark Communications, Inc., Norfolk, VA; *U.S. Private*, pg. 647
Patterson, Thomas L., Pres.-Nichols TXEN--Nichols Research Corporation, Huntsville, AL; *U.S. Public*, pg. 1182
Patton, James P., M.D., Pres.-Renaissance Women's Centers--Universal Health Services, Inc., King of Prussia, PA; *U.S. Public*, pg. 1696
Patton, Michael A., Pres.-Southern Reg.--Community Bank N.A., De Witt, NY; *U.S. Public*, pg. 416
Patty, Tom, Pres.-WW Nissan Acct. Dir.--TBWA Chiat/Day, New York, NY; *U.S. Private*, pg. 1062
Paul, Charles S., Pres.-MCA Enterprises, Inc. & Exec. V.P.--Universal Studios, Inc., Universal City, CA; *Int'l*, pg. 1215
Paul, Kathryn A., Pres.-Rocky Mountain Division & Sr. V.P.--Kaiser Permanente, Oakland, CA; *U.S. Private*, pg. 605
Pauze, Jean-Charles, Pres.-Steelcase Strafor--Groupe Strafor Facom, Morangis, France; *Int'l*, pg. 569
Pavelka, Patrick, Pres.-Interior Sys. Division--Cambridge Industries Inc., Madison Heights, MI; *U.S. Private*, pg. 202
Pavese, Tony, Pres.-Intl. Division--AFC Enterprises, Atlanta, GA; *U.S. Private*, pg. 5
Paxton, John, Pres.-Printing Solutions & Exec. V.P.--PAXAR Corporation, White Plains, NY; *U.S. Public*, pg. 1266
Payne, Barrie, Pres.-Sunrise Europe--Sunrise Medical, Inc., Carlsbad, CA; *U.S. Public*, pg. 1535
Pearo, William R., Pres.--Sun Life of Canada Benefit Management Limited, Montreal, Canada; *Int'l*, pg. 1319
Pearson, Douglas N., Pres.-North America Opers. & Exec. V.P.--Exide Corporation, Reading, PA; *U.S. Public*, pg. 600
Pearson, H. William, Pres.-AGRA Devel.--Agra Inc., Calgary, Canada; *Int'l*, pg. 30
Pearson, John M., Pres.-ABC Coke--Drummond Company, Inc., Jasper, AL; *U.S. Private*, pg. 343
Peck, Richard, Pres.-North American--Ranir Corporation/DCP, Grand Rapids, MI; *U.S. Private*, pg. 909
Pedersen, Ray, Sr. V.P. & Pres.-Princess Tours--Princess Cruise Lines, Los Angeles, CA; *Int'l*, pg. 1035
Peer, Ronald J., Pres.-Magnivision--American Greetings Corporation, Cleveland, OH; *U.S. Public*, pg. 77
Peled, Zui, Pres.-Geotek Technologies--Geotek Communications, Montvale, NJ; *U.S. Public*, pg. 739
Pellegrini, Benjamin J., Pres.-Day & Zimmermann LLC--Day & Zimmermann, Inc., Philadelphia, PA; *U.S. Private*, pg. 316
Peller, J.B., Pres.-Systems Devel. Center--Boeing North American, Seal Beach, CA; *U.S. Public*, pg. 241
Penrose, Gary S., Mng. Dir.-Fin. Institutions Grp.--Scott & Stringfellow, Inc., Richmond, VA; *U.S. Public*, pg. 1445
Penttila, Hannu, Dep. Pres.-Department Stores & Intl. Opers.--OY Stockmann AB, Helsinki, Finland; *Int'l*, pg. 1301
Perkel, Gerald K., V.P. & Pres.-Color Printing & Imaging--Tektronix, Inc., Wilsonville, OR; *U.S. Public*, pg. 1567
Perlberg, Mark C., Sr. V.P. & Pres.-Fin. Mkt. Div.--John H. Harland Company, Decatur, GA; *U.S. Public*, pg. 785
Perozzi, Donald J., Grp. Pres.-Adv. & Publ.--BellSouth Enterprises, Inc., Atlanta, GA; *U.S. Public*, pg. 208
Perry, Arlin R., Pres.-Gear Products, Inc.--Blount International, Inc., Montgomery, AL; *U.S. Public*, pg. 237
Persson, Olof, Pres.--ICA Handlarna Mellansverige AB, Vasteras, Sweden; *Int'l*, pg. 642
Pescatore, John, Pres.-SMR Opers.--Nextel Communications, Mc Lean, VA; *U.S. Public*, pg. 1180
Peters, Frederick C., III, Exec. V.P. & Pres.-First Main Line Bank Div.--National Penn Bank, Boyertown, PA; *U.S. Public*, pg. 1159
Peterson, James L., Vice Chm. & Pres.-Intl. Opers.--Haemonetics Corporation, Braintree, MA; *U.S. Public*, pg. 773
Peterson, Ronald G., Grp. Pres.-Govt., Environ. & Telecomm.--Fluor Daniel Inc., Irvine, CA; *U.S. Public*, pg. 660
Petkus, Donald A., Pres.-Unicom Thermal Tech. & Sr. V.P.--ComEd, Chicago, IL; *U.S. Public*, pg. 1664
Petru, Suzanne M., Pres.-Healthcare Div.--American Home Assurance Co., New York, NY; *U.S. Public*, pg. 84
Pettinella, Edward J., Pres.-Retail Div.--Rochester Community Savings Bank, Rochester, NY; *U.S. Public*, pg. 336
Petty, James, Pres.-Mortgage Opers.--U.S. Home Corporation, Houston, TX; *U.S. Public*, pg. 1682
Petty, Mark E., Pres.--Inland Motor Div., Radford, VA; *U.S. Public*, pg. 965
Pew, R. Anderson, Pres.-Leasing--Sun Company, Inc. (R&M), Philadelphia, PA; *U.S. Public*, pg. 1530
Pfeffer, Eric E., Pres.-HFS Global Services Div.--HFS, Incorporated, Parsippany, NJ; *U.S. Public*, pg. 321
Pfeiffer, Eckhard, Pres. & Chief Exec. Officer--COMPAQ Computer Corporation, Houston, TX; *U.S. Public*, pg. 417
Pfleider, James K., Pres.-Gage Travel--Gage Marketing Group, Minneapolis, MN; *U.S. Private*, pg. 437
Philipps, Linda A., Chief Info. Officer & Sr. V.P.--Allcity Insurance Co., New York, NY; *U.S. Public*, pg. 990
Phillips, Gregory M., Pres.-MTM International--International Family Entertainment, Inc., Virginia Beach, VA; *Int'l*, pg. 927
Phillips, Robert, Pres.-Home & Personal Care/N. America--Unilever Plc, London, United Kingdom; *Int'l*, pg. 1433
Phillips, Robert G., Pres.-El Paso Energy & Resource Co.--El Paso Natural Gas Co., Houston, TX; *U.S. Public*, pg. 567
Phillips, William K., Pres.-Eastern Territory--World Book Educational Products, Elk Grove Village, IL; *U.S. Public*, pg. 218
Philpott, Barry R., Chief Admin. Officer & Pres.-European Opers.--PAREXEL International Corporation, Waltham, MA; *U.S. Public*, pg. 1257
Pickering, Jeff, Pres.-Direct Mktg. & Sls.--Pickering Inc., Tacoma, WA; *U.S. Private*, pg. 864
Pickton, S., Pres.-Safety Systems Div.--Whittaker Controls, Inc., North Hollywood, CA; *U.S. Public*, pg. 1767
Picot, Claude, Pres.-Containers Div. & Sr. V.P.--Saint-Gobain, Courbevoie, France; *Int'l*, pg. 1170
Pierce, J. Raymond, Pres.-Men's Div.--JC Penney Company, Inc., Plano, TX; *U.S. Public*, pg. 916
Pietrangelo, Michael, Pres.-Personal Care Prods. Grp.--IVAX Corporation, Miami, FL; *U.S. Public*, pg. 914
Pietrangelo, Michael, Pres.-Personal Care Products Grp.--Johnson Products Co., Inc., Chicago, IL; *U.S. Public*, pg. 915
Pignataro, Richard G., V.P. & Pres.-Professional & Printing Imaging--Eastman Kodak Company, Rochester, NY; *U.S. Public*, pg. 550
Pillar, Russ, Pres. & Chief Exec. Officer-Prodigy Internet--Prodigy Inc., White Plains, NY; *U.S. Private*, pg. 888
Pilliter, Charles J., Pres. & Sr. V.P.-Northern California--Certified Grocers of California, Los Angeles, CA; *U.S. Private*, pg. 226
Pinchuk, Nicholas T., Pres.-Asia Pacific Opers.--Carrier Corporation, Indianapolis, IN; *U.S. Public*, pg. 1689
Pinot, Martin, Pres.-Fibers & Polymers--Rhone-Poulenc S.A., Courbevoie, France; *Int'l*, pg. 1108
Pinto, William D., Grp. Pres.--Hardin Construction Group, Inc., Atlanta, GA; *U.S. Private*, pg. 501
Pitsch, Karl-Heinz, Chm. Bd., Pres. & Chief Exec. Officer--The Wella Corporation, Montvale, NJ; *Int'l*, pg. 1489
Pittman, Bob, Pres. & Chief Exec. Officer-AOL Networks--America Online Incorporated, Dulles, VA; *U.S. Public*, pg. 66
Pladsen, Keith, Grp. Pres.-Northeast Grp.--Beneficial Corporation, Wilmington, DE; *U.S. Public*, pg. 211
Platt, Marc, Pres.-Production--Universal Pictures, Universal City, CA; *Int'l*, pg. 1216
Pleasant, Dan M., Principal Branch Mgr.-Southern Division--Dewberry & Davis, Fairfax, VA; *U.S. Private*, pg. 329
Plucinski, Rob S., Pres.-HLS Disease Management Systems--CommonHealth USA, Parsippany, NJ; *Int'l*, pg. 1483
Plumbley, Michael, Pres.-Dana Industrial Components--Dana Corporation, Toledo, OH; *U.S. Public*, pg. 479
Poe, Alfred, Pres.-Meal Enhancement--Campbell Soup Company, Camden, NJ; *U.S. Public*, pg. 298
Polansky, Terry, Pres.-Rainbow Adv.--Rainbow Rentals, Inc., Canfield, OH; *U.S. Private*, pg. 907
Pollack, Lawrence J., Pres.-T.V. Stations & V.P.--ABC, Inc, New York, NY; *U.S. Public*, pg. 511
Pollard, David, Pres.-Personal Insurance Div.--Fireman's Fund Insurance Company, Novato, CA; *Int'l*, pg. 58
Polumbo, John, Pres.-Consumer Communications Services--Pacific Bell, San Ramon, CA; *U.S. Public*, pg. 1416
Pope, Steven F., Pres.-Grubb & Ellis Affiliates, Inc.--Grubb & Ellis Company, Northbrook, IL; *U.S. Public*, pg. 767
Port, George, Pres.-Anchor Bay Entertainment--Handleman Company, Troy, MI; *U.S. Public*, pg. 779
Porter, Edward L., V.P. & Pres.-Argus Health Systems, Inc.--DST Systems, Inc., Kansas City, MO; *U.S. Public*, pg. 943
Porter, Scott D., Pres.-Parsons Tech. Division--Broderbund Software, Inc., Novato, CA; *U.S. Public*, pg. 258
Posa, Sandy, Exec. V.P. & Pres.-Consumer Imaging Grp.--Polaroid Corporation, Cambridge, MA; *U.S. Public*, pg. 1313
Poses, Frederick M., Exec. V.P. & Pres.-Engineered Materials--AlliedSignal Inc., Morristown, NJ; *U.S. Public*, pg. 49
Postle, Richard C., Pres.-St. Louis Bread Co.--Au Bon Pain Co., Inc., Boston, MA; *U.S. Public*, pg. 146
Postlethwait, Robert N., Pres.-Neuroscience Bus. Unit--Eli Lilly and Company, Indianapolis, IN; *U.S. Public*, pg. 992
Potter, Robert B., Grp. Pres.-Sys.--Bowthorpe plc, Crawley, United Kingdom; *Int'l*, pg. 207
Powell, Michael N., Pres.-Amcast Flow Control--Amcast Industrial Corporation, Dayton, OH; *U.S. Public*, pg. 63
Powell, Michael N., Pres.-Amcast Flow Control--Elkhart Products Corp.-Plumbing Division, Elkhart, IN; *U.S. Public*, pg. 63
Powers, Richard G., Pres.-Personal Prods. Div.--Playtex Products Inc., Westport, CT; *U.S. Public*, pg. 1310
Powers, Sean, Pres.-Anthem Distribution--Anthem Electronics Inc., San Jose, CA; *U.S. Public*, pg. 134
Pozniak, A.R., Pres. & Chief Exec. Officer-Canac International Inc.--Canadian National Railway Company, Montreal, Canada; *Int'l*, pg. 258
Pratt, Joel, Pres.--Arthrotek, Inc., Ontario, CA; *U.S. Public*, pg. 231
Preble, Clayton H., V.P. & Pres.-The Energy Spring, Inc.--AGL Resources, Atlanta, GA; *U.S. Public*, pg. 6
Price, Terry W., Pres.-Commercial/Indus. Worldwide Opers. & Sr. V.P.--Sensormatic Electronics Corporation, Boca Raton, FL; *U.S. Public*, pg. 1457
Priem, Windle B., Vice Chm. & Pres.-N. America--Korn/Ferry International, New York, NY; *U.S. Private*, pg. 633
Probert, Timothy J., V.P. & Pres.-Baker Hughes INTEQ--Baker Hughes Incorporated, Houston, TX; *U.S. Public*, pg. 165
Procopio, Frank, Sr. V.P. & Pres. Commercial Business--Mohawk Industries, Inc., Calhoun, GA; *U.S. Public*, pg. 1121
Prosser, George T., Inspector Gen.--Tennessee Valley Authority, Knoxville, TN; *U.S. Public*, pg. 1580
Proud, Jack, Pres.-Healthcare Systems Div.--The Reynolds and Reynolds Company, Dayton, OH; *U.S. Public*, pg. 1384
Pudles, Stephen, Pres.-ECO--EA Industries, West Long Branch, NJ; *U.S. Public*, pg. 541
Purbowo, Risbadi, Pres. & Dir.--P.T. Merincorp Securities Indonesia, Jakarta, Indonesia; *Int'l*, pg. 1310
Purslow, Bill, Pres.-Automotive Sealing Div.--Freudenberg-NOK, Plymouth, MI; *U.S. Private*, pg. 427
Purvis, Ed, Pres.-Refrigeration--Copeland Corporation, Sidney, OH; *U.S. Public*, pg. 573
Puskar, George, Pres.-Equitable Real Estate--The Equitable Companies Incorporated, New York, NY; *U.S. Public*, pg. 588
Putman, T. Jeff, Grp. Pres.-Diversified Svcs.--Fluor Daniel Inc., Irvine, CA; *U.S. Public*, pg. 660
Pyatt, Donald, Pres.-Tool Prods.--Quadion Corporation, Minneapolis, MN; *U.S. Private*, pg. 898
Pyatt, Michael, V.P.-Corn Prods. & Pres.-Casco--Casco Inc., Etobicoke, Canada; *U.S. Public*, pg. 448
Pylvanainen, Erkki, Pres.-Valmuet Power Transmission Inc.--Valmet Corporation, Helsinki, Finland; *Int'l*, pg. 1447
Pyott, David, Pres.-Nutrition--Novartis AG, Basel, Switzerland; *Int'l*, pg. 971
Quadracci, Thomas A., Pres.-Quad/Tech. & V.P.-Mfg. & Tech.--Quad/Graphics, Inc., Pewaukee, WI; *U.S. Private*, pg. 897
Qualters, Irene M., Sr. V.P.-Tech. Computing & Pres.-Cray Research--Silicon Graphics, Inc., Mountain View, CA; *U.S. Public*, pg. 1473
Queenan, James P., V.P. & Pres.-Collision Repair Equipment Group--Hein-Werner Corporation, Waukesha, WI; *U.S. Public*, pg. 805
Quezada, Miguel, Pres.-Canandaigua Concentrate--Canandaigua Wine Co., Canandaigua, NY; *U.S. Public*, pg. 300
Quinlan, William J., Pres.-ARCOTOYS--Mattel, Inc., El Segundo, CA; *U.S. Public*, pg. 1057
Quinnell, Bruce A., Pres. & Chief Oper. Officer-Walden--Borders Group, Inc., Ann Arbor, MI; *U.S. Public*, pg. 245
Raba, Bruce, Pres.-Uno Intl.--Uno Restaurant Corporation, West Roxbury, MA; *U.S. Public*, pg. 1698
Radcliffe, Frederick R., Jr., V.P. & Pres.-The Flexaust Co. Division--Callahan Mining Corporation, Coeur D'Alene, ID; *U.S. Public*, pg. 394
Rafferty, William, Pres.-Tuffseal--Kelley Company, Inc., Milwaukee, WI; *U.S. Private*, pg. 612
Ragavan, Vivek, V.P. & Pres.-Broadbank Comml. Division--ADC Telecommunications, Inc., Minnetonka, MN; *U.S. Public*, pg. 4
Raghavan, Asuri, Sr. V.P. & Pres.-Equipment Div.--Kulicke & Soffa Industries, Inc., Willow Grove, PA; *U.S. Public*, pg. 968
Ramas, Guillermo N., Sr., Sr. V.P. & Pres.-SMS Intl.--Shared Medical Systems Corporation, Malvern, PA; *U.S. Public*, pg. 1463
Ramierz, Mario, V.P. & Pres.-Southern Div.--Circuit City Stores, Inc., Richmond, VA; *U.S. Public*, pg. 374
Ramsey, P., Pres.-New Bus. & Engrng.--Royle Systems Group, Pompton Lakes, NJ; *U.S. Private*, pg. 949
Ransby, Edward J., Pres.-GWL Investment Mngmt. Ltd.--The Great-West Life Assurance Company, Winnipeg, Canada; *Int'l*, pg. 557
Ransdell, Thomas R., Pres.--Vulcan Gulf Coast Materials, Inc., Birmingham, AL; *U.S. Public*, pg. 1726
Ransom Rose, Stuart Alan, Chief Exec.-Burtons Menswear, DP, Evans & Principles--The Burton Group PLC, London, United Kingdom; *Int'l*, pg. 237
Rao, Shankar, Pres.-LM Division--Anorad Corporation, Hauppauge, NY; *U.S. Private*, pg. 75
Rathgeber, Kenneth A., Pres.-Institutional Brokerage--Fidelity Investments (FMR Corp.), Boston, MA; *U.S. Private*, pg. 402
Rauch, Marc F., Pres.-Sls.--Rauch Industries, Inc., Gastonia, NC; *U.S. Private*, pg. 1061
Ravencroft, Thomas, Sr. V.P. & Pres.-Dairy Div.--Dean Foods Company, Franklin Park, IL; *U.S. Public*, pg. 489
Rawle, Robert H., Pres. & Chief Oper. Officer-J. Ray McDermott, S.A.--McDermott International, Inc., New Orleans, LA; *U.S. Public*, pg. 1067
Ray, J. Billie, Jr., State Pres.-North Carolina--BellSouth Telecommunications, Inc., Atlanta, GA; *U.S. Public*, pg. 209
Ray, Jim, V.P.-Opers.--Samsonite Corporation, Denver, CO; *U.S. Public*, pg. 1430
Raymond, Gary, Pres.-Resort Devel. Grp.--Intrawest Corporation, Vancouver, Canada; *Int'l*, pg. 685
Razek, Edward, Pres.-Mktg.--The Limited, Inc., Columbus, OH; *U.S. Public*, pg. 995
Reardon, J. Michael, Exec. V.P.-Opers. & Pres.-Home Shopping Club Outlet, Inc.--Home Shopping Network, Inc., Saint Petersburg, FL; *U.S. Public*, pg. 1685
Rearic, Donald E., Pres.-Brady Financial Co.--W.H. Brady Co., Milwaukee, WI; *U.S. Public*, pg. 250
Reasor, William S., Pres.-Modular Housing--Schult Homes Corporation, Middlebury, IN; *U.S. Public*, pg. 1442
Recone, Max, Pres.-Consumer Prods.--Playtex Products Inc., Westport, CT; *U.S. Public*, pg. 1310
Reddersen, William F., Grp. Pres.-Value Added Networks--BellSouth Corporation, Atlanta, GA; *U.S. Public*, pg. 207

Rediger, Chris B., Pres.-Mountain Opers.--U.S. Home Corporation, Houston, TX; *U.S. Public*, pg. 1682
Rediker, Dennis, Pres.--ECC International Inc., Atlanta, GA; *Int'l*, pg. 455
Redon, Leonard E., V.P. & Pres.-Customer Equipment Services--Eastman Kodak Company, Rochester, NY; *U.S. Public*, pg. 550
Reduzzi, Dave, Pres.-JM&A Grp. & Exec. V.P.-JM Family--JM Family Enterprises Inc., Deerfield Beach, FL; *U.S. Private*, pg. 577
Reeb, William R., Corp. V.P. & Pres.-Wilsonart Intl.--Premark International, Inc., Deerfield, IL; *U.S. Public*, pg. 1321
Reed, David P., Pres.-App. Ceramics Grp. & V.P.--Ceradyne, Inc, Costa Mesa, CA; *U.S. Public*, pg. 330
Reed, Vincent J., Pres.-Emerging Applications Grp.--TDS Telecommunications Corporation, Madison, WI; *U.S. Public*, pg. 1570
Reeds, Arthur C., Pres.-CIGNA Inves. Mgmt.--Cigna Corp., Philadelphia, PA; *U.S. Public*, pg. 356
Reeves, W. H., Pres.-Carolina Steel Fabrication--Carolina Steel Corporation, Greensboro, NC; *U.S. Private*, pg. 214
Regulinski, Stephan G., Pres.-UAL Svcs.--United Air Lines, Inc., Elk Grove Village, IL; *U.S. Public*, pg. 1653
Reichmann, Andre, Chief Oper. Officer--Dri Mark Products, Inc., Port Washington, NY; *U.S. Private*, pg. 342
Reid, Harry, Pres, Intl.-London--FCB, New York, NY; *U.S. Private*, pg. 389
Reid, R. Randolph, Area Pres.--New Fortis Corp., King, NC; *U.S. Public*, pg. 843
Reilly, Timothy G., Pres.-North American Commercial Bus.--Fort James Corporation, Richmond, VA; *U.S. Public*, pg. 670
Reinert, James H., V.P. & Pres.-Support Resources, Inc.--DST Systems, Inc., Kansas City, MO; *U.S. Public*, pg. 943
Reisch, Marc L., Grp. Pres.-Sls., Chief Oper. Officer & Exec. V.P.--World Color Press, Inc., Greenwich, CT; *U.S. Public*, pg. 1778
Renshaw, James E., Pres. & Gen. Mgr.-Eastern Div., Paint Stores Grp.--The Sherwin-Williams Company, Cleveland, OH; *U.S. Public*, pg. 1465
Rensing, Victor, Pres.-Quest & Unichema--Unilever Plc, London, United Kingdom; *Int'l*, pg. 1433
Reyes, Greg, Pres. & Gen. Mgr.-Wireless Access Grp.--Glenayre Technologies, Inc., Charlotte, NC; *U.S. Public*, pg. 746
Reynolds, Kathy, Pres.-Womens Div.--Jockey International, Inc., Kenosha, WI; *U.S. Private*, pg. 588
Reynolds, Robert D., Pres.-Sls. Grp. & Sr. V.P.--Newsprint South, Inc., Jackson, MS; *U.S. Private*, pg. 797
Reynolds, Robert L., Pres.-Fidelity Institutional Retirement Services Company--Fidelity Investments (FMR Corp.), Boston, MA; *U.S. Private*, pg. 402
Reynolds, Ross B., Pres.-MCA Records Canada--MCA Records, Inc., Universal City, CA; *Int'l*, pg. 1215
Rhemus, Thomas, Pres.-DEFS--Superior Coffee and Foods, Bensenville, IL; *U.S. Public*, pg. 1434
Ribolla, Luigi, Exec. V.P. & Pres.-Heinz Europe--H.J. Heinz Company, Pittsburgh, PA; *U.S. Public*, pg. 805
Rice, John G., Pres. & Rep. Dir.-G.E. Plastics Pacific--G.E. Plastics, Pittsfield, MA; *U.S. Public*, pg. 710
Rice, William A., Pres.-Industrial Distr.--Airgas, Inc., Radnor, PA; *U.S. Public*, pg. 33
Rich, Gerry, Pres.-Worldwide Mktg.--Metro-Goldwyn-Mayer Inc., Santa Monica, CA; *U.S. Public*, pg. 1101
Rich, Lawrence S., Pres.-AutoNation USA--Republic Industries, Inc., Fort Lauderdale, FL; *U.S. Public*, pg. 1378
Richards, Daniel J., Pres.-Eastern Div.--International Total Services, Independence, OH; *U.S. Public*, pg. 908
Richards, Robert A., Pres.-StoneBridge Village--Cooper Communities, Inc., Bella Vista, AR; *U.S. Private*, pg. 273
Richardson, Michael T., Pres.-S. Opers.--U.S. Home Corporation, Houston, TX; *U.S. Public*, pg. 1682
Richey, Joseph B., II, Sr. V.P.-Total Quality Mngmt. & Pres.-Invacare Technologies--Invacare Corporation, Elyria, OH; *U.S. Public*, pg. 911
Rickard, Norman E., Jr., Pres.-Xerox Bus. Services & V.P.--Xerox Corporation, Stamford, CT; *U.S. Public*, pg. 1783
Ricker, Charles W., Jr., Pres.-Plng. & Network Grp.--TDS Telecommunications Corporation, Madison, WI; *U.S. Public*, pg. 1570
Rickman, Ronald L., Pres.-Publishing Grp.--Lee Enterprises, Incorporated, Davenport, IA; *U.S. Public*, pg. 983
Riddle, W. Curtis, Sr. Grp. Pres.-East Newspaper Grp.--Gannett Company, Inc., Arlington, VA; *U.S. Public*, pg. 698
Rieck, Erwin J., Pres.-Europe--Renaissance Hotel Group N.V., Central, Hong Kong; *U.S. Public*, pg. 1048
Riese, Phillip J., Pres.-Member Card Financial Services Grp./Travel Related--American Express Company, New York, NY; *U.S. Public*, pg. 73
Riese, Phillip J., Pres.-Cardmember Fin. Services Grp.--American Express Travel Related Services Co., Inc., New York, NY; *U.S. Public*, pg. 73
Rifkin, Marty, V.P. & Grp. Pres.--Omnisource Corporation, Fort Wayne, IN; *U.S. Private*, pg. 817
Riley, Lester W., Sr. V.P. & Pres.-Dermatology & Skin Care--Advanced Polymer Systems, Redwood City, CA; *U.S. Public*, pg. 22
Riley, Michael R., Pres.-Books & Journals--Mosby-Year Book, Inc., Saint Louis, MO; *U.S. Public*, pg. 1616
Riley, T.J., Pres.-Aero Tech Mfg. Inc--Toromont Industries Ltd., Concord, Canada; *Int'l*, pg. 1400
Riley, Thomas P., Pres.-Truckers Bank Plan--1st Source Bank Consolidated, South Bend, IN; *U.S. Public*, pg. 638
Rinaldi, Anthony J., V.P. & Pres.-Tredegar Film Products--Tredegar Industries Inc., Richmond, VA; *U.S. Public*, pg. 1633
Ring, Timothy M., Grp. Pres.--C.R. Bard, Inc., Murray Hill, NJ; *U.S. Public*, pg. 189
Ringo, William R., Jr., Pres.-Infectious Diseases Business Unit--Eli Lilly and Company, Indianapolis, IN; *U.S. Public*, *pg. 992*
Ringrose, Peter S., Pres.-Bristol-Myers Squibb Pharmaceutical Research Institute--Bristol-Myers Squibb Company, New York, NY; *U.S. Public*, pg. 253
Riordan, Thomas J., Pres.-Service Solutions--SPX Corporation, Muskegon, MI; *U.S. Public*, pg. 1420
Rioux, Paul, Pres.-Universal New Media Grp.--Universal Studios, Inc., Universal City, CA; *Int'l*, pg. 1215
Risberg, Per, Pres.-Saab Combilech AB--Saab AB, Linkoping, Sweden; *Int'l*, pg. 686
Rislakki, Jaakko, Pres.-Packaging Materials--UPM-Kymmene Corporation, Helsinki, Finland; *Int'l*, pg. 1427
Rison, Townes, Pres.-Telmark--The Martin Agency, Richmond, VA; *U.S. Private*, pg. 678
Rison, Townes, Pres.-Telmark--The Martin Agency, Richmond, VA; *U.S. Public*, pg. 909
Ritchie, Robert, Pres.-Aerospace Div.--Special Devices, Incorporated, Newhall, CA; *U.S. Public*, pg. 1496
Rittinghaus, Erhard, Exec. V.P. & Pres.-Agfa Division--Bayer Corporation, Pittsburgh, PA; *Int'l*, pg. 172
Rittinghaus, Erhard, Pres.-AGFA Div. & Exec. V.P.--Bayer Corporation, Pittsburgh, PA; *Int'l*, pg. 172
Rittinghaus, Erhard, Exec. V.P. & Pres.-Agfa Div.--Bayer Corporation, Parsippany, NJ; *Int'l*, pg. 172
Ritz, Jurgen, Dr., Pres.--Herberts GmbH, Wuppertal, Germany; *Int'l*, pg. 625
Riutta, Juhani, Pres.-Valmet Automotive Inc.--Valmet Corporation, Helsinki, Finland; *Int'l*, pg. 1447
Rivas, Joyce, Partner-Strategic Plng.--Earle Palmer Brown/Philadelphia, Philadelphia, PA; *U.S. Private*, pg. 174
Rives, Chip, Pres.-Sports & Entertainment Mktg.--Woolf Associates, Boston, MA; *U.S. Private*, pg. 84
Robb, Walter, Pres.-Northern California Region--Whole Foods Market, Inc., Austin, TX; *U.S. Public*, pg. 1767
Roberts, C. Frank, Pres.-Broadcast Grp.--The New York Times Company Broadcasting Group, Memphis, TN; *U.S. Public*, pg. 1173
Roberts, David A., V.P. & Pres.-AM Multigraphics--Multigraphics Inc., Mount Prospect, IL; *U.S. Public*, pg. 1141
Roberts, Eddy C., Jr., State Pres.-Kentucky--BellSouth Telecommunications, Inc., Atlanta, GA; *U.S. Public*, pg. 209
Roberts, John, Pres.-OCS--J.B. Hunt Transport Services, Inc., Lowell, AR; *U.S. Public*, pg. 849
Roberts, John B., Chm. Bd. & Pres.-Busch Entertainment Corp.--Anheuser-Busch Companies, Inc., Saint Louis, MO; *U.S. Public*, pg. 113
Roberts, Michael, Pres.-Div.--McDonald's Corporation, Oak Brook, IL; *U.S. Public*, pg. 1068
Roberts, Paul, Pres.-NYC--Phillips Fine Art Auctioneers, New York, NY; *U.S. Private*, pg. 861
Robertson, Clive, Pres.-Circuit Protection Div.--Delta plc, London, United Kingdom; *Int'l*, pg. 389
Robertson, Larry M., Grp. Pres.--Inman Construction Corporation, Memphis, TN; *U.S. Private*, pg. 564
Robertson, Peter J., Corp. V.P. & Pres.-Chevron U.S.A. Production Co.--Chevron Corporation, San Francisco, CA; *U.S. Public*, pg. 347
Robinson, Andrew, Pres.-Frozen Div.--Parmalat Canada Ltd., Etobicoke, Canada; *Int'l*, pg. 1023
Robinson, Ron A., Pres.-Svedala Inc.--Svedala Industri AB, Malmo, Sweden; *Int'l*, pg. 1323
Robuste V., Fidias, Pres. & Mng. Dir.-MONACA--International Multifoods Corporation, Minneapolis, MN; *U.S. Public*, pg. 900
Rocco, Nikki, Pres.-Distribution--Universal Pictures, Universal City, CA; *Int'l*, pg. 1216
Rochel, Roger, Pres.-Great Plains Agriculture Division--Great Plains Manufacturing, Inc., Salina, KS; *U.S. Private*, pg. 475
Rochon, David A., Pres.-Super Markets Online, Inc.--Catalina Marketing Corporation, Saint Petersburg, FL; *U.S. Public*, pg. 314
Rockafellow, Gordon, Pres.--First Trust Corporation, Denver, CO; *U.S. Public*, pg. 647
Rodek, Jeffrey, Pres.-Worldwide--Ingram Micro Inc., Santa Ana, CA; *U.S. Public*, pg. 878
Rodenberg, Dan, Pres.-Midwest Region--Whole Foods Market, Inc., Austin, TX; *U.S. Public*, pg. 1767
Rodoni, Alma C., Pres.-Banner Blue--Broderbund Software, Inc., Novato, CA; *U.S. Public*, pg. 258
Rodriguez-Fiol, Manuel, Pres.-Latin America Grp.--Phelps Dodge Intl. Corp., Coral Gables, FL; *U.S. Public*, pg. 1286
Rodriguez, Jose Andres, Pres.-Intl. Div.--Gerber Products Company, Fremont, MI; *Int'l*, pg. 973
Roe, Robert L., Dr., Pres.-Syntex Devel. Res. & Sr. V.P.--Syntex, Palo Alto, CA; *Int'l*, pg. 1120
Rogalin, Roger, Pres.-School Division Unit--The McGraw-Hill Companies, New York, NY; *U.S. Public*, pg. 1069
Rogers, Johnathan, Pres.-Discovery Networks--Discovery Communications, Inc., Bethesda, MD; *U.S. Private*, pg. 334
Rogers, Stephen C., Pres.-Inland Steel Bar Co.--Inland Steel Industries, Inc., Chicago, IL; *U.S. Public*, pg. 879
Rogers, Thomas S., Pres.-NBC Cable & Business Devel.--National Broadcasting Co., Inc., New York, NY; *U.S. Public*, pg. 712
Rohrbeck, John, Pres.-NBC Television Stations--National Broadcasting Co., Inc., New York, NY; *U.S. Public*, pg. 712
Roland, R. Douglas, Grp. V.P.--MascoTech, Inc., Taylor, MI; *U.S. Public*, pg. 1055
Romero, Carol, Grp. Pres. & Pub. Rels. Dir.--Keyes Martin, East Hanover, NJ; *U.S. Private*, pg. 618
Romine, Maurice G., Pres.-Nichols InfoTec--Nichols Research Corporation, Huntsville, AL; *U.S. Public*, pg. 1182
Ronan, Joel, Pres.-AMANO Pioneer Credit--Pioneer/Eclipse Corp., Sparta, NC; *Int'l*, pg. 71
Ronning, Randy S., Pres.-Home & Leisure Div.--JC Penney Company, Inc., Plano, TX; *U.S. Public*, pg. 916
Roovers, Jerry, Grp. Pres.-Polymer Tech.--Menasha Corporation, Neenah, WI; *U.S. Private*, pg. 731
Roscitt, Richard R., Pres.-AT&T Solutions & Exec. V.P.--AT&T Corporation, Basking Ridge, NJ; *U.S. Public*, pg. 10
Rose, L.N., Pres.-Maple Leaf Grocery Products--Maple Leaf Foods Inc., Toronto, Canada; *Int'l*, pg. 841
Rosebrough, Walter M., Jr., Pres. & Chief Exec. Officer--Hill-Rom Company, Inc., Batesville, IN; *U.S. Public*, pg. 828
Rosen, Elaine D., Pres.-UNUM Life Insurance Co.--UNUM Corporation, Portland, ME; *U.S. Public*, pg. 1699
Rosenauer, James, Pres.-Missouri--World Acceptance Corporation, Greenville, SC; *U.S. Public*, pg. 1778
Rosenband, Phillip, Pres.-Morgan Marshall Indus.--RHC/Spacemaster Corporation, Melrose Park, IL; *U.S. Private*, *pg. 904*
Rosenberg, Joseph, Pres.-Lawton General Corp.--Loews Corporation, New York, NY; *U.S. Public*, pg. 1010
Rosenecker, Joseph A., Pres.-Flat Rolled Prods. Grp.--Gibraltar Steel Corp., Buffalo, NY; *U.S. Public*, pg. 742
Rosenfeld, J.A., Pres.-IWC Utilities--IWC Resources Corporation, Indianapolis, IN; *U.S. Public*, pg. 1185
Rosenthal, Cary, Dir.-SED & Pres.-Phoenix Communications, Inc.--Southern Electronics Corporation, Tucker, GA; *U.S. Public*, pg. 1490
Rosenthal, William E., Sr. V.P. & Pres.-KPR Foods Div.--Foodbrands America, Inc., Oklahoma City, OK; *U.S. Public*, pg. 852
Rosequist, Daniel E., Grp. Pres.-Mid-Atlantic Grp.--Beneficial Corporation, Wilmington, DE; *U.S. Public*, pg. 211
Rosier, Grady, Pres. & Chief Exec. Officer-McLane Co., Inc.--Wal-Mart Stores, Inc., Bentonville, AR; *U.S. Public*, pg. 1732
Ross, David R., Pres.--Clear Results Marketing, Fort Lauderdale, FL; *U.S. Public*, pg. 383
Ross, Edward C., Pres.-Tech. & Mfg. Grp.--Cirrus Logic, Inc., Fremont, CA; *U.S. Public*, pg. 375
Ross, G.L., Pres.-ICI Polyurethanes Grp.--ICI Americas, Inc., Wilmington, DE; *Int'l*, pg. 663
Ross, Gary, Pres.-Superstores--Musicland Group Inc., Minnetonka, MN; *U.S. Public*, pg. 1142
Ross, Steve, Pres.-Reseller Div. & Corp. Mktg.--Inacom Corp., Omaha, NE; *U.S. Public*, pg. 873
Rossbach, Walt, Pres.-Aerospace/Defense Grp. & Sr. V.P.--Stackig Advertising and Public Relations, Mc Lean, VA; *U.S. Private*, pg. 1028
Rossi, Randall C., V.P. & Pres.-Scotsman Ice Systems Div.--Scotsman Industries, Inc., Vernon Hills, IL; *U.S. Public*, pg. 1444
Rossman, Richard H., Pres.-Northern Div.--Prudential Metal Supply Corp., East Dedham, MA; *U.S. Private*, pg. 893
Rotatori, Frank J., Pres.-Healthcare Div.--Executone Information Systems, Inc., Milford, CT; *U.S. Public*, pg. 599
Roth, John A., Chief Exec. & Oper. Officer & Pres.-Nortel North America--Northern Telecom Limited, Brampton, Canada; *Int'l*, pg. 968
Roth, Vincent F., Pres.-ABS Europe--American Bureau of Shipping, New York, NY; *U.S. Private*, pg. 51
Rothaupt, Daniel J., Pres.-AES Thames, Inc.--AES Corporation, Arlington, VA; *U.S. Public*, pg. 5
Rothe, Bill, Pres.-Koll Mngmt. Services--Koll Co., Newport Beach, CA; *U.S. Private*, pg. 631
Rothkopf, Robert H., Pres.-Formed Prod. Grp.--Elco Textron, Rockford, IL; *U.S. Public*, pg. 1590
Rowe, Murray A., Pres.-Bid-Well Div.--CMI Corporation, Oklahoma City, OK; *U.S. Public*, pg. 278
Rowe, Thomas E., Pres.-Comml. Insurance Div.--Fireman's Fund Insurance Company, Novato, CA; *Int'l*, pg. 58
Rowland, Lawrence, Pres. & Chief Exec. Officer-Reinsurance--Lincoln National Corporation, Fort Wayne, IN; *U.S. Public*, pg. 997
Rowland, Thomas H., Exec. V.P. & Pres.-Home Prods. Div.--First Brands Corporation, Danbury, CT; *U.S. Public*, pg. 626
Roy, Drew A., Pres.-OK--Southwestern Bell Telephone Co., Saint Louis, MO; *U.S. Public*, pg. 1416
Rubiera, Miguel G., Pres.-Cone International Marketing Div.--Cone Apparel Products, Greensboro, NC; *U.S. Public*, pg. 430
Rubin, Seymour, V.P. & Pres.-RFI--Del Global Technologies, Valhalla, NY; *U.S. Public*, pg. 493
Rubinfeld, Gerald A., Pres.-Blends Div.--Texfi Industries, Inc., Raleigh, NC; *U.S. Public*, pg. 1588
Rubright, James A., Pres.-Southern Naturalo Gas Co.--Sonat Inc., Birmingham, AL; *U.S. Public*, pg. 1484
Rudloff, Hans-Jorg, Vice Chm.--Novartis AG, Basel, Switzerland; *Int'l*, pg. 971
Rugaber, Walter, Pres.-Landmark Publ. Grp. & The Roanoke Times--Landmark Communications, Inc., Norfolk, VA; *U.S. Private*, pg. 647
Ruhe, Jeffrey R., Pres.-SportsChannel America--Rainbow Programming Holdings, Inc., Woodbury, NY; *U.S. Public*, pg. 288
Ruiz, Eduardo, Pres.-Latin America--The Weather Channel, Atlanta, GA; *U.S. Private*, pg. 647
Rurka, James E., V.P. & Pres.-Cetus Oncology--Chiron Corporation, Emeryville, CA; *U.S. Public*, pg. 349
Rush, Ronald B., Pres.-Southern Div.--Airgas, Inc., Radnor, PA; *U.S. Public*, pg. 33
Russell, Lawrence, Exec. V.P. & Pres.-Info. Services--Unisys Corporation, Blue Bell, PA; *U.S. Public*, pg. 1671
Russell, Robert M., Pres.-Info. Service Grp.--The McGraw-Hill Companies, New York, NY; *U.S. Public*, pg. 1069
Russo, Patricia F., Pres.-Bus. Communications Systems--Lucent Technologies Inc., Murray Hill, NJ; *U.S. Public*, pg. 1017
Rutledge, D.W., Pres.-Latin America--Ingram Micro Inc., Santa Ana, CA; *U.S. Public*, pg. 878

Rutledge, Phillip, Pres. & Chief Exec. Officer-Pizza Hut Grp.--Lundy Enterprises, Inc., New Orleans, LA; *U.S. Private*, pg. 681

Ryan, Marsha P., Pres.-AEP Ohio--American Electric Power Company, Inc., Columbus, OH; *U.S. Public*, pg. 71

Ryder, Thomas, Pres.-Establishment Services Worldwide--American Express Travel Related Services Co., Inc., New York, NY; *U.S. Public*, pg. 73

Ryder, Thomas O., Pres.-Travel Related Services Intl./American Express Travel--American Express Company, New York, NY; *U.S. Public*, pg. 73

Rygiel, Edward K., Sr. V.P.-Corp. Devel. & Pres.-MDS Capital Corp.--MDS Inc., Etobicoke, Canada; *Int'l*, pg. 826

Rypien, John M., Pres.-O.J. Pipelines Corp.--Ocelot Energy Inc., Calgary, Canada; *Int'l*, pg. 996

Sada, Pablo Gonzalez, Pres.-Chemical Fibers & Mining Div. & Sec.-Bd. of Dirs.--Vitro, Sociedad Anonima, Garza Garcia, Mexico; *Int'l*, pg. 1469

Sada, Thomas Gonzalez, Pres.-Household Prods. Div.--Vitro, Sociedad Anonima, Garza Garcia, Mexico; *Int'l*, pg. 1469

Sadler, Gregg R., Pres.-HORL--Lab One, Lenexa, KS; *U.S. Public*, pg. 1449

Sadove, Stephen I., Pres.-Worldwide Beauty Care Grp.--Bristol-Myers Squibb Company, New York, NY; *U.S. Public*, pg. 253

Safrit, Lynn Scott, Pres.-N. American Commercial Opers.--Castle & Cooke Inc., Los Angeles, CA; *U.S. Public*, pg. 313

Saganski, Moira, Sr. V.P. & Pres.-M.R.S. Trust Company--Mackenzie Financial Corporation, Toronto, Canada; *Int'l*, pg. 828

Sahene, James M., Pres. & Chief Oper. Officer-TCBY Systems, Inc.--TCBY Enterprises Inc., Little Rock, AR; *U.S. Public*, pg. 1553

Said, Mohand Sidi, V.P., Sr. V.P.-Pfizer Pharm. Grp. & Area Pres.-Asia/Africa/Mid. E--Pfizer Inc., New York, NY; *U.S. Public*, pg. 1281

Sakaguchi, Kiyofumi, Pres.-Prudential Intl. Insurance--The Prudential Insurance Company of America, Newark, NJ; *U.S. Private*, pg. 892

Sakurada, Yutaka, Sr. V.P. & Pres.-Haemonetics Japan--Haemonetics Corporation, Braintree, MA; *U.S. Public*, pg. 773

Sakus, Gedas A., Chm. Bd.-Bell Northern Research & Pres.-Nortel Tech.--Northern Telecom Limited, Brampton, Canada; *Int'l*, pg. 968

Salamon, Ed, Pres.-Formats--Westwood One, Inc., New York, NY; *U.S. Public*, pg. 1763

Salles, Paulo, Pres.-DMB&B Americas--DMB&B Communications, New York, NY; *U.S. Private*, pg. 302

Salmon, Stephen J., Grp. Pres.-Cable Mgmnt.--Bowthorpe plc, Crawley, United Kingdom; *Int'l*, pg. 207

Salter, William L., Pres.-Home Stores--Sears, Roebuck and Co., Hoffman Estates, IL; *U.S. Public*, pg. 1452

Samo, Wolfgang, Dr., Pres.-Crop Protection--Novartis AG, Basel, Switzerland; *Int'l*, pg. 971

Sanderson, Len, Pres.-Eisner/Sanderson Public Affairs--Eisner & Associates, Inc., Baltimore, MD; *U.S. Private*, pg. 366

Sangster, R. Hugh B., Pres. & Chief Oper. Officer-Lakehead--Interprovincial Pipe Line Inc., Edmonton, Canada; *Int'l*, pg. 652

Sanitsky, Bob, Pres.-Television Production--Polygram N.V., Baarn, Netherlands; *Int'l*, pg. 1051

Sanlley, Salvador A., Pres.-Asia Pacific Grp.--Phelps Dodge Intl. Corp., Coral Gables, FL; *U.S. Public*, pg. 1286

Santini, Gino, Pres.-Women's Health--Eli Lilly and Company, Indianapolis, IN; *U.S. Public*, pg. 992

Sanzone, Salvatore V., Pres. & Gen. Mgr.-Southeastern Div., Paint Stores Grp.--The Sherwin-Williams Company, Cleveland, OH; *U.S. Public*, pg. 1465

Saphir, Nicholas, Chief Exec.-Fresh Produce--The Albert Fisher Group PLC, Stoke Poges, United Kingdom; *Int'l*, pg. 491

Sappenfield, Richard W., V.P. & Pres.-Svcs. Grp.--DeVlieg-Bullard Inc., Westport, CT; *U.S. Public*, pg. 502

Sargent, Ronald L., Pres.-Staples Contract & Commercial--Staples, Inc., Westborough, MA; *U.S. Public*, pg. 1509

Saueracker, Paul R., Pres.-Specialty Minerals Inc.--Minerals Technologies, Inc., New York, NY; *U.S. Public*, pg. 1115

Saul, Sanford, Pres.-Susan Gail Div.--Jaclyn, Inc., West New York, NJ; *U.S. Public*, pg. 920

Sawada, T., Pres--Kodak Japan Industries Ltd., Yokohama, Japan; *U.S. Public*, pg. 552

Sawyer, Nancy M., Jr., Pres.-Vernon Sawyer--KLLM Transport Services, Inc., Jackson, MS; *U.S. Public*, pg. 939

Sayeski, Peter F., Pres.--SRA McGraw Hill, Worthington, OH; *U.S. Public*, pg. 1070

Scafuri, Louis, Pres.-Corometrics Medical Systems--Marquette Medical Systems, Inc., Milwaukee, WI; *U.S. Public*, pg. 1047

Scaminace, Joseph M., Pres. & Gen. Mgr.-Automotive Finishes--The Sherwin-Williams Company, Cleveland, OH; *U.S. Public*, pg. 1465

Scardina, Frank, Pres.-West--The Ryland Group, Inc., Columbia, MD; *U.S. Public*, pg. 1414

Schacht, Andy, Partner & Gen. Mgr.--Earle Palmer Brown/Bethesda, Bethesda, MD; *U.S. Private*, pg. 174

Schadowski, Werner, Pres.-Packaging Systems Div. & Member-Exec. Board--SIG Schweizerische Industrie-Gesellschaft Holding AG, Neuhausen, Switzerland; *Int'l*, pg. 1156

Schaeffer, Geoff, Pres.-Yeast & Bakery--Burns, Philp & Company Limited, Sydney, Australia; *Int'l*, pg. 236

Schaefle, Jean, Pres.-Pigments Div.--Ciba Specialty Chemicals, Tarrytown, NY; *Int'l*, pg. 291

Schaller, David, Pres.-New Communications--Ammirati Puris Lintas Worldwide, New York, NY; *U.S. Public*, pg. 908

Schaller, Heinz, Pres.-Intl. Export--A. Racke GmbH, Bingen, Germany; *Int'l*, pg. 1083

Schaller, Herman, Ph.D., Pres.--Haarmann & Reimer Food Ingredients Div., Elkhart, IN; *Int'l*, pg. 173

Schanck, John W., Grp. V.P. & Pres.-Spirit Energy 76--Unocal Corporation, El Segundo, CA; *U.S. Public*, pg. 1698

Scheerder, Janpieter T., Pres.-SunSoft, Inc.--Sun Microsystems, Inc., Palo Alto, CA; *U.S. Public*, pg. 1531

Schelfhaudt, Peter, Partner--Kerry Kelly Thompson, Greenwich, CT; *U.S. Private*, pg. 174

Schick, Richard, Pres.-Bolle America--BEC Group, Inc., Rye, NY; *U.S. Public*, pg. 160

Schlais, Rudolph A., V.P. & Pres.-China--General Motors Corporation, Detroit, MI; *U.S. Public*, pg. 718

Schmalz, Brian F., Pres.--Creations Aromatiques, Inc., Englewood Cliffs, NJ; *Int'l*, pg. 173

Schmedding, Gary, Pres.-Broadcast Grp.--Lee Enterprises, Incorporated, Davenport, IA; *U.S. Public*, pg. 983

Schmidt-Holtz, Rolf, Pres. & Chief Exec. Officer--CLT-UFA, Luxembourg, Luxembourg; *Int'l*, pg. 561

Schmidt, Pierre, Pres.-Bongard--Groupe Strafor Facom, Morangis, France; *Int'l*, pg. 569

Schmidt, Ted, Pres. & Mng. Dir.-Ball Asia Pacific Ltd., Hong Kong--Ball Corporation, Muncie, IN; *U.S. Public*, pg. 170

Schmuhl, William J., Jr., Pres.-Heywood Williams--LaSalle Bristol Corp., Elkhart, IN; *Int'l*, pg. 618

Schmutte, Daniel P., V.P. & Pres.-Defense Systems--General Dynamics Corporation, Falls Church, VA; *U.S. Public*, pg. 708

Schneebeli, Ernst, Co-Pres.-European Div.--The Swiss Life/Rentenanstalt Group, Zurich, Switzerland; *Int'l*, pg. 1332

Schneiderman, Marc B., Pres.-Northeast Div.--Calton Homes, Inc., Manalapan, NJ; *U.S. Public*, pg. 296

Schnoz, Martin, Pres.-Neuhansen Div. & Member-Exec. Board--SIG Schweizerische Industrie-Gesellschaft Holding AG, Neuhausen, Switzerland; *Int'l*, pg. 1156

Schnuck, Mark J., Pres.-DESCO--Schnuck Markets, Inc., Saint Louis, MO; *U.S. Private*, pg. 971

Schofield, John A., V.P. & Pres. ADC Sys. Integration Inc.--ADC Telecommunications, Inc., Minnetonka, MN; *U.S. Public*, pg. 4

Schoonyoung, Frank H., Pres.-Ingredient Technology--Crompton & Knowles Corporation, Stamford, CT; *U.S. Public*, pg. 459

Schrader, Ralph W., Pres.-Worldwide Technology Bus.--Booz, Allen & Hamilton Inc., New York, NY; *U.S. Private, pg. 157*

Schreiber, Gregory, Pres.-ASCO Valves/The Americas--Automatic Switch Co., Florham Park, NJ; *U.S. Public*, pg. 573

Schroeder, Gary P., Sr. V.P. & Pres.-Western Grp.--Coca-Cola Enterprises Inc., Atlanta, GA; *U.S. Public*, pg. 393

Schroeder, Vern, Pres.-Weiser Worldwide--Weiser Lock, Tucson, AZ; *U.S. Public*, pg. 1053

Schrutt, Norman S., Pres.-Group II--Capital Cities/ABC Owned Radio Stations, New York, NY; *U.S. Public*, pg. 512

Schubel, Ronald L., V.P. & Reg. Pres.-Far East South--Molex Incorporated, Lisle, IL; *U.S. Public*, pg. 1121

Schubert, B. Kingsley, Pres.-CIGNA International--Cigna Corp., Philadelphia, PA; *U.S. Public*, pg. 356

Schuessler, John T., Pres. & Chief Oper. Officer-US. Opers.--Wendy's International Inc., Dublin, OH; *U.S. Public*, pg. 1754

Schultz, Norman L., Reg. Pres.--Citizens Bank of Illinois, Mount Vernon, IL; *U.S. Public*, pg. 280

Schulz, John, Pres.-Rogerson Equipment Grp.--Rogerson Aircraft Corporation, Irvine, CA; *U.S. Private*, pg. 940

Schumann, William F., Sr. V.P. & Pres-Old Republic Insured Credit Services, Inc.--Old Republic International Corporation, Chicago, IL; *U.S. Public*, pg. 1218

Schuster, Ron, Pres.-Construction Grp.--Pettibone Corporation, Lisle, IL; *U.S. Private*, pg. 859

Schwabero, Mark D., Pres.-Automotive Prods. Div.--Libbey Owens Ford Co., Toledo, OH; *Int'l*, pg. 1056

Schwartz, Sanford M., Dr., Exec. V.P. & Pres.-Market Facts-New York--Market Facts, Inc., Arlington Heights, IL; *U.S. Public*, pg. 1046

Schwarz, John H., Exec. V.P.-Fin. & Admin.--Perini Corporation, Framingham, MA; *U.S. Public*, pg. 1278

Schwiem, Wolfgang, Pres.-Saucony--Hyde Athletic Industries, Inc., Peabody, MA; *U.S. Public*, pg. 851

Scibelli, Stephen P., Pres.-Asia--Foamex International Inc., Linwood, PA; *U.S. Private*, pg. 1094

Scolnick, Edward M., M.D., Exec. V.P. & Pres.-Merck Res. Laboratories--Merck & Co., Inc., Whitehouse Station, NJ; *U.S. Public*, pg. 1090

Scorsone, L.V., Pres.-PDM Engineered Construction--Pitt-Des Moines, Inc., Pittsburgh, PA; *U.S. Public*, pg. 1304

Scott, Alan, Pres.-TELUS Communications--Telus Corporation, Edmonton, Canada; *Int'l*, pg. 1374

Scott, Benjamin, Pres. & Chief Exec. Officer-PCS PrimeCo--Bell Atlantic Corporation, New York, NY; *U.S. Public*, pg. 201

Scott, Bryant, Pres.-Expo Div.--The Home Depot, Inc., Atlanta, GA; *U.S. Public*, pg. 831

Scott, Kip, Pres.-North--The Ryland Group, Inc., Columbia, MD; *U.S. Public*, pg. 1414

Scruggs, Steven D., Pres.-Corp. Svcs. Grp.--Grubb & Ellis Company, Northbrook, IL; *U.S. Public*, pg. 767

Segura, Judith Garrett, Pres. & Exec. Dir.-A.H. Belo Corporation Foundation--A.H. Belo Corporation, Dallas, TX; *U.S. Public*, pg. 209

Seitz, Larry, Pres.- O L Fasteners--Service Supply Co. Inc. of Indiana, Indianapolis, IN; *U.S. Private*, pg. 987

Seitz, Melvin C., Jr., Pres.-Foundation--Service Supply Co. Inc. of Indiana, Indianapolis, IN; *U.S. Private*, pg. 987

Selky, John L., Pres.-I/N Tek & I/N Kote--Inland Steel Products Company, East Chicago, IN; *U.S. Public*, pg. 879

Selland, Howard M., Exec. V.P. & Pres.-Aeroquip Corp.--Aeroquip-Vickers, Inc., Maumee, OH; *U.S. Public*, pg. 24

Sellemond, Oswald, Dr., Pres.-Generics--Novartis AG, Basel, Switzerland; *Int'l*, pg. 971

Serrano, George, Pres.-Nuclear Prods., V.P. & Sec.--Packard BioScience Company, Meriden, CT; *U.S. Private*, pg. 833

Servais, Michael G., Sr. V.P. & Pres.-Acute Care--Universal Health Services, Inc., King of Prussia, PA; *U.S. Public*, pg. 1696

Servin, Larry, Pres.-Scancem Real Estate--Scancem AB, Malmo, Sweden; *Int'l*, pg. 1198

Sessoms, Walter W., Grp. Pres.-Services--BellSouth Telecommunications, Inc., Atlanta, GA; *U.S. Public*, pg. 209

Sewell, George, Pres.-Cereals/Europe--International Quaker Food Products, Chicago, IL; *U.S. Public*, pg. 1347

Shahinian, Vahan, Pres.-Tech. Opers.--Computer Methods Corporation, Livonia, MI; *U.S. Private*, pg. 260

Shank, Gordon, Pres.-Levi Strauss-Americas--Levi Strauss & Co., San Francisco, CA; *U.S. Private*, pg. 662

Shank, Mary, Dir.-Environ./Natural Resources--PVS Chemicals, Inc., Detroit, MI; *U.S. Private*, pg. 828

Shannon, Robert J., Pres.-Floor Prods./Worldwide--Armstrong World Industries, Inc., Lancaster, PA; *U.S. Public*, pg. 131

Shapiro, Mark A., Pres.-Golden Grain--U.S. & Canadian Food Products, Chicago, IL; *U.S. Public*, pg. 1347

Sharif, Yaz N., Pres.-Engineered Pump Grp.--Ingersoll-Dresser Pump Company, Liberty Corner, NJ; *U.S. Public, pg. 529*

Sharkey, David B., Pres.-Electric Lightwave, Inc.--Citizens Utilities Company, Stamford, CT; *U.S. Public*, pg. 379

Sharp, William J., Pres.-Global Support Opers.--The Goodyear Tire & Rubber Company, Akron, OH; *U.S. Public*, pg. 752

Sharp, William R., Pres.-Adams Resources Exploration Corp.--Adams Resources & Energy, Inc., Houston, TX; *U.S. Public*, pg. 18

Sharpe, John, Pres.-Buntin Out-of-Home Media--The Buntin Group, Nashville, TN; *U.S. Private*, pg. 181

Sharpe, John, Pres.-Home & Personal Care/Europe--Unilever Plc, London, United Kingdom; *Int'l*, pg. 1433

Shatz, Petar P., Pres.-New Bus. Ventures--Duracell International Inc., Bethel, CT; *U.S. Public*, pg. 743

Shaw, Jeffrey P., Grp. V.P. & Pres.-Dean Foods Vegetable Co.--Dean Foods Company, Franklin Park, IL; *U.S. Public*, pg. 489

Shaw, William J., Pres.-Marriott Service Grp. & Exec. V.P.--Fairfield Inn, Washington, DC; *U.S. Public*, pg. 1048

Shea, Christina L., V.P. & Pres.-Betty Crocker--General Mills, Inc., Minneapolis, MN; *U.S. Public*, pg. 717

Shell, William L., II, Pres.-Music Go Round--Grow Biz International, Inc., Minneapolis, MN; *U.S. Public*, pg. 767

Shelton, James D., Pres.-Central Grp.--Columbia/HCA Healthcare Corporation, Nashville, TN; *U.S. Public*, pg. 403

Shelton, Paul G., Chief Fin. Officer, Sr. V.P. & Pres.-Americo Carriers--AMCOL International Corp., Arlington Heights, IL; *U.S. Public*, pg. 63

Shen, Jimmy H.T., Pres.-Varity Asia/Pacific--LucasVarity Inc., Buffalo, NY; *Int'l*, pg. 820

Shepard, William A., Grp. Pres.-Pkgng.--Menasha Corporation, Neenah, WI; *U.S. Private*, pg. 731

Shepherd, James M., Pres. & Chief Exec. Officer-Japan Johnson & V.P.-SC Johnson & Son--S.C. Johnson & Son, Inc., Racine, WI; *U.S. Private*, pg. 592

Sherard, Jack, Pres.-Dock Div.--Kelley Company, Inc., Milwaukee, WI; *U.S. Private*, pg. 612

Sherard, Jack, Pres.-Dock Div.--Kelley Dock Systems, Milwaukee, WI; *U.S. Private*, pg. 612

Sherlock, Gary F., Grp. Pres.-Atlantic Newspaper Grp.--Gannett Company, Inc., Arlington, VA; *U.S. Public*, pg. 698

Sherlock, Michael J., Pres.-New Technology--National Broadcasting Co., Inc., New York, NY; *U.S. Public*, pg. 712

Sherman, Christopher R., Pres.-Pacific Enterprises Intl.--Pacific Enterprises, Los Angeles, CA; *U.S. Public*, pg. 1249

Sherwood, Ned L., Dir.-SED & Pres.-Zaleski, Sherwood & Co., Inc.--Southern Electronics Corporation, Tucker, GA; *U.S. Public*, pg. 1490

Shields, Robert E., Pres.-Military Health Svcs. Division--Humana Inc., Louisville, KY; *U.S. Public*, pg. 847

Shih, Willy C., Pres.-Digital & Applied Imaging & V.P.--Eastman Kodak Company, Rochester, NY; *U.S. Public*, pg. 550

Shipley, Richard, V.P. & Pres.-Shipley Co.--Rohm and Haas Company, Philadelphia, PA; *U.S. Public*, pg. 1403

Shoaf, Ben, Pres.-Fashion Fabrics--Milliken & Company, Spartanburg, SC; *U.S. Private*, pg. 748

Shoen, Mark, Pres.-Mktg.--U-Haul International, Inc., Phoenix, AZ; *U.S. Private*, pg. 49

Sholder, Jason, V.P. & Pres.-Cardiac Assist Div.--Datascope Corp., Montvale, NJ; *U.S. Public*, pg. 487

Shull, Joseph A., Pres.-Grove Crane--Grove WorldWide, Shady Grove, PA; *Int'l*, pg. 593

Shultz, Edward J., Pres.-Dana Credit Corp.--Dana Corporation, Toledo, OH; *U.S. Public*, pg. 479

Shutt, Buffy, Pres.-Mktg.--Universal Pictures, Universal City, CA; *Int'l*, pg. 1216

Sibley, Dawn, Pres.-Spot Brdcst. Div.--Western International Media Corporation, Los Angeles, CA; *U.S. Private*, pg. 1165

Sickler, John J., Sr. V.P. & Pres.-TFX Equites--Teleflex Incorporated, Plymouth Meeting, PA; *U.S. Public*, pg. 1569

Siddiqui, A. Sami, Pres./Gen. Mgr.-Credit Card Div., North America--Citicorp, New York, NY; *U.S. Public*, pg. 376

Siebert, Mark, Pres.-MarketSmart & Chief Information Officer--The Sunflower Group, Overland Park, KS; *U.S. Private*, pg. 1052

Siegel., N. Tice, Jr., Pres.-Children's & Family Shoes--JC Penney Company, Inc., Plano, TX; *U.S. Public*, pg. 916

Siegenthaler, Kurt E., V.P. & Pres.-Emhart Glass--The Black & Decker Corporation, Towson, MD; *U.S. Public*, pg. 233

Sights, Jack W., Grp. V.P.--Guardian Industries Corp., Auburn Hills, MI; *U.S. Private*, pg. 485
Sigrist, Rainer, Grp. Pres.-Plant Engrng.--Georg Fischer Ltd., Schaffhausen, Switzerland; *Int'l*, pg. 488
Sihler, Helmut, Prof. Dr., Vice Chm.--Novartis AG, Basel, Switzerland; *Int'l*, pg. 971
Sikes, Alfred C., Pres.-Hearst New Media & Tech.--The Hearst Corporation, New York, NY; *U.S. Private*, pg. 515
Sikowitz, Peter, Editor-in-Chief, Men's Fitness--Weider Publications, Inc., Woodland Hills, CA; *U.S. Private*, pg. 1159
Silvestri, Chester J., Pres.-Sun Microelectronics--Sun Microsystems, Inc., Palo Alto, CA; *U.S. Public*, pg. 1531
Simmons, Hardwick, Pres. & Chief Exec. Officer-Prudential Securities, Inc.--The Prudential Insurance Company of America, Newark, NJ; *U.S. Private*, pg. 892
Simmons, Juanita G., Pres.-Ada Crude Oil Company--Adams Resources & Energy, Inc., Houston, TX; *U.S. Public*, pg. 18
Simon, Vawgh, Pres.--Hartco Flooring Company, Oneida, TN; *U.S. Public*, pg. 1322
Simpson, William A., Pres.-Life Insurance Div.--USLIFE Corporation, New York, NY; *U.S. Public*, pg. 77
Simpson, William A., Sr. V.P.-Mortgage Guaranty & Pres.-Republic Mortgage Ins. Co.--Old Republic International Corporation, Chicago, IL; *U.S. Public*, pg. 1218
Simpson, William H., Pres.-Pfaltzgraff Co.--The Pfaltzgraff Co., York, PA; *U.S. Private*, pg. 860
Singer, Frederick D., V.P.-Food & Indus. Divs.--Rochester Midland Corporation, Rochester, NY; *U.S. Private*, pg. 937
Sipe, Gene H., Exec. V.P. & Grp. Pres.--Bremer Financial Corporation, Saint Paul, MN; *U.S. Private*, pg. 167
Sirvaitis, Richard L., Pres.-IFE Adv. Sls.--International Family Entertainment, Inc., Virginia Beach, VA; *Int'l*, pg. 927
Sitkoff, Robert P., Pres.-Maui Tacos International, Inc.--Blimpie International, Inc., Atlanta, GA; *U.S. Public*, pg. 236
Skiles, Allen C., Pres.-Tolk, Inc.--Dewberry & Davis, Fairfax, VA; *U.S. Private*, pg. 329
Skillern, Frank L., Jr., Pres.-Consumer Card Grp./USA--American Express Travel Related Services Co., Inc., New York, NY; *U.S. Public*, pg. 73
Skinner, Ned, Global Pres.-Indus. Food Services--Tone Brothers Inc., Ankeny, IA; *Int'l*, pg. 237
Skinner, P.D., Pres. & Mng. Dir.-Shell Intl. Trading & Shipping Co. Ltd.--Royal Dutch/Shell Group of Companies, Hague, Netherlands; *Int'l*, pg. 1135
Skinner, Peter G., Sr. V.P., Gen. Counsel, Sec. & Pres.-Television--Dow Jones & Company, Inc., New York, NY; *U.S. Public*, pg. 524
Sknoecke, Steve, Div. Pres.-Bennigan's--Bennigan's, Dallas, TX; *U.S. Private*, pg. 736
Skroder, Christian, Pres.-Europe--Tupperware Corporation, Orlando, FL; *U.S. Public*, pg. 1644
Slark, Martin P., V.P. & Reg. Pres.-Americas--Molex Incorporated, Lisle, IL; *U.S. Public*, pg. 1121
Slattery, William, Pres.-Cargo--Northwest Airlines, Inc., Saint Paul, MN; *U.S. Public*, pg. 1200
Slattery, William D., Pres.-Northwest Cargo & Charter--Northwest Airlines Corp., Saint Paul, MN; *U.S. Public*, pg. 1199
Slay, Joe, Pres.-Martin Pub. Rels.--The Martin Agency, Richmond, VA; *U.S. Private*, pg. 678
Slay, Joe, Pres.-Martin Pub. Rels.--The Martin Agency, Richmond, VA; *U.S. Public*, pg. 909
Sloan, Dick, Pres.-Hose, Fittings & Indus. Prods.--United Technologies Automotive, Dearborn, MI; *U.S. Public*, pg. 1691
Sloan, Jim, Pres.-Detail Div.--Blue Coral Systems, Tucson, AZ; *U.S. Public*, pg. 1348
Sloss, Merle, Pres.-Ralph Lauren Footwear--Reebok International Ltd., Stoughton, MA; *U.S. Public*, pg. 1369
Slusarchuk, William A., Pres.-AGRA Earth & Environmental Limited--Agra Inc., Calgary, Canada; *Int'l*, pg. 30
Slusser, Daniel E., V.P., Sr. V.P. & Gen. Mgr.-Universal City--Universal Studios, Inc., Universal City, CA; *Int'l*, pg. 1215
Smetana, Joseph, Pres.-AIG Risk Mngmt.--American International Group, Inc., New York, NY; *U.S. Public*, pg. 83
Smith, Albert E., Pres.-Electronic Systems Sector--Harris Corporation, Melbourne, FL; *U.S. Public*, pg. 791
Smith, Brian J., Exec. V.P. & Pres.-BLP Sls. Support Div.--Boron LePore Group, Fair Lawn, NJ; *U.S. Public*, pg. 246
Smith, D.L., Pres.-Kimmel-Motz Refrigeration Corp.--Toromont Industries Ltd., Concord, Canada; *Int'l*, pg. 1400
Smith, Daryl, Pres.-World Omni Financial Corp. & Exec. V.P.--JM Family Enterprises Inc., Deerfield Beach, FL; *U.S. Private*, pg. 577
Smith, Dewitt, Pres.-Savannah Lakes--Cooper Communities, Inc., Bella Vista, AR; *U.S. Private*, pg. 273
Smith, Douglas A., Pres.-Kraft Canada Inc.--Kraft Foods, Inc., Northfield, IL; *U.S. Public*, pg. 1287
Smith, Geoffrey W., Pres.-Kaiser Alumina & Commodities--Kaiser Aluminum & Chemical Corporation, Pleasanton, CA; *U.S. Public*, pg. 1062
Smith, Glen, Pres.-Hunt Foods Co.--Hunt-Wesson, Inc., Fullerton, CA; *U.S. Public*, pg. 428
Smith, J. Andrew, Pres.-Core Markets Grp.--Brown-Forman Beverages Worldwide, Louisville, KY; *U.S. Public*, pg. 261
Smith, Jerry M., Pres.-Intl.--Triarc Beverage Group, White Plains, NY; *U.S. Public*, pg. 1635
Smith, John R., Pres.-Consumer & Specialty Products Div.--IMC Agribusiness, Collinsville, IL; *U.S. Public*, pg. 856
Smith, Joseph E., Pres.-Shaving Products Grp. & V.P.--Warner-Lambert Company, Morris Plains, NJ; *U.S. Public*, pg. 1738
Smith, Londeo A., Vice Chm.-The Hartford & Pres. & Chief Exec. Officer-H. Life--The Hartford Financial Services Group Inc., Hartford, CT; *U.S. Public*, pg. 794
Smith, Marc C., Pres.-Crestar Mortgage Corp.--Crestar Financial Corporation, Richmond, VA; *U.S. Public*, pg. 458
Smith, Marc C., Pres.-Crestar Mortgage Corp.--Crestar Bank, Richmond, VA; *U.S. Public*, pg. 458
Smith, Michael A., Pres.-Lockheed Martin Ocean--Lockheed Martin Corporation, Bethesda, MD; *U.S. Public*, pg. 1006
Smith, Michael L., Pres.-Somerset Financial Services--The Somerset Group, Inc., Indianapolis, IN; *U.S. Public*, pg. 1484
Smith, P.B., Pres.-Rocketdyne Div.--Boeing North American, Seal Beach, CA; *U.S. Public*, pg. 241
Smith, R.L., Pres--Eastman Kodak Asia Pacific Ltd., Tokyo, Japan; *U.S. Public*, pg. 552
Smith, Randall S., Pres.-Intl. Opers. Grp.--Information Resources, Inc., Chicago, IL; *U.S. Public*, pg. 875
Smith, Robert, Pres.-Frankfurt Balkind West/AV--Frankfurt Balkind Partners, New York, NY; *U.S. Private*, pg. 424
Smith, Robert A., Grp. Pres.--Hardin Construction Group, Inc., Atlanta, GA; *U.S. Private*, pg. 501
Smith, Robert A., Pres.-Indus. Prod. Grp.--Haskel International, Inc., Burbank, CA; *U.S. Public*, pg. 798
Smith, Roy L., Pres.-Polymer Div.--American Buildings Co., Eufaula, AL; *U.S. Public*, pg. 69
Smith, Scott, Pres.-Fabrication Div.--Hunter Douglas, Inc., Upper Saddle River, NJ; *Int'l*, pg. 639
Smith, Stephen D., Pres.-Reda Grp.--Camco International Inc., Houston, TX; *U.S. Public*, pg. 297
Smith, Steven D., Pres.-REDA Grp.--Camco International Inc., Houston, TX; *U.S. Public*, pg. 298
Smith, Wayne A., V.P. & Pres.-Vehicle Sealing Div.--GenCorp Inc., Fairlawn, OH; *U.S. Public*, pg. 705
Smits, P.M.A.M., Pres.-America--Delta plc, London, United Kingdom; *Int'l*, pg. 389
Smolev, Steven P., Pres.-DVM Pharmaceuticals--IVAX Corporation, Miami, FL; *U.S. Public*, pg. 914
Smyth, George C., Pres.-Bell Northern Res. & Sr. V.P.--Northern Telecom Limited, Brampton, Canada; *Int'l*, pg. 968
Smythe, Hugh, Pres.-Resort Opers. Grp.--Intrawest Corporation, Vancouver, Canada; *Int'l*, pg. 685
Snapp, Manco L., Pres.-Masonite--International Paper Company, Purchase, NY; *U.S. Public*, pg. 901
Snider, Stacey, Co-Pres.-Production--Universal Pictures, Universal City, CA; *Int'l*, pg. 1216
Snider, Stephen A., Pres.--Tidewater Compression Service, Inc., Houston, TX; *U.S. Public*, pg. 1608
Sny, Sharon, Pres.-Plastic Pkgng. & Sr. V.P.--Duro-Last Roofing, Inc., Saginaw, MI; *U.S. Private*, pg. 349
Snyder, Bruce, Pres.-Domestic Distr., Motion Picture Div.--Twentieth Century Fox Film Corp., Los Angeles, CA; *Int'l*, pg. 926
Snyder, John, Grp. Pres.-Mtl. Handling--Menasha Corporation, Neenah, WI; *U.S. Private*, pg. 731
Snyder, Michael, Pres.--ADT Security Services, Boca Raton, FL; *U.S. Public*, pg. 1648
Snyder, Ross B., Pres.-Grp. Life & Health & Sr. V.P.--Blue Cross & Blue Shield of Texas, Inc., Richardson, TX; *U.S.* Private, pg. 152
Soderberg, Jerry P., Pres.-Newsprint Grp.--Avenor, Inc., Montreal, Canada; *Int'l*, pg. 101
Soga, Hiromu, Pres.--Eidesign Technologies, Inc., Mountain View, CA; *Int'l*, pg. 940
Sogame, Hiromitsu, Deputy Pres.-Admin./Corp. Plng.--Daiwa Securities Co. Ltd., Tokyo, Japan; *Int'l*, pg. 374
Sohn, Young K., Pres.-Desktop & Portable Storage Grp.--Quantum Corporation, Milpitas, CA; *U.S. Public*, pg. 1350
Solakoglu, Cengiz, Pres.-Consumer Goods Grp.--Koc Holding A.S., Istanbul, Turkey; *Int'l*, pg. 741
Solari, Joseph G., Jr., Pres.-ConvaTec--Bristol-Myers Squibb Company, New York, NY; *U.S. Public*, pg. 253
Solberg, Robert A., Pres.-Intl. Production & V.P.--Texaco Inc., White Plains, NY; *U.S. Public*, pg. 1582
Solberg, Robert A., Pres.-Intl. Production--Texaco Worldwide Exploration & Production, Scroggins, TX; *U.S.* Public, pg. 1583
Solley, Michael W., Pres.-Nichols InfoFed--Nichols Research Corporation, Huntsville, AL; *U.S. Public*, pg. 1182
Solomon, Jerry, Pres.-Natl. Brdcst.--SFM Media Corporation, New York, NY; *U.S. Private*, pg. 956
Solomon, Ken, Pres.-Universal TV--Universal Studios TV, Universal City, CA; *Int'l*, pg. 1215
Solomon, Zachary, Pres. & Chief Exec. Officer-Adrienne Vittadini Division--Marisa Christina Inc., New Hyde Park, NY; *U.S. Public*, pg. 1044
Somerhalder, John W., II, Pres.-Tennessee Gas & Pipeline--El Paso Natural Gas Co., Houston, TX; *U.S. Public*, pg. 567
Sonheim, Richard, Reg. V.P.--American Mail-Well Envelope, Englewood, CO; *U.S. Public*, pg. 1038
Sonnenberg, Ronnie, Pres.-Business Group--Ziff-Davis Publishing Company, New York, NY; *Int'l*, pg. 1276
Sorrels, James P., Pres.-Contract Logistics--KLLM Transport Services, Inc., Jackson, MS; *U.S. Public*, pg. 939
Southard, Donald, V.P. & Pres.-Patient Monitoring Div.--Datascope Corp., Montvale, NJ; *U.S. Public*, pg. 487
Spackman, G. Lawrence, Pres.-Gas Mktg. Group & Transcanada Energy Mngmnt.--Transcanada Pipelines Limited, Calgary, Canada; *Int'l*, pg. 1416
Spackman, G. Lawrence, Pres.-Gas Mktg. Grp.--TransCanada Energy Ltd., Calgary, Canada; *Int'l*, pg. 1417
Spaulding, Peter C., Pres.-Tool Group--Wilton Corporation, Palatine, IL; *U.S. Private*, pg. 1181
Spears, William E., Pres.-North America--Tupperware Corporation, Orlando, FL; *U.S. Public*, pg. 1644
Specht, John, Pres.-Media Div.--Danka Business Systems, La Grange, IL; *Int'l*, pg. 379
Speirs, John R., Pres.-Intl.--The Pillsbury Company, Minneapolis, MN; *Int'l*, pg. 411
Spencer, Dan S., Jr., Pres.-North Banking Region--United Missouri Bank N.A., Kansas City, MO; *U.S. Public*, pg. 1654
Spezio, Carl P., Pres.-Heat Treating Grp.--Gibraltar Steel Corp., Buffalo, NY; *U.S. Public*, pg. 742
Spiessbach, Michael, Pres.-King World Ventures--King World Productions, Inc., New York, NY; *U.S. Public*, pg. 961
Springer, William C., Pres.-Heinz North America--Heinz U.S.A. Div., Pittsburgh, PA; *U.S. Public*, pg. 805
Spungin, Lawrence D., V.P. & Pres.-Universal Studios Devel.--Universal Studios, Inc., Universal City, CA; *Int'l*, pg. 1215
Squier-Dow, Mae H., Pres.-ACC TeleCom--ACC Corp., Rochester, NY; *U.S. Public*, pg. 2
Srere, Linda, Pres. & Chief Exec. Officer-Y&RNY--Young & Rubicam Inc., New York, NY; *U.S. Private*, pg. 1196
St. Amour, Paul R., Pres.-Pinkerton's of Canada--Pinkerton's Inc., Encino, CA; *U.S. Public*, pg. 1296
St. Pe, Gerald J., Sr. V.P. & Pres.-Ingalls Shipbuilding--Litton Industries, Inc., Woodland Hills, CA; *U.S. Public*, pg. 1002
Stahl, Brian E., Pres.-RTR Div.--Aaron Rents, Inc., Atlanta, GA; *U.S. Public*, pg. 12
Stahl, Jack L., Pres.-North America Grp.--The Coca-Cola Company, Atlanta, GA; *U.S. Public*, pg. 392
Stahl, Roy H., Pres.--Utility & Municipal Services, Inc., Bryn Mawr, PA; *U.S. Public*, pg. 1287
Staiano, Edward F., Exec. V.P. & Pres. & Gen. Mgr.-General Systems--Motorola, Inc., Schaumburg, IL; *U.S. Public*, pg. 1136
Staley, Gregory R., Pres.-Intl. Div.--Toys "R" Us, Inc., Paramus, NJ; *U.S. Public*, pg. 1626
Stamp, Philip B., Pres.-Fluid Connectors--Parker Hannifin Corporation, Hemel Hempstead, United Kingdom; *U.S. Public*, pg. 1263
Stanek, Frank, Pres.-Intl. New Bus. Devel.--Universal Studios Recreation Services Group, Universal City, CA; *Int'l*, pg. 1216
Stanley, A. Jack, Sr. V.P. & Pres.-Engrg. & Construction Group--Dresser Industries, Inc., Dallas, TX; *U.S. Public*, pg. 528
Stanton, Tom, Pres.-Nelson/Word Direct--Thomas Nelson Inc., Nashville, TN; *U.S. Public*, pg. 1167
Stanzione, Dan, Pres.-Network Systems & Bell Labs--Lucent Technologies Inc., Murray Hill, NJ; *U.S. Public*, pg. 1017
Stapley, David W., Pres.-Spar Applied Systems--Spar Aerospace Limited, Toronto, Canada; *Int'l*, pg. 1287
Stark, Alan, Pres.-Canada--American Express Travel Related Services Co., Inc., New York, NY; *U.S. Public*, pg. 73
Staton, Robert E., Pres.-Colonial Life & Accident Ins. Co.--UNUM Corporation, Portland, ME; *U.S. Public*, pg. 1699
Staudt, Daniel E., Pres.-Mfg. & Distribution--Shoney's, Inc., Nashville, TN; *U.S. Public*, pg. 1467
Stauffer, Thomas G., Pres.-Americas--Renaissance Hotel Group N.V., Central, Hong Kong; *U.S. Public*, pg. 1048
Staves, Steven G., Pres.-Commercial Opers. & V.P.--Duracell International Inc., Bethel, CT; *U.S. Public*, pg. 743
Stecklein, A.L., Pres.-North American Rubber Opers.--The Gates Rubber Company, Denver, CO; *Int'l*, pg. 1396
Steele, Denny W., Pres.-Interplex--Bergen Brunswig Corporation, Orange, CA; *U.S. Public*, pg. 213
Steffan, Mike, Pres.-Distr. & Opers. & Corp. Sec.--Inacom Corp., Omaha, NE; *U.S. Public*, pg. 873
Steffens, Gretchen, Pres.-Pub. Rels. & Sls. Promo.--Key Communications, Inc., San Juan, PR; *U.S. Private*, pg. 318
Stein, Bruce L., Pres.-Mattel Worldwide & Chief Oper. Officer--Mattel, Inc., El Segundo, CA; *U.S. Public*, pg. 1057
Stein, Phyllis, Pres.-List Brokerage--LCS Industries, Inc., Clifton, NJ; *U.S. Public*, pg. 970
Steinecker, Brent, Pres.-Crowley Marine Services--Crowley Maritime Corporation, Oakland, CA; *U.S. Private*, pg. 292
Stephen, Randall W., V.P. & Pres.-Northeast Div.--Circuit City Stores, Inc., Richmond, VA; *U.S. Public*, pg. 374
Stephenson, Robert, Grp. Pres.-Mainframes & Computer Chips, Grp. Exec. & Sr. V.P.--International Business Machines Corporation, Armonk, NY; *U.S. Public*, pg. 895
Sterlin, Larry O., Pres.-Asia-Pacific Opers.--Zurn Industries, Inc., Erie, PA; *U.S. Public*, pg. 1794
Stern, Brian E., Sr. V.P. & Pres.-Office Documents Product Group--Xerox Corporation, Stamford, CT; *U.S. Public*, pg. 1783
Stern, Evan P., Pres.-Staples National Advantage--Staples, Inc., Westborough, MA; *U.S. Public*, pg. 1509
Stern, Ronald, Pres.-Slim Fast--Slim-Fast Foods Company, West Palm Beach, FL; *U.S. Private*, pg. 1006
Steuck, Gary R., Pres.-Japan--Lands' End, Inc., Dodgeville, WI; *U.S. Public*, pg. 977
Stevens, Meri, Pres.-Waverly Div.--F. Schumacher & Co., New York, NY; *U.S. Private*, pg. 973
Stevens, R.N., Pres.--BOC Canada Ltd., Mississauga, Canada; *Int'l*, pg. 121
Stevenson, Wade, Pres.-Eastman Export--Eastman Worldwide, Buffalo, NY; *U.S. Private*, pg. 358
Stewart, Alistair C., Pres.-G.E. Middle East, Africa, Central & Eastern Europe--General Electric International Operations, London, United Kingdom; *U.S. Public*, pg. 713
Stewart, Allan B., Pres.-Retail Stores--Sears, Roebuck and Co., Hoffman Estates, IL; *U.S. Public*, pg. 1452
Stewart, George, Pres.-Medical Devices-Hospital Products Grp.--Pfizer Inc., New York, NY; *U.S. Public*, pg. 1281
Stier, Mary P., Grp. Pres.-Midwest Newspaper Grp.--Gannett Company, Inc., Arlington, VA; *U.S. Public*, pg. 698
Stirnimann, Kurt, Dr., Grp. Pres.-Mfg. Tech. Grp.--Georg Fischer Ltd., Schaffhausen, Switzerland; *Int'l*, pg. 488

Stoecker, Randy, Pres.-Midwest Div.--Murphy Family Farms, Rose Hill, NC; *U.S. Private*, pg. 768
Stone, David, Second V.P. & Dir.-Adv. & Video--Transamerica Life Companies, Los Angeles, CA; *U.S. Public*, pg. 1630
Stoner, Janet L., Pres.-H.R. Div. & V.P.--Texaco Inc., White Plains, NY; *U.S. Public*, pg. 1582
Storrison, William E., Pres.-C.I.S. Division--Ciber, Inc., Englewood, CO; *U.S. Public*, pg. 356
Story, Edward T., V.P.-Intl. & Pres.-SOCO Intl., Inc.--Snyder Oil Corporation, Fort Worth, TX; *U.S. Public*, pg. 1481
Stoudt, Craig, Pres.-Ampad Div.--American Pad and Paper Company, Dallas, TX; *U.S. Public*, pg. 88
Stout, Harry Lee, Pres.-Natural Gas Mktg. & Transportation--KCS Energy Inc., Edison, NJ; *U.S. Public*, pg. 938
Stoutenburgh, Dennis J., Pres.-Communications Grp.--Intellicall, Inc., Carrollton, TX; *U.S. Public*, pg. 887
Strachan, Rick, V.P. & Pres.-Mfg.--Clayton Homes, Inc., Knoxville, TN; *U.S. Public*, pg. 382
Straeter, Terry A., Dr., V.P., Pres. & Chief Exec. Officer-Tracor Info. Sys.--Tracor, Inc., Austin, TX; *U.S. Public*, pg. 1627
Strahler, Ron, Pres.-The Ink Well--International Center for Entrepreneurial Development, Inc., Cypress, TX; *U.S. Private*, pg. 568
Strand, James W., Pres.-Diversified Opers.--Aliant Communications Inc., Lincoln, NE; *U.S. Public*, pg. 40
Strasser, Alain, Pres.-Campbell Biscuits Europe--Campbell Soup Company, Camden, NJ; *U.S. Public*, pg. 298
Strasser, Alain, Pres.-Campbell Biscuits Europe--Bakery & Confectionary Division, Camden, NJ; *U.S. Public*, pg. 299
Strauss, Charles, Pres.-Latin America--Unilever Plc, London, United Kingdom; *Int'l*, pg. 1433
Straw, Edward M., Pres.-Ryder Integrated Logistics--Ryder System, Inc., Miami, FL; *U.S. Public*, pg. 1413
Straw, Edward M., Pres.-Ryder Integrated Logistics, Inc.--Vehicle Leasing & Services Div., Miami, FL; *U.S. Public*, pg. 1414
Streiff, Christian, Pres.-Pipe Div.--Saint-Gobain, Courbevoie, France; *Int'l*, pg. 1170
Streiff, Christina, Pres.-Paper Div.--Pont-a-Mousson SA, Nancy, France; *Int'l*, pg. 1176
Streit, Clint, Pres.-Paging Network-Southwestern Region, Inc.--Paging Network, Inc., Plano, TX; *U.S. Public*, pg. 1252
Stretmater, Robert L., V.P. & Pres.-Foodservice--General Mills, Inc., Minneapolis, MN; *U.S. Public*, pg. 717
Stroh, B. Gregory, Pres.-Packaging--Fort James Corporation, Richmond, VA; *U.S. Public*, pg. 670
Stroik, Gregory J., Sr. V.P., Dir.-Investments, Taxes & Internal Audit & Asst. Treas.--Federated Mutual Insurance Company, Owatonna, MN; *U.S. Private*, pg. 399
Stroucken, Albert P.L., Exec. V.P. & Pres.-Indus. Chemicals Div.--Bayer Corporation, Parsippany, NJ; *Int'l*, pg. 172
Strouken, Albert P.L., Pres.-Industrial Chemicals Div. & Exec. V.P.--Bayer Corporation, Pittsburgh, PA; *Int'l*, pg. 172
Stuart, Ian, V.P. & Pres.-Latin American Grp.--The Black & Decker Corporation, Towson, MD; *U.S. Public*, pg. 233
Stubbs, Robert W., Pres.-Fin. Services--Bell Atlantic Enterprises Corporation, Philadelphia, PA; *U.S. Public*, pg. 202
Stucki, Hans-Rudolf, Dr., Head.-N. America Division--Winterthur Schweizerische Versicherungs Gesellschaft, Winterthur, Switzerland; *Int'l*, pg. 345
Stuteville, Mick R., Pres.-ONEOK Prods. Company--Energy Companies Of ONEOK, Tulsa, OK; *U.S. Public*, pg. 1226
Stutz, Ferdinand, Grp. Pres.-Automotive Products Grp.--Georg Fischer Ltd., Schaffhausen, Switzerland; *Int'l*, pg. 488
Stutz, Todd M., Pres.-Rottlund of MN--The Rottlund Company, Inc., Roseville, MN; *U.S. Public*, pg. 1406
Subasi, Hasan, Pres.-Household Appliance Grp.--Koc Holding A.S., Istanbul, Turkey; *Int'l*, pg. 741
Subin, Robert, Sr. V.P.-Global Sourcing & Engrng.--Campbell Soup Company, Camden, NJ; *U.S. Public*, pg. 298
Subotnick, Stuart, Deputy Pres.--Metromedia International Group, Inc., East Rutherford, NJ; *U.S. Public*, pg. 1102
Suchomel, James M., V.P., Pres. & Gen. Mgr.-FDM Electronics--Fairbanks Morse Engine Division, Beloit, WI; *U.S. Public*, pg. 401
Sullivan, Barry W., V.P.-Internet & Electronics Bus. Unit--Electronic Data Systems Corporation, Plano, TX; *U.S. Public*, pg. 569
Sullivan, Mike, Pres.-Entertainment--UPN-United Paramount Network, Los Angeles, CA; *U.S. Public*, pg. 352
Sullivan, Mike, Pres.-Entertainment--UPN-United Paramount Network, Los Angeles, CA; *U.S. Private*, pg. 777
Sullivan, Stephen F., Pres.--Ling Electronics Ltd., Suffolk, United Kingdom; *U.S. Public*, pg. 1077
Sullivan, Timothy, Pres.-Pneumatic Scales--Barry-Wehmiller Company, Saint Louis, MO; *U.S. Private*, pg. 118
Suminski, Len, Pres.-PCA, the Americas--Philip Crosby Associates, Inc., Winter Park, FL; *Int'l*, pg. 1072
Suominen, Hanna, Pres.-Nokia Industrial Electronics--Oy Nokia Ab/Nokia Group, Helsinki, Finland; *Int'l*, pg. 951
Sur, Larry M., Pres.-Schneider Logistics--Schneider National, Inc., Green Bay, WI; *U.S. Private*, pg. 971
Sutherland, Allan R., Pres. & Chief Oper. Officer-Industrial Technologies--Derlan Industries Limited, Toronto, Canada; *Int'l*, pg. 395
Sutton, William P., Pres.-Exec. Committee--The Bank of Nova Scotia, Toronto, Canada; *Int'l*, pg. 155
Suzuki, Kiichi, Exec. Deputy Pres.--The Nikko Securities Co., Ltd., Tokyo, Japan; *Int'l*, pg. 930
Swain, Terrence P., Pres. & Chief Oper. Officer-Aerospace Opers.--Derlan Industries Limited, Toronto, Canada; *Int'l*, pg. 395
Swan, Alfred W., Jr., Sr. Exec. V.P. & Pres. & Head-Commercial Banking-AmSouth Bank FL--AmSouth Bancorporation, Birmingham, AL; *U.S. Public*, pg. 105
Swanston, David, Pres.-Pub. Rels. Div.--Stackig Advertising and Public Relations, Mc Lean, VA; *U.S. Private*, pg. 1028
Swearingen, Carl E., State Pres.-Georgia--BellSouth Telecommunications, Inc., Atlanta, GA; *U.S. Public*, pg. 209
Sweatt, Blaine, III, Exec. V.P. & Pres.-New Bus. Devel.--Darden Restaurants, Inc., Orlando, FL; *U.S. Public*, pg. 483
Sweetwood, John, Pres.-Holiday Inn Express--Holiday Inn Worldwide, Atlanta, GA; *Int'l*, pg. 170
Swim, Christopher L., Pres.-Folding Carton Div.--Artistic Carton Company, Elgin, IL; *U.S. Private*, pg. 87
Swoyer, Katherine W., Pres.-Intl. Corp. Travel Svcs., Inc.--Roy F. Weston, Inc., West Chester, PA; *U.S. Public*, pg. 1761
Sykes, James, Pres.-Intl.--The Holland Hitch Company, Holland, MI; *U.S. Private*, pg. 534
Sykes, John, Pres.-VH-1--MTV Networks, New York, NY; *U.S. Private*, pg. 779
Szescila, Andrew J., Sr. V.P. & Pres.-Hughes Christensen Co.--Baker Hughes Incorporated, Houston, TX; *U.S. Public*, pg. 165
Szlasa, John P., Pres. & Chief Exec. Officer-Ferguson Consulting--CommonHealth USA, Parsippany, NJ; *Int'l*, pg. 1483
Taaffe, Paul, Pres. & Chief Exec. Officer-Europe, Africa, Middle East--Hill and Knowlton, Inc., New York, NY; *Int'l*, pg. 1483
Tagliarino, Scott, Pres., Exec. V.P. & Gen. Mgr.-New York Corp. & Fin.--Edelman Worldwide, Inc., New York, NY; *U.S. Private*, pg. 362
Tait, Brad D., Pres.-Disc Go Round & It's About Games--Grow Biz International, Inc., Minneapolis, MN; *U.S. Public*, pg. 767
Takada, H., Pres.Dir.--NSK-RHP UK Limited, Ruddington, United Kingdom; *Int'l*, pg. 904
Takagi, Y., Pres.--Shimadzu (Asia Pacific) Pte. Ltd., Singapore, Singapore; *Int'l*, pg. 1232
Takahashi, Katsuya, Pres.--NSK do Brasil Industria e Comercio de Rolamentos Ltda., Bela Vista, Brazil; *Int'l*, pg. 904
Talagrand, Noel, Pres.-Facom & Mng. Dir.-Strafor facom--Groupe Strafor Facom, Morangis, France; *Int'l*, pg. 569
Talbot, Pamela, Pres. & Chief Oper. Officer-Edelman U.S.--Edelman Public Relations Worldwide, Chicago, IL; *U.S. Private*, pg. 362
Tamaru, K., Pres.--NSK-RHP Europe Limited, Ruddington, United Kingdom; *Int'l*, pg. 904
Tangney, Michael, Pres.-Latin America--Colgate-Palmolive Company, New York, NY; *U.S. Public*, pg. 397
Tanguay, Louis A., Pres.-Bell Quebec--Bell Canada, Montreal, Canada; *Int'l*, pg. 115
Tanner, Roy H., V.P. & Pres.-Control Laser Intl. Corp.--Excel Technology, Inc., New York, NY; *U.S. Public*, pg. 599
Tanner, Travis, Pres.- Carlson Travel Grp.--Carlson Companies, Inc., Minnetonka, MN; *U.S. Private*, pg. 211
Tanner, Travis, Pres.-Carlson Travel Grp.; Co-Pres. & Chief Exec. Officer CWT--Carlson Wagonlit Travel, Minneapolis, MN; *U.S. Private*, pg. 212
Targoff, Michael B., Pres.-Loral Space & Communications--Lockheed Martin Corporation, Bethesda, MD; *U.S. Public*, pg. 1006
Tarney, Julie, Pres.-Pub. Rels.--Laughlin/Constable, Inc., Milwaukee, WI; *U.S. Private*, pg. 653
Tarorick, Felix, Pres.-RB&W Metal Forming--RB&W Corporation, Cleveland, OH; *U.S. Public*, pg. 1259
Tassie, John M., Pres. & Chief Oper. Officer-AAA Fin. Service Corp.--American Automobile Association, Heathrow, FL; *U.S. Private*, pg. 50
Taub, Stephen, Pres. & Chief Oper. Officer--Mafco Worldwide Corp., Camden, NJ; *U.S. Private*, pg. 690
Taxter, Michael W., Pres.-South Reg.--JC Penney Company, Inc., Plano, TX; *U.S. Public*, pg. 916
Taylor, Loren L., Pres.-NSP Electric--Northern States Power Company, Minneapolis, MN; *U.S. Public*, pg. 1195
Temkin, Laura W., Co-Pres. & Acct. Exec.--Temkin & Temkin, Northbrook, IL; *U.S. Private*, pg. 1074
Templeton, Bill, Pres.-Motgage Div.--The Money Store, Sacramento, CA; *U.S. Public*, pg. 1124
Terpack, Daniel, V.P. & Pres.-Measurement Bus.--Tektronix, Inc., Wilsonville, OR; *U.S. Public*, pg. 1567
Terry, Bruce, Pres. & Chief Exec. Officer--Mayfran International, Inc., Cleveland, OH; *Int'l*, pg. 1397
Teruel, Javier, Pres.-Europe--Colgate-Palmolive Company, New York, NY; *U.S. Public*, pg. 397
Testwuide, R.R., Pres.-Seal Div.--BW/IP International, Inc., Long Beach, CA; *U.S. Public*, pg. 658
Testwuide, Richard R., V.P. & Pres.-Seal Div.--Flowserve Corporation, Long Beach, CA; *U.S. Public*, pg. 658
Tevis, G. Phillip, Sr. V.P. & Pres.-Global Marketing Group--Dresser Industries, Inc., Dallas, TX; *U.S. Public*, pg. 528
Thaman, Michael H., V.P. & Pres.-Global Fabrication/Sys.--Owens Corning, Toledo, OH; *U.S. Public*, pg. 1236
Tharp, Paul E., Grp. Pres.-Midwest Grp.--Beneficial Corporation, Wilmington, DE; *U.S. Public*, pg. 211
Theeuwes, Felix, Dr., Pres.-ALZA Technology Institute & Chief Scientist--Alza Corporation, Palo Alto, CA; *U.S. Public*, pg. 62
Thibodeau, Kevin, Pres.-Waverly, N.A.--Waverly, Inc., Baltimore, MD; *U.S. Public*, pg. 1748
Thies, Steve, Pres.- Automotive Aftermarkets--Dayco Products Inc., Miamisburg, OH; *U.S. Public*, pg. 1045
Thom, Preston, Pres.--Comdisco Canada Ltd., Montreal, Canada; *U.S. Public*, pg. 408
Thoma, Walter, Pres.-Philip Morris European Union--Philip Morris International Inc., Rye Brook, NY; *U.S. Public*, pg. 1289
Thomas, Larry R., Pres.-MK Centennial--Morrison Knudsen Corp.-Engineering & Construction, Cleveland, OH; *U.S. Public*, pg. 1134
Thomas, Leo J., Exec. V.P. & Pres.-Imaging Grp.--Scientific Imaging Systems, New Haven, CT; *U.S. Public*, pg. 550
Thomas, Roger, Pres.-Strategic Mktg. Services--Total Research Corporation, Princeton, NJ; *U.S. Public*, pg. 1625
Thompson, David, Pres.-Value City Furniture--Schottenstein Stores Corporation, Columbus, OH; *U.S. Private*, pg. 972
Thompson, David J., Pres.-GWI Properties Inc.--The Great-West Life Assurance Company, Winnipeg, Canada; *Int'l*, pg. 557
Thompson, Evan C., Pres.-Television Div.--Chris-Craft Industries, Inc., New York, NY; *U.S. Public*, pg. 351
Thompson, Jane J., Pres.-Home Svcs.--Sears, Roebuck and Co., Hoffman Estates, IL; *U.S. Public*, pg. 1452
Thompson, Richard L., Grp. Pres.--Caterpillar Inc., Peoria, IL; *U.S. Public*, pg. 315
Thompson, Thomas C., Pres.-Bus. Info.--Phillips Publishing International, Inc., Potomac, MD; *U.S. Private*, pg. 862
Thonet, John A., Pres.-Thonet Assoc.--Herley Industries, Inc., Lancaster, PA; *U.S. Public*, pg. 811
Thorell, Algot F., Jr., Sr. V.P. & Pres.-Chestnut Hill National Bank Div.--National Penn Bank, Boyertown, PA; *U.S. Public*, pg. 1159
Thorne, Oakleigh B., Pres. & Chief Exec. Officer--CCH Incorporated, Riverwoods, IL; *Int'l*, pg. 1513
Thorsteinson, Timothy E., Pres.-Video & Networking--Tektronix, Inc., Wilsonville, OR; *U.S. Public*, pg. 1567
Thrasher, F. Martin, Pres.-Intl. Grocery--Campbell Soup Company, Camden, NJ; *U.S. Public*, pg. 298
Tiefel, William R., Exec. V.P. & Pres.-Marriott Lodging Grp.--Marriott International, Inc., Washington, DC; *U.S. Public*, pg. 1047
Tiefel, William R., Pres.-Marriott Lodging Grp. & Exec. V.P.--Fairfield Inn, Washington, DC; *U.S. Public*, pg. 1048
Tighe, Jim, Pres.-Marketreach--J. Brown/LMC Group, Stamford, CT; *U.S. Public*, pg. 764
Tilghman, Richard H., Pres.-Pepper Environ. Tech.& Sr. V.P.--The Pepper Companies, Inc., Chicago, IL; *U.S. Private*, pg. 851
Tillema, Janice M., Pres.-Community Trust Deed Services--CVB Financial Corp., Ontario, CA; *U.S. Public*, pg. 286
Tilton, Glenn F., Pres.-Global Bus. & Sr. V.P.--Texaco Inc., White Plains, NY; *U.S. Public*, pg. 1582
Timbers, Stephen B., Pres.-Northern Trust Global Investments--Northern Trust Corporation, Chicago, IL; *U.S. Public*, pg. 1195
Tinsley, J. David, Grp. V.P. & Pres.-Water & Waste Treatment Div.--Nalco Chemical Company, Naperville, IL; *U.S. Public*, pg. 1150
Tobias, Kal, Pres.-DHL Canada--DHL International Express Ltd., Mississauga, Canada; *U.S. Private*, pg. 302
Todman, Michael, V.P. & Pres.-Product Teams NAAG--Whirlpool Corporation, Benton Harbor, MI; *U.S. Public*, pg. 1764
Tokuyama, Goro, V.P., Reg. Pres.-Far East North & Pres.-Molex-Japan Co., Ltd.--Molex Incorporated, Lisle, IL; *U.S. Public*, pg. 1121
Tolensky, Steven M., Pres.-Men's & Intl. Divisions--Jockey International, Inc., Kenosha, WI; *U.S. Private*, pg. 588
Tolworthy, Thomas A., Pres.-Barnes & Noble Superstores, Inc.& Exec. V.P--Barnes & Noble Inc., New York, NY; *U.S. Public*, pg. 189
Toohey, Jim, Pres.-Hallmark Intl.--Hallmark Cards, Inc., Kansas City, MO; *U.S. Private*, pg. 495
Tookes, Hansel E., Pres.-Large Military Engines--Pratt & Whitney Operations, East Hartford, CT; *U.S. Public*, pg. 1690
Toole, David G., Pres.-White Paper Grp.--Avenor, Inc., Montreal, Canada; *Int'l*, pg. 101
Townsend, Theodore N., Pres.-Intl.--Badger Meter, Inc., Milwaukee, WI; *U.S. Public*, pg. 164
Toyoda, Masahiro, Dep. Pres.--Daido Hoxan Inc., Tokyo, Japan; *Int'l*, pg. 363
Tracy, Larry, Pres.-Intl. Radionics, Inc.--Detection Systems, Inc., Fairport, NY; *U.S. Public*, pg. 501
Tracy, Toni, V.P.-Publisher Rels. & Pres.-Medical Division--Franklin Electronic Publishers, Inc., Burlington, NJ; *U.S. Public*, pg. 679
Trahan, Jay P., V.P. & Pres.-Baker Hughes Solutions--Baker Hughes Incorporated, Houston, TX; *U.S. Public*, pg. 165
Tralies, Philip, Pres.--Jacobsen Textron, Racine, WI; *U.S. Public*, pg. 1589
Trapp, Robert J., Pres.-Southern California Opers.--J.M. Peters Co., Newport Beach, CA; *U.S. Public*, pg. 302
Travis, R. Neal, State Pres.-Alabama--BellSouth Telecommunications, Inc., Atlanta, GA; *U.S. Public*, pg. 209
Tremblay, John F., Exec. V.P. & Pres.-Bank of Mid-Jersey--B.M.J. Financial Corp., Bordentown, NJ; *U.S. Public*, pg. 1528
Trias, Jennie, Pres.-Children's Programming--ABC Television Network, New York, NY; *U.S. Public*, pg. 511
Tridle, David, Chief Oper. Officer--Frankel & Company, Chicago, IL; *U.S. Private*, pg. 424
Triplett, Dennis L., Pres.-South Banking Region--United Missouri Bank N.A., Kansas City, MO; *U.S. Public*, pg. 1654
Trogen, Karl-Erling, Pres.-Volvo Truck Corp.--AB Volvo, Goteborg, Sweden; *Int'l*, pg. 1476
Trotter, Thomas R., Pres.-Critical Care--Mallinckrodt Inc., Saint Louis, MO; *U.S. Public*, pg. 1039
Truderung, Harry, Pres.-TELUS Mobility--Telus Corporation, Edmonton, Canada; *Int'l*, pg. 1374
Trujillo, Sol, Pres. & Chief Exec. Officer--U S West Communications Group, Inc., Englewood, CO; *U.S. Public*, pg. 1689
Tsai, Ken, Sr. V.P. & Pres.-Solectron Asia--Solectron Corporation, Milpitas, CA; *U.S. Public*, pg. 1483
Tsakos, Andy, Pres.-Construction Grp.--Gibraltar Steel Corp., Buffalo, NY; *U.S. Public*, pg. 742
Tucker, Brian, Pres.-Intl. Opers.--Bozell Worldwide, Inc., New York, NY; *U.S. Public*, pg. 1642
Tucker, F. Byron, Pres.-Lighthouse Studios--Eisner & Associates, Inc., Baltimore, MD; *U.S. Private*, pg. 366

Tucker, Richard B.C., Jr., Pres.-Unifoam Div. & Exec. V.P.--Wm. T. Burnett & Co., Inc., Baltimore, MD; *U.S. Private*, pg. 186

Turgeon, Robert, Pres.--Trans Quebec & Maritimes Pipeline, Montreal, Canada; *Int'l*, pg. 1417

Twiner, Don, Pres.-Consumer Foods--International Multifoods Corporation, Minneapolis, MN; *U.S. Public*, pg. 900

Twyver, David A., Pres.-Wireless Systems & Sr. V.P.--Northern Telecom Limited, Brampton, Canada; *Int'l*, pg. 968

Tylka, Patrick, Pres.-Worldwide Sls.--Scientific-Atlanta, Inc., Norcross, GA; *U.S. Public*, pg. 1443

Uhrich, Carole, Exec. V.P. & Pres.-Commercial Imaging Grp.--Polaroid Corporation, Cambridge, MA; *U.S. Public*, pg. 1313

Ulbrich, Frederick C., III, Pres.-Service Ctr. Grp.--Ulbrich Stainless Steels & Special Metals, Inc., North Haven, CT; *U.S. Private*, pg. 1115

Uller, Frank, Pres.-Automatic Div.--Gage Marketing Group, Minneapolis, MN; *U.S. Private*, pg. 437

Ullman, S. Peter, V.P. & Pres.-Harris Calorific Div.--The Lincoln Electric Company, Cleveland, OH; *U.S. Public*, pg. 996

Ulug, Tunc, Pres.-Foreign Trade Grp.--Koc Holding A.S., Istanbul, Turkey; *Int'l*, pg. 741

Umans, Craig, Pres.-RHC Spacemaster & Chief Oper. Officer--RHC/Spacemaster Corporation, Melrose Park, IL; *U.S. Private*, pg. 904

Upton, Donald, Pres.-Worldwide Services--Scientific-Atlanta, Inc., Norcross, GA; *U.S. Public*, pg. 1443

Urbanic, Joseph, Pres.-Northern Div.--Centimark Corporation, Canonsburg, PA; *U.S. Private*, pg. 222

Urdi, John, Pres.-Mktg.--Attitash Bear Peak, Bartlett, NH; *U.S. Private*, pg. 61

Urrutia, J., Pres.-Latin American Opers.--Hunter Douglas N.V., Rotterdam, Netherlands; *Int'l*, pg. 639

Urso, R.J., Pres. & V.P.-Plastics Div.--The Budd Company, Troy, MI; *Int'l*, pg. 1388

Usilton, Jim, Pres.-Performance Polymers--Ciba Specialty Chemicals, Tarrytown, NY; *Int'l*, pg. 291

Ussery, Joan, Pres.-Doncaster Div.--Tanner Co., Rutherfordton, NC; *U.S. Private*, pg. 1068

Valentini, Robert M., Pres. & Chief Exec. Officer-Bell Atlantic Pennsylvania, Inc.--Bell Atlantic Corporation, New York, NY; *U.S. Public*, pg. 201

Valhos, Dean, Pres.--Champps Entertainment, Inc., Wayzata, MN; *Int'l*, pg. 325

Valkenaar, Lee, Pres.-Southwest Region--Whole Foods Market, Inc., Austin, TX; *U.S. Public*, pg. 1767

Van Cullens, E., Pres.-Commun. Sector--Harris Corporation, Melbourne, FL; *U.S. Public*, pg. 791

van Cuylenburg, Peter, Pres. & Gen. Mgr.-Specialty Storage Prods. Grp.--Quantum Corporation, Milpitas, CA; *U.S. Public*, pg. 1350

van Dalen, C. H., Pres.-Polyethylenes--DSM N.V., Heerlen, Netherlands; *Int'l*, pg. 352

van den Bergh, Frederick, V.P. & Pres.-Europe--The Black & Decker Corporation, Towson, MD; *U.S. Public*, pg. 233

van der Veer, J., Pres.-Shell Chemical Co.--Shell Oil Company, Houston, TX; *Int'l*, pg. 1136

van Heek, G. Jan, V.P. & Pres.-Therapeutics Divison--Genzyme Corporation, Cambridge, MA; *U.S. Public*, pg. 733

van Heemstra, Andre, Pres.-South East Asia & Australasia--Unilever Plc, London, United Kingdom; *Int'l*, pg. 1433

Van Houten, G. David, Jr., Sr. V.P. & Pres.-Central Grp.--Coca-Cola Enterprises Inc., Atlanta, GA; *U.S. Public*, pg. 393

van Oostrom, Richard M., Pres.-Europe, Middle East & Africa--Guidant Corporation, Indianapolis, IN; *U.S. Public*, *pg. 768*

Van Oostrum, Bert, V.P. & Pres.-Sun International--Sun Electric, Lincolnshire, IL; *U.S. Public*, pg. 1480

Van Patten, Robert M., Pres.-Agribusiness Div.--IMC Agribusiness, Collinsville, IL; *U.S. Public*, pg. 856

van Vuuren, Jeremiah J.J., Pres.-Intl.--Wang Laboratories, Inc., Billerica, MA; *U.S. Public*, pg. 1737

Van Zandt, Russell, V.P. & Pres.-InterVascular, Inc.--Datascope Corp., Montvale, NJ; *U.S. Public*, pg. 487

VanBuskirk, David, Pres.-Catalina Mktg. Intl.--Catalina Marketing Corporation, Saint Petersburg, FL; *U.S. Public*, *pg. 314*

Vandenberg, N. Allen, Pres.-Comml. Grp.--The Lehigh Press, Inc., Cherry Hill, NJ; *U.S. Private*, pg. 658

VandenBergh, Albertus J., Pres.-European, Middle East & Africa Opers.--Eli Lilly and Company, Indianapolis, IN; *U.S. Public*, pg. 992

Vander Heyden, William H., Pres. Indus. Div.--Badger Meter, Inc., Milwaukee, WI; *U.S. Public*, pg. 164

Vandiver, F. William, Pres.-Global Finance--NationsBank Corporation, Charlotte, NC; *U.S. Public*, pg. 1162

Varner, Ted, Pres. & Chief Oper. Officer-Convenience Store Distr.--Marsh Supermarkets, Inc., Indianapolis, IN; *U.S. Public*, pg. 1049

Vassalluzzo, Joseph S., Pres.-Staples Realty--Staples, Inc., Westborough, MA; *U.S. Public*, pg. 1509

Vaughan, James W., Jr., Pres.-NUS Div.--Brown & Root Power & Mfg., Houston, TX; *U.S. Public*, pg. 775

Vaughn, John, Pres.-Tellabs Intl.--Tellabs Operations, Inc., Lisle, IL; *U.S. Public*, pg. 1572

Vaughn, Stuart F., Mng. Dir.-NC--Scott & Stringfellow, Inc., Richmond, VA; *U.S. Public*, pg. 1445

Vaught, John C., Pres.-Stainless & Specialty Steels Div.--Republic Engineered Steels, Inc., Massillon, OH; *U.S. Public*, pg. 1378

Veerjee, Nooruddin, Pres.-Transamerica Asset Management--Transamerica Life Companies, Los Angeles, CA; *U.S. Public*, pg. 1630

Vegas, Pete, Pres.-Comet Rice Ingredients--Comet Ventures, Inc., Los Angeles, CA; *U.S. Public*, pg. 591

Veitch, Arthur J., V.P. & Pres.-Land Systems--General Dynamics Corporation, Falls Church, VA; *U.S. Public*, pg. 708

Velasquez, Carlos, Pres.-Intl. Bus. Devel.--Colgate-Palmolive Company, New York, NY; *U.S. Public*, pg. 397

Venderbos, D. J., Pres.-Fine Chemicals--DSM N.V., Heerlen, Netherlands; *Int'l*, pg. 352

Vermylen, David, Pres.-Keebler Brands--Keebler Company, Elmhurst, IL; *U.S. Public*, pg. 657

Verstegen, J.D.M., Pres.-Agro--DSM N.V., Heerlen, Netherlands; *Int'l*, pg. 352

Vertucci, Lawrence, Exec. V.P. & Capital Reg. Pres.--Marine Midland Bank, Buffalo, NY; *Int'l*, pg. 581

Vetal, Bradley S., Pres.-Matrix Services, Inc.--Matrix Service Company, Tulsa, OK; *U.S. Public*, pg. 1057

Veuger, Fred, Pres.-Indus. Tech. Grp.--CAE Inc., Toronto, Canada; *Int'l*, pg. 237

Vezeau, Claude, Dr., Pres.-IAF BioVac Inc.--BioChem Pharma Inc., Laval, Canada; *Int'l*, pg. 196

Viarengo, Robert P., Pres.-Perf. Mtls.--AlliedSignal Inc., Engineered Materials, Morristown, NJ; *U.S. Public*, pg. 51

Viault, Raymond G., Pres. & Chief Exec. Officer-Kraft Jacobs Suchard--Kraft Foods International, Rye Brook, NY; *U.S. Public*, pg. 1288

Villa, Carlos, Pres.-Southern Div.--Prudential Metal Supply Corp., East Dedham, MA; *U.S. Private*, pg. 893

Villante, Richard, Pres.-Allied Communication Group--The Interpublic Group of Companies, Inc., New York, NY; *U.S. Public*, pg. 908

Villarreal L., Marcelino, Pres.-Flat Galss Div.--Vitro, Sociedad Anonima, Garza Garcia, Mexico; *Int'l*, pg. 1469

Vincent, Stephen W., Pres.--Columbia Analytical Services, Inc., Kelso, WA; *U.S. Public*, pg. 571

Vitale, David J., Vice Chm. & Pres.-First National Bank of Chicago--First Chicago NBD Corporation, Chicago, IL; *U.S. Public*, pg. 627

Vitulli, Clark, Sr. V.P. & Pres.-OMC Boat Group--Outboard Marine Corporation, Waukegan, IL; *U.S. Private*, pg. 478

Vivian, David J., Pres.-RMC West Div.--Rochester Midland Corporation, Rochester, NY; *U.S. Private*, pg. 937

Voelkert, Joel, Pres.-Construction Products Group of ABC--American Buildings Co., Eufaula, AL; *U.S. Public*, pg. 69

Voraz, Philippe, Pres.-Food & Mngmt. Service/South American Opers.--Sodexho S.A., Montigny-le-Bretonneux, France; *Int'l*, pg. 1274

Vos, Arend W.D., Pres.-PPG Asia/Pacific & V.P.-Coatings/Asia Pacific--PPG Industries, Inc., Pittsburgh, PA; *U.S. Public*, pg. 1245

Votaw, Timothy, Pres.-Americas Sls. & Sr. Dir.-Channel Sls.--Iomega Corporation, Roy, UT; *U.S. Public*, pg. 912

Vowell, J. Larry, Corp. V.P., Pres. & Chief Exec. Officer-Hussmann Corp.--Whitman Corporation, Rolling Meadows, IL; *U.S. Public*, pg. 1766

Waddell, W.H., Pres.-CN Exploration Inc.--Canadian National Railway Company, Montreal, Canada; *Int'l*, pg. 258

Wagner, Robert J., Pres.-UAM Shareholder Service Center, Inc.--United Asset Management Corporation, Boston, MA; *U.S. Public*, pg. 1672

Wagoner, G. Richard, Jr., Exec. V.P. & Pres. N. American Opers.--General Motors Corporation, Detroit, MI; *U.S. Public*, pg. 718

Waguespack, Raymond L., Pres.--Bancomm, Anaheim, CA; *U.S. Public*, pg. 488

Walborsku, Eric, Pres.-Chem Fleur Co.--Firmenich Incorporated, Plainsboro, NJ; *Int'l*, pg. 486

Walcot, Donald T., Pres.--Sun Life of Canada Investment Management Limited, Toronto, Canada; *Int'l*, pg. 1319

Waldo, Dana E., Pres.-AEP West Virginia--American Electric Power Company, Inc., Columbus, OH; *U.S. Public*, pg. 71

Walker, Cecil L., Pres.-Broadcasting Div.--Gannett Company, Inc., Arlington, VA; *U.S. Public*, pg. 698

Walker, Norman C., Exec. V.P. & Pres.-Intl.--Hasbro, Inc., Pawtucket, RI; *U.S. Public*, pg. 797

Walker, Ronald E., Pres.-Captain D's--Shoney's, Inc., Nashville, TN; *U.S. Public*, pg. 1467

Walker, Stephen, Pres.-Business Forms & Systems Canada--Moore Corporation Limited, Toronto, Canada; *Int'l*, pg. 888

Walker, Thomas K., Pres.-Amcast Automotive--Amcast Industrial Corporation, Dayton, OH; *U.S. Public*, pg. 63

Wall, Douglas J., V.P. & Pres.-Hughes Christensen Company--Baker Hughes Incorporated, Houston, TX; *U.S. Public*, pg. 165

Wall, James, Sr. V.P. & Pres.-AMREP Southwest, Inc.--AMREP Corporation, New York, NY; *U.S. Public*, pg. 104

Wallace, J. Keith, Pres. & Chief Exec. Officer-Showboat Indiana, Inc.--Showboat, Incorporated, Las Vegas, NV; *U.S. Public*, pg. 1469

Wallace, Roger, Sr. V.P. & Co-Pres.-Ag. Svcs.--Data Transmission Network Corporation, Omaha, NE; *U.S. Public*, pg. 486

Walnes, Jack R., Pres.-Varity Zecal--LucasVarity Inc., Buffalo, NY; *Int'l*, pg. 820

Walpole, Robert H., Reg. Pres.-Asia Pacific--Walbro Corporation, Cass City, MI; *U.S. Public*, pg. 1733

Walsh, Philip J., Pres.-N. Opers. & CA. Opers.--U.S. Home Corporation, Houston, TX; *U.S. Public*, pg. 1682

Walter, John F., Pres.-Constellation Power--Constellation Holdings, Inc., Baltimore, MD; *U.S. Public*, pg. 172

Walton, Al, Pres.-Los Angeles Editel Div.--Unitel Video, Inc., New York, NY; *U.S. Public*, pg. 1692

Ward, Jonathan, Grp. Pres.--R.R. Donnelley & Sons Company, Chicago, IL; *U.S. Public*, pg. 517

Ward, Lawrence C., Pres.-North American Reg.--Walbro Corporation, Cass City, MI; *U.S. Public*, pg. 1733

Ware, Carl, Pres.-Africa Grp.--The Coca-Cola Company, Atlanta, GA; *U.S. Public*, pg. 392

Warner, Jack, Pres.-Kerry Ingredients U.S.--Kerry Group PLC, Tralee, Ireland; *Int'l*, pg. 731

Warner, James, Pres.-Magazine Grp.--Primedia Inc., New York, NY; *U.S. Public*, pg. 1327

Warren, Anthony J., Pres.-Illinois National Insurance Co.--American International Group, Inc., New York, NY; *U.S. Public*, pg. 83

Warren, Roger F., Pres.-Intl. Micro Power--RAYOVAC Corporation, Madison, WI; *U.S. Private*, pg. 912

Warrington, George, Acting Chm. Bd., Pres. & Chief Exec. Officer--Amtrak-National Railroad Passenger Corp., Washington, DC; *U.S. Private*, pg. 68

Washburn, Don, Exec. V.P.-Flight Opers. & Pres./Northwest Cargo--Northwest Airlines, Inc., Saint Paul, MN; *U.S. Public*, pg. 1200

Wassen, W. J., Pres.-Engineering Plastic Products--DSM N.V., Heerlen, Netherlands; *Int'l*, pg. 352

Waterman, Jack, Pres.-Worldwide Pay Television--Paramount Pictures Corporation, Los Angeles, CA; *U.S. Private*, pg. 776

Waters, William J., Jr., Pres.-World & Zenith Sls. Div.--World Carpets, Inc., Dalton, GA; *U.S. Private*, pg. 1190

Watkins, Glenn G., V.P. & Pres.-Adult Women's Medical Div.--IntegraMed America, Purchase, NY; *U.S. Public*, pg. 883

Watkins, Jay, III, Pres.-Minimally Invasive Sys. Grp.--Guidant Corporation, Indianapolis, IN; *U.S. Public*, pg. 768

Watson, David, Grp. Pres.-ICF Kaiser Engineers & Constructors Grp. & Exec. V.P.--ICF Kaiser International Inc., Fairfax, VA; *U.S. Public*, pg. 852

Watson, David N., Sr. V.P. & Pres.-Comcast Cellular Communications--Comcast Corporation, Philadelphia, PA; *U.S. Public*, pg. 406

Watson, Gary L., Pres.-Newspaper Div.--Gannett Company, Inc., Arlington, VA; *U.S. Public*, pg. 698

Watson, Gordon R., Pres.-Fidelity Brokerage Grp.--Fidelity Investments (FMR Corp.), Boston, MA; *U.S. Private*, pg. 402

Watts, Lawrence L., Pres.-Kaiser Intl.--Kaiser Aluminum & Chemical Corporation, Pleasanton, CA; *U.S. Public*, pg. 1062

Watzl, Edward L., Pres.-NSP Generation--Northern States Power Company, Minneapolis, MN; *U.S. Public*, pg. 1195

Waxman, Hy, Pres.-Sys. Integration Div.--Systems & Computer Technology Corporation, Malvern, PA; *U.S. Public*, pg. 1552

Waxman, Laurance, Sr. V.P. & Pres.-Waxman Consumer Prods.--WOC Inc., Bedford, OH; *U.S. Public*, pg. 1748

Waxman, Laurance, Sr. V.P. & Pres.-Waxman Consumer Prods.--Waxman USA Inc., Bedford, OH; *U.S. Public*, pg. 1749

Waye, Ron W., Pres.-Rentway--Trimac Corporation, Calgary, Canada; *Int'l*, pg. 1423

Weadock, Daniel P., Sr. V.P.-Hotels & Pres.-ITT Sheraton Corporation--ITT Corporation, New York, NY; *U.S. Public*, *pg. 1512*

Wears, James A., Pres.-Northern Reg.--Community Bank N.A., De Witt, NY; *U.S. Public*, pg. 416

Wearsch, E.A., Pres.-Consumer Paints--ICI Paints, Cleveland, OH; *Int'l*, pg. 664

Weaver, John, Exec. V.P. & Pres.-Newsprint Opers. & Sls.--Abitibi-Consolidated Inc., Montreal, Canada; *Int'l*, pg. 19

Webb, Barry, Pres.-Daniel Measurement & Control, Eastern Hemisphere--Daniel Industries, Inc., Houston, TX; *U.S. Public*, pg. 482

Webb, Reginald, Pres.-Datametrics Systems Corp.--Zitel Corporation, Fremont, CA; *U.S. Public*, pg. 1793

Weber, John H., Exec. V.P. & Pres.-Vickers, Incorporated--Aeroquip-Vickers, Inc., Maumee, OH; *U.S. Public*, pg. 24

Wedaman, David H., Chief Oper. Officer, Exec. V.P. & Pres.-Mark VII Transportation--Mark VII, Inc., Memphis, TN; *U.S. Public*, pg. 1046

Weg, Kenneth E., Exec. V.P. & Pres.-Worldwide Medicines Grp.--Bristol-Myers Squibb Company, New York, NY; *U.S. Public*, pg. 253

Wehlitz, George W., Jr., Pres.-Bombay Canada--The Bombay Company, Inc., Fort Worth, TX; *U.S. Public*, pg. 244

Wehlitz, George, Jr., Pres.-Bombay Canada--The Bombay Company, Fort Worth, TX; *U.S. Public*, pg. 244

Weida, Gregg R., V.P. & Pres.-Penn Racquet Sports Div.--GenCorp Inc., Fairlawn, OH; *U.S. Public*, pg. 705

Weiden, Michael, Pres.-Adv. Sls.--All American Television, Inc., New York, NY; *U.S. Public*, pg. 41

Weiland, John H., Grp. Pres.--C.R. Bard, Inc., Murray Hill, NJ; *U.S. Public*, pg. 189

Weiler, Robert K., Sr. V.P. & Pres.-Software--Wang Laboratories, Inc., Billerica, MA; *U.S. Public*, pg. 1737

Weinert, Eileen, Pres.-Media Wise--Gleason/Calise/Associates, Inc., Dallas, TX; *U.S. Private*, pg. 455

Weinstein, Jerry L., V.P. & Pres.-Exterior Sys.--Owens Corning, Toledo, OH; *U.S. Public*, pg. 1236

Weisbarth, Jake, Pres.-King World Direct--King World Productions, Inc., New York, NY; *U.S. Public*, pg. 961

Weiss, Albrecht, Pres.-Prods.--Home and Building Control, Minneapolis, MN; *U.S. Public*, pg. 833

Weisskopf, Markus, Co-Pres.-Swiss Div.--The Swiss Life/Rentenanstalt Group, Zurich, Switzerland; *Int'l*, pg. 1332

Weiswasser, Stephen A., Pres.-Capital Cities/ABC Media Grp., Sr. V.P. & Gen. Counsel--ABC, Inc, New York, NY; *U.S. Public*, pg. 511

Weitzen, Stephen, Pres.-Golden Value Books & Special Markets--Golden Books Family Entertainment Inc., New York, NY; *U.S. Public*, pg. 749

Welch, John K., V.P. & Pres.-Electric Boat--General Dynamics Corporation, Falls Church, VA; *U.S. Public*, pg. 708

Weller, Craig, Pres.-Texas Health Distributors--Whole Foods Market, Inc., Austin, TX; *U.S. Public*, pg. 1767

Wells, Thomas J., V.P.-Mfg. & Pres.-Machine & Tool Div.--Leggett & Platt, Incorporated, Carthage, MO; *U.S. Public*, *pg. 985*

Welp, David, Pres.-Raytheon TI Systems & Sr. V.P.--Raytheon TI Systems, Lewisville, TX; *U.S. Public*, pg. 1365

Welsh, Cathy L., Pres.-Tech. Mngmt. Div.--Systems & Computer Technology Corporation, Malvern, PA; *U.S. Public*, pg. 1552

Wenger, Robert, Pres.--ENVIRON International, Arlington, VA; *U.S. Public*, pg. 1285

Wenzel, Robert J., Pres.-LaserMaster Corp. & Chief Oper. Officer--LaserMaster Technologies, Inc., Eden Prairie, MN; *U.S. Public*, pg. 979

Werner, Hermann R., Exec. V.P. & Pres.-Fibers, Organics & Rubber Div.--Bayer Corporation, Parsippany, NJ; *Int'l*, pg. 172

Werner, Richard A., Pres.-Smith Drilling And Completions--Smith International, Inc., Houston, TX; *U.S. Public*, pg. 1478

Werrell, Terry S., Pres.-Industrial Prod. Division--Cambridge Industries Inc., Madison Heights, MI; *U.S. Private*, pg. 202

West, Dan L., Pres.-Hush Puppies Intl.--Wolverine World Wide, Inc., Rockford, MI; *U.S. Public*, pg. 1775

West, Randall E., Pres.--Axis Group, Decatur, GA; *U.S. Public*, pg. 48

Westerberg, L. John, Grp. V.P. & Pres.-North Amer. Pasta Prods.--Borden, Inc., Columbus, OH; *U.S. Private*, pg. 157

Westlake, Blair, Pres.-Unviersal Pay Television & Television Bus. Devel.--Universal Studios TV, Universal City, CA; *Int'l*, pg. 1215

Weyne, Angela, Pres.--Caribbean American Life Assurance Company, Hato Rey, PR; *U.S. Public*, pg. 67

Whalen, David G., Pres.-N. American Eyewear--Bausch & Lomb Incorporated, Rochester, NY; *U.S. Public*, pg. 194

Whalen, Edward J., Pres.-JAIX Leasing Co.--Johnstown America Industries, Chicago, IL; *U.S. Public*, pg. 933

Wheeler, Jonathan R., Exec. V.P. & Pres.-CT Film--Rexene Corporation, Dallas, TX; *U.S. Private*, pg. 549

Wheeler, Robert C., Pres.-Hill's Pet Prods.--Colgate-Palmolive Company, New York, NY; *U.S. Public*, pg. 397

Whelan, J. Douglas, Pres.-Forgings Div.--Wyman-Gordon, North Grafton, MA; *U.S. Public*, pg. 1782

Whelehan, Kathleen, Exec. V.P. & Rochester Reg. Pres.--Marine Midland Bank, Buffalo, NY; *Int'l*, pg. 581

Whitby, Robert, Pres.-Americas--Proudfoot plc, Richmond, United Kingdom; *Int'l*, pg. 1071

Whitcher, Geoffrey A., Pres.-Fletcher Challenge Industries--Fletcher Challenge Limited, Auckland, New Zealand; *Int'l*, pg. 494

White, Creighton, Pres-Healthcare Div.--Getinge/Castle Inc., Rochester, NY; *Int'l*, pg. 551

White, David R., Pres.-America Grp.--Columbia/HCA Healthcare Corporation, Nashville, TN; *U.S. Public*, pg. 403

White, John, Pres.-Columbia Div.--Thomas & Howard Co., Columbia, SC; *U.S. Private*, pg. 1081

White, Marshall, Jr., Pres.-Consumer Div.--Ciba Specialty Chemicals, Tarrytown, NY; *Int'l*, pg. 291

White, Ph. D., Richard L., Exec. V.P. & Pres.-Fibers, Organics & Rubber Division--Bayer Corporation, Pittsburgh, PA; *Int'l*, pg. 172

White, Reed, Pres.--Dura Convertible Systems, Inc., Adrian, MI; *U.S. Public*, pg. 399

White, Richard L., Pres.-Fibers, Organics & Rubber Div. & Exec. V.P.--Bayer Corporation, Pittsburgh, PA; *Int'l*, pg. 172

White, Thomas W., Pres.-Telephone Opers.--GTE Corporation, Stamford, CT; *U.S. Public*, pg. 696

Whitehead, Richard H., III, Reg. Pres.--Walbro Corporation, Cass City, MI; *U.S. Public*, pg. 1733

Whiteley, Sharon, Pres.-Creative Svcs.--Contempo Colors, Kalamazoo, MI; *U.S. Private*, pg. 267

Whitley, Douglas L., Pres.-Ameritech Illinois--Ameritech Corporation, Chicago, IL; *U.S. Public*, pg. 97

Whitlock, A. James, Pres.-Retail Prods. Div.--Ontario Foods, Inc., Albion, NY; *U.S. Public*, pg. 728

Whitlock, Janice L., Pres.-Dyersburg Mktg.--Dyersburg Corporation, Dyersburg, TN; *U.S. Public*, pg. 538

Whittaker, Bob, Pres.-Grand Ole Opry Grp.--Gaylord Entertainment Co., Nashville, TN; *U.S. Public*, pg. 704

Wiaderek, Slawomir, Pres.--EMTEC Magnetics Polska Sp. z.o.o., Warsaw, Poland; *Int'l*, pg. 743

Widdis, William J., Pres.-Leather Div.--Wolverine World Wide, Inc., Rockford, MI; *U.S. Public*, pg. 1775

Wiggenhorn, A. William, Sr. V.P. & Pres.-Motorola University--Motorola, Inc., Schaumburg, IL; *U.S. Public*, pg. 1136

Wiggins, Dwight L., Exec. V.P. & Pres.-Tosco Refining Co.--Tosco Corporation, Stamford, CT; *U.S. Public*, pg. 1624

Wilcauskas, Eugene, Pres. & Chief Oper. Officer-Special Prods. Div.--Church & Dwight Co., Inc., Princeton, NJ; *U.S. Public*, pg. 355

Wilcox, Denis G., Grp. Pres.--Mercantile Bank of Iowa, Des Moines, IA; *U.S. Public*, pg. 1087

Wild, Anthony, Pres.-Pharmaceutical Sector--Warner-Lambert Company, Morris Plains, NJ; *U.S. Public*, pg. 1738

Wild, Anthony H., Pres. & V.P.-Pharmaceutical Sector--Parke-Davis Group, Morris Plains, NJ; *U.S. Public*, pg. 1739

Wiley, G. Martin, Pres.-Pacific Region--Loctite Corporation, Rocky Hill, CT; *Int'l*, pg. 611

Wilfong, A. Scott, Pres.-Maryland Region--Crestar Financial Corporation, Richmond, VA; *U.S. Public*, pg. 458

Wilhelm, Paul J., Pres.-U.S. Steel Grp.--USX Corporation, Pittsburgh, PA; *U.S. Public*, pg. 1661

Wilhelm, Paul J., Pres.-U.S. Steel Grp.--U.S. Steel International, Inc., Pittsburgh, PA; *U.S. Public*, pg. 1661

Wilkens, Horace, Jr., Pres.-MO--Southwestern Bell Telephone Co., Saint Louis, MO; *U.S. Public*, pg. 1416

Wilkey, Jerry B., V.P. & Pres.-Aluminum Prods.--Leggett & Platt, Incorporated, Carthage, MO; *U.S. Public*, pg. 985

Wilkey, Jerry B., Pres.-Aluminum Prods.--Pace Industries, Inc., Fayetteville, AR; *U.S. Public*, pg. 986

Wilkinson, Dave, Pres.-Color Your World (Canada)--ICI Paints, Cleveland, OH; *Int'l*, pg. 664

Wilks, David, Pres.-Mktg. & Svcs.--New Century Energies, Inc., Denver, CO; *U.S. Public*, pg. 1170

Willcox, P.J., Exec. Gen. Mgr. & Chief Exec. Officer-BHP Petroleum--The Broken Hill Proprietary Company Limited, Melbourne, Australia; *Int'l*, pg. 223

Williams, Edward D., Pres.-Strategic Outsourcing Services Inc.--Computer Horizons Corp., Mountain Lakes, NJ; *U.S. Public*, pg. 421

Williams, James, Pres. & Chief Oper. Officer-Food Service Group--Cara Operations Limited, Toronto, Canada; *Int'l*, pg. 266

Williams, Peter, Pres.--Anacomp Magnetics, Inc., Atlanta, GA; *U.S. Public*, pg. 107

Williams, Richard B., Pres. & Chief Oper. Officer--Lone Star Gas Co., Dallas, TX; *U.S. Public*, pg. 1587

Williams, Robert, Pres.-Asia Pacific--Tupperware Corporation, Orlando, FL; *U.S. Public*, pg. 1644

Williamson, Bryon, Pres.-Publishing Div.--Word, Incorporated, Dallas, TX; *U.S. Public*, pg. 704

Williamson, Byron, Pres.-Nelson Word Publishing Grp.--Thomas Nelson Inc., Nashville, TN; *U.S. Public*, pg. 1167

Williamson, Delbert L., Pres. & Reg. Exec.-Asia--G.E. Power Systems, Schenectady, NY; *U.S. Public*, pg. 711

Williamson, Guy K., Pres. & V.P.-Xomed Intl.--Xomed Surgical Products, Jacksonville, FL; *U.S. Public*, pg. 253

Willis, Geoff L., Mng. Dir.-Amcor Printing Papers Grp.--Amcor Limited, Melbourne, Australia; *Int'l*, pg. 71

Willis, John, Pres.-Raytheon Aircraft Services--Raytheon Aircraft Company, Wichita, KS; *U.S. Public*, pg. 1365

Willis, William H., Pres.-Reader's Digest Europe--The Reader's Digest Association, Inc., Pleasantville, NY; *U.S. Public*, pg. 1367

Willison, Bruce, Pres.-Home Savings & Chief Oper. Officer--H.F. Ahmanson & Co., Irwindale, CA; *U.S. Public*, pg. 29

Willow, Terry, Pres.-Apparel--Coach, New York, NY; *U.S. Public*, pg. 1433

Wilson, Alan D., V.P. & Pres.-Textile Services--Angelica Corporation, Chesterfield, MO; *U.S. Public*, pg. 113

Wilson, Barry, Pres.-Medtronic Europe, Middle East & Africa--Medtronic Europe S.A./N.V., Lausanne, Switzerland; *U.S. Public*, pg. 1083

Wilson, Barry W., Pres.-Medtronic Europe, Middle East, Africa--Medtronic, Inc., Minneapolis, MN; *U.S. Public*, pg. 1082

Wilson, David C., Pres.-Ethyl Canada--Ethyl Corporation, Richmond, VA; *U.S. Public*, pg. 595

Wilson, Debora, Pres.-US Weather Prods. & Distrib.--The Weather Channel, Atlanta, GA; *U.S. Private*, pg. 647

Wilson, E. Dave, Pres.-Americas--Hasbro, Inc., Pawtucket, RI; *U.S. Public*, pg. 797

Wilson, Joanne, Pres.-Mid-Atlantic Reg.--FPA Medical Management, Inc., San Diego, CA; *U.S. Public*, pg. 608

Wilson, John, Grp. Pres. & Chief Oper. Officer-Transportation Sys. Grp.--Amtech Corporation, Dallas, TX; *U.S. Public*, pg. 105

Wilson, John O., Pres.-Prime Group Realty Services, Inc.--Prime Group Realty Trust, Chicago, IL; *U.S. Public*, pg. 1326

Wilson, Walter W., Sr. V.P. & Pres.-Solectron Americas--Solectron Corporation, Milpitas, CA; *U.S. Public*, pg. 1483

Wilson, William T., V.P.-Commodity Trading & Risk Mngmt. & Pres.-Unocal Global Trade--Unocal Corporation, El Segundo, CA; *U.S. Public*, pg. 1698

Wiltz, James W., Pres.-Patterson Dental Supply, Inc.--Patterson Dental Company, Saint Paul, MN; *U.S. Public*, pg. 1265

Windham, Robert E., Pres.-Church St. Station--Constellation Holdings, Inc., Baltimore, MD; *U.S. Public*, pg. 172

Winebaum, Jake, Pres.-Disney On-Line--The Walt Disney Company, Burbank, CA; *U.S. Public*, pg. 511

Wingfield, Hartsell, Pres.-TCBY Intl.--TCBY Enterprises Inc., Little Rock, AR; *U.S. Public*, pg. 1553

Wingfield, Hartsell, Pres.-TCBY Intl.--TCBY Systems, Inc., Little Rock, AR; *U.S. Public*, pg. 1554

Winick, Leila, Pres.-Multicultural Grp.--Western International Media Corporation, Los Angeles, CA; *U.S. Private*, pg. 1165

Winters, Walter B., Pres.-TCBY Specialty Prods. Div.--TCBY Systems, Inc., Little Rock, AR; *U.S. Public*, pg. 1554

Wipf, Gerald L., V.P. & Pres.-Valvoline Instant Oil Change--Valvoline Company, Lexington, KY; *U.S. Public*, pg. 139

Wipff, Dan R., Pres.-Telxon Prods.--Telxon Corporation, Akron, OH; *U.S. Public*, pg. 1573

Withka, Thomas F., Pres.-Electric Energy Mktg.--KCS Energy Inc., Edison, NJ; *U.S. Public*, pg. 938

Witt, John R., Pres.-Restaurant Svcs.--Darling International, Inc, Irving, TX; *U.S. Public*, pg. 484

Witzleben, Charles, Pres.-SUPERVALU Intl.--SuperValu, Inc., Eden Prairie, MN; *U.S. Public*, pg. 1540

Woelffer, Gale, Pres.-Southwest Div.--Leslie Paper, Minneapolis, MN; *U.S. Public*, pg. 903

Wolaner, Robin, Pres.-Sunset Publishing Corp.--Time Inc., New York, NY; *U.S. Public*, pg. 1612

Wolf, Ken, Pres.-Metropolitan Resources, Inc.--H.B. Zachry, San Antonio, TX; *U.S. Private*, pg. 1203

Wolf, Linda, Grp. Pres.-North America--Leo Burnett Company, Inc., Chicago, IL; *U.S. Private*, pg. 183

Wolf, Martin D., Sr. V.P. & Pres.-Merisel FAB, Inc.--Merisel, Inc., El Segundo, CA; *U.S. Public*, pg. 1095

Wolf, Rudolph C., Pres.--Barksdale, Inc., Los Angeles, CA; *U.S. Public*, pg. 457

Wolfe, Robert, V.P. & Pres.-Aerojet--GenCorp Inc., Fairlawn, OH; *U.S. Public*, pg. 705

Wolfson, Bernardo, Pres.-Beverages, Latin America & Europe--Worldwide Quaker Beverages, Chicago, IL; *U.S. Public*, pg. 1347

Wolgemuth, Sam, Pres.-Freedom Magazine & Sr. V.P.--Freedom Communication Inc., Irvine, CA; *U.S. Private*, pg. 425

Wolpert, Michael, Grp. Pres. & Chief Oper. Officer-Cardkey Systems, Inc.--Amtech Corporation, Dallas, TX; *U.S. Public*, pg. 105

Womble, Ralph H., V.P. & Pres.-Indus. Fabrics--Leggett & Platt, Incorporated, Carthage, MO; *U.S. Public*, pg. 985

Wood, Bruce J., Pres. & Chief Exec. Officer-Nabisco Brands Ltd.--Nabisco Inc., Parsippany, NJ; *U.S. Public*, pg. 1355

Wood, Charles R., Sr. V.P. & Pres.-Fin. Svcs.--Data Transmission Network Corporation, Omaha, NE; *U.S. Public*, pg. 486

Wood, Stephen R., Pres.-Distr. Svcs. Div.--LG & E Energy Corp., Louisville, KY; *U.S. Public*, pg. 970

Woodard, James A., Pres.-Pioneer Container Div.--Weston Paper & Manufacturing Co., Terre Haute, IN; *U.S. Private*, pg. 1169

Woodard, Ronald B., Sr. V.P. & Pres.-Boeing Comml. Airplane Grp.--The Boeing Company, Seattle, WA; *U.S. Public*, pg. 239

Woodhouse, Charles F., Pres. & Chief Exec. Officer--MariFarms, Inc., Woodbridge, NJ; *Int'l*, pg. 593

Woods, Jacqueline F., Pres.-Ameritech Ohio--Ameritech Corporation, Chicago, IL; *U.S. Public*, pg. 97

Woodson, Dillard, Pres.-Intl. Div.--International Total Services, Independence, OH; *U.S. Public*, pg. 908

Woodward, Bruce P., Pres.-Preferred Resources--Lexford Residential Trust, Columbus, OH; *U.S. Public*, pg. 991

Woodward, Richard H., Jr., V.P. & Pres.-AGL Investments--AGL Resources, Atlanta, GA; *U.S. Public*, pg. 6

Wortley, Mark D., Exec. V.P.--Beverly Enterprises, Inc., Fort Smith, AR; *U.S. Public*, pg. 227

Wozniak, Charles, Pres.-Fisher Scientific Company/Safety Div.--Fisher Scientific Company, Pittsburgh, PA; *U.S. Private*, pg. 658

Wrench, W. David, Pres.--Fleck Manufacturing Inc., Tillsonburg, Canada; *Int'l*, pg. 955

Wright, Cyprian C., Pres.-American Opers.--Xerox Corporation, Stamford, CT; *U.S. Public*, pg. 1783

Wright, David, Pres.-Sls. & Mktg. Div.--Duraliner U.S.A., Lapeer, MI; *U.S. Public*, pg. 537

Wright, Frank, V.P. & Pres.-American Colloid Co.--AMCOL International Corp., Arlington Heights, IL; *U.S. Public*, pg. 63

Wright, John W., Pres.-New England Employee Benefits--The New England, Boston, MA; *U.S. Private*, pg. 737

Wright, Thomas J., Pres.-Phosphate--Potash Corporation of Saskatchewan Inc., Saskatoon, Canada; *Int'l*, pg. 1064

Wymore, Kenneth T., Pres.-Gas Service--Western Resources, Inc., Topeka, KS; *U.S. Public*, pg. 1759

Wynn, H.D., Pres.-Pump Div.--BW/IP International, Inc., Long Beach, CA; *U.S. Public*, pg. 658

Wynn, Howard D., V.P. & Pres.-Pump Div.--Flowserve Corporation, Long Beach, CA; *U.S. Public*, pg. 658

Yallop, T. Drew, Pres.-Petroleum Div.--Canadian Tire Corporation Limited, Toronto, Canada; *Int'l*, pg. 259

Yamamoto, Hisao, Deputy Pres.--The Haokkaido Takushoku Securities Co. (Sapporo), Sapporo, Japan; *Int'l*, pg. 626

Yamasaki, Toshiyuki, Pres.-Burr-Brown Japan--Burr-Brown Corporation, Tucson, AZ; *U.S. Public*, pg. 270

Yaschuk, Jim, Pres.-Gas Tech Canada--Gas Tech, Newark, CA; *U.S. Public*, pg. 1593

Yong, Sam, Pres.-Intl. & Trade Channels--Au Bon Pain Co., Inc., Boston, MA; *U.S. Public*, pg. 146

Yoshida, Fuminori, Pres.-Amgen K.K. & Corp. V.P.--Amgen Inc., Thousand Oaks, CA; *U.S. Public*, pg. 100

Yoshino, Yasuo, Deputy Pres.--Sumitomo Life Insurance Company, Osaka, Japan; *Int'l*, pg. 1315

Yost, Larry D., Pres.-Heavy Vehicle Systems--Rockwell International Corporation, Costa Mesa, CA; *U.S. Public*, pg. 1397

Younes, Rami E., Pres.-Container Div.--CCL Industries, Inc., Willowdale, Canada; *Int'l*, pg. 238

Young, David A., V.P. & Pres.-Office Components--Leggett & Platt, Incorporated, Carthage, MO; *U.S. Public*, pg. 985

Young, Edward W., Pres.-Intl., Reinsurance & Specialty Lines--The Allstate Corporation, Northbrook, IL; *U.S. Public*, pg. 55

Young, Miles, Pres.-Asia & Pacific--Ogilvy & Mather Worldwide, Inc., New York, NY; *Int'l*, pg. 1483

Young, Peter G., Pres. & Chief Oper. Officer-AAA Life Insurance Co.--American Automobile Association, Heathrow, FL; *U.S. Private*, pg. 50

Youngblood, H.L., Sr. V.P. & Pres.-Western Cement Region--Lafarge Corporation, Reston, VA; *Int'l*, pg. 788

Yuceulug, Cetin, Pres.-DiverseyLever--Unilever Plc, London, United Kingdom; *Int'l*, pg. 1433

Yuki, Masao, Exec. Deputy Pres.--The Nikko Securities Co., Ltd., Tokyo, Japan; *Int'l*, pg. 930

Zachary, John, Pres.-Indus. Grp.--H.B. Zachry, San Antonio, TX; *U.S. Private*, pg. 1203

Zadel, C. William, V.P. & Pres.-Ciba Corning Diagnostics Corp.--Chiron Corporation, Emeryville, CA; *U.S. Public*, pg. 349

Zagorski, Richard M., Pres.-Response Mktg. Services--Moore Corporation Limited, Toronto, Canada; *Int'l*, pg. 888

Zaki, Galal, Pres.--Intermarkets Egypt, Cairo, Egypt; *Int'l*, pg. 680

Zalak, Timothy F., Chief Fin. Officer, Treas. & Sec.--Multi-Local Media Corporation, Rockville Centre, NY; *U.S. Private*, pg. 767

Zaleski, Andrew B., Pres.-Trimac Transportation Systems--Trimac Corporation, Calgary, Canada; *Int'l*, pg. 1423

Zamboni, Helen, Pres.-Frontier Communications Intl. Opers.--Frontier Communications Services, Bingham Farms, MI; *U.S. Public*, pg. 684

Zander, Edward J., Pres.-Sun Microsystems Computer Co.--Sun Microsystems, Inc., Palo Alto, CA; *U.S. Public*, pg. 1531

Zandomeneggo, Giacomo, Grp. Pres.-Latin America--Leo Burnett Company, Inc., Chicago, IL; *U.S. Private*, pg. 183

Zandomenengo, Giacomo, Grp. Pres.-Latin America--Leo Burnett Worldwide, Latin American Hdqtrs., Coral Gables, FL; *U.S. Private*, pg. 184

Zaremba, James W., Pres.-Publishing Grp.--Penton Publishing, Inc., Cleveland, OH; *U.S. Public*, pg. 1306

Zatcoff, Roy, Pres.-SCT Mfg. & Distr. Sys., Inc.--Systems & Computer Technology Corporation, Malvern, PA; *U.S. Public*, pg. 1552

Zehelein, Ernst-Jorg, Pres.-Dietetics Div.--Altana AG, Bad Homburg, Germany; *Int'l*, pg. 65

Zeleski, Joe, Pres.-Carsey-Werner Distribution--Carsey-Werner Company, LLC, Studio City, CA; *U.S. Private*, pg. 216
Zerbe, Mark A., Pres.--Kent Datacomm Corp., Houston, TX; *U.S. Public*, pg. 951
Zetcher, Arnold B., Pres. & Chief Exec. Officer-The Talbots, Inc.--AEON Group, Chiba, Japan; *Int'l*, pg. 28
Ziegler, George, Div. Pres.--Ferro Union, Inc., Torrance, CA; *U.S. Private*, pg. 402
Zima, Marvin W., V.P. & Pres.-Specialty Polymers Div.--GenCorp Inc., Fairlawn, OH; *U.S. Public*, pg. 705
Zimmel, Peter, Pres.-Technics--Henkel Austria Group, Vienna, Austria; *Int'l*, pg. 611
Zimmerman, Thomas L., Pres.-H&R Block Tax Services, Inc.--H & R Block, Inc., Kansas City, MO; *U.S. Public*, pg. 770
Zoghbi, Sami, Sr. V.P. & Pres.-Africa & Middle East--ITT Sheraton Corporation, Boston, MA; *U.S. Public*, pg. 1512
Zohouri, Saeed, Ph.D., Sr. V.P., Chief Tech. Officer & Pres.-Solectron California Corp.--Solectron Corporation, Milpitas, CA; *U.S. Public*, pg. 1483
Zona, Chuck, Pres.-Men's Grp.--Salant Corporation, New York, NY; *U.S. Public*, pg. 1429
Zorn, Donald B., Grp. Pres.-Industrial & Power Equipment--Blount International, Inc., Montgomery, AL; *U.S. Public*, pg. 237
Zugel, Frank J., Pres.-Castings--Wyman-Gordon, North Grafton, MA; *U.S. Public*, pg. 1782

PUBLIC RELATIONS

Aarnio, Raoul A.R., Dir.-Press Rels.--Opel Oy, Espoo, Finland; *U.S. Public*, pg. 723
Aaronson, Morton C., Chief Mktg. Officer & V.P.--K N Energy, Inc., Lakewood, CO; *U.S. Public*, pg. 937
Abbett, Barbara A., V.P.-Communications--Mallinckrodt Inc., Saint Louis, MO; *U.S. Public*, pg. 1039
Abbot, P., Mgr.-Mktg. Commun.--Air New Zealand Ltd., Auckland, New Zealand; *Int'l*, pg. 38
Abel, Gary V., Pres.--C.R. Daniels, Inc., Ellicott City, MD; *U.S. Private*, pg. 310
Abels, Mark, V.P.-Corp. Communications--Trans World Airlines, Inc., Saint Louis, MO; *U.S. Public*, pg. 1629
Aberg, Helena, Mgr.-Pub. Rels.--Victor Hasselblad AB, Goteborg, Sweden; *Int'l*, pg. 1468
Abraham, Brenda, Communications Specialist--Honeywell Limited, North York, Canada; *U.S. Public*, pg. 835
Abram, Ted, Dir.-Pub. Rels.--Jeld-Wen, Inc., Klamath Falls, OR; *U.S. Private*, pg. 585
Abu Bakar, Datin Rosnah, Head-Human Resources--Standard Chartered Bank Malaysia Berhad, Kuala Lumpur, Malaysia; *Int'l*, pg. 1295
Acerna, Emilio, Assoc. Mgr.-Gen. Affairs & Pub. Rels.--IRI Istituto Ricostruzione Industriale, Rome, Italy; *Int'l*, pg. 652
Acker, Rolf-Dieter, Dr., Head-Adv. & Pub. Rels.--BASF AG, Ludwigshafen, Germany; *Int'l*, pg. 103
Ackerman, Stephanie C., Staff V.P.-Corp. & Govt. Affairs--Aloha Airgroup, Inc., Honolulu, HI; *U.S. Private*, pg. 44
Ackerman, Stephanie C., Staff V.P.-Corp. & Govt. Affairs--Aloha Airlines, Inc., Honolulu, HI; *U.S. Private*, pg. 44
Ackerman, Stephanie C., Mgr.-Pub. Rels.--Island Air, Honolulu, HI; *U.S. Private*, pg. 44
Adam, Olivier, Mgr.-Commun.--Aerospatiale, Paris, France; *Int'l*, pg. 28
Adamov, Robert M., V.P.-Human Resources & Investor Rels.--Corrpro Companies, Inc., Medina, OH; *U.S. Public*, pg. 451
Adams, Audrey, Dir.-Corp. Pub. Rels.--Essence Communications Inc., New York, NY; *U.S. Private*, pg. 383
Adams, Raymond T., V.P.-Corp. Commun.--DSC Communications Corporation, Plano, TX; *U.S. Public*, pg. 475
Adams, Roger, Dir.-Corp. Affairs & Special Advisor--European Investment Bank, Luxembourg, Luxembourg; *Int'l*, pg. 465
Adams, Stephen P., Mgr.-Investor Rels.--Zurn Industries, Inc., Erie, PA; *U.S. Public*, pg. 1794
Adduci, Liane, Pub. Rels. Dir.--Frankel & Company, Chicago, IL; *U.S. Private*, pg. 424
Ades, Julie-Emilie, Corp. Commun.--Havas Advertising, Levallois-Perret, France; *Int'l*, pg. 600
Adkins, Brooke, V.P.-Catalogue, Mktg. & Pub. Rels.--F.A.O. Schwarz, New York, NY; *Int'l*, pg. 750
Adkins, Pamela, Dir.-Pub. Rels.--Aramark Corporation, Philadelphia, PA; *U.S. Private*, pg. 79
Adler, David, V.P.-Corp. Communications--Primedia Inc., New York, NY; *U.S. Public*, pg. 1327
Adler, Michelle, Dir.-Communication Svcs.--Tampa Electric Co., Tampa, FL; *U.S. Public*, pg. 1565
Adler, Stephanie, Mktg. Communications Specialist--Axiom Inc., Moorestown, NJ; *U.S. Public*, pg. 157
Adolphs, Gesa, Mgr.-Pub. Rels.--Alte Leipziger Versicherung Aktiengesellschaft, Oberursel, Germany; *Int'l*, pg. 66
Agnese, Carlos E., Exec. V.P.-Bus. Devel., Mktg., Estimating & Contract Admin.--Norfolk Shipbuilding & Drydock Corporation, Norfolk, VA; *U.S. Private*, pg. 802
Agosti, Jennifer, Dir.-Mktg. Commun.--The National Super Service Co., Toledo, OH; *U.S. Private*, pg. 787
Agresta, Sue, V.P.-Newspaper Rels.--USA Weekend, New York, NY; *U.S. Public*, pg. 701
Aguirre, Joe, Mgr.-Pub. Rels.--Disneyland Hotel, Anaheim, CA; *U.S. Public*, pg. 513
Aguirre, Jose M., Mgr.-Corp. Communications--Hispano Olivetti Office, Barcelona, Spain; *Int'l*, pg. 1003
Aguren, Mats, Sr. V.P.-Corp. Communications--Stora Kopparbergs Bergslags AB, Falun, Sweden; *Int'l*, pg. 1302
Aharoni, Talia, Pub. Rels. Div. Dir.--Gitam/BBDO, Ramat Gan, Israel; *Int'l*, pg. 552
Ai, Lee Kuo, Mgr.-Corp. Affairs & Devel.--Orchard Parade Holdings Limited, Singapore, Singapore; *Int'l*, pg. 1007
Aide, Townley, Mgr.-Pub. Rels.--The Greenbrier, White Sulphur Springs, WV; *U.S. Public*, pg. 284
Aihara, Hiromichi, Gen. Mgr.-Pub. Rels.--Rohm Co., Ltd., Kyoto, Japan; *Int'l*, pg. 1124
Aijala, Tauno, V.P.-Programming--MTV Finland, Helsinki, Finland; *Int'l*, pg. 827
Aiken, Barry H., Dir.-Human Resources & Pub. Affairs--S.C. Johnson, Camberley, United Kingdom; *U.S. Private*, pg. 593
Aker, Michael, Pub. Rels. Rep.--Nippondenso Co., Ltd., Kariya, Japan; *Int'l*, pg. 1412
Akerman, Martin, Dir.-Customer Support Centres--Messier-Dowty Customer Support Centre- Europe, Gloucester, United Kingdom; *Int'l*, pg. 1340
Akers, Barry J., Mgr.-Corp. Commun.--Fletcher Challenge Limited, Auckland, New Zealand; *Int'l*, pg. 494
Akkerman, J., Mgr.-Pub. Rels.--Campina Melkunie BV, Zaltbommel, Netherlands; *Int'l*, pg. 254
Albanesi, Ed, Pub. Rels. Consultant--William Cook Public Relations, Inc., Jacksonville, FL; *U.S. Private*, pg. 273
Albee, Doyle, Dir.-Corp. Communications--Maxtor Corporation, Milpitas, CA; *Int'l*, pg. 641
Albert, Paul J., Mgr.-Mktg. Communications--Krautkramer-Branson, Inc., Lewistown, PA; *U.S. Public*, pg. 574
Albrecht, Patrice, V.P.-Communications--Arianespace SA, Evry, France; *Int'l*, pg. 81
Albright, Judy, Dir.-Pub. Rels.--The Genie Company, Alliance, OH; *U.S. Private*, pg. 823
Albus, Adolf, Dir.-Pub. Rels.--Frankfurter Sparkasse, Frankfurt, Germany; *Int'l*, pg. 504
Alcorn, Susan, Mgr.-Public Rels.--FINAST, Maple Heights, OH; *Int'l*, pg. 750
Alden, Alison, Sr. V.P.-Sls., Service & Human Resources--Boston Edison Company, Boston, MA; *U.S. Public*, pg. 247
Alden, Barbara, Mgr.-Pub. Rels.--FTP Software Inc., Andover, MA; *U.S. Public*, pg. 609
Alderson, Pauline, Mgr.-Pub. Rels.--Union Camp Chemicals, Durham, United Kingdom; *U.S. Public*, pg. 1666
Aldridge, Ellen, Dir.-Pub. Rels.--Jacques Moret, Inc., New York, NY; *U.S. Private*, pg. 580
Alexander, Bruno, Mgr.-Pub. Affairs--Lilly France S.A., Saint Cloud, France; *U.S. Public*, pg. 994
Alexander, Stuart, V.P.-Corp. Commun.--Deluxe Corporation, Shoreview, MN; *U.S. Public*, pg. 498
Alexoff, Carl, Mgr.-Pub. Rels.--Provident Financial Group, Inc., Cincinnati, OH; *U.S. Public*, pg. 1338
Alfirevich, Mary Jo, Dir.-Pub. Rels.--Renaissance International Hotels, Cleveland, OH; *U.S. Public*, pg. 1048
Alfonso, Marida G., V.P.-Corp. Public Involvement--Aetna Inc., Hartford, CT; *U.S. Public*, pg. 26
Alhpuro, Jorma, Mgr.-Pub. Rels.--Olivetti (Suomi) OY, Espoo, Finland; *Int'l*, pg. 1003
Alizart, Robert, V.P.-Corp. Commun.--Airbus Industrie, Blagnac, France; *Int'l*, pg. 39
Alladin, Mohammad, Publicity Asst.--Barneys Inc., New York, NY; *U.S. Private*, pg. 116
Allain, Dea, Mgr.-Corp. Communications--Ruby Tuesday, Inc., Mobile, AL; *U.S. Public*, pg. 1411
Allan, Deborah, Dir.-Pub. Rels.--Spar Aerospace Limited, Toronto, Canada; *Int'l*, pg. 1287
Allen, Barry K., Sr. V.P.-Communications & Info. Prods.--Ameritech Corp., Chicago, IL; *U.S. Public*, pg. 98
Allen, Brad, Dir.-Investor Rels.--Imation Corporation, Oakdale, MN; *U.S. Public*, pg. 870
Allen, Darwin, Dir.-Pub. Rels.--Pontiac-GMC Division, Detroit, MI; *U.S. Public*, pg. 720
Allen, David A., Sr. V.P.-Pub. Rels.--Inco Limited, Toronto, Canada; *Int'l*, pg. 672
Allen, David C., Mgr.-Communications--Inland Steel Industries, Inc., Chicago, IL; *U.S. Public*, pg. 879
Allen, Don, Dir.-Corp. Rels.--Wonderware Corporation, Irvine, CA; *U.S. Public*, pg. 1775
Allen, Ed, V.P.-Strategic Communications--Reliance Electric, Cleveland, OH; *U.S. Public*, pg. 1397
Allen, Gloria, V.P.-Public Rel.--Deposit Guaranty Corp., Jackson, MS; *U.S. Public*, pg. 500
Allen, James R., V.P.-Pub. Rels. & Adv.--CNF Transportation Inc., Palo Alto, CA; *U.S. Public*, pg. 281
Allen, Jay, V.P.-Corp. Affairs--Wal-Mart Stores, Inc., Bentonville, AR; *U.S. Public*, pg. 1732
Allen, Joseph, V.P.-Commun.--Cognizant Corporation, Westport, CT; *U.S. Public*, pg. 395
Allen, Neil, Mgr.-Pub. Rels.--HFS, Incorporated, Parsippany, NJ; *U.S. Public*, pg. 321
Allen, Rich, Dir.-Communications--Coachmen Industries, Inc., Elkhart, IN; *U.S. Public*, pg. 387
Allen, Robert E., Dir.-Corp. Commun.--Guidant Corporation, Indianapolis, IN; *U.S. Public*, pg. 768
Allen, Tammy, Mgr.-Communications Coord.--DePuy, Inc., Warsaw, IN; *Int'l*, pg. 331
Allesina, Tiffany, Mgr.-Pub. Rels.--Attachmate, Bellevue, WA; *U.S. Private*, pg. 98
Allison, Jay, Mgr.-Pub. Rels.--Pizza Hut, Inc., Dallas, TX; *U.S. Public*, pg. 1636
Allo, Leo, V.P.-Commun.--Valmet Corporation, Helsinki, Finland; *Int'l*, pg. 1447
Allsop, Mark, Mgr.-Corp. Commun.--Daily Mail & General Trust PLC, London, United Kingdom; *Int'l*, pg. 366
Alm, Mats, Sr. Dir.-Communications--Stora Billerud AB, Skoghall, Sweden; *Int'l*, pg. 1302
Almeida, Rodrigo de, Mgr.-Corp. Communications--Monsanto do Brasil Ltda. (Mobra S.A.), Sao Paulo, Brazil; *U.S. Public*, pg. 1125
Almgren, Eva, Corp. Communications Asst.--Atlas Copco AB, Stockholm, Sweden; *Int'l*, pg. 95
Almoney, Annette L., Mgr.-Mktg. Communications--ESAB Welding & Cutting Products, Hanover, PA; *Int'l*, pg. 281
Alston, Jack, Dir.-Commun.--Burgess & Niple, Limited, Columbus, OH; *U.S. Private*, pg. 182
Altavilla, Roseanne, Mgr.-Communications--Domtar Inc., Montreal, Canada; *Int'l*, pg. 416
Altemus, James, Dir.-Pub. Rels.--Carton Div., Saint Louis, MO; *Int'l*, pg. 1269
Altemus, James R., Dir.-Communications--Jefferson Smurfit Corporation, Saint Louis, MO; *Int'l*, pg. 1269
Alter, Stewart, Sr. V.P.-Communications-WW--McCann-Erickson Worldwide, New York, NY; *U.S. Public*, pg. 909
Alton, John W., Pres.--Minerallac Co., Addison, IL; *U.S. Private*, pg. 750
Alvarez, Francisco Casanova, Mgr.-Information & Public Rels.--Petroleos Mexicanos, Mexico, Mexico; *Int'l*, pg. 1046
Ambroson, Tom, Dir.-Promotions--The Phoenix Learning Group, Inc., Saint Louis, MO; *U.S. Private*, pg. 863
Amdursky, Jon, Dir.-Worldwide Adv. & Communications--International Specialty Products, Inc., Wayne, NJ; *U.S. Public*, pg. 858
Amestoy, Jay, V.P.-Corp. Affairs & Communications--Mazda Motor of America, Inc., Irvine, CA; *Int'l*, pg. 849
Amig, Eric P., V.P. & Dir.-Bank Rels.--Federal Home Loan Bank of New York, New York, NY; *U.S. Private*, pg. 399
Amle, Charlotte, Mgr.-Pub. Rels.--Den norske Bank ASA, Oslo, Norway; *Int'l*, pg. 392
Amos, Clifton E., Mgr.-Pub. Rels.--Miller Brewing Company, Fort Worth, TX; *U.S. Public*, pg. 1289
AmRhein, Dick, Mgr.- Mktg. Communications & Training--Miller Fluid Power Corp., Bensenville, IL; *U.S. Private*, pg. 747
Amsden, Deborah C., Mgr.-Bus. Devel.--Alliance Construction Solutions, Inc., Fort Collins, CO; *U.S. Private*, pg. 38
Amundson, Jerry, Dir.-Pub. Rels.--Electronic Products Division, Austin, TX; *U.S. Public*, pg. 1605
Anckaert, Jacques, V.P.-External Commun.--N.V. Bekaert S.A., Kortrijk, Belgium; *Int'l*, pg. 183
Anderf, Marion, Dir.-Pub. Rels.--Herlitz PBS Aktiengesellschaft, Berlin, Germany; *Int'l*, pg. 616
Anderia, Bruce, Dir.-Pub. Rels.--Bashas, Chandler, AZ; *U.S. Private*, pg. 120
Andersch, Jennifer, Mktg. Communicaitons Specialist--Metrologic Instruments, Inc., Blackwood, NJ; *U.S. Public*, pg. 1102
Andersen, Beth, Mgr.-Adv. & Pub. Rels.--Recoton Auto Corporation, Lincolnshire, IL; *U.S. Public*, pg. 1369
Andersen, David C., V.P.-Public Affairs--Cox Communications, Inc., Atlanta, GA; *U.S. Public*, pg. 454
Andersen, Grith, Corp. Commun. Asst.--GN Great Nordic Ltd., Copenhagen, Denmark; *Int'l*, pg. 536
Anderson, Barbara, Dir.-Mktg. Communications--Applied Biosystems, Foster City, CA; *U.S. Public*, pg. 1279
Anderson, Barbara, Coord.-Communications--DuBois Chemicals, Cincinnati, OH; *Int'l*, pg. 1437
Anderson, Caroline, Mgr.-Mktg., Promo. & Pub. Rels.--The News Tribune, Tacoma, WA; *U.S. Public*, pg. 1066
Anderson, Charles S., V.P.-Corp. Rels. & Human Resources--Encore Computer Corporation, Fort Lauderdale, FL; *U.S. Public*, pg. 580
Anderson, Dana, Coord.-Pub. Rels.--The Washington Water Power Company, Spokane, WA; *U.S. Public*, pg. 1744
Anderson, Deborah, Corp. Commun. Mgr.--Poppe Tyson, New York, NY; *U.S. Public*, pg. 1642
Anderson, Don, Dir.-Pub. Rels.--Lyon Metal Products, Inc., Montgomery, IL; *U.S. Private*, pg. 638
Anderson, Donald, Dir.-Corp. Commun.--Courtaulds plc, London, United Kingdom; *Int'l*, pg. 338
Anderson, Edie, V.P.-Corp. Communications--Pepperidge Farm, Incorporated, Norwalk, CT; *U.S. Public*, pg. 299
Anderson, Holly, V.P.-Corp. Communications--Safecard Services, Inc., Jacksonville, FL; *U.S. Public*, pg. 320
Anderson, Jayne, Mgr.-Communications & Mktg.--Evans & Sutherland Computer Corporation, Salt Lake City, UT; *U.S. Public*, pg. 595
Anderson, Jeff, Dir.-Adv.--The Rottlund Company, Inc., Roseville, MN; *U.S. Public*, pg. 1406
Anderson, Julie, Mgr.-Pub. Rels.--United Technologies, Chemical Systems Div., San Jose, CA; *U.S. Public*, pg. 1690
Anderson, Karen, Communications Specialist--International Multifoods Corporation, Minneapolis, MN; *U.S. Public*, pg. 900
Anderson, Keith, Mgr.-Pub. Rels.--Travelers Property Casualty Corp., Hartford, CT; *U.S. Public*, pg. 1633
Anderson, Lisa A., Mgr.-Mktg. Communications--Dexter Nonwovens Division, Windsor Locks, CT; *U.S. Public*, pg. 504
Anderson, Nina, Dir.-Adv.--The Hotsy Corporation, Englewood, CO; *U.S. Private*, pg. 500
Anderson, Patricia, Mgr.-Pub. Rels.--Sargent & Lundy, Chicago, IL; *U.S. Private*, pg. 965
Anderson, Romilda, Dir.-Pub. Affairs--Connecticut Energy Corporation, Bridgeport, CT; *U.S. Public*, pg. 431
Anderson, Sam, Mgr.-Pub. Rels.--Brookshire Grocery, Tyler, TX; *U.S. Private*, pg. 172
Anderson, Suzanne, Fund Asst.--Center Partners Management LLC, New York, NY; *U.S. Private*, pg. 222
Anderson, Thomas, Dir.-Corp. Communications--Millipore Corporation, Bedford, MA; *U.S. Public*, pg. 1112
Anderson, Tracy, Mgr.-Pub. Rels.--Comtech Antenna Systems, Inc., Saint Cloud, FL; *U.S. Public*, pg. 425
Andersson, Bo, Mgr.-Service--Atlet AB, Molnlycke, Sweden; *Int'l*, pg. 97
Andersson, Gunnar, Dir.-Corp. Communications--Swedbank, Stockholm, Sweden; *Int'l*, pg. 1328
Andersson, Niclas, Mktg. Communications Officer--Sodra Cell AB, Vaxjo, Sweden; *Int'l*, pg. 1275
Andrade, Luiz, Corp. Relations Dir.--Salles/DMB&B Publicidade S.A., Sao Paulo, Brazil; *U.S. Private*, pg. 305
Andras, Robert, Sr. Dir.-Communications Services--Petro-Canada, Calgary, Canada; *Int'l*, pg. 1041
Andresen, Trond, Sr. V.P.-Corp. Communications--Kvaerner a.s.a., Lysaker, Norway; *Int'l*, pg. 766
Andrew, Gordon G., V.P.-Corp. Commun.--Travelers Group, New York, NY; *U.S. Public*, pg. 1632

Andrews, Bill, Sr. V.P., Dir.-Mktg., Response & Pub. Rels.--Union Planters Bank, Memphis, TN; *U.S. Public*, pg. 1669
Andrews, Dwayne C., V.P.-Labor Rels.--US Airways, Inc., Arlington, VA; *U.S. Public*, pg. 1680
Andrews, Ed, Sr. V.P.-Governmental Affairs-SunTrust Banks, Inc.--SunTrust Banks of Georgia, Inc., Atlanta, GA; *U.S. Public*, pg. 1538
Andrews, Mark, Mgr.-Adv. & Public Relations--Century Telephone Enterprises, Inc., Monroe, LA; *U.S. Public*, pg. 329
Andrews, Tom, Pres.--Lubriquip, Inc., Cleveland, OH; *U.S. Public*, pg. 862
Andrews, William H., Jr., Sr. V.P.-Mktg.--Union Planters Corporation, Cordova, TN; *U.S. Public*, pg. 1668
Andriessen, E., Chief Info. Officer--Schering Nederland B.V., Weesp, Netherlands; *Int'l*, pg. 1204
Anell, Lars, Chief-Pub. Affairs--AB Volvo, Goteborg, Sweden; *Int'l*, pg. 1476
Angell, Rosalind J., Dir.-Communications--George S. May International Company, Park Ridge, IL; *U.S. Private*, pg. 717
Anglin, Joann, Mgr.-Customer Service--Thermoplastics, Inc., Mishawaka, IN; *U.S. Public*, pg. 1590
Anixter, Benjamin M., V.P.-External Affairs--Advanced Micro Devices, Inc., Sunnyvale, CA; *U.S. Public*, pg. 21
Anneberg, Karen, Mgr.-Mktg.--NTH Consultants, Ltd., Farmington, MI; *U.S. Private*, pg. 772
Annesi, P., Dir.-Legal Affairs & Personnel--Sigma-Tau Finanziaria S.p.A., Rome, Italy; *Int'l*, pg. 1248
Annesley, David, Dir.-Govt. & Pub. Affairs--Transcanada Pipelines Limited, Calgary, Canada; *Int'l*, pg. 1416
Annibaldi,Cesare, Exec. V.P.-Public Affairs--Fiat Auto SpA, Turin, Italy; *Int'l*, pg. 480
Ansenault, Brian, V.P.-Corp. Commun.--Peoples Heritage Financial Group, Inc., Portland, ME; *U.S. Public*, pg. 1275
Antoinin, Henrietta, V.P. & Dir.-Pub. Rels.--Atlanta Life Insurance Company, Atlanta, GA; *U.S. Private*, pg. 94
Antonini, Fabrizio, Mgr.-Central Affairs & Pub. Rels.--IRI Istituto Ricostruzione Industriale, Rome, Italy; *Int'l*, pg. 652
Apollonj Ghetti, Luca, Pub. Rels. Dir.--General Motors Italia, S.p.A., Rome, Italy; *U.S. Public*, pg. 722
Appel, Marcia, Sr. V.P.-Adv., Natl. Promo. & Corp. Communications--Musicland Group Inc., Minnetonka, MN; *U.S. Public*, pg. 1142
Applebaum, Stuart, Sr. V.P.-Publicity & Pub. Rels.--Bantam Doubleday Dell Publishing Group, Inc., New York, NY; *Int'l*, pg. 191
Appleton, Diane, V.P.-Pub. Services--The Faxon Company, Inc., Westwood, MA; *Int'l*, pg. 385
Arai, Junichi, Mng. Dir.-Publications, Pub. Rels. & Legal Affairs--Nihon Keizai Shimbun, Inc., Tokyo, Japan; *Int'l*, pg. 929
Araki, Fumiko, Mgr.-Intl. Pub. Rels. & Corp. Communications--Mazda Motor Corporation, Hiroshima, Japan; *Int'l*, pg. 849
Archer, Kelly, Project Coord.--Svedala Industries-Universal Engineering, Cedar Rapids, IA; *Int'l*, pg. 1326
Archer, William C., III, Exec. V.P.-External Affairs--Georgia Power Co., Atlanta, GA; *U.S. Public*, pg. 1490
Arellano, Palmira, V.P. & Pub. Rels. Dir.--Bromley, Aguilar & Associates, San Antonio, TX; *U.S. Private*, pg. 692
Arena, Mafalda, Mgr.-Corp. Commun.--Merit Behavioral Care Corp., Park Ridge, NJ; *U.S. Public*, pg. 1036
Argentin, Sil, Mgr.-Mktg. Commun.--S-B Power Tool Company, Chicago, IL; *Int'l*, pg. 205
Armatis, Leo R., V.P.-Corp. Rels.--Meredith Corporation, Des Moines, IA; *U.S. Public*, pg. 1094
Armour, Karen A., Mgr.-Pub. Information--ABB Inc., Norwalk, CT; *Int'l*, pg. 3
Armstrong, Andrea, Mgr.-Pub. Rels.--CH2M Hill Companies, Ltd., Greenwood Village, CO; *U.S. Private*, pg. 195
Armstrong, Bob, Dir.-Customer Services--North West Water Limited, Warrington, United Kingdom; *Int'l*, pg. 1444
Armstrong, James C., First V.P.-Investor Rels.--SunTrust Banks, Inc., Atlanta, GA; *U.S. Public*, pg. 1537
Armstrong, John, Dir.-Corp. Programs & Events, Corp. Rels.--CBS Corporation, Pittsburgh, PA; *U.S. Public*, pg. 273
Armstrong, Kim, Mgr.-Communications--Killington Limited, Killington, VT; *U.S. Private*, pg. 61
Armstrong, Tom, Mgr.-Pub. Rels.--Cannondale Corporation, Bethel, CT; *U.S. Public*, pg. 301
Arnav, Javier, Dir.-Communications--Bancomer, S.A., Mexico, Mexico; *Int'l*, pg. 145
Arndt, Betty, Dir.-Mktg. & Pub. Rels.--Johnson Controls, Inc., Controls Group, Milwaukee, WI; *U.S. Public*, pg. 932
Arnold, Cassie, Asst. Dir.-Adv. & Pub. Rels.--Ernst & Young, LLP, New York, NY; *U.S. Private*, pg. 381
Arnold, Edwina, Dir.-Pub. Rels.--Club Med Sales, Inc., New York, NY; *Int'l*, pg. 298
Arnold, Jim, Mgr.-Adv. & Pub. Affairs--Helena Chemical Company, Memphis, TN; *Int'l*, pg. 845
Arnold, Marg, Creative Services Dir. & Pub. Rels. Dir.--Leo Burnett Company Ltd., Toronto, Canada; *U.S. Private*, pg. 185
Arnold, Martin, Dir.-Corp. Communications--Rayonier Inc., Stamford, CT; *U.S. Public*, pg. 1363
Aron, Mark G., Exec. V.P.-Law & Pub. Affairs--CSX Corporation, Richmond, VA; *U.S. Public*, pg. 284
Aronson, Sheree, Dir.-Investor Rels.--Apria Healthcare Group Inc., Costa Mesa, CA; *U.S. Public*, pg. 125
Arthurs, Kerry, Dir.-Pub. Rels.--North Limited, Melbourne, Australia; *Int'l*, pg. 967
Artimo, Eeva, Sr. V.P.-Corp. Communications--Tamrock Corp., Tampere, Finland; *Int'l*, pg. 1352
Asaba, Yoshiaki, Mng. Dir.--Citizen Watch Company, Ltd., Tokyo, Japan; *Int'l*, pg. 293
Ashby, Audrey, Dir.-Pub. Rels.--Wyeth-Ayerst Laboratories, Inc., Philadelphia, PA; *U.S. Public*, pg. 80
Ashetty, Bob, Mgr.-Mktg. Commun. & Res.--BMW of North America, Inc.-Eastern Region, Ramsey, NJ; *Int'l*, pg. 177
Ashley, Kathleen M., Coord.-Investor Rels.--Jefferies Group, Inc., Los Angeles, CA; *U.S. Public*, pg. 924
Ashley, Kenneth, Chief Fin. Officer & Sec.--National R.V., Inc., Perris, CA; *U.S. Public*, pg. 1159
Ashooh, Nicholas J., V.P.-Pub. Affairs & Corp. Communications--Niagara Mohawk Power Corporation, Syracuse, NY; *U.S. Public*, pg. 1181
Ashworth, Paul W., Dir.-Corp. Communications--DIMON, Incorporated, Danville, VA; *U.S. Public*, pg. 509
Askaw, Christine, Mgr.-Natl. Mktg. & Pub. Rels.--Shiseido (Australia) Pty. Limited, Pyrmont, Australia; *Int'l*, pg. 1235
Asolese, Michael, Dir.-Pub. Rels.--Price Waterhouse L.L.P. - U.S., New York, NY; *U.S. Private*, pg. 883
Ast, Eileen, V.P.-Corp. Communications--The Mutual Life Insurance Company of New York, New York, NY; *U.S. Private*, pg. 769
Astar, David R., V.P.-Customer Service & Quality--Humana Inc., Louisville, KY; *U.S. Public*, pg. 847
Astrom, Hakan, Sr. V.P.-Strategic Plng. & Investor Rels.--Pharmacia & Upjohn, Inc., Windsor, United Kingdom; *Int'l*, pg. 1047
Atherton, Mary, Mgr.-Pub. Rels.--Matrix Essentials, Inc., Solon, OH; *U.S. Public*, pg. 254
Atkin, Mary, Sr. V.P. & Mgr.-Corp. Communications--A.G. Edwards, Inc., Saint Louis, MO; *U.S. Public*, pg. 565
Atkin, Mary V., V.P.-Corp. Communications--A.G. Edwards & Sons, Inc., Saint Louis, MO; *U.S. Public*, pg. 565
Atkins, Debbie, Mgr.-Pub. Rels.--Advantica Restaurant Group, Inc., Spartanburg, SC; *U.S. Public*, pg. 22
Atkins, Sharon, Dir.-Pub. Affairs & Promo.--WAXY (FM), Fort Lauderdale, FL; *U.S. Public*, pg. 925
Atkinson, Paul, Mgr.-Pub. Rels.--Nationwide Building Society, Swindon, United Kingdom; *Int'l*, pg. 912
Atkiss, A.W., V.P.-Pub. Affairs--Exxon Corporation, Irving, TX; *U.S. Public*, pg. 601
Aubusson, Peter J., Head-Corp. Affairs--Courtaulds Textiles Plc, London, United Kingdom; *Int'l*, pg. 339
Auer, Jacky, Dir.-Pub. Rels.--BNP Finance, Paris, France; *Int'l*, pg. 163
Aufmuth, George, Mgr.-Mktg. Commun./Uniroyal Brand--Michelin Americas Small Tires (MAST), Greenville, SC; *Int'l*, pg. 322
Augustine, L., Pub. Rels. Specialist--Tracor Aerospace Electronics Systems, Inc., Lansdale, PA; *U.S. Public*, pg. 1627
Austin, Jesse, Sr. Writer--Best Power, Necedah, WI; *U.S. Private*, pg. 140
Austin, Michael C., V.P.-Corp. Commun.--Utica Mutual Insurance Company, New Hartford, NY; *U.S. Private*, pg. 1129
Aversano, John, Pres. & Chief Exec. Officer--Air Conditioning Co., Inc., Glendale, CA; *U.S. Private*, pg. 28
Avery, Lorraine, Sr. V.P. & Mgr.-Customer & Acct. Services--First Financial Bank, FSB, Stevens Point, WI; *U.S. Public*, pg. 140
Awrey, Betty Jean, V.P.-Pub. Rels.--Awrey Bakeries, Inc., Livonia, MI; *U.S. Private*, pg. 103
Awsumb, Judi, V.P.-Mktg. & Pub. Rels.--Ikon Office Solutions, Orlando, FL; *U.S. Public*, pg. 863
Axley, Dixie, Asst. V.P.-Pub. Affairs--State Farm Mutual Automobile Insurance Company, Bloomington, IL; *U.S. Private*, pg. 1036
Ayers, Dean, Dir.-Pub. Rels.--Warren Petroleum Company, Houston, TX; *U.S. Public*, pg. 1146
Ayuso, Javier, Dir.-Corp. Communications--Argentaria Corporacion Bancaria de Espana, S.A., Madrid, Spain; *Int'l*, pg. 80
Azzarone, Stephanie, Dir.-Pub. Rels.--Duncan Toys Company, Middlefield, OH; *U.S. Private*, pg. 409
Babb, Ruth, Coord.-Pub. Rels.--Builders Square, Inc., San Antonio, TX; *U.S. Private*, pg. 477
Babicz, Gregory, Dir.-Commun.--Union Switch & Signal Inc., Pittsburgh, PA; *Int'l*, pg. 77
Babin, Daphne, Dir.-Pub. Rels.--Petroleum Helicopters, Inc., Metairie, LA; *U.S. Public*, pg. 1281
Babington, Catherine, V.P.-Investor Rels. & Pub. Affairs--Abbott Laboratories, Abbott Park, IL; *U.S. Public*, pg. 12
Bacar, Werner, Dir.-Pub. Relations--Henkel KGaA, Dusseldorf, Germany; *Int'l*, pg. 609
Bacardi, Jose Argamasilla, Asst. V.P.-Pub. Rels.--Bacardi-Martini, USA, Inc., Miami, FL; *U.S. Private*, pg. 109
Bach, Caroline, V.P.-Pub. Rels. & Mktg.--Bravo Network, Woodbury, NY; *U.S. Public*, pg. 288
Bachelier, Nicole Grisoni, Dir.-Pub. Rels.--Saint-Gobain, Courbevoie, France; *Int'l*, pg. 1170
Bachleda, Lauren, Mgr.-Pub. Rels. & Adv.--Arrow Pneumatics Co. Inc., Lake Zurich, IL; *U.S. Private*, pg. 85
Bachmann, Karen, V.P.-Corp. Communications--Foodmaker, Inc., San Diego, CA; *U.S. Public*, pg. 661
Backman, Charalette, Mgr.-Communications--E.F. Johnson Radio Systems, Lincoln, NE; *U.S. Public*, pg. 1630
Bader, Victor, Dir.-Corp. Communications--Von Roll AG, Gerlafingen, Switzerland; *Int'l*, pg. 1480
Badger, Timothy C., V.P.-Mktg.--Arrow Financial Corporation, Glens Falls, NY; *U.S. Public*, pg. 135
Badilla, Ivan, Dir.-Commun.--CODELCO Chile (Corporacion Nacional Del Cobre De Chile), Santiago, Chile; *Int'l*, pg. 302
Badler, Dick, V.P.-Corp. Commun.--General Instrument Corporation, Horsham, PA; *U.S. Public*, pg. 716
Baedeker, Rick, V.P.-Mktg. & Pub. Rels.--Hollywood Park, Inc., Inglewood, CA; *U.S. Public*, pg. 830
Baez, Ivan, Dir.-Pub. Rels.--Puerto Rican Cement Co., Inc., Guaynabo, PR; *U.S. Public*, pg. 1341
Baez, Ivan, Dir.-Pub. Rels.--Ponce Cement Div., Ponce, PR; *U.S. Public*, pg. 1342
Baggett, William B., Mgr.-Human Resources--Americold Compressor Co., Cullman, AL; *Int'l*, pg. 439
Baggs, Monica, Mgr.-Sls.--Maxcor Manufacturing, Inc., Colorado Springs, CO; *U.S. Private*, pg. 716
Bagley, Rachel, Dir.-Corp. Commun.--Public Service Company of North Carolina, Inc., Gastonia, NC; *U.S. Public*, pg. 1340
Baglivo, Vince, Pub. Rels. Dir.--DKB & Partners, Inc., Morristown, NJ; *U.S. Private*, pg. 302
Bagnall, P.C., Gen. Dir.-Customer Support--General Motors of Canada Ltd., Oshawa, Canada; *U.S. Public*, pg. 722
Bailey, Lisa J., Mgr.-Pub. Rels.--Midwest Express Holdings, Inc., Oak Creek, WI; *U.S. Public*, pg. 1111
Bailey, Mattie, Mgr.-Customer Rels.--Seattle City Light, Seattle, WA; *U.S. Private*, pg. 979
Bailey, Maureen, V.P.-Public Affairs--American Express Travel Related Services Co., Inc., New York, NY; *U.S. Public*, pg. 73
Bailey, Natalie, Mgr.-Corp. Communications--Hershey Chocolate U.S.A., Hershey, PA; *U.S. Public*, pg. 812
Bailie, Barbara, Mgr.-Pub. Rels.--The Family Channel Inc., Toronto, Canada; *Int'l*, pg. 1482
Bailleux, Didier, Dir.-Mktg. & Comminications--Voyage, Issy-les-Moulineaux, France; *U.S. Private*, pg. 647
Bain, Marilyn, Mgr.-Pub. Rels.--Storck International GmbH, Halle, Germany; *Int'l*, pg. 1304
Baird, Anna M., Chief Fin. Officer & V.P.--Black Box Corporation of PA, Lawrence, PA; *U.S. Public*, pg. 235
Baird, Debbie, Dir.-Mktg. Commun.--Mrs. Baird's Bakeries, Inc., Fort Worth, TX; *U.S. Private*, pg. 765
Baird, Jane A., V.P.-Corp. Commun.--Cognos Inc., Ottawa, Canada; *Int'l*, pg. 305
Baker, Bridget, Dir.-Corp. Pub. Rels. & Corp. Sec.--Guard Publishing Company, Eugene, OR; *U.S. Private*, pg. 485
Baker, Frederick W., Asst. V.P.-Communications--Harleysville Group, Harleysville, PA; *U.S. Public*, pg. 786
Baker, Hilary, Dir.-Pub. Rels.--Hilton International Co., Coral Gables, FL; *Int'l*, pg. 787
Baker, Karen, Pub. Rels. Specialist--GenRad, Inc., Westford, MA; *U.S. Public*, pg. 731
Baker, Marybeth, Mgr.-Adv. & Pub. Rels.--Galpin Motors, North Hills, CA; *U.S. Private*, pg. 438
Baker, Melody, Mktg. Communications Assoc.--GIW Industries, Inc., Grovetown, GA; *Int'l*, pg. 721
Baker, Roger W., Dir.-Commun.--Fortune Brands, Inc., Old Greenwich, CT; *U.S. Public*, pg. 674
Baker, T.R., Gen. Mgr.-Mktg., Communication & IT Policy--MLC Limited, Sydney, Australia; *Int'l*, pg. 806
Bakker, Anna Marie, Mgr.-Communications--Nikon Inc., Melville, NY; *Int'l*, pg. 931
Balangue, Alice, Pub. Rels. Dir.--Hemisphere-Leo Burnett, Inc., Manila, Philippines; *U.S. Private*, pg. 184
Balas, Antoine, External Rels., Pub. Rels. Europe--AlliedSignal Aftermarket Europe S.A., Drancy, France; *U.S. Public*, pg. 53
Baldi, Laurel, Asst. to Pres.--Speedling Incorporated, Sun City, FL; *U.S. Private*, pg. 1024
Baldwin, Ann T., V.P.-Corp. Communications--AAR Corp., Wood Dale, IL; *U.S. Public*, pg. 1
Baldwin, Cathy, V.P.-Corp. Communications--Willamette Industries, Inc., Portland, OR; *U.S. Public*, pg. 1768
Baldwin, Ellen, Mgr.-Customer Commun.--Vanguard Cellular Systems, Inc., Greensboro, NC; *U.S. Public*, pg. 1707
Baldwin, Paula, V.P. & Pub. Rels. Dir.--Campbell Mithun Esty, Minneapolis, MN; *U.S. Private*, pg. 204
Baldwin, Roger M., Dir.-Mktg. & Bus. Devel.--Dugan & Meyers Interests, Inc., Cincinnati, OH; *U.S. Private*, pg. 345
Balfoort, M., Mgr.-Pub. Rels.--Ballast Nedam Bouwmaterieel B.V., Almere, Netherlands; *Int'l*, pg. 133
Balian, Cheryl, Pub. Rels. Specialist--Syratech Corporation, East Boston, MA; *U.S. Private*, pg. 1060
Ball, James A., Sr. V.P.-Corp. Communications--Dr Pepper/Seven Up No. America, Dallas, TX; *Int'l*, pg. 248
Ball, James A., Sr. V.P.-Corp. Communications--Dr. Pepper Co., Dallas, TX; *Int'l*, pg. 248
Ballard, John W., III, Chief Fin. Officer & Sec.--TCI International Inc., Sunnyvale, CA; *U.S. Public*, pg. 1555
Ballinger, Tim, Mgr.-Mktg. Communications--Sloan Technology, Santa Barbara, CA; *U.S. Public*, pg. 1711
Balocco, R.J., V.P.-Pub. Rels.--SJW Corp., San Jose, CA; *U.S. Public*, pg. 1418
Balthazar, Sabrina, Mgr.-Pub. Rels.--Hammacher, Schlemmer & Co., Inc., Chicago, IL; *U.S. Private*, pg. 497
Bane, Marc, Dir.-Mktg. Commun.--Information Builders, New York, NY; *U.S. Private*, pg. 561
Banks, J.R., V.P.-Health, Environment & Safety--Sun Company, Inc., Philadelphia, PA; *U.S. Public*, pg. 1530
Banks, J.R., Mgr.-Communications--Sun Refining & Marketing Co. Lubes Div., Philadelphia, PA; *U.S. Public*, pg. 1530
Bankus, G. Kent, V.P.-Govt. Rels.--General Dynamics Corporation, Falls Church, VA; *U.S. Public*, pg. 708
Bannwolf, Donna, Mgr.-Corp. Commun.--Greate Bay Casino Corporation, Atlantic City, NJ; *U.S. Public*, pg. 760
Bannwolf, Donna, Mgr.-Corp. Commun.--Hollywood Casino Corp, Atlantic City, NJ; *U.S. Public*, pg. 830
Banta, Ben, Dir.-Corp. Communications--Nextel Communications, Mc Lean, VA; *U.S. Public*, pg. 1180
Baracho, Maria Luisa, Mgr.-Corp. Commun.--Central de Cervejas, S.A., Lisbon, Portugal; *Int'l*, pg. 279
Barbas, J.P.E., Dir.-Corp. Communication & Sec.--N.V. Koninklijke KNP BT, Amsterdam, Netherlands; *Int'l*, pg. 756
Barber, Dave, V.P.-Newspaper Rels.--USA Weekend, New York, NY; *U.S. Public*, pg. 701
Barber, Kevin, Dir.-Pub. Rels.--Kemper Insurance Companies, Long Grove, IL; *U.S. Private*, pg. 614
Barber, Peggy, Assoc. Exec. Dir.-Pub. Policy & Prog.-American Library--American Library Association, Chicago, IL; *U.S. Private*, pg. 58
Bardwick, Catherine M., V.P.-Corp. Commun.--International Murex Technologies Corporation, Guelph, Canada; *Int'l*, pg. 684
Barendregt, G., Mgr.-Publicity--DSM Resins B.V., Zwolle, Netherlands; *Int'l*, pg. 353
Barkai, Judith, Gen. Counsel, Sec. & Dir.-Investor Rels.--American Israeli Paper Mills Ltd., Hadera, Israel; *Int'l*, pg. 74

Barker, Angela, Communications Officer--WIC Western International Communications Ltd., Vancouver, Canada; *Int'l*, pg. 1481
Barker, Kea, Coord.-Corp. Commun.--Cominco, Ltd., Vancouver, Canada; *Int'l*, pg. 307
Barker, Ronald E., V.P.-Indus. Rels.--Emerson Power Transmission Corporation, Ithaca, NY; *U.S. Public*, pg. 573
Barker, Stephanie, Pub. Rels. Counselor--William Cook Public Relations, Inc., Jacksonville, FL; *U.S. Private*, pg. 273
Barker, Steve, V.P.-Mktg. & Communications--Rexel, Inc., Coral Gables, FL; *Int'l*, pg. 1107
Barlow, Sharon, Mgr.-Pub. Rels.--Hyatt International Corporation, Chicago, IL; *U.S. Private*, pg. 551
Barnes, B., V.P.-Human Resources--The UCS Group, Toronto, Canada; *Int'l*, pg. 792
Barnes, Margo L., Sr. V.P.-Corp. Communications--Bayer Corporation, Pittsburgh, PA; *Int'l*, pg. 172
Barnes, P.T., V.P.-Far East Opers.--Van Melle N.V., Breda, Netherlands; *Int'l*, pg. 1450
Baron, Diana, Sr. V.P.-Publicity--A&M Records, Hollywood, CA; *Int'l*, pg. 1052
Barone, Jodi, Dir.-Mktg.--The Children's Place Retail Stores, Inc., West Caldwell, NJ; *U.S. Private*, pg. 237
Barr, P.C., Dir.-Corp. Communications--Consolidated Communications, Mattoon, IL; *U.S. Public*, pg. 1073
Barr, Thomas, Mgr.-Mktg. & Commun.--Sellstrom Manufacturing Co., Palatine, IL; *U.S. Private*, pg. 983
Barraza, Liz, Mgr.-Communications & Adv.--Courtaulds Aerospace, Glendale, CA; *Int'l*, pg. 339
Barrera, Benjamin A., V.P.-Corp. Rels.--National Bank of Alaska, Anchorage, AK; *U.S. Public*, pg. 1153
Barrera, Rosie, Dir.-Public Affairs--Port of Houston Authority, Houston, TX; *U.S. Private*, pg. 876
Barrett, Allen M., Jr., V.P.-Corp. Commun.--McCormick & Company, Incorporated, Sparks, MD; *U.S. Public*, pg. 1066
Barrett, Carmie G., Mgr.-Pub. Rels.--Riser Foods, Inc., Bedford, OH; *U.S. Private*, pg. 450
Barrett, Colleen C., Exec. V.P.-Customers & Corp. Sec.--Southwest Airlines Co., Dallas, TX; *U.S. Public*, pg. 1493
Barrett, Denise P., Coordinator-Public Relations & Mktg. Events--Keyes Asset Managemet, Miami, FL; *U.S. Private*, pg. 618
Barrett, Diane, Personnel Specialist--Chrysler Capital Corp., Stamford, CT; *U.S. Public*, pg. 354
Barrett, M. Patricia, V.P.-Corp. Commun.--AmerenUE, Saint Louis, MO; *U.S. Public*, pg. 66
Barrett, Michael, Dir.-Corp. Communications--Moore Corporation Limited, Toronto, Canada; *Int'l*, pg. 888
Barrett, William R., Dir.-Pub. Rels. & Adv.--Service Corporation International, Houston, TX; *U.S. Public*, pg. 1460
Barrow, Steven, V.P.-Corp. Devel. & Sec.--Wall Street Deli, Inc., Birmingham, AL; *U.S. Public*, pg. 1734
Barrowman, Rob, Dir.-Pub.--CAP Nationwide Motor Research, Skipton, United Kingdom; *Int'l*, pg. 451
Barry, Cameron, V.P. & Pub. Rels. Dir.--Gray Kirk/VanSant Advertising, Inc., Baltimore, MD; *U.S. Private*, pg. 472
Barry, Robin, Mgr.-Pub. Rels.--Koss Corporation, Milwaukee, WI; *U.S. Public*, pg. 966
Barry, Robin, Mgr.-Pub. Rels.--Koss Classics Ltd., Milwaukee, WI; *U.S. Public*, pg. 966
Barry, Tina S., V.P.-Corp. Commun.--Kimberly-Clark Corporation, Dallas, TX; *U.S. Public*, pg. 958
Barsky, Fran, Dir.-Investor Rels. & Communications--Intelligent Electronics, Inc., Exton, PA; *U.S. Public*, pg. 887
Barth, Monica, Communications Specialist--ABB in Canada, Saint-Laurent, Canada; *Int'l*, pg. 7
Barthe, Marcel, V.P.-Pub. Rels.--Cossette Communication Marketing, Quebec, Canada; *Int'l*, pg. 335
Bartholomew, Linda Curry, V.P.-Public Affairs--PP&L Resources, Allentown, PA; *U.S. Public*, pg. 1244
Bartl, James F., Sec.--National Presto Industries, Inc., Eau Claire, WI; *U.S. Public*, pg. 1159
Barwick, T.G., Dir.-Corp. Affairs--Vodafone Group PLC, Newbury, United Kingdom; *Int'l*, pg. 1469
Basave, Jose Manuel, Mgr.-Pub. Rels. & Communications--CYDSA S.A., Garza Garcia, Mexico; *Int'l*, pg. 246
Basave, Jose Manuel, Mgr.-Pub. Rels. & Communication--Grupo Cydsa, S.A. de C.V., Garza Garcia, Mexico; *Int'l*, pg. 246
Basham, J.D., Mgr.-Investor & Pub. Rels.--Dresser Industries, Inc., Dallas, TX; *U.S. Public*, pg. 528
Bass, Amy, Dir.-Corp. Communications--The Empire District Electric Company, Joplin, MO; *U.S. Public*, pg. 579
Bassett, Amanda, Head-Corp. Rels.--The Burton Group PLC, London, United Kingdom; *Int'l*, pg. 237
Bassewitz, Susanne, Mgr.-Pub. Rels.--Veba AG, Dusseldorf, Germany; *Int'l*, pg. 1454
Bastian, Kimberly S., Mgr.-Adv. & Corp. Info.--Public Service Company of North Carolina, Inc., Gastonia, NC; *U.S. Public*, pg. 1340
Bastian, Michael, Mgr.-Adv. & Pub. Rels.--Sotheby's International Realty, New York, NY; *U.S. Public*, pg. 1487
Bastien, Philippe, Dir.-Pub. Rels.--Groupe Casino, Saint Etienne, France; *Int'l*, pg. 562
Bateman, Lesley, Dir.-Mktg. Commun. & Pub. Rels.--Paradyne, Largo, FL; *U.S. Private*, pg. 838
Batka, Pat, Consumer Svcs.--The Ertl Company, Inc, Dyersville, IA; *U.S. Public*, pg. 1684
Batson, Paula, Sr. V.P.-Public Relations--Universal Studios Music Entertainment Group, Universal City, CA; *Int'l*, pg. 1215
Battaglia, Carol, Mgr.-Mktg. & Commun.--Dataram Corporation, Princeton, NJ; *U.S. Public*, pg. 487
Battaglia, Jean-Luc, Dir.-Communications--Lotto S.p.A., Montebelluna, Italy; *Int'l*, pg. 819
Batyko, R.J., Mgr.-Pub. Rels.--Babcock & Wilcox Co., Barberton, OH; *U.S. Public*, pg. 1068
Baud, Andrew, Dir.-Pub. Rels.--Eagle Star, Cheltenham, United Kingdom; *Int'l*, pg. 110
Bauer, Cathy, Dir.-Field Commun.--Midland National Life Insurance Co., Sioux Falls, SD; *U.S. Private*, pg. 963
Bauer, Debbie, Coord.-Communications--Air Products and Chemicals, Inc., Allentown, PA; *U.S. Public*, pg. 30
Bauer, Julie, Mgr.-Pub. Rels.--Famous Footwear, Madison, WI; *U.S. Public*, pg. 262
Bauer, Laurie, Supvr.-Pub. Rels.--Best Buy Co., Inc., Eden Prairie, MN; *U.S. Public*, pg. 223
Bauer, Liz, Mgr.-Adv. Comm.--Keystone Financial Inc., Harrisburg, PA; *U.S. Public*, pg. 956
Bauguitte, Andre, Mgr.-Pub. Rels.--RWE Entsorgung AG, Essen, Germany; *Int'l*, pg. 1081
Baumgarten, Matthias, Dir.-Pub. Rels.--Triumph Adler Group, Nuremberg, Germany; *Int'l*, pg. 1424
Baxter, Dana, Sr. Mgr.-Corp. Communications--Polygram Records, Inc., New York, NY; *Int'l*, pg. 1052
Baxter, Ellen, Mgr.-Pub. Rels.--Orlane, Inc., New York, NY; *Int'l*, pg. 1011
Baxter, Leslie, Mgr.-Mktg Communication Accts.--Sun Data Inc., Norcross, GA; *U.S. Private*, pg. 1050
Bayhack, Joanie, Dir.-Corp. Communications--WTTW (Channel 11), Chicago, IL; *U.S. Private*, pg. 1145
Bayless, Laurie, Sr. V.P.- Corp. Relations--Transamerica Life Companies, Los Angeles, CA; *U.S. Public*, pg. 1630
Bazelides, L. Diane, V.P.-Pub. Rels.--Enron Corp., Houston, TX; *U.S. Public*, pg. 584
Beach, Bob, V.P.-Corp. Communications--Traveling Software Inc., Bothell, WA; *U.S. Private*, pg. 1098
Beadle, Roy, Mgr.-Pub. Rels.--LASMO plc, London, United Kingdom; *Int'l*, pg. 803
Beale, R. Michelle, Sr. V.P.-H.R., Pub. Affairs & Admin. Svcs.--The Minute Maid Company, Houston, TX; *U.S. Public*, pg. 392
Beamer, Kathleen, V.P.-Pub. Affairs--Recreational Equipment, Inc., Kent, WA; *U.S. Private*, pg. 914
Bean, Barbara, Dir.-Communications--Kitchell Corporation, Phoenix, AZ; *U.S. Private*, pg. 624
Beatson, D., Mgr.-Pub. Rels.--Air New Zealand Ltd., Auckland, New Zealand; *Int'l*, pg. 38
Beattie, John, Gen. Mgr.-Corp. Rels.--Brierley Investments Limited, Wellington, New Zealand; *Int'l*, pg. 215
Beauchamp, Patricia F., V.P.-Commun.--The Penn Mutual Life Insurance Company, Philadelphia, PA; *U.S. Private*, pg. 849
Beauchamp, Paul, Dir.-Pub. Affairs--Cooperative Federee de Quebec, Montreal, Canada; *Int'l*, pg. 330
Beaucock, Robert, Dir.-Pub. Rels.--Winchester Electronics, Watertown, CT; *U.S. Public*, pg. 1003
Beaudry, O. LeRoy, V.P.-Consumer & Pub. Affairs--Cascade Natural Gas Corporation, Seattle, WA; *U.S. Public*, pg. 311
Beaudry, Roseanne, Pub. Rels.--Waring Products, New Hartford, CT; *U.S. Public*, pg. 286
Beauregard, Suzanne, Pub. Rels. Mgr.--Rainoldi, Kerzner & Radcliffe, San Francisco, CA; *U.S. Public*, pg. 1224
Becce, Michael, Public Rels.--The Sawtooth Group, Woodbridge, NJ; *U.S. Private*, pg. 969
Beck, Alois, V.P.-Customer Desk & Dealing Support--Liechtenstein Global Trust Limited, Vaduz, Liechtenstein; *Int'l*, pg. 809
Becker, Dick, Mgr.-Corp. Rels.--Steelcase Inc., Grand Rapids, MI; *U.S. Private*, pg. 1038
Becker, Don, Specialist-Corp. Communications--Rheometric Scientific, Piscataway, NJ; *U.S. Public*, pg. 1387
Becker, Jamie, Coord.-Mktg. Commun. Projects--Trendway Corporation, Holland, MI; *U.S. Private*, pg. 1099
Becker, Patricia, Dir.-Mktg. Commun.--Gelco Information Network, Inc., Eden Prairie, MN; *U.S. Private*, pg. 442
Becker, Patricia, Dir.-Corp. Communications--Electronic Arts, San Mateo, CA; *U.S. Public*, pg. 569
Becker, Suzanne, Dir.-Consumer Affairs--The Promotion in Motion Companies, Closter, NJ; *U.S. Private*, pg. 890
Beckley, Karyn, V.P.-Corp. Admin. Svcs.--SpaceLabs Medical, Inc., Redmond, WA; *U.S. Public*, pg. 1494
Becton, Robert, Dir.-Pub. Rels.--Moody's Investors Service, Inc., New York, NY; *U.S. Public*, pg. 536
Bedard, Kipp A., V.P.-Corp. Affairs--Micron Technology Inc., Boise, ID; *U.S. Public*, pg. 1105
Bedford, Steve, Dir.-Human Resources--BHS Plc, London, United Kingdom; *Int'l*, pg. 1304
Bee, Francis, Dir.-Newspaper Rels.--Metropolitan Sunday Newspapers, Inc., New York, NY; *U.S. Private*, pg. 739
Bee, Kathleen, Mgr.-Adv. & Pub. Rels.--Micro Motion Inc., Boulder, CO; *U.S. Public*, pg. 574
Beede, John, Brand Mgr.-Communications--Vauxhall Motors Limited, Luton, United Kingdom; *U.S. Public*, pg. 724
Beekler, Amy, Mgr.-Mktg. Communications--Northrup King Co., Golden Valley, MN; *Int'l*, pg. 974
Beer, Lorilei, Pub. Rels. Dir.--FGI Inc., Chapel Hill, NC; *U.S. Private*, pg. 389
Beerbower, David A., V.P.-Safety & Quality--Peabody Holding Company, Inc., Saint Louis, MO; *Int'l*, pg. 594
Behagen, Renee, Asst.-Corp. Communications--Guilford of Maine, Inc., Guilford, ME; *U.S. Public*, pg. 889
Behan, Simon, Mgr.-Adv. & Sls. Promo.--Texaco (Ireland) Ltd., Dublin, Ireland; *U.S. Public*, pg. 1584
Behr, Joan, V.P.-Commun.--Foremost Farms USA Cooperative, Baraboo, WI; *U.S. Private*, pg. 418
Belanger, Jim, Dir.-Communications & Adv.--Rockbestos-Suprenant Cable Corp., Clinton, MA; *U.S. Private*, pg. 938
Belding, Joan, Mgr.-Pub. Rels.--Union Bank & Trust Co., North Vernon, IN; *U.S. Public*, pg. 633
Belikove, Paula, Dir.-Global Mktg. Communications--VeriFone, Inc., Redwood City, CA; *U.S. Public*, pg. 815
Belin, Marie-Anne, Mgr.-Commun.--Compagnie Generale Maritime et Financiere, Suresnes, France; *Int'l*, pg. 322
Beliunas, Linda, Mgr.-H.R.--GHM Industries, Inc., Worcester, MA; *U.S. Private*, pg. 435
Belknap, William C., Dir.-Pub. Rels.--H.B. Fuller Company, Saint Paul, MN; *U.S. Public*, pg. 686
Bell, Adrian, Mgr.-Mktg. Communications--Metromail Corporation, Lombard, IL; *U.S. Public*, pg. 1102
Bell, Dan, V.P.-Customer Support--3Com Personal Communications Div., Skokie, IL; *U.S. Public*, pg. 1604
Bell, John, V.P.-Acct. Services/Pub. Rels.--Greenstone Roberts Public Relations, Coconut Creek, FL; *U.S. Public*, pg. 763
Bell, Paul, Dir.-Pub. Rels.--Dow Jones Interactive Publishing, Princeton, NJ; *U.S. Public*, pg. 524
Bell, Sandy, Dir.-Communications--Sterling Electronics Corporation, Houston, TX; *U.S. Public*, pg. 1051
Bellamy, Debbie, C.B.C., Dir.-Mktg. Services--American Software, Inc., Atlanta, GA; *U.S. Public*, pg. 91
Benard, Michael P., V.P. & Dir.-Communications & Public Affairs--Eastman Kodak Company, Rochester, NY; *U.S. Public*, pg. 550
Bendix, Richard C., V.P.-Mktg.--Lindal Cedar Homes, Inc., Seattle, WA; *U.S. Public*, pg. 998
Beneski, Barron, Dir.-Pub. Rels.--Orbital Sciences Corporation, Dulles, VA; *U.S. Public*, pg. 1229
Bengston, Linda, Mgr.-Communications--Ferrellgas Partners, L.P., Liberty, MO; *U.S. Public*, pg. 618
Benhard, Mark, Corp. Commun. & Pub. Rels.--Countrywide Home Loans Inc., Pasadena, CA; *U.S. Public*, pg. 452
Benitez, Pedro, Dir.-Telecommunications--Banco Quilmes, Buenos Aires, Argentina; *Int'l*, pg. 142
Benn, Elizabeth, Mgr.-Mkt. Communications--Pease Industries, Inc., Fairfield, OH; *U.S. Private*, pg. 845
Benner, Brian, Mgr.-Mktg. Communications--Mutoh America Inc., Phoenix, AZ; *Int'l*, pg. 897
Benner, Tony, Grp. Mgr.-Media & Information--Westpac Banking Corporation, Sydney, Australia; *Int'l*, pg. 1495
Bennett, Brenda, Dir.-Pub. Rels.--Western Digital Corporation, Irvine, CA; *U.S. Public*, pg. 1758
Bennett, Douglas M., Dir.-Mktg.--The Turner Corporation, New York, NY; *U.S. Public*, pg. 1645
Bennett, Farren E., Dir.-Mktg. Communications--Hilti Inc., Tulsa, OK; *Int'l*, pg. 620
Bennett, Jessica Ann, Dir.-Adv. & Mktg.--Carfel, Inc., Miami, FL; *U.S. Private*, pg. 210
Bennett, Philip, V.P.-Communication & Mktg.--Lafarge PlatresInternational, Sorges, France; *Int'l*, pg. 789
Benninga, Hans, Dir.-Mkt. Devel. & External Rels.--Heidemij N.V., Arnhem, Netherlands; *Int'l*, pg. 606
Bennyhoff, George R., Sr. V.P.-Human Resources & Pub. Affairs--The West Company, Incorporated, Lionville, PA; *U.S. Public*, pg. 1755
Benoit, Tom, Mgr.-Corp. Mktg.--Phoenix Technologies Ltd., San Jose, CA; *U.S. Public*, pg. 1292
Bensheidt, Carl, Dir.-Corp. Communications--The Washington Water Power Company, Spokane, WA; *U.S. Public*, pg. 1744
Benson, Jo-Dee, Mgr.-Mktg. Communications--Crystal Semiconductor Corporation, Austin, TX; *U.S. Public*, pg. 375
Beranek, Sue, V.P.-Mktg.--Taco John's International, Inc., Cheyenne, WY; *U.S. Private*, pg. 1066
Berdine, Jamie, Mgr.-Mktg. Commun.--CENTRIA, Moon Township, PA; *U.S. Private*, pg. 225
Berecz, Illya, Mgr.-Commun.--Subway Franchise Advertising Fund Trust, Milford, CT; *U.S. Private*, pg. 1048
Beresin, Jody, Asst. V.P.-Communications--Phoenix Home Life Mutual Insurance Co., Hartford, CT; *U.S. Private*, pg. 863
Berg, Bjorn, Dir.-Public Affairs--Hydro Aluminium Ardal Verk, Ovre Ardal, Norway; *Int'l*, pg. 959
Berg, Dick, Dir.-Customer Services--Lancaster Colony Automotive Group, Dublin, OH; *U.S. Public*, pg. 977
Berg, Tanya, V.P.-Communications--Old Kent Bank, Grand Rapids, MI; *U.S. Public*, pg. 1216
Bergen, Jack, Sr. V.P.-Corp. Rels.--CBS, New York, NY; *U.S. Public*, pg. 273
Bergen, Terry, Mgr.-Promo. & Pub. Affairs--The Gazette Company, Cedar Rapids, IA; *U.S. Private*, pg. 442
Bergene, John C., Asst. Dir.-Communications & Pub. Affairs/U.S.--Canadian Pacific Railway, Minneapolis, MN; *Int'l*, pg. 259
Berger, Luc, Dir.-Info.--Dassault Aviation Group, Vaucresson, France; *Int'l*, pg. 383
Bergeson, Margo R., Corp. Sec.--Alta Gold Co., Henderson, NV; *U.S. Public*, pg. 58
Bergh, Gloria, Mgr.-Pub. Rels.--Modern Woodmen of America, Rock Island, IL; *U.S. Private*, pg. 755
Berghley, Kristine, Mgr.-Mktg. Communications--Datapro Information Services Grp., Delran, NJ; *U.S. Public*, pg. 1070
Berghoef, Julie, Mgr.-Mktg. Commun.--Trendway Corporation, Holland, MI; *U.S. Private*, pg. 1099
Bergmann, Richard, Mgr.-Distr. & Customer Service--Ato-Findley, Inc., Wauwatosa, WI; *Int'l*, pg. 445
Berick, Rob, Mgr.-Corp. Commun.--Figgie International Inc., Cleveland, OH; *U.S. Public*, pg. 622
Berke, Art, Dir.-Communications--Sports Illustrated, New York, NY; *U.S. Public*, pg. 1613
Berkun, Judy, Mgr.-Copr. Mktg.--Malcolm Pirnie, Inc., White Plains, NY; *U.S. Private*, pg. 867
Berkus, David, Mgr.-Corp. Mktg. Communications--Sanyo Fisher Company, Chatsworth, CA; *Int'l*, pg. 1191
Berkus, David, Mgr.-Sls. Promo., Mdsg., Pub. Rels. & Adv.--Sanyo Office Automation, Chatsworth, CA; *Int'l*, pg. 1191
Berkwitt, Glenn, Mgr.-Mktg. Commun.--Applied Microsystems Corporation, Redmond, WA; *U.S. Public*, pg. 123
Berliner, Debra, Dir.-Investor Rels.--Overseas Shipholding Group, Inc., New York, NY; *U.S. Public*, pg. 1236
Berman, Bob, Mgr.-Adv. & Pub. Rels.--Market Facts, Inc., Arlington Heights, IL; *U.S. Public*, pg. 1046
Berman, Ira W., Chm. Bd. & Chief Fin. Officer--CCA Industries, Inc., East Rutherford, NJ; *U.S. Public*, pg. 276
Berman, Rich, Pub. Rels. Acct. Mgr.--Keiler & Company, Farmington, CT; *U.S. Private*, pg. 611
Bermio, Rene B., Asst. V.P. & Dir.-Corp. Rels--La Tondena Distillers, Inc., Manila, Philippines; *Int'l*, pg. 785

Bernardy, Laurie, V.P.-Corp. Communications--W.H. Brady Co., Milwaukee, WI; *U.S. Public*, pg. 250
Bernett, Paula, Mgr.-Pub. Rels.--Guideposts Associates, Inc., Carmel, NY; *U.S. Private*, pg. 487
Bernhiem, Claudie, Mgr.-Pub. Rels. & Communications--SCOR, Paris, France; *Int'l*, pg. 1152
Bernier, Marie, V.P.-Communications & Pub. Affairs--Provigo Inc., Montreal, Canada; *Int'l*, pg. 1072
Bernish, Paul, Dir.-Pub. Rels.--The Kroger Co., Cincinnati, OH; *U.S. Public*, pg. 967
Bernstein Winfield, Judy, Pub. Rels. Dir.--Marshall Jaccoma Mitchell Advertising, New York, NY; *U.S. Private*, pg. 708
Bernstein, Jill, Dir.-N.Y. Pub. Rels.--Country Home Magazine, Des Moines, IA; *U.S. Public*, pg. 1094
Bernstein, Paul, V.P.-Communications--Precision Tune Autocare Inc., Leesburg, VA; *U.S. Public*, pg. 1321
Berrett, John C., V.P.-Global Commun.--Haworth, Inc., Holland, MI; *U.S. Private*, pg. 511
Berrey, Sheila, Mgr.-Pub. Rels.--The Swiss Colony, Inc, Monroe, WI; *U.S. Private*, pg. 1059
Berrier, Roy, Dir.-Personnel--Porcelanite, Inc., Lexington, NC; *Int'l*, pg. 573
Berris, Brian, Partner-Private Client--Brown Brothers Harriman & Co., New York, NY; *U.S. Private*, pg. 173
Berry, Benjamin, V.P.-Mktg.--AMATI Communications Corp., San Jose, CA; *U.S. Public*, pg. 1585
Berry, H., Mgr.-Pub. Affairs--British Aerospace Airbus Limited, Chester, United Kingdom; *Int'l*, pg. 217
Berry, Phyllis, V.P.-Corp. Communications--Sun Healthcare Group Inc., Albuquerque, NM; *U.S. Public*, pg. 1530
Berry, Ralph, V.P.-Communications & Pub. Affairs--Harrah's Entertainment, Inc., Memphis, TN; *U.S. Public*, pg. 790
Bert, M.C., Deputy Dir.-Commun.--Compagnie Generale Maritime et Financiere, Suresnes, France; *Int'l*, pg. 322
Berthu, Mr. D., Dir.-Communications--Valeo Research Sooal, Paris, France; *Int'l*, pg. 240
Bertolini, Gary, Dir.-Customer Services--Delco-Electronics Customer Support, Troy, MI; *U.S. Public*, pg. 720
Beshore, Lance G., V.P.-Public Affairs & Govt. Rels.--Leggett & Platt, Incorporated, Carthage, MO; *U.S. Public*, *pg. 985*
Bess, Gordon, Dir.-Mktg. Communications--General American Life Insurance Co., Saint Louis, MO; *U.S. Private*, pg. 443
Besse, Jean, V.P.-Public Affairs--SNECMA - Societe Nationale d'Etude et de Construction de Moteurs d'Aviation, Paris, France; *Int'l*, pg. 1165
Best, Allison Stein, Dir.-Media Rels.--Cerner Corporation, Kansas City, MO; *U.S. Public*, pg. 331
Betlejewski, Tina, Mgr.-Corp. Commun.--SPX Corporation, Muskegon, MI; *U.S. Public*, pg. 1420
Beutel, Katy, Coord.-Communications--Rossignol Ski Co., Williston, VT; *Int'l*, pg. 1127
Bevil, C.K., Jr., Dir.-Mktg. Communications--Shaw Industries, Inc., Dalton, GA; *U.S. Public*, pg. 1464
Bevis, Harold L., V.P.-Pub. Affairs--Delta Air Lines, Inc., Atlanta, GA; *U.S. Public*, pg. 497
Beyer, Jeffrey C., V.P.-Corp. Communications--Farmers Group, Inc., Los Angeles, CA; *Int'l*, pg. 110
Bezandres, Mercedes, Coord.-Corp. Commun.--MarketSource Corporation, Cranbury, NJ; *U.S. Private*, pg. 705
Bezem, Dick, Dir.-Pub. Rels. & Communications--SmithKline Beecham Farma B.V., Rijswijk, Netherlands; *Int'l*, pg. 1266
Bhide, Roopa, Dir.-Pub. Rels.--IRI Software, Waltham, MA; *U.S. Public*, pg. 876
Bibler, Laurie, Chief Fin. Officer, Treas. & Sec.--Bibler Brothers, Inc., Russellville, AR; *U.S. Private*, pg. 142
Bidwell, Donald, Jr., Dir.-Mktg. & Pub. Relations--Bidwell Industrial Group, Inc., Middletown, CT; *U.S. Private*, pg. 142
Bidwell, Donald, Sr., Dir.-Mktg. & Pub. Rels.--Blu-Ray, Middletown, CT; *U.S. Private*, pg. 142
Bielski, John, Asst. V.P.-Commun.--CUNA Mutual Insurance Society, Madison, WI; *U.S. Private*, pg. 296
Bihary, Kristen M., V.P.-Public Affairs--LucasVarity Inc., Buffalo, NY; *Int'l*, pg. 820
Billecard, Georges, Dir.-Pub. Affairs & Legal--3M France, Cergy-Pontoise, France; *U.S. Public*, pg. 1606
Billing, Paul, Dir.-Pub. Rels.--Compass Design Automation Inc., San Jose, CA; *U.S. Public*, pg. 1703
Bilodeau, Alain, Sr. V.P.-Corp. Affairs--Steinberg Inc., Montreal, Canada; *Int'l*, pg. 1272
Biltz, Timothy G., Pres.-U.S. Wireless Opers.--Vanguard Cellular Systems, Inc., Greensboro, NC; *U.S. Public*, pg. 1707
Bind, Barbara Perry, Mgr.-Promos. & Pub. Affairs--The Advocate, Stamford, CT; *U.S. Public*, pg. 1616
Bingaman, Larry L., V.P.-Corp. Rels. & Sec.--Aquarion Company, Bridgeport, CT; *U.S. Public*, pg. 126
Bingaman, Larry L., Mgr.-Pub. Rels.--Hydrocorp, Inc., Bridgeport, CT; *U.S. Public*, pg. 126
Binzer, Corrina, Mgr.-Pub. Rels.--Knurr AG, Munich, Germany; *Int'l*, pg. 739
Binzer, Dan, Dir.-Pub. Rels.--DuBois Chemicals, Cincinnati, OH; *Int'l*, pg. 1437
Birtcil, Bill, V.P.-Community & Gov't. Affairs--The Pillsbury Company, Minneapolis, MN; *Int'l*, pg. 411
Bis, Don, Mgr.-Corp. Rels.--The Allstate Corporation, Northbrook, IL; *U.S. Public*, pg. 55
Bishop, Brad, Dir.-Communications--Zimmer, Inc., Warsaw, IN; *U.S. Public*, pg. 254
Bishop, Larry, V.P.-Commun. & Inv. Rels.--The Boeing Company, Seattle, WA; *U.S. Public*, pg. 239
Bismuth, J., Sr. V.P.-Media, Studies--Danone Group, Paris, France; *Int'l*, pg. 379
Bisschops, Theo P.M., Sec. & Dir.-Investor Rels.--Gamma Holding N.V., Helmond, Netherlands; *Int'l*, pg. 539
Bissell, Ronald, Dir.-Commun.--Furon Company, Laguna Niguel, CA; *U.S. Public*, pg. 688
Bissett, Wm. J., V.P.-Govt. Affairs & Community Rel.--Delaware North Companies, Inc., Buffalo, NY; *U.S. Private*, pg. 321
Bittner, Daniel P., Sr. V.P.-Fin. & Corp. Svcs.--Wisconsin Public Service Corporation, Green Bay, WI; *U.S. Public*, pg. 1728
Bitz, Rod, Dir.-Corp. Communication--Alliant Techsystems, Hopkins, MN; *U.S. Public*, pg. 47
Bitz, Rod, Dir.-Corp. Communications--Alliant Techsystems (Aerospace Division), Wilmington, DE; *U.S. Public*, pg. 47
Bixler, Colleen, Coord.-Mktg. Communications--Shimadzu Scientific Instruments, Inc., Columbia, MD; *Int'l*, pg. 1232
Black, Graham, Mgr.-Mktg. Communications--Case United Kingdom Limited, Doncaster, United Kingdom; *U.S. Public*, pg. 1579
Black, Marv, Dir.-Mktg. Communications--Northrup King Co., Golden Valley, MN; *Int'l*, pg. 974
Black, R. Charles, V.P.-Communications--GPU Service Corp., Parsippany, NJ; *U.S. Public*, pg. 695
Blackburn, Kathy, Mgr.-Pub. Rels.--Kaiser Permanente, California Division, Oakland, CA; *U.S. Private*, pg. 605
Blackburn, Tem, Mgr.-Communications & Trng.--Rose's Stores, Inc., Henderson, NC; *U.S. Public*, pg. 1405
Blackmon, Rod, Mgr.-Adv. & Pub. Rels.--The M.W. Kellogg Company, Houston, TX; *U.S. Public*, pg. 528
Blackmore, Brian, Dir.-Pub. Rels.--Electro-Voice, Inc., Buchanan, MI; *U.S. Private*, pg. 479
Blackmore, Jim, Mgr.-Pub. Rels.--Carrington Laboratories, Inc., Irving, TX; *U.S. Public*, pg. 309
Blain, Michelle, Mgr.-Intl. Sls. & Communications Div.--Titeflex Corporation, Springfield, MA; *Int'l*, pg. 1340
Blakeslee, H. Ed, V.P.-Customer Services & Mktg.--Mississippi Power Co., Gulfport, MS; *U.S. Public*, pg. 1490
Blancett-Scott, Meloyde, Staff V.P.-Corp. Communications--Thrifty Rent-a-Car System, Inc., Tulsa, OK; *U.S. Public*, pg. 354
Blanchard, Larry H., Sr. V.P.-Commun. & Pub. Rels.--CUNA Mutual Insurance Society, Madison, WI; *U.S. Private*, pg. 296
Blanchat, Nancy, Dir.-Mktg. Communications--The Coleman Company, Inc., Golden, CO; *U.S. Private*, pg. 690
Blanco-Belda, Javier, Dir.-Communications--SEPI, Madrid, Spain; *Int'l*, pg. 1223
Blanco, Maria Jose, Mgr.-Mktg. & Communications--A.C. Nielsen Company S.A., Madrid, Spain; *U.S. Public*, pg. 1183
Blank, William, V.P.-Mktg.--VGF Corporation, Lake Success, NY; *U.S. Public*, pg. 15
Blatman, J., Dir.-Public Rels.--Princess Hotels International Inc., New York, NY; *Int'l*, pg. 818
Blaylock, Lou Ann, V.P.-Corp. Rels.--Tandy Corporation, Fort Worth, TX; *U.S. Public*, pg. 1560
Blazier, Nicola, Coord.-Pub. Rels.--Four Seasons Hotels Inc., Don Mills, Canada; *Int'l*, pg. 502
Blickens, George, Dir.-Personnel--Haddon Craftsmen, Inc., Scranton, PA; *U.S. Public*, pg. 518
Bliesath, Nick, Market Anayst--Plastic Suppliers, Inc., Columbus, OH; *U.S. Private*, pg. 871
Bliffen, Rebekka, Mgr.-Pub. Rels.--Fossil Inc., Richardson, TX; *U.S. Private*, pg. 420
Blizman, Wayne, V.P.-Corp. Plng. & Devel.--Durakon Industries, Inc., Lapeer, MI; *U.S. Public*, pg. 537
Bloch, Edward, Mgr.-Pub. Rels.--The Perkin-Elmer Corporation, Norwalk, CT; *U.S. Public*, pg. 1279
Block, Bill, Mgr.-Corp. Communications--Bandag, Incorporated, Muscatine, IA; *U.S. Public*, pg. 177
Block, Eric, Dir.-Pub. Rels.--Datapro Information Services Grp., Delran, NJ; *U.S. Public*, pg. 1070
Block, H., Dir.-Pub. Rels.--Ruhrgas Aktiengesellschaft, Essen, Germany; *Int'l*, pg. 1148
Bloom, Brian, V.P. & Sr. Pub. Rels. Program Mgr.--Liggett-Stashower, Inc., Cleveland, OH; *U.S. Private*, pg. 667
Bloom, Elliot, V.P.-Corp. Communications--HFS, Incorporated, Parsippany, NJ; *U.S. Public*, pg. 321
Bloomfield, Karen, Mgr.-Pub. Rels.--Management Recruiters International, Inc., Cleveland, OH; *U.S. Public*, pg. 277
Blouin, Jean, Dir.-Pub. Rels.--G.T.C. Transcontinental Group Ltd., Montreal, Canada; *Int'l*, pg. 538
Blount, Girard M., V.P.-Pub. Rels.--Sands Investments, Inc., Myrtle Beach, SC; *U.S. Private*, pg. 964
Blum, Jonathan D., Sr. V.P.-Pub. Affairs--Tricon Global Restaurants, Inc., Louisville, KY; *U.S. Public*, pg. 1636
Blum, Stephen D., Sr. V.P.-Corp. Commun.--Quaker State Corporation, Irving, TX; *U.S. Public*, pg. 1348
Boatwright, P.J., Dir.-Mktg. & Communications--Fortune, New York, NY; *U.S. Public*, pg. 1613
Bobone, Manuel, Mgr.-Pub. Rels.--Nestle Portugal, S.A., Carnaxide, Portugal; *Int'l*, pg. 921
Bochert, Jodi, Pub. Rels. Asst.--Newmont Mining Corporation, Denver, CO; *U.S. Public*, pg. 1178
Bockstiegel, Julie, Dir.-Media--Hasbro, Cincinnati, OH; *U.S. Public*, pg. 797
Bodensteiner, Carol A., Pres.-CMF&Z Pub. Rels.--Creswell, Munsell, Fultz & Zirbel, L.P., Cedar Rapids, IA; *U.S. Private*, pg. 1197
Bodkin, David G., Dir.-Asian Pub. Affairs--GMOC Japan, Tokyo, Japan; *U.S. Public*, pg. 723
Bodvig, Colleen, Mgr.-Mktg.--Bourton Group, Rockford, IL; *U.S. Private*, pg. 162
Boegler, Pierre, Exec. V.P.-Communications--N. Schlumberger & Cie, Guebwiller, France; *Int'l*, pg. 1206
Boegli, DeAnne, Mgr.-Corp. Communications--RAYOVAC Corporation, Madison, WI; *U.S. Private*, pg. 912
Boehme, Tom, Gen. Mgr.-Customer Service--G.E. Appliances, Louisville, KY; *U.S. Public*, pg. 710
Boehne, Rich, V.P.-Corp. Communications & Investor Rels.--The E.W. Scripps Company, Cincinnati, OH; *U.S. Public*, *pg. 1447*
Boel, Yvonne, Mgr.-Pub. Rels.--Bel RTL, Brussels, Belgium; *Int'l*, pg. 561
Boelhouser, William, Dir.-Investor Rels.--Gamma Holding N.V., Helmond, Netherlands; *Int'l*, pg. 539
Boesch, Katy, Dir.-Adv. & Pub. Rels.--Williams-Sonoma, Inc., San Francisco, CA; *U.S. Public*, pg. 1770
Bogard, Stacy, Coord.-Mktg. Communications--Cold Spring Granite Company, Cold Spring, MN; *U.S. Private*, pg. 250
Boggiano, Phil, Dir.-Community Rels.--Universal Forest Products, Inc., Grand Rapids, MI; *U.S. Public*, pg. 1696
Boggs, Roger, Mgr.-Mktg. Communications--DePuy, Inc., Warsaw, IN; *Int'l*, pg. 331
Boggs, Timothy A., Sr. V.P.-Public Policy--Time Warner Inc., New York, NY; *U.S. Public*, pg. 1610
Bohannon, Nancy C., Sr. V.P. & Dir.-Mktg.--First Farmers & Merchants National Bank, Columbia, TN; *U.S. Private*, pg. 407
Bohl, Julie A., Dir.-Pub. Rels.--Combe Incorporated, White Plains, NY; *U.S. Private*, pg. 257
Bohn, Susan B., Exec. V.P.-Corp. Dev., Communications & Pub. Rels.--PNC Bank Corp., Pittsburgh, PA; *U.S. Public*, *pg. 1242*
Bolding, Debbie, Mgr.-Communications--Star-Kist Foods Inc., Newport, KY; *U.S. Public*, pg. 805
Boldrini, Ezo, Mgr.-Corp. Mktg.--3M Chile S.A., Santiago, Chile; *U.S. Public*, pg. 1606
Bolduc, A., V.P.-Pub. Affairs--La Brasserie Labatt Limitee, La Salle, Canada; *Int'l*, pg. 679
Bolek, Bernice, Mgr.-Pub. Rels.--ICI Paints, Cleveland, OH; *Int'l*, pg. 664
Boll, James C., V.P.-Law & Corp. Communications--Madison Gas and Electric Company, Madison, WI; *U.S. Public*, pg. 1032
Bologna, Karen, Mgr.-Mktg. Communications--Hexcel Corporation, Pleasanton, CA; *U.S. Public*, pg. 824
Bolt, Jos, Dir.-Pub. Rels.--Ballast Nedam NV, Amstelveen, Netherlands; *Int'l*, pg. 133
Bolte, Rene, Prin. Advisor--Gaz Metropolitain & Company, Montreal, Canada; *Int'l*, pg. 541
Bolton, Catherine A., Dir.-Corp. Communications--Cargill Salt Inc., Minneapolis, MN; *Int'l*, pg. 48
Bombay, Bruno, Mgr.-Pub. Rels.--Parsons Power Group, Inc., Reading, PA; *U.S. Private*, pg. 841
Bonaddio, Vincent A., V.P.-Opers. & Engrng.--Pennsylvania Enterprises Inc., Wilkes-Barre, PA; *U.S. Public*, pg. 1271
Bonanno, Milton, Mgr.-Pub. Rels.--Philips do Brasil-Walita Div., Sao Paulo, Brazil; *Int'l*, pg. 1055
Boncy, R. Richard, V.P.-Law, Pub. Affairs & Corp. Devel.--Medtronic Europe S.A./N.V., Lausanne, Switzerland; *U.S. Public*, pg. 1083
Bond, David E., V.P.-Govt. & Pub. Affairs & Chief Economist--HongKong Bank of Canada, Vancouver, Canada; *Int'l*, pg. 583
Bond, Joe, Pub. Rels. Specialist--Goodwill Industries International, Bethesda, MD; *U.S. Private*, pg. 464
Bondy, Danielle, V.P.-Communication--C.E.P. Communication Group, Paris, France; *Int'l*, pg. 239
Bondy, Sherri, Mgr.-Corp. Commun.--O&Y Properties Corporation, Toronto, Canada; *Int'l*, pg. 993
Boner, Elisabeth, Mgr.-Pub. Rels.--Oerlikon-Contraves AG, Zurich, Switzerland; *Int'l*, pg. 998
Bones, Martin, V.P.-Mktg. Communications--Everex Systems Inc., Fremont, CA; *Int'l*, pg. 498
Boneta, Carol, Mgr.-Personnel & Pub. Rels.--Lectrodryer Div., Ajax Magnethermic Corp., Richmond, KY; *Int'l*, pg. 113
Bonis, Maryann, Communications Admin.--Huls America Inc., Somerset, NJ; *Int'l*, pg. 1455
Bonn, Robin, Press Officer--Fortis, Utrecht, Netherlands; *Int'l*, pg. 498
Bonnet, Michel, Sr. V.P.-Mktg. & Public Affairs--Elf Aquitane, Paris, France; *Int'l*, pg. 444
Bonnett, Madelyn C., Supvr.-Mktg. Commun.--EBSCO Industries, Inc., Birmingham, AL; *U.S. Private*, pg. 358
Boon Khim, Ong, Mgr.-Customer Affairs--Singapore Airlines, Los Angeles, CA; *Int'l*, pg. 1374
Boone Isaacs, Cheryl, Sr. V.P.-Worldwide Publicity--Paramount Pictures Corporation, Los Angeles, CA; *U.S. Private*, pg. 776
Boone, Rhonda G., Mgr.-Corp. Communications--Western Geophysical, Houston, TX; *U.S. Public*, pg. 1757
Boone, Rhonda G., Mgr.-Corp. Communications--Western Atlas International, Inc., Houston, TX; *U.S. Public*, pg. 1757
Boorks, Vivian, Dir.-Pub. Affairs--Friendly Ice Cream Corp., Wilbraham, MA; *U.S. Public*, pg. 682
Booth, William B., V.P.-Investor & Pub. Affairs--Hecla Mining Company, Coeur D'Alene, ID; *U.S. Public*, pg. 803
Borches, Susan M., Dir.-Corp. Communications--ABB Inc., Norwalk, CT; *Int'l*, pg. 3
Boren, LaRita R., V.P.-Pub. Rels.--Avis Industrial Corporation, Upland, IN; *U.S. Private*, pg. 102
Borg, M. Vincent, V.P.-Pub. Affairs & Communications--Barrick Gold Corporation, Toronto, Canada; *Int'l*, pg. 168
Borghs, Horst P., Dir.-Pub. Affairs--Adam Opel AG, Russelsheim, Germany; *U.S. Public*, pg. 721
Borgman, Patt, Coord.-Pub. Rels.--Quill Corp., Lincolnshire, IL; *U.S. Private*, pg. 901
Borrington, H., Mgr.-Reg. Pub. Rels.--British Aerospace Regional Aircraft, Avro Intl. Aerospace Div., Woodford, United Kingdom; *Int'l*, pg. 218
Borrington, H., Mgr.-Reg. Pub. Rels.--British Aerospace Regional Aircraft Limited, Middleton, United Kingdom; *Int'l*, pg. 218
Borsari, R., Gen. Mgr.-Pub. Rels.--Nuovo Pignone S.p.a., Florence, Italy; *Int'l*, pg. 990
Boss, Rhonda, Corp. Commun. Asst.--CPAC, Inc., Leicester, NY; *U.S. Public*, pg. 282
Boster, Kari, Dir.-Mktg.--Bluewater, Mora, MN; *U.S. Private*, pg. 153
Bostic, James E., Jr., Sr. V.P.-Environment, Govt. Affairs & Communications--Georgia-Pacific Corporation, Atlanta, GA; *U.S. Public*, pg. 735
Boswell, L. Blaine, V.P.-Pub. Affairs--PPG Industries, Inc., Pittsburgh, PA; *U.S. Public*, pg. 1245
Bothe, Brooke, Sec.--H.W. Kaufman Financial Group, Inc., Farmington, MI; *U.S. Private*, pg. 609
Botticher, Pam, Mgr.-Mktg. Coord.--Manatron, Inc., Kalamazoo, MI; *U.S. Public*, pg. 1040

Bottrell, Ronald G., Dir.-Pub. Rels.--The Quaker Oats Company, Chicago, IL; *U.S. Public*, pg. 1347
Boucher, Nicole, Dir.-Communications--Entreprise Miniere et Chimique, Paris, France; *Int'l*, pg. 458
Boulais, Dee, Mgr.-Sls. & Service--Lan-O-Sheen, Inc., Saint Paul, MN; *U.S. Private*, pg. 645
Bourgeois, Alison, Dir.-Commun.--Bertrand Faure, Boulogne, France; *Int'l*, pg. 192
Bourque, Marilyn, Supvr.-Mktg. Communications--FMC-Crosby Valve, Inc., Wrentham, MA; *U.S. Public*, pg. 605
Bouster, Ariza, Dir.-Communications--Moulinex S.A., Bagnolet, France; *Int'l*, pg. 896
Boutwell, Julie, Mgr.-Mktg. Communications--Genicom Corporation, Chantilly, VA; *U.S. Public*, pg. 729
Bouwmeester, Erick, V.P.-Pub Rels. & Corp. Communications--DSM N.V., Heerlen, Netherlands; *Int'l*, pg. 352
Bovaird, B.H., V.P.-Customer Svc. & Sls.--Bovaird Supply Co., Tulsa, OK; *U.S. Private*, pg. 162
Boven, Steve, Corp. Communications--Food Services of America, Seattle, WA; *U.S. Private*, pg. 874
Boveroux, Brooks, V.P.-Investor Rels.--The Liposome Company, Inc., Princeton, NJ; *U.S. Public*, pg. 1000
Boville, Ramon Sanjuan, Dir.-Mktg., Pub. Rels., Sls. & Adv.--Cabinas Telefonicas, S.A. (Cabitel), Madrid, Spain; *Int'l*, pg. 1371
Bowen, Denise, Mgr.-Customer Service--Standard Manufacturing Co., Inc., Troy, NY; *U.S. Private*, pg. 1031
Bower, Barbara, Sr. V.P.-Mktg. Services--Trammell Crow Company, Dallas, TX; *U.S. Public*, pg. 1628
Bower, Jan, Coord.-Communications--GATX Corporation, Chicago, IL; *U.S. Public*, pg. 690
Bowersock, Lisa, Dir.-Pub. Rels.--AirTouch Cellular - Western Region, Bellevue, WA; *U.S. Public*, pg. 34
Bowlby, Rita L., V.P.-Corp. Affairs--United Illuminating Company, New Haven, CT; *U.S. Public*, pg. 1678
Bowler, Denise, Mgr.-Pub. Rels.--The B.F. Goodrich Company, Richfield, OH; *U.S. Public*, pg. 751
Bowman, Roberta B., V.P.-Pub. Affairs--Duke Energy Corporation, Charlotte, NC; *U.S. Public*, pg. 534
Boxer, Peter, Dir.-External Rels.--Vickers PLC, London, United Kingdom; *Int'l*, pg. 1466
Boyce, Raymond A, V.P.-Communications & Pub. Rels.--Joseph E. Seagram & Sons, Inc., New York, NY; *Int'l*, pg. 1215
Boyd, Charles A., V.P.-Corp. Rel.--Sundt Corp., Tucson, AZ; *U.S. Private*, pg. 1051
Boyd, James, Dir.-Pub. Rels.--Air New Zealand Ltd. (U.S.A.), El Segundo, CA; *Int'l*, pg. 38
Boyer, Alan, Dir.-Corp. Communications--First Data Corporation, Hackensack, NJ; *U.S. Public*, pg. 630
Boyle, Charlie, Mgr.-External Affairs--Bell Atlantic-DE, Wilmington, DE; *U.S. Public*, pg. 202
Boyle, Jim, V.P.-Corp. Commun.--Discovery Networks, Inc., Bethesda, MD; *U.S. Private*, pg. 334
Boyle, Tom, Dir.-Mktg. Worldwide Communications--PerSeptive Biosystems, Inc., Framingham, MA; *U.S. Public*, pg. 1279
Bozarth, Glenn, Sr. V.P.-Corp. Commun.--Mattel, Inc., El Segundo, CA; *U.S. Public*, pg. 1057
Bracken, Alexander E., V.P.-Pub. Affairs--Ball Aerospace & Technologies Corp., Broomfield, CO; *U.S. Public*, pg. 171
Bracken, H.A., Grp. V.P.-Parts, Service & Customer Rels.--Toyota Motor Sales, U.S.A., Inc., Torrance, CA; *Int'l*, pg. 1412
Brackett, Regina P., V.P.-Mktg.--Home Federal Bank, Hamilton, OH; *U.S. Public*, pg. 633
Bradley, Todd, Mgr.-Investor Rels.--Hutchinson Technology Inc., Hutchinson, MN; *U.S. Public*, pg. 850
Bradshaw, Charlie, Dir.-Corp. Commun.--Safeguard Business Systems, Inc., Fort Washington, PA; *U.S. Private*, pg. 960
Bradshaw, Laura, Product Publicist--General Datacomm Industries, Inc., Middlebury, CT; *U.S. Public*, pg. 708
Brady, Cheryl, Coord.-Pub. Rels.--Pacificare Health Systems, Santa Ana, CA; *U.S. Public*, pg. 1251
Brak, A.J.C., Coordinator-Grp. Public Affairs--Royal Dutch/Shell Group of Companies, Hague, Netherlands; *Int'l*, pg. 1135
Braman, Marvin L., Dir.-Communications--Sanders, A Lockheed Martin Company, Nashua, NH; *U.S. Public*, pg. 1008
Bramblett, Michael T., Exec. V.P.--Jones Medical Industries Inc., Saint Louis, MO; *U.S. Public*, pg. 933
Brancoli, David, Dir.-Pub. Rels.--Visa U.S.A. Inc., San Francisco, CA; *U.S. Private*, pg. 1141
Brandtner, Andreas, Dir.-Pub. Rels.--VARTA AG, Hannover, Germany; *Int'l*, pg. 1451
Branger, Kathy, Mktg. Communications & Media Specialist--Applied Power Inc., Butler, WI; *U.S. Public*, pg. 124
Brangier, Natalie, Mgr.-Fin., Commun.& Adv.--Compagnie Financiere de Paribas, Paris, France; *Int'l*, pg. 319
Branson, Robert J., Gvmt. & Pub. Rels. Dir.--United Australian Automotive Industries Ltd., Saint Kilda, Australia; *U.S. Public*, pg. 725
Branson, Robert J., Gvmt. & Pub. Rels. Dir.--United Australian Automotive Industries Ltd., Saint Kilda, Australia; *Int'l*, pg. 1414
Branston, Robert F., Dir.-Creative Services--Regal Ware, Inc., Kewaskum, WI; *U.S. Private*, pg. 917
Brantingham, Julie, Mgr.-Mktg & Communications--Dionex Corporation, Sunnyvale, CA; *U.S. Public*, pg. 510
Brash, Steven L., Mgr.-Pub. Affairs--Union Light, Heat and Power Co., Cincinnati, OH; *U.S. Public*, pg. 369
Brashear, Albert R., Corp. V.P. & Dir.-Corp. Communications--Motorola, Inc., Schaumburg, IL; *U.S. Public*, pg. 1136
Braswell, B., Mgr.-Mktg. Svcs.--SCANA Corporation, Columbia, SC; *U.S. Public*, pg. 1436
Braswell, Cruse C., Jr., Exec. Dir.-Pub. Rels.--BellSouth Corporation, Atlanta, GA; *U.S. Public*, pg. 207
Braswell, Fred O., III, V.P.-External Affairs--Russell Corporation, Alexander City, AL; *U.S. Public*, pg. 1413
Brattstrom, Kjell, Pub. Rels. Officer--Svenska Handelsbanken, Stockholm, Sweden; *Int'l*, pg. 1327
Bratz, Keith, Dir.-Communications--Provident Mutual Life Insurance Co., Berwyn, PA; *U.S. Private*, pg. 891
Braumann, Elisabeth, Mgr.-Pub. Rels.--Windmoeller & Hoelscher, Lengerich, Germany; *Int'l*, pg. 1510
Braumann, Hans Hugo, Press Office--Villeroy & Boch AG, Mettlach, Germany; *Int'l*, pg. 1468
Braun, Dena, Publications Coord.--Baker & McKenzie, Attorneys At Law, Chicago, IL; *U.S. Private*, pg. 111
Braun, Jane, Mgr.-Pub. Rels.--Schneider Automation, Inc., North Andover, MA; *Int'l*, pg. 1208
Brauner, Susan, Dir.-Communications--Blue Diamond Growers, Sacramento, CA; *U.S. Private*, pg. 152
Bray, Hugh, Dir.-Worldwide Adv. & Communications--BMCA Insulation Products, Inc., Ontario, CA; *U.S. Private*, pg. 433
Bray, Maggie, Mgr.-Mktg.--Tippins Incorporated, Pittsburgh, PA; *U.S. Private*, pg. 1088
Brayton, Stephen, Mgr.-Corp. Pub. Rels.--The Gillette Company, Boston, MA; *U.S. Public*, pg. 743
Brazell, Amelia, Dir.-Mktg.--Zoological Society of San Diego, San Diego, CA; *U.S. Private*, pg. 1207
Breau, Angela, Mgr.-Communications--SierraCom, Hopkinton, MA; *U.S. Private*, pg. 999
Brechbiel, Steve, Mgr.-Communications--Reichhold Chemicals, Inc., Durham, NC; *Int'l*, pg. 370
Bredemeier, Sonning, Dr., Exec. V.P. & Dir.-Pub. Rels.--Norddeutsche Landesbank (NORD/LB), Hannover, Germany; *Int'l*, pg. 957
Bredwell, Jo, Sr. V.P. & Corp. Mktg. Comm. Dir.--Bernard Hodes Group, New York, NY; *U.S. Public*, pg. 1224
Bregenzer, Robert, Sr. V.P.-Communications--Information Resources, Inc., Chicago, IL; *U.S. Public*, pg. 875
Brei, Linda G., Dir.-Corp. Commun.--Wisconsin Power & Light Company, Madison, WI; *U.S. Public*, pg. 1728
Breitenbach, Bernard, Dir.-Pub. Rels.--Mercantile Stores Company, Inc., Fairfield, OH; *U.S. Public*, pg. 1089
Breitenbach, E. Allen, Dr., Chm. Bd. & Chief Exec. Officer--Scientific Software-Intercomp, Inc., Denver, CO; *U.S. Public*, pg. 1443
Breitsprecher, Frank-Ulrich, Dir.-Pub. Rels.--Robert Bosch GmbH, Gerlingen, Germany; *Int'l*, pg. 203
Brendle, Ronnie, Dir.-Commun.--Americal Corporation, Henderson, NC; *U.S. Private*, pg. 49
Brennan, Robert, Mgr.-Communications--The Southern Connecticut Gas Company, Bridgeport, CT; *U.S. Public*, pg. 431
Brennen, Fran, Mgr.-Mktg. Communications/Veeco-NY--Sloan Technology, Santa Barbara, CA; *U.S. Public*, pg. 1711
Brenner, Stanley, Pres.--CV Reit, Inc., West Palm Beach, FL; *U.S. Public*, pg. 286
Breotta, Pat, Mgr.-Pub. Rels.--Lafarge Corporation, Reston, VA; *Int'l*, pg. 788
Breth, Robin, Dir.-Mktg. & Adv.--Gold Medal Products Co., Cincinnati, OH; *U.S. Private*, pg. 459
Brett, Derwood, Mgr.-Corp. Communications--Arkansas Electric Cooperatives Inc., Little Rock, AR; *U.S. Private*, pg. 82
Brett, Pat, Pub. Rels. Specialist--3Com Corporation, Santa Clara, CA; *U.S. Public*, pg. 1603
Brevard, Mary, Dir.-Investor Rels. & Commun.--Borg Warner Automotive, Inc., Chicago, IL; *U.S. Public*, pg. 245
Brewer, Dee, Mgr.-Pub. Affairs--Pacificare of Utah, Salt Lake City, UT; *U.S. Public*, pg. 1251
Brewer, Mitzi, Corp. Communications--Spelling Television, Los Angeles, CA; *U.S. Private*, pg. 776
Brewster, Cynthia, Sec. & Mgr.-Adv.--Labelon Corporation, Canandaigua, NY; *U.S. Private*, pg. 641
Brice, Mary, Mgr.-Pub. Rels.--EG & G Rotron, Woodstock, NY; *U.S. Public*, pg. 543
Bricker, C., Dir.-Pub. Affairs--Labatt Breweries of Canada - Prairie Region, Edmonton, Canada; *Int'l*, pg. 679
Bridges, Jeff, V.P.-Customer Service--Helly-Hansen (US), Inc., Redmond, WA; *Int'l*, pg. 1010
Bridges, Maurice, Sr. V.P.-Diversity Affairs--Hardee's Food Systems, Inc., Rocky Mount, NC; *U.S. Public*, pg. 278
Bright, David E., V.P. & Dir.-Communications--Trace International Holdings, Inc., New York, NY; *U.S. Private*, pg. 1094
Brightman, Patrick, Pub. Rels. Dir.--SSD&W Integrated Marketing Communications, Montville, NJ; *U.S. Private*, pg. 958
Brill, Linda, Dir.-Communications--DirecTV Inc., El Segundo, CA; *U.S. Public*, pg. 720
Brinch, S. Peter, Dir.-Pub. Rels. & External Communications--PHH Corporation, Hunt Valley, MD; *U.S. Public*, pg. 321
Brink, C., Dir.-Corp. Commun.--Koninklijke Hoogovens N.V., Ijmuiden, Netherlands; *Int'l*, pg. 753
Brink, C., Corp. Commun. Chief--Hoogovens Groep B.V., Ijmuiden, Netherlands; *Int'l*, pg. 753
Britnell, Keith, Mgr.-Corp. Pub. Rels.--Intergraph Corporation, Huntsville, AL; *U.S. Public*, pg. 890
Britton, Rob, Mng. Dir.-Corp. Communications--AMR Corporation, Fort Worth, TX; *U.S. Public*, pg. 9
Broadbent, M., Head-Grp. Pub. Affairs/Asia--The Hongkong and Shanghai Banking Corporation Limited (HongkongBank), Central, Hong Kong; *Int'l*, pg. 583
Brock, Nancy, V.P.--First Empire State Corporation, Buffalo, NY; *U.S. Public*, pg. 631
Broder, Matt, Dir.-Issues Communication--United Technologies Corporation, Hartford, CT; *U.S. Public*, pg. 1689
Broderick, Peter, Mgr.-Mktg. Communications--AGFA EPS Division, Wilmington, MA; *Int'l*, pg. 172
Brody, Carolyn, Dir.-Pub. Rels.--Harry Winston, Inc., New York, NY; *U.S. Private*, pg. 1183
Broekhuis, J. W., Dir.-External Affairs--CSM Food Division, Diemen, Netherlands; *Int'l*, pg. 243
Broge, Elizabeth, V.P.-Communications & Press Relations--Avions de Transport Regional - ATR, Blagnac, France; *Int'l*, pg. 654
Bromberg, Leslie, Dir.-Mktg. Communications--Artisoft, Inc., Tucson, AZ; *U.S. Public*, pg. 136
Brondi, Dennis, Dir.-Mktg.--Power-One, Inc., Camarillo, CA; *U.S. Private*, pg. 878
Bronk, Gregg, Dir.-Corp. Commun.--Owens Corning, Toledo, OH; *U.S. Public*, pg. 1236
Brook, J.A., V.P.- Mktg. & Commun.--Alabama Electric Cooperative, Inc., Andalusia, AL; *U.S. Private*, pg. 30
Brook, John, Customer Service--IDP Vertical Turbine Pump Division, Hastings, NE; *U.S. Public*, pg. 877
Brookes, H.M., Treas. & Sec--Powerscreen International Plc, Dungannon, United Kingdom; *Int'l*, pg. 1066
Brooklier, John L., V.P.-Corp. Communications--Heller Financial, Inc., Chicago, IL; *Int'l*, pg. 519
Brooks, Carl, V.P.-Matls. & Svc.--GPU Service Corp., Parsippany, NJ; *U.S. Public*, pg. 695
Brooks, Vivian, Dir.-Pub. Affairs--Friendly Ice Cream Corp., Wilbraham, MA; *U.S. Public*, pg. 682
Brooks, William C., V.P.-Community & Urban Affairs--General Motors Corporation, Detroit, MI; *U.S. Public*, pg. 718
Brookter, Carolyn, Mgr.-Media Rels.--Target Stores, Minneapolis, MN; *U.S. Public*, pg. 489
Broom, Mike, Dir.-Pub. Affairs--AlliedSignal Commercial Avionics Systems, Redmond, WA; *U.S. Public*, pg. 50
Broome, Rich, Asst. V.P. & Dir.-Corp. Communications--Selective Insurance Group, Inc, Branchville, NJ; *U.S. Public*, pg. 1455
Brophy, Mary, Sr. V.P. & Pub. Rels. Dir.--Grant/Jacoby, Inc., Chicago, IL; *U.S. Private*, pg. 470
Bross, Bernard P., Mgr.-Communications--AgrEvo USA Company, Wilmington, DE; *Int'l*, pg. 1203
Brossard, John, Mgr.-Commun.--The Oilgear Company, Milwaukee, WI; *U.S. Public*, pg. 1215
Brotha, Greta, Mgr.-Pub. Rels.--South African Breweries, Ltd., Johannesburg, South Africa; *Int'l*, pg. 1286
Brotman, Phyllis, V.P. & Pub. Rels. Dir.--Gray Kirk/VanSant Advertising, Inc., Baltimore, MD; *U.S. Private*, pg. 472
Browe, David, V.P.-Consumer Rels.--Thermador, Los Angeles, CA; *U.S. Public*, pg. 1053
Brower, Lee, Mgr.-Pub. Rels.--Aeroquip Corporation, Maumee, OH; *U.S. Public*, pg. 24
Brower, Mardyne, Mgr.-Pub. Rels.--Farmers State Bank, Liberty, IN; *U.S. Public*, pg. 633
Brower, Paul G., V.P.-Commun.--Gold Kist, Inc., Atlanta, GA; *U.S. Private*, pg. 459
Brown, Bryan, Grp. Mgr.-Communications--Iams Company, Dayton, OH; *U.S. Private*, pg. 556
Brown, Cheri, Mgr.-Consumer Rels.--HMI Industries, Cleveland, OH; *U.S. Public*, pg. 771
Brown, Debbie, Mgr.-Pub. Rels.--Irwin Toy Ltd., Toronto, Canada; *Int'l*, pg. 688
Brown, Deborah Elliott, Mgr.-Corp. Commun.--York Wallcoverings Inc., York, PA; *U.S. Private*, pg. 1196
Brown, Dennis, Chief Fin. Officer, V.P. & Treas.--Sybron International Corporation, Milwaukee, WI; *U.S. Public*, pg. 1544
Brown, Elizabeth, Dir.-Corp. Rels.--The Bureau of National Affairs, Inc., Washington, DC; *U.S. Private*, pg. 181
Brown, Herbert R., V.P. & Dir.-Pub. Rels.--The Western and Southern Life Insurance Company, Cincinnati, OH; *U.S. Private*, pg. 1164
Brown, James M., V.P. & Chief Information Officer--COM/Energy Services Co., Cambridge, MA; *U.S. Public*, pg. 414
Brown, Jimm, Dir.-Community Rels.--Fisher Broadcasting Inc., Seattle, WA; *U.S. Public*, pg. 648
Brown, Jody A., Dir.-Bus. Commun.--CACI International Inc, Arlington, VA; *U.S. Public*, pg. 272
Brown, John W., V.P.-Pub. Rels.--Arvin Industries, Inc., Columbus, IN; *U.S. Public*, pg. 136
Brown, Judy Simms, Mgr.-Mktg. Communications--Watlow Winona, Inc., Winona, MN; *U.S. Private*, pg. 1153
Brown, Kelley A., Mgr.-Pub. Rels.--Miller Brewing Company, Fulton, NY; *U.S. Public*, pg. 1289
Brown, Kirk, Dir.-Commun.--Farmland Industries, Inc., Kansas City, MO; *U.S. Private*, pg. 395
Brown, Larry L., Mgr.-Pub. Rels.--Volkswagen of America Administration Center West, Westlake Village, CA; *Int'l*, pg. 1474
Brown, Loretta, Coord.-Mktg.--Boyer Candy Company Inc., Altoona, PA; *U.S. Private*, pg. 162
Brown, Marion, Dir.-Publicity & Adv.--Pantheon Books, Inc., New York, NY; *U.S. Private*, pg. 21
Brown, Mark Malloch, V.P.-External Affairs--The World Bank, Washington, DC; *U.S. Private*, pg. 1188
Brown, Marvin L., Mgr.-Communications--Destec Energy, Inc., Houston, TX; *U.S. Public*, pg. 1146
Brown, Michael, V.P.-Corp. Rels. & Sec.--Consolidated Freightways Corp., Menlo Park, CA; *U.S. Public*, pg. 435
Brown, Morry, Mgr.-Sls., Mktg. & Customer Service--Northern Cable Holdings Ltd., Montreal, Canada; *Int'l*, pg. 241
Brown, P.J., Dir.-Commun.--Cooper Tire & Rubber Company, Findlay, OH; *U.S. Public*, pg. 445
Brown, P.J., Dir.-Communications--The Cooper Tire Company, Findlay, OH; *U.S. Public*, pg. 445
Brown, Steve, Dir.-Corp. Communications--Chattanooga Group, Inc., Hixson, TN; *U.S. Private*, pg. 231
Brown, Suzi, Mgr.-Public Relations--CKE Restaurants Inc., Anaheim, CA; *U.S. Public*, pg. 278
Brownlee, Scott, Dir.-Corp. Communications--Toyota (Great Britain) Limited, Redhill, United Kingdom; *Int'l*, pg. 1414
Brownley, Dorothy, Sr. V.P.-Pub. Rels.--Huntington Bancshares Inc., Columbus, OH; *U.S. Public*, pg. 849
Brubeck, Daniel J., Dir.-Communications Adv. & Corp. Identity--Eaton Corporation, Cleveland, OH; *U.S. Public*, pg. 555
Bruce, Jason R., Communications Specialist--Hooker Industries, Ontario, CA; *U.S. Private*, pg. 538
Bruce, Steve, Mgr.-Corp. Communications--The Daiwa Bank Limited, Osaka, Japan; *Int'l*, pg. 373
Bruck, M., Dir.-Mktg. & Pub. Rels.--ALZ N.V., Genk, Belgium; *Int'l*, pg. 79

Bruell, Gary, Sr. Mgr.-Public Affairs--Astra Merck Inc., Wayne, PA; *Int'l*, pg. 93

Brugioni, Cindy, Mgr.-CE Pub. Rels.--Case Corporation, Racine, WI; *U.S. Public*, pg. 311

Brukardt, David, Dir.-Corp. Commun.--Harnischfeger Industries, Inc., Saint Francis, WI; *U.S. Public*, pg. 788

Brunetti, Franco, Grp. V.P.-H.R. & Corp. Commun.--Montedison S.p.A., Milan, Italy; *Int'l*, pg. 324

Brunicardi, Pat, Mgr.-Mktg.--Cracker Barrel Old Country Store, Inc., Lebanon, TN; *U.S. Public*, pg. 455

Brush, Sue, V.P.-Adv. & Pub. Rels.--Westin Hotels & Resorts, Seattle, WA; *U.S. Public*, pg. 1512

Brusher, Nancy C., Dir.-Mktg. Communications & Adv.--Stiles Corporation, Fort Lauderdale, FL; *U.S. Private*, pg. 1043

Brussow, Micheline, Mgr.-Pub. Rels.--Renault USA, Southfield, MI; *Int'l*, pg. 1102

Brust, Marissa, Dir.-Pub. Rels.--Baume Mercier, Inc., New York, NY; *U.S. Private*, pg. 124

Brustad, Reidar G., Dir.-Pub. Rels.--Opel Norge AS, Skedsmokorset, Norway; *U.S. Public*, pg. 723

Bruyn, Kim, Corp. Communications--Amway Corporation, Ada, MI; *U.S. Private*, pg. 69

Bryan, J.L., V.P.--Sverdrup Corporation, Maryland Heights, MO; *U.S. Private*, pg. 1057

Bryant, Carole Y., Exec. V.P.-Corp. & Business Svcs.--SaskPower, Regina, Canada; *Int'l*, pg. 1195

Bryant, Nancy, Mgr.-Mktg. Commun.--Aerolyte Systems, Washington, MO; *U.S. Private*, pg. 24

Bryant, Stephen H., V.P.-Mktg. & Customer Rels.--Commonwealth Gas Co., Cambridge, MA; *U.S. Public*, pg. 415

Bryce, Dale, Mgr.-Pub. Rels.--Melbourne Port Corporation, Melbourne, Australia; *Int'l*, pg. 856

Brylewski, Jim, Mgr.-Adv. & Promotions--The Orioles, Inc., Baltimore, MD; *U.S. Private*, pg. 819

Bryson, Polly, Sr. V.P.-Mktg.--Spaulding & Slye, Boston, MA; *U.S. Private*, pg. 1021

Bubin, Christopher J., V.P.-Pub. Rels. & Investor Rels.--First Citizens Banc Shares, Inc., Raleigh, NC; *U.S. Public*, pg. 628

Bucci, Dick, Dir.-Corp. Communications--Comdial Corporation, Charlottesville, VA; *U.S. Public*, pg. 407

Bucci, Jon, Mgr.-Interactive Communications--Toyota Motor Sales, U.S.A., Inc., Torrance, CA; *Int'l*, pg. 1412

Buchacher, Manfred, Dir.-Adv. & Commun.--Creditanstalt-Bankverein, Vienna, Austria; *Int'l*, pg. 346

Buchan, Claire E., V.P.-Corp. Commun.--The ServiceMaster Company, Downers Grove, IL; *U.S. Public*, pg. 1461

Buck, Allan, Dir.-Pub. Rels.--Kyocera America, Inc., San Diego, CA; *Int'l*, pg. 775

Buckler, Dave, V.P.-Client Devel.--Chyron Corp., Melville, NY; *Int'l*, pg. 1372

Buckley, John, Sr. V.P.-Communications--Federal National Mortgage Association (Fannie Mae), Washington, DC; *U.S. Public*, pg. 615

Buckley, Lindy, Mgr.-Corp. Communications--CCI/Triad Corporation, Austin, TX; *U.S. Private*, pg. 193

Buckley, Michael, Dir.-Corp. Commun.--Tennant Company, Minneapolis, MN; *U.S. Public*, pg. 1577

Buckley, Michael F., Dir.-Public Information--Allmerica Financial Corporation, Worcester, MA; *U.S. Public*, pg. 54

Buckwalter, Randy, Dir.-Pub. Rels.--Harleysville Group, Harleysville, PA; *U.S. Public*, pg. 786

Budd, Patti, Coord.-Mktg. Communications--Philips Automotive Electronics, Cheshire, CT; *Int'l*, pg. 1054

Buechel, Yvonne, Mgr.-Corp. Commun.--Oerlikon-Buhrle Holding AG, Zurich, Switzerland; *Int'l*, pg. 996

Buenz, A.R., Dir.-Pub. Rels.--Oldsmobile Div. General Motors Corp., Lansing, MI; *U.S. Public*, pg. 720

Bugge, Anne Marie, V.P.-Corp. & Investor Rels.--ATL Ultrasound, Inc., Bothell, WA; *U.S. Public*, pg. 11

Buldak, Gerald E., Sr. V.P.-Pub. Affairs--First Chicago NBD Corporation, Chicago, IL; *U.S. Public*, pg. 627

Buldak, Jerry, V.P.-Corp. Rels.--The Allstate Corporation, Northbrook, IL; *U.S. Public*, pg. 55

Bulin, Ron, V.P.-Customer Satisfaction--Memorex Telex Corp., Irving, TX; *Int'l*, pg. 857

Bullard, Joan, V.P.-Publicity--Universal Studios Hollywood, Universal City, CA; *Int'l*, pg. 1216

Bullock, Brian, Sec. & Mgr.-Commercial & Legal Affairs--Australian Oil & Gas Corporation Limited, Sydney, Australia; *Int'l*, pg. 101

Bullock, Cynthia, Mgr.-Grants & Meetings--Globus & Cosmos, Littleton, CO; *U.S. Private*, pg. 458

Bullock, Gene, Mgr.-Mktg. Communications--Data Instruments, Inc., Acton, MA; *U.S. Private*, pg. 312

Bullock, Jennifer, Mgr.-Communications--Velsicol Chemical Corporation, Rosemont, IL; *U.S. Private*, pg. 1135

Bullock, Randye, Pub. Rels. Exec.--Don Coleman Advertising, Inc., Southfield, MI; *U.S. Private*, pg. 251

Bullwinkel, Mary, Dir.-Pub. Rels.--The Pacific Lumber Company, Scotia, CA; *U.S. Public*, pg. 1062

Bultz, P.M., Mgr.-Adv. & Pub. Rels.--Crane Limited U.K., Ipswich, United Kingdom; *U.S. Public*, pg. 458

Bunnell, Alan, Dir.-Corp. Commun.--Tucson Electric Power Company, Tucson, AZ; *U.S. Public*, pg. 1670

Burak Melchione, Janet, Sr. V.P., Gen. Counsel & Sec.--Everest Reinsurance Holdings, Liberty Corner, NJ; *U.S. Public*, pg. 597

Burch-Deluca, Kerrie, V.P.-Corp. Communications--United States Fidelity & Guaranty Company, Baltimore, MD; *U.S. Public*, pg. 1659

Burch, Howe, Sr. V.P.-Adv. & Communications--Fila USA, Sparks, MD; *Int'l*, pg. 484

Burdett, Bonnie, V.P.-Corp. & Investor Rels.--Alza Corporation, Palo Alto, CA; *U.S. Public*, pg. 62

Burdon, E.D., Mgr.-Pub. Rels.--Elopak A/S, Lierstranda, Norway; *Int'l*, pg. 1389

Burford, Helen, V.P.-Mktg. Communications--Celebrity Cruises, Inc., Miami, FL; *U.S. Public*, pg. 1410

Burgay, Stephen P., Second V.P.-Adv. & Pub. Affairs--John Hancock Mutual Life Insurance Company, Boston, MA; *U.S. Private*, pg. 589

Burger, Beverly, Mgr.-Corp. Communications--Hamilton Beach/Proctor-Silex, Inc., Glen Allen, VA; *U.S. Public*, pg. 1149

Burger, Monika, Mgr.-Pub. Rels.--Neuebaum Woll-Spinnerei Und Weberei Hof A.G., Hof, Germany; *Int'l*, pg. 922

Burgert, Laura, Sec.-Corp. Rels.--OGE Energy Corp., Oklahoma City, OK; *U.S. Public*, pg. 1207

Burgess, Linda K., Controller & Corp. Sec.--Maynard Oil Co., Dallas, TX; *U.S. Public*, pg. 1064

Burgess, Phillip, 1st V.P. & Dir.-Communications--Republic New York Corporation, New York, NY; *U.S. Public*, pg. 1380

Burick, Joseph, V.P.-Customer Services--Northern Telecom Inc., Rochester, NY; *Int'l*, pg. 970

Burk, Paula, Mgr.-Pub. Rels.--Precision Systems, Inc., Saint Petersburg, FL; *U.S. Public*, pg. 1321

Burk, Ted, V.P.-Customer Service--Greyhound Lines, Inc., Dallas, TX; *U.S. Public*, pg. 765

Burke, Catherine, Mgr.-Grp. Media Rels.--Allied Irish Banks, p.l.c., Dublin, Ireland; *Int'l*, pg. 64

Burke, Donna, Dir.-Mktg. Communications--Computer Network Technology Corporation, Minneapolis, MN; *U.S. Public*, pg. 421

Burke, Louise, V.P.-Adv., Promo. & Pub.--Berkley Publishing Corp., New York, NY; *Int'l*, pg. 1027

Burke, Nancy, Mgr.-Mktg. & Communications--Hubbell Lighting Inc., Christiansburg, VA; *U.S. Public*, pg. 844

Burke, R., Dir.-Communications--Cochrane, Inc., King of Prussia, PA; *U.S. Public*, pg. 456

Burke, R., Gen. Mgr.-Grp. Corp. Rels.--National Australia Bank Limited, Melbourne, Australia; *Int'l*, pg. 906

Burke, Sharon L., Pub. Rels. & Mktg. Officer--United Missouri Bank of Monett, Monett, MO; *U.S. Public*, pg. 1655

Burke, Sheila, Mgr.-Regulatory Affairs & External Rels.--Sterling Pulp Chemicals, Ltd., Etobicoke, Canada; *U.S. Public*, pg. 1580

Burke, William P., V.P.-H.R.--Cadbury Beverages North America, Stamford, CT; *Int'l*, pg. 248

Burkett, Bud, Dir.-Adv. & Mktg. Commun.--Cosco, Inc., Columbus, IN; *U.S. Private*, pg. 277

Burkett, Cynthia, Mktg. Strategist--GS Electric, Carlisle, PA; *U.S. Public*, pg. 726

Burkett, Larry, Sr. V.P.-Corp. & Member Rels.--Ag Processing Inc., A Cooperative, Omaha, NE; *U.S. Private*, pg. 26

Burkhardt, Brent, V.P.-Pub. Rels.--Trahan, Burden & Charles, Inc., Public Relations, Baltimore, MD; *U.S. Private*, pg. 1095

Burkhardt, James, V.P.-Customer Service--BHC Securities, Inc., Philadelphia, PA; *U.S. Public*, pg. 647

Burkhardt, Sheila, Dir.-Member Rels.--Michigan Milk Producers Association, Novi, MI; *U.S. Private*, pg. 741

Burkit, Donna, Mgr.-Customer Svcs.--Just Born, Inc., Bethlehem, PA; *U.S. Private*, pg. 602

Burley, Pat, Mgr.-Communications--Great Clips, Inc., Minneapolis, MN; *U.S. Private*, pg. 473

Burnett, Iris, Sr. V.P.-Corp. Communications & Pub. Affairs--USA Networks, New York, NY; *U.S. Public*, pg. 1686

Burnett, R. Curtis, V.P.-Pub. Affairs--Questar Corporation, Salt Lake City, UT; *U.S. Public*, pg. 1352

Burney, Michael J., V.P.-Corp. Affairs--Jefferson-Pilot Corporation, Greensboro, NC; *U.S. Public*, pg. 925

Burns, Hannah, Mng. Dir.-Corp. Communications--The Bear Stearns Companies Inc., New York, NY; *U.S. Public*, pg. 197

Burns, Hannah, Mgr.-Pub. Rels.--Bear, Stearns & Co. Inc., New York, New York, NY; *U.S. Public*, pg. 198

Burns, M.I., Mgr.-Adv. & Sls. Promo.--Netherlands Car B.V., Born, Netherlands; *Int'l*, pg. 876

Burns, Mary, Pub. Rels. Counselor--Sawyer Riley Compton Inc., Atlanta, GA; *U.S. Private*, pg. 969

Burnside, Frank B., Dir.-Corp. Commun.--Commonwealth Telephone Enterprises, Inc., Dallas, PA; *U.S. Public*, pg. 415

Burnworth, Mark, Dir.-Corp. Communications--Alcatel Telecom, Richardson, TX; *Int'l*, pg. 55

Burnworth, Mark, Dir.-Corp. Communications--Alcatel Network Systems, Inc. (TX), Richardson, TX; *Int'l*, pg. 55

Burr, Debbie, Mgr.-Pub. Rels.--Reed Travel Publishing, Dunstable, United Kingdom; *Int'l*, pg. 1097

Burris, Brenda, Dir.-Pub. Affairs--Ross Products, Columbus, OH; *U.S. Public*, pg. 13

Burris, Mary Ellen, Dir.-Consumer Affairs--Wegmans Food Markets, Inc., Rochester, NY; *U.S. Private*, pg. 1158

Burton, A.J., Mgr.-Pub. Rels.--Meyer International PLC, London, United Kingdom; *Int'l*, pg. 864

Burton, Colleen, Dir.-Media Rels.--Port of Houston Authority, Houston, TX; *U.S. Private*, pg. 876

Bury, James, V.P.-Fin.--PremiumWear, Inc., Minneapolis, MN; *U.S. Public*, pg. 1323

Busby, Robert L., III, Chief Fin. & Admin. Officer, Sr. V.P. & Treas.--National Western Life Insurance Company, Austin, TX; *U.S. Public*, pg. 1161

Buser, Laura, Assoc. Mgr.-Pub. Rels.--Prudential Real Estate Affiliates Inc., Costa Mesa, CA; *U.S. Private*, pg. 892

Bush, Madelyn, Sr. Mgr.-Pub. Rels.--Boeing Helicopters, Ridley Park, PA; *U.S. Public*, pg. 241

Bushkin, Nancy, V.P.-Corp. Commun.--Spelling Entertainment Group, Inc., Los Angeles, CA; *U.S. Private*, pg. 776

Butch, Melissa, Mgr.-Pub. Rels.--Arizona Instrument Corporation, Phoenix, AZ; *U.S. Public*, pg. 129

Butcher, Paul A.N., V.P.-Bus. Commun. Sys./Europe, Middle East & Africa--Mitel Corporation, Kanata, Canada; *Int'l*, pg. 870

Butenas, Carole F., V.P.-Investor Rels.--Lydall, Inc., Manchester, CT; *U.S. Public*, pg. 1020

Butkus, Al, Dir.-Corp. Communications--UtiliCorp United Inc., Kansas City, MO; *U.S. Public*, pg. 1700

Butler, Ellen, Dir.-Pub. Rels.--May & Speh, Inc., Downers Grove, IL; *U.S. Public*, pg. 1063

Butler, K.H., Dir.-Mktg. Communications--Columbus McKinnon Corp., Amherst, NY; *U.S. Public*, pg. 405

Butler, Skip, Dir.-Communications--Carriage Industries, Inc., Calhoun, GA; *U.S. Public*, pg. 514

Butner, James S., V.P.-Indus. & Pub. Rels.--Cone Mills Corporation, Greensboro, NC; *U.S. Public*, pg. 430

Butt, Jan, Mgr.-Mktg. Communications--Dow Corning Corporation, Midland, MI; *U.S. Public*, pg. 523

Butt, Khalid, Gen. Mgr.-Pub. Affairs--Pakistan International Airlines Corporation, Karachi, Pakistan; *Int'l*, pg. 1021

Butterfield, Keith, Public Information Rep.--Caterpillar Inc., Peoria, IL; *U.S. Public*, pg. 315

Buttice, Darrel, Dir.-Pub. Affairs--Port of Portland, Portland, OR; *U.S. Private*, pg. 876

Buus, David, Dir.-Corp Commun.--Burr-Brown Corporation, Tucson, AZ; *U.S. Public*, pg. 270

Byck, Joseph S., V.P.-Strategic Plng., Investor Rels. & Pub. Affairs--Union Carbide Corporation, Danbury, CT; *U.S. Public*, pg. 1666

Byers, P.G., Mgr.-Mktg. Communications, Engrng., Plastics, Flouropolymer--Du Pont Polymer Products, Wilmington, DE; *U.S. Public*, pg. 531

Byrnes, Christopher R., Dir.-Investor Rels.--PAR Technology Corporation, New Hartford, NY; *U.S. Public*, pg. 1256

Byrnes, Danielle, Press Officer--Tesco PLC, Cheshunt, United Kingdom; *Int'l*, pg. 1376

Byrnes, Edward, Coord.-Communications--Dairylea Cooperative Inc., East Syracuse, NY; *U.S. Private*, pg. 307

Byrnes, Richard, Dir.-Pub. Rels.--Crestline Div., Norwalk, CT; *U.S. Public*, pg. 1543

Bystrom, Asa Lindell, Dir.-Commun. & Pub. Rels.--BTL AB, Goteborg, Sweden; *Int'l*, pg. 123

Bystry, Marianne, Mgr.-Pub. Rels.--Jagenberg AG, Neuss, Germany; *Int'l*, pg. 1108

Cabrero, Belinda, Pub. Rels. Coord.--Leo Burnett S.A. de C.V., Mexico, Mexico; *U.S. Private*, pg. 185

Cabri, Julie, Mgr.-Corp. Programs--CAE Inc., Toronto, Canada; *Int'l*, pg. 237

Caccamo, Al M., V.P.-Pub. Affairs--Chevron Corporation, San Francisco, CA; *U.S. Public*, pg. 347

Cadet, Etienne, Mgr.-Pub. Rels. & Commun.--Iveco France S.A., Trappes, France; *Int'l*, pg. 696

Caffrey, Mike, Dir.-Natl. Mktg. & Sls.--Duncan Toys Company, Middlefield, OH; *U.S. Private*, pg. 409

Cagner, Shelly, Press Rels.--The Arbitron Company, New York, NY; *U.S. Public*, pg. 331

Cahalan, Joseph M., Dir.-Corp. Communications--Xerox Corporation, Stamford, CT; *U.S. Public*, pg. 1783

Cain, Mark, Dir.-Commun.--Pentair, Inc., Saint Paul, MN; *U.S. Public*, pg. 1273

Cajacob, Peter, V.P.-Human Resources--McClatchy Newspapers Inc., Sacramento, CA; *U.S. Public*, pg. 1065

Cala, Vince, V.P.-Consumer Sls.--Refined Sugars, Inc., Yonkers, NY; *Int'l*, pg. 699

Calahan, Katie, Dir.-Mktg.--Country Home Bakery, Inc., Bridgeport, CT; *U.S. Private*, pg. 278

Calderon, Cristian, Mgr.-Commun.--CODELCO Chile (Corporacion Nacional Del Cobre De Chile), Santiago, Chile; *Int'l*, pg. 302

Caldwell, Henry, V.P.-Mktg. & Communications--Anixter Inc., Skokie, IL; *U.S. Public*, pg. 115

Calek, Terry A., Sr. V.P.-Pub. Affairs--Mutual of Omaha Insurance Company, Omaha, NE; *U.S. Private*, pg. 769

Caliendo, Valerie, Adv. & Pub. Rels. Assoc.--Benetton U.S.A. Corporation, New York, NY; *Int'l*, pg. 186

Callahan, Howard M., Mgr.-Communications--McArdle Printing Co., Inc., Upper Marlboro, MD; *U.S. Private*, pg. 182

Callander, Steve, Dir.-Exec. Communications--Pharmacia & Upjohn, Inc., Windsor, United Kingdom; *Int'l*, pg. 1047

Callas, Kayla, Mgr.-Pub. Affairs--Pacificare of Nevada, Las Vegas, NV; *U.S. Public*, pg. 1251

Calmeyer, John, V.P.-Mktg. & Pub. Rels.--Callaway Vineyard & Winery, Temecula, CA; *Int'l*, pg. 63

Calton, John, Dir.-Mktg. Communications--Owens Corning/Foamular, Parsippany, NJ; *U.S. Public*, pg. 1237

Calvin, Amy, Dir.-Commun. & Corp. Librarian--Edison Brothers Stores, Inc., Saint Louis, MO; *U.S. Public*, pg. 563

Camden, Carl, Exec. V.P.-Mktg., Sls. & Pub. Rels.--Kelly Services, Inc., Troy, MI; *U.S. Public*, pg. 949

Camerlengo, Justin, V.P.-Corp. Communications--Matsushita Electric Corporation of America, Secaucus, NJ; *Int'l*, pg. 847

Cameron, Donald, Grp. Head-Pub. Rels.--Schroders PLC, London, United Kingdom; *Int'l*, pg. 1210

Cameron, John, Dir.-Corp. Communications--Ace Hardware Corporation, Oak Brook, IL; *U.S. Private*, pg. 12

Cameron, Kenneth A., Div. Dir.-Public Affairs & Communications--Delphi Energy & Engine Management Systems, Flint, MI; *U.S. Public*, pg. 719

Camerota, Tony, Dir.-Corp. Commun.--BetzDearborn Inc., Trevose, PA; *U.S. Public*, pg. 226

Campanella, Thomas, Exec. V.P.-Adv. & Promo.--Paramount Pictures Corporation, Los Angeles, CA; *U.S. Private*, pg. 776

Campbell, Bob, Mgr.-Pub. Rels. & Adv.--Inter-Continental Hotels & Resorts Corporation, New York, NY; *Int'l*, pg. 1178

Campbell, George L., V.P.-Pub. Affairs--Florida Power Corporation, Saint Petersburg, FL; *U.S. Public*, pg. 655

Campbell, Robin W., Mgr.-Mktg. Svcs. & Adv.--Stanley Furniture Co. Inc., Stanleytown, VA; *U.S. Public*, pg. 1508

Campo, Tom, Mgr.-Press Rels.--The Hearst Corporation, New York, NY; *U.S. Private*, pg. 515

Campobasso, Richard, V.P.-Standard Prods.--Binks Sames Corporation, Franklin Park, IL; *U.S. Public*, pg. 229

Canary, Glenn, Dir.-Investor Rels.--Claire's Stores Inc., Pembroke Pines, FL; *U.S. Public*, pg. 381

Canaval, Marisa, Mgr.-Pub. Rels.--Aero Peru Corporation, Coral Gables, FL; *U.S. Private*, pg. 24
Canciani, A., Gen. Affairs & External Rels.--Electrolux San Jose, Pordenone, Italy; *Int'l*, pg. 442
Canfield, Jim, V.P.-Pub. Rels.--Universal Studios Florida, Orlando, FL; *Int'l*, pg. 1087
Cania, Becky, Mgr.-Corp. Commun.--ACC Corp., Rochester, NY; *U.S. Public*, pg. 2
Cania, Becky, Mgr.-Pub. Rels.--ACC TeleCom, Rochester, NY; *U.S. Public*, pg. 3
Cannan, Patrick F., Dir.-Corp. Rels.--The Wackenhut Corporation, Palm Beach Gardens, FL; *U.S. Public*, pg. 1731
Canning, Donald, Dir.-Pub. Rels.--Robin Hood Multifoods Inc., Markham, Canada; *U.S. Public*, pg. 901
Cannon, Anne, Coord.-Pub. Rels.--Ultramar Diamond Shamrock Corporation, San Antonio, TX; *U.S. Public*, pg. 1663
Cannon, John, Mgr.-Mktg. Communications--InterVoice, Inc., Dallas, TX; *U.S. Public*, pg. 910
Canonaco, Laura, Dir.-Mktg.--Hinckley & Schmitt, Inc., Chicago, IL; *Int'l*, pg. 1322
Cantafio, A.W., V.P.-Corp. Communications--Northrop Grumman Corporation, Los Angeles, CA; *U.S. Public*, pg. 1197
Cantin, Robert L., Dir.-Communications & Adv.--Karsten Manufacturing Corporation, Phoenix, AZ; *U.S. Private*, pg. 608
Cantor, Steve, Mgr.-Corp. Communications--Dynatech Corporation, Burlington, MA; *U.S. Public*, pg. 539
Canzi, Clara, Dir.-Human Resources & Mgr.-Pub. Rels.--Johnson Wax S.p.A., Milan, Italy; *U.S. Private*, pg. 593
Capdevila, Joaquen, Mgr.-Mktg.--Banco Espanol de Credito SA, Madrid, Spain; *Int'l*, pg. 143
Capellini, Osvaldo, Mgr.-Pub. Rels.--Sancor Cooperativas Unidas Limitadas, Buenos Aires, Argentina; *Int'l*, pg. 1183
Caple, Dorry, Dir.-H.R. & Pub. Rels.--Fischer Packing Co., Louisville, KY; *Int'l*, pg. 201
Capone, Joe, V.P.-H.R. & Pub. Rels.--Canac Kitchens Ltd, Thornhill, Canada; *U.S. Private*, pg. 630
Caputo, Lisa, V.P.-Corp. Communications--CBS, New York, NY; *U.S. Public*, pg. 273
Caraco, Andre, V.P.-Publicity--Columbia Pictures, Culver City, CA; *Int'l*, pg. 1281
Carazo, Dan, Mgr.-Mktg. Communications--Sulzer Metco (Westbury) Inc., Westbury, NY; *Int'l*, pg. 1307
Carballosa, Maria, Dir.-Corp. Communications--CRSS Inc., Houston, TX; *Int'l*, pg. 1415
Card, Keith, Dir.-Mktg. & Pub. Rels.--Benihana, Inc., Miami, FL; *U.S. Public*, pg. 211
Card, Keith, Dir.-Mktg. & Pub. Rels.--Benihana International, Inc., Miami, FL; *U.S. Public*, pg. 212
Cardin, France, Corp. Communications Officer--Pratt & Whitney Canada Inc., Longueuil, Canada; *U.S. Public*, pg. 1690
Cardina, Fred, V.P.-Human Resources--Siemens Business Communication Systems, Inc., Santa Clara, CA; *Int'l*, pg. 1245
Carey, Earl T., V.P.-Reg. Opers. & Customer Service--FirstEnergy Corp., Akron, OH; *U.S. Public*, pg. 644
Carlin, Lisa, Dir.-Mktg. Communications--General Signal Networks, Shelton, CT; *U.S. Public*, pg. 727
Carlino, Peter, Dir.-Corp. Communications--Summa Four, Inc., Manchester, NH; *U.S. Public*, pg. 1527
Carlson, Angela, Coord.-Corp. Commun.--Fair, Isaac and Company, Inc., San Rafael, CA; *U.S. Public*, pg. 609
Carlson, George W., Dir.-Publicity--Saratoga Equine Sports Center, Saratoga Springs, NY; *U.S. Private*, pg. 965
Carlson, James W., V.P.-Corp. Commun.--Jones Intercable, Inc., Englewood, CO; *U.S. Private*, pg. 597
Carlson, Julie, Mgr.-Mktg. Communications--Harris Corp., Digital Telephone Systems Div., Novato, CA; *U.S. Public*, *pg. 791*
Carlson, Kathleen, V.P.-Mktg. & Commun.--Grubb & Ellis Company, Northbrook, IL; *U.S. Public*, pg. 767
Carlson, Ria, V.P.-Pub. & Investor Rels.--Sierra Health Services, Inc., Las Vegas, NV; *U.S. Public*, pg. 1469
Carlson, Ria, Mgr.-Pub. Rels.--Health Plan of Nevada, Inc., Las Vegas, NV; *U.S. Public*, pg. 1469
Carlson, Ria, Mgr.-Pub. Rels.--Sierra Health and Life Insurance Company, Inc., Las Vegas, NV; *U.S. Public*, pg. 1469
Carlson, Ria, Mgr.-Pub. Rels.--Family Healthcare Services, Inc., Las Vegas, NV; *U.S. Public*, pg. 1469
Carlson, Ria, Mgr.-Pub. Rels.--Family Home Hospice, Inc., Las Vegas, NV; *U.S. Public*, pg. 1469
Carlson, Ria, Mgr.-Pub. Rels.--Sierra Healthcare Options, Inc., Las Vegas, NV; *U.S. Public*, pg. 1469
Carlson, Ria, Mgr.-Pub. Rels.--Behavioral Healthcare Options, Inc., Las Vegas, NV; *U.S. Public*, pg. 1469
Carlson, Ria, Mgr.-Pub. Rels.--Southwest Medical Associates, Inc., Las Vegas, NV; *U.S. Public*, pg. 1470
Carlson, Ria Marie, V.P.-Pub. Rels.--Pacificare Health Systems, Santa Ana, CA; *U.S. Public*, pg. 1251
Carlson, Robert, Gen. Mgr.-Pub. Rels.--Porsche Cars North America, Inc., Reno, NV; *Int'l*, pg. 1063
Carlsson, Lars O., Dir.-Pub. Rels.--NCC HUS, Goteborg, Sweden; *Int'l*, pg. 899
Carlton, Roberta, Mgr.-Pub. Rels.--Cognos Corp., Burlington, MA; *Int'l*, pg. 306
Carlton, Ron, Ph.D., Dir.-Mktg.--AmeriPath, Inc., Riviera Beach, FL; *U.S. Public*, pg. 96
Carmichael, Alan, Sr. V.P.-Communications--Tennessee Valley Authority, Knoxville, TN; *U.S. Public*, pg. 1580
Carmichael, Jill, Mgr.-Corp. Commun.--Ingersoll International Inc., Rockford, IL; *U.S. Private*, pg. 562
Carmichael, Richard, Mgr.-Customer Accts.--CCL Custom Manufacturing, Niles, IL; *Int'l*, pg. 238
Carmona, Luisa, Asst.-Pub. Rels.--Portuguese Railways (CP), Lisbon, Portugal; *Int'l*, pg. 1063
Carney, Ed, Dir.-Pub. Rels.--Western Regional Off Track Betting, Batavia, NY; *U.S. Private*, pg. 1168
Carney, Mike, Dir.-Mktg. Commun.--Lowrance Electronics, Inc., Tulsa, OK; *U.S. Public*, pg. 1015
Carp, Lisa, Dir.-Human Resources--Bird Products Corporation, Palm Springs, CA; *U.S. Public*, pg. 1591
Carpanelli, Jane, Mgr.-Pub. Rels.--Federal Kemper Life Assurance Company, Long Grove, IL; *Int'l*, pg. 1530
Carpenter, Carla O., Mgr.-Corp. Communications--Phoenix Home Life Mutual Insurance Company, Hartford, CT; *U.S. Private*, pg. 863
Carpenter, Carla O., Mgr.-Corp. Communications--Phoenix Home Life Mutual Insurance Co., Hartford, CT; *U.S. Private*, pg. 863
Carpenter, Elaine, Dir.-Corp. Communications--Aliant Communications Co., Lincoln, NE; *U.S. Public*, pg. 40
Carpenter, Kay, Dir.-Corp. Rels.--Hunt-Wesson, Inc., Fullerton, CA; *U.S. Public*, pg. 428
Carpenter, Kay, Dir.-Pub. Rels.--Wesson/Peter Pan Foods Co., Fullerton, CA; *U.S. Public*, pg. 428
Carpenter, Marian J., Dir.-Corp. Communications--Republic Engineered Steels, Inc., Massillon, OH; *U.S. Public*, pg. 1378
Carpenter, Patrick, Mgr.-Pub. Rels.--Alcan Aluminum Corporation, Cleveland, OH; *Int'l*, pg. 50
Carpenter, Richard A., Mgr.-Adv. & Sales Promo.--Hauck Mfg. Co., Cleona, PA; *U.S. Private*, pg. 510
Carpenter, Suzanne W., Dir.-Pub. Rels.--Bachman Company, Reading, PA; *U.S. Private*, pg. 109
Carpenter, Virginia, Coord.-Mktg. Communications--Uvex Safety, Inc., Smithfield, RI; *Int'l*, pg. 132
Carr, Charles, Dir.-Pub. Affairs--British Aerospace Defence Limited (Dynamics), Stevenage, United Kingdom; *Int'l*, pg. 217
Carr, Logan, Dir.-Pub. Rels.--Dick Clark Productions, Inc., Burbank, CA; *U.S. Public*, pg. 382
Carr, Steve, V.P.-Pub. Rels.--Cramer-Krasselt, Chicago, IL; *U.S. Private*, pg. 285
Carra, Phillip C., V.P.-Pub. Rels.--Pharmacia & Upjohn, Kalamazoo, MI; *Int'l*, pg. 1048
Carrasco, Patricia A., Mgr.-Pub. Rels., Adv. & Mktg.--Casio, Inc., Dover, NJ; *Int'l*, pg. 274
Carrell, Ronald H., V.P.-Customer Service--Indianapolis Water Company, Indianapolis, IN; *U.S. Public*, pg. 1185
Carriere, Roland, Dir.-Communication--Societe Generale, Paris, France; *Int'l*, pg. 1273
Carroll, Bruce, Mgr.-Govt. Affairs--Centocor, Inc., Malvern, PA; *U.S. Public*, pg. 323
Carroll, Lorri, Dir.-Commun. Svcs.--NJ Transit, Newark, NJ; *U.S. Private*, pg. 794
Carroll, Pat, Mgr.-Adv. & Pub. Rels--Kubota Tractor Corp., Torrance, CA; *Int'l*, pg. 762
Carroll, Patricia, Pub. Rels. Consultant--William Cook Public Relations, Inc., Jacksonville, FL; *U.S. Private*, pg. 273
Carroll, Robert G. H. III, V.P.-Communications--Pratt & Whitney Government Engine & Space Propulsion, West Palm Beach, FL; *U.S. Public*, pg. 1690
Carter, Kristen, Mgr.-Strategic Communications--Allen-Bradley Global Sales & Support Group, Milwaukee, WI; *U.S. Public*, pg. 1397
Carter, Susan, V.P.-Pub. Corp. Communications--National Trustco Inc., Toronto, Canada; *Int'l*, pg. 909
Carter, Theresa, Dir.-Community Rels.--GenCorp Inc., Fairlawn, OH; *U.S. Public*, pg. 705
Carter, Tim, V.P.-Pub. Affairs--The Oshawa Group Limited, Etobicoke, Canada; *Int'l*, pg. 1012
Cartwright, James C., Mgr.-Corp. Commun.--Commercial Intertech Corp., Youngstown, OH; *U.S. Public*, pg. 411
Carullo, Carmine, Coord.-External Reporting--Mobil Oil Corporation, Fairfax, VA; *U.S. Public*, pg. 1118
Carwoski, Christopher, Mgr.-Communications--The DIALOG Corporation, New York, NY; *Int'l*, pg. 412
Casarella, R. G., Adv. & Communications Mgr.--Permacel Tape, North Brunswick, NJ; *U.S. Public*, pg. 153
Casey, Marilyn, V.P. & Sr. Pub. Rels. Program Mgr.--Liggett-Stashower, Inc., Cleveland, OH; *U.S. Private*, pg. 667
Casey, Walter H., V.P.-Corp. Communications--ConAgra, Inc., Omaha, NE; *U.S. Public*, pg. 425
Cash, D.R., V.P.-Human Resources & Communications--Texas-New Mexico Power Co., Fort Worth, TX; *U.S. Public*, pg. 1557
Cason, Kenny, Dir.-Adv. & Pub. Affairs--Chief Auto Parts, Dallas, TX; *U.S. Private*, pg. 236
Caspersen, Dan, Sr. V.P.-Community Rels.--Mervyn's California, Hayward, CA; *U.S. Public*, pg. 489
Casselman, Caroline, Mgr.-Pub. Affairs--Falconbridge Limited, Toronto, Canada; *Int'l*, pg. 433
Cassidy, Madelaine, Admin.-Mktg. Communications--Pentax Corporation, Englewood, CO; *Int'l*, pg. 85
Cassidy, Pat, Mgr.-Legislative & Corp. Affairs--Quanex Corporation, Houston, TX; *U.S. Public*, pg. 1349
Castagna, Adalberto, Gen. Mgr.-Gen. Affairs--Pirelli S.p.A., Milan, Italy; *Int'l*, pg. 1058
Castaldi, Thomas E., V.P.-Pub. Rels.--Essex International, Inc., Fort Wayne, IN; *U.S. Public*, pg. 593
Castell, J. Ronald, Sr. V.P.-Investor Rels. & Communications--Florida Panthers Holdings, Inc., Fort Lauderdale, FL; *U.S. Public*, pg. 654
Castro Almeida, Luis Torres, Gen. Mgr.-Sls Promo, Adv. & Pub. Rels.--Banco Totta & Acores, Lisbon, Portugal; *Int'l*, *pg. 144*
Castro, Christine, Dir.-Corp. Communications--SunAmerica Inc., Los Angeles, CA; *U.S. Public*, pg. 1532
Cates, Max, Dir.-Mtkg. Communications--Associated Electric Co-op Inc., Springfield, MO; *U.S. Private*, pg. 89
Cation, Kenneth L., Grp. Pres.--Atlas/Soundolier, Fenton, MO; *U.S. Private*, pg. 64
Cauble, Toni M., Dir.-Corp. Communications & Pub. Rels.--WestPoint Stevens Inc., West Point, GA; *U.S. Public*, pg. 1762
Caudill, Larry, Dir.-External Communications & Strategic Alliance--Nissan Motor Corporation in U.S.A., Gardena, CA; *Int'l*, pg. 945
Caughlan, Carma, Dir.-Corp. Communications--Circle International Group, Inc., San Francisco, CA; *U.S. Public*, *pg. 370*
Cavalier, Janet, Mgr.-Investor Commun.--Glenayre Technologies, Inc., Charlotte, NC; *U.S. Public*, pg. 746
Cavello, Butch, Mgr.-Mktg.--American Louver Co., Skokie, IL; *U.S. Private*, pg. 58
Cayrol, Gabrielle, Mgr.-Communication--Poliet, Courbevoie, France; *Int'l*, pg. 1177
Cecil, Allan V., V.P.-Investor Rels. & Corp. Commun.--Sonoco Products Company, Hartsville, SC; *U.S. Public*, pg. 1485
Cekirge, Arzu, Mgr.-Adv. & Pub. Rels.--Sabanci Holding A.S., Istanbul, Turkey; *Int'l*, pg. 1167
Cerpa, Leonardo, Mgr.-Pub. Rels.--Banco do Brasil, Brasilia, Brazil; *Int'l*, pg. 141
Cersosimo, Bonita, Mgr.-Corp. Communication Services--Aluminum Company of America, Pittsburgh, PA; *U.S. Public*, pg. 60
Chadwick, Clarence, V.P.-Indus. Rels.--Grocers Supply Co. Inc., Houston, TX; *U.S. Private*, pg. 483
Chaine, Nicolas, Head-Corp. Commun.--Credit Lyonnais S.A., Paris, France; *Int'l*, pg. 343
Chalgren, William, Mgr.-Mktg.--Holmatro, Inc., Glen Burnie, MD; *Int'l*, pg. 632
Challis, Georgina, Sr. V.P.-Corp. Communications & Legal Counsel--BPI Communications Inc., New York, NY; *Int'l*, pg. 1446
Chamberlain, Sara, Pub. Rels. Assoc.--SPSS Inc., Chicago, IL; *U.S. Public*, pg. 1420
Chandler, Jon, Mgr.-Grp. Communications--Varity Perkins, Peterborough, United Kingdom; *Int'l*, pg. 820
Chaney, Barbara, Coord.-Pub. Rels. & Adv.--Parlux, Ltd., Fort Lauderdale, FL; *U.S. Public*, pg. 1264
Chant, B., Dir.-Pub. Rels.--Labatt Breweries of Canada, Toronto, Canada; *Int'l*, pg. 679
Chapel, Ronny, Communications Specialist--ARCO Alaska Inc., Anchorage, AK; *U.S. Public*, pg. 144
Chapman, Brad, V.P.-Human Resources Devel.--Peter Kiewit Sons Inc., Omaha, NE; *U.S. Private*, pg. 619
Chapman, Wade, Chief Oper. Officer--Idaho Supreme Company, Firth, ID; *U.S. Private*, pg. 557
Characon, Remi, Mgr.-Corp. Communications--Air Liquide S.A., Paris, France; *Int'l*, pg. 37
Charbet, Jacques, Dir.-Corp. Commun.--Accor S.A., Evry, France; *Int'l*, pg. 20
Charlton, Richard G., V.P.-Corp. Commun.--Parker Hannifin Corporation, Cleveland, OH; *U.S. Public*, pg. 1259
Charmelo, Dominic, Supvr.-Mktg. Communications--Dukane Corporation, Saint Charles, IL; *U.S. Private*, pg. 345
Charness, Wayne, V.P.-Corp. Communications--Hasbro, Inc., Pawtucket, RI; *U.S. Public*, pg. 797
Charney, M. Jeffrey, V.P.-Mktg. & Commun.--Kaufman and Broad Home Corporation, Los Angeles, CA; *U.S. Public*, pg. 944
Charron, Jacques, V.P.-H.R. & Commun.--Gaz Metropolitain & Company, Montreal, Canada; *Int'l*, pg. 541
Chase, Catherine, Dir.-Pub. Rels.--Bombardier Aerospace, Dorval, Canada; *Int'l*, pg. 200
Chase, Helen, Dir.-Pub. Rels.--Hannaford Bros. Co., Scarborough, ME; *U.S. Public*, pg. 781
Chase, Ralph W., Jr., Dir.-Human Resources--Brown & Sharpe Manufacturing Company, North Kingstown, RI; *U.S. Public*, pg. 260
Chase, Ronald J., Dir.-Human Relations & Pub. Communications--Green Bay Packaging Inc., Green Bay, WI; *U.S. Private*, pg. 476
Chaseman, Joanne, Dir.-Pub. Rels.--Times Mirror Magazines, Inc., New York, NY; *U.S. Public*, pg. 1616
Chaves, D. Doc, Asst. V.P.-Corp. Communications--Ameritas Life Insurance Corp., Lincoln, NE; *U.S. Private*, pg. 65
Chavez, Julie, Dir.-Community Rels.--Bank of America Illinois, Chicago, IL; *U.S. Public*, pg. 180
Chazen, Barbara G., Sr. V.P. & Dir.-Corp. Pub. Affairs--Nationsbank/Tennessee, Nashville, TN; *U.S. Public*, pg. 1163
Cheatham, E.W., V.P.-Corp. Communications--The Racal Corporation, New York, NY; *Int'l*, pg. 1083
Cheatham, Edward W., V.P.-Corp. Communications--The Racal Corporation, Sunrise, FL; *Int'l*, pg. 1082
Cheatham, James L., Asst. to Pres.--Eskimo Pie Corporation, Richmond, VA; *U.S. Public*, pg. 592
Chen, Jane, Special Asst.-Pub. Rels.--Acer Incorporated, Taipei, Taiwan; *Int'l*, pg. 22
Chen, S.Y., Mgr.-Pub. Rels.--China Steel Structure Co., Ltd., Kao-hsiung, Taiwan; *Int'l*, pg. 286
Cheng, Eng Hwee, Sr. V.P.-Corp. Affairs--Superior Metal Printing Limited, Singapore, Singapore; *Int'l*, pg. 1322
Cheng, Heng Lee, V.P.-Public Affairs--DBS Bank Ltd., Singapore, Singapore; *Int'l*, pg. 350
Cheng, M.L., Dir.--Taiwan Power Company, Taipei, Taiwan; *Int'l*, pg. 1348
Chepely, Gina, Dir.-Pub. Rels.--International Center for Entrepreneurial Development, Inc., Cypress, TX; *U.S. Private*, pg. 568
Chernoff Salzman, Sue, Dir.-Pub. Rels. & Promo.--Lettuce Entertain You Enterprises, Inc., Chicago, IL; *U.S. Private*, *pg. 661*
Chernowetz, Laura, Mgr.-Adv. & Promotions & Communications--Wallace Laboratories, Cranbury, NJ; *U.S. Public*, pg. 310
Chiariello, Michele, Dir.-Mktg.--Danielli & C. Officine Meccaniche S.p.A., Udine, Italy; *Int'l*, pg. 378
Chieger, Kathryn J., V.P.-Corp. Investor Rels.--Brunswick Corporation, Lake Forest, IL; *U.S. Public*, pg. 265
Chihaya, Mari, V.P.-Adv. & Pub. Rels.--Shiseido Cosmetics (America) Ltd., New York, NY; *Int'l*, pg. 1235
Chihocky, Janet, Mgr.-Corp. Commun.--Orbital Sciences Corporation, Dulles, VA; *U.S. Public*, pg. 1229
Chilabato, Oscar, Dir.-Adv. & Public Rels.--The Richman Brothers Co., Fall River, MA; *U.S. Public*, pg. 1777
Chilcoh, Sharon, Head-Corp. Commun.--Bristol & West Building Society, Bristol, United Kingdom; *Int'l*, pg. 216
Ching, Meredith J., V.P.-Govt. & Community Rels.--Alexander & Baldwin, Inc., Honolulu, HI; *U.S. Public*, pg. 39

Chinnery, R.J., Mktg. Communications Asst.--Thermal Ceramics Inc., Augusta, GA; *Int'l*, pg. 894
Chipperfield, Lynn, V.P., Gen. Counsel & Sec.--Furniture Brands International Inc., Saint Louis, MO; *U.S. Public*, pg. 688
Chizmadia, Thomas A., V.P.-Corp. Communications--Holnam Inc., Dundee, MI; *Int'l*, pg. 628
Chmel, Valentine, V.P.-Communications--West Coast Life Insurance Co., San Francisco, CA; *U.S. Public*, pg. 1336
Chong, Y.T., Mgr.-Customer Svc.--Showpla Asia Limited, Singapore, Singapore; *Int'l*, pg. 1237
Chrietzberg, Gloria, Dir.-Mktg.--One Price Clothing Stores, Inc., Duncan, SC; *U.S. Public*, pg. 1225
Christensen, Jennifer, Asst. Pub. Rels. & Adv.--OshKosh B'Gosh, Inc., Oshkosh, WI; *U.S. Public*, pg. 1232
Christensen, Marc D., Sr. V.P.-Customer Service & Pub. Affairs--Public Service Company of New Mexico, Albuquerque, NM; *U.S. Public*, pg. 1339
Christian, Robert G., V.P. & Dir.-Corp. Communications--Stevens International, Inc., Fort Worth, TX; *U.S. Public*, pg. 1517
Christoffersen, Petter A., Grp. V.P.-Public Affairs--Jotun A/S, Sandefjord, Norway; *Int'l*, pg. 714
Christopherson, Cathleen M., V.P.-Corp. Communications--MDU Resources Group, Inc., Bismarck, ND; *U.S. Public*, pg. 1025
Chu, C.L., Mgr.-Pub. Rels.--China Ecotek Corporation, Kaohsiung, Taiwan; *Int'l*, pg. 285
Chunharas, Somrit, Cust. Svc. Opers. Dir.--Avon Cosmetics (Thailand) Ltd., Bangkok, Thailand; *U.S. Public*, pg. 156
Churchill, Peter, Dir.-Corp. Affairs--Kleinwort Benson Ltd., London, United Kingdom; *Int'l*, pg. 420
Cihock, Steve, Mgr.-Adv. & Pub. Rels.--Komatsu America International Company, Vernon Hills, IL; *Int'l*, pg. 744
Cimbora, Alicia, V.P.-Pub. Rels.--Harrison & Star, New York, NY; *U.S. Private*, pg. 506
Cinquegrani, Sal, V.P.-Corp. Commun.--360 Degrees Communications Company, Chicago, IL; *U.S. Public*, pg. 1607
Cinquegrani, Sal, Mgr.-Pub. Rels.--360 Degrees Long Distance, Cary, NC; *U.S. Public*, pg. 1607
Cislak, Lauren, Mgr.-Corp. Communications & Public Rels.--DowBrands, L.P., Indianapolis, IN; *U.S. Public*, pg. 523
Claassen, Jurgen, Dir.-Commun. & Central Bureau--Fried. Krupp AG, Essen, Germany; *Int'l*, pg. 507
Clap, Isabelle, Head-Pub. Rels.--Banque Nationale de Paris, Paris, France; *Int'l*, pg. 163
Clapp, Amy, Mgr.-Mktg. Commun.--TelCom Semiconductor, Inc., Mountain View, CA; *U.S. Public*, pg. 1569
Clapper, Sarah, Mgr.-Mktg. Communications--Nalge Company, Rochester, NY; *U.S. Public*, pg. 1545
Clark, Cheryl M., Corp. Clerk--The Berkshire Gas Company, Pittsfield, MA; *U.S. Public*, pg. 216
Clark, Donna, Mgr.-Natl. Community Affairs--St. Petersburg Times, Saint Petersburg, FL; *U.S. Private*, pg. 1088
Clark, G. Reynolds, Exec. Dir.-Corp. Services & Community Affairs--CBS Corporation, Pittsburgh, PA; *U.S. Public*, pg. 273
Clark, Janet F., Chief Fin. Officer & V.P.--Santa Fe Energy Resources, Inc., Houston, TX; *U.S. Public*, pg. 1431
Clark, Kristin, Exec. V.P.-Bus. Devel. & Customer Rels.--Seattle Pacific Industries, Inc., Seattle, WA; *U.S. Private*, pg. 980
Clark, Lisa, Mgr.-Corp. Communications--Envoy Corporation, Nashville, TN; *U.S. Public*, pg. 587
Clark, Sarah, Dir.-Pub. Rels.--ALLTEL Corporation, Little Rock, AR; *U.S. Public*, pg. 55
Class, Kelly McCarthy, V.P. & Corp. Communications Dir.--Meldrum & Fewsmith Communications Inc., Cleveland, OH; *U.S. Private*, pg. 730
Claterbaugh, Steve, Mgr.-Pub. Rels.--Continental Electronics Corporation, Dallas, TX; *U.S. Public*, pg. 1563
Claus, Catherine, Mktg. Communications Specialist--Carborundum Abrasives North America, High Point, NC; *Int'l*, pg. 1174
Claus, David, Supvr.-Pub. Rels.--Sanyo Fisher Company, Chatsworth, CA; *Int'l*, pg. 1191
Clauser, Fred, Sec.--Koh-I-Noor, Inc., Bloomsbury, NJ; *U.S. Private*, pg. 629
Clawson, Carol, V.P.-Communications--GPU Nuclear Corp., Parsippany, NJ; *U.S. Public*, pg. 695
Claypoole, Joanne, Mgr.-Commun.--A. Schulman, Inc., Akron, OH; *U.S. Public*, pg. 1441
Clayton, Marybeth, Dir.-Communications--Six Flags Great Adventure Theme Park & Wild Safari Animal Park, Jackson, NJ; *U.S. Public*, pg. 1611
Cleary, William F., V.P.- Investor & Corp. Rels.--AMETEK, Inc., Paoli, PA; *U.S. Public*, pg. 99
Clem, Patricia, Mgr.-Mktg. Communications--UTILX Corporation, Kent, WA; *U.S. Public*, pg. 1701
Clements, Colleen P., Dir.-Corp. Commun.--LaBarge, Inc., Saint Louis, MO; *U.S. Public*, pg. 973
Clements, Marion, Commun. Officer--Fletcher Challenge Limited, Auckland, New Zealand; *Int'l*, pg. 494
Clendenan, R.E., Dir.-Human Resources, Admin, Sec.--Chemetics International Company Ltd Vancouver Operations, Vancouver, Canada; *Int'l*, pg. 774
Clerc, G.E. "Mickey", V.P.-Pub. Rels.--Winn-Dixie Stores, Inc., Jacksonville, FL; *U.S. Public*, pg. 1771
Cline, Amy, Dir.-Mktg.--ATCOM, Inc., Research Triangle Park, NC; *U.S. Private*, pg. 94
Cline, Robbie, Supvr.-Mktg. Communications--Siecor Corporation, Hickory, NC; *U.S. Public*, pg. 449
Cline, Robbie, Supvr.-Mktg. Communications--Siecor Corporation, Hickory, NC; *Int'l*, pg. 1245
Clonan, Jeanette, V.P.-Corp. Communications & Adv.--Loral Space & Communications, New York, NY; *U.S. Public*, pg. 1014
Close, Tim, Dir.-Communications--Serta, Inc., Itasca, IL; *U.S. Private*, pg. 985
Clouse, Debra, Dir.-Pub. Rels.--Pharmacia & Upjohn Adria Laboratories, Kalamazoo, MI; *Int'l*, pg. 1049

Coale, Joseph M., Dir.-Corp. Commun.--Crown Central Petroleum Corporation, Baltimore, MD; *U.S. Public*, pg. 462
Cobb, Karen, Mgr.-Communications--Fieldcrest Cannon, Inc., Kannapolis, NC; *U.S. Public*, pg. 1296
Cobb, Verlene P., V.P.-Corp. Commun.--AGL Resources, Atlanta, GA; *U.S. Public*, pg. 6
Cocco, Dennis A., Dir.-Corp. & Investor Affairs--The Geon Company, Avon Lake, OH; *U.S. Public*, pg. 733
Cochran, Mary M., Dir.-Corp. Communications--Amtran, Inc., Indianapolis, IN; *U.S. Public*, pg. 106
Cocker, Graham, Dir.-Human Resources--Michelin North America (Canada) Inc., Laval, Canada; *Int'l*, pg. 322
Cody, Doug, V.P.-Pub. Rels. & Pub. Affairs--Carlson Wagonlit Travel, Minneapolis, MN; *U.S. Private*, pg. 212
Cody, Douglas, V.P.-Pub. Rels. & Pub. Affairs--Carlson Companies, Inc., Minnetonka, MN; *U.S. Private*, pg. 211
Coello, Enrique, Mgr.-Pub. Affairs--Petroleos de Venezuela S.A., Caracas, Venezuela; *Int'l*, pg. 1045
Coes, Ben, Dir.-External Affairs--Canadian American Railroad Company, Bangor, ME; *U.S. Private*, pg. 575
Coes, Ben, Dir.-External Affairs--Bangor & Aroostook Railroad Co., Bangor, ME; *U.S. Private*, pg. 575
Coes, J. Ben, Dir.-External Affairs--Iron Road Railways Inc., Washington, DC; *U.S. Private*, pg. 575
Coffey, Paula, Admin. Asst.-Corp. Communications--Federated Department Stores, Inc., Cincinnati, OH; *U.S. Public*, pg. 617
Coffey, Sue, Mgr.-Sls. Service--Bontex, Buena Vista, VA; *U.S. Public*, pg. 734
Coffman, H. Frank, V.P.-Customer Service & Communications--The Standard Register Company, Dayton, OH; *U.S. Public*, pg. 1505
Cohen, Dana, Mgr.-Mktg. Commun.--IIS Intelligent Information Systems Ltd., Yokneam, Israel; *Int'l*, pg. 645
Cohen, Rhea, Dir.-Pub. Rels.--Atomic Energy of Canada Ltd., Mississauga, Canada; *Int'l*, pg. 97
Cohen, Shari, Dir.-Mktg. Communications--The Detroit Medical Center, Detroit, MI; *U.S. Private*, pg. 328
Cohen, William M., Dir.-Communications & Pub. Affairs--Bangor Hydro-Electric Company, Bangor, ME; *U.S. Public*, pg. 178
Cohoon, Scott, Mgr.-Pub. Rels.--AlliedSignal, Automotive Aftermarket, Rumford, RI; *U.S. Public*, pg. 51
Cokier, Dana, Dir.-Pub. Rels.--Neff (UK) Limited, Milton Keynes, United Kingdom; *Int'l*, pg. 912
Cole, Chuck, Dir.-Mktg.--Utility Trailer Manufacturing Co., City of Industry, CA; *U.S. Private*, pg. 1130
Cole, Joe C., V.P.-Corp. Commun.--Aztar Corporation, Phoenix, AZ; *U.S. Public*, pg. 158
Cole, Kenneth, V.P.-Govt. Rels.--AlliedSignal Inc., Morristown, NJ; *U.S. Public*, pg. 49
Cole, Laurie, Dir.-Corp. Communications--Providian Financial Corporation, San Francisco, CA; *U.S. Public*, pg. 1338
Coleman, Elisabeth, V.P.-Intl. Pub. Affairs--American Express Travel Related Services Co., Inc., New York, NY; *U.S. Public*, pg. 73
Coleman, John M., Sr. V.P.-Law & Pub. Affairs--Campbell Soup Company, Camden, NJ; *U.S. Public*, pg. 298
Coleman, Mary, V.P.-Mktg.--M. Kamenstein, Inc., Elmsford, NY; *U.S. Private*, pg. 606
Colford, S., Pub. Rels. Dir.--Howard, Merrell & Partners, Inc., Raleigh, NC; *U.S. Private*, pg. 542
Colgan, Kevin, Dir.-Media Rels. & Communications--Merck & Co., Inc., Whitehouse Station, NJ; *U.S. Public*, pg. 1090
Collier, Ann, V.P.-Fin. & Pub. Rels.--Circuit City Stores, Inc., Richmond, VA; *U.S. Public*, pg. 374
Collier, Sharon, Dir.-Information Services--Golden Peanut Company, Alpharetta, GA; *U.S. Private*, pg. 459
Collin, Emmanuelle, V.P.-Communications & Govt. Affairs--Avenor, Inc., Montreal, Canada; *Int'l*, pg. 101
Collin, Emmanuelle, Dir.-Pub. Affairs--Canadian Forest Products Ltd., Vancouver, Canada; *Int'l*, pg. 260
Collin, Jacques, V.P.-University CGS--CAP Gemini S.A., Paris, France; *Int'l*, pg. 263
Collins, Christine, Dir.-Pub. Affairs--Waste Management, Inc., Oak Brook, IL; *U.S. Public*, pg. 1744
Collins, Dan, Pub. Rels. Grp. Mgr.--Caldwell VanRiper, Inc., Indianapolis, IN; *U.S. Private*, pg. 200
Collins, Dana, Dir.-Corp. Commun.--Hellmuth, Obata & Kassabaum, Inc., Saint Louis, MO; *U.S. Private*, pg. 520
Collins, Howard, V.P.-Pub. Rels.--Occidental Petroleum Corporation, Los Angeles, CA; *U.S. Public*, pg. 1210
Collins, John, Dir.-Corp. Commun.--Mid-America Dairymen, Inc., Springfield, MO; *U.S. Private*, pg. 743
Collins, Michael, Mgr.-Pub. Affairs--Recreational Equipment, Inc., Kent, WA; *U.S. Private*, pg. 914
Collins, Rose Ann, Mgr.-Communications--Sherwood-Davis & Geck, Saint Louis, MO; *U.S. Public*, pg. 80
Colloc'h, Francoise, Sr. Exec. V.P.-Grp. Human Resources & Communications--AXA-UAP, Paris, France; *Int'l*, pg. 18
Collova, Camilla, V.P. & Dir.-Corporate Rels.--Armstrong World Industries, Inc., Lancaster, PA; *U.S. Public*, pg. 131
Colmar, Barbara, Mgr.-Pub. Rels.--Six Flags Astroworld/Six Flags Waterworld/Six Flags Houston, Houston, TX; *U.S. Public*, pg. 1611
Colombo, Larry, Mgr.-Pub. Rels.--Techsonic Industries, Inc., Eufaula, AL; *U.S. Public*, pg. 1570
Colosimo, Perry, Mgr.-Corp. Communications--Calgon Corporation, Pittsburgh, PA; *Int'l*, pg. 455
Colquett, Jeann E., Mgr.-Pub. Rels.--SouthTrust Corporation, Birmingham, AL; *U.S. Public*, pg. 1491
Colton, Guy, Dir.-Media Commun.--Outdoor Technologies Group, Spirit Lake, IA; *U.S. Private*, pg. 822
Colver, H., Dir.-Pub. Affairs--British Aerospace Defence Limited (Military Aircraft), Preston, United Kingdom; *Int'l*, pg. 217
Colwell, Tim, Dir.-Pub. Rels.--Parker Drilling Company, Tulsa, OK; *U.S. Public*, pg. 1259
Combot, Jean-Pierre, Grp. Dir.-Bldg., Pub. Works & Offshore--Bouygues, Saint Quentin-en-Yvelines, France; *Int'l*, pg. 206

Companyo, Louis, Dir.-Intl. Affairs.--Alcatel N.V., Amsterdam, Netherlands; *Int'l*, pg. 55
Comstock, Beth, Sr. V.P.-Communications--National Broadcasting Co., Inc., New York, NY; *U.S. Public*, pg. 712
Conboy, Connie, Dir.-Communications--Bayer Corporation, Pittsburgh, PA; *Int'l*, pg. 172
Cone, Amy, Mgr.-Pub. Rels.--Ag-Chem Equipment Co., Inc., Minnetonka, MN; *U.S. Public*, pg. 6
Conenello, Jim, Dir.-Corp. Communications--Pall Corporation, Greenvale, NY; *U.S. Public*, pg. 1253
Conkel, Debra K., Publications Editor--State Automobile Mutual Insurance Co., Columbus, OH; *U.S. Private*, pg. 1036
Conkle, Hope, Corp. Communications Specialist--Pan-American Life Insurance Company, New Orleans, LA; *U.S. Private*, pg. 836
Conklin, Dean C., Mgr.-Corp. Communications--Montana Power Company, Butte, MT; *U.S. Public*, pg. 1126
Conklin, Margaret N., Mgr.-Mktg. Communications--Strathmore Paper, Granby, CT; *U.S. Public*, pg. 903
Conlan, James, Dir.-Pub. Rels.--M&M/Mars, Hackettstown, NJ; *U.S. Private*, pg. 707
Conlin, Thomas R., V.P.-Pub. Affairs--Hubbell Incorporated, Orange, CT; *U.S. Public*, pg. 844
Connelly, Timothy, V.P.-Media Rels.--Fleet Bank, N.A., Jersey City, NJ; *U.S. Public*, pg. 649
Conner, Janet, Mgr.-Corp. Communications--Jeppesen Sanderson, Englewood, CO; *U.S. Public*, pg. 1616
Conner, Stephen D., V.P.-Corp. Commun.--Piedmont Natural Gas Co., Inc., Charlotte, NC; *U.S. Public*, pg. 1295
Connolly, Charles H., V.P.-Corp. Affairs & Investor Rels.--Whitman Corporation, Rolling Meadows, IL; *U.S. Public*, pg. 1766
Connors, Lynne, Dir.-Mktg. Communications--Encore Computer Corporation, Fort Lauderdale, FL; *U.S. Public*, pg. 580
Conrad, Christy, Dir.-Pub. Rels.--Enterprise Rent-A-Car Company, Saint Louis, MO; *U.S. Private*, pg. 377
Conrad, Rita, Pub. Rels.--CDR Pigments & Dispersions, Elizabethtown, KY; *U.S. Private*, pg. 413
Conrad, Rita A., Dir.-Corp. Commun.--Flint Ink Corp., Detroit, MI; *U.S. Private*, pg. 413
Conroy, Amanda, V.P.-Corp. Communications--PolyGram International Ltd., London, United Kingdom; *Int'l*, pg. 1053
Conroy, Carolyn, Dir.-Media & Pub. Rels.--Jacoby & Meyers Law Offices, New York, NY; *U.S. Private*, pg. 580
Conroy, Catherine M., Sr. V.P. & Dir.-Corp. Communications--Donaldson, Lufkin, & Jenrette, Inc., New York, NY; *U.S. Public*, pg. 589
Conroy, James T., Sr. V.P.-Corp. Affairs--MacAndrews & Forbes Holdings Inc., New York, NY; *U.S. Private*, pg. 689
Conroy, James T., Sr. V.P.-Pub. Affairs--Andrews Group, Incorporated, New York, NY; *U.S. Private*, pg. 689
Conroy, Paul, Mgr.-Pub. Affairs--Pacificare of Ohio, Cincinnati, OH; *U.S. Public*, pg. 1251
Conti, Barbara, Dir.-Communications--John Crane Mechanical Seals, Morton Grove, IL; *Int'l*, pg. 1339
Conti, Elisa, Mgr.-Pub. Rels.--Candy S.p.A., Brugherio, Italy; *Int'l*, pg. 259
Conti, John, Dir.-Commun.--Consolidated Natural Gas Company, Pittsburgh, PA; *U.S. Public*, pg. 435
Contos, Dixie, V.P.-Adv. & Dir.-Pub. Rels.--Pay Less Super Markets, Inc., Anderson, IN; *U.S. Private*, pg. 844
Conway, Charles T., Asst. V.P. & Dir.-Corp. Commun. & Adv.--Policy Management Systems Corporation, Blythewood, SC; *U.S. Public*, pg. 1314
Conway, Heather, Sr. V.P.-Pub. Rels. & Corp. Commun.--The Toronto Dominion Bank, Toronto, Canada; *Int'l*, pg. 1401
Conway, Joe, Pub. Rels.--Towers Perrin, New York, NY; *U.S. Private*, pg. 1093
Conyers, Rita, Exec. V.P.-Corp. Commun. & Trng. & Leadership--Mutual of America Life Insurance Company, New York, NY; *U.S. Private*, pg. 769
Cook, John, Sr. V.P.-Communications--Nationwide Insurance Enterprise, Columbus, OH; *U.S. Private*, pg. 788
Cooley, Doug, V.P.-Service--Picker International, Inc., Cleveland, OH; *Int'l*, pg. 545
Coolican, Murray, V.P.-Pub. Affairs--Nova Scotia Power Inc., Halifax, Canada; *Int'l*, pg. 971
Cooling, Michael, Mgr.-Corp. Rels.--Reuters Holdings PLC, London, United Kingdom; *Int'l*, pg. 1105
Coombs, Kevin, V.P.-Corp. Affairs--Fishery Products International Ltd., Saint Johns, Canada; *Int'l*, pg. 492
Coons, Robert C., Mgr.-Corp. Commun.--BJ Services Company, Houston, TX; *U.S. Public*, pg. 161
Cooper, Bobbie, Commun. Specialist--Bourns, Inc., Riverside, CA; *U.S. Private*, pg. 161
Cooper, Cathy, V.P.-Mktg. & Investor Rels.--Washington Federal Savings, Seattle, WA; *U.S. Public*, pg. 1740
Cooper, Claire, V.P.-Human Resources--Gasco, Inc., Honolulu, HI; *Int'l*, pg. 225
Cooper, Doris, Asst. Sec. & Mgr.-Communications--General Employment Enterprises, Inc., Oak Brook Terrace, IL; *U.S. Public*, pg. 714
Cooper, Gordon, Dir.-Mktg. & Communications--Stone Container Corporation, Chicago, IL; *U.S. Public*, pg. 1520
Cooper, Jerry W., Dir.-Corp. Commun.--Asarco Incorporated, New York, NY; *U.S. Public*, pg. 137
Cooper, Kimberly, Mgr.-Corp. Communications--Enzon, Inc., Piscataway, NJ; *U.S. Public*, pg. 587
Cooper, Phil, V.P.-Publicity & Adv.--Caesars World, Inc., Las Vegas, NV; *U.S. Public*, pg. 1512
Cooper, Phil, V.P.-Pub. Rels. & Adv.--Caesars Palace, Las Vegas, NV; *U.S. Public*, pg. 1512
Cooper, Renee, Dir.-Pub. Rels.--United Distillers USA, Inc., Stamford, CT; *Int'l*, pg. 412
Coots, Frank, Mgr.-Pub. Rels.--Ryobi America Corp., Anderson, SC; *Int'l*, pg. 1151

Copel, Margurite, Dir.-Pub. Rels.--Sandoz Agro, Inc., Des Plaines, IL; *Int'l*, pg. 974

Copeland, R. Bruce Jr., V.P.-Mktg. & Pub. Rels.--First Financial Holdings, Inc., Charleston, SC; *U.S. Public*, pg. 634

Copes, Rodney, Dir.-Investor Rels.--Harley-Davidson, Inc., Milwaukee, WI; *U.S. Public*, pg. 786

Coppersmith, Syd, Mgr.-Mktg. Commun.--Dallas Semiconductor Corporation, Dallas, TX; *U.S. Public*, pg. 478

Coppinger, Donna, V.P.-Mktg. Services--Duke Realty Investments, Inc., Indianapolis, IN; *U.S. Public*, pg. 535

Copps, Thomas R., Exec. V.P.-Pub. Rels.--The Copps Corp., Stevens Point, WI; *U.S. Private*, pg. 275

Corbel, Tony, Dir.-Pub. Rels. & Tech.--Hasselblad USA, Inc., Fairfield, NJ; *Int'l*, pg. 1468

Corbett, Gerard F., Dir.-Corp. Communications--Hitachi America, Ltd., Tarrytown, NY; *Int'l*, pg. 622

Corbett, Michael, Chief Fin. Officer--Sholodge, Inc., Hendersonville, TN; *U.S. Public*, pg. 1467

Corbitt, Sharon, Mgr.-Pub. Rels.--Broadband Networks Group, Hatboro, PA; *U.S. Public*, pg. 716

Cordes, Charles, Dir.-Mktg. & Communications--American Annuity Group, Cincinnati, OH; *U.S. Public*, pg. 74

Corello, Matt, Mgr.-Customer Service--Excel Technology, Inc., New York, NY; *U.S. Public*, pg. 599

Cornelis, E., Mgr.-Corp. Communications--Union Miniere, Brussels, Belgium; *Int'l*, pg. 1441

Cornwell, John, Mgr.-Corp. Mktg. & Pub. Affairs--3M, Saint Paul, MN; *U.S. Public*, pg. 1604

Corrigan, Gary, Dir.-Corp. Commun.--Dana Corporation, Toledo, OH; *U.S. Public*, pg. 479

Corso, Joy, Mgr.-Mktg.--GZA GeoEnvironmental Technologies, Inc., Newton, MA; *U.S. Public*, pg. 697

Corsten, Josefine, Dir.-Corp. Commun.--KSB Aktiengesellschaft, Frankenthal, Germany; *Int'l*, pg. 721

Corti, Miguel A., Mgr.-Pub. Rels.--Sancor Cooperativas Unidas Limitadas, Buenos Aires, Argentina; *Int'l*, pg. 1183

Cosby, Mark, V.P.-Adv. & Pub. Rels.--Giant Food Stores Inc., Carlisle, PA; *Int'l*, pg. 750

Cosby, Paige, Dir.-Corp. Communications--Coram Healthcare Corporation, Denver, CO; *U.S. Public*, pg. 446

Cosley, Jerry, Sr. Dir.-Corp. Communications--UtiliCorp United Inc., Kansas City, MO; *U.S. Public*, pg. 1700

Costa Lima, Jose, Dir.-Pub. Rels.--General Motors de Portugal, Sociedade Anonima, Lisbon, Portugal; *U.S. Public*, pg. 722

Costello, Connie, Pub. Rels.--Six Flags Great America, Inc., Gurnee, IL; *U.S. Public*, pg. 1611

Costello, Michael B., V.P.-Admin. & Corp. Commun.--Shared Medical Systems Corporation, Malvern, PA; *U.S. Public*, pg. 1463

Costello, Wade, Mgr.-Mktg.--Bodine Assembly and Test Systems, Bridgeport, CT; *U.S. Private*, pg. 154

Cotton, Bruce C., Sr. V.P.-Pub. Affairs--Long John Silver's, Inc., Lexington, KY; *U.S. Private*, pg. 674

Cottraux, Suzanne, V.P.-Corp. Commun. & Investor Rels.--Patriot American Hospitality, Inc., Dallas, TX; *U.S. Public*, *pg. 1265*

Couch, Heidi, Mgr.-Pub. Rels.--Hitachi Koki U.S.A. Ltd., Norcross, GA; *Int'l*, pg. 620

Couke, J., Mgr.-Pub. Rels.-Belgium--Interbrew S.A., Leuven, Belgium; *Int'l*, pg. 679

Coulter, Cynthia, V.P.-Corp. Communications--Blue Cross of California, Woodland Hills, CA; *U.S. Private*, pg. 152

Coulter, David G., Dir.-Govt. & Pub. Rels.--General Motors New Zealand Ltd., Upper Hutt, New Zealand; *U.S. Public*, pg. 722

Coulter, Patrick C.G., V.P.-Commun.--Boeing Commercial Airplane Group, Renton, WA; *U.S. Public*, pg. 240

Courjault, J., V.P.-External Rels.--Compagnie Generale de Geophysique, Massy, France; *Int'l*, pg. 241

Courtney, James D., Dir.-Mktg. Communications--Bethlehem Steel Corporation, Bethlehem, PA; *U.S. Public*, pg. 226

Cousins, Basil, Mgr.-Corp. Communications--Olivetti U.K. Ltd., London, United Kingdom; *Int'l*, pg. 1003

Cousins, Wayne, Coord.-Pub. Affairs--B.C. Hydro, Vancouver, Canada; *Int'l*, pg. 114

Coutre, Denis, V.P.-Communications & Govt. Rels.--Domtar Inc., Montreal, Canada; *Int'l*, pg. 416

Coventry, Mary, V.P.-Corp. Devel.--Sealed Air Corporation, Saddle Brook, NJ; *U.S. Public*, pg. 1450

Covey, Jim, Dir.-Commun.--Central Mutual Insurance Co., Van Wert, OH; *U.S. Private*, pg. 223

Covington, Joyce, Mgr.-Pub. Rels.--Hypermedia Communications, Inc., San Mateo, CA; *U.S. Public*, pg. 851

Cox, C. Stewart, Gen. Mgr.-Pub. Affairs--Swire Pacific Limited, Central, Hong Kong; *Int'l*, pg. 1328

Cox, Douglas B., V.P. & Dir.-Mktg. Services & Corp. Communications--SmithKline Beecham Consumer Healthcare, U.S., Pittsburgh, PA; *Int'l*, pg. 1264

Cox, Jason, Pub. Rels. Dept.--Goldman, Sachs & Co., New York, NY; *U.S. Private*, pg. 462

Coy, Bill, Mgr.-Support Communications--Royal Insurance Company of America, Charlotte, NC; *Int'l*, pg. 1131

Coyle, Carolyn, Corp. Affairs Specialist--Subaru of America, Inc., Cherry Hill, NJ; *Int'l*, pg. 523

Coyne, Debby, Mgr.-Product Publicity--Fluke Corporation, Everett, WA; *U.S. Public*, pg. 659

Crabtree, David H., V.P.-Customer Svcs.--American Electric Power Service Corp., Columbus, OH; *U.S. Public*, pg. 72

Cradit, Lisa, Mgr.-Pub. Rels.--BMC Software, Inc., Houston, TX; *U.S. Public*, pg. 162

Cram, Karin, Mgr.-Corp. Communications--Exide Electronics Group, Inc., Raleigh, NC; *Int'l*, pg. 126

Crane, Kasey, Coord.-Pub. Affairs--Alcoa of Australia Limited, Melbourne, Australia; *U.S. Public*, pg. 62

Cranois, Nicole, Sr. V.P.-Corp. Communications--Elf Aquitane, Paris, France; *Int'l*, pg. 444

Crawford, Ann, Dir.-Corp. Relations--Resort Condominiums International, Indianapolis, IN; *U.S. Public*, pg. 322

Crawford, Edward, Chm. Bd., Pres & Chief Exec. & Oper. Officer--Park-Ohio Industries, Inc., Cleveland, OH; *U.S. Public*, pg. 1258

Crawford, Jane, Mgr.-Corp. Communications--Elf Atochem North America, Inc., Philadelphia, PA; *Int'l*, pg. 445

Crawford, Judith, Dir.-Corp. Communications--YKK (U.S.A.), Marietta, GA; *Int'l*, pg. 1515

Crawford, Norman, V.P.-Consumer & Indus. Prods.--Dayco Swan Corporation, Worthington, OH; *U.S. Public*, pg. 1045

Crawford, Robin, Pub. Rels.--Mack Trucks, Inc., Allentown, PA; *Int'l*, pg. 1102

Crawford, Shannon, Dir.-Customer Satisfaction--American Freightways Corporation, Harrison, AR; *U.S. Public*, pg. 75

Crespo, Javier, Dir.-Commun.--Sol Melia, Palma de Mallorca, Spain; *Int'l*, pg. 1277

Cresto, Pedro, Dir.-Pub. Rels.--Peugeot Talbot Espana, Madrid, Spain; *Int'l*, pg. 1021

Cripe, Danny, Pub. Rels.--Sweco, Florence, KY; *U.S. Public*, *pg. 574*

Crisman, Anita, Mgr.-Communications--Barton Malow Enterprises, Inc., Southfield, MI; *U.S. Private*, pg. 120

Crisman, Richard, V.P.-Pub. Rels. & Adv.--The Gap, Inc., San Francisco, CA; *U.S. Public*, pg. 702

Crisp, Patrick, Mgr.-Pub. Rels.--Caere Corporation, Los Gatos, CA; *U.S. Public*, pg. 291

Critchlow, Paul, Sr. V.P.-Mktg. & Communications--Merrill Lynch & Co., Inc., New York, NY; *U.S. Public*, pg. 1097

Croken, Ken, Dir.-Commun.--Norstan, Inc., Plymouth, MN; *U.S. Public*, pg. 1192

Cromack, Keith, Sr. Mgr.-Corp. Communications--Comverse Network Systems, Wakefield, MA; *U.S. Public*, pg. 425

Cromer, Deb, Dir.-Pub. Rels. & Consultant Rels.--Tandem Computers Inc., Cupertino, CA; *U.S. Public*, pg. 417

Cronk, Julian, Grp. Sec.--The Hartstone Group PLC, London, United Kingdom; *Int'l*, pg. 599

Croot, Heidi, Dir.-Communications--Extendicare Inc., Markham, Canada; *Int'l*, pg. 468

Crosier, Thelma, Mgr.-Export & Customer Svcs.--The Keller Manufacturing Co., Inc., Corydon, IN; *U.S. Private*, pg. 612

Crosland, Jo, Mgr.-Adv. & Corp. Communications-London Office--Investcorp International, New York, NY; *Int'l*, pg. 686

Cross, Cindy, Assoc. Media & Consumer Rels.--Procter & Gamble Inc., North York, Canada; *U.S. Public*, pg. 1332

Cross, Ian, Dir.-Mktg. Commun.--Wang Laboratories, Inc., Billerica, MA; *U.S. Public*, pg. 1737

Cross, Lori, Dir.-Pub. Rels.--Symantec Corporation - Beaverton Site, Beaverton, OR; *U.S. Public*, pg. 1545

Crosslin, Carole, Pub. Rels. Rep.--R.J. Reynolds Tobacco Company, Winston Salem, NC; *U.S. Public*, pg. 1355

Crouse, Nancy, V.P.-Sls. Admin.--Superba, Inc., Los Angeles, CA; *U.S. Private*, pg. 1054

Crowe, Jan, Mgr.-Mktg. & Communications--Mobil Oil Corporation, Fairfax, VA; *U.S. Public*, pg. 1118

Crowley, James W., Jr., V.P.-Customer Service--NUI Corporation, Bedminster, NJ; *U.S. Public*, pg. 1147

Crowley, Maureen, Mgr.-Corp. Commun.--Furon Company, Laguna Niguel, CA; *U.S. Public*, pg. 688

Crowley, Neely, Supvr.-Pub. Rels.--Atlantic Electric Co., Pleasantville, NJ; *U.S. Public*, pg. 430

Crozes, Helene, Mgr.-Pub. Rels.--Avions de Transport Regional - ATR, Blagnac, France; *Int'l*, pg. 654

Cruickshank, Bert, Dir.-Communications--Bombardier Regional Aircraft Division, Downsview, Canada; *U.S. Public*, pg. 242

Cruickshank, Burt, Dir.-Commun. & Mktg.-Reg. Aircraft--Bombardier Aerospace, Dorval, Canada; *Int'l*, pg. 200

Cruickshank, Jim, V.P.-Commun.--Fender Musical Instruments, Scottsdale, AZ; *U.S. Private*, pg. 400

Crum, Kathleen, Pub. Rels. Officer--James Hardie Industries Ltd., Sydney, Australia; *Int'l*, pg. 596

Crum, Lorrie Paul, Dir.-Corp. Commun.--Rubbermaid Incorporated, Wooster, OH; *U.S. Public*, pg. 1411

Crump, Harold, V.P.-Pub. Affairs--Hubbard Broadcasting, Inc., Saint Paul, MN; *U.S. Private*, pg. 543

Crump, Jane, Public Rels. Specialist--Viking Range Corp., Greenwood, MS; *U.S. Private*, pg. 1140

Cruncher, Jeremiah, V.P.-Corp. Communications--CD Products, Inc., New Providence, NJ; *U.S. Public*, pg. 276

Crunkhorn, Michael, Dir.-Communications--Toronto Star Newspapers Ltd., Toronto, Canada; *Int'l*, pg. 1402

Csanadi, Peter, Dir.-Pub. Rels.--Adidas AG, Herzogenaurach, Germany; *Int'l*, pg. 24

Csinicsek, Kenneth, Sr. V.P.-Mktg., Investor & Pub. Rels.--First Financial Bank, FSB, Stevens Point, WI; *U.S. Public*, pg. 140

Cubell, Lee, Dir.-Mktg., Adv. & Pub. Rels.--Kingsdown, Inc., Mebane, NC; *U.S. Private*, pg. 622

Cudahy, Mike, Dir.-Mktg. Commun.--Farmers and Traders Life Insurance Co., Syracuse, NY; *U.S. Private*, pg. 394

Cudney, Rose, Mgr.-Communications--Toronto Star Newspapers Ltd., Toronto, Canada; *Int'l*, pg. 1402

Cuizio, Ellen, Dir.-Pub. Rels.--International Home Foods Inc., Parsippany, NJ; *U.S. Private*, pg. 526

Cullen, Cheryl, Mgr.-Pub. Rels.--Trumpf Inc., Farmington, CT; *U.S. Private*, pg. 1108

Cullen, Karon, Corp. Dir.-Pub. Rels.--The Ritz-Carlton Hotel Company LLC, Atlanta, GA; *U.S. Private*, pg. 594

Culley, P.L., Mgr.-Mktg. Communications--ABB Kent Plc, Luton, United Kingdom; *Int'l*, pg. 2

Culp, E. Ronald, V.P.-Pub. Affairs--Sears, Roebuck and Co., Hoffman Estates, IL; *U.S. Public*, pg. 1452

Cummings, John, Dir.-Corp. Rels.--Johns Manville Corporation, Denver, CO; *U.S. Public*, pg. 927

Cummins, Lin, V.P.-Communications Coord.--United Technologies Automotive, Dearborn, MI; *U.S. Public*, pg. 1691

Cunnigham, Edward A., Dir.-Corp. Commun. & Investor Rels.--Tredegar Industries Inc., Richmond, VA; *U.S. Public*, pg. 1633

Cunningham, Philip, Dir.-Corp. Commun.--MFI Furniture Center PLC, London, United Kingdom; *Int'l*, pg. 827

Curley, Anne, V.P.-Pub. Affairs--Firstar Corporation, Milwaukee, WI; *U.S. Public*, pg. 642

Curran, Joanne, V.P. & External Communications Mgr.--Union Bank of California, San Francisco, CA; *Int'l*, pg. 157

Curran, Joel, V.P. & Pub. Rels. Acct. Supvr.--Price/McNabb, Inc., Charlotte, NC; *U.S. Private*, pg. 883

Curran, Thomas, V.P.-Distr. Sls.--The Wm. Powell Company, Cincinnati, OH; *U.S. Private*, pg. 877

Current, Gloster, V.P.-Mktg. & Pub. Rels.--Lincoln National Corporation, Fort Wayne, IN; *U.S. Public*, pg. 997

Curtin, Dennis, Mgr.-Corp. Communications--Weis Markets, Inc., Sunbury, PA; *U.S. Public*, pg. 1751

Curwen, Martin, Dir.-Corp. Affairs--European Investment Bank, Luxembourg, Luxembourg; *Int'l*, pg. 465

Cury, Oscar, Dir.-Mktg. & Corp. Communications--Travel Channel-Latin America, Miami, FL; *U.S. Private*, pg. 647

Cusick, Mary L., V.P.-Corp. Communications--Bob Evans Farms, Inc., Columbus, OH; *U.S. Public*, pg. 596

Cusick, Mary L., V.P.-Corp. Communications--Bob Evans Farms, Inc. Sausage Division, Columbus, OH; *U.S. Public*, pg. 596

Custer, John, Mgr.-Mktg. & Communications--Sigma Chemical Co., Saint Louis, MO; *U.S. Public*, pg. 1472

Custer, Kim, Dir.-Reg. & Govt. Affairs--Mitsubishi Motor Sales of America, Inc., Cypress, CA; *Int'l*, pg. 875

Cusumano, Jan, Mgr.-Corp. Communications--May & Speh, Inc., Downers Grove, IL; *U.S. Public*, pg. 1063

Cutler, Katie, Sr. V.P.-Corp. Commun.--Crown Vantage Inc., Oakland, CA; *U.S. Public*, pg. 465

Cyprus, Beth, Mgr.-Communications--International Comfort Products Corp., Lewisburg, TN; *U.S. Public*, pg. 898

Czelusniak, Judith A., V.P.-Corp. Rels.--AGCO Corporation, Duluth, GA; *U.S. Public*, pg. 28

d'Ambly, Lorraine, Mgr.-Pub. Rels.--Serie Club, Paris, France; *Int'l*, pg. 562

D'Amour, Claire M., V.P.-Corp. Affairs--Big Y Foods Inc., Springfield, MA; *U.S. Private*, pg. 143

D'Amour, Holly H., Dir.-Pub. Affairs--Mead Johnson & Co., Evansville, IN; *U.S. Public*, pg. 254

d'Arbeloff, George V., V.P.-Corp. Rels.--Teradyne, Inc., Boston, MA; *U.S. Public*, pg. 1580

D'Armond, Jackson, Mgr.-Mktg. Communications--Stihl Inc., Virginia Beach, VA; *Int'l*, pg. 1301

D'Eliscu, Jeffrey B., V.P.-Corp. Communications--Allergan, Inc., Irvine, CA; *U.S. Public*, pg. 46

d'Oleon, Diane, Mgr.-Corp. Commun.--Danone Group, Paris, France; *Int'l*, pg. 379

Da Rola, Sonia, Mgr.-Pub. Rels.--Opticos S.r.l., Brembate di Sopra, Italy; *Int'l*, pg. 1007

Dabney, Fred E., Corp. Communications Officer--Royal Insurance, Charlotte, NC; *Int'l*, pg. 1130

Daboshi, Yoshikuni, Exec. Mng. Dir.--Kubota Corp., Osaka, Japan; *Int'l*, pg. 762

Dacanay, Aurelio B., Sr. Mgr.-Corp. Communications--Philippine Long Distance Telephone Company, Manila, Philippines; *Int'l*, pg. 1051

Dacey, Michael, Mgr.-Mktg. Communications--Hayward Industries, Inc., Elizabeth, NJ; *U.S. Private*, pg. 513

Dacruz, Ed, Dir.-Corp. Communications--North Safety Products, Charleston, SC; *Int'l*, pg. 1243

Dadoun, Joy, Mgr.-Corp. Communications--Fox River Paper Company, Appleton, WI; *U.S. Private*, pg. 422

Dages, Walter E., V.P.-Pub. Rels.--The F.A. Bartlett Tree Expert Co., Stamford, CT; *U.S. Private*, pg. 119

Daggett, John, Dir.-Mktg. Svcs. & Corp. Communication--RAYOVAC Corporation, Madison, WI; *U.S. Private*, pg. 912

Daily, Alice, Mgr.-Corp. Communications--Cordis, a Johnson & Johnson Company, Miami, FL; *U.S. Public*, pg. 928

Dale, David, Dir.-Grp. Corp. Communications--Tate & Lyle PLC, London, United Kingdom; *Int'l*, pg. 1356

Dale, Steven, V.P.-Public Rels.--Starbanc Corporation, Cincinnati, OH; *U.S. Public*, pg. 1510

Daley, Michel, Mgr.-Media Rels.--Bell Atlantic-Washington, D.C., Inc., Washington, DC; *U.S. Public*, pg. 203

Dallal, Elias, V.P.-Personnel & Admin.--El Al Airlines Ltd., Lod, Israel; *Int'l*, pg. 435

Dallow, K. S., Mgr.-Mktg. Communications--Sensall, Div. of Rosemount, Inc., Hauppauge, NY; *U.S. Public*, pg. 574

Damianakes, Amy, Dir.-Corp. Communications--AirTouch Communications, Inc., San Francisco, CA; *U.S. Public*, pg. 34

Damico, Pam, Sr. Pub. Rels. Mgr.--Wolf Mansfield Bolling Advertising Inc., Buffalo, NY; *U.S. Private*, pg. 1185

Damm, Jens M., Mgr.-Pub. Rels.--Olivetti A/S, Copenhagen, Denmark; *Int'l*, pg. 1003

Danenberg, Alan M., Mgr.-Mdsg. & Mktg. Commun.--Elkay Manufacturing Company, Oak Brook, IL; *U.S. Private*, pg. 372

Daniel, C.D., Mgr.-Integrated Communications--General Motors of Canada Ltd., Oshawa, Canada; *U.S. Public*, pg. 722

Daniello, Debra, Mgr.-Pub. Affairs Information Center--Merck & Co., Inc., Whitehouse Station, NJ; *U.S. Public*, pg. 1090

Daniels, Brigitte, Mgr.-Pub. Affairs--Vickers PLC, London, United Kingdom; *Int'l*, pg. 1466

Daniels, Kim, Exec. Admin. Asst.--The Scoular Company, Omaha, NE; *U.S. Private*, pg. 977

Daniels, Kristin, Pub. Rels. & Mktg. Communications--Williams Worldwide, Santa Monica, CA; *U.S. Private*, pg. 1179

Daniels, Mitchell E., Jr., V.P.-Corp. Policy & Govt. Rels.--Eli Lilly and Company, Indianapolis, IN; *U.S. Public*, pg. 992

Danielsen, Pete, V.P.-Mktg. & Communications--MTV Networks, New York, NY; *U.S. Private*, pg. 779

Danielson, John, Sr. V.P.-Corp. Rels.--U.S. Bancorp, Minneapolis, MN; *U.S. Public*, pg. 1680

Danish, Dina, Dir.-Communications--The Wella Corporation, Montvale, NJ; *Int'l*, pg. 1489

Danni, Joe, V.P.-Corp. Rels.--Placer Dome Inc., Vancouver, Canada; *Int'l*, pg. 1060

Danos, Andras, Dir.-Pub. Rels.--General Motors Hungary, Budapest, Hungary; *U.S. Public*, pg. 722

Dansk, Anna, Mgr.-Pub. Rels.--Skandia Insurance Company Limited, Stockholm, Sweden; *Int'l*, pg. 1256

Darby, Cheryl, Dir.-Human Resources--DuBois Chemicals, Cincinnati, OH; *Int'l*, pg. 1437

Dardess, Margaret, Sr. V.P.-Corp. Affairs--Glaxo Wellcome Inc., Research Triangle Park, NC; *Int'l*, pg. 552

Darlow, Sheldon J., V.P.--Unidigital/Cardinal Corp., New York, NY; *U.S. Public*, pg. 1664

Darmstadt, Rolf, Dr., Dir.-Pub. Rels.--Commerzbank AG, Frankfurt, Germany; *Int'l*, pg. 308

Darwin, Allen, Pres.--Cardinal Inc., Rahway, NJ; *U.S. Private*, pg. 208

Das, Anthony, V.P.-Corp. & Intl. Affairs--Startec Global Communications Corporation, Bethesda, MD; *U.S. Public*, pg. 1511

DaSilva, Suzanne, Mgr.-Mktg. & Communications--Clicquot, Inc., New York, NY; *Int'l*, pg. 781

Datz, Jeanne, Dir.-Commun.--Hilton Hotels Corporation, Beverly Hills, CA; *U.S. Public*, pg. 828

Daugherty, Paul J., Mgr.-Adv. & Mkt. Analyst--Sandusky International Inc., Sandusky, OH; *U.S. Private*, pg. 964

Davey, Beth, V.P. & Dir.-Publicity--Little, Brown & Co., New York, NY; *U.S. Public*, pg. 1612

Davey, Carol, Sr. Corp. Affairs Officer--Standard Chartered Bank PLC, London, United Kingdom; *Int'l*, pg. 1294

David, Len, V.P.-Pub. Rels.--Henry Schein, Inc., Melville, NY; *U.S. Public*, pg. 1437

Davidowitz, Suzie, V.P.-Corp. Pub. Rels.--Cosmair, Inc., New York, NY; *Int'l*, pg. 818

Davids, Hollace, V.P.-Publicity & Special Projects--TriStar Pictures, Culver City, CA; *Int'l*, pg. 1283

Davidson, Bo, Mgr.-Communications--Atlas Copco Rockdrilling Equipment, Stockholm, Sweden; *Int'l*, pg. 96

Davidson, Christopher, Dir.-Pub. Rel. & Corp. Communications--Guinness Plc, London, United Kingdom; *Int'l*, pg. 412

Davidson, Janis, Mgr.-Pub. Rels.--Toronto Blue Jays Baseball Club, Inc., Toronto, Canada; *Int'l*, pg. 680

Davidson, Peter, Mgr.-Media & Pub. Rels.--Weetabix Limited, Kettering, United Kingdom; *Int'l*, pg. 1488

Davidson, Richard A., Dir.-Human Resources--American Mail-Well Envelope, Englewood, CO; *U.S. Public*, pg. 1038

Davies, Russ, Mgr.-Mktg. Communications--Aro Fluid Products Division, Bryan, OH; *U.S. Public*, pg. 877

Davis-Salisbury, Julie, Pres.-Julie Davis Associates--Fitzgerald & Co., Atlanta, GA; *U.S. Private*, pg. 409

Davis, Aaron L., V.P.-Mktg.--American Power Conversion Corporation, West Kingston, RI; *U.S. Public*, pg. 89

Davis, Bill, Mgr.-Mktg. Communications--Toko America, Inc., Mount Prospect, IL; *Int'l*, pg. 1393

Davis, Bob, Mgr.-Mktg. Commun.--Sunnen Products Company, Saint Louis, MO; *U.S. Private*, pg. 1053

Davis, Bob, Mgr.-Human Resources--Jacobsen Textron, Racine, WI; *U.S. Public*, pg. 1589

Davis, Dan, Mgr.-Pub. Rels.--Marilyn Miglin, L.P., Chicago, IL; *U.S. Private*, pg. 745

Davis, Deb, Mgr.-Communications--Onan Corporation, Minneapolis, MN; *U.S. Public*, pg. 468

Davis, Don, Dir.-Public Rels.--Altera Corporation, San Jose, CA; *U.S. Public*, pg. 59

Davis, Kassie, Dir.-Pub. Affairs--Marshall Field, Chicago, IL; *U.S. Public*, pg. 489

Davis, Kurt, V.P.-Public Relations--Foundation Health Systems, Inc., Pueblo, CO; *U.S. Public*, pg. 678

Davis, Kurt R., V.P.-Pub. Affairs & Corp. Communications--Rural Metro Corporation, Scottsdale, AZ; *U.S. Public*, pg. 1412

Davis, Lee, V.P.-H.R.--Packerland Packing Co., Green Bay, WI; *U.S. Private*, pg. 833

Davis, Leslie, Mgr.-Pub. Rels.--3Com Corporation, Santa Clara, CA; *U.S. Public*, pg. 1603

Davis, Marci, V.P.-Mktg. & Communications--Cineplex Odeon Corporation, Toronto, Canada; *Int'l*, pg. 292

Davis, Mariko, Mgr.-Mktg. Commun.--Rollerblade, Inc., Minnetonka, MN; *U.S. Private*, pg. 941

Davis, Michelle, Mktg. & Adv.--Howell Instruments Inc., Fort Worth, TX; *U.S. Private*, pg. 543

Davis, Mitch, Sr. V.P.-People Affairs--C & S Wholesale Grocery Inc., Brattleboro, VT; *U.S. Private*, pg. 192

Davis, Ronald E., V.P.-Corp. Commun.--Franchise Finance Corp. of America, Scottsdale, AZ; *U.S. Public*, pg. 679

Davis, Shea, Asst. V.P. & Dir.-Corp. Commun.--Quorum Health Group, Inc., Brentwood, TN; *U.S. Public*, pg. 1353

Davis, Sheila M., Mgr.-Pub. Rels.--Winnebago Industries, Inc., Forest City, IA; *U.S. Public*, pg. 1772

Davis, Tim J., Dir.-Communications & Admin.--Dowty Aerospace, Abingdon, United Kingdom; *Int'l*, pg. 1337

Davison, Dean, V.P.-Pub. Rels.--Barkley & Evergreen Advertising, Inc., Kansas City, MO; *U.S. Private*, pg. 116

Dawson, Bill, Dir.-Corp. Communications--Gelman Sciences, Inc., Ann Arbor, MI; *U.S. Public*, pg. 1253

Dawson, David C., Dir.-Pub. Rels.--Ryder System, Inc., Miami, FL; *U.S. Public*, pg. 1413

Dawson, J., Mgr.-Communications--Forge Division, Marion, OH; *U.S. Public*, pg. 557

Dawson, Joseph R., Mgr.-Contract Packaging Rels.--Bunker Hill Foods Inc., Bedford, VA; *U.S. Private*, pg. 219

Day, Mark, Mgr.-Pub. Rels. & Mktg. Communications--Teledyne Ryan Aeronautical, San Diego, CA; *U.S. Public*, pg. 43

Day, Stephanie, Dir.-External Rels.--Repsol S.A., Madrid, Spain; *Int'l*, pg. 1104

Day, Stephanie M., V.P.-Corp. Commun.--California Microwave, Inc., Sunnyvale, CA; *U.S. Public*, pg. 293

de al Vega, Sophie, Dir.-Communications--Reckitt & Colman S.A., Massy, France; *Int'l*, pg. 1090

De Andres, Eduardo Gonzales, Dir.-Pub. Rels.--Argentaria Corporacion Bancaria de Espana, S.A., Madrid, Spain; *Int'l*, pg. 80

de Barbe, Mr., Supvr.-Mktg. & Communications--N.V. Kodak S.A., Vilvoorde, Belgium; *U.S. Public*, pg. 554

de Jongh, Nick, Dir.-Pub. Affairs--GKN plc, Redditch, United Kingdom; *Int'l*, pg. 534

de la Cruz, Jennifer, Mgr.-Pub. Rels.--Carnival Corporation, Miami, FL; *U.S. Public*, pg. 306

de La Nove, Sophie, Press Rels.--AGF Assurances, Paris, France; *Int'l*, pg. 14

de La Vaissiere, Vincent, Mgr.-Communication--Lyonnaise des Eaux S.A., Nanterre, France; *Int'l*, pg. 822

de Lavennat, Christine, Dir.-Communications--Compagnie Generale Des Eaux, Paris, France; *Int'l*, pg. 321

de Leede, P.S.M., Staff-Corp. Communications--N.V. Koninklijke KNP BT, Amsterdam, Netherlands; *Int'l*, pg. 756

de Leeuw, C., Mgr.-Pub. Rels.--DSM N.V., Heerlen, Netherlands; *Int'l*, pg. 352

de Lima, Altamir C., Corp. Communications & Govt. Rels.--Banco Chase Manhattan, S.A., Santo Amaro, Brazil; *U.S. Public*, pg. 339

De Llano, Luis, Mgr.-Pub. Rels.--C.A. Cigarrera Bigott, Sucs., Caracas, Venezuela; *Int'l*, pg. 111

de Pierrebourg, Olivier, Dir.-Communications--AGF Assurances, Paris, France; *Int'l*, pg. 14

de Segogne, Bruno, Dir.-Communication--Calberson, Paris, France; *Int'l*, pg. 1163

de Soto, Maria Isabel, Pub. Rels. Dir. & Promo. Dir.--Leo Burnett Inc., Santo Domingo, Dominican Republic; *U.S. Private*, pg. 185

de St. Germain, Herve, Dir.-Human Resources & Communications--Arjo Wiggins Appleton plc, Basingstoke, United Kingdom; *Int'l*, pg. 567

De Waal, John, Dir.-Adv.--New Era Cap. Co., Derby, NY; *U.S. Private*, pg. 793

Dean, Alan V., V.P.-Pub. & Corp. Affairs--EdperBrascan Corporation, Toronto, Canada; *Int'l*, pg. 433

Dean, N., Advisor-Human Resources, Pub. Rels. & Communications--British Aerospace Defence Limited (Military Aircraft), Preston, United Kingdom; *Int'l*, pg. 217

Dean, Shannon C., Mgr.-Corp. Commun.--Dominguez Services Corporation, Long Beach, CA; *U.S. Public*, pg. 516

Dean, Virginia, Exec. Dir.-Commun.--The American Bankers Association, Washington, DC; *U.S. Private*, pg. 51

Deane, Steve, Dir.-Pub. Rels.--International Research & Evaluation, Eagan, MN; *U.S. Private*, pg. 571

Dear, Derek, Gen. Mgr.-Mktg. Communications--British Airways PLC, London, United Kingdom; *Int'l*, pg. 218

Deary, Doreen, Dir.-Communications--Howmet Corporation, Greenwich, CT; *U.S. Private*, pg. 213

Deary, Doreen, Dir.-Communications--Howmet Corporation, Greenwich, CT; *U.S. Public*, pg. 1597

DeBoer, Tana, Mgr.-Corp. Commun.--Medical Graphics Corp., Saint Paul, MN; *U.S. Public*, pg. 1080

Debrosse, Gayle, Sr. V.P.-Pub. Rels.--El Torito Restaurants Inc., Irvine, CA; *U.S. Private*, pg. 393

DeCarolis, Donna, Gen. Mgr.-Corp. Commun. & H.R.--National Fuel Gas Company, Buffalo, NY; *U.S. Public*, pg. 1156

DeCarolis, Donna, Gen. Mgr.-Corp. Commun. & H.R.--National Fuel Gas Distribution Corp., Buffalo, NY; *U.S. Public*, pg. 1156

Decker, Virginia, Mgr.-Pub. Rels.--William M. Mercer Companies, Inc., New York, NY; *U.S. Public*, pg. 1049

Decressac, Anne, Exec. V.P.-Personnel & Communication--Technip, Paris, France; *Int'l*, pg. 1360

Dedera, Nancy, Mgr.-Pub. Rels.--Glacier Park, Inc., Phoenix, AZ; *U.S. Public*, pg. 1718

Dees, Steve, Exec. V.P.-Corp. Rels., Commun. & Intl. Svcs.--Farmland Industries, Inc., Kansas City, MO; *U.S. Private*, pg. 395

DeFatta, Ron, Mgr.-Corp. Communications--Public Service Company of Oklahoma, Tulsa, OK; *U.S. Public*, pg. 324

Dege, Paul, Dir.-Mktg. Commun. & Food Pkgng. Prod./Mkt.--Oliver Products Company, Grand Rapids, MI; *U.S. Private*, pg. 815

DeGood, Paul W., Mgr.-Mktg. Services--M.C. Gill Corporation, El Monte, CA; *U.S. Private*, pg. 453

DeiDolori, Janice, Dir.-Sls. Promo. & Communications--ADVO, Inc., Windsor, CT; *U.S. Public*, pg. 23

Deitler, Ursula, Dir.-Pub. Rels.--Asea Brown Boveri AG, Baden, Switzerland; *Int'l*, pg. 1

Dekker, H., Dir.-Fleet Personnel--Nedlloyd Fleet Services, Rotterdam, Netherlands; *Int'l*, pg. 1145

Del Beccaro, Lisa, Dir.-Adv. & Pub. Rels.--International Flavors & Fragrances, Inc., New York, NY; *U.S. Public*, pg. 898

Del Regno, Nancy, V.P.-Communications & Pub. Affairs--Fleming Companies, Inc., Oklahoma City, OK; *U.S. Public*, pg. 652

Delaborde, Michel, V.P.-Corp. Communications--Total S.A., Paris, France; *Int'l*, pg. 1408

Delafon, Blandine, Dir.-Corp. Commun.--Bouygues, Saint Quentin-en-Yvelines, France; *Int'l*, pg. 206

Delaney, Marnie, Sr. V.P. & Dir.-Adv. & Mktg. Communcaitons--BankAmerica Corporation, San Francisco, CA; *U.S. Public*, pg. 179

Delea, Lois, Mgr.-Corp. Communications--Selective Insurance Group, Inc, Branchville, NJ; *U.S. Public*, pg. 1455

Delenne, Susan C., Mgr.-Energen Communications--Energen Corporation, Birmingham, AL; *U.S. Public*, pg. 581

Dell, Cary, Communications--Lockheed Martin Tactical Defense Systems (Akron), Akron, OH; *U.S. Public*, pg. 1009

DeLoach, Paul O., Mgr.-Pub. Rels.--Miller Brewing Company, Albany, GA; *U.S. Public*, pg. 1289

Delpha, Vernique, V.P.-Commun.--3M France, Cergy-Pontoise, France; *U.S. Public*, pg. 1606

DeLuca, Atila, Mgr.-Pub. Rels.--Gedy S.p.A., Senago, Italy; *Int'l*, pg. 542

DeMallie, Robert W., Dir.-External Commun.--Corning Incorporated, Corning, NY; *U.S. Public*, pg. 448

Demarest, David, Sr. V.P. & Dir.-Corp. Communications--BankAmerica Corporation, San Francisco, CA; *U.S. Public*, pg. 179

DeMaria, Benedict, V.P.-H.R. & Corp. Commun.--Mine Safety Appliances Co., Pittsburgh, PA; *U.S. Public*, pg. 1114

DeMars, Tim, Mgr.-Mktg. Communications--Miller Electric Manufacturing Co., Appleton, WI; *U.S. Public*, pg. 867

DeMatteo, Carol, Mgr.-Pub. Rels.--Keane, Inc., Boston, MA; *U.S. Public*, pg. 946

Dembinski, Susie, Mgr.-Publicity--Daily Racing Form, Inc., Phoenix, AZ; *U.S. Public*, pg. 1327

DeMers, Cynthia A., Dir.-Corp. Commun.--Corning Incorporated, Corning, NY; *U.S. Public*, pg. 448

Demitros, Kathleen A., V.P.-Communications--Harley-Davidson Motor Company, Milwaukee, WI; *U.S. Public*, pg. 786

Denham, Bob, V.P.-Pub. Rels.--BB&T Corporation, Winston Salem, NC; *U.S. Public*, pg. 159

Denney, Cindy, Mgr.-Corp. Commun.--Ohio Casualty Corporation, Hamilton, OH; *U.S. Public*, pg. 1214

Dennison, Helen C., Mgr.-Pub. Rels.--Miller Brewing Company, Eden, NC; *U.S. Public*, pg. 1289

Denny, Brock, R., Chief Fin. Officer, V.P.-Fin. & Treas.--Medusa Corporation, Cleveland, OH; *U.S. Public*, pg. 1084

Denny, Cecilia, Mgr.-Pub. Rels.--Informix Software, Menlo Park, CA; *U.S. Public*, pg. 876

DeNunzio, Janet, Mgr.-Pub. Rels.--American Arbitration Association, New York, NY; *U.S. Private*, pg. 50

DePinto, David, Sr. V.P. & Pub. Rels. Dir.--Ketchum Public Relations, Los Angeles, CA; *U.S. Private*, pg. 617

Depuy, Shelley, Dir.-Mktg.--Tokheim Corporation, Fort Wayne, IN; *U.S. Public*, pg. 1620

Derbyshire, David, Mgr.-Tech. Communications & Regulations--Georg Fischer Disa Inc., Oswego, IL; *Int'l*, pg. 382

Deremo, Mark, Dir.-Corp. Communications--Universal Forest Products, Inc., Grand Rapids, MI; *U.S. Public*, pg. 1696

DeRose, Gaby, Asst. V.P.-Corp. Commun.--Rich Products Corp., Buffalo, NY; *U.S. Private*, pg. 928

DeRousse, Edwina, Mgr.-Corp. Commun.--Coherent, Inc., Santa Clara, CA; *U.S. Public*, pg. 395

Derrough, Anne, V.P.-Commun. & Trng.--Long John Silver's, Inc., Lexington, KY; *U.S. Private*, pg. 674

Desart, Isabel, Dir.-Corp. Commun.--Merial Ltd., London, United Kingdom; *U.S. Public*, pg. 1092

Desart, Isabel, Dir.-Corp. Commun.--Merial Ltd., London, United Kingdom; *Int'l*, pg. 1110

Desch, Theodore E., Sr. V.P.-Law & Corp. Affairs--Blue Cross & Blue Shield of Illinois, Chicago, IL; *U.S. Private*, pg. 151

Desjardins-Siciliano, Yves, V.P.-Law--BCE Mobile Communications Inc., Saint-Laurent, Canada; *Int'l*, pg. 115

Desnick, Pamela, V.P.-Commun.--Lutheran Brotherhood, Minneapolis, MN; *U.S. Private*, pg. 681

Dessers, Jos, Mgr.-Pub. Rels.--Tessenderlo Plant, Tessenderlo, Belgium; *U.S. Public*, pg. 1291

Dessler, Larry, Dir.-Pub. Rels.--Holland America Line Westours, Seattle, WA; *U.S. Public*, pg. 306

Detweiler, Richard, Dir.-Pub. Affairs--PepsiCo, Inc., Purchase, NY; *U.S. Public*, pg. 1276

Deutsch, Ellen, V.P.-Mktg.--The Hain Food Group Inc., Uniondale, NY; *U.S. Public*, pg. 774

Deutshe, Tom, Mgr.-Pub. Rels.--Travelodge, El Cajon, CA; *U.S. Public*, pg. 322

Devany, S., Mgr.-Pub. Affairs--Ladbroke Group Plc, London, United Kingdom; *Int'l*, pg. 787

Devenzio, Huck, Mgr.-Adv. & Pub. Rels.--Hickson Corporation, Smyrna, GA; *Int'l*, pg. 619

Devine, Jacqueline, Corp. Communications Dir. & Acct. Supvr.--Kragie/Newell, Des Moines, IA; *U.S. Private*, pg. 634

DeVinney, Betty W., V.P.-Commun. & Pub. Affairs--Eastman Chemical Company, Kingsport, TN; *U.S. Public*, pg. 550

Devissbher, Luc, Mgr.-Pub. Rels.--Agfa-Gevaert N.V., Antwerp, Belgium; *Int'l*, pg. 174

DeVita, Jan, Corp. Communications Assco.--A.C. Nielsen Company, Schaumburg, IL; *U.S. Public*, pg. 1183

Devlin, Joe, Dir.-Corp. Communications--Mitsubishi Fuso Truck of America, Inc., Bridgeport, NJ; *Int'l*, pg. 875

Devroy, Neil, V.P.-Communications & Pub. Affairs--Rexene Corporation, Dallas, TX; *U.S. Private*, pg. 549

Dewar, Janet, V.P.-Corp. Communications & Pub. Affairs--COMSAT Corporation, Bethesda, MD; *U.S. Public*, pg. 424

Dewar, Susan, V.P.-Mktg. & Adv.--Markel Corporation, Glen Allen, VA; *U.S. Public*, pg. 1046

Dewey, Teri, Dir.-Pub. Rels. & Communications--Star Tribune, Minneapolis-St. Paul, Minneapolis, MN; *U.S. Private*, pg. 281

Dey, Rebecca, Mgr.-Adv. & Pub. Rels.--Whitney Holding Corporation, New Orleans, LA; *U.S. Public*, pg. 1766

Di Elsi, M., Mgr.-Mktg. Communications--The Torrington Co., Torrington, CT; *U.S. Public*, pg. 877

Dias, Elaine, Adv.-Pub. Rels.--Westamerica Bancorporation, Fairfield, CA; *U.S. Public*, pg. 1756

Diaz-Ambrona, Juan Antonio Ortega, Dir.-Corp. Affairs--Repsol S.A., Madrid, Spain; *Int'l*, pg. 1104

Diaz, Luz P., Mgr.-Personnel--Medtronic Med Rel, Inc., Humacao, PR; *U.S. Public*, pg. 1083

Dickard, Paul, Dir.-Pub. Rels.--Ingersoll-Rand Company, Woodcliff Lake, NJ; *U.S. Public*, pg. 876

Dicken, Cindy, Mgr.-Communications & Adv.--Providian Agency Group, Louisville, KY; *Int'l*, pg. 27

Dickinson, Carol, Dir.-Customer Rels.--Seattle City Light, Seattle, WA; *U.S. Private*, pg. 979

Dickman, C., V.P.-Customer Support--Pratt & Whitney Canada Inc., Longueuil, Canada; *U.S. Public*, pg. 1690

Dickson, James G., Jr., Sr. V.P.--Prime Bancshares Inc., Houston, TX; *U.S. Public*, pg. 1326

DiClemente, Mike, Communications--The Lord Group, New York, NY; *U.S. Private*, pg. 325

Diebert, Beth, Mgr.-Mktg. & Customer Services--Decora', Jasper, IN; *U.S. Public*, pg. 675
Diehl, Leann R., Mgr.-Public & Government Affairs--Maine Yankee, Brunswick, ME; *U.S. Public*, pg. 325
Diehl, Stephen, Dir.-Commun.--The Orvis Company, Inc., Manchester, VT; *U.S. Private*, pg. 820
Diemand, Alfonso, Mgr.-Corp. Commun.--Sasol Limited, Johannesburg, South Africa; *Int'l*, pg. 1196
Dier, Adelaide, Pub. Rels.--3M Do Brasil Ltda., Sao Paulo, Brazil; *U.S. Public*, pg. 1606
Dietzel, Alfred S., V.P.-Pub. Rels. & Investor Rels.--The Limited, Inc., Columbus, OH; *U.S. Public*, pg. 995
DiGesu, John, Dir.-Communications--Osram Sylvania Inc., Malvern, PA; *Int'l*, pg. 1245
Dilorio, Joe, Dir.-Client Devel.--DeMaria Building Co. Inc., Novi, MI; *U.S. Private*, pg. 323
diLeo, Alicia, Coord.-Pub.--Merriam-Webster, Inc., Springfield, MA; *U.S. Private*, pg. 375
Dillard, Richard, Dir.-Pub. Affairs--Milliken & Company, Spartanburg, SC; *U.S. Private*, pg. 748
Dillen, Charles R.(Chick), Mgr.-Pub. Rels.--Ward Trucking Corp., Altoona, PA; *U.S. Private*, pg. 1149
Dillon, Laura, V.P.-Communications--J.P. Morgan Co. Incorporated, New York, NY; *U.S. Public*, pg. 1129
DiMaggio, Paige, Mgr.-Investor Rels.--Weatherford Enterra Incorporated, Houston, TX; *U.S. Public*, pg. 1749
Dimarucut, Eloisa, Mgr.-Design/Communications--Zee Medical, Inc., Irvine, CA; *U.S. Public*, pg. 1073
DiMingo, Ed, Dir.-Corp. Commun.--Kulicke & Soffa Industries, Inc., Willow Grove, PA; *U.S. Public*, pg. 968
Dimke, Kerri, Mgr.-Pub. Rels.--Hayes Corporation, Norcross, GA; *U.S. Public*, pg. 800
Dimouski, Jim, Coord.-Pub. Rels.--General Electric Canada Inc., Mississauga, Canada; *U.S. Public*, pg. 713
Dingledy, Carol, Mgr.-Corp. Commun.--Cosco, Inc., Columbus, IN; *U.S. Private*, pg. 277
Dingledy, Thomas G., V.P.-Corp. Commun./Pub. Rels.--Medpartners Inc., Birmingham, AL; *U.S. Public*, pg. 1082
DiNicola, R.J., Dir.-Pub. Rels.--FirstEnergy Corp., Akron, OH; *U.S. Public*, pg. 644
DiNicola, R.J., Dir.-Public Relations--Ohio Edison Co.-Akron Div., Akron, OH; *U.S. Public*, pg. 645
Dinnick, Victoria, Dir.-Corp. Communications--Imax Corporation, Mississauga, Canada; *Int'l*, pg. 661
Dinon, Rick, V.P.-Corp. Communications--20th Century Industries, Woodland Hills, CA; *U.S. Public*, pg. 1646
Dinwiddy, Paul, Mgr.-Pub. Rels.--Tioxide Group Limited, London, United Kingdom; *Int'l*, pg. 663
Dippel, Tom, Mgr.-Commun.--Wyse Technology Inc., San Jose, CA; *U.S. Private*, pg. 1194
DiPrimio, Anne, Mgr.-Commun.--Cole Hersee Company, Boston, MA; *U.S. Private*, pg. 251
Dirat, Henri, Mgr.-Communications--Compaq Computer S.A.R.L., Les Ulis, France; *U.S. Public*, pg. 418
Dirkes, Robert, Dir.-Corp. Commun.--BTI Americas, Inc., Northbrook, IL; *U.S. Private*, pg. 108
Dishart, Stephen K., V.P. & Dir.-Corp. Commun.--Mellon Bank Corporation, Pittsburgh, PA; *U.S. Public*, pg. 1084
Diukarev, Roman, Pub. Rels. Mgr.--Young & Rubicam/Sovero, Moscow, Russia; *U.S. Private*, pg. 1199
Dixon, Annie, Pub. Rels. Dir.--Dewe Rogerson Limited, London, United Kingdom; *Int'l*, pg. 408
Dixon, Diane B., V.P.-Worldwide Communications & Adv.--Avery Dennison Corporation, Pasadena, CA; *U.S. Public*, pg. 152
Dixon, Maureen, Supvr.-Mktg. Commun.--Teledyne Laars/Jandy Products, Novato, CA; *U.S. Public*, pg. 43
do Vale, Jose, Dir.-Pub. Rels.--INLAN-Industria de Componentes Mecanicos, S.A., Ponte de Sor, Portugal; *U.S. Public*, pg. 723
Doat, Nathalia, Dir.-Communications--Lever S.A., Levallois-Perret, France; *Int'l*, pg. 1438
Doba, M., Mgr.-Pub. Rels.--Nichiro Corporation, Tokyo, Japan; *Int'l*, pg. 928
Dobbie, Clare, Dir.-Communications--Nike (U.K.) Limited, Sunderland, United Kingdom; *U.S. Public*, pg. 1184
Dobkowski, F., V.P.-Customer Rels.--Ascom Hasler Mailing Systems, Inc., Shelton, CT; *Int'l*, pg. 86
Dodea, Renee, Admin.-Mktg. Communications--Thomas & Betts Electronics Division, Memphis, TN; *U.S. Public*, pg. 1597
Dodson, Graham, Dir.-Corp. Communications--Central and South West Corporation, Dallas, TX; *U.S. Public*, pg. 324
Dodson, Jan W., Dir.-Corp. Commun.--American Management Systems, Inc., Fairfax, VA; *U.S. Public*, pg. 86
Doerr, Bettina, Press Officer--Preussag AG, Hannover, Germany; *Int'l*, pg. 1069
Doff, Moira M., Mgr.-Corp. Commun.--Bowthorpe plc, Crawley, United Kingdom; *Int'l*, pg. 207
Dolan, Brian P., V.P.-Market Devel. & Pub. Affairs--MTA Long Island Rail Road, Jamaica, NY; *U.S. Private*, pg. 739
Dollahon, Gary, Dir.-Mktg. Communications--Brunswick Outdoor Recreation Group, Tulsa, OK; *U.S. Public*, pg. 265
Dollins, Mark, Dir.-Corp. Commun.--The Quaker Oats Company, Chicago, IL; *U.S. Public*, pg. 1347
Dolphin, John A., V.P. & Dir.-Investor Rels.--Green Tree Financial Corporation, Saint Paul, MN; *U.S. Public*, pg. 761
Dombrowski, Bernie, Indus. Pub. Rels.--Bacharach Inc., Pittsburgh, PA; *U.S. Private*, pg. 109
Domeischel, Jack, V.P.-Public Affairs--Searle Laboratories, Skokie, IL; *U.S. Public*, pg. 1125
Domenge, Muriel, Dir.-Pub. Rels.--Bongrain S.A., Viroflay, France; *Int'l*, pg. 201
Donahue, James J., V.P.-Corp. Commun.--Republic Industries, Inc., Fort Lauderdale, FL; *U.S. Public*, pg. 1378
Donaldson, D.A., Mgr.-Pub. Affairs--Vulcan Chemicals, Birmingham, AL; *U.S. Public*, pg. 1725
Donaldson, Randal W., V.P. & Dir.-Corp. Commun.--The Coca-Cola Company, Atlanta, GA; *U.S. Public*, pg. 392
Donaldson, Yvonne, Dir.-Worldwide Pub. Rels.--Trivoli Systems Inc., Austin, TX; *U.S. Public*, pg. 896
Donato, Barbara R., Supvr.-Pub. Rels.--Norton Company, Worcester, MA; *Int'l*, pg. 1173
Donches, Stephen G., V.P.-Pub. Affairs--Bethlehem Steel Corporation, Bethlehem, PA; *U.S. Public*, pg. 226
Donnely, Ann Marie, Communications Specialist--Fasson Films, Painesville, OH; *U.S. Public*, pg. 153
Donohue, Judy, V.P. & Pub. Rels. Dir.--MARC, Pittsburgh, PA; *U.S. Private*, pg. 701
Donohue, Robert W., Jr., V.P.-Queens Customer Svc.--Consolidated Edison Company of New York, Inc., New York, NY; *U.S. Public*, pg. 434
Donovan, Gerry, Mgr.-Pub. Rels.--The Gates Corporation, Denver, CO; *Int'l*, pg. 1396
Donovan, Mary, Sr. V.P.-Publicity--New Line Cinema Corporation, New York, NY; *U.S. Public*, pg. 1614
Donovan, Thomas, Dir.-Mktg.--The Richman Brothers Co., Fall River, MA; *U.S. Public*, pg. 1777
Doolan, Laurie, Gen. Mgr.-Corp. Affairs & H.R.--Air New Zealand Ltd., Auckland, New Zealand; *Int'l*, pg. 38
Doran, Janine, Media Affairs Officer--BNFL, Warrington, United Kingdom; *Int'l*, pg. 120
Doran, Kim, V.P. & Pub. Rels. Dir.--Trone Advertising, Inc., Greensboro, NC; *U.S. Private*, pg. 1104
Dorn, Gail, V.P.-Communications & Community Rels.--Target Stores, Minneapolis, MN; *U.S. Public*, pg. 489
Dornbusch, Carol, Dir.-Pub. Rels.--Whitehall-Robins Healthcare, Madison, NJ; *U.S. Public*, pg. 80
Doster, Jill, Mgr.-Public Relations--Hammermill Papers, Memphis, TN; *U.S. Public*, pg. 902
Dotterer, Herbert T., Chief Fin. Officer, Sr. V.P.-Fin. & Admin. & Sec.--Eagle Food Centers, Inc., Milan, IL; *U.S. Public*, pg. 547
Dougherty, Kevin, Dir.-Pub. Rels.--Caisse de depot et placement du Quebec, Montreal, Canada; *Int'l*, pg. 249
Douglas, Stephanie W., Dir.-Mktg. Svcs. & Corp. Communications--Harza Engineering Co., Chicago, IL; *U.S. Private*, pg. 509
Douxchamps, Alain, Mgr.-Pub. Affairs--UCB, S.A., Brussels, Belgium; *Int'l*, pg. 1427
Dove, Janice, V.P.-Pub. Affairs--Federal National Mortgage Association (Fannie Mae), Washington, DC; *U.S. Public*, pg. 615
Dow, Jerry, Mgr.-Mktg. Commun.--Pella Corporation, Pella, IA; *U.S. Private*, pg. 848
Dowding, Thelma, Dir.-Consumer Affairs--Foodarama Supermarkets, Inc., Freehold, NJ; *U.S. Public*, pg. 661
Dowell, Valoree, V.P.-Commun.--Immunex Corporation, Seattle, WA; *U.S. Public*, pg. 871
Dowling, Anne T., Dir.-CC&CR--Texaco Inc., White Plains, NY; *U.S. Public*, pg. 1582
Dowling, Jeralyn C., Emerging Media & Plng. Dir.--Corbett HealthConnect, A Frank J. Corbett, Inc., Company, Chicago, IL; *U.S. Public*, pg. 1223
Downey, Tom, Gen. Mgr.-Pub. Rels.--McDonnell Aircraft & Missile Systems Div., Berkeley, MO; *U.S. Public*, pg. 241
Downie, Timothy, V.P.-Customer Service--Uforma Shelby Business Forms, Shelby, OH; *U.S. Private*, pg. 740
Downs, Jennifer, Dir.-Pub. Consumer Affairs--Meijer, Inc., Grand Rapids, MI; *U.S. Private*, pg. 729
Downs, Jill, Mgr.-Corp. Affairs--Potomac Electric Power Company, Washington, DC; *U.S. Public*, pg. 1318
Downs, John H., V.P.-Public Affairs--Coca-Cola Enterprises Inc., Atlanta, GA; *U.S. Public*, pg. 393
Doyal, Steve, V.P.-Hallmark Pub. Affairs & Commun.--Hallmark Cards, Inc., Kansas City, MO; *U.S. Private*, pg. 495
Doyle, Carol, Dir.-Pub. Rels.--Ultra Electronics Holdings plc, Greenford, United Kingdom; *Int'l*, pg. 1431
Doyle, J., Controller--Asahi Glass America, Inc., New York, NY; *Int'l*, pg. 84
Doyle, Jennifer, Pub. Rels.--Air Nova, Bedford, Canada; *Int'l*, pg. 36
Dozier, Dow, Dir.-Corp. Communications--Kerr-McGee Corporation, Oklahoma City, OK; *U.S. Public*, pg. 952
Dragomier, Lynne S., V.P.-Pub. Rels.--Hoover Company, Canton, OH; *U.S. Public*, pg. 1065
Drake, Eileen, V.P.-Pub. Rels.--Karakas, VanSickle, Ouellette Advertising & Public Relations, Portland, OR; *U.S. Private*, pg. 607
Drake, Roger, Dir.-Commun.--Morton's Restaurant Group, Inc., New Hyde Park, NY; *U.S. Public*, pg. 1136
Draper, Douglas G., Grp. Mgr.-Commun.--The Dow Chemical Company, Midland, MI; *U.S. Public*, pg. 522
Draznin, Michael, Sr. V.P. & Corp. Communications Dir.--Lowe & Partners/SMS, New York, NY; *U.S. Private*, pg. 678
Dresner, Mark, Dir.-Corp. Communications--Engelhard Corporation, Iselin, NJ; *U.S. Public*, pg. 582
Drew, Jane, Dir.-Pub. Affairs--American Express Europe Limited, London, United Kingdom; *U.S. Public*, pg. 74
Dreyer, John, V.P.-Corp. Communications--The Walt Disney Company, Burbank, CA; *U.S. Public*, pg. 511
Driscoll, Kathleen F., V.P.-Corp. Communications--John Hancock Mutual Life Insurance Company, Boston, MA; *U.S. Private*, pg. 589
Driver, Jody, Mgr.-Adv. & Pub. Rels.--Kraft Food Ingredients Corp., Memphis, TN; *U.S. Public*, pg. 1288
Drogemuller, Mike, Grp. Mgr.-Commun.--Brierley Investments Limited, Wellington, New Zealand; *Int'l*, pg. 215
Drotch, Amy, Coord.-Mktg. & Public Rels.--Thermal Industries, Inc., Pittsburgh, PA; *U.S. Private*, pg. 490
Druiz, Fae, Dir.-Pub. Rels.--Bulova Corporation, Woodside, NY; *U.S. Public*, pg. 1010
Drumm, Hughes D., V.P.-Adv. & Pub. Rels.--Stewart Enterprises, Inc., Metairie, LA; *U.S. Public*, pg. 1518
Drummond, Cece, Dir.-Corp. Communications--Rail Europe Inc., Harrison, NY; *Int'l*, pg. 1165
Drysdale, Andrew S., Dir.-Paper & Environmental Communications--Boise Cascade Paper Div., Boise, ID; *U.S. Public*, pg. 243
du Bois, Patrick, Exec. V.P. & Sec. Gen.--Sabena, Zaventem, Belgium; *Int'l*, pg. 1168
Dubbeldam, C., Mgr.-Internal & External Rels.--Grolsch N.V., Enschede, Netherlands; *Int'l*, pg. 559
Dubeau, Daniel, V.P.-Communications--Hydro-Quebec, Montreal, Canada; *Int'l*, pg. 640
Dubois-Dumee, Alain, Sr. V.P.-Corp. Commun.--Renault, Boulogne-Billancourt, France; *Int'l*, pg. 1102
DuCharme, Darlene, Coord.-Public Relations--Sonoma Mission Inn & Spa, Sonoma, CA; *U.S. Private*, pg. 1014
Duckett, Stacy, V.P.-Corp. Commun.--TCBY Enterprises Inc., Little Rock, AR; *U.S. Public*, pg. 1553
Ducksworth, Marilyn, Dir.-Pub. Rels.--Penguin Putnam Inc., New York, NY; *Int'l*, pg. 1027
Duckworth, Amanda, Dir.-Corp. Commun.--NationsBank Montgomery Securities LLC, San Francisco, CA; *U.S. Public*, pg. 1162
Dudha, A., Dir.-Customer Svcs.--National Bank of Malawi, Blantyre, Malawi; *Int'l*, pg. 1296
Duff-Bloom, Gale, Pres.-Mktg. & Co. Communications--JC Penney Company, Inc., Plano, TX; *U.S. Public*, pg. 916
Duff, Avery, Dir.-Human Resources--Westpac Banking Corporation, Sydney, Australia; *Int'l*, pg. 1495
Duffus, Cheryl, Asst. V.P. & Mgr.-Mktg.--Pacific Capital Bancorp, Salinas, CA; *U.S. Public*, pg. 1247
Duffy, David L., Sr. V.P.-Corp. Commun.--The Chubb Corporation, Warren, NJ; *U.S. Public*, pg. 354
Duffy, Megan, Mgr.-Communications--United Media, New York, NY; *U.S. Public*, pg. 1448
Dufour, Marie Christine, V.P.-Commun. & Pub. Affairs--Coscient Group Inc., Montreal, Canada; *Int'l*, pg. 335
Dugan, Sherman E., Chief Info. Officer & V.P.-Pub. Rels.--Dugan Production Corp., Farmington, NM; *U.S. Private*, pg. 345
Duggan, Holly, Mgr.-Customer Service--Eastern Color Printing Company, Avon, CT; *U.S. Private*, pg. 357
Duguid, Mike, Dir.-Adv., Pub. Rels. & Mktg.--York International Corporation, York, PA; *U.S. Public*, pg. 1789
Dula, Bob, Mgr.-Customer Service--Keller Ladders Inc., Fort Lauderdale, FL; *U.S. Public*, pg. 1684
Dulle, Mary, Dir.-Professional Rels.--Alcon Laboratories, Inc., Fort Worth, TX; *Int'l*, pg. 916
Dumaine, Sylvie, Mgr.-Communications--Thomson S.A., Paris, France; *Int'l*, pg. 1381
Dumaine, Sylvie, Mgr.-Corp. Communications--Thomson-CSF S.A., Paris, France; *Int'l*, pg. 1383
Dumas, Kathleen, Coord.-Mktg. Commun.--Magnetrol International, Downers Grove, IL; *U.S. Private*, pg. 696
Dumas, Patricia, Sr. Dir.-Communications & Pub. Rels.--Canadian Satellite Communications Inc., Mississauga, Canada; *Int'l*, pg. 1481
Dumortier, Dominique, Mgr.-Adv. & Pub. Rels.--Michelin North America (Canada) Inc., Laval, Canada; *Int'l*, pg. 322
Duncan, Collin, Mgr.-Pub. Rels.--BNFL, Warrington, United Kingdom; *Int'l*, pg. 120
Duncan, Michael, Mgr.-Pub. Rels.--Royale Coach, Elkhart, IN; *U.S. Public*, pg. 1123
Duncan, Michael F., Mgr.-Pub. Rels.--Monaco Coach Corporation, Coburg, OR; *U.S. Public*, pg. 1123
Duncan, N.P., Mgr.-Mktg. Communications--Curtis 1000, Inc., Atlanta, GA; *U.S. Public*, pg. 70
Duncan, Sarah R., Supervisor-Corp. Communications--LaRoche Industries Inc., Atlanta, GA; *U.S. Private*, pg. 651
Dunlap, Gary, Pub. Rels. Counselor--William Cook Public Relations, Inc., Jacksonville, FL; *U.S. Private*, pg. 273
Dunn, Kathy, Dir.-Customer Svc.--Polymer Plastics Corporation, Hauppauge, NY; *U.S. Private*, pg. 875
Dunn, Marsha, Corp. Commun.--Unitech Industries, Inc., Tempe, AZ; *U.S. Public*, pg. 1672
Dunn, Michael G., Dir.-Corp. Communications--Coltec Holdings Inc, Charlotte, NC; *U.S. Public*, pg. 401
Dunn, Mike, Dir.-Corp. Communications--Coltec Industries Inc., Charlotte, NC; *U.S. Public*, pg. 401
Dunn, Norma F., V.P.-Investor & Pub. Rels.--El Paso Natural Gas Co., Houston, TX; *U.S. Public*, pg. 567
Dunn, Paul, Mgr.-Communications--ABC Rail Cogifer Industries, Cincinnati, OH; *U.S. Public*, pg. 2
Dunn, Paul, Mgr.-Communications--Cogifer SA, Croissy-sur-Seine, France; *Int'l*, pg. 386
Dunn, Terrence C., Jr., Dir.-Corp. Communications--Alliant Foodservice, Inc., Deerfield, IL; *U.S. Private*, pg. 244
Dunn, Tom, Pub. Rels.--Credit Union National Association, Madison, WI; *U.S. Private*, pg. 288
Dunnigan, Jim, Dir.-Adv. & Pub. Rels.--City National Corporation, Beverly Hills, CA; *U.S. Public*, pg. 380
Dupras, Andre, V.P.-Commun. & Pub. Affairs--Donohue Inc., Quebec, Canada; *Int'l*, pg. 1075
Dupuy, William L., V.P.-Corp. Communications--Charter One Financial, Inc., Cleveland, OH; *U.S. Public*, pg. 336
Durcan, Kelly, V.P. & Pub. Rels. Dir.--Partners & Shevack, Inc., New York, NY; *U.S. Private*, pg. 842
Durdin, Martha, V.P.-Commun.--Bank of Montreal, Toronto, Canada; *Int'l*, pg. 153
Durfee, John, Dir.-Corp. Commun.--New York State Electric & Gas Corporation, Binghamton, NY; *U.S. Public*, pg. 1173
Durinsky, Stephen A., Dir.-Adv. & Pub. Rels.--Myers Industries, Inc., Akron, OH; *U.S. Public*, pg. 1143
Durlam, Joyce, Dir.-Mktg.--Anderson Erickson Dairy Company, Des Moines, IA; *U.S. Private*, pg. 72
Durward, Clare, Mktg. Dir.--Leo Burnett Limited, London, United Kingdom; *U.S. Private*, pg. 185
Dusar, Geert, V.P.-Commun. & Pub. Affairs--Sabena, Zaventem, Belgium; *Int'l*, pg. 1168
Dusossoit, Janine, V.P.-Investor Rels.--Teleflex Incorporated, Plymouth Meeting, PA; *U.S. Public*, pg. 1569
Duval, Rene, Dir.-Information & Publications--Telediffusion de France, Paris, France; *Int'l*, pg. 503
Duvall, Martine, Mgr.-Adv. & Pub. Rels.--Perdue Farms, Inc., Showell, MD; *U.S. Private*, pg. 852

Dye, Robert M., V.P.-Corp. Commun.--Journal Communications Inc., Milwaukee, WI; *U.S. Private*, pg. 601

Dyer, Dan, Mgr.-Pub. Rels.--Cincom Systems, Inc., Cincinnati, OH; *U.S. Private*, pg. 240

Dyott, Gordon M., Exec. V.P.-Opers. & Consumer Banking--Wilmington Savings Fund Society (FSB), Wilmington, DE; *U.S. Public*, pg. 1729

Dzenski, Elaine, Mgr.-Pub. Rels.--Siemens Transportation Systems, Inc., Iselin, NJ; *Int'l*, pg. 1246

Eacott, J. Graham, V.P.-Investor Rels.--Royal Oak Mines Inc., Kirkland, WA; *U.S. Public*, pg. 1410

Eagon, Donald E., Jr., V.P.-Corp. Communications--Diebold, Incorporated, Canton, OH; *U.S. Public*, pg. 506

Eames, Steve, V.P.-Corp. Communications--The Coastal Corporation, Houston, TX; *U.S. Public*, pg. 389

Earl, Bryan R., Dir.-Mktg. Communications & Adv.--American Woodmark Corporation, Winchester, VA; *U.S. Public*, pg. 96

Earl, Richard, V.P.-Communications--Reliance Insurance Company, Philadelphia, PA; *U.S. Public*, pg. 1374

Earle, Wendy, Pub. Rels. Dir. & Sls. Promo. Dir.--The McClure Group, Wayne, PA; *U.S. Private*, pg. 719

Early, Gregg, Dir.-Pub. Rels.--KCI Communications, Inc, Mc Lean, VA; *U.S. Private*, pg. 784

Eastman, Tracey, Mgr.-Corp. Commun.--Computer Task Group, Inc. (CTG), Buffalo, NY; *U.S. Public*, pg. 423

Easton, Donna C., V.P.-Corp. Communications & Pub. Affairs--PHH Corporation, Hunt Valley, MD; *U.S. Public*, pg. 321

Eaterling, Mike, Mgr.-Public Communications--WJZ-TV, Baltimore, MD; *U.S. Public*, pg. 275

Eaton, Esther, Coord.-Adv. & Media--Seaman Furniture Company, Inc., Woodbury, NY; *U.S. Public*, pg. 1452

Ebbing, Mike, Mgr.-P.R.--Franchise Services, Inc., Mission Viejo, CA; *U.S. Private*, pg. 423

Ebeling, Gary A., Dir.-Investor Rels.--CILCORP Inc., Peoria, IL; *U.S. Public*, pg. 367

Ebeling, Glen, Dir.-Pur.--Carland, Inc., Kansas City, MO; *U.S. Public*, pg. 944

Ebert, Carol, Dir.-Mktg. Communications--Iomega Corporation, Roy, UT; *U.S. Public*, pg. 912

Echols, Bill, Mgr.-Indus. Rels.--RE/MAX International, Inc., Englewood, CO; *U.S. Private*, pg. 912

Echter, Michael, Mng. Partner-Pub. Rels.--Gillespie, Lawrenceville, NJ; *U.S. Private*, pg. 453

Eck, Steve, Mgr.-Pub. Rels.--Ikon Office Solutions, Inc., Malvern, PA; *U.S. Public*, pg. 862

Eckley, Michael, V.P.-Corp. Commun.--Interphase Corporation, Dallas, TX; *U.S. Public*, pg. 908

Eddinger, John W., Dir.-Corp. Comm.--The Kiplinger Washington Editors, Inc., Washington, DC; *U.S. Private*, pg. 623

Edison, Mary Alice, Mgr.-Commun.--T & S Brass & Bronze Works, Inc., Travelers Rest, SC; *U.S. Private*, pg. 1061

Edmund, Nicole, Dir.-Adv.--Edmund Scientific Company, Barrington, NJ; *U.S. Private*, pg. 364

Edwards, Danita, Dir.-P.R.--Anthem, Inc., Indianapolis, IN; *U.S. Private*, pg. 76

Edwards, Diane, Sr. V.P. & Pub. Rels. Dir.--Mintz & Hoke Inc., Avon, CT; *U.S. Private*, pg. 751

Edwards, Douglas, Mgr.-Mktg. Communications--San Jose Mercury News, San Jose, CA; *U.S. Public*, pg. 964

Edwards, Florine, V.P. & Mgr.-Adv. & Corp. Rels.--Allendale Mutual Insurance Co., Johnston, RI; *U.S. Private*, pg. 37

Edwards, George, Corp. Communications & Pub. Rels.--Tasco Sales Inc., Miramar, FL; *U.S. Private*, pg. 928

Edwards, John, Mgr.-Mktg. & Pub. Rels.--Porsche Cars Great Britain Ltd., Reading, United Kingdom; *Int'l*, pg. 1063

Edwards, John, Sr. V.P.-Corp. Rels.--Texas-New Mexico Power Co., Fort Worth, TX; *U.S. Public*, pg. 1557

Edwards, Katherine, Mgr.-Pub. Rels.--Axent Technologies, Rockville, MD; *U.S. Public*, pg. 157

Edwards, Larry W., Dir.-Pub. Rels.--United Metering Inc., Long Island City, NY; *U.S. Public*, pg. 1692

Edwards, Mike, Dir.-Distr.--Sherwood-Davis & Geck, Saint Louis, MO; *U.S. Public*, pg. 80

Edwards, Stephanie, Dir.-Intl. & Pub. Rels.--American Automobile Association, Heathrow, FL; *U.S. Private*, pg. 50

Edwards, Warren, Sr. V.P.--Affiliated Computer Services, Inc., Dallas, TX; *U.S. Public*, pg. 27

Effler, Geno, Mgr.-Public Rels.--Kia Motors America, Inc., Irvine, CA; *Int'l*, pg. 733

Egan, James J., III, Dir.-Sys. Mktg. & Pub. Rels.--Fallon Community Health Plan, Worcester, MA; *U.S. Private*, pg. 392

Egert, Dana, Chm.--Jaclo Inc., Mountainside, NJ; *U.S. Private*, pg. 349

Eggenberger, Jorg, Dir.-Corp. Affairs--Panalpina Welttransport (Holding) AG, Binningen, Switzerland; *Int'l*, *pg. 1022*

Eggleston, Kathy, V.P.-Corp. Communications--JM Family Enterprises Inc., Deerfield Beach, FL; *U.S. Private*, pg. 577

Eguchi, Hiroaki, Gen. Mgr.-Info. & Public Rels.--"K" Line (Kawasaki Kisen Kaisha, Ltd.), Tokyo, Japan; *Int'l*, pg. 717

Ehlers, Elizabeth, Mgr.-Pub. Rels.--Arrington Travel Center Inc., Chicago, IL; *U.S. Private*, pg. 85

Ehrsam, Eric, Dir.-Communications--Automobiles Citroen, Neuilly, France; *Int'l*, pg. 1020

Eich, Susan, Dir.-Corp. Pub. Rels.--Dayton Hudson Corporation, Minneapolis, MN; *U.S. Public*, pg. 489

Eichman, Margaret, V.P.-Investor Rels. & Corp. Affairs--The Quaker Oats Company, Chicago, IL; *U.S. Public*, pg. 1347

Eichstaedt, Vickie, Dir.-Mktg.--Triple S Plastics, Inc., Vicksburg, MI; *U.S. Public*, pg. 1639

Eickmann, Brittne, Pub. Rels. Specialist--Tracor, Inc., Austin, TX; *U.S. Public*, pg. 1627

Eigner, Carole, Coord.-Pub. Rels. & Adv.--Cubic Corporation, San Diego, CA; *U.S. Public*, pg. 466

Eisele, Dana, Mgr.-Corp. Commun.--Yellow Corporation, Overland Park, KS; *U.S. Public*, pg. 1788

Eisenhauer, Clint, V.P.-Corp. Communications--Sea-Land Service, Inc., Charlotte, NC; *U.S. Public*, pg. 284

Eisner, David, Dir.-Commun.--America Online Incorporated, Dulles, VA; *U.S. Public*, pg. 66

Ekdahl, Goran, V.P.-Corp. Commun. & Corp. Affairs--Swedish Match S.A., Stockholm, Sweden; *Int'l*, pg. 1328

Ekrek, Sekita, Exec. Dir.-Publicity & Promo.--Allied Advertising Agency, Public Relations, Washington, DC; *U.S. Private*, pg. 38

Ekstedt, Goran, V.P.-Communications & Public Affairs--Saab Automobile AB, Nykoping, Sweden; *Int'l*, pg. 687

Ekstedt, Goran, V.P.-Communications & Public Affairs--Saab Automobile AB, Nykoping, Sweden; *U.S. Public*, pg. 725

Elder, Dick, V.P.-Corp. Communications--Fort James Corporation, Richmond, VA; *U.S. Public*, pg. 670

Elder, Susan, Mgr.-Corp. Commun.--Invacare Corporation, Elyria, OH; *U.S. Public*, pg. 911

Eleazer, Carol, V.P.-Communications--UNUM Corporation, Portland, ME; *U.S. Public*, pg. 1699

Elek, Edward E., Exec. V.P.-Mktg.--Cosco Fire Protection Inc., Gardena, CA; *U.S. Public*, pg. 1795

Elfstrom, Carol, Dir.-Pub. Rels.--CompUSA, Dallas, TX; *U.S. Public*, pg. 420

Elkin, Lisa, Corp. Communications--Compuware Corporation, Farmington Hills, MI; *U.S. Public*, pg. 423

Eller, Betty Lynn, Dir.-Adv. & Consumer Mktg.--Drexel Heritage Furnishings Inc., Drexel, NC; *U.S. Private*, pg. 432

Ellickson, Nancy, V.P.-Bus. Mktg.--Genus Inc., Sunnyvale, CA; *U.S. Public*, pg. 732

Elliott, David, Mgr.-Pub. Rels.--Brooklyn Union, Brooklyn, NY; *U.S. Public*, pg. 259

Elliott, Paula, Mgr.-Investor Rels.--Summit Technology, Inc., Waltham, MA; *U.S. Public*, pg. 1528

Ellis, Debbie, V.P.-Pub. Rels.--Minyard Food Stores, Inc., Coppell, TX; *U.S. Private*, pg. 752

Ellis, Jeff, V.P.-Personal Lines--VASA North Atlantic Insurance Company, Indianapolis, IN; *Int'l*, pg. 464

Ellis, Lynda, Mrg.-Mktg.--Spirol International Corp., Cuyahoga Falls, OH; *U.S. Private*, pg. 1026

Ellixson, Marita, Mktg. Editor--Game Time, Inc., Fort Payne, AL; *U.S. Public*, pg. 1543

Ellsworth, Diane, Communications & Promo. Coord.--Jacobsen Textron, Racine, WI; *U.S. Public*, pg. 1589

Elrod, Michele, V.P.-Pub. Rels.--AmSouth Bancorporation, Birmingham, AL; *U.S. Public*, pg. 105

Elyard, Vicky, Mgr.-Corp. Affairs--Geest PLC, Spalding, United Kingdom; *Int'l*, pg. 542

Emerson, Frances E., V.P.-Commun.--Honeywell Inc., Minneapolis, MN; *U.S. Public*, pg. 833

Emerson, Mike, Mgr.-Worldwide Mktg. & Corp. Communication--Rainbow Technologies, Inc., Irvine, CA; *U.S. Public*, pg. 1359

Emin, Lesley, Dir.-Corp. Commun.--Premier Farnell plc, Wetherby, United Kingdom; *Int'l*, pg. 1068

Emms, Nigel, Mgr.-Externa Rels.--Iveco-Ford Truck Ltd., Watford, United Kingdom; *Int'l*, pg. 484

Ena, Teruhiko, Pres.-Space Communications Corp.--Mitsubishi Corporation, Tokyo, Japan; *Int'l*, pg. 871

Engel, Brian, Dir.-Pub. Affairs--Mitchell Energy & Development Corp., Spring, TX; *U.S. Public*, pg. 1117

Engel, Lee, Supvr.-Customer Svc.--Monfort, Inc., Greeley, CO; *U.S. Public*, pg. 427

England, Laura E., Mgr.-Pub. Rels.--Land O'Lakes, Inc., Southampton, PA; *U.S. Private*, pg. 646

Engle, Roger, Pres.-Superior Water Light & Power--Minnesota Power, Duluth, MN; *U.S. Public*, pg. 1116

Englehart, Sue, Mgr.-Corp. Communication--M.A. Hanna Company, Cleveland, OH; *U.S. Public*, pg. 780

English, Roderick, Sr. V.P.-Human Resources & Communications--Delco Remy America, Inc., Anderson, IN; *U.S. Public*, pg. 495

Engstroem, Haaken E.G., Dir.-Pub. Rels.--General Motors Nordiska AB, Haninge, Sweden; *U.S. Public*, pg. 722

Epenoy, Pierre, Dir.-Pub. Rels.--BS Continental S.A. Utilidades Domesticas, Sao Paulo, Brazil; *Int'l*, pg. 123

Eperon, A., Dir.-Corp. Affairs--The Boots Company PLC, Nottingham, United Kingdom; *Int'l*, pg. 202

Epp, Phyllis, Dir.-Community Affairs & Prod. Publicity--Union Camp Corporation, Wayne, NJ; *U.S. Public*, pg. 1665

Epperson, Eric, Mgr.-Pub. Rels.--AutoZone, Inc., Memphis, TN; *U.S. Public*, pg. 150

Epstein, Scott, Dir.-Adv. & Pub. Rels.--Excite, Inc., Redwood City, CA; *U.S. Public*, pg. 599

Erdner, Thomas E., Mgr.-Mktg. Communications--Calgon Corporation, Pittsburgh, PA; *Int'l*, pg. 455

Erickson, Bob, Mgr.-Adv. & Pub. Rels.--Hennessy Industries, Inc., La Vergne, TN; *U.S. Public*, pg. 481

Erickson, Jim, Dir.-Communications--Harvest States Cooperatives, Saint Paul, MN; *U.S. Private*, pg. 508

Ericson, Alice, Dir.-Pub. Rels.--Phoenix Home Life Mutual Insurance Company, Hartford, CT; *U.S. Private*, pg. 863

Ericson, Alice, Dir.-Pub.Rels.--Phoenix Home Life Mutual Insurance Co., Hartford, CT; *U.S. Private*, pg. 863

Erkelens, L., Grp. Mgr.-Pub. Rels.--KTI Group B.V., Zoetermeer, Netherlands; *Int'l*, pg. 837

Ernie, Ann M., Mgr.-Mktg. Communicatons--Thoro, Jacksonville, FL; *U.S. Private*, pg. 505

Ernst, Katharina, Communications--MD Papier GmbH, Dachau, Germany; *Int'l*, pg. 864

Eshow, Joanne, Mgr.-Pub. Rels.--Trus Joist MacMillan, Boise, ID; *Int'l*, pg. 829

Eshow, Joanne, Mgr.-Pub. Rels.--Trus Joist MacMillan, Boise, ID; *U.S. Public*, pg. 1556

Esmele, Jaymelina, Pub. Rels.--Wall Data Incorporated, Kirkland, WA; *U.S. Public*, pg. 1734

Espalioux, Jean-Marc, Exec. V.P.-Investor Rels.--Compagnie Generale Des Eaux, Paris, France; *Int'l*, pg. 321

Esposito, Sharyn, Bus. Affairs Dir.--Griffin Bacal Inc., New York, NY; *U.S. Private*, pg. 480

Essen, Arthur, Mgr.-Mktg. & Adv.--American Express Service Europe Ltd., Amsterdam, Netherlands; *U.S. Public*, pg. 74

Essman, Alyn V., Chm. Bd. & Chief Exec. Officer--CPI Corp., Saint Louis, MO; *U.S. Public*, pg. 283

Esson, Penny, Dir.-Pub. Affairs--Simon Engineering plc, London, United Kingdom; *Int'l*, pg. 1251

Estabillo, Rolando G., V.P.-Corp. Commun.--Philippine Airlines, Inc., Manila, Philippines; *Int'l*, pg. 1050

Estabillo, Rolando G., Asst. V.P.-Corp. Commun.--Philippine Airlines, Inc., Manila, Philippines; *Int'l*, pg. 1050

Estes, Wayne, Dir.-Pub. Rels.--Bristol Motor Speedway, Bristol, TN; *U.S. Public*, pg. 1498

Estony, Robert J., Dir.-Communications--Ikegami Electronics (U.S.A.), Inc., Maywood, NJ; *Int'l*, pg. 660

Etherington, Martyn, Sr. Dir.-Corp. Communications--Sequent Computer Systems, Inc., Beaverton, OR; *U.S. Public*, pg. 1459

Evangelista, Thomas E., V.P.-Corp. Devel. & Commun.--Stanhome Inc., Westfield, MA; *U.S. Public*, pg. 1508

Evans, Anita, Asst. V.P.-Corp. Communications--Duncanson & Holt, New York, NY; *U.S. Public*, pg. 1699

Evans, Carolyn, Exec. Dir. & Customers Relations--Saladmaster, Inc., Arlington, TX; *U.S. Private*, pg. 917

Evans, Cynthia, Mng. Dir.-Corp. Commun.--New Century Energies, Inc., Denver, CO; *U.S. Public*, pg. 1170

Evans, Cynthia, Mgr.-Corp. Commun.--Public Service Company of Colorado, Denver, CO; *U.S. Public*, pg. 1170

Evans, Jim, Dir.-Internal Commun.--Ipalco Enterprises, Inc., Indianapolis, IN; *U.S. Public*, pg. 912

Evans, Jim, Dir.-Internal Communications--Indianapolis Power & Light Company, Indianapolis, IN; *U.S. Public*, pg. 913

Evans, John, Sr. V.P. & Pub. Rels. Dir.--Al Paul Lefton Co., Inc., Philadelphia, PA; *U.S. Private*, pg. 658

Evans, Philip, Mgr.-Mktg. & Bus. Devel.--Pipetronix Ltd., Concord, Canada; *Int'l*, pg. 1071

Evans, Tony, V.P.-Communications--White Consolidated Industries, Inc., Cleveland, OH; *Int'l*, pg. 439

Everaars, Ad, Mgr.-Pub. Rels.--RTL4, Luxembourg, Luxembourg; *Int'l*, pg. 561

Everett, Samuel, Dir.-Corp. Communications--JPS Elastomerics Corp., Holyoke, MA; *U.S. Private*, pg. 578

Everhart, Judd, Mgr.-Public Rels.--Xerox Corporation, Stamford, CT; *U.S. Public*, pg. 1783

Ewald, Jessica, Mgr.-Mktg.--Plastag Corporation, Elk Grove Village, IL; *U.S. Private*, pg. 870

Ewigleben, Donald, V.P.-Environ. & Pub. Affairs--Echo Bay Mines Ltd., Englewood, CO; *U.S. Public*, pg. 561

Ewing, Donna, Mgr.-Pub. Rels.--EG & G Sealol Engineered Products Division, Warwick, RI; *U.S. Public*, pg. 542

Eyre, John, Dir.-Communications--Kingfisher plc, London, United Kingdom; *Int'l*, pg. 733

Faber, Charles P., V.P.-Corp. Devel.--Belden & Blake Corporation, Canton, OH; *U.S. Private*, pg. 1078

Facer, Tom, V.P.-Agricultural Service--Comstock Michigan Fruit, Rochester, NY; *U.S. Private*, pg. 887

Fader, Ellen, V.P.-Corp. Commun.--Katz Media Group, Inc., New York, NY; *U.S. Public*, pg. 335

Faigle, Angelika, Mgr.-Pub. Rels.--Pilatus Flugzeugwerke AG, Stans, Switzerland; *Int'l*, pg. 998

Fairbairn, Kelly, Dir.-Employment Services--The Seibels Bruce Group, Inc., Columbia, SC; *U.S. Public*, pg. 1453

Fallon, Jill, Dir.-Corp. Communications--Duracell International Inc., Bethel, CT; *U.S. Public*, pg. 743

Fama, Maureen C., Mgr.-Communications--Uniroyal Chemical Company, Inc., Middlebury, CT; *U.S. Public*, pg. 460

Fancher, Charles, V.P.-Communications & Pub. Affairs--Philadelphia Daily News, Philadelphia, PA; *U.S. Public*, pg. 964

Fanfa, Luiz C.T., Mgr.-Pub. Rels.--General Motors do Brasil Ltda., Sao Caetano do Sul, Brazil; *U.S. Public*, pg. 722

Fanning, Michael, V.P.-Corp. Commun.--Liberty Corporation, Greenville, SC; *U.S. Public*, pg. 991

Fant, Robert, Dir.-Adv.--Sears Tire Group, Hoffman Estates, IL; *U.S. Public*, pg. 1452

Farina, Nick, V.P.-Pub. Rels. & Pub. Affairs--Encyclopaedia Britannica, Inc., Chicago, IL; *U.S. Private*, pg. 375

Farley, John W., Dir.-Pub. Rels.--Phillips Publishing International, Inc., Potomac, MD; *U.S. Private*, pg. 862

Farley, Michele U., V.P.-Communications--Phoenix Home Life Mutual Insurance Co., Hartford, CT; *U.S. Private*, pg. 863

Farmer, Ann, Mgr.-Corp. Communications--DPL Inc., Dayton, OH; *U.S. Public*, pg. 473

Farmer, Christine, Dir.-Communications--AON Risk Services Inc. of Illinois, Chicago, IL; *U.S. Public*, pg. 117

Farmer, David, Dir.-Corp. Communications--Sierra Pacific Resources, Reno, NV; *U.S. Public*, pg. 1470

Farmer, H. Randolph, Sr. V.P.-Corp. Commun. & Investor Rels.--Lawyers Title Insurance Corporation, Richmond, VA; *U.S. Public*, pg. 981

Farmer, Jim, V.P.-Pub. Rels.--The Saturn Corporation, Troy, MI; *U.S. Public*, pg. 721

Farnesi, Michael, Mgr.-Corp. Commun. & Investor Rels.--Banyan Systems Inc., Westborough, MA; *U.S. Public*, pg. 189

Farnsworth, Barbara, Mgr.-Commun.--Rexall Sundown Inc., Boca Raton, FL; *U.S. Public*, pg. 1384

Farr, Anna, Mgr.--Boral Limited, Sydney, Australia; *Int'l*, pg. 203

Farr, David, Sr. V.P. & Gen. Mgr.-Corp. Communications Div.--Canon U.S.A., Inc., Lake Success, NY; *Int'l*, pg. 262

Farrell, Christopher C., Dir.-Corp. Communications & Govt. Rels. Specialist--The Berkshire Gas Company, Pittsfield, MA; *U.S. Public*, pg. 216

Farrow, Jason, Sr. V.P.-Public Affairs--Sony Electronics, Park Ridge, NJ; *Int'l*, pg. 1281

Farwell, Peter, V.P.-Corp. Rels.--Harcourt General, Inc., Chestnut Hill, MA; *U.S. Public*, pg. 782

Fasolino, Jo, Dir.-Commun. & Mgr.-Office of Chm.--Shieffelin Somerset Co., New York, NY; *Int'l*, pg. 412

Fausch, David A., V.P.-Pub. Rels.--The Gillette Company, Boston, MA; *U.S. Public*, pg. 743
Fawcett, Laura C., Mgr.-Mktg. Communications--Garlock Sealing Technologies, Palmyra, NY; *U.S. Public*, pg. 402
Feck, Luke M., Sr. V.P.-Corp. Communications--American Electric Power Service Corp., Columbus, OH; *U.S. Public*, pg. 72
Feeley, John F., Mgr.-Pub. Rels.--Safety-Kleen Corp., Elgin, IL; *U.S. Public*, pg. 1425
Feeney, Anne, Mgr.-Special Events--Marshall Field, Chicago, IL; *U.S. Public*, pg. 489
Fehring, Thomas H., Sec.--Wisconsin Energy Corporation, Milwaukee, WI; *U.S. Public*, pg. 1773
Feighery, Mark, Mgr.-Pub. Rels.--The Mead Corporation, Dayton, OH; *U.S. Public*, pg. 1074
Feinseth, Miriam, Dir.-Adv. & Communication--Hunter Douglas, Inc., Upper Saddle River, NJ; *Int'l*, pg. 639
Felderman, Douglas, Chief Fin. Officer--Strouds, Inc., City of Industry, CA; *U.S. Public*, pg. 1525
Feldman, Alan, V.P.-Pub. Rels.--Mirage Resorts Incorporated, Las Vegas, NV; *U.S. Public*, pg. 1116
Feldman, B., V.P.-Indus. Rels.--NI Industries, Inc., Seal Beach, CA; *U.S. Public*, pg. 1054
Feldman, Leon D., Exec. V.P., Treas. & Sec.--P & F Industries, Inc., Farmingdale, NY; *U.S. Public*, pg. 1239
Feldman, Peter, Sr. Mktg. Specialist--Computer Language Research, Inc., Carrollton, TX; *U.S. Public*, pg. 421
Feldman, Susan, Sr. V.P.-Corp. Commun.--Counsel Corporation, Toronto, Canada; *Int'l*, pg. 338
Feldscher, Sharla, Dir.-Pub. Rels.--Sesame Place, Langhorne, PA; *U.S. Public*, pg. 114
Felici, Ann-Marie, Publicity & Promo. Dir.--Allied Advertising Agency, Public Relations, Philadelphia, PA; *U.S. Private*, pg. 38
Feller, Millicent A., Sr. V.P.-Pub. Affairs & Govt. Rels.--Gannett Company, Inc., Arlington, VA; *U.S. Public*, pg. 698
Fels, Xavier, Exec. V.P.-Pub. Affairs--PSA Peugeot Citroen, Paris, France; *Int'l*, pg. 1020
Femenia, Jaime Bellido, Dir.-Pub. Res. & Corp. Image--Banca March S.A., Palma de Mallorca, Spain; *Int'l*, pg. 136
Fenelon, Marcio, Investor Rels. Analyst--Iochpe-Maxion S.A., Sao Paulo, Brazil; *Int'l*, pg. 688
Fenimore, George W., Sr. V.P.-Pub. Affairs--Peck Jones Construction, Los Angeles, CA; *U.S. Private*, pg. 846
Fennings, Roger, Gen. Mgr.-Pub. Rels. Div. (Dubai)--Intermarkets Advertising, Beirut, Lebanon; *Int'l*, pg. 680
Fennings, Roger, Gen. Mgr.-Pub. Rels. Div.--Intermarkets U.A.E., Dubai, United Arab Emirates; *Int'l*, pg. 680
Fenrich, Jean Ann, Mgr.-Mktg. Communications--Weigh-Tronix, Inc., Fairmont, MN; *Int'l*, pg. 1299
Fenton, Geoffrey D., V.P.-Pub. Affairs--Allegiance Healthcare Corp., McGaw Park, IL; *U.S. Public*, pg. 44
Fenton, Geoffrey D., Mgr.-Pub. Rels.--Convertors/Custom Sterile, McGaw Park, IL; *U.S. Public*, pg. 44
Fenton, Geoffrey D., Mgr.-Pub. Rels.--Cost Management Services, McGaw Park, IL; *U.S. Public*, pg. 44
Fenton, Geoffrey D., Mgr.-Pub. Rels.--Distribution, McGaw Park, IL; *U.S. Public*, pg. 44
Fenton, Geoffrey D., Mgr.-Pub. Rels.--V. Mueller, Deerfield, IL; *U.S. Public*, pg. 44
Fenton, Geoffrey D., Mgr.-Pub. Rels.--Medi-Vac/Airlife Respiratory Care, McGaw Park, IL; *U.S. Public*, pg. 44
Fenton, Geoffrey D., Mgr.-Pub. Rels.--West Hudson, Inc. (Healthcare Consulting Services), Dallas, TX; *U.S. Public*, *pg. 45*
Fenton, Maebeth, Mgr.-Pub. Rels.--FINNAIR, New York, NY; *Int'l*, pg. 485
Ferazzi, Frank J., V.P.-Customer Service & Rates--Transcontinental Gas Pipe Line Corp., Houston, TX; *U.S. Public*, pg. 1769
Ferestein, June, Mgr.-Community Rels.--CVS Corp., Woonsocket, RI; *U.S. Public*, pg. 287
Fergus, Holly, V.P.-Mktg. & Communications--ATC Communications Group, Inc., Dallas, TX; *U.S. Public*, pg. 11
Ferguson, J., Asst. V.P. & Dir.-Mktg. Svcs.--American National Insurance Company, Galveston, TX; *U.S. Public*, pg. 87
Ferguson, James, Dir.-Customer Svc.--Lakeside Foods, Inc., Manitowoc, WI; *U.S. Private*, pg. 643
Ferguson, Patrick, Dir.-Communication--Nobel Insurance Limited, Hamilton, Bermuda; *Int'l*, pg. 951
Ferguson, R.A., Dir.-Public Affairs--Canadian Pacific Railway, Calgary, Canada; *Int'l*, pg. 258
Fernandes, Raul Alves, Dir.-Commun. & Pub. Rels.--Transportes Aereos Portugueses, Lisbon, Portugal; *Int'l*, pg. 1418
Fernandez, Lorenzo, Mgr.-Adv. & Pub. Rels.--Degussa Corporation, Ridgefield Park, NJ; *Int'l*, pg. 388
Fernandez, Suzanne, Mgr.-Corp. Commun.--Superior Telecommunications, Atlanta, GA; *U.S. Public*, pg. 58
Fernandez, Suzanne D., Mgr.-Corp. Commun.--The Alpine Group, Inc., New York, NY; *U.S. Public*, pg. 58
Fernando Monteiro Alve, Jose, Dir.-Mkt. Rels.--Sadia Group, Barueri, Brazil; *Int'l*, pg. 1168
Fernette, Jacqueline, Corp. Commun.--Reilly Industries, Inc., Indianapolis, IN; *U.S. Private*, pg. 919
Ferrant, Catherine, Mgr.-Pub. Rels.--Petrofina S.A., Brussels, Belgium; *Int'l*, pg. 1043
Ferrari, Luigi, V.P.-Pub. Rels.--Istituto Bancario San Paolo Di Torino S.p.A., Turin, Italy; *Int'l*, pg. 691
Ferrari, Nicholas J., Dir.-Mktg. Communications--Advertising Age, Chicago, IL; *U.S. Private*, pg. 284
Ferraz Queimado, Margarida, Deputy Mgr.-Pub. Rels.--Caixa Geral de Depositos, Lisbon, Portugal; *Int'l*, pg. 250
Ferreira, Cheryl, Dir.-Corp. Communications Opers.--Bose Corporation, Framingham, MA; *U.S. Private*, pg. 160
Ferrel, Celia, Mgr.-Pub. Rels.--Commercial Federal Corporation, Omaha, NE; *U.S. Public*, pg. 411
Ferrigno, Kathleen, Pub. Rels. Acct. Mgr.--Keiler & Company, Farmington, CT; *U.S. Private*, pg. 611
Fetherston, Rick, Dir.-Pub. Rels--American Family Mutual Insurance Co., Madison, WI; *U.S. Private*, pg. 53
Fetterman, James M., V.P.-Customer Services Grp.--Acuson Corporation, Mountain View, CA; *U.S. Public*, pg. 18
Fichtner, Lawrence C., Exec. V.P.-Corp. Commun.--Veritas DGC Inc., Houston, TX; *U.S. Private*, pg. 1136
Fields, Jeannine, Mgr.-Pub. Rels.--Cosmicar Lens Div., Englewood, CO; *Int'l*, pg. 85
Filion, Michel, V.P.-Communications & Pub. Affairs--ABB in Canada, Saint-Laurent, Canada; *Int'l*, pg. 7
Filppu, Len, Sr. V.P.-Pub. Rels.--Karakas, Vansickle, Ouellette Advertising & Public Relations, Mountain View, CA; *U.S. Private*, pg. 607
Finco, John, Pub. Rels. Dir.--Select Communications, L.P., New York, NY; *U.S. Private*, pg. 982
FinderStaan, Ama, Dir.-Pub. Rels.--Koninklijke BolsWessanen nv, Amstelveen, Netherlands; *Int'l*, pg. 750
Findlay, Mary, V.P.-Customer Opers.--MichCon, Detroit, MI; *U.S. Public*, pg. 1025
Fine, Mike, Mgr.-Pub. Rels.--Remington Arms Company, Inc., Madison, NC; *U.S. Private*, pg. 921
Fine, Steve, Dir.-Integrated Communications--Moore Document Solutions, Lake Forest, IL; *Int'l*, pg. 890
Fineran, James V., Mgr.-Adv.--Dresser Industries Wayne Division, Austin, TX; *U.S. Public*, pg. 528
Finger, Larry E., Chief Fin. Officer & Sr. V.P.--Washington Real Estate Investment Trust, Kensington, MD; *U.S. Public*, pg. 1743
Fink, K.W., V.P.-H.R.--Roquette America Inc., Keokuk, IA; *U.S. Private*, pg. 944
Finkelman, David, Sr. V.P.-Corp. Commun.--BankAtlantic Bancorp, Inc., Fort Lauderdale, FL; *U.S. Public*, pg. 183
Finkelstein, Gayle, Coord.-Mktg. & Pub. Rels.--Billboard Magazine, New York, NY; *Int'l*, pg. 1446
Finkle, James P., V.P. & Dir.-Grower Rels.--Canandaigua Wine Company, Inc., Canandaigua, NY; *U.S. Public*, pg. 300
Finlay, Peter, Dir.-Corp. Rels.-The Americas--The BOC Group Inc. (Delaware), Murray Hill, NJ; *Int'l*, pg. 121
Finley, Richard L., Sr. V.P.-Sls. & Mktg.--Allied Security, Inc., Pittsburgh, PA; *U.S. Private*, pg. 40
Finn, Anne, Commun. Analyst--Electronic Tele-Communications, Inc., Waukesha, WI; *U.S. Public*, pg. 570
Finnegan, Margaret, Dir.-Pub. Rels.--Schroder & Co. Inc., New York, NY; *Int'l*, pg. 1210
Finney, Beverly, V.P.-Pub. Rels. Grp.--Blue Ridge Electric Membership Corp., Lenoir, NC; *U.S. Private*, pg. 153
Finney, Deryl, Dir.-Corp. Commun.--General Automation, Inc., Irvine, CA; *U.S. Public*, pg. 706
Finney, Kate, Mgr.-Mktg. Communications--Duquesne Light Company, Pittsburgh, PA; *U.S. Public*, pg. 474
Fiorani, R.P., Dir.-Corp. Communications--Square D Company, Palatine, IL; *Int'l*, pg. 1208
Fiore, Liza, Mgr.-Corp. Communications--Interim Services Inc., Fort Lauderdale, FL; *U.S. Public*, pg. 892
Fiorentino, T.M., V.P.-Corp. Communications--CSX Transportation, Inc., Jacksonville, FL; *U.S. Public*, pg. 284
Fischer, Dorothy, Mgr.-Corp. Pub. Rels.--Brother International Corporation, Somerset, NJ; *Int'l*, pg. 229
Fischer, Meredith B., V.P.-Communications, Mktg. & Strategy--Pitney Bowes Inc., Stamford, CT; *U.S. Public*, pg. 1303
Fischerbacher, Robert, Dir.-Pub. Rels.--Knurr AG, Munich, Germany; *Int'l*, pg. 739
Fiser, Phyllis S., Sr. V.P.--Clyde Savings Bank Company, Clyde, OH; *U.S. Public*, pg. 632
Fish, Julia C., Dir.-Corp. Commun.--Sedgwick Group plc, London, United Kingdom; *Int'l*, pg. 1217
Fishbeck, James, Dir.-Corp. Communications & Investor Rels.--Analog Devices, Inc., Norwood, MA; *U.S. Public*, pg. 107
Fisher, Alice, Sr. V.P.-Public Rels.--Greenstone Roberts Public Relations, Coconut Creek, FL; *U.S. Public*, pg. 763
Fisher, C., Mgr.-Pub. Rels.--Bombardier Regional Aircraft Division, Downsview, Canada; *U.S. Public*, pg. 242
Fisher, Debbie, Dir.-Corp. Communications--Mettler-Toledo, Inc., Hightstown, NJ; *U.S. Private*, pg. 4
Fisher, Jim W., Mgr.-Community Rels.--Fisher Gauge Limited, Peterborough, Canada; *Int'l*, pg. 491
Fisher, Lori, Mgr.-Pub. Rels.--Monsanto Company, Saint Louis, MO; *U.S. Public*, pg. 1124
Fisher, M.A., Dir.-Pub. Rels. & Communications--Purina Mills, Inc., Saint Louis, MO; *U.S. Private*, pg. 895
Fisher, Steve, Mgr.-Pub. Rels.--Outboard Marine Corporation, Waukegan, IL; *U.S. Private*, pg. 478
Fisher, Susan, Mgr.-Adv. Corp. Info. & Public Affairs--B.A.T Industries P.L.C., London, United Kingdom; *Int'l*, pg. 110
Fitch, Donna, Dir.-Corp. Commun.--National Life Insurance Company, Montpelier, VT; *U.S. Private*, pg. 785
Fitzgerald, Brian, Dir.-Adv. & External Rels.--Ameritech Corporation, Chicago, IL; *U.S. Public*, pg. 97
Fitzgerald, Joan G., Dir.-Corp. Pub. Rels.--The Gillette Company, Boston, MA; *U.S. Public*, pg. 743
Fitzgerald, Kathy, Sr. V.P.-Pub. Rels. & Investor Rels.--Lucent Technologies Inc., Murray Hill, NJ; *U.S. Public*, pg. 1017
Fitzgerald, Margaret, Sr. V.P. & Community Rels. Dir.--Hill, Holliday, Connors, Cosmopulos, Inc., Boston, MA; *U.S. Private*, pg. 529
Fitzgerald, Patrick J., Dir.-Communications--Varity Kelsey Hayes, Livonia, MI; *Int'l*, pg. 820
Fitzgerald, Tom, Mgr.-Pub. Affairs--Brown & Williamson Tobacco Corp., Louisville, KY; *Int'l*, pg. 111
Fitzwater, Jim, Mgr.-N. American Communications--FMC Corp., Agricultural Products Group, Philadelphia, PA; *U.S. Public*, pg. 605
Fixa, Charles W., Dir.-Sls. & Mktg. & Mgr.-Adv. & Pub. Rels.--Spectrol Electronics Corporation, Ontario, CA; *U.S. Private*, pg. 351
Flaemig, Horst, Dir.-Mktg.--Girmes GmbH, Grefrath, Germany; *Int'l*, pg. 552
Flaiano, Jennifer, Mgr.-Corp. Rels.--Delphi Financial Group, Inc., Wilmington, DE; *U.S. Public*, pg. 496
Flamberg, Fern, V.P.-Pub. Rels.--Pedone & Partners Adv., Inc., New York, NY; *U.S. Private*, pg. 846
Flanagan, Kathleen A., V.P.-Corp. Communications--San Diego Gas & Electric Company, San Diego, CA; *U.S. Public*, pg. 584
Flanagan, Marianne, Dir.-Pub. Rels.--Oxford Health Plans Inc., Norwalk, CT; *U.S. Public*, pg. 1238
Flanagan, Patrick, Mgr.-Pub. Rels.--Central Steel & Wire Company, Chicago, IL; *U.S. Public*, pg. 327
Flancbaum, Paul, Mgr.-Communications--The Budd Company, Troy, MI; *Int'l*, pg. 1388
Fleisher, Peter, V.P.-Commun. Grp.--Rich Products Corp., Buffalo, NY; *U.S. Private*, pg. 928
Fleming, James, V.P.-Communications--Barrick Gold Corporation, Toronto, Canada; *Int'l*, pg. 168
Fleming, Mark A., Mgr.-Corp. Communications--Banta Corporation, Menasha, WI; *U.S. Public*, pg. 187
Fleming, Richard D., Gen. Dir.-Personnel & Pub. Rels., Locomotive Grp.--Electro-Motive Division, La Grange, IL; *U.S. Public*, pg. 719
Fleshner, Barrie, Dir.-Investor Rels.--Holiday RV Superstores, Inc., Orlando, FL; *U.S. Public*, pg. 829
Fletcher-Rogers, H., Mgr.-Legal & Corp. Rels.--Kodak Limited, Hemel Hempstead, United Kingdom; *U.S. Public*, pg. 553
Flick, Earl D., Dir.-Pub. Affairs--Aerospace Corporation, El Segundo, CA; *U.S. Private*, pg. 24
Flinkerbusch, R., Mgr.-Pub. Rels.--Ballast Nedam Dredging, Zeist, Netherlands; *Int'l*, pg. 133
Flo, Kjell, Mgr.-Pub. Rels.--Christiania Bank og Kreditkasse ASA, Oslo, Norway; *Int'l*, pg. 289
Florence, Anthony A., V.P.-Corp. & Investor Rels.--Ansaldo Signal N.V., Amsterdam, Netherlands; *Int'l*, pg. 77
Flores, Dana, Dir.-Communications--Philip Industrial Services Group, Houston, TX; *Int'l*, pg. 1050
Flowers, Arhlene, Dir.-Pub. Rels.--Four Seasons Hotels Inc., Don Mills, Canada; *Int'l*, pg. 502
Fluhrer, David R., V.P.-Corp. Communications--Olsten Corporation, Melville, NY; *U.S. Public*, pg. 1220
Fluor, J. Robert, II, V.P.-Community Rels.--Fluor Corporation, Irvine, CA; *U.S. Public*, pg. 659
Flynn, Lucy A., Sr. V.P.-Corp. Mktg. & Commun.--Wang Laboratories, Inc., Billerica, MA; *U.S. Public*, pg. 1737
Foden, Jennifer, Mgr.-Mktg.--Advanced Circuit Technology, Nashua, NH; *U.S. Private*, pg. 21
Fodor, Odette, Mgr.-Pub. Rels.--KLM Royal Dutch Airlines, Elmsford, NY; *Int'l*, pg. 719
Foerderer, Norma, Dir.-Pub. Rels.--Trump Organization, New York, NY; *U.S. Private*, pg. 1108
Foerster, Molly, Dir.-Investor Rels.--QUALCOMM, San Diego, CA; *U.S. Public*, pg. 1348
Fogarty, Richard, V.P.-Customer Service--Olsy North America Inc., Liberty Lake, WA; *Int'l*, pg. 1002
Fogelson, Dave, Dir.-Pub. Rels.--Reebok International Ltd., Stoughton, MA; *U.S. Public*, pg. 1369
Fokma, A. G., Dir.-Investor Rels.--Koninklijke Van Ommeren NV, Rotterdam, Netherlands; *Int'l*, pg. 758
Folds, Susan, Mgr.-Communications--Printpack Inc., Atlanta, GA; *U.S. Private*, pg. 886
Foley, Carol, Mktg. Commun.--Labelon Corporation, Canandaigua, NY; *U.S. Private*, pg. 641
Foley, Janice, Mgr.-Corp. Communications & Adv.--Keyport Life Insurance Company, Boston, MA; *U.S. Private*, pg. 666
Foley, Mike, V.P.-Corp. Affairs--St. Petersburg Times, Saint Petersburg, FL; *U.S. Private*, pg. 1088
Foley, William, V.P.-Communications--Euclid Hitachi, Cleveland, OH; *Int'l*, pg. 622
Folkes, Sally, Dir.-Mktg. Communications--General Binding Corporation, Northbrook, IL; *U.S. Public*, pg. 707
Folts, Jacque, Mgr.-Mktg. & Pub. Rels.--Atalanta Corporation, Elizabeth, NJ; *U.S. Private*, pg. 93
Foltz, Nancy J., V.P.-Corp. Commun.--Ceridian Corporation, Bloomington, MN; *U.S. Public*, pg. 330
Fonkalsrud, David, Mgr.-Mktg. Communications--DHL Worldwide Express, Redwood City, CA; *U.S. Private*, pg. 301
Fontana, Agostino, Mgr.-Public Sector--European Investment Bank, Luxembourg, Luxembourg; *Int'l*, pg. 465
Forbes, Rob, V.P.-Bus. Devel.--Smith & Hawken, Mill Valley, CA; *U.S. Public*, pg. 279
Ford, Andrew, Grp. Corp. Communications--Calor Group plc, Warwick, United Kingdom; *Int'l*, pg. 1155
Ford, Debi, Dir.-Corp. Communications & Investor Rels.--Starwood Hotels & Resorts, Phoenix, AZ; *U.S. Public*, pg. 1512
Ford, Dennis, Dir.-Mktg. & Communications--USG Interiors, Inc., Chicago, IL; *U.S. Public*, pg. 1660
Ford, H. Dallas, Jr., V.P.-Residential & Commercial Mktg. & Communications--Entex, Houston, TX; *U.S. Public*, pg. 843
Ford, Mary Ann, Mgr.-Pub. Affairs--Rhone-Poulenc Basic Chemicals Co., Shelton, CT; *Int'l*, pg. 1110
Forestell, Linda, Gen. Mgr.-Corp. Commun.--Bruncor, Inc., Saint John, Canada; *Int'l*, pg. 230
Forman, John, Dir.-Pub. Rels.--R.W. Beck, Inc., Seattle, WA; *U.S. Private*, pg. 128
Forman, Lisa, Pub. Rels. Specialist--Eatelcorp Inc., Gonzales, LA; *U.S. Private*, pg. 358
Forman, Victor, V.P.-Postal & Latin American Affairs--Group 1 Software, Inc., Lanham, MD; *U.S. Public*, pg. 417
Formanek, Nicolaus, V.P.-Press Rels.--CLT-UFA, Luxembourg, Luxembourg; *Int'l*, pg. 561
Fornataro, Mark, Mgr.-Mktg. Communications--Overnite Transportation Co., Richmond, VA; *U.S. Public*, pg. 1668
Forneck, Guenter, Mgr.-Corp. Commun.--Bayer AG, Leverkusen, Germany; *Int'l*, pg. 171
Forsblad, Peter, Chief Information Officer & Sr. V.P.--Nordbanken AB, Stockholm, Sweden; *Int'l*, pg. 957

Forssman, Peter, Sr. V.P.-Public Relations & Gov. Affairs--Scandinavian Airlines System (SAS), Solna, Sweden; *Int'l*, pg. 1201

Forst, Dan, Pub. Rels. Grp. Acct. Supvr.--Caldwell VanRiper, Inc., Indianapolis, IN; *U.S. Private*, pg. 200

Fort, Robert C., V.P.-Pub. Rels.--Norfolk Southern Corporation, Norfolk, VA; *U.S. Public*, pg. 1190

Fort, Robert C., V.P.-Pub. Rels.--Norfolk Southern Railway Company, Norfolk, VA; *U.S. Public*, pg. 1191

Forte, Kathy, Dir.-Corp. Pub. Rels.--Du Pont (E.I. Du Pont De Nemours & Co.), Wilmington, DE; *U.S. Public*, pg. 530

Fortney, Cynthia M., V.P.--Fidelity Federal Savings Bank, Marion, IN; *U.S. Public*, pg. 632

Foss, Adam, Corp. Commun. Officer--GN Great Nordic Ltd., Copenhagen, Denmark; *Int'l*, pg. 536

Foster, Erin, Pub. Rels. Dir.--Eric Mower and Associates, Rochester, NY; *U.S. Private*, pg. 765

Foster, Michel, Public Rels. Dir.--Young & Rubicam Bogota, Bogota, Colombia; *U.S. Private*, pg. 1200

Foster, Myra, Mgr.-Pub. Rels.--Stratton Corporation, Stratton Mountain, VT; *Int'l*, pg. 685

Foster, Robert, Sr. V.P.-Pub. Affairs--Edison International, Rosemead, CA; *U.S. Public*, pg. 564

Foster, Robert G., Sr V.P.-Pub. Affairs--Southern California Edison Company, Rosemead, CA; *U.S. Public*, pg. 564

Foster, Sheila, V.P.-Mktg. Communications--Database America Companies, Montvale, NJ; *U.S. Private*, pg. 312

Foster, Thomas M., Mgr.-Pub. Rels.--Phelps Dodge Industries, Phoenix, AZ; *U.S. Public*, pg. 1286

Fouquet, Doug, Coord.-Pub. Rels.--General Atomics, San Diego, CA; *U.S. Private*, pg. 443

Fowler, Frank, V.P.--D.C. Taylor Co., Cedar Rapids, IA; *U.S. Private*, pg. 1070

Fowler, Ian, Dir.-Media Rels.--BP America Inc., Cleveland, OH; *Int'l*, pg. 220

Fowlstone, G., Pres.-Corp. Affairs--Burns, Philp & Company Limited, Sydney, Australia; *Int'l*, pg. 236

Foy, Denise, Corp. Commun.--Beneficial Corporation, Wilmington, DE; *U.S. Public*, pg. 211

Foy, Jim, V.P.-Public Rels.--Corporate Foods Ltd., Etobicoke, Canada; *Int'l*, pg. 841

Fradette, Amy, Pub. Rels. Dir.--AIC-FSS Advertising, Minneapolis, MN; *U.S. Private*, pg. 5

Fraine, Bill, Sr. V.P.-Worldwide Sls.--FDX Corporation, Memphis, TN; *U.S. Public*, pg. 603

Framke, Donna, V.P.-Adv. & Mktg.--Beverly Bancorporation Inc., Chicago, IL; *U.S. Public*, pg. 227

Franca, Franco, Mgr.-Pub. Rels.--Olivetti Advanced Technology Center, Inc., Cupertino, CA; *Int'l*, pg. 1002

France, Richard E., V.P.-H.R. & Pub. Rels.--Caraustar Industries, Inc., Austell, GA; *U.S. Public*, pg. 303

Franchini, Arlene, Dir.-Corp. Commun. & Pub. Rels.--Ortronics, Inc., Pawcatuck, CT; *Int'l*, pg. 806

Franco, Victor M., Mgr.-Pub. Rels.--Miller Brewing Company, Irwindale, CA; *U.S. Public*, pg. 1289

Frank, Becky, V.P.-Pub. Rels.--BOK Financial Corp., Tulsa, OK; *U.S. Public*, pg. 163

Frank, Rudy, Mgr.-Adv. & Pub. Rels.--Kennametal Inc., Latrobe, PA; *U.S. Public*, pg. 950

Frankel, Marc, Dir.-Corp. Communications--Polychrome Corp. Div., Fort Lee, NJ; *Int'l*, pg. 370

Frankel, Ron A., V.P.-Corp. Commun. & Investor Rels.--New Plan Realty Trust, New York, NY; *U.S. Public*, pg. 1172

Frankiewicz, Anita, Dir.-Mktg.--Restonic Mattress Corporation, Rosemont, IL; *U.S. Private*, pg. 925

Franklin, John R., Mgr.-Mktg. & Adv.--Baltimore Stationery Co./Total Office, Baltimore, MD; *U.S. Private*, pg. 113

Franklin, Nick, Sr. V.P.-Pub. Affairs--Pacificare Health Systems, Santa Ana, CA; *U.S. Public*, pg. 1251

Franks, J.E., Mgr.-Mktg. Communications--WESCO Distribution, Inc., Pittsburgh, PA; *U.S. Private*, pg. 244

Franssila, Markku, V.P.-Corp. Communications--UPM-Kymmene Corporation, Helsinki, Finland; *Int'l*, pg. 1427

Franzen, Marci, Mgr.-Pub. Rels.--First Team Sports Inc., Anoka, MN; *U.S. Public*, pg. 638

Fraquelli, Marco, Mgr.-Press Rels.--Cassa di Risparmio delle Provincie Lombarde SpA (CARIPLO), Milan, Italy; *Int'l*, pg. 274

Fraser, Valerie, Mgr.-Communications--Southern Progress Corporation, Birmingham, AL; *U.S. Public*, pg. 1612

Frausin, Alberto, Dir.-Consumer Business--Johnson Wax S.p.A., Milan, Italy; *U.S. Private*, pg. 593

Frautschi, Deanna L., V.P.-Commun. & H.R.--Country Life Insurance Company, Bloomington, IL; *U.S. Private*, pg. 278

Frazier, Kenneth, V.P.-Pub. Affairs--Merck & Co., Inc., Whitehouse Station, NJ; *U.S. Public*, pg. 1090

Frederic, Christy, Gen. Mgr.-Corp. Information & Communication--Central Louisiana Electric Company, Inc., Pineville, LA; *U.S. Public*, pg. 325

Frederick, Robert A., V.P. & Dir.-Mktg. & Pub. Rels.--Peoples National Bank of Central Pennsylvania, State College, PA; *U.S. Public*, pg. 1222

Fredericksen, Jay A., V.P.-Corp. Rels.--Rayonier Inc., Stamford, CT; *U.S. Public*, pg. 1363

Frederickson, Mark, Mgr.-Pub. Rels.--EMC Corporation, Hopkinton, MA; *U.S. Public*, pg. 545

Fredo, Anthony J., V.P.-Public Affairs--Ford Motor Co. of Canada Ltd, Oakville, Canada; *U.S. Public*, pg. 666

Fredstrom, B.A., Dir.-P.R.--McCain Foods Limited, Florenceville, Canada; *Int'l*, pg. 850

Freedman, Alan M., Dir.-Pub. Policy & Communications--Orange and Rockland Utilities, Inc., Pearl River, NY; *U.S. Public*, pg. 1229

Freedman, Barbara, Dir.-Mktg. Communications--Greenwood Mills, Inc., New York, NY; *U.S. Private*, pg. 479

Freeman-Cardone, Marian, Mgr.-Mktg. Communications--Anorad Corporation, Hauppauge, NY; *U.S. Private*, pg. 75

Freeman, Clara, Exec. Dir.-Personnel--Marks & Spencer PLC, London, United Kingdom; *Int'l*, pg. 842

Freeman, James W., V.P.-Corp. Communications--American United Life Insurance Company, Indianapolis, IN; *U.S. Private*, pg. 64

Freese, Howard L., Mgr.-Mktg. Communications--Allvac, Monroe, NC; *U.S. Public*, pg. 43

Freeze, Bob, V.P.-Pub. Rels.--Great Financial Bank FSB, Louisville, KY; *U.S. Private*, pg. 473

Frei, Robert, Dir.-Corp. Affairs--Panalpina Welttransport (Holding) AG, Binningen, Switzerland; *Int'l*, pg. 1022

French, B.J., Sr. V.P.-Corp. Communications--Dain Rauscher Corporation, Minneapolis, MN; *U.S. Public*, pg. 476

Freschi, Susan, Dir.-Investor Rels.--Nellcor Puritan Bennett Incorporated, Pleasanton, CA; *U.S. Public*, pg. 1039

Fresne, Thierry, Adv. & Communications--Elf Aquitane, Paris, France; *Int'l*, pg. 444

Frey, A. Christopher, Dir.-Special Projects--The Goldhirsh Group, Boston, MA; *U.S. Private*, pg. 461

Frey, Deborah, Dir.-Consumer Mktg.--Catholic Digest, Saint Paul, MN; *U.S. Private*, pg. 220

Frey, Geraldine R., Dir.-Pub. Rels.--John S. Frey Enterprises, Los Angeles, CA; *U.S. Private*, pg. 428

Frey, James, Mgr.-Pub. Affairs--Pacificare of Arizona, Phoenix, AZ; *U.S. Public*, pg. 1251

Frey, James E., V.P.-Bus. Devel.--J.S. Alberici Construction Co., Inc., Saint Louis, MO; *U.S. Private*, pg. 32

Frick, Urs, Mng. Dir.-Madrid, Creative & Pub. Rels. Dir.--Grupo Barro Testa, Madrid, Spain; *Int'l*, pg. 1377

Fridling, David, V.P.-Corp. Pub. Rels.--NovaCare Inc., King of Prussia, PA; *U.S. Public*, pg. 1203

Friedling, Cheryl, Dir.-Corp. Commun.--Montgomery Watson, Pasadena, CA; *U.S. Private*, pg. 759

Friedman, Kent, Dir.-Pub. Rels.--The Grandoe Corp., Gloversville, NY; *U.S. Private*, pg. 469

Friedman, Kim, Dir.-Pub. Rels.--Lalique North America, Carlstadt, NJ; *Int'l*, pg. 797

Friedman, Marc, Pub. Rels.--Computer Associates International, Inc., Islandia, NY; *U.S. Public*, pg. 420

Frisch, Maureen S., V.P.-Pub. Affairs--Simpson Investment Co., Seattle, WA; *U.S. Private*, pg. 1003

Frisz, Bob, Mgr.-Corp. Communications--Aesculap, Inc., South San Francisco, CA; *Int'l*, pg. 29

Frith, Marlene, Dir.-Integrated Commun. & Investor Rels.--Brite Voice Systems, Inc., Heathrow, FL; *U.S. Public*, pg. 257

Fritzsche, Linda, V.P.-Mktg. Commun.--Platinum Technology, Inc., Oak Brook Terrace, IL; *U.S. Public*, pg. 1309

Fromager, Isabelle, Mgr.-Pub. Rels.--Clarins, Neuilly-sur-Seine, France; *Int'l*, pg. 295

Frosh, Kirsten, Dir.-Pub. Rels.--Ingram Micro Inc., Santa Ana, CA; *U.S. Public*, pg. 878

Frost, Ron, Dir.-Pub. Affairs--Fleming Companies, Inc., Oklahoma City, OK; *U.S. Public*, pg. 652

Frost, William J., V.P.-Admin.--EDO Corporation, New York, NY; *U.S. Public*, pg. 541

Frugier, Laurie, Corp. Commun.--Havas Advertising, Levallois-Perret, France; *Int'l*, pg. 600

Fry, Charles, Sr. V.P.-Pub. Affairs--Searle & Co., Skokie, IL; *U.S. Public*, pg. 1125

Fryer, Mark, Pub. Rel.--Woods Equipment Company, Oregon, IL; *U.S. Private*, pg. 249

Frysztak, Corie, Mgr.-Pub. Rels.--Barton Incorporated, Chicago, IL; *U.S. Public*, pg. 300

Frysztak, Corie, Mgr.-Pub. Rels.--Barton Beers, Ltd., Chicago, IL; *U.S. Public*, pg. 300

Fuchs, Manfred, Dr., Chm. Bd.--Fuchs Petrolub AG Oel + Chemie, Mannheim, Germany; *Int'l*, pg. 517

Fujii, M., Dir.-Personnel & Pub. Rels.--Otto Sumisho Inc., Tokyo, Japan; *Int'l*, pg. 1015

Fukutome, Yasuhiro, Mgr.-Pub. Rels.--Nippon Oil Company, Limited (NiSSEKI), Tokyo, Japan; *Int'l*, pg. 936

Fullagar, Nick, Mgr.-Pub. Rels.--Mirror Group plc, London, United Kingdom; *Int'l*, pg. 869

Fuller, Devra, Mgr.-Mktg. Communications--Decibel Products, Inc., Dallas, TX; *U.S. Public*, pg. 46

Fuller, Sue, Dir.-Personnel & Pub. Rels.--Litton Systems, Inc. Advanced Circuitry Div., Springfield, MO; *U.S. Public*, pg. 1003

Fulton, Louisa, Mgr.-Communications--Bayer Corporation/Diagnostics Division, Tarrytown, NY; *Int'l*, pg. 173

Fultz, Linda, Corp. Commun.--Archer Daniels Midland Company (ADM), Decatur, IL; *U.S. Public*, pg. 127

Fung, Joyce, Global Communications Coord.--Levi Strauss & Co., San Francisco, CA; *U.S. Private*, pg. 662

Fung, Wang Look, Gen. Mgr.-Pub. Affairs--Keppel Corporation Limited, Singapore, Singapore; *Int'l*, pg. 731

Funk, Ernst, Mgr.-Sls. & Customer Rels.--The Swissair Group, Zurich, Switzerland; *Int'l*, pg. 1333

Fuortes, Beverly, Dir.-Corp. Devel.--Amtech Corporation, Dallas, TX; *U.S. Public*, pg. 105

Furfar, Ricardo, V.P.-Human Resources & Legal Afairs--Johnson & Johnson de Argentina, S.A., Buenos Aires, Argentina; *U.S. Public*, pg. 930

Furniss, Roger, Mgr.-Pub. Rels.--South West Water PLC, Exeter, United Kingdom; *Int'l*, pg. 1287

Furth, Daniel R., Dir.-Corp. Rels.--MTL Inc., Plant City, FL; *U.S. Public*, pg. 1028

Furth, Daniel R., Dir.-Corp. Rels.--Montgomery Tank Lines, Inc., Plant City, FL; *U.S. Public*, pg. 1028

Fusco, Dave, Mgr.-Mktg. Communications--Seal Products Incorporated, Naugatuck, CT; *U.S. Public*, pg. 849

Fusco, Joseph S., V.P.-Communications--Casella Waste Systems, Inc., Rutland, VT; *U.S. Public*, pg. 312

Fusilli, Jim, V.P.-Corp. Communications--Sanofi Beaute Inc., New York, NY; *Int'l*, pg. 445

Gabelier, Philippe, V.P.-Pub. Affairs--Caisse de depot et placement du Quebec, Montreal, Canada; *Int'l*, pg. 249

Gabrynowicz, Elisabeth, Dir.-Corp. Communications--CSX Corporation, Richmond, VA; *U.S. Public*, pg. 284

Gady, Richard L., V.P.-Pub. Affairs--ConAgra, Inc., Omaha, NE; *U.S. Public*, pg. 425

Gaeb, Hans-Wilhelm, Dir.-Pub. Affairs--General Motors (Europe) AG, Glattbrugg, Switzerland; *U.S. Public*, pg. 721

Gaffney, Erin, Dir.-Pub. Rels.--Hartmarx Corporation, Chicago, IL; *U.S. Public*, pg. 795

Gaffney, Erin, Dir.-Pub. Rels.--Hart Schaffner & Marx Clothes, Chicago, IL; *U.S. Public*, pg. 795

Gaffney, Erin, Dir.-Pub. Rels.--Hickey-Freeman/Bobby Jones, Rochester, NY; *U.S. Public*, pg. 795

Gagliardi, Joseph, V.P.-Mktg.--Hertz Equipment Rental Corp., Park Ridge, NJ; *U.S. Public*, pg. 664

Gagnier, Daniel, V.P.-Corp. Affairs--Alcan Aluminium Limited, Montreal, Canada; *Int'l*, pg. 50

Gahlon, Dan E., Exec. Dir.-Pub. Rels. & Corp. Commun.--3M, Saint Paul, MN; *U.S. Public*, pg. 1604

Gail, Brian, Sr. V.P.-Corp. Communications--Aramark Corporation, Philadelphia, PA; *U.S. Private*, pg. 79

Gair, Bill, Mgr.-Communications--DoFasco, Inc., Hamilton, Canada; *Int'l*, pg. 414

Galia, Lynn, Mgr.-Pub. Rels.--Marshall Field, Chicago, IL; *U.S. Public*, pg. 489

Gallagher, James P., V.P.-Pub. Rels.--ITT Corporation, New York, NY; *U.S. Public*, pg. 1512

Gallagher, Sheila E., V.P.-Corp. Communications--Centex Corporation, Dallas, TX; *U.S. Public*, pg. 322

Gallagher, Tim, V.P.-Pub. Rels.--Carnival Corporation, Miami, FL; *U.S. Public*, pg. 306

Gallaspy, Greg, Mgr.-Consumer Relations--Builders Square, Inc., San Antonio, TX; *U.S. Private*, pg. 477

Galletly, Donald R., V.P.-Commun. & Investor Rels.--Dresser Industries, Inc., Dallas, TX; *U.S. Public*, pg. 528

Galligan, Bill J., Asst. V.P.-Corp. Affairs--The Kansas City Southern Railway Co., Kansas City, MO; *U.S. Public*, pg. 944

Gallone, Larry, Mgr.-Mktg. Communications--Powell Electronics Inc., Philadelphia, PA; *U.S. Private*, pg. 877

Galloway, Alice, Mgr.-Commun.--SRI International, Menlo Park, CA; *U.S. Private*, pg. 958

Galyon, Doug, Dir.-Public Affairs--Guilford Mills, Inc., Greensboro, NC; *U.S. Public*, pg. 768

Gambill, Anita, Mktg. Communications Specialist--Seradyn, Inc., Indianapolis, IN; *Int'l*, pg. 871

Gand, Jeanne-Marie, V.P.-Communications--Rossignol Ski Co., Williston, VT; *Int'l*, pg. 1127

Gannon, Barbara, V.P.-Public Relations--Sargento Foods Inc., Plymouth, WI; *U.S. Private*, pg. 966

Gans, Mary Anne, Dir.-Mktg.--Globelle Corporation, Mississauga, Canada; *Int'l*, pg. 554

Gant, Edmund R., Jr., Mgr.-Pub. Rels.--Glen Raven Mills, Inc., Glen Raven, NC; *U.S. Private*, pg. 456

Gantly, Joe, Mgr.-Pub. Rels.--Fiat Auto Ireland Ltd., Dublin, Ireland; *Int'l*, pg. 481

Ganzell, Larry, V.P.-Strategic Partners & Pub. Rels.--ScanTron Corporation, Tustin, CA; *U.S. Public*, pg. 786

Garabedian, Theresa, Pub. Rels.--Waring Products, New Hartford, CT; *U.S. Public*, pg. 286

Garbeaux, Jean-Marie, Sr. V.P.-Corp. Communications--Elf Aquitane, Paris, France; *Int'l*, pg. 444

Garber, Lisa, Dir.-Corp. Communications--Lam Research Corporation, Fremont, CA; *U.S. Public*, pg. 975

Garbuzinski, Kathy, Coord. & Mgr.-Corp. Communications--Morgan Keegan, Inc., Memphis, TN; *U.S. Public*, pg. 1131

Garcia, Raquel, Mgr.-Mktg. Communications--BAX Global, Irvine, CA; *U.S. Public*, pg. 1305

Gardner, Betsy, Dir.-Corp. Commun.--Forstmann & Company, Inc., New York, NY; *U.S. Public*, pg. 670

Gardner, Betsy, Mgr.-Pub. Rels.--Gensym Corporation, Cambridge, MA; *U.S. Public*, pg. 731

Gardner, Cindy, Dir.-Corp. Communications--Universal Studios, Inc., Universal City, CA; *Int'l*, pg. 1215

Gardner, David L., Dir.-Pub. Rel.--Cleveland-Cliffs Inc, Cleveland, OH; *U.S. Public*, pg. 386

Gardner, Gary E., V.P.-Human Res. & Public Affairs--The Valspar Corporation, Minneapolis, MN; *U.S. Public*, pg. 1707

Gardner, William G., Dir.-Pub. Rels.--Apogee Enterprises, Inc., Minneapolis, MN; *U.S. Public*, pg. 120

Garfinkle, Shirley, Mgr.-Adv. & Corp. Communications--Mitchel-Lincoln Packaging, Saint-Laurent, Canada; *Int'l*, pg. 870

Garicano, Jose, Dir.-Pub. Rels.--Opel Espana, Zaragoza, Spain; *U.S. Public*, pg. 724

Garner, James, Mgr.-Mktg. Communications--Camco International Inc., Houston, TX; *U.S. Public*, pg. 297

Garnett, Neil, Mgr.-Group Corp. Commun.--Grand Metropolitan Plc, London, United Kingdom; *Int'l*, pg. 408

Garofalo, Tom, Assoc.-Commun.--Catholic Relief Services, Baltimore, MD; *U.S. Private*, pg. 220

Garratt, Alan, Mgr.-Pub. Rels.--MCI International Inc., Rye Brook, NY; *U.S. Public*, pg. 1024

Garren, Ruth, Mgr.-Commun. & Pub. Rels.--McKee Foods Corporation, Collegedale, TN; *U.S. Private*, pg. 723

Garrett, David, Gen. Mgr.-Customer Service--Sun Life and Provincial Holdings plc, London, United Kingdom; *Int'l*, pg. 1318

Garrison, Karen, Dir.-Commun.--Payless Cashways, Inc., Kansas City, MO; *U.S. Public*, pg. 1267

Garrison, Scott, Mgr.-Customer Svcs.--Instant Web, Inc., Chanhassen, MN; *U.S. Private*, pg. 565

Garvick, Debra, Mgr.-Mktg.--Buck Knives, Inc., El Cajon, CA; *U.S. Private*, pg. 177

Gary, Alice Lardus, Exec. Asst.- Pub. Rels.--Itam Tech Italimplianti, Inc., Coraopolis, PA; *Int'l*, pg. 655

Gary, Kathleen N., V.P.-Pub. Affairs & Communications--Syntex, Palo Alto, CA; *Int'l*, pg. 1120

Gary, Liz, Coord.-Pub. Rels.--Phelps Dodge Tyrone, Tyrone, NM; *U.S. Public*, pg. 1287

Gasprock, Nancy, Sr. Dir.-Communications--Cable & Wireless Communications Inc., Vienna, VA; *Int'l*, pg. 247

Gass, Jerry H., Dir.-Communications & Govt. Affairs--Southern States Cooperative, Inc., Richmond, VA; *U.S. Private*, pg. 1017

Gates, M., Mgr.-Public Rels.--Cyanamid of Great Britain Ltd., Gosport, United Kingdom; *U.S. Public*, pg. 81
Gattis, Jerry, Pres. & Chief Oper. Officer--Cagle's Inc., Atlanta, GA; *U.S. Public*, pg. 291
Gauci, Dennis J., Dir.-Corp. Communications--Calspan SRL Corporation, Washington, DC; *U.S. Private*, pg. 1136
Gaul, Richard, Pub. Rels.--Bayerische Motoren Werke Aktiengesellschaft, Munich, Germany; *Int'l*, pg. 177
Gaulton, Ann, Mgr.-Corp. Communications--General Electric Canada Inc., Mississauga, Canada; *U.S. Public*, pg. 713
Gaut, Steve, Dir.-Pub. Affairs--Delphi Saginaw Steering Systems, Saginaw, MI; *U.S. Public*, pg. 719
Gavigan, Peter, Mgr.-Pub. Rels.--The BOC Group Inc. (Delaware), Murray Hill, NJ; *Int'l*, pg. 121
Gavighan, Joe, Dir.-Pub. Rels.--Marcam Solutions, Inc., Newton, MA; *U.S. Public*, pg. 1042
Gaviser, Judy, Dir.-Pub. Affairs--American Express Financial Advisor, Minneapolis, MN; *U.S. Public*, pg. 73
Gazzarri, Jeff, Dir.-Artist Rels.--Westwood One, Inc., New York, NY; *U.S. Public*, pg. 1763
Geddes, Kristine M., Mgr.-Mktg. Communications--Woods Equipment Company, Oregon, IL; *U.S. Private*, pg. 249
Gefen, Sharon, Sr. V.P.-Corp. Intl. Commun. & Pub. Rels.--Bank Hapoalim, Tel Aviv, Israel; *Int'l*, pg. 149
Geib, Bob, Mgr.-Mktg. Communications--Aeroflex Laboratories Inc., Plainview, NY; *U.S. Public*, pg. 24
Geiger, Sylvie, Mktg. Dir.--EURO RSCG Babinet, Erra, Tong Cuong, Levallois-Perret, France; *Int'l*, pg. 600
Geiselman, R.D., Mgr.-Mktg. Communications--Houghton International Inc., Valley Forge, PA; *U.S. Private*, pg. 541
Geisler, Jim, Mgr.-Mktg. Communications--Killark Electric Manufacturing Co., Saint Louis, MO; *U.S. Public*, pg. 844
Geiss, Valerie, Mgr.-Pub. Rels.--American Kennel Club, Inc., New York, NY; *U.S. Private*, pg. 58
Gellens, Martha, Mgr.-Public Affairs--Mitsubishi International Corporation, New York, NY; *Int'l*, pg. 871
Geller-Hawtof, Jamie, V.P.-Publicity--TriStar Pictures, Culver City, CA; *Int'l*, pg. 1283
Gelt, Iris, Exec. Dir.-Corp. Communications--Universal Studios, Inc., Universal City, CA; *Int'l*, pg. 1215
Gemmel, Kari, Dir.-Mktg.--Jackson Hole Ski Resort, Teton Village, WY; *U.S. Private*, pg. 579
Gendall, Stuart, Mgr.-Pub. Rels.--BTR plc, London, United Kingdom; *Int'l*, pg. 124
Gendron, Tom, Mgr.-Customer Support & Bus. Devel.--Woodward Governor Company, Rockford, IL; *U.S. Public*, pg. 1776
Genest, David, Dir.-Mktg. & Corp. Communications--Brown & Sharpe Manufacturing Company, North Kingstown, RI; *U.S. Public*, pg. 260
Genrett, Gretchen, Exec. Dir.-Adv. Communications--MCI Communications Corp., Atlanta, GA; *U.S. Public*, pg. 1023
Geoffroy, Caroline, Asst.-Communications--Lafarge Materiaux de Specialites, Montrouge, France; *Int'l*, pg. 789
Gerace, Jim, Exec. Dir.-Public Relations--Bell Atlantic Mobile, Bedminster, NJ; *U.S. Public*, pg. 202
Geraci, Lucrezia, Dir.-Corp. Affairs--Compart SpA, Milan, Italy; *Int'l*, pg. 324
Gerbeaux, Jean-Marie, Dir.-Commun.--SNCF, Paris, France; *Int'l*, pg. 1163
Gerber, Bill, V.P.-Investor & Pub. Rels.--Acceptance Insurance Co., Inc., Omaha, NE; *U.S. Public*, pg. 14
Gerchenson, Jeffery H., Pres. & Chief Oper. Officer--Alva/Amco Pharmacal Companies, Inc., Chicago, IL; *U.S. Private*, pg. 47
Gerdemann, Gary, V.P.-Communications--Einstein/Noah Bagel Corp., Golden, CO; *U.S. Public*, pg. 247
Gerrard, Rob, Gen. Mgr.-Pub. Affairs--Australia & New Zealand Banking Group Limited, Melbourne, Australia; *Int'l*, pg. 98
Gerst, Terri, Media Rels. Specialist--West Information Publishing Group, Saint Paul, MN; *U.S. Public*, pg. 1602
Gerstein, Mel, Treas. & Dir.-Mktg., Adv. & Pub. Rels.--Thermwell Products Co., Inc., Paterson, NJ; *U.S. Private*, pg. 1081
Gervasi, John, Dir.-Pub. Rels.--Dreis & Krump Manufacturing Company, Chicago, IL; *U.S. Private*, pg. 342
Ghezzi, Gianluigi, Dir.-Pub. Rels. & Gen. Affairs--Agusta S.P.A., Varese, Italy; *Int'l*, pg. 32
Ghio, Marta, Mgr.-Pub. Rels.--MDS Inc., Etobicoke, Canada; *Int'l*, pg. 826
Giammarchi, Dirce, Dir.-Pub. Rels.--Metropolitana Milanese S.P.A., Milan, Italy; *Int'l*, pg. 863
Giangiulio, Mary Ellen, Mgr.-Mktg.--Streamlight Inc., Norristown, PA; *U.S. Private*, pg. 1047
Giannoni, Kay, Dir.-Mktg.--J.F. Ahern Co., Fond Du Lac, WI; *U.S. Private*, pg. 27
Giaramita, Phillip S., V.P.-Corp. Communications--International Paper Company, Purchase, NY; *U.S. Public*, pg. 901
Gibb, Richard, Dir.-Corp. Affairs--Scottish & Newcastle plc, Edinburgh, United Kingdom; *Int'l*, pg. 1211
Gibbs, Marcus C., Sr. V.P.-Customer Services--American General Life & Accident Insurance Co., Nashville, TN; *U.S. Public*, pg. 76
Gibson, Grant S., Dir.-Corp. Commun.--Protocol Systems, Inc., Beaverton, OR; *U.S. Public*, pg. 1336
Gibson, Holly, Mgr.-Pub. Rels.--Franklin Resources, Inc., San Mateo, CA; *U.S. Public*, pg. 679
Gibson, Roberta J., V.P.-Adv. & Pub. Rels.--Hill-Behan Lumber Company, Saint Louis, MO; *U.S. Private*, pg. 529
Gibson, William, Mgr.-Customer Service--Cone-Blanchard Machine Company, Windsor, VT; *U.S. Private*, pg. 262
Gidito, Luisa, Press Relations--Olivetti SpA, Turin, Italy; *Int'l*, pg. 1002
Giguere, Francine, Dir.-Public Affairs--Bell Canada, Montreal, Canada; *Int'l*, pg. 115
Gilbert, John, V.P. & Pub. Rels. Dir.--Bernstein-Rein Advertising, Inc., Kansas City, MO; *U.S. Private*, pg. 137
Gilbert, Nancy, Dir.-Pub. Rels.--Simi Winery, Healdsburg, CA; *Int'l*, pg. 781
Gilbert, Timothy, Mgr.-Mktg. Communications--The Raymond Corporation, Greene, NY; *Int'l*, pg. 123
Gilbertson, Cydney, Mgr.-Mktg. Communications--Chemical Leaman Corporation, Exton, PA; *U.S. Private*, pg. 233
Gilhuly, Kevin, Dir.-Mktg. Communications--Pirelli Armstrong Tire Corporation, New Haven, CT; *Int'l*, pg. 1058
Gill, Robert, V.P.-Vendor Rels.--Border States Industries, Inc., Fargo, ND; *U.S. Private*, pg. 160
Gill, Zoreen B., Coord.-Investors/Pub. Rels.--St. Paul Bancorp, Inc., Chicago, IL; *U.S. Public*, pg. 1428
Gilles, Pierre, Dir. Gen. Adj.-Rels. Exterieures--Telediffusion de France, Paris, France; *Int'l*, pg. 503
Gillespie, Andrew, Mgr.-Communications--IBM United Kingdom Holdings Limited, Portsmouth, United Kingdom; *U.S. Public*, pg. 897
Gillespie, Rick, Dir.-Corp. Comm.--GMAC Mortgage Corporation, Horsham, PA; *U.S. Public*, pg. 720
Gillespie, Robert C., Second V.P.-Adv. & Corp. Communications--The Guardian Life Insurance Company of America, New York, NY; *U.S. Private*, pg. 486
Gillespie, Timothy J., Jr., Asst. V.P.-Govt. & Pub. Affairs--Amtrak-National Railroad Passenger Corp., Washington, DC; *U.S. Private*, pg. 68
Gillette, Heather, Pub. Rels. Acct. Mgr.--Keiler & Company, Farmington, CT; *U.S. Private*, pg. 611
Gillette, Patty, Dir.-Mktg.--Colonial Gas Company, Lowell, MA; *U.S. Public*, pg. 400
Gilligan, Fernanda K., Sr. V.P.-Pub. Rels.--Tiffany & Co., New York, NY; *U.S. Public*, pg. 1608
Gilliland, Harold, Safety Coord.--Plant Maintenance Service Corporation, Memphis, TN; *U.S. Private*, pg. 869
Gillott, Roger Lee, Assoc. Dir.-Pub. Rels.--Occidental Petroleum Corporation, Los Angeles, CA; *U.S. Public*, pg. 1210
Gillum, Gary, Dir.-Communications--Ingersoll-Dresser Pump Company, Liberty Corner, NJ; *U.S. Public*, pg. 529
Gilmore, Daniel E., Dir.-Communications--The Foxboro Company, Foxboro, MA; *Int'l*, pg. 1243
Gilmore, Lynne, Mgr.-Pub. Rels.--Phelps Dodge Magnet Wire Co., Fort Wayne, IN; *U.S. Public*, pg. 1286
Gilpin, Larry, Exec. V.P.-Team, Guest & Community Rels.--Target Stores, Minneapolis, MN; *U.S. Public*, pg. 489
Gilroy, Kathleen, Mgr.-Mktg. Communications--The Forum Corporation, Boston, MA; *U.S. Private*, pg. 420
Gilston, Lillian, Mgr.-Client Rels. & Events--USA Weekend, New York, NY; *U.S. Public*, pg. 701
Giovanni, Bianchini, Dir.-Public Relations--Banca Popolare di Milano, Milan, Italy; *Int'l*, pg. 137
Gipson, Jim L., Jr., V.P.-Corp. Communications--The Williams Companies, Inc., Tulsa, OK; *U.S. Public*, pg. 1769
Girardi, Frank, Dir.-Inv. Rels.--IGI, Inc., Buena, NJ; *U.S. Public*, pg. 855
Githens, Suzanne, Mgr.-Communications--Cyro Industries, Rockaway, NJ; *Int'l*, pg. 1454
Gitter, Blossom, Mktg. Commun. & Res. Coord.--BMW of North America, Inc.-Eastern Region, Ramsey, NJ; *Int'l*, pg. 177
Giuseppetti, Susan, Mgr.-Mktg. Communications--Harris Corp., RF Communications Group Marketing Division, Rochester, NY; *U.S. Public*, pg. 792
Given, Richard, Exec. Dir.-Mktg. & Pub. Rels.--Mann Theatres, Encino, CA; *U.S. Private*, pg. 239
Gjersik, Eva, Mgr.-Pub. Rels.--Hapag-Lloyd AG, Hamburg, Germany; *Int'l*, pg. 596
Gjestvang, Rosie, Mgr.-Adv. & Commun.--MLT Vacations, Inc., Minnetonka, MN; *U.S. Public*, pg. 1200
Glass, Terri, Community Relations Coord.--Meijer, Inc., Grand Rapids, MI; *U.S. Private*, pg. 729
Glazer, Charles T., Mgr.-Corp. Pub. Rels.--Kennametal Inc., Latrobe, PA; *U.S. Public*, pg. 950
Glazer, Dana, Dir.-Pub. Rels.--Guerlain, Inc., New York, NY; *Int'l*, pg. 780
Glazer, Libby, V.P.-Adv., Pub. Rels. & Corp. Commun.--Credit Lyonnais Americas, New York, NY; *Int'l*, pg. 344
Glazer, Vickie, Dir.-Pub. Rels.--Sylvan Learning Systems Inc., Baltimore, MD; *U.S. Public*, pg. 1545
Glenn, Lyn, Dir.-Commun.--Kaibab Industries, Phoenix, AZ; *U.S. Private*, pg. 605
Glenn, T. Michael, Sr. V.P.-Worldwide Mktg., Customer Service & Corp. Communications--FDX Corporation, Memphis, TN; *U.S. Public*, pg. 603
Glover, Gill, Head-Commun.--Cheltenham & Gloucester plc, Gloucester, United Kingdom; *Int'l*, pg. 283
Glovka, Lynn, Mgr.-Commun.--Borg-Warner Security Corporation, Chicago, IL; *U.S. Public*, pg. 245
Glynn, Meghan, Mgr.-Media Rels.--Comair Holdings, Inc., Erlanger, KY; *U.S. Public*, pg. 406
Goad, Cheryl, Mgr.-Communications--Radian International LLC, Austin, TX; *U.S. Public*, pg. 522
Gobby, Thomas, V.P.-Pub. Rels.--LaSalle-Talman Bank, Chicago, IL; *Int'l*, pg. 11
Gobby, Tom, Sr. V.P.-Community Rels.--LaSalle Cragin Bank, Chicago, IL; *Int'l*, pg. 10
Gobes, Hans, Sr. V.P.-Communications--Koninklijke Ahold NV, Zaandam, Netherlands; *Int'l*, pg. 749
Goddard, Alan B., V.P.-Corp. Affairs--Canadian Tire Corporation Limited, Toronto, Canada; *Int'l*, pg. 259
Godfrey, Richard, Dir.-Public Rels.--The Eureka Company, Bloomington, IL; *Int'l*, pg. 440
Godsell, R.M., Dir. Public Affairs & Indus. Rels.--Anglo American Corporation of South Africa Limited, Johannesburg, South Africa; *Int'l*, pg. 76
Godwin, I.D., Grp. Mgr.-Pub. Rels.--Johnson Matthey Public Limited Company, London, United Kingdom; *Int'l*, pg. 713
Goerke, Brian, Mgr.-Pub. Rels.--PNC Bank, Philadelphia, PA; *U.S. Public*, pg. 1243
Goetz, Christine, Mgr.-Pub. Rels.--Intermec Technologies Corporation, Everett, WA; *U.S. Public*, pg. 1699
Goff, C., Mgr.-Pub. Rels.--Kraft Jacobs Suchard, Velizy-Villacoublay, France; *U.S. Public*, pg. 1290
Goggins, Timothy, Devel. Officer--American Mathematical Society, Inc., Providence, RI; *U.S. Private*, pg. 59
Golatka, B.J., Dir.-Customer Services & Admin.--AP North American Aftermarket Division, Goldsboro, NC; *U.S. Private*, pg. 230
Gold, Michael, Sr. V.P.-Corp. Commun. & Adv.--Packard Bell NEC, Sacramento, CA; *U.S. Private*, pg. 833
Goldbach, Courtney, Dir.-Pub. Rels. & Communications--Holoubek Inc., Waukesha, WI; *U.S. Private*, pg. 536
Goldberg, Marshall, Mgr.-Mktg. Prod.--Sigma Designs, Inc., Fremont, CA; *U.S. Public*, pg. 1472
Goldman, Marcia, Dir.-Communications--The Baltimore Sun Newspapers, Baltimore, MD; *U.S. Public*, pg. 1616
Goldschmidt, Gerry, Dir.-Promo. & Pub. Rels.--Markel Corporation, Glen Allen, VA; *U.S. Public*, pg. 1046
Goldstein, Jonathan, Mgr.-Pub. Rels.--Metropolitan Life Insurance Co., New York, NY; *U.S. Private*, pg. 737
Goldstein, Martha H., V.P.-Corp. Communications--The Times Mirror Company, Los Angeles, CA; *U.S. Public*, pg. 1615
Goldstein, Sandra, Corp. & Pub. Rels. Specialist--Louisiana Gas Service Co., Harvey, LA; *U.S. Public*, pg. 380
Goldstein, Steve, V.P.-Public Relations--Heublein, Inc., Hartford, CT; *Int'l*, pg. 410
Goldstein, Wendy, Mgr.-Mktg. Communications--ITT Sheraton Corporation, Boston, MA; *U.S. Public*, pg. 1512
Gollattscheck, Nick, Dir.-Pub. Rels.--Sea World of California, San Diego, CA; *U.S. Public*, pg. 114
Gomez, Sonia, Dir.-Institutional Rels. Mngmt.--Corporacion Grupo Quimico, S.A.C.A., Caracas, Venezuela; *Int'l*, pg. 331
Gomez, Tracy, Mgr.-Pub. Rels.--Comtech Systems, Inc., Saint Cloud, FL; *U.S. Public*, pg. 425
Gomi, Haruo, Mgr.-Pub. Rels.--Yamaha Corporation, Hamamatsu, Japan; *Int'l*, pg. 1515
Gondolf, Warren, Dir.-Communications--SKF USA Inc., King of Prussia, PA; *Int'l*, pg. 1157
Gonos, G., Dir.-Mktg.--Leader Instruments Corporation, Hauppauge, NY; *U.S. Private*, pg. 655
Gonring, Matthew P., V.P.-Corp. Communications--USG Corporation, Chicago, IL; *U.S. Public*, pg. 1660
Gonsalles, M.B., Mgr.-Corp. Affairs--JCI Limited, Johannesburg, South Africa; *Int'l*, pg. 696
Gonzales, Jay, Mgr.-Pub. Affairs--Tucson Electric Power Company, Tucson, AZ; *U.S. Public*, pg. 1670
Gonzalez, Elysa, Dir.-Corp. Commun.--Geotek Communications, Montvale, NJ; *U.S. Public*, pg. 739
Gonzalez, H.W., Mgr.-Commun.--Celotex Corporation, Tampa, FL; *U.S. Private*, pg. 221
Gonzalez, Laura Padilla, Mgr.-Pub. Rels.--Banca Serfin, S.N.C., Mexico, Mexico; *Int'l*, pg. 137
Gonzalez, Richard J., Chief Fin. Officer, V.P., Treas. & Sec.--Bayou Steel Corporation, La Place, LA; *U.S. Public*, pg. 197
Gonzalez, Rita, Dir.-Mktg.--Lennar Homes Inc., Miami, FL; *U.S. Public*, pg. 988
Gonzalez, Steve, Mgr.-Corp. Communications--Houston Industries Incorporated, Houston, TX; *U.S. Public*, pg. 842
Good, James L., V.P.-Corp. Commun. & Mktg.--California Water Service Co., San Jose, CA; *U.S. Public*, pg. 294
Goodell, Stephanie, Supvr.-Media Rels.--Marine World Africa USA, Vallejo, CA; *U.S. Private*, pg. 703
Goodman, Milda C., Dir.-Adv. & Pub. Rels.--Pacific Life Insurance Company, Newport Beach, CA; *U.S. Private*, pg. 831
Goodwin, Alyssa G., Mgr.-Pub. Rels.--The Greenbrier, White Sulphur Springs, WV; *U.S. Public*, pg. 284
Goransson, Grace, Mgr.-Corp. Communications--Scotts Holdings Limited, Singapore, Singapore; *Int'l*, pg. 1212
Gordon, Edward A., Mgr.-Corp. Communications--Orix Corporation, Tokyo, Japan; *Int'l*, pg. 1008
Gordon, John, V.P.-Human Resources & Corp. Affairs--Methanex Corporation, Vancouver, Canada; *Int'l*, pg. 862
Gordon, Lainie, Dir.-Pub. Rels.--Houston Chronicle, Houston, TX; *U.S. Private*, pg. 517
Gordon, Larry, Mgr.-Pub. Rels.--Information Builders, New York, NY; *U.S. Private*, pg. 561
Gordon, Robert, V.P.-Pub. Rels.--Computer Associates International, Inc., Islandia, NY; *U.S. Public*, pg. 420
Gordon, Sam, Dir.-Prod. Devel.--A-Dec, Inc., Newberg, OR; *U.S. Private*, pg. 2
Gorham, Christine, Dir.-Press & Publicity/MTV Europe--MTV Networks, New York, NY; *U.S. Private*, pg. 779
Gorius, Leola R., V.P.-Bus. Affairs, CBS Productions--CBS Entertainment, Los Angeles, CA; *U.S. Public*, pg. 274
Gorlich, Jochen, Mgr.-Corp. Comm.--Schwing Gmbh, Herne, Germany; *Int'l*, pg. 1211
Gornowicz, Suzanne, Pub. Rels. Specialist--Valassis Communications, Inc., Livonia, MI; *U.S. Public*, pg. 1704
Gosselio, Carolyn, First V.P.-Pub. Rels.--SunTrust, Orlando, FL; *U.S. Public*, pg. 1537
Gosset, Gerard, V.P.-H.R. & Commun.--Ciments Francais, Paris, France; *Int'l*, pg. 292
Gotlieb, Lawrence B., Dir.-Govt. & Pub. Rels.--Kaufman and Broad Home Corporation, Los Angeles, CA; *U.S. Public*, pg. 944
Gotlin, Amy, Mgr.-Pub. Rels. & Promo.--800-FLOWERS, Inc., Westbury, NY; *U.S. Private*, pg. 366
Gott, Leigh, Dir.-Mktg.--Wisconsin Machine and Tool Corporation, Milwaukee, WI; *U.S. Private*, pg. 1185
Gouin, Suzanne, Gen. Mgr.-News & Pub. Affairs--CFCF 12, Montreal, Canada; *Int'l*, pg. 241
Gould, Barbara A., Dir.-Investor Rels. & Pub. Affairs--M.A. Hanna Company, Cleveland, OH; *U.S. Public*, pg. 780
Gould, Brenda, Dir.-Corp. Commun.--Olympic Steel Inc., Cleveland, OH; *U.S. Public*, pg. 1221
Gould, Gerard J., Dir.-Investor Rels. & Communications--The Stanley Works, New Britain, CT; *U.S. Public*, pg. 1508
Gould, John T., Dir.-Corp. Affairs--Unilever United States Inc., New York, NY; *Int'l*, pg. 1435
Gould, Mark, Dir.-Pub. Rels.--Paterno Imports Limited, Lake Bluff, IL; *U.S. Private*, pg. 843
Gould, Patrick, Mgr-Corp. Commun.--Kemper Insurance Companies, Long Grove, IL; *U.S. Private*, pg. 614

Gouldthorpe, Hugh F., Jr., V.P.-Quality & Communications--Owens & Minor Inc., Glen Allen, VA; *U.S. Public,* pg. 1236

Gove, Peter, V.P.-Corp. Rels.--St. Jude Medical, Inc., Saint Paul, MN; *U.S. Public,* pg. 1427

Goyette, Paul, Dir.-Corp. Commun.--Newbridge Networks Corporation, Kanata, Canada; *Int'l,* pg. 923

Goyette, Susan, Dir.-Corp. Mktg.--The Mills Corporation, Arlington, VA; *U.S. Public,* pg. 1113

Graf, Hans-Jurgen, Dir.-Pub. Rels.--Boehringer Mannheim GmbH, Mannheim, Germany; *Int'l,* pg. 331

Graham-Peterson, Lisa, Dir.-Corp. Commun.--MSI Insurance Companies, Arden Hills, MN; *U.S. Private,* pg. 688

Graham, Jennifer L., Corp. V.P.-Commun.--Allegiance Healthcare Corp., McGaw Park, IL; *U.S. Public,* pg. 44

Graham, Jim, Dir.-Pub. Rels.--Lockheed Martin Missiles & Space, Sunnyvale, CA; *U.S. Public,* pg. 1008

Graham, John, V.P.-Corp. Affairs--BTG, Inc., Fairfax, VA; *U.S. Public,* pg. 164

Granden, Christian, Dir.-Commun.--3M France, Cergy-Pontoise, France; *U.S. Public,* pg. 1606

Granum, James L., V.P.-Pub. Affairs--Norfolk Southern Corporation, Norfolk, VA; *U.S. Public,* pg. 1190

Grasser, Stephanie, Mgr.-Pub. Rels.--RTL Radio-Die Grossten Oldies, Luxembourg, Luxembourg; *Int'l,* pg. 561

Grattoni, Rodolfo, Dir.-Communications--AGCO Argentina S.A., Haedo, Argentina; *Int'l,* pg. 30

Grauel, N. Stuart, V.P.-Pub. Affairs--Ipalco Enterprises, Inc., Indianapolis, IN; *U.S. Public,* pg. 912

Gravely, George, V.P.-Corp. Communications--Greyhound Lines, Inc., Dallas, TX; *U.S. Public,* pg. 765

Graves, Eric, V.P.-Corp. Communications--Browning-Ferris Industries, Inc., Houston, TX; *U.S. Public,* pg. 262

Graves, Jim, Dir.-Corp. Communications--Burdick, Inc., Milton, WI; *U.S. Private,* pg. 181

Gravley, George, V.P.-Corp. Communications--Greyhound Lines, Inc., Dallas, TX; *U.S. Public,* pg. 765

Gray, Jim, Dir.-Mktg. Svcs.--Aearo Company, Boston, MA; *U.S. Private,* pg. 23

Gray, John, Sr. V.P.-Corp. Communications--R.T.M. Winners, Atlanta, GA; *U.S. Private,* pg. 906

Gray, Roland, V.P.-Mktg.--Blue Bird Corporation, Macon, GA; *U.S. Private,* pg. 151

Green, Anita, V.P.-Pub. Rels.--Citibank, Federal Savings Bank (Illinois), Chicago, IL; *U.S. Public,* pg. 378

Green, Barry A., Mgr.-Pub. Rels.--Glynwed International PLC, Birmingham, United Kingdom; *Int'l,* pg. 554

Green, Carolyn, Dir.-Govt. & Pub. Affairs--Ultramar Diamond Shamrock Corporation, San Antonio, TX; *U.S. Public,* pg. 1663

Green, Cindy, Mgr.-Customer Svc.--Mill-Rose Company, Mentor, OH; *U.S. Private,* pg. 746

Green, D.P., Dir.-Communications--Thrall Car Mfg. Co., Chicago Heights, IL; *U.S. Private,* pg. 344

Green, David C., Dir.-Corp. Communications--PPG Industries, Inc., Pittsburgh, PA; *U.S. Public,* pg. 1245

Green, Jan, Mgr.-Pub. Rels.--Union Trust Bank, Union City, IN; *U.S. Public,* pg. 633

Green, Mary, V.P.-Corp. Commun.--The Reader's Digest Association, Inc., Pleasantville, NY; *U.S. Public,* pg. 1367

Green, Mary Ann, V.P.-Pub. Rels.--MBL Life Assurance Corporation, Newark, NJ; *U.S. Private,* pg. 685

Green, Mary Jo, V.P.-Pub. Rels.--Warner Cable Communications, Inc., Columbus, OH; *U.S. Public,* pg. 1611

Green, Nancy H., Sr. V.P.-Corp. Rels.--The Equitable Companies Incorporated, New York, NY; *U.S. Public,* pg. 588

Green, Pam, Dir.-Artist Rels.--Westwood One, Inc., New York, NY; *U.S. Public,* pg. 1763

Greenberg, Mark, Exec. V.P.-Mktg. & Communications--Showtime Networks Inc., New York, NY; *U.S. Private,* pg. 779

Greenberg, Mark E., V.P.-Pub. Rels. & External Communications--AlliedSignal Inc., Morristown, NJ; *U.S. Public,* pg. 49

Greenberg, Robert, V.P. & Gen. Mgr.-Communications--Panasonic Consumer Electric Co., Secaucus, NJ; *Int'l,* pg. 847

Greenberg, Steve, V.P.-New Ball Devel. & Commun.--Pittsburgh Associates, Pittsburgh, PA; *U.S. Private,* pg. 867

Greenberg, Susan, Sr. V.P.-H.R.--New York Life Insurance Company, New York, NY; *U.S. Private,* pg. 794

Greene, Gilbert K., Mgr.-Mktg. Svcs.--Victaulic Company of America, Easton, PA; *U.S. Private,* pg. 1138

Greene, Wendy, Mgr.-Pub. Rels.--Hughes Communications, Inc., Long Beach, CA; *U.S. Public,* pg. 721

Greenman, Jill, Dir.-Pub. Rels.--Philips Consumer Electronics, Knoxville, TN; *Int'l,* pg. 1054

Greenstein, Davina, Publ. Rels. Specialist--Dataproducts Corporation, Simi Valley, CA; *Int'l,* pg. 620

Greer, Jana Waring, Pres.-SunAmerica Mktg. Inc. & Sr. V.P. SunAmerica, Inc. Affairs--SunAmerica Inc., Los Angeles, CA; *U.S. Public,* pg. 1532

Greer, John, Dir.-Adv. & Pub. Rels.--Arkansas Best Corporation, Fort Smith, AR; *U.S. Public,* pg. 130

Greer, Lou, V.P.-Partners Mktg.--Network Computing Devices, Inc., Mountain View, CA; *U.S. Public,* pg. 1168

Greer, Michael D., V.P.-Human Resources & Corp. Rels.--CNG Transmission Corporation, Clarksburg, WV; *U.S. Public,* pg. 435

Gregg, Lou, V.P.-Comm.--Hughes Electronics Corporation, Westchester, CA; *U.S. Public,* pg. 720

Gregory, Anne, Dir.-Pub. Rels.--Staff Builders Inc., Lake Success, NY; *U.S. Public,* pg. 1501

Gregory, Donna, Asst. Mgr.-Corp. Commun.--E'Town Corporation, Westfield, NJ; *U.S. Public,* pg. 540

Greisman, Harvey W., V.P.-Pub. Affairs & Communications--GTE Corporation, Stamford, CT; *U.S. Public,* pg. 696

Gremaud, Laurent, Chief Information Officer & Sr. V.P.-Mktg.--UMS Swiss Metalworks Holding Ltd, Dornach, Switzerland; *Int'l,* pg. 1427

Gressak, Cathy, Exec. Dir.-Communications--Countrywide Funding Corporation, Pasadena, CA; *U.S. Public,* pg. 453

Grey, Ruthann E., V.P.-Commun. & Pub. Affairs--Hoechst Marion Roussel, Inc., Bridgewater, NJ; *Int'l,* pg. 624

Griffey, J.I., Mgr.-Human Resources--HPM Corporation, Mount Gilead, OH; *U.S. Private,* pg. 492

Griffin, Gale L., V.P.-Corp. Communications--Bestfoods, Englewood Cliffs, NJ; *U.S. Public,* pg. 223

Griffin, Therese, Mgr.-Corp. Communications--South Carolina Electric & Gas Co. (SCE&G), Columbia, SC; *U.S. Public,* pg. 1436

Griffith, Greg, Dir.-Pub. Affairs & Admin.--Great Lakes Chemical Corporation, West Lafayette, IN; *U.S. Public,* pg. 760

Griffith, James M., Sr. V.P.-Investor Rels. & Corp. Communication--Beverly Enterprises, Inc., Fort Smith, AR; *U.S. Public,* pg. 227

Griffith, Mary H., Sr. V.P.-Mktg. Commun.--National City Corporation, Cleveland, OH; *U.S. Public,* pg. 1154

Grimm, Dan, Dir.-Mktg. & Communications--Becton Dickinson & Company, Franklin Lakes, NJ; *U.S. Public,* pg. 199

Grimm, Kathy, Dir.-Corp. Rels.--Tasty Baking Company, Philadelphia, PA; *U.S. Public,* pg. 1561

Grimmaldi, C.D., Dir.-Corp. Affairs--Rentokil Initial plc, East Grinstead, United Kingdom; *Int'l,* pg. 1285

Grimshaw, Kimberly, Coord.-Special Proj.--Chicago Reader, Inc., Chicago, IL; *U.S. Private,* pg. 235

Griner, Lyn, Pres.-Mktg. & Co. Communications--JC Penney Company, Inc., Plano, TX; *U.S. Public,* pg. 916

Grinnell, Jane, Mgr.-Mktg. Communications--Magna International Inc., Markham, Canada; *Int'l,* pg. 829

Grinnell, Suzanne, Mktg. Specialist--Frank Consolidated Enterprises Inc., Des Plaines, IL; *U.S. Private,* pg. 423

Griscom, Thomas C., Exec. V.P.-External Rels.--R.J. Reynolds Tobacco Company, Winston Salem, NC; *U.S. Public,* pg. 1355

Grizzaffi, Betty M., Coord.- Communications--Philip Morris Companies Inc., New York, NY; *U.S. Public,* pg. 1287

Grobet, Arnaud, Acting Dir.-Adv. & Pub. Rels.--Banque Edouard Constant, Geneva, Switzerland; *U.S. Public,* pg. 1197

Grobman, Richard, V.P. & Buyer-Non-Foods--Dan's Supreme Super Markets Inc., Hempstead, NY; *U.S. Private,* pg. 310

Groce, Barbara, Mgr.-Public Affairs--Fisher Broadcasting Inc., Seattle, WA; *U.S. Public,* pg. 648

Groh, K.L., Mgr.-Corp. & Mktg. Communications--The Timken Company, Canton, OH; *U.S. Public,* pg. 1617

Grohoski, Cheryl, Mgr.-Mktg. Communications--GM Powertrain Group, Pontiac, MI; *U.S. Public,* pg. 719

Groner, Joan, Mgr.-Communications--General Binding Corporation, Northbrook, IL; *U.S. Public,* pg. 707

Groom, Karen, Dir.-Pub. Rels. & Hospitality Mktg.--Gaylord Entertainment/Opryland USA, Nashville, TN; *U.S. Public, pg. 704*

Groome, John, Mgr.-Pub. Rels.--Northern Foods plc, Hull, United Kingdom; *Int'l,* pg. 967

Grosges, Jean, Mgr.-Pub. Rels.--Credit Europeen, Luxembourg, Luxembourg; *Int'l,* pg. 148

Grosse-Leege, Detmar, Dir.-Corp. Communications--Daimler-Benz Aerospace AG, Munich, Germany; *Int'l,* pg. 367

Grosse-Leege, Dirk, Dir.-Pub. Rels.--Heidelberger Druckmaschinen A.G., Heidelberg, Germany; *Int'l,* pg. 604

Grossman, Jerry, Gen. Mgr.-Communications-Nikon Inc.--Nikon Inc., Melville, NY; *Int'l,* pg. 931

Grossman, Marv, Mgr.-Communications--Allen Telecom Inc., Solon, OH; *U.S. Public,* pg. 45

Groves, Steve, Mgr.-Communications Grp.--Andersen Corporation, Bayport, MN; *U.S. Private,* pg. 71

Gruehl, Douglas, Dir.-Mktg. Communications--Amdahl Corporation, Sunnyvale, CA; *Int'l,* pg. 527

Gruman, Rick, Dir.-Pub. Rels. & Mgr.-Govt. Rels.--Southern Union Company, Austin, TX; *U.S. Public,* pg. 1491

Grunberg, Linda, Dir.-Pub. Rels.--Data Transmission Network Corporation, Omaha, NE; *U.S. Public,* pg. 486

Grunkin, Sharon, Mgr.-Public Relations--Omaha Steaks, Omaha, NE; *U.S. Private,* pg. 815

Guadalupe, Daisy, V.P.-Corp. Communications--Andrea Electronics Corporation, Long Island City, NY; *U.S. Public,* pg. 112

Guay, Richard F., V.P.-Intergovernmental Rels.--Jacobs Engineering Group Inc., Arlington, VA; *U.S. Public,* pg. 921

Gubernick, Lisa, V.P.-Corp. Communications--Golden Books Family Entertainment Inc., New York, NY; *U.S. Public,* pg. 749

Gudrian, Henry D., Dir.-Communications--Millennium Petrochemicals, Inc., Cincinnati, OH; *Int'l,* pg. 594

Guenther, Nancy, Dir.-Adv. & Pub. Rels.--ITT Fluid Handling, Morton Grove, IL; *U.S. Public,* pg. 860

Gueriat, Jean-Louis, Mgr.-Corp. Commun.--Groupe GTM, Nanterre, France; *Int'l,* pg. 823

Guertin, Joseph A., Dir.-Mktg. Commun.--TRW Inc., Cleveland, OH; *U.S. Public,* pg. 1558

Guida, Rosy, Dir.-Communications--Lotto S.p.A., Montebelluna, Italy; *Int'l,* pg. 819

Guilbault, Jodi, Mgr.-Pub. Rels.--Philips Semiconductors, Sunnyvale, CA; *Int'l,* pg. 1054

Guillet, Benoit, Dir.-Adv. & Pub. Rels.--Riber, Rueil-Malmaison, France; *Int'l,* pg. 1114

Guillot-Pelpel, Veronique, Dir.-Commun.--Compagnie Financiere de Paribas, Paris, France; *Int'l,* pg. 319

Guimard, Anne, Mgr.-Investor Rels.--Alcatel Alsthom Compagnie Generale D'Electricite, Paris, France; *Int'l,* pg. 52

Guin, James M., V.P.-H.R. & Pub. Rels.--Burlington Industries, Inc., Greensboro, NC; *U.S. Public,* pg. 268

Guis, A., Mgr.-Pub. Rels.--Van Leeuwen Pipe and Tube Group B.V., Zwijndrecht, Netherlands; *Int'l,* pg. 1449

Gulien, Richard, Dir.-Mktg. Corp. Communications--Sextant Avionique, Meudon, France; *Int'l,* pg. 29

Gullberg, Odd S., Dir.-Pub. Affairs--Norsk Hydro a.s, Oslo, Norway; *Int'l,* pg. 959

Gunnarsson, Helene, Mgr.-Investor Rels.--Sandvik AB, Sandviken, Sweden; *Int'l,* pg. 1185

Gura, Jerry, Dir.-Pub. Affairs--Amsted Industries Incorporated, Chicago, IL; *U.S. Private,* pg. 68

Gurda, Richard J., Sr. V.P.-Corp. Communications--Telxon Corporation, Akron, OH; *U.S. Public,* pg. 1573

Gurovsky, Tony, Dir.-Customer Devel.--Showboat, Incorporated, Las Vegas, NV; *U.S. Public,* pg. 1469

Gus, Helene, Dir.-Pub. Rels.--Russ Berrie and Company, Inc., Oakland, NJ; *U.S. Public,* pg. 222

Gustafson, Ingemar, Dir.-Pub. Rels.--Strabruken AB, Sollentuna, Sweden; *Int'l,* pg. 899

Gustafson, Judy, Dir.-Corp. Commun.--Montgomery Ward & Co., Inc., Chicago, IL; *U.S. Private,* pg. 758

Gustafsson, Lars, Mgr.-Pub. Rels.--Atlet AB, Molnlycke, Sweden; *Int'l,* pg. 97

Gustin, L. Carl, Sr. V.P.-Corp. Rels.--Boston Edison Company, Boston, MA; *U.S. Public,* pg. 247

Guterl, Stephanie, Mgr.-Pub. Rels.--Gitano Fashions Ltd., Bowling Green, KY; *U.S. Public,* pg. 686

Guthrie, Paul S., V.P.-Corp. Communications--The Reynolds and Reynolds Company, Dayton, OH; *U.S. Public,* pg. 1384

Gutkencht, Peter, Gen. Mgr.-Corp. Communications--The Swissair Group, Zurich, Switzerland; *Int'l,* pg. 1333

Gutshall, Audrey, Mgr.-Promotions & Desktop Publishing--The Homestead L.C., Hot Springs, VA; *U.S. Private,* pg. 247

Gutterman, Alison, V.P.-Mktg.--Jelmar Company, Lincolnwood, IL; *U.S. Private,* pg. 585

Gvwinner, Pierre, Dir.-Mktg. & Pub. Rels.--Brauerei Eichhof, Lucerne, Switzerland; *Int'l,* pg. 213

Gwyn, Tom, V.P.-Pub. Affairs--Blue Shield of California, San Francisco, CA; *U.S. Private,* pg. 153

Gymburch, David, Mgr.-Pub. Rels.--Oneida Ltd., Oneida, NY; *U.S. Public,* pg. 1225

Haag, Carolyn, Coord.-Adv. & Promos.--Heath Consultants Incorporated, Houston, TX; *U.S. Private,* pg. 518

Haag, J.A., Pub. Rels. Coord.--Highway Equipment Company, Cedar Rapids, IA; *U.S. Private,* pg. 529

Haapalinna, Helena, Mgr.-Communications--Neste Oy, Espoo, Finland; *Int'l,* pg. 912

Haas, Thomas, Mgr.-Mktg. Communications--Siemens Corporation, New York, NY; *Int'l,* pg. 1245

Hackett, L., Mgr.-Publicity & Promotions--British Steel Tubes & Pipes, Corby, United Kingdom; *Int'l,* pg. 221

Hackney, David, Mgr.-Pub. Rels.--PECO Energy Company, Philadelphia, PA; *U.S. Public,* pg. 1268

Hadden, Laura, Mgr.-Pub. Rels.--Rohm and Haas Company, Philadelphia, PA; *U.S. Public,* pg. 1403

Hadders, J.H.J. Zegering, Gen. Mgr.-Corp. Commun.--ING Groep N.V., Amsterdam, Netherlands; *Int'l,* pg. 647

Hadley, Debra, Dir.-Investor Rels.--Cardinal Health Inc., Dublin, OH; *U.S. Public,* pg. 304

Hadley, Jacqueline H., Dir.-Govt. & Pub. Rels.--The Union Central Life Insurance Co., Cincinnati, OH; *U.S. Private,* pg. 1118

Hagan, Kenneth, Dir.-Corp. Commun.--Cowen & Company, New York, NY; *U.S. Private,* pg. 280

Hagan, Thomas M., Sr. V.P.-External Affairs--Central and South West Corporation, Dallas, TX; *U.S. Public,* pg. 324

Hagberg, Nancy, Mgr.-Communications--EMPI, Inc., Saint Paul, MN; *U.S. Public,* pg. 545

Hage, Phil, Mgr.-Communications--Occupational Health & Environmental Safety Division, Saint Paul, MN; *U.S. Public,* pg. 1605

Hager, Kathy E., V.P.-Pub. Affairs--Santa Fe Energy Resources, Inc., Houston, TX; *U.S. Public,* pg. 1431

Hager, Peggy, Mgr.-Commun.--Wicks 'n Sticks, Ltd, Houston, TX; *U.S. Private,* pg. 1175

Hagi, Kurt, Exec. V.P. & Sec.--Sulzer Ltd., Winterthur, Switzerland; *Int'l,* pg. 1305

Hagley, Thomas R., Dir.-Pub. Affairs--Alumax Inc., Atlanta, GA; *U.S. Public,* pg. 59

Haglind, Juergen, Dir.-Communications--Tetra Laval Group, Lund, Sweden; *Int'l,* pg. 1377

Hahn, Alan C., Sr. V.P.-Deal Direct Mktg.--Jackson National Life Insurance Company, Lansing, MI; *Int'l,* pg. 1073

Hahn, David, Mgr.-Mktg. Communications--Davol Inc., Cranston, RI; *U.S. Public,* pg. 189

Haines, Lee, Mgr.-Pub. Rels. & Advertising--AAR Corp., Wood Dale, IL; *U.S. Public,* pg. 1

Haji Idrus, Puan Zaiton, Sr. Mgr.-Communications--Standard Chartered Bank Malaysia Berhad, Kuala Lumpur, Malaysia; *Int'l,* pg. 1295

Hale, Charlie, Mgr.-Pub. Rels.--Mycogen Seeds, Saint Paul, MN; *U.S. Public,* pg. 1142

Hale, Joseph, Gen. Mgr.-Corp. Communications & Investor Rels.--Cinergy Corp., Cincinnati, OH; *U.S. Public,* pg. 369

Hale, Lynne, Dir.-Commum.--Lucasfilm Ltd., San Rafael, CA; *U.S. Private,* pg. 679

Halferd, Tim, Dir.-Corp. Affairs--Standard Chartered Bank PLC, London, United Kingdom; *Int'l,* pg. 1294

Hall, Alan, V.P.-Corp. Communications--Gaylord Entertainment/Opryland USA, Nashville, TN; *U.S. Public, pg. 704*

Hall, Lawrie Platt, Mgr.-Pub. Rels.--Tupperware U.S., Inc., Orlando, FL; *U.S. Public,* pg. 1644

Hall, Melanie, Dir.-Commun.--Heavy Machines, Inc., Memphis, TN; *U.S. Private,* pg. 518

Hall, William C. Jr., Asst. V.P.-Corp. Communications--Dominion Resources, Inc., Richmond, VA; *U.S. Public,* pg. 516

Hallam, Barry, Mgr.-Mktg. Communications--SNE Enterprises, Inc., Mosinee, WI; *U.S. Public,* pg. 1193

Hallberg, Lennart, Sr. V.P.-Grp. Pub. Rels.--Skanska AB, Danderyd, Sweden; *Int'l,* pg. 1260

Halldin, Annika, V.P.-Grp. Commun.--Skandinaviska Enskilda Banken, Stockholm, Sweden; *Int'l,* pg. 1258

Hallett, RichardP., V.P. & Dir.-Pub. Rels.--Ohio Gas Company, Bryan, OH; *U.S. Private,* pg. 812

Halliburton, Roberta, Mgr.-Mktg. Communications--Astec America Inc., Carlsbad, CA; *Int'l*, pg. 93
Hallwyler, Laurie, Dir.-Corp. Communications--Acuson Corporation, Mountain View, CA; *U.S. Public*, pg. 18
Hamblin, Connie, Sec. & Dir.-Corp. Commun.--Gentex Corporation, Zeeland, MI; *U.S. Public*, pg. 731
Hambrick, Harold, V.P.-Corp. Pub. Rels. Commun.--UHP Healthcare, Inglewood, CA; *U.S. Private*, pg. 1113
Hamburg, Ruth, Mgr.-Corp. Communications--Distribution America, Des Plaines, IL; *U.S. Private*, pg. 335
Hamilton, Dean C., Mgr.-Mktg. Communications--ATMI, Inc., Danbury, CT; *U.S. Public*, pg. 12
Hamilton, Fred, Dir.-Mktg. & Communications--The Franklin Institute, Philadelphia, PA; *U.S. Private*, pg. 424
Hamilton, Ian, V.P.-Pub. Rels.--Borden Foods Canada, Etobicoke, Canada; *U.S. Private*, pg. 159
Hamilton, James L., III, Gen. Mgr.-Pub. Affairs--USX Corporation, Pittsburgh, PA; *U.S. Public*, pg. 1661
Hamilton, Rae, Dir.-Commun.--National Electrical Manufacturers Association, Arlington, VA; *U.S. Private*, pg. 782
Hamilton, W.W., V.P.-Customer Service Residential & Small Business--Florida Power & Light Company, North Palm Beach, FL; *U.S. Public*, pg. 608
Hamlin, Hatti, Sr. V.P. & Gen. Mgr.-Pub. Rels.--EvansGroup, San Francisco, CA; *U.S. Private*, pg. 385
Hamm, William R., V.P.-Admin.--Day & Zimmermann, Inc., Philadelphia, PA; *U.S. Private*, pg. 316
Hammond, Jennifer, Mgr.-Community Rels.--CVS Corp., Woonsocket, RI; *U.S. Public*, pg. 287
Hammons, Lora Cassano, Coord.-Pub. Rels. Mktg.--Cassano's Inc., Dayton, OH; *U.S. Private*, pg. 218
Hampton, Wade, V.P.-Mktg.--Koger Equity Inc., Jacksonville, FL; *U.S. Public*, pg. 965
Hand, Leanne, Pub. Rels. Dir.--WestWayne, Inc., Atlanta, GA; *U.S. Private*, pg. 1170
Handley, Lynn, Mgr.-Mktg. & Communications--GTE Supply, Irving, TX; *U.S. Public*, pg. 697
Haney, William V., Exec. V.P.-Corp. & Public Affairs--The MacManus Group, Inc., New York, NY; *U.S. Private*, pg. 692
Hanford, Denton R., V.P.-Information & Communication--Boeing Defense & Space Group, Kent, WA; *U.S. Public*, pg. 240
Hankin, Adrienne, Dir.-Pub. Rels.--Mindscape, Inc., Novato, CA; *Int'l*, pg. 1026
Hanlon, Pamela, Exec. Dir.-Pub. Affairs--American Express Bank Ltd., New York, NY; *U.S. Public*, pg. 73
Hannagan, John, Mgr.-Corp. Affairs--Alcoa of Australia Limited, Melbourne, Australia; *U.S. Public*, pg. 62
Hannity, Vincent, V.P.-Corp. Commun. & Investor Rels.--Boise Cascade Corporation, Boise, ID; *U.S. Public*, pg. 242
Hanock, Lisa, Mgr.-Commun.--Dakotah, Inc., Webster, SD; *U.S. Public*, pg. 477
Hansen, Barbara, Customer Service Rep.--Concord Camera Corporation, Avenel, NJ; *U.S. Public*, pg. 429
Hansen, Joan, Mgr.-Communications--Interstate Electronics Corp., Anaheim, CA; *U.S. Public*, pg. 622
Hansen, Meryll, Mgr.-Corp. Communications & Pub. Rels.--Vishay Intertechnology, Inc., Malvern, PA; *U.S. Public*, pg. 1721
Hansen, Wayne, Dir.-Communications--Quebecor Printing (USA) Corp., Boston, MA; *Int'l*, pg. 1076
Hanson, Barbara, Dir.-Mktg.--Thomas Publishing Company, New York, NY; *U.S. Private*, pg. 1082
Hanson, Burtchell, Mgr.-Customer Rels.--Goodyear Jamaica Limited, Kingston, Jamaica; *U.S. Public*, pg. 753
Hanson, Charles G., III, Chm. Bd. & Chief Exec. Officer--American Pad and Paper Company, Dallas, TX; *U.S. Public*, pg. 88
Hanson, Matthew, Supvr.-Pub. Rels.--TruServ Corporation, Chicago, IL; *U.S. Private*, pg. 1108
Hanson, Maureen, Mgr.-Mktg. & Communications--GN Nettest Fiber Optic Division, Utica, NY; *Int'l*, pg. 536
Harakal, Joe, Mgr.-Mktg. & Commun.--Digital Link Corporation, Sunnyvale, CA; *U.S. Public*, pg. 508
Harbord, Clara, Mgr.-Pub. Affairs--Eagle Star, Cheltenham, United Kingdom; *Int'l*, pg. 110
Harbula, Gene, V.P.-Govt. Mktg. & Corp. Communications--Sabreliner Corporation, Saint Louis, MO; *U.S. Private*, pg. 959
Harcourt, Patricia A., Dir.-Corp. Commun.--Belden & Blake Corporation, Canton, OH; *U.S. Private*, pg. 1078
Hardage, Ginger, V.P.-Pub. Rels. & Corp. Communications--Southwest Airlines Co., Dallas, TX; *U.S. Public*, pg. 1493
Harding, Bryan L., Dir.-Mktg. Commun.--Entergy Corporation, New Orleans, LA; *U.S. Public*, pg. 585
Harding, Bryan L., Dir.-Mktg. Communications--Entergy Louisiana, Inc., New Orleans, LA; *U.S. Public*, pg. 586
Harding, Bryan L., Dir.-Mktg. Communications--Entergy New Orleans, Inc., New Orleans, LA; *U.S. Public*, pg. 586
Hardman, Chris, Mgr.-Pub. Pels.--J.D. Edwards & Company, Denver, CO; *U.S. Private*, pg. 365
Hardwick, Phil, V.P.-Pub. & Govt. Rels.--Mississippi Valley Gas Co., Jackson, MS; *U.S. Private*, pg. 753
Hardwick, Ron, V.P.-H.R.--Miniature Precision Components, Walworth, WI; *U.S. Private*, pg. 750
Hardy, Beth, Pub. Rels. Dir.--Paradigm Communications, Tampa, FL; *U.S. Private*, pg. 838
Hargraves, Richard N., Dir.-Corp. Communications--Laclede Gas Company, Saint Louis, MO; *U.S. Public*, pg. 973
Harley, Louise, Mgr.-Press & Pub. Rels.--Scottish & Newcastle plc, Edinburgh, United Kingdom; *Int'l*, pg. 1211
Harlin, Marlene, Mgr.-Corp. Communications--Comark Communications, Inc., Chalfont, PA; *Int'l*, pg. 1383
Harmon, Greg, Dir.-Pub. Rels.--McKinney & McKinney Advertising, Redondo Beach, CA; *U.S. Private*, pg. 723
Harmon, Pam, Mgr.-Communications--Moto Photo, Inc., Dayton, OH; *U.S. Public*, pg. 1136
Harner, James F., Sr. V.P.-Customer Service & Opers.--The May Department Stores Company, Saint Louis, MO; *U.S. Public*, pg. 1063
Harp Jirschele, Mary, V.P.-Commun.--Aid Association for Lutherans, Appleton, WI; *U.S. Private*, pg. 27
Harper, Jack, Investor Rels.--Tom Brown, Inc., Midland, TX; *U.S. Public*, pg. 262
Harrah, David, Dir.-Pub. Rels.--VLSI Technology, Inc., San Jose, CA; *U.S. Public*, pg. 1703
Harrell, Eileen, V.P.-Corp. Communications--Six Flags Theme Parks Inc., Parsippany, NJ; *U.S. Public*, pg. 1611
Harrington, Peter N., V.P.-Corp. Communications--The New England, Boston, MA; *U.S. Private*, pg. 737
Harrington, Peter N., Dir.-Public Rels.--The New England, Boston, MA; *U.S. Private*, pg. 737
Harris, Carl, Dir.-Pub. Affairs & Adv.--Bell Helicopter Textron, Hurst, TX; *U.S. Public*, pg. 1588
Harris, Hank J., V.P.-Service--Brunswick Indoor Recreation Group, Lake Forest, IL; *U.S. Public*, pg. 265
Harris, Jennifer S., Mgr.-Mktg.--Scott & Stringfellow Financial, Inc., Richmond, VA; *U.S. Public*, pg. 1445
Harris, Marie, Dir.-Investor Rels. & Pub. Rels.--Kronos Incorporated, Waltham, MA; *U.S. Public*, pg. 967
Harris, Martha, Coord.-Corp. Commun.--The Cincinnati Cordage & Paper Company, Cincinnati, OH; *U.S. Private*, pg. 239
Harris, R. Macy, III, V.P., Sec. & Mgr.-Adv.--The Ailing & Cory Company, Rochester, NY; *U.S. Public*, pg. 1666
Harris, Richard J., V.P. & Treas.--Nortek, Inc., Providence, RI; *U.S. Public*, pg. 1192
Harris, Richard W., Dir.-Corp. Communications--Norfolk Southern Corporation, Norfolk, VA; *U.S. Public*, pg. 1190
Harris, Sondra, Mgr.-Corp. Commun.--Fair, Isaac and Company, Inc., San Rafael, CA; *U.S. Public*, pg. 609
Harris, Titus H., Jr., Chm. Bd.--The GNI Group, Inc., Deer Park, TX; *U.S. Public*, pg. 693
Harrison, Dan, V.P.-Corp. Affairs--Whirlpool Corporation, Benton Harbor, MI; *U.S. Public*, pg. 1764
Harrison, George, V.P.-Corp. Mktg. & Corp. Communications--Nintendo of America, Redmond, WA; *Int'l*, pg. 932
Harrison, Lynn, Dir.-Investor Rels.--CML Group, Inc., Acton, MA; *U.S. Public*, pg. 279
Harrison, Ronald E., V.P.-Community Affairs--PepsiCo, Inc., Purchase, NY; *U.S. Public*, pg. 1276
Harrison, Sam D., Sr. V.P.-Creative Svcs.--John H. Harland Company, Decatur, GA; *U.S. Public*, pg. 785
Harrison, Sonia, V.P.-Pub. Rels.--Karakas, VanSickle, Ouellette Advertising & Public Relations, Portland, OR; *U.S. Private*, pg. 607
Harrmann, Terry O., Dir.-Pub. Affairs & Consumer Services--Interstate Power Company, Dubuque, IA; *U.S. Public*, pg. 910
Harrower, Nancy, Dir.-Corp. Commun.--Lawson Software, Minneapolis, MN; *U.S. Private*, pg. 654
Harsanyi, Fruzsina M., V.P.-Pub. Affairs & Corp. Communications--ABB Inc., Norwalk, CT; *Int'l*, pg. 3
Hart, Denis, Dir.-Corp. Communications--Reed Business Information, Sutton, United Kingdom; *Int'l*, pg. 1094
Hart, James, Mgr.-Public Info.--Northrop Grumman Corporation, Los Angeles, CA; *U.S. Public*, pg. 1197
Hart, Paul, Sr. Corp. Commun. Specialist--Tesoro Petroleum Corporation, San Antonio, TX; *U.S. Public*, pg. 1581
Hart, Robert M., Sr. V.P., Gen. Counsel & Sec.--Alleghany Corporation, New York, NY; *U.S. Public*, pg. 42
Hart, Susan, V.P.-Communications--Corrections Corporation of America, Nashville, TN; *U.S. Public*, pg. 450
Hartfield, Marianne, Mgr.-Mkt. Communication--Thermo Separation Products, San Jose, CA; *U.S. Public*, pg. 1594
Hartje, Keith, V.P.-Corp. Communications--MidAmerican Energy Holdings, Des Moines, IA; *U.S. Public*, pg. 1109
Hartl, William P., V.P.-Investor Rels.--Ashland, Inc., Russell, KY; *U.S. Public*, pg. 138
Hartlage, Charles, Mgr.-Corp. Pub. Commun.--Haworth, Inc., Holland, MI; *U.S. Private*, pg. 511
Hartman, Ellen, V.P.-Corp. Commun.--AFC Enterprises, Atlanta, GA; *U.S. Private*, pg. 5
Hartman, Mary, Dir.-Pub. Rels.--Ultramar Diamond Shamrock Corporation, San Antonio, TX; *U.S. Public*, pg. 1663
Hartweg, Chris, Dir.-Pub. Rels.--LaSalle National Bank, Chicago, IL; *Int'l*, pg. 10
Hartz, Karen, Dir.-Mktg. & Communications--Brooktree Rockwell Semiconductor Systems Div., San Diego, CA; *U.S. Public*, pg. 1398
Harvey, Kenny, Dir.-Pub. Rels.--Jazzercise, Inc., Carlsbad, CA; *U.S. Private*, pg. 584
Haschke, Lynda, Sr. V.P.--Ackerman McQueen, Inc., Tulsa, OK; *U.S. Private*, pg. 13
Hasegawa, Isao, Dir.-Pub. Rels.--Narumi China Corporation, Nagoya, Japan; *Int'l*, pg. 906
Hasek, Ronald W., Mgr.-Mktg. Services & Pub. Rels.--Ampco-Pittsburgh Corporation, Pittsburgh, PA; *U.S. Public*, pg. 103
Hasen, Jeff, V.P.-Pub. Rels., Sports Div.--EvansGroup, Salt Lake City, UT; *U.S. Private*, pg. 385
Hashem, M.A., Dir.-Intl. Media Rels.--Otis Elevator Company, Farmington, CT; *U.S. Public*, pg. 1690
Hashida, Akira, Gen. Mgr.-Pub. Rels.--Sapporo Breweries Ltd., Tokyo, Japan; *Int'l*, pg. 1193
Hasimoto, Hiroshi, Dir.-Pub. Rels.--Yamaha Corporation, Hamamatsu, Japan; *Int'l*, pg. 1515
Haskell, Robert G., Sr. V.P.-Public Affairs--Pacific Life Insurance Company, Newport Beach, CA; *U.S. Private*, pg. 831
Hassler, Cindy, V.P. & Pub. Rels. Dir.--Black Rogers Sullivan Goodnight, Inc., Houston, TX; *U.S. Private*, pg. 147
Hatem, R.F., Mgr.-Customer Rels.--Raytheon Electronics Systems, Bedford, MA; *U.S. Public*, pg. 1364
Hatfield, M.A., Sr. V.P. & Sec.--Marshall & Ilsley Corporation, Milwaukee, WI; *U.S. Public*, pg. 1049
Hatfield, Michele, Mgr.-Mktg. Communications-Paper Prods.--ABB Industrial Systems, Inc., Columbus, OH; *Int'l*, pg. 4
Hatley, Donald E., V.P.-Pub. Affairs--Duke Energy Corporation, Charlotte, NC; *U.S. Public*, pg. 534
Hattangadi, Manohar, Dir.-Mktg.--Bachmann Industries, Inc., Philadelphia, PA; *U.S. Private*, pg. 109
Hattox, Patsy L., Chief Admin. Officer, V.P. & Sec.--Nichols Research Corporation, Huntsville, AL; *U.S. Public*, pg. 1182
Hauge, Marilyn I., Dir.-Corp. Compliance & Investor Rels.--Fremont General Corporation, Santa Monica, CA; *U.S. Public*, pg. 681
Hausner, Barbara, Mgr.-Pub. Rels.--Melitta U.S.A., Inc., Clearwater, FL; *Int'l*, pg. 857
Hawk, Bob, V.P.-Corp. Comm.--Fairchild Aerospace Corporation, San Antonio, TX; *U.S. Private*, pg. 391
Hawkins, Jennifer, Pub. Rels.--Orient-Express Hotels Inc., New York, NY; *Int'l*, pg. 1213
Hawkins, John, Dir.-Corp. Communications--Promus Hotel Corporation, Memphis, TN; *U.S. Public*, pg. 1335
Hawkins, Kevin, Dir.-Communications--Safeway PLC, Hayes, United Kingdom; *Int'l*, pg. 1169
Hawks, Eric B., Mgr.-Mkt. Communications--Steelcraft Manufacturing Company, Cincinnati, OH; *U.S. Public*, pg. 877
Hawthorne, Joel, Dir.-Pub. & Investor Rels.--Acme Metals Incorporated, Riverdale, IL; *U.S. Public*, pg. 16
Hawtof, Jamie Geller, V.P.-Publicity--Columbia Pictures, Culver City, CA; *Int'l*, pg. 1281
Hayashi, Masatoshi, Mgr.-Pub. Rels.--Sumitomo Rubber Industries Ltd., Kobe, Japan; *Int'l*, pg. 1316
Hayden, John F., V.P.-State & Local Gov't Affairs & Community Rels.--The Boeing Company, Seattle, WA; *U.S. Public*, pg. 239
Hayden, Thomas, Sr. V.P.-Bus. Plng. & Communications--Showtime Networks Inc., New York, NY; *U.S. Private*, pg. 779
Hayden, William F., Dir.-Customer Satisfaction--Columbus McKinnon Corp., Amherst, NY; *U.S. Public*, pg. 405
Hayes, Chuck, Mgr.-Corp. Commun.--Merchants Group, Inc., Buffalo, NY; *U.S. Public*, pg. 1090
Hayes, Frank, Dir.-Corp. Affairs--Kerry Group PLC, Tralee, Ireland; *Int'l*, pg. 731
Hayes, John, Sr. Pub. Rels. Counsel--Hadeler Sullivan Ewing, Dallas, TX; *U.S. Private*, pg. 493
Hayes, Kelsey, Dir.-Mktg.--Lincoln Property Company, Dallas, TX; *U.S. Private*, pg. 668
Hayes, Lawson, Jr., Dir.-Pub. Rels. & Quality--Collins & Aikman Corporation, Charlotte, NC; *U.S. Public*, pg. 399
Hayes, Linda, V.P.-Mktg. Communications--Zenith Data Systems, Deerfield, IL; *Int'l*, pg. 317
Hayes, P.M., Mgr.-Pub. Affairs--Salt River Project Agricultural Improvement and Power District, Tempe, AZ; *U.S. Private*, pg. 962
Hayes, Tom, Mgr.-Corp. Rels.--Applied Materials, Inc., Santa Clara, CA; *U.S. Public*, pg. 123
Hayman, Leah, Dir.-Pub. Rels.--Corel Corporation, Ottawa, Canada; *Int'l*, pg. 331
Haynes, Jenny, V.P.-Investor Rels. & Pub. Rels.--Paging Network, Inc., Plano, TX; *U.S. Public*, pg. 1252
Hayter, Ryan, Coord.-Corp. Media Rels.--Hallmark Cards, Inc., Kansas City, MO; *U.S. Private*, pg. 495
Hayworth, Steve, V.P. & Pub. Rels.--CNN (Cable News Network), Atlanta, GA; *U.S. Public*, pg. 1614
Hazelbaker, Steven R., Chief Fin. Officer, V.P. & Treas.--Meridian Insurance Group, Inc., Indianapolis, IN; *U.S. Public*, pg. 1095
Hazelrigg, Robert C., V.P.-Mktg. & Pub. Rels.--Delta Natural Gas Company, Inc., Winchester, KY; *U.S. Public*, pg. 497
Hazelton, Warren, Dir.-Corp. Rels.--Tenneco Packaging, Evanston, IL; *U.S. Public*, pg. 1579
Head, Ian, Mgr.-Corp. Communications--Comalco Limited, Brisbane, Australia; *Int'l*, pg. 307
Headler, Robert, Grp. Mgr.-Corp. Affairs--Goodman Fielder Limited, Sydney, Australia; *Int'l*, pg. 555
Healey, Anoushka, Exec.-Pub. Rels.--The Financial Times Ltd., London, United Kingdom; *Int'l*, pg. 1025
Healey, Marsha, Mgr.-Corp. Communications--Plantronics Inc., Santa Cruz, CA; *U.S. Public*, pg. 1308
Healey, Robert E., V.P.-Customer Opers.--Commonwealth Electric Co., Cambridge, MA; *U.S. Public*, pg. 415
Healy, Margie, Dir.-Pub. Rels.--F. Korbel Bros. Inc., Guerneville, CA; *U.S. Private*, pg. 632
Hearn, Kathleen, Mgr.-Community & Government Rels.--Boston Gas Company, Boston, MA; *U.S. Public*, pg. 549
Hearn, Sue, Mgr.-Commun.--Pete's Brewing Company, Palo Alto, CA; *U.S. Public*, pg. 1280
Heartwell, Frances G., V.P.-Human Resources & Admin.--Oryx Energy, Dallas, TX; *U.S. Public*, pg. 1232
Heath, H. Anthony, V.P.-Plng. & Communications--Sun Life Assurance Company of Canada (U.K.) Limited, Basingstoke, United Kingdom; *Int'l*, pg. 1319
Heath, Mary Van, Dir.-Corp. Communicaitons--ALARIS Medical Systems, Inc., San Diego, CA; *U.S. Public*, pg. 35
Heber, Tom, V.P.-Human Resources--United States Sugar Corporation, Clewiston, FL; *U.S. Private*, pg. 1126
Hedegaard, Michael, Mgr.-Corp. Information & Pub. Rels.--Lego System A/S, Billund, Denmark; *Int'l*, pg. 805
Hedlund, Fredrik, Dir.-Pub. Rels.--NCC Industry, Solna, Sweden; *Int'l*, pg. 899
Hedman, Corey, Dir.-Pub. Affairs--Dominick's Finer Foods, Northlake, IL; *U.S. Private*, pg. 1202
Heffke, Jodi, Mktg. Communications Asst.--Pioneer-Standard Electronics, Inc., Cleveland, OH; *U.S. Public*, pg. 1300
Heffron, Howard, Sr. Mgr.-Communications--Sandoz Agro, Inc., Des Plaines, IL; *Int'l*, pg. 974
Heggen, Dewey, Mgr.-Pub. Communications--Basin Electric Power Cooperative, Bismarck, ND; *U.S. Private*, pg. 121
Heggie, Betty-Ann, Sr. V.P.-Corp. Rels.--Potash Corporation of Saskatchewan Inc., Saskatoon, Canada; *Int'l*, pg. 1064
Hegyi, Terry M., Mgr.-Pub. Rels.--Firmenich Incorporated, Plainsboro, NJ; *Int'l*, pg. 486
Heide, David, Mgr.-Adv.--Snap-On Tools Corporation, Kenosha, WI; *U.S. Public*, pg. 1480

Heikkinen, M., V.P.-Corp. Communications--Kesko Ltd., Helsinki, Finland; *Int'l*, pg. 732

Heimers, Trish, V.P.-Communications--Bertelsmann Music Group, Wilmington, DE; *Int'l*, pg. 191

Heimert, Chrystie, Dir.-Pub. Rels.--Farnam Companies, Inc., Phoenix, AZ; *U.S. Private*, pg. 396

Heimert, Chrystie, Dir.-Pub. Rels.--Security Lawn & Garden Co., Phoenix, AZ; *U.S. Private*, pg. 397

Heine, Rick, Mgr.-Communication--Sta-Rite Water Systems, Delavan, WI; *U.S. Public*, pg. 1767

Heinz, Christian, Dir.-Mktg., Adv. & Pub. Rels.--Credit Suisse, Zurich, Switzerland; *Int'l*, pg. 345

Heitzer, H. Sylvia, Press Sec.--Schwarz Pharma AG, Monheim, Germany; *Int'l*, pg. 1211

Heivert, Ylva, Dir.-Pub. Rels.--ICA Handlarnas AB, Solna, Sweden; *Int'l*, pg. 642

Hekeler, Manfred, Mgr.-Mktg. & Communications--Traub AG, Reichenbach, Germany; *Int'l*, pg. 1419

Heldreth, Nick E., V.P.-H.R. & Corp. Rels.--Harris Corporation, Melbourne, FL; *U.S. Public*, pg. 791

Helewicz, Joe S., V.P.-Pub. Affairs--Brown & Williamson Tobacco Corp., Louisville, KY; *Int'l*, pg. 111

Helgerud, Frode, Mgr.-Pub. Rels.--Union Bank of Norway, Oslo, Norway; *Int'l*, pg. 1439

Heller, John, Dir.-Opers. & Asst. to the Pres.--The IDI Group Companies, Arlington, VA; *U.S. Private*, pg. 554

Helmstetter, Dave, Publicity Coord.--Crown Equipment Corporation, New Bremen, OH; *U.S. Private*, pg. 292

Helstab, Susan, V.P.-Corp. Communications--Four Seasons Hotels Inc., Don Mills, Canada; *Int'l*, pg. 502

Hemberger, Barb, Dir.-Communications & Pub. Relations--Carlson Wagonlit Travel, Minneapolis, MN; *U.S. Private*, pg. 212

Hemlepp, Catherine, Dir.-Publ. Rels.--Parade Publications Inc., New York, NY; *U.S. Private*, pg. 20

Henderson, Barbara, Sr. V.P. & Mng. Dir.-Pub. Rels.--Ingalls, Boston, MA; *U.S. Private*, pg. 562

Henderson, D.R., Dir.-Human Resources & Communications--Du Pont Canada Inc., Mississauga, Canada; *U.S. Public*, pg. 532

Henderson, Theresa, Dir.-Corp. Comm.--Current Technology, Inc., Irving, TX; *U.S. Public*, pg. 480

Hendon, Gerald A., V.P.-Pub. Affairs--The Boeing Company, Seattle, WA; *U.S. Public*, pg. 239

Hendriks-Venema, A., Corp. Commun. Coord.--Akzo Nobel N.V., Arnhem, Netherlands; *Int'l*, pg. 42

Hendrix, Phyllis, Mgr.-Mktg. Services--Wyandot Inc., Marion, OH; *U.S. Private*, pg. 1193

Hengelbrok, Janet, Dir.-Communications--General Electric Investment Corp., Stamford, CT; *U.S. Public*, pg. 712

Hennesy, Larry, Dir.-Mktg. Communications--The Gates Rubber Company, Denver, CO; *Int'l*, pg. 1396

Henning, Pam, Dir.-Publicity--Loews Theatre Management Corp., New York, NY; *Int'l*, pg. 1282

Henning, Richard, Mgr.-Media Rels. & Special Events--United Water Management & Services, Harrington Park, NJ; *U.S. Public*, pg. 1692

Henry, Albert J., V.P.-Community Affairs--Alexander's, Inc., Saddle Brook, NJ; *U.S. Public*, pg. 1725

Henry, Brian J., V.P.-Fin. & Treas.--Terex Corporation, Westport, CT; *U.S. Public*, pg. 1581

Henry, Harlene, Mgr.-Global Communications--Videojet Systems International, Inc., Wood Dale, IL; *Int'l*, pg. 545

Henry, Roni, Mgr.-Admin. & Human Resources & Asst. Sec.--Waters Instruments, Inc., Rochester, MN; *U.S. Public*, pg. 1745

Herasimchuk, David A., V.P.-Mktg. Devel.--Global Marine Inc., Houston, TX; *U.S. Public*, pg. 748

Herbert, John A., Dir.-Corp. Communications--Scandinavian Airlines System (SAS), Solna, Sweden; *Int'l*, pg. 1201

Herbst, David, Dir.-Corp. Rels.--Mercury Air Group Inc., Los Angeles, CA; *U.S. Public*, pg. 1092

Hergenhan, Joyce, V.P.-Pub. Rels.--General Electric Company, Fairfield, CT; *U.S. Public*, pg. 709

Herling, Lisa, V.P.-Corp. Communications--Barnes & Noble Inc., New York, NY; *U.S. Public*, pg. 189

Herman, Cindy, Dir.-Corp. Consumer Adv. & Pub. Rels.--OshKosh B'Gosh, Inc., Oshkosh, WI; *U.S. Public*, pg. 1232

Herman, R., Liaison Communications--KDI Precision Products, Inc., Cincinnati, OH; *U.S. Private*, pg. 603

Hernandez Exparza, Abdon, V.P.-Law & Pub. Rels.--Industrias Penoles S.A. de C.V., Cuauhtemoc, Mexico; *Int'l*, pg. 677

Hernandez, Mary, Admin.-Pub. Affairs--Lever Brothers Co., New York, NY; *Int'l*, pg. 1435

Herndon, Wanda, Sr. V.P.-Communications & Pub. Affairs--Starbucks Coffee Company, Seattle, WA; *U.S. Public*, pg. 1510

Herr, W., Mgr.-Pub. Rels. & Adv.--Deminex-Deutsche GmbH, Essen, Germany; *Int'l*, pg. 1460

Herreid, Beth, Mgr.-Corp. Commun.--Graybar Electric Company, Inc., Clayton, MO; *U.S. Private*, pg. 472

Herring, Sandra, V.P. & Pub. Rels. Dir.--DMB&B St. Louis, Saint Louis, MO; *U.S. Private*, pg. 303

Herrington, Checky, Sr. Staff Commun. Specialist--Entergy Corporation, New Orleans, LA; *U.S. Public*, pg. 585

Herrlin, Rosemary, Dir.-Human Resources & Communications--Fiatallis North America, Inc., Carol Stream, IL; *Int'l*, pg. 483

Herrmann, Michael, Dr., Dir.-Pub. Rels.--Deutsche Unilever Gmbh, Hamburg, Germany; *Int'l*, pg. 1436

Herron, Bonnie L., V.P. & Sec.--Intelligent Systems Corp., Norcross, GA; *U.S. Public*, pg. 888

Herron, Michael, Dir.-Communications--Environmental Resources Management, Exton, PA; *U.S. Private*, pg. 378

Hersey, Liz, Dir.-Pub. Rels./Investor Rels.--Tricord Systems, Inc., Plymouth, MN; *U.S. Public*, pg. 1637

Herz, Suzanne, Dir.-Publicity--Doubleday Publishing Company, New York, NY; *Int'l*, pg. 191

Herzgsell, Willi, Mgr.-Plng., Info. & Control--CIBA-GEIGY Australia Ltd., Pendle Hill, Australia; *Int'l*, pg. 976

Herzog, Jim, Mgr.-Corp. Communications, Sls., Mktg. & Adv.--Armco Inc., Pittsburgh, PA; *U.S. Public*, pg. 131

Herzog, Robert, V.P.-Indus. Rels.--General Felt Industries, Inc., Linwood, PA; *U.S. Private*, pg. 1094

Hess, Cindy, Dir.-Corp. Commun.--Michigan Physicians Mutual Liability Inc., East Lansing, MI; *U.S. Private*, pg. 741

Hess, Cynthia, Dir.-Corp. Commun.--Kentucky Medical Insurance Company (KMIC), Louisville, KY; *U.S. Private*, pg. 741

Hess, Don, V.P.-Customer Satisfaction--Rutt Custom Cabinetry, Goodville, PA; *U.S. Private*, pg. 507

Hess, G.N., Dir.-Pub. Rels.--The Kelly-Springfield Tire Company, Cumberland, MD; *U.S. Public*, pg. 753

Hess, Jill C., Corp. Communications/Pub. Rels.--Aloette Cosmetics, Inc., West Chester, PA; *U.S. Public*, pg. 57

Hess, Phil, Dir.-Customer Rels.--Sacramento Kings, Sacramento, CA; *U.S. Private*, pg. 959

Hesse, Paul A., V.P.-Communications & Sec.--General Dynamics Corporation, Falls Church, VA; *U.S. Public*, pg. 708

Heuberger, Mark, Officer-Corp. Communications--Memphis Light, Gas & Water, Memphis, TN; *U.S. Private*, pg. 731

Hewitt, Lisa, V.P.-Corp. Communications--Bank of America Illinois, Chicago, IL; *U.S. Public*, pg. 180

Heyen, Sean, Mgr.-Mktg. Communications--Transcrypt International, Lincoln, NE; *U.S. Public*, pg. 1630

Heying, Mary Beth, Principal-Pub. Rels.--Edward Jones, Saint Louis, MO; *U.S. Private*, pg. 597

Hibbs, Maria P., Dir.-Pub. Affairs--Inland Steel Industries, Inc., Chicago, IL; *U.S. Public*, pg. 879

Hice, Joe, Dir.-Commun./Marine Products--Bombardier Recreational Products, Montreal, Canada; *Int'l*, pg. 200

Hickey, Jerry D., Dir.-Mktg. Communications--IMO Industries Inc., Lawrenceville, NJ; *U.S. Public*, pg. 856

Hicks, Carol, V.P.-Communication--Home & Garden Television, Knoxville, TN; *U.S. Public*, pg. 1447

Hidinger, Jim, Mgr.-Corp. & Mktg. Communications--LeFebure Corp., Cedar Rapids, IA; *Int'l*, pg. 387

Hier, Mark, Dir.-Pub. Rels. & Adv.--The Minnesota Mutual Life Insurance Company, Saint Paul, MN; *U.S. Private*, pg. 750

Higbee, Ann G., Mng. Partner-EMA Pub. Rels. Services--Eric Mower and Associates, Inc., Syracuse, NY; *U.S. Private*, pg. 765

Higbee, Ann G., Mng. Partner-EMA Pub. Rels. Services--Eric Mower and Associates/Buffalo, Inc., Buffalo, NY; *U.S. Private*, pg. 765

Higbee, Ann G., Mng. Partner-EMA Pub. Rels.--Eric Mower & Associates, Albany, NY; *U.S. Private*, pg. 765

Higbee, Ann G., Mng. Partner-EMA Pub. Rels. Services--Eric Mower & Associates, Atlanta, GA; *U.S. Private*, pg. 765

Higgins, Barbara, Mgr.-Pub. Rels. & Personnel Training & Devel.--Bata Shoe Co., Inc., Belcamp, MD; *U.S. Private*, pg. 195

Higgins, Dennis P., Sr. V.P.-Publicity--Columbia Pictures, Culver City, CA; *Int'l*, pg. 1281

Higgins, Dennis P., V.P.-East Coast Publicity--TriStar Pictures, Culver City, CA; *Int'l*, pg. 1283

Higgins, Roland, Dir.-Corp. Commun.--GIB Group, Brussels, Belgium; *Int'l*, pg. 532

Higgins, Sandra, Mgr.-Commun.--Physio-Control Corporation, Redmond, WA; *U.S. Public*, pg. 1294

Higgins, Thomas J., V.P.-Corp. Communications--Edison International, Rosemead, CA; *U.S. Public*, pg. 564

Higgins, Thomas J., V.P.-Corp. Communications--Southern California Edison Company, Rosemead, CA; *U.S. Public*, pg. 564

High, Lynne, Mgr.-Corp. Commun.--ADC Telecommunications, Inc., Minnetonka, MN; *U.S. Public*, pg. 4

Highly, Ann Marie, Mgr.-Adv. Pub. Rels.--Reuters Holdings PLC, London, United Kingdom; *Int'l*, pg. 1105

Higie, David G., Dir.-Corp. Communications--Michael Baker Corporation, Pittsburgh, PA; *U.S. Public*, pg. 168

Hildebrand, Wilton J., V.P.-Engrng. Support & Customer Rels.--Cablevision, Woodbury, NY; *U.S. Public*, pg. 288

Hildebrandt, Jeffrey A., Mgr.-Corp. Communications--CareerTrack Inc., Boulder, CO; *U.S. Public*, pg. 1555

Hildreth, Burgess, V.P.-Admin.--Anchor Continental Incorporated, Columbia, SC; *U.S. Private*, pg. 70

Hill, Bill, Dir.-Communications--Diversey Water Technologies, Inc., Chagrin Falls, OH; *U.S. Public*, pg. 1150

Hill, Dave, Dir.-Mktg. Communications--Symantec Corporation - Beaverton Site, Beaverton, OR; *U.S. Public*, pg. 1545

Hill, David, Dir.-Mktg. Communications--Symantec Corporation, Cupertino, CA; *U.S. Public*, pg. 1545

Hill, James, Dr., Sr. V.P. & Dir.-Corp. Affairs--SmithKline Beecham plc, Brentford, United Kingdom; *Int'l*, pg. 1264

Hill, James, Dr., V.P.-Corp. Affairs--SmithKline Beecham Corporation, Philadelphia, PA; *Int'l*, pg. 1264

Hill, Michelle, Mgr.-Publicity--Ibstock Plc, Lutterworth, United Kingdom; *Int'l*, pg. 658

Hiller, Donald T., Mgr.-Investor Rels.--Professional Auto Warehouse, Rochester, NY; *U.S. Public*, pg. 774

Hilliers, Cynthia J., Mgr.-Corp. Commun.--Cannon, Grand Island, NY; *U.S. Private*, pg. 205

Hillman, Charles F., V.P.-New Market Devel.--Berryman Products, Inc., Arlington, TX; *U.S. Private*, pg. 138

Hillman, Sandra, Exec. V.P. & Pub. Rels. Dir.--Trahan, Burden & Charles, Inc., Baltimore, MD; *U.S. Private*, pg. 1095

Hilmarsson, Thorsteinn, Mgr.-Info.--Landsvirkjun - The National Power Co., Reykjavik, Iceland; *Int'l*, pg. 801

Hilton, Michael R., Pub. Rels. Dir.--SmithKline Beecham Laboratories, Bristol, TN; *Int'l*, pg. 1264

Himes, Susan, Mgr.-Communications--ANGUS Chemical Company, Buffalo Grove, IL; *U.S. Private*, pg. 75

Hindes, Van, Dir.-Corp. Affairs--Gerber Products Company, Fremont, MI; *Int'l*, pg. 973

Hindman, Donald D., V.P.-Sls. & Mktg.--Clark Foodservice, Inc., Elk Grove Village, IL; *U.S. Private*, pg. 242

Hinds, Sharlene Harrison, Dir.-Pub. Rels. & Copy--Color Tile, Inc., Fort Worth, TX; *Int'l*, pg. 686

Hines, Carolyn, Mgr.-Pub. Rels.--Cone Mills Corporation, Greensboro, NC; *U.S. Public*, pg. 430

Hines, Carolyn, Mgr.-Pub. Rels.--Cone Apparel Products, Greensboro, NC; *U.S. Public*, pg. 430

Hinks, Tom, Mgr.-Communications--Atlas Copco Compressors, Inc., Holyoke, MA; *Int'l*, pg. 96

Hinson, Will, Mgr.-Public Affairs--Georgia Gulf Corporation, Atlanta, GA; *U.S. Public*, pg. 734

Hinte, Michael, Mgr.-Adv. & Pub. Rels.--GESTRA GmbH, Bremen, Germany; *Int'l*, pg. 549

Hinterser, Jake, Dir.-Commun.--Basler Electric Company, Highland, IL; *U.S. Private*, pg. 121

Hinton, Bruce, Sr. Dir.-Pub. Rels.--Long John Silver's, Inc., Lexington, KY; *U.S. Private*, pg. 674

Hintze, Glenn, Asst. V.P.-Pub. Rels.--U.S. Trust Corporation, New York, NY; *U.S. Public*, pg. 1688

Hinze, David H., V.P.-Corp. Commun.--Outsource International, Deerfield Beach, FL; *U.S. Public*, pg. 1236

Hirantner, Peter, Mgr.-Pub. Rels.--Mazda Austria GmbH, Klagenfurt, Austria; *Int'l*, pg. 849

Hironaka, Akio, Mgr.-Gen. Affairs Section--Narumi China Corporation, Nagoya, Japan; *Int'l*, pg. 906

Hirose, Hiromitsu, Mgr.-Pub. Rels.--Matsuya Company Ltd., Tokyo, Japan; *Int'l*, pg. 848

Hirotani, S., Mgr.-Pub. Rels.--Nissho Iwai Corporation, Tokyo, Japan; *Int'l*, pg. 946

Hirsh, Ethan, Sr. Dir.-Corp. Communications--UtiliCorp United Inc., Kansas City, MO; *U.S. Public*, pg. 1700

Hirshberg, Jennifer, Dir.-Pub. Rels.--Metromedia International Group, Inc., East Rutherford, NJ; *U.S. Public*, pg. 1102

Hiznay, Paul A., Sr. V.P.-Sls. & Adv.--Mona Industries, Inc., Paterson, NJ; *U.S. Private*, pg. 756

Ho, Claire, Mgr.-Communications--Quad/Graphics, Inc., Pewaukee, WI; *U.S. Private*, pg. 897

Ho, Roh-Seo, Mgr.-Pub. Rels.--KIA Motors Corp., Seoul, Korea; *Int'l*, pg. 732

Hoadley, Russell S., Exec. V.P.-Employee & Pub. Rels.--Hibernia Corporation, New Orleans, LA; *U.S. Public*, pg. 825

Hoavenka, Joe, Dir.-Mktg. & Communications--Sulzermedica USA Inc., Angleton, TX; *Int'l*, pg. 1307

Hobbs, Harry Jr., Dir.-Indus. Rels.--Western Atlas International, Inc., Houston, TX; *U.S. Public*, pg. 1757

Hobel, Marlene, Dir.-Corp. Communications--Camp Dresser & McKee Inc., Cambridge, MA; *U.S. Private*, pg. 203

Hobor, Nancy A., V.P.-Commun. & Investor Rels.--Morton International Inc., Chicago, IL; *U.S. Public*, pg. 1134

Hobson, Tony, Pres.-AG Mktg. & Commun.--Adair Greene Advertising, Atlanta, GA; *U.S. Private*, pg. 16

Hochberg, David C., V.P.-Pub. Affairs--Lillian Vernon Corporation, New Rochelle, NY; *U.S. Public*, pg. 1716

Hock, Stanley, Dir.-Pub. Rels.--Sutter Home Winery, Inc., Saint Helena, CA; *U.S. Private*, pg. 1057

Hocklander, Daniel, Dir.-Pub. Rels.--D.W. Newcomer's Sons, Inc., Kansas City, MO; *U.S. Private*, pg. 796

Hockstad, Doug, Dir.-Corp. Communications--Comshare, Incorporated, Ann Arbor, MI; *U.S. Public*, pg. 425

Hodges, Arlene, Mgr.-Communications & Employee Svcs.--Outokumpu American Brass Co., Buffalo, NY; *Int'l*, pg. 1016

Hodges, Charles, V.P.-Pub. Rels.--Larkin Meeder & Schweidel, Dallas, TX; *U.S. Private*, pg. 651

Hodges, John E., Jr., V.P.-Customer Service & Div. Opers.--Gulf Power Company, Pensacola, FL; *U.S. Public*, pg. 1490

Hoefer, Stephen H., Sr. V.P.-Pub. Affairs--Agway, Inc., De Witt, NY; *U.S. Private*, pg. 27

Hoelsher, Pete, Dir.-Mktg.--Acxiom Corporation, Conway, AR; *U.S. Public*, pg. 18

Hoerger, Bill, Assoc. Dir.-Corp. Commun.--Praxair Inc., Danbury, CT; *U.S. Public*, pg. 1319

Hofcaehs, Rudolf, Mgr.-Public Rels.--Andreas Stihl, Waiblingen, Germany; *Int'l*, pg. 1301

Hoff, Doan, Mgr.-Adv. & Pub. Rels.--Yamaha Electronics Corp. USA, Buena Park, CA; *Int'l*, pg. 1516

Hoff, John E., Dir.-Corp. Commun. & Pub. Rels.--Owens-Illinois, Inc., Toledo, OH; *U.S. Public*, pg. 1238

Hoff, Susan, V.P.-Communications & Pub. Rels.--Best Buy Co., Inc., Eden Prairie, MN; *U.S. Public*, pg. 223

Hoffman, Brad, Dir.-Communications--Bailey Controls Company, Wickliffe, OH; *Int'l*, pg. 654

Hoffman, Brad A., Dir.-Communications--ELSAG Bailey Process Automation N.V., Schiphol, Netherlands; *Int'l*, pg. 449

Hoffman, David, Mgr.-Mktg.--HomeGoods, Framingham, MA; *U.S. Public*, pg. 1557

Hoffman, Don, Mgr.-Pub. Rels.--NIBCO, Inc., Elkhart, IN; *U.S. Private*, pg. 798

Hoffman, Gayla J., V.P.-Pub. Rels.--Peabody Holding Company, Inc., Saint Louis, MO; *Int'l*, pg. 594

Hoffman, Gregory M., V.P.-Bus. Devel.--Santa Fe Energy Resources, Inc., Houston, TX; *U.S. Public*, pg. 1431

Hoffman, Howard, V.P. & Mgr.-S.W. Newspaper Rels.--Parade Publications Inc., New York, NY; *U.S. Private*, pg. 20

Hoffman, Joan W., Mgr.-Info. Svcs.--BNA PLUS, Washington, DC; *U.S. Private*, pg. 182

Hoffman, Marv, V.P.-Mktg. Communications & Franchise Sls.--National Real Estate Services, Inc., Vancouver, Canada; *Int'l*, pg. 909

Hoffman, Ronald R., Exec. V.P.-Human Resources, Quality & Communications--Aluminum Company of America, Pittsburgh, PA; *U.S. Public*, pg. 60

Hoffman, Steven D., Dir.-Corp. Affairs & Mktg.--American Axle & Manufacturing, Detroit, MI; *U.S. Private*, pg. 51

Hoffman, Thomas, V.P.-Pub. Rels.--Consol, Pittsburgh, PA; *U.S. Public*, pg. 531

Hoffman, Thomas, V.P.-Pub. Rels.--Consol, Pittsburgh, PA; *Int'l*, pg. 1081

Hoffner, Jennifer, Dir.-Personnel--Kidron Inc., Kidron, OH; *U.S. Private*, pg. 619
Hoglund, Kathleen, Mgr.-Mktg. Communications--AmClyde Engineered Products Co., Inc., Saint Paul, MN; *U.S. Public*, pg. 778
Hol, Jan, V.P.-Pub. Rels.--Koninklijke Ahold NV, Zaandam, Netherlands; *Int'l*, pg. 749
Holbeck, Frau, Mgr.-Pub. Rels.--Diebels Private Brewery, Issum, Germany; *Int'l*, pg. 413
Holbrook, Michele, Sr. Mgr.-Corp. Commun.--National Fuel Gas Distribution Corp., Buffalo, NY; *U.S. Public*, pg. 1156
Holden, David, V.P.-Public Affairs--Bank of Ireland, Dublin, Ireland; *Int'l*, pg. 152
Hollaar, P., Asst. Dir.-Corp. Communications--Oce-van der Grinten N.V., Venlo, Netherlands; *Int'l*, pg. 993
Holland, E.J., Jr., Sr. V.P.-H.R. & Sec.--Payless Cashways, Inc., Kansas City, MO; *U.S. Public*, pg. 1267
Holleran, Charles B., V.P.-Communications--Digital Equipment Corporation, Maynard, MA; *U.S. Public*, pg. 507
Hollis, Clayton, V.P.-Pub. Affairs--Publix Supermarkets Inc., Lakeland, FL; *U.S. Private*, pg. 893
Hollis, Mark, Sr. V.P.-Sls. & Mktg.--Inverness Corp., Fair Lawn, NJ; *U.S. Private*, pg. 574
Holm, Wolsten, Dir.-Pub. Rels.--Firth-Rixson Plc, Sheffield, United Kingdom; *Int'l*, pg. 487
Holman, Bernice, Mgr.-Public Rels.--Volkswagen Canada, Inc., Ajax, Canada; *Int'l*, pg. 1475
Holman, Sharon, V.P.-Pub. Rels.--Excel Communications, Inc., Dallas, TX; *U.S. Public*, pg. 598
Holmes, B.P., Dir.-Pub. Rels.--BSL Engineering Limited, Manchester, United Kingdom; *Int'l*, pg. 212
Holmes, Beverly, Dir.-Pub. Rels--Lands' End, Inc., Dodgeville, WI; *U.S. Public*, pg. 977
Holmes, Carla, Mgr.-Corp. Communications--Fina, Inc., Dallas, TX; *Int'l*, pg. 1044
Holmes, David, Dir.-Corp. Resources--British Airways PLC, London, United Kingdom; *Int'l*, pg. 218
Holmes, David, Mgr.-Commun.--Yorkshire Building Society, Bradford, United Kingdom; *Int'l*, pg. 1522
Holmes, Margaret, Dir.-Communications--Buick Motor Div. General Motors Corp., Flint, MI; *U.S. Public*, pg. 720
Holmes, Nicole, Coord.-Communications--First Interstate Bank of Texas N.A., Houston, TX; *U.S. Public*, pg. 1753
Holmstrom-Lindgren, Inger, Sr. V.P.-Corp. Rels. & Communications--Vattenfall AB, Stockholm, Sweden; *Int'l*, pg. 1452
Holshouser, Kim, Communications Supvr.--U.S. Electrical Motor Division, Saint Louis, MO; *U.S. Public*, pg. 573
Holt, Barry, Sr. V.P.-Communications--A.C. Nielsen, Stamford, CT; *U.S. Public*, pg. 1183
Holzwasser, Joel D., V.P.-Adv. & Pub. Rels.--Arrow Automotive Industries, Inc., Framingham, MA; *U.S. Public*, pg. 133
Homen De Mello, Nelson, Dir.-Pub. Rels.--Souza Cruz, S.A., Rio de Janeiro, Brazil; *Int'l*, pg. 112
Homle, Karen, Mgr.-Pub. Rels.--St. Paul Fire and Marine Insurance Co., Saint Paul, MN; *U.S. Public*, pg. 1429
Honda, Ken, Mgr.-Pub. Rels. Dept.--Fuji Heavy Industries, Ltd., Aircraft Div., Utsunomiya, Japan; *Int'l*, pg. 522
Hong, Wee Siew, Mgr.-Pub. Rels--Singapore Land Limited, Singapore, Singapore; *Int'l*, pg. 1252
Hood, Christy, Mng. Dir.-Pub. Rels.--Donna Karan, New York, NY; *U.S. Public*, pg. 517
Hood, Elizabeth, Dir.-Corp. Rels.--Continental Europe, West Drayton, United Kingdom; *Int'l*, pg. 1442
Hood, Melinda B., Mgr.-Commun.--Mississippi Chemical Corporation, Yazoo City, MS; *U.S. Public*, pg. 1117
Hood, Sarah W., Mgr.-Pub. Rels.--Intertek Testing Services, Andover, MA; *Int'l*, pg. 672
Hooker, Jeff, Dir.-Prod. Mktg. Devel.--British Steel Plc, London, United Kingdom; *Int'l*, pg. 220
Hoopes, Tobi, Dir.-Pub. Rels.--RELTEC Systems, Bedford, TX; *U.S. Private*, pg. 921
Hopkins, Dom, Dir.-Mktg. Communications--Lafarge Canada Inc., Montreal, Canada; *Int'l*, pg. 789
Hopkins, Sandy, Mgr.-Corp. Marcom--Teknor Apex Company, Pawtucket, RI; *U.S. Private*, pg. 1073
Hopkins, Steve, Mgr.-Corp. Commun.--Standard Insurance Co., Portland, OR; *U.S. Private*, pg. 1031
Hopkins, Wayne W., V.P.-Communications--TECO Energy, Inc., Tampa, FL; *U.S. Public*, pg. 1565
Hopkins, Wayne W., V.P.-Corp. Comm.--Tampa Electric Co., Tampa, FL; *U.S. Public*, pg. 1565
Hoppin, Thomas E., V.P.-Corp. Communications--CSX Corporation, Richmond, VA; *U.S. Public*, pg. 284
Hopson, Andy, Pres.-Pub. Rels. & Dir.--EvansGroup, Salt Lake City, UT; *U.S. Private*, pg. 385
Hopson, Andy, Pres.-Corp. Pub. Rels.--EvansGroup, Seattle, WA; *U.S. Private*, pg. 385
Horden, Julia, Mgr.-Press & Pub. Rels.--Travel U.K., London, United Kingdom,; *U.S. Private*, pg. 647
Horel, Tom, V.P.-Mktg., Sls. & Pub. Rels.--American Metal Products, Olive Branch, MS; *U.S. Public*, pg. 1053
Horner, Tricia, Mgr.-Pub. Rels.--Traveling Software Inc., Bothell, WA; *U.S. Private*, pg. 1098
Hornstein, Alvin S., Dir.-Pub. Rels.--Maaco Enterprises Inc., King of Prussia, PA; *U.S. Private*, pg. 689
Horswill, Douglas H., V.P.-Environ. & Corp. Affairs--Cominco, Ltd., Vancouver, Canada; *Int'l*, pg. 307
Horton, Catherine, Mgr.-Adv. & Commun.--Safety 1st, Inc., Chestnut Hill, MA; *U.S. Public*, pg. 1425
Hosford, Chris, Dir.-Public Rels.--Hyundai Motor America, Fountain Valley, CA; *Int'l*, pg. 641
Hoskins, Ken, Pres.-Pub. Rels. & Pub. Affairs--Creative Alliance, Inc., Louisville, KY; *U.S. Private*, pg. 287
Hoskins, Trevor C., V.P.-Pub. Affairs--Bridgestone/Firestone, Inc., Nashville, TN; *Int'l*, pg. 213
Hostetter, Jerry, V.P.-Corp. Commun.--The Singer Company, Hong Kong, Hong Kong; *Int'l*, pg. 1220
Hotinger, Lizette, Dir.-Pub. Rels.--Paisano Publications, Inc., Agoura, CA; *U.S. Private*, pg. 834
Hougaard, Henrik, Sr. V.P.-Communications--Nykredit, Copenhagen, Denmark; *Int'l*, pg. 993
Houghtby, David, V.P.-New Energy Services--Minnegasco, Minneapolis, MN; *U.S. Public*, pg. 843
House, Bonnie, Corp. Commun. Specialist--Skyway Freight Systems, Inc., Watsonville, CA; *U.S. Private*, pg. 1005
House, Edie, V.P.-Pub. Rels.--Trahan, Burden & Charles, Inc., Baltimore, MD; *U.S. Private*, pg. 1095
House, Edith, V.P.-Pub. Rels.--Trahan, Burden & Charles, Inc., Public Relations, Baltimore, MD; *U.S. Private*, pg. 1095
House, John H., Dir.-Communications--Dassault Falcon Jet Corp., South Hackensack, NJ; *Int'l*, pg. 383
Houts, Jan, Mgr.-MARCommunications & Direct Mktg.--Xilinx, Inc., San Jose, CA; *U.S. Public*, pg. 1786
Howald, Beatrice, Mgr.-Communications & Publ. Rels.--SMH Swiss Corporation for Micro Electronics & Watchmaking Indus. Ltd., Bienne, Switzerland; *Int'l*, pg. 1160
Howard, Chanta, Sec.-Mktg. & Communications Dept.--Shell Chemical Co., Houston, TX; *Int'l*, pg. 1136
Howard, G.E., Chief Exec.-Corp. Affairs--BBA Group plc, London, United Kingdom; *Int'l*, pg. 112
Howard, Patricia M., Dir.-Communications--Datapoint Corporation, San Antonio, TX; *Int'l*, pg. 384
Howard, Richard M., Dir.-Mktg.--Shafer Commercial Seating Inc., Denver, CO; *U.S. Private*, pg. 988
Howard, Susan, Dir.-Commun.--A. Duda & Sons Inc., Oviedo, FL; *U.S. Private*, pg. 344
Howard, William, Mgr.-Adv.--Atotech U.S.A. Inc., Rock Hill, SC; *U.S. Private*, pg. 97
Howatt, Neels, Gen. Mgr.-Human Resources & Pub. Relations--Iscor, Pretoria, South Africa; *Int'l*, pg. 688
Howie, David, Mgr.-Corp. Communications--Rolls-Royce plc, London, United Kingdom; *Int'l*, pg. 1126
Howlett, C.A., V.P.-Public Affairs--America West Holdings Corporation, Phoenix, AZ; *U.S. Public*, pg. 66
Howlett, C.A., V.P.-Public Affairs--America West Airlines, Inc., Phoenix, AZ; *U.S. Public*, pg. 67
Howlett, John, Dir.-Mktg. Communication US--Merial Ltd., Iselin, NJ; *U.S. Public*, pg. 1092
Howlett, John, Dir.-Mktg. Communication US--Merial Ltd., Iselin, NJ; *Int'l*, pg. 1109
Hruska, Susan, Mgr.-Pub. Rels.--The Homestead L.C., Hot Springs, VA; *U.S. Private*, pg. 247
Hubbard, Charles G., Mgr.-Corp. Commun.--Baldor Electric Company, Fort Smith, AR; *U.S. Public*, pg. 168
Hubbard, Danley T., V.P.-Revenues & Public Affairs--Southwestern Bell Telephone Co., Saint Louis, MO; *U.S. Public*, pg. 1416
Hubbel, Robert C., Mng. Dir.-Commun.--Andersen Worldwide, New York, NY; *U.S. Private*, pg. 72
Huber, Jill, Mgr.-Corp. Communications--Intertec Publishing, Overland Park, KS; *U.S. Public*, pg. 1327
Hublou, Heather, Mgr.-Corp. Communications--CorVel Corporation, Irvine, CA; *U.S. Public*, pg. 451
Hudelson, Warren F., Mgr.-Communications--Minnesota Power, Duluth, MN; *U.S. Public*, pg. 1116
Hudgins, Cheryl G., Dir.-Pub. Rels.--Procter & Gamble Cosmetics Co., Hunt Valley, MD; *U.S. Public*, pg. 1330
Hudson, David, Dir.-Corp. Communications--Nestle U.K. Ltd., Croydon, United Kingdom; *Int'l*, pg. 922
Hudson, Douglas K., Sr. V.P.--Poe & Brown, Inc., Daytona Beach, FL; *U.S. Public*, pg. 1312
Hudson, John, V.P.-Investor Rels.--Parametric Technology Corporation, Waltham, MA; *U.S. Public*, pg. 1257
Hudson, Susan, Dir.-Pub. Rels.--Yenkin-Majestic Paint Corporation, Columbus, OH; *U.S. Private*, pg. 1195
Hue, Henri, Dir.-Communications--AMP de France, Pontoise, France; *U.S. Public*, pg. 8
Huebner, Keith, Mgr.-Mktg. & Communications--Cherry Electrical Products Corporation, Waukegan, IL; *U.S. Public*, pg. 346
Huesner, Martin, Dr., Dir.-Pub. Rels.--Bayerische Vereinsbank Group, Munich, Germany; *Int'l*, pg. 178
Hueston, Robin, Mgr.-Pub. Rels.--Security Pacific Financial Services Inc., San Diego, CA; *U.S. Public*, pg. 181
Huff, Pam, Dir.-Corp. Commun.--Medpartners Inc., Birmingham, AL; *U.S. Public*, pg. 1082
Huggins, Catherine, Mgr.-Pub. Rels.--Preferred Risk Mutual Insurance, West Des Moines, IA; *U.S. Private*, pg. 880
Hughes, Ann, V.P.-Pub. Affairs--A&E Television Networks, New York, NY; *U.S. Private*, pg. 515
Hughes, Betty A., Dir.-Consumer Affairs--Weber-Stephen Products Co., Palatine, IL; *U.S. Private*, pg. 1157
Hughes, Charles, Dir.-Pub. Rels.--Cooper Communities, Inc., Bella Vista, AR; *U.S. Private*, pg. 273
Hughes, Gunnar, Mgr.-Media Rels.--American Century Companies, Inc., Kansas City, MO; *U.S. Private*, pg. 52
Hughes, Kim, Mgr.-Mktg. & Adv.--Clothestime Stores, Inc., Anaheim, CA; *U.S. Public*, pg. 387
Hughes, Larry, Sr. V.P.-Field Services & Customer Service--DHL Airways, Inc., Redwood City, CA; *U.S. Private*, pg. 302
Hugill, Gail, Dir.-Corp. Commun.--Sears plc, London, United Kingdom; *Int'l*, pg. 1217
Hugot, Claude, Mgr.-Pub. Rels.--Sonauto S.A., Saint Ouen, France; *Int'l*, pg. 1063
Hull, Jeff, Mgr.-Pub. Rels.--Matson Navigation Company, Inc., San Francisco, CA; *U.S. Public*, pg. 39
Hull, Jeff, Mgr.-Pub. Rels.--Matson Intermodal System, Inc., San Francisco, CA; *U.S. Public*, pg. 40
Hull, John L., Vice Chm. & Sec.--Hull Corporation, Hatboro, PA; *U.S. Private*, pg. 547
Hull, Phyllis, Dir.-Personnel--Megapulse, Inc., Bedford, MA; *U.S. Private*, pg. 729
Hullman, Klaus, Dir.-Mktg. Commun.--Dresdner Bank AG, Frankfurt/Main, Germany; *Int'l*, pg. 417
Hulsey, Slona, Dir.-Mktg. & Pub. Rels.--Pancho's Mexican Buffet, Inc., Fort Worth, TX; *U.S. Public*, pg. 1255
Hultgren, Dennis N., Dir.-Environmental & Pub. Affairs--Appleton Papers Inc., Appleton, WI; *Int'l*, pg. 567
Hummer, Jim, Dir.-Bus. Opers.--Wilcox Electric, Inc., Kansas City, MO; *Int'l*, pg. 1384
Humphrey, Debra, Dir.-Corp. Commun.--Bowater Incorporated, Greenville, SC; *U.S. Public*, pg. 247
Hunnicut, John, Sr. V.P.-Pub. Rels.--American Institute of C.P.A.'s Inc., New York, NY; *U.S. Private*, pg. 57
Hunsinger, Harold, Mgr.-Communications--Nordyne Inc., Saint Louis, MO; *U.S. Public*, pg. 1193
Hunt, Dave, Mgr.-Mktg. Svcs.--The HON Co., Muscatine, IA; *U.S. Public*, pg. 772
Hunter, Andrew, Mgr.-Corp. Affairs & Inv. Rels.--Hillsdown Holdings Plc, London, United Kingdom; *Int'l*, pg. 619
Hunter, Lisa, Press Officer--Scottish Widows' Fund & Life Assurance Society, Edinburgh, United Kingdom; *Int'l*, pg. 1212
Huntington, Mike, Gen. Mgr. & Dir.-Mktg. & Public Affairs--Intermountain Gas Co., Boise, ID; *U.S. Private*, pg. 568
Huntsberry, Judy, Coord.-Adv. Services--Rheem Water Heater, Montgomery, AL; *Int'l*, pg. 1022
Huot, Isaselle, Dir.-Communications--Degremont Inc., Rueil-Malmaison, France; *Int'l*, pg. 822
Hurcomb, Thomas J., V.P.-Mktg. & Public Affairs--Central Vermont Public Service Corporation, Rutland, VT; *U.S. Public*, pg. 327
Hurelbrink, Gene, Dir.-Personnel--Sangamon Industries, Taylorville, IL; *U.S. Private*, pg. 965
Hurt, Suzanne, Mgr.-Mktg. Communications--U.S. Filter, Lowell, MA; *U.S. Public*, pg. 1682
Hurwitz, A. Richard, V.P.-Corp. Communications--Atlantis Plastic, Inc., Atlanta, GA; *U.S. Public*, pg. 145
Hurwitz, A. Richard, V.P.-Corp. Communications--Biscayne Apparel Inc., Clifton, NJ; *U.S. Public*, pg. 232
Hushen, John W., V.P.-Corp. Affairs--Eaton Corporation, Cleveland, OH; *U.S. Public*, pg. 555
Hussey, John F., V.P.-Corp. Affairs--Nestle Holdings, Inc., Stamford, CT; *Int'l*, pg. 916
Hutchings, John, Dir.-Pub. Rels.--TI Group plc, Abingdon, United Kingdom; *Int'l*, pg. 1337
Hutchins, Sid, Sr. Exec. V.P.-Communications--Maritz Inc., Fenton, MO; *U.S. Private*, pg. 703
Hutchinson, Eileen, Dir.-Mktg. Commun.--Humana Inc., Louisville, KY; *U.S. Public*, pg. 847
Hutchinson, John, Mgr.-Corp. Communications--Gulf Power Company, Pensacola, FL; *U.S. Public*, pg. 1490
Huurdeman, G.H., Dir.-Pub. Rels--Stork N.V., Naarden, Netherlands; *Int'l*, pg. 1304
Hwang, Jennifer, Mgr.-Pub. Rels.--Yahoo!, Inc., Santa Clara, CA; *U.S. Public*, pg. 1787
Hyams, Fair, Dir.-Client Communications--First Commerce Corporation, New Orleans, LA; *U.S. Public*, pg. 629
Hyams, Fair, Dir.-Client Communications--First National Bank of Commerce, New Orleans, LA; *U.S. Public*, pg. 629
Hyatt, Les, Mgr.-Mktg.--Andersen Group, Inc., Bloomfield, CT; *U.S. Public*, pg. 111
Hyde, Tom, Mgr.-Adv. & Customer Rels.--Colorado Interstate Gas Co., Colorado Springs, CO; *U.S. Public*, pg. 390
Hynes, Peter, V.P.-Corp. Pub. Rels.--Unisys Corporation, Blue Bell, PA; *U.S. Public*, pg. 1671
Iacovetti, Benedict J., Treas.--American Travellers Corporation, Bensalem, PA; *U.S. Public*, pg. 433
Ide, Masanori, Gen. Mgr.--Chiyoda Mutual Life Insurance Company, Tokyo, Japan; *Int'l*, pg. 286
Iglesias, Carolyn, Dir.-Corp. Commun.--United Water Resources, Harrington Park, NJ; *U.S. Public*, pg. 1691
Iglesias, Carolyn, Dir.-Pub. Rels.--United Water New Jersey, Inc., Harrington Park, NJ; *U.S. Public*, pg. 1692
Iglesias, Carolyn, Dir.-Pub. Rels.--United Water Works, Harrington Park, NJ; *U.S. Public*, pg. 1692
Ikard, Lance, V.P.-Human Resources--American Color Graphics, Brentwood, TN; *U.S. Public*, pg. 1132
Ikehara, Nancy, Pub. Rels. Specialist--Tosoh Corporation, Tokyo, Japan; *Int'l*, pg. 1407
Ildau, Peter M., V.P.-Corp. Commun.--Recoton Corporation, Lake Mary, FL; *U.S. Public*, pg. 1369
Illig, Lynn, Mgr.-Mktg. Commun.--Matthews International Corp., Pittsburgh, PA; *U.S. Public*, pg. 1059
Imeson, Thomas J., V.P.-Pub. Affairs & Communications--PacifiCorp, Portland, OR; *U.S. Public*, pg. 1251
Imeson, Tom, V.P.-Communications--Utah Power & Light, Salt Lake City, UT; *U.S. Public*, pg. 1251
Imia, Christine, Mgr.-Corp. Commun.--Skyway Freight Systems, Inc., Watsonville, CA; *U.S. Private*, pg. 1005
Imperiale, Carole, Coord.-Pub. Rels.--Schering-Plough Corporation, Madison, NJ; *U.S. Public*, pg. 1438
Infanti, Daniel, V.P.-Corp. Communications & Mktg.--Sharp Electronics Corporation, Mahwah, NJ; *Int'l*, pg. 1228
Ingle, Don, Sr. V.P. & Pub. Rels. Dir.--Rockett, Burkhead, Lewis & Winslow, Raleigh, NC; *U.S. Private*, pg. 938
Ingoldsby, John, Dir.-Investor Rels.--Palomar Medical Technologies, Lexington, MA; *U.S. Public*, pg. 1255
Ingra, Elaine, Mgr.-Pub. Rels.--Tri-City Electrical Contractors Inc., Altamonte Springs, FL; *U.S. Private*, pg. 1100
Ingram, Dale, Dir.-Pub. Rels.--Wal-Mart Stores, Inc., Bentonville, AR; *U.S. Public*, pg. 1732
Ingram, Karen, Dir.-Corp. Commun.--USLD Communications Corp., San Antonio, TX; *U.S. Public*, pg. 969
Ingram, Martha, Dir.-Pub. Affairs--Ingram Industries Inc., Nashville, TN; *U.S. Private*, pg. 562
Ingram, Melinda, Mgr.-Communications--Piggly Wiggly Co., Memphis, TN; *U.S. Public*, pg. 653
Ingrassia, Patrice, Dir.-Adv. & Pub. Rels.--Ernst & Young, LLP, New York, NY; *U.S. Private*, pg. 381
Ingui, Richard, Mgr.-Communications--Atlas Copco Comptec Inc., Voorheesville, NY; *Int'l*, pg. 96
Inkel, H. Albert, Sr. V.P.-Assoc. Rels. & Communication--Horace Mann Educators Corporation, Springfield, IL; *U.S. Public*, pg. 835
Inker, Emrys, Mgr.-Pub. Rels.--Weir Group PLC, Glasgow, United Kingdom; *Int'l*, pg. 1488
Innals, Ann-Charlotte, Dir.-Communications--Stora Forest AB, Falun, Sweden; *Int'l*, pg. 1303
Innes, Jan L., V.P-Communications--Rogers Communications, Inc., Toronto, Canada; *Int'l*, pg. 1122
Innes, Robin, Dir.-Pub. Rels.--Cedar Point, Sandusky, OH; *U.S. Public*, pg. 319

Innes, Robin B., Dir.-Pub. Rels.--Cedar Fair, L.P., Sandusky, OH; *U.S. Public*, pg. 319

Innocent, Jean, Mgr.-Mktg. Communications--TRC Companies, Inc., Windsor, CT; *U.S. Public*, pg. 1557

Insco, Jeff, Mktg., Res. & Pub. Rels. Dir.--AGA Catalog Marketing & Design, New York, NY; *U.S. Private*, pg. 5

Insel, Jackie, Dir.-Mktg., Pub. Rels. & Adv.--Phillips Fine Art Auctioneers, New York, NY; *U.S. Private*, pg. 861

Inston, Clive, Dir.-Corp. Affairs--Imperial Tobacco Group, Ltd., Bristol, United Kingdom; *Int'l*, pg. 666

Irelan, Robert W., V.P.-Pub. Rels.--Maxxam Inc., Houston, TX; *U.S. Public*, pg. 1062

Irelan, Robert W., V.P.-Pub. Rels.--Kaiser Aluminum Corporation, Houston, TX; *U.S. Public*, pg. 1062

Irons, Keith D., V.P.-Public Affairs--Minorco, Luxembourg, Luxembourg; *Int'l*, pg. 77

Isherwood, Madeleine, Dir.-Mktg. Sls. Admin.--Winthrop-Atkins Co., Inc., Middleboro, MA; *U.S. Private*, pg. 1183

Ishibashi, Katsuoki, Mgr.-Pub. Rels.--Tomen Corporation, Osaka, Japan; *Int'l*, pg. 1395

Ishika, Mika, Corp. Communications--Sony Corporation, Tokyo, Japan; *Int'l*, pg. 1280

Ising, E. James, 2nd V.P.-Field Incentives & Communications--Providian Agency Group, Louisville, KY; *Int'l*, pg. 27

Isman, Barbara, Asst. V.P. & Mgr.-Corp. Affairs--Cargill Ltd., Winnipeg, Canada; *U.S. Private*, pg. 210

Isola, Rainer, Mgr.-Pub. Rels.--Mazda Austria GmbH, Klagenfurt, Austria; *Int'l*, pg. 849

Issler, Jurg, Mgr.-Pub. Rels.--Oerlikon Buhrle Immobilien AG, Zurich, Switzerland; *Int'l*, pg. 998

Issler, Jurg, Mgr.-Pub. Rels.--Uto Albis AG, Zurich, Switzerland; *Int'l*, pg. 998

Itoi, Nobuo, Mng. Dir.-Corp. Plng., Pub. Rels., Environmental Affairs & Opers.--Nikon Corporation, Tokyo, Japan; *Int'l*, pg. 931

Iverson, Mark, Dir.-Adv. & Pub. Rels.--DataCard Corporation, Minnetonka, MN; *U.S. Private*, pg. 312

Ivic, Bart, V.P.-Mktg. Communications--Blue Coral/Slick 50, Cleveland, OH; *U.S. Public*, pg. 1348

Ivins, Chrystele, Mgr.-Communications--Groupe Usinor, Paris, France; *Int'l*, pg. 570

Iwashita, K.M., Mgr.-Pub. Affairs--The Lubrizol Corporation, Wickliffe, OH; *U.S. Public*, pg. 1016

Izawa, Hirotoshi, Gen. Mgr.--The Tokio Marine & Fire Insurance Company, Ltd., Tokyo, Japan; *Int'l*, pg. 1391

Jabinger, Harald, Mgr.-Pub. Rels.--Novartis-Pharma GmbH, Vienna, Austria; *Int'l*, pg. 984

Jachetti, Richard, Sr. V.P. & Pub. Rels. Dir.--Dugan Valva Contess Inc., Morristown, NJ; *U.S. Private*, pg. 345

Jackson, Dave, Mgr.-Direct Mktg. & Pub. Rels.--Hechinger Company Investors II, L.P., Largo, MD; *U.S. Private*, pg. 477

Jackson, Graham H., Div. V.P.-Govt. Rels. & Corp. Communications--Nalco Chemical Company, Naperville, IL; *U.S. Public*, pg. 1150

Jackson, Mary Ann, Sr. Mgr.-Corp. Pub. Rels. & Adv.--InterBold, Canton, OH; *U.S. Public*, pg. 506

Jackson, Nina, Coord.-Publications--Alimed, Inc., Dedham, MA; *U.S. Private*, pg. 34

Jackson, Peter, Grp. Mgr.-Communications--Royal & Sun Alliance Insurance Group plc, London, United Kingdom; *Int'l*, pg. 1130

Jackson, Wayne, Dir.-Corp. Communications & Investor Rels.--GRC International, Inc., Vienna, VA; *U.S. Public*, pg. 695

Jacob, John E., Chief Communications Officer & Exec. V.P.--Anheuser-Busch Companies, Inc., Saint Louis, MO; *U.S. Public*, pg. 113

Jacob, Maureen, Asst. to V.P.- Corp.Communications/ Pub.Rels.--Joseph E. Seagram & Sons, Inc., New York, NY; *Int'l*, pg. 1215

Jacobi, Mary Jo, Grp. Mgr.-Public Affairs--HSBC Holdings plc, London, United Kingdom; *Int'l*, pg. 579

Jacobs, Daniel F., Dir.-Mktg.--RNL Facilities Corporation, Denver, CO; *U.S. Private*, pg. 905

Jacobs, Franklin A., Chm. Bd. & Chief Exec. Officer--Falcon Products, Inc., Saint Louis, MO; *U.S. Public*, pg. 611

Jacobs, Fred, Dir.-Pub. Rels.--Busch Entertainment Corp., Clayton, MO; *U.S. Public*, pg. 114

Jacobs, Fred, Dir.-Pub. Rels.--Sea World of California, San Diego, CA; *U.S. Public*, pg. 114

Jacobsen, Mary Jeane, V.P. & Dir.-Pub. Affairs--National Geographic Society, Washington, DC; *U.S. Private*, pg. 783

Jacoby, Jeff, Dir.-Pub. Affairs--FMC Corp., Agricultural Products Group, Philadelphia, PA; *U.S. Public*, pg. 605

Jacques, Serge A., V.P.-Human Resources & Communications--St. Lawrence Cement Inc., Montreal, Canada; *Int'l*, pg. 628

Jadwin, Linda J., V.P.-H.R.--Ceridian Corporation, Bloomington, MN; *U.S. Public*, pg. 330

Jaeschke, Monica, Mgr.-Promo.--A&W Food Services of Canada Inc., North Vancouver, Canada; *Int'l*, pg. 1

Jaffe, Stewart, Mgr.-Mktg.--Surgical Laser Technologies, Inc., Montgomeryville, PA; *U.S. Public*, pg. 1542

Jagerfelt, Lars, Exec. V.P.-Corp. Communications & Pub. Affairs--Saab AB, Linkoping, Sweden; *Int'l*, pg. 686

Jaggi, Andreas, Dir.-Pub. Rels.--Swiss Reinsurance Company, Zurich, Switzerland; *Int'l*, pg. 1332

Jake, Peggy, Dir.-Pub. Rels.--Parsons & Whittemore, Inc., Rye Brook, NY; *U.S. Private*, pg. 840

James, Betty M., Pres. & Dir.-Mktg. & Pub. Rels.--James Industries Inc., Hollidaysburg, PA; *U.S. Private*, pg. 580

Jandahl, Keith E., V.P.-Agency Rels.--Tri-State Insurance Company of Minnesota, Luverne, MN; *U.S. Public*, pg. 215

Janeway, Barbara, Pub. Rels. Coord.--Ralphs Grocery Company, Compton, CA; *U.S. Private*, pg. 1202

Jani, Rosana, Mgr.-Pub. Affairs--Liang Court Holdings Ltd., Singapore, Singapore; *Int'l*, pg. 807

Janis, Ann H., Pub. Rels. Assoc.--Dynatech Corporation, Burlington, MA; *U.S. Public*, pg. 539

Janisch, Patrick, Dir.-Mktg. & Pub. Rels.--Bridgeman's Restaurants Inc., Minnetonka, MN; *U.S. Private*, pg. 167

Janke, W., V.P.-Customer Services--Transalta Corporation, Calgary, Canada; *Int'l*, pg. 1416

Jarboe, Greg, Dir.-Pub. Rels.--Ziff-Davis Publishing Company, New York, NY; *Int'l*, pg. 1276

Jarcho, Wendy, Mgr.-Intl. Promo.--National Geographic Magazine, Paris, France; *U.S. Private*, pg. 784

Jardim, Carlos Eduardo, V.P.-Corp. Affairs--Cervejarias Kaiser Brasil Ltda., Campinas, Brazil; *Int'l*, pg. 279

Jarman, Mark W., Mgr.-Corp. Commun. & New Bus. Devel.--Dynamic Materials Corporation, Lafayette, CO; *U.S. Public*, pg. 539

Jascot, Paul S., Mgr.-Public Rels.--General Electric Canada Inc., Mississauga, Canada; *U.S. Public*, pg. 713

Jaspert, Mr., Dir.-Pub. Rels & Communications--Lux GmbH & Co. KG, Wermelskirchen, Germany; *Int'l*, pg. 993

Javier, Rey M., V.P.-Corp. Dev.--EEI Corporation, Manila, Philippines; *Int'l*, pg. 425

Jaxtimer, Joanne, V.P.-Corp. Affairs & Mtkg.--The Boston Company, Inc., Boston, MA; *U.S. Public*, pg. 1085

Jaxtimer, Joanne, V.P.-Corp. Affairs & Corp. Mktg.--Boston Safe Deposit & Trust Co., Boston, MA; *U.S. Public*, pg. 1085

Jayne-Bell, Jennifer, Dir.-Media & Pub. Rels.--Warmington Homes, Costa Mesa, CA; *U.S. Private*, pg. 1150

Jaynes, Roger, Dir.-Pub. Rels.--Times Printing Company, Inc., Random Lake, WI; *U.S. Private*, pg. 1087

Jeffers, David, V.P.-Corp. Rels.--Federal National Mortgage Association (Fannie Mae), Washington, DC; *U.S. Public*, pg. 615

Jefferson, Gary S., V.P.-Pub. Affairs--UAL Corporation, Elk Grove Village, IL; *U.S. Public*, pg. 1652

Jeffreys, Robert, Mgr.-Corp. Commun.--Scott Specialty Gases, Plumsteadville, PA; *U.S. Private*, pg. 977

Jehlik, Ann, Mgr.-Customer Svc.--The Promotion in Motion Companies, Closter, NJ; *U.S. Private*, pg. 890

Jellen, Steve, Mgr.-Service--Fairway Ford, Inc., Greenville, SC; *U.S. Private*, pg. 392

Jemerson, Valerie, Asst. V.P.-Corp. Communications--Citizens Banking Corporation, Flint, MI; *U.S. Public*, pg. 379

Jenkins, Ezra, Mgr.-Employee Rels.--C. B. Fleet Co., Inc., Lynchburg, VA; *U.S. Private*, pg. 410

Jenkins, Shelly, Mgr.-Corp Communications--Norcen Energy Resources Limited, Calgary, Canada; *Int'l*, pg. 434

Jenks, Alison, Mgr.-Pub. Rels.--Cobra Golf Incorporated, Carlsbad, CA; *U.S. Public*, pg. 675

Jenni, Peter, Head-Corp. Communications--Ascom Holding AG, Bern, Switzerland; *Int'l*, pg. 86

Jennings, Jon, Pur. Rep.--Phoenix Home Life Mutual Insurance Company, Hartford, CT; *U.S. Private*, pg. 863

Jennings, Roberta R., Mgr.-Pub. Rels.--Fifth Third Bancorp, Cincinnati, OH; *U.S. Public*, pg. 621

Jennings, Roberta R., V.P.-Pub. Rels.--The Fifth Third Bank, Cincinnati, OH; *U.S. Public*, pg. 621

Jensen, Paul, Dir.-Pub. Rels.--Arizona Cardinals, Phoenix, AZ; *U.S. Private*, pg. 81

Jensen, Robert K., Pres.--Fleischli Oil Company, Inc., Cheyenne, WY; *U.S. Private*, pg. 410

Jensen, Sharon, Dir.-Corp. Communications--Cold Spring Granite Company, Cold Spring, MN; *U.S. Private*, pg. 250

Jensen, V. E., Mgr.-Adv. & Pub. Rels.--Square D Automation Products, Milwaukee, WI; *Int'l*, pg. 1208

Jenter, Juergen, Mgr.-Press--Richard Hirschmann GmbH & Co., Neckartenzlingen, Germany; *Int'l*, pg. 1108

Jeofforry, Carolyn, Dir.-Pub. Rels.--Lafarge Refractaires Monolithiques, Montrouge, France; *Int'l*, pg. 789

Jerome, Jane, Corp. Communications Admin.--The Chase Manhattan Bank, N.A., London, United Kingdom; *U.S. Public*, pg. 339

Jerome, Melissa, Dir.-Pub. Rels.--Sachs Holding Company, Chesterfield, MO; *U.S. Private*, pg. 959

Jerome, P.A., Corp. Dir.-Human Resources--John Brown Plastics Machinery, Attleboro, MA; *Int'l*, pg. 773

Jeske, Erich R., Dir.-Pub. Rels.--Quelle Group, Furth, Germany; *Int'l*, pg. 1078

Jessie, Janelle M., Asst. V.P. & Dir.-Adv. & Pub. Rels.--Chemed Corporation, Cincinnati, OH; *U.S. Public*, pg. 343

Jessup, Jan, Pub. Rels.--Calico Corners, Kennett Square, PA; *U.S. Private*, pg. 386

Jewell, Nancy, Dir.-Publicity--VWS, Inc., Cleveland, OH; *Int'l*, pg. 440

Jewell, Rob, Staff V.P.-Corp. Commun.--The B.F. Goodrich Company, Richfield, OH; *U.S. Public*, pg. 751

Jewels, Bob, Mgr.-Pub. Rels.--Waccamaw Corporation, Myrtle Beach, SC; *U.S. Private*, pg. 1145

Jezequel, Joelle, Mgr.-Fin. Commun.--Remy Cointreau, Paris, France; *Int'l*, pg. 1102

Jirsa, Robert J., Dir.-Environmental & Corp. Affairs--Plum Creek Timber Co., L.P., Seattle, WA; *U.S. Public*, pg. 1311

Joffray, Jeffrey J., V.P.-Corp. & Consumer Affairs--Rexair, Inc., Troy, MI; *U.S. Public*, pg. 1684

Johannsen, Linda, Sr. Mgr.-Mktg. Services--Sensormatic Electronics Corporation, Boca Raton, FL; *U.S. Public*, pg. 1457

Johansson, Jan, Mgr.-Pub. Rels.--Ford Motor Norge A/S, Kolbotn, Norway; *U.S. Public*, pg. 666

Johansson, Lars Goran, Dir.-Communications & Pub. Affairs--Electrolux, AB, Stockholm, Sweden; *Int'l*, pg. 438

Johnson, Alberto K., Mgr.-Pub. Rels. & Adv.--Neumaticos Goodyear SA, Buenos Aires, Argentina; *U.S. Public*, pg. 753

Johnson, Bill, Dir.-Pub. Rels.--Purity Dairies Inc., Nashville, TN; *U.S. Private*, pg. 895

Johnson, Carol, Mgr.-Pub. Rels.--Mervyn's California, Hayward, CA; *U.S. Public*, pg. 489

Johnson, Cheryl, Mgr.-Communications--MRC Bearings, Jamestown, NY; *Int'l*, pg. 1157

Johnson, David H., Mgr.-Mktg. Communications--Twin Disc, Incorporated, Racine, WI; *U.S. Public*, pg. 1646

Johnson, Diane, Mgr.-Pub. Rels.--Harris Farms, Inc., Coalinga, CA; *U.S. Private*, pg. 505

Johnson, Dwayne, Mgr.-Mktg. Communications & Adv.--Republic Automotive-AEA Division, Charlotte, NC; *U.S. Public*, pg. 1377

Johnson, Eileen, V.P.-Corp. Communications--Pan-American Life Insurance Company, New Orleans, LA; *U.S. Private*, pg. 836

Johnson, Fred, Sr. V.P. & Dir.-Newspaper Rels.--Parade Publications Inc., New York, NY; *U.S. Private*, pg. 20

Johnson, Geralyn A., Dir.-Corp. Commun.--Yankee Energy System, Inc., Meriden, CT; *U.S. Public*, pg. 1787

Johnson, H. Gene, Mgr.-Mktg. Commun.--Telsco Industries, Garland, TX; *U.S. Private*, pg. 1074

Johnson, J.L., V.P.-Personnel & Indus. Rels.--General Dynamics Land Systems Div., Muskegon, MI; *U.S. Public*, pg. 709

Johnson, Janilee, V.P.-Pub. Affairs, Promo. & Adv.--Bellcore, Morristown, NJ; *U.S. Private*, pg. 976

Johnson, Lea, Mgr.-Communications--Duff-Norton, Charlotte, NC; *U.S. Public*, pg. 406

Johnson, Leland P., Sr. V.P.-Claims--Berkley Risk Services, Inc., Minneapolis, MN; *U.S. Public*, pg. 215

Johnson, Linda, Mgr.-Adv., Sls. Promo. & Pub. Rels.--Chloride Industrial Batteries Ltd., Manchester, United Kingdom; *Int'l*, pg. 125

Johnson, Mike, Dir.-Communications--G. Leblanc Corporation, Kenosha, WI; *U.S. Private*, pg. 656

Johnson, Noreen, Asst. V.P. & Dir.-Corp. Communications--State Automobile Mutual Insurance Co., Columbus, OH; *U.S. Private*, pg. 1036

Johnson, Paul R., Dir.-Pub. Rels.--Tenneco Automotive, Deerfield, IL; *U.S. Public*, pg. 1577

Johnson, Shelly, Mgr.-Mktg. & Pub. Rels.--MCO Properties Inc., Fountain Hills, AZ; *U.S. Public*, pg. 1062

Johnson, Steve, Sr. V.P.-Pub. Rels.--Union Bank of California, San Francisco, CA; *Int'l*, pg. 157

Johnson, Steven A., V.P.-Customer Svc., Gen. Counsel & Sec.--Maine Public Service Company, Presque Isle, ME; *U.S. Public*, pg. 1038

Johnson, Thomas D., Dir.-Investor Rels.--Blount International, Inc., Montgomery, AL; *U.S. Public*, pg. 237

Johnson, Turner, Mgr.-Communications--Measuring Systems Division, North Kingstown, RI; *U.S. Public*, pg. 260

Johnston, Bill, Dir.-Pub. Rels.--San Diego Chargers, San Diego, CA; *U.S. Private*, pg. 964

Johnston, Libby, Mgr.-Public Affairs--Andersen Corporation, Bayport, MN; *U.S. Private*, pg. 71

Johnston, Steve, Mgr.-Pub. Rels.--Nationwide Life Insurance Co., Columbus, OH; *U.S. Private*, pg. 789

Johnston, Steve, Mgr.-Pub. Rels.--Public Employees Benefit Services Corp., Columbus, OH; *U.S. Private*, pg. 789

Joiner, Lynn, Mgr.-Media Rels.--Port of Oakland, Oakland, CA; *U.S. Private*, pg. 876

Jolley, Don, Mgr.-Adv. & Mktg. Communications--Thermal Ceramics Inc., Augusta, GA; *Int'l*, pg. 894

Jolly, Al, Sr. V.P.-Human Resources--CVS Corp., Woonsocket, RI; *U.S. Public*, pg. 287

Joly, John, Dir.-Pub. Affairs--Seattle Post-Intelligencer, Seattle, WA; *U.S. Private*, pg. 517

Jones Turner, Marta, V.P.-Pub. Affairs--Flowers Industries, Inc., Thomasville, GA; *U.S. Public*, pg. 656

Jones, Annabel, Mgr.-Corp. Devel.--Coats Viyella plc, Manchester, United Kingdom; *Int'l*, pg. 299

Jones, D.M., Mgr.-Customer Service--British Gypsum Ltd., Loughborough, United Kingdom; *Int'l*, pg. 122

Jones, Diane S., Mgr.-Corp. Rels. & Bus. Devel.--Westmoreland Coal Co., Colorado Springs, CO; *U.S. Public*, pg. 1761

Jones, Grant, Mgr.-Pub. Rels.--Ore-Ida Foods, Inc., Boise, ID; *U.S. Public*, pg. 805

Jones, Harvey, Pub. Rels.--Kimberly-Clark Inc., Mississauga, Canada; *U.S. Public*, pg. 959

Jones, John P., Dir.-Indus. Rels.--YSD Industries, Youngstown, OH; *U.S. Private*, pg. 1194

Jones, Jon, V.P.-Distr. & Matls. Mgmt.--Igloo Products Corporation, Houston, TX; *U.S. Public*, pg. 265

Jones, Lloyd, Exec. V.P.--A.G. Simpson Co. Limited, Scarborough, Canada; *Int'l*, pg. 1252

Jones, Mike, Mgr.-Pub. Rels.--Royal & Sun Alliance Insurance Group plc, London, United Kingdom; *Int'l*, pg. 1130

Jones, N.R., Mgr.-Pub. Rels.--LucasVarity plc, London, United Kingdom; *Int'l*, pg. 819

Jones, Patty, Dir.-Commun.--Reckitt & Colman Inc., Montvale, NJ; *Int'l*, pg. 1090

Jones, Robert, Mgr.-Media Rels.--Lincoln National Corporation, Fort Wayne, IN; *U.S. Public*, pg. 997

Jones, Roy, Mgr.-Corp. Commun.--MDIS Group plc, Hemel Hempstead, United Kingdom; *Int'l*, pg. 826

Jones, Stephanie, Mgr.-Mktg. & Communications--Instrument Specialties Company, Delaware Water Gap, PA; *U.S. Private*, pg. 565

Jones, Susan S., Mgr.-Mktg. Communications--BNA Software, Washington, DC; *U.S. Private*, pg. 182

Jones, Y., Pub. Rels.--Ceco Door Products, Brentwood, TN; *U.S. Public*, pg. 1676

Jonson, Bjorn, Dir.-Grp. Info.--Sandvik AB, Sandviken, Sweden; *Int'l*, pg. 1185

Jonsson, Lennart, Dir.-Pub. Rels.--Celsius AB, Stockholm, Sweden; *Int'l*, pg. 276

Jordan, James, Dir.-Mktg. & Adv.--Multiple Allied Services, Inc., Hayward, CA; *U.S. Private*, pg. 767

Jordan, Lani, Dir.-Corp. Commun.--CENEX, Inc., Inver Grove Heights, MN; *U.S. Private*, pg. 221

Jordan, Lynn, Mktg. Communications Specialist--Curtis 1000, Inc., Atlanta, GA; *U.S. Public*, pg. 70

Jorgensen, Ken, Mgr.-Pub. Rels.--Smith & Wesson Corp., Springfield, MA; *Int'l*, pg. 1397

Jorgensen, Virgil, Mgr.-Adv. & Pub. Rels.--Hydro-Aire, Burbank, CA; *U.S. Public*, pg. 457

Joseph, Mark M., Mgr.-Mktg. Communications--Fel-Pro Incorporated, Skokie, IL; *U.S. Private*, pg. 399

Joseph, Meril, Sr. V.P.-Mktg. & Communications--Fortis, Inc., New York, NY; *Int'l*, pg. 499
Joseph, Thad, Asst. V.P.-Adv. & Pub. Rels.--Miracle Recreation Equipment Company, Monett, MO; *U.S. Private*, pg. 752
Jost, Gabriele, Mgr.-Pub. Rels.--Filterwerk Mann & Hummel GmbH, Ludwigsburg, Germany; *Int'l*, pg. 484
Joubert, Marie-Pierre, Mgr.-Communications--Banco Banque Nationale de Paris Brasil S/A, Sao Paulo, Brazil; *Int'l*, pg. 164
Jouett, Jeff, Mgr.-Pub. Rels.--Marine World Africa USA, Vallejo, CA; *U.S. Private*, pg. 703
Joustra, M.P.F., Dir.-Pub. Rels.--Ballast Nedam IGB B.V., Amstelveen, Netherlands; *Int'l*, pg. 133
Joyce, Thomas J., V.P.-Investor & Community Rels.--Rockwell International Corporation, Costa Mesa, CA; *U.S. Public*, pg. 1397
Joyner, Henry, V.P.-Mktg. Plng.--American Airlines, Inc., Fort Worth, TX; *U.S. Public*, pg. 9
Judy, Deborah, Admin. Asst.--United Dominion Realty Trust, Inc., Richmond, VA; *U.S. Public*, pg. 1677
Juenger, Teresa, Dir.-Mktg.--ICI Explosives USA Inc., Dallas, TX; *Int'l*, pg. 663
Juhler-Kjaer, Annette, Mgr.-Grp. Commun.--Danisco A/S, Copenhagen, Denmark; *Int'l*, pg. 378
Jurek, Noreen, Sr. Mgr.-Mktg. Commun.--Tekelec, Calabasas, CA; *U.S. Public*, pg. 1566
Jurgen, H., Product Mgr.-Publicity--Rohm GmbH, Darmstadt, Germany; *Int'l*, pg. 1454
Jusko, Jackie, Pub. Rels. Dir.--Stern Advertising, Inc., Cleveland, OH; *U.S. Private*, pg. 1041
Kaar, Alison, Sr. Dir.-Communications & Public Relations--Lenscrafters, Cincinnati, OH; *Int'l*, pg. 822
Kaburaki, K., Mgr.-Customer Svc.--BancTec Japan Inc., Tokyo, Japan; *U.S. Public*, pg. 177
Kado, Tom, Asst. Gen. Mgr.-Publicity--Matsushita Electric Works, Ltd., Osaka, Japan; *Int'l*, pg. 847
Kaelin, W.E., V.P. & Gen Mgr.-Communications Div.--Lambda Advanced Analog, Santa Clara, CA; *Int'l*, pg. 1241
Kagan, Dave, Dir.-Communications--Bissell Inc., Grand Rapids, MI; *U.S. Private*, pg. 145
Kahen, Wendy, Mktg. Commun. Specialist--Dann Dee Display Fixtures, Niles, IL; *U.S. Private*, pg. 310
Kahle, Shawn McGee, V.P.-Corp. Affairs--Kmart Corporation, Troy, MI; *U.S. Public*, pg. 963
Kahn, Bette, Mgr.-Pub. Rels. & Community Affairs--Euromarket Designs, Inc., Northbrook, IL; *U.S. Private*, pg. 384
Kahn, Judith, Mgr.-Pub. Rels.--Ark Restaurants Corp., New York, NY; *U.S. Public*, pg. 129
Kahn, Judy, V.P.-Publ. Rels. & Strategic Devel.--Shafer, Irvine, CA; *U.S. Private*, pg. 988
Kahnert, Peter, Mgr.-Pub. Rels.--Midland Walwyn Capital Inc., Toronto, Canada; *Int'l*, pg. 865
Kahre, Annette, Dr., Mgr.-Pub. Rels.--Melitta Unternehmensgruppe Bentz KG, Minden, Germany; *Int'l*, *pg. 856*
Kai, Brenda, V.P.-Communications--TIG Holdings, Inc., New York, NY; *U.S. Public*, pg. 1555
Kaine, Mike, Mgr.-Communications--Bell Atlantic-NJ, Newark, NJ; *U.S. Public*, pg. 202
Kainulainen, Eeva, V.P.-Corporate Communications--Metra Corporation, Helsinki, Finland; *Int'l*, pg. 862
Kaiser, Kurt, Dir.-Corp. Affairs--Panalpina Welttransport (Holding) AG, Binningen, Switzerland; *Int'l*, pg. 1022
Kaiser, Patrick, Head-Corp. Commun.--Danzas Holding Ltd., Basel, Switzerland; *Int'l*, pg. 382
Kal, Alison, V.P.-Mktg. Commun.--Hilton Hotels Corporation, Beverly Hills, CA; *U.S. Public*, pg. 828
Kalata, J., Sr. V.P.-Mktg. & Prod. Devel.--Air Canada Vacations Inc., Montreal, Canada; *Int'l*, pg. 36
Kalell, Susan, Mgr.-Pub. Rels.--SPSS Inc., Chicago, IL; *U.S. Public*, pg. 1420
Kalette, Stephen R., V.P.-Admin. & Gen. Counsel--Pubco Corporation, Cleveland, OH; *U.S. Public*, pg. 1339
Kalis, David B., V.P.-Communications--International Business Machines Corporation, Armonk, NY; *U.S. Public*, pg. 895
Kalmar, Janice, Dir.-Corp. Commun.--Grubb & Ellis Company, Northbrook, IL; *U.S. Public*, pg. 767
Kamarinopoulos, J., Mgr.-Pub. Rels.--Karelia Tobacco Company Inc., Kalamata, Greece; *Int'l*, pg. 724
Kamel, Rick, Dir.-Pub. Rels.--J.W. Messner, Inc., Grand Rapids, MI; *U.S. Private*, pg. 734
Kamins, Aaron J., Chief Fin. Officer--Accurate Perforating Co., Chicago, IL; *U.S. Private*, pg. 12
Kaminski, Teri, Dir.-Pub. Rels.--Brach & Brock Confections, Inc., Chicago, IL; *U.S. Private*, pg. 163
Kamiya, D., Mgr.-Pub. Rels./Wharton Unit--British Aerospace Defence Limited (Military Aircraft), Preston, United Kingdom; *Int'l*, pg. 217
Kamp, Dave, Mgr.-Pub. Rels.--VTEL Corporation, Austin, TX; *U.S. Public*, pg. 1703
Kamp, Gregg, V.P. & Pub. Rels.--P.W. Minor & Son, Inc., Batavia, NY; *U.S. Private*, pg. 751
Kamp, Kim, Mgr.-Pub. Rels.--Scott & Stringfellow Financial, Inc., Richmond, VA; *U.S. Public*, pg. 1445
Kanatomi, Nobuyuki, Mgr.-Pub. Rels.--Komatsu Ltd., Tokyo, Japan; *Int'l*, pg. 743
Kandel, Charlotte, Sr. V.P.-Worldwide Publicity & Promotion--Warner Bros. Studios, Inc., Burbank, CA; *U.S. Public*, pg. 1611
Kane, Terry, Mgr.-Adv. & Pub. Rels.--G.E. Superabrasives, Worthington, OH; *U.S. Public*, pg. 711
Kanner, Dianne, Mgr.-Pub. Rels.--AC Martin Partners, Los Angeles, CA; *U.S. Private*, pg. 708
Kaplan, I., Dir.-Pub. Rels.--Elbit Computers Ltd., Haifa, Israel; *Int'l*, pg. 644
Kaplan, Karen, Dir.-Pub. Rels.--Solvay Pharmaceuticals, Inc., Marietta, GA; *Int'l*, pg. 1278
Kaplan, Marcie, Mktg. Communications--Stone Container Corporation, Chicago, IL; *U.S. Public*, pg. 1520
Kaplan, Perrin, Dir.-Corp. Affairs--Nintendo of America, Redmond, WA; *Int'l*, pg. 932
Kappi, Markku, Mgr.-Pub. Rels.--Valmet Automation Inc., Helsinki, Finland; *Int'l*, pg. 1449
Karales, Marci, Mgr.-Pub. Rels.--Reed & Barton Corporation, Taunton, MA; *U.S. Private*, pg. 916
Karasic, Lisa, Mgr.-Bus. Communications--Engelhard Corp.-Quincy Operations, Quincy, FL; *U.S. Public*, pg. 582
Karass, Audrey, V.P.-Mktg. & Dir.-Corp. Video Systems & Telecommunications--Caristrap International Inc., Laval, Canada; *Int'l*, pg. 271
Karber, Wolfgang, Mgr.-Pub. Rels.--Olivetti Austria G.m.b.H., Vienna, Austria; *Int'l*, pg. 1003
Karch, Cheri, Mgr.-Corp. Affairs--Worzalla Publishing Co., Inc., Stevens Point, WI; *U.S. Private*, pg. 1191
Karlsson, Hans-Olof, Sr. V.P.-Corp. Communications--NCC AB, Solna, Sweden; *Int'l*, pg. 898
Karn, Cheri, V.P.-Corp. Communications--Mercantile Bancorporation Inc., Saint Louis, MO; *U.S. Public*, pg. 1087
Karna, Laura, Commun. Asst.--Valmet Corporation, Helsinki, Finland; *Int'l*, pg. 1447
Kashiwakura, Luke, Sr. Mgr.-Corp. Affairs--Hitachi America, Ltd., Tarrytown, NY; *Int'l*, pg. 622
Kasper, Kevin, V.P.-Corp. Communications--Fiserv, Inc., Brookfield, WI; *U.S. Public*, pg. 647
Kate, Lynda, Dir.-Communications--American Eurocopter Corp., Grand Prairie, TX; *Int'l*, pg. 29
Kato, Norio, Gen. Mgr.-Investor Rels.--Cosmo Oil Co., Ltd., Tokyo, Japan; *Int'l*, pg. 335
Katz, Carl, Pub. Rels.--G-III Apparel Group, Ltd., New York, NY; *U.S. Public*, pg. 690
Katzenberg, Noemi, Dir.-Pub. Rels.--NCC Real Estate, Solna, Sweden; *Int'l*, pg. 899
Kaufman, Carol, Dir.-Adv.--Fred V. Fowler Company, Inc., Newton, MA; *U.S. Private*, pg. 422
Kaufman, Lawrence H., Mng. Dir.-Corp. Communications--Union Pacific Railroad Company, Omaha, NE; *U.S. Public*, pg. 1668
Kaufman, Lawrence H., Mng. Dir.-Corp. Communications--Southern Pacific Rail Corporation, San Francisco, CA; *U.S. Public*, pg. 1668
Kaufmann, Denise, V.P.-Pub. Rels.--Marketing Support, Incorporated, Chicago, IL; *U.S. Private*, pg. 705
Kaufmann, Muriel, Press Officer--Iveco France S.A., Trappes, France; *Int'l*, pg. 696
Kaukas, Bruce, V.P.-Commun.--ABB Asea Brown Boveri (Holding) Ltd., Zurich, Switzerland; *Int'l*, pg. 1
Kaul, Kim, Mgr.-Pub. Rels.--Piper Capital Management, Incorporated, Minneapolis, MN; *U.S. Public*, pg. 1303
Kavarana, F.K., Exec. Dir.-Corp. Affairs--Tata Engineering & Locomotive Co. Ltd. (TELCO), Mumbai, India; *Int'l*, pg. 369
Kawachi, Shinjiro, Gen. Mgr.-Pub. Rels.--Kawasho Corporation, Tokyo, Japan; *Int'l*, pg. 726
Kawakatsu, Shotaro, Pub. Rels.--Showa Denko K.K., Tokyo, Japan; *Int'l*, pg. 1236
Kawasaki, Tatsuo, Mgr.-Pub. Rels.--Nemic-Lambda KK, Tokyo, Japan; *Int'l*, pg. 1242
Kaye, David, Assoc. Dir.-Corp. Communications--Amgen Inc., Thousand Oaks, CA; *U.S. Public*, pg. 100
Kays, Margaret J., V.P.-Human Resources--Investors Heritage Life Insurance Co., Frankfort, KY; *U.S. Public*, pg. 952
Kaz, Noma, Dir.-Pub. Rels.--Pacific Crest Capital, Inc., Agoura Hills, CA; *U.S. Public*, pg. 1248
Keane, Kathleen A., Corp. Sec.--Stanley Consultants, Inc., Muscatine, IA; *U.S. Private*, pg. 1033
Keating, Anne, Corp. V.P.-Pub. Rels.--Bloomingdale's, New York, NY; *U.S. Public*, pg. 617
Keating, MaryJo, V.P.-Commun.--Northeast Utilities, Berlin, CT; *U.S. Public*, pg. 1194
Keating, Richard P., V.P.-Corp. Communications & Adv.--USLIFE Corporation, New York, NY; *U.S. Public*, pg. 77
Keating, William M., V.P. & Controller--Lane Industries, Inc., Northbrook, IL; *U.S. Private*, pg. 649
Keck, Paula, Commun. Coord.--Woodcraft Industries, Inc., Saint Cloud, MN; *U.S. Private*, pg. 1187
Keech, Jeanette, Mgr.-Pub. Rels.--Taunton Cider Company P.L.C., Taunton, United Kingdom; *Int'l*, pg. 849
Keegan, Denise, Mgr.-Pub. Rels.--Almay, Inc., New York, NY; *U.S. Private*, pg. 689
Keegan, Hugh, Adv. & Mkt. Res.--Ventre Packing Company, Inc., Syracuse, NY; *U.S. Private*, pg. 1135
Keelty, Richard, V.P.-Pub. Affairs--Warner-Lambert Company, Morris Plains, NJ; *U.S. Public*, pg. 1738
Keelty, Richard W., V.P.-Pub. Affairs--Adams U.S.A., Morris Plains, NJ; *U.S. Public*, pg. 1739
Keenan, Heather, Mktg. Commun. Specialist--IEC Electronics Corp., Newark, NY; *U.S. Public*, pg. 854
Keenan, Leslie, Sr. Dir.-Communications--Manor Healthcare Corp., Gaithersburg, MD; *U.S. Public*, pg. 1041
Keifer, Scott, Communications Editor--The Vernon Company, Newton, IA; *U.S. Private*, pg. 1137
Keir, Gerald J., Sr. V.P.-Corp. Communications Div.--First Hawaiian Bank, Honolulu, HI; *U.S. Public*, pg. 634
Keithley, Don, Partner & Dealer Rels.--J.D. Power and Associates, Agoura Hills, CA; *U.S. Private*, pg. 878
Kelai, Merle A.K., V.P.-Community Rels.--Matson Navigation Company, Inc., San Francisco, CA; *U.S. Public*, pg. 39
Kelberg, Maria, Media Dir. & Pub. Rels. Dir.--Styx & Leo Burnett, Almaty, Kazakhstan; *U.S. Private*, pg. 186
Kelleher, Timothy J., Sr. V.P.-Labor Rels.--Detroit Newspapers, Detroit, MI; *U.S. Public*, pg. 965
Kellenberger, Mike, V.P.-Client Relations--Leon Shaffer Golnick Advertising, Inc., Fort Lauderdale, FL; *U.S. Private*, pg. 463
Keller, Candace, Dir.-Mktg. Commun.--Jami, Inc., Shawnee Mission, KS; *U.S. Private*, pg. 581
Keller, Conni, Mktg. Communications Coord.--Ohmeda, Inc., Liberty Corner, NJ; *Int'l*, pg. 121
Keller, Michael, Exec. V.P.-Mktg.--Koo Koo Roo, Inc., Los Angeles, CA; *U.S. Public*, pg. 966
Keller, Thomas J., V.P.-Corp. Communications--Siemens Corporation, New York, NY; *Int'l*, pg. 1245
Kelley, Alice, Dir.-Mktg. Communications & Services--Andersen Corporation, Bayport, MN; *U.S. Private*, pg. 71
Kelley, Barbara M., V.P.-Corp. Communications--Bausch & Lomb Incorporated, Rochester, NY; *U.S. Public*, pg. 194
Kelley, James J., Grp. Exec. V.P. & Dir.-Human Resources--Crestar Bank, Richmond, VA; *U.S. Public*, pg. 458
Kelley, Marian Herbst, Dir.-Pub. Rels.--Tracor, Inc., Austin, TX; *U.S. Public*, pg. 1627
Kelley, W.T., V.P.-Public Affairs & Adv.--Canadian National Railway Company, Montreal, Canada; *Int'l*, pg. 258
Kelly-Bartley, Kim, Dir.-Mktg. & Pub. Rels.--White Castle System, Inc., Columbus, OH; *U.S. Private*, pg. 1171
Kelly, Barbara, V.P.-Sls., Mktg. & Customer Service--Time Warner Cable of New York City, New York, NY; *U.S. Public*, pg. 1611
Kelly, David, Mgr.-Pub. Rels.-External Communications--Rhone-Poulenc Rorer Ltd., West Malling, United Kingdom; *Int'l*, pg. 1110
Kelly, Freddye, Dir.-Corp. Comm.--Weingarten Realty Investors, Houston, TX; *U.S. Public*, pg. 1751
Kelly, Julia, Dir.-Adv. & Pub. Rels.--Suncor Development Company, Phoenix, AZ; *U.S. Public*, pg. 1298
Kelly, Loraine, Mgr.-Communications--ICI Acrylics Inc., Cordova, TN; *Int'l*, pg. 663
Kelly, Mary, Mgr.-Pub. Rels.--Kaiser Permanente, Southwest Division, Dallas, TX; *U.S. Private*, pg. 605
Kelly, Susan, Dir.-Pub. Affairs--Hudson's, Southfield, MI; *U.S. Public*, pg. 489
Kelly, W., Mgr.-Adv., Sls. Promo. & Pub. Rels.--Arnotts plc, Dublin, Ireland; *Int'l*, pg. 81
Kelmar, Steven B., II, V.P.-Govt. Affairs & Corp. rels.--Medtronic, Inc., Minneapolis, MN; *U.S. Public*, pg. 1082
Kelsay, Kris, V.P.-Mktg. Commun.--Wall Data Incorporated, Kirkland, WA; *U.S. Public*, pg. 1734
Kemp, Tori, Mgr.-Pub. Rels.--Merit Medical Systems, Inc., South Jordan, UT; *U.S. Public*, pg. 1096
Kempner, Katie, Pub. Rels. Dir.--Crispin Porter & Bogusky Advertising, Miami, FL; *U.S. Private*, pg. 290
Kennedy, Judi, Dir.-Worldwide Media Rels.--American Power Conversion Corporation, West Kingston, RI; *U.S. Public*, pg. 89
Kennedy, Kay, V.P.-Worldwide Mktg. Communications--Korn/Ferry International, Los Angeles, CA; *U.S. Private*, pg. 632
Kennedy, Thomas B., Sr. V.P.-Community Affairs--BayBanks, Inc., Boston, MA; *U.S. Public*, pg. 184
Kenney, Danielle, Mgr.-Mktg. Communications--Alnor Instrument Company, Skokie, IL; *U.S. Public*, pg. 1559
Kenney, Mary J., V.P.-Human Resources--Converse Inc., North Reading, MA; *U.S. Public*, pg. 441
Kenney, Susan M., Dir.-Mktg.--The Seibels Bruce Group, Inc., Columbia, SC; *U.S. Public*, pg. 1453
Kenny, Colleen, Dir.-Commun.--Security Mutual Life Insurance Co. of New York, Binghamton, NY; *U.S. Private*, pg. 981
Kenny, Katharine, V.P.-Investor Rels.--Ruddick Corporation, Charlotte, NC; *U.S. Public*, pg. 1412
Kenrick, Rick, Dir.-Commun.--International Research & Evaluation, Eagan, MN; *U.S. Private*, pg. 571
Kenville, Mark, Dir.-Member Relations & Communications--Dairylea Cooperative Inc., East Syracuse, NY; *U.S. Private*, pg. 307
Kenward, A.T., V.P.-Winery Communications--Wine World Estates Company, Saint Helena, CA; *Int'l*, pg. 917
Kenyon, Jeff, Dir.-Mktg. Communications--Keithley Instruments, Inc., Cleveland, OH; *U.S. Public*, pg. 946
Kenyon, Jeff, Mgr.-Mktg. Communications--Keithley Test Instrumentation Group, Cleveland, OH; *U.S. Public*, pg. 946
Keogh, Brian, Dir.-Corp. Commun.--Esterline Technologies Corporation, Bellevue, WA; *U.S. Public*, pg. 594
Keowen, Matt, Dir.-Mktg. & Public Rels.--Fujitsu Computer Products of America, Inc., San Jose, CA; *Int'l*, pg. 526
Ker, Alan S., Chief Fin. Officer & Treas.--Universal Standard HealthCare of Ohio Inc., Southfield, MI; *U.S. Public*, pg. 1698
Kerbel, Barbara, V.P.-Corp. Commun.--CMP Media, Inc., Manhasset, NY; *U.S. Public*, pg. 279
Kercher, Idella, V.P.-Customer Rels.--J.D. Edwards & Company, Denver, CO; *U.S. Private*, pg. 365
Kern, E.F., Jr., Sr. V.P.-Service & Customer Satisfaction--American Isuzu Motors Inc., Whittier, CA; *Int'l*, pg. 692
Kerr, Mary Ann, Dir.-Mktg.--US SerVis, West Orange, NJ; *U.S. Public*, pg. 1687
Kerr, Peter, V.P.-Commun.--Empire Blue Cross & Blue Shield, New York, NY; *U.S. Private*, pg. 374
Kerrigan, Juanita I., V.P. & Sec.--Avatar Holdings Inc., Coral Gables, FL; *U.S. Public*, pg. 151
Kerrigon, Frank, Dir.-Corp. Commun.--E-Z-Em, Inc., Westbury, NY; *U.S. Public*, pg. 540
Kerringe, Paul, Mgr.-Pub. Rels.--Country 103.5, London, United Kingdom; *Int'l*, pg. 561
Kersey, Jessica, Dir.-Pub. Rels.--Acer America Corporation, San Jose, CA; *Int'l*, pg. 22
Kershaw, Tess, Head of Media Rels.--Centrica Plc, Slough, United Kingdom; *Int'l*, pg. 279
Kessler, Lori, Dir.-Pub. Info. & Media Rels.--DTE Energy Company, Detroit, MI; *U.S. Public*, pg. 475
Kesten, Dan, V.P.-Customer Services--El Al Airlines Ltd., Lod, Israel; *Int'l*, pg. 435
Keszler, Charles J., V.P.-Fin. & Corp. Rels. & Treas.--Lone Star Technologies, Inc., Dallas, TX; *U.S. Public*, pg. 1012
Kettwig, K.A., Mgr.-Pub. Rels.--Ozone Research & Equipment Corp., Phoenix, AZ; *U.S. Public*, pg. 1234
Kettwig, K.A., Mgr.-Pub. Rels.--MACE Products, Upland, CA; *U.S. Public*, pg. 1234
Kettwig, Kay A., Mgr.-Corp. Commun.--Osmonics, Inc., Minnetonka, MN; *U.S. Public*, pg. 1233
Key, James A., V.P.-Mktg. Services--Continental Conveyor & Equipment Company, Winfield, AL; *U.S. Private*, pg. 791

Key, K.F., Gen. Mgr.-Communications & Public Affairs--Canadian Pacific Railway, Calgary, Canada; *Int'l*, pg. 258
Keyes, Kimberly, Dir-Corp. Commun.--C & S Wholesale Grocery Inc., Brattleboro, VT; *U.S. Private*, pg. 192
Keyser, John, V.P.-Customer Support Services--Memorex Telex Corp., Irving, TX; *Int'l*, pg. 857
Khail, Steve, Mgr.-Corp. Communications--The Manitowoc Company, Inc., Manitowoc, WI; *U.S. Public*, pg. 1040
Kiat, Neo Poh, Mgr.-Pub. Rels.--DBS Asia Capital Ltd., Central, Hong Kong; *Int'l*, pg. 351
Kidd, Douglas, Sr. Mng. Dir.-Corp. Affairs--Bankers Trust New York Corporation, New York, NY; *U.S. Public*, pg. 185
Kidd, Marvin R., Dir.-H.R.--Caddock Electronics, Inc., Riverside, CA; *U.S. Private*, pg. 198
Kidder, Brian, Dir.-Pub. Rels.--Allright Corporation, Houston, TX; *U.S. Private*, pg. 42
Kieckhefer, Robert, V.P.-Pub. Affairs & Adv.--Blue Cross & Blue Shield of Illinois, Chicago, IL; *U.S. Private*, pg. 151
Kierce, Diane, V.P. & Pub. Rels. Dir.--Integrated Marketing Group, Harrison, NY; *U.S. Private*, pg. 566
Kietzmann, Ellen, V.P.-H.R.--Automatic Equipment Mfg. Co., Pender, NE; *U.S. Private*, pg. 101
Kiguchi, Stafford J., Mgr.-Corp. Commun.--Gasco, Inc., Honolulu, HI; *Int'l*, pg. 225
Kiker, John D., V.P.-Corp. Communications--UAL Corporation, Elk Grove Village, IL; *U.S. Public*, pg. 1652
Kiker, John D., V.P.-Corp. Communications--United Air Lines, Inc., Elk Grove Village, IL; *U.S. Public*, pg. 1653
Kiker, Vickie, Dir.-Mktg. Communications--CEM Corporation, Matthews, NC; *U.S. Public*, pg. 277
Kilburn, Jane, Dir.-Corp. Commun.--Puget Sound Energy, Inc., Bellevue, WA; *U.S. Public*, pg. 1342
Kilgannon, Susan B., V.P.-Mktg. & Commun.--URS Corporation, San Francisco, CA; *U.S. Public*, pg. 1655
Kilgannon, Susan B., V.P.-Mktg. & Commun.--URS Greiner, New York, NY; *U.S. Public*, pg. 1659
Kilpatrick, Kay, Dir.-Corp. Commun.--Sonat Inc., Birmingham, AL; *U.S. Public*, pg. 1484
Kilpatrick, Michael, V.P.-Communications--Ikon Office Solutions, Inc., Malvern, PA; *U.S. Public*, pg. 862
Kimball, Barbara, Communications Coord.--Phoenix Home Life Mutual Insurance Company, Hartford, CT; *U.S. Private*, pg. 863
Kimber, Iris A., Corp. Communications Specialist--Millipore Corporation, Bedford, MA; *U.S. Public*, pg. 1112
Kimberley, Iain, Mgr.-Pub. Rels.--Trafalgar House PLC, London, United Kingdom; *Int'l*, pg. 772
Kimman, R.M., Mgr.-Pub. Rels.--Bayer B.V., Mijdrecht, Netherlands; *Int'l*, pg. 175
Kimmel, Lisa, Pub. Rels. Coord.--Griffin Bacal Volny, Toronto, Canada; *U.S. Private*, pg. 480
Kimrey, Karla, Mgr.-Pub. Rels.--Sociedad Industrial Minera Yamin Ltda., Denver, CO; *U.S. Public*, pg. 1723
Kincaid, Steve, Dir.-Customer Svcs.--Williams, White & Co., Moline, IL; *U.S. Private*, pg. 1179
King, Becky, Sr. Mktg. Communications Specialist--Aurora Pump, North Aurora, IL; *U.S. Public*, pg. 726
King, Debi, V.P.-Human Resources--Nordion International Inc., Kanata, Canada; *Int'l*, pg. 827
King, Edward H., Dir.-Trade & Corp. Rels.--Walgreen Co., Deerfield, IL; *U.S. Public*, pg. 1733
King, Gary, Corp. Commun.--Outdoor Technologies Group, Spirit Lake, IA; *U.S. Private*, pg. 822
King, Geoffrey, Dir.-Commun.--Cambior Inc., Montreal, Canada; *Int'l*, pg. 253
King, Gwendolyn S., Sr. V.P.-Corp. & Pub. Affairs--PECO Energy Company, Philadelphia, PA; *U.S. Public*, pg. 1268
King, Judith, Dir.-Pub. Rels.--Genzyme Genetics Div., Santa Fe, NM; *U.S. Public*, pg. 733
King, Regina, Mgr.-Mktg. Communications--Ohmeda, Inc., Liberty Corner, NJ; *Int'l*, pg. 121
King, Tim, Mgr.-Corp. Communications--The E.W. Scripps Company, Cincinnati, OH; *U.S. Public*, pg. 1447
Kingsbry, Liz, Grp. Mgr.- Commun.--AMEC Plc, Northwich, United Kingdom; *Int'l*, pg. 16
Kinney, Bryant, Dir.-Media Rels.--Duke Energy International, L.L.C., Houston, TX; *U.S. Public*, pg. 534
Kinney, Jan, V.P.-Corp. Opers.--Jazzercise, Inc., Carlsbad, CA; *U.S. Private*, pg. 584
Kirby, Kristin, Mgr.-Pub. Rels.--DonTech, Chicago, IL; *U.S. Public*, pg. 98
Kirk, Donald A., V.P.-GM American Commun.--American Systems Corporation, Chantilly, VA; *U.S. Private*, pg. 63
Kirk, Lise, Dir.-Adv. & Promo.--Midland Life Insurance Co., Columbus, OH; *U.S. Private*, pg. 744
Kirkendall, Robert E., Sec. & Asst. Treas.--The Gorman-Rupp Company, Mansfield, OH; *U.S. Public*, pg. 754
Kirkley, Lenora, V.P.-Adv. & Corp. Communications--Ethan Allen, Inc., Danbury, CT; *U.S. Public*, pg. 595
Kirkwood, Karen, Mgr.-Corp. Communications--Thermo Electron Corporation, Waltham, MA; *U.S. Public*, pg. 1591
Kirkwood, Paul, Dir.-Corp. Communications--Nestle-Rowntree Ltd., York, United Kingdom; *Int'l*, pg. 921
Kirtlink, Lee, Mgr.-Communications--Precision Tools Div., North Kingstown, RI; *U.S. Public*, pg. 260
Kirueshov, Henrik, Mgr.-Pub. Rels.--Hewlett-Packard A/S, Birkerod, Denmark; *U.S. Public*, pg. 818
Kish, Martin A., V.P.-Pub. Rels.--Valvoline Company, Lexington, KY; *U.S. Public*, pg. 139
Kissinger, Nancy E., Coord.-Communications--Pepper, Hamilton & Scheetz, Philadelphia, PA; *U.S. Private*, pg. 851
Kistner, Brenda, Corp. Communications/Pub. Rels.--Wang's International, Inc., Memphis, TN; *U.S. Private*, pg. 1149
Kistner, Louis, Dir.-Communications--Millennium Inorganic Chemicals, Hunt Valley, MD; *Int'l*, pg. 593
Kitamura, Mr., Mgr.-Corp. Commun.--Descente Ltd., Osaka, Japan; *Int'l*, pg. 395
Kitchens, Becky, Mgr.-Customer Svc.--Morgan Keegan, Inc., Memphis, TN; *U.S. Public*, pg. 1131
Kivela, Pekka, Sr. V.P.-Grp. Communications Affairs--Metsa-Serla Corporation, Espoo, Finland; *Int'l*, pg. 863
Kivinen, M., V.P.-Communications--Oy Nokia Ab/Nokia Group, Helsinki, Finland; *Int'l*, pg. 951
Klarfeld, Patricia, Mgr.-Corp. Communications--The Gillette Company, Boston, MA; *U.S. Public*, pg. 743
Klassen, Marlene, Mgr.-Corp. Communications--The Great-West Life Assurance Company, Winnipeg, Canada; *Int'l*, pg. 557
Klein, Carol, Sr. V.P.-Communications--Red Roof Inns, Inc., Hilliard, OH; *U.S. Public*, pg. 1369
Klein, Kathy, V.P.-Corp. Communications--Federal Realty Investment Trust, Rockville, MD; *U.S. Public*, pg. 616
Kleinert, Matthias, Dir.-Pub. Affairs & Intl. Rels.--Daimler-Benz Aktiengesellschaft, Stuttgart, Germany; *Int'l*, pg. 366
Klemens, Joseph F., Mgr.-Commun. Svcs.--The Lubrizol Corporation, Wickliffe, OH; *U.S. Public*, pg. 1016
Klevecz, Lu Ann, Sec. & Dir.-Corp. Commun. & Investor Rels.--nVIEW Corporation, Newport News, VA; *U.S. Public*, pg. 1206
Kling, Mats, V.P.-Pub. Rels.--Stena Line AB, Goteborg, Sweden; *Int'l*, pg. 1300
Klinger, Andy, V.P.-Publicity--SudwestLB, Stuttgart, Germany; *Int'l*, pg. 1304
Klinger, Ernest T., Chief Fin. Officer--Gelson's Markets, Encino, CA; *U.S. Public*, pg. 129
Klink, Bruce C., V.P.-Sls., Rates & Pub. Affairs--The East Ohio Gas Co., Cleveland, OH; *U.S. Public*, pg. 435
Kluttz, Glenda, Dir.-Consumer Rels. & Asst. Sec.--Food Lion, Inc., Salisbury, NC; *Int'l*, pg. 463
Knapp, Lori, Mgr.-Mktg. Services--Eaton Corporation, Engineered Fasteners Division, Brunswick, OH; *U.S. Public*, pg. 556
Knaut, John M., Dir.-Mktg. & Sls.--United Receptical, Inc., Pottsville, PA; *U.S. Private*, pg. 1123
Knerler, A.R., Dir.-Pub. Affairs--J & L Specialty Products Corp., Pittsburgh, PA; *Int'l*, pg. 572
Knicely, Howard V., Exec. V.P.-Human Resources & Communications--TRW Inc., Cleveland, OH; *U.S. Public*, pg. 1558
Knief, Wallace W., Mgr.-Corp. Commun. & Investor Rels.--Blockbuster Entertainment Group, Dallas, TX; *U.S. Private*, pg. 775
Knight, Connie, Dir.-Corp. Commun.--Clariant Corporation, Charlotte, NC; *Int'l*, pg. 624
Knight, Guyon H., III, V.P.-Corp. Communications--The Washington Post Company, Washington, DC; *U.S. Public*, pg. 1742
Knight, Sandra, Corp. Commun.--Albert Kahn Associates, Inc., Detroit, MI; *U.S. Private*, pg. 604
Knobel, Paul, Mgr.-Pub. Rels.--Brauerei AG, Zurich, Switzerland; *Int'l*, pg. 479
Knopfler, Gail, Pub. Rels. Specialist--Outsource International, Deerfield Beach, FL; *U.S. Public*, pg. 1236
Knoppa, Noreen, Mgr.-Adv.--David White, L.L.C., Germantown, WI; *U.S. Public*, pg. 1765
Knoppa, Noreen, Mgr.-Adv.--David White, L.L.C., Germantown, WI; *U.S. Private*, pg. 1765
Knouse, Mark S., V.P.-Govt. Rels. & Pub. Affairs--Union Pacific Resources Company (UPRC), Fort Worth, TX; *U.S. Public*, pg. 1668
Knowles, Douglas, Dir.-Investor Rels.--Serologicals Corporation, Clarkston, GA; *U.S. Public*, pg. 1460
Knowlton, Tim, Dir.-Corp. Communications--Kellogg Company, Battle Creek, MI; *U.S. Public*, pg. 947
Knutson, Marlys, Mgr.-Mktg. Communications--Polaris Industries, Inc., Minneapolis, MN; *U.S. Public*, pg. 1313
Kober, Lori, Dir.-Communications--Foot Locker, New York, NY; *U.S. Public*, pg. 1777
Koch, Allan, Mgr.-Pub. Rels.--Sonofon, Horsholm, Denmark; *Int'l*, pg. 537
Kodweis, John B., V.P.-Human Resources & Pub. Affairs--The Gleason Works, Rochester, NY; *U.S. Public*, pg. 746
Koenig, Marvin, Pub. Rels. Coord.--Renco Group, New York, NY; *U.S. Private*, pg. 922
Koerber, Dirk, V.P.-Corp. Communications, Investor Rels. & Civic Affairs--Western Atlas Inc., Houston, TX; *U.S. Public*, pg. 1757
Koester, Karen, Dir.-Corp. Pub. Rels.--Countrymark Cooperative, Inc., Indianapolis, IN; *U.S. Private*, pg. 279
Kogure, S., Dir.-Systems--Otto Sumisho Inc., Tokyo, Japan; *Int'l*, pg. 1015
Kohl, Kermit K., V.P.-External Customer Service--Furman Foods, Inc., Northumberland, PA; *U.S. Private*, pg. 431
Kohler, Dr., Dir.-Pub. Rels.--Thyssen Stahl AG, Duisburg, Germany; *Int'l*, pg. 1388
Kohler, Laura E., Dir.-Public Affairs--Kohler Company, Kohler, WI; *U.S. Private*, pg. 630
Kohls, Kris, Exec. V.P.-Strategic Devel.--Dart Transit Company, Eagan, MN; *U.S. Private*, pg. 311
Kojima, Kikuo, Mng. Dir.-Inquiry & Audit Depts., Admin. & Pub. Rels.--East Japan Railway Company, Tokyo, Japan; *Int'l*, pg. 431
Kola, Francine, Dir.-Pub. Rels.--Tretorn, Brockton, MA; *Int'l*, pg. 1072
Kolb, James D., V.P.-Mktg.--EMCOR Group, Inc., Norwalk, CT; *U.S. Public*, pg. 571
Kolias, Gus, V.P.-Customer Service--COMPAQ Computer Corporation, Houston, TX; *U.S. Public*, pg. 417
Koling, Barry, Sr. V.P.-Corp. Commun.--Crestar Financial Corporation, Richmond, VA; *U.S. Public*, pg. 458
Kolivosky, E.M., Dir.-Corp. Commu.--Auto-Owners Insurance, Lansing, MI; *U.S. Private*, pg. 100
Kolleda, Leslie, Specialist-Pub. Rels.--The Progressive Corporation, Cleveland, OH; *U.S. Public*, pg. 1334
Koller, Diane, Dir.-Govt. Rels./Pub. Rels.--Vicorp Restaurants, Inc., Denver, CO; *U.S. Public*, pg. 1719
Kolligian, Mark, Dir.-Res. & Customer Rels.--CVS Corp., Woonsocket, RI; *U.S. Public*, pg. 287
Kollmeyer, Julie, Supvr.-Mktg. Commun.--Modernfold, Inc., New Castle, IN; *U.S. Private*, pg. 755
Kolstad, James L., V.P.-Pub. & Govt. Rels.--American Automobile Association, Heathrow, FL; *U.S. Private*, pg. 50
Komschlies, Andrea, Dir.-Mktg.--Witcher Construction Co., Minneapolis, MN; *U.S. Private*, pg. 1185
Kondo, Junichiro, Deputy Gen. Mgr.-Pub. Rels.--Nissho Iwai Corporation, Tokyo, Japan; *Int'l*, pg. 946
Kondor, George J., Jr., Exec. V.P.--BT Financial Corporation, Johnstown, PA; *U.S. Public*, pg. 163
Koning, Annemiek, Mgr.-Pub. Rels., Sls. & Promo.--Lips United B.V., Drunen, Netherlands; *Int'l*, pg. 812
Kono, Yuhei, Gen. Mgr.--OYO Corporation, Tokyo, Japan; *Int'l*, pg. 1019
Konrad, Don, Dir.-Adv. & Pub. Rels.--Fleischer Manufacturing, Inc., Columbus, NE; *U.S. Private*, pg. 410
Konviser, Arthur, Sr. V.P.-Pub. Affairs--Shoppers Drug Mart, Ltd., Toronto, Canada; *Int'l*, pg. 112
Koral, Mary, Mgr.-Mktg. Communications--Sanyo Energy (U.S.A.) Corporation, San Diego, CA; *Int'l*, pg. 1191
Kosanke, Marilyn, Sr. Communications Representative--Texas Utilities Company, Dallas, TX; *U.S. Public*, pg. 1586
Kosick, David, V.P.-Pub. Rels.--The St. George Group, Inc., Pittsburgh, PA; *U.S. Private*, pg. 960
Kosie, Kathy E., Coord.-Catalog--EBSCO Industries, Inc., Birmingham, AL; *U.S. Private*, pg. 358
Koslowski, Richard J., Mgr.-Plng. & Analysis--Simpson Industries, Inc., Plymouth, MI; *U.S. Public*, pg. 1474
Kosman, William, Dir.-Corp. Communications--Henkel Corporation - Chemicals Group, Cincinnati, OH; *Int'l*, pg. 610
Kosman, William D., Dir.-Corp. Communications--Henkel Corporation, King of Prussia, PA; *Int'l*, pg. 610
Kosola, Markku, Dir.-Info. Services & Pub. Rels.--Tapiola-Yhtiot, Espoo, Finland; *Int'l*, pg. 1354
Koss, David, Dir.-Mktg. Communications--Liberty Life Insurance Company, Greenville, SC; *U.S. Public*, pg. 992
Kostenbauer, John, Mgr.-Human Resources--Atlas Cylinder, Eugene, OR; *U.S. Public*, pg. 1261
Kotz, Hans-Helmut, Dir.-Pub. Rels. & Mktg.--Deutsche Girozentrale-Deutsche Kommunalbank, Frankfurt/Main, Germany; *Int'l*, pg. 406
Kouno, Akio, Exec. V.P.-Pub. Rels.--Japan Airlines Company, Ltd., Tokyo, Japan; *Int'l*, pg. 699
Kovacik, Rob, Mgr.-Customer Service--Hollymatic Corporation, Countryside, IL; *U.S. Private*, pg. 535
Kracht, Barbara, Gen. Mgr.- Press & Info. Svcs.--Airbus Industrie, Blagnac, France; *Int'l*, pg. 39
Kraemer, Larry, Dir.-Mktg.--Harkins Builders, Inc., Silver Spring, MD; *U.S. Private*, pg. 502
Krakowsky, Philippe, Sr. V.P. & Corp. Communications Dir.--Young & Rubicam Inc., New York, NY; *U.S. Private*, pg. 1196
Kralik, Carol, Mgr.-Customer & Sls. Support--Bard Diagnostic Sciences, Redmond, WA; *U.S. Public*, pg. 189
Kramer, Charlene, V.P.-Communications--Federal National Mortgage Association (Fannie Mae), Washington, DC; *U.S. Public*, pg. 615
Kramer, Jack, Sr. V.P.-Adv. & Corp. Communications--CVS Corp., Woonsocket, RI; *U.S. Public*, pg. 287
Kramer, Jane M., Exec. Dir.-Communications--Consumers Energy, Jackson, MI; *U.S. Public*, pg. 280
Kramer, Michael, Dir.-Publicity--New Line Cinema Corporation, New York, NY; *U.S. Public*, pg. 1614
Kranz, Karen, Dir.-Image & Comm.--Diners Club Inc., Chicago, IL; *U.S. Public*, pg. 377
Krasselt, Cramer, Mgr.-Pub. Rels.--Ragold, Inc., Chicago, IL; *Int'l*, pg. 1084
Kraus, Rick, Mgr.--Federated Mutual Insurance Company, Owatonna, MN; *U.S. Private*, pg. 399
Kraus, Stephen R., Mgr.-Media Rels.--Madison Gas and Electric Company, Madison, WI; *U.S. Public*, pg. 1032
Krause, Carolyn F., Admin.-Investor Rels.--Plains Resources Inc., Houston, TX; *U.S. Public*, pg. 1307
Krause, Joan Mascio, Mgr.-Pub. Rels. & Adv.--The Austin Company, Cleveland, OH; *U.S. Private*, pg. 99
Kraut, Lori R., Mgr.-Global Media Rels.--Hoechst Marion Roussel, Inc., Bridgewater, NJ; *Int'l*, pg. 624
Krebs, Sue, Mgr.-Pub. Rels.--Seer Technologies, Inc., Cary, NC; *U.S. Public*, pg. 1453
Kreis, Patrice, Dir.-Commun.--Aerospatiale, Paris, France; *Int'l*, pg. 28
Krejci, Allan, Dir.-Pub. Rels.--Hormel Foods Corp., Austin, MN; *U.S. Public*, pg. 840
Kremer, Manfred, Dir.-Adv. & Pub. Rels.--3M Deutschland GmbH, Neuss, Germany; *U.S. Public*, pg. 1606
Krieger, Anne, Coord.-Corp. Communications--Glaxo Wellcome Inc., Research Triangle Park, NC; *Int'l*, pg. 552
Krier, Mary, Mgr.-Communications--Flowers Industries, Inc., Thomasville, GA; *U.S. Public*, pg. 656
Kristapovich, Mary Jo, Dir.-Investor Rels.--D & N Financial Corporation, Hancock, MI; *U.S. Public*, pg. 472
Kritzer, Andrew, Sr. Mgr.-Mktg. Communications--Samsung Electronics America, Inc., Ridgefield Park, NJ; *Int'l*, pg. 1183
Kritzer, Andrew, Mgr.-Adv. & Pub. Rels.--Samsung Electronics North America Inc., Ridgefield Park, NJ; *Int'l*, pg. 1183
Kroft, Gina, Dir.-Commun. & Special Events--Crested Butte Mountain Resort, Inc., Crested Butte, CO; *U.S. Private*, pg. 289
Krogh, Lee, Dir.-Corp. Commun.--Otter Tail Power Company, Fergus Falls, MN; *U.S. Public*, pg. 1234
Kroll, Richard C., Dir.-Adv. & Pub. Rels.--Foster Wheeler Corporation, Clinton, NJ; *U.S. Public*, pg. 676
Kroll, Ursula, Mgr.-Pub. Affairs--Nova Scotia Power Inc., Halifax, Canada; *Int'l*, pg. 971
Kromer, Mary Lou, V.P.-Corp. Communications--W.R. Grace & Co., Boca Raton, FL; *U.S. Public*, pg. 754
Krosen, Marie, Mgr.-Pub. Rels.--HomeBase, Inc., Irvine, CA; *U.S. Public*, pg. 832
Krueger, Ted, Mgr.-Mktg. & Adv.--Rockford Acromatic Product Co., Rockford, IL; *U.S. Private*, pg. 938
Krueger, Wolfgang, Mgr.-Pub. Rels.--Thyssen Handelsunion AG, Dusseldorf, Germany; *Int'l*, pg. 1388

Krulak, Allan C., V.P. & Dir.-Community Affairs--Forest City Enterprises, Inc., Cleveland, OH; *U.S. Public*, pg. 667
Kruse, Jochen, Dir.-Press Rels.--Adam Opel AG, Russelsheim, Germany; *U.S. Public*, pg. 721
Kryza, Frank, Mgr.-Pub. Rels.--ARCO Intl. Oil & Gas Co., Plano, TX; *U.S. Public*, pg. 144
Kubiak, Connie M., Dir.-Public Relations--Tauber Oil Company, Houston, TX; *U.S. Private*, pg. 1069
Kuborn, Max, Mgr.-Pub. Rels.--RTL Tele Letzebuerg, Luxembourg, Luxembourg; *Int'l*, pg. 561
Kuborn, Max, Mgr.-Pub. Rels.--RTL Radio Letzebuerg, Luxembourg, Luxembourg; *Int'l*, pg. 561
Kudatgobilik, Tugrul, V.P.-Indus. & Pub. Rels.--Koc Holding A.S., Istanbul, Turkey; *Int'l*, pg. 741
Kuelb, Irene, Dir.-Communications--Bayerische Hypotheken- und Wechsel-Bank Aktiengesellschaft, Munich, Germany; *Int'l*, pg. 175
Kuhn, Lynda, Dir-Corp. & Community Relations--Philip Services Corp., Hamilton, Canada; *Int'l*, pg. 1050
Kuhner, David L., Mgr.-Mktg. Communications--Pioneer-Standard Electronics, Inc., Cleveland, OH; *U.S. Public*, pg. 1300
Kuhnie, Jay B., Mgr.-Chrysler Plymouth Communications--Chrysler Corporation, Auburn Hills, MI; *U.S. Public*, pg. 352
Kukuca, Kathleen E., Mgr.-Pub. Rels.--Nordson Corporation, Westlake, OH; *U.S. Public*, pg. 1188
Kulcsar, Edward, Dir.-Opers. & Mktg.--Associated Testing Laboratories, Inc., Wayne, NJ; *U.S. Public*, pg. 1341
Kulesza, Barbara, Coord.-Communications--American National Can Company, Chicago, IL; *Int'l*, pg. 1029
Kumagai, Hitoshi, Mgr.--Sumikin Bussan Corporation, Osaka, Japan; *Int'l*, pg. 1308
Kummer, Nancy, Corp. Communications--Metrologic Instruments, Inc., Blackwood, NJ; *U.S. Public*, pg. 1102
Kun, J.M., Mgr.-Admin. & Human Resources--Davy International, Canada, Toronto, Canada; *Int'l*, pg. 775
Kunda, Ken, V.P.--Inductotherm Industries, Inc., Rancocas, NJ; *U.S. Private*, pg. 560
Kunsman-Mizulo, Patti, Dir.-Commun.--Active Software, Inc., Santa Clara, CA; *U.S. Private*, pg. 15
Kunz, Petra, Mgr.-Pub. Rels.--PKL Verpackungssysteme GmbH, Linnich, Germany; *Int'l*, pg. 1020
Kunzler, Maja, Pub. Rels. Dir.--Impuls Advertising AG, Kusnacht, Switzerland; *Int'l*, pg. 666
Kuparinen, Leena, Mgr.-Corp. Commun.--FinnAir Oy, Helsinki, Finland; *Int'l*, pg. 485
Kupec, Evelyn, Mgr.-Adv. & Communications--Joseph T. Ryerson & Son, Inc., Chicago, IL; *U.S. Public*, pg. 879
Kupferman, Spencer, Mgr.-Mktg.--Global Software, Inc., Raleigh, NC; *U.S. Private*, pg. 457
Kurokawa, Katsuhiko, Dir.-Publicity Dept.--Matsushita Electric Works, Ltd., Osaka, Japan; *Int'l*, pg. 847
Kurten, George W., Sec. & Dir.-H.R.--Walsworth Publishing Company, Inc., Marceline, MO; *U.S. Private*, pg. 1148
Kurtz, Larry, Dir.-Corp. Communications--Chiron Corporation, Emeryville, CA; *U.S. Public*, pg. 349
Kurtz, Larry, V.P.-Corp. Communications--McKesson Corporation, San Francisco, CA; *U.S. Public*, pg. 1072
Kusher, J.M., Admin.-Pub. & Investor Rels.--Stepan Company, Northfield, IL; *U.S. Public*, pg. 1514
Kushner, Denise D., Mgr.-Communications--L.M. Scofield Company, Los Angeles, CA; *U.S. Private*, pg. 976
Kuss, Wolfgang, Mgr.-Pub. Rels.--Landesbank Hessen-Thuringen Girozentrale, Frankfurt/Main, Germany; *Int'l*, pg. 798
Kutchin, Jill Pollack, V.P.-Corp. Affairs & Clerk--Parlex Corporation, Methuen, MA; *U.S. Public*, pg. 1264
Kwong, Linda, Mgr.-Pub. Rels.--BIC Corporation, Milford, CT; *Int'l*, pg. 1273
Kyriakou, Linda G., V.P.-Commun.--Sequa Corporation, New York, NY; *U.S. Public*, pg. 1458
La Fourdade, Severine, Dir.-Communications--SKF France S.A., Clamart, France; *Int'l*, pg. 1158
Labonte, Alain P., V.P.-Corp. Affairs--Kruger Inc., Montreal, Canada; *Int'l*, pg. 761
Labonte, Alain P., V.P.-Corp. Affairs--Trois-Rivieres Mill, Trois-Rivieres, Canada; *Int'l*, pg. 761
Labonte, Alain P., V.P.-Corp. Affairs--Place Turcot Mill, Montreal, Canada; *Int'l*, pg. 761
Labonte, Alain P., V.P.-Corp. Affairs--Ville LaSalle Plant, La Salle, Canada; *Int'l*, pg. 761
Labonte, Alain P., V.P.-Corp. Affairs--Rexdale Plant, Rexdale, Canada; *Int'l*, pg. 761
Laboon, Corinne M., Mgr.-Pub. Rels. & Media--Matthews International Corp., Pittsburgh, PA; *U.S. Public*, pg. 1059
Lack, Ruth V.H., Dir.-Communications--First Gibraltar Bank, Irving, TX; *U.S. Public*, pg. 181
Lackey, Brandon, Mgr.-Pub. Rels.--Halliburton Energy Services, Houston, TX; *U.S. Public*, pg. 776
Lackey, Melissa, Mgr.-Pub. Rels.--Edward Jones, Saint Louis, MO; *U.S. Private*, pg. 597
Lackey, William G., V.P.-Investor Rels.--Ideon Group, Inc., Jacksonville, FL; *U.S. Public*, pg. 320
Lackman, Susan, Mgr.-Pub. Rels.--Lackman Food Service, Woodbury, NY; *U.S. Private*, pg. 642
LaCosta, Michael J., Pub. Rels. Acct. Supvr.--SSD&W Integrated Marketing Communications, Montville, NJ; *U.S. Private*, pg. 958
Lacourt, Liliane, Exec. V.P.-Commun.--PSA Peugeot Citroen, Paris, France; *Int'l*, pg. 1020
LaCourt, Liliane, Dir.-Communications--Peugeot S.A., Paris, France; *Int'l*, pg. 1020
Lacross, Lisa, Dir.-H.R. & Pub. Rels.--Nor-Cal Beverage Co., Inc., West Sacramento, CA; *U.S. Private*, pg. 801
Lacter, Barry, Mgr.-Pub. Rels.--Louisiana Pacific Corporation, Portland, OR; *U.S. Public*, pg. 1015
Lacy, J. Dan, V.P.-Corp. Communications--Ashland, Inc., Russell, KY; *U.S. Public*, pg. 138
Lacy, Mary Beth, Mgr.-Mktg. Pub. Rels.--Lynx Golf, Inc., City of Industry, CA; *U.S. Private*, pg. 684
Ladds, H.P., Jr., Pres. & Chief Exec. Officer--Columbus McKinnon Corp., Amherst, NY; *U.S. Public*, pg. 405
Ladnier, Cheryl Jan, Sr. V.P.-Mktg. & Corp. Communication--The Bon Ton Stores, Inc., York, PA; *U.S. Public*, pg. 244
Ladzinski, Greg S., Dir.-Pub. Rels.--Broderick & Bascom Rope Co., Sedalia, MO; *U.S. Private*, pg. 68
Laffoon, Polk, IV, V.P.-Corp. Rels.--Knight-Ridder, Inc., Miami, FL; *U.S. Public*, pg. 963
LaFleur, Denise, Mgr.-Internal Commun.--Dana Corporation, Toledo, OH; *U.S. Public*, pg. 479
Lafrennie, David, Grp. Mgr.-Mktg. Communications--LEGO Systems, Inc., Enfield, CT; *Int'l*, pg. 805
Lagny, Claude, Dir.-Corp. Communications--Elida Faberge, Paris, France; *Int'l*, pg. 1437
Lagoni, Suzanne, Mgr.-Pub. Rels.--ARCO Alaska Inc., Anchorage, AK; *U.S. Public*, pg. 144
Laguette, Louisa, Supvr.-Mktg. & Pub. Rels.--Del Taco, Inc., Laguna Hills, CA; *U.S. Private*, pg. 321
Laird-Dunn, Lisa, V.P.-Sls.--Laird & Company, Eatontown, NJ; *U.S. Private*, pg. 642
Laird, Paul, Assoc. Dir.-External Affairs--BP Exploration (Alaska) Inc., Anchorage, AK; *Int'l*, pg. 220
Lalka, Virginia, Mgr.-Communications--The Gleason Works, Rochester, NY; *U.S. Public*, pg. 746
Lamb, Mei Li, Communications Specialist--UB Networks, Santa Clara, CA; *Int'l*, pg. 924
Lambert, Bob, Supvr.-Mktg. Svcs.--Methode Electronics Inc., Chicago, IL; *U.S. Public*, pg. 1101
Lambert, Debra, Dir.-Pub. Affairs--Safeway Inc., Pleasanton, CA; *U.S. Public*, pg. 1426
Lambrechts, John, Mgr.-Fin. Communications--Pharmacia & Upjohn, Kalamazoo, MI; *Int'l*, pg. 1048
Lambrix, T.G., V.P.-Communications--Union Camp Corporation, Wayne, NJ; *U.S. Public*, pg. 1665
Lamere, Joyce, Pub. Rels.--SunGard Financial Systems, Inc., Canoga Park, CA; *U.S. Public*, pg. 1534
Lammers, Henry P., V.P.-Mktg.--Marketing Communications, Lenexa, KS; *U.S. Public*, pg. 794
LaMontagne, Lisa, Mgr.-Pub. Rels. & Asst. to the Pres.--Tax Management, Inc., Washington, DC; *U.S. Private*, pg. 182
Lampe, Stanford H., Dir.-Media Rels.--Ashland, Inc., Russell, KY; *U.S. Public*, pg. 138
Lamps, Christopher, V.P.-Corp. Affairs & Investor Rels.--Ares-Serono S.A., Geneva, Switzerland; *Int'l*, pg. 80
Land, Frank, Assoc. V.P.-Adv. & Pub. Rels.--First Colony Life Insurance Co., Lynchburg, VA; *U.S. Public*, pg. 711
Landeche, Dean, Dir.-Training & Communications--Hobart Corporation, Troy, OH; *U.S. Public*, pg. 1322
Lander, Gerald A., Mgr.-Pub. Affairs--Du Pont de Nemours International S.A., Geneva, Switzerland; *U.S. Public*, pg. 532
Lane, Barry, Mgr.-Pub. Rels.--Unocal Corporation, El Segundo, CA; *U.S. Public*, pg. 1698
Lane, Kathleen, Dir.-Pub. Rels.--The Weather Channel, Atlanta, GA; *U.S. Private*, pg. 647
Lane, Lynda, Exec. V.P.-Admin. Corp. Communications--Koll Co., Newport Beach, CA; *U.S. Private*, pg. 631
Lane, Mike, Pub. Rels. Dir.--EvansGroup, Denver, CO; *U.S. Private*, pg. 385
Lang, E.M., V.P.-External Affairs--Pacific Telesis Group, San Francisco, CA; *U.S. Public*, pg. 1415
Lang, Joan, Mgr.-Corp. Commun.--AEP Industries, Inc., South Hackensack, NJ; *U.S. Public*, pg. 4
Langdon, Julie, Dir.-Pub. Rels.--Sun Life and Provincial Holdings plc, London, United Kingdom; *Int'l*, pg. 1318
Lange, Elizabeth A., V.P.-Customer Rels.--Tiffany & Co., New York, NY; *U.S. Public*, pg. 1608
Lange, Oddjan, Mgr.-Information--Statoil, Stavanger, Norway; *Int'l*, pg. 1297
Langer, Caroline, Mgr.-Corp. Commun.--J.M. Huber Corporation, Edison, NJ; *U.S. Private*, pg. 544
Langhorst, S., Mgr.-Pub. Rels.--Ballast Nedam Beton en Waterbouw B.V., Amstelveen, Netherlands; *Int'l*, pg. 133
Lanter, D.M., Dir.-Corp. Commun.--Black & Veatch, Kansas City, MO; *U.S. Private*, pg. 146
Lantigua, Jose R., Pub. Rels. Dir.--Publicitaria Cumbre, Santo Domingo, Dominican Republic; *U.S. Public*, pg. 1422
Lanzilloti, Dom, Dir.-Personnel--Crystal Oil Company, Shreveport, LA; *U.S. Public*, pg. 466
Lapartina, Marcia, Mgr.-Pub. Rels.--3M Do Brasil Ltda., Sao Paulo, Brazil; *U.S. Public*, pg. 1606
Laporte, Andre, V.P.-Aboriginal & Community Affairs--Hydro-Quebec, Montreal, Canada; *Int'l*, pg. 640
LaPorte, Joseph J., V.P.-Corp. Rels.--General Binding Corporation, Northbrook, IL; *U.S. Public*, pg. 707
Lappan, George, Dir.-Corp. Communications--Rochester Gas And Electric Corporation, Rochester, NY; *U.S. Public*, pg. 1395
Larance, Charles Larry, V.P.-Corp. Rels.--General American Life Insurance Co., Saint Louis, MO; *U.S. Private*, pg. 443
LaResche, Stephen D., V.P.-Pub. Communications--Anheuser-Busch Companies, Inc., Saint Louis, MO; *U.S. Public*, pg. 113
Larick, Dena, Mgr.-Pub. Rels.--Bose Corporation, Framingham, MA; *U.S. Private*, pg. 160
Lark, Tracy, Mgr.-Media Rels. & Publications--Little Caesar Enterprises, Inc., Detroit, MI; *U.S. Private*, pg. 671
Laroche, Christine, Dir.-Pub. Rels.--Au Bon Marche, Paris, France; *Int'l*, pg. 97
Larsen, Anita M., Dir.-Editorial Svcs.--Texaco Inc., White Plains, NY; *U.S. Public*, pg. 1582
Larsen, E., Mgr.-Media Rels.--Standard Bank Investment Corporation Limited, Johannesburg, South Africa; *Int'l*, pg. 1293
Larsen, John S., V.P.-Office of the Environ.--Weyerhaeuser Company, Federal Way, WA; *U.S. Public*, pg. 1764
Larsen, Mark, Mgr.-Communications--Eveready Battery Co., Saint Louis, MO; *U.S. Public*, pg. 1360
Larsson, Inger, Dir.-Corp. Communications--Gambro AB, Lund, Sweden; *Int'l*, pg. 666
Larter, Paul, Dir.-Mktg. Communications--Du Pont (Australia) Ltd., Sydney, Australia; *U.S. Public*, pg. 532
Laru, Tuula, Mgr.-Commun.--Tapiola-Yhtiot, Espoo, Finland; *Int'l*, pg. 1354
Lasecke, Margaret, Dir.-Pub. Rels.--Oracle Corporation, Redwood City, CA; *U.S. Public*, pg. 1227
Lashlee, Kerry, V.P.-Life Underwriting & Policy Owner Svcs.--Alfa Life Insurance Corp., Montgomery, AL; *U.S. Public*, pg. 40
Laske, Michael, Dir.-Adv. & Pub. Rels.--Pittler Maschinenfabrik AG, Langen, Germany; *Int'l*, pg. 1128
Laskey, Christine, V.P.-Mktg. & Corp. Communications--National Trustco Inc., Toronto, Canada; *Int'l*, pg. 909
Laskowski, Joe, Dir.-Mktg. & Communications--Analog Devices, Santa Clara, CA; *U.S. Public*, pg. 108
Laskowski, Joseph, Dir.-Mktg. Communications--Analog Devices, Inc., Norwood, MA; *U.S. Public*, pg. 107
Laszlo, Matt, Mgr.-Corp. Mktg. Commun.--The Middleby Corporation, Rolling Meadows, IL; *U.S. Public*, pg. 1109
Lau, May, Mgr.-Pub. Rels. & Corp. Communications--Sun Hung Kai Properties Ltd., Wan Chai, Hong Kong; *Int'l*, pg. 1318
Laub, Mark, V.P.-Mktg. & Pub. Affairs--United Power Association, Elk River, MN; *U.S. Private*, pg. 1123
Laudisio, Glenda, Mgr.-Adv. & Pub. Rels.--Checkpoint Systems Inc., Thorofare, NJ; *U.S. Public*, pg. 343
Lauf, Lisa, Dir.-Pub. Rels.--Adventure Island, Tampa, FL; *U.S. Public*, pg. 114
Laufer, Esther, V.P. & Dir.-Promo.--Ladies' Home Journal, New York, NY; *U.S. Public*, pg. 1094
Lauffer, Marlee, V.P.-Corp. Commun.--The Newhall Land And Farming Company, Valencia, CA; *U.S. Public*, pg. 1178
Laurent, Frangoisc, Mgr.-Pub. Rels.--C.M.C. SA, Saint Quentin-en-Yvelines, France; *Int'l*, pg. 792
Lausterer, Mary, Corp. Sec.--Hope's Architectural Products Inc., Jamestown, NY; *U.S. Private*, pg. 538
Lavin, Joseph, V.P.-External Affairs--Sandoz Corporation, New York, NY; *Int'l*, pg. 974
Lavine, Gary J., Sr. V.P.-Legal & Corp. Rels.--Niagara Mohawk Power Corporation, Syracuse, NY; *U.S. Public*, pg. 1181
LaVite, Chris, Coord.-Mktg. Communications--Butler Manufacturing Company, Kansas City, MO; *U.S. Public*, pg. 271
Lavut, Cipora Kurtzman, Sr. V.P.-Corp. Communications--Aura Systems, Inc., El Segundo, CA; *U.S. Public*, pg. 147
Lawler, Steve, Mgr.-Pub. Rels. & Sls. Promo.--Yamaha Motor Corp., U.S.A., Cypress, CA; *Int'l*, pg. 1516
Lawless, Karla, Mgr.-Pub. Rels.--BASF Ireland Limited, Blackrock, Ireland; *Int'l*, pg. 106
Lawlor, John, Mgr.-Pub. Rels.--Ocean Spray Cranberries, Inc., Middleboro, MA; *U.S. Private*, pg. 811
Lawlor, John, V.P.-Corp. Commun.--Newbridge Networks Corporation, Kanata, Canada; *Int'l*, pg. 923
Lawrence, Amanda, Dir.-Investor Rels.--Netscape Communications Corp., Mountain View, CA; *U.S. Public*, pg. 1168
Lawrence, Lisa, Mgr.-Pub. Rels.--Mediatex Communications Corporation, Austin, TX; *U.S. Private*, pg. 727
Lawrence, Steve, Mgr.-Communications--Sea Containers Ltd., Hamilton, Bermuda; *Int'l*, pg. 1213
Lawson, Chris, Dir.-Mktg. Communications--Grace Construction Products, Cambridge, MA; *U.S. Public*, pg. 755
Lawson, Mike, Dir.-Corp. Communications--Granite Construction Incorporated, Watsonville, CA; *U.S. Public*, pg. 759
Lawson, Ron, Sr. V.P.-Sls. & Customer Service--Howmedica, Inc., Rutherford, NJ; *U.S. Public*, pg. 1282
Lawson, Steve, Mgr.-Pub. Rels.--Thiokol Corporation, Ogden, UT; *U.S. Public*, pg. 1596
Lawton, Peter, Pub. Rels. Specialist--BetzDearborn Inc., Trevose, PA; *U.S. Public*, pg. 226
Lawyer, Jean B., Dir.-Corp. Commun--Country Life Insurance Company, Bloomington, IL; *U.S. Private*, pg. 278
Lawyer, Jean B., Dir.-Corp. Communications--CC Services, Bloomington, IL; *U.S. Private*, pg. 279
Lax, David, V.P.-Sls. & Adv.--John Hassall, Inc., Westbury, NY; *U.S. Private*, pg. 509
Layfield, Allen W., V.P. & Pres.-Communication Works--Cadmus Marketing Services, Atlanta, GA; *U.S. Public*, pg. 291
Layne, Stuart, Exec. V.P.-Mktg. & Sls.--Boston Celtics Limited Partnership, Boston, MA; *U.S. Public*, pg. 246
Layton, Mitzi, Mgr.-Mktg. Communications--Coburn Optical Industries Inc., Tulsa, OK; *U.S. Private*, pg. 248
Lazar, Maureen, Coord.-Mktg. Communications--Safeskin Corporation, San Diego, CA; *U.S. Public*, pg. 1425
Lazarus, Robert J., Dir.-Mktg.--L&R Manufacturing Co., Kearny, NJ; *U.S. Private*, pg. 638
Lazenby, Mark, Mgr.-Corp. Communications--Dominion Resources, Inc., Richmond, VA; *U.S. Public*, pg. 516
Le Gall, Karen, Mgr.-Mktg. Communications--Capintec Inc., Ramsey, NJ; *U.S. Private*, pg. 205
Le Lay, Patrick, Grp. Dir.-Commun.--Bouygues, Saint Quentin-en-Yvelines, France; *Int'l*, pg. 206
Leach, Lois A., Dir.-Media Rels.--U S West Inc., Englewood, CO; *U.S. Public*, pg. 1688
Leaf, Greg, Sr. V.P.-Pub. Rels.--Miller Meester Advertising Inc., Minneapolis, MN; *U.S. Private*, pg. 747
Leaf, Mark, Mgr.-Pub. Affairs--Pinkerton's Inc., Encino, CA; *U.S. Public*, pg. 1296
Leahy, Beth, V.P.-Pub. Rels.--Centeon, L.L.C., King of Prussia, PA; *Int'l*, pg. 626
Leahy, Kelly, Dir.-Pub. Rels.--Zoological Society of San Diego, San Diego, CA; *U.S. Private*, pg. 1207
Leber, Laura, Sr. Dir.-Corp. Communications--Genentech, Inc., South San Francisco, CA; *Int'l*, pg. 1120
Leblanc, Marcella, Dir.-Public Affairs--New Brunswick Power Corporation, Fredericton, Canada; *Int'l*, pg. 923
Lebowitz, Sharon, Pub. Rels.-Photo Group--Nikon Inc., Melville, NY; *Int'l*, pg. 931

LeBrescu, Betty, Mgr.-Community & Pub. Rels.--Murphy Oil Corporation, El Dorado, AR; *U.S. Public*, pg. 1141
Lechner, Helen, Mgr.-Communications & Design--Raychem Corporation, Menlo Park, CA; *U.S. Public*, pg. 1362
LeClair, Kelly, Customer Presentations--Mirro Company, Manitowoc, WI; *U.S. Public*, pg. 1177
Lecompte, Veronique, Dir.-Commun.--Coflexip S.A., Paris, France; *Int'l*, pg. 304
Lederman, John, Mgr.-Mktg. Communications--The BOC Group Inc. (Delaware), Murray Hill, NJ; *Int'l*, pg. 121
Ledesma, Arleen P., Dir.-Consumer Health--SmithKline Beecham Research Limited, Pasig, Philippines; *Int'l*, pg. 1266
Lee, C.K., Dir.-Pub. Rels.--LG Group Inc., Englewood Cliffs, NJ; *Int'l*, pg. 779
Lee, Dallas, Sr. V.P.-Communications--NationsBank South, Atlanta, GA; *U.S. Public*, pg. 1163
Lee, Dani, Sls. & Mktg. Coord.--Gilliam Candy Brands, Edwardsville, KS; *U.S. Private*, pg. 454
Lee, Loretta, Mgr.-Pub. Affairs--Cycle & Carriage Industries (1986) Pte. Limited, Singapore, Singapore; *Int'l*, pg. 350
Lee, R. Marilyn, V.P.-Pub. Affairs--Los Angeles Times, Los Angeles, CA; *U.S. Public*, pg. 1616
Lee, Ronald C., Mktg. & Pub. Rels. Officer--Community First Bankshares, Inc., Fargo, ND; *U.S. Public*, pg. 416
Lee, Sammy, Mgr.-Mktg. Communications--Samsung Electronics America, Inc., Ridgefield Park, NJ; *Int'l*, pg. 1183
Lee, Terry, Sr. V.P. & Mgr.-Corp. Commun.--First Tennessee National Corporation, Memphis, TN; *U.S. Public*, pg. 638
Lee, Terry, Sr. V.P. & Mgr.-Corp. Communications--First Tennessee Bank National Association, Memphis, TN; *U.S. Public*, pg. 639
Leedom, John N., Sr., Chm. Bd., Chief Exec. Officer--Wholesale Electronic Supply, Dallas, TX; *U.S. Private*, pg. 1174
Leeds, Candace, V.P.-Pub. Affairs--Loews Corporation, New York, NY; *U.S. Public*, pg. 1010
Leflar, Helen, Mgr.-Pub. Rels.--Bristol Hotels & Resorts, Dallas, TX; *U.S. Public*, pg. 253
LeFort, G. Neil, V.P.-Investor Rels.--Molex Incorporated, Lisle, IL; *U.S. Public*, pg. 1121
LeGault, Sharon, Mgr.-Mktg.--Cooper Instrument Corp., Middlefield, CT; *U.S. Private*, pg. 274
Leggatt, Hugh, Mgr.-Corp. Commun.--Placer Dome Inc., Vancouver, Canada; *Int'l*, pg. 1060
Legros, Brigitte, Mgr.-Pub. Rels.--RTL9, Metz, France; *Int'l*, pg. 561
Lehman, Alice, Sr. V.P. & Mng. Dir.-Corp. Rels.--First Union Corporation, Charlotte, NC; *U.S. Public*, pg. 639
Lehnhard, Mary Nell, Sr. V.P.-Policy & Representation--Blue Cross and Blue Shield Association, Chicago, IL; *U.S. Private*, pg. 151
Lehnhof, Don, Corp. Communications/Pub. Rels--Nature's Sunshine Products, Inc., Provo, UT; *U.S. Public*, pg. 1166
Lehtinen, Veikko, Deputy Pres.-Legal Affairs, Human Resources & Corp. Communication--Outokumpu Oyj, Espoo, Finland; *Int'l*, pg. 1015
Leibundgut, Brice, Mgr.-Pub. Rels.--Union des Assurances Federales, Paris, France; *Int'l*, pg. 344
Leichsering, Volker, Sr. V.P.-Corp. Commun.--ABB Asea Brown Boveri (Holding) Ltd., Zurich, Switzerland; *Int'l*, pg. 1
Leicht, Lars, V.P. & Dir.-Pub. Rels.--Banfi Vintners, Old Brookville, NY; *U.S. Private*, pg. 113
Leinfuss, Ellen, V.P.-Mktg. & Commun.--EA Engineering, Science & Technology, Inc., Hunt Valley, MD; *U.S. Public*, pg. 540
Leipold, Erika M., Coord.-Adv. & Pub. Rels.-Commercial Div.--Continental General Tire, Inc., Charlotte, NC; *Int'l*, pg. 327
Lekang, Jim, V.P.-Customer Srvc.--GE Capital/IT Solutions, Minneapolis, MN; *U.S. Public*, pg. 711
Lemaire, Chantal, Mgr.-Pub. Rels.--Radio Contact, Brussels, Belgium; *Int'l*, pg. 561
Lenart, Nina, Dir.-Pub. Rels.--American International Industries, City of Commerce, CA; *U.S. Private*, pg. 57
Leneghan, Anne, Specialist-Pub. Rels.--Informix Software, Menlo Park, CA; *U.S. Public*, pg. 876
Lennon, Christine, V.P.-Corp. Commun.--BioChem Pharma Inc., Laval, Canada; *Int'l*, pg. 196
Lenoir, J.P., Dir.-Customer Service--Charmilles Technologies SA, Meyrin, Switzerland; *Int'l*, pg. 489
Lentini, Anthony R., V.P.-Public & Intl. Affairs--Apache Corporation, Houston, TX; *U.S. Public*, pg. 119
Lenzer, Sara, Communications Consultant--Hawaiian Electric Company, Inc., Honolulu, HI; *U.S. Public*, pg. 800
Leonard, Earl T., Sr. V.P.-Corp. Affairs--The Coca-Cola Company, Atlanta, GA; *U.S. Public*, pg. 392
Leone, Gina, Dir.-Adv. & Publicity--Aladdin Hotel & Casino, Las Vegas, NV; *U.S. Private*, pg. 30
LePeu, Jean-Marc, V.P.-Pub. Affairs--Renault, Boulogne-Billancourt, France; *Int'l*, pg. 1102
Lepore, Pascal, Dir.-Commun./Snowmobiles--Bombardier Recreational Products, Montreal, Canada; *Int'l*, pg. 200
Lerman, Jeanette, V.P.-Communications--Time Warner Inc., New York, NY; *U.S. Public*, pg. 1610
Leroux, Gerard, Dir.-Pub. Affairs--Facom, Morangis, France; *Int'l*, pg. 570
Leroy, Muriel, Press Relationship--Young & Rubicam France, Paris, France; *U.S. Private*, pg. 1199
Les, Jennifer, Dir.-Information Services & Shareholder Rels.--The McGraw-Hill Companies, New York, NY; *U.S. Public*, pg. 1069
Lesko, Robert E., V.P.-Corp. Communications--Hussmann Corp., Bridgeton, MO; *U.S. Public*, pg. 1766
Lestelle, James F., Sr. V.P.-Corp. Commun.--Hibernia Corporation, New Orleans, LA; *U.S. Public*, pg. 825
Lester, Clayton F., V.P.-Adv.--Associated Grocers, Inc., Baton Rouge, LA; *U.S. Private*, pg. 90
Lester, Keith, Mgr.-Pub. Rels.--Broan Mfg. Co., Inc., Hartford, WI; *U.S. Public*, pg. 1193
Lester, Keith, Mgr.-Pub. Rels.--Aubrey Manufacturing Company, Hartford, WI; *U.S. Public*, pg. 1193
Letta, Giampaolo, Mgr.-Pub. Rels.--Ferrari North America, Inc., Englewood Cliffs, NJ; *Int'l*, pg. 483
Leuchtmann, Lisa, Mgr.-Communications & Adv.--InteCom, Dallas, TX; *Int'l*, pg. 794
Leutas, Tony, Mgr.-Mktg. Commun.--Waters Corporation, Milford, MA; *U.S. Public*, pg. 1745
Leuthe, Paul, Mgr.-Corp. Mktg.--Sub-Zero Freezer Co., Inc., Madison, WI; *U.S. Private*, pg. 1048
Levari, Henry, Sr. V.P.- External Affairs--Atlantic Electric Co., Pleasantville, NJ; *U.S. Public*, pg. 430
Levene, Jane, Sr. Mgr.- Communications & Intl. Pub. Rels.--MCI International Inc., Rye Brook, NY; *U.S. Public*, pg. 1024
Levene, Nancy Boyle, Assoc. Dir.-Pub. Rels. & Events--Sharp Electronics Corporation, Mahwah, NJ; *Int'l*, pg. 1228
Levengood, Robert, Dir.-Commun.--Quality Bakers of America Cooperative, Inc., Greenwich, CT; *U.S. Private*, pg. 898
Levenson, Stanley R., Chief Exec.-Pub. Rels.--Levenson & Hill, Inc., Dallas, TX; *U.S. Private*, pg. 662
Levesque, Christine, Dir.-Corp. Communications--Aetrium Inc., Saint Paul, MN; *U.S. Public*, pg. 27
Levesque, Marie, Pub. Rels. Coord.--Leo Burnett Company, Ltd.-Taiwan Branch, Taipei, Taiwan; *U.S. Private*, pg. 185
Levin, Karen, V.P.-Commun. & Sec.--Biospherics Incorporated, Beltsville, MD; *U.S. Public*, pg. 232
Levin, Robert J., Exec. V.P.-Mktg.--Federal National Mortgage Association (Fannie Mae), Washington, DC; *U.S. Public*, pg. 615
Levin, Susan, V.P.-Publicity--Columbia Pictures, Culver City, CA; *Int'l*, pg. 1281
Levina, Melinda, Dir.-Corp. Communications--Micro Warehouse, Inc., Norwalk, CT; *U.S. Public*, pg. 1104
Levine, Kate, Mgr.-Adv. Design--American Technical Ceramics Corp., Huntington Station, NY; *U.S. Public*, pg. 93
Levine, Stuart Z., Ph.D., Dir.-Investor Rels.--Roberts Pharmaceutical Corporation, Eatontown, NJ; *U.S. Public*, pg. 1393
Levy, Bret W., V.P.-Credit & Customer Service & Treas.--Gottschalks Inc., Fresno, CA; *U.S. Public*, pg. 754
Levy, David, Sr. V.P.-Tech. & Customer Service--MidAmerican Energy Holdings, Des Moines, IA; *U.S. Public*, pg. 1109
Levy, Harry, Mgr.-Pub. Rels.--Foster Wheeler Corporation, Clinton, NJ; *U.S. Public*, pg. 676
Lewandowski, David, V.P.-Pub. Rels.--Al Paul Lefton Co., Inc., Philadelphia, PA; *U.S. Private*, pg. 658
Lewin, Sandra, Dir.-Corp. Communications & Pub. Rels.--George Wimpey PLC, London, United Kingdom; *Int'l*, pg. 1510
Lewis, Ann, Dir.-Media Services & Publicity and Information--B.A.S.S., Inc., Montgomery, AL; *U.S. Private*, pg. 105
Lewis, Barry L., Dir.-Pub. Rels. & Adv.--Huls America Inc., Somerset, NJ; *Int'l*, pg. 1455
Lewis, Caroline A., Sr. V.P.-Pub. Rels. Div.--Serino Coyne Public Relations, Potomac, MD; *U.S. Private*, pg. 985
Lewis, D., Dir.-Communications--SmithGroup, Inc., Detroit, MI; *U.S. Private*, pg. 1010
Lewis, Linda, Mktg. Asst.--Bender Shipbuilding & Repair Company, Inc., Mobile, AL; *U.S. Private*, pg. 132
Lewis, Rhonda S., Mgr.-Pub. Rels. & Promo.--JanSport, Appleton, WI; *U.S. Public*, pg. 1702
Lewis, Richard, V.P.-Pub. Rels.--Hanna-Barbera Productions, Inc., Hollywood, CA; *U.S. Public*, pg. 1614
Lewis, S. D., Dir.-Corp. Affairs--National Westminster Bank PLC, London, United Kingdom; *Int'l*, pg. 910
Lewis, Sandra, Mgr.-Pub. Rels.--Miller Brewing Company, Trenton, OH; *U.S. Public*, pg. 1289
Lewis, Simon, Dir.-Corp. Affairs--Centrica Plc, Slough, United Kingdom; *Int'l*, pg. 279
Lewis, Terry, V.P.-Industry Relations--Yamaha Corporation of America, Buena Park, CA; *Int'l*, pg. 1516
Lewitzke, Gary, Corp. Dir.-Indus. Rels.--Pabst Brewing Co., San Antonio, TX; *U.S. Private*, pg. 954
Leyden, Paul, Sr. V.P.-Pub. Rels.--The Bank of New York, New York, NY; *U.S. Public*, pg. 178
Leyden, Paul J., Sr. V.P.-Pub. Rels.--The Bank of New York Company, Inc., New York, NY; *U.S. Public*, pg. 178
Leys, Marie Christine, Dir.-Corp. Commun.--Bank Brussels Lambert, Brussels, Belgium; *Int'l*, pg. 146
Lichtgarn, Peter, Dir.-Communications--Matthew Bender & Company, Incorporated, New York, NY; *U.S. Public*, pg. 1616
Lichtman, Howard, Exec. V.P.-Mktg. & Communications--Cineplex Odeon Corporation, Toronto, Canada; *Int'l*, pg. 292
Lickstein, Mark, Dir.-Mktg., Pub. Rels. & Commun.--Farmers & Merchants Bank of Central California, Lodi, CA; *U.S. Private*, pg. 394
Lieberman, Mark, Exec. V.P.-Entertainment, Commun. & Media--Reed Elsevier Business Information, Newton, MA; *Int'l*, pg. 1095
Lieske, Laura, Mgr.-Mktg. Communications--Sennheiser Electronic Corp., Old Lyme, CT; *U.S. Private*, pg. 984
Lightford, Arlene, V.P.-Corp. Communications--Cylink Corp., Sunnyvale, CA; *U.S. Public*, pg. 1306
Lightstone, Herb, V.P.-Pub. Rels.--ICN Pharmaceuticals, Inc., Costa Mesa, CA; *U.S. Public*, pg. 853
Lilja, Lu Ann, Dir.-Corp. Communications--Dean Foods Company, Franklin Park, IL; *U.S. Public*, pg. 489
Lim, Joanne, Mgr.-Pub. Rels.--Yeo Hiap Seng Limited, Singapore, Singapore; *Int'l*, pg. 1008
Limbach, Vickie, Mgr.-Communications--J.M. Smucker Company, Orrville, OH; *U.S. Public*, pg. 1480
Limbaugh, Al, Mgr.-Pub. Affairs--Blue Cross & Blue Shield of Illinois, Chicago, IL; *U.S. Private*, pg. 151
Lin, Michael, Mgr.-P.R.--Cytec Fiberite Inc., Tempe, AZ; *U.S. Public*, pg. 471
Lincoln, Greg, Dir.-Brand Communications--The Haagen-Dazs Company Inc., Minneapolis, MN; *Int'l*, pg. 411
Lind, Kathy, Dir.-Customer Service--Brumko Magnetics, Elkhorn, NE; *U.S. Private*, pg. 696
Lindahl, Carol A., Dir.-Corp. Communications--Guidant Corporation-Cardiac Rhythm Management Group, Saint Paul, MN; *U.S. Public*, pg. 768
Lindeke, Ronald C., Dir.-Communications--Lockheed Martin Skunk Works, Palmdale, CA; *U.S. Public*, pg. 1007
Lindeman, Martha, V.P.-Corp. Commun. & Investor Rels.--Playboy Enterprises, Inc., Chicago, IL; *U.S. Public*, pg. 1309
Linder, Suzanne, Mgr.-Communications--Anadarko Petroleum Corporation, Houston, TX; *U.S. Public*, pg. 107
Lindner, Patty L., Dir.-Pub. Rels.--Artesian Resources Corporation, Newark, DE; *U.S. Public*, pg. 135
Lindroos, Merja, Mgr.-Communications--OY Stockmann AB, Helsinki, Finland; *Int'l*, pg. 1301
Lindsay, B., Mgr. Public Rels. & Adv./Europe--Alcoa S.A., Lausanne, Switzerland; *U.S. Public*, pg. 62
Lines, Alan, Coord.-Commun.--Mrs. Fields' Original Cookies, Inc., Salt Lake City, UT; *U.S. Private*, pg. 688
Link, Gary F., V.P. & Dir.-Mktg. & Communication Services--HNTB Corporation, Kansas City, MO; *U.S. Private*, pg. 492
Linke, Curtis, V.P.-Corp. Commun.--Deere & Company, Moline, IL; *U.S. Public*, pg. 491
Linton, Nicolete, Assoc. Editor-Grp. Pub. Affairs--The Hongkong and Shanghai Banking Corporation Limited (HongkongBank), Central, Hong Kong; *Int'l*, pg. 583
Lintz, Connie, Mgr.-Mktg.-Customer Service--Snyder Industries, Inc., Lincoln, NE; *U.S. Private*, pg. 1011
Lipovitch, Gerard, Pub. Rels. Dir.--Crehalet Pouget Poussielgues, Paris, France; *U.S. Private*, pg. 1152
Lipscomb, Pete, Dir.-External Affairs--Guinness Plc, London, United Kingdom; *Int'l*, pg. 412
Liscik, Raymond, V.P.-Adv., Mktg., Sls. & Pub. Rels.--JCI Data Processing, Inc., Cinnaminson, NJ; *U.S. Private*, pg. 577
Lisi, Edward E., Dir.-Mktg. Communications--Southern New England Telecommunications Corporation, New Haven, CT; *U.S. Public*, pg. 1490
Liss, Louisa, Mgr.-Public Relations--Weider Publications, Inc., Woodland Hills, CA; *U.S. Private*, pg. 1159
Liss, Mona, Dir.-Pub. Rels.--The Franklin Mint, Franklin Center, PA; *U.S. Private*, pg. 941
Litterst, Jean, Mgr.-Pub. Affairs--Kentucky Fried Chicken Corporation (KFC), Louisville, KY; *U.S. Public*, pg. 1636
Little, Ann, Dir.-Mktg. Communications--Wavetek Corporation, San Diego, CA; *U.S. Private*, pg. 1154
Little, Bradley A., Chief Fin. Officer, Sr. V.P.-Fin. & Treas.--Calton, Inc., Manalapan, NJ; *U.S. Public*, pg. 296
Little, Cathy, Mgr.-Corp. Commun.--Reflectone, Inc., Tampa, FL; *Int'l*, pg. 218
Little, Philip, Mgr.-Pub. Rels.--Candle Corporation, Santa Monica, CA; *U.S. Private*, pg. 204
Little, R., Mgr.-Communications--British Gypsum Ltd., Loughborough, United Kingdom; *Int'l*, pg. 122
Little, Stephen A., V.P.-Corp. Information Systems--Square D Company, Palatine, IL; *Int'l*, pg. 1208
Lively-Yost, Diane, Mgr.-Pub. Rels.--Apple South, Inc., Madison, GA; *U.S. Public*, pg. 121
Livesey, Marie, Mgr.-Public Rels.- Europe--Astec International Limited, Wan Chai, Hong Kong; *Int'l*, pg. 92
Lividini, Jackie, V.P.-Pub. Rels.--Saks Fifth Avenue, New York, NY; *U.S. Public*, pg. 1429
Livonius, Detlev, Dir.-Pub. Rels.--Otto Versand (GmbH & Co.), Hamburg, Germany; *Int'l*, pg. 1014
Ljungman, Mauritz, Dir.-Info.--SAS Airline, Stockholm, Sweden; *Int'l*, pg. 1201
Llewellyn-Slade, Mark, Mgr.-Corp. Pub. Rels.--Bristol & West Building Society, Bristol, United Kingdom; *Int'l*, pg. 216
Lloyd, Deborah, Communications Specialist--Thermal Ceramics Inc., Augusta, GA; *Int'l*, pg. 894
Locke, Maureen, Mgr.-Mktg. Communications--Capintec Inc., Ramsey, NJ; *U.S. Private*, pg. 205
Lockhart, Harriette, Mgr.-Admin.--Associated Grocers, Inc., Seattle, WA; *U.S. Private*, pg. 90
Lockhart, James B., V.P.-Pub. Affairs--Transamerica Corporation, San Francisco, CA; *U.S. Public*, pg. 1629
Locklear, Susan, Pub. Rels.--3ummit Performance Dist. Inc., Channelview, TX; *U.S. Public*, pg. 1233
Lodge, Helen, Coord.-Pub. Affairs--Gillette France, S.A., Levallois-Perret, France; *U.S. Public*, pg. 744
Loechner, Barbara, Mgr.-Adv. & Communications--Nikon Inc., Melville, NY; *Int'l*, pg. 931
Loeffler, Arthur G., Dir.-Communications--Ashland Chemical, Dublin, OH; *U.S. Public*, pg. 139
Lofland, Cheri, Head-Grp. Commun.--Reckitt & Colman plc, London, United Kingdom; *Int'l*, pg. 1089
Loftus, Jack, V.P.-Communications--Nielsen Media Research, New York, NY; *U.S. Public*, pg. 395
Logan, Lacey, Sr. Dir.-Corp. Commun. & Pub. Rels.--The Stroh Brewery Company, Detroit, MI; *U.S. Private*, pg. 1047
Logerquist, Jim, Corp. Communicaitons--Agripac Inc., Salem, OR; *U.S. Private*, pg. 26
Loh-Kaiser, Sabine Eiser, Mgr.-Mktg. Commun.--Texas Micro, Inc., Houston, TX; *U.S. Public*, pg. 1586
Loh, R. Daniel, Mgr.-Investor Rels.--Alumax Inc., Atlanta, GA; *U.S. Public*, pg. 59
Loiacono, John, Dir.-Corp. Commun.--Sun Microsystems, Inc., Palo Alto, CA; *U.S. Public*, pg. 1531
Lokitus, Tom, Mgr.-Commun.--Conestoga Wood Specialties Corp., East Earl, PA; *U.S. Private*, pg. 262
Lollar, Joan Horne, Mgr.-Corp. Communications--Maybelline, Inc., New York, NY; *Int'l*, pg. 819
Lomax, Brendan, Mgr.-Media Rels.--Mobil Oil Company, Ltd., Milton Keynes, United Kingdom; *U.S. Public*, pg. 1119
Lomax, Susan, Mgr.-Communications Services--Paramount Parks, Charlotte, NC; *U.S. Private*, pg. 776

Lombard, Michael, Mgr.-Customer Svc.--Raffi & Swanson, Inc., Wilmington, MA; *U.S. Private*, pg. 907
Lomelino, Susan, Pres.-Publicis Pub. Rels.--Publicis/Bloom Inc., New York, NY; *Int'l*, pg. 470
Long, Charles F., Dir.-Pub. Rels.--Tellabs Operations, Inc., Lisle, IL; *U.S. Public*, pg. 1572
Long, Elizabeth, Mgr.-Pub. Rels.--Spicer Axle Div., Fort Wayne, IN; *U.S. Public*, pg. 479
Long, James, Dir.-Commun.--The Atlantic Monthly Magazine, Boston, MA; *U.S. Private*, pg. 95
Long, Jeanette, Mgr.-Mktg. Commun.--American Standard Inc., Piscataway, NJ; *U.S. Public*, pg. 91
Long, John C., Dir.-Corp. Commun.--Hershey Foods Corporation, Hershey, PA; *U.S. Public*, pg. 811
Longacre, Robert, Mgr.-Adv.--Hehr International Inc., Los Angeles, CA; *U.S. Private*, pg. 519
Longanecker, Caroline, Mgr.-Pub. Rels.--Enterprise Management, Reston, VA; *U.S. Private*, pg. 351
Longden, Marianne, Mgr.-Adv.--Purity Products Inc., Miami, FL; *U.S. Private*, pg. 896
Longendyke, Rob, Mgr.-Pub. Rels.--Pillsbury Co., Minneapolis, MN; *Int'l*, pg. 411
Loper, LeAnn, Mgr.-Pub. Rels.--Showboat, Incorporated, Las Vegas, NV; *U.S. Public*, pg. 1469
Lopez M., Jose Antonio, Pres.-Legal, Pub. & Banking Rels. Div.--Vitro, Sociedad Anonima, Garza Garcia, Mexico; *Int'l*, pg. 1469
Lopez, Rob, Dir.-Pub. Rels.--Sears Point Raceway, Sonoma, CA; *U.S. Public*, pg. 1498
Lord, Michel, V.P.-Commun. & Pub. Rels.--Bombardier Inc., Montreal, Canada; *Int'l*, pg. 199
Lorenz-Meyer, Eckart, Div. Mgr.--Durkopp Adler AG, Bielefeld, Germany; *Int'l*, pg. 468
Lorenz, Deborah S., V.P.-Investor Rels. & Corp. Commun.--EG & G, Inc., Wellesley, MA; *U.S. Public*, pg. 542
Lorriaux, Bernard, Dir.-Communications--Goodyear, Rueil-Malmaison, France; *U.S. Public*, pg. 753
Losie, Paul M., V.P.-Far West--Amwest Surety Insurance Company, Calabasas, CA; *U.S. Public*, pg. 106
Lot, Thierry, Dir.-Mktg.--Polive/Tricosteril, Courbevoie, France; *U.S. Public*, pg. 673
Lotsberg, Warren K., V.P.-Public Affairs--Northwestern Public Service, Huron, SD; *U.S. Public*, pg. 1200
Lotti, Marta, Mgr.-Pub. Rels.--Alitalia Airlines, New York, NY; *Int'l*, pg. 652
Lougee, R.W., Jr., V.P.-Investor Rels. & Corp. Commun.--Arch Communications Group, Inc., Westborough, MA; *U.S. Public*, pg. 127
Loughrey, Dan, Dir.-Corp. Affairs--Aer Lingus, Dublin, Ireland; *Int'l*, pg. 28
Louis, Murray A., V.P.-Communications & Asst. Sec.--SEI Investments, Oaks, PA; *U.S. Public*, pg. 1417
Lourdelle, Michele, Mgr.-Pub. Rels.--M6, Paris, France; *Int'l*, *pg. 561*
Loux, Michael, Dir.-Mkt. Research--Jervis B. Webb Company, Farmington Hills, MI; *U.S. Private*, pg. 1156
Lovelace, Nancy, Sr. V.P.-Corp. Communications--Wachovia Corporation, Winston Salem, NC; *U.S. Public*, pg. 1730
Lovelace, Nancy P., Dir.-Pub. Rels.--Wachovia Bank of South Carolina, N.A., Columbia, SC; *U.S. Public*, pg. 1730
Lovell, Richard E., Dir.-Communications--Kellogg Company, Battle Creek, MI; *U.S. Public*, pg. 947
Loverd, William T., V.P. & Dir.-Publicity--Alfred A. Knopf, Inc., New York, NY; *U.S. Private*, pg. 21
Lovoy, Cynthia, Mgr.-Publicity--American Cast Iron Pipe Co., Birmingham, AL; *U.S. Private*, pg. 51
Lovstrom, Rolf, V.P.-Pub. Affairs--Norske Skogindustrier A.S, Skogn, Norway; *Int'l*, pg. 965
Low, S., Dir.-Govt. Rels. & Pub. Affairs--General Motors of Canada Ltd., Oshawa, Canada; *U.S. Public*, pg. 722
Low, William H., V.P.-Corp. Communications--R.R. Donnelley & Sons Company, Chicago, IL; *U.S. Public*, pg. 517
Lowe, M.W., Mgr.-Customer Services--Salt River Project Agricultural Improvement and Power District, Tempe, AZ; *U.S. Private*, pg. 962
Lowenfish, Edward, V.P.-Assoc. Rels. & Affairs--Kings Super Markets Inc., West Caldwell, NJ; *Int'l*, pg. 843
Lowman, George S., Dir.-Communications--GATX Corporation, Chicago, IL; *U.S. Public*, pg. 690
Lucas, Barbara B., Sr. V.P.-Pub. Affairs & Corp. Sec.--The Black & Decker Corporation, Towson, MD; *U.S. Public*, pg. 233
Ludwig, Kim, Mgr.-Communications--Energy Absorption Systems, Inc., Chicago, IL; *U.S. Public*, pg. 1353
Lueck, Guada, Mgr.-Adv. & Pub. Rels.--The PBS&J Corporation, Miami, FL; *U.S. Private*, pg. 825
Luest, Helga, Mgr.-Media Rels.--Goodwill Industries International, Bethesda, MD; *U.S. Private*, pg. 464
Luftman, Michael, V.P.-Corp. Communications--Time Warner Cable, Stamford, CT; *U.S. Public*, pg. 1610
Luginbuhl, Dan R., V.P.-Commun.--Penske Corporation, Detroit, MI; *U.S. Private*, pg. 850
Lui, Susan, Mgr.-Corp. & Intl. Rels.--International Factors (Singapore) Ltd., Singapore, Singapore; *Int'l*, pg. 684
Lui, Susan, Mgr.-Pub. Rels.--International Factors Leasing Pte Ltd., Singapore, Singapore; *Int'l*, pg. 684
Lukas, Barney, Dir.-Public Affairs--Weyerhaeuser Canada Ltd., Kamloops, Canada; *U.S. Public*, pg. 1764
Lukas, Joan, Mgr.-Pub. Rels.--ConAgra, Inc., Omaha, NE; *U.S. Public*, pg. 425
Lukas, Julie, Pub. Rels. Coord.--Tredegar Industries Inc., Richmond, VA; *U.S. Public*, pg. 1633
Lukkari, Esko, V.P.-Corp. Communications--Rautaruukki Oy, Helsinki, Finland; *Int'l*, pg. 1088
Lukowski, Dieter, V.P.-Public Affairs--Reemtsma Cigarettenfabriken GmbH, Hamburg, Hamburg, Germany; *Int'l*, pg. 1100
Luljak, Tom, Dir.-Corp. Communications--United Wisconsin Services, Inc., Milwaukee, WI; *U.S. Public*, pg. 1692
Lundquist, Gene A., V.P. & Corp. Sec.--Calcot, Ltd., Bakersfield, CA; *U.S. Private*, pg. 200
Luntz, Gail, Coord.-Mktg. Communications--Fujitsu Systems of America, Inc., La Jolla, CA; *Int'l*, pg. 526
Lurndal, Art, V.P.-Adv., Promo. & Pub. Rels.--Kent Feeds Inc., Muscatine, IA; *U.S. Private*, pg. 1134
Luscomb, Brian, Dir.-Corp. Communications--Jenny Craig, Inc., La Jolla, CA; *U.S. Public*, pg. 926
Lute, Graham, Dir.-Communications--Nestle S.A., Vevey, Switzerland; *Int'l*, pg. 915
Luthringer, Paul J., Dir.-Pub. Rels.--Hearst Magazines Division, New York, NY; *U.S. Private*, pg. 516
Lutz, Jeralyn, Coord.-Communications--Intertec Publishing, Overland Park, KS; *U.S. Public*, pg. 1327
Lybeck, Katarina, Sr. V.P.-Corp. Commun.--Outokumpu Oyj, Espoo, Finland; *Int'l*, pg. 1015
Lydic, Tammy, Dir.-Shareholder Communication--Northwestern Public Service, Huron, SD; *U.S. Public*, pg. 1200
Lyman, Kerry B., Mktg. Dir. & Pub. Rels. Dir.--CheckMark Communications, Saint Louis, MO; *U.S. Private*, pg. 231
Lyn, Sharon, Commun. Asst.--BankAtlantic Bancorp, Inc., Fort Lauderdale, FL; *U.S. Public*, pg. 183
Lynch, Carol, Mgr.-Mktg. Communications, Consumer Prods.--Leviton Mfg. Co., Inc., Little Neck, NY; *U.S. Private*, pg. 663
Lynch, Dennis, V.P.-Communications--Wendy's International Inc., Dublin, OH; *U.S. Public*, pg. 1754
Lynch, Kevin P., V.P.--ELXSI Corporation, Orlando, FL; *U.S. Public*, pg. 545
Lynch, Michael, Dir.-Pub. Affairs--Illinois Tool Works Inc., Glenview, IL; *U.S. Public*, pg. 865
Lynch, Pat, Mgr.-Investor Rels.--The Washington Water Power Company, Spokane, WA; *U.S. Public*, pg. 1744
Lynch, Philip J., V.P. & Dir.-Corp. Commun.--Brown-Forman Corporation, Louisville, KY; *U.S. Public*, pg. 261
Lyndon, J., Mgr.-Adv., Pub. Rels. & Mktg. Communications--Aer Lingus, Melville, NY; *Int'l*, pg. 28
Lynn, Sharon, Mgr.-Commun.--NTS Development Company, Louisville, KY; *U.S. Private*, pg. 772
Lyon, Marina, Dir.-Pub. Affairs--Piper Jaffray Companies, Inc., Minneapolis, MN; *U.S. Public*, pg. 1300
Lyons, Arthur, Mgr.-Corp. Communications--Beckman Coulter, Miami, FL; *U.S. Public*, pg. 199
Lyons, Norine, Dir.-Public Affairs--General Dynamics Corporation, Falls Church, VA; *U.S. Public*, pg. 708
Maatta, Usko, Dir.-Corp. Commun.--FinnAir Oy, Helsinki, Finland; *Int'l*, pg. 485
Mabantsela, K., Gen. Mgr.--Transnet Ltd., Parkview, South Africa; *Int'l*, pg. 1417
MacDonald, Becky, Mgr.-Pub. Affairs--Breed Technologies, Sterling Heights, MI; *U.S. Public*, pg. 251
MacDonald, John A., Dir.-Investor Relations--EEX Corporation, Houston, TX; *U.S. Public*, pg. 542
MacDonald, Martin, Dir.-Pub. Rels.--Bass Pro Shops, Inc., Springfield, MO; *U.S. Private*, pg. 122
MacDonald, S. Kelley, V.P.-Corp. Communications--Unitrode Corporation, Merrimack, NH; *U.S. Public*, pg. 1694
MacFadyen, Scott, P.R. Officer--McCain Foods Limited, Florenceville, Canada; *Int'l*, pg. 850
Machu, Ann Marie, Dir.-Pub. Rels.--France Telecom, Paris, France; *Int'l*, pg. 503
Macius, Mindaugas A., Dir.-Adv. & Pub. Rels.--Houston Foods Company, Franklin Park, IL; *U.S. Private*, pg. 542
Mack, Dennis A., V.P.-Customer Services & Support--FileNet Corporation, Costa Mesa, CA; *U.S. Public*, pg. 622
Mack, Lisbeth, V.P.-Adv. & Mktg. Programs--Trans World Airlines, Inc., Saint Louis, MO; *U.S. Public*, pg. 1629
MacKay, Gordon D., V.P.-Pub. Affairs/Pub. Rels.--The New England, Boston, MA; *U.S. Private*, pg. 737
MacKay, Jackie, Pub. Rels. Dir.--Cramer-Krasselt, Orlando, FL; *U.S. Private*, pg. 286
MacKay, Jackie, Pub. Rels. Dir.-Orlando--Cramer-Krasselt Public Relations, Milwaukee, WI; *U.S. Private*, pg. 286
Mackay, William L., Staff V.P.-Pub. Affairs--Alaska Airlines, Inc., Seattle, WA; *U.S. Public*, pg. 35
MacKenzie, Bruce, Mgr.-Pub. Rels.--Paramount Canada's Wonderland, Vaughan, Canada; *U.S. Private*, pg. 776
MacKenzie, Tod, Sr. V.P.-Pub. Affairs--Frito-Lay Company, Plano, TX; *U.S. Public*, pg. 1277
MacKenzie, Tod, V.P.-Pub. Affairs--Smartfoods, Inc., Plano, TX; *U.S. Public*, pg. 1277
Maclam, Don, Mgr.-Mktg.--The Canadian Coleman Co., Ltd., Toronto, Canada; *U.S. Private*, pg. 691
Macmaster, Kirsty, Mgr.-Pud. Rels.--Mirror Group plc, London, United Kingdom; *Int'l*, pg. 869
MacMillan, Andrew J., Dir.-Pub. Rels.--Credit Suisse First Boston, Inc., New York, NY; *Int'l*, pg. 345
MacNab, Craig, Dir.-Pub. Rels.--AM General Corporation, South Bend, IN; *U.S. Private*, pg. 922
Macomber, Laurie, Dir.-Mktg. Communications & Adv.--International Paper Company, Purchase, NY; *U.S. Public*, *pg. 901*
MacQueen, Craig R., V.P.-Corp. Communications--Conrail, Inc., Philadelphia, PA; *U.S. Public*, pg. 431
MacReynolds, Neil, Mgr.-Pub. Rels.--Kaiser Permanente, Northwest Division, Portland, OR; *U.S. Private*, pg. 605
Madden, Mike, Mgr.-Mktg. & Communications-Global Access Deposit--MasterCard International-Cirrus Brand, Purchase, NY; *U.S. Private*, pg. 714
Madden, Sharon, Dir.-Investor Rels.--Daw Technologies, Inc., Salt Lake City, UT; *U.S. Public*, pg. 489
Madden, Thomas J., Chief Fin. & Acctg. Officer, V.P.-Fin. & Treas.--Daisytek International Corporation, Plano, TX; *U.S. Public*, pg. 477
Madison, Anne C., V.P.-Communications--The Ryland Group, Inc., Columbia, MD; *U.S. Public*, pg. 1414
Maeda, Ichiro, Mgr.-Intl. Commun.--Toray Industries, Inc., Tokyo, Japan; *Int'l*, pg. 1399
Maenza, Drew, Asst. V.P. & Dir.-Mktg.--Crawford & Company, Atlanta, GA; *U.S. Public*, pg. 458
Maeren, Vande, Dir.-Pub. Rels.--L'Oreal Technique Professional Div., Brussels, Belgium; *Int'l*, pg. 819
Magatomy, S., Mgr.-Customer Rels.--Mitsubishi Motors Corporation, Tokyo, Japan; *Int'l*, pg. 875
Maggipinto, Donata, Mgr.-Adv. & Pub. Rels.--Williams-Sonoma, Inc., San Francisco, CA; *U.S. Public*, pg. 1770
Magner, Heidi, Dir.-Corp. Commun.--ADAC Laboratories Inc., Milpitas, CA; *U.S. Public*, pg. 3
Magruder, Logan, V.P.-Corp. Rels. & Bus. Devel.--Barrett Resources Corporation, Denver, CO; *U.S. Public*, pg. 191
Magyar, Mary K., V.P.-Corp. Communications--Associated Banc-Corp, Green Bay, WI; *U.S. Public*, pg. 140
Mahar, Michael C., Sr. V.P.--The Troy Savings Bank, Troy, NY; *U.S. Private*, pg. 1106
Maher, Cindi, Communications Specialist--ANGUS Chemical Company, Buffalo Grove, IL; *U.S. Private*, pg. 75
Maher, Tom, Mgr.-Mktg. Communications--Alcoa Building Products, Inc., Sidney, OH; *U.S. Public*, pg. 61
Mahkorn, Richard, Mgr.-Pub. Rels.--RTL Television, Cologne, Germany; *Int'l*, pg. 561
Mahlanza, Sam, Mgr.-Pub. Rels.--Zimbabwe Electricity Supply Authority, Harare, Zimbabwe; *Int'l*, pg. 1528
Mahmoud-Treimer, Helga, Dir-Publicity--Mosaik Verlag, Munich, Germany; *Int'l*, pg. 190
Mahoney, George R., Jr., Exec. V.P., Gen. Counsel & Sec.--Family Dollar Stores, Inc., Matthews, NC; *U.S. Public*, pg. 612
Mahoney, Robert, Dir.-Media Rels.--Brooklyn Union, Brooklyn, NY; *U.S. Public*, pg. 259
Mahony, Sheila A., V.P.-Govt. Rels. & Pub. Affairs--Cablevision, Woodbury, NY; *U.S. Public*, pg. 288
Mahuka, E., Customer Service--National Bank of Malawi, Blantyre, Malawi; *Int'l*, pg. 1296
Maier, Karen F., V.P.-Mktg.--Frisch's Restaurants, Inc., Cincinnati, OH; *U.S. Public*, pg. 682
Maines Simone, Kristi, Dir.-Mktg. Communications--Max & Erma's Restaurants, Columbus, OH; *U.S. Public*, pg. 1060
Maire, Dominique, Dir.-Communications (France)--The Eurotunnel Group, London, United Kingdom; *Int'l*, pg. 466
Majers, Jacqueline, Dir.-Pub. Rels.--Worldvision Enterprises, New York, NY; *U.S. Private*, pg. 776
Makrush, Theresa, Pub. Rels. Consultant--William Cook Public Relations, Inc., Jacksonville, FL; *U.S. Private*, pg. 273
Male, Montye, V.P.-External Commun.--Weyerhaeuser Company, Federal Way, WA; *U.S. Public*, pg. 1764
Malie, Robert L., Mgr.-Mktg.--Elkins Constructors, Inc., Jacksonville, FL; *U.S. Private*, pg. 372
Malkerson, Elizabeth A., V.P. & Sr. Commun. Officer--United HealthCare Corporation, Minnetonka, MN; *U.S. Public*, pg. 1677
Mallory, Krista, Mgr.-Investor Rels.--Callaway Golf Company, Carlsbad, CA; *U.S. Public*, pg. 294
Malmer, Lars G., Dir.-Pub. Affairs & Investor Rels.--AB SKF, Goteborg, Sweden; *Int'l*, pg. 1156
Malone, Frank, Dir.-Media Rels.--Metra Commuter Rail, Chicago, IL; *U.S. Private*, pg. 919
Maloney, Carlene, Dir.-Mktg. Communications--Waterford Crystal, Inc., Wall, NJ; *Int'l*, pg. 1487
Maloude, Paige, Mgr.-Mktg. Svcs.--Progress Lighting, Spartanburg, SC; *U.S. Public*, pg. 1684
Maloy, A. Cory, Mgr.-Pub. Rels.--Iomega Corporation, Roy, UT; *U.S. Public*, pg. 912
Mammorella, Nancy, V.P.-Mktg. & Pub. Rels.--Mail Boxes Etc., San Diego, CA; *U.S. Public*, pg. 1687
Mammoser, Thomas L., Dir.-Corp. Communications--Walgreen Co., Deerfield, IL; *U.S. Public*, pg. 1733
Manardo, Karen, Mgr.-Corp. Commun.--American Axle & Manufacturing, Detroit, MI; *U.S. Private*, pg. 51
Manbeck, Lois, Dir.-Worldwide Communications--Mead Packaging, Atlanta, GA; *U.S. Public*, pg. 1074
Mander, Lois, V.P.-Pub. Rels.-Lancome--Cosmair, Inc., New York, NY; *Int'l*, pg. 818
Mandeville, Mary, Mgr.-Communications--Aerovox Inc., New Bedford, MA; *U.S. Public*, pg. 25
Mandt, David, Mgr.-Pub. Rels.--Paramount Carowinds, Charlotte, NC; *U.S. Private*, pg. 776
Mandy, Kirk K., V.P.-Bus. Commun. & Semiconductor Div.--Mitel Corporation, Kanata, Canada; *Int'l*, pg. 870
Maneval, J.C., Mgr.-Mktg. Communications--Du Pont Chemicals, Wilmington, DE; *U.S. Public*, pg. 531
Manfredi, John F., Exec. V.P.-Corp. Affairs--Nabisco Inc., Parsippany, NJ; *U.S. Public*, pg. 1355
Mangione, Mike, Mktg. & Communications Specialist--Edwards High Vacuum, International, Grand Island, NY; *Int'l*, pg. 121
Mangione, Mike, Mktg. & Communications Specialist--Edwards High Vacuum International, Wilmington, MA; *Int'l*, pg. 121
Manigan, Liz, Dir.-Promo.--Parade Publications Inc., New York, NY; *U.S. Private*, pg. 20
Manis, Cheri, Mgr.-Commun. & Investor Rels.--Mycogen Corporation, San Diego, CA; *U.S. Public*, pg. 1142
Manley, Jennifer, Mgr.-Adv.--Tanning Research Labs., Inc., Ormond Beach, FL; *U.S. Private*, pg. 1068
Mann, Allan, V.P.-Commun.--Kaiser Permanente, Oakland, CA; *U.S. Private*, pg. 605
Mann, David, Mgr.-Corp. Communications & Inv. Rels.--Talisman Energy Inc., Calgary, Canada; *Int'l*, pg. 1352
Mann, Judy, Mgr.-Corp. Rels.--Medic Computer Systems, Inc., Raleigh, NC; *Int'l*, pg. 870
Manners, Sandy, Dir.-Communications--Westinghouse Canada Inc., Hamilton, Canada; *U.S. Public*, pg. 275
Manroe, Katie, V.P.-Corp. Communications--Pier 1 Imports, Inc., Fort Worth, TX; *U.S. Public*, pg. 1295
Mansell, Frank, Dir.-Pub. Info. & Adv.--Cascade Natural Gas Corporation, Seattle, WA; *U.S. Public*, pg. 311
Manson, Michelle, Mgr.-Mktg. Communications--Interpoint, Redmond, WA; *U.S. Public*, pg. 457
Manta, Anny, Mgr.-Public Relations--Olympic Airways, S.A., Athens, Greece; *Int'l*, pg. 1004
Manuel, Beth, Mktg. Services--Seco Warwick Corporation, Meadville, PA; *U.S. Private*, pg. 980
Maor, Dov, Dr., Chief Scientist--Elscint Ltd., Haifa, Israel; *Int'l*, pg. 450

Maradei, Jose Luis, Mgr.-Pub. Rels.--Aracruz Europe S.A., Nyon, Switzerland; *Int'l*, pg. 78
Marcalus, Peter A., V.P.-Corp. Communications--Marcal Paper Mills, Inc., Elmwood Park, NJ; *U.S. Private*, pg. 701
Marcello, Joan, Dir.-Pub. Rels.--Northville Industries Corp., Melville, NY; *U.S. Private*, pg. 806
Marchand, Jorge E., V.P.-Corp. & Public Affairs--Banco Popular de Puerto Rico, San Juan, PR; *U.S. Public*, pg. 175
Marcheterre, Robert, Dir.-Customer Service--Prepress Solutions, Inc., Billerica, MA; *U.S. Private*, pg. 882
Marcos, Reyes, Gen. Mgr.-Pub. Rels.--Caja de Madrid Group, Madrid, Spain; *Int'l*, pg. 251
Mariam, Tom, Sr. Mgr.-Pub. Rels.--Booz, Allen & Hamilton Inc., New York, NY; *U.S. Private*, pg. 157
Mariano, Waldemar, Mgr.-Communications--IBM Brasil-Industria Maquinas e Servicos Ltda., Rio de Janeiro, Brazil; *U.S. Public*, pg. 896
Marioni, Jennifer, Coord.-Pub. Rels.--Pentax Precision Instrument Corp., Orangeburg, NY; *Int'l*, pg. 85
Markey, Stephen P., V.P.-Corp. & Govt. Affairs--Canadian Airlines Corporation, Calgary, Canada; *Int'l*, pg. 255
Markley, Christopher, V.P.-Corp. Communications--Penn National Insurance, Harrisburg, PA; *U.S. Private*, pg. 850
Markos, Ron, Mgr.-Pub. Rels.--Nationwide Acceptance, Arlington, TX; *U.S. Private*, pg. 917
Markovski, Mike, V.P.-Mktg. & Corp. Communications--U.S. Filter/Arrowhead Inc., Rockford, IL; *U.S. Public*, pg. 1682
Markow, Alan, V.P.-Corp. Communications--National Semiconductor Corporation, Santa Clara, CA; *U.S. Public*, pg. 1159
Marks, Amy, Project Mgr.-Mktg.--Noville, South Hackensack, NJ; *U.S. Private*, pg. 808
Marks, Jeffrey, Dir.-Mktg. & Communications--Epson America Inc., Torrance, CA; *Int'l*, pg. 1219
Marks, John, Dir.-Corp. Commun.--Medline Industries, Inc., Mundelein, IL; *U.S. Private*, pg. 728
Marks, S., Mgr.-Customer Service--General Microwave Corporation, Amityville, NY; *U.S. Public*, pg. 717
Marr, Pearle E., V.P.-Community Rels.--Imperial Litho & Dryography, Inc., Phoenix, AZ; *U.S. Private*, pg. 558
Marriott, Lisa, Mgr.-Pub. Rels.--The Beverly Hills Hotel, Beverly Hills, CA; *U.S. Private*, pg. 142
Marrouchi, C.H., Mgr.-Communications & Adv.--CGC Inc., Mississauga, Canada; *U.S. Public*, pg. 1660
Marsh, Dave, Dir.-Corp. Rels.--Simplicity Manufacturing, Inc., Port Washington, WI; *U.S. Private*, pg. 1002
Marsh, G. J., AGM-Corp. Affairs--Halifax plc, Halifax, United Kingdom; *Int'l*, pg. 589
Marsh, Jim, Mgr.-Mktg. Communications--Graphic Controls Corporation, Buffalo, NY; *U.S. Private*, pg. 470
Marshal, Douglas, V.P.-Pub. Affairs, Gen. Counsel & Sec.--Darigold, Inc., Seattle, WA; *U.S. Private*, pg. 311
Marshall, Betty, Sr. V.P.-Corp. Communications & Community Rels.--Shoney's, Inc., Nashville, TN; *U.S. Public*, pg. 1467
Marshall, Ed, Sr. V.P.-Corp. Communications & Pub. Rels.--First Commerce Corporation, New Orleans, LA; *U.S. Public*, pg. 629
Marshall, K.B., Mgr.-Communications & Admin. Services--Carpenter Technology Corporation, Reading, PA; *U.S. Public*, pg. 307
Marshall, Laura, Mktg. Commun. Specialist--Zoll Medical Corporation, Burlington, MA; *U.S. Private*, pg. 1207
Marshall, Quintin G., Sr. V.P.-Corp. Devel.--Ogden Corporation, New York, NY; *U.S. Public*, pg. 1213
Marshall, Shari, Mgr.-Corp. Communications--Tetra Tech NUS, Inc., Gaithersburg, MD; *U.S. Public*, pg. 1582
Marshall, Teresa A., Mgr.-Corp. Commun.--Dodson Group, Kansas City, MO; *U.S. Private*, pg. 338
Marshall, Vicky, Mgr.-Commun.--Nationwide Building Society, Swindon, United Kingdom; *Int'l*, pg. 912
Marsigliano, Mike, Mgr.-Mktg. Communications--Thermo Electric Co., Inc., Saddle Brook, NJ; *U.S. Private*, pg. 1080
Marsik, Larae, Dir.-Corp. Commun.--TCI Communications, Inc., Englewood, CO; *U.S. Public*, pg. 1554
Martin, Andrew, Dir.-Publicity, Adv. & Promo.--Crown Publishers, Inc., New York, NY; *U.S. Private*, pg. 21
Martin, Angela, Dir.-Employee Communications & Adv.--Dollar General Corporation, Nashville, TN; *U.S. Public*, pg. 515
Martin, Brian, Sr. V.P.-Corp. Communications--Avon Products, Inc., New York, NY; *U.S. Public*, pg. 155
Martin, David, Dir.-Pub. Affairs--Kansas City Power & Light Company, Kansas City, MO; *U.S. Public*, pg. 943
Martin, James, Mgr.-Mktg. Communications--Instron Corporation, Canton, MA; *U.S. Public*, pg. 882
Martin, John R., Jr., V.P.-Corp. Rels. & Mktg.--CBL & Associates Properties, Inc., Chattanooga, TN; *U.S. Public*, pg. 273
Martin, John S., Dir.-Mktg. Services & Pub. Rels.--Healthtex, Greensboro, NC; *U.S. Public*, pg. 1702
Martin, Kim, Dir.-Corp. Communications--Pneumatic Scale Corporation, Cuyahoga Falls, OH; *U.S. Private*, pg. 118
Martin, N.H., Mgr.-Pub. Rels.--New Zealand Dairy Board, Wellington, New Zealand; *Int'l*, pg. 923
Martin, R.V., Dir.-Communications--Lockheed Aeronautical Systems Company, Marietta, GA; *U.S. Public*, pg. 1007
Martin, Richard, V.P.-Pub. Rels.--AT&T Corporation, Basking Ridge, NJ; *U.S. Public*, pg. 10
Martin, Robert P., III, Mgr.-Creative Services--Snap-Tite, Inc., Erie, PA; *U.S. Private*, pg. 1010
Martin, Sallie, Corp. Sec. & Admin. Asst.--Hickory Printing Group, Inc., Conover, NC; *U.S. Private*, pg. 525
Martin, Steve, Dir.-Corp. Communications--M/A-COM Inc., Lowell, MA; *U.S. Public*, pg. 8
Martin, Thomas, V.P.-Corp. Rels.--ITT Industries, Inc., White Plains, NY; *U.S. Public*, pg. 859
Martin, Tim, Mgr.-Corp. Commun.--Pioneer Hi-Bred International, Inc., Des Moines, IA; *U.S. Public*, pg. 1298
Martin, Virginia, Mgr.-Adv.--Henderson Auctions, Livingston, LA; *U.S. Private*, pg. 577
Martincic, Stephen, Presentations Mgr. & Pub. Rels. Mgr.--Australie, Levallois-Perret, France; *Int'l*, pg. 600
Martinez, Alejandro Montano, Dir.-Corp. Communication--Telefonos de Mexico S.A. de C.V., Mexico, Mexico; *Int'l*, pg. 1373
Martinez, Alicia, Dir.-Mktg. & Corp. Commun.--Metropolitan Transportation Authority, New York, NY; *U.S. Private*, pg. 739
Martinez, Maritza, Sr. Assoc.-Adv. Communications--Howmedica, Inc., Rutherford, NJ; *U.S. Public*, pg. 1282
Martini, Hugo, V.P.-Institutional Rels.--Y.P.F., S.A., Buenos Aires, Argentina; *Int'l*, pg. 1515
Martins Pinto, Carlos Albertos, Dir.-Press Rels.--Petrobras - Petroleo Brasileiro S.A., Rio de Janeiro, Brazil; *Int'l*, pg. 1041
Martinsen, Dan, V.P.-Media Rels.--USA Networks, New York, NY; *U.S. Public*, pg. 1686
Marty-Gauquie, Henry, Dir.-Info. & Commun.--European Investment Bank, Luxembourg, Luxembourg; *Int'l*, pg. 465
Martyak, J.J., V.P.-Public Affairs--ICI Americas, Inc., Wilmington, DE; *Int'l*, pg. 663
Martz, Pat, Mgr.-Commun.--Hercules Chemical Co., Inc., Passaic, NJ; *U.S. Private*, pg. 523
Maruszak, Patricia, Mgr.-Mktg. Communications--Justrite Manufacturing Company, Des Plaines, IL; *U.S. Public*, pg. 617
Marzullo, Dinah, Dir.-Pub. Rels.--Costa Cruise Lines, N.V., Miami, FL; *U.S. Private*, pg. 278
Masaki, Shinji, Dir.-Pub. Rels.--Otsuka Pharmaceutical Co., Ltd., Tokyo, Japan; *Int'l*, pg. 1013
Mascheroni, Eleanor, Sr. V.P.-Pub. Rels.--Scudder Kemper Investments, Inc., New York, NY; *Int'l*, pg. 1530
Mascik, Ray, Dir.-Commun.--Duro-Last Roofing, Inc., Saginaw, MI; *U.S. Private*, pg. 349
Mason, Don E., V.P.-External Affairs & Corp. Services--Mississippi Power Co., Gulfport, MS; *U.S. Public*, pg. 1490
Mason, Frederick L., Mgr.-Corp. Communications--Providence Energy Corporation, Providence, RI; *U.S. Public*, pg. 1337
Mason, James L., Dir.-Pub. & Community Affairs--Eaton Corporation, Cleveland, OH; *U.S. Public*, pg. 555
Mason, Paige A., V.P.-Pub. Rels.--Legg Mason, Inc., Baltimore, MD; *U.S. Public*, pg. 984
Massa, Barbara K., Sr. V.P.-Corp. Communications--First Union Corporation, Charlotte, NC; *U.S. Public*, pg. 639
Massaro, Teresa, Mgr.-Corp. Commun.--Western Gas Resources, Inc., Denver, CO; *U.S. Public*, pg. 1758
Massart, G., Dir.-Mktg. & Europe Communications--Gates Europe, Erembodegem, Belgium; *Int'l*, pg. 1396
Masse, Julie, Mgr.-Mktg. Communications--Transportation Equipment Group-North America, Saint-Bruno, Canada; *Int'l*, pg. 200
Massee, Ned W., V.P.-Pub. Affairs--Westvaco Corporation, New York, NY; *U.S. Public*, pg. 1762
Massey, Kristin, Dir.-Mktg.--Jackson MSC, Nashville, TN; *U.S. Private*, pg. 579
Massey, Sarah, Communications Specialist--The Hartford Financial Services Group Inc., Hartford, CT; *U.S. Public*, pg. 794
Masson, Christina, Mgr.-Corp. Communications--Sodexho USA, Waltham, MA; *Int'l*, pg. 1274
Masson, Michel, Mgr.-Pub. Rels.--Cegelec, Levallois-Perret, France; *Int'l*, pg. 52
Mastalski, Stanley, Mgr.-Customer Svcs.--H. Freeman & Son, Inc., Philadelphia, PA; *U.S. Private*, pg. 426
Mastrangelo, Laura A., V.P.-Corp. Commun.--VIMRx Pharmaceuticals, Inc., Wilmington, DE; *U.S. Public*, pg. 1702
Masumoto, Yuzuru, Mng. Dir.--All Nippon Airways Co. Ltd., Tokyo, Japan; *Int'l*, pg. 57
Mata, Vikki, Dir.-Commun.--Sealaska Corporation, Juneau, AK; *U.S. Private*, pg. 978
Mataya, Robert J., V.P.-Bus. Plng. & Devel.--Material Sciences Corporation, Elk Grove Village, IL; *U.S. Public*, pg. 1056
Mathes, Diane, Mgr.-Mktg. Communications--Vactor Mfg. Inc., Streator, IL; *U.S. Public*, pg. 617
Mathews, Jim, Mgr.-Mktg. Com--Electronic Products Division, Austin, TX; *U.S. Public*, pg. 1605
Mathews, Odonna, V.P.-Consumer Affairs--Giant Food Inc., Landover, MD; *U.S. Public*, pg. 741
Mathias, Lawrence L., V.P.-H.R. & Pub. Rels.--American Crystal Sugar Company, Moorhead, MN; *U.S. Private*, pg. 52
Matijevich, Barbara, Pub. Rels. Dir.--SicolaMartin Inc., Austin, TX; *U.S. Private*, pg. 998
Matsch, Terri, Corp. Commun. & Pub. Rels.--Columbia Paint & Coatings, Spokane, WA; *U.S. Private*, pg. 256
Matson, Patricia J., V.P.-Corp. Communications--ABC, Inc, New York, NY; *U.S. Public*, pg. 511
Matson, Patricia J., V.P.-Corp. Communications--ABC News, Inc., New York, NY; *U.S. Public*, pg. 511
Matsumoto, N., Dir.-Pub. Rels.--Nissho Iwai (Shanghai) Corporation, Shanghai, China; *Int'l*, pg. 948
Matteo, Maxine, Exec. V.P.-Adv., Mktg. & Bus. Devel.--INMC Mortgage Holdings, Inc., Pasadena, CA; *U.S. Public*, pg. 857
Matteson, Richard A., Dir.-Corp. Communications--Consumers Energy, Jackson, MI; *U.S. Public*, pg. 280
Matteson, Rochard A., Dir.-Corp. Commun.--CMS Energy Corporation, Dearborn, MI; *U.S. Public*, pg. 279
Matthews, Don, V.P.-Sls. & Mktg.--Wahl Clipper Corp., Sterling, IL; *U.S. Private*, pg. 1146
Matthews, Donna Duda, V.P.-Communications--A. Duda & Sons Inc., Oviedo, FL; *U.S. Private*, pg. 344
Matthews, Gayle, Banking Officer & Pub. Rels. Specialist--Whitney Holding Corporation, New Orleans, LA; *U.S. Public*, pg. 1766
Matthews, Nigel F., Sec. & Dir.-Pub. Affairs--J. Sainsbury plc, London, United Kingdom; *Int'l*, pg. 1169
Matthiesen, JoAnn, V.P.-Pub. Rels. & Organizational Devel. & Asst. to Chm. Bd.--The Washington Water Power Company, Spokane, WA; *U.S. Public*, pg. 1744
Mattich, Mario, Dir.-Pub. Rels.--Leviton Mfg. Co., Inc., Little Neck, NY; *U.S. Private*, pg. 663
Mattich, Mario, Mgr.-Pub. Rels.--Leviton Mfg. Co., Inc., Little Neck, NY; *U.S. Private*, pg. 663
Mattos, William, Mgr.-Pub. Rels.--Spirol West, Corona, CA; *U.S. Private*, pg. 1026
Mattos, William J., Mgr.-Promo. Svcs.--Spirol International Corp., Danielson, CT; *U.S. Private*, pg. 1026
Matusik, Valerie, V.P.-Pub. Rels.--Kokosing Construction Company, Inc., Fredericktown, OH; *U.S. Private*, pg. 631
Mauney, Harold C., Jr., V.P.-Pub. Affairs--Norfolk Southern Corporation, Norfolk, VA; *U.S. Public*, pg. 1190
Maurer, John S., Dir.-Public Affairs--Aristech Chemical Corporation, Pittsburgh, PA; *Int'l*, pg. 872
Maurice, Marianne, Mgr.-Pub. Rels.--GEODIS, Paris, France; *Int'l*, pg. 549
Mauro, Judy, Dir.-Corp. Communications--Chyron Corp., Melville, NY; *Int'l*, pg. 1372
Maury, Nicole F., Dir.-Corp. Communications--Fremont General Corporation, Santa Monica, CA; *U.S. Public*, pg. 681
Maxie, Debbie, Mgr.-Trade Show--Elo TouchSystems, Inc., Fremont, CA; *U.S. Public*, pg. 1362
Maxon, Roger, V.P.-Industrial Rels.--BernzOmatic, Medina, NY; *U.S. Public*, pg. 1177
Maxwell, Robert, Mgr.-Pub. Rels.--National Steel Corp., Granite City Division, Granite City, IL; *Int'l*, pg. 902
May, Hilary, Mgr.-Mktg. Svcs., Adv. & Pub. Rels.--Atalanta Corporation, Elizabeth, NJ; *U.S. Private*, pg. 93
May, Patricia, Dir.-Pub. Rels.--Rocco Inc., Harrisonburg, VA; *U.S. Private*, pg. 937
May, Patty, Dir.-Pub. Rels.--Rocco Quality Foods, Timberville, VA; *U.S. Private*, pg. 937
Mayer, Linda, Dir.-Communications--Knoll Pharmaceutical Company, Whippany, NJ; *Int'l*, pg. 105
Mayo, John, Dir.-Communications--Hamilton Standard, Windsor Locks, CT; *U.S. Public*, pg. 1690
Mayr, Charles, Dir.-Corp. Communications--Barr Laboratories Inc., Pomona, NY; *U.S. Public*, pg. 191
Mazin, Rafael, Dir.-Mktg. Services & External Rels.--Procter & Gamble Espana S.A., Madrid, Spain; *U.S. Public*, pg. 1332
Mc Dougall, Ann, Dir.-Corp. & Mktg. Communications--StarSight Telecast, Inc., Fremont, CA; *U.S. Public*, pg. 705
McAlister, Sheryl, Mgr.-Media Rels.--NationsBank Florida, Tampa, FL; *U.S. Public*, pg. 1162
McAllister, Tom, Mgr.-Mktg.--Alpha Microsystems, Santa Ana, CA; *U.S. Public*, pg. 57
McAndrews, Joy, V.P.-Mktg.--Nobel Education Dynamics, Inc., Media, PA; *U.S. Public*, pg. 1185
McAuliff, Julie, Mgr.-Pub. Rels.--Broadway & Seymour, Inc., Charlotte, NC; *U.S. Public*, pg. 258
McAuliffe, Mary E., V.P.-External Rels.--Union Pacific Corporation, Dallas, TX; *U.S. Public*, pg. 1667
McAuliffe, Robert P., V.P.-Customer Service & Opers.--BTU International, Inc., North Billerica, MA; *U.S. Public*, pg. 164
McBride, Anne, Mgr.-Corp. Commun.--Pharmaceutical Marketing Services Inc., Phoenix, AZ; *U.S. Public*, pg. 1284
McBride, Katie, Dir.-Communications--GM Powertrain Group, Pontiac, MI; *U.S. Public*, pg. 719
McBride, Peter, V.P.-Communications & Investor Relations--Imasco Limited, Montreal, Canada; *Int'l*, pg. 112
McBride, Robert, Mktg. Communications-Voice Prods. & Svcs.--U S West Inc., Englewood, CO; *U.S. Public*, pg. 1688
McCabe, Dora, Group Mgr.-Pub. Rels.--Cadbury Schweppes p.l.c., London, United Kingdom; *Int'l*, pg. 247
McCabe, Lawrence E., V.P.-Corp. & Govt. Rels.--Mesaba Aviation, Inc., Minneapolis, MN; *U.S. Public*, pg. 1099
McCahon, Jane W., V.P.-Corp. Rels.--Eastern Enterprises, Weston, MA; *U.S. Public*, pg. 548
McCain, Kate, Mgr.-Adv. & Pub. Rels.--Doron Precision Systems, Inc., Binghamton, NY; *U.S. Private*, pg. 341
McCall, Carolyn, Dir.-Bus. Communications--Olin Microelectronic Materials, Inc., Norwalk, CT; *U.S. Public*, pg. 1219
McCall, James W., V.P.-Personnel & Public Affairs--Chesebrough-Pond's USA Co., Greenwich, CT; *Int'l*, pg. 1435
McCallum, Tony, Dir.-Pub. Affairs--Transcanada Pipelines Limited, Calgary, Canada; *Int'l*, pg. 1416
McCann, Clark, Dir.-Corp. Commun.--The Boeing Company, Seattle, WA; *U.S. Public*, pg. 239
McCann, Frank V., Mgr.-Pub. Rels.--Thomson Consumer Electronics Inc., Indianapolis, IN; *Int'l*, pg. 1383
McCann, Joseph F., Sr. V.P.-Pub. Affairs--PepsiCo, Inc., Purchase, NY; *U.S. Public*, pg. 1276
McCann, M.J., Mgr.-Employee & Pub. Rels.--Babcock & Wilcox Co., Barberton, OH; *U.S. Public*, pg. 1068
McCarthy, Daniel J., Dir.-Corp. Communications--PP&L Resources, Allentown, PA; *U.S. Public*, pg. 1244
McCarthy, James, Mgr.-Pub. Rels.--Citgo Petroleum Corporation, Tulsa, OK; *Int'l*, pg. 1045
McCarthy, John, Grp. Dir.-Communications & Human Resources--Legal & General Group PLC, London, United Kingdom; *Int'l*, pg. 805
McCarthy, Joseph, Dir.-Corp. Commun.--Cypress Semiconductor Corporation, San Jose, CA; *U.S. Public*, pg. 470
McCarthy, Michael W., Dir.-Investor Rels. & Corp. Commun.--Photronics, Inc., Brookfield, CT; *U.S. Public*, pg. 1293
McCarthy, Peter J., V.P.-Public Affairs--Elf Atochem North America, Inc., Philadelphia, PA; *Int'l*, pg. 445
McCartney, Glenda S., Dir.-Corp. Communications--Nevada Power Company, Las Vegas, NV; *U.S. Public*, pg. 1169
McCarty, Scott, Mgr.-Corp. Commun.--Ball Corporation, Muncie, IN; *U.S. Public*, pg. 170

McCarty, Valerie, Dir.-Intl. Pub. Rels., Latin America--Turner Broadcasting System Inc., Atlanta, GA; *U.S. Public*, pg. 1614
McClain, Thomas E., V.P.-Commu.--Battelle Memorial Institute, Columbus, OH; *U.S. Private*, pg. 123
McClave, William H., Jr., V.P.-Commun.--Transamerica Corporation, San Francisco, CA; *U.S. Public*, pg. 1629
McClelland, Valorie, Mgr.-Corp. Commun.--Rohr, Inc., Chula Vista, CA; *U.S. Public*, pg. 751
McCloskey, Colleen A., V.P.-Public Policy--Bell Atlantic-NJ, Newark, NJ; *U.S. Public*, pg. 202
McCluney, Nancy, Dir.-Communications--John H. Harland Company, Decatur, GA; *U.S. Public*, pg. 785
McClung, Debbie, Mgr.-Pub. Rels.--Vermeer Manufacturing Company, Pella, IA; *U.S. Private*, pg. 1137
McClure, Valencia, Mgr.-Community Svc.--The Dallas Morning News, Inc., Dallas, TX; *U.S. Public*, pg. 209
McCluskey, Connie, Dir.-Pub. Rels.--ICS Learning Systems, Inc., Scranton, PA; *U.S. Public*, pg. 783
McCluskey, Connie, Dir.-Pub. Rels.--ICS Intangibles Holding Company, Irvine, CA; *U.S. Public*, pg. 783
McCluskey, Connie, Dir.-Pub. Rels.--National Learning Systems, Inc., Scranton, PA; *U.S. Public*, pg. 783
McCluskey, Connie, Dir.-Pub. Rels.--NBD Incorporated, Scranton, PA; *U.S. Public*, pg. 783
McCluskey, Connie, Dir.-Pub. Rels.--Steck-Vaughn Company, Austin, TX; *U.S. Public*, pg. 784
McCluskey, Connie, Dir.-Pub. Rels.--National Educational International Corp., Irvine, CA; *U.S. Public*, pg. 784
McCluskey, Connie, Dir.-Pub. Rels.--International Correspondence Schools (Australasia) Limited, Lane Cove, Australia; *U.S. Public*, pg. 784
McCluskey, Connie, Dir.-Pub. Rels.--International Correspondence Schools Canadian Ltd., Montreal, Canada; *U.S. Public*, pg. 784
McCluskey, Connie, Dir.-Pub. Rels.--International Correspondence Schools Ltd., Glasgow, United Kingdom; *U.S. Public*, pg. 784
McCluskey, Connie, Dir.-Pub. Rels.--Intertext Group, Ltd., Glasgow, United Kingdom; *U.S. Public*, pg. 784
McCluskey, Connie, Dir.-Pub. Rels.--The School of Accountancy, Glasgow, United Kingdom; *U.S. Public*, pg. 784
McCluskey, Connie, Dir.-Pub. Rels.--NETG Limited, London, United Kingdom; *U.S. Public*, pg. 784
McCluskey, Connie, Dir.-Pub. Rels.--NETG Applied Learning GmbH, Dusseldorf, Germany; *U.S. Public*, pg. 784
McCluskey, Connie, Dir.-Pub. Rels.--NETG Holding, Inc., Irvine, CA; *U.S. Public*, pg. 784
McCluskey, Connie, Dir.-Pub. Rels.--NETG Applied Learning GmbH, Vienna, Austria; *U.S. Public*, pg. 784
McCluskey, Connie, Dir.-Pub. Rels.--A.S.I. (Computer Training) Netherlands B.V., Amsterdam, Netherlands; *U.S. Public*, pg. 784
McCluskey, Connie, Dir.-Pub. Rels.--Steck-Vaughn Publishing Corporation, Austin, TX; *U.S. Public*, pg. 784
McCollam, Stephanie, Mktg. Communicatons--BAX Global, Irvine, CA; *U.S. Public*, pg. 1305
McComb, E., Mgr.-Corp. Communications--Benjamin Moore & Co., Montvale, NJ; *U.S. Private*, pg. 133
McConnaughy, Tom, Chm. & Chief Creative Officer--McConnaughy Stein Schmidt Brown, Chicago, IL; *U.S. Private*, pg. 720
McCormack, Jean, Mgr.-Communications--Medic Computer Systems, Inc., Raleigh, NC; *Int'l*, pg. 870
McCormey, William, Dir.-Corp. Communications--Shell Quimica de Venezuela, C.A., Caracas, Venezuela; *Int'l*, pg. 1142
McCormick, Antoinette, Mgr.-Mktg. Communications--Alfa Laval Separation Inc., Warminster, PA; *Int'l*, pg. 1378
McCormick, Laura, Mgr.-Corp. Commun.--Kinko's Corporation, Ventura, CA; *U.S. Private*, pg. 622
McCormick, Marcia E., Mktg. & Office Admin.--Williams, White & Co., Moline, IL; *U.S. Private*, pg. 1179
McCoy, Angie, Mgr.-Pub. Rels.--Kimberly-Clark Corporation, Dallas, TX; *U.S. Public*, pg. 958
McCoy, Kendra, Mgr.-Corp. Commun.--Trimble Navigation Limited, Sunnyvale, CA; *U.S. Public*, pg. 1638
McCracken, Larry, V.P.-Communications--McDonnell Aircraft & Missile Systems Div., Berkeley, MO; *U.S. Public*, pg. 241
McCracken, Pat, Dir.-Corp. Communications & Mktg. Programs--BMC Software, Inc., Houston, TX; *U.S. Public*, *pg. 162*
McCreary, Gordon A., V.P.-Inv. Rels.--Kinross Gold Corporation, Toronto, Canada; *Int'l*, pg. 734
McCrudden, Linda, Mgr.-Pub. Rels.--Carolina Power & Light Company, Raleigh, NC; *U.S. Public*, pg. 306
McCullen, Sharon, Mgr.-Pub. Rels.--American Home Products Corporation, Madison, NJ; *U.S. Public*, pg. 79
McCullough, Bob, Dir.-Pub. Rels.--Sea World of Texas, San Antonio, TX; *U.S. Public*, pg. 114
McCully, Duncan J., V.P.-Special Risks--Commercial Travelers Mutual Insurance Company, Utica, NY; *U.S. Private*, pg. 258
McDaniel, William B., V.P.-Pub. Affairs--Olin Corporation, Norwalk, CT; *U.S. Public*, pg. 1218
McDermott, C.J., Mgr.-Pub. Information--PECO Energy Company, Philadelphia, PA; *U.S. Public*, pg. 1268
McDermott, John, Dir.-Corp. Commun.--Highmark Inc., Pittsburgh, PA; *U.S. Private*, pg. 528
McDermott, Mary, Sr. V.P.-Commun.--Travelers Group, New York, NY; *U.S. Public*, pg. 1632
McDonald, Moira, Pub. Affairs Coord.--Maritime Telegraph & Telephone Company, Ltd., Halifax, Canada; *Int'l*, pg. 116
McDonaugh, Adam, Mgr.-Media Relations--European Investment Bank, Luxembourg, Luxembourg; *Int'l*, pg. 465
McDonnell, Joseph W., Sr. V.P.-Mktg. & External Affairs--Long Island Lighting Company, Hicksville, NY; *U.S. Public*, pg. 1013
McDougall, Linda, Asst. V.P.-Corp. Communications--H & R Block, Inc., Kansas City, MO; *U.S. Public*, pg. 770
McDougall, Tom, Mgr.-Publicity--Land Instruments International Ltd., Dronfield, United Kingdom; *Int'l*, pg. 798
McDowell, Jerry, Mgr.-Pub. Rels.--Objective Systems Integrators, Inc., Folsom, CA; *U.S. Public*, pg. 1209
McEachin, Scott, Dir.-Pub. Rels.--Hondo Oil & Gas Company, Roswell, NM; *Int'l*, pg. 818
McElfresh, John, Dir.-Mktg. Communicatons--Schneider Automation, Inc., North Andover, MA; *Int'l*, pg. 1208
McElroy, Chris, Mktg. Commun. Specialist--Pella Corporation, Pella, IA; *U.S. Private*, pg. 848
McElwreath, Sally C., Sr. V.P.-Corp. Communications--UtiliCorp United Inc., Kansas City, MO; *U.S. Public*, pg. 1700
McEneny, Lee, Grp. Dir.-Pub. Rels.--Sega of America Inc., Redwood City, CA; *Int'l*, pg. 1218
McEwan, Feona, Dir.-Commun.--WPP Group plc, London, United Kingdom; *Int'l*, pg. 1482
McFadden, Jeanmarie, V.P.-Corp. Communications--Morgan Stanley Dean Witter & Co., New York, NY; *U.S. Public*, pg. 1132
McFadden, Jeanmarie, V.P.-Corp. Communications--Morgan Stanley Group Inc., New York, NY; *U.S. Public*, pg. 1132
McFall, Michael, Asst. Dir.-Mdsg., Adv. & Communications--General Motors Acceptance Corporation (GMAC), Detroit, MI; *U.S. Public*, pg. 719
McFarlane, Larry, V.P.-Corp. Commun.--Nu Skin International, Provo, UT; *U.S. Private*, pg. 808
McGaughey, Heather, Mgr.-Human Resources--Sunset Publishing Corporation, Menlo Park, CA; *U.S. Public*, pg. 1613
McGavin, Robert J., Sr. V.P.-Institutional & Community Rels.--The Toronto Dominion Bank, Toronto, Canada; *Int'l*, pg. 1401
McGenee, Robert B., Sr. V.P. & Gen. Counsel-Pub. & Corp. Rels.--Carolina Power & Light Company, Raleigh, NC; *U.S. Public*, pg. 306
McGilvery, Jennifer, Dir.-Pub. Rels.--Intelligent Controls Inc., Lynnwood, WA; *U.S. Private*, pg. 566
McGinnity, Dan, Mgr.-Corp. Commun.--Sentry Insurance, A Mutual Company, Stevens Point, WI; *U.S. Private*, pg. 984
McGlothlin, Kathryn, V.P.-Claims--VASA North Atlantic Insurance Company, Indianapolis, IN; *Int'l*, pg. 464
McGovern, Terilyn, V.P. & Dir.-Corp. Devel.--Federal Farm Credit Banks Funding Corporation, Jersey City, NJ; *U.S. Private*, pg. 398
McGowan, Michael, V.P.-Communications--The CIT Group Holdings, Inc., New York, NY; *Int'l*, pg. 360
McGowan, Susan, Dir.-Media Rels.--MTA Long Island Rail Road, Jamaica, NY; *U.S. Private*, pg. 739
McGowen-Carnes, Kathy, Dir.-Mktg.--Advertising Display Co., Englewood Cliffs, NJ; *U.S. Private*, pg. 23
McGrade, Kristin, Mgr.-Pub. Rels.--Kruse International, Auburn, IN; *U.S. Private*, pg. 636
McGrail, Fred, Dir.-Corp. Communications--CVS Corp., Woonsocket, RI; *U.S. Public*, pg. 287
McGrail, Kelly, Mgr.-Corp. Commun.--Oil-Dri Corporation of America, Chicago, IL; *U.S. Public*, pg. 1214
McGrath, Donald, Dir.-Community Affairs--Textron Inc., Providence, RI; *U.S. Public*, pg. 1588
McGrath, James, V.P.-Human Relations--McCormick/ Schilling, Hunt Valley, MD; *U.S. Public*, pg. 1066
McGrath, Tara, Mgr.-Pub. Rels.--The Great Frame Up Systems, Inc., Franklin Park, IL; *U.S. Private*, pg. 473
McGraw, M.J., Sr. V.P.- Law, Human Resources & Pub. Affairs--Brown & Williamson Tobacco Corp., Louisville, KY; *Int'l*, pg. 111
McGreal, Jim, Mgr.-Pur.--D.A. Stuart Company, Warrenville, IL; *U.S. Private*, pg. 1048
McGuigan, James A., Mgr.-Communications--Acheson Colloids Company, Port Huron, MI; *U.S. Private*, pg. 12
McGuire, Bruce, Dir.-Investor Rels. & Pub. Rels.--Tyco Toys, Inc., Mount Laurel, NJ; *U.S. Public*, pg. 1058
McGuire, Carol Lee, Asst. V.P.-Customer Svcs.--Fidelity Mutual Life Insurance Co., Radnor, PA; *U.S. Private*, pg. 403
McGuire, Peter, Mgr.-Pub. Rels.--REAL Applications, Ltd., Woodland Hills, CA; *U.S. Private*, pg. 366
McGuirk, Peter, Dir.-Communications--El Camino Resources, Ltd., Woodland Hills, CA; *U.S. Private*, pg. 366
McHale, Jack F., V.P.-Investor & Corp. Communications--Unisys Corporation, Blue Bell, PA; *U.S. Public*, pg. 1671
McHale, Lauren, Mgr.-Pub. Rels.--Royal Doulton USA Inc., Somerset, NJ; *Int'l*, pg. 1135
McHugh, James J., V.P.-Labor Rels.--Coltec Holdings Inc, Charlotte, NC; *U.S. Public*, pg. 401
McIlwaine, Charles B., V.P.-Communications--The Coleman Company, Inc., Golden, CO; *U.S. Private*, pg. 690
McIngvale, Jim, Dir.-Pub. Affairs & Adv.--Ingalls Shipbuilding, Pascagoula, MS; *U.S. Public*, pg. 1003
McIntire, Brian, V.P.-Communications--National Basketball Association, New York, NY; *U.S. Private*, pg. 780
McIntire, Jan, Dir.-Corp. Commun.--The Cessna Aircraft Co., Wichita, KS; *U.S. Public*, pg. 1589
McIntosh, Sheila M., V.P.-Corp. Commun. & Investor Rels.--Canadian Pacific Limited, Calgary, Canada; *Int'l*, pg. 258
McIntrye, Diane, Dir.-Pub. Rels.--Dreyer's Grand Ice Cream, Inc., Oakland, CA; *U.S. Public*, pg. 529
McIntyre, Tim, Div. V.P.-Pub. Rels.--Domino's Pizza Inc., Ann Arbor, MI; *U.S. Private*, pg. 339
Mckee, Bob, Dir.-Pub. Rels.--Watson Wyatt Worldwide, Bethesda, MD; *U.S. Private*, pg. 1154
McKeever, Thomas P., V.P.-Corp. Affairs & H.R.--Blair Corporation, Warren, PA; *U.S. Public*, pg. 236
McKeithan, Patty, V.P.-Corp. Affairs--Miller Brewing Company, Milwaukee, WI; *U.S. Public*, pg. 1289
McKenna, Lore, Mgr.-Natl. Adv. & Pub. Rels.--American Suzuki Motor Corporation, Brea, CA; *Int'l*, pg. 1323
McKenzie, Dave, V.P.-Service & Product Engrng.--Mitsubishi Motor Sales of America, Inc., Cypress, CA; *Int'l*, pg. 875
McKenzie, Joan, Mgr.-Customer Service--Temco Fireplace Products, Inc., Nashville, TN; *U.S. Public*, pg. 1576
McKeogh, John F., Dir.-Commun.--Rohm and Haas Company, Philadelphia, PA; *U.S. Public*, pg. 1403
McKinley, James, Mgr.-Corp. Commun.--AMETEK, Inc., Paoli, PA; *U.S. Public*, pg. 99
McKinney, Mary, Exec. Dir.-Mktg. Communications & Innovation--Merck & Co., Inc., Whitehouse Station, NJ; *U.S. Public*, pg. 1090
McKinney, Mary, Exec. Dir.-Mktg., Communications & Innovation--Merck Human Health Division (U.S. Human Health), West Point, PA; *U.S. Public*, pg. 1091
McKittrick, G., Mgr.-Communications--Eaton Corporation, Specific Industry Control Division, Milwaukee, WI; *U.S. Public*, pg. 557
McLachlan, Angela D., Corp. Dir.-Communications & Pub. Affairs--LaRoche Industries Inc., Atlanta, GA; *U.S. Private*, pg. 651
McLaughlin, Anne, Coord.-Pub. Rels.--Au Bon Pain Co., Inc., Boston, MA; *U.S. Public*, pg. 146
McLaughlin, Deborah A., V.P.-Customer Svcs.--Commonwealth Energy System, Cambridge, MA; *U.S. Public*, pg. 414
McLaughlin, Diane, Mgr.-Pub. Rels.--Harry and David, Medford, OR; *Int'l*, pg. 1518
McLaughlin, Mary, V.P.-Corp. Communications--Ontario Hydro, Toronto, Canada; *Int'l*, pg. 1007
McLean, Clare, Coord.-Pub. Rels. & Publicity--Maidenform Worldwide, New York, NY; *U.S. Private*, pg. 697
McLean, Gina, Specialist-Corp. Communications--Breed Technologies, Inc., Lakeland, FL; *U.S. Public*, pg. 251
McLean, I., Mgr.-Indus. & Govern. Rels.--National Australia Bank Limited, Melbourne, Australia; *Int'l*, pg. 906
McLean, Jill, Mktg.-Communications--DSM Sheffield Plastics, Sheffield, MA; *Int'l*, pg. 354
McLean, Patricia, Dir.-Corp. Commun.--Witco Corporation, Greenwich, CT; *U.S. Public*, pg. 1773
McLemore, Kathy, Corp. Communications Specialist--Hyundai Electronics America, San Jose, CA; *Int'l*, pg. 641
McMahon, Paul, Mgr.-Mktg. & Communications--LoJack Corporation, Dedham, MA; *U.S. Public*, pg. 1012
McManus, Dawn, Coord.-Mktg. Communications--Louisiana Gas Service Co., Harvey, LA; *U.S. Public*, pg. 380
McManus, Joni, Mgr.-Adv.--Paychex, Inc., Rochester, NY; *U.S. Public*, pg. 1267
McMeekin, S.C., Jr., V.P.-Customer Rels.--South Carolina Electric & Gas Co. (SCE&G), Columbia, SC; *U.S. Public*, pg. 1436
McMonigle, Robert M., Exec. V.P.-Corp. Rels.--International Game Technology, Reno, NV; *U.S. Public*, pg. 900
McMurray, Kim, Mgr.-Texas Communication--Entergy Gulf States, Inc., Beaumont, TX; *U.S. Public*, pg. 586
McMurray, Sharon R., First V.P. & Dir.-Corp. Pub. Rels.--Comerica Incorporated, Detroit, MI; *U.S. Public*, pg. 408
McNabb, Lee Ann, Mgr.-Pub. Rels.--Trimble Navigation Limited, Sunnyvale, CA; *U.S. Public*, pg. 1638
McNally, Edward C., V.P.-Corp. Rels. & Sec.--Rand McNally & Company, Skokie, IL; *U.S. Private*, pg. 908
McNamara, Marie, Mgr.-Pub. Rels.--The F.X. Matt Brewing Co., Utica, NY; *U.S. Private*, pg. 714
McNeely, James B., Dir.-Employee Communications--Northrop Grumman Corporation, Los Angeles, CA; *U.S. Public*, pg. 1197
McNeill, Jim, Dir.-Information--Brown Brothers & Company Ltd., Edinburgh, United Kingdom; *Int'l*, pg. 1466
McNiel, Robert C., V.P.-Pub. Affairs--El Paso Electric Company, El Paso, TX; *U.S. Public*, pg. 567
McRae, D. Gary, Chm. Bd., Pres. & Chief Exec. Officer--McRae Industries, Inc., Mount Gilead, NC; *U.S. Public*, pg. 1073
McStay, William J., Sr. V.P.-Mktg. Communication--Jiffy Lube International, Inc., Houston, TX; *U.S. Public*, pg. 1272
McVinnie, Debbie, Pub. Rels. Counselor--Sawyer Riley Compton Inc., Atlanta, GA; *U.S. Private*, pg. 969
McWade, Robert S., V.P.-Corp. Affairs & Commun.--Raytheon Company, Lexington, MA; *U.S. Public*, pg. 1364
Mead, David, Dir.-Pub. Rels.--PacifiCorp, Portland, OR; *U.S. Public*, pg. 1251
Mead, David, Dir.-Communications--Utah Power & Light, Salt Lake City, UT; *U.S. Public*, pg. 1251
Mead, Susan W.A., V.P.-Communications & Community Rels.--ReliaStar Financial Corp., Minneapolis, MN; *U.S. Public*, pg. 1375
Mead, Suzanne, V.P.-Corp. Communications--Rite Aid Corporation, Camp Hill, PA; *U.S. Public*, pg. 1390
Meakins, Gene, V.P.-Indus. & Pub. Rels.--Monfort, Inc., Greeley, CO; *U.S. Public*, pg. 427
Meaney, Dan, Mgr.-Pub. Rels.--Connecticut Water Service, Inc., Clinton, CT; *U.S. Public*, pg. 431
Meaney, Martin M., V.P.-Mktg. Communications--Wyeth-Ayerst Laboratories, Inc., Philadelphia, PA; *U.S. Public*, pg. 80
Medina, Elaina, Pub. Rels. Coord.--Western Staff Services, Walnut Creek, CA; *U.S. Public*, pg. 1760
Medina, Elaina, Mgr.-Pub. Rels.--Western Light Industrial Services, Walnut Creek, CA; *U.S. Public*, pg. 1760
Meecham, Bob, Dir.-Comml.--Britannic Aviation Limited, Albourne, United Kingdom; *Int'l*, pg. 215
Meek, Pamela, Mgr.-Media Rels.--SAS Institute Inc., Cary, NC; *U.S. Private*, pg. 966
Megat Khas, Putri Rafidah bt, Grp. Mgr.-Commun.--Sime Darby Berhad, Kuala Lumpur, Malaysia; *Int'l*, pg. 1249
Mehrhof, Ken, Adv. & Pub. Rels. Consultant--Kathabar Incorporated, Somerset, NJ; *U.S. Private*, pg. 609
Mehring, Scott, Mgr.-Mktg. Services--Wagner Spray Tech Corp., Plymouth, MN; *U.S. Private*, pg. 1146
Meier, Stephen C., V.P.-Pub. & Govt. Affairs--The Times Mirror Company, Los Angeles, CA; *U.S. Public*, pg. 1615
Meijer-Jentink, N.L.H., Mgr.-Adv. & Sls. Promo.--Delft Instruments N.V., Delft, Netherlands; *Int'l*, pg. 388
Meili, Barbara, Mgr.-Pub. Rels.--Rieter Holdings, Winterthur, Switzerland; *Int'l*, pg. 1116

Meinecke, Patricia J., Dir.-Corp. Commun. & Mktg.--Giddings & Lewis, Inc., Fond Du Lac, WI; *Int'l*, pg. 1389
Meinz, Thomas P., V.P.-Pub. Affairs--Wisconsin Public Service Corporation, Green Bay, WI; *U.S. Public*, pg. 1728
Meinz, Tom, V.P.-Pub. Affairs--WPS Resources Corp., Green Bay, WI; *U.S. Public*, pg. 1728
Meisenheimer, Danny, V.P.-Mktg.--Furr's/Bishops, Inc., Lubbock, TX; *U.S. Public*, pg. 689
Meisnor, Rick, V.P.-Human Rels.--United Technologies Automotive, Dearborn, MI; *U.S. Public*, pg. 1691
Meissner, Dan, Dir.-Corp. Communications--Gulf States Paper Corporation, Tuscaloosa, AL; *U.S. Private*, pg. 487
Melick, Arden, V.P.-Pub. Rels.--Brooklyn Union, Brooklyn, NY; *U.S. Public*, pg. 259
Melillo, Laura, V.P.-Pub. Affairs--Kentucky Fried Chicken Corporation (KFC), Louisville, KY; *U.S. Public*, pg. 1636
Mell, Debbie, Mgr.-Customer Catogory--Baker's Supermarkets, Inc., Omaha, NE; *U.S. Public*, pg. 652
Mellman, Barbara, Mgr.-Pub. Rels.--Bushnell Corporation, Overland Park, KS; *U.S. Private*, pg. 1191
Mellon, William D., V.P.-Pub. Rels.--Rockwell International Corporation, Costa Mesa, CA; *U.S. Public*, pg. 1397
Melo, Gloria, Mgr.-Pub. Rels. (U.S.A.)--TAP Air Portugal, Newark, NJ; *Int'l*, pg. 1418
Melo, John, Dir.-Customer Service--Bradford & Bingley Building Society, Bingley, United Kingdom; *Int'l*, pg. 210
Meloni, Vittorio, Corp. Press Officer--Olivetti SpA, Turin, Italy; *Int'l*, pg. 1002
Melton, Carol, V.P.-Public Policy--Time Warner Inc., New York, NY; *U.S. Public*, pg. 1610
Melvage, Kathy, Mgr.-Investor Rels.--Schawk, Inc., Des Plaines, IL; *U.S. Public*, pg. 1437
Menke, Lori, Mgr.-Mktg. Communications--Indiana Gas Company, Inc., Indianapolis, IN; *U.S. Public*, pg. 875
Menna, Christine, V.P.-Corp. Communications & Mktg.--Crown American Realty Trust, Johnstown, PA; *U.S. Public*, pg. 461
Menville, Jane, Corp. Communications--United Companies Realty & Development Co., Inc., Baton Rouge, LA; *U.S. Public*, pg. 1675
Menz, Christine, Mgr.-Corp. Commun.--Alusuisse-Lonza Holding Ltd., Zurich, Switzerland; *Int'l*, pg. 66
Merandi, Jane, Sec.--Alamco, Inc., Charleston, WV; *U.S. Public*, pg. 403
Mercer, Howard R., Dir.-Pub. Rels. & Adv.--Griffon Corp., Jericho, NY; *U.S. Public*, pg. 766
Mercier, Lise, Pub. Affairs Asst.--Imasco Limited, Montreal, Canada; *Int'l*, pg. 112
Meredith, Edie L., Exec. Asst.--Steel Technologies Inc., Louisville, KY; *U.S. Public*, pg. 1513
Meriage, Lawrence P., V.P.-Exec. Svcs. & Pub. Affairs--Occidental Oil & Gas Corporation, Bakersfield, CA; *U.S. Public*, pg. 1210
Merkin, Harry, Dir.-Corp. Communications--INSO Corporation, Boston, MA; *U.S. Public*, pg. 882
Merkovsky, Juli, Sr. Pub. Rels. Specialist--Odetics Inc., Anaheim, CA; *U.S. Public*, pg. 1212
Merlis, Bob, Sr. V.P. & Dir.-Media Rels.--Warner Bros. Records, Inc., Burbank, CA; *U.S. Public*, pg. 1611
Merrill, Don, Dir.-Pub. Affairs--Littlefield, Adams & Company, Huber Heights, OH; *U.S. Public*, pg. 1001
Merry, Carol, Dir.-Corp. & Shareholder Commun.--Lexford Residential Trust, Columbus, OH; *U.S. Public*, pg. 991
Mersereau, Marilyn, Dir.-Communications--IBM Canada Limited, Markham, Canada; *U.S. Public*, pg. 897
Meshke, Sheryl, Dir.-Communications--North Central AMPI, Inc., New Ulm, MN; *U.S. Private*, pg. 804
Metzenbaves, Heike, Mgr.-Corp. Commun.--Continental AG, Hannover, Germany; *Int'l*, pg. 327
Meyer, John A., V.P. & Mgr.-Midwest Newspaper Rels.--Parade Publications Inc., New York, NY; *U.S. Private*, pg. 20
Meyer, Leslie, Coord.-Commun.--Therma-Tru Corp., Maumee, OH; *U.S. Private*, pg. 1079
Meyer, Madame, Dir.-Communications--JS Telecommunications S.A., Louveciennes, France; *Int'l*, pg. 706
Meyer, Mary, Dir.-Pub. Affairs--KSTP-TV, Saint Paul, MN; *U.S. Private*, pg. 544
Meyers, Robert S., V.P.-Corp. Communications & Investor Rels.--Scientific-Atlanta, Inc., Norcross, GA; *U.S. Public*, pg. 1443
Meyers, Stephanie, Mgr.-Pub. Rels.--Maryland & Virginia Milk Producers Cooperative Association, Inc., Reston, VA; *U.S. Private*, pg. 711
Michael, Jack W., V.P.-Indus. Rels. & Real Estate--Western Atlas International, Inc., Houston, TX; *U.S. Public*, pg. 1757
Michaels, C. Rand, Vice. Chm.--Lomak Petroleum Inc., Fort Worth, TX; *U.S. Public*, pg. 1012
Michaels, C. Rand, Mgr.-Pub. Rels.--Lomak Production Company, Hartville, OH; *U.S. Public*, pg. 1012
Michaels, C. Rand, Mgr.-Pub. Rels.--Lomak Operating Company, Hartville, OH; *U.S. Public*, pg. 1012
Michalak, Rob, Mgr.-Pub. Rels.--Ben & Jerry's Homemade Inc., South Burlington, VT; *U.S. Public*, pg. 210
Michel, Monique, Mgr.-Pub. Rels.--Royal Packaging Industries Van Leer B.V., Amstelveen, Netherlands; *Int'l*, pg. 1145
Michel, Nicole, Commun. Officer--Charbonnages de France, Rueil-Malmaison, France; *Int'l*, pg. 280
Micheletti, Nicole, Corp. Communications--Essilor International Compagnie Generale d'Optique, Charenton-le-Pont, France; *Int'l*, pg. 462
Michelic, Geri, V.P.-Corp. Commun. & Programs--Inacom Corp., Omaha, NE; *U.S. Public*, pg. 873
Michell, Margaret, Head-Communications--Waterford Wedgwood UK Plc, Stoke on Trent, United Kingdom; *Int'l*, pg. 1487
Michener, Sally R., Sec. & Dir.-Personnel & Pub. Rels.--Scott Specialty Gases, Plumsteadville, PA; *U.S. Private*, pg. 977
Middleton, Lee, Sr. Dir.-Public Affairs--American Express Bank Ltd., New York, NY; *U.S. Public*, pg. 73
Middleton, Susan A., V.P.-Mktg.--Brothers Gourmet Coffees, Inc., Boca Raton, FL; *U.S. Public*, pg. 259
Midora, Kathleen, Dir.-Mktg. Svcs.--Angelo Brothers Co., Philadelphia, PA; *U.S. Private*, pg. 74
Mielke, John, Mgr.-Communications & Promo.--Jacobsen Textron, Racine, WI; *U.S. Public*, pg. 1589
Mies. John, Mgr.-Public Rels.--Mack Trucks, Inc., Allentown, PA; *Int'l*, pg. 1102
Milburn, Chris, Dir.-Corp. Affairs--BTR plc, London, United Kingdom; *Int'l*, pg. 124
Miles, Ellen, Mgr.-Corp. Commun.--The Dexter Corporation, Windsor Locks, CT; *U.S. Public*, pg. 504
Miles, Michelle T., Asst. V.P. & Dir.-Devel.--Hayes, Seay, Mattern & Mattern, Inc., Roanoke, VA; *U.S. Private*, pg. 513
Miley, Judith, Mgr.-Communications--Clairson International Corp., Ocala, FL; *U.S. Public*, pg. 575
Miller-Lee, Jennifer, Mgr.-Corp. Communications--Trans Financial, Inc., Bowling Green, KY; *U.S. Public*, pg. 1628
Miller, Alan, Mgr.-Pub. Rels.--Siemens Medical Systems, Inc., Iselin, NJ; *Int'l*, pg. 1246
Miller, Amy, Mgr.-Commun.--Plains Electric Generation Transmission Co-Op, Inc., Albuquerque, NM; *U.S. Private*, pg. 868
Miller, Bill, Dir.-Pub. Rels.--The United Company, Bristol, VA; *U.S. Private*, pg. 1121
Miller, Christen, Mgr.-Communications & Mktg.--Elo TouchSystems, Inc., Fremont, CA; *U.S. Public*, pg. 1362
Miller, Chuck, Mgr.-Corp. Communications--Tech Data Corporation, Clearwater, FL; *U.S. Public*, pg. 1562
Miller, Cindy, Dir.-Pub. Rels. (Ohio)--The Edward J. DeBartolo Corporation, Youngstown, OH; *U.S. Private*, pg. 319
Miller, Cliff, Mgr.-Pub. Rels.--Shamrock Holdings, Inc., Burbank, CA; *U.S. Private*, pg. 989
Miller, Dalene, Dir.-Pub. Rels.--D.A. Davidson & Co., Great Falls, MT; *U.S. Private*, pg. 314
Miller, David, Dir.-Pub. Rels.--Apple Computer (UK) Ltd., Uxbridge, United Kingdom; *U.S. Public*, pg. 121
Miller, David, Corp. Communications & Pub. Rels.--Etec Systems, Inc., Hayward, CA; *U.S. Public*, pg. 594
Miller, Gregg P., V.P.-Human Resources--Dwyer Instruments Inc., Michigan City, IN; *U.S. Private*, pg. 350
Miller, Irene, Mgr.-Corp. Communications--Robern, Inc., Bristol, PA; *U.S. Private*, pg. 630
Miller, Karla, Mgr.- Corp. Commun.--Archer Daniels Midland Company (ADM), Decatur, IL; *U.S. Public*, pg. 127
Miller, Kristen Koca, Mgr.-Mktg. Rels.--Broadmoor Hotel, Inc., Colorado Springs, CO; *U.S. Private*, pg. 170
Miller, Larry D., V.P.-Commun. & Investor Rels.--Alltrista Corporation, Muncie, IN; *U.S. Public*, pg. 56
Miller, Mark, V.P.-Pub. Affairs--Jaguar Cars, Mahwah, NJ; *U.S. Public*, pg. 664
Miller, Matthew M., Mgr.-Corp. Pub. Rels.--The Gillette Company, Boston, MA; *U.S. Public*, pg. 743
Miller, Mike, Dir.-External Communications--AT&T Strategy & New Service Innovations, Parsippany, NJ; *U.S. Public*, pg. 11
Miller, N., Dir.-Pub. Affairs--Oland Breweries Limited, Halifax, Canada; *Int'l*, pg. 679
Miller, Nadine, Mgr.-Pub. Rels.--Land O'Lakes, Inc., Kiel, WI; *U.S. Private*, pg. 646
Miller, Nancy, Dir.-Corp. Rels.--GenRad, Inc., Westford, MA; *U.S. Public*, pg. 731
Miller, Pam, Mgr.-Mktg. Commun.--Simpson Dura-Vent Co., Inc., Vacaville, CA; *U.S. Public*, pg. 1474
Miller, Pam, Mktg. Communications-Wireless (Communications Grp.)--U S West Inc., Englewood, CO; *U.S. Public*, pg. 1688
Miller, Richard, Sr. V.P. & Mng. Dir.-Pub. Rels.--Northlich Stolley LaWarre Public Relations, Cincinnati, OH; *U.S. Private*, pg. 806
Miller, Robin, Pub. Rels. Consultant--William Cook Public Relations, Inc., Jacksonville, FL; *U.S. Private*, pg. 273
Miller, Shira, Dir.-Mktg. Commun.--Morrison Health Care Inc., Smyrna, GA; *U.S. Public*, pg. 1133
Miller, Sue, Head-Corp. Communications--T & N Plc, Manchester, United Kingdom; *Int'l*, pg. 1334
Miller, Susan, V.P.-Fin. Pub. Rels.--American Express Travel Related Services Co., Inc., New York, NY; *U.S. Public*, pg. 73
Miller, Suzanne, Mgr.-Commun.--Clark Refining & Marketing Inc., Saint Louis, MO; *U.S. Private*, pg. 243
Millot, Daniel, V.P.-Sls. & Customer Service--CF Cable TV Inc., Montreal, Canada; *Int'l*, pg. 240
Mills, Angela, Mgr.-Communications--American Rehability Services, Inc., Brentwood, TN; *U.S. Public*, pg. 1257
Mills, Laura, Representative-Corp. Communications--Alza Corporation, Palo Alto, CA; *U.S. Public*, pg. 62
Milne, Jack G., V.P.-Corp. Commun.--FPL Group, Inc., North Palm Beach, FL; *U.S. Public*, pg. 608
Minella, Nancy J., Dir.-H.R.--Worthington Foods Inc., Worthington, OH; *U.S. Public*, pg. 1780
Minerman, Jennifer, Dir.-Mktg. Communications--Weider Nutrition Intl., Salt Lake City, UT; *U.S. Private*, pg. 1159
Minet, Jacques, Dir.-Promos. & Publicity--Peugeot S.A., Paris, France; *Int'l*, pg. 1020
Mineta Clapp, Mari, V.P.-Corp. Rels.--UB Networks, Santa Clara, CA; *Int'l*, pg. 924
Minter, George, Dir.-Pub. Policy--Pacific Enterprises, Los Angeles, CA; *U.S. Public*, pg. 1249
Mintz, Bill, Dir.-Pub. & Intl. Affairs--Apache Corporation, Houston, TX; *U.S. Public*, pg. 119
Miraben, George, Sr. V.P.-Policy & H.R.--Tucson Electric Power Company, Tucson, AZ; *U.S. Public*, pg. 1670
Misakian, Jeffrey D., Sr. V.P. & Dir.-Corp. Rels.--Glendale Federal Bank, F.S.B., Glendale, CA; *U.S. Public*, pg. 747
Mischo, Elke, Dir.-Pub. Rels.--Braun AG, Kronberg, Germany; *U.S. Public*, pg. 744
Missad, Matthew, Exec. V.P.-Corp. Compliance--Universal Forest Products, Inc., Grand Rapids, MI; *U.S. Public*, pg. 1696
Misumi, Setsuo, Gen. Mgr.-Pub. Rels.--Yasuda Mutual Life Insurance Co., Tokyo, Japan; *Int'l*, pg. 1519
Mita, Norio, Gen. Mgr.-Corp. Commun.--Seiko Corporation, Tokyo, Japan; *Int'l*, pg. 1218
Mitchell, Dawn, Mgr.-Corp. Commun.--Canadian Pacific Limited, Calgary, Canada; *Int'l*, pg. 258
Mitchell, Jeanne, V.P.-Investor Rels. & Corp. Communications--Hanover Direct, Inc., Weehawken, NJ; *U.S. Public*, pg. 782
Mitchell, Jeanne, V.P.-Inv. Rels.--Hanover Direct Pennsylvania, Inc., Hanover, PA; *U.S. Public*, pg. 782
Mitchell, Jeanne, V.P.-Inv. Rels.--Scandia Down Shops Limited, La Crosse, WI; *U.S. Public*, pg. 782
Mitchell, Kelly, Communicaton Specialist--Weatherby Health Care, Norwalk, CT; *U.S. Private*, pg. 1155
Mitchell, Mary, Mgr.-Mtkg. & Communications--Go-Video, Inc., Scottsdale, AZ; *U.S. Public*, pg. 748
Mitchell, Michelle, Mgr.-Coord. Mktg.--Advanstar Communications, Cleveland, OH; *U.S. Private*, pg. 22
Mitchell, Nancy, Mgr.-Corp. Commun.--Charles Schwab & Co. Inc., San Francisco, CA; *U.S. Public*, pg. 1443
Mitchell, Ruth, Asst. V.P.-Commun.--Hy-Vee Food Stores Incorporated, West Des Moines, IA; *U.S. Private*, pg. 550
Mitchell, Shannon, Publicity Coord.--Florida Tile Industries, Inc., Lakeland, FL; *U.S. Public*, pg. 1322
Mitchell, Thomas J., Coord.-Commun.--EBSCO Industries, Inc., Birmingham, AL; *U.S. Private*, pg. 358
Mitro, Monica, Dir.-Pub. Rels.--Victoria's Secret Stores, Reynoldsburg, OH; *U.S. Public*, pg. 995
Mitton, Liz, Mgr.-Communications--The Minute Maid Company, Houston, TX; *U.S. Public*, pg. 392
Miyauchi, Tetsuzo, Mgr.-Pub. Rels.--The Siam Sanitary Fittings Co., Ltd., Pathum Thani, Thailand; *Int'l*, pg. 1239
Miyazaki, Yoshimi, Gen. Mgr.-Pub. Rels. & Legal Affairs--Maruha Corporation, Tokyo, Japan; *Int'l*, pg. 845
Mizuno, Toshiro, V.P.-Passenger Mktg. & Adv.--Japan Airlines American Region, New York, NY; *Int'l*, pg. 700
Mizutani, M., Mgr.-Corp. Rels.--Tokyo Gas Co., Ltd., Tokyo, Japan; *Int'l*, pg. 1394
Mobile, Jane, V.P.-Corp. Planning & Communications--France Telecom Inc., New York, NY; *Int'l*, pg. 504
Mocarsky, Thomas F., V.P.-Communications--The Arbitron Company, New York, NY; *U.S. Public*, pg. 331
Mocho, Antonio, Dr., Dir.-Pub. Affairs--Petrogal, s.a., Lisbon, Portugal; *Int'l*, pg. 1044
Modeer, Bengt, Sr. V.P.-Corp. Communications--Incentive AB, Stockholm, Sweden; *Int'l*, pg. 666
Mogavero, Stephanie, Mgr.-Mktg. Communications--Du Pont Fibers, Wilmington, DE; *U.S. Public*, pg. 531
Mohlin, Katarina, Exec. V.P. & Corp. Commun. Officer--Skandia Insurance Company Limited, Stockholm, Sweden; *Int'l*, pg. 1256
Moine, Gerard, Exec. Dir.-Pub. Affairs--France Telecom, Paris, France; *Int'l*, pg. 503
Molineaux, Christopher, V.P.-Commun.--Blue Cross and Blue Shield Association, Chicago, IL; *U.S. Private*, pg. 151
Moller, Soren, Treas. & Mgr.-Communications--Sophus Berendsen A/S, Soeborg, Denmark; *Int'l*, pg. 1284
Molleur, E. Claude, V.P.-Legal & Public Affairs--Ivanhoe, Montreal, Canada; *Int'l*, pg. 249
Moloney, Tania, V.P.-Pub. Rels.--Buena Vista Home Video, Burbank, CA; *U.S. Public*, pg. 513
Molter, Ted, Dir.-Pub. Rels.--Sea World of Ohio, Aurora, OH; *U.S. Public*, pg. 114
Molvin, Lennart, Mgr.-Pub. Rels.--ACTIVE BioTech AB, Malmo, Sweden; *Int'l*, pg. 23
Momber, H.G., Dir.-Communications--DAF Trucks N.V., Eindhoven, Netherlands; *U.S. Public*, pg. 1247
Monaco, Susan, V.P.-Strategic Plng. & Corp. Affairs--Engelhard Corporation, Iselin, NJ; *U.S. Public*, pg. 582
Monahan, Terri, V.P.-Pub. Rels.--American Classic Voyagers Company, New Orleans, LA; *U.S. Private*, pg. 380
Monfried, David, V.P.-Pub. Rels.--The Dun & Bradstreet Corporation, Murray Hill, NJ; *U.S. Public*, pg. 535
Monroe, Jean Ann, Dir.-Communications--Pennaco Hosiery, New York, NY; *U.S. Public*, pg. 483
Monroe, Michael J., V.P.-Corp. Rels.--Cigna Corp., Philadelphia, PA; *U.S. Public*, pg. 356
Montero, Tovar, Mgr.-Communications--Industrias Gessy Lever Ltda., Sao Paulo, Brazil; *Int'l*, pg. 1437
Montgomery, Monte D., V.P.-Customer Rels.--Northrop Grumman Corporation, Los Angeles, CA; *U.S. Public*, pg. 1197
Montgomery, William, Mgr.-Mktg. Communications--Prairie Farms Dairy, Inc., Carlinville, IL; *U.S. Private*, pg. 878
Montlouis, Michele, Mgr.-Pub. Rels.--Dassault Aviation Group, Vaucresson, France; *Int'l*, pg. 383
Montseny, Josep, Asst. Gen. Mgr.--Caixa d'Estalvis de Catalunya, Barcelona, Spain; *Int'l*, pg. 249
Moody, Howard, Dir.-Corp. Affairs--The Royal Bank of Scotland plc, Edinburgh, United Kingdom; *Int'l*, pg. 1132
Mooney, Dave, Dir.-Pub. Rels.--Equifax Inc., Atlanta, GA; *U.S. Public*, pg. 588
Mooney, Dianne, V.P.-Custom Publ. & Promo.--Southern Progress Corporation, Birmingham, AL; *U.S. Public*, pg. 1612
Moore, Betty, Coord.-Corp. Communications--Delta Air Lines, Inc., Atlanta, GA; *U.S. Public*, pg. 497
Moore, Bob, Dir.-Pub. Rels.--Kansas City Chiefs Football Club, Inc., Kansas City, MO; *U.S. Private*, pg. 607
Moore, C.D., Dir.-Pub. Rels.--Pilkington Plc, Saint Helens, United Kingdom; *Int'l*, pg. 1056
Moore, Jay, Dir.-Corp. Commun.--Bassett Furniture Industries, Incorporated, Bassett, VA; *U.S. Public*, pg. 193
Moore, Jennifer, Pub. Rels. & Commun.--Items International/Airwalk, Inc., Altoona, PA; *U.S. Private*, pg. 576
Moore, John E., Sr. V.P.-Personnel & Community Rels.--The Cessna Aircraft Co., Wichita, KS; *U.S. Public*, pg. 1589
Moore, Kate D., Mgr.-Community Rels.--Midlantic Bank, N.A., Edison, NJ; *U.S. Public*, pg. 1242

Moore, Kelly, Mgr.-Pub. Rels.--Spicer Driveshaft Div., Toledo, OH; *U.S. Public*, pg. 479
Moore, Laura, V.P.-Corp. Communications--Zale Corporation, Irving, TX; *U.S. Public*, pg. 1789
Moore, Meredith C., Media Rels.--The Minnesota Mutual Life Insurance Company, Saint Paul, MN; *U.S. Private*, pg. 750
Moore, Mike, Dir.-Pub. Rels.--Cleaning Solutions Group/Cello, Havre De Grace, MD; *U.S. Public*, pg. 1466
Moore, Patricia K., Dir.-Investor Rels.--ESCO Electronics Corporation, Saint Louis, MO; *U.S. Public*, pg. 546
Moore, Steven D., Dir.-Corp. Commun.--Halliburton Company, Dallas, TX; *U.S. Public*, pg. 775
Moore, Steven D., Dir.-Corp. Communications--Halliburton Energy Services, Inc., Dallas, TX; *U.S. Public*, pg. 776
Moran, Tracey, Mgr.-Mktg. Commun.--IDX Systems Corporation, Burlington, VT; *U.S. Public*, pg. 854
Morano, Jerry, Exec. V.P.-Mktg. & Commun.--Quality Bakers of America Cooperative, Inc., Greenwich, CT; *U.S. Private*, pg. 898
More, Shelly, Mgr.-Pub. Affairs--Great Lakes Chemical Corporation, West Lafayette, IN; *U.S. Public*, pg. 760
Moreau, Segolene, Corp. Commun. Dept.--Accor S.A., Evry, France; *Int'l*, pg. 20
Moretensen, Nancy, V.P.-Mktg. & Services--Zions Co-operative Mercantile Institution, Salt Lake City, UT; *U.S. Public*, pg. 1793
Moretti, Peggy M., V.P.-Pub. Rels.--Maguire Partners, Los Angeles, CA; *U.S. Private*, pg. 696
Morgan, Doug, Dir.-Mktg. Communications--Mosler Inc., Hamilton, OH; *U.S. Private*, pg. 763
Morgan, Elizabeth, Mgr.-Pub. Rels.--Hitox Corporation of America, Corpus Christi, TX; *U.S. Public*, pg. 829
Morgan, Laura, Dir.-Communications--Los Angeles Times, Los Angeles, CA; *U.S. Public*, pg. 1616
Morgan, Mary Beth, Pub. Rels. Specialist--Applied Industrial Technologies, Cleveland, OH; *U.S. Public*, pg. 122
Morgan, Rob, Sr. V.P.-Mktg., Sls. & Engrng.--Buck Knives, Inc., El Cajon, CA; *U.S. Private*, pg. 177
Morgan, Susan, Mgr.-Pub. Rels.--Bostonian Shoe Co., Newton, MA; *Int'l*, pg. 297
Morita, Yasuhiko, Mgr.-Pub. Rels.--NSK Ltd., Tokyo, Japan; *Int'l*, pg. 903
Moritz, Jan, Dir.-Information--Stora Cell AB, Gavle, Sweden; *Int'l*, pg. 1303
Moritz, Paula, Publicity & Promo. Dir.--Allied Advertising Agency, Public Relations, Philadelphia, PA; *U.S. Private*, pg. 38
Moriya, Wataru, Sr. Mng. Dir.-Public & Employee Rels. & Gen. Admin.--Japan Energy Corporation, Tokyo, Japan; *Int'l*, pg. 702
Morris, David, Mgr.-Pub. Rels.--General Communication, Inc., Anchorage, AK; *U.S. Public*, pg. 708
Morris, John, V.P.-Pub. Rels.--Griffin Bacal Volny, Toronto, Canada; *U.S. Private*, pg. 480
Morris, Keith, Pub. Rels. Specialist--Wal-Mart Stores, Inc., Bentonville, AR; *U.S. Public*, pg. 1732
Morris, Scott, Exec. V.P.-External Affairs & Sec.--AT&T Wireless Services, Kirkland, WA; *U.S. Public*, pg. 11
Morrison, Fran, Mgr.-Media Rels.--Shell International Petroleum Co. Ltd., London, United Kingdom; *Int'l*, pg. 1139
Morrison, John, Mgr.-Pub. Rels.--General Motors-Holden's Automotive Limited, Melbourne, Australia; *U.S. Public*, pg. 723
Morrison, Linda R., Dir.-Communications--Florida Tile Industries, Inc., Lakeland, FL; *U.S. Public*, pg. 1322
Morrison, Mary, Sr. Mgr.-Mktg. Communications--Oki Semiconductor Group, Sunnyvale, CA; *Int'l*, pg. 1000
Morrison, Paul, Mgr.-Public Rels.--Network Equipment Technologies, Inc., Redwood City, CA; *U.S. Public*, pg. 1168
Morrison, Peter, Dir.-Adv.--Bassett Furniture Industries, Incorporated, Bassett, VA; *U.S. Public*, pg. 193
Morrison, Tracy, Mgr.-Communications--TCG International Inc., Burnaby, Canada; *Int'l*, pg. 1336
Morrisroe, Chris, Mgr.-Pub. Rels.--Hudson's, Southfield, MI; *U.S. Public*, pg. 489
Morrissey, Christopher, Mgr.-Mktg. Commun.--Rogers Corporation, Rogers, CT; *U.S. Public*, pg. 1402
Morrocchi, Lorenzo, V.P.-Communications & Adv.--New Holland Ltd., Brentford, United Kingdom; *Int'l*, pg. 484
Morrow, Mary Ann, Mgr.-Pub. Rels.--Rust International Inc., Birmingham, AL; *U.S. Public*, pg. 1366
Morrow, Michael, V.P.-Mktg.--Kelly Services, Inc., Troy, MI; *U.S. Public*, pg. 949
Morrow, Robert, V.P.-Corp. Communications--Stone & Webster Engineering & Constructors Corp., Boston, MA; *U.S. Public*, pg. 1519
Morrow, Roy, Dir.-Corp. Pub. Rels.--CBS Corporation, Pittsburgh, PA; *U.S. Public*, pg. 273
Morrow, Roy, Dir.-Corp. Communications--The Lincoln Electric Company, Cleveland, OH; *U.S. Public*, pg. 996
Morse, Barbara, V.P.-Corp. Communications--Copley Pharmaceuticals, Inc., Canton, MA; *U.S. Public*, pg. 446
Mortensen, Susan, V.P.-Pub. Affairs--Full House Sports & Entertainment, Seattle, WA; *U.S. Public*, pg. 16
Mortine, Neil, Exec. V.P., Pub. Rels. Dir. & Investor Rels. Dir.--Lord, Sullivan & Yoder Inc. Marketing Communications, Columbus, OH; *U.S. Private*, pg. 676
Mortine, Neil R., Exec. V.P., Pub. Rels. Dir. & Investor Rels. Dir.--Lord, Sullivan & Yoder Public Relations, Columbus, OH; *U.S. Private*, pg. 676
Morton, James, V.P.-Pub. Rels.--Michelin North America, Greenville, SC; *Int'l*, pg. 322
Morton, Jim, V.P.-Pub. Rels. & Govt. Rels.--Michelin Americas Small Tires (MAST), Greenville, SC; *Int'l*, pg. 322
Moschello, Jean, Dir.-Corp. Communications--SBC Warburg Dillon Read Inc., New York, NY; *Int'l*, pg. 1329
Moschello, Joan, Dir.-Corp. Communications--SBC Warburg Dillon Read, Stamford, CT; *Int'l*, pg. 1329
Mosconi, Jean Claude, Dir.-Pub. Affairs--General Motors France, Gennevilliers, France; *U.S. Public*, pg. 724
Moseley, Joe, V.P.& Gen. Counsel--Shelter Mutual Insurance Company, Columbia, MO; *U.S. Private*, pg. 992
Moser, Laura, Mgr.-Communications--Michigan Milk Producers Association, Novi, MI; *U.S. Private*, pg. 741
Moskowitz, Ilene, Head-Mktg. & Pub. Rels.--Bank Leumi Trust Company of New York, New York, NY; *Int'l*, pg. 150
Mosley, Harold, Coord.-Communications--Unison Industries, Jacksonville, FL; *U.S. Private*, pg. 1120
Moss, Bonnie, Dir.-Community Affairs--Browning-Ferris Industries, Inc., Houston, TX; *U.S. Public*, pg. 262
Mossberg, Per, Exec. V.P.-Corp. & Mktg. Communications--Telia AB, Farsta, Sweden; *Int'l*, pg. 1373
Mossburg, Kelley, Sr. V.P.-H.R.--Long John Silver's, Inc., Lexington, KY; *U.S. Private*, pg. 674
Moster, Mary C., V.P.-Corp. Commun.--Comdisco, Inc., Rosemont, IL; *U.S. Public*, pg. 407
Motau, Sej, Gen. Mgr.-Corp. Affairs--Sasol Limited, Johannesburg, South Africa; *Int'l*, pg. 1196
Moth, M., Head-Corp. Communications--Taylor Woodrow plc, London, United Kingdom; *Int'l*, pg. 1358
Mott, Betty, Dir.-Admin. & Human Resources--McBride and Associates, Inc., Albuquerque, NM; *U.S. Private*, pg. 719
Moukakou, Tatiana, Pub. Rels. Dir.--DMB&B Athens, Athens, Greece; *U.S. Private*, pg. 303
Mouren, Henri, Dir.-Communications & Personnel--Compagnie des Machines Bull, Louveciennes, France; *Int'l*, pg. 315
Mowins, Gregg, Dir.-Pub. Rels.--Ikea North America, Inc., Plymouth Meeting, PA; *Int'l*, pg. 660
Moye, Tammy, Dir.-Promo.--WAXY (FM), Fort Lauderdale, FL; *U.S. Public*, pg. 925
Moyer, Steven K., V.P.-Human Resources--Hatfield Quality Meats, Hatfield, PA; *U.S. Private*, pg. 510
Muchow, Jennifer, Pub. Rels. Assoc.--Software Publishing Corporation, Fairfield, NJ; *U.S. Public*, pg. 1483
Muckleroy, Jim, Dir.-Pub. Rels.--Brookshire Grocery, Tyler, TX; *U.S. Private*, pg. 172
Mudd, Michael, V.P.-Corp. Affairs--Kraft Foods, Inc., Northfield, IL; *U.S. Public*, pg. 1287
Muelboeck, Erwin, Mgr.-Adv. & Public Rels.--Agrolinz Melamin GmbH, Lienz, Austria; *Int'l*, pg. 356
Muelenberg, Gary, Mgr.-Mktg. Communications--TSI Incorporated, Shoreview, MN; *U.S. Public*, pg. 1559
Muench, Erwin, Dr., Dir.-Pub. Rels.--RWE Energie AG, Essen, Germany; *Int'l*, pg. 1081
Muenzer, Thomas, Mgr.-Public Relations--Eckes AG, Nieder-Olm, Germany; *Int'l*, pg. 432
Muir, Nigel D., V.P.-Corp. Commun. & Pub. Rels.--Praxair Inc., Danbury, CT; *U.S. Public*, pg. 1319
Mularoni, Betsy, Dir.-Corp. Communications--Materials Research Corporation, Gilbert, AZ; *Int'l*, pg. 1283
Mulberry, Cathy, Coord.-Commun.--Burlington Motor Holdings Inc., Daleville, IN; *U.S. Private*, pg. 183
Mulcahy, Amy, Mgr.-Communications--Agromac International, Inc., Gering, NE; *U.S. Private*, pg. 27
Mulcahy, Kimberly, V.P.-Corp. Communications--Budget Rent A Car Corporation, Lisle, IL; *U.S. Private*, pg. 178
Muldowney, Kevin, Mgr.-Commun.--TimeMed Labeling Systems, Inc., Burr Ridge, IL; *U.S. Private*, pg. 1087
Mulieri, Richard, Dir.-Media Rels.--Consolidated Edison Company of New York, Inc., New York, NY; *U.S. Public*, pg. 434
Muller, Cindy, Coord.-Mktg. Communications--Rheem Water Heater, Montgomery, AL; *Int'l*, pg. 1022
Muller, Karen, Dir.-Community Affairs & Corp. Grants Contact--H.B. Fuller Company, Saint Paul, MN; *U.S. Public*, pg. 686
Muller, Nancy, V.P.-Pub. Affairs--American Express Travel Related Services Co., Inc., New York, NY; *U.S. Public*, pg. 73
Mulligan, Rosemary L., V.P.-Investor & Pub. Rels.--Centris Group Inc., Costa Mesa, CA; *U.S. Public*, pg. 328
Mullins, Dennis, V.P.-Pub. Affairs, Sec. & Gen. Counsel--Tejon Ranch Company, Lebec, CA; *U.S. Public*, pg. 1566
Mullins, Kevin, V.P.-Sls. & Mktg.--LoJack Corporation, Dedham, MA; *U.S. Public*, pg. 1012
Mullins, Suzanne, V.P.-Opers. & Cust. Svc.--Smart & Final, Vernon, CA; *Int'l*, pg. 563
Mumma, J. Stephen, Sr. V.P.-Mktg. & Pub. Rels.--Atlas Van Lines, Inc., Evansville, IN; *U.S. Private*, pg. 97
Mumper-Dickerson, Melanie, V.P.-Mktg. Services & Pub. Rels.--NFO Research, Inc., Greenwich, CT; *U.S. Public*, pg. 1146
Munder, Barbara A., Sr. V.P.-Public Affairs--The McGraw-Hill Companies, New York, NY; *U.S. Public*, pg. 1069
Mundt, Ken, Mgr.-Corp. Communications--Flow International Corporation, Kent, WA; *U.S. Public*, pg. 656
Mundt, Thomas P., V.P.-Strategic Plng., Investor Rels. & Communications--Wolverine World Wide, Inc., Rockford, MI; *U.S. Public*, pg. 1775
Munk, Karen C., Pub. Rels. Dir.--TMP Worldwide, Inc., New York, NY; *U.S. Private*, pg. 1064
Munkres, Kimberli, Pub. Rels.--Experience In Software, Inc., Berkeley, CA; *U.S. Private*, pg. 388
Munsey, Evarard, V.P.-Pub. Policy--Dominion Resources, Inc., Richmond, VA; *U.S. Public*, pg. 516
Munson, Dorothy, Dir.-Communications--Ciba Specialty Chemicals, Tarrytown, NY; *Int'l*, pg. 291
Mura-Smith, Kit, V.P.-Corp. Commun.--Trimble Navigation Limited, Sunnyvale, CA; *U.S. Public*, pg. 1638
Murata, Norihiko, Mgr.-Press & Public Rels.--Dai Nippon Printing Co., Ltd., Tokyo, Japan; *Int'l*, pg. 363
Murphy, Brain, Mgr.-Corp. Commun.--Waters Corporation, Milford, MA; *U.S. Public*, pg. 1745
Murphy, Evelyn, Exec. V.P.-Corp. Affairs--Blue Cross and Blue Shield of Massachusetts, Boston, MA; *U.S. Private*, pg. 151
Murphy, J., V.P.-Corp. Communications--BASF Corporation, Mount Olive, NJ; *Int'l*, pg. 105
Murphy, Karyn, V.P.--State Street Corporation, Boston, MA; *U.S. Public*, pg. 1513
Murphy, Kim, Dir.-Corp. Commun.--Genus Inc., Sunnyvale, CA; *U.S. Public*, pg. 732
Murphy, Margaret R., Asst. Mgr.-Stockholder Svcs. & Community Rels.--Lydall, Inc., Manchester, CT; *U.S. Public*, pg. 1020
Murphy, Russell P., Mgr.-Grp. Communicatons--Henkel Surface Technologies, Madison Heights, MI; *Int'l*, pg. 610
Murphy, William K., V.P.-Corp. Communications, Adv. & Pub. Rels.--Atlantic Mutual Companies, New York, NY; *U.S. Private*, pg. 95
Murrah, Judy, Sr. V.P.-Mktg. Communicaitons--Symbol Technologies, Inc., Holtsville, NY; *U.S. Public*, pg. 1546
Murray, Doug, Dir.-Customer Svc.--Croft Metals, Inc., McComb, MS; *U.S. Private*, pg. 290
Murray, Jan, Gen. Mgr.-External Rels.--North Limited, Melbourne, Australia; *Int'l*, pg. 967
Murray, Julia, Mgr.-Corp. Communcations--Oakite Products, Inc., Berkeley Heights, NJ; *Int'l*, pg. 861
Murray, Marcia Y., Mgr.-Investor Rels.--Wolverine Tube Inc., Huntsville, AL; *U.S. Public*, pg. 1774
Murray, Nancy, V.P.-Public Relations & Mktg.--Treasure Chest Advertising Co., Inc., Glendora, CA; *U.S. Public*, pg. 228
Murray, Robert A., V.P.-Corp. Communications--Colgate-Palmolive Company, New York, NY; *U.S. Public*, pg. 397
Murray, Robert W., V.P.-Communications--MagneTek, Inc., Nashville, TN; *U.S. Public*, pg. 1037
Murtaugh, Dave, Mgr.-Mktg. Commun./Michelin Brand--Michelin Americas Small Tires (MAST), Greenville, SC; *Int'l*, pg. 322
Musacchio, A. Dominick, V.P.-Bus. Devel. & Opers.--Warner-Chilcott Laboratories, Inc., Rockaway, NJ; *Int'l*, pg. 436
Musil, Jerome A., Mgr.-Corp. Commun. & Pub. Affairs--St. Joseph Light & Power Co., Saint Joseph, MO; *U.S. Public*, pg. 1427
Musil, Ruthellyn, V.P.-Corp. Rels.--Tribune Company, Chicago, IL; *U.S. Public*, pg. 1635
Muskof, Amyjean, Coord.-Corp. Communications--Fortis, Inc., New York, NY; *Int'l*, pg. 499
Myatt, Carl, Dir.-Corp. Communications--Hawaiian Electric Company, Inc., Honolulu, HI; *U.S. Public*, pg. 800
Myers, Collin, Gen. Mgr.-Corp. Affairs--M.I.M. Holdings Ltd., Brisbane, Australia; *Int'l*, pg. 827
Myers, Percy, Dir.-Pub. Rels.--GDE Systems, Inc., San Diego, CA; *U.S. Public*, pg. 1627
Myers, Raymond F., V.P. & Mgr.-Adv.--Southwest National Corporation, Greensburg, PA; *U.S. Public*, pg. 1493
Myers, Robert R., Chm. Bd. & Chief Exec. Officer--Kocolene Oil Corp., Seymour, IN; *U.S. Private*, pg. 629
Myers, Ronald W., Chief Fin. Officer & V.P.-Fin. & Admin.--GF Office Furniture Ltd., Gallatin, TN; *U.S. Private*, pg. 434
Myers, Truman, Sr. V.P.-Pub. Rels.--Yesawich, Pepperdine & Brown, Orlando, FL; *U.S. Private*, pg. 1195
Myland, Larry, Mgr.-Mktg.--Humphrey Products Company, Kalamazoo, MI; *U.S. Private*, pg. 547
Nabhan, Lou Anne J., Dir.-Public Relations--Reynolds Metals Company, Richmond, VA; *U.S. Public*, pg. 1385
Nack, Lori, Dir.-Commun.--Jerell, Inc., Dallas, TX; *U.S. Private*, pg. 586
Nadal, Christian, Exec. V.P.-Corp. Communication & Pub. Affairs--Electricite de France, Paris, France; *Int'l*, pg. 437
Naggiar, Caroline, V.P.-Mktg. Communications--Tiffany & Co., New York, NY; *U.S. Public*, pg. 1608
Nagle, Terry, Dir.-Communications--Land O'Lakes, Inc., Arden Hills, MN; *U.S. Private*, pg. 645
Nagle, Thomas, Dir.-Personnel & Labor Rels.--King Kullen Grocery Co., Inc., Westbury, NY; *U.S. Private*, pg. 621
Nakagawa, Yasuhito, Gen. Mgr.-Computers & Communications Systems Div.--Sumitomo Corporation, Tokyo, Japan; *Int'l*, pg. 1312
Nakamura, Jun-ichi, Gen. Mgr.-Pub. Rels.--West Japan Railway Company, Osaka, Japan; *Int'l*, pg. 1490
Nakamura, Waichi, Gen. Mgr.--Hitachi Zosen Corporation, Osaka, Japan; *Int'l*, pg. 622
Namandusa, D., Dir.-Human Resources--National Bank of Malawi, Blantyre, Malawi; *Int'l*, pg. 1296
Namias, Charles, V.P.-Corp. Alliances--Encore Computer Corporation, Fort Lauderdale, FL; *U.S. Public*, pg. 580
Namiot, Milton, Pres. & Chief Exec. Officer--Deering Ice Cream, Inc., Portland, ME; *U.S. Private*, pg. 403
Nance, Larry, Mgr.-Corp. Commun.--Global Industrial Technologies, Dallas, TX; *U.S. Public*, pg. 747
Nank, Reese, V.P.-Corp. Communications--First Maryland Bancorp, Baltimore, MD; *Int'l*, pg. 64
Narborogh, Colin, V.P.-Corp. Communications--ISS-International Service System A/S, Holte, Denmark; *Int'l*, pg. 656
Nash, Charlotte, Dir.-Trade Shows & Mktg. Communications-OEM--Leviton Mfg. Co., Inc., Little Neck, NY; *U.S. Private*, pg. 663
Nash, Garrett J., V.P.-Mkt. Planning & Dealer Support--Mitsubishi Motor Sales of America, Inc., Cypress, CA; *Int'l*, pg. 875
Nash, Malcolm, Pub. Rels. Dir.--Dewe Rogerson Limited, London, United Kingdom; *Int'l*, pg. 408
Nasshan, J. Kenneth, V.P.-Pub. Rels.--Kaman Corporation, Bloomfield, CT; *U.S. Public*, pg. 941
Nathanson, Alice, Mgr.-Pub. Rels.--Kal Kan Foods, Inc., Vernon, CA; *U.S. Private*, pg. 707
Natz, Daryl C., V.P.-Pub. Affairs--Continental Grain Company, New York, NY; *U.S. Private*, pg. 268
Naughton, Beth, Mgr.-Mktg. Communications--Weiser Lock, Tucson, AZ; *U.S. Public*, pg. 1053
Naughton, Jim, Dir.-Corp. Commun.--Eaton Vance Corp., Boston, MA; *U.S. Public*, pg. 559
Naughton, Jim, Mgr.-Pub. Rels.--Eaton Vance Distributors, Inc., Boston, MA; *U.S. Public*, pg. 559
Naylor, B. Phyllis, Dir.-Corp. Commun.--Amcast Industrial Corporation, Dayton, OH; *U.S. Public*, pg. 63

Naylor, G.F., Dir.-Investor Rels. & Pub. Rels.--The RTZ Corporation PLC, London, United Kingdom; *Int'l*, pg. 1118

Naylor, Joe, Mgr.-Commun./AGCO Brands--AGCO Corporation, Duluth, GA; *U.S. Public*, pg. 28

Nazarian, Arda, V.P.-Pub. Rels. & Media Rels.--The American Stock Exchange, New York, NY; *U.S. Private*, pg. 62

Nazziola, Thomas E., V.P.-Mktg.--Ilco Unican Corp., Simplex Access Controls Division, Winston Salem, NC; *Int'l*, pg. 1432

Neafsy, Kathryn, Dir.-Commun.--Rust Environment & Infrastructure, Inc., Greenville, SC; *U.S. Public*, pg. 1745

Neal, Bruce, Dir.-Communications--Six Flags Over Texas, Arlington, TX; *U.S. Public*, pg. 1612

Neal, Clinton H., Jr., Dir.-Human Resources--GoodMark Foods, Inc., Raleigh, NC; *U.S. Public*, pg. 751

Neal, Rick J., V.P.-Corp. Affairs & Admin.--Mapco Inc., Tulsa, OK; *U.S. Public*, pg. 1042

Neale'siemon, Betsy, Mgr.-Mktg. Communications--Bristol Babcock, Inc., Watertown, CT; *Int'l*, pg. 472

Nebbeling, Leidi, Mgr.-Pub. Rels.--Fortis, Utrecht, Netherlands; *Int'l*, pg. 498

Nedjib, Chantal, Sr. V.P.-Corp. Commun.--Credit Commercial de France, Paris, France; *Int'l*, pg. 341

Neel, J.C., Dir.-Communications--Inco Alloys International, Inc., Huntington, WV; *Int'l*, pg. 672

Neighbors, Sue, Mgr.-Communications--Baker Hughes Incorporated, Houston, TX; *U.S. Public*, pg. 165

Neil, D., Mgr.-Mktg. Communications--Du Pont Agricultural Products, Wilmington, DE; *U.S. Public*, pg. 531

Neimark, Tanya, Dir.-Corp. Communications--Macmillan Publishing USA, Indianapolis, IN; *U.S. Private*, pg. 777

Neininger, Wendy, Dir.-Corp. Communications--Schering Berlin Inc., Cedar Knolls, NJ; *Int'l*, pg. 1204

Nellis, James, Sr. V.P.-Pub. Rels.--The St. George Group, Inc., Pittsburgh, PA; *U.S. Private*, pg. 960

Nelson, Alex, Mgr.-Pub. Rels.--Thorn plc, Chertsey, United Kingdom; *Int'l*, pg. 1385

Nelson, Beth, Dir.-Corp. Communications--Carnival Hotels & Casinos, Miami, FL; *U.S. Public*, pg. 1265

Nelson, Carol, Admin.-Investor Rels.--WTD Industries, Inc., Portland, OR; *U.S. Public*, pg. 1729

Nelson, Debra, Dir.-Pub. Rels.--General Reinsurance Corp., Stamford, CT; *U.S. Public*, pg. 725

Nelson, Gregg, Dir.-Adv. & Pub. Rels.--Wenger Corporation, Owatonna, MN; *U.S. Private*, pg. 1162

Nelson, John, Dir.-Communications--Elco Textron, Rockford, IL; *U.S. Public*, pg. 1590

Nelson, Melvin, Dir.-Mktg. & Pub. Rels.--Minnkota Power Cooperative, Inc., Grand Forks, ND; *U.S. Private*, pg. 751

Nelson, Nancy C., V.P.-Human Resources--The HON Co., Muscatine, IA; *U.S. Public*, pg. 772

Nelson, Rachel, Dir.-Investor Rels. & Copr. Communs.--Jumbo Sports Inc., Tampa, FL; *U.S. Public*, pg. 935

Nelson, Richard, Mgr.-Pub. Rels.--Thorn Security Group, Ltd., Sunbury, United Kingdom; *Int'l*, pg. 1386

Nelson, Susan, Dir.-Corp. Relations--Bank of America Illinois, Chicago, IL; *U.S. Public*, pg. 180

Nelson, Terry, Coord.-Pub. Rels.--Biospherics Incorporated, Beltsville, MD; *U.S. Public*, pg. 232

Neonan, Michael D., Mgr.-Investor Rels.--Sterling Chemicals Holdings, Inc., Houston, TX; *U.S. Public*, pg. 1515

Nerenberg, Shelly, Pub. Rels.--Waring & LaRosa, Inc., New York, NY; *U.S. Private*, pg. 1150

Nestor, David L., Natl. Dir.-Corp. Commun.--Coopers & Lybrand, New York, NY; *U.S. Private*, pg. 274

Netkovick, Michael J., Mgr.-Public Rels. & Investor Rels.--EnergyNorth, Inc., Manchester, NH; *U.S. Public*, pg. 581

Neubarth, Ellen, Mgr.-Pub. Rels.--Feodor Burgmann Dichtungswerke GmbH, Wolfratshausen, Germany; *Int'l*, pg. 233

Neubert, Richard, Dir.-Mktg.--Duro-Test Corporation, Fairfield, NJ; *U.S. Private*, pg. 349

Neubronner, Ernst, Mgr.-Pub. Rels.--BHF-BANK AG, Frankfurt, Germany; *Int'l*, pg. 119

Neudorfer, Gail, Shareholder Communications Mgr.--Allen Nelson & Co., Seattle, WA; *U.S. Private*, pg. 790

Neut, Jean-Pierre, Dir.-Commun.--Ciments Francais, Paris, France; *Int'l*, pg. 292

Nevin, Tony, Dir.-Commun.--The Glen Dimplex Group, Dunleer, Ireland; *Int'l*, pg. 553

Newbould, Bill, Mgr.-Inv. Rels.--Centocor, Inc., Malvern, PA; *U.S. Public*, pg. 323

Newcomer, John A., Corp. Affairs Officer--Pinnacle Financial Services Inc., Saint Joseph, MI; *U.S. Public*, pg. 1297

Newham, Liz, Pub. Rels. Coord.--Odetics Inc., Anaheim, CA; *U.S. Public*, pg. 1212

Newhouse, Steve, Dir.-Mktg., Sls. & Adv.--Atlantic Builders Group Inc., Baltimore, MD; *U.S. Private*, pg. 95

Newman, Carole, V.P.-Corp. Commun.--Hambrecht & Quist LLC., San Francisco, CA; *U.S. Public*, pg. 778

Newquest, Susan D., Dir.-Pub. Rels.--American Ecology Corporation, Boise, ID; *U.S. Public*, pg. 71

Newsham, Davina, Communications Exec.--Smith & Nephew PLC, London, United Kingdom; *Int'l*, pg. 1263

Newton, J., Dir.-Pub. Affairs--Metro Brewery, Etobicoke, Canada; *Int'l*, pg. 679

Neyer, Thomas L., Jr., V.P.-Mktg.--Al Neyer, Inc., Cincinnati, OH; *U.S. Private*, pg. 797

Nicholes, Walter, V.P.-Corp. Communications & Public Rels.--L.J. Minor Corporation, Solon, OH; *Int'l*, pg. 917

Nichols, Donna C., V.P.-Corp. Communications--Agouron Pharmaceuticals, Inc., La Jolla, CA; *U.S. Public*, pg. 28

Nichols, Melissa M., V.P.-Corp. Commun.--Comcast Cellular Communications, Inc., Wayne, PA; *U.S. Public*, pg. 407

Nichols, Paul, V.P.-Media Rels.--All American Communications, Inc., Santa Monica, CA; *U.S. Public*, pg. 41

Nicholson, Debra, Dir.-Pub. Affairs--Freightliner Corp., Portland, OR; *Int'l*, pg. 368

Nickerson, Greg, V.P. & Pub. Rels. Dir.--Bader Rutter & Assoc., Inc., Brookfield, WI; *U.S. Private*, pg. 110

Nickle, Dwayne, V.P.-Mktg.--Fabwel Inc., Elkhart, IN; *U.S. Private*, pg. 390

Nicoll, Andrea, Mgr.-Mktg. Communications--The BOC Group Inc. (Delaware), Murray Hill, NJ; *Int'l*, pg. 121

Nielsen, Nancy, V.P.-Corp. Commun.--The New York Times Company, New York, NY; *U.S. Public*, pg. 1173

Nielsen, Nancy, V.P.-Corp. Communications--The New York Times, New York, NY; *U.S. Public*, pg. 1174

Nielsen, Sharon, Corp. Rels. Asst.--Genesco Inc., Nashville, TN; *U.S. Public*, pg. 728

Nielsen, Willard D., V.P.-Corp. Commun.--Johnson & Johnson, New Brunswick, NJ; *U.S. Public*, pg. 927

Nielson, Kellie, Mgr.-Pub. Rels.--Mity-Lite, Inc., Orem, UT; *U.S. Public*, pg. 1118

Niemeier, Laura Lee, Supvr.-Communications--Maytag Galesburg Refrigeration Products, Galesburg, IL; *U.S. Public*, pg. 1064

Nievergelt, Monika, Pub. Rels.--Editor AG Multimedia und Design, Kusnacht, Switzerland; *Int'l*, pg. 666

Nimmer, Ron, Mgr.-Mktg. Communications--The Falk Corporation, Milwaukee, WI; *U.S. Public*, pg. 1534

Nisar, Doering, Mgr.-Pub. Rels.--VARTA AG, Hannover, Germany; *Int'l*, pg. 1451

Nishijima, Takao, Mgr.-Adv. & Pub. Rels.--Hitachi Zosen Corporation, Osaka, Japan; *Int'l*, pg. 622

Nishikawa, Sugao, Assoc. Dir.-Pub. Rels.--Asahi Breweries Ltd., Tokyo, Japan; *Int'l*, pg. 83

Nkoma, Z.J., Dir.-Corp. Svcs.--Zimbabwe Electricity Supply Authority, Harare, Zimbabwe; *Int'l*, pg. 1528

Noagy, Jennifer, Sr. Mktg. Commun. Specialists--Countrymark Cooperative, Inc., Indianapolis, IN; *U.S. Private*, pg. 279

Noah, Sandi J., Dir.-Commun.--GenCorp Inc., Fairlawn, OH; *U.S. Public*, pg. 705

Noble, Lisa, Pub. Rels. Dir.--Cramer-Krasselt, Phoenix, AZ; *U.S. Private*, pg. 285

Noble, Terry, Mgr.-Sls. & Customer Svc.--Pipetronix Ltd., Concord, Canada; *Int'l*, pg. 1071

Nobori, Tsuyoshi, Dir.-Pub. Rels.--Sankyo Company Limited, Tokyo, Japan; *Int'l*, pg. 1189

Noceti, R., Mgr.-Pub. Rels.--Nuovo Pignone S.p.a., Florence, Italy; *Int'l*, pg. 990

Node-Langlois, Patrick, Exec. V.P.-Environment & Public Affairs--Lafarge S.A., Paris, France; *Int'l*, pg. 788

Noftall, Bob, Mgr.-Pub. Rels.--Cadbury Chocolate Canada, Inc., Toronto, Canada; *Int'l*, pg. 248

Noga, Katie, Dir.-Mktg. Communications--Chicago Rawhide, Elgin, IL; *Int'l*, pg. 1157

Nogue, Francois, Dir.-H.R. & Commun.--Framatome SA, Paris, France; *Int'l*, pg. 502

Nogues, M., Dir.-Commun. & Press--Schneider S.A., Boulogne-Billancourt, France; *Int'l*, pg. 1207

Nolan, Christopher W., Dir.-Investor Relations--GAF Corporation, Wayne, NJ; *U.S. Private*, pg. 433

Nolan, Frankie, V.P.-Social Responsibility & Pres.-Borden Foundation--Borden, Inc., Columbus, OH; *U.S. Private*, pg. 157

Nolan, Robert, V.P.-Corp. Rels.--The Hartford Financial Services Group Inc., Hartford, CT; *U.S. Public*, pg. 794

Nolan, Tom, Dir.-Mktg. Plng. & Commun.--Medusa Corporation, Cleveland, OH; *U.S. Public*, pg. 1084

Noland, Pat, Mgr.-Communications--Graphic Technology, Inc., New Century, KS; *Int'l*, pg. 950

Nolte, Brenda, Pub. Affairs Officer--Payless Cashways, Inc., Kansas City, MO; *U.S. Public*, pg. 1267

Noonan, James F., Sr. V.P.-Corp. Communications--Warner Music Group, Inc., New York, NY; *U.S. Public*, pg. 1612

Norcott, Dave, Dir.-Corp. Services--PSDI, Bedford, MA; *U.S. Private*, pg. 828

Nordquist, M., Mgr.-Pub. Rels.--Robert Bosch Corporation, Broadview, IL; *Int'l*, pg. 204

Nore, Peter, V.P.-External Affairs--Saga Petroleum ASA, Sandvika, Norway; *Int'l*, pg. 1169

Norman, Rick, Mgr.-Pub. Rels. & Market Res.--E Z Loader Corporate, Airway Heights, WA; *U.S. Private*, pg. 352

Norris, Christopher M.F., Dir.-Corp. Communications--Compuware Corporation, Farmington Hills, MI; *U.S. Public*, pg. 423

Norris, Jan, Personnel Coord.--Oliver Rubber Co., Athens, GA; *U.S. Public*, pg. 1504

Norton, Eydie, Dir.-Guest Rels.--The Accor Group, Inc., Corona Del Mar, CA; *Int'l*, pg. 21

Norton, Paula, V.P.-Corp. & Investor Rels.--Terra Industries, Inc., Sioux City, IA; *U.S. Public*, pg. 1581

Norton, Shirley, V.P.-Communications--BankAmerica Corporation, San Francisco, CA; *U.S. Public*, pg. 179

Norwitz, Steve, V.P.-Pub. Rels.--T. Rowe Price Associates, Inc., Baltimore, MD; *U.S. Public*, pg. 1324

Nosal, Bob, Dir.-Mktg., Adv. & Pub. Rels.--Unichema U.S.A., Chicago, IL; *Int'l*, pg. 1436

Noto, Blaise J., Sr. V.P.-Natl. Publicity--Paramount Pictures Corporation, Los Angeles, CA; *U.S. Private*, pg. 776

Nott, Marty, Dir.-Mktg. Communications--Niagara Mohawk Power Corporation, Syracuse, NY; *U.S. Public*, pg. 1181

Nottoli, Nivaldo, Dir.-Communications--Fiat Automiseis S.A., Sao Paulo, Brazil; *Int'l*, pg. 483

Nouchy, Chantal, Mgr.-Pub. Rels.--RTL 2, Paris, France; *Int'l*, pg. 561

Novak, Maria, Mgr.-Mktg. Communications--Bailey, Fischer & Porter Company, Warminster, PA; *Int'l*, pg. 449

Novakoff, Amy, Mgr.-Pub. Rels.--Microcom, Norwood, MA; *U.S. Public*, pg. 417

Nowak, Pat, Dir.-Pub. Rels. & Consumer Affairs--Seaway Food Town, Inc., Maumee, OH; *U.S. Public*, pg. 1452

Noyer, Liz, Sr. V.P.-Communications--Nickelodeon/Nick At Nite, New York, NY; *U.S. Private*, pg. 779

Noyes, Donald, Mgr.-Adv. & Pub. Rels.--Asarco Incorporated, New York, NY; *U.S. Public*, pg. 137

Nuetzel, Barbara, Mgr.-Corp. Communications--Loral Space & Communications, New York, NY; *U.S. Public*, pg. 1014

Nugent, Anne, Mgr.-Pub. Rels.--Del Laboratories, Inc., Farmingdale, NY; *U.S. Public*, pg. 494

Nugent, Anne, Mgr.-Pub. Rels.--Sally Hansen, Farmingdale, NY; *U.S. Public*, pg. 494

Nunemaker, Richard A., Chief Fin. Officer & V.P.-Fin.--Varlen Corporation, Naperville, IL; *U.S. Public*, pg. 1710

Nusch, Friedmar, Dr., Dir.-Commun.--Hoechst Aktiengesellschaft, Frankfurt/Main, Germany; *Int'l*, pg. 624

Nyberg, Riitta, Mgr.-Adv. & Communications--Oy Algol AB, Espoo, Finland; *Int'l*, pg. 15

Nylander, Mark C., Exec. V.P. & Gen. Mgr. Pub. Rels.--Liggett-Stashower, Inc., Cleveland, OH; *U.S. Private*, pg. 667

O'Brien, Candice, Exec. Dir.-Corp. communications--Tenneco Inc., Greenwich, CT; *U.S. Public*, pg. 1577

O'Brien, Jack, Dir.-Mktg. Commun.--Eclipse Inc., Rockford, IL; *U.S. Private*, pg. 360

O'Brien, Laraine, Mgr.-Customer Communications--Wisconsin Gas Company, Milwaukee, WI; *U.S. Public*, pg. 1767

O'Brien, Stephen, Dir.-Corp. Affairs--Dixons Group plc, Hemel Hempstead, United Kingdom,; *Int'l*, pg. 413

O'Brien, Steven, Dir.-Corp. Communications & Grp. Sec.--Redland PLC, Reigate, United Kingdom; *Int'l*, pg. 1090

O'Brien, Thomas R., Sr. V.P. & Gen. Counsel--Foster Wheeler Corporation, Clinton, NJ; *U.S. Public*, pg. 676

O'Callaghan, Jay, Dir.-Corp. Communication--MicroAge, Inc., Tempe, AZ; *U.S. Public*, pg. 1104

O'Connell, John J., Jr., V.P.-Corp. Commun.--Hvide Marine Incorporated, Fort Lauderdale, FL; *U.S. Public*, pg. 851

O'Connell, Richard L., V.P.-Customer Opers.--Hawaiian Electric Company, Inc., Honolulu, HI; *U.S. Public*, pg. 800

O'Connor, Edward J., V.P.-Human Resources & Public Affairs--A.O. Smith Corporation, Milwaukee, WI; *U.S. Public*, pg. 1476

O'Connor, Karen, Mgr.-Mktg. Communications--Jacobs Vehicle Equipment Company, Bloomfield, CT; *U.S. Public*, pg. 481

O'Connor, T.L., V.P.-External Affairs--ARCO Coal Company, Denver, CO; *U.S. Public*, pg. 144

O'Connor, Terry, Dir.-Mktg. Svcs.--BASF Corporation, Mount Olive, NJ; *Int'l*, pg. 105

O'Dell, Julie, Mgr.-U.S. Media Rels.--Hoechst Marion Roussel, Inc., Bridgewater, NJ; *Int'l*, pg. 624

O'Der, Linda L., V.P.-Customer Service--Willis Corroon Corp. of New Hampshire, Rochester, NH; *Int'l*, pg. 1506

O'Dochartaigh, Aodgh, Dir.-Commun.--Bass PLC, London, United Kingdom; *Int'l*, pg. 169

O'Donnell, Christine, Dir.-Corp. Commun.--GAI Consultants, Inc., Monroeville, PA; *U.S. Private*, pg. 433

O'Donnell, James F., Dir.-Corp. Commun.--The Hearst Corporation, New York, NY; *U.S. Private*, pg. 515

O'Donnell, Marybeth, Dir.-Communications--Federal National Mortgage Association (Fannie Mae), Washington, DC; *U.S. Public*, pg. 615

O'Flanagan, Sean, Mgr.-Communications--BNP Capital Finance Limited - Ireland, Dublin, Ireland; *Int'l*, pg. 163

O'Grady, Laura S., V.P.-Adv. & Mktg.--S & K Famous Brands, Inc., Glen Allen, VA; *U.S. Public*, pg. 1414

O'Hara, Kevin, Mgr.-Mktg. Communications--AlliedSignal Commercial Avionic Systems, Olathe, KS; *U.S. Public*, pg. 50

O'Hearn, Ed, Mgr.-Customer Service--Fansteel VR/Wesson-Plantsville, Plantsville, CT; *U.S. Public*, pg. 612

O'Keefe, Mary, V.P.-Corp. Rels.--The Principal Financial Group, Des Moines, IA; *U.S. Private*, pg. 885

O'Keefe, Mary, V.P.-Corp. Rels.--Principal Mutual Life Insurance Co., Des Moines, IA; *U.S. Private*, pg. 886

O'Keefe, Mary, Mgr.-Corp. Commun.--Veryfine Products, Inc., Westford, MA; *U.S. Private*, pg. 1137

O'Keene, Patricia, V.P.-Customer Activities--Providence Energy Corporation, Providence, RI; *U.S. Public*, pg. 1337

O'Leary, Robert J., Gen. Mgr.-Public Rels.--Mobil Oil Corporation, Fairfax, VA; *U.S. Public*, pg. 1118

O'Malia, Daniel J., Pres. & Chief Exec. Officer--O'Malia Food Markets Inc., Carmel, IN; *U.S. Private*, pg. 816

O'Malley, Tom, Mgr.-Human Resources--CCI/Triad Automotive, Livermore, CA; *U.S. Private*, pg. 193

O'Neal, Joy, V.P.-Customer Svcs.--Key Industries, Inc., Fort Scott, KS; *U.S. Private*, pg. 618

O'Neal, Peg, Mgr.-Mktg. Commun.--Avo International, Blue Bell, PA; *U.S. Private*, pg. 9

O'Neal, Ron, Mgr.-West Coast Newspaper Rels.--Parade Publications Inc., New York, NY; *U.S. Private*, pg. 20

O'Neil, Frank B., Sr. V.P.-Corp. Commun.--Medical Assurance, Inc., Birmingham, AL; *U.S. Public*, pg. 1079

O'Neill, Kevin M., Sr. V.P.-Bus. Devel. & Strategy--Anacomp, Inc., Indianapolis, IN; *U.S. Public*, pg. 106

O'Neill, Michael J., Sr. V.P.-Corp. Communications--American Express Company, New York, NY; *U.S. Public*, *pg. 73*

O'Neill, Michael J., Sr. V.P.-Public Affairs & Communications--American Express Travel Related Services Co., Inc., New York, NY; *U.S. Public*, pg. 73

O'Reilly, Jr., Charlie, Chm. Bd.--O'Reilly Automotive Inc., Springfield, MO; *U.S. Public*, pg. 1230

O'Reilly, Pat, Dir.-Corp. Communications--Suncor Inc., Calgary, Canada; *Int'l*, pg. 1320

O'Rourke, Tom, Mgr.-Pub. Rels.--Goss Graphic Systems, Westmont, IL; *U.S. Private*, pg. 466

O'Shea, Karen, V.P.-Commun. & Pub. Rels.--Lennox International Inc., Richardson, TX; *U.S. Private*, pg. 659

O'Sullivan, Jerry, Head-Corp. Rels.--Telecom Eireann, Dublin, Ireland; *Int'l*, pg. 1362

Oakley, Bryan K., Dir.-Pub. Rels.--Maxxam Inc., Houston, TX; *U.S. Public*, pg. 1062

Oakley, Melissa F., Mgr.-Corp. Comm.--McDonald's Corporation, Oak Brook, IL; *U.S. Public*, pg. 1068

Oatman, Carolyn, Dir.-Information Services--Harte-Hanks Communications, Inc., San Antonio, TX; *U.S. Public*, pg. 793

Obana, Mary, Dir.-Mktg. & Communications-Keds--The Stride Rite Corporation, Lexington, MA; *U.S. Public*, pg. 1524
Oberg, Leeny, Asst. V.P.-Investor Rels.--SLM Holding Corp., Washington, DC; *U.S. Public*, pg. 1419
Obermeyer, Peggy, Coord.-Customer Service--Amurol Confections Co., Yorkville, IL; *U.S. Public*, pg. 1781
Oberressl, Wolfgang, Mgr.-Pub. Rels.--Haindl Papier GmbH, Augsburg, Germany; *Int'l*, pg. 586
Oberritter, Claudia, Mgr.-Adv. & Corp. Sec.--Deutsche Bahn, Frankfurt/Main, Germany; *Int'l*, pg. 401
Obriotti Green, Cathy, V.P.-Pub. Affairs--H.B. Zachry, San Antonio, TX; *U.S. Private*, pg. 1203
Ocampo, Aminta, Pub. Rels.--Young & Rubicam, S.A. de C.V., Mexico, Mexico; *U.S. Private*, pg. 1200
Ockrent, Isabelle, V.P.-Corp. Communications & External Rels.--SEITA, Societe Nationale D'Exploitation Industrielle des Tabacs et des Allumettes, Paris, France; *Int'l*, pg. 1219
Odenthal, Susan, Dir.-Communications--Ethicon, Inc., Somerville, NJ; *U.S. Public*, pg. 928
Odenthal, Susan, Dir.-Communications--Janssen Pharmaceutica, Inc., Titusville, NJ; *U.S. Public*, pg. 928
Odenthal, Susan, Dir.-Communications--Ortho-McNeil Pharmaceutical Corporation, Raritan, NJ; *U.S. Public*, pg. 929
Oder, Kenneth W., Exec. V.P.-Labor Rels., Human Resources, Law & Pub. Affairs--Safeway Inc., Pleasanton, CA; *U.S. Public*, pg. 1426
Odillard, Martine, V.P.-Corp. Commun. & H.R.--Chargeurs, Paris, France; *Int'l*, pg. 280
Odiseos, Susan, Dir.-Mktg. & Communications--Trigen Energy Corporation, White Plains, NY; *U.S. Public*, pg. 1637
Oelman, Bradford C., V.P.-Govt. & Pub. Rels.--Owens Corning, Toledo, OH; *U.S. Public*, pg. 1236
Oesterle, Karl, Mgr.-Consumer Communications--Fisher-Price, Inc., East Aurora, NY; *U.S. Public*, pg. 1058
Ogasawara, Takeshi, Mgr.-Pub. Rels.--Nissan Mutual Life Insurance Company, Tokyo, Japan; *Int'l*, pg. 945
Ogburn, Emily, Mgr.-Marcom--Oliver Rubber Co., Athens, GA; *U.S. Public*, pg. 1504
Ogburn, Fred, Mgr.-Corp. Commun.--Cogsdill Tool Products, Inc., Lugoff, SC; *U.S. Private*, pg. 250
Ogden, John, Dir.-Pub. Rels.--Portec, Inc.-Construction Equipment Div., Yankton, SD; *U.S. Public*, pg. 1318
Ogden, Tom, Supvr.-Mktg. Commun.--Magnetrol International, Downers Grove, IL; *U.S. Private*, pg. 696
Ogiso, Yuko, Asst. Mgr.-Corp. Commun.--Konica Corporation, Tokyo, Japan; *Int'l*, pg. 748
Ogle, Branka, Pub. Rels.--Abbott Laboratories, Abbott Park, IL; *U.S. Public*, pg. 12
Oglesby, Donna, Dir.-Corp. Communications--Adams Resources & Energy, Inc., Houston, TX; *U.S. Public*, pg. 18
Oguri, Hiroshi, Sr. Mgr.-Pub. Rels.--Asatsu Inc., Tokyo, Japan; *Int'l*, pg. 85
Ohm, Dave, Mgr.-Pub. Rels.--Chr. Hansen, Inc., Milwaukee, WI; *Int'l*, pg. 288
Ohmer, Chris, Mgr.-Pub. Rels. & Special Events--Parisian, Inc., Birmingham, AL; *U.S. Public*, pg. 1333
Ojert, Leno, V.P.-Communications & Pub. Affairs--Scancem AB, Malmo, Sweden; *Int'l*, pg. 1198
Okle, Debbie L., Dir.-Pub. Rels.--Commercial Metals Company, Dallas, TX; *U.S. Public*, pg. 411
Okner, Mike, Grp. Mgr.-Communications--Du Pont Printing & Publishing, Wilmington, DE; *U.S. Public*, pg. 531
Okon, Joseph, V.P.-Adv. & Mktg. Communications--Marriott International, Inc., Washington, DC; *U.S. Public*, pg. 1047
Okonski, Tracy, Sls. & Mkgt. Asst.--Surgical Specialties, Reading, PA; *U.S. Private*, pg. 1056
Oldenzeel, C. Vlaanderen, Sr. Dir.-Personnel & Gen. Affairs--Hoogovens Aluminium BV, Amstelveen, Netherlands; *Int'l*, pg. 753
Oldfield, Chris, Mgr.-Public Affairs--North Limited, Melbourne, Australia; *Int'l*, pg. 967
Oliver, Al, Customer Rels.--Formex, Inc. - Permanent Steel Forms, Richmond, VA; *U.S. Public*, pg. 1222
Oliver, John, Dir.-Pub. Affairs--L.L. Bean, Inc., Freeport, ME; *U.S. Private*, pg. 639
Olmi, Jean Claude, Dir.-Corp. Commun.--Alcatel Cit (S.A.), Velizy-Villacoublay, France; *Int'l*, pg. 56
Olmsted, Bonnie, Mgr.-Project-Communications--Adecco Employment Services, Redwood City, CA; *Int'l*, pg. 24
Olsen, W.C., Mgr.-Pub. Affairs--Illinois Power Company, Decatur, IL; *U.S. Public*, pg. 869
Olson, Dolores, Community Rels. Coord.--Lawry's Foods, Inc., Monrovia, CA; *Int'l*, pg. 1435
Olson, Donald P., Mgr.-Mktg. & Employee Communications--Inland Steel Industries, Inc., Chicago, IL; *U.S. Public*, pg. 879
Olson, Jeanette, Office Mgr.--E.T. Browne Drug Co., Inc., Englewood Cliffs, NJ; *U.S. Private*, pg. 175
Olson, Jon, Dir.-Corp. Commun.--Stratus Computer, Inc., Marlborough, MA; *U.S. Public*, pg. 1524
Olson, Kathleen, Mgr.-Corp. Communications--Erie Family Life Insurance Company, Erie, PA; *U.S. Public*, pg. 590
Olson, Sheree, Dir.-Pub. Rels. & Special Events--ShopKo Stores, Inc., Green Bay, WI; *U.S. Public*, pg. 1467
Olson, Susan, Dir.-Adv. & Communications--Shenandoah Mfg. Co. Inc., Harrisonburg, VA; *U.S. Private*, pg. 992
Ondera, Ritsuko, Mgr.-Pub. Relations--Corporate Software Ltd., KK, Tokyo, Japan; *U.S. Public*, pg. 519
Ong, C.T., Gen. Mgr.-Pub. Affairs--China Steel Corporation, Kao-hsiung, Taiwan; *Int'l*, pg. 285
Ong, John, Dir.-Corp. Rels.--Ladd Furniture, Inc., Greensboro, NC; *U.S. Public*, pg. 974
Onoda, John C., V.P.-Corp. Communications--General Motors Corporation, Detroit, MI; *U.S. Public*, pg. 718
Onodera, Yasuo, Gen. Mgr.-Corp. Commun.--Toyo Tire & Rubber Co., Ltd., Osaka, Japan; *Int'l*, pg. 1411
Opfer, James E., Dir.-Media Programs--Read-Rite Corporation, Milpitas, CA; *U.S. Public*, pg. 1366
Opolko, Phyllis, Corp. Commun. & Pub. Rels.--Monarch Avalon, Inc., Baltimore, MD; *U.S. Public*, pg. 1123
Opperthauser, Ellen, Pub. Rels.--ATC Communications Group, Inc., Dallas, TX; *U.S. Public*, pg. 11
Ordona, John, Mgr.-Pub. Rels.--Esprit de Corp., San Francisco, CA; *U.S. Private*, pg. 383
Orem, Glen, Dir.-Mktg.--SouthCo. Inc., Concordville, PA; *U.S. Private*, pg. 1014
Orenstein, Jerry M., Mgr.-Programs & Sls. Communications--PP&L Resources, Allentown, PA; *U.S. Public*, pg. 1244
Orland, Glenda, Mgr.-Pub. Affairs--H.J. Heinz Company Australia Ltd., Dandenong, Australia; *U.S. Public*, pg. 807
Orr, George H., V.P.-Human Resources--American Paging, Inc., Minneapolis, MN; *U.S. Public*, pg. 1570
Orr, John, V.P. & Pub. Rels. Mgr.--Al Paul Lefton Co., Inc., Philadelphia, PA; *U.S. Private*, pg. 658
Orr, Katherine R., V.P.-Public Relations--Harlequin Enterprises Ltd., Don Mills, Canada; *Int'l*, pg. 1402
Orr, Tommy, Sr. V.P.--Harbor Financial Mortgage Corp., Houston, TX; *U.S. Public*, pg. 644
Ortiz, Ana Maria, Mgr.-Adv. & Pub. Rels.--Sony Corporation of Panama, Panama, Panama; *Int'l*, pg. 1284
Ortiz, Rafael Mendoza, Dir.-Customer Service & Support--Telefonos de Mexico S.A. de C.V., Mexico, Mexico; *Int'l*, pg. 1373
Orzechowski, Darren, Dir.-Pub. Rels.--Cabletron Systems, Inc., Rochester, NH; *U.S. Public*, pg. 288
Osborn, Mike, Sr. V.P.-Mktg.--Robson Communities, Sun Lakes, AZ; *U.S. Private*, pg. 937
Osborne, Francine, V.P.-Communications--Pratt & Whitney Canada Inc., Longueuil, Canada; *U.S. Public*, pg. 1690
Osinski, Patrick, V.P.-Corp. Devel. & Govt. Affairs--Organon Inc., West Orange, NJ; *Int'l*, pg. 48
Ospelt, Werner, V.P.-Public Relations--Liechtenstein Global Trust Limited, Vaduz, Liechtenstein; *Int'l*, pg. 809
Ostenson, R.A., Mgr.-Communications Services--Salt River Project Agricultural Improvement and Power District, Tempe, AZ; *U.S. Private*, pg. 962
Oster, Helen P., Sec.--Baldwin Technology Company, Inc., Norwalk, CT; *U.S. Public*, pg. 169
Ots, Tania, Mgr.-Corp. Svcs.--Melbourne Port Corporation, Melbourne, Australia; *Int'l*, pg. 856
Ott, Rene B., Sr. V.P.-External Relations--Liechtenstein Global Trust Limited, Vaduz, Liechtenstein; *Int'l*, pg. 809
Ott, Rene B., Mng. Dir.-External Rels.--LGT Bank in Liechtenstein Aktiengesellschaft, Vaduz, Liechtenstein; *Int'l*, pg. 809
Otte, Hans, Mgr.-Customer Svc.--BancTec Benelux B.V., Amsterdam, Netherlands; *U.S. Public*, pg. 177
Ottervik, Barbara, Mgr.-Adv. & Promo.--The H.W. Wilson Co., Bronx, NY; *U.S. Private*, pg. 1180
Otto, Bonnie, Mgr.-Media Rels.--AEGON USA, Inc., Louisville, KY; *Int'l*, pg. 26
Otto, Charlotte R., Sr. V.P.-Pub. Affairs--The Procter & Gamble Company, Cincinnati, OH; *U.S. Public*, pg. 1330
Overland, Keith, Mgr.-Pub. Rels.--Sunflower Electric Power Corporation, Hays, KS; *U.S. Private*, pg. 1052
Oviedo, Rodolfo, Dir.-Corp. Communications--Embraer-Empresa Brasileira de Aeronautica S.A., Sao Jose dos Campos, Brazil; *Int'l*, pg. 452
Owen, Barbara, Dir.-Promo. & Pub. Rels.--Sport Obermeyer Ltd., USA, Aspen, CO; *U.S. Private*, pg. 1026
Owen, D.D., Pub. Rels.--PQ Corporation, Berwyn, PA; *U.S. Private*, pg. 827
Owen, Robert E., Pres. & Mng. Dir.--Paxton & Vierling, Omaha, NE; *U.S. Private*, pg. 824
Owens, Beth, Pub. Rels. Specialist--Haworth, Inc., Holland, MI; *U.S. Private*, pg. 511
Oxberry, E.D., Mgr.-Corp. Affairs--Rothmans (UK) Ltd., Aylesbury, United Kingdom; *Int'l*, pg. 1130
Oxford, W. Cliff, Sr. V.P.-Corp. & Human Devel.--Lowe's Companies, Inc., North Wilkesboro, NC; *U.S. Public*, pg. 1015
Oyster, William, Pres., Chief Oper. Officer & Mgr.-Adv., Sls. & Mktg.--Dallas Gold & Silver Exchange, Inc., Dallas, TX; *U.S. Public*, pg. 478
Pacheco, Samantha, Commun. Officer--The Bank of Bermuda Limited, Hamilton, Bermuda; *Int'l*, pg. 150
Pachtner, John, Dir-Corp. Communications--APL Limited, Oakland, CA; *Int'l*, pg. 912
Pacini, Martha, Dir.-Corp. Communications--Heery International, Inc., Atlanta, GA; *U.S. Private*, pg. 519
Padelford, Claire, Mgr.-Mktg. Communications--National Health Enhancement Systems, Inc., Phoenix, AZ; *U.S. Public*, pg. 1157
Paff, Connie, Coord.-Corp. Communications--Cinergy Corp., Cincinnati, OH; *U.S. Public*, pg. 369
Page-Whitehead, Theda, Mgr.-Pub. Rels.--JC Penney Company, Inc., Plano, TX; *U.S. Public*, pg. 916
Page, Janis, Corp. Commun. & Pub. Rels.--Sampler Publications Inc., Saint Charles, IL; *U.S. Private*, pg. 963
Pahwa, Ashok, V.P.-Global Mktg. Communications--Mary Kay, Inc., Dallas, TX; *U.S. Private*, pg. 711
Pailing, Caroline, Dir.-Pub. Affairs--Oxford University Press, Oxford, United Kingdom; *Int'l*, pg. 1018
Paillet, Bruno, Mgr.-Communications--Groupe GAN, Paris, France; *Int'l*, pg. 563
Pain, Steven, Dir.-Corp. Affairs & Pub. Rels.--Storehouse PLC, London, United Kingdom; *Int'l*, pg. 1304
Painter, Graham, V.P.-Pub. Rels.--Houston Lighting & Power Company, Houston, TX; *U.S. Public*, pg. 843
Palangio, Robert J., Mgr.-Pub. Rels.--BetzDearborn Inc., Trevose, PA; *U.S. Public*, pg. 226
Palermo, Cynthia A., Mgr.-Mktg. Communications--The NutraSweet Kelco Company, San Diego, CA; *U.S. Public*, pg. 1125
Palladino, Robert, Dir.-Investor Rels.--C.P. Clare Corporation, Beverly, MA; *U.S. Public*, pg. 382
Palm, S., Head-Info. & Commun.--Assa Abloy AB, Stockholm, Sweden; *Int'l*, pg. 17
Palmer, Charlotte, Mgr.-Adv. & Mkt. Planning--WHX Corporation, New York, NY; *U.S. Public*, pg. 1726
Palmer, Charlotte, Mgr.-Adv.--Wheeling Corrugating Co., Wheeling, WV; *U.S. Public*, pg. 1727
Palmer, Edward M., Dir.-Customer Svcs.--Finch, Pruyn & Co., Inc., Glens Falls, NY; *U.S. Private*, pg. 405
Palmer, Jim, Dir.-Govt. & External Affairs--BP Exploration (Alaska) Inc., Anchorage, AK; *Int'l*, pg. 220
Palmer, Marsha, Mgr.-Corp. Communication Programs--Picker International, Inc., Cleveland, OH; *Int'l*, pg. 545
Palmerio, Carol A., V.P.-Corp. Communications--CoreStates Financial Corp., Philadelphia, PA; *U.S. Public*, pg. 446
Palombi, David, V.P.-Community Rels.--Federal Home Loan Mortgage Corporation, Mc Lean, VA; *U.S. Public*, pg. 615
Paluszek, John L., Pres.-Pub. Affairs--Ketchum Public Relations Worldwide, New York, NY; *U.S. Private*, pg. 617
Panagos, Gregory S., V.P.-Corp. Commun.--Pennzoil Company, Houston, TX; *U.S. Public*, pg. 1272
Panetta, Barbara, Dir.-Pub. Rels. & Special Events--Parfums International Ltd., New York, NY; *Int'l*, pg. 1435
Pangritz, Dirk, Dir.-Pub. Rels.--British-American Tobacco (Germany) GmbH, Hamburg, Germany; *Int'l*, pg. 111
Paolini, Bruce P., V.P.-Labor Rels.--Albertson's, Inc., Boise, ID; *U.S. Public*, pg. 38
Papagni, Elizabeth, Mgr.-Mktg. Commun.--Industrial Electronic Engineers, Inc., Van Nuys, CA; *U.S. Private*, pg. 561
Pappas, Danielle, Dir.-Mktg. & Pub. Rels.--Logo of the Americas, Fort Lauderdale, FL; *Int'l*, pg. 462
Paraboni, Pinuccia, Pub. Rels. Dir.--Leo Burnett Co., S.r.l., Milan, Italy; *U.S. Private*, pg. 185
Paradossi, Pete, Mgr.-Pub. Rels.--Mead Johnson Nutritional Group, Evansville, IN; *U.S. Public*, pg. 254
Pardee, Diane Berry, V.P.-Corp. Commun.--Journal Register Company, Trenton, NJ; *U.S. Public*, pg. 934
Parente, Joseph A., V.P. & Dir.-Consumer Rels.--Central Reserve Life Corporation, Strongsville, OH; *U.S. Public*, pg. 326
Parente, Joseph A., Asst. V.P. & Dir.-Consumer Rels.--Central Reserve Life of North America Insurance Co., Strongsville, OH; *U.S. Public*, pg. 326
Parham, Barry, Dir.-Pub. Rels. & News Media--George W. Park Seed Co., Inc., Greenwood, SC; *U.S. Private*, pg. 839
Paris, Florence, Pub. Rels. Dir. & New Bus. Contact--Young & Rubicam France, Paris, France; *U.S. Private*, pg. 1199
Parisella, John, V.P.-Strategic Communications & Pub. Affairs--BCP Group Ltd., Montreal, Canada; *Int'l*, pg. 116
Parisella, John, V.P.-Strategic Communications & Pub. Affairs--Publicis BCP Montreal Inc., Montreal, Canada; *Int'l*, pg. 116
Parisi, Frank J., V.P.-Commun.--Cowles Media Company, Minneapolis, MN; *U.S. Private*, pg. 280
Park, H.E., Grp. Gen. Mgr.-Corp. Pub. Rels.--National Australia Bank Limited, Melbourne, Australia; *Int'l*, pg. 906
Parker, Bob, Sr. Dir.-Regulatory Affairs--Medeva Pharmaceuticals, Rochester, NY; *Int'l*, pg. 852
Parker, Linda, Mgr.-Public Relations--Videotron Holdings Plc, London, United Kingdom; *Int'l*, pg. 247
Parker, Linda, V.P. & Pub. Rels. Dir.--Hutchins/Young & Rubicam, Rochester, NY; *U.S. Private*, pg. 1197
Parker, Phil, Mgr.-Corp. Commun.--Number Nine Visual Technology, Lexington, MA; *U.S. Public*, pg. 1206
Parker, S. Victoria, Sr. V.P.--John Wieland Homes Inc., Atlanta, GA; *U.S. Private*, pg. 1175
Parker, Sara, Head of Corp. Commun.--The Dialog Corporation plc, London, United Kingdom; *Int'l*, pg. 412
Parker, Steven, Sr. V.P.-Mktg. & Sls.--Red Roof Inns, Inc., Hilliard, OH; *U.S. Public*, pg. 1369
Parker, Tammi, Admin. Asst.--Experience In Software, Inc., Berkeley, CA; *U.S. Private*, pg. 388
Parlato, Roberto, Mgr.-Pub. Rels.--Nestle Industrial e Commercial Ltda., Sao Paulo, Brazil; *Int'l*, pg. 921
Parmeter, Jack, V.P.-On-Air Promo.--CBS Broadcast Group, New York, NY; *U.S. Public*, pg. 274
Parrish, J.P., Pres.-Shell Services Co.--Shell Oil Company, Houston, TX; *Int'l*, pg. 1136
Parrish, Theda, Dir.-Corp. Communications--BTG, Inc., Fairfax, VA; *U.S. Public*, pg. 164
Parsons, Craig A., Sr. V.P.-Corp. Commun. & Investor Rels.--Metro-Goldwyn-Mayer Inc., Santa Monica, CA; *U.S. Public*, pg. 1101
Parsons, Joanie, Pub. Rels.--The Good Guys, Inc., Brisbane, CA; *U.S. Public*, pg. 750
Parsons, Peter, Mgr.-Media Rels., Vickers--Aeroquip-Vickers, Inc., Maumee, OH; *U.S. Public*, pg. 24
Parsons, Peter, Mgr.-Pub. Rels.--Vickers, Incorporated, Maumee, OH; *U.S. Public*, pg. 24
Partridge, Jack W., Grp. V.P.-Corp. Affairs--The Kroger Co., Cincinnati, OH; *U.S. Public*, pg. 967
Paschal, Annelle, Dir.-Pub. Rels.--U.S. Can Company, Oak Brook, IL; *U.S. Public*, pg. 1681
Pasewark, Richard, Dir.-Mktg. & Pub. Relations--Edwards Super Food Stores, Carlisle, PA; *Int'l*, pg. 749
Pasewark, Richard, Dir.-Mktg. & Pub. Rels.--Edwards Super Food Stores, Long Island Div., Garden City, NY; *Int'l*, pg. 750
Paskal, Randy, Sec.--J & R Film / Moviola Digital Co., Hollywood, CA; *U.S. Private*, pg. 576
Pasley, George W., V.P.-Commun.--Global Industrial Technologies, Dallas, TX; *U.S. Public*, pg. 747
Pastor, Beth, V.P.-Corp. Communications--The Leap Partnership, Chicago, IL; *U.S. Private*, pg. 655
Pate, William, V.P.-Adv. & Pub. Rels.--BellSouth Corporation, Atlanta, GA; *U.S. Public*, pg. 207
Paterson, David, V.P.-Corp. Affairs--Agra Inc., Calgary, Canada; *Int'l*, pg. 30
Paterson, David, Mgr.-Pub. Rels.--AGRA Inc., Oakville, Canada; *Int'l*, pg. 30
Paterson, Jeff, Mgr.-Pub. Rels.--Lindsay Manufacturing Company, Lindsay, NE; *U.S. Public*, pg. 999
Patrick, Barbara A., Mgr.-Adv. & Communications--Tax Management, Inc., Washington, DC; *U.S. Private*, pg. 182

Patten, Michael, Mgr.-Corp. Affairs--Avonmore Waterford Group plc, Kilkenny, Ireland; *Int'l*, pg. 102
Patten, Michael, Mgr.-Corp. Affairs--Avenmore Waterford Foods plc, Waterford, Ireland; *Int'l*, pg. 102
Patterson, Carol, Dir.-Prod. Mktg.--Digital Sound Corporation, Carpinteria, CA; *U.S. Public*, pg. 508
Pattie, N., Mgr.-Pub. Rels.--Siebe plc, Windsor, United Kingdom; *Int'l*, pg. 1240
Patton, William, V.P.-Pub. Rels.--Flanigan's Enterprises, Inc., Fort Lauderdale, FL; *U.S. Public*, pg. 648
Paul, M.J., Mgr.-Corp. Commun.--Prescolite Moldcast Lighting Company, San Leandro, CA; *U.S. Public*, pg. 1684
Paul, S., Exec. V.P.-Pub. Affairs--Labatt Breweries of Canada, Toronto, Canada; *Int'l*, pg. 679
Paul, Valerie, Mgr.-Pub. Rels.--Jani King International, Inc., Dallas, TX; *U.S. Private*, pg. 581
Paulus, Monica, Admin.-Interline--Austrian Airlines, Whitestone, NY; *Int'l*, pg. 101
Paxton, Cecilia, Mgr.-Communications--General Medical Corp., Richmond, VA; *U.S. Public*, pg. 1073
Peapples, George A., V.P.-Indus. Govt. Rels.--General Motors Corporation, Detroit, MI; *U.S. Public*, pg. 718
Pearce, Susan, V.P.-Corp. Communications--Lockheed Martin Corporation, Bethesda, MD; *U.S. Public*, pg. 1006
Pearson, Diana, Corp. Communications--Newsweek, Inc., New York, NY; *U.S. Public*, pg. 1743
Pease, Doug, Mgr.-Customer & Vendor Rels.--Bose Corporation, Framingham, MA; *U.S. Private*, pg. 160
Peck, David, Dir.-Fin. & Investor Rels.--Mitchell Energy & Development Corp., Spring, TX; *U.S. Public*, pg. 1117
Peck, Lori J., Mgr.-Communications--Netzsch Incorporated, Exton, PA; *U.S. Private*, pg. 792
Peck, Mike, Dir.-Mktg. Commun.--Modernfold, Inc., New Castle, IN; *U.S. Private*, pg. 755
Peckham, Terry, Mgr.-Marcom-Mktg.--Brown and Caldwell, Pleasant Hill, CA; *U.S. Private*, pg. 173
Pecoraro, Russ, Mgr.-Pub. Rels.--Frost & Sullivan, Mountain View, CA; *U.S. Private*, pg. 430
Peden, Sue, Pub. Rels. Coord.--Leo Burnett/Connaghan & May (VIC.) Pty. Ltd., Melbourne, Australia; *U.S. Private*, pg. 185
Pedersen, Gitte Finnich, Dir.-Commun.--Bayer A/S, Skytta, Norway; *Int'l*, pg. 174
Pederson, Eric, Dir.-Pub. Rels. & Adv.--Allison Engine Company Inc., Indianapolis, IN; *Int'l*, pg. 1127
Peel, Iris H., V.P.-Consumer Affairs--J.H. Harvey Company, Nashville, GA; *U.S. Private*, pg. 508
Peerson, Dennis, Dir.-Mdse. & Pub. Rels.--Godfather's Pizza, Inc., Omaha, NE; *U.S. Private*, pg. 458
Pegg, Daniel O., Sr. V.P.-Pub. Affairs--QUALCOMM, San Diego, CA; *U.S. Public*, pg. 1348
Peier, Heino, Mgr.-Communication--Coop Switzerland, Basel, Switzerland; *Int'l*, pg. 329
Peikoff, Michael, V.P.-Pub. Rels. & Prod. Devel.--Warner Bros. Consumer Products, Burbank, CA; *U.S. Public*, pg. 1610
Pelger, T.P., Mgr.-Mktg. Communications--Caterpillar Inc., Peoria, IL; *U.S. Public*, pg. 315
Peltier, William H., V.P.-Pub. Rels. & Adv.--Viad Corp, Phoenix, AZ; *U.S. Public*, pg. 1718
Penas, Alicia, Dir.-Corp. & Consumer Affairs--Baker's Supermarkets, Inc., Omaha, NE; *U.S. Private*, pg. 652
Pendergast, Ellen, V.P.-Adv. & Pub. Rels.--Trans-Lux Corporation, Norwalk, CT; *U.S. Public*, pg. 1628
Pennington, Mike, Dir.-Mktg. Commun.--Meritor Automotive, Inc., Troy, MI; *U.S. Public*, pg. 1096
Penrose, Anthea, Mgr.-Pub. Rels.--The Times Publishing Co., Saint Petersburg, FL; *U.S. Private*, pg. 1087
Pensec, John, Dir.-Communications--John H. Harland Company, Decatur, GA; *U.S. Public*, pg. 785
Pensec, John, Dir.-Corp. Communications-Atlanta--The Check Store, Lakewood, CO; *U.S. Public*, pg. 785
Perduyn, John P., V.P.-Pub. Affairs--The Goodyear Tire & Rubber Company, Akron, OH; *U.S. Public*, pg. 752
Pereira, Garciela, Pub. Rels. Coord.--Causa Publicidad, Lima, Peru; *U.S. Private*, pg. 184
Peress, Beverly, Mgr.-Publications--MTA Long Island Rail Road, Jamaica, NY; *U.S. Private*, pg. 739
Perez, Lourdez, V.P.-Corp. Communications--Bacardi Corporation, San Juan, PR; *Int'l*, pg. 131
Perier, Philippe, Dir.-Corp. Information & Affairs--Credit Nationale, Paris, France; *Int'l*, pg. 344
Perille, Christopher J., Dir.-Corp. Communications--Wm. Wrigley Jr. Company, Chicago, IL; *U.S. Public*, pg. 1781
Perkins, Deborah, Dir.-Pub. Rels.--Delphi Packard Electric Systems, Beachwood, OH; *U.S. Public*, pg. 719
Perkins, Sherry, Dir.-Mktg. & Adv.--J.E. Higgins Lumber Co., Concord, CA; *U.S. Private*, pg. 527
Perkins, Yvonne, Dir.-Pub. Affairs--Citizens Gas & Coke Utility, Indianapolis, IN; *U.S. Private*, pg. 241
Perl, Maurie, V.P.-Pub. Rels.--The New Yorker Magazine, New York, NY; *U.S. Private*, pg. 795
Perlberg, William, V.P.-Res. & Devel.--The Hartz Mountain Corp., Secaucus, NJ; *U.S. Private*, pg. 508
Perlmutter, Barbara, V.P.-Pub. Affairs--Marsh & McLennan Companies, Inc., New York, NY; *U.S. Public*, pg. 1048
Pernice, Thomas J., V.P.-Pub. Affairs--Dole Food Company, Inc., Westlake Village, CA; *U.S. Public*, pg. 515
Pernigotti, Stefano, Dir.-Corp. Communications--Recordati Industria Chimica e Farmaceutica S.p.A., Milan, Italy; *Int'l*, pg. 1090
Pero, Dan, V.P.-Communications & Dir.-Pub. Rels.--Eckerd Corporation, Largo, FL; *U.S. Public*, pg. 917
Perotto, Greg, Dir.-Creative & Adv. Admin.--Esco Corporation, Portland, OR; *U.S. Private*, pg. 382
Perreault, Gina, Pub. Rels. Officer--Davie Industries Inc., Levis, Canada; *Int'l*, pg. 385
Perrin, Cheryl, Sr. V.P.-Pub. Affairs--Fred Meyer Stores, Portland, OR; *U.S. Public*, pg. 1103
Perron, John T., V.P.-Admin.--AmClyde Engineered Products Co., Inc., Saint Paul, MN; *U.S. Public*, pg. 778
Perroud, S. X., Mgr.-Corp. Communications--Nestle S.A., Vevey, Switzerland; *Int'l*, pg. 915
Perry, Elisabeth L., Mgr.-Bus. Commun.--Consumers Water Company, Portland, ME; *U.S. Public*, pg. 438
Perry, Gregg, Dir.-Adv. & Pub. Rels.--Mackie Designs, Inc., Woodinville, WA; *U.S. Public*, pg. 1030
Perry, Joseph M., Mgr.-Pub. Rels.--General Shale Products Corp., Johnson City, TN; *Int'l*, pg. 843
Perry, Kathie, Dir.-Communications--NuTone, Inc., Cincinnati, OH; *Int'l*, pg. 1499
Perry, Michele, Dir.-Communications--Molten Metal Technology, Inc., Fall River, MA; *U.S. Public*, pg. 1123
Perry, Tracy, V.P.-Corp. Commun.--Maxwell Technologies, Inc., San Diego, CA; *U.S. Public*, pg. 1061
Persico, Patricia, Mgr.-Communications--Master Builders Inc., Cleveland, OH; *Int'l*, pg. 1465
Pertrausch, Robert J., Dir.-Worldwide Communications--Uniroyal Chemical Company, Inc., Middlebury, CT; *U.S. Public*, pg. 460
Pestillo, Peter J., Exec. V.P.-Corp. Rels.--Ford Motor Company, Dearborn, MI; *U.S. Public*, pg. 661
Pestovic, Edward J., V.P.-Adv.--Crowley, Milner & Company, Detroit, MI; *U.S. Public*, pg. 461
Peterman, Donna C., Sr. V.P. & Dir.-Corp. Communications--PaineWebber Group Incorporated, New York, NY; *U.S. Public*, pg. 1252
Peterman, Donna C., Sr. V.P. & Dir. Corp. Communications--PaineWebber Incorporated, New York, NY; *U.S. Public*, pg. 1252
Peters, Aileen, V.P.-Pub. Affairs--Ajinomoto U.S.A., Inc., Teaneck, NJ; *Int'l*, pg. 40
Peters, C.H., Mgr.-Pub. Relations--Sunkist Growers, Inc., Sherman Oaks, CA; *U.S. Private*, pg. 1052
Peters, David, Pres.--Peters Construction Corp., Waterloo, IA; *U.S. Private*, pg. 856
Peters, Dean, Dir.-Communications--International Dairy Queen, Inc., Minneapolis, MN; *U.S. Public*, pg. 220
Peters, Laura, Dir.-Mktg.--Burnham, Atlanta, GA; *Int'l*, pg. 686
Peters, Mike, Exec. Commun.--British Aerospace p.l.c., Farnborough, United Kingdom; *Int'l*, pg. 217
Peters, Rich, 2nd V.P.-Mktg. Svcs. & Pub. Rels.--Woodmen Accident & Life Co., Lincoln, NE; *U.S. Private*, pg. 1187
Peterson, Barry, Mgr.--Federated Mutual Insurance Company, Owatonna, MN; *U.S. Private*, pg. 399
Peterson, Dave, Mgr.-Human Resources & Pub. Rels.--Southern Minnesota Beet Sugar Cooperative, Renville, MN; *U.S. Private*, pg. 1016
Peterson, Kelly, Coord.-Customer Service--Tenax Corporation, Danbury, CT; *Int'l*, pg. 193
Peterson, Richard, Mgr.-Pub. Rels.--Chino Mines Company, Hurley, NM; *U.S. Public*, pg. 1287
Peterson, Richard, Mgr.-Pub. Rels.--Phelps Dodge Hidalgo, Playas, NM; *U.S. Public*, pg. 1287
Peterson, Tracy, Corp. Communications Specialist--Broadcast Electronics, Inc., Quincy, IL; *U.S. Private*, pg. 531
Petray, Gloria, Mgr.-Communications--Circon Video Div., Santa Barbara, CA; *U.S. Public*, pg. 373
Petterson, Lorri, Mgr.-Mktg. Communications--Pentax Corporation, Englewood, CO; *Int'l*, pg. 85
Peyrache, Marie-Claude, Exec. Dir.-Communications--France Telecom, Paris, France; *Int'l*, pg. 503
Peyrot, Catherine, Mgr.-Pub. Rels.--Fun Radio, Neuilly-sur-Seine, France; *Int'l*, pg. 561
Pfeiffer, Brigitte, Pub. Rels. Dir.--Kabelwerke Reinshagen GmbH, Wuppertal, Germany; *U.S. Public*, pg. 723
Pfenninger, Allen, Dir.-Public Affairs--Moen Incorporated, North Olmsted, OH; *U.S. Public*, pg. 675
Pfunder, Martin, Pub. Rels. Dir.--General Motors Austria Ges.m.b.H., Vienna, Austria; *U.S. Public*, pg. 721
Phalan, Tom, Dir.-Corp. Communications & Pub. Rels.--Foley's, Houston, TX; *U.S. Public*, pg. 1063
Phares, Lynn L., V.P.-Pub. Rels.--ConAgra, Inc., Omaha, NE; *U.S. Public*, pg. 425
Philipps, K., Dir.-Communications--Case France S.A., Paris, France; *U.S. Public*, pg. 1579
Phillips-Parker, Rebecca, V.P.-Communications & Bus. Devel.--Indian Head Industries Inc., Charlotte, NC; *U.S. Private*, pg. 559
Phillips, Diana, Sr. V.P.-Pub. Rels.--Sotheby's Holdings Inc., New York, NY; *U.S. Public*, pg. 1487
Phillips, Helen E., V.P.-Bus. Commun. & Adv.--Rockwell International Corporation, Costa Mesa, CA; *U.S. Public*, pg. 1397
Phillips, Jim, Dir.-Mktg., Mdsg. & Pub. Rels.--Control Systems Inc., Saint Paul, MN; *U.S. Private*, pg. 271
Phillips, John C., Jr., Mng. Dir.-Client Rels.--AEW Capital Management, L.P., Boston, MA; *U.S. Private*, pg. 737
Phillips, Joy L., Dir.-Logistics & Pub. Affairs--Vulcan Chemicals, Birmingham, AL; *U.S. Public*, pg. 1725
Phillips, Leonard, Mgr.-Corp. Rels.--Zoom Telephonics, Inc., Boston, MA; *U.S. Public*, pg. 1794
Phillips, Steven D., Exec. V.P.-Consumer Div.--Countrywide Funding Corporation, Pasadena, CA; *U.S. Public*, pg. 453
Piano, Phyllis J., V.P.-Pub. Affairs--Cooper Industries, Inc., Houston, TX; *U.S. Public*, pg. 442
Piantanida, Nancy, Mgr.-Adv.--Lindal Cedar Homes, Inc., Seattle, WA; *U.S. Public*, pg. 998
Piar-Katter, Madalyn, Mgr.-Mktg. Communications--Cascade Corporation, Troutdale, OR; *U.S. Public*, pg. 310
Piastrelli, Denise, Dir.-Pub. Rels.--ICF Kaiser International Inc., Fairfax, VA; *U.S. Public*, pg. 852
Picazo, Tessie, Dir.-Pub. Rels.--Grupo Synkro, S.A. de C.V., Mexico, Mexico; *Int'l*, pg. 576
Pickard, Geoffrey, V.P.-Pub. Rels. & Commun.--American Institute of C.P.A.'s Inc., New York, NY; *U.S. Private*, pg. 57
Pickman, Steve, Dir.-Pub. & Investor Rels.--Midwest Grain Products, Inc., Atchison, KS; *U.S. Public*, pg. 1111
Pidgeon, Matt, Dir.-Commun.--Manufacturers' News, Inc., Evanston, IL; *U.S. Private*, pg. 700
Pierce, Beverly, Mgr.-Pub. Rels.--Bosch Braking Systems-North America, South Bend, IN; *Int'l*, pg. 204
Pierce, Ed, Dir.-Mktg. Communications & Mgr.-Adv.--Automotive Rentals, Inc. (ARI), Mount Laurel, NJ; *U.S. Private*, pg. 535
Pierce, Frank, V.P.-Communications--National Health Enhancement Systems, Inc., Phoenix, AZ; *U.S. Public*, pg. 1157
Pierce, Justin, Publicity--Columbia TriStar Television, Culver City, CA; *Int'l*, pg. 1282
Piersma, Craig, Mgr.-Mktg. Communications--Haworth, Inc., Holland, MI; *U.S. Private*, pg. 511
Piet, William M., V.P.-Corp. Affairs & Sec.--Wm. Wrigley Jr. Company, Chicago, IL; *U.S. Public*, pg. 1781
Pietinen, Markku, Dir.-Pub. Rels.--Huhtamaki Oy, Espoo, Finland; *Int'l*, pg. 638
Pietinen, Markku, Mgr.-Pub. Rels.--Leaf Group B.V., Espoo, Finland,; *Int'l*, pg. 638
Pietinen, Markku, Grp. V.P.-Commun.--Polarcup Group Headquarters, Espoo, Finland; *Int'l*, pg. 638
Pigford, Nancy M., Mgr.-Mktg. Communications--Raytheon Engineers & Constructors International, Inc., Lexington, MA; *U.S. Public*, pg. 1366
Pile, Ted, V.P.-Corp. Communications--Lafarge Corporation, Reston, VA; *Int'l*, pg. 788
Piliero, Zoe, Dir.-Corp. Communications--CVC Products, Inc., Rochester, NY; *U.S. Private*, pg. 197
Pilliod, Barbara Kane, Mgr.- Investor Rels.--MapInfo Corp., Troy, NY; *U.S. Public*, pg. 1042
Pinellas, Tom, Dir.-Corp. Commun.--Encyclopaedia Britannica, Inc., Chicago, IL; *U.S. Private*, pg. 375
Pinet, Paul, V.P.-Corp. Communications--Genzyme Corporation, Cambridge, MA; *U.S. Public*, pg. 733
Pinguet, Christophe, Pub. Rels. Dir.--Select Communications, Paris, Paris, France; *U.S. Private*, pg. 982
Pinheiro Neto, Jose C.S., Dir.-Pub. & Govern. Rels.--General Motors do Brasil Ltda., Sao Caetano do Sul, Brazil; *U.S. Public*, pg. 722
Pinneo, Jeffrey D., V.P.-Customer Service--Horizon Air Industries, Seattle, WA; *U.S. Public*, pg. 35
Pippen, Mann, Dir.-Pub. Rels.--Coastal Lumber Company, Weldon, NC; *U.S. Private*, pg. 248
Pirrmann, Christine, Mgr.-Sls. & Cust. Svc.--Thompson Medical Company, Inc., West Palm Beach, FL; *U.S. Private*, pg. 1083
Pistone, Pete, Mgr.-Pub. Rels.--Bridgestone/Firestone Inc. Retail Operations, Rolling Meadows, IL; *Int'l*, pg. 213
Pitcher, Sarah, V.P.-Corp. Commun.--Mesa Air Group, Las Vegas, NV; *U.S. Public*, pg. 1098
Pitcher, Sarah, V.P.-Corp. Commun.--Air Midwest, Inc., Wichita, KS; *U.S. Public*, pg. 1099
Pitcher, Sarah, V.P.-Corp. Commun.--Westair Commuter Airlines, Inc., Fresno, CA; *U.S. Public*, pg. 1099
Pitcher, Sarah, V.P.-Corp. Commun.--Mesa Airlines, Inc., Farmington, NM; *U.S. Public*, pg. 1099
Pitfield, Rosemary, Mgr.-Pub. Rels.--The Sports Network (TSN), Willowdale, Canada; *Int'l*, pg. 1343
Pittman, David, Dir.-Mktg. Commun.--SPSS Inc., Chicago, IL; *U.S. Public*, pg. 1420
Pitzer, Jurgen, Dir.-Pub. Rels.--Landesbank Rheinland-Pfalz, Mainz, Germany; *Int'l*, pg. 799
Pizzica, Dennis S., V.P. & Treas.--Hunt Corporation, Philadelphia, PA; *U.S. Public*, pg. 848
Pizzo, Thomas V., Exec. V.P.--Century Business Credit Corporation, New York, NY; *U.S. Private*, pg. 225
Plaisance, Melissa, Sr. V.P.-Fin. & Pub. Affairs--Safeway Inc., Pleasanton, CA; *U.S. Public*, pg. 1426
Plamtema, S., Mgr.-Pub. Rels.--CIBA-GEIGY (Pty.) Ltd., Isando, South Africa; *Int'l*, pg. 978
Plantema, Suzette, Dir.-Pharma Policy & Pub. Affairs--CIBA-GEIGY (Pty.) Ltd., Isando, South Africa; *Int'l*, pg. 978
Platt Hall, Laurie, Dir.-External Affairs--Tupperware Corporation, Orlando, FL; *U.S. Public*, pg. 1644
Platt, James R., Sr. V.P.-Corp. Affairs--The News Corporation Limited, Sydney, Australia; *Int'l*, pg. 925
Plazak, Kathryn F., Second V.P.-Pubs. Rels.--The New England, Boston, MA; *U.S. Private*, pg. 737
Plepler, Richard L., Sr. V.P.-Corp. Communication--Home Box Office, Inc., New York, NY; *U.S. Public*, pg. 1612
Plevyak, Laura, V.P.-Corp. Communications & Investor Rels.--CUC International, Inc., Stamford, CT; *U.S. Public*, pg. 320
Plewes, Len, Customer Svc.--Plastomer Products Div., Newtown, PA; *U.S. Public*, pg. 402
Plonski, Ken, Dir.-Pub. & Community Rels.--Del Webb Corporation, Phoenix, AZ; *U.S. Public*, pg. 494
Plotkin, Ron, V.P.-Pub. Rels.--TMP Worldwide, Inc., Westlake Village, CA; *U.S. Private*, pg. 1064
Plowman, C. Bruce, V.P.-Corp. & Mktg. Communications--Computer Sciences Corporation, El Segundo, CA; *U.S. Public*, pg. 422
Pluhowski, John, Dir.-Corp. Communications--American General Corporation, Houston, TX; *U.S. Public*, pg. 76
Plumley, Marion, Mgr.-Pub. Rels.--The Texwipe Co., Inc., Upper Saddle River, NJ; *U.S. Private*, pg. 1079
Plumley, Russell, Dir.-Pub. Affairs--Smiths Industries plc, London, United Kingdom; *Int'l*, pg. 1266
Plumtree, Lada, Mgr.-Media Communications--RAM Golf Corporation, Melrose Park, IL; *U.S. Private*, pg. 908
Plunket, Jim, Dir.-Pub. Rels.--The Pilot Pen Corp. of America, Trumbull, CT; *Int'l*, pg. 1057
Plunkett, William J., V.P.-Fin. & Investor Rels.--Waste Management, Inc., Oak Brook, IL; *U.S. Public*, pg. 1744
Poccio, Kathy, Mgr.-Mktg.--Acorn Structures, Acton, MA; *U.S. Private*, pg. 320
Poe, Sam R., Mgr.-Pub. Rels.--AmerenCIPS, Springfield, IL; *U.S. Public*, pg. 65
Pohlmann, Andreas, Dr., Dir.-Pub. & Govt. Affairs--Hoechst Aktiengesellschaft, Frankfurt/Main, Germany; *Int'l*, pg. 624
Polet, Rudolf, Dir.-Corp. Communications--ING Groep N.V., Amsterdam, Netherlands; *Int'l*, pg. 647
Polkinghorne, Douglas B., Dir.-Creative Svcs.--DTE Energy Company, Detroit, MI; *U.S. Public*, pg. 475

Pollini, Laura, Mgr.-Pub. Rels.--Benetton Group S.p.A., Ponzano Veneto, Italy; *Int'l*, pg. 186
Pollino, Patrick, Dir.-Corp. Communications--Mercer Management Consulting, Inc., New York, NY; *U.S. Public*, pg. 1049
Pollock, LaRhesa, Dir.-Communications--Clarke American Corp., San Antonio, TX; *Int'l*, pg. 267
Pollock, Mayer, II, Pres., Chief Exec. Officer & Chief Oper. Officer--The Pollock Corp., Pottstown, PA; *U.S. Private*, pg. 874
Polski, Tom, Chief Pub. Rels. Officer--Radisson Hotel Corporation, Minneapolis, MN; *U.S. Private*, pg. 212
Poltera, Franz, Dir.-Public Relations--Cerberus AG, Männeforf, Switzerland; *Int'l*, pg. 1246
Pomeroy, Joseph, V.P.-Legal & Indus. Affairs--Mercury Marine, Fond Du Lac, WI; *U.S. Public*, pg. 265
Pommier, Bernard, V.P.-Corp. Communications--Lagardere Groupe, Paris, France; *Int'l*, pg. 791
Ponci, Jean-Bernard, V.P.-Pub. Rels.--Banque Cantonale Vaudoise, Lausanne, Switzerland; *Int'l*, pg. 160
Ponczak, Glen L., Mgr.-External Communication--Johnson Controls, Inc., Controls Group, Milwaukee, WI; *U.S. Public*, pg. 932
Pond, Terri, V.P.-Corp. Communications--Genicom Corporation, Chantilly, VA; *U.S. Public*, pg. 729
Pontal, Jean-Francois, Exec. V.P.-Consumer Services--France Telecom, Paris, France; *Int'l*, pg. 503
Poole, D.E., Dir.-Pub. Rels.--Service Parts Operations, Flint, MI; *U.S. Public*, pg. 720
Poole, Darren W., Mgr.-Gen. Affairs & Personnel--Pioneer/Eclipse Corp., Sparta, NC; *Int'l*, pg. 71
Pope, Don L., V.P.-Investor Rels.--Burlington Resources Inc., Houston, TX; *U.S. Public*, pg. 269
Pophema, Gerard, Mgr.-Trng., Devel. & Pub. Rels.--Elsevier Bedrijfinformatie B.V., Doetinchem, Netherlands; *Int'l*, pg. 1099
Portenueve, Lea, Dir.-Corp. Communications--Metro-Goldwyn-Mayer Inc., Santa Monica, CA; *U.S. Public*, pg. 1101
Porter-Kuchay, Suzanne, Mgr.-Pub. Rels.--COMNET Corporation, Lanham, MD; *U.S. Public*, pg. 416
Porter-Kuchay, Suzanne, Mgr.-Pub. Rels.--Group 1 Software, Inc., Lanham, MD; *U.S. Public*, pg. 417
Porter, Jeff, Dir.-Pub. Affairs--Glaxo Wellcome plc, London, United Kingdom; *Int'l*, pg. 552
Porter, Robin, Supvr.-Corp. Commun.--Valassis Communications, Inc., Livonia, MI; *U.S. Public*, pg. 1704
Porter, William, Dir.-Corp. Rels.--Green Mountain Power Corporation, South Burlington, VT; *U.S. Public*, pg. 761
Portera, Juan Astorqui, Mng. Dir.-Corp. Communications--Caja de Madrid Group, Madrid, Spain; *Int'l*, pg. 251
Posey, Bob, Dir.-Sls. & Mktg.--Aeroglide Corporation, Cary, NC; *U.S. Private*, pg. 24
Posinski, Frank J., Pres. & Chief Oper. Officer--Cincinnati Gear Company, Cincinnati, OH; *U.S. Private*, pg. 240
Posner, Eberhard, Dir.-Corp. Commun.--Siemens AG, Munich, Germany; *Int'l*, pg. 1244
Post, Alfred T., Dir.-Corp. Communications--Century Aluminum Company, Monterey, CA; *U.S. Public*, pg. 328
Post, Jeffrey, V.P.-Design & Mktg.--ATHOL Corporation, Butner, NC; *U.S. Private*, pg. 94
Poston, R. C., Dir.-Corp. Communications--Racal Electronics Plc, Bracknell, United Kingdom; *Int'l*, pg. 1082
Potman, Janelle, Dir.-Commun.--Brim, Inc., Portland, OR; *U.S. Private*, pg. 168
Potter, Muffie, V.P.-Mktg. & Pub. Rels.--Van Cleef & Arpels, Inc., New York, NY; *U.S. Private*, pg. 1132
Potts, Anne Marie, Sr. Dir.-Corp. Commun.--Mobile Telecommunications Technologies Corp., Jackson, MS; *U.S. Public*, pg. 1120
Pouchnik, Mary Jo, Coord.-Commun.--Bemis Company, Inc., Minneapolis, MN; *U.S. Public*, pg. 210
Powderly, Robert G., Exec. V.P.--Eastern Utilities Associates, Boston, MA; *U.S. Public*, pg. 549
Powell, Angela, Mgr.-Reatil Mktg. & Pub. Rels.--Camping World, Inc., Bowling Green, KY; *U.S. Private*, pg. 204
Powell, Chris, Mgr.-Communications--Greenfield Industries, Cleveland, OH; *U.S. Public*, pg. 950
Powell, Eleanor, V.P.-Pub. Rels. & Corp. Travel Planner--Ko-Rec-Type, Brooklyn, NY; *U.S. Private*, pg. 117
Powell, Marian R., V.P.-Communications--General Electric Capital Railcar Services, Chicago, IL; *U.S. Public*, pg. 712
Powell, Shirley, V.P.-Pub. Rels.--The Cartoon Network, Atlanta, GA; *U.S. Public*, pg. 1614
Powers, Ed, Dir.-Pub. Rels.--Raytheon Environmental Services Company, Houston, TX; *U.S. Public*, pg. 1366
Powers, Edward J., Dir.-Communications--Raytheon Engineers & Constructors International, Inc., Lexington, MA; *U.S. Public*, pg. 1366
Powers, Jane, Pub. Affairs Coord.--Delco Electronics Corporation, Kokomo, IN; *U.S. Public*, pg. 720
Powers, Patricia, Dir.-Commun.--Wheelabrator Technologies Inc., Hampton, NH; *U.S. Public*, pg. 1745
Powers, Ron, Dir.-Personnel & Pub. Rels.--Ward Leonard Electric Company, Inc., Mount Vernon, NY; *U.S. Private*, pg. 1118
Poythress, James H., Exec. V.P.-Servicing--United Companies Financial Corporation, Baton Rouge, LA; *U.S. Public*, pg. 1675
Prange, John, Dir.-H.R.--Miles Kimball Company, Oshkosh, WI; *U.S. Private*, pg. 745
Prange, John, Sr. V.P.-Prof. Rels.--Alpo Pet Foods, Inc., Allentown, PA; *Int'l*, pg. 917
Praschak, Kurt, Supvr.-Pub. Rels.--Matsushita Electric Corporation of America, Secaucus, NJ; *Int'l*, pg. 847
Prather, Susan, Sr. V.P. & Pub. Rels. Dir.--Cramer-Krasselt, Chicago, IL; *U.S. Private*, pg. 285
Premoli, Miguel, Dir.-Human Resources--Colgate-Palmolive S.A.I.C., Lavalle, Argentina; *U.S. Public*, pg. 399
Preston, P.J., Gen. Mgr.-Pub. Affairs--Zeneca Inc., Wilmington, DE; *Int'l*, pg. 1525
Preston, Tony, Mgr.-Communications--National Westminster Bank PLC, London, United Kingdom; *Int'l*, pg. 910
Price, Brent, Mgr.-Mktg. Commun.--Desa International, Bowling Green, KY; *U.S. Private*, pg. 326
Price, Gail E., Dir.-Corp. Communications-WLR Foods, Inc.--WLR Foods, Inc., Timberville, VA; *U.S. Public*, pg. 1727
Price, Keith A., V.P.-Mktg.--The Hotsy Corporation, Englewood, CO; *U.S. Private*, pg. 500
Prichard, Dave, V.P.-Investor Rels. & Corp. Commun.--IMC Global, Bannockburn, IL; *U.S. Public*, pg. 856
Prideaux, Michael, Dir.-Grp. Pub. Affairs--B.A.T Industries P.L.C., London, United Kingdom; *Int'l*, pg. 110
Prien, Stephan, Asst. Mgr.-Pub. Rels.--Otto Versand (GmbH & Co.), Hamburg, Germany; *Int'l*, pg. 1014
Prinsen, W.A., Mgr.-Pub. Rels. & Govt. Affairs--Procter & Gamble Benelux S.A., Strombeek-Bever, Belgium; *U.S. Public*, pg. 1332
Prior, Bob, Pub. Rels. Task Force--Anchor Glass Container Corporation, Tampa, FL; *Int'l*, pg. 327
Pritchard, Rod, Dir.-Communications, Pub. Rels. & Adv.--Vigortone AG Products, Inc., Cedar Rapids, IA; *Int'l*, pg. 1357
Pritchard, William, Asst. Gen. Mgr.-Corp. Affairs Div.--Panasonic Consumer Electric Co., Secaucus, NJ; *Int'l*, pg. 847
Privitera, Lorri, Mgr.-Media Rels.--The Pfaltzgraff Co., York, PA; *U.S. Private*, pg. 860
Privitera, Lorri, Mgr.-Media Relations--The Pfaltzgraff Co., York, PA; *U.S. Private*, pg. 860
Proell, Marge, Mgr.-Commun.--Piper Jaffray Companies, Inc., Minneapolis, MN; *U.S. Public*, pg. 1300
Prohaska, Julia, Mgr.-Pub. Rels.--Pleasant Company, Middleton, WI; *U.S. Private*, pg. 872
Pronin, Barbara, Coord.-Pub. Rels.--Bergen Brunswig Corporation, Orange, CA; *U.S. Public*, pg. 213
Prosceno, Mike, Mgr.-Pub. Rels.--Remington Arms Company, Inc., Madison, NC; *U.S. Private*, pg. 921
Proudfit, Donna, Dir.-Mktg.--Pickering Inc., Tacoma, WA; *U.S. Private*, pg. 864
Proveaux, Terry, Dir.-Investor Rels.--National Income Realty Trust, New York, NY; *U.S. Public*, pg. 1157
Pruett, Greg, V.P.-Corp. Comm.--PG&E Corporation, San Francisco, CA; *U.S. Public*, pg. 1240
Pryor, Anne, Mgr.-Natl. Promos. & Pub. Rels--Lifetouch, Portrait Studios, Eden Prairie, MN; *U.S. Private*, pg. 667
Pryor, John, V.P.-Human Rels. & Pub. Rels.--Builders Transport, Incorporated, Camden, SC; *U.S. Public*, pg. 267
Ptacek, Anna M., Mgr.-Communications--Calgon Vestal Laboratories, Saint Louis, MO; *U.S. Public*, pg. 1515
Puccia, Vincent, V.P.-Sls. & Mktg.--American International Airways, Ypsilanti, MI; *U.S. Private*, pg. 57
Puffer, Richard A., Dir.-Corp. Commun.--Sonoco Products Company, Hartsville, SC; *U.S. Public*, pg. 1485
Pulda, Ellen, Mgr.-Pub. Rels.--Converse Inc., North Reading, MA; *U.S. Public*, pg. 441
Pulizzi, Louise E., Dir.-Corp. Communications--Clark Construction Group, Inc., Bethesda, MD; *U.S. Private*, pg. 242
Pulizzi, Matthew S., V.P.-Customer Rels.--Kit Manufacturing Company, Long Beach, CA; *U.S. Public*, pg. 962
Pulley, Charles, Corp. V.P.-Communications--National Car Rental System, Inc., Minneapolis, MN; *U.S. Public*, pg. 1379
Pulver, Kenneth, V.P.-Corp. Commun.--Albany International Corp., Albany, NY; *U.S. Public*, pg. 36
Purdy, John W., Jr., V.P.-Mktg. & Pub. Affairs--Essex County Gas Company, Amesbury, MA; *U.S. Public*, pg. 593
Push, Steve, V.P.-Corp. Communications--Genzyme Corporation, Cambridge, MA; *U.S. Public*, pg. 733
Putnam, Lucinda, Mktg. Communications Admin.--Dexter Axle Div., Elkhart, IN; *Int'l*, pg. 1396
Putnam, Spencer, Chief Oper. Officer & Sec.--The Vermont Teddy Bear Company, Inc., Shelburne, VT; *U.S. Public*, pg. 1716
Putterman, Arlene, V.P.-Pub. Rels. & Events--Fortunoff, Uniondale, NY; *U.S. Private*, pg. 420
Puuri, Cory, Specialist-Mktg. Communications--J.J. Keller & Associates, Inc., Neenah, WI; *U.S. Private*, pg. 612
Pyle, Cabot, Dir.-Corp. Communications--Dollar General Corporation, Nashville, TN; *U.S. Public*, pg. 515
Pyzik, John, Dir.-Pub. Rels.--Delco Remy International, Inc., Anderson, IN; *U.S. Public*, pg. 495
Pyzik, John, Dir.-Pub. Rels.--Delco Remy America, Inc., Anderson, IN; *U.S. Public*, pg. 495
Quadt, Gabriele, Dir.-Corp. Commun. & Investor Rels.--Dyckerhoff AG, Wiesbaden, Germany; *Int'l*, pg. 422
Quah, Michelle, Asst.-Admin. Pub. Rels.--GP Batteries International Ltd., Singapore, Singapore; *Int'l*, pg. 537
Quan, David, Dir.-Corp. Commun.--TrizecHahn Corporation, Toronto, Canada; *Int'l*, pg. 1424
Quan, Janet, Coord.-Pub. Rels.--Pentel of America, Ltd., Torrance, CA; *Int'l*, pg. 1035
Queimado, Margarita, Mgr.-Public Rels.--Caixa Geral de Depositos, Lisbon, Portugal; *Int'l*, pg. 250
Quek, Donald, Sr. Mgr.-Corp. Affairs--Singapore Land Limited, Singapore, Singapore; *Int'l*, pg. 1252
Quick, Mary, Pub. Affairs Specialist--AlliedSignal Commercial Avionics Systems, Redmond, WA; *U.S. Public*, pg. 50
Quincy, Scott, Mgr.-Corp. Communications--Labatt U.S.A., Darien, CT; *Int'l*, pg. 679
Quinn, Joellyn, V.P.-Corp. Rels. & Asst. Sec.--Credit Union National Association, Madison, WI; *U.S. Private*, pg. 288
Quinn, John T., Dir.-Pub. Affairs--Sanders, A Lockheed Martin Company, Nashua, NH; *U.S. Public*, pg. 1008
Quiros, Pedro, Exec. Dir.-Commun. Network--WorldServ, Herndon, VA; *U.S. Public*, pg. 767
Rabe, Pam, Corp. Commun.--Immunex Corporation, Seattle, WA; *U.S. Public*, pg. 871
Rabjohn, Bonnie, Mgr.-Pub. Rels. & Promo.--Six Flags Magic Mountain & Six Flags Hurricane Harbor, Valencia, CA; *U.S. Public*, pg. 1611
Rachmann, K., Dir.-Communications--Dumez-GTM, Nanterre, France; *Int'l*, pg. 823
Racine, Paul, V.P.-Regulatory, Corp. & Native Affairs--Canadian Satellite Communications Inc., Mississauga, Canada; *Int'l*, pg. 1481
Racine, Robert, Sr. V.P.-Pub. Affairs & Investor Rels.--SNC-Lavalin Group Inc., Montreal, Canada; *Int'l*, pg. 1161
Racine, Robert, V.P.-Pub. Affairs--SNC-Lavalin Inc., Montreal, Canada; *Int'l*, pg. 1162
Rackoff, Laurie, Dir.-Mktg.--Shonac Corporation, Columbus, OH; *U.S. Private*, pg. 996
Radaj, Trish, Mgr.-Mktg. Commun.--Richco Inc., Chicago, IL; *U.S. Private*, pg. 929
Radau, Gene, Dir.-Corp. Communications--Ford, Bacon & Davis Companies Inc., Duluth, GA; *Int'l*, pg. 401
Radin, Harvey, V.P.-Communications--BankAmerica Corporation, San Francisco, CA; *U.S. Public*, pg. 179
Radler, Toni, Dir.-Mktg. & Adv.--Hohner/HSS Inc., Ashland, VA; *U.S. Private*, pg. 533
Radziviluk, Samuel J., Corp. Commun.--Lukens Inc., Coatesville, PA; *U.S. Public*, pg. 1019
Raeder, Caroline, V.P.-Communications--MasterCard International-Cirrus Brand, Purchase, NY; *U.S. Private*, pg. 714
Rafael Rivas, Jose, Mgr.-Pub. Rels. & Govt. Affairs--Procter & Gamble Venezuela, C.A., Caracas, Venezuela; *U.S. Public*, pg. 1332
Raffa, Connie L., Coord.-Mktg.--Giffels Associates, Inc., Southfield, MI; *U.S. Private*, pg. 452
Raffa, Louise M., V.P.-Corp. Communications & Adv.--Molded Fiber Glass Co., Union City, PA; *U.S. Private*, pg. 756
Rafferty, Mary Katherine, Dir.-Mktg. & Pub. Rels.--Bulgari Corporation of America, New York, NY; *Int'l*, pg. 232
Raffignone, Lisa, Mgr.-Pub. Rels.--The Burke Institute, Covington, KY; *U.S. Private*, pg. 120
Rageas, Sue A., Sr. V.P.-Pub. Rels.--Northern Trust Corporation, Chicago, IL; *U.S. Public*, pg. 1195
Ragland, Christine, Mgr.-Bus. Promo.--Sealright Company, Inc., De Soto, KS; *U.S. Public*, pg. 1451
Ragland, David, Pres. & Chief Exec. Officer--Duncan Equipment Company, Oklahoma City, OK; *U.S. Private*, pg. 346
Rahmberg, Rolf, V.P.-Corp. Communications--Perstorp AB, Perstorp, Sweden; *Int'l*, pg. 1036
Rakowitz, Cindy, V.P.-Pub. Rels. & Promo.--Playboy Enterprises, Inc., Chicago, IL; *U.S. Public*, pg. 1309
Raleigh, John, Chief Fin. Officer & V.P.-Fin.--C.H. Heist Corp., Clearwater, FL; *U.S. Public*, pg. 807
Ramalho, Americo, Dr., Mgr.-Pub. Rels.--Portuguese Railways (CP), Lisbon, Portugal; *Int'l*, pg. 1063
Ramm, Ulrich, Dir.-Pub. Rels.--Commerzbank AG, Frankfurt, Germany; *Int'l*, pg. 308
Ramos, Elias, Dir.-Corp. Communication--Caja de Madrid Group, Madrid, Spain; *Int'l*, pg. 251
Ramsby, Robert, Supvr.-Mktg. Communications--CTS Corporation, Elkhart, IN; *U.S. Public*, pg. 285
Ramsey, McClain, Mgr.-Pub. Rels.--Nike, Inc., Beaverton, OR; *U.S. Public*, pg. 1184
Randall, Karen F., Dir.-Pub. Rels.--Advantica Restaurant Group, Inc., Spartanburg, SC; *U.S. Public*, pg. 22
Rangel, John J., Sr. V.P.-Fin.--K2 Inc., Los Angeles, CA; *U.S. Public*, pg. 940
Raniszeski, Ed, Mgr.-Mktg. Communications--Rheem Air Conditioning Div., Fort Smith, AR; *Int'l*, pg. 1022
Rank, Bob, Mgr.-Mktg. Communications--Paragon Electric Co., Inc., Two Rivers, WI; *Int'l*, pg. 1243
Rankin, Pamela, Mgr.-Mktg. Communications--X-Rite, Incorporated, Grandville, MI; *U.S. Public*, pg. 1783
Rankin, R.A., Jr., Sr. V.P.-Corp. Relations--Fairfield Inn, Washington, DC; *U.S. Public*, pg. 1048
Ransdell, Darrell, Dir.-Customer Rels.--A.P. Green Industries, Inc., Mexico, MO; *U.S. Public*, pg. 761
Ranvier, Monique, Mgr.-Pub. Rels.--Messier-Bugatti S.A., Velizy-Villacoublay, France; *Int'l*, pg. 1165
Rapp, James R., Dr., V.P.-Corp. Rels.--Hercules Incorporated, Wilmington, DE; *U.S. Public*, pg. 809
Rapp, Marilyn, Communications Coordinator--Sunmark Inc., Saint Louis, MO; *Int'l*, pg. 917
Rasmussen, Julie, Mgr.-Pub. Rels.--Delta Gold N.L., Sydney, Australia; *Int'l*, pg. 389
Rassfeld, Martin, Mgr.-Press & Pub. Rels.--Bankgesellschaft Berlin, Berlin, Germany; *Int'l*, pg. 159
Rasuli, Darryl, Mgr.-Communications--Niagara Frontier Transit & Metro System, Buffalo, NY; *U.S. Private*, pg. 798
Ratcliff, C. Michael, Dir.-External Communications--AMP Incorporated, Harrisburg, PA; *U.S. Public*, pg. 7
Raterink, Jill, Pub. Rels. Counselor--Sawyer Riley Compton Inc., Atlanta, GA; *U.S. Private*, pg. 969
Rathers, Jan, V.P.-Communications--Lockheed Martin Missiles & Space, Sunnyvale, CA; *U.S. Public*, pg. 1008
Rau, Lisa, Dir.-Publicity--Silver Dollar City, Inc., Branson, MO; *U.S. Private*, pg. 1000
Rava, Victorio, Dr., Dir.-Adv.--Fiat Auto SpA, Turin, Italy; *Int'l*, pg. 480
Ray, Jennifer, Dir.-Mktg. & Pub. Rels.--Louisiana Downs, Bossier City, LA; *U.S. Private*, pg. 319
Ray, Monica, Dir.-Pub. Affairs--Kennecott Holdings Corporation, Magna, UT; *Int'l*, pg. 1119
Raymond, Dennis M., V.P.-H.R.--The Austin Company, Cleveland, OH; *U.S. Private*, pg. 99
Razouki, Seham Abdul Razzak, Mng. Dir.-Fin., Admin. & External Relations--Kuwait Petroleum Corporation, Safat, Kuwait; *Int'l*, pg. 764
Reader, Marty, V.P.-Mktg.--G&K Services, Inc., Minnetonka, MN; *U.S. Public*, pg. 690
Ream, Marcy, Mgr.-Mktg. Commun. & Adv.--Republic Storage Systems Company Inc., Canton, OH; *U.S. Private*, pg. 924
Reckford, Jonathan, Sr. V.P.-Plng. & Communications--Circuit City Stores, Inc., Richmond, VA; *U.S. Public*, pg. 374
Redditt, Bruce, Sr. V.P.-Corp. Communications & Pub. Affairs--Sony Pictures Entertainment, Culver City, CA; *Int'l*, pg. 1281

Redlinger, Donald J., Sr. V.P.-Human Resources & Communications--AlliedSignal Inc., Morristown, NJ; *U.S. Public*, pg. 49
Redpath, Tim, Dir.-Mktg. & Commun.--Mitel Corporation, Kanata, Canada; *Int'l*, pg. 870
Reed, Bill J., V.P.-Corp. Commun. & Pub. Affairs--Riceland Foods, Inc., Stuttgart, AR; *U.S. Private*, pg. 928
Reed, D., Dir.-Pub. Rels.--Whitbread PLC, London, United Kingdom; *Int'l*, pg. 1498
Reed, Wanda, Dir.-Customer Accts.--American Freightways Corporation, Harrison, AR; *U.S. Public*, pg. 75
Reese, Amy, Pub. Rels. Specialist--The McClure Group, Wayne, PA; *U.S. Private*, pg. 719
Reeves, Dale, Dir.-Communications, Mktg. & Adv.--John Brown Plastics Machinery, Attleboro, MA; *Int'l*, pg. 773
Reeves, Helen, V.P.-Communications--Noranda Inc., Toronto, Canada; *Int'l*, pg. 433
Reeves, Lisa, Communications Specialist--Equifax Inc., Atlanta, GA; *U.S. Public*, pg. 588
Regan, Patrick L., Dir.-Customer Svcs. & Pub. Affairs--East Ascension Telephone Company, Inc., Gonzales, LA; *U.S. Private*, pg. 358
Reichman, David, Dir.-Pub. Rels.--Granite State Gas Transmission, Inc., Portsmouth, NH; *U.S. Public*, pg. 197
Reichman, David M., Leader-Pub. & Govt. Rels.--Bay State Gas Company, Westborough, MA; *U.S. Public*, pg. 196
Reid, David, Mgr.-Pub. Rels.--Storage Technology Corporation, Louisville, CO; *U.S. Public*, pg. 1522
Reid, Gerald, Sr. V.P.-Customer Service--Zenith Electronics Corp., Glenview, IL; *U.S. Public*, pg. 1790
Reid, Timothy J., V.P.-Corp. Commun.--Brush Wellman Inc., Cleveland, OH; *U.S. Public*, pg. 266
Reidie, Dave, V.P.-Reader Sls. & Svc.--The Edmonton Journal, Edmonton, Canada; *Int'l*, pg. 631
Reilly, Michelle, Mgr.-Communications--Bird Products Corporation, Palm Springs, CA; *U.S. Public*, pg. 1591
Reilly, Mona, Dir.-Pub. Rels.--Paul Stuart, Inc., New York, NY; *U.S. Private*, pg. 844
Reily, Brett, Mktg. Communications Specialist--Samuel Cabot, Inc., Newburyport, MA; *U.S. Private*, pg. 198
Reiman, Beverly J., Dir.-Corp. Communication--The Standard Register Company, Dayton, OH; *U.S. Public*, pg. 1505
Reinhardt, Aura, V.P.-Pub. Rels.--Schieffelin & Somerset Co., New York, NY; *Int'l*, pg. 412
Reiser, Carol A., Dir.-Community Affairs--Rich's/Lazarus/Goldsmith's, Atlanta, GA; *U.S. Public*, pg. 618
Reiss, Nancy, Mgr.-Investor Communications--Southern New England Telecommunications Corporation, New Haven, CT; *U.S. Public*, pg. 1490
Remmert, Joe, Mgr.-Adv.--Springs Window Fashions Division, Middleton, WI; *U.S. Public*, pg. 1500
Renault, Gillian, V.P.-Pub. Rels.--The Travel Channel, Atlanta, GA; *U.S. Private*, pg. 647
Rendine, Robert, V.P.-Corp. Commun.--GTECH Corporation, West Greenwich, RI; *U.S. Public*, pg. 767
Renfrow, Paul, Mgr.-Corp. Commun.--OGE Energy Corp., Oklahoma City, OK; *U.S. Public*, pg. 1207
Renner, Otto W., III, Dir.-Commun.--UGI Corporation, King of Prussia, PA; *U.S. Public*, pg. 1653
Rennison, Peter, Mgr.-Pub. Rels.--Olivetti Research Ltd., Cambridge, United Kingdom; *Int'l*, pg. 1003
Renouard, Ed S., Jr., Mgr.-Mktg. Communications--The Washington Water Power Company, Spokane, WA; *U.S. Public*, pg. 1744
Renstron, Hans, Dir.-Cultural & VIP Rels.--AB Volvo, Goteborg, Sweden; *Int'l*, pg. 1476
Renzel, Werner, Dir.-Pub. Rels.--AGIV Group, Frankfurt, Germany; *Int'l*, pg. 14
Resar, Carolyn, Dir.-Mktg., Commun. & Direct Mktg./Direct Response--Signature Brands USA, Inc., Solon, OH; *U.S. Public*, pg. 1472
Resnik, Leslie R., V.P. & Sr. Pub. Rels. Program Mgr.--Liggett-Stashower, Inc., Cleveland, OH; *U.S. Private*, pg. 667
Restaino, Lisa, Mgr.-Mktg. Communications--Universal-Rundle Corp., New Castle, PA; *U.S. Public*, pg. 1193
Reuland, Brenda, Dir.-Communications--American Eurocopter Corp., Grand Prairie, TX; *Int'l*, pg. 29
Reuning, Karl, Mktg. Communications--Frequency and Time Systems, Inc., Beverly, MA; *U.S. Public*, pg. 488
Reuter, Joel P., Media Rels.--Southwire Company, Carrollton, GA; *U.S. Private*, pg. 1019
Reuwee, Dan, Dir.-Commun.--Mid-America Dairymen, Inc., Springfield, MO; *U.S. Private*, pg. 743
Revak, Crystal L., Dir.-Investor Rels.--RMI Titanium Company, Niles, OH; *U.S. Public*, pg. 1662
Reville, David, Dir.-Corp. Commun.--Banknorth Group Inc., Burlington, VT; *U.S. Public*, pg. 186
Reynolds, Julie, Dir.-Pub. Affairs--National Fire Protection Association, Quincy, MA; *U.S. Private*, pg. 782
Reynolds, Michael S., Mgr.-Pub. Affairs--Condea Vista Company, Houston, TX; *Int'l*, pg. 325
Reynolds, Paul, Dir.-Communications--Pinnacle West Capital Corporation, Phoenix, AZ; *U.S. Public*, pg. 1297
Rhee, Thomas, Dir.-Mktg. Communications & Research--Samsung Electronics America, Inc., Ridgefield Park, NJ; *Int'l*, pg. 1183
Rhoades, Kay, Mgr.-Customer Service--Integrated Metal Technologies, Inc., Spring Lake, MI; *U.S. Public*, pg. 1112
Rhoads, John, Mgr.-Adv. & Pub. Rels.--Heat Controller, Inc., Jackson, MI; *U.S. Private*, pg. 518
Rhodes, Gary, Dir.-Investor Rels.--Gibson Greetings, Inc., Cincinnati, OH; *U.S. Public*, pg. 742
Rhodes, Gary L., Dir.-Corp. Commun.--Omnicare, Inc., Covington, KY; *U.S. Public*, pg. 1223
Rhodes, George R., V.P.-Corp. Commun. & Professional Rels.--Dentsply International Inc., York, PA; *U.S. Public*, pg. 498
Rhodes, Jim, V.P.-H.R. & Dir.-Pub. Rels.--Publix Supermarkets Inc., Lakeland, FL; *U.S. Private*, pg. 893
Rhudy, Marilee, V.P.- Pub. Affairs--Wyeth-Ayerst Laboratories, Inc., Philadelphia, PA; *U.S. Public*, pg. 80
Rhudy, Marily H., V.P.-Pub. Affairs--American Home Products Corporation, Madison, NJ; *U.S. Public*, pg. 79
Ricat, Nicholas, Dir.-Mktg. & Communications--Societe Hoteliere Paris Vanves, Evry, France; *Int'l*, pg. 20
Rice, Harold E., Jr., V.P.-Admin. & Fin.--Pittway Real Estate, Wesley Chapel, FL; *U.S. Public*, pg. 1306
Riceman, Ron, Dir.-Pub. Rels. & Adv.--Elizabethtown Gas Co., Union, NJ; *U.S. Public*, pg. 1147
Rich, Joe, Mgr.-Customer Service--Acme Electric Corporation, East Aurora, NY; *U.S. Public*, pg. 16
Rich, Michael, Dir.-Promo.--Money, New York, NY; *U.S. Public*, pg. 1613
Richards, Barbara, Admin.-H.R.--Future Foam, Inc., Council Bluffs, IA; *U.S. Private*, pg. 433
Richards, J.J., Dir.-Pub. Affairs--Black & Veatch, Kansas City, MO; *U.S. Private*, pg. 146
Richards, Marcia, Mgr-Consumer Affairs--Edwards Baking Co., Norcross, GA; *U.S. Private*, pg. 365
Richards, Paul, Mgr.-Corp. Communications--American Hardware Mutual Insurance Co., Columbus, OH; *U.S. Private*, pg. 764
Richards, Paul J., Mgr.-Corp. Communications & Mktg. Svcs.--Motorists Mutual Insurance Co., Columbus, OH; *U.S. Private*, pg. 764
Richards, Thomas J., Business Mgr.--Strathmore Paper, Granby, CT; *U.S. Public*, pg. 903
Richardson, Bruce, Mgr.-Pub. Rels.--Phelps Dodge Morenci Inc., Morenci, AZ; *U.S. Public*, pg. 1287
Richardson, Charles, Dir.-Corp. Affairs--3i Group plc, London, United Kingdom; *Int'l*, pg. 1386
Richardson, Lindy B., Sr. V.P.-Mktg. & Public Affairs--Columbia/HCA Healthcare Corporation, Nashville, TN; *U.S. Public*, pg. 403
Richfield, Mark, Mgr.-Mktg. Svcs.--Vilter Manufacturing Corporation, Cudahy, WI; *U.S. Private*, pg. 1140
Richterich, Guido, Dr., Mng. Dir.-Law & Communications--F. Hoffmann-La Roche Ltd., Basel, Switzerland; *Int'l*, pg. 1119
Ricks, Gloria, V.P. & Dir.-Pub. Rels.--Hearst Magazines Division, New York, NY; *U.S. Private*, pg. 516
Ricks, Ronald, V.P.-Govt. Affairs--Southwest Airlines Co., Dallas, TX; *U.S. Public*, pg. 1493
Riddle, Virginia, Dir.-Pub. Rels.--Allen-Edmonds Shoe Corp., Port Washington, WI; *U.S. Private*, pg. 36
Ridulfo, S., Mgr.-Pub. Rels. & Mktg.--Olivetti Australia Pty. Ltd., Silverwater, Australia; *Int'l*, pg. 1003
Rieker, David M., Mgr.-Communications Programs--Unitary Products Group, York, PA; *U.S. Public*, pg. 1788
Riera, Lisette, Dir.-Pub. Rels.--Telemundo Group, Inc., Hialeah, FL; *U.S. Public*, pg. 1570
Riess, Frank, V.P.-Mktg. Communications--The Stolle Corporation, Sidney, OH; *U.S. Public*, pg. 61
Riffle, JoLaine, Dir.-Communications--The Lathrop Company, Toledo, OH; *U.S. Public*, pg. 1645
Rigazio, Gloria, Coord.-Pub. Rels.--McKesson Corporation, San Francisco, CA; *U.S. Public*, pg. 1072
Rigdon, Pamela, Mgr.-Corp. Communication--Odetics Inc., Anaheim, CA; *U.S. Public*, pg. 1212
Riley, Barbara, Dir.-Media--Four Seasons Solar Products Corp., Holbrook, NY; *U.S. Private*, pg. 422
Riley, Dick, V.P.-Media Relations--The Prudential Insurance Company of America, Newark, NJ; *U.S. Private*, pg. 892
Riley, Joan R., Gen. Counsel, Sec. & Dir.-Investor Rels.--Quixote Corporation, Chicago, IL; *U.S. Public*, pg. 1353
Riley, John, V.P.-Corp. Communications--Massachusetts Financial Services Company (MFS), Boston, MA; *Int'l*, pg. 1319
Riley, Michael T., Sr. V.P.-Mktg., Infosvcs. & Opers.--First Financial Bancorp, Hamilton, OH; *U.S. Public*, pg. 632
Riley, Paula, Mgr.-Communications--Mitsubishi Silicon America, Palo Alto, CA; *Int'l*, pg. 875
Riley, Richard, Exec. V.P., Media Dir. & Pub. Rels. Dir.--Sawyer Riley Compton Inc., Atlanta, GA; *U.S. Private*, pg. 969
Riley, Tim, Mgr.-Pub. Rels.--Kaiser Permanente, Northeast Division, Farmington, CT; *U.S. Private*, pg. 605
Rinaldo, Nelson P., Mgr.-External Rels.--General Motors do Brasil Ltda., Sao Caetano do Sul, Brazil; *U.S. Public*, pg. 722
Rindfleisch, Bev, Dir.-Mktg. Commun.--Centigram Communications Corporation, San Jose, CA; *U.S. Public*, pg. 323
Ringel, Ellen, Mgr.-Pub. Rels.--Deloitte & Touche LLP, Wilton, CT; *U.S. Private*, pg. 322
Ringer, Grant, Dir.-Corp. Commun.--LG & E Energy Corp., Louisville, KY; *U.S. Public*, pg. 970
Rio, Catherine, Pub. Rels.--Sodexho S.A., Montigny-le-Bretonneux, France; *Int'l*, pg. 1274
Riordan, Lisa, Dir.-Investor Rels. & Pub. Rels.--Bergen Brunswig Corporation, Orange, CA; *U.S. Public*, pg. 213
Riordan, Sue, Dir.-Communications--Wisconsin Gas Company, Milwaukee, WI; *U.S. Public*, pg. 1767
Rios, Vanessa, Sr. Pub. Rels. Specialist--NEC Electronics Inc., Santa Clara, CA; *Int'l*, pg. 900
Ripley, Clinton E., V.P.-Customer Svcs.--Advance Packaging Corporation, Grand Rapids, MI; *U.S. Private*, pg. 18
Risac, Claude, V.P.-Communications--Groupe Pernod Ricard, Paris, France; *Int'l*, pg. 566
Rish, Stephen A., V.P.-Corp. Pub. Involvement--Nationwide Insurance Enterprise, Columbus, OH; *U.S. Private*, pg. 788
Riste, LaDonna, Community Rels. Coord.--Dakota Electric Association, Farmington, MN; *U.S. Private*, pg. 308
Ritchie, Michelle, Mgr.-Commun.--Roy F. Weston, Inc., West Chester, PA; *U.S. Public*, pg. 1761
Ritchie, Roger, Dir.-Communications--FlightSafety International Inc., Flushing, NY; *U.S. Public*, pg. 218
Ritter, Amy, Mgr.-Pub. Rels.--John G. Shedd Aquarium, Chicago, IL; *U.S. Private*, pg. 991
Ritter, Elmas, Dr., Mgr.-Pub. Rels.--Balzers, Balzers, Switzerland; *Int'l*, pg. 997
Rivera, Angela, Mgr.-Corp. Communications--FPA Medical Management, Inc., San Diego, CA; *U.S. Public*, pg. 608
Rizzi, Deborah, Mgr.-Commun.--United Water Resources, Harrington Park, NJ; *U.S. Public*, pg. 1691
Roache, Kathryn, Mgr.-Pub. Rels.--Bright National Bank, Flora, IN; *U.S. Public*, pg. 633
Robb, Ian, Dir.-Corp. Communications--Siemens Nixdorf Information Systems Inc., Burlington, MA; *Int'l*, pg. 1245
Robben, Julie, Pub. Rels. Specialist--Clayton Corporation, Fenton, MO; *U.S. Private*, pg. 244
Robbins, Bob, Dir.-Mktg. Services & Corp. Communications--Mentor Corporation, Santa Barbara, CA; *U.S. Public*, pg. 1086
Robbins, Stanley, Mgr.-Human Resources--Mrs. Giles Country Kitchens, Inc., Lynchburg, VA; *U.S. Public*, pg. 596
Roberson, Donald, Dir.-Mktg. & Sls.--Theradyne Corporation, Jordan, MN; *U.S. Private*, pg. 637
Roberts-Myers, Tammy, Mgr.-Pub. Rels.--Bob Evans Farms, Inc. Restaurant Division, Columbus, OH; *U.S. Public*, pg. 596
Roberts, Alison, Mgr.-Grp. Corp. Affairs--Halifax plc, Halifax, United Kingdom; *Int'l*, pg. 589
Roberts, Carolyn F., Corp. Dir.-Pub. Rels.--Armstrong International, Inc., Three Rivers, MI; *U.S. Private*, pg. 83
Roberts, Deborah, Dir.-Mktg. Communications--Overnite Transportation Co., Richmond, VA; *U.S. Public*, pg. 1668
Roberts, John, Mgr.-Adv. & Customer Service--Parks Products, Inc., Hollywood, CA; *U.S. Private*, pg. 840
Roberts, John F., Dir.-Corp. Admin.--Morrison Knudsen Corporation, Boise, ID; *U.S. Public*, pg. 1133
Roberts, P.A., V.P.-Public Affairs--Emerson Electric Co., Saint Louis, MO; *U.S. Public*, pg. 572
Roberts, Paul, Dir.-Corp. Commun.--Analogic Corporation, Peabody, MA; *U.S. Public*, pg. 109
Roberts, W. Scott, V.P.-Bus. Rels.--The Gillette Company, Gillette Grooming Products, USA, Boston, MA; *U.S. Public*, pg. 744
Roberts, William E., Chief Fin. Officer, V.P., Controller & Treas.--Lone Star Industries, Inc., Stamford, CT; *U.S. Public*, pg. 1012
Robertson, Mike, Dir.-Communications--Cole-Haan, Yarmouth, ME; *U.S. Public*, pg. 1184
Robertson, Nancy, Sr. Dir.-Corp. Commun.--Sonic Corporation, Oklahoma City, OK; *U.S. Public*, pg. 1485
Robidoux, Roy, Sr. V.P.-Mktg. & Sls.--The Cerplex Group, Inc., Tustin, CA; *U.S. Public*, pg. 332
Robillard, Jean-Pierre, Dir.-Commun.--Dassault Aviation Group, Vaucresson, France; *Int'l*, pg. 383
Robinette, Garland, V.P.-Communications--Freeport-McMoRan Inc., New Orleans, LA; *U.S. Public*, pg. 680
Robinette, P.J., Dir.-Consumer Affairs--Delta Air Lines, Inc., Atlanta, GA; *U.S. Public*, pg. 497
Robinson, Carole, V.P.-Press Rels., MTV--MTV Networks, New York, NY; *U.S. Private*, pg. 779
Robinson, Ellen, V.P.-Communications--Case Corporation, Racine, WI; *U.S. Public*, pg. 311
Robinson, Kurt, V.P.-Prod. Support--Robinson Helicopter Company, Torrance, CA; *U.S. Private*, pg. 936
Robinson, Melissa, Dir.-Corp. Commun.--Kaufman and Broad Home Corporation, Los Angeles, CA; *U.S. Public*, pg. 944
Robinson, Pam, Coord.-Communications--Owen Health Care, Inc., Houston, TX; *U.S. Public*, pg. 304
Robinson, Patrick, Dir.-Corp. Communications & Sls. Devel.--Reed Exhibition Companies-Europe, Paris, France; *Int'l*, pg. 1096
Robinson, Patrick, Dir.-Corp. Communications & Sls. Devel.--Reed Exhibition Companies, Richmond, United Kingdom; *Int'l*, pg. 1096
Robles, Emilio, Dir.-Mktg. Communications--Philips Semiconductors, Sunnyvale, CA; *Int'l*, pg. 1054
Robling, Chris, Dir.-Commun.--Regional Transportation Authority (RTA), Chicago, IL; *U.S. Private*, pg. 918
Rocca, Rino, Exec. V.P.-Intl. Rels.--Istituto Bancario San Paolo Di Torino S.p.A., Turin, Italy; *Int'l*, pg. 691
Rocco, Giancarlo, Dir.-Adv. & Pub. Rels.--Pirelli S.p.A., Milan, Italy; *Int'l*, pg. 1058
Rochowansky, Thomas, Mgr.-Adv. & Pub. Rels.--AGA Ges.m.b.H., Vienna, Austria; *Int'l*, pg. 13
Rockwell, Arthur E., V.P.-Corp. Rels.--MGM Entertainment Company, Culver City, CA; *U.S. Public*, pg. 1614
Rockwell, Rick, Mgr.-Pub. Rels.--Denison Hydraulics, Inc., Marysville, OH; *U.S. Private*, pg. 324
Rodefeld, James A., Sr. V.P.-Mktg.--Jacobson Stores Inc., Jackson, MI; *U.S. Public*, pg. 922
Rodgers, Doug, Grp. Mgr.-Corp. Affairs.--CSR Limited, Sydney, Australia; *Int'l*, pg. 245
Rodgers, John, Mgr.-Pub. Rels.--Harris Calorific Co., Gainesville, GA; *U.S. Public*, pg. 996
Rodgers, Mary, Pub. Rels.--Cuisinart Inc., Stamford, CT; *U.S. Private*, pg. 261
Rodriguez Marquez, Jorge H., V.P.-Corp. Communication--Bacardi Services (North America) Corp., Coral Gables, FL; *Int'l*, pg. 131
Rodriguez, Enrique Flores, V.P.-Corp. Communications--Alfa, S.A. de C.V., Garza Garcia, Mexico; *Int'l*, pg. 56
Rodriguez, Jim, Dir.-Corp. Communications--CMI Corporation, Oklahoma City, OK; *U.S. Public*, pg. 278
Rodriguez, Larissa, Mgr.-Pub. Rels.--Hammel, Green & Abrahamson, Inc., Minneapolis, MN; *U.S. Private*, pg. 497
Rodriguez, Ron, V.P.-Special Events & Publ.--Burdines, Miami, FL; *U.S. Public*, pg. 618
Rodriguez, Virginia, Dir.-Pub. Rels.--The Washington Post, Washington, DC; *U.S. Public*, pg. 1743
Rodriquez, Maria, Corp. & Pub. Affairs Officer--Banco Popular de Puerto Rico, San Juan, PR; *U.S. Public*, pg. 175
Roeder, Gil M., Dir.-Mktg. Communications--APL Limited, Oakland, CA; *Int'l*, pg. 912
Roeder, Jerry, Dir.-Communications--Uniroyal Goodrich Canada Inc., Kitchener, Canada; *Int'l*, pg. 322
Roedig, Cynthia, Mgr.-Mktg. Commun.--Burr-Brown Corporation, Tucson, AZ; *U.S. Public*, pg. 270

Roenning, Robert, Corp. Communications--Stabburet A/S, Skien, Norway; *Int'l*, pg. 1011
Rogde, Per Terje, Chief Information Officer--Frionor A/S, Lysaker, Norway; *Int'l*, pg. 516
Roger, Ian, Mgr.-Adv. & Pub. Intl.--Reuters Holdings PLC, London, United Kingdom; *Int'l*, pg. 1105
Rogers, Bruce H., Dir.-Corp. Communications--Forbes, Inc., New York, NY; *U.S. Private*, pg. 417
Rogers, Cathy, Investor Rels.--RPM, Inc., Medina, OH; *U.S. Public*, pg. 1356
Rogers, Jeff, Sr. V.P.-Investor Rels.--The Money Store, Sacramento, CA; *U.S. Public*, pg. 1124
Rogers, Jerry, Dir.-Pub. Rels.--Inco Limited, Ontario Division, Copper Cliff, Canada; *Int'l*, pg. 672
Rogers, John, Dir.-Pub. Rels.--ULLICO Inc., Washington, DC; *U.S. Private*, pg. 1115
Rogers, Larry, V.P.-Consumer Affairs--Kaufman and Broad of Northern California, Inc., San Ramon, CA; *U.S. Public*, *pg. 945*
Rogers, Peter J., Jr., Dir.-Investor Rels. & Bus. Devel.--Micros Systems Inc., Beltsville, MD; *U.S. Public*, pg. 1106
Rogers, Randy, Dir.-Pub. Rels.--Kenny Rogers Roasters, Fort Lauderdale, FL; *U.S. Private*, pg. 939
Rogers, Ron, Mgr.-External Res. & Devel. Commun.--Hoechst Marion Roussel, Inc., Bridgewater, NJ; *Int'l*, pg. 624
Rogers, Stanley C., V.P.-Agriservices Div.--Gold Kist, Inc., Atlanta, GA; *U.S. Private*, pg. 459
Rogers, Susan, V.P.-Corp. Communications--Abitibi-Consolidated Inc., Montreal, Canada; *Int'l*, pg. 19
Rogers, Susan, Mgr.-Pub. Rels.--Horizon Investment Group, Taylor, MI; *U.S. Private*, pg. 539
Rogers, Susan, Mgr.-Pub. Rels.--Business Air, Grosse Ile, MI; *U.S. Private*, pg. 539
Rogers, Susan, Mgr.-Pub. Rels.--Horizon Properties, Taylor, MI; *U.S. Private*, pg. 539
Rogers, Susan, Mgr.-Pub. Rels.--Horizon Technology Group LLC, Taylor, MI; *U.S. Private*, pg. 539
Rogers, Terry, V.P.-Corp. Admin., Benefits & Human Resources--Herff Jones Inc., Indianapolis, IN; *U.S. Private*, pg. 523
Rogerson, Steve, Mgr.-Pub. Rels.--Lost Arrow Corporation, Ventura, CA; *U.S. Private*, pg. 676
Roh, Il-Hwan, Gen. Mgr.--Cho Hung Bank, Seoul, Korea; *Int'l*, pg. 287
Rohrbach, Kate, Sr. V.P.-Corp. Commun.--The Charles Schwab Corporation, San Francisco, CA; *U.S. Public*, pg. 1442
Rohweder, Elena, Mgr.-Pub. Rels.--Quaker State Corporation, Irving, TX; *U.S. Public*, pg. 1348
Roker, Deborah W., Corp. Dir.-Pub. Rels.--Sonesta International Hotels Corporation, Boston, MA; *U.S. Public*, pg. 1485
Rolland, Andre, Dir.-Rels. Sociales & Human Resources--Kodak Pathe S.A., Paris, France; *U.S. Public*, pg. 554
Rolle, Michelle, Mgr.-Mktg. Communications--Orbotech Inc., Billerica, MA; *Int'l*, pg. 1007
Rollins, Fred H., III, Exec. V.P. & Pub. Rels. Dir.--EvansGroup, Salt Lake City, UT; *U.S. Private*, pg. 385
Rollins, Jenelle, Asst. Publicist--Tri-Star Pictures, Inc., Culver City, CA; *Int'l*, pg. 1282
Rombach, C. Scott, V.P.-Corp. Communications--Summit Bancorp, Princeton, NJ; *U.S. Public*, pg. 1527
Rombouts, A., Dir.-Sls. & Mktg.--Holmatro Industrial & Rescue Equipment, Raamsdonksveer, Netherlands; *Int'l*, pg. 632
Rome, Martin, Dir.-Pub. Rels.--Kelly Services, Inc., Troy, MI; *U.S. Public*, pg. 949
Romero, Carol, Grp. Pres. & Pub. Rels. Dir.--Keyes Martin, East Hanover, NJ; *U.S. Private*, pg. 618
Ronnebaum, Linda, Coord.-Mktg. Communications--Batesville Casket Company, Inc., Batesville, IN; *U.S. Public*, pg. 828
Rooney, Dave, Mgr.-Dodge Car & Truck Communications--Dodge Car/Truck Division, Auburn Hills, MI; *U.S. Public*, pg. 353
Root, Tim, Dir.-Corp. Communications--Copeland Corporation, Sidney, OH; *U.S. Public*, pg. 573
Roper, Carole, Pub. Rels. Dir.--Sive/Young & Rubicam L.P., Cincinnati, OH; *U.S. Private*, pg. 1197
Roquemore, Carole, Dir.-Corp. Commun.--Alta-Dena Certified Dairy, City of Industry, CA; *Int'l*, pg. 201
Rosa, Antonio Carlos Fonseca, Dir.-Labor Rels.--Sao Paulo Alpargatas S.A., Sao Paulo, Brazil; *Int'l*, pg. 1193
Rosado Penna, Carlos Leonam, Dir.-Public Affairs--Petrobras - Petroleo Brasileiro S.A., Rio de Janeiro, Brazil; *Int'l*, pg. 1041
Rosasco, John, Dir.-Pub. Rels.--New York Rangers Hockey Club, New York, NY; *U.S. Public*, pg. 288
Rosati, Janet, Dir.-Consumer Relations--Fruit of the Loom, Inc., Chicago, IL; *U.S. Public*, pg. 685
Rose, Bob, V.P.-Commun.--San Francisco Giants Baseball Club, San Francisco, CA; *U.S. Private*, pg. 964
Rose, Harry, Asst. V.P.-Mktg. & Corp. Communications--Atlantic Gulf Communities Corporation, Miami, FL; *U.S. Public*, pg. 144
Rose, Marc M., Dir.-Corp. Communications & Govt. Rels.--Wheat First Butcher Singer, Inc., Richmond, VA; *U.S. Public*, pg. 640
Rosecrance, Kathleen, Mgr.-Pub. Rels.--Computational Systems Inc., Knoxville, TN; *U.S. Public*, pg. 572
Rosello, Josianne, Mgr.-Mktg. & Pub. Rels.--First Leasing & Rental Corporation, Toa Baja, PR; *U.S. Public*, pg. 644
Rosello, Jossiane, Sr. V.P.-Mktg. & Pub. Rels.--Firstbank Puerto Rico, Santurce, PR; *U.S. Public*, pg. 644
Rosello, Jossiane, Mgr.-Mktg. & Pub. Prels.--First Federal Finance Corporation, Santurce, PR; *U.S. Public*, pg. 644
Rosen, Deborah, Sr. V.P.-Corp. Communications & Pub. Affairs--Universal Studios, Inc., Universal City, CA; *Int'l*, pg. 1215
Rosenbaum, Linda, V.P. & Gen. Mgr.-Pub. Rels. Div.--Girgenti, Hughes, Butler & McDowell, New York, NY; *U.S. Private*, pg. 455
Rosenberg, Fred, V.P., Pub. Rels. Dir. & Real Estate Dir.--Pace Advertising, New York, NY; *Int'l*, pg. 1483
Rosenberg, Marc, V.P.-Pub. Rels.--Tiger Electronics, Inc., Vernon Hills, IL; *U.S. Private*, pg. 1086
Rosenberg, Rickie, Pub. Rels. Dir.--Rives Carlberg, Houston, TX; *U.S. Private*, pg. 934
Rosenberg, Susan, Mgr.-Communications--AirTouch Communications, Inc., San Francisco, CA; *U.S. Public*, pg. 34
Rosenblum, Phyllis, First V.P. & Community Affairs Officer--Republic National Bank of New York, New York, NY; *U.S. Public*, pg. 1380
Rosenfeld, Stephan, Asst. Gen. Mgr.-Pub. Affairs--Southeastern Pennsylvania Transportation Authority, Philadelphia, PA; *U.S. Private*, pg. 1015
Rosenstein, David L., Pub. Rels.--Bowne & Co., Inc., New York, NY; *U.S. Public*, pg. 248
Rosenthal, Caroline, Dir.-Pub. Rels.--Schieffelin & Somerset Co., New York, NY; *Int'l*, pg. 412
Roskvist, Christer, Dir.-Pub. Rels.--Cardo AB, Malmo, Sweden; *Int'l*, pg. 268
Ross-Sirola, Heather, Mgr.-Mktg. & Corp Adv.--Partek Corporation, Helsinki, Finland; *Int'l*, pg. 1024
Ross, Georgette, V.P.-Customer Svcs.--CMP Media, Inc., Manhasset, NY; *U.S. Public*, pg. 279
Ross, Jerrell, Mgr.-Fin. Pub. Rels.--Ameritech Corporation, Chicago, IL; *U.S. Public*, pg. 97
Ross, Lezlea, Mgr.-Mktg.--Hygeia Dairy Co., Inc., Harlingen, TX; *U.S. Private*, pg. 552
Ross, Pamela J., Dir.-Corp. Commun.--Overhead Door Corporation, Dallas, TX; *U.S. Private*, pg. 822
Ross, Sharon, Dir.-Pub. Rels.--Jostens Learning Corporation, San Diego, CA; *U.S. Private*, pg. 601
Ross, Sherylyn, Mgr.-Natl. Adv. & Pub. Rels.--TDK Electronics Corporation, Port Washington, NY; *Int'l*, pg. 1336
Ross, Stuart C., V.P.-Pub. Rels.--The Reader's Digest Association, Inc., Pleasantville, NY; *U.S. Public*, pg. 1367
Ross, Thomas, V.P.-Government Rels.--Loral Space & Communications, New York, NY; *U.S. Public*, pg. 1014
Ross, Thomas, Sr. V.P.-Adv. & Creative Services--Oneida Ltd., Oneida, NY; *U.S. Public*, pg. 1225
Rosser, Jay, Dir.-Corp. Communications--Koch Industries, Incorporated, Wichita, KS; *U.S. Private*, pg. 628
Rossi, James J., V.P.-Human Resources--Kewaunee Scientific Corporation, Statesville, NC; *U.S. Public*, pg. 953
Rossiter, Gregory M., Mng. Dir.-Pub. Rels.--FDX Corporation, Memphis, TN; *U.S. Public*, pg. 603
Rotchford, Robert, V.P.- Sls. & Mktg.--Massachusetts Envelope Co., Somerville, MA; *U.S. Private*, pg. 712
Roth, Rick, V.P.-Corp. Communications--Corporate Express, Inc., Broomfield, CO; *U.S. Public*, pg. 449
Roth, S.K., Mgr.-Media Rels.--ICI Americas, Inc., Wilmington, DE; *Int'l*, pg. 663
Rothenburg, Steve S., V.P.-Communications--Reliance Group Holdings, Inc., New York, NY; *U.S. Public*, pg. 1374
Rothrock, Judith, V.P.-Corp. Commun.--Lawson Software, Minneapolis, MN; *U.S. Private*, pg. 654
Rotival, L., Gen. Mgr.-Sys., Pub. Rels. & Bus. Devel.--Nuovo Pignone S.p.a., Florence, Italy; *Int'l*, pg. 990
Roudier, Francois, Dir.-Communications--SNECMA - Societe Nationale d'Etude et de Construction de Moteurs d'Aviation, Paris, France; *Int'l*, pg. 1165
Rounds, D. Michael, Dir.-Commun.--Cyprus Amax Minerals Company, Englewood, CO; *U.S. Public*, pg. 470
Rouot, Jean-Paul, V.P.-Pub. Rels. & Commun.--SNECMA - Societe Nationale d'Etude et de Construction de Moteurs d'Aviation, Paris, France; *Int'l*, pg. 1165
Rourke, Michael J., Sr. V.P.-Communications & Corp. Affairs--The Great Atlantic & Pacific Tea Company, Inc., Montvale, NJ; *Int'l*, pg. 1375
Rouse, Charles, Dir.-Ext. Communications Svcs.--Hoechst Marion Roussel North America, Kansas City, MO; *Int'l*, pg. 625
Rouse, Charles F., Dir.-North American Commun.--Hoechst Marion Roussel, Inc., Bridgewater, NJ; *Int'l*, pg. 624
Roush, Ella M., Asst. V.P.-Plng. & Communication--Moyer Packing Company, Souderton, PA; *U.S. Private*, pg. 765
Roush, Rita, Mgr.-Sls. Promo. & Adv.--Autry Greer & Sons, Inc., Prichard, AL; *U.S. Private*, pg. 479
Rousseau, Pierre, V.P.-Corp. Affairs--Assurance vie Desjardins-Laurentienne, Levis, Canada; *Int'l*, pg. 396
Roussel, Daniel, V.P.-Pub. Affairs--Assurance vie Desjardins-Laurentienne, Levis, Canada; *Int'l*, pg. 396
Rovzer, Pat, Mgr.-Commun.--Commercial Credit Company, Baltimore, MD; *U.S. Public*, pg. 1633
Rowe, Julie, Mgr.-Pub. Rels.--Great Plains Manufacturing, Inc., Salina, KS; *U.S. Private*, pg. 475
Rowe, Sharon H., Dir.-Adv. & Pub. Rels.--The Greenbrier, White Sulphur Springs, WV; *U.S. Public*, pg. 284
Rowell, Catherine, Mktg. Communications Specialist--Veeder-Root Company, Simsbury, CT; *U.S. Public*, pg. 482
Rowley, Ellen, Mgr.-Mktg. & Communications--Modcomp, Fort Lauderdale, FL; *U.S. Public*, pg. 283
Rowse, Steve, V.P.-Bus. Devel.--Veryfine Products, Inc., Westford, MA; *U.S. Private*, pg. 1137
Roy, Andre, V.P.-Corp. Affairs--Societe Generale de Financement du Quebec, Montreal, Canada; *Int'l*, pg. 1274
Rozzi, S.J., Mgr.-Dealer Rels.--Benjamin Moore & Co., Montvale, NJ; *U.S. Private*, pg. 133
Rubenstein, Marke, Sr. V.P. & Pub. Rels. Dir.--North Castle Partners Advertising, Inc., Stamford, CT; *U.S. Private*, pg. 804
Rubis, Anastasia, Pub. Rels. Dir.--TBWA Chiat/Day New York, New York, NY; *U.S. Private*, pg. 1062
Ruch, John S., Supvr.-Media Rels.--PPG Industries, Inc., Pittsburgh, PA; *U.S. Public*, pg. 1245
Rudden, Eileen, Sr. V.P.-Communications Devel.--Lotus Development Corporation, Cambridge, MA; *U.S. Public*, pg. 896
Rudderow, Amy, Pub. Rels. Counselor--Sawyer Riley Compton Inc., Atlanta, GA; *U.S. Private*, pg. 969
Ruddock, Jennifer, Mgr.-Investor Rels.--Catellus Development Corporation, San Francisco, CA; *U.S. Public*, pg. 314
Rudnay, Darcy F., V.P.-Pub. Rels.--Advanta Corp., Spring House, PA; *U.S. Public*, pg. 22
Rudolph, Hans Peter, Dir.-Pub.Rels.--Puma AG Rudolf Dassler Sport, Herzogenaurach, Germany; *Int'l*, pg. 1072
Ruecke, Kurt, Dir.-Communications--MascoTech Tubular Products, Inc., Canton, MI; *U.S. Public*, pg. 1055
Ruf, Bruno, Dir.-Pub. Rels.--Migros, Zurich, Switzerland; *Int'l*, pg. 865
Rufe, Ellen, Mgr.-Pub. Rels.--Volt Information Sciences, Inc., New York, NY; *U.S. Public*, pg. 1724
Ruff, Jim, Dir.-H.R.--Concordia Publishing House, Saint Louis, MO; *U.S. Private*, pg. 261
Rugen, Karen, V.P.-Communications--Boston Chicken, Inc., Golden, CO; *U.S. Public*, pg. 247
Rugen, Karen, V.P.-Pub. Rels.--Hyatt Hotels Corporation, Chicago, IL; *U.S. Private*, pg. 551
Ruggiero, Albert V., V.P.--South Jersey Gas Co., Folsom, NJ; *U.S. Public*, pg. 1488
Ruhl, Bruce, Dir.-Public Rels.--Worthington Industries, Inc., Columbus, OH; *U.S. Public*, pg. 1780
Ruiz Huarte, Jose F., Dir.-Pub. Rels.--Transportacion Maritima Mexicana S.A. de C.V., Mexico, Mexico; *Int'l*, pg. 1418
Rukeyser, Robert J., Sr. V.P.-Corp. Affairs--Fortune Brands, Inc., Old Greenwich, CT; *U.S. Public*, pg. 674
Rumac, Barry, Dir.-Corp. Comm.--VTEL Corporation, Austin, TX; *U.S. Public*, pg. 1703
Rummel, Frieder, Dir.-Pub. Rels.--Procter & Gamble Austria GmbH, Vienna, Austria; *U.S. Public*, pg. 1332
Rumpf, Francois, Sr. V.P.--Ferrier Lullin & Cie SA, Geneva, Switzerland; *Int'l*, pg. 480
Rund, Brian, Pub. Rels. Dir.--Rhea & Kaiser Marketing Communications, Naperville, IL; *U.S. Private*, pg. 927
Runquist, Al, Dr., Mgr.-Publications & Promo.--Aldrich Chemical Co., Inc., Milwaukee, WI; *U.S. Public*, pg. 1471
Runtzler, Michael, Dir.-Pub. Rels.--Trimble Navigation Limited, Sunnyvale, CA; *U.S. Public*, pg. 1638
Rupin, Ellen, V.P.-Pub. Rels.--QVC, Inc., West Chester, PA; *U.S. Private*, pg. 897
Ruschak, William S., Exec. V.P.-Mktg. & Company Rels.--Willis Corroon Corp. of Michigan, Livonia, MI; *Int'l*, pg. 1506
Rusin, Pat, Admin.-Corp Communications--OCE USA, Inc., Chicago, IL; *Int'l*, pg. 994
Ruskowski, Carol, Mgr.-Pub. Rels.--NGC Corporation, Houston, TX; *U.S. Public*, pg. 1146
Rusnak, Joseph N., Mgr.-Communications--Bank of Boston Connecticut, Hartford, CT; *U.S. Public*, pg. 184
Russ, Dennis, Mgr.-Mktg. & Communications--AAF-International, Louisville, KY; *U.S. Private*, pg. 3
Russ, Joe, Dir.-Pub. Rels.--National-Standard Co., Niles, MI; *U.S. Public*, pg. 1160
Russ, Lauren, Pub. Rels. Acct. Supvr.--Jack Levy Associates, Public Relations Dept., Chicago, IL; *U.S. Private*, pg. 664
Russ, Terry, Dir.-Corp. Communications--Telxon Corporation, Akron, OH; *U.S. Public*, pg. 1573
Russack, Richard A., V.P.-Corp. Rels.--Burlington Northern Santa Fe Corporation, Fort Worth, TX; *U.S. Public*, pg. 268
Russek, H., V.P.-Employee Rels.--Astronautics Corporation of America, Milwaukee, WI; *U.S. Private*, pg. 93
Russell, Anita, Dir.-Corp. Commun.--Adolph Coors Company, Golden, CO; *U.S. Public*, pg. 445
Russell, Ed, Exec. V.P.-Worldwide Publicity--Columbia Pictures, Culver City, CA; *Int'l*, pg. 1281
Russell, Georgia, V.P.-Corp. Communications--Southwestern Life Insurance Company, Dallas, TX; *U.S. Private*, pg. 1018
Russell, J.C., Mgr.-Corp. Communications--Wavin Bv, Zwolle, Netherlands; *Int'l*, pg. 1135
Russell, Jane, Dir.-Commun.--HATCO, Inc., Garland, TX; *U.S. Private*, pg. 510
Russell, John A., Dir.-Corp. Commun.--Banc One Corporation, Columbus, OH; *U.S. Public*, pg. 172
Russell, Johnatha, Gen. Mgr.-Strategic Communications--PPP hc, Tunbridge Wells, United Kingdom; *Int'l*, pg. 1020
Russell, Lisa, Mgr.-Pub. Rels.--Batesville Casket Company, Inc., Batesville, IN; *U.S. Public*, pg. 828
Russo, Elizabeth L., V.P.-Corp. Commun.--The Mead Corporation, Dayton, OH; *U.S. Public*, pg. 1074
Russo, Joseph M., V.P.-Pub. Affairs--The Hertz Corporation, Park Ridge, NJ; *U.S. Public*, pg. 664
Russo, Karen L., Dir.-Intl. Sls. & Mgr.-Promo.--Eastern Air Devices, Inc., Dover, NH; *U.S. Private*, pg. 357
Russo, Patricia, Corp. Communications--Movado Group, Inc., Lyndhurst, NJ; *U.S. Public*, pg. 1140
Rustad, David, Mgr.-Pub. Rels.--Lutheran Brotherhood, Minneapolis, MN; *U.S. Private*, pg. 681
Rutledge, Betty, Coord.-Mktg. Communications--Whataburger, Inc., Corpus Christi, TX; *U.S. Private*, pg. 1170
Rutledge, Joseph R., V.P.-Commun.--General Mills, Inc., Minneapolis, MN; *U.S. Public*, pg. 717
Ruuskanen, Antti, Mgr.-Corp. Communications--Imatran Voima Oy, Helsinki, Finland; *Int'l*, pg. 660
Ryan, Debe, Mgr.-Pub. Rels.--Trus Joist MacMillan Limited, Surrey, Canada; *Int'l*, pg. 829
Ryan, Debe, Mgr.-Pub. Rels.--Trus Joist MacMillan Limited, Surrey, Canada; *U.S. Public*, pg. 1556
Ryan, Debe, Mgr.-Pub. Rels.--Trus Joist (Western) Ltd., Surrey, Canada; *U.S. Public*, pg. 1556
Ryan, Dede, Dir.-Commun.--Trus Joist MacMillan, Boise, ID; *Int'l*, pg. 829
Ryan, Dede, Dir.-Commun.--TJ International, Inc., Boise, ID; *U.S. Public*, pg. 1556
Ryan, Dede, Dir.-Commun.--Trus Joist MacMillan, Boise, ID; *U.S. Public*, pg. 1556

Ryan, Denise, Dir.-Commun.-Consumer Div.--The Black & Decker Corporation, Towson, MD; *U.S. Public*, pg. 233

Ryan, Helen, Mgr.-Pub. Rels.--NationsBank Virginia, Richmond, VA; *U.S. Public*, pg. 1163

Ryan, Locksley, Dir.-Commun.--British Aerospace p.l.c., Farnborough, United Kingdom; *Int'l*, pg. 217

Ryan, Nancy E., Dir.-Communications & Media--Klockner Pentaplast of America, Inc., Gordonsville, VA; *Int'l*, pg. 737

Ryan, Sally Mason, Creative Dir./Writer--W. Braun Company, Chicago, IL; *U.S. Private*, pg. 166

Ryan, Tom, Dir.-Commun.--SkyePharma PLC, London, United Kingdom; *Int'l*, pg. 1262

Ryder, Paul R., V.P.-Investor Rels.--Echlin Inc., Branford, CT; *U.S. Public*, pg. 560

Rydeski, Phil, Mgr.-Pub. Rels.--Harbison-Walker Refractories, Pittsburgh, PA; *U.S. Public*, pg. 748

Rygiel, Edward K., Sr. V.P.-Corp. Devel. & Pres.-MDS Capital Corp.--MDS Inc., Etobicoke, Canada; *Int'l*, pg. 826

Rymek, Edwin, Corp. Commun.--Artra Group Incorporated, Northfield, IL; *U.S. Public*, pg. 136

Saarinen, Matti, V.P.-Corp. Communications--Neste Oy, Espoo, Finland; *Int'l*, pg. 912

Sabado, Debra, Dir.-Customer Service--Mizuno USA, Inc., Norcross, GA; *Int'l*, pg. 885

Sabala, Edward, Mgr.-Corp. Communications--ISK Biotech, Mentor, OH; *Int'l*, pg. 689

Sabath, Tim, Mgr.-Pub. Rels. & New Media--Picker International, Inc., Cleveland, OH; *Int'l*, pg. 545

Saber, Janine S., Dir.-Pub. Rels. & Sls. Promo.-Home Fashions Div.--WestPoint Stevens Inc., West Point, GA; *U.S. Public*, pg. 1762

Sabin, David, Mgr.-Customer Service--Harig Products, Elgin, IL; *U.S. Public*, pg. 252

Sabinash, E., Dir.-Mktg. Communications--Eaton Corporation, Electric Drives Division, Kenosha, WI; *U.S. Public*, pg. 556

Sable, Diane, Dir.-News & Pub. Rels.--PG&E Corporation, San Francisco, CA; *U.S. Public*, pg. 1240

Sabota, Dave, Dir.-Information Services--The J.M. Ney Company, Bloomfield, CT; *U.S. Public*, pg. 111

Sabourin, Jim, Gen. Dir.-Media & Community Rels.--Burlington Northern Santa Fe Corporation, Fort Worth, TX; *U.S. Public*, pg. 268

Sacco, Frances, Dir.-Mktg. Communications--Microcom, Norwood, MA; *U.S. Public*, pg. 417

Sackler, Art, V.P.-Public Policy--Time Warner Inc., New York, NY; *U.S. Public*, pg. 1610

Sagalski, Laura, Dir.-Commun.--Omni Hotels, Irving, TX; *U.S. Private*, pg. 1065

Sagan, E.D., Mgr.-Pub. Rels.--Alberta Power Limited, Edmonton, Canada; *Int'l*, pg. 95

Sage, Connie, Dir.-Corp. Communications--Landmark Communications, Inc., Norfolk, VA; *U.S. Private*, pg. 647

Saito, Kazuyoshi, Dir.-Pub. Rels.--Futaba Corporation, Mobara, Japan; *Int'l*, pg. 531

Saiucci, Diane, Dir.-Commun.--DeVry Institutes, Oak Brook Terrace, IL; *U.S. Public*, pg. 503

Sajkowski, Debra, Mgr.-Adv.--Milwaukee Electric Tool Corp., Brookfield, WI; *Int'l*, pg. 96

Sakata, Hiroshi, Mgr.--Sakata Seed Corporation, Yokohama, Japan; *Int'l*, pg. 1178

Salah, Sandra, V.P.-Corp. Rels.--Western Micro Technology, Inc., Campbell, CA; *U.S. Public*, pg. 1759

Salazar, Veronica, V.P.-Community Rels.--San Antonio Express News, San Antonio, TX; *U.S. Private*, pg. 517

Salber, Daniel, Dr., Mgr.-Adv. & Pub. Rels.--Rheinische Olefinwerke GmbH, Wesseling, Germany; *Int'l*, pg. 105

Salcido, Lorene, Dir.-Adv. & Pub. Rels.--Bridgford Foods Corporation, Anaheim, CA; *U.S. Public*, pg. 252

Saldivar, Margaret, Communication Specialist--Mettler-Toledo Inc., Worthington, OH; *U.S. Private*, pg. 4

Salem, Richard, Mgr.-Pub. Rels.--Novartis Pharmaceuticals, East Hanover, NJ; *Int'l*, pg. 973

Saliba, John, Grp. Head-Pub. Rels. & Mktg.--Air Malta Co. Ltd., Luqa, Malta; *Int'l*, pg. 37

Salisbury, Henry H., V.P.-Pub. Affairs--Kansas City Southern Industries, Inc., Kansas City, MO; *U.S. Public*, pg. 943

Salkind, Susan, Mgr.-Corp. Commun.--CSE Insurance Group, San Francisco, CA; *U.S. Private*, pg. 197

Salky, Molly, Dir.-Inv. Rels. & Corp. Communications--The Earthgrains Company, Clayton, MO; *U.S. Public*, pg. 547

Salmans, Charles, Mgr.-Corp. Commun.--The Quick & Reilly Group Inc., Palm Beach, FL; *U.S. Public*, pg. 650

Salminen, Susan, Mgr.-Mktg. Communications--Cylink Corp., Sunnyvale, CA; *U.S. Public*, pg. 1306

Salomon, Peter, Mgr.-Pub. Rels.--IL Returpapper, Stockholm, Sweden; *Int'l*, pg. 646

Salomons, M.E.J., Sec.-Bd. Mgmnt. & Pub. Rels. Officer--Internatio-Muller N.V., Rotterdam, Netherlands; *Int'l*, pg. 680

Saltzman, Nancy B., V.P. & Assoc. Counsel--Chartwell Re Corporation, Stamford, CT; *U.S. Public*, pg. 336

Salvatore, G.E., Mgr.-Distributor Rels.--Carborundum Abrasives North America, High Point, NC; *Int'l*, pg. 1174

Salyer, Sandra, V.P.-Pub. Affairs--Mervyn's California, Hayward, CA; *U.S. Public*, pg. 489

Sammis, Elizabeth, Sr. Dir.-Communications--Mid Atlantic Medical Services, Inc., Rockville, MD; *U.S. Public*, pg. 1109

Sammons, John, V.P.-Corp. Communications--Van Waters & Rogers, Kirkland, WA; *Int'l*, pg. 1147

Samson, Antonio R., Sr. V.P.-Corp. Services--Philippine Long Distance Telephone Company, Manila, Philippines; *Int'l*, pg. 1051

Samson, Brad, Dir.-Investor & Pub. Rels.--Wallace Computer Services, Inc., Lisle, IL; *U.S. Public*, pg. 1735

Samson, David, V.P.-Corp. Commun.--Levi Strauss & Co., San Francisco, CA; *U.S. Private*, pg. 662

Samuel, J., Mgr.-Public Rels. & Govt. Affairs--London International Group plc, London, United Kingdom; *Int'l*, pg. 815

Sanborn, Sally, Dir.-Trade Rels.--Save Mart Supermarkets, Modesto, CA; *U.S. Private*, pg. 968

Sanchez, Judy, Dir.-Corp. Communications--United States Sugar Corporation, Clewiston, FL; *U.S. Private*, pg. 1126

Sandall, Laura, Dir.-Special Events & Pub. Rels.--The Department Store Division of Dayton Hudson Corporation, Minneapolis, MN; *U.S. Public*, pg. 489

Sandbach, Henry A., V.P.-Public Rels.--Nabisco Inc., Parsippany, NJ; *U.S. Public*, pg. 1355

Sandberg, Walter G., Mgr.-Pub. Affairs--Wisconsin Public Service Corporation, Green Bay, WI; *U.S. Public*, pg. 1728

Sanders, Jo, Mgr.-Pub. Rels.--Britannia Music Co. Ltd., Ilford, United Kingdom; *Int'l*, pg. 1052

Sanders, Mary Brady, Dir.-Governmental Affairs & Mktg. Communications--The Homestead L.C., Hot Springs, VA; *U.S. Private*, pg. 247

Sanders, Mike, Mgr.-MarCom--Micropolis Corporation, Chatsworth, CA; *U.S. Private*, pg. 742

Sanders, Richard, Dir.-Corp. Communications--United News & Media plc, London, United Kingdom; *Int'l*, pg. 1443

Sanders, Susan, Dir.-Corp. Communications--Evening Post Publishing Co., Charleston, SC; *U.S. Private*, pg. 385

Sanders, Walter, Dir.-Pub. Affairs--Diners Club Inc., Chicago, IL; *U.S. Public*, pg. 377

Sanders, William H., V.P.-Customer Service--The Coleman Company, Inc., Golden, CO; *U.S. Private*, pg. 690

Sandler, Norm, Dir.-Pub. Rels.--Motorola, Inc., Schaumburg, IL; *U.S. Public*, pg. 1136

Sands, John F., Jr., Dir.-Pub. Affairs--Barnes Group Inc., Bristol, CT; *U.S. Public*, pg. 189

Sanger, Carol, V.P.-Corp. Communications--Macy's East, New York, NY; *U.S. Public*, pg. 618

Sankey, Kelly, Coord.-Customer Communications--MidAmerican Energy Holdings, Des Moines, IA; *U.S. Public*, pg. 1109

Sanscartier, Cecile, Dir.-Pub. Affairs--Donohue Inc., Quebec, Canada; *Int'l*, pg. 1075

Santanasto, Jim, Dir.-Corp. Commun.--Union Pacific Corporation, Dallas, TX; *U.S. Public*, pg. 1667

Santoni, Ellen, Mgr.-Corp. Commun.--Everett Charles Technologies, Pomona, CA; *U.S. Private*, pg. 386

Santosuosso, Vincent, Jr., V.P.-Exec. Admin. & Pub. Rels.--Technical Aid Corporation, Newton, MA; *U.S. Private*, pg. 1072

Saras, Amy, Mgr.-Mktg. Communications--The Kendall Company, Mansfield, MA; *U.S. Public*, pg. 1647

Sargent, Tina, Admin. Asst.--Inter-Tel, Incorporated, Phoenix, AZ; *U.S. Public*, pg. 888

Sarkisian, G.C., Mgr.-Communications & Media Relations--Salt River Project Agricultural Improvement and Power District, Tempe, AZ; *U.S. Private*, pg. 962

Sarko, Cindy, Dir.-Pub. Rels.--Busch Gardens Williamsburg, Williamsburg, VA; *U.S. Public*, pg. 114

Sarmanian, Ronni, Dir.-Corp. Communications--Autodesk, Inc., San Rafael, CA; *U.S. Public*, pg. 148

Sarnow, Beatrice, Pub. Rels. Dir.--American Television Time, Inc., Austin, TX; *U.S. Private*, pg. 63

Sarsaty, Ruth, Pub. Rels.--Radio City Productions, New York, NY; *Int'l*, pg. 873

Sartorius, John, Dir.-Mktg. Team-Communications--Busch Entertainment Corp., Clayton, MO; *U.S. Public*, pg. 114

Sasaki, Tadashi, Dir.--Duskin Co., Ltd., Osaka, Japan; *Int'l*, pg. 422

Sasso, Greg W., V.P.-Corp. Devel. & Commun.--Biomet, Inc., Warsaw, IN; *U.S. Public*, pg. 231

Sato, Kotaro, Sr. V.P.-Pub. Rels.--Japan Airlines Company, Ltd., Tokyo, Japan; *Int'l*, pg. 699

Sato, Masaru, Gen. Mgr.-Personnel--Maruha Corporation, Tokyo, Japan; *Int'l*, pg. 845

Saurer, D.W., Mgr.-Pub. Rels.--Lord Corporation, Cary, NC; *U.S. Private*, pg. 675

Sauter, Markus, Mgr.-Pub. Rels.--Georg Fischer Ltd., Schaffhausen, Switzerland; *Int'l*, pg. 488

Sauther, Melissa, Mgr.-Mktg. Communications--Key Tronic Corporation, Spokane, WA; *U.S. Public*, pg. 953

Sauvage, Robert, Mgr.-Corp. Communications--Herstal S.A., Herstal, Belgium; *Int'l*, pg. 617

Savage, Sheryl, Coord.-Pub. Rels. & Trade Shows--Oki Telecom Group, Suwanee, GA; *Int'l*, pg. 1000

Savner, Rich, Pub. Affairs Rep.--Pathmark Stores Incorporated, Woodbridge, NJ; *U.S. Private*, pg. 843

Sawyer, Russ, Reg. Mgr.-Affairs--Riverdale Chemical Co., Glenwood, IL; *U.S. Private*, pg. 934

Saxenmeyer, Susan J., V.P.-Commun.--TCA Cable TV, Inc., Tyler, TX; *U.S. Public*, pg. 1553

Saxton, Cliff, V.P.-Corp. Communications--UniGroup, Inc., Fenton, MO; *U.S. Private*, pg. 1117

Sayer, David C., Exec. Dir.-Adv. & Pub. Rels.--Publishers Clearing House, Port Washington, NY; *U.S. Private*, pg. 893

Sayre, Larry, Chief Fin. Officer, V.P.-Fin., Controller & Treas.--Collins Industries, Inc., Hutchinson, KS; *U.S. Public*, pg. 399

Scaduto, James A., V.P.-Rels.--Barron's The Dow Jones Business & Financial Weekly, New York, NY; *U.S. Public*, pg. 524

Scaglione, Rich, V.P. & Gen. Mgr.-Buntin Pub. Rels.--The Buntin Group, Nashville, TN; *U.S. Private*, pg. 181

Scarpato, George, Dir.-Pub. Rels. & Communications--Industrial Indemnity Company, San Francisco, CA; *U.S. Public*, pg. 681

Schaber, Josef, Dr., Mgr.-Pub. Rels.--RWE Entsorgung AG, Essen, Germany; *Int'l*, pg. 1081

Schade, Harold C., Asst. V.P.-Public Rels.--USAA (United Services Automobile Association), San Antonio, TX; *U.S. Private*, pg. 1114

Schaefer, Debra G., V.P.-H.R. & Commun., Aeroquip--Aeroquip-Vickers, Inc., Maumee, OH; *U.S. Public*, pg. 24

Schaeffer, Raymond, V.P.-New Bus.--Fay, Spofford & Thorndike, Inc., Burlington, MA; *U.S. Private*, pg. 397

Schafer, Dan A., Dir.-Pub. Affairs--The Minute Maid Company, Houston, TX; *U.S. Public*, pg. 392

Schaffer, Archie, Dir.-Media, Public & Govt. Affairs--Tyson Foods, Inc., Springdale, AR; *U.S. Public*, pg. 1652

Schapdick, Chris, Product Mgr.--Rosenthal U.S.A. Limited, Carlstadt, NJ; *Int'l*, pg. 1127

Schauble, Judith, Mgr.-Pub. Rels.--Durr AG, Stuttgart, Germany; *Int'l*, pg. 421

Schaus, Cynthia M., Mgr.-Corp. Commun.--Equitable of Iowa Companies, Des Moines, IA; *Int'l*, pg. 647

Schawacker, William H., Mgr.-Corp. Commun.--Nooter Corporation, Saint Louis, MO; *U.S. Private*, pg. 801

Scheffer, Carl, Dir.-GMC Truck Pub. Rels.--Pontiac-GMC Truck Division, Pontiac, MI; *U.S. Public*, pg. 720

Schein, Dennis, Mgr.-Pub. Rels.--The Hartford Courant Company, Hartford, CT; *U.S. Public*, pg. 1616

Schellenberg, Ted, Mgr.-External Rels.--BC Gas Inc., Vancouver, Canada; *Int'l*, pg. 114

Scher, Barry F., V.P.-Pub. Affairs--Giant Food Inc., Landover, MD; *U.S. Public*, pg. 741

Scherer, Beatrice, V.P.-Customer Svcs.--Graham-Field Health Products, Inc., Hauppauge, NY; *U.S. Public*, pg. 757

Scherf-Pompa, Martha, Mgr.-Publicity--Gale Research Inc., Detroit, MI; *U.S. Public*, pg. 1600

Schiciano, Jason C., Pres.--The Coon-De Visser Co., Royal Oak, MI; *U.S. Private*, pg. 273

Schick, Thomas, Exec. V.P.-Corp. Affairs & Communications--American Express Company, New York, NY; *U.S. Public*, pg. 73

Schiele, Patty, Supvr.-Pub. Rels.--CCH Incorporated, Riverwoods, IL; *Int'l*, pg. 1513

Schiffmacher, William G., Sr. V.P.-Customer Rels., Information Systems & Tech.--Long Island Lighting Company, Hicksville, NY; *U.S. Public*, pg. 1013

Schikker, M.M.A., Dir.-Pub. Rels.--VNU Verenigde Nederlandse Uitgeversbedrijven B.V., Haarlem, Netherlands; *Int'l*, pg. 1445

Schilling, Nicole, Mgr.-Pub. Rels.--Merinos, Saint Quentin-en-Yvelines, France; *Int'l*, pg. 858

Schillinger, Jorg, Mgr.-Pub. Rels.--Spar Handels AG, Schenefeld, Germany; *Int'l*, pg. 1288

Schindler, Dana, Asst. Dir.-Mktg. & Communications--Great Lakes Window, Inc., Toledo, OH; *U.S. Public*, pg. 1193

Schintgen, Karin, V.P.-Pub. Rels. & Internal Communications--CLT-UFA, Luxembourg, Luxembourg; *Int'l*, pg. 561

Schintgen, Karin, Dir.-Communications--CLT-UFA, Luxembourg, Luxembourg; *Int'l*, pg. 561

Schirmer, Andre, Mgr.-Pub. Rels.--RTL 2, Grunwald, Germany; *Int'l*, pg. 562

Schirmer, James, Dir.-Brand Strategy, Media Group--U S West Inc., Englewood, CO; *U.S. Public*, pg. 1688

Schlatter, Lee Ann, Dir.-Corp. Communications--Knight-Ridder, Inc., Miami, FL; *U.S. Public*, pg. 963

Schlegel, Mike, Admin.-Sls. & Communications--Bunton Division, Louisville, KY; *U.S. Public*, pg. 1589

Schleiter, Astrid, Asst.-Pub. Rels. & Mktg.--Wurzner Dauerbackwaren GmbH, Wurzen, Germany; *Int'l*, pg. 1514

Schlesier, Tony, Mgr.-Member Communications--Milk Marketing Inc., Strongsville, OH; *U.S. Private*, pg. 745

Schmeling, Adrian, Mgr.-Pub. Rels.--Hartmarx Corporation, Chicago, IL; *U.S. Public*, pg. 795

Schmid, Alfons, V.P.-Pub. Affairs--Koninklijke Ahold NV, Zaandam, Netherlands; *Int'l*, pg. 749

Schmidt, Adrien, Corp. Communications Dept.--Union Bank of Switzerland, Zurich, Switzerland; *Int'l*, pg. 1439

Schmidt, Christian, Tech. Editor--GESTRA GmbH, Bremen, Germany; *Int'l*, pg. 549

Schmidt, Donald J., V.P.-Corp. Commun.--National Travelers Life Co., West Des Moines, IA; *U.S. Private*, pg. 787

Schmidt, Gert, Dr., Dir.-Investor Rels. & Press Office--IKB Deutsche Industriebank AG, Dusseldorf, Germany; *Int'l*, pg. 645

Schmidt, Jill, V.P.-Corp. Communications--International Multifoods Corporation, Minneapolis, MN; *U.S. Public*, pg. 900

Schmidt, Jo, Mgr.-Pub. Rels.--Schwarz Pharma Inc., Mequon, WI; *Int'l*, pg. 1211

Schmidt, Uwe, Mng. Dir.-Social Affairs--STAHLwerke Bremen GmbH, Bremen, Germany; *Int'l*, pg. 79

Schmierser, Ann, Pub. Rels. Asst.--Univest Financial Services, LLC, Atlanta, GA; *U.S. Private*, pg. 1128

Schmitt, Karl F., Jr., V.P.-Commun.--Churchill Downs, Inc., Louisville, KY; *U.S. Public*, pg. 356

Schnetzer, Angie L., Coord.-Pub. & Shareholder Rels.--Chemed Corporation, Cincinnati, OH; *U.S. Public*, pg. 343

Schoenberger, Diana L., V.P.-Mktg. Commun. & Investor Rels.--CitFed Bancorp, Inc., Dayton, OH; *U.S. Public*, pg. 376

Schoeneck, David, Dir.-Pub. Rels.--National Car Rental System, Inc., Minneapolis, MN; *U.S. Public*, pg. 1379

Schoenmakers, J.J.J.G., Dir.-Corp. Communications--Royal Gist-Brocades N.V., Delft, Netherlands; *Int'l*, pg. 1142

Schoettl, Brigitte, Dr., Sec.-Pub. Rels.--Bayerische Vereinsbank Group, Munich, Germany; *Int'l*, pg. 178

Schollhammer, Stefan, Mng. Dir.--Klafs Saunabau GmbH & Co. KG Medizinische Technik, Schwabisch Hall, Germany; *Int'l*, pg. 736

Scholz Barber, Mary, Pub. Rels. Dir.--Kupper Parker Communications Inc., Saint Louis, MO; *U.S. Private*, pg. 637

Schon, Cecilia, Sr. V.P.-Corp. Commun.--Trygg-Hansa, Stockholm, Sweden; *Int'l*, pg. 1425

Schoonover, Gary, Mgr.-Corp. Communications--The At-A-Glance Group, Sidney, NY; *U.S. Private*, pg. 295

Schopp, Keith, Mgr.-Corp. Commun.--Ralston Purina Company, Saint Louis, MO; *U.S. Public*, pg. 1359

Schrader, Dwayne, Mgr.-Commun.--The Ward Machinery Company, Hunt Valley, MD; *U.S. Private*, pg. 1149

Schrader, Lynn, Pub. Affairs Staff Assoc.--Krazy Glue Inc., New York, NY; *U.S. Private*, pg. 158

Schraeder, Marsha, Dir.-Customer Service--G.E. Capital Fleet Services, Eden Prairie, MN; *U.S. Public*, pg. 712

Schreiber, Elliot S., Sr. V.P.-Corp. Commun.--Northern Telecom Limited, Brampton, Canada; *Int'l*, pg. 968
Schreiber, Hans, Mng. Dir.--Metallgesellschaft AG, Frankfurt, Germany; *Int'l*, pg. 860
Schroeder, Heinz, Mgr.-Pub. Rels.--Bayer de Chile S.A., Santiago, Chile; *Int'l*, pg. 175
Schropp, Mary Lou, Dir.-Corp. Communications--PHP Healthcare Corporation, Reston, VA; *U.S. Public*, pg. 1241
Schruth, Peter, Sr. V.P.-Affiliate Rels. Div.--CBS Broadcast Group, New York, NY; *U.S. Public*, pg. 274
Schuetz-Spoerl, Georgia, Mgr.-Pub. Rels.--Osterreichische Postsparkasse AG, Vienna, Austria; *Int'l*, pg. 1012
Schukies, Gert, Dr., Dir.-Corp. Comm.--Deutsche Post AG, Bonn, Germany; *Int'l*, pg. 407
Schuler, Carol, V.P.-Communication & Pub. Rels.--Clarins USA Inc., New York, NY; *Int'l*, pg. 295
Schuler, Nancy, Mktg. Svcs. Specialist--Brinkmann Instruments, Inc., Westbury, NY; *U.S. Private*, pg. 169
Schulert, Sanford, Dir.-Mktg. Communications--Amoco Chemicals, Chicago, IL; *U.S. Public*, pg. 102
Schulte, Lynne M., Mgr.-Sls. Service--Dixon Ticonderoga Company, Heathrow, FL; *U.S. Public*, pg. 514
Schultz, James, Dir.-Corp. Communications--Whittaker Corporation, Simi Valley, CA; *U.S. Public*, pg. 1766
Schultz, Jim, Dir.-Pub. Rels.--Atlanta National League Baseball Club, Inc., Atlanta, GA; *U.S. Public*, pg. 1614
Schultz, Nancy E., Dir.-Corp. Commun. & Investor Rels.--Merit Medical Systems, Inc., South Jordan, UT; *U.S. Public*, pg. 1096
Schultz, Patricia, V.P.-Entertainment Press & Publicity--National Broadcasting Co., Inc., New York, NY; *U.S. Public*, pg. 712
Schultz, Robert F., V.P.-Indus. Rels. & Sr. Counsel--Ampco-Pittsburgh Corporation, Pittsburgh, PA; *U.S. Public*, pg. 103
Schultz, Stephanie, Acting Dir.-Corp. Communications--Computer Data Systems, Inc., Rockville, MD; *U.S. Public*, pg. 28
Schulze, Laura, Mgr.-Adv. & Pub. Rels.--Furman Lumber Company, Inc., Billerica, MA; *U.S. Private*, pg. 431
Schumacher, Laura, Dir.-Pub. Rels.--Kyocera America, Inc., San Diego, CA; *Int'l*, pg. 775
Schumacher, Yves, Pub. Rels. Dir.--Impuls Advertising AG, Kusnacht, Switzerland; *Int'l*, pg. 666
Schurman, Mark, Dir.-Corp. Communications--Herman Miller, Inc., Zeeland, MI; *U.S. Public*, pg. 1111
Schuster, Gary F., V.P.-Corp. Rels.--Union Pacific Corporation, Dallas, TX; *U.S. Public*, pg. 1667
Schutter, Martin, Mgr.-Pub. Rels.--Warsteiner Brauerei Haus Cramer GmbH & Co., Warstein, Germany; *Int'l*, pg. 1486
Schwabenlender, Ron, Mgr.-Pub. Rels.--Okuma America Corporation, Charlotte, NC; *Int'l*, pg. 1001
Schwartz, Diane, V.P.-Adv. & Pub. Rels.--Christian Dior Perfumes Inc., New York, NY; *Int'l*, pg. 781
Schwartz, Gil, Sr. V.P.-Communications--CBS, New York, NY; *U.S. Public*, pg. 273
Schwartz, Gil, Sr. V.P.-Communications--CBS Broadcast Group, New York, NY; *U.S. Public*, pg. 274
Schwartz, Nancy, V.P.-Adv. & Pub. Rels.--Medicine Shoppe International, Inc., Saint Louis, MO; *U.S. Public*, pg. 304
Schwartz, Paula, Mgr.-Corp. Rels.--Overseas Shipholding Group, Inc., New York, NY; *U.S. Public*, pg. 1236
Schwartz, Stephanie, Mgr.-Corp. Communications--Wind River Systems, Inc., Alameda, CA; *U.S. Public*, pg. 1770
Schwartz, Thomas P., V.P.-Communications--Maytag Corporation, Newton, IA; *U.S. Public*, pg. 1064
Schweber, Dennis, V.P.-Mktg.--Jaco Electronics, Inc., Hauppauge, NY; *U.S. Public*, pg. 920
Schwegler, Janet, Mgr.-Mdsg.--Integrated Device Technology, Inc., Santa Clara, CA; *U.S. Public*, pg. 884
Schwegman, Jennifer, Mgr.-Corp. Commun.--Lawson Software, Minneapolis, MN; *U.S. Private*, pg. 654
Schweikhart, Gary, V.P.-Pub. Rels.--Office Depot Inc., Delray Beach, FL; *U.S. Public*, pg. 1212
Schweikher, Karen, Dir.-Corp. Communications & Investor Rels.--Ampex Corporation, Redwood City, CA; *U.S. Public*, pg. 104
Schweitzer, George, Exec. V.P.-Mktg. Communications--CBS, New York, NY; *U.S. Public*, pg. 273
Schwietzer, Jeff, Mgr.-Pub. Rels.--American Crystal Sugar Company, Moorhead, MN; *U.S. Private*, pg. 52
Scipione, Marianne, V.P.-Corp. Communications--U.S. Surgical Corp., Norwalk, CT; *U.S. Public*, pg. 1687
Scisson, Brenda, Exec. V.P. & Pub. Rels. Dir.--Cranford Johnson Robinson Woods, Little Rock, AR; *U.S. Private*, pg. 286
Sclafani, Ernestine, Mgr.-Pub. Rels.--Bally Management, New Rochelle, NY; *Int'l*, pg. 998
Scofield, Dave, Dir.-Communications--Minolta Corporation, Ramsey, NJ; *Int'l*, pg. 869
Scofield, David, Dir.-Adv. & Pub. Rels.--Office Products Div., Ramsey, NJ; *Int'l*, pg. 869
Scott, Billie, Dir.-Pub. Rels. (Indianapolis)--The Edward J. DeBartolo Corporation, Youngstown, OH; *U.S. Private*, pg. 319
Scott, Billie, Dir.-Pub. Rels.--Simon DeBartolo Group, Inc., Indianapolis, IN; *U.S. Public*, pg. 1474
Scott, Chery, Dir.-Pub. Rels.--Farmers Telephone Co-Op, Kingstree, SC; *U.S. Private*, pg. 395
Scott, David W., V.P.-Pub. Affairs--Ford Motor Company, Dearborn, MI; *U.S. Public*, pg. 661
Scott, Debbie, Mgr.-Pub. Rels. & Media-North America--IceLandAir, Columbia, MD; *Int'l*, pg. 658
Scott, John, Dir.-Mktg. & Communication--Allsteel, Inc., Aurora, IL; *U.S. Public*, pg. 772
Scott, L., Mgr.-Communications--The Simba Group, Isando, South Africa; *Int'l*, pg. 496
Scott, Mark R., Dir.-Investor Rels. & Fin. Analyst--Autocam Corporation, Grand Rapids, MI; *U.S. Public*, pg. 148
Scotti, Paul, Dir.-Pub. Rels.--Amrion Inc., Boulder, CO; *U.S. Public*, pg. 1767
Scoular, Valerie, Dir.-Customer Service--British Airways PLC, London, United Kingdom; *Int'l*, pg. 218
Scovie, Jay, Asst. Mgr.-Corp. Communications--Kyocera International, Inc., San Diego, CA; *Int'l*, pg. 775
Scroggins, John, Pub. Rels. Dir.--Noble & Associates Public Relations, Chicago, IL; *U.S. Private*, pg. 800
Scroggins, Troy, Dir.-Pub. Rels.--Belarus Machinery, Inc., Milwaukee, WI; *Int'l*, pg. 101
Searcy, Alice, Mgr.-Pub. Rels.--Michelin North America, Greenville, SC; *Int'l*, pg. 322
Searcy, Diane L., Dir.-Commun.--MFA Oil Company, Columbia, MO; *U.S. Private*, pg. 687
Sedlenieks, Maris, Dir.-Corp. Commun.--AGA AB, Lidingo, Sweden; *Int'l*, pg. 12
Sedwick, Lindsay M., Chief Fin. Officer & Sr. V.P.--Standex International Corporation, Salem, NH; *U.S. Public*, pg. 1505
Seeley, Lynne, Mgr.-Pub. Rels.--Brigham's, Inc., Arlington, MA; *U.S. Private*, pg. 483
Seeliger, Michael, V.P.-Investor Rels. & Corp. Rels.--Horizon/CMS Healthcare Corporation, Albuquerque, NM; *U.S. Public*, pg. 836
Segrelles, Jorge, Dir.-External Rels., Mktg. & Sls. Network--Repsol S.A., Madrid, Spain; *Int'l*, pg. 1104
Seheley, Christine, Dir.-Pub. Rels.--The Acacia Group - Acacia Life Insurance Co., Bethesda, MD; *U.S. Private*, pg. 10
Seibert, Dane, Sr. V.P.-Sls. & Mktg.--Glacier Water Services Inc., Carlsbad, CA; *U.S. Public*, pg. 745
Seidman, Allan, Sr. V.P.-Pub. rels.--Charles of the Ritz Group Ltd., New York, NY; *U.S. Private*, pg. 689
Seidman, Allan, Sr. V.P.-Pub. Rels.--Almay, Inc., New York, NY; *U.S. Private*, pg. 689
Seidman, Allyn, Sr. V.P.-Corp. Communications--Revlon, Inc., New York, NY; *U.S. Private*, pg. 689
Seidman, Allyn, Sr. V.P.-Pub. Rels.--Revlon-Realistic Professional Products, Inc., New York, NY; *U.S. Private*, pg. 690
Seither, Mike, Dir.-Corp. Communications--Xilinx, Inc., San Jose, CA; *U.S. Public*, pg. 1786
Seitz, Mark, Mgr.-Sls., Mktg., Adv. & Pub. Rels.--Service Supply Co. Inc. of Indiana, Indianapolis, IN; *U.S. Private*, pg. 987
Sekul, Nadine, Mgr.-Pub. Rels.--Vanstar Corporation, Pleasanton, CA; *U.S. Public*, pg. 1708
Selland, Clay E., Treas. & Asst. Sec.--Longs Drug Stores Corporation, Walnut Creek, CA; *U.S. Public*, pg. 1013
Sellers, Tracy, Mgr.-Adv.--ASICS Tiger Corporation, Fountain Valley, CA; *U.S. Private*, pg. 89
Selsor, Jill, Mgr.-Distributor Rels.--Hobart Brothers Co., Troy, OH; *U.S. Public*, pg. 866
Seltzer, Sherwin, V.P., Gen. Sls. Mgr. & Mgr.-Sls. Promo., Pub. Rels. & Adv.--Villazon Company Inc., Upper Saddle River, NJ; *U.S. Private*, pg. 1140
Sepulveda, Carmen, V.P. & Pub. Rels. Dir.--The Bravo Group, New York, NY; *U.S. Private*, pg. 1197
Serada, Syuji, Pres.--Nissho Iwai New Zealand Limited, Auckland, New Zealand; *Int'l*, pg. 948
Serafin, Kristine, Dir.-Adv. & Pub. Rels.--Omni Hotels, Irving, TX; *U.S. Private*, pg. 1065
Serell, Andrew, Dir.-Investor Rels.--Apertus Technologies Incorporated, Eden Prairie, MN; *U.S. Public*, pg. 119
Servoss, Judith A., V.P.-Pub. Rels.--U S West Inc., Englewood, CO; *U.S. Public*, pg. 1688
Sessler, Andrea, Sr. V.P., Human Resources & Pub. Rels. Dir.--Ammirati, Puris & Lintas, Inc., New York, NY; *U.S. Private*, pg. 66
Setnicka, Lu, Dir.-Pub. Rels.--Lost Arrow Corporation, Ventura, CA; *U.S. Private*, pg. 676
Settle, Bob, Dir.-Mktg. Communications--Siemens Energy & Automation Inc., Alpharetta, GA; *Int'l*, pg. 1245
Sevcik, Fran, Dir.-Pub. Rels.--Norwegian Cruise Line, Miami, FL; *U.S. Private*, pg. 808
Severts, Mark, Mgr.-Media Svcs.--New Century Energies, Inc., Denver, CO; *U.S. Public*, pg. 1170
Sexton, Martin, Mgr.-Corp. Communications--Unisys Limited, Uxbridge, United Kingdom; *U.S. Public*, pg. 1671
Seyler, P., Pub. Rels.--TradeARBED S.A., Luxembourg, Luxembourg; *Int'l*, pg. 79
Seymour, Ann, V.P. & Dir.-Communications--JC Penney Company, Inc., Plano, TX; *U.S. Public*, pg. 916
Shaba, Annie, Mgr.-Pub. Rels.--National Bank of Malawi, Blantyre, Malawi; *Int'l*, pg. 1296
Shaffer, Gill, Mgr.-Pub. Rels.--Fuller, Smith & Turner Plc, London, United Kingdom; *Int'l*, pg. 529
Shaffer, James W., V.P.-Corp. Affairs--IWC Resources Corporation, Indianapolis, IN; *U.S. Public*, pg. 1185
Shah, Debra Ann, V.P.-Pub. Rels.--Accra Pac Group, Elkhart, IN; *U.S. Private*, pg. 11
Shakespear, George, V.P.-Corp. Mktg. Communications & Adv.--J.P. Morgan Co. Incorporated, New York, NY; *U.S. Public*, pg. 1129
Shalop, Lorraine, Mgr.-Pub. Rels.--Air-India, New York, NY; *Int'l*, pg. 37
Shamprois, Thomas, Dir.-Pub. Rels.--The Vermont Teddy Bear Company, Inc., Shelburne, VT; *U.S. Public*, pg. 1716
Shaner, John A., V.P.-Corp. Rels.--Dana Corporation, Toledo, OH; *U.S. Public*, pg. 479
Shanks, David C., V.P.-Human Resources--Sun Company, Inc., Philadelphia, PA; *U.S. Public*, pg. 1530
Shannon, MaryAnn, Dir.-Corp. Communications--Federated Department Stores, Inc., Cincinnati, OH; *U.S. Public*, pg. 617
Shapiro, Barbara L., V.P.-Corp. Commun.--3Com Corporation, Santa Clara, CA; *U.S. Public*, pg. 1603
Shapiro, David, V.P.-Mktg.--Pressman Toy Corp., New York, NY; *U.S. Private*, pg. 882
Shapiro, Karen, V.P.-Mktg. & Pub. Rels. Dir.--Hill, Holliday/Altschiller, New York, NY; *U.S. Private*, pg. 529
Sharga, Rick, V.P. & Grp. Supvr.-Adv. & Pub. Rels.--Shafer, Irvine, CA; *U.S. Private*, pg. 988
Sharnoff, Elana, Publicist--Yale University Press, New Haven, CT; *U.S. Private*, pg. 1195
Sharp, Carolyn L., Dir.-Mktg.--Virginia Metal Industries, Inc., Orange, VA; *U.S. Private*, pg. 1141
Sharp, Liz, V.P.-Corp. Rels.--Three-Five Systems, Tempe, AZ; *U.S. Public*, pg. 1604
Sharp, Tim, Dir.-Corp. Communications--BICC plc, London, United Kingdom; *Int'l*, pg. 120
Sharpe, Jane, V.P.-Corp. Communications--People's Bank, Bridgeport, CT; *U.S. Public*, pg. 1274
Sharrock, Lynda, Mgr.-Communications & Mktg. Assoc.--BOC Coating Technology, Fairfield, CA; *Int'l*, pg. 121
Shaughnessy, J.G., Mgr.-Pub. Rels.--Shanks & McEwan Group Plc, Bourne, United Kingdom; *Int'l*, pg. 1228
Shaw, Brad, Dir.-Pub. Rels.--Pepsi-Cola Company, Somers, NY; *U.S. Public*, pg. 1277
Shaw, G. Martin, Dir.-Public Rels.--Rock-Tenn Company, Norcross, GA; *U.S. Public*, pg. 1396
Shaw, Richard C., V.P.-Commun., Organizational Learning & Quality Standards--Applied Industrial Technologies, Cleveland, OH; *U.S. Public*, pg. 122
Shaw, Roy, Mgr.-Customer Service--U.S. Borax Inc., Valencia, CA; *Int'l*, pg. 1119
Shawe, Jan, Dir.-Corp. Rels.--Prudential Corporation PLC, London, United Kingdom; *Int'l*, pg. 1073
Shay, Tom, Dir.-Corp. Communications--Fuji Photo Film U.S.A., Inc., Elmsford, NY; *Int'l*, pg. 524
Shea, Dave, Dir.-Media Rels.--Raytheon Systems Company, Arlington, VA; *U.S. Public*, pg. 1364
Shea, Martin M., Sr. V.P.-Corp. Commun.--Triarc Companies, Inc., New York, NY; *U.S. Public*, pg. 1634
Shea, Patrick, Dir.-Pub. Rels.--Caremark International Inc, Northbrook, IL; *U.S. Public*, pg. 1082
Sheard, Kelly, Dir.-Corp. Communications--The Canada Life Assurance Company, Toronto, Canada; *Int'l*, pg. 254
Shechtman, Allen L., Mgr.-Adv. & Pub. Rels.--W.W. Grainger, Inc., Lincolnshire, IL; *U.S. Public*, pg. 758
Shelley, Donna, Mgr.-Adv.--Graphic Enterprises of Ohio, Inc., Canton, OH; *U.S. Private*, pg. 471
Shelton, Mark, Dir.-Corp. Commun.--Roadway Express, Inc., Akron, OH; *U.S. Public*, pg. 1392
Shelton, Suzanne, Dir.-Corp. Communications--Michaels Stores, Inc., Irving, TX; *U.S. Public*, pg. 1104
Shenk, Larry, V.P.-Pub. Rels.--The Phillies-A Limited Partnership, Philadelphia, PA; *U.S. Private*, pg. 861
Shepard, Kathy, V.P.-Corp. Commun.--Hilton Hotels Corporation, Beverly Hills, CA; *U.S. Public*, pg. 828
Shepherd, Kathleen, V.P.-Program Production & Community Affairs--WPIX, Inc., New York, NY; *U.S. Public*, pg. 1636
Sherbin, Robert, Grp. V.P.-Corp. Commun.--First Pacific Company Limited, Hong Kong, Hong Kong; *Int'l*, pg. 487
Sherbow, Susan, V.P.-Corp. Commun.--Little Caesar Enterprises, Inc., Detroit, MI; *U.S. Private*, pg. 671
Sherburn, Roger, Mgr.-Corp. Services--Sanden International (U.S.A.), Inc., Wylie, TX; *Int'l*, pg. 1184
Sheridan, Rosemary, Asst. Exec. Dir.-Mktg. & Commun.--NJ Transit, Newark, NJ; *U.S. Private*, pg. 794
Sherman, James, Sr. V.P. & Dir.-Corp. Communications--LaSalle Cragin Bank, Chicago, IL; *Int'l*, pg. 10
Sherman, James, Sr. V.P.-Corp. Commun.--LaSalle-Talman Bank, Chicago, IL; *Int'l*, pg. 11
Sherwood, Amy, Dir.-Pub. Rels.--Taco Bell Corp., Irvine, CA; *U.S. Public*, pg. 1637
Shibata, Ms., Mgr.-Pub. Rels.--Isuzu Motors Limited, Tokyo, Japan; *Int'l*, pg. 692
Shiffman, Mark, V.P.-Corp. Communications--The Coleman Company, Inc., Golden, CO; *U.S. Private*, pg. 690
Shima, Marian, Mgr.-Special Events & Guest Communications--Disneyland Hotel, Anaheim, CA; *U.S. Public*, pg. 513
Shimauchi, Yasuyuki, V.P.-Pub. Rels.--Sapporo U.S.A., Inc., New York, New York, NY; *Int'l*, pg. 1193
Shimizu, Tsuyoshi, Mng. Dir.-Pub. Rels & Adv.--Ajinomoto Company Inc., Tokyo, Japan; *Int'l*, pg. 40
Shinohara, Takuya, Dir.-Pub. Rels.--Nissho Iwai Hong Kong Corporation Limited, Hong Kong, Hong Kong; *Int'l*, pg. 948
Shintani, Keiko, Mgr.-Pub. Rels.--Rohto Pharmaceutical Co., Osaka, Japan; *Int'l*, pg. 1126
Shipley, Sam, Dir.-Pub. Rels.--Kao Corporation of America (DE), Wilmington, DE; *Int'l*, pg. 717
Shirai, Scott, Dir.-Community Rels.--Hawaiian Electric Industries, Inc., Honolulu, HI; *U.S. Public*, pg. 799
Shirai, Scott, Dir.-Community Relations, HEI--Hawaiian Electric Company, Inc., Honolulu, HI; *U.S. Public*, pg. 800
Shirashi, Yasuji, Mgr.-Mktg. & Communicaitons--Kirin USA, Inc., New York, NY; *Int'l*, pg. 736
Shirilla, John, Mgr.-Gen. Sls.--Photogenic Machine Company, Inc., Youngstown, OH; *U.S. Private*, pg. 864
Shirley, B., Gen. Mgr.-Pub. Affairs--Qantas Airways Ltd., Mascot, Australia; *Int'l*, pg. 1074
Shirvanian, Hacob, V.P.-Pub. Rels.--Western Waste Industries, Torrance, CA; *U.S. Public*, pg. 1686
Shively, Naomi, V.P.-Human Resources--IHOP Corp., Glendale, CA; *U.S. Public*, pg. 862
Shiver, William, V.P. & Mgr.-S.E. Newspaper Rels.--Parade Publications Inc., New York, NY; *U.S. Private*, pg. 20
Shoemaker, Jane P., Mgr.-Pub. Rels.--Interstate/Johnson Lane, Inc., Charlotte, NC; *U.S. Public*, pg. 909
Shoemaker, Joseph C., Mgr.-H.R. & Pub. Rels.--Zoeller Co., Louisville, KY; *U.S. Private*, pg. 1207
Sholl, Dan, Mgr.-Pub. Rels.--Eaton Corporation, Hydraulics Division, Eden Prairie, MN; *U.S. Public*, pg. 557
Shomake, Beth, Mgr.-Corp. Communication--Reeves Southeastern Corporation, Tampa, FL; *U.S. Private*, pg. 916
Shook, Gregory R., Sr. V.P.-Admin. & Sec.--Branford Savings Bank, Branford, CT; *U.S. Public*, pg. 250
Shore, Laura, Asst. V.P.-Commun. & Promo. Svcs.--Mohawk Paper Mills, Inc., Cohoes, NY; *U.S. Private*, pg. 755
Short, Donna, Mgr.-Customer Svc.--Schlumberger Industries, Owenton, KY; *U.S. Public*, pg. 1439
Shuck, Michael, Pres.--Overholtzer Church Furniture, Inc., Modesto, CA; *U.S. Private*, pg. 823
Shultz, Michael, Mgr.-Communications--The Baltimore Sun Newspapers, Baltimore, MD; *U.S. Public*, pg. 1616

Shuman, Kathy, Sr. Mgr.-Corp. Comm.--Software AG Americas, Inc., Reston, VA; *U.S. Public*, pg. 1482
Shumate, Aza, Mgr.-Customer Service--Lectrodryer Div., Ajax Magnethermic Corp., Richmond, KY; *Int'l*, pg. 113
Sias, Spencer R., Mgr.-Publ. Rels.--Raychem Corporation, Menlo Park, CA; *U.S. Public*, pg. 1362
Sibold, Ronald G., Treas.--SCI Systems, Inc., Huntsville, AL; *U.S. Public*, pg. 1416
Sibrac, Joel, Sr. Exec. & V.P.-Pub. Rels.--Bank of the West, Walnut Creek, CA; *Int'l*, pg. 163
Sichert, P., Chief Information Officer & V.P.-Pub. Affairs--The Budd Company, Troy, MI; *Int'l*, pg. 1388
Sickels, Linda, V.P.-Pub. Rels.--Trinity Industries Inc., Dallas, TX; *U.S. Public*, pg. 1638
Sickman, William J., V.P.-Corp. Rels.--Figgie International Inc., Cleveland, OH; *U.S. Public*, pg. 622
Sicot-Kelly, Steven, Mgr.-Info. Svcs.--United Grocers Inc., Portland, OR; *U.S. Private*, pg. 1122
Sicree, Joseph, V.P. & Chief Acctg. Officer--Toll Brothers, Inc., Huntingdon Valley, PA; *U.S. Public*, pg. 1620
Sieber, Arlyn, Pub. Rels. Coord.--Krause Publications, Inc., Iola, WI; *U.S. Private*, pg. 635
Sieff, David, The Hon., Exec. Dir.-Corp. & External Affairs--Marks & Spencer PLC, London, United Kingdom; *Int'l*, pg. 842
Siegal, Dean, Dir.-Corp. Communications & Pub. Rels.--Block Drug Company, Inc., Jersey City, NJ; *U.S. Public*, pg. 236
Siegal, Laura, Dir.-Pub. Rels./Viacom Interactive Media--Viacom Broadcasting Inc., New York, NY; *U.S. Private*, pg. 778
Siegel, Fred, Sr. V.P.-Mktg.--QVC, Inc., West Chester, PA; *U.S. Private*, pg. 897
Siegel, Megan, Mgr.-Communications--Genzyme Genetics Div., Santa Fe, NM; *U.S. Public*, pg. 733
Siegel, Richard E., Exec. V.P.-Pub. Rels.--Supertex, Inc., Sunnyvale, CA; *U.S. Public*, pg. 1539
Siegfried, Debbie, Sr. V.P.-Pub. Affairs--Texas Commerce Bank, Houston, TX; *U.S. Public*, pg. 339
Sieracki, Eric P., Mng. Dir.-Corp. Fin. & Commun.--Countrywide Home Loans Inc., Pasadena, CA; *U.S. Public*, pg. 452
Siever, H., Mgr.-Fin., Publicity & Statistics--Volkswagen AG, Wolfsburg, Germany; *Int'l*, pg. 1473
Siewert, Monica, Mgr.-Media & Mktg. Svcs.--Sacramento Municipal Utility District, Sacramento, CA; *U.S. Private*, pg. 959
Sifford, Leon, Dir.-Svcs.--McNamara Pontiac Isuzu Inc., Orlando, FL; *U.S. Private*, pg. 724
Sigman, Richard, Chief Fin. Officer--IWI Holding Limited, Westmont, IL; *U.S. Public*, pg. 861
Sigurdson, Leigh, Pub. Rels.--McKim Communications Limited, Winnipeg, Canada; *U.S. Private*, pg. 104
Silberman, Joe, Mgr.-Mktg./Pub. Rels.--Baker & McKenzie, Attorneys At Law, Chicago, IL; *U.S. Private*, pg. 111
Silbermann, Ronald, Dir.-Corp. Affairs--Panalpina Welttransport (Holding) AG, Binningen, Switzerland; *Int'l*, *pg. 1022*
Siles, Marc, Dir.-External Rels.--Club Mediterranee SA, Paris, France; *Int'l*, pg. 298
Silva, Karen A., Mgr.-Investor Rels.--SpeedFan International, Inc., Chandler, AZ; *U.S. Public*, pg. 1497
Silver, Gillian, Dir.-Public Rels.--Best Western International, Inc., Phoenix, AZ; *U.S. Private*, pg. 140
Silver, Lawrence A., Sr. V.P.-Investor Rels.--Raymond James Financial, Inc., Saint Petersburg, FL; *U.S. Public*, pg. 923
Silver, Michael, Dir.-Communications-CBS--CBS, New York, NY; *U.S. Public*, pg. 273
Silvers, Robert, Sr. V.P., Exec. Publr. & Sec.--Benjamin Franklin Literary & Medical Society, Inc., Indianapolis, IN; *U.S. Private*, pg. 133
Simmer, Rita, Dir.-Communications--SuperValu, Inc., Eden Prairie, MN; *U.S. Public*, pg. 1540
Simmons, Amy Beth, Dir-Corp. Commun., Direct Mktg. & Direct Response--Litecontrol Corporation, Hanson, MA; *U.S. Private*, pg. 669
Simmons, Victoria L., Mktg. Administrator--NavCom Defense Electronics, Inc., El Monte, CA; *U.S. Private*, pg. 789
Simms-Brown, Judy, Mgr.-Mktg. Commun.--Watlow Electric Manufacturing Company, Saint Louis, MO; *U.S. Private*, pg. 1153
Simms, Patricia, Pub. Rels.--RainSoft Water Treatment Systems, Elk Grove Village, IL; *U.S. Private*, pg. 78
Simola, Marja-Leena, V.P.-Communications--Amer Group Ltd., Helsinki, Finland; *Int'l*, pg. 72
Simolin, Botho, Dir.-Communications--Kemira Oy, Helsinki, Finland; *Int'l*, pg. 727
Simon, Liz, Mgr.-Pub. Rels.--Kaiser Aluminum & Chemical Corporation, Pleasanton, CA; *U.S. Public*, pg. 1062
Simon, Susan, Dir.-Pub. Rels.--Staples, Inc., Westborough, MA; *U.S. Public*, pg. 1509
Simoncelli, Morris G., Dir.-Pub. Rels.--Japan Airlines Company, Ltd., Tokyo, Japan; *Int'l*, pg. 699
Simonelli, B., Mgr.-Info. Desk--European Investment Bank, Luxembourg, Luxembourg; *Int'l*, pg. 465
Simonetti, Randall, V.P.-Adv. & Mktg. Communications--Frontier Communications Services, Bingham Farms, MI; *U.S. Public*, pg. 684
Simons, Deb, Mgr.-Human Resources--Spartech Plastics, Portage, WI; *U.S. Public*, pg. 1496
Simons, Steve, Mgr.-Corp. Commun.--Northwestern Public Service, Huron, SD; *U.S. Public*, pg. 1200
Simonson-Berge, Lena, Mgr.-Internal Communications--Ikea North America, Inc., Plymouth Meeting, PA; *Int'l*, pg. 660
Simpkins, Maurice, V.P.-Pub. Affairs--The Ryland Group, Inc., Columbia, MD; *U.S. Public*, pg. 1414
Simpson, Andrea, V.P.-Corp. Commun.--BHP Hawaii, Inc., Honolulu, HI; *Int'l*, pg. 225
Simpson, Andrea L., V.P.-Corp. Commun.--Gasco, Inc., Honolulu, HI; *Int'l*, pg. 225
Simpson, Derek, Dir.-Corp. Communications--Fort Dodge Animal Health, Overland Park, KS; *U.S. Public*, pg. 79
Simpson, Dick, V.P.-Pub. Rels.--Crowley Maritime Corporation, Oakland, CA; *U.S. Private*, pg. 292
Simpson, Gale, Mgr.-Pub. Rels.--Canadian Western Natural Gas Company Limited, Calgary, Canada; *Int'l*, pg. 95
Simpson, Gary E., V.P.-Corp. & Mktg. Commun.--Varian Associates, Inc., Palo Alto, CA; *U.S. Public*, pg. 1710
Simpson, Kathy, Dir.-Mktg.--The Kansas City Southern Railway Co., Kansas City, MO; *U.S. Public*, pg. 944
Sims, Katie, Dir.-Pub. Rels.--Stimson Lane Ltd., Woodinville, WA; *U.S. Public*, pg. 1661
Sinatra, Lisa Marie, Mgr.-Communications--GZA GeoEnvironmental Technologies, Inc., Newton, MA; *U.S. Public*, pg. 697
Sinclair-Brown, Jacqueline, Mgr.-Corp. Communications--Blue Circle Industries PLC, London, United Kingdom; *Int'l*, pg. 197
Singer, Ben, Dir.-Media Rels.--PacifiCare Health Systems, Inc., Cypress, CA; *U.S. Public*, pg. 1250
Singleton, Jill, Mgr.-Pub. Rels.--Cargill Salt, Newark, CA; *U.S. Private*, pg. 210
Sivacek, Chris, Dir.-Communications--Lifetime Hoan Corp., Westbury, NY; *U.S. Public*, pg. 992
Siverts, Mary Sylvia, V.P.-Pub. Affairs--Brown Group, Inc., Saint Louis, MO; *U.S. Public*, pg. 262
Skaare, Richard A., Dir.-Corp. Communications--AMP Incorporated, Harrisburg, PA; *U.S. Public*, pg. 7
Skaggs, Eric, Mgr.-Pub. Rels.--Metropolitan Mortgage & Securities Co., Inc., Spokane, WA; *U.S. Private*, pg. 738
Skiles, Robin, Mgr.-Pub. Rels.--Diamond Star Motors, Normal, IL; *Int'l*, pg. 875
Skipper, Sheila A., Mgr.-Corp. Commun.--ChemFirst Inc., Jackson, MS; *U.S. Public*, pg. 344
Skochdopole, Angela, Mgr.-Commun. & Adv./AGCO Brands--AGCO Corporation, Duluth, GA; *U.S. Public*, pg. 28
Skog, Bary L., Chief Mktg. Officer--Harley Ellington Design, Southfield, MI; *U.S. Private*, pg. 503
Skovholt, Glen, V.P.-Govt. & Pub. Affairs--Honeywell Inc., Minneapolis, MN; *U.S. Public*, pg. 833
Skramstad, Per Arne, Chief Info. Officer & Mgr.-Pub. Rels.--Toyota Norge A/S, Drammen, Norway; *Int'l*, pg. 1414
Skup, David A., Chief Fin. Officer--Legacy Marketing Group, Petaluma, CA; *U.S. Private*, pg. 658
Skyba, Kirsten, Mgr.-Mktg. Svcs.--Oshkosh Truck Corporation, Oshkosh, WI; *U.S. Public*, pg. 1233
Skyba, Kirsten, Mgr.-Pub. Rels.--Pierce Manufacturing, Inc., Appleton, WI; *U.S. Public*, pg. 1233
Slade, Peter, Mgr.-Pub. Rels.--R. Hirschmann Electronics UK Ltd., Sunning Hill, United Kingdom; *Int'l*, pg. 1108
Slakter, Ann, Pub. Rels. Coord.--The Reynolds and Reynolds Company, Dayton, OH; *U.S. Public*, pg. 1384
Slate, Ron, V.P.-Corp. Communications--EMC Corporation, Hopkinton, MA; *U.S. Public*, pg. 545
Slate, Ron, Dir.-Corp. Communications--EMC Corporation, Hopkinton, MA; *U.S. Public*, pg. 545
Slater, Kelly, Dir.-Mktg. Communications--Apertus Technologies Incorporated, Eden Prairie, MN; *U.S. Public*, pg. 119
Slaton, Jeanita K., V.P.-Employee Benefits--Piccadilly Cafeterias, Inc., Baton Rouge, LA; *U.S. Public*, pg. 1294
Slattery, Nora Jane, Sr. Partner & Corp. Communications Dir.--Ogilvy & Mather Worldwide, Inc., New York, NY; *Int'l*, pg. 1483
Slaughter, Susan, Mgr.-Mktg. Communications--Wavetek Corporation, San Diego, CA; *U.S. Private*, pg. 1154
Slaughter, Tony, Head-Press & Corp. Affairs--British Film Institute, London, United Kingdom; *Int'l*, pg. 219
Slayback, Jean, Mgr.-Pub. Rels.--Cytogen Corporation, Princeton, NJ; *U.S. Public*, pg. 471
Slaybaugh, David, Mgr.-Consumer Pub. Rels.--The Scotts Company, Marysville, OH; *U.S. Public*, pg. 1446
Slizewski, Bea, V.P.-Corp. Communications--Curtice Burns Foods, Rochester, NY; *U.S. Private*, pg. 887
Slizewski, Bea, Pub. Rels.--Comstock Michigan Fruit, Rochester, NY; *U.S. Private*, pg. 887
Slizewski, Bea, V.P.-Corp. Comm.--Agrilink Foods, Inc., Rochester, NY; *U.S. Private*, pg. 887
Slocum, Thomas J., V.P.-Corp. Communications--Delta Air Lines, Inc., Atlanta, GA; *U.S. Public*, pg. 497
Smalley, Richard, Mgr.-Communications & Sls. Promo.--Balderson Inc., Wamego, KS; *U.S. Public*, pg. 315
Smart, R., Mgr.-Grp. Exhibitions--Cobham plc, Wimborne Minster, United Kingdom; *Int'l*, pg. 301
Smart, Susanna, Dir.-Corp. Rels.--Reed Elsevier plc, London, United Kingdom; *Int'l*, pg. 1093
Smethers, Mary Kay, Mgr.-Communications--Hardware Wholesalers, Inc., Fort Wayne, IN; *U.S. Private*, pg. 502
Smidebush, James C., V.P.-Pub. Affairs--Delco Electronics Corporation, Kokomo, IN; *U.S. Public*, pg. 720
Smidt, Mike, Mgr.-Mktg. Communications--Garst Seed Company, Slater, IA; *Int'l*, pg. 1524
Smiley, Doug, Mgr.-Investor Rels.--Sundstrand Corporation, Rockford, IL; *U.S. Public*, pg. 1533
Smit, Marilyn, Dir.-Communications--Honeywell's Micro Switch Division, Freeport, IL; *U.S. Public*, pg. 834
Smith-Sanderson, Dianne, V.P.-Adv. & Corp. Communications--CT Financial Services, Inc., Toronto, Canada; *Int'l*, pg. 112
Smith, Alane, Mgr.-Consumer Services--Ridg's Finer Foods, Garland, TX; *U.S. Public*, pg. 1288
Smith, Andrea, Mgr.-Corp. & Mktg. Communications--Concurrent Computer Corporation, Fort Lauderdale, FL; *U.S. Public*, pg. 430
Smith, Ann C., Dir.-Pub. Rels.--Cummins Engine Company, Inc., Columbus, IN; *U.S. Public*, pg. 467
Smith, Anne, Mgr.-Mktg. Communications--LORAD Corporation, Danbury, CT; *U.S. Public*, pg. 1595
Smith, Cameron, Mgr.-Mktg. Communications--Barry Controls, Brighton, MA; *U.S. Public*, pg. 124
Smith, Carol, Dir.-Pub. Rels.--Peoples Energy Corporation, Chicago, IL; *U.S. Public*, pg. 1274
Smith, Chet, Mgr.-Mktg. Comm.--Spectronics Corporation, Westbury, NY; *U.S. Private*, pg. 1024
Smith, Colleen, Dir.-Commun. & Investor Rels.--Dominion Textile Inc., Montreal, Canada; *Int'l*, pg. 415
Smith, Craig, V.P.-Worldwide Pub. Rels. & Commun.--Holiday Inn Worldwide, Atlanta, GA; *Int'l*, pg. 170
Smith, Craig, V.P. & Dir.-Mktg.--FirstFed Financial Corp., Santa Monica, CA; *U.S. Public*, pg. 645
Smith, Dan, V.P.-Stauffer Communications--Stauffer Communications, Inc., Augusta, GA; *U.S. Private*, pg. 995
Smith, Debbie, Mktg. Communications Specialist--Power-One, Inc., Camarillo, CA; *U.S. Private*, pg. 878
Smith, Debbie, Communications Specialist--Kerr-McGee Corporation, Oklahoma City, OK; *U.S. Public*, pg. 952
Smith, Debbie, Mgr.-Customer Service--Champ/Pik-A-Nut Service Line, Edwardsville, KS; *U.S. Public*, pg. 1503
Smith, Denis, V.P.-Pub. Rels.--Weichert Realtors, Inc., Bethesda, MD; *U.S. Private*, pg. 1159
Smith, Donna, Mgr.-Adv./Discus Athletic--Tultex Corporation, Martinsville, VA; *U.S. Public*, pg. 1644
Smith, Donna J., Mgr.-Commun.--Tuboscope Incorporated, Houston, TX; *U.S. Public*, pg. 1643
Smith, Gail L., Adv. & Mktg. Specialist--Harrington Hoists, Inc., Manheim, PA; *U.S. Private*, pg. 504
Smith, Jeffrey, Dir.-Intl. Communications & Media Rels.--Sara Lee Corporation, Chicago, IL; *U.S. Public*, pg. 1432
Smith, Jeffrey, Dir.-Pub. Rels.--Sara Lee Bakery Worldwide, Chicago, IL; *U.S. Public*, pg. 1433
Smith, K.L., Mgr.-Water Customer Service & Planning--Salt River Project Agricultural Improvement and Power District, Tempe, AZ; *U.S. Private*, pg. 962
Smith, Karla G., V.P.-Corp. Commun.--International Comfort Products, Franklin, TN; *U.S. Public*, pg. 898
Smith, Kathy, Corp. Sec.--Lund International Holdings, Inc., Anoka, MN; *U.S. Public*, pg. 1020
Smith, Ken, Mgr.-Mktg. Communications--Lista International Corporation, Holliston, MA; *Int'l*, pg. 812
Smith, Laura, Dir.-Pub. Rels. & Adv.--Cross Creek Apparel, Inc., Mount Airy, NC; *U.S. Public*, pg. 1413
Smith, Linda, Dir.-Corp. Commun.--Westlake Hardware, Inc., Lenexa, KS; *U.S. Private*, pg. 1169
Smith, Lisa, Asst. V.P.-Mktg. Communications--Old Kent Bank, Grand Rapids, MI; *U.S. Public*, pg. 1216
Smith, Lisa, Mgr.-Pub. Rels.--Shoreline Financial Corp., Benton Harbor, MI; *U.S. Public*, pg. 1467
Smith, Lorraine, Mgr.-Mktg. Communications--Dacon Electronics Plc., Hemel Hempstead, United Kingdom; *U.S. Public*, pg. 395
Smith, Marcie M., Asst.-Communications--Oceaneering International, Inc., Houston, TX; *U.S. Public*, pg. 1211
Smith, Maureen, Mgr.-Public Rels.--TransTec Plc, Birmingham, United Kingdom; *Int'l*, pg. 1418
Smith, Michael, Mgr.-Mktg. Communications--Parker Hannifin Corp., Quick Coupling Div., Minneapolis, MN; *U.S. Public*, pg. 1260
Smith, Morris, Dir.-Mktg. Communications--Fujitsu Systems of America, Inc., La Jolla, CA; *Int'l*, pg. 526
Smith, Murray R., V.P.-Corp. Communications--K N Energy, Inc., Lakewood, CO; *U.S. Public*, pg. 937
Smith, P., Dir.-Pub. Affairs--Labatt Breweries British Columbia, New Westminster, Canada; *Int'l*, pg. 679
Smith, Peter, Dir.-Corp. Affairs--The Peninsular and Oriental Steam Navigation Company, London, United Kingdom; *Int'l*, pg. 1032
Smith, Richard, Mgr.-Mktg. Communications--The Lincoln Electric Company, Cleveland, OH; *U.S. Public*, pg. 996
Smith, Richard C., Jr., Sr. V.P.-Quality Devel. & Pub. Rels.--Sprint Corporation, Westwood, KS; *U.S. Public*, pg. 1500
Smith, Rick, Mgr.-Mktg. Commun./BFGoodrich Brand--Michelin Americas Small Tires (MAST), Greenville, SC; *Int'l*, pg. 322
Smith, Roger S., Mgr.-Corp. Adv. & Pub. Affairs--A.O. Smith Corporation, Milwaukee, WI; *U.S. Public*, pg. 1476
Smith, Sheri, Sr. V.P. & Pub. Rels. Dir.--EvansGroup, Dallas, TX; *U.S. Private*, pg. 385
Smith, Steve, V.P.-Production Svcs.--California Offset Printers, Inc., Glendale, CA; *U.S. Private*, pg. 196
Smith, Susannah G., V.P.-Corp. Communications--Ringling Bros., Barnum & Bailey Combined Shows, Inc., Vienna, VA; *U.S. Private*, pg. 400
Smith, Taylor, Gen. Mgr.-Corp. Communications--Jardine Pacific Ltd., Quarry Bay, Hong Kong; *Int'l*, pg. 704
Smith, Tom, Dir.-Corp. Communications--Trafalgar House PLC, London, United Kingdom; *Int'l*, pg. 772
Smith, Venee, Dir.-Human Resources--Aaron Brothers, Inc., City of Commerce, CA; *U.S. Public*, pg. 1104
Smith, Wayman F., III, V.P.-Corp. Affairs--Anheuser-Busch Companies, Inc., Saint Louis, MO; *U.S. Public*, pg. 113
Smuddraprabhut, Panthong, Mgr.-Pub. Rels.--Bangkok Bank Public Company Limited, Bangkok, Thailand; *Int'l*, pg. 146
Smyre, Calvin, Exec. V.P.-Corp. Affairs--Synovus Financial Corp., Columbus, GA; *U.S. Public*, pg. 1548
Smyth, D. Edward I., V.P.-Corp. Affairs--H.J. Heinz Company, Pittsburgh, PA; *U.S. Public*, pg. 805
Sneed, Jan, Exec. V.P. & Corp. Communications Dir.--BDDP North America, Inc., New York, NY; *Int'l*, pg. 117
Snepp, Karen, V.P.-Consumer Insights--Frito-Lay Company, Plano, TX; *U.S. Public*, pg. 1277
Snover, Larry, Dir.-Pub. Rels.--Iveco Trucks Of North America Inc., Bensalem, PA; *Int'l*, pg. 484
Snyder, Kathy M., Dir.-Communications & Shareholder Rels.--The First American Financial Corporation, Santa Ana, CA; *U.S. Public*, pg. 624
Snyder, Kristin, Mgr.-Pub. Rels.--Kaiser Permanente, Rocky Mountain Division, Denver, CO; *U.S. Private*, pg. 605
Snyder, Mike, V.P., Pub. Rels. Dir. & Acct. Exec.--Caldwell VanRiper, Inc., Indianapolis, IN; *U.S. Private*, pg. 200
Snyder, Molly, Pub. Rels. Coord.--Marshall Field, Chicago, IL; *U.S. Public*, pg. 489
Snyder, Susan, Mgr.-Customer Service & Traffic--Cab-o-Sil Div. Cabot Corp., Tuscola, IL; *U.S. Public*, pg. 289
Snyder, Vickie, Mktg. & Communications Specialist--Farinon Div. Harris Corp., Redwood City, CA; *U.S. Public*, pg. 791

Soares, Almir, Pub. Rels. Dir.--DPZ-Duailibi, Petit, Zaragoza, Propaganda S.A., Sao Paulo, Brazil; *Int'l*, pg. 352
Soeda, Kazuya, Dir.-Pub. Rels.--The Bank of Fukuoka, Ltd., Fukuoka, Japan; *Int'l*, pg. 152
Sohleder, Irene, V.P.-Community Relations--Summit Bancorp, Princeton, NJ; *U.S. Public*, pg. 1527
Sohler, Bernadette M., Community Rels. Rep.--Middlesex Water Company, Iselin, NJ; *U.S. Public*, pg. 1110
Sohn, Harold L., V.P.-Corp. Rels.--Ball Corporation, Muncie, IN; *U.S. Public*, pg. 170
Sokolowski, Gail, Dir.-Intl. Pub. Affairs--Bristol-Myers Squibb International, Princeton, NJ; *U.S. Public*, pg. 254
Soland, Norman R., V.P., Gen. Counsel & Sec.--Nash Finch Company, Edina, MN; *U.S. Public*, pg. 1151
Solomito, John P., V.P.-Customer Service--Hawaiian Airlines, Inc., Honolulu, HI; *U.S. Public*, pg. 799
Solomon, Hadar, Esq., V.P., Gen. Counsel & Sec.--Laser Industries Ltd., Tel Aviv, Israel; *Int'l*, pg. 429
Solomon, Larry, V.P.-Corp. Communications--SBC Communications Inc., San Antonio, TX; *U.S. Public*, pg. 1415
Solon, Tony, Mgr.-Mktg. Commun.--AGCO Corporation, Duluth, GA; *U.S. Public*, pg. 28
Soltero, Sharon, Mgr.-Corp. Commun.--Nebraska Public Power District, Columbus, NE; *U.S. Private*, pg. 789
Soltis, Karen, Mgr.-Mktg. & Commun.--Bacharach Inc., Pittsburgh, PA; *U.S. Private*, pg. 109
Somers, Julie, Mgr.-Pub. Rels.--BJ's Wholesale Club, Inc., Natick, MA; *U.S. Public*, pg. 162
Somerville, Anne, Mktg. Commun.--Carl Zeiss Optical, Inc., Petersburg, VA; *Int'l*, pg. 1523
Sommer, Ron W., V.P.-Investor Rels. & Communications--Dravo Corporation, Pittsburgh, PA; *U.S. Public*, pg. 527
Sommer, Ronald, V.P.-Indus. Rels. & Communications--Dravo Lime Company, Pittsburgh, PA; *U.S. Public*, pg. 527
Somoza, Kelly Fawcett, V.P.-Investor Rels.--U.S. Home Corporation, Houston, TX; *U.S. Public*, pg. 1682
Sonis, Larry, Pres.-Pub. Rels.--The William Cook Agency, Inc., Jacksonville, FL; *U.S. Private*, pg. 273
Sonntag, Willi, Sr. V.P.-Adv. & Pub. Rels.--Commerzbank AG, Frankfurt, Germany; *Int'l*, pg. 308
Soper, P. Wayne, V.P.-Environment & Communications--Westcoast Energy Inc., Vancouver, Canada; *Int'l*, pg. 1492
Sorensen, Richard T., Mgr.-Adv. & Pub. Rel.--International Game Technology, Reno, NV; *U.S. Public*, pg. 900
Sota, Alejandro de la, Dir.-Corp. Rels.--Telefonica de Espana, S.A., Madrid, Spain; *Int'l*, pg. 1371
Soucy, Philip, Mgr.-Pub. Affairs--British Aerospace Holdings Inc., Chantilly, VA; *Int'l*, pg. 218
Sousa, David, Pub. Rels. Mgr.--MRA, An Integrated Marketing Communications Agency, Overland Park, KS; *U.S. Private*, pg. 687
South, John R., Pres. & Chief Exec. Officer--Staodyn Inc., Longmont, CO; *U.S. Public*, pg. 1509
Soventino, Tony, Dir.-Pub. Rels.--The Franklin Institute, Philadelphia, PA; *U.S. Private*, pg. 424
Sowards, Kathy, Pub. Rels. Assoc.--Convex Technology Center - Hewlett-Packard, Richardson, TX; *U.S. Public*, pg. 815
Sowers, Richard, Exec. Dir.-Pub. Rels.--Atlanta Motor Speedway, Hampton, GA; *U.S. Public*, pg. 1498
Spadaccino, Sandra, Mgr.-Sls. & Asst. Gen. Mgr.--Philadelphia Reserve Supply Company, Croydon, PA; *U.S. Private*, pg. 861
Spademan, Rob, Dir.-Corp. Communications--Picker International, Inc., Cleveland, OH; *Int'l*, pg. 545
Spahl, Hannelore, Mgr.-Public Rels.--Zwick/Roell Group, Ulm, Germany; *Int'l*, pg. 1532
Spak, Deborah G., Mgr.-Media Rels.--Baxter International Inc., Deerfield, IL; *U.S. Public*, pg. 196
Spalding, Tony, Dir.-Pub. Affairs--Vauxhall Motors Limited, Luton, United Kingdom; *U.S. Public*, pg. 724
Spataro, John, V.P.-Mktg.--Ensoniq, Malvern, PA; *U.S. Private*, pg. 377
Speakman, Ian, Mgr.-Corp. Commun.--T & N Plc, Manchester, United Kingdom; *Int'l*, pg. 1334
Speakman, W.A. III, Pres. & Chief Exec. Officer--Speakman Company, Wilmington, DE; *U.S. Private*, pg. 1021
Spear, Gary, Dir.-Mktg. Communications--Finnigan Corporation, San Jose, CA; *U.S. Public*, pg. 1591
Specht, Tracy, Mgr.-Pub. Rels.--White Pine Software, Nashua, NH; *U.S. Private*, pg. 1173
Spector, Howard B., Sr. V.P.-Govt. Affairs & Communications--Guardsmark, Inc., Memphis, TN; *U.S. Private*, pg. 486
Speights, Debra, V.P. & Mng. Dir.-Burrell Pub. Rels.--Burrell Communications Group, Inc., Atlanta, GA; *U.S. Private*, pg. 188
Spellman, Leo, Dir.-Adv. & Pub. Rels.--Steinway Musical Instruments, Inc., Waltham, MA; *U.S. Public*, pg. 1514
Spencer, James E., Mgr.-Customer Rels.--Wilhold Inc., Cleveland, OH; *U.S. Public*, pg. 78
Spencer, Kathelen, Sr. V.P. & Dir.-Corp. Communications--AFLAC Incorporated, Columbus, GA; *U.S. Public*, pg. 28
Sperlich, Lutz, V.P.-Communications--Osterreichische Industrieholding AG, Vienna, Austria; *Int'l*, pg. 1012
Sperling, Karen, Dir.-Pub. Rels.-English--Goya Foods, Inc., Secaucus, NJ; *U.S. Private*, pg. 468
Spetner, Don, V.P.-Communications--SunAmerica Inc., Los Angeles, CA; *U.S. Public*, pg. 1532
Spicer, Meri, Mgr.-Special Events--Stratton Corporation, Stratton Mountain, VT; *Int'l*, pg. 685
Spiegel, Karen, Dir.-Corporate Communications--Sony Pictures Entertainment, Culver City, CA; *Int'l*, pg. 1281
Spiegel, Merle, Dir.-Corp. Comm.--The Perkin-Elmer Corporation, Norwalk, CT; *U.S. Public*, pg. 1279
Spigelmyer, Toni R., Asst. V.P.-Investor & Media Rels.--Sysco Corporation, Houston, TX; *U.S. Public*, pg. 1550
Spilka, Susan, Dir.-Corp. Commun.--John Wiley & Sons, Inc., New York, NY; *U.S. Public*, pg. 1768
Spindell, Lynn, Dir.-Communications--Phillips-Van Heusen Corporation, New York, NY; *U.S. Public*, pg. 1291
Spinelli, Amy, Mktg. Commun. Asst.--Putzmeister, Inc., Sturtevant, WI; *U.S. Private*, pg. 896
Spiro, Anthony, V.P.-Corp. Pub. Rels.--The Gates Corporation, Denver, CO; *Int'l*, pg. 1396
Spiro, Dee, Mgr.-Pub. Rels.--The Travel Channel, Atlanta, GA; *U.S. Private*, pg. 647
Spiro, Mark F., Chief Fin. Officer, V.P.-Fin., Treas. & Sec.--Calprop Corporation, Marina Del Rey, CA; *U.S. Public*, pg. 296
Sponsler, Linda, V.P.-Adv. & Pub. Commun.--Blue Cross and Blue Shield of Oklahoma, Tulsa, OK; *U.S. Private*, pg. 151
Spooner, Nancy, Pub. Rels. Dir.--McKim Advertising Ltd., Vancouver, Canada; *U.S. Private*, pg. 104
Spraetz, R.L., V.P.-External Affairs--National Starch and Chemical Company, Bridgewater, NJ; *Int'l*, pg. 1435
Sprauve, Anthony A., Sr. Dir.-Corp. Communications--LEXIS-NEXIS, Miamisburg, OH; *Int'l*, pg. 1096
Spreng, C., Mgr.-Commun. & Media--General Accident Fire and Life Assurance Corporation p.l.c., Perth, United Kingdom; *Int'l*, pg. 542
Springer, Heiner, Dir.-Corp. Commun.--Bayer AG, Leverkusen, Germany; *Int'l*, pg. 171
Springer, Hugh, Grp. Mgr.-Clinical Prods. Div.--Novartis Nutrition Corporation, Saint Louis Park, MN; *Int'l*, pg. 974
Springfield, James, Tech. Editor--Belcan Corporation, Cincinnati, OH; *U.S. Private*, pg. 131
Sprunt, Julia W., V.P.-Mktg. & Communictions--Turner Broadcasting System Inc., Atlanta, GA; *U.S. Public*, pg. 1614
Spurlock, Nancy, Dir.-Corp. Commun.--United Dominion Industries, Ltd., Charlotte, NC; *U.S. Public*, pg. 1675
Sraudt, Kelly, V.P. & Gen. Mgr.-Customer Svc.--SaskPower, Regina, Canada; *Int'l*, pg. 1195
St. Amour, Wayne, Mgr.-Pub. Affairs--Transalta Corporation, Calgary, Canada; *Int'l*, pg. 1416
St. Clair, Eleanor M., Dir.-Pub. Rels.--General Assurance Company, Melville, NY; *Int'l*, pg. 543
St. Clair, Eleanor M., Dir.-Pub. Rels.--General Assurance Insurance Company of New York, Melville, NY; *Int'l*, pg. 543
St. Clair, Eleanor M., Dir.-Pub. Rels.--Pennsylvania General Insurance Company of New York, Melville, NY; *Int'l*, pg. 543
St. Dennis, Donald, Dir.-Pub. Rels. & Pres.-The Toro Foundation--The Toro Company, Bloomington, MN; *U.S. Public*, pg. 1623
St. John, Charlotte, Dir.-Pub. Affairs--American Water Works Association, Denver, CO; *U.S. Public*, pg. 94
St. Laurent, Lucie, Communications Counselor--Sico Inc., Longueuil, Canada; *Int'l*, pg. 1239
St. Peter, Dave, Dir.-Commun.--Minnesota Twins Baseball Club, Minneapolis, MN; *U.S. Private*, pg. 750
St. Pierre, Nancy, Pub. Rels.--Six Flags Over Texas, Arlington, TX; *U.S. Public*, pg. 1612
St-Denis, Tracy, Pub. Rels.--Northwest Territorial Airways Ltd., Yellowknife, Canada; *Int'l*, pg. 36
Sta, Jan J.A., Mgr.-Mktg. Communications--Quest International, Naarden, Netherlands; *Int'l*, pg. 1438
Stack, Nathan, Mktg. & Corp. Communications--UBS Management North America, New York, NY; *Int'l*, pg. 1440
Stagaman, Kay C., Pub. Rels. Specialist--Fifth Third Bancorp, Cincinnati, OH; *U.S. Public*, pg. 621
Stahles, Lee Anne, V.P.-Corp. Sponsorship & Promotion--Universal Studios Hollywood, Universal City, CA; *Int'l*, pg. 1216
Staib, Michel, Exec. V.P. & V.P.-Corp. Communications--Schneider S.A., Boulogne-Billancourt, France; *Int'l*, pg. 1207
Stake, Randy J., Mgr.-Mktg. Commun.--Weber Marking Systems, Inc., Arlington Heights, IL; *U.S. Private*, pg. 1157
Stakun, David, Dir.-Corp. Communications--Technitrol, Inc., Trevose, PA; *U.S. Public*, pg. 1564
Stalberg, Lars A., Sr. V.P.-Corp. Rels.--Telefonaktiebolaget LM Ericsson, Stockholm, Sweden; *Int'l*, pg. 1363
Stallfort, Katherine E., Second V.P.--General Re Corporation, Stamford, CT; *U.S. Public*, pg. 725
Standish, Debbie, Mgr.-Corp. Communications--The Tetley Group Limited, Greenford, United Kingdom; *Int'l*, pg. 1377
Stangarone, Angela, Publicist--Owen Comora Associates, New York, NY; *U.S. Private*, pg. 985
Stangarone, Robert, Dir.-Corp. Commuunications--Litton Industries, Inc., Woodland Hills, CA; *U.S. Public*, pg. 1002
Stanhope, Phillip, Dir.-Corp. Commun.--Titan International, Inc., Quincy, IL; *U.S. Public*, pg. 1618
Stanhope, Phillip, Dir.-Corp. Commun.--Titan Wheel Corporation, Walcott, IA; *U.S. Public*, pg. 1618
Staniar, Linda B., Sr. V.P.-Corp. Communications, Adv. & Video Systems--New York Life Insurance Company, New York, NY; *U.S. Private*, pg. 794
Stankey, Tammy, Mgr.-Pub. Rels.--Six Flags St. Louis, Eureka, MO; *U.S. Public*, pg. 1612
Stanley, Brian C., V.P.-Investor Rels. & Controller--Valmont Industries, Inc., Valley, NE; *U.S. Public*, pg. 1706
Stanley, Travis, Dir.-Media Rels.--Sacramento Kings, Sacramento, CA; *U.S. Private*, pg. 959
Stanoch, Ruth, Mgr.-Government Rels. & Media Rels.--West Information Publishing Group, Saint Paul, MN; *U.S. Public*, pg. 1602
Stansu, Gwen, Mgr.-Pub. Rels.--Farley Candy Company, Chicago, IL; *U.S. Private*, pg. 397
Stanyon, Jack, V.P.-Adv. & Pub. Rels.--Fortis, Inc., New York, NY; *Int'l*, pg. 499
Stark, Joel, Sr. V.P.-Mktg. & Devel.--Providence Journal-Bulletin, Providence, RI; *U.S. Public*, pg. 209
Stark, Melissa, Mgr.-Pub. Rels.--The Department Store Division of Dayton Hudson Corporation, Minneapolis, MN; *U.S. Public*, pg. 489
Starkman, Howard, Dir.-Pub. Rels.--Toronto Blue Jays Baseball Club, Inc., Toronto, Canada; *Int'l*, pg. 680
Starmann, Richard G., Sr. V.P.-Communications--McDonald's Corporation, Oak Brook, IL; *U.S. Public*, pg. 1068
Starr, Richard, Admin. & Pub. Rels. Asst.--McKinney & McKinney Advertising, Redondo Beach, CA; *U.S. Private*, pg. 723
States, Judy, Dir.-Corp. Communications--APS, Phoenix, AZ; *U.S. Public*, pg. 1297
Stathas, Karen, Sls. Promo. & Pub. Rels.--Mirro Company, Manitowoc, WI; *U.S. Public*, pg. 1177
Statler, Dan, Project Leader-Pub. Rels. & Special Prods.--SKF USA Inc., King of Prussia, PA; *Int'l*, pg. 1157
Staub, Ronald J., V.P.-Employee Rels.--S-B Power Tool Company, Chicago, IL; *Int'l*, pg. 205
Staven, Carolyn, Mgr.-Mktg. Communications--John Crane Mechanical Seals, Morton Grove, IL; *Int'l*, pg. 1339
Stavropulos, Peter, Dir.-Commun.--Bull Electronics, Lowell, MA; *Int'l*, pg. 316
Stay, Christine, Mgr.-Mktg. Communications--Philips Components, Jupiter, FL; *Int'l*, pg. 1054
Stechmesser, Gary, V.P.-Corp. Communications--Allegheny Teledyne Incorporated, Pittsburgh, PA; *U.S. Public*, pg. 43
Steck, Rich, Mgr.-Public Rels.--Royal Caribbean Cruises Ltd., Miami, FL; *U.S. Public*, pg. 1410
Steel, Dianne, Dir.-Mktg. Communications--Greenfield Industries Inc., Evans, GA; *U.S. Public*, pg. 950
Steele, Lauren, V.P.-Corp. Affairs--Coca-Cola Bottling Co. Consolidated, Charlotte, NC; *U.S. Public*, pg. 391
Steele, Toby B., Mgr.-Customer Service--Luwa Bahnson, Inc., Winston Salem, NC; *U.S. Private*, pg. 682
Steelman, Sheila, Mktg. Communications--Atlas/Soundolier, Fenton, MO; *U.S. Private*, pg. 64
Steeves, Michael A., Dir.-Investor Rels.--Homestake Mining Company, San Francisco, CA; *U.S. Public*, pg. 832
Steffens, Gretchen, Pres.-Pub. Rels. & Sls. Promo.--Key Communications, Inc., San Juan, PR; *U.S. Private*, pg. 318
Steffens, Paul E., Dir.-Pub. Rels.--General Motors Continental, Antwerp, Belgium; *U.S. Public*, pg. 722
Steffy, Andrea R., Dir.-Corp. Rels.--The Allstate Corporation, Northbrook, IL; *U.S. Public*, pg. 55
Stefik, Lynn, Mgr.-Mktg. Communications--Pitney Bowes Software Systems, Glen Ellyn, IL; *U.S. Public*, pg. 1304
Stehr, Richard, Mgr.-Pub. Rels.--CalComp Technology, Inc., Anaheim, CA; *U.S. Public*, pg. 1007
Steilen, Monika, Member-Mngmt. Bd.--Hugo Boss AG, Metzingen, Germany; *Int'l*, pg. 637
Stein, Othmar M., V.P.-Pub. Affairs--Chrysler Canada Ltd., Windsor, Canada; *U.S. Public*, pg. 354
Stein, Sheryl, Mgr.-Pub. Rels. & Adv.--El Al Israel Airlines, Ltd., New York, NY; *Int'l*, pg. 435
Steinback, Michael, Pres.--Communications Instruments Inc., Fairview, NC; *U.S. Private*, pg. 259
Steinberg, Terry, V.P.-Admin.--Aceto Corporation, Lake Success, NY; *U.S. Public*, pg. 15
Steiner, Jeff, Mgr.-Mktg Communications--Johnson Controls, Inc., Plymouth, MI; *U.S. Public*, pg. 932
Steinkamp, Mark, Coord.-Pub. Rels & Adv.--Daktronics, Inc., Brookings, SD; *U.S. Public*, pg. 478
Steinkrauss, Carol, Mgr.-Public Relations--Parker Brothers, Beverly, MA; *U.S. Public*, pg. 797
Stek, Anthony, Mgr.-Pub. Rels.--Rabobank Nederland, Utrecht, Netherlands; *Int'l*, pg. 1082
Stenberg, Hakan, Dir.-Pub. Rels.--Silja Line AB, Stockholm, Sweden; *Int'l*, pg. 899
Stengel, Terry, Corp. Communications--Moore Document Solutions, Lake Forest, IL; *Int'l*, pg. 890
Stephens, Bonnie, Mgr.-Mktg. Communications--Branson Ultrasonics, Danbury, CT; *U.S. Public*, pg. 574
Stephenson, Catherine, Mgr.-Mktg.--Scan-Optics, Inc., Manchester, CT; *U.S. Public*, pg. 1436
Stern, Nancy C., V.P.-Corp. Affairs--The Dial Corporation, Phoenix, AZ; *U.S. Public*, pg. 505
Sternberg, Ira, Dir.-Pub. Rels.--Tropicana Resort & Casino, Las Vegas, NV; *U.S. Public*, pg. 159
Sternfeld, Ilana, Corp. Adv. & Foreign Press--Israel Aircraft Industries Ltd., Israel; *Int'l*, pg. 689
Stetson, Bob, Dir.-Integrated Communications--Tandem Computers Inc., Cupertino, CA; *U.S. Public*, pg. 417
Stevens, Andrew E., Chm. Bd., Pres. & Dir.-Mktg. & Pub. Rels.--GWP, Inc., Los Angeles, CA; *U.S. Private*, pg. 437
Stevens, Ann, Dir.-Corp. Communications--Harte-Hanks Communications, Inc., San Antonio, TX; *U.S. Public*, pg. 793
Stevens, C.G., Dir.-Pub. Rels.--The Ziegler Companies, Inc., West Bend, WI; *U.S. Public*, pg. 1791
Stevens, Elizabeth, V.P.-Human Resources & Pub. Rels.--The Chase Manhattan Bank of Canada, Toronto, Canada; *U.S. Public*, pg. 340
Stevens, Frank, V.P.-Sls. & Mktg.--Boler Company, Itasca, IL; *U.S. Private*, pg. 155
Stevens, James D., Chief Admin. Officer & V.P.--Atkinson, San Bruno, CA; *U.S. Public*, pg. 143
Stevens, Peter, Dir.-Corp. Communications--Willis Corroon Group PLC, London, United Kingdom; *Int'l*, pg. 1501
Stevens, Sandy L., Mgr.-Pub. Rels.--Witco Corporation, Greenwich, CT; *U.S. Public*, pg. 1773
Stewart-Cox, Charlie, Dir.-Pub. Rels.--Swire Pacific Limited, Central, Hong Kong; *Int'l*, pg. 1328
Stewart, Anita, V.P.-Corp. Communications--MobileComm, Ridgefield Park, NJ; *U.S. Public*, pg. 1120
Stewart, Charles, Sr. V.P.-Pub. Affairs--First Commercial Bank, N.A., Little Rock, AR; *U.S. Public*, pg. 630
Stewart, David R., Dir.-Pub. Rels.--Stewart & Stevenson Services, Inc., Houston, TX; *U.S. Public*, pg. 1517
Stewart, Ed, Dir.-Pub. Rels.--Southwest Airlines Co., Dallas, TX; *U.S. Public*, pg. 1493
Stewart, John G., V.P.-Customer Satisfaction--Applied Materials, Inc., Santa Clara, CA; *U.S. Public*, pg. 123
Stewart, Jolanda, Corp. Communications Specialist--Pan-American Life Insurance Company, New Orleans, LA; *U.S. Private*, pg. 836

Stewart, Joseph M., Sr. V.P.-Corp. Affairs--Kellogg Company, Battle Creek, MI; *U.S. Public*, pg. 947
Stewart, Lynda J., Dir.-Communications--Cox Enterprises, Inc., Atlanta, GA; *U.S. Private*, pg. 281
Stewart, Patti, Mgr.-Community Rels.--The Edmonton Journal, Edmonton, Canada; *Int'l*, pg. 631
Stewart, Robert, Mgr.-Pub. Rels.--Occidental De Colombia, Inc., Bogota, Colombia; *U.S. Public*, pg. 1210
Stier, John, Dir.-Pub. Rels.--Lincoln Foodservice Products, Inc., Fort Wayne, IN; *Int'l*, pg. 188
Stiffle, Dolly, Mgr.-Pub. Relations--Kodak (Australasia) Pty. Ltd., Coburg, Australia; *U.S. Public*, pg. 552
Stiffler, Carolyn S., Pres. & Chief Exec. Officer--Classic Markets Corp., Norcross, GA; *U.S. Private*, pg. 244
Stigi, Peter, Sr. V.P.-Sls. & Mktg.--Tuscan/Lehigh Dairies LP, Union, NJ; *U.S. Private*, pg. 1110
Stilley, Richard K., Dir.-Pub. Rels.--NationsBank Corporation, Charlotte, NC; *U.S. Public*, pg. 1162
Stillitano, P.J., Mgr.-Mktg. & Communications--Babcock & Wilcox Co., Barberton, OH; *U.S. Public*, pg. 1068
Stillwell, Rob, V.P.-Corp. Commun.--Boyd Gaming Corporation, Las Vegas, NV; *U.S. Public*, pg. 249
Stingone, Felicia, V.P. & Pub. Rels. Dir.--Kirshenbaum, Bond & Partners, New York, NY; *U.S. Private*, pg. 624
Stirling, Debra, Gen. Mgr.-Public Affairs--Coles Myer Ltd., Tooronga, Australia; *Int'l*, pg. 306
Stites, Tom, V.P.-Communications--Advanced Micro Devices, Inc., Sunnyvale, CA; *U.S. Public*, pg. 21
Stix, Louise A., Mgr.-Corp. Communications--Savin Corporation, Stamford, CT; *Int'l*, pg. 1114
Stockman, Jo, Mgr.-Corp. Office--Zeller Corp., Defiance, OH; *U.S. Private*, pg. 1204
Stoddard, John, V.P.-Mktg. & Communications--The Butcher Company, Marlborough, MA; *U.S. Private*, pg. 189
Stoddard, Rob, V.P.--MediaOne, Boston, MA; *U.S. Public*, pg. 1688
Stoddart, George A., V.P.-Corp. Commun.--McDermott International, Inc., New Orleans, LA; *U.S. Public*, pg. 1067
Stoessel, William, Dir.-Cardiovascular Communications--Medtronic, Inc., Minneapolis, MN; *U.S. Public*, pg. 1082
Stoffer, Diana, Sr. Public Affairs Editor--Public Service Company of New Mexico, Albuquerque, NM; *U.S. Public*, *pg. 1339*
Stoffere, Lisa, Sr. Mgr.-Commun. & Investor Rels.--NovaCare Inc., King of Prussia, PA; *U.S. Public*, pg. 1203
Stoilen, Sheldon T., Grp. V.P.-Corp. Services & Plng. & Public Affairs--Canfor Corporation, Vancouver, Canada; *Int'l*, pg. 260
Stoltenberg, Jessica, Mgr.-Pub. Rels.--Medtronic, Inc., Minneapolis, MN; *U.S. Public*, pg. 1082
Stone, Daniel B., V.P.-Corp. Commun.--Alberto-Culver Company, Melrose Park, IL; *U.S. Public*, pg. 37
Stone, Donna, Asst. Dir.-Corp. Communications--Marshfield Clinic, Marshfield, WI; *U.S. Private*, pg. 708
Stone, Ira N., Sr. V.P.-Mktg., Communications & Pub. Affairs--Stone Container Corporation, Chicago, IL; *U.S. Public*, pg. 1520
Stone, Laurie, Mgr.-Corp. Commun.--American Management Systems, Inc., Fairfax, VA; *U.S. Public*, pg. 86
Stone, Laurie, Dir.-Corp. Communications--Landmark Systems Corporation, Vienna, VA; *U.S. Private*, pg. 649
Stone, W. Arthur, Grp. Dir.-Pub. Rels. & Adv.--Ryder System, Inc., Miami, FL; *U.S. Public*, pg. 1413
Stonebraker, Barbara J., Sr. V.P.-External Affairs--Cincinnati Bell Telephone Company, Cincinnati, OH; *U.S. Public*, pg. 367
Stonehouse, Kate, Mgr.-Adv., Mktg. & Communications--SLM Holding Corp., Washington, DC; *U.S. Public*, pg. 1419
Stops, Emma, Mgr.-Commun. & Corp. Affairs--Staveley Industries PLC, Croydon, United Kingdom; *Int'l*, pg. 1298
Storat, Richard E., V.P.-Corp. Affairs--Gaylord Container Corporation, Deerfield, IL; *U.S. Public*, pg. 704
Storer, Madeleine A., Mgr.-Pub. Rels.--Consumers Maine Water, Rockport, ME; *U.S. Public*, pg. 438
Storey, Jim, V.P. & Pub. Rels. Mngmt. Supvr.--Price/McNabb, Inc., Charlotte, NC; *U.S. Private*, pg. 883
Stout, Eleanor, Dir.-Corp. Communications--Fresenius Medical Care, Inc., Lexington, MA; *Int'l*, pg. 505
Stout, Eleanor, Dir.-Corp. Communications--Fresenius Medical Care (North America), Lexington, MA; *Int'l*, pg. 505
Stout, Michael, Dir.-Pub. Rels.--Tidewater Inc., New Orleans, LA; *U.S. Public*, pg. 1608
Stout, Michael, Dir.-Pub. Rels.--Tidewater Compression Service, Inc., Houston, TX; *U.S. Public*, pg. 1608
Stout, Michael, Dir.-Pub. Rels.--Tidewater Marine International, Inc., New Orleans, LA; *U.S. Public*, pg. 1608
Stout, Michael, Dir.-Pub. Rels.--Tidewater Marine Western, Inc., New Orleans, LA; *U.S. Public*, pg. 1608
Stout, Michael, Dir.-Pub. Rels.--Point Marine, Inc., New Orleans, LA; *U.S. Public*, pg. 1608
Stout, Michael, Dir.-Pub. Rels.--Tidewater Offshore Services, Inc., New Orleans, LA; *U.S. Public*, pg. 1608
Stovall, Juli, Mgr.-Mktg. & Commun.--Paul Mueller Company, Springfield, MO; *U.S. Public*, pg. 1141
Stracham, Jeremy, Exec. Dir.-Legal & Corp. Affairs--Glaxo Wellcome plc, London, United Kingdom; *Int'l*, pg. 552
Stracner, S.D., V.P.-Commun. & Pub. Affairs--Ameron International Corporation, Pasadena, CA; *U.S. Public*, pg. 98
Strain, Laura, Sr. V.P.-Mktg. & Communications--First Bank N.A., Milwaukee, WI; *U.S. Public*, pg. 1680
Strange, Jeanne, Dir.-Mktg. & Adv.--First Southwest Company, Dallas, TX; *U.S. Private*, pg. 407
Stratton, J.L., Mgr.-Pub. Rels.--Albright & Wilson plc, Oldbury, United Kingdom; *Int'l*, pg. 49
Stratton, Maureen, Dir.-Mktg., Pub. Rels. & Trade Rels.--American Greetings Corporation, Cleveland, OH; *U.S. Public*, pg. 77
Straub, Terrence D., V.P.-Pub. Affairs-Washington D.C.--USX Corporation, Pittsburgh, PA; *U.S. Public*, pg. 1661
Straus, David J., Chm. Bd. & Chief Exec. Officer--STRAFCO, Inc., San Antonio, TX; *U.S. Private*, pg. 1046
Street, Alex, Creative Svcs. & Communications Dir.--Western International Media Corporation, Los Angeles, CA; *U.S. Private*, pg. 1165
Streeter, Laura, Mgr.-Corp. Communications--Memorex Telex Corp., Irving, TX; *Int'l*, pg. 857
Strickland, Eleanor, V.P. & Mgr.-Adv.--Compass Bancshares, Inc., Birmingham, AL; *U.S. Public*, pg. 418
Strickland, J.C., Mgr.-Mktg. Communications--Ericsson North America, Inc., Richardson, TX; *Int'l*, pg. 1364
Strickland, James H., Dir.-Pub. Rels.--Drummond Company, Inc., Jasper, AL; *U.S. Private*, pg. 343
Striegel, Dave, Dir.-Mktg. Svcs.--Growmark, Inc., Bloomington, IL; *U.S. Private*, pg. 484
Strigari, Gerald, Dir.-Telecomm. & Network Plng.--NJ Transit, Newark, NJ; *U.S. Private*, pg. 794
Strobeck, Ken, Mgr.-Communications--Regence BlueCross BlueShield of Oregon, Portland, OR; *U.S. Private*, pg. 917
Strode, Jan, V.P.-Corp. Communications--Jenny Craig, Inc., La Jolla, CA; *U.S. Public*, pg. 926
Stroh, Richard, Mktg. & Communications Specialist--Anaren Microwave Inc., East Syracuse, NY; *U.S. Public*, pg. 110
Strom, Tag, Dir.-Mktg.--Rosenthal U.S.A. Limited, Carlstadt, NJ; *Int'l*, pg. 1127
Stroman, Randy, Dir.-Mktg. Communications--Stainless Incorporated, Deerfield Beach, FL; *U.S. Private*, pg. 1029
Stroman, Randy, Dir.-Mktg. Communications--Charter House Incorporated, Holland, MI; *U.S. Private*, pg. 1029
Strommer, Eva, Communications Officer--Neste Oy, Espoo, Finland; *Int'l*, pg. 912
Strong, Gary, Dir-Investor Rels.--Berg Electronics, Saint Louis, MO; *U.S. Public*, pg. 212
Struble, Robert J., Mgr.-Mktg. Communications--Harbison-Walker Refractories, Pittsburgh, PA; *U.S. Public*, pg. 748
Strumpf, Jeff, Dir.-Adv. & mgr.-Corp. Rels.--Alpha Metals, Inc., Jersey City, NJ; *Int'l*, pg. 328
Stubbs, A.C., V.P.-Public Affairs--MacMillan Bloedel Limited, Vancouver, Canada; *Int'l*, pg. 828
Stucki, Connie, Mgr.-Mktg. & Export--U.S. Safety, Lenexa, KS; *U.S. Private*, pg. 1125
Stukenberg, Susan, Dir.-Corp. Communications--QST Environmental Inc., Peoria, IL; *U.S. Public*, pg. 367
Stulc, Dennis, Dir.-Opers.--Abu Garcia Inc., Spirit Lake, IA; *U.S. Private*, pg. 822
Stuntz, Susan M., V.P.-Mktg. Commun. & Pub. Rels.--Colonial Williamsburg Foundation, Williamsburg, VA; *U.S. Private*, pg. 254
Suart, Jacques, V.P.-Corp. Communications--Lafarge S.A., Paris, France; *Int'l*, pg. 788
Sudour, Daniel, Dir.-Corp. Communications--Renault V.I., Suresnes, France; *Int'l*, pg. 1102
Suech, Holli, Admin. Asst.--AIC-FSS Advertising, Minneapolis, MN; *U.S. Private*, pg. 5
Suerg, Jacques, Mgr.-Communications Dept.--Lafarge S.A., Paris, France; *Int'l*, pg. 788
Sufferini, F., Grp. Mgr.-Corp. Affairs & Plng.--Australian National Industries Limited, Pyrmont, Australia; *Int'l*, pg. 100
Sufi, A. Waseem, Mgr.-Personnel--Parke-Davis & Company, Limited, Karachi, Pakistan; *U.S. Public*, pg. 1739
Suga, Akihisa, Mgr.-Pub. Rels.--Chugai Pharmaceutical Co., Ltd., Tokyo, Japan; *Int'l*, pg. 290
Suhr, Hugh R., Mgr.-Pub. Rels.--SunTrust Banks of Georgia, Inc., Atlanta, GA; *U.S. Public*, pg. 1538
Suiminen, Aiya, Dir.-Communications--Nokia Telecommunications, Espoo, Finland; *Int'l*, pg. 952
Sullivan, Brian R., Gen. Mgr.-Human Resources & Pub. Affairs--Elders Limited, Adelaide, Australia; *Int'l*, pg. 500
Sullivan, Michael E., V.P.-Opers. & Customer Service--Vermont Gas Systems, Inc., South Burlington, VT; *Int'l*, pg. 542
Sullivan, Nicholas, Fashion Press Officer--Liberty PLC, London, United Kingdom; *Int'l*, pg. 807
Sullivan, Regina A., V.P.-Govt. & Pub. Affairs--A.H. Belo Corporation, Dallas, TX; *U.S. Public*, pg. 209
Sullivan, Terrence P., V.P.-Mdsg., Adv. & Communications--General Motors Acceptance Corporation (GMAC), Detroit, MI; *U.S. Public*, pg. 719
Sulzbach, Christi R., Sr. V.P.-Pub. Affairs & Assoc. Gen. Counsel--Tenet Healthcare Corporation, Santa Barbara, CA; *U.S. Public*, pg. 1576
Sundsbo, Svein, Sr. V.P.-Corp. Communications & Energy--Elkem ASA, Oslo, Norway; *Int'l*, pg. 446
Sundstrom, Mona Odhnoff, Dir.-Pub. Rels.--NCC Civil Engineering, Solna, Sweden; *Int'l*, pg. 899
Sunseri, Patricia, V.P.-Investor & Pub. Rels.--Mylan Laboratories, Inc., Pittsburgh, PA; *U.S. Public*, pg. 1143
Sunseri, Patricia A., Dir.-Pub. Rels.--Mylan Pharmaceuticals Inc., Morgantown, WV; *U.S. Public*, pg. 1143
Supic, Mark, V.P.-Pub. Rels.--Primerica Financial Services, Duluth, GA; *U.S. Public*, pg. 1633
Surma, Jean, Mgr.-Mktg. Communications--DEZurik, Sartell, MN; *U.S. Public*, pg. 726
Suslik, D., Dir.-Corp. Communications--Israel Aircraft Industries Ltd., Israel; *Int'l*, pg. 689
Sussex, Thomas M., Jr., Dir.-Corp. Communications--Sparton Corporation, Jackson, MI; *U.S. Public*, pg. 1496
Suter, Hans, Mgr.-Pub. Rels. & Commun.--Forbo Holding SA, Eglisau, Switzerland; *Int'l*, pg. 496
Sutterly, Mark, Dir.-Customer Service & Logistics--Arm & Hammer Consumer Products, Princeton, NJ; *U.S. Public*, *pg. 356*
Sutton, Howard, V.P.-Corp. Rels.--Steelcase Inc., Grand Rapids, MI; *U.S. Private*, pg. 1038
Sutton, Lori, Dir.-Corp. Communications--Jostens, Minneapolis, MN; *U.S. Public*, pg. 934
Suver, Susan M., V.P.-Org. Devel. & Commun.--Phelps Dodge Corporation, Phoenix, AZ; *U.S. Public*, pg. 1286
Suzuki, Shigeo, Gen. Mgr.-Pub. Rels.--Tosoh Corporation, Tokyo, Japan; *Int'l*, pg. 1407
Svec, Vic, Mgr.-Communications--Zeigler Coal Holding Company, Fairview Heights, IL; *U.S. Public*, pg. 1790
Swaney, Joe, Dir.-Pub. Rels.--The Cartoon Network, Atlanta, GA; *U.S. Public*, pg. 1614
Swanson, Jill S., V.P.-Devel. & H.R.-Uni-Marts, Inc., State College, PA; *U.S. Public*, pg. 1664
Swanson, Neal, Mgr.-Mktg. Commun.--Standard Duplicating Machines Corp., Andover, MA; *U.S. Private*, pg. 1031
Swanston, David, Pres.-Pub. Rels. Div.--Stackig Advertising and Public Relations, Mc Lean, VA; *U.S. Private*, pg. 1028
Swartz, Thomas, Mgr.-Pub. Communications--Rochester Gas And Electric Corporation, Rochester, NY; *U.S. Public*, pg. 1395
Sweda, G.J., Dir.-Pub. & Investor Rels.--Modine Manufacturing Company, Racine, WI; *U.S. Public*, pg. 1121
Sweeney, Kerry E., Mgr.-N. American Pub. Rels.--Brown & Sharpe Manufacturing Company, North Kingstown, RI; *U.S. Public*, pg. 260
Sweeney, Michael, Dir.-Pub. Rels.--Symantec Corporation, Cupertino, CA; *U.S. Public*, pg. 1545
Sweeney, Patricia A., Mgr.-Pub. Rels.--P.H. Glatfelter Company, Spring Grove, PA; *U.S. Public*, pg. 746
Swenson, Mike, Pres.-Pub. Rels.--Barkley & Evergreen Advertising, Inc., Kansas City, MO; *U.S. Private*, pg. 116
Swetnam, Monte, Mgr.-Govt. & Corp. Affairs--Giant Industries Inc., Scottsdale, AZ; *U.S. Public*, pg. 741
Swiller, Ari, V.P.-External Affairs--Ralphs Grocery Company, Compton, CA; *U.S. Private*, pg. 1202
Swinburn, Paul, Dir.-Corp. Communications--Eagle Star, Cheltenham, United Kingdom; *Int'l*, pg. 110
Swinburne, Peter, Dir.-Customer Service & Sls.--Bass Brewers Ltd., Burton on Trent, United Kingdom; *Int'l*, pg. 170
Swyden, Pam, V.P.-Customer Support--Lodgistix, Inc., Phoenix, AZ; *U.S. Public*, pg. 1527
Sykes, Michael C., Pub. Rels. Officer--Renishaw plc, Wotton-under-Edge, United Kingdom; *Int'l*, pg. 1103
Symigton, Doug, Dir.-Pub. Relations--Consumers Packaging Inc., Etobicoke, Canada; *Int'l*, pg. 326
Szczepanik, David, Sr. Mgr.-Mktg. Communications--J.J. Keller & Associates, Inc., Neenah, WI; *U.S. Private*, pg. 612
Szerlag, Traci, Mgr.-Communications & Adv.--Sciaky, Inc., Chicago, IL; *U.S. Private*, pg. 862
Szlemp, Maureen, Mgr.-Mktg. Communications & Svcs.--Norand Mobile Systems Div., Cedar Rapids, IA; *U.S. Public*, pg. 1699
Szyfter, Agnieszka, Pub. Rels. Dir.--EURO RSCG Poland, Warsaw, Poland; *Int'l*, pg. 603
Taback, Cara, Dir.-Pub. Rels.--Madison Square Garden Network, New York, NY; *U.S. Public*, pg. 288
Tabora, Cristina, Dir.-Mktg. & Corp. Communications--Hyatt International Corporation, Chicago, IL; *U.S. Private*, pg. 551
Tada, Ryokichi, Dir.-Pub. Rels. & Adv.--Japan Airlines American Region, New York, NY; *Int'l*, pg. 700
Taggart, Tom, Dir.-Corp. Commun.--The Charles Schwab Corporation, San Francisco, CA; *U.S. Public*, pg. 1442
Tait, Nancy, Sr. V.P.-Stratagic Plng. & Mktg. Communications--Olsten Health Services, Melville, NY; *U.S. Public*, pg. 1221
Takahashi, Akiko, Corp. Communications--Toshiba America Inc., New York, NY; *Int'l*, pg. 1405
Takahashi, Jin, Sec. & Dir.-Pub. Rels.--Mercian Corporation, Tokyo, Japan; *Int'l*, pg. 858
Takashima, Mamoru, Dir.-Pub. Rels.--Dainichiseika Colour & Chemicals Mfg. Co., Ltd., Tokyo, Japan; *Int'l*, pg. 369
Takebayashi, Mamoru, Exec. V.P.-Personnel, Admin. & Pub. Affairs--Mazda Motor Corporation, Hiroshima, Japan; *Int'l*, pg. 849
Takeda, Rebecca, Dir.-Investor Rels.--Smart Modular Technologies, Fremont, CA; *U.S. Public*, pg. 1476
Talavera, Juan C., Dir.-Pub. Rels.--GM Espana Fisher Guide, Logrono, Spain; *U.S. Public*, pg. 724
Talbot, James, Pub. Rels. Grp. Supvr.--Al Paul Lefton Co., Inc., Philadelphia, PA; *U.S. Private*, pg. 658
Talreja, Prem, Dir.-Mktg. & Pub. Rels.--Sigma Designs, Inc., Fremont, CA; *U.S. Public*, pg. 1472
Tamura, Norihisa, Dir.-Pub. Rels.--Chubu Electric Power Company, Inc., Nagoya, Japan; *Int'l*, pg. 290
Tan, C.G., Mgr.-Pub. Affairs--Mobil Oil Singapore Pte. Ltd., Singapore, Singapore; *U.S. Public*, pg. 1119
Tanaka, Yasuo, Sr. Mng. Dir.-Acct. Service & Promo.--Sogei Inc., Tokyo, Japan; *Int'l*, pg. 1277
Tang, Quinly, Pub. Rels. Dir.--Leo Burnett Worldwide Asia/Pacific Hdqtrs., Hong Kong, Hong Kong; *U.S. Private*, pg. 186
Tanner, Susan, Dir.-Investor Rels.--Isolyser Company, Inc., Norcross, GA; *U.S. Public*, pg. 914
Tanzman, Linn, V.P. & Dir.-Mktg. Communications--Rolling Stone Magazine, New York, NY; *U.S. Private*, pg. 1162
Tanzman, Linn, V.P.-Corp. Pub. Rels.--Us Magazine, New York, NY; *U.S. Private*, pg. 1162
Tarello, John A., Pres.--Analogic Foreign Sales Corp., Saint Thomas, VI; *U.S. Public*, pg. 109
Tarney, Julie, Pres.-Pub. Rels.--Laughlin/Constable, Inc., Milwaukee, WI; *U.S. Private*, pg. 653
Tarpey, Michael T., Sr. V.P.-Pub. Rels.--NCR Corporation, Dayton, OH; *U.S. Public*, pg. 1146
Tarsia, Carlo, Dir.-Communications--Eridania Beghin-Say Group, Neuilly-sur-Seine, France; *Int'l*, pg. 324
Tashijian, Lee C., Jr., V.P.-Commun.--Atlantic Richfield Company, Los Angeles, CA; *U.S. Public*, pg. 144
Tatay, Sandy, Dir.-Pub. Rels.--The Somerset Group, Inc., Indianapolis, IN; *U.S. Public*, pg. 1484
Tate, D.A., Dir.-Corp. Affairs--Tate & Lyle PLC, London, United Kingdom; *Int'l*, pg. 1356
Tattersall, P., V.P.-Pub. Rels.--British Aerospace Regional Aircraft, Avro Intl. Aerospace Div., Woodford, United Kingdom; *Int'l*, pg. 218
Taube, Cindy, Mgr.-Commun.--Red Wing Shoe Co., Inc., Red Wing, MN; *U.S. Private*, pg. 915

Taylor, A. Paul, Jr., V.P.-Corp. Communications--Anadarko Petroleum Corporation, Houston, TX; *U.S. Public*, pg. 107
Taylor, Caroline, Mgr.-Communications Project--Imperial Oil Limited, Toronto, Canada; *U.S. Public*, pg. 602
Taylor, Chris, Sr. Admin.-Pub. Rels.--Peabody Holding Company, Inc., Saint Louis, MO; *Int'l*, pg. 594
Taylor, D.A., Mgr.-Pub. Rels.--ATCO Structures Inc., Calgary, Canada; *Int'l*, pg. 95
Taylor, Diane, Mgr.-Employee Benefits--S & C Electric Company, Chicago, IL; *U.S. Private*, pg. 954
Taylor, Elwyn, Dir.-Human Resources--Gaylord Entertainment/Opryland USA, Nashville, TN; *U.S. Public*, *pg. 704*
Taylor, John, V.P.-Pub. Rels. & Adv.--Intermountain Health Care Inc., Salt Lake City, UT; *U.S. Private*, pg. 568
Taylor, John I., V.P.-Pub. Affairs & Communications--Zenith Electronics Corp., Glenview, IL; *U.S. Public*, pg. 1790
Taylor, Karen, Mgr.-MarCom--Encore Computer Corporation, Fort Lauderdale, FL; *U.S. Public*, pg. 580
Taylor, Kevin, Dir.-Mktg. Services & Communications--Steering and Suspension Division, Saint Louis, MO; *U.S. Public*, pg. 443
Taylor, Kristin Clark, V.P.-External Affairs--SLM Holding Corp., Washington, DC; *U.S. Public*, pg. 1419
Taylor, Lynn, V.P.-Corp. Commun.--Robert Half International Inc., Menlo Park, CA; *U.S. Public*, pg. 774
Taylor, Mike, Dir.-Publications--Oakland Raiders, Alameda, CA; *U.S. Private*, pg. 809
Taylor, Pamela C., V.P.-Corp. Commun.--Jacor Communications, Inc., Covington, KY; *U.S. Public*, pg. 922
Taylor, Patrick, Dir.-Commun.--Rodale Press, Inc., Emmaus, PA; *U.S. Private*, pg. 939
Taylor, S. Martin, V.P.-Community & Pub. Affairs--DTE Energy Company, Detroit, MI; *U.S. Public*, pg. 475
Taylor, Sandra E., V.P. & Dir.-Pub. Affairs--Eastman Kodak Company, Rochester, NY; *U.S. Public*, pg. 550
Taylor, T., Mgr.-Reg. Pub. Rels.--British Aerospace Regional Aircraft, Avro Intl. Aerospace Div., Woodford, United Kingdom; *Int'l*, pg. 218
Tear, Chris, Mgr.-Pub. Affairs--British Aerospace (Systems and Equipment) Ltd., Plymouth, United Kingdom; *Int'l*, pg. 217
Tebierio, Linda, Mgr.-Corp. Pub. Rels.--Emcee Broadcast Products, Inc., White Haven, PA; *U.S. Public*, pg. 570
Teeley, Peter B., V.P.-Govt. & Pub. Rels.--Amgen Inc., Thousand Oaks, CA; *U.S. Public*, pg. 100
Teenor, Kelly, Mgr.-Corp. Communications--Yokohama Tire Corporation, Fullerton, CA; *Int'l*, pg. 1521
Teig, Eva S., V.P.-Pub. Affairs--Virginia Electric and Power Company, Richmond, VA; *U.S. Public*, pg. 516
Temmel, Karen, Mgr.-Corp. Commun. & Pub. Rels.--Correct Craft, Inc., Orlando, FL; *U.S. Private*, pg. 276
Temple, Nancy H., Dir.-Corp. Commun.--Carolina Power & Light Company, Raleigh, NC; *U.S. Public*, pg. 306
Tenenbaum, Bob, V.P.-Pub. Rels.--HMS/Cincinnati, Cincinnati, OH; *U.S. Private*, pg. 492
Tenenbaum, Robert, V.P.-Pub. Rels.--HMS Partners-Columbus, Columbus, OH; *U.S. Private*, pg. 492
Teoli, Ida, Asst. V.P.-Corp. Communications--BCE Inc., Montreal, Canada; *Int'l*, pg. 114
Terashima, Ushio, Pub. Rels. Asst.--Shiseido Company Ltd., Tokyo, Japan; *Int'l*, pg. 1235
Termain, A. Cole, Sr. V.P.-Indus. Rels. & Pub. Affairs--The LTV Corporation, Cleveland, OH; *U.S. Public*, pg. 971
Ternby, Staffan, Dir.-Pub. Rels. & Info.--Astra AB, Sodertalje, Sweden; *Int'l*, pg. 93
Terrone, Michael R., Sr. V.P.--Indiana Lawrence Bank, North Manchester, IN; *U.S. Public*, pg. 633
Terry, Eileen, Mgr.-Mdse. & Pub. Rels.--The Southland Corporation, Willow Grove, PA; *Int'l*, pg. 694
Tesman, Patricia, V.P. & Pub. Rels. Dir.--Gianettino & Meredith Advertising, Short Hills, NJ; *U.S. Private*, pg. 450
Tevis, Carla, Mgr.-Pub. Rels.--Phelps Dodge Refining Corp., El Paso, TX; *U.S. Public*, pg. 1287
Teyssier, Elisabeth, Mng. Dir.-Fin. Info.--Pinault Printemps, Paris, France; *Int'l*, pg. 1057
Tezerskat, T., Pub. Rels.--C.A. Cigarrera Bigott, Sucs., Caracas, Venezuela; *Int'l*, pg. 111
Thacker, Louise, Mgr.-Mktg.--Hart Graphics Inc., Austin, TX; *U.S. Private*, pg. 507
Thaden, Rogene A., V.P.-Communications--Northwestern Public Service, Huron, SD; *U.S. Public*, pg. 1200
Thanepohn, Julie, Publicist--Circus Circus - Las Vegas, Las Vegas, NV; *U.S. Public*, pg. 374
Theisen, Diane, Dir.-Invest Rels.--Guarantee Life Insurance Co., Omaha, NE; *U.S. Public*, pg. 768
Theron, J.M., Exec. V.P.-Grp. Bus. Communication & Corp. Communications--Compagnie de Suez, Paris, France; *Int'l*, pg. 313
Therrien, Denise, V.P.-Environment & Community Affairs--Hydro-Quebec, Montreal, Canada; *Int'l*, pg. 640
Thiel, Sally, Mgr.-Corp. Communications--C-COR Electronics, Inc., State College, PA; *U.S. Public*, pg. 272
Thielen, Lenore J., Mgr.-Mktg. & Pub. Rels.--Dillingham Construction Corporation, Pleasanton, CA; *U.S. Private*, pg. 333
Thiem, Carl W., V.P.-Customer Svcs.--Schneider National, Inc., Green Bay, WI; *U.S. Private*, pg. 971
Thirstrup, Barbara, Mgr.-Pub. Affairs--Black Hills Corporation, Rapid City, SD; *U.S. Public*, pg. 235
Tholen, Steven W., Chief Fin. Officer, V.P. & Treas.--Penn Virginia Corporation, Radnor, PA; *U.S. Public*, pg. 1271
Thoma, Ann, Corp. Rels. Officer--Illinois Central Corporation, Chicago, IL; *U.S. Public*, pg. 864
Thomas-Lowe, Julie, Mgr.-Pub. Rels.--McKesson Water Products Company, Pasadena, CA; *U.S. Public*, pg. 1073
Thomas, Diana Lyn, Sec.--Cornerstone Natural Gas, Inc., Dallas, TX; *U.S. Public*, pg. 567
Thomas, Don, Dir.-Communications--Price Pfister, Inc., Pacoima, CA; *U.S. Public*, pg. 234
Thomas, George, Dir.-Pub. Rels.--H.P. Bulmer Holdings Plc, Hereford, United Kingdom; *Int'l*, pg. 232
Thomas, Hue, III, V.P.-Corp. Rels.--Owens & Minor Inc., Glen Allen, VA; *U.S. Public*, pg. 1236
Thomas, Jeff, Dir.-Corp. Communications--Cardinal Health Inc., Dublin, OH; *U.S. Public*, pg. 304
Thomas, Joannie, Corp. Commun.--Wang Laboratories, Inc., Billerica, MA; *U.S. Public*, pg. 1737
Thomas, Julian, Mgr.-Comml.--Sasol Petroleum International (Pty) Ltd., Rosebank, South Africa; *Int'l*, pg. 1197
Thomas, Larry, Mgr.-Import & Cust. Service--Continental/Midland, Inc., Park Forest, IL; *U.S. Private*, pg. 268
Thomas, Linda, Dir.-Investor Rels.--Unit Corporation, Tulsa, OK; *U.S. Public*, pg. 1672
Thomas, Linda K., V.P.-Communications--Transalta Corporation, Calgary, Canada; *Int'l*, pg. 1416
Thomas, Mary Ellen, Mgr.-Mktg. Commun.--Security Plastics, Inc., Hialeah, FL; *U.S. Private*, pg. 981
Thomas, Owen, Dir.-Pub. Rels. & Adv.--Integrated Marketing Services, Omaha, NE; *U.S. Public*, pg. 631
Thomas, Paula, Dir.-Corp. Rels.--Ace Hardware Corporation, Oak Brook, IL; *U.S. Private*, pg. 12
Thomas, Shelley, V.P.-Pub. Affairs--Smith's Food & Drug Centers, Inc., Salt Lake City, UT; *U.S. Public*, pg. 1103
Thomas, W. Dennis, V.P.-Govt. Relations--International Paper Company, Purchase, NY; *U.S. Public*, pg. 901
Thomases, Martha, Mgr.-Publicity--DC Comics, Inc., New York, NY; *U.S. Public*, pg. 1614
Thompson, Bobbie, Sr. Mgr.-Mktg. & Communications--American Tourister, Inc., Warren, RI; *U.S. Public*, pg. 1430
Thompson, Dave, Mgr.-Corp. Communications--Philips Electronics North America Corporation, New York, NY; *Int'l*, pg. 1053
Thompson, Joseph S., Dir.-Pub. Rels.--United Properties Group, Fairfield, NJ; *U.S. Public*, pg. 1692
Thompson, Kim, Dir.-Customer Commun.--Northwestern Public Service, Huron, SD; *U.S. Public*, pg. 1200
Thompson, Robert L., Jr., V.P.-Pub. Affairs--Springs Industries, Inc., Fort Mill, SC; *U.S. Public*, pg. 1499
Thompson, Sarah J., Asst. V.P.-Adv. & Pub. Rels.--Avemco Corporation, Frederick, MD; *U.S. Public*, pg. 151
Thompson, Sheri C., Commun. Specialist--EBSCO Industries, Inc., Birmingham, AL; *U.S. Private*, pg. 358
Thompson, Terry J., V.P.-Pub. Rels.--The Pillsbury Company, Minneapolis, MN; *Int'l*, pg. 411
Thompson, Tony, V.P.-Pub. & Media Rels.--First of America Bank Corporation, Kalamazoo, MI; *U.S. Public*, pg. 636
Thomsen, Buo, V.P. & Gen. Mgr.--Lincoln Steel, Lincoln, NE; *U.S. Private*, pg. 824
Thomson, C.R.B., Mgr.-Employee Rels.--Kodak Limited, Hemel Hempstead, United Kingdom; *U.S. Public*, pg. 553
Thomson, David B., V.P.-Mkt. Communications--CNA Insurance Companies, Chicago, IL; *U.S. Public*, pg. 1010
Thomson, Mac, Dir.-Asia Pacific External Affairs--Du Pont (Australia) Ltd., Sydney, Australia; *U.S. Public*, pg. 532
Thore, Thom, Exec. Dir.-Publicity & Promo.--Allied Advertising Agency, Public Relations, Washington, DC; *U.S. Private*, pg. 38
Thorn, G., Mgr.-Pub. Rels.--Canon (U.K.) Ltd., Wallington, United Kingdom; *Int'l*, pg. 263
Thornhill Jones, Lisa, Dir.-Mktg. Communications Trusted Div.--CyberGuard Corporation, Fort Lauderdale, FL; *U.S. Public*, pg. 470
Thornton, Jerry, V.P.-Member Relations--Better Homes and Gardens Real Estate Service, Des Moines, IA; *U.S. Public*, pg. 1094
Thorson, Ardie, Dir.-Pub. Communications--Grist Mill Company, Lakeville, MN; *U.S. Public*, pg. 766
Thorstenson, T., Dir.-Corp. Pub. Affairs--Caterpillar Inc., Peoria, IL; *U.S. Public*, pg. 315
Tibbetts, Ivana, Dir.-Mktg. Commun.--Union Carbide Corporation, Danbury, CT; *U.S. Public*, pg. 1666
Ticco, John A., Mgr.-Mktg.--Louis P. Ciminelli Construction Co. Inc., Buffalo, NY; *U.S. Private*, pg. 239
Tice, Marjo, Media Buyer & Communications Admin.--Mentor Corporation, Santa Barbara, CA; *U.S. Public*, pg. 1086
Tieger, Jeff, V.P.-Adv., Pub. Rels. & Sls. Promo.--Starbrite Corp., Fort Lauderdale, FL; *U.S. Public*, pg. 1510
Tilles, Lois, Mgr.-Pub. Rels.--Autodesk, Inc., San Rafael, CA; *U.S. Public*, pg. 148
Tillman, Wesley, Mgr.-Mktg. Communications--W.M. Barr & Co., Inc., Memphis, TN; *U.S. Private*, pg. 117
Tintle, Carmel J., V.P.-Pub. Rels.--Banfi Vintners, Old Brookville, NY; *U.S. Private*, pg. 113
Tippens, Steve, V.P.-Human Resources & Pub. Rels.--Abingdon Press, Nashville, TN, *U.S. Private*, pg. 1123
Tirado, Patricia, Mgr.-Pub. Rels.--Grupo Simec, S.A. de C.V., Guadalajara, Mexico; *Int'l*, pg. 576
Tissot, Anthony, Dir.-Pub. Rels.--Siemens Business Communication Systems, Inc., Santa Clara, CA; *Int'l*, pg. 1245
Tjelmeland, Gordon D., Mgr.-Media Rels. & Commun. Svcs.--Deere & Company, Moline, IL; *U.S. Public*, pg. 491
Tobey, Bill, Mgr.-Mktg. Communicaitons--Eimco Process Equipment Co., Salt Lake City, UT; *U.S. Public*, pg. 166
Tobia, Peter M., Mgr.-Pub. Rels.--Kepner-Tregoe, Inc., Skillman, NJ; *U.S. Public*, pg. 1659
Tobias, Maura, Mgr.-Pub. Affairs--Friendly Ice Cream Corp., Wilbraham, MA; *U.S. Public*, pg. 682
Tocci, Lynda, Asst. V.P. & Dir.-Pub. Rels.--UST Corporation, Boston, MA; *U.S. Public*, pg. 1660
Tod, Shawna, Mgr.-Pub. Rels.--Rockwell Automation, Milwaukee, WI; *U.S. Public*, pg. 1397
Toda, Atsuko, Mgr.-Corp. Commun.--The Nomura Securities Co., Ltd., Tokyo, Japan; *Int'l*, pg. 955
Tokarchuk, Betty, Mgr.-Corp. Affairs--Cargill Ltd., Winnipeg, Canada; *U.S. Private*, pg. 210
Toliver, Harold, Dir.-Mktg.--Golden State Mutual Life Insurance Company, Los Angeles, CA; *U.S. Private*, pg. 461
Tolleson, Laurie, Dir.-Communications--Lockheed Aeronautical Systems Company, Marietta, GA; *U.S. Public*, pg. 1007
Tomack, John K., Sr. V.P.-Mktg. Communications--First Chicago NBD Corporation, Chicago, IL; *U.S. Public*, pg. 627
Tomack, John K., Sr. V.P.-Mktg. Communications--First National Bank of Chicago, Chicago, IL; *U.S. Public*, pg. 627
Tomasch, Mark, Sr. Dir.-Corp. Affairs--The LTV Corporation, Cleveland, OH; *U.S. Public*, pg. 971
Tomasso, Mary Ann, Assoc. Dir.-Corp. Healthcare Affairs--Centeon, L.L.C., King of Prussia, PA; *Int'l*, pg. 626
Tomb, Gordon, Dir.-Communications/Reading--GPU Energy, Johnstown, PA; *U.S. Public*, pg. 695
Tomlinson, Pam, Mgr.-Graphic Communications--Batesville Casket Company, Inc., Batesville, IN; *U.S. Public*, pg. 828
Tommasini, S., Mgr.-Pur.--Zanussi Componenti Plastica S.p.A., Oderzo, Italy; *Int'l*, pg. 442
Toner, Jeffrey M., V.P.-Mfg.--Kingsbury Corporation, Keene, NH; *U.S. Private*, pg. 621
Toohey, Helen, Dir.-Community Rels.--Providence Gas Co., Providence, RI; *U.S. Public*, pg. 1337
Toombs, Emmett, V.P.-Admin.--Hardaway Construction Corp. of Tennessee, Inc., Nashville, TN; *U.S. Private*, pg. 501
Toomey, Kate, Supvr.-Pub. Rels.--The Rockport Company, Marlborough, MA; *U.S. Public*, pg. 1370
Toothman, Bob, Dir.-Communications--National Steel Corporation, Mishawaka, IN; *Int'l*, pg. 902
Topinka, Thomas, V.P. & Dir.-Communications--The Life Insurance Co. of Virginia, Richmond, VA; *U.S. Public*, pg. 712
Toplin, Irving, Mgr.-Mktg. Services--Carl Zeiss, Inc., Thornwood, NY; *Int'l*, pg. 1523
Topping, Karin, Dir.-Pub. Rels.--Shaklee Corporation, San Francisco, CA; *Int'l*, pg. 1518
Torbert, Martin, Dir.-Mktg. Communications & Pub. Rels.--National Starch and Chemical Company, Bridgewater, NJ; *Int'l*, pg. 1435
Toro, Ralph, Dir.-Pub. Rels.-Spanish--Goya Foods, Inc., Secaucus, NJ; *U.S. Private*, pg. 468
Tortorella, Albert J., Sr. V.P.-Communications--UST Inc., Greenwich, CT; *U.S. Public*, pg. 1660
Toscano, Barbara, V.P.-Human Resources & Corp. Communications--Neuman Distributors, Inc., Ridgefield, NJ; *U.S. Public*, pg. 1169
Totaro, David J., Chief Mktg. Officer & Exec. V.P.--The Dime Savings Bank of New York, New York, NY; *U.S. Public*, pg. 509
Towers, Thomas W., Assoc. Dir.-Pub. Rels.--Northwestern Mutual Life Insurance Co., Milwaukee, WI; *U.S. Private*, pg. 807
Townsend, David L., V.P.-Admin.--Walter Industries, Inc., Tampa, FL; *U.S. Public*, pg. 1736
Townsend, David L., Mgr.-Pub. Rels.--Best Insurors, Inc., Tampa, FL; *U.S. Public*, pg. 1736
Traboulsi, Jean, Mng. Dir. & Pub. Rels. Coord.--AMA Leo Burnett, Giza, Egypt; *U.S. Private*, pg. 184
Trace, Debra B., Mgr.-Corp. Commun.--STV Group, Inc., Douglassville, PA; *U.S. Public*, pg. 1421
Tracey, John, Dir.-Pub. Affairs--Procter & Gamble AG, Geneva, Switzerland; *U.S. Public*, pg. 1332
Trachter, Frances E., V.P.-Pub. Affairs--Woolworth Corporation, New York, NY; *U.S. Public*, pg. 1777
Trager, Doreen, Dir.-Communications--Congoleum Corporation, Mercerville, NJ; *U.S. Public*, pg. 69
Trainor, Barbara H., Dir.-Pub. Rels. & Adv.--Providence Gas Co., Providence, RI; *U.S. Public*, pg. 1337
Traub, Pat, V.P.-Pub. Rels.--EvansGroup, Indianapolis, IN; *U.S. Private*, pg. 385
Traum, Robin, Dir.-Pub. Rels.--AT&T Wireless Services, Paramus, NJ; *U.S. Public*, pg. 11
Travaille, Hubert D., V.P.-Pub. Affairs--Potlatch Corporation, Spokane, WA; *U.S. Public*, pg. 1318
Trdinich, Jim, Dir.-Media Rels.--Pittsburgh Pirates, Pittsburgh, PA; *U.S. Private*, pg. 867
Trebour, Burton, V.P.-Labor & Admin.--A-P-A Transport Corp., North Bergen, NJ; *U.S. Private*, pg. 2
Tregenza, Arthur R., Dir.-Personnel & Pub. Rels.--Allison Transmission, Indianapolis, IN; *U.S. Public*, pg. 719
Treiber, David, Dir.-Adv.--United Dairymen of Arizona, Tempe, AZ; *U.S. Private*, pg. 1121
Treloar, Phil, Dir.-Pub. Rels.--The General Electric Company, p.l.c., London, United Kingdom; *Int'l*, pg. 543
Trelut, Lynda, V.P.-Adv. & Pub. Rels.--Nob Hill General Store, Inc., Gilroy, CA; *U.S. Private*, pg. 799
Tremblay, Betsy, Mgr.-Communications--The Cascades Group, Kingsey Falls, Canada; *Int'l*, pg. 273
Triantafillopoulou, N., Dir.-Pub. Rels.--General Motors Marketing Services Hellas AEE, Russelsheim, Germany; *U.S. Public*, pg. 722
Trice, Pat, Mgr.-Pub. Rels.--Allison Transmission, Indianapolis, IN; *U.S. Public*, pg. 719
Triefus, Robert, Sr. V.P.-Global Communications & Promo.--Calvin Klein, Inc., New York, NY; *U.S. Private*, pg. 202
Trifelitti, Tony, Dir.-Human Resources--Johnson Matthey Inc., Wayne, PA; *Int'l*, pg. 713
Trigardi, John, Sr. V.P.-Corp. Affairs & Franchise Opers.--TCG International Inc., Burnaby, Canada; *Int'l*, pg. 1336
Trigg, Mary, Sr. V.P.-Pub. Rels.--H.F. Ahmanson & Co., Irwindale, CA; *U.S. Public*, pg. 29
Trilling, Howard, V.P.-Mktg. & Commun.--American Marketing Industries, Inc., Kansas City, MO; *U.S. Private*, *pg. 58*
Trilling, Howard, V.P.-Communications--Swingster Company, Kansas City, MO; *U.S. Private*, pg. 58
Tripp, Daniel B., V.P.-H.R. & Pub. Rels.--Thomaston Mills, Inc., Thomaston, GA; *U.S. Public*, pg. 1599
Tripp, David L., V.P. & Dir.-Investor Rels.--The Rouse Company, Columbia, MD; *U.S. Public*, pg. 1407

Tritt, Jeff, Dir.-Mktg. Communications--Sherwin-Williams Consumer Brands Division, Cleveland, OH; *U.S. Public*, pg. 1466

Tritt, Jeff, Dir.-Mktg. Communications--Pratt & Lambert United, Inc., Cleveland, OH; *U.S. Public*, pg. 1466

Tron, Dionn, V.P.-Corp. Communications--AGFA Division of Bayer Corporation, Ridgefield Park, NJ; *Int'l*, pg. 172

Trostel, Otto P., V.P.-Mktg.--Penn Security Bank and Trust Co., Scranton, PA; *U.S. Public*, pg. 1270

Troyer, Bob, Dir.-Pub. Rels.--Midas-International Corp., Chicago, IL; *U.S. Public*, pg. 1766

Truffaut, Fabicnne, Mgr.-Pub. Rels.--Editions du Juris-Classeur, Paris, France; *Int'l*, pg. 1095

Trumble, David, Dir.-Corp. Communications--Doubletree Corporation, Memphis, TN; *U.S. Public*, pg. 1335

Tsao, C.M., Mgr.-Pub. Affairs--China Steel Corporation, Kao-hsiung, Taiwan; *Int'l*, pg. 285

Tsuda, Kenicharo, Mgr.-Pub. Rels.--Sankyo Company Limited, Tokyo, Japan; *Int'l*, pg. 1189

Tunchumrus, Boonsom, Exec. V.P.--Siam City Bank Public Company Limited, Bangkok, Thailand; *Int'l*, pg. 1239

Tuner, Susanne, Coord.-Corp. Commun. Project--Berkshire Life Insurance Company, Pittsfield, MA; *U.S. Private*, pg. 136

Turett, Nancy, Mng. Dir.-Edelman Healthcare Communications--Edelman Worldwide, Inc., New York, NY; *U.S. Private*, pg. 362

Turk, Penny, Mgr.-Mktg. Commun.--Multigraphics Inc., Mount Prospect, IL; *U.S. Public*, pg. 1141

Turkay, Levent, Mgr.-Pub. Rels.--Arcelik A.S., Istanbul, Turkey; *Int'l*, pg. 741

Turman, Del, Mgr.-Mktg. Commun.--Computer Language Research, Inc., Carrollton, TX; *U.S. Public*, pg. 421

Turner, Becky, Mgr.-Human Resources--Dayco PTI, Inc., Red Wing, MN; *U.S. Public*, pg. 1045

Turner, Harvey S., Dir.-Pub. Rels.--Union Pacific Corporation, Dallas, TX; *U.S. Public*, pg. 1667

Turner, Janet M., V.P.-Investor Rels.--PLM International, Inc., San Francisco, CA; *U.S. Public*, pg. 1241

Turner, Jeff, V.P.-Mktg.--Swiss Army Brands, Inc., Shelton, CT; *U.S. Public*, pg. 1544

Turner, Lisa, Mgr.-Mktg. Communications--Bergen Brunswig Medical Corporation, Orange, CA; *U.S. Public*, pg. 214

Turner, Robert W., V.P.-Pub. Affairs--Champion International Corp., Stamford, CT; *U.S. Public*, pg. 333

Tuthill, James G., Jr., Pres. & Chief Exec. Officer--Tuthill Corporation, Hinsdale, IL; *U.S. Private*, pg. 1110

Tutor, Dean, Dir.-Adv., Media & Pub. Rels.--L.A. Gear, Inc., Santa Monica, CA; *U.S. Public*, pg. 969

Tuzee, John, Dir.-Corp. Communications--Genmar Holdings, Inc., Minneapolis, MN; *U.S. Private*, pg. 447

Twitty, Roy, Mgr.-Pub Rels.--Linear Technology Corp., Milpitas, CA; *U.S. Public*, pg. 1000

Tyler, Cyrus L., V.P.-Corp. Communications--Konica Business Machines USA, Inc., Windsor, CT; *Int'l*, pg. 748

Tyson, Jeff, Mgr.-Corp. Affairs--Methanex Corporation, Vancouver, Canada; *Int'l*, pg. 862

Tysse, John, Dir.-Pub. Affairs--The Dow Chemical Company, Midland, MI; *U.S. Public*, pg. 522

Tytler-Fisher, Linn, Mgr.-Communications & Pub. Affairs--Honeywell Defense Avionics Systems, Albuquerque, NM; *U.S. Public*, pg. 834

Ueda, Koichi, Mng. Dir.-Customer Service, Office Systems Plng. & Admn.--Yasuda Mutual Life Insurance Co., Tokyo, Japan; *Int'l*, pg. 1519

Uehlinger, Hans-Martin, Mng. Dir.-Corp. Communications--Landis & Staefa AG, Zug, Switzerland; *Int'l*, pg. 800

Uggla, Gustaf, V.P.-Corp. Communications & Pub. Affairs--Electrolux, AB, Stockholm, Sweden; *Int'l*, pg. 438

Uhlman, Tom, Sr. V.P.-Corp. Strategy, Devel. & Pub. Affairs--Lucent Technologies Inc., Murray Hill, NJ; *U.S. Public*, pg. 1017

Uhrich, Marie, Mng. Dir.-Corp. Commun.--Piper Jaffray Companies, Inc., Minneapolis, MN; *U.S. Public*, pg. 1300

Uhring, Stephen J., Mgr.-Customer Mngmt.--CCH Incorporated, Riverwoods, IL; *Int'l*, pg. 1513

Uiedh, Manando, Dir.-Corp. Communications--SmithKline Beecham Pharmaceuticals, Tokyo, Japan; *Int'l*, pg. 1266

Ulbrandt, Laura, Sec.--Leucadia National Corporation, New York, NY; *U.S. Public*, pg. 989

Ulinger, Beth S., Mgr.-Communications--Peabody Western Coal Company, Flagstaff, AZ; *Int'l*, pg. 594

Ulterino, Stacey, Promotions Dir. & Pub. Rels. Dir.--Jay Advertising, Inc., Rochester, NY; *U.S. Private*, pg. 583

Umpleby, D.J., III, V.P.-Customer Services--Solar Turbines Incorporated, San Diego, CA; *U.S. Public*, pg. 316

Undurraga, Jaime, Dir.-Pub. Affairs--CODELCO Chile (Corporacion Nacional Del Cobre De Chile), Santiago, Chile; *Int'l*, pg. 302

Untermeyer, Chase, Dir.-Pub. Affrs.--COMPAQ Computer Corporation, Houston, TX; *U.S. Public*, pg. 417

Upton, Erica, Pub. Rels. Counselor--Sawyer Riley Compton Inc., Atlanta, GA; *U.S. Private*, pg. 969

Urbanetti, Susan J., Mgr.-Communications--Cabot Corporation, Boston, MA; *U.S. Public*, pg. 288

Urbas, Daniel, Pub. Rels. Mgr.--Wunderman Cato Johnson, New York, NY; *U.S. Private*, pg. 1197

Uri, Noelle, Dir.-Pub. Rels.--Credit Mutuel, Paris, France; *Int'l*, pg. 344

Urian, W.E., Mgr.-Mktg. Communications--Vapor, Niles, IL; *U.S. Public*, pg. 1761

Uschold, John G., Dir.-Corp. Communicarions--Santa Fe Drilling Co., Alhambra, CA; *Int'l*, pg. 765

Usinger, Debra, Dir.-Corp. Services--Fred Usinger, Inc., Milwaukee, WI; *U.S. Private*, pg. 1129

Usmani, M. Masood A., Pub. Rels. Officer--National Refinery Limited, Karachi, Pakistan; *Int'l*, pg. 909

Uttermohlen, Dee, Mgr.-Mktg., Adv. & Pub. Rels.--Safelite AutoGlass, Columbus, OH; *U.S. Private*, pg. 960

Vachon, Brian, V.P.-Communications--National Life Insurance Company, Montpelier, VT; *U.S. Private*, pg. 785

Vaillancourt, Donald C., V.P.-Commun.--The Grand Union Company, Wayne, NJ; *U.S. Public*, pg. 758

Vainikka, Pia, Asst.-Personnel & Commun.--Metsa-Serla Corporation, Espoo, Finland; *Int'l*, pg. 863

Vainio, Kari, V.P.-Corp. Communications--Enso Oyj, Helsinki, Finland; *Int'l*, pg. 455

Vala, Elizabeth A., Asst. V.P.-Consumer Affairs--The Franklin Life Insurance Company, Springfield, IL; *U.S. Public*, pg. 76

Valent, Nancy, Dir.-Communications--Fasson Films, Painesville, OH; *U.S. Public*, pg. 153

Valentin, Jacques, Asst. Dir.-Pub. Rels.--Saint-Gobain, Courbevoie, France; *Int'l*, pg. 1170

Valeriola, Jean-Pierre, Dir.-Corp. Communications & Public Rels.--L'Oreal S.A., Clichy, France; *Int'l*, pg. 818

Valladigham, Gisela, Asst. V.P.-Corp. Communications--SLM Holding Corp., Washington, DC; *U.S. Public*, pg. 1419

Vallin, Rose, Corp. Communications Coord.--Auto-Owners Insurance, Lansing, MI; *U.S. Private*, pg. 100

Van Allen, Barbara, Mng. Dir.-Corp. Communications--Cushman & Wakefield, Inc., New York, NY; *Int'l*, pg. 873

Van Brandmeyer, Rick, V.P.-Adv. & Mdsg.--JTS Corporation, San Jose, CA; *U.S. Public*, pg. 919

van Bueren, H.C. Lammerts, Mgr.-Pub. Rels. & Affairs--Royal Nedlloyd Group N.V., Rotterdam, Netherlands; *Int'l*, pg. 1143

van Dongen, Gerard, V.P.-Grp. Communications--AEGON N.V., Hague, Netherlands; *Int'l*, pg. 25

Van Dyke, Lester F., Dir.-Investor Rels. & Corp. Commun.--Battle Mountain Gold Company, Houston, TX; *U.S. Public*, pg. 193

Van Dyne, Denese D., V.P.-Corp. Communications--Landmark Graphics Corporation, Houston, TX; *U.S. Public*, pg. 776

van Essen, G., Mgr.-Pub. Rels.--Ballast Nedam International B.V., Amstelveen, Netherlands; *Int'l*, pg. 133

Van Evans, Catherine, Mgr.-Communications & Public Affairs--Cadbury Beverages, Stamford, CT; *Int'l*, pg. 248

Van Gendt, G., Dir.-Mktg.--Bac Color Franseweg, Steenbergen, Netherlands; *Int'l*, pg. 131

Van Gostenyck, Christine, Mgr.-Pub. Rels.--Almanij N.V., Antwerp, Belgium; *Int'l*, pg. 65

van Luyk, A.B., Exec. V.P.-Commercial Service--KLM Royal Dutch Airlines, Elmsford, NY; *Int'l*, pg. 719

van Meene, R.C., Mgr.-Pub. Rels.--Ballast Nedam Grond en Wegen B.V., Amstelveen, Netherlands; *Int'l*, pg. 133

van Opijnen, S., Dir.-Pub. Rels.--Fortis, Utrecht, Netherlands; *Int'l*, pg. 498

Van Parys, Henri, Mgr.-Pub. Rels.--Kulicke & Soffa Industries, Inc., Willow Grove, PA; *U.S. Public*, pg. 968

Van Riper, Lisa, Dir.-Communications--Popeye's Chicken & Biscuits, Atlanta, GA; *U.S. Private*, pg. 5

Van Ryan, Jane, V.P.-Public Affairs--Science Applications International Corp., San Diego, CA; *U.S. Private*, pg. 975

Van Vleet, Rick, Dir.-Telecommunications & Personnel--Diversco, Inc., Spartanburg, SC; *U.S. Private*, pg. 336

Van Waart, Caron, Mgr.-Adv. & Public Rels.--Relm Communications, Inc., Indianapolis, IN; *U.S. Public*, pg. 1376

Van Warner, Rick, V.P.-Corp. Rels.--Darden Restaurants, Inc., Orlando, FL; *U.S. Public*, pg. 483

Van Wijhe, J.L., Dir.-Human Resources--Schering Nederland B.V., Weesp, Netherlands; *Int'l*, pg. 1204

van Wyk, Johan, Mgr.-Pub. Rels.--Sappi Limited, Braamfontein, South Africa; *Int'l*, pg. 1193

Vanasse, Tanya, V.P.-Mktg.--Bank of the Hudson, Poughkeepsie, NY; *U.S. Public*, pg. 1319

VanBuren, Denise Doring, Dir.-Media Rels.--Central Hudson Gas & Electric Corporation, Poughkeepsie, NY; *U.S. Public*, pg. 324

Vance, David, Dir.-Corp. Mktg. & Communications--Austin Industries, Inc., Dallas, TX; *U.S. Private*, pg. 99

Vance, Dodie, Mgr.-Pub. Rels.--Blimpie International, Inc., Atlanta, GA; *U.S. Public*, pg. 236

Vance, Phyllis, Mgr.-Pub. Affairs--BASF Corporation Fiber Products Division, Charlotte, NC; *Int'l*, pg. 105

VanCor, Norman W., Mgr.-Public Affairs--Yankee Energy System, Inc., Meriden, CT; *U.S. Public*, pg. 1787

VanCor, Norman W., Mgr.-Pub. Affairs--Yankee Gas Services Company, Meriden, CT; *U.S. Public*, pg. 1788

Vanderhorst, Dwaynne, Pub. Rels. Specialist--Symantec Corporation, Cupertino, CA; *U.S. Public*, pg. 1545

Vanderwicken, Peter, Sr. V.P.-Corp. Communications--Morgan Guaranty Trust Company of New York, New York, NY; *U.S. Public*, pg. 1129

Vandewater, S. Terry, Dir.-Pub. Affairs--The Stop & Shop Companies, Inc., Quincy, MA; *Int'l*, pg. 750

Vandiver, Gina, Mgr.-Corp. Communications--Earle M. Jorgensen Company, Brea, CA; *U.S. Private*, pg. 600

VanDuzer, M. Keith, V.P.-Human Resources & Admin.--GTE Mobile Communications Incorporated, Atlanta, GA; *U.S. Public*, pg. 696

VanSickle, Sharon, Principal & Pub. Rels.--Karakas, VanSickle, Ouellette Advertising & Public Relations, Portland, OR; *U.S. Private*, pg. 607

VanTassel, Daniel R., Dir.-Corp. Communications--CF Industries, Inc., Long Grove, IL; *U.S. Private*, pg. 193

Varela, Lucy, Mgr.-Customer Svc.--Williams Electronics Games, Inc., Chicago, IL; *U.S. Public*, pg. 1727

Varney, Thomas, Dir.-Pub. Rels.--Siemens Corporation, New York, NY; *Int'l*, pg. 1245

Vaselaney, Stacey, Mgr.-Pub. Rels.--Royal Appliance Mfg. Co., Cleveland, OH; *U.S. Public*, pg. 1410

Vasilenko, Janet, Dir.-Public Rels.--Tootsie Roll Industries, Inc., Chicago, IL; *U.S. Public*, pg. 1621

Vaskelis, L., Mgr.-Communications--Kruger Inc., Montreal, Canada; *Int'l*, pg. 761

Vassiliades, Thomas A., Pres.-Customer Service--Bell Atlantic Enterprises Corporation, Philadelphia, PA; *U.S. Public*, pg. 202

Vaterlaus, Walter, Head-Corp. Commun.--Clariant International Ltd., Muttenz, Switzerland; *Int'l*, pg. 624

Vattimo, F. D., Dir.-Mktg.--Bradford-White Corporation, Ambler, PA; *U.S. Private*, pg. 164

Vaughan, Adrienne C., Mgr.-Pub. Rels.--Aquarion Company, Bridgeport, CT; *U.S. Public*, pg. 126

Vaughan, Amy, Publicity Dir. & Promo. Dir.--Allied Advertising Agency, Public Relations, Syracuse, NY; *U.S. Private*, pg. 38

Vaughan, Marcia P., Dir.-Corp. Commun.--Sunrise Medical, Inc., Carlsbad, CA; *U.S. Public*, pg. 1535

Vaughn, Shelly, Dir.-Investor Rels.--American Business Information, Inc., Omaha, NE; *U.S. Public*, pg. 69

Vay, Tina, Publicity & Promo.--Allied Advertising, Cleveland, OH; *U.S. Private*, pg. 38

Vea, Amy, Mgr.-Corp. Communications--Televideo, Inc., San Jose, CA; *U.S. Public*, pg. 1572

Veach-Lytle, Tracy, Coord.-Adv.--Star Bronze Company, Alliance, OH; *U.S. Private*, pg. 1034

Veitenheimer, Lynette, Mktg. Communications-DIRECT Yellow Pages--U S West Inc., Englewood, CO; *U.S. Public*, pg. 1688

Vela, Al, Mgr.-Pub. Affairs--Exxon Corporation, Irving, TX; *U.S. Public*, pg. 601

Velbeck, John, Dir.- Communications--Dayco Products Inc., Miamisburg, OH; *U.S. Public*, pg. 1045

Velez, Agnes, Dir.-Press--Puerto Rico Tourism Company, San Juan, PR; *U.S. Private*, pg. 894

Velmosky, Dave, V.P.-H.R.--Isolyser Company, Inc., Norcross, GA; *U.S. Public*, pg. 914

VeltKamp, Vicki J., Mgr.-Corp. Commun.--Hecla Mining Company, Coeur D'Alene, ID; *U.S. Public*, pg. 803

Venechanos, Steven, Chief Fin. Officer & Sec.--Suprema Specialties, Inc., Paterson, NJ; *U.S. Public*, pg. 1541

Venezia, Francesca, Dir.-Corp. Commun.--Atmel Corporation, San Jose, CA; *U.S. Public*, pg. 145

Ventimiglia, Peter J., V.P.-External Affair--Bell Atlantic-NJ, Newark, NJ; *U.S. Public*, pg. 202

Venz, David, V.P.-Commun.--Airbus Industrie of North America, Inc., Herndon, VA; *Int'l*, pg. 39

Veran, Jean-Marc, Mgr.-Pub. Rels.--RTL, Paris, France; *Int'l*, *pg. 561*

Vergara, Sophie, Dir.-Communications--Henkel France S.A., Boulogne-Billancourt, France; *Int'l*, pg. 612

VerSteegh, Jerry, Dir.-Adv. & Commun. Production--Growmark, Inc., Bloomington, IL; *U.S. Private*, pg. 484

Vester-Johannes, J.W., Mgr.-Pub. Rels.--OPEL Nederland B.V., Sliedrecht, Netherlands; *U.S. Public*, pg. 723

Vetter, Don, Pub. Rels.--Dunn Reber Glenn Marz, Reno, NV; *U.S. Private*, pg. 347

Videau, Mrs., Dir.-Communication--Lafarge Refractaires Monolithiques, Montrouge, France; *Int'l*, pg. 789

Videira, Isabel, Dir.-Pub. Rels.--Ford Espana S.A., Madrid, Spain; *U.S. Public*, pg. 665

Vier, Christian, Mgr.-Pub. Rels.--Procter & Gamble France, Neuilly-sur-Seine, France; *U.S. Public*, pg. 1332

Vikkula, Kaisa, V.P.-Corp. Commun. & Investor Rels.--Partek Corporation, Helsinki, Finland; *Int'l*, pg. 1024

Villard, Jean-Claude, Dir.-Pub. Rels.--General Motors Suisse S.A., Bienne, Switzerland; *U.S. Public*, pg. 723

Villeneuve, Carole, Dir.-Public Rels.--The Cascades Group, Kingsey Falls, Canada; *Int'l*, pg. 273

Villiers, R. Child, Dir.-Communications--Rexam PLC, London, United Kingdom; *Int'l*, pg. 1106

Vincent, D., V.P.-Human Resources--John Brown E & C Corporate Offices (U.S.), Houston, TX; *Int'l*, pg. 774

Vincent, Rollie, V.P.-Pub. Relations/Strategic Planning--Bombardier, Learjet Inc., Wichita, KS; *Int'l*, pg. 200

Vinson, Jennifer, Publicity Mgr. & Promo. Mgr.--Allied Advertising, Cleveland, OH; *U.S. Private*, pg. 38

Violaris, Harry, Client Service Dir.--Producta-TBWA, Athens, Greece; *U.S. Private*, pg. 1062

Virgets, Thomas L., V.P.-Customer Rels.--Anco Insulations, Inc., Baton Rouge, LA; *U.S. Private*, pg. 71

Virkelyst, Bob, Mgr.-Mktg. Communications--Fluke Corporation, Everett, WA; *U.S. Public*, pg. 659

Viscardi, Robert, Dir.-Media & Consumer Commmunications--Bestfoods, Englewood Cliffs, NJ; *U.S. Public*, pg. 223

Viscomi, A.J., Dir.-Mktg. Communications--ADT Security Services, Inc., Aurora, CO; *U.S. Public*, pg. 1649

Vita, John S., Mgr.-Pub. Rels.--Arthur Andersen, Chicago, IL; *U.S. Private*, pg. 72

Vitelli, Tom, Dir.-Pub. Rels. & Adv.--Intermountain Health Care Inc., Salt Lake City, UT; *U.S. Private*, pg. 568

Vitlanlic, Tom, Mgr.-Pub. Rels.--New York Islanders Hockey Club, Uniondale, NY; *U.S. Private*, pg. 794

Vivier de Vaugouin, Christian, Mgr.-Pub. Rels.--Laboratoire LaChartre S.A., Blois, France; *U.S. Public*, pg. 1331

Vlk, Leroy F., Exec. Sec.--The Florists Assn. of Greater Cleveland, Inc., Cleveland, OH; *U.S. Private*, pg. 415

Voch, Roland, Dir.-Pub. Commun.--Siemens AG, Munich, Germany; *Int'l*, pg. 1244

Voellinger, Korinn, Dir.-Commun.--BGW Systems, Inc., Hawthorne, CA; *U.S. Private*, pg. 107

Vogelzang, C.F., Mgr.-Investor Rels. & Pub. Rels.--Wolters Kluwer N.V., Amsterdam, Netherlands; *Int'l*, pg. 1512

Vogler, Sharlene, Dir.-Investor Rels.--Mark IV Industries Inc., Amherst, NY; *U.S. Public*, pg. 1044

Voith, Nancy, Mgr.-Media Rels.--Electronic Data Systems Corporation, Plano, TX; *U.S. Public*, pg. 569

Volpone, April, Mktg. Communs. Mgr.--Continental Promotion Group, Tempe, AZ; *U.S. Private*, pg. 269

Volstad, Stephen A., Mgr.-Customer Commun.--Carolina Power & Light Company, Raleigh, NC; *U.S. Public*, pg. 306

von Alten, Gottfried, Dir.-Pub. Rels. & Adv.--O&K Orenstein & Koppel Aktiengesellschaft, Dortmund, Germany; *Int'l*, pg. 516

von der Rott, Dietrech, Mgr.-Pub. Rels.--Freudenberg & Company, Weinheim, Germany; *Int'l*, pg. 505

von Freymann, Cindy, Mgr.-Pub. Rels.--T.J. Maxx, Framingham, MA; *U.S. Public*, pg. 1557

Von Herz, Dr. Dieter, Dir.-Pub. Rels.--Continental AG, Hannover, Germany; *Int'l*, pg. 327

von Hofsten, Erik, Pub. Rels. Officer--Skanska AB, Danderyd, Sweden; *Int'l*, pg. 1260

Vorce, Betsy, Sr. V.P.-Pub. Rels.--Viacom Entertainment, New York, NY; *U.S. Private*, pg. 779

Vorsheim, George A., Jr., Dir.-Commun.--Environment/One Corporation, Niskayuna, NY; *U.S. Public*, pg. 586
Vorster, E.J., Dir.-Corp.--Dorbyl Limited, Bedfordview, South Africa; *Int'l*, pg. 416
Voser, Hans, Dir.-Pub. Rels.--Providentia, Nyon, Switzerland; *Int'l*, pg. 1072
Vu, Theresa, Mktg. Programs Specialist--Advanced Logic Research, Inc., Irvine, CA; *U.S. Public*, pg. 703
Vudri, Jukkapekka, Mgr.-Communications--Metsa-Serla Corporation, Espoo, Finland; *Int'l*, pg. 863
Vumbaco, Frank J., V.P.-Health, Safety & Corp. Communications--Starmet Corporation, Concord, MA; *U.S. Public*, pg. 1511
Vuorijarvi, Pala, Dir.-Pub. Rels.--Olivetti (Suomi) OY, Espoo, Finland; *Int'l*, pg. 1003
Wackerman, Dorothy C., V.P.-Corp. Communications--CertainTeed Corporation, Valley Forge, PA; *Int'l*, pg. 1170
Waddle, Allan C., Sr. V.P.-Pub. Affairs--National City Corporation, Cleveland, OH; *U.S. Public*, pg. 1154
Wade, Janis M., Sr. V.P.-H.R. & Corp. Commun.--CCL Industries, Inc., Willowdale, Canada; *Int'l*, pg. 238
Wade, Robert, V.P.-Corp. & Community Affairs--Beneficial Management Corporation, Peapack, NJ; *U.S. Public*, pg. 211
Wade, Stewart H., V.P.-Mktg. & Adv.--American Bureau of Shipping, New York, NY; *U.S. Private*, pg. 51
Wadsworth, Thomas, Mgr.-Communications--Raynor Garage Doors, Dixon, IL; *U.S. Private*, pg. 912
Waffen, Bruce, Dir.-Corp. Commun.--Nordson Corporation, Westlake, OH; *U.S. Public*, pg. 1188
Wagner, Dave, Dir.-Pub. Rels.--Vinum Inc., Old Brookville, NY; *U.S. Private*, pg. 113
Wagner, Keoni, Sr. Dir.-Corp. Communications--Hawaiian Airlines, Inc., Honolulu, HI; *U.S. Public*, pg. 799
Wagner, Michael, Dir.-Pub. Rels.--Hilti AG, Schaan, Liechtenstein; *Int'l*, pg. 619
Wagner, Randy, Dir.-Pub. Rels.--Brunswick Indoor Recreation Group, Lake Forest, IL; *U.S. Public*, pg. 265
Wagner, Robert, V.P.-Customer Satisfaction--Novellus Systems, Inc., San Jose, CA; *U.S. Public*, pg. 1204
Wagovich, Joseph M., Mgr.-Pub. Rels. & Adv.--Sanders, A Lockheed Martin Company, Nashua, NH; *U.S. Public*, pg. 1008
Wailes, Kathleen M., V.P.-Corp. Commun. & Investor Rels.--Litton Industries, Inc., Woodland Hills, CA; *U.S. Public*, pg. 1002
Waite, Robert E., V.P.-Corp. Rels. & Mktg.--CAE Inc., Toronto, Canada; *Int'l*, pg. 237
Wakefield, T.A., V.P.-Corp. Affairs--General Motors of Canada Ltd., Oshawa, Canada; *U.S. Public*, pg. 722
Walack, Molly, Dir.-Mktg. Communications--Leica Inc., Deerfield, IL; *Int'l*, pg. 806
Walch, Gerhard, V.P.-Client Relations & New Business Devel.--Liechtenstein Global Trust Limited, Vaduz, Liechtenstein; *Int'l*, pg. 809
Walikis, Elizabeth, Dir.-Corp. Commun.--The Vermont Teddy Bear Company, Inc., Shelburne, VT; *U.S. Public*, pg. 1716
Walker, J., Mgr.-Customer Service--Portec, Inc., Shipping Systems Div., Oak Brook, IL; *U.S. Public*, pg. 1318
Walker, James, V.P.-Mktg.--Koger Equity Inc., Jacksonville, FL; *U.S. Public*, pg. 965
Walker, Jennifer, Promo. & Pub. Rels. Specialist--Quality Stores Inc., Muskegon, MI; *U.S. Private*, pg. 899
Walker, Joan, Sr. V.P.-Corp. Communications--Ameritech Corporation, Chicago, IL; *U.S. Public*, pg. 97
Walker, Joan, Sr. V.P.-Corp. Communications--Ameritech Corp., Chicago, IL; *U.S. Public*, pg. 98
Walker, John E., V.P.-Corp. Commun.--Continental Airlines, Houston, TX; *U.S. Public*, pg. 439
Walker, Joseph, Mgr.-Media & Pub. Rels.--Geneva Steel, Vineyard, UT; *U.S. Public*, pg. 729
Walker, Roland, Dir.-Corp. Communications--Holderbank Financiere Glaris Ltd., Glaris, Switzerland; *Int'l*, pg. 628
Walker, Ruth, Mgr.-Pub. Rels.--Foremost Corporation of America, Caledonia, MI; *U.S. Public*, pg. 667
Walker, Sharon, Exec. Sec.-Corp. Commun.--Canadian Pacific Limited, Calgary, Canada; *Int'l*, pg. 258
Walker, Sylvia, Dir.-Adv. & Corp. Rels.--Blue Cross and Blue Shield Association, Chicago, IL; *U.S. Private*, pg. 151
Wallace, David, Dir.-Media Rels.--American Enterprise Institute for Public Policy Research, Washington, DC; *U.S. Private*, pg. 53
Wallace, James M., Mgr.-Corp. Communications--Cargill, Wayzata, MN; *U.S. Private*, pg. 210
Wallace, Linda, Grp. Mgr.-Communications--Colgate-Palmolive Ltd., Guildford, United Kingdom; *U.S. Public*, pg. 398
Walle-Hanren, Jorgen, Mgr.-Corp. Pub. Rels.--Tiedemanns - Joh.H.Andresen ANS, Oslo, Norway; *Int'l*, pg. 1389
Waller, D.A., Mgr.-Pub. Rels.--Halma p.l.c., Amersham, United Kingdom; *Int'l*, pg. 589
Wallman, Susan, Admin. Corp. Social Responsibility--The McGraw-Hill Companies, New York, NY; *U.S. Public*, pg. 1069
Walsh, Ellie, Dir.-Admin. Services--ABM Industries, San Francisco, CA; *U.S. Public*, pg. 2
Walsh, F. Michael, V.P.--First Marathon Inc., Toronto, Canada; *Int'l*, pg. 486
Walston, Suzanne, Mgr.-Corp. Communications--CSX Corporation, Richmond, VA; *U.S. Public*, pg. 284
Walter, John, Mgr.-Corp. Commun.--Burns & McDonnell Engineers-Architects-Consultants, Kansas City, MO; *U.S. Private*, pg. 187
Walters, Charles D., Chm. Bd. & Chief Exec. Officer--World Acceptance Corporation, Greenville, SC; *U.S. Public*, pg. 1778
Walters, Mary Dale, Dir.-Pub. Rels.--CCH Incorporated, Riverwoods, IL; *Int'l*, pg. 1513
Wampler, Jon R., Exec. Consultant-Pub. Affairs--PacifiCare Health Systems, Inc., Cypress, CA; *U.S. Public*, pg. 1250
Wanat, Jeff, Mgr.-Pub. Rels.--Azon Corporation, Johnson City, NY; *U.S. Private*, pg. 104
Wangstad, Kristi Rollag, V.P.-Pub. Affairs--Alliant Techsystems, Hopkins, MN; *U.S. Public*, pg. 47
Wanlin, Beth, Mgr.-Pub. Rels.--Hoffmann-La Roche Ltd., Mississauga, Canada; *Int'l*, pg. 1121
Ward, Diane, Dir.-Credit & Customer Service--Bumble Bee Seafoods Inc., San Diego, CA; *U.S. Private*, pg. 526
Ward, Michael, V.P.-Corp. Rels.--OzEmail Limited, Sydney, Australia; *Int'l*, pg. 1019
Ward, R.D., Mgr.-Pub. Affairs--Laporte plc, Luton, United Kingdom; *Int'l*, pg. 801
Ward, Terri, Mgr.-Pub. Rels.--Six Flags Over Georgia, Austell, GA; *U.S. Public*, pg. 1612
Ward, Thomas J., V.P.-Admin. & Sec.--Pennsylvania Enterprises Inc., Wilkes-Barre, PA; *U.S. Public*, pg. 1271
Warner-Bean, Sue, Mgr.-Pub. Affairs--Horizon Air Industries, Seattle, WA; *U.S. Public*, pg. 35
Warner, Bob, Dir.-Mktg. Communications--Freightliner Corp., Portland, OR; *Int'l*, pg. 368
Warner, Dominique-Paul, Dir-Gen. Affairs & Communications--Coflexip S.A., Paris, France; *Int'l*, pg. 304
Warner, Donald G., Dir.-Mktg.--NewAge Industries Inc., Willow Grove, PA; *U.S. Private*, pg. 796
Warner, Jodi L., Mgr.-AMCOL Commun. & Investor Rels.--AMCOL International Corp., Arlington Heights, IL; *U.S. Public*, pg. 63
Warner, Jodi L., Mgr.-Pub. Rels.--Ameri-Co Carriers, Inc., Scottsbluff, NE; *U.S. Public*, pg. 63
Warner, Linda, Mgr.-Mktg. Communications--Advanced Instruments, Inc., Norwood, MA; *U.S. Private*, pg. 22
Warner, Mary Kay, Mgr.-Pub. Rels.--Cargill Salt Inc., Minneapolis, MN; *Int'l*, pg. 48
Warner, Nicola, Mgr.-Communications--Marketforce (UK) Limited, London, United Kingdom; *Int'l*, pg. 651
Warner, Susan B., Dir.-Communications--General Signal Corporation, Stamford, CT; *U.S. Public*, pg. 726
Warren-Merrick, Gerri, V.P.-Public Affairs--Time Warner Cable of New York City, New York, NY; *U.S. Public*, pg. 1611
Warren, Betsey, Mgr.-Mktg. Communications--Loctite Corp. North American Group, Rocky Hill, CT; *Int'l*, pg. 611
Warren, Eric, Dir.-Pub. Rels.--Ascend Communications, Inc., Alameda, CA; *U.S. Public*, pg. 138
Warren, Gregg S., Dir.-Corp. Commun. & Govt. Rels.--Weirton Steel Corporation, Weirton, WV; *U.S. Public*, pg. 1751
Warren, J. Sandy, Mgr.-Commun.--Southwest Water Company, West Covina, CA; *U.S. Public*, pg. 1494
Warren, Janice, Mgr.-Corp. Commun.--FiberMark Inc., Brattleboro, VT; *U.S. Public*, pg. 620
Warren, Polly C., Dir.-Communications--Pepper, Hamilton & Scheetz, Philadelphia, PA; *U.S. Private*, pg. 851
Warren, Sheila A., Mgr.-Corp. Commun.--Biomet, Inc., Warsaw, IN; *U.S. Public*, pg. 231
Washington, Earl S., Sr. V.P.-Communications--Rockwell International Corporation, Costa Mesa, CA; *U.S. Public*, pg. 1397
Washington, George, Mgr.-Mktg. Commun.--The Flood Company, Hudson, OH; *U.S. Private*, pg. 414
Washington, Lawrence J., Jr., V.P.-Environ., Health & Safety/Pub. Affairs--The Dow Chemical Company, Midland, MI; *U.S. Public*, pg. 522
Wasner, Laurie, Mgr.-Global Commun.--Reedspectrum, Holden, MA; *Int'l*, pg. 624
Wasser, Debra, Dir.-Pub. Rels.--Orthofix International N.V., Curacao, Netherlands Antilles; *Int'l*, pg. 1011
Wasserman, Gail, V.P.-Pub. Affairs--American Express Travel Related Services Co., Inc., New York, NY; *U.S. Public*, pg. 73
Wasserman, Linda, Mgr.-Corp. Communications--Rhone-Poulenc Inc., Princeton, NJ; *Int'l*, pg. 1112
Waters, Kathy, Corp. Librarian--Information Systems & Network Corporation, Bethesda, MD; *U.S. Private*, pg. 561
Watkin-Jones, Howard, Mgr.-Communications--Adidas (UK) Ltd., Stockport, United Kingdom; *Int'l*, pg. 25
Watkins, Barry, Sr. V.P.-Pub. Rels.--Madison Square Garden Corporation, New York, NY; *U.S. Public*, pg. 288
Watkins, Wendy, Dir.-Corp. Commun. & Pub. Rels.--Host Marriott Services Corporation, Bethesda, MD; *U.S. Public*, pg. 841
Watson, Margaret, Dir.-Corp. & Employee Communications--Atmos Energy Corporation, Dallas, TX; *U.S. Public*, pg. 145
Watson, Patricia R., Mgr.-Pub. & Community Rels.--GTECH Corporation, West Greenwich, RI; *U.S. Public*, pg. 767
Watson, Russell A., Dir.-Mktg.--The Pepper Companies, Inc., Chicago, IL; *U.S. Private*, pg. 851
Watson, Susie E., Dir.-Adv. & Pub. Rels.--Timex Corporation, Middlebury, CT; *U.S. Private*, pg. 1088
Watson, Thomas A.G., V.P.-Communications--Laidlaw Inc., Burlington, Canada; *Int'l*, pg. 259
Watt, Phillip, Mgr.-Pub. Rels.--Glaxo Wellcome plc, London, United Kingdom; *Int'l*, pg. 552
Watt, William F., Exec. V.P. & Dir.-Mktg./Retail Banking--FirstFed Financial Corp., Santa Monica, CA; *U.S. Public*, pg. 645
Wattman, Kathy, Dir.-Pub. Rels.--Executive Software, Glendale, CA; *U.S. Private*, pg. 388
Watts, Samuel J., V.P.-Customer Service & Sls.--Atlantic Southeast Airlines Inc., Atlanta, GA; *U.S. Public*, pg. 144
Wawrynek, Edward C., V.P.-Pub. Rels. Communications--Tiffany & Co., New York, NY; *U.S. Public*, pg. 1608
Wayman, Jerry, Mgr.-Jeep Eagle Communications--Jeep, Auburn Hills, MI; *U.S. Public*, pg. 353
Wayman, Reva, Sr. V.P. & Mng. Dir.-Pub. Rels.--Harrison & Star, Inc., New York, NY; *U.S. Private*, pg. 506
Waytula, Carol, Mgr.-Mktg. Communications--OMRON Systems, Inc., Schaumburg, IL; *Int'l*, pg. 1005
Weaver, Donna B., Mgr.-Corp. Communications--Kellwood Company, Chesterfield, MO; *U.S. Public*, pg. 948
Webb, Andy, Mgr.-Telecommunications--Royal Insurance, Charlotte, NC; *Int'l*, pg. 1130
Webb, Mary Sue, Mktg. Communications--Evenflo Company, Inc., Piqua, OH; *U.S. Private*, pg. 629
Webb, Stacey, Pub. Rels. Specialist--Wal-Mart Stores, Inc., Bentonville, AR; *U.S. Public*, pg. 1732
Webb, Theora G., Dir.-Public Affairs--Duracell International Inc., Bethel, CT; *U.S. Public*, pg. 743
Webber, Michelle, Specialist-Pub. Rels.--Informix Software, Menlo Park, CA; *U.S. Public*, pg. 876
Weber-Milsten, Karen, Mgr.-Corp. Commnuications--Van Waters & Rogers, Kirkland, WA; *Int'l*, pg. 1147
Weber, Ann, Mgr.-Corp. Communications--The Andersons Incorporated, Maumee, OH; *U.S. Public*, pg. 111
Weber, Dwight E., Dir.-Communications--Precision Castparts Corp., Portland, OR; *U.S. Public*, pg. 1320
Weber, Gloria R., Dir.-Corp. Communications--Comair, Inc., Erlanger, KY; *U.S. Public*, pg. 406
Weber, Holly, Mktg. Coord.--Camosy, Inc., Russell, IL; *U.S. Private*, pg. 203
Weber, L.G., Mgr.-Consumer Rels.--Salt River Project Agricultural Improvement and Power District, Tempe, AZ; *U.S. Private*, pg. 962
Weddleton, Ann, Mgr.-Human Resources--Loomis, Sayles & Co., Boston, MA; *U.S. Private*, pg. 737
Wee, Michelle, Div. Mgr.-Corp Pub. Rels. & Investor--F. J. Benjamin Holdings Ltd., Singapore, Singapore; *Int'l*, pg. 187
Wee, Michelle, Div. Mgr.-Investor Rels. & Pub. Rels.--F.J. Benjamin Multimedia Pte Ltd., Singapore, Singapore; *Int'l*, pg. 187
Weed, Joe K., V.P.-Mktg. & Commun.--EBSCO Industries, Inc., Birmingham, AL; *U.S. Private*, pg. 358
Weeden, Jeffrey B., Chief Fin. Officer, Sr. V.P., & Treas.--Firstar Corporation-Iowa, Des Moines, IA; *U.S. Public*, pg. 643
Weekem, Ulrich B., Dir.-Corp. Communications--Philip Morris Gmbh, Munich, Germany; *U.S. Public*, pg. 1290
Weeks, Cynthia, Communications Coord.--SRA International Inc., Arlington, VA; *U.S. Private*, pg. 957
Weerts, Christophe, Mgr.-Pub. Rels.--Cockerill Sambre, Brussels, Belgium; *Int'l*, pg. 301
Wegscheid, Laura, Mgr.-Pub. Affairs.--Pacificare of Colorado, Englewood, CO; *U.S. Public*, pg. 1251
Wehling, Robert, Sr. V.P.-Mktg. Research & Govt. Rels.--Richardson-Vicks, Inc., Health Care Products, Cincinnati, OH; *U.S. Public*, pg. 1331
Weidel, Birca, Mgr.-Pub. Rels.--Dun & Bradstreet Deutschland GmbH, Frankfurt/Main, Germany; *U.S. Public*, pg. 536
Weidman, Sheila, Corp. Dir.-External Communication--Georgia-Pacific Corporation, Atlanta, GA; *U.S. Public*, pg. 735
Weigel, Joe, Dir.-Mktg. & Corp. Communications--Batesville Casket Company, Inc., Batesville, IN; *U.S. Public*, pg. 828
Weiman, Lori, Dir.-Corp. Commun. & Investor Rels.--MGI PHARMA INC., Minneapolis, MN; *U.S. Public*, pg. 1026
Weinberg, Dennis, Dir.-Mktg./Communications--Howmedica, Inc., Rutherford, NJ; *U.S. Public*, pg. 1282
Weiner, Lowell B., Asst. V.P., Pub. Rels.--American Home Products Corporation, Madison, NJ; *U.S. Public*, pg. 79
Weingardt, G. Greg, Mgr.-Mktg. Commun.--Union Carbide Corporation, Danbury, CT; *U.S. Public*, pg. 1666
Weinhart, Thomas, Mgr.-Pub. Rels.--Bayer AG, Leverkusen, Germany; *Int'l*, pg. 171
Weinstein, Adrienne, Mgr.-Communications--Bachman's, Inc., Minneapolis, MN; *U.S. Private*, pg. 109
Weinstein, Steve, V.P.-Sls. & Mktg.--Ventre Packing Company, Inc., Syracuse, NY; *U.S. Private*, pg. 1135
Weir, Timothy G., Dir.-Corp. Communications--Breed Technologies, Inc., Lakeland, FL; *U.S. Public*, pg. 251
Weisband, Mimi, Dir.-Pub. Rels.--Crystal Cruises, Inc., Los Angeles, CA; *Int'l*, pg. 941
Weisberg, R., Dir.-Pub. Rels.--Technic Incorporated, Cranston, RI; *U.S. Private*, pg. 1071
Weischer, Carsten, Mgr.-Pub. Rels.--Knurr AG, Munich, Germany; *Int'l*, pg. 739
Weisfeld, Brian, Mng. Dir.-Imax Theatres & Commun.--Imax Corporation, Mississauga, Canada; *Int'l*, pg. 661
Weiss, Ellen R., Sr. V.P.-Mktg. & Communications--Binswanger, Philadelphia, PA; *U.S. Private*, pg. 144
Weiss, Sam, Chm. Bd., Pres. & Chief Exec. Officer--United Receptical, Inc., Pottsville, PA; *U.S. Private*, pg. 1123
Weiss, Skid, Dir.-Publicity--WEA Corp., Burbank, CA; *U.S. Public*, pg. 1612
Weiss, Steven, Sr. Dir.-Corp. Communications--The McGraw-Hill Companies, New York, NY; *U.S. Public*, pg. 1069
Weitman, Jean, Mgr.-Corp. Communications--Cleveland-Cliffs Inc, Cleveland, OH; *U.S. Public*, pg. 386
Welch, Kimberly A., V.P.-Corp. Commun.--Federal-Mogul Corporation, Southfield, MI; *U.S. Public*, pg. 615
Welch, Margaret G., Mgr.-Pub. Rels.--A.G. Edwards, Inc., Saint Louis, MO; *U.S. Public*, pg. 565
Welch, Susan S., Dir.-Corp. Commun.--The Associated Press, New York, NY; *U.S. Private*, pg. 92
Welch, Victoria C., Mgr.-Mktg. Srvcs., Pub. Rels. & Media--Reynolds Metals Co.-Flexible Packaging Products Division, Richmond, VA; *U.S. Public*, pg. 1386
Wells, Andrew, Communication Specialist--Willis Corroon Corp., Nashville, TN; *Int'l*, pg. 1504
Wells, Earl, Pub. Rels. Dir.--Eric Mower and Associates/Buffalo, Inc., Buffalo, NY; *U.S. Private*, pg. 765
Wells, Gill, Mgr.-Pub. Rels.--Trebor Bassett Ltd., Maple Cross, United Kingdom; *Int'l*, pg. 248
Wells, John, Mgr.-Mktg. Communications--Fisher Controls International, Inc., Marshalltown, IA; *U.S. Public*, pg. 573
Wells, John, Mgr.-Mktg. Conmmunications--Fisher Controls International, Inc., North Stonington, CT; *U.S. Public*, pg. 573
Welsh, Magnes, Dir.-Pub. Rels.--Chiquita Brands International, Inc., Cincinnati, OH; *U.S. Public*, pg. 349
Welsh, T.M., Mgr.-Communications Services--FirstEnergy Corp., Akron, OH; *U.S. Public*, pg. 644

Welte, Philip, Dir.-Pub. Rels.--Burda Holding GmbH & Co., KG, Munich, Germany; Int'l, pg. 233

Welty, Susan, Mgr.-Pub. Rels.--Budget Rent A Car Corporation, Lisle, IL; U.S. Private, pg. 178

Wendell, R., Mgr.-Communications--Telephonics Command Systems Div., Farmingdale, NY; U.S. Public, pg. 558

Wengen, Christine, Mgr.-Corp. Commun.--Seed Restaurant Group, Inc., Lexington, KY; U.S. Private, pg. 981

Wentworth, John, Exec. V.P.-Mktg. Paramount T.V. Div.--Paramount Pictures Corporation, Los Angeles, CA; U.S. Private, pg. 776

Wentworth, Roseann, Pub. Rels. Consultant--William Cook Public Relations, Inc., Jacksonville, FL; U.S. Private, pg. 273

Wenzl, Sharon, V.P.-Corp. Rels.--Freudenberg-NOK, Plymouth, MI; U.S. Private, pg. 427

Werderman, Kurt, Corp. Communications Asst.--Fremont General Corporation, Santa Monica, CA; U.S. Public, pg. 681

Werker, Michael, Dir.-Pub. Rels.--Deutz AG, Cologne, Germany; Int'l, pg. 407

Werneck, Mauricio, Mgr.-Corp Rels.--Aracruz Celulose S.A., Rio de Janeiro, Brazil; Int'l, pg. 78

Wesman, Paul, Dir.-Pub. Rels.--Right Management Consultants, Inc., Philadelphia, PA; U.S. Public, pg. 1390

Wessel, James A., Pres.--Becton Dickinson Canada Inc., Mississauga, Canada; U.S. Public, pg. 200

West, Ed, Dir.-Pub. Rels.--Eli Lilly and Company, Indianapolis, IN; U.S. Public, pg. 992

West, Elena F., Mgr.-Mktg. Svcs.--The Ohio Art Company, Inc., Bryan, OH; U.S. Public, pg. 1214

West, Kim, Asst. Mgr.-Investor Rels.--Collins & Aikman Corporation, Charlotte, NC; U.S. Public, pg. 399

West, Krista, Mgr.-Pub. Rels.--Advanced Input Devices, Inc., Coeur D'Alene, ID; U.S. Private, pg. 21

West, Lois J., Dir.-Commun. & Community Rels.--Ecolab Inc., Saint Paul, MN; U.S. Public, pg. 562

West, Rhonda K., V.P.-Corp. Communications--The May Department Stores Company, Saint Louis, MO; U.S. Public, pg. 1063

West, Ross D., Dir.-Mktg.--American Felt & Filter, Newburgh, NY; U.S. Private, pg. 54

West, Sue, Head-Corp. Affairs--Booker PLC, London, United Kingdom; Int'l, pg. 202

Westberg, Bjorn, Sr. V.P.--Nordbanken AB, Stockholm, Sweden; Int'l, pg. 957

Westcott, Gayle, Communications Specialist--Southam Inc., Don Mills, Canada; Int'l, pg. 631

Westerbeck, David F., Sr. V.P., Gen. Counsel & Sec.--The Union Central Life Insurance Co., Cincinnati, OH; U.S. Private, pg. 1118

Westman, Tim, Dir.-Corp. Commun.--Costain Group PLC, London, United Kingdom; Int'l, pg. 336

Whalen, Brian B., V.P.-Pub. Affairs--Navistar International Corporation, Chicago, IL; U.S. Public, pg. 1167

Whalen, Kevin M., V.P.-Corp. Communications & Community Rels. & Exec. Dir.--Jostens, Minneapolis, MN; U.S. Public, pg. 934

Wharton, Martha L., V.P.-Customer Rels.--Indianapolis Water Company, Indianapolis, IN; U.S. Public, pg. 1185

Whatcott, Lee, Mgr.-Pub. Rels.--Western Financial Bank, Irvine, CA; U.S. Public, pg. 1757

Wheat, Ted W., Dir.-Community Rels.--American Mutual Life Holding Co., Des Moines, IA; U.S. Private, pg. 59

Wheeler, Kimberly, Mgr.-Mktg. Services--The New Piper Aircraft, Inc., Vero Beach, FL; U.S. Private, pg. 794

Wheeler, Patrick J., Dir.-Corp. Communications--Consolidated Edison Company of New York, Inc., New York, NY; U.S. Public, pg. 434

Wheeler, Paula, Supvr.-Pub. Rels.--UGI Corporation, King of Prussia, PA; U.S. Public, pg. 1653

Wheeless, Charlene, Dir.-Corp. Commun.--DynCorp, Reston, VA; U.S. Private, pg. 351

Wheeless, Charlene, Mgr.-Pub. Rels.--Aerospace Technology, Fort Worth, TX; U.S. Private, pg. 351

Whelan, Gerard, Mgr.-Corp. Communications--IMI Plc, Witton, United Kingdom; Int'l, pg. 646

Whelan, Veronica, Dir.-Mktg. & Communications--Bell Atlantic New England, Boston, MA; U.S. Public, pg. 202

Whewell, Jo, Mgr.-Corp. Comm.--National & Provincial Building Society, Bradford, United Kingdom; Int'l, pg. 906

Whipp, Donald H., Dir.-Corp. Communications--Allegheny Power System, Inc., Hagerstown, MD; U.S. Public, pg. 42

White, Brian, Coord.-Mktg. Commun.--Hypermedia Communications, Inc., San Mateo, CA; U.S. Public, pg. 851

White, Cheri, Dir.-Media Relations--Full House Sports & Entertainment, Seattle, WA; U.S. Public, pg. 16

White, James D., Mgr.-Adv. & Pub. Rels.--ITT Jabsco, Costa Mesa, CA; U.S. Public, pg. 860

White, Katherine, Pub. Affairs Coord.--Seattle Post-Intelligencer, Seattle, WA; U.S. Private, pg. 517

White, Monica D., Mgr.-Customer Svc.--Flexible Steel Lacing Company, Downers Grove, IL; U.S. Private, pg. 413

White, Vince, Dir.-Investor Rels.--Devon Energy Corporation, Oklahoma City, OK; U.S. Public, pg. 503

White, Virginia, V.P.-Commun. & Asst. Sec.--Staple Cotton Cooperative Association, Greenwood, MS; U.S. Private, pg. 1033

White, W. Ward, V.P.-Communications--Northwestern Mutual Life Insurance Co., Milwaukee, WI; U.S. Private, pg. 807

Whitehouse, Donald, Mgr.-Tech. Cmmunications--Emerson & Cuming Specialty Polymers, Lexington, MA; Int'l, pg. 1435

Whitford, Richard D., Mgr.-Customer Service--Bundy Tubing Co. (Australia) Pty. Ltd., Adelaide, Australia; Int'l, pg. 1341

Whitlatch, Rebecca, Mgr.-Communications--Leslie Controls, Inc., Tampa, FL; U.S. Public, pg. 1746

Whitlow, Michael D., V.P.-External Affairs--Albemarle Corporation, Richmond, VA; U.S. Public, pg. 37

Whitman, Marcus, Mgr.-Pub. Rels.--Tho-Ro Products, Inc., Carlstadt, NJ; U.S. Private, pg. 354

Whitmore, Birge, Supvr.-Pub. Rels.--Snap-On Tools Corporation, Kenosha, WI; U.S. Public, pg. 1480

Whitmyre, Richard D., Dir.-Commun.--Lukens Inc., Coatesville, PA; U.S. Public, pg. 1019

Whitmyre, Richard D., Dir.-Communications--Lukens Steel Company, Coatesville, PA; U.S. Public, pg. 1020

Whittaker, Enez, Mgr.-Adv. & Pub. Rels.--Jamaica Flour Mills, Ltd., Kingston, Jamaica; Int'l, pg. 411

Whittal, Helen, Mgr.-Pub. Rels. & Communications--Birds Eye Walls Ltd., Walton-on-Thames, United Kingdom; Int'l, pg. 1434

Whittle, Roni, Dir.-Communications--Huntsman Corporation, Salt Lake City, UT; U.S. Private, pg. 549

Whittle, Ronnie, Dir.-Communications--Huntsman Corporation, Salt Lake City, UT; U.S. Private, pg. 549

Whittman, Bryan, V.P.-Promo., Publicity & Special Events--Disneyland, Anaheim, CA; U.S. Public, pg. 511

Wholley, Gina, V.P.-Mktg. & Human Resources--Lait Purser & Associates, Charlotte, NC; U.S. Private, pg. 896

Whyte, Ann Marie, Mgr.-Communications--Cedar Fair, L.P., Sandusky, OH; U.S. Public, pg. 319

Whyte, Ann Marie, Mgr.-Communications--Cedar Point, Sandusky, OH; U.S. Public, pg. 319

Wick, D., V.P.-Customer Service--Whittaker Communications, Inc., Santa Clara, CA; U.S. Public, pg. 1767

Wickham, D. M., Dir.-Corp. & Pub. Affairs--Carter Holt Harvey Limited, Auckland, New Zealand; U.S. Public, pg. 904

Wideness, Sarah, Pub. Rels.--Orient-Express Hotels Inc., New York, NY; Int'l, pg. 1213

Widmayer, Karen, V.P.-Commun.--CarrAmerica Realty, Washington, DC; U.S. Public, pg. 308

Widmeyer, Chris, Dir.-Pub. Rels.--National Football League Properties, Inc., New York, NY; U.S. Private, pg. 783

Wiemer, Wilma, Mgr.-Commun. & Pub. Affairs--Celanese Canada, Inc., Montreal, Canada; Int'l, pg. 625

Wienke, Torger, Dir.-Pub. Rels.--Saarbergwerke Aktiengesellschaft, Saarbruecken, Germany; Int'l, pg. 1166

Wiese, Nancy J., Dir.-Worldwide Mktg. Communications--Xerox Corporation, Stamford, CT; U.S. Public, pg. 1783

Wiese, Tracy, Dir.-Commun.--Lund Food Holdings, Inc., Edina, MN; U.S. Private, pg. 680

Wieties, Cynthia P., Dir.-Communications--The Franklin Life Insurance Company, Springfield, IL; U.S. Public, pg. 76

Wightman, Kerri, Pub. Rels. Officer--Holiday Inn Worldwide, Atlanta, GA; Int'l, pg. 170

Wilbrecht, Chris, Mgr.-Communications--Jackson Hole Ski Resort, Teton Village, WY; U.S. Private, pg. 579

Wilbur, Laura, Mgr.-Mktg. Communications--American Tool Companies, Inc., Lincoln, NE; U.S. Private, pg. 63

Wilcox, D.W., Mgr.-Corp. Public Rels. & Communications--Kodak Limited, Hemel Hempstead, United Kingdom; U.S. Public, pg. 553

Wilcox, Kerry L., Mgr.-Pub. Rels. & Events Coord.--The Keyes Company Realtors, Miami, FL; U.S. Private, pg. 618

Wilcox, Marna, Mgr.-Corp. Adv. & Communications--Utah Power & Light, Salt Lake City, UT; U.S. Public, pg. 1251

Wilcox, Richard, Dir.-Commun.--Hubbard Hall Inc., Waterbury, CT; U.S. Private, pg. 544

Wildermuth, Ron E., Dir.-Corp. Rels.--Parsons Corporation, Pasadena, CA; U.S. Private, pg. 841

Wile, Janet, Dir.-Communications--Honeywell Limited, North York, Canada; U.S. Public, pg. 835

Wiley, Deborah E., Sr. V.P.-Corp. Commun.--John Wiley & Sons, Inc., New York, NY; U.S. Public, pg. 1768

Wiley, Dorothy M., V.P.-Pub. Rels.--Paragon Health Network, Inc., Atlanta, GA; U.S. Public, pg. 1256

Wiley, Patricia, Dir.-Mktg.--Ziebart International Corporation, Troy, MI; U.S. Private, pg. 1205

Wilks, Marylaurel E., V.P.-Commun., Gen. Counsel & Sec.--Speedway Motorsports, Inc., Concord, NC; U.S. Public, pg. 1498

Willard, Julia, Pub. Rels. Supvr.--Ingalls, Boston, MA; U.S. Private, pg. 562

Willard, Sheila R., V.P.-Pub. Affairs--Comcast Cable Communications, Inc., Philadelphia, PA; U.S. Public, pg. 407

Willardson, Kris, Dir.-Communications--Wagner Spray Tech Corp., Plymouth, MN; U.S. Private, pg. 1146

Willersdorf, R. Graeme, Sr. V.P.-Pub. Affairs--Foster's Brewing Group Limited, Southbank, Australia; Int'l, pg. 500

Williams, Ann, Mgr.-Mktg.--G.S. Blodgett Corporation, Burlington, VT; U.S. Public, pg. 1064

Williams, Ann E., Mgr.-Mktg., Adv. & Pub. Rels.--The Blodgett Oven Co., Inc., Burlington, VT; U.S. Public, pg. 1064

Williams, Chris, Dir.-Consumer Affairs--Weaver Popcorn Company, Inc., Van Buren, IN; U.S. Private, pg. 1156

Williams, Frank J., Jr., V.P.-Pub. Affairs & Sr. Counsel--The May Department Stores Company, Saint Louis, MO; U.S. Public, pg. 1063

Williams, Gary, Corp. Communications--Omaha Public Power District, Omaha, NE; U.S. Private, pg. 815

Williams, Holly, Mgr.-Communications--Bio-Logic Systems Corp., Mundelein, IL; U.S. Public, pg. 230

Williams, Jonathan, V.P.-Media Rels.--PNC Bank Corp., Pittsburgh, PA; U.S. Public, pg. 1242

Williams, Judy, Sr. V.P.-Corp. Communications (Media Contact)--CoreStates Financial Corp., Philadelphia, PA; U.S. Public, pg. 446

Williams, Katerine, Mgr.-Pub. & Rels.--Greyhound Lines, Inc., Dallas, TX; U.S. Public, pg. 765

Williams, Katherine, Mgr.-Pub. Rels.--Greyhound Lines, Inc., Dallas, TX; U.S. Public, pg. 765

Williams, Lance, Dir.-Human Resources--Fujisawa U.S.A. Inc., Deerfield, IL; Int'l, pg. 525

Williams, R. James, Dir.-Commun.--Keeneland Assoc., Inc., Lexington, KY; U.S. Private, pg. 611

Williams, Robert E., V.P. & Dir.-Investor/Pub. Rels.--St. Paul Bancorp, Inc., Chicago, IL; U.S. Public, pg. 1428

Williams, Steve Lee, Mgr.-Pub. & Employee Communications--Texas Utilities Company, Dallas, TX; U.S. Public, pg. 1586

Williams, Wayne, Mgr.-Corp. Employee Rels.--Hydril Company, Houston, TX; U.S. Private, pg. 551

Williamson, Charles, Mgr.-Communications--Toastmaster, Inc., Columbia, MO; U.S. Public, pg. 1619

Williamson, Patricia, Asst. V.P.--DRS Technologies, Inc., Parsippany, NJ; U.S. Public, pg. 474

Willice, Grieme, Mgr.-Communications--Nestle S.A., Vevey, Switzerland; Int'l, pg. 915

Willis, Elizabeth, Dir.-Communications--Northern States Power Company, Minneapolis, MN; U.S. Public, pg. 1195

Willis, Joyce, Asst. V.P.-Pub. Rels.--The Hartford Financial Services Group Inc., Hartford, CT; U.S. Public, pg. 794

Willoughby, James, Grp. Mgr.-Commun.--Australian Mutual Provident, Sydney, Australia; Int'l, pg. 100

Willox, Bruce A., Mgr.-Mktg. Communications--A.T. Cross Co., Lincoln, RI; U.S. Public, pg. 460

Wills, Karen, Mgr.-Pub. Rels.--Viewlogic Systems Group, Marlborough, MA; U.S. Public, pg. 1548

Wilmsen, Tammie, Mgr.-Corp. Communications--Tecmar Technologies, Inc., Longmont, CO; Int'l, pg. 1361

Wilson, Allan, V.P.-Sls. & Cust. Service--Western Data Systems, Calabasas, CA; U.S. Private, pg. 1165

Wilson, Bob, Mgr.-Pub. Rels.--Manufacturers Technologies, Inc., West Springfield, MA; U.S. Private, pg. 701

Wilson, Cleo F., Exec. Dir.-Pub. Affairs--Playboy Enterprises, Inc., Chicago, IL; U.S. Public, pg. 1309

Wilson, Curt, Dir.-Real Estate--Folmar & Associates, Mobile, AL; U.S. Private, pg. 417

Wilson, Des, Dir.-Corp. & Pub. Affairs.--BAA plc, London, United Kingdom; Int'l, pg. 103

Wilson, Holly, Mgr.-Adv.--Michael Business Machines Corporation, Charleston, SC; U.S. Private, pg. 740

Wilson, Jackie, Dir.-Pub. Rels.--Lyondell Petrochemical Company, Houston, TX; U.S. Public, pg. 1022

Wilson, Jill, Mgr.-Mktg.--James N. Gray Construction Co., Inc., Lexington, KY; U.S. Private, pg. 472

Wilson, Patrick J., Dir.-Indus. Rels.--Northrop Grumman Corporation, Los Angeles, CA; U.S. Public, pg. 1197

Wilson, Paula, Dir.-Mktg.& Communication--The Life Insurance Co. of Virginia, Richmond, VA; U.S. Public, pg. 712

Wilson, Richard H., Dir.-Pub. Affairs--Alberta Energy Company, Ltd., Calgary, Canada; Int'l, pg. 48

Wilson, Rita P., Sr. V.P.-Corp. Rels.--The Allstate Corporation, Northbrook, IL; U.S. Public, pg. 55

Wilson, Robert, Chief Fin. Officer & Pub. Rels.--Supreme Corporation, Goshen, IN; U.S. Public, pg. 1542

Wilson, Robert, Chief Fin. Officer & V.P.--Supreme Corporation of Texas, Cleburne, TX; U.S. Public, pg. 1542

Wilson, Robert, Chief Fin. Officer--Supreme MidAtlantic Corporation, Jonestown, PA; U.S. Public, pg. 1542

Wilson, Robert, Chief Fin. Officer--Supreme Murphy Corp., Wilson, NC; U.S. Public, pg. 1542

Wilson, Ryan, V.P.-Pub. Rels.--Karakas, VanSickle, Ouellette Advertising & Public Relations, Portland, OR; U.S. Private, pg. 607

Wilson, Wayne, V.P.-Corp. Affairs--Hayward Industries, Inc., Elizabeth, NJ; U.S. Private, pg. 513

Windham, C. Richard, Dir.-Pub. Rels. & Burlington Foundation--Burlington Industries, Inc., Greensboro, NC; U.S. Public, pg. 268

Winfrey, Jane, Dir.-Communications--CHF Industries, Inc., New York, NY; U.S. Private, pg. 1094

Winfrey, Savona, Dir.-Pub. Rels.--Texas Motor Speedway, Fort Worth, TX; U.S. Public, pg. 1498

Wink, Kathy, Mgr.-Graphics & Communications--Borden Decorative Products, Saint Louis, MO; U.S. Private, pg. 158

Winner, Pam, Acting V.P.-Commun.--Lexmark International Group, Inc., Lexington, KY; U.S. Public, pg. 991

Winner, Pam, Acting V.P.-Commun.--Lexmark International, Inc., Lexington, KY; U.S. Public, pg. 991

Winnett, Greg, V.P.-Commun.--Service Merchandise Company, Inc., Brentwood, TN; U.S. Public, pg. 1461

Winston, Mark, Mgr.-Mktg.-Consumer Prods.--Wagner Spray Tech Corp., Plymouth, MN; U.S. Private, pg. 1146

Winston, Rick, Corp. Communications & Adv.--Sun Life Assurance Company of Canada, Toronto, Canada; Int'l, pg. 1318

Winter, Ed, Mgr.-Employee Rels.--Avondale Industries, Inc., Avondale, LA; U.S. Public, pg. 156

Winterflood, Claire, Exec.-Corp. Commun.--Taylor Woodrow plc, London, United Kingdom; Int'l, pg. 1358

Winzig, Otmar, Dir.-Communications--Preussag AG, Hannover, Germany; Int'l, pg. 1069

Wires, Brendan, Coord.-Publications--Romac Industries, Inc., Seattle, WA; U.S. Private, pg. 942

Wirth, Peter, Dr., Pres. & Chief Exec. Officer--Mikron Holding AG, Biel, Switzerland; Int'l, pg. 866

Wirth, Rick, Mgr.-Communications--Robicon, New Kensington, PA; U.S. Private, pg. 528

Wirthmann-Rado, Julianna, Dir.-Pub. Rels. & H.R.--Budapest Marriott Hotel, Budapest, Hungary; Int'l, pg. 232

Wischnia, Abe, Dir.-Corp. Commun.--Cubic Corporation, San Diego, CA; U.S. Public, pg. 466

Wise, Eileen, Dir.-Pub. Rels.--The National Magazine Company Ltd., London, United Kingdom; U.S. Private, pg. 518

Wise, Jim, Dir.-Corp. Commun.--Greate Bay Casino Corporation, Atlantic City, NJ; U.S. Public, pg. 760

Wise, Jim, Dir.-Corp. Commun.--Hollywood Casino Corp, Atlantic City, NJ; U.S. Public, pg. 830

Wisner, Franz, V.P.-Govt. Rels.--The Irvine Company, Newport Beach, CA; U.S. Private, pg. 575

Wisniewski, Robert E., Treas. & Sec.--Moore Products Co., Spring House, PA; U.S. Public, pg. 1128

Wissum, Mikael, Dir.-Corp. Affairs--Time/System International A/S, Allerod, Denmark; Int'l, pg. 73

Wiszniewska, Elzbieta, Dir.-Pub. Rels.--LOT Polish Airlines SA, New York, NY; *Int'l*, pg. 1062
Witmer, Mark D., Asst. Treas.--Michael Foods, Inc., Minneapolis, MN; *U.S. Public*, pg. 1103
Witmer, Stephen B., Mgr.-Corp. Communications--Watkins-Johnson Company, Palo Alto, CA; *U.S. Public*, pg. 1745
Wittenzellner, Herman, Mgr.-Pub. Rels.--Kermi GmbH, Plattling, Germany; *Int'l*, pg. 1069
Wittig, Paul, Dir.-Corp. Services--Federal Signal Corporation, Oak Brook, IL; *U.S. Public*, pg. 616
Wittmann, Andrea, Mgr.-Communications--Sauer Sundstrand Gmbh & Co., Neumunster, Germany; *Int'l*, pg. 1198
Witty, Esti, V.P.-Customer Base Mngmt.--MobileComm, Ridgefield Park, NJ; *U.S. Public*, pg. 1120
Wixted, Kevin, Dir.-Adv. & Pub. Rels.--La-Z-Boy Incorporated, Monroe, MI; *U.S. Public*, pg. 972
Wolfe, Rita, Mgr.-Customer Service--BernzOmatic, Medina, NY; *U.S. Public*, pg. 1177
Wolfe, Suzanne, Dir.-Human Resources--SCIEX, Concord, Canada; *Int'l*, pg. 827
Wolfe, William C., Jr., V.P.-Community Rels.--The Dispatch Printing Company, Columbus, OH; *U.S. Private*, pg. 334
Wolfenbarger, Todd, Mgr.-Corp. Communications--AT&T Wireless Services, Kirkland, WA; *U.S. Public*, pg. 11
Wolff, Mane-Luise, Dr., Dir.-Pub. Rels.--Veba AG, Dusseldorf, Germany; *Int'l*, pg. 1454
Wolfington, John F., Chm. Bd.--Wolfington Body Company, Exton, PA; *U.S. Private*, pg. 1186
Wollman, Rick, Mgr.-Media Rels.--Terra Industries, Inc., Sioux City, IA; *U.S. Public*, pg. 1581
Wolski, Christine M., Asst. Corp. Sec.--Commerce Group Corp., Milwaukee, WI; *U.S. Public*, pg. 410
Wolties, K., Dir.-Pub. Rels.--Heineken N.V., Amsterdam, Netherlands; *Int'l*, pg. 608
Wong, Audrey, Sr. Mgr.-Mktg. Commun.--F. J. Benjamin Holdings Ltd., Singapore, Singapore; *Int'l*, pg. 187
Wood, Carol, Dir.-Mktg. & Affiliate Rels.--The Sports Network (TSN), Willowdale, Canada; *Int'l*, pg. 1343
Wood, Jan, V.P.-Mktg. & Commun.--Credit Union National Association, Madison, WI; *U.S. Private*, pg. 288
Wood, Richard, Dir.-Corp. Communications--Laserscope Surgical Systems, San Jose, CA; *U.S. Public*, pg. 979
Wood, Robert E., V.P.-Pub. Affairs & Environmental Policy--MDU Resources Group, Inc., Bismarck, ND; *U.S. Public*, pg. 1025
Wood, Sandra, Dir.-Pub. Rels. & Adv.--ITT Cannon, Santa Ana, CA; *U.S. Public*, pg. 859
Woodbeck, Milford E., Jr., Pres.--Overhead Conveyor Co., Ferndale, MI; *U.S. Private*, pg. 822
Woodmore, Michael, Dir.-Human Resources--Ranks Hovis McDougall Limited, Marlow, United Kingdom; *Int'l*, pg. 1395
Woodruff, Jay, Mgr.-Communications--Molten Metal Technology, Inc., Fall River, MA; *U.S. Public*, pg. 1123
Woods-Turner, Barry, Pub. Rels. Officer--British Aerospace p.l.c., Farnborough, United Kingdom; *Int'l*, pg. 217
Woods, Richard, Sr. V.P. & Dir.-Pub. Rels.--Mastercard International, Inc., Purchase, NY; *U.S. Private*, pg. 714
Woodward, Craig, Dir.-Commun. & Adv.--Kappler Safety Group, Inc., Guntersville, AL; *U.S. Private*, pg. 607
Woodward, Lee, Mgr.-Mktg. Communications--AM General Corporation, South Bend, IN; *U.S. Private*, pg. 922
Wooster, John, V.P.-Communications--National Union Fire Ins. Co. of Pittsburgh, Pa., New York, NY; *U.S. Public*, pg. 84
Wooster, John T., Jr., V.P.-Communications--American International Group, Inc., New York, NY; *U.S. Public*, pg. 83
Worley, Phil, V.P.-Commun.--Taylor Capital Group, Wheeling, IL; *U.S. Private*, pg. 1070
Worrall, Sandra E., Mgr.-Mktg.--N.G. Bailey & Co. Ltd., Ilkley, United Kingdom; *Int'l*, pg. 132
Worthington, Lisa, Dir.-Pub. Rels.--Justin Boot Company, Fort Worth, TX; *U.S. Public*, pg. 937
Worthington, Lisa, Dir.-Pub. Rels.--Nocona Boot Co., Nocona, TX; *U.S. Public*, pg. 937
Worthington, Lisa, Dir.-Pub. Rels.--Tony Lama Co., Inc., El Paso, TX; *U.S. Public*, pg. 937
Wortmann, Tom, Mgr.-Mktg. Svcs.--Littelfuse, Inc., Des Plaines, IL; *U.S. Public*, pg. 1001
Wrenn, Thomas, Mgr.-Information Services--Hawaiian Electric Company, Inc., Honolulu, HI; *U.S. Public*, pg. 800
Wright, Charles S., Mgr.-Corp. Communications--A.O. Smith Corporation, Milwaukee, WI; *U.S. Public*, pg. 1476
Wright, David L., V.P.-Govt. Affairs--PepsiCo, Inc., Purchase, NY; *U.S. Public*, pg. 1276
Wright, Gail, Dir.-Mktg. Communications--SunAmerica Inc., Los Angeles, CA; *U.S. Public*, pg. 1532
Wright, Gregory A., V.P. & Treas.--Tesoro Petroleum Corporation, San Antonio, TX; *U.S. Public*, pg. 1581
Wright, Karen B., Dir.-Adv.--Ariel Corporation, Mount Vernon, OH; *U.S. Private*, pg. 81
Wroblewski, Patti, V.P.-Customer Srevice--M & I Bank of Eagle River, Eagle River, WI; *U.S. Public*, pg. 1050
Wulfkuhle, Ron, Mgr.-Communications & Product Mgr.-Sorghum Seeds--CIBA Seeds, Greensboro, NC; *Int'l*, pg. 973
Wunderink, R.C.J., Sr. V.P.-Pub. Rels.--KLM Royal Dutch Airlines, Amstelveen, Netherlands; *Int'l*, pg. 719
Wustrach, Klaus, Dir.-Communications--Alcatel Business Systems (France), Colombes, France; *Int'l*, pg. 55
Wyatt, Amy, Asst. Dir.-Pub. Rels.--Wal-Mart Stores, Inc., Bentonville, AR; *U.S. Public*, pg. 1732
Wyatt, Joanna, Dir.-Pub. Rels.--BC Telecom Inc., Burnaby, Canada; *U.S. Public*, pg. 697
Wyckoff, Richard, Dir.-Pub. Rels.--Cadence Design Systems, Inc., San Jose, CA; *U.S. Public*, pg. 290
Wylock, Monique, Mgr.-Pub. Rels.--Digital Equipment N.V./S.A., Brussels, Belgium; *U.S. Public*, pg. 508
Wynands, Henny, Dir.-Pub. Rels.--Reed Elsevier Nederland BV, Amsterdam, Netherlands; *Int'l*, pg. 1100
Wyrwas, Margaret E., V.P.-Corp. Communications & Investor Relations--Ames Department Stores, Inc., Rocky Hill, CT; *U.S. Public*, pg. 99
Yacker, Jeffrey B., Mgr.-Communications--BPA International, New York, NY; *U.S. Private*, pg. 107
Yadav, Dave, Communications & Res. Advisor--Suncor Inc., Calgary, Canada; *Int'l*, pg. 1320
Yaeger, Riff, Sr. V.P. & Pub. Rels. Dir.--Colle & McVoy Marketing Communications, Minneapolis, MN; *U.S. Private*, pg. 252
Yamada, Ronald H., Sr. V.P.-Info. Strategies & Corp. Affairs--MDS Inc., Etobicoke, Canada; *Int'l*, pg. 826
Yamaguchi, Kenji, Deputy Pres., Dir.-Plng., Pub. Rels., Gen. Affairs & Sec.--Yasuda Mutual Life Insurance Co., Tokyo, Japan; *Int'l*, pg. 1519
Yamaguchi, Richard, Mgr.-Mktg. & Pub. Rels.--Tropitone Furniture Co. Inc., Irvine, CA; *U.S. Private*, pg. 1105
Yamao, Mahito, Dir.--Tonen Corporation, Tokyo, Japan; *Int'l*, pg. 1398
Yang, Brett, Sr. V.P. & Dir.-Corp. Commun.--J. & W. Seligman & Co., New York, NY; *U.S. Private*, pg. 982
Yang, C.S., Mgr.-Pub. Rels. & Pur.--China Hi-Ment Corp., Kao-hsiung, Taiwan; *Int'l*, pg. 285
Yang, Steve C., Dir.-Pub. Rels.--China Airlines Ltd., Taipei, Taiwan; *Int'l*, pg. 284
Yanny, John, Mgr.-Training & Communications--Payco American Corporation, Brookfield, WI; *U.S. Public*, pg. 1267
Yatar, Stacy, Mgr.-Pub. Affairs--Pacificare of Guam, Tamuning, GU; *U.S. Public*, pg. 1251
Yates, Connie, Dir.-Pub. Rels.--Tom Thumb Food & Pharmacy, Dallas, TX; *U.S. Private*, pg. 909
Yates, Herbert S., Chief Fin. Officer & Sr. V.P.--Camco International Inc., Houston, TX; *U.S. Public*, pg. 297
Yates, Mike, Mgr.-Pub. Rels.--Tactair Fluid Controls Corp., Liverpool, NY; *U.S. Private*, pg. 1196
Yaw, William R., Jr., Sr. V.P.--Standard Federal Bank, Troy, MI; *Int'l*, pg. 10
Yeager, Riff, Sr. V.P. & Pub. Rels. Dir.--Colle & McVoy, Inc., Minneapolis, MN; *U.S. Private*, pg. 252
Yeager, Tracy, Dir.-Commun.--People's Choice TV Corp., Shelton, CT; *U.S. Public*, pg. 1274
Yeo, Julie, Asst. V.P.-Public Affairs--DBS Bank Ltd., Singapore, Singapore; *Int'l*, pg. 350
Yi, Goh Mei, Corp. Rels. Exec.--Singapore Press Holdings Ltd., Singapore, Singapore; *Int'l*, pg. 1253
Yiatchos, Gary, Sr. V.P.-Mktg. & Sls. Promo.--The Bon Marche, Inc., Seattle, WA; *U.S. Public*, pg. 617
Yingling, Edward L., Exec. Dir.-Govt. Rels.--The American Bankers Association, Washington, DC; *U.S. Private*, pg. 51
Yoder, Patricia D., Sr. V.P.-Corp. Affairs--Avis Rent A Car System, Inc., Garden City, NY; *U.S. Public*, pg. 321
Yonekura, Hidekazu, Sr. Mng. Dir.-Corp. Communication & Domestic Mktg. & Sls.--Mazda Motor Corporation, Hiroshima, Japan; *Int'l*, pg. 849
Yonker, Pat, Dir.-Mktg. Svcs.--GraphLine Inc., Tamarac, FL; *U.S. Private*, pg. 471
York, Andrea, Pub. Rels. Specialist--Holstein Association USA, Inc., Brattleboro, VT; *U.S. Private*, pg. 536
Yoshida, Yuko, Customer Rels.--Mitsubishi Motors Corporation, Tokyo, Japan; *Int'l*, pg. 875
Yoshioka, T., Gen. Mgr.-Pub. Rels.--Nissho Iwai Corporation, Tokyo, Japan; *Int'l*, pg. 946
Yoshizawa, Yoshio, Mng. Dir.-Public Rels.--Hino Motors, Ltd., Tokyo, Japan; *Int'l*, pg. 620
Youmans, Bruce, Mgr.-Mktg. Communications & Adv.--TDK Electronics Corporation, Port Washington, NY; *Int'l*, pg. 1336
Younanpour, Ailen, Asst. Corp. Sec.--Pacific Scientific Company, Newport Beach, CA; *U.S. Public*, pg. 1250
Young, Alan, Mgr.-Commun.--Scottish Widows' Fund & Life Assurance Society, Edinburgh, United Kingdom; *Int'l*, pg. 1212
Young, Andrew, Mgr.-Communications--Jagenberg, Inc., Enfield, CT; *Int'l*, pg. 1108
Young, B., Mgr.-Pub. Rels.--Oil Drilling & Exploration Limited, Sydney, Australia; *Int'l*, pg. 101
Young, Fiona, Press Officer--Alliance & Leicester Building Society, London, United Kingdom; *Int'l*, pg. 57
Young, Kathy, Adv. & Pub. Rels. Coord.--Pearle Inc., Dallas, TX; *U.S. Public*, pg. 396
Young, Linette, Dir.-Corp. Communications--Honeywell-Measurex Corporation, Cupertino, CA; *U.S. Public*, pg. 833
Young, Lisa, Dir.-Commun.--J.B. Hunt Transport Services, Inc., Lowell, AR; *U.S. Public*, pg. 849
Young, Melissa, Dir.-Pub. Rels.--Honeywell Inc., Minneapolis, MN; *U.S. Public*, pg. 833
Young, Mike, V.P.-Community Affairs--Delta Air Lines, Inc., Atlanta, GA; *U.S. Public*, pg. 497
Young, Sally Benjamin, V.P.-Corp. Commun.--MMI Companies, Inc., Deerfield, IL; *U.S. Public*, pg. 1027
Younts, Rosemary, Sr. V.P.-Commun.--GenCorp Inc., Fairlawn, OH; *U.S. Public*, pg. 705
Yowell, Skip, V.P.-Global Communications--JanSport, Appleton, WI; *U.S. Public*, pg. 1702
Yuckert, Greg, V.P.-Labor Rels.--Weyerhaeuser Company, Federal Way, WA; *U.S. Public*, pg. 1764
Yudys, Kathy, V.P.-Customer Service--Colfax Envelope Corporation, Buffalo Grove, IL; *U.S. Private*, pg. 252
Yuen, Chua Mun, Public Rels. Officer--Singapore Petroleum Company Ltd., Singapore, Singapore; *U.S. Public*, pg. 102
Yurkovich, Cheryl, Dir.-Media Rels.--The Detroit Medical Center, Detroit, MI; *U.S. Private*, pg. 328
Yuro, George M., Dir.-Pub. & Community Affairs--Cytec Industries Inc., West Paterson, NJ; *U.S. Public*, pg. 471
Zabaleta, Juan Romero, Dir.-Pub. Communications--Amper, S.A., Madrid, Spain; *Int'l*, pg. 1372
Zabetakis, David B., Asst. V.P.-Market Devel.--Unitil Corporation, Hampton, NH; *U.S. Public*, pg. 1692
Zaccara, Glenn, Mgr.-Corp. Communications--Entex Information Services, Rye Brook, NY; *U.S. Private*, pg. 378
Zaccaria, Joe, Dir.-Mktg. Communications--Leviton Mfg. Co., Inc., Little Neck, NY; *U.S. Private*, pg. 663
Zachem, Harry M., Sr. V.P.-Pub. Affairs--Ashland, Inc., Russell, KY; *U.S. Public*, pg. 138
Zallon, Larry, Dir.-Corp. Communications--Amplex/SGNIC, Bloomfield, CT; *Int'l*, pg. 1173
Zanca, Bruce J., Dir.-Corp. Communications--U.S. News & World Report, New York, NY; *U.S. Private*, pg. 1125
Zanelli, Janine, Mgr.-Investor Rels.--Alliance Semiconductor Corp., San Jose, CA; *U.S. Public*, pg. 47
Zanichelli, Marco, Dir.-Corp. Communications--Alitalia Linee Aeree Italiane S.P.A., Rome, Italy; *Int'l*, pg. 652
Zanzalari, Gerry, Mgr.-Pub. Rels.--Ricoh Corporation, West Caldwell, NJ; *Int'l*, pg. 1114
Zapapas, Jan, V.P.-Software Devel.--J.D. Edwards & Company, Denver, CO; *U.S. Private*, pg. 365
Zapciz, David, Dir.-Mktg. Commun.--The First Years Inc., Avon, MA; *U.S. Public*, pg. 642
Zarenkim, Lior, Exec. V.P.-Mktg. & Customer Rels.--The Israel Electric Corporation Ltd., Haifa, Israel; *Int'l*, pg. 690
Zarzecki, Jeff, Regulatory Coord.-Govern. Affairs--Dennis Chemical Co., Inc., Saint Louis, MO; *U.S. Private*, pg. 324
Zatorski, Karen, Corp. Commun.--Viacom Inc., New York, NY; *U.S. Private*, pg. 775
Zawel, Susan Fein, V.P.-Corp. Commun., Sec. & Assoc. Gen. Counsel--United Industrial Corporation, New York, NY; *U.S. Public*, pg. 1679
Zeddun, Wallace E., V.P.-Performance Devel. & Shared Services--Wisconsin Gas Company, Milwaukee, WI; *U.S. Public*, pg. 1767
Zeiner, Wendy, Dir.-Corp. Mktg.--Open Market, Inc., Burlington, MA; *U.S. Public*, pg. 1226
Zekind, Diane, Dir.-Advanced Plng. & Admin.--CMI International Inc., Southfield, MI; *U.S. Private*, pg. 195
Zelasko, Barbara, Mgr.-Corp. Commun.--J.M. Huber Corporation, Edison, NJ; *U.S. Private*, pg. 544
Zentz, Peter, Mgr.-Commun.--Benthos, Inc., North Falmouth, MA; *U.S. Public*, pg. 212
Zepf, Stephen J., Chief Fin. Officer & Treas.--Hughes Supply, Inc., Orlando, FL; *U.S. Public*, pg. 846
Zepp, Alison, Dir.-Mktg. Commun.--W.W. Grainger, Inc., Lincolnshire, IL; *U.S. Public*, pg. 758
Zerza, Fred, V.P.-Pub. Rels. & Govt. Affairs--J.R. Simplot Company, Boise, ID; *U.S. Private*, pg. 1002
Ziegele, Jon, Dir.-Labor Rels.--Keystone Steel & Wire Co., Peoria, IL; *U.S. Public*, pg. 955
Zieger, Henning, Dir.-Mktg. & Adv.--Interbath, Inc., City of Industry, CA; *U.S. Private*, pg. 566
Zielinski, Bella P., Dir.-Mktg. Communications--The Inland Group, Inc., Oak Brook, IL; *U.S. Private*, pg. 564
Zielinski, Pat, Dir.-Mktg.--CompuDyne Corporation, Willimantic, CT; *U.S. Public*, pg. 419
Zieverts, Pete, Dir.-Pub. Rels.--Integrated Payment Systems, Englewood, CO; *U.S. Public*, pg. 631
Zimbalatti, Lory, Mgr.-Brandname & Pub. Rels.--New England Confectionery Co., Cambridge, MA; *U.S. Private*, pg. 1113
Zimmerman, Terri, Mgr.-Adv. & Pub. Rels.--Oak Grigsby, Sugar Grove, IL; *U.S. Public*, pg. 1209
Zimmermann, Steve, Mgr.-Mktg. Communications--Rockwell Automation, Milwaukee, WI; *U.S. Public*, pg. 1397
Zinngrabe, Mary, Mgr.-Commun.--Apple Vacations West Inc., Elk Grove Village, IL; *U.S. Private*, pg. 78
Zitel, Michelle, Mgr.-Mktg. Communications--CEM Corporation, Matthews, NC; *U.S. Public*, pg. 277
Zito, Robert, Dir.-Public Affairs--Sony U.S.A., New York, NY; *Int'l*, pg. 1281
Zlotnik, Arnold, Pres.--Surco Products, Inc., Pittsburgh, PA; *U.S. Private*, pg. 1056
Zoffmann, Beth C., V.P.-Corp. Communications--Georgia-Pacific Corporation, Atlanta, GA; *U.S. Public*, pg. 735
Zschiesche, Alexandra, Pub. Rels. Consultant--WOB MarketingKommunikation AG, Viernheim, Germany; *Int'l*, pg. 1482
Zuazua, Rafael Garcia, Dir.-Pub. Rels.--Altos Hornos de Mexico, S.A., Monclova, Mexico; *Int'l*, pg. 66
Zuckerman, Susan, V.P.-Corp. Commun.--Goldman, Sachs & Co., New York, NY; *U.S. Private*, pg. 462
Zuehl, Roger A., Mgr.-Ag Pub. Rels.--Case Corporation, Racine, WI; *U.S. Public*, pg. 311
Zuissler, Susan, Mgr.-Mktg. Commun.--Morrison Health Care Inc., Smyrna, GA; *U.S. Public*, pg. 1133
Zukawski, Lee, Mgr.-Communications--The Check Store, Lakewood, CO; *U.S. Public*, pg. 785
Zukowski, Lee, Mgr.-Communications--John H. Harland Company, Decatur, GA; *U.S. Public*, pg. 785
Zutz, Denise M., V.P.-Communications--Johnson Controls, Inc., Milwaukee, WI; *U.S. Public*, pg. 932
Zvonck, Dan, V.P.-Pub. & Investor Rels.--American Stores Company, Salt Lake City, UT; *U.S. Public*, pg. 92
Zweck, Brad, Mgr.-Pub. Rels.--Employers Insurance of Wausau, Wausau, WI; *U.S. Private*, pg. 788

PURCHASING

Aaron, Marvin, Pur. Agent--Creative Productions, Pittsburgh, PA; *U.S. Private*, pg. 288
Abbott, M., Mgr.-Pur.--KDI Precision Products, Inc., Cincinnati, OH; *U.S. Private*, pg. 603
Abercrombie, Steve, Dir.-Pur.--T & S Brass & Bronze Works, Inc., Travelers Rest, SC; *U.S. Private*, pg. 1061
Abfalter, Nancy, Mgr.-Pur.--Fiskars-Gerber, Portland, OR; *Int'l*, pg. 492
Abicht, Elaine C., V.P.-Pur.--Smithfield Foods, Inc., Norfolk, VA; *U.S. Public*, pg. 1479
Abraham, Gerry, V.P.-Corp. Pur.--Carnival Corporation, Miami, FL; *U.S. Public*, pg. 306
Abrahams, E.W., Pur. Agent--BS & B Process Systems, Inc., Houston, TX; *U.S. Private*, pg. 572

Abrahamson, Bryce D., V.P.-Pur.--Arctic Cat Inc., Thief River Falls, MN; *U.S. Public*, pg. 128

Abram, Tim, Mgr.-Pur.--United Design Corporation, Noble, OK; *U.S. Private*, pg. 1121

Abramowitz, Sandy, Dir.-Pur.--Best Kosher Sausage Co., Chicago, IL; *U.S. Public*, pg. 1433

Ackerman, Dennis, Mgr.-Pur.--Bel Fuse Inc., Jersey City, NJ; *U.S. Public*, pg. 200

Ackerman, Roger, Dir.-Pur.--Menasha Corporation, Neenah, WI; *U.S. Private*, pg. 731

Ackroyd, Jeff, Pur. Agent--Cortland Line Co., Inc., Cortland, NY; *U.S. Private*, pg. 277

Acosta, Anthony, Mgr.-Pur.--A & B Properties, Inc., Honolulu, HI; *U.S. Public*, pg. 39

Acosta, Anthony, Mgr.-Pur.--A & B-Hawaii, Inc., Honolulu, HI; *U.S. Public*, pg. 39

Acosta, Anthony K., Mgr.-Pur. & Office Svcs.--Alexander & Baldwin, Inc., Honolulu, HI; *U.S. Public*, pg. 39

Adam, Michael, Pur. Agent--General American Door Company, Montgomery, IL; *U.S. Private*, pg. 732

Adamczyck, Tom, Dir.-Pur.--Amurol Confections Co., Yorkville, IL; *U.S. Public*, pg. 1781

Adams, Austin A., Exec. V.P.-Automation & Opers.--First Union Corporation, Charlotte, NC; *U.S. Public*, pg. 639

Adams, Dave, V.P.-Pur.--John Wieland Homes Inc., Atlanta, GA; *U.S. Private*, pg. 1175

Adams, Franklin J., Dir.-Pur.--SK Hand Tool Corp., Chicago, IL; *Int'l*, pg. 570

Adams, Gerry, Admin. Mgr. & TV Buying Mgr.--The Media Centre, London, United Kingdom; *Int'l*, pg. 852

Adams, Jerry, V.P.-Music Pur.--Handleman Company, Troy, MI; *U.S. Public*, pg. 779

Adams, Richard, Mgr.-Pur.--Candela Corporation, Wayland, MA; *U.S. Public*, pg. 300

Adams, Sam, Pur. Agent--Amgen Boulder, Inc., Boulder, CO; *U.S. Public*, pg. 101

Adams, Tony, Dir.-Pur.--C.A. Muer Corp., Detroit, MI; *U.S. Private*, pg. 766

Adcox, Bill, Buyer--Autry Greer & Sons, Inc., Prichard, AL; *U.S. Private*, pg. 479

Adkins, David, Dir.-Pur.--Doehler-Jarvis, Inc., Toledo, OH; *U.S. Public*, pg. 796

Adler, Fred, Dir.-Pur.--Thrifty Oil Co., Santa Fe Springs, CA; *U.S. Private*, pg. 1084

Adowski, Kim, Mgr.-Pur--Colad Group Inc., Buffalo, NY; *U.S.* Private, pg. 250

Agnello, Gary, Mgr.-Pur.--Nasco Industries Inc., Medina, OH; *U.S. Private*, pg. 774

Agullo, Criso Renovell, Dir.-Pur.--Union Naval de Levante, S.A., Madrid, Spain; *Int'l*, pg. 1442

Ahern, J.R., Mgr.-Strategic Matls.--PQ Corporation, Berwyn, PA; *U.S. Private*, pg. 827

Ahrens, James T., Asst. V.P.-Construction--Oriole Homes Corp., Delray Beach, FL; *U.S. Public*, pg. 1230

Ahuja, Dushant, Dir.-Pur.--Computer Sciences Corporation, El Segundo, CA; *U.S. Public*, pg. 422

Aimetti, William B., Dir.-Pur.--Nomura Securities International, Inc., New York, NY; *Int'l*, pg. 956

Aitken, Robert, Dir.-Pur.--Bundy North America, Warren, MI; *Int'l*, pg. 1340

Akchin, Mark, Mgr.-Pur.--Network Long Distance, Inc., Baton Rouge, LA; *U.S. Public*, pg. 1169

Akers, Dennis, Dir.-Pur. & Mgr.-Subcontracting--Norfolk Shipbuilding & Drydock Corporation, Norfolk, VA; *U.S. Private*, pg. 802

Akkawi, Wagas, Mgr.-Pur.--Trans Leasing International Inc., Northbrook, IL; *U.S. Public*, pg. 1628

Albright, Eric, Pur. Mgr.--Pressure Products Div., Dallas, TX; *U.S. Public*, pg. 1268

Alexander, Bill, Dir.-Pur.--First Tennessee National Corporation, Memphis, TN; *U.S. Public*, pg. 638

Alexander, Bob, Dir.-Pur.--M&W, Gibson City, IL; *U.S. Public*, pg. 35

Alexander, J., Mgr.-Pur.--The Will-Burt Company, Orrville, OH; *U.S. Private*, pg. 1177

Alexander, John R., Dir.-Pur.--Sonoco Products Company, Hartsville, SC; *U.S. Public*, pg. 1485

Alisauskas, C., Pur. Agent--Broderick & Bascom Rope Co., Sedalia, MO; *U.S. Private*, pg. 68

Alisauskas, Chas. E., Pur. Agent--Macwhyte Co., Kenosha, WI; *U.S. Private*, pg. 68

Aljets, Lori, Mgr.-Pur.--Norpac Foods, Inc., Stayton, OR; *U.S. Private*, pg. 802

Alkire, Tom, Dir.-Pur.--American Woodmark Corporation, Winchester, VA; *U.S. Public*, pg. 96

Allen, Douglas, V.P.-Pur.--J.W. Allen & Company, Wheeling, IL; *U.S. Private*, pg. 37

Allen, Eileen, Buyer--Centigram Communications Corporation, San Jose, CA; *U.S. Public*, pg. 323

Allen, William, Pur. Agent--Raven Industries Sportswear Div., Sioux Falls, SD; *U.S. Public*, pg. 1361

Allison, Monti, Mgr.-Pur.--Glen Raven Mills, Inc., Glen Raven, NC; *U.S. Private*, pg. 456

Allmann, N., Dir.-Pur.--Howard Maschinenfabrik GmbH, Michelstadt, Germany; *Int'l*, pg. 1387

Allred, Jim, Pur. Agent--Six Flags Over Texas, Arlington, TX; *U.S. Public*, pg. 1612

Alquist, Gil, Gen. Mgr.-Mfg.--Lund International Holdings, Inc., Anoka, MN; *U.S. Public*, pg. 1020

Altaba Nanez, Sergio, Sr. V.P.-Pur.--Grupo Acerero del Norte S.A. de C.V. (GAN), Mexico, Mexico; *Int'l*, pg. 572

Alterman, Joe, Dir.-Pur.--Alterman Transport Lines, Inc., Opa Locka, FL; *U.S. Private*, pg. 47

Altier, William H., Pur. Agent--National Gas & Oil Company, Newark, OH; *U.S. Public*, pg. 1156

Altomare, Arlene S., Mgr.-Pur.--MBIA Inc., Armonk, NY; *U.S.* Public, pg. 1023

Aluise, David A., V.P.-Logistics--Pease Industries, Inc., Fairfield, OH; *U.S. Private*, pg. 845

Alvarez Villafane, Primo, Dir.-Sls., Mktg. & Pur.--Grupo Comercial Chedraui S.A. de C.V., Veracruz, Mexico; *Int'l, pg. 573*

Alvarez Villafane, Primo, Dir.-Sls., Mktg. & Pur.--Tiendas Chedraui S.A. de C.V., Veracruz, Mexico; *Int'l*, pg. 573

Amann, R. William, V.P.-Pur.--Flexible Steel Lacing Company, Downers Grove, IL; *U.S. Private*, pg. 413

Amburger, Joyce, Mgr.-Pur.--CSE Insurance Group, San Francisco, CA; *U.S. Private*, pg. 197

Ammons, D.L., Mgr.-Pur.--L & D Group, Aurora, IL; *U.S. Private*, pg. 638

Amoroso, Anthony J., Spec. V.P.-Pur.--Erie Plastics, Corry, PA; *U.S. Private*, pg. 381

Anderson, Dave, Mgr.-Pur.--Flexfab Horizons International, Inc., Hastings, MI; *U.S. Private*, pg. 412

Anderson, David, Mgr.-Pur.--Seaboard Farms of Elberton, Elberton, GA; *U.S. Public*, pg. 1449

Anderson, Eloise, Pur. Agent--Smith Enterprises, Rock Hill, SC; *U.S. Private*, pg. 1007

Anderson, Eric, Mgr.-Pur.--Beaver Foods Limited, London, Canada; *Int'l*, pg. 266

Anderson, Gary, Dir.-Pur.--Arrow Tank & Engineering Co., Minneapolis, MN; *U.S. Private*, pg. 85

Anderson, J.R., Mgr.-Pur.--Delphi Packard Electric Systems, Beachwood, OH; *U.S. Public*, pg. 719

Anderson, Joe, Dir-Pur.--Raynor Garage Doors, Dixon, IL; *U.S. Private*, pg. 912

Anderson, K. Barr, Mgr.-Pur.--Daw Technologies, Inc., Salt Lake City, UT; *U.S. Public*, pg. 489

Anderson, Mark, Pur. Agent--Reading Body Works, Inc., Reading, PA; *U.S. Private*, pg. 913

Anderson, Nolan, Pur. Agent--Electrical Wholesale Supply Company, Inc., Idaho Falls, ID; *U.S. Private*, pg. 368

Anderson, Phil, Mgr.-Pur.--The Holland Hitch Company, Holland, MI; *U.S. Private*, pg. 534

Anderson, Richard J., V.P.-Pur.--Metropolitan Life Insurance Co., New York, NY; *U.S. Private*, pg. 737

Anderson, Roy, Central Pur. Mgr.--Alcon Laboratories, Inc., Fort Worth, TX; *Int'l*, pg. 916

Anderson, Susan, Adv. Mgr.--Development Association, Inc., Fort Worth, TX; *U.S. Public*, pg. 1561

Anderson, Ted, Dir.-Pur.--Flojet Corporation, Irvine, CA; *U.S.* Private, pg. 414

Anderson, Tom N., Dir.-Matls. Mngmt.--Minnesota Power, Duluth, MN; *U.S. Public*, pg. 1116

Andersson, Bo, V.P.-Pur.--Saab Automobile AB, Nykoping, Sweden; *Int'l*, pg. 687

Andersson, Bo, V.P.-Pur.--Saab Automobile AB, Nykoping, Sweden; *U.S. Public*, pg. 725

Andersson, Roland, Dir.-Pur. & Export Control--ABB Asea Brown Boveri (Holding) Ltd., Zurich, Switzerland; *Int'l*, pg. 1

Andreini, Carlo, Dir.-Pur. & Logistics--Opticos S.r.l., Brembate di Sopra, Italy; *Int'l*, pg. 1007

Andrew, A.J., Mgr.-Queensland Logistics--Q.U.F. Industries Ltd., Brisbane, Australia; *Int'l*, pg. 1074

Andrews, Dan, Dir.-Gen. Svcs.--Roney & Co., Detroit, MI; *U.S. Private*, pg. 943

Angel, Joe, Buyer-Frozen Seafood & Poultry--Alliant Foodservice, Bensenville, IL; *U.S. Private*, pg. 244

Angus, Alyn, Mgr.-Pur.--Dakota Electric Association, Farmington, MN; *U.S. Private*, pg. 308

Anich, John, Pur. Agent--Koken Mfg. Co. Inc., Saint Louis, MO; *Int'l*, pg. 1349

Ankerson, Perry, Pres.-Point of Pur. Div.--Everbrite, Inc., Greenfield, WI; *U.S. Private*, pg. 386

Ann Romano, Rose, Admin. Asst.--Center Partners Management LLC, New York, NY; *U.S. Private*, pg. 222

Annas, Rick, Dir.-Pur.--Hickory Printing Group, Inc., Conover, NC; *U.S. Private*, pg. 525

Ansuini, Tracie, V.P.-Pur.--Kenny Rogers Roasters, Fort Lauderdale, FL; *U.S. Private*, pg. 939

Anthony, Raymond, Pur. Agent--Overhead Conveyor Co., Ferndale, MI; *U.S. Private*, pg. 822

Antler, W., Dir.-Corp. Services--The Canada Life Assurance Company, Toronto, Canada; *Int'l*, pg. 254

Anton, Richard, Pur. Agent--Homasote Company, Trenton, NJ; *U.S. Public*, pg. 831

Antonucci, Gus, Dir.-Pur.--Quaker Fabric Corporation, Fall River, MA; *U.S. Public*, pg. 1347

Appledorn, J., Dir.-Pur.--Montair Andersen B.V., Sevenum, Netherlands; *U.S. Public*, pg. 462

Aquino, Manolo E., Exec. V.P.-Admin. & Procurement--Philippine Airlines, Inc., Manila, Philippines; *Int'l*, pg. 1050

Arb, James, Pur. Agent--Universal Flavors-U.S.A., Indianapolis, IN; *U.S. Public*, pg. 1696

Archambault, Bruce, Dir.-Pur.--Papa Gino's Inc., Dedham, MA; *U.S. Private*, pg. 837

Archer, Simon, TV Buying Grp. Dir.--The Media Centre, London, United Kingdom; *Int'l*, pg. 852

Arendsen, L.D., Mgr.-Inventory Control--Bergen Brunswig Medical Corporation (Durr Drug), Montgomery, AL; *U.S. Public*, pg. 214

Arens, Lowell, Dir.-Pur.--Rosco Manufacturing Co., Madison, SD; *U.S. Private*, pg. 944

Arlt, Tom, Dir.-Pur.--Gulf States Asphalt Company, Inc., South Houston, TX; *U.S. Private*, pg. 487

Armlay, Anthony, Pur. Agent--Triplett Corporation, Bluffton, OH; *U.S. Private*, pg. 1104

Arneson, Paul, Mgr.-Pur.--Andis Company, Sturtevant, WI; *U.S. Private*, pg. 73

Arnolis, Jacques, Dir.-Pur.--Cockerill Sambre, Brussels, Belgium; *Int'l*, pg. 301

Arseniadis, George, Mgr.-Pur.--Shieffelin Somerset Co., New York, NY; *Int'l*, pg. 412

Artuz, Edwin, Asst. V.P.-Corp. Svcs.--Federal Home Loan Bank of New York, New York, NY; *U.S. Private*, pg. 399

Asata, Dominic, Dir.-Pur.--Maxitrol Co., Southfield, MI; *U.S. Private*, pg. 716

Asen, Shel F., Sr. V.P.-Mfg. & Pur.--The McGraw-Hill Companies, New York, NY; *U.S. Public*, pg. 1069

Ash, Robert, Div. Mgr.-Procurement--Metra, Commuter Rail Service Board, Chicago, IL; *U.S. Private*, pg. 919

Ash, Teresa, Pur. Agent--Spectrum Industries, Inc., Chippewa Falls, WI; *U.S. Private*, pg. 1024

Aspden, David H., Mgr.-Pur.--Sea Containers Ltd., Hamilton, Bermuda; *Int'l*, pg. 1213

Athanasiou, Henry, Dir.-Pur.--Armatron International, Inc., Melrose, MA; *U.S. Public*, pg. 131

Atkeisson, Ray, Mgr.-Pur.--J.E. Dunn Construction Co., Kansas City, MO; *U.S. Private*, pg. 347

Atkin, David, Pur. Agent--H.B. Smith Co., Inc., Westfield, MA; *U.S. Private*, pg. 1008

Atkins, Kenneth, Dir.-Pur.--Oxford Industries, Inc., Atlanta, GA; *U.S. Public*, pg. 1239

Audet, Richard, Dir.-Pur.--Sulphite Pulp, Temiscaming, Canada; *Int'l*, pg. 1375

Auger, David P., Mgr.-Pur.--Wausau Papers of New Hampshire, Inc., Groveton, NH; *U.S. Public*, pg. 1748

Augustin, Mary, Mgr.-Pur.--TCI International Inc., Sunnyvale, CA; *U.S. Public*, pg. 1555

Augustin, Mary, Mgr.-Pur.--Technology for Communications International, Sunnyvale, CA; *U.S. Public*, pg. 1555

Augustyne, Joe, Dir.-Pur.--Martin Universal Design, Inc., Detroit, MI; *U.S. Private*, pg. 709

Ausmus, Wayne, V.P.-Pur.--Bristol Metals, L.P., Bristol, TN; *U.S. Public*, pg. 1548

Austin, Jay T., Dir.-Pur. & Leasing--Medusa Corporation, Cleveland, OH; *U.S. Public*, pg. 1084

Austin, Jay T., Dir.-Pur.--Medusa Aggregate Co., Cleveland, OH; *U.S. Public*, pg. 1084

Austin, Ken, Dir.-Pur.--Wide-Lite, San Marcos, TX; *U.S. Public*, pg. 730

Austin, Terry, Dir.-Mktg.-London Region--Shoppers Drug Mart, Ltd., London, Canada; *Int'l*, pg. 112

Austreng, Wayne, Dir.-Pur.--IMI Cornelius Inc. (MN), Anoka, MN; *Int'l*, pg. 646

Avans, Rebecca, Dir.-Pur.--Peebles, Inc., South Hill, VA; *U.S. Private*, pg. 846

Avant, DeWitt, Pur. Agent--Burgess Pigment Co., Sandersville, GA; *U.S. Private*, pg. 182

Avard, Rick, Mgr.-Pur.--Pacesetter Corporation, Omaha, NE; *U.S. Private*, pg. 830

Avery, Ann, Pur. Agent--East Coast Steel, Inc., Claremont, NH; *U.S. Private*, pg. 356

Axelsson, Olle, Pur. Agent--Skanska Vast, Goteborg, Sweden; *Int'l*, pg. 1261

Ayers, Gary, Dir.-Pur.--TIE/Communications, Inc., Overland Park, KS; *U.S. Private*, pg. 1085

Ayers, James, Dir.-Pur.--Spencer's Inc., Mount Airy, NC; *U.S. Private*, pg. 1025

Ayers, Steve, Sr. V.P.-Contracts & Procurement--Science Applications International Corp., San Diego, CA; *U.S. Private*, pg. 975

Babin, G., Mgr.-Pur.--Bromptonville Mill, Bromptonville, Canada; *Int'l*, pg. 761

Bach, James, Dir.-Pur.--C-Tech Systems, Plymouth, MN; *U.S. Public*, pg. 865

Bacharach, Steve, Dir.-Pur.--Friendship Dairies, Inc., Jericho, NY; *U.S. Private*, pg. 429

Bachter, Len, Dir.-Materials--International Electronic Research Corp., Burbank, CA; *U.S. Public*, pg. 286

Badehorst, N.J.K., Mgr.-Matls. Mgmnt.--Iscor, Pretoria, South Africa; *Int'l*, pg. 688

Badenhop, Glenn, V.P.-Corp. Opers.--Fulton Industries Inc., Wauseon, OH; *U.S. Private*, pg. 431

Baderschneider, Earl, Dir.-Opers.--American Arbitration Association, New York, NY; *U.S. Private*, pg. 50

Baer, Jacque, Mgr.-Pur.--Cab-o-Sil Div. Cabot Corp., Tuscola, IL; *U.S. Public*, pg. 289

Baesel, Manfred, Mgr.-Pur.--BOMAG, Boppard, Germany; *U.S. Public*, pg. 1677

Baez, Lyle, Mgr.-Pur.--Credit Union National Association, Madison, WI; *U.S. Private*, pg. 288

Bagetta, Don, Pur. Dir.--Doodle Art Div., Los Angeles, CA; *Int'l*, pg. 1215

Bagwell, Charles F., V.P. & Dir.-Mfg. & Pur.--The Kent Manufacturing Co., Pickens, SC; *U.S. Private*, pg. 615

Bahm, Jack, Production, Pur. & Print Production Mgr.--Creative Alliance, Inc., Louisville, KY; *U.S. Private*, pg. 287

Bailey, John, Mgr.-Central Pur.--Midland Enterprises Inc., Cincinnati, OH; *U.S. Public*, pg. 549

Bailey, Vic, Mgr.-Pur.--Bay West Paper Corp. Towel & Tissue Div., Middletown, OH; *U.S. Public*, pg. 1747

Bailly, R. Jeffrey, Dir.-Pur.--UFP Technology, Georgetown, MA; *U.S. Private*, pg. 1112

Bairos, Jose S., Mgr.-Pur.--Arthur D. Little, Inc., Cambridge, MA; *U.S. Private*, pg. 670

Baker, Allan, Dir.-Pur.--Hyde Manufacturing Co., Southbridge, MA; *U.S. Private*, pg. 551

Baker, C. David, Dir.-Facilities--Watt Publishing Co., Mount Morris, IL; *U.S. Private*, pg. 1154

Baker, Earl, Pur. Agent--Scanforms, Inc., Bristol, PA; *U.S. Public*, pg. 228

Baker, Freada, Asst. V.P.-Pur.--Lance, Inc., Charlotte, NC; *U.S. Public*, pg. 977

Baker, George, Mgr.-Pur.--Tetko, Inc., Briarcliff Manor, NY; *U.S. Private*, pg. 1078

Baker, Herman, Dir.-Pur.--Dry Manufacturing Co., Winters, TX; *U.S. Public*, pg. 1795

Baker, Howard, Dir.-Pur.--Coats North America, Charlotte, NC; *Int'l*, pg. 300

Baker, James N., Pur. Agent--Thermal Transfer Corp., Monroeville, PA; *U.S. Public*, pg. 29

Baker, Marvin, Mgr.-Pur. Dept.--UMI, Ann Arbor, MI; *U.S. Public*, pg. 201

Baker, Trent, Dir.-Pur.--Wilson Products Co., Salt Lake City, UT; *U.S. Private*, pg. 1181

Bakkler, Robyn, Mgr.-Pur.--JPE Canada Inc., Peterborough, Canada; *U.S. Public*, pg. 919

Balchun, Debbie, Dir.-Pur.--American Bankers Insurance Group, Inc., Miami, FL; *U.S. Public*, pg. 67

Baldacci, June, Pur. Agent--Bangor Hydro-Electric Company, Bangor, ME; *U.S. Public*, pg. 178

Balderrama, Suzanne, Mgr.-Pur.--Acorn Engineering Company, City of Industry, CA; *U.S. Private*, pg. 14

Baldwin, Amanda, Dir.-Pur.--Chattem (U.K.) Ltd., Basingstoke, United Kingdom; *U.S. Public*, pg. 342

Bales, Larry, Mgr.-Pur.--Alco Chemical, Chattanooga, TN; *Int'l*, pg. 1435

Ball, Chris, Mgr.-Pur.--Carolina Builders Corporation, Marietta, GA; *Int'l*, pg. 1512
Ball, Dareth, Mgr.-Pur.--Baxter Research Medical, Inc., Midvale, UT; *U.S. Public*, pg. 196
Ball, Darreth, Dir.-Pur.--Research Industries Corp., Midvale, UT; *U.S. Public*, pg. 196
Ball, Robert, Mgr.-Pur.--Hein-Werner Corporation, Waukesha, WI; *U.S. Public*, pg. 805
Ballantyne, Tom, Mgr.-Matls.--Haskel International, Inc., Burbank, CA; *U.S. Public*, pg. 798
Ballard, William, Dir.-Matls. & Pur.--Varity Dayton Walther, Dayton, OH; *Int'l*, pg. 820
Baltz, William, Grp. V.P.-Engrng., Pur. & Construction--Monfort, Inc., Greeley, CO; *U.S. Public*, pg. 427
Bangs, Michael, Dir.-Pur.--Great Lakes Lithograph Co., Cleveland, OH; *U.S. Private*, pg. 474
Bankos, Steve, Mgr.-Pur.--Dayton Parts, Inc., Harrisburg, PA; *U.S. Public*, pg. 919
Banks, David, Dir.-Mats. Mngmnt.--Cincinnati Gear Company, Cincinnati, OH; *U.S. Private*, pg. 240
Banks, Gary, Mgr.-Pur.--Battey Machinery Company, Rome, GA; *U.S. Private*, pg. 123
Baranowski, Joe, Mgr.-IC Business Unit--Siliconix, Inc., Santa Clara, CA; *Int'l*, pg. 367
Barber, Herbert F., Dir.-Pur.--McAnally Enterprises, Inc., Yucaipa, CA; *U.S. Private*, pg. 718
Barber, James, Dir.-Pur.--The Genesee Brewing Company, Inc., Rochester, NY; *U.S. Public*, pg. 728
Barber, Mike, Mgr.-Matls.--Murphy-Phoenix Co., Solon, OH; *U.S. Public*, pg. 397
Barekman, Cheryl, Dir.-Pur.--Bass Enterprises Production Company, Fort Worth, TX; *U.S. Private*, pg. 122
Barker, Keith, Dir.-Pur.--Carolina Biological Supply Co., Burlington, NC; *U.S. Private*, pg. 213
Barlow, David T., V.P.-Pur. & Prod. Devel.--Cara Operations Limited, Toronto, Canada; *Int'l*, pg. 266
Barnes, Barbara, Mgr.-Materials--Despatch Industries, Minneapolis, MN; *U.S. Private*, pg. 327
Barnes, Jesse, Dir.-Corp. Personnel--Commercial Metals Company, Dallas, TX; *U.S. Public*, pg. 411
Barnett, Joseph C., Dir.-Pur.--Henkels & McCoy, Inc., Blue Bell, PA; *U.S. Private*, pg. 522
Barr, David, V.P.-Pur. & Plng.--Bollinger Industries Inc., Grand Prairie, TX; *U.S. Public*, pg. 243
Barrell, Tom, Pur. Agent--Air Gage Company, Livonia, MI; *U.S. Public*, pg. 1676
Barresi, C., Dir.-Pur.--Monarch Luggage Co. Inc., Brooklyn, NY; *U.S. Private*, pg. 757
Barrett, Becky, Mgr.-Pur.--American Automobile Association, Heathrow, FL; *U.S. Private*, pg. 50
Barrett, Dave, Mgr.-Pur.--Dallas Semiconductor Corporation, Dallas, TX; *U.S. Public*, pg. 478
Barrett, Michael, Mgr.-Pur.--Shopsmith, Inc., Dayton, OH; *U.S. Public*, pg. 1467
Barrick, Nathalie, Mgr.-Pur.--Maxon Industries, Inc., Huntington Park, CA; *U.S. Private*, pg. 717
Barry, Bob, Pur. Agent--Blue Cross and Blue Shield of Massachusetts, Boston, MA; *U.S. Private*, pg. 151
Barry, Clint, Dir.-Pur.--Wisconsin Gas Company, Milwaukee, WI; *U.S. Public*, pg. 1767
Barth, Hans-Jorg, Dir.-Matls. Mngmt.--Fried. Krupp AG, Essen, Germany; *Int'l*, pg. 507
Barth, Manfred, Dir.-Corp. Pur.--Siemens Corporation, New York, NY; *Int'l*, pg. 1245
Bartholomew, Kevin, Mgr.-Pur.--Rundel Products, Inc., Portland, OR; *U.S. Private*, pg. 951
Bartolo, A., Dir.-Pur.--C.R. Gibson Co., Norwalk, CT; *U.S. Public*, pg. 1168
Bashaw, Ed, Mgr.-Pur.--Optical Coating Laboratory, Inc., Santa Rosa, CA; *U.S. Public*, pg. 1227
Basil, George, Mgr.-Pur.--Eastman Worldwide, Buffalo, NY; *U.S. Private*, pg. 358
Basiliere, Steve, Mgr.-Pur.--Muro Pharmaceutical, Inc., Tewksbury, MA; *U.S. Private*, pg. 767
Baskinger, Michele, Mgr.-Purchasing--The Children's Place Retail Stores, Inc., West Caldwell, NJ; *U.S. Private*, pg. 237
Basler, Greg, Dir.-Pur. Magnetics--Basler Electric Company, Highland, IL; *U.S. Private*, pg. 121
Bass, Michael C., Dir.-Admin.--Krystal Company, Chattanooga, TN; *U.S. Private*, pg. 636
Bateman, Judy, Coord.-Admin. Service--Baker Hughes INTEQ, Houston, TX; *U.S. Public*, pg. 166
Bates, Jim, Dir.-Pur.--Titan Linkabit, San Diego, CA; *U.S. Public*, pg. 1618
Batha, Dianna, Pur. Agent--Centrifugal & Mechanical Industries, Saint Louis, MO; *U.S. Private*, pg. 370
Bathke, John, Pur. Agent--Smith System Manufacturing Company, Plano, TX; *U.S. Private*, pg. 1009
Batliner, Doug, Dir.-Production & Pur.--Beach Mold & Tool Inc., New Albany, IN; *U.S. Private*, pg. 125
Batroung, Herb, Dir.-Pur.--Evcon Industries, Inc., Wichita, KS; *U.S. Public*, pg. 1788
Battaglia, Russell A., Dir.-Pur.--Farmers & Merchants Bank of Central California, Lodi, CA; *U.S. Private*, pg. 394
Batten, Jerry, Mgr.-Pur.--Recreational Vehicle Div., Caldwell, ID; *U.S. Public*, pg. 962
Battoe, E., Mgr.-Pur.--Brooks Foods, Mount Summit, IN; *U.S. Private*, pg. 887
Battuello, Dennis P., Supvr.-Matls. & Records--Superior Water, Light & Power Company, Superior, WI; *U.S. Public*, pg. 1116
Bauer, Margaret, Asst. V.P.--Reliability Incorporated, Houston, TX; *U.S. Public*, pg. 1373
Bauer, Robert E., V.P.-Pur.--Wendy's International Inc., Dublin, OH; *U.S. Public*, pg. 1754
Baugstat, Harald, Dir.-Pur. & Engrng.--Baumann Springs USA, Inc., Pineville, NC; *Int'l*, pg. 171
Baum, Floyd, V.P.--Elyria Foundry Company, Elyria, OH; *U.S. Private*, pg. 373
Baumgarther, Lec, V.P.-Admin. & Opers.--CSE Insurance Group, San Francisco, CA; *U.S. Private*, pg. 197
Baxter, Donald C., Dir.-Pur.--Elco Textron, Rockford, IL; *U.S. Public*, pg. 1590
Baxter, Philip, Mgr.-Pur.--Fuller, Smith & Turner Plc, London, United Kingdom; *Int'l*, pg. 529
Bayly, Malcolm, Dir.-Pur.--E. Moss Limited, Feltham, United Kingdom; *Int'l*, pg. 58
Bazcerzak, Thomas, Mgr.-Pur.--Louis P. Ciminelli Construction Co. Inc., Buffalo, NY; *U.S. Private*, pg. 239
Beach, Sharon, V.P.-Pur.--Bristol Hotels & Resorts, Dallas, TX; *U.S. Public*, pg. 253
Beaird, Mike, Dir.-Pur.--Dr Pepper/Seven Up No. America, Dallas, TX; *Int'l*, pg. 248
Beale, A., Mgr.-Pur.--Air UK Engineering Ltd., Stansted, United Kingdom; *Int'l*, pg. 39
Beasley, Charles, V.P.-Pur.--Top Flight, Inc., Chattanooga, TN; *U.S. Private*, pg. 1091
Beasley, Joel, V.P.-Distr.--Thomas Nelson Inc., Nashville, TN; *U.S. Public*, pg. 1167
Beatty, Lois, Dir.-Pub.--Ward Leonard Electric Company, Inc., Mount Vernon, NY; *U.S. Private*, pg. 1118
Bechtold, Wolfgang, Dir.-Pur.--Schering AG, Berlin, Germany; *Int'l*, pg. 1203
Beck, J., Mgr.-Pur.--Scan-Optics, Inc., Manchester, CT; *U.S. Public*, pg. 1436
Becker, A. Carl, V.P.-Pur. & Engrng.--Nuttall Gear Corporation, Niagara Falls, NY; *U.S. Private*, pg. 809
Becker, Larry K., Chief Fin. Officer & Exec. V.P.--Horace Mann Educators Corporation, Springfield, IL; *U.S. Public*, *pg. 835*
Becker, Sharon, Pur. Agent--Eagle Zinc Co., Hillsboro, IL; *U.S. Private*, pg. 331
Beckert, C. Norman, Dir.-Matl. Resources/Paper Div.--Boise Cascade Corporation, Boise, ID; *U.S. Public*, pg. 242
Beckert, Norm, Dir.-Matls. Resources, Energy & Procurement--Boise Cascade Paper Div., Boise, ID; *U.S. Public*, pg. 243
Beckett, Rick, Pur. Agent--Williams Patent Crusher and Pulverizer Co., Saint Louis, MO; *U.S. Private*, pg. 1178
Becking, Bob, Mgr.-Pur.--Agromac International, Inc., Gering, NE; *U.S. Private*, pg. 27
Beckman, James, Mgr.-Pur.--Acrometal-Brainerd, Brainerd, MN; *U.S. Private*, pg. 14
Beckmann, James, Dir.-Pur.--Acrometal Companies, Inc., Plymouth, MN; *U.S. Private*, pg. 14
Bedell, Doug, Pur. Agent--McBee Systems, Inc., Parsippany, NJ; *U.S. Private*, pg. 718
Bedell, Neil, Dir.-Pur.--Molin Auto Parts Inc., Buffalo, NY; *U.S. Private*, pg. 756
Beery, L. Merl, Sr. V.P.-Pur. & Tech. Services--Bob Evans Farms, Inc., Columbus, OH; *U.S. Public*, pg. 596
Beilero, Mary, Mgr.-Pur.--Banfi Vintners, Old Brookville, NY; *U.S. Private*, pg. 113
Belinge, Wayne, Dir.-Pur.--First Electric Cooperative, Corp., Jacksonville, AR; *U.S. Private*, pg. 407
Bell, James, Mgr.-Pur.--Interphase Corporation, Dallas, TX; *U.S. Public*, pg. 908
Bell, Marty, Mgr.-Pur.--American Family Mutual Insurance Co., Madison, WI; *U.S. Private*, pg. 53
Bell, Nolan, Dir.-Pur.--Holiday RV Superstores of New Mexico Inc., Las Cruces, NM; *U.S. Public*, pg. 830
Bell, Randy J., V.P.--Levy Security Corp., Chicago, IL; *U.S. Private*, pg. 664
Bell, Sharon, Dir.-Pur.--Process Systems Inc., Memphis, TN; *U.S. Private*, pg. 888
Bell, Tom, Mgr.-Pur.--Enzopac, Inc., Sheboygan, WI; *U.S. Private*, pg. 379
Belmont, Don, V.P.-Pur.--Werthan Packaging, Inc., Nashville, TN; *U.S. Private*, pg. 1162
Belock, Gary, Mgr.-Procurement Process--Central Vermont Public Service Corporation, Rutland, VT; *U.S. Public*, pg. 327
Belzile, Anita, Dir.-Admin. & Pur.--Cara Operations Limited, Toronto, Canada; *Int'l*, pg. 266
Bement, Jerry, Pur. Agent--Ederer Inc., Seattle, WA; *U.S. Private*, pg. 363
Bement, Jerry, Mgr.-Pur.--Ederer Cranes, Seattle, WA; *U.S. Private*, pg. 363
Bencivenga, Barbara, Pur. Agent--Brooks Brothers, New York, NY; *Int'l*, pg. 843
Bender, Steven, Mgr.-Pur.--Boss Manufacturing Company, Kewanee, IL; *U.S. Private*, pg. 1142
Benefield, Don, Mgr.-Pur.--Commerce Bank, N.A., Clayton, MO; *U.S. Public*, pg. 409
Beneson, Paul A., V.P.-Pur.--Stevens-Lee Company, Minneapolis, MN; *U.S. Private*, pg. 1042
Benjamin, F.L., V.P.-Pur., Opers., Personnel & Data Processing--Morris Kirschman & Company, Inc., New Orleans, LA; *U.S. Private*, pg. 623
Benjamin, Joe, Mgr.-Pur.--Genesee Metal Stampings, Inc., West Henrietta, NY; *U.S. Private*, pg. 446
Benjamin, Wayne, V.P. & Pur. Agent--The Times-Picayune Publishing Corp., New Orleans, LA; *U.S. Private*, pg. 1087
Benner, John, Pur. Agent--Snokist Growers, Yakima, WA; *U.S. Private*, pg. 1011
Bennett, Janice, Mgr.-Pur.--Letraset UK, London, United Kingdom; *Int'l*, pg. 462
Bennett, John, V.P.-Pur.--Taylor-Morley, Inc., Saint Louis, MO; *U.S. Private*, pg. 1071
Bennett, Mark, Mgr.-Pur.--Tillamook County Creamery Assn., Tillamook, OR; *U.S. Private*, pg. 1086
Bennett, Richard, Mgr.-Opers.--Ariel Corporation, Mount Vernon, OH; *U.S. Private*, pg. 81
Bennett, Shirley, Mgr.-Pur. & Traffic--Witt Company, Cincinnati, OH; *U.S. Private*, pg. 1185
Benoit, Louis, Pur. Agent--Carver, Inc., Savannah, GA; *U.S. Private*, pg. 217
Bensman, William F., V.P.-Matls. Mngmt.--Pratt & Lambert United, Inc., Cleveland, OH; *U.S. Public*, pg. 1466
Benson, Paul, Mgr.-Pur.--Orbit Valve Co., Little Rock, AR; *U.S. Private*, pg. 819
Bentley, Richard M., Mgr.-Matls.--Accu-Sort Systems, Inc., Telford, PA; *U.S. Private*, pg. 11
Berchem, Allen R., V.P.-Fin. & Pur.--Torke Coffee Roasting Company, Sheboygan, WI; *U.S. Private*, pg. 1092
Berckmans, Walter, Mgr.-Pur.--Credit Lyonnais Belgium, Brussels, Belgium; *Int'l*, pg. 344
Berg, Jim, Pur. Agent--Ohmite Manufacturing Company, Skokie, IL; *U.S. Private*, pg. 813
Berg, Robert G., Mgr.-Pur.--Science Applications International Corp., San Diego, CA; *U.S. Private*, pg. 975
Bergmann, Burkhard, Dr., Dir.-Gas Pur.--Ruhrgas Aktiengesellschaft, Essen, Germany; *Int'l*, pg. 1148
Berkowitz, Ira, V.P.-Pur.--Melard Manufacturing Corporation, Passaic, NJ; *U.S. Private*, pg. 729
Berlin, Elizabeth, Mgr.-Pur.--Metropolitan Mortgage & Securities Co., Inc., Spokane, WA; *U.S. Private*, pg. 738
Berman, Bernard, Gen. Mgr.--Butler Ventamatic Corp., Mineral Wells, TX; *U.S. Private*, pg. 190
Berman, Lee, Mgr.-Pur.--Gans Ink & Supply Company, Inc., Los Angeles, CA; *U.S. Private*, pg. 440
Berman, Richard C., V.P.-Pur.--Kaman Industrial Technologies Corp., Bloomfield, CT; *U.S. Public*, pg. 942
Bernhardt, Russ, Contract Procurement--Sargent & Lundy, Chicago, IL; *U.S. Private*, pg. 965
Bernier, Cecile, Mgr.-Pur.--Galileo Corp., Sturbridge, MA; *U.S. Public*, pg. 698
Berryman, Garry, Dir.-Pur.--Harley-Davidson, Inc., Milwaukee, WI; *U.S. Public*, pg. 786
Berryman, Garry, Dir.-Pur.--Harley-Davidson Motor Company, Milwaukee, WI; *U.S. Public*, pg. 786
Betts, Bruce, Pur. Agent--Target Stamped Products Corp., Kinsman, OH; *U.S. Private*, pg. 1069
Betz, Robert, Dir.-Pur.--Centocor, Inc., Malvern, PA; *U.S. Public*, pg. 323
Bevere, Richard, V.P.-Pur.--Jaclyn, Inc., West New York, NJ; *U.S. Public*, pg. 920
Beyer, Ron, Mgr.-Pur.--IMC Magnetics Corp., Tempe, AZ; *Int'l*, pg. 868
Beyer, Steven C., Pur. Agent--Peter Kiewit Sons Inc., Omaha, NE; *U.S. Private*, pg. 619
Biddle, Kevin, Dir.-Pur.--Mader Construction Corp, Elma, NY; *U.S. Private*, pg. 693
Biek, J., Dir.-Pur.--The Lincoln Electric Company, Cleveland, OH; *U.S. Public*, pg. 996
Bielski, Eugene, Pur. Agent--Diebel Manufacturing Co., Morton Grove, IL; *U.S. Private*, pg. 331
Bien, Timothy E., Sr. V.P.-Professional Services & Pur.--Omnicare, Inc., Covington, KY; *U.S. Public*, pg. 1223
Bienefeld, George, Pur. Agent--Rolled Steel Products Corporation, Los Angeles, CA; *U.S. Private*, pg. 941
Bigliamo, E., Pur. Agent--Edwards Engineering Corporation, Pompton Plains, NJ; *U.S. Private*, pg. 365
Bilderback, Gilbert, V.P.-Pur.--Borden Decorative Products, Saint Louis, MO; *U.S. Private*, pg. 158
Binet, Dominique, Dir.-Pur.--Arjo Wiggins Appleton plc, Basingstoke, United Kingdom; *Int'l*, pg. 567
Bingham, R.S., Dir. Pur.--Atlantic Electric Co., Pleasantville, NJ; *U.S. Public*, pg. 430
Birch, Robert, Dir.-Pur.--Rolland Inc., Fine Papers Division, Saint-Jerome, Canada; *Int'l*, pg. 274
Bird, Peter, Dir.-Pur./Essentials--Dixons Group plc, Hemel Hempstead, United Kingdom,; *Int'l*, pg. 413
Birdsall, Jim, Mgr.-Pur.--L.R. Nelson Corporation, Peoria, IL; *U.S. Private*, pg. 790
Biron, Philippe, V.P.-Procurement & Services--Hydro-Quebec, Montreal, Canada; *Int'l*, pg. 640
Bisbing, Ed, Dir.-Pur.--Advanced Circuit Technology, Nashua, NH; *U.S. Private*, pg. 21
Bishop, Guy M., III, Mgr.-Pur.--Jefferson Mills, Inc., Pulaski, VA; *U.S. Private*, pg. 584
Bishop, Wayne, Pur. Agent--Stanco Metal Products, Inc., Grand Haven, MI; *U.S. Private*, pg. 1030
Bivens, John, V.P.-Pur.--Whataburger, Inc., Corpus Christi, TX; *U.S. Private*, pg. 1170
Bixler, Bruce, Dir.-Pur.--Mack Molding Company Inc., Arlington, VT; *U.S. Private*, pg. 691
Bizios, Harry, V.P.-Mfg.--Lennox International Inc., Richardson, TX; *U.S. Private*, pg. 659
Bizios, Harry, Mgr.-Pur.--Lennox Industries Inc., Richardson, TX; *U.S. Private*, pg. 659
Bjalobok, Frank A., Jr., Pur. Agent--James Austin Co., Mars, PA; *U.S. Private*, pg. 99
Bjerk, Kenneth I., V.P.-Pur.--Ecolab Inc., Saint Paul, MN; *U.S. Public*, pg. 562
Black, Steve, Mgr.-Pur.--Cargill Detroit Corp., Clawson, MI; *U.S. Private*, pg. 210
Blackburn, Gordon, Mgr.-Pur.--E Wood Limited, Northallerton, United Kingdom; *Int'l*, pg. 858
Blackwell, Robert, Dir.-Pur.--Richco Inc., Chicago, IL; *U.S. Private*, pg. 929
Blair, S.E., Mgr.-Pur.--Wheland Foundry Div.--North American Royalties, Inc., Chattanooga, TN; *U.S. Private*, pg. 803
Blakely, Scott, Dir.-Matls. Mngmt.--The National Super Service Co., Toledo, OH; *U.S. Private*, pg. 787
Blakley, Carolyn, Mgr.--Standing Rock Campground, Milwaukee, WI; *U.S. Public*, pg. 410
Blanc, Claude H., V.P.-Strategic Procurement--Quebecor Printing, Inc., Montreal, Canada; *Int'l*, pg. 1076
Blanchette, Karen, Mgr.-Pur.--Victor Corporation, West Warwick, RI; *U.S. Private*, pg. 1138
Blanckaert, Jan, Mgr.-Export & Pur.--Digital Equipment N.V./S.A., Brussels, Belgium; *U.S. Public*, pg. 508
Blanco, Sergio, Mgr.-Import & Pur.--Cervejarias Kaiser Brasil Ltda., Campinas, Brazil; *Int'l*, pg. 279
Blankenship, Brenda, Mgr.-Pur.--Lectrodryer Div., Ajax Magnethermic Corp., Richmond, KY; *Int'l*, pg. 113
Blasdell, Mike, V.P.-Pur.--Furr's/Bishops, Inc., Lubbock, TX; *U.S. Public*, pg. 689
Blaum, Winifred, V.P.-Admin. & Opers.--Arrow Financial Corporation, Glens Falls, NY; *U.S. Public*, pg. 135
Blevins, Bill, Mgr.-Pur.--Polyloom Corp. of America, Dayton, TN; *U.S. Private*, pg. 875
Bligh, Skip, Mgr.-Pur.--Truelove & Maclean Inc., Waterbury, CT; *U.S. Private*, pg. 1107
Bliman, Sam, Mgr.-Corp. Pur.--Malcolm Pirnie, Inc., White Plains, NY; *U.S. Private*, pg. 867
Bloom, Jim, Pur. Agent--Neapco, Inc., Pottstown, PA; *U.S. Private*, pg. 1113

Bloom, William, V.P.-Distr.--Alexander's, Inc., Saddle Brook, NJ; *U.S. Public,* pg. 1725
Bloomstrom, James M., V.P.-Oper. Support--La Quinta Inns, Inc., San Antonio, TX; *U.S. Public,* pg. 972
Blough, John, V.P.-Pur.--Snyder Berlin, Berlin, PA; *U.S. Private,* pg. 887
Blutstein, Morton, Exec. V.P. & Mgr.-Pur.--Halper Bros., Milwaukee, WI; *U.S. Private,* pg. 920
Blystone, Bev, Dir.-Pur. & Personnel--Union City Chair Co., Union City, PA; *U.S. Private,* pg. 170
Board, Daniel L., Asst. V.P.-Pur.--Roanoke Electric Steel Corporation, Roanoke, VA; *U.S. Public,* pg. 1392
Bobik, John A., Dir.-Matl. Mngmt.--Tellabs Operations, Inc., Lisle, IL; *U.S. Public,* pg. 1572
Bobroski, Lance, Mgr.-Pur.--Turnbull Enterprises, Inc., Baltimore, MD; *U.S. Private,* pg. 1109
Bobzin, Joe, Pur. Agent--Young Supply Company, Detroit, MI; *U.S. Private,* pg. 1202
Bocchino, J.C., Dir.-Pur.--Iveco France S.A., Trappes, France; *Int'l,* pg. 696
Bodden, Ralph, Dir.-Matls.--Aero Systems Aviation Corp., Miami, FL; *U.S. Private,* pg. 24
Boeddeker, Cynthia, V.P. & Gen. Mgr.-Mdsg.--PremiumWear, Inc., Minneapolis, MN; *U.S. Public,* pg. 1323
Bogner, Dean, Natl. Product Mgr. Conveyor Comp.--Webster Industries Inc., Tiffin, OH; *U.S. Private,* pg. 1157
Bogoyevac, Pete, Mgr.-Matls.--Westlake Medical Center, Westlake Village, CA; *U.S. Public,* pg. 1697
Bohaty, Robert J., V.P- Pur.--Bank of America Illinois, Chicago, IL; *U.S. Public,* pg. 180
Bohl, Sue, Mgr.-Pur.--Hubbard Scientific, Chippewa Falls, WI; *U.S. Public,* pg. 71
Boike, Steve, Buyer--The Flecto Co., Inc., Oakland, CA; *U.S. Private,* pg. 410
Boissin, Henri, Dir.-Pur.--Merinos, Saint Quentin-en-Yvelines, France; *Int'l,* pg. 858
Boitz, Randall D., Dir.-Pur.--Turtle Wax, Inc., Chicago, IL; *U.S. Private,* pg. 1110
Bolding, Ron, Dir.-Mdsg. & Pur.--UHP Healthcare, Inglewood, CA; *U.S. Private,* pg. 1113
Boll, Dick, Mgr.-Pur.--Broadcast Electronics, Inc., Quincy, IL; *U.S. Private,* pg. 531
Bollinger, Ed, V.P.-Pur.--Royal Caribbean Cruises Ltd., Miami, FL; *U.S. Public,* pg. 1410
Bollmann, Juergen, V.P.-Matls.--Rheem Manufacturing Co., New York, NY; *Int'l,* pg. 1022
Bolton, George C., Sr. V.P. & Dir.-Pur. & Sls.--The Law Company, Inc., Wichita, KS; *U.S. Private,* pg. 653
Boltz, Rick, Sr. Buyer--Ludlow Composites Corporation, Fremont, OH; *U.S. Private,* pg. 680
Bonas, Sharon, Dir.-Pur.--SEI Investments, Oaks, PA; *U.S. Public,* pg. 1417
Bond, Gene P., V.P.-Matls.--Hehr International Inc., Los Angeles, CA; *U.S. Private,* pg. 519
Boneck, Michael, Pur. Agent--Lasko Metal Products, Inc., West Chester, PA; *U.S. Private,* pg. 652
Bonk, Ronald, Mgr.-Pur.--Citibank, Federal Savings Bank (Illinois), Chicago, IL; *U.S. Public,* pg. 378
Boo, Chen Kean, Mgr.-Pur.--Malaysian Tobacco Co./B.A.T. Indust., Kuala Lumpur, Malaysia; *Int'l,* pg. 111
Boockholdt, Keith, Dir.-Pur.--Benihana, Inc., Miami, FL; *U.S. Public,* pg. 211
Booden, J.M., Exec. Dir.-Pur.--Pharmacia & Upjohn, Kalamazoo, MI; *Int'l,* pg. 1048
Boodry, William, Dir.-Pur.--Reebok International Ltd., Stoughton, MA; *U.S. Public,* pg. 1369
Boorshtein, Steven, Mgr.-Pur.--Spire Corporation, Bedford, MA; *U.S. Public,* pg. 1499
Booth, James, V.P.-Worldwide Pur.--Bourns, Inc., Riverside, CA; *U.S. Private,* pg. 161
Booth, Peter, Dir.-Materials--Messier-Dowty Ltd., Gloucester, United Kingdom; *Int'l,* pg. 1340
Boothby, Stan, Dir.-Pur.--Standard Duplicating Machines Corp., Andover, MA; *U.S. Private,* pg. 1031
Boothe, Robert S., Pur. Agent--Farmers Marine Copper Works, Galveston, TX; *U.S. Private,* pg. 422
Borchert, James, Mgr.-Pur.--Riceland Foods, Inc., Stuttgart, AR; *U.S. Private,* pg. 928
Borchi, M., Gen. Mgr.-Sourcing--Nuovo Pignone S.p.a., Florence, Italy; *Int'l,* pg. 990
Borden, Lester, V.P. & Gen. Mgr.-Pur.--TriStar Pictures, Culver City, CA; *Int'l,* pg. 1283
Borg, James F., Dir.-Pur. & Transport--Gaylord Container Corporation, Deerfield, IL; *U.S. Public,* pg. 704
Borggreu, Caj, Pur. Agent--Skanska Prefab AB, Malmo, Sweden; *Int'l,* pg. 1261
Boring, Bill, Pur. Agent--Aristokraft, Inc., Jasper, IN; *U.S. Public,* pg. 675
Born, Len, Mgr.-Pur.--Natural Fuels Corporation, Denver, CO; *U.S. Public,* pg. 1170
Borsaglia, Barry, Dir.-Pur.--Bell-Carter Foods, Inc., Lafayette, CA; *U.S. Private,* pg. 131
Bosaw, John, Dir.-Pur.--Danisco Ingredients USA, Inc., New Century, KS; *Int'l,* pg. 378
Bosco, Fred, Mgr.-Pur.--Engine Components Div., Saginaw, MI; *U.S. Public,* pg. 557
Bose, P., Pur. Agent--Economy Folding Box Corp., Chicago, IL; *U.S. Private,* pg. 362
Bothwell, Bill, Dir.-Pur.--Northern Telecom, Nashville, TN; *Int'l,* pg. 969
Bottiglia, Louis J., Pur. Dir.--The United States Life Ins. Co. In the City of New York, New York, NY; *U.S. Public,* pg. 77
Bottoms, Chris, Mgr.-Pur.--The Pierce Co., Inc., Upland, IN; *U.S. Private,* pg. 102
Bouchard, Earl, V.P.-Pur.--Union Bank of California, San Francisco, CA; *Int'l,* pg. 157
Bouche, Ron, Dir.-Pur.--American Foods Group, Inc., Green Bay, WI; *U.S. Private,* pg. 54
Boulka, Steve, Dir.-Pur.--Eateries, Inc., Oklahoma City, OK; *U.S. Public,* pg. 555
Boulka, Steve, Dir.-Pur.--Pepperoni Grill, Oklahoma City, OK; *U.S. Public,* pg. 555
Bourgeois, A.J., Dir.-Pur.--Schenectady International, Inc., Schenectady, NY; *U.S. Private,* pg. 969
Bourgeois, Rick, Mgr.-Pur.--Performance Contractors Inc., Baton Rouge, LA; *U.S. Private,* pg. 853
Boutin, George, Pur.-Dir.--Allied Plywood Corporation, Concord, MA; *U.S. Public,* pg. 1193
Bouvier, James, Mgr.-Pur.--Moscom Corporation, Pittsford, NY; *U.S. Public,* pg. 1136
Bowen, Walter E., Mgr.-Matls.--McInnes Steel Company, Corry, PA; *U.S. Private,* pg. 722
Bower, Wayne, Dir.-Pur.--Security Plastics, Inc., Hialeah, FL; *U.S. Private,* pg. 981
Bowers, Bruce, V.P.-Pur.--Foodmaker, Inc., San Diego, CA; *U.S. Public,* pg. 661
Bowers, Joe, Grp. V.P.-Pur. & Warehousing--Total System Services, Inc., Columbus, GA; *U.S. Public,* pg. 1550
Bowles, Bob, Mgr.-Pur.--Haws Drinking Faucet Co., Berkeley, CA; *U.S. Private,* pg. 512
Bowman, Lloyd, Pur. Agent & Plant Supvr.--Overholtzer Church Furniture, Inc., Modesto, CA; *U.S. Private,* pg. 823
Bowman, Richard, Dir.-Pur.--Smart & Final, Vernon, CA; *Int'l,* pg. 563
Bowser, Lillian, Dir.-Pur.--North Carolina Mutual Life Insurance Co., Durham, NC; *U.S. Private,* pg. 804
Boyd, Jim, Dir.-Pur.--Collins Oldsmobile Inc., Indianapolis, IN; *U.S. Private,* pg. 253
Boyd, John, Pur. Agent--John Bouchard & Sons Company, Nashville, TN; *U.S. Private,* pg. 161
Boyd, Robert, Pur. Agent--Dana Perfumes Corp., New York, NY; *U.S. Private,* pg. 922
Boyer, Johann, Mgr.-Pur.--AGA Ges.m.b.H., Vienna, Austria; *Int'l,* pg. 13
Boykin, C. Dave, Dir.-Pur.--Power & Telephone Supply Company, Memphis, TN; *U.S. Private,* pg. 877
Bracey, Robert, Dir.-Pur.--Modern Drop Forge Co., Blue Island, IL; *U.S. Private,* pg. 754
Brackhahn, Thomas, Dir.-Corp. Pur.--Tension Envelope Corp., Kansas City, MO; *U.S. Private,* pg. 1077
Braden, William F., Dir.-Materials Mngmt.--NIPSCO Industries, Inc., Hammond, IN; *U.S. Public,* pg. 1185
Bradley, John, Mgr.-Pur.--Bel-Art Products, Pequannock, NJ; *U.S. Private,* pg. 130
Brady, Dennis, Pur. Agent--Anderson Erickson Dairy Company, Des Moines, IA; *U.S. Private,* pg. 72
Brady, Neal, Dir.-Pur.--Manhattan Accessories Div., New York, NY; *U.S. Public,* pg. 1429
Brainard, Al, Mgr.-Pur.--Tremco, Inc., Beachwood, OH; *U.S. Public,* pg. 1358
Bramble, Jody, Supvr.-Pur.--PST Vans, Inc., Salt Lake City, UT; *U.S. Public,* pg. 1246
Branch, Ken, Dir.-Pur.--Plastigage Corporation, Jackson, MI; *U.S. Private,* pg. 871
Brandao, Rui Alves, Dir.-Pur.--LPC Industrias Alimenticias S.A., Vila Jaguara, Brazil; *Int'l,* pg. 380
Brandt, Ben, Mgr.-Pur.--OGE Energy Corp., Oklahoma City, OK; *U.S. Public,* pg. 1207
Brannock, Larry, V.P.-Matls. Mngmt.--Clariant Corporation, Charlotte, NC; *Int'l,* pg. 624
Branson, Dick, Mgr.-Pur.--W.A. Roosevelt Co., La Crosse, WI; *U.S. Private,* pg. 943
Bratton, Donald, Dir.-Pur.--Lampert Yards, Inc., Saint Paul, MN; *U.S. Private,* pg. 645
Braverman, Douglas, Dir.-Pur.--Renault USA, Southfield, MI; *Int'l,* pg. 1102
Braziunas, Ruta, Mgr.-Pur.--Midwest Express Holdings, Inc., Oak Creek, WI; *U.S. Public,* pg. 1111
Brecher, Benjamin, V.P.-Opers.--The Hain Food Group Inc., Uniondale, NY; *U.S. Public,* pg. 774
Breest, John, Buyer--Helwig Carbon Products, Inc., Milwaukee, WI; *U.S. Private,* pg. 521
Brehm, Tim, Pur. Agent--A&A Manufacturing Co., New Berlin, WI; *U.S. Private,* pg. 1
Breining, Gerard, Dir.-Pur.--Compagnie des Machines Bull, Louveciennes, France; *Int'l,* pg. 315
Bremmer, John, V.P.-Estimating & Pur.--R.M. Shoemaker Co., West Conshohocken, PA; *U.S. Private,* pg. 996
Brendel, Arthur, Dir.-Pur.--Lawter International, Inc., Kenosha, WI; *U.S. Public,* pg. 980
Brennan, L.T., V.P.-Pur. & Matls. Mgmnt.--Simmons Company, Atlanta, GA; *Int'l,* pg. 686
Bretz, Robert, Dir.-Pur.--Pitney Bowes Inc., Stamford, CT; *U.S. Public,* pg. 1303
Brewer, Bill, Pur. Agent--Carolina Absorbent Cotton Co., Charlotte, NC; *U.S. Private,* pg. 117
Brewer, Lois, Pur. Mgr.--Finishline Industries Inc. of Georgia, Conyers, GA; *U.S. Private,* pg. 428
Brewster, Bob, Dir.-Pur.--Prime Tanning Co., Inc., Rochester, NH; *U.S. Private,* pg. 884
Breyne, Norma, Mgr.-Pur.--Capsonic Group, Inc., Elgin, IL; *U.S. Private,* pg. 207
Bria, Kim, Mgr.-Pur.--Norwalk Co., Inc., Norwalk, CT; *U.S. Private,* pg. 807
Brice, Tom R., Dir.-Matls. Mngmt.--Madison Gas and Electric Company, Madison, WI; *U.S. Public,* pg. 1032
Bridge, F.J., V.P.-Pur.--Svedala Industries Inc., York, PA; *Int'l,* pg. 1325
Bridwell, Richard L., Dir.-Purch. & Facility Mgmt.--United Missouri Bank of St. Louis, Saint Louis, MO; *U.S. Public, pg. 1655*
Brieck, Gene, Dir.-Pur.--Ash Grove Cement Company, Shawnee Mission, KS; *U.S. Private,* pg. 87
Briggs, John V., V.P.-Matls.--Bard Mfg. Co., Bryan, OH; *U.S. Private,* pg. 116
Briggs, Kurt, V.P.-Pur.--The Hotsy Corporation, Englewood, CO; *U.S. Private,* pg. 500
Brighan, Gene, Dir.-Pur.--Diversco, Inc., Spartanburg, SC; *U.S. Private,* pg. 336
Briick, Gerald, Dir.-Mfg. & Customer Services-Midwest--W. Braun Company, Chicago, IL; *U.S. Private,* pg. 166
Brill, Richard, Dir.-Pur.--The Okonite Company, Ramsey, NJ; *U.S. Private,* pg. 813
Brininger, Dave, V.P.-Pur.--AmeriServe of Norcross, Norcross, GA; *U.S. Private,* pg. 533
Brinker, Kenneth J., Dir.-Pur. & World Trade--Warner-Lambert Company, Morris Plains, NJ; *U.S. Public,* pg. 1738
Brinker, Richard, Dir.-Pur.--Durakon Industries, Inc., Lapeer, MI; *U.S. Public,* pg. 537
Brisa, Oyvind, Mgr.-Pur.--Frionor A/S, Lysaker, Norway; *Int'l,* pg. 516
Brisendine, Harley, Pur. Agent--Rochester Gauges Inc. Of Texas, Dallas, TX; *U.S. Private,* pg. 440
Briski, Kathy, Dir.-Pur.--Metro-Goldwyn-Mayer Inc., Santa Monica, CA; *U.S. Public,* pg. 1101
Brittan, Kent, V.P.-Pur.--United Technologies Corporation, Hartford, CT; *U.S. Public,* pg. 1689
Britton, Jas, Mgr.-Pur.--Dale Industries Inc., Dearborn, MI; *U.S. Private,* pg. 308
Britton, Michael, Pur. Agent--La Marche Mfg. Co., Des Plaines, IL; *U.S. Private,* pg. 640
Broadhurst, Nigel, Dir.-Buying--Iceland Frozen Foods plc., Deeside, United Kingdom; *Int'l,* pg. 658
Broadwater, Peg, Dir.-Pur.--Photogenic Machine Company, Inc., Youngstown, OH; *U.S. Private,* pg. 864
Broadwell, James, Dir.-Pur.--The Cloister, Sea Island, GA; *U.S. Private,* pg. 978
Brockest, Lorne, Mgr.-Pur.--The Citadel Assurance Companies, Toronto, Canada; *Int'l,* pg. 346
Brodeur, Jean, Mgr.-Pur.--Bird Machine Company, South Walpole, MA; *U.S. Public,* pg. 166
Brofft, Jerome V., Sr. V.P.-Pur. & Logistics--World Color Press, Inc., Greenwich, CT; *U.S. Public,* pg. 1778
Brofft, Jerry, Dir.-Pur.--Golden Books Publishing, New York, NY; *U.S. Public,* pg. 749
Broman, D. Edward, V.P.-Pur.--Robinson Helicopter Company, Torrance, CA; *U.S. Private,* pg. 936
Bromley, Andrew, Mgr.-Pur.--Asko, Inc, Homestead, PA; *U.S. Private,* pg. 89
Bromley, Ann, Mgr.-Mdsg.--The Popcorn Factory, Lake Forest, IL; *U.S. Private,* pg. 421
Brooker, Bob, Asst. V.P.-Gen. Svcs.--FirstFed Financial Corp., Santa Monica, CA; *U.S. Public,* pg. 645
Brooks, Barry, Mgr.-Pur.--Snyder's of Hanover, Inc., Hanover, PA; *U.S. Private,* pg. 1011
Brooks, Carl X., Mgr.-Pur.--GPU, Inc., Morristown, NJ; *U.S. Public,* pg. 695
Brooks, Cyndi, Sr. Buyer--McNaughton & Gunn, Inc., Saline, MI; *U.S. Private,* pg. 724
Brooks, Michael, Mgr.-Pur.--Cascade Natural Gas Corporation, Seattle, WA; *U.S. Public,* pg. 311
Brooks, Pamela, Mgr.-Pur.--SouthCo. Inc., Concordville, PA; *U.S. Private,* pg. 1014
Brooks, Steve B., Dir.-Pur.--Hollingsworth & Vose Co., East Walpole, MA; *U.S. Private,* pg. 534
Broucke, Bruno, Mgr.-Pur.--Dexter S.A., Tournus, France; *U.S. Public,* pg. 505
Brown, Alan, Pur. Agent--Martin/F. Weber Company, Philadelphia, PA; *U.S. Private,* pg. 710
Brown, Allen, Mgr.-Pur.--Electronic Systems Div., Sioux Falls, SD; *U.S. Public,* pg. 1361
Brown, Charles, Mgr.-Pur.--The Felters Company, Roebuck, SC; *U.S. Private,* pg. 400
Brown, Donna, Dir.-Pur.--Lakeland Industries, Inc., Ronkonkoma, NY; *U.S. Public,* pg. 975
Brown, Ed, Dir.-Pur.--John Wieland Homes Inc., Atlanta, GA; *U.S. Private,* pg. 1175
Brown, Herb, Sr. Buyer--Landis, Waynesboro, PA; *U.S. Public,* pg. 1699
Brown, Joe, Dir.-Pur.--Giant Cement Company, Harleyville, SC; *U.S. Public,* pg. 741
Brown, Linda, Dir.-Purchasing--Christy's Markets, Inc., Brockton, MA; *U.S. Private,* pg. 238
Brown, Pam, Sr. Mgr.-Pur.--Agouron Pharmaceuticals, Inc., La Jolla, CA; *U.S. Public,* pg. 28
Brown, Robert, Pur. Agent--AirTronics Co., Elgin, IL; *U.S. Public,* pg. 944
Brown, Sharon, Mgr.-Pur.--Southern Guaranty Insurance Companies, Montgomery, AL; *Int'l,* pg. 346
Brown, Tony, Exec. Dir.-Pur.--QMS, Inc., Mobile, AL; *U.S. Public,* pg. 1346
Brown, Walter, Dir.-Pur.--Thomaston Mills, Inc., Thomaston, GA; *U.S. Public,* pg. 1599
Brown, William T., Pur. Agent--Collins Electric Company, Inc., Chicopee, MA; *U.S. Private,* pg. 253
Browne, Avis, Dir.-Pur.--Hydrite Chemical Company, Brookfield, WI; *U.S. Private,* pg. 551
Browne, Robert, Mgr.-Pur. & Properties--The Davey Tree Expert Company, Kent, OH; *U.S. Private,* pg. 314
Browning, Steve, Mgr.-Pur.--Walsworth Publishing Company, Inc., Marceline, MO; *U.S. Private,* pg. 1148
Browns, Barrie, Dir.-Pur.--The Rival Company, Kansas City, MO; *U.S. Public,* pg. 1391
Bruemmer, Arlon W., V.P.-Pur.--Bartlett Cocke, Inc., San Antonio, TX; *U.S. Private,* pg. 249
Brumbeloe, Corbie, Mgr.-Pur.--Syncor International Corporation, Woodland Hills, CA; *U.S. Public,* pg. 1548
Brumfield, Donald L., V.P.-Pur. & Engrng.--Treasure Chest Advertising Co., Inc., Glendora, CA; *U.S. Public,* pg. 228
Brunckhorst, Jane, V.P.-Leasing--Commercial Federal Corporation, Omaha, NE; *U.S. Public,* pg. 411
Brundage, Gary L., Dir.-Pur.--Golden Gem Growers Inc., Umatilla, FL; *U.S. Private,* pg. 460
Bruneau, G., Corp. Pur.--Danone Group, Paris, France; *Int'l, pg. 379*
Brunjes, Henry, Mgr.-Matls. Procurement--Kingsbury Corporation, Keene, NH; *U.S. Private,* pg. 621
Brunner, Chrissy, Mgr.-Pur.--Streamlight Inc., Norristown, PA; *U.S. Private,* pg. 1047
Bruno, Frank, Pur.--Propper Manufacturing Co., Inc., Long Island City, NY; *U.S. Private,* pg. 891
Brunswick, Steve, V.P.-Office Svcs.--Downey Savings & Loan Association, F.A., Newport Beach, CA; *U.S. Public, pg. 526*
Brush, Wayne, Dir.-Pur.--Magna International Inc., Markham, Canada; *Int'l,* pg. 829
Bryan, James A., V.P.-Distr.--The Pep Boys-Manny, Moe & Jack, Philadelphia, PA; *U.S. Public,* pg. 1276

Bryson, Carolyn, Mgr.-Pur.--Integon Corporation, Winston Salem, NC; *U.S. Public*, pg. 719
Buch, Dennis, Pur. Agent--ISI Norgen, Inc., Fraser, MI; *Int'l*, pg. 646
Buchanan, Don, Dir.-Comml. Services--Akzo Nobel Inc., Chicago, IL; *Int'l*, pg. 47
Buchholz, Eugene, Pur. Agent--The Shaler Company, Waupun, WI; *U.S. Private*, pg. 786
Buckingham, Tom, Dir.-Pur.--Norwalk Furniture Corporation, Norwalk, OH; *U.S. Private*, pg. 807
Buckler, Stephen, Dir.-Pur.--Real World, Andover, MA; *U.S. Private*, pg. 913
Buckles, Juli, Pur. Agent--Taco John's International, Inc., Cheyenne, WY; *U.S. Private*, pg. 1066
Buckley, Mark F., V.P.-Facilities, Mngmt. & Pur.--Staples, Inc., Westborough, MA; *U.S. Public*, pg. 1509
Buckley, W.L., Dir.-Procurement--Atwood & Morrill Co., Inc., Salem, MA; *Int'l*, pg. 1489
Buckmier, Chuck, Dir.-Pur.--Dunn-Edwards Corporation, Los Angeles, CA; *U.S. Private*, pg. 347
Bucknall, C.D., Dir.-Pur.--Compass Group plc, Chertsey, United Kingdom.; *Int'l*, pg. 324
Buehl, Eddie, Mgr.-Pur.--Bosch Braking Systems-North America, South Bend, IN; *Int'l*, pg. 204
Buehler, Darrin, Dir.-Pur.--Russell Stover Candies, Inc., Kansas City, MO; *U.S. Private*, pg. 953
Bugher, LeRoy, Dir.-Pur.--Venturian Corp., Hopkins, MN; *U.S. Public*, pg. 1716
Bullock, Jessie, Mgr.-Admin. Services--PLM International, Inc., San Francisco, CA; *U.S. Public*, pg. 1241
Bult, Albert J., Mgr.-Pur.--E.W. Knauss & Son, Inc., Quakertown, PA; *U.S. Private*, pg. 626
Bumbalo, P., Pur. Agent--Krupp Robins, Inc., Englewood, CO; *Int'l*, pg. 511
Bumgarner, Glenda, Mgr.-Pur.--Gaston County Dyeing Machine Co., Mount Holly, NC; *U.S. Private*, pg. 441
Bunk, Debbie, Mgr.-Pur.--Moore-O-Matic, Inc., Waupaca, WI; *U.S. Public*, pg. 1193
Bunker, Jerry, Mgr.-Matl. Mngmt. & Pur.--Schilling Plant, Salinas, CA; *U.S. Public*, pg. 1066
Burch, Elmer, Mgr.-Pur.--Gulf States, Inc., Freeport, TX; *U.S. Private*, pg. 487
Burck, Bruce, Pur. Agent--Mulberry Metal Products, Inc., Union, NJ; *U.S. Private*, pg. 766
Burfield, James, Mgr.-Pur.--Interstate/Johnson Lane, Inc., Charlotte, NC; *U.S. Public*, pg. 909
Burger, Leslie, Mgr.-Prod. Schedule Div.--Farnam Companies, Inc., Phoenix, AZ; *U.S. Private*, pg. 396
Burgess, Mike, Dir.-Pur.--Morrison Textile Machinery Co., Fort Lawn, SC; *U.S. Private*, pg. 762
Burke, John M., V.P.-Pur. & H.R.--Osco Industries Inc., Portsmouth, OH; *U.S. Private*, pg. 820
Burke, Ken, V.P.-Pur.--Printpack Inc., Atlanta, GA; *U.S. Private*, pg. 886
Burke, Robert K., Mgr.-Pur.--Allied Mineral Products, Inc., Columbus, OH; *U.S. Private*, pg. 39
Burkhardt, Fritz, Dir.-Pur.--Burda GmbH, Offenburg, Germany; *Int'l*, pg. 233
Burks, Bob, Mgr.-Purch.--SA-SO Company, Dallas, TX; *U.S. Private*, pg. 955
Burleson, Harold, Mgr.-Pur.--Buccaneer Homes, Inc., Hamilton, AL; *U.S. Public*, pg. 318
Burnett, Vanessa, Mgr.-Pur.--CPAC, Inc., Leicester, NY; *U.S. Public*, pg. 282
Burnham, Tom, Mgr.-Pur. & Matls.--Consumers Energy, Jackson, MI; *U.S. Public*, pg. 280
Burnip, Tony, Dir.-Pur.--Vauxhall Motors Limited, Luton, United Kingdom; *U.S. Public*, pg. 724
Burns, John, Dir.-Matls.--PSC Inc., Webster, NY; *U.S. Public*, pg. 1245
Burrell, Cindy, Dir.-Pur.& Admin.--Sun Data Inc., Norcross, GA; *U.S. Private*, pg. 1050
Burrell, David, Mgr.-Pur.--B/E Aerospace Seating Products, Winston Salem, NC; *U.S. Public*, pg. 159
Burrell, Jackie, Gen. Mdse. IHBA Buyer--The Food Emporium, Bronx, NY; *Int'l*, pg. 1375
Burris, Jeoffrey A., V.P.-Matls. Mngmt. & Engine/N.V.H. Americas--Simpson Industries, Inc., Plymouth, MI; *U.S. Public*, pg. 1474
Burs, Paul, Dir.-Matls.--Tech Industries, Inc., Woonsocket, RI; *U.S. Private*, pg. 1071
Burton, Gregory, Sr. Dir.-World Purchasing--Emulex Corporation, Costa Mesa, CA; *U.S. Public*, pg. 579
Burton, Warren, V.P.-Mktg. & Pur.--Multifoods Specialty Distribution Inc., Denver, CO; *U.S. Public*, pg. 901
Burzynski, James, Pur. Agent--James Steel & Tube Company, Madison Heights, MI; *U.S. Private*, pg. 102
Busch, Celeste, Dir.-Matl.--Williams International, Walled Lake, MI; *U.S. Private*, pg. 1178
Bushman, Janet, Dir.-Pur.--Pascoe Building Systems, Inc., Columbus, GA; *U.S. Private*, pg. 842
Butcher, Doug, Mgr.-Matls.--Industrial Bag Division - Des Moines Plant, Des Moines, IA; *U.S. Public*, pg. 1521
Butcher, Randye, Pur. Agent-Office Supplies--Southern States Cooperative, Inc., Richmond, VA; *U.S. Private*, pg. 1017
Butler, Dean, Sr. V.P.-Misc. Pur.--Reinalt-Thomas Corp., Ann Arbor, MI; *U.S. Private*, pg. 919
Butler, Jennifer, Mgr.-Pur.--Whitin Roberts Co., Sanford, NC; *U.S. Private*, pg. 309
Butler, Todd, Dir.-Pur.--Ultrak Inc., Lewisville, TX; *U.S. Public*, pg. 1663
Butler, Todd, Dir.-Pur.--Diamond Electronics, Inc., Carroll, OH; *U.S. Public*, pg. 1663
Butt, L., Pur. Mgr.--Cochrane, Inc., King of Prussia, PA; *U.S. Public*, pg. 456
Butterfield, David, Mgr.-Pur.--A. Duda & Sons Inc., Oviedo, FL; *U.S. Private*, pg. 344
Butts, Wes, Mgr.-Pur.--Franklin Electric Co., Inc., Bluffton, IN; *U.S. Public*, pg. 679
Buydos, J. J., Dir.-Pur.--Rockbestos-Suprenant Cable Corp., Clinton, MA; *U.S. Private*, pg. 938
Byrd, Amy, Sr. Buyer--Reuter Manufacturing Inc., Hopkins, MN; *U.S. Public*, pg. 1383
Byrne, Dick, Mgr.-Pur.--Golf Grip Division, Laurinburg, NC; *U.S. Public*, pg. 557
Bystrom, Asa Lindell, Dir.-Commun. & Pub. Rels.--BTL AB, Goteborg, Sweden; *Int'l*, pg. 123
Bytnar, Robert, Buyer--Replogle Globes, Inc., Broadview, IL; *U.S. Private*, pg. 923
Cahlink, George, Dir.-Pur.--Checkpoint Systems Inc., Thorofare, NJ; *U.S. Public*, pg. 343
Cahlink, George, Jr., Dir.-Pur.--Wyeth-Ayerst Laboratories, Inc., Philadelphia, PA; *U.S. Public*, pg. 80
Cain, Dom, Dir.-Pur.--Eight O'Clock Coffee, Hyattsville, MD; *Int'l*, pg. 1375
Calafati, Rodney, Dir.-Pur.--Frank Briscoe Co. Inc., Kenilworth, NJ; *U.S. Private*, pg. 169
Caldon, Daniel, Chief Fin. Officer & Sr. V.P.--Bissell Inc., Grand Rapids, MI; *U.S. Private*, pg. 145
Caldwell, Clifford R., V.P.-Pur.--Johns Manville Corporation, Denver, CO; *U.S. Public*, pg. 927
Call, Lisa, Mgr.-Pur.--Zoom Telephonics, Inc., Boston, MA; *U.S. Public*, pg. 1794
Call, Mike, Mgr.-Pur.--OEC Medical Systems, Inc., Salt Lake City, UT; *U.S. Public*, pg. 1207
Callahan, Irene, Mgr.-Pur.--S.A.S.I. Corporation, Collinsville, IL; *U.S. Private*, pg. 955
Callegaro, Romeo, Mgr.-Pur. & Matl. Control--Flowserve Duriron Canada, Woodbridge, Canada; *U.S. Public*, pg. 659
Calloway, Otis, Dir.-Drug Pur.--Bergen Brunswig Medical Corporation, Montgomery, AL; *U.S. Public*, pg. 214
Calvo, Barbara, Pur. Agent--American Institute of C.P.A.'s Inc., New York, NY; *U.S. Private*, pg. 57
Cameron, John M., Engr.--Ingles Markets, Incorporated, Black Mountain, NC; *U.S. Public*, pg. 878
Camoia, Art, Dir.-Pur.--Armor All Products Group, Oakland, CA; *U.S. Public*, pg. 387
Camp, Doreen, Mgr.-Pur.--The Producto Machine Co., Bridgeport, CT; *U.S. Private*, pg. 889
Campbell, Debbie, Mgr.-Pur.--California Water Service Co., San Jose, CA; *U.S. Public*, pg. 294
Campbell, Ike, Pur. Agent--Ward Manufacturing, Inc., Blossburg, PA; *U.S. Private*, pg. 1149
Campbell, Marty, Mgr.-Pur.--Alimed, Inc., Dedham, MA; *U.S. Private*, pg. 34
Campbell, Scott, V.P.-Pur.--Greenwich Air Services, Miami, FL; *U.S. Public*, pg. 710
Campbell, Susan, Pur. Agent--Bennington Iron Works, Inc., Bennington, VT; *U.S. Private*, pg. 133
Campbell, Tom, Sr. V.P.-Pur.--Brinker International, Inc., Dallas, TX; *U.S. Public*, pg. 253
Campbell, W.J., V.P.-Pur.--NVF Company, Yorklyn, DE; *U.S. Private*, pg. 772
Campeur, Jim, Dir.-Pur.--Universal Standard Healthcare, Inc., Southfield, MI; *U.S. Public*, pg. 1697
Candilora, Kim, V.P.-Pur. Dir.--First Security Service Company, Salt Lake City, UT; *U.S. Public*, pg. 638
Caniglia, Dave, Mgr.-Pur.--McNeil & NRM., Inc., Akron, OH; *U.S. Private*, pg. 725
Cannatella, Sal, Mgr.-Pur.--Polk Audio, Inc., Baltimore, MD; *U.S. Public*, pg. 1315
Cannon, Bruce, Mgr.-Pur.--TCA Cable TV, Inc., Tyler, TX; *U.S. Public*, pg. 1553
Cannon, Bruce, Mgr.-Pur.--TCA Management Company, Tyler, TX; *U.S. Public*, pg. 1553
Cannon, Rudy, V.P.-Pur.--Wix Div., Gastonia, NC; *U.S. Public*, pg. 479
Cantrell, Jim, V.P.-Pur.--Hutchens Industries Inc., Springfield, MO; *U.S. Private*, pg. 550
Cantwell, James, Pur. Agent--Reading Anthracite Co., Pottsville, PA; *U.S. Private*, pg. 913
Caouette, Paula, Mgr.-Matls.--Elkay Products, Inc., Shrewsbury, MA; *U.S. Private*, pg. 372
Caple, Mona, Pur. Agent--American Electronics, Inc., Fullerton, CA; *U.S. Private*, pg. 5
Caponigro, Leonard, V.P.-Opers.--Tork, Inc., Mount Vernon, NY; *U.S. Private*, pg. 1092
Capponetto, Danielle, Dir.-Pur.--Morgan Stanley Group Inc., New York, NY; *U.S. Public*, pg. 1132
Cappel, Sheila, V.P.-Pur.--Lykes Pasco Inc., Dade City, FL; *U.S. Private*, pg. 682
Cardy, Jaime, V.P.-Pur.--Four Seasons Hotels Inc., Don Mills, Canada; *Int'l*, pg. 502
Carey, Dan, Mgr.-Pur.--Structural Foam Plastics, Inc., Somerville, NJ; *U.S. Private*, pg. 1047
Carey, Gary, Dir.-Pur. & Logistics--Tree Top, Inc., Selah, WA; *U.S. Private*, pg. 1098
Carey, John, Dir.-Pur.--Liqui-Box Corporation, Worthington, OH; *U.S. Public*, pg. 1000
Carlew, Jerry, Dir.-Pur.--Klipsch, Inc., Hope, AR; *U.S. Private*, pg. 626
Carlson, J.R., Pur. Agent--Brad Foote Gear Works, Inc., Cicero, IL; *U.S. Private*, pg. 417
Carlson, Manuel, Mgr.-Pur.--Holiday RV Superstores West, Inc., Bakersfield, CA; *U.S. Public*, pg. 830
Carlson, Terry A., V.P.-Pur.--Maytag Corporation, Newton, IA; *U.S. Public*, pg. 1064
Carlton, Donald, Dir.-Pur.--Tennant Company, Minneapolis, MN; *U.S. Public*, pg. 1577
Carofalo, Sam, Mgr.-Pur.--Acrison, Inc., Moonachie, NJ; *U.S. Private*, pg. 14
Carr, Micheal, Mgr.-Pur.--Carver Corporation, Lynnwood, WA; *U.S. Public*, pg. 310
Carr, Robert W., Dir.-Corp. Pur.--Masco Corporation, Taylor, MI; *U.S. Public*, pg. 1052
Carree, Alain-Claude, Mng. Dir.-Pur.--Automobiles Citroen, Neuilly, France; *Int'l*, pg. 1020
Carrier, Richard, Dir.-Pur.--Lapp Insulator Company, Le Roy, NY; *U.S. Private*, pg. 473
Carroll, Charles J., Pur. Agent--Milton Can Co., Inc., Elizabeth, NJ; *U.S. Private*, pg. 749
Carroll, Helen, Dir.-Bank Svcs.--Great Lakes Financial Resources, Inc., Matteson, IL; *U.S. Private*, pg. 474
Carroll, Helen, Mgr.-Pur.--First National Bank of Blue Island, Blue Island, IL; *U.S. Private*, pg. 474
Carroll, Helen, Mgr.-Pur.--Bank of Homewood, Homewood, IL; *U.S. Private*, pg. 474
Carroll, Helen, Mgr.-Pur.--Bank of Matteson, Matteson, IL; *U.S. Private*, pg. 474
Carruth, L. Brent, V.P.-Opers.--Maynard Oil Co., Dallas, TX; *U.S. Public*, pg. 1064
Carswell, Doug, Pur. Agent--Vermont American Corporation-Fountain Inn Div., Fountain Inn, SC; *U.S. Public*, pg. 575
Caruso, Carlton, Dir.-Pur.--Hickory Hill Furniture Corporation, Valdese, NC; *U.S. Private*, pg. 808
Casagrande, P., Dir.-Purchasing--Zanussi Grandi Impianti S.p.A., Pordenone, Italy; *Int'l*, pg. 442
Casarrubios, J., Dir.-Pur.--Praxair Espania S.A., Madrid, Spain; *U.S. Public*, pg. 1320
Casciere, Frank, Mgr.-Pur.--Better Baked Foods, Inc., North East, PA; *U.S. Private*, pg. 141
Cascio, Chrissy, Dir.-Pur.--Muskin Leisure Products, Inc., Wilkes-Barre, PA; *U.S. Private*, pg. 768
Case, C., Mgr.-Pur.--Marsh Company, Belleville, IL; *U.S. Private*, pg. 707
Case, Jeff, Mgr.-Pur.--Standard Locknut, Inc., Westfield, IN; *U.S. Private*, pg. 1031
Casey, Don L., V.P.-Pur.--The Pep Boys-Manny, Moe & Jack of California, Los Angeles, CA; *U.S. Public*, pg. 1276
Casey, Hugh, Dir.-Pur.--Ziegler Chemical & Mineral Corp., Jericho, NY; *U.S. Private*, pg. 1205
Casey, Patricia, V.P.-Matls. Mngmt.--Success Development International, Jacksonville, FL; *U.S. Private*, pg. 1048
Cash, Glenda, Dir.-Pur.--Commercial National Bank, Shreveport, LA; *U.S. Public*, pg. 500
Casino, Karleen Zita P., V.P.-Matls. Mngmt.--La Tondena Distillers, Inc., Manila, Philippines; *Int'l*, pg. 785
Cason, Richard, Dir.-Corp. Pur. & Disbursements--Tribune Company, Chicago, IL; *U.S. Public*, pg. 1635
Casper, Nina, Mgr.-Pur.--Right Management Consultants, Inc., Philadelphia, PA; *U.S. Public*, pg. 1390
Cassady, Donald J., Div. Dir.-Matls. Mngmt.--Delphi Energy & Engine Management Systems, Flint, MI; *U.S. Public*, pg. 719
Cassidy, C. Maxwell, Mgr.-Pur.--J.H. Fletcher & Co., Huntington, WV; *U.S. Private*, pg. 412
Cassity, Henry, Dir.-Pur.--Dole Food Company, Inc., Westlake Village, CA; *U.S. Public*, pg. 515
Casso, Ed, Specialty Foods Buyer--The Food Emporium, Bronx, NY; *Int'l*, pg. 1375
Castoral, Roger, V.P.-Leasing & Pur.--The Equitable Companies Incorporated, New York, NY; *U.S. Public*, pg. 588
Catalano, Bill, Pur. Agent--Aydin Displays (East), Horsham, PA; *U.S. Public*, pg. 158
Catalano, Mark, Dir.-Pur.--New Hampshire Ball Bearings, Inc., Peterborough, NH; *Int'l*, pg. 868
Caterfino, Sam, Mgr.-Corp. Pur.--SPS Technologies, Inc., Jenkintown, PA; *U.S. Public*, pg. 1419
Cates, Stephanie, Mgr.-Pur.--Objective Systems Integrators, Inc., Folsom, CA; *U.S. Public*, pg. 1209
Cavanaugh, J.C., Pur. Agent--Waterbury Farrel Technologies, Cheshire, CT; *U.S. Private*, pg. 461
Cayce, Dan, Dir.-Pur.--Hopkinsville Milling Co., Hopkinsville, KY; *U.S. Private*, pg. 538
Cea, Fernando, Dir.-Matls.--Duracell de Mexico S.A. de C.V., Naucalpan, Mexico; *U.S. Public*, pg. 743
Cebula, James, Mgr.-Pur. & Supplier Rels.--Kennametal Inc., Latrobe, PA; *U.S. Public*, pg. 950
Cecil, Tom, Dir.-Pur.--America West Airlines, Inc., Phoenix, AZ; *U.S. Public*, pg. 67
Cefarati, Michael, Dir.-Pur.--The Great Lakes Cheese Co., Newbury, OH; *U.S. Private*, pg. 473
Cervi, Laura, Dir.-Pur.--Continental Circuits Corp., Phoenix, AZ; *U.S. Public*, pg. 440
Cesere, Peter, V.P.-Pur.--East Jordan Iron Works, East Jordan, MI; *U.S. Private*, pg. 356
Cesta, Anthony, Pur. Agent--Ace Glass Incorporated, Vineland, NJ; *U.S. Private*, pg. 12
Cetner, Rob, Mgr.-Pur.--U.S. Tsubaki, Inc., Wheeling, IL; *Int'l*, pg. 1425
Champagne, Conrad, Dir.-Pur.--Aliments Flamingo, Iberville, Canada; *Int'l*, pg. 57
Champe, Ronald, V.P.-Pur.--Eat N Park Restaurants, Pittsburgh, PA; *U.S. Private*, pg. 358
Chancey, William F., Mgr.-Pur.--Mead School & Office Products, Dayton, OH; *U.S. Public*, pg. 1074
Chang, Chang, Mgr.-Pur./Torrance--Virco Mfg. Corporation, Torrance, CA; *U.S. Public*, pg. 1721
Chang, Jeong-Ik, Mgr.-Pur.--Ssangyong Engineering & Construction Co., Ltd., Seoul, Korea; *Int'l*, pg. 1291
Channell, Jeff, Coord.-Pur.--Max & Erma's Restaurants, Columbus, OH; *U.S. Public*, pg. 1060
Chapin, Alfred, V.P.-Pur.--Bright Star Industries, Inc., Wilkes-Barre, PA; *U.S. Public*, pg. 1341
Chapman, Carl, Dir.-Steel Plant--Artco-Bell Corporation, Temple, TX; *U.S. Private*, pg. 86
Chapman, Carl, Mgr.-Pur.--Production Operators Inc., Houston, TX; *U.S. Public*, pg. 298
Chapman, Greg, Mgr.-Pur.--Superior Label Systems, Inc., Mason, OH; *U.S. Private*, pg. 1055
Chapman, Janie, Mgr.-Pur.--Wholesale Electronic Supply, Dallas, TX; *U.S. Private*, pg. 1174
Chapman, Vondel, Dir.-Pur.--Idaho Supreme Company, Firth, ID; *U.S. Private*, pg. 557
Chappel, Jim, Pur. Agent--Jones Chemicals, Inc., Le Roy, NY; *U.S. Private*, pg. 596
Chappell, Charles G., Asst. Sec.--Helix Technology Corp., Mansfield, MA; *U.S. Public*, pg. 808
Charney, Edward, Mgr.-Pur.--New Brunswick Scientific Co., Inc., Edison, NJ; *U.S. Public*, pg. 1169
Charpentier, Sandy, Dir.-Pur.--Robby Len Fashions, New York, NY; *U.S. Public*, pg. 121
Charrier, Jean Jacques, Mgr.-Pur.--Alcatel Cit (S.A.), Velizy-Villacoublay, France; *Int'l*, pg. 56
Charvat, Frank, Dir.-Pur.--Keithley Instruments, Inc., Cleveland, OH; *U.S. Public*, pg. 946

Chase, L. Curtis, Gen. Mgr.-Pur.--Steel Technologies Inc., Louisville, KY; U.S. Public, pg. 1513
Chasseur, Jack, Dir.-Pur.--Robert Bosch Corporation, Broadview, IL; Int'l, pg. 204
Chatt, Peter A., Mgr.-Pur. & Traffic--Caribe Express, Aguadilla, PR; U.S. Private, pg. 211
Cheesebro, Joe, Mgr.-Pur.--Mayville Engineering Co., Inc., Mayville, WI; U.S. Private, pg. 718
Chen, Austin, V.P.--Acer Incorporated, Taipei, Taiwan; Int'l, pg. 22
Cheng, T.M., Mgr.-Pur.--China Steel Structure Co., Ltd., Kao-hsiung, Taiwan; Int'l, pg. 286
Chesnutt, James, V.P.-Matls. Mngmt.--Harriet & Henderson Yarns, Inc., Henderson, NC; U.S. Private, pg. 504
Chestnut, Gary, Mgr.-Pur.--Ag Processing Inc., A Cooperative, Omaha, NE; U.S. Private, pg. 26
Chestnut, Kathie T., Sr. V.P.-Res. & Devel., Quality Assurance & Pur.--Wendy's International Inc., Dublin, OH; U.S. Public, pg. 1754
Cheves, Michael, Mgr.-Pur.--Pangburn Candy Company, Fort Worth, TX; U.S. Private, pg. 836
Chewning, Debbie, Dir.-Pur.--Coastal Wholesale, Inc., Kinston, NC; U.S. Private, pg. 248
Chicki, Steve, Dir.-Pur.--Steiner Co., Inc., Chicago, IL; U.S. Private, pg. 1039
Childerhose, W., Pur. Agent--S & C Electric Canada Ltd., Toronto, Canada; U.S. Private, pg. 954
Chin, Carol, V.P.-Pur.--Interval International Inc., Miami, FL; U.S. Public, pg. 320
Chittaro, Al, Dir.-Matls.--John Crane North America, Morton Grove, IL; Int'l, pg. 1339
Chiziniski, David, Mgr.-Pur.--NAPCO, Inc., Terryville, CT; U.S. Public, pg. 1592
Choi, Nam-Reul, Mgr.-Pur.--Dongseong Express Tourists Co., Ltd., Busan, Korea; Int'l, pg. 1292
Choiniere, Robert, Supvr.-Pur. & Suuport Servcies--The Berkshire Gas Company, Pittsfield, MA; U.S. Public, pg. 216
Chojnowski, John T., Mgr.-Pur.--EnviroTech PumpSystems, Salt Lake City, UT; Int'l, pg. 1489
Choronzuk, Bob, Mgr.-Pur.--Bar-S Foods Co., Phoenix, AZ; U.S. Private, pg. 114
Chowanec, Ernest, Dir.-Pur.--Juno Lighting, Inc., Des Plaines, IL; U.S. Public, pg. 935
Christel, Don, Pur. Agent--Miller-St. Nazianz, Inc., Saint Nazianz, WI; U.S. Private, pg. 748
Christian, Art, Mgr.-Pur.--American Econo-Therm, Tulsa, OK; U.S. Private, pg. 858
Christiano, Charles, Mgr.-Pur.--Bolt Technology Corporation, Norwalk, CT; U.S. Public, pg. 244
Christianson, Don, Mgr.-Pur.--Martin Door Mfg., Inc., Salt Lake City, UT; U.S. Private, pg. 708
Christil, Don, Mgr.-Pur.--Badger Farm Systems, Inc., Saint Nazianz, WI; U.S. Private, pg. 748
Christopher, Shawn, Dir.-Pur.--Magnasync Moviola Corporation, Hollywood, CA; U.S. Private, pg. 576
Christophersen, Gary, Mgr.-Pur.--Ripon Foods, Inc., Ripon, WI; U.S. Private, pg. 931
Chronowski, Larry, Dir.-Pur.--Dann Dee Display Fixtures, Niles, IL; U.S. Private, pg. 310
Chua, Jimmy C., V.P.-Logistics & Pur.--Philippine Airlines, Inc., Manila, Philippines; Int'l, pg. 1050
Church, Linda, Supvr.-Pur.--Alban Tractor Co. Inc., Baltimore, MD; U.S. Private, pg. 32
Chuu, C.H., Dir.-Matl. & Pur. Div.--Chinese Petroleum Corporation, Taipei, Taiwan; Int'l, pg. 286
Ciavardini, Andrew, Mgr.-Pur.--Rynone Manufacturing Corporation, Sayre, PA; U.S. Private, pg. 953
Cicaglao, Ross, V.P.-Pur.--Handy Store Fixtures, Inc., Newark, NJ; U.S. Private, pg. 499
Ciecko, Andrew S., V.P.-Pur.--MNP Corp., Utica, MI; U.S. Private, pg. 687
Cieslak, Henry E., Pur. Agent--Thermo Fibertek, Inc., Waltham, MA; U.S. Public, pg. 1593
Cillo, James, Dir.-Pur.--Hoogovens Aluminium Corp., Secaucus, NJ; Int'l, pg. 755
Cinealis, Richard J., Dir.-Corp. Pur.--Kohler Company, Kohler, WI; U.S. Private, pg. 630
Cioffi, John, Dir.-Pur.--Parlux Fragrances Inc., Fort Lauderdale, FL; U.S. Public, pg. 1264
Cioni, Richard W., Mgr.-Gen. Svcs./Matls.--Potomac Electric Power Company, Washington, DC; U.S. Public, pg. 1318
Ciringione, Dave, Mgr.-Pur.--Comtech PST Corp., Melville, NY; U.S. Public, pg. 425
Cirrani, Michelina, Mgr.-Pur.--Dri Mark Products, Inc., Port Washington, NY; U.S. Private, pg. 342
Cislo, Tim, Dir.-Pur.--Hall Financial Group, Inc., Dallas, TX; U.S. Private, pg. 495
Claney, C.A., Dir.-Pur.--Moore Europe, Lausanne, Switzerland; Int'l, pg. 889
Clark, Bruce, Dir.-Matls. Mngmt.--Hycor Biomedical, Inc., Irvine, CA; U.S. Public, pg. 851
Clark, Dennis, Pur. Agent--Porcelain Products, Carey, OH; U.S. Public, pg. 308
Clark, Diane, Dir.-Pur.--Cains Foods, L.P., Ayer, MA; U.S. Private, pg. 199
Clark, Joe, Pur. Agent--Advance Mechanical Systems, Inc., Mount Prospect, IL; U.S. Private, pg. 18
Clark, Melvin, V.P.-Pur.--Stanley Furniture Co. Inc., Stanleytown, VA; U.S. Public, pg. 1508
Clark, Sandra, Supervisor-Pur.--Holstein Association USA, Inc., Brattleboro, VT; U.S. Private, pg. 536
Clarke, Steve, Dir.-Pur.--Russell Harrington Cutlery Inc., Southbridge, MA; U.S. Private, pg. 551
Clarke, Wallace G., Dir.-Pur.--Mona Industries, Inc., Paterson, NJ; U.S. Private, pg. 756
Class, Richard, Dir.-Pur.--SuperValu, Inc.-Keene Div., Keene, NH; U.S. Public, pg. 1540
Clawson, Marci, Mgr.-Matls.--Utah Medical Products, Inc., Midvale, UT; U.S. Public, pg. 1700
Clear, Thomas, Dir.-Pur.--Noteworthy Industries Inc., Amsterdam, NY; U.S. Private, pg. 808
Cleaver, W., Pur. Agent--STV Group, Inc., Douglassville, PA; U.S. Public, pg. 1421
Clement, Bob, Dir.-Pur.--Barclay Furniture Company, Sherman, MS; U.S. Private, pg. 974
Clement, Martin, Dir.-Pur.--Regal Marine Industries Inc., Orlando, FL; U.S. Private, pg. 917
Clerke, William E., Dir.-Pur.--Cogentrix Incorporated, Charlotte, NC; U.S. Private, pg. 249
Clifford, Peter, Dir.-Pur.--Courier Corporation, North Chelmsford, MA; U.S. Public, pg. 453
Clowers, Sharon, Dir.-Pur. & Corp. Travel Planner--K & R Express Systems Inc., Hinsdale, IL; U.S. Private, pg. 602
Coats, Timothy W., V.P.-Pur.--The Pillsbury Company, Minneapolis, MN; Int'l, pg. 411
Cochran, Gayle, Dir.-Purchasing--Dearborn Gage Company, Garden City, MI; U.S. Private, pg. 319
Cochrane, James, Mgr.-Pur.--Overton Gear & Tool Corp., Addison, IL; U.S. Private, pg. 823
Cockfield, Matt, Pur. Agent--Reily Foods & Co., Knoxville, TN; U.S. Private, pg. 919
Cocks, Bruce, Mgr.-Pur. & Matl. Mgmnt.--Long Island Lighting Company, Hicksville, NY; U.S. Public, pg. 1013
Coelho, Cheryl, Mgr.-Matls.--E.C.D., Inc., Hillside, NJ; U.S. Private, pg. 353
Coggins, Wade A., Mgr.-Pur.--Today's Kids, Booneville, AR; U.S. Private, pg. 1020
Cohen, Alexander, Dir.-Pur.--Exolon-Esk Company, Tonawanda, NY; U.S. Public, pg. 600
Cohn, Norman, V.P.-Piece Goods--Jerell, Inc., Dallas, TX; U.S. Private, pg. 586
Coker, Larry, Dir.-Pur.--Texas Micro, Inc., Houston, TX; U.S. Public, pg. 1586
Colantuone, John N., V.P.-Matls.--The First Years Inc., Avon, MA; U.S. Public, pg. 642
Colasurdo, John, Dir.-Pur.--Giles & Ransome, Inc., Bensalem, PA; U.S. Private, pg. 453
Colby, L., Mgr.-Pur.--Melroe Company, Fargo, ND; U.S. Public, pg. 877
Cole, Bob, Dir.-Pur.--Indiana Glass Company, Cincinnati, OH; U.S. Public, pg. 976
Coleman, Al, Mgr.-Pur.--Ancra International LLC, Hawthorne, CA; U.S. Private, pg. 71
Coleman, James, Dir.-Pur.--Marcam Solutions, Inc., Newton, MA; U.S. Public, pg. 1042
Coleman, Monica, Pur. Agent-Services--SGD International Corp., Riverdale, NY; U.S. Private, pg. 957
Coley, Steve, Mgr.-Pur.--The Amalgamated Sugar Company LLC, Ogden, UT; U.S. Private, pg. 48
Colford, William D., V.P.-Support Svcs.--United Water Management & Services, Harrington Park, NJ; U.S. Public, pg. 1692
Colford, William D., V.P.-Pur.--United Water New Jersey, Inc., Harrington Park, NJ; U.S. Public, pg. 1692
Colling, John, Dir.-Pur. & Traffic--Rama Group of Companies, Cheektowaga, NY; U.S. Private, pg. 908
Collins, Jim, Mgr.-Pur.--Tidewater Inc., New Orleans, LA; U.S. Public, pg. 1608
Collins, Ken, Dir.-Matls.--Taylor Machine Works, Inc., Louisville, MS; U.S. Private, pg. 1070
Colmer, Buddy, Sr. V.P.--Brookshire Bros., Ltd., Lufkin, TX; U.S. Private, pg. 172
Colson, Carl, Pur. Agent--Kayem Foods, Inc., Chelsea, MA; U.S. Private, pg. 610
Comer, Kelley, Mgr.-Pur.--Hydraulics Div., Hutchinson, KS; U.S. Public, pg. 557
Compton, Doug, Asst. to V.P. of Pur.--Overland Transportation System, Inc., Indianapolis, IN; Int'l, pg. 1469
Concepcion, Nellie, Dir.-Pur.--Sterling Healthcare Group, Inc., Miami, FL; U.S. Public, pg. 608
Condict, Pete, V.P.-Pur.--Celebrity Incorporated, Tyler, TX; U.S. Public, pg. 319
Conditt, Don, Mgr.-Matls.--Electronics Div., San Diego, CA; U.S. Public, pg. 396
Cone, Stephen, Chief Fin. Officer--Southern Pilot Insurance Company, Greensboro, NC; Int'l, pg. 346
Coniglio, Phil, Dir.-Pur. & Facilities--Robotic Vision Systems, Inc., Hauppauge, NY; U.S. Public, pg. 1395
Conley, Morgan, Pur. Agent--Western Extrusions, Carrollton, TX; U.S. Private, pg. 1165
Conlift, Ken, Mgr.-Pur.--Brudi, Inc., Ridgefield, WA; U.S. Private, pg. 675
Conner, Brian, Mgr.-Pur.--Grease Monkey International Inc., Denver, CO; U.S. Public, pg. 759
Conner, R. Horace, Mgr.-Pur.--Luwa Bahnson, Inc., Winston Salem, NC; U.S. Private, pg. 682
Conner, W.M., Dir.-Pur.--McJunkin Corporation, Charleston, WV; U.S. Private, pg. 722
Connolly, E.J., Dir.-Buying--Somerfield Stores Ltd., Bristol, United Kingdom; Int'l, pg. 1280
Connolly, Edward J., Dir.-Buying--Somerfield PLC, Bristol, United Kingdom; Int'l, pg. 1280
Connolly, Jim, Dir.-Pur.--Tidelands Oil Production Co., Long Beach, CA; U.S. Private, pg. 1084
Connor, G., Dir.-Pur.--Peterson American Corp., Southfield, MI; U.S. Private, pg. 857
Conrad, Jean, Pur. Agent--Houston Fearless 76 Inc., Compton, CA; U.S. Private, pg. 542
Conrad, Thomas, Dir.-Pur.--Svedala Pumps & Process, Colorado Springs, CO; Int'l, pg. 1325
Conroy, Dan, Dir.-Pur.--Daubert Coated Products, Inc., Westchester, IL; U.S. Private, pg. 313
Conty, Ann Marie, Dir.-Pur.--American White Cross, Dayville, CT; U.S. Public, pg. 694
Cook, Greg, Pres. & Chief Oper. Officer--Cook Manufacturing Corporation, Duncan, OK; U.S. Private, pg. 272
Cook, Norman, Chief Oper. Officer & Pur. Dir.--Hang Ten, Montreal, Canada; Int'l, pg. 549
Cook, R.W., Pur. Agent--Svedala Industries Inc., Appleton, WI; Int'l, pg. 1325
Cook, Stephen, Chief Oper. Officer & Pur. Dir.--Kamik, Montreal, Canada; Int'l, pg. 549
Cook, Thomas E., Asst. V.P.--Commerce Bancshares, Inc., Kansas City, MO; U.S. Public, pg. 409
Cook, Tom, Mgr.-Pur.--Commerce Bank N.A., Kansas City, MO; U.S. Public, pg. 409
Cooper, William, Mgr.-Traffic & Pur. Agent--Mutual Welding Co., Ltd, Honolulu, HI; U.S. Private, pg. 770
Copley, Donald D., Supvr.-Pur.--Monarch Cement Co., Humboldt, KS; U.S. Public, pg. 1123
Corbi, Carlos, Mgr.-Pur.--Nuevo Federal S.A., Buenos Aires, Argentina; Int'l, pg. 990
Corbie, L., Mgr.-Pur.--Lever Brothers West Indies Ltd., Champs Fleurs, Trinidad & Tobago; Int'l, pg. 1437
Corich, Steve, Mgr.-Pur.--Rapid Mounting & Finishing, Union City, CA; U.S. Private, pg. 910
Cormier, Gary P., Mgr.-Pur.--Esselte Meto Canada, Mississauga, Canada; Int'l, pg. 461
Cormier, John, Dir.-Materials--Genetics Institute, Inc., Cambridge, MA; U.S. Public, pg. 79
Corradi, Kathryn, Dir.-Pur.--Lee Pharmaceuticals, South El Monte, CA; U.S. Public, pg. 984
Corrigan, Alan, Mgr.-Pur.--Wahl Clipper Corp., Sterling, IL; U.S. Private, pg. 1146
Corroon, Joe, Pur. Agent--Printed Circuit Corporation, Woburn, MA; U.S. Private, pg. 886
Cosgrove, Pat, V.P. & Pur. Agent--Ardell Industries Inc., Union, NJ; U.S. Private, pg. 597
Cost, John C., Mgr.-Pur.--Moore Products Co., Spring House, PA; U.S. Public, pg. 1128
Costedio, Warren, Pur. Agent--Raytheon Marine, Manchester, NH; U.S. Public, pg. 1366
Costello, Michael, Dir.-Pur.--The Bear Stearns Companies Inc., New York, NY; U.S. Public, pg. 197
Costello, Paul, Pur. Agent--Calgon Vestal Laboratories, Saint Louis, MO; U.S. Public, pg. 1515
Cotton, Vicki, Sr. V.P.-Pur.--Ingram Micro Inc., Santa Ana, CA; U.S. Public, pg. 878
Couch, James, Dir.-Pur.--Packerland Packing Co., Green Bay, WI; U.S. Private, pg. 833
Coughlin, Christopher, Mgr.-Pur.--LoJack Corporation, Dedham, MA; U.S. Public, pg. 1012
Coughlin, Michelle, Dir.-Pur.--Bradley Printing Company, Des Plaines, IL; U.S. Public, pg. 1778
Cougland, Tom, Dir.-Pur.--Driv-Lok, Inc., Sycamore, IL; U.S. Private, pg. 343
Court, Arthur, Dir.-Pur.--Reed & Barton Corporation, Taunton, MA; U.S. Private, pg. 916
Courtney, P., Mgr.-Pur.--B/E Aerospace Seating Products Group, Litchfield, CT; U.S. Public, pg. 159
Coutu, Dave, Dir.-Pur.--Banknorth Group Inc., Burlington, VT; U.S. Public, pg. 186
Cowan, David, Mgr.-Pur.--Pride International, Inc., Houston, TX; U.S. Public, pg. 1324
Cowles, Daniel S., Dir.-Pur.--Bluff City Distributing Co., Inc., Memphis, TN; U.S. Private, pg. 153
Cox, Jack, Mgr.-Pur.--IGI, Inc., Buena, NJ; U.S. Public, pg. 855
Cox, Ray, Mgr.-Pur.--E.C. Barton & Company, Jonesboro, AR; U.S. Private, pg. 119
Cox, Stephen, V.P.-Corp. Pur.--Montgomery KONE Inc., Moline, IL; Int'l, pg. 746
Coxall, John A., V.P.-Pur.--Dimeo Construction Company, Providence, RI; U.S. Private, pg. 333
Coy, James, Mgr.-Pur.--EXAR Corporation, Fremont, CA; U.S. Public, pg. 597
Coyle, Jack, Mgr.-Pur.--Keen Compressed Gas Co., Wilmington, DE; U.S. Private, pg. 611
Craig, Dwight, Dir.-Pur.--Dynamic Metal Products Company, Manchester, CT; U.S. Private, pg. 350
Craig, Kirkley, Mgr.-Pur.--Teleflex Fluid Systems Inc., Suffield, CT; U.S. Public, pg. 1569
Cramer, Ron, Pur. Agent--Monrovia Nursery Co., Azusa, CA; U.S. Private, pg. 757
Crane, Larry, Mgr.-Pur.--Sub-Zero Freezer Co., Inc., Madison, WI; U.S. Private, pg. 1048
Crank, Thomas, Dir.-Pur.--Maritz Inc., Fenton, MO; U.S. Private, pg. 703
Cranor, Timothy W., Sr. V.P.-Pur.--Interstate Bakeries Corporation, Kansas City, MO; U.S. Public, pg. 909
Crehan, Kathy, Pur. Agent--ESA, Inc., Chelmsford, MA; U.S. Private, pg. 354
Crenwelge, Lorence, Mgr.-Pur.--Mooney Aircraft Corporation, Kerrville, TX; U.S. Private, pg. 759
Crews, Ron, Pur. Agent--Hooker Furniture Corporation, Martinsville, VA; U.S. Private, pg. 538
Crigger, Dick, Dir.-Pur.--Gebo Distributing Co., Inc., Plainview, TX; U.S. Private, pg. 442
Crimmins, Pete, Pur. Agent--Correct Craft, Inc., Orlando, FL; U.S. Private, pg. 276
Critzer, Jim, Dir.-Pur.--National Semiconductor Corporation, Santa Clara, CA; U.S. Public, pg. 1159
Crocker, William G., Mgr.-Pur.--Lee Company, Westbrook, CT; U.S. Private, pg. 657
Croke, Nancy, Mgr.-Pur.--Comdisco, Inc., Rosemont, IL; U.S. Public, pg. 407
Croner, William N., Dir.-Pur.--McGraw-Hill Continuing Education Center, Washington, DC; U.S. Public, pg. 1070
Cropper, James, Dir.-Pur.--Dettra Flag Company, Oaks, PA; U.S. Private, pg. 328
Cross, Nicholas, Pur.-Agent--Federal Chicago Corporation, North Chicago, IL; U.S. Private, pg. 398
Crossland, Paul, Dir.-Pur.--Bergelectric Corporation, Los Angeles, CA; U.S. Private, pg. 135
Crosthwait, Kent, V.P.-Sls. & Pur.--Neill-LaVielle Supply Co., Louisville, KY; U.S. Private, pg. 790
Crow, Tommy, Dir.-Pur.--Delta Woodside Industries, Inc., Greenville, SC; U.S. Public, pg. 497
Crowley, Diane N., Corp. Sec.--Superior Auctioneers & Marketing, Inc., San Antonio, TX; U.S. Private, pg. 1054
Crumley, Ron, Dir.-Pur.--J.L. Lester & Son, Inc., Rockmart, GA; U.S. Private, pg. 660
Crump, Don, Mgr.-Pur.--Gibbs Die Casting Corp., Henderson, KY; U.S. Private, pg. 628
Crumpton, Joe, Dir.-MIS, Matls. & Facilities--Amtech Corporation, Dallas, TX; U.S. Public, pg. 105

Cruze, Frank, Mgr.-Pur. & Distr.--Bufkor, Inc., Clearwater, FL; *U.S. Private*, pg. 179
Cuellar, Carmen, Dir.-Pur.--El Chico Restaurants, Inc., Dallas, TX; *U.S. Private*, pg. 283
Cujawa, James M., Mgr.-Pur.--Poly-Seal Corporation, Baltimore, MD; *U.S. Private*, pg. 875
Cullon, Mark, Mgr.-Matls.--Powell Electrical Mfg. Co., Houston, TX; *U.S. Public*, pg. 1319
Culpepper, Jim, Asst. V.P.-Pur. & Inventory--ICO, Inc., Houston, TX; *U.S. Public*, pg. 853
Cunningham, Ronald, Mgr.-Pur.--Encore Computer Corporation, Fort Lauderdale, FL; *U.S. Public*, pg. 580
Curran, Camron, Mgr.-Pur.--Wheel Tronic Inc., Mississauga, Canada; *U.S. Public*, pg. 1481
Curran, Tom, Mgr.-Pur.--Derby Cycle Corporation, Kent, WA; *Int'l*, pg. 394
Curtis, Jim, Dir.-Pur.--Marshall Erdman and Associates, Inc., Madison, WI; *U.S. Private*, pg. 380
Curtis, Tim, Pur. Agent--Mallory, Inc., Carson City, NV; *U.S. Private*, pg. 698
Cushatt, Frank, V.P.-Terminal Opers.--Fleischli Oil Company, Inc., Cheyenne, WY; *U.S. Private*, pg. 410
Cust, Allen, Pur. Agent--H.E. Sargent, Inc., Stillwater, ME; *U.S. Private*, pg. 966
Custer, Janice, Mgr.-Plant--Laird & Company, Eatontown, NJ; *U.S. Private*, pg. 642
Czaja, Wolfgang, Dir.-Materials Pur.--Mercedes-Benz AG, Stuttgart, Germany; *Int'l*, pg. 368
Czernia, Norbert, Pur. Agent--Midway Products Corporation, Monroe, MI; *U.S. Private*, pg. 744
Czerniejewski, Lori, Exec. Asst.--SRDS, Des Plaines, IL; *U.S. Private*, pg. 958
Czysz, Laura A., Office Mgr.--Federal Farm Credit Banks Funding Corporation, Jersey City, NJ; *U.S. Private*, pg. 398
D'Amico, Joseph, V.P.-Matls.--Superior Industries International, Inc., Van Nuys, CA; *U.S. Public*, pg. 1539
D'Antuono, John, Mgr.-Pur.--Woodward-Clyde Federal Services, Denver, CO; *U.S. Public*, pg. 1657
Dabbs, Nathan, Pur. Agent--Cogsdill Tool Products, Inc., Lugoff, SC; *U.S. Private*, pg. 250
Dahl, Gus, V.P.-Materials Mngmt.--Chemtex International, Inc., New York, NY; *Int'l*, pg. 872
Dahlberg, Christer, Sr. V.P.-Pur.--Svedala Industri AB, Malmo, Sweden; *Int'l*, pg. 1323
Daigle, Bill, Pur. Asst.--Megapulse, Inc., Bedford, MA; *U.S. Private*, pg. 729
Daigle, Brynn, Mgr.-Pur.--Tetra Technologies, Woodlands, TX; *U.S. Public*, pg. 1582
Dairy, Bill, Dir.-Pur.--Brush Wellman Inc., Cleveland, OH; *U.S. Public*, pg. 266
Dakes, Robert, Mgr.-Pur.--Gould Instrument Systems, Inc., Valley View, OH; *U.S. Public*, pg. 1592
Daley, Bob, Dir.-Pur.--Wisconsin Energy Corporation, Milwaukee, WI; *U.S. Public*, pg. 1773
Dalton, R. Phillip, V.P. & Dir.-Pur.--Bassett Furniture Industries, Incorporated, Bassett, VA; *U.S. Public*, pg. 193
Daly, Christopher W., Pur. Agent--Berkshire Life Insurance Company, Pittsfield, MA; *U.S. Private*, pg. 136
Damron, Gordon, Mgr.-Pur.--Citizens National Bank, Evansville, IN; *U.S. Public*, pg. 281
Dandie, R., Exec. Gen. Mgr.-Purchasing--Qantas Airways Ltd., Mascot, Australia; *Int'l*, pg. 1074
Danziger, L., Dir.-Pur.--Isfel Company, Inc., Rahway, NJ; *U.S. Private*, pg. 576
Darlington, John, Mgr.-Pur.--Scottish Widows' Fund & Life Assurance Society, Edinburgh, United Kingdom; *Int'l*, pg. 1212
Darmanian, John, Mgr.-Pur.--The Keyes Company Realtors, Miami, FL; *U.S. Private*, pg. 618
Darnold, John, Dir.-Pur.--Justin Boot Company, Fort Worth, TX; *U.S. Public*, pg. 937
Darrold, Peck, Pur. Agent--Bedford Industries, Inc., Worthington, MN; *U.S. Private*, pg. 129
Darrow, Terry, Mgr.-Pur.--McGill Manufacturing Company, Inc., Valparaiso, IN; *U.S. Public*, pg. 573
Dauscher, Jim, Dir.-Pur.--Modern Concrete Septic Tank Company, Ottsville, PA; *U.S. Private*, pg. 754
Dautenhahn, Roland, Mgr.-Pur.--Feodor Burgmann Dichtungswerke GmbH, Wolfratshausen, Germany; *Int'l*, pg. 233
Davenport, Hal, Mgr.-Pur.--Electron Corp., Littleton, CO; *U.S. Private*, pg. 370
Davenport, Sam, Mgr.-Pur.--Temco Fireplace Products, Inc., Nashville, TN; *U.S. Public*, pg. 1576
Davi, S., Pur. Agent--Sargent Manufacturing Company, New Haven, CT; *Int'l*, pg. 18
Davidson, Mason, Dir.-Pur.--West Texas Utilities Co., Abilene, TX; *U.S. Public*, pg. 324
Davidson, Neil, Mng. Dir.-Dairy--Northern Foods plc, Hull, United Kingdom; *Int'l*, pg. 967
Davidson, Robert R., Mgr.-Mfg. & Pur. Agent--Oildyne, Minneapolis, MN; *U.S. Public*, pg. 411
Davis, Bruce, V.P.-Global Pur. & Logistics--Witco Corporation, Greenwich, CT; *U.S. Public*, pg. 1773
Davis, Connie, V.P.-Corp. Pur.--La Petite Academy Inc., Overland Park, KS; *U.S. Private*, pg. 640
Davis, David, Mgr.-Pur.--Holiday RV Superstores West, Inc., Sacramento, CA; *U.S. Public*, pg. 830
Davis, Diana, Dir.-Pur.--Tri-K Industries, Inc., Northvale, NJ; *U.S. Private*, pg. 1100
Davis, Glen, Mgr.-Pur.--Howell Packaging, Burlington, Canada; *Int'l*, pg. 417
Davis, Glenn, Mgr.-Pur.--Red Devil Inc., Union, NJ; *U.S. Private*, pg. 915
Davis, Gordon F., V.P.-Pur.--Sawhill Tubular Div., Sharon, PA; *U.S. Public*, pg. 131
Davis, Greg, Mgr.-Pur.--BLH Electronics, Inc., Canton, MA; *Int'l*, pg. 1289
Davis, Harvey, Dir.-Pur.--Orange-Co., Inc., Bartow, FL; *U.S. Public*, pg. 1229
Davis, Jim, Mgr.-Pur.--The Accor Group, Inc., Corona Del Mar, CA; *Int'l*, pg. 21
Davis, John, Mgr.-Pur.--Sunnen Products Company, Saint Louis, MO; *U.S. Private*, pg. 1053
Davis, Kathy, Mgr.-Pur.--The Washington Water Power Company, Spokane, WA; *U.S. Public*, pg. 1744
Davis, Lynn, V.P.-Sls., Mktg., Pur. & Mfg.--Lithotype Company, Inc., South San Francisco, CA; *U.S. Private*, pg. 670
Davis, Mike, Pur. Agent--Jacobsen Manufacturing, Inc., Safety Harbor, FL; *U.S. Private*, pg. 580
Davis, Ron, V.P.-Pur.--Edwards Baking Co., Norcross, GA; *U.S. Private*, pg. 365
Davis, Ruth, Dir.-Pur.--Systems & Computer Technology Corporation, Malvern, PA; *U.S. Public*, pg. 1552
Dawson, Rita, Dir.-Pur.--Georgia-Bonded Fibers, Inc., Newark, NJ; *U.S. Public*, pg. 734
Day, Dean, Dir.-Pur.--Alza Corporation, Palo Alto, CA; *U.S. Public*, pg. 62
de Castelnav, Nicolas, Head-Pur. Dept.--Credit Lyonnais S.A., Paris, France; *Int'l*, pg. 343
De Dios, Julian B., Grp. Mgr.-Pur.--EEI Corporation, Manila, Philippines; *Int'l*, pg. 425
de Groot, G., Mgr.-Pur.--Moore Nederland B.V., Amsterdam, Netherlands; *Int'l*, pg. 890
De Nardis, Pietro, Dir.-Pur.--Candy S.p.A., Brugherio, Italy; *Int'l*, pg. 259
de Ponti, L., Mgr.-Pur.--Oce-van der Grinten N.V., Venlo, Netherlands; *Int'l*, pg. 993
De Saenz, Marianne, Mgr.-Pur.--Aviateca, Guatemala, Guatemala; *Int'l*, pg. 102
De Witt, R., Mgr.-Opers.--Tosas (Pty) Ltd., Wadeville, South Africa; *Int'l*, pg. 1197
Deal, Mike, Mgr.-Pur.--Alba-Waldensian, Inc., Valdese, NC; *U.S. Public*, pg. 35
DeAlmeida, Tony, Mgr.-Pur.--Interbath, Inc., City of Industry, CA; *U.S. Private*, pg. 566
Dean, Doug, Mgr.-Bldg. Svcs.--Medical Assurance, Inc., Birmingham, AL; *U.S. Public*, pg. 1079
Dean, Gary, V.P.-Matls.--Integrated Device Technology, Inc., Santa Clara, CA; *U.S. Public*, pg. 884
Dean, Terry, Dir.-Pur.--Reliable Castings Corporation, Cincinnati, OH; *U.S. Private*, pg. 920
Deas, Robert, Dir.-Pur.--Miller & Co., Selma, AL; *U.S. Private*, pg. 746
DeBelly, Dean, Mgr.-Pur. & Engrng.--Southern Minnesota Beet Sugar Cooperative, Renville, MN; *U.S. Private*, pg. 1016
DeBruin, D., Dir.-Pur.--Mercon Steel Structures B.V., Gorinchem, Netherlands; *Int'l*, pg. 858
Decker, Carol, Mgr.-Pur.--Thermoplastics, Inc., Mishawaka, IN; *U.S. Public*, pg. 1590
Decker, Kathy, Dir.-Pur.--Prime Technology, Inc., Grand Rapids, MI; *U.S. Private*, pg. 884
Decker, Richard, V.P.-Pur.--Dealers Electrical Supply Co., Waco, TX; *U.S. Private*, pg. 318
Decker, Tim, Mgr.-Pur.--Kennedy Valve, Elmira, NY; *U.S. Private*, pg. 725
Decre, Yvon, V.P.-Pur.--Docks de France S.A., Tours, France; *Int'l*, pg. 98
Dedic, Lori, Mgr.-Pur.--KineticSystems Corporation, Lockport, IL; *U.S. Private*, pg. 620
Deeds, Art, Mgr.-Corp. Pur.--Monaco Coach Corporation, Coburg, OR; *U.S. Public*, pg. 1123
Deeds, Art, Mgr.-Pur.--Monaco Coach Corporation, Coburg, OR; *U.S. Public*, pg. 1123
Deeny, Alice, Mgr.-Pur.--Philadelphia Reserve Supply Company, Croydon, PA; *U.S. Private*, pg. 861
Defilipo, Bob, Dir.-Pur.--Hunter Marine Corporation, Alachua, FL; *U.S. Private*, pg. 549
Defonte, Robert G., Sr. V.P.-Mdsg. & Sec.--E & B Marine Incorporated, Edison, NJ; *U.S. Public*, pg. 1756
Degilio, Helen, Dir.-Pur.--S L C Graphics, LP, Pittston, PA; *U.S. Private*, pg. 955
Deguchi, Kyuzo, Dir.--Duskin Co., Ltd., Osaka, Japan; *Int'l*, pg. 422
Dehler, Bruno, Dir.-Pur.--BMW (US) Holding Corporation, Woodcliff Lake, NJ; *Int'l*, pg. 177
Deiner, Debbie, Mgr.-Pur.--Comtech Antenna Systems, Inc., Saint Cloud, FL; *U.S. Public*, pg. 425
Del Moral, Anthony, Dir.-Pur.--Analogic Corporation, Peabody, MA; *U.S. Public*, pg. 109
Del Priore, Jorge, Mgr.-Pur. & Import--Fate S.A., San Fernando, Argentina; *Int'l*, pg. 478
Del Sasso, John M., V.P.-Distr.--Lawson Products, Inc., Des Plaines, IL; *U.S. Public*, pg. 980
Delea, Guy, Mgr.-Pur.--Imperia Bros., Inc., Pelham Manor, NY; *U.S. Private*, pg. 558
Delin, Richard L., Mgr.-Information Services--BPA International, New York, NY; *U.S. Private*, pg. 107
Della Rocca, Frank, Dir.-Pur.--Saratoga Equine Sports Center, Saratoga Springs, NY; *U.S. Private*, pg. 965
Deloache, Lee, Sr. Exec. Dir.-Pur. & Bldgs.--Magellan Health Services, Inc., Atlanta, GA; *U.S. Public*, pg. 1033
Delperdang-Weber, Cindy, Pur. Agent--Advantage Companies, Inc., Wichita, KS; *U.S. Private*, pg. 22
DeMarco, Lou, Mgr.-Pur.--Beacon Container Corporation, Birdsboro, PA; *U.S. Private*, pg. 125
Demas, J., Dir.-Pur.--Periphonics Corp., Bohemia, NY; *U.S. Public*, pg. 1278
Demastus, Fred E., Mgr.-Pur.--ComSonics, Inc., Harrisonburg, VA; *U.S. Private*, pg. 260
Dembiczak, Anita, V.P.-Pur.--Sun Hill Industries, Inc., Stamford, CT; *U.S. Private*, pg. 1051
Demenna, Gary, Pur. Agent--Oxford Health Plans Inc., Norwalk, CT; *U.S. Public*, pg. 1238
Demne, Marv, Mgr.-Pur.--SL Montevideo Technology, Inc., Montevideo, MN; *U.S. Public*, pg. 1419
den Hartog, A., Mgr.-Pur. & Sls. Admin.--Bakery Ingredients Division, Delft, Netherlands; *Int'l*, pg. 1142
Denbaas, David, Dir.-Pur.--Comerica Incorporated, Detroit, MI; *U.S. Public*, pg. 408
Denburg, Ronnie, Dir.-Pur. & Environmental Compliance--Barton Press, Inc., West Orange, NJ; *U.S. Private*, pg. 120
Denges, James, V.P.-Mktg. & Pur.--Central Grocers Co-op, Franklin Park, IL; *U.S. Private*, pg. 223
Dennard, Richard L., V.P.-Pur.--Pillowtex Corporation, Dallas, TX; *U.S. Public*, pg. 1296
Denning, Robert W., V.P.-Pur. & Distr.--Motion Industries, Inc., Irondale, AL; *U.S. Public*, pg. 732
Denny, Gregg, Mgr.-Pur.--Oneida Ltd., Oneida, NY; *U.S. Public*, pg. 1225
Deowdhat, Sukree, Mgr.-Pur.--Holiday RV Superstores, Inc., Orlando, FL; *U.S. Public*, pg. 829
Depew, J.E., V.P. & Dir.-Pur.--ICI Paints, Cleveland, OH; *Int'l*, pg. 664
Derico, Robert, Mgr.-Pur.--Dotronix, Inc., New Brighton, MN; *U.S. Public*, pg. 520
Dermyer, William, V.P.--Omaha Public Power District, Omaha, NE; *U.S. Private*, pg. 815
DeRossett, Dick, Mgr.-Pur.--Dacon Electronics Plc., Hemel Hempstead, United Kingdom; *U.S. Public*, pg. 395
Derry, Malcolm, Dir.-Pur./PC Peripherals--Dixons Group plc, Hemel Hempstead, United Kingdom,; *Int'l*, pg. 413
Derryberry, William D., Dir.-Admin. Services--DynCorp, Reston, VA; *U.S. Private*, pg. 351
DeRune, Julie, Mgr.-Pur.--Recreational Equipment, Inc., Kent, WA; *U.S. Private*, pg. 914
Derush, Pat, Dir.-Pur.--Quiksilver, Inc., Costa Mesa, CA; *U.S. Public*, pg. 1353
DeSena, Darleen, Mgr.-Pur.--Dimensional Merchandising, Inc., Wharton, NJ; *U.S. Private*, pg. 333
Desmarais, Ann, V.P.-Materials--Worcester Controls Corp., Marlborough, MA; *Int'l*, pg. 128
Desrochers, Jean-Claude, V.P.-Mdsg. & Procurement/ Provigo & Loeb--Provigo Distribution, Montreal, Canada; *Int'l*, pg. 1073
desTombe, Frans, Mgr.-Supply & Distr.--Henkel Canada Ltd., Mississauga, Canada; *Int'l*, pg. 612
Detjer, Jack, Mgr.-Pur.--Power Distribution Div., Lincoln, IL; *U.S. Public*, pg. 557
Detota, Tony, Mgr.-Pur.--Allen Telecom Inc., Solon, OH; *U.S. Public*, pg. 45
Detrick, Terrell, Mgr.-Pur.--Industrial Construction, Inc., Idaho Falls, ID; *U.S. Private*, pg. 560
Detweiler, Dale, Mgr.-Pur.--Harleysville Group, Harleysville, PA; *U.S. Public*, pg. 786
Deuel, Brian, Dir.-Pur.--Pridgeon & Clay, Inc., Grand Rapids, MI; *U.S. Private*, pg. 883
Devens, Mike, Dir.-Pur.--Kaufman and Broad of San Diego, Inc., San Diego, CA; *U.S. Public*, pg. 945
Devine, William, Dir.-Pur.--Essex Chemical Corporation, Clifton, NJ; *U.S. Public*, pg. 523
DeVirgilio, C.J., Gen. Mgr.-Corp. Services--Latrobe Special Products Div., Latrobe, PA; *U.S. Public*, pg. 1617
Devore, Rob, Pur. Agent--Massman Construction Company, Kansas City, MO; *U.S. Private*, pg. 713
Dew, Roger, Mgr.-Pur.--Dixons Group plc, Hemel Hempstead, United Kingdom,; *Int'l*, pg. 413
DeWalt, Sherry, Pur. Officer--AMCORE Bank N.A., Rock River Valley, Sterling, IL; *U.S. Public*, pg. 64
Dewing, Wanda, Mgr.-Purchasing--Montana-Dakota Utilities Co., Bismarck, ND; *U.S. Public*, pg. 1025
Dey, Tom, Mgr.-Pur.--Conap Inc., Olean, NY; *U.S. Private*, pg. 261
Diamond, Lawrence, Chm. Bd., Pres., Chief Exec. & Chief Oper. Officer & Dir.-Pur.--Triangle Marketing Corp., New York, NY; *U.S. Private*, pg. 1102
Diaz, Myriam, Mgr.-Pur.--Microsemi Corporation, Santa Ana, CA; *U.S. Public*, pg. 1107
Dickerson, Robin C., Mgr.-Pur.--Metal Masters Foodservice Equipment, Clayton, DE; *U.S. Private*, pg. 734
DiDonato, Joe, Dir.-Pur.-Aerospace--Tracor, Inc., Austin, TX; *U.S. Public*, pg. 1627
Diener, P., Mgr.-Pur.--H.A. Schlatter AG, Schlieren, Switzerland; *Int'l*, pg. 1205
DiGeorge, Michael, Dir.-Pur.--Arinc Inc. (Consolidated), Annapolis, MD; *U.S. Private*, pg. 81
DiGeorge, Michael, Mgr.-Pur.--Aeronautical Radio, Inc., Annapolis, MD; *U.S. Private*, pg. 81
DiGrassi, Paul, Mgr.-Pur.--People's Choice TV Corp., Shelton, CT; *U.S. Public*, pg. 1274
Dilisio, Bernie, Mgr.-Pur.--CEM Corporation, Matthews, NC; *U.S. Public*, pg. 277
Dilley, L.D., V.P.-Opers. & Matls.--North American Refractories Company, Cleveland, OH; *U.S. Private*, pg. 803
Dillon, James, Dir.-Pur.--Augat, Inc., Wiring Systems & Components Group, Montgomery, AL; *U.S. Public*, pg. 1598
Dillon, Sherry, Pur. Agent--Xerxes Corporation, Minneapolis, MN; *U.S. Private*, pg. 1194
Dimambro, Christine, Mgr.-Pur.--Hershey Pasta and Grocery Group, Hershey, PA; *U.S. Public*, pg. 812
DiMatteo, Don, V.P.-Pur.--DeVault Foods, Devault, PA; *U.S. Private*, pg. 329
DiMiglio, Lucile, Dir.-Personnel & Pur.--Norwalk Powdered Metals, Inc., Norwalk, CT; *U.S. Private*, pg. 808
Dindinger, Glen, Dir.-Pur.--Tetra Tech NUS, Inc., Gaithersburg, MD; *U.S. Public*, pg. 1582
Dines, Richard, Mgr.-Pur.--Latrobe Brewing Co., Latrobe, PA; *Int'l*, pg. 680
Dinges, Jerry, Dir.-Pur.--Union City Body Company, L.P., Union City, IN; *U.S. Private*, pg. 1118
DiNicola, Al, Mgr.-Materials--DSM Sheffield Plastics, Sheffield, MA; *Int'l*, pg. 354
Dircks, Kevin, Dir.-Pur. & Replenishment--Edward Don & Company, North Riverside, IL; *U.S. Private*, pg. 339
Dismukes, Alan, Buyer--Anderson Wholesale Company, Muskogee, OK; *U.S. Private*, pg. 73
Disoh, Dick, Mgr.-Pur.--Rockford Products Corp., Rockford, IL; *U.S. Private*, pg. 938
Ditto, Tom E., Pur. Agent--Kasper Machine Company, Madison Heights, MI; *U.S. Private*, pg. 608
Dittrich, Michael, Pur. Agent--Hopple Plastics, Inc., Florence, KY; *U.S. Private*, pg. 538
Djahanbani, Anush, Mgr.-Opers. & Pur.--Ronson Corporation, Somerset, NJ; *U.S. Public*, pg. 1405

Dlugos, Richard, Pur. Agent--Connecticut Drive Shaft, Inc., Milford, CT; *U.S. Private*, pg. 263

Do Dios, Julian B., Grp. Mgr.-Pur.--EEI-Construction Div., Manila, Philippines; *Int'l*, pg. 426

Dobbs, D., Dir.-Pur.--Remcor Products Co., Glendale Heights, IL; *Int'l*, pg. 646

Dobbs, David L., Exec. V.P.-Pur.--Shoney's, Inc., Nashville, TN; *U.S. Public*, pg. 1467

Dobson, Thomas, Pur. Agent--Airline Hydraulics Corporation, Bensalem, PA; *U.S. Private*, pg. 29

Doddridge, Debbie, Mgr.-Pur.--Vencor, Inc., Louisville, KY; *U.S. Public*, pg. 1711

Doe, Randy, Dir.-Pur.--Pullman Industries, Inc., Pullman, MI; *U.S. Private*, pg. 894

Doedoerlein, Debbie, Dir.-Pur.--NicSand, Inc., Cleveland, OH; *U.S. Private*, pg. 799

Doganiero, Richard, Mgr.-Pur.--Argo-Tech Corporation, Cleveland, OH; *U.S. Private*, pg. 81

Doherty, Frank, Dir.-Pur.--Comptek Research, Inc., Buffalo, NY; *U.S. Public*, pg. 419

Dohmen-Torres, Cindy, Dir.-Pur.--The F. Dohmen Company, Germantown, WI; *U.S. Private*, pg. 338

Dolan, Ted, V.P.-Pur.--Ames Safety Envelope Company, Inc., Somerville, MA; *U.S. Private*, pg. 66

Domandle, Bernie, Pur. Agent--Coleman Powermate, Inc., Omaha, NE; *U.S. Private*, pg. 691

Domanski, Fred, Dir.-Pur.--Snyder Tank Corp., Buffalo, NY; *U.S. Private*, pg. 1011

Donahue, Faye, Dir.-Procurement--Printronix, Inc., Irvine, CA; *U.S. Public*, pg. 1329

Donham, Paul, Dir.-Pur.--Quik Print Inc., Wichita, KS; *U.S. Private*, pg. 421

Donley, Richard, Supvr.-Pur.--Safety-Kleen Corp., Elgin, IL; *U.S. Public*, pg. 1425

Donnelly, John, Mgr.-Pur.--Aydin Raytor Div., Montgomeryville, PA; *U.S. Public*, pg. 158

Donnelly, Lisa, Mgr.-Pur.--M & C Specialties Company, Southampton, PA; *U.S. Private*, pg. 684

Donnenberg, Joel, V.P.-Pur.--Blackman Uhler Chemical Co., Spartanburg, SC; *U.S. Public*, pg. 1548

Donohoe, Robert, Buyer-Indus. Prods. Grp.--De-Sta-Co, A Dover Resources Co., Troy, MI; *U.S. Public*, pg. 521

Donohue, Ryan, Mgr.-Pur.--Stebbins Engineering & Mfg. Co., Watertown, NY; *U.S. Private*, pg. 1037

Dooley, Ron, Pur. Agent--Danuser Machine Co., Fulton, MO; *U.S. Private*, pg. 310

Doorley, Tom, Dir.-Pur.--Cres-Cor, Cleveland, OH; *U.S. Private*, pg. 288

Doran, Cork, Mgr.-Adv. & Office Mgr.--Ace Doran Hauling & Rigging Company, Cincinnati, OH; *U.S. Private*, pg. 340

Doran, Mike, Dir.-Pur.--County Seat Stores, Inc., Dallas, TX; *U.S. Private*, pg. 279

Dorio, Gail, Dir.-Pur.--Schott Brothers, Inc., Perth Amboy, NJ; *U.S. Private*, pg. 972

Dorn, Gordon H., Dir.-Pur.--Chr. Hansen, Inc., Milwaukee, WI; *Int'l*, pg. 288

Dorn, Rick, Dir.-Pur.--Information Systems & Network Corporation, Bethesda, MD; *U.S. Private*, pg. 561

Dorsey, Harold G., Mgr.-Information Systems & Pur.--O.I. Corporation, College Station, TX; *U.S. Public*, pg. 1208

Dossier, David, Mgr.-Pur.--Lowrance Electronics, Inc., Tulsa, OK; *U.S. Public*, pg. 1015

Douglas, Judy, Mgr.-Pur.--KCL Corporation, Shelbyville, IN; *U.S. Private*, pg. 603

Douthitt, Jerry D., Pur. Agent--BWI Kartridg Pak, Davenport, IA; *Int'l*, pg. 130

Dove, Webster, Dir.-Pur.--Revere Electric Supply Co., Chicago, IL; *U.S. Private*, pg. 926

Dover, Paul, Dir.-Pur.--Parkdale Mills, Gastonia, NC; *U.S. Private*, pg. 840

Dowdy, David A., Pur. Agent--Tinius Olsen Testing Machine Co., Inc., Willow Grove, PA; *U.S. Private*, pg. 1088

Doyle, Gene, Pur. Agent--Bituminous Casualty Corp., Rock Island, IL; *U.S. Public*, pg. 1218

Doyle, J., Controller--Asahi Glass America, Inc., New York, NY; *Int'l*, pg. 84

Doyle, Jim, Mgr.-Corp. Pur.--Gold Kist, Inc., Atlanta, GA; *U.S. Private*, pg. 459

Doyle, John B., Mgr.-Materials--RELA, Inc., Boulder, CO; *U.S. Public*, pg. 401

Draffin, Ken, Pur. Agent--Wurzburg, Inc., Memphis, TN; *U.S. Private*, pg. 1192

Drain, C.L., Dir.-Pur.--Storage Technology Corporation, Louisville, CO; *U.S. Public*, pg. 1522

Drake, D., Mgr.-Pur.--Quality Bakers New Zealand Ltd., Auckland, New Zealand; *Int'l*, pg. 556

Drake, Ronald C., Pur. Agent--H & H Tube & Manufacturing Co., Vanderbilt, MI; *U.S. Private*, pg. 489

Drane, Alan, Pur. Agent--Transamerican Natural Gas Corporation, Houston, TX; *U.S. Private*, pg. 1096

Drane, Lupe, Mgr.-Pur.--Ameron International Corporation, Pasadena, CA; *U.S. Public*, pg. 98

Drasher, Carl, Mgr.-Pur.--Conestoga Wood Specialties Corp., East Earl, PA; *U.S. Private*, pg. 262

Dredske, Doug, Mgr.-Matls. Mngmt.--TriEnda Corporation, Portage, WI; *U.S. Private*, pg. 1103

Dreesen, P.D., Dir.-Pur.--Science Applications International Corp., San Diego, CA; *U.S. Private*, pg. 975

Dresch, Peggy, Mgr.-Pur.--Ancira Enterprises Inc., San Antonio, TX; *U.S. Private*, pg. 71

Dressler, Donald, Dir.-Pur.--International Game Technology, Reno, NV; *U.S. Public*, pg. 900

Drew, Robert, Dir.-Pur.--Dean Foods Company, Franklin Park, IL; *U.S. Public*, pg. 489

Drewes, Robert W., V.P.-Procurement & Mfg.--Raytheon Company, Lexington, MA; *U.S. Public*, pg. 1364

Driver, Daryle, V.P.-Matls. Mngmt.--Management Dynamics, New Providence, NJ; *U.S. Public*, pg. 1040

Driver, Steve, Dir.-Corp. Pur.--Shuford Mills, Inc., Hickory, NC; *U.S. Private*, pg. 996

Drotos, Steve, Dir.-Pur.--Flambeau Products Corp., Middlefield, OH; *U.S. Private*, pg. 409

Drumm, Patricia, Mgr.-Pur.--Whitney Holding Corporation, New Orleans, LA; *U.S. Public*, pg. 1766

Drumm, Patricia, Dir.-Pur.--Whitney National Bank, New Orleans, LA; *U.S. Public*, pg. 1766

Ducharme, Lee, Mgr.-Pur.--Semiconductor Equipment Division, Beverly, MA; *U.S. Public*, pg. 557

Duckham, William E., Dir.-Pur.--Porta Systems Corp., Syosset, NY; *U.S. Public*, pg. 1317

Ducklow, Deb, Mgr.-Pur.--St. Croix Press, Inc., New Richmond, WI; *U.S. Private*, pg. 960

Dudek, R.T., V.P. & Pur. Mgr.--Modern Equipment Co., Inc., Port Washington, WI; *U.S. Private*, pg. 33

Duffy, Ken, Mgr.-Pur.--Thermalloy, Inc., Farmers Branch, TX; *Int'l*, pg. 208

Duke, Joseph P., Mgr.-Pur.--Dunmore Corporation, Newtown, PA; *U.S. Private*, pg. 346

Dulude, Jim, V.P.-Pur. & Mfg.--Quaker Fabric Corporation, Fall River, MA; *U.S. Public*, pg. 1347

Dulus, Thomas, Pur. Agent-Texas-New Mexico Power Co.--TNP Enterprises, Inc., Fort Worth, TX; *U.S. Public*, pg. 1557

Duncan, Don, Mgr.-Pur.--Benchmark Electronics Inc., Angleton, TX; *U.S. Public*, pg. 210

Duncan, George A., Dir.-Pur.--Delco Electronics Corporation, Kokomo, IN; *U.S. Public*, pg. 720

Duncan, Scott, Mgr.-Pur.--Binks Sames Corporation, Franklin Park, IL; *U.S. Public*, pg. 229

Dunham, Dick, Mgr.-Inventory Control--Reagan Equipment Company, Inc., Gretna, LA; *U.S. Private*, pg. 913

Dunigan, James, Dir.-Pur.--Bommer Industries, Inc., Landrum, SC; *U.S. Private*, pg. 156

Dunlop, David D., V.P.-Pur. & Mktg.--Bindley Western Industries, Inc., Indianapolis, IN; *U.S. Public*, pg. 228

Dunn, John, Dir.-Pur.--Cliftex, New Bedford, MA; *U.S. Public*, pg. 1777

Dunn, Peggy, Dir.-Pur.--Galaxy Carpet Mills, Inc., Chatsworth, GA; *U.S. Public*, pg. 1121

Dunn, William H., Jr., Sr. V.P.-Pur.--J.E. Dunn Construction Co., Kansas City, MO; *U.S. Private*, pg. 347

DuPont, Wilbur A., Mgr.-Pur.--Mobile Gas Service Corp., Mobile, AL; *U.S. Public*, pg. 1120

Durkan, J., Dir.-Corp. Pur.--Princess Hotels International Inc., New York, NY; *Int'l*, pg. 818

Durso, Joseph, V.P.-Pur.--Slant/Fin Corporation, Greenvale, NY; *U.S. Private*, pg. 1005

Dutridge, Bill, Dir.-Opers.--Sentinel Consumer Products, Inc., Mentor, OH; *U.S. Private*, pg. 984

Duzan, Jean-Batiste, Sr. V.P.-Pur.--Renault, Boulogne-Billancourt, France; *Int'l*, pg. 1102

Dyer, Vernon, V.P.-Opers. Support--Bombardier, Learjet Inc., Wichita, KS; *Int'l*, pg. 200

Dyson, Vickie R., Mgr.-Procurement--Morrison Knudsen Corporation, Boise, ID; *U.S. Public*, pg. 1133

Dziuba, Pat, V.P.-Pur.--AMCORE Bank N.A., Northwest, Woodstock, IL; *U.S. Public*, pg. 64

Earle, E.C., Gen. Pur. Agent--Corner Brook Pulp & Paper Limited, Corner Brook, Canada; *Int'l*, pg. 761

Eastlack, Tom, Mgr.-Pur.--Bird Products Corporation, Palm Springs, CA; *U.S. Public*, pg. 1591

Eaton, John C., V.P. & Gen. Mgr.--The Mudge Paper Co., Hyattsville, MD; *U.S. Public*, pg. 902

Eavey, Russ, Mgr.-Matls.--North American Capacitor Co., Indianapolis, IN; *U.S. Private*, pg. 803

Ebler, Arlene, Dir.-Pur.--Sentry Technology Corp., Hauppauge, NY; *U.S. Public*, pg. 1458

Ebright, Robert L., V.P.-Distr.--Big Bear Stores Company, Columbus, OH; *U.S. Public*, pg. 1270

Ebsen, Amy, Mgr.-Pur.--Merrill Corporation, Saint Paul, MN; *U.S. Public*, pg. 1097

Eck, Toby, Mgr.-Pur.--Cubix Corporation, Carson City, NV; *U.S. Private*, pg. 294

Eckels, Charlie, Mgr.-Pur.--Team, Inc., Alvin, TX; *U.S. Public*, pg. 1562

Eckerling, Sara, Dir.-Sls., Pur. & Adv.--Universal Overall Company, Chicago, IL; *U.S. Private*, pg. 1127

Edkins, Brian, Dir.-Pur.--Vacu-Dry Company, Sebastopol, CA; *U.S. Public*, pg. 1704

Edkins, Brian, Dir.-Pur.--Vacu-Dry Company Plant, Sebastopol, CA; *U.S. Public*, pg. 1704

Edler, James H., V.P.-Matls. Mngmt.--American Greetings U.S. Greeting Card Division, Cleveland, OH; *U.S. Public*, pg. 78

Edlund, Steve, Mgr.-Pur.--Twin City Foods, Inc., Stanwood, WA; *U.S. Private*, pg. 1111

Edmund, James B., Pur. Agent-Special Projects--Peter Pan Seafoods, Inc., Seattle, WA; *Int'l*, pg. 928

Edvinsson, Kent, Mgr.-Pur.--Atlet AB, Molnlycke, Sweden; *Int'l*, pg. 97

Edwards, C., Dir.-Pur.--The Gerstenslager Company, Wooster, OH; *U.S. Public*, pg. 1780

Edwards, Carol, Mgr.-Pur.--All-Luminum Products, Inc., Philadelphia, PA; *U.S. Private*, pg. 34

Edwards, Dan, Dir.-Pur.--Garland Commercial Industries, Inc., Freeland, PA; *Int'l*, pg. 188

Edwards, John, Mgr.-Pur.--American Manufacturing Company, Chattanooga, TN; *U.S. Private*, pg. 58

Edwards, Kip, V.P.-Natl. Svcs.--Kaiser Permanente, Oakland, CA; *U.S. Private*, pg. 605

Edwards, Michele, V.P.-Matls.--Sheldahl, Inc., Northfield, MN; *U.S. Public*, pg. 1465

Edwards, Richard, Pur. Agent--Plant Maintenance Service Corporation, Memphis, TN; *U.S. Private*, pg. 869

Edwards, Robert, Mgr.-Pur.--Paychex, Inc., Rochester, NY; *U.S. Public*, pg. 1267

Eenhuis, Loretta, Controller & Treas.--Westin, Inc., Omaha, NE; *U.S. Private*, pg. 1169

Eggland, Al, Mgr.-Pur.--Pella Corporation, Pella, IA; *U.S. Private*, pg. 848

Eggleston, Jay, Mgr.-Pur.--Spartech Plastics, Portage, WI; *U.S. Public*, pg. 1496

Ehlers, Kathy, V.P.-Pur.--Tropicana Casino & Resort, Atlantic City, NJ; *U.S. Public*, pg. 159

Ehlert, Dirk, Mgr.-Pur.--Hermal Kurt Herrmann & Co., Reinbek, Germany; *Int'l*, pg. 616

Einhorn, Jacob, Dir.-Pur.--Hahn Automotive Warehouse, Inc., Rochester, NY; *U.S. Public*, pg. 774

Einhorn, Jacob, Mgr.-Pur.--Professional Auto Warehouse, Rochester, NY; *U.S. Public*, pg. 774

Eisele, Charles R., V.P.-Pur.--Union Pacific Railroad Company, Omaha, NE; *U.S. Public*, pg. 1668

Eisele, Todd, Mgr.-Pur.--Innovex, Inc., Hopkins, MN; *U.S. Public*, pg. 880

Ekstrom, Dean E., V.P.-Admin.--IES Industries Inc., Cedar Rapids, IA; *U.S. Public*, pg. 855

Elder, D., Dir.-Pur.--Delta International Machinery Corp., Pittsburgh, PA; *U.S. Public*, pg. 1273

Eldredge, Larry, Dir.-Pur.--Ballard Medical Products, Draper, UT; *U.S. Public*, pg. 171

Elesenbast, Dave, Dir.-Pur.--Milk Specialties Company, Dundee, IL; *U.S. Private*, pg. 746

Elias, Ed, Mgr.-Pur.--Hausted, Medina, OH; *U.S. Private*, pg. 1001

Eliasek, Donald, Dir.-Pur.--Harris Steel Co., Cicero, IL; *U.S. Private*, pg. 506

Elliott, Paul, Dir.-Pur.--Long Equipment Co., Tarboro, NC; *U.S. Private*, pg. 675

Ellis, Homer, Dir.-Pur.--American Classic Voyagers Company, New Orleans, LA; *U.S. Private*, pg. 380

Ellis, Jim, Dir.-Pur. & Traffic--Zoeller Co., Louisville, KY; *U.S. Private*, pg. 1207

Ellis, Pat, Mgr.-Pur.--Blumenthal/Lansing Company, Lansing, IA; *U.S. Public*, pg. 1187

Elvin, Joseph, V.P.-Pur.--Marcal Paper Mills, Inc., Elmwood Park, NJ; *U.S. Private*, pg. 701

Embry, W.L., V.P.-Matls.--Crane Defense Systems, Conroe, TX; *U.S. Public*, pg. 456

Emerson, David, Mgr.-Pur.--Kennedy Tank & Manufacturing Co., Inc., Indianapolis, IN; *U.S. Private*, pg. 614

Emery, Earl, Dir.-Pur. & Traffic--CF & I Steel, L.P., Pueblo, CO; *U.S. Public*, pg. 1230

Emery, Kenneth C., V.P.-Info. Sys., Tech. & Opers.--CMS Energy Corporation, Dearborn, MI; *U.S. Public*, pg. 279

Emery, Pete, Mgr.-Pur.--ICI Acrylics Inc., Cordova, TN; *Int'l*, pg. 663

Emmrich, Bob, Mgr.-Mdsg.--WICO, Niles, IL; *U.S. Private*, pg. 1144

Emory, Mike, Mgr.-Pur.--Mayfair Mills, Inc., Arcadia, SC; *U.S. Private*, pg. 718

Endick, Murray, Dir.-Pur.--Aberdeen Mfg. Corporation, New York, NY; *U.S. Private*, pg. 1094

Engberg, John C., Mgr.-Media Pur.--Kohler Company, Kohler, WI; *U.S. Private*, pg. 630

Engelage, Dean, Asst. Dir.-Adv. & Mgr.-Matls.--Woodard Inc., Owosso, MI; *U.S. Private*, pg. 192

Engle, Todd, Mgr.-Pur. & Export--Apertus Technologies Incorporated, Eden Prairie, MN; *U.S. Public*, pg. 119

Engstrom, Paul, Dir.-Pur.--St. Paul Metalcraft, Inc., Saint Paul, MN; *U.S. Private*, pg. 961

Ensminger, Sharon, Dir.-Pur.--Visible Changes, Houston, TX; *U.S. Private*, pg. 1141

Erani, Dennis, Exec. V.P. & Gen. Mgr.--A&E Stores, Inc., Teterboro, NJ; *U.S. Private*, pg. 1

Erdman, Steve, Pur. Agent--Federated Mutual Insurance Company, Owatonna, MN; *U.S. Private*, pg. 399

Erickson, Bill, Mgr.-Matls.--Continental/Midland, Inc., Park Forest, IL; *U.S. Private*, pg. 268

Erickson, Charles D., Mgr.-Equipment--Bacco Construction Co., Iron Mountain, MI; *U.S. Private*, pg. 109

Erickson, E., Dir.-Pur.--Lightnin Mixers, Rochester, NY; *U.S. Public*, pg. 726

Erickson, Jim, Dir.-Pur.--Employers Life Ins. Co. of Wausau, Wausau, WI; *U.S. Private*, pg. 789

Erwin, B.W., Pur. Agent.--American Cast Iron Pipe Co., Birmingham, AL; *U.S. Private*, pg. 51

Erwin, Thomas, Mgr.-Opers.--Midco International Inc., Chicago, IL; *U.S. Private*, pg. 744

Esposito, James, Dir.-Pur.--Wilcox Electric, Inc., Kansas City, MO; *Int'l*, pg. 1384

Esposito, Jim, Pur. Agent--American Specialties Inc., Yonkers, NY; *U.S. Private*, pg. 62

Esposito, William, V.P.-Pur.--Hasbro, Inc., Pawtucket, RI; *U.S. Public*, pg. 797

Estabrooks, Ron, Dir.-Pur.--Palm Beach Beauty Products Co., Minneapolis, MN; *U.S. Private*, pg. 834

Estabrooks, Ron, Pur. Agent--Dayco PTI, Inc., Red Wing, MN; *U.S. Public*, pg. 1045

Estand, Ray, Dir.-Pur.--Silbrico Corporation, Hodgkins, IL; *U.S. Private*, pg. 1000

Estes, Doug, Jr., Mgr.-Production--Moeller Products Co., Inc., Greenville, MS; *U.S. Private*, pg. 755

Estremo, Al, Dir.-Pur.--Astec America Inc., Carlsbad, CA; *Int'l*, pg. 93

Etheridge, Oliver, V.P.-Pur.--Lea Industries, Greensboro, NC; *U.S. Public*, pg. 974

Etter, Mike, Mgr.-Pur.--Fedders North America, Inc., Effingham, IL; *U.S. Public*, pg. 615

Eubanks, Billy, Mgr.-Pur.--Tupperware U.S., Inc., Orlando, FL; *U.S. Public*, pg. 1644

Evans, Dave, Pur. Agent--Gold Medal Products Co., Cincinnati, OH; *U.S. Private*, pg. 459

Evans, Jerry, Pur. Agent--Peterson Tractor Company, San Leandro, CA; *U.S. Private*, pg. 858

Evans, Judy, Dir.-Pur.--Federated Department Stores, Inc., Cincinnati, OH; *U.S. Public*, pg. 617

Evans, Mike, Mgr.-Pur.--Ohio Crankshaft Div., Cleveland, OH; *U.S. Public*, pg. 1258

Evans, Richard S., Mgr.-Pur.--Hynes Industries Inc., Youngstown, OH; *U.S. Private*, pg. 552

Evans, Thomas W., V.P.-Matls. Mngmt.--Weirton Steel Corporation, Weirton, WV; *U.S. Public*, pg. 1751

Everett, Amy, Mgr.-Pur.--Service Corporation International, Houston, TX; *U.S. Public*, pg. 1460

Everett, Jim, V.P.-Procurement--Long John Silver's, Inc., Lexington, KY; *U.S. Private*, pg. 674

Ewald, William G., Dir.-Pur.--Walbro Corporation, Cass City, MI; *U.S. Public*, pg. 1733

Ewen, Tim, Dir.-H.R. & Pur.--Applied Magnetics Corporation, Goleta, CA; *U.S. Public*, pg. 123

Ewing, James C., V.P.-H.R.--Belden & Blake Corporation, Canton, OH; *U.S. Private*, pg. 1078

Ewing, Joe, Dir.-Distr. & Pur.--Mississippi Chemical Corporation, Yazoo City, MS; *U.S. Public*, pg. 1117
Fagan, Michael, Dir.-Pur.--Action Manufacturing Co., Philadelphia, PA; *U.S. Private*, pg. 15
Fahey, James, V.P.-Mdsg. & Pur.--United Stationers Inc., Des Plaines, IL; *U.S. Public*, pg. 1689
Fairbanks, Walter, Grp. V.P.-Defense--Cubic Corporation, San Diego, CA; *U.S. Public*, pg. 466
Fakes, Ray, Dir.-Pur.--Wynn's-Precision, Inc., Lebanon, TN; *U.S. Public*, pg. 1783
Falcofsky, Thomas, V.P.-Pur.--General Cable Corporation, Highland Heights, KY; *Int'l*, pg. 1486
Falcon, A., Dir.-Purch.--Gator Industries Inc., Hialeah, FL; *U.S. Private*, pg. 441
Falcone, Greg, Dir.-Pur.--United States Bronze Powders, Inc., Flemington, NJ; *U.S. Private*, pg. 1124
Faller, Gene, V.P.-Pur.--Fruit of the Loom, Inc., Chicago, IL; *U.S. Public*, pg. 685
Fallstich, Jay, Pur. Agent--Great Neck Saw Manufacturers, Inc., Mineola, NY; *U.S. Private*, pg. 475
Falter, Alfred, V.P.-Pur.--Church & Dwight Co., Inc., Princeton, NJ; *U.S. Public*, pg. 355
Fann, Raymond, Mgr.-Pur.--Mission Industries, Las Vegas, NV; *U.S. Private*, pg. 752
Farmer, Jim, Dir.-Pur.--Hazel Bishop International, Englewood Cliffs, NJ; *U.S. Private*, pg. 514
Farnadas, Jack, Mgr.-Pur.--Guidant Corporation-Vascular Intervention Group, Santa Clara, CA; *U.S. Public*, pg. 768
Farrar, Clarence, Chief Oper. Officer & V.P.--JG Industries, Inc., Chicago, IL; *U.S. Public*, pg. 917
Farrar, Scott, V.P.-Matls. Resource Grp.--Quorum Health Group, Inc., Brentwood, TN; *U.S. Public*, pg. 1353
Farrell, Vivian, Dir.-Pur.--Vicon Industries, Inc., Hauppauge, NY; *U.S. Public*, pg. 1719
Fath, Beth, Mgr.-Pur.--Spec's Music, Inc., Miami, FL; *U.S. Public*, pg. 1497
Fawler, Ron, Mgr.-Matls.--Engine Components Div., Kearney, NE; *U.S. Public*, pg. 557
Fazzio, Joe, Mgr.-Pur.--Fischer Imaging Corporation, RMS Manufacturing Division, Addison, IL; *U.S. Public*, pg. 647
Federspiel, Jim, Dir.-Pur.--Coleman Powermate, Inc., Omaha, NE; *U.S. Private*, pg. 691
Feehan, Jim, Dir.-Admin.--Black Hills Corporation, Rapid City, SD; *U.S. Public*, pg. 235
Fegert, Lawrence M., Dir.-Pur.--Tri-Mark Metal Corp., Shelby, MI; *U.S. Private*, pg. 1100
Feihl, Juergen, Dir.-Matls.--Cherry Mikroschalter GmbH, Auerbach, Germany; *U.S. Public*, pg. 346
Felder, Anton, Gen. Mgr.-Food Pur.--Coop Switzerland, Basel, Switzerland; *Int'l*, pg. 329
Feldmeyer, Cindy, Pur. Agent--Dakotah, Inc., Webster, SD; *U.S. Public*, pg. 477
Felix, Dave, Mgr.-Pur.--Kaufman and Broad Inland Empire, Anaheim, CA; *U.S. Public*, pg. 945
Felix, Edward R., V.P.-Warehouse Distr.--Bashas, Chandler, AZ; *U.S. Private*, pg. 120
Felix, W.S., Dir.-Pur.--Miller Chemical & Fertilizer Corp., Hanover, PA; *U.S. Private*, pg. 33
Felizzi, Tony, Pur. Agent--Channel Master, Smithfield, NC; *U.S. Private*, pg. 228
Felman, Mark, Dir.-Adv.--Allou Health & Beauty Care, Inc., Brentwood, NY; *U.S. Public*, pg. 55
Feltner, Homer, Dir.-Pur.--Quality Foods Inc., Little Rock, AR; *U.S. Private*, pg. 898
Fender, Karen, Mgr.-Pur.--Hampton Print Works, Inc., Johnson City, TN; *U.S. Private*, pg. 498
Fergus, P., Mgr.-Pur.--The Peoples Gas Light & Coke Co., Chicago, IL; *U.S. Public*, pg. 1275
Fergus, Patrick G., Mgr.-Purchasing & Stores--Peoples Energy Corporation, Chicago, IL; *U.S. Public*, pg. 1274
Ferguson, Dave, Dir.-Matls.--Champion Pneumatic Machinery Co., Inc., Princeton, IL; *U.S. Private*, pg. 228
Ferguson, Jim, Mgr.-Pur.--Hershey Pasta and Grocery Group, Hershey, PA; *U.S. Public*, pg. 812
Ferguson, Michelle, Dir.-Pur.--Levlad, Inc., Chatsworth, CA; *U.S. Private*, pg. 663
Ferguson, W., Dir.-Pur.--Wilkinson Company, Inc., Stow, OH; *U.S. Private*, pg. 368
Ferguson, William, Dir.-Pur.--Electric Furnace Co., Salem, OH; *U.S. Private*, pg. 367
Ferrante, Anthony, Pur. Agent--Star Cutter Co., Farmington, MI; *U.S. Private*, pg. 1034
Ferraro, Vincent, Dir.-Pur.--Dimco-Gray Company, Centerville, OH; *U.S. Private*, pg. 333
Ferrer, Cruz A., V.P.-Pur.--Banco Popular de Puerto Rico, San Juan, PR; *U.S. Public*, pg. 175
Ferrise, Mike, Mgr.-Pur.--MTS Systems Corporation, Eden Prairie, MN; *U.S. Public*, pg. 1028
Ferro, Roy, Dir.-Pur.--Edwin B. Stimpson Company, Inc., Bayport, NY; *U.S. Private*, pg. 1043
Fersch, Bill, Dir.-Pur.--AM Cosmetics Inc., Nyack, NY; *U.S. Private*, pg. 6
Fetzer, Shelly, Coord.-Pur.--Moto Photo, Inc., Dayton, OH; *U.S. Public*, pg. 1136
Fickett, Robert, Mgr.-Pur.--Kingston-Warren Corporation, Newfields, NH; *U.S. Public*, pg. 796
Fickling, Tom, Dir.-Pur.--Birmingham Steel Corporation, Birmingham, AL; *U.S. Public*, pg. 232
Fiedler, Elfriede, Mng. Dir.-Produce Buying--Julius Meinl AG, Vienna, Austria; *Int'l*, pg. 856
Fiedler, Joe, Mgr.-Pur.--Magnetrol International, Downers Grove, IL; *U.S. Private*, pg. 696
Fields, Gary H., V.P.-Purchasing--Ball Packaging Holdings Corp., Westminster, CO; *U.S. Public*, pg. 171
Fields, Theresa, Pur. Mgr.--The Toy Factory, Elizabeth, NJ; *U.S. Private*, pg. 883
Filo, Jerry, Pur. Agent--Wisconsin Pharmacal Co., Inc., Jackson, WI; *U.S. Private*, pg. 1185
Finan, Don, Mgr.-Fibre Procurement--Woodlands License Management/Fibre Procurement, Marathon, Canada; *U.S. Public*, pg. 672
Finelli, Ron, Mgr.-Pur.--Piper Jaffray Companies, Inc., Minneapolis, MN; *U.S. Public*, pg. 1300
Fingerhut, Augie, Dir.-Sls. & Pur., Mgr.-Adv.--Manhattan Industries Intl. Div., New York, NY; *U.S. Public*, pg. 1429
Fingerle, Mark M., V.P. & Dir.-Pur.--Fingerle Lumber Co., Ann Arbor, MI; *U.S. Private*, pg. 405
Finnegan, Charles E., V.P.-Metal Pur.--Crown Cork & Seal Company, Inc., Philadelphia, PA; *U.S. Public*, pg. 462
Finnegan, Michael, Dir.-Pur.--Chattem, Inc., Consumer Products Division, Chattanooga, TN; *U.S. Public*, pg. 341
Finnegan, Roger, Mgr.-Corp. Pur.--Don E. Williams Co., Rock Island, IL; *U.S. Private*, pg. 1177
Finnegan, Roger, Mgr.-Pur.--Dewco Chicago, Rolling Meadows, IL; *U.S. Private*, pg. 1178
Fischer, Jack, Pur. Agent--Al Larson Boat Shop, Inc., Terminal Island, CA; *U.S. Private*, pg. 652
Fish, Jed, Dir.-Pur.--Chiron Corporation, Emeryville, CA; *U.S. Public*, pg. 349
Fish, Julia C., Dir.-Corp. Commun.--Sedgwick Group plc, London, United Kingdom; *Int'l*, pg. 1217
Fish, William, Dir.-Pur.--Dennison Stationery Products Company, Holyoke, MA; *U.S. Public*, pg. 153
Fisher, Mark, Dir.-Pur.--Cooker Restaurant Corporation, West Palm Beach, FL; *U.S. Public*, pg. 442
Fisher, R.W., Pur. Agent--Wurzburg, Inc., Memphis, TN; *U.S. Private*, pg. 1192
Fisher, Robert, Mgr.-Pur.--Conbraco Industries Inc., Matthews, NC; *U.S. Private*, pg. 261
Fisher, Tom, Mgr.-Pur.--Big Joe Manufacturing Co., Lincolnwood, IL; *U.S. Private*, pg. 143
Fisher, William, Dir.-Pur.--Winnebago Industries, Inc., Forest City, IA; *U.S. Public*, pg. 1772
Fissasloo, Bill, Sec. , Treas. & Dir.-Pur.--Gress Foods Inc., Gainesville, GA; *U.S. Private*, pg. 480
Fitzgerald, Joyce, V.P.-Pur.--Mellon Bank (MD), Rockville, MD; *U.S. Public*, pg. 1085
Fitzgerald, Phyllis, Mgr.-Pur.--Executive Car Leasing Company, Los Angeles, CA; *U.S. Private*, pg. 388
Fitzgerald, Thomas, Mgr.-Pur.--Tropar Mfg. Co., Inc., Florham Park, NJ; *U.S. Private*, pg. 1105
Fitzsimmons, Jerry, Pur. Agent--Arrow Fastener Co., Inc., Saddle Brook, NJ; *U.S. Private*, pg. 85
Fitzsimmons, Robert J., V.P.-Pur.--Day & Zimmermann, Inc., Philadelphia, PA; *U.S. Private*, pg. 316
Fix, L., Pur. Agent--Century Fence Company, Pewaukee, WI; *U.S. Private*, pg. 226
Fjeld, David L., Mgr.-Pur.--Compaction America, Kewanee, IL; *U.S. Public*, pg. 1676
Flanagan, Dorothy, Mgr.-Pur.--J. Baker, Inc., Canton, MA; *U.S. Public*, pg. 167
Flanagan, J., Mgr.-Pur.--Litton Solid State, Santa Clara, CA; *U.S. Public*, pg. 1003
Flasco, John, Dir.-Pur.--The Akro Corporation, Canton, OH; *U.S. Public*, pg. 399
Fleeher, Donald G., Dir.-Matls. Mngmt. & Pur.--Greer Steel Co., Dover, OH; *U.S. Private*, pg. 479
Fleming, William, Buyer--Prestige Stamping, Inc., Warren, MI; *U.S. Private*, pg. 882
Fletcher, Robert, V.P.-Procurement--The Stanley Works, New Britain, CT; *U.S. Public*, pg. 1508
Flom, Roger, V.P.-Comml. Sls. & Pur.--Standard Publishing, Cincinnati, OH; *U.S. Public*, pg. 1506
Flores, Diana, Dir.-Pur.--Andrea Electronics Corporation, Long Island City, NY; *U.S. Public*, pg. 112
Flory, James R., Pur. Mgr.--Gorman-Rupp Industries Div., Bellville, OH; *U.S. Public*, pg. 754
Flowers, Timi, Mgr.-Pur.--Kaufman and Broad Coastal, Newport Beach, CA; *U.S. Public*, pg. 945
Floyd, Shirley, Mgr.-Matls. Mngmt.--El Paso Electric Company, El Paso, TX; *U.S. Public*, pg. 567
Foate, Jack L., Dir.-Pur.--Utility Trailer Manufacturing Co., City of Industry, CA; *U.S. Private*, pg. 1130
Foehner, Denny, Dir.-Central Pur.--Basler Electric Company, Highland, IL; *U.S. Private*, pg. 121
Foley, Steve, Dir.-Non-Resale Pur.--AMI Leasing Corporation, Worcester, MA; *U.S. Private*, pg. 7
Follett, B., Dir.-Pur.--The Glen Dimplex Group, Dunleer, Ireland; *Int'l*, pg. 553
Fones, Jack, Mgr.-Pur.--Weiss Scientific Glass Blowing Co., Inc., Portland, OR; *Int'l*, pg. 1408
Forbes, Karen, Dir.-Pur.--Farm Progress Publications, Carol Stream, IL; *U.S. Public*, pg. 513
Ford, Libby, Mgr.-Inventory Control--Bergen Brunswig Medical Corporation, Meridian, MS; *U.S. Public*, pg. 214
Ford, Paul, Dir.-Pur.--Tenax Corporation, Danbury, CT; *Int'l*, pg. 193
Ford, Roger, Pur. Agent--Solar Communications, Inc., Naperville, IL; *U.S. Private*, pg. 1012
Forman, S., Mgr.-Pur.--Teradyne, Inc., Boston, MA; *U.S. Public*, pg. 1580
Formanek, Matthew J., Mgr.-Pur.--Milwaukee Cylinder Division, Cudahy, WI; *U.S. Public*, pg. 124
Forti, Richard F., V.P.-Fin. & Pur.--Ragu Foods, Inc., Trumbull, CT; *Int'l*, pg. 1436
Fortney, Donald, Pur. Agent--Brunner & Lay, Inc., Springdale, AR; *U.S. Private*, pg. 176
Fortune, Richard, Dir.-Pur.--Molded Fiber Glass Companies, Ashtabula, OH; *U.S. Private*, pg. 755
Foss, Thomas T., Dir.-Pur.--Eskimo Pie Corporation, Richmond, VA; *U.S. Public*, pg. 592
Fossum, Jeffrey J., Chief Fin. Officer & V.P.--Effective Management Systems, Milwaukee, WI; *U.S. Public*, pg. 565
Foster, Glenn, Mgr.-Facilities--Database America Companies, Montvale, NJ; *U.S. Private*, pg. 312
Foster, James, Mgr.-Pur.--The Fibre-Metal Products Company, Concordville, PA; *U.S. Private*, pg. 402
Fountain, Terry L., V.P.--Peoples Electric Contractor, Inc., Saint Paul, MN; *U.S. Private*, pg. 851
Fountain, William H., V.P.-Prod. Mngmt.--Kent Electronics Corp., Houston, TX; *U.S. Public*, pg. 951
Fournier, Donald, Pur. Agent--Peck Spring Company, Plainville, CT; *U.S. Private*, pg. 846
Fox, Alan, Sr. V.P.-Pur.--Uno Restaurant Corporation, West Roxbury, MA; *U.S. Public*, pg. 1698
Fox, Brent, Dir.-Pur.--ABC Supply Company, Inc., Beloit, WI; *U.S. Private*, pg. 3
Fox, David, Mgr.-Pur.--Duro-Test Corporation, Fairfield, NJ; *U.S. Private*, pg. 349
Fox, Larry, Dir.-Pur.--Collins & Aikman Corporation, Charlotte, NC; *U.S. Public*, pg. 399
Fox, Raymond A., Chief Oper. Officer, V.P. & Sec.--Active Electrical Supply Company, Chicago, IL; *U.S. Private*, pg. 15
Frady, Paul, Mgr.-Pur.--Hoffco/Comet Industries, Inc., Richmond, IN; *U.S. Private*, pg. 532
Fragomeni, Antonio Sergio P., Dir.-Procurement & Pur.--Petrobras - Petroleo Brasileiro S.A., Rio de Janeiro, Brazil; *Int'l*, pg. 1041
Fraleigh, John E., Sr. V.P.-Tobacco Procurement--Swisher International Group, Inc., Darien, CT; *U.S. Public*, pg. 1543
France, Mike, Dir.-Pur.--BHS Plc, London, United Kingdom; *Int'l*, pg. 1304
Frank, Craig, Mgr.-Pur.--L.A. Gear, Inc., Santa Monica, CA; *U.S. Public*, pg. 969
Frank, Ray, Mgr.-Matls.--The Kendall-Betham Division, Piscataway, NJ; *U.S. Public*, pg. 1647
Frankel, Donna, Dir.-Pur.--Thompson Medical Company, Inc., West Palm Beach, FL; *U.S. Private*, pg. 1083
Franklin, Dick, Mgr.-Pur.--Standun, Inc., Inglewood, CA; *U.S. Private*, pg. 1032
Franklin, Dick, Mgr.-Pur.--Zephyr Mfg. Co., Inglewood, CA; *U.S. Private*, pg. 1032
Frankowski, Chester, Pur. Agent--Edwards High Vacuum, International, Grand Island, NY; *Int'l*, pg. 121
Frantz, Dave, Mgr.-Pur.--Algood Food Company, Louisville, KY; *U.S. Private*, pg. 34
Franz, David, Mgr.-Materials--Industrial Bag Division - Cantonment Plant, Cantonment, FL; *U.S. Public*, pg. 1521
Fratilla, Gary, Mgr.-Pur.--Cintas Corporation, Mason, OH; *U.S. Public*, pg. 370
Frayseth, Douglas, Mgr.-Matls.--Schult Homes Corporation, Redwood Falls, MN; *U.S. Public*, pg. 1442
Frazee, Gary, Dir.-Pur.--Frisch's Restaurants, Inc., Cincinnati, OH; *U.S. Public*, pg. 682
Frazier, Charles, Buyer--Anderson Wholesale Company, Muskogee, OK; *U.S. Private*, pg. 73
Frazier, Jerry, Dir.-Pur. & Mdsg.--Anderson Wholesale Company, Muskogee, OK; *U.S. Private*, pg. 73
Frazier, Mike, Mgr.-Pur.--Spectra-Physics Scanning Systems Inc., Eugene, OR; *U.S. Public*, pg. 1594
Frechette, Mark, Pur. Agent--National Computer Print, Inc., Birmingham, AL; *U.S. Private*, pg. 780
Freed, Mike, Buyer--Accu-Sort Systems, Inc., Telford, PA; *U.S. Private*, pg. 11
Freel, Dale L., V.P.-Pur. & Tooling--Cambridge Industries Inc., Madison Heights, MI; *U.S. Private*, pg. 202
Freeman, Larry, Mgr.-Pur.--Universal Coach Parts, Inc., Des Plaines, IL; *Int'l*, pg. 326
Frei, Pat, Pur. Agent--Southwest Marine, Inc., San Diego, CA; *U.S. Private*, pg. 213
Frese, M., Mng. Dir.-Fin. Control, Pur. & Strategy--Hoogovens Ijmuiden, Ijmuiden, Netherlands; *Int'l*, pg. 753
Friday, Gordon D., Sr. V.P.-Pur.--R.R. Donnelley & Sons Company, Chicago, IL; *U.S. Public*, pg. 517
Friedrich, Debra, Asst. Treas.--Bank of the Hudson, Poughkeepsie, NY; *U.S. Public*, pg. 1319
Frobeen, S., Mgr.-Pur.--HPM Corporation, Mount Gilead, OH; *U.S. Private*, pg. 492
Fromm, James, Mgr.-Pur. & Inventory Control--Lutheran Brotherhood, Minneapolis, MN; *U.S. Private*, pg. 681
Frost, Susan, Pur. Agent--Standard Insurance Co., Portland, OR; *U.S. Private*, pg. 1031
Fruscione, Nicholas, V.P.-Pur.--Wallace Laboratories, Cranbury, NJ; *U.S. Public*, pg. 310
Fry, G.E., Mgr.-Materials & Purchasing--Irex Corporation, Lancaster, PA; *U.S. Public*, pg. 913
Fryling, Dick, Dir.-Pur.--MFG Tray Co., Linesville, PA; *U.S. Private*, pg. 756
Fugate, Donna M., Mgr.-Office Svc.--United Fire & Casualty Company, Cedar Rapids, IA; *U.S. Public*, pg. 1677
Fujii, Tsunetsugu, Gen. Mgr.-Pur.--Tosoh Corporation, Tokyo, Japan; *Int'l*, pg. 1407
Fukazawa, Tsuneo, Dir.-Mer.--Kosugi Sangyo Co., Ltd., Tokyo, Japan; *Int'l*, pg. 759
Fukuda, Miyoji, Mgr.-Pur.--Acos Villares Mechanical Engineering Unit, Sao Paulo, Brazil; *Int'l*, pg. 23
Fulco, Albert, V.P.-Pur.--Lukens Steel Company, Coatesville, PA; *U.S. Public*, pg. 1020
Fulco, Albert P., V.P.-Pur.--Lukens Inc., Coatesville, PA; *U.S. Public*, pg. 1019
Fuller, Chuck, Dir.-Pur.--Kappler Safety Group, Inc., Guntersville, AL; *U.S. Private*, pg. 607
Fullerton, Robin, Dir.-Pur.--Nematron Corp., Ann Arbor, MI; *U.S. Private*, pg. 791
Fulmer, Joe, V.P.--Prime Bancshares Inc., Houston, TX; *U.S. Public*, pg. 1326
Furuta, Otto, V.P.-Pur. & Logistics--Great Lakes Chemical Corporation, West Lafayette, IN; *U.S. Public*, pg. 760
Gabay, David, Pur. Agent--Ain Plastics, Inc., Mount Vernon, NY; *Int'l*, pg. 1388
Gabler, Gerald, Mgr.-Matls.--Eaton Corporation, Engineered Fasteners Division, Brunswick, OH; *U.S. Public*, pg. 556
Gagliardi, Richard J., V.P.-Admin.--Allegheny Power System, Inc., Hagerstown, MD; *U.S. Public*, pg. 42
Gagne, Daniel, Dir.-Pur.--GE Hydro, Lachine, Canada; *U.S. Public*, pg. 713
Gahan, Thomas, V.P.-Pharmacy Pur.--Arbor Drugs, Inc., Troy, MI; *U.S. Public*, pg. 126
Gales, Bonnie, Dir.-Pur.--Neill-LaVielle Supply Co., Louisville, KY; *U.S. Private*, pg. 790
Gallagher, George, Pur. Agent--Atlantic Metals Corporation, Philadelphia, PA; *U.S. Private*, pg. 95
Gallagher, Gerry, Mgr.-Matls.--Mallinckrodt Medical, Athlone, Ireland; *U.S. Public*, pg. 1040

Gallauresi, Richard, Supvr.-Office Svcs.--Farmers and Traders Life Insurance Co., Syracuse, NY; *U.S. Private*, pg. 394
Gallay, Antoine, Dir.-Pur.--Clarins, Neuilly-sur-Seine, France; *Int'l*, pg. 295
Galley, P., Mgr.-Pur.--Ransomes Plc, Ipswich, United Kingdom; *Int'l*, pg. 1087
Galloway, C.M., Mgr.-Matls.--Solvay Animal Health, Inc., Mendota Heights, MN; *Int'l*, pg. 1277
Galyen, Thomas, Mgr.-Pur.--Institution Food House, Inc., Hickory, NC; *U.S. Private*, pg. 657
Gamber, Brice, Dir.-Leasing--The Chubb Corporation, Warren, NJ; *U.S. Public*, pg. 354
Gamble, Roger, Gen. Mgr.-Pur.--Ultramar Diamond Shamrock Corporation, San Antonio, TX; *U.S. Public*, pg. 1663
Gann, Russell, Mgr.-Pur.--Southwest Chemical/Services, Houston, TX; *U.S. Public*, pg. 781
Gantt, Laurie, Mgr.-Pur.--Fred B. Johnston Company, Inc., Chapin, SC; *U.S. Private*, pg. 595
Garcia Cruz, Arturo, Dir.-Pur.--Grupo SYR, S.A. de C.V., Mexico, Mexico; *Int'l*, pg. 576
Garcia, Ed, Dir.-Pur.--Peoples Telephone Company, Inc., Miami, FL; *U.S. Public*, pg. 1275
Garcia, J., Pur. Agent--Spirite Industries, Inc., Englewood, NJ; *U.S. Private*, pg. 1026
Gardner, Betty, Mgr.-Purch.--Public Service Company of New Mexico, Albuquerque, NM; *U.S. Public*, pg. 1339
Gardner, Robert, Pur. Agent--Kulite Semiconductor Products, Inc., Leonia, NJ; *U.S. Private*, pg. 636
Garia, Michael, Mgr.-Pur.--Quarterdeck Corp., Marina Del Rey, CA; *U.S. Public*, pg. 1350
Garnier, F.G., Pur. Agent-Cotton--Fieldcrest Cannon, Inc., Kannapolis, NC; *U.S. Public*, pg. 1296
Garret, Len, Mgr.--The Medical Protective Company, Fort Wayne, IN; *U.S. Private*, pg. 728
Garrett, Lewis, V.P.-Pur.--Camelot Music, Inc., Canton, OH; *U.S. Private*, pg. 203
Garrison, Craig, Pur. Agent--The Johnson Corporation, Three Rivers, MI; *U.S. Private*, pg. 591
Gartner, Stephen R., V.P.-Distr. Opers.--The Pillsbury Company, Minneapolis, MN; *Int'l*, pg. 411
Garven, R. Lee, Chief Fin. Officer & Mgr.-Pur.--Directory Distributing Associates, Inc., Scarborough, Canada; *U.S. Private*, pg. 334
Gary, Jackie, Dir.-Pur.--Elsinore Corporation, Las Vegas, NV; *U.S. Public*, pg. 570
Gasiorek, Robert, Buyer-Frozen Foods-Shortening & Oils--Alliant Foodservice, Bensenville, IL; *U.S. Private*, pg. 244
Gaspari, Robert, Buyer--Accu-Sort Systems, Inc., Telford, PA; *U.S. Private*, pg. 11
Gasper, S., Mgr.-Pur.--CM Shredder Div., Sarasota, FL; *U.S. Public*, pg. 405
Gasperack, Gary, Dir.-Procurement & Matls.--Spalding Sports Worldwide, Chicopee, MA; *U.S. Private*, pg. 630
Gattis, Jerry, Pres. & Chief Oper. Officer--Cagle's Inc., Atlanta, GA; *U.S. Public*, pg. 291
Gaul, Joseph, Pur. Agent--Coppus Murray Group, Tuthill Corporation, Millbury, MA; *U.S. Private*, pg. 1110
Gauthier, Nelson, Dir.-Pur.--MFE Instruments, Salem, NH; *U.S. Public*, pg. 1518
Gauvreau, Raymond, Dir.-Purchase Fleet & Bldg. Mngmt.--Gaz Metropolitain & Company, Montreal, Canada; *Int'l*, pg. 541
Gavdette, Michael A., Supvr.-Pur. & Facilities--Fay, Spofford & Thorndike, Inc., Burlington, MA; *U.S. Private*, pg. 397
Gavelin, Ernst, Pur. Agent--Skanska Norr AB, Sundsvall, Sweden; *Int'l*, pg. 1260
Gavin, Raymond, Mgr.-Pur.--Armada Corporation, Detroit, MI; *U.S. Private*, pg. 82
Gavin, Raymond, Mgr.-Pur.--Hoskins Mfg. Co., Detroit, MI; *U.S. Private*, pg. 83
Gavinski, Donna, Pur. Agent--Ampco Metal Incorporated, Milwaukee, WI; *U.S. Private*, pg. 67
Gaylor, Leonard, Pur. Agent--Republic Die & Tool Company, Belleville, MI; *U.S. Private*, pg. 923
Gaynord, Thomas, Dir.-Pur.--Haddon Craftsmen, Inc., Scranton, PA; *U.S. Public*, pg. 518
Gear, Chip, Mgr.-Pur.--Royal Appliance Mfg. Co., Cleveland, OH; *U.S. Public*, pg. 1410
Gehrig, R., Dir.-Pur.--Positech Corporation, Laurens, IA; *U.S. Public*, pg. 406
Geib, M.A., Mgr.-Matls.--Universal Composites-U.S.C., Manheim, PA; *U.S. Private*, pg. 1126
Geib, Walter, Dir.-Procurement--Kearfott Guidance & Navigation Corp., Wayne, NJ; *U.S. Private*, pg. 93
Geiger, Kenneth C., V.P. & Mgr.-Materials--Geiger Brothers, Lewiston, ME; *U.S. Private*, pg. 442
Geise, Philip, Dir.-Pur.--Jayco Inc., Middlebury, IN; *U.S. Private*, pg. 583
Geiss, Bill, Dir.-Pur.--Thomas L. Green & Co., Inc., Indianapolis, IN; *U.S. Private*, pg. 477
Gellerman, David, Sr. V.P.-Opers.--Jaydon Incorporated, Rock Island, IL; *U.S. Private*, pg. 584
Gennai, Tsuneo, Gen. Mgr.--Toyo Tire & Rubber Co., Ltd., Osaka, Japan; *Int'l*, pg. 1411
Gensler, John C., V.P.-Pur.--Seaway Food Town, Inc., Maumee, OH; *U.S. Public*, pg. 1452
Gentle, R.M., Mgr.-Matls.--M M Systems Corporation, Tucker, GA; *U.S. Private*, pg. 685
Gentry, Jeff, Sr. V.P.-Purchasing--Home Shopping Network, Inc., Saint Petersburg, FL; *U.S. Public*, pg. 1685
Genuite, Philippe, Dir.-Pur.--Facom, Morangis, France; *Int'l*, pg. 570
George, Robert E., V.P.--Southwest National Corporation, Greensburg, PA; *U.S. Public*, pg. 1493
George, Robert E., V.P.-Pur.--Southwest National Bank of Pennsylvania, Greensburg, PA; *U.S. Public*, pg. 1493
Gerbel, D.A., Dir.-Matls.--National-Standard Co., Niles, MI; *U.S. Public*, pg. 1160
Gerchenson, Jeffery H., Pres. & Chief Oper. Officer--Alva/Amco Pharmacal Companies, Inc., Chicago, IL; *U.S. Private*, pg. 47
Geri, Mati, Deputy Gen. Mgr.-Pur.--American Israeli Paper Mills Ltd., Hadera, Israel; *Int'l*, pg. 74
Germiniasi, Andrea, Mgr.-Pur.--Cassa di Risparmio delle Provincie Lombarde SpA (CARIPLO), Milan, Italy; *Int'l*, pg. 274
Germscheid, Mike, Mgr.-Pur.--WINCO, Le Center, MN; *U.S. Private*, pg. 350
Gerorgian, Alexis, Mgr.-Pur.--Kaufman and Broad Multi-Housing Group, Long Beach, CA; *U.S. Public*, pg. 945
Gerrity, Thomas E., V.P.-Sls. & Mktg.--E-Z Serve Corp., Houston, TX; *U.S. Public*, pg. 540
Gerstner, Wm., Pur. Agent--Penreco, Karns City, PA; *U.S. Public*, pg. 1273
Gertz, Dick, Mgr.-Pur.--R.S. Owens, Chicago, IL; *U.S. Private*, pg. 824
Gessner, M., Dir.-Pur.--Hill-Rom Company, Inc., Batesville, IN; *U.S. Public*, pg. 828
Gibboney, William M., Mgr.-Pur. & Printing--Jefferson-Pilot Corporation, Greensboro, NC; *U.S. Public*, pg. 925
Gibbons, Michael D., Dir.-Plng. & Sched.--National Steel Corp., Granite City Division, Granite City, IL; *Int'l*, pg. 902
Gibbs, Charlie, Mgr.-Pur.--Aeroflex Laboratories Inc., Plainview, NY; *U.S. Public*, pg. 24
Gibbs, Eddie, Dir.-Pur.--Hughes Supply, Inc., Orlando, FL; *U.S. Public*, pg. 846
Giesbrecht, Michael, Pur. Agent--Microflect Company, Inc., Salem, OR; *U.S. Public*, pg. 1707
Gifford, Lance, Mgr.-Pur.--Pacific Handy Cutter, Inc., Costa Mesa, CA; *U.S. Private*, pg. 831
Giglio, James, Dir.-Pur.--Hostmark Management Group, Rolling Meadows, IL; *U.S. Private*, pg. 541
Gilbert, G.P., Mgr.-Pur.--Crown Central Petroleum Corporation, Baltimore, MD; *U.S. Public*, pg. 462
Gildersleeve, John, Dir.-Trading & Comml.--Tesco PLC, Cheshunt, United Kingdom; *Int'l*, pg. 1376
Gill, A. Lee, Dir.-Pur.--The Dixie Group, Inc., Chattanooga, TN; *U.S. Public*, pg. 514
Gill, Brian, Mgr.-Pur.--Dudek & Bock Spring Manufacturing Company, Chicago, IL; *U.S. Private*, pg. 344
Gill, Pam W., Pur. Agent--Evening Post Publishing Co., Charleston, SC; *U.S. Private*, pg. 385
Gill, Terrence, Dir.-Matls.--Fairbanks Morse Engine Division, Beloit, WI; *U.S. Public*, pg. 401
Gill, William H., Dir.-Matls. Mngmt.--Cambridge Electric Light Co., Cambridge, MA; *U.S. Public*, pg. 414
Gillebo, Rolf, Dir.-Metro Div.--AS OSLO Sporveier, Oslo, Norway; *Int'l*, pg. 1012
Gillen, Greg, Mgr.-Pur.--Paragon Electric Co., Inc., Two Rivers, WI; *Int'l*, pg. 1243
Gillespie, Robert, Pur. Agent--Southern Ohio Fabricators, Inc., Batavia, OH; *U.S. Private*, pg. 1017
Gilley, Burnie, V.P.-Pur.--Singleton Seafood Co., Tampa, FL; *U.S. Public*, pg. 427
Gillmer, Wayne, Buyer--Genova Products, Inc., Davison, MI; *U.S. Private*, pg. 447
Gillmore, Bill, Dir.-Pur.--Field Container Company, L.P., Elk Grove Village, IL; *U.S. Private*, pg. 403
Gilpin, Dallas, Dir.-Pur.--Novell Inc., San Jose, CA; *U.S. Public*, pg. 1203
Gin, Jeff, Mgr.-Pur.--Kaufman and Broad-Monterey Bay, Inc., Salinas, CA; *U.S. Public*, pg. 945
Gingras, L., Dir.-Pur.--Place Turcot Mill, Montreal, Canada; *Int'l*, pg. 761
Ginsberg, Jerry, V.P.-Pur.--Milton Industries, Inc., Chicago, IL; *U.S. Private*, pg. 749
Gipson, David, V.P. & Pur. Dir.-Commercial Printing--The Caxton Printers Ltd., Caldwell, ID; *U.S. Private*, pg. 220
Gipson, Scott, Pur. Dir.-Textbooks--The Caxton Printers Ltd., Caldwell, ID; *U.S. Private*, pg. 220
Giralt, Jaime Villorbina, Mgr.-Pur.--Agropecuaria de Guissona, S. Coop. Ltda., Guisona, Spain; *Int'l*, pg. 31
Giroud, George, Dir.-Pur.--RFI Corp., Bay Shore, NY; *U.S. Public*, pg. 494
Givan, Bud, Dir.-Pur.--Nashville Wire Product Co., Nashville, TN; *U.S. Private*, pg. 775
Gjurich, Lou, Mgr.-Pur.--Johnstown Corporation, Johnstown, PA; *U.S. Private*, pg. 595
Glass, Ron, Mgr.-Pur.--Le Tourneau, Inc., Longview, TX; *U.S. Public*, pg. 1410
Glassman, Bruce, V.P.-Pur.--Tasco Sales Inc., Miramar, FL; *U.S. Private*, pg. 928
Glaub, Robert, Pur. Agent--Dennis Chemical Co., Inc., Saint Louis, MO; *U.S. Private*, pg. 324
Gloeckle, Patrick, Dir.-Pur.--Cracker Jack Division, Northbrook, IL; *U.S. Private*, pg. 157
Glosson, William, Mgr.-Corp. Pur.--Sealing Equipment Products Co., Inc., Pelham, AL; *U.S. Private*, pg. 978
Glover, M.D., Dir.-Pur.--H.P. Bulmer Holdings Plc, Hereford, United Kingdom; *Int'l*, pg. 232
Gnaccarini, A., Exec V.P.-Pur.--Caleffi S.p.A., Viadana, Italy; *Int'l*, pg. 252
Gneuhs, Martin, Dir.-Pur.--Teleflex Automotive, Troy, MI; *U.S. Public*, pg. 1569
Gochenour, Ken L., Supvr.-Office Services--IMO Industries Inc., Lawrenceville, NJ; *U.S. Public*, pg. 856
Gockley, Barbara, Mgr.-Pur.--Dexter Packaging Products, Waukegan, IL; *U.S. Public*, pg. 504
Godlove, Deborah, Dir.-Pur.--Argo Instruments Inc., Winchester, VA; *Int'l*, pg. 839
Godwin, Steve, Mgr.-Pur.--Embers Charcoal Company, Inc., Conway, SC; *U.S. Private*, pg. 373
Goenaga, Al, V.P.-Pur.--BankAtlantic Bancorp, Inc., Fort Lauderdale, FL; *U.S. Public*, pg. 183
Goering, George L., V.P.-Pur.--Weasler Engineering Inc., West Bend, WI; *U.S. Private*, pg. 249
Goerlich, K., Pur. Agent--J.M. Huber, Calcium Carbonate Division, Quincy, IL; *U.S. Private*, pg. 545
Gohmann, John R., Chief Oper. Officer, V.P., Sec. & Dir.-Pur.--Gohmann Asphalt & Construction Inc., Clarksville, IN; *U.S. Private*, pg. 459
Goldacker, Kenneth, Mgr.-Pur.--Warner-Jenkinson Co., Saint Louis, MO; *U.S. Public*, pg. 1696
Goldberg, Mark, Dir.-Data Processing & Pur.--Condor D.C. Power Supplies Inc., Oxnard, CA; *U.S. Public*, pg. 1419
Golden, Michael P., V.P.-Pur.--Southwest Airlines Co., Dallas, TX; *U.S. Public*, pg. 1493
Goldman, Charlie, V.P.-Pur.--Tollman/Hundley Hotels, Hopewell Junction, NY; *U.S. Private*, pg. 1090
Goldman, Greta, Pur. Agent--TimeMed Labeling Systems, Inc., Burr Ridge, IL; *U.S. Private*, pg. 1087
Golliher, Chuck, Mgr.-Pur.--MidAmerican Energy Holdings, Des Moines, IA; *U.S. Public*, pg. 1109
Golubic, John, Dir.-Pur.--YSD Industries, Youngstown, OH; *U.S. Private*, pg. 1194
Golubski, Jennifer, Pur. Agent--B & P Manufacturing, Cadillac, MI; *U.S. Private*, pg. 105
Gomez, C.J., Dir.-Pur.--The U.S. Baird Corporation, Stratford, CT; *U.S. Private*, pg. 1124
Gomez, Max, Dir.-Pur.--UST Inc., Greenwich, CT; *U.S. Public*, pg. 1660
Goncalves, Dolores, Pur. Agent--Merriam-Webster, Inc., Springfield, MA; *U.S. Private*, pg. 375
Gonce, Allan, Dir.-Pur.--Corrections Corporation of America, Nashville, TN; *U.S. Public*, pg. 450
Gonthier, Robert, Mgr.-Pur.--Gould Electronics Inc., Shawmut Circuit Protection Division, Newburyport, MA; *U.S. Public*, pg. 1592
Gonzalez, C., Treas., Sec. & Pur. Agent--Villazon Company Inc., Upper Saddle River, NJ; *U.S. Private*, pg. 1140
Gooch, Rose, Dir.-Pur.--Republic Automotive Parts, Inc., Brentwood, TN; *U.S. Public*, pg. 1377
Goodell, K., Dir.-Pur.--Hofley Manufacturing Company, Roseville, MI; *U.S. Private*, pg. 532
Gooding, Dale, Dir.-Pur.--Bear Creek Corporation, Medford, OR; *Int'l*, pg. 1518
Gooding, Don, Dir.-Admin. & Matls. Mngmt.--Meridian Medical Tech., Saint Louis, MO; *U.S. Public*, pg. 1095
Goodkind, Jane, Pur. Mgr.--Copperweld Chicago Division, Chicago, IL; *Int'l*, pg. 662
Goodman, Milton L., Dir.-Pur.--Air Conditioning Co., Inc., Glendale, CA; *U.S. Private*, pg. 28
Goodman, Paul, V.P.-Pur.--Knapp Shoes Inc., Penn Yan, NY; *U.S. Private*, pg. 401
Goodwin, Jim, Mgr.-Pur.--Leblanc Communications, Inc., Richardson, TX; *U.S. Private*, pg. 656
Goolesby, Ted, V.P.-Cotton Pur.--Fruit of the Loom, Inc., Chicago, IL; *U.S. Public*, pg. 685
Goransson, Rosemary, Dir.-Pur.--NeoRx Corporation, Seattle, WA; *U.S. Private*, pg. 791
Gordon, Thomas M., Dir.-Pur.--American Consumer Products, Solon, OH; *U.S. Private*, pg. 1142
Gore, B. Joe, Mgr.-Procurement--Central and South West Corporation, Dallas, TX; *U.S. Public*, pg. 324
Gore, Joe, Mgr.-Procurement--Central and South West Services, Inc., Dallas, TX; *U.S. Public*, pg. 324
Gore, Katie, Dir.-Pur.--Clayton Industries Co., El Monte, CA; *U.S. Private*, pg. 245
Gore, Patrick, Dir.-Pur.--RAYOVAC Corporation, Madison, WI; *U.S. Private*, pg. 912
Gorton, Les, Mgr.-Pur.--Contempri Homes, Inc., Taylor, PA; *U.S. Public*, pg. 439
Gosling, Andrew, Dir.-Pur.-Catalog Div.--Delta Education, Inc., Hudson, NH; *Int'l*, pg. 1402
Goss, Allan J., Pur. Agent--Penco Products, Oaks, PA; *U.S. Private*, pg. 848
Gossage, Ron, Mgr.-Indus. Pur.--Parker Kalon, Shelton, CT; *U.S. Public*, pg. 233
Gosz, Jude, Pur. Agent--Invincible Office Furniture, Manitowoc, WI; *U.S. Private*, pg. 575
Gottesman, Neil, Dir.-Pur.--Switchcraft, Inc., Chicago, IL; *U.S. Public*, pg. 1366
Gouje, Jerry, Mgr.-Pur.--Jordon Commercial Refrigerator Co., Philadelphia, PA; *U.S. Private*, pg. 599
Gould, Robert, Dir.-Matls. & Pur.--Stokely USA, Inc., Oconomowoc, WI; *U.S. Public*, pg. 1518
Graber, D.K., Dir.-Pur.--Harwick Standard Distribution Corporation, Akron, OH; *U.S. Private*, pg. 509
Grabowski, T.S., Dir.-Pur.--Danaher Tool Group, Chicago, IL; *U.S. Public*, pg. 481
Grace, Carl, Dir.-Pur.--Frequency and Time Systems, Inc., Beverly, MA; *U.S. Public*, pg. 488
Graczyk, Terry, Pur. Agent--The Wyco Tool Co., Racine, WI; *U.S. Private*, pg. 906
Graef, Paul, Mgr.-Fin.--Holiday RV Superstores, Inc.-Ft. Myers, Fort Myers, FL; *U.S. Public*, pg. 830
Grafton, Donald J., Pur. & Inventory Control Supv.--ALLTEL Answering Service, Inc., Export, PA; *U.S. Public*, pg. 55
Grafton, Donald J., Pur. & Inventory Control Supvr.--Brookville Telephone Company, Brookville, PA; *U.S. Public*, pg. 56
Graham, Evelyn, Dir.-Pur.--American Foundry Group, Inc., Bixby, OK; *U.S. Private*, pg. 54
Graham, Jack, Dir.-Pur.--Republic Automotive-AEA Division, Charlotte, NC; *U.S. Public*, pg. 1377
Graham, Joe, Mgr.-Pur.--Powermatic, McMinnville, TN; *U.S. Public*, pg. 502
Graham, L., Pur. Agent--Marlite, Dover, OH; *U.S. Private*, pg. 705
Grandmaison, George, Dir.-Pur.--Flexible Circuit Products Division, Methuen, MA; *U.S. Public*, pg. 1264
Grasse, John, Sr. V.P.-Pur. & Quality Control--Serigraph, Inc., West Bend, WI; *U.S. Private*, pg. 985
Grasu, Wanda, Dir.-Estimating--Atlantic Builders Group Inc., Baltimore, MD; *U.S. Private*, pg. 95
Gravatt, J. Glenn, V.P.-Pur.--TBC Corporation, Memphis, TN; *U.S. Public*, pg. 1553
Grave, Carlos, Dir.-Pur.--Copamex Industrias S.A. de C.V., Garza Garcia, Mexico; *Int'l*, pg. 330
Gravel, Guy, Dir.-Pur.--Panneaux Malette-OSB Inc., Saint-Georges, Canada; *Int'l*, pg. 833
Gravenhorst, Ted, Jr., Mgr.-Sls.--John Boos & Company, Effingham, IL; *U.S. Private*, pg. 156
Graves, Michael, V.P.-Pur. & Mktg.--D & K Healthcare Resources, Inc., Saint Louis, MO; *U.S. Public*, pg. 471
Gravina, John, Dir.-Pur.--The Stride Rite Corporation, Lexington, MA; *U.S. Public*, pg. 1524
Gray, Archie, Dir.-Matls.--Petroleum Helicopters, Inc., Metairie, LA; *U.S. Public*, pg. 1281

Gray, Charles, Dir.-Pur.--Kastle Systems LLC, Arlington, VA; *U.S. Private*, pg. 608
Grayson, Sandra, Dir.-Pur.--Power Conversion, Inc., Elmwood Park, NJ; *Int'l*, pg. 127
Greaves, Ian, Stock/Stores Controller--CiMatrix Ltd., Stourbridge, United Kingdom; *U.S. Public*, pg. 1395
Grebic, Robert, Pur. Agent--Hollymatic Corporation, Countryside, IL; *U.S. Private*, pg. 535
Greear, Paul L., Asst. V.P.-Procurement Services--Equifax Inc., Atlanta, GA; *U.S. Public*, pg. 588
Green, Butch, Pur. Agent--Metal Trades, Inc., Hollywood, SC; *U.S. Private*, pg. 734
Green, Robert, V.P.-Matls. Mngmt.--Ciba Specialty Chemicals, Tarrytown, NY; *Int'l*, pg. 291
Greenberg, Eugene R., V.P. & Pres.-Alumax Materials Management--Alumax Inc., Atlanta, GA; *U.S. Public*, pg. 59
Greene, Ed, V.P.-Pur.--Ponderosa Steakhouse, Dallas, TX; *U.S. Private*, pg. 736
Greene, Ed, Sr. V.P.-Pur.--Bennigan's, Dallas, TX; *U.S. Private*, pg. 736
Greenwood, Teresa, Mgr. Procurement Services--Oglethorpe Power Corp., Tucker, GA; *U.S. Private*, pg. 812
Greesey, Leslie, Dir.-Pur.--Oracle Corporation, Redwood City, CA; *U.S. Public*, pg. 1227
Greeson, Jerry, Mgr.-Pur.--Cleveland Electric Co., Atlanta, GA; *U.S. Private*, pg. 246
Gregory, Steve, Dir.-Pur.--Horton Homes, Inc., Eatonton, GA; *U.S. Private*, pg. 540
Gregory, Walter, Dir.-Pur.--Nationwide Homes, Inc., Martinsville, VA; *U.S. Private*, pg. 788
Gremillet, Bernard, V.P.-Engrng. & Tech.--Y.P.F., S.A., Buenos Aires, Argentina; *Int'l*, pg. 1515
Grenon, R., Buyer--Valley Gas Co., Cumberland, RI; *U.S. Public*, pg. 1706
Grenon, Richard, Mgr.-Pur.--Valley Resources, Inc., Cumberland, RI; *U.S. Public*, pg. 1706
Gribas, John, Dir.-Pur.--The Midland Grocery Company, Westville, IN; *U.S. Private*, pg. 948
Griffin, J.E., III, Dir.-Pur.--Union Camp Fine Paper Div., Franklin, VA; *U.S. Public*, pg. 1666
Griffith, Floyd, Mgr.-Pur.--Allison Corporation, Livingston, NJ; *U.S. Private*, pg. 41
Griffiths, Sandra, Mgr.-Pur.--Marietta Canada, Inc., Toronto, Canada; *U.S. Private*, pg. 703
Grimaldi, Ivan, V.P.-Global Procurement--Cott Corporation, Pointe-Claire, Canada; *Int'l*, pg. 337
Grimm, Bud, Dir.-Matls. Mngmt.--Central Illinois Light Company, Peoria, IL; *U.S. Public*, pg. 367
Grimm, Sherry, Dir.-Pur.--Battle Mountain Gold Company, Houston, TX; *U.S. Public*, pg. 193
Grinstead, Scott, Dir.-Pur.--Fresh America Corp., Dallas, TX; *U.S. Public*, pg. 681
Grinter, Tom, V.P.-Pur.--American Marketing Industries, Inc., Kansas City, MO; *U.S. Private*, pg. 58
Groener, Dr., Dir.-Pur.--Battenfeld GmbH, Meinerzhagen, Germany; *Int'l*, pg. 825
Gronan, Bob, Mgr.-Pur.--Britannia Music Co. Ltd., Ilford, United Kingdom; *Int'l*, pg. 1052
Groot, M.L., Dir.-Pur.--Prenatal B.V., Almere, Netherlands; *Int'l*, pg. 750
Grosshvesch, Bob, Mgr.-Pur.--Polar Ware Company, Sheboygan, WI; *U.S. Private*, pg. 873
Grotsch, Werner, Dir.-Pur.--Suspa Compart AG, Altdorf, Germany; *Int'l*, pg. 1322
Grubbs, Don, Mgr.-Pur. Petroleum--The Parman Corporation, Nashville, TN; *U.S. Private*, pg. 840
Gruber, Charles, Pur. Agent--Advance Business Graphics, Mira Loma, CA; *U.S. Private*, pg. 18
Grunewald, Ann, Mgr.-Pur--Marilyn Miglin, L.P., Chicago, IL; *U.S. Private*, pg. 745
Gu, Suqi, Pur. Agent--Harold Leonard & Company, Inc., Union, NJ; *U.S. Private*, pg. 660
Guadagho, Lou, Pur. Agent--Dothan Apparel, Inc., New York, NY; *U.S. Private*, pg. 540
Guarino, John, Mgr.-Pur.--General Railway Signal Corp., Rochester, NY; *Int'l*, pg. 1194
Gubotosi, Diane, Dir.-Pur.--Donnkenny, Inc., New York, NY; *U.S. Public*, pg. 519
Guerriero, Henry, Mgr.-Pur.--Exide Electronics Group, Inc., Raleigh, NC; *Int'l*, pg. 126
Guetens, Jack, Pur. Agent--O.F. Mossberg & Sons, Inc., North Haven, CT; *U.S. Private*, pg. 764
Guillory, Grace, Dir.-Food Pur.--IHOP Corp., Glendale, CA; *U.S. Public*, pg. 862
Guillory, Grace, Dir.-Pur.--International House of Pancakes, Inc., Glendale, CA; *U.S. Public*, pg. 862
Guipe, Dave, Dir.-Pur.--Alcoa Building Products, Inc., Sidney, OH; *U.S. Public*, pg. 61
Gullett, Scott, V.P.--First National Bank of Southwestern Ohio, Hamilton, OH; *U.S. Public*, pg. 633
Gum, Sherwood, Mgr.-Pur.--Instrument Specialties Company, Delaware Water Gap, PA; *U.S. Private*, pg. 565
Gunning, Frank, Pur. Agent--Del Mar Avionics, Irvine, CA; *U.S. Private*, pg. 321
Gurin, Ron, V.P.-Pur. & Prod. Devel.--Pressman Toy Corp., New York, NY; *U.S. Private*, pg. 882
Gustafsson, Goran, Sr. V.P.-Pur.--Skanska AB, Danderyd, Sweden; *Int'l*, pg. 1260
Gutierrez Melgar, Oscar, V.P.-Pur., Pharmaceutical Prods.--Grupo Casa Autrey, Mexico, Mexico; *Int'l*, pg. 573
Haas, Frank, Pur. Agent--Calcor Space Facility, Inc., Whittier, CA; *U.S. Private*, pg. 200
Haas, Frank, Dir.-Pur.--Grede Foundries, Inc., Milwaukee, WI; *U.S. Private*, pg. 476
Haas, G. A., Mgr.-Pur.--Bud Industries, Inc., Willoughby, OH; *U.S. Private*, pg. 178
Haas, Gary F., Mgr.-Pur.--Rudolph/Libbe, Inc., Walbridge, OH; *U.S. Private*, pg. 950
Haas, Norman, Pur. Agent--Fritz Industries Inc., Mesquite, TX; *U.S. Private*, pg. 429
Haberkorn, Charlie, V.P.-Pur.--The Dannon Co., Tarrytown, NY; *Int'l*, pg. 379
Hadden, Scott, Dir.-Pur.--Keystone Automotive Industries, Inc., Pomona, CA; *U.S. Public*, pg. 955
Haddock, David, V.P.-Pur.--Cox Wood Preserving Co., Orangeburg, SC; *U.S. Private*, pg. 283
Haddow, William, V.P.-Pur. & Trans.--Northland Cranberries, Inc., Wisconsin Rapids, WI; *U.S. Public*, pg. 1197
Hadley, Donald H., II, V.P.-Admin. Services--WSFS Financial Corporation, Wilmington, DE; *U.S. Public*, pg. 1728
Haga, Leif, Mgr.-Pur.--Wisaforest Oy Ab, Pietarsaari, Finland; *Int'l*, pg. 1429
Hagan, Mark D., Asst. V.P.--Scott & Stringfellow Financial, Inc., Richmond, VA; *U.S. Public*, pg. 1445
Hagedorn, Gene, V.P.-Matls.--Baldor Electric Company, Fort Smith, AR; *U.S. Public*, pg. 168
Hageman, Mary, Dir.-Inventory--Viking Office Products, Torrance, CA; *U.S. Public*, pg. 1720
Hager, Dan, Mgr.-Pur.--Gilroy Foods, Inc., Gilroy, CA; *U.S. Public*, pg. 428
Hagerty, Bruce, Dir.-Pur.--Hubbard Broadcasting, Inc., Saint Paul, MN; *U.S. Private*, pg. 543
Hagerty, Patrick, V.P.-Mktg. & Pur.--VSA, Inc., Denver, CO; *U.S. Public*, pg. 901
Hagsbrand, Alan, Dir.-Pur.--Cadbury Beverages North America, Stamford, CT; *Int'l*, pg. 248
Haigler, Jerry, Pur. Agent--Signtech USA, Ltd., San Antonio, TX; *U.S. Private*, pg. 999
Haines, Ron, Mgr.-Pur.--National Machinery, Tiffin, OH; *U.S. Private*, pg. 785
Haislip, Wallace, V.P.-Pur.--Scientific-Atlanta, Inc., Norcross, GA; *U.S. Public*, pg. 1443
Hakansson, Leif, V.P.-Pur.--SAS Airline, Stockholm, Sweden; *Int'l*, pg. 1201
Halberg, Flemming, Mgr.-Corp. Pur.--Sophus Berendsen A/S, Soeborg, Denmark; *Int'l*, pg. 1284
Haley, Darryl, Mgr.-Pur.--PSS, Cincinnati, OH; *U.S. Public*, pg. 1294
Halfacre, William E., Sr. V.P.-Retail & Pur.--Regis Corporation, Minneapolis, MN; *U.S. Public*, pg. 1373
Halfaker, Carol, Dir.-Pur.--Farmer Brothers Company, Torrance, CA; *U.S. Public*, pg. 613
Hall, Brian, Mgr.-Pur.--Thetford Corporation, Ann Arbor, MI; *U.S. Private*, pg. 352
Hall, Charles, Mgr.-Pur.--Wagner Systems Corporation, Greenville, SC; *Int'l*, pg. 1418
Hall, James, Dir.-Pur.--Swank, Inc., Attleboro, MA; *U.S. Public*, pg. 1543
Hall, Joseph, Dir.-Pur.--Westgate Inc., Port Allen, LA; *U.S. Private*, pg. 1169
Hall, Rod, Mgr.-Pur.--Mycogen Corporation, San Diego, CA; *U.S. Public*, pg. 1142
Hall, Ruby T., Pur. Agent--Johnson Supply & Equipment Corp., Houston, TX; *U.S. Private*, pg. 594
Hall, Tom, Dir.-Pur.--GNWC Wire, Cable & Network Products, Downers Grove, IL; *U.S. Private*, pg. 259
Hall, William, Mgr.-Pur.--United Aluminum Corporation, North Haven, CT; *U.S. Private*, pg. 1120
Hallam, W., Dir.-Pur.--Waring Products, New Hartford, CT; *U.S. Public*, pg. 286
Halldorsson, Thorbergur, Mgr.-Pur.--Landsvirkjun - The National Power Co., Reykjavik, Iceland; *Int'l*, pg. 801
Halleen, Jim, Dir.-Pur.--Big Horn Co-Op Marketing Association, Greybull, WY; *U.S. Private*, pg. 143
Hallier, Robert G., Mgr.-Pur. (Ice Cream)--Birds Eye Walls Ltd., Walton-on-Thames, United Kingdom; *Int'l*, pg. 1434
Halsted, Gordon G., Mgr.-Pur.--Reynolds Extrusion Company, Richmond Hill, Canada; *U.S. Public*, pg. 1387
Halsted, Irving, Jr., Mgr.-Pur.--Castle Rubber Co., East Butler, PA; *U.S. Public*, pg. 1258
Halyn, Walter, Pur. Agent--The Coe Manufacturing Company, Painesville, OH; *U.S. Private*, pg. 249
Hamann, James, Pur. Agent--Wausau Homes, Inc., Rothschild, WI; *U.S. Private*, pg. 1154
Hamelin, P., Corp. Dir.-Pur.--Kruger Inc., Montreal, Canada; *Int'l*, pg. 761
Hamelin, P., Dir.-Pur.--Kruger Inc., Montreal, Canada; *Int'l*, pg. 761
Hames, Frank, Mgr.-Pur.--Yardney Technical Products, Inc., Pawcatuck, CT; *U.S. Private*, pg. 376
Hamilton, Keith, Mgr.-Pur.--ECP Incorporated, Westchester, IL; *U.S. Private*, pg. 313
Hamilton, Loretta, Pur. Dir.--General Physics Corporation, Columbia, MD; *U.S. Public*, pg. 694
Hamilton, Thomas, Mgr.-Pur.--Wabash Magnetics, Huntington, IN; *U.S. Private*, pg. 351
Hamlin, S.C., Dir.-Pur. & Matls.--Bangor & Aroostook Railroad Co., Bangor, ME; *U.S. Private*, pg. 575
Hammann, Vada, Dir.-Pur.--Perry & Derrick Co., Cincinnati, OH; *U.S. Private*, pg. 854
Hammer, Chuck, Dir.-Pur.--Allied Plywood Corp., Alexandria, VA; *U.S. Private*, pg. 40
Hammerstein, John, Dir.-U.S. Pur.--Genicom Corporation, Chantilly, VA; *U.S. Public*, pg. 729
Hammons, Ron L., Sr. V.P.-Human Resources & Pur.--Johns Manville Corporation, Denver, CO; *U.S. Public*, pg. 927
Hampel, Albert, Mgr.-Admin. Services--Brazos Electric Power Cooperative, Inc., Waco, TX; *U.S. Private*, pg. 166
Hamper, Mark, Facilities Admin.--Amwest Surety Insurance Company, Calabasas, CA; *U.S. Public*, pg. 106
Hampton, Kristopher D., Sr. Mgr.-Pur.--Auto Glass Specialists, Madison, WI; *U.S. Private*, pg. 100
Hamre, Gus, Sr. Buyer--Acme Design Technology, Co., Crozet, VA; *U.S. Private*, pg. 13
Han, Kae Jeung, V.P.-Pur.--Korean Airlines Co., Ltd., Seoul, Korea; *Int'l*, pg. 758
Hanado, Kenji, Mng. Dir.--Kayaba Industry Co., Ltd., Tokyo, Japan; *Int'l*, pg. 727
Hanes, Dick, Dir.-Pur.--Aldan Industries, Philadelphia, PA; *U.S. Private*, pg. 33
Haney, Bill, Pur. Agent--Mafco Worldwide Corp., Camden, NJ; *U.S. Private*, pg. 690
Hankins, Charles, Mgr.-Pur.--Columbian Rope Company, Guntown, MS; *U.S. Private*, pg. 256
Hanks, Keith, Mgr.-Pur. & Traffic--Geneva Steel, Vineyard, UT; *U.S. Public*, pg. 729
Hanley, R.D., Pur. Agent--J.M. Huber, Oil & Gas Div., Houston, TX; *U.S. Private*, pg. 545
Hanley, Reba, Dir.-Matls. Production--Diagraph Corporation, Earth City, MO; *U.S. Private*, pg. 330
Hansel, Clark, Dir.-Pur.--Dutton-Lainson Co., Hastings, NE; *U.S. Private*, pg. 350
Hansen, Norman, Mgr.-Pur.--Mosinee Converted Products, Columbus, WI; *U.S. Public*, pg. 1747
Hansen, Paul, Pres. & Chief Exec. Officer--Penobscot Shoe Company, Old Town, ME; *U.S. Public*, pg. 1273
Hansen, Staale, Mgr.-Pur.--Scancem AB, Malmo, Sweden; *Int'l*, pg. 1198
Hanson, Chris, Mgr.-Pur.--Nady Systems, Inc., Emeryville, CA; *U.S. Private*, pg. 773
Hanson, Dale, Dir.-Pur.--Elizabethtown Gas Co., Union, NJ; *U.S. Public*, pg. 1147
Hanson, Linda A., V.P.-Mdsg. & Gemstone Acquisition--Tiffany & Co., New York, NY; *U.S. Public*, pg. 1608
Hanson, Wayne, Mgr.-Pur.--Andersen Corporation, Bayport, MN; *U.S. Private*, pg. 71
Hanson, Will, Dir.-Pur.--A.T. Cross Co., Lincoln, RI; *U.S. Public*, pg. 460
Hanson, Win, Dir.-Materials--Power-One, Inc., Camarillo, CA; *U.S. Private*, pg. 878
Harden, Jim, Dir.-Pur.--A.J. Gerrard and Company, Des Plaines, IL; *U.S. Private*, pg. 449
Hardinger, John M., V.P.-Pur. & Logistics--Du Pont (E.I. Du Pont De Nemours & Co.), Wilmington, DE; *U.S. Public*, pg. 530
Hardman, John, Mgr.-Procurement & Admin.--Nissan Motor Corporation in U.S.A., Gardena, CA; *Int'l*, pg. 945
Hardy, Ray, Dir.-Pur. & Asst. Treas.--Builders Transport, Incorporated, Camden, SC; *U.S. Public*, pg. 267
Hardyment, M.L., Pur. Agent--Airport Group International, Inc., Glendale, CA; *U.S. Public*, pg. 1009
Harmel, Bruce, Mgr.-Mdsg. & Procurement-Non-Food--Clark Foodservice, Inc., Elk Grove Village, IL; *U.S. Private*, pg. 242
Harmon, Baxter, Pur. Agent & Transportation--Blue Ridge Electric Membership Corp., Lenoir, NC; *U.S. Private*, pg. 153
Harmon, Jane Rae, Pur. Agent--Hilton Equipment Corp., Beverly Hills, CA; *U.S. Public*, pg. 829
Harper, Charles, Dir.-Matl. Procurement--Duo-Fast Corporation, Huntley, IL; *U.S. Private*, pg. 347
Harpring, Bud, Mgr.-Pur.--Amos-Hill Associates, Inc., Edinburgh, IN; *U.S. Private*, pg. 67
Harrell, Ray, Pur. Agent--Stones, Inc., Bainbridge, GA; *U.S. Private*, pg. 1045
Harrelson, Allen, Dir.-Pur.--Gilman Paper Co., Saint Marys, GA; *U.S. Private*, pg. 454
Harris, D.A., Dir.-Pur.--Pluess-Staufer Industries, Inc., Proctor, VT; *Int'l*, pg. 1061
Harris, David J., Dir.-Pur.--The Flood Company, Hudson, OH; *U.S. Private*, pg. 414
Harris, J., Pur. Agent--Hypertronics Corporation, Hudson, MA; *Int'l*, pg. 1268
Harris, Mocllelland, III, Chief Fin. Officer & V.P.-Fin.--Southern California Water Company, San Dimas, CA; *U.S. Public*, pg. 1489
Harris, Robert L., Mgr.-Pur.--Xtek, Inc., Cincinnati, OH; *U.S. Private*, pg. 1194
Harris, Tom, Dir.-Pur.--Stonecutter Mills Corp., Spindale, NC; *U.S. Private*, pg. 1044
Harrison, Jon, Pur. Mgr.--Bender Shipbuilding & Repair Company, Inc., Mobile, AL; *U.S. Private*, pg. 132
Harrod, Donald, V.P.-Engrng.--Farnam Sealing Systems Division, Troy, MI; *U.S. Public*, pg. 401
Harrod, Riley G., Dir.-Pur. & Matl. Control--SIGCORP, Inc., Evansville, IN; *U.S. Public*, pg. 1471
Harrod, Riley G., Dir.-Pur.--Southern Indiana Gas & Electric Co., Evansville, IN; *U.S. Public*, pg. 1471
Hart-Miller, Robin, Dir.-Pur.--OHM Corporation, Findlay, OH; *U.S. Public*, pg. 1207
Hart, Peter, Mgr.-Pur.--Esselte Meto BV, Nieuwegein, Netherlands; *Int'l*, pg. 461
Hart, William, V.P.-Steak 'n Shake--Consolidated Products, Inc., Indianapolis, IN; *U.S. Public*, pg. 436
Hart, William H., V.P.-Steak 'n Shake, Inc., Indianapolis, IN; *U.S. Public*, pg. 437
Hartford, John, Mgr.-Pur.--R & R Plastics, Swanton, OH; *U.S. Private*, pg. 431
Hartley, Sherry, Mgr.-Pur.--Faber Enterprises, Inc., Canoga Park, CA; *U.S. Private*, pg. 390
Hartman, Brenda, Pur. Agent--Herbalife International of America, Inc., Century City, CA; *U.S. Public*, pg. 809
Harty, Arlene, V.P.-Pur.--Bank of Boston Connecticut, Hartford, CT; *U.S. Public*, pg. 184
Hartz, William, Mgr.-Pur. & Real Estate--General Re Corporation, Stamford, CT; *U.S. Public*, pg. 725
Harvey, Wilson, Mgr.-Pur.--Mississippi Chemical Corporation, Yazoo City, MS; *U.S. Public*, pg. 1117
Hasborough, Donna, Mgr.-Pur.--American Modular Technologies, Liberty, NC; *U.S. Public*, pg. 69
Hasegawa, Hiroshi, Dir.-Pur.--Kikkoman International, Inc., San Francisco, CA; *Int'l*, pg. 733
Hassan, Khalid Shamshul, Dir.-Pur.--National Bank of Pakistan, Karachi, Pakistan; *Int'l*, pg. 907
Hastetler, Robert, Mgr.-Pur.--Bailey Controls Company, Wickliffe, OH; *Int'l*, pg. 654
Hastings, Penny, Mgr.-Pur.--Taylor Impression, Inc., Nashville, TN; *U.S. Private*, pg. 1070
Hatfield, Howard, Mgr.-Pur.--Nalle Plastics Inc., Austin, TX; *U.S. Private*, pg. 773
Hauer, Oscar, V.P.-Pur.--Fleer-Skybox International Inc., Mount Laurel, NJ; *U.S. Public*, pg. 1052
Haupt, William J., Pur. Agent--Rexair, Inc., Troy, MI; *U.S. Public*, pg. 1684
Hausmann, Bernadette, Dr., Dir.-Pur. & Strategic Tire Tech.--Continental AG, Hannover, Germany; *Int'l*, pg. 327

Hautz, Erich, Dir.-Pur. & Logistics--Siemens AG, Munich, Germany; *Int'l*, pg. 1244
Havey, Mary, Dir.-Pur.--Weyco Group, Inc., Milwaukee, WI; *U.S. Public*, pg. 1763
Hawkins, Robert, Mgr.-Pur.--Clairson International Corp., Ocala, FL; *U.S. Public*, pg. 575
Hayes, C.A., Dir.-Pur., Adv. & Mktg.--Blevins Inc., Nashville, TN; *U.S. Private*, pg. 149
Hayes, Joseph V., Dir.-Pur.--John Hancock Mutual Life Insurance Company, Boston, MA; *U.S. Private*, pg. 589
Hayes, Kim, Dir.-Pur.--Weider Nutrition Intl., Salt Lake City, UT; *U.S. Private*, pg. 1159
Hayes, Linda, Mgr.-Pur.--Harman Speaker Manufacturing, Northridge, CA; *U.S. Public*, pg. 787
Haywes, Steve, Dir.-Pur.--Suntory Water Group, Inc., Marietta, GA; *Int'l*, pg. 1321
Hazama, John, Pur. Agent--Diversified Compounders, Los Angeles, CA; *U.S. Private*, pg. 324
Hazuda, Pat, Pur. Agent--Royle Systems Group, Pompton Lakes, NJ; *U.S. Private*, pg. 949
Head, Gerry, Mng. Dir.-Mfg., Logistics & Quality--Thorn Security Group, Ltd., Sunbury, United Kingdom; *Int'l*, pg. 1386
Head, Holman, V.P.-Pur.--O'Neal Steel Inc., Birmingham, AL; *U.S. Private*, pg. 817
Head, Michael, Dir.-Pur.--Syntex, Palo Alto, CA; *Int'l*, pg. 1120
Head, Richard, Dir.-Pur.--Cummings Inc., Nashville, TN; *U.S.* Private, pg. 295
Healey, John, Mgr.-Pur.--Holiday Rambler, Wakarusa, IN; *U.S. Public*, pg. 1123
Heath, Cynthia C., V.P.-Fin. & Pur.--Inland Steel Products Company, East Chicago, IN; *U.S. Public*, pg. 879
Hebert, Patrick, Pur. Agent--American Plastic Toys Inc., Walled Lake, MI; *U.S. Private*, pg. 60
Heed, Lynn, Mgr.-Corp. Admin. Svcs.--Herff Jones Inc., Indianapolis, IN; *U.S. Private*, pg. 523
Hefner, Larry D., V.P.-Procurement--WSMP, Inc., Claremont, NC; *U.S. Public*, pg. 1729
Heidorf, Paul, Mgr.-Pur.--Ridge Tool Co., Elyria, OH; *U.S. Public*, pg. 574
Heiland, Gene, Mgr.-Pur.--York Barbell Co., Inc., York, PA; *U.S. Private*, pg. 1196
Heiman, Mark, Exec. V.P.--Standard Textile Co., Inc., Cincinnati, OH; *U.S. Private*, pg. 1032
Heimbach, Wayne, Pur. Dir.--Hawthorne Adv., Inc., Philadelphia, PA; *U.S. Private*, pg. 512
Heinl, R.D., V.P.-Pur.--ESAB Consumables, Hanover, PA; *Int'l*, pg. 281
Heinz, William, Pur. Agent & Plant Mgr.--Charles Jacquin et Cie, Inc., Philadelphia, PA; *U.S. Private*, pg. 580
Heisley, Connie, Chief Buyer & Pur.--Griffin Manufacturing Co., Muskogee, OK; *U.S. Private*, pg. 481
Helal, E., Dir.-Pur.--Abbott Laboratories/Ashland, Ashland, OH; *U.S. Public*, pg. 13
Helbley, W.C., Dir.-Pur.--Thomas Steel Strip Corp., Warren, OH; *Int'l*, pg. 756
Heller, Cyrus, V.P.-Pur.--Marquette Coppersmithing Co., Inc., Philadelphia, PA; *U.S. Private*, pg. 706
Hellmann, Allen, Asst. V.P.-Pur.--CPI Corp., Saint Louis, MO; *U.S. Public*, pg. 283
Helmrick, R., Pur. Mgr.--ITT Cannon Sealectro, New Britain, CT; *U.S. Public*, pg. 859
Helnes, Bill, Mgr.-Pur.--Pneumafil Corporation, Charlotte, NC; *U.S. Private*, pg. 873
Hence, Bobbie, Mgr.-Pur.--First Tennessee Bank National Association, Memphis, TN; *U.S. Public*, pg. 639
Hendee, M.H., V.P.-Pur.--The Murray Ohio Mfg. Co., Brentwood, TN; *Int'l*, pg. 1397
Hendershot, Judy, Pur. Agent--Fimbel Door Corporation, Whitehouse, NJ; *U.S. Private*, pg. 404
Henderson, D., Pur. Agent--Burnham Foundry Div., Zanesville, OH; *U.S. Public*, pg. 270
Henderson, S.H., Dir.-Pur.--J.M. Huber, Clay Div., Macon, GA; *U.S. Private*, pg. 545
Hendrix, Billy, Buyer--Kleer-Vu Plastics Corp., Compton, CA; *U.S. Public*, pg. 962
Henningsen, Lee, Mgr.-Pur.--Omega World Travel, Inc., Fairfax, VA; *U.S. Private*, pg. 816
Henry, Nancy, Pur. Mgr.--Bongrain Cheese USA, New Holland, PA; *Int'l*, pg. 201
Henry, Robin, Dir.-Pur.--Skyline Chili, Inc., Fairfield, OH; *U.S.* Public, pg. 1475
Hepple, John, Mng. Dir.--Lightcraft, Jeannette, PA; *U.S. Private*, pg. 749
Herchenroder, Frank, Dir.-Procurement & Mdsg.--Bozzuto's Inc., Cheshire, CT; *U.S. Public*, pg. 249
Herin, Jean, Dir.-Pur.--Iveco-Unic S.A., Trappes, France; *Int'l*, pg. 484
Hernandez, Anne, Mgr.-Pur.--Ceco Door Products, Milan, TN; *U.S. Public*, pg. 1676
Hernandez, Bonnie, Mgr.-Pur.--River Ranch Northeast, Inc., Buffalo, NY; *U.S. Private*, pg. 934
Herold, Lad, Mgr.-Pur.--H.B. Zachry, San Antonio, TX; *U.S. Private*, pg. 1203
Heroux, Kathie M., Pur. Agent--Badger Paper Mills, Inc., Peshtigo, WI; *U.S. Public*, pg. 165
Herpai, Sandor, Dir.-Pur.--Aeroplex of Central Europe Ltd., Budapest, Hungary; *Int'l*, pg. 834
Herpai, Sandor, Dir.-Pur.--Aeroplex of Central Europe Ltd., Budapest, Hungary; *U.S. Public*, pg. 1006
Herrenbruck, Ronald, Dir.-Pur. & Terminal Services--Atlas Van Lines, Inc., Evansville, IN; *U.S. Private*, pg. 97
Herrenbruck, Stanley, Dir.-Pur.--Medicalodges, Inc., Coffeyville, KS; *U.S. Private*, pg. 728
Herron, Bruce, Mgr.-Matls.--American Locker Group, Inc., Jamestown, NY; *U.S. Public*, pg. 85
Herron, Bruce, Mgr.-Pur.--American Locker Security Systems, Inc., Jamestown, NY; *U.S. Public*, pg. 86
Herron, Bruce, Mgr.-Pur.--Canadian Locker Co., Ltd., Scarborough, Canada; *U.S. Public*, pg. 86
Hershner, Warren, Mgr.-Pur. & Stores--Otter Tail Power Company, Fergus Falls, MN; *U.S. Public*, pg. 1234
Hesbon, Bruce, Pur. Agent--Everfresh Beverages Inc., Chicago, IL; *U.S. Public*, pg. 1153
Hesmond, Thomas, Dir.-Pur.--National Engineering & Contracting Co., Strongsville, OH; *U.S. Private*, pg. 782
Hess, Donald, Dir.-Continuous Process Improvement & Pur.--OshKosh B'Gosh, Inc., Oshkosh, WI; *U.S. Public*, pg. 1232
Hessinger, Ray, Pur. Agent--Eberline Instrument Corporation, Santa Fe, NM; *U.S. Public*, pg. 1593
Heubel, Lucia, Dir.-Pur.--Magnetic Analysis Corp., Mount Vernon, NY; *U.S. Private*, pg. 695
Heuser, Mike, V.P.-Pur.--Kitchen Kompact, Inc., Jeffersonville, IN; *U.S. Private*, pg. 624
Hewitt, Dave, Mgr.-Pur.--Dayton Rogers Mfg. Co., Blaine, MN; *U.S. Private*, pg. 318
Hewitt, R.S., Mgr.-Pur.--Kaufman Footwear, Kitchener, Canada; *Int'l*, pg. 725
Hewlett, Mary, Dir.-Pur.--Cigna Corp., Philadelphia, PA; *U.S. Public*, pg. 356
Hewlett, Steve, Mgr.-Pur.--Earp Distribution Center, Kansas City, KS; *U.S. Private*, pg. 356
Hieland, David, Dir.-Pur.--Rawlings Sporting Goods Company, Fenton, MO; *U.S. Public*, pg. 1361
Hielman, L., Pur. Agent--Ajax Magnethermic Corp., Warren, OH; *Int'l*, pg. 113
Higdon, Lawrence, V.P.-Pur.--Morgan Foods, Inc., Austin, IN; *U.S. Private*, pg. 761
Higgins, Jerry, Dir.-Pur.--Georgia/Durango Boot Company, Franklin, TN; *U.S. Public*, pg. 1684
Higginson, William J., V.P.-Production--Journal Register Company, Trenton, NJ; *U.S. Public*, pg. 934
Highley, A., Sr. Buyer--Firestone Textiles Company, Woodstock, Canada; *Int'l*, pg. 214
Hilbert, William A., Dir.-Pur.--Paragon Health Network, Inc., Atlanta, GA; *U.S. Public*, pg. 1256
Hilbrant, Richard, Pur. Agent--Williams, White & Co., Moline, IL; *U.S. Private*, pg. 1179
Hill, Greg, Mgr.-Pur.--GF Office Furniture Ltd., Gallatin, TN; *U.S. Private*, pg. 434
Hill, Greg, Mgr.-Pur.--GF Office Furniture, Canfield, OH; *U.S.* Private, pg. 435
Hill, Jerry, Dir.-Pur.--United Service Equipment Company, Murfreesboro, TN; *U.S. Public*, pg. 1507
Hill, Jim, Dir.-Pur.--Key Cadillac, Inc., Edina, MN; *U.S. Private*, pg. 617
Hill, Joseph G., Chief Fin. Officer, V.P.-Fin., Treas. & Sec.--DMI Furniture Inc., Louisville, KY; *U.S. Public*, pg. 473
Hill, Linda, Dir.-Pur. & Mfg.--Blue Coral Systems, Tucson, AZ; *U.S. Public*, pg. 1348
Hill, Maria, Mgr.-Pur.--Federal Screw Works, Detroit, MI; *U.S. Public*, pg. 616
Hill, Sharon, Pur. Agent--Advanced Telemarketing Corp., Irving, TX; *U.S. Public*, pg. 11
Hill, W.J., Dir.-Matls.--Comdial Corporation, Charlottesville, VA; *U.S. Public*, pg. 407
Hillas, D.K.N., Mgr.-Pur.--Meyer International PLC, London, United Kingdom; *Int'l*, pg. 864
Hillas, Douglas, Dir.-Pur.--Meyer Forest Products Ltd, London, United Kingdom; *Int'l*, pg. 864
Hillebrond, E., Dir.-Pur.--F.B. Wright Co., Dearborn, MI; *U.S. Private*, pg. 1192
Hiller, Judy, Buyer--McLaughlin Manufacturing Company, Greenville, SC; *U.S. Private*, pg. 724
Hilliker, Addis T., Dir.-Matls. & Logistics--Banta Corporation, Menasha, WI; *U.S. Public*, pg. 187
Hillpot, William, V.P.-Materials Mngmt. & Wire Opers.--Northwestern Steel & Wire Co., Sterling, IL; *U.S. Public*, pg. 1201
Himes, Patti, Pur. Agent--Apollo Colors Inc., Northbrook, IL; *U.S. Private*, pg. 77
Hindman, David, Dir.-Pur.--NCH Corporation, Irving, TX; *U.S.* Public, pg. 1145
Hineman, James, Dir.-Pur.--Tri-City Electrical Contractors Inc., Altamonte Springs, FL; *U.S. Private*, pg. 1100
Hinrichsen, Ross A., Dir.-Global Pur.--Binks Sames Corporation, Franklin Park, IL; *U.S. Public*, pg. 229
Hipple, Richard J., Sr. V.P.-Pur., Engrng. & Strategic Plng.--The LTV Corporation, Cleveland, OH; *U.S. Public*, pg. 971
Hira, Jack, Mgr.-Pur.--Salton/Maxim Housewares, Inc., Mount Prospect, IL; *U.S. Public*, pg. 1430
Hirako, Shozo, Dir.-Pur.--Toyota Motor Corporation, Tokyo, Japan; *Int'l*, pg. 1411
Hirsch, Jamie, V.P.-Mfg. & Pur.--Structural Industries, Inc., Hicksville, NY; *U.S. Private*, pg. 1048
Hitch, Arthur, Pur. Agent--Allied Old English, Inc., Port Reading, NJ; *U.S. Private*, pg. 39
Hitzeman, Francis, Dir.-Pur.--World's Finest Chocolate, Inc., Chicago, IL; *U.S. Private*, pg. 1191
Hlavacek, James C., V.P.--Minerallac Co., Addison, IL; *U.S. Private*, pg. 750
Hnatyshin, Don, V.P.-Corp. Procurement--Newbridge Networks Corporation, Kanata, Canada; *Int'l*, pg. 923
Hoag, Joel, Mgr.-Pur.--WildHawk, Inc., Wisconsin Rapids, WI; *U.S. Public*, pg. 1197
Hockensmith, Charlie, Dir.-New Homes--The Van Metres Companies, Burke, VA; *U.S. Private*, pg. 1132
Hodges, James, Dir.-Pur.--KONE Lifts Ltd., Hounslow, United Kingdom; *Int'l*, pg. 747
Hodges, Robert, Dir.-Pur.--Sommer Metalcraft Corporation, Crawfordsville, IN; *U.S. Private*, pg. 1013
Hodgson, Terry May, Pur. Agent--Hilton Equipment Corp., Beverly Hills, CA; *U.S. Public*, pg. 829
Hoel, Jim, Dir.-Pur.--Harvest States Cooperatives, Saint Paul, MN; *U.S. Private*, pg. 508
Hoepner, Larry R., Dir.-Pur.--National Presto Industries, Inc., Eau Claire, WI; *U.S. Public*, pg. 1159
Hoffman, Bob, Dir.-Pur.--Netzsch Incorporated, Exton, PA; *U.S. Private*, pg. 792
Hoffman, Emma, V.P.-Pur.--TII Industries, Inc., Copiague, NY; *U.S. Public*, pg. 1556
Hoffman, Joe, Dir.-Pur.--Hale-Halsell Company, Tulsa, OK; *U.S. Private*, pg. 494
Hoffman, Minna, Dir.-Pur.--Forest Laboratories, Inc., New York, NY; *U.S. Public*, pg. 670
Hoffman, Robert, Mgr.-Pur.--FWD/Seagrave Fire Apparatus, Inc., Clintonville, WI; *U.S. Private*, pg. 390
Hoffman, S., Pur. Agent--American Crane & Equipment Corp., Douglassville, PA; *U.S. Private*, pg. 52
Hoffman, Steve, Mgr.-Pur.--Excel Technology, Inc., New York, NY; *U.S. Public*, pg. 599
Hofmann, W.H., Jr., Dir.-Pur.--Sandvik Sorting Systems, Louisville, KY; *Int'l*, pg. 1186
Hogan, Ned, Pur. Mgr.--Grizzard, Atlanta, GA; *U.S. Private*, pg. 482
Hogle, Gloria, Pur. Agent--Preferred Utilities Manufacturing Corp., Danbury, CT; *U.S. Private*, pg. 881
Hoglen, Geny, Office Mgr. & Pur. Agent--Wellco Enterprises, Inc., Waynesville, NC; *U.S. Public*, pg. 1752
Hogue, Brad, Mgr.-Pur.--Barber Industries, Inc., Edmonton, Canada; *Int'l*, pg. 164
Hogye, Tom, Pur. Agent--Salz Leathers, Inc., Santa Cruz, CA; *U.S. Private*, pg. 963
Hojvall, Leif, Mgr.-Pur.--Iggesund Paperboard AB, Iggesund, Sweden; *Int'l*, pg. 886
Holden, John, Mgr.-Pur. & Adv.--Victory Packaging, Plymouth, MI; *U.S. Private*, pg. 1139
Holderman, Jan, Mgr.-Pur.--ATMI, Inc., Danbury, CT; *U.S. Public*, pg. 12
Holgado, R.V., V.P.-Quality & Pur.--Houghton International Inc., Valley Forge, PA; *U.S. Private*, pg. 541
Holifield, Steve, Dir.-Engrng. & Pur.--Peavey Electronics Corp., Meridian, MS; *U.S. Private*, pg. 845
Holland, Steve, Dir.-Pur.--Carolina Builders Corporation, Marietta, GA; *Int'l*, pg. 1512
Hollnagel, Daryl, Dir.-Human Resources & Pur.--Continental General Tire, Inc., Charlotte, NC; *Int'l*, pg. 327
Holloway, Michael, Pur. Agent--Hershey Chocolate U.S.A.-Western Plant, Oakdale, CA; *U.S. Public*, pg. 812
Holman, Donald R., Div. V.P.-Pur. & Mdsg.--Walgreen Co., Deerfield, IL; *U.S. Public*, pg. 1733
Holman, John, Mgr.-Matls.--Spangler Candy Company, Bryan, OH; *U.S. Private*, pg. 1020
Holmes, Jason, Dir.-Pur.--ACS Mistermesh, Houston, TX; *U.S. Private*, pg. 4
Holmes, Roland, Pur. Agent--Metalloy Corporation, Hudson, MI; *U.S. Private*, pg. 735
Holt, Billy, Pur. Agent--Carroll's Foods, Inc., Warsaw, NC; *U.S. Private*, pg. 215
Holtman, Danny, Pur.-Agent--Hirschfeld, Inc., San Angelo, TX; *U.S. Private*, pg. 530
Holtman, Danny S., Pur. Agent--Hirschfeld Steel Company, Inc., San Angelo, TX; *U.S. Private*, pg. 531
Holtman, Ray, Dir.-Pur.--The Barden Corporation, Danbury, CT; *Int'l*, pg. 468
Honeycutt, Tim, Dir.-Procurement--Food Lion, Inc., Salisbury, NC; *Int'l*, pg. 463
Hong, Dong-Peu, Mng. Dir.--Ssangyong Oil Refining Co. Ltd., Seoul, Korea; *Int'l*, pg. 1292
Hong, Sa-Seung, Chief Fin. Officer--Ssangyong Cement Industrial Co., Ltd., Seoul, Korea; *Int'l*, pg. 1291
Hoover, Richard J., Dir.-Pur.--York International Corporation, York, PA; *U.S. Public*, pg. 1789
Hopkins, James, V.P.-Pur.--Southern Electric Supply Co., Inc., Meridian, MS; *Int'l*, pg. 1107
Hopkins, Tom, Pur. Agent--C.W. Zumbiel Company, Norwood, OH; *U.S. Private*, pg. 1207
Hopper, Frank, Asst. Exec. Dir.-Procurement & Support Svcs.--NJ Transit, Newark, NJ; *U.S. Private*, pg. 794
Horensky, Tom, Mgr.-Pur.--CENTRIA, Moon Township, PA; *U.S. Private*, pg. 225
Horne, Carol, Dir.-Pur.--Narrow Fabric Industries, Inc., Reading, PA; *U.S. Private*, pg. 774
Hornsby, Kathy, Mgr.-Pur.--Doctors Hospital of Shreveport, Shreveport, LA; *U.S. Public*, pg. 1697
Horsfall, Jana, Mgr.-Pur.--Sunflower Electric Power Corporation, Hays, KS; *U.S. Private*, pg. 1052
Horta, Carmen, Mgr.-Pur.--Gingiss International, Addison, IL; *U.S. Private*, pg. 455
Hottinger, Richard L., Chief Procurement Officer & V.P.--Owens Corning, Toledo, OH; *U.S. Public*, pg. 1236
Hougland, Steve, Dir.-Pur.--KYB Industries Inc., Franklin, IN; *Int'l*, pg. 727
Houle, Jean Claude, Dir.-Pur.--Davie Industries Inc., Levis, Canada; *Int'l*, pg. 385
Hourigan, Jerry, Mgr.-Pur.--Charter One Bank, Cleveland, OH; *U.S. Public*, pg. 336
Houser, Lynn, Mgr.-Matls.--Schult Homes Corporation, Plainville, KS; *U.S. Public*, pg. 1442
Housey, Daniel H., V.P. & Dir.-Pur.--Orleans Materials & Equipment Co., Inc., New Orleans, LA; *U.S. Private*, pg. 820
Howard, Hagnes, Mgr.-Pur.--Rocco Farm Foods, Inc., Edinburg, VA; *U.S. Private*, pg. 937
Howard, Steve, Dir.-Pur.--Florida Rock Industries, Inc., Jacksonville, FL; *U.S. Public*, pg. 655
Howell, John, Mgr. Pur.--Electrical Insulation Suppliers, Atlanta, GA; *U.S. Private*, pg. 368
Huang, Kenny, Mgr.-Pur.--China Steel Chemical Corp., Kaohsiung, Taiwan; *Int'l*, pg. 286
Hub, Christopher, Dir.-Pur.--Ed Miniat, Inc., Chicago, IL; *U.S.* Private, pg. 750
Hubbard, Bob M., Sr. V.P.-Pur. & Engrng.--TBC Corporation, Memphis, TN; *U.S. Public*, pg. 1553
Hubbard, Frank, V.P.-Pur.--Huls America Inc., Somerset, NJ; *Int'l*, pg. 1455
Hubbard, Stephen H., Dir.-Matls.--Meridian Diagnostics, Inc., Cincinnati, OH; *U.S. Public*, pg. 1094
Huber, R.E., Dir.-Matls. & Pur. Svcs.--Orange and Rockland Utilities, Inc., Pearl River, NY; *U.S. Public*, pg. 1229
Hubler, Richard, Mgr.-Pur.--Provident Mutual Life Insurance Co., Berwyn, PA; *U.S. Private*, pg. 891
Huck, Gary J., Dir.-Matls.--Crenlo, Inc., Rochester, MN; *U.S.* Private, pg. 288
Hudak, Eugene, Mgr.-Pur.--TRW Inc., Cleveland, OH; *U.S. Public*, pg. 1558

Hudash, Ronald, Dir.-Pur.--MTL Inc., Plant City, FL; *U.S. Public*, pg. 1028
Hudash, Ronald, Dir.-Pur.--Montgomery Tank Lines, Inc., Plant City, FL; *U.S. Public*, pg. 1028
Hudepohl, Robert, Dir.-Pur.--ITT A-C Pump/ITT Marlow, Cincinnati, OH; *U.S. Public*, pg. 860
Hudson, Sandy, Dir.-Pur.--VASA Brougher, Inc., Indianapolis, IN; *Int'l*, pg. 464
Huff, Robert J., Gen. Mgr.-Pur.--Steelox Systems Inc., Mason, OH; *U.S. Private*, pg. 1038
Huffman, H., Mgr.-Matls.--American Welding & Manufacturing Co., Warren, OH; *U.S. Private*, pg. 425
Huffman, Wes, Pur. Agent--Lee Grocery Company, Everett, WA; *U.S. Private*, pg. 657
Huggins, Richard, Plant Mgr.--Sackner-Southeast Div., Statesville, NC; *U.S. Public*, pg. 924
Huggins, T.G., Mgr.-Pur.--Central Hudson Gas & Electric Corporation, Poughkeepsie, NY; *U.S. Public*, pg. 324
Hughes, Marion, Mgr.-Pur.--Grist Mill Company, Danville, IL; *U.S. Public*, pg. 766
Hughs, Bill, Mgr.-Pur.--Troy Corporation, Florham Park, NJ; *U.S. Private*, pg. 1105
Hulings, Henry B., Pur. Agent--McCourt Label Co., Lewis Run, PA; *U.S. Private*, pg. 720
Hull, Frank, Dir.-Pur.--BE & K, Inc., Birmingham, AL; *U.S. Private*, pg. 106
Hull, Joe, Dir.-Natl. Pur.--Elixir Industries, Gardena, CA; *U.S. Private*, pg. 371
Hulsey, C.B., Jr., V.P.-Pur.--Unisource, Doraville, GA; *U.S. Public*, pg. 1671
Humby, W. S., Dir.-Grp. Pur.--National Westminster Bank PLC, London, United Kingdom; *Int'l*, pg. 910
Humphries, R.A., Buyer-Raw Matls.--American Welding & Manufacturing Co., Warren, OH; *U.S. Private*, pg. 425
Hunt, Elizabeth, Mgr.-Pur.--The Grieve Corporation, Round Lake, IL; *U.S. Private*, pg. 480
Hunt, Peter, Pur. Agent--Quintron Systems, Inc., Santa Maria, CA; *U.S. Private*, pg. 901
Huntley, R., Mgr.-Stock & Pur.--Australian Oil & Gas Corporation Limited, Sydney, Australia; *Int'l*, pg. 101
Huntley, William, V.P.-Opers.--Autotote Corporation, Newark, DE; *U.S. Public*, pg. 150
Hurs, M., Dir.-Pur.--Boon Edam Inc., Salt Lake City, UT; *Int'l*, pg. 202
Hurst, Frank, Sr. V.P.--Carpenter Co., Richmond, VA; *U.S. Private*, pg. 214
Hurst, Louis, Mgr.-Pur.--Universal Dynamics, Inc., Woodbridge, VA; *Int'l*, pg. 484
Husband, Kenneth W., V.P.-Pur.--R&B, Inc., Colmar, PA; *U.S. Public*, pg. 1354
Huschke, Wolfram, Dir.-Purchasing--Zappa Plastics, Phillipsburg, NJ; *U.S. Private*, pg. 172
Husted, Robert D., V.P. & Dir.-Pur.--ANESCO, Kingston, PA; *U.S. Private*, pg. 74
Hutchenson, Jim, Dir.-Pur.--Hardee's Food Systems, Inc., Rocky Mount, NC; *U.S. Public*, pg. 278
Hutchins, Janet, Sr. Mgr.-Admin. Services--Port of Portland, Portland, OR; *U.S. Private*, pg. 876
Hutchins, Warren, V.P.-Purchasing--Ground Round Inc., Braintree, MA; *U.S. Public*, pg. 766
Hutchinson, B.J., Mgr.-Pur.--A.P. Green Industries, Inc., Mexico, MO; *U.S. Public*, pg. 761
Hutchinson, James, Sr. V.P.-Pur.--Fast Food Merchandisers Inc., Rocky Mount, NC; *U.S. Public*, pg. 278
Hutchinson, Milt, Dir.-Pur.--Modern Equipment Rentals Inc., Wilmington, DE; *U.S. Private*, pg. 754
Hutchison, George, Dir.-Pur.--Dataproducts Corporation, Simi Valley, CA; *Int'l*, pg. 620
Hutton, Nancy, Controller, Treas. & Sec.--Crustbuster, Inc., Dodge City, KS; *U.S. Private*, pg. 293
Huybreckts, Yan, Non-TV Buying Dir.--The Media Centre, London, United Kingdom; *Int'l*, pg. 852
Hvizda, Bill, Mgr.-Pur.--Emcee Broadcast Products, Inc., White Haven, PA; *U.S. Public*, pg. 570
Hynes, John, Mgr.-Engrng.--Samtec Inc., New Albany, IN; *U.S. Private*, pg. 963
Hyttel, Chuck, V.P.-Pur.--Sta-Rite Industries, Inc., Delavan, WI; *U.S. Public*, pg. 1767
Hyvarinen, Pirjo K., Dir.-Pur.--Sesto, Helsinki, Finland; *Int'l*, pg. 1301
Ibach, Thomas, Pur. Agent--Western States Envelope Co., Milwaukee, WI; *U.S. Private*, pg. 1168
Ibraham, Nestor, Dir.-Pur.--Stainless Incorporated, Deerfield Beach, FL; *U.S. Private*, pg. 1029
Ierardi, Dominic, Dir.-Pur.--Marson/Creative Fastener, Inc., Stoughton, MA; *U.S. Private*, pg. 708
Iesalniks, Ray, Mgr- Pur.--Lincoln Steel, Lincoln, NE; *U.S. Private*, pg. 824
Igicl, Bob, Exec. V.P.-Brdcst. Programming & Pur.--Young & Rubicam New York, New York, NY; *U.S. Private*, pg. 1198
Ignasiak, Gordon K., Mgr.-Pur.--Rapid Engineering Inc., Comstock Park, MI; *U.S. Private*, pg. 910
Ihrake, Steve, Dir.-Pur.--Krier Foods, Inc., Brown Deer, WI; *U.S. Private*, pg. 636
Iino, Bungo, Dir.-Tech. Mgmt. Coord.--National Steel Corp., Granite City Division, Granite City, IL; *Int'l*, pg. 902
Ilberman, Barry, V.P.-Pur.--Northeast Utilities, Berlin, CT; *U.S. Public*, pg. 1194
Imel, Cindy,, Mgr.-Pur.--Caddock Electronics, Inc., Riverside, CA; *U.S. Private*, pg. 198
Indahl, Sonya, Mgr.-Pur.--Barr Laboratories Inc., Pomona, NY; *U.S. Public*, pg. 191
Indeck, Michael, Dir.-Pur.--Miniature Precision Components, Walworth, WI; *U.S. Private*, pg. 750
Ingargiola, John, Mgr.-Pur.--Chase Corporation, Braintree, MA; *U.S. Public*, pg. 337
Ingargiola, John, Mgr.-Pur.--Chase & Sons Division, Randolph, MA; *U.S. Public*, pg. 337
Ingle, Herston, Dir.-Pur.--Affiliated Foods Southwest, Little Rock, AR; *U.S. Private*, pg. 26
Ingram, Robert J., V.P.-Pur.--Installation Products Div., Lancaster, PA; *U.S. Public*, pg. 132
Ingram, William, Mgr.-Pur.--Artistic Greetings, Inc., Elmira, NY; *U.S. Public*, pg. 136
Inoue, T., Dir.-Pur.--Mikuni Corporation, Tokyo, Japan; *Int'l*, pg. 867
Instone, John, Mgr.-Pur.--SL Waber, Inc., Mount Laurel, NJ; *U.S. Public*, pg. 1419
Instone, John, Mgr.-Pur.--SL Waber, Nogales, AZ; *U.S. Public*, pg. 1419
Iozzo, Virginia, Dir.-Pur.--Sigmund Cohn Corp., Mount Vernon, NY; *U.S. Private*, pg. 250
Irizarry, Henry, Dir.-Pur.--Hinkley Lighting Inc., Cleveland, OH; *U.S. Private*, pg. 530
Irwin, Clark, Grp. V.P.-Distr. & Commodity Pur.--Tyson Foods, Inc., Springdale, AR; *U.S. Public*, pg. 1652
Irwin, W.P., Mgr.-Matls.--Crane Resistoflex/Defense, Jacksonville, FL; *U.S. Public*, pg. 457
Isenberg, Gary, Pur. Agent--Larson Manufacturing Company, Brookings, SD; *U.S. Private*, pg. 652
Ishida, Youichi, Dir.-Pur.--Sankyo Company Limited, Tokyo, Japan; *Int'l*, pg. 1189
Isleib, L. R., Pur. Agent--Permacel Tape, North Brunswick, NJ; *U.S. Public*, pg. 153
Itoh, Jiko, Dir.-Pur.--Matsushita Electric Works, Ltd., Osaka, Japan; *Int'l*, pg. 847
Jackson, Craig, V.P.-Pur.--Chancellor Corporation, Boston, MA; *U.S. Public*, pg. 335
Jackson, Jeannine, Mgr.-Pur.--Nuttall Gear Corporation, Niagara Falls, NY; *U.S. Private*, pg. 809
Jackson, Randy, Mgr.-Pur.--Southwest Gas Corporation, Las Vegas, NV; *U.S. Public*, pg. 1493
Jackson, Riley, V.P.-Mktg., Pur. & Adv.--Federal Savings Bank, Fort Smith, AR; *U.S. Private*, pg. 614
Jackson, Sandy, Pur. Agent-Equipment--SGD International Corp., Riverdale, NY; *U.S. Private*, pg. 957
Jackson, Vanessa, Mgr.-Pur.--Elgin Dairy Foods, Inc., Chicago, IL; *U.S. Private*, pg. 370
Jacobs, Barbara, Mgr.-Pur.--Dean Operations Inc., Kansas City, MO; *U.S. Private*, pg. 318
Jacobs, Eli, Dir.-Pur.--Nuarc Company, Inc., Niles, IL; *U.S. Private*, pg. 808
Jacobs, Jack, V.P.-Pur. & Sec.--Allou Health & Beauty Care, Inc., Brentwood, NY; *U.S. Public*, pg. 55
Jacobs, Joe, Dir.-Matls. & Service Mngmt.--Kansas City Power & Light Company, Kansas City, MO; *U.S. Public*, pg. 943
Jacobson, Rick, Dir.-Pur.--Colorado National Bank, Denver, CO; *U.S. Public*, pg. 1680
Jacobusse, David, V.P.-Purchasing--AmeriServe of Grand Rapids, Grand Rapids, MI; *U.S. Private*, pg. 533
Jacquays, Collen, Mgr.-Pur.--The F.X. Matt Brewing Co., Utica, NY; *U.S. Private*, pg. 714
Jaffarian, Franklin Z., Dir.-Matls.--Commonwealth Gas Co., Cambridge, MA; *U.S. Public*, pg. 415
Jaffe, Gerald, Dir.-Matls. Mngmt.--Velsicol Chemical Corporation, Rosemont, IL; *U.S. Private*, pg. 1135
Jager, Frans, Mgr.-Pur.--Lesco, Inc., Rocky River, OH; *U.S. Public*, pg. 989
Jagger, Nikki, Mgr.-Pur.--DSP Technology Inc., Fremont, CA; *U.S. Public*, pg. 475
Jakobek, Fred, Dir.-Matls.--OmniQuip International, Inc., Port Washington, WI; *U.S. Private*, pg. 500
Jamison, Gary, Pur. Agent--Bates Container, Inc., North Richland Hills, TX; *U.S. Private*, pg. 122
Janczak, Barbara, Pur. Agent--Telsmith, Inc., Mequon, WI; *U.S. Public*, pg. 141
Jankowiak, Uwe, Mgr.-Intl. Pur. & Quality Control--Traub AG, Reichenbach, Germany; *Int'l*, pg. 1419
Jansen, J.K., V.P.-Pur.--Electric Power Equipment Co., Columbus, OH; *U.S. Private*, pg. 368
Janson, Charles, Dir.-Pur.--Great Lakes Confectionery, Cleveland, OH; *Int'l*, pg. 865
Jarder, Jerome C., Grp. Mgr.-Pur.--Benguet Corporation, Manila, Philippines; *Int'l*, pg. 186
Jarred, Sandy, Mgr.-Pur. & Admin.--Lodgistix, Inc., Phoenix, AZ; *U.S. Public*, pg. 1527
Jarvi, Tom C., V.P.-Maintenance & Pur.--Consolidated Freightways Corp., Menlo Park, CA; *U.S. Public*, pg. 435
Jarvis, Perry, Gen. Mgr.-Logistics--Bruncor, Inc., Saint John, Canada; *Int'l*, pg. 230
Jarzonski, Marty, Dir-Pur. & Distr.--Patrick Industries Inc., Elkhart, IN; *U.S. Public*, pg. 1264
Jastrow, William A., Dir.-Pur.--Amdahl Corporation, Sunnyvale, CA; *Int'l*, pg. 527
Je, Man-Ho, Chief Fin. Officer--Ssangyong Information & Communication Corporation, Seoul, Korea; *Int'l*, pg. 1292
Jech, Z.O., Mgr.-Pur.--Nalco Chemical Company, Naperville, IL; *U.S. Public*, pg. 1150
Jefferlone, Mike, Pur. Agent--Gaymar Industries, Inc., Orchard Park, NY; *U.S. Private*, pg. 442
Jefferson, John, Dir.-Tech. Svcs.-Ayer--Cains Foods, L.P., Ayer, MA; *U.S. Private*, pg. 199
Jenkins, Mary, Sec.--Coral Oil & Gas Inc., Houston, TX; *U.S. Private*, pg. 275
Jensen, Don, Pur. Agent--Hanna-Sherman International, Inc., Portland, OR; *U.S. Private*, pg. 499
Jensen, Jack, Dir.-Pur.--Lawson Mechanical Contractors, Sacramento, CA; *U.S. Private*, pg. 654
Jensen, Peggy, Dir.-Pur.--American Antenna Corp, Elgin, IL; *U.S. Private*, pg. 207
Jenz, Jung, Mgr.-Central Nonfood Pur.--Coop Switzerland, Basel, Switzerland; *Int'l*, pg. 329
Jerin, Joseph, Pur. Agent--Laubeck Corporation/Cross, Carbondale, PA; *U.S. Private*, pg. 652
Jeter, Carl L., Mgr.-Pur.--Consumer Products Div., San Francisco, CA; *U.S. Public*, pg. 1318
Johanson, Roland, Mgr.-Pur.--Esselte Wensbo AB, Malmo, Sweden; *Int'l*, pg. 459
Johansson, Bernt, Mgr.-Pur.--Cementa AB (Degerhamn), Degerhamn, Sweden; *Int'l*, pg. 1199
Johansson, Gerhard, Mgr.-Pur.--Svenskt Papper AB, Stockholm, Sweden; *Int'l*, pg. 886
Johansson, Hakan, Pur. Agent--Myresjo AB, Vetlanda, Sweden; *Int'l*, pg. 1260
Johansson, Kenth, Mgr.-Pur.--Cementa AB (Skovde), Skovde, Sweden; *Int'l*, pg. 1199
Johansson, Ulf, Pur. Agent--Skanska Stalteknik AB, Kalmar, Sweden; *Int'l*, pg. 1261
John, Pamela, V.P.--Versar Inc., Springfield, VA; *U.S. Public*, pg. 1717
John, Sam, Dir.-Pur.--Sanderson Plumbing Products Inc., Columbus, MS; *U.S. Private*, pg. 964
John, Sam, Pur.--Beneke, Columbus, MS; *U.S. Private*, pg. 964
Johnson, Bobby L., Jr., V.P.-Distr.--Gwaltney of Smithfield, Ltd., Smithfield, VA; *U.S. Public*, pg. 1479
Johnson, Bruce, V.P.-Pur.--A.G. Simpson Co. Limited, Scarborough, Canada; *Int'l*, pg. 1252
Johnson, Craig, Dir.-Pur.--Hubbard Feeds Inc., Mankato, MN; *Int'l*, pg. 1116
Johnson, D., Mgr.-Pur.--Bryant Grinder Corp., Springfield, VT; *U.S. Private*, pg. 461
Johnson, Darrel, Mgr.-Pur.--Olympic Steel Inc., Cleveland, OH; *U.S. Public*, pg. 1221
Johnson, David, Dir.-Pur. & Telecommunications--Heery International, Inc., Atlanta, GA; *U.S. Private*, pg. 519
Johnson, Dee, Dir.-Pur.--O'Sullivan Corporation, Winchester, VA; *U.S. Public*, pg. 1234
Johnson, Dennis, Dir.-Pur.--Guilford Mills, Inc., Greensboro, NC; *U.S. Public*, pg. 768
Johnson, Don, Dir.-Pur.--American Metal & Plastics Inc., Grand Rapids, MI; *U.S. Private*, pg. 59
Johnson, Don, Pur. Dir.--Sloan Technology, Santa Barbara, CA; *U.S. Public*, pg. 1711
Johnson, Ernie, Dir.-Pur.--Alaska Airlines, Inc., Seattle, WA; *U.S. Public*, pg. 35
Johnson, John, V.P.-Mfg. & Pur.--Reliable Knitting Works, Milwaukee, WI; *U.S. Private*, pg. 920
Johnson, Junior, Pur. Agent--American Fast Print, Limited, Spartanburg, SC; *U.S. Private*, pg. 53
Johnson, Kimberly F., Mgr.-Pur. & Matl. Control--Illinois Power Company, Decatur, IL; *U.S. Public*, pg. 869
Johnson, Lynn, Pur. Agent--Quill Corp., Lincolnshire, IL; *U.S. Private*, pg. 901
Johnson, Mark K., Chm. Bd. & Chief Exec. Officer--Johnson Storage Moving Co, Denver, CO; *U.S. Private*, pg. 594
Johnson, Mark K., Mgr.--Johnson Moving & Storage, Naperville, IL; *U.S. Private*, pg. 594
Johnson, Raymond L., V.P.-Procurement--Carmun International, San Antonio, TX; *Int'l*, pg. 646
Johnson, Tom, Mgr.-Pur.--Sierracin Corporation, Sylmar, CA; *U.S. Private*, pg. 999
Johnson, Tom, Dir.-Pur.--Sierracin/Sylmar Corporation, Sylmar, CA; *U.S. Private*, pg. 999
Johnson, Wendy, Mgr.-Pur.--Unitrode Corporation, Merrimack, NH; *U.S. Public*, pg. 1694
Johnston, Stephan, Dir.-Pur.--UniSea Foods, Inc., Redmond, WA; *Int'l*, pg. 940
Jolliff, K.L., V.P.-Pur.--The Cooper Tire Company, Findlay, OH; *U.S. Public*, pg. 445
Jolliff, Keith L., V.P.-Pur.--Cooper Tire & Rubber Company, Findlay, OH; *U.S. Public*, pg. 445
Jones, Bob, Mgr.-Plant--United States Lock & Hardware Co., Columbia, PA; *U.S. Private*, pg. 1196
Jones, Donald M., Sr. V.P.-Pur.--Owen Health Care, Inc., Houston, TX; *U.S. Public*, pg. 304
Jones, Ed, Mgr.-Pur.--Todd & Sargent, Inc., Ames, IA; *U.S. Private*, pg. 1089
Jones, F.T., Dir.-Pur.--Oasis Corp., Columbus, OH; *U.S. Private*, pg. 810
Jones, Harry, Mgr.-Pur.--Printing House, Inc., Quincy, FL; *U.S. Private*, pg. 886
Jones, Jacob, Dir.-Pur.--World Carpets, Inc., Dalton, GA; *U.S. Private*, pg. 1190
Jones, Jim, Dir.-Pur.--Atmos Energy Corporation, Dallas, TX; *U.S. Public*, pg. 145
Jones, Jim, Mgr.-Pur.--Circle International Group, Inc., San Francisco, CA; *U.S. Public*, pg. 370
Jones, Jim, Dir.-Pur.--Circle Freight International (U.S.A.), San Francisco, CA; *U.S. Public*, pg. 370
Jones, Jon, Mgr.-Matls.--Schult Homes Corporation, Middlebury, IN; *U.S. Public*, pg. 1442
Jones, Ken, V.P.-Pur. & Matls. Control--Columbus Show Case Company, Columbus, OH; *U.S. Private*, pg. 257
Jones, Melinda, Dir.-Pur.--Southwire Company, Carrollton, GA; *U.S. Private*, pg. 1019
Jones, Mervyn B., Mgr.-Pur.--Raleigh Industries Ltd., Nottingham, United Kingdom; *Int'l*, pg. 394
Jones, Monica, Mgr.-Pur.--Anorad Corporation, Hauppauge, NY; *U.S. Private*, pg. 75
Jones, P.N., Dir.-Pur.--Chloride Industrial Batteries Ltd., Manchester, United Kingdom; *Int'l*, pg. 125
Jones, R.D., Mgr.-Pur.--Atchison/St. Joe Division, Atchison, KS; *U.S. Public*, pg. 142
Jones, Roy, Pur. Agent--Smith Enterprises, Rock Hill, SC; *U.S. Private*, pg. 1007
Jones, Terry, Mgr.-Matls.--Fisher Gauge Limited, Peterborough, Canada; *Int'l*, pg. 491
Jooster, B.P.A., Mgr.-Pur.--CSM Suiker BV, Diemen, Netherlands; *Int'l*, pg. 243
Jordan, Diane, Mgr.-Pur. & Facilities--San Diego Union Tribune, San Diego, CA; *U.S. Private*, pg. 275
Jordan, Edward, Mgr.-Pur.--Engineered Fasteners Div., Massillon, OH; *U.S. Public*, pg. 557
Jordens, Andre, Dir.-Pur.--Ethyl Corporation, Richmond, VA; *U.S. Public*, pg. 595
Jorgensen, Joe, Dir.-Pur.--Motek Engineering & Manufacturing Company, Cambridge, MN; *U.S. Private*, pg. 764
Jorgensen, Robert, Pur. Agent--Pemco Die Casting Corporation, Bridgman, MI; *U.S. Private*, pg. 848
Jorgensen, Roger, Pur. Dir.--Tiffin Enterprises, Inc., Tiffin, OH; *U.S. Public*, pg. 98
Joron, Philippe, V.P.-Pur.--Labinal SA, Montigny-le-Bretonneux, France; *Int'l*, pg. 785
Josefsson, Gunnar, Mgr.-Pur.--JM Byggnads och Fastighets AB, Stockholm, Sweden; *Int'l*, pg. 1260

Joslin, Marion, Mgr.-Pur.--William Bayley/Folger Adam Security, Inc., Springfield, OH; U.S. Private, pg. 125
Jovanelly, Ronald, Mgr.-Pur.--Lyman Products Corporation, Middletown, CT; U.S. Private, pg. 683
Jubinville, Mike, Mgr.-Pur.--Esco Corporation, Portland, OR; U.S. Private, pg. 382
Juliano, Marilyn, Dir.-Pur.--Framesi USA, Inc./Roffler Industries, Inc./Casa di Colore, Inc., Coraopolis, PA; U.S. Private, pg. 419
Julum, Brad, Mgr.-Pur.--Wall Data Incorporated, Kirkland, WA; U.S. Public, pg. 1734
Jun, Richard A., V.P. & Dir.-Corp. Pur.--Owens-Illinois, Inc., Toledo, OH; U.S. Public, pg. 1238
Junk, Ron, Pur. & Natls.--Portec Inc., Railway Maintenance Products Div., Pittsburgh, PA; U.S. Public, pg. 1318
Jurcenko, Esther, Buyer--Namco Controls Corporation, Highland Heights, OH; U.S. Public, pg. 482
Jusslin, Jukka, Dir.-Pur.--FINNAIR, New York, NY; Int'l, pg. 485
Kaberlein, Mark, Mgr.-Pur.--Kaufman and Broad New Mexico Division, Albuquerque, NM; U.S. Public, pg. 945
Kachur, J.M., Pur. Agent--The Hall China Company, East Liverpool, OH; U.S. Private, pg. 494
Kadell, Sharon, V.P.-Adv. & Pur.--Waremart Inc., Boise, ID; U.S. Private, pg. 1150
Kadoyama, Tetsuo, Mng. Dir.-Personnel & Pur.--UBE Industries Ltd., Tokyo, Japan; Int'l, pg. 1426
Kaeser, Eduard, Mgr.-Central Pur.--Mikron Holding AG, Biel, Switzerland; Int'l, pg. 866
Kaiser, Klaus, Mgr.-Logistics--Klafs Saunabau GmbH & Co. KG Medizinische Technik, Schwabisch Hall, Germany; Int'l, pg. 736
Kaiser, Mark P., Sr. V.P.-Sls., Mktg. & Procurement--JP Foodservice, Inc., Columbia, MD; U.S. Public, pg. 918
Kalkosch, Herb, Dir.-Pur.--Interstate Electronics Corp., Anaheim, CA; U.S. Public, pg. 622
Kaloyanides, Stephen, Jr., Dir.-Pur.--New England Coffee Company, Malden, MA; U.S. Private, pg. 792
Kamats, George, Dir.-Pur.--American International Airways, Ypsilanti, MI; U.S. Private, pg. 57
Kameen, Larry, Pur. Agent--Courtaulds Aerospace, Glendale, CA; Int'l, pg. 339
Kaminski, Hank, Mgr.-Matls.--Fiskars Inc., Wausau, WI; Int'l, pg. 492
Kaminski, Jennifer, Mgr.-Pur.--W. Braun Co., Lyndhurst, NJ; U.S. Private, pg. 166
Kaminski, Ron, Dir.-Pur.--Nordson Corporation, Westlake, OH; U.S. Public, pg. 1188
Kamps, Frederick K., Mgr.-Pur.--CUNA Mutual Insurance Society, Madison, WI; U.S. Private, pg. 296
Kanai, Hiroshi, Dir.-Fin. & Pur.--Bridgestone Corporation, Tokyo, Japan; Int'l, pg. 213
Kanaly, Tim, V.P.-Pur.--VICOM Production and Distribution Co., Denver, CO; U.S. Public, pg. 1719
Kanaly, Timothy, V.P.-Pur., Prod. & Distrib.--Vicorp Restaurants, Inc., Denver, CO; U.S. Public, pg. 1719
Kane, Todd, Mgr.-Pur.--Ben & Jerry's Homemade Inc., South Burlington, VT; U.S. Public, pg. 210
Kangas, Mike, Dir.-Pur.--Alaska Industrial Hardware Inc., Anchorage, AK; U.S. Private, pg. 31
Kao, Deborah, Dir.-Pur.--Liuski International, Inc., Norcross, GA; U.S. Public, pg. 1005
Kaplan, Dave, V.P.-Pur.--Magnolia Hi-Fi, Inc., Kent, WA; U.S. Private, pg. 696
Kaplan, Samuel, Pres., Chief Exec. Officer, Sec. & Dir.-Sls. & Pur.--Admiration Hosiery Mills, Inc., Charlotte, NC; U.S. Private, pg. 528
Karalis, Michael, Mgr.-Pur.--Olympic Airways, New York, NY; Int'l, pg. 1004
Karen, Victor, Pur. Agent-Findings--Eastland Shoe Manufacturing Corporation, Freeport, ME; U.S. Private, pg. 357
Karger, Bruce, Pur. Agent--Louis Padnos Iron & Metal Co., Holland, MI; U.S. Private, pg. 834
Karkut, Ernest W., V.P.-Pur. & Plant Services--The Southern Connecticut Gas Company, Bridgeport, CT; U.S. Public, pg. 431
Karlsen, Einar, Grp. V.P.-Purchase--Jotun A/S, Sandefjord, Norway; Int'l, pg. 714
Karlson, Gene, V.P.-Opers.--Northland Aluminum Products, Inc., Minneapolis, MN; U.S. Private, pg. 805
Karosich, Jim, Mgr.-Procurement--Seattle City Light, Seattle, WA; U.S. Private, pg. 979
Karst, Pat, Dir.-Pur.--Construction Counsellors, Inc., Montville, NJ; U.S. Private, pg. 266
Kasahara, K., Dir.-Pur.--Miyata Industry Co., Ltd., Chigasaki, Japan; Int'l, pg. 884
Kasate, Teresa, Mgr.-Pur.--Pulitzer Publishing Company, Saint Louis, MO; U.S. Public, pg. 1343
Kasate, Teresa, Mgr.-Pur.--St. Louis Post-Dispatch, Saint Louis, MO; U.S. Public, pg. 1343
Kasmer, Lou, Dir.-Pur.--WLR Foods, Inc., Timberville, VA; U.S. Public, pg. 1727
Kasper, Herbert, Mng. Dir.-Buying--Julius Meinl AG, Vienna, Austria; Int'l, pg. 856
Kass, Guenter C., V.P.-Pur.--The Elder-Beerman Stores Corp., Dayton, OH; U.S. Private, pg. 367
Kastan, David, Sr. V.P. & Mgr.-Pur. Dept.--Mitsui Foods, Inc., Norwood, NJ; Int'l, pg. 879
Kaszynski, James F., Pur. Agent--Maze Nails, Peru, IL; U.S. Private, pg. 718
Katz, Bernie, Pur. Agent--The Toro Company Irrigation Products, Riverside, CA; U.S. Public, pg. 1624
Kauer, George W., Mgr.- Office Services & Pur.--Tri-Continental Corporation, New York, NY; U.S. Private, pg. 982
Kaufman, Frank, Dir.-Pur.--Cold Spring Granite Company, Cold Spring, MN; U.S. Private, pg. 250
Kaufman, Jay, V.P.-Pur.--Crown Andersen Inc., Peachtree City, GA; U.S. Public, pg. 462
Kaufman, Jay, Dir.-Pur.--Andersen 2000 Inc., Peachtree City, GA; U.S. Public, pg. 462
Kaufman, Stanley, V.P.-Mfg.--Lebhar-Friedman, Inc., New York, NY; U.S. Private, pg. 656
Kaufmann, Robert, Mgr.-Pur.--CSP Inc., Billerica, MA; U.S. Public, pg. 283
Kaup, Marcia, Dir.-Pur.--Armstrong International, Inc., Three Rivers, MI; U.S. Private, pg. 83
Kay, David, Dir.-Pur.--Jones Medical Industries Inc., Saint Louis, MO; U.S. Public, pg. 933
Keane, Richard, V.P.-Grocery Procurement & Pur.--The Stop & Shop Companies, Inc., Quincy, MA; Int'l, pg. 750
Keck, Dick, Mgr.-Pur.--Fiberesin Industries Inc., Oconomowoc, WI; U.S. Private, pg. 402
Kee, B., Dir.-Pur.--Castrol Canada Inc., Toronto, Canada; Int'l, pg. 235
Keegstra, James E., Dir.-Pur.--Wolverine World Wide, Inc., Rockford, MI; U.S. Public, pg. 1775
Keenan, Matt, Mgr.-Pur.--System Software Associates, Inc., Chicago, IL; U.S. Public, pg. 1552
Kees, Dennis, Mgr.-Matls.--Industrial Bag Division - Los Angeles Plant, Los Angeles, CA; U.S. Public, pg. 1521
Kegler, Gary, Pur. Agent--Sealing Devices Inc., Lancaster, NY; U.S. Private, pg. 978
Keibel, B.A., Mgr.-Pur.--Pembina Pipeline Corporation, Calgary, Canada; Int'l, pg. 1032
Keins, Jerry, Mgr.-Parts & Pur.--Holiday RV Superstores of South Atlanta, Inc., Forest Park, GA; U.S. Public, pg. 830
Keller, Hans-Peter, Mgr.-Pur.--Baumann Federn AG, Ruti, Switzerland; Int'l, pg. 171
Kelley, Davis, Pur. Agent--Taylor Machine Works, Inc., Louisville, MS; U.S. Private, pg. 1070
Kelly-Green, Edith, V.P.-Pur.--FDX Corporation, Memphis, TN; U.S. Public, pg. 603
Kelly, Arnold, Dir.-Pur.--Western Regional Off Track Betting, Batavia, NY; U.S. Private, pg. 1168
Kelly, Gregory A., Pur. Agent--The F.D. Lawrence Electric Co., Cincinnati, OH; U.S. Private, pg. 654
Kelly, James, Pur. Dir.--Universal Voltronics Corporation, Mount Kisco, NY; U.S. Public, pg. 1596
Kelly, Kathleen M., V.P.-Admin. & Sec.--American Technical Ceramics Corp., Huntington Station, NY; U.S. Public, pg. 93
Kelly, Michael, Pur. Agent--Litecontrol Corporation, Hanson, MA; U.S. Private, pg. 669
Kelly, Ray, Sr. Buyer--Leupold & Stevens, Inc., Beaverton, OR; U.S. Private, pg. 662
Kelly, Sherry, Mgr.-Pur.--Gusher Pumps, Inc., Dry Ridge, KY; U.S. Private, pg. 488
Kelly, Steve, Sr. V.P.-Pur. & Distr.--AFC Enterprises, Atlanta, GA; U.S. Private, pg. 5
Kelps, Charlotte, Mgr.-Pur.--G. Leblanc Corporation, Kenosha, WI; U.S. Private, pg. 656
Kelsch, Mike, Dir.-Pur.--E & A Industries, Inc., Indianapolis, IN; U.S. Private, pg. 352
Kelsey, Lana, Mgr.-Pur.--The Bakersfield Californian, Bakersfield, CA; U.S. Private, pg. 112
Kelso, Earl F., Pur. Agent--Continental Forge Company, Compton, CA; U.S. Private, pg. 268
Kemerer, Floyd L., Dir.-Pur.--Amtrak-National Railroad Passenger Corp., Washington, DC; U.S. Private, pg. 68
Kemp, Clara E., Dir.-Pur.--Kellwood Company, Chesterfield, MO; U.S. Public, pg. 948
Kempe, Bill, Pur. Agent--Trapp Family Lodge, Inc., Stowe, VT; U.S. Private, pg. 1098
Kempinsky, James, Mgr.-Pur.--Serfilco, Ltd., Northbrook, IL; U.S. Private, pg. 985
Kennedy, Daniel B., Dir.-Global Pur.--John Crane Mechanical Seals, Morton Grove, IL; Int'l, pg. 1339
Kennedy, J.A., V.P.-Matls. Mngmt.--Reading & Bates Corporation, Houston, TX; U.S. Public, pg. 1354
Kennedy, Richard, Mgr.-Pur.--Maxcor Manufacturing, Inc., Colorado Springs, CO; U.S. Private, pg. 716
Kenney, James W., Mgr.-Pur.--Crown Holdings, Inc., Roseville, MN; U.S. Private, pg. 293
Kennon, George, Dir.-Opers.--Stanback Company, Salisbury, NC; U.S. Private, pg. 1030
Kennon, P., Mgr.-Pur.--Philip Morris Limited, Moorabbin, Australia; U.S. Public, pg. 1290
Kent, Ken, Dir.-Pur.--Bayco Industries, Winnipeg, Canada; Int'l, pg. 395
Kent, Kimberly, Mgr.-Pur.--GAI Consultants-NC, Inc., Raleigh, NC; U.S. Private, pg. 434
Kenyon, Kerry, V.P.-Pur.--Peterson Farms, Decatur, AR; U.S. Private, pg. 857
Kenyon, Steven D., Corp. Dir.-Pur.--LaRoche Industries Inc., Atlanta, GA; U.S. Private, pg. 651
Kern, Mark E., V.P.-Pur.--Overland Transportation System, Inc., Indianapolis, IN; Int'l, pg. 1469
Kerschner, Dale, Mgr.-Pur.--Gehl Company, West Bend, WI; U.S. Public, pg. 704
Kershaw, Brigette, Mgr.-Grp. Pur.--T & N Plc, Manchester, United Kingdom; Int'l, pg. 1334
Kershey, Robert D., Dir.-Pur.--HMI Industries, Cleveland, OH; U.S. Public, pg. 771
Kerus, Darlene, Dir.-Pur.--Fujitsu Computer Products of America, Inc., San Jose, CA; Int'l, pg. 526
Kesman, Anthony K., Corp. V.P.-Distr.--Allegiance Healthcare Corp., McGaw Park, IL; U.S. Public, pg. 44
Ketterer, Steve J., Gen. Mgr.-Pur.--Mobil Oil Corporation, Fairfax, VA; U.S. Public, pg. 1118
Kettler, William H., Jr., V.P.-H.R. & Facility Svcs.--Kaneb Services, Inc., Richardson, TX; U.S. Public, pg. 942
Kettlewell, J. F., V.P.-Pur.--Nickles Bakery of Indiana Inc., Elkhart, IN; U.S. Private, pg. 799
Kettlewell, J.F., V.P.-Pur.--Alfred Nickles Bakery, Inc., Navarre, OH; U.S. Private, pg. 799
Keyes, Dewey, Pur. Agent--Jarke Corporation, Niles, IL; U.S. Private, pg. 583
Khan, Imran A., Dir.-Stores & Pur.--Pakistan International Airlines Corporation, Karachi, Pakistan; Int'l, pg. 1021
Khan, M. Anwar, Mgr.-Matls.--Parke-Davis & Company, Limited, Karachi, Pakistan; U.S. Public, pg. 1739
Khawaja, Meraj A., Mgr.-Pur.--National Refinery Limited, Karachi, Pakistan; Int'l, pg. 909
Kibiloski, John, Dir.-Matls. Mgmt.--Howard Miller, Zeeland, MI; U.S. Private, pg. 747
Kibiloski, John, Dir.-Pur.--Trendway Corporation, Holland, MI; U.S. Private, pg. 1099
Kickel, Daniel, Dir.-Pur.--The Geon Company, Avon Lake, OH; U.S. Public, pg. 733
Kidd, Charles C., Mgr.-Procurement--Phillips Petroleum Company, Bartlesville, OK; U.S. Public, pg. 1290
Kidd, Neal, Supv.-Wharehouse--Kelso Oil Company, Knoxville, TN; U.S. Private, pg. 613
Kidwell, Debra K., V.P.-Retail Pur.--Cracker Barrel Old Country Store, Inc., Lebanon, TN; U.S. Public, pg. 455
Kiehnau, Jeannette, Mgr.-Procurement--Peterson Builders, Inc., Sturgeon Bay, WI; U.S. Private, pg. 857
Kieran, James, Pur. Agent--Textron Systems, Wilmington, MA; U.S. Public, pg. 1589
Kievit, Arie, Mgr.-Pur.--Lips United B.V., Drunen, Netherlands; Int'l, pg. 812
Kiggins, Joe, Pur. Agent--Mele Manufacturing Co., Inc., Utica, NY; U.S. Private, pg. 730
Kilander, R., Dir.-Pur.--Great Lakes Dredge & Dock Co., Oak Brook, IL; U.S. Private, pg. 474
Kilderbran, Sandy, Pur. Agent--Hilland Dairy Company, Wichita, KS; U.S. Private, pg. 879
Killeen, Bill, Mgr.-Pur.--Dixon Ticonderoga Company, Heathrow, FL; U.S. Public, pg. 514
Killough, Ray B., Sr. V.P.-Opers.--Piedmont Natural Gas Co., Inc., Charlotte, NC; U.S. Public, pg. 1295
Kilpin, Mark, Mgr.-Pur. & Plng.--Benjamin Obdyke, Inc., Warminster, PA; U.S. Private, pg. 810
Kim, Gerri, Pur. Specialist--Avery Dennison Corporation, Pasadena, CA; U.S. Public, pg. 152
Kim, Hong-Sik, Chief Fin. Officer--Ssangyong Precision Industry Co., Ltd., Inchon, Korea; Int'l, pg. 1292
Kim, M.C., Mgr.-Pur.--Hyundai Electronics America, San Jose, CA; Int'l, pg. 641
Kim, Young, Dir.-Pur. & Sourcing--The Pfaltzgraff Co., York, PA; U.S. Private, pg. 860
Kim, Young-Ik, Mng. Dir.--Ssangyong Motor Company, Seoul, Korea; Int'l, pg. 1292
Kimball, Morrison B., V.P.-Distr. Ctr.--Catherines Stores Corporation, Memphis, TN; U.S. Public, pg. 317
Kincaid, Gary L., V.P.-Matls. & Logistics--Altec Industries, Inc., Birmingham, AL; U.S. Private, pg. 47
King, Fred M., Pur. Agent--Medeco Security Locks, Inc., Salem, VA; U.S. Public, pg. 828
King, Joe, Dir.-Pur.--Pollo Tropical, Inc., Miami, FL; U.S. Public, pg. 1315
King, Kerrie, Dir.-Pur.--Cowden Metal Specialties, Inc., Chino, CA; U.S. Private, pg. 280
King, Milton Chung Jen, Dir.-Mktg.--China Hi-Ment Corp., Kao-hsiung, Taiwan; Int'l, pg. 285
King, Pat, Dir.-Pur.--New Mexico & Arizona Land Co., Phoenix, AZ; U.S. Public, pg. 1172
King, Steve, Dir.-Pur.--Tyler Elevator Products, Inc., Valley View, OH; U.S. Private, pg. 1112
Kinney, Alan, Mgr.-Pur.--BAT Office Products, Zion, IL; U.S. Public, pg. 1686
Kinney, Charles L., V.P.-Matls.--The JPM Company, Lewisburg, PA; U.S. Public, pg. 919
Kinney, Richard, Exec. V.P.--All-Phase Electric Supply Co., Benton Harbor, MI; U.S. Private, pg. 35
Kinney, Steven, Exec. V.P.--All-Phase Electric Supply Co., Benton Harbor, MI; U.S. Private, pg. 35
Kinser, Dennis, V.P.-Procurement--Associated Wholesale Grocers, Inc., Kansas City, KS; U.S. Private, pg. 93
Kirby, Tony, Dir.-Pur.--Bridgeport Machines, Inc., Bridgeport, CT; U.S. Public, pg. 251
Kirk, Danny, Mgr.-Pur.--Madison, Inc., Tulsa, OK; U.S. Private, pg. 428
Kirk, John, V.P.-Central Pur.--The Great Atlantic & Pacific Tea Company, Inc., Montvale, NJ; Int'l, pg. 1375
Kiska, Ed, Mgr.-Pur.--Cleveland City Forge, Cleveland, OH; U.S. Public, pg. 1258
Kitterman, Paul, Pur. Agent--The Keller Manufacturing Co., Inc., Corydon, IN; U.S. Private, pg. 612
Kittle, Ronald F., Mgr.-Pur.--Amstore Corporation, Muskegon, MI; U.S. Private, pg. 68
Kitzmiller, Randy, Mgr.-Pur.--Steiner Turf Equipment Inc., Orrville, OH; Int'l, pg. 1088
Klaas, Kurt, Dir.-Pur.--Kampgrounds of America, Inc., Billings, MT; U.S. Private, pg. 603
Klaasen, R., Pur. Mgr.--Rapistan Demag Corp., Grand Rapids, MI; Int'l, pg. 837
Klar, Jim, Mgr.-Pur.--Gunver Manufacturing Co., Manchester, CT; U.S. Private, pg. 488
Klausner, Robert, Dir.-Pur.--Raytheon Systems Co., Kirkwood, NY; U.S. Public, pg. 1364
Klehm, Marlin, Dir.-Pur.--Hagie Manufacturing Co., Clarion, IA; U.S. Private, pg. 493
Klein, Jim, Mgr.-Pur.--Voyager Emblems, Inc., Sanborn, NY; U.S. Private, pg. 1143
Kleinsorge, Jerry, Mgr.-Matls.--U.S. Safety, Lenexa, KS; U.S. Private, pg. 1125
Klemer, David, Mgr.-Pur.--Faribault Woolen Mill Co., Faribault, MN; U.S. Private, pg. 394
Klien, Larry, Mgr.-Matls.--United Air Specialists, Inc., Cincinnati, OH; U.S. Public, pg. 382
Kline, Daniel, V.P.-Pur.--Gibraltar Steel Corp., Buffalo, NY; U.S. Public, pg. 742
Kloese, Leroy, Pur. Agent--Kaspar Wire Works, Inc., Shiner, TX; U.S. Private, pg. 608
Klopsis, Peter, Mgr.-Pur.--Frequency Electronics, Inc., Uniondale, NY; U.S. Public, pg. 681
Kmiecik, Daniel, Mgr.-Pur.--La-Co Industries Markal Company, Elk Grove Village, IL; U.S. Private, pg. 640
Kneider, Larry, Mgr.-Pur.--Service Merchandise Company, Inc., Brentwood, TN; U.S. Public, pg. 1461
Knight, Paul, Dir.-Pur.--Pfaudler, Inc., Rochester, NY; U.S. Public, pg. 1393
Knipper, P.A., V.P.-Pur.--Energy & Process Corp., Tucker, GA; Int'l, pg. 1512
Knobblock, Denise, Sr. V.P.-Pur., Facilities, Administration & Travel--Compuware Corporation, Farmington Hills, MI; U.S. Public, pg. 423

Knoff, Mike, Pur. Agent--J.R. Simplot Company, Minerals & Chemicals Group, Pocatello, ID; *U.S. Private*, pg. 1002
Knorr, John A., V.P.-Crude Oil Supply & Trading--Holly Corporation, Dallas, TX; *U.S. Public*, pg. 830
Knowles, Janet, V.P.-Admin. & Dir.-Pur.--Metrologic Instruments, Inc., Blackwood, NJ; *U.S. Public*, pg. 1102
Knowlton, L. Gordon, Pur. Agent--The Kerite Company, Seymour, CT; *U.S. Public*, pg. 844
Knox, Karen A., Dir.-Pur.--The First American Financial Corporation, Santa Ana, CA; *U.S. Public*, pg. 624
Knudsen, R.D., Dir.-Pur. & Logistics--The Timken Company, Canton, OH; *U.S. Public*, pg. 1617
Koblick, Jeffrey, Sr. V.P.-Pur. & Opers.--K-Tel International, Inc., Minneapolis, MN; *U.S. Public*, pg. 937
Koch, Robert, Dir.-Procurement--Briggs & Stratton Corporation, Wauwatosa, WI; *U.S. Public*, pg. 252
Koch, Steve, Mgr.-Pur.--Pentel of America, Ltd., Torrance, CA; *Int'l*, pg. 1035
Koegel, Dorothy, Dir.-Pur.--Wilhold Inc., Cleveland, OH; *U.S. Public*, pg. 78
Koehle, William, Mgr.-Pur.--Plastek Group, Erie, PA; *U.S. Private*, pg. 870
Koehling, B., Mgr.-Pur.--Dukane Corporation, Saint Charles, IL; *U.S. Private*, pg. 345
Koelle, David A., Dir.-Pur.--Boyer Candy Company Inc., Altoona, PA; *U.S. Private*, pg. 162
Koenig, Elmer, Pur. Agent--The United States Playing Card Company, Cincinnati, OH; *U.S. Private*, pg. 1125
Koepke, John, Mgr.-Pur.--General Filters, Inc., Novi, MI; *U.S. Private*, pg. 444
Kohanski, Gerald P., Gen. Mgr.-Pur.--Cleveland-Cliffs Inc, Cleveland, OH; *U.S. Public*, pg. 386
Kohl, D., Mgr.-Pur.--Penn Engineering & Manufacturing Corp., Danboro, PA; *U.S. Public*, pg. 1269
Kohl, Rich, Dir.-Pur.--Lyke Corporation, Ripon, WI; *U.S. Private*, pg. 682
Kohn, Robin, Pur. Agent--Washington Scientific Industries, Inc., Long Lake, MN; *U.S. Public*, pg. 1744
Kokinda, Wayne, Mgr.-Matls.--Sentry Group, Rochester, NY; *U.S. Private*, pg. 984
Kolbaba, Jerold P., Second V.P.-Pur.--American National Bank & Trust Co. of Chicago, Chicago, IL; *U.S. Public*, pg. 628
Konecny, Leonard J., V.P.-Pur.--Cannondale Corporation, Bethel, CT; *U.S. Public*, pg. 301
Kong, Wayne, Mgr.-Pur.--Aesculap, Inc., South San Francisco, CA; *Int'l*, pg. 29
Koning, G.T., Dir.-Pur.--DSM Resins B.V., Zwolle, Netherlands; *Int'l*, pg. 353
Koo, Hubert, Dir.-Pur.--Springfield Precision Instruments, Inc., Wood Ridge, NJ; *U.S. Private*, pg. 1027
Kopelson, Richard, Purchasing--Brookwood Companies Inc., New York, NY; *U.S. Public*, pg. 777
Koplitz, Richard A., V.P.-Pur.--Simon & Schuster, New York, NY; *U.S. Private*, pg. 777
Kopscik, Douglas, Mgr.-Mtls.--Eaton Corp., Supercharger Div., Athens, GA; *U.S. Public*, pg. 556
Korba, Paul, Pur. Agent-Supplies--4C Foods Corporation, Brooklyn, NY; *U.S. Private*, pg. 421
Kornowske, Barb, Pur. Assoc.--Sierra Coating Technologies, De Pere, WI; *U.S. Private*, pg. 998
Korst, Noni, Mgr.-Pur.--Ferrellgas Partners, L.P., Liberty, MO; *U.S. Public*, pg. 618
Koschmeder, Dir.-Pur.--Rinker Materials Corp., West Palm Beach, FL; *Int'l*, pg. 246
Koser, Carroll, Mgr.-Pur.--Anderson Bakery Co., Inc., Lancaster, PA; *U.S. Private*, pg. 65
Koshiba, Masato, Gen. Mgr.-Pur.--Tekken Corporation, Tokyo, Japan; *Int'l*, pg. 1362
Kostich, Linda, Mgr.-Pur.--Allied Chucker & Engineering Company, Jackson, MI; *U.S. Private*, pg. 38
Kotys, Gregory S., Dir.-Finishing--National Steel Corp., Granite City Division, Granite City, IL; *Int'l*, pg. 902
Kough, Gene, Dir.-Pur.--American Fluorescent Corporation, Waukegan, IL; *U.S. Private*, pg. 54
Kovac, Rae Lareau, Mgr.-Pur.--Holiday RV Rental/Leasing, Inc., Orlando, FL; *U.S. Public*, pg. 829
Kovac, Steve, Mgr.-Material Control--Ausco Products, Inc., Benton Harbor, MI; *U.S. Private*, pg. 299
Kovacs, Darrell, Pur. Agent--Clark Grave Vault Co., Columbus, OH; *U.S. Private*, pg. 243
Kovarna, Dale, Mgr.-Matls.--Sioux Tools, Inc., Sioux City, IA; *U.S. Public*, pg. 1480
Kowaleski, Carol, Dir.-Pur.--Lockformer Company, Lisle, IL; *U.S. Public*, pg. 1100
Kowalkowski, Sonia, Pur. Agent--Microphase Corporation, Norwalk, CT; *U.S. Private*, pg. 742
Kowieski, Ronald, Dir.-Pur.--Farley Candy Company, Chicago, IL; *U.S. Private*, pg. 397
Kozak, Gary G., Pur. Officer--BT Financial Corporation, Johnstown, PA; *U.S. Public*, pg. 163
Kozell, Joseph, Mgr.-Stock & Pur. Agent--Hesco, Inc., Teterboro, NJ; *U.S. Private*, pg. 524
Kraft, Paul, Office Admin.--Quanex Corporation, Houston, TX; *U.S. Public*, pg. 1349
Krahn, Gerald, Dir.-Pur.--Marvin Lumber & Cedar Company, Warroad, MN; *U.S. Private*, pg. 710
Kralik, Patricia, Pur. Agent--George S. May International Company, Park Ridge, IL; *U.S. Private*, pg. 717
Kramer, Walt, V.P.-Pur. Paper--Duro Bag Manufacturing Co., Ludlow, KY; *U.S. Private*, pg. 348
Kranz, George E., V.P.-Pur. & Supply Worldwide--The Standard Products Company, Dearborn, MI; *U.S. Public*, pg. 1504
Kranzler, R.L., Mgr.-Pur. & Stores--Northwestern Public Service, Huron, SD; *U.S. Public*, pg. 1200
Krause, Bruce, Mgr.-Pur.--Spartan Tool, Mendota, IL; *U.S. Private*, pg. 860
Krause, D., V.P. Supply & Distr.--Automotive, Wayne, NJ; *Int'l*, pg. 234
Krause, D.R., V.P.-Matls.--The Budd Company, Troy, MI; *Int'l*, pg. 1388
Krause, Yvonne, Pur. Agent--Farmers Group, Inc., Los Angeles, CA; *Int'l*, pg. 110
Krauss, Ken, V.P.-Raw Matls. Procurement--Angelica Image Apparel, Saint Louis, MO; *U.S. Public*, pg. 113
Krebs, Al, Pur. Agent--Tennessee Tubebending Inc., Knoxville, TN; *U.S. Private*, pg. 762
Kretsch, Clayton, Buyer--Coleman Powermate Compressors, Springfield, MN; *U.S. Private*, pg. 691
Kretsch, Lynn, Dir.-Pur.--A.L. Hansen Manufacturing Co., Waukegan, IL; *U.S. Private*, pg. 500
Kretzmer, David, Mgr.-Pur.--Strahman Valves, Inc., Florham Park, NJ; *U.S. Private*, pg. 1046
Kreuger, James A., Sr. V.P.-Matls. Mngmt.--Corning Incorporated, Corning, NY; *U.S. Public*, pg. 448
Krider, George L., Dir.-Pur.--Mrs. Smith's Bakeries, Inc., Thomasville, GA; *U.S. Public*, pg. 657
Krieger, James F., Sr. V.P.--Standard Medical Imaging, Inc., Columbia, MD; *U.S. Private*, pg. 1032
Kripal, Josef, V.P. & Dir.-Pur.--Reinke Manufacturing Co., Inc., Deshler, NE; *U.S. Private*, pg. 920
Kristiansen, John, V.P.-Sls. & Distr. & Dir.-Pur.--Frionor A/S, Lysaker, Norway; *Int'l*, pg. 516
Kropfelder, Dave, Dir.-Pur.--First National Mortgage Corporation, Glen Burnie, MD; *Int'l*, pg. 64
Kropfl, Richard, Mgr.-Matls.--Puritan/Churchill Chemical Company, Atlanta, GA; *U.S. Private*, pg. 895
Kruck, Thomas, Div. Mgr.--Durkopp Adler AG, Bielefeld, Germany; *Int'l*, pg. 468
Krueger, Dann F., Mgr.-Fin. & Acctg.--MGI PHARMA INC., Minneapolis, MN; *U.S. Public*, pg. 1026
Kruger, John, Dir.-Pur.--Continental Health Affiliates, Inc., Englewood Cliffs, NJ; *U.S. Public*, pg. 440
Krum, Paul, V.P.-Pur.--Crown Crafts, Inc., Atlanta, GA; *U.S. Public*, pg. 465
Krupp, James A.G., V.P.-Matls.--Echlin Inc., Branford, CT; *U.S. Public*, pg. 560
Kruse, Dave, Pur. Agent--Kiewit Construction Group, Inc., Omaha, NE; *U.S. Private*, pg. 619
Kruse, Dave, Pur. Agent--Kiewit Mining Group, Inc., Omaha, NE; *U.S. Private*, pg. 619
Krush, Tom, Mgr.-Matls.--Inland Valley Regional Medical Center, Wildomar, CA; *U.S. Public*, pg. 1697
Krzykowski, Kenneth, Dir.-Pur.--Wrought Washer Mfg., Inc., Milwaukee, WI; *U.S. Private*, pg. 1192
Kucharik, D., Pur. Agent--American Inks & Coatings Corp., Phoenixville, PA; *U.S. Private*, pg. 56
Kuchler, Louis, V.P.-Pur.--Angelo Brothers Co., Philadelphia, PA; *U.S. Private*, pg. 74
Kudick, Rob, Mgr.-Pur.--Pulp & Paper Div., Mosinee, WI; *U.S. Public*, pg. 1747
Kuhn, John, Dir.-Pur.--Denison Hydraulics, Inc., Marysville, OH; *U.S. Private*, pg. 324
Kuhns, Paul, Dir.-Pur.--VR/Wesson Hydro Carbide, Latrobe, PA; *U.S. Public*, pg. 612
Kuilman, B., Dir.-Pur.--OPEL Nederland B.V., Sliedrecht, Netherlands; *U.S. Public*, pg. 723
Kujawa, J., Mgr.-Pur.--C.A. Cigarrera Bigott, Sucs., Caracas, Venezuela; *Int'l*, pg. 111
Kulbeth, Alan, Mgr.-Pur.--Kit Manufacturing Company, Long Beach, CA; *U.S. Public*, pg. 962
Kulbeth, Alan, Mgr.-Pur.--R-4 KIT Mfg. Co., Mc Pherson, KS; *U.S. Public*, pg. 962
Kulikowski, Eric, Dir.-Pur.--Respironics, Inc., Pittsburgh, PA; *U.S. Public*, pg. 1383
Kulkarni, V.R., Dir.-Stores & Pur.--Air India, Mumbai, India; *Int'l*, pg. 37
Kunda, Ken, V.P.-Pur. & Mfg.--Inductotherm Corp., Rancocas, NJ; *U.S. Private*, pg. 560
Kuntz, James, V.P.-Pur.--AmTran Corporation, Conway, AR; *U.S. Public*, pg. 1167
Kupris, Eleanor M., V.P.-Admin. & Sec.--Bowles Fluidics Corporation, Columbia, MD; *U.S. Public*, pg. 248
Kuramoto, Toyohisa, Mng. Dir.-Prod., Procurement, Quality Control & Prod. Liability--Nikon Corporation, Tokyo, Japan; *Int'l*, pg. 931
Kurtenbach, Larry, Mgr.-Pur.--Lindsay Manufacturing Company, Lindsay, NE; *U.S. Public*, pg. 999
Kurtzweil, Joe, Pur. Agent--Andes Candies Inc., Delavan, WI; *U.S. Private*, pg. 163
Kuyper, Dale, Dir.-Pur.--Wenger Corporation, Owatonna, MN; *U.S. Private*, pg. 1162
Kuzma, Andrew, Dir.-Pur.--C. B. Fleet Co., Inc., Lynchburg, VA; *U.S. Private*, pg. 410
Kwartler, Irwin E., V.P.-Sys.--New Plan Realty Trust, New York, NY; *U.S. Public*, pg. 1172
Kwiatek, Joe, Dir.-Pur.--First American Metro Corp., Mc Lean, VA; *U.S. Public*, pg. 640
Kyle, Dick, V.P.-Pur.--Plasti-Kote Company Inc., Medina, OH; *U.S. Private*, pg. 870
La Belle, Paul, Dir.-Pur.--Waterville TG Inc., Waterville, Canada; *Int'l*, pg. 1487
La Monte, Nancy, Mgr.-Pur.--Northwestern Mutual Life Insurance Co., Milwaukee, WI; *U.S. Private*, pg. 807
La Plante, Carl, Mgr.-Pur.--New Era Cap. Co., Derby, NY; *U.S. Private*, pg. 793
Laakko, Veikko, Mgr.-Pur.--Nokia Mobile Phones, Espoo, Finland; *Int'l*, pg. 951
Labat, Shelly, Dir.-Pur.--Bayou Steel Corporation, La Place, LA; *U.S. Public*, pg. 197
LaBonte, Jim, Mgr.-Pur.--National R.V., Inc., Perris, CA; *U.S. Public*, pg. 1159
Lackey, Steve, Mgr.-Pur.--Rudolph Foods Company, Lima, OH; *U.S. Private*, pg. 950
Lacour, Denis, Dir.-Human Resources--Groupe Strafor Facom, Morangis, France; *Int'l*, pg. 569
Lacox, Dick, Mgr.-Pur.--Anaheim Manufacturing Company, Anaheim, CA; *U.S. Private*, pg. 70
LaDue, Gary, Dir.-Pur.--The Coon-De Visser Co., Royal Oak, MI; *U.S. Private*, pg. 273
Laferlita, Vito, V.P.-Pur.--Atlas Consolidated Mining & Development Corporation, Manila, Philippines; *Int'l*, pg. 95
Laflame, David, Mgr.-Pur.--Keeney Manufacturing Co., Newington, CT; *U.S. Private*, pg. 611
Lafortune, Alain, V.P.-Pur. & Merchandising--The Jean Coutu Group (PJC) Inc., Longueuil, Canada; *Int'l*, pg. 340
Lafrance, George, Dir.-Materials Mgmnt.--New Brunswick Power Corporation, Fredericton, Canada; *Int'l*, pg. 923
LaGrega, Andrew T., Sr. V.P.-Sls., Mktg. & Adv.--The Wilder Companies, Boston, MA; *U.S. Private*, pg. 1176
Laksola, Reijo, Dir.-Pur.--Bronto Skylift Oy AB, Tampere, Finland; *U.S. Public*, pg. 617
Lamar, Bill, Dir.-Pur.--Progress Paint Mfg. Co., Louisville, KY; *U.S. Private*, pg. 890
Lamb, David, Mgr.-Pur.--Heat Controller, Inc., Jackson, MI; *U.S. Private*, pg. 518
Lamb, Kathi A., Mgr.-Matls. Dept.--Lamb Engineering & Construction Co., Salt Lake City, UT; *U.S. Private*, pg. 644
Lamb, Rodney, Dir.-Pur.--Farmers Mutual Hail Insurance Co. of Iowa, Des Moines, IA; *U.S. Private*, pg. 395
Lambert, J.D., Dir.-Pur.--Wells/Bloomfield, Verdi, NV; *U.S. Public*, pg. 1497
Lamison, Russell, Buyer-Pur.--American Machine & Tool Company, Inc., Royersford, PA; *U.S. Private*, pg. 58
Lanard, Tom, Pur. Agent--Univex Corporation, Salem, NH; *U.S. Private*, pg. 1128
Lancaster, Stan, Dir.-Pur.--Colonial Oil Industries, Savannah, GA; *U.S. Private*, pg. 253
Lancett, Tony, Mgr.-Pur.--Interplastic Corp., Saint Paul, MN; *U.S. Private*, pg. 572
Landry, W., Pur. Agent--Jonathan Manufacturing Corp., Fullerton, CA; *U.S. Private*, pg. 595
Landsfra, Steven W., Dir.-Pur.--Monsey-Bakor, Kimberton, PA; *U.S. Private*, pg. 757
Landwehr, Joseph, Dir.-Pur.--Walk, Haydel & Associates, Inc., New Orleans, LA; *Int'l*, pg. 624
Lane, Gordon, Mgr.-Pur.--Tuboscope Incorporated, Houston, TX; *U.S. Public*, pg. 1643
Lane, John, Mgr.-Pur. & Leasing--Dresser Industries, Inc., Dallas, TX; *U.S. Public*, pg. 528
Lane, L., Dir.-Pur.--Conklin Instrument Corporation, Pleasant Valley, NY; *U.S. Private*, pg. 263
Lane, Steven, Mgr.-Pur.--Merrimac Industries, Inc., West Caldwell, NJ; *U.S. Public*, pg. 1098
Lanenga, H., Mgr.-Pur.--Wavin Bv, Zwolle, Netherlands; *Int'l*, pg. 1135
Lang, Bill, Mgr.--E Z Loader Boat Trailers, Inc., Spokane, WA; *U.S. Private*, pg. 353
Lang, Ernest, Asst. V.P.-Pur.--Wasserstrom Company, Columbus, OH; *U.S. Private*, pg. 1152
Lang, Thomas R., Mgr.-Pur.--Green Mountain Power Corporation, South Burlington, VT; *U.S. Public*, pg. 761
Langdon, Stanley, Dir.-Pur.--Austin Group, Flint, MI; *U.S. Private*, pg. 99
Lange, Karen M., Grp. Coord.-Sls.--Glastic Corporation, Cleveland, OH; *Int'l*, pg. 740
Langford, Doyle, Mgr.-Pur.--Circle A.W. Products, Co., Portland, OR; *U.S. Public*, pg. 1471
Langseth, Harold, Dir.-Pur.--Fluke Corporation, Everett, WA; *U.S. Public*, pg. 659
Langston, Howard, Mgr.-Pur.--Pannier Corporation, Pittsburgh, PA; *U.S. Private*, pg. 837
Lanier, Donald S., V.P.-Pur.--Bryant Electric Supply Company, Inc., Lowell, NC; *U.S. Private*, pg. 177
Lanman, K.W., Mgr.-Pur.--Colonial Pipeline Company, Atlanta, GA; *U.S. Private*, pg. 254
Lanno, Dino, Dir.-Pur.--Safelite AutoGlass, Columbus, OH; *U.S. Private*, pg. 960
Lantman, Art, Dir.-Opers.--Mercantile Stores Company, Inc., Fairfield, OH; *U.S. Public*, pg. 1089
Lantz, Frank, Pur. Agent--Ruhle Companies, Inc., Valhalla, NY; *U.S. Private*, pg. 950
Lantz, Frank, Mgr.-Pur.--Farrand Controls, Valhalla, NY; *U.S. Private*, pg. 951
Lapin, Gene, V.P.-Pur.--Clayton Corporation, Fenton, MO; *U.S. Private*, pg. 244
LaPointe, J.J., V.P.-Supply Mngmt.--Raytheon Aircraft Company, Wichita, KS; *U.S. Public*, pg. 1365
Larson, Gregory L., V.P.-Corp. Pur.--Ag-Chem Equipment Co., Inc., Minnetonka, MN; *U.S. Public*, pg. 6
Larson, Kenneth, Exec. V.P.--Monico Alloys, Inc., Los Angeles, CA; *U.S. Private*, pg. 757
Larsson, Bert F., V.P.-Worldwide Metal Pur.--American National Can Company, Chicago, IL; *Int'l*, pg. 1029
Lartieve, Roland, V.P.-Pur.--United Technologies Automotive, Dearborn, MI; *U.S. Public*, pg. 1691
Laschever, Jack, Publ.-North American Edition--Departures, New York, NY; *U.S. Public*, pg. 74
Lasher, Larry, Dir.-Pur.--Meadville Forging Co., Meadville, PA; *U.S. Private*, pg. 726
Latham, J.M., Dir.-Pur.--Cussons (U.K.) LTD., Cheadle, United Kingdom; *Int'l*, pg. 1024
Latimer, Jim, Mgr.-Pur.--Genentech, Inc., South San Francisco, CA; *Int'l*, pg. 1120
Lauer, David, Dir.-Pur.--Inland Associates, Olathe, KS; *U.S. Private*, pg. 563
Laughlin, Rich, Dir.-Pur.--The Wella Corporation, Montvale, NJ; *Int'l*, pg. 1489
Laurro, Linda, Mgr.-Matls.--Wellington Regional Medical Center, West Palm Beach, FL; *U.S. Public*, pg. 1697
Lausterer, Dan, Mgr.-Pur. & Traffic--Hope's Architectural Products Inc., Jamestown, NY; *U.S. Private*, pg. 538
Lavin, James A., Dir.-Plng.--FlightSafety International Inc., Flushing, NY; *U.S. Public*, pg. 218
Law, Danny, Material, Planner & Handler--Sun Microsystems of California Ltd., Kowloon, Hong Kong; *U.S. Public*, pg. 1532
Lawdis, Rebecca, Pur. Mgr.--Coastcast Corporation, Gardena, CA; *U.S. Public*, pg. 391
Lawrence, Charles, Dir.-Pur.--Sauder Woodworking Co., Archbold, OH; *U.S. Private*, pg. 967
Lawrence, Chuck, Dir.-Admin.--Structural Dynamics Research Corp., Milford, OH; *U.S. Public*, pg. 1525
Lawrence, Dianna, Material Mgr.--Industrial Bag Division - New Philadelphia Plant, New Philadelphia, OH; *U.S. Public*, pg. 1521
Layden, Pat, Mgr.-Pur.--Anchor Continental Incorporated, Columbia, SC; *U.S. Private*, pg. 70

Lazzaro, Frank, Dir.-Pur.--Robert James Sales Inc., Buffalo, NY; *U.S. Private*, pg. 935
Le Shiong, Kong, Mgr.-Pur.--Bensons Metal Products Sdn Bhd, Shah Alam, Malaysia; *Int'l*, pg. 460
Leach, J.K., Mgr.-Non-Resale Pur.--JC Penney Company, Inc., Plano, TX; *U.S. Public*, pg. 916
Leahy, James, Dir.-Pur.--ADVO, Inc., Windsor, CT; *U.S. Public*, pg. 23
Leary, Michael J., V.P.-Pur. & Distr.--International Dairy Queen, Inc., Minneapolis, MN; *U.S. Public*, pg. 220
Leasburg-Kramer, Linda, Dir.-Pur.--Tiger Direct, Inc., Miami, FL; *U.S. Public*, pg. 747
Leasburg-Kramer, Linda, Dir.-Pur.--Tiger Direct, Inc. (d/b/a Tiger Software, Inc.), Miami, FL; *U.S. Public*, pg. 747
LeBas, Gina, Buyer-Chinaware Kitchenware-Janitorial--Alliant Foodservice, Bensenville, IL; *U.S. Private*, pg. 244
Lecavalier, Christian, Dir.-Pur.--Genfoot Inc., Montreal, Canada; *Int'l*, pg. 549
Leckie, Bruce, Mgr.-Pur.--Schumacher Electric Corporation, Mount Prospect, IL; *U.S. Private*, pg. 973
Ledebuhr, Bob, Mgr.-Pur.--Waters Instruments, Inc., Rochester, MN; *U.S. Public*, pg. 1745
Lee, Doo-Hwan, Pres.--Ssangyong Uni-Charm Co., Ltd., Kumi, Korea; *Int'l*, pg. 1291
Lee, Glenda, Pur. Agent--Hilton Equipment Corp., Beverly Hills, CA; *U.S. Public*, pg. 829
Lee, Helena, Dir.-Pur.--Camerican International, Paramus, NJ; *U.S. Public*, pg. 426
Lee, N., Mgr.-Pur.--Thilmany Division, Kaukauna, WI; *U.S. Public*, pg. 903
Lee, S.C., Mgr.-Pur.--China Ecotek Corporation, Kao-hsiung, Taiwan; *Int'l*, pg. 285
Lee, S.C., Dir.--Taiwan Power Company, Taipei, Taiwan; *Int'l*, pg. 1348
Lee, Sang-Jun, Mng. Dir.--Ssangyong Paper Co., Ltd., Seoul, Korea; *Int'l*, pg. 1292
Lee, Yong-Hae, V.P.--Ssangyong Corporation, Seoul, Korea; *Int'l*, pg. 1291
Leeb, Peter, Chm. Bd. & Chief Exec. Officer--King Wire Inc., North Chicago, IL; *U.S. Private*, pg. 621
Lefeuvre, Jacques, Dir.-Pur.--Etablissement de Velizy, Velizy-Villacoublay, France; *Int'l*, pg. 383
LeGette, Norman, Mgr.-Matls.--Phoenix Medical Technology, Inc., Andrews, SC; *U.S. Public*, pg. 1292
Lehman, Dean, Pur. Agent--Northwest Pipe Fittings, Inc., Billings, MT; *U.S. Private*, pg. 806
Lehner, Mary, Mgr.-Pur.--South Bend Plastics, Inc., Mishawaka, IN; *U.S. Private*, pg. 1014
Lehoczky, John, V.P.-Pur.--Yellow Corporation, Overland Park, KS; *U.S. Public*, pg. 1788
Leibensperger, J.S., Gen. Mgr.-Pur.--Carpenter Specialty Alloys Operations, Reading, PA; *U.S. Public*, pg. 307
Lekram, Frank, Dir.-Pur.--Everlast World Boxing Corp., Bronx, NY; *U.S. Private*, pg. 386
Lekram, Frank, Dir.-Pur.--Everlast Sports Manufacturing Corp., Bronx, NY; *U.S. Private*, pg. 386
LeMaster, Curt H., V.P.-Mktg. Pur. & Sys.--Wolohan Lumber Co., Saginaw, MI; *U.S. Public*, pg. 1774
Lemieux, Donald, Mgr.-Pur.--Jordan's Foods-Westbrook Division, Westbrook, ME; *U.S. Private*, pg. 599
Lemley, Mike, Dir.-Pur.--Bearden Lumber Company, Inc., Bearden, AR; *U.S. Private*, pg. 127
Lemonde, Pierre, Dir.-Forms Mngmt. & Supply--Assurance vie Desjardins-Laurentienne, Levis, Canada; *Int'l*, pg. 396
Lenard, Harry, Dir.-Pur.--Aurora Pump, North Aurora, IL; *U.S. Public*, pg. 726
Lenk, Edward, V.P.--Unisystems, Inc., New York, NY; *U.S. Private*, pg. 1120
Lennon, Frank T., V.P.-H.R. & Admin.--The Pittston Company, Glen Allen, VA; *U.S. Public*, pg. 1305
Leonard, Richard, Pur. Agent--Somat Corporation, Coatesville, PA; *U.S. Public*, pg. 1322
Leovati, Francs, Mgr.-Pur.--Marcegaglia SpA, Mantova, Italy; *Int'l*, pg. 841
Lerch, Howard D., Jr., V.P.--Mazo Lerch Company, Inc., Alexandria, VA; *U.S. Public*, pg. 918
Leskiw, Robert, Dir.-Pur.--Miken Companies, Inc., Cheektowaga, NY; *U.S. Private*, pg. 745
Lester, Darrell, V.P.-Mktg. Services--Publishers Clearing House, Port Washington, NY; *U.S. Private*, pg. 893
Lettner, Mark, V.P.-Pur.--Johnson & Johnson, New Brunswick, NJ; *U.S. Public*, pg. 927
Letts, Robert, V.P.-Production & Pur.--Bantam Doubleday Dell Publishing Group, Inc., New York, NY; *Int'l*, pg. 191
Leutheuser, K.P., Mgr.-Pur.--Townsend & Bottum, Inc., Ann Arbor, MI; *U.S. Private*, pg. 146
Levey, Harry, V.P.-Pur.--Sico North America Inc., Minneapolis, MN; *U.S. Private*, pg. 997
Levicoff, Louis, Pur. Agent--Pearl-Pressman-Liberty Communications Group, Philadelphia, PA; *U.S. Private*, pg. 845
Levine, Mel, Principal Dir.-Contracts Directorate--Aerospace Corporation, El Segundo, CA; *U.S. Private*, pg. 24
Levine, Melvin L., V.P.-Pur.--Syratech Corporation, East Boston, MA; *U.S. Private*, pg. 1060
Levine, Richard L., V.P.-Pur. & Distr.--Aaron Rents, Inc., Atlanta, GA; *U.S. Public*, pg. 12
Levinson, Steve, Dir.-Pur.--E.T. Browne Drug Co., Inc., Englewood Cliffs, NJ; *U.S. Private*, pg. 175
Levy, Candy, V.P.-Admin./Pur.--Global Van Lines, Inc., Orange, CA; *U.S. Private*, pg. 458
Levy, Kenneth, Mgr.-Pur.--Analysis & Technology, Inc., North Stonington, CT; *U.S. Public*, pg. 109
Levy, Larry, Mgr.-Pur.--B/E Aerospace, Inc./In Flight Entertainment Group, Irvine, CA; *U.S. Public*, pg. 159
Levy, Philippe, Coord.-Pur.--GIB Group, Brussels, Belgium; *Int'l*, pg. 532
Lewenhagen, Stig, Mgr.-Mktg. & Pur.--Skanska Installation AB, Sundbyberg, Sweden; *Int'l*, pg. 1260
Lewis, Diane, Pur. Agent--MarketSource Corporation, Cranbury, NJ; *U.S. Private*, pg. 705
Lewis, Janice, Dir.-Pur.--Butterick Company, Inc., New York, NY; *U.S. Private*, pg. 190
Lewis, Mary, Mgr.-Pur.--Candle Corporation, Santa Monica, CA; *U.S. Private*, pg. 204
Lewis, Sherry, Mgr.-Pur.--Emerson Radio Corp., Parsippany, NJ; *U.S. Public*, pg. 578
Li, Andy Y., Mgr.-Pur.--Philippine Airlines, Inc., San Francisco, CA; *Int'l*, pg. 1051
Liddy, T A. III, Pur. Agent--Lubriplate Div. of Fiske Bros. Refining Co., Newark, NJ; *U.S. Private*, pg. 409
Liermann, R., V.P.-Materials-Food Service Grp.--Manitowoc Ice, Inc., Manitowoc, WI; *U.S. Public*, pg. 1041
Lilley, Marvin, V.P.-Matls.--Marathon Electric Manufacturing Corp., Wausau, WI; *U.S. Public*, pg. 1371
Lim, T., Pur. Agent--Santa Rosa Steel Forming, Inc., Santa Rosa, CA; *U.S. Private*, pg. 965
Limay, Luis A., Dir.-Mktg., Pur. & Sls.--San Sebastian Gold Mines, Inc., Milwaukee, WI; *U.S. Public*, pg. 410
Lin, Jackson, Asst. V.P.--Acer Incorporated, Taipei, Taiwan; *Int'l*, pg. 22
Lin, K.Y., Gen. Mgr.-Pur.--China Steel Corporation, Kao-hsiung, Taiwan; *Int'l*, pg. 285
Linakis, John S., Sr. V.P.-Transportation--American Institute for Foreign Study, Greenwich, CT; *U.S. Private*, pg. 56
Lincoln, John, Pres.--Revenue Collection Group, San Diego, CA; *U.S. Public*, pg. 466
Lind, William, Mgr.-Produce--Affiliated Foods Southwest, Little Rock, AR; *U.S. Private*, pg. 26
Lindeen, Steve, Dir.-Pur.--Wallace Computer Services, Inc., Lisle, IL; *U.S. Public*, pg. 1735
Lindenkohl, George, Asst. V.P.--O.A. Newton & Son Co., Bridgeville, DE; *U.S. Private*, pg. 797
Lindhorn, Jim, V.P.-Procurement--Coachmen Industries, Inc., Elkhart, IN; *U.S. Public*, pg. 387
Lindic, Dan, Mgr.-Pur.--Hoover Company, Canton, OH; *U.S. Public*, pg. 1065
Lindley, David M., Dir.-Corp. Pur.--Sealright Company, Inc., De Soto, KS; *U.S. Public*, pg. 1451
Lindquist, Paul, Mgr.-Pur.--Union Industries, Inc., Providence, RI; *U.S. Private*, pg. 1119
Lindsey, Kris, Exec. V.P.--All Star Gas Corporation, Lebanon, MO; *U.S. Private*, pg. 35
Lindsey, Virginia, Dir.-Pur.--Protocol Systems, Inc., Beaverton, OR; *U.S. Public*, pg. 1336
Lineberry, Jerry, Supvr.-Materials--The Flight International Group, Inc., Newport News, VA; *U.S. Public*, pg. 654
Linehan, James B., Chief Fin. Officer, V.P.-Fin., Treas. & Controller--Ruslander & Sons, Inc., Buffalo, NY; *U.S. Private*, pg. 952
Lingo, Edward J., Dir.-Pur.--Applied Materials, Inc., Santa Clara, CA; *U.S. Public*, pg. 123
Linhart, Alice, Dir.-Pur.--Mesa Laboratories, Inc., Wheat Ridge, CO; *U.S. Public*, pg. 1099
Linser, Marge, Mgr.-Pur.--Kennedy Manufacturing Company, Van Wert, OH; *U.S. Private*, pg. 614
Linsolas, Brouno, V.P.-Pur.--Mack Trucks, Inc., Allentown, PA; *Int'l*, pg. 1102
Lipman, Robert, Pur. Agent--Sika Corporation, Lyndhurst, NJ; *Int'l*, pg. 1249
Lippa, John, Mgr.-Pur.--First Maryland Credit Corp., Baltimore, MD; *Int'l*, pg. 64
Lippa, John, Mgr.-Pur.--First Maryland Leasecorp, Baltimore, MD; *Int'l*, pg. 64
Lippa, John, Mgr.-Pur.--First Maryland Intl. Banking Corp., York, PA; *Int'l*, pg. 64
Lippa, John, Mgr.-Pur.--First Maryland Brokerage Corporation, Baltimore, MD; *Int'l*, pg. 64
Lippa, John, Mgr.-Pur.--First Maryland Annuities Agency Corporation, Baltimore, MD; *Int'l*, pg. 64
Lippa, John, Mgr.-Pur.--The York Bank and Trust Company, York, PA; *Int'l*, pg. 65
Lippe, Gary, V.P.-Corp. Pur.--American Greetings Corporation, Cleveland, OH; *U.S. Public*, pg. 77
Lippetti, Aldo, V.P.-Pur.--Silver State Disposal Service, Inc., Las Vegas, NV; *U.S. Public*, pg. 1380
Lippiat, P., Dir.-Pur.--Smythson of Bond Street, London, United Kingdom; *Int'l*, pg. 707
Lipscomb, Samuel, V.P.-Milk Procurement--Broughton Foods Company, Marietta, OH; *U.S. Public*, pg. 259
Lira, Teri, Dir.-Pur.--Brush Research Manufacturing Company, Los Angeles, CA; *U.S. Private*, pg. 176
Lisker, Harvey, V.P.-Pur.--Antwerp Diamond Distributors Inc., New York, NY; *U.S. Private*, pg. 76
Lister, David, Dir.-Pur.--First National Bank of Commerce, New Orleans, LA; *U.S. Public*, pg. 629
Lister, David, Asst. V.P.-Pur.--Marquis Investments, New Orleans, LA; *U.S. Public*, pg. 629
Littfin, Jack, Mgr.-Mktg. & Pur.--Littfin Lumber Company, Winsted, MN; *U.S. Private*, pg. 670
Little, David, Mgr.-Pur.--Detection Systems, Inc., Fairport, NY; *U.S. Public*, pg. 501
Little, John, Mgr.-Production--Marietta, Inc., Olive Branch, MS; *U.S. Private*, pg. 703
Little, Robert, Mgr.-Matls. & Contract Svcs.--Sacramento Municipal Utility District, Sacramento, CA; *U.S. Private*, pg. 959
Litwin, Adrienne, Dir.-Pur.--Euromarket Designs, Inc., Northbrook, IL; *U.S. Private*, pg. 384
Ljungquist, Pentti, V.P.-Pur.--Partek Corporation, Helsinki, Finland; *Int'l*, pg. 1024
Lloveras, Lowell, Dir.-Pur.--LEGO Systems, Inc., Enfield, CT; *Int'l*, pg. 805
Lloyd, Ian, Dir.-Procurement--Rolls-Royce plc, London, United Kingdom; *Int'l*, pg. 1126
Locke, Jim, Mgr.--Commemorative Brands, Inc., Austin, TX; *U.S. Private*, pg. 258
Locke, Neil, V.P.-Pur.--Hyatt Corporation, Chicago, IL; *U.S. Private*, pg. 551
Lockhart, William, Sr. V.P.-Asset Mngmt.--National Income Realty Trust, New York, NY; *U.S. Public*, pg. 1157
Loe, Tim, Pur. Agent--Mico Inc., North Mankato, MN; *U.S. Private*, pg. 741
Loeffler, Curt, Dir.-Pur.--Nasco International, Inc., Fort Atkinson, WI; *U.S. Private*, pg. 446
Loewer, Paul, Dir.-Pur.--First Omni Bank, N.A., Millsboro, DE; *Int'l*, pg. 65
Lofgren, Paul, Buyer--The Bartell Drug Company, Seattle, WA; *U.S. Private*, pg. 118
Logan, Candace, Mgr.-Pur.--Planning Systems Inc., Mc Lean, VA; *U.S. Private*, pg. 869
Logghe, John, Pur. Agent--Logghe Stamping Company, Fraser, MI; *U.S. Private*, pg. 672
Lohr, Kathi, Dir.-Pur.--Newage Industries Inc., Testing Instruments Group, Willow Grove, PA; *U.S. Private*, pg. 796
Loiselle, Twig, Mgr.-Pur.--Aquarion Company, Bridgeport, CT; *U.S. Public*, pg. 126
Loiselle, Twig, Mgr.-Pur.--BHC Company, Bridgeport, CT; *U.S. Public*, pg. 126
Loizou, Angelo, Mgr.-Pur.--Becton Dickinson Canada Inc., Mississauga, Canada; *U.S. Public*, pg. 200
Lollymore, Robert, Dir.-Pur.--Dixons Group plc, Hemel Hempstead, United Kingdom.; *Int'l*, pg. 413
Lombardi, Robert, Pur. Agent--Alloy Products Corp, Waukesha, WI; *U.S. Private*, pg. 42
Lone, William A., V.P.-Pur. Div.--WestPoint Stevens Inc., West Point, GA; *U.S. Public*, pg. 1762
Long, Bill, Mgr.-Pur.--Uni-Marts, Inc., State College, PA; *U.S. Public*, pg. 1664
Long, Haney A., Sr. V.P.-Pur. & Distr.--Shoney's, Inc., Nashville, TN; *U.S. Public*, pg. 1467
Long, Mark, Pur.-Agent--Imperial Litho & Dryography, Inc., Phoenix, AZ; *U.S. Private*, pg. 558
Long, Pamela, Mgr.-Pur.--Stanley Steemer International, Inc., Dublin, OH; *U.S. Private*, pg. 1033
Long, Steve, Mgr.-Ingredient Procurement--Interstate Brands Corporation, Kansas City, MO; *U.S. Public*, pg. 909
Long, Tony, Dir.-Pur.--Telsco Industries, Garland, TX; *U.S. Private*, pg. 1074
Longe, Martha, Pur. Agent--Edlund Company, Inc., Burlington, VT; *U.S. Private*, pg. 364
Longo, Grace, Sr. Buyer--Stocker & Yale, Inc., Salem, NH; *U.S. Public*, pg. 1518
Lontz, Richard, Dir.-Pur.--DeSoto Inc., Joliet, IL; *U.S. Public*, *pg. 956*
Lopert, Paul, Gen. Mgr.--Boral Limited, Sydney, Australia; *Int'l*, pg. 203
Lopes, Dra. Anabela, Head-Pur.--Transportes Aereos Portugueses, Lisbon, Portugal; *Int'l*, pg. 1418
Lopez, Aurelio, Mgr.-Pur.--Sanitaria Mexicana S.A. de C.V., Mexico, Mexico; *Int'l*, pg. 614
Lopez, Faustino, Dir.-Distr.--Spec's Music, Inc., Miami, FL; *U.S. Public*, pg. 1497
LoPiano, Steve, Mgr.-Pur.--The American Group, Ferndale, WA; *U.S. Private*, pg. 56
Loprest, Jay, Asst. V.P.-Mfg. & Purchasing--Naz-Dar Company, Chicago, IL; *U.S. Private*, pg. 1084
Lorch, Frank, Dir.-Non-Resale Pur.--Golub Corporation, Schenectady, NY; *U.S. Private*, pg. 463
Lorek, Kathy, Dir.-Pur.--Gray Printing Co., Fostoria, OH; *U.S. Private*, pg. 472
Lorenzo, Bart, Pur. Agent--M.A. Bruder & Sons, Incorporated, Broomall, PA; *U.S. Private*, pg. 175
Lorson, Don, Dir.-Pur.--Selfix, Inc., Chicago, IL; *U.S. Public*, pg. 832
Loupe, Diane, Mgr.-Pur.--East Ascension Telephone Company, Inc., Gonzales, LA; *U.S. Private*, pg. 358
Loux, Gerry, Buyer--Replogle Globes, Inc., Broadview, IL; *U.S. Private*, pg. 923
Low, Miriam, Pur. Agent--Sensall, Div. of Rosemount, Inc., Hauppauge, NY; *U.S. Public*, pg. 574
Lowder, Dewey, Dir.-Pur.--Pic'n Pay Stores, Inc., Matthews, NC; *U.S. Private*, pg. 864
Lowe, Art, Mgr.-Pur.--Spectronics Corporation, Westbury, NY; *U.S. Private*, pg. 1024
Lowery, G.L., Pur. Admin.--Airport Group International, Inc., Glendale, CA; *U.S. Public*, pg. 1009
Lowery, Mitch, Mgr.-Corp. Pur.--Valassis Communications, Inc., Livonia, MI; *U.S. Public*, pg. 1704
Luca, Albert, Dir.-Pur. & Personnel--AFA Protective Systems, Inc., Syosset, NY; *U.S. Public*, pg. 5
Lucero, Mike, V.P.-Pur.--Crowley Maritime Corporation, Oakland, CA; *U.S. Private*, pg. 292
Luciano, Mike, V.P.--UST Corporation, Boston, MA; *U.S. Public*, pg. 1660
Luckman, Jeffrey M., V.P.-Livestock Procurement--Smithfield Foods, Inc., Norfolk, VA; *U.S. Public*, pg. 1479
Lukasewych, Agnes, Sr. Radio Buyer--SFM Media Corporation, New York, NY; *U.S. Private*, pg. 956
Lukeman, Karen, Mgr.-Pur.--Media 100, Inc., Marlborough, MA; *U.S. Public*, pg. 1079
Lum, Ed, Pur. Agent--Kenwood USA, Long Beach, CA; *Int'l*, *pg. 730*
Lumley, J., Mgr.-Pur.--Aydin Vector Div., Newtown, PA; *U.S. Public*, pg. 158
Luppino, J.E., Dir.-Pur.--J.M. Huber, Chemicals Division, Havre De Grace, MD; *U.S. Private*, pg. 545
Luscombe, A.B., Mgr.-Pur.--WBB Devon Clays Ltd., Newton Abbot, United Kingdom; *Int'l*, pg. 1487
Lustig, Mark, Dir.-Matls. Mngmt.--Allen-Edmonds Shoe Corp., Port Washington, WI; *U.S. Private*, pg. 36
Luty, Jeff, Dir.-Pur.--Smith & Wesson Corp., Springfield, MA; *Int'l*, pg. 1397
Lutz, Augusto, Asst. Mgr.-Procurement--CODELCO Chile (Corporacion Nacional Del Cobre De Chile), Santiago, Chile; *Int'l*, pg. 302
Lutz, Bob, Exec. Dir.-Pur.--Certified Grocers of California, Los Angeles, CA; *U.S. Private*, pg. 226
Lux, Jim, Materials Mgr.--Inverness Corp., Fair Lawn, NJ; *U.S. Private*, pg. 574
Lux, Jim, Mgr.-Pur.--ERI Laboratories, Fair Lawn, NJ; *U.S. Private*, pg. 574
Luxem, Paul, Pur. Agent--Berger Transfer & Storage, Inc., Saint Paul, MN; *U.S. Private*, pg. 135
Luya, Bill, Mgr.-Natl. Pur. & Support--Meadow Lea Foods Ltd., Mascot, Australia; *Int'l*, pg. 555
Lymer, Jim, Dir.-Pur.--Frigidaire Home Products-Specialty Power Equipment, Shreveport, LA; *Int'l*, pg. 440

Lynch, Linda, Mfr.-Pur.--Analog Devices, Santa Clara, CA; *U.S. Public*, pg. 108
Lynch, Pat, Dir.-Pur.--Perdue Farms, Inc., Showell, MD; *U.S. Private*, pg. 852
Lynch, R., Dir.-Pur.--Hussmann Store Equipment Limited, Brantford, Canada; *U.S. Public*, pg. 1766
Lyon, Gary, Dir.-Pur.--Burlington Industries, Inc., Greensboro, NC; *U.S. Public*, pg. 268
Lyon, Lydia, Dir.-Pur.--Club Med Sales, Inc., New York, NY; *Int'l*, pg. 298
Lyons, B.F., Grp. Pur. Officer--Jefferson Smurfit Group p.l.c., Dublin, Ireland; *Int'l*, pg. 1269
Lyons, Jim, Dir.-Pur.--Rex Moore Electrical Contractors & Engineers, West Sacramento, CA; *U.S. Private*, pg. 760
Lyons, O.T., Mgr.-Matls. & Transportation--Babcock & Wilcox Co., Barberton, OH; *U.S. Public*, pg. 1068
Lyons, Richard, V.P.-Procurement--King & Prince Seafood Corporation, Brunswick, GA; *U.S. Private*, pg. 620
Lyrla, Louis, Dir.-Pur.--Vita Food Products, Inc., Chicago, IL; *U.S. Private*, pg. 1142
Lytle, Jim, Mgr.-Pur.--UnionTools, Inc., Columbus, OH; *U.S. Public*, pg. 17
Maack, Robert, V.P.-Opers.--Russell Stover Candies, Inc., Kansas City, MO; *U.S. Private*, pg. 953
Mabie, Dan, Pur. Agent--Hamlin, Inc., Lake Mills, WI; *U.S. Public*, pg. 251
MacConnell, George A., Sr. V.P.-Distr. & Specialty Opers.--Georgia-Pacific Building Products Division, Atlanta, GA; *U.S. Public*, pg. 735
MacDonald, Donald, V.P.-Pur. & Engrng.--Amway Corporation, Ada, MI; *U.S. Private*, pg. 69
MacDonald, Roberta, Mgr.-Pur.--Intermetrics, Inc., Burlington, MA; *U.S. Private*, pg. 567
MacFarland, William, Pur. Agent--Roy F. Weston, Inc., West Chester, PA; *U.S. Public*, pg. 1761
Machala, Edward W., V.P.-Opers., Mfg. & Treas.--American Power Conversion Corporation, West Kingston, RI; *U.S. Public*, pg. 89
Macho, Jerome, Pur. Agent--Unifoil Corporation, Passaic, NJ; *U.S. Private*, pg. 1117
Machulak, Walter A., Sec. & Mgr.-Pur.--Homespan Realty Co., Inc., Milwaukee, WI; *U.S. Public*, pg. 410
MacInnes, D.C., Dir.-Supply Mngmt.--MacMillan Bloedel Limited, Vancouver, Canada; *Int'l*, pg. 828
MacIsaac, Mel, Mgr.-Pur.--Corporate Foods Ltd., Etobicoke, Canada; *Int'l*, pg. 841
Mack, Harry, Mgr.-Pur.--F.H. Chase, Inc., Mansfield, MA; *U.S. Private*, pg. 230
Mackey, Randy, Mgr.-Pur.--Efco Corporation, Monett, MO; *U.S. Private*, pg. 353
Macko, G., Dir.-Pur.--USG Corporation, Chicago, IL; *U.S. Public*, pg. 1660
MacLea, Rod, Dir.-Pur.--Tekelec, Calabasas, CA; *U.S. Public*, pg. 1566
MacLean, John P., V.P.-Pur.--AMR Corporation, Fort Worth, TX; *U.S. Public*, pg. 9
MacLean, Scott, Mgr.-Materials--Barber Industries, Inc., Edmonton, Canada; *Int'l*, pg. 164
MacLellan, James S., V.P.-Materials--Binkley Company, Warrenton, MO; *U.S. Private*, pg. 534
Macricostas, Steve, Dir.-Pur.--Photronics, Inc., Brookfield, CT; *U.S. Public*, pg. 1293
Madden, Michael J., V.P.-Physical Distr.--Toys "R" Us United States, Paramus, NJ; *U.S. Public*, pg. 1626
Maddona, Nancy D., Dir.-Personnel--Gudebrod, Inc., Pottstown, PA; *U.S. Private*, pg. 486
Madewell, J.F., Dir.-Advanced Programs Pur.--Lockheed Space Operations Co., Titusville, FL; *U.S. Public*, pg. 1009
Madison, Robert, Dir.-Pur.--Webcraft Technologies, Inc., North Brunswick, NJ; *U.S. Public*, pg. 228
Madrid, Gerry, Dir.-Fleet/Pur.--Airborne Freight Corporation, Seattle, WA; *U.S. Public*, pg. 32
Madsen, Barbara, Mgr.-Pur.--View-Master, Inc., Mount Laurel, NJ; *U.S. Public*, pg. 1058
Maehl, Doug, Sr. V.P.-Mfg., Pur. & Distr.--Safelite AutoGlass, Columbus, OH; *U.S. Private*, pg. 960
Magee, David, Mgr.-Resource Plng.--T.D. Williamson, Inc., Tulsa, OK; *U.S. Private*, pg. 1179
Mager, Norbert, Dir.-Pur.--RHC/Spacemaster Corporation, Melrose Park, IL; *U.S. Private*, pg. 904
Magnano, Joe, Pur. Agent--Arrow Fluid Power, Broadview, IL; *U.S. Private*, pg. 85
Magnuson, Dale, Mgr.-Pur.--Reading Tube Corp., Reading, PA; *U.S. Private*, pg. 202
Magoon, Stephen, Mgr.-Pur.--Intesys Technologies, Gilbert, AZ; *U.S. Private*, pg. 574
Mahan, Steve, Pur. Agent--Manning & Lewis Engineering Co., Union, NJ; *U.S. Private*, pg. 700
Mahl, Larry, Dir.-Pur.--Wells-Gardner Electronics Corp., Chicago, IL; *U.S. Public*, pg. 1753
Mahnami, Margaret E., Dir.-Pur.--Cedar Fair, L.P., Sandusky, OH; *U.S. Public*, pg. 319
Mahon, Bridget, Mgr.-Pur.--Cooper Instrument Corp., Middlefield, CT; *U.S. Private*, pg. 274
Maiioch, Daniel, Mgr.-Pur.--Hillsdale Tool & Mfg. Co., Hillsdale, MI; *U.S. Private*, pg. 355
Main, Barbara, V.P.-Pur.--Texas Refinery Corp., Fort Worth, TX; *U.S. Private*, pg. 1078
Maita, Paul, Dir.-Pur.--Gendex-Del Medical Imaging Corp., Franklin Park, IL; *U.S. Public*, pg. 494
Maitland, T., Mgr.-Pur.--Propak Systems Ltd., Airdrie, Canada; *Int'l*, pg. 1071
Makiaris, Jim, Dir.-Pur.--Invacare Corporation, Elyria, OH; *U.S. Public*, pg. 911
Makkencherry, Bob, Mgr.-Pur.--Haydon Switch & Instrument, Inc., Waterbury, CT; *U.S. Private*, pg. 513
Malch, Jim, Pur. Agent--Electro Kinetics Div., Santa Barbara, CA; *U.S. Public*, pg. 1250
Malcolm, William, V.P.-Pur.--Tristate Electrical Supply Co., Inc., Hagerstown, MD; *U.S. Private*, pg. 1104
Malee, Kris, Pur. Supvr.--Uniflow Manufacturing Co., Erie, PA; *U.S. Private*, pg. 1117
Malefyt, Tim, Dir.-Pur.--Grocers Baking Co., Grand Rapids, MI; *U.S. Private*, pg. 482
Malick, Al, Mgr.-Facilities--Western Staff Services, Walnut Creek, CA; *U.S. Public*, pg. 1760
Mall, Saurabh, Pur. Agent--Automotive Moulding Company, Warren, MI; *U.S. Private*, pg. 485
Mall, Udo, Mgr.-Pur.--Traub AG, Reichenbach, Germany; *Int'l*, pg. 1419
Mallette, Jean, Gen. Mgr.-Admin. Svcs.--EBSCO Industries, Inc., Birmingham, AL; *U.S. Private*, pg. 358
Mallette, R., Dir.-Pur.--Eureka Manufacturing Co., Inc., Norton, MA; *U.S. Private*, pg. 916
Malone, Dick, V.P.-Pur.--Spring Arbor Distributors, Belleville, MI; *U.S. Private*, pg. 563
Maltby, Laurie, Mgr.-Pur.--Group 1 Software, Inc., Lanham, MD; *U.S. Public*, pg. 417
Manar, Scott, Head Buyer--Banner Wholesale Grocers, Inc., Chicago, IL; *U.S. Private*, pg. 114
Manchester, Robert, Dir.-Pur.--Multiple Allied Services, Inc., Hayward, CA; *U.S. Private*, pg. 767
Mandli, Pete, Mgr.-Pur.--Sun Electric, Lincolnshire, IL; *U.S. Public*, pg. 1480
Manfreda, Lou, Mgr.-Pur.--National Micronetics, Inc., Kingston, NY; *Int'l*, pg. 1347
Mango, Stephen, Mgr.-Pur.--MBL Life Assurance Corporation, Newark, NJ; *U.S. Private*, pg. 685
Manguel, Nancy, Mgr.-Pur.--Plastag Corporation, Elk Grove Village, IL; *U.S. Private*, pg. 870
Mann, Robert A., Chief Fin. Officer & Exec. V.P.-Fin. & Admin.--Park Foods L.P., Barrington, IL; *U.S. Private*, pg. 839
Mannes, Kenneth, Pur. Agent--Merchants Publishing Co., Kalamazoo, MI; *U.S. Private*, pg. 732
Manning, Bill, Dir.-Pur.--People, New York, NY; *U.S. Public*, pg. 1613
Manning, J., Mgr.-Pur.--Wacker Silicones Corporation, Adrian, MI; *Int'l*, pg. 625
Manning, John, Dir.-Pur.--BIW Cable Systems, Inc., Franklin, MA; *Int'l*, pg. 417
Manno, Samuel F., V.P.-Pur. & Corp. Svcs.--Niagara Mohawk Power Corporation, Syracuse, NY; *U.S. Public*, pg. 1181
Manoni, Dave, Mgr.-Purch.--Hudson Valley Paper Company, Albany, NY; *U.S. Private*, pg. 546
Mansfield, Fred, Dir.-Opers.--Karnak Corporation, Clark, NJ; *U.S. Private*, pg. 607
Manson, Sandra, Pur. Agent--Automatic Machine Products Company, Attleboro, MA; *U.S. Private*, pg. 101
Manter, Amelia, Mgr.-Pur.--Crowe Rope Industries L.L.C., Waterville, ME; *U.S. Private*, pg. 291
Marcy, Bob, Dir.-Pur.--The National Latex Products Co., Ashland, OH; *U.S. Private*, pg. 785
Mards, Rolf, Dir.-Pur.--Korsnas AB, Gavle, Sweden; *Int'l*, pg. 759
Maresca, John, Pur. Mgr.--Hayward Industries, Inc., Elizabeth, NJ; *U.S. Private*, pg. 513
Margate, Alicia, Pur. Dir.--Alpha One Exchange, New Providence, NJ; *U.S. Private*, pg. 45
Mari, Dennis, Dir.-Pur.--La Victoria Foods, Inc., City of Industry, CA; *U.S. Private*, pg. 641
Mariniello, Gabriel, Mgr.-Pur.--Macromedia Incorporated, Hackensack, NJ; *U.S. Private*, pg. 693
Mariniello, Gabriel, Mgr.-Pur.--Bergen Record Corp., Hackensack, NJ; *U.S. Private*, pg. 693
Marino, T., Dir.-Pur.--EnviroSource-International Mill Service, Inc., Horsham, PA; *U.S. Public*, pg. 587
Markmann, Dan E., V.P.-Matls. Mngmt.--Mead Johnson Nutritional Group, Evansville, IN; *U.S. Public*, pg. 254
Marks, Sam, Exec. V.P., Corp. Sec. & Dir.-Pur.--Triangle Marketing Corp., New York, NY; *U.S. Private*, pg. 1102
Marks, Sam, Exec. V.P., Corp. Sec. & Dir.-Pur.--New Brook Paper, New York, NY; *U.S. Private*, pg. 1102
Marlowe, Terry, Sr. Pur. Agent--Sentry Group, Rochester, NY; *U.S. Private*, pg. 984
Marotta, Martin, Pur. Agent--Philadelphia Sign Company, Palmyra, NJ; *U.S. Private*, pg. 861
Marquez, Rudy, Sr. Dir.-Procurement--Catalina Marketing Corporation, Saint Petersburg, FL; *U.S. Public*, pg. 314
Marriott, William, Mgr.-Pur.--Family Smacks, Inc., Liberty, MO; *U.S. Private*, pg. 393
Marsh, Charles L., Sr. Exec. V.P.-Pur. & Mktg.--Southern Electronics Distributors International, Tucker, GA; *U.S. Public*, pg. 1490
Marshall, Richard, V.P.-Pur.--Harris Corp., RF Communications Group Marketing Division, Rochester, NY; *U.S. Public*, pg. 792
Martens, Jeanette, Dir.-Pur.--Automatic Equipment Mfg. Co., Pender, NE; *U.S. Private*, pg. 101
Martin, Danny, Dir. Pur.--Sanderson Farms, Inc., Laurel, MS; *U.S. Public*, pg. 1430
Martin, James L., Jr., V.P.-Pur.--Paragon Health Network, Inc., Atlanta, GA; *U.S. Public*, pg. 1256
Martin, Jane, Mgr.-Pur.--A.I. Root Company, Medina, OH; *U.S. Private*, pg. 944
Martin, Joelle, Mgr.-Facilities--The Leslie Fay Companies, Inc., New York, NY; *U.S. Public*, pg. 989
Martin, Kathie, Buyer--Benthos, Inc., North Falmouth, MA; *U.S. Public*, pg. 212
Martin, Melvin, Exec. Dir.-Pur.--Bridgestone/Firestone, Inc., Nashville, TN; *Int'l*, pg. 213
Martin, Robert, Mgr.-Pur.--Raytech Corporation, Shelton, CT; *U.S. Public*, pg. 1363
Martincic, Joseph, Sr. V.P.-Admin. Services--Regence BlueCross BlueShield of Oregon, Portland, OR; *U.S. Private*, pg. 917
Martineau, P.R., V.P. & Treas.--GSW Inc., Guelph, Canada,; *Int'l*, pg. 538
Martinez Soberanes, German, Dir.-Pur.--Grupo SYR, S.A. de C.V., Mexico, Mexico; *Int'l*, pg. 576
Martinez, Jerry, Mgr.-Pur.--American Computer Assembly/Compas, Ogdensburg, NY; *Int'l*, pg. 36
Martino, Josep Lluis, Head-Pur.--Caixa d'Estalvis de Catalunya, Barcelona, Spain; *Int'l*, pg. 249
Marulli, Eugene, V.P.-Mtls.--Telephonics Command Systems Div., Farmingdale, NY; *U.S. Public*, pg. 558
Mascaro, Alan J., Mgr.-Facilities & Matls.--Yankee Energy System, Inc., Meriden, CT; *U.S. Public*, pg. 1787
Mashburn, Phil, Dir.-Pur.--Magic Circle Manufacturing Div., Coffeyville, KS; *U.S. Private*, pg. 13
Maskill, Karen, Mgr.-Pur.--Kenwal Products Corp., Dearborn, MI; *U.S. Private*, pg. 615
Masley, John, V.P. & Dir.-Pur.--Hofmann Industries, Inc., Sinking Spring, PA; *U.S. Private*, pg. 533
Mason, Brad, Dir.-Pur.--Zions Co-operative Mercantile Institution, Salt Lake City, UT; *U.S. Public*, pg. 1793
Mason, Charlie J., Dir.-Pur.--Octagon Process Inc., Edgewater, NJ; *U.S. Private*, pg. 811
Mason, Clarence, Mgr.-Pur.--National Forge Company, Irvine, PA; *U.S. Private*, pg. 783
Mason, Clive, Dir.-Pur.--British Airways PLC, London, United Kingdom; *Int'l*, pg. 218
Mason, Dee, Mgr.-Pur.--Unger Company, Cleveland, OH; *U.S. Private*, pg. 1117
Mason, J., Mgr.-Pur.--Duraco Products, Inc., Streamwood, IL; *U.S. Private*, pg. 348
Massolini, Malinda, Mgr.-Office Services--Resort Condominiums International, Indianapolis, IN; *U.S. Public*, pg. 322
Masters, Dorothy, Pur.--Phoenix Technologies Ltd., San Jose, CA; *U.S. Public*, pg. 1292
Masters, Fran, Dir.-Pur.--Mar-Mac Manufacturing Company, Inc., McBee, SC; *U.S. Private*, pg. 701
Masters, Tony, Dir.-Pur.--Suitt Construction Company, Inc., Greenville, SC; *U.S. Private*, pg. 106
Mastro, Don, Dir.-Pur.--North America Foods, Minnetonka, MN; *U.S. Public*, pg. 901
Mastrojohn, James, Dir.-Pur.--Computer Power Incorporated, High Bridge, NJ; *U.S. Public*, pg. 421
Masui, Kenichiro, Dir.-Matls. & Purchasing--Asahi Breweries Ltd., Tokyo, Japan; *Int'l*, pg. 83
Mataway, Kathleen S., Mgr.-Customer Service--Hano Document Printers, Inc., Mount Olive, IL; *U.S. Public*, pg. 1686
Matherne, Flo, Dir.-Pur.--Bollinger Shipyards, Inc., Lockport, LA; *U.S. Private*, pg. 155
Mathews, Candace M., Dir.-Pur.--Vitatech International, Inc., Tustin, CA; *U.S. Private*, pg. 1142
Mathews, Dana, Dir.-Mktg.--Interface Electronics Corporation, Hopkinton, MA; *U.S. Private*, pg. 567
Mathews, Foster, Sr. Corp. Pur. Officer--Regions Financial Corporation, Birmingham, AL; *U.S. Public*, pg. 1371
Mathews, Garry, V.P.-Pur. & Mfg.--All-Luminum Products, Inc., Philadelphia, PA; *U.S. Private*, pg. 34
Mathey, Tom, Dir.-Mdse. & Pur.--O'Malia Food Markets Inc., Carmel, IN; *U.S. Private*, pg. 816
Mattas, Clair, Pur. Agent--Woolrich, Inc., Woolrich, PA; *U.S. Private*, pg. 1188
Matthews, David J., Sr. V.P.-Pur. & Gen. Mdse.--Hill-Behan Lumber Company, Saint Louis, MO; *U.S. Private*, pg. 529
Mattingly, John, Mgr.-Pur.--The New Piper Aircraft, Inc., Vero Beach, FL; *U.S. Private*, pg. 794
Mattingly, Joseph, Dir.-Pur.--MacNeal-Schwendler Corp., Costa Mesa, CA; *U.S. Public*, pg. 1031
Mattson, Dave, Mgr.-Logistics--The Lubrizol Corporation, Wickliffe, OH; *U.S. Public*, pg. 1016
Maxon, Joe, V.P.-Pur.--Playtex Products Inc., Westport, CT; *U.S. Public*, pg. 1310
Maxwell, David W., Dir.-Matls. Mngmt.--Worthington Foods Inc., Worthington, OH; *U.S. Public*, pg. 1780
May, Charles E., Mgr.-Pur.--May Supply Company, Inc., Harrisonburg, VA; *U.S. Public*, pg. 1727
May, Jim, Mgr.-Pur.--Dover Flour Mills, Cambridge, Canada; *Int'l*, pg. 417
May, Nelson, Mgr.-Pur.--Oklahoma City Division, Oklahoma City, OK; *U.S. Public*, pg. 279
May, Steve, Pur. Agent--DMI Furniture Inc., Louisville, KY; *U.S. Public*, pg. 473
Mayer, Terry, Mgr.-Corp. Pur.--IEC Electronics Corp., Newark, NY; *U.S. Public*, pg. 854
Mayes, Coy, Produce Buyer--Stanley Stores, Inc., Vidor, TX; *U.S. Private*, pg. 1033
Mayfield, Gary, Dir.--Shelter Mutual Insurance Company, Columbia, MO; *U.S. Private*, pg. 992
Maynard, Greg, Mgr.-Pur.--Snap-Tite, Inc., Erie, PA; *U.S. Private*, pg. 1010
Mazany, Stanley J., II, Mgr.-Matl. Control & Dir.-Pur.--Besser Company, Alpena, MI; *U.S. Private*, pg. 139
Mazarella, Chris, Mgr.-Pur.--Amprobe Instrument, Lynbrook, NY; *U.S. Public*, pg. 1676
Mazer, Allan, Dir.-Pur.--NCC Industries, Inc., Cortland, NY; *U.S. Private*, pg. 697
Mazurek, Stanley, Pur. Agent--Peerless Confection Company, Chicago, IL; *U.S. Private*, pg. 847
Mazzorin, Carlos E., V.P.-Pur.--Ford Motor Company, Dearborn, MI; *U.S. Public*, pg. 661
McAdams, Linda, Pur. Agent--Anemostat Products, Scranton, PA; *U.S. Public*, pg. 286
McAdoo, James C., Dir.-Transportation & Pur.--Potlatch Corporation, Spokane, WA; *U.S. Public*, pg. 1318
McArthur, D., Mgr.-Pur.--Portec, Inc., Shipping Systems Div., Oak Brook, IL; *U.S. Public*, pg. 1318
McArthur, Ron, V.P.-Pur.--Cheesecake Factory Incorporated, Calabasas Hills, CA; *U.S. Public*, pg. 343
McAvoy, Robert, Mgr.-Pur.--Bailey, Fischer & Porter Company, Warminster, PA; *Int'l*, pg. 449
McBride, Bill, Mgr.-Pur.--Hull/Finmac, Inc., Warminster, PA; *U.S. Private*, pg. 547
McBride, John, Dir.-Pur.--Prince Sports Group Inc., Bordentown, NJ; *U.S. Private*, pg. 884
McCabe, Ken, Mgr.-Pur.--AMW Industries Inc., Conway, AR; *U.S. Public*, pg. 457
McCabe, Ron L., Mgr.-Pur.--Cajun Electric Power Co-op, Baton Rouge, LA; *U.S. Private*, pg. 199
McCaffrey, Patrick, Dir.-Materials--Wisconsin Machine and Tool Corporation, Milwaukee, WI; *U.S. Private*, pg. 1185

McCaffrey, Thomas R., V.P.-Procurement & Suppy Chain Services--American Electric Power Service Corp., Columbus, OH; *U.S. Public*, pg. 72
McCain, Irby, Mgr.-Pur.--Earle Industries, Inc., Earle, AR; *U.S. Private*, pg. 356
McCain, S.L., Dir.-Pur.--The Kansas City Southern Railway Co., Kansas City, MO; *U.S. Public*, pg. 944
McCain, Sam L., Mgr.-Pur.--Kansas City Southern Industries, Inc., Kansas City, MO; *U.S. Public*, pg. 943
McCamey, M.J., Pur. Agent--Cincinnati Sub-Zero Products, Inc., Cincinnati, OH; *U.S. Private*, pg. 240
McCard, Tony, Mgr.-Pur.--Homestead Homes, Cordele, GA; *U.S. Public*, pg. 318
McCarley, James, Mgr.-Pur.--Riverchase Homes, Haleyville, AL; *U.S. Public*, pg. 319
McCarthy, Donald J., Dir.-Pur.--Petro Chem Development Company, New York, NY; *U.S. Private*, pg. 858
McCarthy, Ed, Mgr.-Pur.--Interform Corporation, Bridgeville, PA; *U.S. Public*, pg. 333
McCarthy, Richard, V.P.-Pur. & Distr.--Jay Instrument & Specialty Co., Cincinnati, OH; *U.S. Private*, pg. 583
McCarty, Michael J., Mgr.-Pur.--Rohrer Corporation, Wadsworth, OH; *U.S. Private*, pg. 940
McClure, Howard, Pur. Agent--F. D. Kees Power Equipment, Beatrice, NE; *U.S. Private*, pg. 1195
McCluskey, Phillip, Mgr.-Pur.--Airguard Industries Inc., Louisville, KY; *U.S. Public*, pg. 382
McConkey, Hugh, Dir.-Matls. & Pur.--The Airolite Company, Marietta, OH; *U.S. Private*, pg. 29
McCooey, Don, Mgr.-Pur.--Kulicke & Soffa Industries, Inc., Willow Grove, PA; *U.S. Public*, pg. 968
McCormack, John, Dir.-Matls. Mngmt.--Regal Ware, Inc., Kewaskum, WI; *U.S. Private*, pg. 917
McCormick, Michael D., Pres.--BW Transportation Services, Inc., Indianapolis, IN; *U.S. Public*, pg. 228
McCoy, Michael, Dir.-Pur.--LeaRonal, Inc., Freeport, NY; *U.S. Public*, pg. 982
McCranie, G. Edwin, Exec. V.P.-Pur.--Ryan's Family Steak Houses, Inc., Greer, SC; *U.S. Public*, pg. 1413
McCrea, Steve, Pur. Agent--Ohio Gas Company, Bryan, OH; *U.S. Private*, pg. 812
McCready, Howard, Mgr.-Pur.--Hazen Paper Company, Holyoke, MA; *U.S. Private*, pg. 514
McCright, Pat, Buyer II--Tucson Electric Power Company, Tucson, AZ; *U.S. Public*, pg. 1670
McCue, Michael, V.P.-Pur.--Skyland Scientific Services, Inc., Bozeman, MT; *U.S. Public*, pg. 1515
McCurry, Rick, Sr. Dir.-Pur.--Ruiz Food Products, Inc., Dinuba, CA; *U.S. Private*, pg. 951
McDaniel, Walter C., Dir.-Pur. & Plng.--Blue Diamond Growers, Sacramento, CA; *U.S. Private*, pg. 152
McDermott, Mike, Dir.-Pur.--Semtech Corporation, Newbury Park, CA; *U.S. Public*, pg. 1456
McDermott, Sharon, Mgr.-Pur.--Crown American Realty Trust, Johnstown, PA; *U.S. Public*, pg. 461
McDermott, William, Dir.-Pur.--General Printing Ink, Northlake, IL; *Int'l*, pg. 370
McDonough, James, Dir.-Pur.--Ocean Spray Cranberries, Inc., Middleboro, MA; *U.S. Private*, pg. 811
McElwee, A. Joseph, Pur. Agent--Zenith Products Corp., New Castle, DE; *U.S. Public*, pg. 1054
McEwan, Darlene, Dir.-Pur.--FaceMate Corp., Somersworth, NH; *U.S. Private*, pg. 391
McFarland, Pat, Mgr.-Matls.--Electric Research and Manufacturing Cooperative, Inc. (ERMCO), Dyersburg, TN; *U.S. Private*, pg. 82
McGary, Francis H., V.P.-Mfg.--Star Bronze Company, Alliance, OH; *U.S. Private*, pg. 1034
McGee, Gary L., Treas.--Devon Energy Corporation, Oklahoma City, OK; *U.S. Public*, pg. 503
McGinnis, Tomert, Mgr.-Pur.--Moltrup Steel Products Company, Beaver Falls, PA; *U.S. Private*, pg. 756
McGinty, Thomas D., Sr. V.P.-Matls. Mngmt.--Sterling Electronics Corporation, Houston, TX; *U.S. Public*, pg. 1051
McGirt, Brad, Mgr.-Pur.--Town & Country Homes, Fort Worth, TX; *U.S. Public*, pg. 319
McGonigle, Dave, Mgr.-Pur.--Edmund Scientific Company, Barrington, NJ; *U.S. Private*, pg. 364
McGuire, John R., Dir.-Matls. Mngmt.--United Illuminating Company, New Haven, CT; *U.S. Public*, pg. 1678
McIlveen, Robert, Mgr.-Pur.--Liebert Corporation, Columbus, OH; *U.S. Public*, pg. 573
McIntire, Harley, V.P.--AFLAC Incorporated, Columbus, GA; *U.S. Public*, pg. 28
McIntosh, Julia, Pur. Agent--Ghent Manufacturing, Inc., Lebanon, OH; *U.S. Private*, pg. 450
McIntosh, Merle, V.P.-Pur.--Micro Warehouse, Inc., Norwalk, CT; *U.S. Public*, pg. 1104
McIntyre, James W., V.P.-Support Svcs.--USAA (United Services Automobile Association), San Antonio, TX; *U.S. Private*, pg. 1114
McIntyre, James W., Mgr.--Property & Casualty Insurance, San Antonio, TX; *U.S. Private*, pg. 1114
McIntyre, John, Dir.-Pur.--Capital City Press, Inc., Berlin, VT; *U.S. Private*, pg. 205
McKay, Douglas, Mgr.-Pur.--Candle-Lite, A Lancaster Colony Co., Cincinnati, OH; *U.S. Public*, pg. 976
McKeown, John C., Dir.-Pur.--Mitchel & Scott Machine Co., Inc., Indianapolis, IN; *U.S. Private*, pg. 753
McKim, Ron, Dir.-Pur.--Woodward-Clyde Group, Inc., Denver, CO; *U.S. Public*, pg. 1655
McKnight, Penny, V.P.-Pur.--Siouxland Galvanizing Corp., Sioux City, IA; *U.S. Private*, pg. 656
McLaughlin, Kathie, Pur. Agent--Morris Coupling Co., Erie, PA; *U.S. Private*, pg. 762
McLaughlin, Philip K., Dir.-Procurement--S & C Electric Company, Chicago, IL; *U.S. Private*, pg. 954
McLean, Charles, Mgr.-Matls. & Logistics--Du Pont (Australia) Ltd., Sydney, Australia; *U.S. Public*, pg. 532
McMinn, Rory, Dir.-Pur.--Hondo Oil & Gas Company, Roswell, NM; *Int'l*, pg. 818
McMullen, David, Project Mgr.--Sun Healthcare Group Inc., Albuquerque, NM; *U.S. Public*, pg. 1530
McMullen, Jerry, Asst. V.P.-Pur.--Deposit Guaranty Corp., Jackson, MS; *U.S. Public*, pg. 500
McMullen, Jerry, Asst. V.P.-Pur.--Deposit Guaranty National Bank, Jackson, MS; *U.S. Public*, pg. 500
McPartland, Deborah, Exec. V.P. & Buying Opers. Dir.--Cash Plus, Inc., Minneapolis, MN; *U.S. Private*, pg. 218
Meaders, Mark A., V.P.-Corp. Pur. & Logistics--Oshkosh Truck Corporation, Oshkosh, WI; *U.S. Public*, pg. 1233
Meagher, Gary, Pur. Agent--Sandvik/Milford Corporation, Branford, CT; *Int'l*, pg. 1185
Means, Carol, Dir.-Pur.--Group Insurance Inc. of Louisiana, Baton Rouge, LA; *U.S. Private*, pg. 484
Means, Rick, Buyer--The Bartell Drug Company, Seattle, WA; *U.S. Private*, pg. 118
Means, Rod, Dir.-Logistics--Omniflight, Inc., Dallas, TX; *U.S. Private*, pg. 816
Means, Rod, Dir.-Logistics--Omniflight Helicopters, Inc., Dallas, TX; *U.S. Private*, pg. 817
Mearns, Joe, Dir.-Pur.--UniFirst Corporation, Wilmington, MA; *U.S. Public*, pg. 1665
Mears, J., Dir.-Pur.--Sandusky International Inc., Sandusky, OH; *U.S. Private*, pg. 964
Meeks, Cathy, Pur. Agent--Wurzburg, Inc., Memphis, TN; *U.S. Private*, pg. 1192
Meglio, L.D., Dir.-Pur. & Mgr.-Office--Norwalk Powdered Metals, Inc., Norwalk, CT; *U.S. Private*, pg. 808
Mehling, Gary, Dir.-Pur.--Communications Instruments Inc., Fairview, NC; *U.S. Private*, pg. 259
Meidinger, Bruce, Mgr.-Pur.--American Crystal Sugar Company, Moorhead, MN; *U.S. Private*, pg. 52
Meinhold, Jeanne, Mgr.-Pur.--Sequus Pharmaceuticals, Inc., Menlo Park, CA; *U.S. Public*, pg. 1460
Meissner, W.G., Dir.-Pur.--Asarco Incorporated, New York, NY; *U.S. Public*, pg. 137
Melchiori, Tim, Mgr.-Pur.--Rice Growers Association of California, West Sacramento, CA; *U.S. Private*, pg. 927
Melson, Norma, Mgr.-Pur.--The Kay Company, Inc., Frankfort, IN; *U.S. Private*, pg. 610
Melton, David, Dir.-Pur.--Home Beneficial Corporation, Richmond, VA; *U.S. Public*, pg. 76
Menard, Andy, Mgr.-Pur.--Smith Pipe & Steel Co., Phoenix, AZ; *U.S. Private*, pg. 1009
Menard, Robert, Dir.-Pur.--ACS Industries, Inc., Woonsocket, RI; *U.S. Private*, pg. 3
Menda, Bill, V.P.-Admin.--Federal Home Loan Mortgage Corporation, Mc Lean, VA; *U.S. Public*, pg. 615
Mennitto, Valentino, Mgr.-Pur.--Seed Restaurant Group, Inc., Lexington, KY; *U.S. Private*, pg. 981
Mentges, Debra, Mgr.-Pur.--Ross Aluminum Foundries, Sidney, OH; *U.S. Private*, pg. 355
Mentzer, Jim, Dir.-Pur.--Ellwood City Forge, Ellwood City, PA; *U.S. Private*, pg. 373
Menzel, Leigh, Dir.-Pur.--Perry's Ice Cream Co., Inc., Akron, NY; *U.S. Private*, pg. 855
Merchant, Steve, Mgr.-Pur.--Griswold Industries, Inc., Costa Mesa, CA; *U.S. Private*, pg. 482
Merilott, Sandie, Mgr.-Office Svcs.--Sundt Corp., Tucson, AZ; *U.S. Private*, pg. 1051
Merrill, Kaj, Dir.-Pur.--Nordsten, Skive, Denmark; *Int'l*, pg. 1386
Merritt, C., Mgr.-Pur.--AP North American Aftermarket Division, Goldsboro, NC; *U.S. Private*, pg. 230
Merritt, Hugh, Mgr.-Pur.--Marotta Scientific Controls, Inc., Montville, NJ; *U.S. Private*, pg. 706
Meske, Dan, V.P.-Pur.--Deluxe Homes Of PA., Inc., Berwick, PA; *U.S. Private*, pg. 323
Messemer, R.C., Dir.-Distr. & Pur.--Rhone-Poulenc Basic Chemicals Co., Shelton, CT; *Int'l*, pg. 1110
Messick, Rich, Mgr.-Pur.--American Vanguard Corporation, Newport Beach, CA; *U.S. Public*, pg. 94
Metzer, Andreas, Exec. Dir.-Mktg., Buying & Store Opers.--Julius Meinl AG, Vienna, Austria; *Int'l*, pg. 856
Meyer, Glenn, Mgr.-Pur.--Wavetek Communications Div., Indianapolis, IN; *U.S. Private*, pg. 1155
Micek, A.M., Mgr.-Pur.--Kester Solder, Des Plaines, IL; *U.S. Public*, pg. 1003
Miceli, M., Dir.-Pur.--Esquire Radio & Electronics Inc., Brooklyn, NY; *U.S. Private*, pg. 383
Michal, George T., V.P.-Procurement--Sunbeam Corporation, Delray Beach, FL; *U.S. Public*, pg. 1533
Michalak, Jeannine, Pur. Agent--Giant Industries, Toledo, OH; *U.S. Private*, pg. 451
Michl, Joe, Dir.-Pur.--Oregon Metallurgical Corporation, Albany, OR; *U.S. Public*, pg. 43
Middleton, T., Mgr.-Procurement--Lockheed Space Operations Co., Titusville, FL; *U.S. Public*, pg. 1009
Mielcarek, W., Pur. Agent--Thomas & Betts Reznor Division, Memphis, TN; *U.S. Public*, pg. 1598
Migliaccio, Nick, Mgr.-Pur.--Power Systems Inc., Bloomfield, CT; *Int'l*, pg. 868
Miles, Christine, Pur. Agent--Vibra Screw Inc., Totowa, NJ; *U.S. Private*, pg. 1138
Miles, Steve, Master-Schedules--Watts Fluidair, Kittery, ME; *Int'l*, pg. 1243
Milhoan, J., Dir.-Pur.--Imperial Holly Corporation, Sugar Land, TX; *U.S. Public*, pg. 872
Militano, Jerry, V.P.-Pur.--Leonard Wholesale, Inc., Springfield, NJ; *U.S. Private*, pg. 660
Milkie, Robert, Dir.-Pur.--Aetna Bearing Company, Chicago, IL; *U.S. Private*, pg. 25
Miller, Ann, Dir.-Pur.--Roanoke Gas Company, Roanoke, VA; *U.S. Public*, pg. 1392
Miller, B., Pur. Agent--Advance Seed Co., Fulton, KY; *Int'l*, pg. 566
Miller, Bernhard, Mgr.-Pur.--Wandel & Goltermann GmbH & Co., Elektronische Messtechnik, Eningen, Germany; *Int'l*, pg. 1485
Miller, Bob, Dir.-Pur.--Highlights for Children, Inc., Columbus, OH; *U.S. Private*, pg. 528
Miller, Bob, Dir.-Pur.--Safeguard Business Systems, Inc., Fort Washington, PA; *U.S. Private*, pg. 960
Miller, Charles, Mgr.-Pur.--Mansion Homes, Robbins, NC; *U.S. Public*, pg. 318
Miller, Clifford, Dir.-Pur.--AmeriPath, Inc., Riviera Beach, FL; *U.S. Public*, pg. 96
Miller, Dolores, Dir.-Pur.--Rosen Associates Management Corp., Jericho, NY; *U.S. Private*, pg. 945
Miller, E.H., Pur. Agent--Magnetic Metals Corp., Camden, NJ; *U.S. Private*, pg. 560
Miller, F.J., Dir.-Pur.--Skyline Corporation, Elkhart, IN; *U.S. Public*, pg. 1476
Miller, Gary, Dir.-Pur.--Hill & Griffith Company, Cincinnati, OH; *U.S. Private*, pg. 529
Miller, Gary A., V.P.-Pur.--The Goodyear Tire & Rubber Company, Akron, OH; *U.S. Public*, pg. 752
Miller, George, Mgr.-Pur.--Rocco Quality Foods, Timberville, VA; *U.S. Private*, pg. 937
Miller, John, Dir.-Pur.--Ulbrich Stainless Steels & Special Metals, Inc., North Haven, CT; *U.S. Private*, pg. 1115
Miller, Mark F., V.P.-Contracts & Pricing--B-2 Division, Pico Rivera, CA; *U.S. Public*, pg. 1198
Miller, Raymond L., V.P.-Pur.--Midwest Grain Products, Inc., Atchison, KS; *U.S. Public*, pg. 1111
Miller, Richard, Dir.-Pur.--Urschel Labs Incorporated, Valparaiso, IN; *U.S. Private*, pg. 1129
Miller, Rory, Pur. Agent--Facemate Corporation, Chicopee, MA; *U.S. Private*, pg. 391
Miller, S., Mgr.-Pur.--Morrison Berkshire Inc., North Adams, MA; *U.S. Private*, pg. 762
Milliron, Frank, Dir.-Pur.--Mountain States Pipe & Supply Company, Colorado Springs, CO; *U.S. Private*, pg. 764
Mills, M., Dir.-Pur.--Courtaulds Coatings Inc., Louisville, KY; *Int'l*, pg. 338
Mills, Patrick, Dir.-Bus. & Tech. Services--Associated Electric Co-op Inc., Springfield, MO; *U.S. Private*, pg. 89
Milne, George, Div. Mgr.-Pur.--Delta Faucet Corporation, Indianapolis, IN; *U.S. Public*, pg. 1053
Min, Woo-Ki, Mng. Dir.--Bum-A Petroleum Co., Ltd., Seoul, Korea; *Int'l*, pg. 1292
Minami, Fumi, Mgr.-Pur.--Nissin Foods (U.S.A.) Co. Ltd., Gardena, CA; *Int'l*, pg. 949
Minnis, Joyce, Pur. Agent--Mary Maxim, Inc., Port Huron, MI; *U.S. Private*, pg. 716
Minter, Edwin, Dir.-Pur.--Moog Incorporated, East Aurora, NY; *U.S. Public*, pg. 1127
Minutoli, Nancy, Mgr.-Pur.--Dataram Corporation, Princeton, NJ; *U.S. Public*, pg. 487
Mioni, Kim, Mgr.-Pur.--Eversharp Pen Co., Franklin Park, IL; *U.S. Private*, pg. 386
Mirizzi, Ray, Dir.-Pur.--Advanced Micro Devices, Inc., Sunnyvale, CA; *U.S. Public*, pg. 21
Mitchell, Gail, Dir.-Pur. & Prod. Devel.--Arden International Kitchens, Inc., Lakeville, MN; *U.S. Private*, pg. 972
Mitchell, Jerry, Head Buyer--Southco Distributing Company, Goldsboro, NC; *U.S. Private*, pg. 1014
Mitchell, Raymond C., V.P.-Pur.--Kocolene Oil Corp., Seymour, IN; *U.S. Private*, pg. 629
Mitchell, Troy, Dir.-Pur.--Dewberry & Davis, Fairfax, VA; *U.S. Private*, pg. 329
Mix, S., Pur.--Turner Machine Company, Salem, OH; *U.S. Private*, pg. 368
Mizuno, Toshiro, V.P.-Passenger Mktg. & Adv.--Japan Airlines American Region, New York, NY; *Int'l*, pg. 700
Mocarsky, Hank, Dir.-Pur.--Craftex Mills Inc. of Pennsylvania, Blue Bell, PA; *U.S. Private*, pg. 284
Mochon, Don, Mgr.-Pur.--Eaton Corporation Automotive Controls Division, Carol Stream, IL; *U.S. Public*, pg. 557
Moe, Tim, Mgr.-Pur.--Good Companies, Carson, CA; *U.S. Private*, pg. 463
Moerike, Wolfgang, Div. Head-Raw Matls. Pur.--BASF AG, Ludwigshafen, Germany; *Int'l*, pg. 103
Moffit, Carla, Pur. Mgr.-Fine Paper--Dillard, A ResourceNet International Company, Greensboro, NC; *U.S. Public*, pg. 901
Moleski, John, Mgr.-Matls.--Evans Tempcon Inc., Grand Rapids, MI; *U.S. Private*, pg. 7
Mollomo, Paul R., V.P.-Pur.--Miller Brewing Company, Milwaukee, WI; *U.S. Public*, pg. 1289
Molton, Royal, Dir.-Pur.--Complast, Inc., Bloomington, MN; *U.S. Private*, pg. 259
Mondron, Bob, Pur. Agent.--Engelhard Corp.-Quincy Operations, Quincy, FL; *U.S. Public*, pg. 582
Mongell, James A., Dir.-Procurement--Northrop Grumman Corporation, Los Angeles, CA; *U.S. Public*, pg. 1197
Mongeon, Mark, Dir.-Matls. Mngmt. & Pur.--Providence Energy Corporation, Providence, RI; *U.S. Public*, pg. 1337
Monkell, Roy, Mgr.-Matl.--Hannay Reels, Westerlo, NY; *U.S. Private*, pg. 499
Monroe, Jane L., Mktg. Officer--AMCORE Bank, Rock River Valley, Dixon, IL; *U.S. Public*, pg. 64
Monroe, R., Dir.-Pur.--L.B. Smith, Inc., Camp Hill, PA; *U.S. Private*, pg. 1009
Montaclair, Roland, Dir.-Pur.--Ferembal S.A., Clichy, France; *U.S. Public*, pg. 440
Montana, Michael J., V.P.-Supply Service--AmerenUE, Saint Louis, MO; *U.S. Public*, pg. 66
Montano, Michelle, Mgr.-Pur.--McBride and Associates, Inc., Albuquerque, NM; *U.S. Private*, pg. 719
Montgomery, T.L., V.P.-Contracts & Procurement--Raytheon Engineers & Constructors, Inc., Englewood, CO; *U.S. Public*, pg. 1366
Mooney, Robert, Dir.-Pur.--Outboard Marine Corporation, Waukegan, IL; *U.S. Private*, pg. 478
Moore, Brian, Asst. V.P.-Admin. Opers.--The Allstate Corporation, Northbrook, IL; *U.S. Public*, pg. 55
Moore, Greg, Dir.-Pur.--Central Maine Power Company, Augusta, ME; *U.S. Public*, pg. 325
Moore, J.W., Mgr.-Pur.--Pace Industries, Inc., Fayetteville, AR; *U.S. Public*, pg. 986
Moore, Jennifer, Mgr.-Pur.--Gundle/SLT Environmental, Inc., Houston, TX; *U.S. Public*, pg. 769
Moore, M., Dir.-Opers.--Alva/Amco Pharmacal Companies, Inc., Chicago, IL; *U.S. Private*, pg. 47
Moore, Peggy, Purchasing Agent--Gannett Offset-Springfield Plant, Springfield, VA; *U.S. Public*, pg. 700

Moore, Sidney A., Mgr.-Pur.--AmerenCIPS, Springfield, IL; *U.S. Public*, pg. 65
Moorman, Thomas, Buyer--Citizens Gas & Coke Utility, Indianapolis, IN; *U.S. Private*, pg. 241
Moran, John J., Sr. V.P. & Controller--Anchor Financial Corporation, Myrtle Beach, SC; *U.S. Public*, pg. 111
Moreau, Marion, Pur. Agent--Strathmore Paper, Granby, CT; *U.S. Public*, pg. 903
Moreland, Donald J., Dir.-Pur.--Steel of West Virginia, Inc., Huntington, WV; *U.S. Public*, pg. 1513
Moreland, Jim, Dir.-Pur.--EMC Corporation, Hopkinton, MA; *U.S. Public*, pg. 545
Morgan, Damon, Dir.-Bulk Power Svcs.--Alabama Electric Cooperative, Inc., Andalusia, AL; *U.S. Private*, pg. 30
Morgan, Joan, Mgr.-Pur.--Waverly, Inc., Baltimore, MD; *U.S. Public*, pg. 1748
Morgan, John, V.P.-Pur.--Duron, Inc., Beltsville, MD; *U.S. Private*, pg. 349
Morgan, Larry, Dir.-Pur.--Fort Dodge Animal Health, Overland Park, KS; *U.S. Public*, pg. 79
Morgan, M.D., Dir.-Grocery & Intl. Buying--J. Sainsbury plc, London, United Kingdom; *Int'l*, pg. 1169
Morgan, Steve, Dir.-Pur.--Integrated Material Handling Company, Mount Sterling, OH; *Int'l*, pg. 1397
Morones, Richard, Mgr.-Pur.--Grant Thornton LLP, Chicago, IL; *U.S. Private*, pg. 470
Morookian, Tom J., Dir.-Pur.--Cyro Industries, Rockaway, NJ; *Int'l*, pg. 1454
Morrell, Dave, Dir.-Procurement--Pico Products, Inc., Lake View Terrace, CA; *U.S. Public*, pg. 1294
Morris, Linda, Mgr.-Pur.--Eaton Corp., Aerospace & Commercial Controls Div., Costa Mesa, CA; *U.S. Public*, pg. 557
Morris, Owen, Dir.-Pur.--Tasty Baking Company, Philadelphia, PA; *U.S. Public*, pg. 1561
Morris, Wendell, Mgr.-Pur.--Chattanooga Group, Inc., Hixson, TN; *U.S. Private*, pg. 231
Morris, William, Pur. Agent--Peter Paul, Naugatuck, CT; *U.S. Public*, pg. 812
Morrison, David, V.P.-Distr.--Ross Stores, Inc., Newark, CA; *U.S. Public*, pg. 1405
Morrison, Steve, Parts Mgr.--D.S.U.-Peterbilt & GMC, Inc., Portland, OR; *U.S. Private*, pg. 306
Morrison, Terrell, Dir.-Pur.--Daisy Manufacturing Company, Inc., Rogers, AR; *U.S. Private*, pg. 308
Morrisson, James, Pur. Agent--Batson-Cook Company, West Point, GA; *U.S. Private*, pg. 123
Mosesson, Larry, Dir.-Matls. Mngmt.--UniHealth, Burbank, CA; *U.S. Private*, pg. 1117
Moskal, Richard, V.P.-Pur.--Prime Hospitality Corp., Fairfield, NJ; *U.S. Public*, pg. 1326
Mossman, Jill, Mgr.-Pur.--Gould Packaging, Inc., Vancouver, WA; *U.S. Private*, pg. 466
Motyka, Dave, Dir.-Pur.--Oakland Tool & Manufacturing Company, Fraser, MI; *U.S. Private*, pg. 809
Moullet, Barry, Sr. V.P.-Pur.--Darden Restaurants, Inc., Orlando, FL; *U.S. Public*, pg. 483
Moulton, John, Dir.-Pur.--Southwestern/Great American Inc., Nashville, TN; *U.S. Private*, pg. 1018
Mozafrar, Shakeel, Dir.-Pur.--Polaroid Corporation, Cambridge, MA; *U.S. Public*, pg. 1313
Mrock, Tom, Mgr.-Pur.--Chicago White Metal Casting, Inc., Bensenville, IL; *U.S. Private*, pg. 236
Mrozinski, JoAnn, Sec. & Pur. Agent--Facemate Corporation, Chicopee, MA; *U.S. Private*, pg. 391
Mueller, Barbara, Mgr.-Pur.--The Minnesota Mutual Life Insurance Company, Saint Paul, MN; *U.S. Private*, pg. 750
Mueller, Colleen, Pur. Agent--Alumacraft Boat Co., Saint Peter, MN; *U.S. Private*, pg. 1088
Mueller, Terry, V.P.-Pur.--Kohl's Corporation, Menomonee Falls, WI; *U.S. Public*, pg. 965
Muhlhan, Robert, V.P.-Matl. Procurement--AmeriSteel, Tampa, FL; *U.S. Private*, pg. 65
Muldoon, James E., Gen. Mgr.-Pur.--USX Corporation, Pittsburgh, PA; *U.S. Public*, pg. 1661
Mulieri, Mike, V.P. & Brdcst., Prog. & Pur. Grp. Supvr.--Young & Rubicam New York, New York, NY; *U.S. Private*, pg. 1198
Muller, R., Mgr.-Pur.--Sulzer Ltd., Winterthur, Switzerland; *Int'l*, pg. 1305
Mullins, H.G., Controller & Mgr.-Mfg.--Flowserve Corporation, Foundry Div., Dayton, OH; *U.S. Public*, pg. 658
Mumby, Tom, Dir.-Pur.--DHL Worldwide Express, Redwood City, CA; *U.S. Private*, pg. 301
Mumby, Tom, Dir.-Pur.--DHL Airways, Inc., Redwood City, CA; *U.S. Private*, pg. 302
Mundell, Mick, Mgr.-Corp. Pur.--FiberMark Inc., Brattleboro, VT; *U.S. Public*, pg. 620
Munsell, Kerry, Dir.-Pur.--Au Bon Pain Co., Inc., Boston, MA; *U.S. Public*, pg. 146
Murai, Yoichi, Mgr.-Pur.--Nippon Keystone Corporation, Kobe, Japan; *U.S. Public*, pg. 1650
Murawski, T., Pur. Agent--Electroid Co., Springfield, NJ; *U.S. Private*, pg. 369
Murdock, Roy, Pur. Agent--Meco Corporation, Greeneville, TN; *U.S. Private*, pg. 726
Murphy, Don, Mgr.-Pur.--Bou-Matic, Madison, WI; *U.S. Private*, pg. 301
Murphy, Kenneth, V.P.-Pur.--Chiswick Trading Inc., Sudbury, MA; *U.S. Private*, pg. 237
Murphy, Kevin J., V.P.-Mktg.--Recoton Corporation, Lake Mary, FL; *U.S. Public*, pg. 1369
Murphy, Neil, Dir.-Pur.--Irish Biscuits Ltd., Dublin, Ireland; *Int'l*, pg. 688
Murphy, Thomas M., Gen. Mgr.-Pur. & Svcs.--Murphy Oil Corporation, El Dorado, AR; *U.S. Public*, pg. 1141
Murray, Lynn, Dir.-Pur.--Bush Brothers & Company, Knoxville, TN; *U.S. Private*, pg. 189
Murray, Pete, Mgr.-Pur.--Foremost Corporation of America, Caledonia, MI; *U.S. Public*, pg. 667
Murray, Thomas S., Jr., Mgr.-Matls. Mngmt.--Boston Edison Company, Boston, MA; *U.S. Public*, pg. 247
Murrin, Tim, Dir.-Pur.--White Castle System, Inc., Columbus, OH; *U.S. Private*, pg. 1171
Musser, Thomas M., Mgr.-Pur.--Kunzler & Company, Inc., Lancaster, PA; *U.S. Private*, pg. 636
Myers, Jay K., V.P.-Project Mngmt. Estimating--Jennings & Churella Construction Company, Wellington, OH; *U.S. Private*, pg. 586
Myers, Joyce, Dir.-Pur.--North Fork Bancorporation, Inc., Melville, NY; *U.S. Public*, pg. 1194
Myers, Judy, Pur. Agent--Harig Products, Elgin, IL; *U.S. Public*, pg. 252
Myers, Larry, Mgr.-Pur.--Richmond Technology Inc., Redlands, CA; *U.S. Private*, pg. 929
Myers, Mike, V.P.-Pur.--Sea Ray, Knoxville, TN; *U.S. Public*, pg. 266
Myers, P.L., Dir.-Corp. Svcs., Pur. & Security--Texaco Inc., White Plains, NY; *U.S. Public*, pg. 1582
Myers, Paul, Mgr.-Pur.--Barrister Information Systems Corporation, Buffalo, NY; *U.S. Public*, pg. 192
Myers, Richard, Dir.-Pur.--March Manufacturing Inc., Glenview, IL; *U.S. Private*, pg. 702
Myers, Richard C., V.P.-Admin.--Hutchinson Technology Inc., Hutchinson, MN; *U.S. Public*, pg. 850
Myers, Wray, Dir.-Pur.--The Liposome Company, Inc., Princeton, NJ; *U.S. Public*, pg. 1000
Myette, Tom, Mgr.-Matls.--FMC-Crosby Valve, Inc., Wrentham, MA; *U.S. Public*, pg. 605
Nadler, Paul, Buyer-Canned Goods--Alliant Foodservice, Bensenville, IL; *U.S. Private*, pg. 244
Nagy, Al, Chief Admin. Officer--Ferolie Group, Montvale, NJ; *U.S. Private*, pg. 401
Nakajima, Hiroshi, Gen. Mgr.--Cosmo Oil Co., Ltd., Tokyo, Japan; *Int'l*, pg. 335
Nall, Michele, Mgr.-Pur.--Gamma Biologicals Inc., Houston, TX; *U.S. Public*, pg. 698
Nana, David, Mgr.-Pur.--Howden Fluid Systems, Santa Barbara, CA; *U.S. Public*, pg. 1045
Nanez, Sergio Altaba, Dir.-Pur.--Altos Hornos de Mexico, S.A., Monclova, Mexico; *Int'l*, pg. 66
Naquin, Gasper K., Treas. & Sec.--Intrepid Enterprises, Inc., Harvey, LA; *U.S. Private*, pg. 574
Nardo, Guy, Dir.-Gen. Svcs.--Dow Jones & Company, Inc., New York, NY; *U.S. Public*, pg. 524
Nash, Gary, Pur. Agent--C.I. Hayes, Inc., Cranston, RI; *U.S. Private*, pg. 513
Naughton, Dan, Mgr.-Pur.--Master Appliance Corp., Racine, WI; *U.S. Private*, pg. 713
Navarro, Maria E., Mgr.-Pur.--American International Container, Inc., Miami, FL; *U.S. Private*, pg. 57
Navickas, Irene, Pur. Sec.--Skinner Macaroni, Omaha, NE; *U.S. Public*, pg. 812
Neal, Carol, Mgr.-Pur.--International Lottery & Totalizator Systems, Inc., Carlsbad, CA; *U.S. Public*, pg. 900
Neal, David G., V.P.-Opers.--JRN, Inc., Columbia, TN; *U.S. Private*, pg. 578
Neal, Terry, V.P.-Pur.--Kinro, Inc., Arlington, TX; *U.S. Public*, pg. 529
Neale, Allen R., V.P.-Supply Plng.--Essex County Gas Company, Amesbury, MA; *U.S. Public*, pg. 593
Nee, Nancy, Mgr.-Project Pur.--Hilton Equipment Corp., Beverly Hills, CA; *U.S. Public*, pg. 829
Nehmad, Edward, V.P.-Domestic Pur.--SDI Technologies Inc., Rahway, NJ; *U.S. Private*, pg. 956
Neidhardt, Richard J., V.P.-Pur.--Newly Weds Foods Inc., Chicago, IL; *U.S. Private*, pg. 796
Nelms, Jim, Mgr.-Pur.--Automatic Power, Inc., Houston, TX; *Int'l*, pg. 1289
Nelsen, Harlam, Mgr.-Pur.--Recon/Optical, Inc., Barrington, IL; *U.S. Private*, pg. 914
Nelson, Barry, Mgr.-Pur.--American Louver Co., Skokie, IL; *U.S. Private*, pg. 58
Nelson, Donald A., Dir.-Pur.--Hormel Foods Corp., Austin, MN; *U.S. Public*, pg. 840
Nelson, Larry, Dir.-Material--Greenlee Textron, Rockford, IL; *U.S. Public*, pg. 1589
Nelson, Marty, Mgr.-Pur.--Fike Corporation, Blue Springs, MO; *U.S. Private*, pg. 404
Nelson, Nancy, Mgr.-Pur.--Bluewater, Mora, MN; *U.S. Private*, pg. 153
Nelson, Paula, Mgr.-Pur.--Glacier Water Services Inc., Carlsbad, CA; *U.S. Public*, pg. 745
Nelson, R. David, V.P.-Supply Mngmt.--Deere & Company, Moline, IL; *U.S. Public*, pg. 491
Nelson, R.E., Pur. Agent--American Welding & Manufacturing Co., Warren, OH; *U.S. Private*, pg. 425
Neptune, Homer, Mgr.-Pur.--Gish Biomedical, Inc. Irvine, CA; *U.S. Public*, pg. 745
Neptune, Homer, Mgr.-Pur.--Gish International, Inc., Irvine, CA; *U.S. Public*, pg. 745
Neto, Carlos Alberto, Mgr.-Pur.--Central de Cervejas, S.A., Lisbon, Portugal; *Int'l*, pg. 279
Neubeck, Ken, Mgr.-Matls.--Dealers Manufacturing Company, Minneapolis, MN; *U.S. Private*, pg. 318
Neuroth, Robert, Dir.-Pur.--Electro Scientific Industries, Inc., Portland, OR; *U.S. Public*, pg. 568
Neuzil, Steve, Mgr.-Pur.--Thrifty Rent-a-Car System, Inc., Tulsa, OK; *U.S. Public*, pg. 354
New, E.I., Dir.-Pur.--Flexible Technologies Inc., Abbeville, SC; *Int'l*, pg. 1267
Newman, A.G., Pur. Supvr.--BC Gas Inc., Vancouver, Canada; *Int'l*, pg. 114
Newman, George, V.P.--Best Manufacturing, Inc., New York, NY; *U.S. Private*, pg. 139
Newman, Janet, Mgr.-Pur.--Micropure Medical, Inc., White Bear Lake, MN; *U.S. Private*, pg. 743
Newsom, David, Mgr.-Pur.--BGF Industries Inc., Greensboro, NC; *U.S. Private*, pg. 106
Ney, Wolfgang, Dir.-Pur.--Saarbergwerke Aktiengesellschaft, Saarbruecken, Germany; *Int'l*, pg. 1166
Neyer, William L., Sec.--Al Neyer, Inc., Cincinnati, OH; *U.S. Private*, pg. 797
Niccum, Mike, Dir.-Matls.--Harris-Kayot, Inc., Fort Wayne, IN; *U.S. Private*, pg. 506
Nicholas, Linda, Mgr.-Pur.--Myers Foods Company, Plumsteadville, PA; *U.S. Private*, pg. 499
Nicholas, Steve, Pur. Agent--Topflight Corp., York, PA; *U.S. Private*, pg. 1091
Nicholes, J., Dir.-Pur.--Battenfeld Gloucester Engineering Co. Inc., Gloucester, MA; *U.S. Private*, pg. 123
Nichols, Roseann, Asst. Radio Buyer--SFM Media Corporation, New York, NY; *U.S. Private*, pg. 956
Nicholson, A.C., Dir.-Raw Matls. & Pur.--British Mohair Spinners Limited, Bradford, United Kingdom; *Int'l*, pg. 219
Nickeson, Bill D., Mgr.-Pur.--Nebraska Public Power District, Columbus, NE; *U.S. Private*, pg. 789
Nicklos, Bonnie, Supvr.-Pur.--Staodyn Inc., Longmont, CO; *U.S. Public*, pg. 1509
Niman, Eric, Mgr.-Pur.--Cerprobe Corporation, Gilbert, AZ; *U.S. Public*, pg. 332
Nimmo, Terry R., Chief Information Officer & V.P.-Mfg. & Matls.--Lowrance Electronics, Inc., Tulsa, OK; *U.S. Public*, pg. 1015
Nimmo, Terry R., Dir.-Pur.--Eagle Electronics, Catoosa, OK; *U.S. Public*, pg. 1016
Nishimura, Tadashi, Dir.-Pur.--Rohto Pharmaceutical Co., Osaka, Japan; *Int'l*, pg. 1126
Nithart, Philippe, Dir.-Personnel--Laboratoire LaChartre S.A., Blois, France; *U.S. Public*, pg. 1331
Noble, Bill, Dir.-Pur.--Lincoln Electric Systems, Lincoln, NE; *U.S. Private*, pg. 668
Nobriga, John, Mgr.-Pur.--Portland General Electric Co., Portland, OR; *U.S. Public*, pg. 584
Noguchi, Koichiro, Gen. Mgr.-Intl. Pur.--Toyota Motor Corporation, Tokyo, Japan; *Int'l*, pg. 1411
Nohalty, Bryant, Mgr.-Pur.-Louisville--Grindmaster Corporation, Louisville, KY; *U.S. Private*, pg. 482
Nokovich, Joseph, Mgr.-Matl. & Sls.--Hempt Brothers, Inc., Camp Hill, PA; *U.S. Private*, pg. 521
Nolte, Richard, Dir.-Pur.--Arkansas Best Corporation, Fort Smith, AR; *U.S. Public*, pg. 130
Norcia, Mike, Mgr.-Pur.--Mautz Paint Co., Madison, WI; *U.S. Private*, pg. 715
Nordhues, Denton, Mgr.-Pur.--Owen Industries, Inc., Carter Lake, IA; *U.S. Private*, pg. 824
Nordhues, Denton, Mgr.-Pur.--Paxton & Vierling, Omaha, NE; *U.S. Private*, pg. 824
Nordoe, J.W., Mgr.-Pur.--Royal Copenhagen A/S, Frederiksberg, Denmark; *Int'l*, pg. 1134
Norgaard, Ryan, Mgr.-Pur.--Flow Control Division, Sioux Falls, SD; *U.S. Public*, pg. 1361
Norlington, Larry, Pur. Agent--Weil-McLain, Michigan City, IN; *U.S. Public*, pg. 1676
Normandin, Jim, Pur. Agent--Beauty Enterprises Inc., Hartford, CT; *U.S. Private*, pg. 128
Norton, Curt, V.P.-Support Opers.--Essex International, Inc., Fort Wayne, IN; *U.S. Public*, pg. 593
Nowak, Laura, Pur. Agent--Treibacher Schleifmittel Corp., Niagara Falls, NY; *U.S. Private*, pg. 1099
Nownoy, Gene, Mgr.-Pur.--Active Tool & Manufacturing Co., Inc., Roseville, MI; *U.S. Private*, pg. 16
Noyes, Adam P., Dir.-Restaurant Support Services & Pur.--Checkers Drive-In Restaurants, Inc., Clearwater, FL; *U.S. Public*, pg. 342
Nugent, Wallace O., V.P.-Logistics & Pur.--The Mead Corporation, Dayton, OH; *U.S. Public*, pg. 1074
Null, R. Dean, Dir.-Pur.--Higginbotham-Bartlett Co., Lubbock, TX; *U.S. Private*, pg. 527
Nummell, Tom, Mgr.-Pur.--Beechmont Hyundai, Cincinnati, OH; *U.S. Private*, pg. 129
Nussear, David L., Mgr.-Pur.--Hecla Mining Company, Coeur D'Alene, ID; *U.S. Public*, pg. 803
O'Briant, Stonie, V.P.-Mdse.--Dollar General Corporation, Nashville, TN; *U.S. Public*, pg. 515
O'Brien, John, Mgr.-Pur.--The Spencer Turbine Co., Windsor, CT; *U.S. Private*, pg. 1025
O'Connell, Jerry, Pur. Agent--Seymour of Sycamore, Inc., Sycamore, IL; *U.S. Private*, pg. 988
O'Connoh, Gerry, Dir.-Acctg. Opers.--Advanta Corp., Spring House, PA; *U.S. Public*, pg. 22
O'Connor, Diane, Mgr.-Pur.--Hooper Holmes Corporation, Basking Ridge, NJ; *U.S. Public*, pg. 835
O'Connor, Frank, Mgr.-Matls. Procurement & Pur.--Vance Industries, Inc., Chicago, IL; *U.S. Private*, pg. 1133
O'Connor, Jim, Mgr.-Pur.--Equitrac Corporation, Coral Gables, FL; *U.S. Public*, pg. 590
O'Donnell, John, Dir.-Human Resources--Fairfax Lumber & Millwork Company Inc., Springfield, VA; *U.S. Private*, pg. 391
O'Donnell, Joyce, Mgr.-Pur.--Electro Methods Inc., South Windsor, CT; *U.S. Private*, pg. 369
O'Hagen, Liz, Dir.-Pur.(USA)--Synergistics Industries Limited, Mississauga, Canada; *U.S. Public*, pg. 734
O'Hagen, Liz, Mgr.-Pur.--Synergistics Industries (NJ) Inc., Farmingdale, NJ; *U.S. Public*, pg. 734
O'Hagen, Liz, Mgr.-Pur.--Synergistics Industries (TX) Inc., Conroe, TX; *U.S. Public*, pg. 734
O'Keefe, John, Jr., V.P.-Pur.--International Specialty Products, Inc., Wayne, NJ; *U.S. Public*, pg. 858
O'Keette, Brian, Dir.-Pur.--AMD Industries Inc., Cicero, IL; *U.S. Private*, pg. 6
O'Loughlin, J.M., Dir.-Pur.--SJW Corp., San Jose, CA; *U.S. Public*, pg. 1418
O'Mara, J., Dir.-Pur.--Talley Defense Systems, Inc., Mesa, AZ; *U.S. Public*, pg. 308
O'Neil, Vincent, Pur. Agent--The Greenbrier, White Sulphur Springs, WV; *U.S. Public*, pg. 284
O'Neill, John, Mgr.-Pur. & Matls. Mngmt.--AGA Gas, Inc., Independence, OH; *Int'l*, pg. 13
O'Neill, Joyce, V.P.-Human Resources--Data Dimensions, Inc., Culver City, CA; *U.S. Public*, pg. 485
O'Rourke, Ed, Mgr.-Pur.--Westin Hotels & Resorts, Seattle, WA; *U.S. Public*, pg. 1512
O'Rourke, Michael, Dir.-Pur.--Naylor Pipe Company, Chicago, IL; *U.S. Private*, pg. 789
O'Rourke, T., Pur. Agent--Air Cruisers Co., Belmar, NJ; *Int'l*, pg. 572

O'Toole, Rita, Dir.-Pur.--Creative Publications, Mountain View, CA; *U.S. Private*, pg. 288
Oakey, Steve, Dir.-Pur.--Galpin Motors, North Hills, CA; *U.S. Private*, pg. 438
Oakley, Charles, V.P.-Opers.--Inter-Tel, Incorporated, Phoenix, AZ; *U.S. Public*, pg. 888
Oates, Keith, Dep. Chm. & Joint Mng. Dir.--Marks & Spencer PLC, London, United Kingdom; *Int'l*, pg. 842
Obara, Junichi, Dir.--Sakata Seed Corporation, Yokohama, Japan; *Int'l*, pg. 1178
Oberg, Glen, Dir.-Pur.--Video Display Corporation, Tucker, GA; *U.S. Public*, pg. 1720
Oberschlake, Cathie, Mgr.-Pur.--The Sorg Paper Co., Middletown, OH; *U.S. Public*, pg. 1747
Ocelus, Edward, Pur. Agent--Florig Equipment Company, Inc., Conshohocken, PA; *U.S. Private*, pg. 415
Ochoa, Richard, V.P.-Products & Pur.--Alamo Industrial Group, San Antonio, TX; *U.S. Private*, pg. 31
Oday, Mike, Dir.-Pur. & Opers.--Roofing Wholesale Co., Inc., Phoenix, AZ; *U.S. Private*, pg. 943
Odle, John H., Exec. V.P.-Commercial, Mfg. & Pur.--RMI Titanium Company, Niles, OH; *U.S. Public*, pg. 1662
Ogura, Hironori, Mng. Dir.-Pur. Opers.--Yamaha Motor Co., Ltd., Iwata, Japan; *Int'l*, pg. 1516
Oh, J.O., Mgr.-Pur.--Televideo, Inc., San Jose, CA; *U.S. Public*, pg. 1572
Oitzinger, Doug, Mgr.-Pur.--Marinette Marine Corporation, Marinette, WI; *U.S. Private*, pg. 703
Ojersson, Jan, Mgr.-Pur.--Euroc Beton AB, Vaxjo, Sweden; *Int'l*, pg. 1199
Oldweiler, John, Dir.-Pur.--Ark Restaurants Corp., New York, NY; *U.S. Public*, pg. 129
Oleary, Rima, Pur. Agent--Hoboken Wood Flooring Corporation, Wayne, NJ; *U.S. Private*, pg. 532
Olinger, Andrew, V.P.-Distr.--DMI Furniture Inc., Louisville, KY; *U.S. Public*, pg. 473
Olinger, Donald E., V.P.-Procurement--Totes Incorporated, Loveland, OH; *U.S. Private*, pg. 111
Oliver, Tracy, Pur. Agent--Thoro, Jacksonville, FL; *U.S. Private*, pg. 505
Olivieri, Kenneth, Dir.-Materials--National Micronetics, Inc., Kingston, NY; *Int'l*, pg. 1347
Oloroso, Gus, Dir.-Pur.--Beverly Bancorporation Inc., Chicago, IL; *U.S. Public*, pg. 227
Olpak, Ahmet, Exec. V.P.-Pur.--Arcelik A.S., Istanbul, Turkey; *Int'l*, pg. 741
Olson, Jon, V.P.-Pur. & Food Devel.--Lyon's Restaurants, Inc., Foster City, CA; *U.S. Private*, pg. 684
Onaga, Stephen, Mgr.-Pur.--Hawaiian Commercial & Sugar Co., Puunene, HI; *U.S. Public*, pg. 39
Opitz, Ron, Dir.-Procurement Svcs.--Public Service Company of Oklahoma, Tulsa, OK; *U.S. Public*, pg. 324
Orman, Ray, Buyer--Anderson Wholesale Company, Muskogee, OK; *U.S. Private*, pg. 73
Orpe, Carole, Pur. Agent--The Zippertubing Co., Los Angeles, CA; *U.S. Private*, pg. 1207
Orr, Cathleen, Mgr.-Procurement & Traffic--TelCom Semiconductor, Inc., Mountain View, CA; *U.S. Public*, pg. 1569
Orth, Dietmar, Mgr.-Pur.--Groschopp & Co. GmbH EMW Elektromotoren-Feinbauwerk, Viersen, Germany; *Int'l*, pg. 559
Ortiz Andrade, Hector Joaquin, Dir.-Pur.--Coppel S.A. de C.V., Culiacan, Mexico; *Int'l*, pg. 330
Ortlieb, Arthur, Pur. Agent--EG & G Rotron, Woodstock, NY; *U.S. Public*, pg. 543
Ory, Robert, Dir.-Pur.--Wilton Industries, Inc., Woodridge, IL; *U.S. Private*, pg. 1181
Osbeck, Nils, Pur. Agent--Skanska International Civil Engineering AB, Danderyd, Sweden; *Int'l*, pg. 1260
Oslo, Sandy, Dir.-Pur.--Stella Foods Division, Branch, WI; *U.S. Private*, pg. 1040
Osorio, Janio, Dir.-Logistics--CIBA-GEIGY Colombiana S.A., Bogota, Colombia; *Int'l*, pg. 976
Ossam, Seymour, Pur. Agent--International Cutlery, LTD, New York, NY; *U.S. Private*, pg. 569
Ostander, Cathy, Mgr.-Pur.--Harrington & King, South, Inc., Cleveland, TN; *U.S. Private*, pg. 504
Osteen, M.S., Dir.-Pur.--Perfection-Schwank Inc., Waynesboro, GA; *U.S. Private*, pg. 853
Osterfoss, Steve, Mgr.-Pur.--Engineered Films Div., Flexible Films Dept., Sioux Falls, SD; *U.S. Public*, pg. 1361
Osterman, Joseph L., Sr. Mgr.-Quality Assurnace--National Steel Corp., Granite City Division, Granite City, IL; *Int'l*, pg. 902
Ostman, R., Dir.-Pur.--Peerless Tube Company, Bloomfield, NJ; *U.S. Public*, pg. 1269
Ostroski, Matthew, V.P.-Pur.--Rieter Automotive North America Inc, Farmington Hills, MI; *Int'l*, pg. 1117
Ott, Richard, Dir.-Pur.--The Brulin Corporation, Indianapolis, IN; *U.S. Private*, pg. 176
Ottoni, Franco, Dir.-Pur.--Merloni Elettrodomestici S.P.A., Fabriano, Italy; *Int'l*, pg. 860
Ounjian, George E., Pres.--Careers USA Inc., Philadelphia, PA; *U.S. Private*, pg. 209
Over, Dale, Mgr.-Matls.--Schult Homes Corporation, Milton, PA; *U.S. Public*, pg. 1442
Overacker, Donna, V.P.-Pur.--Vienna Sausage Mfg. Co., Chicago, IL; *U.S. Private*, pg. 1139
Overman, William G., V.P.-Pur.--Noland Company, Newport News, VA; *U.S. Public*, pg. 1187
Overturf, Jan, Pur. Agent--Valley Bank & Trust, Brighton, CO; *U.S. Private*, pg. 1132
Owen, David, Mgr.-Pur.--Pass & Seymour/Legrand, Syracuse, NY; *Int'l*, pg. 806
Owen, Steve, Dir.-Pur.--Southwest Airlines Co., Dallas, TX; *U.S. Public*, pg. 1493
Owens, Roger, Dir.-Pur.--Excel Communications, Inc., Dallas, TX; *U.S. Public*, pg. 598
Oxenholm, Pat, Mgr.-Admin.--Computer Task Group, Inc. (CTG), Buffalo, NY; *U.S. Public*, pg. 423
Ozanic, T., Dir.-Pur.--Rauland-Borg Corporation, Skokie, IL; *U.S. Private*, pg. 911
Ozcowicz, James, Pur. Agent--Unity Manufacturing Co., Chicago, IL; *U.S. Private*, pg. 1126
Pace, Kevin, Dir.-Pur.--Megas Beauty Care, Inc., Cleveland, OH; *U.S. Private*, pg. 729
Pacek, Tom, Mgr.-Materials--Wayne Steel, Inc., Wooster, OH; *U.S. Public*, pg. 1101
Pack, Greg, Mgr.-Pur.--SBE, Inc., San Ramon, CA; *U.S. Public*, pg. 1416
Paddor, Earl, Dir.-Matls.--Adams Rite Manufacturing Co., City of Industry, CA; *U.S. Private*, pg. 17
Paeper, Carol, Dir.-Pur.--Xentek, Inc., San Marcos, CA; *Int'l*, pg. 1349
Page, Jim, Mgr.-Pur.--M.C. Gill Corporation, El Monte, CA; *U.S. Private*, pg. 453
Page, Robert, V.P.-Corp. Pur. & Services--Northwest Airlines, Inc., Saint Paul, MN; *U.S. Public*, pg. 1200
Page, William, Dir.-Pur.--Thiele Kaolin Co., Sandersville, GA; *U.S. Private*, pg. 1081
Paguio, Mario C., V.P.-Purchasing--Philippine Long Distance Telephone Company, Manila, Philippines; *Int'l*, pg. 1051
Pahidis, Peter, Pres. & Chief Exec. Officer--Cedar Farms Company, Inc., Philadelphia, PA; *U.S. Private*, pg. 221
Palko, John, Pur. Agent--Rapid Industries, Inc., Louisville, KY; *U.S. Private*, pg. 910
Palmer, Brian, Dir.-Logistics--Tom's Foods, Inc., Columbus, GA; *U.S. Private*, pg. 1090
Palmer, Chuck, Dir.-Pur.--American Meter Company, Horsham, PA; *Int'l*, pg. 1149
Palmer, James A., Sr. V.P.-Opers.--VeriFone, Inc., Redwood City, CA; *U.S. Public*, pg. 815
Palmer, Robert, V.P.-Pur.--Liberty Paper & Bag Co., Auburn Hills, MI; *Int'l*, pg. 233
Palmer, S.W., Mgr.-Pur.--Flowserve Corporation, Valve Div., Cookeville, TN; *U.S. Public*, pg. 658
Palmer, Wendy, Dir.-Pur.--Horizon Enterprises Group LLC, Taylor, MI; *U.S. Private*, pg. 539
Palmitier, John, Dir.-Pur. & Distr.--Taco John's International, Inc., Cheyenne, WY; *U.S. Private*, pg. 1066
Panagoulias, Stephanie, Dir.-Pur.--The F.A. Bartlett Tree Expert Co., Stamford, CT; *U.S. Private*, pg. 119
Panchyshyn, John P., Dir.-Pur.--Hershey Canada Inc., Mississauga, Canada; *U.S. Public*, pg. 812
Pandrea, Kathy, Mgr.-Pur.--Pickering Inc., Tacoma, WA; *U.S. Private*, pg. 864
Pane, Philip, V.P.-Mfg. & Pur.--White Pine Software, Nashua, NH; *U.S. Private*, pg. 1173
Panis, Donna, Mgr.-Pur.--Wonderware Corporation, Irvine, CA; *U.S. Public*, pg. 1775
Panos, Nick, Buyer-Paper Prods.--Alliant Foodservice, Bensenville, IL; *U.S. Private*, pg. 244
Pantzlaff, Don, Pur. Agent--Intertape Polymer Group, Green Bay, WI; *Int'l*, pg. 685
Paoli, Donald, Pur. Agent--General Bearing Corp., West Nyack, NY; *U.S. Public*, pg. 706
Paolino, Tom, Mgr.-Pur.--Paper Enterprises, Inc., Bronx, NY; *U.S. Private*, pg. 837
Paquette, A., Mgr.-Pur.--Eastern Air Devices, Inc., Dover, NH; *U.S. Private*, pg. 357
Paquette, C., Mgr.-Pur.--Synergistics Industries Limited, Saint Remi-de-Napierville, Canada; *U.S. Public*, pg. 734
Paquette, Claude, Dir.-Pur.(Canada)--Synergistics Industries Limited, Mississauga, Canada; *U.S. Public*, pg. 734
Paquette, Raymond, Mgr.-Transportation & Pur.--Uniboard Canada Inc., Laval, Canada; *Int'l*, pg. 1431
Park, Byung-Keun, Mng. Dir.--Ssangyong Shipping Co. Ltd., Seoul, Korea; *Int'l*, pg. 1292
Park, Dave, Mgr.-Pur.--Furman Foods, Inc., Northumberland, PA; *U.S. Private*, pg. 431
Park, I.M., Mgr.-Purchasing--Ensign-Bickford, Bromhof, South Africa; *Int'l*, pg. 1196
Parker, Pat, V.P.-Pur.--Kaufman and Broad Home Corporation, Los Angeles, CA; *U.S. Public*, pg. 944
Parker, Paul, Pur. Agent--Telescope Casual Furniture, Inc., Granville, NY; *U.S. Private*, pg. 1074
Parkhill, Jon, Dir.-Purchasing--Berry Bearing Company, Lyons, IL; *U.S. Public*, pg. 732
Parkhurst, John, Dir.-Pur.--Procon Products, Murfreesboro, TN; *U.S. Public*, pg. 1506
Parks, Dave, Mgr.-Materials--Hydraulics Div., Spencer, IA; *U.S. Public*, pg. 557
Parks, Ken, Mgr.-Pur.--The Buschman Co., Cincinnati, OH; *U.S. Private*, pg. 188
Parks, Ken, V.P.-Opers. & Pur.--Mutual Manufacturing & Supply Co., Cincinnati, OH; *U.S. Private*, pg. 769
Parks, Vern, Mgr.-Pur.--Renosol Corp., Saline, MI; *U.S. Private*, pg. 922
Parrish, John, Dir.-Distr. Systems--Mead Packaging, Atlanta, GA; *U.S. Public*, pg. 1074
Parsche, Phillip C., V.P.-Matls.--Independent Metals, Germantown, WI; *U.S. Private*, pg. 559
Parske, Mike, Dir.-Quality & Indus. Rels.--A. Finkl & Sons Co., Chicago, IL; *U.S. Private*, pg. 405
Partlow, Ken, Mgr.-Pur.--Allsop, Inc., Bellingham, WA; *U.S. Private*, pg. 44
Partridge, Bill, Dir.-Pur.--Grandy's, Inc., Lewisville, TX; *U.S. Private*, pg. 61
Paskal, Marv, Pur. Agent--J & R Film / Moviola Digital Co., Hollywood, CA; *U.S. Private*, pg. 576
Pastrana Orellano, Irma, V.P.-Pur., Consumer Prods.--Grupo Casa Autrey, Mexico, Mexico; *Int'l*, pg. 573
Pate, Karina, Mgr.-Pur.--Williamson-Dickie Mfg. Co., Fort Worth, TX; *U.S. Private*, pg. 1179
Patejdl, Michael J., Dir.-Pur.-PBQD, Inc.--Parsons Brinckerhoff Inc., New York, NY; *U.S. Private*, pg. 841
Patel, A.J., Mgr.-Pur.--Philway Products, Inc., Ashland, OH; *U.S. Private*, pg. 862
Patel, Mahendra A., V.P.-Engrng. & Pur.--Tembec Inc., Montreal, Canada; *Int'l*, pg. 1374
Patel, Raj, Mgr.-Pur.--Brown & Haley, Tacoma, WA; *U.S. Private*, pg. 173
Paterson, Brian D., Sr. V.P.-Pur. & Mktg.--Southern Electronics Corporation, Tucker, GA; *U.S. Public*, pg. 1490
Paterson, Michael, Mgr.-Pur.--Xicor, Inc., Milpitas, CA; *U.S. Public*, pg. 1785
Patka, Warren, Mgr.-Matls.--Schult Homes Corporation, Middlebury, IN; *U.S. Public*, pg. 1442
Patton, Michael, V.P.-Pur.--Huntington Bancshares Inc., Columbus, OH; *U.S. Public*, pg. 849
Patton, Nancy, Mgr.-Pur.--Farmland Dairies, Wallington, NJ; *U.S. Private*, pg. 395
Paul, Mark R., Div. V.P.-Pur. & Mdsg.--Walgreen Co., Deerfield, IL; *U.S. Public*, pg. 1733
Pauline, Kenneth, Jr., Sr. V.P.--First Empire State Corporation, Buffalo, NY; *U.S. Public*, pg. 631
Paulus, Wilhelm, Dir.-Pur.--O&K Orenstein & Koppel Aktiengesellschaft, Dortmund, Germany; *Int'l*, pg. 516
Pauzus, Bruce J., V.P.-Pur.--Restaura, Inc., Phoenix, AZ; *U.S. Public*, pg. 1718
Pavell, Chip, Pur. Agent--Baldwin Filters, Kearney, NE; *U.S. Public*, pg. 381
Pawloski, Mary T., Mgr.-Procurement--Genesee Corporation, Rochester, NY; *U.S. Public*, pg. 728
Payne, Sandra F., Mgr.-Pur.--Woolpert, Dayton, OH; *U.S. Private*, pg. 1188
Paz, Adan, Dir.-Pur.--San Cristobal Mill & Plant, San Salvador, El Salvador; *U.S. Public*, pg. 410
Pearce, R.I., Dir.-Pur.--Rochester & Pittsburgh Coal Company, Indiana, PA; *U.S. Public*, pg. 1395
Pearl, Marcia, Asst. V.P.-Pur.--Lackman Food Service, Woodbury, NY; *U.S. Private*, pg. 642
Pearman, William P., Dir.-Pur.--Franklin Baking Co., Inc., Goldsboro, NC; *U.S. Private*, pg. 424
Pearson, Anthony, Mgr.-Pur.--Rogers Tool Works, Inc., Rogers, AR; *U.S. Public*, pg. 950
Peet, M., Dir.-Pur.--Royal Gist-Brocades N.V., Delft, Netherlands; *Int'l*, pg. 1142
Peglow, Scott, Dir.-Pur.--Indianapolis Newspapers, Inc., Indianapolis, IN; *U.S. Public*, pg. 326
Pehanich, John, Mgr.-Pur.--Simplex Industries, Inc., Scranton, PA; *U.S. Private*, pg. 1001
Peller, Eric, Dir.-Pur.--Carfel, Inc., Miami, FL; *U.S. Private*, pg. 210
Pellerin, Ronald, Mgr.-Pur.--Schleicher & Schuell, Inc., Keene, NH; *Int'l*, pg. 1206
Pence, Robert R., Mgr.-Pur.--D.C. Taylor Co., Cedar Rapids, IA; *U.S. Private*, pg. 1070
Pendleton, C. L., Dir.-Pur.--Courtaulds Fibers Inc., Axis, AL; *Int'l*, pg. 339
Penn, Donald W., V.P.-Matls. & Facilities Services--Healthsouth Corporation, Sunnyvale, CA; *U.S. Public*, pg. 803
Pennell, Eric, Pur. Agent--H.B. Reese Candy Co., Hershey, PA; *U.S. Public*, pg. 812
Pennell, Richard, V.P.-Matls. & Distr.--Bush Industries Inc., Jamestown, NY; *U.S. Public*, pg. 270
Penny, Grover, Mgr.-Pur.--Colonial Gas Company, Lowell, MA; *U.S. Public*, pg. 400
Percy, Gordon K., Mgr.-Pur. & Freight--Ampco-Pittsburgh Corporation, Pittsburgh, PA; *U.S. Public*, pg. 103
Pereira, Hugo Dantas, Dir.-Tech. & Matl. Resources--Banco do Brasil, Brasilia, Brazil; *Int'l*, pg. 141
Pereira, Luis, Mgr.-Pur.--Moran Towing Corporation, Greenwich, CT; *U.S. Private*, pg. 760
Perez, Joseph, V.P.-Pur.--Goya Foods, Inc., Secaucus, NJ; *U.S. Private*, pg. 468
Perez, Ofelia, V.P.-Opers.--Mason Distributors, Inc., Hialeah, FL; *U.S. Private*, pg. 712
Perez, Ramon M., Exec. V.P.-Pur.--Cardinal Health Inc., Dublin, OH; *U.S. Public*, pg. 304
Perez, Ramon M., Exec. V.P.-Pur.--Cardinal Distribution, Dublin, OH; *U.S. Public*, pg. 304
Perez, Thea, Dir.-Pur.--BOK Financial Corp., Tulsa, OK; *U.S. Public*, pg. 163
Peritz, Jurg, Mgr.-Nonfood Pur.--Coop Switzerland, Basel, Switzerland; *Int'l*, pg. 329
Perkins, Ted, Mgr.-Pur.--Moss Telecommunications Services, Grand Rapids, MI; *U.S. Private*, pg. 763
Perkis, Michael, V.P.-Pur.--Coca-Cola Bottling Co. Consolidated, Charlotte, NC; *U.S. Public*, pg. 391
Perlow, Jeff, Dir.-Pur.--Diamond Power Specialty Co., Lancaster, OH; *U.S. Public*, pg. 1068
Perron, Robert, Dir.-Pur.--Donohue Inc., Quebec, Canada; *Int'l*, pg. 1075
Perry, D.M., Pur. Agent--IMI Cash Valve, Inc., Cullman, AL; *Int'l*, pg. 646
Pershing, Doug, Mgr.-Pur.--Plastic Suppliers, Inc., Columbus, OH; *U.S. Private*, pg. 871
Peters, Connie, V.P. & Pur. Dir.--Western International Media Corporation, Los Angeles, CA; *U.S. Private*, pg. 1165
Peters, James R., Pur. Agent--Peters Machinery Co., Chicago, IL; *U.S. Public*, pg. 944
Peters, Joe, Dir.-Adv. & Pur.--McKee Door, Inc., Aurora, IL; *U.S. Public*, pg. 69
Peters, Linda S., Pur. Agent--E.R. Moore Co., Chicago, IL; *U.S. Private*, pg. 759
Peters, Richard, Mgr.-Pur.--Sanwa Bank California, Los Angeles, CA; *Int'l*, pg. 1189
Petersen, Dale L., Pur. Agent--Henningsen Foods, Inc., White Plains, NY; *Int'l*, pg. 1074
Peterson, Dennis A., Mgr.-Pur.--The C.P. Hall Company, Chicago, IL; *U.S. Private*, pg. 495
Peterson, Mark R., V.P.-Pur.--IBP, Inc., Dakota City, NE; *U.S. Public*, pg. 852
Peterson, Mike, Pur. Agent--Brown-Minneapolis Tank & Fabricating Co., Eagan, MN; *U.S. Public*, pg. 914
Peterson, Paul, V.P.-Procurement--Doane Products Co., Joplin, MO; *U.S. Private*, pg. 337
Peterson, R.F., Pur. Agent--Research Products Corporation, Madison, WI; *U.S. Private*, pg. 924
Peterson, Robert, Pur. Agent--Yorktown Tool & Die Corporation, Yorktown, IN; *U.S. Private*, pg. 1196
Peterson, Roger, Dir.-Pur.--Wausau Papers - Printing & Writing Div., Brokaw, WI; *U.S. Public*, pg. 1747
Peterson, Steve, Mgr.-Pur.--Kaufman and Broad of Arizona, Inc., Phoenix, AZ; *U.S. Public*, pg. 945

Petrakis, Tina, Mgr.-Pur.--Precision Systems, Inc., Saint Petersburg, FL; *U.S. Public*, pg. 1321
Petrovich, Steve, Pur. Agent--Sokol & Company, Countryside, IL; *U.S. Private*, pg. 1012
Petrusek, David W., Dir.-Pur.--Atwood Oceanics, Inc., Houston, TX; *U.S. Public*, pg. 146
Petrusky, Brian, Mgr.-Purchasing--Microtouch Systems, Inc., Methuen, MA; *U.S. Public*, pg. 1108
Petry, Max, Dir.-Pur. & Mgr.-Traffic--Beach Mold & Tool Inc., New Albany, IN; *U.S. Private*, pg. 125
Petsch, Gregory, Sr. V.P.-Corp. Opers.--COMPAQ Computer Corporation, Houston, TX; *U.S. Public*, pg. 417
Pettersson, Jan, Pur. Agent--Skanska Syd, Malmo, Sweden; *Int'l*, pg. 1260
Pettit, Donald J., Dir.-Pur.--Interstate Power Company, Dubuque, IA; *U.S. Public*, pg. 910
Pexa, Craig, Dir.-Pur.--Bongards Creameries Inc., Norwood, MN; *U.S. Private*, pg. 156
Peyton, Teresa, Mgr.-Pur.--Attorneys' Title Insurance Fund, Orlando, FL; *U.S. Private*, pg. 98
Pfaff, Mark, Dir.-Pur.--The Gibson-Homans Company, Twinsburg, OH; *U.S. Private*, pg. 451
Pfeffer, Martha, Pur. Mgr.--Delmonico Foods, Louisville, KY; *U.S. Public*, pg. 812
Pfenning, Lowell, Pur. Agent--Miss Elaine Inc., Saint Louis, MO; *U.S. Private*, pg. 752
Pfouts, Rich, Mgr.-Pur.--Easco Inc., Girard, OH; *U.S. Public*, pg. 548
Phelan, Doug, Mgr.-Pur. & Sls.--Canadian Occidental Petroleum Ltd., Calgary, Canada; *U.S. Public*, pg. 1210
Phelps, Sue, Mgr.-Pur.--Advanced Input Devices, Inc., Coeur D'Alene, ID; *U.S. Private*, pg. 21
Philippi, Mike, V.P.-Pur.--W.C. Caye & Company, Inc., Augusta, GA; *U.S. Private*, pg. 220
Phillipa, Tom, V.P.-Pur.--Consolidated Industries Corp., Lafayette, IN; *Int'l*, pg. 188
Phillips, Baxter F., Jr., V.P.-Pur. & Admin.--A.T. Massey Coal Company, Inc., Richmond, VA; *U.S. Public*, pg. 660
Phillips, F.T., Dir.-Pur.--Delta Air Lines, Inc., Atlanta, GA; *U.S. Public*, pg. 497
Phillips, Karla, Mgr.-Pur.--Insurance Brokers & Managers, Inc., New Orleans, LA; *U.S. Public*, pg. 1677
Phillips, Karla, Mgr.-Pur.--Lafayette Insurance Company, New Orleans, LA; *U.S. Public*, pg. 1677
Phillips, Rick, Dir.-Pur.--Cheraw Yarn Mills, Inc., Cheraw, SC; *U.S. Private*, pg. 233
Phipps, Martin, Dir.-Pur.--Flying J. Inc., Brigham City, UT; *U.S. Private*, pg. 415
Picard, Martin, Dir.-Matls.--Rodney Hunt Company, Orange, MA; *U.S. Private*, pg. 549
Pickem, Michael M., Mgr.-Pur.--Sackner Products, Grand Rapids, MI; *U.S. Public*, pg. 924
Piekos, Greg, V.P.-Pur.--Clark Foodservice, Inc., Elk Grove Village, IL; *U.S. Private*, pg. 242
Pielach, Henry, Mgr.-Pur.--Beltone Electronics Corporation, Chicago, IL; *U.S. Private*, pg. 132
Pieper, George, Pur. Agent--Wabash Magnetics, Huntington, IN; *U.S. Private*, pg. 351
Pierce, Edwin, Treas. & Mgr.-Pur.--Tolleson Lumber Company, Inc., Perry, GA; *U.S. Private*, pg. 1090
Pierce, Joe, Dir.-Pur.--Douglas/Quikut, Walnut Ridge, AR; *U.S. Public*, pg. 217
Pierce, Peggy, Mgr.-Inventory--Bergen Brunswig Medical Corporation, Mobile, AL; *U.S. Public*, pg. 214
Piers, E., Mgr.-Pur.--Campina Melkunie BV, Zaltbommel, Netherlands; *Int'l*, pg. 254
Pietrangeli, Joseph J., V.P.-Pur.--Jervis B. Webb Company, Farmington Hills, MI; *U.S. Private*, pg. 1156
Pietrok, Luke, Mgr.-Pur.--Cascade Steel Rolling Mills, Inc., McMinnville, OR; *U.S. Public*, pg. 1440
Pigaty, Charles, Mgr.-Pur.--Bridgeport Fittings, Inc., Stratford, CT; *U.S. Private*, pg. 168
Pignatelli, Samuel, V.P.-Pur.--South Jersey Gas Co., Folsom, NJ; *U.S. Public*, pg. 1488
Pijanowski, Brian, V.P.-Buying & Mdsg.--Shaw's Supermarkets, Inc., East Bridgewater, MA; *Int'l*, pg. 1170
Ping, Alyce, Mgr.-Pur.--GB Holdings, Jurong, Singapore; *Int'l*, pg. 531
Ping, Alyce, Mgr.-Pur.--American Marine Pte. Ltd., Jurong, Singapore; *Int'l*, pg. 531
Pinkney, Michael, Mgr.-Pur.--CAIRE, Inc., Burnsville, MN; *U.S. Private*, pg. 751
Piosa, J., Dir.-Pur.--Woodstream Corporation, Lititz, PA; *U.S. Public*, pg. 566
Pippenger, Richard, V.P.-Pur.--Supreme Industries, Inc., Goshen, IN; *U.S. Public*, pg. 1541
Pippenger, Richard, V.P.-Pur.--Supreme Corporation of Texas, Cleburne, TX; *U.S. Public*, pg. 1542
Pippenger, Richard, V.P.-Pur.--Supreme MidAtlantic Corporation, Jonestown, PA; *U.S. Public*, pg. 1542
Pippenger, Richard, V.P.-Pur.--Supreme Murphy Corp., Wilson, NC; *U.S. Public*, pg. 1542
Pirie, Robin B., Dir.-Grain--Pauls Malt Limited, Newmarket, United Kingdom; *Int'l*, pg. 598
Pirklbauer, Harald E., Dir.-Pur.--Voest-Alpine International Corporation, New York, NY; *Int'l*, pg. 1470
Pittman, Gary, Chm. Bd., Pres., Chief Exec., Chief Oper. & Chief Fin. Officer--PCI, Austin, TX; *U.S. Private*, pg. 826
Pitts, John, Pur. Agent--Sugar Cane Growers Cooperative of Florida, Belle Glade, FL; *U.S. Private*, pg. 1049
Pizzino, J., Mgr.-Pur.--Flowserve Corporation, Foundry Div., Dayton, OH; *U.S. Public*, pg. 658
Place, Duke, Pur. Agent--Honeywell-Measurex Corporation, Cupertino, CA; *U.S. Public*, pg. 833
Plamondon, Simon, Mgr.-Pur.--Security Chimneys International Ltd., Laval, Canada; *Int'l*, pg. 1217
Platz, Neil L., Dir.-Pur.--The Turner Corporation, New York, NY; *U.S. Public*, pg. 1645
Plautz, Dale, Dir.-Pur.--Coleman Cable Systems, Inc., North Chicago, IL; *U.S. Public*, pg. 968
Plaz, Urz, Dir.-Pur.--Nestle Industrial e Commercial Ltda., Sao Paulo, Brazil; *Int'l*, pg. 921
Plazak, Cary, Dir.-Pur.--John B. Sanfilippo & Son, Inc., Elk Grove Village, IL; *U.S. Public*, pg. 1431
Plona, Daniel, Pur. Agent--Glastic Corporation, Cleveland, OH; *Int'l*, pg. 740
Plowman, Peter, Dir.-Pur.--Emery Waterhouse Company, Portland, ME; *U.S. Private*, pg. 373
Pohlman, David, Dir.-Pur.--Crouch Supply Company, Inc., Fort Worth, TX; *U.S. Private*, pg. 291
Poiesz, William, Dir.-Facilities Mgr.--La France Corporation, Philadelphia, PA; *U.S. Private*, pg. 640
Pokorn, James, V.P.-Pur.--Rapid Mounting & Finishing Co., Chicago, IL; *U.S. Private*, pg. 910
Polczynski, Tom, Pur. Agent--Oberg Industries Corp., Freeport, PA; *U.S. Private*, pg. 810
Polk, Donald, Mgr.-Matls.--Schult Homes Corporation, Buckeye, AZ; *U.S. Public*, pg. 1442
Pollack, John, Dir.-Pur.--West Chemical Products, Inc., Princeton, NJ; *U.S. Private*, pg. 1158
Pollnow, Claes, Dir.-Pur., Logistics & Information Systems--AB SKF, Goteborg, Sweden; *Int'l*, pg. 1156
Polucha, Dave, Dir.-Pur.--Hach Company, Loveland, CO; *U.S. Public*, pg. 773
Pomeroy, William D., Dir.-Pur.--United Companies Financial Corporation, Baton Rouge, LA; *U.S. Public*, pg. 1675
Pompilio, Michael F., Mgr.-Pur.--Hano Document Printers, Inc., Conyers, GA; *U.S. Public*, pg. 1686
Ponzetti, Randy, Dir.-Pur.--Tomco Auto Products, Inc., Los Angeles, CA; *U.S. Private*, pg. 1090
Poole, Rodney M., Dir.-Pur.--Cone Mills Corporation, Greensboro, NC; *U.S. Public*, pg. 430
Poon, Bob, Dir.-Pur.--Four Seasons Hotels Inc., Don Mills, Canada; *Int'l*, pg. 502
Pope, Chuck, Dir.-Corp. Pur. & Quality--Freudenberg-NOK, Plymouth, MI; *U.S. Private*, pg. 427
Pope, Reid V., Dir.-Pur.--Famous Restaurants Inc., Scottsdale, AZ; *U.S. Private*, pg. 393
Popik, Charles M., V.P.-Pur.--APS Holding Corporation, Houston, TX; *U.S. Public*, pg. 10
Popik, Charles M., V.P.-Pur.--A.P.S., Inc., Houston, TX; *U.S. Public*, pg. 10
Popovitch, Gary, Gen. Mgr.--Toledo Milk Processing, Inc., Toledo, OH; *U.S. Public*, pg. 1453
Porhola, Marlene, Mgr.-Pur.--W. Braun Co., Sun Valley, CA; *U.S. Private*, pg. 166
Porkert, Helmut F., Chief Procurement Officer--Atlantic Richfield Company, Los Angeles, CA; *U.S. Public*, pg. 144
Pornet, Jean-Marc, Dir.-Corp. Pur.--Alcatel N.V., Amsterdam, Netherlands; *Int'l*, pg. 55
Porter, James E., Dir.-Pur.--Plano Molding Co., Plano, IL; *U.S. Private*, pg. 869
Posewick, J., V.P.-Pur.--Natural Gas Pipeline Co. America, Lombard, IL; *U.S. Public*, pg. 1210
Posinski, Sam, Mgr.-Pur.--RJO Enterprises, Inc., Lanham, MD; *U.S. Private*, pg. 904
Potter, Douglas, Dir.-Pur. & Facilities--Betac International Corporation, Alexandria, VA; *U.S. Private*, pg. 140
Potts, J., Dir.-Pur.--Astronautics Corporation of America, Milwaukee, WI; *U.S. Private*, pg. 93
Potts, John, Dir.-Pur. & Mgr.-Mfg.--World Dryer Corp., Berkeley, IL; *U.S. Public*, pg. 1497
Powell, Kevin, Mgr.-Supply Services--Numac Energy Inc., Calgary, Canada; *Int'l*, pg. 990
Powers, Herman L., Mgr.-Pur.--Pennsylvania Crusher Corp., Broomall, PA; *U.S. Private*, pg. 850
Powers, John M., V.P.-Energy Supply--Commonwealth Electric Co., Cambridge, MA; *U.S. Public*, pg. 415
Prabe, Dave, Dir.-Pur.--Vilter Manufacturing Corporation, Cudahy, WI; *U.S. Private*, pg. 1140
Praet, Norman, Dir.-Pur.--Russ Berrie and Company, Inc., Oakland, NJ; *U.S. Public*, pg. 222
Prasad, Kumar, Dir.-Pur.--Contadina Dalla Casa Buitoni, Glendale, CA; *Int'l*, pg. 916
Pratt, Keith, Dir.-U.S. Pur.--Colgate U.S.A., New York, NY; *U.S. Public*, pg. 397
Pratt, Rick, Mgr.-Matls.--Industrial Bag Division - Kansas City Plant, Kansas City, MO; *U.S. Public*, pg. 1521
Press, David, Dir.-Pur.--Tootsie Roll Industries, Inc., Chicago, IL; *U.S. Public*, pg. 1621
Press, David, Dir.-Pur.--World Trade & Marketing, LTD., Chicago, IL; *U.S. Public*, pg. 1621
Preston, Andrew J., Dir.-Pur.--Birds Eye Walls Ltd., Walton-on-Thames, United Kingdom; *Int'l*, pg. 1434
Pretty, Jim, Corp. Mgr.--Nova Scotia Power Inc., Halifax, Canada; *Int'l*, pg. 971
Preysner, Gary, V.P.-Pur.--USF&G Corporation, Baltimore, MD; *U.S. Public*, pg. 1659
Price, Daniel, Mgr.-Pur.--The Crystal Tissue Co., Middletown, OH; *U.S. Private*, pg. 294
Price, Ed, Mgr.-Pur.--Atlas Electric Devices Co., Chicago, IL; *U.S. Private*, pg. 96
Price, Jack, Dir.-Pur.--Tops Appliance City, Edison, NJ; *U.S. Public*, pg. 1622
Price, Robert J., Chief Fin. Officer, V.P. & Treas.--The Suddath Companies, Jacksonville, FL; *U.S. Private*, pg. 1049
Primm, Mike, Mgr.-Pur.--Electrical Equipment Company, Raleigh, NC; *U.S. Private*, pg. 368
Prior, Dennis, Dir.-Pur.--Cranston Print Works Company, Cranston, RI; *U.S. Private*, pg. 286
Prior, Larry, V.P.-Mdsg.--O'Reilly Automotive Inc., Springfield, MO; *U.S. Public*, pg. 1230
Pritchard, E., Dir.-Pur.--The Mead Corporation, Dayton, OH; *U.S. Public*, pg. 1074
Privott, Tom, Pur. Agent--National Welders Supply Co. Inc., Charlotte, NC; *U.S. Private*, pg. 788
Profaci, Robert J., V.P.-Pur. & Sec.--Colivita USA, Inc., Linden, NJ; *U.S. Private*, pg. 252
Progar, Melvin, Dir.-Pur. & Matls. Control--Bumble Bee Seafoods Inc., San Diego, CA; *U.S. Private*, pg. 526
Proksch, Fritz, Controller--Osterreichischen Bundesbahnen GmbH, Vienna, Austria; *Int'l*, pg. 1012
Proto, Domenic, Mgr.-Pur.--Blauer Manufacturing Co., Inc., Boston, MA; *U.S. Private*, pg. 149
Pryor, Doug, Mgr.-Pur.--Sport Supply Group, Inc., Dallas, TX; *U.S. Public*, pg. 1499
Pryor, Jess, Mgr.-Pur.--Carter Chambers Supply, Inc., Baton Rouge, LA; *U.S. Private*, pg. 216
Pryor, Phillip, Dir.-Pur.--Progress Printing Company, Lynchburg, VA; *U.S. Private*, pg. 890
Puglisi, Vincent, Mgr.-Pur.--Michael Anthony Jewelers, Inc., Mount Vernon, NY; *U.S. Public*, pg. 1103
Pulsifer, Matt, Supvr.-Matls. Procurement--Tucson Electric Power Company, Tucson, AZ; *U.S. Public*, pg. 1670
Purcel, Irene, Asst. Radio Buyer--SFM Media Corporation, New York, NY; *U.S. Private*, pg. 956
Purcell, David, Pur. Agent--B.H. Aircraft Co., Inc., Farmingdale, NY; *U.S. Private*, pg. 107
Purdue, Pat, Pur. Agent--Gem-Dandy, Inc., Madison, NC; *U.S. Private*, pg. 442
Purvis, Ellen, Pur. Agent--The Homestead L.C., Hot Springs, VA; *U.S. Private*, pg. 247
Purvis, R., Pur. Agent--J.M. Huber, Wood Products Div., Charlotte, NC; *U.S. Private*, pg. 545
Push, James, Mgr.-Pur.--Beiersdorf, Inc., Norwalk, CT; *Int'l*, pg. 182
Putman, Ben, Dir.-Pur.--Carolina Tractor & Equipment Co., Charlotte, NC; *U.S. Private*, pg. 214
Putman, Cheryl, Dir.-Pur.--Frank Industries, Inc., Brown City, MI; *U.S. Private*, pg. 423
Putnum, Charles, Pur. Agent--S. Bent & Brothers, Inc., Gardner, MA; *U.S. Private*, pg. 134
Puttrich, Paul M., V.P. & Pur. Agent--Crafty Beaver Home Center, Skokie, IL; *U.S. Private*, pg. 284
Pyles, William, Dir.-Inventory Mngmt.--Clariant Corporation, Charlotte, NC; *Int'l*, pg. 624
Pyszka, Robert E., V.P. & Dir.-Pur.--United Missouri Bank N.A., Kansas City, MO; *U.S. Public*, pg. 1654
Quasey, Richard L., Dir.-Pur.--The Edward J. DeBartolo Corporation, Youngstown, OH; *U.S. Private*, pg. 319
Queen, Bob, Mgr.-Pur.--Stoneville Furniture Co. Inc., Stoneville, NC; *U.S. Private*, pg. 1045
Queeno, Frank, Mgr.-Materials--F.N. Burt Company, Inc., Buffalo, NY; *U.S. Private*, pg. 188
Quick, Ron, Sr. Buyer--Maxwell Macmillan Professional & Business Reference Publishing, Englewood Cliffs, NJ; *U.S. Public*, pg. 1602
Quigney, Pete, Dir.-Global Pur. Grp.--Electronic Data Systems Corporation, Plano, TX; *U.S. Public*, pg. 569
Quiner, Jodi D., Mgr.-Corp. Transportation & Pur.--International Multifoods Corporation, Minneapolis, MN; *U.S. Public*, pg. 900
Quinn, P. William, V.P.-Pur.--SCI Systems, Inc., Huntsville, AL; *U.S. Public*, pg. 1416
Raap, Patricka, Mgr.-Facilities--Stark Candy Company, Pewaukee, WI; *U.S. Private*, pg. 1113
Rabakon, Brent, Mgr.-Matls.--Kurdziel Industries, Inc., Muskegon, MI; *U.S. Private*, pg. 637
Racioppi, Mike, V.P.-Mdsg.--Henry Schein, Inc., Melville, NY; *U.S. Public*, pg. 1437
Radomski, Jurgen, Dir.-Pur., Logistics & Infrastructure Svcs./Europe--Siemens AG, Munich, Germany; *Int'l*, pg. 1244
Radziewicz, John, Dir.-Pur.--Trumpf Inc., Farmington, CT; *U.S. Private*, pg. 1108
Rafter, Chuck, Pur. Agent--Cablewave Systems, North Haven, CT; *U.S. Private*, pg. 197
Raftis, Alex, Dir.-Pur.--Coilcraft, Inc., Cary, IL; *U.S. Private*, pg. 250
Rahn, Steve, Dir.-Pur.--The Vollrath Company, L.L.C., Sheboygan, WI; *U.S. Private*, pg. 1143
Raimondi, Frank, Pur. Agent--Carstens Inc., Chicago, IL; *U.S. Private*, pg. 216
Rakes, Alton, Pur. Agent--Hanover Wire Cloth, Hanover, PA; *U.S. Private*, pg. 193
Ralston, Bob D., Exec. V.P.-Maintenance--J.B. Hunt Transport Services, Inc., Lowell, AR; *U.S. Public*, pg. 849
Ramalho, Jairo, Mgr.-Pur.--SmithKline Beecham Laboratorios Ltda., Rio de Janeiro, Brazil; *Int'l*, pg. 1266
Ramas, Roberto, Mgr.-Procurement--Ponce Cement Div., Ponce, PR; *U.S. Public*, pg. 1342
Ramclam, Jeff, Mgr.-Pur.--Harrison Div., Burbank, CA; *U.S. Private*, pg. 999
Ramirez, Arnel, Dir.-Pur.--The Beverly Hills Hotel, Beverly Hills, CA; *U.S. Private*, pg. 142
Ramirez, Frank, Mgr.-Pur.--Madison Industries, Los Angeles, CA; *U.S. Private*, pg. 428
Ramoni, Fred J., Dir.-Pur.--Holm Industries, Inc., Scottsburg, IN; *U.S. Public*, pg. 1504
Ramos, Roberto, Mgr.-Procurement--Puerto Rican Cement Co., Inc., Guaynabo, PR; *U.S. Public*, pg. 1341
Ramras, Jeff, V.P.-Logistics--Applied Industrial Technologies, Cleveland, OH; *U.S. Public*, pg. 122
Ramsay, Noville, Dir.-Pur.--Milkco, Inc., Asheville, NC; *U.S. Public*, pg. 878
Ramsbacher, Charles F., V.P.-Mktg.--Nash Finch Company, Edina, MN; *U.S. Public*, pg. 1151
Ramsbottom, N.D., V.P.-Pur. & Transportation--Purina Mills, Inc., Saint Louis, MO; *U.S. Private*, pg. 895
Ramsey, Tim, Gen. Mgr.-Procurement--Sanden International (U.S.A.), Inc., Wylie, TX; *Int'l*, pg. 1184
Ramsey, Tom, Mgr.-Pur.--Michigan Tube Co., Eau Claire, MI; *U.S. Private*, pg. 533
Ranaghan, Tom, Dir.-Pur.--Turtle Bay Hilton Golf & Tennis Resort, Kahuku, HI; *U.S. Public*, pg. 829
Rance, Donna, Pur. Agent--Florida Public Utilities Company, West Palm Beach, FL; *U.S. Public*, pg. 655
Rankin, J. Martin, Pur. Agent--Lift-All Co., Inc., Manheim, PA; *U.S. Private*, pg. 667
Raphael, Lisa, Buyer--The Bartell Drug Company, Seattle, WA; *U.S. Private*, pg. 118
Rasmascola, N., Mgr.-Purchasing--RFL Electronics, Inc., Boonton, NJ; *U.S. Private*, pg. 903
Rasmussen, Jack C., Mgr.-Pur. & Stores--Wisconsin Public Service Corporation, Green Bay, WI; *U.S. Public*, pg. 1728
Rasp, Robert, Mgr.-Matls.--Amot Controls Corporation, Richmond, CA; *U.S. Public*, pg. 1405
Rattee, Bill, Dir.-Pur.--Air BC, Richmond, Canada; *Int'l*, pg. 36

Ratti, J., Dir.-Pur.--WHX Corporation, New York, NY; *U.S. Public*, pg. 1726
Raulerson, John P., Dir.-Pur.--EnergyNorth, Inc., Manchester, NH; *U.S. Public*, pg. 581
Raup, Thomas S., Deputy Dir.-Pur.--American Systems Corporation, Chantilly, VA; *U.S. Private*, pg. 63
Rawston, C., Dir.-Pur.--AAH Pharmaceuticals Limited, Runcorn, United Kingdom; *Int'l*, pg. 591
Ray, David, Exec. V.P.--Bill Ray Nissan, Inc., Longwood, FL; *U.S. Private*, pg. 911
Ray, Thomas, Dir.-Matls. Mngmt.--Shaklee Corporation, San Francisco, CA; *Int'l*, pg. 1518
Raymer, Jim, V.P.-Pur.--State Industries Inc., Ashland City, TN; *U.S. Private*, pg. 1036
Raynsford, Peter, Pur. Agent--Harden Furniture Company, McConnellsville, NY; *U.S. Private*, pg. 501
Rea, Jane, Dir.-Corp. Services--B.A.S.S., Inc., Montgomery, AL; *U.S. Private*, pg. 105
Read, John R., Mgr.-Production Matls. Pur.--Moorman's Inc., Quincy, IL; *U.S. Private*, pg. 760
Reale, Joseph, Dir.-Pur.--Jarvis (East), Palmer, MA; *U.S. Public*, pg. 1506
Reddy, Bill, Dir.-Pur.--Castex Incorporated, Holland, MI; *U.S. Public*, pg. 1577
Redman, N.H., Mgr.-Pur.--Moore Paragon U.K. Limited, London, United Kingdom; *Int'l*, pg. 889
Reece, Bill, Mgr.-Pur.--Niagara Cutter, Inc., Amherst, NY; *U.S. Private*, pg. 798
Reece, Jeff, Pur. Agent--John Roberts Company, Minneapolis, MN; *U.S. Private*, pg. 935
Reed, Douglas, Dir.-Contracts Admin.--Mason & Hanger Corporation, Inc., Lexington, KY; *U.S. Private*, pg. 711
Reed, Maria Y., Human Resources Dir.--Don Coleman Advertising, Inc., Southfield, MI; *U.S. Private*, pg. 251
Reed, Peter, V.P.-Distr. Service--The Oshawa Group Limited, Etobicoke, Canada; *Int'l*, pg. 1012
Reed, Todd, Dir.-Pur.--Kova Fertilizer Inc., Greensburg, IN; *U.S. Private*, pg. 634
Reed, Wilma, Buyer--Falcon Products, Inc., Saint Louis, MO; *U.S. Public*, pg. 611
Reeder, H., Mgr.-Pur.--Moore Ges.m.b.H., Vienna, Austria; *Int'l*, pg. 889
Rees, C., Mgr.-Pur.--Pennsylvania General Insurance Company, Philadelphia, PA; *Int'l*, pg. 543
Reese, Bill, Mgr.-Matls.--Fleischer Manufacturing, Inc., Columbus, NE; *U.S. Private*, pg. 410
Regan, Gordon E., Jr., V.P.-Pur. & Transportation--AmeriGas Partners, L.P., Valley Forge, PA; *U.S. Public*, pg. 1653
Reilly, James, Dir.-Material Control--Standard Microsystems Corp., Hauppauge, NY; *U.S. Public*, pg. 1502
Reilly, Jeffry, Mgr.-Corp. Pur.--Gibbs Wire & Steel Company, Inc., Southington, CT; *U.S. Private*, pg. 451
Rein, Carl, Dir.-Procurement--International Research & Evaluation, Eagan, MN; *U.S. Private*, pg. 571
Reines, Larry B., Gen. Counsel & Dir.-Pur.--Vivian & Elliette, Inc., Vernon, CA; *U.S. Private*, pg. 1142
Reinschild, Barbara, Dir.-Pur.--The Fifth Third Bank of Kentucky, Louisville, Louisville, KY; *U.S. Public*, pg. 621
Reiss, Richard T., II, Pur. Agent--R.C.A. Rubber Company, Akron, OH; *U.S. Private*, pg. 902
Relf, Steve, Dir.-Pur. & Logistics--Brown Jordan Company, El Monte, CA; *U.S. Private*, pg. 174
Remy, Dennis K., Pur. Agent--Mansfield Div., Mansfield, OH; *U.S. Public*, pg. 754
Remy, Jerald C., V.P.-Pur.--Auto Glass Specialists, Madison, WI; *U.S. Private*, pg. 100
Renick, Judy, Dir.-Pur.--Alvey Systems, Inc, Saint Louis, MO; *U.S. Private*, pg. 47
Renner, Joe, Mgr.-Purchasing--Advance Circuits, Inc., Minnetonka, MN; *Int'l*, pg. 713
Rentel, Richard O., Dir.-Pur.--Marine Construction & Design Co., Seattle, WA; *U.S. Private*, pg. 703
Renzi, John, Mgr.-Mtls.--Buck Knives, Inc., El Cajon, CA; *U.S. Private*, pg. 177
Ressler, Bernard, Mgr.-Matls.--Wiltron Company, Morgan Hill, CA; *Int'l*, pg. 77
Reszutek, Gregory E., Dir.-Pur.--Hoxan America Incorporated, Piscataway, NJ; *Int'l*, pg. 363
Revell, Phillip A., Pur. Agent--Office Electronics, Inc., Itasca, IL; *U.S. Private*, pg. 812
Rex, Linda, Dir.-Pur.--Crescive Die & Tool, Inc., Saline, MI; *U.S. Private*, pg. 289
Rexroad, Arnold L., Mgr.-Pur.--The Acacia Group - Acacia Life Insurance Co., Bethesda, MD; *U.S. Private*, pg. 10
Reynolds, Michelle, Pur. Clerk--American Beauty Macaroni, Kansas City, KS; *U.S. Public*, pg. 812
Rezendes, Dan, V.P.-Pur.--The Harodite Finishing Company Inc., North Dighton, MA; *U.S. Private*, pg. 503
Rhein, Shirley, Dir.-Pur.--Brencal Contractors Inc., Detroit, MI; *U.S. Private*, pg. 106
Rhoda, Linda, Mgr.-Pur.--Thomas & Skinner, Inc., Indianapolis, IN; *U.S. Private*, pg. 1082
Rhodes, Barry, Chief Oper. Officer--Turner Machine Company, Salem, OH; *U.S. Private*, pg. 368
Rhodes, Rick, Pur. Agent--Continental Eagle Corporation, Prattville, AL; *U.S. Private*, pg. 267
Rice, Jerry, Mgr.-Pur.--Eaton Corporation, Electric Drives Division, Kenosha, WI; *U.S. Public*, pg. 556
Rice, John, Assoc. Dir.-Corp. Pur.--Alcatel N.V., Amsterdam, Netherlands; *Int'l*, pg. 55
Rice, Timothy, V.P.-Pur.--Standard Federal Bank, Troy, MI; *Int'l*, pg. 10
Richard, Dennis, Mgr.-Pur.--Iowa Precision Industries, Cedar Rapids, IA; *U.S. Public*, pg. 1100
Richard, Robert, Dir.-Pur.--Reactive Metals & Alloys Corporation (REMACOR), West Pittsburg, PA; *U.S. Private*, pg. 913
Richards, Brian, Grp. Pur. Mgr.--Birds Eye Walls Ltd., Walton-on-Thames, United Kingdom; *Int'l*, pg. 1434
Richards, Joel, III, Exec. V.P.-Human Resources--El Paso Natural Gas Co., Houston, TX; *U.S. Public*, pg. 567
Richards, Joseph, Pur. Agent--Stephenson, Inc., Alexandria, VA; *U.S. Private*, pg. 1040
Richards, Maureen, Mgr.-Pur.--Environmental Tectonics Corporation (ETC), Southampton, PA; *U.S. Public*, pg. 587
Richards, Patti, Mgr.-Pur.--Texas Utilities Company, Dallas, TX; *U.S. Public*, pg. 1586
Richards, Robert D., Dir.-Pur.--Ames Company, Parkersburg, WV; *U.S. Public*, pg. 1683
Richardson, Bob, Mgr.-Pur.--Kaufman and Broad of Nevada, Inc., Las Vegas, NV; *U.S. Public*, pg. 945
Richardson, Gary, Mgr.-Pur.--Ardent Software, Inc., Westborough, MA; *U.S. Public*, pg. 129
Richenberg, Richard E., V.P.-Matl. Mngmt.--Graham Manufacturing Co., Inc., Batavia, NY; *U.S. Public*, pg. 757
Richey, James, Dir.-Pur.--Precision Parts Corp., Morristown, TN; *U.S. Private*, pg. 879
Richhart, James K., V.P.-Pur. & Distr.--Pancho's Mexican Buffet, Inc., Fort Worth, TX; *U.S. Public*, pg. 1255
Richter, Earl, Dir.-Pur.--Pacesetter Corporation, Omaha, NE; *U.S. Private*, pg. 830
Rickard, Robert, Pur. Agent--Reactive Metals & Alloys Corporation (REMACOR), West Pittsburg, PA; *U.S. Private*, pg. 913
Ridd, Brian, V.P.-Pur.--Huntsman Corporation, Salt Lake City, UT; *U.S. Private*, pg. 549
Riddell, Steve, Mgr.-Pur., Facilities & Warehouse--Epson Canada Limited, Willowdale, Canada; *Int'l*, pg. 1219
Ridewood, Chip, Pur. Agent--Phototype Color Graphics, Inc., Pennsauken, NJ; *U.S. Private*, pg. 864
Ridings, Bill, Sr. Dir.-Pur.--International Comfort Products, Franklin, TN; *U.S. Public*, pg. 898
Riefenstahl, Eckart, Dir.-Pur.--Porsche AG, Stuttgart, Germany; *Int'l*, pg. 1063
Riegert, Werner, V.P.-Pur.--Swissmetal Plant Dornach, Dornach, Switzerland; *Int'l*, pg. 1427
Riggs, James L., Pur. Agent--The Wooster Brush Company, Wooster, OH; *U.S. Private*, pg. 1188
Riley, Bruce, Sr. Property Admin.--The Cafaro Co., Youngstown, OH; *U.S. Private*, pg. 198
Riley, David R., V.P.-Pur.--Interstate Steel Supply Company, Philadelphia, PA; *U.S. Public*, pg. 1100
Rinehart, Brenda, Buyer-Valve Grp.--De-Sta-Co, A Dover Resources Co., Troy, MI; *U.S. Public*, pg. 521
Rinella, Gus, Dir.-Pur.--Freeway Corporation, Cleveland, OH; *U.S. Private*, pg. 426
Ringstedt, Lars, Pur. Agent--Skanska Bostader Stockholm AB, Solna, Sweden; *Int'l*, pg. 1260
Ripatti, Eero, Mgr.-Pur.--Koltek Oy, Vantaa, Finland; *Int'l*, pg. 1379
Ripley, John, Mgr.-Pur.--Pool Energy Services Co., Houston, TX; *U.S. Public*, pg. 1316
Riquelme, Jim, Dir.-Pur.--Olga Div., Bridgeport, CT; *U.S. Public*, pg. 1738
Risley, Jim, V.P.-Pur.--Certified Grocers Midwest, Inc., Hodgkins, IL; *U.S. Private*, pg. 226
Ritchie, Berry, Mgr.-Pur.--Nocona Boot Co., Nocona, TX; *U.S. Public*, pg. 937
Ritchie, Marlene, Pur. Agent--UTA Holland Plant, Holland, MI; *U.S. Public*, pg. 1691
Ritenour, Jim, Dir.-Pur.--Best Western International, Inc., Phoenix, AZ; *U.S. Private*, pg. 140
Ritger, Drew, V.P.-Pur.--Sonic Corporation, Oklahoma City, OK; *U.S. Public*, pg. 1485
Ritger, Drew, V.P.-Pur.--Sonic Restaurants, Inc., Oklahoma City, OK; *U.S. Public*, pg. 1485
Ritter, Gary, Mgr.-Pur.--Mail Boxes Etc., San Diego, CA; *U.S. Public*, pg. 1687
Rivas, Guillermo, Sprvr.-Construction & Pur.--Windsor Fashions, Los Angeles, CA; *U.S. Private*, pg. 1182
Rivera, Joseph M., Dir.-Pur.--Southern California Gas Co., Los Angeles, CA; *U.S. Public*, pg. 1249
Rix, Jane M., Corp. Sec.--Manatron, Inc., Kalamazoo, MI; *U.S. Public*, pg. 1040
Roady, Art, Mgr.-Pur.--East Moline Metal Products Company, East Moline, IL; *U.S. Private*, pg. 357
Robb, Jerry, V.P.-Procurement/Prod. Control--Sargento Foods Inc., Plymouth, WI; *U.S. Private*, pg. 966
Robbins, Charles R., V.P. & Mgr.-Pur.--J.E. Higgins Lumber Co., Concord, CA; *U.S. Private*, pg. 527
Robbins, Charles R., V.P.-Pur. & Div. Mgr.--Higgins Lumber Purchasing, Union City, CA; *U.S. Private*, pg. 527
Robbins, Charles R., V.P.-Pur.--Higgins Sacramento/Purch, Rancho Cordova, CA; *U.S. Private*, pg. 527
Robbins, Jeff, Mgr.-Pur.--Daktronics, Inc., Brookings, SD; *U.S. Public*, pg. 478
Roberson, Billy, Pur. Agent--Wurzburg, Inc., Memphis, TN; *U.S. Private*, pg. 1192
Roberti, Jackie, Pur. Agent--ATF, Inc., Lincolnwood, IL; *U.S. Private*, pg. 8
Roberts, J.C., Pur. Agent--AVEX Electronics, Inc., Huntsville, AL; *U.S. Private*, pg. 545
Roberts, Joseph, Dir.-Pur.--Field Packing Company, Owensboro, KY; *U.S. Private*, pg. 403
Roberts, Steve, Mgr.-Pur.--ICF Kaiser International Inc., Fairfax, VA; *U.S. Public*, pg. 852
Robertson, Art, Dir.-Pur.--Blitz USA, Inc., Miami, OK; *U.S. Private*, pg. 149
Robey, Craig W., Mgr.-Pur.--Washington Gas Light Co., Springfield, VA; *U.S. Public*, pg. 1740
Robinson, Ian, Dir.-Pur.--Conwood Company L.P., Memphis, TN; *U.S. Private*, pg. 272
Robinson, Jerry, Mgr.-Pur.--Connecting Point Computer Services, Canton, OH; *U.S. Private*, pg. 471
Robinson, Rick, Mgr.--J.F. Ahern Co., Fond Du Lac, WI; *U.S. Private*, pg. 27
Robinson, Rob, Dir.-Pur.--Davis Electrical Constructors, Inc., Greenville, SC; *U.S. Private*, pg. 315
Robitaille, Pierre, V.P.-Pur.--UAP, Inc., Montreal, Canada; *Int'l*, pg. 1426
Robling, Janet, Dir.-Pur. Agent--E.A. Sween Company, Eden Prairie, MN; *U.S. Private*, pg. 1058
Robson, William E., Exec. V.P.-Opers.--Luby's Cafeterias, Inc., San Antonio, TX; *U.S. Public*, pg. 1017
Rocha, Carl, Dir.-Distr. Services--VWR Canlab, Mississauga, Canada; *U.S. Public*, pg. 1704
Rock, Pam, Mgr.-Pur.--EMS Central Regional Office (Corporate), Milwaukee, WI; *U.S. Public*, pg. 565
Rock, William C., Chief Fin. Officer--CompuDyne Corporation, Willimantic, CT; *U.S. Public*, pg. 419
Rockwell, Stuart, Pur. Agent--Felton Brush Inc., Manchester, NH; *U.S. Private*, pg. 400
Rodgers, W.E., Jr., Dir.-Pur.--Dan River Inc., Danville, VA; *U.S. Public*, pg. 478
Rodriguez, Manuel, V.P.-Grocery & Dairy--Pueblo International, Inc.-P.R. Div., Carolina, PR; *U.S. Private*, pg. 894
Rodriguez, Marie, Mgr.-Pur.--Mid-Continent Screw Products Co., Lincolnwood, IL; *U.S. Private*, pg. 743
Roemer, Dave, Pur. Agent--Six Flags St. Louis, Eureka, MO; *U.S. Public*, pg. 1612
Rogers, Cindy, Pur. Agent--Projects Unlimited, Inc., Dayton, OH; *U.S. Private*, pg. 890
Rogers, David, Pur. Agent--First Financial Holdings, Inc., Charleston, SC; *U.S. Public*, pg. 634
Rogers, Linda, Dir.-Pur. & Admin.--Entex, Houston, TX; *U.S. Public*, pg. 843
Rogers, Rocky, Mgr.-Pur.--Carpeteria, Inc., Valencia, CA; *U.S. Private*, pg. 215
Rogers, Samuel H., III, V.P.-Pur.--Wilkins-Rogers Incorporated, Ellicott City, MD; *U.S. Private*, pg. 1176
Rogers, Serrane, Mgr.-Pur.--Guerlain, Inc., New York, NY; *Int'l*, pg. 780
Rogers, Tracy, V.P.-Pur.--Montoi Mattel Toys, Laredo, TX; *U.S. Public*, pg. 1058
Rogus, Jeri, Pur. Agent--Plibrico Co., Chicago, IL; *U.S. Private*, pg. 872
Roig, Rafael, Dir.-Pur.--La Hacienda S.A. de C.V., Mexico, Mexico; *U.S. Public*, pg. 901
Roman, Lavinia, Mgr.-Pur.--The Levy Organization, Chicago, IL; *U.S. Private*, pg. 664
Rombach, Klaus, Pur. Agent--Press Enterprise Company, Riverside, CA; *U.S. Public*, pg. 209
Romeo, Pat, Mgr.-Pur.--Robinson Cone, Burlington, Canada; *Int'l*, pg. 417
Romero, C.V., Pur. Agent--Sunkist Growers, Inc., Sherman Oaks, CA; *U.S. Private*, pg. 1052
Romero, O.J., Dir.-Pur.--Beaird Industries, Inc., Shreveport, LA; *U.S. Public*, pg. 1639
Rompa, F., Mgr.-Pur.--Steelweld Division Zweigniederlassung Bonn der Ambac B.V., Saint Augustin, Germany; *Int'l*, pg. 71
Ronan, John C., V.P.-Pur.--The Gillette Company, Gillette Grooming Products, USA, Boston, MA; *U.S. Public*, pg. 744
Ronbinson, Charles, Mng. Dir.--Progress International Limited, Plainview, NY; *U.S. Public*, pg. 141
Ronge, Joe, V.P.-Central Pur.--Super 8 Motels, Inc., Aberdeen, SD; *U.S. Public*, pg. 322
Ronne, Hans G., Dir.-Pur.--Pronova Oleochemicals a.s., Sandefjord, Norway; *Int'l*, pg. 961
Roose, Bob, V.P.-Matls. Mngmt.--Coram Healthcare Corporation, Denver, CO; *U.S. Public*, pg. 446
Root, Lynal A., Sr. V.P.-Chief Pur. Officer--McDonald's Corporation, Oak Brook, IL; *U.S. Public*, pg. 1068
Rosa, Bruno, V.P.-Engrng. & Pur.--AP North American Aftermarket Division, Goldsboro, NC; *U.S. Private*, pg. 230
Rose, Dave, Dir.-Pur.--Cargill Salt, Newark, CA; *U.S. Private*, *pg. 210*
Rose, Richard, Dir.-Pur.--NDS, Columbus, OH; *Int'l*, pg. 918
Rose, S., Mgr.-Pur.--Midland Forge Division, Cedar Rapids, IA; *U.S. Public*, pg. 406
Rose, Tom, V.P.& Dir.-Pur.--Dillard, A ResourceNet International Company, Greensboro, NC; *U.S. Public*, pg. 901
Rosenbaum, Lynn, Mgr.-Matls.--Conley Frog/Switch & Forge Co., Memphis, TN; *U.S. Private*, pg. 263
Rosenbaum, Stuart, Dir.-Pur.--David Michael & Co. Inc., Philadelphia, PA; *U.S. Private*, pg. 740
Rosenberger, Richard, Mgr.-Matls.--Elastomeric Technologies, Inc., Hatboro, PA; *U.S. Public*, pg. 1598
Rosengarten, Zev, V.P.-Pur.--Crystal Clear Industries, Ridgefield Park, NJ; *U.S. Private*, pg. 293
Rosengren, Theodore, Mgr.-Pur.--Snap-On Tools Corporation, Kenosha, WI; *U.S. Public*, pg. 1480
Ross, D.L., Pur. Agent--Eriez Magnetics, Erie, PA; *U.S. Private*, pg. 381
Ross, Ron, Dir.-Pur.--Hvide Marine Incorporated, Fort Lauderdale, FL; *U.S. Public*, pg. 851
Rossman, Charles A., Mgr.-Pur.--Autocam Corporation, Grand Rapids, MI; *U.S. Public*, pg. 148
Rossman, Douglas D., V.P.-Pur.--Harvard Industries, Inc., Tampa, FL; *U.S. Public*, pg. 796
Rossman, Robert L., Mgr.-Energy--Cleveland-Cliffs Inc, Cleveland, OH; *U.S. Public*, pg. 386
Rostollan, Jean C., Exec. V.P.-Pur. & Asst. Sec.--Buffets, Inc., Eden Prairie, MN; *U.S. Public*, pg. 267
Roth, L. Jack, Exec. V.P.-Buying--Universal International, Inc., New Hope, MN; *U.S. Public*, pg. 1697
Rotrou, Gilbert, Mgr.-Facilities--Arianespace Kourou, Kourou, French Guiana; *Int'l*, pg. 81
Rottman, Colleen, Mgr.-Pur.--Walle Corporation, Harahan, LA; *U.S. Private*, pg. 1148
Roush, Judy, Pur. Agent--Abbey Etna Machine Company, Perrysburg, OH; *U.S. Private*, pg. 9
Rowan, Jerold, Mgr.-Materials Mngmnt.--Brooklyn Union, Brooklyn, NY; *U.S. Public*, pg. 259
Rowan, Steven M., V.P.-Materials & Transportation--Oregon Steel Mills Inc., Portland, OR; *U.S. Public*, pg. 1230
Royal, Donald, V.P.-Pur.--Hilton Hotels Corporation, Beverly Hills, CA; *U.S. Public*, pg. 828
Royal, Donald L., V.P.-Pur.--Hilton Hotels Div., Beverly Hills, CA; *U.S. Public*, pg. 829
Royer, Bernard, V.P.-Pur.--Sodexho USA, Waltham, MA; *Int'l*, pg. 1274
Rozensweig, Arye, Dir.-Pur.--Elscint Ltd., Haifa, Israel; *Int'l*, pg. 450

Rozewicz, James, Pur. Agent--Roman Electric Company, Inc., Milwaukee, WI; *U.S. Private*, pg. 942
Rubin, Eric, V.P.-Adv. & Pur.--M. Rubin & Sons Inc., Long Island City, NY; *U.S. Private*, pg. 949
Rubin, Phillip, V.P.-Pur.--M. Rubin & Sons Inc., Long Island City, NY; *U.S. Private*, pg. 949
Ruckstuhl, L.E., V.P.-Pur.--Newpark Environmental Services, Inc., Lafayette, LA; *U.S. Public*, pg. 1179
Rudd, J.G., Mgr.-Pur.--Crane & Co., Inc., Dalton, MA; *U.S. Private*, pg. 286
Rudnick, Harold, Sr. V.P.-Retail Pur.--The Vons Companies, Inc., Arcadia, CA; *U.S. Public*, pg. 1426
Rudz, Doug, Dir.-Pur.--Smith McDonald Corp., Buffalo, NY; *U.S. Private*, pg. 1009
Rudz, Doug, Dir.-Pur.--Smith Metal Arts Company, Inc., Buffalo, NY; *U.S. Private*, pg. 1009
Rudzki, Robert A., V.P.-Pur. & Transportation--Bethlehem Steel Corporation, Bethlehem, PA; *U.S. Public*, pg. 226
Ruehle, Guenther, Corp. Dir.-Pur.--Pabst Brewing Co., San Antonio, TX; *U.S. Private*, pg. 954
Ruehle, Guenther, Corp. Dir.-Pur.--Pabst Brewing Co./Tumwater, Tumwater, WA; *U.S. Private*, pg. 954
Ruehle, Guenther, Dir.-Corp. Pur.--Pearl Brewing Company, San Antonio, TX; *U.S. Private*, pg. 954
Rumney, F., Mgr.-Domestic Pur.--Shure Brothers Incorporated, Evanston, IL; *U.S. Private*, pg. 997
Rumore, Salvatore, Mgr.-Matls.--SI Handling Systems, Inc., Easton, PA; *U.S. Public*, pg. 1418
Runnion, David, Mgr.-Pur.--Oglebay Norton Refractories & Minerals, Inc., Cleveland, OH; *U.S. Public*, pg. 1214
Runyon, Mike, Dir.-Pur.--North American Salt Company, Overland Park, KS; *U.S. Private*, pg. 505
Rupert, Joseph, Dir.-Pur.--Time Warner Cable Liberty Division, Ferndale, NY; *U.S. Public*, pg. 1611
Rusemberger, Jorge, Dir.-Pur.--Sancor Cooperativas Unidas Limitadas, Buenos Aires, Argentina; *Int'l*, pg. 1183
Rush, Margurite, Mgr.-Pur.--Doron Precision Systems, Inc., Binghamton, NY; *U.S. Private*, pg. 341
Rushlow, Paul, V.P.-Pur.--Acklands Limited, Toronto, Canada; *Int'l*, pg. 23
Rusk, John A., V.P.-Pur. & Plng.--Conair Corporation, Stamford, CT; *U.S. Private*, pg. 261
Russell, Dan, Pur. Agent--Thomas & Betts Electronics Division, Memphis, TN; *U.S. Public*, pg. 1597
Russell, Dean, Mgr.-Pur.--Astro Homes, Shippenville, PA; *U.S. Public*, pg. 318
Russell, Joyce, Dir.-Pur.--The Suddath Companies, Jacksonville, FL; *U.S. Private*, pg. 1049
Russell, Paul, Mgr.-Pur.--John Dusenbery Co., Inc., Randolph, NJ; *U.S. Private*, pg. 349
Ryan, Don, Dir.-Pur.--Western States Machine Company, Hamilton, OH; *U.S. Private*, pg. 1168
Ryan, F. Don, V.P. & Gen. Mgr.-Specialty Polyolefins--Union Carbide Corporation, Danbury, CT; *U.S. Public*, pg. 1666
Ryan, H., Dir.-Pur.--The Canadian Coleman Co., Ltd., Toronto, Canada; *U.S. Private*, pg. 691
Ryan, John, Dir.-Pur.--Waterford Wedgwood UK Plc, Stoke on Trent, United Kingdom; *Int'l*, pg. 1487
Ryan, Richard M., Mgr.-Pur.--American Felt & Filter, Newburgh, NY; *U.S. Private*, pg. 54
Ryan, Thomas R., V.P.-Pur.--Hershey Creamery Company, Harrisburg, PA; *U.S. Private*, pg. 524
Rynkowski, Donald, Gen. Mgr.-Matls. Mngmt.--National Fuel Gas Company, Buffalo, NY; *U.S. Public*, pg. 1156
Saari, Stuart, Mgr.-Pur.--H.O. Trerice Company, Oak Park, MI; *U.S. Private*, pg. 1099
Saarinen, Elaine, Mgr.-Pur.--Community Bank N.A., De Witt, NY; *U.S. Public*, pg. 416
Sabal, Jerry, Mgr.-Pur.--Luxor, Waukegan, IL; *U.S. Private*, pg. 359
Sabin, Cathie, Dir.-Pur.--John O. Butler Co., Chicago, IL; *Int'l*, pg. 1320
Sad, Angela, Supvr.-Pur.--Compuware Corporation, Farmington Hills, MI; *U.S. Public*, pg. 423
Sailor, Flawn, Mgr.-Pur.--Bock Industries Inc., Elkhart, IN; *Int'l*, pg. 265
Sais, Maria, Mgr.-Pur.--Pinkerton's Inc., Encino, CA; *U.S. Public*, pg. 1296
Salisbury, D., Pur. Agent--J.M. Huber, Calcium Carbonate Division, Quincy, IL; *U.S. Private*, pg. 545
Sallee, Barbara, Mgr.-Pur.--White Microelectronics, Phoenix, AZ; *U.S. Public*, pg. 248
Salter, M.A.W., Dir.-Pur., Legal & Estates--Britvic Soft Drinks Ltd., Chelmsford, United Kingdom; *Int'l*, pg. 170
Samuelson, Gunnar, Pur. Agent--Skanska Stockholm Malardalen, Danderyd, Sweden; *Int'l*, pg. 1260
San Pedro, Jose Luis, Controller, Treas. & Mng. Dir.-Economy & Fin.--Iberdrola, S.A., Bilbao, Spain; *Int'l*, pg. 657
Sanders, Lori, Pur. Agent--Conso Products Company, Union, SC; *U.S. Public*, pg. 434
Sanderson, J.L., Dir.-Matls. Mngmt.--Kelco International Ltd., London, United Kingdom; *U.S. Public*, pg. 1091
Sanderson, Jim, Dir.-Pur.--Berryman Products, Inc., Arlington, TX; *U.S. Private*, pg. 138
Sandifer, Linda, Pur. Agent--Fabricon Products, River Rouge, MI; *U.S. Private*, pg. 355
Sanford, Frank W., V.P.-Pur. & Mktg.--Sanford & Hawley, Inc., Unionville, CT; *U.S. Private*, pg. 965
Sangster, Gordon W., V.P.-Opers.--Research, Incorporated, Eden Prairie, MN; *U.S. Public*, pg. 1382
Sanner, K.A., Mgr.-Matls. & Pur.--Hobbs Corporation, Springfield, IL; *Int'l*, pg. 127
Santoli, Agelo, Mgr.-Matls.--Center Laboratories, Inc., Port Washington, NY; *U.S. Public*, pg. 813
Santos, Antonio Feliciano Oliveira, Dir.-Pur.--Portuguese Railways (CP), Lisbon, Portugal; *Int'l*, pg. 1063
Sarfati, Andre, Mgr.-Pur.--A.G. Simpson Co. Limited, Scarborough, Canada; *Int'l*, pg. 1252
Sather, Steve, Mgr.-Pur.--Peco Mfg. Co., Inc., Portland, OR; *U.S. Private*, pg. 846
Satterfield, G.J., Mgr.-Pur.--La-Z-Boy Incorporated, Monroe, MI; *U.S. Public*, pg. 972
Satterley, Eric O., Dir.-Purchasing--Sofamor Danek Group, Inc., Memphis, TN; *U.S. Public*, pg. 1482
Sauer, Frederick J., V.P. & Sec.--Alliance Construction Solutions, Inc., Fort Collins, CO; *U.S. Private*, pg. 38
Saunders, Dean, Dir.-Pur.--The Wackenhut Corporation, Palm Beach Gardens, FL; *U.S. Public*, pg. 1731
Sauve, Dan, Mgr.-Pur. & Contracts--TVX Gold Inc., Toronto, Canada; *Int'l*, pg. 1345
Savoni, Stephen, Dir.-Pur.--Selas Corporation of America, Dresher, PA; *U.S. Public*, pg. 1454
Savran, Mike, Chief Buyer--Rapid Power Technologies, Inc., Brookfield, CT; *U.S. Private*, pg. 910
Sawyer, Lou, Pur. Agent--Hyer Industries Inc./Thayer Scale, Pembroke, MA; *U.S. Private*, pg. 552
Sawyer, W.I., Dir.-Pur.--Trion, Inc., Sanford, NC; *U.S. Public*, pg. 1639
Saxon, Jean, Mgr.-Pur.--Zoological Society of San Diego, San Diego, CA; *U.S. Private*, pg. 1207
Scales, Rosemary, Mgr.-Pur.--Elco Precision Stamping Div., Logansport, IN; *U.S. Public*, pg. 1590
Scalzo, Donald, Mgr.-Pur.--Kewaunee Scientific Corporation, Statesville, NC; *U.S. Public*, pg. 953
Scanlon, Thomas, V.P.-Matls.--Tyco Toys, Inc., Mount Laurel, NJ; *U.S. Public*, pg. 1058
Scanzillo, Kathryn E., Dir.-Pur. & Mgr.-Gen. Svcs.--EG & G, Inc., Wellesley, MA; *U.S. Public*, pg. 542
Scaperdine, Donald, Pur. Agent--Commercial Light Company, Hillside, IL; *U.S. Private*, pg. 258
Scarano, Virginia, Asst. V.P.--General Accident Insurance, Philadelphia, PA; *Int'l*, pg. 543
Scarmazzi, Joseph, V.P.-Pur. & Technical Services--Centimark Corporation, Canonsburg, PA; *U.S. Private*, pg. 222
Schaedler, Henry, V.P.-Pur.--Schaedler Brothers, Inc., Harrisburg, PA; *U.S. Private*, pg. 969
Schaefer, Stuart, Mgr.-Pur.--Johnson Ross Corporation, Champaign, IL; *U.S. Public*, pg. 279
Schafer, Elizabeth, Pur. Agent--Hickey-Freeman/Bobby Jones, Rochester, NY; *U.S. Public*, pg. 795
Schafer, John A., V.P.-Pur.--Wm. Wrigley Jr. Company, Chicago, IL; *U.S. Public*, pg. 1781
Schaffer, Paul, V.P.-Pur.--Cook Composites & Polymers Inc., Kansas City, MO; *Int'l*, pg. 1409
Schaub, Sherry J., V.P.-Pur.--The Quaker Oats Company, Chicago, IL; *U.S. Public*, pg. 1347
Schauer, Jo, Mgr.-Pur.--Bibler Brothers, Inc., Russellville, AR; *U.S. Private*, pg. 142
Schebece, Lisa, Mgr.-Pur.--Holiday RV Superstores, Inc.-Orlando, Orlando, FL; *U.S. Public*, pg. 830
Schechter, Lou, V.P.-Mdsg.--Rockbottom Stores, Inc., Lake Success, NY; *U.S. Private*, pg. 938
Scheffel, J.H., Dir.-Pur.--Prenatal B.V., Almere, Netherlands; *Int'l*, pg. 750
Scheide, Bob, Mgr.-Pur.--Life-Like Products, Inc., Baltimore, MD; *U.S. Private*, pg. 666
Scheidt, David, Mgr.--PacifiCare Health Systems, Inc., Cypress, CA; *U.S. Public*, pg. 1250
Scheller, Bill, Dir.-Pur.--Patterson Dental Company, Saint Paul, MN; *U.S. Public*, pg. 1265
Schelter, Marcia, Pur. Agent--American Plastic Toys Inc., Walled Lake, MI; *U.S. Private*, pg. 60
Scherb, Joan, V.P.-Pur. & Plng.--Universal Folding Box Company, Inc., Hoboken, NJ; *U.S. Private*, pg. 1127
Scherden, Patrick, Dir.-Pur.--Mitchell Corporation of Owosso, Owosso, MI; *U.S. Private*, pg. 753
Scherden, Patrick, Dir.-Pur.--Benzonia Manufacturing, Benzonia, MI; *U.S. Private*, pg. 753
Scherden, Patrick, Dir.-Pur.--Mitchell Corporation, Clare Div., Clare, MI; *U.S. Private*, pg. 753
Scherer, Robert, Dir.-Pur.--Gates Canada Inc., Brantford, Canada; *Int'l*, pg. 1396
Scheuner, Bernd, V.P.-Corp. Coord. Pur.--The Braas Group, Oberursell, Germany; *Int'l*, pg. 1091
Schiavone, Ralph, Dir.-Pur.--Roman, Inc., Roselle, IL; *U.S. Private*, pg. 942
Schickler, Joanne, Pur. Agent--Triangle Services, Inc., Valley Stream, NY; *U.S. Private*, pg. 1102
Schirm, Matt, Mgr.-Pur.--Atotech U.S.A. Inc., Rock Hill, SC; *U.S. Private*, pg. 97
Schirmang, Kenneth C., V.P.-Pur.--Skokie Valley Beverage Co., Wheeling, IL; *U.S. Private*, pg. 1005
Schlau, R., Mgr.-Pur.--Van Pelt Corporation, Detroit, MI; *U.S. Private*, pg. 1133
Schlegel, J., Dir.-Pur.--Turco Products Division, Long Beach, CA; *Int'l*, pg. 446
Schlegel, James, Dir.-Pur.--Turco Products Division, Westminster, CA; *Int'l*, pg. 446
Schlensker, Fred, Pur. Agent--Imperial Pools, Inc., Latham, NY; *U.S. Private*, pg. 558
Schlm, Wayne, Dir.-Material Control--Troy Mills, Inc., Troy, NH; *U.S. Private*, pg. 1106
Schlosser, Rita, Pur. Agent--Channellock, Inc., Meadville, PA; *U.S. Private*, pg. 229
Schmeiden, Gary, Mgr.-Pur.--Safway Steel Products Inc., Waukesha, WI; *Int'l*, pg. 1389
Schmidlapp, C.J., III, V.P.-Pur.--Medtech Inc., Jackson, WY; *U.S. Private*, pg. 728
Schmidt, Gary, Pur. Agent--Aurora Casket Company, Aurora, IN; *U.S. Private*, pg. 99
Schmidt, Herr, Mgr.-Pur.--Intertractor Zweigniederlassung der Wirtgen GmbH, Gevelsberg, Germany; *Int'l*, pg. 1511
Schmidt, James F., Dir.-Pur.--Chicago Rivet & Machine Company, Naperville, IL; *U.S. Public*, pg. 348
Schmidt, Jim, Mgr.-Pur.--Kaufman and Broad Central Valley Div., Modesto, CA; *U.S. Public*, pg. 945
Schmidt, R.J., Pur. Agent--KTI Fish, Houston, TX; *U.S. Private*, pg. 604
Schmitt, Eric, Dir.-Pur., Fin. & Organization--Audi AG, Ingolstadt, Germany; *Int'l*, pg. 1473
Schmitz, Jeff, Pur. Agent--McLaughlin Industrial Distributors, Inc., Pico Rivera, CA; *U.S. Private*, pg. 724
Schmitz, Volker, Dir.-Pur.--Lux GmbH & Co. KG, Wermelskirchen, Germany; *Int'l*, pg. 993
Schneider, Rudy, Mgr.-Pur.--Wyandot Inc., Marion, OH; *U.S. Private*, pg. 1193
Schnieders, Richard J., Sr. V.P.-Mdsg. & Multi-Unit Sls.--Sysco Corporation, Houston, TX; *U.S. Public*, pg. 1550
Schnitzer, Carol, Mgr.-Pur.--Environment/One Corporation, Niskayuna, NY; *U.S. Public*, pg. 586
Schodlatz, William, Mgr.-Pur.--UNR Home Products Div., Ruston, LA; *U.S. Public*, pg. 1404
Schofield, V.J., Pur. Agent--Kysor/Warren, Conyers, GA; *U.S. Public*, pg. 1445
Scholler, James, Dir.-Pur.--Times Printing Company, Inc., Random Lake, WI; *U.S. Private*, pg. 1087
Scholtens, G.B., Mgr.-Pur.--Fokker Aircraft Services B.V., Hoogerheyde, Netherlands; *Int'l*, pg. 1304
Schrieks, Jim, Dir.-Pur.--Atlas Hotels, Inc., San Diego, CA; *U.S. Private*, pg. 96
Schrock, Sandra, V.P.-Pur.--Starcraft Automotive Group, Inc., Goshen, IN; *U.S. Public*, pg. 1511
Schrodt, R.L., V.P.-Matls. & Systems--Rheem Air Conditioning Div., Fort Smith, AR; *Int'l*, pg. 1022
Schroeder, Kermit, Asst. V.P.-Logistics--National Fruit Product Company, Winchester, VA; *U.S. Private*, pg. 783
Schroer, Bill, Pur. Agent--Dualite Inc., Williamsburg, OH; *U.S. Private*, pg. 344
Schuck, Bruce, V.P.-Production & Pur.--Houghton International Inc., Valley Forge, PA; *U.S. Private*, pg. 541
Schuermann, C., Dir.-Pur.--Ferguson Machine Co., Saint Louis, MO; *U.S. Public*, pg. 457
Schuette, Thomas, Chief Info. Officer & V.P.-Opers. & Matls.--Wausau Homes, Inc., Rothschild, WI; *U.S. Private*, pg. 1154
Schuetze, Klaus, Mgr.-Pur.--OMRON Systems, Inc., Schaumburg, IL; *Int'l*, pg. 1005
Schulte, Fred, Dir.-Pur.--Quest Medical, Inc., Allen, TX; *U.S. Public*, pg. 1352
Schultz, Larry, Dir.-Pur.--U.S. Home Corporation, Houston, TX; *U.S. Public*, pg. 1682
Schultz, Ron, Mgr.-Matls.--Marlette Homes, Inc., Lewistown, PA; *U.S. Public*, pg. 1442
Schulz, Roger, Mgr.-Pur.--Motor Products Div., Rockford, IL; *U.S. Public*, pg. 1250
Schulze, Jurgen H., Sr. V.P.-Pur.--Deutz AG, Cologne, Germany; *Int'l*, pg. 407
Schwartz, Alice, Dir.-Pur.--Puerto Rico Tourism Company, San Juan, PR; *U.S. Private*, pg. 894
Schwartz, Daniel, Mgr.-Pur.--Hatfield Quality Meats, Hatfield, PA; *U.S. Private*, pg. 510
Schwartz, Robert, Buyer--Lepel Corporation, Edgewood, NY; *U.S. Private*, pg. 560
Schwartz, Stuart, Dir.-Pur.--Alexander Doll Company, Inc., New York, NY; *U.S. Private*, pg. 33
Schwind, Wolfgang, Dir.-Pur.--Schroff, Straubenhardt, Germany; *U.S. Public*, pg. 1274
Schwori, Bill, Dir.-Pur.--M.A. Hanna Color, Suwanee, GA; *U.S. Public*, pg. 781
Sciascia, Roslyn, V.P.-Pur.--Brimms Inc., Tonawanda, NY; *U.S. Private*, pg. 169
Scolavino, Michael, Dir.-Pur. & Sls.--Furman Lumber Company, Inc., Billerica, MA; *U.S. Private*, pg. 431
Scoons, Sandra, Pur. Coordinator--The Troy Savings Bank, Troy, NY; *U.S. Private*, pg. 1106
Scott, Gary, Mgr.-Pur.--The Dispatch Printing Company, Columbus, OH; *U.S. Private*, pg. 334
Scott, Jay, Mgr.-Pur.--Concorde Career Colleges, Inc., Kansas City, MO; *U.S. Public*, pg. 430
Scott, Kimberly, Dir.-Pur.--Sentinel Technologies Inc., Downers Grove, IL; *U.S. Private*, pg. 984
Scott, Pat, Mgr.-Pur.--Mark Andy, Inc., Chesterfield, MO; *U.S. Public*, pg. 521
Scott, R., Pur. Agent--Mellon Corporation, New York, NY; *U.S. Private*, pg. 730
Scott, Raymond, V.P.-Pur.--Sullivan Paper Company, West Springfield, MA; *U.S. Private*, pg. 1050
Scott, Steven P., Dir.-Matls.--Morgan Construction Co., Worcester, MA; *U.S. Private*, pg. 761
Scotto, D., Dir.-Logistics--Zanussi Elettrodomestici S.p.A., Pordenone, Italy; *Int'l*, pg. 442
Scribner, Jim, Pur. Agent--Pizza Haven Inc., Bellevue, WA; *U.S. Private*, pg. 868
Scrivner, Richard, Dir.-Pur.--Star Fine Foods, Inc., Fresno, CA; *U.S. Private*, pg. 1034
Scully, Edward A., Mgr.-Pur.--Whiting Corporation, Harvey, IL; *U.S. Private*, pg. 1173
Sears, Cindy, Mgr.-Pur.--Sunstone Hotel Investors, Inc., San Clemente, CA; *U.S. Public*, pg. 1536
Sears, R.W., Pur. Agent--Peerless Pottery, Inc., Rockport, IN; *U.S. Private*, pg. 847
Sedar, Donald, Mgr.-Pur.--Utica Boilers Inc., Utica, NY; *U.S. Private*, pg. 1129
Seefeldt, Robert, Mgr.-Matls.--E.D. Bullard Company, Cynthiana, KY; *U.S. Private*, pg. 180
Segal, Milton, Dir.-Pur.--J & J Snack Foods Corporation, Pennsauken, NJ; *U.S. Public*, pg. 916
Segarra, Hilda, Second V.P.--Firstbank Puerto Rico, Santurce, PR; *U.S. Public*, pg. 644
Seitz, Edgar c., III, Pres.--Service Supply Co. Inc. of Indiana, Indianapolis, IN; *U.S. Private*, pg. 987
Sekscinski, Susan E., Dir.-Pur.--Spang & Company, Butler, PA; *U.S. Private*, pg. 1020
Seland, Stale, Mgr.-Pur.--Esselte A/S, Oslo, Norway; *Int'l*, pg. 460
Selander, Herbert V., V.P.-Pur.--The Testor Corporation, Rockford, IL; *U.S. Public*, pg. 1358
Self, Joe, Dir.-Pur.--Affiliated Foods, Inc., Amarillo, TX; *U.S. Private*, pg. 25
Self, Mickey, Pur. Agent--Tennsco Corporation, Dickson, TN; *U.S. Private*, pg. 1077
Sell, Vicki, Dir.-Pur.--Koss Corporation, Milwaukee, WI; *U.S. Public*, pg. 966
Sell, Vicki, Dir.-Pur.--Koss Classics Ltd., Milwaukee, WI; *U.S. Public*, pg. 966
Sellheim, Dean, Mgr.-Matls.--United Power Association, Elk River, MN; *U.S. Private*, pg. 1123

Selling, Vern, Dir.-Pur.--Koo Koo Roo, Inc., Los Angeles, CA; *U.S. Public*, pg. 966

Sensing, Carson, Pur. Agent--Enco Materials, Inc., Nashville, TN; *U.S. Private*, pg. 375

Senta, William, Mgr.-Pur.--Atkinson, San Bruno, CA; *U.S. Public*, pg. 143

Sesholtz, Walter J., V.P.-Pur.--The Hartz Mountain Corp., Secaucus, NJ; *U.S. Private*, pg. 508

Sewell, Dave, Mgr.-Pur. & Inventory Control--The Langer Biomechanics Group, Inc., Deer Park, NY; *U.S. Public*, pg. 978

Sewell, Lewis, Mgr.-Meats--Affiliated Foods Southwest, Little Rock, AR; *U.S. Private*, pg. 26

Shachar, Sam, Mgr.-Pur.--Laser Industries Ltd., Tel Aviv, Israel; *Int'l*, pg. 429

Shaffer, M. Todd, Dir.-Pur. & Mfg. Svcs.--Tru-Weld Grating, Inc., Wexford, PA; *U.S. Private*, pg. 1107

Shanahan, Robert, Mgr.-Pur.-Res. & Devel.--Mitsui Foods, Inc., Norwood, NJ; *Int'l*, pg. 879

Shane, Jerry, V.P.-Pur.--Mac Papers, Inc., Jacksonville, FL; *U.S. Private*, pg. 689

Shannon, Katie, Dir.-Internal Fin. Reporting--Legacy Marketing Group, Petaluma, CA; *U.S. Private*, pg. 658

Shapiro, Hannon, Dir.-Pur.--Intermagnetics General Corporation, Latham, NY; *U.S. Public*, pg. 893

Shapiro, Marshall, Pur. Agent--White Systems, Incorporated, Kenilworth, NJ; *U.S. Private*, pg. 866

Shapiro, Samuel D., V.P.-Distr.--Liz Claiborne Outlet Division, Secaucus, NJ; *U.S. Public*, pg. 1006

Sharber, Robert, Dir.-Pur.--Nashville Machine Co. Inc., Nashville, TN; *U.S. Private*, pg. 774

Sharif, Samiullah, Gen. Mgr.-Pur. & Commercial--National Refinery Limited, Karachi, Pakistan; *Int'l*, pg. 909

Sharkey, Phillip, Dir-Personnel--National Insurance Agency, Inc., Miami, FL; *U.S. Public*, pg. 67

Sharp, Roger L., Exec. V.P. & Chief-Global Opers.--Witco Corporation, Greenwich, CT; *U.S. Public*, pg. 1773

Shave, Paul, Mgr.-Pur.--Zenith Electronics Corp., Glenview, IL; *U.S. Public*, pg. 1790

Shaw, Scott, Mgr.-Pur.--Jacobsen Textron, Racine, WI; *U.S. Public*, pg. 1589

Shea, James, Pur. Agent--Scott's Liquid Gold-Inc., Denver, CO; *U.S. Public*, pg. 1447

Shearer, Sandra, Buyer--Accu-Sort Systems, Inc., Telford, PA; *U.S. Private*, pg. 11

Sheets, David, Mgr.-Pur.--SafetyMaster Corporation, Billings, MT; *U.S. Public*, pg. 1523

Sheldon, John A., V.P.-Pur.--Finch, Pruyn & Co., Inc., Glens Falls, NY; *U.S. Private*, pg. 405

Shelly, T., Dir.-Pur.--Guest Services, Inc., Fairfax, VA; *U.S. Private*, pg. 486

Shelton, Carter, Dir.-Pur.--AFG Industries, Inc., Kingsport, TN; *Int'l*, pg. 84

Shelton, T., Dir.-Pur.--Kyanite Mining Corporation, Dillwyn, VA; *U.S. Private*, pg. 638

Shenber, James A., V.P.-Procurement & Mfg. Services--Materials Group North America, Painesville, OH; *U.S. Public*, pg. 153

Shendow, Harry S., Sr. V.P.--S & K Famous Brands, Inc., Glen Allen, VA; *U.S. Public*, pg. 1414

Shepard, Kathy, Mgr.-Pur.--R.A. Mueller, Inc., Cincinnati, OH; *U.S. Private*, pg. 766

Sherbit, Betty, Pur. Mgr.--Grizzard, Atlanta, GA; *U.S. Private, pg. 482*

Sherbit, Betty C., Estimator--TABS Direct (Operating Div.), Stafford, TX; *U.S. Private*, pg. 482

Sherril, Mike, Pur. Agent--Trimfoot Company, Farmington, MO; *U.S. Public*, pg. 1684

Sherrill, Leslie, Mgr.-Pur.--Laboratory Supply Company, Nashville, TN; *U.S. Private*, pg. 642

Sherry, Kieran, Dir.-Pur. & Real Estate--NovaCare Inc., King of Prussia, PA; *U.S. Public*, pg. 1203

Sherwin, Marilyn, Dir.-Logistics & Pur.--Colgate Oral Pharmaceutical, Canton, MA; *U.S. Public*, pg. 397

Shiavo, Anthony, V.P.-Pur.--J.A. Sexauer, Inc., Scarsdale, NY; *U.S. Private*, pg. 352

Shield, Hank, Dir.-Buying & Mktg.--Associated Grocers of the South, Inc., Birmingham, AL; *U.S. Private*, pg. 91

Shimizu, Hiroharu, Dir.--Chiyoda Mutual Life Insurance Company, Tokyo, Japan; *Int'l*, pg. 286

Shimon, Cathy, Pur. Agent--Land O'Lakes, Inc., Kiel, WI; *U.S. Private*, pg. 646

Shing, Steve, V.P.-Pur.--GSC Enterprises, Inc., Sulphur Springs, TX; *U.S. Private*, pg. 436

Shinmura, Takuji, Mng. Dir. & Gen. Mgr.-Pur.--Mitsubishi Electric Corporation, Tokyo, Japan; *Int'l*, pg. 872

Shinn, Dana, Mgr.-Pur.--Action Instruments, Inc., San Diego, CA; *U.S. Private*, pg. 15

Shirley, Steven, Mgr.-Matls.--J.H. Fletcher & Co., Huntington, WV; *U.S. Private*, pg. 412

Shive, James, Mgr.-Pur. & Real Estate--Met-Pro Corporation, Harleysville, PA; *U.S. Public*, pg. 1100

Shoemaker, Suzanne, Dir.-Admin. Services--Playboy Enterprises, Inc., Chicago, IL; *U.S. Public*, pg. 1309

Shores, Ritchie, Mgr.-Pur.--Tetko, Inc., Briarcliff Manor, NY; *U.S. Private*, pg. 1078

Short, Don, Asst. V.P.--City National Corporation, Beverly Hills, CA; *U.S. Public*, pg. 380

Shoup, Sharon, Pur. Agent--Imax Corporation, Mississauga, Canada; *Int'l*, pg. 661

Shufflebotham, John, Mgr.-Pur.--Teleflex (Canada) Ltd., Vancouver, Canada; *U.S. Public*, pg. 1570

Shulman, Isaac, Sr. V.P.-Special Drug Pur. & Analysis--MEDCO Containment Services, Inc., Montvale, NJ; *U.S. Public*, pg. 1091

Shumaker, Frank, Supvr.-Program Plng.--Biomet, Inc., Warsaw, IN; *U.S. Public*, pg. 231

Siegel, Terry, Pres.--Butler Ventamatic Corp., Mineral Wells, TX; *U.S. Private*, pg. 190

Siegert, Doug, Pur. Agent--Haviland Enterprises, Grand Rapids, MI; *U.S. Private*, pg. 511

Siewertsen, Don, Dir.-Pur.--Worthington Industries, Inc., Columbus, OH; *U.S. Public*, pg. 1780

Sigler, George R., Pur. Agent--Peter Pan Seafoods, Inc., Seattle, WA; *Int'l*, pg. 928

Siladi, Michael, V.P.-Pur. & Distr.--A&W Restaurants, Inc., Livonia, MI; *U.S. Private*, pg. 1

Silberstein, Bruce Jay, Pres.--Columbus Pipe & Equipment Company, Columbus, OH; *U.S. Private*, pg. 257

Silberstein, Carl, Buyer--Southwestern Electric Power Co., Shreveport, LA; *U.S. Public*, pg. 324

Silkey, Roger, Mgr.-Matls.--Steiger Tractor, Fargo, ND; *U.S. Public*, pg. 311

Siltanen, Hannu, V.P.-Supply Mngmt.--Valmet Corporation, Helsinki, Finland; *Int'l*, pg. 1447

Silva, Ricardo Fonseca e, Mgr.-Pur.--Acos Villares Steel Unit, Sao Paulo, Brazil; *Int'l*, pg. 23

Silverio, James A., Asst. V.P.-Pur.--Moore Medical Corp., New Britain, CT; *U.S. Public*, pg. 1128

Silvestri, Vincent E., V.P.-Corp. Communications--Rockefeller Group, Inc., New York, NY; *Int'l*, pg. 873

Simerly, Carolyn, Mgr.-Pur.--Kaufman and Broad Colorado Division, Denver, CO; *U.S. Public*, pg. 945

Simerly, Walt, Mgr.-Pur.--Blue Bird Corporation, Macon, GA; *U.S. Private*, pg. 151

Simmers, Neil, Mgr.-Pur.--N.G. Bailey & Co. Ltd., Ilkley, United Kingdom; *Int'l*, pg. 132

Simmers, Robert, Mgr.-Pur.--Tippins Incorporated, Pittsburgh, PA; *U.S. Private*, pg. 1088

Simmons, Janet, Sr. V.P.-Pur.--Del Taco, Inc., Laguna Hills, CA; *U.S. Private*, pg. 321

Simon, Kathy, Mgr.-Pur.--American Freightways Corporation, Harrison, AR; *U.S. Public*, pg. 75

Simon, Steve, Dir.-Pur.--Pentech International, Inc., Edison, NJ; *U.S. Public*, pg. 1274

Simonds, Paulette, Exec. Dir.-Pur.--The Swiss Colony, Inc, Monroe, WI; *U.S. Private*, pg. 1059

Simonet, John, Mgr.-Pur.--NAO, Inc., Philadelphia, PA; *U.S. Private*, pg. 771

Simonton, James, V.P.-Matls. Mngmt.--Navistar International Transportation Corp., Chicago, IL; *U.S. Public*, pg. 1167

Simpson, Bill, Dir.-Pur.--John H. Harland Company, Decatur, GA; *U.S. Public*, pg. 785

Simpson, James, V.P.-Matls.--Continental Conveyor & Equipment Company, Winfield, AL; *U.S. Private*, pg. 791

Simpson, Lee A., V.P.-Pur.--Rubbermaid Incorporated, Wooster, OH; *U.S. Public*, pg. 1411

Sims, Almon, Jr., Dir.-Pur.--Union Light, Heat and Power Co., Cincinnati, OH; *U.S. Public*, pg. 369

Sims, R.D., Mgr.-Opers.--Stamco Industries Inc., Euclid, OH; *U.S. Private*, pg. 1029

Sines, James V., V.P.-Pur.--UAL Corporation, Elk Grove Village, IL; *U.S. Public*, pg. 1652

Singer, Burton, Dir.-Pur.--New Age Intimates Inc., Long Island City, NY; *U.S. Private*, pg. 792

Singleton, Maryann, Pur. Agent--Speakman Company, Wilmington, DE; *U.S. Private*, pg. 1021

Sinke, Sharon, Dir.-Pur.--Weiser Lock, Tucson, AZ; *U.S. Public*, pg. 1053

Sirianni, O., Pur. Agent--The Homer Laughlin China Company, Newell, WV; *U.S. Private*, pg. 653

Sitaram, Dev, Dir.-Pur.--Mercury Air Group Inc., Los Angeles, CA; *U.S. Public*, pg. 1092

Sitz, Janine, Mgr.-Pur.--Exabyte Corporation, Boulder, CO; *U.S. Public*, pg. 597

Sitzler, Keith, Pur. Agent--Gemtron Corporation, Sweetwater, TN; *Int'l*, pg. 1523

Skarbinski, Jay, Pur. Agent--Branch Electric Supply Co., Inc., Boston, MA; *U.S. Private*, pg. 165

Skelton, Larry, Pur. Agent--Traylor Chemical & Supply Co., Orlando, FL; *U.S. Private*, pg. 1098

Skidmore, Chad, Dir.-Matls. Mngmnt.--Sierra Health Services, Inc., Las Vegas, NV; *U.S. Public*, pg. 1469

Skobel, C., Dir.-Pur.--Pyle Inc., Elmhurst, IL; *U.S. Private*, pg. 629

Skoda, Frank, Dir.-Logistics--Acme United Corporation, Fairfield, CT; *U.S. Public*, pg. 17

Skramovsky, Carla, Mgr.-Pur.--Ritchie Industries, Inc., Conrad, IA; *U.S. Private*, pg. 933

Skrbensky-Meinl, Jeanette, Mng. Dir.-Buying--Julius Meinl AG, Vienna, Austria; *Int'l*, pg. 856

Slagle, Scott, Mgr.-Pur.--Graphic Enterprises of Ohio, Inc., Canton, OH; *U.S. Private*, pg. 471

Slattery, Pat, Mgr.-Pur.--Dassault Falcon Jet Corp., South Hackensack, NJ; *Int'l*, pg. 383

Sleik, Jonathan C., V.P.-Pur. & Distr.--Cracker Barrel Old Country Store, Inc., Lebanon, TN; *U.S. Public*, pg. 455

Sloan, Deb, Pur. Agent--The Vernon Company, Newton, IA; *U.S. Private*, pg. 1137

Slocum, Diane, Supv.-Pur.--Utica Mutual Insurance Company, New Hartford, NY; *U.S. Private*, pg. 1129

Slomke, M.E., Dir.-Pur.--Military Avionics Division, Minneapolis, MN; *U.S. Public*, pg. 834

Slusarczyk, Carl H., Dir.-Pur.--Milton Bradley Company, East Longmeadow, MA; *U.S. Public*, pg. 797

Small, R.L., Mgr.-Pur.--Acme Metals Incorporated, Riverdale, IL; *U.S. Public*, pg. 16

Smalley, Robert A., Jr., Chief Oper. Officer & Exec. V.P.--Cruise America, Inc., Mesa, AZ; *U.S. Private*, pg. 178

Smigielski, Daniel E., V.P.-Pur. & Traffic--Armco Inc., Pittsburgh, PA; *U.S. Public*, pg. 131

Smiley, Susan, Dir.-Pur.--The Entwistle Company, Hudson, MA; *U.S. Private*, pg. 378

Smith, Alan, Mgr.-Pur.--Goddess Bra Company, East Boston, MA; *U.S. Private*, pg. 458

Smith, Andrew, TV Buying Grp. Dir.--The Media Centre, London, United Kingdom; *Int'l*, pg. 852

Smith, Bob, Mgr.-Pur.--Virco Mfg. Corporation, Torrance, CA; *U.S. Public*, pg. 1721

Smith, Clyde, Mgr.-Pur.--Power Distribution Div., Cleveland, TN; *U.S. Public*, pg. 557

Smith, David, Dir.-Pur.-Fleet Leasing--Toledo Blade Co., Toledo, OH; *U.S. Private*, pg. 147

Smith, David J., Dir.-Pur.--John Crane Polymer Engineering, Tewkesbury, United Kingdom; *Int'l*, pg. 1338

Smith, Don, Dir.-Pur.--Brookshire Bros., Ltd., Lufkin, TX; *U.S. Private*, pg. 172

Smith, Donnie, V.P.-Pur.--Tyson Foods, Inc., Springdale, AR; *U.S. Public*, pg. 1652

Smith, Fred, Mgr.-Matl. & Pur.--Power Control Div., Bowling Green, KY; *U.S. Public*, pg. 556

Smith, J., Dir.-Pur.--Benjamin Moore & Co., Montvale, NJ; *U.S. Private*, pg. 133

Smith, Jeff, Pur. Agent--FMC Corp., Lithium Division, Gastonia, NC; *U.S. Public*, pg. 605

Smith, Joe, Dir.-Pur.--Laser Systems, Apopka, FL; *U.S. Public*, pg. 1002

Smith, Joyce, Pur. Agent--Southern Mills, Inc., Union City, GA; *U.S. Private*, pg. 1016

Smith, Judith, Dir.-Pur.--Nabi, Boca Raton, FL; *U.S. Public*, pg. 1148

Smith, Ken, Mgr.-Pur.--Electrospace Systems, Inc., Richardson, TX; *U.S. Public*, pg. 1365

Smith, Lawrence, Mgr.-Pur.--Dialight Corporation, Manasquan, NJ; *Int'l*, pg. 1130

Smith, Leah, Mgr.-Pur.--Erlanger Tubular Corporation, Catoosa, OK; *U.S. Public*, pg. 1147

Smith, Linda, Pur. Agent--Transus Intermodal L.L.C., Atlanta, GA; *U.S. Private*, pg. 1097

Smith, M.M., Mgr.-Pur.--Longview Fibre Company, Longview, WA; *U.S. Public*, pg. 1013

Smith, Marty, Dir.-Pur.--Long MFG. NC, Inc., Tarboro, NC; *U.S. Private*, pg. 674

Smith, Marvin W., Sr. V.P.-Opers. Admin.--NationsBank West, Saint Louis, MO; *U.S. Public*, pg. 1164

Smith, Mike, Mgr.-Pur.--Swiss Army Brands, Inc., Shelton, CT; *U.S. Public*, pg. 1544

Smith, Nancy, Dir.-Pur.--Edelbrock Corp., Torrance, CA; *U.S. Public*, pg. 563

Smith, Pam, Mgr.-Pur.--Magnedyne Div., Vista, CA; *U.S. Private*, pg. 999

Smith, Ralph, Dir.-Pur.--Interactive Technologies, Inc., Saint Paul, MN; *U.S. Public*, pg. 888

Smith, Rich, Mgr.-Pur.--The Franklin Institute, Philadelphia, PA; *U.S. Private*, pg. 424

Smith, Ronald D., Pur. Agent--Target Oilfield Pipe & Supply Company (TOPS), Canton, OH; *U.S. Private*, pg. 1078

Smith, Ruth, Mgr.-Pur.--Eaton Corporation, Engine Components Division, Marshall, MI; *U.S. Public*, pg. 556

Smith, Ryland, Mgr.-Pur./Inventory--Case-Swayne Co. Inc., Corona, CA; *U.S. Private*, pg. 218

Smith, Stan, V.P.-Opers. & Dir.-Pur.--Exact Equipment Corporation, Langhorne, PA; *U.S. Private*, pg. 387

Smith, Steve, Dir.-Pur.--Outdoor Technologies Group, Spirit Lake, IA; *U.S. Private*, pg. 822

Smith, T., Dir.-Pur.--Econolite Control Products, Inc., Anaheim, CA; *U.S. Private*, pg. 361

Smith, Thomas, V.P.-Pur.--Merle Norman Cosmetics, Inc., Los Angeles, CA; *U.S. Private*, pg. 733

Smith, Tom, V.P.-Procurement--GSW Water Heating Company, Fergus, Canada; *Int'l*, pg. 538

Smollen, Laura, Mgr.-Pur.--Caswell-Massey Co. Ltd., Edison, NJ; *U.S. Private*, pg. 219

Smoot, Cindy, Pur. Dir.--Environmental Resources Management, Exton, PA; *U.S. Private*, pg. 378

Smullin, Edgar, Pur. Agent--Arrow Pneumatics Co. Inc., Lake Zurich, IL; *U.S. Private*, pg. 85

Smuts, Lex K. , Mgr.-Pur.--San Diego Gas & Electric Company, San Diego, CA; *U.S. Public*, pg. 584

Snabes, James, Dir.-Pur.--Horizon Investment Group, Taylor, MI; *U.S. Private*, pg. 539

Snijder, J., Dir.-Pur.--DAF Trucks N.V., Eindhoven, Netherlands; *U.S. Public*, pg. 1247

Snitzer, Fred, Mgr.-Corp. Pur.--Hughes-Peters, Inc., Cincinnati, OH; *U.S. Private*, pg. 546

Snow, Cal, Mgr.-Pur.--Kit Manufacturing Company, Long Beach, CA; *U.S. Public*, pg. 962

Snow, Cal, Mgr.-Pur.--R-2 KIT Mfg. Co., Caldwell, ID; *U.S. Public*, pg. 962

Snowden, John, V.P.-Opers.--Daisytek International Corporation, Plano, TX; *U.S. Public*, pg. 477

Snyder, Craig, Dir.-Pur.--Adams Business Forms, Topeka, KS; *U.S. Private*, pg. 16

Snyder, Mary, Mgr.-Pur.--Pegasus International Corporation, Pennington, NJ; *U.S. Private*, pg. 1046

Snyder, Richard, Mgr.-Pur.--Superior Surgical Mfg. Co., Inc., Seminole, FL; *U.S. Public*, pg. 1539

Snyder, Todd, Dir.-Pur.--American Furniture Company, Incorporated, Martinsville, VA; *U.S. Public*, pg. 974

Sober, David W., V.P.-Human Resources & Sec.--Performance Food Group Company, Richmond, VA; *U.S. Public*, pg. 1278

Sodaro, Doris, Mgr.-Pur.--Buss (America) Inc., Bloomingdale, IL; *Int'l*, pg. 490

Soehnlen, J.P., Mgr.-Matls.--Superior Dairy, Inc., Canton, OH; *U.S. Private*, pg. 1054

Soeldner, D., Mgr.-Pur.--Manitowoc Ice, Inc., Manitowoc, WI; *U.S. Public*, pg. 1041

Sogno, Gunther, Mgr.--Koh-I-Noor, Inc., Bloomsbury, NJ; *U.S. Private*, pg. 629

Sohm, Woo-Heon, Pres.--Ssangyong Investment Management Co., Ltd., Seoul, Korea; *Int'l*, pg. 1292

Sohm, Woo-Heun, Chief Fin. Officer--Ssangyong Investment & Securities Co., Ltd., Seoul, Korea; *Int'l*, pg. 1292

Soifer, Leonard, V.P.-Production & Converting--Croscill, Inc., New York, NY; *U.S. Private*, pg. 290

Sokol, L., Mgr.-Pur.--Raytheon Engineers & Constructors International, Inc., Lexington, MA; *U.S. Public*, pg. 1366

Sokoloff, Steven, V.P.-Mktg. & Pur.--Milgray/Montreal, Pointe-Claire, Canada; *U.S. Public*, pg. 207

Solan, Debra, V.P.-Pur.--Deerskin Trading Post, Inc., North Bergen, NJ; *U.S. Public*, pg. 879

Solari, Al, Dir.-Pur.--Rex Lumber Company, Acton, MA; *U.S. Private*, pg. 926

Solda, Cesar, Pur. Agent--Jamison Plastic Corporation, Allentown, PA; *U.S. Private*, pg. 581

Solecitto, Frank, Pur. Agent--Carnival Creations, Linden, NJ; *U.S. Private*, pg. 213

Sollenberger, Susan, Dir.-Equipment Pur. & Maintenance--Food Lion, Inc., Salisbury, NC; *Int'l*, pg. 463

Soon, Ong Kian, Dir.-Pur.--Motorola Singapore Pte., Ltd., Singapore, Singapore; *U.S. Public*, pg. 1140

Sorensen, David, Mgr.-Pur.--General Mills, Inc., Minneapolis, MN; *U.S. Public*, pg. 717

Sorensen, Jamey, V.P.-Pur.--RK Mechanical, Inc., Denver, CO; *U.S. Private*, pg. 904

Sorensen, Ken, Dir.-Pur.--Intermountain Farmers Association, Salt Lake City, UT; *U.S. Private*, pg. 568

Sorenson, Jean, Mgr.-Pur.--LubeCon Systems, Inc., White Cloud, MI; *U.S. Private*, pg. 679

Sorrells, Gary, Mgr.-Pur.--Positronic Industries, Inc., Springfield, MO; *U.S. Private*, pg. 876

Sosebee, Dennis, Dir.-Pur.--Rubatex Corporation, Roanoke, VA; *U.S. Private*, pg. 56

Sotek, Ray, Dir.-Pur.--Nelmor Co., Inc., North Uxbridge, MA; *U.S. Private*, pg. 1041

Sour, Jared, V.P.-Opers.--GE Capital/IT Solutions, Minneapolis, MN; *U.S. Public*, pg. 711

Souther, Alan L., Mgr.-Materials--Essex County Gas Company, Amesbury, MA; *U.S. Public*, pg. 593

Southerlin, Art, Mgr.-Matls.--Associated Industrial Supply, Inc., Columbia, SC; *U.S. Private*, pg. 91

Soviero, Joseph C., V.P.-Corp. Ventures & Pur.--Union Carbide Corporation, Danbury, CT; *U.S. Public*, pg. 1666

Sowizral, Gloria, Dir.-Pur.--Stephen Gould Paper Co., Inc., Whippany, NJ; *U.S. Private*, pg. 467

Soza, Marti, Office Pur.--Empire Southwest Co., Mesa, AZ; *U.S. Private*, pg. 374

Spanos, William, V.P.-Pur.--UNR-Leavitt Div., Chicago, IL; *U.S. Public*, pg. 1404

Sparks, Terry, Mgr.-Pur.--CCAIR, Inc., Charlotte, NC; *U.S. Public*, pg. 276

Spear, Joseph, Dir.-Pur.--Alcatel Telecom, Richardson, TX; *Int'l*, pg. 55

Spedale, Robert J., V.P.-Pur. & Prod. Devel.--Lawson Products, Inc., Des Plaines, IL; *U.S. Public*, pg. 980

Spence, Joe, Mgr.-Pur.--Kit Manufacturing Company, Long Beach, CA; *U.S. Public*, pg. 962

Spence, Joe, Mgr.-Pur.--M1 KIT Mfg. Co., Caldwell, ID; *U.S. Public*, pg. 962

Spense, Bill, Dir.-Pur.--C.J. Rush Inc., Scarborough, Canada; *Int'l*, pg. 395

Sponski, John J., Exec. V.P.--Nationsbank/Tennessee, Nashville, TN; *U.S. Public*, pg. 1163

Spooner, Heather, Mgr.-Pur. & Corp. Travel Planner--U.S.S. Seko Worldwide, Elk Grove Village, IL; *U.S. Private*, pg. 1115

Spradling, Eldon, V.P.-MIS--General Communication, Inc., Anchorage, AK; *U.S. Public*, pg. 708

Spraggins, J.D., Supvr.-Pur. & Stores--Southwestern Electric Service Co., Dallas, TX; *U.S. Public*, pg. 1588

Springer, Thomas, Dir.-Pur.--WinCup, Phoenix, AZ; *U.S. Private*, pg. 1182

Spude, R., Dir.-Pur. & Matl. Control--Bay Shipbuilding Co., Sturgeon Bay, WI; *U.S. Public*, pg. 1041

Spurrell, Bruce, Dir.-Admin. Svcs.--Calavo Growers of California, Santa Ana, CA; *U.S. Private*, pg. 199

Squadrito, Anthony J., Dir.-Pur.--Brown & Sharpe Manufacturing Company, North Kingstown, RI; *U.S. Public*, pg. 260

Squillante, Judith, V.P.-Pur. & Employee Benefits--The PBS&J Corporation, Miami, FL; *U.S. Private*, pg. 825

St. Clair, Bob, Dir.-Pur.--Gra-Gar Inc., Omaha, NE; *U.S. Public*, pg. 1755

St. Clair, Robert, V.P.-Pur.--SOLOCO, Inc., Lafayette, LA; *U.S. Public*, pg. 1179

Stackhouse, Brenda M., V.P.-Pur.--Thornton Oil Corp., Louisville, KY; *U.S. Private*, pg. 1084

Stacy, Kay, Mgr.-Pur.--Hitox Corporation of America, Corpus Christi, TX; *U.S. Public*, pg. 829

Stadheim, Terry, Exec. Dir.-Pur--Certified Grocers of California, Los Angeles, CA; *U.S. Private*, pg. 226

Stagg, Alan, Mgr.-Pur.--Rose Art Industries, Livingston, NJ; *U.S. Private*, pg. 945

Stahl, Don, Mgr.-Matls.--Wheeled Coach Industries, Inc., Winter Park, FL; *U.S. Public*, pg. 400

Stallings, Max, Dir.-Pur.--Seagull Energy Corporation, Houston, TX; *U.S. Public*, pg. 1450

Stamper, J.W., V.P.-Pur. & Distr.--The White Lily Foods Co., Knoxville, TN; *U.S. Private*, pg. 866

Stampf, Robert, Dir.-Pur.--CCL Custom Manufacturing, Niles, IL; *Int'l*, pg. 238

Stanley, Mike, Dir.-Pur.--James Burn International Limited, Esher, United Kingdom; *U.S. Public*, pg. 1507

Stanley, Philip, Pur. Agent--Magnacraft, Struthers, Dunn, Inc., Northfield, IL; *U.S. Private*, pg. 695

Starr, Ron, Dir.-Pur. & Opers.--R.J. Corr Naturals, Inc., Posen, IL; *U.S. Private*, pg. 276

Starrett, Joan, Dir.-Pur.--The L.S. Starrett Company, Athol, MA; *U.S. Public*, pg. 1511

Statucki, G.W., Dir.-Pur.--The Standard Register Company, Dayton, OH; *U.S. Public*, pg. 1505

Staub, Catherine, Dir.-Pur.--Kemps Foods, Inc., Lancaster, PA; *Int'l*, pg. 752

Steel, Bernard, Publ.-Intl. Editions--Departures, New York, NY; *U.S. Public*, pg. 74

Steen, Bonnie, Mgr.-Pur. & Telecommunications--Raven Industries, Inc., Sioux Falls, SD; *U.S. Public*, pg. 1361

Stefanchik, Randy, Pur. Agent--Tekni-Plex, Inc., Somerville, NJ; *U.S. Private*, pg. 1073

Stefanek, N.R., Dir.-Pur.--Vertex Communications Corporation, Kilgore, TX; *U.S. Public*, pg. 1717

Stefaniak, Len, Mgr.-Pur.--VAW of America, Inc., Ellenville, NY; *Int'l*, pg. 1466

Stegrnd, Jan-Ake, Mgr.-Pur.--Cementa AB, Danderyd, Sweden; *Int'l*, pg. 1198

Steil, Mark E., V.P.-Pur.--Harrington & King, Chicago, IL; *U.S. Private*, pg. 504

Steiner, Len, V.P.-Pur.--Jac Pac Foods, Ltd., Manchester, NH; *U.S. Private*, pg. 579

Steinhauer, Raymond, Pur.--Fleet Engineers, Inc., Muskegon, MI; *U.S. Private*, pg. 410

Steinlege, Cyril, Dir.-Pur.--H & H Distributing Company, Inc., West Union, IA; *U.S. Private*, pg. 489

Steinmeyer, Philip, Mgr.-Pur.--Andrea Electronics Corporation, Long Island City, NY; *U.S. Public*, pg. 112

Stenger, John P., V.P.-Pur.--Westgate Fabrics, Inc., Grand Prairie, TX; *U.S. Private*, pg. 1169

Stephen, George A., Jr., V.P.-Pur.--Weber-Stephen Products Co., Palatine, IL; *U.S. Private*, pg. 1157

Stephens, R., Dir.-Pur.--The Valspar Corporation, Minneapolis, MN; *U.S. Public*, pg. 1707

Stephens, Rod, Dir.-Pur. & Production Plng.--Sun-Maid Growers of California, Kingsburg, CA; *U.S. Private*, pg. 1051

Stephens, Ron, Dir.-Pur.--Petro-Hunt Corporation, Dallas, TX; *U.S. Private*, pg. 858

Stern, Laura, Mgr.-Pur.--Jackson MSC, Nashville, TN; *U.S. Private*, pg. 579

Sterpka, Carol, Pur. Agent--Hitchcock Chair Company LTD, New Hartford, CT; *U.S. Private*, pg. 531

Stevens, Duane A., Pur. Agent--Curt G. Joa, Inc., Sheboygan Falls, WI; *U.S. Private*, pg. 588

Stevenson, Robert, Pur. Agent--Technicolor, Inc., North Hollywood, CA; *Int'l*, pg. 272

Stewart, A., Mgr.-Pur.--Bruntons Areo Product, Musselburgh, United Kingdom; *Int'l*, pg. 268

Stewart, Carrie, Dir.-Pur.--Allied Diagnostic Imaging Resources, Inc., Norcross, GA; *U.S. Public*, pg. 282

Stewart, Chuck, Dir.-Pur.--Flexible Products Company, Marietta, GA; *U.S. Private*, pg. 412

Stewart, Claire, Dir.-Material--Sabreliner Corporation, Saint Louis, MO; *U.S. Private*, pg. 959

Stewart, Harry, Dir.-Pur.--Santa Fe Gaming Corporation, Las Vegas, NV; *U.S. Public*, pg. 1432

Stewart, John, Dir.-Pur.--JLG Industries, Inc., McConnellsburg, PA; *U.S. Public*, pg. 918

Stewart, Kathy, Pur. Agent--Stark Candy Company, Pewaukee, WI; *U.S. Private*, pg. 1113

Stewart, Larry R., Dir.-Pur.--ACF Industries, Inc., Saint Charles, MO; *U.S. Private*, pg. 556

Stewart, W.G., V.P.-Mtls. & Distr.--Union Camp Corporation, Wayne, NJ; *U.S. Public*, pg. 1665

Stidham, Frank, Mgr.-Pur.--Riverchase Homes, Haleyville, AL; *U.S. Public*, pg. 319

Stier, John K., Dir.-Pur.--Production Tool Supply Co., Warren, MI; *U.S. Private*, pg. 889

Stinson, Beth, Pur. Agent--Farmers Copper & Industrial Supply, Galveston, TX; *U.S. Private*, pg. 422

Stobenrock, K., V.P.-Pur.--Busch-Jaeger Ludenscheider Metallwerk GmbH, Ludenscheid, Germany; *Int'l*, pg. 1427

Stockman, Neil, Dir.-Pur.--Beatrice Cheese Co., Waukesha, WI; *U.S. Public*, pg. 426

Stolarczyk, Mark, Dir.-Pur.--Tropicana Resort & Casino, Las Vegas, NV; *U.S. Public*, pg. 159

Stone, George, Mgr.-Import & Pur.--Union Special Corp., Huntley, IL; *Int'l*, pg. 716

Stone, Robert, V.P.-Pur. & Plng.--Key Industries, Inc., Fort Scott, KS; *U.S. Private*, pg. 618

Stormes, Barry, Dir.-Pur.--Designatronics, Inc., New Hyde Park, NY; *U.S. Private*, pg. 327

Stos, Charles J., V.P.-Non-Retail Procurement--The Vons Companies, Inc., Arcadia, CA; *U.S. Public*, pg. 1426

Stoudt, Rich, Mgr.-Matls.--Advanced Energy Industry, Fort Collins, CO; *U.S. Public*, pg. 20

Stough, Robert, Dir.-Pur.--McCauley Propeller Systems, Vandalia, OH; *U.S. Public*, pg. 1589

Stout, James R., V.P.-Pur.--John H. Harland Company, Decatur, GA; *U.S. Public*, pg. 785

Stover, Gary L., Dir.-Pur. & Services--The Empire District Electric Company, Joplin, MO; *U.S. Public*, pg. 579

Straite, C., Dir.-Pur. & Prod. Mgr.--Welbilt Varimixer, Shreveport, LA; *Int'l*, pg. 189

Strandberg, Kaj, Mgr.-Pur.--Finnsementti Oy Ab, Pargas, Finland; *Int'l*, pg. 1198

Strange, Bob, Dir.-Pur.--Fawn Industries, Inc., Hunt Valley, MD; *U.S. Private*, pg. 397

Stratil, Peter, Mgr.-Matls.--Victaulic Company of America, Easton, PA; *U.S. Private*, pg. 1138

Stratman, Carol, Dir.-Pur.--Lewis Brothers Bakeries, Inc., Evansville, IN; *U.S. Private*, pg. 665

Strickland, Sid, V.P.-Pur. & Admin.--Hughes Supply, Inc., Orlando, FL; *U.S. Public*, pg. 846

Strickler, Steve, Mgr.-Pur.--Royal Waterbeds, Maryland Heights, MO; *U.S. Private*, pg. 949

Strockbine, John, Buyer--Accu-Sort Systems, Inc., Telford, PA; *U.S. Private*, pg. 11

Strohmeyer, Ted, Mgr.-Pur.--Foley-PLP Company, Rochester, NY; *U.S. Private*, pg. 416

Strominger, Mark, Pur. Mgr.--Dayton Superior Corporation, Miamisburg, OH; *U.S. Private*, pg. 931

Strong, Donna, Pur. Agent--Smith Enterprises, Rock Hill, SC; *U.S. Private*, pg. 1007

Strong, Wayne, Mgr.-Pur.--Spectrum Control, Inc., Erie, PA; *U.S. Public*, pg. 1497

Strouse, Charles, Corp. V.P.-Pur.--Ferro Union, Inc., Torrance, CA; *U.S. Private*, pg. 402

Struble, Spencer, V.P. & Div. Mgr.-Supplies--Markem Corporation, Keene, NH; *U.S. Private*, pg. 704

Struffer, Wally, V.P.-Produce Procurement--Shurfine International, Inc., Northlake, IL; *U.S. Private*, pg. 997

Stuart, J., Pur. Agent--Valcor Engineering Corp., Springfield, NJ; *U.S. Private*, pg. 1131

Studebaker, Dan, Mgr.-Mdsg. & Pur.--Van Dyne-Crotty, Inc., Dayton, OH; *U.S. Private*, pg. 1132

Stupar, Richard, V.P.-Pur., Mylan Pharmaceuticals--Mylan Laboratories, Inc., Pittsburgh, PA; *U.S. Public*, pg. 1143

Stupar, Richard F., V.P.-Pur.--Mylan Pharmaceuticals Inc., Morgantown, WV; *U.S. Public*, pg. 1143

Sturgill, J.A., V.P.-Pur.--Marley Mouldings Inc., Marion, VA; *Int'l*, pg. 843

Sturm, Sandy K., Dir.-Pur. & Matl.--Mesaba Holdings, Inc., Minneapolis, MN; *U.S. Public*, pg. 1099

Stuve, Jeff, Dir.-Pur.--Horizon/CMS Healthcare Corporation, Albuquerque, NM; *U.S. Public*, pg. 836

Sull, Norman D., V.P.-Pur.--Tranzonic Industrial Textiles Division, Highland Heights, OH; *U.S. Public*, pg. 1632

Sullan, Gary, Mgr.-Pur.--Capitol Group, Springfield, IL; *U.S. Private*, pg. 206

Sullivan, Bonnie, Mgr.-Pur.--Sequent Computer Systems, Inc., Beaverton, OR; *U.S. Public*, pg. 1459

Sullivan, Gene, Dir.-Pur.--Capital Industries, Inc., Seattle, WA; *U.S. Private*, pg. 206

Sullivan, Jim, Mgr.-Pur.--Liberty Bancorp, Inc., Oklahoma City, OK; *U.S. Public*, pg. 174

Sullivan, Mark, Mgr.-Pur.--ULLICO Inc., Washington, DC; *U.S. Private*, pg. 1115

Sullivan, Michael, Mgr.-Pur.--Caere Corporation, Los Gatos, CA; *U.S. Public*, pg. 291

Sullivan, S., Dir.-Matls. Mngmt.--Plymouth Rubber Company, Inc., Canton, MA; *U.S. Public*, pg. 1311

Sumas, William, Exec. V.P.--Village Super Market Inc., Springfield, NJ; *U.S. Public*, pg. 1721

Summerall, Fraizer, Mgr.-Pur.--Smith Industries, Inc., Montgomery, AL; *U.S. Private*, pg. 1008

Sundberg, Randal, Dir.-Pur.--Jarvis (West), South El Monte, CA; *U.S. Public*, pg. 1506

Sussman, Don, V.P.-Grocery & Meat--The Stop & Shop Companies, Inc., Quincy, MA; *Int'l*, pg. 750

Sussman, Marvin, Exec. V.P.-Pur.--Philipp Brothers Chemicals, Inc., Fort Lee, NJ; *U.S. Private*, pg. 861

Sutton, James, Dir.-Pur.--J.H. Harvey Company, Nashville, GA; *U.S. Private*, pg. 508

Sutton, Stanley E., V.P.-Pur.--Wabash National Corp., Lafayette, IN; *U.S. Public*, pg. 1730

Suzuki, Yukuo, Mng. Dir.-Plng. & Pur., Logistics & Pur., Fertilizer--UBE Industries Ltd., Tokyo, Japan; *Int'l*, pg. 1426

Svedahl, Milt, Mgr.-Pur.--North Coast Electric Company, Bellevue, WA; *U.S. Private*, pg. 804

Svenson, Dick, Mgr.-Pur.--Lytron Incorporated, Woburn, MA; *U.S. Private*, pg. 684

Swaback, James, Mgr.-Pur.--Pennsylvania Enterprises Inc., Wilkes-Barre, PA; *U.S. Public*, pg. 1271

Swan, A.W., Sec. & Dir.-Human Resources--Energizer Eveready Ltd., London, United Kingdom; *U.S. Public*, pg. 1360

Swan, D.L., Dir. & Pur. Agent--Dexter Company, Fairfield, IA; *U.S. Private*, pg. 329

Swanson, R.N., Pur. Agent--United States Pipe & Foundry Company, Inc., Birmingham, AL; *U.S. Public*, pg. 1736

Swanson, Sharon, Dir.-Pur.--Mallinckrodt Inc., Saint Louis, MO; *U.S. Public*, pg. 1039

Swanson, W.F., Dir.-Pur.--P.H. Glatfelter Company, Spring Grove, PA; *U.S. Public*, pg. 746

Swanzey, Robert, Sr. V.P.-H.R. & Opers.--Century Business Credit Corporation, New York, NY; *U.S. Private*, pg. 225

Swatt, Len, Dir.-Procurement--Riser Foods, Inc., Bedford, OH; *U.S. Private*, pg. 450

Sweet, Jack, V.P.-Pur.--Apache Hose & Belting Company, Inc., Cedar Rapids, IA; *U.S. Private*, pg. 76

Sweigart, H., Pur. Agent--Burnham Hydronics Div., Lancaster, PA; *U.S. Public*, pg. 270

Swenson, Ron, Dir.-Pur.--The Dartnell Corporation, Chicago, IL; *U.S. Private*, pg. 312

Swigert, Terry, Dir.-Pur.--Mohawk Paper Mills, Inc., Cohoes, NY; *U.S. Private*, pg. 755

Swiss, Maria, Mgr.-Pur.--Aydin Controls Div., Fort Washington, PA; *U.S. Public*, pg. 158

Switzer, Erik P., Mgr.-Pur.--Osmonics, Inc., Minnetonka, MN; *U.S. Public*, pg. 1233

Switzer, Robert, Pur. Agent--Diehl Inc., Defiance, OH; *U.S. Private*, pg. 332

Swoards, Charles, Pur. Agent--Detroit Coil Company, Ferndale, MI; *U.S. Private*, pg. 328

Swope, Gary L., Mgr.-Pur. & Stores--St. Joseph Light & Power Co., Saint Joseph, MO; *U.S. Public*, pg. 1427

Sylvia, Amy, Dir.-Pur.--The Vermont Teddy Bear Company, Inc., Shelburne, VT; *U.S. Public*, pg. 1716

Syme, Hugh, Mgr.-Pur.--SkyWest Inc., Saint George, UT; *U.S. Public*, pg. 1476

Syverstad, Tor, Dir.-Pur.--Stabburet A/S, Skien, Norway; *Int'l*, pg. 1011

Syvertsen, Kurt, Dir.-Pur.--Aerco International Inc., Northvale, NJ; *U.S. Private*, pg. 23

Szwak, Tom, V.P.-Pur., Consumer Div.--Blockbuster Entertainment Group, Dallas, TX; *U.S. Private*, pg. 775

Tabet, Kenneth, Dir.-Pur.--The Hennegan Company, Florence, KY; *U.S. Private*, pg. 522

Taddy, John, Supvr.-Pur.--Marine Travelift, Inc., Sturgeon Bay, WI; *U.S. Private*, pg. 703

Taddy, John, Mgr.-Pur.--Shuttlelift, Inc., Sturgeon Bay, WI; *U.S. Private*, pg. 703

Tallent, Clyde, Pur. Mgr.--Grizzard, Atlanta, GA; *U.S. Private*, pg. 482

Talmon, Douglas E., Pur. Agent.--Schultz Steel Company, South Gate, CA; *U.S. Private*, pg. 973

Tan, Louis, Mgr.-Mktg. & Matls.--G.E. (U.S.A.) Aviation Service Operation Pte. Ltd., Singapore, Singapore; *U.S. Public*, pg. 713

Tanaka, Nobuki, Exec. Mng. Dir.--Kokusai Electric Co., Ltd., Tokyo, Japan; *Int'l*, pg. 743

Tangney, James, V.P.-Pur.--Emkay, Inc., Itasca, IL; *U.S. Private*, pg. 374

Tangredi, Mike, Mgr.-Opers.--Universal Builders Supply, Inc., Mount Vernon, NY; *U.S. Private*, pg. 1126

Tank, M.O., Dir.-Pur.--Barber Dairies, Inc., Birmingham, AL; *U.S. Private*, pg. 115

Tanselle, Tom, Dir.-Pur.--Manning Equipment, Inc., Louisville, KY; *U.S. Private*, pg. 700

Taphorn, Robert J., Exec. V.P.--S & K Famous Brands, Inc., Glen Allen, VA; *U.S. Public*, pg. 1414

Tarr, Jeffrey A., Mgr.-Matls.--Industrial Bag Division - Wellsburg Plant, Wellsburg, WV; *U.S. Public*, pg. 1521

Tarver, Joe, Sr. V.P.-Pur.--Minyard Food Stores, Inc., Coppell, TX; *U.S. Private*, pg. 752

Tate, Debra, Mgr.-Pur.--Electronic Center, Dallas, TX; *U.S. Private*, pg. 1174

Tatum, W. Earl, Sr. V.P.-Matls., Logistics & Services--Du Pont (E.I. Du Pont De Nemours & Co.), Wilmington, DE; *U.S. Public*, pg. 530

Taura, Akio, Mgr.-Pur.--Asahi/America, Inc., Malden, MA; *U.S. Public*, pg. 137
Taylor, Charles, Mgr.-Pur.--Yorktowne, Inc., Red Lion, PA; *U.S. Private*, pg. 1196
Taylor, Chuck, Gen. Mgr.-Supply Chain--Albemarle Corporation, Richmond, VA; *U.S. Public*, pg. 37
Taylor, Darlene, Mgr.-Bus. & Pur.--Rogers Corporation, Rogers, CT; *U.S. Public*, pg. 1402
Taylor, George, Dir.-Opers. & Matl.--UTILX Corporation, Kent, WA; *U.S. Public*, pg. 1701
Taylor, Jim, V.P.-Pur.--Nature's Bounty Inc., Bohemia, NY; *U.S. Public*, pg. 1166
Taylor, John, Sr. V.P.-Opers.--Tropical Sportswear International, Tampa, FL; *U.S. Private*, pg. 1105
Taylor, Michael, Dir.-Pur.--Jarvis-Pemco, Kalamazoo, MI; *U.S. Public*, pg. 1506
Taylor, Pam, Dir.-Pur.--Color Spot Nursery, Inc., Pleasant Hill, CA; *U.S. Private*, pg. 254
Taylor, Paul A., Pur. Agent--Svedala Industries-Universal Engineering, Cedar Rapids, IA; *Int'l*, pg. 1326
Taylor, Robert, Mgr.-Pur.--Symons Corporation, Des Plaines, IL; *U.S. Private*, pg. 932
Taylor, Terry A., V.P.-Pur.--Browning-Ferris Industries, Inc., Houston, TX; *U.S. Public*, pg. 262
Taylor, Tim, Dir.-Msdg. & Pur.--Maverik Country Stores, Inc., Salt Lake City, UT; *U.S. Private*, pg. 715
Taylors, Fred, Mgr.-Pur.--Spiegel Meats, Inc., Miami, FL; *U.S. Private*, pg. 1025
Teague, Carol R., V.P.-Pur.--Calibron, Inc., Lake Mary, FL; *U.S. Public*, pg. 1369
Tebo, Kenneth, Mgr.-Pur.--Windmoeller & Hoelscher Corp., Lincoln, RI; *Int'l*, pg. 1511
Teeple, Roberta, Dir.-Pur. & Admin.--Parmalat Canada Ltd., Etobicoke, Canada; *Int'l*, pg. 1023
Teichman, Michael, Buyer--Stock Yards Packing Co., Inc., Chicago, IL; *U.S. Private*, pg. 1043
Temple, R., Dir.-Pur. & Admin.--Caterpillar Inc., Peoria, IL; *U.S. Public*, pg. 315
Tenzer, Gerd, Head-Networks, Pur. & Environ. Protection--Deutsche Telekom AG, Bonn, Germany; *Int'l*, pg. 407
Terena, B., Dir.-Matls.--Hydro-Aire, Burbank, CA; *U.S. Public*, pg. 457
Terricciano, David, Pur. Dir.--AlliedSignal Aerospace, Stratford, CT; *U.S. Public*, pg. 50
Terry, Larry, Dir.-Pur.--United Farm Family Life Insurance Co., Indianapolis, IN; *U.S. Private*, pg. 1122
Teske, Robert, Mgr.-Pur.--National Presto Industries, Inc., Eau Claire, WI; *U.S. Public*, pg. 1159
Testa, Al, Dir.-Pur.--Motch Corporation, Cleveland, OH; *Int'l*, *pg. 1128*
Tew, J.J., Dir.-Matls.--Lockheed Aeronautical Systems Company, Marietta, GA; *U.S. Public*, pg. 1007
Thacker, Cheryl, Mgr.-Matls.--Standard Locknut, Inc., Westfield, IN; *U.S. Private*, pg. 1031
Thackray, John C., V.P.-Pur.--Rolled Alloys, Inc., Temperance, MI; *U.S. Private*, pg. 941
Tharp, Doug, Mgr.-Pur.--Norcold, Sidney, OH; *U.S. Private*, pg. 352
Tharpe, Larry, Dir.-Pur., Plng. & Inventory Control--Heckethorn Mfg. Company, Inc., Dyersburg, TN; *U.S. Private*, pg. 519
Theile, Ralph, V.P.-Opers.--GraphLine Inc., Tamarac, FL; *U.S. Private*, pg. 471
Thieme, Larry, Dir.-Pur.--Daniel Valve Company, Houston, TX; *U.S. Public*, pg. 483
Thiry, Richard, Mgr.-Pur.--Cable Constructors, Inc., Iron Mountain, MI; *U.S. Private*, pg. 197
Thoma, Ronald R., Exec. V.P.-Procurement & Traffic--Crown Cork & Seal Company, Inc., Philadelphia, PA; *U.S. Public*, pg. 462
Thomas, Brad, Pur. Agent--Thomas Built Buses, Inc., High Point, NC; *U.S. Private*, pg. 1082
Thomas, C.P., Dir.-Pur.--Consolidated Papers, Inc., Wisconsin Rapids, WI; *U.S. Public*, pg. 436
Thomas, David, Mgr.-Pur.--Sandoz Agro, Inc., Des Plaines, IL; *Int'l*, pg. 974
Thomas, Jim, V.P.-Pur.--Freightliner Corp., Portland, OR; *Int'l*, pg. 368
Thomas, Joseph, Dir.-Pur.--Sara Lee Sock Company, High Point, NC; *U.S. Public*, pg. 1434
Thomas, Karen, Dir.-Pur.--Erdle Perforating Co., Rochester, NY; *U.S. Private*, pg. 380
Thomas, Mark, V.P.-Circulation Mktg.--Milwaukee Journal Sentinel, Milwaukee, WI; *U.S. Private*, pg. 601
Thomas, Mark, Mgr.-Pur.--Autologic Information International, Inc., Thousand Oaks, CA; *U.S. Public*, pg. 1724
Thomas, Philippe, Dir.-Pur.--Au Bon Marche, Paris, France; *Int'l*, pg. 97
Thomas, Ralph, Sr. V.P.-Matls.--Fender Musical Instruments, Scottsdale, AZ; *U.S. Private*, pg. 400
Thomas, Roger, Pur. Agent--J.E. Berkowitz, LP, Westville, NJ; *U.S. Private*, pg. 135
Thomas, Roy, V.P.-Opers.--Ensoniq, Malvern, PA; *U.S. Private*, pg. 377
Thompson, Bill, V.P.-Mfg.--Oil-Dri Corporation of America, Chicago, IL; *U.S. Public*, pg. 1214
Thompson, Bruce, Dir.-Pur.--Biltbest Windows, Saint Genevieve, MO; *U.S. Public*, pg. 1683
Thompson, Chris, Mgr.-Pur.--EZ Paintr Corp., Saint Francis, WI; *U.S. Public*, pg. 1177
Thompson, Jeff, Dir.-Distr.--Wood Industries, Indianapolis, IN; *U.S. Public*, pg. 944
Thompson, John, Mgr.-Opers.--Iomega Corporation, Roy, UT; *U.S. Public*, pg. 912
Thompson, John, Dir.-Pur.--Reeves Southeastern Corporation, Tampa, FL; *U.S. Private*, pg. 916
Thompson, John, Mgr.-Pur.--Sargent & Greenleaf, Inc., Nicholasville, KY; *U.S. Private*, pg. 965
Thompson, Joyce, Mgr.-Pur.--The J.M. Ney Company, Bloomfield, CT; *U.S. Public*, pg. 111
Thompson, Joyce E., Dir.-Pur.--Ney Dental International, Bloomfield, CT; *Int'l*, pg. 388
Thompson, Peggie, Mgr.-Pur. & Personnel--Virginia Metal Industries, Inc., Orange, VA; *U.S. Private*, pg. 1141
Thormann, Fred, V.P.-Corp. Resources--The Conde Nast Publications Inc., New York, NY; *U.S. Private*, pg. 20
Thorn, Mike, V.P.-Pur.--Industrial Americas Group, Maumee, OH; *U.S. Public*, pg. 24
Thorne, Jim, Mgr.-Pur.--The Colonial BancGroup, Inc., Montgomery, AL; *U.S. Public*, pg. 400
Thorne, Jim, Mgr.-Pur.--Colonial Bank, Montgomery, AL; *U.S. Public*, pg. 400
Thorner, Liz, Dir.-Pur.--Gilrichco, Inc., Oxnard, CA; *U.S. Private*, pg. 454
Thornton, Nelson, Dir.-Pur.--Shell West Exploration & Production Inc., Brandon, MS; *Int'l*, pg. 1142
Throgmorton, Jerry, Dir.-Pur.--American Fuel Cell & Coated Fabrics Co. (Amfuel), Magnolia, AR; *U.S. Private*, pg. 55
Thurston, Samuel E., Sr. V.P.-Distr.--Giant Food Inc., Landover, MD; *U.S. Public*, pg. 741
Thweatt, Bill, Mgr.-Pur. Dept.--Tandy Leather Co., Fort Worth, TX; *U.S. Public*, pg. 1561
Thygesen, Jerry, Dir.-Logistics--Red Wing Shoe Co., Inc., Red Wing, MN; *U.S. Private*, pg. 915
Till, David W., V.P.-Supply--Columbian Chemicals Company, Atlanta, GA; *U.S. Public*, pg. 1286
Tinsley, William N., Dir.-Pur.--Duracell International Inc., Bethel, CT; *U.S. Public*, pg. 743
Tipton, Harrell, Dir.-Pur., Automotive Div.--STRAFCO, Inc., San Antonio, TX; *U.S. Private*, pg. 1046
Tirkkonen, Esa, Dir.--Kemira Agro Oy, Helsinki, Finland; *Int'l*, pg. 727
Tjosvold, Richard, Mgr.-Pur.--Computer Network Technology Corporation, Minneapolis, MN; *U.S. Public*, pg. 421
Tkacz, Dick, Pur. Agent--Welded Tube, Chicago, IL; *Int'l*, pg. 101
Toavs, Jay, Supvr.-Pur.--A & S Tribal Industries, Poplar, MT; *U.S. Private*, pg. 1
Tobey, Bruce, Dir.-Pur.--Hampshire Chemical Corp., Lexington, MA; *U.S. Private*, pg. 498
Tobias, Paula, Pur. Agent--All Seasons Services, Inc., Braintree, MA; *U.S. Private*, pg. 35
Todd, Richard J., Dir.-Pur.--Santa Fe Drilling Co., Alhambra, CA; *Int'l*, pg. 765
Todres, Michael, V.P.-Distr. & Non-Resale Pur.--JC Penney Company, Inc., Plano, TX; *U.S. Public*, pg. 916
Tokar, Karen, V.P.-Opers.--Jack Lenor Larsen, Inc., New York, NY; *U.S. Private*, pg. 652
Tollafield, Mark, Mgr.-Pur.--Hickok Incorporated, Cleveland, OH; *U.S. Public*, pg. 825
Tomas, Antonio Condal, Dir.-Legal, Pur. & Personnel--Agropecuaria de Guissona, S. Coop. Ltda., Guisona, Spain; *Int'l*, pg. 31
Tomaseski, John, Pur. Agent--Philips Components, Jupiter, FL; *Int'l*, pg. 1054
Tomasini, Franco, Dir.-Pur. & Logistics--Recordati Industria Chimica e Farmaceutica S.p.A., Milan, Italy; *Int'l*, pg. 1090
Tomei, Egidio, Dir.-Pur. & Quality Control--SASIB SpA, Bologna, Italy; *Int'l*, pg. 1194
Tomku, Regis, Mgr.-Pur.--Hart Graphics Inc., Austin, TX; *U.S. Private*, pg. 507
Tomsic, Carl, Dir.-Pur.--Ohio Sealants Inc., Mentor, OH; *Int'l*, pg. 802
Toney, Larry, V.P.-Pur.--Foxworth-Galbraith Lumber Co., Dallas, TX; *U.S. Private*, pg. 423
Tooley, Darian, Dir.-Pur.--Brewster Transport Co. Ltd., Banff, Canada; *U.S. Public*, pg. 1719
Torcivia, Bryan, V.P.-Plng. & Pur.--The Earthgrains Company, Clayton, MO; *U.S. Public*, pg. 547
Torres, Nelson, Dir.-Pur.--Sein Mendez Laboratories, Inc., Rio Piedras, PR; *U.S. Public*, pg. 670
Torres, Nino, Buyer-Salad Dressings, Coffee, Tea & Cereals--Alliant Foodservice, Bensenville, IL; *U.S. Private*, pg. 244
Torres, Tom, Mgr.-Pur.--Spectra-Physics Lasers, Inc., Mountain View, CA; *U.S. Public*, pg. 1594
Tortora, Michael, Pur. Agent--Kevlin Corporation, Wilmington, MA; *U.S. Public*, pg. 953
Toth, Ruth, Pur. Supervisor--Hershey Chocolate U.S.A., Hazleton, PA; *U.S. Public*, pg. 812
Touchette, Thomas, Pur. Agent--Laclede Gas Company, Saint Louis, MO; *U.S. Public*, pg. 973
Trager, Louis W., V.P.-Pur.--Bachman Company, Reading, PA; *U.S. Private*, pg. 109
Trask, Gardner, Dir.-Pur.--Freudenberg Nonwovens, Durham, NC; *Int'l*, pg. 505
Traup, Robert, Mgr.-Matls.--New Standard Corporation, Mount Joy, PA; *U.S. Private*, pg. 794
Traveller, Seth H., V.P.-Fin. Svcs., Facilities & Pur.--Wyle Electronics, Irvine, CA; *Int'l*, pg. 1457
Travers, Pat, Mgr.-Pur.--nVIEW Corporation, Newport News, VA; *U.S. Public*, pg. 1206
Traviglini, D., Pur. Agent--Munroe, Inc., Pittsburgh, PA; *U.S. Private*, pg. 767
Treen, Ray, V.P.-Pur.--Hardware Wholesalers, Inc., Fort Wayne, IN; *U.S. Private*, pg. 502
Triana, Guillermo, Mgr.-Pur.--Vitromex, S.A., Saltillo, Mexico; *Int'l*, pg. 1469
Triano, Nicholas D., V.P.-Matls. Mngmt.--Reynolds Metals Company, Richmond, VA; *U.S. Public*, pg. 1385
Triantafellou, Michael, V.P.-Retail Opers.--FFP Marketing Company, Inc., Fort Worth, TX; *U.S. Public*, pg. 604
Trin, Maurice, Dir.-Pur.--Sciaky S.A., Vitry-sur-Seine, France; *Int'l*, pg. 1211
Trippacher, Kurt, Mng. Dir.-Global Procurement--Landis & Staefa AG, Zug, Switzerland; *Int'l*, pg. 800
Trischett, Kevin, V.P.-Pur.--American Pad and Paper Company, Dallas, TX; *U.S. Public*, pg. 88
Trotter, Gerry, Mgr.-Pur.--Kemper Insurance Companies, Long Grove, IL; *U.S. Private*, pg. 614
Troxtel, Don, Mgr.-Pur.--Game Time, Inc., Fort Payne, AL; *U.S. Public*, pg. 1543
Truby, Charles, Chief Oper. Officer--Isomedix Inc., Whippany, NJ; *U.S. Public*, pg. 1515
Truby, Charles, Chief Oper. Officer--Isomedix Operations Inc., Whippany, NJ; *U.S. Public*, pg. 1515
Truby, Charles, Chief Oper. Officer--Isomedix Management Inc., Whippany, NJ; *U.S. Public*, pg. 1515
Trumbull, David, Mgr.-Pur.--Taylor Made Group, Inc., Gloversville, NY; *U.S. Private*, pg. 1070
Tsuruta, Kuniaki, Sr. V.P.-Pur.--Continental Airlines, Houston, TX; *U.S. Public*, pg. 439
Tubilewicz, Joseph J., V.P.-Global Pur.--Kellogg Company, Battle Creek, MI; *U.S. Public*, pg. 947
Tubito, Vincent, Sr. V.P.-HR--Jan Bell Marketing Inc., Sunrise, FL; *U.S. Public*, pg. 207
Tucker, Gary, Mgr.-Pur.--Titan International, Inc., Quincy, IL; *U.S. Public*, pg. 1618
Tucker, Janet, Mgr.-Pur.--Oklahoma Publishing Company, Oklahoma City, OK; *U.S. Private*, pg. 813
Tucker, Larry, Dir.-Pur.--Empire Airlines, Coeur D'Alene, ID; *U.S. Private*, pg. 374
Tucker, V.L., Pur. Agent--Anderson-Tully Co., Memphis, TN; *U.S. Private*, pg. 73
Tudor, W., Pur. Agent--Lockheed Martin Missiles & Space, Sunnyvale, CA; *U.S. Public*, pg. 1008
Tukel, Mehmet, Mgr.-Pur.--Arcelik A.S., Istanbul, Turkey; *Int'l*, pg. 741
Tuma, Rick, V.P.-Grocery & Procurement--Shurfine International, Inc., Northlake, IL; *U.S. Private*, pg. 997
Tunchumrus, Boonsom, Exec. V.P.--Siam City Bank Public Company Limited, Bangkok, Thailand; *Int'l*, pg. 1239
Turbyfill, Hoyt, Dir.-Pur./Construction Materials Group--Vulcan Materials Company, Birmingham, AL; *U.S. Public*, *pg. 1725*
Turkett, Tom, V.P.-Pur.--Taco Cabana, San Antonio, TX; *U.S. Public*, pg. 1559
Turley, Sally, Supervisor-Corp. Facilities--James Hardie Industries Ltd., Sydney, Australia; *Int'l*, pg. 596
Turner, Daniel A., V.P.-Admin. Services--MainStreet BankGroup Incorporated, Martinsville, VA; *U.S. Public*, pg. 1038
Turner, Jan, Pur. Agent--Warner Electric Industrial Products Division, South Beloit, IL; *U.S. Public*, pg. 480
Turner, Rod, Dir.-Pur.--Valvoline Instant Oil Change, Inc., Lexington, KY; *U.S. Public*, pg. 139
Turpin, Joe, Pur. Agent--Sturgis Iron & Metal Company, Inc., Sturgis, MI; *U.S. Private*, pg. 1048
Tutor, Larry, Pur. Agent--Hilton Equipment Corp., Beverly Hills, CA; *U.S. Public*, pg. 829
Twohig, Faye, Mgr.--J.F. Ahern Co., Fond Du Lac, WI; *U.S. Private*, pg. 27
Tye, Chris, Pur. Agent--Six Flags Astroworld/Six Flags Waterworld/Six Flags Houston, Houston, TX; *U.S. Public*, pg. 1611
Tyler, Bill, Dir.--ElectroCom Automation L.P., Arlington, TX; *Int'l*, pg. 1244
Tyson, Jim, Dir.-Pur.--Pier 1 Imports, Inc., Fort Worth, TX; *U.S. Public*, pg. 1295
Tyson, Robert, Pur. Dir.-School Supplies--The Caxton Printers Ltd., Caldwell, ID; *U.S. Private*, pg. 220
Uhlemann, William R., V.P.-Pur. & Matls.--Semiconductor Equipment Group, Scotts Valley, CA; *U.S. Public*, pg. 1745
Ulberg, Jean, Mgr.-Pur.--Hydraulics International, Inc., Chatsworth, CA; *U.S. Private*, pg. 551
Ulibee, Steve, Plant Mgr.--General Housewares Corp., Terre Haute, IN; *U.S. Public*, pg. 715
Ulrich, John, Dir.-Pur.--Inductotherm Industries, Inc., Rancocas, NJ; *U.S. Private*, pg. 560
Umberhocker, Bill, Pur.--Indian Head Industries Inc., Charlotte, NC; *U.S. Private*, pg. 559
Underwood, W.W., Mgr.-Personnel--Alamco, Inc., Charleston, WV; *U.S. Public*, pg. 403
Unfal, Ed, Dir.-Pur.--Alliant Foodservice, Bensenville, IL; *U.S. Private*, pg. 244
Urbancic, John, V.P.-Pur.--Freeman Energy Corporation, Springfield, IL; *U.S. Public*, pg. 709
Urquhart, R.D., V.P.-Supply & Transportation--Murphy Oil Co., Ltd., Calgary, Canada; *U.S. Public*, pg. 1142
Utzinger, Tedd, Mgr.-Risk--LGC Management, Englewood, CO; *U.S. Private*, pg. 639
Uy, Conrad, Sec., Dir.-Personnel, & Pur. Agent--Atalanta Corporation, Elizabeth, NJ; *U.S. Private*, pg. 93
Vaillancourt, Paul, Sr. V.P.-Pur.--DHP Limited Partnership, Chicopee, MA; *U.S. Private*, pg. 302
Vakil, Iqbal U., V.P.-Pur.--Lights Of America, Inc., Walnut, CA; *U.S. Private*, pg. 667
Valdez, Frank, Mgr.-Pur.--Punch Press Products, Inc., Los Angeles, CA; *U.S. Private*, pg. 895
Valentine, Christopher, Dir.-Pur.--Comverse Network Systems, Wakefield, MA; *U.S. Public*, pg. 425
Valone, Anthony J., V.P.-Pur.--Leviton Mfg. Co., Inc., Little Neck, NY; *U.S. Private*, pg. 663
Van Antwerp, Jim, Adv. Mgr.--Cargo Furniture & Accents, Fort Worth, TX; *U.S. Public*, pg. 1561
Van Bragt, Robert, Dir.-Pur.--Suspa, Inc., Grand Rapids, MI; *Int'l*, pg. 1322
Van Brunt, Gary, Exec. V.P.-Pur.--Reinalt-Thomas Corp., Ann Arbor, MI; *U.S. Private*, pg. 919
Van Der Laan, Heinz, Mgr.-Pur.--Kao Infosystems Company (MA), Plymouth, MA; *Int'l*, pg. 717
van der Merwe, A., Mgr.-Purchasing--Sasol Oil, Rosebank, South Africa; *Int'l*, pg. 1197
Van Dyke, J.W., Dir.-Pur.--Reynolds Metals Company, Richmond, VA; *U.S. Public*, pg. 1385
Van Edema, Errol, Mgr.-Pur.--Open Market, Inc., Burlington, MA; *U.S. Public*, pg. 1226
Van Houdt, Joan, Dir.-Pur.--Knape & Vogt Mfg. Co., Grand Rapids, MI; *U.S. Public*, pg. 963
Van Howe, David, V.P.-Pur.--Arbor Drugs, Inc., Troy, MI; *U.S. Public*, pg. 126
van Kolfschoten, B., Dir.-Pur.--Amici, Houten, Netherlands; *Int'l*, pg. 750
van Maele, Max, Mgr.-Pur.--Mueller's Muehle GmbH, Gelsenkirchen, Germany; *Int'l*, pg. 896
Van Norman, Daniel, V.P.-Matls. Mngmt.--Farnam Sealing Systems Division, Troy, MI; *U.S. Public*, pg. 401

Wexler, Paul R., Sr. V.P.-Procurement & Distr.--Advantica Restaurant Group, Inc., Spartanburg, SC; *U.S. Public*, pg. 22
Weyland, Francine, Pur.--Millipore S.A., Molsheim, France; *U.S. Public*, pg. 1113
Wharton, Stephanie, Dir.-Pur.--The Garber Company, Ashland, OH; *U.S. Public*, pg. 303
Wheeler, Steve, Dir.-Pur.--The Excellence Group, Stamford, CT; *U.S. Private*, pg. 387
Wheet, Gary, Pur. Agent--Hilliard Corporation, Elmira, NY; *U.S. Private*, pg. 530
Whetstone, Dean, Mgr.-Matls.--National Cooperative Refinery Association, Mc Pherson, KS; *U.S. Private*, pg. 781
Whitaker, Kenneth, Mgr.-Pur.--General Shale Products Corp., Elizabethton, TN; *Int'l*, pg. 843
Whitaker, Kenneth L., Mgr.-Pur.--General Shale Products Corp., Johnson City, TN; *Int'l*, pg. 843
Whitaker, Ron, Dir.-Pur.--Schwegmann Giant Super Markets, New Orleans, LA; *U.S. Private*, pg. 629
White, Alex, Buyer--Austron Inc., Austin, TX; *U.S. Public*, pg. 488
White, Peter, Mgr.-Pur.--International Rectifier Corporation, El Segundo, CA; *U.S. Public*, pg. 906
White, Ray, Dir.-Pur.--W-B Supply Co., Pampa, TX; *U.S. Private*, pg. 1144
White, Wilson R., Sr. V.P.-Pur.--First Citizens Banc Shares, Inc., Raleigh, NC; *U.S. Public*, pg. 628
Whitehead, Darryle, V.P.-Pur.--Duncan Equipment Company, Oklahoma City, OK; *U.S. Private*, pg. 346
Whitley, Gene, Mgr.-Pur.--Madison Industries Inc. of Georgia, Conyers, GA; *U.S. Private*, pg. 428
Whitley, Ken, Pur. Agent--Antenna Products Corp., Mineral Wells, TX; *U.S. Public*, pg. 289
Whitlock, Barbara, Mgr.-Pur.--Matson Navigation Company, Inc., San Francisco, CA; *U.S. Public*, pg. 39
Whitman, M., Mgr.-Procurement--Eagle Button Co., Inc., Carlstadt, NJ; *U.S. Private*, pg. 354
Whitman, Marcus, Dir.-Pur.--Supertex, Inc., Sunnyvale, CA; *U.S. Public*, pg. 1539
Whittaker, Dick, Dir.-Pur.--Multilin, Markham, Canada; *U.S. Public*, pg. 713
Whittaker, Tom, Dir.-Matls.--Michigan Wheel Corporation, Grand Rapids, MI; *U.S. Private*, pg. 741
Whittle, Steve, Mgr.-Pur.--Scott Resources, Fort Collins, CO; *U.S. Public*, pg. 71
Wholey, Rick, Dir.-Intl. Sourcing--Rockford International Group, Rockford, IL; *U.S. Private*, pg. 938
Wiberg, Olle, Mgr.-Pur.--Esselte Chrono AB, Solna, Sweden; *Int'l*, pg. 459
Wick, Richard, Pur. Agent--Wagner Casters and Wheels, Hustisford, WI; *U.S. Private*, pg. 1146
Widgel, Brad, Mgr.-Pur.--R.A. Jones & Co. Inc., Covington, KY; *U.S. Private*, pg. 597
Widmann, Brad, Mgr.-Pur.--MagneTek, Inc., Nashville, TN; *U.S. Public*, pg. 1037
Widmer, Fred, Dir.-Fin.--Computer Task Group, Inc. (CTG), Buffalo, NY; *U.S. Public*, pg. 423
Wiedeman, Wayne, Gen. Mgr.--Sherms Thunderbird Market, Medford, OR; *U.S. Private*, pg. 993
Wiencek, Donald, Dir.-Mfg. & Pur.--Continental Web Press, Inc., Itasca, IL; *U.S. Private*, pg. 269
Wiesenberg, M., Mgr.-Pur.--Schlegel Corporation, Rochester, NY; *Int'l*, pg. 128
Wightman, Lynn, Dir.-Pur.--Perlmuter Printing Company, Cleveland, OH; *Int'l*, pg. 1177
Wigs, Carole, Dir.-Pur.--Brown Industries, Inc., Dalton, GA; *U.S. Private*, pg. 174
Wilbur, Lee, Mgr.-Pur.--Dawn Food Products, Inc., Jackson, MI; *U.S. Private*, pg. 316
Wilcox, Anne, Mgr.-Pur.--The Kiplinger Washington Editors, Inc., Washington, DC; *U.S. Private*, pg. 623
Wilhoite, Dennis, V.P.-Pur.--The Starflo Corporation, Orangeburg, SC; *U.S. Private*, pg. 877
Wiliszewski, George, Dir.-Pur.--Thermometrics, Inc., Edison, NJ; *Int'l*, pg. 208
Wilkenson, Kevin, Pur. Agent--Tennessee Tubebending Inc., Knoxville, TN; *U.S. Private*, pg. 762
Wilkey, Donald, Dir.-Pur.--Growmark, Inc., Bloomington, IL; *U.S. Private*, pg. 484
Willeford, S., Mgr.-Pur.--Besser/APPCO, San Antonio, TX; *U.S. Private*, pg. 139
Willems, Charlene, Mgr.-Pur.--Spotnails, Rolling Meadows, IL; *U.S. Private*, pg. 845
Willems, Leon, Dir.-Sourcing--Medtronic, Inc., Minneapolis, MN; *U.S. Public*, pg. 1082
Willhoite, Dennis, V.P.-Pur.--The Wm. Powell Company, Cincinnati, OH; *U.S. Private*, pg. 877
Williams, A. Warren, Asst. V.P.-Admin.--DIMON, Incorporated, Danville, VA; *U.S. Public*, pg. 509
Williams, An, Pur. Agent--Four-S Baking Company, Los Angeles, CA; *U.S. Private*, pg. 422
Williams, Byron, Dir.-Pur.--American Pacific Corporation, Las Vegas, NV; *U.S. Public*, pg. 88
Williams, Dan, Dir.-Personnel & Pur.--M.A.B. Paints, Terre Haute, IN; *U.S. Private*, pg. 175
Williams, Eldon, Dir.-Purchasing--Nasco Modesto, Modesto, CA; *U.S. Private*, pg. 446
Williams, Graham, Dir.-Pur.--Power Process Piping, Inc., Plymouth, MI; *U.S. Private*, pg. 878
Williams, Jamie, Pur. Agent--UTA Thompson Plant, Thomson, GA; *U.S. Public*, pg. 1691
Williams, Jim, Pur. Agent--Maghielse Tool Corporation, Grand Rapids, MI; *U.S. Private*, pg. 694
Williams, John, Mgr.-Pur.--Sellers Cleaning Systems, Piqua, OH; *U.S. Public*, pg. 457
Williams, Keith, Dir.-Pur.--Young-Phillips Sales Co., Clemmons, NC; *U.S. Private*, pg. 1201
Williams, Larry, Sr. V.P.-Pur.--American Color Graphics, Brentwood, TN; *U.S. Public*, pg. 1132
Williams, Leo, Pur. Agent & Maintenance Supvr.--Staple Cotton Cooperative Association, Greenwood, MS; *U.S. Private*, pg. 1033
Williams, Lisa, Mgr.-Pur.--Griffin Envelope, Inc., Seattle, WA; *U.S. Public*, pg. 1038
Williams, Phil, Mgr.-Pur.--Martin Industries, Inc. (AL), Florence, AL; *U.S. Private*, pg. 709
Williams, Roger D., Exec. V.P.-Food Products, Mktg., Pur., & Tech. Services--Bob Evans Farms, Inc., Columbus, OH; *U.S. Public*, pg. 596
Williamson, Bruce, Dir.-Pur.--The Oilgear Company, Milwaukee, WI; *U.S. Public*, pg. 1215
Williamson, William, Dir.-Pur.--Espey Mfg. & Electronics Corp., Saratoga Springs, NY; *U.S. Public*, pg. 592
Willis, Chuck, V.P.-Pur.--Trelleborg YSH, Inc., South Haven, MI; *Int'l*, pg. 1422
Willis, Edward B., V.P.-UKI Pur.--Dyersburg Corporation, Dyersburg, TN; *U.S. Public*, pg. 538
Willis, Edward B., V.P.-Pur.--United Knitting, Inc., Cleveland, TN; *U.S. Public*, pg. 538
Willis, James L., Dir.-Pur.--Russell Corporation, Alexander City, AL; *U.S. Public*, pg. 1413
Wilmes, Jody, Sr. V.P.-Pur.--Metz Baking Company, Deerfield, IL; *U.S. Private*, pg. 1022
Wilmes, Jody, V.P.-Pur.--Metz Baking Company, Deerfield, IL; *U.S. Private*, pg. 1022
Wilp, David, Mgr.-Pur.--Hardel Mutual Plywood Corporation, Olympia, WA; *U.S. Private*, pg. 501
Wilson, Alvis, Dir.-Pur.--HDS Services, Farmington Hills, MI; *U.S. Private*, pg. 490
Wilson, Darrel K., Mgr.-Pur.--Battelle Memorial Institute, Columbus, OH; *U.S. Private*, pg. 123
Wilson, Don, Mgr.-Pur.--Jerr-Dan Corporation, Greencastle, PA; *U.S. Public*, pg. 537
Wilson, Jimmy, Dir.-Pur.--TCBY Enterprises Inc., Little Rock, AR; *U.S. Public*, pg. 1553
Wilson, Mary M., V.P. & Product Actuary--Southwestern Life Insurance Company, Dallas, TX; *U.S. Private*, pg. 1018
Wilson, R.J., Dir.-Pur.--Modo Merchants Ltd., Byfleet, United Kingdom; *Int'l*, pg. 886
Wilson, Tom, Pur. Agent--Mill-Rose Company, Mentor, OH; *U.S. Private*, pg. 746
Wilson, W., Mgr.-Pur.--American National Insurance Company, Galveston, TX; *U.S. Public*, pg. 87
Windgassen, Wulf, Dir.-Pur.--Lux GmbH & Co. KG, Wermelskirchen, Germany; *Int'l*, pg. 993
Windh, Steve, Dir.-Pur.--Ruiz Food Products, Inc., Dinuba, CA; *U.S. Private*, pg. 951
Winn, David, Pur. Agent--NT Dor-omatic, Harwood Heights, IL; *U.S. Private*, pg. 771
Winters, Doris, Mgr.-Pur--Tighe Industries, Inc., York, PA; *U.S. Private*, pg. 1086
Winters, R.U., III, Dir.-Pur.--Auto-Owners Insurance, Lansing, MI; *U.S. Private*, pg. 100
Wirth, J. Albert, Dir.-Pur.--Legg Mason, Inc., Baltimore, MD; *U.S. Public*, pg. 984
Wise, Kevin, Pur. Agent--Ross Technology Corp., Leola, PA; *U.S. Private*, pg. 946
Wishart, Donald, Dir.-Pur.--McCain Foods Limited, Florenceville, Canada; *Int'l*, pg. 850
Wisniewski, Debbie, Pur. Agent--Corrections Corporation of America, Nashville, TN; *U.S. Public*, pg. 450
Wisniewski, Richard K., Dir.-Opers.--American Home Products Corporation, Madison, NJ; *U.S. Public*, pg. 79
Witt, Edward E., Sr. V.P.-Pur. & Sls.--Miller Electric Company, Jacksonville, FL; *U.S. Private*, pg. 747
Witte, Jay, Dir.-East Opers.--Hackney and Sons, Inc., Washington, NC; *U.S. Private*, pg. 1097
Witter, Marty, Mgr.-Pur.--United Engine & Machine Company, Carson City, NV; *U.S. Private*, pg. 1121
Wlodarski, Arthur, V.P.-Pur.--Houston Foods Company, Franklin Park, IL; *U.S. Private*, pg. 542
Wojedwoda, R.T., V.P.-Pur.--IMC Global, Bannockburn, IL; *U.S. Public*, pg. 856
Wolfe, Jim, Dir.-Pur.--I. Spiewak & Sons, Inc., New York, NY; *U.S. Private*, pg. 1025
Wolfe, Robert A., Mgr.-Pur.--Airflex Div. Eaton Corp., Cleveland, OH; *U.S. Public*, pg. 556
Wolfer, Dianna, Pur. Agent--Dreis & Krump Manufacturing Company, Chicago, IL; *U.S. Private*, pg. 342
Wolfinger, John, Pur. Agent--Johnson & Towers, Inc., Mount Laurel, NJ; *U.S. Private*, pg. 590
Wollenkamp, Mark, Pur.--Sporlan Valve Company, Washington, MO; *U.S. Private*, pg. 1026
Woltman, Sue, Dir.-Pur.--Siemer Milling Company, Teutopolis, IL; *U.S. Private*, pg. 998
Wondolowski, George, Dir.-Pur.--Sun Chemical General Printing Inc., Northlake, IL; *Int'l*, pg. 370
Wong, Linda, Deputy Mgr.-Pur.--Sun Hung Kai Properties Ltd., Wan Chai, Hong Kong; *Int'l*, pg. 1318
Wood, Donald, Dir.-Oper.--BioChem ImmunoSystems, Inc., Allentown, PA; *Int'l*, pg. 196
Wood, E.L., IV, Chm. Bd.--Southeastern Steel Company, Florence, SC; *U.S. Private*, pg. 1015
Wood, Mike, Mgr.-Pur.--Duro-Last Roofing, Inc., Saginaw, MI; *U.S. Private*, pg. 349
Wood, Thomas L., V.P.-Pur. & Logistics--The Valspar Corporation, Minneapolis, MN; *U.S. Public*, pg. 1707
Woodard, William, V.P.-Pur.--Recoton Corporation, Lake Mary, FL; *U.S. Public*, pg. 1369
Wooderd, Candy, Pur. Agent--Harlan Electric Co., Rochester Hills, MI; *U.S. Public*, pg. 1029
Woods, Jim, Pur. Agent--Lloyd Controls, Inc., Mountlake Terrace, WA; *U.S. Private*, pg. 672
Woods, John, Mgr.-Pur.--Inter-Tel, Incorporated, Phoenix, AZ; *U.S. Public*, pg. 888
Woodward, Jack, Dir.-Pur.--VLSI Technology, Inc., San Jose, CA; *U.S. Public*, pg. 1703
Wooten, David, Mgr.-Pur.--Pioneer/Eclipse Corp., Sparta, NC; *Int'l*, pg. 71
Worthey, C. Mark, V.P.-Pur./Flowers Bakeries Div.--Flowers Industries, Inc., Thomasville, GA; *U.S. Public*, pg. 656
Worthington, Susan, Mgr.-Pur.--O'Keeffe's, Inc., San Francisco, CA; *U.S. Private*, pg. 813
Worthy, Mark, Dir.-Pur./Bakery Group--Flowers Industries, Inc., Thomasville, GA; *U.S. Public*, pg. 656
Worzella, Bradley, Mgr.-Matls.--Pioneer Plastics Corporation, Auburn, ME; *U.S. Private*, pg. 867
Wozniak, Dennis, Sr. V.P.-Pur. & Mktg.--Arbor Drugs, Inc., Troy, MI; *U.S. Public*, pg. 126
Wright, B.G., Dir.-Pur.--Kentucky Utilities Company, Lexington, KY; *U.S. Public*, pg. 941
Wright, Doug, Mgr.-Pur.--Hamilton Co., Inc., Reno, NV; *U.S. Private*, pg. 497
Wright, Gary L., Mgr.-Pur.--Idaho Power Company, Boise, ID; *U.S. Public*, pg. 861
Wright, Jeremiah F., Jr., Mgr.-Pur.--Delmarva Power & Light Company, Wilmington, DE; *U.S. Public*, pg. 430
Wright, Robert E., Dir.-Pur.--Millennium Petrochemicals, Inc., Cincinnati, OH; *Int'l*, pg. 594
Wright, Roger, Pur. Agent--The Cardwell Machine Company, Richmond, VA; *U.S. Private*, pg. 209
Wright, Sandy, Dir.-Pur.--Aladdin Hotel & Casino, Las Vegas, NV; *U.S. Private*, pg. 30
Wright, Thomas H., Mgr.-Pur.--Keystone Powdered Metal Company, Saint Marys, PA; *U.S. Private*, pg. 619
Wroldson, Holly, Pur. Agent--Petricca Industries, Inc., Pittsfield, MA; *U.S. Private*, pg. 858
Wu, Max, Dir.-Pur.--Acer America Corporation, San Jose, CA; *Int'l*, pg. 22
Wullings, J., Dir.-Pur.--KTI Group B.V., Zoetermeer, Netherlands; *Int'l*, pg. 837
Wust, Pierre, Treas., Controller & Chief Fin. Officer--Sandoz Pharma Ltd., Eden Terrace, New Zealand; *Int'l*, pg. 985
Wykoff, Jeffery S., Dir.-Pur.--HPS, Inc., Indianapolis, IN; *U.S. Private*, pg. 492
Wylie, P., Dir.-Pur.--Sequa Chemicals, Inc., Chester, SC; *U.S. Public*, pg. 1459
Wyman, J., V.P.-Pur.--R & B Machine Tool Co., Saline, MI; *U.S. Private*, pg. 901
Yagi, Shannon, Mgr.-Pur.--Herbert Malarkey Roofing Company, Portland, OR; *U.S. Private*, pg. 698
Yale, William E., Dir.-Pur.--J.M. Huber Corporation, Edison, NJ; *U.S. Private*, pg. 544
Yang, C.S., Mgr.-Pub. Rels. & Pur.--China Hi-Ment Corp., Kao-hsiung, Taiwan; *Int'l*, pg. 285
Yankes, Mary Ann, Buyer--Thermal Industries, Inc., Pittsburgh, PA; *U.S. Private*, pg. 490
Yanowitz, Harry, Sr. V.P.-Pur.--Chapters Inc., Etobicoke, Canada; *Int'l*, pg. 280
Yarbrough, C., V.P.-Pur.--Wyman-Gordon Forgings, North Grafton, MA; *U.S. Public*, pg. 1782
Yarbrough, C., V.P.-Matl.--Wyman-Gordon Forgings, Inc., Houston, TX; *U.S. Public*, pg. 1782
Yarbrough, Carl, Pur. Dir.--Separation Systems Div., Denton, TX; *U.S. Public*, pg. 1269
Yasuo, Katsumata, Dir.-Pur.--Mutual Trading Co., Inc., Los Angeles, CA; *U.S. Private*, pg. 770
Yates, Rene, Pur. Agent--B.A. Ballou & Co. Inc., East Providence, RI; *U.S. Private*, pg. 112
Yeager, Dennis A., Mgr.-Pur.--PMC Industries Inc., Wickliffe, OH; *U.S. Private*, pg. 827
Yeaman, Kevin, Mgr.-Pur.--MediaNews Group, Eastern Operations, Woodbury, NJ; *U.S. Private*, pg. 727
Yeamans, Gerald R., Dir.-Pur.--Capitol Manufacturing Co., Westerville, OH; *U.S. Public*, pg. 793
Yonkers, Henry, Pur. Agent--Rose Printing Company, Inc., Tallahassee, FL; *U.S. Private*, pg. 945
York, Paul, Mgr.-Pur.--Ambac International Corp., Columbia, SC; *U.S. Private*, pg. 48
Young, Curtis, Dir.--Quaker State Corporation, Irving, TX; *U.S. Public*, pg. 1348
Young, David D., Dir.-Pur.--Wausau-Mosinee Papers Specialty Papers Group, Rhinelander, WI; *U.S. Public*, pg. 1747
Young, Don, Mgr.-Pur.--Ingrid Division of Lawnware, Morton Grove, IL; *U.S. Private*, pg. 654
Young, Gary, Pur. Agent--Y & S Candies, Lancaster, PA; *U.S. Public*, pg. 812
Young, Herb, Dir.-Pur.--Mohawk Commercial Carpet, Atlanta, GA; *U.S. Public*, pg. 1121
Young, Katherine Curtin, V.P.-Supply Mngmt.--AST Research Inc., Irvine, CA; *Int'l*, pg. 1181
Young, Les, Pur. Agent--First District Association, Litchfield, MN; *U.S. Private*, pg. 406
Young, Michael, Mgr.-Pur.--Andover Bank, Andover, MA; *U.S. Public*, pg. 112
Young, Nancy, Mgr.-Pur.--Fischer Imaging Corporation, Denver, CO; *U.S. Public*, pg. 647
Young, Scott, Asst. V.P.--Harbor Financial Mortgage Corp., Houston, TX; *U.S. Public*, pg. 644
Young, Warner, Mgr.-Matls.--Kauffman Products, Inc., Carmel, IN; *U.S. Private*, pg. 609
Young, William J., V.P.--Edison Brothers Stores, Inc., Saint Louis, MO; *U.S. Public*, pg. 563
Youngs, Lynn, Pur. Agent--Goody's Family Clothing, Inc., Knoxville, TN; *U.S. Public*, pg. 753
Yu, Johnson, Mgr.-Pur.--Paramount Fitness Corp., Los Angeles, CA; *U.S. Private*, pg. 838
Yurco, T.J., V.P.-Matls. Mngmt. & Logistics--U.S. Can Company, Oak Brook, IL; *U.S. Public*, pg. 1681
Yurkanin, Joseph J., Mgr.-Pur.--Buckeye Partners, L.P., Allentown, PA; *U.S. Public*, pg. 266
Zaffarano, Thomas, Mgr.-Pur. Div.--PECO Energy Company, Philadelphia, PA; *U.S. Public*, pg. 1268
Zamansky, Alan, Dir.-Pur.--Eastern Utilities Associates, Boston, MA; *U.S. Public*, pg. 549
Zander, Carl W., V.P.-Head Fabrics Buyer--Hancock Fabrics, Inc., Tupelo, MS; *U.S. Public*, pg. 779
Zanga, Lawrence A., Dir.-Pur.--Erving Paper Mills, Inc., Erving, MA; *U.S. Private*, pg. 382
Zantop, Duane G., Sr. V.P.--Zantop International Airlines, Inc., Ypsilanti, MI; *U.S. Private*, pg. 1204
Zanzig, Sandra, Mgr.-Pur.--Nicklaus Golf Company, L.C., West Palm Beach, FL; *U.S. Private*, pg. 799
Zapp, Dennis, Dir.-Pur.--Dexter Nonwovens Division, Windsor Locks, CT; *U.S. Public*, pg. 504
Zary, Jerome E., Dir.-Matls. & Mgr.-Sys.--Frog Switch & Manufacturing Company, Carlisle, PA; *U.S. Private*, pg. 429

Zecca, Mike, V.P.-Meat Procurement--Shurfine International, Inc., Northlake, IL; *U.S. Private*, pg. 997
Zecchini, James F., V.P.-Resort Svcs.--Fairfield Communities, Inc., Little Rock, AR; *U.S. Public*, pg. 610
Zehnder, Mark, Mgr.-Pur.--Igloo Products Corporation, Houston, TX; *U.S. Public*, pg. 265
Zeindler, Franz, Mgr.-Personnel & Purchasing--Oerlikon Buhrle Immobilien AG, Zurich, Switzerland; *Int'l*, pg. 998
Zeinert, Dale, Dir.-Pur.--Fastenal Company, Winona, MN; *U.S. Public*, pg. 614
Zeman, Bruce, Dir.-Pur.--A-P-A Transport Corp., North Bergen, NJ; *U.S. Private*, pg. 2
Zenger, Corey, Pur. Agent--Smith Frozen Foods, Inc., Weston, OR; *U.S. Private*, pg. 1008
Zeratsky, Drew, Pur. Agent--National Rivet & Manufacturing Company, Waupun, WI; *U.S. Private*, pg. 786
Ziebel, Kitch, Dir.-Pur.--Precision Twist Drill Co., Crystal Lake, IL; *Int'l*, pg. 1185
Ziegler, Jim, Mgr.-Pur.--Shady Brook Farms, Dayton, VA; *U.S. Private*, pg. 937
Ziegler, Lynn, Dir.-Pur.--Johnson Matthey Inc., Wayne, PA; *Int'l*, pg. 713
Zielinski, Avon, Dir.-Pur.--SGS-Thomson Microelectronics, Inc., Carrollton, TX; *Int'l*, pg. 1153
Zielke, Keith, Dir.-Pur.--The Gates Rubber Company, Denver, CO; *Int'l*, pg. 1396
Ziesler, Michael G., Dir.-Pur.--Saarbergwerke Aktiengesellschaft, Saarbruecken, Germany; *Int'l*, pg. 1166
Zigbell, Barb, Dir.-Pur.--Photo Control Corporation, Minneapolis, MN; *U.S. Public*, pg. 1292
Ziino, Joe, Pur. Agent--Badger Meter, Inc., Milwaukee, WI; *U.S. Public*, pg. 164
Zimet, Dean, Sls. Rep.--Via Tech Publishing Solutions, Bay Shore, NY; *U.S. Private*, pg. 1138
Zimmerman, E.B., Treas. & Pur. Agent--Lancaster Malleable Castings Company, Lancaster, PA; *U.S. Private*, pg. 645
Zimmerman, Robert, Mgr.-Pur.--Sierra West Bancorp, Truckee, CA; *U.S. Public*, pg. 1470
Zimmerman, Robert, Mgr.-Pur.--Sierra West Bank, Truckee, CA; *U.S. Public*, pg. 1470
Zinn, Bob, Pur. Agent--Electroglas, Inc., Santa Clara, CA; *U.S. Public*, pg. 727
Zirkle, Roger, Mgr.-Pur.--Hershey Chocolate U.S.A.-Stuarts Draft Plant, Stuarts Draft, VA; *U.S. Public*, pg. 812
Zitomer, Bernard, V.P.-Pur.--Sunshine Biscuits, Inc., Woodbridge, NJ; *U.S. Private*, pg. 434
Zitomer, Bernard, V.P.-Pur.--Sunshine Biscuits, Inc., Woodbridge, NJ; *U.S. Public*, pg. 657
Zizik, Ray, V.P.-Procurement--Cytec Industries Inc., West Paterson, NJ; *U.S. Public*, pg. 471
Zoldos, Jerry, Mgr.-Pur.--Donlee Technologies Inc., York, PA; *U.S. Private*, pg. 339
Zuckerman, Henry, V.P.-Pur.--Zuckerman-Honickman Inc., King of Prussia, PA; *U.S. Private*, pg. 1207
Zuckero, Carl, Sr. V.P.-Pur.--Tweddle Litho Company, Clinton Township, MI; *U.S. Private*, pg. 1111
Zuehlke, T.L., Mgr.-Pur.--Wells Mfg. Corp., Fond Du Lac, WI; *U.S. Private*, pg. 1113
Zurawski, Mary, Supvr.-Pur.--Worzalla Publishing Co., Inc., Stevens Point, WI; *U.S. Private*, pg. 1191
Zytkowicz, Gregory G., Mgr.-Pur.--Essex Corporation, New York, NY; *U.S. Public*, pg. 320

RESEARCH & DEVELOPMENT

Abadiano, Delia, Dir.-Res. & Devel.--Levlad, Inc., Chatsworth, CA; *U.S. Private*, pg. 663
Abbey, Nelson D., III, Pres. & Chief Exec. Officer--Abbey Etna Machine Company, Perrysburg, OH; *U.S. Private*, pg. 9
Abdullah, Shafiq Sit, Dr., Grp. Gen. Mgr.-Corp. Plng.--Sime Darby Berhad, Kuala Lumpur, Malaysia; *Int'l*, pg. 1249
Abe, Takehiko, Mng. Dir.-Real Estate & Leisure Business--Nippon Shinpan Co., Ltd., Tokyo, Japan; *Int'l*, pg. 939
Abell, Steve, V.P.-Res. & Devel.--Penford Products Co., Cedar Rapids, IA; *U.S. Public*, pg. 1269
Adamo, Susan, V.P.-Res. & Devel.--Pressman Toy Corp., New York, NY; *U.S. Private*, pg. 882
Adams, John R., V.P.-Res. & Devel.--Milcare, Inc., Grandville, MI; *U.S. Public*, pg. 1112
Adamson, Fletcher D., V.P.-Res.--Russell Corporation, Alexander City, AL; *U.S. Public*, pg. 1413
Adler, Danny, Mgr.-Res. & Devel.--General Microwave Corporation, Amityville, NY; *U.S. Public*, pg. 717
Adler, Irving, V.P.-Tech.--Essex International, Inc., Fort Wayne, IN; *U.S. Public*, pg. 593
Ahmed, Salah U., Sr. V.P.-Prod. & Devel.--Barr Laboratories Inc., Pomona, NY; *U.S. Public*, pg. 191
Akimoto, Akira, Gen. Mgr.-Yokkaichi Res. Ctr.--Tosoh Corporation, Tokyo, Japan; *Int'l*, pg. 1407
Akiyama, Sumio, Sr. Mng. Dir.-Res. & Devel.--Tokuyama Corporation, Tokyo, Japan; *Int'l*, pg. 1393
Aldred, Derrick, V.P.-Engrng.--Haskel International, Inc., Burbank, CA; *U.S. Public*, pg. 798
Aldridge, Roger, Exec. Dir.-Store Devel., Equipment & Grp. Estates--Marks & Spencer PLC, London, United Kingdom; *Int'l*, pg. 842
Alfano, Michael C., Dr., D.M.D., Ph.D., Sr. V.P. & Dir.-Res. & Tech.--Block Drug Company, Inc., Jersey City, NJ; *U.S. Public*, pg. 236
Alix, Didier, Dir.-Res.--Societe Generale, Paris, France; *Int'l, pg. 1273*
Alkstrom, Dave, Mgr.-Res. & Devel.--Hope's Architectural Products Inc., Jamestown, NY; *U.S. Private*, pg. 538
Allahand, Robert B., V.P.-Corp. Res.--BetzDearborn Inc., Trevose, PA; *U.S. Public*, pg. 226
Allain, Ronald J., Sr. V.P.-Res. & Devel.--Nalco Chemical Company, Naperville, IL; *U.S. Public*, pg. 1150
Allen, Morgan, V.P.-Devel. & Construction--Seed Restaurant Group, Inc., Lexington, KY; *U.S. Private*, pg. 981
Allspach, Eugene R., Grp. V.P.-Tech. & Mfg.--Millennium Petrochemicals, Inc., Cincinnati, OH; *Int'l*, pg. 594
Aloise, Art, Mgr.-Res. & Devel.--Cooper Instrument Corp., Middlefield, CT; *U.S. Private*, pg. 274
Alperi, Eero, Dir.-Plng. & Devel.--Amer Group Ltd., Helsinki, Finland; *Int'l*, pg. 72
Alscher, Arnold, Dr., Mng. Dir.-Processing, Research & Devel.--Haltermann AG, Hamburg, Germany; *Int'l*, pg. 590
Alston, Jim, Dr., Dir.-Res. & Devel.--George W. Park Seed Co., Inc., Greenwood, SC; *U.S. Private*, pg. 839
Alton, N. Kirby, Sr. V.P.-Devel.--Amgen Inc., Thousand Oaks, CA; *U.S. Public*, pg. 100
Altrock, Bruce W., V.P.-Res.--Amgen Inc., Thousand Oaks, CA; *U.S. Public*, pg. 100
Alvarez, Tony, V.P.-Res. & Devel.--Cypress Semiconductor Corporation, San Jose, CA; *U.S. Public*, pg. 470
Amaria, Merzi, Mgr.-Quality Assurance--Green Spot Packaging Inc., Claremont, CA; *U.S. Private*, pg. 477
Ambrose, R. J., Dir.-Chemical Res. & Devel.--Lord Research & Development, Cary, NC; *U.S. Private*, pg. 676
Amonette, Jan, V.P.-Media, Mktg. Res. & Database Mktg.--Caldwell VanRiper, Inc., Indianapolis, IN; *U.S. Private*, pg. 200
Amstutz, Douglas D., V.P.-Res. & Devel.--Amstore Corporation, Muskegon, MI; *U.S. Private*, pg. 68
Anaokar, Sunil, Mgr.-Res. & Dev.--Seradyn, Inc., Indianapolis, IN; *Int'l*, pg. 871
Anderson, Byron, V.P.-Res. & Devel.--Immtech International, Inc., Evanston, IL; *U.S. Public*, pg. 459
Anderson, David J., V.P.-Intl. & Corp. Development--CLARCOR, Inc., Rockford, IL; *U.S. Public*, pg. 381
Anderson, David L., Chief Tech. Officer & V.P.-Enterprise Server Devel.--Amdahl Corporation, Sunnyvale, CA; *Int'l*, pg. 527
Anderson, Ed, Mgr.-Mktg. & Brand Devel.--PYA/Monarch, Inc., Greenville, SC; *U.S. Public*, pg. 1433
Anderson, Forrest, Sr. V.P. & Res. Dir.--Golin/Harris Communications, Inc., Chicago, IL; *Int'l*, pg. 1226
Anderson, G. Paul, V.P.-Bus. Devel.--Kerr-McGee Coal Corp., Oklahoma City, OK; *U.S. Public*, pg. 952
Anderson, Michael, Mgr.-Res.--Magneco/Metrel, Inc., Addison, IL; *U.S. Private*, pg. 695
Andersson, Lennart, Mgr.-Res. & Devel., Trailers--Eldon AB, Nassjo, Sweden; *Int'l*, pg. 436
Andrassy, George, V.P.-Res. & Devel.--Dep Corporation, Rancho Dominguez, CA; *U.S. Public*, pg. 500
Angell, Robin, Res. Dir. & Systems Dir.--The Media Centre, London, United Kingdom; *Int'l*, pg. 852
Anton, Mary Breitbach, Sr. V.P. & Consumer Res. & Acct. Grp. Dir.--Creswell, Munsell, Fultz & Zirbel, L.P., Cedar Rapids, IA; *U.S. Private*, pg. 1197
Anwar, Iqbal, V.P.-Res. & Devel.--Environmental Tectonics Corporation (ETC), Southampton, PA; *U.S. Public*, pg. 587
Apleberger, Lennart, Head-Tech., Res. & Devel.--NCC AB, Solna, Sweden; *Int'l*, pg. 898
Aramoto, Magohiro, Sr. Exec. Dir.-Corp. Res. & Devel.--Sharp Corporation, Osaka, Japan; *Int'l*, pg. 1228
Arbelaez, Martha, Mgr.-Res. & Devel.--Salz Leathers, Inc., Santa Cruz, CA; *U.S. Private*, pg. 963
Argent, V., Dir.-Res. & Devel.--Palintest Limited, Gateshead, United Kingdom; *Int'l*, pg. 589
Armstrong, T. Paul, Sr. V.P. & Gen. Mgr.-Table Service Restaurant Bus. Grp.--Micros Systems Inc., Beltsville, MD; *U.S. Public*, pg. 1106
Arnold, David B., V.P. & Chief Tech. Officer--Kennametal Inc., Latrobe, PA; *U.S. Public*, pg. 950
Arnold, Mary T., V.P.-Res. & Devel.--W.H. Brady Co., Milwaukee, WI; *U.S. Public*, pg. 250
Artzt, Russell M., Exec. V.P.-Research & Devel.--Computer Associates International, Inc., Islandia, NY; *U.S. Public*, pg. 420
Ashe, Robert G., Sr. V.P.-Application Devel. Tools--Cognos Inc., Ottawa, Canada; *Int'l*, pg. 305
Atkins, Thomas J., Ph.D., V.P.-Res. & Devel.--Hercon Laboratories Corp., New York, NY; *U.S. Public*, pg. 802
Atwood, Glen W., Sr. Geologist--Coeur Explorations, Inc., Coeur D'Alene, ID; *U.S. Public*, pg. 394
Avdalovic, Nebojsa, V.P.-Res. & Devel.--Dionex Corporation, Sunnyvale, CA; *U.S. Public*, pg. 510
Averett, Devron, Sr. V.P.-Res. & Devel.--ICN Pharmaceuticals, Inc., Costa Mesa, CA; *U.S. Public*, pg. 853
Avery, Roger, Dir.-Prod. Devel.--Today's Kids, Booneville, AR; *U.S. Private*, pg. 1020
Avramescu, S., Mgr.-Res. & Devel.--Electrovert, Grand Prairie, TX; *Int'l*, pg. 328
Awit, Nemesis A., Grp. Mgr.-Tech. Res.--Benguet Corporation, Manila, Philippines; *Int'l*, pg. 186
Ayalla Boto, Joao, Sr. Mgr.-Devel.--Caixa Geral de Depositos, Lisbon, Portugal; *Int'l*, pg. 250
Babcock, Elaine H., Sr. V.P.--ITC Learning Corp., Herndon, VA; *U.S. Public*, pg. 859
Babel, Bernard, Mng. Dir.-Res. & Devel--AGIE AG (Fur Industrielle Elektronik), Lausanne, Switzerland; *Int'l*, pg. 488
Baccei, Louis J., Dr., Pres.-Res. & Devel.--Loctite Corporation, Rocky Hill, CT; *Int'l*, pg. 611
Bach, W. Douglas, V.P.-Mktg. & Bus. Devel.--Herberts-O'Brien Inc., Houston, TX; *Int'l*, pg. 626
Bacon, Mathew, V.P.-Devel.--Delta Education, Inc., Hudson, NH; *Int'l*, pg. 1402
Bader, Fredric G., Sr. V.P.-Mfg. & Pharmaceutical Devel.--Genetics Institute, Inc., Cambridge, MA; *U.S. Public*, pg. 79
Bailey, J., Prof., Dir.-Clay Res.--Redland Technologies Ltd., Crawley, United Kingdom; *Int'l*, pg. 1091
Bailey, Richard N., V.P.-Res. & Devel.--Norgren Co., Littleton, CO; *Int'l*, pg. 647
Bain, Ronald A., Mgr. Geoscience-Exploration & Production--Anadarko Petroleum Corporation, Houston, TX; *U.S. Public*, pg. 107
Baines, J.E., Dir.-Res. & Devel.--British Gypsum Ltd., Loughborough, United Kingdom; *Int'l*, pg. 122
Baker, Howard A., Sr. V.P.-Derivative Securities Admin. & Res.--The American Stock Exchange, New York, NY; *U.S. Private*, pg. 62
Baker, Jeff, Res. Dir.--BrandSolutions, Seattle, WA; *U.S. Private*, pg. 385
Baker, Joffre B., Ph.D., V.P.-Res. Discovery--Genentech, Inc., South San Francisco, CA; *Int'l*, pg. 1120
Baker, Kenneth R., V.P.-Res. & Devel. Center--General Motors Corporation, Detroit, MI; *U.S. Public*, pg. 718
Bakker, M., Mgr.-Res. & Tech.--Oce-van der Grinten N.V., Venlo, Netherlands; *Int'l*, pg. 993
Balaban, Larry, V.P.-Real Estates--Chapters Inc., Etobicoke, Canada; *Int'l*, pg. 280
Baldwin, Chris, Dir.-Devel.--Marine World Africa USA, Vallejo, CA; *U.S. Private*, pg. 703
Balsells, Angel, Head-Res. & Devel.--Caixa d'Estalvis de Catalunya, Barcelona, Spain; *Int'l*, pg. 249
Banashek, Ed, Mgr.-Special Projects--Falcon Products, Inc., Saint Louis, MO; *U.S. Public*, pg. 611
Bane, James E., Mgr.-Research & Devel.--Steadly Company, Carthage, MO; *U.S. Public*, pg. 986
Banks, Donna J., V.P.-Res. & Devel.--Kellogg Company, Battle Creek, MI; *U.S. Public*, pg. 947
Barber, Robley T., Sr. V.P-Corp. Devel.--Hilton Hotels Div., Beverly Hills, CA; *U.S. Public*, pg. 829
Barbosa, Celso A., Mgr.-Res. & Devel.--Acos Villares S.A., Sao Paulo, Brazil; *Int'l*, pg. 23
Barclay, James, Mgr.-Chief Chemist--Electric Furnace Co., Salem, OH; *U.S. Private*, pg. 367
Bardoliwalla, D.F., V.P.-Res. & Tech.--Oakite Products, Inc., Berkeley Heights, NJ; *Int'l*, pg. 861
Barendregt, S., Dir.-Research & Devel.--KTI Group B.V., Zoetermeer, Netherlands; *Int'l*, pg. 837
Barker, R.G., Dr., Dir.-Corp. Res. & Devel.--Union Camp Corporation, Wayne, NJ; *U.S. Public*, pg. 1665
Barlow, W., Mgr.-Res. & Devel.--Marsh Bellofram Corp., Newell, WV; *U.S. Private*, pg. 707
Barnett, Richard, Dir.-Res. & Devel./General Datacomm Advanced Research Ctr. Ltd.--General Datacomm Industries, Inc., Middlebury, CT; *U.S. Public*, pg. 708
Baron, Rene, Exec. V.P.-Plng. & Devel.--N. Schlumberger & Cie, Guebwiller, France; *Int'l*, pg. 1206
Barone, Anthony, V.P.-New Product Devel.--McGraw-Hill Financial Information Services Group, New York, NY; *U.S. Public*, pg. 1071
Barrett, Adam, Mgr.-Prod. Devel.--Thermalloy, Inc., Farmers Branch, TX; *Int'l*, pg. 208
Barro, Dan, V.P. & Corp. Sec.--Lamp Post Franchise Corporation, Tustin, CA; *U.S. Private*, pg. 644
Barry, Steve, Res. Mgr.--Utica Mutual Insurance Company, New Hartford, NY; *U.S. Private*, pg. 1129
Barth, Roy, V.P.-Res. & Devel.--Thermon Manufacturing Company, San Marcos, TX; *U.S. Private*, pg. 1080
Bartlett, D.W., V.P.-Intl. Bus. Devel.--Raytheon Engineers & Constructors, Inc., Englewood, CO; *U.S. Public*, pg. 1366
Bartsch, Art, V.P.-Bakery / R&D--The Swiss Colony, Inc, Monroe, WI; *U.S. Private*, pg. 1059
Baskett, Forest, Ph.D., Chief Tech. Officer & Sr. V.P.-Res. & Devel.--Silicon Graphics, Inc., Mountain View, CA; *U.S.* Public, pg. 1473
Bassi, Sukh, V.P.-Wheat Gluten Mktg. & Dir.-Res. & Devel.--Midwest Grain Products, Inc., Atchison, KS; *U.S. Public*, pg. 1111
Bates, Christa, Bus. Devel. & Mktg. Coord.--Lafarge Construction Materials, Canfield, OH; *Int'l*, pg. 788
Bauch, Thomas, Mgr.-Res. & Devel.--LPC Industrias Alimenticias S.A., Vila Jaguara, Brazil; *Int'l*, pg. 380
Baughn, Alan L., V.P.-Corp. Plng. & Devel. & Sec.--The Standard Register Company, Dayton, OH; *U.S. Public*, pg. 1505
Baumann, Jurgen, Mng. Dir.-Materials Tech. & Chemistry--Landis & Staefa AG, Zug, Switzerland; *Int'l*, pg. 800
Baumann, Werner, Dr., Dir.-Res. & Devel.--Clariant International Ltd., Muttenz, Switzerland; *Int'l*, pg. 624
Bayle, Michel, Exec. V.P.-Res.--Gaz de France, Paris, France; *Int'l*, pg. 541
Bayne, Jay S., V.P.-Engrng., Res. & Devel.--Bailey Controls Company, Wickliffe, OH; *Int'l*, pg. 654
Beasty, Larry, Dir.-Res. & Devel.--A. Duda & Sons Inc., Oviedo, FL; *U.S. Private*, pg. 344
Beauchamp, Bob, Sr. V.P.-Res. & Devel.--BMC Software, Inc., Houston, TX; *U.S. Public*, pg. 162
Beaudin, Timothy, Sr. V.P.-Property Opers. & Indus. Devel.--Catellus Development Corporation, San Francisco, CA; *U.S. Public*, pg. 314
Beck, Dan, Sr. V.P.-Mktg./Artist Devel.--Sony Music Entertainment, Inc., New York, NY; *Int'l*, pg. 1281
Beck, Rolf, Mgr.-Nonfood Devel.--Coop Switzerland, Basel, Switzerland; *Int'l*, pg. 329
Becks, Michael, Dir.-Res.--The Brulin Corporation, Indianapolis, IN; *U.S. Private*, pg. 176
Bedbrook, John R., Dr., Exec. V.P. & Dir.-Science--DNAP Holding Corp., Oakland, CA; *Int'l*, pg. 454
Beers, Richard, V.P.--Geo-Centers, Inc., Newton, MA; *U.S. Private*, pg. 447
Beickovsky, Alex, Sr. V.P.-Research & Technology--Amperif Corporation, Chatsworth, CA; *U.S. Public*, pg. 1523
Beicos, Steve, Dir.-Engrng.--Magnetrol International, Downers Grove, IL; *U.S. Private*, pg. 696
Bell, Ian, Dr., V.P.-Research & Devel.--Ruetgers-Nease Corporation, State College, PA; *Int'l*, pg. 1148
Bell, Peter, V.P.-Research & Chief Scientist--Norton Company, Worcester, MA; *Int'l*, pg. 1173
Bell, Robert A., Dr., V.P.-Res. & Devel.--Consolidated Edison Company of New York, Inc., New York, NY; *U.S. Public*, pg. 434
Bellessa, James L., Jr., V.P.-Res.--D.A. Davidson & Co., Great Falls, MT; *U.S. Private*, pg. 314
Belletto, Owen W., V.P.-Processed Prods. & Res. & Tech. Svcs.--Sunkist Growers, Inc., Sherman Oaks, CA; *U.S. Private*, pg. 1052
Bellmonz, Jurgen, Mgr.-Tech. & Engrng.--Groschopp & Co. GmbH EMW Elektromotoren-Feinbauwerk, Viersen, Germany; *Int'l*, pg. 559

Beltz, Gerald, Ph.D, Sr. V.P.-Res. & Devel.--Aquila Biopharmaceuticals, Inc., Worcester, MA; *U.S. Public*, pg. 126

Bement, Christian, Chief Oper. Officer & Exec. V.P.--Earl Scheib, Inc., Beverly Hills, CA; *U.S. Public*, pg. 1437

Bendure, Raymond, V.P.-Research & Devel.--Arm & Hammer Consumer Products, Princeton, NJ; *U.S. Public*, *pg. 356*

Bengen, Bob, Dir.-Dir. Mktg. & Res.--Lark Luggage Company, Inc., Denver, CO; *U.S. Public*, pg. 1430

Benito, Richard, V.P.-New Product Devel.--Peoples Telephone Company, Inc., Miami, FL; *U.S. Public*, pg. 1275

Benninger, Gary, Exec. V.P.-Engrng., Res. & Dev.--Magna International Inc., Markham, Canada; *Int'l*, pg. 829

Berecz, Imre, V.P.-Res. & Devel.--KTI, Orange, CA; *U.S. Public*, pg. 939

Berendt, Ph.D., Michael J., Sr. V.P.-Res. Pharmaceutical Division--Bayer Corporation, Pittsburgh, PA; *Int'l*, pg. 172

Bergelin, Ingemar, Dir.-Research & Devel.--Perstorp Pharma AB, Lund, Sweden; *Int'l*, pg. 1036

Berger, Greg, Mgr.-Engrng.--Fulton Industries Inc., Wauseon, OH; *U.S. Private*, pg. 431

Berger, R.M., V.P.-Res. & Devel.--Filtrona Richmond Company, Richmond, VA; *Int'l*, pg. 232

Bergin, J.F., Dir.-Res. & Devel.--Consolidated Papers, Inc., Wisconsin Rapids, WI; *U.S. Public*, pg. 436

Bergstrom, John H., V.P.-Mktg. Research--The New England, Boston, MA; *U.S. Private*, pg. 737

Berkheimer, John, Chief Engineer--Go-Video, Inc., Scottsdale, AZ; *U.S. Public*, pg. 748

Berlin, Roger, Ph.D., Sr. V.P.-Scientific Affairs Worldwide--Whitehall-Robins Healthcare, Madison, NJ; *U.S. Public*, pg. 80

Berlin, S. R., Media Dir. & Res.--Brown Marketing Communications, Chicago, IL; *U.S. Private*, pg. 174

Bernal, Enrique G., Dir.-Corp. Devel.--Galileo Corp., Sturbridge, MA; *U.S. Public*, pg. 698

Bernarducci, Ernest, Ph.D., V.P.-Res. & Devel.--Block Drug Company, Inc., Jersey City, NJ; *U.S. Public*, pg. 236

Bertelli, David, V.P.-Organization Devel.--Mercury Computer Systems, Inc., Chelmsford, MA; *U.S. Private*, pg. 732

Bessler, Paul, Dir.-Mktg. Res.--Del Webb Corporation, Phoenix, AZ; *U.S. Public*, pg. 494

Betbeze, Jean-Paul, Mgr.-Economic & Fin. Res.--Credit Lyonnais S.A., Paris, France; *Int'l*, pg. 343

Bettis, John, V.P.-Dev. Laboratories--Glaxo Wellcome PLC, Research Triangle Park, NC; *Int'l*, pg. 553

Betz, Dennis L., Sr., Dir.-Res.--P.H. Glatfelter Company, Spring Grove, PA; *U.S. Public*, pg. 746

Beutels, R., Inspector Gen.-Research--Banque Nationale de Belgique, Brussels, Belgium; *Int'l*, pg. 162

Bey, Philippe, V.P.-Res./U.S.--Hoechst Marion Roussel, Inc., Bridgewater, NJ; *Int'l*, pg. 624

Bierbaum, Robert, Dir.-Res. & Devel.--Nalle Plastics Inc., Austin, TX; *U.S. Private*, pg. 773

Bilger, Mark, Sr. V.P.-Prod. Devel.--Hyperion Software, Stamford, CT; *U.S. Public*, pg. 851

Bilhartz, H.L., Sr. V.P.-ARCO Explorations Tech.--Atlantic Richfield Company, Los Angeles, CA; *U.S. Public*, pg. 144

Bingham, Russ, Dir.-Corp. Research--The Hartford Financial Services Group Inc., Hartford, CT; *U.S. Public*, pg. 794

Bird, Kenneth, Dir.-Engrng.--Norwalk Co., Inc., Norwalk, CT; *U.S. Private*, pg. 807

Birdsall, John, Sr. V.P. & Exec. Chef--Koo Koo Roo, Inc., Los Angeles, CA; *U.S. Public*, pg. 966

Birnbaum, Joel S., Sr. V.P.-Res. & Devel. & Dir.-HP Laboratories--Hewlett-Packard Company, Palo Alto, CA; *U.S. Public*, pg. 813

Bischot, Bob, Dir.-Res. & Devel.--Warner-Jenkinson Co., Saint Louis, MO; *U.S. Public*, pg. 1696

Bisgaard, Nikolai, V.P.-Res. & Devel.--GN Danavox A/S, Taastrup, Denmark; *Int'l*, pg. 537

Bittel, Ralph J., Dr., Mgr.--E.W. Knauss & Son, Inc., Quakertown, PA; *U.S. Private*, pg. 626

Blakeley, John, Dir.-Corp. Devel.--Glynwed International PLC, Birmingham, United Kingdom; *Int'l*, pg. 554

Blanck, Mike, V.P.-Strategic Plng. & Res.--Laughlin/Constable, Inc., Milwaukee, WI; *U.S. Private*, pg. 653

Blank, Norman, V.P.-Res. & Devel.--Sika Corporation, Lyndhurst, NJ; *Int'l*, pg. 1249

Blankenship, Loran, Div. V.P.-Res. & Devel. Engrng.--Stuart Entertainment Inc., Council Bluffs, IA; *U.S. Public*, pg. 1526

Blankenship, Loran, Div. V.P.-Engrng. & Res. & Devel.--Trade Products, Lynnwood, WA; *U.S. Public*, pg. 1526

Blann, Jerry M., Pres.--Jackson Hole Ski Resort, Teton Village, WY; *U.S. Private*, pg. 579

Blanton, James E., Dir.-Res. & Devel.--Pre Finish Metals Incorporated, Elk Grove Village, IL; *U.S. Public*, pg. 1056

Blaschke, Ron, Dir.-Res. & Devel.--Tom's Foods, Inc., Columbus, GA; *U.S. Private*, pg. 1090

Bluhm, Leslie, V.P.-Research & Devel.--Joseph E. Seagram & Sons, Inc., New York, NY; *Int'l*, pg. 1215

Bobb, Barry, Dir.-Res. & Devel.--Concordia Publishing House, Saint Louis, MO; *U.S. Private*, pg. 261

Boehme, Peter, Mng. Dir.-Res. & Devel.--Dr. Th. Boehme KG Chem. Fabrik GmbH & Co., Geretsried, Germany; *Int'l*, pg. 199

Bohm, Georg, Dr., Mgr.-Res.--Bridgestone/Firestone Research Laboratories, Akron, OH; *Int'l*, pg. 213

Bolgiano, D.R., V.P.-Research--InterDigital Communications Corp., King of Prussia, PA; *U.S. Public*, pg. 889

Bolleter, Ulrich, Mgr.-Res. & Devel.--Sulzer Ltd., Winterthur, Switzerland; *Int'l*, pg. 1305

Boncy, R. Richard, V.P.-Law, Pub. Affairs & Corp. Devel.--Medtronic Europe S.A./N.V., Lausanne, Switzerland; *U.S. Public*, pg. 1083

Bond, Bill, Dr., V.P.-Tech. Devel.--The ServiceMaster Company, Downers Grove, IL; *U.S. Public*, pg. 1461

Bondur, James A., Dir.-Plasma Res. & Devel./SEG--Watkins-Johnson Company, Palo Alto, CA; *U.S. Public*, pg. 1745

Bookout, William, V.P.-Res. & Devel.--Medex Inc., Hilliard, OH; *U.S. Public*, pg. 689

Boppart, Loran, Chief Engineer-Res. & Devel.--M&W, Gibson City, IL; *U.S. Public*, pg. 35

Borbolla, Gustavo, Res. Dir.--Leo Burnett S.A. de C.V., Mexico, Mexico; *U.S. Private*, pg. 185

Bosch, Albert, V.P.-Res. & Devel./Quality--Vicorp Restaurants, Inc., Denver, CO; *U.S. Public*, pg. 1719

Boschen, Chris, V.P.-Mktg., Sls. & Business Devel.--L3 Communications Telemetry & Instrumentation Div., San Diego, CA; *U.S. Private*, pg. 639

Bostrom, Meg, V.P.-Res. & Strategic Devel.--Trahan, Burden & Charles, Inc., Baltimore, MD; *U.S. Private*, pg. 1095

Boullianne, George E., V.P.-Corp. Devel.--Western Atlas Inc., Houston, TX; *U.S. Public*, pg. 1757

Bouvier, Pierre, V.P.-Res.--Caisse de depot et placement du Quebec, Montreal, Canada; *Int'l*, pg. 249

Bovendeur, J., Head-Res. & Devel.--Heidemij Realisatie BV, Arnhem, Netherlands; *Int'l*, pg. 607

Bowers, Mark, Dir.-Res. & Devel.--ESA, Inc., Chelmsford, MA; *U.S. Private*, pg. 354

Bowman, Patricia, Sr. V.P.-Res. & Devel.--The Dial Corporation, Phoenix, AZ; *U.S. Public*, pg. 505

Bowrey, Ron, Div. Mgr.-Res. & Devel.--Meadow Lea Foods Ltd., Mascot, Australia; *Int'l*, pg. 555

Boyce, Jeff, V.P.-Engrng. & Quality--Communications Instruments Inc., Fairview, NC; *U.S. Private*, pg. 259

Bozec, Patrick, Exec. V.P.-Res.--Essilor International Compagnie Generale d'Optique, Charenton-le-Pont, France; *Int'l*, pg. 462

Bracho, Rafael, Chief Tech. Officer--Active Software, Inc., Santa Clara, CA; *U.S. Private*, pg. 15

Brachocki, Edward, V.P.-Corp. Devel.--Go-Video, Inc., Scottsdale, AZ; *U.S. Public*, pg. 748

Bracke, William, Dir. Gen.-Res.--Petrofina S.A., Brussels, Belgium; *Int'l*, pg. 1043

Bragg, Sanford B., Mng. Dir.-Ratings Devel.--Standard & Poor's Ratings Services, New York, NY; *U.S. Public*, pg. 1071

Brahmstadt, Clifford A., V.P.-Mfg.--Bachman Company, Reading, PA; *U.S. Private*, pg. 109

Brandenburger, Larry B., V.P.-Res. & Dev.--The Valspar Corporation, Minneapolis, MN; *U.S. Public*, pg. 1707

Brandstatter, Leo, Res. Dir. & Strategic Plng. Dir.--Rubin Ehrenthal & Associates, New York, NY; *U.S. Private*, pg. 949

Brannock, Paul, V.P.-Res. & Devel.--Simmons Company, Atlanta, GA; *Int'l*, pg. 686

Brant, David, V.P.-Program Development--Bombardier, Learjet Inc., Wichita, KS; *Int'l*, pg. 200

Braun, William V., Sr. V.P. & Dir.-Corp. Res. & Devel.--Motorola, Inc., Schaumburg, IL; *U.S. Public*, pg. 1136

Breckenridge, John C., V.P.-Chemicals--Du Pont (E.I. Du Pont De Nemours & Co.), Wilmington, DE; *U.S. Public*, pg. 530

Breda, Bernard, Dir.-Res. & Devel.--Yves Saint Laurent Parfums S.A., Neuilly-sur-Seine, France; *Int'l*, pg. 445

Bredhe, Lauri, Head-Res. & Devel.--Duni AB, Stockholm, Sweden; *Int'l*, pg. 421

Bricknell, Rodger H., V.P.-Res. & Devel.--General Electric Company, Fairfield, CT; *U.S. Public*, pg. 709

Bricout, Jacques, V.P.-Res.--Groupe Pernod Ricard, Paris, France; *Int'l*, pg. 566

Briggs, Mark, V.P.-Res. & Devel.--Thermotron Industries, Holland, MI; *U.S. Private*, pg. 1136

Briggs, Terry, Dir. Mfg. & Res.--Weetabix Limited, Kettering, United Kingdom; *Int'l*, pg. 1488

Bril, John, V.P.-Res. & Devel.--Montgomery KONE Inc., Moline, IL; *Int'l*, pg. 746

Brim, Larry, PhD, Sr. Dir.-Prod. & Process Devel.--HyClone Laboratories Inc., Logan, UT; *Int'l*, pg. 1037

Brinn, Stephen H., V.P.-Res.--Hannaford Bros. Co., Scarborough, ME; *U.S. Public*, pg. 781

Brissette, Peter J., V.P.-Research & Devel.--Shakespeare Monofilament, Columbia, SC; *U.S. Public*, pg. 940

Broberg, Dan, Dir.-Engrng.--Northland Aluminum Products, Inc., Minneapolis, MN; *U.S. Private*, pg. 805

Broder, Samuel, Sr. V.P.-Res. & Devel. & Chief Scientific Officer--IVAX Corporation, Miami, FL; *U.S. Public*, pg. 914

Brokken, Sid, V.P.-Res.--Schering-Plough Animal Health, Union, NJ; *U.S. Public*, pg. 1438

Brolick, Emil J., Sr. V.P.-Strategic Plng. & Res.--Wendy's International Inc., Dublin, OH; *U.S. Public*, pg. 1754

Brookfield, Rowe, PharmD, Exec. Dir.-Res. & Devel.--MET Solutions, LLC, Raleigh, NC; *U.S. Public*, pg. 1642

Brooks, Kelly, Gen. Mgr.--Hitox Corporation of America, Corpus Christi, TX; *U.S. Public*, pg. 829

Brooks, Phil O., Dir.-Tech. & Res. & Devel.--Lance, Inc., Charlotte, NC; *U.S. Public*, pg. 977

Brookshire, Curtis, Dir.-Res. & Devel.--Hackney and Sons, Inc., Washington, NC; *U.S. Private*, pg. 1097

Brophy, Margaret M., Sr. V.P.-Strategic Plng. & Res. Dir.--Young & Rubicam Detroit, Detroit, MI; *U.S. Private*, pg. 1198

Brothers, J.S., Dir.-Res.& Devel.--GEC Plessey Semiconductors, Swindon, United Kingdom; *Int'l*, pg. 544

Brown, Alan, Mgr.-Res. & Devel.--Stanley Steemer International, Inc., Dublin, OH; *U.S. Private*, pg. 1033

Brown, Dennis, Dir.-Res. Maintenance & Acquisitions--Gateway Press, Inc., Louisville, KY; *U.S. Private*, pg. 441

Brown, Dennis L., Dir.-Corp. Devel.--International Multifoods Corporation, Minneapolis, MN; *U.S. Public*, pg. 900

Brown, Felix, Mgr.-Res. & Devel.--Graphic Controls Corporation, Buffalo, NY; *U.S. Private*, pg. 470

Brown, Mark, Mgr.-Res. & Devel.--Virginia Tourism Corp., Richmond, VA; *U.S. Private*, pg. 1141

Brueggeman, Bill, Ph.D., Dir.-Res.--The L & B Group, Dallas, TX; *U.S. Public*, pg. 1673

Brunner, Gordon F., Sr. V.P.-Res. & Devel.--The Procter & Gamble Company, Cincinnati, OH; *U.S. Public*, pg. 1330

Bruns, John, V.P.-Devel.--Renaissance International Hotels, Cleveland, OH; *U.S. Public*, pg. 1048

Brunton, Ellis, Grp. V.P.-Res. & Quality Assurance--Tyson Foods, Inc., Springdale, AR; *U.S. Public*, pg. 1652

Bucher, John H., V.P.-Tech.--Lukens Inc., Coatesville, PA; *U.S. Public*, pg. 1019

Buckley, William N., V.P.-Strategic Plng.--Micros Systems Inc., Beltsville, MD; *U.S. Public*, pg. 1106

Buckman, Thomas W., V.P.-Patents & Tech.--Illinois Tool Works Inc., Glenview, IL; *U.S. Public*, pg. 865

Buckmeier, Ronald, V.P.-Prod. Devel.--Winnebago Industries, Inc., Forest City, IA; *U.S. Public*, pg. 1772

Budzick, James, Mgr.-Prod. Devel.--International Seaway Trading Corporation, Boca Raton, FL; *U.S. Private*, pg. 572

Buettner, Michael L., V.P.-Corp. Devel. & Tech.--Hillenbrand Industries, Inc., Batesville, IN; *U.S. Public*, pg. 828

Bullough, R.P., Mgr.-Res. & Devel.--Chloride Industrial Batteries Ltd., Manchester, United Kingdom; *Int'l*, pg. 125

Bulthuis, K., Dir.-Res.--Philips Electronics N.V., Eindhoven, Netherlands; *Int'l*, pg. 1051

Bumgardner, Clifton Y., Chief Tech. Officer & Sr. V.P.--BTG, Inc., Fairfax, VA; *U.S. Public*, pg. 164

Bumgarner, John C., Jr., Sr. V.P.-Corp. Devel. & Plng. & Pres.-Williams Intl. Co.--The Williams Companies, Inc., Tulsa, OK; *U.S. Public*, pg. 1769

Bupp, Karl, V.P.-Plng. & Admin.--Diamond Technology Partners, Chicago, IL; *U.S. Public*, pg. 1424

Burge, Don, Dir., Res. & Devel.--ConAgra Poultry Co., Duluth, GA; *U.S. Public*, pg. 427

Burger, Richard, Exec. V.P.--Sulzer Ltd., Winterthur, Switzerland; *Int'l*, pg. 1305

Burhardt, Krzysztof, Dr., V.P.-Tech. Devel.--Imation Corporation, Oakdale, MN; *U.S. Public*, pg. 870

Buri, Rudolf, Dr., Mgr.-Res. & Devel.--Coop Switzerland, Basel, Switzerland; *Int'l*, pg. 329

Burk, Richard, V.P.-Strategic Plng.--USLD Communications Corp., San Antonio, TX; *U.S. Public*, pg. 969

Burke, Timothy, Mgr.-Res. & Devel.--Eastern Air Devices, Inc., Dover, NH; *U.S. Private*, pg. 357

Burns, Ralph, Sr. V.P.-Mfg. & Res./Devel.--Peerless Carpet Corporation, Acton Vale, Canada; *Int'l*, pg. 1032

Burrows, Brian W., V.P.-Res. & Tech.--USG Corporation, Chicago, IL; *U.S. Public*, pg. 1660

Burstein, Lonnie, Sr. V.P. & Dir.-Res.--Universal Studios TV, Universal City, CA; *Int'l*, pg. 1215

Burton, John, V.P.-Engrng. & Tech.--Rohr, Inc., Chula Vista, CA; *U.S. Public*, pg. 751

Bush, John B., Jr., Dr., V.P.-Res. & Devel.--The Gillette Company, Boston, MA; *U.S. Public*, pg. 743

Bush, William L., Dir.-Res. & Devel.--Harmon Industries, Inc., Blue Springs, MO; *U.S. Public*, pg. 788

Busse, Charles E., V.P.-Res. Engrng.--Sweetheart Cup Company Inc., Owings Mills, MD; *U.S. Private*, pg. 1058

Butcher, Charles, Mgr.-Market Res.--Scottish Widows' Fund & Life Assurance Society, Edinburgh, United Kingdom; *Int'l*, pg. 1212

Butensky, I., Sr. V.P.-Res. & Devel.--Playtex Beauty Care, Inc., Westport, CT; *U.S. Public*, pg. 1311

Butensky, Irwin S., Sr. V.P.-Res. & Devel.--Playtex Products Inc., Westport, CT; *U.S. Public*, pg. 1310

Butensky, Irwin S., V.P.-Family Prods., Res. & Devel.--Playtex Products Corp., Westport, CT; *U.S. Public*, pg. 1311

Butler, Mike, V.P.-Res. & Devel.--Nokia Mobile Phones (UK) Ltd., Camberley, United Kingdom; *Int'l*, pg. 952

Butterick, Jack L., Dir.-Organizational Devel.--Gerber Products Company, Fremont, MI; *Int'l*, pg. 973

Bybee, Jim L., V.P.-Res. & Devel.--AAI/ACL Technologies, Santa Ana, CA; *U.S. Public*, pg. 1679

Byrne, Michael, V.P.-Res. & Devel.--Global Software, Inc., Raleigh, NC; *U.S. Private*, pg. 457

Byrnes, Ralph R., Sr. V.P.-Automotive Resource Dir.--Consumers Financial Corporation, Camp Hill, PA; *U.S. Public*, pg. 437

Caccese, Arthur, V.P.-Devel.--American Bible Society, New York, NY; *U.S. Private*, pg. 51

Caddock, Richard E. Sr., Pres.--Caddock Electronics, Inc., Riverside, CA; *U.S. Private*, pg. 198

Cain, Kelly, Sr. V.P.-Prod. Devel. & Mdsg.--Stanley Furniture Co. Inc., Stanleytown, VA; *U.S. Public*, pg. 1508

Cain, Mark, Mgr.-Res., Steel Mkts.--Research, Melbourne, Australia; *Int'l*, pg. 227

Calderon, Nissim, V.P.-Res.--The Goodyear Tire & Rubber Company, Akron, OH; *U.S. Public*, pg. 752

Caldwell, Virgil, Mgr.-Prod. Devel.--HyClone Laboratories Inc., Logan, UT; *Int'l*, pg. 1037

Califre, Ronald M., Sr. V.P.-Drug Devel.--Novartis Pharmaceuticals, East Hanover, NJ; *Int'l*, pg. 973

Callahan, Michael S., Dir.--The Harodite Finishing Company Inc., North Dighton, MA; *U.S. Private*, pg. 503

Camille, Gerard, Dir.-Devel. & Mktg.--Credit Mutuel, Paris, France; *Int'l*, pg. 344

Camp, Peter W., V.P.-Project Devel.--Calpine Corporation, San Jose, CA; *U.S. Public*, pg. 296

Campbell, A.J., Res. & Devel.--Quality Bakers New Zealand Ltd., Auckland, New Zealand; *Int'l*, pg. 556

Campbell, Dan, Dir.-Mkt. Res.--CMP Media, Inc., Manhasset, NY; *U.S. Public*, pg. 279

Campbell, Jeff, Sr. V.P.-Brand Devel.--Pepsi-Cola Company, Somers, NY; *U.S. Public*, pg. 1277

Campbell, Kathleen A., V.P. & Mgr.-Market Research--Amcore Financial, Inc., Rockford, IL; *U.S. Public*, pg. 64

Campbell, Melba, V.P.-Bus. Devel. & Dir.-Mktg.--Washington Gas Light Co., Springfield, VA; *U.S. Public*, pg. 1740

Campisi, Frank, V.P.-Res. Quality Control--SFM Media Corporation, New York, NY; *U.S. Private*, pg. 956

Canady, Kathy, Res. Mgr.--The Buntin Group, Nashville, TN; *U.S. Private*, pg. 181

Canal, Patrice, Sr. V.P.-Res.--Compagnie Generale de Geophysique, Massy, France; *Int'l*, pg. 241

Cancilla, Rich, Dir.-Res. & Devel.--Jiffy Lube International, Inc., Houston, TX; *U.S. Public*, pg. 1272

Canclini, D.J., V.P.-Res. & Devel.--Rheem Air Conditioning Div., Fort Smith, AR; *Int'l*, pg. 1022

Cansever, Silas, V.P.-Res. & Devel.--Au Bon Pain Co., Inc., Boston, MA; *U.S. Public*, pg. 146

Capetola, Robert, Dr., V.P.-Res. & Pre-Clinical Devel.--Ohmeda, Liberty Corner, NJ; *Int'l*, pg. 121

Capone, Donald W., V.P.-Engrng. & Construction--AmerenUE, Saint Louis, MO; *U.S. Public*, pg. 66

Caprarola, J., Jr., V.P.-Res. & Devel.--ESAB Consumables, Hanover, PA; *Int'l*, pg. 281

Caprio, James R., V.P. & Chief Scientist--Comptek Federal Systems, Inc., Buffalo, NY; *U.S. Public*, pg. 419

Carpenter, James, V.P.-Res. & Devel.--American Indemnity Financial Corp., Galveston, TX; *U.S. Public*, pg. 83

Carpenter, Sarah, Dir.-Grp. Bus. Devel.--Dixons Group plc, Hemel Hempstead, United Kingdom,; *Int'l*, pg. 413

Carroll, J.R., V.P. & Dir.-Tech.--PQ Corporation, Berwyn, PA; *U.S. Private*, pg. 827

Carruth, L. Brent, V.P.-Opers.--Maynard Oil Co., Dallas, TX; *U.S. Public*, pg. 1064

Carter, Richard, Sr. V.P.-Res. & Prod. Mngmt.--National Bank of Canada, Montreal, Canada; *Int'l*, pg. 907

Carter, William S., V.P.-Res. & Devel.--Xilinx, Inc., San Jose, CA; *U.S. Public*, pg. 1786

Caseau, Paul, Inspector Gen.--Electricite de France, Paris, France; *Int'l*, pg. 437

Cash, Steve, Dir.-Devel.--Progress Paint Mfg. Co., Louisville, KY; *U.S. Private*, pg. 890

Castillon, Pierre, Sr. V.P.-Res., Tech. & Environment--Elf Aquitane, Paris, France; *Int'l*, pg. 444

Catoire, Serge, Corp. V.P.-Res. & Tech.--Aerospatiale, Paris, France; *Int'l*, pg. 28

Catteneo, Giorgio, V.P.-Res. & Devel.--Cassina, Milan, Italy; *Int'l*, pg. 570

Cazes, Roland, Dir.-Res. & Devel.--Sciaky S.A., Vitry-sur-Seine, France; *Int'l*, pg. 1211

Celentano, Domenick A., Jr., V.P.-Mktg. & Adv.--Celentano Bros. Inc., Verona, NJ; *U.S. Private*, pg. 221

Cenna, Timothy J., V.P.-Res.--American Greetings Corporation, Cleveland, OH; *U.S. Public*, pg. 77

Cenna, Timothy J., V.P.-Res.--American Greetings U.S. Greeting Card Division, Cleveland, OH; *U.S. Public*, pg. 78

Chabot, Marc-Andre, Mgr.-Res. & Devel.--Sico Inc., Longueuil, Canada; *Int'l*, pg. 1239

Chakrabati, Subhendu M., V.P.-Res. & Devel.--Gold Medal Div., Minneapolis, MN; *U.S. Public*, pg. 718

Chakravarthy, Padru, Mgr.-Res. & Devel.--Sun Process Converting Company, Elk Grove Village, IL; *U.S. Private*, pg. 1051

Chambliss, Charles W., V.P.-Prod. Devel. & Engrng.--Skyline Corporation, Elkhart, IN; *U.S. Public*, pg. 1476

Chan, Ricky, Exec. V.P.-Far East Opers. & Sr. V.P.-Prod. Devel.--Russ Berrie and Company, Inc., Oakland, NJ; *U.S. Public*, pg. 222

Chance, J. Larry, V.P.-Res. & Devel.--Beloit Corporation, Beloit, WI; *U.S. Public*, pg. 789

Chandler, James, V.P.-Planning & Devel.--PLM International, Inc., San Francisco, CA; *U.S. Public*, pg. 1241

Chang, In-Sung, Mgr.-Strategic Plng.--Samsung Group, Seoul, Korea; *Int'l*, pg. 1181

Chang, William E., V.P.-Res. & Devel.--Stryker Corporation Endoscopy, San Jose, CA; *U.S. Public*, pg. 1526

Chapas, Richard B., V.P.-Res. & Devel.--Rayonier Inc., Stamford, CT; *U.S. Public*, pg. 1363

Chase, Edmund, Exec. V.P.-Strategic Devel.--CPI Corp., Saint Louis, MO; *U.S. Public*, pg. 283

Chaudoin, Elaine, V.P.-Org. Plng. & Devel.--J.B. Hunt Transport Services, Inc., Lowell, AR; *U.S. Public*, pg. 849

Chawla, Ashok, V.P.-Strategic Mngmt.--Mallinckrodt Inc., Saint Louis, MO; *U.S. Public*, pg. 1039

Chawner, Michael, Chief Tech. Officer & V.P.-Product Opers.--Gandalf Technologies Inc., Nepean, Canada; *Int'l*, pg. 540

Chazen, Stephen I., Exec. V.P.-Corp. Devel.--Occidental Petroleum Corporation, Los Angeles, CA; *U.S. Public*, pg. 1210

Chen, C.C., Mgr.-Admin./Res. & Devel.--Taiwan Glass Industry Corp., Taipei, Taiwan; *Int'l*, pg. 1348

Cheng, G.H., V.P.-Tech.--China Steel Corporation, Kao-hsiung, Taiwan; *Int'l*, pg. 285

Chevalier, James L., Dir.-Res. & Devel.--Baltek Corporation, Northvale, NJ; *U.S. Public*, pg. 171

Chicharro, Pedro, Exec. V.P.-Plng. & Res.--Banco Santander, Madrid, Spain; *Int'l*, pg. 143

Ching, Alan, Sr. V.P., Media Plng. & Res. Dir.--Hal Riney & Partners, Inc., San Francisco, CA; *U.S. Private*, pg. 931

Chipperfield, Colin, Mgr.-Res. Opers.--Research, Melbourne, Australia; *Int'l*, pg. 227

Chism, Robert E., V.P.-Devel.--Concurrent Computer Corporation, Fort Lauderdale, FL; *U.S. Public*, pg. 430

Chiu, Y.Y., Dir.--Taiwan Power Company, Taipei, Taiwan; *Int'l*, pg. 1348

Choi, Dong J., Mgr.-Res. & Devel.--Crown Confectionery Co., Ltd., Seoul, Korea; *Int'l*, pg. 348

Chore, Sunlin, V.P. & Dir.-Logic Tech. Devel.--Intel Components Technology & Manufacturing Group, Santa Clara, CA; *U.S. Public*, pg. 886

Chou, Lee, Dr., V.P.-Res. & Devel.--BGF Industries Inc., Greensboro, NC; *U.S. Private*, pg. 106

Choy, Benedict, Sr. V.P. & Sec.--Supertex, Inc., Sunnyvale, CA; *U.S. Public*, pg. 1539

Chrisco, Larry, V.P.-Res. & Devel.--Blitz USA, Inc., Miami, OK; *U.S. Private*, pg. 149

Christensen, Gary S., V.P.-Adv. Devel.--Network Systems Corporation, Minneapolis, MN; *U.S. Public*, pg. 1522

Christianson, William, Dir.-Res. & Devel.--Ed Miniat, Inc., Chicago, IL; *U.S. Private*, pg. 750

Chumney, Jim C., Sr. V.P.-Engrng.--Inter-Tel, Incorporated, Phoenix, AZ; *U.S. Public*, pg. 888

Churchill, G., Dr., Dir.-Govt. Affairs & Quality Control--Theochem Labs., Inc., Tampa, FL; *U.S. Private*, pg. 1079

Ciaramaglia, Frederick J., V.P.-Res. & Devel.--SQA, Inc., Burlington, MA; *U.S. Public*, pg. 1361

Cicci, George, Dir.-Engrng. & Res.--Gehl Company, West Bend, WI; *U.S. Public*, pg. 704

Cintron, Sheri, Audience Res. Mgr.--Western International Media Corporation, Los Angeles, CA; *U.S. Private*, pg. 1165

Cioffi, John, Founder & Chief Tech. Officer--AMATI Communications Corp., San Jose, CA; *U.S. Public*, pg. 1585

Claes, F., Mgr.-Res. & Devel.--Agfa-Gevaert N.V., Antwerp, Belgium; *Int'l*, pg. 174

Clark, Carolyn, Sr. V.P. & Strategic Plng. Dir.--Ingalls, Boston, MA; *U.S. Private*, pg. 562

Clark, Jerry, Dir.-Plng. & Evaluation--CPI Corp., Saint Louis, MO; *U.S. Public*, pg. 283

Clark, Larry D., V.P.-Bus. Devel.--SHL Systemhouse - Latin America Operations, Arlington, VA; *Int'l*, pg. 1154

Clark, Steven C., Sr. V.P.-Discovery Res.--Genetics Institute, Inc., Cambridge, MA; *U.S. Public*, pg. 79

Clary, David, Dir.-Quality Control--Griffin Manufacturing Co., Muskogee, OK; *U.S. Private*, pg. 481

Clausen, Eivind, Sr. Res. & Devel. Engr.--Allsop, Inc., Bellingham, WA; *U.S. Private*, pg. 44

Claypool, Larry, Sr. V.P.- Res. & Quality--Mid-America Dairymen, Inc., Springfield, MO; *U.S. Private*, pg. 743

Clements, Evan, V.P.-Res. & Devel.--Leach International, Buena Park, CA; *U.S. Private*, pg. 655

Clements, M., Dir.-Bus. Devel.--Quadrastat Corp., City of Industry, CA; *U.S. Private*, pg. 17

Clerkin, Tom, V.P. & Dir.-Plng. & Res.--JC Penney Company, Inc., Plano, TX; *U.S. Public*, pg. 916

Clevinger, Norman R., V.P.-Devel. & Plng.--Wolverine Tube Inc., Huntsville, AL; *U.S. Public*, pg. 1774

Clifford, Douglas M., Chief Tech. Officer & V.P.-Res. & Devel.--Iomega Corporation, Roy, UT; *U.S. Public*, pg. 912

Co, Jennifer, Supvr.-Res. & Devel.--Lee Pharmaceuticals, South El Monte, CA; *U.S. Public*, pg. 984

Coblitz, Mark A., V.P.-Strategic Plng.--Comcast Corporation, Philadelphia, PA; *U.S. Public*, pg. 406

Coetzer, J., Mgr.-Res.--Amic Industries Limited, Johanesburg, South Africa; *Int'l*, pg. 76

Cogswell, Theresa, V.P.-Res. & Devel--Interstate Bakeries Corporation, Kansas City, MO; *U.S. Public*, pg. 909

Cole, Allen, Mgr.-Res. & Devel.--Southwest Recreational Industries Inc., Leander, TX; *U.S. Private*, pg. 1018

Cole, Bill, Dir.-Res. & Devel.--Columbine JDS Systems, Inc., Denver, CO; *U.S. Public*, pg. 228

Collings, David A., V.P.-Res. & Devel.--Industrial Acoustics Company, Inc., Bronx, NY; *U.S. Public*, pg. 875

Collins, Harry B., Dr., V.P.-Res.--Delta & Pine Land Company, Scott, MS; *U.S. Public*, pg. 497

Colson, Wendall B., Sr. V.P.-Res. & Devel.--Hunter Douglas, Inc., Upper Saddle River, NJ; *Int'l*, pg. 639

Comley, Ellen, V.P. & Target Plng. Dir.--Miller/Kadanoff/Huber Direct & Interactive, San Francisco, CA; *U.S. Private*, pg. 747

Commender, Linda, V.P. & Res. Dir.--Compton Partners, New York, NY; *U.S. Public*, pg. 1422

Condry, Martin, V.P.-Res. & Devel.--Tyco Preschool, New York, NY; *U.S. Public*, pg. 1058

Conelly, Fred, Dir.-Technical--Star Bronze Company, Alliance, OH; *U.S. Private*, pg. 1034

Connaughton, Alicia G., V.P.-New Business Devel.--Best Foods, Englewood Cliffs, NJ; *U.S. Public*, pg. 224

Conrad, Jeffrey, V.P.-Res. & Devel.--Mattel Games/Puzzles, El Segundo, CA; *U.S. Public*, pg. 1058

Conroy, Patrick, V.P.-Engrng.--MTI Technology Corporation, Anaheim, CA; *U.S. Public*, pg. 1028

Cook, David A., V.P.-Nutritional Res. & Devel. Mead Johnson Nutritional Group--Bristol-Myers Squibb U.S. Pharmaceutical Group, Plainsboro, NJ; *U.S. Public*, pg. 255

Cook, Greg, Pres. & Chief Oper. Officer--Cook Manufacturing Corporation, Duncan, OK; *U.S. Private*, pg. 272

Cook, James C., V.P.-Res. & Devel.--Dodson Group, Kansas City, MO; *U.S. Private*, pg. 338

Cooke, Win, Dir.-Bus.--Alco Chemical, Chattanooga, TN; *Int'l*, pg. 1435

Cooley, Roger B., V.P. & Gen. Mgr.-Res. & Devel.--Binney & Smith Inc., Easton, PA; *U.S. Private*, pg. 496

Coombes, R.S.M., Dir.-Devel.--AEGON Financial Services Group (UK) Ltd., London, United Kingdom; *Int'l*, pg. 28

Cooper, Betty Anne, Mng. Partner-Planning, Segmentation, Lists & Res.--Gillespie, Lawrenceville, NJ; *U.S. Private*, pg. 453

Cooper, David, Chief Tech. Officer--Dentsply New Image, Carlsbad, CA; *U.S. Public*, pg. 499

Cooper, Neal, Mgr.-Prod. Devel.--Ultrak Inc., Lewisville, TX; *U.S. Public*, pg. 1663

Cope, C.W., V.P.-Res.--Marley Mouldings Inc., Marion, VA; *Int'l*, pg. 843

Copeland, Terrence C., V.P.--MacDermid Incorporated, Waterbury, CT; *U.S. Public*, pg. 1029

Corbett, John C., Sr. V.P.-Exploration & Production--Giant Exploration & Production Co., Farmington, NM; *U.S. Public*, pg. 742

Cordery, Alan, Dir.-Global Mktg. & Strategy Devel.--Grand Metropolitan Plc, London, United Kingdom; *Int'l*, pg. 408

Cords, Bruce R., V.P.-Res. & Devel.--Food & Beverage, Saint Paul, MN; *U.S. Public*, pg. 562

Cornell, Linda, V.P.-Plng. & Res.--Sive/Young & Rubicam L.P., Cincinnati, OH; *U.S. Private*, pg. 1197

Corrigan, Donald A., V.P.-Res. & Devel.--Handy & Harman, New York, NY; *U.S. Public*, pg. 780

Corriveau, Christine, Dir.-Research & Devel.--Amurol Confections Co., Yorkville, IL; *U.S. Public*, pg. 1781

Corson, Fred P., V.P.-Res. & Devel.--The Dow Chemical Company, Midland, MI; *U.S. Public*, pg. 522

Costello, Roger, Dir.-Sls. & Devel.--Hollymatic Corporation, Countryside, IL; *U.S. Private*, pg. 535

Cotman, Roger, Chemist--Berryman Products, Inc., Arlington, TX; *U.S. Private*, pg. 138

Cotton, Curran, V.P.-Res. & Devel.--Maytag Company, Newton, IA; *U.S. Public*, pg. 1064

Couder, Alain, Dir.-Info. Tech.--Compagnie des Machines Bull, Louveciennes, France; *Int'l*, pg. 315

Courtin, Olivier, Dr., V.P.-Res. & Devel.--Clarins, Neuilly-sur-Seine, France; *Int'l*, pg. 295

Cox, J. Wesley, Mgr.-Res. & Devel.--Duro-Test Corporation, Fairfield, NJ; *U.S. Private*, pg. 349

Coyne, William E., Sr. V.P.-Res. & Devel.--3M, Saint Paul, MN; *U.S. Public*, pg. 1604

Craft, Quentin D., Dir.-Tech. & Quality--Quaker Chemical Corporation, Conshohocken, PA; *U.S. Public*, pg. 1346

Cramm, Gene F., Sr. V.P. & Dir.-Games & Concept Devel.--ShowBiz Pizza Time, Inc., Irving, TX; *U.S. Public*, pg. 1468

Crasnianski, Serge, Grp. Mng. Dir.-Mfg., Res. & Devel. & Sls.--Photo-Me International plc, Bookham, United Kingdom; *Int'l*, pg. 1055

Cravero, Ricardo, Mgr.-Res. & Devel.--Sancor Cooperativas Unidas Limitadas, Buenos Aires, Argentina; *Int'l*, pg. 1183

Crawford, Gillian, Gen. Mgr.-Project Devel.--Scotts Holdings Limited, Singapore, Singapore; *Int'l*, pg. 1212

Crawford, Jack E., V.P.-Res., Engrng. & Environmental Affairs--Mobil Oil Corporation, Fairfax, VA; *U.S. Public*, pg. 1118

Crecker, Malcolm, Tech. Dir.--Future Foam, Inc., Council Bluffs, IA; *U.S. Private*, pg. 433

Cresswell, Ronald M., Chm.-Parke-Davis Res. & V.P.--Warner-Lambert Company, Morris Plains, NJ; *U.S. Public*, pg. 1738

Crihaldi, Basilio, Mgr.-Res. & Plng.--Cassa di Risparmio delle Provincie Lombarde SpA (CARIPLO), Milan, Italy; *Int'l*, pg. 274

Crispin, George, V.P.-Industrial & Domestic Bus. Devel.--Agripac Inc., Salem, OR; *U.S. Private*, pg. 26

Crockett, Dennis D., V.P.-Consumable Res. & Devel.--The Lincoln Electric Company, Cleveland, OH; *U.S. Public*, pg. 996

Crosby, Kathleen, Mgr.-Res.--Metropolitan Sunday Newspapers, Inc., New York, NY; *U.S. Private*, pg. 739

Cross, Bill, Dir.-Res. & Devel.--Bushnell Corporation, Overland Park, KS; *U.S. Private*, pg. 1191

Crout, Dr. J.R., V.P.-Medical & Scientific Affairs--Boehringer Mannheim Pharmaceuticals Corp., Rockville, MD; *Int'l*, pg. 331

Crowe, Peter, Dir.-Systems Devel.--Mastercare Limited, Hemel Hempstead, United Kingdom; *Int'l*, pg. 414

Crowell, Steve, Mgr.-Mktg.--Cincinnati Gear Company, Cincinnati, OH; *U.S. Private*, pg. 240

Crowley, Larry A., Mgr.-Strategic Plng.--Idaho Power Company, Boise, ID; *U.S. Public*, pg. 861

Culp, Michael, Dir-Res.--PaineWebber Group Incorporated, New York, NY; *U.S. Public*, pg. 1252

Cummings, Timothy J., V.P.-Engrng., Res. & Devel.--Cummings Inc., Nashville, TN; *U.S. Private*, pg. 295

Cybulski, Zach, V.P.-Dev. & Mfg./Tachyarrhythmia Mngmt. Bus.--Medtronic, Inc., Minneapolis, MN; *U.S. Public*, pg. 1082

d'Epinay, Thierry Lalive, Mng. Dir.-Corp. Tech. Innovation--Landis & Staefa AG, Zug, Switzerland; *Int'l*, pg. 800

Dahne, W.D., V.P.-Res. & Devel.--R.J. Reynolds Tobacco Intl., Inc., Geneva, Switzerland; *U.S. Public*, pg. 1355

Dain, R., Dr., Dir.-Res. & Devel.--International Research & Evaluation, Eagan, MN; *U.S. Private*, pg. 571

DalFerro, Gerald, Mgr.-New Project Devel. & Sr. Prod. Engr.--Maxcor Manufacturing, Inc., Colorado Springs, CO; *U.S. Private*, pg. 716

Damiani, Antonio Serafim, Mgr.-Plng. & Fin. Analysis--Sao Paulo Alpargatas S.A., Sao Paulo, Brazil; *Int'l*, pg. 1193

Damlamian, Jean-Jacques, Exec. Dir.-Corp. Devel. & Tech.--France Telecom, Paris, France; *Int'l*, pg. 503

Dana, Charles H., Exec. V.P.-Devel., Plng. & Sourcing--Owens Corning, Toledo, OH; *U.S. Public*, pg. 1236

Daniano, John, V.P.-Res.--National Broadcasting Co., Inc., New York, NY; *U.S. Public*, pg. 712

Daniels, Dennis, Exec. V.P.-Domestic Devel.--United Artists Theatre Circuits Incorporated, Englewood, CO; *U.S. Private*, pg. 1120

Daniels, R.N., V.P.-Devel. & Analysis--Vapor, Niles, IL; *U.S. Public*, pg. 1761

Danielson, Oystein, Mgr.-Res. & Devel.--Frionor A/S, Lysaker, Norway; *Int'l*, pg. 516

Danner, Bonita M., V.P.-Engrng.--Electronic Tele-Communications, Inc., Waukesha, WI; *U.S. Public*, pg. 570

Dansby, Sherri, Res. Analyst--Don Coleman Advertising, Inc., Southfield, MI; *U.S. Private*, pg. 251

Danziger, Itzchak, V.P.-Tech. Devel.--Comverse Technology, Inc., Woodbury, NY; *U.S. Public*, pg. 425

Dapres, Paule, M.D., Sr. V.P.-Res. Opers./Europe--PAREXEL International Corporation, Waltham, MA; *U.S. Public*, pg. 1257

Darby, Michael B., V.P.-Engrng.--Union Pump Company, Battle Creek, MI; *U.S. Private*, pg. 1119

Daud, Razali Mohd, Dir.-Res. Div.--Malaysia Tourism Promotion Board (MTPB), Kuala Lumpur, Malaysia; *Int'l*, pg. 832

Dauphinee, Jim, Sr. V.P.-Programming & Devel.--CBS Enterprises Division, New York, NY; *U.S. Public*, pg. 274

David, Dominique, Devel. Dir.--FCA!BMZ Paris, Suresnes, France; *Int'l*, pg. 469

Davidson Kelly, C. N., Gen. Mgr.-Bus. Devel.--BHP Petroleum, Melbourne, Australia; *Int'l*, pg. 224

Davidson, William, Dir.-Research & Devel.--SCIEX, Concord, Canada; *Int'l*, pg. 827

Davis, Earl E., Exec. V.P.-Commercial--Weirton Steel Corporation, Weirton, WV; *U.S. Public*, pg. 1751

Davis, James W., V.P.-Engrng.--The Raymond Corporation, Greene, NY; *Int'l*, pg. 123

Davis, Ron, Dir.-Engrng. & Res. & Devel.--Hollymatic Corporation, Countryside, IL; *U.S. Private*, pg. 535

Davis, Timothy G., Dir.-Strategic Plng. & Opers.--USDATA Corporation, Richardson, TX; *U.S. Public*, pg. 1425

de Broqueville, Axel, Exec. Dir.-Chemicals, Paints & Res.--Petrofina S.A., Brussels, Belgium; *Int'l*, pg. 1043
De Caprio, Vincent, Chief Tech. Officer & Sr. V.P.--Becton Dickinson & Company, Franklin Lakes, NJ; *U.S. Public*, pg. 199
De Giorgi, Marco, Dr., Mgr.-Res. & Devel.--Lati Industria Termoplastici S.p.A., Vedano Olona, Italy; *Int'l*, pg. 804
de Jesus, Myrna, Dir.-Res.--de la Cruz & Associates, San Juan, PR; *U.S. Private*, pg. 318
de Juniac, Alexandre, Mgr.-Bus. Devel.--Thomson S.A., Paris, France; *Int'l*, pg. 1381
De La Cruz, Dan, Dir.-Res. & Devel.--Zimmer Custom-Made Packaging Co., Indianapolis, IN; *U.S. Private*, pg. 802
De Wit, J.H.W., Sr. Dir.-Corp. Tech.--Koninklijke Hoogovens N.V., Ijmuiden, Netherlands; *Int'l*, pg. 753
Dean, David, Dir.-Res.--The L & B Group, Dallas, TX; *U.S. Public*, pg. 1673
Deans, R.A., Gen. Mgr.-Res. & Devel.--Texaco Inc., White Plains, NY; *U.S. Public*, pg. 1582
Deasy, David, Mgr.-Res. & Devel.--Marietta Corporation, Cortland, NY; *U.S. Private*, pg. 702
DeBord, Donald E., V.P-Technology--Inco Alloys International, Inc., Huntington, WV; *Int'l*, pg. 672
Deck, Bradford B., V.P.-Devel.--Donahue Schriber, Newport Beach, CA; *Int'l*, pg. 253
DeCoursey, J.D., Dir.-New Prods. Plng.--Elanco Animal Health, Indianapolis, IN; *U.S. Public*, pg. 993
Degani, Joshua, Dr., V.P.-Res. & Devel.--Laser Industries Ltd., Tel Aviv, Israel; *Int'l*, pg. 429
Degelman, Scott, Coord.-Res. & Devel.--Degelman Industries Ltd., Regina, Canada; *Int'l*, pg. 388
Degen, Peter, Dr., Sr. V.P. & Dir.-Res. & Devel.--Pall Corporation, Greenvale, NY; *U.S. Public*, pg. 1253
DeJesus, Gigi L., V.P.-Prod. Devel.--Catherines Stores Corporation, Memphis, TN; *U.S. Public*, pg. 317
Delagrave, Pierre, V.P.-Media & Res.--Cossette Communication Marketing, Quebec, Canada; *Int'l*, pg. 335
Delargy, K.J., Dir.-Continuous Improvement--Jefferson Smurfit Corporation, Saint Louis, MO; *Int'l*, pg. 1269
Dellin, Jeff, Mgr.-Res.--Universal Studios TV, Universal City, CA; *Int'l*, pg. 1215
DeLuca, Thomas, V.P.-Imports, Prod. Devel. & Safety Assurance--Toys "R" Us, Inc., Paramus, NJ; *U.S. Public*, *pg. 1626*
Demarmels, Peter, Mgr.-Corp. Devel.--Forbo Holding SA, Eglisau, Switzerland; *Int'l*, pg. 496
DeMeo, Vincent, Jr., Dir.-Res. & Devel.--Bowne & Co., Inc., New York, NY; *U.S. Public*, pg. 248
Deneka, Charles W., Sr. V.P.-Science & Tech.--Corning Incorporated, Corning, NY; *U.S. Public*, pg. 448
Denneny, Joe, Mgr.-Research--The Knight Publishing Co., Charlotte, NC; *U.S. Public*, pg. 964
Denniston, Peter B., Partner-Devel.--Maguire Partners, Los Angeles, CA; *U.S. Private*, pg. 696
Depperman, Warren B., V.P.-Res. & Devel.--Cogsdill Tool Products, Inc., Lugoff, SC; *U.S. Private*, pg. 250
DeRuvo, Alf, Exec. V.P. & Dir.-Res. & Devel.--Svenska Cellulosa Aktiebolaget (SCA), Stockholm, Sweden; *Int'l*, pg. 1326
Desberg, Robert, Mgr.-Res. & Devel.--Hoogovens Aluminium Corp., Secaucus, NJ; *Int'l*, pg. 755
Desmarais, Jean-Pierre, Mgr.-Mdsg., Res. & Devel.--Faucher Industries Inc., Saint Leonard, Canada; *Int'l*, pg. 479
Destival, Claude, Mgr.-Economic Studies, Forecasting & Strategy--Electricite de France, Paris, France; *Int'l*, pg. 437
Dettmann, Peter, Dir.-Res. & Devel.--ICA Handlarnas AB, Solna, Sweden; *Int'l*, pg. 642
Deuling, Deb, Grp. Mgr.-Consumer Research--Gerber Products Company, Fremont, MI; *Int'l*, pg. 973
Devane, John, Ph.D., Exec. V.P.-Res. & Devel. & Acting Chief Scientific Officer--Elan Corporation Plc, Dublin, Ireland; *Int'l*, pg. 435
Dewar, Andrew, Res. Dir.--Dewe Rogerson Limited, London, United Kingdom; *Int'l*, pg. 408
Dewbel, Donald, Dir.-Prod. Devel.--Poly-Seal Corporation, Baltimore, MD; *U.S. Private*, pg. 875
Dhaliwah, Tehsel, V.P.-Science & Tech. Opers.--Soft Sheen Products, Inc., Chicago, IL; *U.S. Private*, pg. 1012
Di Biase, Stephen A., V.P.-Res. & Devel.--The Lubrizol Corporation, Wickliffe, OH; *U.S. Public*, pg. 1016
Diaz, Ariel, Sr. V.P.-Research--Columbia Pictures, Culver City, CA; *Int'l*, pg. 1281
Diaz, David J., Mgr.-Res. & Devel.--Buehler, Limited, Lake Bluff, IL; *U.S. Public*, pg. 574
DiBiagio, A.J. Joseph, Sr. V.P.-Bus. Devel.--Starcraft Corporation, Goshen, IN; *U.S. Public*, pg. 1510
DiCataldo, Emilio, Chief Fin. Officer & V.P.-Res. & Devel.--CVC Products, Inc., Rochester, NY; *U.S. Private*, pg. 197
Dickson, Skeeter, Engr.--Glacier Water Services Inc., Carlsbad, CA; *U.S. Public*, pg. 745
Didier, Ronald, V.P.-Research & Devel.--Groschopp, Inc., Sioux Center, IA; *Int'l*, pg. 559
Diehl, Thomas, V.P.-Res. & Devel.--Diehl Inc., Defiance, OH; *U.S. Private*, pg. 332
Dietrich, Wendell, Chm. Bd. & Chief Exec. Officer--Vidar, Inc., New London, MN; *U.S. Private*, pg. 1139
Dietrich, William V., Exec. V.P.--Kastle Systems LLC, Arlington, VA; *U.S. Private*, pg. 608
Dietz, Paul, Mgr.-Res. & Devel.--Eli Lilly Nederland B.V., Nieuwegein, Netherlands; *U.S. Public*, pg. 994
Diffendal, John, Partner-Res.--J.C. Bradford & Co., Nashville, TN; *U.S. Private*, pg. 163
Digman, Jan, V.P.-Sofware Devel.--Computerized Medical Systems, Inc., Saint Louis, MO; *U.S. Private*, pg. 260
Dionne, Gervais, Ph.D., Exec. V.P.-Res. & Devel.--BioChem Pharma Inc., Laval, Canada; *Int'l*, pg. 196
DiOrio, Joseph J., Dir.-Prod. Res. & Devel.--Computer Systems Research, Inc., Avon, CT; *U.S. Public*, pg. 1070
Dipiazza, Gerald C., V.P.-Res. & Devel--M/A-COM Inc., Lowell, MA; *U.S. Public*, pg. 8
DiQuollo, John, Dir.-Research Services--Federal National Mortgage Association (Fannie Mae), Washington, DC; *U.S. Public*, pg. 615
Discombe, A., Sr. Engr.--Australian Oil & Gas Corporation Limited, Sydney, Australia; *Int'l*, pg. 101
DiSomma, Joseph, Exec. V.P.-Res. & Devel.--Merle Norman Cosmetics, Inc., Los Angeles, CA; *U.S. Private*, pg. 733
DiTonno, Anthony A., Dir.-New Bus. & Devel.--Rhone-Poulenc Rorer - U.S., Collegeville, PA; *Int'l*, pg. 1110
Dixon, Giles, Mgr.-Res. & Devel.--American Buildings Co., Eufaula, AL; *U.S. Public*, pg. 69
Dixon, John R., V.P.-Res. & Devel.--Dawn Food Products, Inc., Jackson, MI; *U.S. Private*, pg. 316
Dobrozsi, John, V.P.-Res.--Farley Candy Company, Chicago, IL; *U.S. Private*, pg. 397
Doddi, Nama, Ph.D., V.P.-Res. & Devel.--Orthofix Inc., Richardson, TX; *Int'l*, pg. 1011
Dolan, Gerry, Mgr.-Res. & Devel.--Genfoot Inc., Montreal, Canada; *Int'l*, pg. 549
Dole, Douglas, Mgr.-Res. & Devel.--Victaulic Company of America, Easton, PA; *U.S. Private*, pg. 1138
Dominguez, Armando Ferriz, Dir.-Tech.--Altos Hornos de Mexico, S.A., Monclova, Mexico; *Int'l*, pg. 66
Dommel, Norbert, Strategic Plng. & Res. Dir.-Germany--DMB&B Frankfurt, Frankfurt/Main, Germany; *U.S. Private*, pg. 303
Donnelly, John, Mgr.-Tech.--M & C Specialties Company, Southampton, PA; *U.S. Private*, pg. 684
Donofrio, Nicholas M., Sr. V.P. & Grp. Exec.-Res., Mfg. & Procurement--International Business Machines Corporation, Armonk, NY; *U.S. Public*, pg. 895
Douma, J., Mgr.-Mktg. & Prod. Devel.--National Electrical Carbon Canada, Mississauga, Canada; *Int'l*, pg. 892
Dowe, James W., III, Chief Scientist--Excalibur Technologies Corporation, Vienna, VA; *U.S. Public*, pg. 598
Dowling, Richard P., Sr. V.P.-Corp. Devel.--General Communication, Inc., Anchorage, AK; *U.S. Public*, pg. 708
Downey, Kevin, V.P. & Assoc. Dir.-Media Res.--Western International Media Corporation, Los Angeles, CA; *U.S. Private*, pg. 1165
Downs, Joe, Dir.-Engrng.--Inkel USA Corporation, La Mirada, CA; *U.S. Private*, pg. 563
Downs, M. Wade, V.P.-Corp. Res. & Analysis--Home Shopping Network, Inc., Saint Petersburg, FL; *U.S. Public*, pg. 1685
Doyal, Linda, Mgr.-Res. & Devel.--Vacu-Dry Company, Sebastopol, CA; *U.S. Public*, pg. 1704
Doza, Douglas K., Dir.-Res. & Devel.--Allied Mineral Products, Inc., Columbus, OH; *U.S. Private*, pg. 39
Draper, Jim, Mgr.-Prod. Devel.--Norbest, Inc., Midvale, UT; *U.S. Private*, pg. 801
Drews, Jurgen, Prof., Mng. Dir.-Research & Devel.--F. Hoffmann-La Roche Ltd., Basel, Switzerland; *Int'l*, pg. 1119
Driscoll, Lisa Clark, V.P.--National Health Care Affiliates, Inc., Buffalo, NY; *U.S. Private*, pg. 784
Driscoll, Timothy J., Dir.-Res. & Devel.--Long Island Lighting Company, Hicksville, NY; *U.S. Public*, pg. 1013
Droz, Claude Francois, Dir.-Res. & Devel.--Nouvelle Lemania S.A., Lorient, Switzerland; *Int'l*, pg. 971
Dryden, Forrest D., V.P.-Res. & Devel.--Hormel Foods Corp., Austin, MN; *U.S. Public*, pg. 840
Dubay, Eugene N., V.P.-Corp. Devel.--ONEOK Inc., Tulsa, OK; *U.S. Public*, pg. 1226
Dube, I., Sr. Officer -Res.--Zimbabwe Electricity Supply Authority, Harare, Zimbabwe; *Int'l*, pg. 1528
DuBois, S.C., V.P.-Res. & Devel.--Wall Colmonoy Corp., Madison Heights, MI; *U.S. Private*, pg. 1148
Duca, James, Dir.-Res. & Devel.--Chyron Corp., Melville, NY; *Int'l*, pg. 1372
Duckwall, Lou, Dir.-Prod. Tech.--Printpack Inc., Atlanta, GA; *U.S. Private*, pg. 886
Duckworth, Charles B., Mgr.-Planning Services--Salt River Project Agricultural Improvement and Power District, Tempe, AZ; *U.S. Private*, pg. 962
Dufour, Eric, Mgr.-Res. & Devel--Security Chimneys International Ltd., Laval, Canada; *Int'l*, pg. 1217
Dulak, John, Mgr.-Product Devel.--The Spencer Turbine Co., Windsor, CT; *U.S. Private*, pg. 1025
Dumen, Thomas, Dir.-Res. & Devel--Forasol S.A., Velizy-Villacoublay, France; *Int'l*, pg. 496
Duncan, Charles L., Dr., V.P.-Res. & Devel.--Hershey Foods Corporation, Hershey, PA; *U.S. Public*, pg. 811
Dunford, James, Jr., Dir.-Bus. Devel.--DRS Precision Echo, Inc., Santa Clara, CA; *U.S. Public*, pg. 474
Dunivant, Noel, Dr., Sr. V.P.-Res. & Strategic Plng.--FGI Inc., Chapel Hill, NC; *U.S. Private*, pg. 389
Duran, Roman, Dr., Dir.-Res. & Devel.--Kalifarma S.A., Barcelona, Spain; *Int'l*, pg. 1279
Durcan, D. Mark, Chief Tech Officer. & V.P.-Res. & Devel.--Micron Technology Inc., Boise, ID; *U.S. Public*, pg. 1105
Dutt, W.H., V.P.-Tech.--Albany International Corp., Albany, NY; *U.S. Public*, pg. 36
Dutton, Dan, Mgr.-Res. & Devel.--Lonza Inc., Fair Lawn, NJ; *Int'l*, pg. 67
Duvall, William R., Sr. V.P.-Opers.--LoJack Corporation, Dedham, MA; *U.S. Public*, pg. 1012
Dykstra, Thomas M., V.P. & Treas.--Effective Management Systems, Milwaukee, WI; *U.S. Public*, pg. 565
Dziewanowska, Zofia E., V.P.-Theraputic Res.--Hoffmann-La Roche Inc., Nutley, NJ; *Int'l*, pg. 1120
Easterbrook, Hugh, V.P.-Intl. Bus. Devel.--Rubbermaid Incorporated, Wooster, OH; *U.S. Public*, pg. 1411
Easton, Dick, Mgr.-Res. & Devel.--LubeCon Systems, Inc., White Cloud, MI; *U.S. Private*, pg. 679
Eberwine, Craig G., V.P.-Corp. Plng. & Devel.--Motorists Mutual Insurance Co., Columbus, OH; *U.S. Private*, pg. 764
Ecker, H. Allen, Ph.D., Chief Oper. Officer & Sr. V.P.-Tech. Opers.--Scientific-Atlanta, Inc., Norcross, GA; *U.S. Public*, pg. 1443
Edelheit, Lewis S., Sr. V.P.-Research & Devel.--General Electric Company, Fairfield, CT; *U.S. Public*, pg. 709
Edwards, D.S., V.P.-Devel.--Edwards Engineering Corporation, Pompton Plains, NJ; *U.S. Private*, pg. 365
Edwards, William, Dir.-Res. & Devel.--Norwalk Powdered Metals, Inc., Norwalk, CT; *U.S. Private*, pg. 808
Efchak, Edward J., V.P.-Strategic Devel.--Macromedia Incorporated, Hackensack, NJ; *U.S. Private*, pg. 693
Effenberger, John A., Dir.-Res. & Devel.--Chemfab Corporation, Merrimack, NH; *U.S. Public*, pg. 344
Efird, Fred, V.P.-Consumer Res.--Advantica Restaurant Group, Inc., Spartanburg, SC; *U.S. Public*, pg. 22
Egberg, David, V.P.-Research--Novartis Nutrition Corporation, Saint Louis Park, MN; *Int'l*, pg. 974
Ehmann, Carl, Grp. Dir.-Global Res. & Devel.--Reckitt & Colman plc, London, United Kingdom; *Int'l*, pg. 1089
Ehmann, Carl W., M.D., Exec. V.P.-Res. & Devel.--R.J. Reynolds Tobacco Company, Winston Salem, NC; *U.S. Public*, pg. 1355
Eide, Melvin O., V.P.-Res. & Devel.--Interpoint, Redmond, WA; *U.S. Public*, pg. 457
Eisenstadt, Samuel, Sr. V.P. & Res. Chm.--Value Line, Inc., New York, NY; *U.S. Private*, pg. 137
Eisler, Susan, Exec. V.P. & Res. Dir.--Gotham Incorporated, New York, NY; *U.S. Private*, pg. 677
El Shami, Said, Chief Scientific Officer & Sr. V.P.-Res. & Devel.--Diagnostic Products Corporation, Los Angeles, CA; *U.S. Public*, pg. 505
Elgin, Jeff, V.P. & Dir.-Devel.--Great Clips, Inc., Minneapolis, MN; *U.S. Private*, pg. 473
Elish, Walter J., Dir.-Economic Devel.--Maine Public Service Company, Presque Isle, ME; *U.S. Public*, pg. 1038
Elisseche, Jean, Mgr.-Devel.--GEODIS, Paris, France; *Int'l*, pg. 549
Ellioff, Cheryl, Mgr.-Q.A. & Res. & Devel.--Enzopac, Inc., Sheboygan, WI; *U.S. Private*, pg. 379
Elliot, Dan D., V.P.-Prod. Devel.--F.E. Myers, Ashland, OH; *U.S. Public*, pg. 1273
Elliot, Tom, Exec. V.P.-Intl. Devel.--United Artists Theatre Circuits Incorporated, Englewood, CO; *U.S. Private*, pg. 1120
Emerson, Peter, Technical Dir.--PRC (UK) Ltd., Newcastle upon Tyne, United Kingdom; *Int'l*, pg. 339
Emery, J. D., Sr. V.P.-Res.--Brown Marketing Communications, Chicago, IL; *U.S. Private*, pg. 174
Epron, Luc, Dir.-Plng. & Mktg.--Automobiles Citroen, Neuilly, France; *Int'l*, pg. 1020
Epstein, Garcy C., Mng. Partner & Bus. Devel. Dir.--EURO RSCG Tatham, Chicago, IL; *Int'l*, pg. 601
Epstein, Philip, V.P.-Res. & Devel.--DAQ Electronics Inc., Piscataway, NJ; *U.S. Private*, pg. 300
Erb, Earl C., Dir.-Technical Services--Hanover Foods Corporation, Hanover, PA; *U.S. Private*, pg. 499
Erhardt, Mark, Sr. Research Analyst--Old Kent Bank, Grand Rapids, MI; *U.S. Public*, pg. 1216
Erickson, Lance, V.P.--Old Kent Bank, Grand Rapids, MI; *U.S. Public*, pg. 1216
Ernest, Jacques, Deputy Dir.-Res. & Tech.--Alcatel N.V., Amsterdam, Netherlands; *Int'l*, pg. 55
Eu, Henry, Res. Dir. & Mkt. Plng. Dir.--Suissa Miller Advertising, Inc., Los Angeles, CA; *U.S. Private*, pg. 1049
Eutsler, Kevin, Dir.-Training--Carrier Corp., Indianapolis, IN; *U.S. Public*, pg. 1690
Evangelista, Thomas E., V.P.-Corp. Devel. & Commun.--Stanhome Inc., Westfield, MA; *U.S. Public*, pg. 1508
Evangelsta, Claro B., Asst. Gen. Mgr.--Benguet Corporation, Manila, Philippines; *Int'l*, pg. 186
Evans, David J.R., V.P.-Tech. & Bus. Devel.--Nordion International Inc., Kanata, Canada; *Int'l*, pg. 827
Evans, Lawrence E., Mgr.-Res. & Devel.--AutoZone, Inc., Memphis, TN; *U.S. Public*, pg. 150
Evans, Ray, V.P.-Tire Engrng.--Titan International, Inc., Quincy, IL; *U.S. Public*, pg. 1618
Evans, Ronald A., V.P.-Strategic Bus. Devel.--Mitel Corporation, Kanata, Canada; *Int'l*, pg. 870
Evans, Russell, Chief Engineer--Fleischer Manufacturing, Inc., Columbus, NE; *U.S. Private*, pg. 410
Evensen, Oystein, V.P.-Res. & Devel.--Aquatic Animal Health, Oslo, Norway; *U.S. Public*, pg. 58
Everett, Edward N., Res. Analyst--Rochester Fund Municipals, Rochester, NY; *U.S. Private*, pg. 937
Everitt, Richard, Grp. Dir.-Strategy & Compliance--BAA plc, London, United Kingdom; *Int'l*, pg. 103
Eynon, Steve, V.P.-Res. & Devel.--Guardian Products, Inc., Simi Valley, CA; *U.S. Public*, pg. 1535
Fair, Lance, V.P.-Acq. & Strategic Plng.--Master Graphic, Inc., Memphis, TN; *U.S. Private*, pg. 713
Fairbanks, M. Kathleen, Proposal Mgr.--Jacobs Engineering Group Inc., Baton Rouge, LA; *U.S. Public*, pg. 921
Falbe, Jurgen, Exec. V.P.-Res. & Tech.--Henkel KGaA, Dusseldorf, Germany; *Int'l*, pg. 609
Falk, Jurgen, Mktg. Res. Dir.--Westag Werbeagentur, Cologne, Germany; *Int'l*, pg. 1491
Fanguy, Dennis, Dir.-Tech., Res. & Devel.--Bollinger Shipyards, Inc., Lockport, LA; *U.S. Private*, pg. 155
Farrell, Dawn L., V.P.-Bus. Devel.--Transalta Corporation, Calgary, Canada; *Int'l*, pg. 1416
Farrell, Moira, Sr. V.P.-Corp. Res. & Sls. Mktg.--King World Productions, Inc., New York, NY; *U.S. Public*, pg. 961
Farrell, Moira, Sr. V.P.-Corp. Res. & Sls. Mktg.--King World Productions, Los Angeles, CA; *U.S. Public*, pg. 961
Fay, John A., V.P.-Opers.--Hull Corporation, Hatboro, PA; *U.S. Private*, pg. 547
Fecher, Doug, Dir.-Prod. Devel.--NIBCO, Inc., Elkhart, IN; *U.S. Private*, pg. 798
Feider, Tom, Mgr.-Engrng.--Marine Travelift, Inc., Sturgeon Bay, WI; *U.S. Private*, pg. 703
Feight, David J., V.P. & Dir.-Bus. Devel.--Armstrong World Industries, Inc., Lancaster, PA; *U.S. Public*, pg. 131
Feimer, Michael P., Dir.-Res. & Devel.--Guarantee Life Insurance Co., Omaha, NE; *U.S. Public*, pg. 768
Felix, Charles R., Sr. V.P.-Devel.--Universal Forest Products, Inc., Grand Rapids, MI; *U.S. Public*, pg. 1696

Ferguson, William D., Mgr.-Res. & Devel.--Delmarva Power & Light Company, Wilmington, DE; *U.S. Public*, pg. 430
Ferm, Martha, Dir.-Business Systems Dev.--Standard & Poor's Compustat Services, Inc., Englewood, CO; *U.S. Public*, pg. 1071
Fernandez, Richard, M.D., Mng. Dir.--AmeriPath, Inc., Riviera Beach, FL; *U.S. Public*, pg. 96
Fernlock, Doug, Dir.-Res. & Strategic Plng.--J.W. Messner, Inc., Grand Rapids, MI; *U.S. Private*, pg. 734
Ferretti, George S., Chief Fin. Officer--The Keyes Company Realtors, Miami, FL; *U.S. Private*, pg. 618
Feuerstein, John, V.P.-Prod. Devel.--The Stiffel Company, Chicago, IL; *U.S. Private*, pg. 1043
Fewell, Ken, Dir.-Res. & Devel.--Peerless Mfg. Co., Dallas, TX; *U.S. Public*, pg. 1268
Fidoten, Douglas, Exec. V.P. & Strategic Plng. Dir.--DCA Advertising, Inc., New York, NY; *Int'l*, pg. 393
Fielder, Virginia Dodge, V.P.-Res.--Knight-Ridder, Inc., Miami, FL; *U.S. Public*, pg. 963
Figdore, Phillip, Dr., Mgr.-Res. & Devel.--West Chemical Products, Inc., Princeton, NJ; *U.S. Private*, pg. 1158
Filis-Burkhardt, Peggy, V.P.-Res.--CBS Enterprises Division, New York, NY; *U.S. Public*, pg. 274
Fillingham, Ashley, Mgr.-Prod. Devel.--BNA International Inc., London, United Kingdom; *U.S. Private*, pg. 182
Fina, Frank, Jr., Sr. V.P.-Bus. Devel.--General Cigar Company, Inc., Bloomfield, CT; *U.S. Public*, pg. 708
Finch, Frank, Dr., Dir.-Res. & Devel.--Andes Candies Inc., Delavan, WI; *U.S. Private*, pg. 163
Fink, Raymond, V.P.-Res. & Devel.--Quark Inc., Denver, CO; *U.S. Private*, pg. 900
Finnelt, Paul, Dir.-Res. & Devel.--Michael Anthony Jewelers, Inc., Mount Vernon, NY; *U.S. Public*, pg. 1103
Fiorivanti, Domenick, Sr. V.P.-Intl. Networks--Discovery Networks, Inc., Bethesda, MD; *U.S. Private*, pg. 334
Fischer, Daniel, V.P.-Res.--Discovery Networks, Inc., Bethesda, MD; *U.S. Private*, pg. 334
Fitzgerel, Barbara S., Dir.-Prod. Mngmt. & Res.--Tax Management, Inc., Washington, DC; *U.S. Private*, pg. 182
Fitzjohn, David, Head-Worldwide Development--Burger King Corporation, Miami, FL; *Int'l*, pg. 411
Fleck, Philip B., V.P.-Res. & Mfg.--Arrow International, Inc., Reading, PA; *U.S. Public*, pg. 135
Fleischner, Albert, Ph.D., V.P.-Pharmaceutical Res. & Devel.--Doak Dermatologics, Westbury, NY; *U.S. Public*, pg. 250
Fleming, Anthony L., V.P.-Res. & Devel.--Biomet, Inc., Warsaw, IN; *U.S. Public*, pg. 231
Fletcher, Don, V.P.-Hallmark/Prod. Devel.--Hallmark Cards, Inc., Kansas City, MO; *U.S. Private*, pg. 495
Flora, Dave, Mgr.-Res. & Devel.--Shopsmith, Inc., Dayton, OH; *U.S. Public*, pg. 1467
Floryan, Daniel E., V.P.-Qual. & Tech.--Phelps Dodge Magnet Wire Co., Fort Wayne, IN; *U.S. Public*, pg. 1286
Foemmel, Richard S., V.P.-New Bus. Devel.--Dianon Systems, Inc., Stratford, CT; *U.S. Public*, pg. 506
Folena-Wasserman, Gail, Ph.D., V.P.-Devel.--MedImmune, Inc., Gaithersburg, MD; *U.S. Public*, pg. 1081
Foley, Jim, V.P.-Res. & Devel.--K-Tron International, Inc., Pitman, NJ; *U.S. Public*, pg. 938
Fontanella, Adrienne, V.P.-Mktg. & Devel.--Sanofi Beaute, Inc., New York, NY; *Int'l*, pg. 445
Foote, Jerrold L., V.P.-Res. & Devel.--Merit Medical Systems, Inc., South Jordan, UT; *U.S. Public*, pg. 1096
Forbes, Rob, V.P.-Bus. Devel.--Smith & Hawken, Mill Valley, CA; *U.S. Public*, pg. 279
Ford, Gary, V.P.-Plng. & Res.--Shelter Mutual Insurance Company, Columbia, MO; *U.S. Private*, pg. 992
Forier, David, Dir.-Research--Ladies' Home Journal, New York, NY; *U.S. Public*, pg. 1094
Forman, Fred L., Chief Info. Officer & Exec. V.P.--American Management Systems, Inc., Fairfax, VA; *U.S. Public*, pg. 86
Forsythe, Dolores, Dir.-Mngmt. Devel.--Viking Office Products, Torrance, CA; *U.S. Public*, pg. 1720
Foster, Alan W., Sr. V.P.-Res. & Devel.--ChemDesign Corporation, Fitchburg, MA; *Int'l*, pg. 173
Foster, Yolanda, Dir.-Res.--WFOR-TV Channel 4, Miami, FL; *U.S. Public*, pg. 275
Fowler, Fred V., III, V.P.-Adv. & Sls.--Fred V. Fowler Company, Inc., Newton, MA; *U.S. Private*, pg. 422
Fox, David, Dr., V.P.-Res. & Devel.--DeKalb Swine Breeders, Inc., De Kalb, IL; *U.S. Public*, pg. 493
Fraedrich, Bruce R., V.P.-Res.--The F.A. Bartlett Tree Expert Co., Stamford, CT; *U.S. Private*, pg. 119
Fraisl, Daniel, V.P.-Res. & Devel.--Software Publishing Corporation, Fairfield, NJ; *U.S. Public*, pg. 1483
Frame, Thomas H., V.P.-Res. & Devel.--Gamma Biologicals Inc., Houston, TX; *U.S. Public*, pg. 698
Francis, Ross, V.P.-Devel.--Brunschwig & Fils, Inc., White Plains, NY; *U.S. Private*, pg. 176
Frangules, Philippe A., V.P.-Strategic Plng. & New Bus.--Boston Edison Company, Boston, MA; *U.S. Public*, pg. 247
Frangules, Philippe A., V.P.-Bus. Devel.--Boston Energy Technology Group, Inc., Boston, MA; *U.S. Public*, pg. 247
Frank, Michael J., V.P.-Bus. Devel.--Learning International, Stamford, CT; *U.S. Public*, pg. 1617
Frank, Paul D., Dr., V.P.-Res. & Devel. & Chief Tech. Officer--Applied Magnetics Corporation, Goleta, CA; *U.S. Public*, pg. 123
Franke, David G., Sr. Process Engrng.--Badger Paper Mills, Inc., Peshtigo, WI; *U.S. Public*, pg. 165
Franke, William, V.P.-Res. & Prod. Devel.--Thomas J. Lipton Company, Englewood Cliffs, NJ; *Int'l*, pg. 1435
Franklin, Ronald, Exec. V.P. & Mktg. Services Dir.--Don Coleman Advertising, Inc., Southfield, MI; *U.S. Private*, pg. 251
Franz, G. Andrew, Chief Oper. Officer & Sr. V.P.-Opers./Pharmaceuticals--Jones Medical Industries Inc., Saint Louis, MO; *U.S. Public*, pg. 933
Freehill, Kate, V.P. & Assoc. Plng. Dir.--Western International Media Corporation, New York, NY; *U.S. Private*, pg. 1166
Freeman, Mark, Mgr.-Sls.-Bus. Devel.--Brite Voice Systems Group, Ltd., Cheadle, United Kingdom; *U.S. Public*, pg. 257
Fresquez, Luis, Chief Info. Officer & Sr. V.P.--American Automobile Association, Heathrow, FL; *U.S. Private*, pg. 50
Frey, Walter, Dr., Div. Head-Engrng, Res. & Devel.--BASF AG, Ludwigshafen, Germany; *Int'l*, pg. 103
Fried, David S., V.P.-Strategic Bus. Devel.-Los Angeles--Leon Shaffer Golnick Advertising, Inc., Fort Lauderdale, FL; *U.S. Private*, pg. 463
Friedlander, Lindy J., Sr. V.P.-Res. & Prod. Devel.--Washington Mutual Inc., Seattle, WA; *U.S. Public*, pg. 1741
Friedman, Lois, V.P.-Res.--Madison Square Garden Network, New York, NY; *U.S. Public*, pg. 288
Friedman, Nadav, PhD., M.D., V.P.-Clinical Research--XOMA Corporation, Berkeley, CA; *U.S. Public*, pg. 1786
Friedrich, Kurt, Sr. V.P. & Gen. Mgr.-Systems Devel.Grp.--Tandem Computers Inc., Cupertino, CA; *U.S. Public*, pg. 417
Friend, J., Gen. Mgr.-Tech. & Res.--Burns, Philp & Company Limited, Sydney, Australia; *Int'l*, pg. 236
Frier, Jim, Mgr.-Res. & Devel.--Tetko, Inc., Briarcliff Manor, NY; *U.S. Private*, pg. 1078
Fritsch, Edward F., V.P.-Prod. Devel.--Genetics Institute, Inc., Cambridge, MA; *U.S. Public*, pg. 79
Froeschle, Thomas, Dir.-Res. & Devel.--Bose Corporation, Framingham, MA; *U.S. Private*, pg. 160
Frohlinger, Debra, Plng. & Res.--Hampel/Stefanides, New York, NY; *U.S. Private*, pg. 498
Frosch, Robert A., V.P.-Res. Labs--General Motors Corporation, Detroit, MI; *U.S. Public*, pg. 718
Fuglevand, Bill, Mgr.-Res., Devel. & Tech.--The Washington Water Power Company, Spokane, WA; *U.S. Public*, pg. 1744
Fujii, Dazuaki, Dir.-Senai Res. Laboratory--Kokusai Electric Co., Ltd., Tokyo, Japan; *Int'l*, pg. 743
Fujii, H., V.P.-Res & Devel.--Kawasaki Motors Corp., U.S.A., Irvine, CA; *Int'l*, pg. 725
Fukui, Hideo, Gen. Mgr.-Res. & Devel.--Terumo Corporation, Tokyo, Japan; *Int'l*, pg. 1375
Fumero, Silvano, Sr. Exec. V.P.-Res. & Devel.--Ares-Serono S.A., Geneva, Switzerland; *Int'l*, pg. 80
Funk, Roger, Dr., V.P.-Human & Technical Resources--The Davey Tree Expert Company, Kent, OH; *U.S. Private*, pg. 314
Funke, William, V.P.-Tech. & Engrng.--Industrial Dielectrics, Inc., Noblesville, IN; *U.S. Private*, pg. 560
Furler, Alan G., Dir.-Res. & Devel./Anesthesia--Vital Signs, Inc., Totowa, NJ; *U.S. Public*, pg. 1723
Furlott, Mike, Mgr.-Dealer Devel.--OmniQuip International, Inc., Port Washington, WI; *U.S. Private*, pg. 500
Furuhashi, Masao, Mng. Dir. & Sr. Gen. Mgr.-Devel.--West Japan Railway Company, Osaka, Japan; *Int'l*, pg. 1490
Gabriel, Lynn, Dir.-Res. & Quality Control--IHOP Corp., Glendale, CA; *U.S. Public*, pg. 862
Gagner, Michael, V.P.-Engrng.--The Will-Burt Company, Orrville, OH; *U.S. Private*, pg. 1177
Gahn, Jerry, Dir.-Prod. Devel.--Diagraph Corporation, Earth City, MO; *U.S. Private*, pg. 330
Galante, Gary, Dir.-Res. & Devel.--Chattem, Inc., Chattanooga, TN; *U.S. Public*, pg. 341
Galdes, Alphonse, Ph.D, Dir.-Protein Engrng. Res.--Biogen, Inc., Cambridge, MA; *U.S. Public*, pg. 230
Galica, James P., Dir.-Laboratory--Springborn Testing & Research, Inc., Enfield, CT; *U.S. Private*, pg. 1027
Galleher, John C., V.P.-Res. & Devel.--Brian Unlimited Distribution Company, Inc., Detroit, MI; *U.S. Private*, pg. 167
Garcia, C.B., Sr. Res. Consultant--Investment Research Company, Rancho Santa Fe, CA; *U.S. Public*, pg. 1673
Gardner, Phyllis, Dr., V.P.-Res.--Alza Corporation, Palo Alto, CA; *U.S. Public*, pg. 62
Garnick, Marc B., V.P.-Clinical Devel.--Genetics Institute, Inc., Cambridge, MA; *U.S. Public*, pg. 79
Garthwaite, Stephen J., Sr. V.P.-Innovation & Tech.--General Mills, Inc., Minneapolis, MN; *U.S. Public*, pg. 717
Garvey, R. Michael, V.P.-Engrng. & Rsch.--Frequency and Time Systems, Inc., Beverly, MA; *U.S. Public*, pg. 488
Garvin-Gowey, Gail, Dir.-Res. & Devel.--Del Taco, Inc., Laguna Hills, CA; *U.S. Private*, pg. 321
Garvin, Deborah, Dir.-Res. Plng.--American Kennel Club, Inc., New York, NY; *U.S. Private*, pg. 58
Gaskill, David M., Jr., V.P.-Res. & Devel.--Astro-Med, Inc., West Warwick, RI; *U.S. Public*, pg. 141
Gastineau, Edward L., Dir.-Res. & Devel.--Central and South West Corporation, Dallas, TX; *U.S. Public*, pg. 324
Gaudette, Roger, V.P.-Res. & Devel.--Hampshire Chemical Corp., Lexington, MA; *U.S. Private*, pg. 498
Gaultiere, Gregory, Dir.-Res. & Devel.--Edwin B. Stimpson Company, Inc., Bayport, NY; *U.S. Private*, pg. 1043
Geaghan, Bernard, V.P.-Res.--Microtouch Systems, Inc., Methuen, MA; *U.S. Public*, pg. 1108
Geertsema, Arie, Mng. Dir.-Res. & Devel. Div.--Sasol Technology (Pty) Ltd., Sasolburg, South Africa; *Int'l*, pg. 1197
Geiler, Cliff, Mgr.-Res. & Devel.--Security Plastics, Inc., Hialeah, FL; *U.S. Private*, pg. 981
Geist, Lee, V.P.-Engrng. & Res. & Devel.--Vital Signs, Englewood, CO; *U.S. Public*, pg. 1723
Georgalas, Art, Dir.-Res. & Devel.--Tri-K Industries, Inc., Northvale, NJ; *U.S. Private*, pg. 1100
Georgian, Paul, Dir.-Mkt. Research--Avis Rent A Car System, Inc., Garden City, NY; *U.S. Public*, pg. 321
Gerber, Hadassa, Exec. V.P.-Media Plng. & Res.--DeWitt Media, Inc., New York, NY; *U.S. Private*, pg. 329
Gerchenson, Emile H., Chm. Bd. & Chief Exec. Officer--Alva/Amco Pharmacal Companies, Inc., Chicago, IL; *U.S. Private*, pg. 47
Germann, Karlel, Dir.-Technical & Res. & Devel.--Fotolabo S.A., Lausanne, Switzerland; *Int'l*, pg. 501
Gershfield, Bruce, Dir.-Corp. Res.--TV Guide Magazine, Radnor, PA; *Int'l*, pg. 925
Gharagozlou, Yahya, V.P. & Corp. Tech. Dir.--Instron Corporation, Canton, MA; *U.S. Public*, pg. 882
Gherini, Steven A., V.P.-Res. & Devel.--Tetra Tech, Inc., Pasadena, CA; *U.S. Public*, pg. 1582
Giachardi, David, Dir.-H.R., Health, Safety & Environment--Courtaulds plc, London, United Kingdom; *Int'l*, pg. 338
Giacoponello, Joseph A., V.P.-Bus. Devel.--Sanders, A Lockheed Martin Company, Nashua, NH; *U.S. Public*, pg. 1008
Giannelli, Ray, V.P.-Res. & Devel.--Cybex International, Inc., Medway, MA; *U.S. Private*, pg. 1114
Giannini, Dennis, V.P.-Design Engrng. & Res. & Devel.--TriEnda Corporation, Portage, WI; *U.S. Private*, pg. 1103
Gibbard, Frank, V.P.-Res. & Devel.--Duracell International Inc., Bethel, CT; *U.S. Public*, pg. 743
Gibbon, Michael A., Sr. V.P.-Tech.--Imax Corporation, Mississauga, Canada; *Int'l*, pg. 661
Gilbert, George G., V.P.-Tech. Svcs.--Simpson Industries, Inc., Plymouth, MI; *U.S. Public*, pg. 1474
Gillett, Anthony F., V.P.-Bus. Plng.--Monier Inc., Irvine, CA; *Int'l*, pg. 1091
Gillis, John, Exec. V.P. & Res./Devel. Dir.--Ross Roy Communications, Inc., Bloomfield Hills, MI; *U.S. Private*, pg. 946
Gilmour, Alan, Dir.-Bus. Devel.--Lloyds TSB Group PLC, London, United Kingdom; *Int'l*, pg. 812
Gilroy, James F., V.P.-Product Strategy--ComputerLand Canada, Brampton, Canada; *Int'l*, pg. 1154
Giminez, Raul, Mgr.-Res. & Devel.--National R.V., Inc., Perris, CA; *U.S. Public*, pg. 1159
Ginis, Asterios M., V.P.-Res. & Devel.--Cereal Partners Worldwide, Morges, Switzerland; *U.S. Public*, pg. 718
Ginis, Asterios M., V.P.-Res. & Devel.--Cereal Partners Worldwide, Morges, Switzerland; *Int'l*, pg. 916
Giordan, Judith, V.P. & Dir.-Res.--International Flavors & Fragrances, Inc., New York, NY; *U.S. Public*, pg. 898
Glass, Robert W., Sr. V.P.-Corp. Devel.--Robert Half International Inc., Menlo Park, CA; *U.S. Public*, pg. 774
Glasson, I. D., Grp Mgr.-Corp. Devel.--Goodman Fielder Limited, Sydney, Australia; *Int'l*, pg. 555
Gleason, John H., Sr. V.P.-Project Plng. & Devel.--Del Webb Corporation, Phoenix, AZ; *U.S. Public*, pg. 494
Gleason, Larry, Dir.-Engr.--Ohmite Manufacturing Company, Skokie, IL; *U.S. Private*, pg. 813
Glodowski, Mark, Mgr.-Research & Devel.--Serfilco, Ltd., Northbrook, IL; *U.S. Private*, pg. 985
Glover, P., V.P.-Bus. Devel.--Coltec Industries Inc., Charlotte, NC; *U.S. Public*, pg. 401
Goble, Wayne, Dir.-Res. & Sls. Promos.--B.A.S.S., Inc., Montgomery, AL; *U.S. Private*, pg. 105
Godfrey, Debbie, Exec. V.P. & Creative Res. Dir.-Y&RNY--Young & Rubicam New York, New York, NY; *U.S. Private*, pg. 1198
Goebel, Dale R., V.P.-Engrng.-Platform Div.--Sequent Computer Systems, Inc., Beaverton, OR; *U.S. Public*, pg. 1459
Goins, Dixie E., V.P.-Res. & Devel.--Albemarle Corporation, Richmond, VA; *U.S. Public*, pg. 37
Gold, Adam, V.P.-Television Res., Los Angeles--CBS Television Network, New York, NY; *U.S. Public*, pg. 274
Goldberg, Lauri, V.P., Assoc. Res. Dir.--Ammirati, Puris & Lintas, Inc., New York, NY; *U.S. Private*, pg. 66
Goldberger, William M., V.P.-Res. & Devel.--Superior Graphite Co., Chicago, IL; *U.S. Private*, pg. 1054
Goldenberg, Jim, Dir.-Res. & Devel.--Cubix Corporation, Carson City, NV; *U.S. Private*, pg. 294
Goldstein, Guy, V.P.-Res. & Devel.--JA/MONT N.V. - Technology Office, Muntzenheim, France; *U.S. Public*, pg. 673
Gomez-Troff, Monica, Strategic Plng. & Devel Mgr.--Western Multicultural Group, Los Angeles, CA; *U.S. Private*, pg. 1167
Gompert, David G., V.P.-Natl. Security Res.--RAND, Santa Monica, CA; *U.S. Private*, pg. 908
Gooch, Ralph, Mgr.-Res. & Devel.--Flexfab Horizons International, Inc., Hastings, MI; *U.S. Private*, pg. 412
Goode, Susan, Asst. V.P.-Res. Svcs.--Lutheran Brotherhood, Minneapolis, MN; *U.S. Private*, pg. 681
Gordon, Bernard M., Chm. Bd. & Chief Exec. Officer--Analogic Corporation, Peabody, MA; *U.S. Public*, pg. 109
Gorka, Chris, Res.--SFM Media Corporation, New York, NY; *U.S. Private*, pg. 956
Gorman, Robert R., Dr., V.P.-Discovery Res.--Pharmacia & Upjohn, Kalamazoo, MI; *Int'l*, pg. 1048
Gothe, Stig, Sr. V.P. Bus. & Strategic Devel.--Vattenfall AB, Stockholm, Sweden; *Int'l*, pg. 1452
Goughenour, Robert J., V.P.-Wholesaler Devel.--Anheuser-Busch, Inc., Saint Louis, MO; *U.S. Public*, pg. 114
Gowans, Jim, Gen. Mgr.-Res. & Design--Placer Dome Inc., Vancouver, Canada; *Int'l*, pg. 1060
Gozlan, Jean-Claude, Dir.-Res.--Facom, Morangis, France; *Int'l*, pg. 570
Grady, James, Mgr.-Res., Devel. & Engrng.--SouthCo. Inc., Concordville, PA; *U.S. Private*, pg. 1014
Graham, Ken, V.P.-Res.--Hyde Athletic Industries, Inc., Peabody, MA; *U.S. Public*, pg. 851
Graney, Patty, Res.--SFM Media Corporation, New York, NY; *U.S. Private*, pg. 956
Granger, Richard, V.P.-Res. & Devel.--U.S. Surgical Corp., Norwalk, CT; *U.S. Public*, pg. 1687
Graser, Mark, V.P.-Business Devel.--The Danis Companies, Dayton, OH; *U.S. Private*, pg. 310
Grau, Stuart, Res. & Acct. Plng. Dir.--Avrett, Free & Ginsberg, Inc., New York, NY; *U.S. Private*, pg. 103
Gray, Kenneth, Dr., Grp. Technical Dir.--EMI Group plc, London, United Kingdom; *Int'l*, pg. 426
Graziano, Frank, Sr. V.P.-Tech.--Material Sciences Corporation, Elk Grove Village, IL; *U.S. Public*, pg. 1056

Green, A., Mng. Dir.-Res., Devel. & Info. Sys.--United Biscuits (Holdings) Plc, West Drayton, United Kingdom; *Int'l*, pg. 1442
Green, Robert, Res. Dir.--DKB & Partners, Inc., Morristown, NJ; *U.S. Private*, pg. 302
Greenbelt, Seth, Mgr.-Res. & Devel.Tech.--Betac International Corporation, Alexandria, VA; *U.S. Private*, pg. 140
Greenberg, N. Geoffrey, V.P.-Res. & Devel.--American & Efird, Inc., Mount Holly, NC; *U.S. Public*, pg. 1412
Greene McChesney, Cynthia, Bus. Devel. Dir.--Fogarty Klein & Partners, Houston, TX; *U.S. Private*, pg. 415
Greenfield, Rick, Mkt. Res.--Colle & McVoy Marketing Communications, Minneapolis, MN; *U.S. Private*, pg. 252
Greenfield, Steve, Exec. Dir.-New Product Devel.--Catalina Marketing Corporation, Saint Petersburg, FL; *U.S. Public*, pg. 314
Greenwood, Donald J., Sr. V.P. & Dir.-Res. & Devel.--Monarch Avalon, Inc., Baltimore, MD; *U.S. Public*, pg. 1123
Gregg, William A., V.P.-Res.--Precision Valve Corporation, Yonkers, NY; *U.S. Private*, pg. 880
Gregory, Mark, Mgr.-Product Design & Devel.--Master Appliance Corp., Racine, WI; *U.S. Private*, pg. 713
Gregory, Michael L., V.P.-Corp. Plng. & Devel.--Ruppman Marketing Technologies, Inc., Peoria, IL; *U.S. Private*, pg. 951
Griffin, Chuck, V.P.-Research & Devel.--Carbomedics, Inc., Austin, TX; *Int'l*, pg. 1307
Griggs, Russel, Dir.-Bus. Devl.--Scottish Enterprise, Glasgow, United Kingdom; *Int'l*, pg. 1212
Grochoski, Gregory, Sr. V.P.-Res. & Devel.--Amway Corporation, Ada, MI; *U.S. Private*, pg. 69
Groennert, C.W., V.P.-Organization Devel.--Emerson Electric Co., Saint Louis, MO; *U.S. Public*, pg. 572
Grollier, Jean Francois, V.P.-Res. & Devel.--L'Oreal S.A., Clichy, France; *Int'l*, pg. 818
Groman, Ernest V., Ph.D., Dir.-Exploratory Res.--Advanced Magnetics, Inc., Cambridge, MA; *U.S. Public*, pg. 20
Grossman, Janine, Dir.-Mktg. Communications--Nation's Business, Washington, DC; *U.S. Private*, pg. 788
Grossman, Sharon, Mgr.-Prod. Devel.--School Annual Publishing Co., Coshocton, OH; *U.S. Private*, pg. 598
Grosz, Ari, V.P.-Advanced Prod. Devel.--Physician Computer Network, Inc., Morris Plains, NJ; *U.S. Public*, pg. 1293
Grower, Ronnie, Asst. V.P.-Quality Initiatives--Sierra Health Services, Inc., Las Vegas, NV; *U.S. Public*, pg. 1469
Guarr, Tom, Ph.D., Dir.-Electrochemical Res.--Gentex Corporation, Zeeland, MI; *U.S. Public*, pg. 731
Gubernick, Joseph, Sr. V.P.-Res. & Devel.--Estee Lauder Companies Inc., New York, NY; *U.S. Public*, pg. 594
Guella, Maria, V.P. & Assoc. Res. Dir--Jordan, McGrath, Case & Taylor Inc., New York, NY; *U.S. Private*, pg. 598
Guengerich, Terri, Dir.-Res.--Goodwill Industries International, Bethesda, MD; *U.S. Private*, pg. 464
Guerci, G., Dir.-Plng. & Mngmt. Control--Banca Nazionale del Lavoro Sj.A., Rome, Italy; *Int'l*, pg. 136
Gueth, Thomas F., V.P.-Res. & Devel.--General Binding Corporation, Northbrook, IL; *U.S. Public*, pg. 707
Guiles, Ron, V.P.-Mfg., Res. & Devel.--Columbia Paint & Coatings, Spokane, WA; *U.S. Private*, pg. 256
Gum, Wilson F., Dr., V.P.-Tech.--Velsicol Chemical Corporation, Rosemont, IL; *U.S. Private*, pg. 1135
Gunderson, Karen, Dir.-Res. & Devel.--Mrs. Smith's Bakeries, Inc., Thomasville, GA; *U.S. Public*, pg. 657
Gussin, Robert Z., PhD., V.P.-Res. & Devel.--Johnson & Johnson, New Brunswick, NJ; *U.S. Public*, pg. 927
Gutman, Harvey, Sr. V.P.-Real Estate & Res. & Devel.--Pathmark Stores Incorporated, Woodbridge, NJ; *U.S. Private*, pg. 843
Guttendorf, Richard A., V.P. & Dir.-Res.--Safeguard Scientifics, Inc., Wayne, PA; *U.S. Public*, pg. 1424
Gwynn, Catherine, V.P. & Res. Dir.--Greenstone Roberts/ Florida, Orlando, FL; *U.S. Public*, pg. 763
Haave, Luther, V.P.-Devel.--WIC Western International Communications Ltd., Vancouver, Canada; *Int'l*, pg. 1481
Habicht, F. Henry, II, Sr. V.P.-Corp. Devel. & Environment--Safety-Kleen Corp., Elgin, IL; *U.S. Public*, pg. 1425
Habres, Joseph P., Mgr.-Engrng.--Lenape Forge, Inc., West Chester, PA; *U.S. Private*, pg. 659
Hacker, Susan, Audience Res. & Acq. Dir.--CPS Direct, Inc., Woburn, MA; *U.S. Private*, pg. 196
Hadley, Peter, V.P.-Res. & Devel.--Claremont Flock Corporation, Claremont, NH; *U.S. Private*, pg. 241
Hafeman, Daniel R., Chief Tech. Officer & V.P.-Advanced Res.--IKOS Systems, Inc., Cupertino, CA; *U.S. Public*, pg. 864
Hagen, Kenneth G., V.P.-Res. & Devel.--Thermo Fibertek, Inc., Waltham, MA; *U.S. Public*, pg. 1593
Hagerlin, Jeffrey R., V.P.-Res. & Devel.--Herberts-O'Brien Inc., Houston, TX; *Int'l*, pg. 626
Hahn, Edward R., V.P.-Res. & Devel.--Albany International Corp., Albany, NY; *U.S. Public*, pg. 36
Halevy, Itai, V.P.-Bus. Devel. & Strategic Plng.--Scitex Corporation Ltd., Holon, Israel; *Int'l*, pg. 644
Haley, Eugene T., Sr. V.P.-Customer Satisfaction--Qualex Inc., Durham, NC; *U.S. Public*, pg. 551
Hall, Deanna L., V.P.-Strategic Plng. & Sec.--Acme Design Technology, Co., Crozet, VA; *U.S. Private*, pg. 13
Hall, Laura, Mgr.-Mktg. Res.--Southern Progress Corporation, Birmingham, AL; *U.S. Public*, pg. 1612
Hall, Nick, Mgr.-Business Devel.--Lex Harvey Ltd., Bedworth, United Kingdom; *Int'l*, pg. 599
Halmrast, Dave, Sr. V.P.-Corp. Plng.--AFLAC Incorporated, Columbus, GA; *U.S. Public*, pg. 28
Halperin, P.J., Mgr.-Systems--Commercial Light Company, Hillside, IL; *U.S. Private*, pg. 258
Hamamoto, Arlene, Dir.-Mfg.--Rice Growers Association of California, West Sacramento, CA; *U.S. Private*, pg. 927
Hammelsvang, Jerk, Mgr.-Res. & Devel, Trailers--Eldon AB, Nassjo, Sweden; *Int'l*, pg. 436
Hammett, Roy, V.P.-Mfg. & Res.--International Container Systems, Tampa, FL; *Int'l*, pg. 685
Hampel, William F., Sr. V.P.-Res. & Devel.--Credit Union National Association, Madison, WI; *U.S. Private*, pg. 288
Hamza, Ezzeldin A., Sr. V.P.-Res. & Devel.--Barr Laboratories Inc., Pomona, NY; *U.S. Public*, pg. 191
Hanagan, John R., V.P.-Worldwide Clinical Devel.--The Procter & Gamble Company, Cincinnati, OH; *U.S. Public*, pg. 1330
Hand, Ed, Dir.-Engrng.--K-D Lamp Company, Cincinnati, OH; *U.S. Private*, pg. 603
Handy, Jim, Mgr.-Res. & Devel.--Nashville Wire Product Co., Nashville, TN; *U.S. Private*, pg. 775
Hanneman, Rodney E., V.P.-Quality Assurance & Technology--Reynolds Metals Company, Richmond, VA; *U.S. Public*, pg. 1385
Hansen, Eric R., V.P.-Technical Dir.--Ash Grove Cement Company, Shawnee Mission, KS; *U.S. Private*, pg. 87
Hansen, Leon A., V.P.-Res.--Rogers N.K. Seed Co., Boise, ID; *Int'l*, pg. 974
Hansen, Lowell, V.P.-Engrng.--Argo-Tech Corporation, Cleveland, OH; *U.S. Private*, pg. 81
Harada, Iki, Dir.-Chemical & Indus. Prods. Tech. Devel.--Bridgestone Corporation, Tokyo, Japan; *Int'l*, pg. 213
Haran, Pranatharthi, V.P.-Res. & Devel.--Smart Modular Technologies, Fremont, CA; *U.S. Public*, pg. 1476
Harari, O., Exec. V.P.--Israel Aircraft Industries Ltd., Israel; *Int'l*, pg. 689
Hardesty, Dorothy B., V.P.-Prod. Devel.--Banana Republic, San Francisco, CA; *U.S. Public*, pg. 702
Hardin, Richard V., Grp. V.P.-Tech.--Oil-Dri Corporation of America, Chicago, IL; *U.S. Public*, pg. 1214
Hargitai, Lilla, Res. Mgr.--EURO RSCG, Budapest, Hungary; *Int'l*, pg. 602
Harris, D.G., Dir.-Res. & Devel.--British Steel Seamless Tubes-Wednesfield Works, Wolverhampton, United Kingdom; *Int'l*, pg. 220
Harris, Dianne, V.P.-Corp. Devel.--Bausch & Lomb Incorporated, Rochester, NY; *U.S. Public*, pg. 194
Harris, Owen, V.P.-Res. & Devel.--F&F Foods, Chicago, IL; *U.S. Private*, pg. 388
Harris, P.M., Dir.-Res. & Tech.--Cookson Matthey Ceramics, West Chester, PA; *Int'l*, pg. 714
Harris, Tom, Dir.-Engrng.--Sanderson Plumbing Products Inc., Columbus, MS; *U.S. Private*, pg. 964
Harrison, Andy, Dir.-Res. & Devel.--J & J Snack Foods Corporation, Pennsauken, NJ; *U.S. Public*, pg. 916
Harrold, Lewis N., V.P.-Engrng.--Waters Instruments, Inc., Rochester, MN; *U.S. Public*, pg. 1745
Harrus, Alain, Chief Tech. Officer & V.P.--Novellus Systems, Inc., San Jose, CA; *U.S. Public*, pg. 1204
Hart, Steven L., V.P.-Mkt. Devel.--SkyWest Airlines, Inc., Saint George, UT; *U.S. Public*, pg. 1476
Harta, P.I., Dir.-Bus. Devel.--Morgan Crucible Co. Plc, Windsor, United Kingdom; *Int'l*, pg. 890
Hartley, Donna, V.P.-Res. & Devel.--The Dannon Co., Tarrytown, NY; *Int'l*, pg. 379
Hartmann, Klaus, Dr., Dir.-Technical Dept.--Boehringer Mannheim GmbH, Mannheim, Germany; *Int'l*, pg. 331
Hartsook, Pieter, V.P.-Mktg. Analysis & Res.--Apple Computer, Inc., Cupertino, CA; *U.S. Public*, pg. 121
Hassman, Howard, Dr., Exec. V.P.-Corp. Devel.--FPA Medical Management, Inc., San Diego, CA; *U.S. Public*, pg. 608
Hassman, Rommey, Res. & Strategic Plng. Dir.--Gitam/ BBDO, Ramat Gan, Israel; *Int'l*, pg. 552
Hatch, Ron, V.P.-Res. & Devel.--Solar Communications, Inc., Naperville, IL; *U.S. Private*, pg. 1012
Hauca, Gregory J., V.P.-Mktg.--Distribution America, Des Plaines, IL; *U.S. Private*, pg. 335
Haugn, Hartwick A., V.P.-Res. & Devel.--TCI, Inc., Ellaville, GA; *U.S. Public*, pg. 1358
Havrilla, J.B., V.P.-Res. & Devel.--Medrad, Inc., Indianola, PA; *Int'l*, pg. 1204
Hawkins, Rody, Dir.-Res. & Devel.--GoodMark Foods, Inc., Raleigh, NC; *U.S. Public*, pg. 751
Hawkins, Wilt, V.P.-Res. & Devel.--Norton Performance Plastics, Wayne, NJ; *Int'l*, pg. 1174
Hawkinson, Eric P., V.P.-Res. & Devel.--Heatilator Inc., Mount Pleasant, IA; *U.S. Public*, pg. 772
Hayashi, I, Dir.-Res. & Devel.--Asahi Glass America, Inc., New York, NY; *Int'l*, pg. 84
Hayashi, Yutaka, Mng. Dir.-Res. & Devel.--Sumitomo Metal Industries, Ltd., Tokyo, Japan; *Int'l*, pg. 1315
Hayes, Dave, Mgr.-Res. & Devel.--Barrister Information Systems Corporation, Buffalo, NY; *U.S. Public*, pg. 192
Haynes, Charles A., V.P.-Engrng.--Trion, Inc., Sanford, NC; *U.S. Public*, pg. 1639
Haynes, Gary, V.P.-Tech. & Research--Tone Brothers Inc., Ankeny, IA; *Int'l*, pg. 237
Haynes, Victoria F., V.P.-Res. & Devel.--The B.F. Goodrich Company, Richfield, OH; *U.S. Public*, pg. 751
Hayouna, Mustapha, Dir.-Research--Karsten Manufacturing Corporation, Phoenix, AZ; *U.S. Private*, pg. 608
Hedman, Christer, Dir.-Research & Devel.--Perstorp Pharma AB, Lund, Sweden; *Int'l*, pg. 1036
Hedstrom, Per G., Dir.-Tech. Res. & Devel.--Electrolux, AB, Stockholm, Sweden; *Int'l*, pg. 438
Hegedus, Louis, Ph.D, V.P.-Research & Devel.--Elf Atochem North America, Inc., Philadelphia, PA; *Int'l*, pg. 445
Heggestad, Robert E., V.P.-Technology--Harmon Industries, Inc., Blue Springs, MO; *U.S. Public*, pg. 788
Heinisch, Roland, Dir.-Res. & Devel.--Deutsche Bahn, Frankfurt/Main, Germany; *Int'l*, pg. 401
Heinrich, Donald M., V.P.-Bus. Devel.--A.O. Smith Corporation, Milwaukee, WI; *U.S. Public*, pg. 1476
Heitmann, G., Dir.-Tech.--Samuel Bingham Co, Bloomingdale, IL; *U.S. Private*, pg. 144
Hekman, Edward W., Mgr.-Corp. Plng.--Autocam Corporation, Grand Rapids, MI; *U.S. Public*, pg. 148
Heller, Chester M., Sr., Dr., Chm. Bd., Pres., Chief Exec. Officer & Chief Engr.--Marquette Coppersmithing Co., Inc., Philadelphia, PA; *U.S. Private*, pg. 706
Henderson, Dan, V.P.-Mfg.--H. R. Kaminsky & Sons, Inc., Fitzgerald, GA; *U.S. Private*, pg. 606
Henderson, Nick, Dir.-Res. & Devel.--Westronics, Inc., Kingwood, TX; *U.S. Public*, pg. 1593
Hennebry, John, Gen. Mgr.-Bus. Devel.--Melbourne Port Corporation, Melbourne, Australia; *Int'l*, pg. 856
Henstra, R., Dir.-Plant Devel.--Hoogovens Ijmuiden, Ijmuiden, Netherlands; *Int'l*, pg. 753
Hentges, Eric, Dir.-Nutrition Res.--National Cattlemen's Beef Association, Chicago, IL; *U.S. Private*, pg. 780
Hepton, Anthony, V.P.-Quality Assurance--Dole Food Company, Inc., Westlake Village, CA; *U.S. Public*, pg. 515
Herasimchuk, David A., V.P.-Mktg. Devel.--Global Marine Inc., Houston, TX; *U.S. Public*, pg. 748
Herman, Robert, Sr. V.P.-Res. & Devel.--Data Transmission Network Corporation, Omaha, NE; *U.S. Public*, pg. 486
Hester, Hilliard H., V.P.-Mngmt. Contracts Division--Allied Clinical Laboratories, Inc., Nashville, TN; *U.S. Public*, pg. 973
Hesterlee, Jerry, V.P.-Wire & Cable Tech.--Southwire Company, Carrollton, GA; *U.S. Private*, pg. 1019
Hettinga, David, V.P.-Res. & Devel.--Land O'Lakes, Inc., Arden Hills, MN; *U.S. Private*, pg. 645
Hiatt, David, Mgr.-Res. & Devel.--Oregon Metallurgical Corporation, Albany, OR; *U.S. Public*, pg. 43
Hichwa, Bryant, V.P.-Res.--Optical Coating Laboratory, Inc., Santa Rosa, CA; *U.S. Public*, pg. 1227
Hickman, R. N., Sr. V.P.- & Grp. Gen. Mgr.--The BHP Copper Group, San Francisco, CA; *Int'l*, pg. 224
Higaki, Taiji, Mng. Dir.-Res. & Devel.--Oji Paper Co., Ltd., Tokyo, Japan; *Int'l*, pg. 998
Hill, George R., Sr. V.P.-Bus. Devel.--The Lubrizol Corporation, Wickliffe, OH; *U.S. Public*, pg. 1016
Hillebrandt, Daren, Dir.-Prod. Devel.--Jenny Craig, Inc., La Jolla, CA; *U.S. Public*, pg. 926
Hiller, Jim, Mgr.-Res. & Devel.--E Z Loader Corporate, Airway Heights, WA; *U.S. Private*, pg. 352
Hillion, Herve, Mng. Dir.-Res. & Devel.--Landis & Staefa AG, Zug, Switzerland; *Int'l*, pg. 800
Hinckley, Robert, V.P.-Strategic Plans & Programs--Xilinx, Inc., San Jose, CA; *U.S. Public*, pg. 1786
Hipp, Christian J., V.P.-Research Environmental & Energy Officer--Moore Corporation Limited, Toronto, Canada; *Int'l*, pg. 888
Hirsch, Erin, Mgr.-Product Devel.--Goddess Bra Company, East Boston, MA; *U.S. Private*, pg. 458
Hirsch, Ted, Mgr.-Engrng.--Benchmark Electronics Inc., Angleton, TX; *U.S. Public*, pg. 210
Hlubek, Werner, Dr., Dir.-Central Res. & Devel.--RWE AG, Essen, Germany; *Int'l*, pg. 1081
Hoagland, James P., Corp. Dir.-Mktg. & Product Devel.--Rocco Inc., Harrisonburg, VA; *U.S. Private*, pg. 937
Hobbs, Robert M., Res.-Steel Focus Programs--Research, Melbourne, Australia; *Int'l*, pg. 227
Hobbs, Robert M., Mgr.-Res.--Port Kembla Laboratories, Port Kembla, Australia; *Int'l*, pg. 227
Hodges-Leinhart, Barbara, V.P.-Quality Control & Res. & Devel.-RANTOVL--Conair Corporation, Stamford, CT; *U.S. Private*, pg. 261
Hodges, John L., V.P. & Dir.-Tech.--Owens-Illinois, Inc., Toledo, OH; *U.S. Public*, pg. 1238
Hoehler, H., Dr., Dir.-Medical--CIBA-GEIGY (Pty.) Ltd., Isando, South Africa; *Int'l*, pg. 978
Hoey, Gerry, Mgr.-Corp. Devel.--Avonmore Waterford Group plc, Killkenny, Ireland; *Int'l*, pg. 102
Hoffait, Alfred, Gen. Mgr.-Res. & Devel.--Solvay S.A., Brussels, Belgium; *Int'l*, pg. 1277
Hoffman, Barbara, Dir.-Bus. Devel.--Amgen Boulder, Inc., Boulder, CO; *U.S. Public*, pg. 101
Hoffman, Donald J., V.P.-Engrng. & Res.--Wallace Computer Services, Inc., Lisle, IL; *U.S. Public*, pg. 1735
Hoffman, Mike, Mgr.-Res. &Devel.--E & A Industries, Inc., Indianapolis, IN; *U.S. Private*, pg. 352
Hoffstadt, Frederick A., Dir.-Res. & Devel.--Insituform Technologies, Inc., Chesterfield, MO; *U.S. Public*, pg. 881
Holland, C.L., V.P.-Bus. Devel.--Parsons Main, Inc., Boston, MA; *U.S. Private*, pg. 842
Holland, Marcia S., V.P.-Promotion & Res.--Journal of Commerce, Inc., New York, NY; *Int'l*, pg. 1026
Holland, Varnum, V.P.-Engrng.--Unitrode Corporation, Merrimack, NH; *U.S. Public*, pg. 1694
Hollis, C.G., V.P.-Res. & Devel.--Buckman Laboratories Inc., Memphis, TN; *U.S. Private*, pg. 180
Holloman, Phillip, V.P.--Cintas Corporation, Mason, OH; *U.S. Public*, pg. 370
Holm, Lynn, Plng. Dir.-West Cost--Western International Media Corporation, Los Angeles, CA; *U.S. Private*, pg. 1165
Holmes, J.A., Grp. Tech. Dir.--Anglo American Corporation of South Africa Limited, Johannesburg, South Africa; *Int'l*, pg. 76
Holt, Mark S., Dr., Dir.-Tech. Service & Devel.--Velsicol Chemical Corporation, Rosemont, IL; *U.S. Private*, pg. 1135
Homa, Arthur, V.P.-Tech.--RAYOVAC Corporation, Madison, WI; *U.S. Private*, pg. 912
Hommes, Jack, Dir.-Product Devel.--Howard Miller, Zeeland, MI; *U.S. Private*, pg. 747
Honeycutt, Travis W., Exec. V.P. & Sec.--Isolyser Company, Inc., Norcross, GA; *U.S. Public*, pg. 914
Hontzas, Thomas H., Exec. V.P.--Deposit Guaranty Corp., Jackson, MS; *U.S. Public*, pg. 500
Hopka, Alex, Mgr.-Res.--Kansas City Power & Light Company, Kansas City, MO; *U.S. Public*, pg. 943
Hopper, Larry, Dir.-Research & Devel.--M.C. Gill Corporation, El Monte, CA; *U.S. Private*, pg. 453
Hopper, Steven, Dir.-Commercial Devel.--The C.P. Hall Company, Chicago, IL; *U.S. Private*, pg. 495
Hopping, J. Mack, Dir.-Engrng.--Staodyn Inc., Longmont, CO; *U.S. Public*, pg. 1509
Horan, David, V.P.-Engrng.--Control Module, Inc., Enfield, CT; *U.S. Private*, pg. 271
Horn, Anne, V.P. & Assoc. Res. Dir.--Cramer-Krasselt, Chicago, IL; *U.S. Private*, pg. 285

Horn, Paul M., Sr. V.P.-Research--International Business Machines Corporation, Armonk, NY; *U.S. Public*, pg. 895
Hoshizaki, T. Blaine, V.P.-Res. & Devel.--Bauer Sports Inc., Montreal, Canada; *U.S. Public*, pg. 1184
Hosokawa, Toyohiro, Mng. Dir.-Res. & Devel.--Tonen Corporation, Tokyo, Japan; *Int'l*, pg. 1398
Houck, Stanley M., Mgr.-Mgmt. & Organizational Devel.--Gerber Products Company, Fremont, MI; *Int'l*, pg. 973
Hsia, James C., Ph.D., Sr. V.P.-Research--Candela Corporation, Wayland, MA; *U.S. Public*, pg. 300
Huang, Cornelius Y.D., V.P.-Research--Electro-Science Laboratories, Inc., King of Prussia, PA; *U.S. Private*, pg. 369
Huard, Tony, V.P.-Prod. Devel.--Jack Schwartz Shoes, Inc., New York, NY; *U.S. Private*, pg. 974
Huber, Charles F., V.P.-Corp. Devel.--Juno Lighting, Inc., Des Plaines, IL; *U.S. Public*, pg. 935
Hubert, Howard, Mgr.-Gas Tech.--AGA Gas, Inc., Independence, OH; *Int'l*, pg. 13
Hudgins, A. Mark, Dir.-New Prod. Devel.--Automatic Signal/Eagle Signal, Austin, TX; *Int'l*, pg. 1245
Hudson, Doranne, V.P.-Hallmark/Emerging Brands & Channels--Hallmark Cards, Inc., Kansas City, MO; *U.S. Private*, pg. 495
Hudson, Michael, V.P.-Res. & Devel./Commun. Div.--Diamond Multimedia Systems, Inc., San Jose, CA; *U.S. Public*, pg. 505
Hughes, Lucy, V.P. & Assoc. Dir.-Media Res.--Western International Media Corporation, Los Angeles, CA; *U.S. Private*, pg. 1165
Hughes, Michael P., Dr., V.P.-Res. & Devel.--Rexene Corporation, Dallas, TX; *U.S. Private*, pg. 549
Hulett, Scott, Sr. Engr.--M K Diamond Products, Inc., Torrance, CA; *U.S. Private*, pg. 684
Humbert, Bruce, V.P.-Strategic & Consumer Research--The Weather Channel, Atlanta, GA; *U.S. Private*, pg. 647
Hundt, Murray, Dir.-Res. & Devel.--Aliments Flamingo, Iberville, Canada; *Int'l*, pg. 57
Hunt, George C., V.P.-Tech.--Kelly-Moore Paint Company, Inc., San Carlos, CA; *U.S. Private*, pg. 613
Hunter, Orville, Jr., V.P.-Refractory Tech.--A.P. Green Industries, Inc., Mexico, MO; *U.S. Public*, pg. 761
Hupf, Charles, Dir.-Prod. Res. & Devel. Grp.--Regal Ware, Inc., Kewaskum, WI; *U.S. Private*, pg. 917
Huppertz, John, Ph.D., Mng. Partner-Mktg. & Res. Services--Eric Mower and Associates/Buffalo, Inc., Buffalo, NY; *U.S. Private*, pg. 765
Huppertz, John, Ph.D., Mng. Partner-Mktg. & Res. Services--Eric Mower & Associates, Albany, NY; *U.S. Private*, pg. 765
Huppertz, John, Ph.D., Mng. Partner-Mkgt. & Res. Services--Eric Mower & Associates, Atlanta, GA; *U.S. Private*, pg. 765
Huppmann, Winfried, Dr., Dir.-Research & Development--Hilti AG, Schaan, Liechtenstein; *Int'l*, pg. 619
Hynes, John, Mgr.-Engrng.--Samtec Inc., New Albany, IN; *U.S. Private*, pg. 963
Idell, Cheryl, Pres.-Res. & Strategic Plng.--Western International Media Corporation, Los Angeles, CA; *U.S. Private*, pg. 1165
Iida, Kazuyoshi, Dir.-Res. & Devel.--Bridgestone Corporation, Tokyo, Japan; *Int'l*, pg. 213
Ilyasuddin, Mir, Mgr.-Quality Control--National Refinery Limited, Karachi, Pakistan; *Int'l*, pg. 909
Indriksson, A., Mgr.-Regulatory--Seradyn, Inc., Indianapolis, IN; *Int'l*, pg. 871
Insco, Jeff, Mktg., Res. & Pub. Rels. Dir.--AGA Catalog Marketing & Design, New York, NY; *U.S. Private*, pg. 5
Irimajiri, Shoichiro, Exec. V.P.-Res., Devel. & Mfg.--Sega Enterprises Ltd., Tokyo, Japan; *Int'l*, pg. 1218
Irons, Edgar T., Chief Scientist--Franklin Electronic Publishers, Inc., Burlington, NJ; *U.S. Public*, pg. 679
Ishida, A., Dir.-Res. & Devel.--The Andrew Jergens Company, Cincinnati, OH; *Int'l*, pg. 717
Ishikawa, Yoichiro, Sr. V.P. & Res. & Devel.--Union Special Corp., Huntley, IL; *Int'l*, pg. 716
Isler, Peter, Sr. V.P.-Res. & Devel.--UMS Swiss Metalworks Holding Ltd, Dornach, Switzerland; *Int'l*, pg. 1427
Ivers, Vic, Mgr.-New Product Devel.--Xtek, Inc., Cincinnati, OH; *U.S. Private*, pg. 1194
Iwamoto, Melanie, Research Analyst--Precor, Inc., Bothell, WA; *U.S. Public*, pg. 1322
Jacklich, John, Dir.-Res. & Devel.--Simpson Dura-Vent Co., Inc., Vacaville, CA; *U.S. Public*, pg. 1474
Jackson, David A., Ph.D., Chief Scientific Officer--VIMRx Pharmaceuticals, Inc., Wilmington, DE; *U.S. Public*, pg. 1702
Jackson, Edwin H., V.P.-Engrng. & Devel.--Crestbrook Forest Industries Ltd., Cranbrook, Canada; *Int'l*, pg. 348
Jackson, Robert, Ph.D., V.P.-Res. & Devel.--Agouron Pharmaceuticals, Inc., La Jolla, CA; *U.S. Public*, pg. 28
Jacobs, Don, Dir.-Res. & Devel.--L.A. Gear, Inc., Santa Monica, CA; *U.S. Public*, pg. 969
Jacobs, Terry, Mgr.-Design Lab--Advance Packaging Corporation, Grand Rapids, MI; *U.S. Private*, pg. 18
Jacoby, Richard E., Dir.-Mkt. Analysis--Zinc Corporation of America, Monaca, PA; *U.S. Private*, pg. 540
Jacques, Gaston, Dir.-Res. & Devel.--Bertrand Faure, Boulogne, France; *Int'l*, pg. 192
James, Adrian, Dir.-Res.--Rogge Global Plc, London, United Kingdom; *U.S. Public*, pg. 1674
James, Louis B., Dir.-Software Engrng. & Chief Engineer--Moscom Corporation, Pittsford, NY; *U.S. Public*, pg. 1136
James, Richard D., V.P.-Small Airplane Devel.--Boeing Commercial Airplane Group, Renton, WA; *U.S. Public*, pg. 240
Janoff, Andrew S., V.P.-Res.--The Liposome Company, Inc., Princeton, NJ; *U.S. Public*, pg. 1000
Jauch, Alice, Dir.-Prod. Devel.--Danaher Tool Group, Chicago, IL; *U.S. Public*, pg. 481
Jefferies, Jerry, Mgr.-Res. & Devel.--Superior Label Systems, Inc., Mason, OH; *U.S. Private*, pg. 1055
Jefferies, Steven, V.P.-Res. & Devel.--Dentsply International Inc., York, PA; *U.S. Public*, pg. 498
Jelkio, Jeffrey A., V.P.-Res.--CyberOptics Corporation, Golden Valley, MN; *U.S. Public*, pg. 470
Jenkins, Len, Dir.-Weirton Tech. Ctr.--Weirton Steel Corporation, Weirton, WV; *U.S. Public*, pg. 1751
Jennings, B.R., Prof., Dir.-Research & Development--English China Clays Plc, Theale, United Kingdom; *Int'l*, pg. 455
Jerphagnon, Jean, Mgr.-Res. & Devel.--Alcatel Cit (S.A.), Velizy-Villacoublay, France; *Int'l*, pg. 56
Johansson, Elof, Exec. V.P.-Res.--Pharmacia & Upjohn Biosystems AB, Uppsala, Sweden; *Int'l*, pg. 1047
John, Peter, MD, V.P.-Health Strategies--Kaiser Permanente, Oakland, CA; *U.S. Private*, pg. 605
Johnannessen, Paul, Chm. Bd.--Megapulse, Inc., Bedford, MA; *U.S. Private*, pg. 729
Johnson, David J., Dr., Dir.-Res. & Devel.--Plasma-Therm, Inc., Saint Petersburg, FL; *U.S. Public*, pg. 1308
Johnson, Edward F., V.P.-Mfg. Resource Devel.--Fruit of the Loom, Inc., Chicago, IL; *U.S. Public*, pg. 685
Johnson, Gerald, Mgr.-Tech. Services, N. America--Ball Metal Food Container Corp., Westminster, CO; *U.S. Public*, pg. 171
Johnson, Nancy M., V.P.-Res. & Devel.--American Family Mutual Insurance Co., Madison, WI; *U.S. Private*, pg. 53
Johnson, Norman E., Sr. V.P.-Tech.--Weyerhaeuser Company, Federal Way, WA; *U.S. Public*, pg. 1764
Johnson, Peter, Dr., Sr. V.P.-Res. & Devel.--Medeva Pharmaceuticals, Rochester, NY; *Int'l*, pg. 852
Johnson, Tom, Mgr.-Quality Control/Res. & Devel.--Grist Mill Company, Danville, IL; *U.S. Public*, pg. 766
Johnston, Peter, Tech. Dept. Leader--APS, Phoenix, AZ; *U.S. Public*, pg. 1297
Jokl, Martin L., V.P. & Dir.-Res.--Barnwell Industries, Inc., Honolulu, HI; *U.S. Public*, pg. 190
Jones, Arthur L., Sr. V.P.-Retail Devel. & Sls.--Associated Grocers, Inc., Seattle, WA; *U.S. Private*, pg. 90
Jones, Jeff, V.P.-Mktg. & Prod. Devel.--Sony Music Entertainment, Inc., New York, NY; *Int'l*, pg. 1281
Jones, Keith, V.P.-Res. & Devel.--Church & Dwight Specialty Products Division, Princeton, NJ; *U.S. Public*, pg. 356
Jones, Kenneth A., V.P.-Res. & Devel.--Quest Medical, Inc., Allen, TX; *U.S. Public*, pg. 1352
Jones, McCall, Res. Analyst--Williams Worldwide, Santa Monica, CA; *U.S. Private*, pg. 1179
Jones, Michael D., Sr. V.P.-Research & Devel.--Jefferson-Pilot Data Services, Inc., Memphis, TN; *U.S. Public*, pg. 925
Jones, Nick, Dir.-Service & Devel.--Iceland Frozen Foods plc., Deeside, United Kingdom; *Int'l*, pg. 658
Jones, S.T., Dir.-Res.--Lorillard Tobacco Company, Greensboro, NC; *U.S. Public*, pg. 1011
Jones, Walt, V.P.-Res. & Devel.--Farmers Mutual Hail Insurance Co. of Iowa, Des Moines, IA; *U.S. Private*, pg. 395
Jordan, Gregory W., Dir.-Business Analysis, Plng. & Engrng.--Northrop Grumman Corporation, Los Angeles, CA; *U.S. Public*, pg. 1197
Jorgensen, John, V.P.-Engrng.--California Micro Devices, Milpitas, CA; *U.S. Public*, pg. 293
Jorgensen, Niels, V.P.-Res., Devel. & Engrg.--Olicom A/S, Lyngby, Denmark; *Int'l*, pg. 1001
Jose Constancio, Maria, Mgr.-Res. & Data Devel.--Caixa Geral de Depositos, Lisbon, Portugal; *Int'l*, pg. 250
Josephson, Lee, Ph.D., Sr. V.P.-Res.--Advanced Magnetics, Inc., Cambridge, MA; *U.S. Public*, pg. 20
Joves, Hakan, Dir.-Res. & Dev.--Korsnas AB, Gavle, Sweden; *Int'l*, pg. 759
Juel, Steinar, Dir.-Bus. Devel.--Christiania Bank og Kreditkasse ASA, Oslo, Norway; *Int'l*, pg. 289
Julian, Jesus, Dir.-Res. & Devel.--Copamex Industrias S.A. de C.V., Garza Garcia, Mexico; *Int'l*, pg. 330
Jullien, Alexis, Dir.-Mktg. Devel.--C.M.C. SA, Saint Quentin-en-Yvelines, France; *Int'l*, pg. 792
Jungwirth, Dieter, Prof. Dr., Mng. Dir.-Res. & Devel.--Dyckerhoff & Widmann AG, Munich, Germany; *Int'l*, pg. 423
Junk, Keith N., V.P.-Corp. Devel.--MascoTech, Inc., Taylor, MI; *U.S. Public*, pg. 1055
Jurdak, Nabil S., Dir.-Devel. & Construction--Securespace Inc., Beauport, Canada; *Int'l*, pg. 253
Kaass, Tore, Dir.-Plng.--AS OSLO Sporveier, Oslo, Norway; *Int'l*, pg. 1012
Kahn, Hameed, Dir.-Research & Devel.--Rieter Automotive North America Inc, Farmington Hills, MI; *Int'l*, pg. 1117
Kakei, Masakazu, Exec. Dir.-Pharmaceuticals--Japan Tobacco Inc., Tokyo, Japan; *Int'l*, pg. 703
Kalantzis, Peter, V.P.-Corp. Devel.--Alusuisse-Lonza Holding Ltd., Zurich, Switzerland; *Int'l*, pg. 66
Kalff, D.J.A., Sr. V.P.-Corp. Devel.--KLM Royal Dutch Airlines, Amstelveen, Netherlands; *Int'l*, pg. 719
Kalgren, Dave, Plant Mgr.--ABC Rail Cogifer Industries, Cincinnati, OH; *U.S. Public*, pg. 2
Kalgren, Dave, Plant Mgr.--Cogifer SA, Croissy-sur-Seine, France; *Int'l*, pg. 386
Kalish, Douglas, Partner--Price Waterhouse L.L.P. - U.S., New York, NY; *U.S. Private*, pg. 883
Kalisik, Frank, V.P.-Res. & Devel.--Continental Plastic Containers, Inc., Norwalk, CT; *U.S. Public*, pg. 440
Kalnoki-Kis, Tibor, Dr., V.P.-Tech.--Gould Electronics Inc., Eastlake, OH; *U.S. Public*, pg. 1591
Kamegai, Kiyoshi, Mng. Dir.-Food Res.--Ajinomoto Company Inc., Tokyo, Japan; *Int'l*, pg. 40
Kamens, Howard, V.P.-Prod. Devel.--Learning International, Stamford, CT; *U.S. Public*, pg. 1617
Kamm, Mary, Dir.-Res. & Devel.--Ben & Jerry's Homemade Inc., South Burlington, VT; *U.S. Public*, pg. 210
Kampe, Scott, Dir.-Engrg. & Res. & Devel.--Merco/Savory Inc., Lakewood, NJ; *Int'l*, pg. 189
Kanalley, Tom, Mgr.-Res. & Devel.--Cortland Line Co., Inc., Cortland, NY; *U.S. Private*, pg. 277
Kaneko, S., Dir.-Res.--Bridgestone/Firestone, Inc., Nashville, TN; *Int'l*, pg. 213
Kanter, Nina, Media Res. Dir.--Griffin Bacal Inc., New York, NY; *U.S. Private*, pg. 480
Kaplan, Bob, Mgr.--Educational Insights, Inc., Carson, CA; *U.S. Public*, pg. 565
Kaplan, Lester J., Ph.D., Corp. V.P.-Res. & Devel.--Allergan, Inc., Irvine, CA; *U.S. Public*, pg. 46
Kaplan, Stanley A., Sr. V.P.-Res. & Devel.--U.S. Pharmaceuticals, Baltimore, MD; *U.S. Public*, pg. 58
Kappelman, David, Mgr.--J.W. Allen & Company, Wheeling, IL; *U.S. Private*, pg. 37
Kariya, Michio, Dir.-Tech. Devel.--Nikon Corporation, Tokyo, Japan; *Int'l*, pg. 931
Karlsson, Anders C., Sr. V.P.-Tech. & Industrial Co.--Skanska AB, Danderyd, Sweden; *Int'l*, pg. 1260
Kartovaara, Ilkka, Dir.-Res. & Devel.--Enso Oyj, Helsinki, Finland; *Int'l*, pg. 455
Kasai, Hiroshi, Exec. V.P.--Oji Paper Co., Ltd., Tokyo, Japan; *Int'l*, pg. 998
Kasianchuk, Walt, Dir.-Engrng. & Tech.--Salem Manufacturing Facility, Salem, OR; *Int'l*, pg. 875
Kato, Hiroki, V.P.-Japan/Asian Devel.--Iomega Corporation, Roy, UT; *U.S. Public*, pg. 912
Kaufman, Stan, Mgr.-Res. & Devel.--TSI Incorporated, Shoreview, MN; *U.S. Public*, pg. 1559
Kawamura, Kouichi, Mgr.-Res. & Devel.--Nippon Oil Company, Limited (NiSSEKI), Tokyo, Japan; *Int'l*, pg. 936
Kawasaki, Nobuhiro, Gen. Mgr.-Tokyo Res. Ctr.--Tosoh Corporation, Tokyo, Japan; *Int'l*, pg. 1407
Kawata, Toru, Dir. & Grp. Gen. Mgr.-Corp. Res. & Devel.--Sharp Corporation, Osaka, Japan; *Int'l*, pg. 1228
Kazle, Scott J., Dir.-Engrng.--HEI, Inc., Victoria, MN; *U.S. Public*, pg. 770
Kearns, Pat, Mgr.-Res. & Devel.--Team, Inc., Alvin, TX; *U.S. Public*, pg. 1562
Kehr, Wolfgang, Dir.-Res. & Devel.--Schering AG, Berlin, Germany; *Int'l*, pg. 1203
Keim, Karl, Mgr.-Res. & Devel.--Battenfeld Gloucester Engineering Co. Inc., Gloucester, MA; *U.S. Private*, pg. 123
Kelley, Larry, Sr. V.P.-Media & Res.--Fogarty Klein & Partners, Houston, TX; *U.S. Private*, pg. 415
Kelly-Bartley, Kim, Dir.-Mktg. & Pub. Rels.--White Castle System, Inc., Columbus, OH; *U.S. Private*, pg. 1171
Kelly, James J., V.P.-Mfg. & Research--M.A. Bruder & Sons, Incorporated, Broomall, PA; *U.S. Private*, pg. 175
Kelly, William, V.P.-Res., Engrng. & Devel.--Johnson Worldwide Associates, Inc., Sturtevant, WI; *U.S. Public*, pg. 932
Kelly, William H., Sr. V.P.-Plng. & Devel.--NorAm Energy Corp., Houston, TX; *U.S. Public*, pg. 843
Kelso, Jennifer, Mgr.-Employee Rels. & Devel.--Cognos Inc., Ottawa, Canada; *Int'l*, pg. 305
Keltner, Thomas, Chief Devel. Officer & Exec. V.P.--Promus Hotel Corporation, Memphis, TN; *U.S. Public*, pg. 1335
Kemppainen, Pekka, Sr. V.P.-Tech.--Kone Corporation, Helsinki, Finland; *Int'l*, pg. 746
Kenney, Jerome P., Exec. V.P.-Corp. Strategy & Research--Merrill Lynch & Co., Inc., New York, NY; *U.S. Public*, pg. 1097
Kenney, William J., Jr., Sr. V.P.-Devel.--Donahue Schriber, Newport Beach, CA; *Int'l*, pg. 253
Kenny, Michael, Mgr.-Res. & Devel.--C.H. Heist Corp., Clearwater, FL; *U.S. Public*, pg. 807
Kerr, Tim, V.P.-Engrng.--Advanced Energy Industry, Fort Collins, CO; *U.S. Public*, pg. 20
Kettunen, Jyrki, Mgr.-Res. & Devel.--Metsa-Serla Corporation, Espoo, Finland; *Int'l*, pg. 863
Kher, Bal, V.P.-Res. & Devel., Tech.--Rockbestos-Suprenant Cable Corp., Clinton, MA; *U.S. Private*, pg. 938
Kiely, Steve, V.P.-Platform Prods.--Stratus Computer, Inc., Marlborough, MA; *U.S. Public*, pg. 1524
Killen, Dale, Dir.-Opers., Res. & Devel.--Frozfruit Corporation, Gardena, CA; *U.S. Private*, pg. 430
Killian, William P., V.P.-Corp. Strategy & Devel.--Johnson Controls, Inc., Controls Group, Milwaukee, WI; *U.S. Public*, pg. 932
Kilpinen, Michael E., Exec. V.P.-Res. & Devel.-Tech. Svcs.--Cambridge Industries Inc., Madison Heights, MI; *U.S. Private*, pg. 202
Kim, David W., Corp. Planner--Sunkyong America, Inc., New York, NY; *Int'l*, pg. 1320
Kim, Leo, Chief Technical Officer & Exec. V.P.--Mycogen Corporation, San Diego, CA; *U.S. Public*, pg. 1142
Kimura, Yasuo, Exec. V.P.-Tech. Res. & Devel., Media Business, C&C Systems--Sumitomo Corporation, Tokyo, Japan; *Int'l*, pg. 1312
Kimzey, James R., Exec. V.P.-Res. & Engrng.--Baldor Electric Company, Fort Smith, AR; *U.S. Public*, pg. 168
Kin, Mak Chi, Sr. Mgr.-Res. & Dev.--Durable Electrical Metal Factory, Ltd., Hong Kong, Hong Kong; *U.S. Public*, pg. 1771
Kincaid, Mary, V.P.-Adv. & Res.--Buena Vista Home Video, Burbank, CA; *U.S. Public*, pg. 513
Kindlund, Newton C., Chm. Bd., Pres., Chief Exec. & Chief Oper. Officer--Holiday RV Superstores, Inc., Orlando, FL; *U.S. Public*, pg. 829
King, Ed, Dr., Dir.-Res. & Devel.--CEM Corporation, Matthews, NC; *U.S. Public*, pg. 277
Kinitsky, Larry, Sr. V.P. & Dir.-Prod., Mngmt. & Research--The Dime Savings Bank of New York, New York, NY; *U.S. Public*, pg. 509
Kinugawa, Motonori, Gen. Mgr.-Plng. & Res.--Meiji Life Insurance Company, Tokyo, Japan; *Int'l*, pg. 854
Kircher, Steven, Mgr.-Res.--The Times Publishing Co., Saint Petersburg, FL; *U.S. Private*, pg. 1087
Kirk, James R., Sr. V.P. & Pres.-Res. & Devel.--Campbell Soup Company, Camden, NJ; *U.S. Public*, pg. 298
Kirkwood, Ronn, V.P. & Mktg. Res. Dir.--Cramer-Krasselt, Milwaukee, WI; *U.S. Private*, pg. 286
Kite, Vern, Dir.-Res. & Analysis--Showboat, Incorporated, Las Vegas, NV; *U.S. Public*, pg. 1469

Kittelson, Marnie, Res. Dir.--Haworth Group Inc., Minneapolis, MN; *U.S. Private*, pg. 511

Kittinger, Kenneth R., Sr. V.P.-Govt. Affairs--Doron Precision Systems, Inc., Binghamton, NY; *U.S. Private*, pg. 341

Kjellerup, Douglas L., V.P.-Mktg. & Devel.--Otter Tail Power Company, Fergus Falls, MN; *U.S. Public*, pg. 1234

Klapmeier, James E., Chm.--Bluewater, Mora, MN; *U.S. Private*, pg. 153

Klein, Dean A., V.P.-Res. & Devel.--Micron Electronics, Inc., Nampa, ID; *U.S. Public*, pg. 1105

Klein, Richard G., Dr., V.P.-Corp. Res. & Tech.--Nordson Corporation, Westlake, OH; *U.S. Public*, pg. 1188

Klein, Robert L., V.P.-Res. & Devel.--ANGUS Chemical Company, Buffalo Grove, IL; *U.S. Private*, pg. 75

Klien, David, Mgr.-Res. & Devel.--Humphrey Products Company, Kalamazoo, MI; *U.S. Private*, pg. 547

Kline, John, Dir.-Engrng.--Presstek, Inc., Hudson, NH; *U.S. Public*, pg. 1324

Klinger, Ernest T., Chief Fin. Officer, V.P.-Fin. & Admin.--Arden Group, Inc., Los Angeles, CA; *U.S. Public*, pg. 128

Klinger, Katherine, Ph.D., V.P.-Science--IG Laboratories, Inc., Framingham, MA; *U.S. Public*, pg. 733

Knepper, T.D., Dir.-Res. & Devel.--The Felters Company, Roebuck, SC; *U.S. Private*, pg. 400

Knowles, Jonathan, Mng. Dir.-Global Pharmaceutical Res.--Roche Holding Ltd., Basel, Switzerland; *Int'l*, pg. 1119

Kobayashi, Isao, Sr. Mng. Dir.-Gen. Store Devel.--Ito-Yokado Co., Ltd., Tokyo, Japan; *Int'l*, pg. 693

Koch, Christopher, Pres.--New Era Cap. Co., Derby, NY; *U.S. Private*, pg. 793

Kodosky, Jeff, V.P.-Res. & Devel.--National Instruments Corp., Austin, TX; *U.S. Public*, pg. 1157

Koenig, Scott, MD, Ph.D., V.P.-Res.--MedImmune, Inc., Gaithersburg, MD; *U.S. Public*, pg. 1081

Kogel, John, V.P.-Res. & Devel.--Candle Corporation, Santa Monica, CA; *U.S. Private*, pg. 204

Kohls, Kris, Exec. V.P.-Strategic Devel.--Dart Transit Company, Eagan, MN; *U.S. Private*, pg. 311

Kohsaka, Masanobu, Exec. Dir.-Prod. Devel. Res.--Fujisawa Pharmaceutical Co. Ltd., Osaka, Japan; *Int'l*, pg. 525

Koike, Hiroshi, Mng. Dir.-Res. & Devel.--Matsushita Electric Works, Ltd., Osaka, Japan; *Int'l*, pg. 847

Kojalo, Jacob, Sr. V.P.-Comml. Lending & Bus. Devel.--Lawrence Savings Bank, North Andover, MA; *U.S. Public*, pg. 980

Kojima, Iwao, Mng. Dir. & Gen. Mgr.-Res. & Tech.--Showa Denko K.K., Tokyo, Japan; *Int'l*, pg. 1236

Kok Leong, Kong, Gen. Mgr.-Res. & Plng.--Singapore Land Limited, Singapore, Singapore; *Int'l*, pg. 1252

Kollman, Ronald E., V.P.-Res. & Devel.--Ethyl Corporation, Richmond, VA; *U.S. Public*, pg. 595

Kolman, Mike, V.P.-Res. & Devel.--Tekra Corporation, New Berlin, WI; *U.S. Private*, pg. 1073

Koltay, Erv, Mgr.-Res. & Devel.--Andes Candies Inc., Delavan, WI; *U.S. Private*, pg. 163

Komatsu, Keiji, Chief Officer-Research & Development--Japan Energy Corporation, Tokyo, Japan; *Int'l*, pg. 702

Komor, Joseph, V.P.-Res. & Devel.--Mona Industries, Inc., Paterson, NJ; *U.S. Private*, pg. 756

Koncel, James E., V.P.-Engrng. & Devel.--Bodine Electric Company, Chicago, IL; *U.S. Private*, pg. 154

Konkler, John, Chief Engr.--Ariel Corporation, Mount Vernon, OH; *U.S. Private*, pg. 81

Konstantin, Peter, Dr., Sr. V.P.-Res. & Devel.--Gelman Sciences, Inc., Ann Arbor, MI; *U.S. Public*, pg. 1253

Konuntakiet, Soonthorn, V.P.-Res. & Devel.--Unicord Public Co. LTD., Bangkok, Thailand; *Int'l*, pg. 1432

Koop, Eileen, Mgr.-Res. & Devel.--Scott's Liquid Gold-Inc., Denver, CO; *U.S. Public*, pg. 1447

Koopman, Jim, Mgr.-Res. & Devel.--Steiner Co., Inc., Chicago, IL; *U.S. Private*, pg. 1039

Korde, Satish, Exec. V.P. & WW Res. Dir.--Young & Rubicam New York, New York, NY; *U.S. Private*, pg. 1198

Korde, Satish, Corp. Res. Dir.-London--Young & Rubicam Holdings Ltd., London, United Kingdom; *U.S. Private*, pg. 1199

Kornhaber, Harvey, Grp. V.P.-Res. & Devel.--Turtle Wax, Inc., Chicago, IL; *U.S. Private*, pg. 1110

Kosco, John, Mgr.-Res. & Devel.--Keystone Powdered Metal Company, Saint Marys, PA; *U.S. Private*, pg. 619

Kotchan, Walter, Dir.-Opers.--Pride Health Care, Inc., Exeter, PA; *U.S. Private*, pg. 883

Koupal, Carl M., Jr., Exec. V.P. & Chief Admin. Officer--Western Resources, Inc., Topeka, KS; *U.S. Public*, pg. 1759

Kovach, Steven, Dr., Mgr.-Res. & Devel.--Speedling Incorporated, Sun City, FL; *U.S. Private*, pg. 1024

Kowalchik, Michael, V.P.-Trng. & Devel.--Auto Driveaway Co., Chicago, IL; *U.S. Private*, pg. 100

Kozal, Mike, Mgr.-Res. & Devel.--Pridgeon & Clay, Inc., Grand Rapids, MI; *U.S. Private*, pg. 883

Koziarz, James J., Ph.D., V.P.-Diagnostic Prods., Res. & Devel.--Abbott Laboratories, Abbott Park, IL; *U.S. Public, pg. 12*

Kramer, William, Dir.-Tech.--Davis Standard Corporation, Pawcatuck, CT; *U.S. Public*, pg. 459

Kraus, Thomas, V.P.-Hardware Devel.--White Pine Software, Nashua, NH; *U.S. Private*, pg. 1173

Krenitsky, Thomas A., V.P.-Res.--Glaxo Wellcome PLC, Research Triangle Park, NC; *Int'l*, pg. 553

Kringstad, Knut, Sr. V.P.-Res. & Devel.--Norske Skogindustrier A.S, Skogn, Norway; *Int'l*, pg. 965

Krish, Leisa, Mgr.-Res. & Prod. Devel.--Great Financial Bank FSB, Louisville, KY; *U.S. Private*, pg. 473

Krueger, Bob, Sr. V.P.-Engrng.--Centigram Communications Corporation, San Jose, CA; *U.S. Public*, pg. 323

Kruger, Franz-Josef, Mgr.-Res. & Devel.--VARTA AG, Hannover, Germany; *Int'l*, pg. 1451

Krupke, LeRoy, V.P.--Overhead Door Corporation, Dallas, TX; *U.S. Private*, pg. 822

Krysh, David, Dir.-New Prod. Development--Esselte Corporation, Garden City, NY; *Int'l*, pg. 459

Ku Kang, In, Exec. V.P.-Res. & Devel.--LG Group, Seoul, Korea; *Int'l*, pg. 778

Kubert, George, V.P.-Res. & Devel.--Edwards Baking Co., Norcross, GA; *U.S. Private*, pg. 365

Kuncar, Edward I., Sr. V.P.-Intl. Devel.--Wackenhut Intl., Inc., Coral Gables, FL; *U.S. Public*, pg. 1731

Kushmaul, Richard, V.P.-Res. & Devel.--Datasouth Computer Corporation, Charlotte, NC; *U.S. Public*, pg. 267

Kusumoto, Koshi, Dir.-Res. & Devel.--Tokuyama Corporation, Tokyo, Japan; *Int'l*, pg. 1393

Kutnick, Robert, V.P.-Strategic Devel.--Quarterdeck Corp., Marina Del Rey, CA; *U.S. Public*, pg. 1350

Kuusi, Juhani, V.P.-Res. & Devel.--Oy Nokia Ab/Nokia Group, Helsinki, Finland; *Int'l*, pg. 951

Kuzminski, Lawrence, V.P.-Tech. Res. & Devel.--Ocean Spray Cranberries, Inc., Middleboro, MA; *U.S. Private*, pg. 811

Kyung-Hun, Nam, Gen. Mgr.--Korea Heavy Industries & Construction Co., Ltd., Seoul, Korea; *Int'l*, pg. 758

Laabs, Tom, Mgr.-New Prods.--Cousins Submarines, Menomonee Falls, WI; *U.S. Private*, pg. 280

LaCapria, Daniel, Res. & Devel.--Gillette Argentina S.A., Buenos Aires, Argentina; *U.S. Public*, pg. 744

Laetz, Curtis J., V.P.-Mktg. & Devel.--OmniQuip International, Inc., Port Washington, WI; *U.S. Private*, pg. 500

Laky, Earnie, Mgr.-Res. & Devel.--Champ/Pik-A-Nut Service Line, Edwardsville, KS; *U.S. Public*, pg. 1503

Lalande, Michel, Dir.-Res. & Devel.--Moulinex S.A., Bagnolet, France; *Int'l*, pg. 896

Laliberte, Antonio M., Vice Chm.-Plng. Res. & Devel.--Ernst & Young, LLP, New York, NY; *U.S. Private*, pg. 381

LaManna, Tom, Dir.-Plng. & Devel.--Dairy Mart Convenience Stores, Inc., Cuyahoga Falls, OH; *U.S. Public*, pg. 476

Lamb, David, Exec. V.P. & Global Bus. Dir.-DeBeers--J. Walter Thompson Company, New York, NY; *Int'l*, pg. 1483

Lamb, Matthew, Engineer--Pacesetter Corporation, Omaha, NE; *U.S. Private*, pg. 830

Lamb, Simon, Mgr.-Res. & Devel., Enclosures--Eldon AB, Nassjo, Sweden; *Int'l*, pg. 436

Lamisse, Michel, Dir.-Res. & Devel.--Kodak Pathe S.A., Paris, France; *U.S. Public*, pg. 554

Lancia, Fred, V.P.-Research & Devel.--Liebert Corporation, Columbus, OH; *U.S. Public*, pg. 573

Landau, Yair, Sr. V.P.-Corp. Devel. & Strategic Plng.--Sony Pictures Entertainment, Culver City, CA; *Int'l*, pg. 1281

Landers, Thomas A., Sr. V.P. & Dir.-Market Res.--Municipal Bond Investors Assurance Corporation, Armonk, NY; *U.S. Public*, pg. 1023

Landt, Jeremy, Dr., Chief Tech. Officer & V.P.--Amtech Corporation, Dallas, TX; *U.S. Public*, pg. 105

Lanfear, Dennis M., V.P.-Process Devel. & Opers. Systems--Amgen Inc., Thousand Oaks, CA; *U.S. Public*, pg. 100

Langdon, Doug, Mgr.-Mktg. Research--Chattem, Inc., Chattanooga, TN; *U.S. Public*, pg. 341

Langford, Virgil R., V.P.-Refining--Holly Corporation, Dallas, TX; *U.S. Public*, pg. 830

Langley, Frank A., V.P.-Mktg. & Prod. Devel.--Intercare Technologies, Inc., Waukesha, WI; *U.S. Public*, pg. 459

Langley, John, Dir.-Res. & Devel.--Kappler Safety Group, Inc., Guntersville, AL; *U.S. Private*, pg. 607

Lankveld, J., Mgr.-Res. & Devel.--Campina Melkunie BV, Zaltbommel, Netherlands; *Int'l*, pg. 254

LaPrade, Steve, Dir.-Res. & Devel.--Georgia-Bonded Fibers, Inc., Newark, NJ; *U.S. Public*, pg. 734

Larkin, Jeremiah B., V.P.-Leasing--World Financial Properties, Inc., New York, NY; *Int'l*, pg. 1004

Larsen, Steve, Dir.-Information Services--Northern States Power Company, Minneapolis, MN; *U.S. Public*, pg. 1195

Larson, Paul Z., V.P.-Chemicals--Du Pont (E.I. Du Pont De Nemours & Co.), Wilmington, DE; *U.S. Public*, pg. 530

Larson, Thomas, V.P.-Mkts. Devel. & Info. Resources--United Power Association, Elk River, MN; *U.S. Private*, pg. 1123

Larsson, Stig-Goran, V.P.-Prod. Devel.--Saab Automobile AB, Nykoping, Sweden; *Int'l*, pg. 687

Larsson, Stig-Goran, V.P.-Prod. Devel.--Saab Automobile AB, Nykoping, Sweden; *U.S. Public*, pg. 725

Lasky, Jack S., V.P.-Res. & Engrng.--The Okonite Company, Ramsey, NJ; *U.S. Private*, pg. 813

Lattote, Dave, V.P.-Aeroquip New Bus. Devel.--Aeroquip-Vickers, Inc., Maumee, OH; *U.S. Public*, pg. 24

Laubner, Gunter, Mgr.-Res.--Bankgesellschaft Berlin, Berlin, Germany; *Int'l*, pg. 159

Laubsch, Ken, Mgr.-Res. & Devel.--Benjamin Obdyke, Inc., Warminster, PA; *U.S. Private*, pg. 810

Lauderback, Sanford, V.P.-Res. & Devel.--Huls America Inc., Somerset, NJ; *Int'l*, pg. 1455

Lauer, Edward, V.P.-Res. & Devel.--Nomaco, Inc., Zebulon, NC; *U.S. Private*, pg. 801

Laughlin, Jim, Consultant--Butler Ventamatic Corp., Mineral Wells, TX; *U.S. Private*, pg. 190

Lavelle, Peter, Chief Res. & Devel. Engr.--Preferred Utilities Manufacturing Corp., Danbury, CT; *U.S. Private*, pg. 881

Lawlor, Thomas, Dir.-Res. & Devel.--Holstein Association USA, Inc., Brattleboro, VT; *U.S. Private*, pg. 536

Lawrence, David L., Treas. & Asst. Sec.--National-Standard Co., Niles, MI; *U.S. Public*, pg. 1160

Lawrence, Robert H., Jr., Sr. V.P.--UST Inc., Greenwich, CT; *U.S. Public*, pg. 1660

Lawson, T., Dr., Dir.-Res. & Devel.--Rentokil Initial plc, East Grinstead, United Kingdom; *Int'l*, pg. 1285

Lawson, Vincent L., V.P.-Res. & Devel.--Texas Refinery Corp., Fort Worth, TX; *U.S. Private*, pg. 1078

Le Fur, Gerard, V.P.-Res.--Elf Aquitaine, Paris, France; *Int'l*, pg. 444

Leach, Antoinette, Mgr.-Bus. Devel.--Saft Nife Ltd., Hampton, United Kingdom; *Int'l*, pg. 55

LeBlanc, Emery P., V.P.-Res., Tech. & Environment--Alcan Aluminium Limited, Montreal, Canada; *Int'l*, pg. 50

Leblanc, Marcel, V.P.-Engnrg. & Devel.--Kruger Inc., Montreal, Canada; *Int'l*, pg. 761

LeBouc, Phillppe, Res. & Devel.--Avions de Transport Regional - ATR, Blagnac, France; *Int'l*, pg. 654

Lederman, Frank L., Sr. V.P. & Dir.-Res.--Noranda Inc., Toronto, Canada; *Int'l*, pg. 433

Lee, David G., V.P.-Engrng.--Echlin Inc., Branford, CT; *U.S. Public*, pg. 560

Lee, Francis H., Dir.-Clinical Res. & Devel.--Fujisawa U.S.A. Inc., Deerfield, IL; *Int'l*, pg. 525

Lee, Pamelia, Sr. Dir.-Devel.--Singapore Tourist Promotion Board, Singapore, Singapore; *Int'l*, pg. 1253

Lee, Peter F., V.P.-Res. & Devel.--International Paper Company, Purchase, NY; *U.S. Public*, pg. 901

Lefler, Kevin D., V.P.-Prod. Engrng. & Devel.--United Air Specialists, Inc., Cincinnati, OH; *U.S. Public*, pg. 382

Legmann, Robert A., V.P.-Res. & Devel.--UOP, Des Plaines, IL; *U.S. Public*, pg. 52

Lehmann, Jean-Claude, Dir.-Res.--Saint-Gobain, Courbevoie, France; *Int'l*, pg. 1170

Leigh, Bradford, Asst. Dir.-Res. & Devel.--The American Stock Exchange, New York, NY; *U.S. Private*, pg. 62

Lemoine, Phillip M., V.P.-Res. & Tech.--Boeing Computer Services, Bellevue, WA; *U.S. Public*, pg. 240

Leong, Alex, Res. & Devel.--Andrea Electronics Corporation, Long Island City, NY; *U.S. Public*, pg. 112

Leppo, Sheldon S., V.P.-Res. & Devel.--Plymouth Rubber Company, Inc., Canton, MA; *U.S. Public*, pg. 1311

Leptos, C. B., Gen. Mgr.-Corp. Devel.--Western Mining Corporation Holdings Limited, Southbank, Australia; *Int'l*, pg. 1494

Lescoffit, Claude, V.P.-Biotech. Devel.--Groupe Limagrain, Chappes, France; *Int'l*, pg. 566

Letendre, N., Dir.-Res. & Devel.--Dynamic Metal Products Company, Manchester, CT; *U.S. Private*, pg. 350

Levine, Howard, V.P.-Res. & Devel.--Columbia Laboratories, Inc., Miami, FL; *U.S. Public*, pg. 405

Levy, Robert, V.P.-Devel. & Franchising--Cara Operations Limited, Toronto, Canada; *Int'l*, pg. 266

Lewicki, John A., Ph.D, V.P.-Res.--Scios Inc., Mountain View, CA; *U.S. Public*, pg. 1444

Lewis, Alan L., Dr., Chief Investment Officer & Dir.-Res.--Analytic TSA Global Asset Management Inc., Los Angeles, CA; *U.S. Public*, pg. 1672

Lewis, Brian, Mgr.-Engrng., Res. & Devel.--GSW Water Heating Company, Fergus, Canada; *Int'l*, pg. 538

Lewis, Frank M., V.P.-Res. & Devel.--Danek Medical Inc., Memphis, TN; *U.S. Public*, pg. 1482

Lewis, Gerard, Sr. V.P.-Res. & Devel.--Boston Chicken, Inc., Golden, CO; *U.S. Public*, pg. 247

Li, Thomas M., V.P.-Res. & Devel.--Hycor Biomedical, Inc., Irvine, CA; *U.S. Public*, pg. 851

Limay, Luis A., Gen. Mgr.-El Salvadoran Opers.--Commerce Group Corp., Milwaukee, WI; *U.S. Public*, pg. 410

Lindbergh, Giles, Sr. V.P.-Research--Fox Broadcasting Company (FBC), Beverly Hills, CA; *Int'l*, pg. 926

Lindenmann, Walter, Dr., Sr. V.P. & Res. Dir.--Ketchum Public Relations Worldwide, New York, NY; *U.S. Private, pg. 617*

Lindsey, Glenn S., V.P.-Res. & Devel.--International Dairy Queen, Inc., Minneapolis, MN; *U.S. Public*, pg. 220

Lindstrom, Tom, Dir.-Res. & Devel.--Mo och Domsjo AB, Stockholm, Sweden; *Int'l*, pg. 885

Lingscheild, Gregory, Mgr.-Engrng.--Solitec Wafer Processing, Inc., San Jose, CA; *U.S. Private*, pg. 1013

Lipsky, Harvey, V.P.-Research & Devel.--Faygo Beverages, Inc., Detroit, MI; *U.S. Public*, pg. 1153

Little, William C., V.P.--Forstmann & Company, Inc., New York, NY; *U.S. Public*, pg. 670

LittleJohn, Judith, V.P.-Clinical Research--Glaxo Wellcome PLC, Research Triangle Park, NC; *Int'l*, pg. 553

Litzinger, Robert A., V.P.-Fin.--Provident Financial Group, Inc., Cincinnati, OH; *U.S. Public*, pg. 1338

Liu, Donald, Dr., Sr. V.P.-Tech.--American Bureau of Shipping, New York, NY; *U.S. Private*, pg. 51

Lizak, Peter, Dir.-Res. & Devel.--Reactor Experiments, Inc., Sunnyvale, CA; *U.S. Public*, pg. 1594

Ljungqvist, Stig-Ove, Mgr.-Res. & Devel, Car Accessories--Eldon AB, Nassjo, Sweden; *Int'l*, pg. 436

Logan, Steve, V.P.-Res. & Devel.--Oxmoor House--Southern Progress Corporation, Birmingham, AL; *U.S. Public*, pg. 1612

Lomazzi, Walter, Dir.-Res. & Devel.--Mazzucchelli 1849 S.p.a., Castiglione Olona, Italy; *Int'l*, pg. 849

Lombardo, William, V.P.-Strategic Devel.--Coats North America, Charlotte, NC; *Int'l*, pg. 300

Longmuir, Alan G., V.P.-Res. & Devel.--Kaiser Aluminum & Chemical Corporation, Pleasanton, CA; *U.S. Public*, pg. 1062

Lorain, Edward J., Dir.-Res.--Hanson Investment Management Company, San Rafael, CA; *U.S. Public*, pg. 1673

Lorenz, C. Edward, V.P.-Chemicals--Du Pont (E.I. Du Pont De Nemours & Co.), Wilmington, DE; *U.S. Public*, pg. 530

Lott, Joseph C., V.P.-Res. & Devel.--Clayton Corporation, Fenton, MO; *U.S. Private*, pg. 244

Loverde, Joseph, V.P.-Res. & Devel.--Wilkins-Rogers Incorporated, Ellicott City, MD; *U.S. Private*, pg. 1176

Lowery, Sandy, Dir.-Res. & Devel.--Meridian Medical Technology, Inc., Columbia, MD; *U.S. Public*, pg. 1095

Lowry, B.E., Dir.-Prod. Devel.--Universal Composites-U.S.C., Manheim, PA; *U.S. Private*, pg. 1126

Lowry, Rick, V.P.-Res. & Devel.--Bryan Foods, West Point, MS; *U.S. Public*, pg. 1433

Luderer, Albert A., Dir.-Res. & Devel.--Dianon Systems, Inc., Stratford, CT; *U.S. Public*, pg. 506

Ludkovsky, Gregory, V.P.-Res. & Devel.--Inland Steel Products Company, East Chicago, IN; *U.S. Public*, pg. 879

Lugones, Olga, Mgr.-Research--American Express Publishing Corporation, New York, NY; *U.S. Public*, pg. 74

Lull, Jack, V.P.-Devel.--Allaire Corporation, Cambridge, MA; *U.S. Private*, pg. 36

Lumsden, Stu, Dir.-Egnrg.--Polk Audio, Inc., Baltimore, MD; *U.S. Public*, pg. 1315
Lund, David, Dir.-Res. & Devel.--Lund International Holdings, Inc., Anoka, MN; *U.S. Public*, pg. 1020
Lund, Robert K., V.P.-Science & Engrng. & Dir.-Tech.--Thiokol Corporation, Ogden, UT; *U.S. Public*, pg. 1596
Lund, Terry L., Mgr.-Research, Devel. & Demo.--San Diego Gas & Electric Company, San Diego, CA; *U.S. Public*, pg. 584
Lupatkin, Bruce, Dir.-Res.--Hambrecht & Quist LLC., San Francisco, CA; *U.S. Public*, pg. 778
Lupyan, David, V.P.-Res. & Devel.--Blue Coral/Slick 50, Cleveland, OH; *U.S. Public*, pg. 1348
Lynam, Niall, Chief Tech. Officer & Sr. V.P.-Res. & Devel.--Donnelly Corporation, Holland, MI; *U.S. Public*, pg. 519
Lynch, Barrett, Dir.-Prod. Devel.--Alba-Waldensian, Inc., Valdese, NC; *U.S. Public*, pg. 35
Lynn, Joe, Chief Devel. Officer--Microlog Corporation, Germantown, MD; *U.S. Public*, pg. 1105
Lyons, John, V.P.-Res. & Devel.--Duro Dyne Corporation, Farmingdale, NY; *U.S. Private*, pg. 349
Ma, Harry, Mgr.-Res. & Devel.--Polyloom Corp. of America, Dayton, TN; *U.S. Private*, pg. 875
MacBean, R.D., Mgr.-Grp. Tech. & Plng.--Q.U.F. Industries Ltd., Brisbane, Australia; *Int'l*, pg. 1074
MacDonald, John R., Ph.D., V.P.-Res. & Devel.--MGI PHARMA INC., Minneapolis, MN; *U.S. Public*, pg. 1026
Macey, James, Dir.-Res. & Devel.--Raytech Corporation, Shelton, CT; *U.S. Public*, pg. 1363
MacInnis, Bob, V.P. & Chief Tech. Officer--Holland Mark Martin, Boston, MA; *U.S. Private*, pg. 534
MacKenzie, Christine, Mgr.-Bus. Plng. & Strategy--Chrysler Corporation, Auburn Hills, MI; *U.S. Public*, pg. 352
Mackey, Catherine, V.P.-Res.--Dekalb Genetics Corporation, De Kalb, IL; *U.S. Public*, pg. 493
MacKinlay, David, Dir.-Corp. Devel.--Vickers PLC, London, United Kingdom; *Int'l*, pg. 1466
Mackrell, G.L., Head-Strategic Plng.--Commonwealth Bank Group, Sydney, Australia; *Int'l*, pg. 312
MacLachlan, Alexander, Sr. V.P.-Res. & Devel.--Du Pont (E.I. Du Pont De Nemours & Co.), Wilmington, DE; *U.S. Public*, pg. 530
Madden, Thomas A., V.P.-Corp. Devel.--Rockwell International Corporation, Costa Mesa, CA; *U.S. Public*, pg. 1397
Maekawa, Yuzo, Dir.--Citizen Watch Company, Ltd., Tokyo, Japan; *Int'l*, pg. 293
Maffey, George, V.P.-Res. & Devel.--Kwikset Corporation, Irvine, CA; *U.S. Public*, pg. 233
Mager, Klaus, Mgr.-Res.--Disneyland Hotel, Anaheim, CA; *U.S. Public*, pg. 513
Maglavy, Daniel B., M.D., Dir.-Medical Research--Biogen, Inc., Cambridge, MA; *U.S. Public*, pg. 230
Magnus, Tom, V.P., Res. Dir. & Strategic Plng. Dir.--The Sawtooth Group, Woodbridge, NJ; *U.S. Private*, pg. 969
Mai, Chao C., Dr., Sr. V.P.-Wafer Fabrication & Tech. Devel.--Dallas Semiconductor Corporation, Dallas, TX; *U.S. Public*, pg. 478
Main, Alan, Sr. V.P.-Research--Novartis Pharmaceuticals, East Hanover, NJ; *Int'l*, pg. 973
Majewski, Gerald L., Dr., V.P.-Res. & Devel.--INCSTAR Corporation, Stillwater, MN; *Int'l*, pg. 483
Mall, Marvin, V.P.-Prod. Devel.--Wall Data Incorporated, Kirkland, WA; *U.S. Public*, pg. 1734
Manber, Susan, V.P., Assoc. Res. Dir.--Ammirati, Puris & Lintas, Inc., New York, NY; *U.S. Private*, pg. 66
Mang, Theo, Dr., Chief Tech. Officer--Fuchs Petrolub AG Oel + Chemie, Mannheim, Germany; *Int'l*, pg. 517
Manley, Warren, V.P.-Res. & Devel.--Cook Composites & Polymers Inc., Kansas City, MO; *Int'l*, pg. 1409
Mann, Gaby, Mgr.-Res.& Devel.--Volkswagen Canada, Inc., Ajax, Canada; *Int'l*, pg. 1475
Manning, Michael, V.P.-Franchise Devel.--Big O Tires Incorporated, Englewood, CO; *U.S. Public*, pg. 1553
Mantz, Rick L., V.P.-Engrng.--General Datacomm Industries, Inc., Middlebury, CT; *U.S. Public*, pg. 708
Manz, George, V.P.-Prod. Mktg., Kimball Office Grp.--Kimball International, Inc., Jasper, IN; *U.S. Public*, pg. 956
Manzo, John, V.P.-Res. & Devel./Carrier Sys.--3Com Corporation, Santa Clara, CA; *U.S. Public*, pg. 1603
Marchart, Horst, V.P.-Research & Devel.--Porsche AG, Stuttgart, Germany; *Int'l*, pg. 1063
Marcus, Stanton C., V.P. & Mgr.-New Business Devel.--Congress Financial Corp., New York, NY; *U.S. Public*, pg. 447
Marek, Helfried, Dir.-Treas. & Investment Banking--Raiffeisen Zentralbank Osterreich, Vienna, Austria; *Int'l*, pg. 1084
Marino, C.A., V.P.-Corp. Devel.--ANSER (Analytic Services Inc.), Arlington, VA; *U.S. Private*, pg. 75
Marks, Ron, Sr. V.P.-Res. & Devel.--Applebee's International, Inc., Overland Park, KS; *U.S. Public*, pg. 122
Marrale, Rick, V.P.-Res. & Devel.--Lennox International Inc., Richardson, TX; *U.S. Private*, pg. 659
Marrone, R.S., V.P.-Strategic Bus. Devel.--Raytheon Engineers & Constructors, Inc., Englewood, CO; *U.S. Public*, pg. 1366
Marrs, Steven, Bus. Devel. Dir.--Blue Marble Advanced Communications Group, New York, NY; *U.S. Private*, pg. 104
Marsh, Dave, Asst. V.P.-Res. & Devel.--Asahi/America, Inc., Malden, MA; *U.S. Public*, pg. 137
Marshall, Scott W., Exec. V.P.-Res. & Devel.--Newbridge Networks Corporation, Kanata, Canada; *Int'l*, pg. 923
Marshall, Scott W., V.P.-Res. & Devel.--Newbridge Networks Corporation, Kanata, Canada; *Int'l*, pg. 924
Martelli, Prof. E. Arrigoni, Dir.-Res. & Devel.--Sigma-Tau Finanziaria S.p.A., Rome, Italy; *Int'l*, pg. 1248
Martensson, Hans, Dir.-Res. & Devel.--Sandvik AB, Sandviken, Sweden; *Int'l*, pg. 1185
Martin, D.L., V.P. & Gen. Mgr.-Southeast Region--Purina Mills, Inc., Saint Louis, MO; *U.S. Private*, pg. 895
Martin, Frank, Ph.D., V.P.-Chief Scientist--Sequus Pharmaceuticals, Inc., Menlo Park, CA; *U.S. Public*, pg. 1460
Martin, James L., V.P.-Res. & Devel.--LeaRonal, Inc., Freeport, NY; *U.S. Public*, pg. 982
Martin, John, Chief Chemist--Vernay Laboratories, Inc., Yellow Springs, OH; *U.S. Private*, pg. 1137
Martin, Linda G., V.P.-Domestic Res.--RAND, Santa Monica, CA; *U.S. Private*, pg. 908
Martin, Michael, V.P.-Res. & Devel.--Deposition Technologies, Inc., San Diego, CA; *U.S. Public*, pg. 1056
Martin, Michael, Dir.-Research--Garst Seed Company, Slater, IA; *Int'l*, pg. 1524
Martin, Mike, Mgr.-Engrng.--Chattanooga Group, Inc., Hixson, TN; *U.S. Private*, pg. 231
Martin, Robert, V.P.-Res. & Devel.--Seymour of Sycamore, Inc., Sycamore, IL; *U.S. Private*, pg. 988
Martinez, Edna Sofia, Res. Dir.--Leo Burnett Columbiana, S.A., Bogota, Colombia; *U.S. Private*, pg. 185
Maseer, Robert K., Jr., Exec. V.P.-Opers. & Systems Devel.--Automated Wagering, Hackensack, NJ; *U.S. Public*, pg. 1319
Mashimo, Tsugio, Gen. Mgr.-Estate Devel.--Gunze Sangyo, Inc., Tokyo, Japan; *Int'l*, pg. 578
Mason, Michael E., Dir.-Facil. Devel.--Eastman Kodak Company, Rochester, NY; *U.S. Public*, pg. 550
Masten, Charles N., V.P.-Chemicals--Du Pont (E.I. Du Pont De Nemours & Co.), Wilmington, DE; *U.S. Public*, pg. 530
Mastrangelo, Peter F., V.P.-Bus. Devel.--Glen Falls National Bank & Trust Company, Glens Falls, NY; *U.S. Public*, pg. 135
Masugata, Masaru, Dir.-Tech. Devel. & Res. & Corp. Plng. & Safety Res. Lab.--East Japan Railway Company, Tokyo, Japan; *Int'l*, pg. 431
Mathieson, John G., Mgr.-Res. Corp. Programs--Research, Melbourne, Australia; *Int'l*, pg. 227
Matievich, Bill, V.P.-Res. & Devel.--SPS Technologies, Inc., Jenkintown, PA; *U.S. Public*, pg. 1419
Matiuk, Greg J., Corp. V.P.-Strategic Plng. & Quality--Chevron Corporation, San Francisco, CA; *U.S. Public*, pg. 347
Matsil, Ellice, V.P.-Mktg. Res. & Plng.--The House of Seagram, New York, NY; *Int'l*, pg. 1217
Matsumura, Mitsuo, Dir.-Res. & Devel.--Tonen Corporation, Tokyo, Japan; *Int'l*, pg. 1398
Matthews, Joseph, Mgr.-Franchise Devel.--Blimpie International, Inc., Houston, TX; *U.S. Public*, pg. 236
Matus, Vickie, Mgr.-Market Research--Linotype-Hell Company, Hauppauge, NY; *Int'l*, pg. 604
Maurer, Henry, Sr. V.P.-Design & Product Devel.--Voyager Emblems, Inc., Sanborn, NY; *U.S. Private*, pg. 1143
Maurer, T., Dir.-Mktg. & Devel.--CorTec Company, Washington Court House, OH; *U.S. Public*, pg. 456
Maurice, Terry, V.P.-Res. & Devel.--Parmalat Canada Ltd., Etobicoke, Canada; *Int'l*, pg. 1023
Mayberry, Donald W., V.P.-Res. & Tests--Norfolk Southern Corporation, Norfolk, VA; *U.S. Public*, pg. 1190
Mayberry, Jack B., V.P.-Res. & Devel.--Edelbrock Corp., Torrance, CA; *U.S. Public*, pg. 563
Mayer, Daniel W., Exec. V.P.--Modern Controls, Inc., Minneapolis, MN; *U.S. Public*, pg. 1120
Mayer, J. M., Mgr.-Res. & Devel.--Conklin Co. Inc., Shakopee, MN; *U.S. Private*, pg. 263
Mayer, Ralph J., V.P.-Devel.--Adra Systems, Inc., Chelmsford, MA; *U.S. Private*, pg. 18
McCall, R., Dir.-Res.--McKinney & McKinney Advertising, Redondo Beach, CA; *U.S. Private*, pg. 723
McClain, Larry D., Dir.-Scientific Affairs--Dade Behring Inc., Westwood, MA; *U.S. Private*, pg. 110
McClendon, Thomas E., V.P. & Dir.-Res.--Cox Broadcasting Inc., Atlanta, GA; *U.S. Private*, pg. 281
McClure, Matt, V.P.-Res. & Devel.--Apollo Colors Inc., Northbrook, IL; *U.S. Private*, pg. 77
McCoy, Kevin C., V.P.-Res. & Devel.--Objective Systems Integrators, Inc., Folsom, CA; *U.S. Public*, pg. 1209
McCurdy, Jill, V.P.-Prod. Devel. & Mktg.--Koss Corporation, Milwaukee, WI; *U.S. Public*, pg. 966
McDaniels, Scott, Dir.-Res. & Devel.--Oregon Metallurgical Corporation, Albany, OR; *U.S. Public*, pg. 43
McDermott, Ronald L., V.P.-Res. & Tech. & Sec.--Worthington Foods Inc., Worthington, OH; *U.S. Public*, pg. 1780
McDonnell, Kevin J., V.P.-Res. & Devel.--Trace Mountain Products, San Jose, CA; *U.S. Private*, pg. 1095
McDougall, Al, Mgr.-Research & Devel.--Auto-trol Technology (Canada) Ltd., Calgary, Canada; *U.S. Public*, pg. 148
McGahay, Christine, Grp. Brand Res. Dir.--EURO RSCG Tatham, Chicago, IL; *Int'l*, pg. 601
McGrady, Dan, Mgr.-Corp. Tech.--Wyandot Inc., Marion, OH; *U.S. Private*, pg. 1193
McGreevy, William T., V.P.-Engrng.--Recoton Corporation, Lake Mary, FL; *U.S. Public*, pg. 1369
McGuinness, Michael E., Exec. V.P.-Res. & Devel.--Parametric Technology Corporation, Waltham, MA; *U.S. Public*, pg. 1257
McIntyre, Greg, Dir.-Bus. Devel. & Plng.--CH2M Hill Companies, Ltd., Greenwood Village, CO; *U.S. Private*, pg. 195
McKain, Rodger W., V.P.-Res. & Devel. Div.--Babcock & Wilcox Co., Barberton, OH; *U.S. Public*, pg. 1068
McKay, Lawrence, Dr., V.P.-Drug Devel.--Ohmeda, Liberty Corner, NJ; *Int'l*, pg. 121
McMahon, Kevin, Dir.-Mktg. & Bus. Devel.--E.D. Bullard Company, Cynthiana, KY; *U.S. Private*, pg. 180
McNamara, Dr. William, V.P.-Research--Osmose Wood Preserving, Inc., Buffalo, NY; *U.S. Private*, pg. 821
McNatton, Gary L., V.P.-Prod. Devel.--The Gap, Inc., San Francisco, CA; *U.S. Public*, pg. 702
McNerney, Jeff, Mgr.-Quality Control--Unger Company, Cleveland, OH; *U.S. Private*, pg. 1117
McRae, Doris, V.P.-Prod. Dev.--Smith Corona Corp., Cortland, NY; *U.S. Private*, pg. 1007
Mead, Jerry, V.P.-Res. & Product Devel.--J.R. Simplot Company, Minerals & Chemicals Group, Pocatello, ID; *U.S. Private*, pg. 1002
Meade, Harry, Ph.D., V.P.-Transgenic Res.--Genzyme Transgenics, Framingham, MA; *U.S. Public*, pg. 733
Medina, Shiela, Mgr.-Res. & Devel.--East Kentucky Power Co-op, Winchester, KY; *U.S. Private*, pg. 356
Medintz, Earl, V.P.-Plng. & Res.--Haworth Group Inc., Minneapolis, MN; *U.S. Private*, pg. 511
Meeder, Bill, Exec. V.P.-Bus. Devel.--Larkin Meeder & Schweidel, Dallas, TX; *U.S. Private*, pg. 651
Meek, John M., V.P.-Prod. Res.--Timberline Software Corporation, Beaverton, OR; *U.S. Public*, pg. 1609
Meeker, Robert, V.P. & Assoc. Plng. Dir.--Western International Media Corporation, New York, NY; *U.S. Private*, pg. 1166
Meers, Urbain, V.P.-Res. & Devel.--Sidmar N.V., Gent, Belgium; *Int'l*, pg. 79
Meiling, Gerald S., Sr. V.P.-Strategy, Science & Tech.--Corning Incorporated, Corning, NY; *U.S. Public*, pg. 448
Mellin, Stephen D., V.P.-Res. & Devel.--Mack Molding Company Inc., Arlington, VT; *U.S. Private*, pg. 691
Mellon, Mike, Sr. V.P.-Res.--Paramount Pictures Corporation, Los Angeles, CA; *U.S. Private*, pg. 776
Melnik, Joseph, Dir.-Res. & Devel.--Johnson & Johnson Ltda., Sao Paulo, Brazil; *U.S. Public*, pg. 931
Meloni, Daniel, Mgr.-Corp. Plng. & Res.--Kemper Insurance Companies, Long Grove, IL; *U.S. Private*, pg. 614
Melson, Christopher M., V.P.-Prod. Devel.--Texas Micro, Inc., Houston, TX; *U.S. Public*, pg. 1586
Melvin, Terry, V.P.-Res. & Engrng.--Spalding Sports Worldwide, Chicopee, MA; *U.S. Private*, pg. 630
Mendenhall, Jan, V.P.-Res. & Devel.--Case-Swayne Co. Inc., Corona, CA; *U.S. Private*, pg. 218
Menjon, Gerard, Exec. V.P. & Head-Res. & Devel.--Electricite de France, Paris, France; *Int'l*, pg. 437
Mercier, C., Research--Danone Group, Paris, France; *Int'l*, pg. 379
Mercurio, Joe, Dir.-Plng. & Res.--Walgreen Co., Deerfield, IL; *U.S. Public*, pg. 1733
Mettinger, Karl L., M.D., Ph.D., Sr. Dir.-Clinical Res.--Baker Norton Pharmaceuticals, Inc., Miami, FL; *U.S. Public*, pg. 914
Meyer, James W., Sr. V.P., Chief Technical Officer & Dir.-Res./Devel.--Eastman Kodak Company, Rochester, NY; *U.S. Public*, pg. 550
Meyer, Michael, Mgr.-Training & Devel.--LEGO Systems, Inc., Enfield, CT; *Int'l*, pg. 805
Meyerhoefer, Carl H., V.P.-Res. Devel.--TII Industries, Inc., Copiague, NY; *U.S. Public*, pg. 1556
Meyers, Michael R., Sr. V.P.-Prod. Research & Devel.--Milton Bradley Company, East Longmeadow, MA; *U.S. Public*, pg. 797
Mezzedimi, V., Gen. Mgr.-Res. & Devel.--Nuovo Pignone S.p.a., Florence, Italy; *Int'l*, pg. 990
Michon, D., Sr. V.P.-Tech. Res.--Compagnie Generale de Geophysique, Massy, France; *Int'l*, pg. 241
Mihm, J.C., Sr. V.P.-Corp. Tech.--Phillips Petroleum Company, Bartlesville, OK; *U.S. Public*, pg. 1290
Miller, Christy, V.P.-Mfg.--Supreme Industries, Inc., Goshen, IN; *U.S. Public*, pg. 1541
Miller, Ellen, Sr. V.P. & Grp. Res. Dir.--Jordan, McGrath, Case & Taylor Inc., New York, NY; *U.S. Private*, pg. 598
Miller, James E., Dr., V.P. & Dir.-Res./Oilseeds & Fire crops--Pioneer Hi-Bred International, Inc., Des Moines, IA; *U.S. Public*, pg. 1298
Miller, L. R., Dir.-Mechanical Res. & Devel.--Lord Research & Development, Cary, NC; *U.S. Private*, pg. 676
Milner, L. Richard, V.P.-Corp. Devel.--Aluminum Company of America, Pittsburgh, PA; *U.S. Public*, pg. 60
Minich, Arthur P., V.P.-Res. & Devel. & Chief Tech. Officer--Proxima Corporation, San Diego, CA; *U.S. Public*, pg. 1339
Mininni, Bob, Dr., V.P.-Res. & Devel.--International Specialty Products, Inc., Wayne, NJ; *U.S. Public*, pg. 858
Minnihan, Richard L., V.P.-Bus. Devel.--Medical Laboratory Automation, Inc., Pleasantville, NY; *U.S. Private*, pg. 727
Mir, Leon, V.P.-Res. & Devel.--Ionics, Incorporated, Watertown, MA; *U.S. Public*, pg. 912
Miracles, Anthony, Dir.-Res. & Devel.--Pace International L.P., Kirkland, WA; *U.S. Private*, pg. 829
Mislang, Gil, Dir.-Res. & Devel.--Dunn-Edwards Corporation, Los Angeles, CA; *U.S. Private*, pg. 347
Mitarai, Akira, Dir. & Grp. Gen. Mgr.-Res. & Devel.--Sharp Corporation, Osaka, Japan; *Int'l*, pg. 1228
Mitchell, Gail, Dir.-Pur. & Prod. Devel.--Arden International Kitchens, Inc., Lakeville, MN; *U.S. Private*, pg. 972
Mixon, Grover C., Chief Oper. Officer & Exec. V.P.--Phoenix Medical Technology, Inc., Andrews, SC; *U.S. Public*, pg. 1292
Mochizuki, David, Research & Devel. & Environment/Natural Rsrcs.--Nabors Industries, Inc., Houston, TX; *U.S. Public*, pg. 1148
Mochizuki, Tateki, Mng. Dir.-Res. & Devel.--Japan Tobacco Inc., Tokyo, Japan; *Int'l*, pg. 703
Modlin, Paul, Mgr.-S/C Devel.--Service Supply Co. Inc. of Indiana, Indianapolis, IN; *U.S. Private*, pg. 987
Moehring, Mary Beth, Asst. V.P.-Trng. & Devel.--Sysco Corporation, Houston, TX; *U.S. Public*, pg. 1550
Moeller, Patrick W., V.P.-Res. & Devel.--Hickory Specialties, Inc., Brentwood, TN; *U.S. Public*, pg. 596
Moeller, Theodore W., V.P.-Res. & Devel.--The Quaker Oats Company, Chicago, IL; *U.S. Public*, pg. 1347
Mohan, Kshitij, V.P.-Res. & Tech. Svcs.--Baxter International Inc., Deerfield, IL; *U.S. Public*, pg. 196
Moldenius, Steve, Dir.-Tech. Res. & Devel.--Sodra Cell AB, Vaxjo, Sweden; *Int'l*, pg. 1275
Moley, Kevin E., Sr. V.P.-Prod. & Bus. Devel.--PCS Health Systems, Inc., Scottsdale, AZ; *U.S. Public*, pg. 993
Monday, Don, V.P.-Res. & Devel.--Brite Voice Systems, Inc., Wichita, KS; *U.S. Public*, pg. 257
Monforte, Joseph, V.P.-Research & Devel.--GeneTrace Systems, Inc., Menlo Park, CA; *U.S. Private*, pg. 958

Monsorno, Richard, Sr. V.P.-Tech.--American Technical Ceramics Corp., Huntington Station, NY; *U.S. Public*, pg. 93
Montgomery, B.J., Sr. V.P.-Res. & Devel. & Bus. Mngmt.--Kerr-McGee Chemical Corp., Oklahoma City, OK; *U.S. Public*, pg. 952
Moore, Bill, V.P.-Devel.--Six Flags Theme Parks Inc., Parsippany, NJ; *U.S. Public*, pg. 1611
Moore, James O., Mgr.-Measurement & Control Div.--Moore Products Co., Spring House, PA; *U.S. Public*, pg. 1128
Moore, Loyd, Dir.-Corp. Creative Design--Inverness Corp., Fair Lawn, NJ; *U.S. Private*, pg. 574
Moore, M.A., Dr., Dir.-Tech. & Mkt. Devel.--Morganite Thermal Ceramics Limited, Norton, United Kingdom; *Int'l, pg. 893*
Moore, Peggy Howard, Dir.-Market Res. & Evaluation--Wisconsin Power & Light Company, Madison, WI; *U.S. Public*, pg. 1728
Moore, Sylvia, V.P.-Res. & Devel.--Alcoa Building Products, Inc., Sidney, OH; *U.S. Public*, pg. 61
Moos, Walter H., Ph.D., V.P.-Chemical Therapeutics Res. & Devel.--Chiron Corporation, Emeryville, CA; *U.S. Public*, pg. 349
Moos, Walter H., Ph.D., V.P.-Res. & Devel.--Chiron Technologies, Emeryville, CA; *U.S. Public*, pg. 350
Morales, Pedro, Dir.-Research & Devel.--CODELCO Chile (Corporacion Nacional Del Cobre De Chile), Santiago, Chile; *Int'l*, pg. 302
Morales, Rodolfo A., V.P.-Res. & Devel.--Farah U.S.A., Inc., El Paso, TX; *U.S. Public*, pg. 613
Moran, John L., V.P.-Bus. Devel.--Apache Corporation, Houston, TX; *U.S. Public*, pg. 119
Moran, M. Marcus, V.P.-Devel. & Real Estate--W.E. Aubuchon Co., Inc., Westminster, MA; *U.S. Private*, pg. 98
Moreau, J. Claude, V.P.-Res. & Devel.--Schneider S.A., Boulogne-Billancourt, France; *Int'l*, pg. 1207
Morel, Donald E., V.P.-Scientific Svcs.--The West Company, Incorporated, Lionville, PA; *U.S. Public*, pg. 1755
Moreno, Victor, V.P.-Mead Johnson Res. Center--Bristol-Myers Squibb U.S. Pharmaceutical Group, Plainsboro, NJ; *U.S. Public*, pg. 255
Morgan, Donald S., Sr. V.P.-Bus. Devel.--WestWayne, Inc., Atlanta, GA; *U.S. Private*, pg. 1170
Morgan, Jack, Dir.-Corp. Devel.--Genetics Institute, Inc., Cambridge, MA; *U.S. Public*, pg. 79
Morgan, James D., V.P. & Chief Scientist--Comptek Research, Inc., Buffalo, NY; *U.S. Public*, pg. 419
Morin, Emmanuel, Dir.-Datech--Gaz Metropolitain & Company, Montreal, Canada; *Int'l*, pg. 541
Morisaki, Katsuhiko, Dir.-Res. & Devel.--Rohto Pharmaceutical Co., Osaka, Japan; *Int'l*, pg. 1126
Morosky, Frank, Res. Dir.--Marketing Support, Incorporated, Chicago, IL; *U.S. Private*, pg. 705
Morrison, Jerry, Mgr.--Commemorative Brands, Inc., Austin, TX; *U.S. Private*, pg. 258
Morse, Randall H., V.P.-Res., Devel. & Regulatory Affairs--Schleicher & Schuell, Inc., Keene, NH; *Int'l*, pg. 1206
Morse, W.F., V.P.-Res.--Columbia Gas Distribution Companies, Columbus, OH; *U.S. Public*, pg. 402
Mosely, L. Max, V.P.-Res.--Computalog Ltd., Calgary, Canada; *Int'l*, pg. 325
Moser, Franz Xaver, Sr. V.P.-Res. & Devel.--Deutz AG, Cologne, Germany; *Int'l*, pg. 407
Moss, Clark, Sr. V.P. & Creative Dir.--Mezzina/Brown Inc., New York, NY; *U.S. Private*, pg. 739
Mosser, Mark, V.P.-Res. & Devel. Laboratory--Teleflex Incorporated, Plymouth Meeting, PA; *U.S. Public*, pg. 1569
Mounday, Donald R., V.P.--Brite Voice Systems, Inc., Heathrow, FL; *U.S. Public*, pg. 257
Mowshowitz, Solomon L., Ph.D., V.P.-Res. & Devel.--AMBI Inc., Tarrytown, NY; *U.S. Public*, pg. 7
Muck, George, Dr., V.P.-Res. & Devel.--Dean Foods Company, Franklin Park, IL; *U.S. Public*, pg. 489
Muller, Owen B., Dir.-Real Estate--Northrop Grumman Corporation, Los Angeles, CA; *U.S. Public*, pg. 1197
Muller, Richard P., V.P.-Res. & Devel., ACMI Div.--Circon Corporation, Santa Barbara, CA; *U.S. Public*, pg. 373
Muntjewerf, A.K., Dir.-Res. & Devel.--Bestuurcentrum der Verenigde Bedrijven Nutricia B.V., Zoetermeer, Netherlands; *Int'l*, pg. 991
Murakami, Edward S., V.P.-Res. & Quality Assurance--Baker Commodities, Inc., Los Angeles, CA; *U.S. Private*, pg. 111
Murata, Yoshihiko, Mng. Dir. & Sr. V.P.-Engrng., Res. & Devel.--Japan Airlines Company, Ltd., Tokyo, Japan; *Int'l*, pg. 699
Murphy, John, Dr., V.P.-Res. & Devel.--Goldwell Cosmetics (USA) Inc., Linthicum Heights, MD; *Int'l*, pg. 718
Murphy, Michael, V.P. & Assoc. Acct. Plng. Dir.--Goldberg Moser O'Neill, San Francisco, CA; *U.S. Private*, pg. 459
Murphy, Ray, V.P.-Sls.--Austin Quality Foods, Cary, NC; *U.S. Private*, pg. 100
Murveit, Hy, V.P.-Research & Devel.--Nuance Communications, Menlo Park, CA; *U.S. Private*, pg. 958
Muston, Bill, Mgr.-Res. & Devel.--Texas Utilities Company, Dallas, TX; *U.S. Public*, pg. 1586
Myatt, J., Mgr.-Research & Devel.--Janesville Products, Norwalk, OH; *U.S. Public*, pg. 924
Myczkowski, Jack, V.P.-Devel. & Tech.--Thinking Machines Corporation, Burlington, MA; *U.S. Private*, pg. 1081
Myers, Mark B., Sr. V.P.-Corp. Res. & Tech.--Xerox Corporation, Stamford, CT; *U.S. Public*, pg. 1783
Nachtigal, Jules, V.P.-Mktg. Res. & Devel.--Conair Corporation, Stamford, CT; *U.S. Private*, pg. 261
Nagano, Sunao, Exec. V.P.--Marubeni Corporation, Osaka, Japan; *Int'l*, pg. 844
Nagasawa, Toshio, Mng. Dir.-Res. & Devel.--UBE Industries Ltd., Tokyo, Japan; *Int'l*, pg. 1426
Naimark, Richard, Sr. V.P.--American Arbitration Association, New York, NY; *U.S. Private*, pg. 50
Nakagawa, Shuichi, V.P.-Res. & Devel.--Yokogawa Electric Corporation, Tokyo, Japan; *Int'l*, pg. 1520
Nakayama, Chiaki, Gen. Mgr.-Res. Center--Toto Ltd., Kitakyushu, Japan; *Int'l*, pg. 1410
Nardone, John, Mng. Dir., Media Dir. & Res. Dir.--Modem Media New York, New York, NY; *U.S. Public*, pg. 1641
Nash, Linn, Res. Dir.--Nestle Ice Cream Co., Columbus, OH; *Int'l*, pg. 918
Nash, Rod, V.P.-Engrng.--Collins Industries, Inc., Hutchinson, KS; *U.S. Public*, pg. 399
Navarette, Dolly, Dir.-Laboratory--Gulf States Asphalt Company, Inc., South Houston, TX; *U.S. Private*, pg. 487
Naylor, Chic, Chief Engr.--Metrologic Instruments, Inc., Blackwood, NJ; *U.S. Public*, pg. 1102
Nedich, Ronald L., Dr., V.P.-Res. & Devel.--Alpharma Inc., Fort Lee, NJ; *U.S. Public*, pg. 57
Neil, G.L., Exec. V.P.-Res. & Devel.--Wyeth-Ayerst Laboratories, Inc., Philadelphia, PA; *U.S. Public*, pg. 80
Neil, Gary, Dir.-Res. & Devel.--Wyeth-Ayerst Laboratories, Inc., Philadelphia, PA; *U.S. Public*, pg. 80
Nelson, Daniel, Mgr.-Res. & Devel.--Pioneer Plastics Corporation, Auburn, ME; *U.S. Private*, pg. 867
Nelson, John, V.P.-Res. & Devel.--Watts Fluidair, Kittery, ME; *Int'l*, pg. 1243
Nethery, Dr. Arthur, V.P.-Res. & Devel.--LiphaTech, Inc., Milwaukee, WI; *Int'l*, pg. 812
Netravali, Arun, V.P.-Res.--Lucent Technologies Inc., Murray Hill, NJ; *U.S. Public*, pg. 1017
Neuner, Mark C., Exec. V.P. & Dir.-Res.--Jefferies & Company, Inc., Los Angeles, CA; *U.S. Public*, pg. 925
Neville, Matthew, Mgr.-Res. & Devl.--Cab-o-Sil Div. Cabot Corp., Tuscola, IL; *U.S. Public*, pg. 289
Newberg, Skip, V.P.-Res. & Devel.--Prudential Real Estate Affiliates Inc., Costa Mesa, CA; *U.S. Private*, pg. 892
Newhouse, Steve, Dir.-Mktg., Sls. & Adv.--Atlantic Builders Group Inc., Baltimore, MD; *U.S. Private*, pg. 95
Newman, Peter A., Sr. V.P.-Ancillary Rights & Special Projects--Viacom Enterprises, New York, NY; *U.S. Private*, pg. 779
Newton, Dennis, Dir.-Strategic Res.--Nextel Communications, Mc Lean, VA; *U.S. Public*, pg. 1180
Nicholas, Philip A., AIA, V.P.--Giffels Associates, Inc., Southfield, MI; *U.S. Private*, pg. 452
Nichols, Roy J., Sr. V.P.--Nichols Research Corporation, Huntsville, AL; *U.S. Public*, pg. 1182
Nishihara, Toru, Dir.-Res. & Devel.--Rohto Pharmaceutical Co., Osaka, Japan; *Int'l*, pg. 1126
Nishimura, Hiroshi, Mng. Dir.-New Business Admin., Res. Labs, New Matls. & Biomed.--Sumitomo Metal Industries, Ltd., Tokyo, Japan; *Int'l*, pg. 1315
Noble, Beth, Dir.-Research & Devel.--Stanback Company, Salisbury, NC; *U.S. Private*, pg. 1030
Noguchi, Hiromasa, Dir.--Sakata Seed Corporation, Yokohama, Japan; *Int'l*, pg. 1178
Nomura, Shinya, Mng. Dir.--Kayaba Industry Co., Ltd., Tokyo, Japan; *Int'l*, pg. 727
Nontapunthawat, Nimit, Exec. V.P. & Gen. Mgr.--Bangkok Bank Public Company Limited, Bangkok, Thailand; *Int'l*, pg. 146
Norman, Earl P., Jr., V.P.-Tech.--Sonoco Products Company, Hartsville, SC; *U.S. Public*, pg. 1485
Notter, Randall P., Dir.-Corp. Res.--Journal Register Company, Trenton, NJ; *U.S. Public*, pg. 934
Novak, Louis R., Chief Oper. Officer & Exec. V.P.--Galoob Toys, Inc., South San Francisco, CA; *U.S. Public*, pg. 698
Novotny, Irv, V.P.-Res. & Quality Assurance--Dean Foods Vegetable Company, Green Bay, WI; *U.S. Public*, pg. 490
Nugent, Marcelle, Dir.-Multifamily Res.--The L & B Group, Dallas, TX; *U.S. Public*, pg. 1673
Nutt, Fred, V.P.-Engrng., Res. & Devel.--Weiler & Company, Inc., Whitewater, WI; *U.S. Private*, pg. 1160
Nuttall, Jan, Dir.-Education & Devel.--Laura Ashley Holdings Plc, Maidenhead, United Kingdom; *Int'l*, pg. 804
O'Brien, D., Dir.-Technical--Cochrane, Inc., King of Prussia, PA; *U.S. Public*, pg. 456
O'Connell, William, Dir.-Res. & Devel.--Nyltech North America Inc., Manchester, NH; *Int'l*, pg. 482
O'Donnell, John P., Dr., V.P.-Res. & Quality Control--Mylan Laboratories, Inc., Pittsburgh, PA; *U.S. Public*, pg. 1143
O'Mahony, J. Sean, V.P.-Res. & Devel.--Rich Products Corp., Buffalo, NY; *U.S. Private*, pg. 928
O'Neil, Thomas J., Exec. V.P.-Opers.--Cleveland-Cliffs Inc, Cleveland, OH; *U.S. Public*, pg. 386
O'Shaughnessy, Mike, Chief Chemist & Mgr.-Production--Sigmund Cohn Corp., Mount Vernon, NY; *U.S. Private*, pg. 250
O'Sullivan, R., Mgr.-Res. & Devel.--Orange and Rockland Utilities, Inc., Pearl River, NY; *U.S. Public*, pg. 1229
Obsenares, Cyndi, Plng. Supvr.--Western Multicultural Group, Los Angeles, CA; *U.S. Private*, pg. 1167
Ogan, Kenneth, V.P.-Res. & Devel.--Hach Company, Loveland, CO; *U.S. Public*, pg. 773
Ohnsorge, Horst, Dir.-Res. & Devel.--Alcatel N.V., Amsterdam, Netherlands; *Int'l*, pg. 55
Okumura, Joao N., Mgr.-Res. & Devel.--Yamaha Motor do Brasil Ltda., Convica, Brazil; *Int'l*, pg. 1516
Okumura, Morio, Dir. & Gen. Mgr.-Intl. Plng.--The Mitsubishi Trust and Banking Corporation, Tokyo, Japan; *Int'l*, pg. 876
Okuyama, Michio, Dir.-Tire Devel. Div. III--Bridgestone Corporation, Tokyo, Japan; *Int'l*, pg. 213
Oldfield, John A., V.P.-Prod. Programs & Powertrain Grp.--Ford of Europe, Incorporated, Dearborn, MI; *U.S. Public*, pg. 664
Oliver, Jerry, Dir.-Quality Assurance--Center Laboratories, Inc., Port Washington, NY; *U.S. Public*, pg. 813
Olsen, Agnar, Dir.-Engrng. & Construction--Landsvirkjun - The National Power Co., Reykjavik, Iceland; *Int'l*, pg. 801
Omohundro, Bill, Dir.-Res.--Carrier Corporation, Indianapolis, IN; *U.S. Public*, pg. 1689
Ophey, Lothar, Dr. Ing., Exec. V.P.-Prod.--Traub AG, Reichenbach, Germany; *Int'l*, pg. 1419
Ornstein, Barry, Mgr.-Res. & Devel.--Blue Cross and Blue Shield of Massachusetts, Boston, MA; *U.S. Private*, pg. 151
Osborne, B.P., V.P.-Research, Technology & Engrng.--Lockheed Aeronautical Systems Company, Marietta, GA; *U.S. Public*, pg. 1007
Osepian, Craig, V.P.-Municipal & Devel.--Western Waste Industries, Torrance, CA; *U.S. Public*, pg. 1686
Osepian, George, V.P.-Corp. Devel.--Western Waste Industries, Torrance, CA; *U.S. Public*, pg. 1686
Osman, Dewaine L., Sr. V.P.--Unisys Corporation, Blue Bell, PA; *U.S. Public*, pg. 1671
Otte, R. Adrian, M.D., Sr. V.P.-Res. Opers./N. America--PAREXEL International Corporation, Waltham, MA; *U.S. Public*, pg. 1257
Owen, William H. III, V.P.-Tech. Devel.--Xicor, Inc., Milpitas, CA; *U.S. Public*, pg. 1785
Oyasu, Hitoshi, Mng. Dir.-Res. & Devel. Div.--Fujisawa Pharmaceutical Co. Ltd., Osaka, Japan; *Int'l*, pg. 525
Paefgen, Franz-Josef, Dir.-Tech. Devel.--Audi AG, Ingolstadt, Germany; *Int'l*, pg. 1473
Paido-Rogues, Guido, Mgr.-Res. & Devel./Prods. Division--Elscint Ltd., Haifa, Israel; *Int'l*, pg. 450
Painter, Stuart T., Dir.-Bus. Devel.--Imperial Tobacco Group, Ltd., Bristol, United Kingdom; *Int'l*, pg. 666
Paisley, John C., V.P.-Sls.--Virginia Metal Industries, Inc., Orange, VA; *U.S. Private*, pg. 1141
Pallone, Thomas J., V.P.-Res. & Devel.--Alberto-Culver Company, Melrose Park, IL; *U.S. Public*, pg. 37
Palmer, Darrel, Dir.-Res. & Devel.--Ballard Medical Products, Draper, UT; *U.S. Public*, pg. 171
Palmer, Robert, Mgr.-Res. & Devel.--Strahman Valves, Inc., Florham Park, NJ; *U.S. Private*, pg. 1046
Palmero, Albert, Dir.-Bus. Res. & Devel.--Haydon Switch & Instrument, Inc., Waterbury, CT; *U.S. Private*, pg. 513
Paluncic, Zdravko, Dir.-Rsch. & Devel.--Lincoln Industrial, Saint Louis, MO; *U.S. Public*, pg. 1273
Pannell, Hershell, Dir.-Res. & Devel.--Barclay Furniture Company, Sherman, MS; *U.S. Public*, pg. 974
Park, John J., Sr. V.P.-Fin., Asst. Treas. & Dir.-Res.--W.P. Carey & Co., Inc., New York, NY; *U.S. Private*, pg. 209
Park, P., V.P.-Res., Devel. & Quality Assurance--Marigold Foods, Inc., Minneapolis, MN; *Int'l*, pg. 752
Parker, Terry L., Corp. Dir.- Res. & Devel.--LaRoche Industries Inc., Atlanta, GA; *U.S. Private*, pg. 651
Parr, Jack, Exec. V.P.-Res. & Devel.--Wright Medical Technology, Arlington, TN; *U.S. Private*, pg. 1192
Parry, Thomas, Mgr.-Res. & Devel., Gen. Pkgng.--Ato-Findley, Inc., Wauwatosa, WI; *Int'l*, pg. 445
Parry, Thomas J., V.P.-Prod. Devel. & Compliance--American Travellers Corporation, Bensalem, PA; *U.S. Public*, pg. 433
Parsons, Robert A., V.P.-Res. & Devel.--Troy Mills, Inc., Troy, NH; *U.S. Private*, pg. 1106
Partlow, Gerald, V.P.-Engrng.--Marsh Company, Belleville, IL; *U.S. Private*, pg. 707
Parziale, John V., V.P.-Plng.--Marathon Oil Company, Houston, TX; *U.S. Public*, pg. 1661
Patarin, Louis, Dir.-Res. & Devel.--COGEMA - Compagnie Generale des Matieres Nucleaires, Velizy-Villacoublay, France; *Int'l*, pg. 304
Patel, Jay, V.P.-Res. & Devel.--Periphonics Corp., Bohemia, NY; *U.S. Public*, pg. 1278
Paterson, Gary A., V.P.-Store Plng.--Albertson's, Inc., Boise, ID; *U.S. Public*, pg. 38
Patino, Hugo, V.P.-Res. & Devel.--Adolph Coors Company, Golden, CO; *U.S. Public*, pg. 445
Patino, Hugo, V.P.-Res. & Devel.--Coors Brewing Company, Golden, CO; *U.S. Public*, pg. 445
Patterson, Sharon, V.P.-Research & Plng.--The Allstate Corporation, Northbrook, IL; *U.S. Public*, pg. 55
Patton, Richard, Exec. V.P.-Res. & Devel.--Lawson Software, Minneapolis, MN; *U.S. Private*, pg. 654
Paul, Donald L., V.P.-Tech. & Environmental Affairs--Chevron Corporation, San Francisco, CA; *U.S. Public*, pg. 347
Paul, Gerhard, Dr., Div. Head-Colorants Laboratory--BASF AG, Ludwigshafen, Germany; *Int'l*, pg. 103
Paul, Jennifer D., Mgr.-Total Quality, Trng. & Devel.--Aquarion Company, Bridgeport, CT; *U.S. Public*, pg. 126
Paulson, David J., Dir.-Res. & Devel.--Osmonics, Inc., Minnetonka, MN; *U.S. Public*, pg. 1233
Paulson, Larry G., V.P.-Res. & Devel.--PPT Vision, Inc., Eden Prairie, MN; *U.S. Public*, pg. 1245
Payan, Jean-Jacques, V.P.-Res.--Renault, Boulogne-Billancourt, France; *Int'l*, pg. 1102
Paydos, Paul, Sr. V.P.-Design Res.--Guilford of Maine, Inc., Guilford, ME; *U.S. Public*, pg. 889
Pedneault, A., V.P.-Devel.--Kruger Inc., Montreal, Canada; *Int'l*, pg. 761
Pekeler, Markus, Exec. V.P. & New Bus. Contact--Impuls Advertising AG, Kusnacht, Switzerland; *Int'l*, pg. 666
Pelerin, Jacques, Dir.-Quality, Res. & Devel.--Cockerill Sambre, Brussels, Belgium; *Int'l*, pg. 301
Pellegrin, J., Dir.-Res.--SNCF, Paris, France; *Int'l*, pg. 1163
Pelligrino, Paul A., V.P.-Engrng.--Twin Disc, Incorporated, Racine, WI; *U.S. Public*, pg. 1646
Pelman, A.I., V.P.-Res. & Devel.--MacMillan Bloedel Limited, Vancouver, Canada; *Int'l*, pg. 828
Penicnak, John, Sr. V.P.-Res. & Devel.--Cosmair, Inc., New York, NY; *Int'l*, pg. 818
Pennington, Alan S., V.P.-Devel.--The Meridian Resource Corporation, Houston, TX; *U.S. Public*, pg. 1095
Peoples, Clarence, V.P.-Res. & Devel.--Collins & Aikman Corporation, Charlotte, NC; *U.S. Public*, pg. 399
Peres, Alvaro M., Dir.-Res. & Devel.--Petrobras - Petroleo Brasileiro S.A., Rio de Janeiro, Brazil; *Int'l*, pg. 1041
Perisse, Laura, Dir.-Bus. Devel.--Fluor Daniel GTI, Inc., Norwood, MA; *U.S. Public*, pg. 660
Perlberg, William, V.P.-Res. & Devel.--The Hartz Mountain Corp., Secaucus, NJ; *U.S. Private*, pg. 508
Perlman, Jane, V.P.-Res.--WPIX, Inc., New York, NY; *U.S. Public*, pg. 1636

Pernet, Andre G., Ph.D., V.P.-Pharmaceutical Prods., Res. & Devel.--Abbott Laboratories, Abbott Park, IL; *U.S. Public, pg. 12*

Perry, Doug, Training & Devel.--Harris Calorific Co., Gainesville, GA; *U.S. Public*, pg. 996

Perry, R.D., V.P.-Personal Lines--Millers Mutual Insurance Assn., Alton, IL; *U.S. Private*, pg. 748

Pesce, James A., Pres.--US SerVis, West Orange, NJ; *U.S. Public*, pg. 1687

Peterman, Charles, Dir.-Research & Devel.--Hydril Technology Center, Houston, TX; *U.S. Private*, pg. 551

Peters, C.A., V.P.-Devel. & Tech.--Emerson Electric Co., Saint Louis, MO; *U.S. Public*, pg. 572

Peters, C.T., Dr., Dir.-Res.--Boart International Limited, Sandton, South Africa; *Int'l*, pg. 76

Peters, Dennis, V.P.-Research & Devel.--Resco Products, Inc., Conshohocken, PA; *U.S. Private*, pg. 924

Petersen, Lee E., Exploration Mgr.-Algeria--Anadarko Petroleum Corporation, Houston, TX; *U.S. Public*, pg. 107

Peterson, Anne, Mgr.-Res.--Westin Hotels & Resorts, Seattle, WA; *U.S. Public*, pg. 1512

Peterson, Don, Mgr.-Material Res.--Spartech Plastics, Portage, WI; *U.S. Public*, pg. 1496

Peterson, Graham H., Mgr.-Res. & Devel.--Speakman Company, Wilmington, DE; *U.S. Private*, pg. 1021

Peterson, Paul, V.P., Assoc. Res. Dir.--Ammirati, Puris & Lintas, Inc., New York, NY; *U.S. Private*, pg. 66

Petri, Eberhard, Exec. V.P.-Res. & Devel.--Siemens Nixdorf Information Systems Inc., Burlington, MA; *Int'l*, pg. 1245

Petroungarung, Songsri, Asst. Mng. Dir.--Bangkok Athletic Co., Ltd., Bangkok, Thailand; *Int'l*, pg. 146

Peyton, Judy, V.P. & Res. Dir.--McConnaughy Stein Schmidt Brown, Chicago, IL; *U.S. Private*, pg. 720

Pfaff, Frederick A., V.P.-Res. & Deve.--Stonhard, Inc., Maple Shade, NJ; *U.S. Public*, pg. 1358

Pfander, Wilhelm, V.P.-Mfg. & Prod. Devel.--Penobscot Shoe Company, Old Town, ME; *U.S. Public*, pg. 1273

Pfizenmaier, Wolfgang, Co-Chief Exec. Officer--Heidelberger Druckmaschinen A.G., Heidelberg, Germany; *Int'l*, pg. 604

Pfund, John, V.P.-Res.--Dekalb Genetics Corporation, De Kalb, IL; *U.S. Public*, pg. 493

Phillips, Amy, Mgr.-Monitoring/Res Svcs.--BNA PLUS, Washington, DC; *U.S. Private*, pg. 182

Phillips, Richard B., Sr. V.P.-Tech.--International Paper Company, Purchase, NY; *U.S. Public*, pg. 901

Pick, Richard, V.P.-Engnrg., Exploration & Devel.--ARCO Coal Company, Denver, CO; *U.S. Public*, pg. 144

Pick, Robert S., V.P.-Corp. Devel.--Comcast Corporation, Philadelphia, PA; *U.S. Public*, pg. 406

Pickard, Murphy, Dir.-Res. & Devel.--Mesa Laboratories, Inc., Wheat Ridge, CO; *U.S. Public*, pg. 1099

Pickow, Peter, Chief Editor--Music Sales Corporation, New York, NY; *U.S. Private*, pg. 768

Piech, Ferdinand, Dr., Chm.-Mngmt. Bd.--Volkswagen AG, Wolfsburg, Germany; *Int'l*, pg. 1473

Pieklo, David A., Dir.-Adv. & Promotions--McDougal/Littell, Evanston, IL; *U.S. Public*, pg. 841

Piepil, Jack, Mgr.-Research & Product Devel.--Andersen Corporation, Bayport, MN; *U.S. Private*, pg. 71

Pierce, Heidi, Art Dir., Acct. Dir. & Res. Dir.--AIC-FSS Advertising, Minneapolis, MN; *U.S. Private*, pg. 5

Pierce, S.C., V.P.-Intl. Bus. Devel.--Amoco Oil Company, Chicago, IL; *U.S. Public*, pg. 102

Pinheiro, Gary, V.P. & Res./Strategic Devel. Dir.--The Bravo Group, New York, NY; *U.S. Private*, pg. 1197

Pitaud, Bernard, Mgr.-Res. & Devel.--Tefal S.A., Rumilly, France; *Int'l*, pg. 569

Pitie, Bernard, V.P.-Res. & Devel.--SEITA, Societe Nationale D'Exploitation Industrielle des Tabacs et des Allumettes, Paris, France; *Int'l*, pg. 1219

Pittauino, Maria, Res. & Devel.--Framesi USA, Inc./Roffler Industries, Inc./Casa di Colore, Inc., Coraopolis, PA; *U.S. Private*, pg. 419

Pittelli, Joseph, Sr. V.P.-Clinical Res. Worldwide--Wyeth-Ayerst Laboratories, Inc., Philadelphia, PA; *U.S. Public*, pg. 80

Platko, Dr. Frank, Res. & Devel.--Propper Manufacturing Co., Inc., Long Island City, NY; *U.S. Private*, pg. 891

Platts, David E., V.P.-Res. & Devel.--Hurco Companies, Inc., Indianapolis, IN; *U.S. Public*, pg. 850

Plotner, Todd, Mgr.-Res. & Devel.--The Airolite Company, Marietta, OH; *U.S. Private*, pg. 29

Podsiadly, C., V.P.-Res. & Devel.--Daubert Coated Products, Inc., Westchester, IL; *U.S. Private*, pg. 313

Polan, George S., V.P.-Res. & Devel.--Central Sprinkler Company, Lansdale, PA; *U.S. Public*, pg. 327

Pollock, Dan, Dir.-Res. & Devel.--Perlmuter Printing Company, Cleveland, OH; *Int'l*, pg. 1177

Poltrack, David, Exec. V.P.-Plng. & Res.--CBS Television Network, New York, NY; *U.S. Public*, pg. 274

Ponnampalam, V., Mgr.-Engrng.--Harrington & King, Chicago, IL; *U.S. Private*, pg. 504

Poole, Gary, Sr. V.P. & Res. Dir.--Lois/EJL New York, New York, NY; *U.S. Public*, pg. 1011

Posen, Miles, V.P.-Res. & Devel.--Beltone Electronics Corporation, Chicago, IL; *U.S. Private*, pg. 132

Powell, Robert, V.P.-Scientific Affairs--SmithKline Beecham Laboratories, Bristol, TN; *Int'l*, pg. 1264

Power, P., Mgr.-Res.--Marathon Petroleum Indonesia, Ltd., Jakarta, Indonesia; *U.S. Public*, pg. 1662

Power, Sarah, Res. Mgr.--Carat MBS, New York, NY; *U.S. Private*, pg. 208

Powers, William F., V.P.-Res.--Ford Motor Company, Dearborn, MI; *U.S. Public*, pg. 661

Pratt, Ronald, Mgr.-Corp. Mfg. Engrng.--IEC Electronics Corp., Newark, NY; *U.S. Public*, pg. 854

Prego, Jose, Dir.-Res. & Devel.--Jac Pac Foods, Ltd., Manchester, NH; *U.S. Private*, pg. 579

Prengaman, R. David, Sr. V.P.-Res. & Devel.--RSR Corporation, Dallas, TX; *U.S. Private*, pg. 900

Preston, Charles, Dir.-Engrng.--BioChem ImmunoSystems, Inc., Allentown, PA; *Int'l*, pg. 196

Preswick, Barry E., Dir.-Res. & Devel. & Quality Assurance--Checkers Drive-In Restaurants, Inc., Clearwater, FL; *U.S. Public*, pg. 342

Price, David, Sr. V.P.-Programs, Res. & Devel.--H.W. Kaufman Financial Group, Inc., Farmington, MI; *U.S. Private*, pg. 609

Price, Doug, Mgr.-Res. & Devel.--Patterson Frozen Foods, Inc., Patterson, CA; *U.S. Private*, pg. 843

Price, Kenneth R., Mgr.-Res. & Devel.--Ludlow Textiles Co., Inc., Ludlow, MA; *U.S. Private*, pg. 680

Priegnitz, Ron, Dir.-Res. & Devel.--Golden Grain Company, Pleasanton, CA; *U.S. Public*, pg. 1348

Primm, Earl, Mgr.-Real Estate & Devel.--Ace Hardware Corporation, Oak Brook, IL; *U.S. Private*, pg. 12

Pronovost, Allan D., Ph.D., V.P.-Res. & Devel.--Quidel Corporation, San Diego, CA; *U.S. Public*, pg. 1352

Provanzand, Salvatore, V.P.-Product & Devel.--QMS, Inc., Mobile, AL; *U.S. Public*, pg. 1346

Prucha, Thomas, V.P.-Tech. & Reliability--CMI International Inc., Southfield, MI; *U.S. Private*, pg. 195

Prue, Nancy J.F., V.P.-Res.--Petroleum & Resources Corp., Baltimore, MD; *U.S. Public*, pg. 1280

Pshtissky, Yacov A., V.P.-Engrng.--Vicon Industries, Inc., Hauppauge, NY; *U.S. Public*, pg. 1719

Pucillo, Barry, Mgr.-Res. & Devel.--American Louver Co., Skokie, IL; *U.S. Private*, pg. 58

Pulaski, Joan, Mgr.-Training & Devel.--Dynamics Research Corporation, Andover, MA; *U.S. Public*, pg. 539

Pulido, Adreienne, V.P., Res. Dir. & Strategic Plng. Dir.--Bromley, Aguilar & Associates, San Antonio, TX; *U.S. Private*, pg. 692

Purcell, Thomas O., Chief Tech. Officer & V.P.--Ferro Corporation, Cleveland, OH; *U.S. Public*, pg. 618

Purkait, Bobby K., V.P.-Res. & Devel.--Mentor Corporation, Santa Barbara, CA; *U.S. Public*, pg. 1086

Putz, Frank J., Mgr.-Training & Devel.--Rheem Water Heater, Montgomery, AL; *Int'l*, pg. 1022

Quadracci, Thomas A., Pres.-Quad/Tech. & V.P.-Mfg. & Tech.--Quad/Graphics, Inc., Pewaukee, WI; *U.S. Private*, *pg. 897*

Quagliara, Ronald P., V.P.-Res. & Devel.--Emulex Corporation, Costa Mesa, CA; *U.S. Public*, pg. 579

Quievre, Claude, Adjoint Dir. Gen. & Dir.-Tech. & Indus.--Arianespace SA, Evry, France; *Int'l*, pg. 81

Quinn, Peter T., V.P.-Org. Devel.--Greenhorne & O'Mara, Inc., Greenbelt, MD; *U.S. Private*, pg. 477

Quisenberry, Richard K., V.P.-Res. & Devel.--Du Pont (E.I. Du Pont De Nemours & Co.), Wilmington, DE; *U.S. Public*, pg. 530

Rachinsky, Joseph W., V.P.-Prod. Devel. & Res.--Reliance Standard Life Insurance Company, Philadelphia, PA; *U.S.* Public, pg. 496

Radcliffe, Julian, Dir.-Political Risks, Overseas Non-Marine, Research & Devel.--Bain Hogg Group plc, London, United Kingdom; *Int'l*, pg. 671

Raddi, William J., Chief Tech. Officer, Sr. V.P. & Gen. Mgr.-Small Systems Grp.--Exide Electronics Group, Inc., Raleigh, NC; *Int'l*, pg. 126

Raisanen, Wally, V.P.-Res. & Devel.--Arizona Instrument Corporation, Phoenix, AZ; *U.S. Public*, pg. 129

Raj, Kuldip, Dr., V.P.-Chief Scientist--Ferrofluidics Corporation, Nashua, NH; *U.S. Public*, pg. 620

Rajfer, Sol I., Sr. V.P.-Clinical Res. & Devel.--Bristol-Myers Squibb Company, New York, NY; *U.S. Public*, pg. 253

Raksis, Joseph, V.P.-Res.--Flint Ink Corp., Detroit, MI; *U.S. Private*, pg. 413

Ralston, Ed, Mgr.-Audit Svcs.--Baldor Electric Company, Fort Smith, AR; *U.S. Public*, pg. 168

Rapetski, Walter, V.P.-Res. & Devel.--Farrel Corporation, Ansonia, CT; *U.S. Public*, pg. 614

Rappange, L., Dir.-Tech. & Prod.--Honig Foods-B.V., Koog aan de Zaan, Netherlands; *Int'l*, pg. 244

Rappoport, Joshua, Assoc.-Center Partners Management LLC, New York, NY; *U.S. Private*, pg. 222

Rashid, Rick, V.P.-Res.--Microsoft Corporation, Redmond, WA; *U.S. Public*, pg. 1107

Rasmussen, James R., Sr. V.P.-Res.--Genzyme Corporation, Cambridge, MA; *U.S. Public*, pg. 733

Rasmussen, Myron, V.P.-Opers.--Farr Company, El Segundo, CA; *U.S. Public*, pg. 613

Rasmussen, Neil E., V.P.-Engrng.--American Power Conversion Corporation, West Kingston, RI; *U.S. Public*, pg. 89

Rattner, Bob, V.P.-Res.--General Media International Inc., New York, NY; *U.S. Private*, pg. 444

Rau, Nelly Maria, Res. Dir.--Leo Burnett Co. Inc., Buenos Aires, Argentina; *U.S. Private*, pg. 185

Raval, Dilip, Exec. V.P.-Res. & Devel.--Alcon Laboratories, Inc., Fort Worth, TX; *Int'l*, pg. 916

Ravindra, Halappa, V.P.-Res. & Devel.--Cirrus Logic, Inc., Fremont, CA; *U.S. Public*, pg. 375

Razon, Eli, V.P.-Tech.--Kulicke & Soffa Industries, Inc., Willow Grove, PA; *U.S. Public*, pg. 968

Ream, Ronald L., Sr. V.P.-Res. & Bus. Devel.--Amurol Confections Co., Yorkville, IL; *U.S. Public*, pg. 1781

Recordati, Alberto, Dir.-Res. & Tech.--Recordati Industria Chimica e Farmaceutica S.p.A., Milan, Italy; *Int'l*, pg. 1090

Reddy, Rama, Dr., V.P.-Res. & Devel.--Peterson Farms, Decatur, AR; *U.S. Private*, pg. 857

Reddy, Tom, V.P.-Engrng.--Yardney Technical Products, Inc., Pawcatuck, CT; *U.S. Private*, pg. 376

Reed, Janet S., V.P.-Res. & Information Services--Bank of America Illinois, Chicago, IL; *U.S. Public*, pg. 180

Reese, Jane, Mgr.-Training & Devel.--Mack Trucks, Inc., Allentown, PA; *Int'l*, pg. 1102

Reeves, Greg, Head Engr.--WINCO, Le Center, MN; *U.S. Private*, pg. 350

Rehberger, Arthur J., V.P.-Brewing & Res.--Miller Brewing Company, Milwaukee, WI; *U.S. Public*, pg. 1289

Rehling, Louise, Sr. V.P.-Devel.--SPSS Inc., Chicago, IL; *U.S. Public*, pg. 1420

Reid, Yolanda, Res. Analyst--Don Coleman Advertising, Inc., Southfield, MI; *U.S. Private*, pg. 251

Reilly, Bill, V.P.-Food & Beverage--Sheetz, Inc., Altoona, PA; *U.S. Private*, pg. 991

Reinhardt, Norm, V.P.-Tech. & Prod.--Pico Products, Inc., Lake View Terrace, CA; *U.S. Public*, pg. 1294

Reinhart, Bill, V.P.-Research & Devel.--The Butcher Company, Marlborough, MA; *U.S. Private*, pg. 189

Rensink, Andrew T., V.P.-Tech.--Osmonics, Inc., Minnetonka, MN; *U.S. Public*, pg. 1233

Resch, Robert J., Dir.-Res. & Devel.--Cyberex, Inc., Mentor, OH; *U.S. Public*, pg. 481

Restaino, Kathy, Dir.-Res.--WGN-TV, Chicago, IL; *U.S. Public*, pg. 1636

Retterath, James E., V.P.-Res. & Devel & Sec.--LaserMaster Technologies, Inc., Eden Prairie, MN; *U.S. Public*, pg. 979

Rettke, Ralph P., V.P.-Devel. & Tech.--W. Braun Company, Chicago, IL; *U.S. Private*, pg. 166

Revellin-Falcoz, Bruno, Exec. V.P.-Engrng. & Res.--Dassault Aviation Group, Vaucresson, France; *Int'l*, pg. 383

Reynolds, Ann Marie, Sr. Res. Analyst--Western International Media Corporation, New York, NY; *U.S. Private*, pg. 1166

Reznek, Steven R., Gen. Mgr.-Chemical Bus. Res. & Devel.--Carbon Black Div., Boston, MA; *U.S. Public*, pg. 289

Ricciardi, Joseph A., Dir.-Res. & Devel.--Ragu Foods, Inc., Trumbull, CT; *Int'l*, pg. 1436

Rice, Thomas B., Dr., V.P. & Dir.-Res.--AgriBioTech, Inc., Las Vegas, NV; *U.S. Public*, pg. 28

Richardson, Tom, Chief Engineer--Electro Scientific Industries, Inc., Portland, OR; *U.S. Public*, pg. 568

Richey, Joseph B., II, Sr. V.P.-Total Quality Mngmt. & Pres.-Invacare Technologies--Invacare Corporation, Elyria, OH; *U.S. Public*, pg. 911

Riddle, Timothy K., V.P.-Mdsg./New Prod. Devel.--Newell Window Furnishings Co., Freeport, IL; *U.S. Public*, pg. 1177

Riedel, John J., Sr. V.P.-Res. Information/Intl.--UMI, Ann Arbor, MI; *U.S. Public*, pg. 201

Riedelon, Norbert, V.P.-Central Res. & Biotechnology--Hoechst Marion Roussel, Inc., Bridgewater, NJ; *Int'l*, pg. 624

Riehm, Charles, V.P.-Devel.--Hayes Microcomputer Products, Inc., Norcross, GA; *U.S. Public*, pg. 801

Riemer, W. John, Sr. V.P.-Engrng.--Replogle Globes, Inc., Broadview, IL; *U.S. Private*, pg. 923

Riha, William E., Dr., Dir.-Research & Devel.--Joseph E. Seagram & Sons, Inc., New York, NY; *Int'l*, pg. 1215

Riley, H. Lee, Mgr.-Res. & Devel.--Bachmann Industries, Inc., Philadelphia, PA; *U.S. Private*, pg. 109

Rindoks, Kurt P., V.P.-Engrng. & New Prod. Devel.--Kewaunee Scientific Corporation, Statesville, NC; *U.S. Public*, pg. 953

Rini, Matt, Dir.-Res. & Devel.--Country Home Bakery, Inc., Bridgeport, CT; *U.S. Private*, pg. 278

Rio, Christopher, V.P.-Devel.--Divi Hotels, Inc., Chapel Hill, NC; *U.S. Private*, pg. 336

Rishell, William A., V.P. & Dir.-Res.--Arbor Acres Farm, Inc., Glastonbury, CT; *Int'l*, pg. 202

Risoldi, Richard M., Dir.-Production--Middlesex Water Company, Iselin, NJ; *U.S. Public*, pg. 1110

Ritgert, Frank, Sr. V.P.-Opers.--American Pad and Paper Company, Dallas, TX; *U.S. Public*, pg. 88

Rittner, Mark, Exec. Dir.-Res. & Devel.--MET Solutions, LLC, Morris Plains, NJ; *U.S. Public*, pg. 1642

Roach, Barrett B., Exec. V.P.-Strategic Devel.--Fair, Isaac and Company, Inc., San Rafael, CA; *U.S. Public*, pg. 609

Robert, Mark, Mgr.-Research & Devel.--Elgin Dairy Foods, Inc., Chicago, IL; *U.S. Private*, pg. 370

Roberts, Alan S., V.P.-Res. & Devel.--Electrovert, Grand Prairie, TX; *Int'l*, pg. 328

Roberts, Sidney, V.P.-Res. & Devel.--Sheldahl, Inc., Northfield, MN; *U.S. Public*, pg. 1465

Robertson, Jack, Mgr.-Res. & Devel.--Ferguson International, Inc., Dallas, TX; *U.S. Private*, pg. 401

Robolin, Claude, Dir.-Res. & Devel.--RHC/Spacemaster Corporation, Melrose Park, IL; *U.S. Private*, pg. 904

Rocchio, John P., V.P.-Project Devel.--Calpine Corporation, San Jose, CA; *U.S. Public*, pg. 296

Rodenstein, Mario, Dir.-Research & Devel.--CPC Latin American Consumer Foods Division, Englewood Cliffs, NJ; *U.S. Public*, pg. 447

Rodgers, James L., V.P.-Research & Devel.--Mutoh America Inc., Phoenix, AZ; *Int'l*, pg. 897

Rodwell, John D., Chief Scientific Officer--Cytogen Corporation, Princeton, NJ; *U.S. Public*, pg. 471

Rogers, Jane, V.P.-Res. Opers.--Reed Elsevier Business Information, Newton, MA; *Int'l*, pg. 1095

Rogers, John, Dir.-Res. & Devel./Tech.--Sandusky International Inc., Sandusky, OH; *U.S. Private*, pg. 964

Rogers, John, Mgr.-Mkt. Research & Analysis--Smith & Wesson Corp., Springfield, MA; *Int'l*, pg. 1397

Rogers, Ron, Mgr.-External Res. & Devel. Commun.--Hoechst Marion Roussel, Inc., Bridgewater, NJ; *Int'l*, pg. 624

Roheim, John, Mgr.-Res. & Devel.--Condea Vista Company, Houston, TX; *Int'l*, pg. 325

Rohling, Edward J., Sr. V.P.-Corp. Devel.--Bristol Hotels & Resorts, Dallas, TX; *U.S. Public*, pg. 253

Roller, Glenn, Dir.-Trng.--Sea Ray, Knoxville, TN; *U.S. Public*, pg. 266

Ronel, Samuel H., Ph.D., V.P.-Res. & Devel.--GP Strategies Corporation, New York, NY; *U.S. Public*, pg. 694

Roney, Kirk, V.P.-Devel.--Nu Skin International, Provo, UT; *U.S. Private*, pg. 808

Ronsin, Philippe, Dir.-Devel. & European Affairs--Ciments Francais, Paris, France; *Int'l*, pg. 292

Rose, Clark, Sr. V.P.-Opers./Oil Recovery & Envirosystems--Safety-Kleen Corp., Elgin, IL; *U.S. Public*, pg. 1425

Rose, Mike, V.P.-Development--IHOP Corp., Glendale, CA; *U.S. Public*, pg. 862

Rosemann, Michael, Div. Mgr.--Durkopp Adler AG, Bielefeld, Germany; *Int'l*, pg. 468

Rosenblum, Harvey, Sr. V.P.-Res. & Statistics & Dir.-Res.--Federal Reserve Bank of Dallas, Dallas, TX; *U.S. Private*, pg. 399

Rosenkotter, Mike, Dir.-Res. & Devel. & Mgr.-H.R.--Long MFG. NC, Inc., Tarboro, NC; *U.S. Private*, pg. 674

Roth, Ed, V.P.-Res. & Devel.--Roussel Corporation, Montvale, NJ; *Int'l*, pg. 625

Rothman, Joan, Sr. V.P.-Strategic Res. & Plng.--The Dun & Bradstreet Corporation, Murray Hill, NJ; *U.S. Public*, pg. 535

Rothman, Mike, V.P.-Engrng. & Tech.--Haynes International, Inc., Kokomo, IN; *U.S. Public*, pg. 801

Roudabush, Mark, V.P.-Technical Devel.--The Cardwell Machine Company, Richmond, VA; *U.S. Private*, pg. 209

Roudebush, James R., Chm. Bd.--Caldwell VanRiper, Inc., Indianapolis, IN; *U.S. Private*, pg. 200

Roumeguere, P., V.P. & Dep. Gen. Mgr.-Devel.--SNCF, Paris, France; *Int'l*, pg. 1163

Rowe, Allan D., Chief Fin. Officer & Sr. V.P.-Fin.--Empire Company Limited, Stellarton, Canada; *Int'l*, pg. 453

Roy, Michel L., Dir.-Mktg.--Gaz Metropolitain & Company, Montreal, Canada; *Int'l*, pg. 541

Royer, Steve, Mgr.-New Product Devel.--DSM Sheffield Plastics, Sheffield, MA; *Int'l*, pg. 354

Rubey, Ray, Dir.-Res. & Devel.--Media Recovery, Inc., Graham, TX; *U.S. Private*, pg. 726

Rudd, Charles, V.P.-Engrng.--Action Instruments, Inc., San Diego, CA; *U.S. Private*, pg. 15

Rudd, T. James, Ph.D., Dir.-Tech.--The Dexter Corporation, Windsor Locks, CT; *U.S. Public*, pg. 504

Rueter, Eric, V.P.-Res. & Devel.--Laserscope Surgical Systems, San Jose, CA; *U.S. Public*, pg. 979

Ruffley, Douglas, Chief Engineer--De-Sta-Co, A Dover Resources Co., Troy, MI; *U.S. Public*, pg. 521

Ruppenthal, Mark, Dir.-Res. & Devel.--Artistic Greetings, Inc., Elmira, NY; *U.S. Public*, pg. 136

Russak, Michael A., Ph.D., V.P.-Res. & Devel.--HMT Technology Corporation, Fremont, CA; *U.S. Public*, pg. 771

Russell, J.L., Dir.-Res.--Procter & Gamble Pharmaceuticals, Inc., Cincinnati, OH; *U.S. Public*, pg. 1331

Rutherford, William F., Mgr.-Research & Devel.--Jefferson Mills, Inc., Pulaski, VA; *U.S. Private*, pg. 584

Rutten, Laura, Plng. Mgr.--Haworth Group Inc., Minneapolis, MN; *U.S. Private*, pg. 511

Ruybal, Jim, Exec. V.P.-New Bus. Dept.--United Artists Theatre Circuits Incorporated, Englewood, CO; *U.S. Private*, pg. 1120

Ryan, T., Div. Mgr.-Bus. Devel.--Meadow Lea Foods Ltd., Mascot, Australia; *Int'l*, pg. 555

Ryan, Thomas, Sr. V.P.-Bus. Devel.--Long John Silver's, Inc., Lexington, KY; *U.S. Private*, pg. 674

Saarinen, Aulis, Exec. V.P.-Res. & Devel.--Rautaruukki Oy, Helsinki, Finland; *Int'l*, pg. 1088

Saarinen, Aulis, Dir.-Research & Devel.--Rautaruukki Oy, Helsinki, Finland; *Int'l*, pg. 1088

Sabharwal, Kulbir, Res. & Devel.--Galaxy Food Company, Orlando, FL; *U.S. Public*, pg. 697

Sacharoff, Alex, V.P.-Res.& Devel.--Summit Technology, Inc., Waltham, MA; *U.S. Public*, pg. 1528

Sacher, Reuven, V.P.-Res. & Devel./Oral Care--Colgate-Palmolive Company, New York, NY; *U.S. Public*, pg. 397

Sadleir, Edmund, V.P.-Devel. & Construction--Landau & Heyman Inc., Chicago, IL; *U.S. Private*, pg. 646

Saintigny, Henri, Dir.-Res. & Devel.--Automobiles Citroen, Neuilly, France; *Int'l*, pg. 1020

Sakus, Gedas A., Chm. Bd.-Bell Northern Research & Pres.-Nortel Tech.--Northern Telecom Limited, Brampton, Canada; *Int'l*, pg. 968

Salce, Ludwig, V.P.-Perm Devel.--Conair Corporation, Stamford, CT; *U.S. Private*, pg. 261

Salcher, Anton, Exec. V.P.-Portfolio Mgnmt. & Res.--Bayerische Landesbank, Munich, Germany; *Int'l*, pg. 176

Saluetti, Alberto, Mgr.-Res. & Devel.--Opticos S.r.l., Brembate di Sopra, Italy; *Int'l*, pg. 1007

Samulski, Paul, V.P.-Creative & Prod. Devel.--Acclaim Entertainment, Inc., Glen Cove, NY; *U.S. Public*, pg. 15

Sanders, Andrea, V.P.-Res. & Devel.--Ato-Findley, Inc., Wauwatosa, WI; *Int'l*, pg. 445

Sanders, Clifton R., Sr. V.P.-Res. & Devel.--BeautiControl Cosmetics, Inc., Carrollton, TX; *U.S. Public*, pg. 198

Sanders, David C., Assoc. V.P.-New Prod. Devel.--Great Lakes Chemical Corporation, West Lafayette, IN; *U.S. Public*, pg. 760

Sanderson, Gary W., Ph.D., V.P.-Tech.--Universal Foods Corporation, Milwaukee, WI; *U.S. Public*, pg. 1695

Sandmeier, Ruedi, V.P.-Research--Sandoz Agro, Inc., Des Plaines, IL; *Int'l*, pg. 974

Sanford, Randy, Dir.-Prod. Devel.--Galaxy Carpet Mills, Inc., Chatsworth, GA; *U.S. Public*, pg. 1121

Sanito, Roberto, Dir.-Res. & Devel.--Rimoldi Necchi S.R.L., Milan, Italy; *Int'l*, pg. 1117

Santangelo, Steven J., Sr. V.P.-Strategic Mktg. & Res. Consultation--Tierney & Partners, Philadelphia, PA; *U.S. Public*, pg. 1641

Santini, William, Dir.--Interphase Corporation, Dallas, TX; *U.S. Public*, pg. 908

Sapakie, Sidney F., V.P.-Intl. Cereal & Snack Res. & Devel.--General Mills, Inc., Minneapolis, MN; *U.S. Public*, pg. 717

Sapan, Christine V., Ph.D., Dir.-Scientific Affairs--Nabi, Boca Raton, FL; *U.S. Public*, pg. 1148

Sargent, Louis K., V.P.-Prod. Devel.--Tri-State Insurance Company of Minnesota, Luverne, MN; *U.S. Public*, pg. 215

Sartani, Avi, Dir.-Res. & Devel.--Recordati Industria Chimica e Farmaceutica S.p.A., Milan, Italy; *Int'l*, pg. 1090

Sasaki, Hiroo, Gen. Mgr.-Nanyo Res. Ctr.--Tosoh Corporation, Tokyo, Japan; *Int'l*, pg. 1407

Saslow, Seymour, Dir.-Sls. & Engrng.--Espey Mfg. & Electronics Corp., Saratoga Springs, NY; *U.S. Public*, pg. 592

Satake, Akihiro, Gen. Mgr.--OYO Corporation, Tokyo, Japan; *Int'l*, pg. 1019

Sater, Barbara, V.P., Mktg. Dir. & Res. Dir.--The Stephenz Group, Inc., San Jose, CA; *U.S. Private*, pg. 1040

Sato, Hideki, Mng. Dir.-Res. & Devel.--Sega Enterprises Ltd., Tokyo, Japan; *Int'l*, pg. 1218

Satti, Marie, Dir.-Mktg. & Prod. Devel.--Supercuts, Inc., San Francisco, CA; *U.S. Public*, pg. 1373

Saunders, R.W., Dr., Dir.-Product Research & Devel. Labs.--Cyanamid of Great Britain Ltd., Gosport, United Kingdom; *U.S. Public*, pg. 81

Saurat, Jean, V.P.-Research & Development--Sofamor, S.N.C., Rang-du-Fliers, France; *U.S. Public*, pg. 1482

Sautter, Edouard, Exec. V.P.-Risk Policy & Indus. Res.--Banque Nationale de Paris, Paris, France; *Int'l*, pg. 163

Sava, Katerina, Res. Dir. & Plng. Dir.--Leo Burnett Athens, Athens, Greece; *U.S. Private*, pg. 184

Schaefer, R. Scott, V.P.-Disk Drive Prod. Bus. Devel.--Hutchinson Technology Inc., Hutchinson, MN; *U.S. Public*, pg. 850

Schaeffer, R.A., V.P.-Prod. Devel.--R.A. Jones & Co. Inc., Covington, KY; *U.S. Private*, pg. 597

Schaible, Dexter, V.P.-Global Prod. Devel.--AGCO Corporation, Duluth, GA; *U.S. Public*, pg. 28

Schalk, Steve, V.P.-Engrng.--Miniature Precision Components, Walworth, WI; *U.S. Private*, pg. 750

Scharf, Rick, Mgr.-Res. & Devel.--Taco John's International, Inc., Cheyenne, WY; *U.S. Private*, pg. 1066

Scheider, Alfred F., V.P.-Research & Devel.--Osborn Manufacturing, Cleveland, OH; *U.S. Public*, pg. 924

Scherer, Richard P., Sr. V.P.-Mktg. & Bus. Devel.--Laser Power Corporation, San Diego, CA; *U.S. Private*, pg. 652

Scheutterle, Bernd, Mgr.-Res. & Devel.--Klafs Saunabau GmbH & Co. KG Medizinische Technik, Schwabisch Hall, Germany; *Int'l*, pg. 736

Schiefen, Michael, V.P.-Corp. Devel.--Siemens Corporation, New York, NY; *Int'l*, pg. 1245

Schindler, Philippe, First V.P.--Ferrier Lullin & Cie SA, Geneva, Switzerland; *Int'l*, pg. 480

Schler, Matt, V.P.-Prod. Devel.--PSC Inc., Webster, NY; *U.S. Public*, pg. 1245

Schlinger, Lisa, V.P. & Assoc. Res. Dir.--Jordan, McGrath, Case & Taylor Inc., New York, NY; *U.S. Private*, pg. 598

Schlissel, Harvey J., V.P.-Research & Devel.--Carter Products Div., Cranbury, NJ; *U.S. Public*, pg. 310

Schmersahl, Peter, Mgr.-Res. & Devel.--Hermal Kurt Herrmann & Co., Reinbek, Germany; *Int'l*, pg. 616

Schmid, Dr. Jung Edgar, V.P.-Sealing & Filtration Prods./Europe--Reinz-Dichtungs-GmbH, Neu-Ulm, Germany; *U.S. Public*, pg. 480

Schmitt, William, Sr. V.P.-Res. & Devel.--Chesebrough-Pond's USA Co., Greenwich, CT; *Int'l*, pg. 1435

Schneider, Al, Dir.-Research & Devel.--Alpha Metals, Inc., Jersey City, NJ; *Int'l*, pg. 328

Schneider, Raymond J., Dir.-Engrng.--ComSonics, Inc., Harrisonburg, VA; *U.S. Private*, pg. 260

Schneider, Robert E., Sr. V.P.-Res. & Devel.--ProBusiness Services, Inc., Pleasanton, CA; *U.S. Public*, pg. 1330

Schnell, Claude, Mgr.-Res. & Devel.--Sika Finanz AG, Baar, Switzerland; *Int'l*, pg. 1248

Schnell, Phillip G., V.P.-Res. & Devel.--Wm. Wrigley Jr. Company, Chicago, IL; *U.S. Public*, pg. 1781

Schnitzler, Gerry, Mgr.-Res. & Devel.--Sunnen Products Company, Saint Louis, MO; *U.S. Private*, pg. 1053

Schoen, Kurt L., V.P.-Res.--David Michael & Co. Inc., Philadelphia, PA; *U.S. Private*, pg. 740

Schorderet, Georges, Exec. V.P.-Corp. Fin. & Devel.--The Swissair Group, Zurich, Switzerland; *Int'l*, pg. 1333

Schott, Dan J., V.P.-Res. & Devel.--Three-Five Systems, Tempe, AZ; *U.S. Public*, pg. 1604

Schreck, Richard H., Pres. & Chief Oper. Officer--Hofmann Industries, Inc., Sinking Spring, PA; *U.S. Private*, pg. 533

Schrenk, Juergen, Dr., V.P.-Res. & Devel.--Wampole Laboratories, Cranbury, NJ; *U.S. Public*, pg. 310

Schrider, Leo A., Sr. V.P.-Tech. Devel.--Belden & Blake Corporation, Canton, OH; *U.S. Private*, pg. 1078

Schubert, Rolf, V.P.-Res. & Devel.--H.B. Fuller Company, Saint Paul, MN; *U.S. Public*, pg. 686

Schuller, Barry, V.P.-Res. & Devel.--Plastics Manufacturing Company, Dallas, TX; *U.S. Public*, pg. 1530

Schutz, C., Dir.-Research & Devel.--Holmatro Industrial & Rescue Equipment, Raamsdonksveer, Netherlands; *Int'l*, pg. 632

Schwab, Mark, V.P.-Hallmark/Strategy & Mktg.--Hallmark Cards, Inc., Kansas City, MO; *U.S. Private*, pg. 495

Schwartz, A., Dir.-Plng. & Econ.--El Al Airlines Ltd., Lod, Israel; *Int'l*, pg. 435

Schwegler, Cornelia, Dir.-Bus. Systems--Brite Voice Systems Group, Ltd., Cheadle, United Kingdom; *U.S. Public*, pg. 257

Schweitzer, Peter, Pres.-J. Walter Thompson, JWT/Americas & Global Bus. Dir.-Ford--J. Walter Thompson Company, New York, NY; *Int'l*, pg. 1483

Scire, Bonita, Mgr.-Res. & Devel.--Robertet Flavors, South Plainfield, NJ; *Int'l*, pg. 1119

Scire, John, V.P.-Res. & Devel.--Robertet Flavors, South Plainfield, NJ; *Int'l*, pg. 1119

Sears, James A., V.P.-Tire Devel.--Continental General Tire, Inc., Charlotte, NC; *Int'l*, pg. 327

Seethaler, Toni, Dr., Dir.-Res. & Devel.--Freudenberg & Company, Weinheim, Germany; *Int'l*, pg. 505

Segelman, Alvin B., Dr., V.P.-Health Sciences--Nature's Sunshine Products, Inc., Provo, UT; *U.S. Public*, pg. 1166

Seggerson, Patrick, Dir.-Design, Res. & Devel.--Dualite Inc., Williamsburg, OH; *U.S. Private*, pg. 344

Seggerson, Patrick J., Dir.-Design & Res.& Devel.--Dualite Sales & Service, Inc., Williamsburg, OH; *U.S. Private*, pg. 344

Seiler, Mark, Mgr.-Quality Control--LubeCon Systems, Inc., White Cloud, MI; *U.S. Private*, pg. 679

Sela, Uri, Dir.-Research & Devel.--Ameda AG, Hunenberg, Switzerland; *U.S. Private*, pg. 535

Seta, Anthony C., V.P.-Res. & Devel.--Perkins Family Restaurants, Memphis, TN; *U.S. Private*, pg. 925

Shackelford, Al, Creative Dir.-Acquisition & Devel.--Lands' End, Inc., Dodgeville, WI; *U.S. Public*, pg. 977

Shanahan, Robert, Mgr.-Pur.-Res. & Devel.--Mitsui Foods, Inc., Norwood, NJ; *Int'l*, pg. 879

Sharma, Amit, V.P.-Strategic Plng. & Bus. Devel.--G.E. Capital Commercial Real Estate Financing, Stamford, CT; *U.S. Public*, pg. 712

Shaughnessy, W. M., V.P.-Engrng.--Rapid Power Technologies, Inc., Brookfield, CT; *U.S. Private*, pg. 910

Shaw, William A., V.P. & Gen. Mgr.-Devel.--Marcam Solutions, Inc., Newton, MA; *U.S. Public*, pg. 1042

Shawlis, Bruce, Dir.-Prod. Devel.--Craftex Mills Inc. of Pennsylvania, Blue Bell, PA; *U.S. Private*, pg. 284

Shea, William H., Jr., Exec. V.P.--Buckeye Partners, L.P., Allentown, PA; *U.S. Public*, pg. 266

Shefchek, Joseph E., Asst. V.P.-Environ. Affairs & Res.--Wisconsin Power & Light Company, Madison, WI; *U.S. Public*, pg. 1728

Sheinfeld, Mark, V.P.-Customer Service & Bus. Devel.--ComputerLand Canada, Brampton, Canada; *Int'l*, pg. 1154

Sherry, Libby, V.P., Res. Dir. & Brand Plng. Dir.--The Weightman Group, Philadelphia, PA; *U.S. Private*, pg. 1159

Shetn, Dinesn, V.P.-Software Devel. & Sys. Integration--Mobile Telecommunications Technologies Corp., Jackson, MS; *U.S. Public*, pg. 1120

Shimano, Bruce, V.P.-Res. & Devel. & Sec.--Adept Technology, Inc., San Jose, CA; *U.S. Public*, pg. 19

Shipp, Ned, V.P.-Engrng. & Prod. Mngmt.--Artisoft, Inc., Tucson, AZ; *U.S. Public*, pg. 136

Shirakawa, Kazuo, Dir.-Strategic Plng.--Hawaiian Electric Industries, Inc., Honolulu, HI; *U.S. Public*, pg. 799

Shirakura, Takeo, Gen. Mgr.-Research & Devel.--Okuma Corporation, Niwa, Japan; *Int'l*, pg. 1000

Shirey, John, V.P.-New Bus. Devel.--First USA Paymentech, Inc., Salem, NH; *U.S. Public*, pg. 174

Shonka, Jeffrey A., Sr. V.P.-New Prods.--Amwest Surety Insurance Company, Calabasas, CA; *U.S. Public*, pg. 106

Shorr, Robert G.L., Dr., V.P.-Res. & Devel.--Enzon, Inc., Piscataway, NJ; *U.S. Public*, pg. 587

Shrader, Gary, V.P.-Systems Devel.--FirstMerit Corporation, Akron, OH; *U.S. Public*, pg. 646

Shumaker, Chris, V.P. & Devel. Dir.--The Martin Agency, Richmond, VA; *U.S. Private*, pg. 678

Shumaker, Chris, V.P.-Bus. Devel.--The Martin Agency, Richmond, VA; *U.S. Public*, pg. 909

Siba, Toshifumi, Dir. & Deputy Sr. Gen. Mgr.-Project Devel.--West Japan Railway Company, Osaka, Japan; *Int'l*, pg. 1490

Sidor, Larry, Corp. Mgr.-Prod. Res. & Devel.--Pabst Brewing Co., San Antonio, TX; *U.S. Private*, pg. 954

Sieben, Paul G., V.P. & Dir.-Devel. & Construction--Health Care & Retirement Corporation, Toledo, OH; *U.S. Public*, pg. 801

Siiteri, Mikko, Sr. V.P.-Res. & Devel.--Valmet Corporation, Helsinki, Finland; *Int'l*, pg. 1447

Silver, William, V.P.-Res. & Devel.--Cognex Corporation, Natick, MA; *U.S. Public*, pg. 394

Silverschotz, Stanford B., V.P.-Technical Services--Webcraft Technologies, Inc., North Brunswick, NJ; *U.S. Public*, pg. 228

Simonsen, John, V.P.-Dealer Devel. & Trng.--Sea Ray, Knoxville, TN; *U.S. Public*, pg. 266

Simpson, Carl, V.P.-Res. & Devel.--Guidant Corporation-Vascular Intervention Group, Santa Clara, CA; *U.S. Public*, pg. 768

Sinclair, C., V.P.-Res. & Engrng.--United Technologies, Chemical Systems Div., San Jose, CA; *U.S. Public*, pg. 1690

Singer, William, V.P.-Res. & Devel.--Troy Corporation, Florham Park, NJ; *U.S. Private*, pg. 1105

Sipila, Pekka, V.P.-Corp. Bus. Devel.--Rautaruukki Oy, Helsinki, Finland; *Int'l*, pg. 1088

Siqueira, C.J.P., Dir.-Res. & Devel.--Souza Cruz, S.A., Rio de Janeiro, Brazil; *Int'l*, pg. 112

Siracusa, Paul, Dir.-Res. & Devel.--Reckitt & Colman Inc., Montvale, NJ; *Int'l*, pg. 1090

Sitarski, Ed, V.P.-Res. & Devel.--Numetrix Ltd., Toronto, Canada; *Int'l*, pg. 990

Siter, Ralph, V.P.-Research & Engrng.--Preformed Line Products, Cleveland, OH; *U.S. Public*, pg. 1321

Six, Howard, V.P.-Res. & Devel.--Connaught Laboratories, Inc., Swiftwater, PA; *Int'l*, pg. 1109

Skelton, Barry, Mgr.-Engrng.--Moeller Products Co., Inc., Greenville, MS; *U.S. Private*, pg. 755

Skibski, Richard, V.P.-Res. & Tech.--Cyborg Systems, Inc., Chicago, IL; *U.S. Private*, pg. 299

Skime, Roger, V.P.-Res. & Devel.--Arctic Cat Inc., Thief River Falls, MN; *U.S. Public*, pg. 128

Skirde, Eckhart, Dir.-Res. & Devel.--Sauer Sundstrand Gmbh & Co., Neumunster, Germany; *Int'l*, pg. 1198

Sklar, Neil, V.P.-Prod. Devel.--Uniflex, Inc., Hicksville, NY; *U.S. Public*, pg. 1665

Slater, Lucy, Sr. V.P.-Prod. Devel.--E-Z Bowz, Inc., Sevierville, TN; *U.S. Private*, pg. 352

Slischel, Karen, V.P.-Res.--Nickelodeon/Nick At Nite, New York, NY; *U.S. Private*, pg. 779

Smalley, Robert A., Jr., Chief Oper. Officer & Exec. V.P.--Cruise America, Inc., Mesa, AZ; *U.S. Private*, pg. 178

Smart, Michael, V.P.-Res. & Devel.--CCX Fiberglass Products, Walterboro, SC; *U.S. Private*, pg. 193

Smeby, Leif, Dir.-Research & Development--Gambro AB, Lund, Sweden; *Int'l*, pg. 666

Smeltzer, D.C., V.P.-Res. & Devel.--Overly Manufacturing Co., Greensburg, PA; *U.S. Private*, pg. 823

Smith-Berntson, Karl, V.P.-Res. & Devel.--Donlee Technologies Inc., York, PA; *U.S. Private*, pg. 339

Smith, Alan E., Sr. V.P.-Res.--Genzyme Corporation, Cambridge, MA; *U.S. Public*, pg. 733

Smith, Andrew, Mgr.-Prod. Devel.--Merisel Austria, Vienna, Austria; *U.S. Public*, pg. 1096

Smith, David, V.P.-Res. & Tech.--IMPCO AirSensors Technologies, Cerritos, CA; *U.S. Public*, pg. 34

Smith, Dr. Edward F., Dir.-Res. & Devel. Div.--Ney Dental International, Bloomfield, CT; *Int'l*, pg. 388

Smith, Edward F., III, Dir.- Research & Devel.--The J.M. Ney Company, Bloomfield, CT; *U.S. Public*, pg. 111

Smith, Edward F., III, Ph.D., V.P.-Res. & Devel.--The J.M. Ney Company, Bloomfield, CT; *U.S. Public*, pg. 111

Smith, Geoffrey A., V.P.-Prod. Devel.--Mitel Corporation, Kanata, Canada; *Int'l*, pg. 870

Smith, George, Dir.-Research & Devel.--Northern Telecom, Nashville, TN; *Int'l*, pg. 969

Smith, Jack A., V.P.-Corp. Plng.--The Reader's Digest Association, Inc., Pleasantville, NY; *U.S. Public*, pg. 1367

Smith, Jonathan, Dir.-Res.--Northland Cranberries, Inc., Wisconsin Rapids, WI; *U.S. Public*, pg. 1197

Smith, Kenard E., V.P.-Area Res.--The May Department Stores Company, Saint Louis, MO; *U.S. Public*, pg. 1063

Smith, Kenneth, Sr. V.P.-Opers.--Marotta Scientific Controls, Inc., Montville, NJ; *U.S. Private*, pg. 706

Smith, Lisa, Mgr.-Research--Weider Publications, Inc., Woodland Hills, CA; *U.S. Private*, pg. 1159

Smith, P.C., V.P.-Res., Devel. & Engrng.--Wesgo Inc., Belmont, CA; *Int'l*, pg. 893

Smith, Paul, Exec. Dir.-Retail Opers., Far East--Marks & Spencer PLC, London, United Kingdom; *Int'l*, pg. 842

Smith, Paul A., Chief Oper. Officer & V.P.-Mfg.--Eversharp Pen Co., Franklin Park, IL; *U.S. Private*, pg. 386

Smith, Robert, Mgr.-Promotional Communications--Rockwell Automation, Milwaukee, WI; *U.S. Public*, pg. 1397

Smith, Robert, V.P.-Quality & Tech.--Spectrum Control, Inc., Erie, PA; *U.S. Public*, pg. 1497

Smith, Robert E., Sr. V.P.-Res.--Nabisco Inc., Parsippany, NJ; *U.S. Public*, pg. 1355

Smith, Robert L., V.P.-Bus. Devel.--Miller Brewing Company, Milwaukee, WI; *U.S. Public*, pg. 1289

Smith, Stephen K., Dir.-Res.--Hamilton, Allen & Associates, Inc, Atlanta, GA; *U.S. Public*, pg. 1673

Smith, William B., Sr. V.P.-Res. & Devel.--U S West Inc., Englewood, CO; *U.S. Public*, pg. 1688

Snook, Bill, Mgr.-Res. & Devel.--Correct Craft, Inc., Orlando, FL; *U.S. Private*, pg. 276

Snow, David, Dir.-Prod. Devel.--American Classic Voyagers Company, New Orleans, LA; *U.S. Private*, pg. 380

Snow, Mike, V.P.-Res. & Devel.--Medical Graphics Corp., Saint Paul, MN; *U.S. Public*, pg. 1080

Snyder, Bob, V.P.-Corp. Devel.--AAF-International, Louisville, KY; *U.S. Private*, pg. 3

Solender, T. Jeff, V.P.-Devel. & Plng.--Grey Asia Pacific, Quarry Bay, Hong Kong; *U.S. Public*, pg. 765

Solheim, Bjoern F., Sr. V.P.-Tech. & Devel.--Saga Petroleum ASA, Sandvika, Norway; *Int'l*, pg. 1169

Solly, Barry, Gen. Mgr.-Res. & Devel.--Fagersta Stainless AB, Fagersta, Sweden; *Int'l*, pg. 476

Solomon, Douglas S., V.P.-Strategic Plng. & Corp. Devel.--Apple Computer, Inc., Cupertino, CA; *U.S. Public*, pg. 121

Solomon, Jonathan H.M., Dir.-New Bus. & Strategy--Cable and Wireless plc, London, United Kingdom; *Int'l*, pg. 247

Sommer, R.A., V.P.-Res.--Ajax Magnethermic Corp., Warren, OH; *Int'l*, pg. 113

Sonneborn, Walter G., V.P.-Program & Prod. Devel.--Bell Helicopter Textron, Hurst, TX; *U.S. Public*, pg. 1588

Sood, Vijay K., V.P.-Res. & Devel.--Big 'G' Div., Minneapolis, MN; *U.S. Public*, pg. 718

Sorensen, Jamey, V.P.-Pur.--RK Mechanical, Inc., Denver, CO; *U.S. Private*, pg. 904

Sorenson, Wayne, V.P.-Res.--State Farm Mutual Automobile Insurance Company, Bloomington, IL; *U.S. Private*, pg. 1036

Soro, Mike, Dir.-Corp. Devel.--The Yorkville Printing Group Limited, Mississauga, Canada; *Int'l*, pg. 538

Sorrells, Kent, Dir.-Res. & Devel.--Alta-Dena Certified Dairy, City of Industry, CA; *Int'l*, pg. 201

Souza, Lawrence M., Sr. V.P.-Res.--Amgen Inc., Thousand Oaks, CA; *U.S. Public*, pg. 100

Spahn, Michael, Dir.-Compensation & Mgmt. Devel.--Philips Electronics North America Corporation, New York, NY; *Int'l*, pg. 1053

Spain, Glenn, Mgr.-Engrng.--American Manufacturing Company, Chattanooga, TN; *U.S. Private*, pg. 58

Spain, William, Sr. V.P.-Res., Govt. Affairs & Indus. Rels.--Del Monte Foods, San Francisco, CA; *U.S. Private*, pg. 321

Spatala, Eileen, Res.--SFM Media Corporation, New York, NY; *U.S. Private*, pg. 956

Spatorico, Tony, V.P.-Res. & Devel.--Anchor Continental Incorporated, Columbia, SC; *U.S. Private*, pg. 70

Spear, Ken, Dir.-Research & Devel.--Ames Company, Parkersburg, WV; *U.S. Public*, pg. 1683

Spencer, Jeffrey, V.P.--A.M. Todd Company, Kalamazoo, MI; *U.S. Private*, pg. 1089

Spigelman, Melvin, V.P.-Res. & Devel.--Knoll Pharmaceutical Company, Whippany, NJ; *Int'l*, pg. 105

Spillane, Robert T., V.P.-Research & Devel.--Guilford Mills, Inc., Greensboro, NC; *U.S. Public*, pg. 768

Sprague, Marsha, V.P.-Res. & Devel.--Faribault Foods Inc., Minneapolis, MN; *U.S. Private*, pg. 393

Spransy, Pete, Mgr.-Res. & Devel.--Daw Technologies, Inc., Salt Lake City, UT; *U.S. Public*, pg. 489

Springett, Linda, Mgr.-Res.--Gruner + Jahr USA Publishing, Inc., New York, NY; *Int'l*, pg. 190

Sproat, Brian, Ph.D., Dir.-Res.--Innovir GmbH, Rosdorf, Germany; *U.S. Public*, pg. 1703

Staby, Ludger W., Chm. Bd.-Mngmt.--Reemtsma Cigarettenfabriken GmbH, Hamburg, Hamburg, Germany; *Int'l*, pg. 1100

Stade, Yngve, Sr. V.P.-Res. & Devel.--Stora Kopparbergs Bergslags AB, Falun, Sweden; *Int'l*, pg. 1302

Staffaroni, Mike, Dir.-Res. & Devel.--L.A. Gear, Inc., Santa Monica, CA; *U.S. Public*, pg. 969

Stamatis, Jim, Sr. V.P.-Devel.--W.M. Grace Development, Phoenix, AZ; *U.S. Private*, pg. 468

Stanbury, Robert G., V.P.-Res./Devel. & Mktg.--Flowserve Corporation, Rotating Equipment Grp., Dayton, OH; *U.S. Public*, pg. 658

Standley, Paul, V.P.-Res. & Devel.--Dayco Products Inc., Miamisburg, OH; *U.S. Public*, pg. 1045

Stanton, Jim L., V.P.-Plng.--Lightnin Mixers, Rochester, NY; *U.S. Public*, pg. 726

Stapley, Roger, Market Research--Michelin North America (Canada) Inc., Laval, Canada; *Int'l*, pg. 322

Starnes, J. Jeter, V.P.-Res. & Devel.--Blackman Uhler Chemical Co., Spartanburg, SC; *U.S. Public*, pg. 1548

Stein, Richard A., Sr. Res. Analyst--Rochester Fund Municipals, Rochester, NY; *U.S. Private*, pg. 937

Steinbach, Bob, Design Engr.--Chicago Lock Company, Pleasant Prairie, WI; *U.S. Private*, pg. 235

Stekly, Z.J.J., V.P.-Advanced Programs--Intermagnetics General Corporation, Latham, NY; *U.S. Public*, pg. 893

Stephens, Bobby W., Exec. V.P.-Asset Mngmt.--Beverly Enterprises, Inc., Fort Smith, AR; *U.S. Public*, pg. 227

Stepner, David E., V.P.-Res. & Devel.--Integrated Systems, Inc., Sunnyvale, CA; *U.S. Public*, pg. 885

Sterling, George, V.P.-Opers.--Perry's Ice Cream Co., Inc., Akron, NY; *U.S. Private*, pg. 855

Stewart, W.W., Dir.-Strategy & Devel.--Scottisch Equitable, Edinburgh, United Kingdom; *Int'l*, pg. 28

Stiles, J.C., Dir.-Res.--Kearfott Guidance & Navigation Corp., Wayne, NJ; *U.S. Private*, pg. 93

Stitley, James, V.P.-Consumer/Prod. Res.--Domino's Pizza Inc., Ann Arbor, MI; *U.S. Private*, pg. 339

Stobart, Philip, V.P.-Prod. Devel.--Crane Plastics Company, Columbus, OH; *U.S. Private*, pg. 286

Stofko, John, Exec. V.P.-Res. & Devel.--Cadbury Beverages North America, Stamford, CT; *Int'l*, pg. 248

Stonehocker, Keith, Sr. V.P.--Christianity Today, Inc., Carol Stream, IL; *U.S. Private*, pg. 238

Stottmeister, Walter, Mgr.-Laboratory--Hardman Division of Harcros Chemicals, Inc., Belleville, NJ; *Int'l*, pg. 598

Stouffer, Peter, V.P.-Engrng. & Mfg.--Code-Alarm, Inc., Madison Heights, MI; *U.S. Public*, pg. 393

Stover, Kim R., Dir.-Devel.--T.D. Williamson, Inc., Tulsa, OK; *U.S. Private*, pg. 1179

Straka, Bobby, Dir.-Research & Devel.--Artco-Bell Corporation, Temple, TX; *U.S. Private*, pg. 86

Strambi, Marybeth, Dir.-Res.--Worldvision Enterprises, New York, NY; *U.S. Private*, pg. 776

Strang, Richard M., Chief Tech. Officer, VLSI Sys.--SBE, Inc., San Ramon, CA; *U.S. Public*, pg. 1416

Strange, David R., V.P.-Bus. Devel.--R.M. Shoemaker Co., West Conshohocken, PA; *U.S. Private*, pg. 996

Straube, Kathleen, Chief Designer--The Vermont Teddy Bear Company, Inc., Shelburne, VT; *U.S. Public*, pg. 1716

Street, J.R., Coordinator-Grp. Res.--Royal Dutch/Shell Group of Companies, Hague, Netherlands; *Int'l*, pg. 1135

Strickland, Danny L., Sr. V.P.-Res. & Devel.--General Mills, Inc., Minneapolis, MN; *U.S. Public*, pg. 717

Strickland, T.L., Sr. V.P.-Intl. Devel.--Morganite Inc., Dunn, NC; *Int'l*, pg. 891

Stuart, Kevin, V.P.-Res. & Devel.--Aerco International Inc., Northvale, NJ; *U.S. Private*, pg. 23

Stull, Pam, Exec. V.P.-Corp. Devel.--Market Place Print, Inc., Pittsburgh, PA; *U.S. Private*, pg. 701

Stump, Kent H., Dir.-Strategy--Southern Indiana Gas & Electric Co., Evansville, IN; *U.S. Public*, pg. 1471

Sudbury, Barry A., Ph.D., V.P.-Res. & Devel.--The Clorox Company, Oakland, CA; *U.S. Public*, pg. 386

Sugathan, Gopakumar, Dir.-Res. & Devel.--Ziegler Chemical & Mineral Corp., Jericho, NY; *U.S. Private*, pg. 1205

Suggett, A., Grp. Dir.-Res. & devel.--Smith & Nephew PLC, London, United Kingdom; *Int'l*, pg. 1263

Sugiyama, K., Mgr.-Plng.--Cosmo Oil Co., Ltd., Tokyo, Japan; *Int'l*, pg. 335

Sukovich, Al, Res. & Devel.--PowderTech Corporation, Valparaiso, IN; *Int'l*, pg. 878

Sullivan, Beth, Sr. V.P. & Dir. Mkt. Res.--Arnold Communications, Inc., Boston, MA; *U.S. Private*, pg. 83

Sullivan, Celine, V.P.-Mkt. Devel.--Cowles Enthusiast Media, Inc., Stamford, CT; *U.S. Private*, pg. 281

Sullivan, Stephen G., V.P.-Bus. Devel.--US SerVis, West Orange, NJ; *U.S. Public*, pg. 1687

Sundstrom, Chris E., V.P.-Corp. Devel.--Wm. Wrigley Jr. Company, Chicago, IL; *U.S. Public*, pg. 1781

Sussman, Ira, Sr. V.P. & Media Res. Dir.--Western International Media Corporation, Los Angeles, CA; *U.S. Private*, pg. 1165

Sustek, Sandra, New Media & Res. Asst.--Quantum Media International, Inc., Chicago, IL; *U.S. Private*, pg. 899

Suter, Brian-Ernest, Gen. Mgr.-Res. & Devel. (Nestec Ltd.)--Nestle S.A., Vevey, Switzerland; *Int'l*, pg. 915

Sutlin, Jerrold, V.P.-Franchise Sls. & Devel.--Gingiss International, Addison, IL; *U.S. Private*, pg. 455

Suzuki, Arata, V.P.-Res. & Devel.--Capintec Inc., Ramsey, NJ; *U.S. Private*, pg. 205

Suzuki, Hisashi, Mng. Dir.-Res. & Devel.--Sega Enterprises Ltd., Tokyo, Japan; *Int'l*, pg. 1218

Suzuki, Yu, Dir.-Res. & Devel.--Sega Enterprises Ltd., Tokyo, Japan; *Int'l*, pg. 1218

Swalls, Tom, Mgr.-Computer Resource--Vogler Motor Company, Inc., Carbondale, IL; *U.S. Private*, pg. 1143

Swenson, Orvil, Dir.-Chemical Res.--Agsco, Inc., Grand Forks, ND; *U.S. Private*, pg. 27

Swigert, J.L., Dir.-Research--Morton International Inc., Chicago, IL; *U.S. Public*, pg. 1135

Sylvanus, Frederick, Dir.-Res. & Devel.--Autotote Corporation, Newark, DE; *U.S. Public*, pg. 150

Synodis, Joseph D., Ph.D., V.P.-Consumer Prods. Res. & Tech.--Block Drug Company, Inc., Jersey City, NJ; *U.S. Public*, pg. 236

Szeto, Wai S., V.P.-Corp. Devel.--AST Research Inc., Irvine, CA; *Int'l*, pg. 1181

Taba, Serge, V.P.-Opers. & Res. & Devel.--U.S. Divers Co., Inc., Santa Ana, CA; *U.S. Private*, pg. 1125

Tada, Koichi, Dr., Gen. Mgr.--Toyo Tire & Rubber Co., Ltd., Osaka, Japan; *Int'l*, pg. 1411

Takai, Koichiro, Assoc. Dir.-Research--Asahi Breweries Ltd., Tokyo, Japan; *Int'l*, pg. 83

Takara, Charlene S., Sr. V.P.-Res. & Devel.--Countrywide Funding Corporation, Pasadena, CA; *U.S. Public*, pg. 453

Takiguchi, Tadahiko, Mng. Dir.-Prod. Planning, Res. & Devel.--Mazda Motor Corporation, Hiroshima, Japan; *Int'l*, pg. 849

Taldu, Gilles, Mgr.-Plng. & Bus. Devel.--Thomson S.A., Paris, France; *Int'l*, pg. 1381

Tallis, Alan, Exec. V.P.-Corp. Devel.--Red Roof Inns, Inc., Hilliard, OH; *U.S. Public*, pg. 1369

Tallman, Jim, Mkt. Res. Dir.--SicolaMartin Inc., Austin, TX; *U.S. Private*, pg. 998

Tamura, Shozo, Dir. & Gen. Mgr.-Project Devel. Bureau--Nihon Keizai Shimbun, Inc., Tokyo, Japan; *Int'l*, pg. 929

Tanaka, Jun-ichi, Sr. Exec. Mng. Dir.--Kokusai Electric Co., Ltd., Tokyo, Japan; *Int'l*, pg. 743

Taneja, Narayan, Dir.-Res. & Devel.--UDT Sensors, Inc., Hawthorne, CA; *U.S. Private*, pg. 1112

Taniguchi, Norihisa, Dir. & Deputy Sr. Gen. Mgr.-Project Devel.--West Japan Railway Company, Osaka, Japan; *Int'l*, pg. 1490

Tanner, Alexandra, Sr. Principal & Strategic Plng. & Res. Dir.--Publicis/Bloom, New York, NY; *Int'l*, pg. 470

Tanner, Anthony A., Asst. V.P.-Res.--Rochester Fund Municipals, Rochester, NY; *U.S. Private*, pg. 937

Tarewicz, R., Dir.-Tech. Opers.--American Inks & Coatings Corp., Phoenixville, PA; *U.S. Private*, pg. 56

Taske, Howard, Res. Dir.--ADWORKS, Inc., Washington, DC; *U.S. Private*, pg. 23

Taylor, Dene, V.P.-Res. & Devel.--Dunmore Corporation, Newtown, PA; *U.S. Private*, pg. 346

Taylor, Jeffrey, Dir.-Res. & Devel.--Standard Textile Co., Inc., Cincinnati, OH; *U.S. Private*, pg. 1032

Taylor, Robert M., V.P.-Engrng. & Tech.--Capital Controls Company Inc., Colmar, PA; *Int'l*, pg. 1226

Taylor, Stephen B., V.P.-Corp. Devel.--Derlan Industries Limited, Toronto, Canada; *Int'l*, pg. 395

Tebo, Paul V., V.P.-Chemicals--Du Pont (E.I. Du Pont De Nemours & Co.), Wilmington, DE; *U.S. Public*, pg. 530

Teixeira, George S., V.P.-Prod. Opers.--Encore Computer Corporation, Fort Lauderdale, FL; *U.S. Public*, pg. 580

Templeton, Christine, Grp. Plng. & Res. Dir.--EURO RSCG Tatham, Chicago, IL; *Int'l*, pg. 601

Terada, Tokio, Pres.--Tsudakoma Corp., Kanazawa, Japan; *Int'l*, pg. 1425

Terhune, Larry L., V.P.-Software Devel.--Manatron, Inc., Kalamazoo, MI; *U.S. Public*, pg. 1040

Terpstra, Wayne R., V.P.-Research & Devel.--Heatilator Inc., Mount Pleasant, IA; *U.S. Public*, pg. 772

Tesic, Mike, V.P.-Engrg.--Fischer Imaging Corporation, Denver, CO; *U.S. Public*, pg. 647

Tesniere, A.J., Dir.-Res. & Devel.--Charmilles Technologies SA, Meyrin, Switzerland; *Int'l*, pg. 489

Testa, Douglas, Ph.D., V.P.-Res.--Interferon Sciences, Inc., New Brunswick, NJ; *U.S. Public*, pg. 694

Thaler, Arnold, Exec. V.P.-Prod. Dev., Engineering & Manufacturing--Windmere-Durable Holdings, Hialeah, FL; *U.S. Public*, pg. 1771

Theeuwes, Felix, Dr., Pres.-ALZA Technology Institute & Chief Scientist--Alza Corporation, Palo Alto, CA; *U.S. Public*, pg. 62

Theno, David, V.P.-Quality Assurance, Res. & Devel. & Prod. Safety--Foodmaker, Inc., San Diego, CA; *U.S. Public*, pg. 661

Thijssen, N.J.W., Dir.-Res. & Works Laboratories--Hoogovens Ijmuiden, Ijmuiden, Netherlands; *Int'l*, pg. 753

Thomas, Joe, Dir.-Research & Devel.--Continental Eagle Corporation, Prattville, AL; *U.S. Private*, pg. 267

Thomas, R.A., V.P.-Engrng. & Res.--Talley Defense Systems, Inc., Mesa, AZ; *U.S. Public*, pg. 308

Thomas, Ramesh Jude, Gen. Mgr., Planning, Res. & Devel.--MAA Communications Bozell, Bangalore, India; *U.S. Public*, pg. 1642

Thompson, David D., V.P.-Hardware Research & Devel.--Cray Research, Eagan, MN; *U.S. Public*, pg. 1473

Thompson, Robin, Dir.-Strategic Devel.--Inchcape PLC, London, United Kingdom; *Int'l*, pg. 671

Thomsen, Jan, Mgr.-Plng. & Devel.--Automatic Equipment Mfg. Co., Pender, NE; *U.S. Private*, pg. 101

Thomson, A., Mgr.-Res. & Devel.--BTR plc, London, United Kingdom; *Int'l*, pg. 124

Thormton, William A., Dir.-Res. & Devel.--Cives Corporation, Roswell, GA; *U.S. Private*, pg. 241

Thornhill, Kathleen A., V.P.-Global Bus. Insights & Consumer Res.--Colgate-Palmolive Company, New York, NY; *U.S. Public*, pg. 397

Tillman, Tod, Dir.-Res. & Devel.--Mico Inc., North Mankato, MN; *U.S. Private*, pg. 741

Timon, Jerry, V.P.-Engrng. & Res. & Devel.--The Johnson Corporation, Three Rivers, MI; *U.S. Private*, pg. 591

Tinker, H. Burnham, V.P.-Res. & Dev.--Mooney Chemicals, Cleveland, OH; *U.S. Public*, pg. 1208

Tinkler, Michael P., V.P.-H.R. & Organizational Devel.--Bombardier Inc., Montreal, Canada; *Int'l*, pg. 199

Tkalcevic, Slobodan, V.P.-Advanced Devel.--TCI International Inc., Sunnyvale, CA; *U.S. Public*, pg. 1555

Tobey, James F., Mgr.-Research & Devel.--Astre Corporate Group, Alexandria, VA; *U.S. Private*, pg. 93

Tobin, Thomas J., V.P.-Res. & Devel.--S & C Electric Company, Chicago, IL; *U.S. Private*, pg. 954

Todaro, Dr. George, Sr. V.P.-Research--Genetic Systems Corporation, Seattle, WA; *Int'l*, pg. 445

Toffler, Van, Sr. V.P.-Prog. Enterprises & Bus. Devel.--MTV Networks, New York, NY; *U.S. Private*, pg. 779

Tom, Glenn M., Ph.D., V.P.-Res. & Devel.--ATMI, Inc., Danbury, CT; *U.S. Public*, pg. 12

Tompkins, Dale B., Dir.-Strategic Plng.--Giddings & Lewis, Inc., Fond Du Lac, WI; *Int'l*, pg. 1389

Toney, John, V.P.-Research--Henningsen Foods, Inc., Omaha, NE; *Int'l*, pg. 1074

Toole, Floyd E., V.P.-Engrng.--Harman International Industries, Inc., Woodbury, NY; *U.S. Public*, pg. 787

Toole, Richard, V.P. & Sr. Telecommunications Analyst--Merrill Lynch & Co., Inc., New York, NY; *U.S. Public*, pg. 1097

Torcivia, Santo, Market Research--Mannington Resilient Floors, Salem, NJ; *U.S. Private*, pg. 700

Torgerson, David F., V.P.-Res. & Prod. Devel.--Atomic Energy of Canada Ltd., Mississauga, Canada; *Int'l*, pg. 97

Tosa, Tetsuya, Ph.D., Sr. Exec. Dir.-Res. & Devel.--Tanabe Seiyaku Co., Ltd., Osaka, Japan; *Int'l*, pg. 1354

Trager, Wesley, V.P.-Advanced Tech. & Engrng.--Acclaim Entertainment, Inc., Glen Cove, NY; *U.S. Public*, pg. 15

Train, M., V.P.-Plng.--Emerson Electric Co., Saint Louis, MO; *U.S. Public*, pg. 572

Treace, D.D., V.P.-Res. & Devel.--Xomed Surgical Products, Jacksonville, FL; *U.S. Public*, pg. 253

Trentham, Charlene, Dir.-Res.--Gruner + Jahr USA Publishing, Inc., New York, NY; *Int'l*, pg. 190

Trimble, M.A., V.P.-Res. & Devel.--IDenticard Systems, Inc., Lancaster, PA; *U.S. Private*, pg. 557

Truax, David, V.P.-Engrng. & Res.-Smith Diamond Tech.--Smith International, Inc., Houston, TX; *U.S. Public*, pg. 1478

Tsai, Bin-Ming Ben, Ph.D., Chief Tech. Officer & V.P.--KLA Tencor Corporation, San Jose, CA; *U.S. Public*, pg. 939

Tsang, Monica, V.P.-Research--Techne Corporation, Minneapolis, MN; *U.S. Public*, pg. 1563

Tsimberg, Lev, Dir.-Tech.--Rose Art Industries, Livingston, NJ; *U.S. Private*, pg. 945

Tsuboshima, Masami, Exec. V.P.-Central Pharmaceutical Res. Institute--Japan Tobacco Inc., Tokyo, Japan; *Int'l*, pg. 703

Tucker, James, V.P.-Bus. Dev.--Smith Corona Corp., Cortland, NY; *U.S. Private*, pg. 1007

Tufenkian, Ralph, V.P.-Projects--Western Waste Industries, Torrance, CA; *U.S. Public*, pg. 1686

Tully, Tom, Exec. V.P.--Marketing Support, Incorporated, Chicago, IL; *U.S. Private*, pg. 705

Tuominen, F. William, Sr. V.P. & Chief Tech. & Environ. Officer--Ecolab Inc., Saint Paul, MN; *U.S. Public*, pg. 562

Turner, Keith, Dir.-Prod. Devel.--Gaston County Dyeing Machine Co., Mount Holly, NC; *U.S. Private*, pg. 441

Turnill, Edwin, Sr., Intl. Res. & Plng.--Grey Europe/London, London, United Kingdom; *U.S. Public*, pg. 765

Twyble, William J., Sr. V.P.-Res. & Devel. Mktg. & Customer Satisfaction--The Lincoln Electric Company, Cleveland, OH; *U.S. Public*, pg. 996

U'Pritchard, David C., Mng. Dir.-Res. & Devel.--SmithKline Beecham plc, Brentford, United Kingdom; *Int'l*, pg. 1264

Ueki, Satoshi, Gen. Mgr.--Chiyoda Mutual Life Insurance Company, Tokyo, Japan; *Int'l*, pg. 286

Ullrich, John F., V.P.-Tech. & Support Services--Masco Corporation, Taylor, MI; *U.S. Public*, pg. 1052

Umbach, Wilfried, Dr., Exec. V.P.-Res. & Tech.--Henkel KGaA, Dusseldorf, Germany; *Int'l*, pg. 609

Underhill, Robert A., Sr. V.P.-Res. & Devel.fficer--Kimberly-Clark Corporation, Dallas, TX; *U.S. Public*, pg. 958

Urdea, Mickey S., Ph.D., V.P.-Nucleic Acid Systems Res. & Devel.--Chiron Corporation, Emeryville, CA; *U.S. Public*, pg. 349

Ureyen, Refik, Mgr.-Res. & Devel.--Arcelik A.S., Istanbul, Turkey; *Int'l*, pg. 741

Vakil, Abubakar U., V.P.-Res. & Devel.--Lights Of America, Inc., Walnut, CA; *U.S. Private*, pg. 667

Valencia de Freitas, Luciano, Dir.-Mfg.--Sao Paulo Alpargatas S.A., Sao Paulo, Brazil; *Int'l*, pg. 1193

Valencia, Gilbert, V.P.-Electronic Res. & Devel.--NT Doromatic, Harwood Heights, IL; *U.S. Private*, pg. 771

Valenzuela, Pablo D.T., Ph.D., Sr. V.P.-Biologicals Res. & Devel.--Chiron Corporation, Emeryville, CA; *U.S. Public*, pg. 349

Valimaki, Pekka, V.P.-Res. & Devel.--Fiskars Power Systems, Espoo, Finland; *Int'l*, pg. 127

Vallet, Dominnique, Exec. V.P.-Research & Corp. Advisory Services--Credit Nationale, Paris, France; *Int'l*, pg. 344

Vallner, Joseph, Ph.D., Sr. V.P.-Res. & Devel.--Sequus Pharmaceuticals, Inc., Menlo Park, CA; *U.S. Public*, pg. 1460

Van Der Broeke, Doug, Dir.-Res. & Devel.--Photronics, Inc., Brookfield, CT; *U.S. Public*, pg. 1293

Van Erden, Donald L., V.P.-Res. & Advanced Devel.--Illinois Tool Works Inc., Glenview, IL; *U.S. Public*, pg. 865

Van Horn, Bob, Exec. V.P. & Strategic Plng. Dir.--Crispin Porter & Bogusky Advertising, Miami, FL; *U.S. Private*, pg. 290

van Suijdam, J.C., Dir.-Central Tech. & Services--Royal Gist-Brocades N.V., Delft, Netherlands; *Int'l*, pg. 1142

Van Wert, James R., Chief Tech. Officer & V.P.-Tech.--Amcast Industrial Corporation, Dayton, OH; *U.S. Public*, pg. 63

Vandegrift, James, V.P.-Res. & Devel.--K2 Corporation, Vashon, WA; *U.S. Public*, pg. 940

Vander Haar, R. William, Sr. V.P.-Res. & Devel./Consumer Care Div.--Bayer Corporation, Pittsburgh, PA; *Int'l*, pg. 172

Vandergrift, James A., V.P.-Res. & Devel.--K2 Inc., Los Angeles, CA; *U.S. Public*, pg. 940

vanderWant, F.A., Dir.-Research & Devel.--Wavin Bv, Zwolle, Netherlands; *Int'l*, pg. 1135

Vanetti, Giulio, Mgr.-Res., Plng. & Control--Cassa di Risparmio delle Provincie Lombarde SpA (CARIPLO), Milan, Italy; *Int'l*, pg. 274

Vanier, Paul, Mgr.-Product Devel.--Fraser Papers, Inc., Stamford, CT; *Int'l*, pg. 434

Vargas, M. Jordan, V.P.-Organizational Devel.--Webcraft Technologies, Inc., North Brunswick, NJ; *U.S. Public*, pg. 228

Varithorn, Premwan, Asst. V.P.-Res. Dept.--The Industrial Finance Corporation of Thailand, Bangkok, Thailand; *Int'l*, pg. 677

Varney, Michael D., Ph.D., V.P.-Res.--Agouron Pharmaceuticals, Inc., La Jolla, CA; *U.S. Public*, pg. 28

Vasquez, Lou, Supvr.-Res. & Devel.--Karnak Corporation, Clark, NJ; *U.S. Private*, pg. 607

Vaughn, David, Exec. V.P.-Bus. Devel.--Trimble Navigation Limited, Sunnyvale, CA; *U.S. Public*, pg. 1638

Vela, Tim, Dir.-Res. & Devel.--Alloy Technology International Inc., West Nyack, NY; *U.S. Private*, pg. 42

Vercoulen, Jan, Dir.-Res. & Devel.--Oce-van der Grinten N.V., Venlo, Netherlands; *Int'l*, pg. 993

Vezina, Serge, Mgr.-Environ. & Res.--Cambior Inc., Montreal, Canada; *Int'l*, pg. 253

Vieira, Manuel Jose Deus, Sr. Gen. Mgr.-Res. & Plng.--Banco Totta & Acores, Lisbon, Portugal; *Int'l*, pg. 144

Vienney, Alain, Gen. Mgr.-Res.--Banque de France, Paris, France; *Int'l*, pg. 160

Vifian, Hugo, V.P.-Res. & Devel.--Harmonic Lightwaves, Sunnyvale, CA; *U.S. Public*, pg. 788

Vihinen, John, Dir.-Plng. & Devel.--Sugarbush, Warren, VT; *U.S. Private*, pg. 62

Vildaurrazaga, Juan, Dir.-Res. & Devel.--Dataproducts Corporation, Simi Valley, CA; *Int'l*, pg. 620

Villadsen, Ove, V.P.-Engrng.--Comdial Corporation, Charlottesville, VA; *U.S. Public*, pg. 407

Vincent, Martha E., V.P.-Clinical Res.--Amgen Inc., Thousand Oaks, CA; *U.S. Public*, pg. 100

Vitale, Harold S., V.P.--LTX Corporation, Westwood, MA; *U.S. Public*, pg. 972

Vogesong, Tom, Dir.-Engrng.--Criticare Systems, Inc., Waukesha, WI; *U.S. Public*, pg. 459

Vohringer, Klaus-Dieter, Dir.-Res. & Tech.--Daimler-Benz Aktiengesellschaft, Stuttgart, Germany; *Int'l*, pg. 366

Volk, Kristin, Exec. V.P. & Consumer Insight Dir.--Arnold Communications, Inc., Boston, MA; *U.S. Private*, pg. 83

Volm, Frank, V.P.-Bus. Devel.--KRC (Hewitt) Inc., Neenah, WI; *Int'l*, pg. 1202

Volpe, Lee, V.P.-Res. & Devel.--Tyco Toys, Inc., Mount Laurel, NJ; *U.S. Public*, pg. 1058

Volpe, Tony, V.P.-Clinical Dental Res.--Colgate-Palmolive Company, New York, NY; *U.S. Public*, pg. 397

Von Mayenburg, Michael, Sr. V.P.-Engrg. & Tech.--Freightliner Corp., Portland, OR; *Int'l*, pg. 368

von Szczepanski, Christoph, Dr., Dir.-Res.--AgrEvo GmbH, Berlin, Germany; *Int'l*, pg. 624

Vondrasek, Robert, V.P. & Chief Engr.--National Fire Protection Association, Quincy, MA; *U.S. Private*, pg. 782

Vydra, Edward J., V.P.-Res. & Devel.--Pre Finish Metals Incorporated, Elk Grove Village, IL; *U.S. Public*, pg. 1056

Wagener, Earl H., V.P.-Res. & Devel.--Stepan Company, Northfield, IL; *U.S. Public*, pg. 1514

Wagle, Patricia, Dir.-Res. & Devel.--The Flood Company, Hudson, OH; *U.S. Private*, pg. 414

Wahlers, Richard L., Dr., Mgr.-Res. & Devel.--Electro-Science Laboratories, Inc., King of Prussia, PA; *U.S. Private*, pg. 369

Wale, N.E., V.P.-Corp. Res. & Devel.--Canadian Pacific Limited, Calgary, Canada; *Int'l*, pg. 258

Walker, John, V.P.-Corp. Devel.--CSR America Inc., Atlanta, GA; *Int'l*, pg. 245

Walker, Scott, Chief Tech. Officer & Sr. V.P.--Delco Electronics Corporation, Kokomo, IN; *U.S. Public*, pg. 720

Walker, Thomas, V.P.-Prod. Mngmt.--Ziebart International Corporation, Troy, MI; *U.S. Private*, pg. 1205

Wall, Joseph, Chief Tech. Officer & V.P.--Pitney Bowes Inc., Stamford, CT; *U.S. Public*, pg. 1303

Wallace, Jerry E., V.P.-Res. & Devel.--Appleton Papers Inc., Appleton, WI; *Int'l*, pg. 567

Wallach, Steven J., Chief Technology Officer--Convex Technology Center - Hewlett-Packard, Richardson, TX; *U.S. Public*, pg. 815

Walling, William Walter, V.P.-Engrng. Svcs.--Gundle/SLT Environmental, Inc., Houston, TX; *U.S. Public*, pg. 769

Walsworth, Edgar, Exec. V.P.-Mfg. & Comml. Sls.--Walsworth Publishing Company, Inc., Marceline, MO; *U.S. Private*, pg. 1148

Walter, Ron A., V.P.-Project Devel.--Calpine Corporation, San Jose, CA; *U.S. Public*, pg. 296

Waltuck, Morey, V.P.-Res. & Devel.--Mentor Opthalmics, Inc., Santa Barbara, CA; *U.S. Public*, pg. 1086

Wang, David, Dir.-Res. & Devel.--Mannington Resilient Floors, Salem, NJ; *U.S. Private*, pg. 700

Wang, Ming, Sr. V.P. & Dir.-Res.--Investment Research Company, Rancho Santa Fe, CA; *U.S. Public*, pg. 1673

Wanner, Paul, Mgr.-Real Estate--Sulzer Ltd., Winterthur, Switzerland; *Int'l*, pg. 1305

Warby, R.J., Devel. Mgr.--Bespak plc, Norfolk, United Kingdom; *Int'l*, pg. 193

Warchol, J.F., V.P.-Technical--Houghton International Inc., Valley Forge, PA; *U.S. Private*, pg. 541

Ward, Charles, Mgr.-Engrng.--Cole Hersee Company, Boston, MA; *U.S. Private*, pg. 251

Ware, James H., V.P.-Tech. & Engrng.--TJ International, Inc., Boise, ID; *U.S. Public*, pg. 1556

Warfield, Nina, V.P. & Assoc. Res. Dir.--Jordan, McGrath, Case & Taylor Inc., New York, NY; *U.S. Private*, pg. 598

Wargo, Chris A., V.P.-Info.--Arinc Inc. (Consolidated), Annapolis, MD; *U.S. Private*, pg. 81

Washida, Kazunobu, Gen. Mgr.-Res. & Devel.--Narumi China Corporation, Nagoya, Japan; *Int'l*, pg. 906

Wasp, Timothy H., Dir.-Mkt. Analysis & Plng.--The M.W. Kellogg Company, Houston, TX; *U.S. Public*, pg. 528

Wassman, David, V.P. & Res. Dir.--Ross Roy Communications, Inc., Bloomfield Hills, MI; *U.S. Private*, pg. 946

Watanabe, August M., M.D., Exec. V.P.-Science & Tech.--Eli Lilly and Company, Indianapolis, IN; *U.S. Public*, pg. 992

Waterson, David, Sr. V.P.-Res. & Devel. & Mktg.--Icon Health & Fitness, Inc., Logan, UT; *U.S. Private*, pg. 556

Watson, Gary M., V.P.-Res. & Devel./Paper Div.--Boise Cascade Corporation, Boise, ID; *U.S. Public*, pg. 242

Watson, Stuart, Ph.D., Sr. V.P.-Res. & Devel.--Carpenter Co., Richmond, VA; *U.S. Private*, pg. 214

Watson, Tom, V.P. & Natl. TV Res. Dir.--Western International Media Corporation, Los Angeles, CA; *U.S. Private*, pg. 1165

Watts, Robert Z., Sr. V.P.-Corp. Res. & Devel.--International Game Technology, Reno, NV; *U.S. Public*, pg. 900

Webb, Dennis W., Grp. V.P.-Intl. Opers. & Bus. Devel.--Navistar International Corporation, Chicago, IL; *U.S. Public*, pg. 1167

Weber, Ronald G., Exec. V.P.-Tech. & Engrng.--Lowrance Electronics, Inc., Tulsa, OK; *U.S. Public*, pg. 1015

Wedlake, R.J., Mgr.-Res.--Amic Industries Limited, Johanesburg, South Africa; *Int'l*, pg. 76

Weeks, Jezabel, Mgr.-Res. & Devel.--Poly Pak America, Inc., Los Angeles, CA; *U.S. Private*, pg. 875

Wehrmeyer, Gunter, Dir.-Research & Devel.--Kali-Chemie Aktiengesellschaft, Hannover, Germany; *Int'l*, pg. 1278

Weinstein, Jan, V.P. & Assoc. Plng. Dir.--Western International Media Corporation, New York, NY; *U.S. Private*, pg. 1166

Weir, Brian R., V.P.-Devel. Engrng.--Pratt & Whitney Canada Inc., Longueuil, Canada; *U.S. Public*, pg. 1690

Weir, Douglas, Dir.-Res. & Devel.--Candle Corporation, Santa Monica, CA; *U.S. Private*, pg. 204

Weir, Ronald, Dir.-Research & Devel.--Morgan Foods, Inc., Austin, IN; *U.S. Private*, pg. 761

Weiss, Paul, Dr., Mgr.-New Business Devel.--Scientific Protein Laboratories, Inc., Waunakee, WI; *U.S. Public*, pg. 80

Weiss, Sam, Chm. Bd., Pres. & Chief Exec. Officer--United Receptical, Inc., Pottsville, PA; *U.S. Private*, pg. 1123

Weiss, Stanley I., V.P. & Gen. Mgr.-Research & Devel. Div.--Lockheed Martin Missiles & Space, Sunnyvale, CA; *U.S. Public*, pg. 1008

Welch, Dean, V.P.-Prod. & Res.--Solvay Animal Health, Inc., Mendota Heights, MN; *Int'l*, pg. 1277

Welch, Dean, V.P.-Prod. & Res.--Salsbury Laboratories, Inc., Charles City, IA; *Int'l*, pg. 1277

Welch, Michael T., V.P.-Opers., Mktg., Restaurant Support Services & Res. & Devel.--Checkers Drive-In Restaurants, Inc., Clearwater, FL; *U.S. Public*, pg. 342

Welch, R.J., Exec. V.P. & Chief Actuary--American National Insurance Company, Galveston, TX; *U.S. Public*, pg. 87

Wells, Pat, V.P.-Res.--Universal Studios TV, Universal City, CA; *Int'l*, pg. 1215

Wencel, Fred, Dir.-Research & Devel.--Papa Gino's Inc., Dedham, MA; *U.S. Private*, pg. 837

Wenninger, Walter, Dr., Mgr.-Res. & Devel.--Bayer AG, Leverkusen, Germany; *Int'l*, pg. 171

Wentler, G.E., Mgr.-Prod. Devel.--Procter & Gamble Pharmaceuticals, Inc., Cincinnati, OH; *U.S. Public*, pg. 1331

Wentworth, Gary, Dr., Dir.-Prod. Devel--The C.P. Hall Company, Chicago, IL; *U.S. Private*, pg. 495

Wernick, Justin, Dr., Exec. V.P. & Sec.--The Langer Biomechanics Group, Inc., Deer Park, NY; *U.S. Public*, pg. 978

Wesber, Manny, V.P.-Res. & Devel.--Select Canfield, Chicago, IL; *U.S. Private*, pg. 982

West, David, V.P.-Prod. Strategy & Plng.--Saab Automobile AB, Nykoping, Sweden; *Int'l*, pg. 687

West, David, V.P.-Prod. Strategy & Plng.--Saab Automobile AB, Nykoping, Sweden; *U.S. Public*, pg. 725

West, J. Thomas, Sr. V.P.-Advanced Devel.--Data General Corporation, Westborough, MA; *U.S. Public*, pg. 485

Westfall, Robert, V.P.-Res. & Devel.--O'Sullivan Corporation, Winchester, VA; *U.S. Public*, pg. 1234

Weston, Clive, Dir.-Thorn Secirity Technology Centre--Thorn Security Group, Ltd., Sunbury, United Kingdom; *Int'l*, pg. 1386

Weyrich, Claus, Dir.-Res. & Devel. & Tech.--Siemens AG, Munich, Germany; *Int'l*, pg. 1244

Whipple, Richard, Exec. V.P.--Kingsbury Corporation, Keene, NH; *U.S. Private*, pg. 621

White, James, V.P.-Bus. Devel.--Washington Gas Light Co., Springfield, VA; *U.S. Public*, pg. 1740

Whiteley, Don, Dir.-Total Quality--Diversey Water Technologies, Inc., Chagrin Falls, OH; *U.S. Public*, pg. 1150

Whitesell, Terry, Exec. V.P.-Sls. & Mktg.--Carpenter Industries, Inc., Richmond, IN; *U.S. Private*, pg. 215

Whitney, John G., Ph.D., V.P.-Lilly Research Labs.--Eli Lilly and Company, Indianapolis, IN; *U.S. Public*, pg. 992

Whitten, Charles E., V.P.-Res. & Devel.--ChemDesign Corporation, Fitchburg, MA; *Int'l*, pg. 173

Whyte, Marcella, Mgr.-Prod. Devel.--Dakotah, Inc., Webster, SD; *U.S. Public*, pg. 477

Wiberger, H. Ingvar, V.P.-Res. & Devel.--Pharmacia & Upjohn Biotech AB, Uppsala, Sweden; *Int'l*, pg. 1047

Wick, Arthur D., V.P.-Res. & Devel.--Lesco, Inc., Rocky River, OH; *U.S. Public*, pg. 989

Wienkoop, Glenn, Exec. V.P.-Engrng. & Mktg./Independant Sys. Grp.--Honeywell-Measurex Corporation, Cupertino, CA; *U.S. Public*, pg. 833

Wiesenfeld, Arnold, Dir.-Laboratory--Octagon Process Inc., Edgewater, NJ; *U.S. Private*, pg. 811

Wiggin, Roger C., V.P.-Exploration & Devel.--Tipperary Corporation, Denver, CO; *U.S. Public*, pg. 1618

Wild, Tim, V.P.-Intl. Mktg. Devel.--UB Networks, Santa Clara, CA; *Int'l*, pg. 924

Wiley, Jo Mark, V.P.-Information Services & Tech.--Bindley Western Drug Company, Indianapolis, IN; *U.S. Public*, pg. 228

Wilkes, John, Pres. & Chief Exec. Officer--John Dusenbery Co., Inc., Randolph, NJ; *U.S. Private*, pg. 349

Wilkie, Ian C., Sr. V.P.-Strategic Devel., Gen. Counsel & Sec.--Cara Operations Limited, Toronto, Canada; *Int'l*, pg. 266

Wilkinson, Maury, Dir.-Res. & Devel.--Seal Products Incorporated, Naugatuck, CT; *U.S. Public*, pg. 849

Willency, Richard, V.P.-Res. & Devel.--DowBrands, L.P., Indianapolis, IN; *U.S. Public*, pg. 523

Williams, Judith A., V.P.-Corp. Plng.--Alexander & Baldwin, Inc., Honolulu, HI; *U.S. Public*, pg. 39

Williams, Richard B., Vice Chm.--Alternative Resources Corporation, Lincolnshire, IL; *U.S. Public*, pg. 59

Williams, Wayne G., Dir.-Project Devel. & Tech. Res.--UFP Technology, Georgetown, MA; *U.S. Private*, pg. 1112

Willis, Bo, Dir.-Res. & Devel.--Oxford Industries, Inc., Atlanta, GA; *U.S. Public,* pg. 1239
Wills, Robert, Mgr.-Res.--Crown Holdings, Inc., Roseville, MN; *U.S. Private,* pg. 293
Wilson, Francis, V.P.-Engrng.--Penn Engineering & Manufacturing Corp., Danboro, PA; *U.S. Public,* pg. 1269
Wilson, G., V.P.-Prod. Devel.--General Railway Signal Corp., Rochester, NY; *Int'l,* pg. 1194
Wilson, Jack, Interactive Media Dir. & Res. Dir.--Berry Network, Inc., Dayton, OH; *U.S. Private,* pg. 137
Wilson, Philip, V.P.-Engrng.--Telco Systems, Inc., Norwood, MA; *U.S. Public,* pg. 1568
Wilson, Robert W., V.P.-Actuarial Res.--Sun Life Assurance Company of Canada, Toronto, Canada; *Int'l,* pg. 1318
Wilson, Warren W., V.P. & Dir.-Site Strategy--The Rouse Company, Columbia, MD; *U.S. Public,* pg. 1407
Wilson, Warren W., V.P. & Dir.-Site Strategy--Rouse Research & Site Strategy Div., Columbia, MD; *U.S. Public,* pg. 1407
Winninghoff, Albert C.M., Corp. Vice Chm., Chief Oper. Officer & Corp. Plng. Dir.--Leo Burnett Company, Inc., Chicago, IL; *U.S. Private,* pg. 183
Wise, Richard, Sr. V.P. & Strategic Plng. Dir.--Mezzina/Brown Inc., New York, NY; *U.S. Private,* pg. 739
Wise, Ted, Exec. V.P.--O'Reilly Automotive Inc., Springfield, MO; *U.S. Public,* pg. 1230
Wissman, Jack L., Mgr.-Engrng. & Res. & Devel.--Flowserve Corporation, Engineered Plastic Products Div., Springboro, OH; *U.S. Public,* pg. 658
Witschonke, Ross P., Mng. Dir.-Prod. Planning, Res. & Devel.--Mazda Motor Corporation, Hiroshima, Japan; *Int'l,* pg. 849
Wolbrink, David W., V.P.-Res. & Devel.--Broan Mfg. Co., Inc., Hartford, WI; *U.S. Public,* pg. 1193
Wolf, Manfred L., V.P.-Devel. & Exec. Dir.-Engrng.--Adam Opel AG, Russelsheim, Germany; *U.S. Public,* pg. 721
Womer, Keith, Dir.-Research & Devel.--M/D Totco Instrumentation, Cedar Park, TX; *U.S. Public,* pg. 1709
Wood, C.F., Sr. V.P.-Mfg., Engrng. & Devel.--Aluma Systems Corp., Toronto, Canada; *Int'l,* pg. 1423
Wood, Jeffrey G., V.P.-Devel.--Donahue Schriber, Newport Beach, CA; *Int'l,* pg. 253
Wood, Richard T., Sr. V.P.-Bus. Devel.--UMI, Ann Arbor, MI; *U.S. Public,* pg. 201
Wood, Tom, Mgr.-Res. & Devel.--C. B. Fleet Co., Inc., Lynchburg, VA; *U.S. Private,* pg. 410
Woods, Derek E., Ph.D., V.P.-Res. & Devel.--Life Technologies, Inc., Rockville, MD; *U.S. Public,* pg. 504
Worley, B.A., V.P.-Res. & Devel.--Springs Industries, Inc., Fort Mill, SC; *U.S. Public,* pg. 1499
Wright, Elizabeth B., Sr. V.P.-Strategic Plng. & Mktg.--National Trustco Inc., Toronto, Canada; *Int'l,* pg. 909
Wright, Joseph, V.P.-Research--Xerox Canada Ltd., North York, Canada; *U.S. Public,* pg. 1785
Wright, T., Dr., Dir.-Res.--Kodak Limited, Harrow, United Kingdom; *U.S. Public,* pg. 553
Wulfert, Ernst, Dir.-Res. & Devel.--UCB SA Pharma Sector, Braine-l'Alleud, Belgium; *Int'l,* pg. 1427
Wurz, David, Mgr.-Res. & Devel.--Accu-Sort Systems, Inc., Telford, PA; *U.S. Private,* pg. 11
Yafe, Albert, V.P.-Res. & Devel.--Orbotech Ltd., Yavne, Israel; *Int'l,* pg. 1007
Yamashita, Ryuichi, Mng. Dir.-Res. & Devel. Opers.--Yamaha Motor Co., Ltd., Iwata, Japan; *Int'l,* pg. 1516
Yi, Ching Sui Arthur, Ph.D., V.P.-Res. & Devel.--Meridian Diagnostics, Inc., Cincinnati, OH; *U.S. Public,* pg. 1094
Yoneno, Masahiro, Dir.-Res. & Devel.--Loctite (Japan) Corp., Yokohama, Japan; *Int'l,* pg. 611
York, Philip D., V.P.-Tech. & Research--Strategic Technology Services, Cerritos, CA; *Int'l,* pg. 1154
Young, James F., Ph.D., Sr. V.P.-Res. & Devel.--MedImmune, Inc., Gaithersburg, MD; *U.S. Public,* pg. 1081
Young, Judy, Asst. Gen. Mgr.-Cooking Light--Southern Progress Corporation, Birmingham, AL; *U.S. Public,* pg. 1612
Young, Keith, V.P.-Res. & Devel.--ABC Rail Products Corp., Chicago, IL; *U.S. Public,* pg. 2
Young, Mark D., V.P.-Mfg. & Process Devel.--Amgen Boulder, Inc., Boulder, CO; *U.S. Public,* pg. 101
Young, Stewart B., Sr. Partner & Grp. Brand Res. Dir.--EURO RSCG Tatham, Chicago, IL; *Int'l,* pg. 601
Yousefi, Cid, V.P.-Prod. Devel. & MIS--Equitrac Corporation, Coral Gables, FL; *U.S. Public,* pg. 590
Zack, Barbara, Dir.-Research & Plng.--Six Flags Theme Parks Inc., Parsippany, NJ; *U.S. Public,* pg. 1611
Zakes, Carin, Assoc. Res. Dir.--The Lord Group, New York, NY; *U.S. Private,* pg. 325
Zampol, Maria Angela, Res. Dir.--Salles/DMB&B Publicidade S.A., Sao Paulo, Brazil; *U.S. Private,* pg. 305
Zanoni, Carl A., V.P.-Res., Devel & Engrng.--Zygo Corporation, Middlefield, CT; *U.S. Public,* pg. 1795
Zavisza, Daniel M., Ph.D., Dir.-Tech.--Raffi & Swanson, Inc., Wilmington, MA; *U.S. Private,* pg. 907
Zeitlin, Bruce A., V.P.-Matls. Tech.--Intermagnetics General Corporation, Latham, NY; *U.S. Public,* pg. 893
Zender, Dean, Mgr.-Research & Devel.--Fred B. Johnston Company, Inc., Chapin, SC; *U.S. Private,* pg. 595
Zhou, Peter Y., Ph.D., V.P.-Tech.--Sentry Technology Corp., Hauppauge, NY; *U.S. Public,* pg. 1458
Zipperian, Donald C., Dr., Gen. Mgr.-Buehler SW Research Center--Buehler, Limited, Lake Bluff, IL; *U.S. Public,* pg. 574
Zkedata, Hideo, Mng. Dir.-Intellectual Property--Nikon Corporation, Tokyo, Japan; *Int'l,* pg. 931
Zoellner, Pam, Dir. & Mgr.-Devel.--GATX Logistics Properties, Inc., Jacksonville, FL; *U.S. Public,* pg. 691
Zuckerberg, David, V.P.-Res. & Devel.--Block Drug Company, Inc., Jersey City, NJ; *U.S. Public,* pg. 236
Zuidam, J., Mgr.-Res.--DSM N.V., Heerlen, Netherlands; *Int'l,* pg. 352
Zurier, Ben, V.P.-Programming & Res.--KPIX-TV, San Francisco, CA; *U.S. Public,* pg. 275

SALES

Aaronson, Morton C., Chief Mktg. Officer & V.P.--K N Energy, Inc., Lakewood, CO; *U.S. Public,* pg. 937
Aasen, Dale, Exec. V.P.- Sls.--Super 8 Motels, Inc., Aberdeen, SD; *U.S. Public,* pg. 322
Abbate, Eileen, V.P.-Adv. & Mktg.--PharmHouse, Inc., New York, NY; *U.S. Public,* pg. 1286
Abbelett, Ron, Mgr.-Sls.--World Aerospace Corporation, Maple Grove, MN; *U.S. Private,* pg. 1188
Abberley, Mike, V.P.-Sls.--Sandvik, Inc., Fair Lawn, NJ; *Int'l, pg. 1185*
Abbey, Robert A., Exec. V.P.- Sls.--Abbey Etna Machine Company, Perrysburg, OH; *U.S. Private,* pg. 9
Abbott, Paul F., Mgr.-Parts & Service--Yarway Corporation, Blue Bell, PA; *U.S. Public,* pg. 1650
Abboud, Dennis, V.P.-Sls. & Mktg.--The Chas. Levy Company, Chicago, IL; *U.S. Private,* pg. 664
Abe, Dave, V.P.-Sls.--Harris Calorific Co., Gainesville, GA; *U.S. Public,* pg. 996
Abeel, Scott, Mgr.-Intl. Sls.--O.I. Corporation, College Station, TX; *U.S. Public,* pg. 1208
Abel, Curtis, V.P.-Sls.--Mitek Systems, Inc., San Diego, CA; *U.S. Public,* pg. 1117
Abels, Terry, Sr. V.P.-Sls. & Mktg.--CFA Holding Company, Charlotte, MI; *U.S. Private,* pg. 194
Abercrombie, George B., V.P.-Sls. & Gen. Mgr.-Bus. Opers.--Glaxo Wellcome Inc., Research Triangle Park, NC; *Int'l,* pg. 552
Abercrombie, Keith, Gen. Sls. Mgr.--KOKI-TV, Tulsa, OK; *U.S. Public,* pg. 384
Abernethy, J.J., V.P.-Sls.--Carolina Glove Co., Newton, NC; *U.S. Private,* pg. 214
Abernethy, J.W., III, V.P.-Sls.--Carolina Glove Co., Newton, NC; *U.S. Private,* pg. 214
Abitalio, Lou, V.P. & Gen. Sls. Mgr.--WNYW, New York, NY; *Int'l,* pg. 926
Abraham, Michael, Mgr.-Sls.--Northern Engineering Corp., Cudahy, WI; *U.S. Private,* pg. 286
Abrams, Dean, V.P.-Sls.--VSA, Inc., Denver, CO; *U.S. Public,* pg. 901
Abrams, Donald J., Mgr.-Drain Valves Sls.--Strahman Valves, Inc., Florham Park, NJ; *U.S. Private,* pg. 1046
Abrams, Howard, Sr. V.P.-Sls.--Tyco Playtime Inc., New York, NY; *U.S. Public,* pg. 1058
Abrunzso, Donna, Mgr.-Sls.--Laporte Inc., Princeton, NJ; *Int'l,* pg. 802
Abruzzo, Chris, Mgr.-Sls.--Great Lakes Technologies Corp., Kalamazoo, MI; *U.S. Private,* pg. 475
Accola, Richard M., V.P.-Sls. & Mktg.--Gravymaster Inc., Branford, CT; *U.S. Private,* pg. 471
Aceuedo, Hiram, Mgr.-Sls.--St. Regis Paper & Bag Div., Guaynabo, PR; *U.S. Public,* pg. 1342
Achtner, S., Mgr.-Sls.--Burns & Roe Enterprises, Inc., Oradell, NJ; *U.S. Private,* pg. 187
Acker, Claud, Asst. V.P.-Domestic Sls.--Calcot, Ltd., Bakersfield, CA; *U.S. Private,* pg. 200
Acker, Don, Dir.-Sls.--Orange-Co., Inc., Bartow, FL; *U.S. Public,* pg. 1229
Acker, Jack, V.P.-Sls. & Gen. Mgr.--Sleepy's The Mattress Professionals, Bethpage, NY; *U.S. Private,* pg. 1005
Acker, Jack, V.P.-Sls. & Gen. Mgr.--Kleinsleep, Port Washington, NY; *U.S. Private,* pg. 1006
Ackerman, Marty, V.P.-Sls.--Hoboken Wood Flooring Corporation, Wayne, NJ; *U.S. Private,* pg. 532
Ackermann, Joe, Sr. V.P.-Sls.--Gateway Press, Inc., Louisville, KY; *U.S. Private,* pg. 441
Adair, Steve, V.P.-Sls.--Southern Phenix Textiles, Inc., Phenix City, AL; *U.S. Public,* pg. 933
Adam, Pierre, Mgr.-Service--Iveco France S.A., Trappes, France; *Int'l,* pg. 696
Adam, Shawn, V.P.-Sls. & Mktg.--Columbia Paint & Coatings, Spokane, WA; *U.S. Private,* pg. 256
Adam, William F., Dir.-Sls.--Mellon Bond Associates Corp., Pittsburgh, PA; *U.S. Public,* pg. 1085
Adams, Annette, Mgr.-Mktg.--Vactor Mfg. Inc., Streator, IL; *U.S. Public,* pg. 617
Adams, D. Scott, Sr. Mgr.-Sls. & Mktg.--Deck House Inc., Acton, MA; *U.S. Private,* pg. 320
Adams, Darlene, Dir.-Sls. & Mktg.--The Beverly Hills Hotel, Beverly Hills, CA; *U.S. Private,* pg. 142
Adams, Ed, Mgr.-Sls.--Hofley Manufacturing Company, Roseville, MI; *U.S. Private,* pg. 532
Adams, Edwin E., V.P.-Field Sls.--Anchor Hocking Consumer Glass, Lancaster, OH; *U.S. Public,* pg. 1177
Adams, Gary, Reg. V.P.-Sls.--Milgray Electronics, Inc., Farmingdale, NY; *U.S. Public,* pg. 205
Adams, J. E., V.P. & Gen. Mgr.-Sls. & Prod. Mdsg. & Distr.--Thomasville Furniture Industries, Inc., Thomasville, NC; *U.S. Public,* pg. 688
Adams, Jane, V.P.-Auto Underwriting--Alfa Insurance Corp., Montgomery, AL; *U.S. Public,* pg. 40
Adams, John, Mgr.-Sls.--Dock Foundry Company, Three Rivers, MI; *U.S. Private,* pg. 337
Adams, John, Mgr.-S.E. Distr. Sls.--King & Prince Seafood Corporation, Brunswick, GA; *U.S. Private,* pg. 620
Adams, John, V.P.-Sls. East--Sutter Home Winery, Inc., Saint Helena, CA; *U.S. Private,* pg. 1057
Adams, Paul, Dir.-Ticket Sls.--Atlanta National League Baseball Club, Inc., Atlanta, GA; *U.S. Public,* pg. 1614
Adams, Richard, V.P.-Sls.--Maynard Steel Casting Company, Milwaukee, WI; *U.S. Private,* pg. 718
Adams, Richard, Dir.-Sls.--Stroehmann Bakeries, Harrisburg, PA; *Int'l,* pg. 1495
Adams, Robert, Dir.-Specialty Sls.--Hydrite Chemical Company, Brookfield, WI; *U.S. Private,* pg. 551
Adams, Robert J., Jr., V.P.-Mktg. & Inside Sls.--Pervasive Software Inc., Austin, TX; *U.S. Public,* pg. 1280
Adams, Roland, Reg. Sls. Mgr.--FINNAIR, Fort Lauderdale, FL; *Int'l,* pg. 486
Adams, Tim, Dir.-Sls. & Mktg.--Ipsen International, Inc., Cherry Valley, IL; *Int'l,* pg. 1149
Adams, William J., Exec. V.P. & Gen. Mgr.-Siding--ABT Building Products Corporation, Neenah, WI; *Int'l,* pg. 20
Adcock, Dwayne, V.P.-Sls.--International Airline Support Group, Inc., Atlanta, GA; *U.S. Public,* pg. 894
Adcock, Fred, V.P.-Sls.--Subaru of America, Inc., Cherry Hill, NJ; *Int'l,* pg. 523
Adcock, Mike, Sr. V.P.-Natl. Sls.--Parmalat Canada Ltd., Etobicoke, Canada; *Int'l,* pg. 1023
Addiego, Joseph, V.P.-North American Sls.--Integrated Systems, Inc., Sunnyvale, CA; *U.S. Public,* pg. 885
Addis, James, Mgr.-Sls.--Gregg Industries, Inc., El Monte, CA; *U.S. Private,* pg. 480
Addison, D., Dir.-Home Sls.--Addison Tube Forming Limited, Preston, United Kingdom; *Int'l,* pg. 448
Adelizzi, Robert F., V.P.-Sls. & Admin.--Temple-Inland Forest Products Corporation, Diboll, TX; *U.S. Public,* pg. 1575
Adelizzi, Robert F., V.P.-Sls. & Admin.--Temple-Inland Forest Products Corp.-Bleached Paperboard Group, Evadale, TX; *U.S. Public,* pg. 1575
Adell, Mike, V.P.-Sls.--3Com Personal Communications Div., Skokie, IL; *U.S. Public,* pg. 1604
Adelson, Max, V.P.-Sls.--Purity Products Inc., Miami, FL; *U.S. Private,* pg. 896
Aden, Matthew, Sr. V.P.-Intl. Sls.--Broadband Networks Group, Hatboro, PA; *U.S. Public,* pg. 716
Adleman, Randall J., V.P.-Sls.-Americas Grp.--Exide Electronics Group, Inc., Raleigh, NC; *Int'l,* pg. 126
Adler, Richard J., Jr., V.P.-Sls.--Fort Dearborn Company, Niles, IL; *U.S. Private,* pg. 419
Adler, Robert J., Exec. V.P. & Dir.-Sls.--Northstar Investment Management Corporation, Greenwich, CT; *U.S. Public,* pg. 1375
Adriasola, Marcela, Mgr.-Sls.--CODELCO Chile (Corporacion Nacional Del Cobre De Chile), Santiago, Chile; *Int'l,* pg. 302
Agee, E. Gill, V.P.-Sls. Support--Distributed Systems Division, Lisle, IL; *U.S. Public,* pg. 1522
Agee, Robert D., V.P.-Sls.--Artco-Bell Corporation, Temple, TX; *U.S. Private,* pg. 86
Agmon, Aharon, V.P.-Intl. Pharmaceutical Sls.--Teva Pharmaceutical Industries Ltd., Petah Tiqwa, Israel; *Int'l,* pg. 1380
Agnese, Carlos E., Exec. V.P.-Bus. Devel., Mktg., Estimating & Contract Admin.--Norfolk Shipbuilding & Drydock Corporation, Norfolk, VA; *U.S. Private,* pg. 802
Agreda, W., Sls. Mgr.--Moore Business Forms de Centro America, S.A. de C.V., San Salvador, El Salvador; *Int'l,* pg. 889
Aheimer, Gary, Dir.-Sls.--LogEtronics Corporation, Springfield, VA; *U.S. Public,* pg. 6
Ahern, Bill, V.P.-Sls. & Mktg.--Lehman Brothers, New York, NY; *U.S. Public,* pg. 987
Ahern, Dan, V.P.-Mktg. & Sls.--Eatelcorp Inc., Gonzales, LA; *U.S. Private,* pg. 358
Ahern, Dan, V.P.-Mktg. & Sls.--East Ascension Telephone Company, Inc., Gonzales, LA; *U.S. Private,* pg. 358
Ahern, James, V.P.-Natl. Sls. & Tech. Services--Precision Carbide Tool Company, Inc., Niles, IL; *U.S. Private,* pg. 879
Ahlenius, Esbjorn, Dir.-Sls.--Sodra Cell AB, Vaxjo, Sweden; *Int'l,* pg. 1275
Ahlrichs, Gary, V.P.-Sls. & Mktg.--Home Juice Co., Melrose Park, IL; *U.S. Private,* pg. 537
Ahlstrom, Craig, Dir.-Adv., Mktg., Opers. & Sls.--Farnsworth Development Co., Mesa, AZ; *U.S. Private,* pg. 397
Ahluwalia, Singh, V.P.-Commercial Tire Sls.--Bridgestone/Firestone, Inc., Nashville, TN; *Int'l,* pg. 213
Ahmer, Al, V.P.-Sls. & Mktg.--Calavo Growers of California, Santa Ana, CA; *U.S. Private,* pg. 199
Ahmer, Al, V.P.-Natl. Sls.--Calavo Foods, Inc., Santa Ana, CA; *U.S. Private,* pg. 199
Aho, Colleen, Mgr.-Sls. Specialist--Howden Fluid Systems, Santa Barbara, CA; *U.S. Public,* pg. 1045
Ahrens, Allan, Dir.-Sls.-Toastmaster--The Middleby Corporation, Rolling Meadows, IL; *U.S. Public,* pg. 1109
Ahrensdorf, Rob, V.P.-Sls. & Mktg.--Coleman Spas, Inc., Chandler, AZ; *U.S. Private,* pg. 691
Aihara, Tamotsu, Sr. V.P. & Gen. Mgr.-NTT Sls.--Anritsu Corporation, Tokyo, Japan; *Int'l,* pg. 77
Aikens, C., V.P.-Sls.--Donohue Paper Sales Corporation, Jericho, NY; *Int'l,* pg. 1075
Ainsworth, Caroline, Mgr.-Sls.--Datapro Services, Maidenhead, United Kingdom; *U.S. Public,* pg. 1072
Aizawa, T., Dir.-Gen. Mktg., Sls. & Adv.--Otto Sumisho Inc., Tokyo, Japan; *Int'l,* pg. 1015
Akemann, John, Natl. Sls. Mgr. & Opers.--Winpower Inc., Saint Peter, MN; *U.S. Private,* pg. 350
Akerhult, H.C., Regional Dir.-Sales--Opel Norge AS, Skedsmokorset, Norway; *U.S. Public,* pg. 723
Akerman, Mark, Mgr.-Sls.--Sealy Mattress Company of Memphis, Memphis, TN; *U.S. Private,* pg. 979
Alaimo, S., Mgr.-Mktg.-Saturn/Saab/Isuzu--General Motors of Canada Ltd., Oshawa, Canada; *U.S. Public,* pg. 722
Alba, Gustave, Reg. Sls. Mgr.--FINNAIR, New York, NY; *Int'l,* pg. 486
Alba, James, Gen. Mgr.--Holiday RV Superstores, Inc., Orlando, FL; *U.S. Public,* pg. 829
Albanese, John, V.P.-Sls. & Mktg.--Friendship Dairies, Inc., Friendship, NY; *U.S. Private,* pg. 429
Alberico, Thomas, Sls. Mgr.-Import--Laird & Company, Eatontown, NJ; *U.S. Private,* pg. 642
Albert, Paul, V.P.-Sls. & Natl. Sls. Mgr.--Kirin USA, Inc., New York, NY; *Int'l,* pg. 736
Albertonni, Jim, V.P.-Sls.--Kendale Industries, Inc., Valley View, OH; *U.S. Private,* pg. 614
Albrecht, John, Sr. V.P.-Sls. & Mktg.--Mexicana Airlines, Los Angeles, CA; *Int'l,* pg. 332
Alcorn, Patrick, V.P.-Transportation Sls.--American Waste Services, Inc., Warren, OH; *U.S. Public,* pg. 94
Alderson, Kristian, Mgr.-Sls. & Mktg. Svcs.--Rexnord Corporation, Milwaukee, WI; *Int'l,* pg. 127
Alexander, Charles, Dr., Mgr.-Sls. & Mktg.--Sasol Alpha Olefins, Rosebank, South Africa; *Int'l,* pg. 1196

Alexander, Don M., V.P.-Sls. Promotion--Proffitt's of Tri-Cities, Inc., Alcoa, TN; *U.S. Public*, pg. 1334

Alexander, Glynn, Regional Mgr.-Midsouth--Columbus Mills, Inc., Columbus, GA; *U.S. Private*, pg. 256

Alexander, Lee, V.P.-Sls.--Amco Folding Cartons, Inc., Towaco, NJ; *U.S. Private*, pg. 48

Alexander, Maurice, V.P.-Sls.--Bailey Hats, Fort Worth, TX; *U.S. Private*, pg. 155

Alexander, Ralph, Jr., V.P.-Sls. & Distr.--Columbia Tri-Star Film Distributors International, Culver City, CA; *Int'l*, pg. 1281

Alexander, Randy, V.P.-Sls. & Mktg.--Chiron Vision, Irvine, CA; *U.S. Public*, pg. 350

Alfieri, John, V.P.-Sls. & Mktg.--Lista International Corporation, Holliston, MA; *Int'l*, pg. 812

Alfred, Toby, Prod. Mgr.--Leader National Insurance Company, Dallas, TX; *U.S. Public*, pg. 75

Algrim, Phyllis, Sls. Representative--PENCO-Illinois, Aurora, IL; *Int'l*, pg. 1508

Alias, Patrick, Exec. V.P.-Sls. & Mktg.--Cognex Corporation, Natick, MA; *U.S. Public*, pg. 394

Alibau, Maite, Sls. & Mktg. Mgr.--Whitehall Spain, Barcelona, Spain; *U.S. Public*, pg. 82

Alioto, Mario, V.P.-Mktg. & Sls.--San Francisco Giants Baseball Club, San Francisco, CA; *U.S. Private*, pg. 964

Allaman, Jim, Mgr.-Sls.--Wire Rope Corporation of America, Inc., Saint Joseph, MO; *U.S. Private*, pg. 1184

Alleman, A.J., Mgr.-Sls. Service--National Frozen Foods Corp., Seattle, WA; *U.S. Private*, pg. 783

Alleman, Ray, V.P.-Specialty Trades & Shoe Care Products--Kiwi Brands, Douglassville, PA; *U.S. Public*, pg. 1433

Allen, Caroline, Mgr.-Sls.--Port Malabar, Palm Bay, FL; *U.S. Public*, pg. 144

Allen, Charles S., Pres. & Chief Exec. Officer--Sloan Valve Company, Franklin Park, IL; *U.S. Private*, pg. 1006

Allen, Dave, Gen. Mgr.-Buildings Div.--American Buildings Co., Eufaula, AL; *U.S. Public*, pg. 69

Allen, David, Chm. Bd., Pres., Chief Exec. Officer & Chief Fin. Officer--AMD Industries Inc., Cicero, IL; *U.S. Private*, *pg. 6*

Allen, Doug, V.P.-Sls.--Allen Canning Company, Siloam Springs, AR; *U.S. Private*, pg. 36

Allen, Fran, V.P.-Sls.--New Balance Athletic Shoe, Inc., Boston, MA; *U.S. Private*, pg. 792

Allen, Frank, V.P.-Sls. & Mktg.--The Arnold Engineering Company, Marengo, IL; *U.S. Public*, pg. 1420

Allen, Gary, V.P.-Retail Opers.--Thriftway, Inc., Louisville, KY; *U.S. Public*, pg. 1771

Allen, George, V.P.-Natl. Sls. Mgr.--Cargo Furniture & Accents, Fort Worth, TX; *U.S. Public*, pg. 1561

Allen, Hugh L., Sr. Exec. V.P.-Sls. & Mktg.--Lawson Products, Inc., Des Plaines, IL; *U.S. Public*, pg. 980

Allen, James, Dir.-Corp. Sls.--Seabrook Wallcoverings, Inc., Memphis, TN; *U.S. Private*, pg. 978

Allen, John, Dir.-Sls.--Dynarad Corporation, Deer Park, NY; *U.S. Public*, pg. 494

Allen, M., Mgr.-Sls. Office--Steelweld Division Zweigniederlassung Bonn der Ambac B.V., Saint Augustin, Germany; *Int'l*, pg. 71

Allen, Melvin, V.P.-Sls.--Vaughan & Sons, Inc., San Antonio, TX; *U.S. Private*, pg. 1134

Allen, Peter R., Dir.-Mktg. & Sls.--Muro Pharmaceutical, Inc., Tewksbury, MA; *U.S. Private*, pg. 767

Allen, Richard, V.P.-Sls.--Allen Foods, Inc., Saint Louis, MO; *U.S. Private*, pg. 37

Allen, Robin, Mgr.-Natl. Sls.--Everfresh Beverages Inc., Chicago, IL; *U.S. Public*, pg. 1153

Allen, Roy, Mgr.-Sls.--Nichifu America, Inc., Pottstown, PA; *Int'l*, pg. 927

Allen, Russ, Exec. V.P.-Corp. Sls.--Glenayre Technologies, Inc., Charlotte, NC; *U.S. Public*, pg. 746

Allen, Stuart, Sr. V.P.-Sls.--Active International, Pearl River, NY; *U.S. Private*, pg. 15

Allen, Thomas G., V.P.-Sls. & Mktg.--Effective Management Systems, Milwaukee, WI; *U.S. Public*, pg. 565

Allen, Tom, Mgr.-Sls.--EMS Central Regional Office (Corporate), Milwaukee, WI; *U.S. Public*, pg. 565

Allen, W.L., Grp. Dir.-Sls.--Avon Products Co., Ltd., Tokyo, Japan; *U.S. Public*, pg. 156

Allen, Wayne E., Dir.-Sls. & Mktg. & Corp. Sec.--Idaho Supreme Company, Firth, ID; *U.S. Private*, pg. 557

Allenback, John, Dir.-Sls.--Danaher Tool Group, Lancaster, PA; *U.S. Public*, pg. 480

Allendorph, Harry, District Sales Mgr.--Varco BJ Oil Tools, New Iberia, LA; *U.S. Public*, pg. 1709

Alleva, Tony, Dir.-Sls. Channel Mngmt.--Andersen Corporation, Bayport, MN; *U.S. Private*, pg. 71

Alley, Fred, V.P.-Sls.--P.W. Minor & Son, Inc., Batavia, NY; *U.S. Private*, pg. 751

Allicock, Simone, Coord.-Incentive Premium--Majorica Jewelry Ltd., New York, NY; *U.S. Private*, pg. 697

Allison, John, Mgr.-Mktg. & Sls.--Ardell Industries Inc., Union, NJ; *U.S. Private*, pg. 597

Allison, John, V.P.-Sls.--The Education Publishing Group, Reading, MA; *Int'l*, pg. 1026

Allman, James, Mgr.-Sls. & Mktg.--The Computer Patch of Joplin, Joplin, MO; *U.S. Private*, pg. 995

Allona, Cesar, Dir.-Sls. & Mktg.--Fate S.A., San Fernando, Argentina; *Int'l*, pg. 478

Alloway, Dan, V.P.-Sls./U.S. & European Opers.--Cannondale Corporation, Bethel, CT; *U.S. Public*, pg. 301

Allsopp, Craig, V.P.-Sls & Mktg.--Dow Jones Telerate Holdings, Inc., Jersey City, NJ; *U.S. Public*, pg. 525

Allsopp, Craig, V.P.-Sls./U.S.A.--Dow Jones Markets, Jersey City, NJ; *U.S. Public*, pg. 525

Allsopp, J.E., III, V.P.-Sls. & Mktg.--Florida Crushed Stone Company, Leesburg, FL; *U.S. Private*, pg. 414

Allsopp, T., Dir.-Sls.--Halifax Rack & Screw Cutting Co., Ltd., Brighouse, United Kingdom; *Int'l*, pg. 448

Almassy, Pamela, Mgr.-Sls.--Brady Marketing Company, Pacheco, CA; *U.S. Private*, pg. 165

Almond, Paul, Mgr.-Sls.--CEM South, Leesburg, FL; *U.S. Private*, pg. 1009

Alore, Ralph, Dir.-Sls.--Karp's Bakery Supply, Taylor, MI; *U.S. Private*, pg. 608

Alperin, Stuart A., V.P.-Sls.--Eastern Smelting & Refining Corporation, Lynn, MA; *U.S. Private*, pg. 357

Alperson, Steven, Exec. V.P.--Rolled Steel Products Corporation, Los Angeles, CA; *U.S. Private*, pg. 941

Alpin, Jerome P., Sr. V.P. & Gen. Mgr.-Intl. Sls. & Mktg.--Dep Corporation, Rancho Dominguez, CA; *U.S. Public*, pg. 500

Alstodt, Harvey, Exec. V.P.-Sls.--Del Laboratories, Inc., Farmingdale, NY; *U.S. Public*, pg. 494

Alter, Mark, Mgr.-Sls.--Electra-Gear Div., Anaheim, CA; *U.S.* Public, pg. 1370

Althaus, James E., V.P.-Sls.--Jockey International, Inc., Kenosha, WI; *U.S. Private*, pg. 588

Altizer, Lance, Dir.-Sls. & Mktg.--Gomar Manufacturing Co., Inc., Linden, NJ; *U.S. Public*, pg. 51

Altman, Barry, Mgr.-Export Sls.--Melitta U.S.A., Inc., Clearwater, FL; *Int'l*, pg. 857

Altman, Geoff, Dir.-Sls.--Agouron Pharmaceuticals, Inc., La Jolla, CA; *U.S. Public*, pg. 28

Altmayer, Larry, Mgr.-Sls./Automotive Aftermarket--Littelfuse, Inc., Des Plaines, IL; *U.S. Public*, pg. 1001

Alton, Sandra, V.P.-Corp. Sls./Eastern Region--Tiffany & Co., New York, NY; *U.S. Public*, pg. 1608

Altrudo, Mike, Pres.-Sls.--Zeigler Coal Holding Company, Fairview Heights, IL; *U.S. Public*, pg. 1790

Alty, Derek, Dir.-Tech. & Sls.--Thermal Processing Group Ltd., Exhall, United Kingdom; *Int'l*, pg. 1338

Alvarez Villafane, Primo, Dir.-Sls., Mktg. & Pur.--Grupo Comercial Chedraui S.A. de C.V., Veracruz, Mexico; *Int'l*, *pg. 573*

Alvarez Villafane, Primo, Dir.-Sls., Mktg. & Pur.--Tiendas Chedraui S.A. de C.V., Veracruz, Mexico; *Int'l*, pg. 573

Alves, Charles, V.P.-Sls. & Mktg.--So-Lo-Food, Inc., Baltimore, MD; *U.S. Private*, pg. 1011

Alvord, George H., Mgr.-Mktg. & Sls.--Dobbs International Services, Inc., Memphis, TN; *U.S. Public*, pg. 1718

Alyn, A., Jr., Mgr.-Sls.--Mellon Corporation, New York, NY; *U.S. Private*, pg. 730

Amabile, Ralph J., Jr., V.P.-Sls., Asian--Prime Tanning Co., Inc., Rochester, NH; *U.S. Private*, pg. 884

Amann, John Robert, V.P.-Single Copy Sales--Murdoch Magazines, New York, NY; *Int'l*, pg. 925

Ames, Chris, Mgr.-Sls.--International Window Corp., South Gate, CA; *U.S. Public*, pg. 895

Ames, David L., V.P.-Sls.--FASTRAC Systems, Inc., San Bruno, CA; *U.S. Public*, pg. 1158

Ames, David L., V.P.-Sls.--FASTRAC Systems, Inc.-Insurance Agent & Broker, South San Francisco, CA; *U.S. Public*, pg. 1158

Ames, Dick, V.P.-Sls.--Intermedics Inc., Angleton, TX; *Int'l*, pg. 1307

Ames, Elizabeth P., V.P.-Retail Sls./New York--Tiffany & Co., New York, NY; *U.S. Public*, pg. 1608

Amico, Robert, Sr. V.P.-Sls.--Rand McNally & Company, Skokie, IL; *U.S. Private*, pg. 908

Amistabi, Richard, V.P.-Sls. & Mktg.--The Doe Run Company, Saint Louis, MO; *U.S. Private*, pg. 922

Ammirati, Lewis, V.P.-Sls.--National Fruit Product Company, Winchester, VA; *U.S. Private*, pg. 783

Ammon, William P., Mgr.-Sls.--Rolock, Inc., Fairfield, CT; *U.S. Private*, pg. 942

Amoruso, Joe, V.P.-Sls.--Jack Schwartz Shoes, Inc., New York, NY; *U.S. Private*, pg. 974

Amsley, Joel, V.P.-Sls./Jerr-Dan--Durakon Industries, Inc., Lapeer, MI; *U.S. Public*, pg. 537

Amsley, Joel, V.P.-Sls. & Mktg.--Jerr-Dan Corporation, Greencastle, PA; *U.S. Public*, pg. 537

Amster, B.R., Sr. V.P.-Mktg. & Sls.--Canadian Airlines International Ltd., Calgary, Canada; *Int'l*, pg. 256

Amster, Eric, V.P.-U.S. Federal & Commercial Sls.--General DataComm, Inc., Middlebury, CT; *U.S. Public*, pg. 708

Anderon, Joe, V.P.-Sls. & Mktg.--Stusser Electric Company, Seattle, WA; *U.S. Private*, pg. 265

Anders, Mary, Dir.-Sls. & Mktg.--Levlad, Inc., Chatsworth, CA; *U.S. Private*, pg. 663

Andersen, Ken, Sls. Rep.--Leblanc Communications, Inc., Richardson, TX; *U.S. Private*, pg. 656

Andersen, Kenneth, V.P.-Sls./N. America--Instron Corporation, Canton, MA; *U.S. Public*, pg. 882

Anderson, Bob, V.P.-Sls.--Selfix, Inc., Chicago, IL; *U.S. Public*, pg. 832

Anderson, Bob, V.P.-Sls.--Arden International Kitchens, Inc., Lakeville, MN; *U.S. Private*, pg. 972

Anderson, Donald, V.P.-Sls. & Mktg.--Minnesota Valley Engineering/Cryogenic Association, Bloomington, MN; *U.S. Private*, pg. 751

Anderson, Doug, V.P.-Sls. & Mktg.--Active Voice Corporation, Seattle, WA; *U.S. Public*, pg. 17

Anderson, Gary, V.P.-Sls. & Mktg. Automotive--American Suzuki Motor Corporation, Brea, CA; *Int'l*, pg. 1323

Anderson, George, V.P.- Sls.--Midland Enterprises Inc., Cincinnati, OH; *U.S. Public*, pg. 549

Anderson, Jack, Sr. V.P.-Sls. & Mktg.--Holland America Line Westours, Seattle, WA; *U.S. Public*, pg. 306

Anderson, Jan, Coord.-Sls. & Co-op Adv.--Berryman Products, Inc., Arlington, TX; *U.S. Private*, pg. 138

Anderson, Joe, Sr. V.P.-Central Retail Div.--Countrywide Funding Corporation, Pasadena, CA; *U.S. Public*, pg. 453

Anderson, John, V.P.-Sls.--General Tours Inc., Keene, NH; *U.S. Private*, pg. 445

Anderson, John T., Mgr.-Sls.--Brower Products, Cincinnati, OH; *U.S. Private*, pg. 172

Anderson, Kathy, Coord.-Sls.--Code-Alarm, Inc., Madison Heights, MI; *U.S. Public*, pg. 393

Anderson, Larry, Gen. Sls. Mgr.--KSL Radio, Salt Lake City, UT; *U.S. Private*, pg. 327

Anderson, Liz, V.P. & Gen. Mgr.-Mktg. & Sls., Vaccines & Pediatrics--Wyeth-Ayerst Laboratories, Inc., Philadelphia, PA; *U.S. Public*, pg. 80

Anderson, Neil, Dir.-Sls. & Mktg.--Simmons American Eagle Airlines, Dallas-Fort Worth Airport, TX; *U.S. Public*, pg. 10

Anderson, Neil, Sr. V.P.-Sls. & Mktg.--Ball Corporation, Muncie, IN; *U.S. Public*, pg. 170

Anderson, Neil M., Sr. V.P.-Mktg. & Sls.--Ball Metal Beverage Container Corp., Westminster, CO; *U.S. Public*, *pg. 171*

Anderson, Orren, V.P. & Mgr.-Sls.--Dakota Drug, Inc., Minot, ND; *U.S. Private*, pg. 308

Anderson, Paul, Mgr.-Western Reg. Sls.--Leach International, Buena Park, CA; *U.S. Private*, pg. 655

Anderson, Pete, V.P.-Sls.--Atlantic Recording Corporation, New York, NY; *U.S. Public*, pg. 1611

Anderson, Richard N., Sr. V.P.-Field Sls. & Gen. Mgr.-Life Cycle Services Group--Vanstar Corporation, Pleasanton, CA; *U.S. Public*, pg. 1708

Anderson, Robert I., Exec. V.P.-Sls.--Gould Paper Corporation, New York, NY; *U.S. Private*, pg. 466

Anderson, Robin, V.P.-Sls. & Mktg.--The Metal Ware Corp., Two Rivers, WI; *U.S. Private*, pg. 734

Anderson, Shy, V.P.-Sls. & Distr.--ALLTEL Corporation, Little Rock, AR; *U.S. Public*, pg. 55

Anderson, Thomas, Staff V.P.-Latin America Sls.--Continental Airlines, Houston, TX; *U.S. Public*, pg. 439

Anderson, Wayne, Sls. Mgr.--Laboratory Supply Company, Oklahoma City, OK; *U.S. Private*, pg. 642

Anderson, William, Mgr.-Sls. Svc.--Agway Energy Products (AEP), Syracuse, NY; *U.S. Private*, pg. 27

Anderton, Peter, Mgr.-Sls.--Sanden International Oceania (Australia) Pty. Ltd., Condell Park, Australia; *Int'l*, pg. 1184

Andolina, John A., Exec. V.P.--Sorrento Cheese Company, Inc., Buffalo, NY; *Int'l*, pg. 323

Andre, Chuck, Mgr.-Sls.--General Office Environments Inc., Rochelle Park, NJ; *U.S. Private*, pg. 445

Andre, Pierre, Mng. Dir.--Beechmont Porsche Audi Inc., Cincinnati, OH; *U.S. Private*, pg. 129

Andreas, Martin L., Sr. V.P.-Sls. & Mktg.--Archer Daniels Midland Company (ADM), Decatur, IL; *U.S. Public*, pg. 127

Andreotti, Cynthia K., Sr. V.P.-West, Bus. Sls. & Service--MCI Communications Corp., Atlanta, GA; *U.S. Public*, pg. 1023

Andrew, Joan Mariani, V.P.-Sls. & Mktg.--X-Rite, Incorporated, Grandville, MI; *U.S. Public*, pg. 1783

Andrews, Steven C., Chief Oper. Officer & Exec. V.P.--Integon Corporation, Winston Salem, NC; *U.S. Public*, pg. 719

Andrews, Todd, V.P.-Eastern Sls.--Shade Foods, Inc., Union City, CA; *U.S. Private*, pg. 802

Andrews, William H., Dir.-Sls.--The Great Lakes Cheese Co., Newbury, OH; *U.S. Private*, pg. 473

Andrus, Candy, Mgr.-Passenger Sls., N.A.--Air New Zealand Ltd. (U.S.A.), El Segundo, CA; *Int'l*, pg. 38

Andrysic, Guy, V.P.-Sls.--Prestone Products Corporation, Danbury, CT; *U.S. Public*, pg. 51

Angelilli, Frank G., Mgr.-Mktg. & Sls.--McGraw-Hill Securities Trading, Inc., New York, NY; *U.S. Public*, pg. 1071

Angeline, Steve, Exec. V.P.-Sls. & Mktg.--Voyager Emblems, Inc., Sanborn, NY; *U.S. Private*, pg. 1143

Angelus, Bud, V.P.-ES Heartland Sls.--Automatic Data Processing, Inc., Roseland, NJ; *U.S. Public*, pg. 150

Angelus, Hellayne, Dir.-Sls.--Procter & Gamble Venezuela, C.A., Caracas, Venezuela; *U.S. Public*, pg. 1332

Angott, Chris, V.P.-Sls.--C.F. Burger Creamery Company, Detroit, MI; *U.S. Private*, pg. 182

Angrick, Roger, Mgr.-Sls.--AT Information Products, Mahwah, NJ; *U.S. Private*, pg. 8

Angst, Pierre, Mgr.-Sls.--Sensormatic AG, Cham, Switzerland; *U.S. Public*, pg. 1457

Angus, Dave, Mgr.-Pipeline Sls.--T.D. Williamson, Inc., Tulsa, OK; *U.S. Private*, pg. 1179

Aniballi, Douglas F., Sr. V.P.-Stores & Sls.--Amlings Flowerland, Hinsdale, IL; *U.S. Private*, pg. 66

Ankenbauer, Jeffrey G., V.P.-Corp. Sls.--Planes Moving And Storage, Inc., Cincinnati, OH; *U.S. Private*, pg. 869

Ankiewicz, Kurt E., V.P.-Sls. & Mktg.--Arnold Transportation Services, Camp Hill, PA; *U.S. Public*, pg. 132

Annel, John, V.P.-Sls.--The Segerdahl Corp., Wheeling, IL; *U.S. Private*, pg. 981

Anthony, Bob, Dir.-Reg. Sls.--Surgical Laser Technologies, Inc., Montgomeryville, PA; *U.S. Public*, pg. 1542

Anthony, Jack, Mgr.-Sls.--Perry Machinery Corporation, Hainesport, NJ; *U.S. Private*, pg. 855

Anthony, Rick, Natl. Sls. Mgr.--Wolf Range Co., Compton, CA; *U.S. Public*, pg. 1322

Antoun, S.D., Pres.-Worldwide Sls.--Dresser-Rand Sales, Houston, TX; *U.S. Public*, pg. 529

Anttikoski, Aimo, Mgr.-Sls.--Kaukas Pulp Mill, Lappeenranta, Finland; *Int'l*, pg. 1428

Anwyll, James, Jr., V.P.-Sls. & Flexible Packaging--Simplex Products, Adrian, MI; *U.S. Public*, pg. 940

Aoyama, Sheni A., Sr. V.P.-Sls. Mngmt.--American Savings Bank, F.S.B., Honolulu, HI; *U.S. Public*, pg. 800

Appel, Rob, Mgr.-Natl. Sls.--Ajay Leisure Products, Inc., Delavan, WI; *U.S. Public*, pg. 34

Applegate, Kathleen, V.P.-U.S. Sls.--GTECH Corporation, West Greenwich, RI; *U.S. Public*, pg. 767

Apthorpe, Bob, Dir.-Sls. & Mktg.--Gast Mfg. Corp., Benton Harbor, MI; *U.S. Private*, pg. 440

Arakelian, David, Dir.-Sls. & Mktg.--Standard Manufacturing Co., Inc., Troy, NY; *U.S. Private*, pg. 1031

Aramagno, Michael, Mgr.-Sls.--Kool Seal, Inc., Twinsburg, OH; *U.S. Private*, pg. 632

Arata, J.R., Dir.-Sls.--American Refractories & Crucible Corporation, North Haven, CT; *Int'l*, pg. 893

Archambault, Richard, V.P.-Sls.--The Miller Company, Meriden, CT; *U.S. Private*, pg. 746

Archer, Mike, Mgr.-Sls.--Dominion Homes, Dublin, OH; *U.S. Public*, pg. 516

Archer, Robert, Sr. V.P.-Sls.--SPS Payment Systems, Inc., Riverwoods, IL; *U.S. Public*, pg. 1132

Arcure, Lee, Mgr.-Sls. & Mktg.--Venturi Inc., Traverse City, MI; *U.S. Private*, pg. 1136

Arcuri, Lou, V.P.-Sls.--E.C.D., Inc., Hillside, NJ; *U.S. Private*, pg. 353
Arend, Bernard, Dir.-Sales--Millipore S.A., Molsheim, France; *U.S. Public*, pg. 1113
Arenstein, Ed, Mgr.-Non-Ferrous Sls.--Sturgis Iron & Metal Company, Inc., Sturgis, MI; *U.S. Private*, pg. 1048
Arenth, Thomas R., V.P.-East Coast Sls.--Fannie May Candy Shops, Inc., Chicago, IL; *U.S. Private*, pg. 598
Aretakis, Tony, Mgr.-Mktg. & Sls.-Silver--Yardney Technical Products, Inc., Pawcatuck, CT; *U.S. Private*, pg. 376
Argeroudis, Nick, V.P.-Sls., Mktg. & Branch Opers.-Film & Advanced Products Div.--Tekra Corporation, New Berlin, WI; *U.S. Private*, pg. 1073
Argiro, John, Mgr.-Intl. Sls.--Kraft Food Ingredients Corp., Memphis, TN; *U.S. Public*, pg. 1288
Arlavskas, Robert, V.P.-Sls., West Zone--Pier 1 Imports, Inc., Fort Worth, TX; *U.S. Public*, pg. 1295
Arledge, Sol, V.P.-Sls. & Mktg.--Discount Labels, Inc., New Albany, IN; *U.S. Public*, pg. 70
Arlequin, Alex, Dir.-Sls.--Eight O'Clock Coffee, Hyattsville, MD; *Int'l*, pg. 1375
Arlt, Randy, Dir.-Sls.--Eaton Corporation, Hydraulics Division, Eden Prairie, MN; *U.S. Public*, pg. 557
Armbruster, Phil, V.P.-Mktg. Devel.--Hillerich & Bradsby Co., Louisville, KY; *U.S. Private*, pg. 530
Armentrout, Kathryn, Dir.-Adv. & Mktg.--Nortel, Nashville, TN; *Int'l*, pg. 970
Armiger, Charlie, V.P.-Sls./Comml. Sys.--Trimble Navigation Limited, Sunnyvale, CA; *U.S. Public*, pg. 1638
Armillei, Ron, V.P.-Sls. & Admin.--Harcourt Brace & Company - Elementary Div., Orlando, FL; *U.S. Public*, pg. 783
Armitage, G. Steven, V.P.-Intl. Sls.--Hilton Hotels Div., Beverly Hills, CA; *U.S. Public*, pg. 829
Armour, Peter, Dir.-Natl. Sls.--Architectural Digest, Los Angeles, CA; *U.S. Private*, pg. 20
Armstrong, Anthony, Mgr.-Mktg. & Sls. Opers.--Semtech Corporation, Newbury Park, CA; *U.S. Public*, pg. 1456
Armstrong, Darril, V.P.-Sls. & Mktg.--Jac Pac Foods, Ltd., Manchester, NH; *U.S. Private*, pg. 579
Armstrong, F. Scott, Mgr.-Sls.--PENCO-Arizona, Phoenix, AZ; *Int'l*, pg. 1508
Armstrong, James, Mgr.-Sls.--B & G Wholesalers, Inc., Nashville, TN; *U.S. Private*, pg. 105
Armstrong, Jean H., V.P.-Sls.--Great Pacific Insurance Company, San Bruno, CA; *U.S. Public*, pg. 1158
Armstrong, Kevin, Dir.-Sls.--Dixons Group plc, Hemel Hempstead, United Kingdom,; *Int'l*, pg. 413
Armstrong, M.F., V.P.-Sls.--Cooper Tire & Rubber Company, Findlay, OH; *U.S. Public*, pg. 445
Armstrong, M.F., V.P.-Sls.--The Cooper Tire Company, Findlay, OH; *U.S. Public*, pg. 445
Armstrong, Rich, Mgr.-Natl. Sls.--King & Prince Seafood Corporation, Brunswick, GA; *U.S. Private*, pg. 620
Armstrong, Stutts, Mgr.-Reg. Sls.--Icicle Seafoods, Inc., Seattle, WA; *U.S. Private*, pg. 556
Armstrong, Thomas E., V.P.-Sls.--Brant Allen Industries, Inc., Greenwich, CT; *U.S. Private*, pg. 165
Arnaud, Tawny, Mgr.-Gen. Sls.--Galpin Motors, North Hills, CA; *U.S. Private*, pg. 438
Arnaudet, Larry, V.P.-Sls.--Freeman Decorating Co., Dallas, TX; *U.S. Private*, pg. 426
Arnold, Bill, V.P., Sls. & Intl. Mktg.--Garvey International, Inc., Saint Charles, IL; *U.S. Private*, pg. 440
Arnold, David P., V.P.-Sls.--Preformed Line Products, Cleveland, OH; *U.S. Public*, pg. 1321
Arnold, Dennis P., V.P.-Sls.--Avibank Mfg., Inc., Burbank, CA; *U.S. Private*, pg. 101
Arnold, Jim, V.P.-Sls.--Continental Web Press Of Kentucky, Walton, KY; *U.S. Private*, pg. 269
Arnold, Kim M., Dir.-Sls. & Mktg.--The Gorman-Rupp Company, Mansfield, OH; *U.S. Public*, pg. 754
Arnold, Kim M., Dir.-Sls.--Mansfield Div., Mansfield, OH; *U.S. Public*, pg. 754
Arnold, Richard E., Exec. V.P. & Dir.-Sls. & Banking Admin.--Bay View Capital Corporation, San Mateo, CA; *U.S. Public*, pg. 197
Arnold, Ron, V.P.-Sls. & Mktg.--Philipp Brothers Chemicals, Inc., Fort Lee, NJ; *U.S. Private*, pg. 861
Arntzen, Sandra, Sr. V.P.-Retail Sls.--Maui Divers of Hawaii, Honolulu, HI; *U.S. Private*, pg. 715
Arollado, Jim, Mgr.-Natl. Sls.--Pen-Tab Industries, Inc., Front Royal, VA; *U.S. Private*, pg. 848
Aronson, Larry, V.P.-Sls.--Adams U.S.A., Morris Plains, NJ; *U.S. Public*, pg. 1739
Arpaia, Steven F., V.P.-Colorforms Sls. & Div. Mgr.--Wallace Computer Services, Inc., Lisle, IL; *U.S. Public*, pg. 1735
Arrabal, Angel, V.P.-Natl. Sls.--Quipp Systems, Inc., Hialeah, FL; *U.S. Public*, pg. 1353
Arriaga, Jorge, Sls. Mgr.-Crop Protection--Monsanto Argentina S.A.I.C., Buenos Aires, Argentina; *U.S. Public*, pg. 1125
Arriola, Eddy, V.P.-Sls. & Mktg.--Inktel Marketing, Miami, FL; *U.S. Private*, pg. 101
Arthur, David R., V.P.-Sls. & Mkyg.--Sunnen Products Company, Saint Louis, MO; *U.S. Private*, pg. 1053
Arthur, Jerry, V.P.-Sls.--Mr. Electric Corporation, Waco, TX; *U.S. Public*, pg. 538
Arthur, Jerry, V.P.-Sls.--Aire Serve Heating & Air Conditioning, Inc., Waco, TX; *U.S. Public*, pg. 538
Arthur, Jerry, V.P.-Sls.--Mr. Rooter Corporation, Waco, TX; *U.S. Public*, pg. 538
Arthur, Kenneth H., V.P.-Consumer Sls.--The Valspar Corporation, Minneapolis, MN; *U.S. Public*, pg. 1707
Arthur, R.B., Mgr.-Mfg. & Sls.--North State Pyrophyllite, Greensboro, NC; *U.S. Private*, pg. 924
Arvia, Paul M., Sr. V.P.-Sls.--Swisher International Group, Inc., Darien, CT; *U.S. Public*, pg. 1543
Arvidson, A.C., Sales Services--Dayco PTI, Inc., Red Wing, MN; *U.S. Public*, pg. 1045
Asalone, Mike, V.P.-Sls.--M. Kamenstein, Inc., Elmsford, NY; *U.S. Private*, pg. 606
Asalone, Pat, V.P.-Natl. Sls.--Beaulieu Vineyard, Rutherford, CA; *Int'l*, pg. 410
Aschinger, Carl, III, V.P.-Intl. Sls.--Columbus Show Case Company, Columbus, OH; *U.S. Private*, pg. 257
Ash, Lowell, V.P.-Sls.--Gould Paper Corporation, New York, NY; *U.S. Private*, pg. 466
Ash, Rich, Mgr.-Inside Sls.--Associated Process Controls, Pleasanton, CA; *U.S. Private*, pg. 92
Ashbaugh, H.S., Sr. V.P.-Sls. & Mktg.--Allvac, Monroe, NC; *U.S. Public*, pg. 43
Ashby, Dennis, V.P.-Sls.--James Steel & Tube Company, Madison Heights, MI; *U.S. Private*, pg. 102
Ashelnejad, Reza, V.P.-Sls.--GE Capital/IT Solutions, Minneapolis, MN; *U.S. Public*, pg. 711
Ashley, Andy, V.P.-Sls.--Thomas Lighting-C&I Indoor Divison, Tupelo, MS; *U.S. Public*, pg. 1599
Ashley, Dan, Mgr.-Industrial Prods. Sls.--Ivex Packaging Corporation-Visalia, Visalia, CA; *U.S. Public*, pg. 915
Ashman, Bruce, V.P.-Endocrine Sls.--Jones Medical Industries Inc., Saint Louis, MO; *U.S. Public*, pg. 933
Ashmore, Clive, Mgr.-Sls.--Brown & Sharpe Limited, Derby, United Kingdom; *U.S. Public*, pg. 260
Ashton, William L., V.P.-U.S. Sls.--Amgen Inc., Thousand Oaks, CA; *U.S. Public*, pg. 100
Ashworth, Catherine, Dir.-Mktg. & Sls.--British Printing Company Ltd., London, United Kingdom; *Int'l*, pg. 220
Askaner, Johan, Mgr.-Mktg.--Svenskt Papper AB, Stockholm, Sweden; *Int'l*, pg. 886
Askew, L. Rudolph, V.P.-Sls. & Mktg.--Jouan, Inc., Winchester, VA; *U.S. Private*, pg. 601
Assad, Dennis, V.P.-Sls. & Mktg.--UniFirst Corporation, Wilmington, MA; *U.S. Public*, pg. 1665
Astafan, Charles, Mgr.-Shredder Sls.--Columbus McKinnon Corp., Amherst, NY; *U.S. Public*, pg. 405
Astorino, Michael, V.P.-Mktg. & Sls.--Kex Products, Inc., La Vergne, TN; *U.S. Private*, pg. 138
Aten, John, Mgr.-Sls.--Dodge Regupol, Inc., Lancaster, PA; *U.S. Private*, pg. 337
Atha, Allen, III, V.P. & Chief Mktg. Officer--Amvestors Financial Corporation, Topeka, KS; *U.S. Private*, pg. 59
Atherley, Darrell, V.P.-Sls. & Mktg.--The Family Channel Inc., Toronto, Canada; *Int'l*, pg. 1482
Athern, Frank, V.P.-Sls. & Mktg./Turbines--Coppus Murray Group, Tuthill Corporation, Millbury, MA; *U.S. Private*, pg. 1110
Atherton, Jerome D., V.P.-Sls. & Engrng.--Bermo, Inc., Circle Pines, MN; *U.S. Private*, pg. 136
Atkins, Charles, V.P.-Sls.--Tennessee Farmers Co-op, La Vergne, TN; *U.S. Private*, pg. 1076
Atkinson, Bob, Mgr.-Sls.--Air Canada, Hounslow, United Kingdom; *Int'l*, pg. 37
Atkinson, John, V.P. & Gen Mgr.-Sls.--Kaepa Inc., Greenville, SC; *U.S. Private*, pg. 604
Atkinson, Mike, V.P.-Sls.-Med/Surg--Graham-Field Health Products, Inc., Hauppauge, NY; *U.S. Public*, pg. 757
Attal, Stephan, Mgr.-Sls.--GN Nettest, Datacom Division, Markham, Canada; *Int'l*, pg. 537
Attar, Isidoro Ambe, Dir.-Sls./Telecorp.--Telefonos de Mexico S.A. de C.V., Mexico, Mexico; *Int'l*, pg. 1373
Atwood, Perry, Chief Sls. Officer & Corp. Sr. V.P.--Brenton Banks, Inc., Des Moines, IA; *U.S. Public*, pg. 251
Atwood, Tom, V.P.-Sls.--Ajinomoto U.S.A., Inc., Teaneck, NJ; *Int'l*, pg. 40
Aucoin, Kenny, Mgr.-Sls.--PENCO-Louisiana, Baton Rouge, LA; *Int'l*, pg. 1508
Audrukonis, Dane, Sr. V.P.-Sls.--Federal Home Loan Mortgage Corporation, Mc Lean, VA; *U.S. Public*, pg. 615
Auer, Mike, Sr. V.P.-Gen. Sls. Mgr.--Fruit of the Loom, Inc., Chicago, IL; *U.S. Public*, pg. 685
Augsburger, Tony, Mgr.-Sls.--Triplett Corporation, Bluffton, OH; *U.S. Private*, pg. 1104
August, Barry, Mgr.-Commercial Papers--Unisource, New York, NY; *U.S. Public*, pg. 1671
Augustin, Denis, Natl. Sls. Mgr.--Tocco, Inc., Boaz, AL; *U.S. Public*, pg. 1259
Augustine, Patrick, V.P.-Sls. & Mktg.--Eva-Tone Inc., Clearwater, FL; *U.S. Private*, pg. 384
Augustine, Peter, V.P.-Sls.--E.T. Browne Drug Co., Inc., Englewood Cliffs, NJ; *U.S. Private*, pg. 175
Augustyn, Richard, V.P.-Mktg. & Sls.--King Group, Inc., Ann Arbor, MI; *U.S. Private*, pg. 620
Auker, John, Mktg.-Sls.--Wilsey Foods, Inc., Atlanta, GA; *Int'l*, pg. 879
Aurilio, D.E., V.P.-Sls.--American Beverage Corporation, Verona, PA; *Int'l*, pg. 752
Aurillo, D.E., V.P.-Sls.--American Beverage Corp. Inc., Akron, OH; *Int'l*, pg. 752
Ausprung, David, V.P.-Sls. & Mdsg.--Roundy's, Milwaukee Division, Milwaukee, WI; *U.S. Private*, pg. 948
Austin, Bill, Mgr.-Mktg. & Sls.--Industra Inc., Portland, OR; *Int'l*, pg. 74
Austin, Harry G., III, V.P.-Natl. Sls.--James Austin Co., Mars, PA; *U.S. Private*, pg. 99
Austin, John T., Jr., V.P.-Regional Sls.--James Austin Co., Mars, PA; *U.S. Private*, pg. 99
Austin, Mike, Mgr.-Sls.--Public Service Company of Oklahoma-Western Div., Lawton, OK; *U.S. Public*, pg. 324
Auth, Greg, V.P.-Mktg. & Sls.--Tenneco Specialty Products, Deerfield, IL; *U.S. Public*, pg. 1579
Averell, Donna J., Coord.-Sls. & Mktg.-Environmental Systems--Environmental Tectonics Corporation (ETC), Southampton, PA; *U.S. Public*, pg. 587
Awrey, Thomas, Vice Chm. & Acting Sr. V.P.-Sls.--Awrey Bakeries, Inc., Livonia, MI; *U.S. Private*, pg. 103
Ayers, James C., Mgr.-Sls.--CTL Steel Co., Columbus, OH; *U.S. Private*, pg. 243
Ayers, Les, Exec. V.P.-Sls. & Mktg.--Simmons Company, Atlanta, GA; *Int'l*, pg. 686
Ayers, P.J., Mgr.-Sls.--Longview Fibre Co. Eastern Container Div., Springfield, MA; *U.S. Public*, pg. 1014
Ayers, Scott, Dir.-Sls. & Mktg.--Mohawk Finishing Products, Inc., Amsterdam, NY; *U.S. Public*, pg. 1357
Ayers, Stan, Mgr.-Natl. Sls.--Clear Springs Foods, Inc., Buhl, ID; *U.S. Private*, pg. 245
Aygard, George, Sr. Exec. V.P.-Sls.--Management Dynamics, New Providence, NJ; *U.S. Public*, pg. 1040
Aylward, A., V.P.-Sls. & Mktg.--Neenah Foundry Company, Neenah, WI; *U.S. Private*, pg. 790
Aylward, Joe, V.P.-Sls.--Fairfield Branson, Branson, MO; *U.S. Public*, pg. 610
Ayre, Michael G., V.P.-Mktg. & Sls.--Davie Industries Inc., Levis, Canada; *Int'l*, pg. 385
Ayres, Darrell, Dir.-Sls.--Essroc Cement, Corp., Speed, IN; *U.S. Private*, pg. 384
Aziz, Douglas, V.P.-Sls. & Mktg.--The Sorg Paper Co., Middletown, OH; *U.S. Public*, pg. 1747
Azurdia, E., Dir.-Sls.--Gran Industria de Neumaticos Centroamericana, S.A., Guatemala, Guatemala; *U.S. Public*, pg. 753
Azzalina, Frank, Mgr.-Govt. Sls.--Victaulic Company of America, Easton, PA; *U.S. Private*, pg. 1138
Baach, Michael K., Exec. V.P.-Sls. & Mktg.--Corrpro Companies, Inc., Medina, OH; *U.S. Public*, pg. 451
Baas, Roger, Mgr.-Sls.--Prince Corporation, Holland, MI; *U.S. Public*, pg. 932
Baasch, Don, Sr. V.P. & Dir.-Mktg. & Franchise Sls.--AVC/Nu-Vision, Inc., Flint, MI; *U.S. Private*, pg. 9
Baba, Masako, Gen. Mgr.-Sls./Japan--Utell International-Japan, Tokyo, Japan; *Int'l*, pg. 1098
Babarik, Paul T., V.P.-Lucent Sls.--Moscom Corporation, Pittsford, NY; *U.S. Public*, pg. 1136
Babcock, Bridgette, Gen. Mgr.-Sls.--Calumet Photographic, Inc., Bensenville, IL; *U.S. Private*, pg. 202
Babcock, Elaine H., Sr. V.P.--ITC Learning Corp., Herndon, VA; *U.S. Public*, pg. 859
Babcock, Kevin, Mgr.-Sls. & Mktg./Tools--Apex Operation, Dayton, OH; *U.S. Public*, pg. 444
Babila, John, Dir.-Sls.-Natl. Accts.--The Middleby Corporation, Rolling Meadows, IL; *U.S. Public*, pg. 1109
Babin, Todd, Mgr.-Sls.--Bollinger Shipyards, Inc., Lockport, LA; *U.S. Private*, pg. 155
Babio, A., Dir.-Sls.--Coats Fabra SA, Barcelona, Spain; *Int'l*, pg. 300
Baboyian, Mal, V.P.-Sls.--OCE-U.S.A., Itasca, IL; *Int'l*, pg. 994
Babrowski, Mike, V.P.-Mktg. & Sls.--Zoeller Co., Louisville, KY; *U.S. Private*, pg. 1207
Bachman, Vernon E., V.P.--Vulcan International Corporation, Wilmington, DE; *U.S. Public*, pg. 1725
Bachus, Richard, V.P.--Southern Missouri Containers Inc., Springfield, MO; *U.S. Private*, pg. 1017
Bacica, Ross, Mgr.-Western Regional Sls.--CTS Corp. Frequency Controls, Sandwich, IL; *U.S. Public*, pg. 285
Back, George, Pres.-Syndication Sls.--All American Television, Inc., New York, NY; *U.S. Public*, pg. 41
Bacon, Vicky, V.P.-Mktg. & Service Oper.--Christenson Electric, Inc., Portland, OR; *U.S. Private*, pg. 238
Bacso, D.W., Mgr.-Sls.--Morgan Matroc Inc.-Electro Ceramics Division, Bedford, OH; *Int'l*, pg. 893
Baden, Marvin, V.P.-Mktg. & Sls., Treas. & Sec.--Producers Rice Mill Inc., Stuttgart, AR; *U.S. Private*, pg. 888
Badger, Timothy C., V.P.-Mktg.--Arrow Financial Corporation, Glens Falls, NY; *U.S. Public*, pg. 135
Badwar, Roger, Mgr.-Northwest Area Sls.--Gensym Corporation, Western Regional Office, Boulder, CO; *U.S. Public*, pg. 731
Baenziger, Douglas A., Mgr.-Sls.--Trim Division, Kalkaska, MI; *U.S. Private*, pg. 355
Baerwald, Leroy, Sls. Mgr.--Besser/APPCO, San Antonio, TX; *U.S. Private*, pg. 139
Bagnato, Thad, V.P.-Sls.--North America Foods, Minnetonka, MN; *U.S. Public*, pg. 901
Bahler, Michael, Mgr.-Mid-Central Reg. Sls.--Sofamor Danek Group, Inc., Memphis, TN; *U.S. Public*, pg. 1482
Bahmueller, Mark, Mgr.-Sls. (Plastics Deflashers)--Hull Corporation, Hatboro, PA; *U.S. Private*, pg. 547
Bahmueller, Mark, Mgr.-Sls. Deflasher--Hull/Finmac, Inc., Warminster, PA; *U.S. Private*, pg. 547
Bahr, John, Reg. Mgr.-Relays--Aromat Northwestern Sales Office, San Jose, CA; *Int'l*, pg. 848
Baiera, Jackie, Sls.--Geyer-McAllister Publications, Inc., New York, NY; *U.S. Private*, pg. 450
Baietti, Carlo, Dir. & Mgr.-Sls.--The IDI Group Companies, Arlington, VA; *U.S. Private*, pg. 554
Bailat, E., Mgr.-Sls.--Swissmetal Plant Boillat, Reconvilier, Switzerland; *Int'l*, pg. 1427
Bailey, Bill, Mgr.-Reg. Sls.--Global Beverage Co., Rochester, NY; *U.S. Private*, pg. 457
Bailey, Dave, V.P.-Sls.--Bussmann Division, Ellisville, MO; *U.S. Public*, pg. 443
Bailey, John R., V.P.-Sls.--Kysor/Warren, Conyers, GA; *U.S. Public*, pg. 1445
Bailey, Robert, Dir.-Sls.--H.J. Heinz Company, Limited, Hayes, United Kingdom; *U.S. Public*, pg. 806
Bailey, Robert, III, Pres.--Mid American Elevator Co., Inc., Chicago, IL; *U.S. Private*, pg. 743
Bailey, Ron, Dir.-Sls. & Mktg.--GSW Jackes-Evans Manufacturing Co., Saint Louis, MO; *Int'l*, pg. 538
Bailey, Ron, V.P.-Sls. & Mktg.--Tempo Products Company, Solon, OH; *U.S. Private*, pg. 870
Bailey, Tim, Mgr.-Sls.--Quest Technologies, Inc., Oconomowoc, WI; *U.S. Private*, pg. 900
Bailey, Wayne, Mgr.-Sls.--Weis Markets, Inc., Sunbury, PA; *U.S. Public*, pg. 1751
Bain, Thom, Dir.-Sls. & Mktg.--Thermometrics, Inc., Edison, NJ; *Int'l*, pg. 208
Bainter, Greg, V.P.- Sls.- Ing.--Tree Top, Inc., Selah, WA; *U.S. Private*, pg. 1098
Bair, Daran, Dir.-Sls.--Martin/F. Weber Company, Philadelphia, PA; *U.S. Private*, pg. 710
Baird, Dan, V.P.-Sls.--Duralam, Inc., Appleton, WI; *U.S. Private*, pg. 966
Baird, Greg, Mgr.-Natl. Sls.--WLKY-TV, Louisville, KY; *U.S. Public*, pg. 1344
Baird, Michael, V.P.-Mktg.--Skyland Scientific Services, Inc., Bozeman, MT; *U.S. Public*, pg. 1515
Baitler, Jay, Sr. V.P.-Contract Sls.--Staples, Inc., Westborough, MA; *U.S. Public*, pg. 1509

Bajaj, Pradeep, Mgr.-Inside Sls.--Ney Dental International, Bloomfield, CT; *Int'l*, pg. 388

Baker, Al, Dir.-Consumer Sls.--San-J Intl. Inc., Richmond, VA; *Int'l*, pg. 1183

Baker, Bill, Mgr.-Gen. Sls.--Regency Lincoln Mercury, Inc., Dallas, TX; *U.S. Private*, pg. 918

Baker, Bridget, V.P.-Natl. Accounts--CNBC, Fort Lee, NJ; *U.S. Public*, pg. 712

Baker, Bruce, Mgr.-Sls.--Plastomer Products Div., Newtown, PA; *U.S. Public*, pg. 402

Baker, Clyde H., Dir.-Sls. & Mktg.--Research Industries Corp., Midvale, UT; *U.S. Public*, pg. 196

Baker, David, V.P.-Sls., Western Reg.--Ash Grove Cement Company, Shawnee Mission, KS; *U.S. Private*, pg. 87

Baker, David R., V.P.-Sales.--Ash Grove Cement Company Sales Office, Portland, OR; *U.S. Private*, pg. 87

Baker, Dwight, V.P.-Sls. & Mktg.--Le Tourneau, Inc., Longview, TX; *U.S. Public*, pg. 1410

Baker, H. Forrest, V.P. & Oper. Mgr.-Filtration Div.--Perry Equipment Corporation, Mineral Wells, TX; *U.S. Private*, pg. 855

Baker, Rick, V.P.-Mktg. & Sls.--Silver Dollar City, Inc., Branson, MO; *U.S. Private*, pg. 1000

Baker, Rick, V.P.-Mktg. & Sls.--Spectra-Physics Scanning Systems Inc., Eugene, OR; *U.S. Public*, pg. 1594

Baker, Robert, Dir.-Intl. Sls.--Fila USA, Sparks, MD; *Int'l*, pg. 484

Bako, Balazs, Reservations Sls. Agent--Utell International-Hungary, Budapest, Hungary; *Int'l*, pg. 1098

Bal, George R., Mgr.-Sls.--Detex Corporation, New Braunfels, TX; *U.S. Private*, pg. 327

Balango, Joe, V.P.-Sls. Western Canada--Western Broadcast Sales Ltd., Toronto, Canada; *Int'l*, pg. 1482

Balart, F., Dir.-Sls.--Neumaticos Goodyear SA, Buenos Aires, Argentina; *U.S. Public*, pg. 753

Balaz, Beverly, Mktg. & Sls.--Grolier Educational Corporation, Danbury, CT; *Int'l*, pg. 794

Balch, Kenna, Dir.-Mktg.--Sholodge, Inc., Hendersonville, TN; *U.S. Public*, pg. 1467

Baldasano, Jeff, V.P.-Sls.--Sky Bros. Inc., Allentown, PA; *U.S. Public*, pg. 918

Baldewein, Uwe, Dir.-Sls.--Georg Sahm Singapore Pte. Ltd., Petaling Jaya, Malaysia; *Int'l*, pg. 1169

Baldovin, Christopher S., V.P.-Sls. & Mktg.--Lava World International/Haggerty Enterprises, Inc., Chicago, IL; *U.S. Private*, pg. 653

Baldwin, Bob, Natl. Sls. Mgr.--Imperial Holly Corporation, Sugar Land, TX; *U.S. Public*, pg. 872

Baldwin, Bob, Mgr.-Natl. Sls.--Holly Sugar Corporation, Sugar Land, TX; *U.S. Public*, pg. 872

Baldwin, Bruce, Mgr.-Sls. & Mktg.--The Entwistle Company, Hudson, MA; *U.S. Private*, pg. 378

Baldwin, Donald D., V.P.-Sls. & Mktg.--Micron Technology Inc., Boise, ID; *U.S. Public*, pg. 1105

Baldwin, Mike, Mgr.-Sls.--Justrite Manufacturing Company, Des Plaines, IL; *U.S. Private*, pg. 617

Baldwin, Robert D., Sr. V.P.-Sls. & Mktg.--Forest Products & Recycled Paperboard Div., Montvale, NJ; *U.S. Public*, pg. 903

Baldwin, Stephen H., Dir.-Retail Opers.--The Greenbrier, White Sulphur Springs, WV; *U.S. Public*, pg. 284

Baldwin, Steve, V.P.-Sls.--BTG, Inc., Fairfax, VA; *U.S. Public*, pg. 164

Baldwin, William W., Sr. V.P.-Aircraft Sls. & Leasing--General Electric Capital Aviation Services, San Francisco, CA; *U.S. Public*, pg. 712

Balicki, Jon, V.P.-Sls.--EZ Paintr Corp., Saint Francis, WI; *U.S. Public*, pg. 1177

Ball, Jim, V.P.-Sls.--Wheeled Coach Industries, Inc., Winter Park, FL; *U.S. Public*, pg. 400

Ball, Toby, V.P.-Sls.--EAC Corporation, Saint Louis, MO; *U.S. Private*, pg. 353

Ballard, Chuck, Dir.-sls.& Mktg.--President Baking-Louisville, Louisville, KY; *Int'l*, pg. 1069

Ballard, Robert, V.P.-Sls.--Benjamin Anselm Company, Saint Louis, MO; *U.S. Private*, pg. 75

Ballard, Steve, Mgr.-Sls.--Madison, Inc., Tulsa, OK; *U.S. Private*, pg. 428

Ballen, Martin, V.P.-Auto Sls.--Troy Mills, Inc., Troy, NH; *U.S. Private*, pg. 1106

Ballmer, Steven A., Exec. V.P.-Sls. & Support--Microsoft Corporation, Redmond, WA; *U.S. Public*, pg. 1107

Balluff, Fred, V.P.-Sls.--Gould Paper Corporation, New York, NY; *U.S. Private*, pg. 466

Balogh, Bob, V.P.-Pulp Sls.--Donohue Inc., Quebec, Canada; *Int'l*, pg. 1075

Balsey, William R., Admin.-Factory Sls.--Crusader Marine Engines, Sterling Heights, MI; *U.S. Public*, pg. 1591

Balthazor, Dennis, Gen. Mgr.-Sls.--Beauchamp Distributing Company, Compton, CA; *U.S. Private*, pg. 127

Baltimore, G., Mgr.-Sls.--Augat, Inc., Interconnection Products-Carol Stream, Glen Ellyn, IL; *U.S. Public*, pg. 1598

Baltimore, Gary, Dir.-Sls.--Corcom, Inc., Libertyville, IL; *U.S. Public*, pg. 446

Baltus, Jerry, V.P.-Mktg. & Sls.--Polar Ware Company, Sheboygan, WI; *U.S. Private*, pg. 873

Balty, Jack, Mgr.-Sls. & Mktg./Groceries--Metro Foods, Inc., Olive Branch, MS; *U.S. Private*, pg. 736

Balzer, Glen, V.P.-Sls. & Mktg., N. America--Philips Semiconductors, Sunnyvale, CA; *Int'l*, pg. 1054

Banach, Todd, Mgr.-Tech. Sls.--Ultra Tool & Plastics, Inc., Amherst, NY; *U.S. Private*, pg. 1116

Bandy, Janell, Sls. & Export Rep.--Gibson Wine Company, Sanger, CA; *U.S. Private*, pg. 452

Bank, Bob, Mgr.-Natl. Mktg.--Cleaning Solutions Group/ Cello, Havre De Grace, MD; *U.S. Public*, pg. 1466

Bankers, Paul, V.P.-Sls.--Multifoods Specialty Distribution Inc., Denver, CO; *U.S. Public*, pg. 901

Banks, James, Mgr.-Sls.--Indimac, Inc., Pasadena, CA; *U.S. Public*, pg. 857

Banks, Katharyn A., V.P.-Intl. Sls.--Martindale-Hubbell, New Providence, NJ; *Int'l*, pg. 1096

Bannon, Bruce, V.P.-Mktg. & Sls.--Whittaker Controls, Inc., North Hollywood, CA; *U.S. Public*, pg. 1767

Bannon, Eugene, Reg. Sls. Mgr.-Eastern Region--GATX Logistics (LWD), Inc., Winston Salem, NC; *U.S. Public*, pg. 691

Barathon, Claude, Exec. V.P.-Worldwide Sls.--Quantum Corporation, Milpitas, CA; *U.S. Public*, pg. 1350

Baratoff, Michael, Dir.-Mktg. & Sls.--Metropolitan Sunday Newspapers, Inc., New York, NY; *U.S. Private*, pg. 739

Baratta, Roland, Mgr.-Central Natl. Sls.--John B. Sanfilippo & Son, Inc., Elk Grove Village, IL; *U.S. Public*, pg. 1431

Barba, Chris, V.P.-Sls. & Mktg.--Warner Books, Inc., New York, NY; *U.S. Public*, pg. 1614

Barbagallo, Dan, V.P.-Sls.--Campbell Soup Company Ltd., Toronto, Canada; *U.S. Public*, pg. 299

Barber, Ed, Reg. Mgr.-Sls.--PENCO-Ohio, Worthington, OH; *Int'l*, pg. 1508

Barber, Jack C., V.P.-Midwest Retail Sls.--Fannie May Candy Shops, Inc., Chicago, IL; *U.S. Private*, pg. 598

Barber, Ken, Mgr.-Natl. Accts./Containerbd & Wave Flute--Boise Cascade Corporation, Boise, ID; *U.S. Public*, pg. 242

Barber, Timothy C., V.P.-Sls. & Mktg.--Expeditors International of Washington, Inc., Seattle, WA; *U.S. Public*, pg. 600

Barbosa, Nelson Brum, Mgr.-Mktg.--Esselte Meto Ind. e. Com. Ltda., Sao Paulo, Brazil; *Int'l*, pg. 461

Bardon, Larry, Dir.-Mktg. & Sls.--The New Piper Aircraft, Inc., Vero Beach, FL; *U.S. Private*, pg. 794

Barendsen, Bud, Mgr.-Natl. Sls.--Rochester Gauges Inc. Of Texas, Dallas, TX; *U.S. Private*, pg. 440

Bareuther, James, Exec. V.P. & Dir.-Sls.--Brown-Forman Corporation, Louisville, KY; *U.S. Public*, pg. 261

Barger, Steve, Gen. Mgr.-Sls.--Arnold Palmer Cadillac Inc., Charlotte, NC; *U.S. Private*, pg. 713

Barhite, James T., V.P.-Sls. & Mktg.--Interface Electronics Corporation, Hopkinton, MA; *U.S. Private*, pg. 567

Barich, Michael, Mgr.-Local Sls.--WFTS-TV, Tampa, FL; *U.S. Public*, pg. 1448

Barina, Dale, Mgr.-Natl. Sls.--Dual-Lite, Cheshire, CT; *U.S. Public*, pg. 726

Barker, Graham, V.P.-Mktg. & Sls.--Norwalk Co., Inc., Norwalk, CT; *U.S. Private*, pg. 807

Barker, S., Mgr.-Natl. Sls.--Quadrastat Corp., City of Industry, CA; *U.S. Private*, pg. 17

Barker, Steven, V.P.-Sls. & Mktg.--Ris Paper Company, Long Island City, NY; *U.S. Private*, pg. 932

Barkes, J.T., Mgr.-Sls.--U.N. Alloy Steel Div., Buena Park, CA; *Int'l*, pg. 1001

Barkman, Floyd, V.P.-Sls. & Mktg.--Collins Bus Corp., South Hutchinson, KS; *U.S. Public*, pg. 400

Barlow, Bryan, V.P.-Sls.--BRW Paper Co., Inc., Farmers Branch, TX; *U.S. Private*, pg. 467

Barma, Ron, Mgr.-Sls. Admin. & Adv.--Simpson Electric Co., Elgin, IL; *U.S. Private*, pg. 1002

Barnabas, Sam, Dir.-Intl. Sls.--Getinge/Castle Inc., Rochester, NY; *Int'l*, pg. 551

Barnard, L. Scott, Exec. V.P.-Sls.--Champion International Corp., Stamford, CT; *U.S. Public*, pg. 333

Barnard, Thomas J., V.P.-Sls. Devel.--United Family Life Insurance Co., Atlanta, GA; *Int'l*, pg. 499

Barnardo, Alan T., Exec. V.P.-Gen. Mgr.-Opers.--Santa Fe Drilling Co., Alhambra, CA; *Int'l*, pg. 765

Barneich, David, V.P.-Bus. Devel. & Sls. Oper.--American Isuzu Motors Inc., Whittier, CA; *Int'l*, pg. 692

Barnes, Chester, Dir.-Sls. & Mktg.--Watts Automatic Control Valves, Inc., Houston, TX; *U.S. Public*, pg. 1747

Barnes, Christopher, V.P.-European Sls.--AMATI Communications Corp., San Jose, CA; *U.S. Public*, pg. 1585

Barnes, Don, Sr. V.P.-Sls. & Mktg.--Presidential Life Corporation, Nyack, NY; *U.S. Public*, pg. 1323

Barnes, Jim, Dir.-Construction Sls.--Gehl Company, West Bend, WI; *U.S. Public*, pg. 704

Barnes, John F., V.P.-Sls.--Temple-Inland Forest Products Corp.-Bleached Paperboard Group, Evadale, TX; *U.S. Public*, pg. 1575

Barnes, Lee, Sr. V.P.-Sls. & Mktg.--Spectrulite Consortium, Inc., Madison, IL; *U.S. Private*, pg. 1024

Barnes, Mary Jean, Mgr.-Sls. Services--Thomas Register, New York, NY; *U.S. Private*, pg. 1082

Barnes, Nancy, V.P.-Sls.--Chittenden Corporation, Burlington, VT; *U.S. Public*, pg. 350

Barnes, R.J., V.P.-Sls.--Preformed Line Products, Cleveland, OH; *U.S. Public*, pg. 1321

Barnes, Roger W., V.P.-Mktg. & Tech.--Valtek International, Springville, UT; *U.S. Public*, pg. 658

Barnett, Dale, Mgr.-Retail Sls.--The Amalgamated Sugar Company LLC, Ogden, UT; *U.S. Private*, pg. 48

Barnett, Dennis, V.P.-Sls. & Mktg.--Republic Beverage Company, Houston, TX; *U.S. Private*, pg. 149

Barnett, Dennis, V.P.-Sls. & Mktg.--Republic Beverage Co., Dallas, TX; *U.S. Private*, pg. 150

Barnett, Kris, Reg. Mgr.-Sls.--Bird Products Corporation, Palm Springs, CA; *U.S. Public*, pg. 1591

Barnett, Marjorie, Exec. V.P.--Farmers Copper & Industrial Supply, Galveston, TX; *U.S. Private*, pg. 422

Barnette, W. E., Mng. Dir.-Low Cost Carrier--Delta Air Lines, Inc., Atlanta, GA; *U.S. Public*, pg. 497

Barnhart, Dale A., Sr. V.P.-Mktg. & Sls.--Wolverine Tube Inc., Huntsville, AL; *U.S. Public*, pg. 1774

Barnhill, Carl, Sr. V.P.-Sls.--Adolph Coors Company, Golden, CO; *U.S. Public*, pg. 445

Barnhill, Carl L., Sr. V.P.-Sls.--Coors Brewing Company, Golden, CO; *U.S. Public*, pg. 445

Barnhill, John W., Jr., Exec. V.P. & Gen. Mgr.-Sls.--Blue Bell Creameries, L.P., Brenham, TX; *U.S. Private*, pg. 150

Baron, Dan, Sr. V.P.-Retail Sls.--Nakano Foods Inc., Arlington Heights, IL; *Int'l*, pg. 883

Baron, Jack, V.P.-Sls./U.S.--ACC Corp., Rochester, NY; *U.S. Public*, pg. 2

Baron, Jack, Mgr.-Sls.--ACC TeleCom, Rochester, NY; *U.S. Public*, pg. 3

Baroni, Robin, Reg. Sls. Dir.--Orient-Express Hotels Inc., New York, NY; *Int'l*, pg. 1213

Baroudi, Roudi E., Gen. Mgr.-Middle East Sls.--Santa Fe Braun Inc., Dhahran, Saudi Arabia; *Int'l*, pg. 765

Barr, Constance, V.P.-Customer Service--Siemer Milling Company, Teutopolis, IL; *U.S. Private*, pg. 998

Barr, Diana, Mgr.-Circulation--St. Louis Business Journal Corp., Saint Louis, MO; *U.S. Private*, pg. 20

Barr, R.G., Dir.-Sls. & Mktg.--Bespak plc, Norfolk, United Kingdom; *Int'l*, pg. 193

Barrera, Fernando Villarreal, Dir.-Sls.--Altos Hornos de Mexico, S.A., Monclova, Mexico; *Int'l*, pg. 66

Barresi, Garry, V.P.-Sls.--BRW Paper Co., Inc., Farmers Branch, TX; *U.S. Private*, pg. 467

Barret, Eileen, Sls. Mgr.--Clarion Corporation of America, Gardena, CA; *Int'l*, pg. 296

Barrett, David, V.P.-Sls.--DePuy, Inc., Warsaw, IN; *Int'l*, pg. 331

Barrett, Edward L., Sr. V.P. & Dir.-Sls.--Marquette Coppersmithing Co., Inc., Philadelphia, PA; *U.S. Private*, pg. 706

Barrett, Jim, V.P.-Sls.--Superior Reprographics, Seattle, WA; *U.S. Private*, pg. 418

Barrett, Lea, Sls. Mgr.-Southern Region--Utell International-Australia, Melbourne, Australia; *Int'l*, pg. 1098

Barrett, Michael P., V.P.-Sls. & Mktg.--Casella Waste Systems, Inc., Rutland, VT; *U.S. Public*, pg. 312

Barrett, Richard, V.P.-Mktg. & Sls.--Hubbell Lighting Inc., Christiansburg, VA; *U.S. Public*, pg. 844

Barrette, Lance, Dir.-Mktg. & Mgr.-Sls.--Dresser Canada, Inc., Mississauga, Canada; *U.S. Public*, pg. 529

Barringer, Thomas, Sr. V.P.-Mass Mktg.--Fieldcrest Cannon, Inc., Kannapolis, NC; *U.S. Public*, pg. 1296

Barrios-LeVeille, Shelly, V.P.-Sls. & Secular Accts.--Bridgestone Multi-Media Group, Chandler, AZ; *U.S. Private*, pg. 168

Barrise, Joesph, Dir.-Sls.--J.M.P. Bakery Co., Inc., Brooklyn, NY; *U.S. Private*, pg. 578

Barron, William, V.P.-Sls. & Mktg.--Littelfuse, Inc., Des Plaines, IL; *U.S. Public*, pg. 1001

Barry, James P., V.P.-Sls. & Mktg.--Remcor Products Co., Glendale Heights, IL; *Int'l*, pg. 646

Barry, Jerry, Dir.-Sls. & Mktg.--Dwyer Instruments Inc., Michigan City, IN; *U.S. Private*, pg. 350

Barry, Tony, Exec. V.P.-Sls.--Sheaffer Pen Crownmark, Lincoln, RI; *Int'l*, pg. 542

Bartek, Bernard M., V.P.-Mktg. & Sls.--Corson Lime Company, Plymouth Meeting, PA; *U.S. Public*, pg. 1685

Bartelt, Bob, Sls. Engr.--Dearborn Gage Company, Garden City, MI; *U.S. Private*, pg. 319

Barth, Clay, V.P.-Sls.--Wilson Products Co., Salt Lake City, UT; *U.S. Private*, pg. 1181

Barth, David S., Sr. V.P.-Western Sls.--VWR Scientific Products, West Chester, PA; *U.S. Public*, pg. 1703

Barth, Wendy, V.P.-Mktg. & Sls.--The Southland Corporation, Dallas, TX; *Int'l*, pg. 693

Bartholomay, A. Eric, V.P.-Intl. Sls.--Astro-Med, Inc., West Warwick, RI; *U.S. Public*, pg. 141

Bartholomew, Allan, Mgr.-Natl. Non Food Sls.--Malco Products, Inc., Barberton, OH; *U.S. Private*, pg. 698

Bartholomew, Charles R., Vice Chm., Client Services Dir. & Dir.--EvansGroup, Salt Lake City, UT; *U.S. Private*, pg. 385

Bartholomew, William J., Dir.-Domestic Sls.--Tellabs Operations, Inc., Lisle, IL; *U.S. Public*, pg. 1572

Bartlet, Jeff L., V.P.-Sls.--Employee Solutions, Inc., Phoenix, AZ; *U.S. Public*, pg. 579

Bartlett, David, Dir.-Sls. & Mktg.--Park Air Electronics Ltd., Peterborough, United Kingdom; *U.S. Public*, pg. 1198

Bartlett, Phil, Sr. V.P.-Sls. & Mktg.--Russell-Stanley Corporation, Red Bank, NJ; *U.S. Private*, pg. 953

Bartley, Roland, Mgr.-Adv. & Sls.--Danuser Machine Co., Fulton, MO; *U.S. Private*, pg. 310

Barto, William, V.P.-Sls.--Robert James Sales Inc., Buffalo, NY; *U.S. Private*, pg. 935

Bartos, Ron, V.P.-Sls. & Mktg.--Savage Arms Inc., Westfield, MA; *U.S. Private*, pg. 968

Bartosch, Scott M, V.P.-Sls.--The Wiremold Company, West Hartford, CT; *U.S. Private*, pg. 1184

Bartosh, Becki, Mgr.-Circulation--Business Journal Publications, Inc., San Antonio, TX; *U.S. Private*, pg. 19

Bartosiak, Tom, Mgr.-Natl. Sls.--Integrated Material Handling Company, Oshkosh, WI; *Int'l*, pg. 1397

Bartosiak, Tom, Mgr.-Natl. Sls.--Integrated Material Handling Company, Mount Sterling, OH; *Int'l*, pg. 1397

Baruch, Karl, Mgr.-Sls. & Admin.--FINNAIR, New York, NY; *Int'l*, pg. 485

Barvero, Alberto, Sls. Mgr.-Crop Protection--Monsanto Argentina S.A.I.C., Buenos Aires, Argentina; *U.S. Public*, pg. 1125

Basacchi, Tom, V.P.-Sls./Europe & Russia--Boeing Commercial Airplane Group, Renton, WA; *U.S. Public*, pg. 240

Basanez, Marc, Mgr.-Mktg. & Sls.--Conrac Display Products, Monrovia, CA; *U.S. Private*, pg. 264

Bascetta, Richard, V.P.-Sls.--Furniture Consultants, New York, NY; *U.S. Public*, pg. 1686

Bascomb, Stuart, Exec. V.P.-Sls. & Mktg.--Express Scripts, Inc., Maryland Heights, MO; *U.S. Public*, pg. 600

Baseler, Theodore, Exec. V.P.-Sls., Mktg. & Corp. Affairs--Stimson Lane Ltd., Woodinville, WA; *U.S. Public*, pg. 1661

Basil, F., Mgr.-Natl. Sls.--Exact Equipment Corporation, Langhorne, PA; *U.S. Private*, pg. 387

Basile, Steve, V.P.-Sls. & Mktg.--Schein Pharmaceutical, Inc., Florham Park, NJ; *U.S. Private*, pg. 969

Basinger, Kirt, V.P.-Spec. Accts.--Kingsdown, Inc., Mebane, NC; *U.S. Private*, pg. 622

Bass, John, Dir.-Sls.--Vishay Components (U.K.) Ltd., Sunderland, United Kingdom; *U.S. Public*, pg. 1722

Bassett, Steve, Pres.--Contempri Homes, Inc., Taylor, PA; *U.S. Public*, pg. 439

Bastian, Dale, V.P.-North American Sls.--Allen Telecom Inc., Solon, OH; *U.S. Public*, pg. 45

Bastian, Doug, Dir.-Sls.--L.L. Olds Seed Company, Madison, WI; *U.S. Private*, pg. 814
Batchelar, Peter, V.P.-Sls.--Jason Industrial, Inc., Fairfield, NJ; *U.S. Private*, pg. 583
Bate, Michael, Mng. Dir.--Totes U.K. Limited, Billericay, United Kingdom; *U.S. Private*, pg. 111
Bateman, Gordon, V.P.-Mktg. & Sls.--AP North American Aftermarket Division, Goldsboro, NC; *U.S. Private*, pg. 230
Batenic, Mark K., Sr. V.P.-Retail Sls. & Mktg.--Fleming Companies, Inc., Oklahoma City, OK; *U.S. Public*, pg. 652
Bates, Laura, Acct. Mgr.--SmithKline Beecham Clinical Laboratories, Nashville, TN; *Int'l*, pg. 1265
Bates, Randy, V.P.-Sls.--Golden Flake Snack Foods, Inc., Birmingham, AL; *U.S. Public*, pg. 750
Batey, Jim, Mgr.-Sls.--Precision Parts Corp., Morristown, TN; *U.S. Private*, pg. 879
Battaglia, Jack, V.P.-Worldwide Sls.--Global Village Communication, Sunnyvale, CA; *U.S. Public*, pg. 748
Battalini, Richard, V.P.-Sls.--Victor Technology, Addison, IL; *U.S. Private*, pg. 1139
Batten, John, V.P.-Mktg.--Malcolm Pirnie, Inc., White Plains, NY; *U.S. Private*, pg. 867
Batterson, D.M., Mgr.-Sls.--Longview Fibre Co. Central Container Div., Cedar Rapids, IA; *U.S. Public*, pg. 1014
Battison, William J., Exec. V.P.-Mktg. & Sls.--Iwerks Entertainment, Burbank, CA; *U.S. Public*, pg. 915
Battles, Richard A., Gen. Mgr.-Sls.--Lapham-Hickey Steel Corp., Chicago, IL; *U.S. Private*, pg. 651
Bauder, Ken, Gen. Sls. Mgr.--WYFF-TV, Greenville, SC; *U.S. Public*, pg. 1344
Baueien, Elisha, Dir.-Natl. Corp. Sales--Henry Birks & Sons (1993) Inc., Montreal, Canada; *Int'l*, pg. 196
Bauer, Bruce, Mgr.-Intl. Sls. & Mktg.--Modern Controls, Inc., Minneapolis, MN; *U.S. Public*, pg. 1120
Bauer, Fred C., V.P.-Natl. Sls. Accts.--Kenan Transport Company, Chapel Hill, NC; *U.S. Public*, pg. 949
Bauer, John W., V.P.-Sls.--Stanley Home Products, Easthampton, MA; *U.S. Public*, pg. 282
Bauer, Lisa, Dir.-Sls.--Midwest Express Holdings, Inc., Oak Creek, WI; *U.S. Public*, pg. 1111
Bauer, Lisa A., Dir.-Sls.--Midwest Express Airlines, Inc., Oak Creek, WI; *U.S. Public*, pg. 1111
Bauer, Mike, Exec. V.P.-Sls. & Mktg.--Empire of Carolina, Inc., Delray Beach, FL; *U.S. Public*, pg. 579
Bauer, Vineeta, Mgr.-Sls. & Retail Mktg.--Firstar Corporation, Milwaukee, WI; *U.S. Public*, pg. 642
Bauernschmidt, William, Dir.-Sls., Allergy Prods.--Bayer Corporation/Pharmaceutical Division, West Haven, CT; *Int'l*, pg. 173
Baughan, Mike, V.P.-Sls. & Mktg.--B/E Aerospace Seating Products Group, Litchfield, CT; *U.S. Public*, pg. 159
Baughard, Buzz, Dir.-Sls.--Universal Flavors-U.S.A., Indianapolis, IN; *U.S. Public*, pg. 1696
Bauler, Beth, V.P.-Sls. & Mktg.--Bridgestone Multi-Media Group, Chandler, AZ; *U.S. Private*, pg. 168
Baum, Barry, V.P.-Records Mngmt. Sls.--International Envelope Company, Exton, PA; *U.S. Public*, pg. 70
Baum, Christopher, V.P.-Sls. & Mktg. Communications--Sonesta International Hotels Corporation, Boston, MA; *U.S. Public*, pg. 1485
Baum, William, V.P.-Sls.--International Specialty Products, Inc., Wayne, NJ; *U.S. Public*, pg. 858
Bauman, John W., Mgr.-Project Devel.--Townsend & Bottum, Inc., Ann Arbor, MI; *U.S. Private*, pg. 146
Baumann, Kaspar, Dir.-Works--Baumann Federn AG, Ruti, Switzerland; *Int'l*, pg. 171
Baumgardt, James R., Pres.-Western Hemishpere Sls.--Guidant Corporation, Indianapolis, IN; *U.S. Public*, pg. 768
Baumgartner, Ed, Sr. V.P.-Sls.--Fruit of the Loom, Inc., Chicago, IL; *U.S. Public*, pg. 685
Baumgartner, Gunter, Dir.-Commercial Vehicles Sls.--Mercedes-Benz AG, Stuttgart, Germany; *Int'l*, pg. 368
Bausch, Heinz-Herbert, Dir.-Passenger Car Sls.--Mercedes-Benz AG, Stuttgart, Germany; *Int'l*, pg. 368
Bause, Jay, V.P.-Mktg. & Sls.--Elco Textron, Rockford, IL; *U.S. Public*, pg. 1590
Bausewine, George, Gen. Mgr.-Sls. & Mktg.--Central Louisiana Electric Company, Inc., Pineville, LA; *U.S. Public*, pg. 325
Bavester, Mika, Sls. Svc. Mgr.--Comet Ventures, Inc., Los Angeles, CA; *U.S. Public*, pg. 591
Bawol, Jeff, V.P.-Corp. Sls.--Computer City, Fort Worth, TX; *U.S. Public*, pg. 1560
Baxter, Brian, Dir.-Mktg. & Sls.--EECO, Switch, Cambridge, United Kingdom; *U.S. Public*, pg. 1631
Baxter, Harry, Vice Chm.--Bancorp South Inc., Tupelo, MS; *U.S. Public*, pg. 176
Baxter, John T., V.P.-Sls. & Mktg.--Alpha Associates, Inc., Woodbridge, NJ; *U.S. Private*, pg. 44
Baxter, Paul, Mgr.-Sls.--Ultra Electronics Ocean Systems, Weymouth, United Kingdom; *Int'l*, pg. 1431
Bayer, Charles, V.P.-Sls. & Mktg.--Crescent Manufacturing Company, Fremont, OH; *U.S. Private*, pg. 289
Baynes, Ron, V.P.-Sls.--Curtis-Toledo, Inc., Saint Louis, MO; *U.S. Private*, pg. 298
Baynes, Scott, Corp. Sls. Mgr.--Florida Panthers Holdings, Inc., Fort Lauderdale, FL; *U.S. Public*, pg. 654
Bazon, Tracy, Mgr.-Local Sls.--WAXY (FM), Fort Lauderdale, FL; *U.S. Public*, pg. 925
Bazzy, Ron, Mgr.-Sls.--Glacier Vandervell, Inc., Troy, MI; *Int'l*, pg. 1334
Beach, Bill, Dir.-Sls.--Andover Controls Securities, Andover, MA; *U.S. Private*, pg. 73
Beach, David, V.P.- Mktg. & Sls.--International Correspondence Schools, Inc., Scranton, PA; *U.S. Public*, pg. 783
Beach, David A., Dir.-Mktg. & Sls.--ICS Learning Systems, Inc., Scranton, PA; *U.S. Public*, pg. 783
Beacham, Wayne, V.P.-Sls. & Mktg.--Corporate Express, Inc., Broomfield, CO; *U.S. Public*, pg. 449
Beal, Steve, V.P.-Mktg. & Sls.--Applied Magnetics Corporation, Goleta, CA; *U.S. Public*, pg. 123
Beals, Michael, Dir.-Sls.--Ross Technology, Inc., Austin, TX; *Int'l*, pg. 526
Beam, Michael W., V.P.-Mktg. & Sls.--Dynamic Materials Corporation, Lafayette, CO; *U.S. Public*, pg. 539
Beam, Pam, Coord.-Sls. & Mktg.--John Boos & Company, Effingham, IL; *U.S. Private*, pg. 156
Bear, Craig, Mgr.-Natl. Accts.--Alloy Products Corp, Waukesha, WI; *U.S. Private*, pg. 42
Bear, J., Mgr.-Sls.--Midland Forge Division, Cedar Rapids, IA; *U.S. Public*, pg. 406
Beard, Bill, V.P.-Sls. Admin.--International Family Entertainment, Inc., Virginia Beach, VA; *Int'l*, pg. 927
Beard, Randy, Mgr.-Sls.--Vulcraft Div., Grapeland, TX; *U.S. Public*, pg. 1206
Beard, Walter, Mgr.-Sls./Wheels--Edgewater Steel Company, Oakmont, PA; *U.S. Private*, pg. 364
Beardslee, Stephen J., V.P.-Sls.--Dremel, Racine, WI; *U.S. Public*, pg. 574
Beasley, B.F., V.P.-Sls. & Mktg.--Parkdale Mills, Gastonia, NC; *U.S. Private*, pg. 840
Beasley, W.B. Rogers, Dir.- Sls.--Keeneland Assoc., Inc., Lexington, KY; *U.S. Private*, pg. 611
Beason, John, Sr. V.P.-Sls. & Mktg.--Guilford of Maine, Inc., Guilford, ME; *U.S. Public*, pg. 889
Beattie, David, Sr. V.P.-Sls. & Mktg.--McNaughton-McKay Electric Co., Madison Heights, MI; *U.S. Private*, pg. 724
Beattie, Douglas, Sr. V.P.-Sls. & Mktg.--Liquid Controls LLC, Lake Bluff, IL; *U.S. Private*, pg. 669
Beattie, Jim, V.P.-Sls. & Mktg.--GSW Heating Products Company, Stoney Creek, Canada; *Int'l*, pg. 538
Beauchine, Fay, V.P.-Reservation Sls. & Svcs.--Northwest Airlines, Inc., Saint Paul, MN; *U.S. Public*, pg. 1200
Beaudin, Timothy, Sr. V.P.-Property Opers. & Indus. Devel.--Catellus Development Corporation, San Francisco, CA; *U.S. Public*, pg. 314
Beaudoin, B. Paul, V.P.-Sls.--Fraser Papers, Inc., Stamford, CT; *Int'l*, pg. 434
Beaulieu, Diane, Mgr.-Adv. & Sls. Promo.--Davis Standard Corporation, Pawcatuck, CT; *U.S. Public*, pg. 459
Beaulieu, Russ, Mgr.-Sls.--International Extrusion Corporation-Texas, Waxahachie, TX; *U.S. Public*, pg. 895
Beaumet, Fern, Mgr.-Sls.--Felton Brush Inc., Manchester, NH; *U.S. Private*, pg. 400
Beaver, Thomas, V.P.-Sls.--McCord Winn Textron Company, Manchester, NH; *U.S. Public*, pg. 1590
Beaver, Tom, V.P.-Sls.--Pollak Division, Boston, MA; *U.S. Private*, pg. 1045
Becher, Hans, V.P.- Sls.--New England Confectionery Co., Cambridge, MA; *U.S. Private*, pg. 1113
Becher, Hans, V.P.-Sls.--Stark Candy Company, Cambridge, MA; *U.S. Private*, pg. 1113
Bechtel, Charles, Exec. V.P.-Sls.--Quaker State Corporation, Irving, TX; *U.S. Public*, pg. 1348
Bechtell, Jim, Mgr.-Sls.--Somerset Pontiac GMC Inc., Troy, MI; *U.S. Private*, pg. 1013
Beck, Douglas A., V.P.-Sls. & Mktg.--Clark Grave Vault Co., Columbus, OH; *U.S. Private*, pg. 243
Beck, Frederick R., V.P.-Retail Acctg.--Riverside/Bi-Lo Division, Du Bois, PA; *U.S. Public*, pg. 1270
Beck, Randy, Mgr.-Natl. Sls.--Triumph Twist Drill Co., Crystal Lake, IL; *Int'l*, pg. 1185
Beck, Richard, V.P.-Intl. Sales--The Cornelius Company, Anoka, MN; *Int'l*, pg. 646
Becker, Dave, Dir.-Flexible Interconnect Sls.--Sheldahl, Inc., Northfield, MN; *U.S. Public*, pg. 1465
Becker, Jim, Pres. & Dir.-Adv. & Sls.--Speedrack Products Group, Ltd., Sparta, MI; *U.S. Private*, pg. 1024
Becker, Patrick J., Sr. V.P.-Sls. & Mktg.--NxTrend Technology, Inc., Colorado Springs, CO; *U.S. Private*, pg. 809
Becker, Richard E., Sr. V.P.-Sls./Major Accts.--Nutmeg Mills Inc., Tampa, FL; *U.S. Public*, pg. 1702
Becks, Peter, Mgr.-Sls. & Mktg.--Kimball Systems BV, Terborg, Netherlands; *Int'l*, pg. 461
Beckum, Randy, Mgr.-Aftermarket Sls.--Thetford Corporation, Ann Arbor, MI; *U.S. Private*, pg. 352
Beckwith, Connie, Mgr.-Sls.--Commercial Intertech Distribution Services, La Porte, IN; *U.S. Public*, pg. 411
Beckwith, Keith M., V.P.-Americas/European Sls.--Digital Sound Corporation, Carpinteria, CA; *U.S. Public*, pg. 508
Bedel, Gregory F., Dir.-Natl. Accounts--Millennium Petrochemicals, Inc., Cincinnati, OH; *Int'l*, pg. 594
Bedingfield, Bob, Mgr.-Mktg. & Sls.--The Kirk & Blum Mfg. Co., Cincinnati, OH; *U.S. Private*, pg. 623
Bednar, Steve, V.P.-Sls.--MB Manufacturing, Valparaiso, IN; *U.S. Private*, pg. 300
Bednaz, Alan J., Dir.-Intl. Sls.--Ney Dental International, Bloomfield, CT; *Int'l*, pg. 388
Bee, Bob, Mgr.-Gen. Sls.--WGAL-TV, Lancaster, PA; *U.S. Public*, pg. 1344
Beebe, Bob, Mgr.-Food & Drug--Magic American Corporation, Cleveland, OH; *U.S. Private*, pg. 695
Beebe, Chris, V.P.-Sls.-Asia/Pacific--Lynx Golf, Inc., City of Industry, CA; *U.S. Private*, pg. 684
Beebe, Larry L., V.P.-WWCP Strategic Sls. Devel.--S.C. Johnson & Son, Inc., Racine, WI; *U.S. Private*, pg. 592
Beebe, Roger W., Mgr.-Natl. Sls., Healthcare Div.--Getinge/Castle Inc., Rochester, NY; *Int'l*, pg. 551
Beech, Wally, Dir.-Sls.--Welbilt Corporation, Stamford, CT; *Int'l*, pg. 188
Beecher, D.J., V.P.-Sls.--Habisat Globe Inc., Buffalo, NY; *Int'l*, pg. 585
Beechey, Cye, Sls. Rep., Canada--Magneco/Metrel, Inc., Addison, IL; *U.S. Private*, pg. 695
Beelar, Eric, V.P.-Fuel Sls.--Mercury Air Group Inc., Los Angeles, CA; *U.S. Public*, pg. 1092
Beeler, Chris, Mgr.-Sls.--Electro Scientific Industries, Inc., Portland, OR; *U.S. Public*, pg. 568
Beeler, Scott, Sls. Mgr.--Harris Broadcast Division, Richmond, IN; *U.S. Public*, pg. 791
Beers, Bob, Sr. V.P.-Mktg. & Bus. Devel.--KTI, Orange, CA; *U.S. Public*, pg. 939
Beeskow, John, V.P.-Sls.--American Plastic Toys Inc., Walled Lake, MI; *U.S. Private*, pg. 60
Beggan, Paul, V.P.-Sls.--Bacardi-Martini, USA, Inc., Miami, FL; *U.S. Private*, pg. 109
Behan, Thomas H., V.P.-Lumber Sls.--Hill-Behan Lumber Company, Saint Louis, MO; *U.S. Private*, pg. 529
Behl, Ron, Mgr.-Natl. Sls.--Playtex Apparel Canada, Ltd., Toronto, Toronto, Canada; *U.S. Public*, pg. 1433
Behnenkamp, Steve, Mgr.-Natl. Sls.--Watlow Electric Manufacturing Company, Saint Louis, MO; *U.S. Private*, pg. 1153
Behnke, William, Sr. V.P.-Sls. & Mktg.--General Communication, Inc., Anchorage, AK; *U.S. Public*, pg. 708
Behrens, Susanne I., V.P.-Natl. Corp. Accts.--Philadelphia American Life Insurance Company, Houston, TX; *U.S. Public*, pg. 853
Behrman, Russell, V.P.-Sls. Plng.--CBS Television Network, New York, NY; *U.S. Public*, pg. 274
Beighley, Sid, V.P.-Eastern Sls.--CBS Enterprises Division, New York, NY; *U.S. Public*, pg. 274
Beigie, Christopher, V.P.-Sls. & Mktg.--Brown-Bridge, Troy, OH; *U.S. Public*, pg. 1022
Beilner, Otto, Dir.-Sls. & Mktg.--AGA Ges.m.b.H., Vienna, Austria; *Int'l*, pg. 13
Beilstein, Kenneth W., Mgr.-Sls.--The J.M. Ney Company, Bloomfield, CT; *U.S. Public*, pg. 111
Beitzel, Thomas, Exec. V.P.-Sls.--Dodge Regupol, Inc., Lancaster, PA; *U.S. Private*, pg. 337
Bejar, Octavio, Mgr.-Sls.--Northrup King y Compania, S.A. de C.V., Guadalajara, Mexico; *Int'l*, pg. 983
Belanger, Sean, V.P.-Sls.--Paradyne, Largo, FL; *U.S. Private*, pg. 838
Belche, Paul, Mng. Dir.-Sls. & Mktg.--STAHLwerke Bremen GmbH, Bremen, Germany; *Int'l*, pg. 79
Belding, Kevin, Dir.-Mktg.--Discover, New York, NY; *U.S. Public*, pg. 513
Beldowski, Ed, Mgr.-Sls.--Gems Sensors, Plainville, CT; *U.S. Public*, pg. 481
Belger, J.H., Mgr.-Sls.--Harrop Industries, Inc., Columbus, OH; *U.S. Private*, pg. 506
Belke, Carl P., V.P.-Sls.--Providence and Worcester Railroad Company, Worcester, MA; *U.S. Public*, pg. 1336
Belkowitz, Mike, Dir.-Sls. & Mktg.--Hochiki America Corporation, Huntington Beach, CA; *Int'l*, pg. 623
Bell, Bill, V.P.-Sls.--Alamo Industrial Group, San Antonio, TX; *U.S. Private*, pg. 31
Bell, David C., Sr. V.P.-Sls.--J. Gibson McIlvain Co., White Marsh, MD; *U.S. Private*, pg. 722
Bell, Ken, V.P.-Sls. West--The Royal China & Porcelain Companies Inc., Moorestown, NJ; *U.S. Private*, pg. 948
Bell, Michael, Mgr.-Sls. & Devel.--A.J. Gerrard and Company, Des Plaines, IL; *U.S. Private*, pg. 449
Bell, Michael, Mgr.-Sls.--Ardell Industries Inc., Union, NJ; *U.S. Private*, pg. 597
Bell, Randy, Reg. Mgr.--Environment/One Corporation, Niskayuna, NY; *U.S. Public*, pg. 586
Bell, Scott, V.P.-Natl. Sls.--MTI Vacations, Inc., Downers Grove, IL; *U.S. Private*, pg. 688
Bell, Will, Mgr.-Sls.--Cleveland City Forge, Cleveland, OH; *U.S. Public*, pg. 1258
Bellini, S., Mgr.-Sls., Scotland & Ireland--OCG Microelectronic Materials Limited, Worcester, United Kingdom; *U.S. Public*, pg. 1220
Bellissimo, Bruno, V.P.-Sls., Canada--Irwin Toy Ltd., Toronto, Canada; *Int'l*, pg. 688
Belliveau, Brodie, V.P.-Sls.--Hartmann Luggage & Leather Goods Group, Lebanon, TN; *U.S. Public*, pg. 261
Bellman, Debra, Admin.-Mktg. & Sls.--F. Korbel Bros. Inc., Guerneville, CA; *U.S. Private*, pg. 632
Bello, Paulo de Souza, Dir.-Sls.--Ceras Johnson Ltda., Rio de Janeiro, Brazil; *U.S. Private*, pg. 593
Bellucci, Louis V., Sr., Exec. V.P. & Mgr.-Natl. Equities Sls.--Jefferies & Company, Inc., Los Angeles, CA; *U.S. Public*, pg. 925
Bellucci, Louis V., Sr., Mgr.-Natl. Equity Sls.--Jefferies & Company, Inc., Short Hills, NJ; *U.S. Public*, pg. 925
Beloff, Jim, Assoc. Publr.-Domestic Sls.--Billboard Magazine, New York, NY; *Int'l*, pg. 1446
Belt, Ed, V.P.-Sls.--Sun City Redi-Mix Inc., El Paso, TX; *Int'l*, pg. 573
Belton, John P., Grp. V.P.-Sls.--American & Efird, Inc., Mount Holly, NC; *U.S. Public*, pg. 1412
Beltran, Fabio, Mgr.-Sls.--Bundy Colombia S.A., Bogota, Colombia; *Int'l*, pg. 1342
Beluze, Gilles, Dir.-Sls.-Mercure--Societe Internationale des Hotels Novotel, Evry, France; *Int'l*, pg. 21
Belyamani, M. Seddik, V.P.-Sls./Africa, Middle East, S. Asia & Pacific--Boeing Commercial Airplane Group, Renton, WA; *U.S. Public*, pg. 240
Bemis, Michael B., Exec. V.P.-Retail Sls.--Entergy Louisiana, Inc., New Orleans, LA; *U.S. Public*, pg. 586
Benassini, George, Dir.-Sls.--Griffith Laboratories Worldwide, Cuautitlan, Mexico; *U.S. Private*, pg. 481
Benavides, Roland, Sr. V.P.-Sls.--The Stiffel Company, Chicago, IL; *U.S. Private*, pg. 1043
Bender, W.D., Gen. Sls. Mgr.--Delphi Packard Electric Systems, Beachwood, OH; *U.S. Public*, pg. 719
Bendixen, Knut, Sr. V.P.-Automotive Sls., Mktg. & Service--Bosch Sales Group, Broadview, IL; *Int'l*, pg. 205
Beneke, Brad, V.P.-Sls.--All Star Gas Co.-Region XIII, Lebanon, MO; *U.S. Private*, pg. 35
Bengtsson, Ake, Export Mgr.--Perstorp Components, Skara, Sweden; *Int'l*, pg. 1040
Benham, Ronald C., Mgr.-Sls.--A & B Plastics-Southwest, Inc., Phoenix, AZ; *Int'l*, pg. 232
Bening, G. J., Dir.-Mktg. & Sls.--PURAC Group, Gorcum, Netherlands; *Int'l*, pg. 244
Beniston, Mal, Mgr.-Sls.--Milk Products Holdings (Latin America) Ltd., Fort Lauderdale, FL; *Int'l*, pg. 923
Benitez, Victor, V.P., Gen. Mgr. & Mgr.-Sls.--Gus Machado Enterprises, Hialeah, FL; *U.S. Private*, pg. 691
Benjamin, G.P., Mgr.-Fleet Sls.--Buick Motor Div. General Motors Corp., Flint, MI; *U.S. Public*, pg. 720

Benjamin, Martin, V.P.-Sls. & Mktg.--Pueblo International, Inc.-P.R. Div., Carolina, PR; *U.S. Private*, pg. 894
Benkovic, James A., V.P.-Consumer Sls.--Acme United Corporation, Fairfield, CT; *U.S. Public*, pg. 17
Benkovich, Jeanine, Coord.-Mktg. & Sls.--LINC Capital Group, Chicago, IL; *U.S. Public*, pg. 996
Bennett, Carl L., Sr. V.P.-Admin. & Sls.--Quad/Graphics, Inc., Pewaukee, WI; *U.S. Private*, pg. 897
Bennett, Constance E., V.P.-Sls.-Northeast Region--Business Week, New York, NY; *U.S. Public*, pg. 1069
Bennett, Craig, Sr. V.P.-Sls. & Mktg.--Utility Trailer Manufacturing Co., City of Industry, CA; *U.S. Private*, pg. 1130
Bennett, Elizabeth, Dir.-Sls. & Mktg.--Kodansha America, Inc., New York, NY; *Int'l*, pg. 742
Bennett, Gary, Exec. V.P.-Sls.--Hitachi Home Electronics, Norcross, GA; *Int'l*, pg. 621
Bennett, George, V.P.-North American Sls.--Memorex Telex Corp., Irving, TX; *Int'l*, pg. 857
Bennett, George, V.P.-Bus. Devel.--Medical Assurance, Inc., Birmingham, AL; *U.S. Public*, pg. 1079
Bennett, James B., V.P.-Sls.--The Raymond Corporation, Greene, NY; *Int'l*, pg. 123
Bennett, June, Staff V.P.-North America Sls.--Continental Airlines, Houston, TX; *U.S. Public*, pg. 439
Bennett, Pat, Asst. V.P.-Sls.--Moran Towing of Maryland, Baltimore, MD; *U.S. Private*, pg. 761
Bennett, Patrick, Dir.-Sls.--Teledyne Portland Forge, Portland, IN; *U.S. Public*, pg. 43
Bennett, R.L., Sr. V.P.-Mktg. & Sls.--Danek Medical Inc., Memphis, TN; *U.S. Public*, pg. 1482
Bennett, R.M., V.P.-Sls. & Mktg.--Smith & Sons Foods, Inc., Macon, GA; *U.S. Private*, pg. 1006
Bennett, Reid, V.P.-Sls.--Jays Foods LLC, Chicago, IL; *U.S. Private*, pg. 584
Bennett, Rex, V.P.-Sls.--Lake Investment Co., Phoenix, AZ; *U.S. Public*, pg. 1563
Bennett, Scott, Dir.-Sls.--Veeder-Root Company, Simsbury, CT; *U.S. Public*, pg. 482
Bennett, Stephen, V.P.-European Sls. & Mktg.--Utility Trailer Manufacturing Co., City of Industry, CA; *U.S. Private*, pg. 1130
Bennett, Tim, Mgr.-Bulk Powert--East Kentucky Power Co-op, Winchester, KY; *U.S. Private*, pg. 356
Bennett, Tony, Dir.-Mktg. & Sls.--Sketchley Plc, Hinckley, United Kingdom; *Int'l*, pg. 1261
Bennett, Wallace, Dir.-Sls. & Mktg.--Kansas City Chiefs Football Club, Inc., Kansas City, MO; *U.S. Private*, pg. 607
Bennier, J.M., V.P.-Sls. & Mktg.--A.Y. McDonald Mfg. Co., Dubuque, IA; *U.S. Private*, pg. 721
Benninger, Brian, V.P.-Sls. & Engrng.--Kingston Warren, Farmington Hills, MI; *U.S. Public*, pg. 796
Bennis, Tom, Dir.-Sls. Opers.--Wallace Laboratories, Cranbury, NJ; *U.S. Public*, pg. 310
Benoit, Giles, Div. Mgr.-East--Pier 1 Imports Canada, Toronto, Canada; *U.S. Public*, pg. 1295
Benrubi, Sam, Exec. V.P. & Dir.-Sls.--Westwood One, Inc., New York, NY; *U.S. Public*, pg. 1763
Bensaid, Eric, V.P.-Sls.--Troy Corporation, Florham Park, NJ; *U.S. Private*, pg. 1105
Bensimon, Ronny A., V.P. & Gen. Mgr.--Dearden's, Los Angeles, CA; *U.S. Private*, pg. 319
Bensinger, Roger, V.P.-Corp. Sls.--The Sharper Image, San Francisco, CA; *U.S. Public*, pg. 1464
Benson, Bill, Mgr.-Natl. Sls.-Automotive After Mkt.--Rockford International Group, Rockford, IL; *U.S. Private*, pg. 938
Benson, Charles, V.P.-Food Svc. Sls.--Nakano Foods Inc., Arlington Heights, IL; *Int'l*, pg. 883
Benson, Frank, V.P.-Sls. & Mktg.--Hill Phoenix, Colonial Heights, VA; *U.S. Public*, pg. 521
Benson, James R., V.P.-Sls.--Utica Boilers Inc., Utica, NY; *U.S. Private*, pg. 1129
Benson, Laurie, Reg. V.P.-New York Ad Sls.--Home & Garden Television, Knoxville, TN; *U.S. Public*, pg. 1447
Benson, Stan M., Sr. V.P.-Sls. & Mktg.--Amgen Inc., Thousand Oaks, CA; *U.S. Public*, pg. 100
Benson, Tom, Mgr.-Sls.--Thermal-Care Div., Niles, IL; *U.S. Public*, pg. 1026
Benson, Wayne A., Chief Sales Officer--CUNA Mutual Insurance Society, Madison, WI; *U.S. Private*, pg. 296
Bent, A. Lopez, Mgr.-Sls. & Mktg.--Moore Portuguesa Limitada, Mem Martins, Portugal; *Int'l*, pg. 890
Benti, Sal, Mgr.-Sls.--Comstream Corporation, San Diego, CA; *Int'l*, pg. 1288
Benun, Eli, Mgr.-Sls.--Bentex Kiddie Corporation, New York, NY; *U.S. Private*, pg. 134
Benzie, J. Peter, Jr., Exec. V.P.-Retail--Fidelity Investments (FMR Corp.), Boston, MA; *U.S. Private*, pg. 402
Berard, David J., V.P.-Domestic Sls.--Unifab International Inc., New Iberia, LA; *U.S. Public*, pg. 1665
Berci, Winton L., V.P.-Mktg. & Sls.--Circon Corporation, Santa Barbara, CA; *U.S. Public*, pg. 373
Berci, Winton L., V.P.-Mktg. & Sls.--Circon ACMI, Stamford, CT; *U.S. Public*, pg. 373
Berg, David, Chief Oper. Officer & Exec. V.P.-Sls.--PremiumWear, Inc., Minneapolis, MN; *U.S. Public*, pg. 1323
Berg, Don, V.P.-Sls. & Mktg.--Channel Master, Smithfield, NC; *U.S. Private*, pg. 228
Berg, George H., V.P.-Mktg. & Sls.--Na-Churs Plant Food Company, Marion, OH; *U.S. Private*, pg. 1096
Bergamin, Mario, V.P.-Mktg. & Sls.--Security Chimneys International Ltd., Laval, Canada; *Int'l*, pg. 1217
Bergen, Douglas, Sr. V.P.-Mktg. & Sales--Forma Scientific Inc., Marietta, OH; *U.S. Public*, pg. 1595
Bergenholz, Tom, V.P.-Sls.--Via Tech Publishing Solutions, Bay Shore, NY; *U.S. Private*, pg. 1138
Berger, Bill, V.P.-Sls.--Elektra Entertainment, New York, NY; *U.S. Public*, pg. 1612
Berger, David, V.P.-Sls. & Distrbution--Datapoint Corporation, Paris, France; *Int'l*, pg. 384
Berger, Ernie, Sr. V.P.-Small Bus. Services Mktg.--American Express Travel Related Services Co., Inc., New York, NY; *U.S. Public*, pg. 73
Berger, Vincent, Dir.-Sls.--AEC/Application Engineering Corporation, Wood Dale, IL; *U.S. Private*, pg. 1041
Berges, Emil H. Jr., V.P.-Sls. & Adv.--Abbott Ball Company, West Hartford, CT; *U.S. Private*, pg. 9
Berglass, David, V.P.-Domestic Sls. & Mktg.--Dep Corporation, Rancho Dominguez, CA; *U.S. Public*, pg. 500
Bergman, Kevin, Dir.-Sls. & Mktg.--The Holiday Inn Lancaster Host Hotel & Conference Center, Lancaster, PA; *U.S. Private*, pg. 534
Bergstein, Barry L., Natl. Sls. & Mktg. Mgr.--BKI, Simpsonville, SC; *U.S. Public*, pg. 1506
Bergstrom, John, Sr. V.P. & Chief Mktg. Officer--Berkshire Life Insurance Company, Pittsfield, MA; *U.S. Private*, pg. 136
Bering, William, V.P.-Sls.--Elmer's Products, Inc., Columbus, OH; *U.S. Private*, pg. 158
Berkbigler, Bill, V.P.-South Central Region Sls.--Thorn Apple Valley, Inc., Southfield, MI; *U.S. Public*, pg. 1602
Berkenbile, Terry, Sr. V.P.-Sls. & Mktg.--Pilgrim's Pride Corporation, Pittsburg, TX; *U.S. Public*, pg. 1296
Berkey, Donald L., Dir.-Sls. & Mktg.--Hollymatic Corporation, Countryside, IL; *U.S. Private*, pg. 535
Berkson, Michael, V.P.-Intl. Sls.--Stanbee Company, Inc., Carlstadt, NJ; *U.S. Private*, pg. 1030
Berlamino, Betty Ellen, Gen. Mgr.-Sls.--WPIX, Inc., New York, NY; *U.S. Public*, pg. 1636
Berling, Henry, Exec. V.P.-Partnership Devel.--Owens & Minor Inc., Glen Allen, VA; *U.S. Public*, pg. 1236
Berlinger, Liz, V.P.-Sls.--Jordache Enterprises, Inc., New York, NY; *U.S. Private*, pg. 597
Berlowski, John, Mgr.-Sls.--Hiniker Company, Mankato, MN; *U.S. Private*, pg. 530
Berman, Bernard, Gen. Mgr.--Butler Ventamatic Corp., Mineral Wells, TX; *U.S. Private*, pg. 190
Berman, David, Sr. V.P.-Mktg. & Bus. Devel.--PHP Healthcare Corporation, Reston, VA; *U.S. Public*, pg. 1241
Berman, Edward, V.P.-Sls.--Mannington Resilient Floors, Salem, NJ; *U.S. Private*, pg. 700
Bermosk, Greg, V.P.-Sls.--SOCO-Lynch Corp., Los Angeles, CA; *Int'l*, pg. 1458
Bermudez, Robert L., V.P. & Mgr.-Natl. Sls.--Marie Brizard Wines & Spirits USA, North Miami, FL; *U.S. Private*, pg. 702
Bermudez, Rodolfo, Mgr.-After Sls.--General Motors Uruguay S.A., Montevideo, Uruguay; *U.S. Public*, pg. 723
Bernacki, Rhonda, Sls. Mgr.--KWWL-TV, Waterloo, IA; *U.S. Private*, pg. 912
Bernal, Yanaka, Corp. Sls. Acct.--Amspec Chemical Corporation, Gloucester City, NJ; *U.S. Private*, pg. 67
Bernard, Larry, Mgr.-Sls.--Scientific Imaging Systems, New Haven, CT; *U.S. Public*, pg. 550
Bernardi, Mark, Mgr.-Sls.--Dark Horse Comics, Inc., Milwaukie, OR; *U.S. Private*, pg. 311
Bernardo, Thomas, Sr. V.P.-Franchise Sls.--Days Inns of America, Inc., Parsippany, NJ; *U.S. Public*, pg. 321
Bernauer, Leonard, Mgr.-Sls.--OEM Div., Hope, AR; *U.S. Public*, pg. 335
Bernauer, Leonard, Mgr.-Sls.--Northeast Div., Beech Creek, PA; *U.S. Public*, pg. 335
Bernier, Judy, Dir.-Intl. Sls.--International Sales, Oshkosh, WI; *U.S. Public*, pg. 1233
Bernlohr, Timothy J., V.P.-Sls. & Mktg.--RBX Corporation, Roanoke, VA; *U.S. Private*, pg. 56
Bernlohr, Timothy J., V.P.-Sls. & Mktg.--Rubatex Corporation, Roanoke, VA; *U.S. Private*, pg. 56
Bernth, Steen, Mgr.-Sls.--Schubert Seals A/S, Horsens, Denmark; *U.S. Public*, pg. 1755
Berry, Daniel H., Sr. V.P.-Sls., Service & Mktg.--Ultratech Stepper, Inc., San Jose, CA; *U.S. Public*, pg. 1663
Berry, Gary L., V.P.-Sls.--Struthers Industries Inc., Gulfport, MS; *U.S. Private*, pg. 1048
Berry, Gordon, Mgr.-Sls.--Bailey Fire Protection, Bradford, United Kingdom; *Int'l*, pg. 133
Berry, Tony, Sls./Mktg. Dir.--CiMatrix Ltd., Stourbridge, United Kingdom; *U.S. Public*, pg. 1395
Bertelli, Rich, V.P.-Mktg. & Sls.--Crosman Corp., East Bloomfield, NY; *U.S. Private*, pg. 291
Bertelli, Rich, V.P.-Sls. & Mktg.--Benjamin Sheridan Co., East Bloomfield, NY; *U.S. Private*, pg. 291
Bertges, Gerhard, Sls. Dir.--Berlitz Schools of Languages GmbH, Frankfurt/Main, Germany; *U.S. Public*, pg. 222
Bertloff, Paula, Mgr.-Natl. Accts./BBQ Grill Prods.--Porcelain Metals Corp., Louisville, KY; *U.S. Private*, pg. 876
Bertoli, L.J., Mgr.-Sls.--The Kirk & Blum Mfg. Co., Cincinnati, OH; *U.S. Private*, pg. 623
Bertram, Jim, V.P.-Sls. & Mktg.Dir.--Primedia Information Inc., Hightstown, NJ; *U.S. Public*, pg. 1328
Beseler, Chris, Sr. V.P.-Mktg. & Sls.--Waccamaw Corporation, Myrtle Beach, SC; *U.S. Private*, pg. 1145
Beshel, Joseph, V.P.-Mktg. & Sls., EDI Lederle--Wyeth-Ayerst Laboratories, Inc., Philadelphia, PA; *U.S. Public*, pg. 80
Bessette, Bill, V.P.-Sls.--Labatt U.S.A., Darien, CT; *Int'l*, pg. 679
Best, Lonnie, Dir.-Sls.--Design Concepts Integration, Inc., Bloomington, MN; *U.S. Private*, pg. 572
Best, Page H., V.P.-Sls.--Eastern Fine Paper, Brewer, ME; *U.S. Private*, pg. 357
Best, Richard L., V.P.-Fin. Opers. & Sls.--General Mills, Inc., Minneapolis, MN; *U.S. Public*, pg. 717
Best, Wayne, Sr. V.P.-Mktg. & Sls.--The Frymaster Corp., Shreveport, LA; *Int'l*, pg. 188
Betchick, Jack, Dir.-Industrial Sls.--Favorite Brands International, Inc., Lincolnshire, IL; *U.S. Private*, pg. 397
Bethards, Brandon C., V.P. & Gen. Mgr.-Global Sls. & Svc.--Babcock & Wilcox Co., Barberton, OH; *U.S. Public*, pg. 1068
Bettencourt, Bob, V.P.--Immunex Corporation, Seattle, WA; *U.S. Public*, pg. 871
Betts, Dave, V.P.-Retail Sls.--Furman Foods, Inc., Northumberland, PA; *U.S. Private*, pg. 431
Betz, Wes, Mgr.-Sls./Regina--SGI Canada Insurance Services Ltd., Regina, Canada; *Int'l*, pg. 1195
Beurskens, Pierre, V.P.-Intl. Sls.--Consolidated Cigar Corporation, Fort Lauderdale, FL; *U.S. Private*, pg. 690
Beverage, Gary, Dir.-Sls.--Cubix Corporation, Carson City, NV; *U.S. Private*, pg. 294
Beverly, Richard, V.P.-Field Sls.-Valve Prods.--Automatic Switch Co., Florham Park, NJ; *U.S. Public*, pg. 573
Bevington, Kim, V.P.-Sls.--Elyria Foundry Company, Elyria, OH; *U.S. Private*, pg. 373
Bevins, Donald E., V.P.-Mktg. & Sls.--Farmers Mutual Hail Insurance Co. of Iowa, Des Moines, IA; *U.S. Private*, pg. 395
Bewoets, F., Mgr.-Sls.--Moore Belgium NV, Gent, Belgium; *Int'l*, pg. 889
Bexon, R., Sr. V.P.-Mktg. Sls.--Brown & Williamson Tobacco Corp., Louisville, KY; *Int'l*, pg. 111
Beyel, Steve, Dir.-Sls.--American Technical Ceramics Corp., Huntington Station, NY; *U.S. Public*, pg. 93
Beyeler, Dana, Dir.-Mktg.--National Forge Company, Irvine, PA; *U.S. Private*, pg. 783
Beyeler, Les, V.P.-Sls. & Mktg.--Graphic Enterprises of Ohio, Inc., Canton, OH; *U.S. Private*, pg. 471
Beyer, Fred, Mgr.-Sls.--NTH Consultants, Ltd., Farmington, MI; *U.S. Private*, pg. 772
Beyer, Ronald, Mgr.-Sls./Services--Microflect Company, Inc., Salem, OR; *U.S. Public*, pg. 1707
Bezak, Sharon, Pres. & V.P.-Sls. & Mktg.--Sharon Concepts, Millburn, NJ; *U.S. Private*, pg. 990
Bhatt, Andrea, V.P.-Sls. & Mktg.--General Alum & Chemical, Holland, OH; *U.S. Private*, pg. 443
Bianchi, Leonard, Mgr.-Sls.--Nasco Modesto, Modesto, CA; *U.S. Private*, pg. 446
Bianchini, Neil L., Sr. V.P. & Natl. Sls. Dir.--Shieffelin Somerset Co., New York, NY; *Int'l*, pg. 412
Bianco, James W., Jr., Dir.-Mktg. & Sls.--Control Module, Inc., Enfield, CT; *U.S. Private*, pg. 271
Biazis, Andrew, V.P.-Sls.--The Wella Corporation, Montvale, NJ; *Int'l*, pg. 1489
Bichsel, Dean, V.P.- Mktg.--Osborn Manufacturing, Cleveland, OH; *U.S. Public*, pg. 924
Bickel, Blair, Mgr.-Sls.--Hy-Tek Material Handling, Inc., Columbus, OH; *U.S. Private*, pg. 550
Bickhart, Stanley, Dir.-Sls.--Wabash Magnetics, Huntington, IN; *U.S. Private*, pg. 351
Bicknell, Bob, Sr. V.P.-Mktg. & Sls.--Campbell Hausfeld Division of Scott Fetzer, Harrison, OH; *U.S. Public*, pg. 217
Bidwell, Michael M., Dir.-Sls.--Bidwell Industrial Group, Inc., Middletown, CT; *U.S. Private*, pg. 142
Bieker, Don, V.P.-Sls. & Mktg. & Adv.--Columbia Manufacturing Inc., Westfield, MA; *U.S. Private*, pg. 255
Bielecki, Bruce, V.P.-Sls. & Opers.--Auto Glass Specialists, Madison, WI; *U.S. Private*, pg. 100
Bieln, Jennifer, V.P.-Sls.--Aloette Cosmetics, Inc., West Chester, PA; *U.S. Public*, pg. 57
Bielski, Richard, Mgr.-Sls.--N.G. Bailey & Co. Ltd.-Reading Branch, Reading, United Kingdom; *Int'l*, pg. 132
Bierman, Norman F., Exec. V.P.-Corp. Mktg. & Sls.--Intellisource, Fairfield, CT; *U.S. Public*, pg. 1425
Biermann, Syl, V.P.-Sls.--RS Electronics, Livonia, MI; *U.S. Private*, pg. 905
Bievenour, Raymond, V.P.-Sls. & Mktg.--Penn Engineering & Manufacturing Corp., Danboro, PA; *U.S. Public*, pg. 1269
Bigelow, Doug, V.P.-Sls.--Eastman Worldwide, Buffalo, NY; *U.S. Private*, pg. 358
Biggers, Jay, Mgr.-Gen. Sls.--Omega Environmental Inc., Richmond, VA; *U.S. Public*, pg. 1222
Biggs, Craig, V.P.-Mktg. & Sls.--Electrovert, Grand Prairie, TX; *Int'l*, pg. 328
Biggs, Mickey, Sr. V.P.-Sls. & Mktg.--Henry Lee Company, Miami, FL; *U.S. Private*, pg. 657
Bigham, Jack, Mgr.-Sls.--Washington Specialty Metals, Buffalo Grove, IL; *U.S. Public*, pg. 1020
Bigoss, Patrick, V.P.-Sls.--Webcraft Technologies, Inc., North Brunswick, NJ; *U.S. Public*, pg. 228
Biles, Homer, Dir.-Grocery Sls. & Mktg.--J.L. Lester & Son, Inc., Rockmart, GA; *U.S. Private*, pg. 660
Biljan, John, V.P.-Sls. & Mktg.--Relm Communications, Inc., Indianapolis, IN; *U.S. Public*, pg. 1376
Billing, Guy, Mgr.-Natl. Sls.--The Excellence Group, Stamford, CT; *U.S. Private*, pg. 387
Billings, Barbara L., Mgr.-Sls. Svcs.--Sutter Home Winery, Inc., Saint Helena, CA; *U.S. Private*, pg. 1057
Billingsley, Dave, Mgr.-AZ Sls.--Dunn-Edwards Corporation, Los Angeles, CA; *U.S. Private*, pg. 347
Billman, Ted, V.P.-Sls.--General American Door Company, Montgomery, IL; *U.S. Private*, pg. 732
Billock, John K., Pres.-Sls. & Mktg.--Home Box Office, Inc., New York, NY; *U.S. Public*, pg. 1612
Bilson, Allen, Mgr.-Sls.--Barrecrafters, Shelburne, VT; *U.S. Private*, pg. 991
Binckli, Erich, Div. Head-Central Europe--BASF AG, Ludwigshafen, Germany; *Int'l*, pg. 103
Bindon, Tom, V.P.- Retail--Singleton Seafood Co., Tampa, FL; *U.S. Public*, pg. 427
Binet, Carole, V.P.-Sls. & Mktg.--Logo of the Americas, Fort Lauderdale, FL; *Int'l*, pg. 462
Bingham, Richard, Mgr.-Circulation--ACBJ Business Publications, Inc., Louisville, KY; *U.S. Private*, pg. 19
Binn, Mike, Mgr.-Sls.--Blue Anchor, Inc., Dinuba, CA; *U.S. Private*, pg. 150
Birch, Larry, V.P.-Sls.--Mueller Industries, Inc., Memphis, TN; *U.S. Public*, pg. 1141
Bird, William, Mgr.-Natl. Sls.--Jensen Industries, Los Angeles, CA; *U.S. Public*, pg. 1193
Birk, James A., V.P.-Mktg. & Sls./Kimball Lodging Group--Kimball International, Inc., Jasper, IN; *U.S. Public*, pg. 956

Birkholz, Kim, Dir.-Sls.--Ingersoll Equipment Co., Inc., Winneconne, WI; *Int'l*, pg. 1129
Birnbaum, Hally, Sls. Mgr.-N.Y.--USA Weekend, New York, NY; *U.S. Public*, pg. 701
Birnie, Bob, V.P.-Mktg. & Sls.--International Tubular Products, Inc., Claremore, OK; *U.S. Private*, pg. 14
Birschbach, Jim, V.P.-Adv. & Sls.--TCI Communications, Inc., Englewood, CO; *U.S. Public*, pg. 1554
Bischoff, Denis, V.P.-Sls.--Anderson Bakery Co., Inc., Lancaster, PA; *U.S. Private*, pg. 65
Biscombe, Barry, Mgr.-Outside Sls.--Wohlert Corp., Lansing, MI; *U.S. Private*, pg. 1185
Bisek, J.D., V.P.-Sls. & Mktg.--WRR Environmental Services Co., Inc., Eau Claire, WI; *U.S. Public*, pg. 1792
Bishop, Ben L., V.P.-Direct Sls.--Armco Inc.-Mansfield Operations, Mansfield, OH; *U.S. Public*, pg. 131
Bishop, Brian T., Gen. Mgr.-Injection Molding Sls.--HPM Corporation, Mount Gilead, OH; *U.S. Private*, pg. 492
Bishop, C.M., III, Mgr.-Women's Mdse.--Pendleton Woolen Mills, Inc., Portland, OR; *U.S. Private*, pg. 848
Bishop, Daniel, V.P.-Sls.-Flat Bed--Anderson Trucking Service Inc., Saint Cloud, MN; *U.S. Private*, pg. 72
Bishop, Don, Grp. V.P.-Sls. & Mktg.--Gulf States Toyota, Inc., Houston, TX; *U.S. Private*, pg. 488
Bishop, Judith A., V.P.-N. America Sls.--UAL Corporation, Elk Grove Village, IL; *U.S. Public*, pg. 1652
Bishop, Robert E., V.P.-Sls. & Mktg.--The Gunlocke Company, Wayland, NY; *U.S. Public*, pg. 772
Bissell, Eugene V.N., V.P.-Sls. & Opers. (Southern Div.)--AmeriGas Partners, L.P., Valley Forge, PA; *U.S. Public*, pg. 1653
Bittker, Ron, Mgr.-Sls.--National Lumber Co., Warren, MI; *U.S. Private*, pg. 785
Bittner, Mark, V.P.-Sls.--Goody Products, Inc., Peachtree City, GA; *U.S. Public*, pg. 1177
Biviano, Michael A., V.P. & Reg. Dir.--Carrols Corporation, Syracuse, NY; *U.S. Private*, pg. 216
Bixby, B.C., Chm. Bd.--Bixby International Corp., Newburyport, MA; *U.S. Private*, pg. 146
Bizzack, Jeffrey M., Sr. V.P.-Sls.--ProBusiness Services, Inc., Pleasanton, CA; *U.S. Public*, pg. 1330
Bjorneboe, Jan, Dir.-Mktg. & Adv. & Sls. Mgr.--ISS Norge a.s., Oslo, Norway; *Int'l*, pg. 656
Bjornsson, Steinn Logi, Sr. V.P.--Icelandair, Reykjavik, Iceland; *Int'l*, pg. 658
Black, Barbara, Dir.-Sls. Promo.--Abdalla's Lafayette, Inc., Lafayette, LA; *U.S. Private*, pg. 10
Black, David, Sr. V.P.-Sls.--Camco International Inc., Houston, TX; *U.S. Public*, pg. 298
Black, Michael, V.P.-U.S. Sales & Mktg.--Datapoint Corporation, San Antonio, TX; *Int'l*, pg. 384
Blackburn, F. Scott, V.P.-Sls.--Clemco Industries Corp., Washington, MO; *U.S. Private*, pg. 24
Blackburn, Linda, Gen. Mgr.-Sls.--KCRG Radio & TV Stations, Cedar Rapids, IA; *U.S. Private*, pg. 442
Blackburn, Scott, V.P.-Sls.--Aerolyte Systems, Washington, MO; *U.S. Private*, pg. 24
Blackman, Mark, V.P.-Sls. & Mktg.--International Division, Chicago, IL; *U.S. Private*, pg. 459
Blackwell, John, Exec V.P.-Sls. & Mktg.--Moulinex Appliances, Inc., Closter, NJ; *Int'l*, pg. 896
Blackwell, John C., V.P.-Mktg. & Sls.--General Housewares Corp., Terre Haute, IN; *U.S. Public*, pg. 715
Blagaich, Alvin, V.P.-Sls. & Mktg.--Fenton Press, Inc., Addison, IL; *U.S. Private*, pg. 400
Blaha, Bill, Pres.-Sls.--Pacesetter Corporation, Omaha, NE; *U.S. Private*, pg. 830
Blahut, Erik, Dr., Mgr.-Equity Sls. & Corp. Fin.--Bankgesellschaft Berlin, Berlin, Germany; *Int'l*, pg. 159
Blaine, Brent, Dir.-Sls.--Binney & Smith Inc., Easton, PA; *U.S. Private*, pg. 496
Blaine, Brent, V.P.-Sls.--Revell-Monogram Inc., Morton Grove, IL; *U.S. Private*, pg. 926
Blaine, Thomas, Mgr.-Adv. & Sls.--Gentex Optics, Inc., Simpson, PA; *Int'l*, pg. 462
Blair, J.S., Mgr.-Intl. Sls.--Trion, Inc., Sanford, NC; *U.S. Public*, pg. 1639
Blair, John C., Mgr.-Sls.--Rohrer Corporation, Wadsworth, OH; *U.S. Private*, pg. 940
Blair, Rick, Exec. V.P.-Sls. & Mktg.--Weider Nutrition Intl., Salt Lake City, UT; *U.S. Private*, pg. 1159
Blair, Robert, Mgr.-Sls.--Wards Cove Packing Company, Seattle, WA; *U.S. Private*, pg. 1149
Blais, Russell A., V.P.-Mktg.--Naylor Pipe Company, Chicago, IL; *U.S. Private*, pg. 789
Blajsczak, Richard J., Pres. & Chief Exec. Officer--RCB Baking Company, Fargo, ND; *U.S. Public*, pg. 1354
Blake, David, Dir.-Adv.--Crain's Chicago Business, Chicago, IL; *U.S. Private*, pg. 285
Blake, Jerry R., V.P.-Sls.--L & L Maintenance & Repair, Metairie, LA; *U.S. Private*, pg. 638
Blake, Lyn, V.P.-Trade Sls. & Mktg.--Macmillan Publishing USA, Indianapolis, IN; *U.S. Private*, pg. 777
Blake, Ron, Regional Sls. Mgr.--Prime Technology, Inc., Indianapolis, IN; *U.S. Private*, pg. 884
Blakely, James, V.P.-Sls.--The Dannon Co., Tarrytown, NY; *Int'l*, pg. 379
Blakemore, Bob, Mgr.-Sls. & Mktg.--Ultra Electronics Magnetics, Cannock, United Kingdom; *Int'l*, pg. 1431
Blakley, Luther, Mgr.--Standing Rock Campground, Milwaukee, WI; *U.S. Public*, pg. 410
Blalock, Adam, V.P.-Sls. & Mktg.--Daisy Manufacturing Company, Inc., Rogers, AR; *U.S. Private*, pg. 308
Blalock, B., V.P.-Sls.--Penske Logistics, Reading, PA; *U.S. Private*, pg. 851
Blanc, Arturo, Gen. Mgr. & Mgr.-Sls.--APLI Combustion, S.A., Barcelona, Spain; *U.S. Private*, pg. 361
Bland, Craig, V.P. & Gen. Mgr.-Sls.--KRIV, Houston, TX; *Int'l*, pg. 926
Blank, Robert E., V.P.-Sls.--BankAmerica Corporation, San Francisco, CA; *U.S. Public*, pg. 179
Blank, Robert E., V.P.- Mktg. & Sls.--Littleford Day Inc., Florence, KY; *U.S. Private*, pg. 671
Blank, Susan, Grp. Sls.--Self, New York, NY; *U.S. Private*, pg. 20
Blankendaal, Cor, Area Sls. Mgr.-Benelux & France--Bourns Benelux B.V., Voorburg, Netherlands; *U.S. Private*, pg. 161
Blankenship, Robert R., V.P.-Activewear Sls.--Fruit of the Loom, Inc., Chicago, IL; *U.S. Public*, pg. 685
Blankenship, Tim, Mgr.-Circulation--Hillsdale Daily News, Hillsdale, MI; *U.S. Private*, pg. 995
Blanton, Graham P., V.P.-Sls. & Mktg.--Asbury Carbons, Inc., Asbury, NJ; *U.S. Private*, pg. 87
Blashill, G.L., Dir.-Sls. & Mktg.--Imperial Tobacco Group, Ltd., Bristol, United Kingdom; *Int'l*, pg. 666
Blatsios, Demethius, Mgr.-Sls.--Henkel Hellas, Moschato, Greece; *Int'l*, pg. 612
Blatz, Steve, Dir.-Sls. Admin.--The Princess Marcella Borghese, Inc., New York, NY; *U.S. Private*, pg. 690
Blauch, Denise A., Product Mgr.-Sls.--Saint-Gobain Advanced Materials Corporation, Louisville, KY; *Int'l*, pg. 1173
Blauer, Stephen, V.P.-Sls.--Blauer Manufacturing Co., Inc., Boston, MA; *U.S. Private*, pg. 149
Blauvelt, Brian, Natl. Sls. Mgr.--Edlon Products, Inc., Avondale, PA; *U.S. Public*, pg. 1393
Blazin, Bernard, Pres.-Intl. Div.--Clarins, Neuilly-sur-Seine, France; *Int'l*, pg. 295
Blazowski, Miriam, Dir.-Sls. Admin.--Appleton Electric Co., Chicago, IL; *U.S. Public*, pg. 572
Bleckheimer, Mark L., V.P.-Sls.--Primary Steel, Inc., Middletown, CT; *U.S. Private*, pg. 884
Blenner, Joel, V.P.-Sls.--Microtouch Systems, Inc., Methuen, MA; *U.S. Public*, pg. 1108
Blessinger, Mike, Dir.-Sls.--Jofco Inc., Jasper, IN; *U.S. Private*, pg. 588
Blink, John, Dir.-Sls.--Rio Hotel & Casino Inc., Las Vegas, NV; *U.S. Public*, pg. 1390
Block, Randolf E., V.P.-Sls. & Promo.--Screw Conveyor Corp., Hammond, IN; *U.S. Private*, pg. 977
Bloemen, Michael, V.P.-Station Opers.--Natural Fuels Corporation, Denver, CO; *U.S. Public*, pg. 1170
Blohm, Chris, Sec.-Sls. & Mktg.--Red Wings Inc., Fredonia, NY; *Int'l*, pg. 1398
Blomgren, Tom Z., Mgr.-Sls.--Oy Nautor AB, Pietarsaari, Finland; *Int'l*, pg. 1428
Blomquist, Kaj, Dir.-Sls.--Wisapak Mertens GmbH, Julich, Germany; *Int'l*, pg. 1430
Blomstrom, Don, Mgr.-Natl. Sls.-Medical--Instrumentarium Imaging, Inc., Milwaukee, WI; *U.S. Private*, pg. 565
Blood, Charles, V.P.-Sls. Admin.--New England Confectionery Co., Cambridge, MA; *U.S. Private*, pg. 1113
Bloom, Allen J., Exec. V.P.-Mktg & Sls.--Ringling Bros., Barnum & Bailey Combined Shows, Inc., Vienna, VA; *U.S. Private*, pg. 400
Bloom, Richard A., Gen. Mgr.-Sls. & Mktg.--Bloom Electric Services, Inc., Oklahoma City, OK; *U.S. Private*, pg. 150
Bloomstein, Edward, Mgr.-Natl. Sls.--Sterilite Corporation, Townsend, MA; *U.S. Private*, pg. 1040
Bloss, David A., Sr., Exec. V.P.--Jameco Industries, Inc., Spindale, NC; *U.S. Public*, pg. 1746
Bloss, Douglas V., V.P.-Mktg. & Sls.--Armstrong International, Inc., Three Rivers, MI; *U.S. Private*, pg. 83
Blot, Edward J., V.P.-Sls. & Mktg., Stainless & Specialty Steels--Republic Engineered Steels, Inc., Massillon, OH; *U.S. Public*, pg. 1378
Blue, Jeff, V.P.-Sls. & Mktg.--Goldsmiths, Inc., Wichita, KS; *U.S. Private*, pg. 462
Blue, Richard N., V.P.-Sls.--Domco Inc., Farnham, Canada; *Int'l*, pg. 415
Bluhm, Leland, Mgr.-Dist. Sls.-S.E.--Singapore Airlines Ltd., Atlanta, GA; *Int'l*, pg. 1374
Blumen, Al, Dir.-Sls.--Tunmore Oldsmobile Inc., Buffalo, NY; *U.S. Private*, pg. 1109
Blumenstock, Mike, V.P.-Mktg. & Sls.--EGA, Seymour, CT; *Int'l*, pg. 436
Blumenthal, Jack, Sls. Mgr.--Lion Brand Yarn Co., New York, NY; *U.S. Private*, pg. 669
Blumenthal, R. Dean, V.P.--Lion Brand Yarn Co., New York, NY; *U.S. Private*, pg. 669
Blumstein, Jerry, V.P. & Asst. Mgr.-Sls.--Gould Paper Corporation, New York, NY; *U.S. Private*, pg. 466
Blundell-Pound, George, Commercial Dir.--Caledonian Airways Ltd, Gatwick, United Kingdom; *Int'l*, pg. 219
Blutstein, Mark, Mgr.-Sls.--Reliable Knitting Works, Milwaukee, WI; *U.S. Private*, pg. 920
Blythe, Daniel, V.P.-Sls.--Central Steel & Wire Company, Chicago, IL; *U.S. Public*, pg. 327
Board, Steve, Dir.-Mktg.--The ARGOS Group, Southfield, MI; *U.S. Private*, pg. 120
Board, T., V.P.-Sls.--Onondaga Litho Supply Co., Inc., Henrietta, NY; *U.S. Public*, pg. 1329
Boardman, Hollis, Mgr.-Gen. Sls.--WXII-TV, Winston Salem, NC; *U.S. Public*, pg. 1344
Boba, Denise, V.P.-Mktg. & Circulation--Sampler Publications Inc., Saint Charles, IL; *U.S. Private*, pg. 963
Bobrick, Neal A., V.P.-Sls. & Store Opers.--Ultimate Electronics, Thornton, CO; *U.S. Public*, pg. 1662
Bocchi, Mark, Dir.-Sls. & Reservations--Horizon Air Industries, Seattle, WA; *U.S. Public*, pg. 35
Bock, Arthur, V.P.-Sls. & Mktg.--Philip Fritze & Sons, Inc., Whippany, NJ; *U.S. Private*, pg. 429
Bockenfeld, Jim, Dir.-Sls. & Mktg.--The Knapheide Mfg. Co., Quincy, IL; *U.S. Private*, pg. 626
Bodenheimer, George W., Exec. V.P.-Mktg. & Sls.--ESPN, Inc., Bristol, CT; *U.S. Private*, pg. 512
Bodill, Len, Dir.-Sls.--United Distillers PLC, Edinburgh, United Kingdom; *Int'l*, pg. 412
Bodkin, Lawrence, V.P.-Mktg. & Sls.--White Rock Products Corp., Whitestone, NY; *U.S. Private*, pg. 1173
Bodweine, Mel, Natl. Sls. Mgr.--The Promotion in Motion Companies, Closter, NJ; *U.S. Private*, pg. 890
Boemer, Stacey, Mgr.-Customer Service--Oriental Motor U.S.A. Corp., Santa Clara, CA; *Int'l*, pg. 1008
Boender, Brian H., V.P.-Sls., Mktg. & Engr. Prods.--Trion, Inc., Sanford, NC; *U.S. Public*, pg. 1639
Bogey, David, Dir.-Natl. Sls.--Nicklaus Golf Company, L.C., West Palm Beach, FL; *U.S. Private*, pg. 799
Boggs, Jim, Mgr.-Gen. Sls.--WYMT-TV, Hazard, KY; *U.S. Public*, pg. 759
Boggs, Marvin K., V.P.-Sls.--Derst Baking Company, Inc., Savannah, GA; *U.S. Private*, pg. 326
Bogin, Brett, V.P.-Sls.--Invincible Office Furniture, Manitowoc, WI; *U.S. Private*, pg. 575
Bohan, Peter, V.P.-Mktg. & Sls.--Bird Machine Company, South Walpole, MA; *U.S. Public*, pg. 166
Bohler, Alan, V.P.-Sls. Uphol.--Bassett Furniture Industries, Incorporated, Bassett, VA; *U.S. Public*, pg. 193
Bohnet, Mike, V.P.-Sls. & Mktg.--Robertshaw Tennessee, Knoxville, TN; *Int'l*, pg. 1243
Boireau, Christian, Exec. V.P.-Sls--Groupe Air France, Roissy, France; *Int'l*, pg. 559
Boldrini, Ezo, Mgr.-Corp. Mktg.--3M Chile S.A., Santiago, Chile; *U.S. Public*, pg. 1606
Boleda, Pat, Mgr.-Intl. Sls.--Rogers N.K. Seed Co., Boise, ID; *Int'l*, pg. 974
Bolen, Mike, Dir.-Sls. & Mktg.--The Zippertubing Co., Los Angeles, CA; *U.S. Private*, pg. 1207
Boles, John W., V.P.-Sls. Northern Reg.--Goody's Family Clothing, Inc., Knoxville, TN; *U.S. Public*, pg. 753
Bollen, Boudewijn, Exec. V.P.-Worldwide Sls., Svcs. & Distr.--Nellcor Puritan Bennett Incorporated, Pleasanton, CA; *U.S. Public*, pg. 1039
Boller-Krakauer, Frances, V.P.-Men's Sls.--G-III Apparel Group, Ltd., New York, NY; *U.S. Public*, pg. 690
Bolles, Doug, Mgr.-Sls, Parts/Accessories--VWS, Inc., Cleveland, OH; *Int'l*, pg. 440
Bollinger, Eric, Dir.- Mktg. & Sls.--Bollinger Shipyards, Inc., Lockport, LA; *U.S. Private*, pg. 155
Bollinger, Eric, Dir.-Sls. & Mktg.--Bollinger Algiers Inc., New Orleans, LA; *U.S. Private*, pg. 155
Bollinger, Tom, Treas. & Mgr.-Sls.--The John C. Groub Company Inc., Seymour, IN; *U.S. Private*, pg. 484
Bollman, G., Mgr.-Sls.--Moore Ges.m.b.H., Vienna, Austria; *Int'l*, pg. 889
Bollmeier, Mark, V.P.-Sls.--Color Arts, Inc., Racine, WI; *U.S. Private*, pg. 254
Bolls, Gend, Printing--Burda GmbH, Offenburg, Germany; *Int'l*, pg. 233
Boltin, George, V.P.-Sls. & Mktg.--Kurz-Kasch, Inc., Wilmington, OH; *U.S. Private*, pg. 637
Bolton, Frances, Administrator-Sls.--Lumonics Inc., Kanata, Canada; *Int'l*, pg. 1314
Bolton, George C., Sr. V.P. & Dir.-Pur. & Sls.--The Law Company, Inc., Wichita, KS; *U.S. Private*, pg. 653
Bonadio, Michael, Dir.-Sls. Promo.--Fruit of the Loom, Inc., Chicago, IL; *U.S. Public*, pg. 685
Bonadurer, Werner, Exec. V.P.--Union Bank of Switzerland, Zurich, Switzerland; *Int'l*, pg. 1439
Bonati, Mr., Mgr.-Sls.--ILRO Srl, Brienza, Italy; *Int'l*, pg. 646
Bonavia, Patricia, V.P.-Sls.--AMCORE Capital Management, Inc., Rockford, IL; *U.S. Public*, pg. 64
Bond, Edward H., Gen. Mgr.-Sls.--Ellicott Machine Corporation International, Baltimore, MD; *U.S. Private*, pg. 372
Bond, Larry, V.P.-Client Svcs.--Atlas Weathering DSET Laboratories, Phoenix, AZ; *U.S. Private*, pg. 96
Bonds, Andrew, Sr. V.P.-Sls.--DeLeuw, Cather & Company, Washington, DC; *U.S. Private*, pg. 841
Bonham, Mike, Sr. V.P.-Sls. & Mktg.--Cerprobe Corporation, Gilbert, AZ; *U.S. Public*, pg. 332
Bonham, Trevor, Mgr.-Intl. Sls.--Miniature Precision Components, Walworth, WI; *U.S. Private*, pg. 750
Bonney, Michael W., V.P.-Sls.--Biogen, Inc., Cambridge, MA; *U.S. Public*, pg. 230
Bonnici, Linda, Gen. Mgr.-Sls.--KLAS, Inc., Las Vegas, NV; *U.S. Private*, pg. 647
Bonvinie, Tony, Mgr.-Retail Sls.--WAXY (FM), Fort Lauderdale, FL; *U.S. Public*, pg. 925
Booker, Steve, V.P.-Sls./Automotive Div.--Armor All Products Group, Oakland, CA; *U.S. Public*, pg. 387
Bookstaver, Chuck, V.P.-Mktg.--Flexible Flyer Toys, West Point, MS; *U.S. Private*, pg. 412
Boone, Pamela, Mgr.-Office Support--Overholtzer Church Furniture, Inc., Modesto, CA; *U.S. Private*, pg. 823
Boone, Sharon, V.P.-Sls. & Mktg.--Johnson Products Co., Inc., Chicago, IL; *U.S. Public*, pg. 915
Boos, Pat, V.P.-Sls. & Mktg.--Lenox Collections, Langhorne, PA; *U.S. Public*, pg. 261
Booth, Doug, Sls. Mgr.--Penn Champ, East Butler, PA; *U.S. Private*, pg. 145
Booth, James E., V.P.-Sls.--McCormick Paint Works Company, Rockville, MD; *U.S. Private*, pg. 720
Booth, Neil, V.P.-Sls. & Mktg.--Brown & Haley, Tacoma, WA; *U.S. Private*, pg. 173
Booth, Scott, Dir.-Sls.--Turner Construction Co., Philadelphia, PA; *U.S. Public*, pg. 1645
Boozer, Larry, V.P.-Sls.--Lancaster Malleable Castings Company, Lancaster, PA; *U.S. Private*, pg. 645
Bordeleau, John, V.P.-Adv. Sls.--Cable Television Division, New Canaan, CT; *U.S. Public*, pg. 329
Bordelon, Clarence J., V.P.-Sls. & Admin.--Tyler Elevator Products, Inc., Valley View, OH; *U.S. Private*, pg. 1112
Borden, Arthur, Dir.-Dir. Response--The Vermont Teddy Bear Company, Inc., Shelburne, VT; *U.S. Public*, pg. 1716
Bordfeld, Glenn R., V.P.-Sls.--Juno Lighting, Inc., Des Plaines, IL; *U.S. Public*, pg. 935
Boren, John, Dir.-Repaint Sls.--Dunn-Edwards Corporation, Los Angeles, CA; *U.S. Private*, pg. 347
Borgan, J., V.P.-Sls. & Mktg.--Crane Valves/North American, Joliet, IL; *U.S. Public*, pg. 457
Borges, Felix R., Grp. Pres.--Rochester Midland Corporation, Rochester, NY; *U.S. Private*, pg. 937
Borgese, Anthony, V.P.-Sls./Consumer Prods.--Alberto-Culver Company, Melrose Park, IL; *U.S. Public*, pg. 37
Borgese, Tony, V.P.-Consumer Product Sls.--Consumer Products Div., Melrose Park, IL; *U.S. Public*, pg. 37

Borghese, Frank, V.P.-N. American Sls.--Symbol Technologies, Inc., Holtsville, NY; *U.S. Public*, pg. 1546
Borja, Raul, Mgr.-Sls.--Banner Wholesale Grocers, Inc., Chicago, IL; *U.S. Private*, pg. 114
Bork, Walter A., V.P.-Sls. & Supply--Mobil Oil Corporation, Fairfax, VA; *U.S. Public*, pg. 1118
Borland, Ralph, V.P.-Sls. & Service--Greyhound Lines, Inc., Dallas, TX; *U.S. Public*, pg. 765
Borland, Ralph, V.P.-Sls. & Services--Greyhound Lines, Inc., Dallas, TX; *U.S. Public*, pg. 765
Bormann, John H., V.P.-Sls. & Mktg.--Rymer Meat Inc., Chicago, IL; *U.S. Public*, pg. 1414
Bornhuetter, Doug, V.P.-Sls. & Mktg.--Gunite Corporation, Rockford, IL; *U.S. Public*, pg. 933
Boroughs, Jean, Dir.-Sls.--Europa Cruises Corporation, Saint Petersburg, FL; *U.S. Public*, pg. 595
Borowiec, John, V.P.-Sls.--GS Electric, Carlisle, PA; *U.S. Public*, pg. 726
Borruso, Joseph V., Sr. V.P.-Sls. & Engrng.--Bosch Automotive Group, Farmington, MI; *Int'l*, pg. 204
Bors, Dan, Dir.-Sls.--Revere Transducers Inc., Cerritos, CA; *U.S. Public*, pg. 790
Borseth, John D., Sr. V.P.-Sls. & Mktg.--Newcor, Inc., Bloomfield Hills, MI; *U.S. Public*, pg. 1176
Borshell, David, Sr. V.P.-Sls. & Mktg.--Image Entertainment, Inc., Chatsworth, CA; *U.S. Public*, pg. 870
Borys, Walter, V.P.-Sls.--Cereal Partners Worldwide, Morges, Switzerland; *U.S. Public*, pg. 718
Borys, Walter, V.P.-Sls.--Cereal Partners Worldwide, Morges, Switzerland; *Int'l*, pg. 916
Bosch, Larry, Dir.-Intl. Sls.--Celestial Seasonings, Boulder, CO; *U.S. Public*, pg. 319
Boschen, Chris, V.P.-Mktg., Sls. & Business Devel.--L3 Communications Telemetry & Instrumentation Div., San Diego, CA; *U.S. Private*, pg. 639
Boshears, Robert, V.P.-Sls.--Welsco Inc., North Little Rock, AR; *U.S. Private*, pg. 1161
Bosken-Diebels, Paul, Dr., Pres.--Diebels Private Brewery, Issum, Germany; *Int'l*, pg. 413
Bosken, Lidy, Sls. Dir.--Berlitz Schools of Languages B.V., Amsterdam, Netherlands; *U.S. Public*, pg. 222
Boskey, William, Dir.-Intl. Sls., Mktg. & Joint Ventures--GM Powertrain Group, Pontiac, MI; *U.S. Public*, pg. 719
Boss, Frank, Dir.-Project Devel.--Jacobs Applied Technology, Inc., Orangeburg, SC; *U.S. Public*, pg. 921
Bossaerts, Nadine, V.P.-Sls./Latin America--Maison Mathieu, S.A., Antwerp, Belgium; *Int'l*, pg. 846
Bosse, Dave, Coord.-Sls.--Yardney Technical Products, Inc., Pawcatuck, CT; *U.S. Private*, pg. 376
Bosticco, Giorgio, Dir.-Sls.--Barbero 1891 SpA, Canale, Italy; *Int'l*, pg. 164
Bostrom, Andrew, V.P.-Sls. & Mktg.--Ace Tank & Equipment Co., Seattle, WA; *U.S. Private*, pg. 12
Bostrom, Susan, V.P.-Sls.--FTP Software Inc., Andover, MA; *U.S. Public*, pg. 609
Boswell, Betsy, Mgr.-Sls.--Washington Business Journal, Inc., Arlington, VA; *U.S. Private*, pg. 20
Boteler, Jack, Natl. Sls. Mgr.--Bran & Luebbe Inc., Buffalo Grove, IL; *Int'l*, pg. 1378
Botha, Kobus, Mgr.-Sls. & Admin.--Sasol Ammonia, Johannesburg, South Africa; *Int'l*, pg. 1196
Botsford, David, Pres.-The Botsford Grp.--Fitzgerald & Co., Atlanta, GA; *U.S. Private*, pg. 409
Bott, Robert L., Sr. V.P.-Opers.--Quick & Reilly, Inc., New York, NY; *U.S. Public*, pg. 650
Botthof, Thomas, Prod. Specialist--Battenfeld of America, West Warwick, RI; *Int'l*, pg. 825
Botti, Vincent, V.P.-Retail Sls.--J.L. Hammett Company, Braintree, MA; *U.S. Private*, pg. 498
Bottino, Ron, V.P.-Sls. & Mktg.--Connecticut Spring & Stamping Corporation, Farmington, CT; *U.S. Private*, pg. 263
Bouchard, Wayne, V.P.-Sls.-Switch Prods.--Automatic Switch Co., Florham Park, NJ; *U.S. Public*, pg. 573
Bouck, Robert, Dir.-Fleet & Leasing--CC Services, Bloomington, IL; *U.S. Private*, pg. 279
Boudour, Abdu, V.P.-Sls. & Mktg.--QC Optics, Inc., Wilmington, MA; *U.S. Public*, pg. 1345
Boudreaux, Frank, V.P.-Sls. & Mktg.--SOLOCO, Inc., Lafayette, LA; *U.S. Public*, pg. 1179
Boudreaux, O'Neil, V.P.-Sls. & Mktg.--General American Life Insurance Co., Saint Louis, MO; *U.S. Private*, pg. 443
Bouffard, Gary, V.P.-Sls. & Mktg.--Ideal Forging Corporation, Southington, CT; *U.S. Private*, pg. 557
Bouffard, Gaston, Sr. V.P./Sls. & Mktg./Paper & Bus. Devel.--Donohue Inc., Quebec, Canada; *Int'l*, pg. 1075
Bouilhol, Christophe, Dir.-Sls.--Rainbow Technologies, Neuilly-sur-Seine, France; *U.S. Public*, pg. 1359
Boulais, Dee, Mgr.-Sls. & Service--Lan-O-Sheen, Inc., Saint Paul, MN; *U.S. Private*, pg. 645
Boulanger, Andre, V.P.-Sls.--Gaz Metropolitain & Company, Montreal, Canada; *Int'l*, pg. 541
Bouley, Dave, V.P.-Sls.--Advanced Circuit Technology, Nashua, NH; *U.S. Private*, pg. 21
Boundy, Edward, V.P.-Sls. & Mktg.--The Weetabix Company, Inc., Clinton, MA; *Int'l*, pg. 1488
Bouquillon, Ed, Mgr.-Sls.--Delta Industries, East Granby, CT; *U.S. Private*, pg. 322
Bourassa, Mike, Mgr.-Sls.--Eland-Brandt, B.V., Amsterdam, Netherlands; *U.S. Public*, pg. 895
Bourdages, Alain, Dir.-Sls.--The Canadian Coleman Co., Ltd., Toronto, Canada; *U.S. Private*, pg. 691
Bourguet, Bruno, Dir.-Sls. & Mktg.--Amtech International, Nanterre, France; *U.S. Public*, pg. 106
Bourke, Jean, V.P.-Sls.--Arrow Pneumatics Co. Inc., Lake Zurich, IL; *U.S. Private*, pg. 85
Bourne, C.V., V.P.-Sls.--Dispatch Consumer Services, Westerville, OH; *U.S. Private*, pg. 335
Bourne, H.S., V.P.-Sls.--Home Beneficial Corporation, Richmond, VA; *U.S. Public*, pg. 76
Boutin, Robert, Mgr.-Sls.--Joseph Kirschner Co., Augusta, ME; *U.S. Private*, pg. 599
Boutsikaris, Peter, Mgr.-Reg. Sls.--ENSI, Inc., Rahway, NJ; *U.S. Public*, pg. 546
Bouvette, William, V.P.-Sls.--TSC Shannock Corporation, Burnaby, Canada; *Int'l*, pg. 1343
Bouwmeester, Frank, Mgr.-Sls., N.W. U.S./San Francisco--Singapore Airlines Ltd., San Francisco, CA; *Int'l*, pg. 1374
Bouy, Claude, Dir.-Sls.-Novotel--Societe Internationale des Hotels Novotel, Evry, France; *Int'l*, pg. 21
Bouzoumet, Mr., Mgr.-Sls.--Sonauto S.A., Saint Ouen, France; *Int'l*, pg. 1063
Bova, Greg, Mgr.-Sls.--SL Montevideo Technology, Inc., Montevideo, MN; *U.S. Public*, pg. 1419
Bovaird, B.H., V.P.-Customer Svc. & Sls.--Bovaird Supply Co., Tulsa, OK; *U.S. Private*, pg. 162
Bovard, Pierre, V.P. & Gen. Mgr.-Radio--The Arbitron Company, New York, NY; *U.S. Public*, pg. 331
Bover, J. Michael, Sr. V.P.-Giftware Div. Sls.--Crystal Clear Industries, Ridgefield Park, NJ; *U.S. Private*, pg. 293
Boville, Ramon Sanjuan, Dir.-Mktg., Pub. Rels., Sls. & Adv.--Cabinas Telefonicas, S.A. (Cabitel), Madrid, Spain; *Int'l*, pg. 1371
Bowater, M., V.P.-Sls.--Kruger Pulp & Paper Sales, Inc., New York, NY; *Int'l*, pg. 762
Bowen, Jack, V.P.-Sls.-Southwest--Crabar Business Systems, Dayton, OH; *U.S. Private*, pg. 283
Bowen, John, V.P.-Sls.--Golden Peanut Company, Alpharetta, GA; *U.S. Private*, pg. 459
Bowen, Mary, Dir.-Mktg.--Power & Telephone Supply Company, Memphis, TN; *U.S. Private*, pg. 877
Bowen, Sheila, Dir.-Sls.--Sunstone Hotel Investors, Inc., San Clemente, CA; *U.S. Public*, pg. 1536
Bower, Don, Salesman--Kern Livestock Supplement Co., Inc., Bakersfield, CA; *U.S. Private*, pg. 46
Bower, Peter, Assoc. Publr.-Sls.--Time Inc., New York, NY; *U.S. Public*, pg. 1612
Bower, Scott, Sr. V.P.-Sls. & Mktg.--AST Research Inc., Irvine, CA; *Int'l*, pg. 1181
Bowes, Bob, V.P.-Sls. & Mktg.--National Truck Leasing System, Oak Brook Terrace, IL; *U.S. Private*, pg. 787
Bowes, Cecil F., V.P.-North American Sls.--PSC Inc., Webster, NY; *U.S. Public*, pg. 1245
Bowes, John, Dir.-Intl. Mktg. & Sls.--Behlen Mfg. Co., Columbus, NE; *U.S. Private*, pg. 130
Bowler, Peter, V.P. & Gen. Mgr.-Sls.--AMR Corporation, Fort Worth, TX; *U.S. Public*, pg. 9
Bowler, Peter M., V.P. & Gen. Sls. Mgr.--American Airlines, Inc., Fort Worth, TX; *U.S. Public*, pg. 9
Bowling, Gene H., V.P.-Corp. & Mgr.-Intl. Sls.--Alkota Cleaning Systems, Inc., Alcester, SD; *U.S. Private*, pg. 34
Bowling, Tim, V.P.-Sls.--Orthofix Inc., Richardson, TX; *Int'l*, pg. 1011
Bowman, Steve E., V.P. & Dir.-Sls. & Mktg.--Shuford Mills, Inc., Hickory, NC; *U.S. Private*, pg. 996
Bowman, Ted, Mgr.-North American Sls. & Mktg.--International Lottery & Totalizator Systems, Inc., Carlsbad, CA; *U.S. Public*, pg. 900
Bowsher, Steven J., V.P.-Sls. & Mktg.--Inland Steel Industries, Inc., Chicago, IL; *U.S. Public*, pg. 879
Bowsher, Steven J., V.P.-Sls. & Mktg./ISFPC--Inland Steel Products Company, East Chicago, IN; *U.S. Public*, pg. 879
Boyce, James, Dir.-Sls.--Trapp Family Lodge, Inc., Stowe, VT; *U.S. Private*, pg. 1098
Boychuk, Robert, V.P.-Sls.-Bus. Prods. Div.--Colad Group Inc., Buffalo, NY; *U.S. Private*, pg. 250
Boychuk, Robert, Mgr.-Sls.--Colad Group Inc., Buffalo, NY; *U.S. Private*, pg. 250
Boyd, Bryan W., V.P.-Natl. Sls. & Distr.--Rogers Cantel Mobile Communications Inc., Saint-Laurent, Canada; *Int'l*, pg. 1122
Boyd, Margaret, Sr. V.P.-Sls. & Mktg.--First Tennessee National Corporation, Memphis, TN; *U.S. Public*, pg. 638
Boyd, Stan, Sr. V.P.-Sls. & Mktg.--The Fairmont Hotels, San Francisco, CA; *U.S. Private*, pg. 391
Boyd, Thomas R., Mgr.-Western Reg. Sls.--Sofamor Danek Group, Inc., Memphis, TN; *U.S. Public*, pg. 1482
Boyer, Henry K., V.P.-Sls.--Comcast Cellular Communications, Inc., Wayne, PA; *U.S. Public*, pg. 407
Boyett, Terry, Coord.-Sls. & Svcs.--Wright Brand Foods, Inc., Vernon, TX; *U.S. Private*, pg. 1192
Boyke, Dale C., V.P.-Mktg. & Sls.--The Oilgear Company, Milwaukee, WI; *U.S. Public*, pg. 1215
Boykin, William, V.P.-Intl. Sls.--Vital Signs, Englewood, CO; *U.S. Public*, pg. 1723
Boylan, John, V.P.-Sls. & Mktg.--Harriss & Covington Hosiery Mills, High Point, NC; *U.S. Private*, pg. 506
Boylan, Mike, Mgr.-Sls.--Wausau Metals, Nanik Division, Wausau, WI; *U.S. Public*, pg. 1500
Boyle, C., Gen. Mgr.-Sls.--Farrell Lines Incorporated, New York, NY; *U.S. Private*, pg. 397
Boyle, Edward J., Jr., V.P.-Sls.-Eastern Div.--Crown Cork & Seal, Eastern Div., Philadelphia, PA; *U.S. Public*, pg. 463
Boyle, Frank J., V.P.-Sls. & Engrng.--Selas Corporation of America, Dresher, PA; *U.S. Public*, pg. 1454
Boyle, John C., V.P. & Gen. Mgr.--Heluva Good Cheese Inc., Sodus, NY; *Int'l*, pg. 752
Boyle, Mike, V.P.-Sls.--M & C Specialties Company, Southampton, PA; *U.S. Private*, pg. 684
Boyle, Ronald, V.P.-Sls.--Frozfruit Corporation, Gardena, CA; *U.S. Private*, pg. 430
Boyles, Brad, Mgr.-Adv., Sls. & Mktg.--Gunver Manufacturing Co., Manchester, CT; *U.S. Private*, pg. 488
Boynton, John, Dir.-Canned Sls.--Icicle Seafoods, Inc., Seattle, WA; *U.S. Private*, pg. 556
Boyum, Ronald L., V.P.-Sls. & Sports Mktg.--The Topps Company, Inc., New York, NY; *U.S. Public*, pg. 1621
Bozsan, Rob, V.P.-Sls.--Hudepohl-Schoenling Brewing Company, Cincinnati, OH; *U.S. Private*, pg. 545
Bozza, Anthony, Mgr.-Sls.--Premier Metal Products Company, Bronx, NY; *U.S. Private*, pg. 881
Bracci, George T., V.P.-Sls. & Mktg.--EAO Switch Corporation, Milford, CT; *Int'l*, pg. 444
Brackemyre, Daniel J., Dir.-Sls., IPL--Ipalco Enterprises, Inc., Indianapolis, IN; *U.S. Public*, pg. 912
Brackman, R., Mgr.-Belgium/Luxembourg Sls.--Bakery Ingredients Division, Delft, Netherlands; *Int'l*, pg. 1142
Bradbury, Phil E., Mgr.-Mktg.--Bradbury Company, Inc., Moundridge, KS; *U.S. Private*, pg. 163
Bradford, Claire V., V.P.-Sls. & Staff Services--The Arnold Palmer Golf Company, Ooltewah, TN; *U.S. Public*, pg. 132
Bradford, Michael, V.P.-Sls. & Mktg.--West Penetone Corporation, Tenafly, NJ; *U.S. Private*, pg. 1158
Bradley, Brian, V.P.-Sls.--Lander Co., Inc., Englewood, NJ; *U.S. Private*, pg. 647
Bradley, Daniel J., Div. V.P.-Sls. & Mktg./N. America--Ethyl Corporation, Richmond, VA; *U.S. Public*, pg. 595
Bradley, Rex, V.P.-Amateur Bat Sls.--Hillerich & Bradsby Co., Louisville, KY; *U.S. Private*, pg. 530
Bradly, Miles, Mgr.-Sls.--Hartley Courseware, San Diego, CA; *U.S. Private*, pg. 601
Bradtke, Robert C., V.P.-Sls.--Pullman Industries, Inc., Pullman, MI; *U.S. Private*, pg. 894
Brady, Don, Sr. V.P.-Sls. & Mktg.--Bruning Paint Company, Baltimore, MD; *U.S. Private*, pg. 176
Brady, Francis, Mgr.-Sls.--Merchants Publishing Co., Kalamazoo, MI; *U.S. Private*, pg. 732
Brady, Frank, Sr. V.P.-Contract Services & Intl. Sls.--Pandrol Jackson, Inc., Ludington, MI; *Int'l*, pg. 280
Brady, Martha, V.P.-Sales--Guerlain, Inc., New York, NY; *Int'l*, pg. 780
Brady, Tom, Mgr.-Eastern Reg. Sls.--The Flood Company, Hudson, OH; *U.S. Private*, pg. 414
Brafford, Donald, Mgr.-Sls./Southern Reg.--AEP Industries, Inc., South Hackensack, NJ; *U.S. Public*, pg. 4
Brahl, Doug, V.P.-Sls. & Mktg.--U.S. Safety, Lenexa, KS; *U.S. Private*, pg. 1125
Brahm, Cliff, Dir.-Sls. & Mktg.--Huffy Service First, Inc., Miamisburg, OH; *U.S. Public*, pg. 846
Brain, Roger A., V.P.-Mktg. & Sls.--Cominco, Ltd., Vancouver, Canada; *Int'l*, pg. 307
Brainard, Douglas M., V.P.-Sls. & Mktg.--Sales Technologies, Atlanta, GA; *U.S. Public*, pg. 395
Brainard, Ken, Dir.-Sls.--Brudi, Inc., Ridgefield, WA; *U.S. Private*, pg. 675
Braithwait, Ross E., Dir.-Sls.--Varco-Pruden Buildings, Memphis, TN; *U.S. Public*, pg. 1677
Brak, P., Dir.-Sls.--Spectra-Physics Belgium BVBA, Antwerp, Belgium; *Int'l*, pg. 1290
Braley, Peter, V.P.-Sls. & Mktg.--WMF/USA, Farmingdale, NY; *U.S. Private*, pg. 1144
Bralley, Candy, Mgr.-Sls. Support--Danzas Corporation, Bellevue, WA; *Int'l*, pg. 382
Bralower, Steve, Sr. V.P.-Leasing--Carr Real Estate Services, Washington, DC; *U.S. Public*, pg. 309
Braly, Gary, Mgr.-Sls.--Public Service Company of Oklahoma, Tulsa, OK; *U.S. Public*, pg. 324
Bramlett, Michael, Dir.-Sls.--Mrs. Smith's Bakeries, Inc., Thomasville, GA; *U.S. Public*, pg. 657
Bramwell, Richard, Mgr.-Sls.--Daubert Chemical Company, Inc., Chicago, IL; *U.S. Private*, pg. 313
Branch, Brenda, V.P.-Sls.--House of Raeford Farms, Inc., Raeford, NC; *U.S. Private*, pg. 542
Brand, J.C., Dir.-Sls.--Charmilles Technologies SA, Meyrin, Switzerland; *Int'l*, pg. 489
Brandi, Ralph, V.P.-Modular Products--Linfinity Microelectronics Inc., Garden Grove, CA; *U.S. Public*, pg. 1547
Brandt, Alan, V.P.-Sls.--N Base Communications, Germantown, MD; *U.S. Public*, pg. 1027
Brandt, C., Corp. Sls. Mgr.--Koyo Corporation of USA, Sales Division, Westlake, OH; *Int'l*, pg. 760
Brandt, Hugh, Mgr.-Commercial--Buehler, Limited, Lake Bluff, IL; *U.S. Public*, pg. 574
Brandt, Ronald D., V.P.-Mktg. & Sls.--United Life Insurance Company, Cedar Rapids, IA; *U.S. Public*, pg. 1677
Branigan, Joseph P., Asst. V.P.-Credit Sls.--Consumers Financial Corporation, Camp Hill, PA; *U.S. Public*, pg. 437
Brannen, Charles A., V.P.--Overton Gear & Tool Corp., Addison, IL; *U.S. Private*, pg. 823
Branning, Harry, Dir.-Sls.--Advest, Inc., Hartford, CT; *U.S. Public*, pg. 23
Brannon, David, Dir.-Sls.--Augat, Inc., Automotive Division, Mount Clemens, MI; *U.S. Public*, pg. 1598
Brannon, Jim, V.P.-Sls.--Trinidad/Benham Corp., Denver, CO; *U.S. Private*, pg. 1103
Branstetter, Tim, Mgr.-Sls.--Bethel Mills, Inc., Bethel, VT; *U.S. Private*, pg. 141
Brant, E.T., Dir.-Sls.--Hepworth Heating Ltd., Belper, United Kingdom; *Int'l*, pg. 615
Brantley, John, Asst. Store Mgr.--Gump's, San Francisco, CA; *U.S. Public*, pg. 782
Branton, Robert, V.P.-Sls. & Mktg.--United Hardware Distributing Co., Plymouth, MN; *U.S. Private*, pg. 335
Brashear, Dessa, Assoc. Publr. & Mgr.-Bus.--HarperCollins San Francisco, San Francisco, CA; *Int'l*, pg. 927
Brasseur, Dave, Sls. Mgr.-North Central District--Fluidtec Engineer Products, Greensboro, NC; *U.S. Public*, pg. 401
Braun, Barbara, Sec.-Sls.--General Microwave Corporation, Amityville, NY; *U.S. Public*, pg. 717
Braun, Grace, Sls. Rep.-Sterilizer Div.--Environmental Tectonics Corporation (ETC), Southampton, PA; *U.S. Public*, pg. 587
Braun, James, V.P.-Mktg. & Sls.--Recoton Auto Corporation, Lincolnshire, IL; *U.S. Public*, pg. 1369
Braunger, Bat, Mgr.-Sls.--CMI Metro Pave, Cedar Falls, IA; *U.S. Public*, pg. 279
Brauss, K.A., V.P.-Sls. & Mktg.--Marley Electric Heating Company, Bennettsville, SC; *U.S. Public*, pg. 1676
Bravata, Doug, V.P.-Sls.--RTG Furniture Corp., Seffner, FL; *U.S. Private*, pg. 905
Bravo, Rick, V.P.-Sls.-Fresh Vegetables--Dole Food Company, Inc., Westlake Village, CA; *U.S. Public*, pg. 515

Braxton, Charles R., Dir.-Gas Mktg. & Sls.--Niagara Mohawk Power Corporation, Syracuse, NY; *U.S. Public*, pg. 1181
Bray, Karen, Sr. V.P.-Sls.--Baltimore Stationery Co./Total Office, Baltimore, MD; *U.S. Private*, pg. 113
Breden, Jeanette, Adv. Coord.--Taube/Violante, Inc., Norwalk, CT; *U.S. Private*, pg. 1069
Breen, Donald, Jr., Sr. V.P.-Sls. & Mktg.--John Morrell & Co., Cincinnati, OH; *U.S. Public*, pg. 1479
Breen, Edward, Pres.--Broadband Networks Group, Hatboro, PA; *U.S. Public*, pg. 716
Breit, Catherine, V.P.-Sls.--Shaker Advertising Agency, Oak Park, IL; *U.S. Private*, pg. 988
Brems, Marc, Dir.-Sls.--Rainbow Technologies, GmbH, Unterschleissheim, Germany; *U.S. Public*, pg. 1359
Brendle, Charles A., Jr., Dir.-Tobacco Paper Sls.--P.H. Glatfelter Company, Spring Grove, PA; *U.S. Public*, pg. 746
Brennan, Bill, Dir.-Sls.--Vishay Intertechnology, Inc., Malvern, PA; *U.S. Public*, pg. 1721
Brennan, Jim, V.P.-Mktg. & Sls./Motors--Marathon Electric Manufacturing Corp., Wausau, WI; *U.S. Public*, pg. 1371
Brennan, John, V.P.-Naperville Sls.--Solar Communications, Inc., Naperville, IL; *U.S. Private*, pg. 1012
Brennan, Vin, V.P.-Community Mkts.--John H. Harland Company, Decatur, GA; *U.S. Public*, pg. 785
Brennan, Vin, V.P.-Community Mkts.Sls.--The Check Store, Lakewood, CO; *U.S. Public*, pg. 785
Brently, Dennis, V.P.-Sls.--Coleman Powermate, Inc., Omaha, NE; *U.S. Private*, pg. 691
Brenton, Keith, V.P.-Sls. & Mktg.--Autoswage Products, Inc., Shelton, CT; *U.S. Private*, pg. 101
Breton, John, V.P.-Sls. & Mktg.--Nalle Plastics Inc., Austin, TX; *U.S. Private*, pg. 773
Brett, Paul, V.P.-Mktg. & Sls.--R.F. Technology, Inc., Norwalk, CT; *Int'l*, pg. 1289
Brevik, John, Exec. V.P.-Sls., Adv. & Mktg.--Exotic Rubber & Plastics Corp., Farmington Hills, MI; *U.S. Private*, pg. 388
Brewer, Ned, Gen. Mgr.-Sls.--McDowell Mfg. Co. Inc., Du Bois, PA; *U.S. Private*, pg. 300
Brewster, Wayne, V.P.-Variable Sls.--Ameritas Life Insurance Corp., Lincoln, NE; *U.S. Private*, pg. 65
Breyer, Gabor, Mgr.-Sls.--Sensormatic kfi, Budapest, Hungary; *U.S. Public*, pg. 1458
Briedenbach, Rainer, Sr. V.P.-Sls. & Mktg.--Deutz AG, Cologne, Germany; *Int'l*, pg. 407
Briggs, David, Dir.-Mktg. & Sls.--Frequency and Time Systems, Inc., Beverly, MA; *U.S. Public*, pg. 488
Briggs, Ray, V.P.-Sls.--Masoneilan North American Operations, Houston, TX; *U.S. Public*, pg. 528
Briggs, Robert, Corp. V.P.-Sls.--National Car Rental System, Inc., Minneapolis, MN; *U.S. Public*, pg. 1379
Briggs, Stephen M., V.P.-Consumer Coatings--The Valspar Corporation, Minneapolis, MN; *U.S. Public*, pg. 1707
Brigham, Debbie, Supvr.-Mktg. Svcs.--Sanderson Plumbing Products Inc., Columbus, MS; *U.S. Private*, pg. 964
Brigham, Lisa, Dir.-Sls.--Kobra International Ltd, New York, NY; *U.S. Private*, pg. 628
Brigham, Sharon A., Asst. Mgr.-Sls.--Rodman Industries, Marinette, WI; *U.S. Private*, pg. 402
Bright, James, Dir.-Mktg. & Mgr.-Natl. Sls.--Sprayway, Inc., Addison, IL; *U.S. Private*, pg. 462
Brightbill, Darlene, Rep.-Adv. & Sls.--Credit Union National Association, Madison, WI; *U.S. Private*, pg. 288
Brinkman, D.B., V.P.-Sls.--Ceco Door Products, Brentwood, TN; *U.S. Public*, pg. 1676
Brinkman, Don, V.P.-Opers.--Mr. Gatti's, Inc., Kerrville, TX; *U.S. Private*, pg. 639
Brinkmann, J.E., V.P.-Intl. Sls.--R.T. Vanderbilt Company, Inc., Norwalk, CT; *U.S. Private*, pg. 1133
Brinkmann, Karl, Mgr.-Inside Sls.--O.I. Corporation, College Station, TX; *U.S. Public*, pg. 1208
Brinks, Jim, Mgr.-Sls. & Mktg.--Reedspectrum, Holden, MA; *Int'l*, pg. 624
Brisco, Robert N., Sr. V.P.-Mktg. & New Bus. Devel.--Los Angeles Times, Los Angeles, CA; *U.S. Public*, pg. 1616
Bristow, A., Dir.-Sls. & Mktg.--Andres Wines (Atlantic) Ltd., Dartmouth, Canada; *Int'l*, pg. 76
Brix, Kenneth G., V.P.-Sls.--Cognitronics Corporation, Danbury, CT; *U.S. Public*, pg. 394
Broady, Craig, V.P.-Wood Sls.--Pope & Talbot, Inc., Portland, OR; *U.S. Public*, pg. 1316
Brocco, Frank A., Dir.-Sls. & Mktg.--First American Title Insurance Co. of N.Y., New York, NY; *U.S. Public*, pg. 626
Brochhausen, Jim, Sr. V.P.-Sls.--Pinnacle Brands, Inc., Dallas, TX; *U.S. Private*, pg. 866
Brock, A.J., Sls. Mgr.-Customer Support--Chevrolet Motor Div. General Motors Corp., Warren, MI; *U.S. Public*, pg. 720
Brock, Gary, V.P.-Children's Wear Sls.--OshKosh B'Gosh, Inc., Oshkosh, WI; *U.S. Public*, pg. 1232
Brock, Lee, V.P.-Sls.--Fairfield Bay, Fairfield Bay, AR; *U.S. Public*, pg. 610
Brock, Stephen P., Sr. V.P.-Sls. & Mktg.--Baldwin Piano & Organ Company, Loveland, OH; *U.S. Public*, pg. 169
Brocker, Paul, Mgr.-Intl. Sls.--FMC FoodTech/Fran Rica, Stockton, CA; *U.S. Public*, pg. 605
Brockett, Patrick J., Exec. V.P.-World Wide Mktg. & Sls.--National Semiconductor Corporation, Santa Clara, CA; *U.S. Public*, pg. 1159
Brockman, Hank, Partner-Institutional Sls.--J.C. Bradford & Co., Nashville, TN; *U.S. Private*, pg. 163
Broderick, Dennis, V.P.-Sls.--In-Sink-Erator, Racine, WI; *U.S. Public*, pg. 573
Broderick, John, Mgr.-Sls.--Subaru Mid-America, Inc., Addison, IL; *Int'l*, pg. 523
Broderick, John, Mgr.-Sls. & Mdsg.--Lee Grocery Company, Everett, WA; *U.S. Private*, pg. 657
Broderick, Joseph E., Exec. V.P.-Client Sls. & Services--Manugistics Group, Inc., Rockville, MD; *U.S. Public*, pg. 1042
Brodey, Larry, Pres.--Jaclo Inc., Mountainside, NJ; *U.S. Private*, pg. 349
Brodin, Ulf, Sr. V.P.-After Sls.--BT Industries AB, Mjolby, Sweden; *Int'l*, pg. 123
Brodsky, Richard, Mgr.-Natl. Sls.--Easy Day Manufacturing Company, Holliston, MA; *U.S. Private*, pg. 358
Brody, John, V.P. & Natl. Sls. Mgr.-Men's--Jockey International, Inc., Kenosha, WI; *U.S. Private*, pg. 588
Brody, Michael, V.P.-Sls. & Mktg.--M.S. Walker, Inc., Somerville, MA; *U.S. Private*, pg. 1147
Broens, James P., Dir.-Sls.--Lips United B.V., Drunen, Netherlands; *Int'l*, pg. 812
Broers, M.A.C., Sls.--Mercon Steel Structures B.V., Gorinchem, Netherlands; *Int'l*, pg. 858
Brogan, Mike, V.P.-Sls. & Mktg./Generator Set--Detroit Diesel Corp., Detroit, MI; *U.S. Private*, pg. 850
Brogan, Pat, V.P.-Mktg. & Sls.--Elo TouchSystems, Inc., Fremont, CA; *U.S. Public*, pg. 1362
Broggi, M., Dir.-Sls.--OWL AG Logistik-Systeme, Buchs, Switzerland; *Int'l*, pg. 490
Brommeland, Olav, Mgr.-Mktg. & Sls.--SAS Park Royal Hotel, Lysaker, Norway; *Int'l*, pg. 1202
Bronaugh, John, Natl. Sls. Mgr.--Haws Drinking Faucet Co., Berkeley, CA; *U.S. Private*, pg. 512
Bronson, Charles, Mgr.-Natl. Sls.--PLM Trailer Leasing, San Francisco, CA; *U.S. Public*, pg. 1241
Brook, Robert P., Sr. V.P.-Sls. & Mktg.--EBP Life Insurnace Co., Minneapolis, MN; *U.S. Public*, pg. 635
Brooker, Gregory, V.P.-Sls.--Nomaco, Inc., Zebulon, NC; *U.S. Private*, pg. 801
Brookes, Ed, V.P.-Sls.--Tropitone Furniture Co. Inc., Irvine, CA; *U.S. Private*, pg. 1105
Brooks, Dave, Mgr.-Sls.--PENCO-Ohio, Worthington, OH; *Int'l*, pg. 1508
Brooks, Gary, V.P.-Sls. & Mktg. & Mgr.-Graphics Prods.--Dunmore Corporation, Newtown, PA; *U.S. Private*, pg. 346
Brooks, Henry A., Dir.-Sls.--Lawter International, Inc., Kenosha, WI; *U.S. Public*, pg. 980
Brooks, John, V.P. & Dir.-Sports Sls.--CBS Television Network, New York, NY; *U.S. Public*, pg. 274
Brooks, Lindsay H., Mgr.-Mktg.--Chattem (Canada) Inc., Mississauga, Canada; *U.S. Public*, pg. 342
Brooks, Michael, V.P.-Sls.--Anheuser-Busch Companies, Inc., Saint Louis, MO; *U.S. Public*, pg. 113
Brooks, Michael J., V.P.-Sls.--Anheuser-Busch, Inc., Saint Louis, MO; *U.S. Public*, pg. 114
Brooks, Paul, Natl. Sls.--Dow Hickam Pharmaceuticals Inc., Sugar Land, TX; *U.S. Public*, pg. 1143
Brooks, TaJuana, Mgr.-Mktg. Svcs.--Carlisle Food Service Products, Oklahoma City, OK; *U.S. Public*, pg. 305
Brooks, William J., Dir.-Sls.--Lay's Fine Foods, Knoxville, TN; *U.S. Private*, pg. 655
Brookshire, John, Mgr.-Sls.--Atlas Copco Comptec Inc., Voorheesville, NY; *Int'l*, pg. 96
Broom, Mike, Dir.-Pub. Affairs--AlliedSignal Commercial Avionics Systems, Redmond, WA; *U.S. Public*, pg. 50
Broome, Rich, Asst. V.P. & Dir.-Corp. Communications--Selective Insurance Group, Inc, Branchville, NJ; *U.S. Public*, pg. 1455
Broschart, Ron, Dir.-Sls.--Six Flags Magic Mountain & Six Flags Hurricane Harbor, Valencia, CA; *U.S. Public*, pg. 1611
Brossard, Gerry, V.P.-Sls. & Mktg.--Laidlaw Environmental Services, Inc., Columbia, SC; *U.S. Public*, pg. 975
Brosset, Michel, Dr., Mgr.-Sanitary/Bathroom Equipment Div.--Villeroy & Boch AG, Mettlach, Germany; *Int'l*, pg. 1468
Brost, Dan, Mgr.-Nonautomotive Sls.--Miniature Precision Components, Walworth, WI; *U.S. Private*, pg. 750
Broth, Tim, Dir.-Mktg. & Sls--National Lamination Co., Des Plaines, IL; *U.S. Private*, pg. 1068
Brothers, Gary, V.P.-Sls.--D&H Distributing Company, Harrisburg, PA; *U.S. Private*, pg. 300
Brothers, Jim, Dir.-Sls.--Six Flags Over Texas, Arlington, TX; *U.S. Public*, pg. 1612
Broughton, Donald, V.P.-Sls.--Broad National Bancorporation, Newark, NJ; *U.S. Public*, pg. 257
Broughton, Donald, V.P.-Sls.--Broad National Bank, Newark, NJ; *U.S. Public*, pg. 257
Broughton, George W., Exec. V.P.-Sls. & Mktg.--Broughton Foods Company, Marietta, OH; *U.S. Public*, pg. 259
Brouillette, Bob, V.P.-Sls.--Outdoor Technologies Group, Spirit Lake, IA; *U.S. Private*, pg. 822
Brouse, William K., V.P.-Sls.--First Alert, Inc., Aurora, IL; *U.S. Private*, pg. 406
Broussard, Steve, Sls. Mgr.-Twine & Netting--Barbour Thread, Inc., Blue Mountain, AL; *Int'l*, pg. 618
Browder, J.W., V.P.-Sls./Lighting Div.--Rangaire Inc., Cleburne, TX; *U.S. Public*, pg. 1193
Brown, Barbara C., Sr. V.P.-Sls. & Opers.--Wherehouse Entertainment, Inc., Torrance, CA; *U.S. Private*, pg. 1171
Brown, Barry L., V.P.-Sls. & Mktg.--Michigan Sugar Company, Saginaw, MI; *U.S. Public*, pg. 873
Brown, Bob, V.P.-Sls. & Mktg.--Robertshaw Controls Company, Richmond, VA; *Int'l*, pg. 1243
Brown, Bobby, Gen. Mgr.-Sls.--Cave City Chevrolet, Cave City, KY; *U.S. Private*, pg. 712
Brown, C. Douglas, V.P.-Sls. & Mktg.--Intermet Corporation, Troy, MI; *U.S. Public*, pg. 894
Brown, Cary, Exec. V.P.-Sls. & Customer Services--American Eurocopter Corp., Grand Prairie, TX; *Int'l*, pg. 29
Brown, Chris, Mgr.-Sls.--Madison Industries Inc. of Georgia, Conyers, GA; *U.S. Private*, pg. 428
Brown, Daniel, Sr. V.P.-Sls. & Mktg.--J.H. Heafner Co. Inc., Lincolnton, NC; *U.S. Private*, pg. 514
Brown, Daniel F., Exec. V.P.-Sls.--CompuCom Systems, Inc., Dallas, TX; *U.S. Public*, pg. 1424
Brown, Darrell, Gen. Mgr.-Sls.--KGTV, San Diego, CA; *U.S. Public*, pg. 1070
Brown, David, V.P.-Sls. & Mktg.--Cargill Detroit Corp., Clawson, MI; *U.S. Private*, pg. 210
Brown, David, V.P.-Sls.--Gates, McDonald & Co., Hilliard, OH; *U.S. Private*, pg. 789
Brown, Dee, Mgr.-Sls.--Ritchie Industries, Inc., Conrad, IA; *U.S. Private*, pg. 933
Brown, Don, Mgr.-Sls.--Atwood Oceanics, Inc., Houston, TX; *U.S. Public*, pg. 146
Brown, Don, V.P.-Sls. & Mktg., Surgical Products--Mentor Urology, Inc., Santa Barbara, CA; *U.S. Public*, pg. 1086
Brown, Earl, Mgr.-Branch--GAI Consultants, Inc., Charleston, WV; *U.S. Private*, pg. 434
Brown, Frank, Dir.-Adv. Sls.--MTV Europe, London, United Kingdom; *U.S. Private*, pg. 779
Brown, Fred, V.P.-APAC Sls.--C-Cube Microsystems, Milpitas, CA; *U.S. Public*, pg. 272
Brown, G. Robert, Sr. V.P.-Mktg. & Sls.--Deltak Inc., Plymouth, MN; *U.S. Public*, pg. 924
Brown, Gene, Exec. V.P.-Sls. & Mktg.--Groendyke Transports, Inc., Enid, OK; *U.S. Private*, pg. 483
Brown, Gregory A., Sr. V.P.-Sls.--Gibson Greetings, Inc., Cincinnati, OH; *U.S. Public*, pg. 742
Brown, Harold Buck, V.P.-Sls.--U.S. Pharmaceuticals, Baltimore, MD; *U.S. Public*, pg. 58
Brown, Holly, Dir.-Sls.--DeVault Foods, Devault, PA; *U.S. Private*, pg. 329
Brown, Howard, Dir.-Sls. & Mktg.--Crown Prince, Inc. (CA), City of Industry, CA; *U.S. Private*, pg. 293
Brown, J.J., V.P.-OE Sls.--Abex Friction Products, Winchester, VA; *U.S. Public*, pg. 443
Brown, Jack, V.P.-Sls. & Mktg.--The Wm. Powell Company, Cincinnati, OH; *U.S. Private*, pg. 877
Brown, James A., V.P.-Sls.--Standard Locknut, Inc., Westfield, IN; *U.S. Private*, pg. 1031
Brown, James A., V.P.-Sls.--Connaught Laboratories, Inc., Swiftwater, PA; *Int'l*, pg. 1109
Brown, James B., V.P.-Sls.--System Sensor Division, Saint Charles, IL; *U.S. Public*, pg. 1306
Brown, Jeff, V.P.-Sls.--Perfecseal Company, Philadelphia, PA; *U.S. Public*, pg. 210
Brown, Jeff, Mgr.-Sls.--Hudson, RCI, Temecula, CA; *U.S. Private*, pg. 546
Brown, Jeff S., Mgr.-Residential Mkt.--Citizens Gas & Coke Utility, Indianapolis, IN; *U.S. Private*, pg. 241
Brown, Jerry, Mgr.-Natl. Sls.--All-Luminum Products, Inc., Philadelphia, PA; *U.S. Private*, pg. 34
Brown, John A., Sr. V.P.-Sls./Fin. Services--The Great-West Life Assurance Company, Winnipeg, Canada; *Int'l*, pg. 557
Brown, Juanita, Sls. Coord.--Bergen Brunswig Medical Corporation, Montgomery, AL; *U.S. Public*, pg. 214
Brown, Kenneth, Mgr.-Sls.--Trimtex Co. Inc., Williamsport, PA; *U.S. Private*, pg. 1103
Brown, Laurie, V.P. & Dir.-Mktg. & Sls.--Farrar, Straus & Giroux, Inc., New York, NY; *Int'l*, pg. 1479
Brown, Martin S., Exec. V.P.-Sls. & Mktg.--Foster Wheeler Environmental Corporation, Livingston, NJ; *U.S. Public*, pg. 677
Brown, Michael, Exec. V.P.--House of Fabrics, Inc., Sherman Oaks, CA; *U.S. Public*, pg. 842
Brown, Michele, Dir.-Adv. Sls.--Butterick Company, Inc., New York, NY; *U.S. Private*, pg. 190
Brown, Mike, Sr. V.P. & Asst. Oper.-Sls. & Mktg.--Alvey Systems, Inc, Saint Louis, MO; *U.S. Private*, pg. 47
Brown, Mike, Mgr.-Sls.--Switchgear & Instrumentation Ltd., Bradford, United Kingdom; *Int'l*, pg. 133
Brown, Mimi, V.P.-Mktg. & Sls.--Denver Nuggets Limited Partnership, Denver, CO; *U.S. Public*, pg. 138
Brown, Morry, Mgr.-Sls., Mktg. & Customer Service--Northern Cable Holdings Ltd., Montreal, Canada; *Int'l*, pg. 241
Brown, P. Kent, Gen. Mgr.-Sls.--Brown Evans Distributing Co., Mesa, AZ; *U.S. Private*, pg. 174
Brown, Patricia, V.P. & Midwest/West Coast Sls. Mgr.--CBS Enterprises Division, New York, NY; *U.S. Public*, pg. 274
Brown, Phillip L., V.P.-Sls. & Mktg.--Pandrol Jackson, Inc., Ludington, MI; *Int'l*, pg. 280
Brown, R. Scott, Sr. V.P.-Worldwide Sls.--Xilinx, Inc., San Jose, CA; *U.S. Public*, pg. 1786
Brown, Renee C., Sr. V.P.-Adv., Sls. & Mktg.--Pro-Line Corporation, Dallas, TX; *U.S. Private*, pg. 887
Brown, Rich, Mgr.-Sls.-Traffic Safety--Radiator Specialty Company, Charlotte, NC; *U.S. Private*, pg. 906
Brown, Richard, Gen. Mgr.-Sls.--Fairfax Lumber & Millwork Company Inc., Springfield, VA; *U.S. Private*, pg. 391
Brown, Richard A., V.P.-Sls. & Mktg.--DMI, Inc., Goodfield, IL; *U.S. Private*, pg. 305
Brown, Robert, Sr. V.P.-Sls.--Gould Paper Corporation, New York, NY; *U.S. Private*, pg. 466
Brown, Robert G., V.P.-Sls.--Ciprico, Inc., Plymouth, MN; *U.S. Public*, pg. 370
Brown, Robert V., Dir.-Natl. Sls.--Tasty Baking Company, Philadelphia, PA; *U.S. Public*, pg. 1561
Brown, Sharon S., Sr. V.P.-Sls. & Service Div.--First Hawaiian Bank, Honolulu, HI; *U.S. Public*, pg. 634
Brown, Steve, Mgr.-Sls.--Utimaco Safeware, Inc., Windsor, CT; *Int'l*, pg. 1444
Brown, T.J., V.P.-Mktg. & Sls.--Alberox Corporation, New Bedford, MA; *Int'l*, pg. 893
Brown, Terry, V.P.-Sls. & Mktg.--Lindberg Corporation, Rosemont, IL; *U.S. Public*, pg. 999
Brown, Warren M., V.P.-Sls.-Southern Region--Carlton & United Breweries Ltd., Southbank, Australia; *Int'l*, pg. 500
Brown, Wayne, Gen. Mgr.-Sls.--Theochem Labs., Inc., Tampa, FL; *U.S. Private*, pg. 1079
Brown, William M., Jr., Dir.-Sls. & Mktg.--Bayou Steel Corporation, La Place, LA; *U.S. Public*, pg. 197
Browne, Fred, Sr. V.P.-Sls.--Zee Medical, Inc., Irvine, CA; *U.S. Public*, pg. 1073
Browne, G., Mgr.-Natl. Sls.--Moore Business Forms & Systems Ltd., Auckland, New Zealand; *Int'l*, pg. 889
Browning, Jane, Dir.-Catalog Sls.--Camping World, Inc., Bowling Green, KY; *U.S. Private*, pg. 204
Browning, Lewis, Dir.-Mktg.--Ambac International Corp., Columbia, SC; *U.S. Private*, pg. 48
Browning, Toni E., Pres.-Mdsg. & Sls.--Proffitt's, Inc., Alcoa, TN; *U.S. Public*, pg. 1333

Broxey, H.K., V.P.-Sls.-Central Container Div.--Longview Fibre Co. Central Container Div., Minneapolis, MN; *U.S. Public*, pg. 1014

Broxterman, Bruce, Exec. V.P.--Richards Industries, Inc., Cincinnati, OH; *U.S. Private*, pg. 929

Brua, Rick, V.P.-Sls. & Mktg.--Mile High Equipment Co., Denver, CO; *Int'l*, pg. 189

Bruce, Jim, V.P.-Sls. & Mktg.--Amrion Inc., Boulder, CO; *U.S. Public*, pg. 1767

Bruce, Stuart, Mgr.-Sls.-Alternate Care Prods.--Conmed Corporation, Utica, NY; *U.S. Public*, pg. 431

Bruchert, Bill, Dir.-Sls. & Mktg.--DeSoto Inc., Joliet, IL; *U.S. Public*, pg. 956

Bruck, Rodney, V.P.-Individual Sls. & Mktg.--Standard Insurance Co., Portland, OR; *U.S. Private*, pg. 1031

Bruder, John, Sr. V.P.-Fin. Svcs. Div.--The Minnesota Mutual Life Insurance Company, Saint Paul, MN; *U.S. Private*, pg. 750

Bruder, Thomas A., III, V.P.-Sls.--M.A. Bruder & Sons, Incorporated, Broomall, PA; *U.S. Private*, pg. 175

Bruggeman, Ron, Dir.-Sls.--Omaha Steaks, Omaha, NE; *U.S. Private*, pg. 815

Brummer, Alfons, Dir.-Grp. Sls.--Knurr AG, Munich, Germany; *Int'l*, pg. 739

Bruneau, Steve, Dir.-Aerospace Sls.--Marotta Scientific Controls, Inc., Montville, NJ; *U.S. Private*, pg. 706

Bruner, Brodi, Mgr.-Natl. Sls.--Telsco Industries, Garland, TX; *U.S. Private*, pg. 1074

Brunetti, Michael, V.P.-Franchise Sls. Devel. & Real Estate--Grease Monkey International Inc., Denver, CO; *U.S. Public*, pg. 759

Bruno, Carl, Mgr.-Inside Sls.--Brad Foote Gear Works, Inc., Cicero, IL; *U.S. Private*, pg. 417

Bruno, John, Sr. V.P.-Sls.--Cagle's Inc., Atlanta, GA; *U.S. Public*, pg. 291

Brush, James, Exec. V.P.-Sls. & Mktg.--Sentry Group, Rochester, NY; *U.S. Private*, pg. 984

Bruton, Thomas R., CLU, ChFC, Asst. V.P.-Sls. Admin.--Farmers and Traders Life Insurance Co., Syracuse, NY; *U.S. Private*, pg. 394

Brwon, Richard, Mgr.-Sls.--Bell Gas, Inc., Roswell, NM; *U.S. Private*, pg. 131

Bryan, Gary G., V.P.-Sls. & Mktg.--Chroma Corporation, McHenry, IL; *U.S. Private*, pg. 238

Bryan, William, Mgr.-Sls.--Dry Manufacturing Co., Winters, TX; *U.S. Public*, pg. 1795

Bryant, Carleton F., III, Chief Oper. Officer, Exec. V.P., Treas. & Sec.--Westerbeke Corporation, Avon, MA; *U.S. Public*, pg. 1757

Bryant, J. Michael, Sr. V.P.-Sls., Svc. & Final Assembly Grp.--Altec Industries, Inc., Birmingham, AL; *U.S. Private*, pg. 47

Bryant, Roy, Exec. V.P.-Sls. & Mktg.--Castleberry/Snow's Brands Inc., Augusta, GA; *U.S. Private*, pg. 219

Bryson, Garff, Sr. V.P.-Sls. & Mktg.--Tropical Sportswear International, Tampa, FL; *U.S. Private*, pg. 1105

Bryson, Lee R., Exec. V.P.-Sls.--Piggly Wiggly Co., Memphis, TN; *U.S. Public*, pg. 653

Bryzgel, John D., V.P.-Machinery Div.--Fenn Manufacturing Co., Newington, CT; *U.S. Public*, pg. 1676

Bubendorff, Jean G., Sr. V.P.-Sls./Quebec--Mackenzie Financial Corporation, Toronto, Canada; *Int'l*, pg. 828

Bucar, John, Sls. Rep.-Sterilizer Div.--Environmental Tectonics Corporation (ETC), Southampton, PA; *U.S. Public*, pg. 587

Bucchi, Richard A., Sr. V.P.-Sls. & Mktg.--Moore Medical Corp., New Britain, CT; *U.S. Public*, pg. 1128

Buccola, Tony, V.P.-Sls. & Mktg.--Cumberland Packing Corp., Brooklyn, NY; *U.S. Private*, pg. 295

Buchanan, James R., Exec. V.P.-Sls.--Central Sprinkler Company, Lansdale, PA; *U.S. Public*, pg. 327

Buchelhofer, Robert, Dr., Dir.-Mktg. & Sls.--Volkswagen AG, Wolfsburg, Germany; *Int'l*, pg. 1473

Bucher, Gene, Mgr.-Industrial Sls.--Jones Blair Company, Dallas, TX; *U.S. Private*, pg. 596

Buck, David N., V.P.-Medical Sls.--Acme United Corporation, Fairfield, CT; *U.S. Public*, pg. 17

Buckalter, Amy, V.P.-Sls. & Mktg., In-line Skates--K2 Corporation, Vashon, WA; *U.S. Public*, pg. 940

Buckingham, George H., V.P.-Field Sls.--Lawson Products, Inc., Des Plaines, IL; *U.S. Public*, pg. 980

Buckingham, Jay, Gen. Mgr.-Sls.--Old Dutch Foods, Inc., Roseville, MN; *U.S. Private*, pg. 814

Buckles, Daniel T., V.P.-Sls.--FARO Technologies, Inc., Lake Mary, FL; *U.S. Public*, pg. 613

Buckley, Maura T., V.P.-Sportswear Sls.--Dyersburg Corporation, Dyersburg, TN; *U.S. Public*, pg. 538

Buckner, Chuck, Sr. V.P.-Sls.--Gelco Information Network, Inc., Eden Prairie, MN; *U.S. Private*, pg. 442

Budd, Dick, Mgr.-Sls.--Handgards Inc., Northbrook, IL; *U.S. Private*, pg. 499

Budd, Mike, Sr. V.P.-Sls--Overhead Door Corporation, Dallas, TX; *U.S. Private*, pg. 822

Buddig, Thomas R., V.P.-Sls. & Mktg.--Carl Buddig & Company, Homewood, IL; *U.S. Private*, pg. 178

Buensuceso, Enrique S., Grp. Mgr.-Mktg. Construction Div.--EEI Corporation, Manila, Philippines; *Int'l*, pg. 425

Buente, Robert, V.P.-Sls. & Mktg.--The Okonite Company, Ramsey, NJ; *U.S. Private*, pg. 813

Buente, Robert W., Mktg. & Sls.--The Okonite Company, Ramsey, NJ; *U.S. Private*, pg. 813

Buetow, Kathleen M., V.P.-Sls. & Mktg.--F.E. Myers, Ashland, OH; *U.S. Public*, pg. 1273

Buettgen, Mary Kay, Gen. Mgr.-Laurentis Sls.--Superior Coffee and Foods, Bensenville, IL; *U.S. Public*, pg. 1434

Buff, Alan, Dir.-Mktg. & Sls.--Reed & Barton Corporation, Taunton, MA; *U.S. Private*, pg. 916

Buffard, Francois, V.P.-Sls.--Consorcio G. Grupo Dina, S.A. de C.V., Mexico, Mexico; *Int'l*, pg. 326

Buganelli, Gianpaolo, Dir.-Sls.--Dateo Import S.P.A., Milan, Italy; *Int'l*, pg. 385

Buhler-Scott, Amy B., V.P.-Retail Div.--Old Dominion Box Co., Inc., Madison Heights, VA; *U.S. Private*, pg. 814

Buisson, Patrick, Mgr.-Intl. Sls.--Axson S.A., Paris, France; *Int'l*, pg. 102

Buist, D., Dir.-Sls.--Principal Marques Meat Co., Etobicoke, Canada; *Int'l*, pg. 841

Buker, Jim, Mgr.-Sls./Indus.--Reuter Manufacturing Inc., Hopkins, MN; *U.S. Public*, pg. 1383

Bukowski, Gary, V.P.-Sls. & Mktg.--Key Industries, Inc., Fort Scott, KS; *U.S. Private*, pg. 618

Bull, Sheryl, Dir.-Adv.--Modern Healthcare, Chicago, IL; *U.S. Private*, pg. 285

Bullert, Rick, V.P.-Sls.--MedTrac, Inc., Minneapolis, MN; *Int'l*, pg. 1504

Bullins, Jerry, V.P.-Sls.--Klaussner Furniture Industry, Asheboro, NC; *U.S. Private*, pg. 625

Bumgardner, Carl L., V.P.-Printing Sls.--Imperial Bondware Corp., Montvale, NJ; *U.S. Public*, pg. 903

Bumpus, Greg, Natl. Sls. Mgr.--K-D Lamp Company, Cincinnati, OH; *U.S. Private*, pg. 603

Bunch, Steve, V.P.-Sls.--Standard Plywoods, Inc., Clinton, SC; *U.S. Private*, pg. 1032

Bunch, Steve, V.P.-Sls.--Anderson Hardwood Floors, Clinton, SC; *U.S. Private*, pg. 1032

Bundy, Merlin, V.P.-Newsprint Sls. & Mktg.--Donohue Inc., Quebec, Canada; *Int'l*, pg. 1075

Bungert, David, Mgr.--Security Life Insurance Company of America, Minnetonka, MN; *U.S. Private*, pg. 980

Bungert, David, Mgr.--Congress Life Insurance Company, Minnetonka, MN; *U.S. Private*, pg. 980

Bunker, Duane, Mgr.-Natl. Sls.--Saunders Brothers, Westbrook, ME; *U.S. Private*, pg. 968

Bunnell, Dale, V.P.-Bus. Devel.--Mark Andy, Inc., Chesterfield, MO; *U.S. Public*, pg. 521

Bunnell, Randy B., Dir.-Sls.--Specialty Coated Products, Merrimack, NH; *U.S. Public*, pg. 1152

Bunner, Hency, V.P.-Mktg. & Sls.--Louis Allis Company, Milwaukee, WI; *U.S. Private*, pg. 677

Buntyn, Ralph, V.P.-Sls.--Motion Industries, Inc., Irondale, AL; *U.S. Public*, pg. 732

Bunworth, David, Dir.-Sls. & Mktg.--Aer Lingus, Dublin, Ireland; *Int'l*, pg. 28

Buonassissi, Mike, V.P.-Sls.--Pepsi-Cola Bottling Co. of Long Island City, Long Island City, NY; *U.S. Public*, pg. 1276

Buono, Tony, V.P.-Sls.--The Hartz Mountain Corp., Secaucus, NJ; *U.S. Private*, pg. 508

Burbach, Lyle, Dir.-Intl. Mktg. & Sls.--Behlen Mfg. Co., Columbus, NE; *U.S. Private*, pg. 130

Burbage, C.T., V.P.-Bus. Devel. & Product Support--Lockheed Aeronautical Systems Company, Marietta, GA; *U.S. Public*, pg. 1007

Burbank, Richard, V.P.-Distr. Sls.--Quaker State Corporation, Irving, TX; *U.S. Public*, pg. 1348

Burbick, Ron L., V.P.-Mktg.--Schneller, Inc., Kent, OH; *U.S. Private*, pg. 971

Burdash, Ann, Mgr.-Sls.--Kenyon Industries, Inc., Kenyon, RI; *U.S. Public*, pg. 778

Burdett, Dan, Dir.-Sls.--Garst Seed Company, Slater, IA; *Int'l*, pg. 1524

Burdick, Curtis, V.P.-Sls. & Sls. Promo--Distribution America, Des Plaines, IL; *U.S. Private*, pg. 335

Buresh, Randy, V.P.-Sls.--The Jel Sert Co., West Chicago, IL; *U.S. Private*, pg. 585

Burfield, Bill, V.P.-Natl. Sls. & Mktg.--TTC Illinois Inc., Kankakee, IL; *U.S. Private*, pg. 1066

Burg, Stanley H., Natl. Sls. Mgr.--Emcee Broadcast Products, Inc., White Haven, PA; *U.S. Public*, pg. 570

Burger, Barbara, Customer Sls. Support--A. Schulman, Inc., Akron, OH; *U.S. Public*, pg. 1441

Burget, Bill, V.P.-Comml. Sls.--York Wallcoverings Inc., York, PA; *U.S. Private*, pg. 1196

Burgette, Dennis, Exec. V.P.-Sls. & Mktg.--Action Industries, Inc., Tupelo, MS; *U.S. Public*, pg. 688

Burghard, Rolf, Chief Exec. Officer & Dir.-Mktg.--Rominger Reisebuero GmbH, Stuttgart, Germany; *Int'l*, pg. 1127

Burgin, James A., Exec. V.P.-Sls.--Bollinger Industries Inc., Grand Prairie, TX; *U.S. Public*, pg. 243

Burgin, Jim, Pres.-Sls.--Bollinger Industries Inc., Grand Prairie, TX; *U.S. Public*, pg. 243

Burk, William, V.P.-Sls.--Monumental Millwork, Inc., Westminster, MD; *U.S. Private*, pg. 759

Burke, Bob, Sr. V.P.-Sls.--Banyan Systems Inc., Westborough, MA; *U.S. Public*, pg. 189

Burke, David, Exec. V.P.-Sls. & Mktg.--B&G Foods, Inc., Roseland, NJ; *U.S. Private*, pg. 105

Burke, Donald B., Exec. V.P.-Mktg. & Sls.--Worthington Foods Inc., Worthington, OH; *U.S. Public*, pg. 1780

Burke, Frederick T., II, V.P.-Field Sls.--Starter Corp., New Haven, CT; *U.S. Public*, pg. 1511

Burke, George, Sr. V.P.-Mktg.--Globe Life And Accident Insurance Co., Oklahoma City, OK; *U.S. Public*, pg. 1622

Burke, Jim, Exec. V.P.- Sls. & Mktg.--Fox Television Stations Inc., Los Angeles, CA; *Int'l*, pg. 926

Burke, John, V.P.-Sls. & Mktg.--Trek Bicycle Corporation, Waterloo, WI; *U.S. Private*, pg. 1099

Burke, John, V.P.-Sls. & Svc.--Staples, Inc., Westborough, MA; *U.S. Public*, pg. 1509

Burke, Mike, V.P.-Worldwide Sls. & Support--Tandem Computers Inc., Cupertino, CA; *U.S. Public*, pg. 417

Burke, Robert, V.P.-Sls.--Motor Products Div., Rockford, IL; *U.S. Public*, pg. 1250

Burke, Robert J., Sr. V.P.--American Appraisal Associates, Inc., Milwaukee, WI; *U.S. Private*, pg. 49

Burke, Robert R., V.P.-Sls.-Kimball Office Grp.--Kimball International, Inc., Jasper, IN; *U.S. Public*, pg. 956

Burke, Therese, Sr. V.P.-Sls. & Mktg. Devel.--HarperCollins Publishers, New York, NY; *Int'l*, pg. 926

Burke, Therese, Dir.-Natl. Sls.--The Putnam & Grosset Group, New York, NY; *Int'l*, pg. 1027

Burke, Thomas, Dir.-Commercial Sls. & Mktg.--Waring Products, New Hartford, CT; *U.S. Public*, pg. 286

Burlingame, Keith, Mgr.-Sls. Admin. & Mktg.--Easco Inc., Girard, OH; *U.S. Public*, pg. 548

Burman, Daniel, V.P.-Sls.--Ballard Medical Products, Draper, UT; *U.S. Public*, pg. 171

Burmester, Klaus, Mgr.-Sls. & Mktg.--Hermal Kurt Herrmann & Co., Reinbek, Germany; *Int'l*, pg. 616

Burnett, John, V.P.-Sls.--Philips Components, Jupiter, FL; *Int'l*, pg. 1054

Burnett, Tom, V.P.-Sls.--Calcitek, Inc., Carlsbad, CA; *Int'l*, pg. 1307

Burnette, John, V.P.-Sls.--Philips Components, Jupiter, FL; *Int'l*, pg. 1054

Burnette, Tab, V.P.-Regional Sls. Mgr.--Fruit of the Loom, Inc., Chicago, IL; *U.S. Public*, pg. 685

Burns, Bob, Mgr.-Natl. Sls.--Correct Craft, Inc., Orlando, FL; *U.S. Private*, pg. 276

Burns, Bob, Dir.-Sls. Admin.--AVX Corporation, Myrtle Beach, SC; *Int'l*, pg. 775

Burns, Jerry N., Sls. Mgr.--American Ductile Iron Pipe Div., Birmingham, AL; *U.S. Private*, pg. 52

Burns, Jim, Mgr.-Used Car Sls.--Fairway Ford, Inc., Greenville, SC; *U.S. Private*, pg. 392

Burns, Larry, V.P.-Sales & Mktg.--Vitamilk Dairy, Inc., Seattle, WA; *U.S. Private*, pg. 1142

Burns, Linda, Gen. Sls. Mgr.--KJYO-FM, Oklahoma City, OK; *U.S. Public*, pg. 384

Burns, Pat, V.P.-Mktg. & Domestic Sls.--Pinnacle Systems, Inc., Mountain View, CA; *U.S. Public*, pg. 1297

Burns, R. Mark, V.P.-Sls.--Digital Courier International Inc., Burnaby, Canada; *Int'l*, pg. 413

Burns, Richard, V.P.--Cornucopia, Inc., Irvine, CA; *U.S. Private*, pg. 276

Burns, Richard, Sr. V.P.-Sls.--GT Interactive Software Corp., New York, NY; *U.S. Public*, pg. 696

Burns, Robert D., V.P.-Sls. & Mktg.--Conway Import Co. Inc., Elmsford, NY; *U.S. Private*, pg. 272

Burns, Samuel D., Area Pres.--New Fortis Corp., King, NC; *U.S. Public*, pg. 843

Burns, Skipper, Dir.-Sls.--Atlanta Motor Speedway, Hampton, GA; *U.S. Public*, pg. 1498

Burns, Tim, Dir.-Sls.--Old World Automotive Products, Northbrook, IL; *U.S. Private*, pg. 814

Burns, William, V.P.-Sls. & Mktg.--Coronet/MTI, Saint Louis, MO; *U.S. Private*, pg. 863

Burns, William, V.P.-Sls. & Mktg.--BFA Educational Media, Saint Louis, MO; *U.S. Private*, pg. 863

Burns, William, V.P.-Sls. & Mktg.--Phoenix Films & Video, Saint Louis, MO; *U.S. Private*, pg. 863

Burnside, Richard M., V.P.-Slots--Boyd Gaming Corporation, Las Vegas, NV; *U.S. Public*, pg. 249

Burnside, Sally, Mgr.-Customer Svcs.--Randa Corp., Kinston, NC; *U.S. Private*, pg. 909

Burnstein, Elyse, Mgr.-Sls./Export--The W.E. Bassett Company, Shelton, CT; *U.S. Private*, pg. 122

Burr, Les, Dir.-Circulation & Commercial--BBC Magazines, London, United Kingdom; *Int'l*, pg. 114

Burr, R., V.P.-Sls.--Steelworks, Inc. Dover Division, Dover, DE; *U.S. Private*, pg. 1039

Burridge, Jeffrey, V.P.-Sls. & Mktg.--Surgical Specialties, Reading, PA; *U.S. Private*, pg. 1056

Burroughs, David L., V.P.-Sls./SED--Southern Electronics Corporation, Tucker, GA; *U.S. Public*, pg. 1490

Burrows, Roger, V.P.-Sls.--Spartan Motors, Inc., Charlotte, MI; *U.S. Public*, pg. 1495

Burrows, Thomas, V.P.-Mktg. & Sls.--Griffith Laboratories Worldwide, Inc., Alsip, IL; *U.S. Private*, pg. 481

Bursh, Thomas, Mgr.-Sls. & Mktg.--Acme Design Technology, Co., Crozet, VA; *U.S. Private*, pg. 13

Burstein, Arnold, V.P.-Intl. Sls. & Mktg.--Inverness Corp., Fair Lawn, NJ; *U.S. Private*, pg. 574

Burstein, Arnold, V.P.-Sls. & Mktg--ERI Laboratories, Fair Lawn, NJ; *U.S. Private*, pg. 574

Burt, Steven R., Sr. V.P.-Field Opers.--Daw Technologies, Inc., Salt Lake City, UT; *U.S. Public*, pg. 489

Burton, C.D., Mgr.-Sls.--Amos-Hill Associates, Inc., Edinburgh, IN; *U.S. Private*, pg. 67

Burton, Lee, Mgr.-Sls.--CNF Transportation Inc., Palo Alto, CA; *U.S. Public*, pg. 281

Bury, Jeffrey D., V.P.-Bus. Devel.--Wyandot Inc., Marion, OH; *U.S. Private*, pg. 1193

Burzillo, Barbara, Mgr.-Natl. Sls.--KOAT-TV, Albuquerque, NM; *U.S. Public*, pg. 1344

Busarow, Jayne, Mgr.-Customer Service--Sierra Coating Technologies, De Pere, WI; *U.S. Private*, pg. 998

Busby, Robert B., Exec. V.P. & Dir.-Sls.--Pawling Corporation, Pawling, NY; *U.S. Private*, pg. 844

Busch, Guy, V.P.-Sls. & Mktg.--Chem-Trend Incorporated, Howell, MI; *Int'l*, pg. 235

Buschmann, Martin, Dir.-Mktg. & Sls.--GESTRA GmbH, Bremen, Germany; *Int'l*, pg. 549

Busey, Jay, V.P.-Sls.--Lea Industries, Greensboro, NC; *U.S. Public*, pg. 974

Bush, Alanna, Mgr.-Sls. Admin.--Star Fine Foods, Inc., Fresno, CA; *U.S. Private*, pg. 1034

Bush, Brent, Dir.-Sls.--Business Mens Insurance Corporation, Coral Gables, FL; *U.S. Private*, pg. 189

Bush, Howard J., V.P.-Mktg. & Sls.--Brenco, Inc., Petersburg, VA; *U.S. Public*, pg. 1710

Bush, James, V.P.-Sls. & Mktg.--The Holland Hitch Company, Holland, MI; *U.S. Private*, pg. 534

Bush, Michael, V.P.-Credit Union Sls.--Telecredit Service Center, Inc., Los Angeles, CA; *U.S. Public*, pg. 588

Bush, Skip, Aircraft Sls.--Cutter Aviation Albuquerque, Inc, Albuquerque, NM; *U.S. Private*, pg. 298

Bushnell, Christopher, V.P.-Acct. Service & Sls.--Corinthian Media, Inc., New York, NY; *U.S. Private*, pg. 275

Buskirk, Jeffrey, Mgr.-Sls.--Rock Hill Materials Company, Catasauqua, PA; *U.S. Private*, pg. 938

Bussi, Hugo, Mgr.-Sls.--Sancor Cooperativas Unidas Limitadas, Buenos Aires, Argentina; *Int'l*, pg. 1183

Bussing, Dave, Mgr.-Gen. Sls.--M.A.B. Paints, Terre Haute, IN; *U.S. Private*, pg. 175

Butensky, Martin, Dir.-Mktg.--Vernitron Sensor Systems, Saint Petersburg, FL; *U.S. Public*, pg. 157

Buth, Douglas P., V.P.-Sls.--Appleton Papers Inc., Appleton, WI; *Int'l*, pg. 567

Butkus, John, Mgr.-New Prod. Sls.--Milford Fastening Systems, Milford, CT; *U.S. Private*, pg. 745

Butkus, Nancy, Dir.-New Bus. Devel. & Mktg. Services--OshKosh B'Gosh, Inc., Oshkosh, WI; *U.S. Public*, pg. 1232
Butler, Charles, Mgr.-Sls. Svc.--Agway Energy Products (AEP), Syracuse, NY; *U.S. Private*, pg. 27
Butler, Charles, Mgr.-Custom Sls.--Maryland Plastics, Inc., Federalsburg, MD; *U.S. Private*, pg. 641
Butler, Gerard F., V.P.-Sls.--Block Drug Company, Inc., Jersey City, NJ; *U.S. Public*, pg. 236
Butler, Kim P., V.P.-Sls., Western Reg.--Magneco/Metrel, Inc., Addison, IL; *U.S. Private*, pg. 695
Butler, LuAnn, V.P.-Sls. & Mktg.--Kaufman and Broad Home Corporation, Los Angeles, CA; *U.S. Public*, pg. 944
Butler, LuAnn, V.P.-Sls. & Mktg.--Kaufman and Broad of Texas, Ltd., San Antonio, TX; *U.S. Public*, pg. 945
Butler, Norman D., V.P.-Sls. & Mktg., Service Parts Div.--Foley-PLP Company, Rochester, NY; *U.S. Private*, pg. 416
Butler, Oliver, V.P.-Mktg. & Sls.,Pharmaceutical--Wyeth-Ayerst Laboratories, Inc., Philadelphia, PA; *U.S. Public*, pg. 80
Butler, Tom, V.P.-Sampling & Natl. Sls. Mgr.--The Sunflower Group, Overland Park, KS; *U.S. Private*, pg. 1052
Butta, Vincent, V.P.-Sls.--Advertising Display Co., Englewood Cliffs, NJ; *U.S. Private*, pg. 23
Butterfield, Robert, Mgr.-Sls.--Buckeye Container, Wooster, OH; *U.S. Private*, pg. 177
Butters, Norm, Sr. V.P.-Sls. & Mktg.--Norpac Foods, Inc., Stayton, OR; *U.S. Private*, pg. 802
Button, Brian T., V.P.-Mktg. & Sls.--Proxim, Inc., Mountain View, CA; *U.S. Public*, pg. 1338
Butts, Lampkin, V.P.-Sls.--Sanderson Farms, Inc., Laurel, MS; *U.S. Public*, pg. 1430
Buyck, Piet, Mgr.-Sls.--Numetrix GmbH, Wiesbaden, Germany; *Int'l*, pg. 990
Buyko, John, V.P.-Sls. & Mktg.--Aeroflex Incorporated, Plainview, NY; *U.S. Public*, pg. 23
Buzzard, James A., V.P.-Fine Paper Sls. & Mktg.--Westvaco Corporation, New York, NY; *U.S. Public*, pg. 1762
Buzzard, James A., V.P. & Mgr.-Div. Sls. & Mktg.--Westvaco Corporation-Fine Papers Div., Richmond, VA; *U.S. Public*, pg. 1762
Bwers, John, Exec. V.P.-Sls.--AEP Industries, Inc., South Hackensack, NJ; *U.S. Public*, pg. 4
Byczynski, Dennis, V.P.-Intl. Sls.--Mohawk Industries, Inc., Calhoun, GA; *U.S. Public*, pg. 1121
Byer, Marion, Dir.-Adv. & Sls.--CNN (Cable News Network), Atlanta, GA; *U.S. Public*, pg. 1614
Byerly, Ron, V.P.-Training, Mktg. & Adv.--O'Reilly Automotive Inc., Springfield, MO; *U.S. Public*, pg. 1230
Byers, Joseph M., V.P.-Sls. & Mktg.--Easco Inc., Girard, OH; *U.S. Public*, pg. 548
Byers, Richard F., V.P.-Sls.--Burke Mills, Inc., Valdese, NC; *U.S. Public*, pg. 267
Byers, Steve, V.P.-Sls.--Goldenberg Group, Inc., Lynwood, CA; *U.S. Public*, pg. 1193
Bykerk, Larry, V.P.-Sls.--Apollo Colors Inc., Northbrook, IL; *U.S. Private*, pg. 77
Byland, Shelley, Sls.--Semac Industries Inc., Millersburg, OH; *U.S. Private*, pg. 983
Byle, Gerald E., V.P.-Intl. Sls.--The Rival Company, Kansas City, MO; *U.S. Public*, pg. 1391
Bynon, W. Lee, V.P.-Natl. Sls.--Daniel Green Co., Dolgeville, NY; *U.S. Private*, pg. 477
Byrd, Vincent C., V.P. & Gen. Mgr.-Consumer Mkt.--J.M. Smucker Company, Orrville, OH; *U.S. Public*, pg. 1480
Byrne, Joseph J., V.P.-Sls. & Mktg.--Mead Specialty Paper, South Lee, MA; *U.S. Public*, pg. 1074
Byrne, Paddy, Dir.-Sls.--Ford Motor Company Limited, Brentwood, United Kingdom; *U.S. Public*, pg. 666
Byrne, Paul, V.P.-Sls. & Mktg.--Precor, Inc., Bothell, WA; *U.S. Public*, pg. 1322
Byrnes, Ed, V.P. & Gen. Mgr.-Sls. & Adv.--The Weather Channel, Atlanta, GA; *U.S. Private*, pg. 647
Byrnes, Ralph R., Sr. V.P.-Automotive Resource Dir.--Consumers Financial Corporation, Camp Hill, PA; *U.S. Public*, pg. 437
Byrnes, Stephen, V.P. & Gen. Mgr. Injection Molding Sls.--HPM Corporation, Mount Gilead, OH; *U.S. Private*, pg. 492
Byrnes, Terrence J., V.P.-Sls. & Mktg.--Enerfab Inc., Cincinnati, OH; *U.S. Private*, pg. 376
Byrnes, Thomas, V.P.-Sls.--Byrnes & Kiefer Company, Callery, PA; *U.S. Private*, pg. 191
Byrnes, Thomas, V.P.-Sls.--Avis Rent A Car System, Inc., Garden City, NY; *U.S. Public*, pg. 321
Byrom, Gary, Mgr.-Sls. & Mktg./U.K. & Ireland--Dexter Specialty Materials, Ltd., Twickenham, United Kingdom; *U.S. Public*, pg. 505
Byron, Terry P., V.P.-Consumer Prods. Grp. Sls.--Chesebrough-Pond's, Trumbull, CT; *Int'l*, pg. 1436
Cabana, Casey, Mgr.-New Car Sls.--Mark Chevrolet Inc., Wayne, MI; *U.S. Private*, pg. 704
Cabiallavetta, Mathis, Exec. V.P.-Trading & Sls. & Risk Mngmt.--Union Bank of Switzerland, Zurich, Switzerland; *Int'l*, pg. 1439
Cabilao, Enriqueto, Sls. Dir.-N. Mindanao--La Tondena Distillers, Inc., Manila, Philippines; *Int'l*, pg. 785
Cabral, G., Mgr.-Sls.--Plymkraft Inc., Newport News, VA; *U.S. Private*, pg. 256
Cabucio, Steve, V.P.-Sport Sls.--Loga Athletic/Headwear Inc., Mattapoisett, MA; *U.S. Public*, pg. 1644
Caddock, Richard E. Jr., V.P.-Engrng. & Mktg.--Caddock Electronics, Inc., Riverside, CA; *U.S. Private*, pg. 198
Cadicamo, Frank, Gen. Dir.-Sls. Admin.--Cadillac Motor Car Division, Warren, MI; *U.S. Public*, pg. 720
Caduto, Julian, Dir.-Sls./Scrubble--ACS Industries, Inc., Woonsocket, RI; *U.S. Private*, pg. 3
Caffrey, Mike, Dir.-Natl. Mktg. & Sls.--Duncan Toys Company, Middlefield, OH; *U.S. Private*, pg. 409
Caggiano, Art, Mgr.-Reg. Sls.--General Microwave Corporation, Amityville, NY; *U.S. Public*, pg. 717
Cagle, James David, V.P.-New Prod. Sls.--Cagle's Inc., Atlanta, GA; *U.S. Public*, pg. 291
Cagliero, Robert J., Exec. V.P. & Mgr.- Natl Sls.--ABC Television Network, New York, NY; *U.S. Public*, pg. 511
Cahill, Chris J., V.P.-Sls.--Canadian Pacific Hotels & Resorts Inc., Toronto, Canada; *Int'l*, pg. 258
Cahoon, R.L., Sr. V.P.-Sls.--Dunlop Tire Corporation, Buffalo, NY; *Int'l*, pg. 1317
Cailliet, Sue, Sls. Broker--Brooks Resources Corporation, Bend, OR; *U.S. Private*, pg. 172
Cain, Bill, V.P.-Sls.--C&L Communications, Inc., Boerne, TX; *U.S. Private*, pg. 191
Caine, J.C., Mgr.-Intl. Sls.--Vicon Industries, Inc., Hauppauge, NY; *U.S. Public*, pg. 1719
Caine, Linda, Dir.-Sls. & Mktg.--Walden Book Company, Ann Arbor, MI; *U.S. Public*, pg. 245
Cala, Vince, V.P.-Consumer Sls.--Refined Sugars, Inc., Yonkers, NY; *Int'l*, pg. 699
Calabrese, Clement, V.P.-Sls.--Hanover Foods Corporation, Hanover, PA; *U.S. Private*, pg. 499
Calabrese, F.P., Mgr.-Natl. Sls.--The Grieve Corporation, Round Lake, IL; *U.S. Private*, pg. 480
Calabrese, P., Mgr.-Sls., Dialysis Div.--Terumo Medical Corporation, Somerset, NJ; *Int'l*, pg. 1376
Calabro, Brian, V.P.-Forms Sls. & Mktg.--The Standard Register Company, Dayton, OH; *U.S. Public*, pg. 1505
Calabro, Brian W., V.P.-Sls. & Document Mngmt. Div.--The Standard Register Company, Dayton, OH; *U.S. Public*, pg. 1505
Caldera, Steve, V.P.-Sls.--Yamaha Electronics Corp. USA, Buena Park, CA; *Int'l*, pg. 1516
Caldu, R., Exec. V.P.-Sls.--Waterville TG Inc., Waterville, Canada; *Int'l*, pg. 1487
Caldwell, James F., V.P.-Intl. Sls.--Telecom Solutions, San Jose, CA; *U.S. Public*, pg. 1547
Caldwell, Robert, Mgr.-Natl. Sls.--Spencer's Inc., Mount Airy, NC; *U.S. Private*, pg. 1025
Calim, Joseph, Dir.-Sls.--WFOR-TV Channel 4, Miami, FL; *U.S. Public*, pg. 275
Call, Jack, Sls. Mgr.-Northeast District--Fluidtec Engineer Products, Greensboro, NC; *U.S. Public*, pg. 401
Callahan, Bob, Sr. V.P.-Sls., Mktg. & Oper.--U.S. Tsubaki, Inc., Wheeling, IL; *Int'l*, pg. 1425
Callahan, George, Dir.-Sls.--Catholic Order of Foresters, Naperville, IL; *U.S. Private*, pg. 220
Callahan, Harry, Mgr.-Gen. Sls.--WAXY (FM), Fort Lauderdale, FL; *U.S. Public*, pg. 925
Callahan, John, Dir.-Sls.-Urethane--JPS Elastomerics Corp., Holyoke, MA; *U.S. Private*, pg. 578
Callahan, John, Mgr.-U.S. Sls.--Gould Electronics Inc., Foil Division, Eastlake, OH; *U.S. Public*, pg. 1592
Callahan, Michael E., V.P.-North American Sls.--Intermec Technologies Corporation, Everett, WA; *U.S. Public*, pg. 1699
Callahan, Neil, Dir.-Mktg. & Flavor Sls.--Robertet Flavors, South Plainfield, NJ; *Int'l*, pg. 1119
Callegari, Louis A., V.P.-Sls.--Hickory Printing Group, Inc., Conover, NC; *U.S. Private*, pg. 525
Calman, Michael, Mgr.-Natl. Sls.--Amerex Children, New York, NY; *U.S. Private*, pg. 49
Caltabiano, Joe, Dir.-Sls. & Mktg.--Camillus Cutlery Co., Camillus, NY; *U.S. Private*, pg. 203
Calthorpe, William A., V.P.-Sls., Adv. & Mktg.--Weeks Dairy Foods, Inc., Concord, NH; *Int'l*, pg. 752
Caltron, Steve, V.P.-Mktg. & Sls.--Kansas City Power & Light Company, Kansas City, MO; *U.S. Public*, pg. 943
Calug, Victor A., Sls. Dir.-Luzon--La Tondena Distillers, Inc., Manila, Philippines; *Int'l*, pg. 785
Calvano, Robert, Mgr.-Jewelry Sls.--B.A. Ballou & Co. Inc., East Providence, RI; *U.S. Private*, pg. 112
Calvert, Denis A., V.P.-U.S. Sls,--VeriFone, Inc., Redwood City, CA; *U.S. Public*, pg. 815
Calvo, Jesus R., Mng. Dir.-Distribution & Customer--Iberdrola, S.A., Bilbao, Spain; *Int'l*, pg. 657
Camara, Paul, Exec. V.P.-Creative, Sls. & Mktg.--TMP Worldwide, Inc., New York, NY; *U.S. Private*, pg. 1064
Cambournac, Gilles, V.P.-Sls. & Mktg.--SEITA, Societe Nationale D'Exploitation Industrielle des Tabacs et des Allumettes, Paris, France; *Int'l*, pg. 1219
Cambria, Peter, Div. Mgr.-Special Applications--Rapid Power Technologies, Inc., Brookfield, CT; *U.S. Private*, pg. 910
Camden, Carl, Exec. V.P.-Mktg., Sls. & Pub. Rels.--Kelly Services, Inc., Troy, MI; *U.S. Public*, pg. 949
Camens, Bernard, Sr. V.P.-Sls.-Lighting Div.--Crystal Clear Industries, Ridgefield Park, NJ; *U.S. Private*, pg. 293
Camerata, Joe, V.P.-Sls. & Mktg.--Atlas Copco Wagner Inc., Portland, OR; *Int'l*, pg. 96
Cameron, Sherry, Mgr.-Sls.--TIE Systems Mid-Atlantic, Columbia, MD; *U.S. Private*, pg. 1085
Camp, Christine, Mgr.-Sls.--A & B Properties, Inc., Honolulu, HI; *U.S. Public*, pg. 39
Camp, Michael, Dir.-Sls.--The Tetley Group Limited, Greenford, United Kingdom; *Int'l*, pg. 1377
Camp, Teri, Dir.-Consumer Sls.--Churchill Downs, Inc., Louisville, KY; *U.S. Public*, pg. 356
Campagna, Fred, V.P.-Intl. Sls. & Mktg.--Aerco International Inc., Northvale, NJ; *U.S. Private*, pg. 23
Campagnola, Gino, Exec. V.P. & Gen. Sls. Mgr.--Paramount Pictures Corporation, Los Angeles, CA; *U.S. Private*, pg. 776
Campbell, A.A., Sr. V.P.-Sls. & Mktg.--Celotex Corporation, Tampa, FL; *U.S. Private*, pg. 221
Campbell, Bernard, V.P.-Sls.--Connelly Containers, Inc., Bala Cynwyd, PA; *U.S. Private*, pg. 264
Campbell, Christopher J., V.P.-Sls.--Marketing Communications, Lenexa, KS; *U.S. Public*, pg. 794
Campbell, D.D., Sls./Service Mgr.-Dealer Network--Chevrolet Motor Div. General Motors Corp., Warren, MI; *U.S. Public*, pg. 720
Campbell, E. Wayne, V.P.-Sls.--Magnetics, Butler, PA; *U.S. Private*, pg. 1020
Campbell, Garry, Dir.-Retail Technology Services--Coles Myer Ltd., Tooronga, Australia; *Int'l*, pg. 306
Campbell, Geoffrey G., V.P.-Intl. Sls.--JLG Industries, Inc., McConnellsburg, PA; *U.S. Public*, pg. 918
Campbell, James L., V.P.-Sls.--Jarvis-Pemco, Kalamazoo, MI; *U.S. Public*, pg. 1506
Campbell, Joe, Dir.-Sls.--Better Living Inc., Charlottesville, VA; *U.S. Private*, pg. 141
Campbell, John, Dir.-Natl. Sls.--Chesapeake Bagel Bakery, Atlanta, GA; *U.S. Private*, pg. 5
Campbell, John, V.P.-Sls. Svcs.--Diagraph Corporation, Earth City, MO; *U.S. Private*, pg. 330
Campbell, John, Dir.-Sls.--Setzer Forest Products, Sacramento, CA; *U.S. Private*, pg. 987
Campbell, Joseph, Mgr.-Natl. Sls.--Star Bronze Company, Alliance, OH; *U.S. Private*, pg. 1034
Campbell, Michael, V.P.-Sls.--Reily Foods Company, New Orleans, LA; *U.S. Private*, pg. 919
Campbell, Nick, V.P.-Sls. & Mdsg.--P & C Food Markets, Inc., Syracuse, NY; *U.S. Public*, pg. 1270
Campbell, Reg, Dir.-Mktg. & Sls.--Kasle Steel Corporation, Dearborn, MI; *U.S. Private*, pg. 608
Campbell, Rick, Mgr.-Sls.--Nucor Steel-South Carolina, Darlington, SC; *U.S. Public*, pg. 1205
Campbell, Scott, V.P.-Sls. & Mktg.--Microdot/Recoil, Placentia, CA; *U.S. Public*, pg. 940
Campbell, Steve, V.P.-Sls.--Alpha Omega Publications, Chandler, AZ; *U.S. Private*, pg. 168
Campbell, Willy, Mgr.-Mdsg. & Sls.--Binney & Smith Ltd., Lindsay, Canada; *U.S. Private*, pg. 496
Campeau, Bob, Mgr.-Natl. Sales--Interlake Material Handling Div., Naperville, IL; *U.S. Public*, pg. 893
Caneri, Olcayto, Mgr.-After Sls. Service--Arcelik A.S., Istanbul, Turkey; *Int'l*, pg. 741
Canniff, Greg, Mgr.-Div. Sls.--AP North American Aftermarket Division, Goldsboro, NC; *U.S. Private*, pg. 230
Cannon, Marv, Dir.-Mktg., Bus. Plng. & Sls.--Delphi Packard Electric Systems, Beachwood, OH; *U.S. Public*, pg. 719
Cannon, Michael J., V.P.-Sls.--Grist Mill Company, Lakeville, MN; *U.S. Public*, pg. 766
Cannon, Roger F., Exec. V.P.-Sls. & Mktg.--Lawson Products, Inc., Des Plaines, IL; *U.S. Public*, pg. 980
Canright, Mark W., Sr. V.P.-Worldwide Sls.--Exabyte Corporation, Boulder, CO; *U.S. Public*, pg. 597
Canterbury, Glenn, Sls. Mgr.-Hyperbarics--Environmental Tectonics Corporation (ETC), Southampton, PA; *U.S. Public*, pg. 587
Canto, Nicholas, Dir.-Sls.--Aerolineas Argentinas, Buenos Aires, Argentina; *Int'l*, pg. 575
Cantor, Lee, V.P.-Sls.--Uniflex, Inc., Hicksville, NY; *U.S. Public*, pg. 1665
Cantrell, Clifford, Sls. Mgr.--Nutter Engineering, Tulsa, OK; *U.S. Public*, pg. 793
Cantrell, Mike, Mgr.-F & I Sls.--Fairway Ford, Inc., Greenville, SC; *U.S. Private*, pg. 392
Cantrelle, Jean, Dir.-Sls. & Opers.--Clestra Hauserman, Strasbourg, France; *Int'l*, pg. 569
Cantu, Eloy, Dir.-Product/Mkt. & Sls.--Oliver Products Company, Grand Rapids, MI; *U.S. Private*, pg. 815
Cantz, Robin, Dir.-Corp. Sls.--The Beverly Hills Hotel, Beverly Hills, CA; *U.S. Private*, pg. 142
Canuso, Thomas A., V.P.-Sls.--Turkey Hill Dairy, Inc., Conestoga, PA; *U.S. Private*, pg. 1109
Capalbo, Francis A., V.P.-Sls.--G.F. Wright Steel & Wire Company, Worcester, MA; *U.S. Private*, pg. 1192
Caparelli, William D., Sr. V.P.-Worldwide Sls.--Cirrus Logic, Inc., Fremont, CA; *U.S. Public*, pg. 375
Capo, Barbara, Mgr.-Key. Accts.--Arrow Group Industries, Inc., Wayne, NJ; *U.S. Private*, pg. 477
Capone, Andrew, Sr. V.P.-Mktg.--National Broadcasting Co., Inc., New York, NY; *U.S. Public*, pg. 712
Capone, Donald W., V.P.-Sls.--Munroe, Inc., Pittsburgh, PA; *U.S. Private*, pg. 767
Capparelli, Nick, V.P.-Sls.--Softmart, Inc., Downingtown, PA; *U.S. Private*, pg. 1012
Cappelletti, A., Mgr.-Optical Div. Sls. Promo--Mazzucchelli 1849 S.p.a., Castiglione Olona, Italy; *Int'l*, pg. 849
Cappelletti, Joe, Sr. V.P.-Sls.--ADI (Ademco Distribution, Inc.), Syosset, NY; *U.S. Public*, pg. 1306
Cappello, John, V.P.-Mktg. & Sls.--MidAmerican Energy Holdings, Des Moines, IA; *U.S. Public*, pg. 1109
Capps, Robert, Sr. V.P. & Gen. Sls. Mgr.--TriStar Pictures, Culver City, CA; *Int'l*, pg. 1283
Caputo, Art, Sr. V.P.-Sls. & Mktg.--Waters Corporation, Milford, MA; *U.S. Public*, pg. 1745
Caradonna, Peter, V.P.-Sls.--J.E. Goold & Company, Portland, ME; *U.S. Public*, pg. 229
Caramela, Laurence M., Dir.-Mktg., Bottle/Can--Central Coca-Cola Bottling Company, Inc., Richmond, VA; *U.S. Private*, pg. 222
Carballo, Bernard A., Exec. V.P.-Sls., Mktg. & Product Line Mngmt.--Seagate Technology Inc., Scotts Valley, CA; *U.S. Public*, pg. 1449
Carbonari, James J., V.P.-Sls. & Mktg.--Osmonics, Inc., Minnetonka, MN; *U.S. Public*, pg. 1233
Carbone, Jack, V.P.-Distr. Sls.--Emerson Motor Company, Sturgeon Bay, WI; *U.S. Public*, pg. 573
Carcone, Joseph A., V.P.-Mktg. & Sls.--Sanyo Energy (U.S.A.) Corporation, San Diego, CA; *Int'l*, pg. 1191
Card, Kerry, Sls. & Mktg. Admin.--LFE Industrial Systems Corporation, Clinton, MA; *U.S. Public*, pg. 1045
Card, Michael, Dir.-Sls.--Millennium Inorganic Chemicals, Hunt Valley, MD; *Int'l*, pg. 593
Cardinal, Jacques, Dir.-Sls.--Charcuterie la Tour Eiffel Inc., Ville Vanier, Canada; *Int'l*, pg. 850
Cardito, John, V.P. & Natl. Sls. Mgr.--Totes Incorporated, Loveland, OH; *U.S. Private*, pg. 111
Cardwell, Greg, Field Mgr.-Sls.--Master Lock Company, Milwaukee, WI; *U.S. Public*, pg. 675
Carey, Breisda, Mgr.-Sls.--Turner Construction Company, Orlando, FL; *U.S. Public*, pg. 1645
Carey, Dale, Mgr.-Mid-Atlantic Reg. Sls.--Vanguard Cellular Systems, Inc., Greensboro, NC; *U.S. Public*, pg. 1707
Carey, Dale, Mgr.-Reg. Sls.--Pennsylvania Cellular Telephone Corp., Bethlehem, PA; *U.S. Public*, pg. 1708
Carey, Dennie, Reg. V.P.-N.W. Sls.--American Freightways Corporation, Harrison, AR; *U.S. Public*, pg. 75

Carey, Jim, V.P.-Sls.--The L.S. Starrett Company, Athol, MA; *U.S. Public*, pg. 1511
Carey, Larry, Mgr.-Sls.--Quincy Design & Manufacturing, Quincy, IL; *U.S. Private*, pg. 176
Carey, Michael, Mgr.-Sls.--Muralo Co., Inc., Bayonne, NJ; *U.S. Private*, pg. 767
Carfolite, David, Gen. Mgr.-Sls.--KERO-TV, Bakersfield, CA; *U.S. Public*, pg. 1070
Carhart, E.J., V.P.-Mktg. & Sls.--Automotive, Wayne, NJ; *Int'l*, pg. 234
Carhart, John, Dir.-Intl. Sls. & Sls. Programs--America West Airlines, Inc., Phoenix, AZ; *U.S. Public*, pg. 67
Cariolo, Cosimo, Dir.-Sls. & Mktg.--Warren E. Collins, Inc., Braintree, MA; *U.S. Private*, pg. 253
Carletti, Steve, V.P.-Sls.--H.B. Ives, Wallingford, CT; *U.S. Private*, pg. 506
Carlin, Dan, V.P.-Sls.--Fishery Products International USA, Danvers, MA; *Int'l*, pg. 492
Carlin, R.E., V.P.-Sls.--Philips Components-Discrete Products Division, Slatersville, RI; *Int'l*, pg. 1054
Carlisle, Todd, Exec. V.P.-Sls.--Croft Metals, Inc., McComb, MS; *U.S. Private*, pg. 290
Carlsen, Dennis, Sls./Mktg.--Cowden Metal-San Jose, San Jose, CA; *U.S. Private*, pg. 280
Carlson, Dick, Sls. Rep.--Leblanc Communications, Inc., Richardson, TX; *U.S. Private*, pg. 656
Carlson, Jim, Mgr.-Corp. Sls.--Scherer Bros. Lumber Company, Minneapolis, MN; *U.S. Private*, pg. 970
Carlson, Keith, Sr. Sls. Advisor--Hovnanian Enterprises, Inc., Red Bank, NJ; *U.S. Public*, pg. 843
Carlson, Linda, V.P.-Worldwide Sls.--ACT Networks, Inc., Camarillo, CA; *U.S. Public*, pg. 3
Carlson, Todd, V.P.-Sls.--Carlson Systems, Omaha, NE; *U.S. Private*, pg. 212
Carlston, Kira, Sls. & Mktg. Coord.--The Zippertubing Co., Los Angeles, CA; *U.S. Private*, pg. 1207
Carlton, Henry, Dir.-Sls.--Cannon Rubber Ltd., London, United Kingdom; *Int'l*, pg. 261
Carlton, Thomas J., V.P.-Sls. & Mktg.--Corrugated Metals, Inc., Bedford Park, IL; *U.S. Private*, pg. 277
Carmen-Fegley, Patricia, V.P.-Sls.--Reed Travel Publishing-Dallas, Dallas, TX; *Int'l*, pg. 1097
Carmona, Francisco, Dir.-Real Estate Sls.--Grupo Sidek, S.A. de C.V., Guadalajara, Mexico; *Int'l*, pg. 576
Carnes, Crais, V.P.-Sls. & Mktg.-Flooring--Burke Industries, Inc., San Jose, CA; *U.S. Private*, pg. 183
Carney, Edward O., V.P.-Sls.--Superior Graphite Co., Chicago, IL; *U.S. Private*, pg. 1054
Caron, Steve, Mgr.-Sls.--Furukawa Electric America Inc. (FEA), Peachtree City, GA; *Int'l*, pg. 530
Carosi, Al, V.P.-Sls. & Mktg.--Hedstrom Corporation, Mount Prospect, IL; *U.S. Private*, pg. 526
Carothers, George E., Gen. Mgr.-Sls.--WHX Corporation, New York, NY; *U.S. Public*, pg. 1726
Carpenter, E.W., V.P.-Mktg. & Sls.--Durametallic Corp., Kalamazoo, MI; *U.S. Public*, pg. 658
Carpenter, Frank, Dir.-Intl. Sls. & Service--HIAC/ROYCO Division, Silver Spring, MD; *U.S. Public*, pg. 1250
Carpenter, Larry, Mgr.-Sls.--Clarklift Of Minnesota, Inc., Bloomington, MN; *U.S. Private*, pg. 243
Carpenter, Mike, V.P.-Sls. & Mktg.--The Vollrath Company, L.L.C., Sheboygan, WI; *U.S. Private*, pg. 1143
Carpenter, Patrick, Mgr.-Pub. Rels.--Alcan Aluminum Corporation, Cleveland, OH; *Int'l*, pg. 50
Carpenter, Robert, V.P.-Sls. & Adv.--Sequa Can Machinery, East Rutherford, NJ; *U.S. Public*, pg. 1458
Carpenter, Rodney S., Dir.-Sls. & Mktg.--Durco GmbH Atomac Division, Ahaus, Germany; *U.S. Public*, pg. 659
Carpenter, Scott R., V.P.-Sls.--Bachman Company, Reading, PA; *U.S. Private*, pg. 109
Carpou, Nick, Exec. V.P. & Natl. Sls. Mgr.-Distribution--Universal Pictures, Universal City, CA; *Int'l*, pg. 1216
Carr, John, V.P.-Sls. Worldwide--Fresenius Medical Care (North America), Lexington, MA; *Int'l*, pg. 505
Carr, Richard, Dir.-Sls.--Kohler Co. Generator Div., Sheboygan, WI; *U.S. Private*, pg. 630
Carr, W. Brad, V.P.-Sls. & Mktg.--Luwa Bahnson, Inc., Winston Salem, NC; *U.S. Private*, pg. 682
Carraro, Umberto, Dir.-Consumer Sls.--Johnson Wax S.p.A., Milan, Italy; *U.S. Private*, pg. 593
Carrejo, Gene, V.P.-Sls. & Mktg.--Price's Creameries, El Paso, TX; *U.S. Public*, pg. 491
Carreon, Richard R., V.P.-Sls.--Federal Cartridge Co., Anoka, MN; *U.S. Public*, pg. 239
Carretta, Frank, Jr., V.P.-Sls.--Digital Microwave Corporation, San Jose, CA; *U.S. Public*, pg. 508
Carrico, David E., Sr. V.P.-Sls.--Churchill Downs, Inc., Louisville, KY; *U.S. Public*, pg. 356
Carrig, Wayne K., Mgr.-Sls.--Sealing Devices Inc., Lancaster, NY; *U.S. Private*, pg. 978
Carrigan, Dennis, Mgr.-Sls.--Tempo Instrument Inc., Commack, NY; *Int'l*, pg. 208
Carrocia, M., Natl. Sls. Dir.--Pyle Inc., Elmhurst, IL; *U.S. Private*, pg. 629
Carroll, Kevin, Mgr.-Sls.--Strahman Valves, Inc., Florham Park, NJ; *U.S. Private*, pg. 1046
Carroll, Michael L., Treas.--Homestake Mining Company, San Francisco, CA; *U.S. Public*, pg. 832
Carroll, Patrick E., Sr. V.P.-Sls.--Payco American Corporation, Brookfield, WI; *U.S. Public*, pg. 1267
Carroll, Ronald, V.P.-Sls. & Mktg.--Hoffman Laces, Ltd., Cobleskill, NY; *U.S. Public*, pg. 769
Carroll, Ruth Ann, V.P.-Sls.-Eastern Region--The Sunflower Group, Overland Park, KS; *U.S. Private*, pg. 1052
Carroll, Ruth Ann, V.P.-Sls.--The Sunflower Group, White Plains, NY; *U.S. Private*, pg. 1052
Carrot, Rosa, Dir.-Retail Sls.--San Antonio Express News, San Antonio, TX; *U.S. Private*, pg. 517
Carruthers, Carl, V.P.-Product Supply & Distr. Sls.--Mitel Corporation, Kanata, Canada; *Int'l*, pg. 870
Carson, Bill, Mgr.-Reg. Sls.--Namco Controls Corporation, Highland Heights, OH; *U.S. Public*, pg. 482
Carson, Charles, Sr. V.P.-Mktg. & Sls.--Genesee Corporation, Rochester, NY; *U.S. Public*, pg. 728
Carson, J. Robert, Exec. V.P.-Sls.--R & B Machine Tool Co., Saline, MI; *U.S. Private*, pg. 901
Carson, Jim, V.P.-Sls.--Associated Process Controls, Pleasanton, CA; *U.S. Private*, pg. 92
Carson, John, Sls. Mgr.-Books--Brodart Company, Williamsport, PA; *U.S. Private*, pg. 170
Carson, Richard, Dir.-Exec. Accts.--Dunn-Edwards Corporation, Los Angeles, CA; *U.S. Private*, pg. 347
Cartagena, Angel, V.P.-Sls.--Bacardi-Martini Caribbean Corporation, Catano, PR; *Int'l*, pg. 132
Carter, Bill, V.P.-Sls.--Aladdin Industries, Incorporated, Nashville, TN; *U.S. Private*, pg. 30
Carter, Edward F., V.P. & Dir.-Bus. Devel.--Harza Engineering Co., Chicago, IL; *U.S. Private*, pg. 509
Carter, Glenn, Dir.-Turkey Sls.--WLR Foods, Inc., Timberville, VA; *U.S. Public*, pg. 1727
Carter, Jerry, V.P.-Sls.--Rapid Mounting & Finishing, Union City, CA; *U.S. Private*, pg. 910
Carter, John M., Chm. Bd. & Chief Exec. Officer--Carco Electronics, Menlo Park, CA; *U.S. Private*, pg. 208
Carter, Kirk T., Mgr.-Bus. Devel.--Potter-Shackelford Construction Co., Greenville, SC; *U.S. Private*, pg. 877
Carter, Leon, Mgr.-Reg. Sls.--Pepsi-Cola Bottling Company of Richmond, Inc., Richmond, VA; *U.S. Public*, pg. 1277
Carter, Michael, V.P.-Sls.--Wells Fargo Alarm Services, Inc., King of Prussia, PA; *U.S. Public*, pg. 246
Carter, Richard G., V.P. & Natl. Sls. Mgr.--Wine World Estates Company, Saint Helena, CA; *Int'l*, pg. 917
Carter, Rick, Mgr.-Local Sls.-KVI AM--Fisher Broadcasting Inc., Seattle, WA; *U.S. Public*, pg. 648
Cartner, Rita, Admin.-Sls.--Baum USA, Sidney, OH; *Int'l*, pg. 1293
Cartolano, P., Dir.-Mktg. & Sls. Services--Shieffelin Somerset Co., New York, NY; *Int'l*, pg. 412
Carton, David, Dir.-Sls.--Union Camp Ireland, Ashbourne, Ireland; *U.S. Public*, pg. 1666
Caruba, Walter J., V.P.-Sls. & Mktg.--Tultex Corporation, Martinsville, VA; *U.S. Public*, pg. 1644
Carus, Inga, V.P.-Sls. & Mktg.--Carus Corporation, Peru, IL; *U.S. Private*, pg. 217
Caruso, Salvatore, Bus. Mgr.--Master Data Center, Southfield, MI; *U.S. Private*, pg. 778
Carvalho, Flavio, V.P.-Mktg. & Sls.--Transbrasil Airlines, Inc., Miami, FL; *Int'l*, pg. 1416
Carvalho, Roger, V.P.-Intl. Sls.--Coleman Powermate, Inc., Omaha, NE; *U.S. Private*, pg. 691
Carver, Norman, V.P.-Sales--Carbone of America, Carbon Brush Div., Boonton, NJ; *Int'l*, pg. 1028
Carway, Ron, Dir.-Sls.--Cam Am Casters, Mississauga, Canada; *U.S. Public*, pg. 1507
Casadei, Loris, Mgr.-Sls.--Porsche Italia S.p.A Padova, Padua, Italy; *Int'l*, pg. 1063
Casalbore, Carl, V.P.-Sls.--Pirelli Armstrong Tire Corporation, New Haven, CT; *Int'l*, pg. 1058
Casale, Jerry N., V.P.-Critical Parts Sls.--Fenn Manufacturing Co., Newington, CT; *U.S. Public*, pg. 1676
Casaletta, Joe, Dir.-Used Machinery--CNB International, L.L.C., Charleston, SC; *U.S. Private*, pg. 196
Casanova, Antonio, Dir.-Sls.--Industrias Lever Portuguesa, Lda., Lisbon, Portugal; *Int'l*, pg. 1437
Casazza, Luis, Mgr.-Sls.--Nuevo Federal S.A., Buenos Aires, Argentina; *Int'l*, pg. 990
Cascade, Susan, Dir.-Adv. & Sls.--Crain's Detroit Business, Detroit, MI; *U.S. Private*, pg. 285
Cascino, J., Sr. V.P.-Sls.--Institutional Financing Services, Benicia, CA; *U.S. Public*, pg. 1652
Cascio, Bill, Exec. V.P.-Natl. Sls. & Mktg.--Fetzer Vineyards California Wines, Hopland, CA; *U.S. Public*, pg. 261
Cascio, James, Mgr.-Sls.--Sethco Division, Hauppauge, NY; *U.S. Public*, pg. 1100
Casella, Billie, Mgr.-Circulation--Pittsburg Morning Sun, Pittsburg, KS; *U.S. Private*, pg. 995
Casellari, Mario R., Dir.-Sls. & Mktg.--IGT-(Australia), Pty. Limited, Rosebery, Australia; *U.S. Public*, pg. 900
Cases, Ramon Rijera, Wholesale Trade-Spain--K & P Leykam Austria, Gratkorn, Austria; *Int'l*, pg. 757
Casey, Christine, Dir.-Mktg. Services--Baccarat, Inc., Edison, NJ; *Int'l*, pg. 132
Casey, James, V.P.-Sls. & Mktg.--IBJ Schroder Bank & Trust Company, New York, NY; *Int'l*, pg. 674
Casey, Joseph H., V.P.-Intl. Sls.--Allied Mineral Products, Inc., Columbus, OH; *U.S. Private*, pg. 39
Casey, Kevin, Dir.-Sls. & Mktg.--Educational Insights, Inc., Carson, CA; *U.S. Public*, pg. 565
Casey, Mary, Dir.-Sls.--Sheraton Hotels (England) Limited, London, United Kingdom; *U.S. Public*, pg. 1512
Casey, Richard, Mgr.-Sls, Billerica--Select Robinson Inc., Billerica, MA; *Int'l*, pg. 274
Casey, Tom, Mgr.-Natl. Sls.--Anthony and Sylvan Pools Corporation, Doylestown, PA; *U.S. Public*, pg. 593
Casimiro, Jose, Dir.-Sales--Vercoope-Uniao Das Adegas Cooperativas da Regiao Dos Vinhoa Verdes, U.C.R.L., Santo Tirso, Portugal; *Int'l*, pg. 1463
Casner, John, V.P.-Sls. & Mktg.--Hayward Industrial Products-Strainer Div., Elizabeth, NJ; *U.S. Private*, pg. 513
Caspall, Ken, V.P.-Sls.--MFA Oil Company, Columbia, MO; *U.S. Private*, pg. 687
Caspar, Dietmar, Dir.-Sls. & Mktg.--EMS Kurierpost GmbH, Bonn, Germany; *Int'l*, pg. 407
Casper, Michael, V.P.-Sls. & Mktg.--KYB Corporation of America, Lombard, IL; *Int'l*, pg. 727
Casperson, Curt, Dir.-Mktg.--The First American Financial Corporation, Santa Ana, CA; *U.S. Public*, pg. 624
Cassafa, Frank, Dir.-Sls. & Plng--JC Penney Company, Inc., Plano, TX; *U.S. Public*, pg. 916
Cassaro, Tom, Natl. Sls. Mgr.--Media General Broadcasting, Inc. (WJWB-TV), Jacksonville, FL; *U.S. Public*, pg. 1078
Cassidy, Brian, Dir.-Incentive Mkt. Sls.--Hyatt Hotels Corporation, Chicago, IL; *U.S. Private*, pg. 551
Cassin, Thomas C., V.P.-Mktg.--Pitco Frialator Inc., Bow, NH; *U.S. Public*, pg. 1065
Castellano, Nicholas, V.P.-Sls.--Lexicon Publications, Inc., Danbury, CT; *Int'l*, pg. 794
Casten, Fred, Dir.-Sls.--Terex Trucks, Tulsa, OK; *U.S. Public*, pg. 1581
Castile, Todd, V.P.-Sls.--Superior Steel Acquisition Corporation, Cheshire, CT; *Int'l*, pg. 75
Castillo, R., Mgr.-Sls.--Formularios Moore de Costa Rica S.A. de CV, Heredia, Costa Rica; *Int'l*, pg. 889
Castro Yllanes, Miguel, Mgr.-Commercial--Quimica S.A. de C.V., Mexico, Mexico; *Int'l*, pg. 614
Castro, J.L., Sr. Representative-Tech. Sls.--Ceramicas Termicas de Guatemala S.A., Guatemala, Guatemala; *Int'l*, pg. 894
Castro, Milt, Mgr.-Western Div. Sls.--Star Fine Foods, Inc., Fresno, CA; *U.S. Private*, pg. 1034
Catalani, Robert L., Dir.-Sls.-Southwest--Guinness Southern Division, Newport Beach, CA; *Int'l*, pg. 412
Catalano, Joe, Sr. V.P.-Sls./Fortis Long Term Care--Time Insurance, Milwaukee, WI; *Int'l*, pg. 499
Catania, Mike, Natl. Sls. Mgr.--Foote-Jones/Illinois Gear, Chicago, IL; *U.S. Public*, pg. 1370
Cates, John, Gen. Sls. Mgr.--WFI International, Inc., Houston, TX; *U.S. Private*, pg. 1144
Catlett, Timothy P., V.P.-Sls. & Mktg.--Barr Laboratories Inc., Pomona, NY; *U.S. Public*, pg. 191
Catona, Fred, V.P.-Sls.--Radio Direct Response, Broomall, PA; *U.S. Private*, pg. 906
Catsicas, Costas, Sls. & Mktg. Mgr.--Whitehall Greece, Athens, Greece; *U.S. Public*, pg. 82
Cattini, Mark, V.P.- Sls. & Mktg.--MapInfo Corp., Troy, NY; *U.S. Public*, pg. 1042
Caudill, Ed, Mgr.-Sls.--Courtaulds Coatings Inc., Louisville, KY; *Int'l*, pg. 338
Caudle, Morris W., V.P.-Sls.--Data Documents, Inc., Omaha, NE; *U.S. Public*, pg. 449
Caudron, Anne Marie, Mgr.-Natl. Sls.--KCCI Television, Inc., Des Moines, IA; *U.S. Public*, pg. 1343
Cauley, Ed, V.P.-Sls.--Sau-Sea Foods, Inc., Tarrytown, NY; *U.S. Private*, pg. 967
Caulfield, Richard J., V.P.-Mktg. & Sls.--Roberts Pharmaceutical Corporation, Eatontown, NJ; *U.S. Public*, pg. 1393
Caumette, Andre, Sls. Dir.--Avions de Transport Regional - ATR, Blagnac, France; *Int'l*, pg. 654
Cavallero, Mike, V.P.-Mktg. & Sls./Fresh Fruit--Dole Food Company, Inc., Westlake Village, CA; *U.S. Public*, pg. 515
Cavanagh, Jim, V.P.-Sls.--The Ertl Company, Inc, Dyersville, IA; *U.S. Public*, pg. 1684
Cavanagh, Ron, V.P.-Sls.--Bohler-Uddeholm Corp., Rolling Meadows, IL; *Int'l*, pg. 1471
Cavanaugh, David, V.P.-Sls. & Mktg.--Airtex Products, Fairfield, IL; *U.S. Private*, pg. 1113
Cavarra, Joseph, V.P.-Sls.--Costa Cruise Lines, N.V., Miami, FL; *U.S. Private*, pg. 278
Cavedon, George F., V.P.-Levi Outlet Stores--Designs, Inc., Needham, MA; *U.S. Public*, pg. 501
Cawley, Jim, Sr. V.P.-Mktg. & Sls.--GRP Records, New York, NY; *Int'l*, pg. 1215
Cawley, Kraig, Dir.-Adv. & Sls.--Tribune Review Publishing Co., Greensburg, PA; *U.S. Private*, pg. 1102
Cawthorne, Mark B., V.P.-Disposal Sls.--American Waste Services, Inc., Warren, OH; *U.S. Public*, pg. 94
Cazares, Arturo, V.P.-Latin America Sls.--3Com Corporation, Santa Clara, CA; *U.S. Public*, pg. 1603
Cekay, Tom, Mgr.-No. East Div.--Carillon Importers, Ltd., Fort Lee, NJ; *Int'l*, pg. 409
Celentano, Craig, V.P.-Sls.--Blue Coral Systems, Tucson, AZ; *U.S. Public*, pg. 1348
Cella, John, Mgr.-Sls./Western Reg.--AEP Industries, Inc., South Hackensack, NJ; *U.S. Public*, pg. 4
Cendella, Michael, Mgr.-Elec. Sls.--New York State Electric & Gas Corporation, Binghamton, NY; *U.S. Public*, pg. 1173
Cepa, Edward, V.P.-Opers.--C.J. Vitner Co., Chicago, IL; *U.S. Private*, pg. 1142
Cepek, Robert L., V.P.-Trade Sls.--Tiffany & Co., New York, NY; *U.S. Public*, pg. 1608
Cephus, Will, Sr. V.P.-Sls. & Mktg.--The Arnold Palmer Golf Company, Ooltewah, TN; *U.S. Public*, pg. 132
Cernohous, Paul, Mgr.-Natl. Sls.--Top Brands, Inc., Oshkosh, WI; *U.S. Private*, pg. 1091
Cerullo, Pat, V.P.-Sls. & Mktg.--Tesma International Inc., Concord, Canada; *Int'l*, pg. 830
Cervantes, Joseph P., V.P.-Sls. & Mktg.--Crowley Foods, Inc., Binghamton, NY; *Int'l*, pg. 752
Cerza, Robert, V.P.-Sls. & Mktg.--Pharmacia & Upjohn Deltec, Inc., Arden Hills, MN; *Int'l*, pg. 1049
Cezauru, Nat, Sr. V.P.-Sls. & Mktg.--4C Foods Corporation, Brooklyn, NY; *U.S. Private*, pg. 421
Cha, In-Sue, Mng. Dir.-Sls. & Beverage Mktg.--Dong-Suh Foods Corporation, Inchon, Korea; *Int'l*, pg. 416
Chabot, Norm, Mgr.-Acct.--Robertson Factories, Inc., Taunton, MA; *U.S. Private*, pg. 936
Chadwick, Douglas, V.P.-Sls.--Starmark, Inc., Sioux Falls, SD; *U.S. Public*, pg. 1054
Chadwick, Trevor, Dir.-Sls.--Carrington Viyella Garments Ltd., Derby, United Kingdom; *Int'l*, pg. 299
Chaffetz, Alex, Dir.-Adv. Sls.--Product Information Network, Englewood, CO; *U.S. Private*, pg. 597
Chainey, David E., Mgr.-Sls. & Mktg.--Amicon Canada Ltd., Oakville, Canada; *U.S. Public*, pg. 1113
Chalermsopone, Sophia, V.P.-Wholesale--Oroamerica, Inc., Burbank, CA; *U.S. Public*, pg. 1232
Chalfin, Sharon, Gen. Mgr.-Sls.--WRTV, Indianapolis, IN; *U.S. Public*, pg. 1070
Chamberlain, R., Mgr.-Natl. Sls.--Norcold, Sidney, OH; *U.S. Private*, pg. 352
Chambers, J.W., Sr. V.P.-Sls. & Mktg.--Hartwell Corporation, Placentia, CA; *U.S. Private*, pg. 1168
Chambers, Rob, V.P.-Sls.--Wright Medical Technology, Arlington, TN; *U.S. Private*, pg. 1192
Champley, Michael E., Sr. V.P.-Customer Energy Solutions--DTE Energy Company, Detroit, MI; *U.S. Public*, pg. 475
Champlin, Charles, V.P.-Sls. & Mktg.--Faribault Woolen Mill Co., Faribault, MN; *U.S. Private*, pg. 394

Champlin, Chris, Gen. Sls. Mgr.--Phil Long Ford, Colorado Springs, CO; *U.S. Private*, pg. 675
Chan, Ernie, Mgr.-Natl. Sls.--TSC Shannock Corporation, Burnaby, Canada; *Int'l*, pg. 1343
Chan, William, Mgr.-Sls.-Asama Pte. Ltd. Singapore--Straube Regional Center LLC, Pennington, NJ; *U.S. Private*, pg. 1046
Chan, William, Mgr.-Sls. & Mktg.--Asama Pte. Ltd., Asia, Singapore, Singapore; *U.S. Private*, pg. 1046
Chandler, Ron, V.P.-Sls.--Antenna Products Corp., Mineral Wells, TX; *U.S. Public*, pg. 289
Chaney, Mark, Mgr.-Circulation--The Grand Island Daily Independent, Grand Island, NE; *U.S. Private*, pg. 995
Channel, Frank, Gen. Mgr.- Sls.--Your Man Tours, Inc., Inglewood, CA; *U.S. Private*, pg. 1202
Channell, Jeff, Area Sls. Mgr.--Analog Devices Ltd. - Eastern Sales Office, Harlow, United Kingdom; *U.S. Public*, pg. 108
Channer, Wayne, Sr. V.P.-Sls. & Mktg.--Interactive Data Corporation, Lexington, MA; *Int'l*, pg. 1025
Chapel, Ed, V.P.-Dealer Sls./Americas--Micros Systems Inc., Beltsville, MD; *U.S. Public*, pg. 1106
Chapelone, Larry, V.P.-Enterprise Sls.--Inacom Corp., Omaha, NE; *U.S. Public*, pg. 873
Chapin, Andrew N., V.P.-Sls.--Combe Incorporated, White Plains, NY; *U.S. Private*, pg. 257
Chaplar, Kenneth, V.P.-Sls.--Astrex, Inc., Plainview, NY; *U.S. Public*, pg. 141
Chaplin, Arthur, Sr. V.P.-Sls.--Gould Paper Corporation, New York, NY; *U.S. Private*, pg. 466
Chaplin, Cliff, Sr. V.P.-Sls.--Gould Paper Corporation, New York, NY; *U.S. Private*, pg. 466
Chaplinski, Joe, Mgr.-Gen. Sls.--WESH Television, Inc., Winter Park, FL; *U.S. Public*, pg. 1344
Chapman, Doug, Mgr.-Distr. Sls.--Liquid Controls LLC, Lake Bluff, IL; *U.S. Private*, pg. 669
Chapman, Jim, Dir.-Residential Sls.--York Wallcoverings Inc., York, PA; *U.S. Private*, pg. 1196
Chapman, P., Dir.-Export Sls.--Addison Tube Forming Limited, Preston, United Kingdom; *Int'l*, pg. 448
Chapman, Randy, Mgr.-Sls./Western Canada--Security Chimneys International Ltd., Laval, Canada; *Int'l*, pg. 1217
Charlas, Lynn, Mgr.-Natl. Sls.--Club Med Sales, Inc., New York, NY; *Int'l*, pg. 298
Charlick, Mike, Mgr.-Sls & Engrng.--Hussmann Store Equipment Limited, Brantford, Canada; *U.S. Public*, pg. 1766
Charney, M. Jeffrey, V.P.-Mktg. & Commun.--Kaufman and Broad Home Corporation, Los Angeles, CA; *U.S. Public*, pg. 944
Charpentier, Mark, Dir.-Sls.--Cannondale Corporation, Bethel, CT; *U.S. Public*, pg. 301
Charpia, Mack, Mgr.-Vehicle Sls.--Fairway Ford, Inc., Greenville, SC; *U.S. Private*, pg. 392
Chase, William, Exec. V.P.-Sls. & Mktg.--American Business Information, Inc., Omaha, NE; *U.S. Public*, pg. 69
Chasm, James G., V.P.-Sls. & Mktg.--SK Hand Tool Corp., Chicago, IL; *Int'l*, pg. 570
Chastain, Roger W., Pres. & Chief Oper. Officer--Mount Vernon Mills, Inc., Greenville, SC; *U.S. Private*, pg. 835
Chastanet, Allen, V.P.-Mktg & Sls.--Air Jamaica Ltd., Miami, FL; *U.S. Private*, pg. 28
Chasteen, Jim, V.P.-Sls.--Gator Freightways, Inc., Wilmington, OH; *U.S. Private*, pg. 441
Chasteen, Lynn, Mgr.-Sls.--American City Business Journals, Inc., Jacksonville, FL; *U.S. Private*, pg. 19
Chatel, Marc, V.P.-Mktg. & Retail Sls.--Logitech International SA, Morges, Switzerland; *Int'l*, pg. 815
Chatfield, Jim, Gen. Mgr.-Sls.--Peerless Importers, Inc., Brooklyn, NY; *U.S. Private*, pg. 847
Chavda, Jiten, Dir.-Intl. Sls.--Heatcraft, Inc.-Refrigeration Products Division, Stone Mountain, GA; *U.S. Private*, pg. 659
Chaves, Ruy A., V.P.-Sls.--Sensormatic Do Brazil Electronica Ltda., Santo Andre, Brazil; *U.S. Public*, pg. 1457
Chavous, Joyce A., Admin.-Sls. & Mktg.--Magnetic Metals Corp., Camden, NJ; *U.S. Private*, pg. 560
Cheben, Mark, Dir.-Sls.--Roto-Rooter, Cincinnati, OH; *U.S. Public*, pg. 344
Chee, Wee Soon, Mgr.-Sls.--Sensormatic Asia/Pacific, Singapore, Singapore; *U.S. Public*, pg. 1457
Cheeseman, Peter, Dir.-Sls. & Mktg.--Wayfarer Transit Systems Ltd., Poole, United Kingdom; *Int'l*, pg. 853
Chen, J.J., Mgr.-Taiwan Sls.--Durco Valtek (Asia Pacific) Pte. Ltd., Taipei, Taiwan; *U.S. Public*, pg. 659
Chen, Paul, Mgr.-Sls.--Liebert Malaysia Sdn. Bhd., Sulang Jaya, Malaysia; *U.S. Public*, pg. 577
Chenoweth, Rick, Dir.-Retail Sls.--Rocco Inc., Harrisonburg, VA; *U.S. Private*, pg. 937
Chenoweth, Rick, Dir.-Sls.--Shady Brook Farms, Dayton, VA; *U.S. Private*, pg. 937
Cherian, Peter, V.P.-Sls. Canada--Combined Insurance Company of America, Chicago, IL; *U.S. Public*, pg. 118
Chernicki, R.L., V.P.-Sls., Food Service--McCain Foods Limited, Florenceville, Canada; *Int'l*, pg. 850
Chernosky, Robert J., Dir.-Natl. Sls.--Air Techniques, Inc., Hicksville, NY; *U.S. Private*, pg. 28
Chesler, Martin, Mgr.-Sls. Training--Knoll Pharmaceutical Company, Whippany, NJ; *Int'l*, pg. 105
Chessman, Frank, Exec. V.P.-Retail--Simon Marketing, Inc., Los Angeles, CA; *U.S. Private*, pg. 1001
Chester, G. Scott, Mgr.-Sls. & Mktg.--Nashua Imaging Supplies Div., Nashua, NH; *U.S. Public*, pg. 1152
Cheung, Alex, Chief Sls. Officer--Getinge AB Beijing, Beijing, China; *Int'l*, pg. 551
Cheung, Ang Ghim, Sls. Mgr.-Commercial Vehicles--Cycle & Carriage Industries (1986) Pte. Limited, Singapore, Singapore; *Int'l*, pg. 350
Cheung, Raymond, Mgr-Sls.--Acessorios Electronicos (Bel Fuse Macao), Limitada, Taipa, Macau; *U.S. Public*, pg. 200
Chew, Christina, Sls. Support--Asama Pte. Ltd., Asia, Singapore, Singapore; *U.S. Private*, pg. 1046
Chia, J., Mgr.-Inland Sales--Mobil Oil Singapore Pte. Ltd., Singapore, Singapore; *U.S. Public*, pg. 1119
Chiam, S.M., Mgr.-Sls.--Morganite Carbon of Singapore Pte. Limited, Singapore, Singapore; *Int'l*, pg. 892
Chiang, Chao-Chang, Mgr.-Sls.--China Hi-Ment Corp., Kaohsiung, Taiwan; *Int'l*, pg. 285
Chiarello, Richard, Sr. V.P.-Sls.--Computer Associates International, Inc., Islandia, NY; *U.S. Public*, pg. 420
Chidester, Craig, Mgr.-Mktg. & Sls.--Eaton Corporation, Electric Drives Division, Kenosha, WI; *U.S. Public*, pg. 556
Chiericozzi, Pete, V.P.-Mktg. & Sls.--Wisconsin Tissue Mills, Inc., Menasha, WI; *U.S. Public*, pg. 347
Childers, Gary, V.P.-Sls.--Vital Signs, Englewood, CO; *U.S. Public*, pg. 1723
Childs, Carl, V.P.-Sls. & Mktg.--Raytheon Aircraft Company, Wichita, KS; *U.S. Public*, pg. 1365
Childs, Donna, Coord.-Sls.--Flint Manufacturing Co., Burton, MI; *U.S. Private*, pg. 413
Childs, Fred, Mgr.-Sls.--Polyloom Corp. of America, Dayton, TN; *U.S. Private*, pg. 875
Childs, Jack, V.P.-Sls.--Parisi Inc./Royal Store Fixture, Philadelphia, PA; *U.S. Private*, pg. 839
Chin, George, V.P.-Sls., Mktg. & Bus. Devel.--Pharmaceutical Formulations, Inc., Edison, NJ; *U.S. Public*, pg. 1284
Chiostergi, Bob, V.P.-Mktg. & Sls.--Southern Mills, Inc., Union City, GA; *U.S. Private*, pg. 1016
Chitkara, Vinod, V.P.-Sls.--L3 Communications Narda-Microwave Div., Hauppauge, NY; *U.S. Private*, pg. 638
Chittaro, Al, V.P.-Sls.--Faygo Beverages, Inc., Detroit, MI; *U.S. Public*, pg. 1153
Chittenden, Jon, V.P. & Mgr.-Sls.--Champssports, Bradenton, FL; *U.S. Public*, pg. 1777
Chmela, Michael, Mgr.-Sls.--Jordan's Foods-Westbrook Division, Westbrook, ME; *U.S. Private*, pg. 599
Chmura, John A., Sr. V.P.-Sls.--Aerovox Inc., New Bedford, MA; *U.S. Public*, pg. 25
Cho, Soo Ho, Exec. V.P.-Sls., Mktg. & Traffic--Korean Airlines Co., Ltd., Seoul, Korea; *Int'l*, pg. 758
Choi, Chong-Hee, Mgr.--Ssangyong Precision Industry Co., Ltd., Inchon, Korea; *Int'l*, pg. 1292
Choi, Jae-Ho, Mgr.--Ssangyong Finance Inc., Seoul, Korea; *Int'l*, pg. 1292
Choinard, Paul, Dir.-Sls.--Tocco, Inc., Boaz, AL; *U.S. Public*, pg. 1259
Chong, Kaye, Mgr.-Admin, Mktg. & Sls.--Air Jamaica Ltd., Miami, FL; *U.S. Private*, pg. 28
Choo, Thomas, Dir.-Sls. & Mktg./RMS Opers.--Dun & Bradstreet Information Services (M) Sdn. Bhd., Kuala Lumpur, Malaysia; *U.S. Public*, pg. 536
Choon, Chim Kar, Sls. Mgr.-Proton Sls.--Cycle & Carriage Industries (1986) Pte. Limited, Singapore, Singapore; *Int'l*, pg. 350
Chorney, Alvan F., Sr. V.P.-Sls. & Mktg.--Ferrofluidics Corporation, Nashua, NH; *U.S. Public*, pg. 620
Chown, Fred L., V.P.-Sls.--Lampert Yards, Inc., Saint Paul, MN; *U.S. Private*, pg. 645
Chrimes, Mike, Dir.-Sls. Cardiac--Datascope Corp., Montvale, NJ; *U.S. Public*, pg. 487
Chrisjohn, Terry, V.P.-Sls.--Kennedy Valve, Elmira, NY; *U.S. Private*, pg. 725
Chrisley, Randy V., V.P.-Sls.--Pulaski Furniture Corporation, Pulaski, VA; *U.S. Public*, pg. 1342
Christ, Michael C., V.P.-Retail Sls./Chicago & Central Reg.--Tiffany & Co., New York, NY; *U.S. Public*, pg. 1608
Christensen, Chris, Sales Mgr.--Systems Engineering Division, Richardson, TX; *U.S. Public*, pg. 46
Christensen, James, Dir.-Natl. Sls. & Mktg.--Decora', Jasper, IN; *U.S. Public*, pg. 675
Christensen, Larry, V.P.-Sls.--General Automation, Inc., Irvine, CA; *U.S. Public*, pg. 706
Christensen, Ted, V.P.-Sls.--Plasti-Line, Inc., Knoxville, TN; *U.S. Public*, pg. 1308
Christenson, Michael, Dir.-Sls.--Acme Boot Co., Inc., El Paso, TX; *U.S. Private*, pg. 394
Christian, Michael, V.P.-Sls.--Frank Consolidated Enterprises Inc., Des Plaines, IL; *U.S. Private*, pg. 423
Christiansen, E.M., V.P.-Sls.--SmithKline Beecham Laboratories, Bristol, TN; *Int'l*, pg. 1264
Christiansen, Kelly, Mgr.-Sls. & Mktg.--Ling Electronics Inc., Anaheim, CA; *U.S. Public*, pg. 1077
Christie, Scott, V.P.-Trade Sls.--Courtaulds Coatings Inc., Louisville, KY; *Int'l*, pg. 338
Christopher, Ken, Mgr.-Sls.--Reily Foods & Co., Knoxville, TN; *U.S. Private*, pg. 919
Christopher, Richard E., V.P.-Sls.--Chips and Technologies, Inc., San Jose, CA; *U.S. Public*, pg. 349
Christy, Tom, Mgr.-Mktg. & Sls.--Comtech Antenna Systems, Inc., Saint Cloud, FL; *U.S. Public*, pg. 425
Chu, Aleda D., Mgr.-Nat. Sls.--SmithKline Beecham Research Limited, Pasig, Philippines; *Int'l*, pg. 1266
Chudyk, Kevin, V.P.-Sls.--AEC, Inc., Wood Dale, IL; *U.S. Private*, pg. 500
Chudyte, Kevin, V.P.-Sls. & Mktg.--Nelmor Co., Inc., North Uxbridge, MA; *U.S. Private*, pg. 1041
Chudyte, Kevin, V.P.-Mktg. & Sls.--AEC/Whitlock, Inc., Wood Dale, IL; *U.S. Private*, pg. 1041
Chung, Jong-Moo, Chief Fin. Officer--Ssangyong Resources Development Co., Ltd., Tonghae, Korea; *Int'l*, pg. 1291
Chura, D.E., Mgr.-Wholesale--Sporlan Valve Company, Washington, MO; *U.S. Private*, pg. 1026
Church, Jack, V.P.-Mktg. & Sls.--Hitchcock Industries, Inc., Bloomington, MN; *U.S. Private*, pg. 531
Churchill, Jerry M., V.P.-U.S. Sls. & Service--Hach Company, Loveland, CO; *U.S. Public*, pg. 773
Churchor, Bob, Mgr.-Sls.--N.G. Bailey & Co. Ltd.-Southampton Branch, Southampton, United Kingdom; *Int'l*, pg. 132
Chwalek, Joe, V.P.-Sls. & Mktg.--IKG Industries, Clark, NJ; *U.S. Public*, pg. 793
Chyrds, Thanassis, Mgr.-Sls.--Cretan Papermill S.A., Ierapetra, Greece; *Int'l*, pg. 864
Chytil, Jiri, Reservations Sls. Agent--Utell International-Czech Republic, Prague, Czech Republic; *Int'l*, pg. 1098
Cianciaruso, C. J., Mgr.-Sls.--Dunn Industries Inc., Kansas City, MO; *U.S. Private*, pg. 347
Ciarlone, Kevin, Dir.-Sls.--Hypro Corporation, New Brighton, MN; *U.S. Public*, pg. 1767
Cicciarella, David, V.P.-Sls.--IG Laboratories, Inc., Framingham, MA; *U.S. Public*, pg. 733
Ciccone, Jeanine, V.P.-Sls.--Elkay Products, Inc., Shrewsbury, MA; *U.S. Private*, pg. 372
Cieslowski, John, Dir.-Sls.--Hoffmann-La Roche Ltd., Mississauga, Canada; *Int'l*, pg. 1121
Cilento, G.C., V.P.-Sls.--Johnson & Johnson Ltda., Sao Paulo, Brazil; *U.S. Public*, pg. 931
Cimalore, Patti, Mgr.-Sls. & Mktg.--Jan-Co., Inc., Cranston, RI; *U.S. Private*, pg. 581
Cini, Joanne, V.P. & Mgr.-Local Sls.--WNYW, New York, NY; *Int'l*, pg. 926
Cinti, David A., V.P.-Sls.--Pinnacle Data Corporation, San Bruno, CA; *U.S. Public*, pg. 1158
Cinti, David A., V.P.-Sls.--FASTRAC Systems, Inc.-Insurance Agent & Broker, South San Francisco, CA; *U.S. Public*, pg. 1158
Cipriani, Diana, Mgr.-Local Sales--WFOR-TV Channel 4, Miami, FL; *U.S. Public*, pg. 275
Civanbay, Osman, Mgr.-Domestic Mktg.--Arcelik A.S., Istanbul, Turkey; *Int'l*, pg. 741
Claassen, James G., Sr. V.P.-Sls. & Sls. Services--Montgomery KONE Inc., Moline, IL; *Int'l*, pg. 746
Clabough, James E., V.P.-Sls.--Ingersoll-Rand Air Centers, Davidson, NC; *U.S. Public*, pg. 876
Claesson, Beugt, Mgr.-Sls. & Mktg.--Ledu International AB, Bohus, Sweden; *Int'l*, pg. 821
Claflin, Bruce L., Sr. V.P.-Sls. & Mktg.--Digital Equipment Corporation, Maynard, MA; *U.S. Public*, pg. 507
Claire, Franklin, V.P.-Distr.--The B. Manischewitz Company, Jersey City, NJ; *U.S. Private*, pg. 699
Clancy, Kevin, Mgr.-Sls.--Homes of Merit Inc., Bartow, FL; *U.S. Private*, pg. 537
Clancy, Terry, V.P.-General Motors Sls.--CMI International Inc., Southfield, MI; *U.S. Private*, pg. 195
Clande, Jim, V.P.-Sls.--United Design Corporation, Noble, OK; *U.S. Private*, pg. 1121
Clare, Jim, Mgr.-Sls.--American Computer Assembly/Compas, Ogdensburg, NY; *Int'l*, pg. 36
Clark, B.G., Mgr.-Sls. Admin.--Algoma Steel Inc., Sault Sainte Marie, Canada; *Int'l*, pg. 56
Clark, Blaine, III, V.P.-Sls.--Access Corporation, Cincinnati, OH; *Int'l*, pg. 994
Clark, David, Mgr.-Sls.--Snap-Tite, Inc., Erie, PA; *U.S. Private*, pg. 1010
Clark, Duane D., V.P.-Gas Mktg.--Belden & Blake Corporation, Canton, OH; *U.S. Private*, pg. 1078
Clark, Gary, Dir.-Sls.--Rainbow Technologies, Ltd., Chertsey, United Kingdom; *U.S. Public*, pg. 1359
Clark, Gerry, Dir.-Sls.--Portec Ltd., Lachine, Canada; *U.S. Public*, pg. 1318
Clark, J., Dir.-Sls. & Mktg.--Oland Breweries Limited, Halifax, Canada; *Int'l*, pg. 679
Clark, Jay D., V.P.-Sls.--Kennedy Tank & Manufacturing Co., Inc., Indianapolis, IN; *U.S. Private*, pg. 614
Clark, Jeff, Mgr.-Sls.--State Electric Supply Co., Huntington, WV; *U.S. Private*, pg. 1036
Clark, John F., Jr., Sr. V.P.--Guardsmark, Inc., Memphis, TN; *U.S. Private*, pg. 486
Clark, Lamar, V.P.-Adv., Mktg. & Sls.--Binning's Building Products, Inc., Lexington, NC; *U.S. Public*, pg. 67
Clark, Lewis, V.P.-Sls. & Mktg.-Controls--Kidde-Fenwal, Inc., Ashland, MA; *Int'l*, pg. 1500
Clark, Marilyn, Mgr.-Sls. & Sls. Svcs.--Peerless Tube Company, Bloomfield, NJ; *U.S. Public*, pg. 1269
Clark, Mitchell J., Sr. V.P.-Sls.--Robert Mondavi Winery, Inc., Oakville, CA; *U.S. Public*, pg. 1393
Clark, Peter, V.P.-Sls. & Mktg.-Protection--Kidde-Fenwal, Inc., Ashland, MA; *Int'l*, pg. 1500
Clark, R., Sls. Dir.--S.O.S. Newall Limited, Stamford, United Kingdom; *Int'l*, pg. 1166
Clark, Richard A., Mgr.-Sls. & Mktg.--Target Oilfield Pipe & Supply Company (TOPS), Canton, OH; *U.S. Private*, pg. 1078
Clark, Richard L., V.P.-Sls.--CCL Custom Manufacturing, Danville, IL; *Int'l*, pg. 238
Clark, Robert, Mgr.-Natl. Sls.--Phoenix Medical Technology, Inc., Andrews, SC; *U.S. Public*, pg. 1292
Clark, Robert, V.P.-Mktg. Strategy & Sls. Plng.--John B. Sanfilippo & Son, Inc., Elk Grove Village, IL; *U.S. Public*, pg. 1431
Clark, Robert J., V.P.-Sls. & Mktg.--Alden Shoe Co., Inc., Middleboro, MA; *U.S. Private*, pg. 33
Clark, Veda, V.P.-Mktg. & Sls.--Litecontrol Corporation, Hanson, MA; *U.S. Private*, pg. 669
Clarke, Adrian, Dir.-Sls. & Opers./UK & Ireland--Clestra Hauserman, Strasbourg, France; *Int'l*, pg. 569
Clarke, Roger, Sls. Rep.--Flowserve Duriron Canada Inc., Port Coquitlam, Canada; *U.S. Public*, pg. 659
Clarke, S., V.P.-Sales--Duraloy Technologies, Scottdale, PA; *U.S. Private*, pg. 839
Clarkson, Colin, Chief Exec. Officer & V.P.-Mktg.--Lotus Cars USA, Inc., Lawrenceville, GA; *Int'l*, pg. 1071
Clarysse, G., Dir.-Sls. & Comml.--Vandemoortele N.V., Izegem, Belgium; *Int'l*, pg. 1451
Class, Bill, V.P. & Dir.-Sls.--Richey Electronics, Inc., Garden Grove, CA; *U.S. Public*, pg. 1388
Claude, Brad, Mgr.-Sls.--Jaco Electronics, Inc., Tustin, CA; *U.S. Public*, pg. 921
Clay, Kermit, V.P.-Sls.--All Star Gas Co.-Region V, Lebanon, MO; *U.S. Private*, pg. 35
Clayton, Keith, Sls. Mgr.--Wisaforest (UK) Ltd., Uxbridge, United Kingdom; *Int'l*, pg. 1429
Clayton, Ted, V.P.-Domestic Sls.--Thomas Built Buses, Inc., High Point, NC; *U.S. Private*, pg. 1082

Cleary, Gerald V., Exec. V.P.-Sls.--Tyco Preschool, New York, NY; U.S. Public, pg. 1058
Cleary, Tom, V.P.-Sls.--Bandai America, Inc., Cypress, CA; Int'l, pg. 145
Cleaver, John W., V.P. & Mgr.-Sls.-West--Gibbs Wire & Steel Company, Inc., Southington, CT; U.S. Private, pg. 451
Clelland, Jim, V.P.-Sls. & Mktg.--Alcoa Forged Products, Cleveland, OH; U.S. Public, pg. 60
Clemente, Tom, Dir.-Sls.--DuBois Chemicals, Cincinnati, OH; Int'l, pg. 1437
Clementi, Frank, V.P.-Sls.--JM Company, Hasbrouck Heights, NJ; U.S. Private, pg. 577
Clements, A.G., Dir.-Sls.--Seven Seas Limited, Hull, United Kingdom; Int'l, pg. 593
Clements, Bill, Mgr.-Sls.--Kewanee Boiler Manufacturing Company, Inc., Kewanee, IL; U.S. Public, pg. 270
Clements, Bob, V.P.-Sls.--Favorite Brands International, Inc., Lincolnshire, IL; U.S. Private, pg. 397
Clements, Bob, Sr. V.P.-Natl. Sls.--Farley Candy Company, Chicago, IL; U.S. Private, pg. 397
Clements, Edward, Mgr.-Sls.--Clements Foods Co., Oklahoma City, OK; U.S. Private, pg. 245
Clements, Rob, Exec. V.P.-Sls. & Mktg.--Clairson International Corp., Ocala, FL; U.S. Public, pg. 575
Clemmer, Jake, Mgr.-Direct Export Sls.--Hatfield Quality Meats, Hatfield, PA; U.S. Private, pg. 510
Clemons, Charlie, V.P.-Sls.--Warren Electric Group, Houston, TX; U.S. Private, pg. 1151
Cleveland, James, Pres.-North American Opers.--Telxon Corporation, Akron, OH; U.S. Public, pg. 1573
Clever, Harry, Mktg. Mgr.-Mechanical Sls.--Fluidtec Engineer Products, Greensboro, NC; U.S. Public, pg. 401
Clifford, John, Dir.-Containerboard Sls. & Mktg.--Gaylord Container Corporation, Deerfield, IL; U.S. Public, pg. 704
Clifford, Paul, V.P.-Sls.--Clifford Paper Inc., Upper Saddle River, NJ; U.S. Private, pg. 246
Clifford, Robert N., V.P.-North American Sls.--Magneco/Metrel, Inc., Addison, IL; U.S. Private, pg. 695
Clifton, Paul H., Jr., Sr. V.P.-Sls. & Mktg.--Colonial Companies, Inc., Columbia, SC; U.S. Public, pg. 1699
Cline, David, Natl. Sls. Mgr.--Elektra Entertainment, New York, NY; U.S. Public, pg. 1612
Cline, Dennis, V.P.-Worldwide Sls.--Network Associates, Inc., Santa Clara, CA; U.S. Public, pg. 1168
Cline, Randy, Sr. V.P.-Mktg.--Regence BlueCross BlueShield of Oregon, Portland, OR; U.S. Private, pg. 917
Clinton, Brad, V.P.-Sls.--City Postal, Inc., New York, NY; U.S. Private, pg. 241
Close, Allyn D., Pres., Chief Exec. Officer & Mgr.-Sls. & Mktg.--Interpacific Investors Services, Seattle, WA; U.S. Private, pg. 572
Close, Ross, V.P.-Sls. & Mktg.--Astra Pharma Inc., Mississauga, Canada; Int'l, pg. 94
Clossey, Dan, V.P.-Sls.--S-B Power Tool Company, Chicago, IL; Int'l, pg. 205
Closson, Clemmy, Mgr.-West Coast Sls.--Parade Publications Inc., New York, NY; U.S. Private, pg. 20
Cloud, Tom, V.P.-Sls.--Cloud Corporation, Des Plaines, IL; U.S. Private, pg. 247
Clough, Ed, V.P.-Sls.--Outsource International, Deerfield Beach, FL; U.S. Public, pg. 1236
Clouse, John, V.P. & Natl. Sls. Mgr.--Nikon Inc., Melville, NY; Int'l, pg. 931
Cloutier, Dennis, V.P.-Sls.--Sierra On-Line, Inc., Bellevue, WA; U.S. Public, pg. 321
Clow, K.C., Dir.-Sls.--Trebor Bassett Ltd., Sheffield, United Kingdom; Int'l, pg. 248
Cloyd, Richard, Gen. Sls. Mgr.--Keystone Steel & Wire Co., Peoria, IL; U.S. Public, pg. 955
Cluett, Geoff, Sr. V.P.-Field Opers./Europe, Middle East & Africa--Comshare, Incorporated, Ann Arbor, MI; U.S. Public, pg. 425
Clunk, James, Mgr.-Sls.--The Hall China Company, East Liverpool, OH; U.S. Private, pg. 494
Clyde, Robert W., Exec. V.P.-Mktg. & Sls.--The Acacia Group - Acacia Life Insurance Co., Bethesda, MD; U.S. Private, pg. 10
Coale, William, Chm. Bd. & Chief Exec. Officer--Alcom Printing Group, Inc., Bethlehem, PA; U.S. Private, pg. 33
Coates, Doug, Sr. V.P.-Natl. Accts.--The Gibson-Homans Company, Twinsburg, OH; U.S. Private, pg. 451
Cobb, Charlie, V.P. & Natl. Sls. Mgr.--Lanier Worldwide Inc., Atlanta, GA; U.S. Public, pg. 791
Cobb, Neil, Dir.-Intl. Tent Sls.--Anchor Industries Inc., Evansville, IN; U.S. Private, pg. 71
Cobbledick, Paul C., Dir.-Sls. & Mktg.--Reynolds Metals Co.-Can Division Headquarters, Richmond, VA; U.S. Public, pg. 1386
Cobelo, H.R., Dr., Dir.-Mktg. & Sls.-USA--Leiner-Davis International Limited, Gladesville, Australia; Int'l, pg. 555
Coben, John B., Exec. V.P.--Nashville Machine Co. Inc., Nashville, TN; U.S. Private, pg. 774
Cochran, Bob, Sr. V.P.--ICF Kaiser International Inc., Fairfax, VA; U.S. Public, pg. 852
Cochran, Charles T., V.P.-Sls. & Mktg., Cold Finished Bar Div.--Republic Engineered Steels, Inc., Massillon, OH; U.S. Public, pg. 1378
Cochran, John, V.P.-Sls.--PRC, Inc., Mc Lean, VA; U.S. Public, pg. 1003
Cochran, Robert, Natl. Sls. Mgr.--Wausau Papers - Printing & Writing Div., Brokaw, WI; U.S. Public, pg. 1747
Cochrane, William, V.P.-Sls.--Caldwell Manufacturing Company, Rochester, NY; U.S. Private, pg. 200
Cockrell, Glenn, V.P.-Sls. & Mktg.--Shealy Electrical Wholesalers, Greenville, SC; U.S. Private, pg. 991
Cockrill, Al, V.P.-Sls. & Mktg.--York Barbell Co., Inc., York, PA; U.S. Private, pg. 1196
Cockrum, Lowell, Dir.-Natl. Sls.--Champion Laboratories, Inc., Albion, IL; U.S. Private, pg. 1113
Cockuyt, Alec, Dir.-Sls. & Mktg.--The Yorkville Printing Group Limited, Mississauga, Canada; Int'l, pg. 538
Codova Tirado, Luis, Ing., Technical Sls. Rep.--Morton Thiokol S.A. de C.V., Mexico, Mexico; U.S. Public, pg. 1136
Coe, Roger, V.P.-Sls. & Mktg.--Andiamo, Inc., Fountain Valley, CA; U.S. Private, pg. 73
Coelho, Laura, Dir.-Sls.--Noville, South Hackensack, NJ; U.S. Private, pg. 808
Coen, Terrence F., V.P. & Dir.-Sls. & Mktg.--Survey Sampling, Inc., Fairfield, CT; U.S. Private, pg. 1056
Coffin, D.M.., V.P. & Dir. Business Devel.--Irex Corporation, Lancaster, PA; U.S. Public, pg. 913
Coffin, Louise, Dir.-Sls.--FaceMate Corp., Somersworth, NH; U.S. Private, pg. 391
Coffman, H.F., Mgr.-National Sls.--Business Equipment and Systems Division, Dayton, OH; U.S. Public, pg. 1505
Cogen, Mitch, Dir.-Sls.--Pyramid Handbags Inc., New York, NY; U.S. Private, pg. 896
Cohen, Eric, V.P.-Sls.--Cardinal Inc., Rahway, NJ; U.S. Private, pg. 208
Cohen, Gary, Mgr.-Reg. Sls.--Pennsylvania Cellular Telephone Corp., Harrisburg, PA; U.S. Public, pg. 1708
Cohen, Gary, Mgr.-Reg. Sls.--Pennsylvania Cellular Telephone Corp., Wormleysburg, PA; U.S. Public, pg. 1708
Cohen, Joel H., V.P.-Sls. & Mktg.--Queen Carpet Corporation, Dalton, GA; U.S. Private, pg. 900
Cohen, Jonathan, V.P.-Wholesale Sls.--PG Vinyl Windows/PG Proglass Construction, Westbrook, ME; U.S. Private, pg. 826
Cohen, Mark J., Exec. V.P.-Sls. & Mktg.--All-Luminum Products, Inc., Philadelphia, PA; U.S. Private, pg. 34
Cohen, Steve, V.P.-Sls.--Falcon Products, Inc., Saint Louis, MO; U.S. Public, pg. 611
Cohlst, C.G., Pres.-Mktg. & Sls.--UBO Verzekeringen, Utrecht, Netherlands; Int'l, pg. 26
Cohn, Derek, Sr. V.P.-Mktg. & Sls.--International Plastics Company, New York, NY; U.S. Private, pg. 571
Cohoon, Joe, Mgr.-Sls.--Spectra-Physics Laserplane Inc., Dayton, OH; U.S. Public, pg. 1594
Coia, John, V.P.-Sls.--Perry Products, Hainesport, NJ; U.S. Private, pg. 855
Coker, Charles, V.P.-Sls.--The Berkline Corporation, Morristown, TN; U.S. Private, pg. 432
Colando, Greg, Sr. V.P.-Sls. & Mktg.--Interface Flooring Systems Inc., La Grange, GA; U.S. Public, pg. 889
Colangelo, Tony, V.P.-North American Sls.--Hyperion Software, Stamford, CT; U.S. Public, pg. 851
Colburn, Robert B., V.P.-Sls. & Mktg.--Bauer Sports Inc., Montreal, Canada; U.S. Public, pg. 1184
Cole, Allan, V.P.-Sls.--AVX Corporation, Myrtle Beach, SC; Int'l, pg. 775
Cole, Bill, Sls.--Etec Systems, Inc., Hayward, CA; U.S. Public, pg. 594
Cole, Charles, Dir.-Sls. & Mktg.--Protective Closures Co., Inc., Buffalo, NY; U.S. Public, pg. 1045
Cole, Donald, V.P.-Sls.--Mountain States Pipe & Supply Company, Colorado Springs, CO; U.S. Private, pg. 764
Cole, Jeane, Mgr.-Mktg. Projects--Lucasfilm Ltd., San Rafael, CA; U.S. Private, pg. 679
Cole, Robert M., V.P.-Mktg. & Sls.--Arkwright, Inc, Fiskeville, RI; Int'l, pg. 994
Cole, Roger M., V.P.-Sls.--Kleer-Vu Plastics Corp., Compton, CA; U.S. Public, pg. 962
Cole, Ron, V.P.-Sls.--America West Airlines, Inc., Phoenix, AZ; U.S. Public, pg. 67
Cole, Sebastian, Dir.-Sls. & Mktg.--Colex International, Ltd., Leicester, United Kingdom; U.S. Private, pg. 796
Cole, Stephen, V.P.-Sls.--Detecto Scale Company, Webb City, MO; U.S. Private, pg. 209
Cole, Steven, V.P.-Sls. & Mktg.--Park Foods L.P., Barrington, IL; U.S. Private, pg. 839
Coleburns, Will, V.P.-Mktg. & Sls.--Koh-I-Noor, Inc., Bloomsbury, NJ; U.S. Private, pg. 629
Coleman, Beverly B., Dir.-Sls.--Colonial Williamsburg Foundation, Williamsburg, VA; U.S. Private, pg. 254
Coleman, Bob, Gen. Mgr.-Sls.--Coleman Dairy LLC, Little Rock, AR; U.S. Private, pg. 251
Coleman, Galya, District Sls. Mgr.--FINNAIR, Falls Church, VA; Int'l, pg. 486
Coleman, James, V.P.-Natl. Sls.--A.W. Chesterton Company, Stoneham, MA; U.S. Private, pg. 234
Coleman, Jay W., Exec. V.P.-Sls. & Service--CVB Financial Corp., Ontario, CA; U.S. Public, pg. 286
Coleman, Nancy, V.P.-Sls. Admin., (N.Y.)--Columbia Tri-Star International Television, Culver City, CA; Int'l, pg. 1281
Coleman, Peter J., Reg. V.P.-N. American Sls.--Pioneer-Standard Electronics, Inc., Cleveland, OH; U.S. Public, pg. 1300
Coleman, Roseanne, Assoc. Project Devel. & Sls. Training Dir.--CoMed Communications, Inc., Philadelphia, PA; U.S. Private, pg. 1083
Coleman, Roxanne, Supvr.-Mktg., Adv. & Sls.--Shakespeare Fishing Tackle, Columbia, SC; U.S. Public, pg. 940
Coletti, Henry, V.P.-Sls.--Vulcan-Hart Corp., Louisville, KY; U.S. Public, pg. 1322
Colgan, Robert T., Exec. V.P. & Asst. Mgr.-Natl. Sls.--Jefferies & Company, Inc., Los Angeles, CA; U.S. Public, pg. 925
Colin, Bill, Mgr.-Natl. Sls.--TSC Shannock Corporation, Burnaby, Canada; Int'l, pg. 1343
Colip, Randy, V.P.-Sls.--Baldor Electric Company, Fort Smith, AR; U.S. Public, pg. 168
Colletti, Gaspare, Dir.-Sls. & Mktg.--Reynolds Extrusion Company, Richmond Hill, Canada; U.S. Public, pg. 1387
Collier, Deanie, V.P.-Adv.--Stein Mart, Inc., Jacksonville, FL; U.S. Public, pg. 1514
Collier, Lance, Mgr.-Natl. Sls.--Yamaha Corp. of America, Sporting Goods Div., Buena Park, CA; Int'l, pg. 1516
Collier, Robert G., Dir.-Sls.--F.W. Myers & Co., Inc., Rouses Point, NY; U.S. Private, pg. 770
Collins, Bill, Mgr.-Sls.--Don Massey Cadillac Inc., Plymouth, MI; U.S. Private, pg. 712
Collins, Carol A., Leader-Services Delivery--Bay State Gas Company, Westborough, MA; U.S. Public, pg. 196
Collins, Chris, V.P.-Sls.--Russ Berrie and Company, Inc., Oakland, NJ; U.S. Public, pg. 222
Collins, Cliff, Mgr.-Sls.--Gem Top Mfg., Inc., Clackamas, OR; U.S. Private, pg. 443
Collins, Dan, V.P.-Sls.--Grace Cocoa/Ambrosia Chocolate, Milwaukee, WI; U.S. Public, pg. 128
Collins, Don, V.P.-Sls.--Fairfield Sapphire Valley, Sapphire, NC; U.S. Public, pg. 611
Collins, Fred, V.P.-Sls.--Gould Paper Corporation, New York, NY; U.S. Private, pg. 466
Collins, Gerry, V.P.-Sls. & Mktg.--M K Diamond Products, Inc., Torrance, CA; U.S. Private, pg. 684
Collins, Harry, Mgr.-Multiwall Regional Sls.--Industrial Bag Division - Des Moines Plant, Des Moines, IA; U.S. Public, pg. 1521
Collins, J.L., Mgr.-Sls.--Electric Furnace Co., Salem, OH; U.S. Private, pg. 367
Collins, John, Gen. Mgr.-Sls.--General Tools Mfg., Co. Inc., New York, NY; U.S. Private, pg. 445
Collins, Phillip E., V.P.-Sls.--United Services Life Insurance Co., Arlington, VA; U.S. Public, pg. 1376
Collins, Randy, V.P.-Sls. & Mktg.--Gorges/Quik-To-Fix Foods, Dallas, TX; U.S. Private, pg. 465
Collins, Richard, Sr. V.P.-Sls. & Mktg.--Golden Books Family Entertainment Inc., New York, NY; U.S. Public, pg. 749
Collins, Ron, V.P.-Sls.--Quality Bakers of America Cooperative, Inc., Greenwich, CT; U.S. Private, pg. 898
Collins, Russ, V.P.-Sls.--Hathaway Corporation, Littleton, CO; U.S. Public, pg. 798
Collins, Sean, Dir.-Sls.--VideoLabs, Inc., Minneapolis, MN; U.S. Public, pg. 1720
Collins, Thomas J., Mgr.-Reg. Sls.--Automotive News, Detroit, MI; U.S. Private, pg. 284
Collison, Donald B., Mgr.-Acq. & Sls.--Potomac Electric Power Company, Washington, DC; U.S. Public, pg. 1318
Colliver, Richard, Sr. V.P.-Automobile Sls.--American Honda Motor Co., Inc., Torrance, CA; Int'l, pg. 634
Colucci, James, Sr. V.P. Sls., Mktg. & Dir.-Creative & Mgr.-Sls. Promo.--Consolidated Cigar Corporation, Fort Lauderdale, FL; U.S. Private, pg. 690
Colucco, Robert, V.P.-Sls.--Gould Paper Corporation, New York, NY; U.S. Private, pg. 466
Colvin, Kit, Mgr.-Natl. Sls.--Colony Paints, Kansas City, MO; U.S. Public, pg. 1707
Colyar, R., Mgr.-Sls.--CM Shredder Div., Sarasota, FL; U.S. Public, pg. 405
Combs, Tom, Gen. Sls. Mgr.--WLFI-TV, West Lafayette, IN; U.S. Private, pg. 148
Comer, Tony, V.P. & District Sls. Mgr.-Life & Health--Willis Corroon Administrative Services Corporation, Cary, NC; Int'l, pg. 1505
Comerford, Gary M., V.P.-Agency Sls.--Sun Life of Canada, Toronto, Canada; Int'l, pg. 1319
Comerford, Vince, Sr. V.P.-Global Sls.--Noville, South Hackensack, NJ; U.S. Private, pg. 808
Compagno, Robert L., V.P.-Sls.--Fellowes Manufacturing Co., Itasca, IL; U.S. Private, pg. 400
Compton, Randy, Dir.-Sls.--The Vendo Company, Fresno, CA; Int'l, pg. 1184
Comstock, Jack, V.P.-Television Sls.--QVC, Inc., West Chester, PA; U.S. Private, pg. 897
Conard, Tom, V.P.-Sls.--Dovatech, Ltd., Beecher, IL; U.S. Public, pg. 520
Conarroe, Richard, V.P.-Mktg. & Sls.--The Thermos Company, Schaumburg, IL; Int'l, pg. 938
Conaty, John R., Dir.-Sls.--Turner Construction Co., Los Angeles, CA; U.S. Public, pg. 1645
Conaway, Ken, Dir.-Mktg. & Sls.--Future Foam, Inc., Council Bluffs, IA; U.S. Private, pg. 433
Conda, Joseph V., V.P.-Glass Container Sls. & Mktg.--Owens-Illinois, Inc., Toledo, OH; U.S. Public, pg. 1238
Conda, Joseph V., V.P.-Sls. & Mktg.--Owens-Brockway Glass Containers, Toledo, OH; U.S. Public, pg. 1238
Condict, Dennis W., V.P.-Sls. & Svcs.--Enogex Inc., Oklahoma City, OK; U.S. Public, pg. 1207
Condiotte, F.S., Mgr.-Sls.--Sterno, Inc., New York, NY; U.S. Public, pg. 397
Condon, Charles, Mgr.-Sls.--Jordan's Foods-Bangor Division, Bangor, ME; U.S. Private, pg. 599
Condon, Michelle, Exec. V.P.-Retail Banking--The Colonial BancGroup, Inc., Montgomery, AL; U.S. Public, pg. 400
Condon, Michelle, Mgr.-Sls.--Colonial Bank, Montgomery, AL; U.S. Public, pg. 400
Cone, Tim, Dir.-Sls. & Mktg.--Hahn Automotive Warehouse, Inc., Rochester, NY; U.S. Public, pg. 774
Conley, David, Natl. Sls. Mgr.-Retail Mkts.--The Homer Laughlin China Company, Newell, WV; U.S. Private, pg. 653
Conley, Deidre, Natl. Wine Mgr.--Marie Brizard Wines & Spirits USA, North Miami, FL; U.S. Private, pg. 702
Conley, E. Renae, Mgr.-Sls.--Cinergy Corp., Cincinnati, OH; U.S. Public, pg. 369
Conlin, Gary, V.P.-Sls. U.S. & Canada--Periphonics Corp., Bohemia, NY; U.S. Public, pg. 1278
Conlin, Tom, Dir.-Sls. Patient Monitoring--Datascope Corp., Montvale, NJ; U.S. Public, pg. 487
Conlon, Terence, Dir.-Sls.--Prism Integrated Sanitation Management, Inc., Miami, FL; U.S. Private, pg. 592
Conlon, William C., V.P.-Worldwide Sls. Fin.--Cisco Systems, Inc., San Jose, CA; U.S. Public, pg. 375
Connell, Dave, V.P.-Sls.--Joern's Sunrise Medical, Stevens Point, WI; U.S. Public, pg. 1536
Conner, Brian R., V.P.-Sls.-Europe, Africa & Middle East--Pinnacle Systems, Inc., Mountain View, CA; U.S. Public, pg. 1297
Conner, Tom, Dir.-Sls.--The Van Metres Companies, Burke, VA; U.S. Private, pg. 1132
Connerotte, Jean-Pierre, Gen. Mgr.-Distribution Centre--Electrabel S.A., Brussels, Belgium; Int'l, pg. 436
Connolly, Brian, V.P.-U.S. Sls. Organization--Avon Products, Inc., New York, NY; U.S. Public, pg. 155
Connolly, Brian, V.P.-Sls. & Mktg.--Emson, Inc., Bridgeport, CT; U.S. Private, pg. 375

Connolly, John, V.P.-Adv. Sls.--The Edmonton Journal, Edmonton, Canada; *Int'l*, pg. 631
Connor, Barry C., Mgr.-Natl. Sls.--Noteworthy Industries Inc., Amsterdam, NY; *U.S. Private*, pg. 808
Connor, Eric, Mgr.-Mktg. & Sls.--Industra Inc., Greenville, SC; *Int'l*, pg. 74
Connor, R.J., V.P.-Sls.--Broderick & Bascom Rope Co., Sedalia, MO; *U.S. Private*, pg. 68
Connors, Charles W., Jr., District Sls. Mgr.-Chicago--Magneco/Metrel, Inc., Addison, IL; *U.S. Private*, pg. 695
Conover, Clay, V.P.-Adv. Specialty--The At-A-Glance Group, Sidney, NY; *U.S. Private*, pg. 295
Conrad, Jeffrey V., Dir.-Sls.--Mooney Aircraft Corporation, Kerrville, TX; *U.S. Private*, pg. 759
Conran, William, Sls. Mgr.-Central Div.--Hunter Douglas, Inc., Upper Saddle River, NJ; *Int'l*, pg. 639
Conroy, Pat, Dir.-Sls. & Service--Interform Corporation, Bridgeville, PA; *U.S. Public*, pg. 333
Conroy, Thomas J., Dir.-Sls. & Mktg.--ChemPump, Warrington, PA; *U.S. Public*, pg. 456
Constantini, Ben, Exec. V.P.-Sls.--Wavetek Corporation, San Diego, CA; *U.S. Private*, pg. 1154
Contardi, James, V.P.-Sls. & Mktg.--Aurora Electronics, Inc., Irvine, CA; *U.S. Public*, pg. 147
Contardi, James N., V.P.-Sls.--PC Service Source, Inc., Dallas, TX; *U.S. Public*, pg. 1240
Conte, Leo, Pres. & Chief Exec. Officer--Montebello Brands Inc., Baltimore, MD; *U.S. Private*, pg. 758
Contella, John, V.P.-Sls.--A & S Building Systems, Inc., Caryville, TN; *U.S. Public*, pg. 1146
Conti, Joe, Sr. V.P.-Sls.--Johnny Carson Apparel, Inc., Buffalo, NY; *U.S. Public*, pg. 796
Conti, Joseph, Sr. V.P.-Sls.--Intercontinental Branded Apparel, Buffalo, NY; *U.S. Public*, pg. 796
Contreras, Jeanette, V.P.-Sls.--Caribe Freight, Aguadilla, PR; *U.S. Private*, pg. 211
Converse-Wilson, Lizabeth, V.P.-Sls.--Apertus Technologies Incorporated, Eden Prairie, MN; *U.S. Public*, pg. 119
Converse, James P., V.P. & Gen. Sls. Mgr.--Sues, Young & Brown Inc., Baldwin Park, CA; *U.S. Private*, pg. 1049
Convey, Mike, V.P.-Sls.--Kwikset Corporation, Irvine, CA; *U.S. Public*, pg. 233
Conway, Barry, Exec. V.P.-Sls. & Mktg.--Adams Business Forms, Topeka, KS; *U.S. Private*, pg. 16
Conway, Matthew, Dir.-Sls.--Dettra Flag Company, Oaks, PA; *U.S. Private*, pg. 328
Conway, Michael, Dir.-Mktg. & Sls.--Sermatech (U.K.) Limited, Ripley, United Kingdom; *U.S. Public*, pg. 1570
Cook, J.W., V.P.-Sls.--Ajax Magnethermic Corp., Warren, OH; *Int'l*, pg. 113
Cook, James R., Jr., Natl. Sls. Mgr.--Stiefel Laboratories, Inc., Coral Gables, FL; *U.S. Private*, pg. 1043
Cook, Jim, Dir.-Sls.--Emery Waterhouse Company, Portland, ME; *U.S. Private*, pg. 373
Cook, John A., V.P. & Dir.-Sls. & Training--Omega Financial Corporation, State College, PA; *U.S. Public*, pg. 1222
Cook, Nancy, V.P.-Southwestern Sls.--CBS Enterprises Division, New York, NY; *U.S. Public*, pg. 274
Cook, Paul, Dir.-Mktg. & Sls.--Labatt Brewing Company Limited, Toronto, Canada; *Int'l*, pg. 679
Cook, Stephen, V.P.-Sls. & Mktg.--Kaufman and Broad Home Corporation, Los Angeles, CA; *U.S. Public*, pg. 944
Cook, Stephen, Mgr.-Mktg. & Sls.--Kaufman and Broad Colorado Division, Denver, CO; *U.S. Public*, pg. 945
Cook, Steve, V.P.-Dedicated Sls.--Builders Transport, Incorporated, Camden, SC; *U.S. Public*, pg. 267
Cook, Tim, V.P.-Sls.--Orders Distributing Co., Greenville, SC; *U.S. Private*, pg. 819
Cookinham, James B., V.P.-Mktg.--Mid-America Energy Resources, Indianapolis, IN; *U.S. Public*, pg. 913
Coomber, Ian M., Exec. Dir.-Sls. & Mktg.--Vauxhall Motors Limited, Luton, United Kingdom; *U.S. Public*, pg. 724
Coomes, Dennis, V.P.-Sls.--Lawson Products, Inc., Des Plaines, IL; *U.S. Public*, pg. 980
Coon, Andy, V.P.-Comml. Mktg.--General Communication, Inc., Anchorage, AK; *U.S. Public*, pg. 708
Cooney, Charles C., V.P.-Sls.--Tellabs Operations, Inc., Lisle, IL; *U.S. Public*, pg. 1572
Cooney, Tom, Mgr.-Sls./Steel Div.--Northwestern Steel & Wire Co., Sterling, IL; *U.S. Public*, pg. 1201
Coons, Robert L., V.P.-Mktg. & Sls.--Burnham, Lancaster, PA; *U.S. Public*, pg. 270
Cooper, Andrew, Dir.-Sls.--Morton Automotive Coatings, Lansing, IL; *U.S. Public*, pg. 1135
Cooper, B. Ray, V.P.-Sls. & Mktg.--Gaston County Dyeing Machine Co., Mount Holly, NC; *U.S. Private*, pg. 441
Cooper, Brace, V.P.-Sls. & Mktg.--Mark Andy, Inc., Chesterfield, MO; *U.S. Public*, pg. 521
Cooper, Candy, Sec.-Sls.Svcs.--Shell Chemical Co., Houston, TX; *Int'l*, pg. 1136
Cooper, David, Dir.-Sls.--SLM Holding Corp., Washington, DC; *U.S. Public*, pg. 1419
Cooper, Dick, Dir.-Sls.--Harvest Brands, Inc., Pittsburg, KS; *U.S. Private*, pg. 46
Cooper, Frank, Dir.-Sls. & Mktg.--Electronic Solutions, San Diego, CA; *U.S. Public*, pg. 1791
Cooper, James, V.P.-North American Sales--Kolmar Laboratories, Inc., Port Jervis, NY; *Int'l*, pg. 239
Cooper, Jim, Mgr.-Natl. Sls.--R.S. Owens, Chicago, IL; *U.S. Private*, pg. 824
Cooper, Larry, Regional Mgr.-Southeast--Columbus Mills, Inc., Columbus, GA; *U.S. Private*, pg. 256
Cooper, Mark A., Dir.-Sls. & Mktg.--Gorman-Rupp Industries Div., Bellville, OH; *U.S. Public*, pg. 754
Copestick, Allan T., V.P.-Soft Drink Sls.--Metal Container Corporation, Saint Louis, MO; *U.S. Public*, pg. 114
Copley, C. Richard, Dir.-Sls.--The Variable Annuity Life Insurance Co., Houston, TX; *U.S. Public*, pg. 76
Copley, John A., Chief Oper. Officer & V.P.--Jennings & Churella Construction Company, Wellington, OH; *U.S. Private*, pg. 586
Coppinger, Gary, Mgr.-Corp. Retail & Niche Adv.--TruServ Corporation, Chicago, IL; *U.S. Private*, pg. 1108
Coppola, Mike, Exec. V.P.-Sls. & Mdsg.--Tops Markets, Inc., Amherst, NY; *Int'l*, pg. 750
Corbett, Dave, V.P.-Sls. & Mktg.--Crane Manufacturing, Cudahy, WI; *U.S. Private*, pg. 286
Corbett, Jeff, Sr. V.P.-Sls. & Mktg.--DHL Worldwide Express, Redwood City, CA; *U.S. Private*, pg. 301
Corbett, Jeff, Sr. V.P.-Mktg. & Sls.--DHL Airways, Inc., Redwood City, CA; *U.S. Private*, pg. 302
Corbett, Martin, Mgr.-Sls. & Adv.--Harold Leonard & Company, Inc., Union, NJ; *U.S. Private*, pg. 660
Corbett, Mike, V.P.-Opers.--Northern Engineering Corp., Cudahy, WI; *U.S. Private*, pg. 286
Corbin, Brad J., V.P.-Sls.--Northern Life Insurance Company, Seattle, WA; *U.S. Public*, pg. 1375
Corbusie, Alain, Dir.-Sls./Medium & Heavy--Iveco France S.A., Trappes, France; *Int'l*, pg. 696
Corcoran, J.C., Dir.-Sls.--Companhia Goodyear do Brasil Produtos de Borracha, Sao Paulo, Brazil; *U.S. Public*, pg. 753
Corcoran, Jerry, Mgr.-Reg. Sls.--Duraliner U.S.A., Lapeer, MI; *U.S. Public*, pg. 537
Corde, Robert, Mgr.-Local Sls.--WQDR, Raleigh, NC; *U.S. Private*, pg. 298
Cordeau, Jacques, Dir.-Mktg. & Sls./Food Sevice--Aliments Flamingo, Iberville, Canada; *Int'l*, pg. 57
Cordier, Tom, V.P.-Sls. & Mktg.--Wah Chang, Albany, OR; *U.S. Public*, pg. 44
Cordoso, Luis Seara, Mgr.-Sls.-Zone I--Central de Cervejas, S.A., Lisbon, Portugal; *Int'l*, pg. 279
Corica, Vincent C., Sr. V.P.-East, Bus. Sls. & Service--MCI Communications Corp., Atlanta, GA; *U.S. Public*, pg. 1023
Corlew, Donald, Dir.-Sls.--American Inks & Coatings Corp., Phoenixville, PA; *U.S. Private*, pg. 56
Cormack, David A., Sr. V.P.-Sls.--IQ Software Corporation, Norcross, GA; *U.S. Public*, pg. 858
Corn, Tammie, Indust. Div. Admin. Asst.--Seymour of Sycamore, Inc., Sycamore, IL; *U.S. Private*, pg. 988
Cornelism, David, V.P.-Sls.--M & C Specialties (Ireland) Limited, Athlone, Ireland; *U.S. Private*, pg. 684
Cornelison, Dave, V.P.-Sls. & Mktg.--M & C Specialties Company, Southampton, PA; *U.S. Private*, pg. 684
Cornelius, Bob, V.P.-Mktg. & Sls.--Saztec International, Inc., Billerica, MA; *U.S. Public*, pg. 1435
Cornelius, Connie, Dir.-Mktg. & Sls.--American Educational Products, Boulder, CO; *U.S. Public*, pg. 71
Cornelius, Jim, V.P.-Sls.--Edward Don & Company, North Riverside, IL; *U.S. Private*, pg. 339
Cornell, Tammy, Mgr.-Sls. Admin.--The Network of City Business Journals, Inc., Kansas City, MO; *U.S. Private*, pg. 19
Corning, L. Avery, V.P.-Opers. & Sls.--Kenan Transport Company, Chapel Hill, NC; *U.S. Public*, pg. 949
Cornish, Joette, Mgr.-Sls. Support--Labelon Corporation, Canandaigua, NY; *U.S. Private*, pg. 641
Cornu, P., Dir.-Sls.-Ag Equipment--Case France S.A., Paris, France; *U.S. Public*, pg. 1579
Cornwall, Pete, Dir.-Sls.--Air UK Ltd., Stansted, United Kingdom; *Int'l*, pg. 38
Corona, Ben, V.P.-Sls. & Mktg.--Americas--Kerr-McGee Chemical Corp., Oklahoma City, OK; *U.S. Public*, pg. 952
Corrasco, Pedro, Mgr.-Sls.--Bundy Venezolana C.A., Valencia, Venezuela; *Int'l*, pg. 1342
Corrigan, C. Rory, Exec. V.P. & Mgr.-N.Y. Sls. Mgr.--Jefferies & Company, Inc., Los Angeles, CA; *U.S. Public*, pg. 925
Cortez, Rene, District Sls. Mgr.--Thai Airways Intl. Ltd.-U.S. Office, El Segundo, CA; *Int'l*, pg. 1381
Cortinez, Juan P., Asst. Mgr.-Sls.--CODELCO Chile (Corporacion Nacional Del Cobre De Chile), Santiago, Chile; *Int'l*, pg. 302
Corto, Frank, District Sls. Mgr.-Baltimore--Magneco/Metrel, Inc., Addison, IL; *U.S. Private*, pg. 695
Cosgrove, Dan, Pres.-Eyemark Media Sls.--CBS Enterprises Division, New York, NY; *U.S. Public*, pg. 274
Cosner, David, Dir.-Sls. & Mktg.--Universal Dynamics, Inc., Woodbridge, VA; *Int'l*, pg. 484
Costa, Joe, Mgr.-Natl. Sls.--Sensormatic New Zealand Ltd., Auckland, New Zealand; *U.S. Public*, pg. 1458
Costello, Fred, V.P.-Sls.--Alliant Foodservice, Bensenville, IL; *U.S. Private*, pg. 244
Costello, James G., Dir.-Sls.--Sugarloaf/USA, Kingfield, ME; *U.S. Private*, pg. 62
Costello, Roger, Dir.-Sls. & Devel.--Hollymatic Corporation, Countryside, IL; *U.S. Private*, pg. 535
Cote, Al, Gen. Mgr.--Dean Industries, Inc., Gardena, CA; *Int'l*, pg. 188
Cote, James R., V.P.-Sls. & Mktg.--ROHN Industries, Inc., Peoria, IL; *U.S. Public*, pg. 1404
Cote, James R., Mgr.-Mktg. & Sls.--UNR-Rohn Div., Peoria, IL; *U.S. Public*, pg. 1404
Cotney, Anita M., V.P.-Sls. & Mktg.--Russell Corporation, Alexander City, AL; *U.S. Public*, pg. 1413
Cottle, Michael, V.P.-Worldwide Sls. & Mktg.--Multigen Inc., San Jose, CA; *U.S. Public*, pg. 1425
Cotton, Graham, V.P.-Sls.--Radica USA Limited, Dallas, TX; *U.S. Private*, pg. 906
Cotton, Robert W., V.P.-Sls. & Mgr.-Mktg.--Hohner/HSS Inc., Ashland, VA; *U.S. Private*, pg. 533
Cottrell, Louise, Dir.-Affiliate Sls. & Mktg.--Travel U.K., London, United Kingdom,; *U.S. Private*, pg. 647
Cotuno, Ken, V.P.-Natl. Accounts & Specialty Sls.--Edward Don & Company, North Riverside, IL; *U.S. Private*, pg. 339
Coucerio, Joseph, Dir.-Mktg. Team, Sls., Promo. & Partnerships--Busch Entertainment Corp., Clayton, MO; *U.S. Public*, pg. 114
Couch, Cecil, Mgr.-Sls.--Nucor Fasteners, Saint Joe, IN; *U.S. Public*, pg. 1205
Coughlan, Basil J., V.P.-Sls.--Ford of Europe, Incorporated, Dearborn, MI; *U.S. Public*, pg. 664
Coughlin, Jim, V.P.-Sls. & Mktg.--Seyfert Foods, Inc., Fort Wayne, IN; *U.S. Private*, pg. 988
Coughlin, Neil P., V.P.-Sls. & Mktg.--Kingsbury Corporation, Keene, NH; *U.S. Private*, pg. 621
Coulter, David, Mgr.-Sls., Special Tran. Grp.--Atlas Specialized Transportation, Evansville, IN; *U.S. Private*, pg. 97
Coulter, Ken, V.P.-Sls. & Mktg.--Mark IV Automotive Canada Inc., Weston, Canada; *U.S. Public*, pg. 1045
Coulter, Sara, Intl. Sls. Mgr.--Harris Broadcast Division, Richmond, IN; *U.S. Public*, pg. 791
Counihan, Jack, Mgr.-Promo.--Newsweek, Inc., New York, NY; *U.S. Public*, pg. 1743
Coupar, John, V.P.-Sls.--Gault Distributors Inc., Richmond, Canada; *Int'l*, pg. 541
Courtade, Judy, Dir.-Sls. & Mktg./Knopt Grp.--Random House, Inc., New York, NY; *U.S. Private*, pg. 20
Courtade, Judy, Dir.-Sls. & Mktg.--Alfred A. Knopf, Inc., New York, NY; *U.S. Private*, pg. 21
Courtney, Chuck, Mgr.-Govt. Sls.--My Own Meals, Inc., Deerfield, IL; *U.S. Private*, pg. 770
Courtney, John, V.P.-Sls. Service & Customer Rels.--Imprimerie Quebecor Canada, Woodbridge, Canada; *Int'l*, pg. 1077
Cousins, Steve, Exec. V.P.-Sls. & Mktg.--Delicato Vineyards, Manteca, CA; *U.S. Private*, pg. 322
Couvert, F., Dir.-Mktg. & Sls.--Steelweld Division Zweigniederlassung Bonn der Ambac B.V., Saint Augustin, Germany; *Int'l*, pg. 71
Covella, Robert, Mgr.-Sls./Midwest Reg.--AEP Industries, Inc., South Hackensack, NJ; *U.S. Public*, pg. 4
Covenko, Howard L., V.P.-Sls. & Mktg.--Major Smith Inc., New Holland, PA; *Int'l*, pg. 201
Coviello, Ken, V.P.-Sls.-Homecare--Graham-Field Health Products, Inc., Hauppauge, NY; *U.S. Public*, pg. 757
Cowan, Joe, V.P.-Sls.--Wonderware Corporation, Irvine, CA; *U.S. Public*, pg. 1775
Cowan, Ronald L., Dir.-Wholesale Svcs.--Wisconsin Power & Light Company, Madison, WI; *U.S. Public*, pg. 1728
Cowan, Thomas R., V.P.-Reg. Sls.--Sealed-Sweet Growers, Inc., Vero Beach, FL; *U.S. Private*, pg. 978
Cowell, Jeff, Dir.-Commercial Mktg. & Sls.--Quaker Oats Limited, Southall, United Kingdom; *U.S. Public*, pg. 1348
Cower, John, V.P.-Sls. & Mktg.--Crouse-Hinds, Syracuse, NY; *U.S. Public*, pg. 444
Cowie, George, V.P.-Sls.--Lipton, Toronto, Canada; *Int'l*, pg. 1438
Cowin, D., Dir.-Sls.--Hepworth Home Products Limited, Belper, United Kingdom; *Int'l*, pg. 615
Cowles, Jim, V.P.-Life & Health & Dir.-Sls.--Willis Corroon Corporation of Louisville, Louisville, KY; *Int'l*, pg. 1505
Cowling, John, Dir.Sls.--Arthur Sanderson and Sons Ltd., Uxbridge, United Kingdom; *Int'l*, pg. 540
Cox, Amalia, Dir.- Sls. & Mktg.--Kitchen Fair, Jacksonville, AR; *U.S. Private*, pg. 917
Cox, Andy, V.P.-Intl. Sls.--Tasco Sales Inc., Miramar, FL; *U.S. Private*, pg. 928
Cox, Barry, Mng. Dir.-U.K. Sls. & Mktg.--Waterford Wedgwood UK Plc, Stoke on Trent, United Kingdom; *Int'l*, pg. 1487
Cox, Gary L., Mgr.-Mktg. & Sls.--Mitchel & Scott Machine Co., Inc., Indianapolis, IN; *U.S. Private*, pg. 753
Cox, Gary M., V.P.-Commercial Sls.--Huntington National Bank, Morgantown, WV; *U.S. Public*, pg. 850
Cox, Jerry, Sls. Mgr.-New Cars--Dean Sellers Ford Inc., Troy, MI; *U.S. Private*, pg. 983
Cox, Jerry, V.P.-Sls. & Mktg.--Union City Body Company, L.P., Union City, IN; *U.S. Private*, pg. 1118
Cox, Lee, V.P.-Sls. & Svcs.--IES Industries Inc., Cedar Rapids, IA; *U.S. Public*, pg. 855
Cox, Lee, V.P.-Sls. & Svcs.--IES Utilities Inc., Cedar Rapids, IA; *U.S. Public*, pg. 855
Cox, Malcolm, Dir.-Sls.--Sanderson Technology Ltd., Sheffield, United Kingdom; *Int'l*, pg. 1184
Cox, Mark, Mgr.-Eastern Sls.--Efco Corporation, Monett, MO; *U.S. Private*, pg. 353
Cox, Mike, Exec. V.P.-Opers.--Monro Muffler/Brake, Inc., Rochester, NY; *U.S. Public*, pg. 1124
Cox, Patrick, V.P.-Sls.--Van Melle USA, Inc., Erlanger, KY; *Int'l*, pg. 1451
Cox, Tim, V.P.-North American Sls.--Linear Technology Corp., Milpitas, CA; *U.S. Public*, pg. 1000
Cox, William, Mgr.-Sls.--Reading Anthracite Co., Pottsville, PA; *U.S. Private*, pg. 913
Cox, William W., Jr., V.P.-Sls./Americas--Molex Incorporated, Lisle, IL; *U.S. Public*, pg. 1121
Coxhead, Chuck, Dir.-Sls.--Tuthill Pump, Alsip, IL; *U.S. Private*, pg. 1111
Coxwell, Doug, V.P.-Sls.--National Sea Products Incorporated, Portsmouth, NH; *Int'l*, pg. 909
Coyle, James E., III, Sr. V.P.-Mdsg. & Sls.--DeCorp, Carrollton, TX; *U.S. Public*, pg. 948
Coyne, Bill, Exec. V.P.-Sls.--Cable & Wireless Communications Inc., Vienna, VA; *Int'l*, pg. 247
Coyne, Martin, V.P.-Eastern & Central Reg.--Racke USA, Sonoma, CA; *Int'l*, pg. 1083
Crabtree, Richard A., V.P.-Retail Opers.--Central Maine Power Company, Augusta, ME; *U.S. Public*, pg. 325
Craggs, Nicholas, Dir.-Sls.--Mead Coated Board U.K. Limited, Rickmansworth, United Kingdom; *U.S. Public*, pg. 1076
Craig, John, Dir.-Sls. & Mktg.--Heil Environmental Industries, Chattanooga, TN; *U.S. Public*, pg. 520
Craig, John, V.P.-Sls./Motive Power--Yuasa-Exide, Inc., Reading, PA; *Int'l*, pg. 1522
Craig, Tom, Sr. V.P.-Sls. & Mktg.--Golden Flake Snack Foods, Inc., Birmingham, AL; *U.S. Public*, pg. 750
Cramer, Barbara, Dir.-Mktg. & Sls. Support--GTE Supply, Irving, TX; *U.S. Public*, pg. 697
Cramer, Neil, Dir.-Sls. Grp.--Sonoma Mission Inn & Spa, Sonoma, CA; *U.S. Private*, pg. 1014
Crandall, Jill, V.P.-Sls. & Mktg.--Crystal Cabinet Works, Inc., Princeton, MN; *U.S. Private*, pg. 293
Crane, D., V.P.-System Sls. & Mktg.--Bran & Luebbe Inc., Buffalo Grove, IL; *Int'l*, pg. 1378

Crane, Frank, V.P.-Sls.--Morton Salt, Chicago, IL; *U.S. Public*, pg. 1135

Cranford, R.W., Gen. Sls. Mgr.--Sawhill Tubular Div., Sharon, PA; *U.S. Public*, pg. 131

Crary, Van, Mgr.- Western Reg. Sls.--Thoro, Jacksonville, FL; *U.S. Private*, pg. 505

Craske, A.G., V.P.-Mktg. & Sls.--Isco, Inc., Lincoln, NE; *U.S.* Public, pg. 913

Crasnianski, Serge, Grp. Mng. Dir.-Mfg., Res. & Devel. & Sls.--Photo-Me International plc, Bookham, United Kingdom; *Int'l*, pg. 1055

Crawford, David, V.P.-Sls.--DOALL Company, Des Plaines, IL; *U.S. Private*, pg. 337

Crawford, David J., V.P.-Sls.--American Home Shield Corporation, Memphis, TN; *U.S. Public*, pg. 1461

Crawford, Doris, Admin. Sls. & Adv.--Envirex Inc., Waukesha, WI; *U.S. Public*, pg. 61

Crawford, John, Chief Info. Officer & V.P.-Sls.--Collin Street Bakery, Corsicana, TX; *U.S. Private*, pg. 252

Crawford, Tom, Exec. V.P.-Sls. & Mktg.--Lozier Corporation, Omaha, NE; *U.S. Private*, pg. 679

Crawford, Tyrone G., V.P.-Sls.--Metallurgical, Inc., Minneapolis, MN; *U.S. Public*, pg. 1594

Creary, Brian, V.P.-Sls. & Mktg.--Global Beverage Co., Rochester, NY; *U.S. Private*, pg. 457

Crecca, A., Sr. V.P.-Sls./Cosmed Div.--Beiersdorf, Inc., Norwalk, CT; *Int'l*, pg. 182

Crecca, Tony, V.P.-Sls.--Futuro Inc., Milford, OH; *Int'l*, pg. 182

Creech, Freda, Coord.-Sls. & Mktg.--National Retail Hardware Assn., Indianapolis, IN; *U.S. Private*, pg. 786

Creed, J. Richard, Dir.-Structural Bus. Unit--Wyman-Gordon, North Grafton, MA; *U.S. Public*, pg. 1782

Crees, Chris, Dir.-Sls.--Britannic Aviation Limited, Albourne, United Kingdom; *Int'l*, pg. 215

Crement, Gale, Mgr.-E. Central Sls.--RAM Golf Corporation, Melrose Park, IL; *U.S. Private*, pg. 908

Cremer, Vivian, V.P.-Intl. Sls.--Sebago, Inc., Gorham, ME; *U.S. Private*, pg. 980

Crenshaw, Helene, Dir.-Intl. Sls. & Mktg.--Farnam Companies, Inc., Phoenix, AZ; *U.S. Private*, pg. 396

Crenshaw, John, District Sls. Mgr.-Cincinnati--Magneco/Metrel, Inc., Addison, IL; *U.S. Private*, pg. 695

Cress, Dave, Dir.-Sales & Mktg.--CTS Corp. Frequency Controls, Sandwich, IL; *U.S. Public*, pg. 285

Crew, Charles E., Jr., V.P.-Sls.--G.E. Plastics, Pittsfield, MA; *U.S. Public*, pg. 710

Cribbin, Dan, Dir.-Sls. & Mktg.--Vile-Goller, Fine Art Printing & Lithography, Kansas City, KS; *U.S. Private*, pg. 1140

Crichton, Sarah, V.P. & Publisher-Adult Trade--Little, Brown & Co., New York, NY; *U.S. Public*, pg. 1612

Crider, Charles, Mgr.-Sls.--United States Aluminum-Carolina, Rock Hill, SC; *U.S. Public*, pg. 895

Crider, Larry, V.P.-Reg. Sls.--Wittnauer International, Inc., New Rochelle, NY; *U.S. Public*, pg. 273

Crilly, James, Sr. V.P.-Sls./Arm & Hammer Div.--Church & Dwight Co., Inc., Princeton, NJ; *U.S. Public*, pg. 355

Crisp, William, Mgr.-Sls.--Knurlet Tool Co., Warren, MI; *U.S. Private*, pg. 608

Cristo, Gus, Exec. V.P. & Dir.-Sls. & Mktg.--Ferguson International, Inc., Dallas, TX; *U.S. Private*, pg. 401

Cristofoli, Nino M., Sr. V.P.-Sls. & Mktg., Nestle Refigerated Food Co.--Nestle Frozen/Refrigerated Food Co., Solon, OH; *Int'l*, pg. 918

Crivelli, Robert, V.P.-Sls. & Mktg.--Santo Tours & Travel, Inc., Buffalo, NY; *U.S. Private*, pg. 23

Croarkin, Tom, Mgr.-Natl. Sls.--Market Data Retrieval, Shelton, CT; *U.S. Public*, pg. 536

Croft, G., Dir.-Sls. & Promo.--Labatt Breweries British Columbia, New Westminster, Canada; *Int'l*, pg. 679

Crolla, Tony, Mgr.-European Sls.--Ling Electronics Ltd., Suffolk, United Kingdom; *U.S. Public*, pg. 1077

Crompton, R.C., V.P.-Sls. & Direct Mktg. Svcs.--May & Speh, Inc., Downers Grove, IL; *U.S. Public*, pg. 1063

Cron, Robert W., V.P.-Indus. Prods. Div.--AEP Industries, Inc., South Hackensack, NJ; *U.S. Public*, pg. 4

Cronin, Mike, V.P.-North American Sls.--VTEL Corporation, Austin, TX; *U.S. Public*, pg. 1703

Cronkhite, Larry, V.P.-Sls.--Chittenden & Eastman Co., Burlington, IA; *U.S. Private*, pg. 237

Cronkite, George F., V.P.-Sls. & Mktg.--Windsor Door, Little Rock, AR; *U.S. Public*, pg. 69

Cronkright, Roger, V.P.-Sls.--Interkal, Inc., Kalamazoo, MI; *Int'l*, pg. 759

Cronovich, David N., V.P.-Auto. & OEM Sls.--MNP Corp., Utica, MI; *U.S. Private*, pg. 687

Crorey, David, Exec. V.P.-Sls. & Mktg.--ISI Norgen, Inc., Fraser, MI; *Int'l*, pg. 646

Crosby, Daniel, Dir.-Retail--Martin Lawrence Limited Editions, Inc., North Hollywood, CA; *U.S. Private*, pg. 709

Cross, Allan, V.P.-Newspaper Sls.--Autologic Information International, Inc., Thousand Oaks, CA; *U.S. Public*, pg. 1724

Cross, Andy, Exec. V.P.-Sls. & Mktg.--MobileComm, Ridgefield Park, NJ; *U.S. Public*, pg. 1120

Cross, G., Sls. Dir.--Moore Business Systems Australia Ltd., Richmond, Australia; *Int'l*, pg. 889

Cross, Maria, V.P.-Sls. & Mktg.--Optimaxx International, Rockleigh, NJ; *U.S. Private*, pg. 818

Cross, Robert, V.P.-Sls.--Ruiz Food Products, Inc., Dinuba, CA; *U.S. Private*, pg. 951

Cross, Steve, V.P.-Sls.--Connectix Corporation, San Mateo, CA; *U.S. Private*, pg. 264

Cross, Steve, Exec. V.P.-Sls.--Northeast Environmental Services, Inc., Canastota, NY; *U.S. Public*, pg. 546

Crossan, Barbara, Dir.-Sls.--Reynen, Bardis & Winn, Sacramento, CA; *U.S. Private*, pg. 926

Crossman, Paul, Asst. V.P.-Mktg. & Sls.--National Fire Protection Association, Quincy, MA; *U.S. Private*, pg. 782

Crosthwait, Kent, V.P.-Sls. & Pur.--Neill-LaVielle Supply Co., Louisville, KY; *U.S. Private*, pg. 790

Crotty, Don, Sls.& Cost Analyst--Takatta Inc., Auburn Hills, MI; *U.S. Private*, pg. 528

Crouch, Bob, Mgr.-Prod. Sls.--KCL Corporation, Shelbyville, IN; *U.S. Private*, pg. 603

Crouch, Robert D., Sr. V.P.-Sls. & Mktg.--Respironics, Inc., Pittsburgh, PA; *U.S. Public*, pg. 1383

Crouse, Nancy, V.P.-Sls. Admin.--Superba, Inc., Los Angeles, CA; *U.S. Private*, pg. 1054

Crow, Phillip W., V.P.-Sls. & Mktg.--Dawn Food Products, Inc., Jackson, MI; *U.S. Private*, pg. 316

Crowder, Toby, Mgr.-Sls. & Customer Service--William Bayley/Folger Adam Security, Inc., Springfield, OH; *U.S. Private*, pg. 125

Crowl, David, V.P.-Sls.--Four Seasons Hotels Inc., Don Mills, Canada; *Int'l*, pg. 502

Crowley, Donald, V.P.-Sls.--Krazy Glue Inc., New York, NY; *U.S. Private*, pg. 158

Crowley, Stephen, V.P.-Mktg. & Sls.--Rome Cable Corporation, Rome, NY; *U.S. Private*, pg. 942

Crown, Michael D., Mgr.-Special Services--School Annual Publishing Co., Coshocton, OH; *U.S. Private*, pg. 598

Cruce, Tom, Mgr.-Sls. & Mktg.--Westvaco Corporation-Envelope Div., Springfield, MA; *U.S. Public*, pg. 1762

Cruke, Gaetan, Dir.-Sls. & Mktg.--Wyeth Australia Pty. Ltd., Baulkham Hills, Australia; *U.S. Public*, pg. 82

Crum, Ben, V.P.-Sls. & Mktg.--Sargent-Welch Scientific Company, Buffalo Grove, IL; *U.S. Public*, pg. 1704

Crumbaugh, Susan, Mgr.-Agency Devel.--State Farm Mutual Automobile Insurance Company, Bloomington, IL; *U.S. Private*, pg. 1036

Crummey, Stephen J., V.P.-World-Wide Sls.--PictureTel, Andover, MA; *U.S. Public*, pg. 1294

Crump, A.J., Dir.-Sls.--Britains Petite Ltd., Nottingham, United Kingdom; *U.S. Public*, pg. 789

Crylen, Ed, Sls. Mgr.--Midwesco Mechanical Energy, Niles, IL; *U.S. Public*, pg. 1026

Cryman, Tim, Sls. Associate--OPT Industries, Inc., Phillipsburg, NJ; *U.S. Public*, pg. 1624

Cudby, P., Dir.-Sls.--Puritan Maid Ltd., Aylesbury, United Kingdom; *Int'l*, pg. 210

Cuddeback, Ron, Mgr.-Sls./New Cars--McNamara Pontiac Isuzu Inc., Orlando, FL; *U.S. Private*, pg. 724

Culberson, Jeff, Dir.-Sls.--Bank One, Wisconsin, Milwaukee, WI; *U.S. Public*, pg. 174

Culbert, William, V.P.-Sls.--John Roberts Company, Minneapolis, MN; *U.S. Private*, pg. 935

Culbreth, Grady, Mgr.-Sls. Admin.--Carl Zeiss Optical, Inc., Petersburg, VA; *Int'l*, pg. 1523

Cullen, R., Dir.-Sls.--Turner Construction Co., Arlington, VA; *U.S. Public*, pg. 1645

Cullen, William P., V.P.-Sls. & Mktg.--Communication Cable, Inc., Sanford, NC; *U.S. Public*, pg. 968

Culligan, Gerald, Dir.-Sls.--Masterfoods Ltd., Dublin, Ireland; *U.S. Private*, pg. 707

Culpepper, Lewis, Mgr.-Sls. & Mktg.--Southern Pilot Insurance Company, Greensboro, NC; *Int'l*, pg. 346

Culver, John A., Dir.-Sls. & Mktg.--Giumarra Vineyards, Edison, CA; *U.S. Private*, pg. 455

Culver, Robert J., V.P.-Retail Sls.--Bunker Hill Foods Inc., Bedford, VA; *U.S. Private*, pg. 219

Cummings, Donald P., V.P.-Professional Hand Tools--Hyde Manufacturing Co., Southbridge, MA; *U.S. Private*, pg. 551

Cummings, Robert, Nat'l Sls. Dir.--Wisconsin Label Corporation, Algoma, WI; *U.S. Private*, pg. 1184

Cummins, Charles W., V.P.-Sls., Southwest Div.--C.R. Gibson Co., Norwalk, CT; *U.S. Public*, pg. 1168

Cuneo, Chris, V.P.-Retail Opers.--Six Flags Great Adventure Theme Park & Wild Safari Animal Park, Jackson, NJ; *U.S. Public*, pg. 1611

Cunha, Ricardo, Mgr.-Sls.-Zone II--Central de Cervejas, S.A., Lisbon, Portugal; *Int'l*, pg. 279

Cunha, Rui, Mgr.-Sls.--Shell de Cabo Verde, Ilha do Sal, Cape Verde; *Int'l*, pg. 1137

Cunningham, Bob, Sr. V.P.-Sls. & Mktg.--Pico Products, Inc., Lake View Terrace, CA; *U.S. Public*, pg. 1294

Cunningham, Jonathan R., Exec. V.P. & Mgr.-N.Y. Reg. Sls.--Jefferies & Company, Inc., Los Angeles, CA; *U.S. Public*, pg. 925

Cunningham, Mark, V.P.-Sls.--Indiana Glass Company, Cincinnati, OH; *U.S. Public*, pg. 976

Cunningham, Michael, Dir.-Mktg. & Sls.--Pawling Corporation, Pawling, NY; *U.S. Private*, pg. 844

Cunnion, Kerry, V.P.-Sls.--Huffy Bicycle Company, Celina, OH; *U.S. Public*, pg. 846

Cupples, Kenneth, V.P.-Sls.--Central States Enterprises, Inc., Heathrow, FL; *U.S. Private*, pg. 225

Curley, C.Z., Mgr.-Sls.--Longview Fibre Co., Merchandise, Grocery & Specialty Bag Div., Waltham, MA; *U.S. Public, pg. 1014*

Curran, John, Dir.-Sls.--Pollio Dairy Products, Mineola, NY; *U.S. Public*, pg. 1288

Curran, Timothy J., Sr. V.P.-Sls.--Tech Data Corporation, Clearwater, FL; *U.S. Public*, pg. 1562

Curren, Martha, V.P.-Sls.-Lenox Collections--Lenox, Incorporated, Lawrenceville, NJ; *U.S. Public*, pg. 261

Currie, Bill, Dir.-Mktg. & Sls.--Canadian Kenworth Co., Mississauga, Canada; *U.S. Public*, pg. 1247

Currier, W. Brent, V.P.-Sls. & Mktg.--General Cigar Company, Inc., Bloomfield, CT; *U.S. Public*, pg. 708

Curry, Gerri, Mgr.-Intl. Customer Service--Spectronics Corporation, Westbury, NY; *U.S. Private*, pg. 1024

Curtin, John F., V.P.-Sls.--Paul Hemmer Construction Company, Fort Mitchell, KY; *U.S. Private*, pg. 521

Curtin, Nick, V.P.-Sls. & Mktg.--Precision Dynamics Corporation, San Fernando, CA; *U.S. Private*, pg. 879

Curtis, Christopher L., V.P.-Sls. & Mktg.--Peabody COALSALES Company, Saint Louis, MO; *Int'l*, pg. 594

Curtis, Michael, Dir.-Sls. & Mktg.--Penn Racquet Sports, Phoenix, AZ; *U.S. Public*, pg. 706

Curto, D., Coord.-Mktg.--Echelon International Corporation, Saint Petersburg, FL; *U.S. Public*, pg. 560

Cusack, Richard J., Jr., V.P.-Sls. & Mktg.--Berkley Risk Managers, Somerset, NJ; *U.S. Public*, pg. 215

Cusano, Tony, V.P.-Sls.--Cape Cod Potato Chip Company, Hyannis, MA; *U.S. Private*, pg. 205

Cusher, Jeffrey D., V.P.-Sls.--Dowty O Rings North America - Charleston, Charleston, SC; *Int'l*, pg. 1338

Cushing, Pat, V.P.-Sls.-Canada--GSW Water Heating Company, Fergus, Canada; *Int'l*, pg. 538

Cusick, Walt, Corp. Mgr.-Sls. & Mktg.--McInnes Steel Company, Corry, PA; *U.S. Private*, pg. 722

Cuss, Martin, Dir.-Sls. & Mktg.-Education--Oxford University Press, Oxford, United Kingdom; *Int'l*, pg. 1018

Cusson, Michel, Dir.-Sls. (Quebec, Ontario East and Atlantique)--Grocery Division, Montreal, Canada; *Int'l*, pg. 348

Custer, Kelly, Mgr.-Sls.--Linn Products, Inc., Charlotte, MI; *U.S. Private*, pg. 669

Cutler, Michael, V.P.-Sls./Western U.S.--Thorn Apple Valley, Inc., Southfield, MI; *U.S. Public*, pg. 1602

Cutler, Timothy, Dir.-Sls.& Mktg.--Miracle Adhesives, Buffalo, NY; *U.S. Public*, pg. 1466

Cuttsforth, Stephen, Mgr.-Intl. Sls.--Hunter Marine Corporation, Alachua, FL; *U.S. Private*, pg. 549

Cvijanovic, Vince, V.P.-Sls.--Rospatch Jessco, Inc., Dowagiac, MI; *U.S. Public*, pg. 98

Cwieka, W.J., V.P.-Sls.--United States Bronze Powders, Inc., Flemington, NJ; *U.S. Private*, pg. 1124

Cychol, John, Dir.-Sls.--Irving Convention & Visitors Bureau, Irving, TX; *U.S. Private*, pg. 575

Cymrot, Andrew, V.P.-Sls.--Austin Productions, Inc., Holbrook, NY; *U.S. Private*, pg. 100

Cyphers, Bill, Mgr.-Sls.--Subaru of America Western, Inc., Portland, OR; *Int'l*, pg. 523

Cyphers, Bill, Mgr.-Sls.--Subaru Northwest Region, Portland, OR; *Int'l*, pg. 523

Cyprell, Ellen, Dir.-Sls.--Beverly National Bank, Wilmington, IL; *U.S. Public*, pg. 227

Cypress, Ellyn, Sr. V.P. & Dir.-Sls. & Svc.--Beverly Bancorporation Inc., Chicago, IL; *U.S. Public*, pg. 227

Cyr, F., V.P.-Sls. & Mktg.--National Rivet & Manufacturing Company, Waupun, WI; *U.S. Private*, pg. 786

Czaja, Michael, V.P.-Sls. & Mktg.--Sentinel Consumer Products, Inc., Mentor, OH; *U.S. Private*, pg. 984

Czarnecki, Joe, Mgr.-Sls.--MFG Union City Operations, Union City, PA; *U.S. Private*, pg. 756

Czerniawski, Kevin, Mgr.-Inside Sls.--Swepco Tube Corporation, Clifton, NJ; *U.S. Private*, pg. 1058

Czyzewski, Ken, Sls. Mgr.--A&A Manufacturing Co., New Berlin, WI; *U.S. Private*, pg. 1

D'Agostino, Walter, V.P.-Sls. & Mdse.--D'Agostino Supermarkets Inc., Larchmont, NY; *U.S. Private*, pg. 306

D'Alessandro, Rich, V.P.-Mktg. & Sls.--Spectra-Physics Laserplane Inc., Dayton, OH; *U.S. Public*, pg. 1594

D'Amaro, Lou, Sr. V.P.-Sls.--Esselte Corporation, Garden City, NY; *Int'l*, pg. 459

D'Amato, Andy, Sr. V.P.-Sls.--Telecredit Service Corp., Tampa, FL; *U.S. Public*, pg. 588

D'Ambrosio, Michael, Dir.-Sls.--Eastco Industrial Safety Corp., Huntington Station, NY; *U.S. Public*, pg. 548

D'Antonio, Frank, Dir.-Sls. & Mktg.--Healthsource Kentucky, Louisville, KY; *U.S. Public*, pg. 360

D'Arcangelo, Marco, Mgr.-Sls.--Opticos S.r.l., Brembate di Sopra, Italy; *Int'l*, pg. 1007

D'Arcy, Paul, Sr. V.P.-Sls. & Mktg.--Sanyo Office Automation, Chatsworth, CA; *Int'l*, pg. 1191

D'Elia, Frank, Mgr.-Sls.--Milgray/Delaware Valley, Inc., Mount Laurel, NJ; *U.S. Public*, pg. 206

D'Jaen, Richard, Dir.-Sls. & Mktg.--Sam Dick Industries, Inc., Seattle, WA; *U.S. Private*, pg. 360

D'Uva, Nick, Dir.-Sls. & Mktg.--Alfa Romeo Distributors of North America, Orlando, FL; *Int'l*, pg. 481

Da Puzzo, Dennis, Dir.-Sls.--Colonna Bros., Inc., North Bergen, NJ; *U.S. Private*, pg. 254

Da Silva Filho, Walter Jesus, Dir.-Footwear Sls.--Sao Paulo Alpargatas S.A., Sao Paulo, Brazil; *Int'l*, pg. 1193

Dabarno, Susan F., Mgr.-Sls.--Midland Walwyn Capital Inc., Toronto, Canada; *Int'l*, pg. 865

Dacres, Claudette, Mgr.-Sls. Audit--Jan Bell Marketing Inc., Sunrise, FL; *U.S. Public*, pg. 207

Dadaian, Paul, District Mgr.-Sls.--Klockner-Moeller Corp., Garfield Heights, OH; *Int'l*, pg. 736

Dadiego, Sharon, Admin.-Sls. & Mktg.--Connors Brunswick, Inc., South Portland, ME; *U.S. Private*, pg. 264

Daggett, Donn, Natl. Sls. Mgr.--Haws Drinking Faucet Co., Berkeley, CA; *U.S. Private*, pg. 512

Dahlager, Ken, V.P.-Sls. & Mkgt.--Smith System Manufacturing Company, Plano, TX; *U.S. Private*, pg. 1009

Dailey, Jay, Natl. Sls. Mgr.--Continental Promotion Group, Tempe, AZ; *U.S. Private*, pg. 269

Dailey, Kenneth E., Gen. Mgr.--Seaman Timber Company, Inc., Montevallo, AL; *U.S. Private*, pg. 979

Daily, H. Pete, V.P.-Crude Supply and Prods. Mktg.--Mapco Petroleum Inc., Tulsa, OK; *U.S. Public*, pg. 1042

Daily, John, Mgr.-Hospital & Indus. Sls.--Ortho-Kinetics, Inc., Waukesha, WI; *U.S. Private*, pg. 820

Dakin, G., V.P.-Sls.--Van Leer Containers, Inc., Alsip, IL; *Int'l*, pg. 1146

Dale, Jimmy H., V.P.-Sls.--Bryant Electric Supply Company, Inc., Lowell, NC; *U.S. Private*, pg. 177

Dale, P., Mgr.-Sls.--Rexdale Plant, Rexdale, Canada; *Int'l*, pg. 761

Dalessio, Joey, V.P.-Sls.--Medeco Security Locks, Inc., Salem, VA; *U.S. Public*, pg. 828

Daley, Alex, V.P.-Sls. & Mktg.--C-Cube Microsystems, Milpitas, CA; *U.S. Public*, pg. 272

Dalgleish, Rod, Sls. Dir.--Engineered Seals, Tewkesbury, United Kingdom; *Int'l*, pg. 1338

Dallaire, Lucien, Mgr.-Sls. & Mktg.--NAPCO, Inc., Terryville, CT; *U.S. Public*, pg. 1592

Dalpe, Liz, Natl. Sls. Mgr.--Steven Manufacturing Co., Hermann, MO; *U.S. Private*, pg. 1042

Dalrymple, E., Mgr.-Sls.--Hypertronics Corporation, Hudson, MA; *Int'l*, pg. 1268

Dalrymple, John, Natl. Sls. Mgr.--KLAS, Inc., Las Vegas, NV; *U.S. Private*, pg. 647

Dalsoglio, D.L., Mgr.-Sls.--Longview Fibre Co. Western Container Div., Twin Falls, ID; *U.S. Public*, pg. 1014

Dalton, James S., V.P.-Sls.--Bardons & Oliver, Inc., Solon, OH; *U.S. Private*, pg. 116

Dalton, Mark, Dir.-Sls.-Central Div.--Clestra Hauserman, Inc., Solon, OH; *Int'l*, pg. 569

Dalton, Mark, Mgr.-Natl. Sls.--OSI, Chicago, IL; *U.S. Private*, *pg. 1068*

Daly, Martin B., V.P. & Dir.-Sls. & Mktg.--CBS Television Network, New York, NY; *U.S. Public*, pg. 274

DAmare, Dennis, V.P.-Sls. & Mktg.--LASCO Bathware, Anaheim, CA; *Int'l*, pg. 1398

Dambold, John, V.P.-Mktg. & Sls.--Fleming Foods of Alabama, Inc., Geneva, AL; *U.S. Public*, pg. 653

Damiano, V. Jay, Sr. V.P.-Sls.--General Datacomm Industries, Inc., Middlebury, CT; *U.S. Public*, pg. 708

Dammeier, Roger, V.P.-Sls.--InterBio Inc., Woodlands, TX; *U.S. Private*, pg. 566

Damson, Glenis, Dir.-Sls.--Sandoz Pharma Ltd., Eden Terrace, New Zealand; *Int'l*, pg. 985

Danczyk, Gary, V.P.-Sls.--Wynn's-Precision, Inc., Lebanon, TN; *U.S. Public*, pg. 1783

Daners, John C., Mgr.-Sls.--New Zealand Milk Products (Pacific) Ltd., Auckland, New Zealand; *Int'l*, pg. 923

Dangelo, Bruce, V.P.-Corp. Sls.--Wallace Computer Services, Inc., Lisle, IL; *U.S. Public*, pg. 1735

Daniels, Dan, V.P.-Sls.--Maremont Exhaust Systems Product Division, Loudon, TN; *U.S. Public*, pg. 137

Daniels, Richard A., V.P.-Transit Sls.--Harmon Industries, Inc., Blue Springs, MO; *U.S. Public*, pg. 788

Daniels, Richard A., Sr. V.P.-Sls.--Periphonics Corp., Bohemia, NY; *U.S. Public*, pg. 1278

Danko, Dick, V.P.-Sls.--Universal Foods Corporation-Bakery Products Div., Milwaukee, WI; *U.S. Public*, pg. 1696

Dann, Earl, Pres.--Dann Dee Display Fixtures, Niles, IL; *U.S.* Private, pg. 310

Danner, Mark E., V.P.-Sls. Admin.--Anheuser-Busch, Inc., Saint Louis, MO; *U.S. Public*, pg. 114

Darby, Everett, V.P.-Sls.--The NutraSweet Company, Deerfield, IL; *U.S. Public*, pg. 1125

Darcy, Thomas B., Mgr.-Reg. Sls.--Burgmann Seals America, Inc., Warwick, RI; *Int'l*, pg. 233

Darnell, Jerry R., Exec. V.P.-Franchise--Sterling Vision, Inc., East Meadow, NY; *U.S. Public*, pg. 1516

Darragh, Mike, Mgr.-Sls.--Anchor Foods Limited, Swindon, United Kingdom; *Int'l*, pg. 923

Darragh, Robert J., Sr. V.P.-Mktg. & Sls.--Copes-Vulcan Inc., Lake City, PA; *U.S. Private*, pg. 274

Darrow, Kurt, V.P.-Sls./Residential--La-Z-Boy Incorporated, Monroe, MI; *U.S. Public*, pg. 972

Dartley, Larry, V.P.-Sls.--Bally Management, New Rochelle, NY; *Int'l*, pg. 998

Daste, Alain, V.P.-Intl. Sls.--Stratus Computer, Inc., Marlborough, MA; *U.S. Public*, pg. 1524

Dattilo, David A., Sr. V.P.-Sls. & Service--Safety-Kleen Corp., Elgin, IL; *U.S. Public*, pg. 1425

Dauer, Stephen J., Sr. V.P.-Sls.--Dyersburg Corporation, Dyersburg, TN; *U.S. Public*, pg. 538

Daugherty, Ed, Dir.-Sls. & Mktg.--Alcan Rolled Products Division, Cleveland, OH; *Int'l*, pg. 50

Daugherty, J.R., Sr. V.P.-Sls. & Mktg.--The Chas. H. Lilly Co., Portland, OR; *U.S. Private*, pg. 667

Daugherty, Paul, Gen. Mgr.--LubeCon Systems, Inc., White Cloud, MI; *U.S. Private*, pg. 679

Dausey, William, Mgr.-Sls./Energy Services--Northwestern Public Service, Huron, SD; *U.S. Public*, pg. 1200

David Guthrie, V.P.-Sls. & Mktg.--Monarch Tile, Inc., Florence, AL; *U.S. Private*, pg. 287

David, John R., Mgr.-Sls.--Beacon Container Corporation, Birdsboro, PA; *U.S. Private*, pg. 125

David, Tim, V.P.-Worldwide Sls. & Service--Data I/O Corporation, Redmond, WA; *U.S. Public*, pg. 486

Davidson, Charles T., Chm. Bd., Pres. & Chief Exec. Officer--J.A. Jones, Inc., Charlotte, NC; *Int'l*, pg. 633

Davidson, Harry, V.P.-North America Sls.--Magline, Inc., Pinconning, MI; *U.S. Private*, pg. 695

Davidson, M.J., Gen. Mgr.-Sls.--Quality Bakers New Zealand Ltd., Auckland, New Zealand; *Int'l*, pg. 556

Davidson, Mark, Gen. Mgr.-W. Region Sls.--Orange County Metal Works, Orange, CA; *U.S. Public*, pg. 411

Davies, B., Mgr.-Sls.--BEAU Interconnect Systems, Gilford, NH; *U.S. Public*, pg. 157

Davies, Barry, V.P. & Gen. Mgr.-Sls. & Mktg.--Fisher Gauge Limited, Peterborough, Canada; *Int'l*, pg. 491

Davies, Barry, V.P. & Gen. Mgr.-Sls.--Fishercast, Peterborough, Canada; *Int'l*, pg. 491

Davies, Barry, V.P. & Gen. Mgr.-Sls.--Fishertech, Peterborough, Canada; *Int'l*, pg. 491

Davies, G. Basil, Sr. V.P.-Sls. & Mktg.--Copperweld Fayetteville Division, Fayetteville, TN; *Int'l*, pg. 662

Davies, G. Basil, Dir.-Sls. & Mktg.--Copperweld Fayetteville Division, Fayetteville, TN; *Int'l*, pg. 662

Davies, G. Basil, Sr. V.P.-Sls. & Mktg.--Copperweld Chicago Division, Chicago, IL; *Int'l*, pg. 662

Davies, John, Mgr.-Sls.--Esselte Chrono AB, Solna, Sweden; *Int'l*, pg. 459

Davies, John, V.P.-Sls.--Alsons Corporation, Hillsdale, MI; *U.S. Public*, pg. 1053

Davies, Peggy, V.P.-Private Label Sls.--Comstock Michigan Fruit, Rochester, NY; *U.S. Private*, pg. 887

Davies, Rachel, Dir.-Sls.--Williams Electronics Games, Inc., Chicago, IL; *U.S. Public*, pg. 1727

Davies, Robert, V.P.-Sls.--Merck Frosst Canada Inc., Kirkland, Canada; *U.S. Public*, pg. 1092

Davis, Alan, Mng. Dir.-U.K.--MDIS Group plc, Hemel Hempstead, United Kingdom; *Int'l*, pg. 826

Davis, B.R., V.P.-Sls.--Conwood Company L.P., Memphis, TN; *U.S. Private*, pg. 272

Davis, Ben, V.P.- Sls.-Natl. Accts.--Fabwel Inc., Elkhart, IN; *U.S. Private*, pg. 390

Davis, Bill, Mgr.-Reg. Sls. Western--Ivex Packaging Corporation-Visalia, Visalia, CA; *U.S. Public*, pg. 915

Davis, Bob, Mgr.-Gen. Sls.--Electrovert, Grand Prairie, TX; *Int'l*, pg. 328

Davis, C., V.P.-Mktg. & Sls.--The Budd Company, Troy, MI; *Int'l*, pg. 1388

Davis, Dan, V.P.-Sls.--Singleton Seafood Co., Tampa, FL; *U.S. Public*, pg. 427

Davis, Dennis, V.P.-Adv., Sls. & Mktg.--Davis Wood Products, Inc., Hudson, NC; *U.S. Private*, pg. 315

Davis, Dewayn, V.P.-Sls. & Mktg.--Auto-trol Technology Corporation, Denver, CO; *U.S. Public*, pg. 148

Davis, Dewayn, V.P.-Sls.--Auto-trol Technology Sales, Troy, MI; *U.S. Public*, pg. 148

Davis, Donna Sue, Dir.-Sls.--Disneyland Hotel, Anaheim, CA; *U.S. Public*, pg. 513

Davis, E.H., V.P.-Sls.--Eveready Battery Co., Saint Louis, MO; *U.S. Public*, pg. 1360

Davis, Earl E., Exec. V.P.-Commercial--Weirton Steel Corporation, Weirton, WV; *U.S. Public*, pg. 1751

Davis, Frank Thomas, V.P.-Sls.--Continental Homes, Inc., Scottsdale, AZ; *U.S. Public*, pg. 440

Davis, Gary, V.P.-Sls.--AmeriPath, Inc., Riviera Beach, FL; *U.S. Public*, pg. 96

Davis, Gary, V.P.-Sls.--Funeral Security Plans, Inc., Kansas City, MO; *U.S. Private*, pg. 796

Davis, Gene A., V.P.-Sls. & Mktg.--Environmental Tectonics Corporation (ETC), Southampton, PA; *U.S. Public*, pg. 587

Davis, Grady, V.P.-Sls. & Mktg.--Tolleson Lumber Company, Inc., Perry, GA; *U.S. Private*, pg. 1090

Davis, J. Dan, V.P.-Sls. & Mktg.--Prym-Dritz Corporation, Spartanburg, SC; *Int'l*, pg. 1499

Davis, J.R., V.P.-Sls. & Mktg.--Atlas Roofing Corp., Meridian, MS; *U.S. Private*, pg. 96

Davis, Jeff, Mgr.-Natl. Sls.--Pawling Corporation, Pawling, NY; *U.S. Private*, pg. 844

Davis, Jeff, Mgr.-Sls.--PENCO-New Mexico, Albuquerque, NM; *Int'l*, pg. 1508

Davis, Joe, V.P.-Life & Health & District Mgr.-Sls.--Willis Corroon Corporation of Louisville, Louisville, KY; *Int'l*, pg. 1505

Davis, John, Asst. V.P.-Pediatric Sls.--Wyeth-Ayerst Laboratories, Inc., Philadelphia, PA; *U.S. Public*, pg. 80

Davis, John, Natl. Sls. Mgr.- Power Transmission Div.--Electron Corp., Littleton, CO; *U.S. Private*, pg. 370

Davis, John, V.P.-Sls.--Road Machinery & Supplies Co., Savage, MN; *U.S. Private*, pg. 934

Davis, John, Dir.-Sls. & Mktg.--Simpson Dura-Vent Co., Inc., Vacaville, CA; *U.S. Public*, pg. 1474

Davis, Kem, Mgr.-Sls. Admin.--T & S Brass & Bronze Works, Inc., Travelers Rest, SC; *U.S. Private*, pg. 1061

Davis, Lloyd, V.P.-Sls. & Mktg.--North American Salt Company, Overland Park, KS; *U.S. Private*, pg. 505

Davis, Lynn, V.P.-Sls., Mktg., Pur. & Mfg.--Lithotype Company, Inc., South San Francisco, CA; *U.S. Private*, pg. 670

Davis, Mary Lou, Gen. Mgr.-Sls.--WGME-TV, Portland, ME; *U.S. Private*, pg. 439

Davis, Mickey, Sr. V.P.-Mktg. & Sls.--American Sign & Marketing Services, Inc., Florence, KY; *U.S. Public*, pg. 1309

Davis, Mike, Mgr.-Sls.--Kaufman and Broad New Mexico Division, Albuquerque, NM; *U.S. Public*, pg. 945

Davis, Mike, V.P. & Natl. Sls. Mgr.--Rauch Industries, Inc., Gastonia, NC; *U.S. Private*, pg. 1061

Davis, Neil, V.P.-Sls.--Madison Square Garden Network, New York, NY; *U.S. Public*, pg. 288

Davis, P. Michael, V.P.-Dedicated Fleet--Builders Transport, Incorporated, Camden, SC; *U.S. Public*, pg. 267

Davis, Parke, Sr. V.P.-Retail--Commemorative Brands, Inc., Austin, TX; *U.S. Private*, pg. 258

Davis, Preston, V.P.-Sls.--K-Swiss Inc., Chatsworth, CA; *U.S. Public*, pg. 937

Davis, Randal R., V.P.-Sls. & Mktg.--Dexter Nonwovens Division, Windsor Locks, CT; *U.S. Public*, pg. 504

Davis, Richard L., Mgr.-Sls.--Bergman Manufacturing, Garland, TX; *U.S. Private*, pg. 313

Davis, Rick A., V.P.-Sls. & Mktg.-Displays--American Manufacturing Company, Chattanooga, TN; *U.S. Private*, pg. 58

Davis, Robert, V.P.-Mktg. & Sales--Ryobi Motor Products, Anderson, SC; *Int'l*, pg. 1151

Davis, Robert B., III, V.P.-Juvenile Prods.--Bassett Furniture Industries, Incorporated, Bassett, VA; *U.S. Public*, pg. 193

Davis, Robert W., Sr. V.P.-Sls. & Mktg.--Andres Wines Ltd., Winona, Canada; *Int'l*, pg. 75

Davis, Ron, Dir.-Sls.--Lake Business Products, Inc., Willoughby, OH; *U.S. Private*, pg. 643

Davis, Ted, Dir.-Baby Care Sales--Gerber Products Division-Baby Care, Reedsburg, WI; *Int'l*, pg. 973

Davis, Terrence D., V.P.-Opers. & Indus. Sls.--North Carolina Natural Gas Corporation, Fayetteville, NC; *U.S. Public*, pg. 1194

Davisson, Bill, Dir.-Sls.- Men's Footwear & Acces.--Cole-Haan, Yarmouth, ME; *U.S. Public*, pg. 1184

Dawahare, A.F., Pres. & Dir.-Sls. & Mktg.--Dawahares, Inc., Lexington, KY; *U.S. Private*, pg. 316

Day, Charles P., V.P.-Engrng. & Sls.--Ambrake Corporation, Elizabethtown, KY; *U.S. Public*, pg. 721

Day, Devin, Mgr.-Sls.--Action Technology Company, Rockaway, NJ; *U.S. Private*, pg. 15

Day, Jack, Dir.-Direct Response Mktg. & Sls./Prof., Ref. & Trade Grp.--John Wiley & Sons, Inc., New York, NY; *U.S. Public*, pg. 1768

Day, Ron, V.P.-Miami--L. Karp & Sons, Inc., Elk Grove Village, IL; *U.S. Private*, pg. 607

Day, Steve, V.P.-Parts, Opers. & Sls.--Komatsu America International Company, Vernon Hills, IL; *Int'l*, pg. 744

Dayot, Alejandro, III, Sls. Dir.-W. Visayas--La Tondena Distillers, Inc., Manila, Philippines; *Int'l*, pg. 785

Dayton, Peter E., Sr. V.P.-Natl. Sls.--Recoton Corporation, Lake Mary, FL; *U.S. Public*, pg. 1369

De Angelis, Christopher, Natl. Sls. Mgr.--Survey Sampling, Inc., Fairfield, CT; *U.S. Private*, pg. 1056

de Backer, H., Mgr.-Sls.--General Motors Hungary (Distribution) Ltd., Budapest, Hungary; *U.S. Public*, pg. 722

de Belloy, Palmick, Mgr.-Sls.--Lafarge Ciments, Saint Cloud, France; *Int'l*, pg. 788

de Bodinat, Henri, Sr. Exec. V.P.-Mktg., Sls. & Prods.--Club Mediterranee SA, Paris, France; *Int'l*, pg. 298

de Brouwer, R.B.P., Dir.-Sls. (Packaging Steel)--Hoogovens Ijmuiden, Ijmuiden, Netherlands; *Int'l*, pg. 753

De Camara, Paul, Mgr.-Sls.--Westwood Computer Corporation, Springfield, NJ; *U.S. Private*, pg. 1170

De Castro-Palomino, Julio, Commercial Dir.--Industrias CH, S.A. de C.V., Tlalnepantla, Mexico; *Int'l*, pg. 677

De Coster, Alain, Mgr.-Retail--Bernheim-Comofi, Brussels, Belgium; *Int'l*, pg. 562

De Filippo, Patrice, Dir.-Sls. & Gen. Mgr.--Milgray/ Connecticut, Inc., Milford, CT; *U.S. Public*, pg. 206

De Forest, Steven J., Dir.-Sls./Private Label--Levlad, Inc., Chatsworth, CA; *U.S. Private*, pg. 663

de Garmo, John, V.P.-Affiliate Sls.--Home & Garden Television, Knoxville, TN; *U.S. Public*, pg. 1447

De Gaulejac, Thibault, Mgr.-Sls.--F.J. Benjamin Fashions (HK) Ltd., Causeway Bay, Hong Kong; *Int'l*, pg. 187

de Haas, Fred, Gen. Mgr.--Sensormatic B.V., Bunnik, Netherlands; *U.S. Public*, pg. 1457

de Heer, William, Dir.-Mktg. & Sls.--OPEL Nederland B.V., Sliedrecht, Netherlands; *U.S. Public*, pg. 723

De Herder, Richard G., Sr. V.P. & Gen. Mgr.-Sls. & Mktg. Support--Mattel, Inc., El Segundo, CA; *U.S. Public*, pg. 1057

de Jaeghere, Simon, Mgr.-Intl. Sls.--Golden Star Inc., Kansas City, MO; *U.S. Private*, pg. 460

De Los Reyes, Wison, Sls. Dir.-Central Visayas--La Tondena Distillers, Inc., Manila, Philippines; *Int'l*, pg. 785

de Monnink, Peter, Dir.-Sls.--Elsevier Bedrijfinformatie B.V., Doetinchem, Netherlands; *Int'l*, pg. 1099

de Moraes, Neide Barros, Mgr.-Sls.--Cia. Niquel Tocantins, Sao Miguel, Brazil; *Int'l*, pg. 677

De Pasquale, Michael, V.P.-Sls.--McGraw-Hill College Division, New York, NY; *U.S. Public*, pg. 1070

de Pere, Arnault, Dir.-European Network--Compagnie Generale Maritime et Financiere, Suresnes, France; *Int'l*, *pg. 322*

de Preux, Philippe, Sr. V.P.-Sls. & Mktg.--Bobst S.A., Lausanne, Switzerland; *Int'l*, pg. 198

De Quesada, Raul, V.P.-Adv. & Sls.--Travel Channel-Latin America, Miami, FL; *U.S. Private*, pg. 647

De Rocco, Beatrice, V.P.-Mktg. & Sls.--Computer Task Group, Inc. (CTG), Buffalo, NY; *U.S. Public*, pg. 423

De Rosa, Jack, Territory Sls.--Jos. M. Herman Shoe Co., Armonk, NY; *U.S. Private*, pg. 524

De Sanctis, P., Dir.-Sls.--Sangemini S.p.A., Rome, Italy; *Int'l*, *pg. 1188*

De Simone, Mark, V.P.-European Sls./Carrier Sys.--3Com Corporation, Santa Clara, CA; *U.S. Public*, pg. 1603

De Sousa, Richard, Sr. V.P.-Sls. & Mdsg.--American Trouser, Inc., Columbus, MS; *U.S. Private*, pg. 64

de Tuya, Jorge, Dir.-Sls., Latin Am. & Caribbean--Golden Eagle Group, Inc., Humble, TX; *U.S. Public*, pg. 749

de Uriarte, Carlos, V.P.-Sls. & Service U.S.--Mexicana Airlines, Los Angeles, CA; *Int'l*, pg. 332

Deacon, Deidre, Mgr.-Sls.--Epson Canada Limited, Willowdale, Canada; *Int'l*, pg. 1219

Deahr, Ronald, V.P.-Sls. & Mktg.--Isomedix Operations Inc., Whippany, NJ; *U.S. Public*, pg. 1515

Deahr, Ronald, V.P.-Sls. & Mktg.--Isomedix Management Inc., Whippany, NJ; *U.S. Public*, pg. 1515

Deakin, Mic, V.P.-Sls.--AR Accessories Group, Inc., Milwaukee, WI; *U.S. Private*, pg. 7

Deakins, John, V.P.-Sls.--The William Carter Company, Morrow, GA; *U.S. Private*, pg. 217

Deakle, Gerald V., Mgr.-Sls.--Bergen Brunswig Medical Corporation, Mobile, AL; *U.S. Public*, pg. 214

Deal, Tom, Mgr.-Gen. Sls.--KTVE, Inc., Channel 10, Monroe, LA; *U.S. Public*, pg. 759

Dean, Ed, V.P.-Sls.--Angelo Brothers Co., Philadelphia, PA; *U.S. Private*, pg. 74

Dear, Roger E., Mgr.-Sls.--Raleigh Industries Ltd., Nottingham, United Kingdom; *Int'l*, pg. 394

Deardoff, Michael, Gen. Mgr.-Sls.--Island Lincoln-Mercury, Merritt Island, FL; *U.S. Private*, pg. 576

DeArmas, Manuel, Mgr.-Natl. Sls--Video Display Corporation, Tucker, GA; *U.S. Public*, pg. 1720

Deaton, Wayne, V.P.-Printing Paper Sls.--Henley Paper Company, Greensboro, NC; *U.S. Private*, pg. 522

Deats, Richard, V.P.-Ticket Opers.--The Phillies-A Limited Partnership, Philadelphia, PA; *U.S. Private*, pg. 861

Debaeke, Luc, V.P.-Sls./Asia--Maison Mathieu, S.A., Antwerp, Belgium; *Int'l*, pg. 846

DeBerge, Gary A., V.P.-Sls.--Pre Finish Metals Incorporated, Elk Grove Village, IL; *U.S. Public*, pg. 1056

Deblois, Bonifacio C., V.P.-Dir. Sls. Opers.--La Tondena Distillers, Inc., Manila, Philippines; *Int'l*, pg. 785

Deborde, Robert M., V.P.-Sls.--Pulp & Paperboard Group, San Francisco, CA; *U.S. Public*, pg. 1318

DeCabia, Philip T., V.P. & Sls. Dir.-RASCO--Rainbow Advertising Sales Corporation (RASCO), Woodbury, NY; *U.S. Public*, pg. 288

DeCamp, Richard, Pres.-Value Brand Sls.--R.G. Barry Corporation, Pickerington, OH; *U.S. Public*, pg. 192

DeCardlis, Anthony, V.P.-Sls. & Mktg.--Fischer Imaging Corporation, Denver, CO; *U.S. Public*, pg. 647

Decaviver, P., Dir.-Belgium Sls.--N.V. Johnson Wax Belgium S.A., Groot-Bijgaarden, Belgium; *U.S. Private*, pg. 593

DeCelis, Howard D., Mgr.-Intl. Sls.--MD Pneumatics, Springfield, MO; *U.S. Private*, pg. 1111

Dechamps, Guy, Dir.-Mktg. & Sls.--Amicon, Inc., Beverly, MA; *U.S. Public*, pg. 1113

Decher, Rick, Dir.-Sls.--Blue Streak-Hygrade Motor Products Ltd., Mississauga, Canada; *U.S. Public*, pg. 1503

Decio, Terrence M., Sr. Exec. V.P.-Sls. & Mktg.--Skyline Corporation, Elkhart, IN; *U.S. Public*, pg. 1476

Decker, John, Mgr.-Natl. Sls.--Ridg-U-Rak, Inc., North East, PA; *U.S. Private*, pg. 930

Decker, Mark, Mgr.-Distr./Sls.--Central Data Corporation, Champaign, IL; *U.S. Private*, pg. 223

Decker, William, V.P.-Sls.--Goldwell Cosmetics (USA) Inc., Linthicum Heights, MD; *Int'l*, pg. 718
DeCoster, Mark, Natl. Sls. Mgr.--National Auto Credit Inc., Solon, OH; *U.S. Public*, pg. 1152
Dedo, Jacqui, Mgr.-Sls.--Bosch Braking Systems-North America, South Bend, IN; *Int'l*, pg. 204
Dedrick, William T., V.P.-U.S. Sls.--SQA, Inc., Burlington, MA; *U.S. Public*, pg. 1361
Dee, Jay, Treas., Sec. & Dir.-Sls.--Dee Paper Company, Chester, PA; *U.S. Private*, pg. 320
Deeds, David C., Dir.-Sls.--Solvay Polymers Inc., Houston, TX; *Int'l*, pg. 1278
Deegan, Joan, Mgr.-Sls.--Letraset UK, London, United Kingdom; *Int'l*, pg. 462
Deephouse, Mel, Mgr.-Sls.--Grove Gear Div., Union Grove, WI; *U.S. Public*, pg. 1370
Deering, Bill, Mgr.-Sls.--Village Car Company, Bangor, ME; *U.S. Private*, pg. 1140
Deering, Christopher, Exec. V.P.-Mktg. & Sls.--Columbia Tri-Star Home Video, Burbank, CA; *Int'l*, pg. 1282
Deffner, David, V.P.-Sls.--New Hermes Incorporated, Duluth, GA; *U.S. Private*, pg. 793
Degelman, Jack, Mgr.-Mktg.--Degelman Industries Ltd., Regina, Canada; *Int'l*, pg. 388
Degelman, Roland, Mgr.-Sls.--Hylar Metal Products, Regina, Canada; *Int'l*, pg. 388
DeGeorge, Sal, Sr. V.P.-Sls. & Mktg.--Bridgford Foods Corporation, Anaheim, CA; *U.S. Public*, pg. 252
Degnan, Tony, V.P.-Sls.--ADM Milling Co., Overland Park, KS; *U.S. Public*, pg. 128
Degracia, Gayle, District Mgr.-Sls.--Austrian Airlines, Whitestone, NY; *Int'l*, pg. 101
DeGregorio, Louis W., Sr. V.P.-Sls.--Paul-Son Gaming Corporation, Las Vegas, NV; *U.S. Public*, pg. 1265
DeHart, Pete, Sr. V.P.-Sls. & Mktg.--Alpha Therapeutic Corp., Los Angeles, CA; *Int'l*, pg. 558
DeHart, W.E., V.P.-Sls. & Mktg.--Powell Electrical Mfg. Co., Houston, TX; *U.S. Public*, pg. 1319
Dehlinger, Leo, Dir.-Intl. Sls.--C & D Technologies, Inc., Blue Bell, PA; *U.S. Public*, pg. 272
Deines, Kathy, Dir.-Sls.--PharmChem Laboratories, Inc., Menlo Park, CA; *U.S. Public*, pg. 1285
Deitz, Harry, Mgr.-Sls.--AirTronics Co., Elgin, IL; *U.S. Public*, *pg. 944*
DeJonghe, Johan, Dir.-Sls.--Haco N.V., Roeselare, Belgium; *Int'l*, pg. 585
Del Neri, Edoardo, Exec. V.P.-Sls. & Mktg.--Merloni Elettrodomestici S.P.A., Fabriano, Italy; *Int'l*, pg. 860
Del Rua, Guido, V.P.-Sls. & Mktg.--Furness North America Inc., Houston, TX; *Int'l*, pg. 530
Del Sontro, Rick, Sr. V.P.-Franchise Sls. & Devel.--Century 21 Real Estate Corp., Parsippany, NJ; *U.S. Public*, pg. 321
DeLaat, Gordon, Mgr.-Sls./Southwest Reg.--AEP Industries, Inc., South Hackensack, NJ; *U.S. Public*, pg. 4
Delahunt, G., Dir.-Sls. & Mktg.--Colgate-Palmolive, Dublin, Ireland; *U.S. Public*, pg. 398
Delaney, Kevin, Mgr.-Sls.--R.A. Mueller, Inc., Cincinnati, OH; *U.S. Private*, pg. 766
Delaney, Richard M., Sr. V.P. & Dir.-Mktg.--UMB Financial Corporation, Kansas City, MO; *U.S. Public*, pg. 1653
Delaney, Ronald, Mgr.-Intl. Sls.--Cargill Detroit Corp., Clawson, MI; *U.S. Private*, pg. 210
Delaney, Sean, V.P.-Sls.--Baton Broadcasting Incorporated, Scarborough, Canada; *Int'l*, pg. 170
Delaplane, Thomas M., V.P.-Sls.--Dreyer's Grand Ice Cream, Inc., Oakland, CA; *U.S. Public*, pg. 529
DeLattre, Frank J., V.P.-Intl. Sls.--Deltec, San Diego, CA; *Int'l*, pg. 126
DelBalso, Jerry, Dir.-Sls. & Technical Svcs.--Better Baked Foods, Inc., North East, PA; *U.S. Private*, pg. 141
Delett, Eugene, Mgr.-Natl. Sls.--National Twist Drill Div., South Beloit, IL; *U.S. Public*, pg. 1370
Deliberato, Carmine J., Dir.-Mktg. & Sls.--Lavelle Company, Philadelphia, PA; *U.S. Private*, pg. 653
Delida, Luke, Sr. Mgr.-Sls.--H.O. Trerice Company, Oak Park, MI; *U.S. Private*, pg. 1099
Delizio, Dale, Sr. Mgr.-Mktg.--Goshen Rubber Co., Inc., Goshen, IN; *U.S. Private*, pg. 465
Della, Frank, V.P.-Pebblecreek Sls.--Robson Communities, Sun Lakes, AZ; *U.S. Private*, pg. 937
Dellamano, Mark, Mgr.-Sls. & D.P.--Patson's Press, Sunnyvale, CA; *U.S. Private*, pg. 843
DellaVecchia, Gene, V.P.-Sls.--Packard Instrument Co., Inc., Meriden, CT; *U.S. Private*, pg. 833
Dellinger, Bob, Pres.-Sls. & Mktg./Bed Div.--Fieldcrest Cannon, Inc., Kannapolis, NC; *U.S. Public*, pg. 1296
Dellinger, Doris, Mgr.-Sls.--Game Time, Inc., Fort Payne, AL; *U.S. Public*, pg. 1543
DelMonte, Ed, V.P.-Sls.--Gould Paper Corporation, New York, NY; *U.S. Private*, pg. 466
DeLoia, Mary Ann Turk, Sls. Administrator--Itam Tech Italimplianti, Inc., Coraopolis, PA; *Int'l*, pg. 655
DeLong, David, V.P.-Sls.--Sequus Pharmaceuticals, Inc., Menlo Park, CA; *U.S. Public*, pg. 1460
Delorenzo, Dick, V.P.-Sls. & Mktg.--Datapro Information Services Grp., Delran, NJ; *U.S. Public*, pg. 1070
Delp, Mark, Sr. V.P.-Sls. & Mktg.--Gemtron Corporation, Sweetwater, TN; *Int'l*, pg. 1523
Delpha, Vernique, V.P.-Commun.--3M France, Cergy-Pontoise, France; *U.S. Public*, pg. 1606
Delvecchio, George, Mgr.-District Sls.--Milgray Electronics/P.R., Inc., Canovanas, PR; *U.S. Public*, pg. 206
Delzio, Jerry, V.P.-Sls. & Mktg.--Bolliger, Inc., Stamford, CT; *U.S. Private*, pg. 155
DeMarco, Jack, V.P.-Sales--Hostess Frito-Lay Co., Mississauga, Canada; *U.S. Public*, pg. 1277
DeMarco, Peter, Mgr.-Sls.--Jordan's Foods-Colchester Division, Colchester, VT; *U.S. Private*, pg. 599
DeMarino, Louis T., Sr. V.P.-Sls. & Mktg.--The Jaydor Corporation, Millburn, NJ; *U.S. Private*, pg. 584
DeMarre, John, Natl. Sls. Mgr.--Belshaw Brothers, Inc., Seattle, WA; *Int'l*, pg. 188
DeMartino, John, V.P.-Sls.--Bradley Pharmaceuticals, Fairfield, NJ; *U.S. Public*, pg. 249
DeMartino, John, V.P.-Sls.--Doak Dermatologics, Westbury, NY; *U.S. Public*, pg. 250
DeMaso, Joseph, Mgr.-Natl. Sls.--Eva-Tone Inc., Clearwater, FL; *U.S. Private*, pg. 384
Dembrow, Jon, V.P.-Sls.--Young Stuff Apparel Group, Inc., New York, NY; *U.S. Private*, pg. 1202
Dement, J.A., V.P.-European Sls.--Global Marine Drilling Co., Houston, TX; *U.S. Public*, pg. 748
Demeo, Joe, Dir.-Sls. & Mktg., Western Reg.--BGW Systems, Inc., Hawthorne, CA; *U.S. Private*, pg. 107
DeMeo, Ronald C., Sr. V.P.-Mktg. & Sls. & Sec.--Marietta Corporation, Cortland, NY; *U.S. Private*, pg. 702
Demers, Richard P., V.P.-Mktg., Sls. & Adv.--EnergyNorth, Inc., Manchester, NH; *U.S. Public*, pg. 581
Demi, Dave, V.P.-Sls.--Hillshire Farm & Kahn's, Cincinnati, OH; *U.S. Public*, pg. 1433
Deming, Derrell, Dir.-Sls. & Mktg.--Polka Dot Dairy/Tom Thumb Food Markets, Hastings, MN; *U.S. Private*, pg. 874
Demirjian, Abraham, Mgr.-Sls., West Coast--Kuwait Airways, West Coast Region, Los Angeles, CA; *Int'l*, pg. 764
Demitry, Thomas, Sr. Mgr.-Sls.--New Era Cap. Co., Derby, NY; *U.S. Private*, pg. 793
DeMory, Chuck, Sr. V.P.-Sls.--Comdisco, Inc., Rosemont, IL; *U.S. Public*, pg. 407
Demos, Dave, V.P.-Sls.--American Axle & Manufacturing, Detroit, MI; *U.S. Private*, pg. 51
Dempsey, James, Mgr.-Sls.--Chesapeake Packaging Co./LeRoy, Le Roy, NY; *U.S. Public*, pg. 346
Dempsey, William F., V.P. & Mng. Dir.-Valvoline Intl.--Valvoline Company, Lexington, KY; *U.S. Public*, pg. 139
Demuth, Otto, Pres.--Dumore Corporation, Mauston, WI; *U.S. Private*, pg. 346
den Hartog, A., Mgr.-Pur. & Sls. Admin.--Bakery Ingredients Division, Delft, Netherlands; *Int'l*, pg. 1142
DeNapoli, Gary, Mgr.-Eastern Regional Sls.--The Kendall-Betham Division, Piscataway, NJ; *U.S. Public*, pg. 1647
Denbosslhe, A. Van, Dir.-Sls.--Sidmar N.V., Gent, Belgium; *Int'l*, pg. 79
Denby, William C., V.P.-Sls. & Mktg.--Agouron Pharmaceuticals, Inc., La Jolla, CA; *U.S. Public*, pg. 28
Deneny, Sean, V.P. & Gen. Sls. Mgr.-First Run--Viacom Enterprises, New York, NY; *U.S. Public*, pg. 779
Dengler, Raymond, V.P.-Sls. Mgr.--D.C. Taylor Co., Cedar Rapids, IA; *U.S. Private*, pg. 1070
Denham, Rick, V.P.-Sls.--Intercraft Company, Taylor, TX; *U.S. Public*, pg. 1177
Denney, Gary, V.P.-Sls.--Multi Metals Div., Louisville, KY; *U.S. Public*, pg. 575
Dennis, Dick, V.P.-Sls.--Transkrit Corporation, Roanoke, VA; *U.S. Private*, pg. 782
Dennis, Dick, Dir.-Sls.--Transkrit Corporation, Roanoke, VA; *U.S. Private*, pg. 782
Dennis, John, Mgr.-Sls.--EnviroTech PumpSystems, Salt Lake City, UT; *Int'l*, pg. 1489
Dennis, John N., V.P.-Sls.--Annin & Company, Roseland, NJ; *U.S. Private*, pg. 75
Dennis, Lou, V.P. & Sls. Dir.--Warner Bros. Records, Inc., Burbank, CA; *U.S. Public*, pg. 1611
Denogeon, Ernie, Dir.-Sls.--Lifetouch, Portrait Studios, Eden Prairie, MN; *U.S. Private*, pg. 667
Densmore, Tom, Dir.-Sls. & Mktg.--Whitfield Foods, Inc., Montgomery, AL; *U.S. Private*, pg. 1173
Denton, Alan, Mgr.-Sls. Promo.--Vauxhall Motors Limited, Luton, United Kingdom; *U.S. Public*, pg. 724
Denton, Debby, Mgr.-W. Sls.--RCR Publications, Denver, CO; *U.S. Private*, pg. 285
Denton, Norman, Sr. V.P.-Sls. & Mktg.--Rainbow Technologies, Inc., Irvine, CA; *U.S. Public*, pg. 1359
DePalma, J., V.P.-Sls.--Zim-American Israeli Shipping Co., New York, NY; *U.S. Private*, pg. 1206
DePalma, Tara, Coord.-Prod. Sls.--Marcel Dekker, Inc., New York, NY; *U.S. Private*, pg. 321
DePeau, Norman, Dir.-Sls. & Mktg.--Lewis Engineering Company, Naugatuck, CT; *U.S. Public*, pg. 402
Depp, Herbert D., V.P.-Mktg. & Sls.--G.E. Aircraft Engines, Cincinnati, OH; *U.S. Public*, pg. 710
DePrinzio, Ken, V.P.-Sls.--All Star Gas Co.-Region VII, Lebanon, MO; *U.S. Private*, pg. 35
Derasmo, Jack, V.P.-Mktg. & Sls. Mgr.--Glen Raven Marketing Corporation, Pearl River, NY; *U.S. Private*, pg. 456
Derderian, John, V.P.-Sls. & Mktg.--Pathmark Stores Incorporated, Woodbridge, NJ; *U.S. Private*, pg. 843
Derleth, April, V.P.-Sls. & Mktg.--Mueller Sports Medicine, Inc., Prairie Du Sac, WI; *U.S. Private*, pg. 766
Deroche, William, Dir.-Sls.--Bud Industries, Inc., Willoughby, OH; *U.S. Private*, pg. 178
Derosa, Dominick A., Sr. V.P.-Sls.--HBOC, Atlanta, GA; *U.S. Public*, pg. 770
DeRosa, Tom, Reg. Mgr.--Cargill Salt, Newark, CA; *U.S. Private*, pg. 210
DeRose, Dino, Dir.-Natl. Sls.--Muzak Limited Partnership, Seattle, WA; *U.S. Private*, pg. 222
Derrick, G. Lynn, Jr., Mgr.-Mktg.--Shakespeare Composites & Electronics, Newberry, SC; *U.S. Public*, pg. 940
Deryes, Phil, Exec. Dir.-Sls. & Mktg. Promo.--Atlanta Motor Speedway, Hampton, GA; *U.S. Public*, pg. 1498
Des Enfants, T., Dir.-Aerospace Bus. Unit--Wyman-Gordon Investment Castings, Inc., Groton, CT; *U.S. Public*, pg. 1782
DeSalvo, Dan, Exec. V.P.-Sls.--American Family Mutual Insurance Co., Madison, WI; *U.S. Private*, pg. 53
Desanti, Tony J., Asst. V.P.-Metal & Concentrate Sls.--Falconbridge Limited, Toronto, Canada; *Int'l*, pg. 433
DeSantis, Michael, Sr. V.P.-Sls.--Chancellor Corporation, Boston, MA; *U.S. Public*, pg. 335
Desbiens, Michel, Sr. V.P.-Sls. & Corp. Devel.--Donohue Matane, Inc., Quebec, Canada; *Int'l*, pg. 1075
Deschene, C.D., Mgr.-Mktg.--Maine Public Service Company, Presque Isle, ME; *U.S. Public*, pg. 1038
Desgagnes, Serge, Mgr.-Sls.--Place Turcot Mill, Montreal, Canada; *Int'l*, pg. 761
Deskin, Suni, V.P.-Sls. Services--CBS Enterprises Division, New York, NY; *U.S. Public*, pg. 274
Despontin, J.P., Dir.-Spa--Spadel SA, Brussels, Belgium; *Int'l*, pg. 1287
DesRoches, Christopher M., V.P.-Sls. & Mktg.--Casella Waste Systems, Inc., Rutland, VT; *U.S. Public*, pg. 312
DesRoches, Grant, Dir.-Sls.--Tennant Company, Minneapolis, MN; *U.S. Public*, pg. 1577
Destasio, Michael J., V.P.-Sls.--Huffy Sports Company, Sussex, WI; *U.S. Public*, pg. 846
DeStefano, Neil, Mgr.-Sls., Southern Reg.--FMC Corp., Agricultural Products Group, Philadelphia, PA; *U.S. Public*, pg. 605
DeTomaso, Steve, Mgr.-Adv. & Sls.--Sachs Boge of America, Westlake, OH; *Int'l*, pg. 835
DeTour, Walter, V.P.-Mktg. & Sls.--Universal Photonics, Inc., Hicksville, NY; *U.S. Private*, pg. 1127
Dettmann, Robert J., V.P.-Sls. & Mktg.--Action Technology Company, Rockaway, NJ; *U.S. Private*, pg. 15
DeVault, Keith D., V.P.-Sls.--Lever Brothers Household Products Div., New York, NY; *Int'l*, pg. 1436
Devaux, Tom, Mgr.-Sls. Natl. Fleet--The Crown Divisions, Wooster, OH; *U.S. Public*, pg. 1631
Devenish, Michael, Dir.-Intl. Sls.--Dorling Kindersley Ltd., London, United Kingdom; *Int'l*, pg. 417
Deverter, Joseph, Mgr.-Sls.--Duferco Steel Inc., Laurence Harbor, NJ; *U.S. Private*, pg. 345
DeVincenzi, Louie, Asst. V.P.-Winery Rels.--F. Korbel Bros. Inc., Guerneville, CA; *U.S. Private*, pg. 632
Devine, John, Dir.-Sls. & Mktg.--Metex Corporation, Edison, NJ; *U.S. Public*, pg. 1674
Devine, Sean F., V.P.-Serials Sls.--UMI, Ann Arbor, MI; *U.S. Public*, pg. 201
Devine, Wayne R., V.P.-Sls., Retail--McCain Foods Limited, Florenceville, Canada; *Int'l*, pg. 850
Devito, Ralph, V.P.-Bakery--Pepperidge Farm, Incorporated, Norwalk, CT; *U.S. Public*, pg. 299
DeVooght, Phil, V.P.-Sls.--S.C. Johnson & Son, Limited, Brantford, Canada; *U.S. Private*, pg. 593
Devor, Cory, V.P.-Sls. & Mktg.--Tricord Systems, Inc., Plymouth, MN; *U.S. Public*, pg. 1637
Devore, Jeanne, Mgr.-Sls.--Rexall Sundown Inc., Boca Raton, FL; *U.S. Public*, pg. 1384
DeVos, Giles, V.P.-Intl. Sls.--Merit Medical Systems, Inc., South Jordan, UT; *U.S. Public*, pg. 1096
DeVoss, Lee, Mgr.-Sls.--Fuel Systems Textron Inc., Zeeland, MI; *U.S. Public*, pg. 1589
Devoto, Earl, V.P.-Sls.--Fitz & Floyd, Dallas, TX; *U.S. Private*, pg. 409
DeVries, Peter, V.P.-Sls.--Bergquist ITC, GmbH, Pinneberg, Germany; *U.S. Private*, pg. 135
DeVries, Peter, V.P.-Sls.--Bergquist UK. Limited, Milton Keynes, United Kingdom; *U.S. Private*, pg. 135
Devroy, Gary, V.P.-Sls.--Intermark World Products, Ltd., Kenilworth, IL; *U.S. Private*, pg. 567
DeWald, Lloyd, V.P.-Mktg. & Sls.--Pierce Manufacturing, Inc., Appleton, WI; *U.S. Public*, pg. 1233
Dewall, Dennie, Mgr.-Sls.--Arrow Tank & Engineering Co., Minneapolis, MN; *U.S. Private*, pg. 85
Dewar, Cathy, Sls. Coord.--Euroclean, Itasca, IL; *Int'l*, pg. 440
Dewey, Pat, V.P.-Sales--Propak Systems Ltd., Airdrie, Canada; *Int'l*, pg. 1071
DeWitt, Lucille, Mgr.-Sls.--New Haven Savings Bank, New Haven, CT; *U.S. Private*, pg. 793
DeWitt, Van, Mgr.-Intl. Sls.--Tidewater Inc., New Orleans, LA; *U.S. Public*, pg. 1608
DeYoung, Jim, V.P.-Sls.--All Star Gas Co.-Region IV, Lebanon, MO; *U.S. Private*, pg. 35
DeZarate, Raymond A., Dir.-Natl. Acct. Sls.--Checkpoint Systems Inc., Thorofare, NJ; *U.S. Public*, pg. 343
Dezek, R.J., V.P.-Sls. & Mktg.--Young Radiator Company, Racine, WI; *U.S. Private*, pg. 1201
Di Marco, M., Gen. Mgr.-Corp. Mktg. & Sls.--Nuovo Pignone S.p.a., Florence, Italy; *Int'l*, pg. 990
Di Zazzo, Elizabeth, V.P.--Oomphies, Inc., Lawrence, MA; *U.S. Private*, pg. 817
Diamond, Harry A., AIA, Exec. V.P. & Treas.--Giffels Hoyem Basso, Inc., Troy, MI; *U.S. Private*, pg. 452
Dias, Georgio, Mgr.-Sls.--Overholtzer Church Furniture, Inc., Modesto, CA; *U.S. Private*, pg. 823
Dias, Richard A., Mgr.-Natl. Sls.--The Valvoline Company, Lexington, KY; *U.S. Public*, pg. 139
Diaz, Cass F., Sr. V.P.-Worldwide Sls. & Mktg.--ATL Ultrasound, Inc., Bothell, WA; *U.S. Public*, pg. 11
Diaz, David, V.P.-Sls.--Cucina Classica Italiana, Inc., Lakewood, NJ; *U.S. Public*, pg. 1435
Diaz, Manuel F., V.P. & Gen. Mgr.-Solutions Sls. & Delivery Grp./Computer Sys. Org--Hewlett-Packard Company, Palo Alto, CA; *U.S. Public*, pg. 813
Diaz, Tony, Mgr.-Sls.--Taca International Airlines, S. A., San Salvador, El Salvador; *Int'l*, pg. 1346
DiBiagio, Dave, Mgr.-Sls.--White Pigeon Paper Company, White Pigeon, MI; *U.S. Private*, pg. 87
DiBona, Anthony P., Div. V.P.-U.S. Sls. Eastern--Data General Corporation, Westborough, MA; *U.S. Public*, pg. 485
Dichak, Pete, Mgr.-Sls.--Southern Post Company, Houston, TX; *U.S. Public*, pg. 412
Dick, Joan, Coord.-Sls.--ENI, Rochester, NY; *U.S. Private*, pg. 354
Dick, Kenneth P., Sr. V.P.-Sls.--TBC Corporation, Memphis, TN; *U.S. Public*, pg. 1553
Dick, M., Sls.--Canefco Limited, Scarborough, Canada; *U.S. Private*, pg. 368
Dickenson, Larry S., V.P.-Sls./Asia & Pacific--Boeing Commercial Airplane Group, Renton, WA; *U.S. Public*, pg. 240
Dickerson, Don, Mgr.-Sls.--PENCO-Indiana, Indianapolis, IN; *Int'l*, pg. 1508
Dickerson, Sid, V.P.-Sls.--Hirschfeld, Inc., San Angelo, TX; *U.S. Private*, pg. 530

Dickerson, Sid, Mgr.-Sls.--Hirschfeld Steel Company, Inc., San Angelo, TX; *U.S. Private*, pg. 531
Dickey, Bob, Reg. V.P.-Image Brands Sls.--R.G. Barry Corporation, Pickerington, OH; *U.S. Public*, pg. 192
Dickhoff, Bill, Dir.-Sls., Mktg. & Adv.--Roofing Wholesale Co., Inc., Phoenix, AZ; *U.S. Private*, pg. 943
Dickinson, Carl, Dir.-Reg. Sls.--Surgical Laser Technologies, Inc., Montgomeryville, PA; *U.S. Public*, pg. 1542
Dickinson, Harry L., Sr. V.P.-Sls.--S3 Incorporated, Santa Clara, CA; *U.S. Public*, pg. 1415
Dickinson, John H., V.P.-Retail Sls./Houston--Tiffany & Co., New York, NY; *U.S. Public*, pg. 1608
Dickinson, William, V.P.-Sales--Yokogawa Corporation of America, Newnan, GA; *Int'l*, pg. 1521
Dicks, Tom, Dir.-Sls. & Mktg.--American Fluorescent Corporation, Waukegan, IL; *U.S. Private*, pg. 54
Dickson, Chris, V.P.-Replacement Sls.-Passenger/Light Truck Div.--Continental General Tire, Inc., Charlotte, NC; *Int'l*, pg. 327
Dickson, Jim, Sr. Dir.-Truck Tires Sls.-Commercial Div.--Continental General Tire, Inc., Charlotte, NC; *Int'l*, pg. 327
DiClemente, M., Mgr.-Sls., Cardiovascular--Terumo Medical Corporation, Somerset, NJ; *Int'l*, pg. 1376
DiCola, Anthony, V.P.-Sls. & Mktg.--Wrought Washer Mfg., Inc., Milwaukee, WI; *U.S. Private*, pg. 1192
Didier, Pascal, V.P.-Worldwide Sls.--GaSonics International, San Jose, CA; *U.S. Public*, pg. 703
Diehl, Ed, V.P.-Sls.--The Felters Company, Roebuck, SC; *U.S. Private*, pg. 400
Diehl, Keith K., V.P.-Sls.--Ward Trucking Corp., Altoona, PA; *U.S. Private*, pg. 1149
Diehr, Jeff S., V.P.-Sls. & Mktg.--The Fremont Co., Fremont, OH; *U.S. Private*, pg. 426
Diem, G., V.P.-Sls./Mid West--Sika Corporation, Lyndhurst, NJ; *Int'l*, pg. 1249
Diener, Jerry L., Sr. V.P.-Sls.--Smith Corona Corp., Cortland, NY; *U.S. Private*, pg. 1007
Diercksen, Doug, Dir.-Sls.--Turner Construction Company, Somerset, NJ; *U.S. Public*, pg. 1645
Dierksen, Paul, V.P.-Sls.--Chris-Craft Boats, Sarasota, FL; *U.S. Private*, pg. 478
Dierres, John, V.P.-Sls., The Americas--Imax Corporation, Mississauga, Canada; *Int'l*, pg. 661
Dieterich, Laurent, Dir. Sls. & Mktg.--Berlitz Schools of Languages AG, Geneva, Switzerland; *U.S. Public*, pg. 222
Dietheln, Zack, Dir.-Adv.--Deutsche Bahn, Frankfurt/Main, Germany; *Int'l*, pg. 401
Dietlin, Paul, Mgr.-Sls.--E.J. Brooks Company, Newark, NJ; *U.S. Private*, pg. 172
Dietrich, Edward, Dir.-Sls. & Mktg.--American Banknote Holographics, Elmsford, NY; *U.S. Public*, pg. 68
Dietrich, Lovonne, V.P.-Sls. & Mktg.--Stella Foods, Inc., Green Bay, WI; *U.S. Private*, pg. 1040
Dietrich, W.V., V.P.-Sls.--Elwell-Parker, Inc., Farmington, MI; *U.S. Private*, pg. 373
Diez, Angel M., V.P.-Pulp Sls.--Pope & Talbot, Inc., Portland, OR; *U.S. Public*, pg. 1316
Diez, Valentin, Mgr.-Sls. & Mktg.--Grupo Modelo S.A., Mexico, Mexico; *U.S. Public*, pg. 115
DiFilippo, Pat A., Dir.-Sls.--Turner Construction Co., New York, NY; *U.S. Public*, pg. 1645
DiGangi, Robert, V.P.-Sls.--Inter-Tel, Incorporated, Phoenix, AZ; *U.S. Public*, pg. 888
DiGangi, Robert, V.P.-Distr. Sls.--Inter-Tel Integrated Systems, Inc., Chandler, AZ; *U.S. Public*, pg. 888
DiGenova, Paul, V.P.-Special Mkt. Sls.--Comstock Michigan Fruit, Rochester, NY; *U.S. Private*, pg. 887
Diggle, Robert, Mgr.-Sls.--Bell Distributing, Sacramento, CA; *U.S. Private*, pg. 664
DiGiacomo, Mike, V.P.-Sls. & Mktg.--Compas Electronics, Inc., Kanata, Canada; *Int'l*, pg. 36
Digrassi, J., Dir.-Sls.--Goodyear de Colombia S.A., Cali, Colombia; *U.S. Public*, pg. 753
Dilcher, Richard, Mgr.-Sls.--Patterson Laboratories, Inc., Detroit, MI; *U.S. Private*, pg. 843
Dilday, Ted, Mgr.-Sls. & Mktg.--Nelsen Steel & Wire Co., Franklin Park, IL; *U.S. Private*, pg. 790
Diliberto, R.A., Mgr.-Insider Sls.--Tamaqua Cable Products Corp., Schuylkill Haven, PA; *Int'l*, pg. 417
Dillahey, Frank, V.P.-Sls.--TV Host Inc., Harrisburg, PA; *U.S. Private*, pg. 1066
Dillenberg, Alan, V.P.-Payment Systems & Sls.--National Computer Print, Inc., Birmingham, AL; *U.S. Private*, pg. 780
Dillon, Joe, V.P.-Sls.--Williams Electronics Games, Inc., Chicago, IL; *U.S. Public*, pg. 1727
Dillon, Matthew, Sr. Acct. Mgr.--Aisin World Corp.-Detroit, Plymouth, MI; *Int'l*, pg. 39
Dillon, Mike, V.P.-Sls.--Prepress Solutions, Inc., Billerica, MA; *U.S. Private*, pg. 882
Dillon, Mimi, Dir. & Sec.-Sls.--Catholic Order of Foresters, Naperville, IL; *U.S. Private*, pg. 220
Dills, Patrick G., Exec. V.P.-Sls.--First Health Group Corp., Downers Grove, IL; *U.S. Public*, pg. 635
Dilschneider, Ray, Pres.-Ing. Div.--Tree Top, Inc., Selah, WA; *U.S. Private*, pg. 1098
DiMarco, Angie, Mgr.-Sls. Admin.--McGraw-Hill Securities Trading, Inc., New York, NY; *U.S. Public*, pg. 1071
DiMarco, Michael A., Sr. V.P.-Natl. Accts. Div.--Paging Network, Inc., Plano, TX; *U.S. Public*, pg. 1252
DiMario, Peter, V.P.-Dealer Sls.--Philips Speech Processing, Atlanta, GA; *Int'l*, pg. 1055
DiMateo, Don, Natl. Sls. Mgr.--The Foreign Candy Co., Inc., Hull, IA; *U.S. Private*, pg. 418
DiMatteo, Carmen, Sr. V.P.-Services & Sls.--Semco Industries Inc., Stoughton, MA; *U.S. Private*, pg. 983
Dimitroff, Mike, Mgr.-Sls. & Mktg.--Chicago White Metal Casting, Inc., Bensenville, IL; *U.S. Private*, pg. 236
Dimmick Jr., Henry M., V.P.-Sls.--AGR International, Inc., Butler, PA; *U.S. Private*, pg. 5
Dimter, Howard, V.P.-Sls.--C. B. Fleet Co., Inc., Lynchburg, VA; *U.S. Private*, pg. 410
DiMuro, Joe, V.P.-Sls.--20th Century Fox Home Entertainment, Los Angeles, CA; *U.S. Public*, pg. 275
DiMuro, Joe, V.P.-Sls.--20th Century Fox Home Entertainment, Los Angeles, CA; *Int'l*, pg. 926
Dineen, Larry, Mgr.-Natl. Sls.--Kennedy Manufacturing Company, Van Wert, OH; *U.S. Private*, pg. 614
Dingwall, Bob, Dir.-Sls.--Poly Pak America, Inc., Los Angeles, CA; *U.S. Private*, pg. 875
Dinkel, Linda, V.P.--Andover Bancorp, Inc., Andover, MA; *U.S. Public*, pg. 111
Dinkins, Greg, Mgr.-Natl. Sls.--Hansberger Precision Golf Inc., Pontotoc, MS; *U.S. Private*, pg. 499
Dinnin, Elizabeth, V.P.-Sls.--Meridian Insurance Group, Inc., Indianapolis, IN; *U.S. Public*, pg. 1095
Dinnin, Elizabeth, Dir.-Sls.--Meridian Security Insurance Company, Indianapolis, IN; *U.S. Public*, pg. 1095
Dinsdale, Chris, Pres.-Tillamook Food Sls.--Tillamook County Creamery Assn., Tillamook, OR; *U.S. Private*, pg. 1086
DiPasquale, Guy, Sls. Mgr.--Holmes Protection of Philadelphia, Inc., Philadelphia, PA; *U.S. Public*, pg. 1649
DiPietro, Peter, Mgr.-Natl. Sls.--Interplastic Corp., Saint Paul, MN; *U.S. Private*, pg. 572
Dippel, Clem, Dir.-Sls. & Adv.--Fishing Tackle Retailer, Montgomery, AL; *U.S. Private*, pg. 105
Disalvo, E.S., V.P.-Sls.--RPS Inc., Coraopolis, PA; *U.S. Public*, pg. 604
Disbury, Brian E., V.P.-Mktg. & Sls.--Magma Metals Company, Tucson, AZ; *Int'l*, pg. 224
Dischner, Jack, Dir.-Intl. Sls.--Computational Systems Inc., Knoxville, TN; *U.S. Public*, pg. 572
Disedouy, Gean, V.P.-Sls.--Colgate-Palmolive France, Courbevoie, France; *U.S. Public*, pg. 398
Diskin, Joe, Sr. V.P.-Sls.--Johnny Carson Apparel, Inc., Buffalo, NY; *U.S. Public*, pg. 796
Disque, Don R., Sr. V.P.-Sls. & Mktg.--Phelps Dodge Magnet Wire Co., Fort Wayne, IN; *U.S. Public*, pg. 1286
Ditch, Randy, V.P.-Sls. & Mktg.--Weldon Machine Tool, Inc., York, PA; *U.S. Private*, pg. 1161
Ditkowich, Jack, V.P.-Sls.--Multimatic Corporation, Northvale, NJ; *U.S. Private*, pg. 767
Dittrich, Ray, V.P.-Sls.--American Color, Phoenix, AZ; *U.S. Public*, pg. 1133
Dix, A., Dir.-Sls.--Herr Voss Ltd., Derby, United Kingdom; *U.S. Private*, pg. 962
Dix, Ron, Sr. V.P.-Mktg. & Sls.--Bush Brothers & Company, Knoxville, TN; *U.S. Private*, pg. 189
Dixon, Harold P., V.P.-Sls. Midrange Central U.S.--EMC Corporation, Hopkinton, MA; *U.S. Public*, pg. 545
Dixon, Peter, V.P.-Intl. Sls.--Computer Network Technology Corporation, Minneapolis, MN; *U.S. Public*, pg. 421
Dixon, Robert, Mgr.-Sls. & Mktg.--Pannier Corporation, Pittsburgh, PA; *U.S. Private*, pg. 837
Djamianto, Mariati, Sls. Dir.--Reed Exhibition Companies-Indonesia, Jakarta, Indonesia; *Int'l*, pg. 1097
Djurle, Gunilla, Sls. & Mktg. Mgr.--Whitehall Sweden, Stockholm, Sweden; *U.S. Public*, pg. 82
Dobbs, Mark, V.P.-Retail & Commercial Markets--Dri Mark Products, Inc., Port Washington, NY; *U.S. Private*, pg. 342
Dobel, Steve, Sr. V.P.-Sls.--WorldCom, Inc., Jackson, MS; *U.S. Public*, pg. 1779
Dobrick, Glenn, Dir.-Sls. & Services--Kentucky Manufacturing Co., Louisville, KY; *U.S. Private*, pg. 615
Dobson, John R., Sr. V.P.-Sls.--Owen Industries, Inc., Carter Lake, IA; *U.S. Private*, pg. 824
Dobson, John R., Mgr.-Sls. & Mktg.--Paxton & Vierling, Omaha, NE; *U.S. Private*, pg. 824
Dobson, Reuben, Mgr.-Natl. Sls. & Mktg.--NUS International Pty. Ltd., Sydney, Australia; *U.S. Private*, pg. 787
Dodd, Dave, V.P.-Sls.--Whiteville Apparel Corp., Whiteville, NC; *U.S. Public*, pg. 796
Dodd, Peter, Mng. Dir.-Sls.--ESAB Group (UK) Ltd., Waltham Cross, United Kingdom; *Int'l*, pg. 282
Dodez, Gary, V.P.-Sls.--Malta Div.-Tomkins Industries, Inc., Malta, OH; *Int'l*, pg. 1398
Dodge, Larry, Dir.-Sls. & Mktg.--Booth Newspapers, Inc., Grand Rapids, MI; *U.S. Private*, pg. 157
Dodge, Les, Mgr.-Sls.--Best Manufacturing, Inc., New York, NY; *U.S. Private*, pg. 139
Dodson, Larry, Mgr.-Sls.--North American Royalties, Inc., Chattanooga, TN; *U.S. Private*, pg. 803
Doell, Don, V.P.-Natl. Sls.--Pfaudler, Inc., Rochester, NY; *U.S. Public*, pg. 1393
Doering, Roy, V.P.-Sls. & Mktg.--Hurd Millwork Company, Inc., Medford, WI; *U.S. Private*, pg. 1113
Doerr, Dave, V.P.-Sls. & Mktg.--The Falk Corporation, Milwaukee, WI; *U.S. Public*, pg. 1534
Doggette, Curtis, V.P. & Gen. Mgr.-Brandon Drying Fabrics--Wangner Systems Corporation, Greenville, SC; *Int'l*, pg. 1418
Doherty, John, Dir.-Sls.- Standard Bus. Sys.--Standard Duplicating Machines Corp., Andover, MA; *U.S. Private*, pg. 1031
Doherty, Kevin, V.P.-Sls.--Cabletel Communications Inc., Markham, Canada; *Int'l*, pg. 17
Doin, David, V.P.-Sls.--Environment/One Corporation, Niskayuna, NY; *U.S. Public*, pg. 586
Dolan, A.J., Sls. Mgr.--Albany International/Industrial Eng Process Fabrics Division, Portland, TN; *U.S. Public*, pg. 36
Dolan, Bob, V.P.-Franchise Sls.--International Center for Entrepreneurial Development, Inc., Cypress, TX; *U.S. Private*, pg. 568
Dolan, Jeff, Sr. V.P.-Sls. & Mktg.--Selfix, Inc., Chicago, IL; *U.S. Public*, pg. 832
Dolan, Jeffrey R., Sr. V.P.-Sls. & Mktg.--Selfix--Home Products International, Inc., Chicago, IL; *U.S. Public*, pg. 832
Dolan, Michael, Exec. V.P.-Hospital Sls. & Devel.--HBE Corporation/Design Build Divisions, Saint Louis, MO; *U.S. Private*, pg. 489
Dolan, Terry, Mgr.-Southern Reg. Sls.--Pennsylvania Cellular Telephone Corp., Lancaster, PA; *U.S. Public*, pg. 1708
Dolan, Terry, Mgr.-Southern Reg. Sls.--Pennsylvania Cellular Telephone Corp., York, PA; *U.S. Public*, pg. 1708
Dolim, Mark, Dir.-Sls.--L.N. Curtis & Sons, Oakland, CA; *U.S. Private*, pg. 297
Dolle, Kevin, V.P.-Retail Sls.--ODL Incorporated, Zeeland, MI; *U.S. Private*, pg. 809
Dollman, Walt, Mgr.-Bus. Unit--Ceramtec North America Applications, Inc., Mansfield, MA; *Int'l*, pg. 860
Dolori, Philip Dei, V.P.-Sls.--Pitco Frialator Inc., Bow, NH; *U.S. Public*, pg. 1065
Domalewski, Chris, Sr. Dir.-Mktg. & Sls.--NJ Transit, Newark, NJ; *U.S. Private*, pg. 794
Domaschossky, Matt, Gen. Mgr.-Sls. & Mktg.--Crestar Food Products, Inc., Brentwood, TN; *U.S. Public*, pg. 805
Domenicali, Dena, V.P.-Member Sls.--Book of the Month Club, New York, NY; *U.S. Public*, pg. 1612
Domingue, Randy, Mgr.-Sls.--Woodfin Pontiac-Isuzu, Baton Rouge, LA; *U.S. Private*, pg. 1187
Domingues Massa, Mizael Jose, Dir.-Sls.--LPC Industrias Alimenticias S.A., Vila Jaguara, Brazil; *Int'l*, pg. 380
Dominguez, Justo, Sls. Mgr.-Crop Protection--Monsanto Argentina S.A.I.C., Buenos Aires, Argentina; *U.S. Public*, pg. 1125
Dominguez, Ron, Gen. Mgr.--Mitsubishi Silicon America-Southwest Regional Sales Office, Dallas, TX; *Int'l*, pg. 875
Domino, Tom, V.P.-Sls.-PCSD--Aromat Corporation, New Providence, NJ; *Int'l*, pg. 847
Donahue, Caroline F., V.P.-Sls.--Intuit, Inc., Mountain View, CA; *U.S. Public*, pg. 911
Donahue, David, Mgr.-Sls.--Spirite Industries, Inc., Englewood, NJ; *U.S. Private*, pg. 1026
Donahue, Jerry, Mgr.-Sls.--Atlantic Concrete Products, Inc., Tullytown, PA; *U.S. Private*, pg. 95
Donahue, Milly, Sls. Mgr.--Robinson Helicopter Company, Torrance, CA; *U.S. Private*, pg. 936
Donars, Rene J., V.P.-Sls. & Mktg.--Porter-Cable Corporation, Jackson, TN; *U.S. Public*, pg. 1274
Donarumo, Mike, Regional Mgr.-Southwest--Columbus Mills, Inc., Columbus, GA; *U.S. Private*, pg. 256
Donatello, D., V.P.-Domestic Sls.--General Railway Signal Corp., Rochester, NY; *Int'l*, pg. 1194
Donegan, Jerry, V.P.-Natl. Sls.--Avedis Zildjian Company, Norwell, MA; *U.S. Private*, pg. 1206
Donelly, Susan, Mgr.-Sls.--Yale University Press, New Haven, CT; *U.S. Private*, pg. 1195
Doney, Bart J., V.P.-Sls. & Admin.--Inland Container-Containerboard Division, Indianapolis, IN; *U.S. Public*, pg. 1575
Doney, Dave, Mgr.-Sls.--Peco Mfg. Co., Inc., Portland, OR; *U.S. Private*, pg. 846
Donlon, Timothy, V.P.-Domestic Sls.--Jet Spray Corp., Norwood, MA; *U.S. Private*, pg. 586
Donnaruma, Tom, Sr. V.P.-Sls.--Sony Music Entertainment, Inc., New York, NY; *Int'l*, pg. 1281
Donnelly, C. R., V.P.-Sls.--Everglades Sugar Refinery, Inc., Clewiston, FL; *U.S. Public*, pg. 873
Donnelly, Dan, V.P.-Cable Sls.--StarSight Telecast, Inc., Fremont, CA; *U.S. Public*, pg. 705
Donnelly, Joann Campo, Gen. Mgr.-Sls.--KSHB-TV, Kansas City, MO; *U.S. Public*, pg. 1448
Donnelly, Lane, V.P.-Sls.--Belcan Corporation, Cincinnati, OH; *U.S. Private*, pg. 131
Donnelly, Michael E., V.P.-Sls. & Mktg.--Starcrest Products of California, Perris, CA; *U.S. Private*, pg. 1035
Donnelly, Richard, V.P.-Sls. & Mktg.--Amtrak-National Railroad Passenger Corp., Washington, DC; *U.S. Private*, pg. 68
Donnelly, Rick, V.P.-Sls.--Cosco, Inc., Columbus, IN; *U.S. Private*, pg. 277
Donnelly, Robert, Exec. V.P.-Sls. & Mktg.--Glastic Corporation, Cleveland, OH; *Int'l*, pg. 740
Donnelly, W.T., Dir.-Sls. & Mktg.--Aston Martin Lagonda of North America, Inc., Mahwah, NJ; *U.S. Public*, pg. 664
Donner, D.A., V.P.-Sls.--Modern Equipment Co., Inc., Port Washington, WI; *U.S. Private*, pg. 33
Donner, Richard W., V.P.-Sls.--Dyersburg Corporation, Dyersburg, TN; *U.S. Public*, pg. 538
Donnowitz, Vicki, V.P.-Retail Store Div.--Rand McNally & Company, Skokie, IL; *U.S. Private*, pg. 908
Donofrio, Al, V.P.-Sls.--Eagle Button Co., Inc., Carlstadt, NJ; *U.S. Private*, pg. 354
Donofrio, Richard M., Sr. V.P.-Mktg. & Sls.--The Southern New England Telephone Company, New Haven, CT; *U.S. Public*, pg. 1491
Donoghue, Thomas F., Mgr.-Mktg. & Sls., Kraft Plng.--Kraft Paper Div., Memphis, TN; *U.S. Public*, pg. 903
Donohoe, Michael P., Sr. V.P.-Sls. & Mktg.--JBB Worldwide, Inc., Deerfield, IL; *U.S. Public*, pg. 675
Donohue, Jim, Sls. Mgr.--Holmes Protection of New York, Incorporated, New York, NY; *U.S. Public*, pg. 1649
Donovan, James M., Exec. Dir.-Mktg. & Sls.--Wyeth-Ayerst Laboratories, Inc., Philadelphia, PA; *U.S. Public*, pg. 80
Donovan, John, Sr. V.P.-Leasing--Carr Real Estate Services, Washington, DC; *U.S. Public*, pg. 309
Donovan, Michael, Gen. Mgr.-Sls.--Republic Automotive Parts Sales, Inc., Charlotte, NC; *U.S. Public*, pg. 1378
Donovan, Stephen M., V.P.-Intl. Sls.--Lattice Semiconductor Corporation, Hillsboro, OR; *U.S. Public*, pg. 979
Donovan, Vincent L., Dir.-Sls. & Mktg.--Manchester Plastics, Troy, MI; *U.S. Public*, pg. 399
Doodson, K., Mgr.-Sls. & Mktg./Meat--Metro Foods, Inc., Olive Branch, MS; *U.S. Private*, pg. 736
Dooey, H.P., Dir.-Sls. & Mktg.--Powerscreen International Plc, Dungannon, United Kingdom; *Int'l*, pg. 1066
Dooley, Robert, Sr. V.P.-Worldwide Computer Sls. & Mktg.--Global Direct Mail Corp, Port Washington, NY; *U.S. Public*, pg. 747
Dooner, Peter S., V.P. & Gen. Mgr.-Sls.--Wheatland Tube Company, Collingswood, NJ; *U.S. Private*, pg. 1170

Doordan, John M., V.P.-Sls./Bus. Devel.--QAD Inc, Carpinteria, CA; *U.S. Public*, pg. 1345
Dorfman, Eliezer, V.P.-Sls. & Procurement Fresh Pork--Thorn Apple Valley, Inc., Southfield, MI; *U.S. Public*, pg. 1602
Dorfman, Jay, Mgr.-Gen. Sls.--The U.S. Baird Corporation, Stratford, CT; *U.S. Private*, pg. 1124
Dorfman, Robert, Pres.--King Wire Inc., North Chicago, IL; *U.S. Private*, pg. 621
Dorn, Jean, Dir.-Sls.--Globus & Cosmos, Littleton, CO; *U.S. Private*, pg. 458
Dornetti, Enzo, Mgr.-Sls.--Gelman Italy S.R.L., Milan, Italy; *U.S. Public*, pg. 1253
Doss, Kent, V.P.-Sls.-U.S.--Tambrands Inc., Cincinnati, OH; *U.S. Public*, pg. 1331
Doster, Gary A., V.P.-Sls. & Mktg.--F.N. Burt Company, Inc., Buffalo, NY; *U.S. Private*, pg. 188
Doster, M.D., Mgr.-Sls.--Turner/On-Site, Tempe, AZ; *U.S. Public*, pg. 1646
Dotson, Dave, Mgr.-Sls.--Dayton Rogers of Ohio, Columbus, OH; *U.S. Private*, pg. 318
Doucet, Theodule J., Jr., V.P.-Strategic Sls.--Pervasive Software Inc., Austin, TX; *U.S. Public*, pg. 1280
Doucette, David, Dir.-Sls.--Spincraft Wisconsin, Milwaukee, WI; *U.S. Public*, pg. 1506
Doucette, William R., Sr. V.P.-Sls.--PG&E Energy Services, San Francisco, CA; *U.S. Public*, pg. 1241
Dougherty, Kevin P., V.P.-Grp. Mktg. & Sls.--Sun Life of Canada, Toronto, Canada; *Int'l*, pg. 1319
Dougherty, Michael F., Dir.-Natl. Sls.--Minnesota Brewing Company, Saint Paul, MN; *U.S. Public*, pg. 1115
Dougherty, Tom, Mgr.-Sls.--Detroit Coil Company, Ferndale, MI; *U.S. Private*, pg. 328
Doughty, Kerry, V.P.-Sls. & Mktg.--Fast Food Merchandisers Inc., Rocky Mount, NC; *U.S. Public*, pg. 278
Douglas, Iain, V.P.-Sls.--La-Z-Boy Canada Ltd., Waterloo, Canada; *U.S. Public*, pg. 973
Douglas, Jim, V.P.-Sls. & Mktg.--AAF-International, Louisville, KY; *U.S. Private*, pg. 3
Douglas, Max, V.P.-Automotive Sls.-Eastern Div.--Berryman Products, Inc., Arlington, TX; *U.S. Private*, pg. 138
Douglass, Tom, V.P.-Marine Sls. & Mktg.--Teleflex Marine, Limerick, PA; *U.S. Public*, pg. 1569
Dountz, K.E., V.P.-Sls.--J.M. Smucker Company, Orrville, OH; *U.S. Public*, pg. 1480
Dover, Mac, Sls. Mgr.-Eastern Reg.--Houston Fearless 76 Inc., Compton, CA; *U.S. Private*, pg. 542
Dowd, Gerard, Sr. V.P.-Foodservice Sls. & Mktg.--Tyson Foods, Inc., Springdale, AR; *U.S. Public*, pg. 1652
Dowey, Mark, Sr. V.P.--Sealright Company, Inc., De Soto, KS; *U.S. Public*, pg. 1451
Dowling, Mary, Mgr.-Sls. Devel.--USA Weekend, New York, NY; *U.S. Public*, pg. 701
Dowling, Stephen E., Sr. V.P.-Sls. & Mktg.--Lincoln Foodservice Products, Inc., Fort Wayne, IN; *Int'l*, pg. 188
Downey, Dennis, Dir.-Sls.--Eclipse Inc., Rockford, IL; *U.S. Private*, pg. 360
Downing, Dolores K., Mngmt. Asst.-Outside Sls.--Linde Hydraulics Corporation, Canfield, OH; *Int'l*, pg. 810
Downs, Barry, V.P.-Sls./Natl. Retailer Grp.--Michelin Americas Small Tires (MAST), Greenville, SC; *Int'l*, pg. 322
Dowse, M., V.P.-Sls.--R.A. Industries, Inc., Lansdale, PA; *U.S. Private*, pg. 902
Doyle, Brian, Publr.--Colonial Homes, New York, NY; *U.S. Private*, pg. 517
Doyle, Brian K., Pres. & Treas.--King Milling Company, Lowell, MI; *U.S. Private*, pg. 621
Doyle, C.E., Mgr.-Sls. & Mktg.--TGM Detectors Inc., Waltham, MA; *Int'l*, pg. 892
Doyle, Daniel, Gen. Mgr.-Sls.--Kowalski Sausage Co., Inc., Hamtramck, MI; *U.S. Private*, pg. 634
Doyle, Dick, Mgr.-Hardware Sls. Div.--Seymour of Sycamore, Inc., Sycamore, IL; *U.S. Private*, pg. 988
Doyle, James, Dir.-Intl. Sls.--Oregon Metallurgical Corporation, Albany, OR; *U.S. Public*, pg. 43
Doyle, Jim, V.P.-Mktg. & Sls.--A. Finkl & Sons Co., Chicago, IL; *U.S. Private*, pg. 405
Doyle, Tom, Dir.-Sls.--Barenbrug Northeast, Ogdensburg, NJ; *Int'l*, pg. 167
Doyle, William J., Pres.-Sls.--Potash Corporation of Saskatchewan Inc., Saskatoon, Canada; *Int'l*, pg. 1064
Dozier, Michael, Pres. & Chief Oper. Officer--TIE/Communications, Inc., Overland Park, KS; *U.S. Private*, pg. 1085
Drafts, G. R., V.P.-Sls.--Loxcreen Company, West Columbia, SC; *U.S. Private*, pg. 679
Drago, Greg F., Mgr.-Sls.--Bison Canning Co., Inc., Angola, NY; *U.S. Private*, pg. 468
Drake, Glenn, Mgr.-Sls.--Tupperware U.S., Inc., Orlando, FL; *U.S. Public*, pg. 1644
Drake, Peter, V.P.-Sls.--Blommer Chocolate Co., Chicago, IL; *U.S. Private*, pg. 150
Drake, W.C., V.P.-Corp. Sls.--The Kendall Company, Mansfield, MA; *U.S. Public*, pg. 1647
Drapeau, Norman, Exec. V.P.-Worldwide Sls. & Mktg.--PSDI, Bedford, MA; *U.S. Private*, pg. 828
Draper, Willis H., V.P.-Sls.--The Flexaust Co., Amesbury, MA; *U.S. Public*, pg. 394
Drassler, Carolyn, V.P.-Mktg. & Sls.--MTI Vacations, Inc., Downers Grove, IL; *U.S. Private*, pg. 688
Draughon, Terry, V.P.-Intl. Export Publishing Sls.--Thomas Nelson Inc., Nashville, TN; *U.S. Public*, pg. 1167
Dreblow, Lutz, Area Sls.--Analog Devices GMBH - Technisches Buero Nord, Buchholz, Germany; *U.S. Public*, pg. 108
Drechsler, David, V.P.-Bus. Unit & Mgr.-Grinders--S.E. Huffman Corp., Clover, SC; *U.S. Private*, pg. 546
Dresch, John, Dir.-Sls.-Compounds--The Geon Company, Avon Lake, OH; *U.S. Public*, pg. 733
Dresser, Steve, Mgr.-Sls.--Trico Products Corporation, Buffalo, NY; *Int'l*, pg. 1397
Drew, Carol, Dir.-Sls.--The Levy Organization, Chicago, IL; *U.S. Private*, pg. 664
Drexinger, Jim, V.P.-Mktg. & Sls.--NIBCO, Inc., Elkhart, IN; *U.S. Private*, pg. 798
Dreyfuss, Norman, V.P.--The IDI Group Companies, Arlington, VA; *U.S. Private*, pg. 554
Driend, Nancy J., Intl. Sls. Mgr.--Schlumberger Industries, Owenton, KY; *U.S. Public*, pg. 1439
Driggs, James J., Natl. Mgr.-Sls.--Crane & Co., Inc., Dalton, MA; *U.S. Private*, pg. 286
Driscoll, Brian J., Pres.-Sls. & Integrated Logistics Co.--Nabisco Inc., Parsippany, NJ; *U.S. Public*, pg. 1355
Driscoll, Donald J., Mgr.-Sls. & Mktg.--Sheet & Coil Products Division, Port Kembla, Australia; *Int'l*, pg. 227
Driscoll, John P., Exec. V.P.--Murata Electronics North America, Inc., Smyrna, GA; *Int'l*, pg. 897
Driscoll, Mike, Mgr.-Sls.--N.G. Bailey & Co. Ltd.-Birmingham Branch, Birmingham, United Kingdom; *Int'l*, pg. 132
Driscoll, Patrick, Dir.-Sls. & Mktg.--Artistic Carton Company, Elgin, IL; *U.S. Private*, pg. 87
Driscoll, Robert, Dir.-Sls.--Buehler, Limited, Lake Bluff, IL; *U.S. Public*, pg. 574
Driscoll, Robert P., Mgr.-Natl. Sls.--Buehler, Limited, Lake Bluff, IL; *U.S. Public*, pg. 574
Drouillard, Charles, Exec. V.P. & Chief Oper. Officer--Maxwell Macmillan Professional & Business Reference Publishing, Englewood Cliffs, NJ; *U.S. Public*, pg. 1602
Drucker, Barry, Sr. V.P.-Sls.--Nature's Bounty Inc., Bohemia, NY; *U.S. Public*, pg. 1166
Drucker, Martin, V.P.-Sls.--Nu Horizons International Corp., Amityville, NY; *U.S. Public*, pg. 1205
Drumgoole, Michael J., Sr. V.P.-Sls. & Mktg.--Medical Resources Inc., Hackensack, NJ; *U.S. Public*, pg. 1080
Drummond, Tom, V.P.-Sls. & Mktg.--Standard Candy Co., Inc., Nashville, TN; *U.S. Private*, pg. 1030
Drury, Tom, Mgr.-Mktg. & Sls.--American White Cross, Dayville, CT; *U.S. Public*, pg. 694
Dryburgh, Douglas T., Sr. V.P.-Sls. & Mktg.--Starter Corp., New Haven, CT; *U.S. Public*, pg. 1511
Dryden, Will, Mgr.-Gen. Branch Sls.--Jones Blair Company, Dallas, TX; *U.S. Private*, pg. 596
Duarte, Mirta, V.P.--Mason Distributors, Inc., Hialeah, FL; *U.S. Private*, pg. 712
Dubay, Doug, Mgr.-Indus. Fabric--Dickson Elberton Mills Inc., Elberton, GA; *U.S. Private*, pg. 331
Dubin, Robert S., V.P.-Managed Care Sls.--Bradley Pharmaceuticals, Fairfield, NJ; *U.S. Public*, pg. 249
Dubin, Robert S., V.P.-Managed Care Sls.--Doak Dermatologics, Westbury, NY; *U.S. Public*, pg. 250
Dubler, Gary, Mgr.-Sls.--Mallery Lumber Corp., Emporium, PA; *U.S. Private*, pg. 698
Dubner, Ron, Mgr.-Natl. Sales--Fuji Photographic Products Div., Elmsford, NY; *Int'l*, pg. 524
Dubois, Colette, Gen. Mgr.-Sls. & Mktg./France, Switzerland, Benelux & Africa--Utell International-France, Paris, France; *Int'l*, pg. 1098
DuBois, Richard, Exec. V.P.-Sls.--Astec America Inc., Carlsbad, CA; *Int'l*, pg. 93
Dudley, Steve, Exec. V.P.-Sls.--Rossignol Ski Co., Williston, VT; *Int'l*, pg. 1127
Duerst, Mark A., V.P.-Sls. & Mktg.--Hologic, Inc., Waltham, MA; *U.S. Public*, pg. 831
Dues, David L., V.P.-Sls.--Caldwell Tanks, Inc., Louisville, KY; *U.S. Private*, pg. 200
Duff, W.M., V.P.-Grocery Sls.--California & Hawaiian Sugar Company Inc., Crockett, CA; *U.S. Public*, pg. 39
Duffield, Albert W., Sr. V.P.-Sls.--PeopleSoft, Inc., Pleasanton, CA; *U.S. Public*, pg. 1276
Dufford, Eric, V.P.-Sls. & Mktg.--Quest Medical, Inc., Allen, TX; *U.S. Public*, pg. 1352
Duffus, Cheryl, Asst. V.P. & Mgr.-Mktg.--Pacific Capital Bancorp, Salinas, CA; *U.S. Public*, pg. 1247
Duffy, Brian, Mgr.-Sls.--Keystone New England Warehouse-Norwood, Norwood, MA; *U.S. Public*, pg. 955
Duffy, John, V.P.-Sls.--Mississippi Chemical Corporation, Yazoo City, MS; *U.S. Public*, pg. 1117
Duffy, Peter A., V.P.-Sls. & Mktg.--Haskel International, Inc., Burbank, CA; *U.S. Public*, pg. 798
Duffy, T.A., Dir.-Consumer Sls.--LePage's Limited, Brampton, Canada; *Int'l*, pg. 613
Duffy, Timothy B., V.P. & Gen. Mgr.-Europe/Md. Est./Af. Sls. & Srvc. Div.--PictureTel, Andover, MA; *U.S. Public*, pg. 1294
Dufour, Gaston, Dir.-Sls.--CANCOM, Westmount, Canada; *Int'l*, pg. 1482
Dufrene, Otis, V.P.-Sls. & Mktg.--The Crosby Group Inc., Tulsa, OK; *Int'l*, pg. 473
Dugan, Daniel R., Sr. V.P.-Worldwide Sls., Service & Mktg.--Acuson Corporation, Mountain View, CA; *U.S. Public*, pg. 18
Dugan, Dennis, Sr. V.P.-Sls. & Mktg.--Burns & Roe Enterprises, Inc., Oradell, NJ; *U.S. Private*, pg. 187
Dugan, Thomas P., Reg. Sls. Mgr.--Anaheim Manufacturing Company, Anaheim, CA; *U.S. Private*, pg. 70
Dugan, Vincent, V.P.-Project Mngmt.--Northern Telecom Inc., Rochester, NY; *Int'l*, pg. 970
Duggan, Dan, Dir.-Direct Sls.-Asia & North America--HMI Industries, Cleveland, OH; *U.S. Public*, pg. 771
Duggan, Michael, Pres.--Melard Manufacturing Corporation, Passaic, NJ; *U.S. Private*, pg. 729
Duggan, Paul, Dir.-Sls.--Sleepeezee Limited, London, United Kingdom; *Int'l*, pg. 1263
Duggan, Peter, Sr. V.P.-Sls. & Mktg.--Lance, Inc., Charlotte, NC; *U.S. Public*, pg. 977
Duitch, Nancy, Mgr.-Natl. Sls.--Kent & Spiegel Direct, Culver City, CA; *U.S. Private*, pg. 615
Duke, Ellen B., Dir.-Sls. & Mktg--Inamed Development Company, Carpinteria, CA; *U.S. Public*, pg. 873
Dull, William B., Dir.-Sls. & Mktg.--Tamura Corporation of America, Temecula, CA; *U.S. Private*, pg. 1067
Dullea, John, V.P.-Sls.--The Andrew Jergens Company, Cincinnati, OH; *Int'l*, pg. 717
DuMont, Robert, Mgr.-Spray Nozzles Sls.--Strahman Valves, Inc., Florham Park, NJ; *U.S. Private*, pg. 1046
Dunagan, C.E., V.P. Sls.--Shell Chemical Co., Houston, TX; *Int'l*, pg. 1136
Dunavant, John, V.P.-Domestic Sls.--Dunavant Enterprises, Inc., Memphis, TN; *U.S. Private*, pg. 346
Duncan, Andrew, Dir.-Mktg.--Van den Bergh Foods Ltd., Crawley, United Kingdom; *Int'l*, pg. 1434
Duncan, Gordon, V.P.-Sls. & Mktg.--LFE Industrial Systems Corporation, Clinton, MA; *U.S. Public*, pg. 1045
Duncan, Michael, Dir.-Mktg. & Sls.--Electro-Motive Division, La Grange, IL; *U.S. Public*, pg. 719
Duncheon, Charles S., Sr. V.P.-Mktg. & Sls.--Adept Technology, Inc., San Jose, CA; *U.S. Public*, pg. 19
Dunham, Mark, Sr. V.P.-Corporation--General Electric Investment Corp., Stamford, CT; *U.S. Public*, pg. 712
Dunkin, Eugene, V.P.-Sls. & Mktg.--Godiva Chocolatier, Inc., New York, NY; *U.S. Public*, pg. 299
Dunlap, Michael, Dir.-Mktg.--Suspa, Inc., Grand Rapids, MI; *Int'l*, pg. 1322
Dunlap, Steve, V.P.-Sls.--Sub-Zero Freezer Co., Inc., Madison, WI; *U.S. Private*, pg. 1048
Dunn, Bryan C., Chief Mktg. Officer & Sr. V.P.--The Western and Southern Life Insurance Company, Cincinnati, OH; *U.S. Private*, pg. 1164
Dunn, Daniel H., V.P.-Sls.-Midwest Region--Business Week, New York, NY; *U.S. Public*, pg. 1069
Dunn, George, Regional Mgr.-Omnitrac Sls. Div.--QUALCOMM, San Diego, CA; *U.S. Public*, pg. 1348
Dunn, Kevin, Natl. Sls. Mgr.--Quantum Sport, New York, NY; *U.S. Private*, pg. 900
Dunn, Mike, Sls. Mgr.--Mid-Western Nursery Division, Tahlequah, OK; *U.S. Private*, pg. 60
Dunn, Mike, V.P.-Natl. Sls. & Mktg--Watkins Manufacturing Corp./Hot Spring Portable Spas, Vista, CA; *U.S. Public*, pg. 1054
Dunn, William, V.P.-Sls. & Mktg.--Durable Specialties Division, Quakertown, PA; *U.S. Public*, pg. 620
Dunne, William, Dir.-Mktg. & Sls.--New Brunswick Scientific Co., Inc., Edison, NJ; *U.S. Public*, pg. 1169
Dunning, F.W., V.P.-Sls.--Shepard Niles, Inc., Montour Falls, NY; *U.S. Private*, pg. 992
Dunworth, Kevin, V.P.-Sls.--Trans Leasing International Inc., Northbrook, IL; *U.S. Public*, pg. 1628
Dupon, Yvan, Gen. Mgr.-Distribution Flanders--Electrabel S.A., Brussels, Belgium; *Int'l*, pg. 436
Dupont-Lauren, Randi, Dir.-Sls.--EMPI, Inc., Saint Paul, MN; *U.S. Public*, pg. 545
Dupont, Arnaud, Dir.-Asian Sls.--Chargeurs Fabrics, Paris, France; *Int'l*, pg. 280
Dupont, James, Mgr.-Sls.--Sani-Tech Inc., Lafayette, NJ; *U.S. Public*, pg. 1545
Duprez, Phillippe, Mgr.-Intl. Sls.--Swiss Army Brands, Inc., Shelton, CT; *U.S. Public*, pg. 1544
Dupuis, Rene-Jeam, Mgr.-Sls.--Calcia, Guerville, France; *Int'l*, pg. 292
Durgin, Harold, Dir.-Sls. & Mktg.--George T. Schmidt, Niles, IL; *U.S. Private*, pg. 970
Durkin, Pat, Natl. Sls. Mgr.-Wire--Thermo Electric Co., Inc., Saddle Brook, NJ; *U.S. Private*, pg. 1080
Durning, Ken, V.P.-Sls. & Mktg.--Galaxy Carpet Mills, Inc., Chatsworth, GA; *U.S. Public*, pg. 1121
Durrani, M., Mgr.-Adv. Sls.--Pakistan International Airlines Corporation, New York, NY; *Int'l*, pg. 1022
Durstberger, B., V.P.-Mktg. & Fin.--Treibacher Schleifmittel Corp., Niagara Falls, NY; *U.S. Private*, pg. 1099
Dust, Robert, Dir.-Sls.--Dow Corning S.T.I., Plymouth, MI; *U.S. Public*, pg. 523
Dustman, Tom, Mgr.-Abrasive Mktg.--Sunnen Products Company, Saint Louis, MO; *U.S. Private*, pg. 1053
Dutka, June, V.P.-Mktg. & Sls.--Bright Star Industries, Inc., Wilkes-Barre, PA; *U.S. Public*, pg. 1341
Duval, James F., V.P.-Designs Stores--Designs, Inc., Needham, MA; *U.S. Public*, pg. 501
DuVall, Dennis, V.P.-Sls.--The Instant Web Companies, Chanhassen, MN; *U.S. Private*, pg. 565
Duvalle, John, Mgr.-Natl. Sls./Pipe Div.--Wheatland Tube Company, Collingswood, NJ; *U.S. Private*, pg. 1170
Dvorak, Nick, Dir.-Mktg. & Sls.--Weather Tec Corporation, Fresno, CA; *U.S. Private*, pg. 1155
Dwiggins, L.K., Gen. Mgr.-Sls. & Service--Ford Parts and Service Div., Dearborn, MI; *U.S. Public*, pg. 662
Dwyer, Herb, V.P.-Sls. & Mktg.--Varity Zecal, Churchville, NY; *Int'l*, pg. 820
Dwyer, Robert, Mgr.-Sls.-Carolina Mtn. Retail--Mountain Valley Spring Company, Hot Springs National Park, AR; *U.S. Private*, pg. 963
Dyck, David L., V.P.-Sls., Western Reg.--Bindley Western Drug Company, Indianapolis, IN; *U.S. Public*, pg. 228
Dyckman, David, V.P.-Mktg. & Intl. Sls.--Veeder-Root Company, Simsbury, CT; *U.S. Public*, pg. 482
Dye, Cecil, Sr. V.P.-Worldwide Sls.--Network Computing Devices, Inc., Mountain View, CA; *U.S. Public*, pg. 1168
Dyer, Clarence, Mgr.-Gen. Sls.--Buccaneer Homes, Inc., Hamilton, AL; *U.S. Private*, pg. 318
Dynek, Robert, Mgr.-Sls.--General Drug Co., Chicago, IL; *U.S. Private*, pg. 1007
Dziomba, M., Dir.-Sls.--Organon Inc., West Orange, NJ; *Int'l*, pg. 48
Eaccarino, Lou, V.P.-Sls.--Natalie Knitting Mills, Chilhowie, VA; *U.S. Public*, pg. 779
Eaccarino, Lou, Exec. V.P.-Sls. & Mktg.--A.J. Brandon, Vernon, CA; *U.S. Public*, pg. 948
Eaccarino, Lou, Exec. V.P.-Sls.--Goodman Knitting Company, Brockton, MA; *U.S. Public*, pg. 948
Eades, Vincent, Sr. V.P.-Specialty Sls. & Mktg.--Starbucks Coffee Company, Seattle, WA; *U.S. Public*, pg. 1510
Eadie, Wayne, Dir.-Adv. Sls. & Adv. Res. & Devel.--The Reader's Digest Association, Inc., Pleasantville, NY; *U.S. Public*, pg. 1367
Eakin, Joe, Consultant-Sls. & Mktg.--Bassick by Kaspar, Shiner, TX; *U.S. Private*, pg. 122
Earhart, Ronald, Mgr.-Sales--Henderson Auctions, Livingston, LA; *U.S. Private*, pg. 577
Earl, Eric, Mgr.-Sls. & Mkt. Res.--Haviland Enterprises, Grand Rapids, MI; *U.S. Private*, pg. 511

Earle, Keith, Sales Mgr.--Dillard, A ResourceNet International Company, Chattanooga, TN; *U.S. Public*, pg. 902
Easley, Richard, Mgr.-Sls.--Trout-Blue Cheliau, Inc., Chelan, WA; *U.S. Private*, pg. 1105
Eason, Forrest K., V.P.-Sls.--Crown Cork & Seal, Southwest Div., Abilene, TX; *U.S. Public*, pg. 463
East, Bob, V.P.-Sls. & Mktg.--GSW Thermoplastics Company, Barrie, Canada; *Int'l*, pg. 538
East, Rick, V.P.-Sls. & Mktg.--Gerry Baby Products Company, Thornton, CO; *U.S. Private*, pg. 629
Eastep, Bob, V.P.-Intl. Sls.--BeefAmerica Operating Co., Inc., Omaha, NE; *U.S. Private*, pg. 130
Easter, Russ, Dir.-Circulation--The Advocate, Newark, OH; *U.S. Private*, pg. 23
Easterly, William, V.P.-Cloth, Bleach & Dyeing Sls.--Johnstown Knitting Mill Co., Johnstown, NY; *U.S. Private*, pg. 595
Easthope, Paul, V.P.-Mktg. & Sls.--ACCO Canada Inc., Willowdale, Canada; *U.S. Public*, pg. 674
Eaton, Charles, Sr. V.P.-Sls.--Shorewood Packaging Corporation, New York, NY; *U.S. Public*, pg. 1468
Ebbels, H.D., Mgr.-Sls.--CGTX Calgary Office, Calgary, Canada; *U.S. Public*, pg. 693
Ebeck, Bill, Mgr.-Reg. Sls. & Mktg.--Ivex Packaging Corporation-Grove City, Grove City, PA; *U.S. Public*, pg. 915
Eberhardt, John, V.P.-Mktg. & Sls.--Delta Faucet Corporation, Indianapolis, IN; *U.S. Public*, pg. 1053
Eberhardt, Josehp W., Jr., V.P.-Sls. & Mktg.--Sanford Beroc Corp., Brentwood, TN; *U.S. Public*, pg. 1178
Eberly, Ken, Dir.-Chain Product Sls.--Acco Chain & Lifting Products, York, PA; *Int'l*, pg. 473
Eberly, Rick, V.P.-Sls. & Mktg.--Meridian Diagnostics, Inc., Cincinnati, OH; *U.S. Public*, pg. 1094
Ebner, George, V.P.-Wholesale Sls.--Broan Mfg. Co., Inc., Hartford, WI; *U.S. Public*, pg. 1193
Ebnet, Paul, V.P.-Sls. & Mktg.--Stearns Manufacturing Company, Sauk Rapids, MN; *U.S. Public*, pg. 940
Ebron, James A., Exec. V.P.-Media Sls.--Black Entertainment Television Holdings Inc., Washington, DC; *U.S. Public*, pg. 235
Ebsen, Greg, Sr. V.P.-Sls. & Mktg.--J.R. Simplot Company Food Group, Boise, ID; *U.S. Private*, pg. 1002
Eccleston, Lou, Dir.-Sls.--Bloomberg L.P., New York, NY; *U.S. Private*, pg. 150
Echevarria, L.A., Mgr.-Sls.--Iberica de Crisoles S.A., Bilbao, Spain; *Int'l*, pg. 894
Echinger, Bernd, Dir.-Sls.--Bols Strothmann Brennereien GmbH & Co. KG, Nordrhein-Westfalen, Germany; *Int'l*, pg. 751
Echsner, T., V.P.-Sls.--CPC Baking Business, Bay Shore, NY; *U.S. Public*, pg. 224
Eck, James C., V.P.-Sls. & Service--Pomeroy Computer Resources, Hebron, KY; *U.S. Public*, pg. 1315
Eckard, Dalthard, Sr. V.P.-Sls. & Mktg.--The Berkline Corporation, Morristown, TN; *U.S. Private*, pg. 432
Eckel, Peter, Mgr.-Regional Sls.--Atlantic Cellular Telephone Corp., Westbrook, ME; *U.S. Public*, pg. 1708
Eckel, Peter, Mgr.-Reg. Sls.--Piscataqua Cellular Telephone Corp., Dover, NH; *U.S. Public*, pg. 1708
Eckerling, Heather, Dir.-Sls. & Adv.--Universal Overall Company, Chicago, IL; *U.S. Private*, pg. 1127
Eckerling, Sara, Dir.-Sls., Pur. & Adv.--Universal Overall Company, Chicago, IL; *U.S. Private*, pg. 1127
Eckert, Craig D., V.P.-Mktg. & Sls.--Century Telephone Enterprises, Inc., Monroe, LA; *U.S. Public*, pg. 329
Eckert, Pat, Sls. Sec.--Milwaukee Seasonings, Inc., Germantown, WI; *U.S. Public*, pg. 224
Eckert, Randy, Mgr.-Export Sls.--Stadelman Fruit L.L.C., Yakima, WA; *U.S. Private*, pg. 1028
Eckert, Steven, V.P.-Sls.--Winstar Global Products, Inc., Fairfield, NJ; *U.S. Public*, pg. 1772
Eckman, John, V.P.-U.S. Sls.--Vicon Industries, Inc., Hauppauge, NY; *U.S. Public*, pg. 1719
Eckman, John, V.P.-Sls.--Vicon Industries-Southern Inc., Norcross, GA; *U.S. Public*, pg. 1719
Eckstein, Helene, V.P.-Sls. & Mktg.--Prep - STAT/Spectrum, Franklin, KY; *U.S. Private*, pg. 882
Ecleberry, Ronald, V.P.-Sls. & Mktg.--Modern Welding Co., Inc., Owensboro, KY; *U.S. Private*, pg. 755
Eda, Shiro, Mng. Dir.-Sls.--Oji Paper Co., Ltd., Tokyo, Japan; *Int'l*, pg. 998
Eddy, Lane, Dir.-Sls.--Dekko Automotive Technologies Iowa Assemblies Div., Osceola, IA; *U.S. Private*, pg. 484
Edell, Dunnan, Sr. Exec. V.P.-Sls.--CCA Industries, Inc., East Rutherford, NJ; *U.S. Public*, pg. 276
Edgar, Jim, Dir.-Domestic Bus.--Marsh Company, Belleville, IL; *U.S. Private*, pg. 707
Edge, A.B., III, V.P.-Intl. Sls.--Columbus Mills, Inc., Columbus, GA; *U.S. Private*, pg. 256
Edgington, Kenen, Exec. V.P.-Sls. & Mktg.--The Wurlitzer Company, Loveland, OH; *U.S. Public*, pg. 169
Edgmon, Bob, Dir.-Sls. & Promo.--Hale-Halsell Company, Tulsa, OK; *U.S. Private*, pg. 494
Edinger, Carol, Mgr.-Retail Adv.--Coast to Coast--TruServ Corporation, Chicago, IL; *U.S. Private*, pg. 1108
Edington, B.D., V.P.-Sls. & Mktg.--Logo 7, Inc., Indianapolis, IN; *U.S. Public*, pg. 1644
Edison, E. Charles, III, Sr. V.P.-Sls.--Asymetrix Learning Systems, Inc., Bellevue, WA; *U.S. Private*, pg. 93
Edmon, Tord, Mgr.-Sls.--Lauderdale Computer AB, Stockholm, Sweden; *U.S. Public*, pg. 580
Edmonds, David B., V.P.-Sls.--Caliber System, Inc., Akron, OH; *U.S. Public*, pg. 604
Edoff, Kenneth, Sr. V.P.-Sls.--Cyrix Corporation, Richardson, TX; *U.S. Public*, pg. 1160
Edward, Linda, V.P.-Sls. & Mktg.--Kaufman and Broad Home Corporation, Los Angeles, CA; *U.S. Public*, pg. 944
Edwards, Allan L., V.P.-Sls. & Mktg.--Simpson Industries, Inc., Plymouth, MI; *U.S. Public*, pg. 1474
Edwards, Benjamin F., IV, Exec. V.P. & Dir.-Sls. & Mktg.--A.G. Edwards, Inc., Saint Louis, MO; *U.S. Public*, pg. 565
Edwards, Crystal, Mgr.-Circulation--Business Journals of North Carolina, LLC, Charlotte, NC; *U.S. Private*, pg. 19
Edwards, Jerry D., V.P.-Sls.--Boca Research Inc., Boca Raton, FL; *U.S. Public*, pg. 239
Edwards, Jessica, Mgr.-Sls.--West Virginia Cellular Telephone Corp., Huntington, WV; *U.S. Public*, pg. 1708
Edwards, Joe, V.P.-Sls.--The Promotion in Motion Companies, Closter, NJ; *U.S. Private*, pg. 890
Edwards, John J., Chief Oper. Officer & V.P.--Edwards Brothers, Inc., Ann Arbor, MI; *U.S. Private*, pg. 365
Edwards, Lee, Mgr.-Intl. Sls.--Schlosser Forge Company, Rancho Cucamonga, CA; *U.S. Private*, pg. 970
Edwards, Linda, V.P.-Sls. & Mktg.--Kaufman and Broad Coastal, Newport Beach, CA; *U.S. Public*, pg. 945
Edwards, Linda, V.P.-Sls. & Mktg.--Kaufman and Broad of San Diego, Inc., San Diego, CA; *U.S. Public*, pg. 945
Edwards, Ralph, Dir.-Sls.--Universal Construction Co., Huntsville, AL; *U.S. Public*, pg. 1646
Edwards, Robert D., Mgr.-Natl. Accounts, Sls.--Boise Cascade Timber & Wood Products Division, Boise, ID; *U.S. Public*, pg. 243
Edwards, Sandra, Mgr.-Sls.--KBAK-TV, Bakersfield, CA; *U.S. Private*, pg. 1170
Edwards, Steve, Mgr.-Natl. Sls.--Thermalloy, Inc., Farmers Branch, TX; *Int'l*, pg. 208
Efthymiou, Nicholas, V.P.-U.S. Sls. & Bus. Devel.--SCM Microsystems, Inc., Los Gatos, CA; *U.S. Public*, pg. 1417
Egan, John R., Exec. V.P.-Prods. & Offerings--EMC Corporation, Hopkinton, MA; *U.S. Public*, pg. 545
Egan, Peter, V.P.-Sls.--Frank Consolidated Enterprises Inc., Des Plaines, IL; *U.S. Private*, pg. 423
Egan, Robert F., V.P.-Distr. Sls.--Federal-Mogul Corporation, Southfield, MI; *U.S. Public*, pg. 615
Egan, Thomas F., V.P.-Mktg. & Sls.--Suprema Specialties, Inc., Paterson, NJ; *U.S. Public*, pg. 1541
Egan, Tom, V.P.-Sls.--Wolf Range Co., Compton, CA; *U.S. Public*, pg. 1322
Egeland, Arnold, Dir.-Sls. & Mktg.--Royal Olympic Cruises, New York, NY; *U.S. Public*, pg. 1411
Egerdahl, Jim, V.P.-N.A. Sls.--MTS Systems Corporation, Eden Prairie, MN; *U.S. Public*, pg. 1028
Egger, Anne M., V.P.-Sls.--Galderma Laboratories, Inc., Fort Worth, TX; *Int'l*, pg. 819
Eggerding, Charles R., V.P.-Sls./Automotive--QAD Inc, Carpinteria, CA; *U.S. Public*, pg. 1345
Egleston, Theodore, V.P.-Sls.--Clearing-Niagara, Buffalo, NY; *U.S. Private*, pg. 196
Eglinton, Dave, V.P.-Sls. & Mktg.--L.R. Nelson Corporation, Peoria, IL; *U.S. Private*, pg. 790
Eguchi, Mike, Natl. Sls. Mgr.--Fisher Broadcasting Inc., Seattle, WA; *U.S. Public*, pg. 648
Eherenfeldt, Gene, V.P.-Sls.--Ha-Lo Industries, Inc., Niles, IL; *U.S. Public*, pg. 773
Ehlers, Fred, Dir.-Sls.--Mazda Motor of America, Inc., Irvine, CA; *Int'l*, pg. 849
Ehrlich, Jay, V.P.-Sls. & Mktg.-Printing Equip.--Wisconsin Automated Machinery Corp., Oshkosh, WI; *U.S. Private*, pg. 1184
Ehrlich, R., Dir.-Mktg. & Sls.- Confectionery--Warner-Lambert K.K., Tokyo, Japan; *U.S. Public*, pg. 1739
Ehrlund, Ronald A., V.P.-Sls. & Mktg./Medical Equipment--Carsen Group Inc., Markham, Canada; *U.S. Public*, pg. 301
Eichenseer, Jeff, Dir.-Furniture Bus.--Conestoga Wood Specialties Corp., East Earl, PA; *U.S. Private*, pg. 262
Eichhorn, J.C., Sls. Dir.-Long Prods.--Hoogovens Ijmuiden Verkoopkantoor B.V., Ijmuiden, Netherlands; *Int'l*, pg. 754
Eichler, Larry, V.P.-Sls. & Mktg.--Prentiss Incorporated, Floral Park, NY; *U.S. Private*, pg. 882
Eickhoff, Dietrich, Div. Mgr.--Durkopp Adler AG, Bielefeld, Germany; *Int'l*, pg. 468
Eiler, R., Sr. V.P.-Mktg. & Sls.--GAB Robins North America, Inc., Parsippany, NJ; *Int'l*, pg. 1153
Einhauser, James G., Exec. V.P.-Sls. & Mktg.--Wigwam Mills, Inc., Sheboygan, WI; *U.S. Private*, pg. 1175
Einwalter, Pat, Mgr.-Fast/Lock Sls.--Deco Products Co., Decorah, IA; *U.S. Private*, pg. 320
Eisenberg, Alan I., V.P.-Sls. & Mktg.--Plymouth Rubber Company, Inc., Canton, MA; *U.S. Public*, pg. 1311
Eisenberg, David M., V.P.-Law, Mktg. & Sls.--Sprint Corporation, Westwood, KS; *U.S. Public*, pg. 1500
Eisenberg, Morton, V.P.-Sls.--Gould Paper Corporation, New York, NY; *U.S. Private*, pg. 466
Eisenbury, Wayne, Mgr.-Sls.--Apex Data, Fremont, CA; *U.S. Public*, pg. 1476
Eisenstein, Les, Sr. V.P.-Mdse. Sls.--Active International, Pearl River, NY; *U.S. Private*, pg. 15
Eitel, Dieter, Dir.-Comml.--Kermi GmbH, Plattling, Germany; *Int'l*, pg. 1069
Eitreim, Jeffrey D., V.P.-Sls. & Mktg.--MediVators, Inc., Eagan, MN; *U.S. Public*, pg. 301
Ek, Carl, Dir.-Sls. & Mktg.--Jonkopings Lantman Ek. For., Jonkoping, Sweden; *Int'l*, pg. 714
El-Haj, Ali, V.P.-Global Business Devel., Sls. & Engrng.--Casco Products Corporation, Bridgeport, CT; *U.S. Public*, pg. 1458
Elberg, Dale, Sr. V.P.-Sls. & Mktg.--Royal Oak Enterprises, Inc., Atlanta, GA; *U.S. Private*, pg. 948
Elefson, Matt, Mgr.-Sls.--L.G. Everist Inc., Sioux Falls, SD; *U.S. Private*, pg. 386
Elfenbein, Reed, V.P.-Sls. & Mktg./Scientific, Tech. & Medical Grp.--John Wiley & Sons, Inc., New York, NY; *U.S. Public*, pg. 1768
Elias, Antonio Fernando, Mgr.-Sls.--Aracruz Celulose S.A., Rio de Janeiro, Brazil; *Int'l*, pg. 78
Elias, William, Dir.-Mktg. & Sls.--Gehl Company, West Bend, WI; *U.S. Public*, pg. 704
Elison, Mike, Intl. Sls. Mgr.--Belshaw Brothers, Inc., Seattle, WA; *Int'l*, pg. 188
Ellen, Don, V.P.-Sls.--Peterson Farms, Decatur, AR; *U.S. Private*, pg. 857
Ellenberger, Richard G., Sr. V.P.-Worldwide Sls.--MCI Business Markets, Atlanta, GA; *U.S. Public*, pg. 1024
Ellenburg, Bob, Dir.-Comml. Sls.--Dunn-Edwards Corporation, Los Angeles, CA; *U.S. Private*, pg. 347
Ellens, Sherwin (Chuck), Pres.-Direct Sls. Worldwide--HMI Industries, Cleveland, OH; *U.S. Public*, pg. 771
Ellenwood, Chuck, V.P.-Sls.--John B. Sanfilippo & Son, Inc., Elk Grove Village, IL; *U.S. Public*, pg. 1431
Eller, Jay E., Mgr.-Mktg.--Twin City Die Castings Co., Minneapolis, MN; *U.S. Private*, pg. 1111
Ellington, Dennis, Projects Officer--Mason & Hanger Corporation, Inc., Lexington, KY; *U.S. Private*, pg. 711
Ellington, Steve, Mgr.-Natl. Sls.--Glen Raven Mills, Inc., Glen Raven, NC; *U.S. Private*, pg. 456
Elliot, Mike, V.P.-Sls.--Don Miguel Mexican Foods, Inc., Anaheim, CA; *U.S. Private*, pg. 339
Elliot, R., Mgr.-Sls.--AAH Pharmaceuticals Limited, Runcorn, United Kingdom; *Int'l*, pg. 591
Elliot, Simon, Dir.-Corp. Business Sls.--Toyota (Great Britain) Limited, Redhill, United Kingdom; *Int'l*, pg. 1414
Elliott, Bill, Dir.-Sls.--Portland General Electric Co., Portland, OR; *U.S. Public*, pg. 584
Elliott, Bill, Mgr.-Sls. & Fin.--Holiday RV Superstores West, Inc., Bakersfield, CA; *U.S. Public*, pg. 830
Elliott, Donald, Natl. Sls. Mgr.--Matec Corporation, Hopkinton, MA; *U.S. Public*, pg. 1056
Elliott, Gary L., V.P.-Mktg. & Sls.-Commodity Chemicals Grp.--Georgia Gulf Corporation, Atlanta, GA; *U.S. Public*, pg. 734
Elliott, Jay A., Sr. V.P.-Natl. Sls.--Jackson National Life Insurance Company, Lansing, MI; *Int'l*, pg. 1073
Elliott, Mark W., Gen. Mgr.-Worldwide Software Sls. & Mktg.--International Business Machines Corporation, Armonk, NY; *U.S. Public*, pg. 895
Elliott, Michael R., V.P.-Sls. & Mktg.--Strattec Securities Corporation, Milwaukee, WI; *U.S. Public*, pg. 1523
Elliott, Ray, Sls. Mgr.--Blaw-Knox Construction Equipment Corporation, Mattoon, IL; *U.S. Public*, pg. 877
Ellis, Gary P., V.P.-Sls. & Mktg.--Crenlo, Inc., Rochester, MN; *U.S. Private*, pg. 288
Ellis, James A., Sr. V.P.-Sls. & Service Div.--CVB Financial Corp., Ontario, CA; *U.S. Public*, pg. 286
Ellis, Robert, V.P.-Mktg.--Watson Wyatt Worldwide, Bethesda, MD; *U.S. Private*, pg. 1154
Ellis, Walter, Dir.-Mktg. & Sls.--SASIB Packaging North America, Skokie, IL; *Int'l*, pg. 1194
Ellison, William, Dir.-Energy Mngmt.--Superior Water, Light & Power Company, Superior, WI; *U.S. Public*, pg. 1116
Elmore, Nan, V.P.-Group Sls.--K-III Media Group, New York, NY; *U.S. Public*, pg. 1328
Elsmore, Mark A., Commercial Dir.--John Crane Mechanical Seals, Morton Grove, IL; *Int'l*, pg. 1339
Elsworth, Patty, Mgr.-Sls.--Shape Inc., Kennebunk, ME; *U.S.* Private, pg. 990
Elwell, Tom, Dir.-Sls.--Mizuno USA, Inc., Norcross, GA; *Int'l, pg. 885*
Emary, Don, V.P.-Sls.--Millstone Coffee, Inc., Everett, WA; *U.S. Public*, pg. 1331
Emerson, Dennis, Sr. V.P.-Sls.-West--Viacom Enterprises, New York, NY; *U.S. Private*, pg. 779
Emerson, John, V.P.-Sls.--Ocean Spray Cranberries, Inc., Middleboro, MA; *U.S. Private*, pg. 811
Emerson, Noel, Mgr.-Central Div.--Pearl Brewing Company, San Antonio, TX; *U.S. Private*, pg. 954
Emmerling, Paul E., V.P.-Sls., Mktg. & Gen. Mgr.--American Welding & Manufacturing Co., Warren, OH; *U.S. Private*, pg. 425
Emmons, Gary F., V.P.-Sls. & Mktg./Semiconductor Group--SpeedFan International, Inc., Chandler, AZ; *U.S. Public*, pg. 1497
Emory, Everett "Skip", Sls. Mgr.--Cone-Blanchard Machine Company, Windsor, VT; *U.S. Private*, pg. 262
Enck, Doug, V.P.-Sls.--Patcraft Commercial Carpet, Chatsworth, GA; *U.S. Private*, pg. 900
Endean, James, Dir.-Sls. & Mktg.--Uniflow Manufacturing Co., Erie, PA; *U.S. Private*, pg. 1117
Endean, James, Mgr.-Sls. & Mktg.--Kold Draft, Erie, PA; *U.S. Private*, pg. 1117
Eng, David, Sr. V.P.-Worldwide Sls.--C-COR Electronics, Inc., State College, PA; *U.S. Public*, pg. 272
Engan, Mike, V.P.-Sls. & Mktg.- Domestic--Miracle Recreation Equipment Company, Monett, MO; *U.S. Private*, pg. 752
Engel, Phil, V.P.-Sls. & Mktg.--Harcros Chemicals Inc., Kansas City, KS; *Int'l*, pg. 598
Engelbrecht, Ralfh, Natl. Sls. Mgr.--Clarion Corporation of America, Gardena, CA; *Int'l*, pg. 296
Engen, James, Dir.-Sls. & Mktg.--Acrometal Companies, Inc., Plymouth, MN; *U.S. Private*, pg. 14
Enger, Trond, V.P.-Sls. & Mktg.--Aquatic Animal Health, Oslo, Norway; *U.S. Public*, pg. 58
England, Don, V.P.-Intl. Sls.--PAR Technology Corporation, New Hartford, NY; *U.S. Public*, pg. 1256
England, Donald, V.P.-Sls. & Mktg.--PAR Microsystems Corporation, New Hartford, NY; *U.S. Public*, pg. 1256
Engle, Don, Mgr.-Sls.--The Mighty Ducks of Anaheim, Anaheim, CA; *U.S. Public*, pg. 513
Englebrecht, Chuck, Mgr.-Sls.--Hathaway Corporation, Littleton, CO; *U.S. Public*, pg. 798
Engler, Dan, Dir.-Branded Jobber Sls.--Ultramar Diamond Shamrock Corporation, San Antonio, TX; *U.S. Public*, pg. 1663
English, Kevin W., V.P.-Sls./Legal Information Services--LEXIS-NEXIS, Miamisburg, OH; *Int'l*, pg. 1096
Enkkela, Erkki, Dir.-Sls.--Finland Travel Bureau Ltd., Helsinki, Finland; *Int'l*, pg. 485
Ennamorato, Robert J., V.P.-Mktg. & Sls.--The Fibre-Metal Products Company, Concordville, PA; *U.S. Private*, pg. 402
Enos, Barry, Mgr.-Sls.--New Standard Corporation, Mount Joy, PA; *U.S. Private*, pg. 794
Enright, Robert, V.P.-Sls.--Cyborg Systems, Inc., Chicago, IL; *U.S. Private*, pg. 299
Enticknap, Chris, Dir.-Sls.--Facts on File News Services, New York, NY; *U.S. Public*, pg. 1327

Epley, Larry Jack, V.P. & Gen. Mgr.-Geschmay Wet Felts--Wangner Systems Corporation, Greenville, SC; *Int'l*, pg. 1418
Epperson, Craig, V.P.-Sls.--Raytheon Environmental Services Company, Houston, TX; *U.S. Public*, pg. 1366
Epps, Nick, Gen. Mgr.-Sls.--Alliance UniChem PLC, Chessington, United Kingdom; *Int'l*, pg. 57
Epstein, Andy, Mgr.-Sls., Bldg. & Devel.--Environment/One Corporation, Niskayuna, NY; *U.S. Public*, pg. 586
Epstein, Ronald M., Mgr.-Sls. & Mktg.--Halocarbon Products Corp., River Edge, NJ; *U.S. Private*, pg. 496
Erb, Pat, Sls. Promo.--Ralston Purina Company, Saint Louis, MO; *U.S. Public*, pg. 1359
Erbin, Mike, V.P.-Sls. & Mktg.--Gunnebo Fastening Corp., Lonoke, AR; *U.S. Private*, pg. 488
Erbland, Leslie, Mgr.-Sls.--Kaufman and Broad of Nevada, Inc., Las Vegas, NV; *U.S. Public*, pg. 945
Erickson, Bill, Sr. V.P. & Pres.-Americas--Medtronic, Inc., Minneapolis, MN; *U.S. Public*, pg. 1082
Erickson, Bob, Mgr.-Adv. & Pub. Rels.--Hennessy Industries, Inc., La Vergne, TN; *U.S. Public*, pg. 481
Erickson, D., Mgr.-Sls. & Retail Adv.--JC Penney Company, Inc., Plano, TX; *U.S. Public*, pg. 916
Erickson, James, Mgr.-Sls. & Cargo Mktg.--Kuwait Airways, Northeast Region, Jamaica, NY; *Int'l*, pg. 764
Ericson, Dennis, Mgr.-Sls.--Village Ford Inc., Dearborn, MI; *U.S. Private*, pg. 1140
Eriksmoen, Eric, V.P.-Program Mngmt. & Product Support--Menasco Aerospace Ltd., Oakville, Canada; *U.S. Public*, pg. 402
Erikson, Liz, V.P. & Natl. Dir.-Reg. Sls.--The Fairmont Hotels, San Francisco, CA; *U.S. Private*, pg. 391
Erins, Pete, Dir.-Sls.--Johanson Manufacturing Corporation, Boonton, NJ; *U.S. Private*, pg. 589
Erkenbrack, William, Mgr.-Western Div.--Harrington Hoists, Inc., Manheim, PA; *U.S. Private*, pg. 504
Erker, Charles F., Mgr.-Mktg. & Sls.--Commerce Bank, N.A., Clayton, MO; *U.S. Public*, pg. 409
Erler, Richard, V.P.-NAPA Sls. & Mktg.--Tenneco Automotive, Deerfield, IL; *U.S. Public*, pg. 1577
Ernst, Reinhard, Mgr.-Sls.--NUS Deutschland GmbH, Dusseldorf, Germany; *U.S. Private*, pg. 787
Ernsting, Kenneth W., Sr. V.P.-Sls. & Mktg.--Physician Computer Network, Inc., Morris Plains, NJ; *U.S. Public*, pg. 1293
Erol, Robert R., V.P.-Sls. & Mktg.-Commericial Prods. Div.--Reading Tube Corp., Reading, PA; *U.S. Private*, pg. 202
Erps, Patti, Mgr.-Natl. Acct.--Colony Paints, Kansas City, MO; *U.S. Public*, pg. 1707
Erridge, Ian, V.P.-Sls. & Mktg.--Blue Diamond Growers, Sacramento, CA; *U.S. Private*, pg. 152
Erskine, Ken J., Mgr.-Natl. Sls. & Mktg.--Precision Roll Grinders, Inc., Allentown, PA; *U.S. Private*, pg. 880
Ervin, J. Patrick, V.P.-Sls. & Mktg.--Hardings, Inc., Elmira, NY; *U.S. Private*, pg. 502
Ervin, Mike, V.P.-Sls. & Distr.--Hercules Engine Company, Canton, OH; *U.S. Private*, pg. 523
Erwin, Robert J., V.P. & Gen. Mgr.-Rohco Div.--McGean-Rohco, Inc., Cleveland, OH; *U.S. Private*, pg. 721
Escarra, Vicki, V.P.-Airport Customer Service--Delta Air Lines, Inc., Atlanta, GA; *U.S. Public*, pg. 497
Escue, Ronald F., V.P.-Sls.--Superior Industries International, Inc., Van Nuys, CA; *U.S. Public*, pg. 1539
Eshoo, Gilbert B., V.P.-Surfactant Sls.--Stepan Company, Northfield, IL; *U.S. Public*, pg. 1514
Eskelson, Randy J., V.P.-Sls. & Estimating--Schuff Steel Co., Phoenix, AZ; *U.S. Private*, pg. 973
Esplin, Brian, Mgr.-Natl. Sls. & Mktg.--Goodman Fielder Mills Ltd., Eastwood, Australia; *Int'l*, pg. 555
Esposito, John, Sr. V.P.-Sls.--Schieffelin & Somerset Co., New York, NY; *Int'l*, pg. 412
Esposito, Louis J., V.P.-Sls.--Roadway Express, Inc., Akron, OH; *U.S. Public*, pg. 1392
Esser, Patrick J., V.P.-Adv. Sls.--Cox Communications, Inc., Atlanta, GA; *U.S. Public*, pg. 454
Esser, R.W., V.P.-Sls.--Knouse Foods Inc., Peach Glen, PA; *U.S. Private*, pg. 627
Essex, J. Michael, V.P.-Sls.--Energy Absorption Systems, Inc., Chicago, IL; *U.S. Public*, pg. 1353
Essig, Barry, Mgr.-Sls.--Converter Power, Inc., Ipswich, MA; *U.S. Public*, pg. 856
Estrada, Mike, Sr. V.P.-Sls.--The Rockport Company, Marlborough, MA; *U.S. Public*, pg. 1370
Estrella, Mario, Natl. Sls. Mgr.--Rockford Acromatic Product Co., Rockford, IL; *U.S. Private*, pg. 938
Etheredge, Charles E., Sr. V.P.-Sls. & Mktg.--Lockwood Greene Engineers, Inc., Spartanburg, SC; *Int'l*, pg. 633
Ettelson, Stephen, V.P., Sec. & Mgr.-Natl. Sls.--Electro Brand, Inc., Chicago, IL; *U.S. Private*, pg. 368
Ettere, John, V.P.--Koch Otto H. York Co., Inc., Parsippany, NJ; *U.S. Private*, pg. 628
Etzweiler, Thomas I., Dir.-Intl. Sls.--WWF Paper Corporation, Bala Cynwyd, PA; *U.S. Private*, pg. 1145
Eugenio, Vincent, V.P.-Sls.--Gould Paper Corporation, New York, NY; *U.S. Private*, pg. 466
Eukovich, Robert, V.P.-Sls. & Mktg.--Pullman/Holt Corp., Tampa, FL; *U.S. Private*, pg. 1173
Euliss, Roger, V.P.-Sls.--MultiQuip, Inc., Carson, CA; *Int'l*, pg. 695
Euson, Gregory S., V.P. & Dir.-Sls.--Houghton Mifflin Trade & Reference Div., Boston, MA; *U.S. Public*, pg. 841
Evans, Bill, Dir.-Sls. & Mktg./Foodservice--Beatrice Cheese Co., Waukesha, WI; *U.S. Public*, pg. 426
Evans, Bob, V.P.-Sls.--Meto, USA, Morris Plains, NJ; *Int'l*, pg. 460
Evans, Bob, Dir.-Sls.--KOB-TV, Inc., Albuquerque, NM; *U.S. Private*, pg. 544
Evans, Bryan D., V.P.-Mktg.--Terra Nitrogen Company, L.P., Tulsa, OK; *U.S. Public*, pg. 1581
Evans, David, Mgr.-Sls.-Composite Prod. Machinery--CAE Machinery Ltd., Vancouver, Canada; *Int'l*, pg. 237
Evans, David, V.P.-Sls.--Westin Hotels & Resorts, Seattle, WA; *U.S. Public*, pg. 1512
Evans, Doug, Mgr.-Sls. & Mktg.--Perstorp Analytical Inc., Silver Spring, MD; *Int'l*, pg. 1039
Evans, G., V.P.-Sls. & Mktg.--Waukesha Foundry Inc., Waukesha, WI; *U.S. Private*, pg. 1154
Evans, Gary, V.P.-Sls.--Grocers Baking Co., Grand Rapids, MI; *U.S. Private*, pg. 482
Evans, Gaylen, Dir.-Domestic Sls.--Harris Corp. Broadcast Div., Quincy, IL; *U.S. Public*, pg. 791
Evans, Jim, Sr. V.P.-Sls.--Hyatt Hotels Corporation, Chicago, IL; *U.S. Private*, pg. 551
Evans, John, Jr., V.P.-Sls.--Gold Medal Products Co., Cincinnati, OH; *U.S. Private*, pg. 459
Evans, Kenneth M., V.P.-Sls. & Mktg.--Waste Management, Inc., Oak Brook, IL; *U.S. Public*, pg. 1744
Evans, Michael, V.P.-Sls. & Mktg.--Kikkoman International, Inc., San Francisco, CA; *Int'l*, pg. 733
Evans, Michael, Mgr.-Sales--Raybestos Aftermarket Products Co., Crawfordsville, IN; *U.S. Public*, pg. 1363
Evans, R.M., V.P.-Sls. & Service--Medrad, Inc., Indianola, PA; *Int'l*, pg. 1204
Evans, Ron, Gen. Mgr.-Sls.--Homestead Homes, Cordele, GA; *U.S. Public*, pg. 318
Evans, Steve, V.P.-Sls.--Perdue Farms Incorporated, Salisbury, MD; *U.S. Private*, pg. 852
Evans, Tom, Natl. Sls. Mgr.--Eager Beaver, Lake Wales, FL; *U.S. Private*, pg. 354
Evans, William, V.P. & Dir.-Sls.--Overland Transportation System, Inc., Indianapolis, IN; *Int'l*, pg. 1469
Evansky, Bebe, Sls. Mgr.-Supplies--Brodart Company, Williamsport, PA; *U.S. Private*, pg. 170
Evelyn, W.D., Dir.-Sls.--Coats Natal Thread, Natal, South Africa; *Int'l*, pg. 300
Everett, B., Mgr.-Natl. Sls.--Northern Rock PLC, Newcastle upon Tyne, United Kingdom; *Int'l*, pg. 968
Everett, D., Mgr.-Sls. & Mktg.--Ensign-Bickford, Bromhof, South Africa; *Int'l*, pg. 1196
Everett, Jim, V.P.-Regional Sls. Mgr.--Fruit of the Loom, Inc., Chicago, IL; *U.S. Public*, pg. 685
Eves, Brian, Gen. Mgr.--Hussmann Store Equipment Limited, Brantford, Canada; *U.S. Public*, pg. 1766
Ewald, Jessica, Mgr.-Mktg.--Plastag Corporation, Elk Grove Village, IL; *U.S. Private*, pg. 870
Ewert, Phillip B., Mgr.-Sls./Western Div.--The Ohio Art Company, Inc., Bryan, OH; *U.S. Public*, pg. 1214
Ewing, Robert, Sls. Mgr.--Faraday, Inc., Tecumseh, MI; *Int'l*, pg. 1246
Eyck, Linda Ten, V.P.-Sls.--Orlane, Inc., New York, NY; *Int'l*, pg. 1011
Eyre, Alvin, Mgr.-Sales & Mktg.--Carbone of America, Ultra Carbon Div., Bay City, MI; *Int'l*, pg. 1028
Eyre, Dennis, Dir.-Intl. Sls.--Ballard Medical Products, Draper, UT; *U.S. Public*, pg. 171
Ezcurra, Gus, V.P.-Worldwide Sls.--Harris Corp. Broadcast Div., Quincy, IL; *U.S. Public*, pg. 791
Ezell, Mark, Sr. V.P.-Sls. & Mktg.--Purity Dairies Inc., Nashville, TN; *U.S. Private*, pg. 895
Fabian, Bud, V.P.-Sls. & Mktg.--Everett Charles Technologies, Pomona, CA; *U.S. Private*, pg. 386
Fabrega, Jorge Grasa, Mgr.-Sls.--Agropecuaria de Guissona, S. Coop. Ltda., Guisona, Spain; *Int'l*, pg. 31
Faccenda, Ian, Dir.-Sls.--Hitchcock Chair Company LTD, New Hartford, CT; *U.S. Private*, pg. 531
Fachet, Greg, V.P.-Sls. & Mktg.--Steiner Co., Inc., Chicago, IL; *U.S. Private*, pg. 1039
Facione, Jan, V.P.-Boston Trading Co.--Designs, Inc., Needham, MA; *U.S. Public*, pg. 501
Fadler, Steve, V.P.-Sls.--Litton Systems, Inc. Advanced Circuitry Div., Springfield, MO; *U.S. Public*, pg. 1003
Fagan, Kenneth, V.P.-Mktg. & Sls.--Fone America, Inc., Portland, OR; *U.S. Public*, pg. 661
Fahey, Jack, V.P.-Sls. & Mktg.--Temco Fireplace Products, Inc., Nashville, TN; *U.S. Public*, pg. 1576
Fahlgren, Jim, Mgr.-Sls.--Economy Folding Box Corp., Chicago, IL; *U.S. Private*, pg. 362
Faigh, Larry, Wholesale Sls.--Staodyn Inc., Longmont, CO; *U.S. Public*, pg. 1509
Fain, John W., Sr. V.P.-Mktg. & Sls.--Overnite Transportation Co., Richmond, VA; *U.S. Public*, pg. 1668
Fair, Roger, V.P.-Sls. & Engrng.--Western States Machine Company, Hamilton, OH; *U.S. Private*, pg. 1168
Fairchild, Bob, Multiwall Regional Sls. Mgr.--Industrial Bag Division - Jacksonville Plant, Jacksonville, AR; *U.S. Public*, pg. 1521
Fairchild, Mel, Mgr.-Sls.--Southco Distributing Company, Goldsboro, NC; *U.S. Private*, pg. 1014
Fairfax, Barry, V.P.-Sls. & Mktg.--Red Ball Corporation, Seattle, WA; *U.S. Private*, pg. 97
Fairleigh, Kenneth F., V.P.-Sls.--Square D Company, Palatine, IL; *Int'l*, pg. 1208
Fairlie, Graeme, V.P.-Sls. & Mktg.--Deposition Technologies, Inc., San Diego, CA; *U.S. Public*, pg. 1056
Falander, Tom, V.P.-Sls.--Philip Metals/Steiner-Liff, Nashville, TN; *Int'l*, pg. 1050
Falcone, John C., V.P.-Sls. & Mktg.--Sennheiser Electronic Corp., Old Lyme, CT; *U.S. Private*, pg. 984
Falduto, Dennis, V.P.-Sls.--Amco Folding Cartons, Inc., Towaco, NJ; *U.S. Private*, pg. 48
Falduto, James M., Exec. V.P.-Sls. & Mktg.--Wilton Corporation, Palatine, IL; *U.S. Private*, pg. 1181
Falk, Jim, Reg. Sls. Mgr.--Just Born, Inc., Bethlehem, PA; *U.S. Private*, pg. 602
Fall, David, Sr. V.P.-Sls.--Eversharp Pen Co., Franklin Park, IL; *U.S. Private*, pg. 386
Fallaway, Doug, Mgr.-Sls., Worldwide--Applied Microsystems Corporation, Redmond, WA; *U.S. Public*, pg. 123
Fallon, James N., Dir.-Mktg. Communications & Adv.--ITW Signode, Glenview, IL; *U.S. Public*, pg. 867
Fallon, John, Dir.-Mktg. & Sls.--Westronics, Inc., Kingwood, TX; *U.S. Public*, pg. 1593
Fallot, John, V.P.-Mktg. & Sls.--Mercer Transportation Co., Louisville, KY; *U.S. Private*, pg. 732
Fallow, Rod, V.P.-Sls. & Mktg.--Swagelok Company, Solon, OH; *U.S. Private*, pg. 1057
Falls, James K., V.P.-Sls. & Mktg.--Sealing Equipment Products Co., Inc., Pelham, AL; *U.S. Private*, pg. 978
Famighette, Joe, V.P.-Sls./Inacom Communications--Inacom Corp., Omaha, NE; *U.S. Public*, pg. 873
Famighette, Joseph, V.P.-Maritime Sls.--COMSAT Mobile Communications, Clarksburg, MD; *U.S. Public*, pg. 424
Fancher, David, V.P.-Mktg. & Sls.--The Cooper Companies, Inc., Irvine, CA; *U.S. Public*, pg. 442
Fantozzi, George V., Dir.-Power Systems Services--S & C Electric Company, Chicago, IL; *U.S. Private*, pg. 954
Farber, Bernard, Sr. V.P.-Sls. & Mdsg.--West Mill Clothes, Inc., Woodside, NY; *U.S. Private*, pg. 1163
Farber, Gerald, Mgr.-Sls.--PP&L Resources, Allentown, PA; *U.S. Public*, pg. 1244
Farerinto, M., Sls.--Key Container Corporation, Pawtucket, RI; *U.S. Private*, pg. 617
Farid, Ted, V.P.-Domestic Bus. Jet Sls.--Raytheon Aircraft Company, Wichita, KS; *U.S. Public*, pg. 1365
Farkas, Scott, Mgr.-Sls.--WPTF, Raleigh, NC; *U.S. Private*, pg. 298
Farland, Jim, V.P.-Sls. & Mktg.--UnionTools, Inc., Columbus, OH; *U.S. Public*, pg. 17
Farley, Jim, Mgr.-Natl. Sls.-Ice Cream--Solon Manufacturing Company, Solon, ME; *U.S. Private*, pg. 1013
Farley, Kevin, Sr. Mgr.-Sls.--Comair Holdings, Inc., Erlanger, KY; *U.S. Public*, pg. 406
Farley, Robert, V.P.-Magazines--Publishers Clearing House, Port Washington, NY; *U.S. Private*, pg. 893
Farley, Terry, V.P.-Sls.--The Echo Design Group, Inc., New York, NY; *U.S. Private*, pg. 359
Farmer, Ralph L., Sr. V.P. & Mgr.-Natl. Sls.--Arandell Corporation, Menomonee Falls, WI; *U.S. Private*, pg. 79
Farmer, Tony, Mgr.-Sls. & Mktg./UK & Ireland--Transnet Group, London, United Kingdom; *Int'l*, pg. 1418
Farmer, Wiliam A., Gen. Mgr.-Sls. & Service--Oldsmobile Div. General Motors Corp., Lansing, MI; *U.S. Public*, pg. 720
Farnan, James R., Mgr.-Reg. Sls.--Automotive News, Detroit, MI; *U.S. Private*, pg. 284
Farqulav, James D., Sls. Mgr.--Elkem Sales & Marketing Service, Hamilton, Canada; *Int'l*, pg. 448
Farrell, Dan, V.P.-Corp. Sls.--St. Louis National Baseball Club L.P., Saint Louis, MO; *U.S. Private*, pg. 961
Farrell, James, V.P.-Sls.--House of Bianchi, Inc., Medford, MA; *U.S. Private*, pg. 541
Farrell, Kevin, V.P.-Sls.--Sechrist Industries, Inc., Anaheim, CA; *U.S. Private*, pg. 980
Farrell, Moira, Sr. V.P.-Corp. Res. & Sls. Mktg.--King World Productions, Inc., New York, NY; *U.S. Public*, pg. 961
Farrell, Moira, Sr. V.P.-Corp. Res. & Sls. Mktg.--King World Productions, Los Angeles, CA; *U.S. Public*, pg. 961
Farris, Michael G., V.P.-Sls. & Mktg.--MW Manufacturers Inc., Rocky Mount, VA; *Int'l*, pg. 593
Farrow, B.D., Dir.-Sls.--NETG Limited, London, United Kingdom; *U.S. Public*, pg. 784
Farwell, W.R.T., Mgr.-Sls.--Ultra Electronics Ocean Systems, Weymouth, United Kingdom; *Int'l*, pg. 1431
Fasano, Tony, V.P.-Sls.--Bridgeport Fittings, Inc., Stratford, CT; *U.S. Private*, pg. 168
Fasbender, David J., Sr. V.P.-Sls.--Smead Manufacturing Company, Hastings, MN; *U.S. Private*, pg. 1006
Fasola, Kenneth J., V.P. & Mgr.-Natl. Sls.--Humana Inc., Louisville, KY; *U.S. Public*, pg. 847
Fasola, Kenneth J., V.P.-Sls.--Humana Wisconsin Health Organization Insurance Corporation, Milwaukee, WI; *U.S. Public*, pg. 848
Fasorile, Tom, Exec. V.P.-Sls.--Bulova Corporation, Woodside, NY; *U.S. Public*, pg. 1010
Fass, Stan, Exec. V.P.-Sls.--Elgin Watch Company, Long Island City, NY; *U.S. Private*, pg. 371
Faubel, Wil, V.P.-Mktg. & Sls.--Hughes Christensen, Houston, TX; *U.S. Public*, pg. 166
Faulkner, J. Ross, V.P.-Sls.--Continental Electronics Corporation, Dallas, TX; *U.S. Public*, pg. 1563
Faulkner, Laurence, Exec. V.P.-Equity Trading & Sls.--Fidelity Investments (FMR Corp.), Boston, MA; *U.S. Private*, pg. 402
Faunce, David B., Jr., V.P.-Adv., Sls. & Mktg.--Mauney Hosiery Mills, Inc., Kings Mountain, NC; *U.S. Private*, pg. 715
Faunce, William, V.P.-Sls.--Western Interactive Media, Los Angeles, CA; *U.S. Private*, pg. 1166
Faura, Joaquin, Mgr.-Sls. & Mktg.--Tabacalera, S.A., Madrid, Spain; *Int'l*, pg. 1345
Faust, Heather, V.P. & Mgr.-Midwest Sls.--Parade Publications Inc., New York, NY; *U.S. Private*, pg. 20
Favazza, Steve, V.P.-Sls./Northern Div.--Schmidt Baking Co., Inc., Baltimore, MD; *U.S. Private*, pg. 970
Favell, G., Dir.-Sls.--Magnet Ltd., Keighley, United Kingdom; *Int'l*, pg. 188
Fawcett, Georgia, Dir.-Natl. Sls.--Riddell Sports, Inc., New York, NY; *U.S. Public*, pg. 1389
Fawcett, Scott, Sr. V.P.-Sls. & Mktg.--Springs Window Fashions Division, Middleton, WI; *U.S. Public*, pg. 1500
Faxon, Scott, Mgr.-Sls.--TIE Systems Georgia, Norcross, GA; *U.S. Private*, pg. 1085
Faxton, Wayne, V.P.-Sls.--Tri-State Motor Transit Co., Joplin, MO; *U.S. Private*, pg. 1101
Fay, Joseph, Mgr.-Sls.--Herlin Press Inc., West Haven, CT; *U.S. Private*, pg. 524
Fay, Peter, V.P.-N.E. Area--Borden Foods Co., Littleton, MA; *U.S. Private*, pg. 158
Fazel, Eddie, Dir.-Sls.--United Distillers USA, Inc., Stamford, CT; *Int'l*, pg. 412
Fazio, Gary, V.P.-Sls.--Sealy Corporation, Cleveland, OH; *U.S. Private*, pg. 978
Fazzari, Anthony, Sr. V.P.-Retail Mktg. & Sls.--Chock Full O' Nuts Corporation, New York, NY; *U.S. Public*, pg. 351
Fazzini, Christopher A., V.P.-Sls. & Mktg.--Reliance Standard Life Insurance Company, Philadelphia, PA; *U.S. Public*, pg. 496
Fazzio, Gary, Dir.-N. CA Sls.--Dunn-Edwards Corporation, Los Angeles, CA; *U.S. Private*, pg. 347

Fea, Gregory, V.P. & Mgr.-Bus. Unit-Evian Water--Great Brands of Europe, Stamford, CT; *Int'l*, pg. 381
Feagin, Alan W., Sr. V.P.-Sls.--United Family Life Insurance Co., Atlanta, GA; *Int'l*, pg. 499
Federico, Nick, V.P.-Sls. & Gen. Mgr.--Blue Coral/Slick 50, Cleveland, OH; *U.S. Public*, pg. 1348
Federle, Mike, Dir.-Adv. & Sls.--Fortune, New York, NY; *U.S. Public*, pg. 1613
Fedock, Paul, Reg. Sls. Mgr.-Relays--Aromat Mid Atlantic Sales, New Providence, NJ; *Int'l*, pg. 848
Fee, James P., Jr., V.P.-Sls. & Mktg.--Protocol Systems, Inc., Beaverton, OR; *U.S. Public*, pg. 1336
Feely, E.P., Jr., Sls./Service Mgr.-Field--Chevrolet Motor Div. General Motors Corp., Warren, MI; *U.S. Public*, pg. 720
Feely, M., V.P.-Sls.--ECP Incorporated, Westchester, IL; *U.S. Private*, pg. 313
Fegely, Glenn, Dir.-Forging Sls.--Ellwood City Forge, Ellwood City, PA; *U.S. Private*, pg. 294
Fehlig, Kenneth L., V.P.-Sls. & Mktg.--Lincoln Automotive, Saint Louis, MO; *U.S. Public*, pg. 1273
Feiereisen, Lee E., V.P.-Sls. & Mktg.--Independent Metals, Germantown, WI; *U.S. Private*, pg. 559
Fein, Mason, Mgr.-Natl. Sls.--Mountain Optech Inc., Boulder, CO; *U.S. Private*, pg. 862
Feit, Saul, V.P.-Natl. Sls.--Sun Hill Industries, Inc., Stamford, CT; *U.S. Private*, pg. 1051
Feldman, Don, V.P.-Sls.--Evy Of California, Inc., Los Angeles, CA; *U.S. Private*, pg. 387
Feldman, Paul, Sr. V.P.-Sls.--Duro Bag Manufacturing Co., Ludlow, KY; *U.S. Private*, pg. 348
Feldman, Trudy, Exec. V.P.-Sls.--Careers USA Inc., Philadelphia, PA; *U.S. Private*, pg. 209
Feldsine, Bill, Mgr.-Sls.--Nucor Bearing Products, Inc., Wilson, NC; *U.S. Public*, pg. 1206
Feldstein, Philip, V.P.-Sls.--Gould Paper Corporation, New York, NY; *U.S. Private*, pg. 466
Felmus, Ron, V.P.-Corporations--General Electric Investment Corp., Stamford, CT; *U.S. Public*, pg. 712
Femmel, Jack, Dir.-Sls.--Simpson Electric Co., Elgin, IL; *U.S. Private*, pg. 1002
Fensterhem, B., V.P.-Sls.--React Magazine, New York, NY; *U.S. Private*, pg. 20
Fentress, Mike, Dir.-Sls.--News & Record, Greensboro, NC; *U.S. Private*, pg. 649
Fenwick, James, V.P.-Sls.--Ohmeda, Liberty Corner, NJ; *Int'l*, pg. 121
Fenwick, Robert, Sr. V.P.-Sls. & Mktg.--Vital Signs, Englewood, CO; *U.S. Public*, pg. 1723
Ferber, Marlene, V.P.-Sls.--LCS Industries, Inc., Clifton, NJ; *U.S. Public*, pg. 970
Ferbert, Dal, Mgr.-Sls./Power Fuse--Littelfuse, Inc., Des Plaines, IL; *U.S. Public*, pg. 1001
Ferdinand, Bob, Mgr.-Reg. Sls. East--WINCO, Le Center, MN; *U.S. Private*, pg. 350
Fererro, Jim, Area Sls. Rep.--Production Operators, Inc. (Denver Office), Englewood, CO; *U.S. Public*, pg. 298
Ferguson, Bob, V.P.-Sls. & Mktg.--Setco, Cincinnati, OH; *U.S. Private*, pg. 987
Ferguson, Donald J., Exec. V.P.-Sls. & Mktg.--Intermatic Inc., Spring Grove, IL; *U.S. Private*, pg. 567
Ferguson, Hugh C., Exec. V.P.-Sls. & Mktg.--Fayette Tubular Products, Troy, MI; *U.S. Public*, pg. 481
Ferguson, Jane, Adv. Sls.--Sky Network Television Limited, Auckland, New Zealand; *U.S. Public*, pg. 204
Ferguson, Larry J., V.P.-Sls. & Mktg.--Master Molded Products Corporation, Elgin, IL; *U.S. Private*, pg. 714
Ferguson, N., V.P.-Sls. & Mktg.-Furnaces--Italimpianti of America, Incorporated, Coraopolis, PA; *Int'l*, pg. 655
Ferguson, Norman T., V.P.-Sls. & Tech.--Itam Tech Italimplianti, Inc., Coraopolis, PA; *Int'l*, pg. 655
Ferguson, Scott, Gen. Mgr.-Sls.--Illinois Auto Electric Midwest Engine Warehouse Div., Elmhurst, IL; *U.S. Private*, pg. 558
Ferin, Roberto, V.P.-Intl. Sls.--Banfi Vintners, Old Brookville, NY; *U.S. Private*, pg. 113
Ferland, Richard, Sls. Mgr.-National Contract--Peerless Carpet Corporation, Acton Vale, Canada; *Int'l*, pg. 1032
Fernald, Peter, Mgr.-Reg. Sls.--Global Beverage Co., Rochester, NY; *U.S. Private*, pg. 457
Fernandez, A., Comml. Dir.--Revlon, S.A., Madrid, Spain; *U.S. Private*, pg. 690
Fernandez, Aurelio E., Sr. V.P.-Worldwide Sls.--EXAR Corporation, Fremont, CA; *U.S. Public*, pg. 597
Fernandez, Joe, Natl. Sls. Mgr.--GSW Jackes-Evans Manufacturing Co., Saint Louis, MO; *Int'l*, pg. 538
Ferraco, Mark, Mgr.-Sls., Brdcst. & Promo.--Pittsburgh Pirates, Pittsburgh, PA; *U.S. Private*, pg. 867
Ferrand, Brian, V.P.-Sls.--Merit Medical Systems, Inc., South Jordan, UT; *U.S. Public*, pg. 1096
Ferrans, Kristine, Mgr.-Mktg. & Sls.--Copperweld Fayetteville Division, Fayetteville, TN; *Int'l*, pg. 662
Ferrans, Kristine, Mgr.-Sls. & Mktg.--Copperweld Chicago Division, Chicago, IL; *Int'l*, pg. 662
Ferrans, Kristine, Mgr.-Sls. & Mktg.--Copperweld Miami Division, Piqua, OH; *Int'l*, pg. 662
Ferrante, Frank, Exec. V.P.-Sls.--Farmland Dairies, Wallington, NJ; *U.S. Private*, pg. 395
Ferreira, Jose Wagner, Gen. Mgr.-Sls.--Viacao Aerea Sao Paulo S.A. (VASP), Sao Paulo, Brazil; *Int'l*, pg. 1464
Ferrell, Edson, V.P.-Sls.--Nicholas Paper, Inc., Fitchburg, MA; *U.S. Private*, pg. 798
Ferrer, R., V.P.-Sls.--Best Foods Caribbean, Inc., Santurce, PR; *U.S. Public*, pg. 224
Ferrino, David, Dir.-Natl. Sls. & Mktg.--Joseph Huber Brewing Co., Inc., Monroe, WI; *U.S. Private*, pg. 545
Ferris, Gerald P., Mgr.-Gen. Sls. & Mktg.--Boston Gear, Quincy, MA; *U.S. Public*, pg. 857
Ferrise, Sam, II, V.P.-Sls. & Mktg.--Bandag, Incorporated, Muscatine, IA; *U.S. Public*, pg. 177
Ferron, Brian, V.P.-Sls.--Lancaster Colony Automotive Group, Dublin, OH; *U.S. Public*, pg. 977
Ferry, William E., Vice Chm.-Sls.--Lands' End, Inc., Dodgeville, WI; *U.S. Public*, pg. 977
Fertig, Jay, V.P.-Sls.--Atlantic Gulf Communities Corporation, Miami, FL; *U.S. Public*, pg. 144
Fervan, Douglas J., Product Mgr.-Sls.--Saint-Gobain Advanced Materials Corporation, Louisville, KY; *Int'l*, pg. 1173
Fetner, W. Ted, V.P.-Natl. Accts.--Yorktowne, Inc., Red Lion, PA; *U.S. Private*, pg. 1196
Ficken, Bill, Sr. V.P.-Sls. & Mktg.--Gerber Plumbing Fixtures Corporation, Chicago, IL; *U.S. Private*, pg. 449
Ficklin, Wade, Mgr.-Industrial Sls.--George Koch Sons, Inc., Evansville, IN; *U.S. Private*, pg. 628
Fieber, V., Mgr.-Sls.--Morgan Thermal Ceramics GmbH, Wiesbaden, Germany; *Int'l*, pg. 894
Fiebiger, Ray, V.P.-Mktg. & Sls.--Laserscope Surgical Systems, San Jose, CA; *U.S. Public*, pg. 979
Fiedler, Eric W., V.P.-Sls. & Mktg.--Crown Fence Co., Long Beach, CA; *U.S. Private*, pg. 292
Field, David, V.P.-Sls. & Mktg.--Trendway Corporation, Holland, MI; *U.S. Private*, pg. 1099
Field, Gerry, V.P.-Sls.--Transnational Motors Inc., Grand Rapids, MI; *U.S. Private*, pg. 1097
Field, Mike, V.P.-Sls.--The Disston Co., Greensboro, NC; *U.S. Public*, pg. 950
Fielding, Bob, Mgr.-Sls.--PENCO-Tennessee, Nashville, TN; *Int'l*, pg. 1508
Fields, Larry, Regional Mgr.-Northwest--Columbus Mills, Inc., Columbus, GA; *U.S. Private*, pg. 256
Fieler, Tony, V.P.-Sls. & Mktg.--Lucas Body Systems - North America, Winona, MN; *Int'l*, pg. 820
Fieweger, Tom E., III, Mgr.-Sls.--American Flow Control, Birmingham, AL; *U.S. Private*, pg. 52
Fife, Michael, Exec. V.P.--Fairfax Lumber & Millwork Company Inc., Springfield, VA; *U.S. Private*, pg. 391
Figg, Marjorie, Mgr.-Mktg.--Georg Fischer Disa, Inc., Holly, MI; *Int'l*, pg. 490
Figueras, Armand, Sr. V.P.-Sls. & Mktg.--M. Kamenstein, Inc., Elmsford, NY; *U.S. Private*, pg. 606
Figuerelli, Thomas, V.P.-Sls., Oral Health Care Div.--Block Drug Company, Inc., Jersey City, NJ; *U.S. Public*, pg. 236
Filho, Cesar M., Mgr.-Timberland Sls.--Sao Paulo Alpargatas S.A., Sao Paulo, Brazil; *Int'l*, pg. 1193
Filiault, Robert, V.P.-Worldwide Sls.--California Micro Devices, Milpitas, CA; *U.S. Public*, pg. 293
Filippelli, Pete, V.P.-Sls.--Eli's Cheese Cake Company, Chicago, IL; *U.S. Private*, pg. 371
Filippi, Dario T., Mgr.-Sls.--NUS Italia, s.r.l., Milan, Italy; *U.S. Private*, pg. 787
Filkins, Dick, Mgr.-Sls.--Admiral Heintz, Inc., Wadsworth, OH; *U.S. Public*, pg. 1143
Filoukatjis, Michael, V.P.-Sls.--Gould Paper Corporation, New York, NY; *U.S. Private*, pg. 466
Finch, Jeff, V.P.-Sls. & Mktg., Aeroquip--Aeroquip-Vickers, Inc., Maumee, OH; *U.S. Public*, pg. 24
Finch, Jeri, V.P.-North America MVSO Sls.--Aurora Electronics, Inc., Irvine, CA; *U.S. Public*, pg. 147
Finch, Sam, Mgr.-Sls.--Seward Inc., Petersburg, VA; *U.S. Private*, pg. 988
Fine, Jay, Chief Oper. Officer & Exec. V.P.--Fort Lock Corporation, River Grove, IL; *U.S. Private*, pg. 419
Fine, Robert, V.P.-Sls.--Security Dynamics Technologies, Bedford, MA; *U.S. Public*, pg. 1453
Fineman, Jerry, Sr. V.P.-Sls.--Tyco Preschool, New York, NY; *U.S. Public*, pg. 1058
Fingerhut, Augie, Dir.-Sls. & Pur., Mgr.-Adv.--Manhattan Industries Intl. Div., New York, NY; *U.S. Public*, pg. 1429
Fink, Alan, V.P.-Intl. Sls.--Conmed Corporation, Utica, NY; *U.S. Public*, pg. 431
Fink, Clemar, Mgr.-Sls.--Sancor Cooperativas Unidas Limitadas, Buenos Aires, Argentina; *Int'l*, pg. 1183
Fink, Jeff, Sr. V.P.-Sls.--LIVE Entertainment Inc., Van Nuys, CA; *U.S. Private*, pg. 671
Fink, Jeffrey, Sr. V.P.-Sls.--LIVE Film & Mediaworks, Van Nuys, CA; *U.S. Private*, pg. 671
Finkelnburg, Karl, V.P.-Sls. America--Netrix, Corp., Herndon, VA; *U.S. Private*, pg. 791
Finley, Bill, V.P. & Natl. Sls. Mgr.--Lerner New York, New York, NY; *U.S. Public*, pg. 996
Finley, C. Sue, V.P.-Opers. & Dir.-Sls.--Spartech Plastics, Portage, WI; *U.S. Public*, pg. 1496
Finley, Dale, Natl. Sls. Mgr.--Poly-Seal Corporation, Baltimore, MD; *U.S. Private*, pg. 875
Finley, Jon, Dir.-Sls. & Mktg.--Rundel Products, Inc., Portland, OR; *U.S. Private*, pg. 951
Finley, Richard L., Sr. V.P.-Sls. & Mktg.--Allied Security, Inc., Pittsburgh, PA; *U.S. Private*, pg. 40
Finn, Bob, V.P.-Sls.--Lynx Golf, Inc., City of Industry, CA; *U.S. Private*, pg. 684
Finn, G.G., Mgr.-Sls.--Morgan Matroc Inc.-West Coast Sales Division, El Toro, CA; *Int'l*, pg. 893
Finn, Larry, Gen. Mgr.-Sls.--Saunders Oil Company, Inc., Richmond, VA; *U.S. Private*, pg. 968
Finn, Robert, V.P.-Sls.--Lane Press, Inc., South Burlington, VT; *U.S. Private*, pg. 650
Finnen, Paula, Mgr.-Category--United Dairy Farmers, Inc., Cincinnati, OH; *U.S. Private*, pg. 1121
Finnerty, Patrick, Dir.-Sls. & Mktg.--Kaufman and Broad Inland Empire, Anaheim, CA; *U.S. Public*, pg. 945
Finney, Deborah, Mgr.-Sls. & Mktg.--ISS London Ltd., London, United Kingdom; *Int'l*, pg. 657
Finney, Mike, Area Sls. Mgr. Comp.--Analog Devices Ltd., Halesowen, United Kingdom; *U.S. Public*, pg. 108
Finney, V. Craig, V.P.-Sls.--The W.E. Bassett Company, Shelton, CT; *U.S. Private*, pg. 122
Fint, Linda, V.P.-Reg. Sls.--Lifetime Television/ABC, New York, NY; *U.S. Public*, pg. 512
Fint, Linda, V.P.-Reg. Sls.--Lifetime Television/ABC, New York, NY; *U.S. Private*, pg. 516
Finucane, Michael F., V.P.-Sls., Mktg. & Devel.--Nichols-Homeshield, Davenport, IA; *U.S. Public*, pg. 1350
Fiora, Ann, Mgr.-Sls.--Dodge Regupol, Inc., Lancaster, PA; *U.S. Private*, pg. 337
Fiore, Anthony, Exec. V.P.-Intl. Sls.--Active International, Pearl River, NY; *U.S. Private*, pg. 15
Fiore, Richard E., V.P.-Domestic Sls.--Comark Communications, Inc., Chalfont, PA; *Int'l*, pg. 1383
Fiorentino, Patrick, Dir.-Sls.--Tiger Direct, Inc. (d/b/a Tiger Software, Inc.), Miami, FL; *U.S. Public*, pg. 747
Fiorini, Peter, V.P.-Sls. & Mktg./Industrial--Rainfair, Inc., Racine, WI; *U.S. Private*, pg. 907
Firenze, Richard, V.P.-Sls.--Franklin Sports, Inc., Stoughton, MA; *U.S. Private*, pg. 424
Fischer, Dale, V.P.-Intl. Sls.--Metrologic Instruments, Inc., Blackwood, NJ; *U.S. Public*, pg. 1102
Fischer, Peter, Mng. Dir.-Sls.--Inka Paletten GmbH, Hoehenkirchen, Germany; *Int'l*, pg. 678
Fischer, Rick, Sls. Mgr.--Manitowoc Ice, Inc., Manitowoc, WI; *U.S. Public*, pg. 1041
Fischer, Samuel C., V.P.-Domestic Sls.--Abbott Diagnostic Products, North Chicago, IL; *U.S. Public*, pg. 13
Fischlin, J.K., V.P.-Sls.--Feintool Equipment Corp., White Plains, NY; *Int'l*, pg. 479
Fisher, Barbara, Adv. & Sls. Dept.--Universal Studios TV, Universal City, CA; *Int'l*, pg. 1215
Fisher, Bob, Dir.-Sls.--Emery Waterhouse Company, Portland, ME; *U.S. Private*, pg. 373
Fisher, Bruce, Gen. Mgr.-Agromac Retail--Agromac International, Inc., Gering, NE; *U.S. Private*, pg. 27
Fisher, George, V.P.-Distributor Sales--Ballantine Books, New York, NY; *U.S. Private*, pg. 21
Fisher, J.A., V.P. Sls. Intl.--Herr-Voss Corp., Callery, PA; *U.S. Private*, pg. 961
Fisher, Jan, V.P.-Sls.--La Quinta Inns, Inc., San Antonio, TX; *U.S. Public*, pg. 972
Fisher, John, V.P. & Mgr.-Sls.--Gould Paper Corporation-Albany, Albany, NY; *U.S. Private*, pg. 467
Fisher, John, Dir.-Sls.--Valley Forest Resources Co., Marcell, MN; *U.S. Private*, pg. 1140
Fisher, Michael D., Mgr.-Sls., Services & Mktg.--Arrow Oilfield Service Company, Canton, OH; *U.S. Private*, pg. 1078
Fisher, Randy, Exec. V.P.-Sls.--John J. Campbell Co., Inc., Memphis, TN; *U.S. Private*, pg. 204
Fisher, Ronald K., Mgr.-Sls.--Bunker Hill Foods Inc., Bedford, VA; *U.S. Private*, pg. 219
Fisher, Thomas, District Sls. Mgr.-Cleveland--Magneco/Metrel, Inc., Addison, IL; *U.S. Private*, pg. 695
Fisher, Warren F., V.P.-Sls. & Mktg.--Moeller Products Co., Inc., Greenville, MS; *U.S. Private*, pg. 755
Fisher, Warren J., V.P.-Sls.--Box Hill Systems Corporation, New York, NY; *U.S. Public*, pg. 249
Fishlin, J., V.P.-Mktg.--U.S. Bioscience, Inc., Conshohocken, PA; *U.S. Public*, pg. 1681
Fishman, Adam, Mgr.-Mktg.--Tribune Entertainment Company, Los Angeles, CA; *U.S. Public*, pg. 1636
Fisk, G.W., Mgr.-Mktg. & Sls.--British Steel Seamless Tubes-Wednesfield Works, Wolverhampton, United Kingdom; *Int'l*, pg. 220
Fiskin, Marty, V.P.-Reg. Sls. Mgr.--Fruit of the Loom, Inc., Chicago, IL; *U.S. Public*, pg. 685
Fissel, Craig, Sls. Mgr.-Mktg.--Peyton Meats, El Paso, TX; *U.S. Public*, pg. 75
Fitz, Peter, Mgr.-Central Sls. Front Plng.--Coop Switzerland, Basel, Switzerland; *Int'l*, pg. 329
Fitzer, Charles, Dir.-Sls.--Blonder-Tongue Laboratories, Inc., Old Bridge, NJ; *U.S. Public*, pg. 237
Fitzgerald, Brian J., V.P.-Leasing--Washington Real Estate Investment Trust, Kensington, MD; *U.S. Public*, pg. 1743
Fitzgerald, Dave, V.P.-Sls.--Wolfington Body Company, Exton, PA; *U.S. Private*, pg. 1186
Fitzgerald, Dick, Mgr.-Sls. Padlock--Master Lock Company, Milwaukee, WI; *U.S. Public*, pg. 675
Fitzgerald, Hope, Sec. & Sls. Admin.--Son Chief Electrics, Inc., Winsted, CT; *U.S. Private*, pg. 1014
Fitzgerald, Mary, Admin.-Sls.--Dri-Print Foils Inc., Rahway, NJ; *U.S. Private*, pg. 343
Fitzgerald, Michael W., V.P.-Sls. & Mktg.--Nice-Pak Products, Inc., Orangeburg, NY; *U.S. Private*, pg. 798
Fitzharris, Michael J., Asst. V.P. & Dir.-Sls.--National Guardian Life Insurance Company, Madison, WI; *U.S. Private*, pg. 784
Fitzpatrick, John, Mgr.-Sls. Personnel Devel.--Bayer Corporation/Pharmaceutical Division, West Haven, CT; *Int'l*, pg. 173
Fitzpatrick, Phil, V.P.-Mktg. & Sls./Packaged Foods--Dole Food Company, Inc., Westlake Village, CA; *U.S. Public*, pg. 515
Fitzpatrick, Tom, V.P.-Mktg. & Sls.--Thermal Ceramics Inc., Augusta, GA; *Int'l*, pg. 894
Fixa, Charles W., Dir.-Sls. & Mktg & Mgr.-Adv. & Pub. Rels.--Spectrol Electronics Corporation, Ontario, CA; *U.S. Private*, pg. 351
Fixel, Gary, Dir.-Sls.--Spectronics Corporation, Westbury, NY; *U.S. Private*, pg. 1024
Fixel, Gary, Dir.-Sls.--Tracer Products, Westbury, NY; *U.S. Private*, pg. 1024
Flaherty, Sharon, V.P.-Sls., Mktg. & Client Svcs.--National Research Corporation, Lincoln, NE; *U.S. Public*, pg. 1159
Flaherty, W., Dir.-Sls.-Rubber--Farrel Corporation, Ansonia, CT; *U.S. Public*, pg. 614
Flam, Donald, Sr. V.P.-Sls. Promo.--Genfoot Inc., Montreal, Canada; *Int'l*, pg. 549
Flam, Donald, Mgr.-Sls.--Hang Ten, Montreal, Canada; *Int'l*, pg. 549
Flament, Alain, Dir.-Mktg.--Giesecke & Devrient Engineering, Inc., Bedford, MA; *U.S. Private*, pg. 452
Flanagan, Frank, Sr. V.P.-Sls.-East--Viacom Enterprises, New York, NY; *U.S. Private*, pg. 779
Flanagan, James, Dir.-Sls. & Mktg.--PCC Specialty Products, Inc., Worcester, MA; *U.S. Public*, pg. 1321
Flanagan, Pat, Mgr.-Sls. Admin.--Crown Cork & Seal Company, Inc., Philadelphia, PA; *U.S. Public*, pg. 462
Flannery, Michael, V.P.-Gen. Sls., Natl.--Duo-Fast Corporation, Huntley, IL; *U.S. Private*, pg. 347
Flannigan, Cynthia, Mgr.-Leupold Sls.--Leupold & Stevens, Inc., Beaverton, OR; *U.S. Private*, pg. 662
Flaskey, Mike, V.P.-Sls.--Fairfield Orlando at Cypruss Palms, Kissimmee, FL; *U.S. Public*, pg. 611

Flaster, S.R., Sr. V.P.-Sls.--Ingram Book Company, La Vergne, TN; *U.S. Private*, pg. 563
Flavin, Denis, V.P.-Product Sls.--OAG, Oak Brook, IL; *Int'l*, pg. 1097
Flavin, Mike, V.P.-Sls. & Mgr.-Natl. Sls.--Heyman Corporation, Niles, IL; *U.S. Private*, pg. 524
Fleig, Gunther, Dir.-Sls. Projects Europe--Mercedes-Benz AG, Stuttgart, Germany; *Int'l*, pg. 368
Fleischmann, Charles, Regional Mgr.-Omnitrac Sls. Div.--QUALCOMM, San Diego, CA; *U.S. Public*, pg. 1348
Fleischner, Fred, V.P.-Mktg.--Dollar Rent A Car, Tulsa, OK; *U.S. Public*, pg. 354
Fleming, Bill, V.P.-Sls. & Mdsg.--Pay Less Super Markets, Inc., Anderson, IN; *U.S. Private*, pg. 844
Fleming, D.N., North Am. Sls. Mgr.--Silica Catalysts & Adsorbents Business, Valley Forge, PA; *U.S. Private*, pg. 827
Fleming, Davis, Mgr.-Natl. Sls.--Laubeck Corporation/Cross, Carbondale, PA; *U.S. Private*, pg. 652
Fleming, Ed, Gen Mgr.-Sls.--Turner Holding LLC, Covington, TN; *U.S. Private*, pg. 1109
Fleming, Fawn, Mgr.-Sls.--ACBJ Business Journals, Inc., Kansas City, MO; *U.S. Private*, pg. 19
Fleming, Frank, V.P.-Sls.--King Press Corporation, Joplin, MO; *U.S. Public*, pg. 1341
Fleming, Jack, Bentree Real Estate Grp.--Calprop Corporation, Marina Del Rey, CA; *U.S. Public*, pg. 296
Fleming, John, Mgr.-Sls.--Kalin Enterprises, Inc., Sarasota, FL; *U.S. Private*, pg. 606
Fleshman, James, V.P.-Mktg. & Sls.--Consumer Products Div., San Francisco, CA; *U.S. Public*, pg. 1318
Fletcher, Wayne, V.P.-Sls.--The Seibels Bruce Group, Inc., Columbia, SC; *U.S. Public*, pg. 1453
Fletcher, Wayne A., V.P.-Sls.--South Carolina Insurance Company, Columbia, SC; *U.S. Public*, pg. 1453
Fletcher, Wayne A., V.P.-Sls.--Consolidated American Insurance Co., Columbia, SC; *U.S. Public*, pg. 1454
Fletcher, Wayne A., V.P.-Sls.--Catawba Insurance Co., Columbia, SC; *U.S. Public*, pg. 1454
Fletcher, Wayne A., V.P.-Sls.--Investors National Life Insurance Co., Columbia, SC; *U.S. Public*, pg. 1454
Fletcher, Wayne A., V.P.-Sls.--Kentucky Insurance Co., Louisville, KY; *U.S. Public*, pg. 1454
Fletcher, Wayne A., V.P.-Sls.--Seibels, Bruce & Co., Columbia, SC; *U.S. Public*, pg. 1454
Fletcher, Wayne A., V.P.-Sls.--Agency Specialty Inc., Columbia, SC; *U.S. Public*, pg. 1454
Fletcher, Wayne A., V.P.-Sls.--Forest Lake Travel Service, Inc., Columbia, SC; *U.S. Public*, pg. 1454
Fletcher, William, V.P.-Engr. Prods.--Hyde Manufacturing Co., Southbridge, MA; *U.S. Private*, pg. 551
Fletcher, William, Mgr.-Sls.--Wilson Machine Knife Co., Inc., Dayville, CT; *U.S. Private*, pg. 551
Fletcher, William A., Pres.-Lemmon Company & V.P.-North American Sls.--Teva Pharmaceutical Industries Ltd., Petah Tiqwa, Israel; *Int'l*, pg. 1380
Flinn, Jeff, V.P.-Sls. & Mktg.--Spartan Tool, Mendota, IL; *U.S. Private*, pg. 860
Flinn, Mark, V.P.-Sls. Devel.--Business Week, New York, NY; *U.S. Public*, pg. 1069
Floisand, John, Sr. V.P.-Worldwide Sls.--Apple Computer, Inc., Cupertino, CA; *U.S. Public*, pg. 121
Floisand, John, V.P.-U.S. Sls.--Borland International, Inc., Scotts Valley, CA; *U.S. Public*, pg. 246
Flom, Roger, V.P.-Comml. Sls. & Pur.--Standard Publishing, Cincinnati, OH; *U.S. Public*, pg. 1506
Flood, John, V.P.-Deli Sls.--Bil Mar Foods, Inc., Zeeland, MI; *U.S. Public*, pg. 1433
Flood, Roy M., Exec. V.P.-Sls. & Mdsg.--Big Bear Stores Company, Columbus, OH; *U.S. Public*, pg. 1270
Flora, Michael J., V.P.-Sls.--GuestInformant, Inc., Woodland Hills, CA; *U.S. Public*, pg. 11
Flores, Roberto, Mgr.-Sls./Latin America--The Vendo Company, Fresno, CA; *Int'l*, pg. 1184
Florian, Susana, V.P.-Sls. & Mktg.--Baker Mellon Stuart Construction, Inc., Pittsburgh, PA; *U.S. Public*, pg. 168
Flowers, Carl A., V.P.-Sls.--BeautiControl Cosmetics, Inc., Carrollton, TX; *U.S. Public*, pg. 198
Flowers, Marianne, Dir.-Sls.--Sea World of California, San Diego, CA; *U.S. Public*, pg. 114
Floyd, Chuck, V.P.-Sls.--Hyatt Corporation, Chicago, IL; *U.S. Private*, pg. 551
Floyd, David F., V.P.-Sls.--Oregon Metallurgical Corporation, Albany, OR; *U.S. Public*, pg. 43
Fluri, D., Dir.-Mktg. & Sls.--Mikron AG Nidau, Nidau, Switzerland; *Int'l*, pg. 866
Flyer, Matthew, Sls.--Fike Corporation, Blue Springs, MO; *U.S. Private*, pg. 404
Flygare, Kurt, Dir.-Sls.--Corel Corporation, Orem, UT; *Int'l*, pg. 331
Flynn, Bob, Mgr.-Natl. Sls.--Standard Duplicating Machines Corp., Andover, MA; *U.S. Private*, pg. 1031
Flynn, James, V.P.-Sls.--Divi Hotels, Inc., Chapel Hill, NC; *U.S. Private*, pg. 336
Flynn, James, Dir.-Sls. & Mktg.--Precision Resource Inc., Shelton, CT; *U.S. Private*, pg. 880
Flynn, Terrance R., Mgr.-Bus. Devel. & Sls.--MBNA Corporation, Wilmington, DE; *U.S. Public*, pg. 1023
Fobare, Pete, Grp. V.P.-Sls. & Mktg.--Oneida Ltd., Oneida, NY; *U.S. Public*, pg. 1225
Fogel, Bob, V.P.-Sls.--Whiteswan/Meta, Libertyville, IL; *U.S. Private*, pg. 342
Foggin, John, Dir.-Sls.--Allied Domecq Spirits & Wine (UK) Ltd., Horsham, United Kingdom; *Int'l*, pg. 63
Folb, Ed, Dir.-Sls.--Yashica, Inc., Somerset, NJ; *Int'l*, pg. 776
Foley, Lisa, V.P.-Mktg. & Sls.--National City Bank, Cleveland, OH; *U.S. Public*, pg. 1154
Foley, Thomas P., V.P.-Sls. & Mktg.--DynaVac, Hingham, MA; *U.S. Private*, pg. 1076
Foley, Vincent P., V.P.-Sls.--Superior Brands, Inc., Quincy, MA; *Int'l*, pg. 917
Folkerth, Robert, V.P.-Field Sls.--Shopsmith, Inc., Dayton, OH; *U.S. Public*, pg. 1467
Fones, Ed, V.P.-Circulation--Rodale Press, Inc., Emmaus, PA; *U.S. Private*, pg. 939
Fong, Joseph, Mgr.-CSD Retail--Kodak (Australasia) Pty. Ltd., Coburg, Australia; *U.S. Public*, pg. 552
Fontana, John A., Sr. V.P.-Sls.--National Insurance Group, South San Francisco, CA; *U.S. Public*, pg. 1157
Fontana, John A., Sr. V.P.-Sls.--Pinnacle Data Corporation, San Bruno, CA; *U.S. Public*, pg. 1158
Fontana, John A., Sr. V.P.-Sls.--FASTRAC Systems, Inc.-Insurance Agent & Broker, South San Francisco, CA; *U.S. Public*, pg. 1158
Fontini, George, Exec. V.P.-Sls.--MUDD Jeans, Inc., New York, NY; *U.S. Private*, pg. 766
Foot, T., Mgr.-U.K. Sls.--Stafford-Miller Limited, Welwyn Garden City, United Kingdom; *U.S. Public*, pg. 237
Footer, Eli, V.P.-Sls. & Mktg.--Schwartz & Benjamin, Inc., New York, NY; *U.S. Private*, pg. 974
Foran, Louis, V.P.-Als. & Mktg.--Legg Mason, Inc., Baltimore, MD; *U.S. Public*, pg. 984
Forassiepi, Lido J., Mgr.-Sls.--Wellsville Fire Brick Company, Wellsville, MO; *U.S. Private*, pg. 194
Forberich, Helmut, Mgr.-Prod. & Sls.--Durkopp Adler AG, Bielefeld, Germany; *Int'l*, pg. 468
Forbes, Jack, Dir.-Sls. & Mktg.--Universal Coach Parts, Inc., Des Plaines, IL; *Int'l*, pg. 326
Forbes, Jim, V.P.-Sls.--Weber-Stephen Products Co., Palatine, IL; *U.S. Private*, pg. 1157
Forbush, James S., Sr. V.P.-Catalog Sls. & Mktg.--Staples, Inc., Westborough, MA; *U.S. Public*, pg. 1509
Ford, Don, V.P.-Sls. & Mktg.--Union Special Corp., Huntley, IL; *Int'l*, pg. 716
Ford, James, Mgr.-Sls.--Uniroyal Chemical Co., Inc,, Fresno, CA; *U.S. Public*, pg. 460
Ford, John, Sr. V.P.-Mktg. & Sls.--UDL Laboratories, Inc., Rockford, IL; *U.S. Public*, pg. 1143
Ford, Mike, Prod. Line Mgr.-SigLab Grp.--DSP Technology Inc., Fremont, CA; *U.S. Public*, pg. 475
Ford, Stephen A., Exec. V.P.-Sls. & Distr.--D & K Healthcare Resources-Lexington Division, Lexington, KY; *U.S. Public*, pg. 472
Ford, V. Kevin, V.P.-Sls. & Mktg.--Kalmbach Publishing Co., Waukesha, WI; *U.S. Private*, pg. 606
Fore, Dewey, Reg. Mgr.-Sls.--Ash Grove Cement Company Sales Office, Little Rock, AR; *U.S. Private*, pg. 87
Forget, Gerard, V.P.-Sls. & Mktg.--Gaz Metropolitain & Company, Montreal, Canada; *Int'l*, pg. 541
Forkovitch, Jim, V.P. & Asst. Gen. Mgr.--Howell Metal Company, New Market, VA; *U.S. Public*, pg. 413
Forman, Geoff, V.P.-Sls.--Wayne Dalton Corporation, Mount Hope, OH; *U.S. Private*, pg. 1155
Formichelli, Anthony, Sls. Mgr.--CRN International, Inc., Hamden, CT; *U.S. Private*, pg. 197
Formisano, Lou, V.P.-Natl. Sls.--Outdoor Systems, Inc.-New York, New York, NY; *U.S. Public*, pg. 1235
Fornal, Bob, V.P.-Sls. & Mktg.--S.P. Richards Co., Smyrna, GA; *U.S. Public*, pg. 732
Fornell, Karen, Mgr.-Catalog--The Popcorn Factory, Lake Forest, IL; *U.S. Private*, pg. 421
Forney, Paul, Sr. V.P.-Sls.--Beverage Canners International Corp., Miami, FL; *U.S. Private*, pg. 106
Forni, Jim, V.P.-Sls. & Mktg.--Bradley Printing Company, Des Plaines, IL; *U.S. Public*, pg. 1778
Forrest, Peter, V.P.-Sls.--VWR Canlab, Mississauga, Canada; *U.S. Public*, pg. 1704
Forster, Michael H., Sr. V.P.-Worldwide Field Opers.--Sybase, Inc., Emeryville, CA; *U.S. Public*, pg. 1544
Forster, Paul, Mgr.-Sls.--Atlet Ltd., Thame, United Kingdom; *Int'l*, pg. 97
Forsythe, Pat, Dir.-Sls.--Hoffmann-La Roche Ltd., Mississauga, Canada; *Int'l*, pg. 1121
Fortenberry, Donnie, V.P.-Sls.--Intellicall, Inc., Carrollton, TX; *U.S. Public*, pg. 887
Fortier, L., V.P.-Sls. & Mktg.--La Brasserie Labatt Limitee, La Salle, Canada; *Int'l*, pg. 679
Fortier, Peter, Mgr.-Domestic Sls.--Tidewater Inc., New Orleans, LA; *U.S. Public*, pg. 1608
Fortini, Paul, V.P.-Sls.--Sullivan Paper Company, West Springfield, MA; *U.S. Private*, pg. 1050
Fortunato, E., Dir.-Sls.--Compania Hulera Goodyear-Oxo Sociedad Anonima, Mexico, Mexico; *U.S. Public*, pg. 753
Fortune, A.H., V.P.-Sls.--Molded Fiber Glass Co., Union City, PA; *U.S. Private*, pg. 756
Fortune, Raymond, Sr. V.P.-Intl. Sls.--EMC Corporation, Hopkinton, MA; *U.S. Public*, pg. 545
Foster, Allan, V.P.-Sls. & Mktg.--J.W. Allen & Company, Wheeling, IL; *U.S. Private*, pg. 37
Foster, Craig, V.P.-Sls. & Mktg.--Capital Pacific Holdings, Newport Beach, CA; *U.S. Public*, pg. 302
Foster, Douglas J., V.P.-Sls. & Mktg.--Emery Worldwide, Redwood City, CA; *U.S. Public*, pg. 281
Foster, Eddie W., V.P. & Mgr.-Natl. Sls.--Stokely USA, Inc., Oconomowoc, WI; *U.S. Public*, pg. 1518
Foster, Ethan G., V.P.-Sls.--Soft Sheen Products, Inc., Chicago, IL; *U.S. Private*, pg. 1012
Foster, Gordon, Mgr.-Sls. & Mktg.--Royale Coach, Elkhart, IN; *U.S. Public*, pg. 1123
Foster, J.A., Dir.-Sls.-Gen. Agency--AEGON Financial Services Group (UK) Ltd., London, United Kingdom; *Int'l*, *pg. 28*
Foster, James, Dir.-Sls.--Mellon Equity Associates Corp., Pittsburgh, PA; *U.S. Public*, pg. 1085
Foster, Jim, V.P.-Sls. & Mktg.--Tweddle Litho Company, Clinton Township, MI; *U.S. Private*, pg. 1111
Foster, John, V.P.-Sls.--John Roberts Company, Minneapolis, MN; *U.S. Private*, pg. 935
Foster, John R., V.P.-Sls. & Mktg.--Caraustar Industries, Inc., Austell, GA; *U.S. Public*, pg. 303
Foster, Ken, Dir.-Sls.--Sanderson Technology Ltd., Sheffield, United Kingdom; *Int'l*, pg. 1184
Foster, Lawrence, V.P.-Sls. & Mktg.--Lawnware Products, Inc., Morton Grove, IL; *U.S. Private*, pg. 653
Foster, Lawrence, V.P.-Sls. & Mktg.--Ingrid Division of Lawnware, Morton Grove, IL; *U.S. Private*, pg. 654
Foster, Mary Lou, Mgr.-Div. Sls. Support-Print Media--Burdines, Miami, FL; *U.S. Public*, pg. 618
Foster, Michael S., V.P.-Worldwide Sls. & Mktg., PC/SF--Shipley Co., LLC, Marlborough, MA; *U.S. Public*, pg. 1403
Foster, Steve, V.P.-Sls.--Roquette America Inc., Keokuk, IA; *U.S. Private*, pg. 944
Fountain, Brad, Controller-Sls. & Mktg.--Jami, Inc., Shawnee Mission, KS; *U.S. Private*, pg. 581
Fournier, Timothy, V.P.-Sls. & Multi-Media--LIVE Film & Mediaworks, Van Nuys, CA; *U.S. Private*, pg. 671
Fourticq, Michael, Jr., V.P.-Sls.--Brown Jordan Company, El Monte, CA; *U.S. Private*, pg. 174
Foust, George, Dir.-Sls.--Delta Foremost Chemical Corp., Memphis, TN; *U.S. Private*, pg. 322
Fowkes, Dan, V.P.-N. American Sls.--USCS International, Inc., Rancho Cordova, CA; *U.S. Public*, pg. 1659
Fowler, James, V.P. & Mgr.-Bus.--Piedmont Publishing Co., Inc., Winston Salem, NC; *U.S. Public*, pg. 1079
Fox, Bob, V.P.-Pharmaceutical Sls.--John D. Lucas Printing Company, Baltimore, MD; *U.S. Private*, pg. 253
Fox, Debbie, V.P.-Sls.--Crested Butte Mountain Resort, Inc., Crested Butte, CO; *U.S. Private*, pg. 289
Fox, Jacob, V.P.-Sls.--Orbotech Inc., Billerica, MA; *Int'l*, pg. 1007
Fox, John, Franchise Sls.--The Barbers, Hairstyling for Men & Women, Inc., Minneapolis, MN; *U.S. Private*, pg. 115
Fox, Roger, Dir.-Sls.--George Philip Limited, London, United Kingdom; *Int'l*, pg. 1093
Fox, Stuart D., V.P.-Consumer Appliance Sls.--Conair Corporation, Stamford, CT; *U.S. Private*, pg. 261
Foxen, Tracy, V.P.-Oper. & Sls.--CORS, Itasca, IL; *U.S. Private*, pg. 196
Foy, Reginald E., V.P. & Dir.-Sls.--Universal Leaf Tobacco Company, Inc., Richmond, VA; *U.S. Public*, pg. 1694
Frabitore, Steve, V.P.-Natl. Accts.--Empire Berol U.S.A., Brentwood, TN; *U.S. Public*, pg. 1178
Frabitore, Steve, V.P.-Sls.--Rexall Sundown Inc., Boca Raton, FL; *U.S. Public*, pg. 1384
Fraine, Bill, Sr. V.P.-Worldwide Sls.--FDX Corporation, Memphis, TN; *U.S. Public*, pg. 603
Fraioli, Dennis, V.P.-Sls. & Mktg.--Jeneric/Pentron Corp., Wallingford, CT; *U.S. Private*, pg. 298
Frampton, Jack, V.P.-Franchise Devel.--Comprehensive Business Services Inc., Mission Viejo, CA; *U.S. Private*, pg. 423
Frances, Owen, V.P.-Sls.--Premisys Communications, Inc., Fremont, CA; *U.S. Public*, pg. 1323
Francis, Bill, Natl. Sls. Mgr.--James Burn Intl., Poughkeepsie, NY; *U.S. Public*, pg. 1506
Francis, Jim, Gen. Mgr.-Sls.--Keystone Master Warehouse-Chicago, Chicago, IL; *U.S. Public*, pg. 955
Francken, Rene, Dir.-Sls. & Mktg.--Montair Andersen B.V., Sevenum, Netherlands; *U.S. Public*, pg. 462
Frangipane, Joe, Exec. V.P.-Sls. & Mktg. (U.S. & Canada)--Alcan Cable Division, Atlanta, GA; *Int'l*, pg. 50
Frank, Dale, Mgr.-Sls.--Illinois Auto Central Div., Chicago, IL; *U.S. Private*, pg. 558
Frank, Jeff, V.P.-Sls. & Mktg.--POLESTAR Labs, Inc., Escondido, CA; *U.S. Private*, pg. 874
Frankel, Norman, V.P.-Sls. & Mktg.--Standard Textile Co., Inc., Cincinnati, OH; *U.S. Private*, pg. 1032
Frankel, Richard, V.P.-Sls. & Mktg.--Universal Industrial Products Co., Pioneer, OH; *U.S. Public*, pg. 1677
Franklin, David, Dir.-Mktg., Sls. & Automation--Brodart Company, Williamsport, PA; *U.S. Private*, pg. 170
Franklin, Ellen, V.P.-Sls. & Mktg.--Wizards of the Coast, Renton, WA; *U.S. Private*, pg. 1185
Franklin, Ellen, V.P.-Sls. & Mktg.--TSR, Inc., Renton, WA; *U.S. Private*, pg. 1185
Franklin, James E., Jr., V.P.-Indus. Sls.--Thomaston Mills, Inc., Thomaston, GA; *U.S. Public*, pg. 1599
Franklin, James R., V.P.-Sls. & Mktg.--Sellstrom Manufacturing Co., Palatine, IL; *U.S. Private*, pg. 983
Franklin, Joann, Mgr.-Circulation--The Hannibal Courier-Post, Hannibal, MO; *U.S. Private*, pg. 995
Franklin, Ken, Sr. V.P.-Sls.--Metz Baking Company, Deerfield, IL; *U.S. Private*, pg. 1022
Franklin, Richard, V.P.-Sls. & Mktg.--Garden State Paper Co., Inc., Elmwood Park, NJ; *U.S. Public*, pg. 1078
Franklin, Robert, Dir.-Sls.--Bertan High Voltage, Hicksville, NY; *U.S. Public*, pg. 494
Franklin, Tony, Mgr.-Used Truck Sls.--Fairway Ford, Inc., Greenville, SC; *U.S. Private*, pg. 392
Franks, Michael D., V.P.-Dir. of Sls.--Ringling Bros., Barnum & Bailey Combined Shows, Inc., Vienna, VA; *U.S. Private*, pg. 400
Franson, Anders, Mgr.-Sls.--Nielsen Design AB, Sollentuna, Sweden; *Int'l*, pg. 459
Franz, Allan L., Mgr.-Home Improvement Sls.--AEP-SPAN, Dallas, TX; *U.S. Public*, pg. 1676
Fraser, Jay, Dir.-Sls.--Turner Construction Company, Shelton, CT; *U.S. Public*, pg. 1645
Fraser, Steven, Exec. V.P.-Global Retail--Regal Ware, Inc., Kewaskum, WI; *U.S. Private*, pg. 917
Frazho, Paul R., Mgr.-Sls. & Admin.--Fastcut Tool Corporation, Troy, MI; *U.S. Public*, pg. 368
Frazier, Barbara, Mgr.-Whsle. Admin.--Contract Interiors Inc., Taylor, MI; *U.S. Private*, pg. 270
Frazier, Roger, Dir.-Intl. Sls.--Gold Medal Products Co., Cincinnati, OH; *U.S. Private*, pg. 459
Frazier, Walter, V.P.-Sls. & Mktg.--Roller Derby Skate Corp., Litchfield, IL; *U.S. Private*, pg. 941
Freay, V. Peter, Mgr.-Natl. Sls.--Intool Rotor Company, Cleveland, OH; *U.S. Private*, pg. 574
Frederick, David M., V.P.-Sls.--Velsicol Chemical Corporation, Rosemont, IL; *U.S. Private*, pg. 1135
Frederick, Gerry, Mgr.-Sls.--TELUS Mobility, Calgary, Canada; *Int'l*, pg. 1374
Frederick, Gordon, V.P.-Sls.--BancTec, Inc., Dallas, TX; *U.S. Public*, pg. 176
Frederick, James, Dir.-Sls.--Kewaunee Scientific Corporation, Statesville, NC; *U.S. Public*, pg. 953

Frederiksen, Helge, V.P.-Sls.--ISS Darenas International A/S, Nivaa, Denmark; *Int'l,* pg. 656
Fredrickson, Gary, Dir.-Sls. & Mktg.--Diehl Machines, Wabash, IN; *U.S. Public,* pg. 944
Freeborn, Bill, V.P.-Sls. & Mktg.--CSC United States, Wilmington, DE; *U.S. Private,* pg. 197
Freed, Vicki, Sr. V.P.-Sls. & Mktg.--Carnival Corporation, Miami, FL; *U.S. Public,* pg. 306
Freeman, John, Chief Oper. Officer, V.P.-Sls. & Mktg.--Johnson & Quin, Inc., Niles, IL; *U.S. Private,* pg. 590
Freeman, Marty, V.P.-Field Sls.--Old Dominion Freight Line, Inc., High Point, NC; *U.S. Public,* pg. 1216
Freeman, Stephen, V.P.-Alloy Prods.--Brush Wellman Inc., Cleveland, OH; *U.S. Public,* pg. 266
Frei, Chris, Terminal Mgr.--Kintetsu World Express Inc., El Paso, TX; *Int'l,* pg. 735
Freidl, Robert, V.P.-Sls.--Victaulic Company of America, Easton, PA; *U.S. Private,* pg. 1138
Freidman, Stan, Dir.-Sls.--Blimpie International, Inc., Atlanta, GA; *U.S. Public,* pg. 236
Freitag, Bob, Dir.-Sls.--Ryobi America Corp., Anderson, SC; *Int'l,* pg. 1151
Freitag, D., Mgr.-North American Sls.--Melroe Company, Fargo, ND; *U.S. Public,* pg. 877
Fremer, Hal, V.P.-Sls. & Mdsg. Admin.--R.G. Barry Corporation, Pickerington, OH; *U.S. Public,* pg. 192
French, Forrest, Sls. Mgr.-Threads--Barbour Thread, Inc., Blue Mountain, AL; *Int'l,* pg. 618
French, John, Mgr.-Export & Sls.--Thomas Equipment Limited, Centreville, Canada; *Int'l,* pg. 850
Frenz, Dean A., Sr. V.P.-Rail--L.B. Foster Company, Pittsburgh, PA; *U.S. Public,* pg. 675
Freschi, John, V.P.-Sls. & Mktg.--Country Home Bakery, Inc., Bridgeport, CT; *U.S. Private,* pg. 278
Freshwater, S., Dir.-Fleet Sls.--General Motors of Canada Ltd., Oshawa, Canada; *U.S. Public,* pg. 722
Frey, Barry, Mng. Dir.-Intl. Sls.--USA Network, New York, NY; *U.S. Public,* pg. 1686
Frey, David, Natl. Sls. Mgr.--Butterball Turkey Company, Downers Grove, IL; *U.S. Public,* pg. 426
Frey, Ernesto, Dir.-Sls.--American Textil, S.A. de C.V., Santa Clara, Mexico; *U.S. Public,* pg. 769
Frey, James E., V.P.-Bus. Devel.--J.S. Alberici Construction Co., Inc., Saint Louis, MO; *U.S. Private,* pg. 32
Frey, Lawrence D., Sr. V.P.-Sls. & Mktg.--The Buschman Co., Cincinnati, OH; *U.S. Private,* pg. 188
Friberg, Peter A., Sr. V.P.-Memorial Sls. & Dir.-Sls. & Mktg.--Rock of Ages Corporation, Graniteville, VT; *U.S. Public,* pg. 1396
Frick, Dave, V.P.-Reg. Sls. Mgr.--Fruit of the Loom, Inc., Chicago, IL; *U.S. Public,* pg. 685
Fried, Lawrence S., Exec. V.P. & Mgr.-Gen. Sls.--ABC Television Network, New York, NY; *U.S. Public,* pg. 511
Frieden, David, V.P.-Sls. & Mktg.--Iowa Precision Industries, Cedar Rapids, IA; *U.S. Public,* pg. 1100
Friedle, Jurgen, Dr., Mng. Dir.--TosoHaas GmbH, Stuttgart, Germany; *Int'l,* pg. 1408
Friedson-Garrett, Barbara, Pres.-Windmere U.S. Sls. & Mktg.--Windmere-Durable Holdings, Hialeah, FL; *U.S. Public,* pg. 1771
Friel, John P., Sr. V.P. & Gen. Mgr.--Medrad, Inc., Indianola, PA; *Int'l,* pg. 1204
Friend, Kent, Sr. V.P.-Sls. & Mktg.--Kraco Enterprises, Inc., Compton, CA; *U.S. Private,* pg. 634
Fries, Donald B., Dir.-Adv. Sls.--Life Magazine, New York, NY; *U.S. Public,* pg. 1613
Friesch, Mark, Gen. Mgr.-Sls.--WICS-TV, Springfield, IL; *U.S. Private,* pg. 439
Friesen, Kelvin, V.P.-Sls.--Sauder Manufacturing Corporation, Archbold, OH; *U.S. Private,* pg. 967
Friesh, Mark, Gen. Mgr.-Sls.--WICD-TV, Champaign, IL; *U.S.* Private, pg. 439
Friessen, Jim, Hotel Mgr.--Circus Circus Hotel Casinos, Inc., Las Vegas, NV; *U.S. Public,* pg. 374
Friman, C.I., Mgr.-Sls.--Moore-Lithorex Direct Marketing Services N.V./S.A., Dusseldorf, Germany; *Int'l,* pg. 889
Frings, Jurgen, V.P.-Sls.--Radiometer A/S, Bronshoj, Denmark; *Int'l,* pg. 1083
Frisk, Lars, Dir.-Sls. & Mktg.--AGA Ges.m.b.H., Vienna, Austria; *Int'l,* pg. 13
Fritts, W. Allen, Sr. V.P.-Sls. & Mktg.--Fire Lite Alarms, Inc./Notifier Co., Northford, CT; *U.S. Public,* pg. 1306
Fritz, Wayne, Pres.--Saladmaster, Arlington, TX; *U.S. Private,* pg. 961
Frix, Brant, V.P.-Sls.--Tyco Toys, Inc., Mount Laurel, NJ; *U.S. Public,* pg. 1058
Frock, Jay, Rep.-Sls.--Scott Environmental Technology, Plumsteadville, PA; *U.S. Public,* pg. 546
Fromfeld, Jim, V.P.-Sls.--Leslie Controls, Inc., Tampa, FL; *U.S. Public,* pg. 1746
Fross, Vern, Sr. V.P.-Sls. & Mktg.--Ingram Entertainment Inc., La Vergne, TN; *U.S. Private,* pg. 563
Frost, Howard, Pres.-Sls.--Bollinger Industries Inc., Grand Prairie, TX; *U.S. Public,* pg. 243
Frosthome, Bob, V.P.-Sls.--SEEQ Technology Inc., Fremont, CA; *U.S. Public,* pg. 1417
Fruhinsholz, Hubert, Dir.-Sls.--Iveco-Unic S.A., Trappes, France; *Int'l,* pg. 484
Fruth, Steve, Dir.-Mktg.--Fostoria Industries, Inc., Fostoria, OH; *U.S. Private,* pg. 421
Fry, G. Rogan, Dir.-Sls. & Mktg.--Conley Frog/Switch & Forge Co., Memphis, TN; *U.S. Private,* pg. 263
Frye, Harvey J., V.P.-Sls. & Mktg.--Trikon Technologies Inc., Chatsworth, CA; *U.S. Public,* pg. 1638
Fryhoff, J.P., Dir.-Sls.--White Cap, Inc., Downers Grove, IL; *Int'l,* pg. 1207
Fryman, Norman, Exec.V.P.-Mdsg. Sls.--Bayer Clothing Group, New York, NY; *U.S. Private,* pg. 124
Fuad, Encik Ahmad, Sr. Mgr.-Sls. Branch Banking--Standard Chartered Bank Malaysia Berhad, Kuala Lumpur, Malaysia; *Int'l,* pg. 1295
Fuchs, Jay, Chief Sls. Officer--American Bankers Insurance Group, Inc., Miami, FL; *U.S. Public,* pg. 67
Fuchs, Wilhelm, Exec. V.P.--Stora Feldmuhle AG, Dusseldorf, Germany; *Int'l,* pg. 1303
Fuchsman, Alan, Mgr.-Sls.--KSHB-TV, Kansas City, MO; *U.S. Public,* pg. 1448
Fuderburk, Mark, V.P.-Sls./Records & Music--Word, Incorporated, Dallas, TX; *U.S. Public,* pg. 704
Fudun, Neil, V.P. & Creative Dir.--Macy's East, New York, NY; *U.S. Public,* pg. 618
Fuentevilla, Ramon, Sr. V.P.-Sls.--Mattel, Inc., El Segundo, CA; *U.S. Public,* pg. 1057
Fuhriman, David H., Sr. V.P.-Branch Sls. & Svc.--Zions First National Bank, Salt Lake City, UT; *U.S. Public,* pg. 1793
Fuhriman, R.R., Mgr.-Sls.--Longview Fibre Co. Western Container Division, Spanish Fork, UT; *U.S. Public,* pg. 1014
Fuhrmann, Curt, Pres.-Fortis Sls.--Time Insurance, Milwaukee, WI; *Int'l,* pg. 499
Fujishima, Hiroyuki, Mgr.-Overseas Sls.--Ikegami Tsushinki Co., Overseas Sales Div., Tokyo, Japan; *Int'l,* pg. 660
Fujiwara, Buheita, Exec. Dir. & Grp. Gen. Mgr.-Intl. Mdsg. & Sls.--Sharp Corporation, Osaka, Japan; *Int'l,* pg. 1228
Fulks, Gary, Dir.-Engrng., Opers. & Plng.--Associated Electric Co-op Inc., Springfield, MO; *U.S. Private,* pg. 89
Fuller, Barbara Brooks, V.P.-Retail Sls.--Rocky Shoes & Boots, Inc., Nelsonville, OH; *U.S. Public,* pg. 1402
Fuller, James, Mgr.-Sls.--Futter Lumber Corporation, Rockville Center, NY; *U.S. Private,* pg. 432
Fuller, Larry, Dir.-Sls.--Clover Club Foods, Inc., Kaysville, UT; *U.S. Private,* pg. 469
Fuller, Michael T., V.P.-Indus. Sls.--The Rival Company, Kansas City, MO; *U.S. Public,* pg. 1391
Fuller, N.J., Dir.-Sls.--Omnifit Ltd., Cambridge, United Kingdom; *Int'l,* pg. 589
Fuller, Richard, Dir.-Free Trade--Fuller, Smith & Turner Plc, London, United Kingdom; *Int'l,* pg. 529
Fullerton, D. Rush, V.P.-Sls. & Mktg., Gen. Mgr.--Sandvik Sorting Systems, Louisville, KY; *Int'l,* pg. 1186
Fulmer, Joseph S., V.P.-Sls.--Marshall & Williams Co., Greenville, SC; *U.S. Private,* pg. 708
Fulton, Amy, Mgr.-Sls.--Bead Industries Inc., Bridgeport, CT; *U.S. Private,* pg. 126
Fulton, Doug, Mgr.-Sls.--Delta Power Co., Rockford, IL; *U.S.* Private, pg. 322
Funes, Victor, Dir.-Sls.--Turner Construction Co., Houston, TX; *U.S. Public,* pg. 1645
Funk, Ernst, Mgr.-Sls. & Customer Rels.--The Swissair Group, Zurich, Switzerland; *Int'l,* pg. 1333
Furman, Barry, V.P.-Vet Sls.--Jones Medical Industries Inc., Saint Louis, MO; *U.S. Public,* pg. 933
Furman, Joel R., V.P.-Foodservice Sls.--Furman Foods, Inc., Northumberland, PA; *U.S. Private,* pg. 431
Furnandez, Donna, V.P.-Sls. & Mktg. Admin.--Johnson & Johnson Medical, Inc., Arlington, TX; *U.S. Public,* pg. 928
Fusarelli, Tony, Exec. V.P.-Worldwide Sls. & Service--General Signal Networks, Shelton, CT; *U.S. Public,* pg. 727
Fusco, John, Mgr.-Gen. Sls.--WNCT-TV, Greenville, NC; *U.S. Public,* pg. 1078
Fusco, Tim, V.P.-Sls., Mktg. & Res. Information--UMI, Ann Arbor, MI; *U.S. Public,* pg. 201
Fuscrardi, Geraldine, Mgr.-Sls.--Numetrix Ltd., Manchester, United Kingdom; *Int'l,* pg. 990
Fuson, Mike, V.P.-Sls.--L & L Nursery Supply, Inc., Chino, CA; *U.S. Private,* pg. 638
Futia, Anthony, Sls. Mgr.--Buss (America) Inc., Bloomingdale, IL; *Int'l,* pg. 490
Futterer, Sally, Supvr.-Sls. & Service--Amurol Confections Co., Yorkville, IL; *U.S. Public,* pg. 1781
Gabe, Jon, V.P.-Sls. & Mktg.--Fred Usinger, Inc., Milwaukee, WI; *U.S. Private,* pg. 1129
Gable, William H., V.P.-Sls. & Mktg.--Alabama Metal Industries Corporation, Birmingham, AL; *U.S. Private,* pg. 30
Gabor, Dick, Mgr.-Adv.--Sommer & Maca Industries, Inc., Cicero, IL; *U.S. Private,* pg. 1013
Gabriel, John, Jr., Asst. Mgr.-Sls.--Bowling Products Div., Cincinnati, OH; *U.S. Public,* pg. 1725
Gabuzda, George, V.P.-Sls. & Mktg.--Electronics Division-Materials, Bear, DE; *U.S. Public,* pg. 165
Gaddum, Andreas, Dir.-Sls.--CWS International A.G., Glattbrugg, Switzerland; *Int'l,* pg. 592
Gaffney, B.M., Mgr.-Sls.--Longview Fibre Co. Central Container Div., Milwaukee, WI; *U.S. Public,* pg. 1014
Gaffney, Matthew, V.P.-Worldwide Mktg. & Sls.--Virginia Tourism Corp., Richmond, VA; *U.S. Private,* pg. 1141
Gafner, Robin, Mgr.-Sls.--Frontier Foundry, Inc., Titusville, PA; *U.S. Private,* pg. 430
Gage, Dirk, Natl. Sls. Mgr.--Hurco Companies, Inc., Indianapolis, IN; *U.S. Public,* pg. 850
Gaggin, Brian, Dir.-Sls.--Ultra Pac, Inc., Rogers, MN; *U.S. Public,* pg. 1662
Gagliardi, Michel, Sls. Coordinator-Intl. Div.--West Penetone Corporation, Tenafly, NJ; *U.S. Private,* pg. 1158
Gagnon, Luc, Dir.-Mktg. & Sls./Retail--Aliments Flamingo, Iberville, Canada; *Int'l,* pg. 57
Gagnon, Paul, V.P.-Canadaian & Intl. Sls./Newsprint--Donohue Inc., Quebec, Canada; *Int'l,* pg. 1075
Gagnon, Pierre, Sr. Grp. V.P.-Sls. & Mktg.--Mitsubishi Motor Sales of America, Inc., Cypress, CA; *Int'l,* pg. 875
Gagnon, Richard, Sr. V.P. & Mgr.-Natl. Sls.--White Cap Industries, Inc., Costa Mesa, CA; *U.S. Public,* pg. 1765
Gahan, Laurie, Mgr.-Sls.--SL Waber, Inc., Mount Laurel, NJ; *U.S. Public,* pg. 1419
Gahan, Laurie, Mgr.-Sls.--SL Waber, Nogales, AZ; *U.S. Public,* pg. 1419
Gahm, Gordon, V.P.-Sls.--Kitchen Kompact, Inc., Jeffersonville, IN; *U.S. Private,* pg. 624
Gaidmore, Jack, V.P.-Retail Sls..--Linear Corporation, Carlsbad, CA; *U.S. Public,* pg. 1193
Gaige, Chris, Dir.-Mktg. & Sls.--MascoTech Tubular Products, Inc., Canton, MI; *U.S. Public,* pg. 1055
Gaines, A., Mgr.-Natl. Sls.--Richmond Screw Anchor Company, Fort Worth, TX; *U.S. Private,* pg. 932
Gaines, Mark, Exec. V.P. & Natl. Sls. Mgr.-Distribution--Universal Pictures, Universal City, CA; *Int'l,* pg. 1216
Gale, Nelson, V.P.-Mtkg. & Sls.--AmeriServe of Norcross, Norcross, GA; *U.S. Private,* pg. 533
Galie, Sandro, Dir.-Sls.--AGIP Deutschland AG, Munich, Germany; *Int'l,* pg. 428
Galin, Robert, V.P.-Sls.--IDX Systems Corporation, Burlington, VT; *U.S. Public,* pg. 854
Galla, Ronald, Mgr.-Sls.--Ohio Crankshaft Div., Cleveland, OH; *U.S. Public,* pg. 1258
Gallagher, Chris, Sls. Coord.-Publications--Florida Panthers Holdings, Inc., Fort Lauderdale, FL; *U.S. Public,* pg. 654
Gallagher, D.H., Gen. Mgr.-Sls., Seafood--Star-Kist Foods Inc., Newport, KY; *U.S. Public,* pg. 805
Gallagher, Dan, Dir.-Sls.--Mission Industries, Las Vegas, NV; *U.S. Private,* pg. 752
Gallagher, Edward, V.P.-Replacement Sls./N. America--The Goodyear Tire & Rubber Company, Akron, OH; *U.S. Public,* pg. 752
Gallagher, Glen, Dir.-Sls.--Canada Malting Co. Limited, Mississauga, Canada; *U.S. Public,* pg. 428
Gallagher, J., Dir.-Sls. & Mktg. Services--Menley & James Laboratories, Inc., Horsham, PA; *U.S. Public,* pg. 1086
Gallagher, Jamie, V.P.-U.S. Retail--Books & Home Entertainment Div., Pleasantville, NY; *U.S. Public,* pg. 1367
Gallagher, Tom, V.P.-Sls.--Michael Business Machines Corporation, Charleston, SC; *U.S. Private,* pg. 740
Gallehawk, Nick, Mgr.-Mktg.--BNA International Inc., London, United Kingdom; *U.S. Private,* pg. 182
Galli, Bryan, Dir.-Sls.--Freeman Energy Corporation, Springfield, IL; *U.S. Public,* pg. 709
Gallian, Robert, Exec. V.P. & V.P.-Sls. & Mktg.--Pet Life Foods, Inc., Willowbrook, IL; *U.S. Private,* pg. 856
Gallion, Steve, V.P.-Sls.--Reed Travel Publishing-Los Angeles, Los Angeles, CA; *Int'l,* pg. 1097
Gallivan, Gary, Mgr.-Findings Sls.--B.A. Ballou & Co. Inc., East Providence, RI; *U.S. Private,* pg. 112
Gallivan, Quentin, V.P.-Sls. & Mktg.--LASCO Fluid Distribution Products, Brownsville, TN; *Int'l,* pg. 1398
Gallivan, Tom, Dir.-Sls.-Roofing--JPS Elastomerics Corp., Holyoke, MA; *U.S. Private,* pg. 578
Gallo, A.J., Dir.-Sls.--Comare Products, Hialeah, FL; *U.S. Public,* pg. 1771
Gallo, Dan, V.P.-Sls., Mass Market--Sanford Corporation, Bellwood, IL; *U.S. Public,* pg. 1178
Gallo, Dan, V.P.-Sls.--Sanford Beroc Corp., Brentwood, TN; *U.S. Public,* pg. 1178
Gallo, Richie, V.P.-Sls.--A&M Records, Hollywood, CA; *Int'l,* pg. 1052
Galluccio, Joseph, Sr. V.P.-Sls.--P.F. Collier LP, New York, NY; *Int'l,* pg. 433
Gallun, Jon, Mgr.-Natl. Sls.--Huffy Sports Company, Sussex, WI; *U.S. Public,* pg. 846
Galser, Robert J., V.P.-Mktg. & Sls.--Merck Vaccine Division, Rahway, NJ; *U.S. Public,* pg. 1091
Galterio, Vinny, V.P.-Sls.--Hampton Print Works, Inc., Johnson City, TN; *U.S. Private,* pg. 498
Galvin, J., Dir.-Grp. Sls. & Mktg.--Beazer Group Plc, Bath, United Kingdom; *Int'l,* pg. 181
Galvin, James, Dir.-Adv. & Mktg. & Mgr.-Sls.--MAC America Communications, Inc., Phoenix, AZ; *U.S. Private,* pg. 685
Galvin, Mike, V.P.-Consumer Sls.--Palm Beach Beauty Products Co., Minneapolis, MN; *U.S. Private,* pg. 834
Gamache, Brian, Dir.-Resort Div. Sls. & Mktg.--Hyatt Hotels Corporation, Chicago, IL; *U.S. Private,* pg. 551
Gamba, Philippe, Sr. V.P.-Europe Mkt.--Renault, Boulogne-Billancourt, France; *Int'l,* pg. 1102
Gandy, Hary, V.P.-Sls. & Mktg.--Signtech USA, Ltd., San Antonio, TX; *U.S. Private,* pg. 999
Gandy, Jim, Mgr.-Sls.--Morgantown Machine & Hydraulics, Inc., Morgantown, WV; *Int'l,* pg. 280
Gangstee, Gary, V.P.-Mktg. & Sls./Medical--Reuter Manufacturing Inc., Hopkins, MN; *U.S. Public,* pg. 1383
Ganot, Harvey, Pres.-Adv. & Promo. Sls.--MTV Networks, New York, NY; *U.S. Private,* pg. 779
Ganskopp, C. Robert, V.P.-Sls. & Mktg.--SouthCo. Inc., Concordville, PA; *U.S. Private,* pg. 1014
Ganz, Ray, V.P.-Sls.--Everest & Jennings, Inc., Earth City, MO; *U.S. Public,* pg. 758
Ganzhorn, Carl, Gen. Mgr.-Sls.--Plymouth Industries, Inc., Plymouth, OH; *U.S. Private,* pg. 873
Garachena, Fernando, Mgr.-Sls.--General Motors Chile S.A., Industria Automotriz, Santiago, Chile; *U.S. Public,* pg. 721
Garand, Ron, Dir.-Mktg. Svcs. & Intl. Sls.--Dynagear Inc., Downers Grove, IL; *U.S. Private,* pg. 350
Garbe, Herve, Dir.-Sls.-France, Sofamor S.N.C.--Sofamor Danek Group, Inc., Memphis, TN; *U.S. Public,* pg. 1482
Garber, George, Mgr.-Incentive Sls.--FINNAIR, New York, NY; *Int'l,* pg. 485
Garber, Sid, V.P.-Field Sls.--Tyco Toys, Inc., Mount Laurel, NJ; *U.S. Public,* pg. 1058
Garcia, Alex, Sr. V.P.-Sls.--BankAtlantic Bancorp, Inc., Fort Lauderdale, FL; *U.S. Public,* pg. 183
Garcia, Debbie, Mgr.-Sls./Market Pulp--Boise Cascade Corporation, Boise, ID; *U.S. Public,* pg. 242
Garcia, Frank, V.P.-Sls.--Good Companies, Carson, CA; *U.S. Private,* pg. 463
Garcia, J., Mgr.-Dental Sls.--Stafford-Miller Limited, Welwyn Garden City, United Kingdom; *U.S. Public,* pg. 237
Gardiner, J., Dir.-Sls.--Senior Moducel Limited, Stoke on Trent, United Kingdom; *Int'l,* pg. 1221
Gardner, Bill, Mgr.-Natl. Sales--Franklin-Burlington Plastics, Kearny, NJ; *U.S. Public,* pg. 1496
Gardner, David A., Exec. V.P., Sls. Mgr. & Sec.--Alfred Nickles Bakery, Inc., Navarre, OH; *U.S. Private,* pg. 799
Gardner, David A., Exec. V.P.-Sls.--Nickles Bakery of Indiana Inc., Elkhart, IN; *U.S. Private,* pg. 799
Gardner, David A., Exec. V.P., Sls. Mgr. & Sec.--Nickles Bakery of Ohio Inc., Lima, OH; *U.S. Private,* pg. 799
Gardner, Edward, Dir.-Sls.--McCormick Ingredients, Hunt Valley, MD; *U.S. Public,* pg. 1066

Gardner, Richard P., Sr. V.P.-Worldwide Sls. & Mktg.--BMC Software, Inc., Houston, TX; *U.S. Public*, pg. 162
Gardner, Rob, V.P.-Hardware Sls.--Safety 1st, Inc., Chestnut Hill, MA; *U.S. Public*, pg. 1425
Gardner, Thomas C., V.P.-Natl. Sls.--Consolidated Freightways Corp., Menlo Park, CA; *U.S. Public*, pg. 435
Garel, John R., Sr. V.P.-Mktg. & Sls.--America West Airlines, Inc., Phoenix, AZ; *U.S. Public*, pg. 67
Gargan, R., Mgr.-Sls. Office--VG Quadrupoles Ltd., Middlewich, United Kingdom; *Int'l*, pg. 1111
Gargas, David E., V.P.-Sls. & Mktg.--Alphabet Division, Warren, OH; *U.S. Private*, pg. 1044
Garing, Kurt, V.P.-Sls.--Advance Business Graphics, Mira Loma, CA; *U.S. Private*, pg. 18
Garland, Frank, V.P.-Adv. Sls.--The Weather Channel, Atlanta, GA; *U.S. Private*, pg. 647
Garlock, Garth, V.P.-Mktg. & Sls.--Midland Life Insurance Co., Columbus, OH; *U.S. Private*, pg. 744
Garmoe, Trent, Supvr.-Sls.--Sigmatech USA, Ltd., San Antonio, TX; *U.S. Private*, pg. 999
Garner, H., Dir.-Sls.--Bridport-Grundy Marine, Dorset, United Kingdom; *Int'l*, pg. 215
Garner, Jerry, V.P.-Hospital Sls.--Jones Medical Industries Inc., Saint Louis, MO; *U.S. Public*, pg. 933
Garnett, Thomas H., Jr., V.P.-Intl. Sls.--Southern States Cooperative, Inc., Richmond, VA; *U.S. Private*, pg. 1017
Garoulfis, Leon, V.P.-Sls.--Composites Distribution Corp., Arlington Heights, IL; *U.S. Private*, pg. 435
Garrabrant, Lori, Dir.-Sls. & Mktg.--Golden Books Family Entertainment Inc., New York, NY; *U.S. Public*, pg. 749
Garrabrant, Lori, Dir.-Sls. & Mktg.--Golden Books Publishing, New York, NY; *U.S. Public*, pg. 749
Garrett, Bob, Dir.-Sls.--Temco Fireplace Products, Inc., Nashville, TN; *U.S. Public*, pg. 1576
Garrett, D. William, V.P.-Sls.--Gencor Industries, Inc., Orlando, FL; *U.S. Public*, pg. 705
Garrett, Daniel, V.P.-Sls.-Music--Ensoniq, Malvern, PA; *U.S. Private*, pg. 377
Garrett, Don, V.P.-Cryogenics--IMI Cash Valve, Inc., Cullman, AL; *Int'l*, pg. 646
Garrett, Gary, V.P.-Sls.--Atlas Supply Company, Atlanta, GA; *U.S. Private*, pg. 96
Garrett, Robert, Sr. V.P.-Mktg. & Adv.--Warehouse Home Furnishings Distributor, Dublin, GA; *U.S. Private*, pg. 1150
Garrett, Robert J., V.P.-Sls.--The Jim Dandy Co., Inc., Atlanta, GA; *Int'l*, pg. 918
Garris, Tom, Mgr.-Natl. Sls.--Robicon, New Kensington, PA; *U.S. Private*, pg. 528
Garrison, John, Sr. V.P.-Sls. & Mktg./Consumer Electronics--Samsung Electronics America, Inc., Ridgefield Park, NJ; *Int'l*, pg. 1183
Garrison, Joseph, Dir.-Sls.--Augat, Inc., Wiring Systems, Montgomery, AL; *U.S. Public*, pg. 1598
Garry, Jeff, Mgr.-Adv., Sls. & Mktg.-Sportswear--Raven Industries, Inc., Sioux Falls, SD; *U.S. Public*, pg. 1361
Garry, Jeffrey R., Dir.-Sls. & Mktg.--Raven Industries Sportswear Div., Sioux Falls, SD; *U.S. Public*, pg. 1361
Garry, William, Mgr.-Natl. Sls.--Inverness Corp., Fair Lawn, NJ; *U.S. Private*, pg. 574
Garston, Priscilla, Dir.-Circulation--Advertising Age, Chicago, IL; *U.S. Private*, pg. 284
Gartman, Sally, Dir.-Sls. & Mktg.-Sterling--Wausau Homes, Inc., Rothschild, WI; *U.S. Private*, pg. 1154
Gartner, Rosalie, Mgr.-Sls.--Tricon Brazing Alloys & Chemical Products Div., Downers Grove, IL; *U.S. Private*, pg. 1103
Garvelink, Steve, Dir.-Sls.--Suspa, Inc., Grand Rapids, MI; *Int'l*, pg. 1322
Garvey, Bill, Reg. Sls. Mgr.--Dillard Paper Co. of Tampa, Tampa, FL; *U.S. Public*, pg. 902
Garvey, James R., V.P.-Mktg. & Sls. Services--Bristol-Myers Squibb U.S. Pharmaceutical Group, Evansville, IN; *U.S. Public*, pg. 254
Gaskarth, Peter, V.P.-Sls.--Polk Audio, Inc., Baltimore, MD; *U.S. Public*, pg. 1315
Gasmovic, David J., Exec. V.P.--McLaughlin Manufacturing Company, Greenville, SC; *U.S. Private*, pg. 724
Gasparini, Donald V., Mgr.-Sls. Promo.--Sullivan Paper Company, West Springfield, MA; *U.S. Private*, pg. 1050
Gasparini, Peter, Mgr.-Natl. Sls.--Heat Controller, Inc., Jackson, MI; *U.S. Private*, pg. 518
Gassel, Jerry, V.P.-Sls.--Guarantee Electrical Company, Saint Louis, MO; *U.S. Private*, pg. 485
Gassman, J.A., V.P.-Sls.--Janesville Products, Norwalk, OH; *U.S. Public*, pg. 924
Gastineau, Roger, Natl. Sls. Mgr.--Oneida Rostone Corporation, Oneida, NY; *U.S. Public*, pg. 1383
Gates, Jerry, Dir.-Sls.--Hankins Lumber Company, Inc., Elliott, MS; *U.S. Private*, pg. 499
Gates, Richard, Mgr.-Natl. Sales--Michelin North America (Canada) Inc., Laval, Canada; *Int'l*, pg. 322
Gattis, J. Michael, Sr. V.P.-Sls.--Bindley Western Drug Company, Indianapolis, IN; *U.S. Public*, pg. 228
Gatto, John, Mgr.-Field Sls.--Jaco Electronics, Inc., Hauppauge, NY; *U.S. Public*, pg. 920
Gaudet, Gilles, Dir.-Sls.--Durco-Valtek (Asia Pacific) Pte. Ltd., Singapore, Singapore; *U.S. Public*, pg. 659
Gaudet, Phil, Dir.-Sls. & Mktg.--The Dee Howard Company, San Antonio, TX; *U.S. Private*, pg. 542
Gaudreau, Robert, Mgr.-Sls.--Ville LaSalle Plant, La Salle, Canada; *Int'l*, pg. 761
Gauger, A. Gary, Mgr.-Sls.--Walbridge Aldinger Company, Detroit, MI; *U.S. Private*, pg. 1146
Gault, Matt, Sls. & Mktg.--Paradigm National Yellow Pages Group, Tampa, FL; *U.S. Private*, pg. 838
Gause, Erich, Mgr.-Sls.--Public Service Company of Oklahoma-Mantulsa Div., Tulsa, OK; *U.S. Public*, pg. 324
Gausnell, Judy, V.P.-Sls.--Bristol Hotels & Resorts, Dallas, TX; *U.S. Public*, pg. 253
Gaver, Charles C., Jr., Mgr.-Sls. & Mktg.--Belmont Metals, Inc., Brooklyn, NY; *U.S. Private*, pg. 132
Gavin, John, Exec. V.P.--Right Management Consultants, Inc., Philadelphia, PA; *U.S. Public*, pg. 1390
Gavin, K.J., Dir.-Sls.--Henry Ford & Son, Limited, Cork, Ireland; *U.S. Public*, pg. 665
Gavin, Moira, Sr. V.P.-Sls.-Lenox Brands--Lenox, Incorporated, Lawrenceville, NJ; *U.S. Public*, pg. 261
Gawriluk, Susie, Dir.-Travel Industry Sls.--Hyatt Hotels Corporation, Chicago, IL; *U.S. Private*, pg. 551
Gawronski, Robert A., National Sls. Mgr.--Alumax Primary Materials Management National Sales Office, Mentor, OH; *U.S. Public*, pg. 60
Gay, Lawrence W., Sr. V.P.-Sls. & Bus. Devel.--GTECH Corporation, West Greenwich, RI; *U.S. Public*, pg. 767
Gaylor, Chris, V.P.-Sls.--Shimadzu Scientific Instruments, Inc., Columbia, MD; *Int'l*, pg. 1232
Gaynor, Elizabeth, Sls.--Geyer-McAllister Publications, Inc., New York, NY; *U.S. Private*, pg. 450
Gdanitz, John A., V.P.-Sls.--Sani-Dairy Div., Johnstown, PA; *U.S. Public*, pg. 1271
Geaber, Diane, Mgr.-Sls.--Providence Energy Corporation, Providence, RI; *U.S. Public*, pg. 1337
Gearey, Susan J., V.P.-Retail Sls./San Francisco & Northwest Region--Tiffany & Co., New York, NY; *U.S. Public*, pg. 1608
Geddeis, Bob, Dir.-Intl. Sls.--Greenlee Textron, Rockford, IL; *U.S. Public*, pg. 1589
Geddes, Bob, V.P.-Mktg. & Sls.--Giga-Tronics Incorporated, San Ramon, CA; *U.S. Public*, pg. 742
Geddis, John, V.P.-Retail Sales--Villeroy & Boch Tableware, Ltd., Princeton, NJ; *Int'l*, pg. 1468
Gee, Robert, V.P.-Sls.--Cloverhill Bakery, Chicago, IL; *U.S. Private*, pg. 247
Geedey, Harry, V.P.-Sls. & Mktg.--Empire Kosher Poultry, Inc., Mifflintown, PA; *U.S. Private*, pg. 374
Geer, Thomas, Dir.-Sls.--Fried. Krupp AG, Essen, Germany; *Int'l*, pg. 507
Geesa, Gilbert, V.P.-Sls.--Graphic Arts Division, Fort Worth, TX; *U.S. Private*, pg. 419
Geffert, Jim, V.P.-Natl. Sls.--Woman's Day, New York, NY; *Int'l*, pg. 795
Gegus, J.A., Dir.-Worldwide Sls.--Dresser-Rand Co. (Wellsville), Wellsville, NY; *U.S. Public*, pg. 529
Geheran, John J., V.P.-Sls.--Bose Corporation, Framingham, MA; *U.S. Private*, pg. 160
Gehrman, Jim, V.P.-Sls.--Fraser Papers, Inc., Stamford, CT; *Int'l*, pg. 434
Geiger, Peter E., V.P.-Sls.--Geiger Brothers, Lewiston, ME; *U.S. Private*, pg. 442
Geisbauer, James, Mgr.-Sls.--Grocers and Merchants Insurance, Inc., Covina, CA; *U.S. Private*, pg. 227
Geisen, Paul, Mgr. Sls.-Natl. Accts.--Temco Fireplace Products, Inc., Nashville, TN; *U.S. Public*, pg. 1576
Geishecker, Edward P., V.P.-U.S. & Canada Sls. & Mktg.--Ionics, Incorporated, Watertown, MA; *U.S. Public*, pg. 912
Geissberger, Heinz, Mgr.-Sls. & Mktg.--K-Tron Switzerland-Soder Division, Niederlenz, Switzerland; *U.S. Public*, pg. 938
Gelb, Mike, Sr. V.P.-Dept. Store Sls.--Crystal Clear Industries, Ridgefield Park, NJ; *U.S. Private*, pg. 293
Gelinski, Larry, Mgr.-Sls.--Baum USA, Sidney, OH; *Int'l*, pg. 1293
Gellman, Bob, V.P.-Sls.--Computer City, Fort Worth, TX; *U.S. Public*, pg. 1560
Gellner, John, Jr., Mgr.-Sls.--Hoffman Import and Distribution Company, Millburn, NJ; *U.S. Private*, pg. 584
Gempko, Rick, V.P.-Grocery Sls.--GSC Enterprises, Inc., Sulphur Springs, TX; *U.S. Private*, pg. 436
Genadry, Elie M., V.P.-Institutional Sls.--The Dreyfus Corporation, New York, NY; *U.S. Public*, pg. 1085
Gendron, Tom, Mgr.-Customer Support & Bus. Devel.--Woodward Governor Company, Rockford, IL; *U.S. Public*, pg. 1776
Gennari, John, V.P.-Sls.--Borden Italian Foods, Columbus, OH; *U.S. Private*, pg. 158
Genovese, Frank, V.P. & Gen. Mgr.-Sls.--The Jaydor Corporation, Millburn, NJ; *U.S. Private*, pg. 584
Genovese, Pat, Regional Mgr.-Central--Columbus Mills, Inc., Columbus, GA; *U.S. Private*, pg. 256
Gensheimer, Karl, V.P. & Dir.-Sls.--KSTP-TV, Saint Paul, MN; *U.S. Private*, pg. 544
Gentilcore, James, V.P.-Sls. & Mktg.--Advanced Energy Industry, Fort Collins, CO; *U.S. Public*, pg. 20
Gentile, Dominic, V.P.-Sls. & Export--The Eureka Company, Bloomington, IL; *Int'l*, pg. 440
Gentili, Gene, V.P.-Sls. & Mktg./Consumer Pkgng. Div.--Ivex Packaging Corporation, Lincolnshire, IL; *U.S. Public*, pg. 915
Gentry, David S., V.P.-Sls.--Current Technology, Inc., Irving, TX; *U.S. Public*, pg. 480
Gentz, Jim, Sr. V.P.-Sls. & Mktg.--Yamaha Motor Corp., U.S.A., Cypress, CA; *Int'l*, pg. 1516
Geocaris, Dan, V.P.-Sls. & Mktg.--Little Lady Foods, Inc., Elk Grove Village, IL; *U.S. Private*, pg. 671
George, Alex, Mgr.-Natl. Sls.--KSHB-TV, Kansas City, MO; *U.S. Public*, pg. 1448
George, David G., V.P.-Sls.--Mackenzie Financial Corporation, Toronto, Canada; *Int'l*, pg. 828
George, John W., Pres.--Autocon Technologies, Inc., Farmington, MI; *U.S. Public*, pg. 850
George, Kim, Sls. & Mktg. Asst.--Jamison Bedding, Inc., Franklin, TN; *U.S. Private*, pg. 581
George, Rodney M., V.P.-Sls.--Melody Foods, Inc., Farmington Hills, MI; *U.S. Private*, pg. 730
Georgells, Nicholas, V.P.-Sls.--Weaber, Inc, Lebanon, PA; *U.S. Private*, pg. 1155
Georgeson, Craig, Sls. Rep.--Leblanc Communications, Inc., Richardson, TX; *U.S. Private*, pg. 656
Georgiadis, Gus P., Exec. V.P.-Sls. & Mktg.--Highmark Inc., Pittsburgh, PA; *U.S. Private*, pg. 528
Gephart, Bruce, V.P.-Sls.--Shiseido Cosmetics (America) Ltd., New York, NY; *Int'l*, pg. 1235
Geraci, James, V.P.-Sls.--Brimms Inc., Tonawanda, NY; *U.S. Private*, pg. 169
Gerardiello, Jerry, Dir.-Natl. Ad Sls.--National Football League Properties, Inc., New York, NY; *U.S. Private*, pg. 783
Gerber, John, V.P.-Sls.--American Drew, Greensboro, NC; *U.S. Public*, pg. 974
Gerber, Michael J., V.P.-Sls.--Custom Laminates, Inc., Dallas, TX; *U.S. Public*, pg. 1530
Gericke, Ed, V.P.-Sls.--True Temper Hardware Company, Camp Hill, PA; *U.S. Public*, pg. 846
Gerlach, Dan, Div. Mgr.-Sls.--The Jel Sert Co., West Chicago, IL; *U.S. Private*, pg. 585
Gerlach, Guy, Reg. Sls. Dir.--Heinemann ELT-Brazil, Sao Paulo, Brazil; *Int'l*, pg. 1479
Germaine, D., Mgr.-Sls.--Union Camp Chemical Products Div., Wayne, NJ; *U.S. Public*, pg. 1666
German, Gary H., V.P.-Sls. & Mktg.--Ultimate Technology Corporation, Victor, NY; *U.S. Public*, pg. 1637
Gerol, Bob, V.P.-Sls.--Photo & Sport Optics Div.--Pentax Corporation, Englewood, CO; *Int'l*, pg. 85
Gerold, Martin, Dir.-Export Sls.--Diebels Private Brewery, Issum, Germany; *Int'l*, pg. 413
Gerosa, Peter R., Gen. Mgr.-Sls. & Svc.--Cadillac Motor Car Division, Warren, MI; *U.S. Public*, pg. 720
Gerrity, Thomas E., V.P.-Sls. & Mktg.--E-Z Serve Corp., Houston, TX; *U.S. Public*, pg. 540
Gerrity, Thomas E., Mgr.-Sls. & Mktg.--E-Z Serve Convenience Stores, Inc., Houston, TX; *U.S. Public*, pg. 540
Gershaw, Gerald, Pres.-Intl. Div.--Therapedic Associates, Inc., Middlesex, NJ; *U.S. Private*, pg. 1079
Gershberg, Jay, Sr. V.P. & Pres.-Travel Nurse Grp.--Hospital Staffing Services, Inc., Fort Lauderdale, FL; *U.S. Public*, pg. 840
Gerstein, Mel, Treas. & Dir.-Mktg., Adv. & Pub. Rels.--Thermwell Products Co., Inc., Paterson, NJ; *U.S. Private*, pg. 1081
Gerthamp, Hans-Hermann, Dir.-Sls.--Mueller's Muehle GmbH, Gelsenkirchen, Germany; *Int'l*, pg. 896
Gervais, Diane, Mgr.-Natl. Sls.--Fisher Broadcasting Inc., Seattle, WA; *U.S. Public*, pg. 648
Gessner, Lee, Sr. V.P.-Sls.--Word, Incorporated, Dallas, TX; *U.S. Public*, pg. 704
Getchis, Randy E., Sr. V.P.-Sls. & Mktg.--Automotive Rentals, Inc. (ARI), Mount Laurel, NJ; *U.S. Private*, pg. 535
Gettman, K.D., Mgr.-Sls.--Longview Fibre Co. Western Div., Seattle, WA; *U.S. Public*, pg. 1014
Getto, Judith, Mgr.-Sls. Service--Hazen Paper Company, Holyoke, MA; *U.S. Private*, pg. 514
Getto, Steven, V.P.-Sls.--Howes Leather Corporation, Curwensville, PA; *U.S. Private*, pg. 543
Gezundhajt, B., Sr. V.P.-Mktg. & Sls.--Zim-American Israeli Shipping Co., New York, NY; *U.S. Private*, pg. 1206
Ghedine, Scott, Sls.--Geyer-McAllister Publications, Inc., New York, NY; *U.S. Private*, pg. 450
Giambalvo, Gina, Mgr.-Natl. Sls. Devel.--People, New York, NY; *U.S. Public*, pg. 1613
Giambra, Ernie, V.P.-Mktg. & Sls.--Pioneer Life Insurance Co. of Illinois, Rockford, IL; *U.S. Public*, pg. 434
Giammarco, Ralph, V.P.-Sls. & Mktg.-Advanced Technologies Grp.--Tekra Corporation, New Berlin, WI; *U.S. Private*, pg. 1073
Giamo, Kathy, Dir.-Sls. & Mktg.--Reckson Associates Realty Corp., Melville, NY; *U.S. Public*, pg. 1368
Gianferante, Richard, V.P.-Mktg. & Sls.--Northwestern Golf Company, Elmhurst, IL; *U.S. Private*, pg. 806
Giangiulo, Randall C., Sr. V.P.-Grp. Sls.--Phoenix Home Life Mutual Insurance Company, Hartford, CT; *U.S. Private*, pg. 863
Giannasi, Susan, Sls. Coord.-Consumer Sls.--San-J Intl. Inc., Richmond, VA; *Int'l*, pg. 1183
Giannola, Paul J., V.P.-IQUE Sls.--Dyersburg Corporation, Dyersburg, TN; *U.S. Public*, pg. 538
Giard, Larry, Dir.-Sls.--Orkin Exterminating Co., Inc., Atlanta, GA; *U.S. Public*, pg. 1404
Giarusso, Joseph, Sr. V.P.-Sls.--Entertainment Partners, Burbank, CA; *U.S. Private*, pg. 554
Gibbey, Brewnan, V.P.-Sls. & Mktg.--Allison-Erwin Co. Inc., Charlotte, NC; *U.S. Private*, pg. 41
Gibbs, Bob, Dir.-US Sls.--Ansul Incorporated, Marinette, WI; *U.S. Public*, pg. 1648
Giblain, Eric, Dir.-Sls.--C.M.C. SA, Saint Quentin-en-Yvelines, France; *Int'l*, pg. 792
Gibney, Robert, Dir.-Pigment Sls. & Mktg./Americas--Kerr-McGee Chemical Corp., Oklahoma City, OK; *U.S. Public*, pg. 952
Gibson, Betsy, Mgr.-Sls.--Shape South, Inc., Dadeville, AL; *U.S. Private*, pg. 990
Gibson, D., Mgr.-Sls. & Mktg.--Air UK Engineering Ltd., Stansted, United Kingdom; *Int'l*, pg. 39
Gibson, G.S., Gen. Mgr.-Sls.--J & L Specialty Products Corp., Pittsburgh, PA; *Int'l*, pg. 572
Gibson, Mark, V.P.-Wholsale Sls.--Copeland Corporation, Sidney, OH; *U.S. Public*, pg. 573
Gibson, P., Mgr.-Sls.--Rolls-Royce Inc., Reston, VA; *Int'l*, pg. 1127
Gibson, Pam, Mgr.-Category--United Dairy Farmers, Inc., Cincinnati, OH; *U.S. Private*, pg. 1121
Gibson, Peter, V.P.-Mktg. & Sls.--U.S. Turbine Corporation, Maineville, OH; *Int'l*, pg. 1127
Gibson, Ronald L., V.P.-Sls.--Duke Energy Corporation, Charlotte, NC; *U.S. Public*, pg. 534
Gibson, Stewart, Mgr.-Sls.--APV Crepaco, Inc., Dryer Div., North Attleboro, MA; *Int'l*, pg. 1240
Giersch, Frederic E., III, V.P.-Sls. Devel.--Anheuser-Busch International, Inc., Saint Louis, MO; *U.S. Public*, pg. 114
Gigena, Leopoldo, Dir.-Sls.--Juan Minetti S.A., Cordoba, Argentina; *Int'l*, pg. 869
Giglio, Phil, V.P.-Sls.--Apache Hose & Belting Company, Inc., Cedar Rapids, IA; *U.S. Private*, pg. 76
Gignac, Jim, Dir.-Sls. & Mktg.--Elgin Dairy Foods, Inc., Chicago, IL; *U.S. Private*, pg. 370
Giguere, Coreen, Mgr.-Medical Sls.--Solon Manufacturing Company, Solon, ME; *U.S. Private*, pg. 1013

Gilbert, Charles, V.P.-Intl. Sls.--Bird Products Corporation, Palm Springs, CA; U.S. Public, pg. 1591
Gilbert, Chris, Sr. V.P.-Sls.--Altec Lansing Technologies, Inc., Milford, PA; U.S. Private, pg. 479
Gilbert, David, V.P.-Resort Sls.--Interval International Inc., Miami, FL; U.S. Public, pg. 320
Gilbert, George A., Mgr.-Sls.--Hansen Corporation, Princeton, IN; Int'l, pg. 868
Gilbert, R.W., Exec. V.P.-Sls. & Mktg. & Treas.--Shure Brothers Incorporated, Evanston, IL; U.S. Private, pg. 997
Gilbert, Robert, V.P.-Sls.--Benchmark Electronics Inc., Angleton, TX; U.S. Public, pg. 210
Gilbert, Tim, V.P.-Sls.--Reyco Industries, Inc., Springfield, MO; U.S. Private, pg. 926
Gilbertson, Michael D., Dir.-Sls.--Faribault Foods Inc., Minneapolis, MN; U.S. Private, pg. 393
Gilchrist, Charles, Dir.-Sls.--Acme Foundry, Inc., Coffeyville, KS; U.S. Private, pg. 13
Giles, Mike, Mgr.-Laminated Prods. Sls.--Anthony Forest Products Co., Inc., El Dorado, AR; U.S. Private, pg. 76
Giles, Roger, V.P.-Intl. Sls.--Sea Ray, Knoxville, TN; U.S. Public, pg. 266
Gill, Andrew, Comml. Dir.--International Thomson Business Publishing, London, United Kingdom; U.S. Public, pg. 1601
Gill, Ed, Sr. V.P.-Sls. Admin.--Jockey International, Inc., Kenosha, WI; U.S. Private, pg. 588
Gill, Jerry A., V.P.-Sls.--Varco BJ Drilling Systems, Orange, CA; U.S. Public, pg. 1709
Gill, Lee, Gen. Mgr.-Natl. Accts. Sls./Container Opers.--Boise Cascade Corporation, Boise, ID; U.S. Public, pg. 242
Gill, Luther, V.P.-Sls.--All Star Gas Co.-Region VIII, Lebanon, MO; U.S. Private, pg. 35
Gillece, Rich, V.P.-Natl. Sls.--All-Luminum Products, Inc., Philadelphia, PA; U.S. Private, pg. 34
Gillespie, D., Mktg. Dir.--Rodenstock Precision Optics, Inc., Rockford, IL; Int'l, pg. 1007
Gillespie, Dennis G., Pres.-Worldwide Mktg. & Domestic Sls.--Viacom Enterprises, New York, NY; U.S. Private, pg. 779
Gillespie, William G., Mgr.-Sls.-Natl. Childcare--J.L. Hammett Company, Braintree, MA; U.S. Private, pg. 498
Gilley, E.J., V.P.-Sls.--Wang's International, Inc., Memphis, TN; U.S. Private, pg. 1149
Gilliam, Doyle, V.P.-Sls.--E.C. Barton & Company, Jonesboro, AR; U.S. Private, pg. 119
Gilligan, Fred, Dir.-Bus. Devel.--Raytheon Optical Systems, Lexington, MA; U.S. Public, pg. 1364
Gilliland, Robert, Dir.-Sls. & Mktg.--Texon Materials Inc., Russell, MA; U.S. Private, pg. 1079
Gillis, Carey, Regional Mgr.-Atlantic Coast--Columbus Mills, Inc., Columbus, GA; U.S. Private, pg. 256
Gillon, Peter, V.P.-Sls.--Harris-Kayot, Inc., Fort Wayne, IN; U.S. Private, pg. 506
Gillott, Terry, V.P.-Sls. & Mktg.--Jacuzzi Bros., Jacuzzi, Inc., Little Rock, AR; U.S. Public, pg. 1684
Gilman, John, Sr. V.P. & Mgr.-Natl. Sls.--Allyn & Bacon, Needham, MA; U.S. Private, pg. 778
Gilmer, William, V.P.-Sls. & Mktg.--The Homestead L.C., Hot Springs, VA; U.S. Private, pg. 247
Gilmore, Bill, V.P.-Sls. & Mktg.--Beloit Lenox, Div., Lenox, MA; U.S. Public, pg. 789
Gilmore, Kathleen, Mgr.-Sls.--Gilmore Envelope Corp., Los Angeles, CA; U.S. Private, pg. 454
Gilreath, Mark, Mgr.-Eastern Region Sls.--Pentax Precision Instrument Corp., Orangeburg, NY; Int'l, pg. 85
Gilson, Pat, Mgr.-Sls.--Circle Freight International USA, Mendota Heights, MN; U.S. Public, pg. 371
Gimber, Peter S.P., V.P.-Eastern Sls.--CBS Enterprises Division, New York, NY; U.S. Public, pg. 274
Ginder, Douglas, V.P.-Sls.--Redco Corporation, Red Lion, PA; U.S. Private, pg. 915
Ginley, John, Mgr.-Malco Automotive Sls.--Malco Products, Inc., Barberton, OH; U.S. Private, pg. 698
Ginsberg, Herb, V.P.-Sls.--Bel-Art Products, Pequannock, NJ; U.S. Private, pg. 130
Ginsberg, Steve, Mgr.-Sls.--Mallory, Inc., Carson City, NV; U.S. Private, pg. 698
Ginsberg, Teri, Sls. Coord.--O'Donnell-Usen Fisheries Corp., Tampa, FL; U.S. Public, pg. 427
Gioia, Giuseppe, Dir.-Sls.--Kabelschlepp GmbH, Siegen, Germany; Int'l, pg. 721
Giordano, Alexander, Exec. V.P. & Chief Mktg. Officer--Standard Security Life Insurance Company of New York, New York, NY; U.S. Private, pg. 446
Giordano, Joan, Supvr.-Customer Svcs.--H. Freeman & Son, Inc., Philadelphia, PA; U.S. Private, pg. 426
Giordano, Sal, Mgr.-Sls.--Honeywell, Inc., Fort Washington, PA; U.S. Public, pg. 804
Giorgianni, George, Exec. V.P.-Sls. & Mktg.--Allegiant Physician Services, Atlanta, GA; U.S. Public, pg. 45
Giorgianni, George, V.P.-Sls.--Surgical Information Systems, Atlanta, GA; U.S. Public, pg. 45
Gipson, William, V.P.-Commercial Opers.--The Empire District Electric Company, Joplin, MO; U.S. Public, pg. 579
Giralt, P., Dir.-Sls.--FIMA-Productos Alimentares, Lda, Lisbon, Portugal; Int'l, pg. 471
Girard, Francis E., Pres. & Chief Exec. Officer--Comverse Network Systems, Wakefield, MA; U.S. Public, pg. 425
Giraudy, John, Dir.-Sls.--Bombardier Regional Aircraft Division, Downsview, Canada; U.S. Public, pg. 242
Giroux, Bob, Mgr.-Sls.--Malette Quebec, Inc., Montreal, Canada; Int'l, pg. 833
Girsky, Charles B., V.P.-Sls.--Jaco Electronics, Inc., Hauppauge, NY; U.S. Public, pg. 920
Gish, Alan, V.P.-Strategic Mktg.--Eagle Electric Mfg. Co., Inc., Long Island City, NY; U.S. Private, pg. 354
Giuffre, N. J., V.P.-Sls.--Bradford-White Corporation, Ambler, PA; U.S. Private, pg. 164
Giuliani, Joe, V.P.-Sales--Duron, Inc., Beltsville, MD; U.S. Private, pg. 349
Giunestress, James, V.P.-Sls.--Cherry Central Cooperative, Traverse City, MI; U.S. Private, pg. 233
Giunte, Dora, Coord.-Sls.--Acclaim Entertainment, Inc., Glen Cove, NY; U.S. Public, pg. 15
Given, Cecil, V.P.-Sls. & Mktg.--The Flood Company, Hudson, OH; U.S. Private, pg. 414
Givens, J.M., Mktg. & Sls.--Autolease Fleets Limited, Birmingham, United Kingdom; Int'l, pg. 216
Gladfelter, Thomas R., V.P.-Sls.,Mktg. & Adv.--Spontex, Inc., Columbia, TN; Int'l, pg. 1409
Glaisyer, Heidi, V.P.-Sls.--J.R. Simplot Company Food Group, Boise, ID; U.S. Private, pg. 1002
Glass, Donald L., Exec. V.P.-Bldg. Prods., Mfg. & Sls.--Georgia-Pacific Corporation, Atlanta, GA; U.S. Public, pg. 735
Glasscock, Rhonda, Admin. Asst.- Toyota Motor Sls., USA--Toyota Motor Corporation, Tokyo, Japan; Int'l, pg. 1411
Glatzau, Sandy, Sr. V.P.-Mktg. & Sls.--Browning-Ferris Industries, Inc., Houston, TX; U.S. Public, pg. 262
Gleason, Daniel S., Staff V.P.-Passenger Sls.--Aloha Airgroup, Inc., Honolulu, HI; U.S. Private, pg. 44
Gleason, Pat, V.P.-Sls.--Willert Home Products, Inc., Saint Louis, MO; U.S. Private, pg. 1177
Gleaves, Leon R., V.P.-Mktg. & Sls.--Wilkins-Rogers Incorporated, Ellicott City, MD; U.S. Private, pg. 1176
Gleeson, David, Dir.-Sls. & Mktg.--Reilly Industries, Inc., Indianapolis, IN; U.S. Private, pg. 919
Gleich, Steven, V.P.-Sls.--Gould Paper Corporation, New York, NY; U.S. Private, pg. 466
Gleicher, Alan A., Sr. V.P.-Sls.--Intuit, Inc., Mountain View, CA; U.S. Public, pg. 911
Glenner, Lori, Dir.-Business Devel.--Aurora Electronics, Inc., Irvine, CA; U.S. Public, pg. 147
Glessner, David, V.P.-Sls. & Mktg. (ARMD)--I.C. System, Inc., Vadnais Heights, MN; U.S. Private, pg. 553
Glibert, P., Dir.-Sls.--Cockerill Sambre, Brussels, Belgium; Int'l, pg. 301
Glick, Ken, Dir.-Sls.--Lennar Homes Inc., Miami, FL; U.S. Public, pg. 988
Glickman, Joseph L., Mgr.-Sls.--Ruslander & Sons, Inc., Buffalo, NY; U.S. Private, pg. 952
Glickman, Joseph L., Mgr.-Sls.--The Jewett Refrigerator Co., Inc., Buffalo, NY; U.S. Private, pg. 952
Gligorovic, Goran, Dir.-Natl. Sls.--Omega World Travel, Inc., Fairfax, VA; U.S. Private, pg. 816
Glockner, Dieter, V.P.-Sls.--Deutsche Girozentrale-Deutsche Kommunalbank, Frankfurt/Main, Germany; Int'l, pg. 406
Glomb, John, Mgr.-Natl. Sls./U.S.A.--HMI Industries, Cleveland, OH; U.S. Public, pg. 771
Glover, M., Dir.-Mktg. & Sls.--Labatt Breweries of Canada - Prairie Region, Edmonton, Canada; Int'l, pg. 679
Glowiak, Matthew, Mgr.-Sls. & Mktg.--H. Wilson Company, South Holland, IL; U.S. Private, pg. 359
Gmunder, Thomas, Dir.-Adv. & Sls.--Schweizer Verband der Raiffeisenbanken, Saint Gallen, Switzerland; Int'l, pg. 1211
Gnat, Larry, Sls. Mgr.--Milgray/Chicago, Inc., Palatine, IL; U.S. Public, pg. 206
Gnesda, Thomas A., V.P.-Sls. & Mktg.--EcoScience Produce Systems Corp., Orlando, FL; U.S. Public, pg. 563
Gobern, June C., Asst. Dir.-Sls. & Tech. Mktg. Opers.--Cytogen Corporation, Princeton, NJ; U.S. Public, pg. 471
Goblet, Michael R., V.P.-Sls.--Ringer Corporation, Bloomington, MN; U.S. Public, pg. 1390
Goddard, Melanie L., Mgr.-Sls. & Mktg.--Koehler Manufacturing Company, Marlborough, MA; U.S. Private, pg. 706
Godfrey, Ralph, Sr. V.P.-Client Access/America Sls.--3Com Corporation, Santa Clara, CA; U.S. Public, pg. 1603
Godfrey, Tony, V.P.-Sls. & Mktg.--Columbus Mills, Inc., Columbus, GA; U.S. Private, pg. 256
Goding, Keith L, Chief Devel. Officer & Exec. V.P.--RehabCare Group, Inc., Saint Louis, MO; U.S. Public, pg. 1373
Goedhart, E., Dir.-Mktg. & Sls.--Fokker Aircraft Services B.V., Hoogerheyde, Netherlands; Int'l, pg. 1304
Goer, Randy, V.P.-Sls.--Goer Manufacturing Co., Charleston, SC; U.S. Private, pg. 904
Goertz, Steve, Mgr.-Natl. Sls.--Data Transmission Network Corporation, Omaha, NE; U.S. Public, pg. 486
Goetz, W.D., Dir.-Worldwide Sls.--Reading & Bates Corporation, Houston, TX; U.S. Public, pg. 1354
Goetzen, Johann, Area Sls.--Analog Devices GMBH - Technisches Buero West, Cologne, Germany; U.S. Public, pg. 108
Goetzke, John, V.P.-Agribus. Sls.--MSI Insurance Companies, Arden Hills, MN; U.S. Private, pg. 688
Goff, Roger, Sr. V.P.-Mktg. & Customer Service--The Cornelius Company, Anoka, MN; Int'l, pg. 646
Goffi, Ernest, V.P.-Mktg. & Sls.--Fosbel, Inc., Berea, OH; Int'l, pg. 234
Goffredo, David B., V.P.-Pharmaceutical Prods. Mktg. & Sls.--Abbott Laboratories, Abbott Park, IL; U.S. Public, pg. 12
Goggin, Jim, Mktg.-Sls.--Wilsey Foods, Inc., Salem, OR; Int'l, pg. 879
Goins, Bill, V.P.-Sls.--Moore Document Solutions, Lake Forest, IL; Int'l, pg. 890
Goins, James, Mgr.-Sls.--International Carolina Glass Corp., Rock Hill, SC; U.S. Public, pg. 895
Goit, Whitney, Exec. V.P.-Mktg. & Sls.--A&E Television Networks, New York, NY; U.S. Private, pg. 515
Goit, Whitney, II, Exec. V.P.-Sls. & Mktg.--Arts & Entertainment Network/ABC/NBC, New York, NY; U.S. Public, pg. 512
Goit, Whitney, II, Exec. V.P.-Sls. & Mktg.--Arts & Entertainment Network/ABC/NBC, New York, NY; U.S. Private, pg. 516
Gola, Oswaldo, Dir.-Commercial Sls. & Mktg.--SmithKline Beecham Laboratorios Ltda., Rio de Janeiro, Brazil; Int'l, pg. 1266
Gold, Isaac, Sr. V.P.-Sls. & Procurement Fresh Pork--Thorn Apple Valley, Inc., Southfield, MI; U.S. Public, pg. 1602
Gold, Kevin, Dir.-Intl. Sls.--Diagraph Corporation, Earth City, MO; U.S. Private, pg. 330
Gold, Rick, Dir.-Mktg. & Sls.--The Eureka Company, Bloomington, IL; Int'l, pg. 440
Gold, William W., V.P.- Car Sls.--Enterprise Rent-A-Car Company, Saint Louis, MO; U.S. Private, pg. 377
Goldberg, Michael, Dir.-Sls.--Raymour and Flanigan Furniture Co., Liverpool, NY; U.S. Private, pg. 912
Goldberg, Michael, V.P.-Juvenile Sls.--Safety 1st, Inc., Chestnut Hill, MA; U.S. Public, pg. 1425
Goldberg, Ron, V.P. & Dir.-Sls.--CLTV News, Oak Brook, IL; U.S. Public, pg. 1635
Goldberg, Steve, Dir.-Sls.--Raymour and Flanigan Furniture Co., Liverpool, NY; U.S. Private, pg. 912
Goldburg, H. Lance, V.P.-Sls.--Improved Blow Molding Equipment Company, Inc., Bedford Park, IL; U.S. Private, pg. 464
Golde, Mark, Rep.-Sls. Promo.--Dillard, A ResourceNet International Company, Charlotte, NC; U.S. Public, pg. 902
Golden, Michael, V.P.-Sls.-Plumbing No. America--Kohler Company, Kohler, WI; U.S. Private, pg. 630
Golden, Paul, V.P.-Mktg.--Dranetz-BMI, Edison, NJ; U.S. Private, pg. 1144
Golden, Steven P., Mgr.-Gen. Sls.--Gasco, Inc., Honolulu, HI; Int'l, pg. 225
Goldenberg, Mindy D., V.P.-Sls.--Goldenberg Candy Company, Philadelphia, PA; U.S. Private, pg. 461
Goldfarb, Al, V.P.-Sls.--Gould Paper Corporation, New York, NY; U.S. Private, pg. 466
Goldfarb, Marc, V.P. & Mgr.-Natl. Sls.--National Banner Company, Inc., Dallas, TX; U.S. Private, pg. 780
Goldklank, Mitchell, Sr. V.P.-Sls. & Mktg.--LCS Industries, Inc., Clifton, NJ; U.S. Public, pg. 970
Goldschmidt, Mark, V.P. & Dir.-Corp. Mktg. & Sls.--Hearst Magazines Division, New York, NY; U.S. Private, pg. 516
Goldsmith, Marvin, Pres.-Sls. & Mktg.-TV Network--ABC, Inc, New York, NY; U.S. Public, pg. 511
Goldsmith, Marvin, Pres.-Sls. & Mktg.--ABC Television Network Group, New York, NY; U.S. Public, pg. 511
Goldstein, Arnold, V.P.-Sls. & Mktg.--Danzas Corporation, Bellevue, WA; Int'l, pg. 382
Goldstein, Mark E., V.P.-Sls. & Mktg.--Stanley Door Systems, Troy, MI; U.S. Public, pg. 1509
Goldstein, Richard J., V.P.-Sls. & Mktg.--Industrial Electronics Division, Collinsville, CT; Int'l, pg. 204
Goman, Stan, Sr. V.P.-Sls.--Tower Records, West Sacramento, CA; U.S. Private, pg. 688
Gomeau, Mary Ellen, V.P.-Sls. & Mktg.--Phonetics, Inc., Aston, PA; U.S. Private, pg. 863
Gomez, Bob, Reg. Sls. Mgr.--Aromat Southwest Sales Office, El Segundo, CA; Int'l, pg. 848
Gomez, Jose, Dir.-Sls. & Mktg.--La Reina, Inc., Los Angeles, CA; U.S. Private, pg. 640
Gomez, Manuel, Sr. V.P.-Intl. Opers.--Renault, Boulogne-Billancourt, France; Int'l, pg. 1102
Goncalves, Jose, Mgr.-Sls.--Swedish Match do Brasil S/A, Rio de Janeiro, Brazil; Int'l, pg. 1328
Gonzalez, Alberto, Mgr.-Sls.--Quimica Henkel S.A. de C.V., Morelos, Mexico; Int'l, pg. 613
Gonzalez, Carlos, Dir.-Sls.--Nepera Inc., Harriman, NY; U.S. Public, pg. 297
Gonzalez, Danelle, Dir.-Sls. & Conservation Svcs.--Puget Sound Energy, Inc., Bellevue, WA; U.S. Public, pg. 1342
Gonzalez, Steve, V.P.-Sls.--AT&T Networked Commerce Services, Parsippany, NJ; U.S. Public, pg. 11
Good, Carl, Mgr.-Industrial Sls.--Homasote Company, Trenton, NJ; U.S. Public, pg. 831
Good, David S., V.P.-Sls. & Mktg.--Engineered Systems Group, Jackson, MI; U.S. Public, pg. 24
Good, Jim, V.P.-Domestic Sls.--Liebert Corporation, Columbus, OH; U.S. Public, pg. 573
Goode, Curtis L., Jr., Mgr.-Southeast Reg. Sls.--Sofamor Danek Group, Inc., Memphis, TN; U.S. Public, pg. 1482
Goodfellow, David, Mng. Dir.-Sls.--Hermann Pfauter GmbH & Co., Ludwigsburg, Germany; Int'l, pg. 617
Goodman, Brian, Dir.-Sls.--Noble House Hotels and Resorts, Kirkland, WA; U.S. Private, pg. 800
Goodman, Jeffrey M., V.P.-Sls.--The Topps Company, Inc., New York, NY; U.S. Public, pg. 1621
Goodman, Larry, Exec. V.P.-CNN Sls.--CNN Headline News, Atlanta, GA; U.S. Public, pg. 1614
Goodman, Larry, Pres.-CNN Sls. & Mktg.--CNN (Cable News Network), Atlanta, GA; U.S. Public, pg. 1614
Goodman, Marc, Dir.-Adv. Sls.--Discovery Networks, Inc., Bethesda, MD; U.S. Private, pg. 334
Goodpaster, Mike, Retail Sls.--Staodyn Inc., Longmont, CO; U.S. Public, pg. 1509
Goodson, John G., Mgr.-Sls.--TransInstruments, Basingstoke, United Kingdom; U.S. Public, pg. 857
Goodwyn, William H., Jr., Exec. V.P.-Sls. & Mktg.--Lawyers Title Insurance Corporation, Richmond, VA; U.S. Public, pg. 981
Goodyear, Bruce, V.P.-Field Sls.--The Blodgett Oven Co., Inc., Burlington, VT; U.S. Public, pg. 1064
Gorak, Michael, Pres.--Martin/F. Weber Company, Philadelphia, PA; U.S. Private, pg. 710
Goranson, Brad A., V.P.-Sls. Midwest--Steel Technologies Inc., Louisville, KY; U.S. Public, pg. 1513
Gorchow, Jonathan R., V.P.-Mktg. & Sls.--Comcast Cable Communications, Inc., Philadelphia, PA; U.S. Public, pg. 407
Gordon, Cary, Mgr.-W. Central Sls.--RAM Golf Corporation, Melrose Park, IL; U.S. Private, pg. 908
Gordon, Cheryl, Dir.-Mktg. & Sls.--Rothschild North America Inc., New York, NY; U.S. Private, pg. 947
Gordon, Cheryl, Dir.-Sls. & Mktg.--Rothschild Inc., New York, NY; U.S. Private, pg. 947
Gordon, Dan, Mgr.-Sls.--Replogle Globes, Inc., Broadview, IL; U.S. Private, pg. 923
Gordon, Dave, Dir.-Mktg.-Swine & Poultry Prods.--Elanco Animal Health, Indianapolis, IN; U.S. Public, pg. 993

Gordon, Kathleen, Sr. Dir.-Sls. & Sls. Programs--Amtrak-National Railroad Passenger Corp., Washington, DC; *U.S. Private*, pg. 68

Gordon, Mark, Dir.-Vehicle Conversions--The Crown Divisions, Wooster, OH; *U.S. Public*, pg. 1631

Gordon, Rick, Sr. V.P.-Sls.--All American Semiconductor, Inc., Miami, FL; *U.S. Public*, pg. 41

Gordon, Russell L., Dir.-Corp. Devel.--RPM, Inc., Medina, OH; *U.S. Public*, pg. 1356

Gordon, S., Mgr.-Natl. Sls.--Crane National Vendors Co., Ltd., Scarborough, Canada; *U.S. Public*, pg. 456

Gordon, Steffan A., Dir.-Prod. & Sls. Support--JLG Industries, Inc., McConnellsburg, PA; *U.S. Public*, pg. 918

Gordon, Steve, Exec. V.P. & Dir.-Sls. & Mktg.--Columbia Paint & Coatings, Spokane, WA; *U.S. Private*, pg. 256

Gorecham, Jim, Reg. Mgr.-Sls.--PENCO-Tennessee, Nashville, TN; *Int'l*, pg. 1508

Gormally, Pat, Mgr.-Prod. Mkt.--Vitramon, Incorporated, Monroe, CT; *U.S. Public*, pg. 1722

Gorman, D., Exec. V.P.-Sls.--R.T. Vanderbilt Company, Inc., Norwalk, CT; *U.S. Private*, pg. 1133

Gorman, Jon, Dir.-Sls. & Mktg.--Power Contracting & Engineering Corp., Schaumburg, IL; *U.S. Private*, pg. 877

Gorman, Joseph P., V.P.-Sls.--Graham Manufacturing Co., Inc., Batavia, NY; *U.S. Public*, pg. 757

Gorman, Tom, Dir.-Sls.--Aydin Telecom Division, Horsham, PA; *U.S. Public*, pg. 158

Gorski, Martin, Mgr.-Natl. Sls.--Charmilles Technologies Corp., Lincolnshire, IL; *Int'l*, pg. 489

Gos, A., Dir.-Sls.--ALZ N.V., Genk, Belgium; *Int'l*, pg. 79

Goshien, Gerald, Controller & Treas.-Sls. For Meats & Produce--The Mad Butcher, Inc., Pine Bluff, AR; *U.S. Private*, pg. 693

Goss, John, Mgr.-Sls.--PENCO-Georgia, Atlanta, GA; *Int'l*, pg. 1508

Goss, R.S., V.P.-Sls., Intermountain Region--Longview Fibre Co. Western Container Div., Twin Falls, ID; *U.S. Public*, pg. 1014

Gosselin, Raymond, V.P.-Sls.--Palmer Manufacturing Company, Malden, MA; *U.S. Private*, pg. 835

Gouett, Charles G., Mgr.-Sls.--Bondware, Toronto, Canada; *Int'l*, pg. 417

Gouett, Charles G., Mgr.-Sls.--Robinson Cone, Burlington, Canada; *Int'l*, pg. 417

Goulakos, George, V.P.-Sls.--CFCF Inc., Montreal, Canada; *Int'l*, pg. 240

Goulakos, Georges, Gen. Sls. Mgr.--CFCF 12, Montreal, Canada; *Int'l*, pg. 241

Gould, Bob, Dir.-Sls.--D. Anderson & Son Ltd., Stretford, United Kingdom; *Int'l*, pg. 659

Gould, Doyle, V.P. & Gen. Mgr.-Flow Measure Div.--Perry Equipment Corporation, Mineral Wells, TX; *U.S. Private*, pg. 855

Gould, William, Mgr.-Sls. & Mktg.--Brady Enterprises, Inc., East Weymouth, MA; *U.S. Private*, pg. 165

Goulding, Cecil, Dir.-Worldwide Sls.--Farr Company, El Segundo, CA; *U.S. Public*, pg. 613

Goulding, Thomas, V.P.-Sls. & Mktg., Interconnect Produdts Div.--Altron Incorporated, Wilmington, MA; *U.S. Public*, pg. 59

Goulson, George, Sr. V.P.-Franchise Devel.--A&W Restaurants, Inc., Livonia, MI; *U.S. Private*, pg. 1

Gourley, Richard, V.P.-Sls.--Adaptec, Inc., Milpitas, CA; *U.S. Public*, pg. 19

Gouze, Stephen P., V.P.-Sls. & Mktg.--INCSTAR Corporation, Stillwater, MN; *Int'l*, pg. 483

Goward, Jim, Mgr.-Sls., W. Coast Opers.--LeaRonal, Inc., Orange, CA; *U.S. Public*, pg. 982

Gower, Myron T., V.P.-Engrng. Sls.--Miller Electric Company, Jacksonville, FL; *U.S. Private*, pg. 747

Goyette, Richard, Sls. Rep.--Bennington Iron Works, Inc., Bennington, VT; *U.S. Private*, pg. 133

Goyette, Richard C., V.P.-Sls. & Mktg.--Scan-Optics, Inc., Manchester, CT; *U.S. Public*, pg. 1436

Grabaskewitz, Bill, V.P.-Western Reg. Sls.--Southwestern Life Insurance Company, Dallas, TX; *U.S. Private*, pg. 1018

Grabia, Leonard, V.P.-Sls.--Pascoe Building Systems, Inc., Columbus, GA; *U.S. Private*, pg. 842

Grable, Marsha, Mgr.-Sls.--International Window-Arizona, Inc., Phoenix, AZ; *U.S. Public*, pg. 895

Grabowski, Dave, V.P.-Sls. & Mktg.--Allied Healthcare Products, Inc., Saint Louis, MO; *U.S. Public*, pg. 48

Grabowski, Richard E., V.P.--Camosy, Inc., Russell, IL; *U.S. Private*, pg. 203

Grady, Bill, Mgr.-Theme Parks Sls.--Ortho-Kinetics, Inc., Waukesha, WI; *U.S. Private*, pg. 820

Grady, Joseph, V.P.-Worldwide Sls.--AMATI Communications Corp., San Jose, CA; *U.S. Public*, pg. 1585

Grady, R. Paul, V.P.-Sls. & Opers. (Northern Div.)--AmeriGas Partners, L.P., Valley Forge, PA; *U.S. Public*, pg. 1653

Grady, Thomas F., Jr., V.P.-Sls./Imperial Bondware Corp.--Imperial Bondware Corp., Montvale, NJ; *U.S. Public*, pg. 903

Grady, Tom, V.P.-Sls.--Imperial Bondware Corp., Montvale, NJ; *U.S. Public*, pg. 903

Graff, Michael, V.P.-Strategic Mktg.--Harris Semiconductor, Melbourne, FL; *U.S. Public*, pg. 792

Graft, Jim, V.P.-Sls.--Coleman Powermate Compressors, Springfield, MN; *U.S. Private*, pg. 691

Graham, Chuck, Mgr.-Intl. Sls.--Rudolph Foods Company, Lima, OH; *U.S. Private*, pg. 950

Graham, Dennis, V.P.-Bus. Devel.--Educational Insights, Inc., Carson, CA; *U.S. Public*, pg. 565

Graham, Doug, V.P.-Sls., Mktg. & Customer Service--Utilimaster Corp., Wakarusa, IN; *U.S. Private*, pg. 1130

Graham, James, Sr. V.P.-European Sls.--Columbia Tri-Star International Television, Culver City, CA; *Int'l*, pg. 1281

Graham, Jim, Sr. V.P.-Corp. Sls. & Mktg.--Time Inc., New York, NY; *U.S. Public*, pg. 1612

Graham, John, Mgr.-Mktg. & Sls.--The Citadel Assurance Companies, Toronto, Canada; *Int'l*, pg. 346

Graham, Mark, V.P.-Sls.--Pameco Corp., Norcross, GA; *U.S. Public*, pg. 1255

Graham, P.M., Gen. Mgr.-Sls.--Research Products Corporation, Madison, WI; *U.S. Private*, pg. 924

Graham, Rod, V.P.-Worldwide Sls.--Siliconix, Inc., Santa Clara, CA; *Int'l*, pg. 367

Graham, Roy, Sr. V.P.-Sls. & Mktg.--Wyse Technology Inc., San Jose, CA; *U.S. Private*, pg. 1194

Graham, Thomas A., V.P. & Reg. Sls. Mgr.--First Financial Bank, FSB, Stevens Point, WI; *U.S. Public*, pg. 140

Graham, Tom, V.P.-Sls.--Florida Tile Industries, Inc., Lakeland, FL; *U.S. Public*, pg. 1322

Grahn, Gustav, Sls. Mgr.--Wisaforest Sverige AB, Stockholm, Sweden; *Int'l*, pg. 1429

Gramelspacher, Glenn, Dir.-Corp. Sls.--Jasper Seating Co., Inc., Jasper, IN; *U.S. Private*, pg. 583

Grammenopoulos, Danny, Dir.-Bus. Devel.--Yogen Fruz Worldwide Inc., Markham, Canada; *Int'l*, pg. 1520

Grammer, Bill, Sr. V.P.-Sls.--Imperial Adhesives & Chemicals, Inc., Cincinnati, OH; *U.S. Public*, pg. 1147

Granata, Gene, Mgr.-Sls.--United Receptical, Inc., Pottsville, PA; *U.S. Private*, pg. 1123

Grandcolas, D., Sls. Exec.-Southwest Reg.--Universal Studios TV, Universal City, CA; *Int'l*, pg. 1215

Grangerois, Michelle, Dir.Retail Sls.--The Philadelphia Inquirer, Philadelphia, PA; *U.S. Public*, pg. 964

Grangerois, Mirelle, Dir.-Retail Sls.--Philadelphia Daily News, Philadelphia, PA; *U.S. Public*, pg. 964

Grant, Bruce, V.P.-Sls. & Mktg.--Engineered Polymers Corporation, Mora, MN; *Int'l*, pg. 328

Grant, Lawrence Hunter, V.P.-Sls. & Mktg.--Matthew Bender & Company, Incorporated, New York, NY; *U.S. Public*, pg. 1616

Grant, Patrick D., Mgr.-Natl. Sls.-Aerosois--Peerless Tube Company, Bloomfield, NJ; *U.S. Public*, pg. 1269

Grant, Wadie, Mgr.-Sls.--Marryat & Scott Egypt-S.A., Cairo, Egypt; *Int'l*, pg. 748

Granucci, Leo, Sr. V.P.-Mktg. & Sls.--Core-Mark International, South San Francisco, CA; *U.S. Private*, pg. 275

Granucci, Leo R., Grp. V.P.-Sls.--Bergen Brunswig Drug Company, Orange, CA; *U.S. Public*, pg. 213

Grass, Harry, Dir.-Sls. & Mktg.--CGF Sign, Inc., Denver, CO; *U.S. Private*, pg. 194

Graubard, Erick H., Mgr.-Sls./Latin America--The Ohio Art Company, Inc., Bryan, OH; *U.S. Public*, pg. 1214

Gravenhorst, Ted, Jr., Mgr.-Sls.--John Boos & Company, Effingham, IL; *U.S. Private*, pg. 156

Graves, Matthew, Pres.--Medusa Minerals Co, Thomasville, PA; *U.S. Public*, pg. 1084

Graves, Peter, V.P.-Prod. Mktg.--Selfix, Inc., Chicago, IL; *U.S. Public*, pg. 832

Gray, Barry, V.P.-Sls. & Mktg.--Weiler & Company, Inc., Whitewater, WI; *U.S. Private*, pg. 1160

Gray, Bobby, V.P.-Sls. & Customer Service--UNC ARTEX, Addison, TX; *U.S. Public*, pg. 710

Gray, Brian, Mgr.-Sls./Intl. Sls. & Exports--United Aluminum Corporation, North Haven, CT; *U.S. Private*, pg. 1120

Gray, Diana, Mgr.-Sls.--U.N. Alloy Steel Div., Buena Park, CA; *Int'l*, pg. 1001

Gray, Donna, Mgr.-Sls. Admin.--Melitta U.S.A., Inc., Clearwater, FL; *Int'l*, pg. 857

Gray, Eric L., V.P.-Sls.--F.H. Chase, Inc., Mansfield, MA; *U.S. Private*, pg. 230

Gray, Jack, Area Sls. Mgr.--Varco BJ Oil Tools, Houston, TX; *U.S. Public*, pg. 1709

Gray, James, V.P.-Sls.--Capintec Inc., Ramsey, NJ; *U.S. Private*, pg. 205

Gray, John H., V.P.-West Coast Sls.--CBS Television Network, New York, NY; *U.S. Public*, pg. 274

Gray, Larry, V.P.-Consumer Sls. & Mktg.--The Fuller Brush Company, Great Bend, KS; *U.S. Public*, pg. 282

Gray, Larry H., V.P.-Consumer Sls. & Mktg.--The Fuller Brush Company, Great Bend, KS; *U.S. Public*, pg. 282

Gray, Richard, V.P.-Sls. & Mktg.--Rochester-Midland ICL, Omaha, NE; *U.S. Private*, pg. 937

Gray, Robert A., Mgr.-Sls.--Eberline Instrument Corporation, Santa Fe, NM; *U.S. Public*, pg. 1593

Gray, Scott A., V.P.-Sls. & Mktg.--Gray Printing Co., Fostoria, OH; *U.S. Private*, pg. 472

Gray, William J., Sr. V.P.-Mktg. & Supply--Holly Corporation, Dallas, TX; *U.S. Public*, pg. 830

Graziano, Mike, V.P.-Sls.--Sanford Corporation, Bellwood, IL; *U.S. Public*, pg. 1178

Greaving, Jim, Dir.-Sls.--M & H Dairy, Nashville, TN; *U.S. Public*, pg. 653

Grecco, Gino, Sls. Mgr.--Astro Div., Laconia, NH; *Int'l*, pg. 868

Grecco, Thomas A., V.P.-Sls. & Opers.--Tandem Computers Canada Limited, Markham, Canada; *U.S. Public*, pg. 417

Greco, Joseph, V.P.-Sls.--LG Group Inc., Englewood Cliffs, NJ; *Int'l*, pg. 779

Greco, M., V.P.-Sls.--Tubed Products, Inc., Easthampton, MA; *U.S. Public*, pg. 1066

Green, Barry, Sr. V.P.-Sls. & Mktg.--Active International, Pearl River, NY; *U.S. Private*, pg. 15

Green, Chuck, Sr. Dir.-Sls.--Ben & Jerry's Homemade Inc., South Burlington, VT; *U.S. Public*, pg. 210

Green, Clifford, V.P.-Sls., Mktg. & Adv.--Highfield Manufacturing Co., Bridgeport, CT; *Int'l*, pg. 127

Green, Connie, Coord.-Sls. Project--Benjamin Moore & Co., Montvale, NJ; *U.S. Private*, pg. 133

Green, J., Mgr.-Contracts--Australian Oil & Gas Corporation Limited, Sydney, Australia; *Int'l*, pg. 101

Green, Michael, V.P.-Worldwide Sls.--FORE Systems, Inc., Warrendale, PA; *U.S. Public*, pg. 667

Green, Paul, Dir.-Bus. Devel.--Replogle Globes, Inc., Broadview, IL; *U.S. Private*, pg. 923

Green, Reynold K., V.P.-Sls.--Merrimac Industries, Inc., West Caldwell, NJ; *U.S. Public*, pg. 1098

Green, Rick, V.P.-Sls. & Mktg.--Sensall, Div. of Rosemount, Inc., Hauppauge, NY; *U.S. Public*, pg. 574

Green, Tom, V.P.-Sls. & Mktg.--North American Capacitor Co., Indianapolis, IN; *U.S. Private*, pg. 803

Greenberg, Gary, Mgr.-Local Sls.-KPLZ-FM--Fisher Broadcasting Inc., Seattle, WA; *U.S. Public*, pg. 648

Greenberg, Irwin, V.P.-Natl. Acct. Sls.--Universal Folding Box Company, Inc., Hoboken, NJ; *U.S. Private*, pg. 1127

Greenberg, Steve, V.P.-Sls.--Jantzen, Portland, OR; *U.S. Public*, pg. 1702

Greenberg, Stuart, Sr. Exec. V.P.-Sls--Bestform Foundations, Inc., Long Island City, NY; *U.S. Private*, pg. 140

Greenberg, Stuart, Sr. Exec. V.P.-Sls.--Lily of France, Inc., New York, NY; *U.S. Private*, pg. 140

Greenblatt, Rob, V.P.-Natl. Sls., Glove Div., & Dress Div.--The Grandoe Corp., Gloversville, NY; *U.S. Private*, pg. 469

Greene, Harold, Sr. V.P.-Sls.--Forever Living Products International, Inc., Scottsdale, AZ; *U.S. Private*, pg. 418

Greenfield, R.H., Dir.-Sls.--Crowley Tubing Div., Crowley, TX; *U.S. Public*, pg. 159

Greenisen, Phil, Mktg.--Turner Machine Company, Salem, OH; *U.S. Private*, pg. 368

Greenlee, Algernon F., Mgr.-Retail Bus.--Blue Diamond Growers, Sacramento, CA; *U.S. Private*, pg. 152

Greenlee, Roy, Mgr.-Circulation--Shawnee News-Star, Shawnee, OK; *U.S. Private*, pg. 995

Greenstein, Mark, V.P.-Intl. Sls.--Safety 1st, Inc., Chestnut Hill, MA; *U.S. Public*, pg. 1425

Greer, Richard, Mgr.-Reg. Sls.--Automotive News, Detroit, MI; *U.S. Private*, pg. 284

Gregg, Edward G., V.P.-Sls. & Mktg.--Roppe Corp., Fostoria, OH; *U.S. Private*, pg. 944

Gregg, JIm, V.P.-N. American Sls.--Truevision, Inc., Santa Clara, CA; *U.S. Public*, pg. 1642

Gregg, W., Dir.-Technical Services--Mikropul Environmental Systems Div., Summit, NJ; *Int'l*, pg. 636

Gregorio, Rick, Mgr.-Retail Sls.--Killington Limited, Killington, VT; *U.S. Private*, pg. 61

Gregory, Michael, Dir.-Sls. & Mktg.--The North American Coal Corporation, Dallas, TX; *U.S. Public*, pg. 1149

Greinor, Robert, Sr. V.P.-CATV Sls.--Pico Products, Inc., Lake View Terrace, CA; *U.S. Public*, pg. 1294

Greiper, Beverly, V.P., Dir.-Sls. Promo. & Merchandising--Longevity International, Ltd., New York, NY; *U.S. Private*, pg. 444

Greisl, Kevin P., V.P.-Sls.--Mid-America Capital Resources, Inc., Indianapolis, IN; *U.S. Public*, pg. 913

Greisl, Kevin P., V.P.-Sls.--Mid-America Energy Resources, Indianapolis, IN; *U.S. Public*, pg. 913

Greminger, Dick, Dir.-Sls. & Mktg.--Biltbest Windows, Saint Genevieve, MO; *U.S. Public*, pg. 1683

Grepp, Dave W., V.P.-Sls. & Mktg.--The Chardon Rubber Co., Chardon, OH; *U.S. Private*, pg. 229

Gresack, Morton, V.P.-Sls.--Glamorise Foundations, Inc., New York, NY; *U.S. Private*, pg. 455

Gress, Peter, V.P.-Intl. Sls.--Gress Foods Inc., Gainesville, GA; *U.S. Private*, pg. 480

Gressak, Anthony, V.P.-Bakery Distributor Sls.--Cheesecake Factory Incorporated, Calabasas Hills, CA; *U.S. Public*, pg. 343

Greubel, Dave, Mgr.-Sls.--WTWC-TV, Tallahassee, FL; *U.S. Private*, pg. 439

Greuter, R.C., Mgr.-Sls., Valves & Hydrants--United States Pipe & Foundry Company, Inc., Birmingham, AL; *U.S. Public*, pg. 1736

Grey, Bob, Sr. V.P.-Sls.--Tyco Toys, Inc., Mount Laurel, NJ; *U.S. Public*, pg. 1058

Grey, Thomas, V.P.-Sls. & Mktg.--Lawson Mardon Flexible Packaging, Inc., Bellwood, IL; *Int'l*, pg. 67

Gribbin, Ed, Sr. V.P.-Hospitality Sls.--Angelica Image Apparel, Saint Louis, MO; *U.S. Public*, pg. 113

Griessel, Richard, Dir.-Mktg. & Sls.--Semikron International, GmbH & Co. KG, Nuremberg, Germany; *Int'l*, pg. 1220

Griffhorn, Richard, V.P.-Opers.--Baker Hughes INTEQ, Houston, TX; *U.S. Public*, pg. 166

Griffin, Alfred, Mgr.-Sls., Western--Atlanta Mfg. Facility, Douglasville, GA; *U.S. Private*, pg. 976

Griffin, Charles, Sr. Dir.-Sls. & Mktg.--Sequus Pharmaceuticals, Inc., Menlo Park, CA; *U.S. Public*, pg. 1460

Griffin, Posey, V.P.-Sls.--Jack Lenor Larsen, Inc., New York, NY; *U.S. Private*, pg. 652

Griffin, Thomas P., Sr. V.P.-Sls. & Opers.--Williams Telecommunications Systems, Inc., Houston, TX; *U.S. Public*, pg. 1769

Griffith, David, V.P.-Sls. & Mktg.--Earle Industries, Inc., Earle, AR; *U.S. Private*, pg. 356

Griffith, Greg, V.P.-Sls. & Mktg.--Delta Pride Catfish, Inc., Indianola, MS; *U.S. Private*, pg. 322

Griffith, Lee, V.P.-Sls.--Sunbeam Corporation, Delray Beach, FL; *U.S. Public*, pg. 1533

Griffiths, M., Dir.-Sls.--ABB Kent-Taylor Ltd., Huntingdon, United Kingdom; *Int'l*, pg. 7

Griggs, Ron, V.P.-Sls.--G. Leblanc Corporation, Kenosha, WI; *U.S. Private*, pg. 656

Grijalva, Manuel, Dir.-OEM Sls.--Private Label Division, Chicago, IL; *U.S. Private*, pg. 459

Grilli, L., Dir.-Sls.--Solplant, Milan, Italy; *Int'l*, pg. 1524

Grimes, Dean, Dir.-Sls.--Reed Asian Information, Singapore, Singapore; *Int'l*, pg. 1094

Grimes, Gary, V.P.-Sls. & Mktg.--Directory Distributing Associates, Inc., Saint Louis, MO; *U.S. Private*, pg. 334

Grimland, Gene, Exec. V.P.-Sls.--United American Insurance Co., Dallas, TX; *U.S. Public*, pg. 1623

Grimm, Clyde, V.P.-U.S. Sls.--Bayer Corporation/ Diagnostics Division, Tarrytown, NY; *Int'l*, pg. 173

Grimm, Clyde L., Sr. V.P.-U.S. Sls., Mktg. & Service & Gen. Mgr.--Bayer Corporation, Pittsburgh, PA; *Int'l*, pg. 172

Grimm, J.E., Sls. Mgr.-OEM--Sporlan Valve Company, Washington, MO; *U.S. Private*, pg. 1026

Grimm, Michael, Exec. V.P.-Sls. & Mktg.--MTL Inc., Plant City, FL; *U.S. Public*, pg. 1028

Grimm, Michael, Exec. V.P.-Sls. & Mktg.--Montgomery Tank Lines, Inc., Plant City, FL; *U.S. Public*, pg. 1028

Grindstaff, Evelyn S., V.P.-Sls.--Chi Systems Division, Ann Arbor, MI; *U.S. Public*, pg. 1539
Grisso, Ed, V.P.-Sls. & Mktg.--Harcrest International, Ltd., Clark, NJ; *U.S. Private*, pg. 500
Grissom, Chip, V.P.-Mktg.--Norrell Services Inc., Atlanta, GA; *U.S. Public*, pg. 1192
Groefsema, Bruce, Sr. V.P.-Sls.--Calcot, Ltd., Bakersfield, CA; *U.S. Private*, pg. 200
Groen, Ron, V.P.-Sls. & Mktg.--Texas Micro, Inc., Houston, TX; *U.S. Public*, pg. 1586
Groetzinger, Stephen H., V.P.-N. American Sls.--Tangram Enterprise Solutions, Inc., Cary, NC; *U.S. Public*, pg. 1424
Groff, James, V.P.-Natl. Sls. Mgr.--Beech Holdings, Inc., Wichita, KS; *U.S. Public*, pg. 1365
Grofik, John, Mgr.-Cargo Sls.--Pakistan International Airlines Corporation, New York, NY; *Int'l*, pg. 1022
Groflin, H., Mgr.-Sls.--Tuflin AG, Basel, Switzerland; *U.S. Public*, pg. 578
Grogan, Ken, V.P. & Mgr.-Gen. Sls.--National Brands, Inc., Phoenix, AZ; *U.S. Private*, pg. 780
Grohs, Fred, Dir.-Sls.--Trumpf Inc., Farmington, CT; *U.S. Private*, pg. 1108
Groothuizen, J.E., Sls. Dir.-Pkgng. Steel--Hoogovens Ijmuiden Verkoopkantoor B.V., Ijmuiden, Netherlands; *Int'l*, pg. 754
Groppe, Matt, Mgr.-Area Sls.--Sky Courier, Reston, VA; *U.S. Public*, pg. 33
Grosbois, Jean-Marie, Mgr.-Sls.--Orangina France, Aix-en-Provence, France; *Int'l*, pg. 566
Grosman, Leo, Mgr.-Sls.--Sensormatic (Belgium) S.A., Groot-Bijgaarden, Belgium; *U.S. Public*, pg. 1457
Gross, Debbie, Dir.-Retail Sls.--The Franklin Institute, Philadelphia, PA; *U.S. Private*, pg. 424
Gross, Lawrence J., V.P.-Mktg.--Wabash National Corp., Lafayette, IN; *U.S. Public*, pg. 1730
Grosse, M., Mgr.-Sls.--Fuchs' Sche Tongruben GmbH & Co. Ltd., Ransbach-Baumbach, Germany; *Int'l*, pg. 1488
Grossestreuer, Joseph, Sr. V.P.-Sls./Outsourcing--May & Speh, Inc., Downers Grove, IL; *U.S. Public*, pg. 1063
Grossman, Bernard, V.P.-Sls., Mktg. & Fin.--M. Grossman & Son, Inc., Passaic, NJ; *U.S. Private*, pg. 483
Grossman, Jeff, Mgr.-Natl. Sls.--Ragold, Inc., Chicago, IL; *Int'l*, pg. 1084
Grossman, Michelle, Mgr.-Sls.--U.N. Alloy Steel Div., Buena Park, CA; *Int'l*, pg. 1001
Grothe, Reed, V.P.-Sls.--Interactive Technologies, Inc., Saint Paul, MN; *U.S. Public*, pg. 888
Group, Peter Colettis-Somerset Sls., Dir.-Sls.--Eastern Division, New York, NY; *Int'l*, pg. 412
Group, Steven Hall-Essex Sls., Dir.-Sls.--Eastern Division, New York, NY; *Int'l*, pg. 412
Grove, James, V.P.-Sls.-Americas--Lincoln Industrial, Saint Louis, MO; *U.S. Public*, pg. 1273
Grover, Don, Dir.-Stores--David Jones Limited, Sydney, Australia; *Int'l*, pg. 714
Grover, William G., Sr. V.P.-Sls. & Mktg.--Comdial Corporation, Charlottesville, VA; *U.S. Public*, pg. 407
Groves, Bob, Dir.-Retail Sls.--White Rose Food, Carteret, NJ; *U.S. Private*, pg. 330
Groves, James S., V.P.-Retail Sls.--The Smithfield Companies, Inc., Portsmouth, VA; *U.S. Public*, pg. 1479
Gruaz, Bruno, V.P.-Intl. Sls.--DOALL Company, Des Plaines, IL; *U.S. Private*, pg. 337
Grubman, James, V.P.-Sls.--Media Printing Corporation, Pompano Beach, FL; *U.S. Private*, pg. 726
Gruen, Judy, Dir.-Mktg. & Ad Sls.--Discovery Communications, Inc., Bethesda, MD; *U.S. Private*, pg. 334
Gruettner, Gary, Mgr.-Natl. Sls.--Crown Prince, Inc. (CA), City of Industry, CA; *U.S. Private*, pg. 293
Grulke, Ted, V.P.-Sls. & Mktg./Govt.--Detroit Diesel Corp., Detroit, MI; *U.S. Private*, pg. 850
Grymes, John, Pres.-Williamhouse Div.--American Pad and Paper Company, Dallas, TX; *U.S. Public*, pg. 88
Guariglia, Michael, V.P. & Dir.-Sls. & Mktg.--CBS Television Network, New York, NY; *U.S. Public*, pg. 274
Guarnaccia, Richard T., V.P. & Dir.-Sls. & Mktg.--Reeves International, Spartanburg, SC; *U.S. Private*, pg. 507
Gudmendsson, Goran, Mgr.-Sls.--Neste Cellplast AB, Norrtalje, Sweden; *Int'l*, pg. 914
Guendel, Douglas, V.P.-Consumer Sls.--Golden Books Publishing, New York, NY; *U.S. Public*, pg. 749
Guenin, Greg, Mgr.-Circulation--Brainerd Daily Dispatch, Brainerd, MN; *U.S. Private*, pg. 995
Guenniwag, Tom, V.P.-Sls.--Master Builders Inc., Cleveland, OH; *Int'l*, pg. 1465
Guerico, Vincent M., Sr. V.P.-Worldwide Sls. & Mktg.--General Semiconductor, Inc., Melville, NY; *U.S. Public*, pg. 726
Guerin, J., Mgr.-Sls.--Alumax Mill Products, Inc., Morris, IL; *U.S. Public*, pg. 59
Guerin, Kelly, Mgr.-Sls.--PSS, Cincinnati, OH; *U.S. Public*, pg. 1294
Guerreau, Bernard, Dir.-Sls. & Mktg. (France)--Automobiles Citroen, Neuilly, France; *Int'l*, pg. 1020
Guerrero, Rick, V.P.-Sls.--Standun, Inc., Inglewood, CA; *U.S. Private*, pg. 1032
Guerrero, Rick, V.P.-Sls.--Zephyr Mfg. Co., Inglewood, CA; *U.S. Private*, pg. 1032
Guest, John, Sr. V.P.-Sls.--Salomon-North America Inc., Georgetown, MA; *Int'l*, pg. 1181
Guffey, Bob, Mgr.-Reg.--Imperial Holly Corporation, Sugar Land, TX; *U.S. Public*, pg. 872
Guffey, Bob, Mgr.-Reg. Sls.--Holly Sugar Corporation, Sugar Land, TX; *U.S. Public*, pg. 872
Guglielmi, Dominic, V.P.-Sls./Eastern Region--Peoples Jewellers Corporation, Don Mills, Canada; *Int'l*, pg. 1036
Guhring, R., Mgr.-Sls.--Dynacast Deutschland GmbH, Braunlingen, Germany; *Int'l*, pg. 300
Guida, Chris, Sr. V.P.-Sls.--International Home Foods Inc., Parsippany, NJ; *U.S. Private*, pg. 526
Guidicci, Mark, Sls.--Inverness France, Paris, France; *U.S. Private*, pg. 574
Guijarro, Pedro Urieta, Dir.-Sls.--Telefonica Publicidad e Informac., Madrid, Spain; *Int'l*, pg. 1372
Guilday, Michael C., Mgr.-Sls.--Longview Fibre Co. Central Container Div., Minneapolis, MN; *U.S. Public*, pg. 1014
Guiles, Tammy, Mgr.-Sls.--Amstore Corporation, Muskegon, MI; *U.S. Private*, pg. 68
Guillory, Winston, Sr. V.P.-Sls., Mktg. & Field Opers.--Amtech Systems Corporation, Dallas, TX; *U.S. Public*, pg. 105
Guilzon, David, Mgr.-Sls.--Hannay Reels, Westerlo, NY; *U.S. Private*, pg. 499
Guin, James P., Jr., V.P.-Consumer Prods. Sls.--American & Efird, Inc., Mount Holly, NC; *U.S. Public*, pg. 1412
Guinn, Chet G., Sr. V.P.-Sls.--Longview Fibre Co. Western Div., Seattle, WA; *U.S. Public*, pg. 1014
Guiod, James J., V.P. & Reg. Sls. Mgr.--Airborne Freight Corporation, Seattle, WA; *U.S. Public*, pg. 32
Guist, Alan, V.P.-Sls.--Sherwin-Williams Diversified Brands, Inc., Solon, OH; *U.S. Public*, pg. 1466
Gukelberger, Armin, Dir.-Sls.--Zwick/Roell Group, Ulm, Germany; *Int'l*, pg. 1532
Gulardo, Richard, V.P.-Sls.--Empire Office Equipment, Inc., New York, NY; *U.S. Private*, pg. 374
Guldalian, Ken, Dir.-Mktg. & Sls.--Guth Lighting Company, Saint Louis, MO; *Int'l*, pg. 821
Gulden, Gary W., V.P.-Mktg. & Sls.--JJI Lighting Group Inc., Greenwich, CT; *Int'l*, pg. 821
Gulledge, Mike, Mgr.-Resale Warehouse--Paramount Carowinds, Charlotte, NC; *U.S. Private*, pg. 776
Gunn, Charlene, Dir.-Mktg. & Industry Sls.--Payless Car Rental System, Inc., Saint Petersburg, FL; *U.S. Private*, pg. 844
Gunn, Larry, Gen. Mgr.-Retail Sls.--Cross Creek Apparel, Inc., Mount Airy, NC; *U.S. Public*, pg. 1413
Gunner, Paul, Mgr.-Sls.--Kenwal Products Corp., Dearborn, MI; *U.S. Private*, pg. 615
Gunter, Bill, V.P.-Sls./Americas--Gelman Sciences, Inc., Ann Arbor, MI; *U.S. Public*, pg. 1253
Guogenti, George G., Mgr.-Sls.--James N. Gray Construction Co., Inc., Lexington, KY; *U.S. Private*, pg. 472
Gurassa, Charles, Dir.-Passenger Bus.--British Airways PLC, London, United Kingdom; *Int'l*, pg. 218
Gurgold, Steven, Dir.-Sls.--Tiffany Extruders, Inc., Paterson, NJ; *U.S. Private*, pg. 1085
Gurka, Dennis, V.P.-Domestic Sls.--Dep Corporation, Rancho Dominguez, CA; *U.S. Public*, pg. 500
Gurkin, Martin, Asst. Gen. Mgr. & Dir.-Sls. & Mktg.--Isco Separation Instruments Division, Lincoln, NE; *U.S. Public*, pg. 914
Gusman, Renee, Exec. Dir.-Sls. Resources--20th Century Fox Home Entertainment, Los Angeles, CA; *U.S. Public*, pg. 275
Gusman, Renee, Exec. Dir.-Sls. Resources--20th Century Fox Home Entertainment, Los Angeles, CA; *Int'l*, pg. 926
Gustafson, Al, Field Mgr.-Sls.--Master Lock Company, Milwaukee, WI; *U.S. Public*, pg. 675
Gustafson, Rob, Reg. Sls. Mgr.-Southeastern US--Atlantic Southeast Airlines Inc., Atlanta, GA; *U.S. Public*, pg. 144
Gute, Joseph, Mgr.-Sls.--IMC Magnetics Corp., Tempe, AZ; *Int'l*, pg. 868
Guthmiller, Richard, V.P.-Produce Sls.--Albertson's, Inc., Boise, ID; *U.S. Public*, pg. 38
Guthridge, Jan, Grp. Sls. Dir.--Cedar Point, Sandusky, OH; *U.S. Public*, pg. 319
Guthridge, Jan R., Dir.-Grp. Sls.-Cedar Point--Cedar Fair, L.P., Sandusky, OH; *U.S. Public*, pg. 319
Guthrie, A. D., Dir.-Adv. & Mgr.- Sls. & Mktg.--Sterling Davis Standard, South Plainfield, NJ; *Int'l*, pg. 1240
Guthrie, Frances, Exec. V.P.-Mktg. & Sls.--Fortis Benefits Insurance Company, Kansas City, MO; *Int'l*, pg. 499
Guthrie, James, Sr. V.P.-Sls. & Mktg.--Petersen Publishing Company, L.L.C., Los Angeles, CA; *U.S. Private*, pg. 856
Guttas, Fred, V.P.-Sls.--Precision Twist Drill Co., Crystal Lake, IL; *Int'l*, pg. 1185
Guy, Wendy, Mgr.-Sls. Admin.--Phildas Ltd., Pontefract, United Kingdom; *Int'l*, pg. 585
Gwinn, Victor L., Mgr.-Sls.--Mrs. Cubbison's Foods, Inc., Montebello, CA; *U.S. Public*, pg. 909
Gwozda, E., Dir.-Sls.--SmithKline Beecham Farma B.V., Rijswijk, Netherlands; *Int'l*, pg. 1266
Gyorkonyi, T., Gen. Mgr.-Sls.--Scitel Telematics Ltd., Budapest, Hungary; *Int'l*, pg. 1195
Gyssler, Keith, V.P.-Sls./Western--InterVoice, Inc., Dallas, TX; *U.S. Public*, pg. 910
Haack, Bob, V.P.-Sls.--City Machine Tool & Die Company, Inc., Muncie, IN; *U.S. Private*, pg. 241
Haas, Mike, V.P.-Sls. & Mktg.--Columbia Paint & Coatings, Spokane, WA; *U.S. Private*, pg. 256
Haas, Robert, Dir.-Direct Sls.-Central & S. America--HMI Industries, Cleveland, OH; *U.S. Public*, pg. 771
Haas, Stephen, V.P.-Sls. Admin.--Barton Beers, Ltd., Chicago, IL; *U.S. Public*, pg. 300
Haas, William H., V.P.-Foodservice Distr.--Sweetheart Cup Company Inc., Owings Mills, MD; *U.S. Private*, pg. 1058
Haasl, Jack, Mgr.-Sls.--Mautz Paint Co., Madison, WI; *U.S. Private*, pg. 715
Haber, John, Mgr.-Sls. Desk--Preferred Utilities Manufacturing Corp., Danbury, CT; *U.S. Private*, pg. 881
Haberl, Claudio, Dir.-Sls.--American Sahm Corporation, Greenville, SC; *Int'l*, pg. 1169
Haberman, Pat, V.P.-Sls.--Thompson Medical Company, Inc., West Palm Beach, FL; *U.S. Private*, pg. 1083
Habermann, Reiner, Mgr.-Export Sls.--Kermi GmbH, Plattling, Germany; *Int'l*, pg. 1069
Habetler, Chuck, Mgr.-Sls. & Mktg.--Atlas Cylinder, Eugene, OR; *U.S. Public*, pg. 1261
Habich, Rick, Mgr.-Sls.--General Office Environments Inc., Rochelle Park, NJ; *U.S. Private*, pg. 445
Haboush, Louis, Sr. V.P. & Mgr.-Natl. Sls./Comdisco Healthcare Group, Inc.--Comdisco, Inc., Rosemont, IL; *U.S. Public*, pg. 407
Habuda, Tamas, Mgr.-Intl. Sls.--Malev Hungarian Airlines, Plc., Budapest, Hungary; *Int'l*, pg. 833
Hachenbung, Rich, Asst. Dir.-Sls.--Beltone Electronics Corporation, Chicago, IL; *U.S. Private*, pg. 132
Hackbarth, Warren A., V.P.-Sls.--Proxim, Inc., Mountain View, CA; *U.S. Public*, pg. 1338
Hackett, Jonathan, V.P.-Sls.--Continental Eagle Corporation, Prattville, AL; *U.S. Private*, pg. 267
Hackett, Thomas, V.P.-Commercial Sls.--World Color-Chicago Div., Elk Grove Village, IL; *U.S. Public*, pg. 1778
Hackman, Dodd, Sr. V.P.-Sls. & Mktg.--TABS Direct (Operating Div.), Stafford, TX; *U.S. Private*, pg. 482
Hackman, Roger D., V.P.-Mktg. & Sls.--Seymour Manufacturing Company, Seymour, IN; *U.S. Private*, pg. 988
Hackney, Hodges, Exec. V.P.-Intl. Sls.--Transportation Technologies, Inc., Washington, NC; *U.S. Private*, pg. 1097
Hackney, R. Hodges, Exec. V.P.-Intl. Sls.--Hackney and Sons, Inc., Washington, NC; *U.S. Private*, pg. 1097
Hadd, Dennis, Gen. Mgr.-Sls.--McNamara Pontiac Isuzu Inc., Orlando, FL; *U.S. Private*, pg. 724
Hadden, Bob, V.P.-North American Sls.--White Pine Software, Nashua, NH; *U.S. Private*, pg. 1173
Haden, Rodney D., V.P.-Sls.--Broderbund Software, Inc., Novato, CA; *U.S. Public*, pg. 258
Hadfield, Mike, Pres.--Robert Bosch Fluid Power Corporation, Racine, WI; *Int'l*, pg. 204
Hadley, Joelle, Mgr.-Sls.--Business Journal Publications, Inc., Phoenix, AZ; *U.S. Private*, pg. 19
Haegerty, Robert, V.P.-Sls.--All Star Gas Co.-Region XII, Lebanon, MO; *U.S. Private*, pg. 35
Haen, Chris, Gen. Mgr.-Sls.--Six Flags Great Adventure Theme Park & Wild Safari Animal Park, Jackson, NJ; *U.S. Public*, pg. 1611
Haffey, Bernard, Dir.-Sls.--Mentor Opthalmics, Inc., Santa Barbara, CA; *U.S. Public*, pg. 1086
Haffner, John, Dir.-Sls. & Mktg.--Integrated Health Concepts, Walnut Creek, CA; *U.S. Public*, pg. 1013
Haga, Hisashi, Dir.-Tableware Sls. Dept.--Narumi China Corporation, Nagoya, Japan; *Int'l*, pg. 906
Hagan, Catherine F., V.P.-Retail Sls./King of Prussia & Philadelphia--Tiffany & Co., New York, NY; *U.S. Public*, pg. 1608
Hagan, Daniel Y., V.P.-Refactory Sls.--A.P. Green Industries, Inc., Mexico, MO; *U.S. Public*, pg. 761
Hagan, Howard, Dir.-Sls.--Ammco Tools, Inc., La Vergne, TN; *U.S. Public*, pg. 480
Hagan, Howard, Dir.-Sls.--Hennessy Industries, Inc., La Vergne, TN; *U.S. Public*, pg. 481
Hagan, Jerry, V.P.-Sls.--Glencoe/Mc-Graw Hill, Westerville, OH; *U.S. Public*, pg. 1070
Hagan, Rick, Mgr.-Sls.--Camellia Food Stores, Inc., Norfolk, VA; *U.S. Private*, pg. 203
Hage, Dave, V.P.-Sls. & Mktg.--Power-One, Inc., Camarillo, CA; *U.S. Private*, pg. 878
Hageman, Bruce, Dir.-Sls.-Cleaning Div.--Church & Dwight Specialty Products Division, Princeton, NJ; *U.S. Public*, pg. 356
Hagen, Allen O., Sr. V.P.-Sls.--Bluewater, Mora, MN; *U.S. Private*, pg. 153
Hagen, Billy, Dir.-D.P. & Software Sls.--The Climatic Corp., Columbia, SC; *U.S. Private*, pg. 246
Hager, Ed, Reg. Mgr.-Key Accts.--Coca-Cola Enterprises - Eastern Group/Southeast Region, Atlanta, GA; *U.S. Public*, pg. 393
Hagerty, Patrick K., V.P. & Dir.-Adv. Sls.--U.S. News & World Report, New York, NY; *U.S. Private*, pg. 1125
Haggerty, Richard, Exec. V.P.-Sls.--Gilman Paper Co., Saint Marys, GA; *U.S. Private*, pg. 454
Hagiwara, Tad, Exec. V.P.-Sls.--Hitachi Home Electronics, Norcross, GA; *Int'l*, pg. 621
Hagorty, Carl, V.P.-Sls. & Mktg.--Fire Control Instruments, Inc., Waltham, MA; *U.S. Private*, pg. 406
Hagwood, Geffrey K., V.P.-Sls.--Aerofin Corp., Lynchburg, VA; *U.S. Public*, pg. 103
Hahn, Alan C., Sr. V.P.-Deal Direct Mktg.--Jackson National Life Insurance Company, Lansing, MI; *Int'l*, pg. 1073
Hahn, John, Dir.-Sls. & Mktg.--Fiatallis North America, Inc., Carol Stream, IL; *Int'l*, pg. 483
Hahn, Kenneth A., V.P.-Sls.--The Wyco Tool Co., Racine, WI; *U.S. Private*, pg. 906
Hahn, Michael, V.P.-Sls.--Shofar Kosher Foods, Linden, NJ; *U.S. Public*, pg. 1433
Hahn, Roy, Mgr.-Sls.--Vulcraft Div., Brigham City, UT; *U.S. Public*, pg. 1206
Haid, Frank, V.P.-Sls.--Globelle Corporation, Mississauga, Canada; *Int'l*, pg. 554
Haik, S.J., V.P.-Sls.--ECP Incorporated, Westchester, IL; *U.S. Private*, pg. 313
Haikins, R.C., Dir.-Sls.--Moore Paragon U.K. Limited, London, United Kingdom; *Int'l*, pg. 889
Haile, Don, V.P. & Sls. Mgr.--Hodgson Mill, Inc., Gainesville, MO; *U.S. Private*, pg. 998
Haines, Bruce A., V.P.-Sls.--U.S. Steel International, Inc., Pittsburgh, PA; *U.S. Public*, pg. 1661
Hainrihar, Gary, V.P.-Sls.--Kalamazoo Holdings, Inc., Kalamazoo, MI; *U.S. Private*, pg. 606
Haire, Ann, Sr. V.P.-Circulation--BPI Communications Inc., New York, NY; *Int'l*, pg. 1446
Hairston, Jim, Dir.-Sls. & Mktg.--Hooker Industries, Ontario, CA; *U.S. Private*, pg. 538
Hakoda, Mary M., V.P.-Sls. & Mktg.--Malama Pacific Corp., Honolulu, HI; *U.S. Public*, pg. 800
Haladyn, Jan, Mgr.-Sls.--KONE Elevator A/S, Copenhagen, Denmark; *Int'l*, pg. 747
Halbach, Hans, Exec. V.P.-Sls. & Mktg.--Saab Automobile AB, Nykoping, Sweden; *Int'l*, pg. 687
Halbach, Hans, Exec. V.P.-Sls. & Mktg.--Saab Automobile AB, Nykoping, Sweden; *U.S. Public*, pg. 725
Hale, Joseph, Gen. Mgr.-Corp. Communications & Investor Rels.--Cinergy Corp., Cincinnati, OH; *U.S. Public*, pg. 369
Hale, Mark, Sr. V.P.-Sls.--EAC-Embraer Aircraft Corporation, Fort Lauderdale, FL; *Int'l*, pg. 452
Hale, Nick, Dir.-Sls.--Cheltenham & Gloucester plc, Gloucester, United Kingdom; *Int'l*, pg. 283

Hale, Thomas, V.P.-Sls. & Mktg.--Ball Metal Food Container Corp., Westminster, CO; *U.S. Public*, pg. 171
Haley, Steven R., V.P.-Worldwide Telco Sls.--Cisco Systems, Inc., San Jose, CA; *U.S. Public*, pg. 375
Haliburda, Dan, Dir.-Sls. & Mktg.--Go-Video, Inc., Scottsdale, AZ; *U.S. Public*, pg. 748
Halkoski, Ross, Dir.-Sls.--Provimi Veal Corporation, Seymour, WI; *U.S. Private*, pg. 892
Hall, Deborah, Mgr.-Sls.--U.N. Alloy Steel Div., Houston, TX; *Int'l*, pg. 1001
Hall, Dulany, Dir.-Grp. Sls.--Sea Island Company, Sea Island, GA; *U.S. Private*, pg. 977
Hall, Jimmy, V.P.-Consumer Prods. Sls.--Thomaston Mills, Inc., Thomaston, GA; *U.S. Public*, pg. 1599
Hall, John, V.P.-Mktg. & Sls.--Dan River, Inc., New York, NY; *U.S. Public*, pg. 479
Hall, John, V.P.-Sls. & Mktg.--The Milnot Company, Saint Louis, MO; *U.S. Private*, pg. 749
Hall, Mark, Exec. V.P. & Dir.-Adv. & Sls.--Monarch Avalon, Inc., Baltimore, MD; *U.S. Public*, pg. 1123
Hall, Medford, Mgr.-Divisional Sls.--Ouimet Corp., Nashville, TN; *U.S. Private*, pg. 821
Hall, Peter, Dir.-Export Sls. & Mktg.--Gaylord Container Corporation, Deerfield, IL; *U.S. Public*, pg. 704
Hall, Steve, V.P.-North American Sls.--Sensormatic Electronics Corporation, Boca Raton, FL; *U.S. Public*, pg. 1457
Hall, Susan G., V.P.-Gypsum Sls.--Republic Group Incorporated, Hutchinson, KS; *U.S. Public*, pg. 1378
Hall, Terry, Sr. V.P.-Worldwide Sls.--Cognos Inc., Ottawa, Canada; *Int'l*, pg. 305
Hall, Terry, V.P.-Sls.--Cognos Corp., Burlington, MA; *Int'l*, pg. 306
Hall, Tom, V.P.-Sls.--International Women's Apparel Group, Easton, PA; *U.S. Public*, pg. 796
Hallenbeck, Jack, Sr. V.P.-Sls. & Mktg.--Beatrice Cheese Co., Waukesha, WI; *U.S. Public*, pg. 426
Hallet, A.J., Mgr.-Sls.--Armitage Shanks Limited, Rugeley, United Kingdom; *Int'l*, pg. 197
Hallingby, Barney, Exec. V.P.-Institutional Sls.--Hambrecht & Quist LLC., San Francisco, CA; *U.S. Public*, pg. 778
Hallman, Russel, Sr. V.P.-Mktg. & Sls.--Electronic Data Magnetics, Inc., High Point, NC; *U.S. Private*, pg. 370
Hallock, Charlott, Sls. Mgr.-Parts--W.N. Best, Danbury, CT; *U.S. Private*, pg. 881
Hallom, William, Dir.-Sls. & Mktg.--DeMert & Dougherty, Inc., Coal City, IL; *U.S. Private*, pg. 323
Halloran, Don, Mgr.-Natl. Sls. & Mktg.--Anemostat Products, Scranton, PA; *U.S. Public*, pg. 286
Hallowell, David, Dir.-Sls.--Ark-Les Corporation, Stoughton, MA; *U.S. Private*, pg. 82
Hallquist, Harlan, V.P.--Adolfson & Peterson, Inc., Minneapolis, MN; *U.S. Private*, pg. 17
Hallstedt, Fred, V.P-Sls. & Mktg.--AmeriServe of Grand Rapids, Grand Rapids, MI; *U.S. Private*, pg. 533
Hallstrom, Ulf, Mgr.-Sls.--Esselte Sverige AB, Solna, Sweden; *Int'l*, pg. 459
Halminak, Mike, Mgr.-Natl. Sls.--WFLD Inc., Chicago, IL; *Int'l*, pg. 926
Halpin, John, Sr. V.P.-Direct Mktg.--Successories, Inc., Aurora, IL; *U.S. Private*, pg. 1049
Halstead, Russ, Mgr.-Sls. & Mktg.--Victor Products, Lisle, IL; *U.S. Public*, pg. 480
Halsten, Bob, Mgr.-Sls.--Nucor Building Systems, Waterloo, IN; *U.S. Public*, pg. 1205
Halston, Mike, Mgr.-Natl. Sls.--Carfel, Inc., Miami, FL; *U.S. Private*, pg. 210
Halverson, Gordon E., Exec. V.P.-Sls.--The Antec Corporation, Rolling Meadows, IL; *U.S. Public*, pg. 116
Hamann, John, V.P.-Ford Sls.--CMI International Inc., Southfield, MI; *U.S. Private*, pg. 195
Hamann, Per, Dir.-Sls. & Mktg.--Time/System International A/S, Allerod, Denmark; *Int'l*, pg. 73
Hamer, Scott, Mgr.-Sls.--Waldo Bros. Company, Boston, MA; *U.S. Private*, pg. 1147
Hamerling, Wayne, Exec. V.P.--Jean Philippe Fragrances, Inc., New York, NY; *U.S. Public*, pg. 924
Hamill, D., V.P.-Sls. & Mktg.--Alumax Mill Products, Inc., Morris, IL; *U.S. Public*, pg. 59
Hamilton, Fred, Dir.-Adv. Sls.--Kalmbach Publishing Co., Waukesha, WI; *U.S. Private*, pg. 606
Hamilton, Kenny, Gen. Mgr.-Sls.--Coleman Oldsmobile, Inc., Baton Rouge, LA; *U.S. Private*, pg. 252
Hamilton, Larry, V.P.-Carrier Sls.--RELTEC Corporation, Cleveland, OH; *U.S. Private*, pg. 921
Hamilton, Lee, Mgr.-Nat. Sls.--Triple A Specialty Company, Chicago, IL; *U.S. Private*, pg. 1103
Hamilton, Michael R., Exec. V.P.-Sls. & Service--Briggs & Stratton Corporation, Wauwatosa, WI; *U.S. Public*, pg. 252
Hamilton, Robert, V.P.-Sls.--Kingsdown, Inc., Mebane, NC; *U.S. Private*, pg. 622
Hamilton, Roland, Div. V.P.-Sls.--Trade Products, Lynnwood, WA; *U.S. Public*, pg. 1526
Hamilton, Tim, V.P.-Sls. & Mktg.--J.M. Peters Co., Newport Beach, CA; *U.S. Public*, pg. 302
Hamlin, Steve, V.P.-Sls.--Gem-Dandy, Inc., Madison, NC; *U.S. Private*, pg. 442
Hamm, David J., V.P. & Gen. Mgr.--Jerry Hamm Chevrolet Inc., Jacksonville, FL; *U.S. Private*, pg. 497
Hammel, George R., Dir.-Sls.--McGraw-Hill Healthcare Publications Group, Minneapolis, MN; *U.S. Public*, pg. 1071
Hammer, Michael C., V.P.-Sls.--Deluxe Corporation, Shoreview, MN; *U.S. Public*, pg. 498
Hammett, Ric, Sr. V.P.-Sls.--Baltimore Stationery Co./Total Office, Baltimore, MD; *U.S. Private*, pg. 113
Hammond, Don, V.P.-Sls.--McCormick Distilling Co., Weston, MO; *U.S. Private*, pg. 720
Hammond, Michael L., Mgr.-Sls.--Humphrey Products Company, Kalamazoo, MI; *U.S. Private*, pg. 547
Hammond, Orville E., Sr. V.P.-Matl. Control & Sys. Grp.--O.A. Newton & Son Co., Bridgeville, DE; *U.S. Private*, pg. 797
Hammonds, R.P., Natl. Sls. Mgr.-Hospital & Medical--Becton Dickinson Canada Inc., Mississauga, Canada; *U.S. Public*, pg. 200
Hampton, Charles, Pres. & Chief Exec. Officer--American Louver Co., Skokie, IL; *U.S. Private*, pg. 58
Hampton, Craig, V.P.-Sls. & Mktg.--DSM Sheffield Plastics, Sheffield, MA; *Int'l*, pg. 354
Hampton, Wade, V.P.-Sls.--Andros Incorporated, Berkeley, CA; *U.S. Private*, pg. 74
Hamre, Henrick, Dir-Sls.--Colgate-Palmolive A/S, Glostrup, Denmark; *U.S. Public*, pg. 398
Hamstreet, Richard, Mgr.-Sls.--Pick's Cove Marina, Tacoma, WA; *U.S. Private*, pg. 865
Han, Sung K., Mgr.-Sls.--Crown Engineering Co., Ltd., Seoul, Korea; *Int'l*, pg. 348
Hancharick, Steve, Mgr.-Sls.--PENCO-North Carolina, Raleigh, NC; *Int'l*, pg. 1508
Hancock, John, V.P.-Sls. & Mktg.--Coburn Optical Industries Inc., Tulsa, OK; *U.S. Private*, pg. 248
Hancock, Kevin, Dir.-Media--Giant Food Inc., Landover, MD; *U.S. Public*, pg. 741
Hancock, Mike, V.P.-Intl. Sls.--Reed Elsevier Business Information, Newton, MA; *Int'l*, pg. 1095
Hancock, Scott, Sr. V.P.-Mktg. & Sls.--Unapix Entertainment Inc., New York, NY; *U.S. Public*, pg. 1664
Hand, Max R., Sr. V.P.-Sls.--MEDCO Containment Services, Inc., Montvale, NJ; *U.S. Public*, pg. 1091
Handen, Keith, Mgr.-Natl. Sls.--Salton/Maxim Housewares, Inc., Mount Prospect, IL; *U.S. Public*, pg. 1430
Handler, N., Mgr.-Sls.--Penny & Giles Inc., Santa Monica, CA; *Int'l*, pg. 208
Handley, John M., Sr. V.P.-Mktg. & Sls.--Industrial Acoustics Company, Inc., Bronx, NY; *U.S. Public*, pg. 875
Hanichak, John J., III, V.P.-Natl. Retail Sls.--Anheuser-Busch, Inc., Saint Louis, MO; *U.S. Public*, pg. 114
Hanisko, Dean, V.P.-Sls.--Great Lakes Lithograph Co., Cleveland, OH; *U.S. Private*, pg. 474
Hanke, Art, V.P.-Sls.--The Dial Corporation, Phoenix, AZ; *U.S. Public*, pg. 505
Hanke, Dean, Mgr.-Sls. Devel. & Adv.--J-Star Industries, Inc., Fort Atkinson, WI; *U.S. Private*, pg. 576
Hanke, James, V.P.-Holly--Handleman Company, Troy, MI; *U.S. Public*, pg. 779
Hankins, Bill, Team Leader-Managed Care--Boehringer Ingelheim Pharmaceuticals, Inc., Ridgefield, CT; *Int'l*, pg. 199
Hankins, Cathy, V.P.-Sls. & Mktg.--Memphis Group, Inc., Memphis, TN; *U.S. Private*, pg. 730
Hanks, Ken, Sr. V.P.-Sls.--Ranir Corporation/DCP, Grand Rapids, MI; *U.S. Private*, pg. 909
Hanley, Declan, V.P.-Sls.-Europe--Koss Corporation, Milwaukee, WI; *U.S. Public*, pg. 966
Hanley, Declan, V.P.-Sls., Europe--Koss Europe, Stabio, Switzerland; *U.S. Public*, pg. 966
Hanley, Joseph C., V.P.-Sls./N. America--Columbian Chemicals Company, Atlanta, GA; *U.S. Public*, pg. 1286
Hanlon, D.E., Jr., V.P.-Mktg. & Sls.--Unimark Plastics Company, Greer, SC; *U.S. Public*, pg. 57
Hanlon, John, Natl. Sls. Mgr.--Barry Controls, Brighton, MA; *U.S. Public*, pg. 124
Hanlon, Ward J., V.P.-Sls.--Robin Hood Multifoods Inc., Markham, Canada; *U.S. Public*, pg. 901
Hanna, David E., Mgr.-Sls. & Mktg.--Owatonna Canning Company, Owatonna, MN; *U.S. Public*, pg. 349
Hannagan, Kathie, V.P.--Publishing Div., Tulsa, OK; *U.S. Public*, pg. 565
Hannah, J., Dir.-Sls. & Mktg.--British Gypsum Ltd., Loughborough, United Kingdom; *Int'l*, pg. 122
Hannah, Ron, V.P.-Sls.--Duracell Canada Inc., Mississauga, Canada; *U.S. Public*, pg. 743
Hannay, Donald, Sr., V.P.-Sls.--Rexhall Industries, Inc., Lancaster, CA; *U.S. Public*, pg. 1384
Hannezo, Hubert, V.P.-Mktg. & Sls./MAST & Flag Brands--Michelin Americas Small Tires (MAST), Greenville, SC; *Int'l*, pg. 322
Hannigan, John, Sls. Dir.- N. America--Devro-Teepak, Inc., Westchester, IL; *Int'l*, pg. 408
Hannigan, William J., V.P.-Bus. Sls.--Pacific Bell, San Ramon, CA; *U.S. Public*, pg. 1416
Hanning, Franz, Sr. V.P.-Corp. Sls.--Fairfield Communities, Inc., Little Rock, AR; *U.S. Public*, pg. 610
Hanno, Marshall W., Sr. V.P.-Sls.--LCI International, Inc., Dublin, OH; *U.S. Public*, pg. 969
Hano, Greg, Dir.-Adv.--Popular Mechanics, New York, NY; *U.S. Private*, pg. 517
Hansbury, Ben, Dir.-Sls. & Mktg.--Nordberg-Read, Inc., Middleboro, MA; *Int'l*, pg. 1428
Hansen, Kent, V.P.-Mktg. Sales & Adv.--Nobel Insurance Limited, Hamilton, Bermuda; *Int'l*, pg. 951
Hansen, Larry, Mgr.-Sls.--Hiniker Company, Mankato, MN; *U.S. Private*, pg. 530
Hansen, Larry, Mgr.-Sls./Filling Sys.--H.C. Miller Company, Milwaukee, WI; *U.S. Private*, pg. 747
Hansen, Odille, Dir.-Opers. & Administrator-Insurance--Windsor Fashions, Los Angeles, CA; *U.S. Private*, pg. 1182
Hansen, R.M., V.P.-Mktg. & Sls.--Pyle Inc., Elmhurst, IL; *U.S. Private*, pg. 629
Hanson, Brenda, Mgr.-Sls. & Mktg.--West Virginia Cellular Telephone Corp., Charleston, WV; *U.S. Public*, pg. 1708
Hanson, Ed, Sr. Mgr.-Mktg.--Jewel-Osco, Melrose Park, IL; *U.S. Public*, pg. 93
Hanson, Geoff, Dir.-Sls. & Prod. Support--Dowty Aerospace Propellers, Gloucester, United Kingdom; *Int'l*, pg. 1337
Hanson, Greg, Dir.-Sls.--Hornady Manufacturing Company, Grand Island, NE; *U.S. Private*, pg. 539
Hanson, Larry, V.P.-Mktg. & Sls.--Twin City Foods, Inc., Stanwood, WA; *U.S. Private*, pg. 1111
Hanson, Peter, Mgr.-Sls. & Mktg. Chicago--Banta Publications Group, Long Prairie, MN; *U.S. Public*, pg. 188
Hanson, Richard, Sr. V.P.-Sls.--Northland Aluminum Products, Inc., Minneapolis, MN; *U.S. Private*, pg. 805
Hanson, Richard, Sr. V.P.-Sls. & Mktg.--Nordic Ware, Minneapolis, MN; *U.S. Private*, pg. 806
Hanson, Rick, Mgr.-Mktg.--Great Plains Manufacturing, Inc., Salina, KS; *U.S. Private*, pg. 475
Hanson, William, V.P.-Sls. & Mktg.--Hamlin, Inc., Lake Mills, WI; *U.S. Public*, pg. 251
Hantranft, Jim, Dir.-Sls.--Cherry Electrical Products Corporation, Waukegan, IL; *U.S. Public*, pg. 346
Hara, Adrienne, Dir.-Sls. & Catering--Ark Restaurants Corp., New York, NY; *U.S. Public*, pg. 129
Harasyn, Ken, Mgr.-Sls.--Hawkins Chemical, Inc., Minneapolis, MN; *U.S. Public*, pg. 800
Harbaugh, Jim, Prod. Mgr.--Welding Products Group, Niles, MI; *U.S. Public*, pg. 1161
Harbold, Lin, Mgr.-Sls. & Mktg.--Iceland Seafood Corporation, Newport, VA; *U.S. Private*, pg. 556
Harcourt, Patricia A., Dir.-Corp. Commun.--Belden & Blake Corporation, Canton, OH; *U.S. Private*, pg. 1078
Hardee, Gary, Mgr.-Sls.--Stihl Inc., Virginia Beach, VA; *Int'l*, pg. 1301
Harden, Jon R., V.P.-Sls.--Avemco Corporation, Frederick, MD; *U.S. Public*, pg. 151
Hardies, Albert C., V.P.-Mktg. & Sls.--Zinc Corporation of America, Monaca, PA; *U.S. Private*, pg. 540
Harding, Jack, V.P.-Sls.--U.S. Bottlers Machinery Co., Charlotte, NC; *U.S. Private*, pg. 1124
Harding, Mark, Gen. Sls. Mgr.--Santa Monica Ford Company, Santa Monica, CA; *U.S. Private*, pg. 965
Hardison, Jack, Dir,-Sls. & Mktg.--Pool Energy Services Co., Houston, TX; *U.S. Public*, pg. 1316
Hardison, Trafton T., Asst. V.P.-Sls.--Estes Express Lines, Inc., Richmond, VA; *U.S. Private*, pg. 384
Hardman, Douglas R., Mgr.-Sls. & Engrng.--J.H. Fletcher & Co., Huntington, WV; *U.S. Private*, pg. 412
Hardmin, Jay, Mgr.-Sls.--Nestle-Rowntree Ltd., York, United Kingdom; *Int'l*, pg. 921
Hardt, Wolfgang, Dir.-Sls.--Saarbergwerke Aktiengesellschaft, Saarbruecken, Germany; *Int'l*, pg. 1166
Hardy, David, Asst. Mgr.-Sls.--Frederick Trading Company, Frederick, MD; *U.S. Private*, pg. 335
Hardy, David L., Pres.-Custom Weave & Wunda Weave Sls. Div.--World Carpets, Inc., Dalton, GA; *U.S. Private*, pg. 1190
Hardy, William M., Jr., V.P.-Reg. Sls./S. Alabama--Alfa Corporation, Montgomery, AL; *U.S. Public*, pg. 40
Hare, Stan, Mgr.-Indus. Sls.--Mapa Pioneer Corporation, Willard, OH; *Int'l*, pg. 1409
Hargrove, George, V.P.-Sls. & Mktg.--Barnhardt Manufacturing Co., Charlotte, NC; *U.S. Private*, pg. 116
Hargrove, George, V.P.-Sls. & Mktg.--Carolina Absorbent Cotton Co., Charlotte, NC; *U.S. Private*, pg. 117
Harker, Gary, Exec. V.P.-Sls.--California Panel & Veneer Company, Cerritos, CA; *U.S. Private*, pg. 201
Harker, R.J., Dir.-Sls., Europe, Africa & West Asia--British Timken Div., Northampton, United Kingdom; *U.S. Public*, pg. 1617
Harkins, Ann, V.P.-Sls. Services--CBS Television Network, New York, NY; *U.S. Public*, pg. 274
Harkless, Brad, Exec. V.P.-Sls. & Mktg.--L & S Bearing Co., Oklahoma City, OK; *U.S. Public*, pg. 970
Harkness, Glenn, V.P. & Dir.-Bus. Devel.--TRC Companies, Inc., Windsor, CT; *U.S. Public*, pg. 1557
Harlan, David M., V.P.-Natl. Sls. & Mktg.--United States Cold Storage, Inc., Cherry Hill, NJ; *U.S. Private*, pg. 1124
Harlan, Richard K., V.P.-Sls. & Mktg.--E.W. Knauss & Son, Inc., Quakertown, PA; *U.S. Private*, pg. 626
Harless, I., Dir.-Mktg. & Sls.--Tri Tech Laboratories, Inc., Lynchburg, VA; *U.S. Private*, pg. 1101
Harlow, Rick, V.P.-Engrng. & Dir.-Mktg. & Sls.--Universal Fasteners Inc., Lawrenceburg, KY; *Int'l*, pg. 1515
Harm, Ray, V.P.-Sls.--BarcaLounger Company, Rocky Mount, NC; *U.S. Private*, pg. 265
Harman, Jon, Natl. Sls. Mgr.--Branson Ultrasonics Corp. - Precision Cleaning Div., Danbury, CT; *U.S. Public*, pg. 574
Harmon, Al, Mgr.-Natl. Sls.--Beutlich, L.P., Waukegan, IL; *U.S. Private*, pg. 141
Harmon, Brad, Dir.-Retail Adv.--The Cincinnati Enquirer, Inc., Cincinnati, OH; *U.S. Public*, pg. 700
Harmon, Eugene, Sls. Rep.--Bennington Iron Works, Inc., Bennington, VT; *U.S. Private*, pg. 133
Harmon, Gary, Exec. V.P.-Sls.--Kraft Foods Inc., Glenview, IL; *U.S. Public*, pg. 1288
Harmon, Tom, Sls. Mgr.--Scott Aviation, Lancaster, NY; *U.S. Public*, pg. 622
Harms, Steve, Exec. V.P.-Sls.--Sika Corporation, Lyndhurst, NJ; *Int'l*, pg. 1249
Harnes, Jay, V.P.-Sls. & Mktg.--A.O. Smith Water Products Company, Irving, TX; *U.S. Public*, pg. 1477
Harness, Larry, Sr., Consultant-Sls. & Mktg.--Bassick by Kaspar, Shiner, TX; *U.S. Private*, pg. 122
Harnist, Charlie L., V.P.-Sls.--Skyline Chili, Inc., Fairfield, OH; *U.S. Public*, pg. 1475
Harold, Ann, Exec. V.P.-Mktg. & Sls.--Weber-Stephen Products Co., Palatine, IL; *U.S. Private*, pg. 1157
Harp, Paul L., V.P.-Sls. & Mktg./Processed Meats--Gwaltney of Smithfield, Ltd., Smithfield, VA; *U.S. Public*, pg. 1479
Harper, Don, Gen. Mgr.-Sls.--Town & Country Homes, Fort Worth, TX; *U.S. Public*, pg. 319
Harper, George C., Dir.-Sls.--Dexter Aerospace Materials Division, Pittsburg, CA; *U.S. Public*, pg. 504
Harper, Georgie, V.P.-Sls.--Dakotah, Inc., Webster, SD; *U.S. Public*, pg. 477
Harradine, Bob, Mgr.-Sls.--Genesee A & B, Inc., Old Hickory, TN; *U.S. Private*, pg. 446
Harradine, Robert P., Mgr.-Sls.--Genesee Metal Stampings, Inc., West Henrietta, NY; *U.S. Private*, pg. 446
Harrell, Francis C., Sr. V.P.-USA Sls.--International Comfort Products, Franklin, TN; *U.S. Public*, pg. 898
Harrell, Frank, V.P.-Sls.--International Comfort Products Corp., Lewisburg, TN; *U.S. Public*, pg. 898

Harrigan, Pat, Mgr.-Sls.--Cleveland Electric Co., Atlanta, GA; *U.S. Private*, pg. 246
Harrington, David, Mgr.-Sls.--Advance Packaging Corporation-Jackson Facility, Jackson, MI; *U.S. Private*, pg. 18
Harrington, Paul, Dir.-Domestic Direct Sls.--Checkpoint Systems Inc., Thorofare, NJ; *U.S. Public*, pg. 343
Harrington, Richard, V.P.-Sls.-Textile Prods.--Raffi & Swanson, Inc., Wilmington, MA; *U.S. Private*, pg. 907
Harris, Alan F., Exec. V.P.-Cereal Div.-Mktg. & Sls.--Kellogg USA Inc., Battle Creek, MI; *U.S. Public*, pg. 947
Harris, Albert, V.P.-Mktg. & Sls.--Johnson & Towers, Inc., Mount Laurel, NJ; *U.S. Private*, pg. 590
Harris, Bob, Dir.-Sls.--Wright Brand Foods, Inc., Vernon, TX; *U.S. Private*, pg. 1192
Harris, Bob, V.P.-Sls. & Mktg.-Durango Boot--Georgia/Durango Boot Company, Franklin, TN; *U.S. Public*, pg. 1684
Harris, Bonnie, Dir.-Natl. Sls.--EB5 Corporation, Portland, OR; *U.S. Private*, pg. 353
Harris, Bruce, Mgr.-Sls.--Steel Form Div., New Braunfels, TX; *U.S. Private*, pg. 932
Harris, David, Natl. Sls. Mgr.--ComPair LeRoi, Sidney, OH; *Int'l*, pg. 1242
Harris, Gregory L., V.P.-Sls. & Mktg.--Ault Incorporated, Minneapolis, MN; *U.S. Public*, pg. 147
Harris, John, Sls. Mgr.-Southeast--Storck U.S.A., L.P., Chicago, IL; *Int'l*, pg. 1304
Harris, K., Mgr.-Natl. Sls. & Mktg.--Goodman Fielder Mills (NZ) Ltd., Auckland, New Zealand; *Int'l*, pg. 556
Harris, Ken, Dir.-Sls.--Email Limited-Major Appliance Group, Riverwood, Australia; *Int'l*, pg. 450
Harris, Ken, Dir.-Sls. & Service/Europe--GenRad, Inc., Westford, MA; *U.S. Public*, pg. 731
Harris, Linda, Mgr.-Sls.--American City Business Journals, Inc., Houston, TX; *U.S. Private*, pg. 19
Harris, Patrick B., Sr. V.P.-Sls. & Retail--News America Marketing, Norwalk, CT; *Int'l*, pg. 925
Harris, Peter, V.P.-Sls. & Mktg.--American Science & Engineering, Inc., Billerica, MA; *U.S. Public*, pg. 90
Harris, Richard L., V.P.-Sls.--American Baler Co., Bellevue, OH; *U.S. Private*, pg. 102
Harris, Robert, Mgr.-Sls.--Koch Container, Victor, NY; *U.S. Private*, pg. 177
Harris, Robert K., Mgr.-Sales/Pipe--United States Pipe & Foundry Company, Inc., Birmingham, AL; *U.S. Public*, pg. 1736
Harris, Thomas, V.P.-Catalog Sls.--World Color-Chicago Div., Elk Grove Village, IL; *U.S. Public*, pg. 1778
Harris, Tom, Dir.-Sls.--The Thompson's Company, Memphis, TN; *U.S. Public*, pg. 1466
Harrison-Dees, Geoffrey, Gen. Mgr.-Sls. & Mktg.--Sun Life and Provincial Holdings plc, London, United Kingdom; *Int'l*, pg. 1318
Harrison, Gerald L., V.P.-Intl. Sls.--Guilford of Maine, Inc., Guilford, ME; *U.S. Public*, pg. 889
Harrison, James F., Sr. V.P.-Sls. & Mktg.--Muzak Limited Partnership, Seattle, WA; *U.S. Private*, pg. 222
Harrison, Lee C., V.P.-Sls.--Foodservice Division, Oklahoma City, OK; *U.S. Public*, pg. 852
Harrison, Lloyd, V.P.-Sls./S.W. Region--Thorn Apple Valley, Inc., Southfield, MI; *U.S. Public*, pg. 1602
Harrison, R. A., V.P.-Sls.--Bryant Grinder Corp., Springfield, VT; *U.S. Private*, pg. 461
Harrison, Tom, Sls. Channel Mgr.--Carhartt, Inc., Dearborn, MI; *U.S. Private*, pg. 210
Harrod, James, Principal-Sls. Trng.--Edward Jones, Saint Louis, MO; *U.S. Private*, pg. 597
Harrold, Jim, Dir.-Sls.--Sensormatic CamEra Ltd., Warwick, United Kingdom; *U.S. Public*, pg. 1457
Hart, Cary, Mgr.-Sls. & Opers.--The Pierce Co., Inc., Upland, IN; *U.S. Private*, pg. 102
Hart, Cynthia L., Sr. V.P. & Dir.-Sls. & Banking Opers.--Bay View Capital Corporation, San Mateo, CA; *U.S. Public*, pg. 197
Hart, David, V.P.-Sls. & Mktg.--American Granby, Inc., Liverpool, NY; *U.S. Private*, pg. 55
Hart, Trevor A., Dir.-Sls.--Weetabix Limited, Kettering, United Kingdom; *Int'l*, pg. 1488
Harte, Kevin, Natl. Sls. Dir.--Avon Cosmetics (Thailand) Ltd., Bangkok, Thailand; *U.S. Public*, pg. 156
Hartenstein, A., Dir.-Sls.--Monarch Luggage Co. Inc., Brooklyn, NY; *U.S. Private*, pg. 757
Harthun, Ken, V.P.-Sls. & Mktg.--Dormeyer Industries, Chicago, IL; *U.S. Private*, pg. 340
Harting, Tom, V.P.-Sls. & Mktg.--Mrs. Alison's Cookie Company, Saint Louis, MO; *U.S. Private*, pg. 765
Hartleib, Chris, Mgr.-Sls.--Rubbermaid Canada Inc. Consumer Products, Mississauga, Canada; *U.S. Public*, pg. 1411
Hartley, Richard, V.P.-Sls. & Mktg.--Mattison Technologies, Inc., Rockford, IL; *U.S. Private*, pg. 714
Hartman, Karen S., V.P.-Mktg. & Sls.--E.R. Moore Co., Chicago, IL; *U.S. Private*, pg. 759
Hartmann, Rolf, Dir.-German Sls.--Knurr AG, Munich, Germany; *Int'l*, pg. 739
Hartnett, Robert B., Pres.-Bus. Sls. & Services--MCI Communications Corp., Atlanta, GA; *U.S. Public*, pg. 1023
Hartnett, Thomas J., V.P.-Sls.--Bird Roofing Products, Inc., Norwood, MA; *Int'l*, pg. 1171
Harvey, Don, Mgr.-Natl. Sls.--Etonic Tretorn, Brockton, MA; *U.S. Private*, pg. 629
Harvey, Mary, Asst. Mgr.-Sls. & Mktg.--Cres-Cor, Cleveland, OH; *U.S. Private*, pg. 288
Harvey, Thomas A., V.P.-Sls. & Mktg.--Faroudja, Inc., Sunnyvale, CA; *U.S. Public*, pg. 613
Harvie, Ed, Mgr.-Sls. & Mktg.--KSB Inc., Richmond, VA; *Int'l*, pg. 721
Harvie, Jeff, Mgr.-Sls. & Mktg.--Kombi, Ltd., Essex Junction, VT; *U.S. Private*, pg. 631
Harward, Dennis, V.P.-Sls.--Leblanc Communications, Inc., Richardson, TX; *U.S. Private*, pg. 656
Harward, Dennis, Dir.-Sls.--Leblanc Communications, Inc., Richardson, TX; *U.S. Private*, pg. 656
Hasbach, Gary, V.P.-Sls. & Mktg.--Florida Tile Industries, Inc., Lakeland, FL; *U.S. Public*, pg. 1322
Hasegawa, Akira, Sr. Exec. V.P.--All Nippon Airways Co. Ltd., Tokyo, Japan; *Int'l*, pg. 57
Haselton, Susan, Customer Service Coord.--Venturi Inc., Traverse City, MI; *U.S. Private*, pg. 1136
Haskins, Bob, V.P.-Mktg. System Tech.--Edwards Systems Tech, Cheshire, CT; *U.S. Public*, pg. 726
Haslam, David, Mgr.-Natl. Sls.--Martin Door Mfg., Inc., Salt Lake City, UT; *U.S. Private*, pg. 708
Hasselbeck, Todd, V.P.-Sls.--Summa Four, Inc., Manchester, NH; *U.S. Public*, pg. 1527
Hassi, James, Mgr.-Intl. Sls.--Allsop, Inc., Bellingham, WA; *U.S. Private*, pg. 44
Hasson, Arthur, Sr. V.P.-Eastern Sls.--Universal Studios TV, Universal City, CA; *Int'l*, pg. 1215
Haste, John, Mng. Dir.-Stores Implementation--PRO Group, Inc., Englewood, CO; *U.S. Private*, pg. 887
Hastings, John A., Dir.-Sls.--C-COR Electronics, Inc., State College, PA; *U.S. Public*, pg. 272
Hatch, Mark, V.P.-Sls. & Mktg.--Data Instruments, Inc., Acton, MA; *U.S. Private*, pg. 312
Hatcher, John L., Corp. V.P.-Health Sys., Sls. Opers., Alternate Care--Allegiance Healthcare Corp., McGaw Park, IL; *U.S. Public*, pg. 44
Hatt, Brad, V.P.-Dometic Beech Sls.--Raytheon Aircraft Company, Wichita, KS; *U.S. Public*, pg. 1365
Hattendorf, J., V.P.-Petroleum Sls.--R.T. Vanderbilt Company, Inc., Norwalk, CT; *U.S. Private*, pg. 1133
Hauck, Al, Natl. Sls. Mgr.--Da-Lite Screen Company, Inc., Warsaw, IN; *U.S. Private*, pg. 306
Hauck, Bob, Mgr.-Sls.--PENCO-Kentucky, Louisville, KY; *Int'l*, pg. 1508
Hauer, Dale, V.P.-Sls. & Mktg.--Ajax Paving Industries Inc., Madison Heights, MI; *U.S. Private*, pg. 29
Haug-Brown, Katrina, Mgr.-Sls.--On Track, Charlotte, NC; *U.S. Private*, pg. 19
Haug-Brown, Katrina, Mgr.-Sls.--Winston Cup Scene, Charlotte, NC; *U.S. Private*, pg. 20
Haug-Brown, Katrina, Mgr.-Sls.--Winston Cup Illustrated, Charlotte, NC; *U.S. Private*, pg. 20
Hauglie, Roy, Mgr.-Sls.--Richardton Mfg. Co., Richardton, ND; *U.S. Public*, pg. 1676
Haugsby, Gary, V.P.-Sls.--Wyandot Inc., Marion, OH; *U.S. Private*, pg. 1193
Haupt, Jill M., V.P. & Reg. Sls. Mgr.--First Financial Bank, FSB, Stevens Point, WI; *U.S. Public*, pg. 140
Hauser, Paul R., V.P. & Dir.-Sls./Bedding Components--Leggett & Platt, Incorporated, Carthage, MO; *U.S. Public*, pg. 985
Hauserman, Tom, Dir.-Sls./Western Div.--Clestra Hauserman, Inc., Solon, OH; *Int'l*, pg. 569
Hausler, Robert J., V.P.-Sls. & Mktg.--Mark Lighting Fixture Co., Inc., Edison, NJ; *U.S. Private*, pg. 704
Haverot, Linda, V.P.-Sls.--Ocean Properties, Ltd., Delray Beach, FL; *U.S. Private*, pg. 811
Hawk, Keith, Sr. Dir.-Sls. & Sls. Support/Bus. Information Systems--LEXIS-NEXIS, Miamisburg, OH; *Int'l*, pg. 1096
Hawken, Doug, Chief Oper. Officer--Karsten Manufacturing Corporation, Phoenix, AZ; *U.S. Private*, pg. 608
Hawkes, Phil, Sr. V.P.-Sls. & Mktg.--Abco Markets, Inc., Phoenix, AZ; *U.S. Private*, pg. 10
Hawley, F.J., Mgr.-Export & Eastern Sls.--Sloan Valve Company, Franklin Park, IL; *U.S. Private*, pg. 1006
Hawley, Sumner, Sls. Mgr.--Airflex Div. Eaton Corp., Cleveland, OH; *U.S. Public*, pg. 556
Haworth, Missy, V.P.-Sls. & Mktg.--Broder Bros. Co., Plymouth, MI; *U.S. Private*, pg. 170
Haws, Larry, Mgr.-Retail Sls./Dehy. Potato--Idaho Supreme Company, Firth, ID; *U.S. Private*, pg. 557
Hay, Bernie, Mgr.-Sls.--Eaton Corporation Commercial Controls Division, Selma, NC; *U.S. Public*, pg. 556
Hay, Bill, V.P.-Sls. & Mktg.--Larson Manufacturing Company, Brookings, SD; *U.S. Private*, pg. 652
Hayden, John, Dir.-Mktg. & Sls. Support--The West Company, Incorporated, Lionville, PA; *U.S. Public*, pg. 1755
Hayden, Mark, Dir.-Food Service Sls.--Lamb-Weston, Inc., Kennewick, WA; *U.S. Public*, pg. 427
Hayden, William F., Dir.-Customer Satisfaction--Columbus McKinnon Corp., Amherst, NY; *U.S. Public*, pg. 405
Haydon, Ted, Sr. V.P.-Sls. & Mktg.--Rock of Ages Canada, Inc., Beebe, Canada; *U.S. Public*, pg. 1396
Hayes, Daniel, V.P.-Sls.--Provident Mutual Life Insurance Co., Berwyn, PA; *U.S. Private*, pg. 891
Hayes, Lisabeth, Reg. V.P.-Midwest Ad Sls.--Home & Garden Television, Knoxville, TN; *U.S. Public*, pg. 1447
Hayes, Lucy, Mgr.-Sls.--American Water Works Association, Denver, CO; *U.S. Public*, pg. 94
Hayes, Marc, Dir.-Sls.--Safety 1st, Inc., Chestnut Hill, MA; *U.S. Public*, pg. 1425
Hayes, Paula, V.P.-Sls.--Premier Cruises, Miami, FL; *U.S. Private*, pg. 293
Hayes, William, Mgr.-Sls.--W.N. Best, Danbury, CT; *U.S. Private*, pg. 881
Haygood, Glenn, Mgr.-Natl. Sls.--WXII-TV, Winston Salem, NC; *U.S. Public*, pg. 1344
Haygood, James F., Jr., V.P.-Apparel Sls.--Thomaston Mills, Inc., Thomaston, GA; *U.S. Public*, pg. 1599
Hayman, Derick, Mgr.-Mktg. Services--The Valspar Corp. Protective Coatings Div., Baltimore, MD; *U.S. Public*, pg. 1707
Hayner, Scott, V.P. & Gen. Sls. Mgr.--Fisher Broadcasting Inc., Seattle, WA; *U.S. Public*, pg. 648
Haynes, J., Dir.-Sls.--Autolease Limited, Birmingham, United Kingdom; *Int'l*, pg. 216
Haynes, Ken, Mgr.-Special Mkts. Sls.--Lamb-Weston, Inc., Kennewick, WA; *U.S. Public*, pg. 427
Haynes, Steven D., V.P.-North American Sls.--Xilinx, Inc., San Jose, CA; *U.S. Public*, pg. 1786
Hays, Brad, V.P.-Sls.--Pennzoil Company, Houston, TX; *U.S. Public*, pg. 1272
Hays, Brad, V.P.-Sls.--Pennzoil Products Co., Houston, TX; *U.S. Public*, pg. 1272
Hays, Brian, Mgr.-Sls.--Holiday Rambler, Wakarusa, IN; *U.S. Public*, pg. 1123
Hays, Bryan, Mgr.-Sls.--Monaco Coach Corporation, Coburg, OR; *U.S. Public*, pg. 1123
Hayward, Anna, Sls. Mgr.--Utell International-New Zealand, Auckland, New Zealand; *Int'l*, pg. 1098
Hayward, Craig, Dir.-Mktg. & Sls.--Acco Chain & Lifting Products, York, PA; *Int'l*, pg. 473
Hazell, Tim, Dir.-Sls.--Matthew Clark Taunton, Ltd., Bristol, United Kingdom; *Int'l*, pg. 848
Hazelwood, Mark A., V.P.-Sls. & Devel.--Pilot Corporation, Knoxville, TN; *U.S. Private*, pg. 865
Hazen, Herman A., V.P.-Sls. & Mktg.--Ferag Inc., Bristol, PA; *Int'l*, pg. 1484
Hazen, Mike, Sls. Mgr.--Mid-Western of Alabama Division, Leesburg, AL; *U.S. Private*, pg. 60
Hazenberg, P.R., Mng. Dir.--Schering Nederland B.V., Weesp, Netherlands; *Int'l*, pg. 1204
Hazleton, John, Mgr. Sls.--Air France (Southwestern Region), Houston, TX; *Int'l*, pg. 561
Head, George V., V.P.-Sls.--Southland Mower Corp., Selma, AL; *U.S. Private*, pg. 1144
Headley, T., V.P. & Dir.-Sls. & Adv.--Midwesco Filter Resources Inc., Winchester, VA; *U.S. Public*, pg. 1026
Headrick, V. Roger, V.P.-Sls. & Mktg.--Dr. T.C. Smith Co. Inc., Asheville, NC; *U.S. Public*, pg. 214
Healey, Patrick J., V.P. & Mgr.-Sls.--Viking Yacht Co., New Gretna, NJ; *U.S. Private*, pg. 1140
Healy, Arthur, Dir.-Sls./Storage Units--Samsung Electronics America, Inc., Ridgefield Park, NJ; *Int'l*, pg. 1183
Healy, Dennis, Mgr.-Mktg. & Sls.--Barko Hydraulics, Superior, WI; *U.S. Private*, pg. 859
Heap, David, Mgr.-Sls.--Mity-Lite, Inc., Orem, UT; *U.S. Public*, pg. 1118
Hearley, David, V.P.-Sls.--Acorn Engineering Company, City of Industry, CA; *U.S. Private*, pg. 14
Heastrup, Jed C., Mgr.-Zero Product Sls.--Clemco Industries Corp., Washington, MO; *U.S. Private*, pg. 24
Heath, Robert S., Sr. V.P.-Sls.--BeautiControl Cosmetics, Inc., Carrollton, TX; *U.S. Public*, pg. 198
Heatley, Chris, Mgr.-Automotive Sls. Div.--Seymour of Sycamore, Inc., Sycamore, IL; *U.S. Private*, pg. 988
Heazlitt, Michael, V.P.-Sls. & Mktg.--Paoli, Inc., Orleans, IN; *U.S. Private*, pg. 837
Hebert, Wally, Dir.-Adv. & Sls. & Mktg.--JRN, Inc., Columbia, TN; *U.S. Private*, pg. 578
Hebranson, Denny, Dir.-Sls. Admin.--Johnson & Johnson Medical, Inc., Arlington, TX; *U.S. Public*, pg. 928
Hecht, Donald W., Dir.-Mktg.-Cattle Prods.--Elanco Animal Health, Indianapolis, IN; *U.S. Public*, pg. 993
Hecht, Stephen, Sr. V.P.-Sls & Mktg.--Centimark Corporation, Canonsburg, PA; *U.S. Private*, pg. 222
Heck, Mike, Mgr.-Sls.--Lithographix, Inc., Los Angeles, CA; *U.S. Private*, pg. 670
Heckman, Mike, Mgr.-Sls.--Pennsylvania Cellular Telephone Corp., Chambersburg, PA; *U.S. Public*, pg. 1708
Hedges, John D., Dir.-Hoffco Power Equip. Div.--Hoffco/Comet Industries, Inc., Richmond, IN; *U.S. Private*, pg. 532
Hedlund, Christer, Dir.-Sls.--Amtech Europe Limited, Cambridge, United Kingdom; *U.S. Public*, pg. 106
Heenan, Paul, V.P.-Sls./U.S.A.--Uniboard Canada Inc., Laval, Canada; *Int'l*, pg. 1431
Heerlyn, Henry, Mgr.-Sls.--Land O'Lakes, Inc., Southampton, PA; *U.S. Private*, pg. 646
Heerwagen, John, Sr. V.P.--Andover Bank, Andover, MA; *U.S. Public*, pg. 112
Hefley, Jim, Mgr.-Circulation--The Ardmore Daily Ardmoreite, Ardmore, OK; *U.S. Private*, pg. 995
Heflin, David, V.P.-Sls.--Industrial Powder Coatings, Inc., Norwalk, OH; *U.S. Public*, pg. 894
Hegel, Henry, Mgr.-Sls.--Outboard Marine Corporation, Waukegan, IL; *U.S. Private*, pg. 478
Hegel, John, Mgr.-Sls.--Warner Electric Industrial Products Division, South Beloit, IL; *U.S. Public*, pg. 480
Heger, Jean, V.P.-Sls.--Rail Europe Inc., Harrison, NY; *Int'l*, pg. 1165
Heiden, Gudrun, Dir.-Mktg. & Mgr.-Sls.--ISS Servisystem GesmbH, Vienna, Austria; *Int'l*, pg. 657
Heidenreich, Vincent J., Mgr.-Adv. & Sls. Promotion--Bayer Corporation/Pharmaceutical Division, West Haven, CT; *Int'l*, pg. 173
Heidl, Deb, Admin. Asst.--Integrated Material Handling Company, Oshkosh, WI; *Int'l*, pg. 1397
Heidrich, R.C., Mgr.-Sls.--Kaufman Footwear, Kitchener, Canada; *Int'l*, pg. 725
Heil, Louis, Sls. & Mktg.--Steel Ceilings Inc., Coshocton, OH; *U.S. Private*, pg. 29
Heilferty, William H., Mgr.-Sls.--Primepak Company, Teaneck, NJ; *U.S. Private*, pg. 884
Heilman, David, Sr. V.P.-Sls. & Mktg.--Photronics, Inc., Brookfield, CT; *U.S. Public*, pg. 1293
Heilmann, Bernd, V.P.-Sls. & Mktg.--Hako-Werke GmbH & Co., Bad Oldesloe, Germany; *Int'l*, pg. 587
Heilstedt, John, V.P.-Sls. & Mktg.--Elkay Manufacturing Company, Oak Brook, IL; *U.S. Private*, pg. 372
Heim, Millie, Dir.-Sls. & Adv.--Jumping Jacks, Monett, MO; *U.S. Private*, pg. 767
Heina, Ed, Dir.-Sls./Middleby--The Middleby Corporation, Rolling Meadows, IL; *U.S. Public*, pg. 1109
Heine, Charles, V.P.-Sls.--Bayer Clothing Group, New York, NY; *U.S. Private*, pg. 124
Heineman, Brett D., V.P., Sec. & Mgr.-East Reg. Sls.--Conway Import Co. Inc., Franklin Park, IL; *U.S. Private*, pg. 272
Heinkel, F.G., V.P.-Sls. & Mktg.--PrimeSource Corporation, Pennsauken, NJ; *U.S. Public*, pg. 1329
Heinrich, Thomas P., V.P.--Apex Broach & Machine Co., Detroit, MI; *U.S. Private*, pg. 77
Heinrich, Wally, Sr. Mgr.-Sls.--New Era Cap. Co., Derby, NY; *U.S. Private*, pg. 793

Heissel, Mgr.-Sls.--Uddeholm Corporation, Itasca, IL; *Int'l*, pg. 1471
Heissenbattel, David, Mgr.-Sls.--Dillard, A ResourceNet International Company, Columbia, SC; *U.S. Public*, pg. 902
Heitzman, Michael, Mgr.-Sls.--Timber Products Co., Germantown, TN; *U.S. Private*, pg. 1086
Helier, Bernard B., V.P.-Mktg. & Sls.--Zero Corporation, Los Angeles, CA; *U.S. Public*, pg. 1791
Hellberg, S.W., Sr. V.P.-Mktg. & Sls.--Creative Productions, Pittsburgh, PA; *U.S. Private*, pg. 288
Helmick, Michael E., V.P.-Sls.-Employee Benefits Div.--Northwestern National Life Insurance Co., Minneapolis, MN; *U.S. Public*, pg. 1375
Helweg, Brian, Mgr.-Wire Prod. Sls.--Kaspar Wire Works, Inc., Shiner, TX; *U.S. Private*, pg. 608
Hemard, Andre, Mgr.-Sls.--Pernod, Creteil, France; *Int'l*, pg. 566
Hemery, Patrick, Natl. Sls. Mgr.--Sensormatic (France) S.A., Antony, France; *U.S. Public*, pg. 1457
Hemmelgarn, Richard A., V.P.-Sls. & Mktg.--Blount, Inc. Forestry & Industrial Equipment Division, Zebulon, NC; *U.S. Public*, pg. 238
Hemmes, Jack, Mgr.-Sls./USA--Security Chimneys International Ltd., Laval, Canada; *Int'l*, pg. 1217
Hemp, John Michael, Sr. V.P.-Sls.--The Lincoln National Life Insurance Co., Fort Wayne, IN; *U.S. Public*, pg. 998
Hemp, Richard, V.P.-Retail Sls.--Jenn-Air, Newton, IA; *U.S. Public*, pg. 1064
Hemperly, Daniel P., Mgr.-Sls.--Vibra-Metrics, Inc., Hamden, CT; *U.S. Private*, pg. 622
Hemple, Robert, Mgr.-Sls.--Architectural Landscape Lighting, Santa Ana, CA; *Int'l*, pg. 821
Hempstead, Gerard, V.P.-Natl. Accts.--Airborne Freight Corporation, Seattle, WA; *U.S. Public*, pg. 32
Henager, Al, Dir.-Retail Sls.--Champion Laboratories, Inc., Albion, IL; *U.S. Private*, pg. 1113
Henaire, Patrice, V.P.-Sls. & Mktg.--Venmar Ventilation, Inc., Drummondville, Canada; *U.S. Public*, pg. 1194
Henceroth, David, Mgr.- Sls. & Mktg.--Testronics, Freeport, TX; *U.S. Private*, pg. 487
Henderson, David, V.P. & Gen. Mgr.--American Locker Group, Inc., Jamestown, NY; *U.S. Public*, pg. 85
Henderson, Jim, Exec. V.P.-Sls. & Mktg.--BGF Industries Inc., Greensboro, NC; *U.S. Private*, pg. 106
Henderson, Jim, V.P.-Sls.--Gulf States Steel, Inc., Gadsden, AL; *U.S. Private*, pg. 488
Henderson, Jim, Exec. V.P.--Poe & Brown, Inc., Daytona Beach, FL; *U.S. Public*, pg. 1312
Henderson, Lloyd, V.P.-Sls.--JAH Enterprises, Inc., Livingston, LA; *U.S. Private*, pg. 577
Henderson, Merrel, V.P.-Sls.--Somerset Refinery Inc., Somerset, KY; *U.S. Private*, pg. 1013
Henderson, Michael, V.P.-Sls. & Mktg.--Northern Telecom Inc., Rochester, NY; *Int'l*, pg. 970
Henderson, R.L., Asst. Gen. Sls. Mgr.-Eastern Area--Buick Motor Div. General Motors Corp., Flint, MI; *U.S. Public*, pg. 720
Henderson, Rick, Dir.-Sls.--Shelter Mutual Insurance Company, Columbia, MO; *U.S. Private*, pg. 992
Henderson, Scott, Mgr.-Retail Adv.-Specialties--TruServ Corporation, Chicago, IL; *U.S. Private*, pg. 1108
Hendren, Michael, Sr. V.P.-N. American Sls.--Ascend Communications, Inc., Alameda, CA; *U.S. Public*, pg. 138
Hendricks, Gerald, V.P.-Sls.--Fargo Glass & Paint Company, Fargo, ND; *U.S. Private*, pg. 393
Hendricks, Jack, Reg. Sls. Mgr.--Aromat South Central Sales Office, Richardson, TX; *Int'l*, pg. 848
Hendricks, Jerry P., V.P.-Sls.--Weldon, Williams & Lick, Inc., Fort Smith, AR; *U.S. Private*, pg. 1161
Hendrickson, Brad A., V.P.-Natl. Sls.--Allied Diagnostic Imaging Resources, Inc., Norcross, GA; *U.S. Public*, pg. 282
Hendrix, Barry, Dir.-Sls.-Resins--The Geon Company, Avon Lake, OH; *U.S. Public*, pg. 733
Heneghan, Frank M., V.P.-Sls. & Mktg.--McArdle Printing Co., Inc., Upper Marlboro, MD; *U.S. Private*, pg. 182
Heneghan, Tom, Reg. Sls. Mgr.-Relays--Aromat North Central Sales Office, Rolling Meadows, IL; *Int'l*, pg. 848
Heng, Koh Ban, V.P.-Intl. Sls.--Singapore Petroleum Company Ltd., Singapore, Singapore; *U.S. Public*, pg. 102
Heniger, Karen, V.P. & Mgr.-Gen. Sls.--Fisher Broadcasting Inc., Seattle, WA; *U.S. Public*, pg. 648
Henke, Gary, V.P.-Sls.--Foulds Inc., Libertyville, IL; *U.S. Private*, pg. 421
Henke, James, Mgr.-Sls--Ruska Instrument Corporation, Houston, TX; *U.S. Private*, pg. 952
Henley, Rob, V.P.-Sls.--Action Instruments, Inc., San Diego, CA; *U.S. Private*, pg. 15
Hennen, Daniel, V.P.-Sls.--ACR Industries Inc., Macomb Township, MI; *U.S. Private*, pg. 3
Hennen, Jerry, Mgr.-Sls. & Mktg.--Arrow Tru-Line, Inc., Archbold, OH; *U.S. Private*, pg. 85
Hennessey, Thomas, V.P.-Sls.--Smith-Lee Co., Inc., Oneida, NY; *U.S. Private*, pg. 1009
Henning, Tim, V.P.-Sls.--ADAC Laboratories Inc., Milpitas, CA; *U.S. Public*, pg. 3
Henning, William W., Sr. V.P.-Sls.--Toter Incorporated, Statesville, NC; *U.S. Private*, pg. 1092
Henningsen, Christopher K., V.P.-Sls.--Henningsen Foods, Inc., White Plains, NY; *Int'l*, pg. 1074
Henningsen, John, V.P. & Natl. Sls. Mgr.--The School Division, Menlo Park, CA; *Int'l*, pg. 1026
Hennington, Rolf, V.P.-Sls. & Mktg.--Industrial Coatings Group, Inc., Chicago, IL; *U.S. Private*, pg. 434
Henriksen, B., Mgr.-Vehicle Sls.--Opel Norge AS, Skedsmokorset, Norway; *U.S. Public*, pg. 723
Henry, Alain, Sr. Sls. Assoc.-European Industry Service--DRI Europe, Inc., Brussels, Belgium; *U.S. Public*, pg. 1072
Henry, Charles, V.P.-Sls. & Mktg.--Xentek, Inc., San Marcos, CA; *Int'l*, pg. 1349
Henry, Ed, Mgr.-Sls. & Mktg.--Viking Electronics, Inc., Chatsworth, CA; *U.S. Private*, pg. 1184
Henry, Marlene, Sls. Assoc.--WJR-AM, Detroit, MI; *U.S. Public*, pg. 512
Henry, Steven, V.P.-Sls.--Alan Lithograph, Inc., Inglewood, CA; *U.S. Private*, pg. 31
Henry, Wes, Sls. Admin.--Akzo Nobel Fortafil Fibers Inc., Rockwood, TN; *Int'l*, pg. 48
Hensarling, Ray, Sls. Mgr.-Southwest District--Fluidtec Engineer Products, Greensboro, NC; *U.S. Public*, pg. 401
Henshell, Morton, V.P.-Sls.--Bagcraft Corporation of America, Chicago, IL; *U.S. Public*, pg. 136
Henson, Mike, Dir.-Sls.--3ummit Performance Dist. Inc., Channelview, TX; *U.S. Public*, pg. 1233
Henson, Ron, Sr. V.P.-Sls.--S&D Coffee Inc., Concord, NC; *U.S. Private*, pg. 954
Hentges, Roger, V.P.-Sls.--Mid America Steel, Inc., Fargo, ND; *U.S. Private*, pg. 743
Henthorn, C.G., V.P.-Sls.--Kiwi Brands Pty. Ltd., Clayton, Australia; *U.S. Public*, pg. 1434
Henwood, Bill, Sr. V.P.-Sls. & Mktg.--Nicklaus Golf Company, L.C., West Palm Beach, FL; *U.S. Private*, pg. 799
Henzl, David, Sr. Sls. Engineer--Kvaerner Hydro Power, Inc.-West Coast Sales Division, San Francisco, CA; *Int'l*, pg. 770
Hepburn, carman D., V.P.-Sls. & Mktg.--Knape & Vogt Canada Inc., Etobicoke, Canada; *U.S. Public*, pg. 963
Hepler, Jay, Dir.-Comet OEM Sls.--Hoffco/Comet Industries, Inc., Richmond, IN; *U.S. Private*, pg. 532
Heraty, Daniel P., V.P.-Travelift Sls.--MI-Jack Products, Inc., Hazel Crest, IL; *U.S. Private*, pg. 740
Herbert, Betsy, V.P.-Mktg. & Sls.--Danco Products, Concordville, PA; *U.S. Public*, pg. 1145
Herbst, Keith S., Dir.-Intl. Sls.--Moore Products Co., Spring House, PA; *U.S. Public*, pg. 1128
Herkamp, W.J., V.P.-Sls. & Mktg.--Sweco, Florence, KY; *U.S. Public*, pg. 574
Herling, Robert, V.P.-Sls. & Mktg.--Atlas Electric Devices Co., Chicago, IL; *U.S. Private*, pg. 96
Herman, Kim, V.P.-Strategic Mktg. & Sls. Support--Olsten Health Services, Melville, NY; *U.S. Public*, pg. 1221
Hermes, Steve, V.P.-Sls. Promo. & Adv.--Waddell & Reed, Inc., Shawnee Mission, KS; *U.S. Public*, pg. 1623
Hern, Roy D., Dir.-Sls. & Mktg.--Hardings, Inc., Elmira, NY; *U.S. Private*, pg. 502
Hernandez, Cynthia, V.P.-Sls. & Mktg.--Chip Supply Inc., Orlando, FL; *U.S. Private*, pg. 237
Hernandez, Gabriel, Dir.-Sls.--CIBA-GEIGY Colombiana S.A., Bogota, Colombia; *Int'l*, pg. 976
Hernandez, Gilbert, Dir.-Intl. Sls.--Ferry-Morse Seed Company, Modesto, CA; *Int'l*, pg. 566
Hernandez, Roland, Dir.-Sls.--Stanback Company, Salisbury, NC; *U.S. Private*, pg. 1030
Herndon, Vince, Pres. & Chief Oper. Officer--Holcomb & Hoke Mfg. Company, Inc., Indianapolis, IN; *U.S. Private*, pg. 533
Heroes, Daniel, Mgr.-Sls.--N.V. Maxon International S.A., Vilvoorde, Belgium; *U.S. Private*, pg. 717
Heron, Elaine J., Ph.D., V.P.-Worldwide Sls. & Mktg.--The Perkin-Elmer Corporation, Norwalk, CT; *U.S. Public*, pg. 1279
Herrin, Elaine, V.P.-Worldwide Sls. & Mktg.--Applied Biosystems, Foster City, CA; *U.S. Public*, pg. 1279
Herring, Donald, V.P.-Aftermarket Sls.--Standard Motor Products Inc., Long Island City, NY; *U.S. Public*, pg. 1503
Herrington, Bill, V.P.-Mktg. Natl. & Intl. Accts.--Manna Pro Corporation, Saint Louis, MO; *U.S. Private*, pg. 700
Herron, Patti, Sls. Coord.--Sigma Designs, Inc., Fremont, CA; *U.S. Public*, pg. 1472
Hersh, Ken, Dir.-Sls.--Starving Students, Inc., Los Angeles, CA; *U.S. Private*, pg. 1035
Hershberger, Jerry, Gen. Sls. Mgr.--Hussmann Store Equipment Limited, Brantford, Canada; *U.S. Public*, pg. 1766
Hershey, Leon, V.P.-Sls. & Mktg.--Sunline Coach Co., Inc., Denver, PA; *U.S. Private*, pg. 1053
Hershman, Robert, Mgr.-Sls.--American Library Association, Chicago, IL; *U.S. Private*, pg. 58
Hershner, A., V.P.-Domestic Sls.--Shure Brothers Incorporated, Evanston, IL; *U.S. Private*, pg. 997
Hertlein, Jackie, Mgr.-Corp. Devel.--Artistic Greetings, Inc., Elmira, NY; *U.S. Public*, pg. 136
Herzog, Jim, Mgr.-Corp. Communications, Sls., Mktg. & Adv.--Armco Inc., Pittsburgh, PA; *U.S. Public*, pg. 131
Hespe, Thomas J., Exec. V.P.-Clinical Sls.--Lab One, Lenexa, KS; *U.S. Public*, pg. 1449
Hess, James T., V.P.-Sls.--Williams Steel & Hardware Company, Minneapolis, MN; *U.S. Private*, pg. 1178
Hess, Jill, Mgr.-Sls.--The Denver Business Journal, LLC, Denver, CO; *U.S. Private*, pg. 19
Hess, Renae L., V.P.-Sls.--W-B Supply Co., Pampa, TX; *U.S. Private*, pg. 1144
Hess, William R., Exec. V.P.-Mktg. & Sls.--Farmers and Traders Life Insurance Co., Syracuse, NY; *U.S. Private*, pg. 394
Hessel, Tom, Mgr.-Export Sls.--J.D. Streett & Co., Inc., Maryland Heights, MO; *U.S. Private*, pg. 1047
Hester, S.R., V.P.-Mktg. & Sls.--Rocky Rococo Corporation, Oconomowoc, WI; *U.S. Private*, pg. 938
Hettrick, Craig, V.P.-Sls. & Mktg.--Frionor U.S.A. Inc., New Bedford, MA; *Int'l*, pg. 516
Hewgley, William M., Jr., Exec. V.P.-Sls. & Mktg.--American Manufacturing Company, Chattanooga, TN; *U.S. Private*, pg. 58
Heyamoto, Dave, Mgr.-Mktg.--The Washington Water Power Company, Spokane, WA; *U.S. Public*, pg. 1744
Heyer, Steven J., Pres.-Worldwide Sls., Mktg., Distr. & Intl. Networks Group--Turner Broadcasting System Inc., Atlanta, GA; *U.S. Public*, pg. 1614
Heyl, Jack, Mgr.-Classified Adv.--Toledo Blade Co., Toledo, OH; *U.S. Private*, pg. 147
Heyward, Ralph, Mgr.-Local Sls.-KOMO-AM--Fisher Broadcasting Inc., Seattle, WA; *U.S. Public*, pg. 648
Hibbard, Fredrick, V.P.-Sls./E. U.S.--Thorn Apple Valley, Inc., Southfield, MI; *U.S. Public*, pg. 1602
Hibbett, C.W., V.P.-Sls.--Emerson Power Transmission Corporation, Ithaca, NY; *U.S. Public*, pg. 573
Hibbett, Chuck, Pres.-Sls.--McGill Manufacturing Company, Inc., Valparaiso, IN; *U.S. Public*, pg. 573
Hibray, Blake, V.P.-Mktg. & Sls., Natl. Accts.--Sigma Chemical Co., Saint Louis, MO; *U.S. Public*, pg. 1472
Hickerson, K. Michael, V.P. & Gen. Mgr.-U.S. Sls. & Srvc. Div.--PictureTel, Andover, MA; *U.S. Public*, pg. 1294
Hickman, Barrett, V.P.-Sls. & Mktg.--Imax Corporation, Mississauga, Canada; *Int'l*, pg. 661
Hickmann, Richard, V.P.-Sls.--Smith Fiberglass Products Inc., Little Rock, AR; *U.S. Public*, pg. 1477
Hickox, Jennifer, Sls. & Mktg. Asst.--Sunroc Corporation, Dover, DE; *U.S. Private*, pg. 1053
Hickox, Jennifer, Sls. & Mktg. Asst.--Telkee, Dover, DE; *U.S. Private*, pg. 1053
Hicks, Frank, Mgr.-Sls.--Dettra Flag Company, Oaks, PA; *U.S. Private*, pg. 328
Hicks, Ken, V.P.-Sls. & Mktg.--Argo-Tech Corporation, Cleveland, OH; *U.S. Private*, pg. 81
Hicks, Lawrence R., Exec. V.P.-Sls. & Mdsg.--Handleman Company, Troy, MI; *U.S. Public*, pg. 779
Hicks, Thomas, V.P.--American Laubscher Corp., Farmingdale, NY; *U.S. Private*, pg. 58
Higdon, Danny, V.P.-Sls.--Fairfield Nashville, Nashville, TN; *U.S. Public*, pg. 611
Higginbotham, Terry, V.P.-Sls.--American Freightways Corporation, Harrison, AR; *U.S. Public*, pg. 75
Higgins, Barry, Mgr.-Sls.--Collins Electric Company, Inc., Chicopee, MA; *U.S. Private*, pg. 253
Higgins, Charlie, V.P.-Natl. Sls.--Rusch, Duluth, GA; *U.S. Public*, pg. 1569
Higgins, Dan, Mgr.-Sls. Admin.--Hercules Engine Company, Canton, OH; *U.S. Private*, pg. 523
Higgins, Donald R., V.P.-Sls.--Roanoke Electric Steel Corporation, Roanoke, VA; *U.S. Public*, pg. 1392
Higgins, Robert, Dir.-Sls. & Mktg.--DHL International Express Ltd., Mississauga, Canada; *U.S. Private*, pg. 302
Hight, David, Dir.-Sls.--Dorling Kindersley Ltd., London, United Kingdom; *Int'l*, pg. 417
Hightower, C.S., Mgr.-Sls.--American Steel Pipe Div., Birmingham, AL; *U.S. Private*, pg. 52
Hightower, George H., Jr., Exec. V.P.-Sls. & Adv.--Thomaston Mills, Inc., Thomaston, GA; *U.S. Public*, pg. 1599
Hightower, Jack, Sr. V.P.-Field Opers.--Jan Bell Marketing Inc., Sunrise, FL; *U.S. Public*, pg. 207
Hightower, Sharon, V.P. & Dir.-Sls. Mngmt.--South Trust Bank of Georgia, Atlanta, GA; *U.S. Public*, pg. 1492
Hilbrands, W.J., Mgr.-Mktg. & Sls.--Corporate New Business Development Div., Delft, Netherlands; *Int'l*, pg. 1142
Hildebrand, James, V.P.-Sls. & Mktg.--GF Office Furniture Ltd., Gallatin, TN; *U.S. Private*, pg. 434
Hildebrand, Loren, Exec. V.P.-Sls.--Galoob Toys, Inc., South San Francisco, CA; *U.S. Public*, pg. 698
Hildebrand, Phillip, Exec. V.P.-Sls. & Mktg.--New York Life Insurance Company, New York, NY; *U.S. Private*, pg. 794
Hildebrand, William, Mgr.-Sls.--Hougen Manufacturing Inc., Swartz Creek, MI; *U.S. Private*, pg. 541
Hildebrandt, David A., Sr. V.P.-Intl. Sls.--Starcraft Automotive Group, Inc., Goshen, IN; *U.S. Public*, pg. 1511
Hildebrandt, John, V.P.-Mktg. & Sls.--Cedar Point, Sandusky, OH; *U.S. Public*, pg. 319
Hildebrandt, Leon, V.P.-Sls.--Canadian Broadcast Sales, Toronto, Canada; *Int'l*, pg. 1482
Hildner, Jack, Exec. V.P.-Sls. & Mktg.--American Color Graphics, Brentwood, TN; *U.S. Public*, pg. 1132
Hilf, Jerry, Mgr.-Natl. Sls./Anderson--Wilton Corporation, Palatine, IL; *U.S. Private*, pg. 1181
Hilfman, Dave, Staff V.P.-Natl. Sls.--Continental Airlines, Houston, TX; *U.S. Public*, pg. 439
Hilinski, Ed, Prod. Mgr.-Standard Products--Bridgeport Machines, Inc., Bridgeport, CT; *U.S. Public*, pg. 251
Hilker, Harold, V.P.-Industrial Sls.--Sun-Maid Growers of California, Kingsburg, CA; *U.S. Private*, pg. 1051
Hill, Bill, V.P.-Sls.--Celebrity Incorporated, Tyler, TX; *U.S. Public*, pg. 319
Hill, Denise, Mgr.-Mktg. & Sls.--Carme' Cosmeceutical Sciences, Inc., Napa, CA; *U.S. Private*, pg. 213
Hill, G., Mgr.-Intl. Sls.--Clearing-Niagara, Buffalo, NY; *U.S. Private*, pg. 196
Hill, Gordon S., Dir.-Intl. Sls.--CNB International, L.L.C., Charleston, SC; *U.S. Private*, pg. 196
Hill, Harvey, Dir.-Natl. Sls.--Philadelphia Daily News, Philadelphia, PA; *U.S. Public*, pg. 964
Hill, Harvey, Dir.-Natl. Sls.--The Philadelphia Inquirer, Philadelphia, PA; *U.S. Public*, pg. 964
Hill, John, Dir.-Sls.--Auto Driveaway Co., Chicago, IL; *U.S. Private*, pg. 100
Hill, Larry D., Sr. Exec. V.P.--Icicle Seafoods, Inc., Seattle, WA; *U.S. Private*, pg. 556
Hill, Mitch, Mgr.-Large Sls.--PENCO-Nevada, Reno, NV; *Int'l*, pg. 1508
Hill, Spencer, V.P.-Sls. & Mktg.--Clover Club Foods, Inc., Kaysville, UT; *U.S. Private*, pg. 469
Hillard, Michael, V.P.-Intl. Sls.--Fieldcrest Cannon, Inc., Kannapolis, NC; *U.S. Public*, pg. 1296
Hillenbrand, Bruce, V.P.-Sls.--Bestfoods, Englewood Cliffs, NJ; *U.S. Public*, pg. 223
Hillenbrand, Bruce, V.P.-Sls.--Best Foods, Englewood Cliffs, NJ; *U.S. Public*, pg. 224
Hillis, Michael, Mgr.-Sls. & Mktg.--Tober Industries, Inc., Saint Louis, MO; *U.S. Private*, pg. 1089
Hillman, Charles F., V.P.-New Market Devel.--Berryman Products, Inc., Arlington, TX; *U.S. Private*, pg. 138
Hills, P.W., Dir. & Gen. Mgr.-Sls.--IRD Mechanalysis (U.K.) Limited, Chester, United Kingdom; *U.S. Public*, pg. 790

Hilmarsson, Hannes, Mgr.-Sls.-U.S.A. & Canada--IceLandAir, Columbia, MD; *Int'l*, pg. 658
Hilsenbeck, Susan, V.P.-Mktg., Sls. & Promo.--General Host Corporation, Stamford, CT; *U.S. Public*, pg. 715
Hilton, Danette, Dir.-Sls. Admin.--Republic Storage Systems Company Inc., Canton, OH; *U.S. Private*, pg. 924
Hilton, John M., V.P.-Sls.--Freedom Forge Corporation, Burnham, PA; *U.S. Private*, pg. 425
Hilton, Mike, Mgr.-Sls. & Adv.--Dexion Group plc, Hemel Hempstead, United Kingdom; *U.S. Public*, pg. 893
Hiltwine, Mike, Sls.--Bateman Brothers Lumber Co., Inc., New Britain, PA; *U.S. Private*, pg. 122
Hinck, Don, V.P.-Sls.--Stella Foods, Inc., Green Bay, WI; *U.S. Private*, pg. 1040
Hindenburg, Marion, Sr. V.P.-Sls.--Gould Paper Corporation, New York, NY; *U.S. Private*, pg. 466
Hindman, Donald D., V.P.-Sls. & Mktg.--Clark Foodservice, Inc., Elk Grove Village, IL; *U.S. Private*, pg. 242
Hines, David C., V.P.-Natl. Sls. Div.--John Morrell & Co., Cincinnati, OH; *U.S. Public*, pg. 1479
Hines, Dennis, V.P. & Sls. Mgr.--Cliftex, New Bedford, MA; *U.S. Public*, pg. 1777
Hines, Mac, Sls.--Edward Hines Lumber Co., Itasca, IL; *U.S. Private*, pg. 530
Hinfray, Francois, Sr. V.P.-France Mkt. Area--Renault, Boulogne-Billancourt, France; *Int'l*, pg. 1102
Hinge, Claus, V.P.-European Sls. & Mktg.--Printronix, Inc., Irvine, CA; *U.S. Public*, pg. 1329
Hinkle, Allen, V.P.-Sls./Indus. Fabrics--Johnston Industries, Inc., Columbus, GA; *U.S. Public*, pg. 933
Hinkle, Jane K., V.P.-Sls. & Mktg.--Octagon Process Inc., Edgewater, NJ; *U.S. Private*, pg. 811
Hinkle, Jeff, Mgr.-Natl. Sls.--Scott's Liquid Gold-Inc., Denver, CO; *U.S. Public*, pg. 1447
Hinkle, Jeffrey, Natl. Sls. Mgr.--SLG Chemicals, Inc., Denver, CO; *U.S. Public*, pg. 1447
Hinkle, Jeffrey, Natl. Sls. Mgr.--Neoteric Cosmetics, Inc., Denver, CO; *U.S. Public*, pg. 1447
Hinman, Mark, V.P., Sec. & Mgr.-Sls.--Rome Strip Steel Co., Inc., Rome, NY; *U.S. Private*, pg. 942
Hinton, James H., Natl. Sls. Mgr.--Protective Benefits Communications, Birmingham, AL; *U.S. Public*, pg. 1336
Hinton, Walter, V.P.-Sls. & Service (Europe)--StorageTek Network Systems Group, Minneapolis, MN; *U.S. Public*, pg. 1522
Hippard, William, V.P.-Sls.--Precoat Metals Division, Saint Louis, MO; *U.S. Public*, pg. 1458
Hipwell, Roger, Sr. V.P.-Sls. & Mktg.--Bay State Milling Co., Quincy, MA; *U.S. Private*, pg. 124
Hirata, Tokusaburo, Dir.-Eastern Japan Sls. Headquarters--Rohm Co., Ltd., Kyoto, Japan; *Int'l*, pg. 1124
Hirose, Yoshihiro, Gen. Mgr.-Sls./Plastics Div,--Showa Denko K.K., Tokyo, Japan; *Int'l*, pg. 1236
Hirsch, Steven, Pres.-Camelot Entertainment Sls., Inc.--King World Productions, Inc., New York, NY; *U.S. Public*, pg. 961
Hirsch, Steven, Pres.-Camelot Entertainment Sls. Inc.--King World Productions, Los Angeles, CA; *U.S. Public*, pg. 961
Hirschfeld, Ron, Exec. V.P.-Intl. Sls. & Mktg.--Galoob Toys, Inc., South San Francisco, CA; *U.S. Public*, pg. 698
Hirschmann, Jim, V.P.-Sls.-Eastern Region--Crabar Business Systems, Dayton, OH; *U.S. Private*, pg. 283
Hirsh, Joe, Sr. V.P. & Dir.-Sls.--National Distributors, Vernon, CA; *U.S. Private*, pg. 781
Hiser, Dennis, Sr. V.P.-Sls. & Mktg.--World Color-Chicago Div., Elk Grove Village, IL; *U.S. Public*, pg. 1778
Hiser, Paul, Mgr.-Intl. Sls.--Damsmith Corp., Sanford, NC; *U.S. Private*, pg. 309
Hisiger, Ronda, V.P.-Stores--Paul Harris Stores, Inc., Indianapolis, IN; *U.S. Public*, pg. 792
Hitchins, Ron, Sr. V.P.-Sls.--U.S. Electrical Motor Division, Saint Louis, MO; *U.S. Public*, pg. 573
Hitchman, A.F., Dir.-Sls. & Tech.--Senior Bigwood Limited, West Bromwich, United Kingdom; *Int'l*, pg. 1220
Hitzig, David, Sls. Mgr.-Easter Div.--Hunter Douglas, Inc., Upper Saddle River, NJ; *Int'l*, pg. 639
Hiznay, Paul A., Sr. V.P.-Sls. & Adv.--Mona Industries, Inc., Paterson, NJ; *U.S. Private*, pg. 756
Hizo, Jozsef, Sls. Engr.--Borland Hungary Online/Delphi-Szoft Kft, Budapest, Hungary; *U.S. Public*, pg. 246
Hjorth, Lars, Deputy Mng. Dir.-Retail Bus. & Support Units--KF/Konsum Coop Group, Stockholm, Sweden; *Int'l*, pg. 718
Hnatek, Richard, Sr. V.P.-Sls. Officer--Falcon Products, Inc., Saint Louis, MO; *U.S. Public*, pg. 611
Ho, Bob, Mgr.-Sls. & Mktg.--Aydin Corporation West, San Jose, CA; *U.S. Public*, pg. 158
Hoadley, James, Gen. Mgr.-Sls. & Mktg.--ITW Screen Process Specialist, Ltd., Plymouth, WI; *U.S. Public*, pg. 867
Hoag, Charles, V.P. & Dir.-Sales--Star Tribune, Minneapolis-St. Paul, Minneapolis, MN; *U.S. Private*, pg. 281
Hoagland, William A., V.P.-Sls.-Load Runners--Osborn Manufacturing, Cleveland, OH; *U.S. Public*, pg. 924
Hoane, Steve, V.P.-Sls.--Arrow Automotive Industries, Inc., Framingham, MA; *U.S. Public*, pg. 133
Hoban, Joe, Mgr.-Mktg. & Sls.--Kaufman and Broad-Monterey Bay, Inc., Salinas, CA; *U.S. Public*, pg. 945
Hoben, James, Dir.-Export Sls.--WLR Foods, Inc., Timberville, VA; *U.S. Public*, pg. 1727
Hobson, Phil, V.P.-Sls./UK, Europe, Africa & Middle East--Reed Travel Publishing-Switzerland, Geneva, Switzerland; *Int'l*, pg. 1097
Hocevar, Greg, V.P.-Sls. & Mktg.--Bata Shoe Co., Inc., Belcamp, MD; *U.S. Private*, pg. 195
Hockin, Jeff, V.P.-Sls. & Mktg.--Crum Electric Supply Co., Inc., Casper, WY; *U.S. Private*, pg. 293
Hodder, Linda, Mgr.-Contract Sls. & Mktg.--Marietta Canada, Inc., Toronto, Canada; *U.S. Private*, pg. 703
Hodes, Ben, V.P.-Sls.--Gould Paper Corporation, New York, NY; *U.S. Private*, pg. 466
Hodge, J., Mgr.-Natl. Sls.--Kiwi Brands Pty. Ltd., Clayton, Australia; *U.S. Public*, pg. 1434
Hodges, Greg, Mgr.-Sls.--Harrington & King, South, Inc., Cleveland, TN; *U.S. Private*, pg. 504
Hodges, Martina J., V.P.-Sls.--Thiele Kaolin Co., Sandersville, GA; *U.S. Private*, pg. 1081
Hodges, Tim, Mgr.-OCTG--Newport Steel Corporation, Newport, KY; *U.S. Public*, pg. 1147
Hodges, Wayne, V.P.-Sls. & Mktg.--The Standard Products Company, Dearborn, MI; *U.S. Public*, pg. 1504
Hodges, Wendell, Exec. V.P.-Sls. & Mktg.--Towne Square Furniture, Inc., Hillsboro, TX; *U.S. Private*, pg. 1093
Hodgkinson, W.M., Chief Gen. Mgr.-Sls. & Mktg.--Pearl Group Plc, Peterborough, United Kingdom; *Int'l*, pg. 100
Hodson, Thomas, Sr. V.P.-Mktg. Sls.--Ford Meter Box Company, Wabash, IN; *U.S. Private*, pg. 418
Hoe, Leong Seow, Mgr.-Malaysia & Singapore Sls.--Singapore Petroleum Company Ltd., Singapore, Singapore; *U.S. Public*, pg. 102
Hoel, Mark, V.P.-Sls./West--BJ Services Company, Houston, TX; *U.S. Public*, pg. 161
Hoel, W. P., Mgr.-Sls. & Mktg.-Specialty Prods.--Masonite Corporation, Chicago, IL; *U.S. Public*, pg. 904
Hoeschen, Donald, V.P.-Sls.--National Presto Industries, Inc., Eau Claire, WI; *U.S. Public*, pg. 1159
Hof, Michael, V.P.-Sls. & Mktg.--Bostrom Seating, Inc., Piedmont, AL; *U.S. Public*, pg. 933
Hofer, Eric, Dir.-Sls. & Mktg.--Arrington Travel Center Inc., Chicago, IL; *U.S. Private*, pg. 85
Hoff, Dave, Sls. Mgr. D.S.D.--Mrs. Alison's Cookie Company, Saint Louis, MO; *U.S. Private*, pg. 765
Hoffer, William, V.P.-Sls.--Hoffer Plastics Corporation, South Elgin, IL; *U.S. Private*, pg. 532
Hoffman, Al, V.P.-Sls. & Mktg.--Pryon Corporation, Menomonee Falls, WI; *U.S. Public*, pg. 1336
Hoffman, Dave, V.P.--Grocers Supply Co. Inc., Houston, TX; *U.S. Private*, pg. 483
Hoffman, Frank, Gen. Mgr.-Mktg. & Sls.--Duquesne Light Company, Pittsburgh, PA; *U.S. Public*, pg. 474
Hoffman, Gary, V.P.-Sls.--Carlisle Equipment Company, Wilder, KY; *U.S. Private*, pg. 211
Hoffman, Howard, V.P. & Mgr.-S.W. Newspaper Rels.--Parade Publications Inc., New York, NY; *U.S. Private*, pg. 20
Hoffman, John, V.P.-Sls. & Mktg.--Outlook Group Corporation, Neenah, WI; *U.S. Public*, pg. 1235
Hoffman, John, Mgr.-Sls.--Waters Instruments, Inc., Rochester, MN; *U.S. Public*, pg. 1745
Hoffman, Judy, Sr. V.P.-Sls. & Mktg.--Lionel LLC, Chesterfield, MI; *U.S. Private*, pg. 669
Hoffman, Marv, V.P.-Mktg. Communications & Franchise Sls.--National Real Estate Services, Inc., Vancouver, Canada; *Int'l*, pg. 909
Hoffman, Michael, V.P.-Canadian Sls.--Fruit of the Loom, Inc., Chicago, IL; *U.S. Public*, pg. 685
Hoffman, Robert, Mgr.-Sls.--Mueller Steam Specialty, Lumberton, NC; *U.S. Public*, pg. 1676
Hoffman, Todd, V.P.-Sls. & Mktg.--Lykes Meat Group, Plant City, FL; *U.S. Public*, pg. 1479
Hoffner, Larry, Pres.-Sls.--National Broadcasting Co., Inc., New York, NY; *U.S. Public*, pg. 712
Hofstetter, Gerhardt, Sales, Mktg., Fin.--Diehl & Eagle-Picher GmbH, Nuremberg, Germany; *U.S. Private*, pg. 355
Hofverberg, U.J., V.P.-Sls. & Mktg.--Mead Pulp Sales, Inc., Dayton, OH; *U.S. Public*, pg. 1074
Hogan, Bob, Dir.-Sls. & Mktg.--Minigrip Zip-Pak, Orangeburg, NY; *U.S. Public*, pg. 867
Hogan, Debra, Mgr.-Adv.--Lee Pharmaceuticals, South El Monte, CA; *U.S. Public*, pg. 984
Hogan, Paul B., V.P.-Sls. & Mktg.--Sealed Air Corporation, Saddle Brook, NJ; *U.S. Public*, pg. 1450
Hogan, William, Exec. V.P.-Sls. & Mktg.--Clestra Hauserman, Inc., Solon, OH; *Int'l*, pg. 569
Hogelind, Linda, Mgr.-Reg. Sls.--Meadowcraft, Inc., Birmingham, AL; *U.S. Private*, pg. 725
Hogg, Michael, Dir.-Sls.--Playtex Apparel Canada, Ltd., Malton, Canada; *U.S. Public*, pg. 1433
Hogg, Sandy, Head-Sls.--Scottish Widows' Fund & Life Assurance Society, Edinburgh, United Kingdom; *Int'l*, pg. 1212
Hoglund, Kenneth, V.P.-Sls.--Pony Express Delivery Services, Inc, Atlanta, GA; *U.S. Public*, pg. 245
Hohing, Laura B., Sr. V.P.-Sls.--Time Insurance, Milwaukee, WI; *Int'l*, pg. 499
Hohing, Laura B., V.P.-Sls.--Fortis Sales, Milwaukee, WI; *Int'l*, pg. 499
Holahan, Mike, Mgr.-Sls.--Travel Ports of America Inc., Rochester, NY; *U.S. Public*, pg. 1632
Holben, Barry, V.P.-Sls.--Allen Organ Company, Macungie, PA; *U.S. Public*, pg. 45
Holborn, Donald C., Sr. V.P.-Natl. Sls. Plng.--FMR Corp., Boston, MA; *U.S. Private*, pg. 403
Holbrook, Henry W., V.P.-Sls./Northeast Reg.--Medical Manager Corporation, Tampa, FL; *U.S. Public*, pg. 1080
Holbrook, Mike, Mgr.-New Car Sls.--James Chevrolet Inc., Clinton Township, MI; *U.S. Private*, pg. 580
Holcomb, John T., 1st V.P.-Sls.--The Berlin Steel Construction Company, Berlin, CT; *U.S. Private*, pg. 136
Holcomb, Steve, Dir.-Contract/Export Bus. Unit--Conestoga Wood Specialties Corp., East Earl, PA; *U.S. Private*, pg. 262
Holden, James P., Exec. V.P.-Sls. & Mktg.--Chrysler Corporation, Auburn Hills, MI; *U.S. Public*, pg. 352
Holden, Jeffrey, V.P.-Sls. & Mktg.--J.L. Hammett Company, Braintree, MA; *U.S. Private*, pg. 498
Holder, Thomas M., V.P.-Sls. & Treas.--Hershey Creamery Company, Harrisburg, PA; *U.S. Private*, pg. 524
Holdridge, John, V.P.-Southeastern Sls.--CBS Enterprises Division, New York, NY; *U.S. Public*, pg. 274
Holert, Gert, V.P.-Domestic Sls. & Exec. Dir.-H.F. & Ph.F. Reemtsma Gmbh--Reemtsma Cigarettenfabriken GmbH, Hamburg, Hamburg, Germany; *Int'l*, pg. 1100
Holiday, Chris, V.P.-Domestic Sls.--Callaway Golf Company, Carlsbad, CA; *U.S. Public*, pg. 294
Hollabaugh, Michael D., V.P.-Worldwide Sls. & Mktg.--GTI Corporation, San Diego, CA; *U.S. Public*, pg. 767
Holland, J. Douglas, Mgr.-Sls.--Barksdale, Inc., Los Angeles, CA; *U.S. Public*, pg. 457
Holland, John, V.P.-European Sls.--Axent Technologies, Rockville, MD; *U.S. Public*, pg. 157
Holland, Marcia S., V.P.-Promotion & Res.--Journal of Commerce, Inc., New York, NY; *Int'l*, pg. 1026
Hollick, Clive, Lord, Chief Exec. Officer--United News & Media plc, London, United Kingdom; *Int'l*, pg. 1443
Hollignsworth, David, Dir.-Sls. & Mktg.--Millennium Technology Services, Inc., White City, OR; *U.S. Private*, pg. 746
Hollingsworth, Claudia, V.P.-Sls.--Oroamerica, Inc., Burbank, CA; *U.S. Public*, pg. 1232
Hollis, David, Dir.-Mktg.--Holstein Association USA, Inc., Brattleboro, VT; *U.S. Private*, pg. 536
Hollis, Mark, Sr. V.P.-Sls. & Mktg.--Inverness Corp., Fair Lawn, NJ; *U.S. Private*, pg. 574
Hollister, Tom, Reg. V.P.-Image Brands Sls.--R.G. Barry Corporation, Pickerington, OH; *U.S. Public*, pg. 192
Holloway, Bill, Dir.-Sls. & Mktg.--Gulf States Manufacturers, Inc., Starkville, MS; *Int'l*, pg. 699
Holloway, Fred, Mgr.-Stevens Sls.--Leupold & Stevens, Inc., Beaverton, OR; *U.S. Private*, pg. 662
Hollowell, Gary, Sr. V.P.-Natl. Acct.--Aladdin Mills, Dalton, GA; *U.S. Public*, pg. 1121
Holm, Kim R., Exec. V.P.-Mktg. & Sls.--Salem Carpet Mills, Inc., Winston Salem, NC; *U.S. Public*, pg. 1464
Holman, Nick, Dir.-Intl. Sls.--Action Instruments, Inc., San Diego, CA; *U.S. Private*, pg. 15
Holmes, Harry, Natl. Sls. Mgr.--The Vernon Company, Newton, IA; *U.S. Private*, pg. 1137
Holmes, James J., V.P. & Natl. Sls.--Old American Insurance Co., Kansas City, MO; *U.S. Public*, pg. 943
Holmes, Jos. T., Mgr.-Sls.--ANESCO, Kingston, PA; *U.S. Private*, pg. 74
Holmes, Mike, V.P. & Gen. Mgr.--Hershey Foods Corporation, Hershey, PA; *U.S. Public*, pg. 811
Holmes, Ronald P., V.P.-Sls.--Weston Paper & Manufacturing Co., Terre Haute, IN; *U.S. Private*, pg. 1169
Holmes, Roy, V.P.-Sls.- Branded Prods.--Chicopee Inc., Dayton, NJ; *Int'l*, pg. 113
Holmquist, Richard, Mgr.-Sls. & Mktg.--Bryan Steam Corporation, Peru, IN; *U.S. Private*, pg. 176
Holodnak, John, Mgr.-Sls., Church Candles--A.I. Root Company, Medina, OH; *U.S. Private*, pg. 944
Holownia, Michael, Reg. Sls. Mgr.--FINNAIR, Boston, MA; *Int'l*, pg. 485
Holstein, Hans-Joachim, Exec. V.P. & Sls. Dir.--Traub AG, Reichenbach, Germany; *Int'l*, pg. 1419
Holstein, Hans-Joachim, Mgr.-Sls.--Traub-Heckert Vertriebs GmbH, Reichenbach, Germany; *Int'l*, pg. 1419
Holstrom, Jeff, V.P.-Mktg. & Sls.--TFP Data Systems, Oxnard, CA; *U.S. Private*, pg. 1070
Holt, Mark, Dir.-Sls.--nVIEW Corporation, Newport News, VA; *U.S. Public*, pg. 1206
Holt, Ralph M., III, V.P.-Sls. & Mktg.--Holt Hosiery Mills, Inc., Burlington, NC; *U.S. Private*, pg. 536
Holt, Scott, Sr. V.P.-Worldwide Sls.--Diamond Multimedia Systems, Inc., San Jose, CA; *U.S. Public*, pg. 505
Holtz, A, Sr. V.P.-Sls.--Penguin Putnam Inc., New York, NY; *Int'l*, pg. 1027
Holz, Robert, V.P.-Selfix Intl. Sls.--Home Products International, Inc., Chicago, IL; *U.S. Public*, pg. 832
Holzapfel, Tony, Exec. V.P.-Sls. & Mktg.--First Data Resources, Omaha, NE; *U.S. Public*, pg. 631
Holzman, Jyll F., V.P.-Adv. Sls.--The New York Times, New York, NY; *U.S. Public*, pg. 1174
Honaker, Jim, Mgr.-Natl. Sls.--Hub City, Inc., Aberdeen, SD; *U.S. Public*, pg. 1371
Honaker, Mark, Mgr.-Sls.--PENCO-Florida, Altamonte Springs, FL; *Int'l*, pg. 1508
Honckler, Roger, Mgr.-Sls.--Holiday RV Superstores, Inc., Greer, SC; *U.S. Public*, pg. 829
Honeycutt, Conrad, Sr. V.P.-Sls.--Gelco Information Network, Inc., Eden Prairie, MN; *U.S. Private*, pg. 442
Hong, Han P., Dir.-Sls.--Crown Confectionery Co., Ltd., Seoul, Korea; *Int'l*, pg. 348
Hong, J.S., Mgr.-Sls.--China Steel Structure Co., Ltd., Kaohsiung, Taiwan; *Int'l*, pg. 286
Hongosh, Edward J., Mgr.-Gen. Sls.--Eberhard Manufacturing, Strongsville, OH; *U.S. Public*, pg. 548
Hoobler, J.V., V.P.-Utility Sls.--Struthers Wells Corp., Warren, PA; *U.S. Private*, pg. 1048
Hood, Dave, V.P.-Sls.--Diamond Hill Plywood Company, Darlington, SC; *U.S. Private*, pg. 311
Hood, Richard, Natl. Sls. Mgr.--Case-Swayne Co. Inc., Corona, CA; *U.S. Private*, pg. 218
Hood, S., Mgr.-Natl. Sls., Bakery--GF Food Services, Alexandria, Australia; *Int'l*, pg. 555
Hoogerwerf, Richard, V.P.-Corp. Sls.--Alro Group, Jackson, MI; *U.S. Private*, pg. 45
Hooker, Tom, V.P.-Intl. Sls.--Townsend Engineering Co., Des Moines, IA; *U.S. Private*, pg. 1094
Hoong, Yeow Kok, Mgr.-Sls.--GB Holdings, Jurong, Singapore; *Int'l*, pg. 531
Hooper, Ken, V.P.-Mktg. & Sls.--Gould Electronics Inc., Shawmut Circuit Protection Division, Newburyport, MA; *U.S. Public*, pg. 1592
Hoorweg, R.P.A., V.P.-Mktg. & Sls.--Europe Combined Terminals B.V., Rotterdam, Netherlands; *Int'l*, pg. 682
Hoover, R.E., V.P.-Sls.--Watkins-Johnson Company, Palo Alto, CA; *U.S. Public*, pg. 1745
Hoover, T.J., V.P.-Sls.--Wilkinson Company, Inc., Stow, OH; *U.S. Private*, pg. 368
Hope, John, V.P.-Mktg., Sls. & Product Dev.--Imprimerie Quebecor Canada, Woodbridge, Canada; *Int'l*, pg. 1077
Hopkins, Jim, V.P.-Sls. & Mktg.--BIW Cable Systems, Inc., Franklin, MA; *Int'l*, pg. 417
Hopkins, Roger, V.P.-Sls. & Mktg.--San Diego Division, San Diego, CA; *U.S. Public*, pg. 27

Hoppe, Ben, Special Projects Coord.--FWD/Seagrave Fire Apparatus, Inc., Clintonville, WI; *U.S. Private*, pg. 390
Hoppe, James, Mgr.-Sls., Golden Hearth Div.--National Baking, Chicago, IL; *U.S. Private*, pg. 1022
Hoque, Jeffery C., Pres. & Mgr.-Sls. & Adv.--Charles Atlas, Ltd., New York, NY; *U.S. Private*, pg. 229
Horack, James F., Mgr.-Natl. Sls.--Linde Hydraulics Corporation, Canfield, OH; *Int'l*, pg. 810
Horan, Gina, Retail Store Coord.--Villeroy & Boch Tableware, Ltd., Princeton, NJ; *Int'l*, pg. 1468
Horan, John, V.P.-Sls./Bed & Bath Div.--Cameo Window Furnishings, New York, NY; *U.S. Private*, pg. 1094
Horan, John, V.P.-Sls./Bed & Bath Div.--Jakson-A CHF Company, New York, NY; *U.S. Private*, pg. 1094
Horel, Tom, V.P.-Mktg., Sls. & Pub. Rels.--American Metal Products, Olive Branch, MS; *U.S. Public*, pg. 1053
Hori, K., Mgr.-American Sls.--Hitachi Sales Corp., Tokyo, Japan; *Int'l*, pg. 621
Horian, Robert L., Sr. V.P.-Sls., OEM--Calibron, Inc., Lake Mary, FL; *U.S. Public*, pg. 1369
Horn, Greg, Sr. V.P.-Sls.--General Nutrition Centers, Pittsburgh, PA; *U.S. Public*, pg. 725
Horn, Gregory T., Sr. V.P.-Retail Sls. & Mktg.--General Nutrition, Inc., Pittsburgh, PA; *U.S. Public*, pg. 725
Horn, Randall C., Exec. V.P.-Grp. Opers.--Mutual of Omaha Insurance Company, Omaha, NE; *U.S. Private*, pg. 769
Horn, Rick, V.P.-Sls. & Mktg.--Supreme Industries, Inc., Goshen, IN; *U.S. Public*, pg. 1541
Horn, Rick, V.P.-Mktg & Sls.--Supreme Corporation, Goshen, IN; *U.S. Public*, pg. 1542
Horn, Rick, V.P.-Sls. & Mktg.--Supreme Corporation of Texas, Cleburne, TX; *U.S. Public*, pg. 1542
Horn, Rick, V.P.-Sls. & Mktg.--Supreme MidAtlantic Corporation, Jonestown, PA; *U.S. Public*, pg. 1542
Horn, Rick, V.P.-Sls. & Mktg.--Supreme Murphy Corp., Wilson, NC; *U.S. Public*, pg. 1542
Horne, Ander, Sr. V.P.-Sls. & Mktg.--Ridgeview, Inc., Newton, NC; *U.S. Private*, pg. 930
Horne, F.L., Jr., V.P. & Gen. Mgr.--Gas-Fired Products, Inc., Charlotte, NC; *U.S. Private*, pg. 440
Horner, Andrea, Mgr.-Dealer Support--Magline, Inc., Pinconning, MI; *U.S. Private*, pg. 695
Hornyan, Janos, Mgr.-Home Sls.--Malev Hungarian Airlines, Plc., Budapest, Hungary; *Int'l*, pg. 833
Horsfall, Stan, Dir.-Sls.--Curries Company, Mason City, IA; *Int'l*, pg. 18
Horstman, John, Mgr.-Specialty Mkts. Sls.--Horsehead Resource Development Company, Inc., Palmerton, PA; *U.S. Private*, pg. 540
Horthrop, Bill, V.P.-Sls.--Spartanburg Steel Products, Spartanburg, SC; *U.S. Private*, pg. 300
Horton, Charles, V.P.-Sls.--Carolina Shoe Company, Morganton, NC; *U.S. Public*, pg. 217
Horton, David C., Sr. V.P.-Sls.--Superior Brands, Inc., Quincy, MA; *Int'l*, pg. 917
Horton, E. Mackie, Dir.-Sls. & Mktg.--Union Camp Container Div., Wayne, NJ; *U.S. Public*, pg. 1666
Horton, John D., Div. V.P.- Sls. & Mktg.--High Density Film Prods. Div., Hartsville, SC; *U.S. Public*, pg. 1486
Horton, Ken, V.P.-Sls.--Martin Industries, Inc. (AL), Florence, AL; *U.S. Private*, pg. 709
Horton, Roger, Dir.-Sls. & Mktg.--Taylor & Francis Group Ltd., London, United Kingdom; *Int'l*, pg. 1357
Horuath, John J., V.P.-Sls. & Mktg.--Bondo/Mar-Hyde Corporation, Cleveland, OH; *U.S. Public*, pg. 1357
Horvat, Frank, Reg. V.P.-N.E. Sls.--American Freightways Corporation, Harrison, AR; *U.S. Public*, pg. 75
Horvawitz, Stephen A., Dir.-Natl. Sls.--Seth Thomas, Norcross, GA; *U.S. Private*, pg. 445
Hosea, Tom, Mgr.-Area Sls.--Gensym Corporation, South Central Regional Office, Spring, TX; *U.S. Public*, pg. 731
Hosenfeld, Marv, V.P.-Natl. Sls.--Callaway Golf Company, Carlsbad, CA; *U.S. Public*, pg. 294
Hoshizaki, Kotaro, Dir.-Sls.--Mutual Trading Co., Inc., Los Angeles, CA; *U.S. Private*, pg. 770
Hoskin, Daniel W., Sr. V.P.-Sls. & Mktg.--Kenney Manufacturing Company, Warwick, RI; *U.S. Private*, pg. 615
Hoskins, Kelly, V.P.-Sls.--California Hardware Company, Ontario, CA; *U.S. Private*, pg. 335
Hoskins, William, V.P.-Sls. & Adv.--Penobscot Shoe Company, Old Town, ME; *U.S. Public*, pg. 1273
Hostetter, Sharon S., V.P.-Mktg. & Sls.--Baltimore Gas and Electric Company, Baltimore, MD; *U.S. Public*, pg. 172
Hotchkin, W.F., Dir.-Mktg. & Sls.--Stamco Industries Inc., Euclid, OH; *U.S. Private*, pg. 1029
Hotchkiss, M., Dir.-Sls.-Plastics--Farrel Corporation, Ansonia, CT; *U.S. Public*, pg. 614
Hotchkiss, Stephen H., V.P.-Sls. & Mktg.--IEC Electronics Corp., Newark, NY; *U.S. Public*, pg. 854
Hough, Blair, Mgr.-Sls.--Mechanical Technology Inc.-Technology Grp.(Latham), Latham, NY; *U.S. Public*, pg. 1077
Houlihan, Bob, Dir.-Sls. & Mktg.--Ashworth Bros., Inc., Fall River, MA; *U.S. Private*, pg. 89
Houlle, J.F., Dir.-Sls.--Laboratoires Polymedic, S.A., Casablanca, Morocco; *U.S. Public*, pg. 1092
House, Mike, V.P.-Sls.--Dana Perfumes Corp., New York, NY; *U.S. Private*, pg. 922
Householder, Jack, V.P.-Intl. Sls.--Accu-Sort Systems, Inc., Telford, PA; *U.S. Private*, pg. 11
Houser, John, Mgr.-Sls.--Lundy Construction Co., Inc., Williamsport, PA; *U.S. Private*, pg. 681
Houston, D., Mgr.-Worldwide Bus.--Silver-Weibull, Aurora, CO; *U.S. Public*, pg. 705
Houston, Donald, V.P.-Sls.--Plantronics Inc., Santa Cruz, CA; *U.S. Public*, pg. 1308
Houston, Donald S., V.P.-Sls.--Proxima Corporation, San Diego, CA; *U.S. Public*, pg. 1339
Houston, Paul G., Mgr.-Sls. Distr.--International Nickel, Inc., Saddle Brook, NJ; *Int'l*, pg. 672
Houston, Stephen E., Mgr.-Nat'l Sls.-Deco Products--Herberts-O'Brien Inc., Houston, TX; *Int'l*, pg. 626
Hovas, Donald, Mgr.-Sls.--Bergen Brunswig Medical Corporation, Meridian, MS; *U.S. Public*, pg. 214
Hoven, Rich, Mgr.-Prod./Brand-R-O Grinders & Asst. Mgr.-Sls.--Seneca Falls Technology Group, Seneca Falls, NY; *U.S. Private*, pg. 984
Hover, Marion, Dir.-Retail--Sonoma Mission Inn & Spa, Sonoma, CA; *U.S. Private*, pg. 1014
Hovind, Kai G., Dir.-Intl. Sls.--Jordan A/S, Oslo, Norway; *Int'l*, pg. 714
Howard, Bob, V.P. & Dir.-NY Sls. & Mktg.--Columbine JDS Systems, Inc., Denver, CO; *U.S. Public*, pg. 228
Howard, Jim, V.P.-Sls.--Howard Manufacturing, Kent, WA; *U.S. Private*, pg. 477
Howard, Kenneth, V.P.-Sls.--Medic Computer Systems, Inc., Raleigh, NC; *Int'l*, pg. 870
Howard, Larry, V.P.-Sls.--The Fabri-Form Company, Byesville, OH; *U.S. Private*, pg. 390
Howard, Lawrence J., V.P.-Sls.--Packaging Business, Milford, OH; *U.S. Public*, pg. 671
Howard, Peter, Sls. Engnr.--Cogsdill-Nuneaton, Ltd., Nuneaton, United Kingdom; *U.S. Private*, pg. 250
Howard, Scott, V.P.-Intl. Sls.--Callaway Golf Company, Carlsbad, CA; *U.S. Public*, pg. 294
Howard, Steve, V.P.-Sls. & Mktg.--American Television Time, Inc., Austin, TX; *U.S. Private*, pg. 63
Howarth, Ken, Sr. V.P.-Sls. & Mktg.--Imax Corporation, Mississauga, Canada; *Int'l*, pg. 661
Howe, Don, Mgr.-Reg. Sls.--DeVault Foods, Devault, PA; *U.S. Private*, pg. 329
Howe, P., Sls. Dir.--Moore Business Systems Australia Ltd., Richmond, Australia; *Int'l*, pg. 889
Howell, J.D., V.P.-Tent Sls.--Anchor Industries Inc., Evansville, IN; *U.S. Private*, pg. 71
Howell, Josh, Sr. V.P.-Corp. Mktg.--MFS WorldCom, Inc., Omaha, NE; *U.S. Public*, pg. 1779
Howells, Robert, Dir.-Sls.--Mardev, New York, NY; *Int'l*, pg. 1094
Howitt, John, Mgr.-Field Sls.--VWS, Inc., Cleveland, OH; *Int'l*, pg. 440
Howlan, Jim, V.P.-Sls.--Orange Motor Company Inc., Albany, NY; *U.S. Private*, pg. 818
Howson, Debra, Dir.-Inside Sls. & Adv.--North American Capacitor Co., Indianapolis, IN; *U.S. Private*, pg. 803
Hoxton, Jerome, Sr. V.P.-Sls. & Mktg.--Renaissance Publishing Co., Inc., Auburn, IN; *Int'l*, pg. 185
Hoyle, John, Grp. V.P.-Sls.--American & Efird, Inc., Mount Holly, NC; *U.S. Public*, pg. 1412
Hoyson, James P., Mgr.-MRO Sls.--ANESCO, Kingston, PA; *U.S. Private*, pg. 74
Hoyt, Deanne, Mgr.-Indus.--Ventura Coastal Corporation, Ventura, CA; *U.S. Private*, pg. 1136
Hoyt, Gunther, V.P.-Mktg. & Sls.--Xaloy, Inc., Pulaski, VA; *U.S. Private*, pg. 1194
Hoyt, Norman G., V.P.-Sls. & Mktg.--Lancaster Glass Corporation, Lancaster, OH; *U.S. Public*, pg. 977
Hricik, Kathleen, Sr. V.P.-Intl. Program Sls.--Nickelodeon/Nick At Nite, New York, NY; *U.S. Private*, pg. 779
Hubbard, Mike, Sr. V.P.-Sls.--Allen Canning Company, Siloam Springs, AR; *U.S. Private*, pg. 36
Hubbard, Peter E., Sr. V.P.-Sls. & Mktg.--Midland Enterprises Inc., Cincinnati, OH; *U.S. Public*, pg. 549
Hubbell, John, Sr. V.P.-Sales--Carnation Grocery Products Div., Glendale, CA; *Int'l*, pg. 916
Hubble, Chris M., V.P.-Sls. & Mktg.--Elastomer Seals - North America, Morton Grove, IL; *Int'l*, pg. 1338
Hubenthal, James, V.P.-Sls., Lithograph--Walle Corporation, Harahan, LA; *U.S. Private*, pg. 1148
Huber, Dave, Gen. Mgr.-Sls.--Ebsco Graphics, Oklahoma City, OK; *U.S. Private*, pg. 359
Huberfeld, Michael J., Div. Sls. Mgr.--Shofar Kosher Foods, Linden, NJ; *U.S. Public*, pg. 1433
Hubner, C.E., Jr., Pres. & Chief Oper. Officer--Central/Shippee, Inc., Bloomingdale, NJ; *U.S. Private*, pg. 224
Hubscher, Albin, V.P.-Sls. & Mktg.--CIBA Seeds, Greensboro, NC; *Int'l*, pg. 973
Hudak, Mike, Mgr.-N. American Sls.--Chronos Richardson, Fairfield, NJ; *Int'l*, pg. 1299
Hudak, Thomas, V.P.- Sls. & Mktg.--O-Z/Gedney Co., Farmington, CT; *U.S. Public*, pg. 727
Hudes, Jack, Mgr.-Sls. & Mktg.--Kaiser Permanente, California Division, Oakland, CA; *U.S. Private*, pg. 605
Hudgins, A. Mark, Dir.-New Prod. Devel.--Automatic Signal/Eagle Signal, Austin, TX; *Int'l*, pg. 1245
Hudgins, Doug, V.P.-Eastern Reg. Sls.--Southwestern Life Insurance Company, Dallas, TX; *U.S. Private*, pg. 1018
Hudson, Bob, Head-Nordic Sls.--Skandia Life Assurance Co. Ltd. - Helsinki, Helsinki, Finland; *Int'l*, pg. 1256
Hudson, Clive, V.P.-Client Access/European Sls.--3Com Corporation, Santa Clara, CA; *U.S. Public*, pg. 1603
Hudson, Jamie, Dir.-Sls.--Century Telephone Enterprises, Inc., Monroe, LA; *U.S. Public*, pg. 329
Hudson, Keith, V.P.-Sls.--Jim Hudson, Pontiac, Oldsmobile GMC, Columbia, SC; *U.S. Private*, pg. 545
Hudson, Mary Swatek, V.P.-Mktg. & Plng.--AMBI Inc., Tarrytown, NY; *U.S. Public*, pg. 7
Hudson, Phillip F., Exec. V.P.-Retail Banking & Mktg. Grp.--First Security Service Company, Salt Lake City, UT; *U.S.* Public, pg. 638
Huebner, Phil, Dir.-Ticket Sls.--Minnesota Twins Baseball Club, Minneapolis, MN; *U.S. Private*, pg. 750
Huesca, Rene, V.P.-Construction Sls.--Robbins Manufacturing Company, Tampa, FL; *U.S. Private*, pg. 935
Huett, Greg, V.P.-Wholesale Club Sls. & Mktg.--Tyson Foods, Inc., Springdale, AR; *U.S. Public*, pg. 1652
Huettel, John, Dir.-Sls.--Numetrix Inc., Santa Clara, CA; *Int'l*, *pg. 990*
Huffman, Deborah, V.P.-Women's Sls.--G-III Apparel Group, Ltd., New York, NY; *U.S. Public*, pg. 690
Hugh, D.C., Dir.-Sls. & Mktg.--Senior Foster Wheeler Power Division, Wembley, United Kingdom; *Int'l*, pg. 1221
Hughes, Bill, V.P.-Sls.--United States Lime & Minerals, Dallas, TX; *U.S. Public*, pg. 1684
Hughes, Bill, V.P.-Mktg. & Sls.--Arkansas Lime Co., Batesville, AR; *U.S. Public*, pg. 1685
Hughes, Bill R., V.P.-Sls. & Mktg.--Texas Lime Co., Cleburne, TX; *U.S. Public*, pg. 1685
Hughes, Dennis, Mgr.-Customer Svc.--Oasis Corp., Columbus, OH; *U.S. Private*, pg. 810
Hughes, Geoff A., Mgr.-Sls.--WBB Pacific Clays Ltd., Singapore, Singapore; *Int'l*, pg. 1488
Hughes, H.D., Chm. Bd., Pres., Chief Exec. Officer & Dir.-Sls.--Diversified Group, Inc., Harahan, LA; *U.S. Private*, pg. 336
Hughes, Jack, V.P.-Consumer Mktg.--General Communication, Inc., Anchorage, AK; *U.S. Public*, pg. 708
Hughes, James, V.P.-Sls. & Mgr.-Mdsg.--Ingrid Division of Lawnware, Morton Grove, IL; *U.S. Private*, pg. 654
Hughes, Kenneth M., V.P. & Natl. Dir.-Bank Sls.--Keyport Life Insurance Company, Boston, MA; *U.S. Private*, pg. 666
Hughes, Patrick, Sr. V.P.-Mktg. & Sls.--Blue Cross and Blue Shield of Massachusetts, Boston, MA; *U.S. Private*, pg. 151
Hugo, Donna, Sls. Asst.--Williams Foods Inc., Lenexa, KS; *U.S. Private*, pg. 1178
Huiid, Flemming, Dir.-Sls.--Sandvik Hard Materials A/S, Espergaerde, Denmark; *Int'l*, pg. 1186
Huizing, M. E., Dir.-Sls.--Bols Benelux B.V., Zoetermeer, Netherlands; *Int'l*, pg. 751
Huizinga, Bruce G., V.P.-Sls. & Mktg.--Magic Valley Foods, Inc., Rupert, ID; *U.S. Private*, pg. 695
Hulbert, Larry, Sr. V.P.-Sls. & Svc.--Alcatel Telecom, Richardson, TX; *Int'l*, pg. 55
Huldt, Patrik, Mgr.-Mktg. & Sls.--Esselte Chrono AB, Solna, Sweden; *Int'l*, pg. 459
Hull, Jim, V.P.-Sls. & Mktg.--Wide-Lite, San Marcos, TX; *U.S. Public*, pg. 730
Hull, Randolph, Dir.-Mktg. & Sls., Caribbean & Central America--Block Drug Company, International Division, Jersey City, NJ; *U.S. Public*, pg. 237
Hulme, J.H., Dir.-Industrial Sls.--LePage's Limited, Brampton, Canada; *Int'l*, pg. 613
Huls, Douglas A., V.P.-Sls.--Empire General Life Assurance Corporation, Birmingham, AL; *U.S. Public*, pg. 1336
Hulsing, Dennis I., Dir.-Sls. & Corp. Mktg.--Omni Hotels, Irving, TX; *U.S. Private*, pg. 1065
Hulsizer, William R., Mgr.-Reg. Sls. Distr.--International Nickel, Inc., Saddle Brook, NJ; *Int'l*, pg. 672
Hultberg, Peter, Mgr.-Sls. & Mktg.--Jimek, Arlov, Sweden; *U.S. Public*, pg. 170
Hulvat, Scott, Sr. V.P.-Sls. & Mktg.--F&F Foods, Chicago, IL; *U.S. Private*, pg. 388
Humbertson, Don, Dir.-Adv.--Chicago Reader, Inc., Chicago, IL; *U.S. Private*, pg. 235
Humphrey, Robert P., Pres. & Gen. Mgr.--Humphrey Products Company, Kalamazoo, MI; *U.S. Private*, pg. 547
Hundt, Doug, Mgr.-Natl. Sls.--Vermeer Manufacturing Company, Pella, IA; *U.S. Private*, pg. 1137
Hunt, Brian, Mgr.-Sls.--N.G. Bailey & Co. Ltd.-Manchester Branch, Manchester, United Kingdom; *Int'l*, pg. 132
Hunt, Dan, V.P.-Mktg. & Devel.--Mason Shoe Mfg. Co., Chippewa Falls, WI; *U.S. Private*, pg. 712
Hunt, J., Dir.-Sls.--Senior Colman Limited, Sale, United Kingdom; *Int'l*, pg. 1220
Hunt, James L., Mgr.-Sls., Hardwoods--TreeSource, Inc., Portland, OR; *U.S. Public*, pg. 1729
Hunt, Mark, V.P.-Medical Sls.--Span-America Medical Systems Inc., Greenville, SC; *U.S. Public*, pg. 1495
Hunt, Ray, Mgr.-Natl. Sls.--GN Nettest Fiber Optic Division, Utica, NY; *Int'l*, pg. 536
Hunt, Roger, V.P. & Regional Mgr.-London--Santa Fe Drilling Co., Alhambra, CA; *Int'l*, pg. 765
Hunter, George J., Exec. V.P.--Bonanza Bus Lines, Inc., Providence, RI; *U.S. Private*, pg. 156
Hunter, J.R., V.P.-Asia-Pacific/Latin America--BMC Software, Inc., Houston, TX; *U.S. Public*, pg. 162
Hunter, Kate, Dir.-Mktg.--Kal Grafx, Kentwood, MI; *U.S. Private*, pg. 387
Hunter, Kathy, Mgr.-Mktg.--K-Tron America, Inc., Pitman, NJ; *U.S. Public*, pg. 938
Hunter, Warren, Exec. V.P. & Chief Mktg. Officer--The McClure Group, Wayne, PA; *U.S. Private*, pg. 719
Hupp, William T., V.P.-Sls.--Estes Express Lines, Inc., Richmond, VA; *U.S. Private*, pg. 384
Hurst, Charles, V.P.-Sls. & Mktg.--Fischer Packing Co., Louisville, KY; *Int'l*, pg. 201
Hurst, Gordon S., Sr. V.P.-Sls.--Waukesha Cherry-Burrell, Delavan, WI; *U.S. Public*, pg. 1677
Hurst, M.J., Dir.-Sls. & Mktg.--Tube Products, Oldbury, United Kingdom; *Int'l*, pg. 1222
Hurst, Timm M., V.P.-Sls. & Mktg.--Serologicals Corporation, Clarkston, GA; *U.S. Public*, pg. 1460
Hurston, Jim, Dir.-Food Svcs. Sls. & Mktg.--Victory Refrigeration Co. LC, Cherry Hill, NJ; *U.S. Private*, pg. 1139
Hurtubise, Ken, Sr. V.P.-Sls. & Mktg.--ECRM, Tewksbury, MA; *U.S. Private*, pg. 353
Hurvitz, Chaim, V.P.-European Pharmaceutical Sls.--Teva Pharmaceutical Industries Ltd., Petah Tiqwa, Israel; *Int'l*, pg. 1380
Husain, E. Ejaz, Mgr.-Sls.--Organon Pakistan (Private) Limited, Karachi, Pakistan; *Int'l*, pg. 45
Huskins, Harold L., Mgr.-Sls.--Marion Machine Company Division, Marion, NC; *U.S. Private*, pg. 1055
Huso, Nathan, Mgr.-Comm. & Mktg.--Dakota Electric Association, Farmington, MN; *U.S. Private*, pg. 308
Hussain, Mohammed, Mgr.-Medical Sls.--Stafford-Miller Limited, Welwyn Garden City, United Kingdom; *U.S. Public*, pg. 237
Hussar, J., Mgr.-Precast Sls.--Terre Hill Concrete Products, Inc., Terre Hill, PA; *U.S. Private*, pg. 1077
Hussey, Tim, Mgr.-Sls.--Lepel Corporation, Edgewood, NY; *U.S. Private*, pg. 560
Hussong, Nancy, V.P.-Sls.--CitFed Bancorp, Inc., Dayton, OH; *U.S. Public*, pg. 376

Huston, Dennis, Mgr.-Sls. & Mktg./LVL--Boise Cascade Corporation, Boise, ID; *U.S. Public*, pg. 242
Huston, Dennis, Mgr.-Sls.--East Moline Metal Products Company, East Moline, IL; *U.S. Private*, pg. 357
Huston, John, V.P.-Sls.--Philips Medical Systems North America Company, Shelton, CT; *Int'l*, pg. 1055
Hutchens, Jim, V.P.-Sls.--Foamex International-Consumer Products Division, Saint Louis, MO; *U.S. Private*, pg. 1094
Hutchins, M.W., Gen. Mgr.-Sls.--Lincoln-Mercury Division, Detroit, MI; *U.S. Public*, pg. 662
Hutchinson, David, Dir.-Sls. & Mktg.-Hosiery--Charnos plc, Ilkeston, United Kingdom; *Int'l*, pg. 280
Hutchinson, Mark, V.P.-Passenger Sls.--American International Airways, Ypsilanti, MI; *U.S. Private*, pg. 57
Hutchinson, Ron, V.P.-Quality Assurance--Simmons Company, Atlanta, GA; *Int'l*, pg. 686
Hutchinson, Ted, Gen. Mgr.-Concrete--Onoda Northwest, Inc., Seattle, WA; *Int'l*, pg. 284
Hutchison, M.N., Sr. V.P.-S.F. Opers. & Dir.-Sls. & Mktg.-Nonferrous Sector--Davy International, San Francisco, San Ramon, CA; *Int'l*, pg. 774
Hutchison, Scott, Mgr.-Contract Sls.--The Flood Company, Hudson, OH; *U.S. Private*, pg. 414
Hutson, William, V.P.-Sls.--Mark III Industries, Ocala, FL; *U.S. Private*, pg. 704
Hutto, Mike, V.P.-Sls.--Fairfield Ocean Ridge, Edisto Island, SC; *U.S. Public*, pg. 610
Hutton, Cameron, V.P. & Mgr.-Southwest Reg.--Universal Studios TV, Universal City, CA; *Int'l*, pg. 1215
Hutton, Robin R., Exec V.P.-Sls./Vallen Safety Supply Company--Vallen Corporation, Houston, TX; *U.S. Public*, pg. 1705
Hutton, Robin R., Exec. V.P.-Sls.--Vallen Safety Supply Company, Houston, TX; *U.S. Public*, pg. 1705
Hwang, Soyen, Dir.-Sls.--Everex Systems Inc., Fremont, CA; *Int'l*, pg. 498
Hwang, Tae-In, Mgr.--Ssangyong Information & Communication Corporation, Seoul, Korea; *Int'l*, pg. 1292
Hyde, Howard, V.P.-Sls.--Baccarat (Cie des Cristalleries), Paris, France; *Int'l*, pg. 132
Hyde, Howard, V.P.-Sls. & Mktg.--Baccarat, Inc., Edison, NJ; *Int'l*, pg. 132
Hyman, Chuck, V.P.-Sls.--Dancker, Sellew & Douglas, Inc., New York, NY; *U.S. Private*, pg. 309
Hyman, Richard, Exec. V.P.-Sls.--Milgray/International, Inc., Farmingdale, NY; *U.S. Public*, pg. 206
Hynes, Dave, Regional Mgr.-Midwest--Columbus Mills, Inc., Columbus, GA; *U.S. Private*, pg. 256
Hynes, Dick, V.P.-Warehouse Sls.--Armour Swift Eckrich, Downers Grove, IL; *U.S. Public*, pg. 426
Hynes, Mike, Mgr.-Corp. Sls.--Samtec Inc., New Albany, IN; *U.S. Private*, pg. 963
Hynes, Thomas, Dir. Mktg. & Dir. Response--Moxness Products, Inc., Racine, WI; *U.S. Public*, pg. 124
Hyslop, Jim, Dir.-Mktg. Sls.--Armco Inc.-Coshocton Operations, Coshocton, OH; *U.S. Public*, pg. 131
Hyter, Steve, Mgr.-Natl. Sls--Transico Incorporated, Santa Ana, CA; *U.S. Public*, pg. 1630
Hytheir, M., Exec. V.P.-Systems Sales--Compagnie Generale de Geophysique, Massy, France; *Int'l*, pg. 241
Iaffaldano, Paul, Mgr.-Natl. Adv. Sls.--The Travel Channel, Atlanta, GA; *U.S. Private*, pg. 647
Iannuzzi, Tony, V.P.-Imprintable Sls.--Russell Corp., Jerzees Div., Alexander City, AL; *U.S. Public*, pg. 1413
Iannuzzi, Vincent, Mgr.-Sls.--Manning & Lewis Engineering Co., Union, NJ; *U.S. Private*, pg. 700
Ibanez, Rafael, Mgr.-Sls.-Latin America--T.D. Williamson, Inc., Tulsa, OK; *U.S. Private*, pg. 1179
Iblings, Michael, Mgr.-Sls.--Quadion Corporation, Minneapolis, MN; *U.S. Private*, pg. 898
Ice, David R., Mgr.-Sls. & Mktg.--U.S. Axle, Inc., Pottstown, PA; *U.S. Private*, pg. 1124
Idjer, Hocine, Dir.-Sls.--Eagle-Picher Fluid Systems Limited, Market Harborough, United Kingdom; *U.S. Private*, pg. 355
Iglesias-Enriquez, Avelina, Gen. Mgr.-Sls. & Mktg./ Mediterranean & Middle East--Utell International-Spain, Madrid, Spain; *Int'l*, pg. 1099
Igo, Mike, Mgr.-Circulation--Glenwood Post, Glenwood Springs, CO; *U.S. Private*, pg. 995
Iguchi, Mitch, V.P.-Sls.--Sanyo Energy (U.S.A.) Corporation, San Diego, CA; *Int'l*, pg. 1191
Iiams, Mike, V.P.-Strategic Partnerships--J.D. Edwards & Company, Denver, CO; *U.S. Private*, pg. 365
Ikeuchi, Shogo, Mgr.-Import Sls.--Kwe-Kintetsu World Express(S)Pte Ltd., Singapore, Singapore; *Int'l*, pg. 735
Ilaria, Peter E., Dir.-Mktg. & Sls.--Tropar Mfg. Co., Inc., Florham Park, NJ; *U.S. Private*, pg. 1105
Iles, B.W., V.P.-Sls.--IDenticard Systems, Inc., Lancaster, PA; *U.S. Private*, pg. 557
Iles, T. Randall, Sr. V.P.-Mktg. & Sls.--Pella Corporation, Pella, IA; *U.S. Private*, pg. 848
Illing, Klaus, Asst. Mgr.-Sls.--Schleicher & Schuell GmbH, Einbeck, Germany; *Int'l*, pg. 1206
Imamura, Eigi, Mng. Dir.--Murata Manufacturing Co., Ltd., Kyoto, Japan; *Int'l*, pg. 897
Imazumi, Michiaki, Mng. Dir.-Sls. & Mktg. Div.--Fujisawa Pharmaceutical Co. Ltd., Osaka, Japan; *Int'l*, pg. 525
Imhoff, William P., Mgr.-Sls.--Peters Machinery Co., Chicago, IL; *U.S. Public*, pg. 944
Imrie, Jim, V.P.-Sls.--Wisconsin Machine and Tool Corporation, Milwaukee, WI; *U.S. Private*, pg. 1185
Imus, Russ, V.P.-Sls.--Efficient Engineering Co., Troy, MI; *U.S. Private*, pg. 365
Inamura, Toshimichi, Gen. Mgr.-Sls. & Mktg.--Kintetsu World Express (H.K.) Ltd., Kowloon, Hong Kong; *Int'l*, pg. 735
Indyk, William, V.P.-Mktg. & Sls.--White Rock Products Corp., Whitestone, NY; *U.S. Private*, pg. 1173
Inglis, G.M., Gen. Mgr.-Sls.--WHX Corporation, New York, NY; *U.S. Public*, pg. 1726
Ingraham, Stan, V.P.-Sls. & Mktg.--VWS, Inc., Cleveland, OH; *Int'l*, pg. 440
Ingram, C.H., Mgr.-Natl. Sls.--Eriez Magnetics, Erie, PA; *U.S. Private*, pg. 381
Ingram, Lynn, Mgr.-Sls. Admin.--Kemet Corporation, Simpsonville, SC; *U.S. Public*, pg. 949
Ingram, O.H., II, Asst. V.P.-Liquid Sls. & Customer Service--Ingram Barge Company, Nashville, TN; *U.S. Private*, pg. 563
Ingram, Robert, V.P.-Sls.--Covington Industries, Atlanta, GA; *U.S. Private*, pg. 280
Ingrassia, John, Sr. V.P.-Columbia Records Group--Sony Music Entertainment, Inc., New York, NY; *Int'l*, pg. 1281
Inman, Jerry, Mgr.-Sls. Promo.--Information Builders, New York, NY; *U.S. Private*, pg. 561
Innamorata, Lori, Dir.-Sls.--Friendly Holidays Inc., Lake Success, NY; *U.S. Private*, pg. 428
Innes, John, V.P.-Sls.--Cable Spinning Equipment Inc., New London, MN; *U.S. Private*, pg. 197
Innes, Roger, Exec. V.P.-Sls.--Comdisco Electronics Group, San Diego, CA; *U.S. Public*, pg. 408
Innes, William D., Mgr.-Tiles Div.--Villeroy & Boch AG, Mettlach, Germany; *Int'l*, pg. 1468
Inoue, Haruo, Gen. Mgr.-Tableware Sls. Dept.--Narumi China Corporation, Nagoya, Japan; *Int'l*, pg. 906
Insognia, Dennis J., V.P.-Sls. & Mktg.--Imperial Nurseries Inc., Granby, CT; *U.S. Public*, pg. 707
Interlandi, Daniel G., Sr. V.P. & Gen. Mgr.-Leisure & Entertainment Prods.--Micros Systems Inc., Beltsville, MD; *U.S. Public*, pg. 1106
Iorio, Robert, V.P. & Mgr.-Sls.-East--Gibbs Wire & Steel Company, Inc., Southington, CT; *U.S. Private*, pg. 451
Ippolito, Gary, V.P.-Natl. Sls.--E. & J. Gallo Winery, Modesto, CA; *U.S. Private*, pg. 438
Ippolito, Joe, V.P.-Field Sls.--Syroco Inc., Peabody, MA; *Int'l*, pg. 844
Iramola, Enrique, V.P.-Mktg. & Sls.--Kaufman y Broad de Mexico SA de CV, Mexico, Mexico; *U.S. Public*, pg. 945
Ireton, Jamie, Natl. Sls. Mgr.--Ascom Canada Limited, Markham, Canada; *Int'l*, pg. 86
Irish, Michael, Gen. Mgr.-Sls.--Brillion Iron Works, Inc., Brillion, WI; *U.S. Public*, pg. 933
Irvine, Albert L., Jr., Grp. V.P.-Sls.--American & Efird, Inc., Mount Holly, NC; *U.S. Public*, pg. 1412
Irwin, Adam J., Chief Fin. Officer--Bensons International Systems Pty. Ltd., Yagoona, Australia; *Int'l*, pg. 460
Irwin, John, Reg. Mgr.--Environment/One Corporation, Niskayuna, NY; *U.S. Public*, pg. 586
Irwin, Rick, Sr. V.P.-Sls. & Gen. Mgr.-Publication Papers Div.--Gould Paper Corporation, New York, NY; *U.S. Private*, pg. 466
Irwin, T. Bryan, Sr. V.P.-Sls.--Irwin Toy Ltd., Toronto, Canada; *Int'l*, pg. 688
Isherwood, Madeleine, Dir.-Mktg. Sls. Admin.--Winthrop-Atkins Co., Inc., Middleboro, MA; *U.S. Private*, pg. 1183
Ishihara, Ken, V.P.-Adv.--Toshiba America Inc., New York, NY; *Int'l*, pg. 1405
Isselmann, Jeff, Mgr.-OEM Sls.--Intertractor America Corporation, Elkhorn, WI; *Int'l*, pg. 1511
Ivon, Susan, Admin. Asst.-Sls. & Mktg.--Dexol, Torrance, CA; *U.S. Public*, pg. 1390
Ix, Charles, Mgr.-Sls.--Frank Ix & Sons, Inc., New York, NY; *U.S. Private*, pg. 423
Izmirlian, Alex, Dir.-Export Sls.--Golden Peanut Company, Alpharetta, GA; *U.S. Private*, pg. 459
Izzard, D.C., Dir.-Sls.--Kelco International Ltd., London, United Kingdom; *U.S. Public*, pg. 1091
Izzo, Diane, Mgr.-Telephone Sls.--The Vermont Teddy Bear Company, Inc., Shelburne, VT; *U.S. Public*, pg. 1716
Jablonski, Brian J., Exec. V.P.-Sls. & Mktg.--Lason, Inc., Troy, MI; *U.S. Public*, pg. 979
Jablonski, S., V.P.-Sls. & Credit--Kruger Inc., Montreal, Canada; *Int'l*, pg. 761
Jablonski, Scott, Analyst-Sls. & Mktg.--The Davey Tree Expert Company, Kent, OH; *U.S. Private*, pg. 314
Jacino, John, 1st V.P.-Sls. & Mktg.--Wetsel-Oviatt Lumber Company, El Dorado Hills, CA; *U.S. Private*, pg. 1170
Jack, Larry, Mgr.-Sls.--Oklahoma City Division, Oklahoma City, OK; *U.S. Public*, pg. 279
Jackino, Dan, Sr. V.P.-Sls.--Gould Paper Corporation, New York, NY; *U.S. Private*, pg. 466
Jackling, Michael, V.P.-Sls. & Mktg.--Ferrari North America, Inc., Englewood Cliffs, NJ; *Int'l*, pg. 483
Jackman, Neil W., V.P.-Sls. & Human Resources--Pease Industries, Inc., Fairfield, OH; *U.S. Private*, pg. 845
Jackson, A., Dir.-Sls. & Mktg.--Oxford University Press, Oxford, United Kingdom; *Int'l*, pg. 1018
Jackson, B., V.P.-Sls.--White Cap, Inc., Downers Grove, IL; *Int'l*, pg. 1207
Jackson, Brett, Exec. V.P.-Sls. & Mktg.--Axent Technologies, Rockville, MD; *U.S. Public*, pg. 157
Jackson, Earle L., V.P.-Sls.--Vanguard Division, Farmington, CT; *Int'l*, pg. 917
Jackson, Gerald, Sls. Mgr.-Automotive--Parker & Amchem, Etobicoke, Canada; *Int'l*, pg. 612
Jackson, Jake, V.P.-Sls. & Mktg.--Dillard, A ResourceNet International Company, Greensboro, NC; *U.S. Public*, pg. 901
Jackson, Owen R., V.P.-Sls. & Mktg.--Technology Research Corporation, Clearwater, FL; *U.S. Public*, pg. 1564
Jackson, Regina, Mgr.-Sls.--Warner Press, Inc., Anderson, IN; *U.S. Private*, pg. 1150
Jackson, Robert, V.P.-Sls.--CPC Specialty Markets Group, Englewood Cliffs, NJ; *U.S. Public*, pg. 224
Jackson, Tom, V.P.-Sls.--Wheaton Van Lines, Inc., Indianapolis, IN; *U.S. Private*, pg. 1171
Jacob, Linda, Admin.-Exec. & Sls.--York Wallcoverings Inc., York, PA; *U.S. Private*, pg. 1196
Jacob, William, V.P.-Mktg. & Sls.--Transicoil, Inc., Valley Forge, PA; *U.S. Private*, pg. 538
Jacobazzi, Ralph, Mgr.-Utility Div. Sls.--W.H. Salisbury & Company, Skokie, IL; *Int'l*, pg. 1244
Jacobs, Jane, V.P.-Sls.--Cricket Lane, West Bridgewater, MA; *U.S. Public*, pg. 948
Jacobs, Jim, Bus. Devel. Mgr.--Advanced Marine Enterprises, Inc., Arlington, VA; *U.S. Public*, pg. 1182
Jacobs, Sol, Natl. Sls. Mgr.--I. Spiewak & Sons, Inc., New York, NY; *U.S. Private*, pg. 1025
Jacobs, T. Paul, V.P.-Sls.--Klipsch, Inc., Hope, AR; *U.S. Private*, pg. 626
Jacobsen, Jarl, Sls. Team Leader--Martin Door Mfg., Inc., Salt Lake City, UT; *U.S. Private*, pg. 708
Jacobsen, Jerry, V.P.-Tissue Sls.--Pope & Talbot, Inc., Portland, OR; *U.S. Public*, pg. 1316
Jacobson, Howard, V.P.-Sls. & Mktg.--Canandaigua Wine Company Div., Canandaigua, NY; *U.S. Public*, pg. 300
Jacobus, Steven, V.P.-Sls. & Mktg.--Subaru Distributor Corp., Orangeburg, NY; *Int'l*, pg. 523
Jacoby, Donald, V.P.-Sls. & Mktg.--Northrup King Co., Golden Valley, MN; *Int'l*, pg. 974
Jacques, Maurice E., V.P.-Mktg. & Sls.--Varco BJ Drilling Systems, Orange, CA; *U.S. Public*, pg. 1709
Jacquoletto, Marcel, Mgr.-Sls.--Lafarge Aluminates, Paris, France; *Int'l*, pg. 789
Jaderholm, Lars, Mgr.-Intl. Sls. & Private Label--Oregon Freeze Dry, Inc., Albany, OR; *U.S. Private*, pg. 819
Jaeger, Ralph, Adjoint Dir. Gen.-Commercial & Intl.--Arianespace SA, Evry, France; *Int'l*, pg. 81
Jaeschke, Monica, Mgr.-Promo.--A&W Food Services of Canada Inc., North Vancouver, Canada; *Int'l*, pg. 1
Jahnke, Keith, Exec. V.P.-Processed Meats--Thorn Apple Valley, Inc., Southfield, MI; *U.S. Public*, pg. 1602
Jahnke, Mike, V.P.-Worldwide Sls. Opers.--Sequent Computer Systems, Inc., Beaverton, OR; *U.S. Public*, pg. 1459
Jakab, Joseph J., Gen. Mgr.-Sls.--Moore Tool Company, Inc., Bridgeport, CT; *U.S. Private*, pg. 889
Jakaboski, Paul, Mgr.-Sls.--Victor Corporation, West Warwick, RI; *U.S. Private*, pg. 1138
Jakel, F., Mgr.-Sls. Office--Steelweld Division Zweigniederlassung Bonn der Ambac B.V., Saint Augustin, Germany; *Int'l*, pg. 71
Jakusz, Wayne, Mgr.-Distr.--Ampco Metal Incorporated, Milwaukee, WI; *U.S. Private*, pg. 67
Jalaba, Jerry J., V.P.-North America Sls./Enterprise Sys.--3Com Corporation, Santa Clara, CA; *U.S. Public*, pg. 1603
Jambe, Charles, Dir.-Institutional Sls.--Value Line, Inc., New York, NY; *U.S. Private*, pg. 137
James, Frank, V.P.-Kelly Brand Sls.--The Kelly-Springfield Tire Company, Cumberland, MD; *U.S. Public*, pg. 753
James, Frank, V.P.-Sls.--Kelly Brands Division, Cumberland, MD; *U.S. Public*, pg. 753
James, M.C., Dir.-Sls.--Watts Blake Bearne & Co. Plc, Newton Abbot, United Kingdom; *Int'l*, pg. 1487
James, Mike, Dir.-Mktg. & Sls.--Carefree of Colorado, Broomfield, CO; *U.S. Public*, pg. 217
James, Richard, Sr. V.P.-Sls.--Princess Cruise Lines, Los Angeles, CA; *Int'l*, pg. 1035
James, Richard T., II, Mgr.-Sls.--James Industries Inc., Hollidaysburg, PA; *U.S. Private*, pg. 580
James, Scott, V.P.-Sls. & Mktg.--National Cabinet Lock, Inc., Mauldin, SC; *U.S. Private*, pg. 270
Jamison, Jim, Dir.-Sls.--Bradford & Bingley Building Society, Bingley, United Kingdom; *Int'l*, pg. 210
Janelli, Mary Jane, Mgr.-Mktg. & Sls.--DeVault Foods, Devault, PA; *U.S. Private*, pg. 329
Janello, Guenter, Mgr.-Sls.--Kulicke & Soffa, AG, Zug, Switzerland; *U.S. Public*, pg. 969
Janiga, Ken, V.P.-Consumer Mktg. & Sls.--The White Lily Foods Co., Knoxville, TN; *U.S. Private*, pg. 866
Janik, John E., Mgr.-Sls.--Southeastern Steel Company, Florence, SC; *U.S. Private*, pg. 1015
Janik, Robert, Mgr.-Sls.--Dielectric Polymers, Inc., Holyoke, MA; *U.S. Public*, pg. 1258
Janke, Burghard, Div. Mgr.-Sls.--Otis GmbH, Berlin, Germany; *U.S. Public*, pg. 1690
Jankovic, Paul, V.P.-Sls. & Mktg.--Gessner/Miller Corporation, Worcester, MA; *U.S. Private*, pg. 435
Janowiak, James N., Sls./Service Promo.--Chevrolet Motor Div. General Motors Corp., Warren, MI; *U.S. Public*, pg. 720
Janowski, Fred A., Gen. Mgr.-Sls. & Prod. Distr.--RMI Titanium Company, Niles, OH; *U.S. Public*, pg. 1662
Janowski, James F., Mgr.-OEM Sls.--Thetford Corporation, Ann Arbor, MI; *U.S. Private*, pg. 352
Jansing, Dan, Natl. Sls. Mgr.--The Flood Company, Hudson, OH; *U.S. Private*, pg. 414
Janssen, Chuck, Dir.-Men's Wear Sls.--Men's Wear, Oshkosh, WI; *U.S. Public*, pg. 1233
Janssens, Jacques, Mgr.-Sls.--ALZ N.V., Genk, Belgium; *Int'l*, pg. 79
Jarchow, Jerry, Chief Oper. Officer & V.P.-Sls.--Kellermeyer Co., Toledo, OH; *U.S. Private*, pg. 612
Jardina, Matt, Asst. V.P.-Sls.--Total System Services, Inc., Columbus, GA; *U.S. Public*, pg. 1550
Jarosinski, Richard, Mgr.-Mktg., Sls. & Services--Portec Inc., Railway Maintenance Products Div., Pittsburgh, PA; *U.S. Public*, pg. 1318
Jarrett, Michael R., Dir.-Natl. Sls.--Label Products Div., Omaha, NE; *U.S. Public*, pg. 1152
Jarvis, Burney K., Sr. V.P. & Dir.-Branch Sls. & Admin.--Barclays American/Mortgage Corp., Charlotte, NC; *Int'l*, pg. 165
Jaskoviak, James, V.P.-Sls. & Mktg.--Winnebago Industries, Inc., Forest City, IA; *U.S. Public*, pg. 1772
Jaster, Eugene N., V.P.-Sls. & Mktg.--Detector Electronics Corporation, Minneapolis, MN; *Int'l*, pg. 1500
Javier, Conrado, Sls. Rep.--Columbia Pictures International Television, Manila, Philippines; *Int'l*, pg. 1282
Jeanquenin, Adrian, Mgr.-Sls.--Tempil Inc., South Plainfield, NJ; *U.S. Private*, pg. 90
Jech, Jean, Mgr.-Sls. & Mktg.--CIBA Seeds, Greensboro, NC; *Int'l*, pg. 973
Jefferson, Robert F., V.P.-Mktg.--Arinc Inc. (Consolidated), Annapolis, MD; *U.S. Private*, pg. 81
Jeffery, John G., Dir.-Sls.--Convesco Vehicle Sales GmbH, Russelsheim, Germany; *U.S. Public*, pg. 724

Jeffries, Jim, V.P.-Industrial Sls., Mktg. & Tech.--Favorite Brands International, Inc., Lincolnshire, IL; *U.S. Private*, pg. 397
Jelkin, Jerry, Dir.-Sls. & Mktg.--Optrex Glass, Plymouth, MI; *Int'l*, pg. 84
Jembelis, Thomas, Sr. V.P.--Nozaki America, Inc., New York, NY; *Int'l*, pg. 990
Jenkins, Barbara, V.P.-Reg. Acct. Sls.--Serta, Inc., Itasca, IL; *U.S. Private*, pg. 985
Jenkins, Carla, Gen. Sls. Mgr.--KTKR-AM, San Antonio, TX; *U.S. Public*, pg. 384
Jenkins, Colin, Dir.-Mktg. & Sls.--Chattem (U.K.) Ltd., Basingstoke, United Kingdom; *U.S. Public*, pg. 342
Jenkins, David, V.P.-Sls. & Mktg.--Chemical Leaman Tank Lines, Inc., Exton, PA; *U.S. Private*, pg. 233
Jenkins, Dennis, V.P.-Sls. & Mktg.--American Security Distribution, Anaheim, CA; *U.S. Private*, pg. 61
Jenkins, H.F., Mgr.-Sls.--Timken Argentina S.R.L., Buenos Aires, Argentina; *U.S. Public*, pg. 1617
Jenkins, Peter, Sr. V.P.-Mktg. & Sls.--Hawaiian Airlines, Inc., Honolulu, HI; *U.S. Public*, pg. 799
Jenkins, Peter W., Sr. V.P.-Mktg. & Sls.--Hawaiian Airlines, Inc., Honolulu, HI; *U.S. Public*, pg. 799
Jenks, Cliff, Exec. V.P.-North American Sls. & Mktg.--Zenith Data Systems, Deerfield, IL; *Int'l*, pg. 317
Jenne, P., Mgr.-Sls.--Penny & Giles Controls Inc., Attleboro, MA; *Int'l*, pg. 208
Jennings, Dale, Mgr.-Sls. & Mktg.--Pacific Handy Cutter, Inc., Costa Mesa, CA; *U.S. Private*, pg. 831
Jennings, Phil, V.P.-Sls. West--Esselte Corporation, Garden City, NY; *Int'l*, pg. 459
Jennings, R.W., Dir.-Intl. Sls.--United States Pipe & Foundry Company, Inc., Birmingham, AL; *U.S. Public*, pg. 1736
Jensen, S., Consultant-Fleet Sls.--Toyota Norge A/S, Drammen, Norway; *Int'l*, pg. 1414
Jensen, Steven, Dir.-Sls.--Dentsply International Inc., York, PA; *U.S. Public*, pg. 498
Jensen, Steven L., V.P.-Worldwide Sls. & Service--Silicon Valley Group, Inc., San Jose, CA; *U.S. Public*, pg. 1474
Jentjens, Pierre, Dir.-Sls.--Wisaforest Benelux B.V., Heerlen, Netherlands; *Int'l*, pg. 1429
Jeoffrey, Dominic, Dir.-Sls.--Jarchem Industries, Inc., Newark, NJ; *U.S. Private*, pg. 582
Jeon, Keon-Ho, Mgr.--Ssangyong Information & Communication Corporation, Seoul, Korea; *Int'l*, pg. 1292
Jepsen, Claudia, Dir.-Sls. Devel.--Life Magazine, New York, NY; *U.S. Public*, pg. 1613
Jericiau, John, Mgr.-Sls.--Potamkin Toyota, Inc., Miami, FL; *U.S. Private*, pg. 877
Jermasek, Doug, Assoc. Dir.-VIRACEPT Prod. Sls.--Agouron Pharmaceuticals, Inc., La Jolla, CA; *U.S. Public*, pg. 28
Jernigan, Michael E., Mgr.-Hospital Sls.--Bergen Brunswig Medical Corporation (Durr Drug), Montgomery, AL; *U.S. Public*, pg. 214
Jernigan, Paul, V.P.-Sls. & Mktg.--Gibson Musical Instruments, Inc., Nashville, TN; *U.S. Private*, pg. 451
Jerome, Louis, V.P.-Daytime & Children's Sls.--CBS Television Network, New York, NY; *U.S. Public*, pg. 274
Jeschonnek, Charlotte, Admin.-Sls.--Premier Mill Corp., Reading, PA; *U.S. Private*, pg. 881
Jespersen, Jim, Prod. Mgr.--Rubber Group, Niles, MI; *U.S. Public*, pg. 1160
Jesukaitis, Tom, Mgr.-Gen. Sls.--Cross Motors Corp., Louisville, KY; *U.S. Private*, pg. 291
Jindra, Martin, V.P.-Sls.--Squire-Cogswell Company, Gurnee, IL; *U.S. Private*, pg. 1027
Jirek, Charles, V.P.-Sls.--Kester Solder, Des Plaines, IL; *U.S. Public*, pg. 1003
Jobe, Michael, Mgr.-Sls. & Mktg.--Rotary Lift, Madison, IN; *U.S. Public*, pg. 521
Jobes, Steven D., V.P.-Mktg., Mdsg, Sls. & Natl. Accts.--CORT Business Services Corporation, Fairfax, VA; *U.S. Public*, pg. 451
Joerges, Dan, Exec. V.P.-Sls.--Green Forest Lumber Corporation, Toronto, Canada; *Int'l*, pg. 828
Johansson, Jan, Sr. V.P.-Electricity Sls.--Vattenfall AB, Stockholm, Sweden; *Int'l*, pg. 1452
Johansson, Stig, Mgr.-Sls.--Rubsteel AB, Perstorp, Sweden; *Int'l*, pg. 1146
John, Joseph J., Jr., Gen. Sls. Mgr.--Ludlow Textiles Co., Inc., Ludlow, MA; *U.S. Private*, pg. 680
John, Stephen, Gen. Mgr.-Sls.--Magnolia Hi-Fi, Inc., Kent, WA; *U.S. Private*, pg. 696
Johns, Bruce, V.P.-Sls.--Axent Technologies, Mountain View, CA; *U.S. Public*, pg. 157
Johns, R.W., Jr., V.P., Gen. Mgr.-Atlanta Opers., & Dir.-Sls.--Electronic Tele-Communications, Inc., Waukesha, WI; *U.S. Public*, pg. 570
Johns, Robert, Mgr.-Sls.--Nucor-Yamato Steel Company, Blytheville, AR; *U.S. Public*, pg. 1206
Johnsen, John, Dir.-Sales--NHT, Benicia, CA; *U.S. Public*, pg. 1369
Johnson, Allen, Mgr.-Mktg. & Sls.--Rubatex Corporation, Roanoke, VA; *U.S. Private*, pg. 56
Johnson, Amy, V.P.-Sls. & Mktg.--Rosemount Measurement Division, Eden Prairie, MN; *U.S. Public*, pg. 574
Johnson, Bob, Dir.-Natl. Sls.--Caswell-Massey Co. Ltd., Edison, NJ; *U.S. Private*, pg. 219
Johnson, Brent, Mgr.-Sls.--Peco Mfg. Co., Inc., Portland, OR; *U.S. Private*, pg. 846
Johnson, Charles, Mgr.-Sls.--J. Hellman Produce, Inc., Los Angeles, CA; *U.S. Private*, pg. 520
Johnson, Charles, V.P.-Sls.--Standex Electronics, Cincinnati, OH; *U.S. Public*, pg. 1507
Johnson, Clarence, Dir.-MIS--WorldCorp, Inc., Herndon, VA; *U.S. Public*, pg. 1779
Johnson, Cliff, V.P.-Sls.--Tyndale House Publishers, Inc., Carol Stream, IL; *U.S. Private*, pg. 1112
Johnson, Craig A., Sr. V.P.-Sls.--Philip Morris U.S.A., New York, NY; *U.S. Public*, pg. 1289
Johnson, Dan, Mgr.-Sls. & Mktg.--Hunter/Krey Foods, Hazelwood, MO; *U.S. Public*, pg. 75
Johnson, Dan, Mgr.-Local Sls.--Fisher Broadcasting Inc., Seattle, WA; *U.S. Public*, pg. 648
Johnson, Daryl, V.P.-Mktg. & Sls.--Pharmaceutical Basics, Inc., Chicago, IL; *Int'l*, pg. 48
Johnson, Dave, V.P.-Sls.--Kampgrounds of America, Inc., Billings, MT; *U.S. Private*, pg. 603
Johnson, David, V.P.-Sls. & Mktg.--National Sea Products Incorporated, Portsmouth, NH; *Int'l*, pg. 909
Johnson, Dennis, V.P.-Mktg. & Sls.--Harper-Wyman Co., Aurora, IL; *U.S. Public*, pg. 1209
Johnson, Dick, Gen. Mgr.-Bldg. Matls.--Onoda Northwest, Inc., Seattle, WA; *Int'l*, pg. 284
Johnson, Ed, Exec. V.P.-Sls. & Mktg.--Star-Kist Foods Inc., Newport, KY; *U.S. Public*, pg. 805
Johnson, Eric, V.P.-Sls. & Mktg.--John Boos & Company, Effingham, IL; *U.S. Private*, pg. 156
Johnson, Eric, Mgr.-Plastic Prods.--T.D. Williamson, Inc., Tulsa, OK; *U.S. Private*, pg. 1179
Johnson, Gary D., V.P.-Sls./Patterson Dental Supply, Inc.--Patterson Dental Company, Saint Paul, MN; *U.S. Public*, pg. 1265
Johnson, Hallett, V.P.-Circulation--Southern Progress Corporation, Birmingham, AL; *U.S. Public*, pg. 1612
Johnson, Heather, Mgr.-Natl. Sls.--Shiseido (Australia) Pty. Limited, Pyrmont, Australia; *Int'l*, pg. 1235
Johnson, Herb, Mgr.-Intl. Sls.--Trippe Mfg. Co., Chicago, IL; *U.S. Private*, pg. 1104
Johnson, J. Dennis, V.P.-Mktg.--Kentucky Medical Insurance Company (KMIC), Louisville, KY; *U.S. Private*, pg. 741
Johnson, J.B., Dir.-Sls.--Birdsong Peanuts, Suffolk, VA; *U.S. Private*, pg. 145
Johnson, J.B., Jr., Sr. V.P.--Birdsong Corporation, Suffolk, VA; *U.S. Private*, pg. 145
Johnson, James E., Sr. V.P.-Group Ins.--The Minnesota Mutual Life Insurance Company, Saint Paul, MN; *U.S. Private*, pg. 750
Johnson, James F., V.P.-Special Sls. Projects--The HON Co., Muscatine, IA; *U.S. Public*, pg. 772
Johnson, James L., V.P.-Sls.--Martin Sprocket & Gear, Inc., Arlington, TX; *U.S. Private*, pg. 709
Johnson, James R., Exec. V.P. & Sec.--Johnson Storage Moving Co, Denver, CO; *U.S. Private*, pg. 594
Johnson, James R., Exec. V.P.--Security Van Lines, Kenner, LA; *U.S. Private*, pg. 594
Johnson, Jim, Dir.-Sls.--FWD/Seagrave Fire Apparatus, Inc., Clintonville, WI; *U.S. Private*, pg. 390
Johnson, Jim, V.P.-Sls.-Seating Division--Harter, Middlebury, IN; *U.S. Private*, pg. 581
Johnson, Jim, V.P.-Sls. & Mktg.--Midwest Mutual Insurance Co., West Des Moines, IA; *U.S. Private*, pg. 881
Johnson, John W., V.P.-Domestic Sls.--Harmon Industries, Inc., Blue Springs, MO; *U.S. Public*, pg. 788
Johnson, Keith A., V.P.-Natl. Sls.--Clear Shield National, Inc., Wheeling, IL; *U.S. Public*, pg. 586
Johnson, Kenneth, V.P.-Sls. & Mktg.--FieldBrook Farms, Inc., Dunkirk, NY; *U.S. Private*, pg. 403
Johnson, Larry, Sr. V.P.-Sls.--Grindmaster Corporation, Louisville, KY; *U.S. Private*, pg. 482
Johnson, Linda, Mgr.-Adv., Sls. Promo. & Pub. Rels.--Chloride Industrial Batteries Ltd., Manchester, United Kingdom; *Int'l*, pg. 125
Johnson, Maryann, V.P.-Sls.--Mellon Bank (MD), Rockville, MD; *U.S. Public*, pg. 1085
Johnson, Michael E., V.P.-Natl. Sls.--Consolidated Freightways Corp., Menlo Park, CA; *U.S. Public*, pg. 435
Johnson, P.R., Dir.-Sls.--Vauxhall, Luton, United Kingdom; *U.S. Public*, pg. 724
Johnson, Pat, V.P.-Sls.--Polymer Composites Inc., Winona, MN; *Int'l*, pg. 624
Johnson, Paul, Natl Sls. Mgr.--Teledyne Laars/Jandy Products, Novato, CA; *U.S. Public*, pg. 43
Johnson, Peter J., Dir.-Corp. Circulation--Crain Communications, Inc., Chicago, IL; *U.S. Private*, pg. 284
Johnson, Richard, V.P.-Retail & Industrial Sls.--Knapp Shoes Inc., Penn Yan, NY; *U.S. Private*, pg. 401
Johnson, Richard, V.P.-Worldwise Sls.--QuickLogic Corporation, Sunnyvale, CA; *U.S. Private*, pg. 901
Johnson, Rick, Exec. V.P.-Automotive Sls.--Radiator Specialty Company, Charlotte, NC; *U.S. Private*, pg. 906
Johnson, Robert, V.P.-Mktg. & Sls.-Midwest Region--ResourceNet International, Shawnee Mission, KS; *U.S. Public*, pg. 903
Johnson, Ron, V.P.-Sls. & Mktg.--AmTran Corporation, Conway, AR; *U.S. Public*, pg. 1167
Johnson, Ronald A., V.P.-Sls. & Mktg.--Key Risk Management Services, Inc., Greensboro, NC; *U.S. Public*, pg. 216
Johnson, Tom, V.P.-Mktg. & Sls.--Atlas/Soundolier, Fenton, MO; *U.S. Private*, pg. 64
Johnson, Wayne, Dir.-Sls.--Rockford Products Corp., Rockford, IL; *U.S. Private*, pg. 938
Johnston, Jeffrey, V.P.-Intl. Sls.--Medstone International, Inc., Aliso Viejo, CA; *U.S. Public*, pg. 1082
Johnston, Jeffrey D., V.P.-Intl. Sls. & Mktg.--Ruslander & Sons, Inc., Buffalo, NY; *U.S. Private*, pg. 952
Johnston, Jeffrey D., V.P.-Sls. & Mktg.--Jewett International Corp., Buffalo, NY; *U.S. Private*, pg. 952
Johnston, Les, Dir.-Sls. & Mktg.--Fasco Controls Corporation, Shelby, NC; *Int'l*, pg. 125
Johnston, Scott, Mgr.-Sls.--Thomas Industries Inc., Sheboygan, WI; *U.S. Public*, pg. 1599
Jokerst, Raymond W., V.P.-Mktg. & Sls.--Magnetek Motors & Generators, Saint Louis, MO; *U.S. Public*, pg. 1037
Jolivette, Jordan, Mgr.-Sls. & Mktg.--E & A Industries, Inc., Indianapolis, IN; *U.S. Private*, pg. 352
Jonakin, Johnny, Mgr.-Comml. Sls.--HMI Electric, Memphis, TN; *U.S. Private*, pg. 518
Jonap, Scott T., V.P.-Sls. & Mktg., Consumer Prods. Div.--Foley-PLP Company, Rochester, NY; *U.S. Private*, pg. 416
Jonas, Mary, Mgr.-Sls.--Business Journal Publications, Inc., San Antonio, TX; *U.S. Private*, pg. 19
Jondahl, Kenneth E., V.P.-Intl. Sls. & Mktg.--Osmonics, Inc., Minnetonka, MN; *U.S. Public*, pg. 1233
Jones, Arthur L., Sr. V.P.-Retail Devel. & Sls.--Associated Grocers, Inc., Seattle, WA; *U.S. Private*, pg. 90
Jones, Bob, Mgr.-Sls.--Executive Car Leasing, Inc., Los Angeles, CA; *U.S. Private*, pg. 388
Jones, Bob, Prod. Mgr. & Sls. Mgr.--Sports & Recreational Prods.--Barbour Thread, Inc., Blue Mountain, AL; *Int'l*, pg. 618
Jones, Carolyn, Mgr.-Sls.--Business First of New York, Inc., Albany, NY; *U.S. Private*, pg. 19
Jones, Charlie, V.P.-Sls.--All Star Gas Co.-Region X, Lebanon, MO; *U.S. Private*, pg. 35
Jones, Chris, Dir.-Sls.--EMAP Direct, Purley, United Kingdom; *Int'l*, pg. 451
Jones, Cliff, Mgr.-Sls.--Watson's Quality Turkey Products, Inc., Turnersville, NJ; *U.S. Private*, pg. 1154
Jones, Craig, Dir.-Sls.--Turner Construction Company, San Jose, CA; *U.S. Public*, pg. 1645
Jones, Daryl, Dir.-Circulation--Memphis Publishing Co., Memphis, TN; *U.S. Public*, pg. 1448
Jones, Dave, Mgr.-Sls.--Matthews International Corp., Pittsburgh, PA; *U.S. Public*, pg. 1059
Jones, Gary, Mgr.-Sls.--GH Hensley Industries, Inc., Dallas, TX; *U.S. Private*, pg. 439
Jones, George, Dir.-Sls.--Great Vacations International, Sedona, AZ; *U.S. Public*, pg. 1172
Jones, Glynn, Mgr.-Sls.--Otto Junker GmbH Lammersdorf, Simmerath, Germany; *Int'l*, pg. 1014
Jones, Gordon, V.P. & Gen. Mgr.-Mkt. Pulp & Export Sls.--Stone Container Corporation, Chicago, IL; *U.S. Public*, pg. 1520
Jones, J.B., V.P.-Sls. & Mktg.--Coldwater Seafood Corporation, Rowayton, CT; *U.S. Private*, pg. 251
Jones, James L., Sr., Chm. Bd. & Chief Exec. Officer--Jones & Jones, Inc., McAllen, TX; *U.S. Private*, pg. 596
Jones, Jerry L., Sr. V.P.-Retail Opers.--Jitney-Jungle Stores of America, Inc., Jackson, MS; *U.S. Private*, pg. 588
Jones, Jim, Dir.-Sls. Devel.--Hyatt Hotels Corporation, Chicago, IL; *U.S. Private*, pg. 551
Jones, John P., V.P.-Sls./Intl.--Equitrac Corporation, Coral Gables, FL; *U.S. Public*, pg. 590
Jones, Lloyd, V.P.- Intl. Sls.--Fire King International, Inc., New Albany, IN; *U.S. Private*, pg. 406
Jones, Michael, V.P.-Sls.--Hitachi Data Systems Inc., Montreal, Canada; *Int'l*, pg. 622
Jones, R.W., Dir.-Sls.--Precision Drawn Tube, West Bromwich, United Kingdom; *Int'l*, pg. 1222
Jones, Richard, V.P.-Builder Sls.--Jenn-Air, Newton, IA; *U.S. Public*, pg. 1064
Jones, Ronald V., Mgr.-Intl. Sls. & Svc. Center--Lukens Inc., Coatesville, PA; *U.S. Public*, pg. 1019
Jones, Scott W., Sr. V.P. & Sls. Mgr.-Midwest--Jefferies & Company, Inc., Los Angeles, CA; *U.S. Public*, pg. 925
Jones, Steve, Mgr.-Retail Sls.--Jones Blair Co., Chattanooga, TN; *U.S. Private*, pg. 596
Jones, T. Roy, V.P.-Sls.--American Uniform Co., Cleveland, TN; *U.S. Private*, pg. 1039
Jones, Thomas, Exec. V.P.-Sales, Mktg. & Cust. Serv.--MDL Information Systems, Inc., San Leandro, CA; *Int'l*, pg. 1100
Jones, Tim, Mgr.-Sls.--The Seattle Business Journal, Inc., Seattle, WA; *U.S. Private*, pg. 20
Jones, Wayne, Mgr.-Sls.--Nucor Steel-Utah, Plymouth, UT; *U.S. Public*, pg. 1205
Jonker, John, Mgr.-Sls.--Caristrap International Inc., Laval, Canada; *Int'l*, pg. 271
Jonscher, Erich, Dir.-Commercial Vehicle Sls.--Mercedes-Benz AG, Stuttgart, Germany; *Int'l*, pg. 368
Jonsdottir, Asa, Sls. Zone Mgr.--Coldwater Seafood Corporation, Rowayton, CT; *U.S. Private*, pg. 251
Joo-Young, Jung, Mng. Dir.--Korea Heavy Industries & Construction Co., Ltd., Seoul, Korea; *Int'l*, pg. 758
Jopek, Larry, Gen. Mgr.-Sls.--WFTS-TV, Tampa, FL; *U.S. Public*, pg. 1448
Jordan, John, V.P.-Sls.--Erisco, Inc., New York, NY; *U.S. Public*, pg. 395
Jordan, Joyce, Exec. V.P.-Sls.--Dart Transit Company, Eagan, MN; *U.S. Private*, pg. 311
Jordan, Lawrence J., Sr. V.P.-Sls.--FileNet Corporation, Costa Mesa, CA; *U.S. Public*, pg. 622
Jordan, Nicholas, Exec. V.P.-Sls. & Mktg.--CPS Corporation, Franklin, TN; *U.S. Private*, pg. 422
Jorgensen, John, Mgr.-Export Sls.--GN Nettest, Telecom Division, Brondby, Denmark; *Int'l*, pg. 536
Jorgensen, Rickey, Mgr.-Sls./New Cars--McNamara Pontiac Isuzu Inc., Orlando, FL; *U.S. Private*, pg. 724
Jorgenson, Bruce, V.P.-Sls. & Mktg.--Rexam Medical Packaging, Inc., Mundelein, IL; *Int'l*, pg. 1107
Jory, Jim, Dir.-Mktg. & Sls. Integration--Clarke American Corp., San Antonio, TX; *Int'l*, pg. 267
Joseph, David, V.P.-Retail--Sun Diamond Growers of California, Pleasanton, CA; *U.S. Private*, pg. 1051
Josephs, Norm, Mgr.-Sls.--Maestro Products Inc., Moreno Valley, CA; *U.S. Public*, pg. 895
Jouan, Sylvie, Dir.-Sls.--Lalique North America, Carlstadt, NJ; *Int'l*, pg. 797
Jouchoux, Yvesde, Dir.-Sls. & Mktg. (Europe)--Automobiles Citroen, Neuilly, France; *Int'l*, pg. 1020
Joyce, Kevin E., V.P.-Sls.--Naylor Pipe Company, Chicago, IL; *U.S. Private*, pg. 789
Joyce, Richard, Mgr.-Sls.--Sony Corporation of Panama, Panama, Panama; *Int'l*, pg. 1284
Joyce, Ted, Reg. Mgr.-Sls.--PENCO-Tennessee, Nashville, TN; *Int'l*, pg. 1508
Joyner, A. Rex, V.P.-Sls.--SAIA Motor Freight Lines, Houma, LA; *U.S. Public*, pg. 1788
Joyner, Barrett, V.P.-North American Mktg. & Sls.--SAS Institute Inc., Cary, NC; *U.S. Private*, pg. 966
Joyner, Don, V.P.-Sls.--Allarcom Pay Television Limited, Edmonton, Canada; *Int'l*, pg. 1481
Juarez, F., Mktg./Sls.--Candy Iberica S.A., Barcelona, Spain; *Int'l*, pg. 260
Judd, Dwayne, V.P.-Sls.-Paper Div.--Burrows Paper Corporation, Little Falls, NY; *U.S. Private*, pg. 188
Judd, Frank, Mgr.-Natl. Sls.--Panel Processing, Inc., Alpena, MI; *U.S. Private*, pg. 836

Juenger, Steven, Dir.-Mktg. & Sls.--Reliance Medical Products, Inc., Mason, OH; *U.S. Private*, pg. 921
Julian, Dennis, V.P.-Packaging Adhesives--Evans Adhesive Corp., Columbus, OH; *U.S. Private*, pg. 384
Julian, Ken, Dir.-Corp. Communications--Harsco Corporation, Camp Hill, PA; *U.S. Public*, pg. 792
Julian, Malcolm, Exec. V.P.-Sls. & Mktg.--Winstar Global Products, Inc., Fairfield, NJ; *U.S. Public*, pg. 1772
Jump, George R., V.P.-Sls.--FASTRAC Systems, Inc., San Bruno, CA; *U.S. Public*, pg. 1158
Jump, George R., V.P.-Sls.--Pinnacle Data Corporation, San Bruno, CA; *U.S. Public*, pg. 1158
Jump, Shelley G., Mgr.-Sls. Admin.--Reynolds Metals Co.-Can Division Headquarters, Richmond, VA; *U.S. Public*, pg. 1386
Junco, Francisco, Dir.-Sls.--Duracell de Mexico S.A. de C.V., Naucalpan, Mexico; *U.S. Public*, pg. 743
Jung, Peter, Sr. V.P.-Sls.--Moen Incorporated, North Olmsted, OH; *U.S. Public*, pg. 675
Jungbluth, Eric, V.P.-Field Sls.--Kirsch, Sturgis, MI; *U.S. Public*, pg. 1176
Junk, Robert L., Mgr.-Sls./Private Label--Doane Products Co., Branded Sales Div., Joplin, MO; *U.S. Private*, pg. 337
Jura, Dan D., V.P.-Sls. (Air Systems)--Engineered Support Systems Inc., Saint Louis, MO; *U.S. Public*, pg. 583
Jurcak, Jim, Mgr.-Sls.--Southgate Ford Inc., Southgate, MI; *U.S. Private*, pg. 1018
Juredine, David, V.P.-Sls. & Mktg.--Ohio Indemnity Company, Columbus, OH; *U.S. Public*, pg. 175
Jusic, Boris, Sls. Mgr.-Central Region--Parker & Amchem, Etobicoke, Canada; *Int'l*, pg. 612
Just, Mark, V.P.-Sls. & Mktg.--Bradley Printing Company, Des Plaines, IL; *U.S. Public*, pg. 1778
Justic, Thomas J., V.P.-Natl. Sls.--Bernina of America Inc., Aurora, IL; *Int'l*, pg. 189
Justice, Hal, Exec. V.P.-Sls. & Mktg.--URS Logistics, Atlanta, GA; *U.S. Private*, pg. 1114
Justice, Michael, Dir.-Sls. & Mktg.--RB&W Corporation, Cleveland, OH; *U.S. Public*, pg. 1259
Kaasa, M.D., V.P.-Sls.--Rheem Air Conditioning Div., Fort Smith, AR; *Int'l*, pg. 1022
Kabella, Albert B., V.P.-Sls. & Mktg.--Calumet Construction Corporation, Hammond, IN; *U.S. Private*, pg. 201
Kacmarynski, John, Dir.-Sls.--Marine Travelift, Inc., Sturgeon Bay, WI; *U.S. Private*, pg. 703
Kacvinsky, Ray C., V.P.-Mktg. & Sls.-Generators--Marathon Electric Manufacturing Corp., Wausau, WI; *U.S. Public*, pg. 1371
Kaczynski, Steve, Exec. V.P.-Sls. & Mktg.--Giant Food Stores Inc., Carlisle, PA; *Int'l*, pg. 750
Kaemmer, Brian, Sls. Mgr.--BOC Coating Technology, Fairfield, CA; *Int'l*, pg. 121
Kafarakis, Phil, V.P.-Sls. & Mktg.--Jones Dairy Farm, Fort Atkinson, WI; *U.S. Private*, pg. 596
Kafkarkou, George, V.P.-Sls. & Mktg.--Infresco Corporation, Sarasota, FL; *U.S. Public*, pg. 420
Kahan, Jeff, Sr. V.P.-Sls.--Tyco Toys, Inc., Mount Laurel, NJ; *U.S. Public*, pg. 1058
Kahl, Tom, Mgr.-Sls.--C.C.K., Inc., Tyrone, PA; *U.S. Private*, pg. 637
Kahle, Douglas, V.P.-Intl. Sls.--Canandaigua Wine Company Div., Canandaigua, NY; *U.S. Public*, pg. 300
Kahn, Jan, Pres., Sls. & Mktg.--Caron International, De Kalb, IL; *U.S. Private*, pg. 786
Kahn, Michael, V.P. & Dir.-Franchise Sls. & Consumer Mktg.--The Great Frame Up Systems, Inc., Franklin Park, IL; *U.S. Private*, pg. 473
Kai, Ho Seow, Gen. Mgr.-Sls.--Cycle & Carriage Industries (1986) Pte. Limited, Singapore, Singapore; *Int'l*, pg. 350
Kain, Bill, Dir.-Corp. Sls.--New York Islanders Hockey Club, Uniondale, NY; *U.S. Private*, pg. 794
Kain, Debbie, Dir.-Sls.-Women's Footwear--Cole-Haan, Yarmouth, ME; *U.S. Public*, pg. 1184
Kaiser, Dave, Mgr.-Sls.--Vance Industries, Inc., Chicago, IL; *U.S. Private*, pg. 1133
Kaiser, Mark P., Sr. V.P.-Sls., Mktg. & Procurement--JP Foodservice, Inc., Columbia, MD; *U.S. Public*, pg. 918
Kaiser, Mark P., Sr. V.P.-Sls., Mktg. & Procurement--JP Foodservice Distributors, Inc., Columbia, MD; *U.S. Public*, pg. 918
Kaiser, Robert J., Sr. V.P.-Sls.--Emkay, Inc., Itasca, IL; *U.S. Private*, pg. 374
Kaiser, Sharon, Mgr.-Sls.--Noll Printing Corporation, Huntington, IN; *U.S. Private*, pg. 821
Kakac, Sharmila, Representative.-Export Sls.--Airtex Products, Fairfield, IL; *U.S. Private*, pg. 1113
Kalata, J., Sr. V.P.-Mktg. & Prod. Devel.--Air Canada Vacations Inc., Montreal, Canada; *Int'l*, pg. 36
Kale, Peter, Dir.-Sls.--H.J. Heinz Company Australia Ltd., Dandenong, Australia; *U.S. Public*, pg. 807
Kalick, Irving B., Exec. V.P.-Affiliate Sls. & Mktg.--QVC, Inc., West Chester, PA; *U.S. Private*, pg. 897
Kalil, A.J., V.P.-Sls. & Mktg.--PHB Die Casting, Fairview, PA; *U.S. Private*, pg. 826
Kalil, A.J., V.P.-Sls.--PHB Machining Division, Fairview, PA; *U.S. Private*, pg. 826
Kalil, A.J., V.P.- Sls.--PHB Tool & Die, Girard, PA; *U.S. Private*, pg. 826
Kalil, A.J., V.P.-Sls.--PHB Plastic & Rubber Molding Division, Fairview, PA; *U.S. Private*, pg. 826
Kalinowski, Richard, Mgr.-Sls.--Armatron International, Inc., Melrose, MA; *U.S. Public*, pg. 131
Kalinta, Nond, Mgr.-Dist. Sls.--Thai Airways Intl. Ltd.-San Francisco, San Francisco, CA; *Int'l*, pg. 1381
Kalmuck, John, V.P.-Sls. & Mktg.--La Marche Mfg. Co., Des Plaines, IL; *U.S. Private*, pg. 640
Kalsow, Dennis, Dir.-Sls. Training--Ohmeda, Liberty Corner, NJ; *Int'l*, pg. 121
Kalt, David, Mgr.-Sls.--Leathers Best, Farmingdale, NY; *U.S. Private*, pg. 656
Kamena, Karl, Mgr.-Sls. & Mktg.--Nanocor, Inc., Arlington Heights, IL; *U.S. Public*, pg. 64
Kamins, Aaron J., Chief Fin. Officer--Accurate Perforating Co., Chicago, IL; *U.S. Private*, pg. 12
Kaminsky, Thomas, Exec. V.P.-Sls.--Domecq Importers Inc., Old Greenwich, CT; *Int'l*, pg. 63
Kammersgard, Dana W., V.P.-Sls. & Mktg.--Artecon, Inc., Carlsbad, CA; *U.S. Private*, pg. 409
Kampman, Kevin, Mgr.-Circulation--The Independence Examiner, Independence, MO; *U.S. Private*, pg. 995
Kamps, P., Dir.-Sls. & Mktg.--Howard Maschinenfabrik GmbH, Michelstadt, Germany; *Int'l*, pg. 1387
Kanabar, Anil, Mgr.-Export Sls.--Conestoga Wood Specialties Corp., East Earl, PA; *U.S. Private*, pg. 262
Kane, Bob, V.P.-Sls.--McBee Systems, Inc., Parsippany, NJ; *U.S. Private*, pg. 718
Kane, Bradley P., V.P.-Strategic Acquisitions--Sensormatic Electronics Corporation, Boca Raton, FL; *U.S. Public*, pg. 1457
Kane, Patrick, Sr. V.P., Corp. Devel. & New Bus. Contact--CRN International, Inc., Hamden, CT; *U.S. Private*, pg. 197
Kane, Richard C., Sr. V.P. & Mgr.-San Francisco Sls.--Jefferies & Company, Inc., Los Angeles, CA; *U.S. Public*, pg. 925
Kane, Tim, V.P.-Sls.--Goodway Technologies Corporation, Stamford, CT; *U.S. Private*, pg. 464
Kangas, Mel, V.P.-Sls. & Mktg.--Capacity of Texas, Inc., Longview, TX; *U.S. Public*, pg. 400
Kania, Gene, Mgr.-Bus. Unit--Senior Flexonics Inc., Bartlett, IL; *Int'l*, pg. 1222
Kanter, Alan R., V.P.-Sls.--Syratech Corporation, East Boston, MA; *U.S. Private*, pg. 1060
Kanter, Don, Dir.-Sls. & Mktg.--F. D. Kees Power Equipment, Beatrice, NE; *U.S. Private*, pg. 1195
Kanther, William P., V.P.-Sls.--Tranzonic Personal Care Division, Pepper Pike, OH; *U.S. Public*, pg. 1632
Kantzler, A., Dir.-Sls. & Mktg.--Moore Business Equipment Div., Dover, NH; *Int'l*, pg. 890
Kaplan, Dean, V.P.-Olympic Sls.--CBS Television Network, New York, NY; *U.S. Public*, pg. 274
Kaplan, Frank, V.P.-Intl. Sls.--VTEL Corporation, Austin, TX; *U.S. Public*, pg. 1703
Kaplan, Jerry, V.P.-Yarn Sls.--Amicale Industries, Inc., New York, NY; *U.S. Private*, pg. 66
Kaplan, Joseph, Mgr.-Export Sls.--Pitco Frialator Inc., Bow, NH; *U.S. Public*, pg. 1065
Kaplan, Michael M., V.P.-Sls. & Mktg.--Life Sciences International, Philadelphia, PA; *U.S. Private*, pg. 317
Kaplan, Samuel, Pres., Chief Exec. Officer, Sec. & Dir.-Sls. & Pur.--Admiration Hosiery Mills, Inc., Charlotte, NC; *U.S. Private*, pg. 528
Kaplan, Steven, V.P.-Sls., Domestic--Prime Tanning Co., Inc., Rochester, NH; *U.S. Private*, pg. 884
Kapp, Matthew, V.P.-Asia Pacific Rim Sls./Enterprise Sys.--3Com Corporation, Santa Clara, CA; *U.S. Public*, pg. 1603
Kappen, Don, Mgr.-Mktg. & Sls.--Bodolay/Pratt Div., Lakeland, FL; *U.S. Private*, pg. 832
Karaga, Steve, V.P.-Sls. & Mktg.--Hitachi Koki U.S.A. Ltd., Norcross, GA; *Int'l*, pg. 620
Karas, Richard, Sr. V.P.-Sls. & Fin. Svcs.--Nationwide Life Insurance Co., Columbus, OH; *U.S. Private*, pg. 789
Karas, Rick, Sr. V.P.-Sls.-Financial Services--Nationwide Insurance Enterprise, Columbus, OH; *U.S. Private*, pg. 788
Kardish, Tim, V.P.-Sls.- Core Microscopy & Histology--Leica Inc., Deerfield, IL; *Int'l*, pg. 806
Kargman, Steve, Mgr.-Natl. Sls.--KNXV-TV, Phoenix, AZ; *U.S. Public*, pg. 1448
Karn, Don, Sr. V.P.-Sls.--Shaklee Corporation, San Francisco, CA; *Int'l*, pg. 1518
Karn, Greg, Mgr.-Sls.-Northeastern Reg.--Temco Fireplace Products, Inc., Nashville, TN; *U.S. Public*, pg. 1576
Karr, James W., V.P.-Major Market Sls.--Moscom Corporation, Pittsford, NY; *U.S. Public*, pg. 1136
Karran, Bill, Sls. Mgr.-Wellhead--Barber Industries Inc., Calgary, Canada; *Int'l*, pg. 164
Karrel, Dean, V.P.-Trade Sls./Prof., Reg. & Trade Grp.--John Wiley & Sons, Inc., New York, NY; *U.S. Public*, pg. 1768
Karrigan, Dean, Mgr.-Sls.--Northern Michigan Veneers, Inc., Gladstone, MI; *U.S. Private*, pg. 805
Karstoff, Nick, Reg. Sls. Mgr.--E.D. Smith, Winona, Canada; *Int'l*, pg. 1263
Kashmer, Bernard A., Chief Oper Officer & Exec. V.P.--Hull Corporation, Hatboro, PA; *U.S. Private*, pg. 547
Kaspar, David, V.P.-Sls.--Bassick by Kaspar, Shiner, TX; *U.S. Private*, pg. 122
Kaspar, David C., Mgr.-Rack & Wire Prod. Sls.--Kaspar Wire Works, Inc., Shiner, TX; *U.S. Private*, pg. 608
Kasper, Ted, Dir.-Adv. & Mktg.--Hutchenson Seal Corporation, Downey, CA; *U.S. Private*, pg. 550
Kass, Daniel B., V.P.-Sls.--CDW Computer Centers, Inc., Vernon Hills, IL; *U.S. Public*, pg. 277
Kass, Jeffrey F., V.P.-Sls.--Hammermill Papers, Memphis, TN; *U.S. Public*, pg. 902
Kassab, Thomas M., Exec. V.P.--Stainless Incorporated, Deerfield Beach, FL; *U.S. Private*, pg. 1029
Kassab, Thomas M., Exec. V.P.--Charter House Incorporated, Holland, MI; *U.S. Private*, pg. 1029
Kastein, Trice A., Mgr.-Customer Svc.--Detex Corporation, New Braunfels, TX; *U.S. Private*, pg. 327
Kasten, Richard J., V.P.-Intl. Sls.--Oregon Steel Mills Inc., Portland, OR; *U.S. Public*, pg. 1230
Kasten, Robert, V.P.-Sls. & Mktg.--Hoffer's Inc., Schofield, WI; *U.S. Private*, pg. 239
Katopis, Christopher, V.P.-Sls. & Mktg.--Cains Foods, L.P., Ayer, MA; *U.S. Private*, pg. 199
Katsafanas, Parry, V.P.-Mktg. & Sls.--UNR-Leavitt Div., Chicago, IL; *U.S. Public*, pg. 1404
Katz, Alan, V.P.-Sls.--CGS Industries, Inc., Long Island City, NY; *U.S. Private*, pg. 194
Katz, Barry, V.P.-Sls.--Unitel Video, Inc., New York, NY; *U.S. Public*, pg. 1692
Katz, Howard, Exec. V.P.--RMT Technology, Bellwood, IL; *U.S. Private*, pg. 927
Katz, Larry J., Dir.-Sls., Use & Miscellaneous Taxes--Ikon Office Solutions, Inc., Malvern, PA; *U.S. Public*, pg. 862
Kauble, Dan R., V.P.-Sls. Food Service--Thorn Apple Valley, Inc., Southfield, MI; *U.S. Public*, pg. 1602
Kaufman, L.C., V.P.-Field Sls.--AFG Industries, Inc., Kingsport, TN; *Int'l*, pg. 84
Kaufmann, David A., V.P.-Natl. Sls.--Fel-Pro Incorporated, Skokie, IL; *U.S. Private*, pg. 399
Kaupa, G., Gen. Mgr.-Sls.--Kintetsu World Express (Deutschland) GmbH, Ratingen, Germany; *Int'l*, pg. 735
Kavanagh, Robert E., Sr. V.P.-Sls. & Employee Benefits--The Great-West Life Assurance Company, Winnipeg, Canada; *Int'l*, pg. 557
Kavanaugh, MaryAnn, Sls. Mgr.-Eastern Equip. Div.--JanSport, Appleton, WI; *U.S. Public*, pg. 1702
Kavazanjian, John, V.P.-Sls.--Casio Phone-Mate, Inc., Torrance, CA; *Int'l*, pg. 274
Kaveney, Peter W., Dir.-Sls.--Haskel Energy Systems Ltd., Sunderland, United Kingdom; *U.S. Public*, pg. 798
Kavois, Steve, Mgr.-Sls.--Triton Industries, Inc., Chicago, IL; *U.S. Private*, pg. 1104
Kawanaka, Katsuo, Mng. Dir.-Tokyo Sls.--Orix Corporation, Tokyo, Japan; *Int'l*, pg. 1008
Kawano, Hidemichi, Dir.-Mktg. & Mgr.-Sls.--Fotograbado Industrial Centro-Americano S.A., San Jose, Costa Rica; *Int'l*, pg. 1349
Kawashima, Masanori, Gen. Mng. Dir.-Sls.--Sapporo Breweries Ltd., Tokyo, Japan; *Int'l*, pg. 1193
Kawaters, A.J., Mgr.-Sls.--Landauer, Inc., Glenwood, IL; *U.S. Public*, pg. 977
Kawczynski, Randy, V.P.-Mktg. & Sls.--Sawhill Tubular Div., Sharon, PA; *U.S. Public*, pg. 131
Kay, Bart, Mgr.-Western Sls.--Efco Corporation, Monett, MO; *U.S. Private*, pg. 353
Kay, Carroll, V.P.-Sls. & Traffic--Kyanite Mining Corporation, Dillwyn, VA; *U.S. Private*, pg. 638
Kay, G., V.P.-Sls.--Zim-American Israeli Shipping Co., New York, NY; *U.S. Private*, pg. 1206
Kay, Mike, V.P.-Sls.--The Kay Company, Inc., Frankfort, IN; *U.S. Private*, pg. 610
Kaye, Gordon H., Sr. V.P.-Sls.--Fair, Isaac and Company, Inc., San Rafael, CA; *U.S. Public*, pg. 609
Kazanowski, Adam, Dir.-Sls. Markets--Johnson & Johnson Poland, Sp.z.o.o., Warsaw, Poland; *U.S. Public*, pg. 931
keane, Michael, V.P.-Sls. & Mktg.--Arburg, Inc., Newington, CT; *U.S. Private*, pg. 79
Keane, Robert S., V.P.-Intl. Sls.--Astronics Corporation, Buffalo, NY; *U.S. Public*, pg. 142
Keane, Terry, V.P.-Sls.-Smith Tool--Smith International, Inc., Houston, TX; *U.S. Public*, pg. 1478
Kearins, Michael, V.P.-Sls. Flooring--Triangle Pacific Corporation, Dallas, TX; *U.S. Public*, pg. 1634
Kearney, George B., Exec. V.P.--Northwestern Industrial Piping, Niles, IL; *U.S. Private*, pg. 806
Kearney, Richard P., Mgr.-Mktg. & Sls.--W.R. Case & Sons Cutlery Company, Bradford, PA; *U.S. Private*, pg. 1207
Kearney, T. Scott, V.P.-Sls. & Mktg./Furniture--Ameriwood Industries International Inc., Grand Rapids, MI; *U.S. Public*, pg. 98
Kearns, Connie, Exec. Sec.--Airmaster Fan Co., Michigan Center, MI; *U.S. Private*, pg. 29
Kearns, Paul, Dir.-Sls. & Mktg.--Lancashire Dairies Ltd., Manchester, United Kingdom; *Int'l*, pg. 798
Kearns, Robert W., Mgr.-Gen. Sls.--Newport Steel Corporation, Newport, KY; *U.S. Public*, pg. 1147
Kearns, Tom, V.P.-Sls.--Mead Johnson Nutritional Group, Evansville, IN; *U.S. Public*, pg. 254
Keasler, Dave, V.P.-Sls.--Steiner Electric Company, Chicago, IL; *U.S. Private*, pg. 1039
Keating, Thomas, V.P.-Sls.--Woodard Inc., Owosso, MI; *U.S. Private*, pg. 192
Keaveney, W.J., Global Sls. Mgr.-Specialty Alloys Opers.--Carpenter Specialty Alloys Operations, Reading, PA; *U.S. Public*, pg. 307
Keaveney, W.J., Mgr.-Global Sls./Steel Div.--Carpenter Technology (Canada) Ltd., Mississauga, Canada; *U.S. Public*, pg. 308
Kebrdle, Dave, Pres.-Sls. & Mktg.--Domore Corporation, Elkhart, IN; *U.S. Private*, pg. 339
Kedijang, Timmy, Dir.-Medical--Novo Nordisk (Pty) Ltd., Woodmead, South Africa; *Int'l*, pg. 988
Kee, Jim, V.P.-Sls.--Yazoo Power Equipment, LLC, Jackson, MS; *U.S. Private*, pg. 1195
Keefer, Eric, V.P.-Environmental Sls.--Perma-Fix Environmental Services, Inc., Gainesville, FL; *U.S. Public*, pg. 1279
Keefer, Ray, Gen. Mgr.-Sls.-Food Svcs. Markets--The Homer Laughlin China Company, Newell, WV; *U.S. Private*, pg. 653
Keefer, Tom B., V.P.-Sls. & Mktg.--AC Corporation, Greensboro, NC; *U.S. Private*, pg. 3
Keegan, Bill, Dir.-Sls. & Mktg.--Central States Can Co., Massillon, OH; *U.S. Public*, pg. 463
Keen, Willard, V.P.-Sls. & Mktg.--Keen Compressed Gas Co., Wilmington, DE; *U.S. Private*, pg. 611
Keenan, Eddie, District Mgr.-Sls.--Autry Greer & Sons, Inc., Prichard, AL; *U.S. Private*, pg. 479
Keenan, James, V.P.-Sls.--Clipper Exxpress, Lemont, IL; *U.S. Public*, pg. 130
Keenan, Joe, Mgr.-Sls. & Mktg.--Hughes-Peters, Inc., Cincinnati, OH; *U.S. Private*, pg. 546
Keene, Milford, V.P. & Gen. Mgr.--North American Products Corp., Jasper, IN; *U.S. Private*, pg. 803
Keene, Ronnie, Mgr.-Sls. N. & S. America--Cascade Corporation, Troutdale, OR; *U.S. Public*, pg. 310
Keenley, James, Mgr.-Sls.--The World Almanac, Mahwah, NJ; *U.S. Public*, pg. 1328
Keep, Randy, Dir.-Sls.--Magna Lomason Corp., Farmington Hills, MI; *Int'l*, pg. 830
Kegley, David, V.P.-Sls.--Blue Grass Quality Meats, Crescent Springs, KY; *U.S. Private*, pg. 152

Kehal, Gerry, Natl. Sls. Mgr.--Bio-Rad Semiconductor Systems Div., Cambridge, MA; *U.S. Public*, pg. 230
Keighley, Donald N., Dir.-Sls.--Stamping & Frame Div., Rochester, MI; *Int'l*, pg. 1388
Keil, David, Mgr.-Sls.--Chesapeake Packaging Co./Scotia, Scotia, NY; *U.S. Public*, pg. 347
Keith, William R., V.P.-Sls.--Crown Cork & Seal, Southern Div., Arden, NC; *U.S. Public*, pg. 463
Kelahan, Mike, Dir.-Sls.--The Rottlund Company, Inc., Roseville, MN; *U.S. Public*, pg. 1406
Kelle, Carl J., V.P.-Sls.--GEICO Indemnity Company, Washington, DC; *U.S. Public*, pg. 220
Kelleher, K.B., Exec. V.P.-Mktg. & Sls.--CNB International, Inc., Charleston, SC; *U.S. Private*, pg. 196
Kelleher, K.B., Exec. V.P.-Mktg. & Sls.--Clearing-Niagara, Buffalo, NY; *U.S. Private*, pg. 196
Keller, Brian, V.P.-Sls. Admin.--Fairfield Communities, Inc., Little Rock, AR; *U.S. Public*, pg. 610
Keller, Carol, Asst. Mgr.-Sls.--Jefferson Smurfit Corporation, Saint Louis, MO; *Int'l*, pg. 1269
Keller, Chris, Mgr.-Natl. Sls.--W.R. Case & Sons Cutlery Company, Bradford, PA; *U.S. Private*, pg. 1207
Keller, James, Dir.-Bus. Devel.--NavCom Defense Electronics, Inc., El Monte, CA; *U.S. Private*, pg. 789
Keller, Jim, V.P.-Mktg.--Houck Industries, Inc., Visalia, CA; *U.S. Private*, pg. 541
Keller, Kurt, V.P.-Mktg. & Sls.--Seal Group, Irvine, CA; *U.S. Public*, pg. 1262
Keller, Michael, Exec. V.P.-Mktg.--Koo Koo Roo, Inc., Los Angeles, CA; *U.S. Public*, pg. 966
Keller, Robert J., V.P.-Sls./Home Care Div.--Armor All Products Group, Oakland, CA; *U.S. Public*, pg. 387
Kellersman, John, V.P.-Sls. & Mktg.--Cooper Instrument Corp., Middlefield, CT; *U.S. Private*, pg. 274
Kelley, Brian, V.P.-Sls. & Distr.--G.E. Appliances, Louisville, KY; *U.S. Public*, pg. 710
Kelley, Ella, Natl. Sls. Coord.--Medical Resources Inc., Murray Hill, NJ; *U.S. Public*, pg. 1080
Kelley, Lauren J., Dir.-Worldwide Sls.--Art Technology Group, Boston, MA; *U.S. Private*, pg. 86
Kelley, O.B., V.P.-Sales--Hunter Douglas, Inc., Upper Saddle River, NJ; *Int'l*, pg. 639
Kelley, Randy, Dir.-Natl. Sls.--Chiron Corporation, Emeryville, CA; *U.S. Public*, pg. 349
Kelley, Rick, V.P.-Sls.--Cardkey Systems, Inc., Simi Valley, CA; *U.S. Public*, pg. 105
Kelley, Robert D., V.P. & Reg. Mgr.-Sls.--Airborne Freight Corporation, Seattle, WA; *U.S. Public*, pg. 32
Kelley, William B., V.P.-N. American Sls. & Service--Candela Corporation, Wayland, MA; *U.S. Public*, pg. 300
Kelley, William E., Sr. V.P.-Sls., Adv. & Mktg.--Mohawk Paper Mills, Inc., Cohoes, NY; *U.S. Private*, pg. 755
Kellman, Cheri, V.P.-Architectural Glass Div.--Globe-Amerada Glass Company, Elk Grove Village, IL; *U.S. Private*, pg. 458
Kellman, John, V.P.-Retail & Wholesale Div.--Globe-Amerada Glass Company, Elk Grove Village, IL; *U.S. Private*, pg. 458
Kellman, Michael, V.P.-Natl. Auto Glass Replacement Program--Globe-Amerada Glass Company, Elk Grove Village, IL; *U.S. Private*, pg. 458
Kellogg, Jeanette, V.P.-Sls. & Mktg.--Genova Products, Inc., Davison, MI; *U.S. Private*, pg. 447
Kelly, Barbara, V.P.-Sls., Mktg. & Customer Service--Time Warner Cable of New York City, New York, NY; *U.S. Public*, pg. 1611
Kelly, Brian T., Sr. V.P.-Global Mktg. & Sls.--Occidental Chemical Corporation, Dallas, TX; *U.S. Public*, pg. 1210
Kelly, David, Mgr.-Sls.--Pittsburgh Tube Co. Fairbury Div., Fairbury, IL; *U.S. Private*, pg. 868
Kelly, Jim, V.P.-Natl. Sls.--The American Companies, Inc., Topeka, KS; *U.S. Private*, pg. 52
Kelly, John, Dir.-Sls.--Underground Construction Co., Inc., Benicia, CA; *U.S. Private*, pg. 1116
Kelly, John M., Exec. V.P.-Mktg. & Sls.--Desa International, Bowling Green, KY; *U.S. Private*, pg. 326
Kelly, Keith, V.P.-Intl. Sls. & Mktg.--Mile High Equipment Co., Denver, CO; *Int'l*, pg. 189
Kelly, Kevin, Mgr.-Division Sls.--Tekra Corporation, New Berlin, WI; *U.S. Private*, pg. 1073
Kelly, Kevin O., Pres.-Michael Sales Group--Michael Foods, Inc., Minneapolis, MN; *U.S. Public*, pg. 1103
Kelly, Leslie, Dir.-Sls.--Review Publishing Company Ltd., Hong Kong, Hong Kong; *U.S. Public*, pg. 525
Kelly, M.L., Dir.-Sls.--Goodyear de Chile S.A.I.C., Santiago, Chile; *U.S. Public*, pg. 753
Kelly, Patrick T., V.P.-Sls. & Mktg.--Haws Drinking Faucet Co., Berkeley, CA; *U.S. Private*, pg. 512
Kelly, Pete, Sr. V.P.-Sls.-Hasbro Toy Grp.--Hasbro, Inc., Pawtucket, RI; *U.S. Public*, pg. 797
Kelly, Pete, Mgr.-Sls.--Playskool, Inc., Pawtucket, RI; *U.S. Public*, pg. 797
Kelly, Peter, Sr. V.P.-Sls.--Hasbro, Cincinnati, OH; *U.S. Public*, pg. 797
Kelly, Robert D., Dir.-Special Sls. Program--The F.X. Matt Brewing Co., Utica, NY; *U.S. Private*, pg. 714
Kelly, Robin, V.P.-Sls. & Mktg.--ENPAC, Eastlake, OH; *U.S. Public*, pg. 592
Kelly, Sean, Dir.-Sls.--Sifco Turbine Components, Ltd., Cork, Ireland; *U.S. Public*, pg. 1471
Kelly, Tom, Mgr.-Sls.--Bill Wink Chevrolet, Dearborn, MI; *U.S. Private*, pg. 144
Kelly, Tom, V.P.-Sls.--Star Transportation, Inc., Nashville, TN; *U.S. Private*, pg. 1035
Kelly, Tony, V.P.-Worldwide Sls.--Gelman Sciences, Inc., Ann Arbor, MI; *U.S. Public*, pg. 1253
Kelly, William, V.P.-Sls.--XRE Corporation, Littleton, MA; *U.S. Public*, pg. 1595
Kelsey, Rich, Pres.--Encore Shoe Corporation, Rochester, NH; *U.S. Private*, pg. 375
Kemp, M., Dir.-Sls. & Mktg.--Decoflex Limited, Hartlepool, United Kingdom; *Int'l*, pg. 889
Kempin, Joachim, Sr. V.P.-OEM Sls.--Microsoft Corporation, Redmond, WA; *U.S. Public*, pg. 1107
Kempner, Irv, V.P.-Sls.--The Gillette Company, Boston, MA; *U.S. Public*, pg. 743
Kenerly, Nancy, Mgr.-Sls.--American Cities Business Journals, Inc., Atlanta, GA; *U.S. Private*, pg. 19
Kenna, John, Mgr.-Sls.-Vending--The O'Boise Corporation, Oak Brook, IL; *U.S. Private*, pg. 810
Kennedy Winstead, Marybeth, V.P.-Sls.--ATCOM, Inc., Research Triangle Park, NC; *U.S. Private*, pg. 94
Kennedy, Bill, Mgr.-Prod. Publicity--Kennametal Inc., Latrobe, PA; *U.S. Public*, pg. 950
Kennedy, Brian, V.P.-Mktg. & Sls.--Hertz Corporation, Newark, NJ; *U.S. Public*, pg. 664
Kennedy, Brian, V.P.-Mktg. & Sls.--Hertz Corporation, Trenton, NJ; *U.S. Public*, pg. 664
Kennedy, Brian, Dir.-ISD Sls.--Samsung Electronics America, Inc., Ridgefield Park, NJ; *Int'l*, pg. 1183
Kennedy, Brian J., Exec. V.P.-Sls. & Mktg.--The Hertz Corporation, Park Ridge, NJ; *U.S. Public*, pg. 664
Kennedy, Edward, Exec. V.P.-sls. & Mktg.--LePage's, Inc., Pittsburgh, PA; *U.S. Private*, pg. 598
Kennedy, Eric, Sls. Exec.--Circle Freight International, Houston, TX; *U.S. Public*, pg. 370
Kennedy, Gene, Gen. Sls. Mgr.--Southern Belle Dairy Company, Somerset, KY; *U.S. Private*, pg. 1015
Kennedy, John, V.P.-Sls.--United Stationers Inc., Des Plaines, IL; *U.S. Public*, pg. 1689
Kennedy, Joseph J., V.P.-Sls., Service & Mktg.--The Saturn Corporation, Troy, MI; *U.S. Public*, pg. 721
Kennedy, Maureen, V.P.& Dir.-Mktg., Illinois--Citibank, Federal Savings Bank (Illinois), Chicago, IL; *U.S. Public*, pg. 378
Kennedy, Richard E., V.P. & Dir.-Snack Sls.--GoodMark Foods, Inc., Raleigh, NC; *U.S. Public*, pg. 751
Kennedy, T.M., Corp. Sls. Admin.--Benjamin Moore & Co., Montvale, NJ; *U.S. Private*, pg. 133
Kennedy, Tom, Gen. Sls. Mgr.-East--Milwaukee Electric Tool Corp., Brookfield, WI; *Int'l*, pg. 96
Kennerly, Keith, Sales Mgr.-Printing Paper--Dillard, A ResourceNet International Company, Doraville, GA; *U.S. Public*, pg. 902
Kenney, William, Dir.-Sls. & Mktg.--The Kent Manufacturing Co., Pickens, SC; *U.S. Private*, pg. 615
Kenny, Terrence, V.P.--Buffalo Pumps, Inc., North Tonawanda, NY; *U.S. Public*, pg. 103
Kent, John, V.P.-Natl. Sls. Admin.--Barton Incorporated, Chicago, IL; *U.S. Public*, pg. 300
Kent, Roy, Dir.-Sls.--Steering and Suspension Division, Saint Louis, MO; *U.S. Public*, pg. 443
Kent, Thomas, Sr. V.P.-Sls.--Gould Paper Corporation, New York, NY; *U.S. Private*, pg. 466
Kenyon, Art, V.P.-Sls. & Mktg.--Red Wing Shoe Co., Inc., Red Wing, MN; *U.S. Private*, pg. 915
Kephart, Craig, Dir.-Sls.--IVTx, Maryland Heights, MO; *U.S. Public*, pg. 601
Kereston, Ron, V.P.-Sls.--Snyder Berlin, Berlin, PA; *U.S. Private*, pg. 887
Kerley, Brad, Mgr.-Sls.-S.W.--Mountain Valley Spring Company, Hot Springs National Park, AR; *U.S. Private*, pg. 963
Kerlin, Kay J., Second V.P.-Sls. Support--Time Insurance, Milwaukee, WI; *Int'l*, pg. 499
Kern, Ed, Mgr.-Export Sls.--SK Hand Tool Corp., Chicago, IL; *Int'l*, pg. 570
Kern, Richard C., Mgr.-Sls. & Mktg.--Kern Industries, City of Industry, CA; *U.S. Private*, pg. 616
Kern, William J., Jr., Sr. V.P.-Sls.--The Pepper Companies, Inc., Chicago, IL; *U.S. Private*, pg. 851
Kerns, Ed, V.P.-Sls. & Mktg.-Plumbing Prods. Div.--Reading Tube Corp., Reading, PA; *U.S. Private*, pg. 202
Kershaw, Peter, V.P.-Sls. & Mktg.--Tenax Corporation, Danbury, CT; *Int'l*, pg. 193
Kersten, James E., V.P.-Direct Sls. West--Wallace Computer Services, Inc., Lisle, IL; *U.S. Public*, pg. 1735
Kersting, Kurt, V.P.-Sls. & Mktg.--Duro-Test Corporation, Fairfield, NJ; *U.S. Private*, pg. 349
Kersting, Kurt, V.P.-Sls. & Mktg.--Duro-Test Intl. Corp., Fairfield, NJ; *U.S. Private*, pg. 349
Keskey, Mike, V.P.-Sls.--Best Buy Co., Inc., Eden Prairie, MN; *U.S. Public*, pg. 223
Kessaratos, Frank, Mng. Dir.-Intl. Sls.--Landis & Staefa AG, Zug, Switzerland; *Int'l*, pg. 800
Kessler, Alan J., Sr. V.P.-Global Sls./Enterprise Sys.--3Com Corporation, Santa Clara, CA; *U.S. Public*, pg. 1603
Kessler, Bruce, Mgr.-Sls.-N.E.--Mountain Valley Spring Company, Hot Springs National Park, AR; *U.S. Private*, pg. 963
Kester, Gary, Natl. Sls. Mgr.--RAM Golf Corporation, Melrose Park, IL; *U.S. Private*, pg. 908
Kesterson, Danny, Exec. V.P.-Sls. & Mktg.--Kesterson Food Company, Inc., Paris, TN; *U.S. Private*, pg. 616
Keveryn, Joe, V.P.-Sls.--Universal Furniture Industries, Inc., High Point, NC; *U.S. Private*, pg. 432
Kevorkian, Chris, Mgr.-Nalt. Sls.--The Hearst Corporation, New York, NY; *U.S. Private*, pg. 515
Kevorkian, Christopher, Dir.-Adv. Sls.--Sunset Publishing Corporation, Menlo Park, CA; *U.S. Public*, pg. 1613
Kewley, Don, V.P.-Sls.--Colgate-Palmolive Canada Inc., Toronto, Canada; *U.S. Public*, pg. 398
Key, Denise, Rep.-Sls. Promo.--Dillard, A ResourceNet International Company, Birmingham, AL; *U.S. Public*, pg. 902
Key, Michael, Dir.-Sls. Promo. & Incentives--People's Security Life Insurance, Durham, NC; *Int'l*, pg. 27
Keyes, Joe, Dir.-Retail Sls.--Parks LLC, Baltimore, MD; *U.S. Private*, pg. 840
Keysor, David, V.P.-Sls. & Mktg.--Prime Matrix Wireless Communications, Calabasas, CA; *U.S. Private*, pg. 884
Khan, Kamran, V.P.-Worldwide Sls.--Excalibur Technologies Corporation, Vienna, VA; *U.S. Public*, pg. 598
Khan, S.R., Regional Sls. Mgr.--Parke-Davis & Company, Limited, Karachi, Pakistan; *U.S. Public*, pg. 1739
Khawaja, Shahid Waheed, Sr. Mgr.-Supply--National Refinery Limited, Karachi, Pakistan; *Int'l*, pg. 909
Khoury, Patrick, Gen. Mgr.-Mktg. & Sls.-The Americas--Asiana Airlines, Los Angeles, CA; *U.S. Private*, pg. 89
Kiarashi, Sonia, Dir.-Mktg. & Sls.--Newcom, Inc., Westlake Village, CA; *U.S. Public*, pg. 147
Kibi, Akio, Mng. Dir.-Sls.--Japan Tobacco Inc., Tokyo, Japan; *Int'l*, pg. 703
Kibort, Mark, Mgr.-Reg. Sls.--Oriental Motor U.S.A. Corp., Santa Clara, CA; *Int'l*, pg. 1008
Kida, Haruo, Sr. Mng. Dir.-Sls., Mktg. & Prod. Devel.--Nisshin Steel Co., Ltd., Tokyo, Japan; *Int'l*, pg. 946
Kidd-Collins, Marsha, Mgr.-Natl. Sls.--WFTS-TV, Tampa, FL; *U.S. Public*, pg. 1448
Kidd, Neal, Supv.-Wharehouse--Kelso Oil Company, Knoxville, TN; *U.S. Private*, pg. 613
Kiedinger, Keith, V.P.-Pkgng. & Mgr.-Sls. & Natl. Sls.--Queens Group, Inc., Long Island City, NY; *U.S. Private*, pg. 900
Kieffer, Gerald, Mgr.-Sls.--Badger Meter Industrial Div., Milwaukee, WI; *U.S. Public*, pg. 165
Kieffer, Kathy, V.P.-Sls. & Dir. Mktg. Svcs.--May & Speh, Inc., Downers Grove, IL; *U.S. Public*, pg. 1063
Kiefus, Steven, Mgr.-Sls.--Big Joe Manufacturing Co., Lincolnwood, IL; *U.S. Private*, pg. 143
Kiehl, J. L., V.P.-Mktg. & Sls.--Carlisle Tire & Wheel Company, Aiken, SC; *U.S. Public*, pg. 305
Kiely, Jack, Mgr.-Natl. Sls.--Stocko Corp., Carlstadt, NJ; *Int'l*, pg. 1301
Kiernan, Nick, V.P.-Affiliate Sls.- CBS Radio Network--CBS Radio Div., New York, NY; *U.S. Public*, pg. 274
Kiever, D., Mgr.-Sls.--Maple Leaf Meats, Winnipeg, Canada; *Int'l*, pg. 841
Kilcoyne, Raymond, V.P.-Foodservice Sls. & Mktg.--Cains Foods, L.P., Ayer, MA; *U.S. Private*, pg. 199
Kildea, Tim, Mgr.-Regional Sls.--Toledo Commutator Co., Owosso, MI; *U.S. Private*, pg. 623
Killgore, Steve, Gen. Sls. Mgr.--Willamette Industries, Inc., Eugene, OR; *U.S. Public*, pg. 1769
Killiam, Greg, Gas Supply Rep.--Enogex Inc., Oklahoma City, OK; *U.S. Public*, pg. 1207
Killingsworth, Deborah, V.P.-Sls. & Mktg.--Total System Services, Inc., Columbus, GA; *U.S. Public*, pg. 1550
Kilman, Gary, V.P.-Sls.--OEC Medical Systems, Inc., Salt Lake City, UT; *U.S. Public*, pg. 1207
Kilpatrick, Allen, V.P.-Mktg. & Sls.--Atomic Energy of Canada Ltd., Mississauga, Canada; *Int'l*, pg. 97
Kim Tiong, Quah, Dir.-Wholesale & Bus. Devel.--F.J. Benjamin Fashions (Singapore) Pte. Ltd., Singapore, Singapore; *Int'l*, pg. 187
Kim, Heung-Sik, Mgr.--Ssangyong Heavy Industries Co., Ltd., Seoul, Korea; *Int'l*, pg. 1292
Kim, Jae-Hong, Mgr.--Ssangyong Investment & Securities Co., Ltd., Seoul, Korea; *Int'l*, pg. 1292
Kim, Jeong-Yoon, Mgr.--Dongseong Express Tourists Co., Ltd., Busan, Korea; *Int'l*, pg. 1292
Kim, Joong-Soo, Mgr.--Ssangyong Engineering Co., Ltd., Seoul, Korea; *Int'l*, pg. 1292
Kim, Myung-Roung, Mgr.--Ssangyong Heavy Industries Co., Ltd., Seoul, Korea; *Int'l*, pg. 1292
Kim, Sang-Kyo, Mgr.--Ssangyong Oil Refining Co. Ltd., Seoul, Korea; *Int'l*, pg. 1292
Kim, Suk-Won, Dir.-Sls.--Grand Hyatt Seoul, Seoul, Korea; *U.S. Private*, pg. 551
Kim, Young-Bok, Mgr.--Ssangyong Cement Industrial Co., Ltd., Seoul, Korea; *Int'l*, pg. 1291
Kimball, Don, V.P.--Don Miguel Mexican Foods, Inc., Anaheim, CA; *U.S. Private*, pg. 339
Kimball, Douglas, V.P.-Oil Equip. & Related Services--Eaton Metal Products Company, Denver, CO; *U.S. Private*, pg. 358
Kimball, John E., V.P.-Sls.--Macromedia Incorporated, Hackensack, NJ; *U.S. Private*, pg. 693
Kimball, John E., Mgr.-Sls.--Bergen Record Corp., Hackensack, NJ; *U.S. Private*, pg. 693
Kimes, Karl, Sr. V.P.-Sls.--Package Service Company, LLC., Kansas City, MO; *U.S. Private*, pg. 833
Kimpel, Lee, Mgr.-Commerical Div. Sls.--Ortho-Kinetics, Inc., Waukesha, WI; *U.S. Private*, pg. 820
Kimpton, Greg, Mgr.-Intl.--Projects Unlimited, Inc., Dayton, OH; *U.S. Private*, pg. 890
Kimura, H., Gen. Mgr.-Sls.--Miyata Industry Co., Ltd., Chigasaki, Japan; *Int'l*, pg. 884
Kimura, Naoya, Exec. Mng. Dir.--Kokusai Electric Co., Ltd., Tokyo, Japan; *Int'l*, pg. 743
Kimura, Yaichi, Dir. & Gen. Mgr.--Cosmo Oil Co., Ltd., Tokyo, Japan; *Int'l*, pg. 335
Kinard, Kenneth, Asst. V.P.-SCR Sls.--Southwire Company, Carrollton, GA; *U.S. Private*, pg. 1019
Kindt, James K., Div. V.P.-Eastern Sls.--Baldwin Piano & Organ Company, Loveland, OH; *U.S. Public*, pg. 169
Kinel, John P. Jr., V.P.-Sls.--The Spencer Turbine Co., Windsor, CT; *U.S. Private*, pg. 1025
King-wan, Law, Exec. Dir.-Sls.--Sun Hung Kai Properties Ltd., Wan Chai, Hong Kong; *Int'l*, pg. 1318
King, Albin, Dir.-Sls.--Bayernland Gmbh & Co. KG, Nuremberg, Germany; *Int'l*, pg. 181
King, Bill, V.P. & Dir.-Sls. & Shipping Mgr.--H. R. Kaminsky & Sons, Inc., Fitzgerald, GA; *U.S. Private*, pg. 606
King, Catherine M., Natl. Sls. Officer--Lincoln Financial Advisors, Fort Wayne, IN; *U.S. Public*, pg. 998
King, Don, Dir.-Sls.--Steelcraft Manufacturing Company, Cincinnati, OH; *U.S. Public*, pg. 877
King, Don, Mgr.-Sls. & Contracts--Starmet Corporation, Concord, MA; *U.S. Public*, pg. 1511
King, Gary, Mgr.-Comml. Sls.--HMI Electric, Memphis, TN; *U.S. Private*, pg. 518
King, George, Mgr.-Sls. & Mktg.--Automatic Machine Products Company, Attleboro, MA; *U.S. Private*, pg. 101
King, H. Alan, V.P.-Sls. & Mktg.--Rogers Tool Works, Inc., Rogers, AR; *U.S. Public*, pg. 950
King, James D., V.P.-Sls. & Mktg.--Consumer Products Company, Muncie, IN; *U.S. Public*, pg. 56
King, Jim, Pres.-Sls.--Things Remembered, Inc., Highland Heights, OH; *U.S. Public*, pg. 397

King, Jim, V.P.-Sls.--Therma-Tru Corp., Maumee, OH; *U.S. Private*, pg. 1079
King, Joe, V.P.-Sls. & Mktg.--American Sightseeing International, San Francisco, CA; *U.S. Private*, pg. 61
King, Joe, V.P.-Sls. & Mktg.--Carmun International, San Antonio, TX; *Int'l*, pg. 646
King, Larry, V.P.-Sls. Ice Cream--Prairie Farms Dairy, Inc., Carlinville, IL; *U.S. Private*, pg. 878
King, Larry, V.P.-Sls. & Mktg.--Ryan Herco Products Corp., Burbank, CA; *U.S. Private*, pg. 953
King, Larry, Jr., V.P.-Direct Sls. & Service--Intuit, Inc., Mountain View, CA; *U.S. Public*, pg. 911
King, Mark A., V.P.-Sls. & Mktg.--Voyager Emblems, Inc., Sanborn, NY; *U.S. Private*, pg. 1143
King, Mike, Mgr.-Natl. Sls.--Cherokee Brick & Tile Co., Macon, GA; *U.S. Private*, pg. 233
King, Neal, V.P.-Grp. Sls. & Mktg.--Standard Insurance Co., Portland, OR; *U.S. Private*, pg. 1031
King, Rod, V.P.-Sls.-Consumer Markets--Fuji Photo Film U.S.A., Inc., Elmsford, NY; *Int'l*, pg. 524
King, Roger, V.P.-Sls. & Mktg.--Software Spectrum, Inc., Garland, TX; *U.S. Public*, pg. 1483
King, Scott, Mgr.-Sls. & Mdsg.--Eaton Corporation, Tort Control Division, Marshall, MI; *U.S. Public*, pg. 557
King, Sid F., Dir.-Sls.--Lincoln Assurance Limited, Uxbridge, United Kingdom; *U.S. Public*, pg. 998
King, Terry L., Mgr.-Sls.--Thermal Transfer Corp., Monroeville, PA; *U.S. Public*, pg. 29
King, Tom, Gen. Mgr.-Sls.--Standard Life Assurance, Edinburgh, United Kingdom; *Int'l*, pg. 1297
Kingsley, Joe, V.P.-Sls.--Thomas Engineering Inc., Hoffman Estates, IL; *U.S. Private*, pg. 1082
Kinney, Ed, Mgr.-Sls.--Monaco Coach Corporation, Coburg, OR; *U.S. Public*, pg. 1123
Kinney, Ed, Mgr.-Sls.--Holiday Rambler, Wakarusa, IN; *U.S. Public*, pg. 1123
Kinney, Ed, Mgr.-Sls.--McKenzie Towables By Monaco, Springfield, OR; *U.S. Public*, pg. 1123
Kinney, Pat, V.P.-Sls.--Ore-Ida Foods, Inc., Boise, ID; *U.S. Public*, pg. 805
Kinning, Rick L., Pres. & Treas.--RK Mechanical, Inc., Denver, CO; *U.S. Private*, pg. 904
Kinning, Ronald L., Chm. Bd. & Chief Exec. Officer--RK Mechanical, Inc., Denver, CO; *U.S. Private*, pg. 904
Kinnison, Jerry W., V.P.-Sls.--Warner-Jenkinson Co., Saint Louis, MO; *U.S. Public*, pg. 1696
Kinowski, Walt, V.P.-Sls.--American Metal & Plastics Inc., Grand Rapids, MI; *U.S. Private*, pg. 59
Kinsman, Mike, Dir.-Sls. & Mktg.--Cal-Air Inc., Whittier, CA; *U.S. Private*, pg. 199
Kippen, John, Sr. V.P.-Mktg.& Sls.--Plano Molding Co., Plano, IL; *U.S. Private*, pg. 869
Kirby, John, V.P.-Sls.--Sulzermedica USA Inc., Angleton, TX; *Int'l*, pg. 1307
Kirby, Michael L., Dir.-Printing, Specialty Paper Sls.--P.H. Glatfelter Company, Spring Grove, PA; *U.S. Public*, pg. 746
Kirby, Paul, V.P.-Sls.& Mktg.--Hodgson Mill, Inc., Gainesville, MO; *U.S. Private*, pg. 998
Kirchbaum, Richard, V.P.-Sls.--Croscill, Inc., New York, NY; *U.S. Private*, pg. 290
Kirchner, C.P., Dir.-Sls. & Distr.--Rothmans (UK) Ltd., Aylesbury, United Kingdom; *Int'l*, pg. 1130
Kirchner, Vinson E., V.P. & Gen. Mgr.-Sls.--Bob Evans Farms, Inc. Sausage Division, Columbus, OH; *U.S. Public*, pg. 596
Kirk, S.F., V.P.-Sls.--The Lubrizol Corporation, Wickliffe, OH; *U.S. Public*, pg. 1016
Kirkman, Paul, Exec. V.P.-Mktg. & Sls.--Beverage Canners International Corp., Miami, FL; *U.S. Private*, pg. 106
Kirkner, Robert E., Dir.-Sls.--John D. Lucas Printing Company, Baltimore, MD; *U.S. Private*, pg. 253
Kirkowski, Michael, Exec. V.P.--Condor D.C. Power Supplies Inc., Oxnard, CA; *U.S. Public*, pg. 1419
Kirpalani, John, V.P.-Mktg. & Sls.--Andrew Sports Club Inc., Secaucus, NJ; *U.S. Private*, pg. 73
Kirrish, Hail, Dir.-Sls. & Mktg.--Continental/Midland, Inc., Park Forest, IL; *U.S. Private*, pg. 268
Kirtley, Melvyn, V.P. & Gen. Mgr.-Retail Sls./New York & New York Region--Tiffany & Co., New York, NY; *U.S. Public*, pg. 1608
Kirz, Steve, Mgr.-Sls.--Micro Motion Inc., Boulder, CO; *U.S. Public*, pg. 574
Kishore, R., Mgr.-Sls.--Kinetics Technology India Ltd., New Delhi, India; *Int'l*, pg. 837
Kislevitz, David, Mng. Dir.-Sls.--Colorforms, Ramsey, NJ; *U.S. Public*, pg. 1625
Kitaoka, Hideo, V.P.-Sls.--Kawasho International (U.S.A.) Inc., Fort Lee, NJ; *Int'l*, pg. 726
Kittelson, Sid, Plant Mgr.--Stella Foods, Inc., Hinesburg, VT; *U.S. Private*, pg. 1040
Kittine, Bob, V.P.-Specialty Sls. & New Product Devel.--Industrial & Retail Bag Division, Chicago, IL; *U.S. Public*, pg. 1521
Kittinger, Mark, Mgr.-Sls.--MW Manufacturers Inc., Rocky Mount, VA; *Int'l*, pg. 593
Kitwaan, Kneoyuki, Dir.-Sls.--SmithKline Beecham Pharmaceuticals, Tokyo, Japan; *Int'l*, pg. 1266
Kivioja, Rod, Dir.-Sls.--Super Sky Products, Inc., Mequon, WI; *U.S. Private*, pg. 1054
Klackle, Michael, Dir.-Fresh Sls.--Michigan Blueberry Growers Assn., Grand Junction, MI; *U.S. Private*, pg. 740
Klaess, Richard, Mgr.-Natl. Sls.--CR LLC, Evanston, IL; *U.S.* Private, pg. 196
Klanac, Mike, Dir.-Sls. & Mktg.--Red Wings Inc., Fredonia, NY; *Int'l*, pg. 1398
Klapholz, Sam, V.P.-Sls.--Jerell, Inc., Dallas, TX; *U.S. Private*, pg. 586
Klasell, T.A., Mgr.-Sls.--Rodman Industries, Marinette, WI; *U.S. Private*, pg. 402
Klass, Joe, Mgr.-Adv., Sls. & Mktg.-Plastics & Industrial--Raven Industries, Inc., Sioux Falls, SD; *U.S. Public*, pg. 1361
Klauber, James, Exec. V.P.-North American Sls.--Adecco S.A., Lausanne, Switzerland; *Int'l*, pg. 23
Klausing, Trisha, Dir.-Mktg. & Sls.--The Commercial Bank, Delphos, OH; *U.S. Public*, pg. 410
Klausman, C. William, V.P.-Franchise Sls.--Diet Center Worldwide, Inc., Akron, OH; *U.S. Private*, pg. 864
Klayko, Michael A., Sr. V.P.-Sls./North American--EMC Corporation, Hopkinton, MA; *U.S. Public*, pg. 545
Klein, Art, V.P.-Sls.--Alantec Corp., San Jose, CA; *U.S. Public*, pg. 667
Klein, Gary, Exec. V.P. & Natl. Sls. Mgr.--Lane Bryant, Reynoldsburg, OH; *U.S. Public*, pg. 995
Klein, Jeffrey S., Sr. V.P.-Mktg.--Los Angeles Times, Los Angeles, CA; *U.S. Public*, pg. 1616
Klein, Jesse, Reg. Mgr.-Sls.--Bird Products Corporation, Palm Springs, CA; *U.S. Public*, pg. 1591
Klein, Kenneth, V.P.-N. American Sls.--Mercury Interactive Corp., Sunnyvale, CA; *U.S. Public*, pg. 1093
Klein, Martin, V.P.-Sls.--Inwood Laboratories, Inc., Inwood, NY; *U.S. Public*, pg. 670
Klein, Michael, Coord.-Sls.--MiTek, Inc., Chesterfield, MO; *Int'l*, pg. 1106
Klein, Robert, Mgr.-Natl. Sls.--Monarch Ware, Inc., Algoma, WI; *U.S. Private*, pg. 735
Klein, Royal, Dir.-Sls.--Lander Co., Inc., Englewood, NJ; *U.S. Private*, pg. 647
Kleine, Mike, V.P.-Mktg. & Sls.--Bird Products Corporation, Palm Springs, CA; *U.S. Public*, pg. 1591
Kleiner, Stanley E., V.P.-Sls.--Wallace Laboratories, Cranbury, NJ; *U.S. Public*, pg. 310
Kleinman, Mel, Exec. V.P.-Sls.--El Camino Resources, Ltd., Woodland Hills, CA; *U.S. Private*, pg. 366
Klemencic, Joy, V.P.-Corp. Mktg.--Hill's Pet Nutrition, Topeka, KS; *U.S. Public*, pg. 397
Klemmt, Andy, Dir.-Industrial Sls.--Danaher Tool Group, Chicago, IL; *U.S. Public*, pg. 481
Klene, Brian C., Exec. V.P.-Sls. & Mktg.--Micron Electronics, Inc., Nampa, ID; *U.S. Public*, pg. 1105
Kleve, Patrick, V.P.-Sheer Hosiery Sls.--Brown Wooten Mills, Inc., Burlington, NC; *U.S. Private*, pg. 174
Klich, H., Mgr.-Sls.--Raybestos Reibtechnik, Leverkusen, Germany; *U.S. Public*, pg. 1364
Klienberg, Lee, Dir.-Ind. Sls.--Green Seed Co., Baltimore, MD; *U.S. Private*, pg. 477
Kliger, Jack, Exec. V.P.--Parade Publications Inc., New York, NY; *U.S. Private*, pg. 20
Klimm, Robert, Dir.-Mktg., Sls. & Service--Semiconductor Equipment Division, Beverly, MA; *U.S. Public*, pg. 557
Kline, Edurado, Mgr.-Sls. Opers.--General Motors Chile S.A., Industria Automotriz, Santiago, Chile; *U.S. Public*, pg. 721
Kline, J.R., Dir.-Bus. Mngmt. Sls.--Lockheed Space Operations Co., Titusville, FL; *U.S. Public*, pg. 1009
Kline, Richard, Mgr.-Divisonal Sls. East--AP North American Aftermarket Division, Goldsboro, NC; *U.S. Private*, pg. 230
Klingner, Mike, Mgr.-Sls./Mobile Homes--Kit Manufacturing Company, Long Beach, CA; *U.S. Public*, pg. 962
Klink, Bruce C., V.P.-Sls., Rates & Pub. Affairs--The East Ohio Gas Co., Cleveland, OH; *U.S. Public*, pg. 435
Klisz, R., Dir.-Sls.--Aerochem, Inc., Orange, CA; *U.S. Public*, *pg. 534*
Klompmaker, D.O., Mgr.-Sls.-Automotive Div.--Young Radiator Company, Racine, WI; *U.S. Private*, pg. 1201
Kloos, John A., Dir.-Mktg. & Sls.--E.V. Roberts & Associates, Inc., Culver City, CA; *U.S. Private*, pg. 935
Klopfer, John, Sr. V.P.-Healthcare Corp. Accts.--Angelica Image Apparel, Saint Louis, MO; *U.S. Public*, pg. 113
Klunp, Bill, V.P.-Mktg. & Retail Deli Sls.--Bil Mar Foods, Inc., Zeeland, MI; *U.S. Public*, pg. 1433
Klustner, Kevin, V.P.-Sls. & Mktg.--WRQ, Inc., Seattle, WA; *U.S. Private*, pg. 1145
Knape, Stephen, Mgr.-Circulation--The Holland Sentinel, Holland, MI; *U.S. Private*, pg. 995
Knarr, Robert A., Exec. V.P.-Sls. & Mktg., N. America--U.S. Surgical Corp., Norwalk, CT; *U.S. Public*, pg. 1687
Knaut, John M., Dir.-Mktg. & Sls.--United Receptical, Inc., Pottsville, PA; *U.S. Private*, pg. 1123
Knecht, Susan, Mgr.-Prof. Svcs.--TransNet Corporation, Somerville, NJ; *U.S. Public*, pg. 1631
Knefel, Raymond, V.P.-Sls.--Diversified Compounders, Los Angeles, CA; *U.S. Private*, pg. 324
Kneip, Dick F., Mgr.-Mktg.--Stahl Specialty Company, Kingsville, MO; *U.S. Private*, pg. 1029
Knibbe, Dave, V.P.-Sls. & Mktg.--Herman Miller, Inc., Zeeland, MI; *U.S. Public*, pg. 1111
Knierman, John, V.P.-Sls. & Mktg.--International Container Systems, Tampa, FL; *Int'l*, pg. 685
Knight, Bob, V.P.-Sls.--Gilman Building Products Co., Saint Marys, GA; *U.S. Private*, pg. 454
Knight, Dennis, Mgr.-Sls. Promotion--BC Gas Inc., Vancouver, Canada; *Int'l*, pg. 114
Knight, Ernest, Exec. V.P.-Sls.& Mktg.- Intl.--Miracle Recreation Equipment Company, Monett, MO; *U.S. Private*, pg. 752
Knight, Lois, Mgr.-Natl. Sls.--Prep - STAT/Spectrum, Franklin, KY; *U.S. Private*, pg. 882
Knight, Steve, Mgr.-Sls.-Coating Prods.--King Industries, Inc., Norwalk, CT; *U.S. Private*, pg. 620
Knipmeyer, Ken, Exec. V.P. & Gen. Mgr.-BASES C1 Svc.--BASES Worldwide, Covington, KY; *U.S. Private*, pg. 120
Knipp, Kurt S., Exec. V.P.-Bankcard Services--National City Processing, Inc., Louisville, KY; *U.S. Public*, pg. 1154
Knodler, Ottmar, Mgr.-Sls.--Velcro GmbH, Sachsenheim, Germany; *Int'l*, pg. 1462
Knoll, Paul, V.P.-Mktg.--Universal Standard Healthcare, Inc., Southfield, MI; *U.S. Public*, pg. 1697
Knook, Cor N., Mgr.-Sls.--NAO, Inc., Philadelphia, PA; *U.S. Private*, pg. 771
Knorr, C.G., V.P.-Sls.--Ano-Coil Corporation, Rockville, CT; *U.S. Private*, pg. 75
Knorr, Carol, Exec. V.P.-Mktg. & Devel.--GMAC Insurance Holdings, Detroit, MI; *U.S. Public*, pg. 719
Knott, Doug, V.P.-Brand Sls.--Comstock Michigan Fruit, Rochester, NY; *U.S. Private*, pg. 887
Knott, Doug, V.P.-Sls. & Mktg.--Brooks Foods, Mount Summit, IN; *U.S. Private*, pg. 887
Knudsen, J., V.P.-Engrng. Sls.--BIF, North Wales, PA; *U.S. Public*, pg. 726
Knudsen, Larry, V.P.-Sls. & Mktg.--Camp Healthcare, Jackson, MI; *Int'l*, pg. 1425
Knudsen, Michael, V.P.-N. American Sls.--Digi International Inc., Minnetonka, MN; *U.S. Public*, pg. 506
Knudson, Gregory H., V.P.-Sls. & Mktg.--Hillsdale Tool & Mfg. Co., Hillsdale, MI; *U.S. Private*, pg. 355
Ko, Jeffrey, Mgr.-Sls. & Mktg.--Superior Metal Printing Limited, Singapore, Singapore; *Int'l*, pg. 1322
Kobayashi, Katsunobu, Mng. Dir.--Ebara Corporation, Tokyo, Japan; *Int'l*, pg. 431
Kobayashi, T., Dir. & Mgr.-Paper Sls.--MacMillan Bloedel K. K., Tokyo, Japan; *Int'l*, pg. 829
Kobayashi, Takashi, Mgr.-Sls. Dept.--Nippon Shokubai Co., Ltd., Osaka, Japan; *Int'l*, pg. 939
Kobberger, Robert, Mgr.-Sls.--ITT A-C Pump/ITT Marlow, Cincinnati, OH; *U.S. Public*, pg. 860
Koch, Clint, Dir.-Sls.--Modern Equipment Rentals Inc., Wilmington, DE; *U.S. Private*, pg. 754
Koch, Dan, V.P.-Sls.--Aetrium Inc., Saint Paul, MN; *U.S. Public*, pg. 27
Koch, Frank, Exec. V.P.-Sls.--Nature's Recipe Pet Foods, Corona, CA; *U.S. Private*, pg. 789
Koch, Paul, V.P.-Sls.--Republic Container Corp., Jersey City, NJ; *U.S. Private*, pg. 923
Koch, Robert J., Jr., V.P.-Food Service Sls.--The Smithfield Companies, Inc., Portsmouth, VA; *U.S. Public*, pg. 1479
Koch, Stevan, Dir.-Mktg. & Sls.--General Motors do Brasil Ltda., Sao Caetano do Sul, Brazil; *U.S. Public*, pg. 722
Koch, Tom, Mgr.-Sls.--Maze Nails, Peru, IL; *U.S. Private*, pg. 718
Kochanski, John A., V.P.-Mktg. & Sls.--Pegasus International Corporation, Pennington, NJ; *U.S. Private*, pg. 1046
Kocielski, John A., V.P.-Sales--Riser Foods, Inc., Bedford, OH; *U.S. Private*, pg. 450
Koedyker, Randall, V.P.-Field Sls.--Fruit of the Loom, Inc., Chicago, IL; *U.S. Public*, pg. 685
Koehler, Don, Reg. Sls. Mgr.-Relays--Aromat Southeast Sales Office, Norcross, GA; *Int'l*, pg. 848
Koenig, Heather, Sls.--R.J. Corr Naturals, Inc., Posen, IL; *U.S. Private*, pg. 276
Koenitzer, Jay G., V.P.-Mktg.--Helwig Carbon Products, Inc., Milwaukee, WI; *U.S. Private*, pg. 521
Koenitzer, John E., Chm. Bd. & Chief Exec. Officer--Helwig Carbon Products, Inc., Milwaukee, WI; *U.S. Private*, pg. 521
Koeppen, Ron, V.P.-Sls. Div.--Kendale Industries, Inc., Valley View, OH; *U.S. Private*, pg. 614
Koestenblatt, Caroline, Sr. V.P.-Mktg.--Novartis Pharmaceuticals, East Hanover, NJ; *Int'l*, pg. 973
Koetje, Mark, V.P.-Sls. & Mktg.--Prime Technology, Inc., Grand Rapids, MI; *U.S. Private*, pg. 884
Koetzier, C., Mng. Dir.-Sls.--Hoogovens Ijmuiden, Ijmuiden, Netherlands; *Int'l*, pg. 753
Kogerup, Alan G., Gen. Sls. Mgr.--Carstens Inc., Chicago, IL; *U.S. Private*, pg. 216
Kogod, Dennis L., V.P.-Sls. & Mktg.--Pilling Weck, Research Triangle Park, NC; *U.S. Public*, pg. 1569
Koh, T.S., Mgr.-Intl. Sls.--Mobil Oil Singapore Pte. Ltd., Singapore, Singapore; *U.S. Public*, pg. 1119
Kohlmann, Herbert, Dir.-Commercial Vehicle Sls.--Mercedes-Benz AG, Stuttgart, Germany; *Int'l*, pg. 368
Koksal, Jeff, Mgr.-Sls. & Mktg.--Diamond Power Specialty Co., Lancaster, OH; *U.S. Public*, pg. 1068
Kolb, David, Mgr.-Mktg.--Lightcraft, Jeannette, PA; *U.S. Private*, pg. 749
Kolb, Donald R., V.P.-Sls.--Manheim Auctions, Inc., Atlanta, GA; *U.S. Private*, pg. 282
Kolb, James D., V.P.-Mktg.--EMCOR Group, Inc., Norwalk, CT; *U.S. Public*, pg. 571
Kolberg, Curtis L., V.P.-Sls.--Kysor/Westran, Byron, IL; *U.S. Public*, pg. 968
Kole, Ronald, V.P.-Online Systems & Applications--Intermetrics, Inc., Burlington, MA; *U.S. Private*, pg. 567
Koleszar, James F., V.P.-Sls.--R&B, Inc., Colmar, PA; *U.S. Public*, pg. 1354
Kolkebeck, W. Charles, V.P.-Mktg. & Sls.--Nuttall Gear Corporation, Niagara Falls, NY; *U.S. Private*, pg. 809
Kollar, Paul T., V.P.-Sls.--Lattice Semiconductor Corporation, Hillsboro, OR; *U.S. Public*, pg. 979
Kollenborn, Don, V.P.-Sls. & Adv.--Hickory Printing Group, Inc., Conover, NC; *U.S. Private*, pg. 525
Kollias, Jack, Sls. Mgr.- Eastern Reg.--Storck U.S.A., L.P., Chicago, IL; *Int'l*, pg. 1304
Kolodziej, Edmond P., Jr., Dir.-Sls./Edmond--GPU Energy, Johnstown, PA; *U.S. Public*, pg. 695
Kolterjahn, Don, Mgr.-Sls.--General Office Environments Inc., Rochelle Park, NJ; *U.S. Private*, pg. 445
Koman, Elizabeth, V.P. & Eastern Sls. Mgr.--CBS Enterprises Division, New York, NY; *U.S. Public*, pg. 274
Kommers, Phil, V.P.-Sls.--Coleman Powermate, Inc., Omaha, NE; *U.S. Private*, pg. 691
Konci, Michael, Dir.-North American Sls.--Velsicol Chemical Corporation, Rosemont, IL; *U.S. Private*, pg. 1135
Konecny, Dave, Sls. Mgr.--International Cold Storage Co., Inc., Andover, KS; *U.S. Private*, pg. 568
Koner, Larry, Mgr.-Sls.--Shokai Far East Ltd., Peekskill, NY; *U.S. Private*, pg. 996
Koning, Annemiek, Mgr.-Pub. Rels., Sls. & Promo.--Lips United B.V., Drunen, Netherlands; *Int'l*, pg. 812
Konradt, Joseph, Sr. V.P.-Sls.--First Federal Capital Corp., La Crosse, WI; *U.S. Public*, pg. 632
Kontney, J., Mgr.-Artist Rels.--Shure Brothers Incorporated, Evanston, IL; *U.S. Private*, pg. 997
Koontz, Quinn, Dir.-Sls.--Capitol Broadcasting Co., Inc., Raleigh, NC; *U.S. Private*, pg. 206
Koop, Brian, Mgr.-Sls./Camera Division--Photo Control Corporation, Minneapolis, MN; *U.S. Public*, pg. 1292

Kopack, Al, Mgr.-Sls.--F.X. Coughlin Co., Taylor, MI; *U.S. Private*, pg. 278
Kopko, Wally, Sr. Dir.-Sls. & Mktg.-Home Impressions--HMI Industries, Cleveland, OH; *U.S. Public*, pg. 771
Koponen, Kari, Sls. Mgr.--Opel Oy, Espoo, Finland; *U.S. Public*, pg. 723
Kops, Charles T., Mgr.-Natl. Sls.--Pemko Manufacturing Company, Ventura, CA; *U.S. Private*, pg. 848
Korbely, Mike, Mgr.-Sls.--Vindicator Technologies, Austin, TX; *U.S. Private*, pg. 1141
Koren, Barbara, V.P.-Sls.--Sterling Plumbing Group, Inc., Rolling Meadows, IL; *U.S. Private*, pg. 630
Korey, Larry, Mgr.-Sls.--Lumber Group Inc., Dothan, AL; *U.S. Private*, pg. 680
Korieneld, Bob, Reg. Sls. Mgr.-Factory Automation--Aromat North Central Sales Office, Rolling Meadows, IL; *Int'l*, pg. 848
Korkalainen, Veikko, Mgr.-Sls.--Kemi Mills, Kemi, Finland; *Int'l*, pg. 863
Korman, Hal, V.P.-Sls.--UDL Laboratories, Inc., Rockford, IL; *U.S. Public*, pg. 1143
Kornfeld, Marvin, Mgr.-Sls.--Deitsch Plastics Company, West Haven, CT; *U.S. Private*, pg. 320
Kornfield, Dan, Dir.-Mktg. & Sls.--Sid Harvey Industries, Valley Stream, NY; *U.S. Private*, pg. 998
Korthaus, Thomas A., V.P.-Sls. & Mdsg.--Riverside/Bi-Lo Division, Du Bois, PA; *U.S. Public*, pg. 1270
Korzenko, E.J., Reg. Sls. Mgr.--Portec, Inc., Shipping Systems Div., Oak Brook, IL; *U.S. Public*, pg. 1318
Koshikawa, Koh, Gen. Mgr.-3rd Sls. Oper.--Anritsu Corporation, Tokyo, Japan; *Int'l*, pg. 77
Koski, L., Gen. Sls. Mgr.--Manistique Papers, Inc., Manistique, MI; *Int'l*, pg. 762
Kosobucki, Bob, V.P.-Worldwide Sls. & Mktg.--Optek Technology, Inc., Carrollton, TX; *U.S. Public*, pg. 1227
Koss, John, Jr., V.P.-Sls.--Koss Corporation, Milwaukee, WI; *U.S. Public*, pg. 966
Koss, John, Jr., V.P.-Sls.--Koss Classics Ltd., Milwaukee, WI; *U.S. Public*, pg. 966
Kostlin, Ulrich, Dr., Exec. Dir.-Mktg. & Sls.--Schering AG, Berlin, Germany; *Int'l*, pg. 1203
Kotaro, Hirota, Dir.-Intl. Sls.--Mikuni Corporation, Tokyo, Japan; *Int'l*, pg. 867
Kotcher, Michele, Dir.-Sls. & Mktg.--F.X. Coughlin Co., Taylor, MI; *U.S. Private*, pg. 278
Koterba, Jeff, Mgr.-Natl. Sls.--Micron Separations, Inc., Westborough, MA; *U.S. Private*, pg. 742
Kottman, Michael, V.P.-Mktg. & Sls.--Clouth Gummiwerke AG, Cologne, Germany; *Int'l*, pg. 297
Koubek, Dave, Gen. Sls. Mgr.--Chief Industries - Buildings Div., Grand Island, NE; *U.S. Private*, pg. 236
Koudelka, Pierre, V.P.-Sls. & Mktg.--Federal APD, Inc., Farmington, MI; *U.S. Public*, pg. 616
Koumoutsakis, John, Sls. Representative--Brian Controls Division, Moncton, Canada; *Int'l*, pg. 711
Kovach, Mark J., V.P.-Sls./TOPS & Div. Mgr.--Wallace Computer Services, Inc., Lisle, IL; *U.S. Public*, pg. 1735
Kovalenko, Yuri, Deputy Dir.-USSR Affairs--Abbott Laboratories-Moscow Sales Office, Moscow, Russia; *U.S. Public*, pg. 14
Kovatch, M.S., V.P.-Sls.--Brown & Williamson Tobacco Corp., Louisville, KY; *Int'l*, pg. 111
Kovdsmeier, Bud, V.P.-OEM Sls.--RELTEC Corporation, Cleveland, OH; *U.S. Private*, pg. 921
Kovich, Ronald H., V.P.-Sls.--Blistex, Inc., Oak Brook, IL; *U.S. Private*, pg. 149
Kovin, James, Mgr.-Sls.--International Research & Evaluation, Eagan, MN; *U.S. Private*, pg. 571
Kowall, Tim, Gen. Mgr.-Sls. & Mktg.--Yamaha Motor Canada Ltd., North York, Canada; *Int'l*, pg. 1516
Kowalski, William, V.P.-Sls. & Mktg.--London House, Rosemont, IL; *U.S. Public*, pg. 1070
Kozel, Al, V.P.-Sls. & Mktg./Marine--Detroit Diesel Corp., Detroit, MI; *U.S. Private*, pg. 850
Koziel, John, Dir.-Sls. & Mktg.--Weldun International, Inc., Bridgman, MI; *Int'l*, pg. 205
Koziol, Chris, Sr. V.P.-Sls.--MicroAge, Inc., Tempe, AZ; *U.S. Public*, pg. 1104
Kozisek, Larry, Mgr. Sls.--Schumacher Electric Corporation, Mount Prospect, IL; *U.S. Private*, pg. 973
Kozlowski, Ken, Mgr.-Natl. Sls.--Symons Corporation, Des Plaines, IL; *U.S. Private*, pg. 932
Kozub, John F., V.P.-Sls.--Janlynn Corporation, Indian Orchard, MA; *U.S. Private*, pg. 582
Kozuk, John, Natl. Sls. Mgr.--The Crosby Group Inc., Tulsa, OK; *Int'l*, pg. 473
Kraft, Michael, Dir.-Off Premise Sls.--Papa Gino's Inc., Dedham, MA; *U.S. Private*, pg. 837
Kragin, Gary, Natl. Sls. Dir.--ITT Jabsco, Costa Mesa, CA; *U.S. Public*, pg. 860
Kraines, Steve, Sr. V.P.-Sls.--Kraco Enterprises, Inc., Compton, CA; *U.S. Private*, pg. 634
Kralik, Carol, Mgr.-Customer & Sls. Support--Bard Diagnostic Sciences, Redmond, WA; *U.S. Public*, pg. 189
Kramer, Burt, Mgr.-Natl. Sls.--Ouimet Corp., Nashville, TN; *U.S. Private*, pg. 821
Kramer, Debra, Mgr.-Sls. & Mktg.--BNA PLUS, Washington, DC; *U.S. Private*, pg. 182
Kramer, Kenneth R., V.P.-Service Delicatessen Sls.--Albertson's, Inc., Boise, ID; *U.S. Public*, pg. 38
Kramer, Larry, V.P.-Mktg. & Sls.--Wilson Products Co., Salt Lake City, UT; *U.S. Private*, pg. 1181
Kramer, R.C., V.P.-Sls. & Mktg.--Fairmont Tamper, West Columbia, SC; *U.S. Public*, pg. 793
Krammer, Anja, Dir.-Mktg. & Channel Sls.--Key Tronic Corporation, Spokane, WA; *U.S. Public*, pg. 953
Krasiewich, Dave, V.P.-Sls. & Mktg.--Cochrane, Inc., King of Prussia, PA; *U.S. Public*, pg. 456
Krassenksy, Ron, Sr. V.P.-Sls. & Mktg.--Air Conditioning Co., Inc., Glendale, CA; *U.S. Private*, pg. 28
Kraus, Arno, Dir.-Sls.--Pittler Maschinenfabrik AG, Langen, Germany; *Int'l*, pg. 1128
Kraus, Charles, Dir.-Sls.--Custom Hoists, Inc., Hayesville, OH; *U.S. Public*, pg. 1506
Kraus, Doug, V.P.-Sls.--BancTec, Inc.-New York, Hauppauge, NY; *U.S. Public*, pg. 177
Kraus, Edward, Dir.-Mktg. Svcs.--Medusa Corporation, Cleveland, OH; *U.S. Public*, pg. 1084
Kraus, Tim, V.P.-Mktg. & Sls.--Manitowoc Ice, Inc., Manitowoc, WI; *U.S. Public*, pg. 1041
Krause, Gary W., V.P. & Dir.-Sls. & Mktg.--Laird & Company, Eatontown, NJ; *U.S. Private*, pg. 642
Krause, Werner, Mgr.-Overseas Sls.--Feodor Burgmann Dichtungswerke GmbH, Wolfratshausen, Germany; *Int'l*, pg. 233
Krautkremer, Steve, Mgr.-Sls. & Mktg.--Old Town Canoe, Old Town, ME; *U.S. Public*, pg. 933
Krautzik, Christian, Dr., Mgr.-Domestic Sls.--O&K Orenstein & Koppel Aktiengesellschaft, Dortmund, Germany; *Int'l*, pg. 516
Kraynik, Jim, V.P.-Natl. Sls.--Pittsburgh Brewing Company, Pittsburgh, PA; *U.S. Private*, pg. 619
Krecl, Robert, V.P.-Mktg. & Sls.--Seth Thomas, Norcross, GA; *U.S. Private*, pg. 445
Kreeft, Jan, Dir.-Sls., Mktg. & Adv.--ISS Servisystem B.V., Amersfoort, Netherlands; *Int'l*, pg. 657
Kreger, James, V.P.-Sls.--Seats Incorporated, Reedsburg, WI; *U.S. Private*, pg. 410
Kreikemeier, Ken, V.P.-Sls.--J-M Manufacturing Co., Inc., Livingston, NJ; *Int'l*, pg. 498
Kreis, Emile, Asst. V.P.-Sls.--Bobst S.A., Lausanne, Switzerland; *Int'l*, pg. 198
Kreitz, Jon, Aftermarket SBU Leader--Warn Industries, Inc., Clackamas, OR; *U.S. Private*, pg. 1150
Kreitzberg, Michael, Mgr.-Sls./Component Prod.--Microflect Company, Inc., Salem, OR; *U.S. Public*, pg. 1707
Kreitzman, Steven, Reg. Mgr.--Environment/One Corporation, Niskayuna, NY; *U.S. Public*, pg. 586
Kreple, Mark, V.P.-Intl. Sls. & Mktg.--Manitowoc Ice, Inc., Manitowoc, WI; *U.S. Public*, pg. 1041
Kress, Bill, Mgr.-Natl. Sls.--Hehr Power Systems, Fort Worth, TX; *U.S. Private*, pg. 519
Kress, Walter, V.P.-Sls.--Everglades Sugar Refinery, Inc., Clewiston, FL; *U.S. Public*, pg. 873
Kreuger, Jim, Dir.-Sls.--Luhrs Corporation, Saint Augustine, FL; *U.S. Private*, pg. 680
Kreusch, Leonard P., III, Pres.--Leonard Kreusch, Inc., Northvale, NJ; *U.S. Private*, pg. 635
Krieg, T.J., Dir.-Sls.--J.M. Huber, Chemicals Division, Havre De Grace, MD; *U.S. Private*, pg. 545
Krier, Jim, Dir.-Sls.--Caddy Corp. of America, Bridgeport, NJ; *U.S. Private*, pg. 198
Krier, Jim, Mgr.-Processing Sls.--Rogers N.K. Seed Co., Boise, ID; *Int'l*, pg. 974
Krikorian, Charles, Mgr.-Natl. Sls.--Printed Circuit Corporation, Woburn, MA; *U.S. Private*, pg. 886
Kril-Dicciani, Mary, Mgr.-Intl. Prod.--Rhone-Poulenc Rorer - U.S., Collegeville, PA; *Int'l*, pg. 1110
Kringen, Stu, Dir.-Sls.--Bongards Creameries Inc., Norwood, MN; *U.S. Private*, pg. 156
Krise, Ed, V.P.-Sls.--Command Plastic Corporation, Akron, OH; *U.S. Private*, pg. 257
Kristensen, J.E., Exec. V.P.-Sls. & Mktg.--APV Crepaco, Inc., Rosemont, IL; *Int'l*, pg. 1240
Kristiansen, John, V.P.-Sls. & Distr. & Dir.-Pur.--Frionor A/S, Lysaker, Norway; *Int'l*, pg. 516
Krivahee, Ken, Dir.-Sls. & Mktg.--Kaufman and Broad Utah Division, Midvale, UT; *U.S. Public*, pg. 945
Kroener, Bix, Sr. V.P.-Mktg. & Sls.--Adaptive Information Systems, Mission Viejo, CA; *Int'l*, pg. 946
Kroetch, Jerry, V.P.-Sls. & Mktg.--Krofam Inc., Philip, SD; *U.S. Private*, pg. 636
Krogh, Jorgen, Dir.-Sls.--Wisapak Multicoate A/S, Skovlunde, Denmark; *Int'l*, pg. 1430
Krol, Bruce, Mgr.-Mktg. & Sls.--Vacudyne Inc., Chicago Heights, IL; *U.S. Private*, pg. 46
Krol, Joseph, V.P.-Sls. & Mktg--Embassy Industries, Inc., Farmingdale, NY; *U.S. Public*, pg. 1240
Krone, Philip S., V.P.-Mktg.--Krone Casting Corp., North Chicago, IL; *U.S. Private*, pg. 636
Kroneberger, Greg, Sr. V.P.-Sls.--Baltimore Stationery Co./ Total Office, Baltimore, MD; *U.S. Private*, pg. 113
Kronen, Terry, Pres. & Mgr.-Natl. Sls.--Graphic Jackets, Seattle, WA; *U.S. Private*, pg. 827
Kronfeld, Andrew S., Grp. V.P.-Sls.--Spirite Industries, Inc., Englewood, NJ; *U.S. Private*, pg. 1026
Krosner, Nancy, Mgr.-Sls.--Webcraft Technologies, Inc., North Brunswick, NJ; *U.S. Public*, pg. 228
Krotman, Howard, Mgr.-Sls.--Pyramid Handbags Inc., New York, NY; *U.S. Private*, pg. 896
Krueger, Jim, Dir.-Sls. & Mktg.--Mainship Corporation, Saint Augustine, FL; *U.S. Private*, pg. 697
Krueger, Richard G., V.P.-Sls. & Mgr.--The F.D. Lawrence Electric Co., Cincinnati, OH; *U.S. Private*, pg. 654
Kruger, John, Exec. V.P.-Sls. & Mktg.--Hazel Bishop International, Englewood Cliffs, NJ; *U.S. Private*, pg. 514
Kruithof, Ken, V.P.-Sls./Natl. Dealer Grp.--Michelin Americas Small Tires (MAST), Greenville, SC; *Int'l*, pg. 322
Krulik, Bob, Mgr.-Sls., Deco Candles--A.I. Root Company, Medina, OH; *U.S. Private*, pg. 944
Krummel, Cardin, Dir.-Sls. & Mktg.--Carnival Creations, Linden, NJ; *U.S. Private*, pg. 213
Kruse, Kent, Dir.-Sls.--Fischer Imaging Corporation, Denver, CO; *U.S. Public*, pg. 647
Kruse, Michael, V.P.-Sls.--Heidtman Steel Products, Inc., Toledo, OH; *U.S. Private*, pg. 519
Krywicki, Gerald, V.P.-Sls.--Heat Bath Park Metallurgical Corp., Indian Orchard, MA; *U.S. Private*, pg. 518
Krzeminski, Jim, V.P.-Sls. & Mktg.--Bissell Inc., Grand Rapids, MI; *U.S. Private*, pg. 145
Kubacki, Theodore J., V.P.-Sls.-Industrial Prods.--Raffi & Swanson, Inc., Wilmington, MA; *U.S. Private*, pg. 907
Kublank, Robert M., V.P. & Reg. Sls. Mgr.--First Financial Bank, FSB, Stevens Point, WI; *U.S. Public*, pg. 140
Kuch, P., Mgr.-Tech. Sls.--Fuchs' Sche Tongruben GmbH & Co. Ltd., Ransbach-Baumbach, Germany; *Int'l*, pg. 1488
Kudlacek, John, Dir.-Sls.--Balkamp, Inc., Indianapolis, IN; *U.S. Public*, pg. 732
Kuebler, Christopher A., V.P.-Mktg. & Sls.--Abbott Pharmaceutical Products Division, Abbott Park, IL; *U.S. Public*, pg. 13
Kuecker, Tobey, Mgr.-Sls. & Svc.--Mosinee Converted Products, Columbus, WI; *U.S. Public*, pg. 1747
Kuester, Joe, Dir.-Mktg. & Sls.--Knudsen & Sons, Inc., Chico, CA; *U.S. Public*, pg. 1480
Kugle, Dennis, Dir.-Sls.--Gast Mfg. Corp., Benton Harbor, MI; *U.S. Private*, pg. 440
Kugler, Kim, Natl. Sls. Mgr.--Master Craft Corp., Kalamazoo, MI; *Int'l*, pg. 267
Kugo, Shozo, Dir.-N.A. Sls.--Hokuriku Electric Industry Co., Ltd., Toyama, Japan; *Int'l*, pg. 627
Kuhn, Frank, Sr. V.P.-Sls.--INX International, Milwaukee, WI; *Int'l*, pg. 1311
Kuhn, Harold, V.P. & Mgr.-Sls.--Park Motor Sales Company, Detroit, MI; *U.S. Private*, pg. 840
Kuhns, David, V.P.-Sls.--McCormick/Schilling, Hunt Valley, MD; *U.S. Public*, pg. 1066
Kuklenski, Charles, Mgr.-Sls.--Ericsson, Inc., Overland Park, KS; *Int'l*, pg. 1364
Kula, Donald, V.P.-Sls. & Treas.--Bloch/New England, Inc., Worcester, MA; *U.S. Private*, pg. 149
Kula, Pat C., V.P.-Mktg. & Sls.--Diamond Electronics, Inc., Carroll, OH; *U.S. Public*, pg. 1663
Kulczycki, Bill, Dir.-Sls. & Mktg.--Lost Arrow Corporation, Ventura, CA; *U.S. Private*, pg. 676
Kulik, M., Dir.-Sls.--NIDEC, Canton, MA; *Int'l*, pg. 933
Kulik, Paul J., Dir.-Sls. & Mktg.--Hennells, Inc., Ferndale, MI; *U.S. Private*, pg. 522
Kulle, Russ, Gen. Mgr.-Sls.--Eagle Lincoln Mercury Inc., Dallas, TX; *U.S. Private*, pg. 355
Kulp, G., Dir.-Sls.--Senior Engineering Co.-Eastern Region, King of Prussia, PA; *Int'l*, pg. 1222
Kumm, Larry, Mgr.-Sls.--Penny Saver, Cedar Rapids, IA; *U.S. Private*, pg. 442
Kumraks, Apichart, 1st V.P.--Siam City Bank Public Company Limited, Bangkok, Thailand; *Int'l*, pg. 1239
Kunkel, Bill, Sr. V.P.-Intl. Media Sls.--CBS Enterprises Division, New York, NY; *U.S. Public*, pg. 274
Kuntz, Michael, V.P.-Sls.--Pennaco Hosiery, New York, NY; *U.S. Public*, pg. 483
Kunz, M., Mgr.-Pulp Sls.--Burrows Paper Corporation, Little Falls, NY; *U.S. Private*, pg. 188
Kunzer, Gary, V.P.-OEM/Custom Sls.--Labelon Corporation, Canandaigua, NY; *U.S. Private*, pg. 641
Kuo, John, Mgr.-Sls.--Ajinomoto U.S.A., Inc., Los Angeles Branch, Torrance, CA; *Int'l*, pg. 40
Kurachi, Yoshihiro, Dir.-Sls.--Oji Paper Co., Ltd., Tokyo, Japan; *Int'l*, pg. 998
Kurata, Paul, V.P.-Sls. Devel./Honolulu--Tiffany & Co., New York, NY; *U.S. Public*, pg. 1608
Kurebayashi, Shunichi, Exec. Mng. Dir.--Sankyo Company Limited, Tokyo, Japan; *Int'l*, pg. 1189
Kurihara, Tetsuo, Deputy Dir.-Sls. Div.--Mitsumi Electric Co., Ltd., Tokyo, Japan; *Int'l*, pg. 884
Kurinsky, Roger, V.P.-Sls. & Mktg./Specialty Prods.--Ivex Packaging Corporation, Lincolnshire, IL; *U.S. Public*, pg. 915
Kurofsky, Harold I., V.P.-Sales--Safeguard Health Enterprises, Inc., Anaheim, CA; *U.S. Public*, pg. 1424
Kurokawa, Kumio, Mgr.-Sls. Admin.--Toto Ltd., Kitakyushu, Japan; *Int'l*, pg. 1410
Kuroyama, Ikuo, Mgr.-Sls.--Koito Manufacturing Co., Tokyo, Japan; *Int'l*, pg. 743
Kurpis, Joseph J., Sr. V.P.-Indus. & Intl. Sls.--Stearns Manufacturing Company, Sauk Rapids, MN; *U.S. Public*, pg. 940
Kurtenbach, Frank, V.P.-Sls.--Daktronics, Inc., Brookings, SD; *U.S. Public*, pg. 478
Kurtis, Bill, V.P.-Mktg. & Sls.--Lifetime Products Inc., Clearfield, UT; *U.S. Private*, pg. 667
Kurtze, Jack, Mgr.-Sls. & Mktg.--Maxcor Manufacturing, Inc., Colorado Springs, CO; *U.S. Private*, pg. 716
Kushnerick, John L., Dir.-Mktg. & Sls.--American Camper, Tulsa, OK; *U.S. Public*, pg. 265
Kusiak, Joe, Mgr.-Sls.--MFG Union City Operations, Union City, PA; *U.S. Private*, pg. 756
Kusnick, Drew, V.P.-Sls. & Mktg.--Kaufman and Broad of Northern California, Inc., San Ramon, CA; *U.S. Public*, pg. 945
Kusnick, Drew, V.P.-Sls. & Mktg.--Kaufman and Broad-South Bay Inc., Fremont, CA; *U.S. Public*, pg. 945
Kussick, Laura, Sr. V.P.-Sales--Full House Sports & Entertainment, Seattle, WA; *U.S. Public*, pg. 16
Kustich, Karen, Mgr.-Sls.--A.M. Castle & Co., Cheswick, PA; *U.S. Public*, pg. 313
Kuypers, Bill, Dir.-Electronics Sls. & Mktg.--Tensolite Company, Saint Augustine, FL; *U.S. Public*, pg. 305
Kwiatkowski, Elaine, V.P.-Sls.--Blue Bird Coach Lines Inc., Olean, NY; *U.S. Private*, pg. 150
Kwon, E.C., Mgr.-Sls.--John Crane (Korea) Co., Ltd., Seoul, Korea; *Int'l*, pg. 1339
Kwong, Ken, V.P.-Mktg./North American Sls.--Atmel Corporation, San Jose, CA; *U.S. Public*, pg. 145
Kyle, Robin A., Rep.-Sls. Promo.--Dillard, A ResourceNet International Company, Richmond, VA; *U.S. Public*, pg. 902
L'Ecuyer, R., Mgr.-Intl. Sls.--Data Instruments, Inc., Acton, MA; *U.S. Private*, pg. 312
L'Empereur, Denis, Mgr.-Canned Private Label Sls.--Dean Foods Vegetable Company, Green Bay, WI; *U.S. Public*, pg. 490
La Dolce, Gary, Div. Mgr.-Sls.--The Jel Sert Co., West Chicago, IL; *U.S. Private*, pg. 585
La Fortune, Michael J., V.P.-Supermarket Sls.--American Greetings U.S. Greeting Card Division, Cleveland, OH; *U.S. Public*, pg. 78
La Magna, Mary, Mgr.-Adv. Sls.--National Business Employment Weekly, Princeton, NJ; *U.S. Public*, pg. 524

La Porte, Tony, Mgr.-Eastern Sls.--RAM Golf Corporation, Melrose Park, IL; *U.S. Private*, pg. 908

La Sada, Jorge, Admin.-Sls.--R.L. Albert & Son, Inc., Greenwich, CT; *U.S. Private*, pg. 32

Labahn, Bill, V.P.-Program Sls.--Delta Education, Inc., Hudson, NH; *Int'l*, pg. 1402

Labas, James, Mgr.-Intl. Sls.--Weaver Popcorn Company, Inc., Van Buren, IN; *U.S. Private*, pg. 1156

Labelle, R., Mgr.-N. American Wintriss Sls.--Data Instruments, Inc., Acton, MA; *U.S. Private*, pg. 312

Labenek, Joseph, V.P. & Dir.-Intl. Sls.--LORAD Corporation, Danbury, CT; *U.S. Public*, pg. 1595

LaBonte, Susan, Mgr.-Sls.--ACBJ Business Publications, Inc., Cincinnati, OH; *U.S. Private*, pg. 19

Laborowski, John V., V.P.-Sls. & Mktg.--Hammary Furniture Co., Lenoir, NC; *U.S. Public*, pg. 973

LaBossiere, Robert L., V.P.-Corp. Parts--Mitsubishi Motor Sales of America, Inc., Cypress, CA; *Int'l*, pg. 875

Labro, Gerard, Dir.-Sls.--Polive/Tricosteril, Courbevoie, France; *U.S. Public*, pg. 673

Labrum, Ron K., Corp. & Grp. V.P.-Reg. Cos. & Health Sys.--Allegiance Healthcare Corp., McGaw Park, IL; *U.S.* Public, pg. 44

Labuschange, J.H., Gen. Mgr.-Sls.--Timken South Africa Proprietary Ltd., Transvaal, South Africa; *U.S. Public*, pg. 1618

Lacey, Norman E., Dir.-Sls. & Mktg.--Thermo Black Clawson, Inc., Middletown, OH; *U.S. Public*, pg. 1593

Lach, E.W., V.P.-Sls.--British Steel, Inc., Schaumburg, IL; *Int'l*, pg. 221

Lachapelle, A.D., Sr. V.P.-Mktg. & Sls.--Reed & Barton Corporation, Taunton, MA; *U.S. Private*, pg. 916

Lacny, Paul J., V.P.-State Sls.--Blue Cross & Blue Shield of Illinois, Chicago, IL; *U.S. Private*, pg. 151

Lacoste, Roy, V.P.-Grocery Sls.--Schwegmann Giant Super Markets, New Orleans, LA; *U.S. Private*, pg. 629

Lacroix, Richard J., Exec. V.P.-Sls.--Potash Corporation of Saskatchewan Inc., Saskatoon, Canada; *Int'l*, pg. 1064

Lacy, George T., V.P.-Grp. Strategic Implementation--General American Life Insurance Co., Saint Louis, MO; *U.S. Private*, pg. 443

Lacy, Thomas, V.P.-Sls. & Mktg.--Bio-Logic Systems Corp., Mundelein, IL; *U.S. Public*, pg. 230

Ladbrook, Peter, Dir.-Sls. Opers.--Bio-Logic Systems Corporation Ltd., Chipping Norton, United Kingdom; *U.S.* Public, pg. 230

Ladden, Steven P., V.P.-Sls. & Mktg.--Yankee Energy System, Inc., Meriden, CT; *U.S. Public*, pg. 1787

Laden, Steven P., V.P.-Sls., Mktg. & External Rels.--Yankee Gas Services Company, Meriden, CT; *U.S. Public*, pg. 1788

LaDoucer, Doug, V.P.-Mktg. & Sls.--E.D. Smith, Winona, Canada; *Int'l*, pg. 1263

Ladue, David, Gen. Mgr.-Sls.--Yale/Chase Materials Handling, Inc., City of Industry, CA; *U.S. Private*, pg. 1195

Lae, Byung-Tae, Chief Oper. Officer & Exec. V.P.--Jaeneung Education Co., Ltd., Seoul, Korea; *Int'l*, pg. 697

Laezza, Joe, V.P.-Mktg. & Sls.--Falconbridge Limited, Toronto, Canada; *Int'l*, pg. 433

LaFaille, Jean-Marc, V.P.-European Sls.--GTECH Corporation, West Greenwich, RI; *U.S. Public*, pg. 767

LaFleur, Dennis W., V.P.-Intl. Sls.--Unifab International Inc., New Iberia, LA; *U.S. Public*, pg. 1665

Laforest, Marcel, Dir.-Sls.--Gaz Metropolitain & Company, Montreal, Canada; *Int'l*, pg. 541

LaGrace, Dick, Dir.-Mktg. & Sls.--Barry Controls Aerospace, Burbank, CA; *U.S. Public*, pg. 124

LaGrega, Andrew T., Sr. V.P.-Sls., Mktg. & Adv.--The Wilder Companies, Boston, MA; *U.S. Private*, pg. 1176

Lahey, Thomas J., V.P.-Sls.-Pacific Rim--Hexcel Corporation, Pleasanton, CA; *U.S. Public*, pg. 824

Lahre, Paul, Mgr.-Export Sls.--ITT A-C Pump/ITT Marlow, Cincinnati, OH; *U.S. Public*, pg. 860

Laidig, Marc, Dir.-Trading & Sls.--Nasinsa Securities, New York, NY; *Int'l*, pg. 904

Laidlaw, Frank, Dir.-Mktg. & Sls.--Berol Corp., Georgetown, KY; *U.S. Public*, pg. 1178

Lainto, Timo, Dir.-Comml., Overseas--Kemira Agro Oy, Helsinki, Finland; *Int'l*, pg. 727

Laird-Dunn, Lisa, V.P.-Sls.--Laird & Company, Eatontown, NJ; *U.S. Private*, pg. 642

Laird, E.T., Sr. V.P. & Mgr.-Atlanta Sls.--Jefferies & Company, Inc., Los Angeles, CA; *U.S. Public*, pg. 925

Laird, John, V.P.-Sls.--Hardware Wholesalers, Inc., Fort Wayne, IN; *U.S. Private*, pg. 502

Lake, Barbara, Sls. Promo. Specialist--McKee Foods Corporation, Collegedale, TN; *U.S. Private*, pg. 723

Lake, Sally, Mgr.-Sls. Promo.--Spartan Stores Inc., Grand Rapids, MI; *U.S. Private*, pg. 1021

Lakin, Kathy, V.P.-Sls.--A.J. Brandon, Vernon, CA; *U.S. Public*, pg. 948

Lalone, Gary L., V.P.-Sls.--The Buckle, Inc., Kearney, NE; *U.S. Public*, pg. 267

Lalwani, P.J., Chief Oper. Officer, Chief Info. Officer, Controller & Sec.--Andrew Sports Club Inc., Secaucus, NJ; *U.S. Private*, pg. 73

Lam, Lit, Dir.-Mktg.--Gatefield Corporation, Fremont, CA; *U.S. Public*, pg. 703

Lam, Perry, Reg. Dir.-Sls.--DHL International (Hong Kong) Ltd., Wan Chai, Hong Kong; *U.S. Private*, pg. 302

LaMarca, Jim, V.P.-Sls.--Broadcast Programming, Seattle, WA; *U.S. Private*, pg. 531

Lamb, Curtis, Mgr.-Circulation--Lake Wales Daily Highlander, Lake Wales, FL; *U.S. Private*, pg. 995

Lamb, R. James, V.P.-Sls.--Bayer Corporation/ Pharmaceutical Division, West Haven, CT; *Int'l*, pg. 173

Lamb, Tim, V.P.-Mktg. & Sls.--Apex Precision Technology Inc., Indianapolis, IN; *U.S. Private*, pg. 77

Lambert, Art, V.P.-Sls.--Heath Company, Benton Harbor, MI; *Int'l*, pg. 317

Lambert, Doug, Mgr.-Western Sls.--Salon Division, Englewood, NJ; *Int'l*, pg. 1489

Lambert, Larry, V.P.-Sls. & Mdsg.--Signal Apparel Company, Inc., Chattanooga, TN; *U.S. Public*, pg. 1472

Lambert, Ron, Sls. Mgr.--Milgray/Kansas City, Inc., Overland Park, KS; *U.S. Public*, pg. 206

Lambley, Ken, Mgr.-Intl. Sls.--Seradyn, Inc., Indianapolis, IN; *Int'l*, pg. 871

Lamer, Allan J., Exec. V.P.-Sls. & Mktg.--Marine Travelift, Inc., Sturgeon Bay, WI; *U.S. Private*, pg. 703

Lamkin, Robert, V.P.-Americas Sls.--Microcom, Norwood, MA; *U.S. Public*, pg. 417

Lammot, Brooke, Dir.-Sls.--Clayton Manufacturing Div., Dynamic Equipment, El Monte, CA; *U.S. Private*, pg. 245

Lamond, Dennis, V.P.-Export--Briggs Industries, Inc., Tampa, FL; *U.S. Private*, pg. 168

Lamone, Gene, V.P.-Sls. & Mktg. & Adv.--Capitol Manufacturing Co., Westerville, OH; *U.S. Public*, pg. 793

LaMont, Peter, Dir.-Sls.--The Vacation Store, Virginia Beach, VA; *U.S. Private*, pg. 649

Lamothe, Walter, V.P.-Sls.--Shirmax Leasing Ltd., Montreal, Canada; *Int'l*, pg. 1235

Lamotte, Mark, V.P.-Sls.--The Gorton Group, Gloucester, MA; *Int'l*, pg. 1434

Lampen, Ron, V.P.-Sls. & Mktg.--Thermotron Industries, Holland, MI; *U.S. Private*, pg. 1136

Lampen, Wayne, Mgr.-Sls.--Kysor Cooling Systems, Cadillac, MI; *U.S. Public*, pg. 968

Lampropolis, Ms., Wholesale Trade-Hungary--K & P Leykam Austria, Gratkorn, Austria; *Int'l*, pg. 757

Lanbot, Francoise, Dir.-Sls. & Mktg./Biotherm--L'Oreal Parfumerie, Brussels, Belgium; *Int'l*, pg. 819

Lancaster, Bill, V.P.-Corp. Sls.--Associated Wholesale Grocers, Inc., Kansas City, KS; *U.S. Private*, pg. 93

Lancaster, Charles L., Mgr.-Natl. Sls.--Laboratory Supply Company, Inc., Louisville, KY; *U.S. Private*, pg. 641

Lancaster, Don, Regional Dir.-Omnitrac Sls. Div.--QUALCOMM, San Diego, CA; *U.S. Public*, pg. 1348

Land, Ron, Sr. V.P.-Mass Market Book & Bible Sls.--Thomas Nelson Inc., Nashville, TN; *U.S. Public*, pg. 1167

Landerman, Bob, V.P.-Sls.--L.A. Gear, Inc., Santa Monica, CA; *U.S. Public*, pg. 969

Landes, George, Jr., Dir.-Sls. & Mktg.--CMS Gilbreth Packaging Systems, Bensalem, PA; *U.S. Private*, pg. 558

Landess, Marsha, Gen. Sls. Mgr.--WRVQ-FM, Richmond, VA; *U.S. Public*, pg. 385

Landis, Dean, Treas. & Sec.--United Credit Corp. & Patroit Funding, New York, NY; *U.S. Private*, pg. 1121

Landolfi, Tony, V.P -Natl. Sls.--4C Foods Corporation, Brooklyn, NY; *U.S. Private*, pg. 421

Landolt, Thomas, CEMS Sls.--Scott Environmental Technology, Plumsteadville, PA; *U.S. Public*, pg. 546

Landreth, Dan, V.P.-Sales & Mktg.--SatCom Technologies Division, Duluth, GA; *U.S. Public*, pg. 424

Landrum, James, Mgr.-Sls.--Vulcraft Div., Florence, SC; *U.S.* Public, pg. 1206

Landrum, Rodney, V.P.-Sls.-Central & S.W. Div.--Time Systems, Inc., Phoenix, AZ; *U.S. Private*, pg. 1086

Landwear, Uwe, Dir.-Sls.--SpeedFam GmbH, Ingelfingen, Germany; *U.S. Public*, pg. 1498

Landy, Michael, V.P.-Sls. & Mktg.--Sanmina Corporation, San Jose, CA; *U.S. Public*, pg. 1431

Lane, Donald, V.P.-Sls.--Makino Inc., Mason, OH; *Int'l*, pg. 831

Lane, Edwin, Mgr. Sls.-Eastern Reg.--W. Braun Co., Lyndhurst, NJ; *U.S. Private*, pg. 166

Lane, Maurice, V.P.-Sls.--Swanson, Camden, NJ; *U.S. Public*, pg. 299

Lane, W.R., Dir.-Sls. & Mktg.--Edward Barber & Co., London, United Kingdom; *U.S. Public*, pg. 1651

Lang, Art, Dir.-Mail Order Sls.--USA Weekend, New York, NY; *U.S. Public*, pg. 701

Lang, Bill, Regional Sls. Mgr.--Dayton Rogers of Texas, Arlington, TX; *U.S. Private*, pg. 318

Lang, Daniel, Dir.-Natl. Sls.--Northland Cranberries, Inc., Wisconsin Rapids, WI; *U.S. Public*, pg. 1197

Lang, Marlen P., Admin.-Mktg. & Sales--Heckett MultiServ, Butler, PA; *U.S. Public*, pg. 793

Lang, Pierre, Asst. V.P.-Sls.--Bobst S.A., Lausanne, Switzerland; *Int'l*, pg. 198

Lang, Richard A., Jr., V.P.-Adv., Sls. & Mktg.--Dad's Products Co., Inc., Meadville, PA; *U.S. Private*, pg. 306

Lang, Richard J., V.P.-Intl. Sls. & Mktg.--DeVlieg-Bullard Inc., Westport, CT; *U.S. Public*, pg. 502

Langan, John, V.P.-Mktg. & Sls.--Clearly Canadian Beverage Corp., Vancouver, Canada; *Int'l*, pg. 297

Lange, Karen M., Grp. Coord.-Sls.--Glastic Corporation, Cleveland, OH; *Int'l*, pg. 740

Lange, Richard, V.P.-Sls.--Spangler Inc., Kansas City, KS; *U.S. Private*, pg. 1020

Langenberg, Oliver M., Sr. V.P.-Institutional Sls.--A.G. Edwards & Sons, Inc., Saint Louis, MO; *U.S. Public*, pg. 565

Langey, Walter, Engr.-Sls.--Baum USA, Sidney, OH; *Int'l*, pg. 1293

Langley, E.J., Mgr.-Lumber Sls.--Anthony Forest Products Co., Inc., El Dorado, AR; *U.S. Private*, pg. 76

Langmead, Chuck, Dir.-Sls.--Food Service Division, Hunt Valley, MD; *U.S. Public*, pg. 1066

Langridge, Jack, V.P.-Sls. & Mktg.--New Hampshire Ball Bearings, Inc., Peterborough, NH; *Int'l*, pg. 868

Langston, Billy, Sr. V.P.-Sls. Admin.--Haggar Corporation, Dallas, TX; *U.S. Public*, pg. 774

Langton, Robert R., V.P.-Sls. & Mktg.--The JPM Company, Lewisburg, PA; *U.S. Public*, pg. 919

Langvardt, Chris, Mgr.-Sls. Devel.--Balderson Inc., Wamego, KS; *U.S. Public*, pg. 315

Lanham, Larkin, V.P.-Mktg. & Sls.--CD Products, Inc., New Providence, NJ; *U.S. Public*, pg. 276

Lanier, John, V.P.-Sls.--MedTrac, Inc., Minneapolis, MN; *Int'l*, pg. 1504

Lanigan, Michael, Pres.-Mi-Jack & Exec. V.P.--MI-Jack Products, Inc., Hazel Crest, IL; *U.S. Private*, pg. 740

Lanigan, Michael, Natl. Sls. Mgr.--TMP Worldwide Pty Limited, Sydney, Australia; *Int'l*, pg. 1342

Lanigan, Patrick, V.P. & W.E.D.--MI-Jack Products, Inc., Hazel Crest, IL; *U.S. Private*, pg. 740

Lanjevin, Hal, V.P.-Sls.--Illinois Fruit & Produce Corp., Streator, IL; *U.S. Public*, pg. 918

Lanning, Al, V.P.-Sls.--Haworth, Inc., Holland, MI; *U.S. Private*, pg. 511

Lanning, Paul, Mgr.-Sls.--Thermoplastics, Inc., Mishawaka, IN; *U.S. Public*, pg. 1590

Lantz, Ron, Mgr.-Sls.--Circle International, Vandalia, OH; *U.S. Public*, pg. 371

Lapiana, Pietro, Component Sls. Engr.--Analog Devices SRL, Rome, Italy; *U.S. Public*, pg. 109

Lapine, Richard, V.P.-Sls. & Mktg.--Essex Specialty Products, Auburn Hills, MI; *U.S. Public*, pg. 523

LaPlaca, Barbara, Dir.-Creative Svcs. & U.S. Adv. Sls.--The Reader's Digest Association, Inc., Pleasantville, NY; *U.S.* Public, pg. 1367

LaPlante, David, V.P.-Sls. & Mktg.--Shurfine International, Inc., Northlake, IL; *U.S. Private*, pg. 997

LaPoff, Gary, V.P.-Sls.--The Manhattan Shirt Co., New York, NY; *U.S. Public*, pg. 1429

LaPointe, Rodger, Mgr.-Export Sls.--York Barbell Co., Inc., York, PA; *U.S. Private*, pg. 1196

Laponte, Phil, Sls. Zone Mgr.--Coldwater Seafood Corporation, Rowayton, CT; *U.S. Private*, pg. 251

LaPort, Larry, V.P.-Sls.--Pearlstine Distributors Inc., Charleston, SC; *U.S. Private*, pg. 845

LaQuintano, Tony, V.P.-Sls. & Mktg.--Dietzgen Corporation, Palatine, IL; *U.S. Private*, pg. 332

Laramy, John E., V.P.-Sls. & Mktg.--The Riverside Publishing Co., Chicago, IL; *U.S. Public*, pg. 841

Largent, James D., V.P.-Sls.--D & K Healthcare Resources Division, Cape Girardeau, MO; *U.S. Public*, pg. 472

Larime, Michael W., V.P.-Sls. & Mktg.--Thetford Corporation, Ann Arbor, MI; *U.S. Private*, pg. 352

Larinto, Vincent, Sr. V.P.-Sls.--20th Century Fox Home Entertainment, Los Angeles, CA; *U.S. Public*, pg. 275

Larinto, Vincent, Sr. V.P.-Sls.--20th Century Fox Home Entertainment, Los Angeles, CA; *Int'l*, pg. 926

Larkin, Jackie, V.P.-Inside Sls.--Reed Elsevier Business Information, Newton, MA; *Int'l*, pg. 1095

Larkin, James A., Sr. Exec. V.P.-Sales--North Shore Movers, Northbrook, IL; *U.S. Private*, pg. 805

Larned, Mark, Sls. Dir.-N.E. Region--Barton Nelson Inc., Kansas City, MO; *U.S. Private*, pg. 120

Laroche, Louis J., Mgr.-Natl. Sls.--General Filters, Inc., Novi, MI; *U.S. Private*, pg. 444

LaRosa, Stephanie, V.P.-Sls. & Mktg.--Quantum Sport, New York, NY; *U.S. Private*, pg. 900

Larsen, Gregory J., Mgr.-Veg-All Sls.--Dean Foods Vegetable Company, Green Bay, WI; *U.S. Public*, pg. 490

Larsen, J.A., V.P.-Mktg. & Sls.--CWC Textron Company, Muskegon, MI; *U.S. Public*, pg. 1590

Larsen, Joanne, Mgr.-Customer Service & Sls.--Intertractor America Corporation, Elkhorn, WI; *Int'l*, pg. 1511

Larsen, Nancy, Supvr.-Sls.--Remcor Products Co., Glendale Heights, IL; *Int'l*, pg. 646

Larsen, Richard, V.P.-Sls. & Mktg.--Arvida, Boca Raton, FL; *U.S. Private*, pg. 578

Larson, Allan G., Reg. Mgr.-Sls.--Cramer Company, Old Saybrook, CT; *U.S. Public*, pg. 1238

Larson, Curt, V.P.-Distr. Sls. & Service--Briggs & Stratton Corporation, Wauwatosa, WI; *U.S. Public*, pg. 252

Larson, Kenneth, Exec. V.P.--Monico Alloys, Inc., Los Angeles, CA; *U.S. Private*, pg. 757

Larson, Rick, Reg. Mgr.-Factory Automation--Aromat Northwestern Sales Office, San Jose, CA; *Int'l*, pg. 848

Larson, Stephen, Mgr.-Sls. & Mktg.--Oildyne, Minneapolis, MN; *U.S. Public*, pg. 411

Larter, Dan, V.P.-Sls. & Mktg.--Burlington Motor Holdings Inc., Daleville, IN; *U.S. Private*, pg. 183

LaSelle, Tony, V.P.-Sls.--Malt-O-Meal Company, Minneapolis, MN; *U.S. Private*, pg. 699

Laseter, Larry, V.P.-Sls. & Mktg.--Florida Power & Light Company, North Palm Beach, FL; *U.S. Public*, pg. 608

Laskey, Christine, V.P.-Mktg. & Corp. Communications--National Trustco Inc., Toronto, Canada; *Int'l*, pg. 909

Laskey, Timothy W., Div. V.P.-Western Sls.--Baldwin Piano & Organ Company, Loveland, OH; *U.S. Public*, pg. 169

Lassalette, Joe, Mgr.-Sls.--International Extrusion Corp., Alhambra, CA; *U.S. Public*, pg. 895

Lasser, Sherman, Sr. V.P.-Sls.--Brown Shoe Company, Saint Louis, MO; *U.S. Public*, pg. 262

Lasser, Sherman H., Sr. V.P. & Mgr.-Sls.--Brown Group, Inc., Saint Louis, MO; *U.S. Public*, pg. 262

Lassiter, Dennis, Gen. Mgr.-Sls.--Jaguar Cars, Mahwah, NJ; *U.S. Public*, pg. 664

Lassy, Ron, V.P.-Sls. & Mktg.--Vlier Engineering, Brighton, MA; *U.S. Public*, pg. 124

Latham, Michael, Dir.-Sls.--Wavetek Corporation, San Diego, CA; *U.S. Private*, pg. 1154

Latham, Michael, Sls.--Wavetek Corp., San Diego, CA; *U.S. Private*, pg. 1155

Latimer, Becky, Mgr.-Sls.--Driv-Lok, Inc., Sycamore, IL; *U.S.* Private, pg. 343

Latour, John, Natl. Sls. Mgr.--Ascom Canada Limited, Markham, Canada; *Int'l*, pg. 86

Latourette, Everett, Reg. Mgr.-Sls. & Adv.--Cramer Company, Old Saybrook, CT; *U.S. Public*, pg. 1238

Latta, John, V.P.--ElectroCom Automation L.P., Arlington, TX; *Int'l*, pg. 1244

Latta, R.M., V.P.-Sls. & Mtkg.--Chrysler Canada Ltd., Windsor, Canada; *U.S. Public*, pg. 354

Latuda, Suzanne, Dir.-Sls. & Mktg.--Wolverine Leather Div., Rockford, MI; *U.S. Public*, pg. 1775

Latzen, Robert, Sr. V.P.-Sls.--Gould Paper Corporation, New York, NY; *U.S. Private*, pg. 466

Lau, B.H., V.P.-Sls. & Mktg.--Ph. Orth Co., Oak Creek, WI; *Int'l*, pg. 244

Lau, K.S., Sls. Mgr.--Delta Electrical & Engineering Services Ltd., Kwai Chung, Hong Kong; *Int'l*, pg. 390

Lau, Timothy J., V.P. & Reg. Sls. Mgr.--First Financial Bank, FSB, Stevens Point, WI; *U.S. Public*, pg. 140

Lauber, Dennis R., V.P.-Sls. & Mktg.--Grede Foundries, Inc., Milwaukee, WI; *U.S. Private*, pg. 476
Lauer, Michael, Mgr.-Area Sls.--Gensym GmbH, Dortmund, Germany; *U.S. Public*, pg. 731
Laughlin, Leo, Exec. V.P.-Sls.--Dribeck Importers, Inc., Greenwich, CT; *U.S. Private*, pg. 343
Laughridge, W.J. III, Mgr.-Natl. Sls.--Bommer Industries, Inc., Landrum, SC; *U.S. Private*, pg. 156
Laumeister, Glenn, V.P.-Fin. Sls.--National Electronics Warranty Corporation, Sterling, VA; *U.S. Private*, pg. 782
Laura, Henry, V.P.-Sls., Mktg. & Adv./Agency Svcs.--The Arbitron Company, New York, NY; *U.S. Public*, pg. 331
Laure, Patrick, Dir.-Sls.--Skandia Life Assurance Co. Ltd. - Paris, Paris, France; *Int'l*, pg. 1256
Lauren, Kai, Mgr.-Oil, Bulk Sls. & Supply--Neste Oy, Espoo, Finland; *Int'l*, pg. 912
Laurent, J.R., Mgr.-Truck Tire Sls.--The Cooper Tire Company, Findlay, OH; *U.S. Public*, pg. 445
Laurenzi, Mark V., Exec. V.P.-Sls. & Mktg.--Marotta Scientific Controls, Inc., Montville, NJ; *U.S. Private*, pg. 706
Laurie, B.L., Dir.-Sls. & Mktg.--Coats Patons, Toronto, Canada; *Int'l*, pg. 300
Laurie, Dick, Mgr.-Sls./Electronic--Littelfuse, Inc., Des Plaines, IL; *U.S. Public*, pg. 1001
Lautzenhiser, Gary, Exec. V.P.-Sls., Mktg. & Bus. Devel.--Aristokraft, Inc., Jasper, IN; *U.S. Public*, pg. 675
Laux, Thomas E., V.P.-Intl. Sls. & Service--Integrated Systems, Inc., Sunnyvale, CA; *U.S. Public*, pg. 885
LaValle, Joseph, Mgr.-Mktg. & Sls.--Washington Scientific Industries, Inc., Long Lake, MN; *U.S. Public*, pg. 1744
Lavelle, Barb, Mgr.-Sls. & Mktg.--Pennsylvania Cellular Telephone Corp., Williamsport, PA; *U.S. Public*, pg. 1708
Lavelle, Patrick, V.P.-Sls.--Audiovox Corporation, Hauppauge, NY; *U.S. Public*, pg. 147
Lavely, Anthony, Sr. V.P.-Sls. & Mktg.--Rally's Hamburgers, Inc., Louisville, KY; *U.S. Public*, pg. 1359
Lavers, Julian P., Sr. V.P.-Sls. & Field Opers.--Wechsler Coffee Corp., Moonachie, NJ; *U.S. Private*, pg. 1158
Laverty, Brian, V.P.-Natl. Sls.--General Mills Canada Inc., Etobicoke, Canada; *U.S. Public*, pg. 718
Lavin, Chris, V.P.-Sls. & Mktg.--U.S. Filter, Lowell, MA; *U.S. Public*, pg. 1682
Lavoie, Raymond L., V.P.-U.S. Cardiac Surgery Sls.--Medtronic, Inc., Minneapolis, MN; *U.S. Public*, pg. 1082
Lavorgna, Anthony N., Mgr.-Mktg. & Sales--Airflex Div. Eaton Corp., Cleveland, OH; *U.S. Public*, pg. 556
Lavota, Ivana, Asst. Mgr.-Sls.--Sensormatic E.C., S.r.l., Milan, Italy; *U.S. Public*, pg. 1457
Law, Bob, Dir.-Sls. & Mktg.--Kenwood USA, Long Beach, CA; *Int'l*, pg. 730
Law, Jerry, V.P.-Sls.--Central Commissary, Inc., Phoenix, AZ; *U.S. Private*, pg. 276
Law, Jim, V.P.-Sls.--Trelleborg YSH, Inc., South Haven, MI; *Int'l*, pg. 1422
Law, R.L., V.P.-Sls.--Tru-Fit Products Corp., Medina, OH; *U.S. Private*, pg. 1107
Law, S., Mgr.-Sls.--Esselte Ltd., Wan Chai, Hong Kong; *Int'l*, pg. 461
Lawless, James, Mgr.-Sls.--Flexible Technologies Inc., Abbeville, SC; *Int'l*, pg. 1267
Lawliss, William, V.P.-Sls., N. American--Prince Sports Group Inc., Bordentown, NJ; *U.S. Private*, pg. 884
Lawrence, Charles, V.P.-Mktg. & Sls.--Zebco, Tulsa, OK; *U.S. Public*, pg. 265
Lawrence, Charles, V.P.-Mktg. & Sls.--Martin Reels, A Division of Zebco, Tulsa, OK; *U.S. Public*, pg. 265
Lawrence, James, V.P.-Fabric Sls.-N.Y.--Woolrich, Inc., Woolrich, PA; *U.S. Private*, pg. 1188
Lawrence, Ken, Mgr.-Indus. Sls.--Progress Paint Mfg. Co., Louisville, KY; *U.S. Private*, pg. 890
Lawrence, Richard J., Natl. Sls. Dir.- Consumer Div.--Ohio Sealants Inc., Mentor, OH; *Int'l*, pg. 802
Lawrie, Dan, Gen. Sls. Mgr.--WKY-AM, Oklahoma City, OK; *U.S. Public*, pg. 385
Lawrie, R.E., Dir.-Export Sls.--Sunkist Growers, Inc., Sherman Oaks, CA; *U.S. Private*, pg. 1052
Lawson, Bruce, Mgr.-Local Sls.--WGAL-TV, Lancaster, PA; *U.S. Public*, pg. 1344
Lawson, Jerry, V.P.-Western Sls.--Apperson Business Forms, Inc., Los Angeles, CA; *U.S. Private*, pg. 78
Lawson, Joe, Sls. Mgr.--Milford Fastening Systems, Milford, CT; *U.S. Private*, pg. 745
Lawson, Louis L., Sr. V.P.-Strategic Sls.--United Family Life Insurance Co., Atlanta, GA; *Int'l*, pg. 499
Lawson, Mike, Dir.-Sls.--PACCAR Winch Division, Broken Arrow, OK; *U.S. Public*, pg. 1246
Lawson, Ron, Sr. V.P.-Sls. & Customer Service--Howmedica, Inc., Rutherford, NJ; *U.S. Public*, pg. 1282
Lawton, John, V.P.-Sls. & Mktg.--Clean Harbors, Inc., Braintree, MA; *U.S. Public*, pg. 383
Lawton, Mike, Pres.-U.S. Baby Care--Gerber Products Company, Fremont, MI; *Int'l*, pg. 973
Lax, David, V.P.-Sls. & Adv.--John Hassall, Inc., Westbury, NY; *U.S. Private*, pg. 509
Lay, T.Y., V.P.-Sls. & Mktg.--Acer Incorporated, Taipei, Taiwan; *Int'l*, pg. 22
Lazar, Stuart, V.P.-Sls.--Glencraft Lingerie, Inc., New York, NY; *U.S. Private*, pg. 456
Lazaran, Frank, Grp. V.P.-Sls. & Mdsg.--Ralphs Grocery Company, Compton, CA; *U.S. Private*, pg. 1202
Lazarro, V.G., Mgr.-Sls.--Turner Construction Co., Cleveland, OH; *U.S. Public*, pg. 1645
Lazerson, Lee, Mgr.-Reg. Sls.--KOAT-TV, Albuquerque, NM; *U.S. Public*, pg. 1344
Lazorchak, E.D., V.P.-Sls.--Electroid Co., Springfield, NJ; *U.S. Private*, pg. 369
Le Blanc, Theodore, Exec. V.P.-Dealer Sls./Dist. Western Hemisphere--Konica Business Machines USA, Inc., Windsor, CT; *Int'l*, pg. 748
Le Lacheur, Robert G., V.P.-Sls.-Northeast Div.--Crown Cork & Seal, Northeast Div., Lawrence, MA; *U.S. Public*, pg. 463
Lea, John, V.P.-Retail Sls. & Mktg.--Tyson Foods, Inc., Springdale, AR; *U.S. Public*, pg. 1652
Leach, David P., V.P.-Sls. & Mktg.--GH Hensley Industries, Inc., Dallas, TX; *U.S. Private*, pg. 439
Leach, Peter, Mgr.-Sls.--D.D. Bean & Sons Co., Jaffrey, NH; *U.S. Private*, pg. 126
Leach, Thomas, Dir.-Sls. & Mktg.--Horton Homes, Inc., Eatonton, GA; *U.S. Private*, pg. 540
Leadabrand, Roger, V.P.-Sls.--Radionics, Inc., Salinas, CA; *U.S. Public*, pg. 501
Leafstone, Howard, V.P.- Sls.--On-Cor Frozen Foods Inc., Northbrook, IL; *U.S. Private*, pg. 817
Leahy, John, Sr. V.P.-Intl. Corp. Sls.--Playtex Beauty Care, Inc., Westport, CT; *U.S. Public*, pg. 1311
Leahy, John D., Sr. V.P.-Intl. Corp. Sls.--Playtex Products Inc., Westport, CT; *U.S. Public*, pg. 1310
Leahy, Peter, V.P.-Sls.--Hill's Pet Nutrition, Topeka, KS; *U.S. Public*, pg. 397
Leahy, Robert B., Sr. V.P.-Sls. & Mktg.--Folger Nolan Fleming Douglas, Washington, DC; *U.S. Private*, pg. 416
Leahy, W., V.P.-Sls.--Moore Data Management Services Div., Saint Louis Park, MN; *Int'l*, pg. 890
Leaky, Ken, V.P. & Natl. Sls. Mgr.--Tandy Brands Accessories, Inc., Arlington, TX; *U.S. Public*, pg. 1560
Leaman, Gordon A., V.P.-Intl. Sls.--Pervasive Software Inc., Austin, TX; *U.S. Public*, pg. 1280
Leavengood, Robert, V.P.-Sls. & Mktg.--UniSea Foods, Inc., Redmond, WA; *Int'l*, pg. 940
Leavitt, John, Sr. V.P.-Sls. & Mktg.--Prime Hospitality Corp., Fairfield, NJ; *U.S. Public*, pg. 1326
LeBed, Orest, V.P.-Sls. & Mktg.--John Dusenbery Co., Inc., Randolph, NJ; *U.S. Private*, pg. 349
Leber, Rudolph, Dir.-Intl. Sls.--Atlas Electric Devices Co., Chicago, IL; *U.S. Private*, pg. 96
LeBlac, Paul, Dir.-Worldwide Sls.--Richfield Hospitality Services, Englewood, CO; *U.S. Private*, pg. 929
LeBlanc, Greg, V.P.-Mktg. & Sls.--CEM Corporation, Matthews, NC; *U.S. Public*, pg. 277
LeBlanc, Joel, Mgr.-Domestic Sls.--Warn Industries, Inc., Clackamas, OR; *U.S. Private*, pg. 1150
Lebreton, Joel, Sr. V.P.-Contracts & Sls. Fin.--Avions de Transport Regional - ATR, Blagnac, France; *Int'l*, pg. 654
Lebrija, Rafael de Haro, V.P.-Sls--Grupo Televisa, S.A. de C.V., Mexico, Mexico; *Int'l*, pg. 576
Leckey, David, V.P.-Circulation--Hachette Filipacchi Magazines Inc., New York, NY; *Int'l*, pg. 794
Leclair, Andre, V.P.-Sls.--Grocery Division, Montreal, Canada; *Int'l*, pg. 348
Ledbetter, Roy, Mgr.-Sls.--National Mine Service Company, Alabama Div., Birmingham, AL; *Int'l*, pg. 281
Ledger, Bob, Mgr.-Sls.--Texas Metal Works, Inc., Beaumont, TX; *U.S. Private*, pg. 1078
Lee Kenning, Kristi, Rep.-Sls.--American Journal of Nursing Company, New York, NY; *Int'l*, pg. 1513
Lee, C.H., Dir.-Sls.--Kodak Korea Ltd., Seoul, Korea; *U.S. Public*, pg. 555
Lee, Dale G., Pres.-U.S. Sls.--Nature's Sunshine Products, Inc., Provo, UT; *U.S. Public*, pg. 1166
Lee, David, V.P.-Semiconductor Equipment Sls.--Leica Inc., Deerfield, IL; *Int'l*, pg. 806
Lee, Dennis, Mgr.-Sls.--S.O.S. Newall, Keighley, United Kingdom; *Int'l*, pg. 1166
Lee, Doo-Hwan, Pres.--Ssangyong Uni-Charm Co., Ltd., Kumi, Korea; *Int'l*, pg. 1291
Lee, Gerry, Dir.-Opers.--Subaru of America, Inc., Cherry Hill, NJ; *Int'l*, pg. 523
Lee, Greg, Exec. V.P.-Sls., Mktg. & Tech. Svcs.--Tyson Foods, Inc., Springdale, AR; *U.S. Public*, pg. 1652
Lee, Jack D., V.P.-Sls. & Mktg.--Associated Industrial Supply, Inc., Columbia, SC; *U.S. Private*, pg. 91
Lee, Jae-Woong, Mgr.--Ssangyong Information & Communication Corporation, Seoul, Korea; *Int'l*, pg. 1292
Lee, Joanna, Mgr.-Mktg.--Orchard Parade Holdings Limited, Singapore, Singapore; *Int'l*, pg. 1007
Lee, John, V.P.-Central Sls.--CBS Television Network, New York, NY; *U.S. Public*, pg. 274
Lee, K.S., Gen. Mgr.-Sls./Korea--Utell International-Korea, Seoul, Korea; *Int'l*, pg. 1098
Lee, Kevin, Mgr.-Natl. Sls.--Grace Taiwan, Inc., Tao-yuan, Taiwan; *U.S. Public*, pg. 756
Lee, Kiwhan, Sr. V.P.-Sls. & Mktg.--American Tape Co., Secaucus, NJ; *Int'l*, pg. 685
Lee, Kwan-Sep, Chief Fin. Officer--Ssangyong Investment & Finance Co., Ltd., Inchon, Korea; *Int'l*, pg. 1292
Lee, Laura Beth, Coord.-Sls.--Universal Flavors-U.S.A., Indianapolis, IN; *U.S. Public*, pg. 1696
Lee, Mark, V.P.-Sls.--Sonoco Engraph, Inc., Atlanta, GA; *U.S. Public*, pg. 1486
Lee, Michael, Dir.-Sls. & Mktg.--Zung Fu Company Ltd., Hong Kong, Hong Kong; *Int'l*, pg. 704
Lee, Rod, Mgr.-Warehouse Sls.--Kwe-Kintetsu World Express(S)Pte Ltd., Singapore, Singapore; *Int'l*, pg. 735
Lee, Trevor, V.P.-Worldwide Aftermarket Sls.--CalComp Technology, Inc., Anaheim, CA; *U.S. Public*, pg. 1007
Lee, Yong-Hae, V.P.--Ssangyong Corporation, Seoul, Korea; *Int'l*, pg. 1291
Leech, Ronald, V.P.-New Business--C P Converters, Inc., York, PA; *U.S. Private*, pg. 192
Leech, W. Michael, V.P.-Sls. & Mktg.--W.G. Carroll, Inc., Atlanta, GA; *U.S. Public*, pg. 1071
Leek, John, Mgr.-Sls. & Mktg.--Baldwin (UK) Ltd., Dunstable, United Kingdom; *U.S. Public*, pg. 170
Leeming, John B., V.P.-Sls. & Mktg.--Nomaco, Inc., Zebulon, NC; *U.S. Private*, pg. 801
Leerink, J., Dir.-Sls. & Mktg.--Hak B.V., Giessen, Netherlands; *Int'l*, pg. 244
Leese, Dennis, Dir.-Sls.--Augat, Inc., Communications Division, Seattle, WA; *U.S. Public*, pg. 1598
LeFebvre, Timothy, V.P.-Domestic Sls. & Mktg.--NESLAB Instruments, Inc., Newington, NH; *U.S. Public*, pg. 1595
LeFevre, Robert M., Sr. V.P.-Mktg. & Sls.--The United States Playing Card Company, Cincinnati, OH; *U.S. Private*, pg. 1125
Leff, Jeffrey, Chief Information Officer & Exec. V.P.-Sls.--Carole Wren, Inc., New York, NY; *U.S. Private*, pg. 1192
Leftwich, James, Mgr.-Intl. Sls.--Buehler, Limited, Lake Bluff, IL; *U.S. Public*, pg. 574
Legan, Gayland, V.P.-Retail Sls.--Family Smacks, Inc., Liberty, MO; *U.S. Private*, pg. 393
Legan, Richard E., V.P.-Sales--Motch Corporation, Cleveland, OH; *Int'l*, pg. 1128
Leggiere, Regina, Mgr.-Sls.--J&J Distribution Company, Millburn, NJ; *U.S. Private*, pg. 584
Legrain, Olivier, Mng. Dir.--Lafarge Materiaux de Specialites, Montrouge, France; *Int'l*, pg. 789
Legris, Bruce, V.P.-Intl. Sls.--Cobra Electronics Corporation, Chicago, IL; *U.S. Public*, pg. 391
Legros, Dick, V.P.-Religious Sls. & Mktg.--Standard Publishing, Cincinnati, OH; *U.S. Public*, pg. 1506
Lehman, Mike, V.P.-Sls. & Mktg.--Bard Mfg. Co., Bryan, OH; *U.S. Private*, pg. 116
Lehmkuhl, John, Asst. Mgr.-Sls.--Fleischer Manufacturing, Inc., Columbus, NE; *U.S. Private*, pg. 410
Lehneis, Walter C., V.P.-Mktg.--Diamond Crystal Specialty Foods, Inc., Wilmington, MA; *U.S. Private*, pg. 330
Lehning, Larry, Mgr.-Sls. & Mktg.--Liberty Precision Industries, Rochester, NY; *U.S. Private*, pg. 666
LeHocky, Robert, V.P.-Sls.--Howard Miller, Zeeland, MI; *U.S. Private*, pg. 747
Lehr, Phil, Gen. Mgr.-Sls.--Swepco Tube Corporation, Clifton, NJ; *U.S. Private*, pg. 1058
Leifheit, John, Mgr.-Gen. Sls.--KETV, Omaha, NE; *U.S. Public*, pg. 1343
Leininger, Edward R., V.P.-Sls. & Mktg.--GSE, Inc., Farmington, MI; *U.S. Public*, pg. 1676
Leiser, Ken, V.P.-Sls.--Akorn, Inc., Lincolnshire, IL; *U.S. Public*, pg. 34
Lekich, Ivo, Dir.-Sls.--GDC Federal Systems, Inc., Reston, VA; *U.S. Public*, pg. 708
LeMayo, Joan, Dir.-Sls. & Mktg./Crown Grp.--Random House, Inc., New York, NY; *U.S. Private*, pg. 20
LeMayo, Joan, Dir.-Mktg. & Sls.--Crown Publishers, Inc., New York, NY; *U.S. Private*, pg. 21
Lemberger, Mark, Sr. V.P.-Sls. & Mktg.--Western States Envelope Co., Milwaukee, WI; *U.S. Private*, pg. 1168
Lembert, Jean Luc, Mgr.-Sls.--Alpha Industries, Inc., Woburn, MA; *U.S. Public*, pg. 57
Lembo, Dick, Mgr.-Intl. Sls.--B.A. Ballou & Co. Inc., East Providence, RI; *U.S. Private*, pg. 112
Lemley, Paul, V.P.--Giffels Technologies, Inc., Southfield, MI; *U.S. Private*, pg. 452
Lemmo, Mark, V.P. & Gen. Mgr.-Sls. & Mktg.--InterDigital Communications Corp., King of Prussia, PA; *U.S. Public*, pg. 889
Lenander, John, V.P.-Sls.--Grove Valve & Regulator Company, Stafford, TX; *U.S. Private*, pg. 484
Lenandowski, Thomas, Sr. V.P.-Mktg.--Jones Medical Industries Inc., Saint Louis, MO; *U.S. Public*, pg. 933
Lenhart, Jim, Dir.-Sls.--Superior Coffee & Foods/Hawaii, Aiea, HI; *U.S. Private*, pg. 191
Lenhart, Larry, V.P.-Sls.--Zimmer Custom-Made Packaging Co., Indianapolis, IN; *U.S. Private*, pg. 802
Lenhart, S.J., Sls. Mgr.--Bedford Chemical Div., Walton Hills, OH; *U.S. Public*, pg. 618
Lenir, Jean-Marie, Mgr.-Sls./France--Axson S.A., Paris, France; *Int'l*, pg. 102
Lennertz, Carl, Sls. Mgr.--Schocken Books, New York, NY; *U.S. Private*, pg. 21
Lennig, Edmund, V.P.-U.S. Sls.--American Meter Company, Horsham, PA; *Int'l*, pg. 1149
Lenny, Rick, V.P.-Mktg. & Sls.--Kraft Foods Inc., Rye Brook, NY; *U.S. Public*, pg. 1288
Lentine, John, V.P.--Rex Lumber Company, Acton, MA; *U.S. Private*, pg. 926
Lenzini, Franco, V.P.-Sls.--Pacific Wine Co., Chicago, IL; *U.S. Private*, pg. 843
Leonard, Chuck, Mgr.-Natl. Sls.--D.C.I., Inc., Saint Cloud, MN; *U.S. Private*, pg. 301
Leonard, Craig, Dir.-Specialty Prod. Sls.--Thomas Built Buses, Inc., High Point, NC; *U.S. Private*, pg. 1082
Leonard, Michael S., V.P.-Mktg. & Sls.--Continental Promotion Group, Tempe, AZ; *U.S. Private*, pg. 269
Leonard, Rick, V.P.-Sls.--Modern Drop Forge Co., Blue Island, IL; *U.S. Private*, pg. 754
Leonardi, Marjorie H., V.P.-Sls., Southeast Div.--C.R. Gibson Co., Norwalk, CT; *U.S. Public*, pg. 1168
Leone, Chuck, V.P., Sales & Mktg.-Nissan--Nissan Forklift Corporation, North America, Marengo, IL; *Int'l*, pg. 944
Leone, Rick, V.P.-Sls. & Mktg.--Bonney Forge Corporation, Allentown, PA; *U.S. Private*, pg. 156
Lepine, Gilles, V.P.-Sls./Canada--Uniboard Canada Inc., Laval, Canada; *Int'l*, pg. 1431
Leppert, Tom, Sr. V.P.-Sls. & Mktg.--Sargent & Greenleaf, Inc., Nicholasville, KY; *U.S. Private*, pg. 965
Leroy, Doug, V.P.-Sls.--Fruit of the Loom, Inc., Chicago, IL; *U.S. Public*, pg. 685
Leroy, Tim, V.P.-Sls.--Meadowcraft, Inc., Birmingham, AL; *U.S. Private*, pg. 725
Lervick, R.M., V.P.-Sls.--Ziegler Inc., Minneapolis, MN; *U.S. Private*, pg. 1205
Leshinski, Bruce A., Sr. V.P.-Sls. & Mktg.--Newly Weds Foods Inc., Chicago, IL; *U.S. Private*, pg. 796
Leslie, Don, Mgr.-Sls.--Plastics Div., Sioux Falls, SD; *U.S. Public*, pg. 1361
Leslie, Michael, V.P.-Sls.--Berg Electronics, Saint Louis, MO; *U.S. Public*, pg. 212
Lesser, Steve, V.P.-N. American Opers.--Marcam Solutions, Inc., Newton, MA; *U.S. Public*, pg. 1042
Lester, D. Nelson, V.P.-Mktg. & Sls.--Porcelain Products, Carey, OH; *U.S. Public*, pg. 308
Lester, Rex A., V.P.-Sls. Devel.--Coors Brewing Company, Golden, CO; *U.S. Public*, pg. 445
Letchford, Peter, Mgr.-Ntl. Sls.--CIBA-GEIGY Australia Ltd., Pendle Hill, Australia; *Int'l*, pg. 976
Leteuier, Gislain, Mgr.-Sls.--Atlet France S.A., Cergy-Pontoise, France; *Int'l*, pg. 97

Letourneau, Joe, V.P.-Sls., W-A, Lederle Vaccines & Pediatrics--Wyeth-Ayerst Laboratories, Inc., Philadelphia, PA; *U.S. Public*, pg. 80
Letourneau, Peter D., V.P.-Sls. Service--Geiger Brothers, Lewiston, ME; *U.S. Private*, pg. 442
Lettie, Ben, Sls. Mgr.-Mass Mdse. & Hardware--Frederick Trading Company, Frederick, MD; *U.S. Private*, pg. 335
Leu, Meg, Mgr.-Intl. Sls.--Seika Electric Co., Ltd., Taipei, Taiwan; *Int'l*, pg. 1218
Leuchtenberger, Mark, V.P.-Mktg. & Sls.--Biogen, Inc., Cambridge, MA; *U.S. Public*, pg. 230
Leuther, Peter, Area Sls. Mgr.--Bourns Electronics, Ltd., Dunfermline, United Kingdom; *U.S. Private*, pg. 161
LeValley, George W., V.P.-Sls.--Bosch Packaging Machinery Division, South Plainfield, NJ; *Int'l*, pg. 204
Levausc, J. F., Mgr.-Sls.--S.A. Cockerill Mechanical Industries C.M.I., Seraing, Belgium; *Int'l*, pg. 301
Levell, Paul, Mgr.-Natl. Acct.--Nestle Lyons Maid, York, United Kingdom; *Int'l*, pg. 918
Leverette, Thomas L., V.P.-Sls.--Patterson Pump Company, Toccoa, GA; *U.S. Public*, pg. 754
Levers, Jeff I., Area Sls. Rep.--Production Operators, Inc. (Lafayette Office), Lafayette, LA; *U.S. Public*, pg. 298
Levia, Jim, V.P.-Corrigated Sls.--Mitchel-Lincoln Packaging, Saint-Laurent, Canada; *Int'l*, pg. 870
Levin, Alan, V.P.-Sls.--TMP Worldwide Ltd., Toronto, Canada; *U.S. Private*, pg. 1065
Levin, Stephen J., Exec. V.P.-Sls.--Telemundo Group, Inc., Hialeah, FL; *U.S. Public*, pg. 1570
Levine, D.S., V.P.-Sls. & Mktg., Indus. Prods. Grp.--Flowserve Corporation, Valve Div., Cookeville, TN; *U.S. Public*, pg. 658
Levine, David, V.P.-Sls.--Human Affairs International Inc., Sandy, UT; *U.S. Public*, pg. 1036
Levine, Jane, Publr.--Chicago Reader, Inc., Chicago, IL; *U.S. Private*, pg. 235
Levine, Ken, Dir.-Sls.--Cabletron Systems, Inc., Rochester, NH; *U.S. Public*, pg. 288
Levine, Mark B., V.P.-Sls. & Mktg.--Watts Fluidair, Kittery, ME; *Int'l*, pg. 1243
Levine, Todd, V.P.-Mktg. & Sls.--Don Alleson, Inc., Rochester, NY; *U.S. Private*, pg. 339
Levinson, Adam, V.P.-Sls. & Mktg.--Sunroc Corporation, Dover, DE; *U.S. Private*, pg. 1053
Levy, Carolyn J., Sr. V.P.-Mktg. & Sls. Information--Philip Morris U.S.A., New York, NY; *U.S. Public*, pg. 1289
Levy, Malcolm, V.P.-Sls. & Mktg.--Racal Instruments, Inc., Irvine, CA; *Int'l*, pg. 1083
Levy, Steven E., V.P.-Sls. & Mktg.--Copperweld Bimetallics Products Co., Fayetteville, TN; *Int'l*, pg. 662
Lewandowski, Len, Sls. Zone Mgr.--Coldwater Seafood Corporation, Rowayton, CT; *U.S. Private*, pg. 251
Lewis, Amy, V.P.-Worldwide Sls.--Allaire Corporation, Cambridge, MA; *U.S. Private*, pg. 36
Lewis, Ari, Dir.-Sls.--Paper Enterprises, Inc., Bronx, NY; *U.S. Private*, pg. 837
Lewis, Barbara, V.P.-Adv. & Sls. Promo.--Wherehouse Entertainment, Inc., Torrance, CA; *U.S. Private*, pg. 1171
Lewis, Daniel L., V.P.-Sls.--Integrated Device Technology, Inc., Santa Clara, CA; *U.S. Public*, pg. 884
Lewis, Dick, Sr. V.P.-Mktg. & Sls.--Fortis Financial Group, Woodbury, MN; *Int'l*, pg. 499
Lewis, Herbert E., Sr. V.P.-Southern Wholesale Div.--Countrywide Funding Corporation, Pasadena, CA; *U.S. Public*, pg. 453
Lewis, John, Sr. V.P.-Sls.--MicroAge, Inc., Tempe, AZ; *U.S. Public*, pg. 1104
Lewis, Kelly, Mgr.-Sls.--Pearlstine Distributors Inc., Charleston, SC; *U.S. Private*, pg. 845
Lewis, Kurt W., V.P.-Mktg. & Sls.--Fujisawa U.S.A. Inc., Deerfield, IL; *Int'l*, pg. 525
Lewis, Les, Dir.-Sls.--Colgate Oral Pharmaceutical, Canton, MA; *U.S. Public*, pg. 397
Lewis, Michael E., Mgr.-Sls. & Mktg.--Ekstrom Industries, Inc., Farmington Hills, MI; *U.S. Private*, pg. 172
Lewis, Norman, V.P.-Sls.--Kasper Machine Company, Madison Heights, MI; *U.S. Private*, pg. 608
Lewis, Paul, Mgr.-Adv. & Sls.--Prodigy Inc., White Plains, NY; *U.S. Private*, pg. 888
Lewis, Ray, Sr. V.P.-European Sls. & New Bus. Devel.--Columbia Tri-Star International Television, Culver City, CA; *Int'l*, pg. 1281
Lewis, Robert B., V.P. & Gen. Mgr.--Asahi/America, Inc., Malden, MA; *U.S. Public*, pg. 137
Lewis, Samuel A., V.P.-Sls.--Elgar Corporation, San Diego, CA; *U.S. Public*, pg. 789
Lewis, William B., V.P.-North American Sls.--CBT Systems USA Ltd., Menlo Park, CA; *U.S. Public*, pg. 275
Lewkowitz, Bill, Dir.-Natl. Sls. & Special Events--Jackson Hole Ski Resort, Teton Village, WY; *U.S. Private*, pg. 579
Lian, Loh, Mgr.-Sls.--CWT Distribution Limited, Singapore, Singapore; *Int'l*, pg. 246
Libbe, Scott Wm., Exec. V.P.-Sls.--Rudolph/Libbe, Inc., Walbridge, OH; *U.S. Private*, pg. 950
Libbey, Michael A., Gen. Mgr.-Vehicle Sls.--Porsche Cars North America, Inc., Reno, NV; *Int'l*, pg. 1063
Libbey, Ruth, V.P.-Sls. Opers.--Valassis Communications, Inc., Livonia, MI; *U.S. Public*, pg. 1704
Libengood, Harry H., Jr., V.P.-Sls.--Roessing Bronze Co., Mars, PA; *U.S. Private*, pg. 939
Librizzi, Joseph A., Sr. V.P.-Mktg. & Sls.--Jevic Transportation, Inc., Delanco, NJ; *U.S. Public*, pg. 927
Librock, Ned T., V.P.-Sls. & Mktg.--Columbus McKinnon Corp., Amherst, NY; *U.S. Public*, pg. 405
Lich, Terry, Mgr.-Sls.--Raynor Garage Doors, Dixon, IL; *U.S. Private*, pg. 912
Lichtenberger, R., Mgr.-Intl. Sls.--Graymills Corp., Chicago, IL; *U.S. Private*, pg. 473
Liddel, Ken, Reg. Sls. Mgr.-Factory Automation--Aromat Mid Atlantic Sales, New Providence, NJ; *Int'l*, pg. 848
Lieber, E., Dir.-Mktg. & Sls.--Presstek, Inc., Hudson, NH; *U.S. Public*, pg. 1324
Lieberman, Daniel, Pres.--A&W Restaurants, Inc.-Carousel Div., Minneapolis, MN; *U.S. Private*, pg. 2
Liebl, Kevin, V.P.- Mktg.--MTI Technology Corporation, Anaheim, CA; *U.S. Public*, pg. 1028
Liebowitz, Michelle, V.P. & Mgr.-Natl. Sls.--WNYW, New York, NY; *Int'l*, pg. 926
Liederbach, Gregg, Natl. Sls. Mgr.--Bradley Corporation, Menomonee Falls, WI; *U.S. Private*, pg. 164
Liegeois, Paul J., Gen. Mgr.-Mktg. & Bus. Devel.--Wisconsin Public Service Corporation, Green Bay, WI; *U.S. Public*, pg. 1728
Lien, Grant, V.P.-Sls. & Mktg.--Tyler Industries, Benson, MN; *U.S. Private*, pg. 1112
Liesem, Paul, V.P.-Sls.--Ohio Machinery Co., Cleveland, OH; *U.S. Private*, pg. 812
Lieto, Tim, V.P.-N. American Sls.--3Com Corporation, Southborough, MA; *U.S. Public*, pg. 1604
Liewald, Kate, Dir.-Sls.--Sun Process Converting Company, Elk Grove Village, IL; *U.S. Private*, pg. 1051
Light, Don, Mgr.-Sls.--Cadaco, Chicago, IL; *U.S. Private*, pg. 910
Light, Doug, Dir.-Sls., Foodservices & Retail Deli--Rocco Inc., Harrisonburg, VA; *U.S. Private*, pg. 937
Light, Ted, V.P.-Sls. & Mktg.--DuBois Chemicals, Cincinnati, OH; *Int'l*, pg. 1437
Lightman, Elliott, V.P.-Sls.--Duck Head Apparel, Winder, GA; *U.S. Public*, pg. 498
Ligon, Susan, V.P.-Mktg.--Word, Incorporated, Dallas, TX; *U.S. Public*, pg. 704
Lillejord, Paul, V.P.-Sls.-U.S. Therapeutics--Genzyme Corporation, Cambridge, MA; *U.S. Public*, pg. 733
Lillig, George, Mgr.-Sls.--Lucent Technologies, Seattle, WA; *U.S. Public*, pg. 1017
Lilly, Lawrence, V.P.-Sls.--Tyco Toys, Inc., Mount Laurel, NJ; *U.S. Public*, pg. 1058
Lim, Alberto A., Mgr.-Sls.--Philippine Airlines, Inc., San Francisco, CA; *Int'l*, pg. 1051
Lim, Lionel, Dir.-Asian Sls.--Sun Microsystems of California Ltd., Singapore, Singapore; *U.S. Public*, pg. 1532
Lim, Ron, Dir.-Mktg. & Sls.--Stonco Genlyte, Union, NJ; *U.S. Public*, pg. 730
Limay, Luis A., Dir.-Mktg., Pur. & Sls.--San Sebastian Gold Mines, Inc., Milwaukee, WI; *U.S. Public*, pg. 410
Limwattanakul, Suebpong, Asst. Mng. Dir.--Siam City-Showa Leasing Co., Ltd., Bangkok, Thailand; *Int'l*, pg. 1239
Lin, Ahwa, Mgr.-Sls. & Mktg.--Seika Electric Co., Ltd., Taipei, Taiwan; *Int'l*, pg. 1218
Lin, Jia-Shyong, V.P.-Mktg./Sls., Sec. & Gen. Mgr.--Amspec Chemical Corporation, Gloucester City, NJ; *U.S. Private*, pg. 67
Lin, Mark, Mgr.-Sls.--China Steel Chemical Corp., Kaohsiung, Taiwan; *Int'l*, pg. 286
Linbeck, Leo, III, Dir.-Sls. & Mktg.--Linbeck Construction Corp, Houston, TX; *U.S. Private*, pg. 667
Lincer, Walt, V.P.-Sls. & Mktg.--Citrus World Inc., Lake Wales, FL; *U.S. Private*, pg. 241
Lincoln, Thomas C., Dir.-Sls. & Mktg.--Cincinnati Industrial Machinery Div., Cincinnati, OH; *U.S. Private*, pg. 355
Lind, Ted, Corp. V.P.-Sls., Mktg. & Technology--The Bethlehem Corporation, Easton, PA; *U.S. Public*, pg. 225
Lind, Ted, Dir.-Mktg. & Sls.--The Bethlehem Corporation, Easton, PA; *U.S. Public*, pg. 225
Lindahl, John, Jr., V.P.-Sls.--State Industries Inc., Ashland City, TN; *U.S. Private*, pg. 1036
Lindberg, Karl, Dir.-Sls. & Mktg.--Locust Street Securities, Inc., Des Moines, IA; *Int'l*, pg. 647
Linde, Ken, Dir.-Sls.--Phase Linear, Lincolnshire, IL; *U.S. Public*, pg. 1369
Lindenboom, Gene, V.P.-Sls. & Mktg.--VAW of America, Inc., Ellenville, NY; *Int'l*, pg. 1466
Lindgren, John, Mgr.-Book Sls.--Krause Publications, Inc., Iola, WI; *U.S. Private*, pg. 635
Lindquist, Dean, Mgr.-Sls.--St. Croix Press, Inc., New Richmond, WI; *U.S. Private*, pg. 960
Lindsay, Steve, Mgr.-Sls.--Applied Materials, Inc., Santa Clara, CA; *U.S. Public*, pg. 123
Lindsey, Ralph, V.P.-Mktg. & Sls.--Barber Dairies, Inc., Birmingham, AL; *U.S. Private*, pg. 115
Lindstrom, Scott, Mgr.-Sls.--Ohio Gear/Richmond Gear - Liberty Div., Liberty, SC; *U.S. Public*, pg. 1370
Linedell, John B., V.P.-Sls.--LaBarge Pipe & Steel Company, Saint Louis, MO; *U.S. Private*, pg. 641
Lines, Bruce, V.P.-Sls.--PSR, Kirkland, WA; *U.S. Private*, pg. 828
Link, Jim, V.P.-Intl. Sls.--Raytheon Aircraft Company, Wichita, KS; *U.S. Public*, pg. 1365
Linney, Jim, V.P.-Indus. Sls.--Watts Regulator Co., Andover, MA; *U.S. Public*, pg. 1747
Linscott, Darlene, Dir.-Mktg.--Gitano Fashions Ltd., Bowling Green, KY; *U.S. Public*, pg. 686
Linssen, Tony, Mgr.-Sls. & Mktg.--Barber Industries Ltd.-Service Center, Grande Prairie, Canada; *Int'l*, pg. 164
Lintelman, Richard, Mgr.-Tech. Sls.--O-Z/Gedney, Nelson Firestop Products, Tulsa, OK; *U.S. Public*, pg. 726
Linton, John, Mgr.-Sls.--Benjamin Metals Company, Gardena, CA; *U.S. Private*, pg. 133
Linville, Christopher, V.P.-Sls. & Mktg.--Chattanooga Group, Inc., Hixson, TN; *U.S. Private*, pg. 231
Linz, Jim, Dir.-Sls.--MFG Tray Co., Linesville, PA; *U.S. Private*, pg. 756
Lipin, E.D., Mgr.-Industrial Sls.--NRI Schools, Washington, DC; *U.S. Public*, pg. 1071
Lipp, Ed, V.P.-Sls. Projects--Perlmuter Printing Company, Cleveland, OH; *Int'l*, pg. 1177
Lippiatt, John, Mgr.-Sls.--N.G. Bailey & Co. Ltd.-Bristol Branch, Bristol, United Kingdom; *Int'l*, pg. 132
Lippold, Larry J., V.P.-Sls. & Mktg.--Schlumberger Malco Inc., Owings Mills, MD; *Int'l*, pg. 1206
Lipschutz, Millt, Gen. Sls. Mgr.--Beech Isuzu, Cincinnati, OH; *U.S. Private*, pg. 129
Lipscomb, William, V.P.-Sls. & Mktg.--Plastic Packaging, Inc., Hickory, NC; *U.S. Private*, pg. 871
Liptak, Dave, Mgr.-Speciality Fitness Sls.--York Barbell Co., Inc., York, PA; *U.S. Private*, pg. 1196
Lipton, Lee, V.P.-Sls.--Biscayne Apparel Inc., Clifton, NJ; *U.S. Public*, pg. 232
Liscik, Raymond, V.P.-Adv., Mktg., Sls. & Pub. Rels.--JCI Data Processing, Inc., Cinnaminson, NJ; *U.S. Private*, pg. 577
Lisman, Ruben, V.P.-Intl. Sls.--Parlux Fragrances Inc., Fort Lauderdale, FL; *U.S. Public*, pg. 1264
Lissandrello, Michael, Mgr.-Sls.-Aviation--EMS-Togo, Taylor, MI; *Int'l*, pg. 981
Lister, Marc D., V.P.-Sls.--Fel-Pro Incorporated, Skokie, IL; *U.S. Private*, pg. 399
Liston, Scott, V.P.-Mktg. & Sls.--Executive Jet Aviation, Inc., Columbus, OH; *U.S. Private*, pg. 388
Litchman, Mike, Mgr.-Sls., Men's Wear--Pendleton Woolen Mills, Inc., Portland, OR; *U.S. Private*, pg. 848
Liter, Jeff, V.P.-Sls.--Consolidated Industries Corp., Lafayette, IN; *Int'l*, pg. 188
Litrun, James, Mgr.-Natl. Sls.--Cab-o-Sil Div. Cabot Corp., Tuscola, IL; *U.S. Public*, pg. 289
Little, Kipp, Mgr.-Sls.--General Wholesale Company, Inc., Atlanta, GA; *U.S. Private*, pg. 445
Little, Stephen, V.P.-Sls. & Mktg.--Ilco Unican Inc. (Electronic Access Controls Division), Montreal, Canada; *Int'l*, pg. 1432
Little, Tillman, Dir.-Sls.--Hankins Lumber Company, Inc., Elliott, MS; *U.S. Private*, pg. 499
Littlefield, Robert, V.P.-Retail Sls.--Veryfine Products, Inc., Westford, MA; *U.S. Private*, pg. 1137
Litzsinger, P.S., Sr. V.P.-Sls. & Mktg.--Carboline Co., Saint Louis, MO; *U.S. Public*, pg. 1357
Liu, Frank, Sls. Engr.--Liebert Hong Kong, Aberdeen, Hong Kong; *U.S. Public*, pg. 577
Livingston, Linda, Mgr.-Circulation & Adv.--Dodge City Daily Globe, Dodge City, KS; *U.S. Private*, pg. 995
Livingstone, William, Mgr.-Sls.--M.S. Walker, Inc., Somerville, MA; *U.S. Private*, pg. 1147
Livorsi, Joseph M., Sr. V.P.-Sls. & Mdsg.--Buttrey Food & Drug Company, Great Falls, MT; *U.S. Public*, pg. 271
Lizotte, Brad, Mgr.-Reg. Sls.--Elastomeric Technologies, Inc., Hatboro, PA; *U.S. Public*, pg. 1598
Llabres, Antonio, Dir. & V.P.-Sls. Resort Div. Europe--Sol Melia, Palma de Mallorca, Spain; *Int'l*, pg. 1277
Llopis, Glenn, Dir.-Sls. & Mktg.--Artichoke Industries, Inc., Castroville, CA; *U.S. Private*, pg. 86
Lloyd-Taylor, Peter, V.P.-Contract & Special Sls.--Thomas Nelson Inc., Nashville, TN; *U.S. Public*, pg. 1167
Lloyd, Chuck, V.P.-Sls.--Maurey Manufacturing Corp., Chicago, IL; *U.S. Private*, pg. 715
Lloyd, Joseph, Mgr.-Sls.--Amlings Landscape Co., Hinsdale, IL; *U.S. Private*, pg. 66
Lloyd, Spence, V.P.-Sls.--Intermountain Farmers Association, Salt Lake City, UT; *U.S. Private*, pg. 568
Lo, Samuel, Sls. Engr.--Moog Controls (Hong Kong) Ltd., Sha Tin, Hong Kong; *U.S. Public*, pg. 1128
Loch, Doug, Mgr.-Sls.--First District Association, Litchfield, MN; *U.S. Private*, pg. 406
Lochner, Bob, Mgr.-Sls.--Mazda Motor of America, Inc. Gulf Region, Sugar Land, TX; *Int'l*, pg. 849
Lock, Dwayne, Dir.-Sls.--Kansas City Power & Light Company, Kansas City, MO; *U.S. Public*, pg. 943
Locke, Todd, Mgr.-Sls. & Mktg.--Superior Dairy, Inc., Canton, OH; *U.S. Private*, pg. 1054
Lockhart, Gregory M., V.P.-Sls.--Lockhart Cadillac Inc., Indianapolis, IN; *U.S. Private*, pg. 672
Lockhart, Gregory M., V.P.-Sls.--Lockhart Cadillac South, Greenwood, IN; *U.S. Private*, pg. 672
Lockhart, Jack, V.P.-Sls.--Melnor Inc., Winchester, VA; *U.S. Public*, pg. 1234
Lockley, Jim, V.P.-Sls. & Mktg.--Cramer Inc., Kansas City, KS; *U.S. Private*, pg. 285
Lockman-Brooks, Linda, Mgr.-Mktg., Adv. & Sls.--Duke Energy Corporation, Charlotte, NC; *U.S. Public*, pg. 534
Lockman, Vincent W., Sls. Mgr.-Pumps & Controls--IMO Industries Inc., Lawrenceville, NJ; *U.S. Public*, pg. 856
Lockwood, Helshi, V.P.-Sls.--Mediatex Communications Corporation, Austin, TX; *U.S. Private*, pg. 727
Lodanski, Ed, Dir.-Sls., Caging Systems--Harford Systems, Inc., Aberdeen, MD; *U.S. Private*, pg. 641
Lodestro, Jim, V.P.-Channel Sls.--Arbor Software Corporation, Sunnyvale, CA; *U.S. Public*, pg. 127
Lodge, Andrew, V.P.-Sls.--Delaware Ribbon Manufacturers, Inc., Philadelphia, PA; *U.S. Private*, pg. 322
Lodge, Jean, Mgr.-Sls. & Mktg.--Salford Electrical Instruments Ltd., Heywood, United Kingdom; *Int'l*, pg. 545
Lodzinski, Pawel, Dir.-Sls.--LOT Polish Airlines SA, New York, NY; *Int'l*, pg. 1062
Loeffler, Dan, Mgr.-Sls. & Mktg.--Mafco Worldwide Corp., Camden, NJ; *U.S. Private*, pg. 690
Loetscher, Fred, V.P.-Automotive Sls.-Western Div.--Berryman Products, Inc., Arlington, TX; *U.S. Private*, pg. 138
Loffredo, Nicholas, V.P.-Sls.--Snap-On Tools Corporation, Kenosha, WI; *U.S. Public*, pg. 1480
Lofgren, R., Dir.-Sls./Electrical Distr.--Eagle Electric Mfg. Co., Inc., Long Island City, NY; *U.S. Private*, pg. 354
Loftus, William A., Exec. V.P.-Retail--Ace Hardware Corporation, Oak Brook, IL; *U.S. Private*, pg. 12
Logan, Donald F., V.P.-Sls. & Mktg.--Russell Corp., Fabrics Div., Alexander City, AL; *U.S. Public*, pg. 1413
Logan, Garey, Reg. Sls. Mgr.--Just Born, Inc., Bethlehem, PA; *U.S. Private*, pg. 602
Logan, Gene, V.P.-Sls.--Wickes Inc., Vernon Hills, IL; *U.S. Public*, pg. 1391
Logan, Robert, Sr. V.P.-European Sls. & Mktg.--R.R. Donnelley & Sons Company, Chicago, IL; *U.S. Public*, pg. 517
Logan, Timothy J., V.P.-U.S. Commercial Sls.--Encore Computer Corporation, Fort Lauderdale, FL; *U.S. Public*, pg. 580
Logsdon, James M., Asst. V.P.-Commercial Mkts.--GTE Supply, Irving, TX; *U.S. Public*, pg. 697
Logue, George A., V.P.-Sls. & Mktg.--Houghton Mifflin School Division, Boston, MA; *U.S. Public*, pg. 841

Logue, Ken, V.P.-Sls. & Mktg.--Variform, Inc., Kearney, MO; *U.S. Public*, pg. 1193
Loh, Larry, Mgr.-Sls.--DBS Trading Pte. Ltd., Singapore, Singapore; *Int'l*, pg. 351
Loharjun, Ton, Mgr.-Sls.--Thai Airways Intl. Ltd.-Washington, Washington, DC; *Int'l*, pg. 1381
Lohr, Cliff, V.P.-Intl. Sls.--Seco Warwick Corporation, Meadville, PA; *U.S. Private*, pg. 980
Lohr, D.G., Pres.-Trade Sls.--California Products Corp., Cambridge, MA; *U.S. Private*, pg. 201
Lohr, Kurt, Mgr.-Aftermarket--Intertractor Zweigniederlassung der Wirtgen GmbH, Gevelsberg, Germany; *Int'l*, pg. 1511
Lohse, Gerhard, Mgr.-Sls.--Wurzner Dauerbackwaren GmbH, Wurzen, Germany; *Int'l*, pg. 1514
Lohwasser, Charles, V.P., Controller & Sls. Mgr.--EG & G Rotron, Woodstock, NY; *U.S. Public*, pg. 543
Lombard, Bob, Mgr.-Sls.--PENCO-Nevada, Reno, NV; *Int'l*, pg. 1508
Lombardo, Tom, V.P.-Mktg. & Sls.--The Little Tikes Company, Hudson, OH; *U.S. Public*, pg. 1411
Lommel, John A., V.P.-Mktg. & Sls.--Kysor/Medallion, Spring Lake, MI; *U.S. Public*, pg. 968
Londino, Thomas, Sr. V.P.-Sls.--Gould Paper Corporation, New York, NY; *U.S. Private*, pg. 466
Long, Donald P., V.P.-Sls.--Chicago Rivet & Machine Company, Naperville, IL; *U.S. Public*, pg. 348
Long, Gary, V.P.-Sls.--IQ Software Corporation, Norcross, GA; *U.S. Public*, pg. 858
Long, J. Shane, V.P.-Sls. & Mktg.--STB Systems, Inc., Richardson, TX; *U.S. Public*, pg. 1421
Long, Jack, Dir.-Sls. & Mktg.--Holsum Bakery, Inc., Phoenix, AZ; *U.S. Private*, pg. 536
Long, John, V.P.-Sls.--All Star Gas Co.-Region IX, Lebanon, MO; *U.S. Private*, pg. 35
Long, John, Sls. Mgr.--Svedala Industries-Universal Engineering, Cedar Rapids, IA; *Int'l*, pg. 1326
Long, Nigel, Dir.-Sls./Eastern Div.--Clestra Hauserman, Inc., Solon, OH; *Int'l*, pg. 569
Longo, Mark, V.P.-Mktg. & Sls.--Ohio Sealants Inc., Mentor, OH; *Int'l*, pg. 802
Loomer, Tim, V.P.-Sls. & Mktg.--ScanTron Corporation, Tustin, CA; *U.S. Public*, pg. 786
Looney, Ken, Dir.-Sls.--National Banner Company, Inc., Dallas, TX; *U.S. Private*, pg. 780
Lopez, Cesar Vacchiano, Dir.-Mktg. & Sls.--Tabacalera, S.A., Madrid, Spain; *Int'l*, pg. 1345
Lopez, Filemon, Sr. V.P.-Adv. Sls.--Comcast Cable Communications, Inc., Philadelphia, PA; *U.S. Public*, pg. 407
Lopresti, Ricardo, Head-Intl. Sls.--Transportes Aereos Portugueses, Lisbon, Portugal; *Int'l*, pg. 1418
Lopus, Jerry, V.P.-Sls.--Peterson Tractor Company, San Leandro, CA; *U.S. Private*, pg. 858
Lorbecki, David, V.P.-Sls.--Sargento Foods Inc.- Food Service Div., Plymouth, WI; *U.S. Private*, pg. 966
Lorenzon, Alfieri, Dir.-Mktg. & Sls.--McGraw-Hill Libri Italia, S.r.l., Milan, Italy; *U.S. Public*, pg. 1072
Lorimor, Randy, Dir.-Corp. Adv. & Sls. Promo.--Country Mutual Insurance Company, Bloomington, IL; *U.S. Private*, pg. 279
Losa, Elvira, Mgr.-Sls./South--Iberia Air Lines of Spain, Miami, FL; *Int'l*, pg. 575
Losier, John, Sr. V.P. & Gen. Mgr.-Worldwide Sls. & Mktg.--Tandem Computers Inc., Cupertino, CA; *U.S. Public*, pg. 417
Losthouse, Roy, Dr., Dir.-Sls. & Mktg.--Union Camp Chemicals, Durham, United Kingdom; *U.S. Public*, pg. 1666
Lott, William, Sls. Mgr.--Humiseal Div., Woodside, NY; *U.S. Public*, pg. 337
Lotving, Per, Mgr.-Sls.--Thomas Publishing Company, New York, NY; *U.S. Private*, pg. 1082
Louden, James A., V.P.-Sls.--Komline-Sanderson Engineering Corp., Peapack, NJ; *U.S. Private*, pg. 631
Loudon, James R.H., Dir.-Grp. Fin.--Blue Circle Industries PLC, London, United Kingdom; *Int'l*, pg. 197
Louis, Richard, Natl. Sls. Mgr.--Turner Electric Corporation, Fairview Heights, IL; *U.S. Public*, pg. 1705
Lounsberry, Fred, V.P.-Sls. & Promo.--Universal Studios Florida, Orlando, FL; *Int'l*, pg. 1087
Lounsberry, Fred, Exec. V.P.-Sls. & Mktg.--Universal Studios Music Australia, Sydney, Australia; *Int'l*, pg. 1216
Louvar, David, Dir.-Sls. & Mktg.-Saws--Wisconsin Automated Machinery Corp., Oshkosh, WI; *U.S. Private*, pg. 1184
Lovas, Ernest, Mgr.-Rte. Sls.--John B. Sanfilippo & Son, Inc., Elk Grove Village, IL; *U.S. Public*, pg. 1431
Love, Bruce, V.P.-Sls.--Stinson Seafood Company, Prospect Harbor, ME; *U.S. Private*, pg. 1043
Love, David, Field Dir.-Natl. Accts.--Master Lock Company, Milwaukee, WI; *U.S. Public*, pg. 675
Love, Tim, Reg. Sls. Dir.--QualMed Plans for Health-Colorado Springs, Colorado Springs, CO; *U.S. Public*, pg. 678
Loveland, Nigel A. D., Mgr.-European Sls.--The Ohio Art Company, Inc., Bryan, OH; *U.S. Public*, pg. 1214
Lovett, Carol, Mgr.-Sls.--Rotary Forms Press, Inc., Hillsboro, OH; *U.S. Private*, pg. 947
Lovold, Norton, Dir.-Sls. & Mktg.--Tone Commander Systems, Mukilteo, WA; *U.S. Private*, pg. 1090
Low, Linda, Mgr.-Export Sls.--Kwe-Kintetsu World Express(S)Pte Ltd., Singapore, Singapore; *Int'l*, pg. 735
Lowe, D.W., Dir.-Sls.--Senior Hargreaves Limited, Bury, United Kingdom; *Int'l*, pg. 1221
Lowe, David, Mgr.-Sls.--Kesterson Food Company, Inc., Paris, TN; *U.S. Private*, pg. 616
Lowman, Blenda, Dir.-Retail Adv.--Drexel Heritage Furnishings Inc., Drexel, NC; *U.S. Private*, pg. 432
Lowndes, Dan, V.P.-Sls. & Mktg.--Glentel Inc., Burnaby, Canada; *Int'l*, pg. 1336
Lowry, Ken, Mgr.-Export Sls.--BGF Industries Inc., Greensboro, NC; *U.S. Private*, pg. 106
Lowry, Paul, V.P.-Retail--OshKosh B'Gosh, Inc., Oshkosh, WI; *U.S. Public*, pg. 1232
Lowry, Paul, V.P.-Retail--Retail, Oshkosh, WI; *U.S. Public*, pg. 1233
Loyne, Todd, Dir.-Sls.--Genzyme Genetics Div., Santa Fe, NM; *U.S. Public*, pg. 733
Loyzaga, Joaquin, Natl. Sls. Dir.-Special Accts.--La Tondena Distillers, Inc., Manila, Philippines; *Int'l*, pg. 785
Lozannof, Michael, Dir.-Sls.--NewAge Industries Inc., Willow Grove, PA; *U.S. Private*, pg. 796
Lozowski, Joseph P., V.P.-Sls., Construction & Bus. Devel.--Contract Interiors Inc., Taylor, MI; *U.S. Private*, pg. 270
Lubar, Bruce, Mgr.-Regional Sls.--Boyer Candy Company Inc., Altoona, PA; *U.S. Private*, pg. 162
Lubin, Myron L., Sr. V.P.-Sls.--ADVO, Inc., Windsor, CT; *U.S. Public*, pg. 23
Lucaro, Alfred R., Reg. Mgr.--Environment/One Corporation, Niskayuna, NY; *U.S. Public*, pg. 586
Lucas, B., Dir.-Sls.--CV Home Furnishings Limited, Manchester, United Kingdom; *Int'l*, pg. 299
Lucas, Brad, V.P.-Sls. & Mktg.--Toter Incorporated, Statesville, NC; *U.S. Private*, pg. 1092
Lucas, Dave, Mgr.-Sls.--Roney Otman, Aurora, IL; *U.S. Private*, pg. 943
Lucas, Patricia, Sls. Mgr.--Hoppe's A Brunswick Company, Coatesville, PA; *U.S. Public*, pg. 266
Lucas, Robert M., Mgr.-Sls.--Hunter Engineering Co., Inc., Riverside, CA; *Int'l*, pg. 474
Lucas, Scott, V.P.-Sls. & Mktg.--Dorner Manufacturing Corp., Hartland, WI; *U.S. Private*, pg. 340
Luchetta, Rodolfo, Div. Mgr.-Mktg.--Y.P.F., S.A., Buenos Aires, Argentina; *Int'l*, pg. 1515
Luchs, Kenneth, Sr. V.P.-Mktg., Sls. & Adv.--Reliable Stores, Inc., Columbia, MD; *U.S. Private*, pg. 920
Luckern, Maurice, V.P.-Sls.--East Coast Steel, Inc., Claremont, NH; *U.S. Private*, pg. 356
Ludington, Deborah, Assoc. V.P.-Sls. & Mktg.--NESLAB Instruments, Inc., Newington, NH; *U.S. Public*, pg. 1595
Ludlam, Ian, Dir.-Sls.--Salem Engineering Co., Ltd., Derby, United Kingdom; *U.S. Private*, pg. 962
Ludlow, Ted, V.P.-Sls. & Mktg.--Bedford Industries, Inc., Worthington, MN; *U.S. Private*, pg. 129
Ludwig, David, Mgr.-Sls.--Blue Cross of California, Woodland Hills, CA; *U.S. Private*, pg. 152
Ludwig, Peter, Area Sls.--Analog Devices GMBH - Technisches Buero Berlin, Berlin, Germany; *U.S. Public*, pg. 108
Ludwig, Phil, Mgr.-Polyflex Sls.--Plastic Suppliers, Inc., Columbus, OH; *U.S. Private*, pg. 871
Ludwig, William, V.P.-Sls.-Latin America & Asia--Pinnacle Systems, Inc., Mountain View, CA; *U.S. Public*, pg. 1297
Luebke, Richard, Gen. Sls. Mgr.--PACCAR Winch Division, Broken Arrow, OK; *U.S. Public*, pg. 1246
Luedke, Keith, V.P.-Sls.--Field Packing Company, Owensboro, KY; *U.S. Private*, pg. 403
Luehrs, Robert, Pres.-Sls. Div.--Henry I. Siegel Company, Inc., New York, NY; *U.S. Private*, pg. 998
Luevano, Maria, Dir.-Intl. Sls.--Berryman Products, Inc., Arlington, TX; *U.S. Private*, pg. 138
Lugioyo, Tony, Dir.-Intl. Sls.--Laramie Tire Distributors Inc., Norristown, PA; *Int'l*, pg. 1312
Luitjens, Steve, V.P.-Sls.--Sathers Inc., Round Lake, MN; *U.S. Private*, pg. 397
Lukaszyk, William R., V.P.-Material Handling Sls.--Universal Dynamics, Inc., Woodbridge, VA; *Int'l*, pg. 484
Luken, Judith P., V.P.-Sls. & Customer Satisfaction--Spiegel, Inc., Downers Grove, IL; *U.S. Public*, pg. 1498
Luker, Mike, V.P.-Sls. & Mktg.--Sunny Fresh Foods, Monticello, MN; *U.S. Private*, pg. 210
Lukeson, David, V.P.-Mktg. & Sls.--Grayson Electronics Corporation, Forest, VA; *U.S. Public*, pg. 46
Lukitsh, Walt, Mgr.-Sls.--Arrow Fluid Power, Broadview, IL; *U.S. Private*, pg. 85
Luksic, Michael, Sls. Rep.--The Lion Brewery, Inc., Wilkes-Barre, PA; *U.S. Public*, pg. 1000
Luktenski, David J., V.P.-Sls.--Welch Foods Inc., A Cooperative, Concord, MA; *U.S. Private*, pg. 784
Lumbatis, David, Mgr.-Bus. Devel.--Gulf States, Inc., Freeport, TX; *U.S. Private*, pg. 487
Lumley, David R., Sr. V.P.-Sls. & Mktg.--Outboard Marine Corporation, Waukegan, IL; *U.S. Private*, pg. 478
Lummis, Larry, V.P.-Worldwide Sls.--Micronics Computers, Inc., Fremont, CA; *U.S. Public*, pg. 1106
Lumpe, Dick, Sls. Mgr.--Dotronix, Inc., New Brighton, MN; *U.S. Public*, pg. 520
Lumsden, Gregory A., Exec. V.P.-Retail Div.--Countrywide Funding Corporation, Pasadena, CA; *U.S. Public*, pg. 453
Lund, Jeffrey, V.P.-Process & Food Sls.--Lakeside Foods, Inc., Manitowoc, WI; *U.S. Private*, pg. 643
Lund, Jerry, Mgr.-Sls. & Mktg.--Simmons Juvenile Products Co., Inc., New London, WI; *U.S. Private*, pg. 1001
Lund, Nancy, V.P.-Intl. Sls.--LIVE Film & Mediaworks, Van Nuys, CA; *U.S. Private*, pg. 671
Lund, Terri, Admin.-Sls.--Rosco Manufacturing Co., Madison, SD; *U.S. Private*, pg. 944
Lunde, Jeff, Coord.-Intl. Sls.--Ciprico, Inc., Plymouth, MN; *U.S. Public*, pg. 370
Lundy, Dee, Dir.-Sls. & Mktg.--Family Inns of America, Inc., Pigeon Forge, TN; *U.S. Private*, pg. 392
Lunetta, Lawerence, Sr. V.P.-Sls. & Service--Caere Corporation, Los Gatos, CA; *U.S. Public*, pg. 291
Luongo, Daniel, Dir.-Sls.--Modern Handling Equipment Co., Bristol, PA; *U.S. Private*, pg. 755
Lupetine, Eugene, Dir.-Sls.--Nissin Foods (U.S.A.) Plant, Memphis, TN; *Int'l*, pg. 950
Luter, Joseph W., IV, Sr. V.P.-Mktg. & Sls./Fresh Pork--The Smithfield Packing Co., Inc., Smithfield, VA; *U.S. Public*, pg. 1479
Lutfy, E.C., Mgr.-N. American Transducer Sls.--Data Instruments, Inc., Acton, MA; *U.S. Private*, pg. 312
Luth, Klaus, Dir.-Sls.--Richardson G.m.b.H., Schwalbach, Germany; *U.S. Public*, pg. 1333
Lutter, Hartmut D., Mgr.-Intl. Sls.--Leupold & Stevens, Inc., Beaverton, OR; *U.S. Private*, pg. 662
Lutzow, Rick, Sls. Rep.--Rockford Mercantile Agency, Rockford, IL; *U.S. Public*, pg. 65
Luxmore, Simon, Dir.-Sls. & Mktg.--Messier-Dowty Ltd., Gloucester, United Kingdom; *Int'l*, pg. 1340
Lwabuchi, Osamu, Mgr.-Hub-Sls.--Nemic-Lambda KK, Tokyo, Japan; *Int'l*, pg. 1242
Lyall, David, Dir.-Sls. & Mktg.--Roush Industries Inc., Livonia, MI; *U.S. Private*, pg. 948
Lyden, Jerry J., Sr. V.P.-Sls.--Apria Healthcare Group Inc., Costa Mesa, CA; *U.S. Public*, pg. 125
Lykens, Tom, Mgr.-Sls.--Telonic Berkeley, Inc., Laguna Beach, CA; *U.S. Private*, pg. 1074
Lynch, Bill, V.P.-Sls. & Mktg.--Dukane Ultrasonics Div., Saint Charles, IL; *U.S. Private*, pg. 346
Lynch, Gerald A., V.P.-Intl. Sls. & Mktg.--Advanced Micro Devices, Inc., Sunnyvale, CA; *U.S. Public*, pg. 21
Lynch, Larry, V.P.-Sls.--Barclay Furniture Company, Sherman, MS; *U.S. Public*, pg. 974
Lynch, Tim, Mgr.-Natl. Sls.--RHC/Spacemaster Corporation, Melrose Park, IL; *U.S. Private*, pg. 904
Lynn, Gary L., V.P.-Sls. & Mktg.--Arrow Gear Company, Downers Grove, IL; *U.S. Private*, pg. 85
Lynn, Gary L., Mgr.-Sls. & Mktg.--Johnson Gear, Lincoln, NE; *U.S. Private*, pg. 85
Lynn, Skip, V.P.-Western Reg. Sls.--Toter Incorporated, Statesville, NC; *U.S. Private*, pg. 1092
Lynne, Mara, Dir.-Sls.--Smith's Personnel Service, Inc., New York, NY; *U.S. Private*, pg. 1010
Lyon, John D., V.P.-Mktg. & Sls.--Safeguard Health Enterprises, Inc., Anaheim, CA; *U.S. Public*, pg. 1424
Lyons, Bernie, V.P.-Mktg. & Sls.--Meadox Medicals, Inc., Oakland, NJ; *U.S. Public*, pg. 247
Lyons, Craig L., V.P.-Sls. & Mktg.--Flambeau Mill, Park Falls, WI; *Int'l*, pg. 434
Lyons, Ellis, Dir.-Sls. & Mktg.--W.H. Salisbury & Company, Skokie, IL; *Int'l*, pg. 1244
Lyons, John, Sr. V.P.-Sls. & Mktg.--Entex Information Services, Rye Brook, NY; *U.S. Private*, pg. 378
Lyons, Norbert, Sr. V.P.-Sls.--Syroco Inc., Peabody, MA; *Int'l*, pg. 844
Lytle, James R., Sr. V.P.-Natl. Sls.--Newspapers First, New York, NY; *U.S. Public*, pg. 964
Lyu, Je-Min, Dir.-Sls.--Dong-Suh Foods Corporation, Inchon, Korea; *Int'l*, pg. 416
Maatman, John S., Mgr.-Sls.--Groschopp, Inc., Sioux Center, IA; *Int'l*, pg. 559
Mabee, William H., Sr. V.P.--Manufacturers & Traders Trust Company, Buffalo, NY; *U.S. Public*, pg. 631
Mabie, S., Sls. Mgr.-Automotive--Waterjet Cutting Systems Division, Farmington, MI; *U.S. Public*, pg. 877
Mabry, Eric, Dir.-Sls./Europe & Far East--I-Flow Corporation, Lake Forest, CA; *U.S. Public*, pg. 851
Mac Wherter, John, V.P.-Mdsg.--Stuart Hall Co., Inc., Kansas City, MO; *U.S. Public*, pg. 1178
Macaluso, Carlos, Exec. V.P.-Sls. & Mktg.--Golden Eagle Group, Inc., Humble, TX; *U.S. Public*, pg. 749
Macaluso, Joe, Mgr.-Sls.--Weaver Popcorn Company, Inc., Van Buren, IN; *U.S. Private*, pg. 1156
Macaluso, Wayne, Mgr.-Sls.--Network Long Distance, Inc., Baton Rouge, LA; *U.S. Public*, pg. 1169
MacArthur, David, V.P.-Natl. Sls.--Anchor Industries Inc., Evansville, IN; *U.S. Private*, pg. 71
Macatavish, F.A., V.P.-Transmission & Distr.--Manitoba Hydro, Winnipeg, Canada; *Int'l*, pg. 834
MacBean, Larry, V.P.-Intl. Sls.--Century Furniture Industries, Hickory, NC; *U.S. Private*, pg. 226
Maccaux, Stephen, Dir.-Sales--Philip Laser Magnetic Storage, Colorado Springs, CO; *Int'l*, pg. 1054
Macchi, Massimo, Prod. Mgr.-Sls. & Mktg.--Bulgari SPA, Rome, Italy; *Int'l*, pg. 232
Macchione, Mike, V.P.-Sls.--Partlow Corporation, New Hartford, NY; *U.S. Public*, pg. 482
MacConnell, Daniel R., V.P.-Sls.--Thomson MacConnell Cadillac, Inc., Cincinnati, OH; *U.S. Private*, pg. 1084
MacCord, G.W., V.P.-Sls. & Mktg.--Controlled Power (CPC), Canton, OH; *Int'l*, pg. 74
Macdonald, A., V.P.-Sls. & Mktg.--ATCO Structures Inc., Calgary, Canada; *Int'l*, pg. 95
MacDonald, R. H., V.P.-Sls. & Dir.-Mktg.--Castrol Canada Inc., Toronto, Canada; *Int'l*, pg. 235
MacDonald, Ross, V.P.-Sls.--Reed Travel Publishing-Australia/South Pacific, Chatswood, Australia; *Int'l*, pg. 1097
MacDonald, Ross, V.P.-Sls.--Reed Travel Publishing-Hong Kong, Chai Wan, Hong Kong; *Int'l*, pg. 1097
MacDonald, Ross, V.P.-Sls.--Reed Travel Publishing-Japan, Tokyo, Japan; *Int'l*, pg. 1097
Mace-Basha, Michelle, Dir.-Natl. Sls. Support--Del Webb Corporation, Phoenix, AZ; *U.S. Public*, pg. 494
Macey, Scott, V.P.-Sls.--Northeastern Graphic Supply, Inc., Portland, ME; *U.S. Private*, pg. 805
Macfarlane, Bud, V.P.-Sls. & Mktg.--Innovative Plastics Corporation, Orangeburg, NY; *U.S. Private*, pg. 565
Machado, Jeff, Mgr.-Sls.--International Window-Northern California, Hayward, CA; *U.S. Public*, pg. 895
Machado, Marshall, V.P.-Sls. & Mktg.--AgrEvo USA Company, Wilmington, DE; *Int'l*, pg. 1203
Machulak, Walter A., Sec. & Mgr.-Pur.--Homespan Realty Co., Inc., Milwaukee, WI; *U.S. Public*, pg. 410
MacInnes, John T., Mgr.-Sls. (Plastics Molding Machinery)--Hull Corporation, Hatboro, PA; *U.S. Private*, pg. 547
MacInnes, John T., Mgr.-Sls. Press--Hull/Finmac, Inc., Warminster, PA; *U.S. Private*, pg. 547
Mack, Brad, V.P.-Sls./Eastern--InterVoice, Inc., Dallas, TX; *U.S. Public*, pg. 910
Mack, Jeffrey W., V.P.-Equipment Sls.--Lesco, Inc., Rocky River, OH; *U.S. Public*, pg. 989
Mack, Michael T., V.P.-Sls. & Mktg.--Mead Publishing Paper, Escanaba, MI; *U.S. Public*, pg. 1074
Mack, Ruth, Exec. V.P.-Sls.--WLR Foods, Inc., Timberville, VA; *U.S. Public*, pg. 1727
Mack, Ruth, Exec. V.P.-Sls. & Mktg.--Wampler Foods, Timberville, VA; *U.S. Public*, pg. 1727

MacKay, Bruce, Div. Mgr.-West--Pier 1 Imports Canada, Toronto, Canada; *U.S. Public*, pg. 1295
MacKenzie, Norman, Mgr.-Inside Sls.--Enidine Incorporated, Orchard Park, NY; *U.S. Private*, pg. 377
MacKenzie, Warren, V.P.-Sls. & Mktg.--Pittsburgh Tube Co., Moon Township, PA; *U.S. Private*, pg. 867
Mackey, David, V.P.-Sls.--OzEmail Limited, Sydney, Australia; *Int'l*, pg. 1019
Mackinnon, G., Mgr.-Sls.--Bloomfield Industries Canada Ltd., Mississauga, Canada; *U.S. Public*, pg. 1497
Macksoud, Edmund, Gen. Mgr.-Sls.--Uncas Manufacturing Company, Providence, RI; *U.S. Private*, pg. 1116
MacLellan, Neil F., III, Exec. V.P.-Sls. & Mktg.--Mac-Gray Corporation, Cambridge, MA; *U.S. Public*, pg. 1029
MacLeod, James S., Sr. V.P.-Sls.--Mortgage Guaranty Insurance Corporation, Milwaukee, WI; *U.S. Public*, pg. 1026
MacLeod, Roxanne, Dir.-Mktg. & Sls.--Nova Scotia Power Inc., Halifax, Canada; *Int'l*, pg. 971
MacMaster, Jim, V.P.-Replacement Sls.--Yokohama Tire Corporation, Fullerton, CA; *Int'l*, pg. 1521
MacNeill, Rich, Dir.-Sls.--John G. Shedd Aquarium, Chicago, IL; *U.S. Private*, pg. 991
Macomber, Dave, V.P.-Sls.--The Garber Company, Ashland, OH; *U.S. Public*, pg. 303
Macsuga, Joseph, V.P.-Oper. Divisions--Stebbins Engineering & Mfg. Co., Watertown, NY; *U.S. Private*, pg. 1037
MacTaggart, John, Reg. Mgr.-Sls.--Bird Products Corporation, Palm Springs, CA; *U.S. Public*, pg. 1591
Madden, Bruce, Exec. V.P.-Sls. & Mktg.--Maharam, Hauppauge, NY; *U.S. Private*, pg. 696
Maddex, Sharon, V.P.-Mktg.--LaSalle National Bank, Chicago, IL; *Int'l*, pg. 10
Maddock, John P., Sr. V.P.-Mktg.--The Ailing & Cory Company, Rochester, NY; *U.S. Public*, pg. 1666
Maddox, Richard, Sr. V.P.-Sls. & Mktg.--Bachmann Industries, Inc., Philadelphia, PA; *U.S. Private*, pg. 109
Maddox, Richard, V.P.-Sls.--Blue Bird Corporation, Macon, GA; *U.S. Private*, pg. 151
Maddox, William O., Mgr.-Sls.--Bergen Brunswig Medical Corporation (Durr Drug), Montgomery, AL; *U.S. Public*, pg. 214
Madison, John, Sr. V.P.-Sls.--Polygram Records, Inc., New York, NY; *Int'l*, pg. 1052
Madlock, Cleve, V.P.-Sls.--ANGUS Chemical Company, Buffalo Grove, IL; *U.S. Private*, pg. 75
Madsen, Donald G., V.P.-Automotive Sls.--Andros Incorporated, Berkeley, CA; *U.S. Private*, pg. 74
Madsen, John, Regional Sls. Mgr.--Dayton Rogers Mfg. Co., Blaine, MN; *U.S. Private*, pg. 318
Maex, Rudy, Dir.-Sls.--Sabena, Zaventem, Belgium; *Int'l*, pg. 1168
Maffei, Nicholas, V.P.-Sls. & Product Devel.--Esquire Radio & Electronics Inc., Brooklyn, NY; *U.S. Private*, pg. 383
Maffeo, Anthony, Sls. Rep.--Bennington Iron Works, Inc., Bennington, VT; *U.S. Private*, pg. 133
Magee, Keith, V.P.-Sls. & Mktg., Europe--Lincoln-Mercury Division, Detroit, MI; *U.S. Public*, pg. 662
Magee, Thomas, V.P.-Sls.--Paul Arpin Vanlines, Inc., West Warwick, RI; *U.S. Private*, pg. 85
Maggied, Brian, V.P.-Sls. & Mktg.--The Akro Corporation, Canton, OH; *U.S. Public*, pg. 399
Magill, Roger L., V.P.-Sls. & Gen. Mgr.--Bates Div., Rockford, MI; *U.S. Public*, pg. 1775
Magnuson-Carson, Mimi, V.P.-Bus. Affairs--Hanna-Barbera Productions, Inc., Hollywood, CA; *U.S. Public*, pg. 1614
Magrann, Robert, V.P.-Sls.--Tetley USA Inc., Shelton, CT; *Int'l*, pg. 1377
Magri, Bill, V.P.-Retail Sls.--Vienna Sausage Mfg. Co., Chicago, IL; *U.S. Private*, pg. 1139
Magrino, Robert, Exec. V.P.-Sls.--Mita Copystar America Inc., Fairfield, NJ; *Int'l*, pg. 870
Maguire, Dennis, Sr. V.P.-Sls.--Buena Vista Home Video, Burbank, CA; *U.S. Public*, pg. 513
Maguire, James V., Sr. V.P.-Sls.--R.J. Reynolds Tobacco Company, Winston Salem, NC; *U.S. Public*, pg. 1355
Maguire, John, Mgr.-Sls.--TNT Vacations, Boston, MA; *U.S. Private*, pg. 1065
Maguire, Peter F., Dir.-Intl. Sls.--Millennium Petrochemicals, Inc., Cincinnati, OH; *Int'l*, pg. 594
Magyar, Judit, Mgr.-Sls./USA--Malev Hungarian Airlines, U.S. Office, New York, NY; *Int'l*, pg. 834
Magyaros, J.M., Mgr.-Intl. Sls.--Electric Furnace Co., Salem, OH; *U.S. Private*, pg. 367
Mahon, Joe, V.P.-Sls.--Zenith Products Corp., New Castle, DE; *U.S. Public*, pg. 1054
Mahoney, Anne, Mgr.-Retail Adv.-True Value--TruServ Corporation, Chicago, IL; *U.S. Private*, pg. 1108
Mahoney, David, Dir.-Sls., Biological Prods.--Bayer Corporation/Pharmaceutical Division, West Haven, CT; *Int'l*, pg. 173
Mahoney, David, Pres.-Pharmaceutical & Retail Sls.--McKesson U.S. Health Care, San Francisco, CA; *U.S. Public*, pg. 1073
Mahoney, James, Exec. V.P.-Sls.--Plasti-Kote Company Inc., Medina, OH; *U.S. Private*, pg. 870
Mahoney, John J., Dir.-Sls.--Fisher Pierce Division, Weymouth, MA; *U.S. Public*, pg. 1250
Mahoney, Thomas F., Sr. V.P.-Sls.--Trans-Lux Corporation, Norwalk, CT; *U.S. Public*, pg. 1628
Mahoney, Tom, Pres.-Consumer Sls. Americas--The Stanley Works, New Britain, CT; *U.S. Public*, pg. 1508
Maile, John, V.P.-Sls., Import & Export--Cold Spring Granite Company, Cold Spring, MN; *U.S. Private*, pg. 250
Maiman, Mort, Sls. Rep.--R.A. Briggs & Co., Lake Zurich, IL; *U.S. Private*, pg. 536
Main, Peter, Exec. V.P.-Mktg. & Sls.--Nintendo of America, Redmond, WA; *Int'l*, pg. 932
Maitland, John, Mgr.-Grp. Prod.--CIBA-GEIGY Australia Ltd., Pendle Hill, Australia; *Int'l*, pg. 976
Maiuccoro, Gary, Dir.-Sls. & Mktg.--Imperial Pools, Inc., Latham, NY; *U.S. Private*, pg. 558
Major, Jason, Reg. Sls. Mgr.--M/D Totco Instrumentation, Jurong, Singapore; *U.S. Public*, pg. 1709
Mak, T.C., Dir.-Sls.--Kulicke & Soffa (Asia), Ltd., Kowloon, Hong Kong; *U.S. Public*, pg. 969
Makabe, Mark, Sr. V.P.-Entertainment Sls. & Mktg.--Pioneer New Media Technologies, Long Beach, CA; *U.S. Private, pg. 866*
Maki, Kirsti, District Sls. Mgr.--FINNAIR, San Francisco, CA; *Int'l*, pg. 486
Malandrakis, Joseph E., V.P.-Sls. & Service/N. America Analytical Instruments Div.--The Perkin-Elmer Corporation, Norwalk, CT; *U.S. Public*, pg. 1279
Malarkey, Gregory B., Sr. V.P.-Sls. & Mktg., Tech. Svcs. & Warehouse Opers.--Herbert Malarkey Roofing Company, Portland, OR; *U.S. Private*, pg. 698
Malarkey, Timothy R., V.P.-Sls.--American Greetings Corporation, Cleveland, OH; *U.S. Public*, pg. 77
Malarkey, Timothy R., V.P.-Sls.--American Greetings U.S. Greeting Card Division, Cleveland, OH; *U.S. Public*, pg. 78
Malcolm, Julie, Dir.-Sls.--Holly's Inc., Grand Rapids, MI; *U.S. Private*, pg. 535
Malen, Art, Dir.-Sls.--Fuji Magnetic Products Div., Elmsford, NY; *Int'l*, pg. 524
Males, Ron, V.P.-Sls.--QuikTrip Corporation, Tulsa, OK; *U.S. Private*, pg. 901
Maley, Patrick, V.P.-Sls. & Mktg.--Zoll Medical Corporation, Burlington, MA; *U.S. Private*, pg. 1207
Malfait, Louis, Mng. Dir.-Italy & European Sales--Chargeurs Wool, Paris, France; *Int'l*, pg. 280
Malham, Joe, Mgr.-Sls. & Mktg.--Pennsylvania Cellular Telephone Corp., Bethlehem, PA; *U.S. Public*, pg. 1708
Mallett, Jill, Mgr.-Sls.--Thomas Pipe & Steel, Inc., Baton Rouge, LA; *U.S. Private*, pg. 508
Mallin, Ed, Sr. V.P.-Natl. Sls.--Database America Companies, Montvale, NJ; *U.S. Private*, pg. 312
Mallis, Harvey, V.P.-Sls.--Manhattan Accessories Div., New York, NY; *U.S. Public*, pg. 1429
Malloy, William, Jr., V.P. & Mgr.-Sls.--Cheraw Yarn Mills, Inc., Cheraw, SC; *U.S. Private*, pg. 233
Malman, Don, V.P.-Sls.--Snorkel, Saint Joseph, MO; *U.S. Private*, pg. 500
Malmstedt, Dave, V.P.-Americas--Candle Corporation, Santa Monica, CA; *U.S. Private*, pg. 204
Malone, George, Mgr.-Sls.--Metal Treating, Inc., Milwaukee, WI; *U.S. Public*, pg. 1592
Malone, Jerry, V.P.-Sls.--Maytag Company, Newton, IA; *U.S. Public*, pg. 1064
Maloney-Koslick, Norma, V.P.-Corp. Sls.--Lettuce Entertain You Enterprises, Inc., Chicago, IL; *U.S. Private*, pg. 661
Maloney, Cissy, Gen. Sls. Mgr.--WHAS-AM, Louisville, KY; *U.S. Public*, pg. 385
Maloney, Dave, Dir.-Sls.--Eagle Window & Door, Inc., Dubuque, IA; *U.S. Public*, pg. 67
Maloney, Jack, Dir.-Sls.--Calgary Flames Hockey Club, Calgary, Canada; *Int'l*, pg. 252
Maloney, John, Exec. V.P.-Sls. & Mktg.--Tacony Corporation, Fenton, MO; *U.S. Private*, pg. 1066
Maloney, Mark, Sr. V.P.-Sls.--Trust Fund Advisors, Inc., Washington, DC; *U.S. Private*, pg. 1116
Maloney, Michael, Dir.-Mktg. & Sls.--Snappy Air Distribution Products, Detroit Lakes, MN; *U.S. Public*, pg. 1506
Maloney, Rick, Mgr.-Sls.--SA-SO Company, Dallas, TX; *U.S. Private*, pg. 955
Maloney, Terry, Sr. V.P. & Gen. Mgr.--American Isuzu Motors Inc., Whittier, CA; *Int'l*, pg. 692
Man Ming, Chan, Dir.-Sls. & Service/Asia--GenRad, Inc., Westford, MA; *U.S. Public*, pg. 731
Manca, Jimmy, Sls. Rep.--T.V. Overseas, S.R.L., Rome, Italy; *Int'l*, pg. 1282
Mancini, Skip, V.P.--B.T. Mancini Co., Inc., Milpitas, CA; *U.S. Private*, pg. 699
Mancini, W., Dr., Mgr.-Sls.--Carbide & Graphite Technologies S.r.l., Pescara, Italy; *Int'l*, pg. 891
Mancuso, Michael V., Dir.-Sls. & Mktg.--C.J. Tower Inc., Buffalo, NY; *U.S. Public*, pg. 1071
Manczak, John E., Sr. V.P.-Retails Sls. & Svcs.--Carolina Power & Light Company, Raleigh, NC; *U.S. Public*, pg. 306
Mandala, Jim, Dir.-Sls. & Mktg.--Epson Canada Limited, Willowdale, Canada; *Int'l*, pg. 1219
Mandel, Bernard, V.P.-Distributor Sls.--American & Efird, Inc., Mount Holly, NC; *U.S. Public*, pg. 1412
Mandel, Lauren, V.P.-Mktg. & Sls.--The Napier Co., Meriden, CT; *U.S. Private*, pg. 774
Mandell, McEwan, V.P.-Sls.--A.M. Best Company, Oldwick, NJ; *U.S. Private*, pg. 139
Manderscheid, Larry, V.P.-Sls. & Mktg.--Aerostar International, Sioux Falls, SD; *U.S. Public*, pg. 1361
Manenti, Thomas J., Sr. V.P.-Mktg. & Sls.--MiTek, Inc., Chesterfield, MO; *Int'l*, pg. 1106
Mangi, Jack, V.P.-Sls.--Pace Press, Inc., Moonachie, NJ; *U.S. Private*, pg. 829
Mangiaracina, Vito, V.P.-Rubber Prods. Sls.--Rubber Products Div., Clarksville, TN; *U.S. Public*, pg. 1725
Mangine, Tony, V.P.-Sls. & Mktg.--FieldBrook Farms, Inc., Dunkirk, NY; *U.S. Private*, pg. 403
Mangini, Ron, Sr. V.P.-Sls.--Jacques Moret, Inc., New York, NY; *U.S. Private*, pg. 580
Mango, Bill, Mgr.-Sls.--Richard Hirschmann of America, Inc., Riverdale, NJ; *Int'l*, pg. 1108
Mangold, Bob, V.P. & Gen. Mgr.-Auto Warehouse Div.--STRAFCO, Inc., San Antonio, TX; *U.S. Private*, pg. 1046
Mangold, Fred, Dir.-Sls.--Jake Sweeney Automotive Inc., Cincinnati, OH; *U.S. Private*, pg. 1058
Manjan, Thomas, Sr. V.P.-Sls. & Mktg.--Microlog Corporation, Germantown, MD; *U.S. Public*, pg. 1105
Manka, Roger, V.P.-America Sls./Carrier Sys.--3Com Corporation, Santa Clara, CA; *U.S. Public*, pg. 1603
Mankamyer, Richard, Mgr.-Mktg. & Sls.--Schubert Industries Inc., Akron, OH; *U.S. Private*, pg. 973
Mankamyer, Richard, Mgr.-Mktg. & Sls.--The Springwall Mattress Co., Akron, OH; *U.S. Private*, pg. 973
Mankovski, Aharon, V.P.-Sls.--Orbotech Ltd., Yavne, Israel; *Int'l*, pg. 1007
Manley, Michael G., V.P. & Reg. Sls. Mgr.--First Financial Bank, FSB, Stevens Point, WI; *U.S. Public*, pg. 140
Mann, Christopher, V.P.-Mktg.--CVC Products, Inc., Rochester, NY; *U.S. Private*, pg. 197
Mann, Raymond R., V.P.-Bus. Devel.--Analytical Surveys, Inc., Colorado Springs, CO; *U.S. Public*, pg. 110
Mannarino, J., Mgr.-O.E.M. Sls.--Eagle Electric Mfg. Co., Inc., Long Island City, NY; *U.S. Private*, pg. 354
Mannerkoski, Lauri, Vice Chm. & Exec. V.P.-Mktg.--Rautaruukki Oy, Helsinki, Finland; *Int'l*, pg. 1088
Manning, John, V.P.-Sls. & Mktg.--Crane Plastics Company, Columbus, OH; *U.S. Private*, pg. 286
Manning, Terry J., V.P.-Mktg. & Sls.--Zoom Telephonics, Inc., Boston, MA; *U.S. Public*, pg. 1794
Manns, D.M., Mgr.-Sls. & Mktg.--Linhas Corrente Ltda., Ipiranga, Brazil; *Int'l*, pg. 301
Manny, Yvon, Mgr.-Sls./Quebec--Security Chimneys International Ltd., Laval, Canada; *Int'l*, pg. 1217
Manor, Moshe, V.P.-Israeli Pharmaceutical Sls.--Teva Pharmaceutical Industries Ltd., Petah Tiqwa, Israel; *Int'l*, pg. 1380
Manos, Eric B., V.P.-Sls. & Mktg.--Buehler U.K. Ltd., Coventry, United Kingdom; *U.S. Public*, pg. 575
Mansfield, Robert, V.P.-Sls./S.W. Region--Thorn Apple Valley, Inc., Southfield, MI; *U.S. Public*, pg. 1602
Manson, Bob, V.P.-Sales--George Fischer Sloane, Inc., Little Rock, AR; *Int'l*, pg. 430
Mantle, Philip, Sr. V.P.-Sls.--Vertel, Woodland Hills, CA; *U.S. Public*, pg. 1717
Mantyla, Gero, Mgr.-Sls.--Kemi Mills, Kemi, Finland; *Int'l*, pg. 863
Mantz, Jason, Exec. Dir.-Creative--Merle Norman Cosmetics, Inc., Los Angeles, CA; *U.S. Private*, pg. 733
Marabito, Keefe, Rep.-Sls.--Mock Seed Company, Pittsburgh, PA; *U.S. Private*, pg. 981
Marassi, C., Mgr.-Sls.--Letraset Italia Srl, Milan, Italy; *Int'l*, pg. 462
Marbry, Tom, Dir.-Sls.--Plant Maintenance Service Corporation, Memphis, TN; *U.S. Private*, pg. 869
Marcellus, Richard, Dir.-N. American Sls.--Simplicity Manufacturing, Inc., Port Washington, WI; *U.S. Private*, pg. 1002
Marchak, Ben, V.P.-Sls. & Dir.-European Opers.--Advanced Logic Research, Inc., Irvine, CA; *U.S. Public*, pg. 703
Marchesini, Sandro, Dir.-Export Sls.--Rimoldi Necchi S.R.L., Milan, Italy; *Int'l*, pg. 1117
Marck, Andy, Div. Mgr.-Sls.--The Jel Sert Co., West Chicago, IL; *U.S. Private*, pg. 585
Marconi, Allan, V.P.-Sls. & Mktg.--Alpha Wire Company, Elizabeth, NJ; *U.S. Public*, pg. 201
Marcotte, Richard, V.P.-Mktg. & Sls.--Nissan Canada Inc., Mississauga, Canada; *Int'l*, pg. 945
Marcus, Stanton C., Sls. & Mktg.--Coast Business Credit, Los Angeles, CA; *U.S. Public*, pg. 872
Mardell, R., Mgr.-Fleet Sls.--Camden Motors Ltd., Leighton Buzzard, United Kingdom; *Int'l*, pg. 165
Marder, Thomas, Mgr.-Sls.--Mikron AG Biel, Nidau, Switzerland; *Int'l*, pg. 866
Margaux, Andre, Mgr.-Sls. & Mktg.--Pacific Handy Cutter, Inc., Costa Mesa, CA; *U.S. Private*, pg. 831
Margerie, Jean, Dir.-Sls./Light Vehicles--Iveco France S.A., Trappes, France; *Int'l*, pg. 696
Margraff, George, Dir.-Sls.--Argo Instruments Inc., Winchester, VA; *Int'l*, pg. 839
Marim, Joel, Mgr.-Sls.--Souza Cruz, S.A., Rio de Janeiro, Brazil; *Int'l*, pg. 112
Marinaro, Richard, V.P.-Mktg. & Sls.--Advanced Telemarketing Corp., Irving, TX; *U.S. Public*, pg. 11
Marini, Jeff, Mgr.-Natl. Sls.--Autoroll Machine Co., LLC, Middleton, MA; *U.S. Private*, pg. 101
Marker, T., Dir.-Sales & Mktg.--Carbone of America, Commutation Components Div., Farmville, VA; *Int'l*, pg. 1028
Markham, Bill, V.P.-Natl. Accts.--American Freightways Corporation, Harrison, AR; *U.S. Public*, pg. 75
Markl, Thomas L., Sr. V.P.--UTILX Corporation, Kent, WA; *U.S. Public*, pg. 1701
Markman, Scott, Dir.-Incentive Sls.--Faribault Woolen Mill Co., Faribault, MN; *U.S. Private*, pg. 394
Marks, Ken, Mgr.-Sls.--Ambar, Inc., Lafayette, LA; *U.S. Private*, pg. 126
Marks, Richard, Dir.-Sls.--Paris Foods Corp., Camden, NJ; *U.S. Private*, pg. 839
Marks, Richard, Exec. V.P.-Sls.--Shadow Broadcast Services, Bala Cynwyd, PA; *U.S. Public*, pg. 1763
Marks, Ron, Mgr.-Sls.--Aetna Industries, Inc., Center Line, MI; *U.S. Private*, pg. 25
Marks, Ted, V.P.-Sls.--Gould Paper Corporation, New York, NY; *U.S. Private*, pg. 466
Marks, Tony J., Gen. Mgr.-Intl. Sls. & Mktg.--Air New Zealand Ltd., Auckland, New Zealand; *Int'l*, pg. 38
Markwart, Robert, V.P.-Mktg. & Sls.--The Chamberlain Group, Inc., Elmhurst, IL; *U.S. Private*, pg. 344
Marmion, Bridget, Dir.-Sls. & Mktg./Random House Grp.--Random House, Inc., New York, NY; *U.S. Private*, pg. 20
Marnock, Ed, Dir.-Sls.--Thonet, Statesville, NC; *U.S. Public*, pg. 1465
Marquard, Mike, V.P.-Sls.--Wyeth-Ayerst Laboratories, Inc., Philadelphia, PA; *U.S. Public*, pg. 80
Marquess, Mike, Gen. Mgr.-Sls.--Biddulph Automotive Group, Glendale, AZ; *U.S. Private*, pg. 142
Marr, A.G., V.P.-Mining Sls.--Road Machinery Company, Phoenix, AZ; *U.S. Private*, pg. 934
Marr, Cliff, V.P.-Sls. & Mktg.--Fiberesin Industries Inc., Oconomowoc, WI; *U.S. Private*, pg. 402
Marr, David G., Mgr.-Fertilizer Sls.--B&W Co-op, Inc., Breckenridge, MI; *U.S. Private*, pg. 105
Marragonnis, Gerard, Mgr.-Sls.--CSR Pampryl, La Courneuve, France; *Int'l*, pg. 566
Marrangoini, Dave, Sls. Devel. Dir. & New Bus. Contact--The St. George Group, Inc., Pittsburgh, PA; *U.S. Private, pg. 960*

Marrinucci, John, V.P.-Sls. & Mktg.--Gai-Tronics Corporation, Mohnton, PA; *U.S. Public*, pg. 1430
Marrold, Robert, Dir.-Corp. Sls.--Gruner + Jahr USA Publishing, Inc., New York, NY; *Int'l*, pg. 190
Marron, George, Sr. V.P.-Sls.--Opp Micolas Mills Inc., Opp, AL; *U.S. Public*, pg. 933
Marsenison, Matthew, Dir.-Sls.--Aero Systems Aviation Corp., Miami, FL; *U.S. Private*, pg. 24
Marsh, Daniel, V.P.-Sls. & Mktg.--Medical Action Industries Inc., Hauppauge, NY; *U.S. Public*, pg. 1079
Marsh, Mike, V.P.-Sls.--ADM Milling Co., Overland Park, KS; *U.S. Public*, pg. 128
Marsh, Ron, V.P.-Sls. & Mktg.--Gwaltney of Smithfield, Ltd., Smithfield, VA; *U.S. Public*, pg. 1479
Marshall, Chris, Mgr.-Sls.--Richardson Electronics Canada Ltd., Mississauga, Canada; *U.S. Public*, pg. 1388
Marshall, Chris, Dir.-European Sls.--AAR Europa, Hounslow, United Kingdom; *U.S. Public*, pg. 1
Marshall, Dan, V.P.-Sls.--Network Power & Light, Fremont, CA; *U.S. Public*, pg. 1144
Marshall, Donna, Mgr.-Sls.--Beldoch Industries, West Hempstead, NY; *U.S. Public*, pg. 519
Marshall, Duff, Mgr.-Sls., Mktg. & Adv.--Marvin Lumber & Cedar Company, Warroad, MN; *U.S. Private*, pg. 710
Marshall, Geoffrey I., V.P.-Natl. Sls.--The Turner Corporation, New York, NY; *U.S. Public*, pg. 1645
Marshall, J.T., V.P.-Sls.--British Steel, Inc., Schaumburg, IL; *Int'l*, pg. 221
Marshall, Richard, V.P.-Sls. & Mktg.--Fred B. Johnston Company, Inc., Chapin, SC; *U.S. Private*, pg. 595
Marshmann, Van, V.P.-Sls. Zone--Wise Foods, Inc., Parsippany, NJ; *U.S. Private*, pg. 157
Marston, Barry, V.P.-Sls. & Mktg.--Medex Inc., Hilliard, OH; *U.S. Public*, pg. 689
Martel, Brian, Dir.-Circulation Sls.--The London Free Press, London, Canada; *Int'l*, pg. 1320
Martensen, Per, Dir.-Sls.--Nordsten, Skive, Denmark; *Int'l*, pg. 1386
Martenson, Tom, V.P.-Indus. Sls.--Amerock Corporation, Rockford, IL; *U.S. Public*, pg. 1177
Martin, Andrew S., V.P.-Sls. & Mktg.--First Protective Insurance Group, Birmingham, AL; *U.S. Public*, pg. 1336
Martin, Bill, V.P.-Sls.--Waxman Industries, Inc., Bedford, OH; *U.S. Public*, pg. 1748
Martin, Bob, Dir.-Construction Sls.--Cleveland Group, Inc., Atlanta, GA; *U.S. Private*, pg. 246
Martin, Bob, Dir.-Sls.--Cleveland Electric Co., Atlanta, GA; *U.S. Private*, pg. 246
Martin, Charles W., V.P.-Sls.--The Allstate Corporation, Northbrook, IL; *U.S. Public*, pg. 55
Martin, Craig L., Sr. V.P.-Gen. Sls. & Mktg.--Jacobs Engineering Group Inc., Pasadena, CA; *U.S. Public*, pg. 921
Martin, Dan T., V.P.-Sls. & Customer Service Dry Bulk--Ingram Barge Company, Nashville, TN; *U.S. Private*, pg. 563
Martin, Duane, V.P.-Retail--IGA, Inc. (Independent Grocers Alliance), Chicago, IL; *U.S. Private*, pg. 555
Martin, Frank, Mgr.-Sls.--Coastal Wood Products, Inc., City of Industry, CA; *U.S. Private*, pg. 720
Martin, Gloria, Admin. Asst.-Sls.--American Locker Security Systems, Inc., Jamestown, NY; *U.S. Public*, pg. 86
Martin, Hugh B., V.P.-Sls.--Ames Company, Parkersburg, WV; *U.S. Public*, pg. 1683
Martin, James, Mgr.-Sls.--N.G. Bailey & Co. Ltd.-Aberdeen Branch, Aberdeen, United Kingdom; *Int'l*, pg. 132
Martin, James L., V.P.-Bleached Bd. Sls. & Mktg.--Westvaco Corporation, New York, NY; *U.S. Public*, pg. 1762
Martin, Jim, Gen. Mgr.-Lubes--J.D. Streett & Co., Inc., Maryland Heights, MO; *U.S. Private*, pg. 1047
Martin, John, Mgr.-Sls.--Dayton Rogers of New York, Rochester, NY; *U.S. Private*, pg. 318
Martin, John, V.P.-Sls.--Dimensional Merchandising, Inc., Wharton, NJ; *U.S. Private*, pg. 333
Martin, John, Sr. V.P.-Sls.--Fruit of the Loom, Inc., Chicago, IL; *U.S. Public*, pg. 685
Martin, Kent, Sr. V.P.--Servo Corporation of America, Westbury, NY; *U.S. Private*, pg. 987
Martin, Leon, Dir.-Sls. U.S.--Capital Controls Company Inc., Colmar, PA; *Int'l*, pg. 1226
Martin, P., Mgr.-Gen. Sls.--Camden Motors Ltd., Leighton Buzzard, United Kingdom; *Int'l*, pg. 165
Martin, Peter, V.P.-Sls. & Mktg.--Captive Plastics, Piscataway, NJ; *U.S. Private*, pg. 207
Martin, Richard, V.P.-Sls.--Network Services Company, Mount Prospect, IL; *U.S. Private*, pg. 791
Martin, Robert, V.P.-Sls. & Mktg.--American Packaging Corporation, Philadelphia, PA; *U.S. Private*, pg. 60
Martin, Rodger, Mgr.-Sls.--Branson Ultrasonics Corp.-Plastics Joining Div., Danbury, CT; *U.S. Public*, pg. 574
Martin, Sam, Mgr.-Intl. Sls.--Tommy Armour Golf, Morton Grove, IL; *U.S. Public*, pg. 1683
Martin, Scott, V.P.-Sls. & Mktg.--Nodak Mutual Insurance Company, Fargo, ND; *U.S. Private*, pg. 800
Martin, Thomas A., Mgr.-Natl. Sls.--Elixir Industries, Gardena, CA; *U.S. Private*, pg. 371
Martin, Thomas O., V.P.-Mktg. & Sec.--Uniflow Manufacturing Co., Erie, PA; *U.S. Private*, pg. 1117
Martin, Thomas O., V.P.-Mktg. & Sls.--Kold Draft, Erie, PA; *U.S. Private*, pg. 1117
Martin, Tilden, V.P.-Sls.--Better Brands Of Atlanta, Inc., Atlanta, GA; *U.S. Private*, pg. 141
Martin, Tim, Mgr.-Sls.--Vicon Industries (U.K.) Ltd., Fareham, United Kingdom; *U.S. Public*, pg. 1719
Martin, Tom, Mgr.-Natl. Sls.-U.S.A.--GSW Water Heating Company, Fergus, Canada; *Int'l*, pg. 538
Martin, William G., Sr. V.P.-Sls.--Siecor Corporation, Hickory, NC; *U.S. Public*, pg. 449
Martin, William G., Sr. V.P.-Sls.--Siecor Corporation, Hickory, NC; *Int'l*, pg. 1245
Martindale, Kenneth A., Sr. V.P.-Sls. & Procurement--Smith's Food & Drug Centers, Inc., Salt Lake City, UT; *U.S. Public*, pg. 1103
Martinez Salinas, Antonio, V.P.-Intl. Sls.--Mexicana Airlines, Los Angeles, CA; *Int'l*, pg. 332
Martinez, Guillermo, Mgr.-Sls.--Sanitaria Mexicana S.A. de C.V., Mexico, Mexico; *Int'l*, pg. 614
Martinez, John, Mgr.-Inside Sls.--TCI Aluminum, Gardena, CA; *U.S. Private*, pg. 1063
Martinez, Luis, Dir.-Sls.--Mattel Espana, S.A., Barcelona, Spain; *U.S. Public*, pg. 1059
Martinez, Paul, V.P.-Sls. & Mktg.--Label-Aire Inc., Fullerton, CA; *U.S. Private*, pg. 641
Martinez, Ramon V., Dir.-Sls. & Mktg./Latin America--Ethyl Corporation, Richmond, VA; *U.S. Public*, pg. 595
Martinez, Steven, Mgr.-Sls.--Auto Trend Products, Los Angeles, CA; *U.S. Private*, pg. 895
Martins, Francis A., V.P.-Sls. & Field Opers.--Applied Industrial Technologies, Cleveland, OH; *U.S. Public*, pg. 122
Martinsen, Tom, V.P.-Mktg. & Sls.--Tool & Hoist Division, Liberty Corner, NJ; *U.S. Public*, pg. 877
Martuchi, R., Mgr.-Sls.--Erie Bronze & Aluminum Co., Erie, PA; *U.S. Private*, pg. 722
Martzolf, Phil, Sls. Mgr.-Northeast Reg.--Universal Studios TV, Universal City, CA; *Int'l*, pg. 1215
Maruyama, Ryoji, Sales Mgr.--Minebea Co., Ltd. - Kuala Lumpur Branch, Kuala Lumpur, Malaysia; *Int'l*, pg. 869
Marvin, Susan I., Sr. V.P.- Sls. & Mktg.--Marvin Lumber & Cedar Company, Warroad, MN; *U.S. Private*, pg. 710
Marwell, Josh, V.P. & Dir.-Sls.--Little, Brown & Co., New York, NY; *U.S. Public*, pg. 1612
Masalunga, Napoleon, Natl. Sls. Dir.-S. Luzon--La Tondena Distillers, Inc., Manila, Philippines; *Int'l*, pg. 785
Maschke, Peter C., Mgr.-Intl. Sls. & Mktg.--Bender Shipbuilding & Repair Company, Inc., Mobile, AL; *U.S. Private*, pg. 132
Mase, A., V.P.-Aftermarket Sls.--Clearing-Niagara, Buffalo, NY; *U.S. Private*, pg. 196
Maser, H. Barry, V.P.-Bus. Devel. & Intl. Sls.--Aydin Corporation, Horsham, PA; *U.S. Public*, pg. 158
Mashburn, Walter, V.P.-Sls.--Sterling Electric, Inc., Irvine, CA; *U.S. Private*, pg. 1041
Mashington, Paul, V.P.-Sls.--Rose Art Industries, Livingston, NJ; *U.S. Private*, pg. 945
Masiello, Diane, Dir.-Sls. & Promotions--MTA Long Island Rail Road, Jamaica, NY; *U.S. Private*, pg. 739
Masilotti, Richard, V.P.-Detroit Sls.--CBS Television Network, New York, NY; *U.S. Public*, pg. 274
Maskal, Vanessa, V.P.-Mktg.--Drake Bakeries, Inc., Wayne, NJ; *Int'l*, pg. 349
Mason, James, Mgr.-Sls.--Amsco School Publications, Inc., New York, NY; *U.S. Private*, pg. 67
Mason, Kent, Mgr.-Sls.--Gardner Denver Machinery Inc., Quincy, IL; *U.S. Public*, pg. 703
Mason, Tim, V.P.-Mktg. & Sls.--Bridon Cordage Inc., Albert Lea, MN; *Int'l*, pg. 215
Mason, Tom, Dir.-Sls. & Mktg.-Wausau--Wausau Homes, Inc., Rothschild, WI; *U.S. Private*, pg. 1154
Mason, William H., V.P.-Natl. Sls.--Consolidated Freightways Corp., Menlo Park, CA; *U.S. Public*, pg. 435
Mason, William R., Sr. V.P. & Gen. Mgr.-Sls.--American Greetings Corporation, Cleveland, OH; *U.S. Public*, pg. 77
Mason, William R., V.P. & Gen. Sls. Mgr.--American Greetings U.S. Greeting Card Division, Cleveland, OH; *U.S. Public*, pg. 78
Mass, Harvey, Sr. V.P.-Sls. & Mktg.--First Central Financial Corporation, Lynbrook, NY; *U.S. Private*, pg. 406
Massalone, Daniel, V.P.-Sls.--Corporate Express Delivery Systems Southwest, Inc., Houston, TX; *U.S. Public*, pg. 449
Masselli, Michael, Sr. V.P.-Sls. & Mktg.--Jordan's Meats, Portland, ME; *U.S. Private*, pg. 599
Massey, Bret, Mgr.-Sls.--Massey Cadillac, Inc., Dallas, TX; *U.S. Private*, pg. 713
Massey, Don, V.P.-Sls./Home Furnishings--Johnston Industries, Inc., Columbus, GA; *U.S. Public*, pg. 933
Massey, John M., V.P.-Plant Sls.--Food & Beverage, Saint Paul, MN; *U.S. Public*, pg. 562
Massey, T.L., V.P.-Valve Sls., N. America--Flowserve Corporation, Valve Div., Cookeville, TN; *U.S. Public*, pg. 658
Massey, Wayne, Mgr.-Sls.--Massey Cadillac, Inc., Dallas, TX; *U.S. Private*, pg. 713
Mast, Larry L., Exec. V.P.-Sls. & Mktg.--The Penn Mutual Life Insurance Company, Philadelphia, PA; *U.S. Private*, pg. 849
Masters, Geoff, Gen. Mgr.-Prod.--Spirol International Corp., Cuyahoga Falls, OH; *U.S. Private*, pg. 1026
Masters, Stan, Sr. V.P.-Sls.--USLD Communications Corp., San Antonio, TX; *U.S. Public*, pg. 969
Masterson, Bill, V.P.-Sls.--Braun, North America, Woburn, MA; *U.S. Public*, pg. 743
Masterson, Michael V., V.P. & Reg. Sls. Mgr.--First Financial Bank, FSB, Stevens Point, WI; *U.S. Public*, pg. 140
Masterson, Tim, V.P.-Western Region Sls.--Vienna Sausage Mfg. Co., Chicago, IL; *U.S. Private*, pg. 1139
Mastro, Donald, V.P.-Sls.--Blumberg Communications Inc., Minneapolis, MN; *U.S. Public*, pg. 305
Mastropolo, Richard, V.P.-Intl. Sls.--Telsmith, Inc., Mequon, WI; *U.S. Public*, pg. 141
Masuda, Koji, Gen. Mgr.--Chiyoda Mutual Life Insurance Company, Tokyo, Japan; *Int'l*, pg. 286
Matarazzo, Nick, Sr. V.P. & Dir.-Corp. Sls.--Hachette Filipacchi Magazines Inc., New York, NY; *Int'l*, pg. 794
Matassoni, David, V.P.-Foodservice Sls.--Tyson Foods, Inc., Springdale, AR; *U.S. Public*, pg. 1652
Mateja, James, V.P.-Sls.--Coats & Clark Inc., Greenville, SC; *Int'l*, pg. 300
Mathison, Donald, Sr. V.P.-Sls. & Mktg.--Media General Cable of Fairfax County Inc., Chantilly, VA; *U.S. Public*, pg. 1078
Matiya, Mary, Mgr.-Human Resources Services--A.E. Staley Manufacturing Co., Decatur, IL; *Int'l*, pg. 1356
Matles, Hal, V.P.-Mktg.--M.H. Rhodes, Inc., Avon, CT; *U.S. Private*, pg. 927
Matlock, Thomas P., V.P.-Sls. & Mktg.--The Brewer Company, Milford, OH; *U.S. Private*, pg. 167
Matson, Bob, V.P.-Sls. Metro.--Seven-Up Bottling Co. of St. Louis, Hazelwood, MO; *U.S. Private*, pg. 142
Matt, Alfred D., V.P.-Mktg. & Sls.--The F.X. Matt Brewing Co., Utica, NY; *U.S. Private*, pg. 714
Matter, John, V.P.-Sls. & Mktg.--Equitable Savings & Loan Association, Wauwatosa, WI; *U.S. Private*, pg. 380
Matteson, John, Exec. V.P.-Sls. & Mktg.--Fleischer Manufacturing, Inc., Columbus, NE; *U.S. Private*, pg. 410
Matteson, Spencer, V.P.-Sls.--United Farm Tools, Inc., Glasgow, KY; *U.S. Private*, pg. 1122
Matthei, Axel, Mgr.-Sls.--Thermoplast und Apparatebau GmbH, Idstein, Germany; *Int'l*, pg. 1381
Matthew, Robert J., Mgr.-Northeast Reg. Sls.--Sofamor Danek Group, Inc., Memphis, TN; *U.S. Public*, pg. 1482
Matthew, Steve, V.P.-Mdsg. & Sls. Devel.--The Wooster Brush Company, Wooster, OH; *U.S. Private*, pg. 1188
Matthews, Don, V.P.-Sls. & Mktg.--Wahl Clipper Corp., Sterling, IL; *U.S. Private*, pg. 1146
Matthews, Jack, Dir.-Intl. Sales--The Crosby Group Inc., Tulsa, OK; *Int'l*, pg. 473
Matthews, John, V.P.-Indus. Prods.--Carolina Mirror Company, North Wilkesboro, NC; *U.S. Private*, pg. 214
Matthews, Milton T., V.P.-Sls.--Hershey Chocolate U.S.A., Hershey, PA; *U.S. Public*, pg. 812
Matthews, Ronald, Mgr.-Sls.--Blackman Uhler Chemical Co., Spartanburg, SC; *U.S. Public*, pg. 1548
Matthews, Terry, Sr. V.P.-Sls. & Mktg.--J.B. Hunt Transport Services, Inc., Lowell, AR; *U.S. Public*, pg. 849
Mattheys, R.D., Dir.-Sls. & Sls. Promo.--Permark International (Pty.) Ltd., Johannesburg, South Africa; *Int'l*, pg. 1036
Matthias, Fred, V.P. & Dir.-Circulation--Pulitzer Publishing Company, Saint Louis, MO; *U.S. Public*, pg. 1343
Matthy, Hank, V.P.-Dir. Sls.--Physician Computer Network, Inc., Morris Plains, NJ; *U.S. Public*, pg. 1293
Mattia, Charles, V.P.-Sls.--Lukens Steel Company, Coatesville, PA; *U.S. Public*, pg. 1020
Mattia, Charles M., V.P.-Comml. Sls.--Lukens Inc., Coatesville, PA; *U.S. Public*, pg. 1019
Mattia, R., Mgr.-Sls.--A.I. Ocean S.A., Buenos Aires, Argentina; *Int'l*, pg. 14
Mattingly, Steve, V.P.-Sls.--O'Bryan Brothers Inc., Chicago, IL; *U.S. Private*, pg. 810
Mattoon, David S., Exec. V.P. & Asst. Mgr.-Natl. Sls.--Jefferies & Company, Inc., Los Angeles, CA; *U.S. Public*, pg. 925
Matura, Thomas, Mgr.-Sls.--John Hassall, Inc., Westbury, NY; *U.S. Private*, pg. 509
Mauersberg, Hans, V.P.-Sls.--Deutsche Girozentrale-Deutsche Kommunalbank, Frankfurt/Main, Germany; *Int'l*, pg. 406
Maughan, Julian, Mgr.-European Sls.--Summit Technology, Inc., Waltham, MA; *U.S. Public*, pg. 1528
Maulden, T. Wayne, Mgr.-Sls.--Lake Placid Groves, Lake Placid, FL; *U.S. Public*, pg. 437
Mauldin, Michael, Exec. V.P.-Black Music--Sony Music Entertainment, Inc., New York, NY; *Int'l*, pg. 1281
Maulsby, Don, V.P.-Sls. & Mktg.--Interphase Corporation, Dallas, TX; *U.S. Public*, pg. 908
Maupin, Patrick, Sr. V.P.-Sls. & Mktg.--Jaydon Incorporated, Rock Island, IL; *U.S. Private*, pg. 584
Maurer, Dr., Dir.-Sls.--Boehringer Mannheim GmbH, Mannheim, Germany; *Int'l*, pg. 331
Mavers, Vaughn E., V.P.-Sls. & Mktg.--Peabody COALSALES Company, Saint Louis, MO; *Int'l*, pg. 594
Mavis, Todd, Exec. V.P.-Mktg. & Sls.--Mitchell International, San Diego, CA; *U.S. Public*, pg. 1601
Max, George, Dir.-Retail--Earl May Seed & Nursery L.c., Shenandoah, IA; *U.S. Private*, pg. 356
May, Benjamin, V.P.-Acct. Devel.-Natl. & Intl. Sls.--Stimson Lane Ltd., Woodinville, WA; *U.S. Public*, pg. 1661
May, David, Mgr.-Sls./New Cars--McNamara Pontiac Isuzu Inc., Orlando, FL; *U.S. Private*, pg. 724
May, David, V.P. & Mng. Dir.-Sls.--The New Yorker Magazine, New York, NY; *U.S. Private*, pg. 795
May, James, V.P.-Sls.--Frontier Foundry, Inc., Titusville, PA; *U.S. Private*, pg. 430
May, James, V.P.-Sls.--The Jel Sert Co., West Chicago, IL; *U.S. Private*, pg. 585
May, Jim, V.P.-Sls. & Opers.--Stella Foods, Inc., Green Bay, WI; *U.S. Private*, pg. 1040
May, Tom L., Exec. V.P.-Sls. & Chief Mktg. Officer--Equitable of Iowa Companies, Des Moines, IA; *Int'l*, pg. 647
May, Warren H., Sr. V.P.-Agency Sls.--The Travelers Life & Annuity Co., Hartford, CT; *U.S. Public*, pg. 1633
Mayer, Mark, Natl. Sls. Mgr.-Grocery Prods.--Hormel Foods Corp., Austin, MN; *U.S. Public*, pg. 840
Mayer, S., Mgr.-Gen. Sls.--Hosokawa MikroPul GmbH, Cologne, Germany; *Int'l*, pg. 636
Mayer, Sam, Dir.-Sls.--Boeing Helicopters, Ridley Park, PA; *U.S. Public*, pg. 241
Mayerick, Joseph Jr., V.P.-Sls.--Bolt Technology Corporation, Norwalk, CT; *U.S. Public*, pg. 244
Mayerick, Joseph, Jr., V.P.-Sls.--Bolt Research Division, Norwalk, CT; *U.S. Public*, pg. 244
Mayher, Kenneth G., V.P.-Sls., Eastern Reg.--Magneco/Metrel, Inc., Addison, IL; *U.S. Private*, pg. 695
Maynard, Dale, V.P.-Sls.--Anchor Tool & Die Company, Cleveland, OH; *U.S. Private*, pg. 71
Mayo, York, V.P.-Sls.-Tool Division--American Saw & Mfg. Company, East Longmeadow, MA; *U.S. Private*, pg. 61
Mayora, Federico, Mgr.-Sls. & Mktg.--General Motors Uruguay S.A., Montevideo, Uruguay; *U.S. Public*, pg. 723
Mayoras, Dave, V.P.-Sls. & Mktg./Hwy.--Detroit Diesel Corp., Detroit, MI; *U.S. Private*, pg. 850
Mazanec, Richard, V.P.-Sls.--Arrow Fastener Co., Inc., Saddle Brook, NJ; *U.S. Private*, pg. 85
Mazantti, Kyle, Bayliner Sales--U.S. Marine Div., Everett, WA; *U.S. Public*, pg. 266

Mazelis, Ed, Mgr.-Sls.--General Office Environments Inc., Rochelle Park, NJ; *U.S. Private*, pg. 445
Mazur, Jack, V.P.-Sls. & Mktg.--Johnstown Corporation, Johnstown, PA; *U.S. Private*, pg. 595
Mazza, Charlie A., Gen. Mgr.-Sls.--Berry Network, Inc., Dayton, OH; *U.S. Private*, pg. 137
Mazzali, Milton, Dir.-Sls.--3M Do Brasil Ltda., Sao Paulo, Brazil; *U.S. Public*, pg. 1606
Mazzola, Ronald A., Exec. Dir.-Mktg. & Sls.--McNaughton & Gunn, Inc., Saline, MI; *U.S. Private*, pg. 724
McAdam, Robert C., Sr. V.P.-Mktg. & Sls.--Facemate Corporation, Chicopee, MA; *U.S. Private*, pg. 391
McAlister, Gary, Mgr.-New Ford Sls.--Fairway Ford, Inc., Greenville, SC; *U.S. Private*, pg. 392
McAlister, Phil, V.P. & Gen. Mgr.-Consumer Mktg. & Sls.--Technology Research Corporation, Clearwater, FL; *U.S. Public*, pg. 1564
McAloon, Brian P., V.P.-Sls.--Analog Devices, Inc., Norwood, MA; *U.S. Public*, pg. 107
McAloon, Gregory A., Dir.-Sls.--Boss Manufacturing Company, Kewanee, IL; *U.S. Private*, pg. 1142
McArthur, David, Dir.-Prod. Sls.--Reed Travel Publishing-Asia/Pacific, Singapore, Singapore; *Int'l*, pg. 1097
McArthur, Lynne, Mgr.-Corp. Devel.--BFC Construction Corporation, Scarborough, Canada; *Int'l*, pg. 118
McAuley, Eileen, Mgr.-Natl. Sls.--Lava World International/Haggerty Enterprises, Inc., Chicago, IL; *U.S. Private*, pg. 653
McAulife, Joe, Sls. Mgr.--Hendrix Wire & Cable, Milford, NH; *U.S. Public*, pg. 1598
McAvoy, Dale, Mgr.-Adv., Sls. & Mktg.-Flow Controls--Raven Industries, Inc., Sioux Falls, SD; *U.S. Public*, pg. 1361
McAvoy, Dale T., Mgr.-Sls. & Mktg.--Flow Control Division, Sioux Falls, SD; *U.S. Public*, pg. 1361
McBain, W.P., V.P.-Sls. & Mktg.--Daubert Coated Products, Inc., Westchester, IL; *U.S. Private*, pg. 313
McBride, Michael, V.P.-Govt. Sls.--Harris Corp., RF Communications Group Marketing Division, Rochester, NY; *U.S. Public*, pg. 792
McBride, Phil, Mgr.-Sls.--Coleman Dairy LLC, Little Rock, AR; *U.S. Private*, pg. 251
McBride, Richard L., Mgr.-Sls.--T. Bruce Sales, Inc., West Middlesex, PA; *U.S. Private*, pg. 175
McBride, Vince, Exec. V.P.-Sls. & Mktg.--The Selmer Co., Inc., Elkhart, IN; *U.S. Public*, pg. 1514
McBride, Vince, Exec. V.P.-Sales & Mktg.--Ludwig Industries, Monroe, NC; *U.S. Public*, pg. 1514
McBryan, Michael E., V.P.-Sls. Div.--Healthcare Services Group, Inc., Huntingdon Valley, PA; *U.S. Public*, pg. 803
McCabe, George, V.P.-Mktg. & Sls.--Mazda Motor of America, Inc., Irvine, CA; *Int'l*, pg. 849
McCabe, James, Sr. V.P.-Sls.--UAD Laboratories, Jackson, MS; *U.S. Public*, pg. 670
McCaffery, James, V.P.-Sales & Mktg.--Mitsumi Electronics Corp., Irving, TX; *Int'l*, pg. 884
McCaffray, K.A., Mgr.-Intl. Sls.--National Frozen Foods Corp., Seattle, WA; *U.S. Private*, pg. 783
McCall, Henry C., III, Sr. V.P.-Assets Sls.--United Companies Financial Corporation, Baton Rouge, LA; *U.S. Public*, pg. 1675
McCall, John, V.P.-Sls. & Field Opers.--Sanofi Pharmaceuticals, Inc., New York, NY; *Int'l*, pg. 445
McCall, Mac, Dir.-Sls.--Broyhill Furniture Industries, Inc., Saint Louis, MO; *U.S. Public*, pg. 688
McCalla, Hal, V.P.-Sls.--Tennsco Corporation, Dickson, TN; *U.S. Private*, pg. 1077
McCallie, James, V.P.-Sls.--Southeastern Freight Lines, Inc., Lexington, SC; *U.S. Private*, pg. 1015
McCamish, Bernie, V.P.-Sls. & Engrng.--Ward Leonard Electric Company, Inc., Mount Vernon, NY; *U.S. Private*, pg. 1118
McCandless, William, V.P.-Sls.--Key Handling Systems, Inc., Moonachie, NJ; *U.S. Private*, pg. 618
McCann, James B., Exec. V.P.-Sls. & Mktg.--Maui Pineapple Co., Ltd., Kahului, HI; *U.S. Public*, pg. 1060
McCarles, Angus, Pres.-Natl. Sls.--Ralston Purina Canada Inc., Mississauga, Canada; *U.S. Public*, pg. 1360
McCarrick, Edward, Dir.-Adv. Sls.--Time, New York, NY; *U.S. Public*, pg. 1613
McCarthy, Bill, Exec. V.P.-Sls.--Risdon Corporation, Naugatuck, CT; *U.S. Public*, pg. 463
McCarthy, Francis J., V.P.-Mktg. & Sls.--A. Duda & Sons Inc., Oviedo, FL; *U.S. Private*, pg. 344
McCarthy, John, Grp. Dir.-Communications & Human Resources--Legal & General Group PLC, London, United Kingdom; *Int'l*, pg. 805
McCarthy, John, V.P.-Mktg. & Sls.--Amersham Corporation, Arlington Heights, IL; *Int'l*, pg. 992
McCarthy, John A., Mgr.-South Central Reg. Sls.--Sofamor Danek Group, Inc., Memphis, TN; *U.S. Public*, pg. 1482
McCarthy, Kevin, Mgr.-Sls.--Benthos, Inc., North Falmouth, MA; *U.S. Public*, pg. 212
McCarthy, Raymond, Asst. V.P.-Sls. & Mktg.--Hornor, Townsend & Kent, Philadelphia, PA; *U.S. Private*, pg. 849
McCarty, John, Dir.-Sls. Dev. Grp.--Ketchum, Inc., Pittsburgh, PA; *U.S. Private*, pg. 617
McCarty, Michael, Dir.-Sls.--Pitney Bowes Software Systems, Glen Ellyn, IL; *U.S. Public*, pg. 1304
McCaslin, Marty, V.P.-Sls. & Mktg.--Siouxland Galvanizing Corp., Sioux City, IA; *U.S. Private*, pg. 656
McCauley, Jim, V.P.-Sls. & Mktg.--SaniServ Manufacturing Corp., Indianapolis, IN; *U.S. Private*, pg. 965
McCauley, L., V.P.-Sls./W.--Sika Corporation, Lyndhurst, NJ; *Int'l*, pg. 1249
McCaw, Debra, Mgr.-Sls.--Business Journal Publications, Inc., Tampa, FL; *U.S. Private*, pg. 19
McCendon, Steve, Asst. V.P.-Sls. & Mktg.--Southwire Company, Carrollton, GA; *U.S. Private*, pg. 1019
McCeudy, Tom, Mgr.-Natl. Sls.--Meadox Medicals, Inc., Oakland, NJ; *U.S. Public*, pg. 247
McClafferty, Pat, V.P.-Sls. Svcs.--Arkansas Electric Cooperatives Inc., Little Rock, AR; *U.S. Private*, pg. 82
McClain, Hugh, Mgr.-Natl. Accts.--Mohawk Commercial Carpet, Atlanta, GA; *U.S. Public*, pg. 1121
McClain, Mike, Mgr.-Sls.--Rotational Molding, Inc., Gardena, CA; *U.S. Public*, pg. 1406
McClain, Todd, Regional Sls. Mgr.--Blitz USA, Inc., Miami, OK; *U.S. Private*, pg. 149
McClarren, Scott, V.P.-Coastal Bend Sls.--Hygeia Dairy Co., Inc., Harlingen, TX; *U.S. Private*, pg. 552
McClelland, John, Corp. V.P.-Consumer Sls.--Scott Paper Limited, Mississauga, Canada; *Int'l*, pg. 762
McClennon, Richard, Sr. V.P.-Mktg.--The Detroit News, Detroit, MI; *U.S. Public*, pg. 700
McClimon, David S., V.P.-Natl. Sls.--Con-Way Transportation Services, Palo Alto, CA; *U.S. Public*, pg. 281
McClinton, Raymond, V.P.-Mktg.--Communications Instruments Inc., Fairview, NC; *U.S. Private*, pg. 259
McClory, Tom, Mgr.-Medical Prods. & Prod. Line--Mine Safety Appliances Co., Pittsburgh, PA; *U.S. Public*, pg. 1114
McCloskey, Daniel, V.P.-Sls. & Mktg.--Lifetime Hoan Corp., Westbury, NY; *U.S. Public*, pg. 992
McCloud, Michael, V.P.-Sls. & Mktg.--Cuisine Solutions, Inc., Alexandria, VA; *U.S. Public*, pg. 466
McClune, Robert C., V.P.-Sls.--Potters Industries, Inc., Valley Forge, PA; *U.S. Private*, pg. 827
McCluskey, Tom, Sls. Mgr.-N.Y.--USA Weekend, New York, NY; *U.S. Public*, pg. 701
McColley, David, Mgr.-Key Accts.--Weinbrenner Shoe Company, Inc., Merrill, WI; *U.S. Private*, pg. 1160
McCollum, Bruce, Exec. V.P.-Adv., Mktg. & Sls.--Tingley Rubber Corporation, South Plainfield, NJ; *U.S. Private*, pg. 1088
McCollum, Wayne E., Sr. V.P.-Supply Chain--Quality Stores Inc., Muskegon, MI; *U.S. Private*, pg. 899
McConnaughy, Dolores, V.P.-Ntl. Accts. & Export Sls.--The Fuller Brush Company, Great Bend, KS; *U.S. Public*, pg. 282
McConnell, Maggie, V.P.-Sls.--Technicolor, Inc., North Hollywood, CA; *Int'l*, pg. 272
McConnell, Michael, V.P.-Intl. Sls.--Universal Security Instruments Inc., Owings Mills, MD; *U.S. Public*, pg. 1697
McCook, George M., V.P.-Sls. & Mktg.--Purcell Co., Inc., Diamondhead, MS; *U.S. Private*, pg. 895
McCool, Paul, Dir.-Intl.Sls.--Appleton Electric Co., Chicago, IL; *U.S. Public*, pg. 572
McCord, R.L., Mgr.-Sls.--American Welding & Manufacturing Co., Warren, OH; *U.S. Private*, pg. 425
McCormack, John, V.P.-Sls. & Mktg.--McArthur Dairy, Inc., Sunrise, FL; *U.S. Public*, pg. 491
McCormack, Vinnie, Dir.-Sls.--Sensall, Div. of Rosemount, Inc., Hauppauge, NY; *U.S. Public*, pg. 574
McCormick, Jim, V.P.-Sls.--Jimlar Corporation, Great Neck, NY; *U.S. Private*, pg. 587
McCormick, John, Exec. V.P.-Tire Equipment Sls.--McNeil & NRM., Inc., Akron, OH; *U.S. Private*, pg. 725
McCormick, John, V.P. & Gen. Mgr.-Sls.--KTTV, Los Angeles, CA; *Int'l*, pg. 926
McCormick, John, V.P.-Sls. & Mktg.--Stokely USA, Inc., Oconomowoc, WI; *U.S. Public*, pg. 1518
McCort, John, V.P.-Sls.--Santa Rosa Steel Forming, Inc., Santa Rosa, CA; *U.S. Private*, pg. 965
McCorvey, William D., Sr. V.P.-Retail Sls.--Helen of Troy Corporation, El Paso, TX; *U.S. Public*, pg. 807
McCourtney, Mark, V.P.-Sls.--Plastech Corporation, Forest Lake, MN; *U.S. Private*, pg. 870
McCoy, Bill, Dir.-Sls. & Mktg.--The Fuller Brush Company, Great Bend, KS; *U.S. Public*, pg. 282
McCoy, Fred, Pres.-Pacific Rim Sls.--Guidant Corporation, Indianapolis, IN; *U.S. Public*, pg. 768
McCoy, Mike, Natl. Sls. Mgr.--Bee Line Company, Bettendorf, IA; *U.S. Private*, pg. 129
McCoy, Walter, V.P.-Sls.--Pacific Combining Corp., Los Angeles, CA; *U.S. Public*, pg. 802
McCracken, William E., Gen. Mgr.-Sls. & Service--International Business Machines Corporation, Armonk, NY; *U.S. Public*, pg. 895
McCraney, Lloyd, V.P.-Sls.--Cadmus Marketing Services, Atlanta, GA; *U.S. Public*, pg. 291
McCranie, Dan, V.P.-Mktg. & Sls.--Cypress Semiconductor Corporation, San Jose, CA; *U.S. Public*, pg. 470
McCranie, James B., V.P.-Intl. Sls.--Sealed-Sweet Growers, Inc., Vero Beach, FL; *U.S. Private*, pg. 978
McCrea, Cecil, Gen. Mgr.-Mill Sls.--Tolko Industries Ltd., Vernon, Canada; *Int'l*, pg. 1395
McCrobie, Ronald N., V.P.-Procurement--Tri-State Wholesale Associated Grocers, Inc., El Paso, TX; *U.S. Private*, pg. 1101
McCrone, Allan, Mgr.-Sls.--Richardson Electronics (Europe) Ltd., Lincoln, United Kingdom; *U.S. Public*, pg. 1388
Mccroy, Jim, Sr. V.P.-Institutional Sls.--Waddell & Reed, Inc., Shawnee Mission, KS; *U.S. Public*, pg. 1623
McCulla, Gary W., Pres. & Dir.-Sls. & Mktg.--Tel-Save Holdings, Inc., New Hope, PA; *U.S. Public*, pg. 1568
McCulloch, Hugh, Gen. Sls. Mgr.--Dunkin' Donuts U.K. Limited, Bourne, United Kingdom; *Int'l*, pg. 63
McCullohs, Neal J., V.P.-Sls./Mill Prods.--AmeriSteel, Tampa, FL; *U.S. Private*, pg. 65
McCullough, Brian, Mgr.-Sls.--Douglas Stephen Plastics, Inc., Paterson, NJ; *U.S. Private*, pg. 341
McCullough, Tom, Mgr.-Sls. & Mktg.--Cortland Line Co., Inc., Cortland, NY; *U.S. Private*, pg. 277
McCune, Robert E., II, Asst. V.P.-Large Comml. & Small Indus. Sls.--North Carolina Natural Gas Corporation, Fayetteville, NC; *U.S. Public*, pg. 1194
McCurdy, W. R., V.P.-Sls.--Bristol-Myers Products, New York, NY; *U.S. Public*, pg. 254
McCurren, Rob, V.P.-Sls. Outstate--Seven-Up Bottling Co. of St. Louis, Hazelwood, MO; *U.S. Private*, pg. 142
McDaniel, Al, Asst. V.P. & Mgr.-Sls.--Nasco Industries Inc., Medina, OH; *U.S. Private*, pg. 774
McDaniel, Terry, V.P.-Sls.--Wise Foods, Inc., Parsippany, NJ; *U.S. Private*, pg. 157
McDannold, Doran E., V.P. & Dir.-Sls. & Mktg.--The Troy Savings Bank, Troy, NY; *U.S. Private*, pg. 1106
McDavid, Dan, Mgr.-Real Estate--Concorp, Inc., Nitro, WV; *U.S. Private*, pg. 262
McDavid, David, Jr., V.P. & Mgr.-Opers.--David McDavid Auto Dealership, Irving, TX; *U.S. Private*, pg. 721
McDermott, Andy, Dir.-Sales--Monroe Forgings Inc., Rochester, NY; *Int'l*, pg. 488
McDermott, Michael, V.P.-Sls. & Mktg.--The Presmet Corp., Worcester, MA; *U.S. Private*, pg. 882
McDermott, Rossa, Sr. Dir.-Intl. Sls.--Cybex International, Inc., Medway, MA; *U.S. Private*, pg. 1114
McDevitt, Robert A., Sr. V.P.-Sls. & Opers.--ADT Automotive, Inc., Nashville, TN; *U.S. Public*, pg. 1648
McDonagh, Jim, V.P.-Sls. & Mktg.--Riker Products, Inc., Toledo, OH; *U.S. Private*, pg. 300
McDonald, Frank, Dir.-Sls., Bioclean Systems--Harford Systems, Inc., Aberdeen, MD; *U.S. Private*, pg. 641
McDonald, James, V.P.-Sls.--Moore Products Co., Spring House, PA; *U.S. Public*, pg. 1128
McDonald, John, Gen. Sls. Mgr.--Columbine JDS Systems, Inc., Denver, CO; *U.S. Public*, pg. 228
McDonald, Joseph, Sr. V.P.-Sls.--Triarc Beverage Group, White Plains, NY; *U.S. Public*, pg. 1635
McDonald, R., Mgr.-Natl. Sls.--The Uncle Toby's Company Ltd., Richmond, Australia; *Int'l*, pg. 555
McDonald, Raymond J., Sr. V.P.-Distr. & Logistics--Canadian Tire Corporation Limited, Toronto, Canada; *Int'l*, pg. 259
McDonald, Thomas P., Div. V.P.-Sls.--New Penn Motor Express, Inc., Lebanon, PA; *U.S. Public*, pg. 132
McDonough, Joseph, Dir.-Sls.--California Drop Forge, Los Angeles, CA; *U.S. Public*, pg. 612
McDonough, Robert T., Sr. V.P.-Mktg. & Sls.--Artistic Greetings, Inc., Elmira, NY; *U.S. Public*, pg. 136
McDonough, Tom, V.P.-N. American Sls.--Axent Technologies, Rockville, MD; *U.S. Public*, pg. 157
McDougall, Douglas, Mgr.-Sls. & Consumer Promotion--Reily Foods Company, New Orleans, LA; *U.S. Private*, pg. 919
McDougall, Sandy, Mgr.-Mktg. Sls. & Adv.--Air BC, Richmond, Canada; *Int'l*, pg. 36
McDowell, Charles T., V.P.-Sls. & Mktg.--First Protective Insurance Group, Birmingham, AL; *U.S. Public*, pg. 1336
McEnroe, Ken, V.P.-Paper Tech. Sls.--The Johnson Corporation, Three Rivers, MI; *U.S. Private*, pg. 591
McEttrick, Rick, Dir.-Sls.--BIC Corporation, Milford, CT; *Int'l*, pg. 1273
McEwen, Bob, Mgr.-Sls.--Harris Ford, Inc., Lynnwood, WA; *U.S. Private*, pg. 506
McEwen, Ian, V.P.-Franchising--Speedy Car-X, Inc., Chicago, IL; *U.S. Public*, pg. 1578
McEwen, Kevin B., Branch Mgr.--Hilland Dairy Company, Wichita, KS; *U.S. Private*, pg. 879
McFadden, Joe, V.P.-Sls.--Capitol Records, Inc., Hollywood, CA; *Int'l*, pg. 428
McFalls, Patricia, Dir.-Corp. Admin.--Careers USA Inc., Philadelphia, PA; *U.S. Private*, pg. 209
McFarland, Malcolm, Mgr.-Sls.--ECC Financial Group, Cleveland, OH; *U.S. Public*, pg. 558
McFarlane, Don, Dir.-New Const. Sls.--Dunn-Edwards Corporation, Los Angeles, CA; *U.S. Private*, pg. 347
McFarling, Robert E., V.P.-Sls. & Treas.--McFarling Foods, Inc., Indianapolis, IN; *U.S. Private*, pg. 721
McFerran, Brian A., V.P.-Sls.--Porth Plastic Co., Des Plaines, IL; *Int'l*, pg. 233
McFillen, R. Leon, V.P.--The IDI Group Companies, Arlington, VA; *U.S. Private*, pg. 554
McFillin, R.K., Dir.-Sls.--Mallinckrodt Baker Inc., Phillipsburg, NJ; *U.S. Public*, pg. 1039
McGaha, Ray, Sr. V.P.-Sls. & Engrng.--Continental Conveyor & Equipment Company, Winfield, AL; *U.S. Private*, pg. 791
McGarry, N.S., Dir.-Sls.--Garryson-Insley Ltd., Ibstock, United Kingdom; *Int'l*, pg. 448
McGarry, Richard D., Mgr.-Sls.--Southwark Metal Manufacturing Company, Philadelphia, PA; *U.S. Private*, pg. 1018
McGee, Millard L., Jr., Grp. V.P.-Sls.--American & Efird, Inc., Mount Holly, NC; *U.S. Public*, pg. 1412
McGee, Rick, V.P.-Sls. & Mktg.--Artisoft, Inc., Tucson, AZ; *U.S. Public*, pg. 136
McGhee, Douglas, Mng. Dir.--Newage Industries Inc., Testing Instruments Group, Willow Grove, PA; *U.S. Private*, pg. 796
McGill, John, Mgr.-Natl. Sls.--Benjamin Obdyke, Inc., Warminster, PA; *U.S. Private*, pg. 810
McGill, Paul E., Area Sls. Rep.--Production Operators, Inc. (Denver Office), Englewood, CO; *U.S. Public*, pg. 298
McGillycuddy, Ray, Mgr.-Sls.--James Burn Binders, Eynsham, United Kingdom; *U.S. Public*, pg. 1507
McGinnis, David, V.P. & Dir.-Sls.--Bostonian Shoe Co., Newton, MA; *Int'l*, pg. 297
McGinnis, Pat, V.P.-Sls.-Pkgng. Div.--Burrows Paper Corporation, Little Falls, NY; *U.S. Private*, pg. 188
McGinnis, Tom, Gen. Mgr.-Sls.--Meadville Forging Co., Meadville, PA; *U.S. Private*, pg. 726
McGinnity, Timothy J., Sr. V.P.-Sls./Consumer Prods.--Signature Brands USA, Inc., Solon, OH; *U.S. Public*, pg. 1472
McGlone, Brian, Dir.-Mktg & Sls.--Hubbell Premise Wiring, Inc., Stonington, CT; *U.S. Public*, pg. 844
McGlothlin, Jim, V.P.--Production Operators Inc., Houston, TX; *U.S. Public*, pg. 298
McGlothlin, Jim, V.P.-Sls.--Production Operators, Inc., Houston, TX; *U.S. Public*, pg. 298
McGough, Mark, Mgr.-Sls.--Energy Products, San Diego, CA; *U.S. Public*, pg. 1061
McGovern, Alice, Sls. Dept.--Edgewater Steel Company, Oakmont, PA; *U.S. Private*, pg. 364
McGovern, Eastmen, Exec. V.P.-Worldwide Sls.--Storage Dimensions, Inc., Milpitas, CA; *U.S. Public*, pg. 1522
McGovern, Renee, Exec. V.P.-Sls.--David Dart, Chatsworth, CA; *U.S. Public*, pg. 948

McGowan, Bill, Sr. V.P.-Discovery Networks & Adv. Sls.--Discovery Communications, Inc., Bethesda, MD; *U.S. Private*, pg. 334

McGowan, Bill, Sr. V.P.-Adv. Sls.--Discovery Networks, Inc., Bethesda, MD; *U.S. Private*, pg. 334

McGrath, Daniel S., V.P.-Sls.--Mico Inc., North Mankato, MN; *U.S. Private*, pg. 741

McGrath, Michael, Dir.-Sls.--Stewart Warner Instruments Corporation, Des Plaines, IL; *U.S. Private*, pg. 1042

McGrath, Mike, Sr. V.P.-Sls.-Independent Bottling Systems--Cadbury Beverages, Stamford, CT; *Int'l*, pg. 248

McGrath, Richard, V.P.-Sls.--Commodity Information Services Group, New York, NY; *U.S. Public*, pg. 1071

McGraw, Scott, V.P.-Sports Sls.--CBS Television Network, New York, NY; *U.S. Public*, pg. 274

McGregor, Andy, V.P.-Sls. & Distr., N. America--Office Pavilion Division (Sls. & Mktg. Div.), Zeeland, MI; *U.S. Public*, pg. 1112

McGregor, J. D., V.P.-Sls.--Pogo Producing Company, Houston, TX; *U.S. Public*, pg. 1312

McGregor, Robert G., Mgr.-Sls. & Mktg.--Brookfield Engineering Laboratories, Inc., Stoughton, MA; *U.S. Private*, pg. 171

McGuff, Rick, Dir.-Sls. & Mktg.--Spalding Canada, Concord, Canada; *U.S. Private*, pg. 630

McGuire, Eugene, Sls. Mgr.-Midwest Reg.--Universal Studios TV, Universal City, CA; *Int'l*, pg. 1215

McGuire, Mac, Dir.-Mktg. & Sls.--Sangamon Industries, Taylorville, IL; *U.S. Private*, pg. 965

McGushin, Terry, V.P.-Sls.--Rite-Hite Corporation, Milwaukee, WI; *U.S. Private*, pg. 933

McHale, John, V.P.-Sls.--Maxitrol Co., Southfield, MI; *U.S. Private*, pg. 716

McHale, John, V.P.-Sls.--Petron Corporation, New Berlin, WI; *U.S. Private*, pg. 1158

McHenry, Brian, V.P.-Sls. & Mktg.--La France Corporation, Philadelphia, PA; *U.S. Private*, pg. 640

McHenry, Scott, Sr. V.P.-Mktg. & Sls.--The Dial Corporation, Phoenix, AZ; *U.S. Public*, pg. 505

McHugh, Joseph, V.P. & Mgr.-Detroit Sls.--Parade Publications Inc., New York, NY; *U.S. Private*, pg. 20

McHugh, Timothy, Mgr.-Sales & Mktg.--Access Corporation, Cincinnati, OH; *Int'l*, pg. 994

McIlvaine, Glen E., Sr. V.P. & Sls. Mgr.-Los Angeles--Jefferies & Company, Inc., Los Angeles, CA; *U.S. Public*, *pg. 925*

McInerney, John J., V.P.-Sls. & Mktg.--McInerney Inc., Oak Park, MI; *U.S. Private*, pg. 722

McInnis, Louisa, Natl. Sales Mgr.--Noel Joanna, Inc., Rancho Santa Margarita, CA; *U.S. Public*, pg. 465

McIntosh, Dick, V.P.-Sls. & Mktg.--Kyocera Canada, Inc., Mississauga, Canada; *Int'l*, pg. 776

McIntosh, Richard S., V.P.-Mktg.--Univex Corporation, Salem, NH; *U.S. Private*, pg. 1128

McIntyre, J.J., Mgr.-Sls.--Longview Fibre Co. Central Container Div., Rockford, IL; *U.S. Public*, pg. 1014

McIntyre, Michael, V.P.-Mktg.--Killark Electric Manufacturing Co., Saint Louis, MO; *U.S. Public*, pg. 844

McKay, Larry, Sr. V.P.-Traditional Sls.--The Spring Air Company, Des Plaines, IL; *U.S. Private*, pg. 1027

McKeand, Bert, Sr. Sls. Representative--PENCO-Virginia, Richmond, VA; *Int'l*, pg. 1508

McKee, Donovan R., V.P.-Sls.--Carlton Cards Division, Cleveland, OH; *U.S. Public*, pg. 78

McKendrick, Bruce, Dir.-Retail Services--The Eurotunnel Group, London, United Kingdom; *Int'l*, pg. 466

McKenna, Andrew J., Jr., V.P-Sls.--Schwarz Paper Company, Morton Grove, IL; *U.S. Private*, pg. 974

McKenna, Fergus, Dir.-Sls.--Batchelors (Ireland) Ltd., Dublin, Ireland; *Int'l*, pg. 968

McKenzie, Jim, Mgr.-Western Reg.--Brillion Iron Works, Inc., Brillion, WI; *U.S. Public*, pg. 933

McKenzie, Joan, Mgr.-Customer Service--Temco Fireplace Products, Inc., Nashville, TN; *U.S. Public*, pg. 1576

McKenzie, Mori, Dir.-Stores--Chico's Fas Inc, Fort Myers, FL; *U.S. Public*, pg. 349

McKenzie, William K., V.P.-Sls.--Baldwin Filters, Kearney, NE; *U.S. Public*, pg. 381

McKeonn, P.J., Sales Exec.--British Steel Seamless Tubes-Wednesfield Works, Wolverhampton, United Kingdom; *Int'l*, pg. 220

McKey, Randy, V.P.-Affiliate Sls.--A&E Television Networks, New York, NY; *U.S. Private*, pg. 515

McKinley, John, V.P.-Engrng., Sls. & Mktg.--Varity Dayton Walther, Dayton, OH; *Int'l*, pg. 820

McKinley, Richard, V.P.-Field Sls.--JII/Sales Promotion Associates, Inc., Coshocton, OH; *U.S. Private*, pg. 598

McKinnell, James A., V.P.-Distr.-Canada--Bauer Sports Inc., Montreal, Canada; *U.S. Public*, pg. 1184

McKinney, Ronald L., V.P.-Sls.--Specialty Industries, Inc., Red Lion, PA; *U.S. Private*, pg. 1022

McKinnon, Alan, V.P.-Sls. & Mktg.--Guilford Europe, Ltd., Derby, United Kingdom; *U.S. Public*, pg. 769

McKinnon, George, Mgr.-Sls.--James Ferrera & Sons, Inc., Canton, MA; *U.S. Private*, pg. 401

McKinnon, James, Dir.-Retail Sls.--Intertek Testing Services, Andover, MA; *Int'l*, pg. 672

McKinnon, Tony, Gen. Mgr.-Sls.--The Howden Fan Co., Buffalo, NY; *U.S. Private*, pg. 543

McKinstry, David, Mgr.-Commercial Sls. & Mktg.--IMO Pump, Monroe, NC; *U.S. Public*, pg. 857

McKissick, Larry, Mgr.-Sls. & Mktg.--Brunner & Lay, Inc., Springdale, AR; *U.S. Private*, pg. 176

McKnight, Robert R., III, V.P.-Sales--Lotus Word Processing Division, Atlanta, GA; *U.S. Public*, pg. 896

McKnight, Ron, Exec. V.P.-Sls.--United States Bakery, Portland, OR; *U.S. Private*, pg. 1124

McLaughin, John G., V.P.-Sls. & Mktg.--Diagnostic Products Corporation, Los Angeles, CA; *U.S. Public*, pg. 505

McLaughlin, Allen, Gen. Sls. Mgr.--KAKC-AM, Tulsa, OK; *U.S. Public*, pg. 384

McLaughlin, Joseph, Dir.-Sales--Berlitz Publishing Company Inc., New York, NY; *U.S. Public*, pg. 221

McLaughlin, Larry, V.P.-Sls. Div.--Kendale Industries, Inc., Valley View, OH; *U.S. Private*, pg. 614

McLaughlin, Lee, Natl. Sls. Mgr.--Bee Line Company, Bettendorf, IA; *U.S. Private*, pg. 129

McLaughlin, Thomas M., V.P.-Sls.-Industrial Foam--Ludlow Composites Corporation, Fremont, OH; *U.S. Private*, pg. 680

McLean, Edwin J., V.P.-Sls.--Advance Packaging Corporation, Grand Rapids, MI; *U.S. Private*, pg. 18

McLean, J.H., V.P.-Sls.--Southern Plastics Co., West Columbia, SC; *Int'l*, pg. 233

McLean, Mark, Mgr.-Railroad Sls.--CF & I Steel, L.P., Pueblo, CO; *U.S. Public*, pg. 1230

McLean, Steve, V.P.-Sls.--The Savogran Company, Norwood, MA; *U.S. Private*, pg. 968

McLeod, Lorn E., Mgr.-Sls./Grocery Div.--Doane Products Co., Branded Sales Div., Joplin, MO; *U.S. Private*, pg. 337

McLoughlin, Brendan A., V.P.-Sls.--COMPAQ Computer Corporation, Houston, TX; *U.S. Public*, pg. 417

McLoughlin, Larry, V.P.-Sls. Zone--Wise Foods, Inc., Parsippany, NJ; *U.S. Private*, pg. 157

McMahon, Frank, Mgr.-Sls. & Mktg.--OPT Industries, Inc., Phillipsburg, NJ; *U.S. Public*, pg. 1624

McMahon, John, Exec. V.P.-Worldwide Sls.--Parametric Technology Corporation, Waltham, MA; *U.S. Public*, pg. 1257

McMahon, Joseph, Mgr.-Sls.--Bock Industries Inc., Elkhart, IN; *Int'l*, pg. 265

McMahon, Kenneth J., V.P.-Corp. Sls.--American Waste Services, Inc., Warren, OH; *U.S. Public*, pg. 94

McManus, Charlie, V.P.-Sls./Stationary--Yuasa-Exide, Inc., Reading, PA; *Int'l*, pg. 1522

McManus, Greg, V.P.-Sls, Distr., NAAG--Whirlpool Corporation, Benton Harbor, MI; *U.S. Public*, pg. 1764

McManus, J.H., V.P.-Indus. Prod. Sls.--California & Hawaiian Sugar Company Inc., Crockett, CA; *U.S. Public*, pg. 39

McManus, Rich, Mgr.-Sls. & Mktg.--Huck International, Inc., Tucson, AZ; *U.S. Public*, pg. 1597

McMartin, Terry, V.P.-Sls.--Nissin Foods (U.S.A.) Co. Ltd., Gardena, CA; *Int'l*, pg. 949

McMath, Michael E., Exec. Dir.-Sls. & Mktg.--Lincoln National (UK) plc, Oxbridge, United Kingdom; *U.S. Public*, pg. 998

McMenamin, William F., V.P.-Sls./Electronics-Indus.--QAD Inc, Carpinteria, CA; *U.S. Public*, pg. 1345

McMillan, Bruce A., V.P.-Sls.--Liberty Homes, Inc., Goshen, IN; *U.S. Public*, pg. 992

McMillan, Mike, V.P.-Sls.--Superior Auctioneers & Marketing, Inc., San Antonio, TX; *U.S. Private*, pg. 1054

McMunn, William H., Pres.--Indigo Development Inc., Daytona Beach, FL; *U.S. Public*, pg. 437

McNab, Peter, Dir.-Admin. & Customer Svcs.--Selecto-Flash, Inc., West Orange, NJ; *U.S. Private*, pg. 982

McNally, J., Dir.-Sls.--Moore Business Forms de Mexico S.A. de C.V., Tlalnepantla, Mexico; *Int'l*, pg. 889

McNamara, Brian, Mgr.-Sls.--Caro Produce & Institutional Foods, Houma, LA; *U.S. Public*, pg. 1278

McNeal, Dennis, Mgr.-Natl. Sls.--Yamaha Motor Corp., U.S.A., Cypress, CA; *Int'l*, pg. 1516

McNeeley, Donald R., Pres. & Chief Oper. Officer--Chicago Tube & Iron Co., Chicago, IL; *U.S. Private*, pg. 235

McNeil, Dwayne, Dir.-Sls.--Six Flags Astroworld/Six Flags Waterworld/Six Flags Houston, Houston, TX; *U.S. Public*, pg. 1611

McNeil, Joe, Sls. Engr.--Marion Machine Company Division, Marion, NC; *U.S. Private*, pg. 1055

McNeil, John, Mgr.-Retail Adv.--Trend-Lines Inc., Revere, MA; *U.S. Private*, pg. 1099

McNeil, Kevin, V.P.-Sls.--The Good Guys, Inc., Brisbane, CA; *U.S. Public*, pg. 750

McNulty, John, Sr. V.P.-Sls. & Mktg.--Brunswick Bicyles Div., Bannockburn, IL; *U.S. Public*, pg. 265

McOllough, Jeff, Mgr.-Adv., Sls., & Mktg.--Hagie Manufacturing Co., Clarion, IA; *U.S. Private*, pg. 493

McPhee, Randy, V.P.-North American Sls.--Computerized Medical Systems, Inc., Saint Louis, MO; *U.S. Private*, pg. 260

McPhee, S., Exec. Gen. Mgr.-Sls., Europe & S.E. Asia--Qantas Airways Ltd., Mascot, Australia; *Int'l*, pg. 1074

McPherson, Bill, Dir.-Sls.--Wicks 'n Sticks, Ltd, Houston, TX; *U.S. Private*, pg. 1175

McPherson, James, V.P.-Sls.--Rodefeld Co., Inc., Richmond, IN; *U.S. Private*, pg. 939

McQueen, Edwin D., V.P.-Sls. & Mktg.--Steelox Systems Inc., Mason, OH; *U.S. Private*, pg. 1038

McQueen, Jeff, V.P.-Sls. & Mktg.--Schwab Corp., Lafayette, IN; *U.S. Private*, pg. 974

McQueston, Robert, Sls. Representative--Brian Controls Division, Halifax, Canada; *Int'l*, pg. 711

McQuiddy, Craig, V.P. & Dir.-Retail Sls.--Bush Brothers & Company, Knoxville, TN; *U.S. Private*, pg. 189

McQuilkin, Allan, Mgr.-Natl. Sls.--Alimak Elevator Company, Bridgeport, CT; *U.S. Private*, pg. 34

McQuillin, David, V.P.-Mktg. & Sls.--Gunther Mele Limited, Brantford, Canada; *Int'l*, pg. 578

McQuiston, Bruce, Dir.-Mktg. & Sls.--Mentholatum Company, Buffalo, NY; *Int'l*, pg. 1126

McQuown, Mark, Dir.-Sls.--Lowrance Electronics, Inc., Tulsa, OK; *U.S. Public*, pg. 1015

McRae, Ed, Dir.-Agency Sls.--MSI Insurance Companies, Arden Hills, MN; *U.S. Private*, pg. 688

McRea, Miles, Dir.-Promo.--Atlanta National League Baseball Club, Inc., Atlanta, GA; *U.S. Public*, pg. 1614

McTernan, H., Dir.-Sls.--Hollandia Weathershields Limited, Birmingham, United Kingdom; *Int'l*, pg. 1463

McWhinnie, David, Mgr.-Sls.--Chase & Sons Division, Randolph, MA; *U.S. Public*, pg. 337

McWilliams, Brent N., V.P.-Sls.--Laidlaw Corporation, Scottsdale, AZ; *U.S. Private*, pg. 642

McWilliams, Gary A., Mgr.-Sls.--McWilliams Forge Co., Rockaway, NJ; *U.S. Private*, pg. 725

McWilliams, Larry S., Sr. V.P.-Sls. U.S. Future Consumption--The Minute Maid Company, Houston, TX; *U.S. Public*, pg. 392

McWilliams, Timothy C., Exec. V.P.--McWilliams Forge Co., Rockaway, NJ; *U.S. Private*, pg. 725

Meade, Mary Pat, Dir.-Sls.--GTCO Corporation, Columbia, MD; *U.S. Private*, pg. 436

Meadows, Jeff, V.P.-Shaw Retail Stores Devel.--Evans-Black Carpet Mills, Dalton, GA; *U.S. Public*, pg. 1464

Meaker, Don, V.P.-Sls.--Borden Foods Canada, Etobicoke, Canada; *U.S. Private*, pg. 159

Meals, Kathy, Dir.-Sls.--Calvin Klein Cosmetics Company, New York, NY; *Int'l*, pg. 1435

Means, Doug, V.P.-Field Sls.--Zenith Data Systems, Deerfield, IL; *Int'l*, pg. 317

Mears, Kirk, V.P.-Sls. & Mktg.--Carrington Laboratories, Inc., Irving, TX; *U.S. Public*, pg. 309

Mechanic, David M., Dir.-Sls. & Mktg.--Rubber Molding Division, Norwich, CT; *U.S. Private*, pg. 355

Mechling, Robert, V.P.-Sls.--Midco International Inc., Chicago, IL; *U.S. Private*, pg. 744

Medeiros, Rick, V.P.-The Americas Sls.--Unify Corporation, San Jose, CA; *U.S. Public*, pg. 1665

Medick, Keith, Gen. Mgr.-Mktg.--Joseph T. Ryerson & Son, Inc., Chicago, IL; *U.S. Public*, pg. 879

Mefford, Dean A., Pres. & Chief Exec. Officer--Viskase Corporation, Chicago, IL; *U.S. Public*, pg. 586

Mehnert, Dana, V.P.-Intl. Sls.--Harris Corp., RF Communications Group Marketing Division, Rochester, NY; *U.S. Public*, pg. 792

Mehrlich, Richard W., Exec. V.P.-Sls & Mktg.--Medical Manager Corporation, Tampa, FL; *U.S. Public*, pg. 1080

Mehtlan, David L., V.P.-Sls. & Mktg.--American Stone-Mix, Inc., Towson, MD; *U.S. Private*, pg. 62

Meier, George, V.P.-Sls.--Autologic Information International Ltd. (Australia), Morabbin, Australia; *U.S. Public*, pg. 1724

Meier, John, Mgr.-Sls.--Armada Corporation, Detroit, MI; *U.S. Private*, pg. 82

Meier, John, Mgr.-Sls.--Hoskins Mfg. Co., Detroit, MI; *U.S. Private*, pg. 83

Meijer-Jentink, N.L.H., Mgr.-Adv. & Sls. Promo.--Delft Instruments N.V., Delft, Netherlands; *Int'l*, pg. 388

Meike, Bill, Dir.-Sls.--Rawal Engravers, Villa Park, IL; *U.S. Public*, pg. 1506

Meinicke, Holger, Mgr.-Sls. & Mktg.--Degussa Corp., Dental Dept., South Plainfield, NJ; *Int'l*, pg. 388

Meis, John, V.P.-Sls. & Mktg.--Cross Creek Apparel, Inc., Mount Airy, NC; *U.S. Public*, pg. 1413

Meisel, James A., V.P.-Sls.--Drake Bakeries, Inc., Wayne, NJ; *Int'l*, pg. 349

Meisel, Julius, V.P.-Sls.--Gould Paper Corporation, New York, NY; *U.S. Private*, pg. 466

Meisinger, Steve, V.P.-Sls. & Mdsg.--Amurol Confections Co., Yorkville, IL; *U.S. Public*, pg. 1781

Meister, Mark A., V.P.-Sls. & Mktg.--Post Glover Resistors Inc., Erlanger, KY; *Int'l*, pg. 590

Mekus, Tom, V.P.-Sls. & Mktg.--Diehl Specialties International, Defiance, OH; *U.S. Private*, pg. 332

Melancon, Rudy, Sls. & Service Mgr.--Varco BJ Drilling Systems, New Iberia, LA; *U.S. Public*, pg. 1709

Melchoir, James, Dir.-Agency Sls.--MSI Insurance Companies, Arden Hills, MN; *U.S. Private*, pg. 688

Melehes, Nicholas, Dir.-Field Sls.--Institution Food House, Inc., Hickory, NC; *U.S. Private*, pg. 657

Melhuish, James P., Mgr.-Retail Sls.--Algood Food Company, Louisville, KY; *U.S. Private*, pg. 34

Melhuish, Nicolas B., Mgr.-Industrial Sls.--Algood Food Company, Louisville, KY; *U.S. Private*, pg. 34

Melien, Doug, V.P.-Mktg. & Sls.--GSW Water Heating Company, Fergus, Canada; *Int'l*, pg. 538

Mellecker, Kirk, V.P.-Sls. Food Services--Ventura Foods, City of Industry, CA; *U.S. Private*, pg. 508

Mellinger, Sandy, Mgr.-Retail Adv.-ServiStar--TruServ Corporation, Chicago, IL; *U.S. Private*, pg. 1108

Melsgaard, Lars, Mgr.-Sls.--All Plast A-S, Havndal, Denmark; *Int'l*, pg. 460

Melson, Erling, Dir.-Sls.--Pronova Oleochemicals a.s., Sandefjord, Norway; *Int'l*, pg. 961

Melton, Bruce C., V.P.-Sls.--Butler Automatic, Inc., Canton, MA; *U.S. Private*, pg. 189

Melton, Harrold, V.P.-Sls.--Acme Brick Co., Fort Worth, TX; *U.S. Public*, pg. 936

Melwid, David, Dir.-Sls. & Mktg.--PTS Electronics Corporation, Bloomington, IN; *U.S. Private*, pg. 828

Menapace, David, V.P.-Representative Sls. & Opers.--Agway Retail Services, Syracuse, NY; *U.S. Private*, pg. 27

Menard, Guy, Mgr.-Mktg.--Alcan Aluminium Limited, Montreal, Canada; *Int'l*, pg. 50

Menard, Luc-Alexandre, Sr. V.P.-Mercosur Unit--Renault, Boulogne-Billancourt, France; *Int'l*, pg. 1102

Menard, Real, V.P.-Sls.--Grocery Division, Montreal, Canada; *Int'l*, pg. 348

Mencher, Stuart, V.P.-Mktg. & Sls.--Teleport Communications Group, Staten Island, NY; *U.S. Public*, pg. 1572

Menconi, Larry, V.P.-Sls.--Midwest Litho Arts, Des Plaines, IL; *U.S. Public*, pg. 1779

Mendelson, Morrie, Exec. V.P.-Intl. Sls.--Shorewood Packaging Corporation of Canada, Ltd., Scarborough, Canada; *U.S. Public*, pg. 1468

Mendelson, Stuart, Sr. V.P.-Sales Div.--Murry's, Inc., Upper Marlboro, MD; *U.S. Private*, pg. 768

Mendez, Abe, V.P.-Sls.--Vertex Computer Cable Products, Farmingdale, NY; *U.S. Public*, pg. 1718

Mendius, L., V.P.-Sls. & Dir.-Mktg.--Silbrico Corporation, Hodgkins, IL; *U.S. Private*, pg. 1000

Mendoza, Andy, V.P.-Sls. & Mktg.--Nor-Cal Beverage Co., Inc., West Sacramento, CA; *U.S. Private*, pg. 801

Menne, J., V.P.-Sls.--TK Gray, Minneapolis, MN; *U.S. Public*, *pg. 1329*

Mentzer, Bob, V.P.-Sls./Southeast--Coram Healthcare Corporation, Denver, CO; *U.S. Public*, pg. 446

Menzies, D. Stephen, Sr. V.P.-Sls. & Mktg.--General American Transportation Corporation, Chicago, IL; U.S. Public, pg. 692
Menzies, Dennis, V.P.-Sls.--Superior Tube Company, Collegeville, PA; U.S. Private, pg. 1056
Meola, Peter, V.P.-Mktg. & Sls.--Castrol North America, Wayne, NJ; Int'l, pg. 235
Mercer, Bruce K., V.P.-Mktg., Sls. & Prod./Brand Mgr.--Swift Instruments, Inc., Dorchester, MA; U.S. Private, pg. 1058
Mercer, Reuben E., V.P.-Credit--Carlyle & Co. Jewelers, Greensboro, NC; U.S. Private, pg. 213
Mercer, Ron, V.P.-Sls.--Coats North America, Charlotte, NC; Int'l, pg. 300
Merello, Agustin, Mgr.-Sls.--Gillette Argentina S.A., Buenos Aires, Argentina; U.S. Public, pg. 744
Merideth, Ed, Exec. V.P.-Sls.--Barton Beers, Ltd., Chicago, IL; U.S. Public, pg. 300
Merkel, Joe, Sls. Mgr.-Western Reg.--Houston Fearless 76 Inc., Compton, CA; U.S. Private, pg. 542
Merker, Dave, Dir.-Sls. & Mktg./Commercial Prods.--Cantex Inc., Mineral Wells, TX; Int'l, pg. 1312
Merkley, Dean, V.P.-Mktg. & Sls.--Litton Solid State, Santa Clara, CA; U.S. Public, pg. 1003
Merling, Eric, Mgr.-Gen. Sls.--Astro Homes, Shippenville, PA; U.S. Public, pg. 318
Merlo, Mark, Mgr.-Sls., Western Reg.--FMC Corp., Agricultural Products Group, Philadelphia, PA; U.S. Public, pg. 605
Merlond, Manuel, Mgr.-Sls.--Standard Supply & Hardware Co., New Orleans, LA; U.S. Private, pg. 1032
Meroni, Giuliano, V.P.-Intl. Sls. & Mktg.--Advanced Micro Devices, Inc., Sunnyvale, CA; U.S. Public, pg. 21
Merrer, P., Mgr.-Sls. Office--Steelweld Division Zweigniederlassung Bonn der Ambac B.V., Saint Augustin, Germany; Int'l, pg. 71
Merrill, Dick, V.P.-Sls. & Mktg.--Mayfran International, Inc., Cleveland, OH; Int'l, pg. 1397
Merrill, Fred, V.P.-Sls. & Mktg.--Bristol Babcock, Inc., Watertown, CT; Int'l, pg. 472
Merrill, Robert L., Sr. V.P.-Mktg. & Sls.--Fraser Papers, Inc., Stamford, CT; Int'l, pg. 434
Merwise, Norm, Sr. V.P.-Sls. & Mktg.--Scripto-Tokai Corp., Fontana, CA; U.S. Private, pg. 977
Mescher, Gary, V.P.-Mktg.--Georgia Tent & Awning Inc., Atlanta, GA; U.S. Private, pg. 448
Mesec, Susan, Sr. V.P.-Mktg. & Sls.--Stern's, Paramus, NJ; U.S. Public, pg. 618
Meska, Richard, Gen. Mgr.-Licensing Sls.--Eskimo Pie Corporation, Richmond, VA; U.S. Public, pg. 592
Meskill, James F., Sr. V.P.-Sls.--Kay Home Products, Inc., Cleveland, OH; U.S. Public, pg. 1258
Messinger, Craig, Exec. V.P.-Fixed Income Trading & Sls.--Fidelity Investments (FMR Corp.), Boston, MA; U.S. Private, pg. 402
Messinger, David G., Sr. V.P.-Sls. & Mktg.--Bush Industries Inc., Jamestown, NY; U.S. Public, pg. 270
Messmer, Daniel A., V.P.-Sls. & Mktg.--Escalade Sports, Evansville, IN; U.S. Public, pg. 591
Metcalf, Linda, V.P.-Admin. Svcs.--Bairnco Corporation, Maitland, FL; U.S. Public, pg. 165
Metcalfe, Frank T., V.P.-Natl. Sls.--Cummings Inc., Nashville, TN; U.S. Private, pg. 295
Metenier, Alain, Dir.-Sls.--Laboratoire LaChartre S.A., Blois, France; U.S. Public, pg. 1331
Methe, Kim, V.P.-Exhibitor Sls. & Service--Freeman Decorating Co., Dallas, TX; U.S. Private, pg. 426
Mettler, Max, Asst. V.P.-Sls.--Bobst S.A., Lausanne, Switzerland; Int'l, pg. 198
Metzgar, Gary, Mgr.-Sls. & Mktg.--North American Products Corp., Jasper, IN; U.S. Private, pg. 803
Metzler, E., V.P.-Sls.--Maghielse Tool Corporation, Grand Rapids, MI; U.S. Private, pg. 694
Meudt, Alan, V.P.-Sls. & Mktg.--MWCA, Rexburg, ID; U.S. Public, pg. 804
Meuser, Dan, V.P.-Sls.--Pride Health Care, Inc., Exeter, PA; U.S. Private, pg. 883
Meyer, Bruce, Dir.-Sls.--Schlumberger Industries, Owenton, KY; U.S. Public, pg. 1439
Meyer, Friedrich, Dir.-Sls.--Fresenius AG, Bad Hamburg, Germany; Int'l, pg. 505
Meyer, Geoffrey E., Dir.-Adv. Sls.--Barron's The Dow Jones Business & Financial Weekly, New York, NY; U.S. Public, pg. 524
Meyer, Greg, V.P.-Sls.--Chemdal Corporation, Palatine, IL; U.S. Public, pg. 64
Meyer, Gregory, V.P.-Sls. & Mktg.--Fluor Daniel GTI, Inc., Norwood, MA; U.S. Public, pg. 660
Meyer, James, Exec. V.P.-Mktg. & Sls., Americas--Thomson Consumer Electronics Inc., Indianapolis, IN; Int'l, pg. 1383
Meyer, Jeff, Mgr.-Reg. Sls. Midwest--Evenflo Company, Inc., Piqua, OH; U.S. Private, pg. 629
Meyer, Joseph, Grp. V.P.-Vegetable Oils, Pet Foods & Ag. Environ. Prod.--Ag Processing Inc., A Cooperative, Omaha, NE; U.S. Private, pg. 26
Meyer, Kent, Sr. V.P.-Imaging--Saztec International, Inc., Billerica, MA; U.S. Public, pg. 1435
Meyer, M., Dir.-Sls.-Construction Equipment--Case France S.A., Paris, France; U.S. Public, pg. 1579
Meyer, Stephen, V.P. & Asst. Mgr.-Sls.--Gould Paper Corporation, New York, NY; U.S. Private, pg. 466
Meyer, Walter, Mgr.-Sls., N.E., NYC & Lat. America--Singapore Airlines Ltd., New York, NY; Int'l, pg. 1374
Meyers, Jan, Dir.-Sls.--Badger Air Brush Company, Franklin Park, IL; U.S. Private, pg. 110
Meyerson, Aaron, Sr. V.P.-Motion Pictures--DIC Entertainment, Burbank, CA; U.S. Public, pg. 513
Miale, Richard, V.P.-Sls.--Industrial Wire Products Corporation, Pomona, CA; U.S. Private, pg. 561
Michaek, Martin, Mgr.-Sls. Promo.--Century Publishing Company, Evanston, IL; U.S. Private, pg. 226
Michael, Dennis M., V.P.-Sls.--Frederick Trading Company, Frederick, MD; U.S. Private, pg. 335
Michaelis, Dana, Sr. V.P.-Affiliate Sls.--The Weather Channel, Atlanta, GA; U.S. Private, pg. 647
Michaelis, Dana, V.P.-Affiliated Sls.--The Travel Channel, Atlanta, GA; U.S. Private, pg. 647
Michaels, Dennis, V.P.-Sls.--Leslie - Locke, Inc., Atlanta, GA; U.S. Public, pg. 989
Michaelson, Edward, V.P.-Sls./New Business Div.--Brother International Corporation, Somerset, NJ; Int'l, pg. 229
Michaelson, Richard, Dir.-Sls.--RFI Corp., Bay Shore, NY; U.S. Public, pg. 494
Michaud, Laura, V.P.-Sls. & Mktg.--Beltone Electronics Corporation, Chicago, IL; U.S. Private, pg. 132
Michaud, William, Dir.-Sls.--MFE Instruments, Salem, NH; U.S. Public, pg. 1518
Michaud, William J., V.P.-Sls. & Mktg.--Stocker & Yale, Inc., Salem, NH; U.S. Public, pg. 1518
Michel, Cyrille, Mgr.-North American Sls.--Blount, Inc. Oregon Cutting Systems Division, Portland, OR; U.S. Public, pg. 238
Michel, John, Assoc. Publr.--Benjamin Franklin Literary & Medical Society, Inc., Indianapolis, IN; U.S. Private, pg. 133
Michel, Pierre, Dir.-Sls.--Hoffmann-La Roche Ltd., Mississauga, Canada; Int'l, pg. 1121
Michella, Steve, V.P.-Sls.--Eggland's Best, Inc., King of Prussia, PA; U.S. Private, pg. 366
Michelotti, Bob, Dir.-Sls.--Roney & Co., Detroit, MI; U.S. Private, pg. 943
Michels, Scott, V.P.-Worldwide Sls.--CBS Enterprises Division, New York, NY; U.S. Public, pg. 274
Michelson, Robert, V.P.-Sls.--Easy Day Manufacturing Company, Holliston, MA; U.S. Private, pg. 358
Mick, Richard, V.P.-Sls. & Mktg.--IWI Holding Limited, Westmont, IL; U.S. Public, pg. 861
Mickey, Scott, V.P.-Sls.--Brent Transportation Co., Greenville, MS; U.S. Public, pg. 961
Middleton, Paul, Mgr.-Mktg. Services--The Marley Cooling Tower Co., Overland Park, KS; U.S. Public, pg. 1676
Middleton, Richard, Dir.-Sls.--CAIRE, Inc., Burnsville, MN; U.S. Private, pg. 751
Miele, Arthur R., V.P.-Mktg. & Pres.-PD Sales Co.--Phelps Dodge Corporation, Phoenix, AZ; U.S. Public, pg. 1286
Miele, Arthur R., Pres.-Phelps Dodge Sales Company--Phelps Dodge Mining Company, Phoenix, AZ; U.S. Public, pg. 1286
Migacz, Frank, V.P.-Sls.--Jarke Corporation, Niles, IL; U.S. Private, pg. 583
Mihalich, James M., V.P.-Sls. & Mktg.--Shakespeare Monofilament, Columbia, SC; U.S. Public, pg. 940
Mihic, Paul, V.P.-Sls., South Zone--Pier 1 Imports, Inc., Fort Worth, TX; U.S. Public, pg. 1295
Milbauer, Jerry, Dir.-Mktg. & Sls.--FWD/Seagrave Fire Apparatus, Inc., Clintonville, WI; U.S. Private, pg. 390
Milburn, Robert, Mgr.-Sls. Office--Rudel Machinery Company, Inc., Shelton, CT; U.S. Private, pg. 950
Milder, Mike, Mgr.-Plant & Sls.--Golden Sun Feeds, Inc., Grinnell, IA; U.S. Private, pg. 895
Miles, Mike, Mgr.-Prod. Sls.--Worcester Controls Corp., Marlborough, MA; Int'l, pg. 128
Miles, Ron, V.P.-Sls. & Mktg.-HVAC--White-Rodgers Div., Emerson Electric Co., Saint Louis, MO; U.S. Public, pg. 573
Miles, Sharon, Mgr.-Sls.--Instructional Fair, Inc., Grand Rapids, MI; U.S. Private, pg. 288
Miley, Stephen R., V.P.-Sls.--Southdown, Inc., Houston, TX; U.S. Public, pg. 1488
Milich, Miguel, Sr. V.P.-Sls. & Mgr.-Natl. Sls.--Amcel Corp., Watertown, MA; U.S. Private, pg. 48
Miliotis, Patrick, Mgr.-Natl. Sls.--National Utility Service, S.A., Paris, France; U.S. Private, pg. 787
Millan, Augusto H., Sr. V.P. & Gen. Mgr.-Intl. Sls.--International Comfort Products, Franklin, TN; U.S. Public, pg. 898
Miller, Alton Wayne, Dir.-Sls. & Mktg.--Affiliated Foods Southwest, Little Rock, AR; U.S. Private, pg. 26
Miller, Anita, V.P.-Fin, Treas. & Sec.--Wholesale Electronic Supply, Dallas, TX; U.S. Private, pg. 1174
Miller, Archie, V.P.-Sls.--Number Nine Visual Technology, Lexington, MA; U.S. Public, pg. 1206
Miller, Ben, V.P.-Mktg. & Sls.--Whaling Industries, Inc., Fall River, MA; U.S. Private, pg. 1170
Miller, Bill, Mgr.-Category--United Dairy Farmers, Inc., Cincinnati, OH; U.S. Private, pg. 1121
Miller, Bob, Mgr.-Natl. Accts./OEM Prods.--Porcelain Metals Corp., Louisville, KY; U.S. Private, pg. 876
Miller, Bob, V.P.-Natl. Sls.--Tomco Auto Products, Inc., Los Angeles, CA; U.S. Private, pg. 1090
Miller, Bruce, V.P.-Mktg. & Sls.--E.A. Miller Company, Hyrum, UT; U.S. Public, pg. 428
Miller, Calvin, Mgr.-Sls.--Republic Die & Tool Company, Belleville, MI; U.S. Private, pg. 923
Miller, Charles, Mgr.-Sls.--Beach Mold & Tool Inc., New Albany, IN; U.S. Private, pg. 125
Miller, David, V.P.-Sls.--Wyle Electronics, Irvine, CA; Int'l, pg. 1457
Miller, David, V.P.-Mktg. & Sls.--Signature Inns, Inc., Indianapolis, IN; U.S. Public, pg. 1473
Miller, David D., V.P.-Franchise Opers., Sls. & Devel.--Checkers Drive-In Restaurants, Inc., Clearwater, FL; U.S. Public, pg. 342
Miller, Denny, Dir.-Sls.--Adventure Island, Tampa, FL; U.S. Public, pg. 114
Miller, Denny, Dir.-Sls.--Busch Gardens Tampa, Tampa, FL; U.S. Public, pg. 114
Miller, Derek, Mgr.-Intl. Sls.--Northland Aluminum Products, Inc., Minneapolis, MN; U.S. Private, pg. 805
Miller, Dick, Gen. Mgr.-Sls.--RS Electronics, Livonia, MI; U.S. Private, pg. 905
Miller, Don, Jr., V.P.-Sls.--IGT North America, Reno, NV; U.S. Public, pg. 900
Miller, Donnie, V.P.-Sls.--Prescolite Moldcast Lighting Company, San Leandro, CA; U.S. Public, pg. 1684
Miller, Doug, V.P.-Sls. & Mktg.--ComPair LeRoi, Sidney, OH; Int'l, pg. 1242
Miller, Gary, Mgr.-Sls. & Mktg.--Erlanger Tubular Corporation, Catoosa, OK; U.S. Public, pg. 1147
Miller, George, Mgr.-Sls.--Mark Lighting Fixture Co., Inc., Edison, NJ; U.S. Private, pg. 704
Miller, George, Sr. V.P.-Sls.--Fisher-Price, Inc., East Aurora, NY; U.S. Public, pg. 1058
Miller, Graham, V.P.-Sls. & Mktg.--WD-40 Company, San Diego, CA; U.S. Public, pg. 1726
Miller, J.C., Jr., V.P.-Sls. & Mktg.--Hanna Corporation, Chicago, IL; U.S. Private, pg. 231
Miller, Jack, V.P.-Sls.-Professional Div.--Andis Company, Sturtevant, WI; U.S. Private, pg. 73
Miller, James, Mgr.-Reg. Sls.--Cres-Cor, Cleveland, OH; U.S. Private, pg. 288
Miller, Jeff, V.P.-Sls. & Mktg.--Gilbert Paper, Menasha, WI; U.S. Public, pg. 1074
Miller, Jerry, Mgr.-Sls.--Fleet Engineers, Inc., Muskegon, MI; U.S. Private, pg. 410
Miller, Jim, V.P.-Sls.--Grocery Division, Montreal, Canada; Int'l, pg. 348
Miller, Jim, Exec. V.P.-Sls. & Mktg.--Sutter Home Winery, Inc., Saint Helena, CA; U.S. Private, pg. 1057
Miller, John L., Sr. V.P.-N. America Sls.--American & Efird, Inc., Mount Holly, NC; U.S. Public, pg. 1412
Miller, LeRoy, Mgr.-Sls.--Ocean Mist Farms Corp., Castroville, CA; U.S. Private, pg. 811
Miller, Mark, Mgr.-Adv.--Hiniker Company, Mankato, MN; U.S. Private, pg. 530
Miller, Mark, V.P.-Adv. Sls.--CNBC, Fort Lee, NJ; U.S. Public, pg. 712
Miller, Marty, Jr., Gen. Sls. Mgr.--Media General Broadcasting, Inc. (WJWB-TV), Jacksonville, FL; U.S. Public, pg. 1078
Miller, Michael, V.P.-Sls.--The Hain Food Group Inc., Uniondale, NY; U.S. Public, pg. 774
Miller, Mike, Dir.-Sls. & Mktg. Svcs.--Beltone Electronics Corporation, Chicago, IL; U.S. Private, pg. 132
Miller, Mira, V.P.-Sls. & Mktg.--Plastigage Corporation, Jackson, MI; U.S. Private, pg. 871
Miller, Oris, Mgr.-Sls.--DMI, Inc., Goodfield, IL; U.S. Private, pg. 305
Miller, Paul, V.P.-Sls.--Parfums International Ltd., New York, NY; Int'l, pg. 1435
Miller, Paul M., V.P.-Sls. & Sec.--Mill-Rose Company, Mentor, OH; U.S. Private, pg. 746
Miller, Raymond, V.P.-Sls. & Mktg.--National Seating Co., Vonore, TN; U.S. Private, pg. 786
Miller, Robert, Ntl. Mgr.--APV Chemical Machinery, Inc., Process Systems Div., Saginaw, MI; Int'l, pg. 1240
Miller, Scott, V.P.-Sls.--Sky Bros. Inc., Altoona, PA; U.S. Public, pg. 918
Miller, Thomas, Mgr.-Sls.-Aerospace & Defense--Enidine Incorporated, Orchard Park, NY; U.S. Private, pg. 377
Miller, Tim, Natl. Sls. Mgr.-Fertilizer--Dempster Industries Inc., Beatrice, NE; U.S. Private, pg. 324
Miller, Timothy B., V.P.-Sls. & Mktg.--Cooper Hand Tools, Raleigh, NC; U.S. Public, pg. 444
Miller, Tom, V.P.-Sls.--Lady Baltimore Foods, Inc., Kansas City, KS; U.S. Public, pg. 975
Miller, Wayne, Mgr.-Sls.--Astrex, Inc., Plainview, NY; U.S. Public, pg. 141
Miller, Wayne, V.P.-Mktg. & Sls.--Micron Separations, Inc., Westborough, MA; U.S. Private, pg. 742
Millermann, Dr., Dir.-Sls.--Boehringer Mannheim GmbH, Mannheim, Germany; Int'l, pg. 331
Millican, Bryan, V.P.-Sls. & Mktg.--Con-Way Transportation Services, Palo Alto, CA; U.S. Public, pg. 281
Milligan, Bill, V.P.-Sls.--Hoffmann-La Roche Ltd., Mississauga, Canada; Int'l, pg. 1121
Millot, Daniel, V.P.-Sls. & Customer Service--CF Cable TV Inc., Montreal, Canada; Int'l, pg. 240
Mills, Fred E., Dir.-Sls.--Lamb Engineering & Construction Co., Salt Lake City, UT; U.S. Private, pg. 644
Mills, Jack, Sr. V.P.-Sls.--Bob Evans Farms, Inc., Columbus, OH; U.S. Public, pg. 596
Mills, Manker, Mgr.-Natl. Sls.--Homasote Company, Trenton, NJ; U.S. Public, pg. 831
Milne, Chris, Dir.-Sls.--Taunton Cider Company P.L.C., Taunton, United Kingdom; Int'l, pg. 849
Milnen, David, Mgr.-Sls.--Campbell Grocery Products Ltd., Kings Lynn, United Kingdom; U.S. Public, pg. 299
Minahan, John, Dir.-Sls.--Federal Industries, Inc., Belleville, WI; U.S. Public, pg. 1506
Minassian, Don, V.P.-Sls.--Master International Corp., Santa Monica, CA; U.S. Private, pg. 713
Minchella, Ken, Sls. Mgr.--PacAero, Burbank, CA; U.S. Public, pg. 187
Mindrum, Mark D., V.P.-Direct Sls. Midwest--Wallace Computer Services, Inc., Lisle, IL; U.S. Public, pg. 1735
Miner, Gary, Dir.-Technology Sls.--Imaging Technologies Corp., San Diego, CA; U.S. Public, pg. 870
Miner, Richard, Sr. V.P.-Sls.--Gould Paper Corporation, New York, NY; U.S. Private, pg. 466
Ming, Grace, V.P.-Sls.--The McGuire Furniture Company, San Francisco, CA; U.S. Private, pg. 630
Minier, Mary, Mgr.-Sls. & Admin.--Allied Carbi-Tech, Inc., Topeka, IN; U.S. Private, pg. 38
Minns, Richard V., Mgr.-Sls.--Kennametal Metalworking Systems Div., Latrobe, PA; U.S. Public, pg. 950
Minogue, Daniel P., V.P.-Sls.--Precision Valve Corporation, Yonkers, NY; U.S. Private, pg. 880
Minor, Bill, V.P.-Mktg.--Ohio Casualty Corporation, Hamilton, OH; U.S. Public, pg. 1214
Minton, James A., V.P.-Sls.--Lovejoy Inc., Downers Grove, IL; U.S. Private, pg. 677
Mintz, Morris, V.P.-Sls.--Lasco Bathware, Anaheim, CA; Int'l, pg. 1397
Mintz, Phil, Mgr.-Natl. Sls.--Head USA, Inc., Columbia, MD; U.S. Private, pg. 514
Mintzer, Keith, V.P.-Sls.--Hayes Microcomputer Products, Inc., Norcross, GA; U.S. Public, pg. 801
Minutillo, Larry, Reg. V.P.-N. Sls.--American Freightways Corporation, Harrison, AR; U.S. Public, pg. 75

Minutolo, Michael V., V.P.-Sls.--F.H. Chase, Inc., Mansfield, MA; *U.S. Private*, pg. 230
Mirabella, Paul J., V.P.-Americas Sls.--G.E. Medical Systems, Milwaukee, WI; *U.S. Public*, pg. 710
Miraselli, Anthony, Sr. V.P.-Mktg. & Sls.--Cobra Electronics Corporation, Chicago, IL; *U.S. Public*, pg. 391
Miripol, Jeff, Mgr.-Sls., Transfusion Div.--Terumo Medical Corporation, Somerset, NJ; *Int'l*, pg. 1376
Misco, Jim, Dir.-Domestic Sls.--Vision-Ease Lens Inc., Brooklyn Park, MN; *U.S. Public*, pg. 162
Mishler, Jim, V.P.-Sls. & Mktg.--Lennox International Inc., Richardson, TX; *U.S. Private*, pg. 659
Mishler, Jim, Mgr.-Mktg. & Sls.--Lennox Industries Inc., Richardson, TX; *U.S. Private*, pg. 659
Mitch, Warren, Mgr.-Inside Sls.--Bel Fuse Inc., Jersey City, NJ; *U.S. Public*, pg. 200
Mitchell, Beverly L., Sr. V.P. & Chief Market Mgr.--MainStreet BankGroup Incorporated, Martinsville, VA; *U.S. Public*, pg. 1038
Mitchell, Brian, Dir.-Sls. & Mktg.--Provident Music Group, Brentwood, TN; *Int'l*, pg. 1529
Mitchell, Carol, Dir.-Sls.--INSO Corporation, Boston, MA; *U.S. Public*, pg. 882
Mitchell, Clay, V.P.-Sls.--The Sperry & Hutchinson Company, Inc., New York, NY; *U.S. Public*, pg. 990
Mitchell, Doug, Rep.-Sls.--American Journal of Nursing Company, New York, NY; *Int'l*, pg. 1513
Mitchell, James, V.P.-Sls.--Shea Communications Co., Smyrna, GA; *U.S. Private*, pg. 990
Mitchell, Jennifer, Mgr.-Sls.--Annabelle Candy Company, Inc., Hayward, CA; *U.S. Private*, pg. 75
Mitchell, Jim, Reg. V.P.-Sls.--Allied Digital Technologies, Elk Grove Village, IL; *U.S. Public*, pg. 48
Mitchell, Jim, V.P.-Development Mkts.--Good Humor/Breyers Ice Cream, Green Bay, WI; *Int'l*, pg. 1435
Mitchell, Ken, R.Ph., V.P.-Managed Care Sls.--Bindley Western Drug Company, Indianapolis, IN; *U.S. Public*, pg. 228
Mitchell, Morris, Mgr.-Sls.--Wemco, Inc., New Orleans, LA; *U.S. Private*, pg. 909
Mitchell, Randy, Dir.-Sls.--Pioneer Express Inc., Indianapolis, IN; *Int'l*, pg. 1469
Mitchell, Roy, V.P.-Sls. & Mktg.--American Furniture Company, Incorporated, Martinsville, VA; *U.S. Public*, pg. 974
Mitchell, Wayne, Sr. Dir.-OTR Tire Sls.--Continental General Tire, Inc., Charlotte, NC; *Int'l*, pg. 327
Mitchell, William, Mgr.-Sls. & Services--Suntec Industries Inc., Rockford, IL; *U.S. Private*, pg. 1054
Mitsuoka, Teruo, Sr. Mng. Dir.-Domestic Mktg. & Sls.--Mazda Motor Corporation, Hiroshima, Japan; *Int'l*, pg. 849
Miyata, Keiichi, Exec. Dir. & Grp. Gen. Mgr.-Sls. & Mktg.--Sharp Corporation, Osaka, Japan; *Int'l*, pg. 1228
Mizell, Sidney C., Sr. V.P.-Sls. & Mktg.--Halter Marine Group, Inc., Gulfport, MS; *U.S. Public*, pg. 778
Mizuno, H., V.P.-Indus. Sls.--TDK Electronics Corporation, Port Washington, NY; *Int'l*, pg. 1336
Moar, Jim, Dir.-Mktg. & Sls.--AlliedSignal Ocean Systems, Sylmar, CA; *U.S. Public*, pg. 50
Moccia, Robert, Dir.-Sls.--Dermik Laboratories, Inc., Collegeville, PA; *Int'l*, pg. 1110
Mock, Joe, Mgr.-Natl. Sls. & Mktg.--Douglas/Quikut, Walnut Ridge, AR; *U.S. Public*, pg. 217
Modlin, Bill, V.P.-Sls. & Mktg.--Hathaway Process Instrumentation, Carrollton, TX; *U.S. Public*, pg. 799
Moehling, Paul M., Mgr.-Sls.--Sommer Metalcraft Corporation, Crawfordsville, IN; *U.S. Private*, pg. 1013
Moeller, Bill, Dir.-Sls./Rational--The Middleby Corporation, Rolling Meadows, IL; *U.S. Public*, pg. 1109
Moeller, Paul, V.P.-American Sls.--VideoServer, Inc., Burlington, MA; *U.S. Public*, pg. 1720
Moen, Doug, V.P.-Sls. & Mktg.--Rea Magnet Wire Company, Inc., Fort Wayne, IN; *U.S. Private*, pg. 913
Moersen, Mark, V.P.-Sls.--Reed Tool Company, Houston, TX; *U.S. Public*, pg. 298
Moffat, Sheree, Dir.-Sls.--Turtle Bay Hilton Golf & Tennis Resort, Kahuku, HI; *U.S. Public*, pg. 829
Moffatt, W., Mgr.-Sls.--Standard Medical Imaging, Inc., Columbia, MD; *U.S. Private*, pg. 1032
Moffit, Robert, V.P.-Sls.-Motorcycles--Kawasaki Motors Corp., U.S.A., Irvine, CA; *Int'l*, pg. 725
Mogol, Alan, V.P.-Sls. & Mktg.--Poly Pak America, Inc., Los Angeles, CA; *U.S. Private*, pg. 875
Mogul, Michael P., V.P.-Sls.--Osteonics Corp., Allendale, NJ; *U.S. Public*, pg. 1526
Mohn, Lou, V.P.-Sls.-Western Region--Business Week, New York, NY; *U.S. Public*, pg. 1069
Mohr, Jeff, Mgr.-Natl. Sls.--Welbilt Varimixer, Shreveport, LA; *Int'l*, pg. 189
Mohr, Nancy, Mgr.-Sales Services--Alsons Corporation, Hillsdale, MI; *U.S. Public*, pg. 1053
Mohr, Terrence B., V.P.-U.S. Grocery--The Quaker Oats Company, Chicago, IL; *U.S. Public*, pg. 1347
Mohr, Terrence B., V.P.-Sls.--U.S. & Canadian Food Products, Chicago, IL; *U.S. Public*, pg. 1347
Mohrm, Ross, Mgr.-Professional Svcs. Sls.--The Golden Touch Division, Chicago, IL; *U.S. Private*, pg. 459
Moidel, Harland E., V.P.-Adv. Sls.--Comcast Cable Communications, Inc., Philadelphia, PA; *U.S. Public*, pg. 407
Moilanen, Karl E., Mgr.-Crane Rental & Sls. Coord.--Cloverdale Equipment Co., Oak Park, MI; *U.S. Private*, pg. 247
Mojica, Sergenti, Mgr.-Sls. & Mktg.--Eurocermex N.V., Brussels, Belgium; *U.S. Public*, pg. 115
Molbury, Kevin T., V.P.-Sls.--Royal Doulton USA Inc., Somerset, NJ; *Int'l*, pg. 1135
Moley, Miriam, Exec. V.P.-Mktg.--Carson Products Company, Savannah, GA; *U.S. Public*, pg. 309
Molina, Lee, Mgr.-Sls.--Earle Industries, Inc., Earle, AR; *U.S. Private*, pg. 356
Molinari, M.V., V.P.-Sls. & Mktg.-North America--The Goodyear Tire & Rubber Company, Akron, OH; *U.S. Public*, pg. 752
Molkup, Kenneth, V.P.-Sls. & Mktg.--Premdor, Inc., Tampa, FL; *Int'l*, pg. 1067
Moll, Bob, Mgr.-Sls.--Tank Division, Fremont, OH; *U.S. Public*, pg. 345
Moloney, Herbert W., Sr. V.P.-Mktg. & Sls.--Treasure Chest Advertising Co., Inc., Glendora, CA; *U.S. Public*, pg. 228
Molyneux, Greg, Mgr.-Intl. Sls., Middle East--Royal Skandia Life Assurance Ltd., Nicosia, Cyprus; *Int'l*, pg. 1257
Momper, Jerry, V.P.-Natl. Sls.--Whiting Manufacturing Co., Inc., Cincinnati, OH; *U.S. Private*, pg. 1174
Monachino, Joseph J., V.P.-Sls. & Mktg.--Alarmguard Holdings, Inc., Orange, CT; *U.S. Public*, pg. 35
Monaco, Gilberto, Dir.-Sls.--Sao Paulo Alpargatas S.A., Sao Paulo, Brazil; *Int'l*, pg. 1193
Monaghan, Pat, V.P.-Retail Sls.--Agripac Inc., Salem, OR; *U.S. Private*, pg. 26
Monahan, Dianne, Dir.-Industry Prods.--MacDermid Incorporated, Waterbury, CT; *U.S. Public*, pg. 1029
Monahan, Jim, V.P.-Sls.--Riverwood International Corporation, Atlanta, GA; *U.S. Public*, pg. 1391
Monahan, William G., V.P.-Sls.--Gould Paper Corporation-New England, Stoughton, MA; *U.S. Private*, pg. 467
Monette, Jerry, Mgr.-Sls., Promo. & Adv.--Allison Transmission, Indianapolis, IN; *U.S. Public*, pg. 719
Mongeau, Jean, Gen. Mgr.-Sls. & Mktg.--Reseau de Television Quatre Saisons Inc., Montreal, Canada; *Int'l*, pg. 241
Mongiello, Patrick A., V.P.-Mktg. & Sls.--Brunschwig & Fils, Inc., White Plains, NY; *U.S. Private*, pg. 176
Monhollen, Ken, Mgr.-Svcs.--Kissimmee Toyota Inc., Kissimmee, FL; *U.S. Private*, pg. 624
Monihan, Robin, V.P.-Adv. & Sls.--SAE Engineering, Inc., Santa Clara, CA; *U.S. Private*, pg. 955
Monken, G.W., V.P.-Corp. Sls.--Emerson Electric Co., Saint Louis, MO; *U.S. Public*, pg. 572
Monocchio, Tony, V.P.-Sls. & Mktg.--The National Latex Products Co., Ashland, OH; *U.S. Private*, pg. 785
Monos, Jean-Francois, Mgr.-Intl. Govt. Sls.--World Trade Transport of Virginia, Sterling, VA; *U.S. Public*, pg. 749
Monroe, Bill, V.P.-Sls.--Bombardier, Learjet Inc., Wichita, KS; *Int'l*, pg. 200
Monroe, Laurie, Dir.-Sls.--Hoxan America Incorporated, Piscataway, NJ; *Int'l*, pg. 363
Monroe, Michael, Reg. V.P.-Sls.--White Cap Industries, Inc., Costa Mesa, CA; *U.S. Public*, pg. 1765
Monroe, Thomas O., Jr., V.P.-Intl. Sls.--The Johnson Corporation, Three Rivers, MI; *U.S. Private*, pg. 591
Monsegur, Santiago, Dir.-Commercial--Renault Argentina, Buenos Aires, Argentina; *Int'l*, pg. 1103
Monsu, Philippe, Gen. Mgr.-Sls. & Mktg.--DynetCom, Guyancourt, France; *Int'l*, pg. 425
Montalvo, Michael A., V.P.-Mktg. & Sls.--Sierra Health Services, Inc., Las Vegas, NV; *U.S. Public*, pg. 1469
Montalvo, Mike, V.P.-Mktg. & Sls.--Sierra Health and Life Insurance Company, Inc., Las Vegas, NV; *U.S. Public*, pg. 1469
Montanaro, Carl, Sr. V.P.-Sls. & Mdsg.--Foodarama Supermarkets, Inc., Freehold, NJ; *U.S. Public*, pg. 661
Montesano, Nick, V.P.-Mdse.--Quill Corp., Lincolnshire, IL; *U.S. Private*, pg. 901
Montgomery, Bob, V.P.-Retail Sls.--McCain Foods Inc., Oak Brook, IL; *Int'l*, pg. 850
Montgomery, David, V.P.-Sls.--Biomet, Inc., Warsaw, IN; *U.S. Public*, pg. 231
Montgomery, Jim, V.P.-Industrial Prods. Sls.--Henley Paper Company, Greensboro, NC; *U.S. Private*, pg. 522
Montiegel, Jim, V.P.-Volume Sls.--Jumping Jacks, Monett, MO; *U.S. Private*, pg. 767
Montisano, Joe, Dir.-Sls.--Sea World of Ohio, Aurora, OH; *U.S. Public*, pg. 114
Montouri, Vin, V.P.-Sls.--Club Med Sales, Inc., New York, NY; *Int'l*, pg. 298
Monzon, Medardo, Mgr.-Sls. & Mktg.--Arizona Chemical Div., Panama City, FL; *U.S. Public*, pg. 901
Moody, Bill, Mgr.-Sls.--Magnacraft, Struthers, Dunn, Inc., Northfield, IL; *U.S. Private*, pg. 695
Moody, H.A., Dir.-Mktg. & Sls.--Ferguson Machine Co., Saint Louis, MO; *U.S. Public*, pg. 457
Moody, John, V.P.-Sls.--Action Industries, Inc., Tupelo, MS; *U.S. Public*, pg. 688
Moody, John R., V.P.-Fresh Meat Sls.--The Smithfield Packing Co., Inc., Smithfield, VA; *U.S. Public*, pg. 1479
Moody, Tim, V.P.-Sls.--United States Filter Corporation, Palm Desert, CA; *U.S. Public*, pg. 1681
Moody, Tim, V.P.-Sls.--U.S. Filter/Arrowhead Inc., Rockford, IL; *U.S. Public*, pg. 1682
Moola, Aslam, Mgr.-Reg. Sls.--Sasol Alpha Olefins, Rosebank, South Africa; *Int'l*, pg. 1196
Moolenburgh, A., Mgr.-Sls.-Forms & Supplies--Moore Nederland B.V., Amsterdam, Netherlands; *Int'l*, pg. 890
Moon, Alan, V.P.-Intl. Sls.--Duo-Fast Corporation, Huntley, IL; *U.S. Private*, pg. 347
Moon, John, V.P.-Sls. & Mktg.--M&W, Gibson City, IL; *U.S. Public*, pg. 35
Moon, Patti, Mgr.-Sls.--American City Business Journals, Inc., Austin, TX; *U.S. Private*, pg. 19
Moone, Robert H., V.P. & Dir.-Sls. & Mktg.--State Auto P & C, Columbus, OH; *U.S. Private*, pg. 1036
Mooradian, Erich, V.P.-Sls.--Johnstown Knitting Mill Co., Johnstown, NY; *U.S. Private*, pg. 595
Moore, Arthur, Mgr.-Sls.--Schaedler Brothers, Inc., Harrisburg, PA; *U.S. Private*, pg. 969
Moore, Barbara, Mktg. & Sls. Coord.--Syseca Inc., Marina Del Rey, CA; *Int'l*, pg. 1384
Moore, Bob, V.P.-Sls.--Bush Hog Division, Selma, AL; *U.S. Public*, pg. 48
Moore, Carl, Mgr.-Sls.--Heidtman Steel Products, Inc., Toledo, OH; *U.S. Private*, pg. 519
Moore, Chris, Mgr.-Sls.--Field Controls Co., Kinston, NC; *U.S. Private*, pg. 860
Moore, Chris, Mgr.-Reg. Sls.--Pepsi-Cola Bottling Company of Richmond, Inc., Richmond, VA; *U.S. Public*, pg. 1277
Moore, Chris, V.P.-Natl. Retail Sls.--Miller Brewing Company, Milwaukee, WI; *U.S. Public*, pg. 1289
Moore, Dan, V.P.-Sls. & Mktg.--Target Stamped Products Corp., Kinsman, OH; *U.S. Private*, pg. 1069
Moore, Dave, V.P.-Sls.--DonTech, Chicago, IL; *U.S. Public*, pg. 98
Moore, David, Dir.-Sls., Asia & Americas--Hycor Biomedical, Inc., Irvine, CA; *U.S. Public*, pg. 851
Moore, Donald, V.P.-Sales--Polytech Netting Industries, Troy, MI; *Int'l*, pg. 1362
Moore, Gary, V.P.-Sls.--Victaulic Company of Canada Limited, Rexdale, Canada; *U.S. Private*, pg. 1138
Moore, Gary D., Dir.-Somerset Sls. Grp.--Guinness Southern Division, Newport Beach, CA; *Int'l*, pg. 412
Moore, Gene, Gen. Mgr. & Sls. Mgr.-Children's Div.--Trimfoot Company, Farmington, MO; *U.S. Public*, pg. 1684
Moore, James, Mgr.-Sls.--Monson Trucking, Inc., Duluth, MN; *U.S. Private*, pg. 758
Moore, Jerry, Dist. Sls. Mgr.-Alabama--Magneco/Metrel, Inc., Addison, IL; *U.S. Private*, pg. 695
Moore, John O., Mng. Dir.--Duncan Equipment Company, Oklahoma City, OK; *U.S. Private*, pg. 346
Moore, Johnny, V.P.-Sls.--Wisdom Imports Sales Co. Inc., Irvine, CA; *Int'l*, pg. 679
Moore, Madeline, V.P.-Sls.- Carbon Dioxide Div.--The BOC Group Inc. (Delaware), Murray Hill, NJ; *Int'l*, pg. 121
Moore, Marvin R., V.P.-Sls.--Riverdale Chemical Co., Glenwood, IL; *U.S. Private*, pg. 934
Moore, Mike, Sr. V.P.-Sls.--Shelby Williams Industries, Inc., Morristown, TN; *U.S. Public*, pg. 1464
Moore, Nancy, V.P.-Sls.--AMCORE Mortgage, Inc., Rockford, IL; *U.S. Public*, pg. 64
Moore, R., Dir.-Sls. & Mktg.--Dowty Aerospace, Wolverhampton, Wolverhampton, United Kingdom; *Int'l*, pg. 1337
Moore, Terry, V.P.-Sls.--Massachusetts Container Corporation, Marlborough, MA; *U.S. Private*, pg. 263
Moore, Tom, Natl. Sls. Mgr.--C-Line Products, Inc., Des Plaines, IL; *U.S. Private*, pg. 192
Moore, William J., V.P.-Sls.--Ortel Corporation, Alhambra, CA; *U.S. Public*, pg. 1232
Moore, William S., Sr. V.P.-Sls. & Mktg.--Rocky Shoes & Boots, Inc., Nelsonville, OH; *U.S. Public*, pg. 1402
Moorhead, J.R., V.P.-Sls.--Airline Hydraulics Corporation, Bensalem, PA; *U.S. Private*, pg. 29
Mooring, Jeff, Mgr.-Gen. Sls.--Brigadier Homes of North Carolina, Nashville, NC; *U.S. Public*, pg. 318
Moose, Bobbi, Mgr.-Program Sls.--Underwriters Management Associates, Inc., Nashville, TN; *Int'l*, pg. 1508
Moquist, Paul A., Exec. V.P.-Sls. & Mktg.--Insignia Systems, Inc., Minnetonka, MN; *U.S. Public*, pg. 881
Moraczewski, Daniel J., V.P.-Sls.--American Greetings U.S. Greeting Card Division, Cleveland, OH; *U.S. Public*, pg. 78
Moraczewski, Daniel L., V.P.-Sls.--American Greetings Corporation, Cleveland, OH; *U.S. Public*, pg. 77
Moran, James, Dir.-Sls.--Jarvis (East), Palmer, MA; *U.S. Public*, pg. 1506
Moran, Joseph G., V.P. & Gen. Sls. Mgr.--Nelson Westerberg, Somerville, NJ; *U.S. Private*, pg. 1164
Moran, Peter J., Sr. V.P. & Sls. Dir.-CNI--Rainbow Advertising Sales Corporation (RASCO), Woodbury, NY; *U.S. Public*, pg. 288
More, Ray, V.P.-Sls.--Zebco, Tulsa, OK; *U.S. Public*, pg. 265
Moreira, Juarez, Dir.-Sls.--SmithKline Beecham Laboratorios Ltda., Rio de Janeiro, Brazil; *Int'l*, pg. 1266
Moreland, Rem, V.P.-Sls.--Orbit Valve International, Inc., Little Rock, AR; *U.S. Private*, pg. 819
Moreno, Lori, Mgr.-Sls.--Southern Union Company, Austin, TX; *U.S. Public*, pg. 1491
Moretensen, Nancy, V.P.-Mktg. & Services--Zions Co-operative Mercantile Institution, Salt Lake City, UT; *U.S. Public*, pg. 1793
Morgan, Ann, Dir.-Sls.--Accecones Ricci U.S.A., Inc., New York, NY; *Int'l*, pg. 445
Morgan, Avon, V.P.-Sls.--Central Data Corporation, Champaign, IL; *U.S. Private*, pg. 223
Morgan, Bill, Dir.-Customer Svcs.--Pneumatic Scale Corporation, Cuyahoga Falls, OH; *U.S. Private*, pg. 118
Morgan, Bob, Sls.--Grayline Housewares, Carol Stream, IL; *U.S. Private*, pg. 472
Morgan, Bob, Mgr.-Natl. Sls.--Yazoo Power Equipment, LLC, Jackson, MS; *U.S. Private*, pg. 1195
Morgan, Forrester L., V.P.-Sls.--Integral Marketing, Inc., Lanham, MD; *U.S. Public*, pg. 883
Morgan, J., V.P.-Sls.--CorTec Company, Washington Court House, OH; *U.S. Public*, pg. 456
Morgan, Larry, V.P.-Sls.--Magee Co., Pocahontas, AR; *U.S. Public*, pg. 1561
Morgan, Neil, Dir.-Sls.--Sanderson Farms, Inc., Laurel, MS; *U.S. Public*, pg. 1430
Morgan, Raymond U., V.P.-Sls. & Mktg.--Barton Nelson Inc., Kansas City, MO; *U.S. Private*, pg. 120
Morgan, Rob, Sr. V.P.-Mktg., Sls. & Engrng.--Buck Knives, Inc., El Cajon, CA; *U.S. Private*, pg. 177
Morgan, Stanley, Mgr.-Sls.--St. Louis Music, Inc., Saint Louis, MO; *U.S. Private*, pg. 960
Morgenroth, Stefan, Dir.-Sls. & Mktg.--Georg Sahm GmbH & Co. KG Maschinenfabrik, Eschwege, Germany; *Int'l*, pg. 1169
Morgenstern, David, Mgr.-Natl. Sls.--Alexander Doll Company, Inc., New York, NY; *U.S. Private*, pg. 33
Morgese, Chris, V.P.-Sls. & Mktg.--Titan Tool, Inc., Oakland, NJ; *U.S. Private*, pg. 500
Mori, Yukiyoshi, Mgr.-Sls.--Eagle-Picher Far East, Inc., Nagoya, Japan; *U.S. Private*, pg. 355
Moriarty, Gene, V.P.-Personal Sls.--Playtex Products Inc., Westport, CT; *U.S. Public*, pg. 1310
Morimoto, Toru, V.P.-Sls.--CBM America Corp., Fort Lee, NJ; *U.S. Private*, pg. 192

Morin, James, Mgr.-Sls.--Bixby International Corp., Newburyport, MA; *U.S. Private*, pg. 146
Morini, Christopher E., V.P.-Retail Sls. & Mktg.--Galaxy Food Company, Orlando, FL; *U.S. Public*, pg. 697
Moriondo, Alberto, Mgr.-Sls. & Mktg.--FMC FoodTech/Fran Rica, Stockton, CA; *U.S. Public*, pg. 605
Morissette, R.L., Mgr.-Mktg.--Firestone Textiles Company, Woodstock, Canada; *Int'l*, pg. 214
Morken, CeCe, V.P.-Natl. Mkts.--John H. Harland Company, Decatur, GA; *U.S. Public*, pg. 785
Morken, Cece, V.P. Natl. Mkts.--The Check Store, Lakewood, CO; *U.S. Public*, pg. 785
Morrey, Robert J., V.P.-Natl. Sls.--Consolidated Freightways Corp., Menlo Park, CA; *U.S. Public*, pg. 435
Morris, Cliff, Dir.-Tech. Matls.--Sheldahl, Inc., Northfield, MN; *U.S. Public*, pg. 1465
Morris, David, Mgr.-Sls.--WJZ-TV, Baltimore, MD; *U.S. Public*, pg. 275
Morris, David, V.P.-Sls.--Crystal Cruises, Inc., Los Angeles, CA; *Int'l*, pg. 941
Morris, Graham John, Dir.-Mktg. & Sls.--Audi AG, Ingolstadt, Germany; *Int'l*, pg. 1473
Morris, Jim, Admin.-Sls. Services--Penreco, Karns City, PA; *U.S. Public*, pg. 1273
Morris, John, Dir.-Sls.--Cannon Rubber Ltd., London, United Kingdom; *Int'l*, pg. 261
Morris, Larry, Dir.-Tech. & Sls.--Georgia-Bonded Fibers, Inc., Newark, NJ; *U.S. Public*, pg. 734
Morris, Larry E., Dir.-Sls./Tech.--Bontex, Buena Vista, VA; *U.S. Public*, pg. 734
Morris, Pat, V.P.-Mktg. & Sls.-U.S.A.--Timex Corporation, Middlebury, CT; *U.S. Private*, pg. 1088
Morris, Ray, Consultant-Sls. & Mktg.--Bassick by Kaspar, Shiner, TX; *U.S. Private*, pg. 122
Morris, Richard T., Mgr.-Customer Service--Mine Safety Appliances Co., Pittsburgh, PA; *U.S. Public*, pg. 1114
Morris, Robert, Mgr.-Sls.--Continental Forge Company, Compton, CA; *U.S. Private*, pg. 268
Morris, Roger, Dir.-Mktg. & Sls.--The Du Pont Merck Pharmaceutical Company, Wilmington, DE; *U.S. Public*, pg. 531
Morris, Shawn D., Sr. V.P.-Mktg.--National General Insurance Co., Earth City, MO; *U.S. Public*, pg. 721
Morrison, Anthony, V.P.-Intl. Sls.--Ford Steel Co., Inc., Maryland Heights, MO; *U.S. Private*, pg. 418
Morrison, Gary, V.P.-Indus. Sls./ACC--AMCOL International Corp., Arlington Heights, IL; *U.S. Public*, pg. 63
Morrison, Gregory, Mgr.-Sls.--Lindenmeyr Munroe, Mansfield, MA; *U.S. Private*, pg. 224
Morrison, Marianne, V.P.-Sls.-Western Div.--Time Systems, Inc., Phoenix, AZ; *U.S. Private*, pg. 1086
Morrison, Ron, V.P.-Sls.--Okidata Group, Mount Laurel, NJ; *Int'l*, pg. 1000
Morrison, Tony, Dir.-Sls. & Mktg.--AmVestors Acquisition Subsidiary, Inc., Topeka, KS; *U.S. Private*, pg. 59
Morrissette IV, Arthur E. (Bud), V.P.--Interstate Van Lines, Inc., Springfield, VA; *U.S. Private*, pg. 573
Morrow, Chester R., Mgr.-Sls.--Ross Aluminum Foundries, Sidney, OH; *U.S. Private*, pg. 355
Morrow, David, V.P.-Sls. & Mktg.--Sanderson Plumbing Products Inc., Columbus, MS; *U.S. Private*, pg. 964
Morrow, David, V.P.-Sls.--Magnolia Division, Columbus, MS; *U.S. Private*, pg. 964
Morrow, David, Mktg. & Sls.--Beneke, Columbus, MS; *U.S. Private*, pg. 964
Morrow, Dennis, Dir.-Mktg. & Sls.--Enidine Incorporated, Orchard Park, NY; *U.S. Private*, pg. 377
Morrow, Melynda, Sls. Training--Atlas Van Lines, Inc., Evansville, IN; *U.S. Private*, pg. 97
Morrow, Randy, Mgr.-Seed & Chemical Sls.--B&W Co-op, Inc., Breckenridge, MI; *U.S. Private*, pg. 105
Mort, Don, Dir.-Sls.--Dekko Heating Technologies, Inc., North Webster, IN; *U.S. Private*, pg. 484
Mortensen, John, Mgr.-Natl. Sls.--La-Co Industries Markal Company, Elk Grove Village, IL; *U.S. Private*, pg. 640
Mortenson, Jim, Exec. V.P.-Sls. & Mktg.--Arrowhead Mills, Inc., Hereford, TX; *U.S. Private*, pg. 86
Mortimer, D., Dir.-Performance Prods. Bus. Unit--Wyman-Gordon Investment Castings, Inc., Groton, CT; *U.S. Public*, pg. 1782
Morton, David R., Mgr.-Natl. Sls.--Conap Inc., Olean, NY; *U.S. Private*, pg. 261
Mosack, Cal C., V.P.-Sls. & Mktg.--Conbraco Industries Inc., Matthews, NC; *U.S. Private*, pg. 261
Mosca, Ken, V.P.-Sls.--DX Communications, Inc., Deerfield Beach, FL; *Int'l*, pg. 694
Moscato, Giuseppe, Mgr.-Sls.--Standex International S.r.L. (Mold-Tech Division), Gorgonzola, Italy; *U.S. Public*, pg. 1508
Mosek, Steve, Dir.-Natl. Distribution--Genicom Corporation, Chantilly, VA; *U.S. Public*, pg. 729
Moseley, Mark, V.P.-Mktg.--Rowe Furniture Corp., Mc Lean, VA; *U.S. Public*, pg. 1410
Moseley, Steven, V.P. & Dir.-Sls.--LORAD Corporation, Danbury, CT; *U.S. Public*, pg. 1595
Moser, Bruce, Mgr.-Natl. Sls.--Coronet/MTI, Saint Louis, MO; *U.S. Private*, pg. 863
Moser, Sam, V.P.-Adv. Sls.--Nickelodeon/Nick At Nite, New York, NY; *U.S. Private*, pg. 779
Moses, Robert, Dir.-Export Sls.--Power & Telephone Supply Company, Memphis, TN; *U.S. Private*, pg. 877
Mosey, Bill, V.P.-Sls. & Mktg.--K-D Lamp Company, Cincinnati, OH; *U.S. Private*, pg. 603
Mosher, William, Sr. Pres.-Sls.--Circle Plastics Products, Inc., Circleville, OH; *U.S. Private*, pg. 240
Mosier, George O., V.P.-Sls. & Mktg., Intl. Div.--Foley-PLP Company, Rochester, NY; *U.S. Private*, pg. 416
Mosier, Steve, Gen. Mgr.-Sls.--Westco Products, Inc., Pico Rivera, CA; *Int'l*, pg. 244
Mosig Zambrano, Guillermo, Exec. V.P.-Sls., Office Prods.--Grupo Casa Autrey, Mexico, Mexico; *Int'l*, pg. 573
Moss, Dale, Exec. V.P.-Sls. & Mktg.--British Airways, Flushing, NY; *Int'l*, pg. 219
Moss, Margie, Dir.-Sls. Admin.--Colorforms, Ramsey, NJ; *U.S. Public*, pg. 1625
Mostek, Charles F., Exec. V.P.-Fresh Meats Sls. & Mktg.--IBP, Inc., Dakota City, NE; *U.S. Public*, pg. 852
Mostin, Mike, V.P.-Sls. & Mktg.--J & R Film / Moviola Digital Co., Hollywood, CA; *U.S. Private*, pg. 576
Mostow, Mark R., Sr. V.P.-Sls. & Mktg.--Beverly Enterprises, Inc., Fort Smith, AR; *U.S. Public*, pg. 227
Motel, George, Mgr.-Sls.--Bozzuto's Inc., Cheshire, CT; *U.S. Public*, pg. 249
Mothes, Carl, V.P.-Natl. Accts.--Triboro Electric Co., Doylestown, PA; *U.S. Private*, pg. 1102
Motika, Kim, V.P.-Sls.--Interplay Productions, Inc., Irvine, CA; *U.S. Private*, pg. 572
Motley, Gerald, Sls. Dir.--Powermatic, McMinnville, TN; *U.S. Public*, pg. 502
Motsay, John M., V.P.-Sls. & Mktg.--Canton Drop Forge, Canton, OH; *U.S. Private*, pg. 205
Mott, Robert, Mgr.-Sls. & Service Pennsylvania--Agway Energy Products (AEP), Syracuse, NY; *U.S. Private*, pg. 27
Moucha, Larry, Dir.-Sls.--Aydin Displays (East), Horsham, PA; *U.S. Public*, pg. 158
Moumousis, Michael F., V.P.-Sls. Opers.--Manheim Auctions, Inc., Atlanta, GA; *U.S. Private*, pg. 282
Mounsey, Andrew, Dir.-Retail--Thorntons PLC, Darbyshire, United Kingdom; *Int'l*, pg. 1386
Mountain, Patrick, Dir.-Sls. & Mktg. Consumer Audio--Carver Corporation, Lynnwood, WA; *U.S. Public*, pg. 310
Mouritsen, Anders, Mgr.-Sls.--Esselte A/S, Frederiksberg, Denmark; *Int'l*, pg. 460
Mouser, Bob, Mgr.-Sls.--Public Service Company of Oklahoma-Eastern Div., McAlester, OK; *U.S. Public*, pg. 324
Mouw, Don, Dir.-Sls.--Kiewit Mining Group, Inc., Omaha, NE; *U.S. Private*, pg. 619
Mowell, Eric, Dir.-Mktg. & Sls.--James Burn International Limited, Esher, United Kingdom; *U.S. Public*, pg. 1507
Mowen, R.K., Jr., V.P.-Worldwide Sls., Customer Service & Matls. Mngmt.--Eastman Chemical Company, Kingsport, TN; *U.S. Public*, pg. 550
Mowry, E.C., Mgr.-Sls.--Longview Fiber Co. Eastern Container Div., Amsterdam, NY; *U.S. Public*, pg. 1014
Mowry, Ron, Mgr.-Sls.--Weatherford US Inc., Grand Junction, CO; *U.S. Public*, pg. 1750
Mowry, Ronald C., V.P.-Sls. Technology--C.I. Hayes, Inc., Cranston, RI; *U.S. Private*, pg. 513
Moyer, Pat, V.P.-Sls.--American Rug Craftsmen, Sugar Valley, GA; *U.S. Public*, pg. 1121
Moylan, J., V.P.-Sales & Mktg.--Fleck Manufacturing Inc., Tillsonburg, Canada; *Int'l*, pg. 955
Mozak, Robert, V.P.-Sls. & Mktg.--Dey Laboratories Inc., Napa, CA; *Int'l*, pg. 812
Mozes, David, V.P.-Sls.--Corinthian Media, Inc., New York, NY; *U.S. Private*, pg. 275
Mroz, Alex R., Mgr.-Natl. Key Accts.--Lane Limited, Tucker, GA; *Int'l*, pg. 1129
Mroz, Gary, V.P.-Sls.--LeFebure Corp., Cedar Rapids, IA; *Int'l*, pg. 387
Muehlhausen, Steve, Mgr.-Sls.--Elco Precision Stamping Div., Logansport, IN; *U.S. Public*, pg. 1590
Mueller, Brett, Pres.-Magnum Div. & V.P.-Sls. & Mktg.--Mueller Sports Medicine, Inc., Prairie Du Sac, WI; *U.S. Private*, pg. 766
Mueller, Mike, V.P.-Sls. & Mktg.--Columbus Show Case Company, Columbus, OH; *U.S. Private*, pg. 257
Mueller, Richard E., Exec. V.P.-Sls.--Mulberry Metal Products, Inc., Union, NJ; *U.S. Private*, pg. 766
Mueller, Terry, Sls. Rep.--Weldotron Corporation, Piscataway, NJ; *U.S. Public*, pg. 1752
Mueller, Tom, V.P.-Sls.--Mutual Manufacturing & Supply Co., Cincinnati, OH; *U.S. Private*, pg. 769
Mueller, U., Dir.-Sales--Raybestos Industrie-Produkte GmbH, Morbach, Germany; *U.S. Public*, pg. 1364
Muir, Chris, V.P.-Mktg.--C.H. Heist Corp., Clearwater, FL; *U.S. Public*, pg. 807
Muir, Robert J., V.P.-Franchise Sls.--Sylvan Learning Systems Inc., Baltimore, MD; *U.S. Public*, pg. 1545
Muirhead, B., Mgr.-Natl. Sls.--Bluebird Foods Ltd, Manukau, New Zealand; *Int'l*, pg. 556
Muise, Steven A., V.P.-Sls.--Conklin Instrument Corporation, Pleasant Valley, NY; *U.S. Private*, pg. 263
Mukai, Isao, Mgr.-Sls.--Hirose Cherry Precision Company Ltd., Kawasaki, Japan; *U.S. Public*, pg. 346
Muklevicz, Joe, V.P.-Mktg. & Sls.--AMI Industries, Inc., Colorado Springs, CO; *U.S. Public*, pg. 401
Mulder, Marco, Sls. Engr.--CiMatrix NV/SA, Zaventem, Belgium; *U.S. Public*, pg. 1395
Muldoon, Doreen, Dir.-Advertiser Sls. Mgmt.--Worldvision Enterprises, New York, NY; *U.S. Private*, pg. 776
Mulhall, John F., V.P.-Sls. & Mktg.--Insituform East, Inc., Hyattsville, MD; *U.S. Public*, pg. 330
Mulkern, John J., V.P.-Govt. Sls.--Paper Corporation of United States, New York, NY; *U.S. Public*, pg. 1671
Mulkey, Terry, V.P.-Sls.--Sunrise Medical Mobility Products, Fresno, CA; *U.S. Public*, pg. 1536
Mullen, Dave, Mgr.-Sls.--Adelphia Lamp & Shade Inc., Philadelphia, PA; *U.S. Private*, pg. 17
Mullen, James, V.P.-Sls.--Russell Harrington Cutlery Inc., Southbridge, MA; *U.S. Private*, pg. 551
Mullen, Terry, Mgr.-Sls.--DEC International, Inc., Madison, WI; *U.S. Private*, pg. 301
Mullendore, Roy, Prod. Mgr. & Sls. Mgr.-Mike Consumer Prods.--Barbour Thread, Inc., Blue Mountain, AL; *Int'l*, pg. 618
Muller, Gregor, V.P.-Sls.--Liechtenstein Global Trust Limited, Vaduz, Liechtenstein; *Int'l*, pg. 809
Muller, Ken, Mgr.-Sls.--E Wood Limited, Northallerton, United Kingdom; *Int'l*, pg. 858
Muller, Patrick, Mgr.-Sls.--TrefilARBED Luxembourg/ Saarbrucken S.a.r.l., Luxembourg, Luxembourg; *Int'l*, pg. 80
Muller, T., Sls. Dir.-Cold Rolled Prods.--Hoogovens Ijmuiden Verkoopkantoor B.V., Ijmuiden, Netherlands; *Int'l*, pg. 754
Mulligan, Michael L., V.P.-Sls. & Mktg.--SuperValu, Inc., Eden Prairie, MN; *U.S. Public*, pg. 1540
Mullins, Ed, V.P.-Sls.-Fluid Milk Div.--Prairie Farms Dairy, Inc., Carlinville, IL; *U.S. Private*, pg. 878
Mullins, Kevin, V.P.-Sls. & Mktg.--LoJack Corporation, Dedham, MA; *U.S. Public*, pg. 1012
Mullins, Michael, Mgr.-Sls.--Salz Leathers, Inc., Santa Cruz, CA; *U.S. Private*, pg. 963
Mullins, Sandi, Mgr.-Sls.--Tupperware U.S., Inc., Orlando, FL; *U.S. Public*, pg. 1644
Mulligan, George, V.P.-Sls.--Appleton Electric Co., Chicago, IL; *U.S. Public*, pg. 572
Mullnix, Steve, V.P.-Sls. & Mktg.--The Todd-AO Corporation, Hollywood, CA; *U.S. Public*, pg. 1619
Mullock, Paul S., Sr. V.P.-Sls.--Alliance America, Norcross, GA; *U.S. Private*, pg. 37
Mulryan, Matt, Sls. Mgr.-Brands--Dacor Corporation, Northfield, IL; *U.S. Private*, pg. 306
Mulvey, M.J., Dist. Mgr.-Sls.--Vanguard Cellular Systems of South Carolina, Inc., Myrtle Beach, SC; *U.S. Public*, pg. 1708
Mumm, Robert, Mgr.-Natl. Sls.--Wilton Tool Div., Palatine, IL; *U.S. Private*, pg. 1181
Mumm, Robert, V.P.-Sls.--Wilton Tool Corp., Schiller Park, IL; *U.S. Private*, pg. 1181
Munch, Bill, V.P.-Sls. & Mktg.--Pyramid Mouldings, Jacksonville, FL; *Int'l*, pg. 1335
Munch, Hans, Sls. Dir.--Intervascular GmbH, Bensheim, Germany; *U.S. Public*, pg. 488
Munchen, Paul, Dir.-Gen. Mktg., Sls. & Adv.--CLT-UFA, Luxembourg, Luxembourg; *Int'l*, pg. 561
Munchschwander, Peter, Dir.-Sls.--Deutsche Bahn, Frankfurt/Main, Germany; *Int'l*, pg. 401
Munger, Bob, Mgr.-Mktg. & Sls.--Sakata Seed America, Inc., Morgan Hill, CA; *Int'l*, pg. 1178
Munn, Robert, Mgr.-Natl. Sls./Indus. Tools--Wilton Corporation, Palatine, IL; *U.S. Private*, pg. 1181
Munska, David, Mgr.-Sls.--P.S.I. Division, Ellington, CT; *U.S. Private*, pg. 832
Munson, Gary A., V.P.-Sls.--Crown Cork & Seal, Western Div., La Mirada, CA; *U.S. Public*, pg. 463
Munte, J., Mgr.-Block Sls.--Terre Hill Concrete Products, Inc., Terre Hill, PA; *U.S. Private*, pg. 1077
Munyon, Paul, V.P.-Sls.--Quoizel Inc., Goose Creek, SC; *U.S. Private*, pg. 901
Murakami, Ryoshichi, Sr. Mgr.-Intl. Sls.--Wako Securities Co., Ltd., Tokyo, Japan; *Int'l*, pg. 1485
Murata, Akiya, Chief Fin. Officer & Gen. Mgr.-Sls. & Mktg.--Okazaki Golf Club KK, Okazaki, Japan; *Int'l*, pg. 1362
Murata, Matahiko, Dir.-Paper Sls.--Oji Paper Co., Ltd., Tokyo, Japan; *Int'l*, pg. 998
Murata, Maysayuki, Mng. Dir.--Murata Manufacturing Co., Ltd., Kyoto, Japan; *Int'l*, pg. 897
Murata, Tsuneo, Mng. Dir.--Murata Manufacturing Co., Ltd., Kyoto, Japan; *Int'l*, pg. 897
Murchison, Nickie, Mgr.-Sls.--American City Business Journals, Inc., Dallas, TX; *U.S. Private*, pg. 19
Murdoch, Douglas, Dir.-Sls. & Mktg.--Puritan-Bennett Canada Ltd., Pickering, Canada; *U.S. Public*, pg. 1040
Murdoch, Roger, Mgr.-Sls.--Miller-St. Nazianz, Inc., Saint Nazianz, WI; *U.S. Private*, pg. 748
Murphey, Sean, Mgr.-Natl. Sls.--Hipotronics, Inc., Brewster, NY; *U.S. Public*, pg. 844
Murphy, Barb, Dir.-Sls. & Adv.--Buttrey Food & Drug Company, Great Falls, MT; *U.S. Public*, pg. 271
Murphy, Brad, Sls. Exec.--Western Interactive Media, Irving, TX; *U.S. Private*, pg. 1166
Murphy, Carl E., Mgr.-Customer Service--Barksdale, Inc., Los Angeles, CA; *U.S. Public*, pg. 457
Murphy, Cliff, V.P.-Sales--Ilco Unican Inc. (Capitol Division), Montreal, Canada; *Int'l*, pg. 1432
Murphy, Dan, V.P.-Sls. & Mktg.--Iceland Seafood Corporation, Newport, VA; *U.S. Private*, pg. 556
Murphy, David, V.P.-Consumer Mktg. & Sls.--Chicago Tribune Co., Chicago, IL; *U.S. Public*, pg. 1635
Murphy, Dennis, V.P.-Sls.--Kayser-Roth Corporation, Inc., Greensboro, NC; *Int'l*, pg. 576
Murphy, Edward, Mgr.-Sls.--Fybroc Division, Telford, PA; *U.S. Public*, pg. 1100
Murphy, Jack, Dir.-Sls.--Turner Construction Co., Boston, MA; *U.S. Public*, pg. 1645
Murphy, Kevin, V.P.-Sls. & Mktg., Fabric--Hoffman Laces, Ltd., Cobleskill, NY; *U.S. Public*, pg. 769
Murphy, L.D., V.P.-Mktg. & Sls.--Marlite, Dover, OH; *U.S. Private*, pg. 705
Murphy, Larry, Natl. Sls. Mgr.--Prime Technology Imports, Ltd., Grand Rapids, MI; *U.S. Private*, pg. 884
Murphy, Lee, V.P.-Sls.--Kent Feeds Inc., Muscatine, IA; *U.S. Private*, pg. 1134
Murphy, Melvin, V.P.-Sls.--Gould Paper Corporation, New York, NY; *U.S. Private*, pg. 466
Murphy, Michael, V.P.-Sls. & Mktg.--Belden Inc., Saint Louis, MO; *U.S. Public*, pg. 200
Murphy, Michael, V.P.-Sls.--Avon Books, New York, NY; *U.S. Private*, pg. 515
Murphy, Michael, V.P.-Sls.--William Morrow & Co., Inc., New York, NY; *U.S. Private*, pg. 515
Murphy, Michael L., Dir.-Sls.--Belden Wire & Cable Company, Richmond, IN; *U.S. Public*, pg. 201
Murphy, Mike, Dir.-Sls.--Barbeque King, Reading, United Kingdom; *U.S. Public*, pg. 1507
Murphy, Patrick, V.P.-Mktg. & Sls.--Coz Plastics Inc., Northbridge, MA; *U.S. Private*, pg. 827
Murphy, Ralph B., V.P.-Corp. Sls.--Offshore Logistics, Inc., Lafayette, LA; *U.S. Public*, pg. 1212
Murphy, Ray, V.P.-Sls.--Austin Quality Foods, Cary, NC; *U.S. Private*, pg. 100
Murphy, Richard D., V.P.-Sls. & Mktg.--Colonial Gas Company, Lowell, MA; *U.S. Public*, pg. 400
Murphy, Robert, V.P.-Sls. & Mktg.--David Clark Company Incorporated, Worcester, MA; *U.S. Private*, pg. 242

Murphy, Tom, Natl. Sls. Mgr.--Cameo Window Furnishings, New York, NY; U.S. Private, pg. 1094
Murray, Adrian, V.P.-Sls.--Edelbrock Corp., Torrance, CA; U.S. Public, pg. 563
Murray, Asa G., V.P.-Sls. & Mktg.--Philadelphia Coca-Cola Bottling Co., Philadelphia, PA; U.S. Private, pg. 861
Murray, David, Exec. V.P.-U.S. Sls. & Prod. Mktg.--The Dun & Bradstreet Corporation, Murray Hill, NJ; U.S. Public, pg. 535
Murray, G., V.P.-Sls. & Mktg.--Prime Systems Group, Tampa, FL; U.S. Public, pg. 1329
Murray, James E., V.P.-Indus. Sls.--Cyberex, Inc., Mentor, OH; U.S. Public, pg. 481
Murray, Joe, Sr. V.P.-Sls. & Mktg.--Frank Industries, Inc., Brown City, MI; U.S. Private, pg. 423
Murray, Mark, Exec. V.P.-Mktg. & Sls.--FAG Bearings Corporation, Danbury, CT; Int'l, pg. 469
Murray, Michael J., Sr. V.P.-Sls. & Mktg.--Pilgrim's Pride Corporation, Pittsburg, TX; U.S. Public, pg. 1296
Murray, Mike, Mgr.-Local Sls.--Fisher Broadcasting Inc., Seattle, WA; U.S. Public, pg. 648
Murray, O.W., V.P.-Intl. Sls. & Export--Doron Precision Systems, Inc., Binghamton, NY; U.S. Private, pg. 341
Murray, R. J., V.P.-Mktg. & Sls.--Timec Company, Vallejo, CA; U.S. Private, pg. 1087
Murray, Roland, Sr. Dir.-North American Sls.--Cybex International, Inc., Medway, MA; U.S. Private, pg. 1114
Murrieta, Jill, Mgr.-Natl. Sls.--Gould Packaging, Inc., Vancouver, WA; U.S. Private, pg. 466
Murzinski, Edward, V.P.-Mktg. & Sls.--Revcor, Inc., Carpentersville, IL; U.S. Private, pg. 925
Muscatello, Frank, V.P.-Consumer Sls.--Playtex Products Inc., Westport, CT; U.S. Public, pg. 1310
Muselman, Roger, Exec. V.P.-Sls.--E.P. Graphics, Inc., Berne, IN; U.S. Private, pg. 354
Muser, Robert J., V.P.-Sls.--Weil-McLain, Michigan City, IN; U.S. Public, pg. 1676
Musial, Cheryl, V.P.-Sls. & Mktg.--Vitalink Pharmacy Services, Inc., Atlanta, GA; U.S. Public, pg. 1042
Musick, Gary D., V.P.-Sls.--Houston Foods Company, Franklin Park, IL; U.S. Private, pg. 542
Musselwhite, John, Mgr.-Sls.--J.T. Davenport & Sons, Inc., Sanford, NC; U.S. Private, pg. 314
Mutchnick, Jerry, V.P.-Sls.--Gould Paper Corporation, New York, NY; U.S. Private, pg. 466
Muth, Steve, Sls.--North Hills Signal Processing, Glen Cove, NY; U.S. Public, pg. 1317
Mutimer, John, V.P.-Sls.--Newell Window Furnishings Co., Freeport, IL; U.S. Public, pg. 1177
Myatt, Paul, Dir.-Inside Sls. & Mktg.--Magnetrol International, Downers Grove, IL; U.S. Private, pg. 696
Mycock, Tony, Dir.-Sls. & Mktg.--Tate & Lyle PLC, London, United Kingdom; Int'l, pg. 1356
Myer, H., Mgr.-Sls. Svcs.--Lenape Forge, Inc., West Chester, PA; U.S. Private, pg. 659
Myers, Dan, V.P.-Natl. Acct. Sls.--Kirsch, Sturgis, MI; U.S. Public, pg. 1176
Myers, David, V.P.-Sls./E. Central Region--Thorn Apple Valley, Inc., Southfield, MI; U.S. Public, pg. 1602
Myers, Frederick J., V.P.-Sls.--Unitrode Corporation, Merrimack, NH; U.S. Public, pg. 1694
Myers, James H., V.P.-Intl. Sls. & Prod. Mngmt.--Simplicity Manufacturing, Inc., Port Washington, WI; U.S. Private, pg. 1002
Myers, Kim, Mgr.-Sls. & Logistics--Artichoke Industries, Inc., Castroville, CA; U.S. Private, pg. 86
Myers, L., Mgr.-ESD--Terre Hill Concrete Products, Inc., Terre Hill, PA; U.S. Private, pg. 1077
Myers, Lilo, Mgr.-Intl. Sls.--Hobart Corporation, Troy, OH; U.S. Public, pg. 1322
Myers, Mike, V.P.-Sls.--Marson/Creative Fastener, Inc., Stoughton, MA; U.S. Private, pg. 708
Myers, Raymond F., V.P. & Mgr.-Adv.--Southwest National Corporation, Greensburg, PA; U.S. Public, pg. 1493
Myers, Robert W., V.P.-Sls. & Mktg.--Morris Coupling Co., Erie, PA; U.S. Private, pg. 762
Myers, Ron, V.P.-Sls. & Mktg./OEM & BIC--Ameriwood Industries International Inc., Grand Rapids, MI; U.S. Public, pg. 98
Myers, Ron, V.P.-Sls.--Tiffin Enterprises, Inc., Tiffin, OH; U.S. Public, pg. 98
Mykoski, William, Mgr.-Sls.--Sifco Industries, Inc., Cleveland, OH; U.S. Public, pg. 1470
Mykytiuk, Tom, Grp. Sls. Mgr.--Arizona Instrument Corporation, Phoenix, AZ; U.S. Public, pg. 129
Nadel, Bernard, Dir.-Sls. & Mdsg.--Ferrero U.S.A., Inc., Somerset, NJ; Int'l, pg. 480
Naff, Charles E., V.P.-Sls.--United Retail Group, Inc., Rochelle Park, NJ; U.S. Public, pg. 1679
Nagahata, Osamu, Mng. Dir.--All Nippon Airways Co. Ltd., Tokyo, Japan; Int'l, pg. 57
Nagel, A., Mgr.-Sls.--Prenatal B.V., Almere, Netherlands; Int'l, pg. 750
Nagels, L., Sls. Mgr.--KTI Belgium N.V., Mol, Belgium; Int'l, pg. 836
Nagle, Andrew, V.P.-Sls. & Mktg.--A-B Emblem Div. of Conrad Industries, Inc., Weaverville, NC; U.S. Private, pg. 2
Nagle, W. Dan, V.P.-Sls. & Mktg.--Tasty Baking Company, Philadelphia, PA; U.S. Public, pg. 1561
Nagorsen, Tony, V.P.-Sls.--Penske Performance, Inc., Detroit, MI; U.S. Private, pg. 850
Nahay, Harry, Sls. Mgr.- Midwest--Storck U.S.A., L.P., Chicago, IL; Int'l, pg. 1304
Naidu, S.K. Ramadas, V.P.-Sls.--R.R. Donnelley Far East Limited, Singapore, Singapore; U.S. Public, pg. 519
Najim, Edward L., Exec. V.P.-Sls. & Mktg.--Horace Mann Educators Corporation, Springfield, IL; U.S. Public, pg. 835
Nakagiri, Toshi, V.P.-Mktg. & Sls.--Permacel, New Brunswick, NJ; Int'l, pg. 950
Nakamoto, Arlene M., Exec. V.P.-Sls. & Mktg.--American Savings Bank, F.S.B., Honolulu, HI; U.S. Public, pg. 800
Nakano, Tadahisa, Gen. Mgr.-Intl. Sls.--Wako Securities Co., Ltd., Tokyo, Japan; Int'l, pg. 1485
Nance, Charles, V.P.-Sls.--Insituform Technologies, Inc., Chesterfield, MO; U.S. Public, pg. 881
Nance, David, Sls. Mgr.--World's Finest Chocolate Australia Pty. Ltd., Stanmore, Australia; U.S. Private, pg. 1191
Nance, Doug, V.P.-Sls.--Grindmaster Corporation, Louisville, KY; U.S. Private, pg. 482
Nanson, Dave, V.P.-Sls. & Mktg.--Tollycraft Yacht Corporation, San Diego, CA; U.S. Public, pg. 1620
Napier, Angus, Mgr.-Sls. & Mktg.--Sasol Fibres, Reunion, South Africa; Int'l, pg. 1196
Napier, Jerry, V.P.-Sls.--Super Sagless Corp., Tupelo, MS; U.S. Public, pg. 986
Napoleon, Dan, Mgr.-Sls.--Roger Holler Chevrolet & GEO Co., Winter Park, FL; U.S. Private, pg. 534
Napoleon, Jeffrey, V.P.-Sls.--Banfi Vintners, Old Brookville, NY; U.S. Private, pg. 113
Nardi, Tom, V.P.-Mktg., Sls. & Treas.--Northern Illinois Gas Company, Naperville, IL; U.S. Public, pg. 1183
Nash, Eloise, V.P.-Natl. Internal Sls./Bedding Components--Leggett & Platt, Incorporated, Carthage, MO; U.S. Public, pg. 985
Nash, Timothy P., V.P.-Sls.--Marten Transport, Ltd., Mondovi, WI; U.S. Public, pg. 1052
Nasky, Thomas G., Exec. V.P.-Mktg. & Sls.--Dualite Inc., Williamsburg, OH; U.S. Private, pg. 344
Nasky, Thomas G., Exec. V.P.-Sls. & Mktg.--Dualite Sales & Service, Inc., Williamsburg, OH; U.S. Private, pg. 344
Nast, Bill, Exec. V.P.-Sls. & Mktg.--Tech Industries, Inc., Woonsocket, RI; U.S. Private, pg. 1071
Nast, Chris, V.P.-Sls.--Colgate U.S.A., New York, NY; U.S. Public, pg. 397
Nast, Nelson, V.P.-Sls.--American Marketing Industries, Inc., Kansas City, MO; U.S. Private, pg. 58
Nastasi, Sam, Mgr.-Sls.--Eagle Button Co., Inc., Carlstadt, NJ; U.S. Private, pg. 354
Natale, James L., Pres.-Corp. Mktg. & Sls.--C.R. Bard, Inc., Murray Hill, NJ; U.S. Public, pg. 189
Natale, Mike, Sales Mgr.--Dillard, A ResourceNet International Company, Richmond, VA; U.S. Public, pg. 902
Nathan, Barry, Mgr.-Sls.--Balson-Hercules Ltd., New York, NY; Int'l, pg. 326
Nathanson, Jerry, V.P.-Mktg. & Sls.--VARTA Batteries Inc., Elmsford, NY; Int'l, pg. 1452
Natoli, Joe, Mgr.-Natl. Sls.--Cleaning Solutions Group/Cello, Havre De Grace, MD; U.S. Public, pg. 1466
Naton, Ray, Natl. Sls. Mgr.--Beckett Papers, East Granby, CT; U.S. Public, pg. 903
Naton, Ray, Mgr.-Natl. Sls.--Strathmore Paper, Granby, CT; U.S. Public, pg. 903
Natonski, Jim, Intl. Sls. Dir.--Velsicol Chemical Corporation, Rosemont, IL; U.S. Private, pg. 1135
Nauffts, Bud, Dir.-Adv.--Crain's Cleveland Business, Cleveland, OH; U.S. Private, pg. 285
Naughton, Eugene, Mgr.-Food & Beverage--Paramount Carowinds, Charlotte, NC; U.S. Private, pg. 776
Nauta, Roger, V.P.-Distribution Sls.--ODL Incorporated, Zeeland, MI; U.S. Private, pg. 809
Nava, Joseph A., V.P.-Worldwide Sls.--Ultratech Stepper, Inc., San Jose, CA; U.S. Public, pg. 1663
Naval, Tomas, Mgr.-Natl. Sls.--Kodak America, Ltda., Lima, Peru; U.S. Public, pg. 554
Navarro, Carmen E., Mgr.-Sls. & Export Mktg.--Benguet Corporation, Manila, Philippines; Int'l, pg. 186
Nawratil, Franz, V.P. & Mng. Dir.-Europe, Africa & Middle East Opers.--Hewlett-Packard Company, Palo Alto, CA; U.S. Public, pg. 813
Nay, Kelly, Gen. Mgr.-Sls.--Rea Magnet Wire Company, Inc., Fort Wayne, IN; U.S. Private, pg. 913
Naylor, Larry, Area Sls. Rep.--Production Operators, Inc. (Oklahoma City Office), Oklahoma City, OK; U.S. Public, pg. 298
Nazario, Richard, Mgr.-Sls.--Bridgestone Cycle (U.S.A.), Inc., San Leandro, CA; Int'l, pg. 213
Nazziola, Thomas E., V.P.-Mktg.--Ilco Unican Corp., Simplex Access Controls Division, Winston Salem, NC; Int'l, pg. 1432
Neal, Bill G., Sr. V.P.-Sls. & Mktg.--Meco Corporation, Greeneville, TN; U.S. Private, pg. 726
Neal, Jim, Mgr.-Gen. Dealer Sls.--Jones Blair Company, Dallas, TX; U.S. Private, pg. 596
Neal, Richard, Mgr.-Sls.--United States Aluminum Corp.-Illinois, Bedford Park, IL; U.S. Public, pg. 895
Neau, Jean Pierre, Mgr.-Sls.--Bontex S.A., Stembert, Belgium; U.S. Public, pg. 734
Necovetich, John, Pres.-Tokheim North America--Tokheim Corporation, Fort Wayne, IN; U.S. Public, pg. 1620
Neels, Henry, Sls. & Mktg. Mgr.--Whitehall Laboratoria B.V., Amsterdam, Netherlands; U.S. Public, pg. 82
Neeve, James B., Mgr.-Sls.--Amcast Industrial Ltd., Burlington, Canada; U.S. Public, pg. 63
Neff, Harry, V.P.-Sls.--Uvex Safety, Inc., Smithfield, RI; Int'l, pg. 132
Negri, Michael, Sr. V.P.-Sls. & Mgr.-Office Prods. Div.--Gould Paper Corporation, New York, NY; U.S. Private, pg. 466
Negrini, Dario, Dir.-Corp. Sls. & Mktg.--Instrument Specialties Company, Delaware Water Gap, PA; U.S. Private, pg. 565
Neidigh, Sam, Mgr.-Large Acct. Sls.--PENCO-Tennessee, Nashville, TN; Int'l, pg. 1508
Neiley, George F., III, V.P.-Sls. & Mktg.--Ring King Visibles, Inc., Muscatine, IA; Int'l, pg. 460
Neill, Joseph, V.P.-Sls.--Gould Paper Corporation, New York, NY; U.S. Private, pg. 466
Neilson, David L., V.P.-Sls. & Mktg.--Intermet Corporation, Troy, MI; U.S. Public, pg. 894
Neiman, Larry, District Sls. Mgr.-St. Louis--Magneco/Metrel, Inc., Addison, IL; U.S. Private, pg. 695
Neiverth, C.J., V.P.-Sls.--Automotive, Wayne, NJ; Int'l, pg. 234
Nelan, Dennis, Mgr.-Sls.--TIE Systems Colorado, Denver, CO; U.S. Private, pg. 1085
Nelles, William A., V.P.-Sls. & Mktg.--Monex Deposit Co., Newport Beach, CA; U.S. Private, pg. 757
Nelso, Kim, Mgr.-Sls.--Standard Restaurant Equipment Co., Las Vegas, NV; U.S. Private, pg. 1031
Nelson, Claude, Mgr.-Sls.--Rolland Inc., Fine Papers Division, Saint-Jerome, Canada; Int'l, pg. 274
Nelson, Dan, Mgr.-Sls.--Granite Furniture Co., Salt Lake City, UT; U.S. Private, pg. 469
Nelson, Dan, V.P.-Sls.--The Dial Corporation, Phoenix, AZ; U.S. Public, pg. 505
Nelson, Glade, V.P.-Sls. & Mktg.--Ampco Metal Incorporated, Milwaukee, WI; U.S. Private, pg. 67
Nelson, Glen, V.P.-Sls. & Mktg.--Roll Forming Corporation, Shelbyville, KY; U.S. Private, pg. 941
Nelson, H. Vincent, V.P.-Sls.--American Safety Razor Company, Verona, VA; U.S. Private, pg. 597
Nelson, James E., Dir.-Sls. & Mktg.--Ederer Inc., Seattle, WA; U.S. Private, pg. 363
Nelson, Jim, Dir.-Sls. & Mktg.--Ederer Cranes, Seattle, WA; U.S. Private, pg. 363
Nelson, John L., V.P.-Sls. & Mktg.--Marlow Industries, Dallas, TX; U.S. Private, pg. 705
Nelson, Kimi, Mgr.-Sls. & Adv.--Westfall GMC Truck Inc., Kansas City, MO; U.S. Private, pg. 1169
Nelson, Kris, V.P.-N. American Sls.--Cognex Corporation, Natick, MA; U.S. Public, pg. 394
Nelson, Mark A., V.P.-Sls.--Wisconsin Pharmacal Co., Inc., Jackson, WI; U.S. Private, pg. 1185
Nelson, Murray A., V.P.-Retail Energy Mktg.--Transalta Corporation, Calgary, Canada; Int'l, pg. 1416
Nelson, Paul, V.P.-Sls.--Midwest Coast Transport L.P., Sioux Falls, SD; U.S. Private, pg. 744
Nelson, Paul A., V.P. & Sec.--Natural Fuels Corporation, Denver, CO; U.S. Public, pg. 1170
Nelson, Phyllis, V.P.-Mktg. & Sls.--Clayton Industries Co., El Monte, CA; U.S. Private, pg. 245
Nelson, Rick, V.P.-Sls.--Zotos International, Darien, CT; Int'l, pg. 1236
Nelson, Roger, V.P.-Sls.--Vermont American Tool Group, Lincolnton, NC; U.S. Public, pg. 575
Nelson, Thomas, Dir.-Mktg. & Sls.--Athey Products Corporation, Wake Forest, NC; U.S. Public, pg. 142
Nelson, Tom, Sr. V.P.-Sls.--Converse Inc., North Reading, MA; U.S. Public, pg. 441
Nelson, Tom, Mgr.-Intl. Sls.--Warn Industries, Inc., Clackamas, OR; U.S. Private, pg. 1150
Nemec, Randy, Natl. Sls. Mgr.--The Benjamin/Cummings Publishing Company, Menlo Park, CA; Int'l, pg. 1026
Nemeth, Al, Dir.-Sls. Collagen Products--Datascope Corp., Montvale, NJ; U.S. Public, pg. 487
Nemeth, Jeff, V.P.-Sls.--Richco Inc., Chicago, IL; U.S. Private, pg. 929
Nemetz, Mike, Dir.-Adv.--Talbots, Inc., Hingham, MA; Int'l, pg. 28
Nemhauser, Bob, V.P.-Sls.--Firstcorp, Portland, OR; U.S. Private, pg. 408
Nenninger, John, Sr. V.P. & Dir.-Mktg.--Starbanc Corporation, Cincinnati, OH; U.S. Public, pg. 1510
Nesbit, Tom, Sls. Representative--PENCO-Alambama, Birmingham, AL; Int'l, pg. 1508
Nesbitt, David, V.P.-Sls. & Engrng.--Williams, White & Co., Moline, IL; U.S. Private, pg. 1179
Ness, Greg, V.P.-Retirement Plans Sls. & Mktg.--Standard Insurance Co., Portland, OR; U.S. Private, pg. 1031
Nestor, Michael, V.P.-Mktg. & Sls., Pediatrics/Vaccines--Wyeth-Ayerst Laboratories, Inc., Philadelphia, PA; U.S. Public, pg. 80
Nesvig, Jon, Pres.-Sls.--Fox Broadcasting Company (FBC), Beverly Hills, CA; Int'l, pg. 926
Nettemeyer, Joe, V.P.-Sls.--Wiegand Industrial-Chromalox, Pittsburgh, PA; U.S. Public, pg. 573
Neubauer, Mark E., V.P.-Sls. & Mktg.--Oriole Homes Corp., Delray Beach, FL; U.S. Public, pg. 1230
Neul, Ralph, V.P.-Store Opers.--Brauns Fashions Corporation, Plymouth, MN; U.S. Public, pg. 251
Neuman, Milt, Sls. Mgr.--World's Finest Chocolate Canada Ltd., Campbellford, Canada; U.S. Private, pg. 1191
Neuman, Richard, Dir.-Special Mkt. Sls.--Hunter Fan Company, Memphis, TN; U.S. Private, pg. 549
Neumann, Mark C., V.P.-Sls.--Badger Paper Mills, Inc., Peshtigo, WI; U.S. Public, pg. 165
Neumann, Vivian F., V.P.-Sls. & Mktg.--St. Paul Metalcraft, Inc., Saint Paul, MN; U.S. Private, pg. 961
Neuwirth, Mark, V.P.-Sls.--Unex Conveying Systems, Inc., Jackson, NJ; U.S. Private, pg. 1117
Neves, Antonio, Dir.-Domestic Sls.--Ferry-Morse Seed Company, Modesto, CA; Int'l, pg. 566
Neville, Shawn, V.P.-U.S. Opers.--Reebok International Ltd., Stoughton, MA; U.S. Public, pg. 1369
Neville, Steve, V.P.-Reg. Sls. & Gen. Mgr.--Tom's Foods, Inc., Columbus, GA; U.S. Private, pg. 1090
Nevins, Kirk M., V.P.-Sls.--Franklin Electric Co., Inc., Bluffton, IN; U.S. Public, pg. 679
Nevsimal, Charles J., Exec. V.P.-Sls. & Mktg--Wisconsin Pharmacal Co., Inc., Jackson, WI; U.S. Private, pg. 1185
Newburn, Lorance H., Dir.-Sls.--Isco Environmental Division, Lincoln, NE; U.S. Public, pg. 914
Newcomer, Charles, V.P.-Sls.--Maxell Corp. Of America, Fair Lawn, NJ; Int'l, pg. 621
Newell, Robert A., V.P.-Mktg.--NewTel Communications, Saint Johns, Canada; Int'l, pg. 115
Newham, D.H., Mng. Dir.--A.C. Labs (Pty.) Ltd., Sebenza, South Africa; U.S. Public, pg. 38
Newhouse, Steve, Dir.-Mktg., Sls. & Adv.--Atlantic Builders Group Inc., Baltimore, MD; U.S. Private, pg. 95
Newiss, S., Dir.-Sls., Terry's Suchard--Kraft Jacobs Suchard, Cheltenham, United Kingdom; U.S. Public, pg. 1290
Newman, Carole, Admin.-Sls.--CAE Machinery Ltd., Vancouver, Canada; Int'l, pg. 237
Newman, Chris, V.P.-Sls.--Advanced Input Devices, Inc., Coeur D'Alene, ID; U.S. Private, pg. 21

Newman, Donald V., V.P.-Massey-Retail--Craddock-Terry Inc., Lynchburg, VA; *U.S. Private*, pg. 284
Newman, Gary L., Exec. V.P.-Sls., Sls. Promo. & Direct Mktg.--Cooper Communities, Inc., Bella Vista, AR; *U.S. Private*, pg. 273
Newman, Larry, Exec. V.P.-Mktg. & Sls.-Angelica Image Apparel--Angelica Corporation, Chesterfield, MO; *U.S. Public*, pg. 113
Newman, Larry, Exec. V.P.-Mktg. & Sls.--Angelica Image Apparel, Saint Louis, MO; *U.S. Public*, pg. 113
Newman, Mark, Dir.-Sls. & Mktg.--Bounty Books, London, United Kingdom; *Int'l*, pg. 1093
Newman, Monte, Exec. V.P.-Sls. & Mktg.-NBC TV Stations--National Broadcasting Co., Inc., New York, NY; *U.S. Public*, pg. 712
Newman, Paul, Mgr.-Sls.--Universal Relay, Bridgeport, CT; *U.S. Private*, pg. 839
Newman, Steve, Sr. V.P.-Adv. Sls.--Home & Garden Television, Knoxville, TN; *U.S. Public*, pg. 1447
Newton, D.P., Mgr.-Sls.--Turner Construction Company, Kansas City, MO; *U.S. Public*, pg. 1645
Newton, Larry, V.P.-Sls.--C & S Wholesale Grocery Inc., Brattleboro, VT; *U.S. Private*, pg. 192
Newton, Ron, V.P.-Sls & Mktg.--Ammco Tools, Inc., La Vergne, TN; *U.S. Public*, pg. 480
Newton, Ron, V.P.-Sls. & Mktg.--Hennessy Industries, Inc., La Vergne, TN; *U.S. Public*, pg. 481
Newton, Ronnie, Mgr.-Sls.--Ira Higdon Grocery, Inc., Cairo, GA; *U.S. Private*, pg. 527
Neyer, David F., V.P.-Sls.--Al Neyer, Inc., Cincinnati, OH; *U.S. Private*, pg. 797
Nibbe, Warner, V.P.-Sls. & Mktg.-Pacal Blades--Paper Calmenson & Co., Saint Paul, MN; *U.S. Private*, pg. 837
Nibbelink, Richard, Reg. Sls. Mgr.--Quinlan Pretzel Co., Inc., Denver, PA; *U.S. Private*, pg. 158
Nice, David, Dir.-Sls.--Neff (UK) Limited, Milton Keynes, United Kingdom; *Int'l*, pg. 912
Nichol, Jeanne, Sr. Adv. Assoc.-Mktg. & Sls.--The Principal Financial Group, Des Moines, IA; *U.S. Private*, pg. 885
Nichola, Frederick S., Mgr.-Sls.--Essex Corporation, New York, NY; *U.S. Public*, pg. 320
Nicholas, Philip A., AIA, V.P.--Giffels Associates, Inc., Southfield, MI; *U.S. Private*, pg. 452
Nichols, Bob, Mgr.-Sls.--Automatic Power, Inc., Houston, TX; *Int'l*, pg. 1289
Nichols, Michael, V.P.-Sls.--Reptron Electronics, Inc., Tampa, FL; *U.S. Public*, pg. 1377
Nichols, William, Gen. Mgr.-Sls.--Craddock-Terry Inc., Lynchburg, VA; *U.S. Private*, pg. 284
Nicholson, P.R., Sec. & Sls. Mgr.--Senior New Zealand Limited, Auckland, New Zealand; *Int'l*, pg. 1223
Nickel, Dave, Mgr.-Sls.-Mass Transit--Intool Rotor Company, Cleveland, OH; *U.S. Private*, pg. 574
Nickerson, Norman F., V.P.-Sls.--Monsey-Bakor, Kimberton, PA; *U.S. Private*, pg. 757
Nicoletos, George, Mgr.-Cutlery & Scientific Sls.--Maryland Plastics, Inc., Federalsburg, MD; *U.S. Private*, pg. 641
Nicolini, Adevanir, Mgr.-Sls.--Sao Paulo Alpargatas S.A., Sao Paulo, Brazil; *Int'l*, pg. 1193
Nicosia, Anthony S., Div. V.P.-Sls.--New Penn Motor Express, Inc., Lebanon, PA; *U.S. Public*, pg. 132
Niederst, James E., Mgr.-Natl. & Export Sls.--Glastic Corporation, Cleveland, OH; *Int'l*, pg. 740
Nielsen, Ed, Mgr.-Sls.--Varco BJ Oil Tools B.V., Etten-Leur, Netherlands; *U.S. Public*, pg. 1709
Nielsen, Jacob P., Mgr.-Nordic Sls.--GN Nettest, Telecom Division, Brondby, Denmark; *Int'l*, pg. 536
Nieman, David, V.P.-Sls. & Mktg. Tire Grp.--Titan International, Inc., Quincy, IL; *U.S. Public*, pg. 1618
Niemeyer, Bart F., V.P.-Sls. & Mktg.--Koppel Steel Corp., Beaver Falls, PA; *U.S. Public*, pg. 1147
Niemeyer, W. Pil, Chief Fin. Officer & Exec. V.P.--Nasco, Fort Atkinson, WI; *U.S. Private*, pg. 446
Niemi, Frank, Dir.-Mktg. & Sls.--Abbott Laboratories/ Ashland, Ashland, OH; *U.S. Public*, pg. 13
Nienhuiys, Winne, Mgr.-Sls. & Mktg./Access Control--Amtech International, Nanterre, France; *U.S. Public*, pg. 106
Nieves, John, Sr. V.P.-Mktg. & Sls.--New England Machinery, Inc., Bradenton, FL; *U.S. Private*, pg. 793
Nieze, Ken, V.P.-Sls., N.A.--Air Express International Corporation, Darien, CT; *U.S. Public*, pg. 30
Niggli, Michael R., Sr. V.P.-Custom Accts. & V.P.-Sls. & Mktg.--Entergy Corporation, New Orleans, LA; *U.S. Public*, pg. 585
Niggli, Michael R., V.P.-Sls. & Mktg.--Entergy New Orleans, Inc., New Orleans, LA; *U.S. Public*, pg. 586
Nine, Jerry, V.P.-Sls. & Mktg.--National Education Training Group, Naperville, IL; *U.S. Public*, pg. 784
Nisson, Max, Mgr.-Sls.--Albert Fisher North America, Dallas, TX; *Int'l*, pg. 491
Nitiss, Joe, Dir.-Mktg.--Appleton Electric Co., Chicago, IL; *U.S. Public*, pg. 572
Nitz, Bruce E., V.P.-Sls. & Mktg.--Stanley Knight Corporation, New Troy, MI; *U.S. Private*, pg. 1033
Nitzkin, Jeff, V.P.-Sls.--Paris Presents, Gurnee, IL; *U.S. Private*, pg. 839
Niwore, Roberta, Mgr.-Sls. Planning--Bayer Corporation/ Pharmaceutical Division, West Haven, CT; *Int'l*, pg. 173
Nix, Gary, Mgr.-Div. Sls. & Mkt. Res.--AP North American Aftermarket Division, Goldsboro, NC; *U.S. Private*, pg. 230
Nix, Tim, Dir.-Promo.--Time, New York, NY; *U.S. Public*, pg. 1613
Nixon, Doug, Mgr.-Sls.--Electrical Equipment Company, Raleigh, NC; *U.S. Private*, pg. 368
Nixon, Gus, V.P.-Sls. & Transportation--Circle International, Dallas-Fort Worth Airport, TX; *U.S. Public*, pg. 372
Nixon, Tom, V.P.-Sls.--McBride and Associates, Inc., Albuquerque, NM; *U.S. Private*, pg. 719
Noack, Hans-Herbert, Mgr.-Sls. & Mktg.--Eagle-Picher Wolverine GmbH, Ohringen, Germany; *U.S. Private*, pg. 355
Noack, Hans-Herbert, Mgr.-Sls. & Mktg.--Eagle-Picher Wolverine Gmbh, Ohringen, Germany; *U.S. Private*, pg. 355
Noble, Terry, Mgr.-Sls. & Customer Svc.--Pipetronix Ltd., Concord, Canada; *Int'l*, pg. 1071
Noe, Brad, Exec. V.P.-Sls. & Mktg.--Henredon Furniture Industries, Inc., Morganton, NC; *U.S. Private*, pg. 432
Noe, Brad, V.P.-Sls.--Henredon Upholstery, High Point, NC; *U.S. Private*, pg. 432
Noe, David P., V.P.-Industrial Sls.--Rev-A-Shelf, Louisville, KY; *U.S. Public*, pg. 925
Noelke, Eric, V.P.-Sls.--Numetrix Ltd., Toronto, Canada; *Int'l*, pg. 990
Noens, Benny, V.P.-European Sls. & Mng. Dir.-Metrologic GmbH--Metrologic Instruments GmbH, Munich, Germany; *U.S. Public*, pg. 1102
Noes, Don, Sr. V.P.-Sls. & MKtg.--Provident Music Group, Brentwood, TN; *Int'l*, pg. 1529
Noes, Don, Sr. V.P.-Sls. & Mktg.--Provident Music Distribution, Nashville, TN; *Int'l*, pg. 1529
Nofsinger, Rowland, V.P.-Mktg. & Sls.--Nofsinger, Inc., Kansas City, MO; *U.S. Private*, pg. 187
Nokovich, Joseph, Mgr.-Matl. & Sls.--Hempt Brothers, Inc., Camp Hill, PA; *U.S. Private*, pg. 521
Nolan, Jim, Dir.-Mktg. & Sls.--Irish Cement Ltd., Stillorgan, Ireland; *Int'l*, pg. 242
Nolan, Joy, Sr. Mgr.-Sls.--Chattanooga Choo-Choo Holiday Inn, Chattanooga, TN; *U.S. Private*, pg. 231
Nolen, George, Sr. V.P.-Sls. & Svc.--Siemens Business Communication Systems, Inc., Santa Clara, CA; *Int'l*, pg. 1245
Noll, Irwin, V.P.-Sls.--Narrow Fabric Industries, Inc., Reading, PA; *U.S. Private*, pg. 774
Noonan, Edward J., Mgr.-Reg. Sls.--Automotive News, Detroit, MI; *U.S. Private*, pg. 284
Noonan, Richard, V.P.-Sls. Opers.--Northern Telecom Inc., Rochester, NY; *Int'l*, pg. 970
Nooney, Charles, Sr. V.P.-Sls. & Mktg.--The Disney Channel, Burbank, CA; *U.S. Public*, pg. 513
Norberg, Dave, Mgr.-Customer Sls. & Service--Hanna Corporation, Chicago, IL; *U.S. Private*, pg. 231
Norcia, Vincent, Mgr.-Sls./Eastern Reg.--AEP Industries, Inc., South Hackensack, NJ; *U.S. Public*, pg. 4
Nordaby, Bill, Dir.-Sls. & Mktg.--Plastic Suppliers, Inc., Columbus, OH; *U.S. Private*, pg. 871
Nordel, Stan, Mgr.-Sls. Padlock--Master Lock Company, Milwaukee, WI; *U.S. Public*, pg. 675
Nordell, Peter, V.P.-Mktg. & Sls.--Edlund Company, Inc., Burlington, VT; *U.S. Private*, pg. 364
Norder, Ali, Asst. Mgr.-Sls.--Great Lakes Kraut Co., Bear Creek, WI; *U.S. Private*, pg. 887
Nordhaus, Scott, V.P.-Sls. & Distrib.--DirecTV Inc., El Segundo, CA; *U.S. Public*, pg. 720
Nordin, Kent, Dir.-Sls. & Range--Ikea North America, Inc., Plymouth Meeting, PA; *Int'l*, pg. 660
Nordman, Jari, Dir.-Sls.--Opel Oy, Espoo, Finland; *U.S. Public*, pg. 723
Nordman, Mike, Mgr.-Sls.--Senco Products, Inc., Cincinnati, OH; *U.S. Private*, pg. 984
Nordquist, Dale A., V.P.-Sls. & Mktg.--HEI, Inc., Victoria, MN; *U.S. Public*, pg. 770
Nordstrom, Jeff, Dir.-Mktg.--Whataburger, Inc., Corpus Christi, TX; *U.S. Private*, pg. 1170
Nordvi, Jan Erik, Sls. & Adv. Mgr.--ISS Catering a.s., Oslo, Norway; *Int'l*, pg. 656
Nordyke, Frank, V.P.-Sls.--Idea Man, Inc., Los Angeles, CA; *U.S. Private*, pg. 557
Noren, Jeff, Mgr.-Sls. & Mktg.Opers.--Tapemark, Saint Paul, MN; *U.S. Private*, pg. 1068
Norkus, Anthony E., V.P.-Intl. Sls.--I-Flow Corporation, Lake Forest, CA; *U.S. Public*, pg. 851
Norman, Bruce E., V.P.-Mktg.--Mercury General Corporation, Los Angeles, CA; *U.S. Public*, pg. 1093
Norman, Cecil, Mgr.-Sls.--Broan Limited, Mississauga, Canada; *U.S. Public*, pg. 1194
Norman, David, V.P.-Sls. & Mktg.--Kobelco Stewart Bolling, Inc., Hudson, OH; *Int'l*, pg. 740
Norman, Gary E., Sr. V.P.-Bus. Devel.--Elkins Constructors, Inc., Jacksonville, FL; *U.S. Private*, pg. 372
Norman, H., Crumpton, V.P.-Sls. & Mktg.--H.H. Robertson Burford Plant, Hamilton, Canada; *U.S. Public*, pg. 1394
Norman, Ken, Mgr.-Sls.--Control Module, Inc., Enfield, CT; *U.S. Private*, pg. 271
Norman, Mark, Dir.-Sls.--Dun & Bradstreet (Australia) Pty. Ltd., Melbourne, Australia; *U.S. Public*, pg. 536
Norman, Rich, Mgr.--E Z Loader Boat Trailers, Inc., Spokane, WA; *U.S. Private*, pg. 353
Normand, Dan, Reg. Mgr.-Sls.--Bird Products Corporation, Palm Springs, CA; *U.S. Public*, pg. 1591
Normandin, Marc, V.P.-Sls. & Mktg.--Nyltech North America Inc., Manchester, NH; *Int'l*, pg. 482
Normandin, Ray, Gen. Sls. & Mktg. Mgr.--Koyo Corporation of USA, Sales Division, Westlake, OH; *Int'l*, pg. 760
Noroovi, Hal, V.P.-Mfg. & Engrng.--Evans Tempcon Inc., Grand Rapids, MI; *U.S. Private*, pg. 7
Norquist, Tom, Dir.-Mktg. & Sls.--Game Time, Inc., Fort Payne, AL; *U.S. Public*, pg. 1543
Norrie, Gordon, Dir.-Sls.--The Calgary Sun, Calgary, Canada; *Int'l*, pg. 1320
Norris, Lynnwood, Mgr.-Sls.--Meherrin Agriculture & Chemical Co., Severn, NC; *U.S. Private*, pg. 729
Northridge, Nigele, Mgr.-Sls. & Mktg.--Gallaher International Limited, Weybridge, United Kingdom; *Int'l*, pg. 539
Northup, Christopher, Dir.-Sls. & Mktg.--Keystone Automotive Industries, Inc., Pomona, CA; *U.S. Public*, pg. 955
Norton, Patrick H., Sr. V.P.-Sls. & Mktg.--La-Z-Boy Incorporated, Monroe, MI; *U.S. Public*, pg. 972
Nosal, Dianne, V.P.-Milk Sls. & Distr.--Dairylea Cooperative Inc., East Syracuse, NY; *U.S. Private*, pg. 307
Noster, Sandy, V.P.-Sls.--Pacific Metal Company, Portland, OR; *U.S. Private*, pg. 832
Nourse, William, Dir.-Sls.--Concord Litho Co., Inc., Concord, NH; *U.S. Private*, pg. 261
Novak, John, Mgr.-Inside Sls.--Spadone-Alfa Corporation, Norwalk, CT; *U.S. Private*, pg. 1020
Novak, John H., Dir.-Sls. Chemicals & Specialties--Millennium Petrochemicals, Inc., Cincinnati, OH; *Int'l*, pg. 594
Novak, R.D., V.P.-Sls.-Brushes--Osborn Manufacturing, Cleveland, OH; *U.S. Public*, pg. 924
Novell, P.M., Gen. Mgr.-Sls.--Ford Division, Detroit, MI; *U.S. Public*, pg. 662
Novotny, Eva, Exec. V.P.-Sls. & Mktg.--Medstone International, Inc., Aliso Viejo, CA; *U.S. Public*, pg. 1082
Nowacki, Michael, V.P.-News Sls.--CBS Television Network, New York, NY; *U.S. Public*, pg. 274
Nowak, Steve, Mgr.-Natl. Sls.--Tab Products Co., Palo Alto, CA; *U.S. Public*, pg. 1559
Nowicki, Len, V.P.-Sls.--Paterno Imports Limited, Lake Bluff, IL; *U.S. Private*, pg. 843
Nozawa, Abazu, Dir.-Sls.--Honda Motor do Brasil Ltda., Sao Paulo, Brazil; *Int'l*, pg. 635
Nugent, John, Gen. Mgr.-Sls.--PSC Bar Code Ltd., Runcorn, United Kingdom; *U.S. Public*, pg. 1246
Nunamann, Robert W., Dir.-Military Sls.--Marotta Scientific Controls, Inc., Montville, NJ; *U.S. Private*, pg. 706
Nunez, Armando, Jr., Pres.-Intl. Distr.--New World Entertainment, Inc., Los Angeles, CA; *Int'l*, pg. 926
Nunn, Don, Sls. Mgr.--Holmes Protection of Long Island, Inc., Islandia, NY; *U.S. Public*, pg. 1649
Nunn, Michael J., V.P. & Reg. Mgr.-Sls.--Airborne Freight Corporation, Seattle, WA; *U.S. Public*, pg. 32
Nunziata, Frank, Mgr.-Natl. Sls.--Bel-Art Products, Pequannock, NJ; *U.S. Private*, pg. 130
Nurmi, James A., V.P.-Sls.--Plastics, Inc., Saint Paul, MN; *U.S. Public*, pg. 1177
Nurton, C.C., Dir.-Sls.--United Flexible, Merthyr Tydfil, United Kingdom; *Int'l*, pg. 1221
Nussbaum, Robert, V.P.-Sls. & Mktg.--The Lenson Coffee Co., Pleasantville, NJ; *U.S. Public*, pg. 351
Nussbaun, Bob, V.P.-Sls. & Mktg.--Ireland Coffee Tea, Inc., Pleasantville, NJ; *U.S. Public*, pg. 351
Nussmeier, Robert, Mgr.-Sls., Eastern--Atlanta Mfg. Facility, Douglasville, GA; *U.S. Private*, pg. 976
Nussmeier, Robert W., Mgr.-North America-Sls. & Service--L.M. Scofield Company, Los Angeles, CA; *U.S. Private*, pg. 976
Nuttall, William N., V.P.-Sls.--Diadora America, Inc., Kent, WA; *U.S. Private*, pg. 330
Nutter, Dale, V.P.-Comml. Sls.--Virco Mfg. Corporation, Torrance, CA; *U.S. Public*, pg. 1721
Nyberg, L.G., Mgr. Sls.-Bus. Forms--Moore Paragon Svenska AB, Vastervik, Sweden; *Int'l*, pg. 890
Nyberg, Stig-Bjorn, Dir.-Retail Book Sls.--Academic Bookstore, Helsinki, Finland; *Int'l*, pg. 1301
Nyblad, Mary Jo, Mgr.-Sls. & Mktg./Structural Panel Prods.--Boise Cascade Corporation, Boise, ID; *U.S. Public*, pg. 242
Nye, Kenneth, Mgr.-Sls.--Buffalo Truck Center, Buffalo, NY; *U.S. Private*, pg. 179
Nyenshuis, Tom, V.P.-Sls.--X-Rite, Incorporated, Grandville, MI; *U.S. Public*, pg. 1783
Nygaard, K.S., V.P.-Sls.--Harwick Standard Distribution Corporation, Akron, OH; *U.S. Private*, pg. 509
Nysten, Juhani, Dir.-Sls.--Voikkaa Paper Mill, Voikkaa, Finland; *Int'l*, pg. 1428
Nytes, Andy, Dir.-Sls.--Milk Specialties Company, Dundee, IL; *U.S. Private*, pg. 746
O'Boyle, Sean, V.P.-Midwestern Sls.--CBS Enterprises Division, New York, NY; *U.S. Public*, pg. 274
O'Brien, Chris, Dir.-Sls.--Sensormatic New Zealand Ltd., Auckland, New Zealand; *U.S. Public*, pg. 1458
O'Brien, J. Michael, V.P.-Sls. & Sec.--American Cast Iron Pipe Co., Birmingham, AL; *U.S. Private*, pg. 51
O'Brien, John, Mgr.-Natl. Sls./Foodservice--Fresh America Corp., Dallas, TX; *U.S. Public*, pg. 681
O'Brien, John, V.P.-Sls.--B & R Foods, Dover, FL; *U.S. Public*, pg. 1278
O'Brien, John M., V.P.-Sls. & Mktg.--Federal Screw Works, Detroit, MI; *U.S. Public*, pg. 616
O'Brien, John W., V.P.-Sls./Western Reg.--Amtran, Inc., Indianapolis, IN; *U.S. Public*, pg. 106
O'Brien, Michael T., V.P.-Sls. & Mktg./Precision & Indus.--Carsen Group Inc., Markham, Canada; *U.S. Public*, pg. 301
O'Brien, Mike, Mgr.-Sls., Water Systems--F.E. Myers, Ashland, OH; *U.S. Public*, pg. 1273
O'Brien, Patrick J., V.P.-North American Consumer Prod. Sls.--S.C. Johnson & Son, Inc., Racine, WI; *U.S. Private*, pg. 592
O'Brien, Philip, Mgr.-Sls.--Perrier UK Ltd., London, United Kingdom; *Int'l*, pg. 919
O'Brien, Ray, Sr. V.P.-Sls. & Mktg.-SkyTel--Mobile Telecommunications Technologies Corp., Jackson, MS; *U.S. Public*, pg. 1120
O'Brien, Thomas W., V.P.-Sls. & Mktg.--Western Industries, Inc., Milwaukee, WI; *U.S. Private*, pg. 1165
O'Connell, Dave, Dir.-Sls.--Carver Boat Corp., Pulaski, WI; *U.S. Private*, pg. 447
O'Connell, James, V.P.-Sls.--LEGO Systems, Inc., Enfield, CT; *Int'l*, pg. 805
O'Connell, Jerry, V.P.-Sls.--CNS-Community News Service Weekly Newspapers, Columbus, OH; *U.S. Private*, pg. 335
O'Connell, Larry, Dir.-Sls./Americas--Gelman Sciences, Inc., Ann Arbor, MI; *U.S. Public*, pg. 1253
O'Connor, Dan, V.P.-Sls. & Mtkg.--Northern Telecom - National Repair & Distribution Center, Nashville, TN; *Int'l*, pg. 970
O'Connor, Daniel P., V.P.-Sls.--Aearo Company, Boston, MA; *U.S. Private*, pg. 23
O'Connor, Mike, V.P.-Sls. & Mktg.--Seitz Foods Inc., Saint Joseph, MO; *U.S. Public*, pg. 1434
O'Conor, Robert B., V.P.-Sls.--BHA Company, Inc., Kansas City, MO; *U.S. Public*, pg. 161

O'Dare, James T., Jr., Grp. V.P.-Sls. & Distr.--Navistar International Corporation, Chicago, IL; *U.S. Public,* pg. 1167
O'Dea, Bill, V.P.-Sls. & Mktg.--Azon Corporation, Johnson City, NY; *U.S. Private,* pg. 104
O'Donnell, Brian, Dir.-Natl. Sls.--Porcelanite, Inc., Lexington, NC; *Int'l,* pg. 573
O'Donnell, Dave, Mgr.-Sls.--Genesee Precision Fabricating, Grand Prairie, TX; *U.S. Private,* pg. 446
O'Donnell, Dave, Mgr.-Sls.--Genesee Stamping, Grand Prairie, TX; *U.S. Private,* pg. 446
O'Donnell, Eddie, Mgr.-Sls.--N.G. Bailey & Co. Ltd.-Edinburgh Branch, Edinburgh, United Kingdom; *Int'l,* pg. 132
O'Donnell, Jack, V.P.-Sls.--Reading Body Works, Inc., Reading, PA; *U.S. Private,* pg. 913
O'Donnell, Kevin, V.P. & Mgr.-Pub. School Sls.--William H. Sadlier, Inc., New York, NY; *U.S. Public,* pg. 1422
O'Donnell, Michael J., V.P.-Assets Mngmt.--Sun Financial Group, Inc., Tampa, FL; *U.S. Public,* pg. 691
O'Driscoll, J.F., Mgr.-Sls.--CGTX Toronto Office, Mississauga, Canada; *U.S. Public,* pg. 693
O'Flaherty, Thomas, Dir.-Mktg. & Sls.--Hercules Chemical Co., Inc., Passaic, NJ; *U.S. Private,* pg. 523
O'Flynn, Terry, Sr. V.P.-OEM Sls.--Recoton Corporation, Lake Mary, FL; *U.S. Public,* pg. 1369
O'Gara, Dennis, V.P.-Worldwide Sls.--Budget Rent A Car Corporation, Lisle, IL; *U.S. Private,* pg. 178
O'Hanlon, Rosemary, Coord.-Sls.--Amphenol Corporation, Wallingford, CT; *U.S. Private,* pg. 629
O'Hara, Jan, Mgr.-Adv. & Sls. Promo.--Buster Brown Apparel, Inc., Chattanooga, TN; *U.S. Private,* pg. 189
O'Hara, Michael J., Sr. V.P.-Franchise Sls.--Knights Franchise Systems, Inc., Parsippany, NJ; *U.S. Public,* pg. 321
O'Hara, Thomas, Mgr.-Sls.--Dorchester, Millburn, NJ; *U.S. Private,* pg. 584
O'Hargan, Jim, V.P.-Sls.--Hubbell Lighting Inc., Christiansburg, VA; *U.S. Public,* pg. 844
O'Keeffe, James, Natl. Sls. Mgr.--Sportcraft Ltd., Mount Olive, NJ; *U.S. Private,* pg. 1026
O'Kray, Len, V.P.-Mktg. & Sls.--Elgin Sweeper Company, Elgin, IL; *U.S. Public,* pg. 617
O'Leary, Dennis, V.P.-Worldwide Sls.--Thinking Machines Corporation, Burlington, MA; *U.S. Private,* pg. 1081
O'Leary, E.J., V.P.-Sls. & Mktg.--Moog Automotive, Inc., Saint Louis, MO; *U.S. Public,* pg. 443
O'Leary, Robert W., V.P.-Mktg., Sls. & Adv.--Scanforms, Inc., Bristol, PA; *U.S. Public,* pg. 228
O'Loughlin, Dennis, V.P.-Intl. Sls.--Harris Waste Mgmt. Group, Inc., Peachtree City, GA; *Int'l,* pg. 473
O'Mahony, Conor, V.P.-Sls. & Customer Opers.--Electroglas, Inc., Santa Clara, CA; *U.S. Public,* pg. 727
O'Mara, Thomas K., Mgr.-Sls. & Mktg.--Autocam Corporation, Grand Rapids, MI; *U.S. Public,* pg. 148
O'Mara, Thomas P., Dir.-Sls.--Curtis Mathes Holding Corp., Dallas, TX; *U.S. Public,* pg. 1057
O'Meara, Maureen, Mgr.-Sls.--ACBJ Business Publications, Inc., Louisville, KY; *U.S. Private,* pg. 19
O'Neil, Bob, Mgr.-Sls./Used Cars--Roger Holler Chevrolet & GEO Co., Winter Park, FL; *U.S. Private,* pg. 534
O'Neil, Charles J., Sr. V.P.-Sls.--Stuart Hall Co., Inc., Kansas City, MO; *U.S. Public,* pg. 1178
O'Neill, Brian, Sls. Rep.-Sterilizer Div.--Environmental Tectonics Corporation (ETC), Southampton, PA; *U.S. Public,* pg. 587
O'Neill, Jeffrey J., V.P.-Sls.--The Quaker Oats Co. of Canada Ltd., Peterborough, Canada; *U.S. Public,* pg. 1348
O'Neill, Jim, Sr. V.P.-Sls. & Mktg.--Alpine Electronics of America, Inc., Torrance, CA; *Int'l,* pg. 65
O'Neill, Kevin, V.P.-Mktg. & Sls.--Wilbur Chocolate Co., Inc., Lititz, PA; *U.S. Private,* pg. 210
O'Neill, Michael J., V.P.-Sls.--Ripon Foods, Inc., Ripon, WI; *U.S. Private,* pg. 931
O'Neill, Peter, V.P.-Worldwide Sls.--Sequent Computer Systems, Inc., Beaverton, OR; *U.S. Public,* pg. 1459
O'Neill, Peter, Mgr.-Sls. Toronto--Western Broadcast Sales Ltd., Toronto, Canada; *Int'l,* pg. 1482
O'Regan, Sean J., V.P.-Data Capture Opers.--Saztec International, Inc., Billerica, MA; *U.S. Public,* pg. 1435
O'Reilly, Gordon, V.P.-Mdsg.--The Bartell Drug Company, Seattle, WA; *U.S. Private,* pg. 118
O'Reilly, Mike, Natl. Sls. Mgr.--Q.U.F. Industries Ltd., Brisbane, Australia; *Int'l,* pg. 1074
O'Reilly, Tom, Dir.-Sls. & Mktg.--Elida Faberge (Ireland) Ltd., Dublin, Ireland; *Int'l,* pg. 1437
O'Rourke, J.B., Dir.-Sls.--Onan Corporation, Minneapolis, MN; *U.S. Public,* pg. 468
O'Rourke, John, V.P.-Sls.--Custom Brands Div., Cumberland, MD; *U.S. Public,* pg. 753
O'Rourke, Patrick H., Dir.-Sls. & Mktg.--Selectone, Inc., Hayward, CA; *U.S. Private,* pg. 982
O'Shea, Michael, Dir.-Sls.--Irish Biscuits, Dublin, Ireland; *Int'l,* pg. 688
O'Shea, Michael G., Dir.-Sls.--Irish Biscuits Ltd., Dublin, Ireland; *Int'l,* pg. 688
O'Shea, Tim, V.P.-Mktg.--Fresh Choice, Inc., Santa Clara, CA; *U.S. Public,* pg. 682
O'Sullivan, James, Dir.-Distr.--Distribution Division, Mansfield, MA; *U.S. Public,* pg. 74
O'Sullivan, John, V.P. & Dir.-Sls. & Mktg.--CBS Television Network, New York, NY; *U.S. Public,* pg. 274
O'Sullivan, Thomas M., Jr., V.P.-Sls.--O'Sullivan Industries Holdings, Lamar, MO; *U.S. Public,* pg. 1234
O'Toole, Mark, V.P.-Retail Sls.-Deli/Club--Bil Mar Foods, Inc., Zeeland, MI; *U.S. Public,* pg. 1433
O'Toole, Matt, V.P.-Domestic Sls.--Tommy Armour Golf, Morton Grove, IL; *U.S. Public,* pg. 1683
Oakley, Brian M., Mgr.-Sls. & Mktg.--Fleet Industries, Fort Erie, Canada; *Int'l,* pg. 829
Oates, Gordon, Jr., V.P.-Sls. & Mktg.--American Wyott Corporation, Cheyenne, WY; *U.S. Private,* pg. 1193
Oats, Corinne, Dir.-Sls.--Lalique North America, Carlstadt, NJ; *Int'l,* pg. 797
Obana, Yuji, Mng. Dir.-Admin., Personnel, Safety, Sls., Adv. & Customer Serv.--Nikon Corporation, Tokyo, Japan; *Int'l,* pg. 931
Oberbillig, D.C., V.P.-Wire Prods. Divison Sls.--Northwestern Steel & Wire Co., Sterling, IL; *U.S. Public,* pg. 1201
Oberleitner, William H., V.P.-Sls.--Badger Meter Utility Div., Milwaukee, WI; *U.S. Public,* pg. 165
Oberling, Jim, V.P.-Sls.--Hayes Brake, Mequon, WI; *U.S. Private,* pg. 299
Obermeier, Roland, Mgr.-Gen. Sls.--Calwer Decken-und Tuchfabriken AG, Calw-Hirsau, Germany; *Int'l,* pg. 253
Ocana, Rafael, Dir.-Sls.--Aviaco, Madrid, Spain; *Int'l,* pg. 574
Ochlind, Markus, Dir.-Sls.--IL Returpapper, Stockholm, Sweden; *Int'l,* pg. 646
Odachowski, Ed, V.P.-Sls.--Learning International, Stamford, CT; *U.S. Public,* pg. 1617
Oddo, Jim, V.P.-Mktg., Adv. & Sls.--Atlas Hotels, Inc., San Diego, CA; *U.S. Private,* pg. 96
Odell, Stephen T., V.P.-Sls. & Mktg.--Jaguar Cars, Mahwah, NJ; *U.S. Public,* pg. 664
Odham, Don, V.P.-Commercial Sls.--Printing House, Inc., Quincy, FL; *U.S. Private,* pg. 886
Odillard, Martine, V.P.-Corp. Commun. & H.R.--Chargeurs, Paris, France; *Int'l,* pg. 280
Oehlert, George, V.P.-Sls.--Concordia Publishing House, Saint Louis, MO; *U.S. Private,* pg. 261
Oehlrich, Kurt, Mgr.-Sls.--Steiner Turf Equipment Inc., Orrville, OH; *Int'l,* pg. 1088
Oertel, Jack, Dir.-Sls. & Mktg.--William A. Randolph, Inc., Morton Grove, IL; *U.S. Private,* pg. 909
Oetelaar, Anthony, Dir.-Natl. Sls., Indus. Div.--Agropur, Granby, Canada; *Int'l,* pg. 31
Ofstun, Richard E., V.P.-Sls.--Dexol, Torrance, CA; *U.S. Public,* pg. 1390
Ogata, Kyoya, Dir.-Sls. Div.--Mitsumi Electric Co., Ltd., Tokyo, Japan; *Int'l,* pg. 884
Ogden, Charles, Dir.-Sls.--North American Recreation Products Company, Wichita, KS; *U.S. Private,* pg. 691
Oh, Dong-Hwee, Pres.--Ssangyong Research Institute, Seoul, Korea; *Int'l,* pg. 1292
Ohl, D.W., V.P.-Sls. & Mktg.--Inco Alloys International, Inc., Huntington, WV; *Int'l,* pg. 672
Ohnmacht, Judy, Dir.-Sls.--Kawasaki Motors Corp., U.S.A., Irvine, CA; *Int'l,* pg. 725
Ohotnicky, Frank, Mgr.-Sls.--Mount Snow Resort, Mount Snow, VT; *U.S. Private,* pg. 61
Ohrenich, Bruce, V.P.-Sls.--Hornor, Townsend & Kent, Philadelphia, PA; *U.S. Private,* pg. 849
Ojanen, Asko, Dir.-Sls.--Dun & Bradstreet Finland Oy., Espoo, Finland; *U.S. Public,* pg. 536
Okada, Takeshi, Chief Oper. Officer, Dir.-Sls.--Takagi Chokoku Co., Ltd.-Hamamatsu Factory, Hamamatsu, Japan; *Int'l,* pg. 1349
Okonski, Tracy, Sls. & Mkgt. Asst.--Surgical Specialties, Reading, PA; *U.S. Private,* pg. 1056
Okosky, Michael, V.P.-Sls. & Mktg.--PAXAR Corporation, White Plains, NY; *U.S. Public,* pg. 1266
Oksanen, Matti, Mgr.-Oil, Mktg. & Sls.--Neste Oy, Espoo, Finland; *Int'l,* pg. 912
Oktavec, Thomas, V.P.-Mktg.--Kocolene Oil Corp., Seymour, IN; *U.S. Private,* pg. 629
Oktela, Michael, Dir.-Mktg. & Sls.--Federal Signal Corporation, Signal Div., University Park, IL; *U.S. Public,* pg. 616
Okuya, Naoyuki, Mgr.-Sls.--Unitika America Corp., New York, NY; *Int'l,* pg. 1444
Olcott, Andy, Industrial/Commercial Sls. Mgr.--Herrmidifier Co., Inc., Lancaster, PA; *U.S. Public,* pg. 1639
Oldham, J. Donald, V.P.-Worldwide Sls.--Stratus Computer, Inc., Marlborough, MA; *U.S. Public,* pg. 1524
Oldham, Mike, Sr. V.P. & Dir.-Sls. & Mktg.--Columbine JDS Systems, Inc., Denver, CO; *U.S. Public,* pg. 228
Olds, Rick, Mgr.-Reg. Sls.--Sloan Technology, Santa Barbara, CA; *U.S. Public,* pg. 1711
Olechiw, Jerry, V.P.-Sls.--Dranetz-BMI, Edison, NJ; *U.S. Private,* pg. 1144
Oler, Debbie, Gen. Mgr.-Sls.--Alliant Foodservice, Bensenville, IL; *U.S. Private,* pg. 244
Oleson, Donald L., Pres.-Natl. Sls. Div.--Allied Digital Technologies, Hauppauge, NY; *U.S. Public,* pg. 48
Olfers, F.A.H.M., Mgr.-Netherlands Sls.--Bakery Ingredients Division, Delft, Netherlands; *Int'l,* pg. 1142
Olin, Greg, Dir.-Sls.--Super Sky Products, Inc., Mequon, WI; *U.S. Private,* pg. 1054
Olin, Scott, V.P.-Sls. & Mktg.--Columbia Paint & Coatings, Spokane, WA; *U.S. Private,* pg. 256
Olin, Thomas F. Jr., Pres.-Sls. & Mktg.--Archway Cookies, Inc., Battle Creek, MI; *U.S. Private,* pg. 80
Olinger, Jack, Exec. V.P.-Adv.--The Hammerblow Corp., Wausau, WI; *U.S. Private,* pg. 498
Olingy, Jeffrey F., Sr. V.P.-Sls. & Mktg.--Provident Companies, Inc., Chattanooga, TN; *U.S. Public,* pg. 1337
Oliva, Bruce, Mgr.-Natl. Sls.--Van Son Holland Ink Corp. of America, Mineola, NY; *U.S. Private,* pg. 1133
Oliva, Thomas, V.P.-Catalog Sls.--World Color-Chicago Div., Elk Grove Village, IL; *U.S. Public,* pg. 1778
Oliver, Peter, Sls. Rep.--Horizon Enterprises Group LLC, Taylor, MI; *U.S. Private,* pg. 539
Olivier, R., Dir.-Sls.-Sugar--Kraft Jacobs Suchard, Velizy-Villacoublay, France; *U.S. Public,* pg. 1290
Ollen, George, Dir.-Sls. & Mktg.--International Electronic Research Corp., Burbank, CA; *U.S. Public,* pg. 286
Oller, Otto, Dir.-Adv.--ITW Plastiglide, Rancho Dominguez, CA; *U.S. Public,* pg. 867
Olley, Peter H., V.P.-Sls. & Mktg.--Day-Glo Color Corp., Cleveland, OH; *U.S. Public,* pg. 1357
Olmen, Richard, V.P.-Sls.--Construction & Mining Group, Bethlehem, PA; *U.S. Public,* pg. 876
Olmos, Pascual, Dir.-Sls.--Repsol S.A., Madrid, Spain; *Int'l,* pg. 1104
Olmsted, D.F. (Dave), Intl. Sls. Mgr.--Barber Industries Inc., Calgary, Canada; *Int'l,* pg. 164
Olschan, Brian S., Sr. V.P.-Mktg. & Sls.--Acme United Corporation, Fairfield, CT; *U.S. Public,* pg. 17
Olsen, E., Consultant-Sls.--Toyota Norge A/S, Drammen, Norway; *Int'l,* pg. 1414
Olsen, Hans, V.P.-Mktg. & Worldwide Sls.--Trident Microsystems, Inc., Mountain View, CA; *U.S. Public,* pg. 1637
Olsen, John F., Sr. V.P.-Worldwide Sls.--Cadence Design Systems, Inc., San Jose, CA; *U.S. Public,* pg. 290
Olsen, Larry A., V.P.-Sls. & Mktg.--Research Products Corporation, Madison, WI; *U.S. Private,* pg. 924
Olsen, Michael, V.P.-Sls.--Joy Mining Machinery, Warrendale, PA; *U.S. Public,* pg. 790
Olsen, Mike, V.P.-Sls.--Joy Mining Machinery, Warrendale, PA; *U.S. Public,* pg. 789
Olson, Charles R., V.P.-Sls. & Mktg.--Aspec Technology, Inc., Sunnyvale, CA; *U.S. Private,* pg. 89
Olson, Dan, Gen. Mgr.-Sls.--KGAN-TV, Cedar Rapids, IA; *U.S. Private,* pg. 439
Olson, Debra, Mgr.-Retail Sls.--Voyager Emblems, Inc., Sanborn, NY; *U.S. Private,* pg. 1143
Olson, Eric, Mgr.-W. Coast Sls.--Advertising Checking Bureau Incorporated, New York, NY; *U.S. Private,* pg. 23
Olson, Kurt, Sr. V.P.-Sls.--Advance Machine Company, Plymouth, MN; *Int'l,* pg. 932
Olson, Larry D., Exec. V.P. & Pres.-Kent Components--Kent Electronics Corp., Houston, TX; *U.S. Public,* pg. 951
Olson, Mark, Mgr.-Sls. & Mktg.--Rodney Metals, New Bedford, MA; *U.S. Public,* pg. 43
Olson, Terry, Exec. V.P.-Sls. & Mktg.--Brothers Gourmet Coffees, Inc., Boca Raton, FL; *U.S. Public,* pg. 259
Olsrud, Steve, V.P.--Sherms Thunderbird Market, Medford, OR; *U.S. Private,* pg. 993
Oltman, Lou, Sr. V.P.-Sls--Simplicity Holdings Inc., New York, NY; *U.S. Private,* pg. 1002
Omidbakhsh, Sohrab, Dir.-Intl. Sls.--Worcester Controls Corp., Marlborough, MA; *Int'l,* pg. 128
Onderson, Leil Skovby, Dir.-Sls.--Fisons A/S, Soeborg, Denmark; *Int'l,* pg. 1111
Ong, Cindy, Mgr.-Sls.--Bensons Metal Products Pte. Ltd., Singapore, Singapore; *Int'l,* pg. 460
Onrubia, Jose Antonio, Gen. Dir.-Sls.--Alicorp S.A., Lima, Peru; *Int'l,* pg. 57
Ontiveros, Victor, V.P.-Sls. Admin.--Farah U.S.A., Inc., El Paso, TX; *U.S. Public,* pg. 613
Onusz, Larry, Mgr.-Western Sls.--RAM Golf Corporation, Melrose Park, IL; *U.S. Private,* pg. 908
Opet, William A., V.P.-Mktg. & Sls.--LIN Cellular Group, Kirkland, WA; *U.S. Public,* pg. 11
Oplinger, Jean, Mgr.-Muzak Promo. Svcs.--Muzak Limited Partnership, Seattle, WA; *U.S. Private,* pg. 222
Oppenheimer, Jim, V.P.-Sls.--AGI Inc., Melrose Park, IL; *U.S. Private,* pg. 5
Orban, David, Dir.-Bus. Devel.--Adams Rite Manufacturing Co., City of Industry, CA; *U.S. Private,* pg. 17
Orbesen, C., V.P.-Retail Sls.--Flexible Products Company, Marietta, GA; *U.S. Private,* pg. 412
Ord, William, V.P.-Sls., Intl.--Ingersoll-Dresser Pump Company, Liberty Corner, NJ; *U.S. Public,* pg. 529
Ordelheide, Gerd, Sr. V.P.-Sls.-European Opers.--BMC Software, Inc., Houston, TX; *U.S. Public,* pg. 162
Orderud, Espen, Mgr.-Sls.--Esselte A/S, Oslo, Norway; *Int'l, pg. 460*
Orenstein, Jerry M., Mgr.-Programs & Sls. Communications--PP&L Resources, Allentown, PA; *U.S. Public,* pg. 1244
Orfao, David, Sr. V.P.-Worldwide Sls.--SQA, Inc., Burlington, MA; *U.S. Public,* pg. 1361
Orlaska, Clark J., V.P.-Sls., Northwest Div.--C.R. Gibson Co., Norwalk, CT; *U.S. Public,* pg. 1168
Orloff, Michael A., Sr. V.P.-Sls. & Mktg.--Roman, Inc., Roselle, IL; *U.S. Private,* pg. 942
Ormes, Kevin, Grp. V.P.-Sls. & Mktg.--Mitsubishi Motor Sales of America, Inc., Cypress, CA; *Int'l,* pg. 875
Orr, C. K., V.P.-Sls.-Houston--Santa Fe Drilling Co., Alhambra, CA; *Int'l,* pg. 765
Orr, Tommy, Sr. V.P.--Harbor Financial Mortgage Corp., Houston, TX; *U.S. Public,* pg. 644
Orrell, Bob, V.P.-Intl. Sls.--NDS, Columbus, OH; *Int'l,* pg. 918
Orrorne, Greg, Mgr.-Natl. Sls.--DeVilbiss Ransburg Industrial Coating Equipment, Maumee, OH; *U.S. Public,* pg. 865
Orseck, Stephen, V.P.-Sales--Esselte Corporation, Garden City, NY; *Int'l,* pg. 459
Orsini, John, V.P.-Sls.--Quala Systems, Inc., Exton, PA; *U.S.* Private, pg. 233
Orth, John, V.P.-Sls & Mktg.--Saab Cars USA, Inc., Norcross, GA; *Int'l,* pg. 687
Orth, Mark, Gen. Mgr.-Telecomm. & Mgr.-Sls.--Times Printing Company, Inc., Random Lake, WI; *U.S. Private,* pg. 1087
Orth, W.J., V.P.-U.S. Sls.--Gould Electronics Inc., Foil Division, Eastlake, OH; *U.S. Public,* pg. 1592
Orth, William, V.P.-U.S. Sls.--Gould Electronics Inc., Eastlake, OH; *U.S. Public,* pg. 1591
Orth, William, Dir.-Sls.--Gould Electronics Inc., Foil Division, Eastlake, OH; *U.S. Public,* pg. 1592
Ortiz, Hector, Exec. V.P. Sls. & Mktg.--Miller Products Company, Inc., North Bergen, NJ; *U.S. Private,* pg. 747
Ortolani, Terrence, Mgr.-Sls.--Carton-Craft Corporation, Buffalo, NY; *U.S. Private,* pg. 217
Ortueta, Antionio, Dir.-Sls. & Mktg., Trade--C.A. Cigarrera Bigott, Sucs., Caracas, Venezuela; *Int'l,* pg. 111
Osberg, Greg, Assoc. Publr.--Newsweek, Inc., New York, NY; *U.S. Public,* pg. 1743
Osborn, Ian, V.P.-Intl. Sls.--Garland Commercial Ranges, Ltd., Mississauga, Canada; *Int'l,* pg. 189
Osborn, Mark, Mgr.-Natl. Sls.--Thomas Conveyor Company, Burleson, TX; *U.S. Private,* pg. 1082
Osborn, Todd, V.P.-Sls.--Gateway 2000, North Sioux City, SD; *U.S. Public,* pg. 703
Osborne, Don, V.P.-Sls. & Mktg.--AMF Bakery Systems, Richmond, VA; *U.S. Private,* pg. 6

Osborne, John M., Exec. V.P.-Franchise Sls. & Devel.--HFS, Incorporated, Parsippany, NJ; *U.S. Public*, pg. 321
Oshone, Akira, Dir.-Sls.--Tekelec, Ltd., Tokyo, Japan; *U.S. Public*, pg. 1566
Osipa, Hank, Mgr.-Sls. Training Projects--Bayer Corporation/Pharmaceutical Division, West Haven, CT; *Int'l*, pg. 173
Osos, Alan, Prod. Mgr.--Specialty Products Group, Niles, MI; *U.S. Public*, pg. 1160
Oss, Arnold C., V.P.-Sls.--Northwest Paper Div., Cloquet, MN; *U.S. Public*, pg. 1318
Ostapowicz, Phil, V.P.-Mktg. & Sls.--Barry-Wehmiller Company, Saint Louis, MO; *U.S. Private*, pg. 118
Ostrom, Anthony D., V.P.-Retail Sls./Boston--Tiffany & Co., New York, NY; *U.S. Public*, pg. 1608
Ostroski, Carol, Mktg. & Sls. Acct. Exec.--Pegasus International Corporation, Pennington, NJ; *U.S. Private*, pg. 1046
Ostrow, Lane, V.P.-Retail Sls.--Ostrow Textile Co., Inc., Rock Hill, SC; *U.S. Private*, pg. 821
Ostrow, Mitch, Dir.-Sls.--Hyatt Regency Lake Tahoe Resort & Casino, Incline Village, NV; *U.S. Private*, pg. 551
Ostrowski, John, Dir.-North American Sls.--Computational Systems Inc., Knoxville, TN; *U.S. Public*, pg. 572
Osumi, T., Exec. V.P.-Mktg. & Sls.--Sumitomo Sitix Silicon, Inc., Fremont, CA; *Int'l*, pg. 1317
Osuszek, Alex, V.P.-Retail Sls./North America--Harlequin Enterprises Ltd., Don Mills, Canada; *Int'l*, pg. 1402
Oswald, Peter W., V.P.-Sls. & Mktg.--Akzo Nobel Fortafil Fibers Inc., Rockwood, TN; *Int'l*, pg. 48
Osweiler, Stanley, Exec. V.P. & Sr. V.P.-Sls.--Service Supply Co. Inc. of Indiana, Indianapolis, IN; *U.S. Private*, pg. 987
Otake, Masafumi, Mgr.-Sls.--Kintetsu World Express (France) S.A., Roissy, France; *Int'l*, pg. 735
Otaki, Yukikatsu, Mng. Dir.-Sls.--Ajinomoto Company Inc., Tokyo, Japan; *Int'l*, pg. 40
Otis, William G., V.P.-Sls. & Mktg./Foodservice--Patrick Cudahy Inc., Cudahy, WI; *U.S. Public*, pg. 1479
Ott, Jim, Sls. Rep.-T.I.--Time Index, Inc., Phoenix, AZ; *U.S. Private*, pg. 1087
Otto, Eric, Mng. Dir.-Worldwide Sls.--Best Western International, Inc., Phoenix, AZ; *U.S. Private*, pg. 140
Otto, Gary, V.P.-Retail Sls.--Sun Data Inc., Norcross, GA; *U.S. Private*, pg. 1050
Otto, Roger, V.P.-Enterprise Sls.--El Camino Resources, Ltd., Woodland Hills, CA; *U.S. Private*, pg. 366
Oueilette, Michael A., V.P.-Sls. & Mktg./Consumer Prods.--Carsen Group Inc., Markham, Canada; *U.S. Public*, pg. 301
Ouellette, Ray, Exec. V.P.-Sls. & Mktg.--IMI Cornelius Inc. (MN), Anoka, MN; *Int'l*, pg. 646
Ouellette, Ray, Exec. V.P.-Sls. & Mktg.--IMI Cornelius, Inc. (IA), Mason City, IA; *Int'l*, pg. 646
Outcalt, Andy, V.P.-Intl. Sls.--MTD Products, Inc., Valley City, OH; *U.S. Private*, pg. 688
Outlaw, J. Thomas Jr., V.P. & Sls. Mgr.--Ingles Markets, Incorporated, Black Mountain, NC; *U.S. Public*, pg. 878
Overbeek, Richard, Mgr.-Sls.--Mid-West Automation Systems, Inc., Buffalo Grove, IL; *U.S. Public*, pg. 475
Overbey, Pam, Gen. Sls. Mgr.--WRNL-FM, Richmond, VA; *U.S. Public*, pg. 385
Overing, Jim, V.P. & Bus. Mgr.-Plastics--Synergistics Industries Limited, Mississauga, Canada; *U.S. Public*, pg. 734
Overland, Dennis, Mgr.-Mktg. & Sls.-Fluid Power--Aro Fluid Products Division, Bryan, OH; *U.S. Public*, pg. 877
Overstreet, David, Dir.-Sls. & Adv.--Duckwall-Alco Stores, Inc., Abilene, KS; *U.S. Public*, pg. 533
Owen, Joseph, Mgr.-Natl. Accts.--The Hall China Company, East Liverpool, OH; *U.S. Private*, pg. 494
Owen, Paul E., V.P.-Deli Meat Sls.--The Smithfield Packing Co., Inc., Smithfield, VA; *U.S. Public*, pg. 1479
Owen, R., Mgr.-Central Sls.--Sloan Valve Company, Franklin Park, IL; *U.S. Private*, pg. 1006
Owens, Allen, Sls. Zone Mgr.--Coldwater Seafood Corporation, Rowayton, CT; *U.S. Private*, pg. 251
Owens, Andy, Dir.-Sls.--The Cloister, Sea Island, GA; *U.S. Private*, pg. 978
Owens, Stephen, V.P.-Sls. & Mktg.--Hofmann Industries, Inc., Sinking Spring, PA; *U.S. Private*, pg. 533
Owensbe, Gary, Mgr.-Sls.--Dayton Parts, Inc., Harrisburg, PA; *U.S. Public*, pg. 919
Oyster, William, Pres., Chief Oper. Officer & Mgr.-Adv., Sls. & Mktg.--Dallas Gold & Silver Exchange, Inc., Dallas, TX; *U.S. Public*, pg. 478
Ozar, Bruce, V.P.-Sls.--Glen Oaks Industries, Inc., New York, NY; *U.S. Private*, pg. 456
Paben, Edward, V.P.-Sls.--Fleetwood Systems, Inc., Romeoville, IL; *U.S. Private*, pg. 410
Pabst, Henry, Jr., Dir.-Sls., Walk-In Coolers & Freezers--Harford Systems, Inc., Aberdeen, MD; *U.S. Private*, pg. 641
Pace, Don, Consultant-Sls. & Mktg.--Bassick by Kaspar, Shiner, TX; *U.S. Private*, pg. 122
Pace, Michael, Sr. V.P.-Sls.--ERO Industries, Inc., Mount Prospect, IL; *U.S. Private*, pg. 526
Pacelli, Robert A., V.P.-Sls. & Mktg.--Weslock National, Inc., Los Angeles, CA; *U.S. Private*, pg. 1163
Pacheco, Enrico, Dir.-Adv. & Sls.--Zivi S.A. Cutelaria, Porto Alegre, Brazil; *Int'l*, pg. 1529
Paciorek, Les A., V.P.-Natl. Sls.--Con-Way Transportation Services, Palo Alto, CA; *U.S. Public*, pg. 281
Pacyga, Robert, Dir.-Sls. & Mktg.--Minnesota Brewing Company, Saint Paul, MN; *U.S. Public*, pg. 1115
Padden, Roger M., Mgr.-Natl. Sls.--Hitox Corporation of America, Corpus Christi, TX; *U.S. Public*, pg. 829
Paddock, David H., Sec. & Sls. Mgr.-NY District--Preferred Utilities Manufacturing Corp., Danbury, CT; *U.S. Private*, pg. 881
Padgett, Tina, Sls. Opers. Admin.--Brooks Foods, Mount Summit, IN; *U.S. Private*, pg. 887
Padjen, Dale N., Gen. Mgr.-Sls.--Chicago Lock Company, Pleasant Prairie, WI; *U.S. Private*, pg. 235
Padnos, Mitchell W., V.P.-Sls. & Mktg.--Louis Padnos Iron & Metal Co., Holland, MI; *U.S. Private*, pg. 834
Padovano, A.A., V.P.-Sls.--The Torrington Co., Torrington, CT; *U.S. Public*, pg. 877
Paff, James, Mgr.-Customer Svcs.--Doron Precision Systems, Inc., Binghamton, NY; *U.S. Private*, pg. 341
Pagano, Paul, V.P.-Sls.--Fairfield Harbour, New Bern, NC; *U.S. Public*, pg. 610
Page, John, Mgr.-Sls.--Ultra Tool & Plastics, Inc., Amherst, NY; *U.S. Private*, pg. 1116
Page, Mark, Mgr.-Commercial Sls. Division--Pemko Manufacturing Company, Ventura, CA; *U.S. Private*, pg. 848
Page, Richard, V.P.-Sls.--Myrick Construction Inc., Biscoe, NC; *U.S. Private*, pg. 771
Pageau, Denis, V.P.-Sls./Eastern--Premier CDN Enterprises Ltd., Dorval, Canada; *Int'l*, pg. 1067
Paguieri, Diego, Mgr.-Sls. & Mktg.--Ferrero Inc., Caguas, PR; *Int'l*, pg. 480
Pailas, Evelyn, Mgr.-Export Sls.--C.R. Gibson Co., Norwalk, CT; *U.S. Public*, pg. 1168
Pajerski, Maureen, V.P.-Sls. & Mktg.--Rauland-Borg Corporation, Skokie, IL; *U.S. Private*, pg. 911
Pakes, Tom, Gen. Mgr.-Sls.--F.E. Myers, Ashland, OH; *U.S. Public*, pg. 1273
Pal, Sujit, Mgr.-Natl. Accts.--SunGard Financial Systems, Inc., Canoga Park, CA; *U.S. Public*, pg. 1534
Palafox, Salvador O., V.P.-Intl. Sls.--S & C Electric Company, Chicago, IL; *U.S. Private*, pg. 954
Palagonia, Joseph A., V.P.-Sls.--J.M.P. Bakery Co., Inc., Brooklyn, NY; *U.S. Private*, pg. 578
Palante, Luke, V.P.-Sls. & Mktg.--Essex Grain Products, Inc., Frazer, PA; *U.S. Private*, pg. 383
Palazzolo, John, V.P.-Residential Sls.--Clopay Corporation, Cincinnati, OH; *U.S. Public*, pg. 766
Paley, William, Sr. V.P.-Sls.--Gould Paper Corporation, New York, NY; *U.S. Private*, pg. 466
Palin, Nick, Sr. V.P.-Sls. & Mktg.--Rexall Sundown Inc., Boca Raton, FL; *U.S. Public*, pg. 1384
Palko, Lorri M., Pres. & Chief Oper. Officer--Dorsey Trailers, Inc., Atlanta, GA; *U.S. Public*, pg. 520
Palladino, Charles, V.P.-Sls.--Kiwi Brands, Douglassville, PA; *U.S. Public*, pg. 1433
Pallenik, Gary, V.P.-Sls & Mktg.--Comprehensive Behavioral Care, Inc., Tampa, FL; *U.S. Public*, pg. 419
Palm, Mats Ola, Dir.-Mktg. Golbal--Electrolux, AB, Stockholm, Sweden; *Int'l*, pg. 438
Palma, Al, Exec. V.P.-Sls.--Eby-Brown Co., Naperville, IL; *U.S. Private*, pg. 359
Palma, Joseph J., V.P.-Sls. & Mktg.--E-Z-Em, Inc., Westbury, NY; *U.S. Public*, pg. 540
Palma, Joseph J., V.P.-Sls. & Mktg.--Enteric Products, Inc., Westbury, NY; *U.S. Public*, pg. 540
Palmatier, Rex, Mgr.-Sls.--Clark Door Co., Inc., Maryland Heights, MO; *U.S. Private*, pg. 242
Palmer, Bruce, Mgr.-Sls.--Cox Wood Preserving Co., Orangeburg, SC; *U.S. Private*, pg. 283
Palmer, G.T., Sls. Mgr.--Household Products Co., Oakland, CA; *U.S. Public*, pg. 387
Palmer, Henry L., V.P.-Fresh Meats Retail/Food Servie Sls.--IBP, Inc., Dakota City, NE; *U.S. Public*, pg. 852
Palmer, Jeffrey H., V.P.-Sls. & Mktg.--Conmed Corporation, Utica, NY; *U.S. Public*, pg. 431
Palmer, Mack, Sr. V.P.--Ocean Beauty Seafoods, Inc., Seattle, WA; *U.S. Private*, pg. 810
Palmer, Richard H., V.P.-Sls.--Yellow Freight System, Inc., Overland Park, KS; *U.S. Public*, pg. 1788
Palmer, Rick, V.P.-Plant Oper.--La Victoria Foods, Inc., City of Industry, CA; *U.S. Private*, pg. 641
Palmer, Robert K., V.P.-Sls.--Eastern Color Printing Company, Avon, CT; *U.S. Private*, pg. 357
Palmieri, Gerardo, Dir.-Sls. & Mktg.--Scotsman Industries, Inc., Vernon Hills, IL; *U.S. Public*, pg. 1444
Palmieri, Gerardo, Dir.-Sls. & Mktg.--Frimont, S.p.A., Bettolino di Pogliano, Italy; *U.S. Public*, pg. 1445
Palucci, Sergio, Mgr.-Intl. Sls.--Pass & Seymour/Legrand, Syracuse, NY; *Int'l*, pg. 806
Panagos, Joan, Sls. Dir.--Spectra-Tech, Shelton, CT; *U.S. Public*, pg. 1593
Pando, Patrick, Dir.-Sls. & Mktg.--Lynch Machinery, Inc., Bainbridge, GA; *U.S. Public*, pg. 1022
Pane, Tom, Mgr.-Sls.-Lubricant & Additives Div.--King Industries, Inc., Norwalk, CT; *U.S. Private*, pg. 620
Pang, Ark W., V.P.-Intl. Sls. & Mktg. & Gen. Mgr.-Equip. Div.--Ionics, Incorporated, Watertown, MA; *U.S. Public*, pg. 912
Panico, Warren, V.P.-Intl. Sls. Div.--Bar-S Foods Co., Phoenix, AZ; *U.S. Private*, pg. 114
Paniel, Georg, Sls. Mgr.--ISS Servisystem S.A., Amarousion, Greece; *Int'l*, pg. 657
Panvini, Mary, V.P.-Sls.--Alfin, Inc., New York, NY; *U.S. Public*, pg. 40
Panyard, Michelle, Dir.-Distributor Accts.--Tokheim Corporation, Fort Wayne, IN; *U.S. Public*, pg. 1620
Panzer, Mark C., V.P.-Adv. & Sls.--American Drug Stores Inc., Oak Brook, IL; *U.S. Public*, pg. 93
Paoletti, Steve, V.P.-Hallmark/Mass Channel Retail Teams--Hallmark Cards, Inc., Kansas City, MO; *U.S. Private*, pg. 495
Paoli, Judy, Mgr.-Sls.--Bennett Brothers, Inc., Chicago, IL; *U.S. Private*, pg. 133
Pape, Gregory, Sr. V.P.-Sls. & Mktg.--American Shared Hospital Services, San Francisco, CA; *U.S. Public*, pg. 91
Papera, Richard D., V.P.-Sls. & Mktg.--Allstate Can Corporation, Parsippany, NJ; *U.S. Private*, pg. 44
Papes, G.A., V.P.-Sls. & Mktg.--U.S. Can Company, Oak Brook, IL; *U.S. Public*, pg. 1681
Papke, Brian J., V.P.-Mktg. & Sls.--WCI Machine Tools & Systems, Cincinnati, OH; *Int'l*, pg. 440
Papke, P.A., V.P.-Original Equipment Sls.--Dunlop Tire Corporation, Buffalo, NY; *Int'l*, pg. 1317
Pappariella, Douglas A., V.P.-Sls.-Grove Manlift--Grove WorldWide, Shady Grove, PA; *Int'l*, pg. 593
Pappariella, Greg, Reg. Sls. Mgr.--Just Born, Inc., Bethlehem, PA; *U.S. Private*, pg. 602
Pappas, George, Natl. Sls. Mgr.--Barouh Eaton Allen Corporation, Brooklyn, NY; *U.S. Private*, pg. 117
Pappert, E. Thomas, V.P.-Sls. & Service--Chrysler Corporation, Auburn Hills, MI; *U.S. Public*, pg. 352
Papreck, Richard T., V.P.-Intl. Sls.--Tommy Armour Golf, Morton Grove, IL; *U.S. Public*, pg. 1683
Paquette, M.W., Pres. & Reg. Dir.-Americas--Devro-Teepak, Inc., Westchester, IL; *Int'l*, pg. 408
Para, Victor, V.P.-Sls. & Mktg.--Atalla Corporation, San Jose, CA; *U.S. Public*, pg. 417
Paradise, Scott E., V.P.-Automotive Sls.--Magna Lomason Corp., Farmington Hills, MI; *Int'l*, pg. 830
Pardo, Roger, Mgr.-Natl. Sls.--Hammermill Papers, Memphis, TN; *U.S. Public*, pg. 902
Pare, Anne, Admin.-Sls. & Mktg.--Admiral Packaging, Inc., Providence, RI; *U.S. Private*, pg. 1119
Parent, Jocelyn, Mgr.-Area Sls.--Sensormatic Canada, Inc., Ville Saint Laurent, Canada; *U.S. Public*, pg. 1457
Parente, Robert, Dir.-Sls.--Mikohn Gaming Corporation, Las Vegas, NV; *U.S. Public*, pg. 1111
Paris, Alan, Dir.-Educational & OEM Sls.--Leica Inc., Deerfield, IL; *Int'l*, pg. 806
Parls, Marion, Dir.-Sls. Promo.--Rama Group of Companies, Cheektowaga, NY; *U.S. Private*, pg. 908
Parizek, Richard J., V.P.-National Accts.--Farley Candy Company, Chicago, IL; *U.S. Private*, pg. 397
Park, Andy, Mgr.-Sls.--Inkel USA Corporation, La Mirada, CA; *U.S. Private*, pg. 563
Park, Byung-Keun, Mng. Dir.--Ssangyong Shipping Co. Ltd., Seoul, Korea; *Int'l*, pg. 1292
Park, Hyo Sung, Sr. V.P.-Passenger Sls., Mktg. & Traffic--Korean Airlines Co., Ltd., Seoul, Korea; *Int'l*, pg. 758
Park, Jerry, Sr. V.P.-CBA Sls., Nelson Word Publishing--Thomas Nelson Inc., Nashville, TN; *U.S. Public*, pg. 1167
Park, Jim, V.P.-Sls.--Hardwick Clothes Inc., Cleveland, TN; *U.S. Private*, pg. 502
Park, K.H., Coord.-Mktg. & Sls.--Hanjin Shipping Company Ltd., Seoul, Korea; *Int'l*, pg. 592
Park, Patrick, V.P.-Bus. Devel.--Tecstar Inc., City of Industry, CA; *U.S. Private*, pg. 1072
Park, Young-Il, V.P.--Ssangyong Paper Co., Ltd., Seoul, Korea; *Int'l*, pg. 1292
Parker, Chris, Sr. V.P.-Sls. & Bus.--A.P.S., Memphis, TN; *U.S. Public*, pg. 10
Parker, Giles, V.P.-Sls.--All Star Gas Co.-Region XI, Lebanon, MO; *U.S. Private*, pg. 35
Parker, Glen, Dir.-Mktg.--Industrial Plastics Company, Fort Smith, AR; *U.S. Public*, pg. 56
Parker, J. Timmons, V.P.-Sls.--BeautiControl Cosmetics, Inc., Carrollton, TX; *U.S. Public*, pg. 198
Parker, James, Mgr.-Sls.--Capital City Press, Inc., Berlin, VT; *U.S. Private*, pg. 205
Parker, Jeff, Dir.-Sls.--Packaging Resources, Incorporated, Lake Forest, IL; *U.S. Private*, pg. 833
Parker, John, V.P.-Mktg. & Sls.--Woodmark Originals Inc., Archdale, NC; *U.S. Private*, pg. 747
Parker, John A. H., Exec. V.P. & Dir.-Sls.--Universal Leaf Tobacco Company, Inc., Richmond, VA; *U.S. Public*, pg. 1694
Parker, Scott, Dir.-Sls.--BioChem ImmunoSystems, Inc., Allentown, PA; *Int'l*, pg. 196
Parker, Steven, Sr. V.P.-Mktg. & Sls.--Red Roof Inns, Inc., Hilliard, OH; *U.S. Public*, pg. 1369
Parker, Tom, V.P.-Sls. & Mktg.--Medeva Pharmaceuticals, Rochester, NY; *Int'l*, pg. 852
Parker, Tom, V.P.-Mktg. & Plng.--Sierra Pacific Resources, Reno, NV; *U.S. Public*, pg. 1470
Parker, W. N., V.P.-Sls. & Service--Camco Inc., Mississauga, Canada; *U.S. Public*, pg. 713
Parker, Wendell W., Chief Oper. Officer--GAI Consultants-NC, Inc., Raleigh, NC; *U.S. Private*, pg. 434
Parker, William S., V.P.-Mktg. & Sls.--American Dental Technologies, Southfield, MI; *U.S. Public*, pg. 70
Parkinson, D., V.P.-Sls. & Mktg.--Eureka Manufacturing Co., Inc., Norton, MA; *U.S. Private*, pg. 916
Parkinson, Robert, Mgr.-Natl. Sls.--Ronson Corporation, Somerset, NJ; *U.S. Public*, pg. 1405
Parlapiano, Joseph, V.P.-Sls.--Ajay Leisure Products, Inc., Delavan, WI; *U.S. Public*, pg. 34
Parlette, J. Samuel, V.P.-Sls. & Mktg.--Cavco Industries, Inc., Phoenix, AZ; *U.S. Public*, pg. 323
Parman, Kenneth W., V.P.-Sls., R&B Automotive--R&B, Inc., Colmar, PA; *U.S. Public*, pg. 1354
Parmentier, Rob, Sr. V.P.-Domestic Sls. & Mktg.--Sea Ray, Knoxville, TN; *U.S. Public*, pg. 266
Paro, John J., V.P.-Mktg. & Sls.--The C.P. Hall Company, Chicago, IL; *U.S. Private*, pg. 495
Parr, Charlie, V.P.-Worldwide Sls.--Gatefield Corporation, Fremont, CA; *U.S. Public*, pg. 703
Parr, Douglas, V.P.-Sls. & Mktg.--Dean Foods Company, Franklin Park, IL; *U.S. Public*, pg. 489
Parrish, Bill, Mgr.-Natl. Sls.--Capro, Inc., Willis, TX; *U.S. Public*, pg. 1569
Parrish, Craig, Mgr.-Sls.--Scan Globe A/S, Havdrup, Denmark; *U.S. Private*, pg. 923
Parrish, Gary, V.P.-Domestic Sls.--Gamma Biologicals Inc., Houston, TX; *U.S. Public*, pg. 698
Parrish, Mark, Exec. V.P.-Sls. & Mktg.--Cardinal Health Inc., Dublin, OH; *U.S. Public*, pg. 304
Parrish, Mark W., Exec. V.P.-Sls. & Mktg.--Cardinal Distribution, Dublin, OH; *U.S. Public*, pg. 304
Parrish, Tom, Dir.-OEM Sls.--Key Tronic Corporation, Spokane, WA; *U.S. Public*, pg. 953
Parrott, Graham, Commercial Dir.--Granada Group PLC, London, United Kingdom; *Int'l*, pg. 556
Parry, David, Dir.-Sls.--Essex Corporation, Columbia, MD; *U.S. Public*, pg. 593
Parry, Kathy, Mgr.-Natl. Sls.--Environment/One Corporation, Niskayuna, NY; *U.S. Public*, pg. 586
Parry, Thomas, V.P.-Interactive Multimedia--Intermetrics, Inc., Burlington, MA; *U.S. Private*, pg. 567

Parson, Larry, V.P.-Sls.--Optical Coating Laboratory, Inc., Santa Rosa, CA; *U.S. Public*, pg. 1227

Parsons, Don, V.P.-Sls. & Mktg.--TNT Vacations, Boston, MA; *U.S. Private*, pg. 1065

Parsons, Grace, Mgr.-Sls./Winnipeg--SGI Canada Insurance Services Ltd., Regina, Canada; *Int'l*, pg. 1195

Parsons, John, V.P.-Sls.--Knoll Pharmaceutical Company, Whippany, NJ; *Int'l*, pg. 105

Parsons, M., Gen. Mgr.-Sls.--Germantown (USA) Co., Broomall, PA; *Int'l*, pg. 555

Parsons, Michael E., V.P.-Sls.--Invacare Corporation, Elyria, OH; *U.S. Public*, pg. 911

Parsons, Richard, V.P.-Sls. & Mktg.--Westec Security Inc., Irvine, CA; *Int'l*, pg. 1217

Parsons, Robert, V.P.-Publr. Sls.--Scoville Press, Inc., Minneapolis, MN; *U.S. Private*, pg. 977

Parsons, Terry N., Sr. V.P.-Sls.--AMCORE Trust Company, Rockford, IL; *U.S. Public*, pg. 65

Parsons, William, Sls. Mgr.-Western Reg.--Storck U.S.A., L.P., Chicago, IL; *Int'l*, pg. 1304

Partridge, Ken, Dir.-Sls.--Rosemount Analytical, Uniloc Div., Irvine, CA; *U.S. Public*, pg. 574

Parunak, H. John, Sr. V.P.-Telephone Services & Sls.--Citizens Savings Bank, Providence, RI; *Int'l*, pg. 1132

Pascale, Anthony, Gen. Mgr. & Mgr.-Mktg. & Sls.--Exsil, Inc., San Jose, CA; *Int'l*, pg. 802

Paschal, Bruce, Pres.-Duda Sls. Division--A. Duda & Sons Inc., Oviedo, FL; *U.S. Private*, pg. 344

Pash, J., V.P.--Kathabar Incorporated, Somerset, NJ; *U.S. Private*, pg. 609

Pasquale, Gabe, Sr. Mktg. Advisor-N.E. Reg.--Hovnanian Enterprises, Inc., Red Bank, NJ; *U.S. Public*, pg. 843

Passe, Luci, Dir.-Sls.--The Kahler Hotel, Rochester, MN; *U.S. Public*, pg. 1537

Patchen, James J., V.P.-Mktg. & Sls., Biological Prods.--Bayer Corporation/Pharmaceutical Division, West Haven, CT; *Int'l*, pg. 173

Pate, Joseph, V.P.-Field Sls.--JII/Sales Promotion Associates, Inc., Coshocton, OH; *U.S. Private*, pg. 598

Pate, Ronald O., Sr. V.P.-Sls. & Mktg.--Horace Small Apparel Company, Nashville, TN; *Int'l*, pg. 635

Patel, Haresh, V.P.-Sls.--PMC Sierra, Inc., Burnaby, Canada; *U.S. Public*, pg. 1470

Paterson, Allister C., V.P.-Sls./North America--Canadian Airlines Corporation, Calgary, Canada; *Int'l*, pg. 255

Paterson, Graham, V.P.-Sls. & Mktg.--Computer Corporation of America, Framingham, MA; *U.S. Private*, pg. 260

Paton, Jack, V.P.-Sls. & Mktg./Lotus--Columbus Mills, Inc., Columbus, GA; *U.S. Private*, pg. 256

Paton, Jack, V.P.-Sls. & Mktg.--Lotus Carpet Division, Phenix City, AL; *U.S. Private*, pg. 257

Patrick, David, Exec. V.P.-World-Wide Sls.--The Learning Co., Inc., Cambridge, MA; *U.S. Public*, pg. 982

Patrick, Scott, V.P.-Corp. Sponsorship Sls. & Brdcst.--Full House Sports & Entertainment, Seattle, WA; *U.S. Public*, *pg. 16*

Patrone, Mary Jane, V.P.-Sls. & Mktg.--Globe Newspaper Company, Boston, MA; *U.S. Public*, pg. 1175

Patt, Jerry, V.P.-Sls.--Ajax Manufacturing Company, Inc., Hillsborough, NJ; *U.S. Private*, pg. 1030

Patterson, Bill, V.P.-Worldwide Sls.--Attachmate, Bellevue, WA; *U.S. Private*, pg. 98

Patterson, David, V.P.-Corp. Services--Williams Telecommunications Systems, Inc., Houston, TX; *U.S. Public*, pg. 1769

Patterson, James R., V.P.-Sls./Solid State & Components--Richardson Electronics, Ltd., Lafox, IL; *U.S. Public*, pg. 1387

Patterson, Leonard, V.P.-Sls.--Whitman's Candies, Inc., Kansas City, MO; *U.S. Private*, pg. 953

Patterson, Mike, V.P.-Sls.--Solvay Animal Health, Inc., Mendota Heights, MN; *Int'l*, pg. 1277

Patterson, Paul, Natl. Sls. Mgr.--ATS Automation Tooling Systems, Inc., Cambridge, Canada; *Int'l*, pg. 18

Patti, Joseph, Reg. Sls. Mgr.--River Ranch Northeast, Inc., Buffalo, NY; *U.S. Private*, pg. 934

Patton, Bob, Sr. V.P.-Sls.--The Genie Company, Alliance, OH; *U.S. Private*, pg. 823

Patton, Steve, Mgr.-Sls.--Alling-Lander, Union Grove, WI; *U.S. Public*, pg. 1370

Pattyjohn, Thad, V.P.-Sls.--Jamison Bedding, Inc., Franklin, TN; *U.S. Private*, pg. 581

Paul, William L., V.P.-Comml.--Asarco Incorporated, New York, NY; *U.S. Public*, pg. 137

Pauley, George, V.P.-Produce Sls. & Perishelde Concepts & Procurement--The Stop & Shop Companies, Inc., Quincy, MA; *Int'l*, pg. 750

Pauley, John, V.P.-Sls.--John Morrell & Co., Cincinnati, OH; *U.S. Public*, pg. 1479

Paulhus, Ron, Dir.-Sls.-Wire--ACS Industries, Inc., Woonsocket, RI; *U.S. Private*, pg. 3

Paull, Jim, Sr. V.P.-Sls. & Mktg.--Competitive Media Reporting, New York, NY; *Int'l*, pg. 1447

Paulsen, Gorgas E., Mgr.-Sls.--Pak-Sher Co., Kilgore, TX; *U.S. Private*, pg. 1062

Paulson, Dave, V.P.-Sls. & Mktg.--Oceana Foods, Shelby, MI; *U.S. Private*, pg. 234

Paulson, David, V.P.-Mktg. & Sls.-Canned--Cherry Central Cooperative, Traverse City, MI; *U.S. Private*, pg. 233

Pavlik, Robert, Dir.-Intl. Sls.--Carver, Inc., Savannah, GA; *U.S. Private*, pg. 217

Pawley, Roger, Dir.-U.S. Sls.--Helly-Hansen (US), Inc., Redmond, WA; *Int'l*, pg. 1010

Paxton, Edgar L., V.P.-Adv. & Sls. Promo.--Family Dollar Stores, Inc., Matthews, NC; *U.S. Public*, pg. 612

Paxton, Johnnie, District Sls. Mgr.-West Coast--Aero Peru, Los Angeles, CA; *U.S. Private*, pg. 24

Paylor, Craig E., V.P.-Sls. & Market Devel.--JLG Industries, Inc., McConnellsburg, PA; *U.S. Public*, pg. 918

Payne, Carolyn, Sls. Mgr.--Sport Obermeyer Ltd., USA, Aspen, CO; *U.S. Private*, pg. 1026

Paypick, Ron, Mgr.-Sls.--Buffelen Woodworking Company, Tacoma, WA; *U.S. Private*, pg. 179

Pazinatto, Nilson, Dir.-Comml.--Duracell do Brasil Industria & Comercio Ltda., Sao Paulo, Brazil; *U.S. Public*, pg. 743

Pazolt, Warren, V.P.-Sls. & Mktg.--Ernest Paper Products, Inc., Los Angeles, CA; *U.S. Private*, pg. 381

Peace, David, V.P.-Sls.--Monroe Auto Equipment Co., Monroe, MI; *U.S. Public*, pg. 1577

Peach, Les, Mgr.-Sls.--PENCO-Illinois, Aurora, IL; *Int'l*, pg. 1508

Pearce, Anthony Michael, Dir.-Sls.--Birds Eye Walls Ltd., Walton-on-Thames, United Kingdom; *Int'l*, pg. 1434

Pearce, Mike, V.P.-Sls. & Mktg.-Smith Diamond Tech.--Smith International, Inc., Houston, TX; *U.S. Public*, pg. 1478

Pearce, Stan, Mgr.-Mktg. & Sls.--AGRA Plastics Inc., Mississauga, Canada; *Int'l*, pg. 30

Pearson, Scott, V.P.-Sls. & Mktg.--Digital Communications of America, Inc., Oklahoma City, OK; *U.S. Private*, pg. 872

Peasley, Michael R., Asst. V.P.-Sls. Svcs.--The Franklin Life Insurance Company, Springfield, IL; *U.S. Public*, pg. 76

Peavy, Mike, V.P.-Sls. & Mktg.--Cherokee Brick & Tile Co., Macon, GA; *U.S. Private*, pg. 233

Pecha, Robert O., V.P.-Sls. & Mktg.--Chemstone Corp., Strasburg, VA; *U.S. Private*, pg. 233

Pechi, Lou, Dir.-Sls.--Power-One, Inc., Camarillo, CA; *U.S. Private*, pg. 878

Peck, A., Dir.-Sls.--Britax Vega Limited, Droitwich, United Kingdom; *Int'l*, pg. 216

Peck, Chuck, Sr. V.P.-Mktg., Prods., Organization & Devel.--American Institute of C.P.A.'s Inc., New York, NY; *U.S. Private*, pg. 57

Peck, Don, V.P.-Sls. & Mktg.--Heat Controller, Inc., Jackson, MI; *U.S. Private*, pg. 518

Peck, Richard, V.P.-Sls. & Mktg.--Levlad, Inc., Chatsworth, CA; *U.S. Private*, pg. 663

Pecoraro, Gerald, V.P.-Sls., Household Prods. Div.--Block Drug Company, Inc., Jersey City, NJ; *U.S. Public*, pg. 236

Peddicord, Herschel, Sr. V.P.-Mktg., Sls. & Engrng.--Criticare Systems, Inc., Waukesha, WI; *U.S. Public*, pg. 459

Pedersen, Erik, V.P.-Sls.--Lynx Golf, Inc., City of Industry, CA; *U.S. Private*, pg. 684

Pederson, Gary, Mgr.-Mktg. & Sls.--Portec, Inc.-Construction Equipment Div., Yankton, SD; *U.S. Public*, pg. 1318

Pedrick, James E., V.P.-Sls.--ContiMortgage Corporation, Horsham, PA; *U.S. Public*, pg. 439

Pedroth, Larry, V.P.-Sls.--Ranco North America, Plain City, OH; *Int'l*, pg. 1243

Pedula, Joe, V.P.-Sls.-Stationary Products--Stationery Products Division, Boston, MA; *U.S. Public*, pg. 744

Peet, Kathy, Gen. Mgr.-Sls.--WTVF, Nashville, TN; *U.S. Private*, pg. 647

Peeters, Peter W., Dir.-Intl. Bus.--Marsh Company, Belleville, IL; *U.S. Private*, pg. 707

Peiker, Butch, Mgr.-Classified Inside Sls.--St. Petersburg Times, Saint Petersburg, FL; *U.S. Private*, pg. 1088

Peikert, Berthold, Sls.-Automotive/Indus.--Suspa Compart AG, Altdorf, Germany; *Int'l*, pg. 1322

Peitler, Michael A., Sr. V.P.-Worldwide Sls.--Emulex Corporation, Costa Mesa, CA; *U.S. Public*, pg. 579

Peka, Duane, Sls. Mgr.-Southeast District--Fluidtec Engineer Products, Greensboro, NC; *U.S. Public*, pg. 401

Pelini, Robert G., V.P.-Industrial Equipment--Struthers Wells Corp., Warren, PA; *U.S. Private*, pg. 1048

Pelisek, Steve, V.P.-Sls.--Cobra Golf Incorporated, Carlsbad, CA; *U.S. Public*, pg. 675

Pellegrino, Don, Gen. Mgr.-Specialty Sls.--Star-Kist Foods Inc., Newport, KY; *U.S. Public*, pg. 805

Pellerin, Antoine, Mgr.-Sls.--Richardson Franc SNC, Colombes, France; *U.S. Public*, pg. 1388

Pelletier, R., Mgr.-Sls.--Les Vins Andres du Quebec Ltee., Saint-Hyacinthe, Canada; *Int'l*, pg. 76

Pellman, Mark, Engr.-Sls.--Baum USA, Sidney, OH; *Int'l*, pg. 1293

Pelly, Michael F., V.P.-Sls.-Northern Region--Carlton & United Breweries Ltd., Southbank, Australia; *Int'l*, pg. 500

Pelosi, M., V.P.-Sls. & Mktg.--Tranter, Inc., Augusta, GA; *U.S. Public*, pg. 521

Peltola, Esa, V.P.-Mktg.--Bronto Skylift Oy AB, Tampere, Finland; *U.S. Public*, pg. 617

Peluso, Nick, V.P.-Sls.--ADT Automotive, Inc., Nashville, TN; *U.S. Public*, pg. 1648

Pemlington, C., Dir.-Sls.--CIBA-GEIGY (Pty.) Ltd., Isando, South Africa; *Int'l*, pg. 978

Pence, David, V.P.-Sls.--Walker Manufacturing Co., Deerfield, IL; *U.S. Public*, pg. 1578

Pendergast, Bert, V.P.--IBM Canada Limited, Markham, Canada; *U.S. Public*, pg. 897

Pendergast, Patrick, Mgr.-Sls.--The Bentley-Harris Manufacturing Co., Lionville, PA; *Int'l*, pg. 1334

Pendleton, Gary, Mgr.-Sls.--Weather Tec Corporation, Fresno, CA; *U.S. Private*, pg. 1155

Pendleton, T., Sr. V.P.-Sls. & Mktg.--Corner Brook Pulp & Paper Limited, Corner Brook, Canada; *Int'l*, pg. 761

Pendleton, T.N., Sr. V.P.-Sls. & Mktg./Paper Prods.--Kruger Inc., Montreal, Canada; *Int'l*, pg. 761

Pendleton, T.N., Sr. V.P.-Sls. & Mktg./Paper Prods.--Bromptonville Mill, Bromptonville, Canada; *Int'l*, pg. 761

Pendleton, T.N., Sr. V.P.-Sls. & Mktg.--Kruger Inc., Montreal, Canada; *Int'l*, pg. 761

Pendleton, Terry, Sr. V.P.-Sls.--Trois-Rivieres Mill, Trois-Rivieres, Canada; *Int'l*, pg. 761

Penn, Richard, V.P.-Sls. & Mktg.--Hutchinson Technology Inc., Hutchinson, MN; *U.S. Public*, pg. 850

Pennavaria, Russell, Dir.-Mktg. & Sls.-Medical Div.--Cincinnati Sub-Zero Products, Inc., Cincinnati, OH; *U.S. Private*, pg. 240

Pennell, Gary B., V.P.-Mktg., Sls. & Adv.--Diamond Chain Company, Indianapolis, IN; *U.S. Private*, pg. 68

Penney, Jay, V.P.-Sls. & Mktg.--Frigidaire Home Products, Dublin, OH; *Int'l*, pg. 439

Pennington, J., Mgr.-Sls.--Akers Packaging Service Inc., Middletown, OH; *U.S. Private*, pg. 29

Pennington, Reid, V.P.-Sls.--Magee Co., Pocahontas, AR; *U.S. Public*, pg. 1561

Penny, Jay, V.P.-Sls. & Mktg.--White Consolidated Industries, Inc., Cleveland, OH; *Int'l*, pg. 439

Penny, Jay, V.P.-Sls. & Mktg.-Appliances--Gibson Appliances, Dublin, OH; *Int'l*, pg. 439

Penny, Jay, V.P.-Sls. & Mktg.-Appliances--Kelvinator Appliances, Dublin, OH; *Int'l*, pg. 440

Penshorn-Montalvo, Cher, Mgr.-Reg'l. Sls.--Southern Union Company, Austin, TX; *U.S. Public*, pg. 1491

Pepin, Denis, Sr. V.P.-Sls. & Brokerage--Meridian Technology Leasing Services, Deerfield, IL; *U.S. Private*, *pg. 732*

Pepp, Denise, Dir.-Mktg. & Sls. Promo.--Stuart Anderson's Black Angus/Cattle Company Restaurants, Los Altos, CA; *U.S. Private*, pg. 61

Pepys Lowe, Renee, Exec. V.P.-Sls. & Mktg.--Noel Joanna, Inc., Rancho Santa Margarita, CA; *U.S. Public*, pg. 465

Percenti, Don, Sr. V.P.-Sls. & Mktg./Balfour--Commemorative Brands, Inc., Austin, TX; *U.S. Private*, pg. 258

Percenti, Don, Sr. V.P.-Sls. & Mktg.--L.G. Balfour Co., Inc., Austin, TX; *U.S. Private*, pg. 258

Perdigao, Joao, Mgr.-Sls.-Zone IV--Central de Cervejas, S.A., Lisbon, Portugal; *Int'l*, pg. 279

Perdoni, Lou, Dir.-Sls. & Service--Air Cruisers Co., Belmar, NJ; *Int'l*, pg. 572

Perelgat, Art, Dir.-Western Sls.--Gatefield Corporation, Fremont, CA; *U.S. Public*, pg. 703

Peres, Edward J., Div. Mgr.--Fuchs Lubricants, Midlantic Div., Baltimore, MD; *Int'l*, pg. 518

Perez, Eridania, V.P.-Mktg., Promotions & Sls.--Marcel Dekker, Inc., New York, NY; *U.S. Private*, pg. 321

Perez, Gabriel, Mgr.-Sls./Northeast--Iberia Air Lines of Spain, Miami, FL; *Int'l*, pg. 575

Perez, John, Dir.-Fourway Golf Sls.--Ortho-Kinetics, Inc., Waukesha, WI; *U.S. Private*, pg. 820

Perez, John L., Mgr.-Sls.--Vilter Manufacturing Corporation, Cudahy, WI; *U.S. Private*, pg. 1140

Perez, Jose A., V.P.-Sys. Sls.--Andrew Corporation, Orland Park, IL; *U.S. Public*, pg. 112

Perez, Ronald, Mgr.-Sls.--Madison Industries, Los Angeles, CA; *U.S. Private*, pg. 428

Perich, Silvio, Sr. V.P.-Sls.--Sigma Designs, Inc., Fremont, CA; *U.S. Public*, pg. 1472

Perkins, Cheryl, Mktg. Asst. & Trade Show Coord.--Prism Integrated Sanitation Management, Inc., Miami, FL; *U.S. Private*, pg. 592

Perkins, Kevin, Sr. Dir.-Cargo Sls. & Mktg.--America West Airlines, Inc., Phoenix, AZ; *U.S. Public*, pg. 67

Perkins, M.G., V.P.-Domestic Sls. & Mktg.--Morganite Inc., Dunn, NC; *Int'l*, pg. 891

Perkins, Michael, Dir.-Sls.--Pneumatic Products Corp., Ocala, FL; *U.S. Public*, pg. 1676

Perkins, Sharon, Sls. & Mktg. Asst.--Saunders Brothers, Westbrook, ME; *U.S. Private*, pg. 968

Perko, Thomas, V.P.-Consumer Electronics Sls.--Conair Corporation, Stamford, CT; *U.S. Private*, pg. 261

Perks, Bob, Dir.-Govt. Sls.--CyberGuard Corporation, Fort Lauderdale, FL; *U.S. Public*, pg. 470

Perks, Lachlan, V.P.-Mktg. & Sls.--Eclipse Inc., Rockford, IL; *U.S. Private*, pg. 360

Perl, Allen S., V.P.--T.L. Diamond Company, New York, NY; *U.S. Private*, pg. 330

Perlberg, Mark, Sr. V.P., Pres., Fin. Sls. Mktg. Division--The Check Store, Lakewood, CO; *U.S. Public*, pg. 785

Perlman, Milton, Consultant--Schott Brothers, Inc., Perth Amboy, NJ; *U.S. Private*, pg. 972

Perlstein, William B., V.P.-Sls.--The Good Guys, Inc., Brisbane, CA; *U.S. Public*, pg. 750

Pernsteiner, Bob, V.P.-Sls.--Okuma America Corporation, Charlotte, NC; *Int'l*, pg. 1001

Peroutka, Michael S., Exec. V.P.-Sls. & Mktg.--Faribault Foods Inc., Minneapolis, MN; *U.S. Private*, pg. 393

Peroutka, Michael S., Exec. V.P.-Sls. & Mktg.--Kuner-Empson Company, Brighton, CO; *U.S. Private*, pg. 393

Perrella, Aurelio, Dir.-Intl. Sls.--Weiser Lock, Tucson, AZ; *U.S. Public*, pg. 1053

Perri-Molina, Lisa, V.P.-Retail Sls./Bal Harbour & Southern Region--Tiffany & Co., New York, NY; *U.S. Public*, pg. 1608

Perrigo, Laurie, Mgr.-Dealer Sls.--Kalmbach Publishing Co., Waukesha, WI; *U.S. Private*, pg. 606

Perrone, Anthony, V.P.-Sls. & Mktg.--Refined Sugars, Inc., Yonkers, NY; *Int'l*, pg. 699

Perry, Becky, Mgr.-Sls.--Standard Restaurant Equipment Co., Phoenix, AZ; *U.S. Private*, pg. 1031

Perry, Dan, V.P.-Sls.--Milwaukee Electric Tool Corp., Brookfield, WI; *Int'l*, pg. 96

Perry, Dwight G., V.P.-Sls.--PMC Industries Inc., Wickliffe, OH; *U.S. Private*, pg. 827

Perry, Jerry, Natl. Sls. Mgr.--Ansco Photo-Optical Products Corp., Elk Grove Village, IL; *Int'l*, pg. 587

Perry, John E., V.P.-Sls.--Shurflo Pump Manufacturing Co., Santa Ana, CA; *U.S. Public*, pg. 1767

Perry, Joseph Z., V.P.-Sls. & Mktg.--ICL, Inc., Irvine, CA; *Int'l*, pg. 529

Perry, Kay, Natl. Sls. Mgr.--Atwood & Morrill Co., Inc., Salem, MA; *Int'l*, pg. 1489

Perry, Lynne, Mgr.-Sls./Special Markets--The W.E. Bassett Company, Shelton, CT; *U.S. Private*, pg. 122

Perry, Mike, Reg. V.P.-S.W. Sls.--American Freightways Corporation, Harrison, AR; *U.S. Public*, pg. 75

Perry, Pat, Mgr.-Sls.--Chemical Group, Gibsonburg, OH; *U.S. Public*, pg. 345

Perry, Robert M., V.P.-Sls.--Amtran, Inc., Indianapolis, IN; *U.S. Public*, pg. 106

Persson, Jan, Regional Product Mgr.--Sandvik South East Asia Ltd., Jurong, Singapore; *Int'l*, pg. 1187

Pesavento, Gilbert, Dir.-Sls. & Mktg.--American Specialties Inc., Yonkers, NY; *U.S. Private*, pg. 62

Pesci, Paul, V.P.-Sls. & Mktg.--Ransomes-Cushman-Ryan, Lincoln, NE; *Int'l*, pg. 1088

Pesin, Larry, V.P.-Global Mktg. & Sls.--Concord Camera Corporation, Avenel, NJ; *U.S. Public*, pg. 429

Peskosky, S.A., Mgr.-Intl. Markets Devel./Canada--Carpenter Technology (Canada) Ltd., Mississauga, Canada; *U.S. Public*, pg. 308

Peter, Larry, Dir.-Sls. & Mktg.--Kinney Vacuum Company, Canton, MA; *U.S. Private*, pg. 1110

Peterman, Sonny, V.P.-Sls. & Distr.--360 Degrees Communications Company, Chicago, IL; *U.S. Public*, pg. 1607

Peters, Anne-Francoise, Mgr.-Mfg. & Site Devel.-Pumps--S.A. Durco Europe N.V., Petit-Rechain, Belgium; *U.S. Public*, pg. 659

Peters, Cecil M., V.P.-Sls.--Pinnacle Data Corporation, San Bruno, CA; *U.S. Public*, pg. 1158

Peters, Cecil M., V.P.-Sls.--FASTRAC Systems, Inc.-Insurance Agent & Broker, South San Francisco, CA; *U.S. Public*, pg. 1158

Peters, Dan, Dir.-Sls.--Akron Brass Company, Wooster, OH; *Int'l*, pg. 1068

Peters, Dave, V.P.-Mktg. & Sls.--Armstrong Air Conditioning Inc., Bellevue, OH; *U.S. Private*, pg. 659

Peters, Donald, Mgr.-Sls.--First Financial Corporation, Stevens Point, WI; *U.S. Public*, pg. 140

Peters, Henry, Exec. V.P.-Sales--Miami Systems Corporation, Cincinnati, OH; *U.S. Private*, pg. 740

Peters, Kay, V.P.-Sls.-Wallcovering Div.--Evans Adhesive Corp., Columbus, OH; *U.S. Private*, pg. 384

Peters, Patrick J., V.P.-Sls.--Chesebrough-Pond's USA Co., Greenwich, CT; *Int'l*, pg. 1435

Peters, William H., V.P.-Sls. & Mktg.--YSD Industries, Youngstown, OH; *U.S. Private*, pg. 1194

Peters, Willie, Natl. Sls. Mgr.--Kenwood USA, Long Beach, CA; *Int'l*, pg. 730

Petersen, Edgar N., V.P. & Gen. Mgr.-Canada, Asia Pacific & Latin America--Diebold, Incorporated, Canton, OH; *U.S. Public*, pg. 506

Petersen, Eric, Exec. Dir.-Sls. & Mktg.--Spartan International Inc., Holt, MI; *U.S. Private*, pg. 1020

Petersen, Rich, Reg. Sls. Mgr.--Aromat New England Sales Office, Marlborough, MA; *Int'l*, pg. 848

Peterson, Brian, V.P.-Sls. & Mktg.--Haydon Switch & Instrument, Inc., Waterbury, CT; *U.S. Private*, pg. 513

Peterson, Christer, Mgr.-Sls.--Iggesund Timber AB Scandinavia, Skanor, Sweden; *Int'l*, pg. 886

Peterson, D., V.P.-Sls.--Bel/Kaukauna USA, Little Chute, WI; *U.S. Private*, pg. 130

Peterson, Duane, Natl. Sls. Mgr.-Mktg.--Gordon & Ferguson of Delaware, Inc., Plymouth, MN; *U.S. Private*, pg. 465

Peterson, Glen, Mgr.-Sls.--Cascade Steel Rolling Mills, Inc., McMinnville, OR; *U.S. Public*, pg. 1440

Peterson, John T., Dir.-Sls. & Mktg.--Hunter Marine Corporation, Alachua, FL; *U.S. Private*, pg. 549

Peterson, Keith, Exec. V.P.-Global Direct--Regal Ware, Inc., Kewaskum, WI; *U.S. Private*, pg. 917

Peterson, Matt, Mgr.-Sls.--Triangle Brass Manufacturing, Los Angeles, CA; *U.S. Private*, pg. 1101

Peterson, Phyllis, Rep.-Adv. & Sls.--Credit Union National Association, Madison, WI; *U.S. Private*, pg. 288

Peterson, Rod, Mgr.-Sls.--H.K. International, Inc., Northbrook, IL; *U.S. Private*, pg. 491

Peterson, Wayne, Mgr.-Mktg. & Sls.--Amite Foundry and Machine, Inc., Amite, LA; *U.S. Public*, pg. 142

Petit, Joseph E., V.P.-Sls.--The Testor Corporation, Rockford, IL; *U.S. Public*, pg. 1358

Petit, Louis, Mgr.-Natl. Grocery Sls.--Malco Products, Inc., Barberton, OH; *U.S. Private*, pg. 698

Petit, Manuela, Sls. Office--Lee Company S.A., Voisins-le-Bretonneaux, France; *U.S. Private*, pg. 657

Petko, Greg, V.P.-Sls. Clark Gum--Clark Gum Company, Buffalo, NY; *U.S. Private*, pg. 243

Petkus, Barbara, Mgr.-Intl. Sls.--Portec Inc., Railway Maintenance Products Div., Pittsburgh, PA; *U.S. Public*, pg. 1318

Petray, O.G., Mgr.-Sls.--Turner Construction Company, West Sacramento, CA; *U.S. Public*, pg. 1645

Petrie, Johnny, V.P.-Natl. Accts.--Kesterson Food Company, Inc., Paris, TN; *U.S. Private*, pg. 616

Petronzi, Gary, V.P.-Sls.--Somerset Knitting Mills, New York, NY; *U.S. Public*, pg. 1291

Petrucelli, John, Sr. V.P.-Sls.--Gould Paper Corporation, New York, NY; *U.S. Private*, pg. 466

Petterson, John S., Sr. V.P.-Corp. Sls.--Tiffany & Co., New York, NY; *U.S. Public*, pg. 1608

Pettis, Edmund, V.P. & Mgr.-Mktg.--Roy F. Weston, Inc., West Chester, PA; *U.S. Public*, pg. 1761

Peverell, Ed, Sr. V.P.-Sls. & Support--Network Equipment Technologies, Inc., Redwood City, CA; *U.S. Public*, pg. 1168

Peychal-Heiling, Gerald, Dr., Dir.-Sls. & Recycling--VAW Aluminum AG, Bonn, Germany; *Int'l*, pg. 1466

Pezzi, Ray, Dir.-Sls.-U.S.A.--Timex Corporation, Middlebury, CT; *U.S. Private*, pg. 1088

Pezzin, M., Mgr.-Sls.--Hunter Douglas do Brazil Ltda., Sao Paulo, Brazil; *Int'l*, pg. 640

Pfaff, Ken, Reg. Sls. Mgr.-Relays--Aromat South Central Sales Office, Richardson, TX; *Int'l*, pg. 848

Pfanstiel, Donald, V.P.-Sls.--Wabash Alloys Division, Wabash, IN; *U.S. Private*, pg. 264

Pfeffer, Marianne, Mgr.-Sls.--Baltimore Business Publications, Inc., Baltimore, MD; *U.S. Private*, pg. 19

Pfeiffer, Ralph, V.P.-Sls. & Mktg.--Acorn Window Systems Inc., Quincy, MI; *U.S. Private*, pg. 14

Pfieffer, V., Mgr.-Sls. Distr.--Norcold, Sidney, OH; *U.S. Private*, pg. 352

Pfister, Robert, V.P.-Sls. & Mktg.--General Office Environments Inc., Rochelle Park, NJ; *U.S. Private*, pg. 445

Pfister, Robert, V.P.-Sls. & Mktg.--General Office Environments Inc., Somerset, NJ; *U.S. Private*, pg. 445

Pflugrad, Jim, V.P.-Sls.--Aeromotor Pump, Inc., Conway, AR; *Int'l*, pg. 538

Pflugrad, Jim, V.P.-Sls. & Mktg./U.S.--GSW Pump Company, Fergus, Canada; *Int'l*, pg. 538

Pfuehler, Mark, V.P.-Sls.-Central North Region--PST Vans, Inc., Salt Lake City, UT; *U.S. Public*, pg. 1246

Phaneuf, Eugene, Dir.-Sls. & Engrng., Ultrasonic Div.--The J.M. Ney Company, Bloomfield, CT; *U.S. Public*, pg. 111

Pheil, D.L., V.P.-Sls.--Landis, Waynesboro, PA; *U.S. Public*, pg. 1699

Phelan, Doug, Mgr.-Pur. & Sls.--Canadian Occidental Petroleum Ltd., Calgary, Canada; *U.S. Public*, pg. 1210

Phelan, J., V.P.-Intl. Sls. & Mktg.--Shure Brothers Incorporated, Evanston, IL; *U.S. Private*, pg. 997

Phelan, Janet, Sls. Support Specialist--The Hartford Financial Services Group Inc., Hartford, CT; *U.S. Public*, pg. 794

Phelan, Sue, V.P.-Sls.--SPSS Inc., Chicago, IL; *U.S. Public*, pg. 1420

Philbin, John W., Dir.-Mktg. & Sls.--Altair Corporation, Lincolnshire, IL; *U.S. Private*, pg. 46

Philbin, Joseph R., V.P.-Sls.--Pinnacle Data Corporation, San Bruno, CA; *U.S. Public*, pg. 1158

Philbin, Joseph R., V.P.-Sls.--FASTRAC Systems, Inc.-Insurance Agent & Broker, South San Francisco, CA; *U.S. Public*, pg. 1158

Philbrick, Chris, Mgr.-Sls. & Mktg.--Weir Floway Inc., Fresno, CA; *Int'l*, pg. 1489

Philipps, Warren C., Mgr.-Sls.--Southeastern Regional Office, Alpharetta, GA; *U.S. Private*, pg. 224

Phillips, Barry, Dir.-Sls.--E.D. Bullard Company, Cynthiana, KY; *U.S. Private*, pg. 180

Phillips, Bill, V.P.-Sls.--Price Pfister, Inc., Pacoima, CA; *U.S. Public*, pg. 234

Phillips, Bill, Sr. V.P.-Sls.--The Coleman Company, Inc., Golden, CO; *U.S. Private*, pg. 690

Phillips, Brad, V.P.-Sls., Eastern Zone--Pier 1 Imports, Inc., Fort Worth, TX; *U.S. Public*, pg. 1295

Phillips, Bryant, V.P.-Sls. & Mktg.--Hatteras Yachts, New Bern, NC; *U.S. Private*, pg. 447

Phillips, Carroll E., V.P.-Sls.--Vulcan Chemicals, Birmingham, AL; *U.S. Public*, pg. 1725

Phillips, Charles Skip, Mgr.-Gen. Sls.--Todco, Marion, OH; *U.S. Private*, pg. 823

Phillips, Daniel D., Jr., V.P.-Worldwide Sls.--Concord Communications, Inc., Marlborough, MA; *U.S. Public*, pg. 429

Phillips, Don, Dir.-Sls.--Kaman Instrumentation Corp., Colorado Springs, CO; *U.S. Public*, pg. 942

Phillips, Glynn M., Exec. V.P.-Sls.--Del Monte Foods, San Francisco, CA; *U.S. Private*, pg. 321

Phillips, J., Mgr.-Sls.--Rolls-Royce Inc., Reston, VA; *Int'l*, pg. 1127

Phillips, John B., V.P.-Sls. & Mktg.--Red Spot Paint & Varnish Co., Evansville, IN; *U.S. Private*, pg. 915

Phillips, John, Jr., V.P.-Mktg. & Sls.--McKee Foods Corporation, Collegedale, TN; *U.S. Private*, pg. 723

Phillips, Mark, Dir.-Sls.--Maxon Corporation, Muncie, IN; *U.S. Private*, pg. 716

Phillips, Mark J., V.P.-Mktg. & Sls.--Barrister Information Systems Corporation, Buffalo, NY; *U.S. Public*, pg. 192

Phillips, R.J., Dir.-Commercial Opers.--Iveco-Ford Truck Ltd., Watford, United Kingdom; *Int'l*, pg. 484

Phillips, Robert, Mgr.-Sls.--GB Holdings, Jurong, Singapore; *Int'l*, pg. 531

Phillips, Scott, Mgr.-Sls. & Mktg.--Fishertech, Peterborough, Canada; *Int'l*, pg. 491

Phillips, William F., Dir.-Sls.--Spartech Corporation, Clayton, MO; *U.S. Public*, pg. 1495

Philpott, Ted, Sr. V.P.-Sls.--Lexington Furniture Industries, Lexington, NC; *U.S. Private*, pg. 432

Phipps, Robin, Grp. Dir.-Sls. & Mktg.--Legal & General Group PLC, London, United Kingdom; *Int'l*, pg. 805

Pichot, G., Mgr.-Intl. Sls.-Skis & Boots--Rossignol S.A., Voiron, France; *Int'l*, pg. 1127

Pickell, Derek A., V.P.-Sls.--US SerVis, West Orange, NJ; *U.S. Public*, pg. 1687

Pickens, William S., Jr., Sls. Mgr.--Sackner-South Div., Verona, MS; *U.S. Public*, pg. 924

Picker, Fred, V.P.-Sls.--Zone VI Studios, Inc., Newfane, VT; *U.S. Private*, pg. 202

Pickering, Arthur W., Sr. V.P.-Domestic Mktg.--National Western Life Insurance Company, Austin, TX; *U.S. Public*, pg. 1161

Pickering, Jeff, Pres.-Direct Mktg. & Sls.--Pickering Inc., Tacoma, WA; *U.S. Private*, pg. 864

Pickert, Steve, V.P.-Sls. & Mktg.--M & S Systems, Inc., Dallas, TX; *U.S. Public*, pg. 1193

Pickett, Jim, V.P.-Eastern Reg. Sls.--Toter Incorporated, Statesville, NC; *U.S. Private*, pg. 1092

Picone, Thomas, V.P.-Sls. & Mktg.--Premier Mill Corp., Reading, PA; *U.S. Private*, pg. 881

Pidgeon, Tom, Dir.-Sls., Americas HPG--Seal Products Incorporated, Naugatuck, CT; *U.S. Public*, pg. 849

Piekos, Frank, V.P.-Corp. Devel.--Philip Industrial Services Group, Houston, TX; *Int'l*, pg. 1050

Piepenbring, Ray, Dir.-Aftermarket Sls. & Mktg.--Casco Products Corporation, Bridgeport, CT; *U.S. Public*, pg. 1458

Pieper, Roel, Sr. V.P. & Gen. Mgr.-Worldwide Sls. & Mktg.--Tandem Computers Inc., Cupertino, CA; *U.S. Public*, pg. 417

Pierce, Chris, Natl. Sls. Mgr.-Joe Boxer Hose--Great American Knitting Mills, New York, NY; *Int'l*, pg. 194

Pierce, David, V.P.-Sls.--Columbia Tri-Star Home Video, Burbank, CA; *Int'l*, pg. 1282

Pierce, Fred, V.P.-Sls.--Hershey Pasta and Grocery Group, Hershey, PA; *U.S. Public*, pg. 812

Pierce, John, Gen. Mgr.-Sls. & Mktg.--Rosenbergers Dairies, Inc., Hatfield, PA; *U.S. Private*, pg. 945

Pierce, Karl W., Asst. Gen. Mgr.-Sls. & Svc.--Cadillac Motor Car Division, Warren, MI; *U.S. Public*, pg. 720

Pierce, Marc, V.P.-Sls. & Mktg.--Pentax Precision Instrument Corp., Orangeburg, NY; *Int'l*, pg. 85

Pierce, Michael G., V.P.-Mktg. & Sls.--The Austin Company, Cleveland, OH; *U.S. Private*, pg. 99

Pierce, Orval, Mgr.-Distribution Systems--T.D. Williamson, Inc., Tulsa, OK; *U.S. Private*, pg. 1179

Piercy, Ed, Reg. Sls. Mgr.--Varco BJ Drilling Systems, Jurong, Singapore; *U.S. Public*, pg. 1709

Pierro, Dave, Mgr.-Natl. Sls.--Lund International Holdings, Inc., Anoka, MN; *U.S. Public*, pg. 1020

Pierson, Robert, V.P.-Sls. & Mktg.--Jervis B. Webb Company, Farmington Hills, MI; *U.S. Private*, pg. 1156

Piessens, Luc, Gen. Mgr.-Mktg.--Wisconsin Gas Company, Milwaukee, WI; *U.S. Public*, pg. 1767

Pietras, Phil, V.P.-Sls. Admin.--Worcester Controls Corp., Marlborough, MA; *Int'l*, pg. 128

Pifer, Norm, Mgr.-Sls.--Alco Chemical, Chattanooga, TN; *Int'l*, pg. 1435

Pigeard, Jean-Pierre, Mgr.-Sls.--Editions Grasset-Fasquelle, Paris, France; *Int'l*, pg. 792

Pike, Bruce, Pres.-Howell Exports--Howell Instruments Inc., Fort Worth, TX; *U.S. Private*, pg. 543

Pike, Jackson, Mgr.-Natl. Sls. & Dealer--Lotus Cars USA, Inc., Lawrenceville, GA; *Int'l*, pg. 1071

Pikus, Carl, Dir.-Sls. & Mktg.--Fyrnetics, Inc., Roselle, IL; *Int'l*, pg. 1499

Pilgrim, Mike, V.P.-Mktg. & Sls.--Serco Company, Dallas, TX; *U.S. Public*, pg. 1676

Pilic, Vlad, V.P.-Sls.--Lepel Corporation, Edgewood, NY; *U.S. Private*, pg. 560

Piliot, Dennis, V.P.-Sls. & Mktg.--Cherokee International LLC, Tustin, CA; *U.S. Private*, pg. 233

Pilliter, Charles J., Pres. & Sr. V.P.-Northern California--Certified Grocers of California, Los Angeles, CA; *U.S. Private*, pg. 226

Pinchot, Roy, Dir.-Bus. Devel.--Biospherics Incorporated, Beltsville, MD; *U.S. Public*, pg. 232

Pinder, Robert, Gen. Mgr.-Sls.--Mitchell Corporation of Owosso, Owosso, MI; *U.S. Private*, pg. 753

Pinder, Robert, Dir.-Mktg. & Sls.--Benzonia Manufacturing, Benzonia, MI; *U.S. Private*, pg. 753

Pinder, Robert, Dir.-Mktg.--Mitchell Corporation, Clare Div., Clare, MI; *U.S. Private*, pg. 753

Pinhard, Richard, Mgr.-Sls., Flooring--R.C.A. Rubber Company, Akron, OH; *U.S. Private*, pg. 902

Pini, Bryan, V.P.-Intl. Sls.--Diamond Multimedia Systems, Inc., San Jose, CA; *U.S. Public*, pg. 505

Pinkans, Michael, V.P.-Sls.--National Life Insurance Company, Montpelier, VT; *U.S. Private*, pg. 785

Pinkham, Rob, Dir.-Sls. & New Bus. Devel.--Coleman Spas, Inc., Chandler, AZ; *U.S. Private*, pg. 691

Pinkley, Steve, Sls.--Adventure Lands of America, Inc., Des Moines, IA; *U.S. Private*, pg. 22

Pinna, John, V.P.-Sls. & Mktg.--Roussel Corporation, Montvale, NJ; *Int'l*, pg. 625

Pinotti, Ennio, Mgr.-Sls.--Marcegaglia SpA, Mantova, Italy; *Int'l*, pg. 841

Pinson, Greg, Field Mgr.-Sls.--Master Lock Company, Milwaukee, WI; *U.S. Public*, pg. 675

Pinte, Christian, Mgr.-Sls.--Banque Paribas Belgique, Brussels, Belgium; *Int'l*, pg. 319

Pinto, Harold, V.P.-Sls. & Mktg.--Jacobsen Textron, Racine, WI; *U.S. Public*, pg. 1589

Pio, Pat, V.P.-Sls.-Band Saw Division--American Saw & Mfg. Company, East Longmeadow, MA; *U.S. Private*, pg. 61

Piontkowski, Richard, V.P.-Sls.--Edward Don & Company-Fort Lauderdale Branch, Fort Lauderdale, FL; *U.S. Private*, pg. 339

Piper, Steve, Exec. V.P.-Sls.--Grassland Equipment & Irrigation Corp., Latham, NY; *U.S. Private*, pg. 471

Pires, Armano, Dir.-Sls.--BS Continental S.A. Utilidades Domesticas, Sao Paulo, Brazil; *Int'l*, pg. 123

Pirnie, Douglas D., Jr., Sr. V.P.-Sls. & Mktg.--IMG, New York, NY; *U.S. Private*, pg. 555

Pirrmann, Christine, Mgr.-Sls. & Cust. Svc.--Thompson Medical Company, Inc., West Palm Beach, FL; *U.S. Private*, pg. 1083

Pirrone, Arthur, V.P.-Sls. & Mktg.--Inverness Corp., Fair Lawn, NJ; *U.S. Private*, pg. 574

Pirtle, William B., Sr. V.P.-Mktg. & Sls.--Barclay Furniture Company, Sherman, MS; *U.S. Public*, pg. 974

Piscitelli, Francis M., V.P.-Mktg. & Sls.--Osram Sylvania Inc., Malvern, PA; *Int'l*, pg. 1245

Piskin, Joe, Sr. V.P.-Sls.--Intercontinental Branded Apparel, Buffalo, NY; *U.S. Public*, pg. 796

Pistner, John, Sr. V.P.-Sls.--Movado Group, Inc., Lyndhurst, NJ; *U.S. Public*, pg. 1140

Pistorese, Todd A., V.P.-Bus. Devel.--Tellus, Inc., Bellevue, WA; *U.S. Public*, pg. 1342

Pitch, Harold, V.P.-Sls.--Liggett Group Inc., Durham, NC; *U.S. Public*, pg. 259

Pitcher, Sarah, V.P.-Corp. Commun.--Mesa Air Group, Las Vegas, NV; *U.S. Public*, pg. 1098

Pitera, Thomas G., V.P.-N. American Sls.--Pioneer-Standard Electronics, Inc., Cleveland, OH; *U.S. Public*, pg. 1300

Pitkin, Jason, Dir.-Natl. Sls.--Frost & Sullivan, Mountain View, CA; *U.S. Private*, pg. 430

Pitman, Jerry, Mgr.-Sls.--Ocean Bio-Chem Inc., Fort Lauderdale, FL; *U.S. Public*, pg. 1211

Pitney, Scott, Mgr.-Sls.--Spring Engineers of Houston Ltd., Houston, TX; *U.S. Private*, pg. 956

Pittman, Jerry, Mgr.-Sls.--Kinpak, Inc., Montgomery, AL; *U.S. Public*, pg. 1211

Pittman, Jerry, Dir.-Sls.--Starbrite Corp., Fort Lauderdale, FL; *U.S. Public*, pg. 1510

Pittman, Robert, Exec. V.P.--Trend Offset Printing Services, Los Alamitos, CA; *U.S. Private*, pg. 1099

Pittman, Rod, V.P.-Mktg. & Sls.--Lufkin Industries, Inc., Lufkin, TX; *U.S. Public*, pg. 1019

Pittroff, Pete, Sr. V.P.-Sls.--Duron, Inc., Beltsville, MD; *U.S. Private*, pg. 349

Pitz, Sandra, Mgr.-Sls.--Wurzner Dauerbackwaren GmbH, Wurzen, Germany; *Int'l*, pg. 1514

Pladna, D.L., V.P.-Sls. & Mktg.--A.Y. McDonald Supply Co. Inc., Dubuque, IA; *U.S. Private*, pg. 721

Plaener, W., Sls. Mgr.--Murray Export Sales B. V., Brentwood, TN; *Int'l*, pg. 1397

Plagens, Steve, V.P.-Sls. Promo.--Colle & McVoy, Inc., Minneapolis, MN; *U.S. Private*, pg. 252
Plagman, Bruce, V.P.-Sls./North America--AGCO Corporation, Duluth, GA; *U.S. Public*, pg. 28
Plain, Charles, V.P.-Sls.--The Kent Company, Elkhart, IN; *Int'l*, pg. 440
Planeta, Geri, Mgr.-Opers. & Sls.--Aiwa America, Inc., Mahwah, NJ; *Int'l*, pg. 1280
Plastino, Joe, Mgr.-Intl. Sales--Precor, Inc., Bothell, WA; *U.S. Public*, pg. 1322
Plath, Tom, V.P.-Sls.--Mack Printing Company, Easton, PA; *U.S. Private*, pg. 691
Platt, H. Russell, V.P.-Mktg.--PLM Railcar Management Services, Inc., Chicago, IL; *U.S. Public*, pg. 1241
Platt, Ron, Sr. V.P.-Sls.--Hutch Sports USA, Inc., Hebron, KY; *U.S. Public*, pg. 1354
Platts, Rich, Natl. Sls. Mgr.--Tech Spray, Inc., Amarillo, TX; *U.S. Private*, pg. 1071
Platz, Mark, Mgr.-Sls.--Gulf State Specialties, Inc., South Houston, TX; *U.S. Private*, pg. 487
Plaumann, Bart L., V.P.-Sls.--Anchor Hocking Plastics, Saint Paul, MN; *U.S. Public*, pg. 1177
Playford, Alyson, Gen. Mgr.-Sls. & Mktg./Northern Europe--Utell International-United Kingdom, Sutton, United Kingdom; *Int'l*, pg. 1098
Pleasant, Gaylon, Dir.-Sls.--General Magnaplate Texas, Arlington, TX; *U.S. Public*, pg. 717
Pleming, Buzz, V.P.-Sls.--M.B. Kahn Construction Co., Inc., Columbia, SC; *U.S. Private*, pg. 604
Pless, Robert H., V.P. & Gen. Mgr.-Davco Div.--U.S. Filter/Davis Water & Waste Industries, Inc., Thomasville, GA; *U.S. Public*, pg. 1682
Plomin, Kathy, Mgr.-Sls.--WKYT-TV, Lexington, KY; *U.S. Public*, pg. 759
Ploss, Gus, V.P.-Sls., Mktg. & Bus. Devel.--Walbro Corporation, Cass City, MI; *U.S. Public*, pg. 1733
Plotzeneder, Thomas, Client Service Dir.--GGK Occidental Holding AG, Vienna, Austria; *Int'l*, pg. 1335
Plourde, Real, V.P.-Sls.--Alimentation Couche Tard Inc., Vimont, Canada; *Int'l*, pg. 57
Pluijmakers, Jos, Dir.-Sls. & Mktg.--Pan European Publishing Co., Brussels, Belgium; *Int'l*, pg. 1099
Plummer, Robert, Mgr.-Sls. & Mktg.--Dean Pump Division, Indianapolis, IN; *U.S. Public*, pg. 1100
Plummer, Terry, V.P.-Sls. & Mktg.--Boise Cascade Paper Div., Boise, ID; *U.S. Public*, pg. 243
Plummer, Terry M., V.P.-Mktg. & Sls./Paper Div.--Boise Cascade Corporation, Boise, ID; *U.S. Public*, pg. 242
Plummer, Tom, V.P.-Sls. & Mktg.--Kilgore Operations, Toone, TN; *U.S. Public*, pg. 47
Pluschke, Christian, Mgr.-Sls.--Helly-Hansen GmbH, Hamburg, Germany; *Int'l*, pg. 1011
Plush, Richard F., V.P.-Field Mktg. & Sls. Support--The Penn Mutual Life Insurance Company, Philadelphia, PA; *U.S. Private*, pg. 849
Podall, James J., Mgr.-Sls.--Jomac, Inc., Warrington, PA; *U.S. Private*, pg. 595
Poe, J.F., V.P.-Sls.--Morton Salt, Chicago, IL; *U.S. Public*, pg. 1135
Poedens, Dr. B., Mgr.-Mktg. & Sls.--Mallinckrodt Medical B.V., Petten, Netherlands; *U.S. Public*, pg. 1040
Poertner, Hank, Dir.-Sls.--A-Dec, Inc., Newberg, OR; *U.S. Private*, pg. 2
Pogorzelski, Donald E., V.P.-Sls. & Mktg.-Diagnostics--Genzyme Corporation, Cambridge, MA; *U.S. Public*, pg. 733
Pohl, Roger, Dir.-Sls.--Porta Systems Co., Charlotte, NC; *U.S. Public*, pg. 1317
Pohlabel, Steven, Mgr.-Terminal--Kintetsu World Express Inc., Cudahy, WI; *Int'l*, pg. 734
Polacheck, Jerry, Exec. V.P.-Sls.--Reliable Knitting Works, Milwaukee, WI; *U.S. Private*, pg. 920
Polacheck, Jerry, V.P.-Sls.--Halper Bros., Milwaukee, WI; *U.S. Private*, pg. 920
Poleo, J. Michael, Mgr.-District Sls.--Mellon Bank, N.A.-Northern Region, Erie, PA; *U.S. Public*, pg. 1085
Polich, Michael L., V.P.-Mktg. & Sls.--Doehler-Jarvis, Inc., Toledo, OH; *U.S. Public*, pg. 796
Polke, Thomas P., V.P.-Sls. & Mktg.--Johnson Products Co., Inc., Chicago, IL; *U.S. Public*, pg. 915
Pollan, Clifford M., V.P.-Sls. & Mktg.--NewsEdge Corporation, Burlington, MA; *U.S. Public*, pg. 1180
Pollard, Tom, Mgr.-Sls.--Progress Paint Mfg. Co., Louisville, KY; *U.S. Private*, pg. 890
Pollic, Gene, Plant Mgr.--Agrotec, Williams Inc., Pendleton, NC; *U.S. Public*, pg. 1769
Pollinger, Richard, Pres.--Stapo Hollander Industries, Lakewood, NJ; *U.S. Private*, pg. 1033
Pollock, Leland M., V.P.-Meat Sls.--Albertson's, Inc., Boise, ID; *U.S. Public*, pg. 38
Polson, Art, Mgr.-Retail Sls./Institutional & Private Lbl.--Idaho Supreme Company, Firth, ID; *U.S. Private*, pg. 557
Polster, Harvey, Dir.-Sls.--Tecumseh Products Co. Engine & Transmission Group, Grafton, WI; *U.S. Public*, pg. 1566
Polston, Peter, V.P.-Sls. & Mktg.--Cowden Metal Specialties, Inc., Chino, CA; *U.S. Private*, pg. 280
Polucha, Jeffrey, V.P.-Mktg. & Devel.--Valley Resources, Inc., Cumberland, RI; *U.S. Public*, pg. 1706
Pond, Bruce, Mgr.-Sls--Rynone Manufacturing Corporation, Sayre, PA; *U.S. Private*, pg. 953
Ponder, Gary, V.P.-Sls.--Colgate-Palmolive Co., Institutional Products Div., Tenafly, NJ; *U.S. Public*, pg. 397
Ponder, Michael H., V.P.-Sls. & Mktg.-Red Star BioProducts--Universal Foods Corporation, Milwaukee, WI; *U.S. Public*, pg. 1695
Pont, Neil F., Sr. V.P.-Sls.--Amwest Insurance Group, Inc., Calabasas, CA; *U.S. Public*, pg. 106
Pont, Neil F., Exec. V.P.-Branch Delivery Sys.--Amwest Surety Insurance Company, Calabasas, CA; *U.S. Public*, pg. 106
Pontell, Irwin, V.P.-Sls.--Browning Chemical Corporation, White Plains, NY; *U.S. Private*, pg. 175
Pontin, Toby J., V.P.-Sls. & Mktg.--Kallista, Inc., San Leandro, CA; *U.S. Private*, pg. 630
Pontious, James C., V.P.-Sls. & Mktg.--Westinghouse Air Brake Company, Wilmerding, PA; *U.S. Public*, pg. 1760
Ponton, Henry E., Sls. Mgr.-Plumbing & Heating--Frederick Trading Company, Frederick, MD; *U.S. Private*, pg. 335
Pontz, Rick, Natl. Sls. Mgr.--Security Lawn & Garden Co., Phoenix, AZ; *U.S. Private*, pg. 397
Pool, Stanley L., V.P.-Sls. & Mktg. & Sec.--Mity-Lite, Inc., Orem, UT; *U.S. Public*, pg. 1118
Popa, Emil, Dir.-Intl. Sls.--U.S. Bottlers Machinery Co., Charlotte, NC; *U.S. Private*, pg. 1124
Popeil, Ron, Pres.--Ronco, Inventions. LLC, Chatsworth, CA; *U.S. Private*, pg. 943
Popkowski, John, Exec. V.P.-Adv. Sls.-MTV Networks--MTV Networks, New York, NY; *U.S. Private*, pg. 779
Popolow, Emma, Natl. Sls. Mgr.-Hotel Div.--WMF/USA, Farmingdale, NY; *U.S. Private*, pg. 1144
Popovitch, Gary, Gen. Mgr.--Toledo Milk Processing, Inc., Toledo, OH; *U.S. Public*, pg. 1453
Popovits, Kim, V.P.-Sls.--Genentech, Inc., South San Francisco, CA; *Int'l*, pg. 1120
Poppele, K., Mgr.-Sales & Mktg.--Carbone of America, Parsippany, NJ; *Int'l*, pg. 1028
Poppen, Sonya, Mgr.-Sls.--Jackson MSC, Nashville, TN; *U.S. Private*, pg. 579
Poppenhoeser, Kathleen, V.P.-Sls.--Clare Rose Inc./Clare Rose of Nassau, Patchogue, NY; *U.S. Private*, pg. 945
Porepp, David, Mgr.-Gen. Sls.--KCCI Television, Inc., Des Moines, IA; *U.S. Public*, pg. 1343
Port, Frederick, Exec. V.P.-Intl. Sls.--Callaway Golf Company, Carlsbad, CA; *U.S. Public*, pg. 294
Portada, Joseph, Mgr.-Intl. Sls.--Dynamics Research Corporation, Andover, MA; *U.S. Public*, pg. 539
Portelli, John, V.P.-Sls.--Advertising Checking Bureau Incorporated, New York, NY; *U.S. Private*, pg. 23
Porteous, Jim, Gen. Mgr.-Sls.--Romac Industries, Inc., Seattle, WA; *U.S. Private*, pg. 847
Porter, Charles A., V.P.-Sls. & Mktg.--Peerless Pottery, Inc., Rockport, IN; *U.S. Private*, pg. 847
Porter, Dwight, V.P.-N. American Sls.--Ag-Chem Equipment Co., Inc., Minnetonka, MN; *U.S. Public*, pg. 6
Porter, J.A., V.P.-Sls. & Mktg.--Solar Turbines Incorporated, San Diego, CA; *U.S. Public*, pg. 316
Porter, Ray, Gen. Sls. Mgr.--Wick Bldg. Systems Inc. Manufactured Homes Div., Marshfield, WI; *U.S. Private*, pg. 1174
Porter, Richard A., Pres.--Lamb-Weston, Inc., Kennewick, WA; *U.S. Public*, pg. 427
Porteret, Jacques, Program Sls. Mgr.--Columbia Pictures Television, Paris, France; *Int'l*, pg. 1282
Portman, Jeff, Exec. V.P.-Sls. & Mktg.--AMC, Inc., Atlanta, GA; *U.S. Private*, pg. 6
Posey, Bob, Dir.-Sls. & Mktg.--Aeroglide Corporation, Cary, NC; *U.S. Private*, pg. 24
Posnock, Leonard H., Dir.-Sls.--Shofar Kosher Foods, Linden, NJ; *U.S. Public*, pg. 1433
Pospisil, Frederick J., 1st V.P.-Customer Sls.--St. Paul Bancorp, Inc., Chicago, IL; *U.S. Public*, pg. 1428
Post, Tom, Natl. Sls. Mgr.--WYFF-TV, Greenville, SC; *U.S. Public*, pg. 1344
Post, Virgil C., V.P.-Mktg., Sls. & Svcs.--Construction Equip. Div., Lubbock, TX; *U.S. Private*, pg. 355
Postlethwait, Jeff, Dir.-Sls. & Mktg.--Micro Networks Corp., Worcester, MA; *U.S. Private*, pg. 969
Pottenger, Linda K., V.P.-Sls.--BeautiControl Cosmetics, Inc., Carrollton, TX; *U.S. Public*, pg. 198
Potter, Alfred K. II, Sr. V.P.-Sls. & Mktg.--Gilbane Building Company, Providence, RI; *U.S. Private*, pg. 452
Potter, James, V.P.-Sls.--Branch Group Inc., Upper Marlboro, MD; *U.S. Private*, pg. 165
Potter, Jay, Mgr.-Sls.--PENCO-Mississippi, Jackson, MS; *Int'l*, pg. 1508
Potter, Larry D., V.P. & Gen. Mgr.-Worldwide Field Opers., Test & Meas. Org.--Hewlett-Packard Company, Palo Alto, CA; *U.S. Public*, pg. 813
Potts, Robert S., V.P. & Gen. Mgr.-Yearbooks--Herff Jones Inc., Indianapolis, IN; *U.S. Private*, pg. 523
Potvin, Bob, Mgr.-Natl. Sls.--Claire Manufacturing Co., Addison, IL; *U.S. Private*, pg. 462
Poucher, Donald A., Dir.-Sls. & Mktg.--Deepwater Chemicals, Inc., Woodward, OK; *Int'l*, pg. 1395
Poulos, Tom, V.P.-Mktg. & Sls.--American Paging, Inc., Minneapolis, MN; *U.S. Public*, pg. 1570
Pourzanjani, Cameron, V.P.-Mktg. & Sls.--Syseca Inc., Marina Del Rey, CA; *Int'l*, pg. 1384
Pow, Lincoln, Sls. Mgr.--Berlitz Escola de Idiomas Ltda., Sao Paulo, Brazil; *U.S. Public*, pg. 221
Powell, James R., Sr. V.P.-Sls. & Mktg.--Daisytek International Corporation, Plano, TX; *U.S. Public*, pg. 477
Powell, James R., Sr. V.P.-Sls. & Mktg.--Daisytek Incorporated, Plano, TX; *U.S. Public*, pg. 477
Powell, James R., Sr. V.P.-Sls. & Mktg.--Daisytek (Canada) Inc., Toronto, Canada; *U.S. Public*, pg. 477
Powell, James R., Sr. V.P.-Sls. & Mktg.--Daisytek Latin America, Miami, FL; *U.S. Public*, pg. 477
Powell, James R., Sr. V.P.-Sls. & Mktg.--Daisytek De Mexico S.A. de C.V., Mexico, Mexico; *U.S. Public*, pg. 477
Powell, James R., Sr. V.P.-Sls. & Mktg.--Priority Fulfillment Services, Inc., Plano, TX; *U.S. Public*, pg. 477
Powell, James R., Sr. V.P.-Sls. & Mktg.--Daisytek Australia Pty. Ltd., Alexandria, Australia; *U.S. Public*, pg. 477
Powell, Jamie, Sls. Mgr.-Western Region--Parker & Amchem, Etobicoke, Canada; *Int'l*, pg. 612
Powell, Jeffrey E., Partner-Retail Sls. & Mktg.--J.C. Bradford & Co., Nashville, TN; *U.S. Private*, pg. 163
Powell, Jenny, Mgr.-Retail Mktg.--Starbanc Corporation, Cincinnati, OH; *U.S. Public*, pg. 1510
Powell, Jim, V.P.-Mktg. & Sls.--Sioux Honey Association, Sioux City, IA; *U.S. Private*, pg. 1003
Powell, Jim, V.P.-Sls.-Consumer Prods.--Dayco Swan Corporation, Worthington, OH; *U.S. Public*, pg. 1045
Powell, Scott, Gen. Sls. Mgr.--Baugher Chevrolet-Buick Inc., Waynesboro, VA; *U.S. Private*, pg. 123
Powell, Teresa M., Dir.-Bus. Devel.--AC Martin Partners, Los Angeles, CA; *U.S. Private*, pg. 708
Power, Larry, Mgr.-Sls.--Hilland Dairy Company, Wichita, KS; *U.S. Private*, pg. 879
Power, William, Reg. V.P.-Sls.--American Security Distribution, Anaheim, CA; *U.S. Private*, pg. 61
Powers, Dave, V.P.-Sls. & Mktg.--King Koil Licensing Company Inc., Saint Paul, MN; *U.S. Private*, pg. 621
Powers, Gordon, V.P.-Sls./Bryant, Day & Night, Payne--Carrier Corp., Indianapolis, IN; *U.S. Public*, pg. 1690
Powers, John J., Exec. V.P.-Sls. & Mktg.--AEP Industries, Inc., South Hackensack, NJ; *U.S. Public*, pg. 4
Powers, Michael, V.P.-Sls.--Glines & Rhodes, Inc., Attleboro, MA; *U.S. Private*, pg. 457
Powers, Rick, V.P.-Sls.--Hodges Division, Chicago, IL; *U.S. Public*, pg. 985
Pozil, Robert, Dir.-Export Sls.--Lander Co., Inc., Englewood, NJ; *U.S. Private*, pg. 647
Pozzi, Luigi, Mgr.-Rumania & Slovenia Sls.--Johnson Wax S.p.A., Milan, Italy; *U.S. Private*, pg. 593
Prais, John, V.P.-Sls.--Worzalla Publishing Co., Inc., Stevens Point, WI; *U.S. Private*, pg. 1191
Pranckh, Ferdinand, V.P.-Extrusion Sls.--HPM Corporation, Mount Gilead, OH; *U.S. Private*, pg. 492
Pranckus, Joseph, V.P.-Sls.--Liqui-Box Corporation, Worthington, OH; *U.S. Public*, pg. 1000
Pranger, Scott, V.P.-Sls. & Mktg.--Kurdziel Industries, Inc., Muskegon, MI; *U.S. Private*, pg. 637
Pranger, Scott, Mgr.-Sls.--Kurdziel Industries, Inc., Muskegon, MI; *U.S. Private*, pg. 637
Pranka, Tom, Mgr.-Mktg.& Sls.--ARDCO/Traverse Lift, Houston, TX; *U.S. Private*, pg. 859
Pratico, Natalie, Dir.-Sls. Admin.--Columbia Tri-Star International Television, Culver City, CA; *Int'l*, pg. 1281
Pratt, Norris, Grp. V.P.-Sls.--Fleischmann's Yeast, Fenton, MO; *Int'l*, pg. 237
Pratt, Sarah, Dir.-Mktg.--Dictaphone Co. U.K. Ltd., Royal Leamington Spa, United Kingdom; *U.S. Private*, pg. 1045
Pregartner, Sue, V.P.-Sls. East--The Royal China & Porcelain Companies Inc., Moorestown, NJ; *U.S. Private*, pg. 948
Preis, David, Dir.-Sls.-New York--Hardwick Clothes Inc., Cleveland, TN; *U.S. Private*, pg. 502
Preis, Peter, V.P.-Western Sls.--CBS Enterprises Division, New York, NY; *U.S. Public*, pg. 274
Preisel, Thomas G., V.P.-Opers., Sls. & Mktg.--Baltek Corporation, Northvale, NJ; *U.S. Public*, pg. 171
Prentice, Mike, Dir.-Sls. & Mktg.--API Harowe, West Chester, PA; *U.S. Public*, pg. 90
Presley, Clay, Sr. V.P.-Sls.--C.R. Gibson Co., Norwalk, CT; *U.S. Public*, pg. 1168
Presley, James L., Chief Info. Officer & V.P.-Sls.--Clark Specialty Co., Inc., Hammondsport, NY; *U.S. Private*, pg. 243
Presley, W. Clay, Sr. V.P.-Sls.-Gift Prods.--Thomas Nelson Inc., Nashville, TN; *U.S. Public*, pg. 1167
Pressley, Robert, Mgr.-Sls.--Marquette Coppersmithing Co., Inc., Philadelphia, PA; *U.S. Private*, pg. 706
Pressley, Rodney L., V.P.-Sls. & Mgr.-Opers.--Industrial Maintenance Overflow Corporation, Fletcher, NC; *U.S. Private*, pg. 561
Preston, Michael L., Sr. V.P.-Sls. & Mktg.--APS Holding Corporation, Houston, TX; *U.S. Public*, pg. 10
Preston, Robert, Dir.-Sls.--Medical Economics Company Inc., Montvale, NJ; *U.S. Public*, pg. 1601
Pretasky, Dan, V.P.-Sls.--Inland Printing Co., Inc., La Crosse, WI; *U.S. Private*, pg. 564
Pretorius, Quintin, Gen. Mgr.-Broker Div. & Devel.--Life Division, Rondebosch, South Africa; *Int'l*, pg. 77
Pretty, David A., Dir.-Sls. & Mktg.--Barratt Developments Plc, Newcastle upon Tyne, United Kingdom; *Int'l*, pg. 167
Prevatt, John W., V.P.-Sls. & Mktg.--Golden Gem Growers Inc., Umatilla, FL; *U.S. Private*, pg. 460
Prevost, Fred, V.P.-Sls.--Southwestern/Great American Inc., Nashville, TN; *U.S. Private*, pg. 1018
Price, Barbara G., Mgr.-Natl. Sls.--WQDR, Raleigh, NC; *U.S. Private*, pg. 298
Price, Bob, V.P.-Sls. & Mktg.--Thomas Built Buses, Inc., High Point, NC; *U.S. Private*, pg. 1082
Price, David A., V.P.-Adv. & Sls.--ACMAT Corporation, New Britain, CT; *U.S. Public*, pg. 16
Price, Judy, Mgr.-Natl. Accts. & Admin.-Sls.--Baume Mercier, Inc., New York, NY; *U.S. Private*, pg. 124
Price, Keith A., V.P.-Mktg.--The Hotsy Corporation, Englewood, CO; *U.S. Private*, pg. 500
Price, Kenneth, Sr. V.P.-Sls. & Mktg.--Toymax International Inc., Plainview, NY; *U.S. Public*, pg. 1626
Price, Kevin, V.P.-Sls. & Mktg.-Track Prods. Div.--ABC Rail Products Corp., Chicago, IL; *U.S. Public*, pg. 2
Price, Mark, Sr. V.P.-New Bus. Devel.--Sterling Healthcare Group, Inc., Miami, FL; *U.S. Public*, pg. 608
Price, Robert, V.P.-Sls.--J.E. Berkowitz, LP, Westville, NJ; *U.S. Private*, pg. 135
Price, Wayne, Dir.-Sls. & Mktg.--Amprobe Instrument, Lynbrook, NY; *U.S. Public*, pg. 1676
Priebe, Robert W., Sr. V.P.-OEM Sls. & Intl.--Stant Corporation, Denver, CO; *Int'l*, pg. 1396
Priem, Troy, Mgr.-Mktg. & Sls.--Nobles Mfg. Inc., Saint Croix Falls, WI; *U.S. Private*, pg. 800
Priestley, Perry V., Mgr.-Intl. Sls.--Comark Communications, Inc., Chalfont, PA; *Int'l*, pg. 1383
Prieto, Robert, Exec. V.P. & Dir.-Corp. Devel.--Parsons Brinckerhoff Inc., New York, NY; *U.S. Private*, pg. 841
Prince, Robert, V.P.-Worldwide Sls.--Richardson Electronics, Ltd., Lafox, IL; *U.S. Public*, pg. 1387
Prince, Robert J., Exec. V.P.-Institutional & Govt. Sls./N. America--FCA International Ltd., Westmount, Canada; *Int'l*, pg. 470
Prinz, Bill, V.P.-Sls. & Mktg.--Jayco Inc., Middlebury, IN; *U.S. Private*, pg. 583
Pritt, Roger, V.P. & Gen. Mgr.-Auto Store Div.--STRAFCO, Inc., San Antonio, TX; *U.S. Private*, pg. 1046

Privette, John C., V.P.-Intl. Opers.--Hach Company, Loveland, CO; *U.S. Public,* pg. 773
Probach, Michael, Mgr.-Natl. Sls.--Lindal Cedar Homes, Inc., Seattle, WA; *U.S. Public,* pg. 998
Probst, Lud A., V.P.-Sls. & Mktg.--Jacobs Engineering Group Inc., Houston, TX; *U.S. Public,* pg. 921
Procassini, Russ, Mgr.-Reg. Sls.--Automotive News, Detroit, MI; *U.S. Private,* pg. 284
Prochaska, Barry, Mgr.-Sls.--Stoneville Furniture Co. Inc., Stoneville, NC; *U.S. Private,* pg. 1045
Proctor, Anthony G., V.P.- Sls. & Mktg. for HPG (UK)--Seal Products Incorporated, Naugatuck, CT; *U.S. Public,* pg. 849
Proctor, Randy B., Dir.-Sls.--Medical Meadow Gold Dairies, Inc., Ogden, UT; *U.S. Private,* pg. 1016
Proffitt, Carol, Mgr.-Sls. Opers.--Kennedy Manufacturing Company, Van Wert, OH; *U.S. Private,* pg. 614
Prohodski, Alex, V.P.-Sls. & Mktg.--Novartis Seeds, Inc., Downers Grove, IL; *Int'l,* pg. 974
Prose, David, V.P.-Sls.--Icon International, Stamford, CT; *U.S. Private,* pg. 556
Proto, Anthony, V.P.-Mktg. & Sls.--CEBCOR (Consolidated Employment Benefits Corp.), Chicago, IL; *U.S. Private,* pg. 220
Protzman, Robert, V.P.-Sls. & Mktg.--Schneider National, Inc., Green Bay, WI; *U.S. Private,* pg. 971
Proud, Caroline, Dir.-Sls. & Mktg.--Mitchell Beazley, London, United Kingdom; *Int'l,* pg. 1093
Proudfit, Randall, Technical Sls. Rep.--Klungess Electronic supply, Iron Mountain, MI; *U.S. Private,* pg. 197
Provonsha, Terry, Mgr.-Retail Sales--Precor, Inc., Bothell, WA; *U.S. Public,* pg. 1322
Provoost, Rudy, V.P.-Grp. Sls.--Whirlpool Europe B.V., Comerio, Italy; *U.S. Public,* pg. 1765
Provost, Gerald, V.P.-Sls.--Bennington Iron Works, Inc., Bennington, VT; *U.S. Private,* pg. 133
Provost, Roy G., Dir.-Sls. & Mktg.-Indus. Div.--Bel-Ray Company, Inc., Farmingdale, NJ; *U.S. Private,* pg. 130
Prudames, Charles, Mgr.-Natl. Sls.--Smith Industries, Inc., Montgomery, AL; *U.S. Private,* pg. 1008
Prudente, Ivano, Mgr.-Sls.--Opticos S.r.l., Brembate di Sopra, Italy; *Int'l,* pg. 1007
Pruett, R., Mgr.-North East Reg.--King & Prince Seafood Corporation, Brunswick, GA; *U.S. Private,* pg. 620
Prugh, J., V.P.-Sls.--Dixie Type & Supply Co., Inc., Birmingham, AL; *U.S. Public,* pg. 1329
Prusnick, L., V.P.-Sls.--Euclid Hitachi, Cleveland, OH; *Int'l,* pg. 622
Pruzansky, Stu, Mgr.-Gen. Sales--WFOR-TV Channel 4, Miami, FL; *U.S. Public,* pg. 275
Pryne, Mark A., Mgr.-Sls. & Air Filtration Brand--American Felt & Filter, Newburgh, NY; *U.S. Private,* pg. 54
Pryor, John P., V.P.-Mktg. & Sls.--BGS Systems, Inc., Waltham, MA; *U.S. Public,* pg. 161
Przybylek, G.P., Dir.-Intl. Sls.--Duraco Products, Inc., Streamwood, IL; *U.S. Private,* pg. 348
Puccia, Vincent, V.P.-Sls. & Mktg.--American International Airways, Ypsilanti, MI; *U.S. Private,* pg. 57
Puckett, L.H., Gen. Mgr.-Mktg. & Sls.--Union Camp Fine Paper Div., Franklin, VA; *U.S. Public,* pg. 1666
Puckett, Michael W., V.P.-Cement Sls. & Concrete Opers.--Lone Star Industries, Inc., Stamford, CT; *U.S. Public,* pg. 1012
Pugatch, Bob, V.P.-Sls.--CMI Holding Corp., Canton, MA; *U.S. Private,* pg. 195
Pugatch, Gary, V.P.-Sls. & Mktg.--Williams Hospitality Group Inc., Carolina, PR; *U.S. Public,* pg. 1265
Pugh, Cathy, Mgr.-Mktg.--Columbus Show Case Company, Columbus, OH; *U.S. Private,* pg. 257
Pugh, Edward F., Mgr.-Sls.--Willis Corroon Corp. of Wash. D.C., Bethesda, MD; *Int'l,* pg. 1507
Pugliese, Joseph, V.P.-Sls.--Centeon, L.L.C., King of Prussia, PA; *Int'l,* pg. 626
Pulk, David R., Sr. V.P.-Sls. & Mktg.--Golden Eagle Group, Inc., Humble, TX; *U.S. Public,* pg. 749
Pullen, Dr. G.R., Mgr.-Sls. Admin.--Terumo (Australia) Pty. Ltd., Mordialloc, Australia; *Int'l,* pg. 1376
Pulner-Mihaly, Stacey, Dir.-Mktg.--Plan International USA, Inc., Warwick, RI; *U.S. Private,* pg. 869
Pulse, Dick, Dir.-Mktg. Services--Liebert Corporation, Columbus, OH; *U.S. Public,* pg. 573
Punzo, Tom G., Mgr.-Sls.--Waldes Truarc/Industrial Retaining Ring, Somerset, NJ; *U.S. Public,* pg. 1632
Purcell, Dennis J., V.P.-Natl. Accts./Sls.--Dean Foods Company, Franklin Park, IL; *U.S. Public,* pg. 489
Purcell, Jacqueline, Dir.-ATS (After the Sale)--HMI Industries, Cleveland, OH; *U.S. Public,* pg. 771
Purcell, Tom, Sr. V.P.-Sls.--Fedders Corp., Liberty Corner, NJ; *U.S. Public,* pg. 614
Purcell, Tom, Sr. V.P.-Sls.--Fedders North America, Inc., Whitehouse, NJ; *U.S. Public,* pg. 614
Purdy, John W., Jr., V.P.-Mktg. & Pub. Affairs--Essex County Gas Company, Amesbury, MA; *U.S. Public,* pg. 593
Purdy, Kevin, Mgr.-Sls.--Anorad Corporation, Hauppauge, NY; *U.S. Private,* pg. 75
Puri, Vijaytt, Dir.-Export Sls.--DEZurik, Sartell, MN; *U.S. Public,* pg. 726
Purigraski, M., Sr. V.P.-Mktg. & Sls.--Mead School & Office Products, Dayton, OH; *U.S. Public,* pg. 1074
Purtill, Tom, V.P.-Sls. & Mktg.--Baylor Company, Sugar Land, TX; *Int'l,* pg. 1134
Purvis, Ron, V.P.-U.S. Ag. Sls.--Carter Day International, Inc., Minneapolis, MN; *U.S. Private,* pg. 217
Purvis, T.W., Exec. V.P.-Mktg. & Sls.--Appleton Electric Co., Chicago, IL; *U.S. Public,* pg. 572
Push, Steve, V.P.-Sls.--Performance Food Group Company, Richmond, VA; *U.S. Public,* pg. 1278
Putnam, Roger G., Dir.-Sls. & Mktg.--Jaguar Cars Limited, Coventry, United Kingdom; *U.S. Public,* pg. 666
Putvinski, Jim, V.P.-Sls. & Mktg.--Tecknit Incorporated, Cranford, NJ; *U.S. Private,* pg. 1072
Pyle, Rick, Mgr.-Sls.--Collegeville Flag & Mfg. Company, Collegeville, PA; *U.S. Private,* pg. 252
Pyle, Roy, V.P.-Sls.--Dayco Products Inc., Miamisburg, OH; *U.S. Public,* pg. 1045
Pyles, David, Sr. V.P.-Sls.--Bentley Mills, Inc., City of Industry, CA; *U.S. Public,* pg. 889
Pype, Pikerre, V.P.-Sls.--Rapid Mounting & Finishing Co., Chicago, IL; *U.S. Private,* pg. 910
Quaine, Tim, Mgr.-Sls.--Hasper Equipment Co., Muskegon, MI; *U.S. Private,* pg. 247
Qualls, Jo E., V.P.-Retail Sls./Costa Mesa--Tiffany & Co., New York, NY; *U.S. Public,* pg. 1608
Quamme, Ralph, V.P.-Sls. & Mktg.--Long Equipment Co., Tarboro, NC; *U.S. Private,* pg. 675
Quaranto, Paul A., Jr., V.P.-Grp. Sls.--Boston Mutual Life Insurance Co., Canton, MA; *U.S. Private,* pg. 161
Quertinmont, Tom, Mgr.-Mktg. Communications--Mettler-Toledo Inc., Worthington, OH; *U.S. Private,* pg. 4
Quesada, Juan, Exec. V.P.-Sls., Mktg. & Adv.--Cox Lumber Co., Saint Petersburg, FL; *U.S. Private,* pg. 283
Quesnel, Roger, V.P.-Pulp Sls.--Donohue Inc., Quebec, Canada; *Int'l,* pg. 1075
Quigley, Don, V.P.-Sls.--Pete's Brewing Company, Palo Alto, CA; *U.S. Public,* pg. 1280
Quigley, Gordon, Dir.-Sls.--Schneider Automation, Inc., North Andover, MA; *Int'l,* pg. 1208
Quimby, Edward D., Sr. V.P.-Sls. & Mktg.--The Turner Corporation, New York, NY; *U.S. Public,* pg. 1645
Quimby, Edward D., Sr. V.P.-Sls. & Mktg.--Turner Construction Company, New York, NY; *U.S. Public,* pg. 1645
Quinley, John, Mgr.-LandPride Mktg. & Sls. Promo.--Great Plains Manufacturing, Inc., Salina, KS; *U.S. Private,* pg. 475
Quinn, James T., V.P.-Consumer Sls.--Durex Consumer Products, Norcross, GA; *Int'l,* pg. 815
Quinn, Pat, Mgr.-Mktg.--Esselte Meto Ltd., Bracknell, United Kingdom; *Int'l,* pg. 461
Quinton, Linda, V.P. & Dir.-Mktg. Tourbook--St. Martins Press, Inc., New York, NY; *Int'l,* pg. 1479
Quirino, Sylvia P., V.P.-Intl. Bus. Opers.--La Tondena Distillers, Inc., Manila, Philippines; *Int'l,* pg. 785
Quirk, Brian, Exec. V.P.-Sls. & Affiliate Rels.--Playboy Entertainment Group, Inc., Beverly Hills, CA; *U.S. Public, pg. 1310*
Quist, James, Dir.-Sls.--Carriage Industries, Inc., Calhoun, GA; *U.S. Public,* pg. 514
Raasch, Jeff, Exec. V.P.-Sls. & Mktg.--Enerfab Inc., Cincinnati, OH; *U.S. Private,* pg. 376
Rabbidge, Charles, Mgr.-Sls. & Mktg.--Scania USA Inc., Orange, CT; *Int'l,* pg. 687
Rabey, Wayne, Dir.-Sales & Mktg.--General Instrument of Canada Ltd., Mississauga, Canada; *U.S. Public,* pg. 716
Rabin, Hal, V.P.-Mktg.--Sonic Couriers of Arizona, Inc., Scottsdale, AZ; *U.S. Private,* pg. 1123
Rabinovitch, Donald, Pres.--AFP Imaging Corporation, Elmsford, NY; *U.S. Public,* pg. 6
Rabon, Rick, Mgr.-Sls.--Sexton Can Co., Inc., Cambridge, MA; *U.S. Private,* pg. 988
Race, J.A., Dir.-Sls.--VG Analytical Ltd., Manchester, United Kingdom; *Int'l,* pg. 1110
Rachels, G.K., Mgr.-Sls./Southeast Reg.--Industrial Maintenance Corp., Charlotte, NC; *U.S. Public,* pg. 562
Raclaw, David, V.P.-Sls.--Schawkgraphics, Des Plaines, IL; *U.S. Public,* pg. 1437
Rademacher, Dave, Mgr.-Sls.--PENCO-Michigan, Lansing, MI; *Int'l,* pg. 1508
Rademacher, Jeni, Sr. Sls. Representative--PENCO-Wisconsin, Racine, WI; *Int'l,* pg. 1508
Rademacher, Kent D., Sr. V.P.-Dental Office Opers., Sls & Mktg.--Safeguard Health Enterprises, Inc., Anaheim, CA; *U.S. Public,* pg. 1424
Rader, Jonathan, Mgr.-Wholesaler Opers.--Amurol Confections Co., Yorkville, IL; *U.S. Public,* pg. 1781
Radford, John, Dir.-Sls.--Ford Motor Co. of Canada Ltd, Oakville, Canada; *U.S. Public,* pg. 666
Radloff, Dick, Mgr.-Natl. Sls.-Contract Div.--Polar Ware Company, Sheboygan, WI; *U.S. Private,* pg. 873
Radshaw, John, Mgr.-N. Amer. Sls. & Mktg.-Metallurgical Prods.--Hennepin Division, Exolon-Esk, Hennepin, IL; *U.S. Public,* pg. 600
Rae, Craig, V.P.-Sls. OEM Accounts--CCX Fiberglass Products, Walterboro, SC; *U.S. Private,* pg. 193
Rafael, Heather, Mgr.-Janitorial Sls.--American Specialties Inc., Yonkers, NY; *U.S. Private,* pg. 62
Rafalowski, R., V.P.-Sls.--Jetcom, Cincinnati, OH; *U.S. Public,* pg. 1329
Rafaniello, Ralph R., Sr. V.P.-Sls.--The American Stock Exchange, New York, NY; *U.S. Private,* pg. 62
Raffaelli, Richard, V.P.-Sls. & Mktg.--Muskin Leisure Products, Inc., Wilkes-Barre, PA; *U.S. Private,* pg. 768
Raffensberger, Larry, V.P.-Boiler Sls.--Donlee Technologies Inc., York, PA; *U.S. Private,* pg. 339
Raffner, Bernard, V.P.-Sls. & Mktg.--Inductotherm Corp., Rancocas, NJ; *U.S. Private,* pg. 560
Raftery, Patrick J., V.P.-U.S. Sls.--Equitrac Corporation, Coral Gables, FL; *U.S. Public,* pg. 590
Ragatz, Jon, Dir.-Mktg. & Sls.--Alta-Dena Certified Dairy, City of Industry, CA; *Int'l,* pg. 201
Ragland, Roger, V.P.-Intl. Sls.--Dean Foods Company, Franklin Park, IL; *U.S. Public,* pg. 489
Ragsdell, Diana, V.P.-Commercial Sls.--Rand McNally & Company, Skokie, IL; *U.S. Private,* pg. 908
Rahim, Yaakob Bin Abdul, Mgr.-Seafreight Sls. & Mktg.--Kwe-Kintetsu World Express(S)Pte Ltd., Singapore, Singapore; *Int'l,* pg. 735
Rahlke, Hans, Gen. Mgr.-Export Sls.--Freightliner Corp., Portland, OR; *Int'l,* pg. 368
Rahn, Terry, V.P.-Direct Response Sls.--Physicians Mutual Insurance Co., Omaha, NE; *U.S. Private,* pg. 864
Raikes, Jeffrey S., Grp. V.P.-Sls. & Mktg.--Microsoft Corporation, Redmond, WA; *U.S. Public,* pg. 1107
Rainey, Brian, V.P.-Sls.--McCormick Canada, Ltd., London, Canada; *U.S. Public,* pg. 1067
Rains, Douglas J., Sr. V.P.-Natl. Sls.--Wm. E. Wright Limited Partnership, West Warren, MA; *U.S. Private,* pg. 1192
Rains, Lindsey, V.P.-Sls.--Heartland Express, Inc., Coralville, IA; *U.S. Public,* pg. 803
Rains, Sidney, V.P.-Sls. & Mktg.--Van Dorn Demag Corporation, Strongsville, OH; *Int'l,* pg. 837
Rajlis, Marcia, Dir.-Sls. & Mktg. Admin.--Columbian Mutual Life Insurance Co., Binghamton, NY; *U.S. Private,* pg. 256
Rakusin, Marshall, V.P.-Sls. & Mktg.--Fred V. Fowler Company, Inc., Newton, MA; *U.S. Private,* pg. 422
Raleigh, Robert E., Sr. V.P.-Domestic Sls.--Worldvision Enterprises, New York, NY; *U.S. Private,* pg. 776
Raley, Gary, V.P.-Sls.--Fruit of the Loom, Inc., Chicago, IL; *U.S. Public,* pg. 685
Ralston, Ronald, Exec. V.P.-Mktg. & Sls.--Parfums International Ltd., New York, NY; *Int'l,* pg. 1435
Ramachandran, M.S., Gen. Mgr.-Sls.--Indian Oil Corporation Limited, New Delhi, India; *Int'l,* pg. 673
Ramaglia, Mary, V.P.-Sls. & Mktg.--Revco Scientific, Asheville, NC; *U.S. Public,* pg. 727
Ramaley, James, V.P.-Circulation Services--Ziff-Davis Publishing Company, New York, NY; *Int'l,* pg. 1276
Rambo, Virgil A., V.P.-Sls. & Mktg.--CorryHiebert Corporation, Corry, PA; *U.S. Public,* pg. 772
Ramey, A.J., V.P.-Sls. & Mktg.--Marley Mouldings Inc., Marion, VA; *Int'l,* pg. 843
Ramos, Rick, Mgr.-F & I Sls.--Fairway Ford, Inc., Greenville, SC; *U.S. Private,* pg. 392
Ramsay, Paddy, Dir.-Natl. Sls.--KTAR-AM, Phoenix, AZ; *U.S. Public,* pg. 1344
Ramsay, Paddy, Dir.-Natl. Sls.--KKLT-FM, Phoenix, AZ; *U.S. Public,* pg. 1344
Ramsey, Jim, Sales Mgr.--Dillard, A ResourceNet International Company, Charlotte, NC; *U.S. Public,* pg. 902
Rance, Michael J., V.P.-Sales & Mktg. Bus. Dev.--ICI Pharmaceuticals Group, Wilmington, DE; *Int'l,* pg. 664
Rand, S., Dir.-Sls.--Comet, Rickmansworth, United Kingdom; *Int'l,* pg. 733
Randall, James W., V.P.-Sls.--Symix Systems, Inc., Columbus, OH; *U.S. Public,* pg. 1546
Randazzo, B., Dir.-Export Sls.--W.W. Grainger, Inc., Lincolnshire, IL; *U.S. Public,* pg. 758
Randazzo, Gary W., V.P.-Sls.--Houston Chronicle, Houston, TX; *U.S. Private,* pg. 517
Randle, Alan, Dir.-Sls.--Dowty O Rings & Actuation Polymers, Qormi, Malta; *Int'l,* pg. 1338
Randon, Jean-Louis, Mgr.-Sls.--Groupe GAN, Paris, France; *Int'l,* pg. 563
Raneiro, Frank A., Gen. Mgr.-Sls.--Magnetic Metals Corp., Camden, NJ; *U.S. Private,* pg. 560
Ranger, G., Dir.-Sls. & Mktg.--BBA Friction LTD., Cleckheaton, United Kingdom; *Int'l,* pg. 112
Ranieri, Tony, V.P.-Sls.--Carrier Corporation, Indianapolis, IN; *U.S. Public,* pg. 1689
Ranieri, Tony, V.P.-Sls./Carrier--Carrier Corp., Indianapolis, IN; *U.S. Public,* pg. 1690
Rankin, Roberta, Sls. Consultant--Jordon Commercial Refrigerator Co., Philadelphia, PA; *U.S. Private,* pg. 599
Rankin, Timothy J., V.P.-Sls./Canada--FCA International Ltd., Westmount, Canada; *Int'l,* pg. 470
Ransom, Chris, Reg. V.P.-Central Sls.--American Freightways Corporation, Harrison, AR; *U.S. Public,* pg. 75
Rantama, Heikki, V.P.-Intl. Sls.--Fiskars Power Systems, Espoo, Finland; *Int'l,* pg. 127
Ranzinger, Rick, V.P.-Sls. & Mktg.--Lyman Products Corporation, Middletown, CT; *U.S. Private,* pg. 683
Rapaport, Steve, Exec. V.P.-Sls. Opers.--Paramount Pictures Corporation, Los Angeles, CA; *U.S. Private,* pg. 776
Raper, Bryant, V.P.-Sls.--Greensboro Sales, Greensboro, NC; *U.S. Public,* pg. 611
Rapp, James F., Exec. V.P.-Intl. Sls.--Plasti-Kote Company Inc., Medina, OH; *U.S. Private,* pg. 870
Rappaport, Neil J., V.P.-Sls.--Vitesse Semiconductor Corporation, Camarillo, CA; *U.S. Public,* pg. 1723
Raptes, Jim, Mgr.-Custom Sls.--Deco Products Co., Decorah, IA; *U.S. Private,* pg. 320
Rarpal, Ricardo, Dir.-Sls.--Sudamtex de Uruguay, S.A., Montevideo, Uruguay; *Int'l,* pg. 1304
Rasen, S., Mgr.-Fleet Sls.--Toyota Norge A/S, Drammen, Norway; *Int'l,* pg. 1414
Rashilla, Richard, V.P.-Sls.--A.O. Smith Electrical Products Company, Tipp City, OH; *U.S. Public,* pg. 1477
Rashkovsky, Gary, V.P.-Intl. Sls. & Mktg.--Del Global Technologies, Valhalla, NY; *U.S. Public,* pg. 493
Rasimas, Ken, Mgr.-Export Sls.--Okuma America Corporation, Charlotte, NC; *Int'l,* pg. 1001
Raskin, Linda, Dir.-Sls. Programs--Dahlberg, Inc., Golden Valley, MN; *U.S. Public,* pg. 194
Rasmmen, Lars, Dir.-Sls.--DAB-Silkeborg a/s, Silkeborg, Denmark; *Int'l,* pg. 350
Rasmussen, Lisa, Dir.-Sls.--William Morrow & Co., Inc., New York, NY; *U.S. Private,* pg. 515
Rasmussen, Liza, Dir.-Sls.--Avon Books, New York, NY; *U.S. Private,* pg. 515
Rasmussen, Pen-Allan, V.P.-Sls./W. Region--Thorn Apple Valley, Inc., Southfield, MI; *U.S. Public,* pg. 1602
Ratajckyk, Scott, Sls. Coord.--Badger Equipment Co., Winona, MN; *U.S. Private,* pg. 102
Ratcliffe, E.E., Mgr.-Sls.--Longview Fibre Co. Western Container Div., Yakima, WA; *U.S. Public,* pg. 1014
Rath, Robert, Dir.-Sls.--Heller Bros. Packing Corp., Winter Garden, FL; *U.S. Private,* pg. 520
Rathbun, Dave, Mgr.-Grp. Sls.--Stratton Corporation, Stratton Mountain, VT; *Int'l,* pg. 685
Rathjen, Dennis, Treas.--Vogler Motor Company, Inc., Carbondale, IL; *U.S. Private,* pg. 1143
Ratkey, Ron, V.P.-Sls. & Mktg.--Access Industries, Grandview, MO; *U.S. Private,* pg. 11
Ratkus, Ted, Sr. V.P.-Sls.--Shorewood Packaging Corporation of Virginia-Williamsburg Operations, Newport News, VA; *U.S. Public,* pg. 1468

Ratkus, Theodore S., Sr. V.P.-Sls. & Mktg.--Shorewood Packaging Corporation, New York, NY; *U.S. Public*, pg. 1468

Ratterman, Debby, Exec. Coord-Sls.--Stegner Food Products Co., Cincinnati, OH; *U.S. Private*, pg. 1039

Ratterman, Frank, Mgr.-Gen. & Natl. Sls.--WDSU Television, Inc., New Orleans, LA; *U.S. Public*, pg. 1344

Rau, Gregory, V.P.-Sls.--Multi-Clean Inc., Shoreview, MN; *Int'l*, pg. 587

Rauch, James, Dir.-Western Sls.--M & C Remco Tape Products Co., North Hollywood, CA; *U.S. Private*, pg. 684

Rauch, Marc F., Pres.-Sls.--Rauch Industries, Inc., Gastonia, NC; *U.S. Private*, pg. 1061

Rauchwerger, Jerry, V.P.-Intl. Sls. & Mktg.--Inverness Corp., Fair Lawn, NJ; *U.S. Private*, pg. 574

Rauscher, Craig D., Mgr.-Mktg.--Stewart-Warner South Wind Corp., Indianapolis, IN; *Int'l*, pg. 127

Rauss, William G., V.P.-Sls. & Mktg.--Edwin B. Stimpson Company, Inc., Bayport, NY; *U.S. Private*, pg. 1043

Raven, David E., V.P.-Sls. Admin.--NBT Bancorp Inc., Norwich, NY; *U.S. Public*, pg. 1144

Rawlins, Candi, Gen. Mgr.-Sls.--Six Flags Over Georgia, Austell, GA; *U.S. Public*, pg. 1612

Rawlins, Robert, Dir.-Sls.--Sentinel Consumer Products, Inc., Mentor, OH; *U.S. Private*, pg. 984

Rawlinson, John T., V.P.-Sls. & Mktg.--Renold, Inc., Westfield, NY; *Int'l*, pg. 1104

Ray, Brian, Dir.-Eastern Regional Sls.--Lynx Golf, Inc., City of Industry, CA; *U.S. Private*, pg. 684

Ray, Diane P., V.P.-Retail Sls./Washington D.C.--Tiffany & Co., New York, NY; *U.S. Public*, pg. 1608

Ray, Lisa D., Dir.-Sls. & Mktg.--Ray Communications, Inc., Kill Devil Hills, NC; *U.S. Private*, pg. 911

Ray, Preston, V.P.-Sls.--Aurora Casket Company, Aurora, IN; *U.S. Private*, pg. 99

Ray, V.E., Dir.-Sls. & Mktg.--Flowserve Corporation, Foundry Div., Dayton, OH; *U.S. Public*, pg. 658

Rayl, Steve, V.P.-Activewear Sls.--Fruit of the Loom, Inc., Chicago, IL; *U.S. Public*, pg. 685

Raymond, Carolyn, Sls. Admin.--Wolfer Printing Company, City of Commerce, CA; *U.S. Private*, pg. 1186

Read, R., Div. Mgr.-Commercial Sls.--Meadow Lea Foods Ltd., Mascot, Australia; *Int'l*, pg. 555

Read, Rock, Mgr.-Sls.--U.N. Alloy Steel Div., Houston, TX; *Int'l*, pg. 1001

Readal, Tom, V.P.-Export Sls.--Penreco, Karns City, PA; *U.S. Public*, pg. 1273

Ready, Jon E., V.P.-Sls. & Mktg.--Sunshine Biscuits, Inc., Woodbridge, NJ; *U.S. Private*, pg. 434

Ready, Jon E., V.P.-Sls. & Mktg.--Sunshine Biscuits, Inc., Woodbridge, NJ; *U.S. Public*, pg. 657

Reantaso, Oscar V., V.P. & Gen Mgr.--Benguet Management Corporation, Manila, Philippines; *Int'l*, pg. 186

Reap, Jeff, Dir.-Sls. & Mktg.--Keith Smith Company, Hot Springs National Park, AR; *U.S. Private*, pg. 1008

Reardon, Patrick C., V.P.-Sls./Hydraulic Sys.--Commercial Intertech Corp., Youngstown, OH; *U.S. Public*, pg. 411

Reaume, Jack, Coord.-Mktg.& Sls.--Air Control Products, Roxboro, NC; *U.S. Public*, pg. 556

Reber, Bill, Sls. Devel.--Beechmont Investments Inc., Cincinnati, OH; *U.S. Private*, pg. 129

Reber, Bill, Mgr.-Sls.--Beechmont Porsche Audi Inc., Cincinnati, OH; *U.S. Private*, pg. 129

Reber, Bill, Mgr.-Sls.--Beechmont Hyundai, Cincinnati, OH; *U.S. Private*, pg. 129

Reber, Rebecca K., Coord.-Sls. Projects--Deck House Inc., Acton, MA; *U.S. Private*, pg. 320

Recke, Judith G., Dir.-Sls.--Merriam-Webster, Inc., Springfield, MA; *U.S. Private*, pg. 375

Rector, Harry, Sr. V.P.-Sls. & Mktg.--Southern Bag Corporation, Madison, MS; *U.S. Private*, pg. 1015

Redd, Shari, Mgr.-Circulation--The Arkansas City Daily Traveler, Arkansas City, KS; *U.S. Private*, pg. 995

Reddy, Colin, V.P.-Sls./ECO--EA Industries, West Long Branch, NJ; *U.S. Public*, pg. 541

Reder, Thomas J., V.P.-Sls. & Mktg.--Fairbanks Morse Engine Division, Beloit, WI; *U.S. Public*, pg. 401

Redetzke, Joe, Mgr.-Sls.-Agr. Prods. Div.--Krause Plow Corp., Hutchinson, KS; *U.S. Private*, pg. 635

Redfeld, Jean, Asst. V.P.-Retail Mktg.--DTE Energy Company, Detroit, MI; *U.S. Public*, pg. 475

Redhouse, John W., V.P.-Sls. & Mktg.--Henkels & McCoy, Inc., Blue Bell, PA; *U.S. Private*, pg. 522

Redinger, Ralph, V.P.-Sls.--CMI International Inc., Southfield, MI; *U.S. Private*, pg. 195

Redlin, Martin N., Sr. V.P.-Mktg. & Sls.--Broan Mfg. Co., Inc., Hartford, WI; *U.S. Public*, pg. 1193

Redman, Ray, Dir.-Sls. & Distr.--Logan Corporation, Huntington, WV; *U.S. Private*, pg. 672

Redmond, John, Mgr.-Sls.--Hopkinsville Milling Co., Hopkinsville, KY; *U.S. Private*, pg. 538

Redmond, John, Pres. & Chief Exec. Officer--Hoover Group, Inc., Alpharetta, GA; *U.S. Private*, pg. 538

Redmond, John M., Reg. Mgr.--Environment/One Corporation, Niskayuna, NY; *U.S. Public*, pg. 586

Redshaw, John, V.P.-Sls. & Mktg.--Exolon-Esk Company, Tonawanda, NY; *U.S. Public*, pg. 600

Reece, Greg, V.P.-Natl. Sls.--Saladmaster, Arlington, TX; *U.S. Private*, pg. 961

Reece, Walter, V.P.-Sls.--Bachmann Industries, Inc., Philadelphia, PA; *U.S. Private*, pg. 109

Reeck, Larry, V.P.-Mktg. & Sls.--Dean Pickle & Specialty Products Co., Green Bay, WI; *U.S. Public*, pg. 490

Reed, David, Mgr.-Natl. Sls.--Western States Envelope Co., Milwaukee, WI; *U.S. Private*, pg. 1168

Reed, Glenn, V.P.-Sls.--800-FLOWERS, Inc., Westbury, NY; *U.S. Private*, pg. 366

Reed, John, Mgr.-Area Sls.--Gensym Corporation, Philadelphia Area Office, Trevose, PA; *U.S. Public*, pg. 731

Reed, Kenneth, V.P.-Sls. & Mktg.--TriEnda Corporation, Portage, WI; *U.S. Private*, pg. 1103

Reed, Mark E., Sr. V.P.-Sls. & Mktg. Service--In Focus Systems, Inc., Wilsonville, OR; *U.S. Public*, pg. 873

Reed, Phil, Dir.-Sls.--Litton Poly-Scientific, Blacksburg, VA; *U.S. Public*, pg. 1003

Reed, Raymond, Gen. Mgr.-Sls. & Treas.--Reed Motors, Inc., Orlando, FL; *U.S. Private*, pg. 916

Reed, William, V.P.-Sls. & Mktg.--C.P. Clare Corporation, Beverly, MA; *U.S. Public*, pg. 382

Reeder, Lloyd, V.P.-Sls.--Greenlee Lighting Inc., Carrollton, TX; *U.S. Public*, pg. 971

Reeder, Robert, Mgr.-Natl. Sls.--Video Display Corporation, Tucker, GA; *U.S. Public*, pg. 1720

Reefman, R., Dir.-Sls. & Mktg.--Holmatro Industrial & Rescue Equipment, Raamsdonksveer, Netherlands; *Int'l*, pg. 632

Reese, J. Barrett, Grp. V.P.-Sls. & Mktg./Expanded Shale & Clay--Texas Industries, Inc., Dallas, TX; *U.S. Public*, pg. 1585

Reeves, Bob, V.P.-Gen. Sls.--The Gibson-Homans Company, Twinsburg, OH; *U.S. Private*, pg. 451

Reeves, Richard, V.P.-Sls.-Tapecoat Div.--T C Manufacturing Company, Inc., Evanston, IL; *U.S. Private*, *pg. 1062*

Reeves, Richard, V.P. & Dir.-Sls.--Tapecoat Company, Evanston, IL; *U.S. Private*, pg. 1062

Reeves, Robert S., Sr. V.P.-Sls.--Kerr Group, Inc., Lancaster, PA; *U.S. Public*, pg. 952

Regan, Joseph, Sr. V.P.-Sls. & Mktg.--Solectron Corporation, Milpitas, CA; *U.S. Public*, pg. 1483

Regan, Tim, Mgr.-Natl. Sls.--Goddess Bra Company, East Boston, MA; *U.S. Private*, pg. 458

Reggin, Elmer, Dir.-Sls.--Minolta Corporation, Ramsey, NJ; *Int'l*, pg. 869

Regier, Jackie, Bus. & Circulation Mgr.--The York News-Times, York, NE; *U.S. Private*, pg. 995

Rehm, Alfred R., V.P.-Sls.--Standard Commercial Tobacco Co., Inc., Wilson, NC; *U.S. Public*, pg. 1502

Rehmer, Carl, Mgr.-Sls.--Williams Patent Crusher and Pulverizer Co., Saint Louis, MO; *U.S. Private*, pg. 1178

Rehor, James, V.P.-Sls.--BRW Paper Co., Inc., Farmers Branch, TX; *U.S. Private*, pg. 467

Reich, William M., Mgr.-Publications--L3 Communications Narda-Microwave Div., Hauppauge, NY; *U.S. Private*, pg. 638

Reichbach, Joseph, Sr. V.P.-Sls. & Mktg.--Merix Corporation, Forest Grove, OR; *U.S. Public*, pg. 1096

Reichel, Jeff, Mgr.-Sls.--Mallet & Co., Carnegie, PA; *U.S. Private*, pg. 698

Reichert, Charles, Reg. Sls. Mgr.--Serfilco, Ltd., Northbrook, IL; *U.S. Private*, pg. 985

Reid, Andrew W., V.P.-Sls.--Moore-Handley, Inc., Pelham, AL; *U.S. Public*, pg. 1128

Reid, Andy, V.P.-Sls.--Biscayne Apparel Inc., Clifton, NJ; *U.S. Public*, pg. 232

Reid, Bob, Exec. V.P.-Mktg. & Sls.--Outdoor Technologies Group, Spirit Lake, IA; *U.S. Private*, pg. 822

Reid, Bob, V.P.-Sls.--Abu Garcia Inc., Spirit Lake, IA; *U.S. Private*, pg. 822

Reid, Bob, V.P.-Sls., Perry Menswear--Perry Ellis, New York, NY; *U.S. Public*, pg. 1429

Reid, Brooks, Mgr.-Natl. Sls.--TimeMed Labeling Systems, Inc., Burr Ridge, IL; *U.S. Private*, pg. 1087

Reid, Edward L., Dir.-Natl. Franchise Sls.--Lawn Doctor Inc., Holmdel, NJ; *U.S. Private*, pg. 653

Reid, J. William, V.P.-Sls. & Mktg.--Del Pharmaceuticals, Inc., Farmingdale, NY; *U.S. Public*, pg. 494

Reid, Odis, V.P.-Franchise Devel.--Mitsubishi Motor Sales of America, Inc., Cypress, CA; *Int'l*, pg. 875

Reid, Phil, V.P.-Res. Sls. & Mktg.--Season-All Industries, Inc., Indiana, PA; *Int'l*, pg. 267

Reid, Richard, Dir.-Sls. & Mktg.--Stadium Limited, Hartlepool, United Kingdom; *Int'l*, pg. 1293

Reider, Thomas D., V.P.-Domestic Sls. & Mktg.--Ruslander & Sons, Inc., Buffalo, NY; *U.S. Private*, pg. 952

Reidie, Dave, V.P.-Reader Sls. & Svc.--The Edmonton Journal, Edmonton, Canada; *Int'l*, pg. 631

Reifenhauser, Ulrich, Sls. Mgr.--Reifenhauser GmbH & Co. Maschinenfabrik, Troisdorf, Germany; *Int'l*, pg. 1101

Reigle, Douglas, V.P.-Eurasia--Regal Ware, Inc., Kewaskum, WI; *U.S. Private*, pg. 917

Reiland, Richard, V.P.-Sls. & Mktg.--Worcester Controls Corp., Marlborough, MA; *Int'l*, pg. 128

Reilly, Dave, Dir.-Mktg. & Sls.--Schleicher & Schuell, Inc., Keene, NH; *Int'l*, pg. 1206

Reilly, Jonathan D., V.P.-Parts Sls. & Service--Pandrol Jackson, Inc., Ludington, MI; *Int'l*, pg. 280

Reilly, Terry, Mgr.-Adv. Sls.--Iowa Farmer Today, Cedar Rapids, IA; *U.S. Private*, pg. 442

Reilly, Thomas P., V.P.-Sls. & Mktg.--Rockbestos-Suprenant Cable Corp., Clinton, MA; *U.S. Private*, pg. 938

Reiman, Stephen W., Pres., Chief Exec. Officer & Mgr.-Sls.--W.A. Roosevelt Co., La Crosse, WI; *U.S. Private*, pg. 943

Reimann, Joachim, V.P.-Sls.--Koenig & Bauer-Albert AG, Wurzburg, Germany; *Int'l*, pg. 742

Reimer, Robert I., Mgr.-Mktg. & Sls.--Escast, Inc., Addison, IL; *U.S. Public*, pg. 612

Reinhardt, Mary, V.P.-Sls.--Fairfield Williamsburg, Williamsburg, VA; *U.S. Public*, pg. 611

Reinhart, Ed, V.P.-Sls.- CPG--Tree Top, Inc., Selah, WA; *U.S. Private*, pg. 1098

Reinke, Kenneth J., V.P.-Sls.--Rolled Alloys, Inc., Temperance, MI; *U.S. Private*, pg. 941

Reinke, Steve, V.P.-Sls.--Berlin Industries, Inc., Carol Stream, IL; *U.S. Private*, pg. 136

Reis, Antonio C., Div. Mgr.-Natl Sls.--TAP Air Portugal, Newark, NJ; *Int'l*, pg. 1418

Reis, R.J., Exec. V.P.--Serigraph, Inc., West Bend, WI; *U.S. Private*, pg. 985

Reiss, Myrna, Dir.-Sls. & Mktg.--Value City Department Stores, Inc., Columbus, OH; *U.S. Private*, pg. 972

Reissig, Robert, Gen. Mgr.--Genzyme Diagnostics, Medix Biotech, San Carlos, CA; *U.S. Public*, pg. 733

Reitan, David, Reg. Mgr.-Sls.--PENCO-Nebraska, Omaha, NE; *Int'l*, pg. 1508

Reiter, Douglas, Sr. V.P.-Sls. & Mktg., Dallas--Safeguard Business Systems, Inc., Fort Washington, PA; *U.S. Private*, pg. 960

Reiter, Othman, Mgr.-Natl. Sls.--Kodak S.A., Lausanne, Switzerland; *U.S. Public*, pg. 554

Reith, Ronald J., Exec. V.P.-Mktg. & Sls.--Merck Medco Managed Care, Independence, OH; *U.S. Public*, pg. 1091

Reitmeier, Debbie, Asst. V.P.-Mktg. & Sls.--Key Pharmaceuticals, Kenilworth, NJ; *U.S. Public*, pg. 1438

Reitz, Bonnie, Sr. V.P.-Mktg. & Sls. Distr.--Continental Airlines, Houston, TX; *U.S. Public*, pg. 439

Rem, Steen, V.P.-Sls. & Mktg.--International Pharmaceuticals, Oslo, Norway; *U.S. Public*, pg. 58

Rembold, Bill, V.P.-Sls.--Patterson Frozen Foods, Inc., Patterson, CA; *U.S. Private*, pg. 843

Remi, Charles, Dir.-Sls.--Liberty Paper & Bag Co., Auburn Hills, MI; *Int'l*, pg. 233

Remied, Charles, Reg. Sls. Mgr.--Serfilco, Ltd., Northbrook, IL; *U.S. Private*, pg. 985

Remington, John, Mgr.-Midwest Sls.--Peerless Tube Company, Bloomfield, NJ; *U.S. Public*, pg. 1269

Remington, Larry, V.P. & Gen. Mgr.-Foot Locker U.S.--Foot Locker, New York, NY; *U.S. Public*, pg. 1777

Remus, Frank, Sr. V.P.-Sls.--Dixon Ticonderoga Company, Heathrow, FL; *U.S. Public*, pg. 514

Renalda, Roy, Exec. V.P.-Sls. & Mktg.--The Faxon Company, Inc., Westwood, MA; *Int'l*, pg. 385

Renberg, Michael, Dir.-Circulation--Lee Enterprises, Incorporated, Davenport, IA; *U.S. Public*, pg. 983

Rendon, Ricardo, Dir.-Sls.--Johnson & Johnson del Ecuador S.A., Guayaquil, Ecuador; *U.S. Public*, pg. 930

Rene, Linda, V.P. & Dir.-Primetime & Late Night Sls.--CBS Television Network, New York, NY; *U.S. Public*, pg. 274

Renich, Tom, Dir.-Sls. & Mktg.--Peabody TecTank, Inc., Parsons, KS; *U.S. Public*, pg. 1477

Renkens, Rick, V.P.-Natl. Sls.--Barton Brands, Ltd., Chicago, IL; *U.S. Public*, pg. 300

Renmert, Rory, V.P.-Sls.--Meadowcraft, Inc., Birmingham, AL; *U.S. Private*, pg. 725

Rennels, Jack, V.P.-Mktg.--Emkay, Inc., Itasca, IL; *U.S. Private*, pg. 374

Rennick, Tom, Natl. Sls. Mgr.--CASI-RUSCO Inc., Boca Raton, FL; *U.S. Private*, pg. 218

Rent, John, Mgr.-Prod. Sls. & Mktg.--Lukens Steel Company, Coatesville, PA; *U.S. Public*, pg. 1020

Rentschler, Karen, Mgr.-Reg. Sls.--Automotive News, Detroit, MI; *U.S. Private*, pg. 284

Rentzel, Becky, Admin.-Sls. & Mktg.--York Wallcoverings Inc., York, PA; *U.S. Private*, pg. 1196

Reodriquez, Ed, V.P.-Sls Grp.--Orbit Semiconductor, Inc., Sunnyvale, CA; *U.S. Private*, pg. 819

Replane, Chuck, V.P.-Sls.--Automotive Products, Elkhart, IN; *U.S. Public*, pg. 285

Replogle, Robert P., V.P. & Dir.-Intl. Sls.--Met-Pro Corporation, Harleysville, PA; *U.S. Public*, pg. 1100

Repp, Gordon, Mgr.-Real Estate--Outboard Marine Corporation, Waukegan, IL; *U.S. Private*, pg. 478

Reppe, Svern, V.P.-Sls.--TiMar Seafood A/S, Trondheim, Norway; *Int'l*, pg. 1390

Reppeto, Jack, V.P.-Sls.--The Royal China & Porcelain Companies Inc., Moorestown, NJ; *U.S. Private*, pg. 948

Resendez, Gilbert, V.P.-Sls. & Mktg.--Monrovia Nursery Co., Azusa, CA; *U.S. Private*, pg. 757

Resnick, Dennis A., V.P.-Sls. & Mktg.--R & R Marketing, West Caldwell, NJ; *U.S. Private*, pg. 902

Resnick, Kevin, V.P.-Sls. Video Games--Interact Accessories, Inc., Hunt Valley, MD; *U.S. Public*, pg. 1369

Restivo, Joseph J., Mgr.-Intl. Sls.--Gaffney-Kroese Electrical Supply Corp., Rahway, NJ; *U.S. Private*, pg. 437

Restivo, Pete, V.P.-Sls.--L & S Bearing Co., Oklahoma City, OK; *U.S. Public*, pg. 970

Restivo, Tom, V.P.-Sls.--The Pilot Pen Corp. of America, Trumbull, CT; *Int'l*, pg. 1057

Restivo, Vincent D., V.P.-Domestic Sls.--Allied Mineral Products, Inc., Columbus, OH; *U.S. Private*, pg. 39

Retsmas, Jim, Mgr.-Sls., Men's Wear--Pendleton Woolen Mills, Inc., Portland, OR; *U.S. Private*, pg. 848

Retter, B., V.P.-Sls. (Motorcycles)--Yuasa-Exide, Inc., Reading, PA; *Int'l*, pg. 1522

Retuerto, Jorge, Mgr.-Intl. Sls.--Theochem Labs., Inc., Tampa, FL; *U.S. Private*, pg. 1079

Reuss, Penny, Dir.-Sls.--Ke-Master, Dover, DE; *U.S. Private*, *pg. 1053*

Rewey, Robert L., Jr., Grp. V.P.-Mktg., Sls. & Service--Ford Motor Company, Dearborn, MI; *U.S. Public*, pg. 661

Reyes, Inez S., Sls. Dir.-GMA--La Tondena Distillers, Inc., Manila, Philippines; *Int'l*, pg. 785

Reyes, Nelson, Dir.-Sls.--KYB Industries Inc., Franklin, IN; *Int'l*, pg. 727

Reyna, Rodulfo, Sls. Mgr.-NutraSweet--Monsanto Argentina S.A.I.C., Buenos Aires, Argentina; *U.S. Public*, pg. 1125

Reynolds, Curt, V.P.-Mktg. & Sls.--Comlinear Corporation, Fort Collins, CO; *U.S. Public*, pg. 1160

Reynolds, Donald, V.P.-Natl. Sls.--ABF Freight System, Inc., Fort Smith, AR; *U.S. Public*, pg. 130

Reynolds, Gary, Sr. V.P.-Sls. & Mktg.--General Electric Capital Railcar Services, Chicago, IL; *U.S. Public*, pg. 712

Reynolds, Gary, Sls. Dir.--Micro-Precision Operations, Berne, IN; *U.S. Public*, pg. 1589

Reynolds, Hugh M., Mgr.-Sls.--Darlington Veneer Company, Darlington, SC; *U.S. Private*, pg. 311

Reynolds, Jean M., V.P.-Sls. & Mktg.--BPI Inc., Kent, WA; *U.S. Public*, pg. 772

Reynolds, John, Mgr.-Institutional--Brown Brothers Harriman & Co., New York, NY; *U.S. Private*, pg. 173

Reynolds, Mike, Mgr.-Natl. Sls.--IPC-International Parts Corp., Chicago, IL; *U.S. Public*, pg. 1766

Reynolds, Randall, Exec. V.P.-Retail Investment Sls.--Compass Bank, Birmingham, AL; *U.S. Public*, pg. 418

Reynolds, Robert D., Pres.-Sls. Grp. & Sr. V.P.--Newsprint South, Inc., Jackson, MS; *U.S. Private*, pg. 797
Reynolds, Sandra, Mgr.-Sls. Admin.--Scott Aviation, Lancaster, NY; *U.S. Public*, pg. 622
Rhees, Herb, V.P.-Sls.--Champion Pneumatic Machinery Co., Inc., Princeton, IL; *U.S. Private*, pg. 228
Rhoads, Steve, Mgr.-Sls.--Watlow Industries, Inc., Hannibal, MO; *U.S. Private*, pg. 1153
Rhodaberger, W.R., V.P.-Sales--Ervin Industries, Inc., Ann Arbor, MI; *U.S. Private*, pg. 382
Rhodes, Amy, V.P. & Dir.-Mktg. & Sls.--Little, Brown & Co., New York, NY; *U.S. Public*, pg. 1612
Rhodes, David L., Jr., Sr. V.P.-Sls. & Mktg.--Unisource Worldwide, Inc., Berwyn, PA; *U.S. Public*, pg. 1670
Rhodes, Steve, V.P.-Mktg. & Sls.--Paramount Fitness Corp., Los Angeles, CA; *U.S. Private*, pg. 838
Rhodes, Tim, Mgr.-Sls. & Promo.--Southland Corp.-Prairies Division, Calgary, Canada; *Int'l*, pg. 694
Rhyne, Dot, Dir.-Adv. & Sls. Promo.--A.H. Belo Corporation, Dallas, TX; *U.S. Public*, pg. 209
Riazzi, Richard, V.P.-Mktg. & Sls.--Idaho Power Company, Boise, ID; *U.S. Public*, pg. 861
Ricard, Michael J., V.P.-Sls.--Selfix, Inc., Chicago, IL; *U.S. Public*, pg. 832
Riccato, Julio, Mgr.-Sls. Promo.--CIBA-GEIGY Uruguaya S.A., Montevideo, Uruguay; *Int'l*, pg. 980
Ricci, Leo, Mgr.-Div. Sls.--AP North American Aftermarket Division, Goldsboro, NC; *U.S. Private*, pg. 230
Ricci, R., V.P.-Sls. & Mktg.--National Vendors, Bridgeton, MO; *U.S. Public*, pg. 457
Ricciardi, Robert J., Exec. V.P.-Sls. & Acquisitions--Enesco Corporation, Itasca, IL; *U.S. Public*, pg. 1508
Riccio, Bruce, Sr. V.P.-Sls.-Hasbro Games Grp.--Hasbro, Inc., Pawtucket, RI; *U.S. Public*, pg. 797
Riccio, Bruce, Sr. V.P.-Sls.--Milton Bradley Company, East Longmeadow, MA; *U.S. Public*, pg. 797
Riccioni, Jerry T., V.P.-Retail/Intl. Sls.--Old World Industries, Inc., Northbrook, IL; *U.S. Private*, pg. 814
Ricco, Michelle, Div. Mgr.--Tekra Corporation, New Berlin, WI; *U.S. Private*, pg. 1073
Rice, Gerald, Dir.-Sls. & Mktg.--Danfoss Fluid Power, Racine, WI; *Int'l*, pg. 377
Rice, Jerry, Sls. Mgr.--Northland Evergreens, Inc., West Olive, MI; *U.S. Private*, pg. 60
Rice, John F., V.P.-Mktg. & Sls.--Kevlin Corporation, Wilmington, MA; *U.S. Public*, pg. 953
Rice, Pete, Mgr.-Natl. Sls.--San Diego Union Tribune, San Diego, CA; *U.S. Private*, pg. 275
Rice, Robert, Mgr.-Sls.--Kern's Bakeries, Incorporated, Knoxville, TN; *U.S. Public*, pg. 547
Rice, Roland, V.P.-North American Sls.--Diamond Multimedia Systems, Inc., San Jose, CA; *U.S. Public*, pg. 505
Rich, Paul, Mgr.-Sls.--Milgray/Cleveland, Inc., Cleveland, OH; *U.S. Public*, pg. 206
Richard, Jean, V.P.-Sls.--Sico Inc., Longueuil, Canada; *Int'l*, pg. 1239
Richard, Mark, V.P.-Sls. & Mktg.--J.W. Allen & Company, Wheeling, IL; *U.S. Private*, pg. 37
Richards, Craig, Sr. V.P.-Sls. & Mktg.--Proteon, Inc., Westborough, MA; *U.S. Public*, pg. 1336
Richards, Denton, V.P.-Retail Sls.--Andis Company, Sturtevant, WI; *U.S. Private*, pg. 73
Richards, Doug, V.P.-Mktg. & Sls.--Weibel Winery, Lodi, CA; *U.S. Private*, pg. 1159
Richards, Grant, Mgr.-Sls. & Promo.--Southland Corp.-British Columbia Division, Burnaby, Canada; *Int'l*, pg. 694
Richards, J.C., V.P.-Mktg. & Sls.--Frog Switch & Manufacturing Company, Carlisle, PA; *U.S. Private*, pg. 429
Richards, Lee, Asst. V.P.-Southwire Tech. Sls .--Southwire Company, Carrollton, GA; *U.S. Private*, pg. 1019
Richards, M.A., Mgr.-Natl. Sls. & Mktg.--Crane Australia Pty. Ltd., Saint Marys, Australia; *U.S. Public*, pg. 457
Richards, Phil, V.P.-Sls.--Alliance Semiconductor Corp., San Jose, CA; *U.S. Public*, pg. 47
Richards, Ron, V.P.-Sls.--Asahi/America, Inc., Malden, MA; *U.S. Public*, pg. 137
Richardson, Bill, Mgr.-Sls.--N.G. Bailey & Co. Ltd.-Glasgow Branch, Glasgow, United Kingdom; *Int'l*, pg. 132
Richardson, Cantey, Sr. V.P.-Sls & Mktg.--Diversco, Inc., Spartanburg, SC; *U.S. Private*, pg. 336
Richardson, Don, Sr. V.P.-Sls.-Home Electronics--Pioneer Electronics (USA) Inc., Long Beach, CA; *Int'l*, pg. 1058
Richardson, F. Shelton, Jr., Chief Fin. Officer & V.P.--Curtis Mathes Holding Corp., Dallas, TX; *U.S. Public*, pg. 1057
Richardson, Jeff, Mgr.-Sls.--PENCO-Kansas, Topeka, KS; *Int'l*, pg. 1508
Richardson, Jim, V.P.-Sls. & Mktg.--Richardson Bros. Co. Div., Sheboygan Falls, WI; *U.S. Private*, pg. 929
Richardson, Jim, V.P.-Sls. & Mktg.--Richardson's Furniture Emporium, Sheboygan Falls, WI; *U.S. Private*, pg. 929
Richardson, Robert L., Mgr.-Sls.--Pepper-Lawson, Katy, TX; *U.S. Private*, pg. 851
Richardson, W. Russel, V.P.-Sls.--Amstore Corporation, Muskegon, MI; *U.S. Private*, pg. 68
Richey, Alvan E., Jr., V.P.-Sls. & Mktg.--NCI Building Systems, Inc., Houston, TX; *U.S. Public*, pg. 1145
Richman, Joshua V., Pres. & Chief Exec. Officer--Straw Hat Cooperative Corp., Dublin, CA; *U.S. Private*, pg. 1046
Richman, Steve, V.P.-Mktg. & Sls.--The Murray Ohio Mfg. Co., Brentwood, TN; *Int'l*, pg. 1397
Richstein, Ernest, Mgr.-Sls.--Tracer Products, Westbury, NY; *U.S. Private*, pg. 1024
Richter, Edward F., V.P.-Sls.--Hostmark Management Group, Rolling Meadows, IL; *U.S. Private*, pg. 541
Richter, George, V.P.-Sls. & Mktg./Meats Grp.--Farmland Industries, Inc., Kansas City, MO; *U.S. Private*, pg. 395
Rickershzuser, Peter J., V.P.-Sls.--Southern Pacific Rail Corporation, San Francisco, CA; *U.S. Public*, pg. 1668
Rickert, Thomas M., Dir.-Adv. Sls.--Catholic Digest, Saint Paul, MN; *U.S. Private*, pg. 220
Riddel, T.O., V.P.-Sls.--Alva/Amco Pharmacal Companies, Inc., Chicago, IL; *U.S. Private*, pg. 47
Riddle, John, V.P.-Sls.--Tuscarora Yarns Inc., Mount Pleasant, NC; *U.S. Private*, pg. 1110
Riddle, Larry, V.P.-Sls. & Mktg.--Ikegami Electronics (U.S.A.), Inc., Maywood, NJ; *Int'l*, pg. 660
Riddle, Richard, Mgr.-Mktg. & Sls.--TFX Medical Inc., Jaffrey, NH; *U.S. Public*, pg. 1570
Ridenour, Glen, V.P.-Sls.--Bushnell Corporation, Overland Park, KS; *U.S. Private*, pg. 1191
Ridge, Colman, Reg. Dir.-Sls. & Mktg.--DHL International (Singapore) Pte. Ltd., Singapore, Singapore; *U.S. Private*, pg. 302
Ridge, Roy M., V.P.-Worldwide Bus. Devel.--Harris Corp. Broadcast Div., Quincy, IL; *U.S. Public*, pg. 791
Ridley, Dave, V.P.-Sls. & Mktg.--Southwest Airlines Co., Dallas, TX; *U.S. Public*, pg. 1493
Ridley, Gerald F., Mgr.-Sls.--Washington Manufacturing Company, Inc., Washington, IA; *U.S. Public*, pg. 612
Ridley, Steve M., Dir.-Sls. & Mktg.--Dowty Aerospace Hydraulics, Cheltenham, Cheltenham, United Kingdom; *Int'l*, pg. 1337
Riebe, Ron, Dir.-Mktg.--Fleming Company, Waukesha, WI; *U.S. Public*, pg. 653
Rieckman, John, V.P.-Sls.--Braden Manufacturing Co., Tulsa, OK; *U.S. Public*, pg. 924
Riedel, Hans, Exec. V.P.-Sls. & Mktg.--Porsche AG, Stuttgart, Germany; *Int'l*, pg. 1063
Riedel, James F., V.P.-Mktg. & Sls.--Webster Industries Inc., Tiffin, OH; *U.S. Private*, pg. 1157
Riefler, Scott, Dir.-Sls. & Mktg.--T.L. Smith Machine, Springville, NY; *U.S. Private*, pg. 1009
Riegel, William S., V.P.-Sls. & Mktg.--The Pacific Lumber Company, Scotia, CA; *U.S. Public*, pg. 1062
Rieger, Bob, Mgr.-Sls. Opers.--Check Technology Corporation, Minnetonka, MN; *U.S. Public*, pg. 342
Riegler, Ernie J., Mgr.-Sls.--Keystone Filter Division, Hatfield, PA; *U.S. Public*, pg. 1100
Riehle, Peter, V.P.-Mktg. & Sls.--Trumpf Inc., Farmington, CT; *U.S. Private*, pg. 1108
Riffle, Don, Sr. V.P.-Sls. & Mktg.--Sea Watch International, Ltd., Easton, MD; *Int'l*, pg. 928
Rigas, Denny A., Sr. V.P.-Mktg., Tech. & Sls.--Innovative Valve Technology, Inc., Houston, TX; *U.S. Public*, pg. 880
Rigby, Gary, Natl. Sls. Mgr.--Marketing Displays International, Farmington Hills, MI; *U.S. Private*, pg. 705
Rigg, Don, Mgr.-Mktg. & Sls. Support--Champion Laboratories, Inc., Albion, IL; *U.S. Private*, pg. 1113
Riggins, Tom, Dir.-Sls.-North America--BWI Kartridg Pak, Davenport, IA; *Int'l*, pg. 130
Riggs, Steven, V.P.-Sls. & Svcs.--Bently Nevada Corporation, Minden, NV; *U.S. Private*, pg. 134
Rigney, Thomas A., Dir.-Sls. Polyethylene--Millennium Petrochemicals, Inc., Cincinnati, OH; *Int'l*, pg. 594
Rigola, James, V.P.-Sls.--The Orr Felt Company, Piqua, OH; *U.S. Private*, pg. 820
Riguardi, Edward A., V.P.-Direct Sls. East--Wallace Computer Services, Inc., Lisle, IL; *U.S. Public*, pg. 1735
Rijks, R., Dir.-Holland Sls.--N.V. Johnson Wax Belgium S.A., Groot-Bijgaarden, Belgium; *U.S. Private*, pg. 593
Riley, Dennis, Sr. V.P.-Sls.--Superior Coffee and Foods, Bensenville, IL; *U.S. Public*, pg. 1434
Riley, Estuardo, Mgr.-Intl. Sls.--Aviateca, Guatemala, Guatemala; *Int'l*, pg. 102
Riley, Jeff, V.P.-Sls.--Hydraulics International, Inc., Chatsworth, CA; *U.S. Private*, pg. 551
Riley, Michael P., V.P.-Foodservice Sls.--The Smithfield Packing Co., Inc., Smithfield, VA; *U.S. Public*, pg. 1479
Riley, Robert, Dir.-Sls.--Fuji Graphic Arts Div., Itasca, IL; *Int'l*, pg. 524
Riley, Stephen, V.P.-Sls.--Boston Celtics Limited Partnership, Boston, MA; *U.S. Public*, pg. 246
Rinaldo, Carolyn, V.P.-Mktg. & Sls.--Marilyn Miglin, L.P., Chicago, IL; *U.S. Private*, pg. 745
Rinaldo, Michael, V.P.-Resale--Paramount Canada's Wonderland, Vaughan, Canada; *U.S. Private*, pg. 776
Rinder, Jerry, V.P.-Sls.--Sperry Top-Sider, Inc., Cambridge, MA; *U.S. Public*, pg. 1525
Ring, David S., V.P.-Sls. & Service--World Dryer Corp., Berkeley, IL; *U.S. Public*, pg. 1497
Ringo, Herb, Mgr.-Natl. Sls.--American Fabrics Company, New York, NY; *U.S. Private*, pg. 53
Rink, James A., V.P.-Engrng.--Prestige Stamping, Inc., Warren, MI; *U.S. Private*, pg. 882
Rink, Jeff, V.P.-Sls. & Office Mgr.--Prestige Stamping, Inc., Warren, MI; *U.S. Private*, pg. 882
Rinn, Russ, Exec. V.P.-Sls./CMC Steel Grp.--Structural Metals, Inc., Seguin, TX; *U.S. Public*, pg. 412
Riordan, Geri, V.P. & Mng. Dir.-Women's Accessories--The Echo Design Group, Inc., New York, NY; *U.S. Private*, pg. 359
Riordan, Joe, Mgr.-Reg. Sls.--Icicle Seafoods, Inc., Seattle, WA; *U.S. Private*, pg. 556
Riordan, Peter, Dir.-Sls./Currys Div.--Dixons Group plc, Hemel Hempstead, United Kingdom,; *Int'l*, pg. 413
Ripple, Louis J., Dir.-Sls. & Mktg./Worldwide--Allen-Edmonds Shoe Corp., Port Washington, WI; *U.S. Private*, pg. 36
Riss, Albert, Dir.-Sls.--Laboratoire LaChartre S.A., Blois, France; *U.S. Public*, pg. 1331
Risser, Timothy, Exec. V.P.-Sls. & Admin.--U.S. Bottlers Machinery Co., Charlotte, NC; *U.S. Private*, pg. 1124
Rissier, Henry, Sr. V.P.-Sls. & Mktg.--Anchor Continental Incorporated, Columbia, SC; *U.S. Private*, pg. 70
Ristaino, Robert A., V.P.-Sls., Mktg. & Service--New England Coffee Company, Malden, MA; *U.S. Private*, pg. 792
Ritchie, John, Sr. V.P.-Sls. & Mktg.--KLLM Transport Services, Inc., Jackson, MS; *U.S. Public*, pg. 939
Ritchie, Joseph, V.P.-Sls. & Mktg.--Griffin Envelope, Inc., Seattle, WA; *U.S. Public*, pg. 1038
Ritter, Kelbourne J., Sr. V.P.-Natl. Sls.--U.S. Healthcare, Inc., Blue Bell, PA; *U.S. Public*, pg. 26
Ritter, P.C., Sr. V.P.-Sls.--Mack Trucks, Inc., Allentown, PA; *Int'l*, pg. 1102
Rittman, Tom, Mgr.-Tech. Sls.--Plastic Suppliers, Inc., Columbus, OH; *U.S. Private*, pg. 871
Riveiro, Vicente, Sls. Mgr.--Agema Infrared Systems AB, Danderyd, Sweden; *Int'l*, pg. 1289
Rivera, Ralph, V.P.-Indus. Sls.--The Gates Rubber Company, Denver, CO; *Int'l*, pg. 1396
Rivers, Charles F., III, Sr. V.P. & Dir.-Retail Sls.--SouthTrust Bank of Charleston, Charleston, SC; *U.S. Public*, pg. 1492
Rivers, David P., V.P.-Mktg. & Sls.--E-Z-GO Textron, Augusta, GA; *U.S. Public*, pg. 1589
Rivest, Robert, Sls. Mgr.-Eastern Region--Parker & Amchem, Etobicoke, Canada; *Int'l*, pg. 612
Riviello, John, Mng. Dir.--Kruger Recycling Inc., Albany, NY; *Int'l*, pg. 762
Rizza, Rick, Mgr.-ETI Business/Airpax Instruments--Philips Automotive Electronics, Cheshire, CT; *Int'l*, pg. 1054
Rizzi, Tim, V.P.-Sls.--Normark Corporation, Minnetonka, MN; *U.S. Private*, pg. 802
Roach, Alfred R., Jr., Exec. V.P.-Mktg., Sls. & Prod. Support--Group Maintenance America Corp., Houston, TX; *U.S. Public*, pg. 766
Roach, Bill, V.P.-Worldwide Sls.--Maxtor Corporation, Milpitas, CA; *Int'l*, pg. 641
Roach, James, V.P.-Mktg., Sls. & Adv.--TII Industries, Inc., Copiague, NY; *U.S. Public*, pg. 1556
Roach, James, V.P.-Mktg. & Sls.--Vulcan Materials Company, Birmingham, AL; *U.S. Public*, pg. 1725
Robb, Ken, Dir.-Sls. & Mktg.--The Gates Rubber Company Ltd., Dumfries, United Kingdom; *Int'l*, pg. 1397
Robb, Thom, Mgr.-Sls.--Cross Creek Apparel, Inc., Mount Airy, NC; *U.S. Public*, pg. 1413
Robbin, Jim, Exec. V.P. & Gen. Mgr.--K & R Express Systems Inc., Hinsdale, IL; *U.S. Private*, pg. 602
Robbins, Bruce, Mgr.-Sls. & Mktg.--Svedala Bulk Materials Handling Engineered Products, Pittsburgh, PA; *Int'l*, pg. 1326
Robbins, Clinton, Dir.-Mktg. & Sls.--General Motors Chile S.A., Industria Automotriz, Santiago, Chile; *U.S. Public*, pg. 721
Robbins, Don, V.P.-Sls. & Mktg.--Orange-Co., Inc., Bartow, FL; *U.S. Public*, pg. 1229
Robbins, Jerome G., V.P.-Sls.--Robbins Manufacturing Company, Tampa, FL; *U.S. Private*, pg. 935
Robbins, Paul, V.P.-Sls.--Butterick Company, Inc., New York, NY; *U.S. Private*, pg. 190
Robbins, Robert W., Sr. V.P.-Sls.--Synovus Financial Corp., Columbus, GA; *U.S. Public*, pg. 1548
Roberson, Donald, Dir.-Mktg. & Sls.--Theradyne Corporation, Jordan, MN; *U.S. Private*, pg. 637
Robert, Dick, V.P.-Sls. & Mktg.--Griswold Industries, Inc., Costa Mesa, CA; *U.S. Private*, pg. 482
Roberts, Chris, V.P.-Sls.--Rentrak Corporation, Portland, OR; *U.S. Public*, pg. 1377
Roberts, Dan, Exec. V.P.-Sls. & Mktg.--Wellington Industries Inc., Madison, GA; *U.S. Private*, pg. 1161
Roberts, Dana, Mgr.-Sls.--Lavelle Industries Inc., Burlington, WI; *U.S. Private*, pg. 653
Roberts, Doug, Mgr.-Sls.--Woodbury Business Forms, Inc., La Grange, GA; *U.S. Private*, pg. 1186
Roberts, Ed, Mgr.-Sls.--GB Holdings, Jurong, Singapore; *Int'l*, pg. 531
Roberts, Ed, Mgr.-Mktg. & Sls.--American Marine Pte. Ltd., Jurong, Singapore; *Int'l*, pg. 531
Roberts, Frank, V.P.-Sls.--Check Technology Corporation, Minnetonka, MN; *U.S. Public*, pg. 342
Roberts, Jill, Coord.-Sls.--Ausco Products, Inc., Benton Harbor, MI; *U.S. Private*, pg. 299
Roberts, John, Mgr.-Nissan New Car Sls.--Jeffrey Buick-Nissan Inc., Roseville, MI; *U.S. Private*, pg. 585
Roberts, John D., V.P.-Sls.--Lift-All Co., Inc., Manheim, PA; *U.S. Private*, pg. 667
Roberts, Matthew, V.P.-Chasis & Suspension--CMI International Inc., Southfield, MI; *U.S. Private*, pg. 195
Roberts, Phil, Dir.-Sls., Natl. & Intl.--Sloan Technology, Santa Barbara, CA; *U.S. Public*, pg. 1711
Roberts, Skip, Sls. Consultant--Columbia Laboratories, Inc., Miami, FL; *U.S. Public*, pg. 405
Roberts, Sue F., V.P.-Sls., N.E. Reg.--SLM Holding Corp., Washington, DC; *U.S. Public*, pg. 1419
Roberts, Sue F., Asst. V.P.-Northeast Reg. Sls.--SLM Holding Corp., Washington, DC; *U.S. Public*, pg. 1419
Roberts, Tanya L., V.P.-Direct Sls.--Intuit, Inc., Mountain View, CA; *U.S. Public*, pg. 911
Roberts, Ted, Exec. V.P.-Sls.--Dean Operations Inc., Kansas City, MO; *U.S. Private*, pg. 318
Roberts, Tom, V.P.-Sls.--The Sunflower Group, Overland Park, KS; *U.S. Private*, pg. 1052
Robertson, B., Dir.-Intl. Sls. & Mktg.--Renold PLC, Manchester, United Kingdom; *Int'l*, pg. 1103
Robertson, Brian, V.P.-Sls.--Maitland-Smith U.S., Inc., High Point, NC; *U.S. Private*, pg. 432
Robertson, Dale K., V.P.-Multi-Unit Sls.--Sysco Corporation, Houston, TX; *U.S. Public*, pg. 1550
Robertson, Graeme, Client Services Dir.--ARC Advertising, London, United Kingdom; *Int'l*, pg. 17
Robertson, Jay L., V.P.-Retail Sls.--Worthington Foods Inc., Worthington, OH; *U.S. Public*, pg. 1780
Robertson, Jennifer, Controller.-Intl;. Sls. & Mktg.--The Gates Rubber Company Ltd., Dumfries, United Kingdom; *Int'l*, pg. 1397
Robertson, Ronald, V.P.-Cemetery Sls.--The Loewen Group, Inc., Burnaby, Canada; *Int'l*, pg. 814
Robertson, Ross, V.P.-Sls.--Hershey Canada Inc., Mississauga, Canada; *U.S. Public*, pg. 812
Robertson, Steve, Sr. V.P.-Sls. & Mktg.--The Keller Manufacturing Co., Inc., Corydon, IN; *U.S. Private*, pg. 612
Robicaux, D., V.P.-Mktg. & Sls.--Bank Building, Manchester, MO; *U.S. Private*, pg. 407
Robicaux, David, V.P.-Natl. Sls. & Mktg.--First Financial Building Corporation, Manchester, MO; *U.S. Private*, pg. 407

Robidoux, Roy, Sr. V.P.-Mktg. & Sls.--The Cerplex Group, Inc., Tustin, CA; *U.S. Public*, pg. 332
Robillard, Anne, Dir.-Sls.--Kinko's Corporation, Ventura, CA; *U.S. Private*, pg. 622
Robinius, Vern, V.P.-Mktg.--Q & B Foods, Inc., Irwindale, CA; *Int'l*, pg. 1074
Robins, Rob, Sr. V.P.--Visa U.S.A. Inc., San Francisco, CA; *U.S. Private*, pg. 1141
Robinson, Barry E., Vice. Chm.-Sls.--Ernst & Young, LLP, New York, NY; *U.S. Private*, pg. 381
Robinson, Chris, Mgr.-Sls.--M1 KIT Mfg. Co., Caldwell, ID; *U.S. Public*, pg. 962
Robinson, Curtis, Mgr.-Sls. Envelopes--Top Flight, Inc., Chattanooga, TN; *U.S. Private*, pg. 1091
Robinson, Ervin, V.P.-Mfg.--Carolina Shoe Company, Morganton, NC; *U.S. Public*, pg. 217
Robinson, George, Mgr.-Natl. Sls.--Top Flight, Inc., Chattanooga, TN; *U.S. Private*, pg. 1091
Robinson, Gordon, V.P.-Sls.--Cogsdill Tool Products, Inc., Lugoff, SC; *U.S. Private*, pg. 250
Robinson, Greg, Mgr.-Sls.--Paramount Canada's Wonderland, Vaughan, Canada; *U.S. Private*, pg. 776
Robinson, Jeff, V.P.-Sls. & Mktg.--Amerford International Corporation, Atlanta, GA; *Int'l*, pg. 1388
Robinson, Jim, Mgr.-Sls.--C. Weaver Chevrolet, Inc., New York Mills, NY; *U.S. Private*, pg. 1156
Robinson, Keith, V.P.-Sls.--Symantec Corporation, Cupertino, CA; *U.S. Public*, pg. 1545
Robinson, Keith, V.P.-Sls.--Symantec Corporation - Beaverton Site, Beaverton, OR; *U.S. Public*, pg. 1545
Robinson, Malcom, V.P.-Sls.--Gant, New York, NY; *U.S. Public*, pg. 1291
Robinson, Mike, Mgr.-Natl. Sls. Mass Mktg.--Top Flight, Inc., Chattanooga, TN; *U.S. Private*, pg. 1091
Robinson, N.M.F., Dir.-Mktg. & Sls.--Gallaher (Dublin) Ltd., Tallaght, Ireland; *Int'l*, pg. 539
Robinson, Neal, V.P.-Natl. Sls.--Bunn-O-Matic Corporation, Springfield, IL; *U.S. Private*, pg. 180
Robinson, Patrick, Dir.-Corp. Communications & Sls. Devel.--Reed Exhibition Companies-Europe, Paris, France; *Int'l*, pg. 1096
Robinson, Patrick, Dir.-Corp. Communications & Sls. Devel.--Reed Exhibition Companies, Richmond, United Kingdom; *Int'l*, pg. 1096
Robinson, Ted, Mgr.-Natl. Sls.--Creative Publications, Mountain View, CA; *U.S. Private*, pg. 288
Robisch, Tim, Mgr.-Natl. Sls.--Alloy Technology International Inc., West Nyack, NY; *U.S. Private*, pg. 42
Robison, David, Mgr.-Sls. & Mktg.--Milton Roy Company, Ivyland, PA; *U.S. Public*, pg. 1534
Robley, Ron, Natl. Sls. Mgr.-Sports Knives--Fiskars-Gerber, Portland, OR; *Int'l*, pg. 492
Robson, Bill, Dir.-North American Sls.--Jacobsen Textron, Racine, WI; *U.S. Public*, pg. 1589
Robson, Mark, Regional Mgr.-California--Columbus Mills, Inc., Columbus, GA; *U.S. Private*, pg. 256
Rocca, Frank H., V.P.-Mktg. & Sls.--Neapco, Inc., Pottstown, PA; *U.S. Private*, pg. 1113
Rocco, John D., Sr. V.P.-Sls.--Sierra Capital Management, Northridge, CA; *U.S. Public*, pg. 1742
Roche, Alexander, Exec. V.P.-Sls. & Mktg.--Fishery Products International Ltd., Saint Johns, Canada; *Int'l*, pg. 492
Roche, Edward, Dir.-Intl. Sls.--H.J. Baker & Bro., Inc., Stamford, CT; *U.S. Private*, pg. 112
Rochester, Ralph G., Sr. V.P.-Sls. & Mktg.--Comcast Cable Communications, Inc., Philadelphia, PA; *U.S. Public*, pg. 407
Rock, Jim, Gen. Sls. Mgr.--WODT-AM, New Orleans, LA; *U.S. Public*, pg. 385
Rockman, Elena, Dir.-Adv. & Sls.--Childrens Press Inc., Danbury, CT; *Int'l*, pg. 794
Rockne, Tom, V.P.-Sls.--MLT Vacations, Inc., Minnetonka, MN; *U.S. Public*, pg. 1200
Rocks, Frank L., V.P.-Sls. & Service--Bell & Howell Document Management Products Company, Chicago, IL; *U.S. Public*, pg. 201
Rockwell, Christine, Mgr.-Sls.--Circle Freight International USA, Grand Rapids, MI; *U.S. Public*, pg. 371
Rodecki, Robert, Mgr.-Sls.--Universal Molding Company, Lynwood, CA; *U.S. Private*, pg. 1127
Rodehorst, D., Mgr.-Intl. Sls.--Radix Wire Company, Cleveland, OH; *U.S. Private*, pg. 907
Rodel, Tom, Exec. V.P.-Sls.--Gilbert & Bennett Manufacturing Company, Georgetown, CT; *U.S. Private*, pg. 453
Rodelli, Gerald N., Sr. V.P.--Stonecutter Mills Corp., Spindale, NC; *U.S. Private*, pg. 1044
Roderick, John, Mgr.-Sls. & Mktg.--The Entwistle Company, Hudson, MA; *U.S. Private*, pg. 378
Rodgers, Lisa, Mgr.-Natl. Sls.--Irma Shorell, Inc., Lynchburg, VA; *U.S. Private*, pg. 1101
Rodman, Rodney F., V.P.-Natl. Acct. Sls.--The Smithfield Packing Co., Inc., Smithfield, VA; *U.S. Public*, pg. 1479
Rodriguez, Luis, Mgr.-Sls. Promo.--CIBA-GEIGY Uruguaya S.A., Montevideo, Uruguay; *Int'l*, pg. 980
Roebuck, Richard, Mgr.-Mktg.--Pneumatic Div., Cannock, United Kingdom; *U.S. Public*, pg. 1264
Roeder, J. Thomas, V.P.-Mktg. & Sls.--Symtron Systems, Inc., Fair Lawn, NJ; *U.S. Public*, pg. 1679
Roehricht, Hans, V.P.-Bus. Opers.--AirSensors, Inc., Seattle, WA; *U.S. Public*, pg. 33
Roesle, Jack, V.P.-Sls. & Mktg.--Alpha/Owens Corning LLC, Collierville, TN; *U.S. Private*, pg. 45
Roessle, Erwin H., V.P.-Mktg.--Dreis & Krump Manufacturing Company, Chicago, IL; *U.S. Private*, pg. 342
Roesslein, Mike, V.P.-Sls., Central Zone--Pier 1 Imports, Inc., Fort Worth, TX; *U.S. Public*, pg. 1295
Rogers, Chuck, V.P.-Sls.--Bell Flavors & Fragrances, Northbrook, IL; *U.S. Private*, pg. 131
Rogers, David A., V.P.-U.S. Sls. & Mktg.--A.T. Cross Co., Lincoln, RI; *U.S. Public*, pg. 460
Rogers, Don D., Dir.-Sls. & Mktg.--Krause Plow Corp., Hutchinson, KS; *U.S. Private*, pg. 635
Rogers, Frank K., Dir.-Mktg. & Sls.--Providence and Worcester Railroad Company, Worcester, MA; *U.S. Public*, pg. 1336
Rogers, Fred, Dir.-Appliance Div.--Rangaire Inc., Cleburne, TX; *U.S. Public*, pg. 1193
Rogers, Jeff, Mgr.-District Sls.--Southwestern/Great American Inc., Nashville, TN; *U.S. Private*, pg. 1018
Rogers, Jerry, Mgr.-Sls.--Dominion Homes, Dublin, OH; *U.S. Public*, pg. 516
Rogers, Ken, Exec. V.P.-Mktg. & Sls. (Canada)--Intertape Polymer Group, Green Bay, WI; *Int'l*, pg. 685
Rogers, Kenneth R., V.P.-Distr. & Sls.--Intertape Polymer Group Inc., Saint-Laurent, Canada; *Int'l*, pg. 684
Rogers, Mark, Dir.-Sls.--First American Real Estate Information Services, Inc., Saint Petersburg, FL; *U.S. Public*, pg. 625
Rogers, Paul, Dir.-OEM Sales--Industrial Distribution and OEM, North America, Dayton, OH; *U.S. Public*, pg. 1045
Rogers, Thomas W., Sr. V.P.-Sls. & Mktg.--IMCO Recycling Inc., Irving, TX; *U.S. Public*, pg. 870
Rohauer, Shelly, Mgr.-Sls.--Business First of New York, LLC, Buffalo, NY; *U.S. Private*, pg. 19
Rohde, Mark R., Sr. V.P.-Sls. & Mktg.--Cincinnati Bell Information Systems Inc., Cincinnati, OH; *U.S. Public*, pg. 367
Rohloff, Winfried, Sr. V.P.-Worldwide Sls., Mktg. & Services--CalComp Technology, Inc., Anaheim, CA; *U.S. Public*, pg. 1007
Rohmann, Eric, Dir.-Sls.--Princeton University Press, Princeton, NJ; *U.S. Private*, pg. 885
Rohr, Paul, V.P.-Sls.--Leach International, Buena Park, CA; *U.S. Private*, pg. 655
Rohrbach, Eric, V.P.-Natl. Sls.--Waxman Industries, Inc., Bedford, OH; *U.S. Public*, pg. 1748
Rohrer, Doug, Sr. V.P.-Adv. Sls.-MTV & VH1--MTV Networks, New York, NY; *U.S. Private*, pg. 779
Roid, Hahns, Exec. V.P.-Sls. & Mktg.--Premier Cruises, Miami, FL; *U.S. Private*, pg. 293
Rojas, Ruben, Dir.-Sls.--Mathieu Chile, Santiago, Chile; *Int'l, pg. 846*
Rojnica, Kruno, V.P.-Intl. Sls. & Mktg.--The Wm. Powell Company, Cincinnati, OH; *U.S. Private*, pg. 877
Roller, Daryl, V.P.-Natl. Sls.--Ward Kraft, Inc., Fort Scott, KS; *U.S. Private*, pg. 634
Rollo, Tom, Dir.-Sls.--Federal APD, Inc., Farmington, MI; *U.S. Public*, pg. 616
Rolls, D., Exec. V.P.-Mktg. & Sls.--The Chamberlain Group, Inc., Elmhurst, IL; *U.S. Private*, pg. 344
Roma, Gary, V.P.-Sls. & Mktg.--Riverside Cement Co., Diamond Bar, CA; *Int'l*, pg. 1293
Roman, Anthony L., Asst. Gen. Sls. Mgr.-Admin. & DAC--Buick Motor Div. General Motors Corp., Flint, MI; *U.S. Public*, pg. 720
Romanelliz, Nick, Regional Mgr.-Northeast--Columbus Mills, Inc., Columbus, GA; *U.S. Private*, pg. 256
Romano, Nadine, Mgr.-Sls. & Promo.--Braun, North America, Woburn, MA; *U.S. Public*, pg. 743
Romer, Dick, V.P.-Sls.--Latshaw Enterprises, Inc., Wichita, KS; *U.S. Public*, pg. 979
Romines, Don, Mgr.-Mdsg.--Uni-Marts, Inc., State College, PA; *U.S. Public*, pg. 1664
Ronbinson, Charles, Mng. Dir.--Progress International Limited, Plainview, NY; *U.S. Public*, pg. 141
Roney, C.H., Dir.-Sls.--Tech-Tran Corporation, Rancocas, NJ; *U.S. Private*, pg. 560
Roney, Reid, V.P.-Sls. & Mktg.--Martin Industries, Inc. (AL), Florence, AL; *U.S. Private*, pg. 709
Ronning, Bruce, Dir.-Sls. & Mktg.--Hays Fluid Controls-Division of Romac Industries, Dallas, NC; *U.S. Private*, pg. 942
Roof, James F., V.P.-Worldwide Sls. & Mktg., Microelectronic Prods.--Shipley Co., LLC, Marlborough, MA; *U.S. Public*, pg. 1403
Rooker, Bill, Mgr.-Sls.--Massey Cadillac, Inc., Detroit, MI; *U.S. Private*, pg. 713
Rooney, Bryan, V.P.-Sls.--Burr-Brown Corporation, Tucson, AZ; *U.S. Public*, pg. 270
Rooney, John, Sr. V.P.-Natl. Sls.--Carillon Importers, Ltd., Fort Lee, NJ; *Int'l*, pg. 409
Rooney, Linda, Mgr.-Reg. Sls.--Duraliner U.S.A., Lapeer, MI; *U.S. Public*, pg. 537
Rooney, Rob, Mgr.-Sls.--Revere Electric Supply Co., Chicago, IL; *U.S. Private*, pg. 926
Rooney, Robert, Mgr.-Mktg. & Sls.--Taylor & Francis Philadelphia, Bristol, PA; *Int'l*, pg. 1358
Roos, Burkard, Exec. V.P.-Sls.--Koenig & Bauer-Albert AG, Wurzburg, Germany; *Int'l*, pg. 742
Root, R.G., Dir.-Sls.--Reynolds Metals Co.-Flexible Packaging Products Division, Richmond, VA; *U.S. Public, pg. 1386*
Root, Steve, V.P.-Sls. & Mktg. Wheel Grp.--Titan International, Inc., Quincy, IL; *U.S. Public*, pg. 1618
Ropson, Ardin, Sr. V.P.-Impulse Sls.--Good Humor/Breyers Ice Cream, Green Bay, WI; *Int'l*, pg. 1435
Rosa, Scott, Exec. V.P.-Sls. & Mktg.--Cannon Equipment, Chattanooga, TN; *Int'l*, pg. 646
Rosado, Dulce, Sls. Mgr.--Aero Peru Corporation, Coral Gables, FL; *U.S. Private*, pg. 24
Rosania, Carl A., V.P.-Sls.--Structural Foam Plastics, Inc., Somerville, NJ; *U.S. Private*, pg. 1047
Rose, Bill, V.P.-Mktg. & Sls.--SRC Vision, Medford, OR; *U.S. Public*, pg. 20
Rose, Herbert A., V.P.-Sls, Mktg. & Consumer Prods.--Trion, Inc., Sanford, NC; *U.S. Public*, pg. 1639
Rose, Jerry, V.P.-Sls./WCO--EA Industries, West Long Branch, NJ; *U.S. Public*, pg. 541
Rose, Jerry, V.P.-Sls.--McLane Company, Inc., Temple, TX; *U.S. Public*, pg. 1733
Rose, Jim, Dir.-Sls. & Mktg.--John Crane Asia Pacific, Singapore, Singapore; *Int'l*, pg. 1339
Rose, John, Dir.-Sls.--Alnor Instrument Company, Skokie, IL; *U.S. Public*, pg. 1559
Rose, Jon, V.P.-Sls.--The Wooster Brush Company, Wooster, OH; *U.S. Private*, pg. 1188
Rose, Ronnie, V.P.-Reg. Sls. & Gen. Mgr.--Tom's Foods, Inc., Columbus, GA; *U.S. Private*, pg. 1090
Rose, Scott, Dir.-Adv. & Sls. Promo.--Sea World of California, San Diego, CA; *U.S. Public*, pg. 114
Rose, Tim, Mgr.-Sls.--Process Color Plate, Chicago, IL; *U.S. Public*, pg. 1437
Rose, William D., V.P.-Integrated Bus. Sys. Bldg. Prods. Mfg. & Sls.--Georgia-Pacific Corporation, Atlanta, GA; *U.S. Public*, pg. 735
Rosebush, Raymond, V.P.-Natl. Accts. & Newsprint Sls.--Donohue Inc., Quebec, Canada; *Int'l*, pg. 1075
Rosen, Amy, V.P.-Sls.--Belvedere Company, Belvidere, IL; *U.S. Private*, pg. 1008
Rosen, Gary, Controller--Puroflow Incorporated, Van Nuys, CA; *U.S. Public*, pg. 1345
Rosenberg, Gerald B., Sr. V.P.-Mktg. & Sls.--Bayer Corporation/Pharmaceutical Division, West Haven, CT; *Int'l*, pg. 173
Rosenberg, Marc, Sr. V.P.-Sls. & Prod. Distr.--Air Canada, Saint-Laurent, Canada; *Int'l*, pg. 36
Rosenberger, Barry, Dir.-Sls.--A. Pomerantz & Company, Philadelphia, PA; *U.S. Private*, pg. 875
Rosenberger, Howard, Exec. V.P.-Sls.--Ellen Tracy Inc., New York, NY; *U.S. Private*, pg. 372
Rosenblum, Kenneth, Sr. V.P.-Sls./Home Entertainment--Shorewood Packaging Corporation, New York, NY; *U.S. Public*, pg. 1468
Rosenecker, Joseph A., Pres.-Flat Rolled Prods. Grp.--Gibraltar Steel Corp., Buffalo, NY; *U.S. Public*, pg. 742
Rosenfeld, Jim, Dir.-Mktg. & Sls.--Fishman & Tobin, Inc., Conshohocken, PA; *U.S. Private*, pg. 408
Rosenthal, Steve, V.P.-Sls.--Empire of Carolina, Inc., Delray Beach, FL; *U.S. Public*, pg. 579
Rosentreter, Paula, Dir.-Adv. & Sls. Promo.--Follett College Stores Corp., Elmhurst, IL; *U.S. Private*, pg. 417
Rosenwald, James B., V.P.-OEM Mktg. & Sls.--Leviton Mfg. Co., Inc., Little Neck, NY; *U.S. Private*, pg. 663
Rosling, Reed V., V.P.-Sls. & Natl. Accts.--Bergen Brunswig Drug Company, Orange, CA; *U.S. Public*, pg. 213
Ross, Austin, Dir.-Sls.--Cruise America, Inc., Mesa, AZ; *U.S. Private*, pg. 178
Ross, Bill, Asst. Mgr.-New Ford Sls.--Fairway Ford, Inc., Greenville, SC; *U.S. Private*, pg. 392
Ross, Daniel, V.P.-Sls.--Open Market, Inc., Burlington, MA; *U.S. Public*, pg. 1226
Ross, Don, Dir.-Sls.--Providence Journal-Bulletin, Providence, RI; *U.S. Public*, pg. 209
Ross, Donald G, Sr. V.P.-Retail Banking--St. Paul Bancorp, Inc., Chicago, IL; *U.S. Public*, pg. 1428
Ross, Ed, V.P.-Sls. & Mktg.--Anderson, Greenwood & Co., Stafford, TX; *U.S. Public*, pg. 1650
Ross, Jack, Sr. V.P. & Gen. Mgr.-Pulp & Paper Div.--ABB Industrial Systems, Inc., Columbus, OH; *Int'l*, pg. 4
Ross, JoAnn, V.P.-Primetime, Late Night & Olympic Sls.--CBS Television Network, New York, NY; *U.S. Public*, pg. 274
Ross, Ken, Dir.-Sls. & Mktg.--Elkem Aluminium ANS, Oslo, Norway; *Int'l*, pg. 446
Ross, Marty, Dir.-Adv.--Business Insurance, Chicago, IL; *U.S. Private*, pg. 285
Ross, Michael A., V.P.-Sls.--Square Two Golf Incorporated, Fairfield, NJ; *U.S. Public*, pg. 1501
Ross, Ronnie E., Mgr.-Sls. Admin.--P.H. Glatfelter Company, Spring Grove, PA; *U.S. Public*, pg. 746
Ross, Sean, Mgr.-Intl. Sls.--Mico Inc., North Mankato, MN; *U.S. Private*, pg. 741
Ross, Thomas, V.P.-Sls. & Admin.--Jack Ross Motors Inc., Tempe, AZ; *U.S. Private*, pg. 946
Rosseau, Randy, Dir.-Sls.--Fiamm Technologies Inc., Cadillac, MI; *Int'l*, pg. 480
Rossi, Endvar, V.P.-Mktg. Sls. & Customer Svc.--Dow Corning Corporation, Midland, MI; *U.S. Public*, pg. 523
Rossi, George, Exec. V.P.-Sls.--WEA Corp., Burbank, CA; *U.S. Public*, pg. 1612
Rosskam, Steve, Exec. V.P.-Sls. & Mktg.--David Michael & Co. Inc., Philadelphia, PA; *U.S. Private*, pg. 740
Rossman, Tom, Mgr.-Western Reg. Sls.--The Flood Company, Hudson, OH; *U.S. Private*, pg. 414
Rotchford, Robert, V.P.- Sls. & Mktg.--Massachusetts Envelope Co., Somerville, MA; *U.S. Private*, pg. 712
Rotenberg, Lesli, Div. Dir.-Ad Sls.--Discovery Communications, Inc., Bethesda, MD; *U.S. Private*, pg. 334
Roth, E.M., Mgr.-Sls.--Graphic Controls Corporation, Buffalo, NY; *U.S. Private*, pg. 470
Roth, Richard, Sr. V.P.-Sls. & Mktg.--Queens Group, Inc., Long Island City, NY; *U.S. Private*, pg. 900
Roth, William, Mgr.-Natl. Svc.--Hitachi Instruments, Inc., San Jose, CA; *Int'l*, pg. 622
Rothe, Philip, Mgr.-Sls.--Teleflex Electrical Systems, Sarasota, FL; *U.S. Public*, pg. 1569
Rothenberg, Harvey, V.P.-Sls.--Sport Supply Group, Inc., Dallas, TX; *U.S. Public*, pg. 1499
Rothfuss, Robert K., V.P.-Sls. & Mktg.--Buckhorn Material Handling Group Inc., Milford, OH; *U.S. Public*, pg. 1143
Rothkopf, Robert H., Pres.-Formed Prod. Grp.--Elco Textron, Rockford, IL; *U.S. Public*, pg. 1590
Rothwell, John D., Sr. V.P. & Mgr.-Natl. Sls.--Mackenzie Financial Corporation, Toronto, Canada; *Int'l*, pg. 828
Rotondi, Robert F., Dir.-Turbine Bus. Unit--Wyman-Gordon, North Grafton, MA; *U.S. Public*, pg. 1782
Rotsch, Jeffrey R., Sr. V.P.-Sls. & Distr.--General Mills, Inc., Minneapolis, MN; *U.S. Public*, pg. 717
Rottering, Quintin, V.P.-Sls. & Mktg.--Beam Industries, Webster City, IA; *Int'l*, pg. 440
Roudebush, Jim, Acct. Exec. & Bus. Devel.--Caldwell VanRiper, Inc., Indianapolis, IN; *U.S. Private*, pg. 200
Rougeau, Jean-Pierre, V.P.-Mktg. & Sls.--COGEMA - Compagnie Generale des Matieres Nucleaires, Velizy-Villacoublay, France; *Int'l*, pg. 304
Rouille, Gregg, Mgr.-Sls.--McKenzies of Vermont, Inc., Burlington, VT; *U.S. Private*, pg. 723

Schneider, Morris, V.P. & Dir.-Circulation--The Times-Picayune Publishing Corp., New Orleans, LA; *U.S. Private*, pg. 1087
Schneider, Robert R., V.P.-Sls. & Mktg.--White Mop Wringer Company, Tampa, FL; *U.S. Private*, pg. 1172
Schneider, Ron, V.P.-Adv. Sls.--A&E Television Networks, New York, NY; *U.S. Private*, pg. 515
Schneider, Steve L., V.P.-Sls. & Mktg.--Lowrance Electronics, Inc., Tulsa, OK; *U.S. Public*, pg. 1015
Schneider, Steven L., Sr. V.P.-Sls. & Mktg.--Eagle Electronics, Catoosa, OK; *U.S. Public*, pg. 1016
Schneider, Steven L., Sr. V.P.-Sls. & Mktg.--Lowrance Avionics, Tulsa, OK; *U.S. Public*, pg. 1016
Schneiderman, Stephanie, Mgr.-Export Sls.--Thermador, Los Angeles, CA; *U.S. Public*, pg. 1053
Schneidewind, Art, V.P.-Sls. & Mktg.--Blue M Electric Co., Watertown, WI; *U.S. Public*, pg. 726
Schneller, John, V.P.-Sls.--B/E Aerospace Seating Products Group, Litchfield, CT; *U.S. Public*, pg. 159
Schnepper, Howard, Sls. & Mktg. Mgr.--Chipico Pickles, Chicago, IL; *U.S. Private*, pg. 1140
Schnese, Kent A., V.P.-Sls. & Mktg.--Naz-Dar Company, Chicago, IL; *U.S. Private*, pg. 1084
Schnieders, Bob, Exec. V.P.-Sls. & Mktg.--Universal Studios, Inc., Universal City, CA; *Int'l*, pg. 1215
Schnieders, Richard J., Sr. V.P.-Mdsg. & Multi-Unit Sls.--Sysco Corporation, Houston, TX; *U.S. Public*, pg. 1550
Schnittgey, Ted, Dir.-Sls.--Crystal Flash Petroleum Corp., Indianapolis, IN; *U.S. Private*, pg. 294
Schnorrenberg, H. K., Dir.-Sls.--Liebert G.m.b.H., Kirchheim, Germany; *U.S. Public*, pg. 577
Schnurstein, Nancy, V.P.-Mktg. & Sls.--Fremont Indemnity Co./Medical Professional Liab. Div., Santa Monica, CA; *U.S. Public*, pg. 681
Schoeffel, Joe, Dir.-Engrng. & Sls.--Holcomb & Hoke Mfg. Company, Inc., Indianapolis, IN; *U.S. Private*, pg. 533
Schoenauer, Thomas E., V.P.-Sls. & Mgr.-Adv.--A&A Manufacturing Co., New Berlin, WI; *U.S. Private*, pg. 1
Schoenbacher, Robert N., V.P.-Sls. & Mktg.--Newhouse Newspapers Metro-Suburbia, Inc., New York, NY; *U.S. Private*, pg. 20
Schoenig, Karl, Mgr.-Prods., Mktg. & Sls.--Medtronic GmbH, Bad Homburg, Germany; *U.S. Public*, pg. 1083
Schoeny, Don, Sr. V.P.-Sls. Worldwide & Service Support--PerSeptive Biosystems, Inc., Framingham, MA; *U.S. Public*, pg. 1279
Schoepplein, Wolfgang, Mgr.-European Sls.--Feodor Burgmann Dichtungswerke GmbH, Wolfratshausen, Germany; *Int'l*, pg. 233
Schoettler, William, V.P.-Sls.--Lightolier Division, Fall River, MA; *U.S. Public*, pg. 730
Schofield, John, V.P.-Sls.--Becton Dickinson Infusion Therapy, Inc., Sandy, UT; *U.S. Public*, pg. 199
Scholl, Tom, V.P.-Sls.--Philway Products, Inc., Ashland, OH; *U.S. Private*, pg. 862
Schollman, Dave, Mgr.-Sls.--Waters Instruments, Inc., Rochester, MN; *U.S. Public*, pg. 1745
Scholma, Doug, V.P.-Grocery--D & W Food Centers, Inc., Grand Rapids, MI; *U.S. Private*, pg. 300
Scholz, Bill, Sls. Mgr.-Photo Prods.--Houston Fearless 76 Inc., Compton, CA; *U.S. Private*, pg. 542
Scholz, J., Dir.-Sls.--RFL Electronics, Inc., Boonton, NJ; *U.S. Private*, pg. 903
Schon, Joe, V.P.-Mktg. & Sls.--Agromac International, Inc., Gering, NE; *U.S. Private*, pg. 27
Schossmann, Wolfgang, Mng. Dir.-Sls.--ESAB GmbH, Solingen, Germany; *Int'l*, pg. 282
Schott, Roz, V.P.-Mktg. & Sls.--Schott Brothers, Inc., Perth Amboy, NJ; *U.S. Private*, pg. 972
Schrader, Karen, Mgr.-Sls.--St. Louis Business Journal Corp., Saint Louis, MO; *U.S. Private*, pg. 20
Schraeder, Mike, V.P.-Worldwide Sls. & Svc.--GenRad, Inc., Westford, MA; *U.S. Public*, pg. 731
Schrage, Cal, Mgr.-Mktg.--Lincoln Steel, Lincoln, NE; *U.S. Private*, pg. 824
Schram, John, Mgr.-Particleboard Sls. & Mktg.--Boise Cascade Timber & Wood Products Division, Boise, ID; *U.S. Public*, pg. 243
Schramm, John, Mgr.-Sls. & Mktg./Particleboard--Boise Cascade Corporation, Boise, ID; *U.S. Public*, pg. 242
Schrandt, Kevin, Mgr.-Natl. Sls.--Bestop, Inc., Broomfield, CO; *Int'l*, pg. 830
Schrantz, Stephen J., Exec. V.P.-Sls. & Intl. Bus.--Fifth Third Bancorp, Cincinnati, OH; *U.S. Public*, pg. 621
Schreck, Tom, Gen. Sls. Mgr.--Bush Hog Division, Selma, AL; *U.S. Public*, pg. 48
Schreiber, Gary, Dir.-Sls. & Mktg.--Power Contracting & Engineering Corp., Schaumburg, IL; *U.S. Private*, pg. 877
Schreiber, Hans, Dir.-Adv. & Sls.--J. Dieffenbacher GmbH & Co., Eppingen, Germany; *Int'l*, pg. 413
Schreiber, James M., V.P.-Natl. Accounts--Dresher, Inc., Carthage, MO; *U.S. Public*, pg. 986
Schreiber, Mike, Mgr.-Sls.--Bill Brown Ford Inc., Livonia, MI; *U.S. Private*, pg. 173
Schreibmaier, Emanuel, Mgr.-Mktg. & Sls.--Sol Melia America, Miami, FL; *Int'l*, pg. 1277
Schrine, Ron, V.P.-Sls. & Adv.--Ingersoll-Rand Company, Woodcliff Lake, NJ; *U.S. Public*, pg. 876
Schroder, Ruediger, Dir.-Sls.--Hako-Werke GmbH & Co., Bad Oldesloe, Germany; *Int'l*, pg. 587
Schroder, Sandi, Dir.-Sls.--Aladdin Hotel & Casino, Las Vegas, NV; *U.S. Private*, pg. 30
Schroeder, B., Dr., Mgr.-Sls.--Morganite GmbH, Dusseldorf, Germany; *Int'l*, pg. 892
Schroeder, Donald R., V.P.-Sls. & Mktg.--CTS Corporation, Elkhart, IN; *U.S. Public*, pg. 285
Schroeder, Michael, V.P.-Sls. & Mktg.--Code-Alarm, Inc., Madison Heights, MI; *U.S. Public*, pg. 393
Schroeder, Michael, V.P.-Natl. Sls.--Code Alarm Security Systems, Madison Heights, MI; *U.S. Public*, pg. 394
Schroeder, Robert, Natl. Sls. Mgr.--Cashco, Inc., Ellsworth, KS; *U.S. Private*, pg. 218
Schroeder, Robert W., V.P. & Gen. Mgr.-McCormick/Schilling Div.--McCormick & Company, Incorporated, Sparks, MD; *U.S. Public*, pg. 1066
Schroeyers, Brian-Jean, Mgr. Sls.--Banque Paribas (Luxembourg) S.A., Luxembourg, Luxembourg; *Int'l*, pg. 320
Schubert, M., Dir.-Sls.--Coats Mez Industrieahfaden G.m.b.H., Braunlingen, Germany; *Int'l*, pg. 300
Schubert, Robert, Dir.-Sls. & Mktg.--Sermatech International, Inc., Limerick, PA; *U.S. Public*, pg. 1569
Schuele, K.W., Jr., Mgr.-Natl. Sls.--Evans Rule Co., Inc., Charleston, SC; *U.S. Public*, pg. 1511
Schuetz, Linda, Dir.-Sls.--FlexRx, North Versailles, PA; *U.S. Public*, pg. 1091
Schuler, Dale E., V.P.-Sls. & Mktg.--Veterinary Medicine Publishing Co., Inc., Lenexa, KS; *U.S. Public*, pg. 1600
Schuler, Edmund W., V.P.-Mktg. & Sls.--Werner & Pfleiderer Corporation, Ramsey, NJ; *Int'l*, pg. 511
Schulis, Tracy W., Mgr.-Sls.--Paradise, Inc., Plant City, FL; *U.S. Public*, pg. 1256
Schulte, Lynne M., Mgr.-Sls. Service--Dixon Ticonderoga Company, Heathrow, FL; *U.S. Public*, pg. 514
Schultheis, Edward, Dir.-Sls. & Mktg.--Healthcare Management Group, New York, NY; *U.S. Public*, pg. 1071
Schultz, Bradford C., Sr. V.P.-Sls. & Mktg.--Accuride Corp., Henderson, KY; *U.S. Public*, pg. 1286
Schultz, Chuck A., V.P.-Sls. & Mktg.--Huck International Industrial Fastener Division, Waco, TX; *U.S. Public*, pg. 1597
Schultz, Gary J., V.P.-N.A. Sls.--Neway Anchorlok International Inc., Muskegon, MI; *U.S. Private*, pg. 796
Schultz, Gordon, Mgr.-Sls., Transit--R.C.A. Rubber Company, Akron, OH; *U.S. Private*, pg. 902
Schultz, Lisa, Dir.-Mktg.--The Keyes Company Realtors, Miami, FL; *U.S. Private*, pg. 618
Schultz, Michael, V.P.-Mktg. & Sls.--Hughes Family Markets, Inc., Irwindale, CA; *U.S. Public*, pg. 1349
Schultz, Michael L., V.P.-North America Sls.--Federal-Mogul Corporation, Southfield, MI; *U.S. Public*, pg. 615
Schultz, Sue, V.P. & Dir.-Sls.--Scott Forseman/Addison Wesley, Glenview, IL; *Int'l*, pg. 927
Schultz, Terry, Dir.-Natl. Sls.--Superior Industries International, Inc., Van Nuys, CA; *U.S. Public*, pg. 1539
Schulz, Jim, Area V.P.--Borden Italian Foods, Northbrook, IL; *U.S. Private*, pg. 158
Schumacher, Joseph, V.P.-Sls.-Central South Region--PST Vans, Inc., Salt Lake City, UT; *U.S. Public*, pg. 1246
Schumacher, Rocky, Gen. Mgr.-Sls. & Mktg.--Agsco, Inc., Grand Forks, ND; *U.S. Private*, pg. 27
Schuman, Guy, Dir.-Sls.--Healthtex, Greensboro, NC; *U.S. Public*, pg. 1702
Schumburg, Noel, V.P.-Sls.--Bioproducts, Inc., Fairlawn, OH; *U.S. Private*, pg. 145
Schuster, Stephen, Sr. V.P.-Sls.--Konica Imaging USA, Inc., Glen Cove, NY; *Int'l*, pg. 749
Schutte, Suzanne, Deputy Mgr.-Private Client--Brown Brothers Harriman & Co., New York, NY; *U.S. Private*, pg. 173
Schutz, John, Exec. V.P.-Sls. & Mktg.--Strombecker Corporation, Chicago, IL; *U.S. Private*, pg. 1047
Schutz, John, V.P.-Sls.--Stride Rite Children's Group-Wholesale Div., Lexington, MA; *U.S. Public*, pg. 1525
Schutz, John E., V.P.-Sls.--Samuel Cabot, Inc., Newburyport, MA; *U.S. Private*, pg. 198
Schwab, Tadd, V.P.-Sls.--S. Schwab Company, Cumberland, MD; *U.S. Private*, pg. 974
Schwall, Lawrence E., III, V.P.-Sls. & Mktg.--Karts International Inc., Covington, LA; *U.S. Public*, pg. 944
Schwan, Vince, V.P.-Direct Sls.--Quaker State Corporation, Irving, TX; *U.S. Public*, pg. 1348
Schwantes, David L., Dir.-Mktg. & Sls.--Worthington Foods Inc., Worthington, OH; *U.S. Public*, pg. 1780
Schwanz, David, Natl. Sls. Mgr.--Parlux Fragrances Inc., Fort Lauderdale, FL; *U.S. Public*, pg. 1264
Schwartz, Bruce, V.P.-Mktg. & Sls.--Boulevard Distillers and Importers Inc., Lawrenceburg, KY; *Int'l*, pg. 567
Schwartz, Cary, V.P.-Mktg. Svcs.--Carillon Importers, Ltd., Fort Lee, NJ; *Int'l*, pg. 409
Schwartz, Jeffrey R., Mgr.-Sls.--System One Control, Saint Paul, MN; *U.S. Private*, pg. 851
Schwartz, Joel, Sr. V.P.-Worldwide Sls.--Data General Corporation, Westborough, MA; *U.S. Public*, pg. 485
Schwartz, Martin B., Exec. V.P.-Sls.--Media Resources International, New York, NY; *U.S. Private*, pg. 727
Schwartz, Robert, V.P.-Sls. & Mdsg.--Kings Super Markets Inc., West Caldwell, NJ; *Int'l*, pg. 843
Schwartz, Robert, V.P.-Foodservice Sls.--Vienna Sausage Mfg. Co., Chicago, IL; *U.S. Private*, pg. 1139
Schwartz, Robert P., V.P.-Sls.--Salton/Maxim Housewares, Inc., Mount Prospect, IL; *U.S. Public*, pg. 1430
Schwarz, Ken, V.P.-Sls. & Mktg.--Industrial Coated Fabrics Group, Spartanburg, SC; *U.S. Private*, pg. 507
Schwarz, Michael, Mgr.-Sls. & Mktg.--Electronic Systems Div., Sioux Falls, SD; *U.S. Public*, pg. 1361
Schweers, Mark E., Mgr.-Sls. & Mktg.--The International Metals Reclamation Company, Inc., Ellwood City, PA; *Int'l*, pg. 672
Schweiker, Gregory, Mgr.-Natl. Sls.--William H. Sadlier, Inc., New York, NY; *U.S. Public*, pg. 1422
Schweitzer, Bruce, Sr. V.P.-Sls. & Mktg.--Jennie-O Foods, Inc., Willmar, MN; *U.S. Public*, pg. 840
Schwerman, Scott, V.P.-Sls.--Vance Industries, Inc., Chicago, IL; *U.S. Private*, pg. 1133
Schweter, Steve, Mgr.-Natl. Sls.--Projects Unlimited, Inc., Dayton, OH; *U.S. Private*, pg. 890
Schwiebert, Kirk, Mgr.-Mktg. & Sls.--Ohmite Manufacturing Company, Skokie, IL; *U.S. Private*, pg. 813
Schwieger, Dennis, V.P.-Mktg. & Sls.-Irrigation--Valmont Industries, Inc., Valley, NE; *U.S. Public*, pg. 1706
Schwister, Tony, V.P.-Retail Sls.--Sargento Foods Inc., Plymouth, WI; *U.S. Private*, pg. 966
Schwoerer, John, V.P.-Sls.--NAO, Inc., Philadelphia, PA; *U.S. Private*, pg. 771
Scmitt, Don, V.P.-Sls.--Tiger Electronics, Inc., Vernon Hills, IL; *U.S. Private*, pg. 1086
Scoboria, Raymond, Dir.-Sls.-Automotive Prods.--ACS Industries, Inc., Woonsocket, RI; *U.S. Private*, pg. 3
Scolavino, Michael, Dir.-Pur. & Sls.--Furman Lumber Company, Inc., Billerica, MA; *U.S. Private*, pg. 431
Scollard, Tom, Dir.-Logistics Sls.--Rollins Logistics Inc., Wilmington, DE; *U.S. Public*, pg. 1405
Scott, Briggs, V.P.-Sls., Flexograph--Walle Corporation, Harahan, LA; *U.S. Private*, pg. 1148
Scott, Bruce B., V.P.-Sls.--Sun Financial Group, Inc., Tampa, FL; *U.S. Public*, pg. 691
Scott, D.A., V.P.-Sls.--Sandusky International Inc., Sandusky, OH; *U.S. Private*, pg. 964
Scott, D.B., V.P.-Intl. Sls.--Ridge Tool Co., Elyria, OH; *U.S. Public*, pg. 574
Scott, David, V.P.-Sls.--Leonard & Harral Packing Co., San Antonio, TX; *U.S. Private*, pg. 660
Scott, David Maxwell, Dir.-Sls. & Mktg.--The Highland Distilleries Company plc, Glasgow, United Kingdom; *Int'l*, pg. 619
Scott, Don, Sls. Mgr.-Mid Atlantic/Mid West District--Fluidtec Engineer Products, Greensboro, NC; *U.S. Public*, pg. 401
Scott, Gary L., V.P.-Natl. Sls. Mgr. & Sec.--Alkota Cleaning Systems, Inc., Alcester, SD; *U.S. Private*, pg. 34
Scott, H., Dir.-Sls.--Livingston UK Ltd., Teddington, United Kingdom; *Int'l*, pg. 212
Scott, J. Barrett, Mgr.-Sls.--Bates Container, Inc., North Richland Hills, TX; *U.S. Private*, pg. 122
Scott, L. Thomas, V.P.-Sls.--Jewell Building Systems, Dallas, NC; *U.S. Private*, pg. 587
Scott, M., Dir.-Sls.--Dictaphone Co. U.K. Ltd., Royal Leamington Spa, United Kingdom; *U.S. Private*, pg. 1045
Scott, Mary Jo, Dir.-Retail Sls.--See's Candy Shops, Inc., South San Francisco, CA; *U.S. Public*, pg. 221
Scott, Newton, Dir.-Mktg. & Sls.--Scottish Widows' Fund & Life Assurance Society, Edinburgh, United Kingdom; *Int'l*, pg. 1212
Scott, Paul, V.P.-Sls. & Mktg.--Richtex Corporation, Columbia, SC; *Int'l*, pg. 699
Scott, Robert L., V.P.-Sls. & Mktg.--Cosmo Communications Corporation, Miami, FL; *U.S. Public*, pg. 451
Scott, Rodney, Dir.-Sls.--April Hill, Inc., Grand Rapids, MI; *U.S. Private*, pg. 483
Scott, Ronald D., Mgr.-Sls.--McDonald Equipment Co., Willoughby, OH; *U.S. Private*, pg. 721
Scott, Scott, Sr. Mgr.-Sls.--Haseko (California) Inc., Los Angeles, CA; *Int'l*, pg. 600
Scott, Terry, V.P.-Sls.--Rollins Truck Leasing Corp., Wilmington, DE; *U.S. Public*, pg. 1405
Scott, William T., V.P.-Sls.--ChemDesign Corporation, Fitchburg, MA; *Int'l*, pg. 173
Scovile, Paul, V.P.-Sls.--Ott Food Products, Carthage, MO; *U.S. Private*, pg. 821
Scowsill, D., Sr. V.P.-Sls. & Mktg.--Hilton International Co., Coral Gables, FL; *Int'l*, pg. 787
Scriven, Scott, Dir.-Sls.-Intl.--BWI Kartridg Pak, Davenport, IA; *Int'l*, pg. 130
Scrupps, Gary L., V.P.-Worldwide Sls.--Acacia Networks, Inc., Lowell, MA; *U.S. Private*, pg. 11
Scudder, Bob, Prod. Mgr.--Martin Reels, A Division of Zebco, Tulsa, OK; *U.S. Public*, pg. 265
Scull, Mike, Dir.-European Opers.--Arrow Group Industries, Inc., Wayne, NJ; *U.S. Private*, pg. 477
Scully, Jim, Sr. V.P.-Sls.--Sony Music Entertainment, Inc., New York, NY; *Int'l*, pg. 1281
Scutt, C., Dir.-Sls.--Aylesbury Automation Ltd., Aylesbury, United Kingdom; *Int'l*, pg. 297
Scwartzman, Stan, V.P.-Activewear Sls.--Fruit of the Loom, Inc., Chicago, IL; *U.S. Public*, pg. 685
Sczcepaniak, Joe, V.P.-Sls. & Mktg./North America--Software Publishing Corporation, Fairfield, NJ; *U.S. Public*, pg. 1483
Seabrook, Brian E., V.P.-Sls.--Seabrook Brothers & Sons, Inc., Seabrook, NJ; *U.S. Private*, pg. 978
Seal, Mark J., V.P.-Polymer Grp.--Georgia Gulf Corporation, Atlanta, GA; *U.S. Public*, pg. 734
Seaman, Dave, V.P.-Sls.--Cole-Haan, Yarmouth, ME; *U.S. Public*, pg. 1184
Searight, Bruce, Mgr.-Mktg., Sls. & Adv.--Energy Systems Industries, Inc., Boston, MA; *U.S. Private*, pg. 376
Searle, Gregg A., V.P.-U.S. Sls. & Mktg.--InterBold, Canton, OH; *U.S. Public*, pg. 506
Sears, David, V.P.-Sls.--Conso Products Company, Union, SC; *U.S. Public*, pg. 434
Seastrom, D.M., Mgr.-Sls.--Turner Construction Company, Irvine, CA; *U.S. Public*, pg. 1645
Seaver, James M., Exec. V.P.-Sls. & Mktg. Grp.--AGCO Corporation, Duluth, GA; *U.S. Public*, pg. 28
Seavey, Ronald D., V.P.-Direct Sls. Southeast--Wallace Computer Services, Inc., Lisle, IL; *U.S. Public*, pg. 1735
Seay, Steve, Mgr.-Mktg.--Microbe Masters, Woodlands, TX; *U.S. Private*, pg. 567
Sebastian, Doug, V.P.-Domestic Sls.--Harris Waste Mgmt. Group, Inc., Peachtree City, GA; *Int'l*, pg. 473
Sebastian, Felix, V.P.-Mktg. & Sls.--Megapulse, Inc., Bedford, MA; *U.S. Private*, pg. 729
Sebastiao, A. Buddy, Mgr.-Mktg. & Intl. Sls.--Centrifugal & Mechanical Industries, Saint Louis, MO; *U.S. Private*, pg. 370
Sechler, William B., Mgr.-Sls.--Fabreeka International, Inc., Stoughton, MA; *U.S. Private*, pg. 390
Secor, Henry, Asst. V.P.- Natl. & Intl. Sls.--Marcel Dekker, Inc., New York, NY; *U.S. Private*, pg. 321
Sector, Don, Mgr.-Natl. Sls.--Rubber & Plastics News, Akron, OH; *U.S. Private*, pg. 285
Sedberry, Steven R., V.P.-Sls. & Mktg.--Century Aluminum Company, Monterey, CA; *U.S. Public*, pg. 328
Sedlak, Bruce, V.P.-Sls.--Three-Five Systems, Tempe, AZ; *U.S. Public*, pg. 1604
Seeger, David, V.P.-Sls. & Mktg.--Welded Tube, Chicago, IL; *Int'l*, pg. 101

Seeley, Bill, V.P.-Dealer Sls.--Mercury Marine, Fond Du Lac, WI; *U.S. Public*, pg. 265

Seeley, Steve, Gen. Sls. Mgr.--Elkay Plastics Company, Inc., Los Angeles, CA; *U.S. Private*, pg. 372

Seeliger, Michael, V.P.-Investor Rels. & Corp. Rels.--Horizon/CMS Healthcare Corporation, Albuquerque, NM; *U.S. Public*, pg. 836

Sefranek, George, V.P.-Sls.--Freeway Corporation, Cleveland, OH; *U.S. Private*, pg. 426

Segel, Walter, Exec. V.P.-Sls.--Hampshire Hosiery, Inc., Spruce Pine, NC; *U.S. Public*, pg. 778

Seger, Charles F., III, V.P.-Sls. & Mktg. & Sec.--Dennis Chemical Co., Inc., Saint Louis, MO; *U.S. Private*, pg. 324

Seguin, Jacques, V.P.-Canadian Sls.--Garland Commercial Ranges, Ltd., Mississauga, Canada; *Int'l*, pg. 189

Seholm, Joachim, Mgr.-Natl. Sls.--Festo Corporation, Hauppauge, NY; *Int'l*, pg. 480

Seibert, Dane, Sr. V.P.-Sls. & Mktg.--Glacier Water Services Inc., Carlsbad, CA; *U.S. Public*, pg. 745

Seibert, John, Mgr.-Reg. Sls. Engrng.--Elastomeric Technologies, Inc., Hatboro, PA; *U.S. Public*, pg. 1598

Seibert, Ron, Gen. Sls. Mgr.--PACCAR Winch Division, Broken Arrow, OK; *U.S. Public*, pg. 1246

Seigel, Paul, Mgr.-Natl. Sls.--Magic American Corporation, Cleveland, OH; *U.S. Private*, pg. 695

Seiler, P., Mgr.-Sls.--Ferrolegeringar AG, Dubendorf, Switzerland; *U.S. Private*, pg. 735

Seiles, Peter Beat, Mgr.-Sls.--Kunz Spinning Mills Ltd., Windisch, Switzerland; *Int'l*, pg. 998

Seiles, Peter Beat, Mgr.-Sls.--Kunz & Dietfurt, Windisch, Switzerland; *Int'l*, pg. 998

Seitz, Thomas, Dir.-Sls. & Mktg.--MPS Corporation, Pittsburgh, PA; *U.S. Private*, pg. 687

Seitz, Thomas D., Mgr.-Sls.--AEP-SPAN, Dallas, TX; *U.S. Public*, pg. 1676

Sekerka, Karl, V.P. & Gen. Mgr.-Sls.--CMI International Inc., Southfield, MI; *U.S. Private*, pg. 195

Selan, Bruce, V.P.-Sls.--Zotos International, Darien, CT; *Int'l*, pg. 1236

Seldeslachts, Marc, Mgr.-Sls.(Benelux)--S.A. Durco Europe N.V., Brussels, Belgium; *U.S. Public*, pg. 659

Seldeslachts, Marc, Mgr.-Sls.--Durco B.V., Breda, Netherlands; *U.S. Public*, pg. 659

Seldin, James, Pres.--Miss Elaine Inc., Saint Louis, MO; *U.S. Private*, pg. 752

Selig, Jeff, Exec. V.P.-Sls./CMC Steel Grp.--Structural Metals, Inc., Seguin, TX; *U.S. Public*, pg. 412

Selig, Jeff, Mgr.-Mill Sls.--SMI Steel South Carolina, Cayce, SC; *U.S. Public*, pg. 412

Seljestokken, Hapald, Mgr.-Sls.--Kaldnes Heavy Lift Trucks A/S, Tonsberg, Norway; *Int'l*, pg. 965

Sell, Joe, V.P.-Sls. Admin.--Gerber Plumbing Fixtures Corporation, Chicago, IL; *U.S. Private*, pg. 449

Sell, Randy, Dir.-Sls.--Krautkramer-Branson, Inc., Lewistown, PA; *U.S. Public*, pg. 574

Sellers, Dave, V.P.-Sls.--L & L Oil Company, Inc., Metairie, LA; *U.S. Private*, pg. 638

Sells, Richard T., Sr. V.P.-Prearranged Sls.--Service Corporation International, Houston, TX; *U.S. Public*, pg. 1460

Sellwood, Peter, Reg. Dir.-Sls. & Mktg.--Willis Corroon South Limited, Maidstone, United Kingdom; *Int'l*, pg. 1503

Seltzer, Sherwin, V.P., Gen. Sls. Mgr. & Mgr.-Sls. Promo., Pub. Rels. & Adv.--Villazon Company Inc., Upper Saddle River, NJ; *U.S. Private*, pg. 1140

Selzler, James, Mgr.-Sls. & Mktg.--McAnally Enterprises, Inc., Yucaipa, CA; *U.S. Private*, pg. 718

Seminoro, J., Mgr.-Natl. Sls.--Polyflon Company, New Rochelle, NY; *U.S. Public*, pg. 457

Sener, Walt, Dir.-Sls. & Mktg.--The Crown Divisions, Wooster, OH; *U.S. Public*, pg. 1631

Sengewalt, Larry, Mgr.-Sales--Forge Division, Marion, OH; *U.S. Public*, pg. 557

Senko, Greg, Mgr.-European Sls.--Comtest Instrumentation B.V., Zoeterwoude-Rijndijk, Netherlands; *U.S. Public*, pg. 1596

Sentell, Greg, Reg. Sls. Mgr.--Varco BJ Oil Tools, Jurong, Singapore; *U.S. Public*, pg. 1709

Sentell, J.P., Mgr.-Sls.--Madison Industries Inc. of Arizona, Phoenix, AZ; *U.S. Private*, pg. 428

Seppala, Eero, Dir.-Sls.--Lappeenranta Paper Mill, Lappeenranta, Finland; *Int'l*, pg. 1428

Sequeria, Jose Ramao, Mgr.-Sls.-Zone V--Central de Cervejas, S.A., Lisbon, Portugal; *Int'l*, pg. 279

Sequin, Brian J., V.P.-Boston Traders Outlet Stores--Designs, Inc., Needham, MA; *U.S. Public*, pg. 501

Serafin, Daniel, V.P.-Sls. & Mktg.--Wolverine Gasket & Manufacturing Co., Inkster, MI; *U.S. Private*, pg. 355

Seratti, Tom, Mgr.-Industrial Sls.--Zack Electronics, San Jose, CA; *U.S. Private*, pg. 1203

Serrano, F., Mgr.-Sls.--McGraw Hill Interamericana de Espana S.A., Madrid, Spain; *U.S. Public*, pg. 1072

Serritella, Mike, Dir.-Sls.--Kirby Building Systems, Inc., Portland, TN; *Int'l*, pg. 699

Serulneck, Lester, Chm. Bd.--Allmetal Screw Products Corp., Deer Park, NY; *U.S. Private*, pg. 41

Servais, G., Mgr.-Sales--Monorail, Inc., Auburn, NY; *U.S. Private*, pg. 256

Sessman, Bernie, Sr. V.P.-Sls. & Mktg.--L&R Manufacturing Co., Kearny, NJ; *U.S. Private*, pg. 638

Setian, Rick, V.P.-Sls. & Mktg.--Isolyser Company, Inc., Norcross, GA; *U.S. Public*, pg. 914

Severino, Donna, Mgr.-Sls.--Circle Frieght International USA, East Boston, MA; *U.S. Public*, pg. 371

Sew, Christine, Coord.-Sls.--Liebert Far East Ltd., Singapore, Singapore; *U.S. Public*, pg. 577

Sewell, Robert, V.P.-Mktg. & Sls.--Telephonics Command Systems Div., Farmingdale, NY; *U.S. Public*, pg. 558

Sexton, Cecil, Outsourcing Sls.--Affiliated Computer Services, Inc., Dallas, TX; *U.S. Public*, pg. 27

Sexton, John, Mgr.-Intl. Sls.--Electro-Voice, Inc., Buchanan, MI; *U.S. Private*, pg. 479

Seymour, Allen, Sr. V.P.-Sls.--Evenflo Company, Inc., Piqua, OH; *U.S. Private*, pg. 629

Seymour, Thomas, V.P.-Western Sls.--Shade Foods, Inc., Union City, CA; *U.S. Private*, pg. 802

Sgro, Bill, Mgr.-Natl. Accts.--Consolidated Electrical Distributors, Westlake Village, CA; *U.S. Private*, pg. 265

Shada, James E., V.P.-Sls.--The Buckle, Inc., Kearney, NE; *U.S. Public*, pg. 267

Shadday, Paul, Mgr.-Sls.--Collins Oldsmobile Inc., Indianapolis, IN; *U.S. Private*, pg. 253

Shaevel, Martin, V.P.-Sls.--Sterilite Corporation, Townsend, MA; *U.S. Private*, pg. 1040

Shafer, Alice, V.P.-Corp. Mktg.--Alimed, Inc., Dedham, MA; *U.S. Private*, pg. 34

Shaffer, Michael, V.P.-Sls.--Breuer/Tornado, Chicago, IL; *U.S. Private*, pg. 167

Shaffer, Scott, V.P.-Consumer Sls.--Rand McNally & Company, Skokie, IL; *U.S. Private*, pg. 908

Shakespeare, Samuel W., V.P.-Sls.--Nabi, Boca Raton, FL; *U.S. Public*, pg. 1148

Shalvoy, James J., V.P.-Sls. & Mktg.-Siding Div.--ABT Building Products Corporation, Neenah, WI; *Int'l*, pg. 20

Shamp. Wesley, Dir.-Sls.--Molded Fiber Glass Co., Union City, PA; *U.S. Private*, pg. 756

Shamshoian, Peter, V.P.-Sls.--ATMI Ecosys Corp., San Jose, CA; *U.S. Public*, pg. 12

Shanahan, David, V.P.-Sls.--Keller Ladders Inc., Fort Lauderdale, FL; *U.S. Public*, pg. 1684

Shanes, Robert, Dir.-Mktg. & Sls.--Talk-A-Phone Co., Chicago, IL; *U.S. Private*, pg. 1067

Shani, Shaul, Mng. Dir.-Sls. Devel.--Sapiens International Corporation N.V., Curacao, Netherlands Antilles; *Int'l*, pg. 1193

Shank, William, Mgr.-Sls. & Service--Agway Energy Products (AEP), Syracuse, NY; *U.S. Private*, pg. 27

Shannon, Bill, Mgr.-Sls.--Derby Cycle Corporation, Kent, WA; *Int'l*, pg. 394

Shannon, Dave, Mng. Dir.-Sls. & Mktg.--Toyota Motor Distributors (Ireland) Ltd., Dublin, Ireland; *Int'l*, pg. 1413

Shannon, Ronald J., V.P.-Sls.--Guinness Southern Division, Newport Beach, CA; *Int'l*, pg. 412

Shannon, Terry, Mgr.-Sls.--International California Glass Corp., South Gate, CA; *U.S. Public*, pg. 895

Shapiro, I. Joseph, V.P.-Sls. & Mktg.--ECI Telecom Ltd., Petah Tiqwa, Israel; *Int'l*, pg. 643

Shapiro, Ilene L., V.P. & Mgr.-Sls. Devel./Prod. Devel.--FirstMerit Corporation, Akron, OH; *U.S. Public*, pg. 646

Shapiro, L.R., Dir.-Sls. & Mktg.--Union Camp Folding Carton Div., Clifton, NJ; *U.S. Public*, pg. 1666

Sharkey, Bonnie, Dir.-Sls.--Kaufman and Broad Central Valley Div., Modesto, CA; *U.S. Public*, pg. 945

Sharkey, David K., Mgr.-Natl. Sls.--Victaulic Company of America, Easton, PA; *U.S. Private*, pg. 1138

Sharp, Bill, Mgr.-Sls.--Anderson Erickson Dairy Company, Des Moines, IA; *U.S. Private*, pg. 72

Sharp, Willis, V.P.-Sls.--Drexel Heritage Furnishings Inc., Drexel, NC; *U.S. Private*, pg. 432

Sharpe, Bradford G., V.P.-Sls.--W.M. Barr & Co., Inc., Memphis, TN; *U.S. Private*, pg. 117

Shattgen, C.F., V.P.-Sls. & Mktg.--Specialty Products and Insulation Company, Lancaster, PA; *U.S. Public*, pg. 913

Shattuck, James A., Exec. V.P.-Mktg. & Sls.--Union Pacific Railroad Company, Omaha, NE; *U.S. Public*, pg. 1668

Shattuck, Jim, V.P.-Mktg. & Sls.--Southern Pacific Rail Corporation, San Francisco, CA; *U.S. Public*, pg. 1668

Shaughnessy, James, Asst. V.P.-Mktg., Sls. & Retail Bus.--Wyeth-Ayerst Laboratories, Inc., Philadelphia, PA; *U.S. Public*, pg. 80

Shaver, Pat, Mgr.-Large Acct. Sls.--PENCO-Ohio, Worthington, OH; *Int'l*, pg. 1508

Shaw, Alec, Mgr.-UK Retail Div.--Bain Hogg Group plc, London, United Kingdom; *Int'l*, pg. 671

Shaw, Bob, V.P.-Sls./Window Div.--Cameo Window Furnishings, New York, NY; *U.S. Private*, pg. 1094

Shaw, Bob, Mgr.-Sls.--Western Waste Industries, Torrance, CA; *U.S. Public*, pg. 1686

Shaw, Clark, V.P.-Sls.--A-P-A Transport Corp., North Bergen, NJ; *U.S. Private*, pg. 2

Shaw, Frederick J., Exec. V.P.-Sls.--Bloomsburg Mills Inc., New York, NY; *U.S. Private*, pg. 150

Shaw, John C., Jr., Exec. V.P. & Asst. Mgr.-Natl. Sls.--Jefferies & Company, Inc., Los Angeles, CA; *U.S. Public*, *pg. 925*

Shaw, John C., Jr., Asst. Mgr.-Natl. Sls.--Jefferies & Company, Inc., Boston, MA; *U.S. Public*, pg. 925

Shaw, Michael S., V.P.-Sls. & Mktg.--Peabody COALSALES Company, Saint Louis, MO; *Int'l*, pg. 594

Shawe, Larry, V.P.-Sls. & Mktg.--Engle Homes, Inc., Boca Raton, FL; *U.S. Public*, pg. 583

Shawver, Todd A., V.P.-Sls. & Mktg.--Union Pump Company, Battle Creek, MI; *U.S. Private*, pg. 1119

Shay, Michael, V.P.-Sls.--CPC Foodservice Group, Franklin Park, IL; *U.S. Public*, pg. 224

Shay, Michael A., V.P.-Sls. & Mktg.--Hauck Mfg. Co., Cleona, PA; *U.S. Private*, pg. 510

Shea, Fred, Dir.-Midwest Div. Sls. & Mktg.--Hyatt Hotels Corporation, Chicago, IL; *U.S. Private*, pg. 551

Shea, John, Mgr.-Sls.--Velvet Drive Transmissions, New Bedford, MA; *U.S. Public*, pg. 1370

Shea, Michael, Sr. V.P.-Sls. & Mktg.--Daw Technologies, Inc., Salt Lake City, UT; *U.S. Public*, pg. 489

Shea, Wayne, V.P.-Worldwide Sls.--The First Years Inc., Avon, MA; *U.S. Public*, pg. 642

Shean, John, V.P.-Sls.--Arizona Cardinals, Phoenix, AZ; *U.S. Private*, pg. 81

Sheargold, Glenn, Branch Sls. Mgr.--Kohler Australia, Wetherill Park, Australia; *U.S. Private*, pg. 631

Shears, Tom, Mktg.-Sls.--Wilsey Foods, Inc., Fort Worth, TX; *Int'l*, pg. 879

Sheble, James, Mgr.-Sls.--Nucor Steel-Texas, Jewett, TX; *U.S. Public*, pg. 1205

Sheehan, Bill, V.P.-Sls., Automotive Div.--Wix Div., Gastonia, NC; *U.S. Public*, pg. 479

Sheehan, Chris, V.P.-Mktg.--Labelon Corporation, Canandaigua, NY; *U.S. Private*, pg. 641

Sheehan, Jack, V.P.-Sls. & Mktg.--Wagner Lighting Products, Chesterfield, MO; *U.S. Public*, pg. 442

Sheehan, Jack, V.P.-Sls. & Mktg.--Cooper Automotive Division, Chesterfield, MO; *U.S. Public*, pg. 443

Sheffield, Syd, Mgr.-Natl. Sls.--Corning Canada Inc., Richmond Hill, Canada; *U.S. Public*, pg. 448

Shelbourne, Jack, V.P.-Sls.--LaBarge Mirrors, Inc., Holland, MI; *U.S. Private*, pg. 432

Shelton, David W., Dir.-U.S. Sls.--Physio-Control Corporation, Redmond, WA; *U.S. Public*, pg. 1294

Shelton, Gary L., Natl. Sls. Mgr.--T & S Brass & Bronze Works, Inc., Travelers Rest, SC; *U.S. Private*, pg. 1061

Shelton, Jack, Sr. V.P.-Mktg.--Fender Musical Instruments, Scottsdale, AZ; *U.S. Private*, pg. 400

Shemesh, Jacob, Exec. V.P.-Sls.--IIS Intelligent Information Systems Ltd., Yokneam, Israel; *Int'l*, pg. 645

Shen, Andrew, Mgr.-Sls.--China Airlines Ltd., Washington, DC; *Int'l*, pg. 285

Shen, Dean, Assoc. Dir.-Sls./Asia Pacific--Mitsubishi Silicon America, Palo Alto, CA; *Int'l*, pg. 875

Shepherd, Malcolm H., Mgr.-Sls. & Mktg.--Arrow Gear Company, Downers Grove, IL; *U.S. Private*, pg. 85

Shepherd, Nick, Gen. Mgr.-Coffee & Food--Kraft Jacobs Suchard, Cheltenham, United Kingdom; *U.S. Public*, pg. 1290

Shepherd, Ted, Pres.--Archibald Candy Company, Chicago, IL; *U.S. Private*, pg. 597

Sheppard, Michael, V.P. & Reg. Sls. Mgr.-West--Mr. Christmas Inc., New York, NY; *U.S. Private*, pg. 765

Sherban, P.J., V.P.-Sls.--Universal Studios Hollywood, Universal City, CA; *Int'l*, pg. 1216

Sheridan, Jerry, Dir.-Central Regional Sls.--Lynx Golf, Inc., City of Industry, CA; *U.S. Private*, pg. 684

Sheridan, Kevin, V.P.-Data Processing Sls.--Database America Companies, Montvale, NJ; *U.S. Private*, pg. 312

Sherlock, Joseph M., Mgr.-Sls. & Adv.--Tinius Olsen Testing Machine Co., Inc., Willow Grove, PA; *U.S. Private*, pg. 1088

Sherlock, Liam, Mgr.-Aftersls.--Fiat Auto Ireland Ltd., Dublin, Ireland; *Int'l*, pg. 481

Sherlock, Mike, Sr. V.P. & Gen. Mgr.--Gitano Fashions Ltd., Bowling Green, KY; *U.S. Public*, pg. 686

Sherman, Bill, Sr. V.P.-Institutional Prod.--Riddell Sports, Inc., New York, NY; *U.S. Public*, pg. 1389

Sherman, Dean, Mgr.-Sls.--Malloy Lithographing Inc., Ann Arbor, MI; *U.S. Private*, pg. 698

Sherman, R.J., Gen. Dir.-Sls. & Mktg., U.S.--Service Parts Operations, Flint, MI; *U.S. Public*, pg. 720

Sherman, Tom, V.P.-Sls & Mktg.--Sunnyland Inc., Thomasville, GA; *U.S. Public*, pg. 1479

Sherow, Donald, Dir.-Sls.--Modern Hilift Equipment Co., West Conshohocken, PA; *U.S. Private*, pg. 755

Sherratt, E.L., Dir.-Sls.--Morganite Industrial Carbon (MIC), Johannesburg, South Africa; *Int'l*, pg. 895

Sherrick, Robert, Exec. V.P.-Sls. & Mdsg.--Edwards Super Food Stores, Carlisle, PA; *Int'l*, pg. 749

Sherrod, Bill, Mgr.-Circulation & Bus.--The Business Journal of Portland, Inc., Portland, OR; *U.S. Private*, pg. 19

Sherry, Jeff, Mgr.-Intl. Sls.--Dukane Ultrasonics Div., Saint Charles, IL; *U.S. Private*, pg. 346

Sherwood, Philip H., Div. V.P.-Sls.--Stuart Entertainment Inc., Council Bluffs, IA; *U.S. Public*, pg. 1526

Sheth, Arun, Dir.-Intl. Sls. & Mktg.--KineticSystems Corporation, Lockport, IL; *U.S. Private*, pg. 620

Shi, Pau Shoon, Mgr.-Sls.--KONE Elevator Pte. Ltd., Singapore, Singapore; *Int'l*, pg. 747

Shields, James E., V.P.-Sls.--MGI PHARMA INC., Minneapolis, MN; *U.S. Public*, pg. 1026

Shiino, K., Mgr.-Sls. & Mktg.--Morinaga Nutritional Foods Deutschland GmbH, Stuttgart, Germany; *Int'l*, pg. 895

Shilcock, George, Mgr.-Parts-Sls.--Sequa Can Machinery, East Rutherford, NJ; *U.S. Public*, pg. 1458

Shiller, Linda, V.P.-Mktg., Sls. & Reservations--Imperial Hotels, El Segundo, CA; *U.S. Private*, pg. 558

Shiller, Linda, V.P.-Adv., Mktg. & Sls.--The Vagabond Inns, San Diego, CA; *U.S. Private*, pg. 558

Shilling, Charles, Dir.-Sls.--Aydin Electro-Fab Div., Croydon, PA; *U.S. Public*, pg. 158

Shimamura, Takeshi, Sr. Mng. Dir.-Kinki & Shikoku Area Sls.--Daiwa Securities Co. Ltd., Tokyo, Japan; *Int'l*, pg. 374

Shimansky, Henry, V.P.-Sls. Admin.--Slim-Fast Foods Company, West Palm Beach, FL; *U.S. Private*, pg. 1006

Shimizu, Keiji, Gen. Mgr.-Airfreight Sls.--Kwe-Kintetsu World Express(S)Pte Ltd., Singapore, Singapore; *Int'l*, pg. 735

Shimizu, Scott E., Exec. V.P.-Sls.--Pillowtex Corporation, Dallas, TX; *U.S. Public*, pg. 1296

Shimomura, Kei, Mgr.-Mktg. & Sls.--Japan Travel Bureau International, Inc., New York, NY; *U.S. Private*, pg. 582

Shind, Steve, V.P.-Sls.--Flavor House Products, Inc., Dothan, AL; *U.S. Private*, pg. 410

Shiner, Donald, V.P.--Deluxe Homes Of PA., Inc., Berwick, PA; *U.S. Private*, pg. 323

Shinoda, Hiroshi, Sr. V.P.-Sls. & Mktg.--Pentel of America, Ltd., Torrance, CA; *Int'l*, pg. 1035

Shirilla, John, Mgr.-Gen. Sls.--Photogenic Machine Company, Inc., Youngstown, OH; *U.S. Private*, pg. 864

Shively, Bill, Exec. V.P.-Worldwide Sls.--Gelco Information Network, Inc., Eden Prairie, MN; *U.S. Private*, pg. 442

Shively, Lynn, Mgr.-Commercial Sls.--Precor, Inc., Bothell, WA; *U.S. Public*, pg. 1322

Shivers, Gary R., Sr. V.P.-Sls.--Advanta Business Services, Voorhees, NJ; *U.S. Public*, pg. 22

Shloub, Michael, Exec. V.P.-Admin.--Crosby & Overton, Inc., Long Beach, CA; *U.S. Private*, pg. 290

Shoaf, Ben, Pres.-Fashion Fabrics--Milliken & Company, Spartanburg, SC; *U.S. Private*, pg. 748

Shoe, Richard L., V.P.-Mktg. & Sls.--Carolina Biological Supply Co., Burlington, NC; *U.S. Private*, pg. 213

Shoemaker, Don, V.P.-Sls.--Lozier Corporation, Omaha, NE; *U.S. Private*, pg. 679

Shogren, James, V.P.-Sls.--Pre Finish Metals Incorporated, Elk Grove Village, IL; *U.S. Public*, pg. 1056
Sholakh, Sam, Gen. Mgr.-Sls.--Nexus Plastics, Inc., Hawthorne, NJ; *U.S. Private*, pg. 797
Shone, Thomas, Dir.-Mktg.--The Cooper Companies, Inc., Irvine, CA; *U.S. Public*, pg. 442
Shook, Bob, Mgr.-Large Acct. Sls.--PENCO-Tennessee, Nashville, TN; *Int'l*, pg. 1508
Shook, Randy, Dir.-Sls.--Danaher Tool Group, Lancaster, PA; *U.S. Public*, pg. 480
Shope, Lissa, Mgr.-Mktg. & Sls.--LINC Quantum Analytics, Foster City, CA; *U.S. Public*, pg. 996
Shope, Roger, Dir.-Domestic Sls.--Tellabs Operations, Inc., Lisle, IL; *U.S. Public*, pg. 1572
Shopoff, Bruce, Sr. V.P.-Reg. Sls./Los Angeles--Swank, Inc., Attleboro, MA; *U.S. Public*, pg. 1543
Shore, Jeffrey, V.P.-Sls. & Mktg.--Kaufman and Broad Home Corporation, Los Angeles, CA; *U.S. Public*, pg. 944
Short, Richard, V.P. & Mgr.-Sls.--NTS-Los Angeles Division, Los Angeles, CA; *U.S. Public*, pg. 1161
Shorthose, Paul G., V.P.-Worldwide Sls.--Art Technology Group, Boston, MA; *U.S. Private*, pg. 86
Shoshani, Avraham, V.P.-Sls.--Elscint Ltd., Haifa, Israel; *Int'l*, pg. 450
Show, Pat, V.P.-Sls.--Compar, New York, NY; *Int'l*, pg. 1073
Showalter, Tom, Dir.-Sls.--Louisiana Downs, Bossier City, LA; *U.S. Private*, pg. 319
Showers, Jacqui, Mgr.-Mktg. & Pub. Rels.--National Electrical Manufacturers Association, Arlington, VA; *U.S. Private*, pg. 782
Showlater, Rick, Dir.-Mktg. & sls.--The Van Metres Companies, Burke, VA; *U.S. Private*, pg. 1132
Shrader, Michael J., V.P.-Gen. Sls./Americas Group--Gateway 2000, North Sioux City, SD; *U.S. Public*, pg. 703
Shrigley, David A., Exec. V.P.-Sls., Service & Mktg.--Bay Networks, Inc., Santa Clara, CA; *U.S. Public*, pg. 196
Shriver, Frank, V.P.-Sls.--Independent Can Company, Belcamp, MD; *U.S. Private*, pg. 559
Shubin, Dennis, V.P.-Sls.--Mother's Cake & Cookie Co., Oakland, CA; *U.S. Private*, pg. 1022
Shulman, Arthur, V.P.-Retail Sls.--National Electronics Warranty Corporation, Sterling, VA; *U.S. Private*, pg. 782
Shum, Amy Y.M., V.P.-Sls.--Smart Shirts Ltd., Kowloon, Hong Kong; *U.S. Public*, pg. 948
Sibbick, Bill, Sr. V.P.-Sls.--Stanley Furniture Co. Inc., Stanleytown, VA; *U.S. Public*, pg. 1508
Sibella, Frank, Mgr.-Sls.--Adams Industries, Inc., Suffield, CT; *U.S. Public*, pg. 187
Sibert, Jean-Cleurg, Dir.-Sls.--Wisaforest France S.A.R.L., Lyon, France; *Int'l*, pg. 1429
Sica, Richard R., Mgr.-Sls.--H.S. Crocker Co., Inc., Huntley, IL; *U.S. Private*, pg. 290
Siden, Debbie S., V.P.-Sls.--Union Industries, Inc., Providence, RI; *U.S. Private*, pg. 1119
Sidler, Norman F., Div. V.P.-Sls.--The Peoples Gas Light & Coke Co., Chicago, IL; *U.S. Public*, pg. 1275
Sidler, Norman F., Jr., Div. V.P.-Sls.--Peoples Energy Corporation, Chicago, IL; *U.S. Public*, pg. 1274
Sieb, Chuck, Dir.-Comet Aftermath Sls.--Hoffco/Comet Industries, Inc., Richmond, IN; *U.S. Private*, pg. 532
Siebers, Bruce, Natl. Sls. Mgr.-Gas Grill--MWCA, Rexburg, ID; *U.S. Public*, pg. 804
Sieckman, Debra, V.P.-Sls. & Mktg.--National Van Lines, Inc., Broadview, IL; *U.S. Private*, pg. 788
Siegel, Jeff, Exec. V.P.-Sls. & Mktg.--Lifetime Hoan Corp., Westbury, NY; *U.S. Public*, pg. 992
Siegel, Todd, V.P.-MTV Adv. Sls.--MTV Networks, New York, NY; *U.S. Private*, pg. 779
Sieger, Carl, Natl. Sls. Mgr.--K-D Lamp Company, Cincinnati, OH; *U.S. Private*, pg. 603
Siembab, Kevin J., Mgr.-Sls.--Mele Manufacturing Co., Inc., Utica, NY; *U.S. Private*, pg. 730
Siemer, Barbara J., Dir.-Sls. & Intl. Mkt. Coord.--Desco Corporation, Columbus, OH; *U.S. Private*, pg. 326
Sienicki, Stephen A., V.P.-Sls.--DiscWasher, Lake Mary, FL; *U.S. Public*, pg. 1369
Sieron, Mark, V.P.-Sls.--The Middleby Corporation, Rolling Meadows, IL; *U.S. Public*, pg. 1109
Sieron, Mark, V.P.-Sls.--Middleby Marshall/CTX, Elgin, IL; *U.S. Public*, pg. 1110
Sierra, Jesus Navarro, Mgr.-Natl. Sls.--Loctite Espana, S.A., Madrid, Spain; *Int'l*, pg. 611
Sierra, Justo, Mgr.-Sls.--Grupo Simec, S.A. de C.V., Guadalajara, Mexico; *Int'l*, pg. 576
Siewert, Monica, Mgr.-Media & Mktg. Svcs.--Sacramento Municipal Utility District, Sacramento, CA; *U.S. Private*, pg. 959
Siewert, Patrick T., Chief Oper. Officer-Mktg. & Sls.--Eastman Kodak Company, Rochester, NY; *U.S. Public*, pg. 550
Sigmar, Bill, Natl. Sls. Mgr.--Fisher Broadcasting Inc., Seattle, WA; *U.S. Private*, pg. 648
Signorelli, Lou, Mgr.-Natl. Sls./Tools Retail--Wilton Corporation, Palatine, IL; *U.S. Private*, pg. 1181
Signorelli, Lou, Dir.-Sls. & Retail--Warren Tool Group, Garrettsville, OH; *U.S. Private*, pg. 1181
Sigvardt, Ole, V.P.-Sls. & Mktg.--Danfoss Fluid Power, Racine, WI; *Int'l*, pg. 377
Sikora, Mike, Mgr.-Mktg. & Sls.-Fluid Handling--Aro Fluid Products Division, Bryan, OH; *U.S. Public*, pg. 877
Silano, Frank, Mgr.-Natl. Sls.--The Turner & Seymour Mfg. Company, Torrington, CT; *U.S. Private*, pg. 1109
Silberman, Michael, Sr. V.P.-Theatrical Sls.--October Films, Inc., New York, NY; *Int'l*, pg. 1216
Silberstein, Bruce Jay, Pres.--Columbus Pipe & Equipment Company, Columbus, OH; *U.S. Private*, pg. 257
Silipigni, Dick, V.P.-Sls.- CBS Radio Network--CBS Radio Div., New York, NY; *U.S. Public*, pg. 274
Silkwood, Charles, Dir.-Sls.--Maddak Inc., Pequannock, NJ; *U.S. Private*, pg. 130
Sillers, Coby, Sr. V.P.-Sls. & Mktg.--Oki Telecom Group, Suwanee, GA; *Int'l*, pg. 1000
Sillick, David, Mgr.-Sls.--Business Journals of North Carolina, LLC, Raleigh, NC; *U.S. Private*, pg. 19
Silver, Bertram R., Pres.--Jenkins Spirits Corp. Ltd., Londonderry, NH; *U.S. Private*, pg. 585
Silver, Edward, Mgr.-Sls.--The Barden Corporation, Danbury, CT; *Int'l*, pg. 468
Silverberg, Al, Dir.-Sls.--Personal Communications Div., Fort Worth, TX; *Int'l*, pg. 1433
Silverman, Gerrald B., Sr. V.P.-Sls. The Keds Corporation--The Stride Rite Corporation, Lexington, MA; *U.S. Public*, pg. 1524
Silvernail, Bob, Mgr.-Dealer Sls.--Jones Blair Company, Dallas, TX; *U.S. Private*, pg. 596
Silvestre, Javier, Dir. & V.P.-Sls./City Div. Europe--Sol Melia, Palma de Mallorca, Spain; *Int'l*, pg. 1277
Silvestri, John, Exec. V.P.-Adv. Sls.--USA Networks, New York, NY; *U.S. Public*, pg. 1686
Silvia, Jason, V.P.-Worldwide Sls. & Service--Ardent Software, Inc., Westborough, MA; *U.S. Public*, pg. 129
Silvire, Ricardo, Dir.-Sls. & Mktg.--Swedish Match do Brasil S/A, Rio de Janeiro, Brazil; *Int'l*, pg. 1328
Simak, Bob, Dir.-Sls.--L&J Technologies, Hillside, IL; *U.S. Private*, pg. 638
Simal, Joao, Mng. Dir.-Sls.--Sensormatic Lda., Lisbon, Portugal; *U.S. Public*, pg. 1458
Simko, Sherri, Mgr.-Sls.--Furniture Consultants, New York, NY; *U.S. Public*, pg. 1686
Simm McDowell, Terri, V.P.-Sls.--Sanofi Beaute, Inc., New York, NY; *Int'l*, pg. 445
Simmons, Don, V.P.-Sls. & Mktg.--Mountain Valley Spring Company, Hot Springs National Park, AR; *U.S. Private*, pg. 963
Simmons, J.K., Dir.-Mktg. & Sls.--Kemlite Company, Joliet, IL; *U.S. Public*, pg. 457
Simmons, Kenneth, Mgr.-Sls.--Public Service Company of Oklahoma-Northern Div., Bartlesville, OK; *U.S. Public*, pg. 324
Simmons, Patrick E., Dir.-Mktg. & Sls.--Yoplait USA, Minneapolis, MN; *U.S. Public*, pg. 718
Simmons, William, V.P.-Sls. Admin.--Ohmeda, Liberty Corner, NJ; *Int'l*, pg. 121
Simms-Brown, Judy, Dir.-Sls. & Mktg.--Watlow Gordon, Richmond, IL; *U.S. Private*, pg. 1153
Simon, Christopher, V.P. & Dir.-Sls. & Mktg.--CBS Television Network, New York, NY; *U.S. Public*, pg. 274
Simon, George, V.P.-Sales--CTB/McGraw Hill, Monterey, CA; *U.S. Public*, pg. 1070
Simon, Jeremy, V.P.-Sls. & Mktg.--Del Global Technologies, Valhalla, NY; *U.S. Public*, pg. 493
Simon, John, V.P.-Sls.--American Tourister, Inc., Warren, RI; *U.S. Public*, pg. 1430
Simon, Mark, Dir.-Sls.--Dowty Aerospace Yakima, Yakima, WA; *Int'l*, pg. 1337
Simon, R., Mgr.-Sls.--Union Camp Chemical Products Div., Wayne, NJ; *U.S. Public*, pg. 1666
Simon, Robert, V.P.-Sls./SED--Southern Electronics Corporation, Tucker, GA; *U.S. Public*, pg. 1490
Simon, Robert, V.P.-Sls.--Southern Electronics Distributors International, Tucker, GA; *U.S. Public*, pg. 1490
Simon, Terry, V.P.-Sls.--Duro Bag Manufacturing Co., Ludlow, KY; *U.S. Private*, pg. 348
Simoncini, Robert P., V.P.-Sls.--Danafilms, Inc., Westborough, MA; *U.S. Private*, pg. 309
Simonds, Brian, Mgr.-Sls.--Kingsbury Machining Center, Div., Keene, NH; *U.S. Private*, pg. 622
Simoneau, Line, Gen. Mgr.-Admin. Sls.--Reseau de Television Quatre Saisons Inc., Montreal, Canada; *Int'l*, pg. 241
Simonetti, Jim, Gen. Sls. Mgr.--WELI-AM, Hamden, CT; *U.S. Public*, pg. 384
Simonetti, Jim, Gen. Sls. Mgr.--WKCI-FM, Hamden, CT; *U.S. Public*, pg. 385
Simons, Craig, V.P.-Sls. & Mktg.--IMI Cash Valve, Inc., Cullman, AL; *Int'l*, pg. 646
Simonsen, M., Dir.-Sls. & Mktg.--Simonsen & Sons Limited, Nykobing, Denmark; *Int'l*, pg. 894
Simpkins, C. M., V.P.-Mktg. & Sls.--Compaction America, Kewanee, IL; *U.S. Public*, pg. 1676
Simpson, J.T., Mgr.-Leasing & Fleet Programs--Lincoln-Mercury Division, Detroit, MI; *U.S. Public*, pg. 662
Simpson, Michael, V.P. Sls.-Southeast Reg.--RS Electronics, Livonia, MI; *U.S. Private*, pg. 905
Simpson, T.M., Gen. Sls. Mgr.--Seven Seas Limited, Hull, United Kingdom; *Int'l*, pg. 593
Simpson, William, Gen. Mgr.-Sls.--Danfoss Fluid Power, Racine, WI; *Int'l*, pg. 377
Sims, Doug, Mgr.-Sls.--Milgray/Atlanta, Inc., Norcross, GA; *U.S. Public*, pg. 206
Sims, Jack, Sr. V.P.-Music Sls.--Queens Group, Inc., Long Island City, NY; *U.S. Private*, pg. 900
Sims, Mike J., Mgr.-Mktg./Siding--ABT Building Products Corporation, Neenah, WI; *Int'l*, pg. 20
Sinclair, Dan, V.P.-Sls.--Sinclair Printing & Litho, Inc., Los Angeles, CA; *U.S. Private*, pg. 1003
Sinclair, John, V.P.-Sls.--Niagara Frontier Hockey, L.P., Buffalo, NY; *U.S. Private*, pg. 798
Singer, Steve, V.P.-Sun Lakes Sls.--Robson Communities, Sun Lakes, AZ; *U.S. Private*, pg. 937
Singfield, Mark, Reg. Dir.-Sls. & Mktg.--Willis Corroon South Limited, Maidstone, United Kingdom; *Int'l*, pg. 1503
Singh, Anil, V.P.-Adv. Sls.--Yahoo!, Inc., Santa Clara, CA; *U.S. Public*, pg. 1787
Singh, Shri, V.P.-Sls.--Ranjit Corporation, Cedar Knolls, NJ; *U.S. Private*, pg. 909
Singleton, David, Dir.-Sls.--International Factors Limited, Brighton, United Kingdom; *Int'l*, pg. 813
Sinha, P.K., Mgr.-USA & Canada--Air-India, New York, NY; *Int'l*, pg. 37
Sinick, Ken, Mgr.-Natl. Sls.--Channel Master, Smithfield, NC; *U.S. Private*, pg. 228
Sinkel, Hank, V.P.-Sls.--Esprit de Corp., San Francisco, CA; *U.S. Private*, pg. 383
Sinkula, David, Mgr.-Freshlike Frozen Sls.--Dean Foods Vegetable Company, Green Bay, WI; *U.S. Public*, pg. 490
Sinnott, Dan, Dir.-Sls.--Turner Construction Co., Detroit, MI; *U.S. Public*, pg. 1645
Sipe, Alan W., V.P.-Sls. & Mktg.--Klein Tools Inc., Skokie, IL; *U.S. Private*, pg. 625
Sirgant, Robert B., V.P.-Corp. Accts.--USG Corporation, Chicago, IL; *U.S. Public*, pg. 1660
Sirko, Randy, Mgr.-Sls.--Manning Equipment, Inc., Louisville, KY; *U.S. Private*, pg. 700
Sirridge, John, V.P.-US Sls. Div.--Bar-S Foods Co., Phoenix, AZ; *U.S. Private*, pg. 114
Sitarz, Jim, V.P.-Sls. & Mktg.--Prospect Foundry, Inc., Minneapolis, MN; *U.S. Public*, pg. 142
Siveiro, Victor, Dir.-Sls.--Binter Canarias, Las Palmas, Spain; *Int'l*, pg. 574
Siwek, Paul, V.P.-Sls. & Mktg.--ELE International, Inc./Soiltest, Lake Bluff, IL; *Int'l*, pg. 1287
Siwicki, Frank, Natl. Sls. Mgr.--Synchro-Start Products, Inc., Niles, IL; *U.S. Private*, pg. 627
Sjamaar, R., Mgr.-Sls. & Mktg.--Honig Merkartikelen B.V., Koog aan de Zaan, Netherlands; *Int'l*, pg. 244
Skaare, Gordon, Dir.-Sls.--IPC-International Parts Corp., Chicago, IL; *U.S. Public*, pg. 1766
Skaggs, Jerry, Dir.-Sls.--O'Reilly Automotive Inc., Springfield, MO; *U.S. Public*, pg. 1230
Skare, Ronald J., V.P.-Sls.--Ecology and Environment, Inc., Lancaster, NY; *U.S. Public*, pg. 562
Skarie, David, V.P.-Sls.--Ralston Foods, Inc., Saint Louis, MO; *U.S. Public*, pg. 1359
Skebba, Bill, Jr., Sr. V.P.-Sls. & Mktg.--M.W. Kasch Company, Mequon, WI; *U.S. Private*, pg. 608
Skelley, William, Mgr.-Sls. Plng.--General Cigar Company, Inc., Bloomfield, CT; *U.S. Public*, pg. 708
Skelly, John, V.P.-Intl. Sls. & Mktg.--Haarmann & Reimer Food Ingredients Div., Elkhart, IN; *Int'l*, pg. 173
Skelton, Don, Sr. V.P.-Mktg. & Sls.--Illinois Central Corporation, Chicago, IL; *U.S. Public*, pg. 864
Skelton, James, Dir.-Sls.--Caddock Electronics, Inc., Riverside, CA; *U.S. Private*, pg. 198
Skemp, Randy, Sr. V.P.-Sls.--HBO & Company/Cycare Business Group, Scottsdale, AZ; *U.S. Public*, pg. 770
Skene, Jerry A., V.P.-Sls. & Mktg.--Peter Pan Seafoods, Inc., Seattle, WA; *Int'l*, pg. 928
Skibinski, Betsy, Mgr.-Mktg.& Sls.--Ansco Photo-Optical Products Corp., Elk Grove Village, IL; *Int'l*, pg. 587
Skibo, Andrew D., Exec. V.P.-Sls. & Mktg.--Life Sciences International, Philadelphia, PA; *U.S. Private*, pg. 317
Skidelsky, S.M., Dir.-Sls.--Turner Construction Co., Miami, FL; *U.S. Public*, pg. 1645
Skinner, Murray, V.P.-Mktg. & Sls.--Metroland Printing & Distributing, Mississauga, Canada; *Int'l*, pg. 1402
Skinner, Robert H., Sr. V.P.-Sls.--Best Software, Inc., Reston, VA; *U.S. Public*, pg. 223
Skipp, Andrew K., Exec. V.P.--Hubbard Hall Inc., Waterbury, CT; *U.S. Private*, pg. 544
Skipper, Skip, V.P.-Distr. Sls.--Great Dane Trailers, Inc., Savannah, GA; *U.S. Private*, pg. 1030
Sklar, Bob, Sr. V.P.-Sls.--Interactive Telecard Services, Inc. (ITS), Miami, FL; *U.S. Private*, pg. 566
Skog, Bary L., Chief Mktg. Officer--Harley Ellington Design, Southfield, MI; *U.S. Private*, pg. 503
Skomoroh, Ed, V.P.-Sls. & Mktg.--Polaris Industries, Inc., Minneapolis, MN; *U.S. Public*, pg. 1313
Skorpinski, Casey J., V.P.-Sls. & Mktg.--Whiting Corporation, Harvey, IL; *U.S. Private*, pg. 1173
Skoulis, Thomas A., V.P.-N. America Sls.--Netopia, Inc., Alameda, CA; *U.S. Public*, pg. 1168
Skow, Lary, V.P.-Sls.--Sico North America Inc., Minneapolis, MN; *U.S. Private*, pg. 997
Skura, Gary, V.P.-Sls.--Buffalo Hospital Supply Co., Inc., Buffalo, NY; *U.S. Private*, pg. 179
Skyrmes, Smokey, V.P.-Sls. & Mktg.--Harcros Chemicals Inc., Kansas City, KS; *Int'l*, pg. 598
Slade, Barry, Dir.-Sls. & Mktg./Intl.--Fountain Powerboat Industries, Inc., Washington, NC; *U.S. Public*, pg. 678
Slade, James M., V.P.-Sls.--Techalloy Co., Inc., Mahwah, NJ; *Int'l*, pg. 572
Slagle, Fred, V.P.-Sls.--Cincinnati Sales, Mason, OH; *U.S. Public*, pg. 611
Slagle, Jim, V.P.-Sls. & Mktg.--Servico, Inc., West Palm Beach, FL; *U.S. Public*, pg. 1462
Slaney, Mary, V.P.-Sales & Mktg.--Delcar Digital, New York, NY; *U.S. Public*, pg. 1642
Slangen, Louis F.J., Sr. V.P.-Sls. & Mktg.--Invacare Corporation, Elyria, OH; *U.S. Public*, pg. 911
Slankard, Marilyn, Dir.-Mktg. & Sls.--Borders, Inc., Ann Arbor, MI; *U.S. Public*, pg. 245
Slate, Robert, Dir.-Sls.--Alabama Farmers Co-op, Decatur, AL; *U.S. Private*, pg. 30
Slattery, Terry, V.P.-Sales--Adidas (Canada) Ltd., Downsview, Canada; *Int'l*, pg. 24
Slaughter, Joe, V.P. & Gen. Mgr.-Scholastic--Herff Jones Inc., Indianapolis, IN; *U.S. Private*, pg. 523
Slaughter, Jon, V.P.-Sls.--Johnson Worldwide Associates, Inc., Sturtevant, WI; *U.S. Public*, pg. 932
Slavik, Robert, V.P.-Sls./Meat Prods.--Hormel Foods Corp., Austin, MN; *U.S. Public*, pg. 840
Slavik, Robert A., V.P.-Sls.--Hormel Meat Products Div., Austin, MN; *U.S. Public*, pg. 840
Slavin, E.A., V.P.-Sls. & Mktg.--NVF Company, Yorklyn, DE; *U.S. Private*, pg. 772
Slayter, Craig K., V.P.-Worldwide Field Opers.--Phoenix Technologies Ltd., San Jose, CA; *U.S. Public*, pg. 1292
Sleeth, Dave, V.P.-Sls.--Recoton Canada Ltd., Markham, Canada; *U.S. Public*, pg. 1369
Slingerland, Oscar, Trader--Coastal (Rotterdam) B.V., Rotterdam, Netherlands; *U.S. Public*, pg. 390
Sliva, Robert D., Mgr.-Natl. Sls.--WXYZ TV - Channel 7 of Detroit, Inc., Southfield, MI; *U.S. Public*, pg. 1448
Sloan, Bruce, Dir.-Sls.--Danisco Ingredients USA, Inc., New Century, KS; *Int'l*, pg. 378

Sloan, Stephen, Sr. V.P. & Gen. Mgr.-Mdse.--The Bon Ton Stores, Inc., York, PA; *U.S. Public*, pg. 244
Sloane, Michael A., V.P.-Sls.--Sportcraft Ltd., Mount Olive, NJ; *U.S. Private*, pg. 1026
Sloane, Steven, V.P.-Intl. Sls.--Chyron Corp., Melville, NY; *Int'l*, pg. 1372
Slone, Carl J., V.P.-Mktg. & Sls.--Trigon Blue Cross & Blue Shield, Richmond, VA; *U.S. Public*, pg. 1637
Slotter, Brian, Sls. Zone Mgr.--Coldwater Seafood Corporation, Rowayton, CT; *U.S. Private*, pg. 251
Slowey, Thomas A., Exec. V.P.-Sls.--Platinum Technology, Inc., Oak Brook Terrace, IL; *U.S. Public*, pg. 1309
Slusarski, Don, Exec. V.P.-Field Opers.--Lawson Software, Minneapolis, MN; *U.S. Private*, pg. 654
Sluss, Greg, Dir.-Sls. & Mktg.--Republic Storage Systems Company Inc., Canton, OH; *U.S. Private*, pg. 924
Slutzky, Elliot, Exec. V.P.-Sls.--LIVE Film & Mediaworks, Van Nuys, CA; *U.S. Private*, pg. 671
Small, Peter, Area Sls. Mgr.--Analog Devices Ltd., Livingston, United Kingdom; *U.S. Public*, pg. 108
Smalley, Robert A., Jr., Chief Oper. Officer & Exec. V.P.--Cruise America, Inc., Mesa, AZ; *U.S. Private*, pg. 178
Smallwood, David B., V.P.-Multi-Unit Sls.--Sysco Corporation, Houston, TX; *U.S. Public*, pg. 1550
Smart, David C., Lab Mgr.-Wholesale--Kodak (Australasia) Pty. Ltd., Coburg, Australia; *U.S. Public*, pg. 552
Smart, William, V.P.-Sls.--Phototype Color Graphics, Inc., Pennsauken, NJ; *U.S. Private*, pg. 864
Smeall, Janice, Mgr.-Sls.--Electro Dynamics Crystal Corporation, Overland Park, KS; *U.S. Private*, pg. 368
Smedley, Graham, Mgr.-Sls.--Bailey Maintenance Services, Newcastle upon Tyne, United Kingdom; *Int'l*, pg. 133
Smeilus, Graham, Sls. Mgr.--SGS U.S. Testing Company, Inc., Fairfield, NJ; *Int'l*, pg. 1153
Smeltzer, Dave, Prod. Mgr.--Welding Products Group, Niles, MI; *U.S. Public*, pg. 1161
Smerchek, E.J., Mgr.-Sls.-Indus. Div.--Young Radiator Company, Racine, WI; *U.S. Private*, pg. 1201
Smiddy, Bob, V.P.-Sls.--Blount, Inc. Sporting Equipment Group, Lewiston, ID; *U.S. Public*, pg. 238
Smit, Jack, Mgr.-Mktg. & Sls.--Miracle Feeds Inc., London, Canada; *U.S. Private*, pg. 432
Smit, Ton, V.P.-Mktg. & Sls.--Wedco Holland B.V., s Gravendeel, Netherlands; *U.S. Public*, pg. 854
Smith, A.G., Dir.-Mktg. & Defence Sls.--Chloride Industrial Batteries Ltd., Manchester, United Kingdom; *Int'l*, pg. 125
Smith, Aileen, Mgr.-Circulation & Bus.--The Seattle Business Journal, Inc., Seattle, WA; *U.S. Private*, pg. 20
Smith, Alan, Sls. Mgr.--BMC Software, Limited, Camberley, United Kingdom; *U.S. Public*, pg. 163
Smith, Angela, Dir.-Sls. & Mktg.--Moran Industries, Inc., Midlothian, IL; *U.S. Private*, pg. 760
Smith, Arthur, V.P.-Sls.--Markin Tubing, Inc., Wyoming, NY; *U.S. Private*, pg. 705
Smith, Barbara, Mgr.-Sls.--Minerallac Co., Addison, IL; *U.S. Private*, pg. 750
Smith, Brian, Sr. V.P.-Sls.--Vail Resorts, Inc., Vail, CO; *U.S. Public*, pg. 1704
Smith, C.E., V.P.-Sls. & Mktg.--The American Group, Ferndale, WA; *U.S. Private*, pg. 56
Smith, Carol, Sls.--Adventure Lands of America, Inc., Des Moines, IA; *U.S. Private*, pg. 22
Smith, Cort O., Mgr.-Sls.--PENCO-Utah, Sandy, UT; *Int'l*, pg. 1508
Smith, Craig, V.P.-Sls. & Mktg.--Leone Food Service Corp., Livonia, MI; *U.S. Private*, pg. 244
Smith, D.C., Dir.-Mktg. & Sls.--Griffin Manufacturing Co., Muskogee, OK; *U.S. Private*, pg. 481
Smith, Dan, Mgr.-Milk Div. Sls.--Trauth Dairy Inc., Newport, KY; *U.S. Private*, pg. 1098
Smith, Dave, Dir.-Sls.--The Griffith Laboratories Ltd., Scarborough, Canada; *U.S. Private*, pg. 481
Smith, David, Mgr.-Sls.--Aydin Controls Div., Fort Washington, PA; *U.S. Public*, pg. 158
Smith, David, V.P. & Reg. Dir.--Carrols Corporation, Syracuse, NY; *U.S. Private*, pg. 216
Smith, David, V.P.-Sls.--Scholls Inc., Arden Hills, MN; *U.S. Private*, pg. 972
Smith, Debbie, Mgr.-Sls.-Johari Brand--Soft Sheen Products, Inc., Chicago, IL; *U.S. Private*, pg. 1012
Smith, Dennis, Exec. V.P.-Sls.--Hobart Corporation, Troy, OH; *U.S. Public*, pg. 1322
Smith, Don, Dir.-Sls. & Mktg.--Chris-Craft Boats, Sarasota, FL; *U.S. Private*, pg. 478
Smith, Donald F., V.P.-Mktg. & Sls.--The Guttman Group, Belle Vernon, PA; *U.S. Private*, pg. 488
Smith, Douglas, V.P.-Sls. & Mktg.--Davox Corp., Westford, MA; *U.S. Public*, pg. 488
Smith, Douglas, V.P.-Channel Sls. & Mktg.--Tecmar Technologies, Inc., Longmont, CO; *Int'l*, pg. 1361
Smith, E.T., Grp. V.P.--Industrial Americas Group, Maumee, OH; *U.S. Public*, pg. 24
Smith, G., Mgr.-Southeast Sls.--Sloan Valve Company, Franklin Park, IL; *U.S. Private*, pg. 1006
Smith, Gary, Sr. V.P.-Sls.--UST Inc., Greenwich, CT; *U.S. Public*, pg. 1660
Smith, Gerry, V.P.-Sls.--Oxford Health Plans Inc., Norwalk, CT; *U.S. Public*, pg. 1238
Smith, Graham, Dir.-Intl. Sls.--Mercury Computer Systems, Inc., Chelmsford, MA; *U.S. Private*, pg. 732
Smith, Grayson, Mgr.-Sls. Promo.--Pontiac-GMC Truck Division, Pontiac, MI; *U.S. Public*, pg. 720
Smith, Greg, Gen. Mgr.-Sls.--Buffalo Rock Company, Birmingham, AL; *U.S. Private*, pg. 179
Smith, Greg, V.P.-Dedicated Sls.--Builders Transport, Incorporated, Camden, SC; *U.S. Public*, pg. 267
Smith, Greg, Sr. V.P.-Sls.--InterVoice, Inc., Dallas, TX; *U.S. Public*, pg. 910
Smith, H.J., V.P.-Sls. & Mktg.--Ravarino & Freschi, Inc., Saint Louis, MO; *U.S. Private*, pg. 158
Smith, Harold, Dir.-Sls. & Mktg.--MTD Products Limited, Kitchener, Canada; *U.S. Private*, pg. 688
Smith, Ian L., V.P.-Sls.--Fenner Drives, Manheim, PA; *U.S. Private*, pg. 400
Smith, James S., Jr., V.P.-Sls. & Distr.--YSI Incorporated, Yellow Springs, OH; *U.S. Private*, pg. 1195
Smith, James U., V.P.-Sls. & Mktg.--Ruetgers-Nease Corporation, State College, PA; *Int'l*, pg. 1148
Smith, Jay, V.P.-Sls. & Mktg.--Voit Sports, Inc., Carlsbad, CA; *U.S. Private*, pg. 1143
Smith, Jimmy, V.P.-Mktg & Sls.--Alden Electronics, Inc., Westborough, MA; *U.S. Private*, pg. 872
Smith, JoAnne, Mgr.-Sls.--American Water Works Association, Denver, CO; *U.S. Public*, pg. 94
Smith, Joseph H., Pres.--40 Fort Eye Associates, Forty Fort, PA; *U.S. Private*, pg. 420
Smith, Kelly, Mgr.-Sls.--Stoneville Furniture Co. Inc., Stoneville, NC; *U.S. Private*, pg. 1045
Smith, Larry, Mgr.-Natl. Sls./RV--Kit Manufacturing Company, Long Beach, CA; *U.S. Public*, pg. 962
Smith, Larry, Mgr.-Sls.--R-2 KIT Mfg. Co., Caldwell, ID; *U.S. Public*, pg. 962
Smith, Lawrence W., Sr. V.P.-Sls. & Mktg./N. America--FCA International Ltd., Westmount, Canada; *Int'l*, pg. 470
Smith, Marc, Exec. V.P.-Sls. & Mktg.--The Stop & Shop Companies, Inc., Quincy, MA; *Int'l*, pg. 750
Smith, Mark, Dir.-Natl. Sls.--Shivers Trading & Operating Co., Augusta, GA; *U.S. Private*, pg. 994
Smith, Mark, Dir.-Natl. Sls.--Morris Communications Corporation, Augusta, GA; *U.S. Private*, pg. 995
Smith, Michael, V.P.-Sls.--PST Vans, Inc., Salt Lake City, UT; *U.S. Public*, pg. 1246
Smith, Nancy, Exec. V.P.-Sls.--Electronic Arts, San Mateo, CA; *U.S. Public*, pg. 569
Smith, Pamela, V.P.-Sls. & Service--Contract Interiors Inc., Taylor, MI; *U.S. Private*, pg. 270
Smith, Patrick, Natl. Sls. Mgr.- Foundry Div.--Electron Corp., Littleton, CO; *U.S. Private*, pg. 370
Smith, Paul, Sr. V.P.-Sls.--Hamilton Beach/Proctor-Silex, Inc., Glen Allen, VA; *U.S. Public*, pg. 1149
Smith, Philip, V.P.-Sales & Mktg.--A.H. Hoffman, Inc., Landisville, PA; *U.S. Private*, pg. 532
Smith, Philip, Pres.--AGEMA Infrared Systems, Inc., Secaucus, NJ; *Int'l*, pg. 1289
Smith, Ray, Exec. V.P.-Sls.--U.N.A. Corporation, Elk Grove Village, IL; *Int'l*, pg. 1001
Smith, Richard, V.P.-Sales--S & C Electric Canada Ltd., Toronto, Canada; *U.S. Private*, pg. 954
Smith, Rick, Reg. Dir.--Ireland Coffee Tea, Inc., Pleasantville, NJ; *U.S. Public*, pg. 351
Smith, Ron, Mgr.-Sls. & Mktg.--GAI Consultants, Inc., Fort Wayne, IN; *U.S. Private*, pg. 434
Smith, Roy C., Exec. V.P.-Store Opers.--Cache, Inc., New York, NY; *U.S. Public*, pg. 289
Smith, Russ, Dir.-Franchise Sls.--The Athlete's Foot Group, Inc., Kennesaw, GA; *U.S. Private*, pg. 94
Smith, Stephen J., V.P.-Sls.--Hazen Paper Company, Holyoke, MA; *U.S. Private*, pg. 514
Smith, T.P., V.P.-Sls.--The Kerite Company, Seymour, CT; *U.S. Public*, pg. 844
Smith, Terryll R., V.P.-European Sls. & Mktg.--Advanced Micro Devices, Inc., Sunnyvale, CA; *U.S. Public*, pg. 21
Smith, Thomas M., Exec. V.P.-Mktg. & Sales--CPS Direct, Inc., Woburn, MA; *U.S. Private*, pg. 196
Smith, Tom, Gen. Mgr.-Sls.--LaSalle Steel Company, Hammond, IN; *U.S. Public*, pg. 1181
Smith, Tom, V.P.-Sls.--Restaura, Inc., Phoenix, AZ; *U.S. Public*, pg. 1718
Smith, Tony, Dir.-Sls.--Van den Bergh Foods Ltd., Crawley, United Kingdom; *Int'l*, pg. 1434
Smith, Wayne, Dir.-Domestic Sls.--Tasco Sales Inc., Miramar, FL; *U.S. Private*, pg. 928
Smith, William J., Sr. V.P.-Sls. & Mktg.--Premisys Communications, Inc., Fremont, CA; *U.S. Public*, pg. 1323
Smits, Staf, Gen. Mgr.-Sales--Bailey-Fischer & Porter N.V., Wilrijk, Belgium; *Int'l*, pg. 449
Smullen, Michael, V.P.-Sls.--MedImmune, Inc., Gaithersburg, MD; *U.S. Public*, pg. 1081
Smurfit, D.F., Deputy Chm. & Exec. V.P.-Worldwide Sls. & Mktg.--Jefferson Smurfit Group p.l.c., Dublin, Ireland; *Int'l*, pg. 1269
Smutny, Chuck, Exec. V.P.-Sls. & Mktg.--Agripac Inc., Salem, OR; *U.S. Private*, pg. 26
Smyth, Greg, Dir.-Mktg. & Sls.--Robert E. Bayley Construction, Seattle, WA; *U.S. Private*, pg. 125
Smyth, Peter, V.P.-Sls.--Altera Corporation, San Jose, CA; *U.S. Public*, pg. 59
Smyth, Robert, Dir.-European Mktg.--NSC European Operations, Ascot, United Kingdom; *U.S. Public*, pg. 1522
Smythe, Robert A., V.P. & Dir.-Sls. & Mktg.--Zygo Corporation, Middlefield, CT; *U.S. Public*, pg. 1795
Sneath, G., Dir.-Sls.--Andres Wines Ltd., Winona, Canada; *Int'l*, pg. 75
Snediker, R.R., Jr., Exec. V.P.-Sls.--Chicago Show Printing Co., Morton Grove, IL; *U.S. Private*, pg. 235
Sneed, Elaine, V.P.-Sls.--Express Scripts, Inc., Maryland Heights, MO; *U.S. Public*, pg. 600
Snell, David J., V.P.-Sls. & Mktg.--Data General (Canada) Ltd., Mississauga, Canada; *U.S. Public*, pg. 485
Snell, Mike, Mgr.-Sls.--Monaco Coach Corporation, Coburg, OR; *U.S. Public*, pg. 1123
Snell, Phyllis, Mgr.-Sls. & Mktg.--Dimco-Gray Company, Centerville, OH; *U.S. Private*, pg. 333
Snider, Alan, V.P.-Sls. & Mktg.--Gussco Manufacturing, Inc., Brooklyn, NY; *U.S. Private*, pg. 488
Snider, Lee, Mgr.-Sls.--Service Supply Co. Inc. of Indiana, Indianapolis, IN; *U.S. Private*, pg. 987
Snider, Terrence Q., V.P.-Sls. & Mktg.--Merck Medco Managed Care, Des Moines, IA; *U.S. Public*, pg. 1091
Snijder, J.A., Dir.-Netherlands--Spadel SA, Brussels, Belgium; *Int'l*, pg. 1287
Snively, Robert, Dir.-Intl. Sls.--F.E. Myers, Ashland, OH; *U.S. Public*, pg. 1273
Snoek, Karel, Mgr.-Natl. Sls.--Lifetime Doors Inc., Farmington, MI; *U.S. Private*, pg. 666
Snoozy, Robert S., V.P.-Sls. & Mktg.--Lindsay Manufacturing Company, Lindsay, NE; *U.S. Public*, pg. 999
Snow, Andy, Sls. Engr.--Frequency and Time Systems, Inc., Beverly, MA; *U.S. Public*, pg. 488
Snow, Pat, V.P.-Sls.--Paco Rabanne Compar, New York, NY; *Int'l*, pg. 1073
Snow, Richard, Mgr.-Sls.--Mitchell Corporation of Owosso, Owosso, MI; *U.S. Private*, pg. 753
Snuttjer, Dave, Mgr.-Sls.--Mid Res Service Div., Niles, IL; *U.S. Public*, pg. 1026
Snyder, Bob, Sls. Mgr.--Miss Elaine Inc., Saint Louis, MO; *U.S. Private*, pg. 752
Snyder, Joseph T., Dir.-Sls. & Mktg.--J.T. Slocomb Company, South Glastonbury, CT; *U.S. Private*, pg. 1006
Snyder, Lawrence, Sls. Mgr.-Paint--Frederick Trading Company, Frederick, MD; *U.S. Private*, pg. 335
Snyder, Robert B., V.P.-Sls.--Haeger Industries, Inc., Dundee, IL; *U.S. Private*, pg. 493
Snyder, Steve, Dir.-Sls.--Hickson Corporation, Smyrna, GA; *Int'l*, pg. 619
Snyder, Tom, Mgr.-Natl. Sls.--Tony Lama Co., Inc., El Paso, TX; *U.S. Public*, pg. 937
So, Alfred, Mgr.-Sls.--Sun Hung Kai Properties Ltd., Wan Chai, Hong Kong; *Int'l*, pg. 1318
Soares, Antonio, Sls. & Mktg. Mgr.--Whitehall Portugal, Lisbon, Portugal; *U.S. Public*, pg. 81
Sobel, Beth, Sr. V.P.-Sls.--Ranir Corporation/DCP, Grand Rapids, MI; *U.S. Private*, pg. 909
Sobic, Dan, Gen. Mgr.-Sls.--Peterbilt Motors Co., Denton, TX; *U.S. Public*, pg. 1247
Sobiran, David, Gen. Mgr.-Sls.--Lever Brothers West Indies Ltd., Champs Fleurs, Trinidad & Tobago; *Int'l*, pg. 1437
Sobolewski, Gary M., V.P.-Sls.--Syntellect, Inc., Phoenix, AZ; *U.S. Public*, pg. 1550
Sobon, Diane, Natl. Sls. Mgr.--R.A. Briggs & Co., Lake Zurich, IL; *U.S. Private*, pg. 536
Sobrero, R.F., Gen. Mgr.-Sls. & Svc.--Chevrolet Motor Div. General Motors Corp., Warren, MI; *U.S. Public*, pg. 720
Soccorsi, Frank, V.P.-North America Dealer Sls.--Ziebart International Corporation, Troy, MI; *U.S. Private*, pg. 1205
Soccorsi, Frank, Mgr.-Sls.--Ziebart Corp., Troy, MI; *U.S. Private*, pg. 1205
Soccorsi, Frank, Mgr.-Sls.--Tidy Car International, Inc., Troy, MI; *U.S. Private*, pg. 1205
Soccorsi, Frank, Mgr.-Sls.--Ziebart Canada, Inc., Concord, Canada; *U.S. Private*, pg. 1205
Soehnlen, Thomas, Mgr.-Key Accts.--Superior Dairy, Inc., Canton, OH; *U.S. Private*, pg. 1054
Soennichsen, Torbin, Dir.-Sls. & Mktg.--Vestjyske Slagterier, Struer, Denmark; *Int'l*, pg. 1464
Sohm, Woo-Heon, Pres.--Ssangyong Investment Management Co., Ltd., Seoul, Korea; *Int'l*, pg. 1292
Sokoloff, Steven, V.P.-Mktg. & Sls.--Milgray/Toronto, Inc., Mississauga, Canada; *U.S. Public*, pg. 207
Sokoly, Jim, Dir.-Sls.--Mayville Engineering Co., Inc., Mayville, WI; *U.S. Private*, pg. 718
Soldner, Jerry, V.P.-Sls.--Swift-Cor Tool Engineering, Gardena, CA; *U.S. Private*, pg. 1058
Sole, Ian, V.P.-Sls. & Mktg.--American Woodmark Corporation, Winchester, VA; *U.S. Public*, pg. 96
Sole, Ian, V.P.-Intl. Sls.--Hamilton Beach/Proctor-Silex, Inc., Glen Allen, VA; *U.S. Public*, pg. 1149
Solis, Kurt, V.P.-Sls.--Ruska Instrument Corporation, Houston, TX; *U.S. Private*, pg. 952
Sollon, John, Sls. Engr.--Instron Canada, Inc., Burlington, Canada; *U.S. Public*, pg. 883
Solomon, Irwin, Mgr.-Sls. Admin.--Getinge/Castle Inc., Rochester, NY; *Int'l*, pg. 551
Solomon, Tom, V.P.-Sls. & Mktg.--Uniblend Spinners, Inc., Conway, SC; *U.S. Private*, pg. 1117
Solow, Philip, Mgr.-Natl. Sls.--Mutoh America Inc., Phoenix, AZ; *Int'l*, pg. 897
Soltis, William T., Mgr.-Indus. Rels. & Sls.--Consolidated Industries, Inc., Cheshire, CT; *U.S. Private*, pg. 265
Soma, Jerry, Dir.-Corp. Communications--Cubix Corporation, Carson City, NV; *U.S. Private*, pg. 294
Somma, Rande, V.P.-Sls. & Mktg.--Johnson Controls, Inc., Plymouth, MI; *U.S. Public*, pg. 932
Sommer, John, Exec. V.P.-Sls. & Mktg.--Kidron Inc., Kidron, OH; *U.S. Private*, pg. 619
Sommers, Gerald, Exec. V.P.-Sls. & Mktg.--Allied Printing Services, Inc., Manchester, CT; *U.S. Private*, pg. 40
Sommerville, Donald J., Dir.-Sls. & Mktg.--ComSonics, Inc., Harrisonburg, VA; *U.S. Private*, pg. 260
Sonaco, Mike, Mgr.-Sls.--Apertus Technologies Incorporated, Eden Prairie, MN; *U.S. Public*, pg. 119
Soncek, Dan, Mgr.-Eastern Regional Sls.--CTS Corp. Frequency Controls, Sandwich, IL; *U.S. Public*, pg. 285
Songer, Jim, V.P.-Worldwide Sls. & Mktg.--Esco Corporation, Portland, OR; *U.S. Private*, pg. 382
Sonntag, Ann, Mgr.-Sls.--Business Journals of North Carolina, LLC, Charlotte, NC; *U.S. Private*, pg. 19
Sontgen, Michael, Mgr.-Export Sls.--Diebels Private Brewery, Issum, Germany; *Int'l*, pg. 413
Sorem, Dave, Dir.-Sls. & Mktg./Oil Centrifuges--Reuter Manufacturing Inc., Hopkins, MN; *U.S. Public*, pg. 1383
Sorensen, Richard, Mgr.-Sls.--Rowe Furniture Corp., Mc Lean, VA; *U.S. Public*, pg. 1410
Sorenson, Dave, Natl. Sls. Mgr.--Fairmont Snack Group, Inc., Independence, OH; *U.S. Private*, pg. 392
Soria, Bob, V.P.-Franchise Sls.--Pizza Inn, Inc., Dallas, TX; *U.S. Public*, pg. 1307
Soriano, M. Paul, Natl. Sls. Dir.-Mineral Water--La Tondena Distillers, Inc., Manila, Philippines; *Int'l*, pg. 785
Soriano, Rafael, Dir.-Sls.--Plaza y Janes S.A., Barcelona, Spain; *Int'l*, pg. 192
Soroczak, Walter, V.P.-Sls.--Voss Industries, Inc., Cleveland, OH; *U.S. Private*, pg. 1143
Sorsby, Cecil, V.P.-Sls.--Grant-Lydick Beverage Co., San Antonio, TX; *U.S. Private*, pg. 470

Sortino, Charles, Mgr.-Sls.--Norwalk Powdered Metals, Inc., Norwalk, CT; *U.S. Private*, pg. 808
Sosville, Dick, V.P.-Sls. & Mktg.--The Dow Chemical Company, Midland, MI; *U.S. Public*, pg. 522
Sosville, Dick, V.P.-Sls. & Mktg.-N. America & Mexico--Dow Chemical Canada, Inc., Sarnia, Canada; *U.S. Public*, pg. 523
Sosville, Richard E., V.P.-Mktg. & Sls.--Dow Chemical North America, Midland, MI; *U.S. Public*, pg. 522
Sotera, John, V.P.-Sls.--Thermo Jarrell Ash Corporation, Franklin, MA; *U.S. Public*, pg. 1594
Souillard, Gerald, Mgr.-Sls.--Spirol S.A., Saint Leu-la-Foret, France; *U.S. Private*, pg. 1026
Soule, Larry, Mgr.-Sls.--Rihm Motor Company, Saint Paul, MN; *U.S. Private*, pg. 931
Soulsby, Jeffrey L., V.P.-Sls.--Processed Plastic Company, Montgomery, IL; *U.S. Private*, pg. 888
Souter, J. Murray, V.P.-Sls. & Mktg.-Canada--Bauer Sports Inc., Montreal, Canada; *U.S. Public*, pg. 1184
Souyias, Soc, V.P.-Sls.--Automotive Moulding Company, Warren, MI; *U.S. Private*, pg. 485
Sowa, Paul J., V.P. & Gen. Mgr.--Nelson Westerberg, Inc., Elk Grove Village, IL; *U.S. Private*, pg. 1163
Sowa, Paul J., V.P. & Gen. Mgr.--Nelson Westerberg of Illinois, Elk Grove Village, IL; *U.S. Private*, pg. 1164
Sowden, R.M., Mgr.-Retail Trng.--General Motors of Canada Ltd., Oshawa, Canada; *U.S. Public*, pg. 722
Sowell, Lee, V.P.-Sls. & Mktg.--Frigidaire Home Products-Specialty Power Equipment, Shreveport, LA; *Int'l*, pg. 440
Sower-Koza, Brenda, Dir.-Sls.--PVC Compounders, Kendallville, IN; *U.S. Private*, pg. 484
Sozonoff, Alex, V.P. & Gen. Mgr.-Sls. & Mktg./Computer Org.--Hewlett-Packard Company, Palo Alto, CA; *U.S. Public*, pg. 813
Spaan, L.P.A., Mgr.-Mktg. & Sls.--Quality Bakers Nederland B.V., Gouda, Netherlands; *Int'l*, pg. 555
Spadaccino, Sandra, Mgr.-Sls. & Asst. Gen. Mgr.--Philadelphia Reserve Supply Company, Croydon, PA; *U.S. Private*, pg. 861
Spain, Leo, Mgr.-Mktg. & Sales--Eaton Corp. Div., Athens, AL; *U.S. Public*, pg. 556
Spalteholz, Bianca, Gen. Mgr.Sls. & Mktg./Germany, Austria & Central/Eastern Europe--Utell International-Germany, Frankfurt, Germany; *Int'l*, pg. 1098
Spaner, Robert L., V.P.-Sls.--Boston Acoustics, Inc., Peabody, MA; *U.S. Public*, pg. 246
Spangian, Richard, V.P.-Sls.--Pony U.S.A., Nashville, TN; *Int'l*, pg. 1036
Spangler, David B., Pres. & Chief Exec. Officer--Jefferson Mills, Inc., Pulaski, VA; *U.S. Private*, pg. 584
Spangler, Kim, Mgr.-Circulation & Bus.--ACBJ Business Publications, Inc., Cincinnati, OH; *U.S. Private*, pg. 19
Spangler, Robert, Mgr.-Sls.--Fincor Electronics, York, PA; *U.S. Public*, pg. 857
Spanjian, Richard, V.P.-Sls.--Mitre Sports (U.S.), Nashville, TN; *Int'l*, pg. 1036
Spano, John W., V.P.-Sls. & Mktg.--Twin Disc, Incorporated, Racine, WI; *U.S. Public*, pg. 1646
Spano, Lori, V.P.-Sls.--Outdoor Systems, Inc. Sales, New York, NY; *U.S. Public*, pg. 1235
Spanos, James, Dir.-Lithium Industrial Sls.--Power Conversion, Inc., Elmwood Park, NJ; *Int'l*, pg. 127
Sparks, Jason, Dir.-Mktg. & Sls.--MAG Innovision Co., Inc., Santa Ana, CA; *U.S. Private*, pg. 694
Sparks, R., Dir.-Sls.--Leader Instruments Corporation, Hauppauge, NY; *U.S. Private*, pg. 655
Sparks, Steve, Dir.-Mktg./Packaged Water--McKesson Water Products Company, Pasadena, CA; *U.S. Public*, pg. 1073
Sparvero, Robert P., Dir.-NAAO Export Sls.--NAAO Marketing, Dearborn, MI; *U.S. Public*, pg. 662
Spath, Friedrich, Dir.-Gas Sls.--Ruhrgas Aktiengesellschaft, Essen, Germany; *Int'l*, pg. 1148
Speak, Craig A., Dir.-Domestic Sls.--Tellabs Operations, Inc., Lisle, IL; *U.S. Public*, pg. 1572
Speakman, James, V.P.-Sls.--United States Ceramic Tile Co., East Sparta, OH; *U.S. Private*, pg. 1124
Spearman, Vivian, V.P.-Sls. Opers.--Weider Publications, Inc., Woodland Hills, CA; *U.S. Private*, pg. 1159
Spears, Jimmy, Dir.-Mktg. & Sls.--Darlington Veneer Company, Darlington, SC; *U.S. Private*, pg. 311
Spector, David, Sr. V.P.-Secondary Mktg./Loan Sales--Countrywide Funding Corporation, Pasadena, CA; *U.S. Public*, pg. 453
Spector, Martin, Sls. Devel. Chief--Weight Watchers Magazine, Birmingham, AL; *U.S. Public*, pg. 1612
Spector, Peter S., Mgr.-Sls.--Eastern Engraving, Stirling, NJ; *U.S. Public*, pg. 1506
Speisman, Robert, V.P.-Sls.--Lazare Kaplan Intl., Inc., New York, NY; *U.S. Public*, pg. 981
Spell, Randy, Sr. V.P.-Sls.--Lorillard Tobacco Company, Greensboro, NC; *U.S. Public*, pg. 1011
Spence, Cam, Mgr.-Sls.--Armstrong Fluid Handling, Three Rivers, MI; *U.S. Private*, pg. 83
Spence, Chester E., V.P.-Mktg. & Sls.--American Technical Ceramics Corp., Huntington Station, NY; *U.S. Public*, pg. 93
Spence, Gavin, V.P.-Sls.--Wells Mfg. Corp., Fond Du Lac, WI; *U.S. Private*, pg. 1113
Spence, Jeffrey E., Chm. Bd., Pres., Controller & Chief Exec. & Fin. Officer--Controlled Systems of Wisconsin, Inc., Nashotah, WI; *U.S. Private*, pg. 271
Spencer, Martin G., V.P.-Sls. & Mktg.--Schwitzer, Inc., Indianapolis, IN; *U.S. Public*, pg. 968
Spencer, Merlee, Mgr.-Indoor Sls.--Bethurum Research & Development, Inc., Texas City, TX; *U.S. Private*, pg. 141
Spencer, Paul, V.P.-Sls. & Mktg.--Cooper Power Tools Division, Lexington, SC; *U.S. Public*, pg. 444
Spencer, Paul, Mgr.-Sls.--New Hampshire Ball Bearings, Precision Products Group, Chatsworth, CA; *Int'l*, pg. 868
Sperco, John J., Sr. V.P.-Consumer Sls. & Service--MCI Communications Corp., Atlanta, GA; *U.S. Public*, pg. 1023
Spessard, Robert W., V.P.-Sls.--Ragu Foods, Inc., Trumbull, CT; *Int'l*, pg. 1436
Spicer, Anthony J., Dir.-Sls.-Intl. Div.--Clayton Industries Co., El Monte, CA; *U.S. Private*, pg. 245
Spicer, Anthony J., Dir.-Sls.--International Div., El Monte, CA; *U.S. Private*, pg. 245
Spicq, Francois, Dir.-Sls./Big Fleets--Iveco France S.A., Trappes, France; *Int'l*, pg. 696
Spiegel, Gary J., V.P.-Sls.--Newport Corporation, Irvine, CA; *U.S. Public*, pg. 1179
Spiegel, Tamio, V.P.-Sls.--Noma-International, Inc., Itasca, IL; *Int'l*, pg. 955
Spielman, John, Dir.-Natl. Sls.--Heller Seasonings & Ingredients, Inc., Bedford Park, IL; *U.S. Private*, pg. 520
Spier, Chris, V.P.-Sls. & Mktg.--Bucyrus Blades Inc., Bucyrus, OH; *U.S. Private*, pg. 383
Spiesshoefer, Peter, Dr., Exec. V.P.-Adv. & Intl. Sls.--Burda Holding GmbH & Co., KG, Munich, Germany; *Int'l*, pg. 233
Spigner, Ray, V.P.-Sls.--St. Louis Sales, Chesterfield, MO; *U.S. Public*, pg. 611
Spillane, Jim, Sr. V.P.-Sls.--Bell Sports Corp., San Jose, CA; *U.S. Public*, pg. 207
Spinazzi, J., V.P.-Sls.--Econolite Control Products, Inc., Anaheim, CA; *U.S. Private*, pg. 361
Spinner, Robert, Sr. V.P.-Worldwide Sls.--Clarify Inc., San Jose, CA; *U.S. Public*, pg. 382
Spivey, Andy, Mgr.-Sls.--House of Raeford Farms, Inc., Raeford, NC; *U.S. Private*, pg. 542
Spivey, Ron, V.P.-Sls.--Bench Craft, Inc., Blue Mountain, MS; *U.S. Private*, pg. 432
Spohn, Chuck, Gen. Sls. Mgr.--WPTY-TV, Memphis, TN; *U.S. Public*, pg. 385
Sponaugle, Charles J., V.P.-Sls.--Haynes International, Inc., Kokomo, IN; *U.S. Public*, pg. 801
Spooner, Worthington, V.P.-Intl. Sls. & Systems--Emcee Broadcast Products, Inc., White Haven, PA; *U.S. Public*, pg. 570
Spoonhoward, Lisa, Sls. Admin.--Childcraft Education Corporation, Lancaster, PA; *U.S. Public*, pg. 513
Spors, Kriss, Admin.-Sls.--UDL Laboratories, Inc., Rockford, IL; *U.S. Public*, pg. 1143
Spragg, Gregory, Exec. V.P.-Sls. & Mdsg.--FINAST, Maple Heights, OH; *Int'l*, pg. 750
Sprague, Lori, Special Sls.--American Mathematical Society, Inc., Providence, RI; *U.S. Private*, pg. 59
Spreenberg, Robert, V.P.--Midwesco Mechanical Energy, Niles, IL; *U.S. Public*, pg. 1026
Spresser, Mark A., Mgr.-Direct Sls.--The Machine Tool Group, Cleveland, OH; *U.S. Public*, pg. 503
Spring, John S., V.P.-Sls.--Eonic Inc., Detroit, MI; *U.S. Public*, pg. 1176
Spruit, Johannes, V.P.-Sls./Alliances--QAD Inc, Carpinteria, CA; *U.S. Public*, pg. 1345
Sprunger, Steve, Mgr.-Sls. & Mktg.--Kelley Company, Inc., Milwaukee, WI; *U.S. Private*, pg. 612
Spyker, Michael P., Dir.-Farm Seed Sls.--Agway Agricultural Products (AAP), Syracuse, NY; *U.S. Private*, pg. 27
Squeglia, Thomas J., V.P.-Sls.--Vistakon Johnson & Johnson Vision Products, Inc., Jacksonville, FL; *U.S. Public*, pg. 929
Squiller, Daniel W., V.P.-Sls.--Deltec, San Diego, CA; *Int'l*, pg. 126
Sramek, Robert, Mgr.-Sls.--Air Gage Company, Livonia, MI; *U.S. Public*, pg. 1676
Sroka, William A., Mgr.-Sls.--Logghe Stamping Company, Fraser, MI; *U.S. Private*, pg. 672
St. John, Mike, V.P.-Sls.--All Star Gas Co.-Region XIV, Lebanon, MO; *U.S. Private*, pg. 36
St. Onge, Claudette, Exec. V.P.-Sls.--Pharmavite Corp., Mission Hills, CA; *U.S. Private*, pg. 860
St. Peter, Jerry, Natl. Field Sls. Mgr.--Muro Pharmaceutical, Inc., Tewksbury, MA; *U.S. Private*, pg. 767
Stacey, Dan, Mgr.-Sls./Comml. Div.--SBS Products, Inc., Saginaw, MI; *U.S. Private*, pg. 955
Stacey, Eric, Mgr.-Natl. Sls.--Deck House Inc., Acton, MA; *U.S. Private*, pg. 320
Stachelrodt, Sarita, Dir.-Sls.--Executive Software, Glendale, CA; *U.S. Private*, pg. 388
Stack, Jim, Dir.-Sls. Warranties--Wynn Oil Company, Azusa, CA; *U.S. Public*, pg. 1782
Stacy, Ron, V.P.-Mktg. & Sls.--American Flange & Manufacturing Co. Inc., Carol Stream, IL; *Int'l*, pg. 1146
Stadel, Ashley M., Mgr.-Prod. Sls.--Enger-Kress Company, West Bend, WI; *U.S. Private*, pg. 376
Stafford, Charlie, V.P.-Sls--Chattem, Inc., Chattanooga, TN; *U.S. Public*, pg. 341
Stafford, Dave, V.P.-Export Sls.--Kysor/Warren, Conyers, GA; *U.S. Public*, pg. 1445
Stafford, David, V.P.-Sls.--Commodore Holdings, Hollywood, FL; *U.S. Public*, pg. 414
Stafford, John, V.P.-Sls. & Mktg.--Systech Computer Corporation, San Diego, CA; *U.S. Private*, pg. 1061
Stager, Robert, Mgr.-Sls.--Sheffield Steel Corporation-Joliet, Joliet, IL; *U.S. Private*, pg. 991
Stahl, Glenn H., Reg. Mgr.--Environment/One Corporation, Niskayuna, NY; *U.S. Public*, pg. 586
Stai, Harlan C., Exec. V.P.-Opers.--Owen Health Care, Inc., Houston, TX; *U.S. Public*, pg. 304
Stak, Gregory, Natl. Sls. Mgr.--R.H. Forschner Division, Shelton, CT; *U.S. Public*, pg. 1544
Stalets, Scott W., Mgr.-West Central Reg. Sls.--Sofamor Danek Group, Inc., Memphis, TN; *U.S. Public*, pg. 1482
Staller, Chris, Dir.-Indus. Sls., Mktg. & Adv.--Vibro-Meter Corp., Long Beach, CA; *U.S. Private*, pg. 1138
Stamos, J.A., V.P.-Sls.--Lee Company, Westbrook, CT; *U.S. Private*, pg. 657
Stamos, Peter, Mgr.-Govt. Sls.--Trippe Mfg. Co., Chicago, IL; *U.S. Private*, pg. 1104
Stamp, Brandley, Dir.-Sls.--CSP Inc., Billerica, MA; *U.S. Public*, pg. 283
Stamper, Edward R., V.P.-Global Sls.-Western Area--Emery Worldwide, Redwood City, CA; *U.S. Public*, pg. 281
Stamper, Gordon, Mgr.-Sls.--PENCO-Pennsylvania, Harrisburg, PA; *Int'l*, pg. 1508
Stanaland, J.O., Dir.-Sls.--Speakman Company, Wilmington, DE; *U.S. Private*, pg. 1021
Stancato, Deborah, Mgr.-Natl. Sls.--Springfield Precision Instruments, Inc., Wood Ridge, NJ; *U.S. Private*, pg. 1027
Stancil, Dave, V.P.-Natl. Sls.--U.S. Divers Co., Inc., Santa Ana, CA; *U.S. Private*, pg. 1125
Stancil, Dave, V.P.-Natl. Sls.--U.S. Divers, Santa Ana, CA; *U.S. Private*, pg. 1125
Stand, Judy, Gen. Sls. Mgr.--Dodge City Shopper's Weekly, Dodge City, KS; *U.S. Private*, pg. 995
Standaert, Randall, Mgr.-Sls.--PENCO-Wyoming, Worland, WY; *Int'l*, pg. 1508
Standen, Bill, Mgr.-Sls. & Mktg.--Abbott Electronics, Inc., Los Angeles, CA; *U.S. Private*, pg. 9
Stander, Gert, Mgr.-Sls.--Tosas (Pty) Ltd., Wadeville, South Africa; *Int'l*, pg. 1197
Standish, Victor J., Chm. Bd., Pres. & Chief Exec. Officer--York Barbell Co., Inc., York, PA; *U.S. Private*, pg. 1196
Stang, Dave C., Dir.-Corp. Environmental Sls.--Jacobs Engineering Group Inc., Houston, TX; *U.S. Public*, pg. 921
Stang, Gary, V.P.-Sls. & Mktg.--Scoville Press, Inc., Minneapolis, MN; *U.S. Private*, pg. 977
Stanghellini, Mario, Dir.-Sls.--Olin Microelectronic Materials, Inc., Norwalk, CT; *U.S. Public*, pg. 1219
Stanko, Chuck, Mgr.-Sls.--Zappa Plastics, Phillipsburg, NJ; *U.S. Private*, pg. 172
Stanley, Bill, Mgr.-Gen. Sls.--WLKY-TV, Louisville, KY; *U.S. Public*, pg. 1344
Stanley, George, V.P. & Dir.-Grp. Sls./Professional, Ref. & Trade Grp.--John Wiley & Sons, Inc., New York, NY; *U.S. Public*, pg. 1768
Stanley, Gregory, Dir.-Sls.--Radiometer America Inc., Westlake, OH; *Int'l*, pg. 1083
Stannard, Bob, V.P.-Sls.--Dahlberg, Inc., Golden Valley, MN; *U.S. Public*, pg. 194
Stanoch, Mark, V.P.-Sls.--TransNet Corporation, Somerville, NJ; *U.S. Public*, pg. 1631
Stanton, E., Mgr.-Sls.--Qualitas Bathrooms Ltd., Burton on Trent, United Kingdom; *Int'l*, pg. 197
Stanton, F. Ronald, V.P. & Gen Mgr.-Sls. & Mktg.--Allen & Hanburys, Research Triangle Park, NC; *Int'l*, pg. 552
Stanton, John, V.P.-Sls.--GE Capital/IT Solutions, Minneapolis, MN; *U.S. Public*, pg. 711
Stapf, Adam, Mgr.-Sls.--Cincinnati Gear Company, Cincinnati, OH; *U.S. Private*, pg. 240
Staple, Ed, V.P.-Sls. & Mktg.--Greenlee Textron, Rockford, IL; *U.S. Public*, pg. 1589
Starek, John, Mgr.-Sls.--Daniel Valve Company, Houston, TX; *U.S. Public*, pg. 483
Stark, Edward, Exec. V.P. & Mgr.-Sls.--Dixie Dairy Company, Gary, IN; *U.S. Private*, pg. 337
Stark, Jim, Sr. V.P.-RV Sls. & Mktg.--The Coast Distribution System, San Jose, CA; *U.S. Public*, pg. 388
Stark, Joe, V.P.-Sls.--Miner Enterprises Inc., Geneva, IL; *U.S. Private*, pg. 749
Stark, Patty, V.P.-Sls./Educational Publ. Grp.--John Wiley & Sons, Inc., New York, NY; *U.S. Public*, pg. 1768
Starks, Richard, Sr. V.P.-Sls. & Mktg.--The Dallas Morning News, Inc., Dallas, TX; *U.S. Public*, pg. 209
Starkweather, Jeff, Dir.-Mktg.--WOKR-TV, Rochester, NY; *U.S. Private*, pg. 439
Starnes, Billy, Pres.--Gold Lance, Inc., Houston, TX; *U.S. Public*, pg. 1625
Starnes, Jerry, Mgr.-Sls.--Nucor Steel-Arkansas, Blytheville, AR; *U.S. Public*, pg. 1205
Starnes, Wayne, Exec. V.P.-Sls. & Mktg.--Stainless Ice-Tainer Co. (SITCO), Roswell, GA; *Int'l*, pg. 646
Starns, Mark, Mgr.-Area Sls.--Gensym Corporation, Mid-Atlantic Area Office, Chantilly, VA; *U.S. Public*, pg. 731
Starr, Randy G., V.P.-Sls.-Mat. & Matting--Ludlow Composites Corporation, Fremont, OH; *U.S. Private*, pg. 680
Starrett, Frederick D., III, Pres. & Treas.--Penobscot Frozen Foods, Inc., Belfast, ME; *U.S. Private*, pg. 850
Stashkiw, Walter, V.P.-Mktg., Sls. & Adv.--The Will-Burt Company, Orrville, OH; *U.S. Private*, pg. 1177
Stasia, R.N., Mgr.-Sls.--Turner Construction Co., Columbus, OH; *U.S. Public*, pg. 1645
Staszkow, Myron, V.P.-Mktg. & Sls.--OMRON Systems, Inc., Schaumburg, IL; *Int'l*, pg. 1005
Stathers, Richard N., Sr. V.P.-Sls. & Mktg.--Centennial Technologies, Inc., Wilmington, MA; *U.S. Public*, pg. 322
Stathis, James H., V.P.-Sls.--Imperial Schrade Corp., Ellenville, NY; *U.S. Private*, pg. 559
Staub, Ray, V.P. & Mgr.-Natl. Sls.--Glen-Gery Corporation, Wyomissing, PA; *Int'l*, pg. 658
Stauber, Jim, V.P.-Sls. Food Svcs.--Wilson Products Co., Salt Lake City, UT; *U.S. Private*, pg. 1181
Stauch, George, V.P.-Sls.--Lamina Inc., Oak Park, MI; *Int'l*, pg. 75
Stauch, Volker, Dir.-Passenger Car Sls.--Mercedes-Benz AG, Stuttgart, Germany; *Int'l*, pg. 368
Staudt, Michael, Dir.-Mktg. & Sls.--Sunkist Growers, Processed Products, Ontario, CA; *U.S. Private*, pg. 1052
Staufer, Al, V.P.-Intl. Sls.--Mooney Aircraft Corporation, Kerrville, TX; *U.S. Private*, pg. 759
Stauffer, Michael G., Dir.-Sls. & Mktg.--Keystone Powdered Metal Company, Saint Marys, PA; *U.S. Private*, pg. 619
Stautzenbach, Edward G., V.P.-Mktg.--Mercury Finance Co., Lake Forest, IL; *U.S. Public*, pg. 1093
Stavros, Nick, V.P.-Sls.--John Sterling Corporation, Richmond, IL; *U.S. Private*, pg. 1041
Stearns, Doug, Dir.-Sls. & Mktg.--Seneca Wire & Manufacturing Co., Fostoria, OH; *U.S. Private*, pg. 984
Steeb, Ray, Dir.-Sls.--Turner Construction Co., Pittsburgh, PA; *U.S. Public*, pg. 1645
Steele, Darryl, Natl. Sls. Mgr.--KSL Radio, Salt Lake City, UT; *U.S. Private*, pg. 327
Steele, Donald K., V.P.-Sls. & Sec.--Industrial Dielectrics, Inc., Noblesville, IN; *U.S. Private*, pg. 560

Steele, Frank C., Sr. V.P.-Sls.--Airborne Freight Corporation, Seattle, WA; *U.S. Public,* pg. 32

Steele, Fred, Natl. Sls. Mgr.--Hunt-Wesson Grocery Sales Division, Fullerton, CA; *U.S. Public,* pg. 428

Steele, Gary, V.P.-Sls.--Loctite Canada Inc., Mississauga, Canada; *Int'l,* pg. 611

Steele, John, V.P.-Sls.--Altron Systems Corporation, Fremont, CA; *U.S. Public,* pg. 59

Steele, John W., Dir.-Sls. & Mktg.--The Uhlmann Co., Kansas City, MO; *U.S. Private,* pg. 1115

Steele, Richard A., V.P.-Reg. Sls. & Newsprint--Donohue Inc., Quebec, Canada; *Int'l,* pg. 1075

Steele, Richard A., Sr. V.P.-Sls. & Mktg.--Printronix, Inc., Irvine, CA; *U.S. Public,* pg. 1329

Steele, Tom, Reg. Sls. Mgr.-Factory Automation--Aromat Southeast Sales Office, Norcross, GA; *Int'l,* pg. 848

Steen, Craig, V.P.-Sls. Logistics & Factored Prods.--Inter-Tel Integrated Systems, Inc., Chandler, AZ; *U.S. Public,* pg. 888

Steever, Daniel J., Grp. V.P. & Gen. Mgr.-Sls.--Broderbund Software, Inc., Novato, CA; *U.S. Public,* pg. 258

Stefano, Mike, Coord.-Sls.--Reactive Metals & Alloys Corporation (REMACOR), West Pittsburg, PA; *U.S. Private,* pg. 913

Stefanski, Larry, V.P.-Sls. & Mktg.--Cattleman's, Inc., Detroit, MI; *U.S. Public,* pg. 318

Steffel, John, Mgr.-Sls., Midwest Reg.--FMC Corp., Agricultural Products Group, Philadelphia, PA; *U.S. Public,* pg. 605

Stefkovich, Emil P., V.P.-Merchant Sls. (Commercial Coated Papers)--Fine Paper Div., Chillicothe, OH; *U.S. Public,* pg. 1074

Stegall, Robert, Sr. V.P.-Sls. & Mktg.--SGI Integrated Graphic Systems, Houston, TX; *U.S. Public,* pg. 971

Stegeman, Tom, Dir.-Franchise Sls.-Eastern Region--A&W Restaurants, Inc., Livonia, MI; *U.S. Private,* pg. 1

Stegner, Noel, V.P.-Sls.--Polychrome Corp. Div., Fort Lee, NJ; *Int'l,* pg. 370

Steichen, Peggy, Coord.-Sls.--Capsonic Group, Inc., Elgin, IL; *U.S. Private,* pg. 207

Steider, Dave, V.P.-Sls.--Urschel Labs Incorporated, Valparaiso, IN; *U.S. Private,* pg. 1129

Steidle, Stephen, V.P.-Intl. Sls.--FiberMark Inc., Brattleboro, VT; *U.S. Public,* pg. 620

Steidle, Stephen A., V.P. & Mgr.-Gen. Sls.--Office Products Division, Brattleboro, VT; *U.S. Public,* pg. 620

Steimer, Peter, V.P.-Sales--TMP Worldwide/Interactive Division, Framingham, MA; *U.S. Private,* pg. 1065

Stein, Andrew B., V.P.-Intl. Sls.--Toymax International Inc., Plainview, NY; *U.S. Public,* pg. 1626

Stein, John, V.P.-Sls./N.E. Region--Thorn Apple Valley, Inc., Southfield, MI; *U.S. Public,* pg. 1602

Stein, Jon, Mgr.-Sls., Women's Wear--Pendleton Woolen Mills, Inc., Portland, OR; *U.S. Private,* pg. 848

Stein, Melvin H., Sr. V.P.-Natl. Sls.--U.S. Healthcare, Inc., Blue Bell, PA; *U.S. Public,* pg. 26

Stein, Michael S., V.P.-Sls. Fin.--Fortis Sales, Milwaukee, WI; *Int'l,* pg. 499

Stein, S., Dir.-Sls.--ABB Simcon, Inc., Bloomfield, NJ; *Int'l,* pg. 5

Stein, Tim, V.P.-Sls. & Mktg.--Abex Friction Products, Winchester, VA; *U.S. Public,* pg. 443

Steinbach, Hilary, Reg. Mgr.-Sls.-Midwest--New England Confectionery Co., Cambridge, MA; *U.S. Private,* pg. 1113

Steinbarth, David, V.P.-Sls.--La Preferida, Inc., Chicago, IL; *U.S. Private,* pg. 640

Steinberg, Bob, Dir.-Sls.--Dormeyer Industries, Chicago, IL; *U.S. Private,* pg. 340

Steinberg, Mark, V.P.-Natl. Sls.--The Stroh Brewery Company, Detroit, MI; *U.S. Private,* pg. 1047

Steinbrook, Vicki, Mgr.-Sls. & Mktg.--White Castle Distributing, Inc., Columbus, OH; *U.S. Private,* pg. 1172

Steiner, Alan, Mgr.-Sls., Mktg., Adv. & Distr.--ITW Switches, Chicago, IL; *U.S. Public,* pg. 867

Steiner, Irene, Dir.-Mktg. & Sls.--The Vermont Teddy Bear Company, Inc., Shelburne, VT; *U.S. Public,* pg. 1716

Steiner, Robert, Mgr. Reg. Sls.--JEOL (U.S.A.), Inc., Rosemont, IL; *Int'l,* pg. 697

Steiner, Wallace W., V.P.-Retail Sls./Beverly Hills & Southwest Region--Tiffany & Co., New York, NY; *U.S. Public,* pg. 1608

Steinhart, Conrad, Controller, Treas. & Sec.--Happy Holiday Tree Farms, Sheridan, MI; *U.S. Private,* pg. 254

Steinkamp, Manfred, V.P.-Exec. Sls. & Dir.-Tech.-SD&C--Smith International, Inc., Houston, TX; *U.S. Public,* pg. 1478

Steinkamp, Mark, Coord.-Pub. Rels & Adv.--Daktronics, Inc., Brookings, SD; *U.S. Public,* pg. 478

Steinke, James E., V.P.-Sls. & Mktg./Retail--Patrick Cudahy Inc., Cudahy, WI; *U.S. Public,* pg. 1479

Steinman, Andrew, V.P.-Mktg. & Sls.--Falcon Safety Products Inc., Somerville, NJ; *U.S. Private,* pg. 392

Steinmayer, Claude, V.P.-Intl. Sls.--Zitel Corporation, Fremont, CA; *U.S. Public,* pg. 1793

Steinmentz, Alton G., V.P.-Intl. Sls.--Boeing Commercial Airplane Group, Renton, WA; *U.S. Public,* pg. 240

Steinweg, Paul, Dir.-Sls.--Danaher Tool Group, Lancaster, PA; *U.S. Public,* pg. 480

Steisel, Catherine, Dir.-Mktg.--Kleer-Vu Plastics Corp., Compton, CA; *U.S. Public,* pg. 962

Stejskal, Michael, Sls. Service Mgr.--Bradford Company, Holland, MI; *U.S. Private,* pg. 163

Stella, Joe, Mgr.-Mktg. & Sls.--Dacor Corporation, Northfield, IL; *U.S. Private,* pg. 306

Stelmach, Leigh S., Exec. V.P.-Opers.--Dollar General Corporation, Nashville, TN; *U.S. Public,* pg. 515

Stembridge, John, Mgr.-Sls.--TreeSource, Inc., Portland, OR; *U.S. Public,* pg. 1729

Stembridge, John C., V.P.-Sls. & Mktg.--WTD Industries, Inc., Portland, OR; *U.S. Public,* pg. 1729

Stemmetz, Herb, V.P.-Catalog Sls.--Mason Shoe Mfg. Co., Chippewa Falls, WI; *U.S. Private,* pg. 712

Stemple, Brad, Mgr.-Sls.--Bridgestone Cycle (U.S.A.), Inc., San Leandro, CA; *Int'l,* pg. 213

Stemple, Tom, V.P.-Sls.--Kwal-Howells, Inc.(Denver), Denver, CO; *Int'l,* pg. 1501

Stempler, Mark, Exec. V.P.-Sls.--Craftmatic Organization, Inc., Trevose, PA; *U.S. Private,* pg. 284

Stentiford, M.J., Mgr.-Tech. Sls.--WBB Devon Clays Ltd., Newton Abbot, United Kingdom; *Int'l,* pg. 1487

Stephan, John, Sr. V.P. & Mgr.-Sls. & Svc.--Great Western Financial Corporation, Chatsworth, CA; *U.S. Public,* pg. 1741

Stephani, Jim, Mgr.-Natl. Sls.-Institution Div.--Polar Ware Company, Sheboygan, WI; *U.S. Private,* pg. 873

Stephen, Doug, Dir.-Sls.--Sensormatic Limited, Hemel Hempstead, United Kingdom; *U.S. Public,* pg. 1458

Stephen, Greg, V.P.-Sls.--Aid Auto Stores, Inc., Westbury, NY; *U.S. Public,* pg. 29

Stephens, Bryon, Dir.-Franchise Sls.-Western Region--A&W Restaurants, Inc., Livonia, MI; *U.S. Private,* pg. 1

Stephens, Dana, Coord.-Sls. & Mktg.--Royston Laboratories, Pittsburgh, PA; *U.S. Public,* pg. 337

Stephens, James R., V.P.-Sls.--Today's Kids, Booneville, AR; *U.S. Private,* pg. 1020

Stephens, Thomas, V.P.-Pulp Sls./U.S.--Donohue Inc., Quebec, Canada; *Int'l,* pg. 1075

Stephenson, Jim, Mgr.-Sls. & Service--NuArc Co., Columbus, OH; *U.S. Private,* pg. 809

Stephenson, R.L., Sr. V.P.-Sls. & Mktg.--Resco Products, Inc., Conshohocken, PA; *U.S. Private,* pg. 924

Stephenson, Sandy, V.P.--Stephenson, Inc., Alexandria, VA; *U.S. Private,* pg. 1040

Sterling, Ron, Mgr.-Sls.--Packerland Packing Co., Green Bay, WI; *U.S. Private,* pg. 833

Stern, Bill, V.P.-Sls. & Bus. Devel.--Recon/Optical, Inc., Barrington, IL; *U.S. Private,* pg. 914

Stern, Dan, Dir.-Mktg. & Sls.--Global Motor Sport Group, Inc., Morgan Hill, CA; *U.S. Public,* pg. 748

Sterrett, James E., Mgr.-Lumber/Plywood Sls. & Mktg.--Boise Cascade Timber & Wood Products Division, Boise, ID; *U.S. Public,* pg. 243

Sterrett, Jim, Gen. Mgr.-Sls./Lumber & Plywood--Boise Cascade Corporation, Boise, ID; *U.S. Public,* pg. 242

Steve, Mark, 1st V.P.-Sls. & New Bus. Devel.--Great Financial Bank FSB, Louisville, KY; *U.S. Private,* pg. 473

Stevens, Adrienne, V.P.-Sls. & Mktg.--BF Goodrich Avionic Systems, Inc., Grand Rapids, MI; *U.S. Public,* pg. 751

Stevens, Allen, Mgr.-Reg. Sls.--Pennsylvania Cellular Telephone Corp., State College, PA; *U.S. Public,* pg. 1708

Stevens, Brian D., V.P.-Sls.--Hilton Hotels Div., Beverly Hills, CA; *U.S. Public,* pg. 829

Stevens, Charles, V.P.-Professonal Sls.--Linear Corporation, Carlsbad, CA; *U.S. Public,* pg. 1193

Stevens, Clement L., V.P.-Meat Sls.--Albertson's, Inc., Boise, ID; *U.S. Public,* pg. 38

Stevens, Ed, Mgr.-Sls.--Skokie Valley Beverage Co., Wheeling, IL; *U.S. Private,* pg. 1005

Stevens, Elliott, Reg. V.P.-Sls.--Milgray Electronics, Inc., Farmingdale, NY; *U.S. Public,* pg. 205

Stevens, Frank, V.P.-Sls. & Mktg.--Boler Company, Itasca, IL; *U.S. Private,* pg. 155

Stevens, Glenn, V.P.--GWP, Inc., Los Angeles, CA; *U.S. Private,* pg. 437

Stevens, R., V.P.-National Accounts--Welded Tube, Chicago, IL; *Int'l,* pg. 101

Stevens, R.L., Gen. Mgr.-Sls.--MelloButtercup Ice Cream Inc., Wilson, NC; *U.S. Private,* pg. 730

Stevens, Richard, Mgr.-Sls. & Service--Agway Energy Products (AEP), Syracuse, NY; *U.S. Private,* pg. 27

Stevens, Robert, Mgr.-Sls.--Tricon Electromechanical Div., Downers Grove, IL; *U.S. Private,* pg. 1103

Stevens, Terrance, Dir.-Sls.--VR/Wesson Hydro Carbide, Latrobe, PA; *U.S. Public,* pg. 612

Stevenson, Andrew, Mgr.-Sls.--Bruntons Areo Product, Musselburgh, United Kingdom; *Int'l,* pg. 268

Stevenson, Denny, V.P.-Worldwide Sls.--Magnetrol International, Downers Grove, IL; *U.S. Private,* pg. 696

Stevenson, John, V.P.-Sls. & Mktg.--Health Economics Corporation, Dallas, TX; *U.S. Public,* pg. 588

Stevenson, Lloyd, V.P.-Mktg. & Sls.--Abbott Ball Company, West Hartford, CT; *U.S. Private,* pg. 9

Stevenson, R.H., Sr. V.P.-Sls. & Mktg.--North State Pyrophyllite, Greensboro, NC; *U.S. Private,* pg. 924

Stevenson, Robert, V.P.-Sls. & Mktg.--Pioneer Plastics Corporation, Auburn, ME; *U.S. Private,* pg. 867

Stewart, Danny, Exec. V.P.-Sls. & Mktg.--Catalina Lighting, Inc., Miami, FL; *U.S. Public,* pg. 314

Stewart, Don, Gen. Sls. Mgr.--Metz Baking Co., Dubuque, IA; *U.S. Private,* pg. 1022

Stewart, Jim, V.P.-Sls.--Alban Tractor Co. Inc., Baltimore, MD; *U.S. Private,* pg. 32

Stewart, John, V.P.-Sls. & Mktg.--Schmidt Baking Co., Inc., Baltimore, MD; *U.S. Private,* pg. 970

Stewart, Mark, Asst. V.P.-Mktg.--Academy Insurance Group, Inc., Alpharetta, GA; *Int'l,* pg. 27

Stewart, Rob, Dir.-Sls.--Stadelman Fruit L.L.C., Yakima, WA; *U.S. Private,* pg. 1028

Stewart, Thomas, V.P.-Sls. & Mktg.--Gaymar Industries, Inc., Orchard Park, NY; *U.S. Private,* pg. 442

Steyn, C.H., Mgr.-Sales--Sasol Oil, Rosebank, South Africa; *Int'l,* pg. 1197

Stibich, Donald C., Sr. V.P.-Paper Sls.--Longview Fibre Company, Longview, WA; *U.S. Public,* pg. 1013

Stidham, J. Michael, Exec. V.P.-Sls.--Oakwood Homes Corporation, Greensboro, NC; *U.S. Public,* pg. 1209

Stiegler, Bob, Mgr.-Sls.--Kansas City Royals Radio Network, Kansas City, MO; *U.S. Private,* pg. 995

Stight, Richard, V.P.-Sls. & Mktg.--Columbian Rope Company, Guntown, MS; *U.S. Private,* pg. 256

Stigi, Peter, Sr. V.P.-Sls. & Mktg.--Tuscan/Lehigh Dairies LP, Union, NJ; *U.S. Private,* pg. 1110

Stiles, Gary M., Mgr.-Sls.--Cloister Pure Spring Water Co., Inc., Lancaster, PA; *U.S. Private,* pg. 247

Still, Annie, Dir.-Sls.--Chattanooga Choo-Choo Holiday Inn, Chattanooga, TN; *U.S. Private,* pg. 231

Stillings, Robert, V.P.-Opers., Sls., Mktg. & Dir.-Personnel--Presto Food Stores, Inc., Plant City, FL; *U.S. Private,* pg. 882

Stimac, Tom, Prod. Mgr.--De-Sta-Co, A Dover Resources Co., Troy, MI; *U.S. Public,* pg. 521

Stine, John, Mgr.-Circulation--The Yankton Printing Company, Yankton, SD; *U.S. Private,* pg. 995

Stinson, David N., V.P.-Sls.--Nemschoff Chairs, Inc., Sheboygan, WI; *U.S. Private,* pg. 791

Stith, Andrew W., Sr. V.P.-Sls. & Mktg.--NovaCare Employee Services, Inc., Norristown, PA; *U.S. Public,* pg. 1203

Stock, Heinz, Mgr.-Sls.--Letraset AG, Glattbrugg, Switzerland; *Int'l,* pg. 461

Stocker, Jeff, V.P.-Sls./East--BJ Services Company, Houston, TX; *U.S. Public,* pg. 161

Stockett, Peter, V.P.-Adv., Sls. & Mktg.--Sun Bancorp, Inc., Selinsgrove, PA; *U.S. Public,* pg. 1529

Stockham, Jim, Mgr.-Mktg. & Sls.--Zacky Farms, Inc., South El Monte, CA; *U.S. Private,* pg. 1203

Stocking, Ronald, Mgr.-Sls.--Fansteel VR/Wesson-Plantsville, Plantsville, CT; *U.S. Public,* pg. 612

Stockstill, Roy, V.P.-Sls.--Smith Environmental Technologies Corp., Plymouth Meeting, PA; *U.S. Public,* pg. 1477

Stoebner, Tom, Mgr.-Adv., Sls. & Mktg.-Films--Raven Industries, Inc., Sioux Falls, SD; *U.S. Public,* pg. 1361

Stoebner, Tom, V.P.-Sls. & Mktg.--Engineered Films Div., Flexible Films Dept., Sioux Falls, SD; *U.S. Public,* pg. 1361

Stoer, Robert, Dir.-Premium Sls.--Animal Fair, Minneapolis, MN; *U.S. Private,* pg. 885

Stoesser, Dieter, Area Sls.--Analog Devices GMBH - Technisches Buero Suedwest, Karlsruhe, Germany; *U.S.* Public, pg. 108

Stoffek, Klaus, Mgr.-Sls.--Georg Sahm GmbH & Co. KG Maschinenfabrik, Eschwege, Germany; *Int'l,* pg. 1169

Stokely, Gregg, V.P.-Commercial Mktg.--BEI Sensors and Systems Company, Sylmar, CA; *U.S. Public,* pg. 160

Stokes, Nick, Mgr.-Mktg. & Sls./Bldg. Matls.--Boise Cascade Corporation, Boise, ID; *U.S. Public,* pg. 242

Stokes, Nick, Mgr.-Division Sls. & Mktg.--Boise Cascade Building Materials Distribution Div., Boise, ID; *U.S. Public,* pg. 243

Stokes, Terry G., V.P.-Sls., Plumbing Hardware--Radiator Specialty Company, Charlotte, NC; *U.S. Private,* pg. 906

Stolarz, Michael, Sr. V.P.-Sls.--The Great Atlantic & Pacific Tea Company, Inc., Montvale, NJ; *Int'l,* pg. 1375

Stoll, Mark, Gen. Sls. Mgr.--Cole Hersee Company, Boston, MA; *U.S. Private,* pg. 251

Stollberg, Scott, Dir.-Adv. Sls.--Kalmbach Publishing Co., Waukesha, WI; *U.S. Private,* pg. 606

Stolls, Steven, Dir.-Sls.--The Power Line, Port Washington, NY; *U.S. Private,* pg. 893

Stollsteimer, G.R., V.P.-Sls.--Reuland Electric Company, City of Industry, CA; *U.S. Private,* pg. 925

Stoltman, Pat, Mgr.-Mktg. & Sls.--Farm Press, Clarksdale, MS; *U.S. Public,* pg. 1328

Stolz, Rich, Mgr.-Sls./Millwork--Sierra Pacific Industries, Anderson, CA; *U.S. Private,* pg. 998

Stone, Bob, Dir.-Sls./Americas--Proxima Corporation, San Diego, CA; *U.S. Public,* pg. 1339

Stone, Brett, Dir.-Retail Sls.--Russell Stover Candies, Inc., Kansas City, MO; *U.S. Private,* pg. 953

Stone, David B., Exec. V.P.-Sls. & Mktg.--Merit Behavioral Care Corp., Park Ridge, NJ; *U.S. Public,* pg. 1036

Stone, Harold, Jr., V.P.-Sls. & Mktg.--Renfro Corp., Mount Airy, NC; *U.S. Private,* pg. 922

Stone, John, Mgr.-Natl.Sls.--Caravan Brokay, Totowa, NJ; *U.S. Private,* pg. 208

Stone, Mitch, Dir.-Sls.--Datum Inc., Irvine, CA; *U.S. Public,* pg. 488

Stone, Richard L., Dir.-Managed Care--Muro Pharmaceutical, Inc., Tewksbury, MA; *U.S. Private,* pg. 767

Stone, Tom, V.P.-Mktg. & Sls.--Crane Pumps & Systems Inc., Piqua, OH; *U.S. Public,* pg. 457

Stone, Tom, V.P.-Sales & Mktg.--Barnes Pumps, Inc., Mansfield, OH; *U.S. Public,* pg. 457

Stonestreet, Bill, Mgr.-Sls.--Sunniland Corporation, Sanford, FL; *U.S. Private,* pg. 1053

Stoops, W.G., Sr. V.P.-Sls., East--Emkay, Inc., Itasca, IL; *U.S. Private,* pg. 374

Storey, Tom, Exec. V.P.-Sales & Mktg.--Doubletree Corporation, Memphis, TN; *U.S. Public,* pg. 1335

Stork, Detlef, Exec. V.P.-Sls.--Koenig & Bauer-Albert AG, Wurzburg, Germany; *Int'l,* pg. 742

Storm, David, Mgr.-Sls.--Eatelcorp Inc., Gonzales, LA; *U.S. Private,* pg. 358

Stormont, James, V.P.-Sls. & Mktg.--Bodine Electric Company, Chicago, IL; *U.S. Private,* pg. 154

Storms, A. James, Dir.-Sls.--ITW Woodworth, Ferndale, MI; *U.S. Public,* pg. 867

Story, F. Paul, V.P.-Aerospace--Beacon Group, Bloomfield, CT; *U.S. Private,* pg. 126

Story, Jim, Mgr.-Sls.--Bandini Fertilizer Company, Los Angeles, CA; *U.S. Private,* pg. 113

Stotts, John, V.P.-Sls. & Mktg.--Conmed Corporation, Utica, NY; *U.S. Public,* pg. 431

Stotts, John, Dir.-Sls. & Mktg.--Conmed Andover Medical, Inc., Haverhill, MA; *U.S. Public,* pg. 431

Stoudt, Craig, Pres.-Ampad Div.--American Pad and Paper Company, Dallas, TX; *U.S. Public,* pg. 88

Stouffs, Arthur J., V.P.-Culinary Sls.--Cuisine Solutions, Inc., Alexandria, VA; *U.S. Public,* pg. 466

Stoupis, George, District Sls. Mgr.-Pittsburgh--Magneco/Metrel, Inc., Addison, IL; *U.S. Private,* pg. 695

Stout, Carl A., V.P.-Sls. & Dir.-Mktg.--Morgan Foods, Inc., Austin, IN; *U.S. Private,* pg. 761

Stout, Dan, V.P.-Sls.--Aristokraft, Inc., Jasper, IN; *U.S. Public,* pg. 675

Stout, R.M., V.P.-Land & Mktg.--Rio Algom Mining Corp., Oklahoma City, OK; *Int'l,* pg. 1118

Stovall, Brian, Dir.-Sls.--Houston Galvanizing Div., Houston, TX; *U.S. Public*, pg. 159
Stover, Robert W., Mgr.-Sls.--Kunzler & Company, Inc., Lancaster, PA; *U.S. Private*, pg. 636
Stowe, Donald, Exec. V.P.-Sls. & Technology--Dravo Lime Company, Pittsburgh, PA; *U.S. Public*, pg. 527
Stowe, Donald H., Jr., V.P.-Sls. & Tech.--Dravo Corporation, Pittsburgh, PA; *U.S. Public*, pg. 527
Straight, David N., Dir.-Sls.--HealthAmerica Pennsylvania, Inc., Pittsburgh, PA; *U.S. Public*, pg. 454
Strand, Doreen L., V.P.-Sls.--PrimeVest Financial Services, Inc., Saint Cloud, MN; *U.S. Public*, pg. 1376
Strange, John, V.P.-Sls.--Tenneco Specialty Products, Deerfield, IL; *U.S. Public*, pg. 1579
Stransky, John, V.P.-Sls. & Service-Worldwide--Brunswick Bowling & Billiards Corp., Muskegon, MI; *U.S. Public*, pg. 265
Strashum, B., Mgr.-Sls.--Crest-Foam Corporation, Moonachie, NJ; *U.S. Public*, pg. 986
Stratford, James, Mgr.-Sls.--Bergquist UK. Limited, Milton Keynes, United Kingdom; *U.S. Private*, pg. 135
Strauss, Robert, Dir.-Mktg. & Sls.--Fastenal Company, Winona, MN; *U.S. Public*, pg. 614
Straw, John E., V.P.-Sls. & Mktg.--Jefferson Smurfit Corporation, Saint Louis, MO; *Int'l*, pg. 1269
Strawn, Steve, V.P.-Sls.--City Club of Charlotte, Fort Mill, SC; *U.S. Public*, pg. 610
Strecker, Al, Mgr.-Sls.--Bradbury Company, Inc., Moundridge, KS; *U.S. Private*, pg. 163
Strecker, William S., V.P.-Sls. & Mktg.--Kingsbury, Inc., Philadelphia, PA; *U.S. Private*, pg. 622
Streeter, Bill, V.P.-Sls.--MFA Incorporated, Columbia, MO; *U.S. Private*, pg. 686
Streeter, Butch, V.P.-Sls. & Mktg.--Amarillo Hardware Company, Amarillo, TX; *U.S. Private*, pg. 335
Streeter, Kenneth, Mgr.-Sls.--Eaton Corp., Supercharger Div., Athens, GA; *U.S. Public*, pg. 556
Stremmel, Rick, Mgr.-Sls.--Subaru Central Region, Inc., Aurora, CO; *Int'l*, pg. 523
Stressing, John, V.P.-Worldwide Sls.--IKOS Systems, Inc., Cupertino, CA; *U.S. Public*, pg. 864
Strickland, Ben, Mgr.-Sls., Food Service--Beaver Street Fisheries, Inc., Jacksonville, FL; *U.S. Private*, pg. 128
Strickland, Bob, V.P.-Sls.--Envoy Corporation, Nashville, TN; *U.S. Public*, pg. 587
Strickland, Dennis, V.P.-Sls.--Pangburn Candy Company, Fort Worth, TX; *U.S. Private*, pg. 836
Strickland, Wyatt, Mgr.-Sls.--Fairfax Building Systems, Culpeper, VA; *U.S. Private*, pg. 391
Stringer, Steve, V.P.-Sls.--GE Capital/IT Solutions, Minneapolis, MN; *U.S. Public*, pg. 711
Stringfellow, Stu, Exec. V.P.-Domestic Television Sls.--King World Productions, Inc., New York, NY; *U.S. Public*, pg. 961
Stringfellow, Tommy, Mgr.-Grp. Sales--Paramount Carowinds, Charlotte, NC; *U.S. Private*, pg. 776
Strong, J., Mgr.-Sls.--Crane Resistoflex/Industrial, Marion, NC; *U.S. Public*, pg. 457
Stropki, John M., Exec. V.P.-Sls. & Mfg.--The Lincoln Electric Company, Cleveland, OH; *U.S. Public*, pg. 996
Stroupe, Rick, V.P.-Worldwide Sls.--SymmetriCom, Inc., San Jose, CA; *U.S. Public*, pg. 1547
Stroupe, Rick, Sr. V.P.-Worldwide Sls.--Telecom Solutions, San Jose, CA; *U.S. Public*, pg. 1547
Strouse, Denise, Mgr.-Sls.--McCourt Label Co., Lewis Run, PA; *U.S. Private*, pg. 720
Strout, Bob, Sls. Rep.--Leblanc Communications, Inc., Richardson, TX; *U.S. Private*, pg. 656
Strouts, Raymond, Mgr.-Sls.--Rock of Ages Corporation, Graniteville, VT; *U.S. Public*, pg. 1396
Strunc, Murray G., Mgr.-Sls. Admin.--Ennis Business Forms, Inc., Ennis, TX; *U.S. Public*, pg. 583
Strunk, Denise, Asst.-Bus. Devel.--Ghent Manufacturing, Inc., Lebanon, OH; *U.S. Private*, pg. 450
Strunk, Gary A., V.P.-Sls. & Mktg.--Peterson American Corp., Southfield, MI; *U.S. Private*, pg. 857
Strup, Richard F., Sr. V.P.-Intl. Mktg.--Miller Brewing Company, Milwaukee, WI; *U.S. Public*, pg. 1289
Stuart, Andrew, Dir.-Sls.--SJL of Kansas Corp., Wichita, KS; *U.S. Public*, pg. 984
Stuart, Dan, V.P.-Field Sls.--Newell Window Furnishings Co., Freeport, IL; *U.S. Public*, pg. 1177
Stuart, David, Mgr.-Sls.--Colin Stewart Minchem Limited, Winsford, United Kingdom; *Int'l*, pg. 858
Stuart, William, V.P.-Mktg. & Sls.--Schulze & Burch Biscuit Company, Chicago, IL; *U.S. Private*, pg. 973
Stuart, William E., Dir.-Sls.-Essex Sls. Grp.--Guinness Southern Division, Newport Beach, CA; *Int'l*, pg. 412
Stubbe, Allen, Mgr.-Sls. & Mktg.--Wagner Casters and Wheels, Hustisford, WI; *U.S. Private*, pg. 1146
Studer, Evan, V.P.-Sls. & Mktg.--Sunstone Hotel Investors, Inc., San Clemente, CA; *U.S. Public*, pg. 1536
Studzinski, Keith, Mgr.-Sls.--Mike Savoie Chevrolet Inc., Troy, MI; *U.S. Private*, pg. 968
Stuff, Steven, Mgr.-Intl. Sls.--Dorner Manufacturing Corp., Hartland, WI; *U.S. Private*, pg. 340
Stuhlman, Dennis, Dir.-Sls. & Mktg./Commercial Prods.--Cantex Inc., Mineral Wells, TX; *Int'l*, pg. 1312
Stukel, V.V., Dir.-Sls.--Turner Construction Co., Chicago, IL; *U.S. Public*, pg. 1645
Stulik, Miroslav, Mgr.-Sls.--PENCO-Washington, Tukwila, WA; *Int'l*, pg. 1508
Stum, Ed, Mgr.-Sls.--PENCO-Oklahoma, Oklahoma City, OK; *Int'l*, pg. 1508
Stumbo, B., Dir.-Sls.--Positech Corporation, Laurens, IA; *U.S. Public*, pg. 406
Stupka, Jerry, V.P.-Intl. Sls.--Allen Telecom Inc., Solon, OH; *U.S. Public*, pg. 45
Sturgell, Brian, V.P.-Sls. & Mktg.--Alcan Rolled Products Division, Cleveland, OH; *Int'l*, pg. 50
Sturgis, Robert, V.P.-Sls.--Lakeside Industries, Issaquah, WA; *U.S. Private*, pg. 644
Sturm, Joe, Mgr.-Inside Sls.--Bunn-O-Matic Corporation, Springfield, IL; *U.S. Private*, pg. 180
Styacich, Robert, V.P.-Sls.--The Hennegan Company, Florence, KY; *U.S. Private*, pg. 522
Stysly, T., V.P.-Sls./S.--Sika Corporation, Lyndhurst, NJ; *Int'l*, pg. 1249
Subramanian, Mani, Country Mgr.--qad.japan k.k., Yokohama, Japan; *U.S. Public*, pg. 1345
Suchanek, Janine T., Mgr.-Mktg. Communications Coord.--Mestek, Inc., Westfield, MA; *U.S. Public*, pg. 1099
Suchordt, Volkert, Chief Oper. Officer--Busch-Jaeger Ludenscheider Metallwerk GmbH, Ludenscheid, Germany; *Int'l*, pg. 1427
Suematsu, Haruhito, Dir.-Western Japan Sls. Headquarters--Rohm Co., Ltd., Kyoto, Japan; *Int'l*, pg. 1124
Suessmilch, Wieland, Dir.-Sls. & Mktg.--Cherry Mikroschalter GmbH, Auerbach, Germany; *U.S. Public*, pg. 346
Suffoletto, Matthew V., Sr. V.P.-Sls.--Primavera Systems, Inc., Bala Cynwyd, PA; *U.S. Private*, pg. 884
Sugarman, Joel, V.P.-Sls.--Bradford Industries, Inc., Lowell, MA; *U.S. Private*, pg. 163
Sugg, D., V.P.-Sls.--Stacoswitch, Inc., Costa Mesa, CA; *U.S. Private*, pg. 260
Sugg, John, Dir.-Premium Sls.--Provident Music Group, Brentwood, TN; *Int'l*, pg. 1529
Sugiura, Atsushi, Asst. Gen. Mgr.-Domestic Sls.--Makita Corporation, Anjo, Japan; *Int'l*, pg. 831
Suitmich, Paul, Sls. Admininistrator--Kamax-G.B. DuPont L.P., Troy, MI; *U.S. Private*, pg. 606
Suits, Reggis, Mgr.-Sls.--American Uniform Co., Cleveland, TN; *U.S. Private*, pg. 1039
Sul, Jay C., Mgr.-Sls.--H.K. International, Inc., Northbrook, IL; *U.S. Private*, pg. 491
Sulick, E., Gen. Mgr.-Sls.-Medical--Graphic Controls Corporation, Buffalo, NY; *U.S. Private*, pg. 470
Sullivan, Brian, V.P.-Natl. Accounts--K-Swiss Inc., Chatsworth, CA; *U.S. Public*, pg. 937
Sullivan, Charles F., V.P.-Sls.--Pepsi-Cola Bottling Company of Charlotte Inc., Charlotte, NC; *U.S. Private*, pg. 852
Sullivan, Dennis, Dir.-Sls.--Mitsubishi Silicon America, Palo Alto, CA; *Int'l*, pg. 875
Sullivan, Frank B., Sr. V.P.-Sls. & Mktg.--Square D Company, Palatine, IL; *Int'l*, pg. 1208
Sullivan, Gary, Exec. V.P.-Sls. & Mktg.--EMPI, Inc., Saint Paul, MN; *U.S. Public*, pg. 545
Sullivan, George R., V.P.-Sls.--Sullivan Paper Company, West Springfield, MA; *U.S. Private*, pg. 1050
Sullivan, James, V.P. & Gen. Mgr.-Nuswitch Grp.--Network Peripherals Inc., Milpitas, CA; *U.S. Public*, pg. 1169
Sullivan, Kevin P., V.P.-Home Theater Div.--Go-Video, Inc., Scottsdale, AZ; *U.S. Public*, pg. 748
Sullivan, Lorraine, Dir.-Sls.--Peter Pan Seafoods, Inc., Seattle, WA; *Int'l*, pg. 928
Sullivan, Mike, V.P.-Sls. & Mgr.-Adv.--Lawrence Paper Company, Lawrence, KS; *U.S. Private*, pg. 654
Sullivan, Mike, V.P.-Sls.--Lambda Advanced Analog, Santa Clara, CA; *Int'l*, pg. 1241
Sullivan, Patrick M., V.P.-Dealer Sales--Royal Appliance Mfg. Co., Cleveland, OH; *U.S. Public*, pg. 1410
Sullivan, Rhonda L., Pres.--Lavelle Industries Inc., Burlington, WI; *U.S. Private*, pg. 653
Sullivan, Robert R., V.P.-Sls. & Mktg.--Southwire Company, Carrollton, GA; *U.S. Private*, pg. 1019
Sullivan, Terrence M., Sr. V.P.-Individual Ins.--The Minnesota Mutual Life Insurance Company, Saint Paul, MN; *U.S. Private*, pg. 750
Sullivan, Terry, V.P. & Dir.-Direct Response Adv. Sls.--Parade Publications Inc., New York, NY; *U.S. Private*, pg. 20
Sullivan, Thomas, V.P.-Sls.--Smead Manufacturing Company, Hastings, MN; *U.S. Private*, pg. 1006
Sullivan, Thomas J., V.P.-Sls. & Mktg.--DuBois Chemicals, Cincinnati, OH; *Int'l*, pg. 1437
Sullivan, Tim W., V.P.-Sls. & Mktg.--Bucyrus International, South Milwaukee, WI; *U.S. Private*, pg. 177
Sullman, Michael, Sls. Dir.--Skandia Life Assurance Co. Ltd., Southampton, United Kingdom; *Int'l*, pg. 1258
Sultenfuss, John H., Sr. V.P.-Mktg. & Sls.--CF Industries, Inc., Long Grove, IL; *U.S. Private*, pg. 193
Summers, Doug, Dir.-Construction & Equipment Sls.--Carolina Tractor & Equipment Co., Charlotte, NC; *U.S. Private*, pg. 214
Summers, Karl, V.P.-Sls. & Mktg.--Feintool U.S. Operations Inc., White Plains, NY; *Int'l*, pg. 479
Summerville, Douglas, V.P.-Sls.--Garlock Sealing Technologies, Palmyra, NY; *U.S. Public*, pg. 402
Sumner, Mark E., Sls. Mgr.-Special Markets--Rice Growers Association of California, West Sacramento, CA; *U.S. Private*, pg. 927
Sumner, Ray, Mgr.-Sls.-Eastern Div.--The Ohio Art Company, Inc., Bryan, OH; *U.S. Public*, pg. 1214
Sun, Conrad, V.P.-Sls.-Asia/Pacific--Lynx Golf, Inc., City of Industry, CA; *U.S. Private*, pg. 684
Sun, T.C., Dir.--Taiwan Power Company, Taipei, Taiwan; *Int'l*, pg. 1348
Sunaway, A., Dir.-Div. Sls. & Mktg.--Ransomes Plc, Ipswich, United Kingdom; *Int'l*, pg. 1087
Sundberg, Carl, Mgr.-Sls.--Holmen Paper AB, Norrkoping, Sweden; *Int'l*, pg. 885
Sundermeyer, Ron, Exec. V.P.--S.A.S.I. Corporation, Collinsville, IL; *U.S. Private*, pg. 955
Sundwick, Robert, V.P.-Sls. & Mktg.--Grote Industries, Madison, IN; *U.S. Private*, pg. 483
Suquet, Jose, Exec. V.P. & Chief Agency Officer--The Equitable Companies Incorporated, New York, NY; *U.S. Public*, pg. 588
Sur, Richard R., Dir.-Mktg. Devel. & Admin.--Polyfibron Technologies Corp., Billerica, MA; *U.S. Private*, pg. 875
Surane, James, Sr. V.P.-Sls.--Vermont American Tool Corp., Louisville, KY; *U.S. Public*, pg. 575
Surasky, P., Art Dir.--Young & Rubicam de Buenos Aires, Buenos Aires, Argentina; *U.S. Private*, pg. 1200
Surbaugh, Gary, V.P.-Natl. Sls.--Tension Envelope Corp., Kansas City, MO; *U.S. Private*, pg. 1077
Sussberg, L., Sr. V.P.-Sls.--SEIKO Corporation of America, Mahwah, NJ; *Int'l*, pg. 1218
Sussman, Dennis, Sr. V.P.-Sls.-Lighting Div.--Crystal Clear Industries, Ridgefield Park, NJ; *U.S. Private*, pg. 293
Sussman, Don, V.P.-Grocery & Meat--The Stop & Shop Companies, Inc., Quincy, MA; *Int'l*, pg. 750
Sutherland, James, Reg. Sls. Mgr.--Serfilco, Ltd., Northbrook, IL; *U.S. Private*, pg. 985
Sutherland, R.L., Div. Mgr.-Prod. Sls.--The Ohio Art Company, Inc., Bryan, OH; *U.S. Public*, pg. 1214
Sutherland, Robert W., Dir.-Sls. & Mktg.--Therm, Inc., Ithaca, NY; *U.S. Private*, pg. 1079
Sutlin, Jerrold, V.P.-Franchise Sls. & Devel.--Gingiss International, Addison, IL; *U.S. Private*, pg. 455
Sutter, Debbie, V.P.-Mktg. & Retail Sls.--Clear Shield National, Inc., Wheeling, IL; *U.S. Public*, pg. 586
Suttles, Chuck, Dir.-Mktg. & Sls.--Duff-Norton, Charlotte, NC; *U.S. Public*, pg. 406
Sutton, Mark, Mgr.-Mktg. & Sls.--Thilmany Division, Kaukauna, WI; *U.S. Public*, pg. 903
Sutton, Michael T., V.P.-Mktg.--General Shale Products Corp., Elizabethton, TN; *Int'l*, pg. 843
Suydam, Mark, V.P.-Sls. & Mktg.--Kirkwood Industries, Inc., Cleveland, OH; *U.S. Private*, pg. 623
Suzanski, Mike, V.P.-Mktg. & Sls.--Monier Inc., Irvine, CA; *Int'l*, pg. 1091
Suzuki, Keisuke, Dir.-Original Equipment Sls.--Bridgestone Corporation, Tokyo, Japan; *Int'l*, pg. 213
Suzuki, Mitsunori, Gen. Mgr.-Sls.--Terumo Corporation, Tokyo, Japan; *Int'l*, pg. 1375
Suzuki, Takao, Dir. & Gen. Mgr.-Paperboard Sls.--Settsu Corporation, Amagasaki, Japan; *Int'l*, pg. 1225
Svensson, Sven-Inge, Reg. Sls. Dir.-Europe--Frionor A/S, Lysaker, Norway; *Int'l*, pg. 516
Svrcek, Rudy, V.P.-Sls. & Mktg.--The Irvine Company, Newport Beach, CA; *U.S. Private*, pg. 575
Swaback, Ray, Pres.-Sls.--Medline Industries, Inc., Mundelein, IL; *U.S. Private*, pg. 728
Swafford, Larry P., V.P.-Sls. & Mktg.--Smithfield Foods, Inc., Norfolk, VA; *U.S. Public*, pg. 1479
Swan, Alex, Gen. Mgr.--ITOCHU Building Products Co., Inc., Miami, FL; *Int'l*, pg. 694
Swan, James, Mgr.-Sls.--Active Electrical Supply Company, Chicago, IL; *U.S. Private*, pg. 15
Swanger, Milo, V.P.-Sls.--Drummond American Corporation, Vernon Hills, IL; *U.S. Public*, pg. 980
Swank, Tom, Dir.-Secondary Mkt. Sls. & Quality Control--Roman, Inc., Roselle, IL; *U.S. Private*, pg. 942
Swanson, Bob, Gen. Mgr.-Sls.--Mansion Homes, Robbins, NC; *U.S. Public*, pg. 318
Swanson, Jim, Mgr.-Sls.--Klockner-Moeller, Kennesaw, GA; *Int'l*, pg. 736
Swanson, Richard, V.P.-Casualwear Sls.--Fruit of the Loom, Inc., Chicago, IL; *U.S. Public*, pg. 685
Swart, Dirk F., V.P.-Sls. & Mktg.--United Sugars Corp., Bloomington, MN; *U.S. Private*, pg. 52
Swarts, Al, Dir.-Sls. & Mktg.--Amgen Inc., Thousand Oaks, CA; *U.S. Public*, pg. 100
Swartz, Dan, V.P.-Private Label Packing--4C Foods Corporation, Brooklyn, NY; *U.S. Private*, pg. 421
Swaw, Robert L., V.P.-Beverage Alcohol Mktg.--Midwest Grain Products, Inc., Atchison, KS; *U.S. Public*, pg. 1111
Swedeen, John, V.P.-Sls. & Mktg.--Weiser Lock, Tucson, AZ; *U.S. Public*, pg. 1053
Sweeney, Gene, Mgr.-Sls.--Dominion Homes, Dublin, OH; *U.S. Public*, pg. 516
Sweeney, James, Dir.-Natl. Sls.--Dianon Systems, Inc., Stratford, CT; *U.S. Public*, pg. 506
Sweeney, Ron, Exec. V.P.-Black Music--Sony Music Entertainment, Inc., New York, NY; *Int'l*, pg. 1281
Sweet, Mark, Mgr.-Sls.--Holiday RV Superstores West, Inc., Sacramento, CA; *U.S. Public*, pg. 830
Sweigart, Michelle, Coord.-Sls. & Mktg.-Aircrew Trng. Systems Div.--Environmental Tectonics Corporation (ETC), Southampton, PA; *U.S. Public*, pg. 587
Sweitzer, Steve, V.P.-Sls.--Continental Eagle Corporation, Prattville, AL; *U.S. Private*, pg. 267
Swenerton, Stephen, V.P.-Retail Sls.--Broan Mfg. Co., Inc., Hartford, WI; *U.S. Public*, pg. 1193
Swenson, Brent, V.P.-Sls.--Linzer Products Corp., Flushing, NY; *U.S. Private*, pg. 669
Swenson, Kathy, Sr. V.P.-Sls., Mktg. & Commun.--Kaiser Permanente, Oakland, CA; *U.S. Private*, pg. 605
Swerdlow, Al, Mgr.-Sls.--Miller Curtain Co., Inc., San Antonio, TX; *U.S. Private*, pg. 746
Swetlik, Don, V.P.-Mktg. & Sls.--Bird Products Corporation, Palm Springs, CA; *U.S. Public*, pg. 1591
Swett, John P., Sr. V.P.-Sls., Mktg. & Tech. Services/ Rubber Div.--Bayer Corporation, Pittsburgh, PA; *Int'l*, pg. 172
Swift, Alison C., Mgr.-Sls.--Swift Instruments, Inc.-Technical Instruments Div., San Jose, CA; *U.S. Private*, pg. 1059
Swift, Tim, Natl. Sls. Mgr.--Majorica Jewelry Ltd., New York, NY; *U.S. Private*, pg. 697
Swinburne, Peter, Dir.-Customer Service & Sls.--Bass Brewers Ltd., Burton on Trent, United Kingdom; *Int'l*, pg. 170
Swingle, David O., Sr. V.P.-Sls.--Wyeth-Ayerst Laboratories, Inc., Philadelphia, PA; *U.S. Public*, pg. 80
Swisher, William, V.P.-Sls.--Hertz Equipment Rental Corp., Park Ridge, NJ; *U.S. Public*, pg. 664
Swiskow, Jonathan D, Sr. V.P.-Sls. & Mktg.--Hickory Specialties, Inc., Brentwood, TN; *U.S. Public*, pg. 596
Swithenbank, Gene W., Exec. V.P.-Sls. & Mktg.--CommScope, Inc., Hickory, NC; *U.S. Public*, pg. 415
Switzer, Scott, Natl. Sls. Mgr.--Hosokawa Micron Powder Systems, Summit, NJ; *Int'l*, pg. 636
Swords, Mary Patricia, V.P. & Dir.-Sls. & Mktg.--The Bureau of National Affairs, Inc., Washington, DC; *U.S. Private*, pg. 181
Syberg, Kenneth E., V.P.-Sls.--Dualite Inc., Williamsburg, OH; *U.S. Private*, pg. 344
Syberg, Kevin M., V.P.-Sls.--Dualite Sales & Service, Inc., Williamsburg, OH; *U.S. Private*, pg. 344

Sykes, Jeremy A.L., Dir.-European Auto Sls.--John Crane Polymer Engineering, Tewkesbury, United Kingdom; *Int'l, pg. 1338*
Sylvester, Jeff, V.P.-Sls. & Mktg./Construction & Industrial--Detroit Diesel Corp., Detroit, MI; *U.S. Private*, pg. 850
Sylvester, Tom, Dir.-Sls.--Modern Handling Equipment of N.J., Inc., Edison, NJ; *U.S. Private*, pg. 755
Sylvia, Kenneth A., Sr. V.P., Grp. Publr. & Publr. Consultant--Cliggott Publishing, Greenwich, CT; *U.S. Private*, pg. 246
Symonds, Curtis N., Exec. V.P.-Affiliate Sls. & Mktg.--Black Entertainment Television Holdings Inc., Washington, DC; *U.S. Public*, pg. 235
Sytsma, Fred, Exec. V.P.-OEM Sls.--Frost Inc., Grand Rapids, MI; *U.S. Private*, pg. 430
Szczepaniak, Joseph, V.P.-Sls.--Grolier Electronic Publishing, Inc., Danbury, CT; *Int'l*, pg. 794
Szile, Donna, Admin.-Sls. & Mktg.--Kirkwood Industries, Inc., Cleveland, OH; *U.S. Private*, pg. 623
Szmigiel, Rick, Mgr.-Nissan New Car Sls.--Jeffrey Buick-Nissan Inc., Roseville, MI; *U.S. Private*, pg. 585
Szostak, Michael J., V.P.-Mktg. & Sls.--Douglas Steel Fabricating Corporation, Lansing, MI; *U.S. Private*, pg. 341
Szostek, John, V.P.-Mktg. & Sls.--BLH Electronics, Inc., Canton, MA; *Int'l*, pg. 1289
Szostek, John J., V.P.-Sls. & Mktg.--BIF, North Wales, PA; *U.S. Public*, pg. 726
Szwack, Tom, Sr. V.P.-Sls.--Republic Entertainment, Inc., Los Angeles, CA; *U.S. Private*, pg. 776
Szymanski, Bob, V.P.-Sls.--Megas Beauty Care, Inc., Cleveland, OH; *U.S. Private*, pg. 729
Tabaksblat, Israel, V.P.-Mktg. & Sls.--Allomatic Products Company, Sullivan, IN; *U.S. Public*, pg. 1363
Taber, Robert M., Jr., V.P.-Worldwide Sls.--QT Optoelectronics, Sunnyvale, CA; *U.S. Private*, pg. 897
Taborek, Eric, V.P.-Sls.--Smart Modular Technologies, Fremont, CA; *U.S. Public*, pg. 1476
Tachuk, Ron, V.P.-Mktg. & Sls.--Breed Technologies, Sterling Heights, MI; *U.S. Public*, pg. 251
Taffe, Vanessa, Sls. Specialist--American Water Works Association, Denver, CO; *U.S. Public*, pg. 94
Taggart, David, Mgr.-Sls. & Mktg.--Aer Lingus, Paris, France; *Int'l*, pg. 28
Taggart, Jack, V.P.-Sls.--Fuji Medical Systems USA, Inc., Stamford, CT; *Int'l*, pg. 524
Taglauer, H.J., Mgr.-Sls.--Groschopp & Co. GmbH EMW Elektromotoren-Feinbauwerk, Viersen, Germany; *Int'l*, pg. 559
Taida, T., Dir.-Sls.--Otto Sumisho Inc., Tokyo, Japan; *Int'l*, pg. 1015
Takada, Osamu, V.P.-Sls.--Yokogawa Electric Corporation, Tokyo, Japan; *Int'l*, pg. 1520
Takahashi, Yasuyuki, Mgr. Sls. & Mktg.--Sapporo U.S.A., Inc., New York, New York, NY; *Int'l*, pg. 1193
Takano, Shinmatsu, V.P.-Replacement Tire Sls.--Bridgestone Corporation, Tokyo, Japan; *Int'l*, pg. 213
Takayama, K., Dir.-Americas Dept. & Intl. Sls.--Anritsu Corporation, Tokyo, Japan; *Int'l*, pg. 77
Takei, Kazuo, Sr. V.P.-Sls.--Kikkoman International, Inc., San Francisco, CA; *Int'l*, pg. 733
Takenada, Yoji, V.P.--Intermetrics, Inc., Burlington, MA; *U.S. Private*, pg. 567
Takeuchi, Kiichiro, Exec. Mng. Dir.--Fujikura Ltd., Tokyo, Japan; *Int'l*, pg. 525
Talarico, R., Mgr.-Sls.--Andres Wines (Alberta) Ltd., Calgary, Canada; *Int'l*, pg. 76
Talbot, Jocelyn, Telesales Dir.--TMP Worldwide/Interactive Division, Framingham, MA; *U.S. Private*, pg. 1065
Taliaferro, Mike, Exec. V.P.-Consumer Mkts. Div./Sls. & Mktg.--Countrywide Home Loans Inc., Pasadena, CA; *U.S. Public*, pg. 452
Tamagawa, Masaru, Exec. Mgr.-Sls. & Promo.--Sony Corporation of Panama, Panama, Panama; *Int'l*, pg. 1284
Tamayo, Peter, V.P.-Mktg. & Sls.--UHP Healthcare, Inglewood, CA; *U.S. Private*, pg. 1113
Tamburri, Anthony, Sls. Mgr.--Paradigm National Yellow Pages Group, Tampa, FL; *U.S. Private*, pg. 838
Tamcsin, Dennis, Sr. V.P.-Agencies--Northwestern Mutual Life Insurance Co., Milwaukee, WI; *U.S. Private*, pg. 807
Tamura, A., V.P.-Mktg. & Sls.--Sumitomo Sitix Silicon, Inc., Fremont, CA; *Int'l*, pg. 1317
Tan, Hendrick, Mgr.-Sls.--Olivetti Singapore Pte. Ltd., Singapore, Singapore; *Int'l*, pg. 1003
Tan, Philip, Asst. V.P.-Distributors--La Tondena Distillers, Inc., Manila, Philippines; *Int'l*, pg. 785
Tan, Ronald, Dir.-Sls.--Malayan Law Journal, Petaling Jaya, Malaysia; *Int'l*, pg. 1095
Tanaka, Masaaki, Mgr.-Sls.--McGraw-Hill Publishing Co.-Japan Ltd., Tokyo, Japan; *U.S. Public*, pg. 1072
Tanaka, Toshio, Sr. Exec. Dir.-Mktg. & Sls./Ethical Prods. Mktg. Div.--Tanabe Seiyaku Co., Ltd., Osaka, Japan; *Int'l*, pg. 1354
Tandy, Don, Dir.-Aerospace Sls.--Tensolite Company, Saint Augustine, FL; *U.S. Public*, pg. 305
Tang, N.C., Sls. Dir.--Pan Malaysia Cement Works (Singapore) Pte. Ltd., Singapore, Singapore; *Int'l*, pg. 198
Tang, Patrick, Pres.--ADC L.P., Wheeling, IL; *U.S. Private*, pg. 4
Tankerlsey, Bobby, V.P.-Mktg. & Sls.--Young Pecan Company (A Partnership), Florence, SC; *U.S. Private*, pg. 1201
Tanklage, Brian, Natl. Sls. Mgr.-Food Service--La Victoria Foods, Inc., City of Industry, CA; *U.S. Private*, pg. 641
Tanklage, John, Natl. Sls. Mgr.--La Victoria Foods, Inc., City of Industry, CA; *U.S. Private*, pg. 641
Tann, Gerald, Asst. V.P.-Sls.--Safelite AutoGlass, Columbus, OH; *U.S. Private*, pg. 960
Tanner, Allan, V.P.-Sls.--Americo Manufacturing Co., Inc., Acworth, GA; *U.S. Private*, pg. 64
Tanner, Carl, Dir.- Sls. & Mktg.--LiphaTech, Inc., Milwaukee, WI; *Int'l*, pg. 812
Tanner, Robert, V.P.-Mktg. & Sls.--Lapp Insulator Company, Le Roy, NY; *U.S. Private*, pg. 473
Tanner, Rusty, Mgr.-Sls.--Western Florida Cellular Telephone Corp., Pensacola, FL; *U.S. Public*, pg. 1708
Tanous, J.H., Sls. Analyst--Curtis 1000, Inc., Atlanta, GA; *U.S. Public*, pg. 70
Tapling, Mark E., Sr. V.P.-Field Opers./Americas--Comshare, Incorporated, Ann Arbor, MI; *U.S. Public*, pg. 425
Tappa, Patti, Dir.-Sls.--A.L. Hansen Manufacturing Co., Waukegan, IL; *U.S. Private*, pg. 500
Tapscott, Judy, Dir. Mtg./Dir. Response, Asst. Dir.-Sls.--National Banner Company, Inc., Dallas, TX; *U.S. Private*, pg. 780
Tarantine, Dan, Mgr.-Sls. & Mktg.--White Microelectronics, Phoenix, AZ; *U.S. Public*, pg. 248
Taratunio, Jim, Exec. V.P.-Field Services--MarketSource Corporation, Cranbury, NJ; *U.S. Private*, pg. 705
Taraze, Juan, V.P.-Sls.--Puerto Rican Cement Co., Inc., Guaynabo, PR; *U.S. Public*, pg. 1341
Tarka, Zbig, Dir.-Sls. & Mktg.--Valtek/Australia, Scoresby, Australia; *U.S. Public*, pg. 659
Tarkanish, Tom, V.P.-Sls. & Mktg./N. America--Greenwich Air Services, Miami, FL; *U.S. Public*, pg. 710
Tarling, M., Gen. Mgr.-Sls. & Distr.--Peters & Brownes Foods Ltd., Balcatta, Australia; *Int'l*, pg. 1040
Tarlo, Jay, Mgr.-Sls.--Brush Research Manufacturing Company, Los Angeles, CA; *U.S. Private*, pg. 176
Tarnat, Jacky, Dir.-Commercial Mkt.--Lati Industria Termoplastici S.p.A., Vedano Olona, Italy; *Int'l*, pg. 804
Tarrant, Roger, V.P.-Sls. & Mktg.--M/A-COM Inc., Lowell, MA; *U.S. Public*, pg. 8
Taskey, Ron, V.P.-Sls.--Fairfield Plantation, Villa Rica, GA; *U.S. Public*, pg. 611
Taskey, Ron, V.P.-Sls.--Atlanta Sales, Duluth, GA; *U.S. Public*, pg. 611
Tasman, Joel, V.P.-Sls. West--Tyco Toys, Inc., Mount Laurel, NJ; *U.S. Public*, pg. 1058
Tatalias, Marilee, Sr. V.P.-Sls. & Oper. Support--DSC Logistics, Inc., Des Plaines, IL; *U.S. Private*, pg. 306
Tataseo, Frank A., V.P.-Sls.--The Clorox Company, Oakland, CA; *U.S. Public*, pg. 386
Tate, Mark, V.P.-Retail Sls.-Knit Apparel Div.--Russell Corp., Jerzees Div., Alexander City, AL; *U.S. Public*, pg. 1413
Tate, Mike, V.P.-Catalog Sls.--Advance Seed Co., Fulton, KY; *Int'l*, pg. 566
Tatemichi, Bob, V.P.-Sls.--Quintus Corporation, Fremont, CA; *U.S. Private*, pg. 901
Tatsutomi, Yasuo, Mng. Dir.-Quality, Cost Plng. & Domestic Mktg. & Sls.--Mazda Motor Corporation, Hiroshima, Japan; *Int'l*, pg. 849
Tatum, Jim, Dir.-Sls.--North Park Lincoln Mercury Inc., San Antonio, TX; *U.S. Private*, pg. 805
Taunton, JT, Jr., Exec. V.P.-Sls. & Mktg.--Russell Corporation, Alexander City, AL; *U.S. Public*, pg. 1413
Taute, Harry, V.P.-Sls. & Mktg.--Communications Systems, Inc., Hector, MN; *U.S. Public*, pg. 415
Taverna, Richard, V.P.-Sls. & Mktg.--Par Industries, Inc., Medina, OH; *U.S. Private*, pg. 838
Taw, Richard, Mgr.-Reg. Sls.--Automotive News, Detroit, MI; *U.S. Private*, pg. 284
Tayler, Joanne, Mgr.-Sls.--Takugin Finance International Ltd., London, United Kingdom; *Int'l*, pg. 627
Taylor, Bob, Sls. Mgr.-Western District--Fluidtec Engineer Products, Greensboro, NC; *U.S. Public*, pg. 401
Taylor, Cal, V.P.-Sls.--Romeo Rim Inc., Romeo, MI; *U.S. Private*, pg. 300
Taylor, Carol, Dir.-Sls.-Western Region--The Beverly Hills Hotel, Beverly Hills, CA; *U.S. Private*, pg. 142
Taylor, Chuck, Mgr.-Sls., Grocery Prods.--ADM Milling Co., Portland, OR; *U.S. Public*, pg. 128
Taylor, Chuck, Mgr.-Sls.--ADM Milling Co., Overland Park, KS; *U.S. Public*, pg. 128
Taylor, Gary E., V.P.-U.S. Implantable Sls.--Medtronic Neurological Div., Minneapolis, MN; *U.S. Public*, pg. 1083
Taylor, Graham, Sls. Dir.--Heinemann English Language Teaching, Oxford, United Kingdom; *Int'l*, pg. 1479
Taylor, Henry L., V.P.-Intl. Sls. & Mktg.--Accuride Corp., Henderson, KY; *U.S. Public*, pg. 1286
Taylor, J.V., Jr., V.P.-Sls.--Filtrona Richmond Company, Richmond, VA; *Int'l*, pg. 232
Taylor, John C., Exec. V.P.-Sls. & Mktg.--John B. Sanfilippo & Son, Inc., Elk Grove Village, IL; *U.S. Public*, pg. 1431
Taylor, John C., Jr., V.P.-Sls. & Mktg.--John B. Sanfilippo & Son, Inc., Elk Grove Village, IL; *U.S. Public*, pg. 1431
Taylor, Marcia, Mgr.-Sls.--Shaw Creations, Inc., Edison, NJ; *U.S. Private*, pg. 990
Taylor, Mike, Dir.-Sls.--Carhartt, Inc., Dearborn, MI; *U.S. Private*, pg. 210
Taylor, Mike, V.P.-Sls. & Mktg.--Vanner, Inc., Hilliard, OH; *Int'l*, pg. 449
Taylor, Mike, V.P.-Sls.--Atari Games Corporation, Milpitas, CA; *U.S. Public*, pg. 1727
Taylor, Peter, Dir.-Sls.--Columbia Tri-Star Films (UK), London, United Kingdom; *Int'l*, pg. 1281
Taylor, Robert, V.P.-Sls.--Wisconsin Label Corporation, Algoma, WI; *U.S. Private*, pg. 1184
Taylor, Sasha, V.P.-Sls. & Mktg.--Sorbee International Ltd., Philadelphia, PA; *U.S. Private*, pg. 1014
Taylor, Steve, Mgr.-Sls.-Midwest--Mountain Valley Spring Company, Hot Springs National Park, AR; *U.S. Private*, pg. 963
Taylor, William, V.P.-Sls.--The Butcher Company, Marlborough, MA; *U.S. Private*, pg. 189
Tazzioli, R., Gen. Mgr.-Sls.--SASIB Railway Electrification S.p.A., Rome, Italy; *Int'l*, pg. 1194
Tedeschi, Robert, Div. Mgr.-Surface Finishing--Rapid Power Technologies, Inc., Brookfield, CT; *U.S. Private*, pg. 910
Teegen, John A., V.P.-Sls.--MMC Networks, Inc., Sunnyvale, CA; *U.S. Public*, pg. 1027
Teeple, Andrew R., V.P.-Sls. & Mktg.--Haddon Craftsmen, Inc., Scranton, PA; *U.S. Public*, pg. 518
Teeple, Mike H., V.P.-Sls.-Southern Reg.--Goody's Family Clothing, Inc., Knoxville, TN; *U.S. Public*, pg. 753
Tegajarin, Annop, Mgr.-Delaers Sls. Div.--The Siam Cement Public Company Limited, Bangkok, Thailand; *Int'l*, pg. 1237
Teich, Robert, Mgr.-Sls. & Mktg.--Duall Division, Owosso, MI; *U.S. Public*, pg. 1100
Teich, Tim, V.P.-Sls. & Mktg.--Advanced Input Devices, Inc., Coeur D'Alene, ID; *U.S. Private*, pg. 21
Teller, James, Mgr.-Natl. Sls.--Unistrut Corporation, Wayne, MI; *U.S. Public*, pg. 1651
Teller, Jeff, Sr. V.P.-Sls.-Natl. Accts.--Crystal Clear Industries, Ridgefield Park, NJ; *U.S. Private*, pg. 293
Tellis, Clifford, Mgr.-Sls., Canada--Kuwait Airways, Canada, Toronto, Canada; *Int'l*, pg. 764
Temple, Cathy, Dir.-Sls. & Mktg.--Conran Octopus Limited, London, United Kingdom; *Int'l*, pg. 1093
Temple, John, V.P.-Passenger Sls.--Northwest Airlines, Inc., Saint Paul, MN; *U.S. Public*, pg. 1200
Temple, Wick, V.P. & Dir.-Newspaper Membership--The Associated Press, New York, NY; *U.S. Private*, pg. 92
Templeman, Miles, Mng. Dir.-Beer Co.--Whitbread PLC, London, United Kingdom; *Int'l*, pg. 1498
Templin, Gary, V.P.-Sls.--Altec Lansing Corp., Buchanan, MI; *U.S. Private*, pg. 479
Templin, J.M., V.P.-Sls. & Mktg.--Mayville Metal Products Division, Mayville, WI; *U.S. Private*, pg. 264
Tenn, Ben, V.P.-Sls.--Activision, Santa Monica, CA; *U.S. Public*, pg. 17
Tentori, Zoe, Dir.-Sls.--Mardev-Australia, Chatswood, Australia; *Int'l*, pg. 1094
Teo, Edgar, Rep.-Sls.--ANGUS Chemical (Singapore) Pte. Ltd., Singapore, Singapore; *U.S. Private*, pg. 75
Tercy, Karyn, Mgr.-Sls.--PENCO-Hawaii, Honolulu, HI; *Int'l*, pg. 1508
Termier, Jean-Pierre, Gen. Mgr.-American Opers. & Sls.--Lipha Chemicals S.A., Lyon, France; *Int'l*, pg. 812
Ternan, Lynn, Dir.-Sls.--Thermotron Industries, Holland, MI; *U.S. Private*, pg. 1136
Terranova, Kim, Dir.-Corp. Sls.--Florida Panthers Holdings, Inc., Fort Lauderdale, FL; *U.S. Public*, pg. 654
Terrell, Andy, Mgr.-Reg. Sls.--Burgmann Seals America, Inc., Conyers, GA; *Int'l*, pg. 233
Terrell, Frank G., Mgr.-Sls.--Bender Shipbuilding & Repair Company, Inc., Mobile, AL; *U.S. Private*, pg. 132
Terreri, David J., V.P.-Distr.-U.S.A.--Bauer Sports Inc., Montreal, Canada; *U.S. Public*, pg. 1184
Terry, Daryl, Product Mgr.-Sls.--Saint-Gobain Advanced Materials Corporation, Louisville, KY; *Int'l*, pg. 1173
Terry, Steve, V.P.-Dental Div.--The Medical Protective Company, Fort Wayne, IN; *U.S. Private*, pg. 728
Tersigni, Gino, V.P.-Sls.--Selfix, Inc., Chicago, IL; *U.S. Public*, pg. 832
Tersigni, Phillip, V.P.-Sls. & Mktg.--Giant Industries, Toledo, OH; *U.S. Private*, pg. 451
Tertenik, Pete, Mgr.-Natl. Sls.--Flambeau Products-Columbus, Columbus, IN; *U.S. Private*, pg. 410
Tescione, G., Dir.-Sls.--Eli Lilly Italia, S.p.A., Sesto Fiorentino, Italy; *U.S. Public*, pg. 994
Tessier, Frank, Sls. Rep.--August West Systems, Worcester, MA; *U.S. Private*, pg. 98
Tessitore, Joseph, Mktg. & Sls.--Childrens Press Inc., Danbury, CT; *Int'l*, pg. 794
Tester, Stephen, Mgr.-Sls.--Berendsen Fluid Power Pty. Ltd., Villawood, Australia; *Int'l*, pg. 1285
Teter, Jim, V.P.-Retail Sls.--ABF Freight System, Inc., Fort Smith, AR; *U.S. Public*, pg. 130
Teter, Todd, V.P.-Natl. Sls.--NuTone, Inc., Cincinnati, OH; *Int'l*, pg. 1499
Tetlow, Charles, Dir.-Sls.--Portec (U.K.) Ltd., Wrexham, United Kingdom; *U.S. Public*, pg. 1318
Teubel, Thomas, V.P.-Sls.--Putzmeister, Inc., Sturtevant, WI; *U.S. Private*, pg. 896
Thalmann, Craig, V.P.-Mktg. & Sls.--National Utility Service, Inc., Park Ridge, NJ; *U.S. Private*, pg. 787
Thalmann, Diane L., V.P.-Mktg. & Bus. Plng.--Waukesha Cherry-Burrell, Delavan, WI; *U.S. Public*, pg. 1677
Thammanajit, Suvit, Mgr.-Sls.--Bangkok Athletic Co., Ltd., Bangkok, Thailand; *Int'l*, pg. 146
Tharp, Jim, Mgr.-Sls. & Service--NuArc Co., Kansas City, MO; *U.S. Private*, pg. 809
Thatcher, Scott, Dir.-Sls.--Information & Engineering Technology, Fairfax, VA; *U.S. Private*, pg. 351
Thather, Kathy, V.P.-Sls. & Mktg.--Broadcast Supply Worldwide, Inc., Tacoma, WA; *U.S. Private*, pg. 170
Theeman, Klaus, Dir.-Mktg. & Sls.--Krups GmbH & Co. KG, Solingen, Germany; *Int'l*, pg. 896
Thees, R.A., V.P.-Sls.--Glens Falls Cement Co., Glens Falls, NY; *Int'l*, pg. 423
Theesfield, Paul, V.P.-Sls.--Batesville Casket Company, Inc., Batesville, IN; *U.S. Public*, pg. 828
Theile, Greg, V.P.-Dist.--B&G Foods, Inc., Roseland, NJ; *U.S. Private*, pg. 105
Theis, H.E., V.P.-Mktg. & Sls.--Herr-Voss Corp., Callery, PA; *U.S. Private*, pg. 961
Thelin, Jean-Noel, Asst. V.P.-Sls.--Bobst S.A., Lausanne, Switzerland; *Int'l*, pg. 198
Theodores, James, V.P.-Sls.--Kaiser Cement Corporation, Pleasanton, CA; *Int'l*, pg. 593
Theriault, Theodore, V.P.-Sls.--C.R. Gibson Co., Norwalk, CT; *U.S. Public*, pg. 1168
Theune, Robert, V.P.-Sls. & Mktg.--Dunbarton Corporation, Dothan, AL; *U.S. Private*, pg. 194
Theut, Joel, Mgr.-New Car Sls.--Jefferson Chevrolet Co., Detroit, MI; *U.S. Private*, pg. 584
Thibodeau, Kevin, Pres.-Waverly, N.A.--Waverly, Inc., Baltimore, MD; *U.S. Public*, pg. 1748
Thiets, Dennis, V.P.-Sls.--Karastan, Calhoun, GA; *U.S. Public*, pg. 1121
Thigpen, Kathy, Dir.-Bus. Devel. & Sls.--Westgate Inc., Port Allen, LA; *U.S. Private*, pg. 1169
Thigpen, Z. Ben, V.P.-Sls.--Pace Industries, Inc., Fayetteville, AR; *U.S. Public*, pg. 986

Thijn, Mark Alberdingk, V.P.-Sls.--Corel Corporation, Ottawa, Canada; *Int'l*, pg. 331
Tholen, J. David, Exec. V.P.-Sls. & Mktg.--Hycor Biomedical, Inc., Irvine, CA; *U.S. Public*, pg. 851
Thoman, Jack, Mgr.-Reg. Sls.--Global Beverage Co., Rochester, NY; *U.S. Private*, pg. 457
Thomas, Brian, Natl. Sls. Mgr.--Goody Canada Limited, Toronto, Canada; *U.S. Public*, pg. 1177
Thomas, Chris, Natl. Dir.-Acct. Sls.--Thomas Built Buses, Inc., High Point, NC; *U.S. Private*, pg. 1082
Thomas, Chuck, Mgr.-Intl. Sls.--Chattanooga Group, Inc., Hixson, TN; *U.S. Private*, pg. 231
Thomas, Dalen D., Sr. V.P.-Sls., Mktg. & Strategic Plng.--Amtran, Inc., Indianapolis, IN; *U.S. Public*, pg. 106
Thomas, Damian A., V.P.-Mktg. & Sls.--PECO Energy Company, Philadelphia, PA; *U.S. Public*, pg. 1268
Thomas, David A., Mgr.-Sls.--Ohio Sealants Inc., Mentor, OH; *Int'l*, pg. 802
Thomas, Geoff, Dir.-Mktg. & Sls.--Bostik Ltd., Leicester, United Kingdom; *Int'l*, pg. 1409
Thomas, George, V.P.-Sls. & Mktg.--R.A. Jones & Co. Inc., Covington, KY; *U.S. Private*, pg. 597
Thomas, Gil, V.P.-Sls. & Mktg.--Double-Cola Co.-USA, Chattanooga, TN; *U.S. Private*, pg. 341
Thomas, Griff, Dir.-Sls. & Customer Svcs.--Telescope Casual Furniture, Inc., Granville, NY; *U.S. Private*, pg. 1074
Thomas, Guy, V.P.-Sls.--The Ohio Art Company, Inc., Bryan, OH; *U.S. Public*, pg. 1214
Thomas, J. Fredric, Gen. Mgr.-Sls. Mktg.--Copperweld Miami Division, Piqua, OH; *Int'l*, pg. 662
Thomas, J.R., V.P.-Sls. & Mktg.--Kaufman Footwear, Kitchener, Canada; *Int'l*, pg. 725
Thomas, Jerry, Mgr.-Sls.--PENCO-Missouri, Jefferson City, MO; *Int'l*, pg. 1508
Thomas, Jim, Plant Mgr.--Craftwell Containers & Packaging Limited, Rexdale, Canada; *Int'l*, pg. 761
Thomas, Mark, Dir.-Sls.--WAMZ-FM, Louisville, KY; *U.S. Public*, pg. 384
Thomas, Mark, Dir.-Sls.--WHAS-AM, Louisville, KY; *U.S. Public*, pg. 385
Thomas, Peter, V.P.-Mktg. & Sls.--Kennecott Holdings Corporation, Magna, UT; *Int'l*, pg. 1119
Thomas, Ralph, V.P.-Sls.--Halm Industries Company, Incorporated, Glen Head, NY; *U.S. Private*, pg. 496
Thomas, Randy, Dir.-Grp. Sls.--Zoological Society of San Diego, San Diego, CA; *U.S. Private*, pg. 1207
Thomas, Stan, Sls. Mgr.--Dover Mills Limited, Halifax, Canada; *Int'l*, pg. 417
Thomas, Ted, V.P.-Sls.--Quality Foods Inc., Little Rock, AR; *U.S. Private*, pg. 898
Thompson, Adam, Natl. Sls. Mgr.--Cetrk USA, Limerick, PA; *U.S. Public*, pg. 1569
Thompson, Anthony, Grp. V.P.-Mktg.--Proudfoot USA Company, West Palm Beach, FL; *Int'l*, pg. 1072
Thompson, Bob, V.P.-Sls.--Aesculap, Inc., South San Francisco, CA; *Int'l*, pg. 29
Thompson, Bob, Mgr.-Sls.--Sturm, Ruger & Co., Inc., Southport, CT; *U.S. Public*, pg. 1526
Thompson, Brent, V.P.-Sls.--Yuba Heat Transfer Division, Tulsa, OK; *U.S. Private*, pg. 264
Thompson, C., V.P.-Sls.--Penny & Giles Aerospace Inc., Santa Monica, CA; *Int'l*, pg. 208
Thompson, C., V.P.-Sls.--Penny & Giles Aerospace Inc., Valley Center, KS; *Int'l*, pg. 208
Thompson, Dewey, V.P.-Sls.--Baltimore Aircoil Company, Jessup, MD; *U.S. Private*, pg. 68
Thompson, Doug, Mgr.-Natl. Sls.--Koch Engineering Company, Inc., Akron, OH; *U.S. Private*, pg. 628
Thompson, Ernest E., III, V.P.-Sls. & Mktg.--CPAC, Inc., Leicester, NY; *U.S. Public*, pg. 282
Thompson, Ernest E., III, V.P.-Sls. & Mktg.--CPAC Equipment Division, Leicester, NY; *U.S. Public*, pg. 282
Thompson, G., V.P.-Sls.--Carole Fabrics Corp., Martinez, GA; *Int'l*, pg. 639
Thompson, Gary, Mgr.-Sls.--Pak-Sher Co., Kilgore, TX; *U.S. Private*, pg. 1062
Thompson, Gary E., V.P.-Retail Sls.--T. Marzetti Company, Columbus, OH; *U.S. Public*, pg. 977
Thompson, Gerald W., Sr. V.P.-Sls.--Town & Country Fine Jewelry Group, Inc., Chelsea, MA; *U.S. Public*, pg. 1625
Thompson, Irv, Dir.-Natl. Accts.--American Buildings Co., Eufaula, AL; *U.S. Public*, pg. 69
Thompson, J. Michael, V.P.-Sls.--Rawlings Sporting Goods Company, Fenton, MO; *U.S. Public*, pg. 1361
Thompson, Jim, V.P.-Sls.--J.T. Davenport & Sons, Inc., Sanford, NC; *U.S. Private*, pg. 314
Thompson, Joe, Div. Mgr.-West--Pabst Brewing Co./ Tumwater, Tumwater, WA; *U.S. Private*, pg. 954
Thompson, John, V.P.-Sls. & Mktg.--Mays Chemical Company, Indianapolis, IN; *U.S. Private*, pg. 718
Thompson, Keith, Mgr.-Sls.--Nielsen & Bainbridge, Paramus, NJ; *Int'l*, pg. 460
Thompson, Ken, V.P.-Sls./Commun. Cords--ACS Industries, Inc., Woonsocket, RI; *U.S. Private*, pg. 3
Thompson, L., Mgr.-Sls.--Coilcraft, Inc., Cary, IL; *U.S. Private*, pg. 250
Thompson, Larry, Mgr.-Sls. Admin.--Crane Pumps & Systems Inc., Piqua, OH; *U.S. Public*, pg. 457
Thompson, Larry, Mgr.-Sls. Admin.--Barnes Pumps, Inc., Mansfield, OH; *U.S. Public*, pg. 457
Thompson, Larry, Mgr.-Sls. Opers.--Sellers Cleaning Systems, Piqua, OH; *U.S. Public*, pg. 457
Thompson, Larry, V.P.-Sls.--Martindale-Hubbell, New Providence, NJ; *Int'l*, pg. 1096
Thompson, Mike, V.P.-Sls.--Multilin, Markham, Canada; *U.S. Public*, pg. 713
Thompson, Mike, V.P.-Food Service--Comstock Michigan Fruit, Rochester, NY; *U.S. Private*, pg. 887
Thompson, Paulm, V.P.-Sls.--Duro Dyne Corporation, Farmingdale, NY; *U.S. Private*, pg. 349
Thompson, Richard, V.P.-Natl. Sls.--Slant/Fin Corporation, Greenvale, NY; *U.S. Private*, pg. 1005
Thompson, Rick, V.P.-Sls. & Mktg.--Burlington Basket Co., Burlington, IA; *U.S. Private*, pg. 183
Thompson, Thomas, Sr. V.P.-Sls. & Mktg.--Friedman Industries, Inc., Houston, TX; *U.S. Public*, pg. 682
Thompson, William, V.P.-Sls.--Kreher Steel Co., Inc., Melrose Park, IL; *U.S. Private*, pg. 635
Thomsen, Jim, Sr. V.P.-Sls.--JanSport, Appleton, WI; *U.S. Public*, pg. 1702
Thorlakson, Brad, Mgr.-Export & Specialty Sls.--Tolko Industries Ltd., Vernon, Canada; *Int'l*, pg. 1395
Thornburg, Dick, V.P.-Sls., Custom Forms--Adams Business Forms, Topeka, KS; *U.S. Private*, pg. 16
Thorne, Dan, Mgr.-Mktg.--Gilster Mary Lee Corp., Chester, IL; *U.S. Private*, pg. 455
Thornton, Daniel P., Sr. V.P.-Sls. & Mktg.--Progress Printing Company, Lynchburg, VA; *U.S. Private*, pg. 890
Thornton, Jim, Natl. Sls. Mgr.--Holm Industries, Inc., Scottsburg, IN; *U.S. Public*, pg. 1504
Thornton, John, V.P.-Mktg. & Sls.--IRD Mechanalysis, Inc. (U.S.A.), Columbus, OH; *U.S. Public*, pg. 789
Thorwart, Bob, Sls. Mgr.-Furniture--Brodart Company, Williamsport, PA; *U.S. Private*, pg. 170
Thrall, Brad, V.P.-Sls.--Border States Industries, Inc., Fargo, ND; *U.S. Private*, pg. 160
Thrasher, Bill, V.P.-Cat Litter Sls.--AMCOL International Corp., Arlington Heights, IL; *U.S. Public*, pg. 63
Thrasher, Scott, Sr. V.P.-Sls. & Mktg.--Toastmaster, Inc., Columbia, MO; *U.S. Public*, pg. 1619
Throop, Daniel, V.P.-Intl. Sls.--Harris Corp., RF Communications Group Marketing Division, Rochester, NY; *U.S. Public*, pg. 792
Thrussell, Dan, V.P.-Sls.--FAG Bearings Corporation, Danbury, CT; *Int'l*, pg. 469
Thull, Steve, V.P.-Sls.--Fairfield Pagosa, Pagosa Springs, CO; *U.S. Public*, pg. 611
Thurer, Stewart, Dir.-Sls.--GE Capital/IT Solutions, South Plainfield, NJ; *U.S. Public*, pg. 711
Thurman, Jimmy, V.P.-Sls. & Mktg.--Harrington & King, Chicago, IL; *U.S. Private*, pg. 504
Thurstone, Peter, Mgr.-Sls.--Radix Wire Company, Cleveland, OH; *U.S. Private*, pg. 907
Thwaites, R., Sls., Mktg. & Comml. Mgr.--Ultra Electrics, Cheltenham, United Kingdom; *Int'l*, pg. 1431
Thybony, James D., Pres.--Thybony Wall Coverings Co., Chicago, IL; *U.S. Private*, pg. 1084
Thyen, John, Sr. Exec. V.P.-Mktg. & Sls.--Kimball International, Inc., Jasper, IN; *U.S. Public*, pg. 956
Tianen, Susan M., V.P.-Opers.--Hoban Foods, Inc., Detroit, MI; *U.S. Private*, pg. 531
Tiarks, Mike, Mgr.-Sls.--Austral Bronze Crane Copper Limited, Wetherill Park, Australia; *Int'l*, pg. 340
Tibbits, Rolland, V.P.-Sls. & Mktg.--Hill & Griffith Company, Cincinnati, OH; *U.S. Private*, pg. 529
Tibbs, Aaron, Mgr.-Sls.--AG Industries, Inc., Redmond, WA; *Int'l*, pg. 40
Tiberi, John J., Dir.-Sls. & Mktg.--Medusa Aggregate Co., Cleveland, OH; *U.S. Public*, pg. 1084
Tiberii, Joe, Dir -Sls.--Edmund Scientific Company, Barrington, NJ; *U.S. Private*, pg. 364
Tierney, Danial J., V.P.-Corp. Sls.--TRM Copy Centers Corporation, Portland, OR; *U.S. Public*, pg. 1558
Tierney, Michael, V.P.-Sls.--Cobra Electronics Corporation, Chicago, IL; *U.S. Public*, pg. 391
Tierney, Michael, V.P.-Sls.--The Robert E. Morris Company, Farmington, CT; *U.S. Private*, pg. 762
Tietjen, Tom, V.P.-Mktg. & Sls.--Xerxes Corporation, Minneapolis, MN; *U.S. Private*, pg. 1194
Tighe, Matthew, Mgr.-Sls.--Ace Glass Incorporated, Vineland, NJ; *U.S. Private*, pg. 12
Tilghman, Richard H., Pres.-Pepper Environ. Tech.& Sr. V.P.--The Pepper Companies, Inc., Chicago, IL; *U.S. Private*, pg. 851
Tillis, Arlen, V.P.-Sls. & Mktg.--Cox Lumber Co., Saint Petersburg, FL; *U.S. Private*, pg. 283
Tilzer, James, V.P.-Sls.--Paper Enterprises, Inc., Bronx, NY; *U.S. Private*, pg. 837
Timber, Jeanne, V.P.-Mktg. & Sls.--AR Accessories Group, Inc., Milwaukee, WI; *U.S. Private*, pg. 7
Timberlake, Roger D., V.P.-Sls., Central Reg.--Magneco/ Metrel, Inc., Addison, IL; *U.S. Private*, pg. 695
Timbie, Mark, V.P.-Sls. & Mktg.--McCormick/Schilling, Hunt Valley, MD; *U.S. Public*, pg. 1066
Timko, Joseph R., V.P.-Circulation--Yankee Publishing Incorporated, Dublin, NH; *U.S. Private*, pg. 1195
Timm, Spencer L., Dir.-Sls.--Franklin Portfolio Associates Trust, Boston, MA; *U.S. Public*, pg. 1085
Timmerann, Jozef, Gen. Mgr.-Sls.--Gebr. Eickhoff Maschinenfabrik und Eisengiesserei mbH, Bochum, Germany; *Int'l*, pg. 542
Timmers, Ted N., Dir.-Dir. Sls.-Europe--HMI Industries, Cleveland, OH; *U.S. Public*, pg. 771
Timp, Gary, Mgr.-Window/Door Sls.--Deco Products Co., Decorah, IA; *U.S. Private*, pg. 320
Timpanelli, Peter, Dir.-Sls. & Mktg.--Skinner Valve Division, New Britain, CT; *U.S. Public*, pg. 1260
Tindall, Mary, Exec. Dir.-Mktg.--Tropicana Casino & Resort, Atlantic City, NJ; *U.S. Public*, pg. 159
Tinebra, Vince, Sr. V.P.-Sls.--Vanstar Corporation, Pleasanton, CA; *U.S. Public*, pg. 1708
Tinghitella, John, V.P.-Sls. & Mktg.--Marinco/AFI, Napa, CA; *U.S. Public*, pg. 1705
Tinkis, David, V.P.-Sls./Central Region--Thorn Apple Valley, Inc., Southfield, MI; *U.S. Public*, pg. 1602
Tinozzi, Renato, Dir.-Domestic Sls.--Rimoldi Necchi S.R.L., Milan, Italy; *Int'l*, pg. 1117
Tippit, Raymond, V.P.-Natl. Railroad Sls.--MI-Jack Products, Inc., Hazel Crest, IL; *U.S. Private*, pg. 740
Tipps, Bill, Sr. V.P.-Sls. & Mktg.--Universal-Rundle Corp., New Castle, PA; *U.S. Public*, pg. 1193
Tipton, Dave, Grp. V.P.-Sls.--Fleischmann's Yeast, Fenton, MO; *Int'l*, pg. 237
Tipton, Dick, V.P.-Sls. & Mktg.--Thermador, Los Angeles, CA; *U.S. Public*, pg. 1053
Titus, Eric, Natl. Sls. Mgr.--Euroclean, Itasca, IL; *Int'l*, pg. 440
Tjerandsen, Tom, Pres. & Gen. Mgr.--California Fresh Apricot Council, San Francisco, CA; *U.S. Private*, pg. 200
Tobey, Bill, Mgr.-Mktg. Communicaitons--Eimco Process Equipment Co., Salt Lake City, UT; *U.S. Public*, pg. 166
Tobias, Sally, Sec. & Adv. Sls.--Warner Cable Communications, Inc., Columbus, OH; *U.S. Public*, pg. 1611
Tobin, Leslie, V.P.-Motion Pictures Sales & Acquisitions--Columbia Tri-Star Television Distribution, Burbank, CA; *Int'l*, pg. 1282
Tobin, Linda, V.P.-Intl. Sls. Admin.--Worldvision Enterprises, New York, NY; *U.S. Private*, pg. 776
Tobin, Pat, Sls. Mgr.--Copperweld Bimetallics Products Co., Fayetteville, TN; *Int'l*, pg. 662
Tochterman, Robert C., Mgr.-Sls.--Packaging and Material Handling Division, Chicago, IL; *U.S. Public*, pg. 606
Todd, Colin, Dir.-Sls.--Taunton Cider Company P.L.C., Taunton, United Kingdom; *Int'l*, pg. 849
Todd, Dale, V.P.-Sls.-Carleton Cards--American Greetings U.S. Greeting Card Division, Cleveland, OH; *U.S. Public*, pg. 78
Todd, John M., Dir.-European Sls.--CBT Systems USA Ltd., Menlo Park, CA; *U.S. Public*, pg. 275
Todd, Leonard D., V.P.-Sls.--Carlton Cards Division, Cleveland, OH; *U.S. Public*, pg. 78
Todd, Virgil, Mgr.- Intl. Sls.--Quincy Compressor Division Coltec Industries, Quincy, IL; *U.S. Public*, pg. 402
Toengi, Ferdi, Mng. Dir.-Mktg. & European Sls.--AGIE AG (Fur Industrielle Elektronik), Lausanne, Switzerland; *Int'l*, pg. 488
Tofalli, John, Mgr.-Sls.--Circle Freight International USA, Lawrence, NY; *U.S. Public*, pg. 371
Togher, Renee, Dir.-Mktg. & Sls.--Azteca Foods, Incorporated, Chicago, IL; *U.S. Private*, pg. 104
Tojo, Harry, Reg. Mgr.-Sls.--Taiyo Yuden (U.S.A) Inc., Vista, CA; *Int'l*, pg. 1349
Tokar, Steven, Mgr.-Domestic Sls.--Ariel Corporation, Mount Vernon, OH; *U.S. Private*, pg. 81
Tokuhisa, Roy T., Sr. V.P.-Direct Sls. Opers.--Servco Pacific Inc., Honolulu, HI; *U.S. Private*, pg. 986
Tolbert, Matt, Mgr.-Sls.--The Business Journal of Portland, Inc., Portland, OR; *U.S. Private*, pg. 19
Tollefsrud, Curt, V.P.-Mktg. & Sls.--The Stolle Corporation, Sidney, OH; *U.S. Public*, pg. 61
Tollefsrud, Curt, V.P.-Mktg. & Sls.--Alcoa Building Products, Inc., Sidney, OH; *U.S. Public*, pg. 61
Tollensdorf, Mark, Mgr.-Sls.--DeVlieg-Bullard Services Group, Rockford, IL; *U.S. Public*, pg. 502
Tollinger, Tom, V.P.-HVAC Sls.--Donlee Technologies Inc., York, PA; *U.S. Private*, pg. 339
Tolmos, M., Mgr.-Sls.--SASIB Railway Iberica S.A., Madrid, Spain; *Int'l*, pg. 1195
Toma, Tony, Dir.-Sls.--March Manufacturing Inc., Glenview, IL; *U.S. Private*, pg. 702
Toma, Yoshiyuki, Sr. Mng. Dir.-Overseas Sls.--Makita Corporation, Anjo, Japan; *Int'l*, pg. 831
Tomao, D.F., Dir.-Sls.-Aftermarket & Original Equipment--Universal Composites-U.S.C., Manheim, PA; *U.S. Private*, *pg. 1126*
Tomick, John J., V.P.-Sls.--Willamette Industries Inc., Cleveland, OH; *U.S. Public*, pg. 1768
Tomins, J., Natl. Sls. Mgr.-Indus. Chemicals Div.--PQ Corporation, Berwyn, PA; *U.S. Private*, pg. 827
Tomins, J., Natl. Sls. Mgr.--Industrial Chemicals Div., Valley Forge, PA; *U.S. Private*, pg. 827
Tomio, Hideharu, Mng. Dir.-Sls.--Kawasho Corporation, Tokyo, Japan; *Int'l*, pg. 726
Tomlin, Merrell, Sr. V.P.-Sls.--RAYOVAC Corporation, Madison, WI; *U.S. Private*, pg. 912
Tomlinson, Mack, Sr. V.P.-Sls. & Mktg.--Carfel, Inc., Miami, FL; *U.S. Private*, pg. 210
Tomohiro, Katsumori, Gen. Sls. Mgr.--Loctite (Japan) Corp., Yokohama, Japan; *Int'l*, pg. 611
Tompkins, C.M., Dir.-Domestic Adv. & Mktg.--Sunkist Growers, Inc., Sherman Oaks, CA; *U.S. Private*, pg. 1052
Tompkins, Jim, Exec. V.P.-Sls. & Mktg.--New Balance Athletic Shoe, Inc., Boston, MA; *U.S. Private*, pg. 792
Tompleins, G.R., Dir.-Sls.--Aztec Industries, Inc., Jackson, MS; *U.S. Public*, pg. 159
Tonjum, James F., Sr. V.P.-Mktg. & Sls.--Wine World Estates Company, Saint Helena, CA; *Int'l*, pg. 917
Tonkon, Ed, Pres. & Gen. Mgr.--Huffy Service First, Inc., Miamisburg, OH; *U.S. Public*, pg. 846
Tookey, Robert, V.P.-Sls.--Sharon Tube Company, Sharon, PA; *U.S. Private*, pg. 990
Toole, Charles E., V.P.-Whlse. Sls.--Fannie May Candy Shops, Inc., Chicago, IL; *U.S. Private*, pg. 598
Toolen, John T., Sr. V.P.-Sls.--WestPoint Stevens Inc., West Point, GA; *U.S. Public*, pg. 1762
Toombs, Chuck, V.P.-Mktg.& Sls.--Cadet Manufacturing Company, Vancouver, WA; *U.S. Private*, pg. 198
Toomey, Kevin, Sr. V.P. & Gen. Mgr.-Sls.--Kayser-Roth Corporation, Inc., Greensboro, NC; *Int'l*, pg. 576
Toomey, Rodger, Sr. V.P.-Mktg. & Bus. Devel.--Food Services of America, Seattle, WA; *U.S. Private*, pg. 987
Topley, Doug, V.P.--Crown Andersen Inc., Peachtree City, GA; *U.S. Public*, pg. 462
Topley, Douglas, V.P.-Sls.--Andersen 2000 Inc., Peachtree City, GA; *U.S. Public*, pg. 462
Topping, Richard C., V.P.-Sls., Northeast Div.--C.R. Gibson Co., Norwalk, CT; *U.S. Public*, pg. 1168
Torkelson, V., Mgr.-Sls.--F.B. Wright Co., Dearborn, MI; *U.S. Private*, pg. 1192
Tornetta, Joe, V.P.-Sls. & Mktg.--Automatic Timing & Controls, Inc., New Holland, PA; *U.S. Private*, pg. 327
Tornio, Russell, Reg. Sls. Mgr.--FINNAIR, Chicago, IL; *Int'l*, pg. 486
Torok, Steven, Exec. Dir.-Sls. & Mktg. Opers.--Chrysler Corporation, Auburn Hills, MI; *U.S. Public*, pg. 352
Torok, Steven, Exec. Dir.-Sls.--Chrysler/Plymouth Division, Detroit, MI; *U.S. Public*, pg. 353

Torres, Alvaro, Dir.-Sls.--Nestle Portugal, S.A., Carnaxide, Portugal; *Int'l*, pg. 921
Torres, Henry, Sls.--Rums of Puerto Rico, New York, NY; *U.S. Private*, pg. 951
Torres, Luisito R., Grp. Mgr.-Overseas Mktg. Construction Div.--EEI Corporation, Manila, Philippines; *Int'l*, pg. 425
Torres, X. Guillamet, Dir.-Mktg. & Sls.--Howard S.A., Barcelona, Spain; *Int'l*, pg. 1387
Torsteinsen, J.T., Mgr.-Aftersales--Opel Norge AS, Skedsmokorset, Norway; *U.S. Public*, pg. 723
Tortorich, Nick, Dir.-Reg. Sls.--Nissan Forklift Corporation, North America, Marengo, IL; *Int'l*, pg. 944
Torzillo, Joseph, Mgr.-Sls.--EAO Switch Corporation, Milford, CT; *Int'l*, pg. 444
Tosto, N., Dir.-Intl. Sls.--Fairmont Tamper, West Columbia, SC; *U.S. Public*, pg. 793
Toth, Rusty, Mgr.-Mktg. & Sls.--Fosbel, Inc., Berea, OH; *Int'l*, pg. 234
Totman, Don, Mgr.-Sls./RV--Kit Manufacturing Company, Long Beach, CA; *U.S. Public*, pg. 962
Totman, Don, Mgr.-Sls.--R-4 KIT Mfg. Co., Mc Pherson, KS; *U.S. Public*, pg. 962
Totten, Tracy, V.P.-Sls. & Mktg.--Totten Tubes, Inc., Los Angeles, CA; *U.S. Private*, pg. 1093
Totzke, Bill, Mgr.-Sls.--WICO, Niles, IL; *U.S. Private*, pg. 1144
Tough, G.G., Dir.-Sls. & Mktg.-Diagnostic--Becton Dickinson Canada Inc., Mississauga, Canada; *U.S. Public*, pg. 200
Tousignant, Kathy, V.P.-Sls.--Minwax Company Div., Upper Saddle River, NJ; *U.S. Public*, pg. 1466
Tousigntant, Tim, Dir.-Sls. & Mktg.--The Toro Company Irrigation Products, Riverside, CA; *U.S. Public*, pg. 1624
Townsend, Rich, Mgr.-Sls.--Central States Diversified, Inc., Saint Louis, MO; *U.S. Private*, pg. 224
Toyooka, Isao, Mng. Dir.--Ebara Corporation, Tokyo, Japan; *Int'l*, pg. 431
Tracas, Steven, V.P.-Sls.--US Airways Group, Inc., Arlington, VA; *U.S. Public*, pg. 1680
Trach, John P., V.P.-Sls. & Mktg.--Daily Express, Inc., Carlisle, PA; *U.S. Private*, pg. 307
Tracy, Laurie, Dir.-Wholesale Admin. Sls. & Mktg.--DFI/ Inflight, Inc., Ridgefield, CT; *Int'l*, pg. 103
Tracy, Sandi, V.P.-Ad Sls., Central Region--Discovery Networks, Inc., Bethesda, MD; *U.S. Private*, pg. 334
Tracy, Steve, Assoc. V.P.-Mktg.--The PBS&J Corporation, Miami, FL; *U.S. Private*, pg. 825
Trads, Carsten, V.P.-Mktg. & Sls.--GN Danavox A/S, Taastrup, Denmark; *Int'l*, pg. 537
Trafford, William F., Exec. V.P.-Sales--Strategic Technology Services, Cerritos, CA; *Int'l*, pg. 1154
Traidman, Michael, V.P.-Sls. & Mktg.--Printco Group, Greenville, MI; *U.S. Public*, pg. 228
Trakselis Avery, Katharine, Mgr.-Sls.--Replogle Globes, Inc., Broadview, IL; *U.S. Private*, pg. 923
Tramont, Mark, Mgr.-Sls.--Int. Vintners, Millburn, NJ; *U.S. Private*, pg. 584
Trapp, Robert, V.P.-Sls.-North Eastern Region--PST Vans, Inc., Salt Lake City, UT; *U.S. Public*, pg. 1246
Trapp, Ron Von, V.P.-Worldwide Sls.--Mylex Corporation, Fremont, CA; *U.S. Public*, pg. 1143
Trapp, Steve, V.P.-Sls. & Mktg.--G.I. Plastek, Elyria, OH; *U.S. Private*, pg. 435
Trask, Jim, V.P.-Brand Sls.--Comstock Michigan Fruit, Rochester, NY; *U.S. Private*, pg. 887
Traub, Ken, Dir.-OEM Sls.--Robert Bosch Fluid Power Corporation, Racine, WI; *Int'l*, pg. 204
Traut, Clem, Domestic Sls. Mgr.--Serfilco, Ltd., Northbrook, IL; *U.S. Private*, pg. 985
Traver, Jerry M., V.P.-Sls.--PC Quote, Inc., Chicago, IL; *U.S. Public*, pg. 1240
Travis, Bruce, Sr. V.P.-Sls.--Duracell International Inc., Bethel, CT; *U.S. Public*, pg. 743
Travis, Clare E., Mgr.-Sls.--Amurol Confections Co., Yorkville, IL; *U.S. Public*, pg. 1781
Travis, Gerald, Mgr.-Sls.--Amcor, Inc., Bountiful, UT; *Int'l*, pg. 242
Treace, John R., V.P.-U.S. Sls.--Xomed Surgical Products, Jacksonville, FL; *U.S. Public*, pg. 253
Tredinnick, David, Mgr.-Natl. Sls.--Miether Bearing Products, Inc., Odessa, TX; *U.S. Private*, pg. 33
Treiber, David, Dir.-Adv.--United Dairymen of Arizona, Tempe, AZ; *U.S. Private*, pg. 1121
Tremblay, George A., V.P.-Sls.--Hunter Fan Company, Memphis, TN; *U.S. Private*, pg. 549
Tremble, Mark, V.P.-Sls.--J.J. Keller & Associates, Inc., Neenah, WI; *U.S. Private*, pg. 612
Tremoulis, James, V.P.-Sls. & Mktg.--O'Sullivan Corporation, Winchester, VA; *U.S. Public*, pg. 1234
Trendowicz, Julie, V.P.-Sls. & Mktg.--Copley Pharmaceuticals, Inc., Canton, MA; *U.S. Public*, pg. 446
Tretor, J.T., Mgr.-Leasing & Fleet Sls.--Lincoln-Mercury Division, Detroit, MI; *U.S. Public*, pg. 662
Trevisan, Jane D., V.P.-Mktg. & Sls.--SLM Holding Corp., Washington, DC; *U.S. Public*, pg. 1419
Trezin, Jean-Claude, Mgr.-Sls.--Nokia Display Products, Romainville, France; *Int'l*, pg. 951
Triantafellou, Michael, V.P.-Retail Opers.--FFP Marketing Company, Inc., Fort Worth, TX; *U.S. Public*, pg. 604
Triffaux, Roland, V.P.-European Sls. & Mktg.--Xilinx, Inc., San Jose, CA; *U.S. Public*, pg. 1786
Trigalet, Harry, Mgr.-Natl. Sls.--Permabond International, Englewood, NJ; *Int'l*, pg. 1435
Triglia, Ruth, V.P.-Sls.--Hobie Cat Company, Oceanside, CA; *U.S. Private*, pg. 531
Trimm, Jim, V.P.-Sls.--Mebane Packaging Group., Kearny, NJ; *U.S. Private*, pg. 726
Trimmer, Gord, V.P.-North American Sls. & Mktg.--A. Schulman, Inc., Akron, OH; *U.S. Public*, pg. 1441
Trinceri, Chris, Dir.-Season & Grp. Ticket Sls.--Florida Panthers Holdings, Inc., Fort Lauderdale, FL; *U.S. Public*, pg. 654
Tripp, Kevin H., Sr. V.P.-Pharmacy Sls. & Opers.--American Drug Stores Inc., Oak Brook, IL; *U.S. Public*, pg. 93
Triquoit, Guy, Asst. Dir.-Sls.--Bacardi-Martini Belgium, Brussels, Belgium; *U.S. Private*, pg. 109
Trocher, John A., V.P.-Mktg. & Sls.--American Credit Indemnity, Baltimore, MD; *Int'l*, pg. 464
Trogden, Tracy, Mgr.-Sls.--Hardel Mutual Plywood Corporation, Olympia, WA; *U.S. Private*, pg. 501
Troje, Mike, Mgr.-Domestic Sls.--Broadcast Electronics, Inc., Quincy, IL; *U.S. Private*, pg. 531
Trondle, Joseph J., Mgr.-Sls.--WXYZ TV - Channel 7 of Detroit, Inc., Southfield, MI; *U.S. Public*, pg. 1448
Troutman, John, V.P.-Sls.-Multimedia--Ensoniq, Malvern, PA; *U.S. Private*, pg. 377
Troxler, Kent, Dir.-Sls.--Transus Intermodal L.L.C., Atlanta, GA; *U.S. Private*, pg. 1097
Troy, Chris, Mgr.-Sls.--Harco, El Segundo, CA; *U.S. Public*, pg. 187
Troy, Heidi, Mgr.-Sls. & Mktg.--Luxor, Waukegan, IL; *U.S. Private*, pg. 359
Troyer, Paul E., V.P.-Sls., Mktg. & Adv.--Hanover Wire Cloth, Hanover, PA; *U.S. Private*, pg. 193
Truax, Terry, Mgr.-Sls.--H & H Distributing Company, Inc., West Union, IA; *U.S. Private*, pg. 489
Truchis, Emmanuel de, Dir.-Sls.--Editions du Juris-Classeur, Paris, France; *Int'l*, pg. 1095
Trudel, Brian, M., V.P.-Sls. & Mktg.--Carrier Vibrating Equipment, Inc., Louisville, KY; *U.S. Private*, pg. 215
Trudel, Michel, V.P.-Sls. & Distr., Central--Camco Inc., Mississauga, Canada; *U.S. Public*, pg. 713
Truelsen, Carl, Mgr.-Sls.--Dayton Rogers of California, Van Nuys, CA; *U.S. Private*, pg. 318
Truesdale, Bill, V.P.-Sls.--Maplehurst Farms, Inc., Indianapolis, IN; *U.S. Public*, pg. 490
Trujillo, Robert R., Exec. V.P. & Dir.-Franchise Mngmt.--Glendale Federal Bank, F.S.B., Glendale, CA; *U.S. Public*, pg. 747
Truran, Ron, Mgr.-Natl. Sls./Machinery--Wilton Corporation, Palatine, IL; *U.S. Private*, pg. 1181
Trybus, Tom, Sr. V.P.-Mktg. & Sls.--Belvedere Company, Belvidere, IL; *U.S. Private*, pg. 1008
Tsai, L.C., Mgr.-Sls.--Tainan Spinning Co., Ltd., Tai-nan, Taiwan; *Int'l*, pg. 1347
Tsay, Imad, Mgr.-Natl. Sls. & Mktg.--Miyano Machinery, Inc., Wood Dale, IL; *U.S. Private*, pg. 754
Tsiakos, John, Mgr.-Natl. Sls.--Univex Corporation, Salem, NH; *U.S. Private*, pg. 1128
Tsuda, Masayuki, Mgr.-Japanese Sls.--Kwe-Kintetsu World Express(S)Pte Ltd., Singapore, Singapore; *Int'l*, pg. 735
Tsujita, Hikaru, Sr. Mng. Dir.-Sls.--Sapporo Breweries Ltd., Tokyo, Japan; *Int'l*, pg. 1193
Tsuruta, Masami, Asst. Gen. Mgr.-Domestic Sls.--Makita Corporation, Anjo, Japan; *Int'l*, pg. 831
Tubman, Shawn, V.P.-Field Sls.--Norwegian Cruise Line, Miami, FL; *U.S. Private*, pg. 808
Tucci, Paul, V.P.-Intl. Sls.--Bell & Howell Holdings, Skokie, IL; *U.S. Public*, pg. 201
Tucker, Gordon, Mgr.-Sls.--Rotex Canada Inc., Scarborough, Canada; *Int'l*, pg. 462
Tucker, Hugh, V.P.-Sls. & Mktg.--Dataram Corporation, Princeton, NJ; *U.S. Public*, pg. 487
Tucker, James E., V.P.-Sls. & Mktg.--R.M. Palmer Company, Reading, PA; *U.S. Private*, pg. 835
Tucker, Jim, V.P.-Mktg. & Sls.--Denison Hydraulics, Inc., Marysville, OH; *U.S. Private*, pg. 324
Tucker, John, Dir.-Mining Sls. & Major Accts.--Komatsu America International Company, Vernon Hills, IL; *Int'l*, pg. 744
Tucker, John W., V.P.-Mktg. & Sls.--ACT Networks, Inc., Camarillo, CA; *U.S. Public*, pg. 3
Tucker, Kevin, V.P.-Sls. & Retail--Suntory Water Group, Inc., Marietta, GA; *Int'l*, pg. 1321
Tucker, Michael, V.P.-Sls. & Mktg.--Hackney and Sons, Inc., Washington, NC; *U.S. Private*, pg. 1097
Tui, Mah Yong, Dir.-Sls.--Malaysian Tobacco Co./B.A.T. Indust., Kuala Lumpur, Malaysia; *Int'l*, pg. 111
Tuit, Debbie, Asst.-Sls. & Mktg.--Koch Otto H. York Co., Inc., Parsippany, NJ; *U.S. Private*, pg. 628
Tulli, Nancy, Mgr.-Natl. Sls.--WGAL-TV, Lancaster, PA; *U.S. Public*, pg. 1344
Tullis, Steve, V.P.-Sls.-Conroc. Div.--Burrows Paper Corporation, Little Falls, NY; *U.S. Private*, pg. 188
Tullo, G., Mgr.-Sls.--British Airways, Zurich, Switzerland; *Int'l*, pg. 219
Tully, Mark R., V.P. & Natl. Dir.-Traditional Sls.--Keyport Life Insurance Company, Boston, MA; *U.S. Private*, pg. 666
Tully, Steve, V.P. & Mgr.-Natl. Sls.--Quiksilver, Inc., Costa Mesa, CA; *U.S. Public*, pg. 1353
Tung, Stephen, Mgr.-Sls.--Sun Hung Kai Properties Ltd., Wan Chai, Hong Kong; *Int'l*, pg. 1318
Tunkel, Alan R., V.P.-Grp. Sls.--Sun Life Assurance Company of Canada (U.S.), Wellesley Hills, MA; *Int'l*, pg. 1319
Tunnessen, James, V.P. & Reg. Dir.--Carrols Corporation, Syracuse, NY; *U.S. Private*, pg. 216
Tuominen, Kari, Mgr.-Sls.--Tako Carton Plant Ltd., Jarvenpaa, Finland; *Int'l*, pg. 863
Tupa, Ed, V.P.-Sls. & Mktg.--Roxane Laboratories, Inc., Columbus, OH; *Int'l*, pg. 199
Tupper, Mark, V.P.-Primetime Sls. & Central Sls.--CBS Television Network, New York, NY; *U.S. Public*, pg. 274
Turcotte, Bruce, V.P.-Sls.--Lilyette Brassiere Co., New York, NY; *U.S. Private*, pg. 697
Turek, Walter, V.P.-Sls.--Paychex, Inc., Rochester, NY; *U.S. Public*, pg. 1267
Turin, George, Dir.-Indus. Sls.--Frigid Products, Inc., Elizabeth, NJ; *U.S. Private*, pg. 883
Turnbull, Gene, Sr. V.P.-Sls.--Genuine Parts Company, Atlanta, GA; *U.S. Public*, pg. 732
Turnbull, John, Reg. Sls. Mgr.--Esselte Meto, Mountain View, CA; *Int'l*, pg. 460
Turner, David, Mgr.-Sls.--ATHOL Corporation, Butner, NC; *U.S. Private*, pg. 94
Turner, Frank, Sr. V.P.-Sls. & Mktg.--Mighty Distributing System, Norcross, GA; *U.S. Private*, pg. 745
Turner, Greg, Dir.-Sls.--qad.australia pty ltd, Hunters Hill, Australia; *U.S. Public*, pg. 1345
Turner, Gregory M., V.P.-Sls./Consumer Prods.--QAD Inc, Carpinteria, CA; *U.S. Public*, pg. 1345
Turner, J. Timothy, Sr. V.P.-Sls. & Mktg.--Old Dominion Freight Line, Inc., High Point, NC; *U.S. Public*, pg. 1216
Turner, Jeff, V.P.-American Sls.--Media 100, Inc., Marlborough, MA; *U.S. Public*, pg. 1079
Turner, John A., V.P.-Sls. & Mktg.--Hatfield Quality Meats, Hatfield, PA; *U.S. Private*, pg. 510
Turner, Mitch, V.P.-Mktg. & Sls.--Corinthian Media, Inc., New York, NY; *U.S. Private*, pg. 275
Turner, Richard, V.P.-Sls.--C & M Corporation, Wauregan, CT; *U.S. Private*, pg. 191
Turner, Robert, Gen. Mgr.-Sls.--Reliable Chevrolet, Richardson, TX; *U.S. Private*, pg. 920
Turpin, Jeff, Dir.-Sls.--Bearden Lumber Company, Inc., Bearden, AR; *U.S. Private*, pg. 127
Turrentine, Tom, V.P.-Sls.--Lone Star Corrugated Container Corporation, Irving, TX; *U.S. Private*, pg. 674
Turse, Bill, V.P.-Mktg. & Sls., Dir.-Adv.--Ferraz Corporation, Parsippany, NJ; *Int'l*, pg. 1028
Turturro, John, Dir.-Sls.--Knoll Pharmaceutical Company, Whippany, NJ; *Int'l*, pg. 105
Turunen, Eero, Sr. V.P.-Sls. & Mktg.--Valmet Corporation, Helsinki, Finland; *Int'l*, pg. 1447
Tutini, Peter, V.P.-Sls. & Mktg.--Perstorp Analytical Inc. Division NIRSystems, Silver Spring, MD; *Int'l*, pg. 1039
Twete, Mark, Mgr.-Sls.--Schlosser Forge Company, Rancho Cucamonga, CA; *U.S. Private*, pg. 970
Twining, Robert, V.P.-Sls., Mktg. & Bus. Plng.--COMSAT World Systems, Bethesda, MD; *U.S. Public*, pg. 424
Twomey, Sean, V.P.-Contract Sls.--Imprimeries Quebecor Canada, Richmond Hill, Canada; *Int'l*, pg. 1077
Tyler, Kent, Sr. V.P.-Sls.--ConAgra Frozen Food Company, Omaha, NE; *U.S. Public*, pg. 427
Tyler, Stephen, Mgr.-Sls.--Master Products Mfg. Co., Los Angeles, CA; *Int'l*, pg. 340
Tyler, William A., V.P.-Sls. & Mktg.--Miller Fluid Power Corp., Bensenville, IL; *U.S. Private*, pg. 747
Tylka, Patrick, Pres.-Worldwide Sls.--Scientific-Atlanta, Inc., Norcross, GA; *U.S. Public*, pg. 1443
Tyrrell, George, V.P.-Sls.--Beauty Enterprises Inc., Hartford, CT; *U.S. Private*, pg. 128
Tyson, Eugene, Mgr.-Sls.--Nucor Steel-Nebraska, Norfolk, NE; *U.S. Public*, pg. 1205
Uclinski, Ron, Dir.-Sls. Ed.--Simmons Company, Atlanta, GA; *Int'l*, pg. 686
Ueno, Mary, Mgr.-Sls.--Kintetsu Intermodal Inc., Carson, CA; *Int'l*, pg. 735
Ueno, Seishi, V.P.-Sls. & Mktg.--Suntory International Corp., New York, NY; *Int'l*, pg. 1321
Ueno, Takafumi, Sr. V.P.-Aerospace Sls.--Japan Aviation Electronics Industry, Ltd., Tokyo, Japan; *Int'l*, pg. 701
Uetz, Carl, V.P.-Sls. & Promo.--The Northern Trust Company, Chicago, IL; *U.S. Public*, pg. 1197
Uhl, Chuck, V.P.-Sls. & Mktg.--Satellite Technology Group, Fort Worth, TX; *Int'l*, pg. 1433
Uhl, Eugene T., Mgr.-Sls.--Delroyd Worm Gear, Trenton, NJ; *U.S. Public*, pg. 857
Uhlen, Bjorn, Dir.-Sls. & Mktg.--Korsnas AB, Gavle, Sweden; *Int'l*, pg. 759
Ulbrich, Chris, V.P.- Mktg. & Sls.--Ulbrich Stainless Steels & Special Metals, Inc., North Haven, CT; *U.S. Private*, pg. 1115
Ulfig, Mark, V.P.-OEM Sls.--Sanden International (U.S.A.), Inc., Wylie, TX; *Int'l*, pg. 1184
Ullom, Art, Mgr.-Sls.--Vulcraft Div., Saint Joe, IN; *U.S. Public*, pg. 1206
Ulrich, Bob, Mgr.-Sls.--Tupperware U.S., Inc., Orlando, FL; *U.S. Public*, pg. 1644
Ulrich, John, Dir.-Natl. Sls.--UTILX Corporation, Kent, WA; *U.S. Public*, pg. 1701
Um, Jusoo, Mgr.-Area Sls.--Hanguke Gensym, Seoul, Korea; *U.S. Public*, pg. 731
Umani, Franco, Dir.-Sls.-Italy--Datapoint Italia S.P.A., Milan, Italy; *Int'l*, pg. 384
Underhill, James F., Sr. V.P. & Controller--McJunkin Corporation, Charleston, WV; *U.S. Private*, pg. 722
Underhill, Jerry D., Sr. V.P.-Sls. & Mktg.--Morrison Health Care Inc., Smyrna, GA; *U.S. Public*, pg. 1133
Underwood, Jim, V.P. & Gen. Mgr.-CV--American Isuzu Motors Inc., Whittier, CA; *Int'l*, pg. 692
Underwood, Mark, V.P.-Sls.--Four-S Baking Company, Los Angeles, CA; *U.S. Private*, pg. 422
Unger, Bob, V.P.-Sls.--Tafa Incorporated, Concord, NH; *U.S. Public*, pg. 866
Unger, Michael D., V.P.-Sls.--Sanifill, Inc., Houston, TX; *U.S. Public*, pg. 1686
Union, Christopher N., V.P.-Sls.--Cameron & Barkley Company, Charleston, SC; *U.S. Private*, pg. 203
Unterwiener, H., V.P.-Mktg. & Sls.--Farrell Lines Incorporated, New York, NY; *U.S. Private*, pg. 397
Upchurch, Steve, V.P.-Sls.--Delta Apparel, Duluth, GA; *U.S. Public*, pg. 498
Updike, Steven, V.P.-Food & Beverage Opers.--Ocean Properties, Ltd., Delray Beach, FL; *U.S. Private*, pg. 811
Updyke, Jerry, V.P.-Sls. & Mktg.--Lance Industries, Sylmar, CA; *U.S. Private*, pg. 645
Upegui, Jose, V.P.-Intl. Sls.--Montgomery KONE Inc., Moline, IL; *Int'l*, pg. 746
Upgaard, E. Terrence, V.P.-Sls. & Mktg.--Slocan Forest Products Ltd., Richmond, Canada; *Int'l*, pg. 1263
Upton, Dan, Dir.-Sls.--Fountain Powerboat Industries, Inc., Washington, NC; *U.S. Public*, pg. 678
Urachez, Lazlo, V.P.-Sls.--Technic Incorporated, Cranston, RI; *U.S. Private*, pg. 1071
Urban, Mike, V.P.--MAGVS, Inc., Cleveland, OH; *U.S. Private*, pg. 696
Urbanek, Joe, V.P.-Sls., Rosemount Measurement Div.--Rosemount Measurement Division, Eden Prairie, MN; *U.S. Public*, pg. 574
Ure, Kent, V.P.-Mktg. & Sls.--Milk Specialties Company, Dundee, IL; *U.S. Private*, pg. 746

Uren, Alan, Mgr.-Sls. Opers.--Dixons Group plc, Hemel Hempstead, United Kingdom,; *Int'l*, pg. 413
Urguhart, Steve, Mgr.-Lighting Sls.--Appleton Electric Co., Chicago, IL; *U.S. Public*, pg. 572
Urso, Joseph, V.P.-Sls., North America--Tippins Incorporated, Pittsburgh, PA; *U.S. Private*, pg. 1088
Usina, Mike, Dir.-Sls. & Mktg.--Silverton Marine Corporation, Millville, NJ; *U.S. Private*, pg. 1000
Uthe, Dwight, V.P.-Brand Sls.--Comstock Michigan Fruit, Rochester, NY; *U.S. Private*, pg. 887
Utteridge, M.A., Dir.-Sls. & Customer Svcs.--Britvic Soft Drinks Ltd., Chelmsford, United Kingdom; *Int'l*, pg. 170
Utton, William W., Gen. Mgr.-Sls.--KVVU Broadcasting Corporation, Henderson, NV; *U.S. Public*, pg. 1094
Uys, Dirk, Mgr.-Sls./Solvents--Sasol Chemicals Pacific Limited, Wan Chai, Hong Kong; *Int'l*, pg. 1196
Vack, Eric, Mgr.-Adv. & Sls.--Abell-Howe Company, Forest Park, IL; *U.S. Private*, pg. 10
Vaill, Brian, Dir.-Sls., U.S. & Canada--George S. May International Company, Park Ridge, IL; *U.S. Private*, pg. 717
Vain, William C., V.P.-Mktg. & Sls.--Penco Products, Oaks, PA; *U.S. Private*, pg. 848
Vakil, Ishaq U., V.P.-Sls.--Lights Of America, Inc., Walnut, CA; *U.S. Private*, pg. 667
Valeiras, Luis, V.P.-Sls., Mktg. & Adv.--Gator Industries Inc., Hialeah, FL; *U.S. Private*, pg. 441
Valencia, Harry T., Sr. V.P.-Sls.--Great Pacific Insurance Company, San Bruno, CA; *U.S. Public*, pg. 1158
Valenti-Thornton, Kathryn, V.P.-Sls. & Mktg.--VV Publishing Corp., New York, NY; *U.S. Private*, pg. 1131
Valenti, John, Dir-Natl. Sls.--Lambda Electronics Inc., Melville, NY; *Int'l*, pg. 1241
Valentine, John, V.P.-Mktg. & Sls.--Belden Inc., Saint Louis, MO; *U.S. Public*, pg. 200
Valentino, Tom, Dir.-Sls. & Mktg.--Mokon, Buffalo, NY; *U.S. Public*, pg. 1045
Valinski, Sandi, Sr. V.P.-Sls.--Thompson Nutritional Products, Boca Raton, FL; *U.S. Public*, pg. 1384
Vallandingham, Tim, V.P. & Gen. Mgr.--Gusher Pumps, Inc., Dry Ridge, KY; *U.S. Private*, pg. 488
Valone, Bob, V.P.-Sls.--Nu Horizons Electronics Corp., Melville, NY; *U.S. Public*, pg. 1205
Valone, Robert, Reg. V.P.-Sls.--Nu Horizons/Merit Electronics Corp., San Jose, CA; *U.S. Public*, pg. 1205
Valovcin, Kenneth, Mgr.-Key Accts.--El Paso Electric Company, El Paso, TX; *U.S. Public*, pg. 567
Valtin, Dan, Sls. Mgr.--Cellular One Buffalo, Cheektowaga, NY; *U.S. Public*, pg. 1415
Valvano, Nick, V.P.-Bus. Devel.--Olsy North America Inc., Liberty Lake, WA; *Int'l*, pg. 1002
Valvo, Gary, V.P.-Sls. & Mktg.--Quincy Compressor Division Coltec Industries, Quincy, IL; *U.S. Public*, pg. 402
van Adrichem, H.J., Mgr.-Sls. & Mktg.--Algemene Sein Industrie B.V., Utrecht, Netherlands; *Int'l*, pg. 1194
Van Allen, Harvey, Mgr.-Sls.--Vulcraft Div., Fort Payne, AL; *U.S. Public*, pg. 1206
van Amerongen, R., Dir.-Mktg. & Sls.--Red Band Venco, Breda, Netherlands; *Int'l*, pg. 244
Van Anken, Richard A., Pres. & Chief Exec. Officer--Jennings & Churella Construction Company, Wellington, OH; *U.S. Private*, pg. 586
Van Arsdale, Dan, Dir.-Sls.--Aeros Instruments, Inc., Gurnee, IL; *U.S. Private*, pg. 1028
van den Brink, R.G.C., Sr. Exec. V.P.-Sls., Services & Intl. Private Banking--ABN-AMRO Holding N.V., Amsterdam, Netherlands; *Int'l*, pg. 8
van der Meer, Jaap, V.P.-Strategic Devel. & Worldwide Sls. & Mktg.--Alpnet Inc., Salt Lake City, UT; *U.S. Public*, pg. 58
van Dijk, Henk, Mgr.-Sls.--Atlet-Multicar BV, Enschede, Netherlands; *Int'l*, pg. 97
Van Dine, Jim, Exec. V.P.-Sls., Mktg. & Customer Services--Deckers Outdoor Corporation, Goleta, CA; *U.S. Public*, pg. 491
Van Doren, Dick, Mgr.-Sls.--Aydin Vector Div., Newtown, PA; *U.S. Public*, pg. 158
Van EE, J., Dir.-Sls.--Boon Edam Inc., Salt Lake City, UT; *Int'l*, pg. 202
van Exter, J.F.H.M., Dir.-Sls. (Flat Products)--Hoogovens Ijmuiden, Ijmuiden, Netherlands; *Int'l*, pg. 753
van Exter, Y.F.H.M., Sls. Dir.-Hot Rolled Prods.--Hoogovens Ijmuiden Verkoopkantoor B.V., Ijmuiden, Netherlands; *Int'l*, pg. 754
Van Farowe, Robert, V.P.-Sls.--DMI Furniture Inc., Louisville, KY; *U.S. Public*, pg. 473
van Gemert, Marnix, Exec.-Sls.--Rogers Cantel Mobile Communications Inc., Saint-Laurent, Canada; *Int'l*, pg. 1122
van Haeften, A.W., Dir.-Sls. (Cold Rolled Products)--Hoogovens Ijmuiden, Ijmuiden, Netherlands; *Int'l*, pg. 753
van Hasselt, Job, Asst. V.P.-Sls.--Bobst S.A., Lausanne, Switzerland; *Int'l*, pg. 198
van Heck, Franz, Mgr.-Sls.--Eli Lilly Nederland B.V., Nieuwegein, Netherlands; *U.S. Public*, pg. 994
Van Kalsbeek, David, Dir.-Mktg. & Sls.--ITT Sheraton Corporation, Boston, MA; *U.S. Public*, pg. 1512
Van Natter, Mike, V.P.-Sls.--Kleinschmidt Inc., Deerfield, IL; *U.S. Private*, pg. 625
Van Norman, Jim, V.P.-Mktg. Svcs.--Jamison Door Company, Hagerstown, MD; *U.S. Private*, pg. 581
Van Ord, Norman, Pres.--Blue Seal Feeds, Inc., Londonderry, NH; *U.S. Private*, pg. 1134
Van Orsow, Bob, Mgr.-Natl. Sls.--Byers Portland Willamette, Portland, OR; *U.S. Private*, pg. 191
van Prooijen, W., Mng. Dir.--Honig Foods-B.V., Koog aan de Zaan, Netherlands; *Int'l*, pg. 244
Van Remortel, Steve, Mgr.-Natl. Sls. & Mktg.--Enzopac, Inc., Sheboygan, WI; *U.S. Private*, pg. 379
Van Steemburg, Kurt, V.P.--Hudson Valley Paper Company, Albany, NY; *U.S. Private*, pg. 546
Van Stralen, Frederik, Dir.-Sls. & Opers./Germany--Clestra Hauserman, Strasbourg, France; *Int'l*, pg. 569
Van Tholen, Pete, V.P.-Sls.--Toccoa Metal Technologies, Inc., Elmhurst, IL; *U.S. Private*, pg. 1089
Van Tholen, Peter, Dir.-Sls.--Dempster Equipment, Toccoa, GA; *U.S. Private*, pg. 1089
Van Tuyle, Jeff, V.P.-Sls.--Serta, Inc., Itasca, IL; *U.S. Private*, pg. 985
Van Valkenburgh, Deborah, Sr. V.P.-Sls. & Mktg.--First Maryland Bancorp, Baltimore, MD; *Int'l*, pg. 64
Van Wel, J., Mgr.-Mktg. & Sls.--McCain Alimentari (Italia) Srl, Bergamo, Italy; *Int'l*, pg. 850
Van Wey, Don, V.P.-Sls.--Weiser Lock, Tucson, AZ; *U.S. Public*, pg. 1053
Van Wunster, Massimo, Dir.-Mktg. & Sls.--Interbrew Italia S.p.A., Comun Nuovo, Italy; *Int'l*, pg. 679
VanAlstne, Gary, V.P.- Sales & Mktg.--PrimeCare Health Plan, Inc., Milwaukee, WI; *U.S. Public*, pg. 1678
Vandekopple, David, Sr. V.P.-Sys. Sls.--The Buschman Co., Cincinnati, OH; *U.S. Private*, pg. 188
Vandenbergh, Jim, V.P.-Sls.--Rose Packing Company, Barrington, IL; *U.S. Private*, pg. 945
Vandepoele, N., Dir.-Belgium & Luxembourg--Spadel SA, Brussels, Belgium; *Int'l*, pg. 1287
Vander Zee, J. Dirk, V.P.-Sls. & Mktg.--Mooney Aircraft Corporation, Kerrville, TX; *U.S. Private*, pg. 759
Vanderbeck, Ed, Jr., V.P.-Sls.--Black Millwork Co., Inc., Allendale, NJ; *U.S. Private*, pg. 147
Vanderberg, William R., V.P.-Sls.--Sunset Life Insurance Co. of America, Olympia, WA; *U.S. Public*, pg. 943
VanDerEems, Karen, Mgr.-Sls.--ACBJ Business Journals, Inc., Miami, FL; *U.S. Private*, pg. 19
Vanderminden, Henry, IV, Mgr.-Sls.--Telescope Casual Furniture, Inc., Granville, NY; *U.S. Private*, pg. 1074
Vandeventer, Orlin, Mgr.-Food Service Sls.--John B. Sanfilippo & Son, Inc., Elk Grove Village, IL; *U.S. Public*, pg. 1431
Vaniscote, T., Dir.-Sls.-Coffee--Kraft Jacobs Suchard, Velizy-Villacoublay, France; *U.S. Public*, pg. 1290
VanLanen, Charles, Mgr.-Reg. Sls.--Interstate Steel Supply Co. of Maryland, Baltimore, MD; *U.S. Public*, pg. 1100
Vann, Gary, Sr. V.P.-Sls. & Mktg.--Mighty Distributing System, Norcross, GA; *U.S. Private*, pg. 745
Vann, Michael J., Sls. Mgr.-Natl. Accts.--Storck U.S.A., L.P., Chicago, IL; *Int'l*, pg. 1304
Vannick, Carroll, Sr. V.P.-Sls./East Coast--Freeman Cosmetic Corp., Los Angeles, CA; *U.S. Private*, pg. 426
Vanos, Russ, Sr. V.P.-Utility Sls.--Itron Inc., Spokane, WA; *U.S. Public*, pg. 914
Vanosdall, David, V.P.-Sls. & Mktg.--CENTRIA, Moon Township, PA; *U.S. Private*, pg. 225
VantHul, Randy, Dir.-Sls. & Mktg.--Sackner Products, Grand Rapids, MI; *U.S. Public*, pg. 924
Vanuum, Jim, Mgr.-Sls.--Melling Forging Company, Lansing, MI; *U.S. Private*, pg. 102
Varela, Sergio, V.P.-Sls.--Anaheim Manufacturing Company, Anaheim, CA; *U.S. Private*, pg. 70
Varella, Joao W., Mgr.-Sls.--TI Brazil Industria E Comerico Ltda., Sao Jose dos Campos, Brazil; *Int'l*, pg. 1342
Vargas, Diana, V.P. & Gen. Sls. Mgr.--Fox Television Stations Inc., Los Angeles, CA; *Int'l*, pg. 926
Vargason, Randy, Mgr.-Sls. Admin.--Mustang Manufacturing Company, Inc., Owatonna, MN; *U.S. Public*, pg. 704
Varvel, Russell E., Sr. V.P.-Sls.--American Classic Voyagers Company, New Orleans, LA; *U.S. Private*, pg. 380
Varzino, Robert, Dir.-Sls. & Retail--Warren Tool Group, Garrettsville, OH; *U.S. Private*, pg. 1181
Vasone, John, Mgr.-Eastern Sls.--Salon Division, Englewood, NJ; *Int'l*, pg. 1489
Vasquez, Julian, Mgr.-Sls.--Wolf Brand Products, Fullerton, CA; *U.S. Public*, pg. 428
Vasquez, O., Dir.-Sls.--Charles Atlas, Ltd., New York, NY; *U.S. Private*, pg. 229
Vaughan, Art, V.P.-Saddlebrooke Sls.--Robson Communities, Sun Lakes, AZ; *U.S. Private*, pg. 937
Vaughan, Frank, Mgr.-Sls.--Tennessee Packaging, Sweetwater, TN; *U.S. Private*, pg. 177
Vaughan, Ken, Supvr.-Sls. Service--Namco Controls Corporation, Highland Heights, OH; *U.S. Public*, pg. 482
Vaughan, Vaughn V., V.P.--American Indemnity Company, Galveston, TX; *U.S. Public*, pg. 83
Vaughn, Chris, Dir.-Sls. & Mktg./Ventilation Prods.--Coppus Murray Group, Tuthill Corporation, Millbury, MA; *U.S. Private*, pg. 1110
Vaughn, Jack, Dir.-Domestic Sls. & Mktg.--Midcoast Aviation, Inc., Saint Louis, MO; *U.S. Private*, pg. 959
Vaughn, Jack L., Dir.-Domestic Sls. & Mktg.--Sabreliner Corporation, Saint Louis, MO; *U.S. Private*, pg. 959
Vaughn, Jeff, Mgr.-Sls.--Boston Whaler, Inc., Edgewater, FL; *U.S. Private*, pg. 689
Vaughn, Jeff, Grp. V.P.-Sls.--Turtle Wax, Inc., Chicago, IL; *U.S. Private*, pg. 1110
Vaughn, Jim, Mgr.-Natl. Sls.--Williams & Company, Inc., Pittsburgh, PA; *U.S. Private*, pg. 1055
Vaughn, Pete, Mgr.- Ice Cream Div. Sls.--Trauth Dairy Inc., Newport, KY; *U.S. Private*, pg. 1098
Vaupere, Aivar, Mgr.-Sls.--AS Neopac-Elkson, Maakond, Estonia; *Int'l*, pg. 863
Vavra, John, Sr. V.P.-Sls. & Mktg.--Ascom Hasler Mailing Systems, Inc., Shelton, CT; *Int'l*, pg. 86
Vazquez, Ricardo, Dir.-Intl. Sls.--Liqui-Box Corporation, Worthington, OH; *U.S. Public*, pg. 1000
Veale, Ernest, V.P.-Sls., Mktg., Mdse. & Adv.--The Stellar Group Inc., Jacksonville, FL; *U.S. Private*, pg. 1040
Vecck, Robert, Dir.-Intl. Sls.--Microsemi Corporation, Santa Ana, CA; *U.S. Public*, pg. 1107
Veenstra, Robert, Natl. Dir.-Technical Sls.--Detection Systems, Inc., Fairport, NY; *U.S. Public*, pg. 501
Veerhorn, Will, Mgr.-Sls.--Good Companies, Carson, CA; *U.S. Private*, pg. 463
Vega, Reynaldo, V.P.-Intl. Div.--Donlee Technologies Inc., York, PA; *U.S. Private*, pg. 339
Vehr, Eric, Mgr.-Mktg. Services & Inside Sls.--Automax, Inc., Cincinnati, OH; *U.S. Public*, pg. 658
Veirs, William, V.P.-Sls. & Mktg.--AmeriServe of Grand Rapids, Grand Rapids, MI; *U.S. Private*, pg. 533
Veji, Jotaro, Sr. Mgr.-Sls.--Mizuno Corporation, Osaka, Japan; *Int'l*, pg. 884
Venarchick, Walter, V.P.-Sls.--Bon Ton Foods, Inc., York, PA; *U.S. Private*, pg. 65
Venie, Michael S., V.P.-Mktg. & Sls.--Northwestern Steel & Wire Co., Sterling, IL; *U.S. Public*, pg. 1201
Venitelli, Mike, Mgr.-Natl. Sls.--Michael Business Machines Corporation, Charleston, SC; *U.S. Private*, pg. 740
Venturato, Maurizio, Mgr.-Sls.--Benetton Group S.p.A., Ponzano Veneto, Italy; *Int'l*, pg. 186
Ver Lee, Doug, V.P.-Sls.-Corp. Acct.--Environetx, Itasca, IL; *U.S. Private*, pg. 378
Verdile, Louis, Mgr.-Sls.--PENCO-New York, Albany, NY; *Int'l*, pg. 1508
Verdonck, Caroline, Mgr.-Sls. & Mktg./Benelux--Utell International-Benelux, Hilversum, Netherlands; *Int'l*, pg. 1098
Verdult, P.L.M., Sr. V.P.-Mktg. & Sales--Van Melle N.V., Breda, Netherlands; *Int'l*, pg. 1450
Verdurme, Philippe, Exec. V.P.-Sls. & Mktg.--Rail Europe Inc., Harrison, NY; *Int'l*, pg. 1165
Vere, Phil, Gen. Mgr.-Sls. & Mktg./Germany--Instron Schenck Testing Systems Limited, High Wycombe, United Kingdom; *U.S. Public*, pg. 883
Vergoni, Paul R., V.P. & Dir.-Insurance Sls. & Mktg.--The Troy Savings Bank, Troy, NY; *U.S. Private*, pg. 1106
Vermeulen, Kevin, V.P.-Sls.--New York Law Journal, New York, NY; *Int'l*, pg. 956
Vermeulen, Theo, Mgr.-Sls. & Mktg.--MoDo Van Gelder, Amsterdam, Netherlands; *Int'l*, pg. 886
Vermudes, Rafael, Dir.-Sls.--Laboratorios Pharmacia & Upjohn, C.A., Caracas, Venezuela; *Int'l*, pg. 1049
Vermylen, Robert A., V.P.-Sls. & Mktg.--A. Zeregas Sons, Inc., Fair Lawn, NJ; *U.S. Private*, pg. 1204
Vernon, Chris, Exec. V.P.-Mktg. & Sls.--The Vernon Company, Newton, IA; *U.S. Private*, pg. 1137
Versteeg, Roger, Mgr.-Sls.--Northern Rock Financial Services Limited, Newcastle upon Tyne, United Kingdom; *Int'l*, pg. 968
Vetter, Hans, V.P.-Sls.--SNE Enterprises, Inc., Mosinee, WI; *U.S. Public*, pg. 1193
Vetterli, Michael O., V.P.-Sls. & Mktg.--The Flecto Co., Inc., Oakland, CA; *U.S. Private*, pg. 410
Vicary, Jack, Gen. Mgr.-Industrial Construction--Keystone Steel & Wire Co., Peoria, IL; *U.S. Public*, pg. 955
Vick, Gary, V.P.-Sls.--Miller Automation, Inc. (MO), Kansas City, MO; *U.S. Public*, pg. 867
Victor, Tom, V.P.-Domestic Sls.--John Fabick Tractor Company, Fenton, MO; *U.S. Private*, pg. 390
Vida, Dan, Mgr.-Sls.--Dover Flour Mills, Cambridge, Canada; *Int'l*, pg. 417
Vidana, Abel, Mgr.-Natl. Sls.--BGW Systems, Inc., Hawthorne, CA; *U.S. Private*, pg. 107
Viesca, Felipe Bueno, Dir.-Sls.--Vitromex, S.A., Saltillo, Mexico; *Int'l*, pg. 1469
Vikner, Paul L., Exec. V.P.-Sls. & Mktg.--Mack Trucks, Inc., Allentown, PA; *Int'l*, pg. 1102
Vilanove, M. Campos, Mgr.-Area Sls.--Thermal Ceramics Espana, S.L., Castellon de la Plana, Spain; *Int'l*, pg. 894
Viljoen, F., Mgr.-Intl. Sls.--Sasol Phenolics, Rosebank, South Africa; *Int'l*, pg. 1196
Villamil, Alberto, V.P.-Mktg. & Sls.--La Hacienda S.A. de C.V., Mexico, Mexico; *U.S. Public*, pg. 901
Villano, Glen J., V.P.-Sls. & Mktg.--Eaglemark Financial Services, Inc., Chicago, IL; *U.S. Public*, pg. 786
Vilmain, Joe, V.P.-Intl. Sls. & Services--Trans World Airlines, Inc., Saint Louis, MO; *U.S. Public*, pg. 1629
Vincent, David, Dir.-Sls. & Mktg.--Johnson Matthey Inc., Wayne, PA; *Int'l*, pg. 713
Vincent, James S., Sr., V.P.-Natl. Accts.--Cobra Golf Incorporated, Carlsbad, CA; *U.S. Public*, pg. 675
Vincent, John, Mgr.-Natl. Sls.--Dayton Tire Company, Oklahoma City, OK; *Int'l*, pg. 213
Vinck, Alex, V.P.-Sls. & Mktg.--Southwest Marine, Inc., San Diego, CA; *U.S. Private*, pg. 213
Vining, Peggy, Mgr.-Sls.--Rocco Farm Foods, Inc., Edinburg, VA; *U.S. Private*, pg. 937
Vinsko, William, Mgr.-Sls.--Medico Industries, Inc., Wilkes-Barre, PA; *U.S. Private*, pg. 728
Vinther, Jorgen Pilgaard, Mgr.-Sls.--Fibo ExClay Polska Sp.z.o.o., Szczecin, Poland; *Int'l*, pg. 1200
Vinzant, S. Benton, V.P.-Sls. & Mktg.--Newport Steel Corporation, Newport, KY; *U.S. Public*, pg. 1147
Viola, Dennis, V.P.-Sls. Opers.--Del Laboratories, Inc., Farmingdale, NY; *U.S. Public*, pg. 494
Viola, George, Div. Mgr.-Ground Power Equip.--Rapid Power Technologies, Inc., Brookfield, CT; *U.S. Private*, pg. 910
Virdone, Joseph F., V.P.-U.S. Commercial Opers.--Quaker Chemical Corporation, Conshohocken, PA; *U.S. Public*, pg. 1346
Virene, Peter, Exec. V.P. & Dir.-Sls. & Mktg.--American Modular Technologies, Liberty, NC; *U.S. Public*, pg. 69
Virgalitte, Stan, Mgr.-Sls.-Northern Div.--Lafarge Construction Materials, Canfield, OH; *Int'l*, pg. 788
Virgona, Kim, Mgr.-Tertiary Sls.-Eastern Region--McGraw-Hill Book Co. Australia Pty. Ltd., Roseville, Australia; *U.S. Public*, pg. 1072
Virrazzi, Fred A., V.P.-Sls.--ENSI, Inc., Rahway, NJ; *U.S. Public*, pg. 546
Visser, L., V.P.-Sls.--KTI Group B.V., Zoetermeer, Netherlands; *Int'l*, pg. 837
Vitko, John, Sls. Mgr.--Vibco Inc., Wyoming, RI; *U.S. Private*, pg. 1138
Vito, James M., V.P.-Sls.--Giles & Ransome, Inc., Bensalem, PA; *U.S. Private*, pg. 453
Vivian, Frank, Mgr.-Sls.--Chief E-Z Breaker, Inc., Grand Island, NE; *U.S. Private*, pg. 236
Vivian, Ken, Dir.-Dental & Consumer Sls. & Mktg.--Stafford-Miller Limited, Welwyn Garden City, United Kingdom; *U.S. Public*, pg. 237
Vivian, Les, V.P.-Sls.--Gould Paper Corporation, New York, NY; *U.S. Private*, pg. 466
Vizcarra, Jorge, Mgr.-Sls.--Alicorp S.A., Lima, Peru; *Int'l*, pg. 57

SALES DIRECTORY OF CORPORATE AFFILIATIONS

Vizcarra, Mike, Mgr.-Standard Sls.--O'Keeffe's, Inc., San Francisco, CA; *U.S. Private*, pg. 813
Vizzini, Paul, V.P.-Mktg. & Sls.--Lifeline Systems, Inc., Cambridge, MA; *U.S. Public*, pg. 992
Vlk, Leroy F., Exec. Sec.--The Florists Assn. of Greater Cleveland, Inc., Cleveland, OH; *U.S. Private*, pg. 415
Voccola, Richard, Mgr.-Inside Sls.--Spadone Inc., Norwalk, CT; *U.S. Private*, pg. 1019
Vogler, Rick, Mgr.-Sls.--Rowenta (USA), Inc., Medford, MA; *Int'l*, pg. 569
Vognar, Daniela, Natl. Sls. Mgr.--Continental Promotion Group, Tempe, AZ; *U.S. Private*, pg. 269
Vogt, Erich, Sls.-Sedia Prods.--Suspa Compart AG, Altdorf, Germany; *Int'l*, pg. 1322
Vogt, Michael W., V.P.-Asia/Pacific Sls.--Proxima Corporation, San Diego, CA; *U.S. Public*, pg. 1339
Vogus, John W., V.P.-Sls. & Mktg.--Knape & Vogt Mfg. Co., Grand Rapids, MI; *U.S. Public*, pg. 963
Vohmann, S.G., Div. Mgr.-Sls.--Meadow Lea Foods Ltd., Mascot, Australia; *Int'l*, pg. 555
Vojik, Ron, V.P.-Sls. & Mktg.--Dudek & Bock Spring Manufacturing Company, Chicago, IL; *U.S. Private*, pg. 344
Vokac, Glen, Mgr.-Natl. Sls.--Kingsley Machine Co., Downers Grove, IL; *U.S. Public*, pg. 866
Voland, Paul, Dir.-Intl., Gov. & Hospitality Sls.--Howe Furniture Corporation, Trumbull, CT; *U.S. Private*, pg. 543
Volcker, Wolfgang, Mgr.-Sls--Reise-und Verkehrs Verlag GmbH, Munich, Germany; *Int'l*, pg. 190
Volk, Rick, V.P.-Sls.--Oliver Rubber Co., Athens, GA; *U.S. Public*, pg. 1504
Volker, M.J., V.P.-Sls. & Mktg.--Merchants Home Delivery Service Inc., Oxnard, CA; *Int'l*, pg. 901
Volkwein, Ed, Sr. V.P.-Mktg. & Sls.--Philips Consumer Electronics, Knoxville, TN; *Int'l*, pg. 1054
Voltz, Gunnar, V.P.-Sls.--Steck-Vaughn Publishing Corporation, Austin, TX; *U.S. Public*, pg. 784
Voltz, Gunnar, V.P.-Sls.--Steck-Vaughn Distribution Company, Austin, TX; *U.S. Public*, pg. 784
Voltz, Gunnar C., V.P.-Sls.--Steck-Vaughn Company, Austin, TX; *U.S. Public*, pg. 784
Von Aspern, Dieter, Dir.-Mktg. & Sls.--Hertie Waren-und Kaufhaus GmbH, Frankfurt/Main, Germany; *Int'l*, pg. 724
von Boch-Galhau, Wendelin, Mgr.-Tableware Div.--Villeroy & Boch AG, Mettlach, Germany; *Int'l*, pg. 1468
Von Duhn, Mark J., Gen. Mgr.-Sls.--Oglebay Norton Refractories & Minerals, Inc., Cleveland, OH; *U.S. Public*, pg. 1214
Von Gillern, Jack, Mgr.-Natl. Sls.--Dallas Semiconductor Corporation, Dallas, TX; *U.S. Public*, pg. 478
von Koskull, Karin, Mng. Dir.-Institutional Sls.--Academic Bookstore, Helsinki, Finland; *Int'l*, pg. 1301
Von Liebermann, Don, Pres.--Cutco Industries, Inc., Syosset, NY; *U.S. Public*, pg. 470
Voorman, Korker, Mgr.-Sls.--Latshaw Enterprises, Inc., Wichita, KS; *U.S. Public*, pg. 979
Vos, M.J., Mgr.-Mktg. & Sls--Meneba Meel B.V., Rotterdam, Netherlands; *Int'l*, pg. 555
Voss, Alan, Dir.-Sls.--Atco/East-West Records, New York, NY; *U.S. Public*, pg. 1611
Voss, Dietmar, Sr. V.P.-Sls. & Mktg. Worldwide--Columbian Chemicals Company, Atlanta, GA; *U.S. Public*, pg. 1286
Voss, Jeff, New Business Mgr.--Safway Steel Products Inc., Waukesha, WI; *Int'l*, pg. 1389
Votaw, Timothy, Pres.-Americas Sls. & Sr. Dir.-Channel Sls.--Iomega Corporation, Roy, UT; *U.S. Public*, pg. 912
Votruba, Larry, Mgr.-Sls.--Ernest Paper Products, Inc., Los Angeles, CA; *U.S. Private*, pg. 381
Vrabac, Mike, Gen. Mgr.-Sls.--KJRH, Tulsa, OK; *U.S. Public*, pg. 1448
Vreeland, R. F., Exec. V.P.-Mktg. & Sls.--Shieffelin Somerset Co., New York, NY; *Int'l*, pg. 412
Vroman, John, Mgr.-Sls.-Western Reg.--Temco Fireplace Products, Inc., Nashville, TN; *U.S. Public*, pg. 1576
Vujnovich, Michael L., Dir.-Natl. Sls. & Mktg.--Ascom Hasler Mailing Systems, Inc., Shelton, CT; *Int'l*, pg. 86
Vukmanic, Frank, Sr. V.P.-Sls. & Mktg.--Amperif Corporation, Chatsworth, CA; *U.S. Public*, pg. 1523
Waack, Gregg, Natl. Sls. Mgr.--DSM Engineering Plastic Products, Reading, PA; *Int'l*, pg. 354
Wachob, Robert D., V.P.-Sls. & Mktg.--Rogers Corporation, Rogers, CT; *U.S. Public*, pg. 1402
Wacker, J.C., Sr. V.P.-Production & Sls., Western & Central Container Div.--Longview Fibre Company, Longview, WA; *U.S. Public*, pg. 1013
Wackerlin, Jim, Exec. V.P.--American Seating Company, Grand Rapids, MI; *U.S. Private*, pg. 61
Wade, Jeffrey, Exec. V.P.-Sls. & Mktg.--Showtime Networks Inc., New York, NY; *U.S. Private*, pg. 779
Wade, Jim, V.P.-Sls. & Mktg.--Crane Carrier Company, Tulsa, OK; *U.S. Private*, pg. 286
Wadsten, Gary, V.P.-Sls.--Fairfield Myrtle Beach, Inc., North Myrtle Beach, SC; *U.S. Public*, pg. 611
Wadsworth, Carl, Dir.-Sls.--Franklin Baking Co., Inc., Goldsboro, NC; *U.S. Private*, pg. 424
Wadsworth, Martha, Dir.-Adv. & Mktg.--Thonet, Statesville, NC; *U.S. Public*, pg. 1465
Waebens, Daniel, Sls. Mgr.--Banque Paribas Nederland N.V., Amsterdam, Netherlands; *Int'l*, pg. 320
Wagahoff, Randy, V.P.-Sls.--Top Air Manufacturing, Inc., Cedar Falls, IA; *U.S. Public*, pg. 1621
Waggoner, Doug, V.P.-Sls.--Yellow Corporation, Overland Park, KS; *U.S. Public*, pg. 1788
Wagner, Bill, Dir.-Sls. Promo.--Penn-Daniels, Inc., Quincy, IL; *U.S. Public*, pg. 1467
Wagner, Dale, V.P.-Sls. & Mktg., Home Fashions--Hoffman Laces, Ltd., Cobleskill, NY; *U.S. Public*, pg. 769
Wagner, David, Dir.-Sls.--Mold-Tech, Villa Park, IL; *U.S. Public*, pg. 1506
Wagner, Eugene M., V.P.-Mktg. & Sls./Rhinelander--Wausau Papers - Printing & Writing Div., Brokaw, WI; *U.S. Public*, pg. 1747
Wagner, Eugene M., V.P.-Mktg. & Sls.--Wausau-Mosinee Papers Specialty Papers Group, Rhinelander, WI; *U.S. Public*, pg. 1747
Wagner, James E., Mgr.-Reg. Sls.--Bunker Hill Foods Inc., Bedford, VA; *U.S. Private*, pg. 219
Wagner, Jeff, Mgr.-Sls. & Mktg.--Barber-Colman Company, Rockford, IL; *Int'l*, pg. 1242
Wagner, K., V.P.-Mktg. & Sls. Foundry--Brillion Iron Works, Inc., Brillion, WI; *U.S. Public*, pg. 933
Wagner, Karsten, Dir.-Sls. & Mktg.--Nordsten, Skive, Denmark; *Int'l*, pg. 1386
Wagner, L.P., Mgr.-Natl. Sls.--Curtis 1000, Inc., Atlanta, GA; *U.S. Public*, pg. 70
Wagner, Mike, Mgr.-Sls.--Nucor Steel-Indiana, Crawfordsville, IN; *U.S. Public*, pg. 1205
Wagner, Paul, Mgr.-Sls.--United States Aluminum Corp., Vernon, CA; *U.S. Public*, pg. 895
Wagner, Richard H., V.P.-Sls.--Clarin, Lake Bluff, IL; *U.S. Private*, pg. 242
Wagner, Rodger, V.P.-Sls. & Mktg.--KYB Corporation of America, Lombard, IL; *Int'l*, pg. 727
Wagner, Steve, V.P.-Mktg., Carrier Sls. & Bus. Devel.--USLD Communications Corp., San Antonio, TX; *U.S. Public*, pg. 969
Wagner, Toby, Mgr.-Natl. Sls.--American Speedy Printing Centers, Inc., Troy, MI; *U.S. Private*, pg. 62
Wah Ying, Chin, Mgr.-Intl. Sls.--Melroe Company, Fargo, ND; *U.S. Public*, pg. 877
Wahl, Claire, Dir.-Intl. Sls.--Mizuno USA, Inc., Norcross, GA; *Int'l*, pg. 885
Wahl, Nicholas F., III, Mgr.-Sls.--Truelove & Maclean Inc., Waterbury, CT; *U.S. Private*, pg. 1107
Wahlin, Helena, Mgr.-Mktg. & Sls.--Foga Systems, Oxnard, CA; *Int'l*, pg. 496
Wait, Larry, Reg. Sls. Mgr.--Just Born, Inc., Bethlehem, PA; *U.S. Private*, pg. 602
Waite, Rick, Mgr.-Sls. & Mktg.--Burke Engineering Company, South El Monte, CA; *U.S. Private*, pg. 183
Wajmer, Mary Jane, Mgr.-Circulation--Buffalo Law Journal, Buffalo, NY; *U.S. Private*, pg. 19
Wakefield, Bob, V.P.-Industrial Cleaning Equip. Sls.--Landa, Inc., Portland, OR; *U.S. Private*, pg. 646
Wakin, Robert H., V.P.-Retail Sls.--Bergen Brunswig Drug Company, Orange, CA; *U.S. Public*, pg. 213
Walberg, Mats, Mgr.-Mktg. & Sls.--Iggesund Paperboard AB, Iggesund, Sweden; *Int'l*, pg. 886
Walborn, Robert L., V.P.-Sls. & Mktg.--Farmer's Pride, Inc., Fredericksburg, PA; *U.S. Private*, pg. 395
Walburn, Mark T., V.P.-Mfg. Sls.--CMC Kalamazoo Inc., Kalamazoo, MI; *U.S. Private*, pg. 1030
Walden, Eric, V.P.-Sls.--American Eurocopter Corp., Grand Prairie, TX; *Int'l*, pg. 29
Walden, John, V.P.-Sls.--Air Liquide Southern Div., Houston, TX; *Int'l*, pg. 37
Waldenburg, Stephen, Mgr.-Reg. Sls.--American Technical Ceramics Corp., Huntington Station, NY; *U.S. Public*, pg. 93
Waldman, Steve, Dir.-Sls.--Showboat, Incorporated, Las Vegas, NV; *U.S. Public*, pg. 1469
Waldoch, Terri, V.P.-Sls. & Mktg.--Fritz Co. Inc., Newport, MN; *U.S. Private*, pg. 429
Waldon, Mike, V.P.-Sls. & Mktg.--Johanna Foods Inc., Flemington, NJ; *U.S. Private*, pg. 589
Waldorf, Jennifer, Asst.-Sls. & Adv.--Parents Magazine, New York, NY; *Int'l*, pg. 191
Waldron, John, Chief Oper. Officer--Lyman Lumber Company, Excelsior, MN; *U.S. Private*, pg. 683
Waldron, John T., Dir.-Sls.--Takeda USA Inc., Orangeburg, NY; *Int'l*, pg. 1350
Waldrop, Richard E., Pres., Chief Oper. Officer & V.P.-Sls.--Edwards Engineering Corporation, Pompton Plains, NJ; *U.S. Private*, pg. 365
Wales, Maureen, Dir.-Sls.--Creative Publications, Mountain View, CA; *U.S. Private*, pg. 288
Walkenhorst, Wayne, V.P. & Dir.-Circulation--Harcourt Brace & Company Farm Publications Inc., Orlando, FL; *U.S. Public*, pg. 783
Walker, Bill, Dir.-Sls. & Mktg.--Superior Machine Systems, Mason, OH; *U.S. Private*, pg. 1055
Walker, Bob, Mgr.-Sls. & Mktg.--Ipsen International, Inc., Cherry Valley, IL; *Int'l*, pg. 1149
Walker, C.G., V.P.-Sls.--Harriet & Henderson Yarns, Inc., Henderson, NC; *U.S. Private*, pg. 504
Walker, Dale W., V.P.-Corp. Sls.--Nalco Chemical Company, Naperville, IL; *U.S. Public*, pg. 1150
Walker, J. Philip, Sr. V.P.-Sls. & Mktg.--Interface Europe B.V., Scherpenzeel, Netherlands; *U.S. Public*, pg. 889
Walker, James, V.P.-Mktg.--Koger Equity Inc., Jacksonville, FL; *U.S. Public*, pg. 965
Walker, James C., Exec. V.P.-Sls.--Ernst W. Dorn Co., Inc., Gardena, CA; *U.S. Private*, pg. 340
Walker, John, Mgr.-Intl. Tech. Sls.--Stanbee Company, Inc., Carlstadt, NJ; *U.S. Private*, pg. 1030
Walker, Ken, Mgr.-Corp. Sls. & Mktg.--Wangner Systems Corporation, Greenville, SC; *Int'l*, pg. 1418
Walker, Lynn, Customer Support--Comverse Network Systems, Marietta, GA; *U.S. Public*, pg. 425
Walker, Marty, Sr. V.P.-Sls. & Mktg.--Iams Company, Dayton, OH; *U.S. Private*, pg. 556
Walker, R.C., Bus. Unit Mgr.--Peerless Faucet Corporation, Indianapolis, IN; *U.S. Public*, pg. 1053
Walker, Rich, Sls. Mgr.--The Corporate Communications Group, Whippany, NJ; *U.S. Private*, pg. 276
Walker, Ronald, V.P.-Sls.--CRC Industries, Inc., Warminster, PA; *U.S. Private*, pg. 138
Walker, Scott, Dir.-Western Div. Sls. & Mktg.--Hyatt Hotels Corporation, Chicago, IL; *U.S. Private*, pg. 551
Walker, Stanley, Mgr.-Sls.--Vulcraft Div., Norfolk, NE; *U.S. Public*, pg. 1206
Walker, Steve, Dir.-Sls.--Basler Electric Company, Highland, IL; *U.S. Private*, pg. 121
Walklet, Judith C., Sr. V.P.-Sls.--Quebecor Printing (USA) Corp., Greenwich, CT; *Int'l*, pg. 1078
Wall, Jack, Pres.--Al Larson Boat Shop, Inc., Terminal Island, CA; *U.S. Private*, pg. 652
Wall, John, Sr. V.P.-Sls. & Mktg.--Owsley & Sons, Inc., Fort Mill, SC; *U.S. Private*, pg. 824
Wall, Tim, Mgr.-Sls.--Mike Castrucci Chevrolet, Milford, OH; *U.S. Private*, pg. 219
Wallace, Jeffrey J., Mgr.-Sls. & Mktg.--Besser Company, Alpena, MI; *U.S. Private*, pg. 139
Wallace, Karen, Mgr.-Sls. Promo.--Midlantic Bank, N.A., Edison, NJ; *U.S. Public*, pg. 1242
Wallace, Scott C., V.P.-Mainland Mktg. & Sls.--Mauna Loa Macadamia Nut Corporation, Hilo, HI; *U.S. Private*, pg. 190
Wallace, Sean, Mgr.-Sls.--Fairways and Swinford (Travel) Ltd., London, United Kingdom; *Int'l*, pg. 1214
Wallace, Thomas T., Pres.--Johnston, Lemon & Co. Inc., Washington, DC; *U.S. Private*, pg. 595
Wallake, Randy, V.P.-Pension Div.--The Minnesota Mutual Life Insurance Company, Saint Paul, MN; *U.S. Private*, pg. 750
Wallis, John, V.P.-Sls. & Mktg.--Hyatt International Corporation, Chicago, IL; *U.S. Private*, pg. 551
Wallis, Robert, V.P.-Mktg.--Laubeck Corporation/Cross, Carbondale, PA; *U.S. Private*, pg. 652
Wally, Fletcher, Mgr.-Natl. Sls.--Vinings Industries Inc., Atlanta, GA; *U.S. Private*, pg. 1141
Walser, Jeff, V.P.-Eastern Region Sls.--Vienna Sausage Mfg. Co., Chicago, IL; *U.S. Private*, pg. 1139
Walsh, Brian A., V.P.-Sls. & Mktg.--Fort James Canada, Inc., Toronto, Canada; *U.S. Public*, pg. 672
Walsh, Gerald C., Exec. V.P.--V-Band Corporation, Elmsford, NY; *U.S. Public*, pg. 1701
Walsh, Jim, V.P.-Mktg., Sls. & Technology--Slater Steels Corporation, Fort Wayne, IN; *Int'l*, pg. 1263
Walsh, Jim, V.P.-Licensing of OEM--The Ertl Company, Inc, Dyersville, IA; *U.S. Public*, pg. 1684
Walsh, John, V.P.-Consumer Mktg.--The Orange County Register, Santa Ana, CA; *U.S. Private*, pg. 425
Walsh, Joseph A., Pres., Chief Exec. Officer & Sls. Dir.--Multi-Local Media Corporation, Rockville Centre, NY; *U.S. Private*, pg. 767
Walsh, Mark, Dir.-Sls.--Crystal Cabinet Works, Inc., Princeton, MN; *U.S. Private*, pg. 293
Walsh, Patrick J., Dir.-Field Svcs.--Ferrellgas Partners, L.P., Liberty, MO; *U.S. Public*, pg. 618
Walsworth, Edgar, Exec. V.P.-Mfg. & Comml. Sls.--Walsworth Publishing Company, Inc., Marceline, MO; *U.S. Private*, pg. 1148
Walter, Mike, Sls. Mgr.--Holmes Protection of New Jersey, Inc., Edison, NJ; *U.S. Public*, pg. 1649
Walters, DeDra A., Mgr.-Sls., Plng. & Admin.--The Ohio Art Company, Inc., Bryan, OH; *U.S. Public*, pg. 1214
Walther, Jean-Jacques, Dir.-Comml.--Nouvelle Lemania S.A., Lorient, Switzerland; *Int'l*, pg. 971
Walther, Lee, Dir.-Intl. Sls.--The New Piper Aircraft, Inc., Vero Beach, FL; *U.S. Private*, pg. 794
Walton, Kent R., Sr. Exec. V.P.-Sls. Promo.--Rexair, Inc., Troy, MI; *U.S. Public*, pg. 1684
Waluszko, Alex, V.P.-Mktg. & Sls.--UVP, Inc., Upland, CA; *U.S. Private*, pg. 1115
Wang, R.C., Dir.-Sls.--Taiwan Glass Industry Corp., Taipei, Taiwan; *Int'l*, pg. 1348
Wankmiller, Albert, V.P.-Sls. & Mktg.--Print-O-Stat, Inc., York, PA; *U.S. Private*, pg. 830
Wanko, Dan, Sls. Mgr.--WVUE-TV, New Orleans, LA; *U.S. Public*, pg. 1685
Wanner, Ken, V.P.-Sls. & Mktg.--Accra Pac Group, Elkhart, IN; *U.S. Private*, pg. 11
Wanous, Craig, Natl. Sls. Mgr.-Equip. Div.--JanSport, Appleton, WI; *U.S. Public*, pg. 1702
Waples, Jim, Dir.-Intl. Sls.--Marine Travelift, Inc., Sturgeon Bay, WI; *U.S. Private*, pg. 703
Warberg, Svein, Dir.-Sls.--Tine-Vestlandsmeieriet, Minde,, Norway; *Int'l*, pg. 1390
Ward, Brian, V.P.-Sls. & Mktg.--Spectrum Control, Inc., Erie, PA; *U.S. Public*, pg. 1497
Ward, Brian, V.P.-Sls.--Spectrum Control, Filter Products Group, Fairview, PA; *U.S. Public*, pg. 1497
Ward, J., Sls. Mgr.--Senior Conflow, Nottingham, United Kingdom; *Int'l*, pg. 1220
Ward, Jim, Mgr.-Tech. Sls.--Eagle Packaging Group, Oakland, CA; *U.S. Private*, pg. 832
Ward, John, Sr. V.P.-Sls. & Mktg.--Boston Whaler, Inc., Edgewater, FL; *U.S. Private*, pg. 689
Ward, Paulette, Mgr.-Sls. & Mdsg.--Magee Co., Pocahontas, AR; *U.S. Public*, pg. 1561
Ward, Richard, Mgr.-Regional Sls.--Boyer Candy Company Inc., Altoona, PA; *U.S. Private*, pg. 162
Warden, Dick, V.P.-Sls. & Mktg.--Structron Corporation, San Marcos, CA; *U.S. Private*, pg. 988
Wardwell, Robert, V.P.-Sls. & Mktg.--Filter Products Division, Richmond, VA; *U.S. Public*, pg. 620
Ware, Dexter, V.P.-Sls. & Mktg.--Courtaulds Fibers Inc., Axis, AL; *Int'l*, pg. 339
Ware, Greg P., V.P.-Field Opers.--Programart Corporation, Cambridge, MA; *U.S. Private*, pg. 890
Ware, J., Mgr.-Materials & Supplies--Philip Morris Limited, Moorabbin, Australia; *U.S. Public*, pg. 1290
Ware, Robert, V.P.-Sls.--Carter Day Industries (Canada) Ltd., Winnipeg, Canada; *U.S. Private*, pg. 217
Ware, Warren, Sr. V.P.-Sls.--Ridge Tool Co., Elyria, OH; *U.S. Public*, pg. 574
Warhurst, C., Gen. Mgr.-Sls.--Lancashire Dairies Ltd., Manchester, United Kingdom; *Int'l*, pg. 798
Warmelink, Martin, Sls. Dir.--Langford Inc., Guelph, Canada; *U.S. Public*, pg. 81
Warner, Glen, Mgr.-Regional Sls.--Molded Fiber Glass Companies, Ashtabula, OH; *U.S. Private*, pg. 755
Warner, Glen, Dir.-Sls.--Molded Fiber Glass Co., Ashtabula, OH; *U.S. Private*, pg. 756
Warrelmann, T., Tool Sls.--Victaulic Tool Company, Easton, PA; *U.S. Private*, pg. 1138
Warren, Bill, Sr. V.P.-Sls.--Tyco Toys, Inc., Mount Laurel, NJ; *U.S. Public*, pg. 1058

Warren, Dan, Mgr.-Mktg.--MW Manufacturers Inc., Rocky Mount, VA; *Int'l*, pg. 593
Warren, Gordon, V.P.-Sls.--Manheim Auctions, Inc., Atlanta, GA; *U.S. Private*, pg. 282
Warren, Mark, V.P.-Consumer Sls.--Amerock Corporation, Rockford, IL; *U.S. Public*, pg. 1177
Warren, Ronald J., V.P.-Sls.--John Crane North America, Morton Grove, IL; *Int'l*, pg. 1339
Warren, Tom, Mgr.-Sls. Opers.--Micromatic Textron, Holland, MI; *U.S. Public*, pg. 1589
Warren, Walter, Mgr.-Sls. & Mktg.--Salwasser Manufacturing Company, Inc., Reedley, CA; *U.S. Private*, pg. 963
Warzniack, Jim, Mgr.-Sls.--Universal Foods Corp.-Dehydrated Products Div., Turlock, CA; *U.S. Public*, pg. 1696
Washington, Felicia, Dir.-Sls.--Pro-Line Corporation, Dallas, TX; *U.S. Private*, pg. 887
Wasielewski, Larry, Mgr.-Sls.--Wedgestone Automotive Corp., Irwindale, CA; *U.S. Public*, pg. 1751
Wasielewski, Larry, Mgr.-Sls.--Fey Mfg. Co., Inc., Irwindale, CA; *U.S. Public*, pg. 1751
Wasikowski, Ronald R., Sr. V.P.-Mktg. & Sls.--World Airways, Inc., Herndon, VA; *U.S. Public*, pg. 1780
Wasil, Tony, Mgr.-Sls.--Lou LaRiche Chevrolet Inc., Plymouth, MI; *U.S. Private*, pg. 651
Wassel, James, V.P.-Sls.--Lynch Machinery, Inc., Bainbridge, GA; *U.S. Public*, pg. 1022
Wassmann, Ernest H., V.P.-Mktg.--Exabyte Corporation, Boulder, CO; *U.S. Public*, pg. 597
Watanabe, Akira, Mng. Dir.-Yokohama Area Sls.--Japan Tobacco Inc., Tokyo, Japan; *Int'l*, pg. 703
Watanabe, Satoru, Sr. Mng. Dir.-Overseas Sls.--Makita Corporation, Anjo, Japan; *Int'l*, pg. 831
Watanabe, Satoshi, Mng. Dir.-Sls. & Mktg.--Yamaha Motor Co., Ltd., Iwata, Japan; *Int'l*, pg. 1516
Waterfield, J.R., Gen. Mgr.-Sls.--ITT Fluid Handling, Morton Grove, IL; *U.S. Public*, pg. 860
Waterman, Win, V.P.-Sls.--Peace Industries Inc., Rolling Meadows, IL; *U.S. Private*, pg. 845
Waterman, Win, V.P.-Mktg. & Sls.--Spotnails, Rolling Meadows, IL; *U.S. Private*, pg. 845
Waters, Mitchell, V.P.-Sls.--ATF, Inc., Lincolnwood, IL; *U.S. Private*, pg. 8
Waters, Tim, V.P.-Sls. & Trng.--All Pro Bumper to Bumper Inc., Florence, KY; *U.S. Private*, pg. 35
Waters, William J., Jr., Pres.-World & Zenith Sls. Div.--World Carpets, Inc., Dalton, GA; *U.S. Private*, pg. 1190
Waterson, David, Sr. V.P.-Res. & Devel. & Mktg.--Icon Health & Fitness, Inc., Logan, UT; *U.S. Private*, pg. 556
Watkins, Jim, Mgr.-Custom Sls.--O'Keeffe's, Inc., San Francisco, CA; *U.S. Private*, pg. 813
Watkins, Pete, Gen. Mgr.-Natl. Sls.--WSLS-TV, Roanoke, VA; *U.S. Public*, pg. 1078
Watmough, Malcolm, Area Sales Mgr.- N. Sea--M/D Totco Instrumentation, Aberdeen, United Kingdom; *U.S. Public*, pg. 1709
Watson, Alice, Mgr.-Sls.--TIE Systems Northern California, Hayward, CA; *U.S. Private*, pg. 1085
Watson, Chris, Dir.-Custom Bus.--Conestoga Wood Specialties Corp., East Earl, PA; *U.S. Private*, pg. 262
Watson, J. Scott, V.P.-Sales--Cyprus Foote Mineral Co., Kings Mountain, NC; *U.S. Public*, pg. 471
Watson, John, Mgr.-Sls.--Neff (UK) Limited, Milton Keynes, United Kingdom; *Int'l*, pg. 912
Watson, R.W., V.P.-Copper Tube Sls.--Mueller Industries, Inc., Memphis, TN; *U.S. Public*, pg. 1141
Watson, Randy, V.P.-Natl. Sls.--Justin Boot Company, Fort Worth, TX; *U.S. Public*, pg. 937
Watt, William A., V.P.-Sls.--Moran Towing Corporation, Greenwich, CT; *U.S. Private*, pg. 760
Watts, Helen M., Mgr.-Sls.--Young Pecan Company (A Partnership), Florence, SC; *U.S. Private*, pg. 1201
Watts, Joan Lane, Mgr.-Sls.--American City Business Journals of Florida, Inc., Orlando, FL; *U.S. Private*, pg. 19
Watts, Randy, V.P.-Sls.--Specialty Brands, San Francisco, CA; *Int'l*, pg. 237
Watts, Samuel J., V.P.-Customer Service & Sls.--Atlantic Southeast Airlines Inc., Atlanta, GA; *U.S. Public*, pg. 144
Way, Bill, Dir.-Mktg.--Network Systems Corporation, Minneapolis, MN; *U.S. Public*, pg. 1522
Wayland, Ken, Gen. Sls. Mgr.--WRVA-AM, Richmond, VA; *U.S. Public*, pg. 385
Wayman, Craig, V.P. & Mgr.-Natl. Sls.-Prentice Hall School--Secondary Division, Upper Saddle River, NJ; *U.S. Private*, pg. 778
Wayne, John, V.P.-Retail Sls.--Armstrong World Industries, Inc., Lancaster, PA; *U.S. Public*, pg. 131
Wayne, Michael, Dir.-Sls. & Mktg.--Pool Energy Services Co., Houston, TX; *U.S. Public*, pg. 1316
Wayworm, Russ, V.P.-Sls.--Robot Research, Inc., San Diego, CA; *U.S. Public*, pg. 1457
Weales, Randall, V.P.-Sls.--Kimball Electronics Group, Jasper, IN; *U.S. Public*, pg. 957
Weary, Brent, V.P.-Sls. & Mktg.--Rentway Inc., Etobicoke, Canada; *Int'l*, pg. 1424
Weatherford, Timothy, Exec. V.P.-Sls.--SofTECH, Inc., Grand Rapids, MI; *U.S. Public*, pg. 1482
Weaver, Chris, Sls. Mgr.--Capital American Finance, Cleveland, OH; *U.S. Public*, pg. 433
Weaver, Donald, V.P.-Sls.--Edward Don & Company-Dallas Branch, Carrollton, TX; *U.S. Private*, pg. 339
Weaver, Mike, Mgr-Sls.--U.N. Alloy Steel Div., Buena Park, CA; *Int'l*, pg. 1001
Weaver, Morten G., V.P.-Pacific Rim Sls.--CBT Systems USA Ltd., Menlo Park, CA; *U.S. Public*, pg. 275
Weaver, Richard, Sls. Mgr.--Pacific Foods, Inc., Kent, WA; *U.S. Private*, pg. 831
Weaver, Robert, V.P.-Sls. & Key Accts.--Windmere-Durable Holdings, Hialeah, FL; *U.S. Public*, pg. 1771
Weaver, Sam, Jr., V.P.-Sls.--Chevy Chase Cars & Geo, Bethesda, MD; *U.S. Private*, pg. 234
Weaver, Scott, V.P.-Sls.--BTG, Inc., Fairfax, VA; *U.S. Public*, pg. 164
Weaver, Tom, V.P.-Sls.--Roman Meal Company, Tacoma, WA; *U.S. Private*, pg. 942
Weba, Richard S., Dr., Dir.-Sls. & Mktg.--Electro-Science Laboratories, Inc., King of Prussia, PA; *U.S. Private*, pg. 369
Webb, Don, V.P.-Sls. & Mktg.--Central Transport, Archdale, NC; *U.S. Private*, pg. 225
Webb, Ian, Dir.-Sls. & Mktg.--Fermec Holdings, Ltd., Manchester, United Kingdom; *U.S. Public*, pg. 312
Webb, J.F., V.P.-Sls. & Mktg.--Jaguar Canada Inc., Bramalea, Canada; *U.S. Public*, pg. 667
Webb, Jon, Dir.-North American Sls.--Rainbow Technologies, Inc., Irvine, CA; *U.S. Public*, pg. 1359
Webb, Leah, Dir.-Sls.--Foster Wheeler Environmental Corporation, Livingston, NJ; *U.S. Public*, pg. 677
Webb, Robert, V.P.-Sls. & Mktg.--Saunders Brothers, Westbrook, ME; *U.S. Private*, pg. 968
Webb, Warren, V.P.-Sls. & Mktg.--Tri-State Armature & Electric Works, Memphis, TN; *U.S. Private*, pg. 1100
Webb, William J., Exec. V.P.-Global Sls. & Svcs.--Picker International, Inc., Cleveland, OH; *Int'l*, pg. 545
Webber, Milton C., Gen. Sls. Mgr.--Hapco/American Div., Abingdon, VA; *U.S. Private*, pg. 351
Webber, Sandy, V.P.-Sls. & Mktg.--Watsco, Inc., Coconut Grove, FL; *U.S. Public*, pg. 1745
Weber, Barbara, Dir.-Mktg. & Sls.--El Paso Energy, Houston, TX; *U.S. Public*, pg. 567
Weber, Bill, Mgr.-Sls.--Interstate Payco Seed Company, West Fargo, ND; *U.S. Private*, pg. 573
Weber, Dick H., V.P.-Sls. & Mktg.--Doane Products Co., Branded Sales Div., Joplin, MO; *U.S. Private*, pg. 337
Weber, Ernie, Dir.-Sls.--National Manufacturing Co., Mendota, IL; *U.S. Private*, pg. 860
Weber, John, Dir.-N. American Sls.--Vernay Laboratories, Inc., Yellow Springs, OH; *U.S. Private*, pg. 1137
Weber, Joseph D., V.P.-Sls.--Burdick, Inc., Milton, WI; *U.S. Private*, pg. 181
Weber, Susan, Dir.-Sls.--The London Free Press, London, Canada; *Int'l*, pg. 1320
Webster, George, Sr. V.P.-Sls.--Sterner Lighting Systems Incorporated, Eden Prairie, MN; *U.S. Private*, pg. 1042
Webster, Jack, V.P.-Sls.--Coty Inc., New York, NY; *Int'l*, pg. 185
Wechsler, Peter, Mgr.-Sls.--The Paper House/Southern Paper, Miami, FL; *U.S. Private*, pg. 467
Wedell, Mark, Dir.-U.S. Sls.--Dorner Manufacturing Corp., Hartland, WI; *U.S. Private*, pg. 340
Wedge, Michael T., Exec. V.P.-Sls. Opers.--BJ's Wholesale Club, Inc., Natick, MA; *U.S. Public*, pg. 162
Wee, Alvin, Mgr.-Sls.--United Pulp & Paper Company Limited, Jurong, Singapore; *Int'l*, pg. 1444
Wee, Sandy, Gen. Mgr.-Sls.-Used Car Div.--Champion Motors (1975) Pte. Ltd., Singapore, Singapore; *Int'l*, pg. 672
Weed, Andrew, Mgr.-Gen. Sls.--Tension Envelope Corp., Kansas City, MO; *U.S. Private*, pg. 1077
Weeks, C. Wallace, V.P.-Sls.--DHP Limited Partnership, Chicopee, MA; *U.S. Private*, pg. 302
Weeks, James, V.P.-Domestic Sls.--Penreco, Karns City, PA; *U.S. Public*, pg. 1273
Weeks, Mike, Mgr.-Sls.--Subaru of America Southeast Region, Austell, GA; *Int'l*, pg. 523
Weeks, Richard S., V.P.-Sls. & Mktg.--Automax, Inc., Cincinnati, OH; *U.S. Public*, pg. 658
Weeks, Robert, V.P.-Sls. & Mktg.--Battenfeld Gloucester Engineering Co. Inc., Gloucester, MA; *U.S. Private*, pg. 123
Wegelius, Curt, V.P.-Sls.--Roosevelt Paper Co., Philadelphia, PA; *U.S. Private*, pg. 943
Weggeland, Ed M., V.P.-Sls. & Mktg.--Richmond Technology Inc., Redlands, CA; *U.S. Private*, pg. 929
Wegher, Mary Beth, Mgr.-Circulation--Business Journal Publications, Inc., Phoenix, AZ; *U.S. Private*, pg. 19
Wehrle, S.D., Sr. V.P.-Sls.--McJunkin Corporation, Charleston, WV; *U.S. Private*, pg. 722
Wehrly, James, V.P.-Sls. & Mktg.--The School Division, Menlo Park, CA; *Int'l*, pg. 1026
Weibel, Diana, Dir.-Export--Weibel Winery, Lodi, CA; *U.S. Private*, pg. 1159
Weibler, Klaus P., Mng. Dir.-Gentex GmbH--Gentex Corporation, Zeeland, MI; *U.S. Public*, pg. 731
Weiden, Michael, Pres.-Adv. Sls.--All American Television, Inc., New York, NY; *U.S. Public*, pg. 41
Weidman, Bill K., Dir.-Mktg. & Sls.--Kentucky-Tennessee Clay Co., Mayfield, KY; *U.S. Public*, pg. 804
Weigel, Mark, V.P.-Sls. & Mktg.--Perry's Ice Cream Co., Inc., Akron, NY; *U.S. Private*, pg. 855
Weigle, Peggy, V.P.-N. America Sls.--Arbor Software Corporation, Sunnyvale, CA; *U.S. Public*, pg. 127
Weihe, Gary, Dir.-Micro Products--Sheldahl, Inc., Northfield, MN; *U.S. Public*, pg. 1465
Weiland, William, V.P.--Carter Chambers Supply, Inc., Baton Rouge, LA; *U.S. Private*, pg. 216
Weill, Sheldon, V.P.-Mktg. & Sls.--Universal Folding Box Company, Inc., Hoboken, NJ; *U.S. Private*, pg. 1127
Weimer, Lynnette, Mgr.-Mktg. & Sls.--Group Dekko, Kendallville, IN; *U.S. Private*, pg. 484
Weinberg, Joseph, V.P.-Sls./Household Prods. Div.--Block Drug Company, Inc., Jersey City, NJ; *U.S. Public*, pg. 236
Weinberg, Keith, Mgr.-Inside Sls.--Advanced Logic Research, Inc., Irvine, CA; *U.S. Public*, pg. 703
Weiner, Martin S., V.P.-Sls.--Sanitary-Dash Manufacturing Co., Inc., North Grosvenordale, CT; *U.S. Public*, pg. 1795
Weiner, Sonny, Dir.-Retail Sls.--Balson-Hercules Ltd., New York, NY; *Int'l*, pg. 326
Weingartner, Ronald, Dir.-Sls.--Schroff, Straubenhardt, Germany; *U.S. Public*, pg. 1274
Weinstein, Cherie, V.P.-Grp. Sls.--Carnival Corporation, Miami, FL; *U.S. Public*, pg. 306
Weinstock, Donna, Dir.-Distr. Sls.--Hydrite Chemical Company, Brookfield, WI; *U.S. Private*, pg. 551
Weir, Anthony, Mgr.-Reg. Sls. West--WINCO, Le Center, MN; *U.S. Private*, pg. 350
Weirback, Terry, Mgr.-Sls. & Mktg.--Perkasie Industries Corporation, Perkasie, PA; *U.S. Private*, pg. 854
Weisbruck, Craig, V.P.-Sls. & Mktg.--National Gypsum Company, Charlotte, NC; *Int'l*, pg. 790
Weiser, John, Sr. V.P.-West Coast Adv. & Sls.--The Guber Peters Entertainment Company, Los Angeles, CA; *Int'l*, pg. 1283
Weisfeld, Marty, Exec. V.P. & Mgr.-Promo Sls.--MUDD Jeans, Inc., New York, NY; *U.S. Private*, pg. 766
Weiskircher, James, V.P.-Retail Sls.--Briggs Industries, Inc., Tampa, FL; *U.S. Private*, pg. 168
Weisman, Gary, Natl. Sls. Mgr.--Fire King International, Inc., New Albany, IN; *U.S. Private*, pg. 406
Weiss, Anthony A., Sr. V.P.-Direct Sls.--CompUSA, Dallas, TX; *U.S. Public*, pg. 420
Weiss, Ed, Mgr.-Natl. Sls.--Emerson Radio Corp., Parsippany, NJ; *U.S. Public*, pg. 578
Weiss, Frank, V.P.-Sls.--Prime Cast, Inc., South Beloit, IL; *U.S. Public*, pg. 142
Weiss, Jonathan, V.P.-Sls.--Oxford University Press, Inc., New York, NY; *Int'l*, pg. 1019
Weiss, Lenny, Natl. Sls. Mgr.--Rosenthal U.S.A. Limited, Carlstadt, NJ; *Int'l*, pg. 1127
Weiss, Martin, Sr. Exec. V.P.-Sls.--Bestform Foundations, Inc., Long Island City, NY; *U.S. Private*, pg. 140
Weiss, Martin, Sr. Exec. V.P.-Sls.--Lily of France, Inc., New York, NY; *U.S. Private*, pg. 140
Weissler, Mindy, Dir.-Mktg.--Advertising Checking Bureau Incorporated, New York, NY; *U.S. Private*, pg. 23
Weisz, Stephen P., Sr. V.P.-Lodging Brands--Marriott Hotels, Resorts, and Suites, Washington, DC; *U.S. Public*, pg. 1048
Weitl, Jim, Dir.-Mktg. & Sls.--Superior Bank, Chicago, IL; *U.S. Private*, pg. 1054
Weitzen, Stephen, V.P.-Sls.--Modern Publishing, New York, NY; *U.S. Private*, pg. 1120
Welch, Charles, Mgr.-Sls.--Bates Container, Inc., North Richland Hills, TX; *U.S. Private*, pg. 122
Welcome, Craig, Mgr.-Opers.--CB North America, Inc., Saratoga Springs, NY; *U.S. Private*, pg. 192
Welcome, Craig, Mgr.-Opers.--CB Sports Inc., Saratoga Springs, NY; *U.S. Private*, pg. 192
Weldy, Owen, V.P.-Sls.--Synergis Technologies Group, Grand Rapids, MI; *U.S. Private*, pg. 1060
Welfelt, Dave, Dir.-Sls. & Mktg.--Excel Industries, Inc., Hesston, KS; *U.S. Private*, pg. 387
Welk, Tom, Dir.-Sls. & Mktg.--Lyke Corporation, Ripon, WI; *U.S. Private*, pg. 682
Wellan, Wayne, V.P.-Indus. Sls.--Carter Day International, Inc., Minneapolis, MN; *U.S. Private*, pg. 217
Weller, Ken, Sr. V.P.-Sls.--Best Buy Co., Inc., Eden Prairie, MN; *U.S. Public*, pg. 223
Weller, Peter, V.P.-Sls.--H.E. Williams, Inc., Carthage, MO; *U.S. Private*, pg. 1178
Wells, Betty, Mgr.-Prod. Sls.--S.T. Research, Newington, VA; *U.S. Private*, pg. 958
Wells, Dave, Mgr.-Sls.--Schutte Lumber Company, Kansas City, MO; *U.S. Private*, pg. 973
Wells, Ellyn, Mgr.-Sls. Promo.--Dillard, A ResourceNet International Company, Greenville, SC; *U.S. Public*, pg. 902
Wells, John, Dir.-Sls. & Mktg.--The Bakersfield Californian, Bakersfield, CA; *U.S. Private*, pg. 112
Wells, Jonathan, Mgr.-Sls.--Omega Environmental Services, Lorton, VA; *U.S. Public*, pg. 1222
Wells, Michael D., V.P.-Sls.--Bondex Intl., Inc., Saint Louis, MO; *U.S. Public*, pg. 1357
Wells, R., Mgr.-Sls.--Kodak Limited-Chemical Division, Liverpool, United Kingdom; *U.S. Public*, pg. 553
Wells, Richard, V.P.-Sls.--Hardaway Concrete Co., Inc., Columbia, SC; *U.S. Private*, pg. 501
Wells, William, Mgr.-Sls.--Mastergear Division, Roscoe, IL; *U.S. Public*, pg. 1370
Welman, Bill, V.P.-Sls.--Brawny Plastics West, Santa Ana, CA; *U.S. Private*, pg. 166
Welsh, Dennis, Gen. Sls. Mgr.--WPMI-TV, Mobile, AL; *U.S. Public*, pg. 385
Welsh, Francis John, Mgr.-Sls.--Apache Plastics, L.P., Lodi, CA; *U.S. Private*, pg. 77
Welsh, John, V.P.-Sls.--USLD Communications Corp., San Antonio, TX; *U.S. Public*, pg. 969
Wemms, Michael, Dir.-Retail--Tesco PLC, Cheshunt, United Kingdom; *Int'l*, pg. 1376
Wender, Sam, Dir.-Adv.--Crain's New York Business, New York, NY; *U.S. Private*, pg. 285
Wenderlich, Raymond L., Mgr.-Energy Sls. & Service--Baltimore Gas and Electric Company, Baltimore, MD; *U.S. Public*, pg. 172
Wendorf, Kathy, Mgr.-Sls. & Mktg.--Wausau Metals, Nanik Division, Wausau, WI; *U.S. Public*, pg. 1500
Weng, Simon, Exec. V.P.-Sls., Asia--Tippins Incorporated, Pittsburgh, PA; *U.S. Private*, pg. 1088
Wenig, Raymond, V.P.-Sls.--The National Super Service Co., Toledo, OH; *U.S. Private*, pg. 787
Wenlock, J.P., Mgr.-Sls.--Britax Puericulture S.A.R.L., Vulaines-sur-Seine, France; *Int'l*, pg. 216
Wenner, Bill, Mgr.-Sls.--Haveg Div., Wilmington, DE; *U.S. Public*, pg. 100
Wentura, Mark, V.P.-Sls.--Buck Knives, Inc., El Cajon, CA; *U.S. Private*, pg. 177
Wenz, George A., V.P.-Sls./Natl. Accts.--American Greetings Corporation, Cleveland, OH; *U.S. Public*, pg. 77
Wenz, George A., V.P.-Sls.-Natl. Accts.--American Greetings U.S. Greeting Card Division, Cleveland, OH; *U.S. Public*, pg. 78
Werbrouck, Eric, Sls. Dir.--Berlitz Schools of Languages of Benelux S.A., Brussels, Belgium; *U.S. Public*, pg. 222
Werner, Gary, Mktg. Sls. Mgr.--Chief Industries - Buildings Div., Grand Island, NE; *U.S. Private*, pg. 236
Werner, George F., Sr. V.P.-Sls.--Damascus Bishop Tube Co., Greenville, PA; *Int'l*, pg. 842
Werner, Lloyd, Sr. V.P.-Sls. & Mktg.--Group W Satellite Communications, Stamford, CT; *U.S. Public*, pg. 275

Werner, Tom, V.P.-Mktg. & Sls.--Commonwealth Industries, Inc., Louisville, KY; *U.S. Public*, pg. 415
Wert, James W., Jr., V.P.-Mktg.--Mead Coated Board, Atlanta, GA; *U.S. Public*, pg. 1074
Wertheimer, C.M., Mgr.-Sls.--Longview Fibre Co. Western Container Div., Oakland, CA; *U.S. Public*, pg. 1014
Werwick, Pete, Dir.-Mktg. & Sls.--McCauley Propeller Systems, Vandalia, OH; *U.S. Public*, pg. 1589
Wesley, Charles, V.P.-Sls. & Mktg.--Hyer Industries Inc./ Thayer Scale, Pembroke, MA; *U.S. Private*, pg. 552
Wessel, Dan, Reg. Sls. Dir.--Comverse Network Systems, Reston, VA; *U.S. Public*, pg. 425
Wessel, Jeffrey W., Mgr.-Sls. & Mktg.--Weiss Scientific Glass Blowing Co., Inc., Portland, OR; *Int'l*, pg. 1408
West, A. Stanley, Sr. V.P.-Sls.--Cleveland-Cliffs Inc, Cleveland, OH; *U.S. Public*, pg. 386
West, A.S., Sr. V.P.-Sls.--The Cleveland-Cliffs Iron Company, Cleveland, OH; *U.S. Public*, pg. 386
West, Barn, Dir.-Sls.--Pharmacia & Upjohn Inter-American Corporation, Auckland, New Zealand; *Int'l*, pg. 1048
West, Charles H., Pres.--Delagra Corporation, Bridgeville, DE; *U.S. Private*, pg. 321
West, Dennis, Dir.-Sls.--The Knight Publishing Co., Charlotte, NC; *U.S. Public*, pg. 964
West, G., V.P.-Sls.--Orval Kent Food Co., Wheeling, IL; *U.S. Private*, pg. 820
West, J.R., V.P.-Sls.--S & C Electric Company, Chicago, IL; *U.S. Private*, pg. 954
West, J.S., Dir.-Sls. & Mktg.-Consumer Prods.--Becton Dickinson Canada Inc., Mississauga, Canada; *U.S. Public*, pg. 200
West, John R., Mgr.-Sls.-Aftermarket--Cole Hersee Company, Boston, MA; *U.S. Private*, pg. 251
West, Lawrence, V.P.-Sls., Processed Fruit--Snokist Growers, Yakima, WA; *U.S. Private*, pg. 1011
West, Lynda, Coord.-Sls. & Mktg.--Exolon-Esk Company, Tonawanda, NY; *U.S. Public*, pg. 600
West, Steve, Mgr.-Sls.--SL Montevideo Technology, Inc., Montevideo, MN; *U.S. Public*, pg. 1419
West, W. Casey, V.P.-Sls. & Mktg.--Stanchem Inc., East Berlin, CT; *U.S. Private*, pg. 1030
Westbrook, Mark, Mgr.-Mktg. & Sls.--Proto Systems of Atlanta, Alpharetta, GA; *U.S. Private*, pg. 891
Wester, Bob, Pres.--WEN Products, Inc., Bensenville, IL; *U.S. Private*, pg. 1144
Westerberg, Jacqueline, V.P.-Sls. & Mktg.--JRC Canida, Inc., Fort Worth, TX; *U.S. Private*, pg. 578
Westhoff, Andy, V.P.-Natl. Sls.--B.B. Walker Company, Asheboro, NC; *U.S. Public*, pg. 1734
Westland, Hans, V.P.-Mdsg. & Sls.--Robert Scott/David Brooks, Dedham, MA; *U.S. Public*, pg. 948
Westland, Scott, Dir.-Intl. Sls.--Shur-Lok Corporation, Irvine, CA; *U.S. Private*, pg. 997
Westmoreland, K.W., Mgr.-Sls.--Rigby Metal Components Limited, Cleckheaton, United Kingdom; *Int'l*, pg. 891
Westphal, Kenneth, V.P.-Bldg. Sys. Svcs. Grp.--Air Conditioning Co., Inc., Glendale, CA; *U.S. Private*, pg. 28
Westring, P., V.P.-Intl. Sls.--Fuller Company, Bethlehem, PA; *Int'l*, pg. 475
Wetherton, Norman C., V.P.-Special Sls.--Rose Packing Company, Barrington, IL; *U.S. Private*, pg. 945
Wetterauer, Michael, Sr. V.P.-Sls. & Mktg.--Case-Swayne Co. Inc., Corona, CA; *U.S. Private*, pg. 218
Wetton, Scott, Mgr.-Sls.--E & E Steel, Inc., Los Angeles, CA; *U.S. Private*, pg. 941
Weum, Ragnar, Mgr. Sls.--Kaldnes Industri A/S, Tonsberg, Norway; *Int'l*, pg. 965
Weyers, Larry, Dir.-Sls.--Woods Equipment Company, Oregon, IL; *U.S. Private*, pg. 249
Wharnsby, William J., V.P.-Sls. & Mktg.--Waterloo Furniture Components Limited, Kitchener, Canada; *U.S. Private*, pg. 270
Wheatley, Terry, V.P.-Sls. West--Sutter Home Winery, Inc., Saint Helena, CA; *U.S. Private*, pg. 1057
Wheaton, Art, V.P.-Mktg. & Sls.--Remington Arms Company, Inc., Madison, NC; *U.S. Private*, pg. 921
Wheaton, Robert, Sr. V.P.-Sls.--Wind River Systems, Inc., Alameda, CA; *U.S. Public*, pg. 1770
Wheeler, Dave, Asst. Sls. Mgr.--Rhodes International, Inc., Salt Lake City, UT; *U.S. Private*, pg. 927
Wheeler, Dianne, Sales Dir.--Passport Books, Lincolnwood, IL; *U.S. Public*, pg. 1636
Wheeler, G., Dir.-Sls. & Mktg.--Salford Electrical Instruments Ltd., Heywood, United Kingdom; *Int'l*, pg. 545
Wheeler, Jon, Mgr.-Sls.--Eagle Iron Works, Des Moines, IA; *U.S. Private*, pg. 354
Wheeler, Ken, Natl. Accts. Mgr.--Master Craft Corp., Kalamazoo, MI; *Int'l*, pg. 267
Wheelwright, Bart, Mgr.-Sls./Containerboard--Boise Cascade Corporation, Boise, ID; *U.S. Public*, pg. 242
Wherry, Ken A., Sr. V.P.-Customer Satisfaction & Sls.--Eddie Bauer, Inc., Redmond, WA; *U.S. Public*, pg. 1499
Whetter, M., V.P.-Aftermarket Sls.--Trico Products Corporation, Buffalo, NY; *Int'l*, pg. 1397
Whipple, Charles, V.P.-Sls. & Mktg.--The Chicago Faucet Co., Des Plaines, IL; *U.S. Private*, pg. 234
Whipple, Dennis, V.P.-Chemical Sls.--Ideal Chemical & Supply Company, Memphis, TN; *U.S. Private*, pg. 557
Whisler, Robert, V.P.-Sls.--Kyocera America, Inc., San Diego, CA; *Int'l*, pg. 775
Whitacre, R. Gregory, V.P.-College & University Prods.--SLM Holding Corp., Washington, DC; *U.S. Public*, pg. 1419
Whitaker, Charles, V.P.-Sls.--Fox River Paper Company, Appleton, WI; *U.S. Private*, pg. 422
Whitaker, Ken, V.P.-Sls.--Kimberly-Clark Inc., Mississauga, Canada; *U.S. Public*, pg. 959
Whitbeck, Earl, Dir.-Sls.--Ginsberg's Institutional Foods, Inc., Hudson, NY; *U.S. Private*, pg. 455
White, Dale, Mgr.-Natl. Sls.--Capsonic Group, Inc., Elgin, IL; *U.S. Private*, pg. 207
White, David, V.P.-Sls.--The HON Co., Muscatine, IA; *U.S. Public*, pg. 772
White, Don, V.P.-Worldwide Sls.--J.D. Edwards & Company, Denver, CO; *U.S. Private*, pg. 365
White, Frank, Sr. V.P.-Sls.--First Commercial Bank, N.A., Little Rock, AR; *U.S. Public*, pg. 630
White, Frank, V.P.-Sls.--Multiplex Technology, Inc., Brea, CA; *U.S. Public*, pg. 1705
White, Garrett, V.P. & Dir.-Sls. & Mktg. Services--Houghton Mifflin College Div., Boston, MA; *U.S. Public*, pg. 841
White, Gary D., Grp. V.P.--Builder Marts of America, Inc., Greenville, SC; *U.S. Private*, pg. 179
White, Gordon, V.P.-Sls.--Cogsdill Tool Products, Inc., Lugoff, SC; *U.S. Private*, pg. 250
White, James, Dir.-Sls.--O.S. Walker Co. Inc., Worcester, MA; *U.S. Private*, pg. 1147
White, James D., Mgr.-Mountain Reg. Sls.--Purina Grocery Products Group, Saint Louis, MO; *U.S. Public*, pg. 1360
White, James L., Dir.-N. American Sls.--Brown & Sharpe Manufacturing Company, North Kingstown, RI; *U.S. Public*, pg. 260
White, James L., North American Mgr.-Sls. & Metrology Srvcs.--Measuring Systems Division, North Kingstown, RI; *U.S. Public*, pg. 260
White, Jeffrey W., V.P.-Sls.--Oceaneering Multiflex, Magnolia, TX; *U.S. Public*, pg. 1211
White, John, V.P.-Sls. & Mktg.-EP--AAF-International, Louisville, KY; *U.S. Private*, pg. 3
White, Ken, Dir.-Sls.--MJB Rice Company, Union City, CA; *Int'l*, pg. 917
White, M., Dir.-Sls.--T.H.E., Newcastle under Lyme, United Kingdom; *Int'l*, pg. 707
White, Marc, Dir.-Adv.--Electronic Media, Chicago, IL; *U.S. Private*, pg. 285
White, Mark, Mgr.-Sls.--Mobil Mining & Minerals Company, Ashland, VA; *U.S. Public*, pg. 1118
White, Matthew, V.P.-Sls.--Thybony Wall Coverings Co., Chicago, IL; *U.S. Private*, pg. 1084
White, Peter, Dir.-Sls.--British Airways PLC, London, United Kingdom; *Int'l*, pg. 218
White, Robert A., Gen. Mgr.-Sls.-SDP--Galileo Corp., Sturbridge, MA; *U.S. Public*, pg. 698
White, Stephen, Dir.-Sls. & Mktg.--First National Mortgage Corporation, Glen Burnie, MD; *Int'l*, pg. 64
White, Steve, Dir.-Sls. & Mktg.--American Speedy Printing Centers, Inc., Troy, MI; *U.S. Private*, pg. 62
White, Thomas G., V.P.-Natl. Accounts--Starter Corp., New Haven, CT; *U.S. Public*, pg. 1511
White, Vern, V.P.-Sls. & Mktg.--Wenger Corporation, Owatonna, MN; *U.S. Private*, pg. 1162
White, Wanda, V.P.-Retail Sls.--American Drug Stores Inc., Oak Brook, IL; *U.S. Public*, pg. 93
Whitehouse, Bevi, Dir.-Sls.--Paisano Publications, Inc,, Agoura, CA; *U.S. Private*, pg. 834
Whitehurst, William, Dir.-Mktg. & Sls.--Pac-Fab, Inc./East, Sanford, NC; *U.S. Public*, pg. 593
Whiteley, A.C., Mgr.-Sls.--Turner Construction Company, Raleigh, NC; *U.S. Public*, pg. 1646
Whiteman, Derek, V.P.-Intl. Sls. & Mktg.--Christie Design, Chatsworth, CA; *U.S. Public*, pg. 1369
Whiteman, John F., V.P.-Sls. & Mktg.--Sentry Technology Corp., Hauppauge, NY; *U.S. Public*, pg. 1458
Whitesell, Terry, Exec. V.P.-Sls. & Mktg.--Carpenter Industries, Inc., Richmond, IN; *U.S. Private*, pg. 215
Whiting, Lawson, Sr. V.P.-Sls.--Asko, Inc, Homestead, PA; *U.S. Private*, pg. 89
Whitley, Mike, V.P.-Sls.--D.P. Fitness, Opelika, AL; *U.S. Public*, pg. 1354
Whitley, Steve A., Sr. V.P.-Retail Banking--Virginia First Savings Bank, F.S.B., Petersburg, VA; *U.S. Public*, pg. 1721
Whitmer, Becky, Engr.-Sls.--Baum USA, Sidney, OH; *Int'l*, pg. 1293
Whitney, Fred, V.P.-Indus. Div.--Tesa Tuck Inc., Sparta, MI; *Int'l*, pg. 182
Whitney, Jim, V.P.-Sls. & Mktg.--Educational Insights, Inc., Carson, CA; *U.S. Public*, pg. 565
Whitt, John R., Sr. V.P.-Mktg., Sls. & Sec.--Sherman & Reilly, Inc., Chattanooga, TN; *U.S. Private*, pg. 993
Whitted, Donald R., V.P.-Sls.-Central Reg.--Goody's Family Clothing, Inc., Knoxville, TN; *U.S. Public*, pg. 753
Whittington, Jeff, Mgr.-Sls.--Flex-O-Glass, Inc., Chicago, IL; *U.S. Private*, pg. 412
Whitwam, D., Dir.-Sls. & Mktg.--British Mohair Spinners Limited, Bradford, United Kingdom; *Int'l*, pg. 219
Wichmann, Hans, Mgr.-Mktg.--Uniroyal Englebert Reifen GmbH, Aachen, Germany; *Int'l*, pg. 327
Wichmann, Robert, V.P.-N. American Seed Sls.--Pioneer Hi-Bred International, Inc., Des Moines, IA; *U.S. Public*, pg. 1298
Wicker, Barry, Exec. V.P.-Sls. & Mktg.--Vital Signs, Inc., Totowa, NJ; *U.S. Public*, pg. 1723
Wickham, Claudia, Mgr.-Local Sls.--WESH Television, Inc., Winter Park, FL; *U.S. Public*, pg. 1344
Wicks, D.J., Dir.-Sls.--Rolls-Royce-Commercial Aero Engines Ltd., Derby, United Kingdom; *Int'l*, pg. 1127
Wicks, Sidney, V.P.-Publ. Sls.--John D. Lucas Printing Company, Baltimore, MD; *U.S. Private*, pg. 253
Wickstrom, Wayne R., V.P. & Dir.-Mktg. & Sls./Furniture & Intl. Export Components--Leggett & Platt, Incorporated, Carthage, MO; *U.S. Public*, pg. 985
Wida, Thomas, V.P.-Sls.--Pharmacia & Upjohn Biotech Inc., Piscataway, NJ; *Int'l*, pg. 1047
Widerkehr, R.L., V.P.-Vet. Sls. & Mktg.--SmithKline Beecham Laboratories, Bristol, TN; *Int'l*, pg. 1264
Widgodsky, John, Exec. V.P.-Sls. & Mktg.--Fruit of the Loom, Inc., Chicago, IL; *U.S. Public*, pg. 685
Widmar, David, Mgr.-OEM Sls.--Electro-Voice, Inc., Buchanan, MI; *U.S. Private*, pg. 479
Wieble, Curtis, Mgr.-Sls.--PENCO-Nebraska, Omaha, NE; *Int'l*, pg. 1508
Wiebusch, Jerry, V.P.-Sls.--L & D Group, Aurora, IL; *U.S. Private*, pg. 638
Wiebusch, Jerry, V.P.-Sls.--Lyon Metal Products, Inc., Montgomery, IL; *U.S. Private*, pg. 638
Wiechman, Duane, V.P.-Admin.--Chance Rides, Inc., Wichita, KS; *U.S. Private*, pg. 228
Wiedenbeck, Ulrich, Sr. V.P.-South America Sls.--K-Tron America, Inc., Pitman, NJ; *U.S. Public*, pg. 938
Wiegand, John, Dir.-Sls.--PAC Manufacturing & Distributing Co., Winchester, VA; *U.S. Public*, pg. 1321
Wiehe, Bill, Sr. V.P.-Adv. Sls.--The Weather Channel, Atlanta, GA; *U.S. Private*, pg. 647
Wiela, Fred, Sr. V.P.-Sls. & Mktg.--Komag, Incorporated, San Jose, CA; *U.S. Public*, pg. 966
Wielgus, Wayne, V.P.-Worldwide Mktg. & Sls.--Best Western International, Inc., Phoenix, AZ; *U.S. Private*, pg. 140
Wielopolski, Mari Kroon, V.P.-Mktg. & Sls.--Awrey Bakeries, Inc., Livonia, MI; *U.S. Private*, pg. 103
Wienholz, Ken, V.P.-Sls & Mktg.--Bell-Carter Foods, Inc., Lafayette, CA; *U.S. Private*, pg. 131
Wiese, Jim, V.P.-Planning--International Comfort Products Corp., Lewisburg, TN; *U.S. Public*, pg. 898
Wiesemes, Kurt, V.P.-Mktg. & Sls.--Quality Packaging Products, Inc., Benton Harbor, MI; *U.S. Private*, pg. 899
Wiesmann, Patric, V.P.-Mktg. & Bus. Devel.--Mackie Designs, Inc., Woodinville, WA; *U.S. Public*, pg. 1030
Wigger, Tim, V.P.-Sls. & Mktg.--The Marley Cooling Tower Co., Overland Park, KS; *U.S. Public*, pg. 1676
Wiggerman, Dawn, Mgr.-Natl. Sls.--Sampler Publications Inc., Saint Charles, IL; *U.S. Private*, pg. 963
Wiggins, Ernie, Reg. Sls. Mgr.--Snyder Bakery, Yakima, WA; *U.S. Private*, pg. 1124
Wiggins, Lawrence, V.P.-Sls.--Tyco Toys, Inc., Mount Laurel, NJ; *U.S. Public*, pg. 1058
Wigodsky, John, Exec. V.P.-Mktg. & Sls.--Delta Apparel, Duluth, GA; *U.S. Public*, pg. 498
Wigodsky, John, Exec. V.P.-Mktg. & Sls.--Union Underwear Co., Inc., Bowling Green, KY; *U.S. Public*, pg. 686
Wiig, Jon J., V.P.-Sls.--Kalas Manufacturing, Inc., Denver, PA; *U.S. Private*, pg. 606
Wilbanks, Dale, Mgr.-Reg. Sls.--Meadow Steel Products, Tampa, FL; *Int'l*, pg. 593
Wilbourn, Brooks, Sls. Exec.--Circle International, Nashville, TN; *U.S. Public*, pg. 371
Wilbur, Jim, Mgr.-F & I Sls.--Fairway Ford, Inc., Greenville, SC; *U.S. Private*, pg. 392
Wilbur, Steve, Dir.-Sls. & Mktg.--David Michael & Co. Inc., Philadelphia, PA; *U.S. Private*, pg. 740
Wilcott, Randolph L., Dir.-Sls.--The Greenbrier, White Sulphur Springs, WV; *U.S. Public*, pg. 284
Wilcox, Jim, V.P. & Gen. Sls. Mgr.--WALB-TV, Inc., Channel 10, Albany, GA; *U.S. Public*, pg. 759
Wildenberg, Michael, V.P.-Sls. & Mktg.--Bay West Paper Corp. Towel & Tissue Div., Middletown, OH; *U.S. Public*, pg. 1747
Wildenberg, Michael, V.P.-Sls. & Mktg.--Bay West Paper Corporation, Harrodsburg, KY; *U.S. Public*, pg. 1747
Wildy, Francis, Mgr.-Sls.--Process & Analytical Instruments Div., Pittsburgh, PA; *U.S. Public*, pg. 100
Wilen, Tom V., Exec. V.P.-Worldwide Sls. & Mktg.--JBB Worldwide, Inc., Deerfield, IL; *U.S. Public*, pg. 675
Wilensky, Ron, V.P.-Bus. Devel.--TCI International Inc., Sunnyvale, CA; *U.S. Public*, pg. 1555
Wiley, Eric, Dir.-Capital Project Sls.--Ahlstrom Machinery, Glens Falls, NY; *Int'l*, pg. 34
Wiley, Marc, Dir.-Sls.--Gaymar Industries, Inc., Orchard Park, NY; *U.S. Private*, pg. 442
Wilhelm, Bob, Sr. V.P.-Sls. & Mktg.--Unitog Company, Kansas City, MO; *U.S. Public*, pg. 1693
Wilhelm, Charles, Mgr.-Sls.--Circon ACMI, Stamford, CT; *U.S. Public*, pg. 373
Wilhelm, Dick, Gen. Sls. Mgr.-West--Milwaukee Electric Tool Corp., Brookfield, WI; *Int'l*, pg. 96
Wilhelm, Steven, Mgr.-Mktg.--Woodcraft Industries, Inc., Saint Cloud, MN; *U.S. Private*, pg. 1187
Wilhide, Robert, V.P.-Sls./U.S. Grocery--The Quaker Oats Company, Chicago, IL; *U.S. Public*, pg. 1347
Wilke, Jerry, V.P.-Sls., Worldwide Mkt. Devel.--Harley-Davidson, Inc., Milwaukee, WI; *U.S. Public*, pg. 786
Wilken, Jon, Exec. V.P.-Sls. & Mdsg.--BI-LO Inc., Greenville, SC; *Int'l*, pg. 749
Wilkerson, Mary, Gen. Mgr.-Sls.--Broadway Chevrolet, Louisville, KY; *U.S. Private*, pg. 170
Wilkes, Anthony, Dir. Sls.--Berlitz de Mexico, S.A. de C.V., Mexico, Mexico; *U.S. Public*, pg. 221
Wilkes, James C., II, Sr. V.P.-Carrier Sls.--MCI Communications Corp., Atlanta, GA; *U.S. Public*, pg. 1023
Wilkey, Ron, Dir.-Sls./Natl. Accts.--The Middleby Corporation, Rolling Meadows, IL; *U.S. Public*, pg. 1109
Wilkinlok, William C., V.P.-Sls. & Mktg.--Metal Container Corporation, Saint Louis, MO; *U.S. Public*, pg. 114
Wilkinson, Jerry, V.P.-Sls.-West--Coram Healthcare Corporation, Denver, CO; *U.S. Public*, pg. 446
Wilkinson, Vincent, Mgr.-Sls.--N.G. Bailey & Co. Ltd.-Sheffield Branch, Sheffield, United Kingdom; *Int'l*, pg. 132
Willard, Walt, V.P.-Sls.--ABF Freight System, Inc., Fort Smith, AR; *U.S. Public*, pg. 130
Willert, Phil, Mgr.-Sls.--SL Auburn, Inc., Auburn, NY; *U.S. Public*, pg. 443
Willes, Mark, V.P.-Retail Sls.--Tyson Foods, Inc., Springdale, AR; *U.S. Public*, pg. 1652
Willey, Glenn, V.P.-Sls.--Allfast Fastening Systems, Inc., City of Industry, CA; *U.S. Private*, pg. 37
Willey, John, V.P.--SL Surface Technology, Inc., Camden, NJ; *U.S. Public*, pg. 1419
Willey, Mark C., V.P.-Opers. & Mktg.--Atlantic Aviation Corp., New Castle, DE; *U.S. Private*, pg. 94
Williams, Al, Sls. Mgr.-Promo.--Frederick Trading Company, Frederick, MD; *U.S. Private*, pg. 335
Williams, Al, Mgr.-Outside Sls.--Jaco Electronics, Inc., San Jose, CA; *U.S. Public*, pg. 921
Williams, Ann, Mgr.-Mktg.--G.S. Blodgett Corporation, Burlington, VT; *U.S. Public*, pg. 1064
Williams, Ann, V.P.-Sls. & Mktg.--Tollman/Hundley Hotels, Hopewell Junction, NY; *U.S. Private*, pg. 1090

Williams, Bill, Dir.-Retail--J. Sainsbury plc, London, United Kingdom; *Int'l*, pg. 1169
Williams, Bob, V.P.-Sls. & Mktg.--G.D. Packaging Machinery Inc., Richmond, VA; *Int'l*, pg. 531
Williams, Brian J.G., Mgr.-Sls.--Coopers Payen Ltd., Slough, United Kingdom; *Int'l*, pg. 1334
Williams, C. Garrett, Dir.-Sls. & Mktg.--Dewey Square Investors Corporation, Boston, MA; *U.S. Public*, pg. 1673
Williams, C.D., Dir.-Sls.--Crowley Galvanizing Div., Crowley, TX; *U.S. Public*, pg. 159
Williams, Carol C., Natl. Dir.-Wholesale Sls.--Abingdon Press, Nashville, TN; *U.S. Private*, pg. 1123
Williams, Clark, V.P.-Sls./Contract--La-Z-Boy Incorporated, Monroe, MI; *U.S. Public*, pg. 972
Williams, Dan J., V.P.-Sls.--The Producto Machine Co., Bridgeport, CT; *U.S. Private*, pg. 889
Williams, Dan L., Mgr.-Canned Food Service Sls.--Dean Foods Vegetable Company, Green Bay, WI; *U.S. Public*, pg. 490
Williams, Daniel J., V.P.-Sls.--The Producto Machine Co., Bridgeport, CT; *U.S. Private*, pg. 889
Williams, Dave, V.P.-Sls.--Tranzonic Industrial Textiles Division, Highland Heights, OH; *U.S. Public*, pg. 1632
Williams, David B., V.P.-Sls./Gatorade U.S.--The Quaker Oats Company, Chicago, IL; *U.S. Public*, pg. 1347
Williams, Derek, Asst. Mgr.-Sls.--Rosco Manufacturing Co., Madison, SD; *U.S. Private*, pg. 944
Williams, Don, Dir.-Sls.--Hankins Lumber Company, Inc., Elliott, MS; *U.S. Private*, pg. 499
Williams, Doug, Mgr.-Natl. Sls.--Universal Fasteners Inc., Lawrenceburg, KY; *Int'l*, pg. 1515
Williams, E. Perkins, V.P.-Sls.--Benson's, Inc., Bogart, GA; *U.S. Private*, pg. 134
Williams, Frank M., V.P.-Central Sls. Reg.--SLM Holding Corp., Washington, DC; *U.S. Public*, pg. 1419
Williams, G., Dir.-Sls.--Kent Introl Ltd., Brighouse, United Kingdom; *Int'l*, pg. 7
Williams, George, Sr. V.P.-Sls.--Hayward Industries, Inc., Elizabeth, NJ; *U.S. Private*, pg. 513
Williams, J.M., V.P. & Dir.-Sls.--CHEMCENTRAL Corporation, Bedford Park, IL; *U.S. Private*, pg. 231
Williams, Joe, Mgr., Sls. & Personnel--T.K.G. International Corp., Macon, GA; *Int'l*, pg. 1349
Williams, Joe, Mgr.-Reg. Sls.--MedTrac, Inc., Atlanta, GA; *Int'l*, pg. 1504
Williams, Jon, Mgr.-Sls.--Energy Products, San Diego, CA; *U.S. Public*, pg. 1061
Williams, Jonas, Dir.-Mktg.--Adams Rite Sabre International, Glendale, CA; *U.S. Private*, pg. 1203
Williams, Lori, Admin.-Sls. & Mktg.--Eaton Corporation, Pressure Sensors Division, Bethel, CT; *U.S. Public*, pg. 557
Williams, Mark, Mgr.-Sls.--Spirol West, Corona, CA; *U.S. Private*, pg. 1026
Williams, Michael, Dir.-Sls.--Golf Host Resorts, Inc., Tarpon Springs, FL; *U.S. Private*, pg. 1036
Williams, Mike, Dir.-Mktg. & Sls.-ICI Paints--ICI Paints, Cleveland, OH; *Int'l*, pg. 663
Williams, Mike, Dir.-Mktg. & Sls-ICI Paints--Devoe Paint, Cleveland, OH; *Int'l*, pg. 663
Williams, Mike, Dir.-Sls. & Service--Varco (U.K.) Ltd. Drilling Systems, Montrose, United Kingdom; *U.S. Public*, pg. 1709
Williams, Phil, Mgr.-Intl. Sls.--George Koch Sons, Inc., Evansville, IN; *U.S. Private*, pg. 628
Williams, Richard, V.P.-Sls.--Fairfield Mountains, Lake Lure, NC; *U.S. Public*, pg. 610
Williams, Richard G., V.P.-Sls.--Lear Corporation, Rochester Hills, MI; *U.S. Public*, pg. 982
Williams, Rick, Mgr.-Sls., Softwoods--TreeSource, Inc., Portland, OR; *U.S. Public*, pg. 1729
Williams, Robert, Sr. V.P. & Mgr.-Natl. Sls.--Waddell & Reed, Inc., Shawnee Mission, KS; *U.S. Public*, pg. 1623
Williams, Roger D., Exec. V.P.-Mktg.-Food Products--Bob Evans Farms, Inc. Sausage Division, Columbus, OH; *U.S. Public*, pg. 596
Williams, Ross, Mgr.-Natl. Sls.--PTA Corporation, Oxford, CT; *U.S. Private*, pg. 828
Williams, Russ, Dir.-Sls.--Kraft Food Ingredients Corp., Memphis, TN; *U.S. Public*, pg. 1288
Williams, Sherman, Dir.-Sls.--Keithley Instruments, Inc., Cleveland, OH; *U.S. Public*, pg. 946
Williams, Stan, Mgr.-Sls.--Ain Plastics, Inc., Mount Vernon, NY; *Int'l*, pg. 1388
Williams, Stephen E., V.P.-Mktg. & Sls.--Indiana Gas Company, Inc., Indianapolis, IN; *U.S. Public*, pg. 875
Williams, Steve, V.P.-Mktg. & Sls.--Macklanburg-Duncan Co., Oklahoma City, OK; *U.S. Private*, pg. 692
Williams, Suzanne, V.P.-Sls. & Mktg.--Ventura Coastal Corporation, Ventura, CA; *U.S. Private*, pg. 1136
Williams, Ted, Reg. V.P.-Southeastern Sls.--American Freightways Corporation, Harrison, AR; *U.S. Public*, pg. 75
Williams, Woody, V.P.-Sls.--Clayton-Marcus Company, Inc., Hickory, NC; *U.S. Public*, pg. 975
Williams, Woody, V.P.-Sls.--Pennsylvania House Casegoods, Lewisburg, PA; *U.S. Public*, pg. 975
Williamson, David, V.P.-Sls., Office Prods. Div.--The At-A-Glance Group, Sidney, NY; *U.S. Private*, pg. 295
Williamson, James, V.P.-Sls.--CCX Fiberglass Products, Walterboro, SC; *U.S. Private*, pg. 193
Williamson, Robert J., Dir.-Sls.--Noland Company, Newport News, VA; *U.S. Public*, pg. 1187
Williford, Greg, V.P.-Sls. & Client Svcs.--Vitatech International, Inc., Tustin, CA; *U.S. Private*, pg. 1142
Willis, Greg, V.P. & Mgr.-Natl. Sls.--Lakeland Industries, Inc., Ronkonkoma, NY; *U.S. Public*, pg. 975
Willis, Mike, Dir.-Sls. & Mktg.-Indus.--Kappler Safety Group, Inc., Guntersville, AL; *U.S. Private*, pg. 607
Willis, S. Craig, V.P.-Intl. Sls. Div.--John Morrell & Co., Cincinnati, OH; *U.S. Public*, pg. 1479
Willison, Blake, V.P.-Sls. & Mktg.--Unitech Industries, Inc., Tempe, AZ; *U.S. Public*, pg. 1672
Willsea, Lou, V.P.-Sls. & Mktg.--Racke USA, Sonoma, CA; *Int'l*, pg. 1083
Willsea, Louis, V.P.-Sls. & Mktg.--Buena Vista Winery, Sonoma, CA; *Int'l*, pg. 1083
Willson, Barry, Gen. Mgr. & Dir.-Mktg., Adv. & Sls.--Eberline Instrument Corporation, Santa Fe, NM; *U.S. Public*, pg. 1593
Willumsen, Anne Kathrine, V.P.-Sls. & Mktg.--Fine Chemicals, Oslo, Norway; *U.S. Public*, pg. 58
Wilner, Jeff, V.P.-Sls. & Mktg.--Mr. Christmas Inc., New York, NY; *U.S. Private*, pg. 765
Wilson, A.H.R., Dir.-Sls. & Mktg.--Butler Newall Limited-Butler Machine Tool Div., Halifax, United Kingdom; *Int'l*, pg. 448
Wilson, Allan, V.P.-Sls. & Cust. Service--Western Data Systems, Calabasas, CA; *U.S. Private*, pg. 1165
Wilson, Bruce, Mgr.-Intl. Sls.--Utah Medical Products, Inc., Midvale, UT; *U.S. Public*, pg. 1700
Wilson, Bryan, Natl. Sls. Mgr.--Howe Furniture Corporation, Trumbull, CT; *U.S. Private*, pg. 543
Wilson, Charles L., Sr. V.P.-Natl. Accts. Sls.--Inland Container-Container Division, Indianapolis, IN; *U.S. Public*, pg. 1575
Wilson, Cheryl, V.P.-Sls.-Wedco--Wedco Technology, Bloomsbury, NJ; *U.S. Public*, pg. 854
Wilson, David G., Jr., Sr. V.P.-Sls. & Mktg--Cadmus Journal Services, Richmond, VA; *U.S. Public*, pg. 291
Wilson, Diane, Mgr.-Local Sls.--Fisher Broadcasting Inc., Seattle, WA; *U.S. Public*, pg. 648
Wilson, Don, Mng. Dir.--Totes Canada Ltd., Etobicoke, Canada; *U.S. Private*, pg. 111
Wilson, Don, V.P.-Sls. & Logistics--Ploof Truck Lines, Inc., Jacksonville, FL; *U.S. Private*, pg. 872
Wilson, Gary E., V.P.-Major Acct. Sls.--RAYOVAC Corporation, Madison, WI; *U.S. Private*, pg. 912
Wilson, Glen, V.P.-Sales--Kraft Canada Inc., Don Mills, Canada; *U.S. Public*, pg. 1288
Wilson, Jack W., II, V.P.-Cuisinarts Sls.--Conair Corporation, Stamford, CT; *U.S. Private*, pg. 261
Wilson, James D., Mgr.-Sls.--Lappin Electric Company, Waukesha, WI; *U.S. Private*, pg. 265
Wilson, James L., V.P.-Mktg. & Sales--First DataBank, San Bruno, CA; *U.S. Private*, pg. 515
Wilson, Jeffrey A., V.P.-Sls. & Mktg.--A.T. Massey Coal Company, Inc., Richmond, VA; *U.S. Public*, pg. 660
Wilson, John, Mgr.-Sls., Indus. Div.--Seymour of Sycamore, Inc., Sycamore, IL; *U.S. Private*, pg. 988
Wilson, John, Dir.-Sls. & Mktg.--IRPC Hinton Limited, Hinckley, United Kingdom; *Int'l*, pg. 1502
Wilson, John J., Mgr.-Area Sls.--Gensym Corporation, Southeast Area Office, Tucker, GA; *U.S. Public*, pg. 731
Wilson, Karin, Coord.-Sls. & Mktg.--Alra Laboratories, Inc., Gurnee, IL; *U.S. Private*, pg. 45
Wilson, Larry, V.P.-Sls. & Mktg./Canada--GSW Pump Company, Fergus, Canada; *Int'l*, pg. 538
Wilson, Larry, Mgr.-Sls.--National Machinery, Tiffin, OH; *U.S. Private*, pg. 785
Wilson, Linette, Adv. Sls. Asst.--Pfaudler, Inc., Rochester, NY; *U.S. Public*, pg. 1393
Wilson, Mike, Mgr.-Natl. Sls.--Carlisle Food Service Products, Oklahoma City, OK; *U.S. Public*, pg. 305
Wilson, Mike, Mgr.-Sls.--Splitfire, Inc., Northbrook, IL; *U.S. Private*, pg. 814
Wilson, Mike, CIM SBU Leader--Warn Industries, Inc., Clackamas, OR; *U.S. Private*, pg. 1150
Wilson, Olen, V.P.-Worldwide Opers.--International Shoe Machine Corp., Nashua, NH; *U.S. Private*, pg. 572
Wilson, P. Rodney, Exec. V.P.-Sls.--Potash Corporation of Saskatchewan Inc., Saskatoon, Canada; *Int'l*, pg. 1064
Wilson, Ray, Gen. Mgr.--Installation Products Div., Lancaster, PA; *U.S. Public*, pg. 132
Wilson, Rick, Mgr.-Sls.--Acme Tube Inc., Somerset, NJ; *U.S. Private*, pg. 14
Wilson, Scott, Gen. Sls. Mgr.--WALA-TV, Mobile, AL; *U.S. Public*, pg. 1685
Wilson, Steven A., Dir.-Sls, Mktg. & Adv.--Music Sales Corporation, New York, NY; *U.S. Private*, pg. 768
Wilson, Wayne, V.P.-Sls. & Mktg.-Georgia/Northlake--Georgia/Durango Boot Company, Franklin, TN; *U.S. Public*, pg. 1684
Wiltfong, Mike, Mgr.-Sls. & Applications--Swartwout Industries, Grandview, MO; *Int'l*, pg. 1398
Wiltshire, Michael, Natl. Sls. Mgr.-Retail--Quality Bakers Australia Ltd., Eastwood, Australia; *Int'l*, pg. 555
Wimbish, Schaffer B., Jr., V.P.-Sls.--Colonial Oil Industries, Savannah, GA; *U.S. Private*, pg. 253
Winch, David, V.P.-Sls. & Mktg.--The Minster Machine Company, Minster, OH; *U.S. Private*, pg. 751
Winder, Edwin C., Sr. V.P.-Sls.--Active Software, Inc., Santa Clara, CA; *U.S. Private*, pg. 15
Winder, Gary, Mgr.-Intl. Sls.--Russell Stover Candies, Inc., Kansas City, MO; *U.S. Private*, pg. 953
Windsor, Hugh, Mgr.-Sls. & Adv.--Thomas & Betts Corporation, Memphis, TN; *U.S. Public*, pg. 1597
Windsor, Hugh, Mgr.-Sls. & Adv.--Thomas & Betts Reznor Division, Memphis, TN; *U.S. Public*, pg. 1598
Windsor, Ray, Mgr.-Sls. & Mktg.--Fujitsu Ten Corp. of America, Torrance, CA; *Int'l*, pg. 526
Windt, Cathy, V.P.-Retail--Six Flags Theme Parks Inc., Parsippany, NJ; *U.S. Public*, pg. 1611
Wine, Melanie, Coord.-Sls. Promo.--WEN Products, Inc., Bensenville, IL; *U.S. Private*, pg. 1144
Winering, Bill, V.P.-Sls.-L.A.--Bergelectric Corporation, Los Angeles, CA; *U.S. Private*, pg. 135
Wing, Howard, V.P.-Sls.--Maxoptix Corp., Fremont, CA; *Int'l*, pg. 762
Winger, Jay, Mgr.-Sls.--Robbins, Inc., Cincinnati, OH; *U.S. Private*, pg. 934
Wingert, Mary, Mgr.-Adv.--Horsehead Resource Development Company, Inc., Palmerton, PA; *U.S. Private*, pg. 540
Winship, Syd, Mgr.-Sls.--N.G. Bailey & Co. Ltd.-Newcastle Branch, Newcastle upon Tyne, United Kingdom; *Int'l*, pg. 132
Winter, Randy, V.P.-Sls.--Sargento Foods Inc., Plymouth, WI; *U.S. Private*, pg. 966
Winterbottom, Warren, Sr. V.P.-Sls.-Americas--Bentley Systems, Inc., Exton, PA; *U.S. Private*, pg. 134
Winterle, Susan, Sls. Mgr.-Office Prods.--Brodart Company, Williamsport, PA; *U.S. Private*, pg. 170
Winters, G., Mgr.-Sls.--Hauck Manufacturing Company Inc., Lebanon, PA; *Int'l*, pg. 1149
Winters, Shaun, Gen. Mgr.-Sls. Admin.--Aiwa America, Inc., Mahwah, NJ; *Int'l*, pg. 1280
Winters, Thomas W., V.P.-Jack Product Sls.--Ausco Products, Inc., Benton Harbor, MI; *U.S. Private*, pg. 299
Wise, Marie, Mgr.-Sls.--Tosoh USA, Inc.-San Francisco Office, San Francisco, CA; *Int'l*, pg. 1407
Wise, Steve, Dir.-Sls.--Jillian's Entertainment Corporation, Boston, MA; *U.S. Private*, pg. 587
Wiseman, N.B., V.P.-Sls.--The NutraSweet Kelco Company, San Diego, CA; *U.S. Public*, pg. 1125
Wisinski, Tom, V.P.-Sls. & Mktg.--Interform Corporation, Bridgeville, PA; *U.S. Public*, pg. 333
Wiskur, Jim, Sr. V.P.-Corp. Sls.--Manufacturers Consolidation Service, Inc., Memphis, TN; *U.S. Private*, pg. 700
Wismer, Eli, V.P.-Sls.--Laserscope Surgical Systems, San Jose, CA; *U.S. Public*, pg. 979
Wiswasser, Kim, Mgr.-Export Sls.--Triplett Corporation, Bluffton, OH; *U.S. Private*, pg. 1104
Witcher, Alan, V.P.-Sls. & Mktg.--Star Fine Foods, Inc., Fresno, CA; *U.S. Private*, pg. 1034
Witek, Gary, V.P.-Sls.--World Tableware, Inc., Dallas, TX; *Int'l*, pg. 1056
Withers, Jonathan, Sls. V.P. & Branch Mgr.--BSA Advertising, Inc., San Diego, CA; *U.S. Private*, pg. 108
Withrow, David, Pres., Chief Exec. Officer & Dir.-Sls.--FATA Production Machinery, Cleveland, OH; *Int'l*, pg. 474
Witkin, Richard, V.P.-Infomercial Sls.--Corinthian Media, Inc., New York, NY; *U.S. Private*, pg. 275
Witko, Ron, V.P.-North Amer. Sls.--Chyron Corp., Melville, NY; *Int'l*, pg. 1372
Witt, Edward E., Sr. V.P.-Pur. & Sls.--Miller Electric Company, Jacksonville, FL; *U.S. Private*, pg. 747
Witt, Gerald, V.P.-Sls., Central Region--Donlen Corp., Northbrook, IL; *U.S. Private*, pg. 340
Witt, Mark, V.P.-Sls.--Fairfield Glade, Fairfield Glade, TN; *U.S. Public*, pg. 610
Witt, Rob, Mgr.-Sls.--Bibler Brothers, Inc., Russellville, AR; *U.S. Private*, pg. 142
Witte, Bob, V.P.-Domestic Sls. & Mktg.--Dri-Print Foils Inc., Rahway, NJ; *U.S. Private*, pg. 343
Witte, J.H., Exec. V.P.-Sls.--AEGON Schadeverzekering N.V., Hague, Netherlands; *Int'l*, pg. 26
Wittenbrock, Manfred, Gen. Mgr.-Sls.--Windmoeller & Hoelscher, Lengerich, Germany; *Int'l*, pg. 1510
Wittig, Detlef, Dir.-Sls. & Mktg.--SKODA, Automobilova a.s., Mlada Boleslav, Czech Republic; *Int'l*, pg. 1475
Wittler, Manfred, Exec. V.P.-Worldwide Sls.--Intergraph Corporation, Huntsville, AL; *U.S. Public*, pg. 890
Wittry, James, V.P.-Sls.--Merisel, Inc., El Segundo, CA; *U.S. Public*, pg. 1095
Witzgall, Annemarie, Gen. Mgr.-Sls. & Mktg.--Essex County Gas Company, Amesbury, MA; *U.S. Public*, pg. 593
Wnek, Gary, Mgr.-Sls.--Vision One, Norwich, CT; *U.S. Private*, pg. 1141
Woelfel, Mark, Mgr.-Pneumatics--Robert Bosch Fluid Power Corporation, Racine, WI; *Int'l*, pg. 204
Woerner, Dennis, V.P.-Mktg.--Six Flags St. Louis, Eureka, MO; *U.S. Public*, pg. 1612
Woerner, Reiner, Mgr.-Sls. Point--VARTA AG, Hannover, Germany; *Int'l*, pg. 1451
Wofford, Gary, V.P.-Sys. Sls. & Support--Grease Monkey International Inc., Denver, CO; *U.S. Public*, pg. 759
Wojcik, John, V.P.-Sls. & Branch Mgr.--Anicom, Troy, MI; *U.S. Public*, pg. 115
Wojcik, Ray, V.P.-Sls.--Fleer-Skybox International Inc., Mount Laurel, NJ; *U.S. Public*, pg. 1052
Wokasch, Michael G., V.P.-Sls.--Abbott Pharmaceutical Products Division, Abbott Park, IL; *U.S. Public*, pg. 13
Wolf, B.D., V.P.-Sls. E & D--Kvaerner Davy, Pittsburgh, PA; *Int'l*, pg. 774
Wolf, Barbara, Dir.-Mktg. & Sls.--Merco/Savory Inc., Lakewood, NJ; *Int'l*, pg. 189
Wolf, C.A., Asst. Gen. Sls. Mgr.-Service--Buick Motor Div. General Motors Corp., Flint, MI; *U.S. Public*, pg. 720
Wolf, Carl, Dir.-Aftermarket Sls.--AlliedSignal Commercial Avionic Systems, Olathe, KS; *U.S. Public*, pg. 50
Wolf, David, Mgr.-Sls.--Central States Can Co.-Composite Operations, Massillon, OH; *U.S. Public*, pg. 463
Wolf, Michael, Dir.-Sls. & Mdsg.--International Seaway Trading Corporation, Boca Raton, FL; *U.S. Private*, pg. 572
Wolf, Michael H., V.P.-Sls.--Kulicke & Soffa Industries, Inc., Willow Grove, PA; *U.S. Public*, pg. 968
Wolf, Robert D., Pres. & Chief Exec. Officer--Howard B. Wolf, Inc., Dallas, TX; *U.S. Public*, pg. 1774
Wolfarth, Ronald, Mgr.-Sales & Mktg.--Axle and Brake Div., Henderson, KY; *U.S. Public*, pg. 556
Wolfe, John, Mgr.-Sls. Support--Buss (America) Inc., Bloomingdale, IL; *Int'l*, pg. 490
Wolfe, Ted, Sr. V.P.-Sls.--Butler Manufacturing Company, Kansas City, MO; *U.S. Public*, pg. 271
Wolk, Doug, Dir.-Natl. Sls.--Sentry Group, Rochester, NY; *U.S. Private*, pg. 984
Wollberg, Royal, V.P.-Sls.--Liquid Controls LLC, Lake Bluff, IL; *U.S. Private*, pg. 669
Wolpert, Ronda, Dir.-Corp. Sls.--Motel 6 Operating L.P., Dallas, TX; *Int'l*, pg. 21
Wolstenholm, Rick, Sls.--Russell Stover Candies, Inc., Kansas City, MO; *U.S. Private*, pg. 953
Wonder, Larry, V.P.-Educational Sls.--Virco Mfg. Corporation, Torrance, CA; *U.S. Public*, pg. 1721
Wong, Michael, Mgr.-Sls.--Kewaunee Scientific Corporation, Statesville, NC; *U.S. Public*, pg. 953
Woo, Seok-Keun, Mgr.--Ssangyong Heavy Industries Co., Ltd., Seoul, Korea; *Int'l*, pg. 1292

Wood, Dave, OEM Intl. SBU Leader--Warn Industries, Inc., Clackamas, OR; *U.S. Private*, pg. 1150
Wood, Gary, Dir.-Natl. Sls.--Gold Medal Products Co., Cincinnati, OH; *U.S. Private*, pg. 459
Wood, Jan, V.P.-Domestic Sls. & Svc. Prods.--Trans World Airlines, Inc., Saint Louis, MO; *U.S. Public*, pg. 1629
Wood, John, V.P.-Mktg. & Sls.--Clark Detroit-Diesel Allison, Cincinnati, OH; *U.S. Private*, pg. 242
Wood, Ken, V.P. & Sec.--Barringer Technologies Inc., New Providence, NJ; *U.S. Public*, pg. 191
Wood, Kevin R., V.P.-Sls.--United Air Specialists, Inc., Cincinnati, OH; *U.S. Public*, pg. 382
Wood, Ray, Mgr.-Mktg. & Sls.--Whitecable, Liverpool, United Kingdom; *Int'l*, pg. 462
Wood, Richard, V.P.-Dallas Sls.--Vaughan & Sons, Inc., San Antonio, TX; *U.S. Private*, pg. 1134
Wood, Ron, V.P.-Intl. Sls.--Truevision, Inc., Santa Clara, CA; *U.S. Public*, pg. 1642
Wood, Steve, V.P.-Sls.--E.P. Graphics, Inc., Berne, IN; *U.S. Private*, pg. 354
Wood, Thomas, Dir.-Sls.--The Challenge Machinery Co., Grand Haven, MI; *U.S. Private*, pg. 227
Woodall, Jake M., Mgr.-Gas Sls.--Anadarko Petroleum Corporation, Houston, TX; *U.S. Public*, pg. 107
Woodard, C., Gen. Mgr.-Natl. Sls. & Mktg.--Australian Poultry Ltd., Beresfield, Australia; *Int'l*, pg. 555
Woodard, Jim, V.P.-Sls.--Vaughan & Sons, Inc., San Antonio, TX; *U.S. Private*, pg. 1134
Woodard, Ken, Dir.-Sls.--Bassmaster Magazine, Montgomery, AL; *U.S. Private*, pg. 105
Woodard, Ken, Dir.-Sls.--Southern Outdoors Magazine, Montgomery, AL; *U.S. Private*, pg. 106
Woodard, R., Sls. Mgr.-IN--Waterjet Cutting Systems Division, Farmington, MI; *U.S. Public*, pg. 877
Woodard, William M., Exec. V.P.-Sls.--I.V. One, Altamonte Springs, FL; *U.S. Public*, pg. 229
Woodbeck, Thomas M., Exec. V.P.--Overhead Conveyor Co., Ferndale, MI; *U.S. Private*, pg. 822
Woodburn, Connie R., Exec. V.P.-Corp. Sls.--Cardinal Health Inc., Dublin, OH; *U.S. Public*, pg. 304
Woodcock, James W., V.P.-Gen. Field Sls.--Milcare, Inc., Grandville, MI; *U.S. Public*, pg. 1112
Woodford, Bill, Dir.-Sls. & Mktg.--Land O'Lakes Dairy Foods, Clear Lake, WI; *U.S. Private*, pg. 646
Woodhouse, J., V.P.-Weiser Sales--Weiser Inc., Burnaby, Canada; *U.S. Public*, pg. 1055
Wooding, J.M., Exec. V.P.-Defense Mktg. Directorate--British Aerospace Defence Limited (Military Aircraft), Preston, United Kingdom; *Int'l*, pg. 217
Woodly, Susan, Dir.-Circulation--Architectural Digest, Los Angeles, CA; *U.S. Private*, pg. 20
Woodmaska, Steve, V.P.-Sls.--ATAPCO Office Products Group, Saint Louis, MO; *U.S. Private*, pg. 64
Woodruff, Don, Jr., Admin.-Sls.--Taylor Machine Works, Inc., Louisville, MS; *U.S. Private*, pg. 1070
Woods, Bob, V.P.-Sls.--Viking Range Corp., Greenwood, MS; *U.S. Private*, pg. 1140
Woods, Donald B., V.P.-Sls. & Mktg./Western Canada--Andres Wines Ltd., Winona, Canada; *Int'l*, pg. 75
Woods, Jack, V.P.-Agency Sls.--Nationwide Insurance Enterprise, Columbus, OH; *U.S. Private*, pg. 788
Woods, Jack, Mgr.-Sls.--Nationwide Mutual Insurance Co., Columbus, OH; *U.S. Private*, pg. 789
Woods, Jim D., V.P.-Sls. Automotive Window & Door Sys.--Excel Industries, Inc., Elkhart, IN; *U.S. Public*, pg. 598
Woods, Larry, V.P.-Sls.-North America--Benckiser Consumer Products Inc., Greenwich, CT; *Int'l*, pg. 185
Woods, Mike, Mgr.-Natl. Sls.--National R.V., Inc., Perris, CA; *U.S. Public*, pg. 1159
Woods, Robert G., V.P.-Sls. Opers.--Combe Incorporated, White Plains, NY; *U.S. Private*, pg. 257
Woodward, Jerry, Gen. Mgr.-Roofing & Architectural Products Div.--American Buildings Co., Eufaula, AL; *U.S. Public*, pg. 69
Woody, M., Coord.-Sls.--Farrell Lines Incorporated, New York, NY; *U.S. Private*, pg. 397
Woolf, Roger, Dir.-Sls. & Distr.--Matthew Clark Brands, Bristol, United Kingdom; *Int'l*, pg. 848
Woolf, Thomas, Reg. V.P.-Sls.--Milgray Electronics, Inc., Farmingdale, NY; *U.S. Public*, pg. 205
Woolf, Tom, V.P.-Sls.--Milgray/Indiana, Inc., Indianapolis, IN; *U.S. Public*, pg. 206
Woolie, M.M., V.P.-N. & S. American Sls.--Global Marine Drilling Co., Houston, TX; *U.S. Public*, pg. 748
Wooten, A. H., Natl. Sls. Mgr.--James Walker & Co. Limited, Woking, United Kingdom; *Int'l*, pg. 1485
Wooten, Sidney C., Jr., V.P.-Mktg. & Sls.--Lane Limited, Tucker, GA; *Int'l*, pg. 1129
Wooton, William D., V.P.-Distr. Sls.--Durakon Industries, Inc., Lapeer, MI; *U.S. Public*, pg. 537
Worcester, Bob, V.P.-Sls.--Dickinson Press, Inc., Grand Rapids, MI; *U.S. Private*, pg. 331
Worley, Kevin, Dir.-Sls.--Signature Flight Support, Orlando, FL; *Int'l*, pg. 114
Worrell, John K., Sr. V.P.-Sls.--Igloo Products Corporation, Houston, TX; *U.S. Public*, pg. 265
Worsham, Lud, Gen. Mgr.-Environmental Products--Hull Corporation, Hatboro, PA; *U.S. Private*, pg. 547
Worton, Geoffrey, V.P.-Sls. & Mktg.--The H.W. Wilson Co., Bronx, NY; *U.S. Private*, pg. 1180
Wortsmann, Michael, V.P. & Gen. Mgr.-Sls.--WTTG, Washington, DC; *Int'l*, pg. 926
Woznicki, Kevin, V.P.-N. American Sls.--Metrologic Instruments, Inc., Blackwood, NJ; *U.S. Public*, pg. 1102
Wrenn, Tim, Mgr.-Sls. & Mktg.--Winchester Electronics, Watertown, CT; *U.S. Public*, pg. 1003
Wrentshler, Kathy, Coord.-Human Resources--A.E. Staley Manufacturing Co., Decatur, IL; *Int'l*, pg. 1356
Wright, Charles, Mgr.-Sls.--Pax World Fund Family, Portsmouth, NH; *U.S. Public*, pg. 1266
Wright, David, Pres.-Sls. & Mktg. Div.--Duraliner U.S.A., Lapeer, MI; *U.S. Public*, pg. 537
Wright, David P., Exec. V.P.-Sls. & Mktg.--MedImmune, Inc., Gaithersburg, MD; *U.S. Public*, pg. 1081
Wright, Gary, Mgr.-Corp. Commun.--RLI Corp., Peoria, IL; *U.S. Public*, pg. 1356
Wright, Lowell, V.P.-Mktg. & Sls.--Caremark International Inc, Northbrook, IL; *U.S. Public*, pg. 1082
Wright, Mark A., V.P. & Dir.-Stores--Value Slacks, Inc., El Paso, TX; *U.S. Public*, pg. 613
Wright, Peter, Dir.-Sls.--SpeedFam Limited, Hinckley, United Kingdom; *U.S. Public*, pg. 1498
Wright, W.H., Dir.-Sls. & Mktg.--Redland Tile & Brick, Crumlin, United Kingdom; *Int'l*, pg. 1091
Wroblewski, Norbert J., Mgr.-Sls.--Plastek Group, Erie, PA; *U.S. Private*, pg. 870
Wu, Alex, Mgr.-Sls.--China Ecotek Corporation, Kao-hsiung, Taiwan; *Int'l*, pg. 285
Wuest, Oskar, Dir.-Domestic Sls. Dept.--Eckes AG, Nieder-Olm, Germany; *Int'l*, pg. 432
Wunderlich, Mini, Dir.-Sls. & Promo.--Republic Entertainment, Inc., Los Angeles, CA; *U.S. Private*, pg. 776
Wurster, Hans C., Exec. V.P.-Mktg. & Sls.--Bel/Kaukauna USA, Little Chute, WI; *U.S. Private*, pg. 130
Wyatt, Jan, V.P.-Sls. & Mktg.--Interval International Inc., Miami, FL; *U.S. Public*, pg. 320
Wyatt, Jeff, V.P.-Sls.--Gilliam Candy Brands, Edwardsville, KS; *U.S. Private*, pg. 454
Wyckoff, Paul, Exec. V.P.-Sls. & Mktg.--Maharam, Hauppauge, NY; *U.S. Private*, pg. 696
Wylan, Corey, V.P.-Sls.--Gould Paper Corporation, New York, NY; *U.S. Private*, pg. 466
Wyland, Harold E., V.P.-Sls.--Patrick Industries Inc., Elkhart, IN; *U.S. Public*, pg. 1264
Wylie, Jenette, Dir.-Sls.--Southbend, Fuquay Varina, NC; *U.S. Public*, pg. 1110
Wyman, K., Mgr.-Sls. & Adv.--Trippe Mfg. Co., Chicago, IL; *U.S. Private*, pg. 1104
Wypyszynski, Keith, V.P.-Sls.--Whitehall-Robins Healthcare, Madison, NJ; *U.S. Public*, pg. 80
Wyse, Michael L., V.P.-Sls. Div.--Healthcare Services Group, Inc., Huntingdon Valley, PA; *U.S. Public*, pg. 803
Wyse, Ross, Mgr.-Natl. Sls.--Sauder Woodworking Co., Archbold, OH; *U.S. Private*, pg. 967
Wysocki, Al, Natl. Sls. Mgr.-Sensors & Instruments--Thermo Electric Co., Inc., Saddle Brook, NJ; *U.S. Private*, pg. 1080
Wysocki, Mike, Dir.-Pacific-Rim Sls.--Media 100, Inc., Marlborough, MA; *U.S. Public*, pg. 1079
Wytvliet, A., Dir.-Sls.--Mercon Steel Structures B.V., Gorinchem, Netherlands; *Int'l*, pg. 858
Yaffa, Glen D., Sr. V.P.-Sls.--Stimson Lane Ltd., Woodinville, WA; *U.S. Public*, pg. 1661
Yajimi, S., Gen. Mgr.-Sls.--TYK Corporation, Tokyo, Japan; *Int'l*, pg. 1345
Yakshe, Stephen, Mgr.-Sls.--Pressure Systems, Inc., Hampton, VA; *Int'l*, pg. 1130
Yamada, Satoshi, Sr. Mng. Dir.-Intl. Bus. Devel. & Overseas Mktg. & Sls.--Mazda Motor Corporation, Hiroshima, Japan; *Int'l*, pg. 849
Yamagata, T., Mgr.-Overseas Sls./Automotive Components--Mitsubishi Cable Industries, Ltd., Tokyo, Japan; *Int'l*, pg. 870
Yamaguchi, Kanzo, Mgr.-Sls.--Kodansha Ltd., Tokyo, Japan; *Int'l*, pg. 742
Yamamoto, Katsuaki, Mng. Dir.-Pur. & Domestic Mktg. & Sls.--Mazda Motor Corporation, Hiroshima, Japan; *Int'l*, pg. 849
Yamanaka, Kuniaki, Dir.-Tire Mktg. & Sls. Div.--Bridgestone Corporation, Tokyo, Japan; *Int'l*, pg. 213
Yanda, David, V.P.-Frozen Food Sls.--Lakeside Foods, Inc., Manitowoc, WI; *U.S. Private*, pg. 643
Yando, Fred, V.P.-Sls. & Mktg.--Christie Design, Chatsworth, CA; *U.S. Public*, pg. 1369
Yanez, Ismail, Dir.-Sls.--John Crane Venezuela, Barquisimeto, Venezuela; *Int'l*, pg. 1340
Yang, Richard, V.P.-Mktg. & Sls.--Garland Commercial Industries, Inc., Freeland, PA; *Int'l*, pg. 188
Yarchin, Jeff, Natl. Sls. Mgr.--Etienne Aigner, New York, NY; *U.S. Private*, pg. 384
Yargus, Richard A., V.P.-Sls.--Dresher, Inc., Carthage, MO; *U.S. Public*, pg. 986
Yarns, Terry, Dir.-Sls. & Mktg.--Art's-Way Manufacturing Co., Inc., Armstrong, IA; *U.S. Public*, pg. 136
Yarrish, Al, V.P.-Intl. Sls.--Macrotech Plyseal, Inc., Salt Lake City, UT; *U.S. Private*, pg. 693
Yarson, Donald D., V.P.-Mktg. & Sls.--The Liposome Company, Inc., Princeton, NJ; *U.S. Public*, pg. 1000
Yaskin, John, V.P.-Sls.--Caesars Palace, Las Vegas, NV; *U.S. Public*, pg. 1512
Yasuba, Shoichi, Gen. Mgr.-Sls. & Mktg--Okuma Corporation, Niwa, Japan; *Int'l*, pg. 1000
Yavorsky, William, V.P.-Worldwide Sls.--In Focus Systems, Inc., Wilsonville, OR; *U.S. Public*, pg. 873
Yaw, Liu K, V.P.-Sls. & Plng.--China Airlines Ltd., Taipei, Taiwan; *Int'l*, pg. 284
Yaw, William R., Jr., Sr. V.P.--Standard Federal Bank, Troy, MI; *Int'l*, pg. 10
Yeager, Truman, V.P.-Sls., Fresh Fruit--Snokist Growers, Yakima, WA; *U.S. Private*, pg. 1011
Yeagley, Scott, Mgr.-Catalog--American Machine & Tool Company, Inc., Royersford, PA; *U.S. Private*, pg. 58
Yeahle, Tom, Mgr.-Sls.--Harmony Engineering Corporation, Minneapolis, MN; *U.S. Private*, pg. 503
Yeates, Rick, Sr. V.P.-Sls.--Steelcase Inc., Grand Rapids, MI; *U.S. Private*, pg. 1038
Yenkner, Charles E., Jr., V.P.-Sls. & Mktg.--Ney Dental International, Bloomfield, CT; *Int'l*, pg. 388
Yenkner, Chuck, Sr. V.P.-Sls. & Mktg.--Ney Dental International, Bloomfield, CT; *Int'l*, pg. 388
Yeo, Gavin, Gen. Mgr.-Sls.--Champion Motors (1975) Pte. Ltd., Singapore, Singapore; *Int'l*, pg. 672
Yeo, George, Gen. Mgr.-Parts--Champion Motors (1975) Pte. Ltd., Singapore, Singapore; *Int'l*, pg. 672
Yeo, Harold, V.P.-Sls.--Wheel Tronic Inc., Mississauga, Canada; *U.S. Public*, pg. 1481
Yepsen, Robert E., Mgr.-Sls.--Damascus Bishop Tube Co., Greenville, PA; *Int'l*, pg. 842
Yevoli, Vince, Mgr.-Mktg. & Sls.-Lithium--Yardney Technical Products, Inc., Pawcatuck, CT; *U.S. Private*, pg. 376
Yglesias, Joe, V.P.-Mktg. & Sls.--Victory Refrigeration Co. LC, Cherry Hill, NJ; *U.S. Private*, pg. 1139
Ying, Hu Shao, Mgr.-District Sls.--China Airlines Ltd., Honolulu, HI; *Int'l*, pg. 285
Yip, P.D., Sr. Exec.-Sls. & Services--The Hongkong and Shanghai Banking Corporation Limited (HongkongBank), Central, Hong Kong; *Int'l*, pg. 583
Yocom, Joel, Dir.-Mktg. & Sls.--Flexible Circuit Products Division, Methuen, MA; *U.S. Public*, pg. 1264
Yokoi, K., V.P.-Consumer Sls.--TDK Electronics Corporation, Port Washington, NY; *Int'l*, pg. 1336
Yokokawa, Norio, Chief Exec. Officer & V.P.--Skylark Co., Ltd., Tokyo, Japan; *Int'l*, pg. 1262
Yokota, Sunao, Exec. V.P.-Domestic Mktg. & Sls. & Parts & Accessories--Mazda Motor Corporation, Hiroshima, Japan; *Int'l*, pg. 849
Yondola, Robert A., Div. V.P.-Sls.--Ethyl Corporation, Richmond, VA; *U.S. Public*, pg. 595
Yonekura, Hidekazu, Sr. Mng. Dir.-Corp. Communication & Domestic Mktg. & Sls.--Mazda Motor Corporation, Hiroshima, Japan; *Int'l*, pg. 849
Yonekura, Shuji, Sr. V.P.-Sls. & Mktg.--Sanden International (U.S.A.), Inc., Wylie, TX; *Int'l*, pg. 1184
Yonenaga, Eiichiro, Assoc. Dir.-Intl. Sls.--Asahi Breweries Ltd., Tokyo, Japan; *Int'l*, pg. 83
Yoon, Cheol-Gu, Mgr.--Ssangyong Motor Company, Seoul, Korea; *Int'l*, pg. 1292
York, Brett, V.P.-Sls. & Mktg.--Hopple Plastics, Inc., Florence, KY; *U.S. Private*, pg. 538
York, Herb, Mgr.-Sls.--Welco Lumber Company, Marysville, WA; *U.S. Private*, pg. 1161
Youkhana, Arminak, Mgr.-Sls.--Kuwait Airways, Central USA, Arlington Heights, IL; *Int'l*, pg. 764
Young, Al, Dir.-Sls.--Oakland Tool & Manufacturing Company, Fraser, MI; *U.S. Private*, pg. 809
Young, Dick, V.P.-Sls.--Merchants Distributors, Inc., Hickory, NC; *U.S. Private*, pg. 657
Young, Donald E., V.P.-Mktg. & Sls.--E.H. Titchener & Company, Binghamton, NY; *U.S. Private*, pg. 1089
Young, Doris, Mgr.-Office Sls.--Cox Cable Greater Ocala, Inc., Ocala, FL; *U.S. Public*, pg. 455
Young, Gary, Natl. Sls. Mgr.--WEN Products, Inc., Bensenville, IL; *U.S. Private*, pg. 1144
Young, Geoffrey R., Mgr.-Sls.--Wentgate Dynaweld Inc., Agawam, MA; *Int'l*, pg. 1337
Young, John, V.P.-Sls. & Mktg.--Diamond Brands, Inc., Cloquet, MN; *U.S. Private*, pg. 330
Young, Joseph, V.P.-Sls. & Mktg./North America--Gundle/SLT Environmental, Inc., Houston, TX; *U.S. Public*, pg. 769
Young, Marty, V.P.-Direct Sls.--Sun Data Inc., Norcross, GA; *U.S. Private*, pg. 1050
Young, Richard, V.P.-Sls.--The Frymaster Corp., Shreveport, LA; *Int'l*, pg. 188
Young, Steve, Dir.-Sls.--American Fine Foods, Inc., Payette, ID; *U.S. Public*, pg. 349
Young, Tim, V.P.-Sls.--Nelson Photo Supplies, San Diego, CA; *U.S. Private*, pg. 791
Yount, Stephen A., V.P.-Sls./Americas--Symix Systems, Inc., Columbus, OH; *U.S. Public*, pg. 1546
Youssefzadeh, Emil, Pres., Chief Exec. Officer & Sec.--STM Wireless, Inc., Irvine, CA; *U.S. Public*, pg. 1421
Ytzen, Jeff, Mgr.-Dealer Sls.--Jones Blair Company, Dallas, TX; *U.S. Private*, pg. 596
Yu, David, Mgr.-Sls.--Thai Airways Intl. Ltd.-Toronto, Toronto, Canada; *Int'l*, pg. 1381
Yu, Emilio C., V.P.-Sls.--Philippine Airlines, Inc., Manila, Philippines; *Int'l*, pg. 1050
Yudis, Charles S., Exec. V.P.-Sls. & Mktg.--Capp, Inc., Clifton Heights, PA; *U.S. Private*, pg. 207
Yuruckso, Robert, Mgr.-Sls.--Comtech PST Corp., Melville, NY; *U.S. Public*, pg. 425
Yvan, Jo, V.P.-Sls. & Mktg.--Pride Products, Inc., Elizabeth, NJ; *U.S. Private*, pg. 883
Zabetakis, David B., Asst. V.P.-Market Devel.--Unitil Corporation, Hampton, NH; *U.S. Public*, pg. 1692
Zaborowski, Jerzy, Mgr.-Sports Sls.--FINNAIR, New York, NY; *Int'l*, pg. 485
Zade, Larry, Gen. Mgr. & Dir.-Sls. & Mktg.-Wood Working--Wisconsin Automated Machinery Corp., Oshkosh, WI; *U.S. Private*, pg. 1184
Zager, Tom V., Mgr.-Sls. & Mktg.--Metron Steel Corp., Chicago, IL; *U.S. Private*, pg. 736
Zago, Armand, District Sls. Mgr.--FINNAIR, Long Beach, CA; *Int'l*, pg. 486
Zakrzewski, Ed, V.P.-P.O. Sls.--Key Handling Systems, Inc., Moonachie, NJ; *U.S. Private*, pg. 618
Zaldavar, Michael, V.P.-Sls. & Mktg.--Whessoe Varec, Cypress, CA; *Int'l*, pg. 1498
Zalewski, Gerald P., Mgr.-Sls. & Mktg.--Ruhle Companies, Inc., Valhalla, NY; *U.S. Private*, pg. 950
Zalewski, Gerald P., Mgr.-Sls. & Mktg.--Farrand Controls, Valhalla, NY; *U.S. Private*, pg. 951
Zambelli, Jean-Claude, V.P.-Worldwide Sls.--EXAR Corporation, Fremont, CA; *U.S. Public*, pg. 597
Zambelli, Jean-Claude, V.P.-Sls. & Mktg.--Semtech Corporation, Newbury Park, CA; *U.S. Public*, pg. 1456
Zambini, Jerry, Dir.-Sls. & Mktg.--Rolland Inc., Saint-Jerome, Canada; *Int'l*, pg. 273
Zambruski, Michael, Mgr.-Reg. Sls.--TRI-S Incorporated, Ellington, CT; *U.S. Public*, pg. 546
Zanchelli, Robert, V.P.-Sls.--General Binding Corporation, Northbrook, IL; *U.S. Public*, pg. 707
Zaneri, Barbara, Sls. Mgr.-Western Reg.--Universal Studios TV, Universal City, CA; *Int'l*, pg. 1215
Zangardi, J. Michael, Dir.-Sls. & Mktg.--Simplex Industries, Inc., Scranton, PA; *U.S. Private*, pg. 1001
Zanzig, John A., Mgr.-Sls.--Finch, Pruyn & Co., Inc., Glens Falls, NY; *U.S. Private*, pg. 405

Zarmati, Maurice, V.P.-Sls.--Carnival Corporation, Miami, FL; *U.S. Public*, pg. 306
Zarookian, Paul A., Sr. V.P.-Sls. & Mktg--A.I. Credit Corp., New York, NY; *U.S. Public*, pg. 85
Zarr, Dale, V.P.-Sls. & Mgr.--Minot Builders Supply Association, Minot, ND; *U.S. Private*, pg. 751
Zastrow, Teresa, Dir.-H-D Sls.--Holoubek Inc., Waukesha, WI; *U.S. Private*, pg. 536
Zavadsky, Tom, Exec. V.P.-Sls. & Mktg.--Noel Olson Group, Stevens Point, WI; *U.S. Private*, pg. 800
Zawadzki, Frank, V.P. & Reg. Sls. Mgr.--Fruit of the Loom, Inc., Chicago, IL; *U.S. Public*, pg. 685
Zawik, Doug, Dir.-Sls.--Winkelman Stores, Inc., Plymouth, MI; *U.S. Private*, pg. 858
Zebarth, Mike, V.P.-Sls. & Mktg.--Packard BioScience Company, Meriden, CT; *U.S. Private*, pg. 833
Zehringer, Vance, Mgr.-Sls.--United Power Association, Elk River, MN; *U.S. Private*, pg. 1123
Zeigler, R.H., Dir.-Sls.--The Gerstenslager Company, Wooster, OH; *U.S. Public*, pg. 1780
Zeilman, Harold, Dir.-Sls. & Industrial Mktg.--Cincinnati Sub-Zero Products, Inc., Cincinnati, OH; *U.S. Private*, pg. 240
Zellmer, Karl, V.P.-Air Conditioning Sls.--Copeland Corporation, Sidney, OH; *U.S. Public*, pg. 573
Zemanek, Thomas, Mgr.-Sls.-Enidine West--Enidine Incorporated, Orchard Park, NY; *U.S. Private*, pg. 377
Zemick, M., Exec. V.P.-Sls. & Mktg.--Industrial Steel & Wire Company, Chicago, IL; *U.S. Private*, pg. 561
Zemke, D.E., Sr. V.P.-Sls. & Mktg.--Cincinnati Bell Telephone, Cincinnati, OH; *U.S. Public*, pg. 367
Zemmin, Richard W., V.P.-Mktg. & Sls.--MichCon, Detroit, MI; *U.S. Public*, pg. 1025
Zenere, Reno P., V.P.-Sls.--Acme Packaging Corporation, Riverdale, IL; *U.S. Public*, pg. 16
Zenk, Jason, V.P.-Fin.--Monico Alloys, Inc., Los Angeles, CA; *U.S. Private*, pg. 757
Zenner, Howard, V.P.-Sls.--Hickey-Freeman/Bobby Jones, Rochester, NY; *U.S. Public*, pg. 795
Zenner, Nico, Asst. Gen. Mgr.--Sabena Belgian World Airlines, Manhasset, NY; *Int'l*, pg. 1168
Zentmyer, David T., Jr., V.P.-Corp. Sls.--Lands' End, Inc., Dodgeville, WI; *U.S. Public*, pg. 977
Zeratsky, J. Bur, Mgr.-Sls. & Mktg.--The Shaler Company, Waupun, WI; *U.S. Private*, pg. 786
Zerbe, Mark A., Exec. V.P.--Kent Electronics Corp., Houston, TX; *U.S. Public*, pg. 951
Zetsche, Dieter, Dr., Dir.-Sls. & Mktg.--Daimler-Benz Aktiengesellschaft, Stuttgart, Germany; *Int'l*, pg. 366
Zeus, William, Jr., Pres. & Chief Exec. Officer--National Tool & Manufacturing Company, Kenilworth, NJ; *U.S. Private*, pg. 787
Ziauddin, M., Natl. Sls. Mgr.--Parke-Davis & Company, Limited, Karachi, Pakistan; *U.S. Public*, pg. 1739
Zidek, Charles, Dir.-Corp. Commun.--U.S.S. Seko Worldwide, Elk Grove Village, IL; *U.S. Private*, pg. 1115
Zieger, Ari, Dir.-Sls. & Mdsg.--Interbath, Inc., City of Industry, CA; *U.S. Private*, pg. 566
Ziegler, Chip, V.P.-Sls.--Ziegler Chemical & Mineral Corp., Jericho, NY; *U.S. Private*, pg. 1205
Ziegler, Seeta, V.P.-Sls., Western Region--USA Network, Los Angeles, CA; *U.S. Public*, pg. 1686
Zielfelt, Henrik, Dir.-Commercial Perfume--L'Oreal Parfumerie, Brussels, Belgium; *Int'l*, pg. 819
Zielinski, Pat, Dir.-Mktg.--CompuDyne Corporation, Willimantic, CT; *U.S. Public*, pg. 419
Zifkin, Dan, V.P. & Natl. Sls. Mgr.-Syndication--Western International Media Corporation, Chicago, IL; *U.S. Private*, pg. 1167
Zimmer, Tim, Mgr.-Mktg. & Sls.--Atchison/St. Joe Division, Atchison, KS; *U.S. Public*, pg. 142
Zimmerman, Ken, V.P.-Sls. & Mktg.--Alumacraft Boat Co., Saint Peter, MN; *U.S. Private*, pg. 1088
Zimmerman, Victor C., Dir.-Sls.--Chemtech Products Inc., Saint Louis, MO; *U.S. Private*, pg. 39
Zimmermann, Don, V.P.-Opers.--Ferguson Manufacturing & Equipment Company, Inc., Dallas, TX; *U.S. Private*, pg. 401
Zimmermann, J., Mgr.-Sls.--Esselte SA, Paris, France; *Int'l*, pg. 461
Zimmermann, Keith, Jr., V.P.-Sls.--Whitney Blake Company of Vermont, Inc., Bellows Falls, VT; *U.S. Private*, pg. 148
Zimpfer, Rick, Mgr.-U.S. Sls.--The New Piper Aircraft, Inc., Vero Beach, FL; *U.S. Private*, pg. 794
Zindel, Al, V.P.-Sls. & Mktg.--Woolrich, Inc., Woolrich, PA; *U.S. Private*, pg. 1188
Zindel, Walter, Sls. Application Engr.--Moore Special Tool AG, Zurich, Switzerland; *U.S. Private*, pg. 889
Zinniker, R., Mgr.-Sls.--Moore Paragon (Suisse) S.A., Lausanne, Switzerland; *Int'l*, pg. 800
Zintmeir, John, Mgr.-Natl. Sls.--Seward Inc., Petersburg, VA; *U.S. Private*, pg. 988
Ziolo, Mike, Sls.--Geyer-McAllister Publications, Inc., New York, NY; *U.S. Private*, pg. 450
Zipin, Larry, V.P.-Adv. & Sls.--Time Warner Cable, Stamford, CT; *U.S. Public*, pg. 1610
Zipkis, Sandy, Dir.-Sls.--Getko Group Inc., Westbury, NY; *U.S. Public*, pg. 320
Zipper, Gary, Sr. V.P.-Sls.--Gould Paper Corporation, New York, NY; *U.S. Private*, pg. 466
Zirbel, Denise, Grp. Mgr.-Sls.--Six Flags Great America, Inc., Gurnee, IL; *U.S. Public*, pg. 1611
Znidar, Paul R., Intl. Sls. Mgr.--PMC Industries Inc., Wickliffe, OH; *U.S. Private*, pg. 827
Zobel, Kim, Mgr.-Customer Svcs., Sls. & Mktg.--Midwest Industries, Inc., Ida Grove, IA; *U.S. Private*, pg. 744
Zobel, Mike, Dir.-Sls. & Mktg.--Vacu-Dry Company, Sebastopol, CA; *U.S. Public*, pg. 1704
Zong, A.C., Mgr.-Sls.--Turner Construction Company, Atlanta, GA; *U.S. Public*, pg. 1645
Zoukis, Paul, Sr. V.P.-Mktg. & Sls.--Hogan Systems, Inc., Dallas, TX; *U.S. Public*, pg. 422
Zubler, R., Dir.-Sls.--Cruspi S.A., Dallikon, Switzerland; *Int'l*, pg. 348
Zucht, Earle, Sr. V.P.-Semiconductor Mktg.--Wyle Electronics, Irvine, CA; *Int'l*, pg. 1457
Zucker, Lloyd, V.P.-Sls.--Shillcraft, Inc., Baltimore, MD; *U.S. Private*, pg. 994
Zuhlke, Kim K., V.P.-Cust. Sls. & Service--Wisconsin Power & Light Company, Madison, WI; *U.S. Public*, pg. 1728
Zuk, T., Dir.-Ontario Sls.--Metro Brewery, Etobicoke, Canada; *Int'l*, pg. 679
Zukowski, Paul, V.P.-Sls. & Adv.--The Hibbert Company, Trenton, NJ; *U.S. Private*, pg. 525
Zummo, Tom, Mgr.-Sls.--Florig Equipment Company, Inc., Conshohocken, PA; *U.S. Private*, pg. 415
Zuponeck, Bob, Dir.-Sls. Admin.--A.J. Gerrard and Company, Des Plaines, IL; *U.S. Private*, pg. 449
Zurcher, T., Trade & Sls.--Danone Group, Paris, France; *Int'l*, pg. 379
Zurich, Richard, V.P.-Sls.--KCL Corporation, Shelbyville, IN; *U.S. Private*, pg. 603
Zweep, James, Mgr.-Field Sls.--Carter Products, Canada, Mississauga, Canada; *U.S. Public*, pg. 310
Zweifel, Bobby, V.P.-Sls.--Fairfield Flagstaff, Flagstaff, AZ; *U.S. Public*, pg. 611
Zwicker, Bruce, V.P.-Mktg. & Sls.--Millennium Inorganic Chemicals, Hunt Valley, MD; *Int'l*, pg. 593
Zyngier, Leonildo, Dir.-Sls. & Mktg.--Schwitzer, Inc., Indianapolis, IN; *U.S. Public*, pg. 968

SENIOR VICE PRESIDENT

Aaabak, Edward, Sr. V.P.-Opers.--Western Gas Resources, Inc., Denver, CO; *U.S. Public*, pg. 1758
Aaron, Hank, Sr. V.P. & Asst. to the Pres.--Atlanta National League Baseball Club, Inc., Atlanta, GA; *U.S. Public*, pg. 1614
Aarseth, Geir, Sr. V.P.-Personnel/Organization--Orkla A.S.A., Oslo, Norway; *Int'l*, pg. 1010
Aasheim, Hilde, Sr. V.P.-Personnel/Health, Safety & Environment--Elkem ASA, Oslo, Norway; *Int'l*, pg. 446
Abassi, Sohaib, Sr. V.P.-Tools--Oracle Corporation, Redwood City, CA; *U.S. Public*, pg. 1227
Abate, Anthony J., Sr. V.P. & Corp. Sec.--North Fork Bancorporation, Inc., Melville, NY; *U.S. Public*, pg. 1194
Abatemarco, Fred, Sr. V.P.--Times Mirror Magazines, Inc., New York, NY; *U.S. Public*, pg. 1616
Abatte, Mark, Sr. V.P.--H.F. Ahmanson & Co., Irwindale, CA; *U.S. Public*, pg. 29
Abbatomarco, Frank, Chief Fin. Officer & Sr. V.P.--DHP Limited Partnership, Chicopee, MA; *U.S. Private*, pg. 302
Abbinante, Christopher, Sr. V.P.-Eastern Div.--Chicago Title Insurance Co., Chicago, IL; *U.S. Public*, pg. 42
Abbott, Rohn D., Sr. V.P.--Shannon & Wilson, Inc., Seattle, WA; *U.S. Private*, pg. 989
Abbrederis, Dale E., Chief Fin. Officer & Sr. V.P.--Unigard Insurance Co., Bellevue, WA; *Int'l*, pg. 345
Abbrederis, Dale E., Chief Fin. Officer & Sr. V.P.--Unigard Indemnity Co., Bellevue, WA; *Int'l*, pg. 345
Abdalla, Evelina, Sr. V.P.--Abdalla's Lafayette, Inc., Lafayette, LA; *U.S. Private*, pg. 10
Abdalla, Irma B., Sr. V.P.--Abdalla's Lafayette, Inc., Lafayette, LA; *U.S. Private*, pg. 10
Abeita, Leonard, Sr. V.P.-Global Professional Services--Telxon Corporation, Akron, OH; *U.S. Public*, pg. 1573
Abel, Marius, Sr. V.P. & Gen. Mgr.-Network Products Div.--UB Networks, Santa Clara, CA; *Int'l*, pg. 924
Abele, William J., Sr. V.P. & Exec. Producer--Ross Roy Communications, Inc., Bloomfield Hills, MI; *U.S. Private*, pg. 946
Abeles, Peter, Sr. V.P.--ContiFinancial Corporation, New York, NY; *U.S. Public*, pg. 439
Abell, Robert, Sr. V.P.-Comml. Lending--First Federal Capital Corp., La Crosse, WI; *U.S. Public*, pg. 632
Abels, Terry, Sr. V.P.-Sls. & Mktg.--CFA Holding Company, Charlotte, MI; *U.S. Private*, pg. 194
Aberle, Patrick, Sr. V.P.-Managed Care--Sutter Health, Sacramento, CA; *U.S. Private*, pg. 1057
Abernathy, Charles C., Jr., Sr. V.P.-Syndicate Dept.--D.A. Davidson & Co., Great Falls, MT; *U.S. Private*, pg. 314
Abernathy, James R., V.P.-Mortgage Loan--Jefferson-Pilot Life Insurance Co., Greensboro, NC; *U.S. Public*, pg. 926
Abernathy, Penelope Muse, Sr. V.P.-Plng. & Human Resources--The New York Times, New York, NY; *U.S. Public*, pg. 1174
Abernethy, Claude S., Jr., Sr. V.P.--Interstate/Johnson Lane Corporation, Charlotte, NC; *U.S. Public*, pg. 910
Abolafio, Rafael Gomez, Sr. V.P.--Banco Santander, Singapore, Singapore; *Int'l*, pg. 144
Abolfathi, Farzad, Sr. V.P.-Systems Devel.--Countrywide Funding Corporation, Pasadena, CA; *U.S. Public*, pg. 453
Abraham, Dean W., Sr. V.P.-Opers.--Hancock Fabrics, Inc., Tupelo, MS; *U.S. Public*, pg. 779
Abraham, William W., Sr. V.P.--Conmed Corporation, Utica, NY; *U.S. Public*, pg. 431
Abrahams, Mark, Sr. V.P. & Gen. Mgr.-Specialty Nets--Applied Extrusion Technologies, Inc., Peabody, MA; *U.S. Public*, pg. 122
Abrahamson, James R., Sr. V.P.-Franchises--Hilton Hotels Div., Beverly Hills, CA; *U.S. Public*, pg. 829
Abrahamson, Jim, Sr. V.P.-Franchising--Hilton Hotels Corporation, Beverly Hills, CA; *U.S. Public*, pg. 828
Abrahamson, Jim, Sr. V.P.-Franchising Select Hotels--Hilton Inns, Inc., Beverly Hills, CA; *U.S. Public*, pg. 829
Abramczyk, Dennis, Sr. V.P. & Gen. Mdse. Mgr.-Men's, Young Men's & Children's--Carson Pirie Scott & Co., Milwaukee, WI; *U.S. Public*, pg. 309
Abramovic, A. Mark, Chief Fin. Officer & Sr. V.P.--NUI Corporation, Bedminster, NJ; *U.S. Public*, pg. 1147
Abramowicz, Daniel A., Sr. V.P.--Crown Cork & Seal Company, Inc.-Corporate Technologies, Alsip, IL; *U.S. Public*, pg. 463
Abrams, Bruce R., Sr. V.P.-Mktg.--Western National Corporation, Houston, TX; *U.S. Public*, pg. 76
Abrams, Bruce R., Sr. V.P.-Mktg.--Western National Life Insurance Co., Houston, TX; *U.S. Public*, pg. 76
Abrams, Gary N., Chief Fin. Officer, Sr. V.P. & Treas.--Somerset Savings Bank, Somerville, MA; *U.S. Public*, pg. 1484
Abrams, Larry, Sr. V.P.--National Restaurant Management, Inc., New York, NY; *U.S. Private*, pg. 786
Abrams, Robin, Sr. V.P.-Apple Americas--Apple Computer, Inc., Cupertino, CA; *U.S. Public*, pg. 121
Abrams, Suzanne, Sr. V.P. & Grp. Media Dir.--Young & Rubicam New York, New York, NY; *U.S. Private*, pg. 1198
Abramson, David M., Sr. V.P. & Gen. Counsel--JP Foodservice, Inc., Columbia, MD; *U.S. Public*, pg. 918
Abramson, Robert, Sr. V.P.--D.L. Blair Inc., Garden City, NY; *U.S. Private*, pg. 148
Accardi, Emelia M., Sr. V.P.--Chubb & Son, Inc., Warren, NJ; *U.S. Public*, pg. 355
Acero, Susan, Sr. V.P. & Brdcst. Opers. Dir.--N.W. Ayer & Partners New York, New York, NY; *U.S. Private*, pg. 104
Ackerly, Mary, Sr. V.P.--Edelman Public Relations Worldwide, Chicago, IL; *U.S. Private*, pg. 362
Ackerman, Philip C., Chief Fin. Officer & Sr. V.P.--National Fuel Gas Company, Buffalo, NY; *U.S. Public*, pg. 1156
Ackerman, Robert, Sr. V.P. & Gen. Mgr.-Mdsg.--Neiman Marcus Co., Dallas, TX; *U.S. Public*, pg. 785
Ackerman, Sanford S., Chief Fin. Officer & Sr. V.P.--Blair Television, New York, NY; *U.S. Private*, pg. 148
Ackermann, Joe, Sr. V.P.-Sls.--Gateway Press, Inc., Louisville, KY; *U.S. Private*, pg. 441
Acosta, Jack, Chief Fin. Officer & Sr. V.P.--Sybase, Inc., Emeryville, CA; *U.S. Public*, pg. 1544
Acree, George T., Sr. V.P. & Admin. Services Dir.--DMB&B Detroit, Troy, MI; *U.S. Private*, pg. 302
Acuff, Keith, Sr. V.P., Chief Mktg. Officer-Consumer Brands & Dir.--Noble & Associates Promotion Group, Springfield, MO; *U.S. Private*, pg. 800
Adam, Douglas K., Sr. V.P.--Empire General Life Assurance Corporation, Birmingham, AL; *U.S. Public*, pg. 1336
Adam, Shmuel, Sr. V.P.-Dan District--The Israel Electric Corporation Ltd., Haifa, Israel; *Int'l*, pg. 690
Adamitza, Jurgen, Sr. V.P.--Bayerische Landesbank Girozentrale - Frankfurt Branch, Frankfurt, Germany; *Int'l*, pg. 176
Adams, Allen R., Sr. V.P.-Strategic Plng.--DSC Communications Corporation, Plano, TX; *U.S. Public*, pg. 475
Adams, Alton W., Sr. V.P.--United States Tobacco Company, Greenwich, CT; *U.S. Public*, pg. 1661
Adams, Betty, Sr. V.P.-Legal Affairs--Delta Life Corporation, Memphis, TN; *U.S. Private*, pg. 59
Adams, Dirk, Grp. Sr. V.P.--Golden West Financial Corporation, Oakland, CA; *U.S. Public*, pg. 750
Adams, John, Sr. V.P.-Opers.--Heublein, Inc., Hartford, CT; *Int'l*, pg. 410
Adams, John, Jr., Sr. V.P. & Mgr.-Opers.--Adams Extract Co., Inc., Austin, TX; *U.S. Private*, pg. 16
Adams, Karen, Sr. V.P. & Worldwide Acct. Dir.--Young & Rubicam San Francisco, San Francisco, CA; *U.S. Private*, pg. 1198
Adams, Kenneth J., Chief Fin. Officer & Sr. V.P.--Movado Group, Inc., Lyndhurst, NJ; *U.S. Public*, pg. 1140
Adams, Mark, Sr. V.P., Treas. & Sec.--Hechinger Company Investors II, L.P., Largo, MD; *U.S. Private*, pg. 477
Adams, Mark S., Sr. V.P.--Eastbridge Capital Inc., New York, NY; *Int'l*, pg. 933
Adams, Paul D., Chief Fin. Officer, Sr. V.P. & Treas.--Old Republic International Corporation, Chicago, IL; *U.S. Public*, pg. 1218
Adams, R.G., Sr. V.P.-Personnel Services--Delta Air Lines, Inc., Atlanta, GA; *U.S. Public*, pg. 497
Adamsen, Julia, Sr. V.P. & Dir.-Corp. Mktg.--Keycorp, Cleveland, OH; *U.S. Public*, pg. 954
Adamson, Julie, Sr. V.P.-Corp. Mktg. Communications--Society National Bank, Cleveland, OH; *U.S. Public*, pg. 954
Adamson, Reggie D., Sr. V.P.-Fin.--Jefferson-Pilot Corporation, Greensboro, NC; *U.S. Public*, pg. 925
Adamson, William J., Jr., Sr. V.P.--Continental Assurance Company, Chicago, IL; *U.S. Private*, pg. 267
Adcock, Aubrey, Sr. V.P.--Huitt-Zollars, Inc., Dallas, TX; *U.S.* Private, pg. 547
Adcock, Mike, Sr. V.P.-Natl. Sls.--Parmalat Canada Ltd., Etobicoke, Canada; *Int'l*, pg. 1023
Addington, William J., Sr. V.P.--Canadian Western Bank, Edmonton, Canada; *Int'l*, pg. 259
Addison, C.H., Sr. V.P.-Systems, Plng. & Computing--American National Insurance Company, Galveston, TX; *U.S. Public*, pg. 87
Adelman, Graham, Sr. V.P., Gen. Counsel & Sec.--Global Industrial Technologies, Dallas, TX; *U.S. Public*, pg. 747
Adelson, Andrew S., Chief Investment Officer-Intl. & Sr. V.P.--Sanford C. Bernstein & Co., Inc., New York, NY; *U.S. Private*, pg. 137
Aden, Matthew, Sr. V.P.-Intl. Sls.--Broadband Networks Group, Hatboro, PA; *U.S. Public*, pg. 716
Adilerri, John, Sr. V.P.-Mktg.--CSE Insurance Group, San Francisco, CA; *U.S. Private*, pg. 197
Adkins, H. Larry, Sr. V.P. & Mgr.-Opers.--Marine Drilling Companies, Inc., Sugar Land, TX; *U.S. Public*, pg. 1044
Adkins, Michael D., Sr. V.P.-Opers.--Cracker Barrel Old Country Store, Inc., Lebanon, TN; *U.S. Public*, pg. 455
Adler, Ira R., Chief Fin. Officer & Sr. V.P.--UniSource Energy Corporation, Tucson, AZ; *U.S. Public*, pg. 1670
Adler, Ira R., Chief Fin. Officer & Sr. V.P.--Tucson Electric Power Company, Tucson, AZ; *U.S. Public*, pg. 1670
Adolfson, Brook P., Sr. V.P.--Adolfson & Peterson, Inc., Minneapolis, MN; *U.S. Private*, pg. 17
Adonetti, Joe, Sr. V.P.--Rockbottom Stores, Inc., Lake Success, NY; *U.S. Private*, pg. 938
Adornetto, J.J., Sr. V.P.--Westfield Companies, Westfield Center, OH; *U.S. Private*, pg. 1169
Aelis, Gary, Chief Fin. Officer & Sr. V.P.--Consolidated Cigar Corporation, Fort Lauderdale, FL; *U.S. Private*, pg. 690

Aerni, Bernhard, Chief Fin. Officer & Sr. V.P.-Fin.--UMS Swiss Metalworks Holding Ltd, Dornach, Switzerland; *Int'l*, pg. 1427

Affonso, Luis Carlos, Sr. V.P.-Engrng.--Embraer-Empresa Brasileira de Aeronautica S.A., Sao Jose dos Campos, Brazil; *Int'l*, pg. 452

Afshar, B. Yamin, Sr. V.P.-Intl.--Cogentrix Incorporated, Charlotte, NC; *U.S. Private*, pg. 249

Agate, Bob, Sr. V.P.-Tile Opers.--Congoleum Corporation, Mercerville, NJ; *U.S. Public*, pg. 69

Agathen, Paul A., Sr. V.P.-Energy Supply Services--AmerenUE, Saint Louis, MO; *U.S. Public*, pg. 66

Agger, James H., Sr. V.P., Gen. Counsel & Sec.--Air Products and Chemicals, Inc., Allentown, PA; *U.S. Public*, pg. 30

Agnew, Donald J., Sr. V.P.--First National Bank of Naples, Naples, FL; *U.S. Public*, pg. 607

Agoos, Andy, Sr. V.P.-Equipment--Hubbard Construction Co., Winter Park, FL; *U.S. Private*, pg. 544

Agosti, Frank E., Sr. V.P.--DTE Energy Company, Detroit, MI; *U.S. Public*, pg. 475

Agostini, Giulio, Sr. V.P.-Fin. & Admin. Svcs.--3M, Saint Paul, MN; *U.S. Public*, pg. 1604

Agren, Christer, Sr. V.P.-Personnel--Stora Kopparbergs Bergslags AB, Falun, Sweden; *Int'l*, pg. 1302

Agrenius, Bertil, Sr. V.P.-Energy--Vattenfall AB, Stockholm, Sweden; *Int'l*, pg. 1452

Aguilera, Luis, Sr. V.P.-Mfg.--Checkpoint Systems Inc., Thorofare, NJ; *U.S. Public*, pg. 343

Aguirre, Annette, Sr. V.P.-Mortgage Lending Services--Advanta Mortgage Corp. USA, Fort Washington, PA; *U.S. Public*, pg. 22

Aguren, Mats, Sr. V.P.-Corp. Communications--Stora Kopparbergs Bergslags AB, Falun, Sweden; *Int'l*, pg. 1302

Ahladas, John A., Sr. V.P.-Corp. Services--Virginia Electric and Power Company, Richmond, VA; *U.S. Public*, pg. 516

Ahlgrimm, Marijo, Sr. V.P. & Controller--ICF Kaiser International Inc., Fairfax, VA; *U.S. Public*, pg. 852

Ahmed, Salah U., Sr. V.P.-Prod. & Devel.--Barr Laboratories Inc., Pomona, NY; *U.S. Public*, pg. 191

Ahner, David L., Sr. V.P.-Corp. Real Estate--NationsBank West, Saint Louis, MO; *U.S. Public*, pg. 1164

Ahotupa, Jaakko, Sr. V.P.-Admin.--Outokumpu Oyj, Espoo, Finland; *Int'l*, pg. 1015

Ahrens, Leavitt, Sr. V.P.-Intl.--Rubbermaid Incorporated, Wooster, OH; *U.S. Public*, pg. 1411

Aiello, Larry, Jr., Sr. V.P.-Intl.--Corning Incorporated, Corning, NY; *U.S. Public*, pg. 448

Aiga, Terunori, Sr. V.P.--Toshiba Corporation, Tokyo, Japan; *Int'l*, pg. 1402

Aiken, Robert M., Jr., Chief Fin. Officer & Sr. V.P.--Sun Company, Inc., Philadelphia, PA; *U.S. Public*, pg. 1530

Aiko, Jiro, Sr. Mng. Dir.--Sony Corporation, Tokyo, Japan; *Int'l*, pg. 1280

Ainsworth, Earl, Sr. V.P. & Publr.--Farm Journal Inc., Philadelphia, PA; *U.S. Private*, pg. 394

Aizawa, Shin-ichi, Sr. V.P.--Nippon Telegraph and Telephone Corporation, Tokyo, Japan; *Int'l*, pg. 940

Aizawa, Tsuneo, Sr. Mng. Dir.--Amada Co., Ltd., Kanagawa, Japan; *Int'l*, pg. 70

Ajani, Amirali G., Sr. V.P.-Swiss Chalet Restaurants--Cara Operations Limited, Toronto, Canada; *Int'l*, pg. 266

Ajram, Elie, Sr. V.P.-Strategic Plng.--Shoppers Drug Mart, Ltd., Toronto, Canada; *Int'l*, pg. 112

Ake, John A., V.P.-Regulatory Affairs--Ameritech, Chicago, IL; *U.S. Public*, pg. 97

Akers, Joe, Sr. V.P.--First Commercial Bank, N.A., Little Rock, AR; *U.S. Public*, pg. 630

Akers, Joseph A., Sr. V.P.-Controlling & Admin./Diagnostics Div.--Bayer Corporation, Pittsburgh, PA; *Int'l*, pg. 172

Akers, Michael J., Sr. V.P. & Chief Actuary--Western National Corporation, Houston, TX; *U.S. Public*, pg. 76

Akerson, Steve, Sr. V.P., Health Care Prods. Mgr. & Acct. Exec.--Colle & McVoy, Inc., Minneapolis, MN; *U.S. Private*, pg. 252

Akerson, Steve, Sr. V.P.-Bus.-to-Bus.--Colle & McVoy Marketing Communications, Minneapolis, MN; *U.S. Private*, pg. 252

Akimoto, Minoru, Sr. V.P. & Mgr.--The Bank of Tokyo-Mitsubishi, Ltd. (Columbus Corporate Banking), Columbus, OH; *Int'l*, pg. 157

Akouris, Elaine, Sr. V.P. & Branch Mgr.--FirstFed Financial Corp., Santa Monica, CA; *U.S. Public*, pg. 645

Akselrad, Harold E., Sr. V.P.-Business Affairs--Home Box Office, Inc., New York, NY; *U.S. Public*, pg. 1612

Al-Zaid, F., Sr. Reg. Dir.--Kuwait Airways Corp., New York, NY; *Int'l*, pg. 764

Alamo, Tony, Sr. V.P.--Circus Circus Hotel Casinos, Inc., Las Vegas, NV; *U.S. Public*, pg. 374

Albada, Jeff, Sr. V.P. & Mgr.-Surety Div.--Willis Corroon Corp. of California, San Francisco, CA; *Int'l*, pg. 1505

Albanese, John M., Sr. V.P.-Customer Svcs. & IS--The Penn Mutual Life Insurance Company, Philadelphia, PA; *U.S. Private*, pg. 849

Alberg, Edward G., Sr. V.P.--Falley's Inc., Topeka, KS; *U.S. Private*, pg. 1202

Albergotti, Ray, Sr. V.P. & Mngmt. Supvr.--Adler Boschetto Peebles & Partners, Inc., New York, NY; *U.S. Private*, pg. 17

Alberici, John S., Vice Chm., Chief Fin. Officer, Sr. V.P. & Sec.--J.S. Alberici Construction Co., Inc., Saint Louis, MO; *U.S. Private*, pg. 32

Alberini, Carlos, Chief Fin. Officer & Sr. V.P.--Footstar Inc., Mahwah, NJ; *U.S. Public*, pg. 661

Albert, Charles M., Sr. V.P.--FootAction USA, Irving, TX; *U.S. Public*, pg. 661

Albert, J.C., Sr. V.P.--Union Camp Corporation, Wayne, NJ; *U.S. Public*, pg. 1665

Albertson, Bob, Sr. V.P.-Direct Mktg.--Fairfield Communities, Inc., Little Rock, AR; *U.S. Public*, pg. 610

Albom, Ira, Sr. V.P.--Teleflex Incorporated, Plymouth Meeting, PA; *U.S. Public*, pg. 1569

Alborelli, Rodolfo, Sr. V.P. & Country Mgr.--Bank of America NT&SA, Buenos Aires, Argentina; *U.S. Public*, pg. 182

Albrecht, John, Sr. V.P.-Sls. & Mktg.--Mexicana Airlines, Los Angeles, CA; *Int'l*, pg. 332

Albright, Wayne, Sr. V.P.-Mfg.--Swingster Company, Kansas City, MO; *U.S. Private*, pg. 58

Albus, Robert E., Sr. V.P. & Pres.-OTC & Specialty--Advanced Polymer Systems, Redwood City, CA; *U.S. Public*, pg. 22

Alchin, John R., Sr. V.P. & Treas.--Comcast Corporation, Philadelphia, PA; *U.S. Public*, pg. 406

Alcorn, Daniel G., Sr. V.P.-Consumer Credit--Chittenden Corporation, Burlington, VT; *U.S. Public*, pg. 350

Alden, Alison, Sr. V.P.-Sls., Service & Human Resources--Boston Edison Company, Boston, MA; *U.S. Public*, pg. 247

Alderman, J. Kenneth, Sr. V.P.-Investments--Regions Financial Corporation, Birmingham, AL; *U.S. Public*, pg. 1371

Alderman, Ken, Chief Fin. Officer & Sr. V.P.--Gilbane Building Company, Providence, RI; *U.S. Private*, pg. 452

Alejo, Gene, Sr. V.P.-Fin. & Admin.--Dailey & Associates, West Hollywood, CA; *U.S. Public*, pg. 909

Alekel, Dennis A., Chief Oper. Officer & Sr. V.P.--Lewis Homes Management Corp., Upland, CA; *U.S. Private*, pg. 665

Alexander, Douglas S., Chief Fin. Officer & Sr. V.P.--London Life Insurance Group, London, Canada; *Int'l*, pg. 835

Alexander, John F., II, Chief Fin. Officer & Sr. V.P.--EG & G, Inc., Wellesley, MA; *U.S. Public*, pg. 542

Alexander, John R., Sr. V.P. & Sec.--Orange-Co., Inc., Bartow, FL; *U.S. Public*, pg. 1229

Alexander, Leigh, Sr. V.P.-Mktg. & Bus. Devel.--Paging Network, Inc., Plano, TX; *U.S. Public*, pg. 1252

Alexander, Nicholas Z., Sr. V.P.-Gen. Counsel & Sec.--ACCEL International Corporation, Dublin, OH; *U.S. Public*, pg. 14

Alexander, R. David, Sr. V.P.-Distribution & Transportation--Family Dollar Stores, Inc., Matthews, NC; *U.S. Public*, pg. 612

Alexander, Tom, Sr. V.P.--First Commerce Bancshares, Inc., Lincoln, NE; *U.S. Public*, pg. 629

Alexy, George N., Chief Mktg. & Prods. Officer--Cirrus Logic, Inc., Fremont, CA; *U.S. Public*, pg. 375

Alfano, Andrea, Sr. V.P. & Acct Dir.--Hal Riney & Partners, Inc., San Francisco, CA; *U.S. Private*, pg. 931

Alford, Timothy, Sr. V.P.--The Lincoln National Life Insurance Co., Fort Wayne, IN; *U.S. Public*, pg. 998

Alford, Timothy, Sr. V.P.--Lincoln National Administrative Services Corp., Fort Wayne, IN; *U.S. Public*, pg. 998

Alford, Timothy J., Sr. V.P.-Grp. Mkts.--Lincoln National Reinsurance Company (Barbados) Limited, Fort Wayne, IN; *U.S. Public*, pg. 998

Alford, Timothy J., Sr. V.P.-Grp. Markets--Lincoln National Reinsurance Company (Bermuda) Limited, Fort Wayne, IN; *U.S. Public*, pg. 998

Alger, Glenn M., Sr. V.P.--Expeditors International of Washington, Inc., Seattle, WA; *U.S. Public*, pg. 600

Allain, Stephanie, Sr. V.P.-Production--Columbia Pictures, Culver City, CA; *Int'l*, pg. 1281

Allan, Norman S., Sr. V.P.--C.S. McKee & Company, Inc., Pittsburgh, PA; *U.S. Public*, pg. 1673

Allard, Leigh W., Sr. V.P.-Admin. Svcs. Grp.--Federal Home Loan Bank of New York, New York, NY; *U.S. Private*, pg. 399

Allatt, Dennis, Sr. V.P.--Willis Corroon Melling Ltd., Vancouver, Canada; *Int'l*, pg. 1509

Allchin, James E., Sr. V.P.-Personal & Bus. Sys. Grp.--Microsoft Corporation, Redmond, WA; *U.S. Public*, pg. 1107

Allen, Barry K., Sr. V.P.-Communications & Info. Prods.--Ameritech Corp., Chicago, IL; *U.S. Public*, pg. 98

Allen, Charles E., Sr. V.P.-Human Resources--The Lamson & Sessions Co., Cleveland, OH; *U.S. Public*, pg. 976

Allen, Clive V., Sr. V.P. & Gen. Counsel--Northern Telecom Limited, Brampton, Canada; *Int'l*, pg. 968

Allen, David A., Sr. V.P.-Pub. Rels.--Inco Limited, Toronto, Canada; *Int'l*, pg. 672

Allen, Don, Sr. V.P. & Trust Officer--First National Bank of Sweetwater, Sweetwater, TX; *U.S. Public*, pg. 633

Allen, Durwood C., Sr. V.P.--Standard Federal Bank, Troy, MI; *Int'l*, pg. 10

Allen, Evelyn R., Sr. V.P.--Liggett-Stashower, Inc., Cleveland, OH; *U.S. Private*, pg. 667

Allen, G. Stephen, Sr. V.P.--Burns & Wilcox Ltd., Farmington, MI; *U.S. Private*, pg. 609

Allen, George Stephen, Sr. V.P. & Dir.-Branch Devel.--H.W. Kaufman Financial Group, Inc., Farmington, MI; *U.S. Private*, pg. 609

Allen, H. David, Sr. V.P. & Gen. Mgr.-Pacific Rim Div.--Manulife Financial (The Manufacturers Life Insurance Company), Toronto, Canada; *Int'l*, pg. 840

Allen, Hugh L., Sr. Exec. V.P.-Sls. & Mktg.--Lawson Products, Inc., Des Plaines, IL; *U.S. Public*, pg. 980

Allen, James A., Sr. V.P.--Chemical Bank Michigan, Clare, MI; *U.S. Public*, pg. 345

Allen, James W., Sr. V.P.-Opers.--Pride International, Inc., Houston, TX; *U.S. Public*, pg. 1324

Allen, Joseph W., Sr. V.P.--Great Lakes Construction Co., Independence, OH; *U.S. Private*, pg. 474

Allen, Judith, Sr. V.P.-Mktg. & Programming--Cable Television Division, New Canaan, CT; *U.S. Public*, pg. 329

Allen, Kathy L., Sr. V.P.--Duro-Last Roofing, Inc., Saginaw, MI; *U.S. Private*, pg. 349

Allen, Lindsey, Chief Fin. Officer & Sr. V.P.--Liquid Controls LLC, Lake Bluff, IL; *U.S. Private*, pg. 669

Allen, Mark K., Sr. V.P.-Opers.--C-Cube Microsystems, Milpitas, CA; *U.S. Public*, pg. 272

Allen, Martin J., Jr., Sr. V.P. & Sec.--Old Kent Financial Corporation, Grand Rapids, MI; *U.S. Public*, pg. 1216

Allen, Michael F., Sr. V.P.--The Forest Hill State Bank, Bel Air, MD; *U.S. Public*, pg. 1089

Allen, Michael L., Sr. V.P.--Trustmark National Bank, Jackson, MS; *U.S. Public*, pg. 1643

Allen, Patrick J., Chief Fin. Officer & Sr. V.P.--Hambrecht & Quist LLC., San Francisco, CA; *U.S. Public*, pg. 778

Allender, Patrick W., Chief Fin. Officer, Sr. V.P. & Sec.--Danaher Corporation, Washington, DC; *U.S. Public*, pg. 480

Aller, Robert L., Sr. V.P.-Fin.--Loctite Corporation, Rocky Hill, CT; *Int'l*, pg. 611

Allerbrand, Tom, Chief Fin. Officer & Sr. V.P.--Vattenfall AB, Stockholm, Sweden; *Int'l*, pg. 1452

Alley, Greg, Sr. V.P. & Mngmt. Supvr.--Laughlin/Constable, Inc., Milwaukee, WI; *U.S. Private*, pg. 653

Allford, Suzanne, Sr. V.P.-Mktg. & Admin.--Sam's Clubs Div., Bentonville, AR; *U.S. Public*, pg. 1733

Allin, Thomas B., Sr. V.P.--McDonald's Corporation, Oak Brook, IL; *U.S. Public*, pg. 1068

Allison, Lin, Sr. V.P.-Systems & Data Processing--Kohl's Corporation, Menomonee Falls, WI; *U.S. Public*, pg. 965

Allonen, Heikki, Sr. V.P.-Plng. Devel.--Metra Corporation, Helsinki, Finland; *Int'l*, pg. 862

Allor, Marilyn, Sr. V.P.-Human Resources--Citizens Banking Corporation, Flint, MI; *U.S. Public*, pg. 379

Allran, Robert R., Sr. V.P.-Opers.--Detroit Diesel Corp., Detroit, MI; *U.S. Private*, pg. 850

Alm, John R., Chief Fin. Officer & Sr. V.P.--Coca-Cola Enterprises Inc., Atlanta, GA; *U.S. Public*, pg. 393

Alm, Robert A., Sr. V.P.-Fin. Mngmt. Grp.--First Hawaiian Bank, Honolulu, HI; *U.S. Public*, pg. 634

Americo, Vincent R., Sr. V.P.--Halter Marine Group, Inc., Gulfport, MS; *U.S. Public*, pg. 778

Almieri, Raymond, Sr. V.P.-West Region--Mobile Technology Inc., Los Angeles, CA; *U.S. Private*, pg. 754

Almog, Rivki, Sr. V.P.-Customers & Trng. Dept.--Bank Hapoalim, Tel Aviv, Israel; *Int'l*, pg. 149

Almond, David R., Sr. V.P., Gen. Counsel & Sec.--Fleming Companies, Inc., Oklahoma City, OK; *U.S. Public*, pg. 652

Almquist, Stephan, Sr. V.P. & Corp. Treas.--Telefonaktiebolaget LM Ericsson, Stockholm, Sweden; *Int'l*, pg. 1363

Aloian, D. Pike, Sr. V.P.--Rothschild Inc., New York, NY; *U.S. Private*, pg. 947

Alpin, Jerome P., Sr. V.P. & Gen. Mgr.-Intl. Sls. & Mktg.--Dep Corporation, Rancho Dominguez, CA; *U.S. Public*, pg. 500

Alscher, Murray J., Sr. V.P.-Acq.--Prime Group Realty Trust, Chicago, IL; *U.S. Public*, pg. 1326

Alt, Claudia J., Sr. V.P.-Individual Markets--Time Insurance, Milwaukee, WI; *Int'l*, pg. 499

Altaba Nanez, Sergio, Sr. V.P.-Pur.--Grupo Acerero del Norte S.A. de C.V. (GAN), Mexico, Mexico; *Int'l*, pg. 572

Alten, Lawrence, Sr. V.P.-Creative Svcs. & Adv.--U.S. Healthcare, Inc., Blue Bell, PA; *U.S. Public*, pg. 26

Altenbaumer, Larry F., Chief Fin. Officer & Sr. V.P.--Illinois Power Company, Decatur, IL; *U.S. Public*, pg. 869

Altiere, Daniel J., Sr. V.P.--Blonder-Tongue Laboratories, Inc., Old Bridge, NJ; *U.S. Public*, pg. 237

Altilio, David C., Chief Fin. Officer & Sr. V.P.--Federal Home Loan Bank of New York, New York, NY; *U.S. Private*, pg. 399

Altman, Dan, Chief Fin. Officer & Sr. V.P.--Intertec Publishing, Overland Park, KS; *U.S. Public*, pg. 1327

Alton, N. Kirby, Sr. V.P.-Devel.--Amgen Inc., Thousand Oaks, CA; *U.S. Public*, pg. 100

Altonen, Aarto, Sr. V.P.--Rauma Ltd., Helsinki, Finland; *Int'l*, pg. 1428

Alvarez, David R., Sr. V.P.-Providian Home Loans--AEGON USA, Inc., Louisville, KY; *Int'l*, pg. 26

Alvarez, Fausto, Sr. V.P.--Banco Santander, Madrid, Spain; *Int'l*, pg. 143

Alves, G.W., Sr. V.P.--KTI Fish, Houston, TX; *U.S. Private*, pg. 604

Am, Knut, Sr. V.P.-Exploration & Production--Phillips Petroleum Company, Bartlesville, OK; *U.S. Public*, pg. 1290

Amadio, Ernest R., Sr. V.P.--The Annapolis Banking & Trust Co., Annapolis, MD; *U.S. Public*, pg. 1088

Amato, A.J. (Nino), Sr. V.P.--Wisconsin Power & Light Company, Madison, WI; *U.S. Public*, pg. 1728

Amato, Albert L., Jr., Sr. V.P.-Policy Admin.--American National Insurance Company, Galveston, TX; *U.S. Public*, pg. 87

Amato, Justo S., Sr. V.P.-Fin.--Swisher International Group, Inc., Darien, CT; *U.S. Public*, pg. 1543

Amato, Susan L., Sr. V.P.-Engrng. & Network Opers.--360 Degrees Communications Company, Chicago, IL; *U.S. Public*, pg. 1607

Ambro, J. Gregory, Sr. V.P.-Fin. & Admin.--Harris Teeter, Inc., Charlotte, NC; *U.S. Public*, pg. 1412

Ambrus, Jozsef, Sr. V.P.-Strategic Plng.--TVX Gold Inc., Toronto, Canada; *Int'l*, pg. 1345

Amelia, Margot A., Sr. V.P. & Grp. Supvr.-Acct. Services--Gray Kirk/VanSant Advertising, Inc., Baltimore, MD; *U.S. Private*, pg. 472

Amell, Hans B., Sr. V.P.-Mktg.--Cognizant Corporation, Westport, CT; *U.S. Public*, pg. 395

Amerman, Tom, Sr. V.P.-Human Resources--Younkers, Inc., Des Moines, IA; *U.S. Public*, pg. 1334

Ames, Kevin, Sr. V.P. & Controller--Bank of the West, Walnut Creek, CA; *Int'l*, pg. 163

Ames, Mike, Chief Oper. Officer & Sr. V.P.--Inner Secrets, Inc., Harrison, NJ; *U.S. Private*, pg. 564

Amico, Robert, Sr. V.P.-Sls.--Rand McNally & Company, Skokie, IL; *U.S. Private*, pg. 908

Amiry, Reda H., Sr. V.P.-Taxes--Crown Cork & Seal Company, Inc., Philadelphia, PA; *U.S. Public*, pg. 462

Amiry, Seyed, Chief Fin. Officer & Sr. V.P.--Heald Colleges, San Francisco, CA; *U.S. Private*, pg. 514

Amlin, Bo, Sr. V.P.-Corp. Affairs--Swedish Match S.A., Stockholm, Sweden; *Int'l*, pg. 1328

Ammons, Larry B., Sr. V.P.--Riverside/Bi-Lo Division, Du Bois, PA; *U.S. Public*, pg. 1270

Amon, Anton, Sr. V.P.--The Coca-Cola Company, Atlanta, GA; *U.S. Public*, pg. 392

Amster, B.R., Sr. V.P.-Mktg. & Sls.--Canadian Airlines International Ltd., Calgary, Canada; *Int'l*, pg. 256

Amundson, Joy A., Sr. V.P.-Chemical & Agricultural Prods.--Abbott Laboratories, Abbott Park, IL; *U.S. Public*, pg. 12

Anantakul, Poonsin, Sr. V.P.-Info. Tech.--The Industrial Finance Corporation of Thailand, Bangkok, Thailand; *Int'l*, pg. 677

Anastasi, Robert E., Sr. V.P.--Helix Technology Corp., Mansfield, MA; *U.S. Public*, pg. 808

Andelin, Gerald, Sr. V.P. & Creative Dir.--Hal Riney & Partners, Inc., San Francisco, CA; *U.S. Private*, pg. 931

Andenmatten, Fredy, Sr. V.P.-Information Systems & Organization--Liechtenstein Global Trust Limited, Vaduz, Liechtenstein; *Int'l*, pg. 809

Anderi, Norris H., Sr. V.P.--Henkels & McCoy, Inc., Blue Bell, PA; *U.S. Private*, pg. 522

Anders, Paul, Sr. V.P.-Info. Sys.--Tropical Sportswear International, Tampa, FL; *U.S. Private*, pg. 1105

Andersen, Shaza L., Sr. V.P.--Century Bancshares, Inc., Washington, DC; *U.S. Public*, pg. 328

Anderson, Allen J., Sr. V.P.-Admin. & Pub. Affairs--Harvest States Cooperatives, Saint Paul, MN; *U.S. Private*, pg. 508

Anderson, Ardys A., Sr. V.P.-Servicing--ReliaStar Mortgage Company, West Des Moines, IA; *U.S. Public*, pg. 1376

Anderson, D.J., Chief Fin. Officer & Sr. V.P.--Newport News Shipbuilding, Inc., Newport News, VA; *U.S. Public*, pg. 1179

Anderson, David S., Sr. V.P. & Controller--Citizens Savings Bank, Providence, RI; *Int'l*, pg. 1132

Anderson, Don, Chief Fin. Officer & Sr. V.P.--Carr Gottstein Foods, Anchorage, AK; *U.S. Public*, pg. 308

Anderson, Forrest, Sr. V.P. & Res. Dir.--Golin/Harris Communications, Inc., Chicago, IL; *Int'l*, pg. 1226

Anderson, Fred, Sr. V.P.-Mergers & Acquisitions--Hanover Direct, Inc., Weehawken, NJ; *U.S. Public*, pg. 782

Anderson, G. Michael, Sr. V.P.-Buying Grp.--Tuesday Morning Corporation, Dallas, TX; *U.S. Public*, pg. 1644

Anderson, Gail Philip, Sr. V.P.-H.R.--Raytheon Company, Lexington, MA; *U.S. Public*, pg. 1364

Anderson, Gregory M., Sr. V.P.--ReliaStar Investment Research, Inc., Minneapolis, MN; *U.S. Public*, pg. 1376

Anderson, Jack, Sr. V.P.-Sls. & Mktg.--Holland America Line Westours, Seattle, WA; *U.S. Public*, pg. 306

Anderson, James, Sr. V.P.-Labor Rels. & Personnel Admin.--Hilton Hotels Corporation, Beverly Hills, CA; *U.S. Public*, pg. 828

Anderson, James E., Sr. V.P. & Chief Admin. Officer--Call Interactive, Omaha, NE; *U.S. Public*, pg. 631

Anderson, James R., Chief Fin. Officer & Sr. V.P.--HNTB Corporation, Kansas City, MO; *U.S. Private*, pg. 492

Anderson, Ken, Sr. V.P.-Fin. & Admin.--Freudenberg-NOK, Plymouth, MI; *U.S. Private*, pg. 427

Anderson, Margaret A., Chief Fin. Officer, Sr. V.P.-Admin. & Treas.--Aerospace Corporation, El Segundo, CA; *U.S. Private*, pg. 24

Anderson, Mark, Sr. V.P.-Educational Svcs. Grp.--Vanstar Corporation, Pleasanton, CA; *U.S. Public*, pg. 1708

Anderson, Marvin R., Sr. V.P. & Controller--AMCORE Trust Company, Rockford, IL; *U.S. Public*, pg. 65

Anderson, Neil, Sr. V.P.-Sls. & Mktg.--Ball Corporation, Muncie, IN; *U.S. Public*, pg. 170

Anderson, Neil M., Sr. V.P.-Mktg. & Sls.--Ball Metal Beverage Container Corp., Westminster, CO; *U.S. Public*, pg. 171

Anderson, Peter J., Sr. V.P.-Investments--American Express Financial Advisor, Minneapolis, MN; *U.S. Public*, pg. 73

Anderson, R. Wayne, Sr. V.P.-H.R.--Amoco Corporation, Chicago, IL; *U.S. Public*, pg. 101

Anderson, Richard, Sr. V.P. & Tech. Dir.--Hunter Douglas, Inc., Upper Saddle River, NJ; *Int'l*, pg. 639

Anderson, Richard, Sr. V.P.-Technical Opers. & Airport Affairs--Northwest Airlines, Inc., Saint Paul, MN; *U.S. Public*, pg. 1200

Anderson, Richard H., Sr. V.P.-Technical Opers. & State Affairs--Northwest Airlines Corp., Saint Paul, MN; *U.S. Public*, pg. 1199

Anderson, Richard N., Sr. V.P.-Field Sls. & Gen. Mgr.-Life Cycle Services Group--Vanstar Corporation, Pleasanton, CA; *U.S. Public*, pg. 1708

Anderson, Richard T., Sr. V.P.--Rothschild Inc., New York, NY; *U.S. Private*, pg. 947

Anderson, Richard T., Sr. V.P.--Rothchild Asset Management Inc., New York, NY; *U.S. Private*, pg. 947

Anderson, Rick J., Sr. V.P.-Fin.--Noranda Inc., Toronto, Canada; *Int'l*, pg. 433

Anderson, Robert, Sr. V.P.-Science & Tech.--Johns Manville Corporation, Denver, CO; *U.S. Public*, pg. 927

Anderson, Robert W., Sr. V.P.-Real Estate Dept.--Zions First National Bank, Salt Lake City, UT; *U.S. Public*, pg. 1793

Anderson, Ronald C., Sr. V.P.-Gen. Merchandise--Fleming Companies, Inc., Oklahoma City, OK; *U.S. Public*, pg. 652

Anderson, Ronald G., Chief Fin. Officer & Sr. V.P.--Aid Association for Lutherans, Appleton, WI; *U.S. Private*, pg. 27

Anderson, Roy, Sr. V.P.-Energy Generation--Florida Power Corporation, Saint Petersburg, FL; *U.S. Public*, pg. 655

Anderson, Russell W., Sr. V.P.--UNUM Life Insurance Company of America, Portland, ME; *U.S. Public*, pg. 1699

Anderson, Sherry E., Sr. V.P. & Sec.--United Companies Financial Corporation, Baton Rouge, LA; *U.S. Public*, pg. 1675

Anderson, William N., Sr. V.P.-GMM Hardlines--Kmart Corporation, Troy, MI; *U.S. Public*, pg. 963

Andersson, Digby, Sr. V.P.-Claims Div.--Trygg-Hansa, Stockholm, Sweden; *Int'l*, pg. 1425

Andersson, Hans, Sr. V.P.--Elof Hansson AB, Goteborg, Sweden; *Int'l*, pg. 595

Andre, Michael G., Sr. V.P.--Methode Electronics Inc., Chicago, IL; *U.S. Public*, pg. 1101

Andre, Stan, Sr. V.P.-Mktg.--Nulaid Foods, Ripon, CA; *U.S. Private*, pg. 809

Andreas, Martin L., Sr. V.P.-Sls. & Mktg.--Archer Daniels Midland Company (ADM), Decatur, IL; *U.S. Public*, pg. 127

Andreotti, Cynthia K., Sr. V.P.-West, Bus. Sls. & Service--MCI Communications Corp., Atlanta, GA; *U.S. Public*, pg. 1023

Andreotti, Lamberto, Sr. V.P.--Pharmacia & Upjohn, Inc., Windsor, United Kingdom; *Int'l*, pg. 1047

Andrepont, Kevin, Sr. V.P. & Treas.--Parish Water Company, Inc., Baton Rouge, LA; *U.S. Private*, pg. 123

Andresen, Trond, Sr. V.P.-Corp. Communications--Kvaerner a.s.a., Lysaker, Norway; *Int'l*, pg. 766

Andrew, S. Lance, Sr. V.P. & Acct. Exec.--Odyssey Reinsurance Corporation, New York, NY; *Int'l*, pg. 1258

Andrews, Ceceilia, Sr. V.P.-Bus. Affairs--MGM Worldwide Television, Group., Santa Monica, CA; *U.S. Public*, pg. 1102

Andrews, Glen F., Sr. V.P. & Grp. Gen. Mgr.--BHP Copper, San Francisco, CA; *Int'l*, pg. 227

Andrews, Lin, Sr. V.P. & Client Services Dir.--Highway One Communications, Integrated Marketing Services, San Francisco, CA; *U.S. Private*, pg. 303

Andrews, William E., Chief Fin. Officer & Sr. V.P.--Varco-Pruden Buildings, Memphis, TN; *U.S. Public*, pg. 1677

Andrews, William H., Jr., Sr. V.P.-Mktg.--Union Planters Corporation, Cordova, TN; *U.S. Public*, pg. 1668

Andrews, Yvonne S., Sr. V.P.-Mngmt. Services--SouthTrust Corporation, Birmingham, AL; *U.S. Public*, pg. 1491

Andriessen, Roel G.M., Sr. V.P.-Intl.--IBP, Inc., Dakota City, NE; *U.S. Public*, pg. 852

Ang, Christopher, Sr. V.P. & Worldwide Grp. Acct. Dir.--DMB&B New York, New York, NY; *U.S. Private*, pg. 302

Ange, Jean-Paul, Sr. V.P.--Banexi International Financial Services (North America) Corp., New York, NY; *Int'l*, pg. 163

Angelozzi, Claire, Sr. V.P.-Special Projects--BankAtlantic Bancorp, Inc., Fort Lauderdale, FL; *U.S. Public*, pg. 183

Angerami, John L., Sr. V.P.--Chubb & Son, Inc., Warren, NJ; *U.S. Public*, pg. 355

Angers, Thomas, Sr. V.P.-Personnel--The Bank of New York Company, Inc., New York, NY; *U.S. Public*, pg. 178

Angle, Richard W., Sr. V.P.--Time Warner Publishing Inc., New York, NY; *U.S. Public*, pg. 1614

Anglewicz, David J., Sr. V.P.-Facility Svcs.--La Petite Academy Inc., Overland Park, KS; *U.S. Private*, pg. 640

Aniballi, Douglas F., Sr. V.P.-Stores & Sls.--Amlings Flowerland, Hinsdale, IL; *U.S. Private*, pg. 66

Anicetti, Richard, Sr. V.P.-Retail Opers./Southeast--Hannaford Bros. Co., Scarborough, ME; *U.S. Public*, pg. 781

Annett, J.M., Sr. V.P. & Natl. Dir.-Long Term Care Fin.--Ziegler Securities Division, Chicago, IL; *U.S. Public*, pg. 1792

Anson, Philip J., Sr. V.P.--STS Services Inc., Nashville, TN; *U.S. Public*, pg. 277

Answine, Emmanuel J., Sr. V.P.-Bus. Sys.--Southwest National Corporation, Greensburg, PA; *U.S. Public*, pg. 1493

Answine, Emmanuel J., Sr. V.P.--Southwest National Bank of Pennsylvania, Greensburg, PA; *U.S. Public*, pg. 1493

Answorth, Louis L., Sr. V.P. & Gen. Counsel--Pentair, Inc., Saint Paul, MN; *U.S. Public*, pg. 1273

Antoine, Rene, Sr. V.P.-Export Div.--Danone Group, Paris, France; *Int'l*, pg. 379

Anton, Denise, Sr. V.P.-Mktg.--Taubman Centers, Inc., Bloomfield Hills, MI; *U.S. Public*, pg. 1561

Anton, Mary Breitbach, Sr. V.P. & Consumer Res. & Acct. Grp. Dir.--Creswell, Munsell, Fultz & Zirbel, L.P., Cedar Rapids, IA; *U.S. Private*, pg. 1197

Antrasian, Robert B., Chief Fin. Officer & Sr. V.P.--Big Y Foods Inc., Springfield, MA; *U.S. Private*, pg. 143

Anylon, Kenneth, Sr. V.P.-Underwriting--Amica Mutual Insurance Co., Lincoln, RI; *U.S. Private*, pg. 66

Anzilotti, Michael G., Sr. V.P. & Reg. Exec. Officer-Northern Reg.--First Virginia Banks, Inc., Falls Church, VA; *U.S. Public*, pg. 641

Aoyama, M., Sr. V.P.--Mitsubishi International Corporation, New York, NY; *Int'l*, pg. 871

Aoyama, Sheni A., Sr. V.P.-Sls. Mngmt.--American Savings Bank, F.S.B., Honolulu, HI; *U.S. Public*, pg. 800

Aparicio, Anthony, Sr. V.P. & Sec.--Banco Santander, Madrid, Spain; *Int'l*, pg. 143

Apatoff, Robert S., Sr. V.P.-Adv.--U.S. Healthcare, Inc., Blue Bell, PA; *U.S. Public*, pg. 26

Apatov, Craig, Sr. V.P.-Strategic Mktg.--The Weather Channel, Atlanta, GA; *U.S. Private*, pg. 647

Aplin, Gregory, Sr. V.P.-Manufactured Housing--Green Tree Financial Corporation, Saint Paul, MN; *U.S. Public*, pg. 761

Appel, Marcia, Sr. V.P.-Adv., Natl. Promo. & Corp. Communications--Musicland Group Inc., Minnetonka, MN; *U.S. Public*, pg. 1142

Appel, Mark E., Sr. V.P.--American Arbitration Association, New York, NY; *U.S. Private*, pg. 50

Apple, John, V.P.-Floor Covering--William M. Bird & Co., Inc., Charleston, SC; *U.S. Private*, pg. 145

Appleby, Pauline A., Sr. V.P.--Hibernia Corporation, New Orleans, LA; *U.S. Public*, pg. 825

Applegate, Henry M., III, Sr. V.P. & Controller--Mirage Resorts Incorporated, Las Vegas, NV; *U.S. Public*, pg. 1116

Appleton, Colin C., Sr. V.P. & Trust Officer--First National Bank of Pennsylvania, Hermitage, PA; *U.S. Public*, pg. 607

Apps, Victor S., Sr. V.P. & Gen. Mgr.-Greater China Div.--Manulife Financial (The Manufacturers Life Insurance Company), Toronto, Canada; *Int'l*, pg. 840

Aps, Albert, Sr. V.P.-Controlling & Coordination--Bayer Corporation, Pittsburgh, PA; *Int'l*, pg. 172

Aragane, Y., Sr. V.P.--Mitsubishi International Corporation, New York, NY; *Int'l*, pg. 871

Arai, Tadayuki, Sr. V.P.--Nippon Telegraph and Telephone Corporation, Tokyo, Japan; *Int'l*, pg. 940

Arakelian, Carol, Sr. V.P.-Fin.--Citizens Bank of Massachusetts, Fairhaven, MA; *Int'l*, pg. 1132

Araki, Toshihiko, Sr. V.P. & Deputy Gen. Mgr.--Bank of Yokohama New York, New York, NY; *Int'l*, pg. 159

Aramini, Ronald A., Sr. V.P.-Opers.--America West Airlines, Inc., Phoenix, AZ; *U.S. Public*, pg. 67

Aramony, Diane, Sr. V.P.-Human Resources--Mutual of America Life Insurance Company, New York, NY; *U.S. Private*, pg. 769

Arant, John E., III, Sr. V.P.-Distr. & Client Services--Keyport Life Insurance Company, Boston, MA; *U.S. Private*, pg. 666

Araya, Hector, Sr. V.P.--Coeur D'Alene Mines Corporation, Coeur D'Alene, ID; *U.S. Public*, pg. 394

Arboleda, Rodrigo, Sr. V.P.-Bus. Devel.-Latin America--Ogden Corporation, New York, NY; *U.S. Public*, pg. 1213

Arbutina, Petra, Sr. V.P. & Media Dir.--Ketchum Advertising/Pittsburgh, Pittsburgh, PA; *U.S. Private*, pg. 616

Archer, Cynthia A., Sr. V.P.-Intermodal Service Group--Conrail, Inc., Philadelphia, PA; *U.S. Public*, pg. 431

Archer, Dennis, Sr. V.P. & Gen. Mgr.-Hosiery/Childrenswear/Casualwear--Fruit of the Loom, Inc., Chicago, IL; *U.S. Public*, pg. 685

Archer, Marie J., Sr. V.P.--Clyde Savings Bank Company, Clyde, OH; *U.S. Public*, pg. 632

Archer, Robert, Sr. V.P.-Sls.--SPS Payment Systems, Inc., Riverwoods, IL; *U.S. Public*, pg. 1132

Archibald, David R., Sr. V.P.-Corp. Mktg.--Huntington National Bank, Columbus, OH; *U.S. Public*, pg. 850

Ard, Anthony E., Sr. V.P.-Corp. Affairs--Indiana Energy, Inc., Indianapolis, IN; *U.S. Public*, pg. 874

Ard, Anthony E., Sr. V.P.-Corp. Affairs--Indiana Gas Company, Inc., Indianapolis, IN; *U.S. Public*, pg. 875

Arend, James W., Sr. V.P.--Atlantic Mutual Companies, New York, NY; *U.S. Private*, pg. 95

Arendt, Steve, Exec. V.P.-Opers.--Remco America, Inc., Wichita, KS; *Int'l*, pg. 1385

Argila, Raymond P., Sr. V.P., Legal & Asst. Sec.--Urstadt Biddle Properties, Inc., Greenwich, CT; *U.S. Public*, pg. 1700

Arisman, A. Thomas, Sr. V.P.-Life Div.--Horace Mann Educators Corporation, Springfield, IL; *U.S. Public*, pg. 835

Ariturk, Haluk, Sr. V.P. & Chief Actuary--The Acacia Group - Acacia Life Insurance Co., Bethesda, MD; *U.S. Private*, pg. 10

Arlo, Marie, Sr. V.P.--Grey Advertising Inc., New York, NY; *U.S. Public*, pg. 764

Armitage, Carol, Sr. V.P.-Tech.--Broadband Networks Group, Hatboro, PA; *U.S. Public*, pg. 716

Armitage, Jeffrey K., Sr. V.P.-Construction--Taubman Centers, Inc., Bloomfield Hills, MI; *U.S. Public*, pg. 1561

Armitrano, Richard, Sr. V.P.--Aceto Corporation, Lake Success, NY; *U.S. Public*, pg. 15

Armstrong, A. Gordon, Sr. V.P.-Fin. & Corp. Services--Canfor Corporation, Vancouver, Canada; *Int'l*, pg. 260

Armstrong, Alex, Sr. V.P.-Product Strategies--Security Pacific Financial Services Inc., San Diego, CA; *U.S. Public*, pg. 181

Armstrong, Bill, Sr. V.P.-Americana Foods--TCBY Enterprises Inc., Little Rock, AR; *U.S. Public*, pg. 1553

Armstrong, Bill, Sr. V.P.--Americana Foods, Inc., Dallas, TX; *U.S. Public*, pg. 1554

Armstrong, T. Paul, Sr. V.P. & Gen. Mgr.-Table Service Restaurant Bus. Grp.--Micros Systems Inc., Beltsville, MD; *U.S. Public*, pg. 1106

Arnesen, Siguard, Sr. V.P.-Property Mngmt.--Lat Purser & Associates, Charlotte, NC; *U.S. Private*, pg. 896

Arnett, James W., Jr., Sr. V.P.-Shoney's Opers.--Shoney's, Inc., Nashville, TN; *U.S. Public*, pg. 1467

Arnholt, John, Sr. V.P. & Dir.-Fin.--HMS Partners, Columbus, OH; *U.S. Private*, pg. 491

Arnold, A. Joel, Sr. V.P.--Drug Emporium, Inc., Powell, OH; *U.S. Public*, pg. 530

Arnold, Dave W., Sr. V.P.-Tech. Grp.--Mississippi Chemical Corporation, Yazoo City, MS; *U.S. Public*, pg. 1117

Arnold, Gary M., Chief Fin. Officer & Sr. V.P.-Fin.--Mosby-Year Book, Inc., Saint Louis, MO; *U.S. Public*, pg. 1616

Arnold, Harry, Sr. V.P.-Airplane Devel. & Definition--Engineering Division, Renton, WA; *U.S. Public*, pg. 240

Arnold, Henry P., Sr. V.P.-Airplane Devel.--Boeing Commercial Airplane Group, Renton, WA; *U.S. Public*, pg. 240

Arnold, Junius H., Jr., Sr. V.P.--COMSAT RSI, Inc., Sterling, VA; *U.S. Public*, pg. 424

Arnold, Michael J., Chief Admin. Officer & Sr. V.P.--Freeport-McMoRan Inc., New Orleans, LA; *U.S. Public*, pg. 680

Arnold, Robert, Sr. V.P. & Dir.-Stores--T.J. Maxx, Framingham, MA; *U.S. Public*, pg. 1557

Arnon, Ehud, Sr. V.P.-Foreign Trade--Bank Hapoalim, Tel Aviv, Israel; *Int'l*, pg. 149

Arnon, Wendy, Sr. V.P. & Assoc. Media Dir.--Grey Direct, New York, NY; *U.S. Public*, pg. 764

Arnone, Philip S., Sr. V.P.-Mdsg.--Riser Foods, Inc., Bedford, OH; *U.S. Private*, pg. 450

Aronaho, Kauko O., Chief Fin. Officer & Sr. V.P.-Fin.--ComputerLand Canada, Brampton, Canada; *Int'l*, pg. 1154

Aronchick, Joel D., Sr. V.P.--Chubb & Son, Inc., Warren, NJ; *U.S. Public*, pg. 355

Arone, Anne, Sr. V.P.-Corp. Devel.--EdperBrascan Corporation, Toronto, Canada; *Int'l*, pg. 433

Aronson, Gary S., Sr. V.P.-Mdse.--Haggar Corporation, Dallas, TX; *U.S. Public*, pg. 774

Aronson, Lewis, Sr. V.P.-Org. Devel. & Strategic Plng.--Bush Industries Inc., Jamestown, NY; *U.S. Public*, pg. 270

Arora, Upkar S., Sr. V.P.-Fin.--TrizecHahn Corporation, Toronto, Canada; *Int'l*, pg. 1424

Aroyan, Edward, Sr. V.P.--Grey Advertising Inc., New York, NY; *U.S. Public*, pg. 764

Arp, Steven, Sr. V.P.--First Mutual of Boston, Boston, MA; *U.S. Public*, pg. 184

Arpey, Gerard J., Chief Fin. Officer & Sr. V.P.--AMR Corporation, Fort Worth, TX; *U.S. Public*, pg. 9

Arrieta, C., Sr. V.P.-Gulf Coast Region--Daher Golden Eagle, Humble, TX; *U.S. Public*, pg. 749

Arrington, David J., Sr. V.P.-Human Resources--Niagara Mohawk Power Corporation, Syracuse, NY; *U.S. Public*, pg. 1181

Artes, Didac, Sr. V.P.--Banco Santander, Madrid, Spain; *Int'l*, pg. 143

Arthur, Magaret K., Sr. V.P. & Gen. Consel--National Life Insurance Company, Montpelier, VT; *U.S. Private*, pg. 785

Artis, Curt, Sr. V.P.-Human Resources--Lucent Technologies Inc., Murray Hill, NJ; *U.S. Public*, pg. 1017

Artolozaga Noriega, Carlos, Sr. V.P.-Sugar Mill Div.--Grupo Continental S.A., Tampico, Mexico; *Int'l*, pg. 573

Arton, Gavin R., Sr. V.P.-Investor Rels. Officer--Exel Insurance Co. Ltd., Hamilton, Bermuda; *Int'l*, pg. 467

Arvantinos, S.C., Sr. V.P. & Treas.--Hope's Architectural Products Inc., Jamestown, NY; *U.S. Private*, pg. 538

Arvela, Pertti, Sr. V.P.--United Paper Mills Ltd., Valkeakoski, Finland; *Int'l*, pg. 1429

Asada, A., Sr. V.P.--Mitsubishi International Corporation, New York, NY; *Int'l*, pg. 871

Aschenbrenner, John, Sr. V.P.-Individual Opers.--The Principal Financial Group, Des Moines, IA; *U.S. Private*, pg. 885

Aschenbrenner, John, Sr. V.P.-Individual Opers.--Principal Mutual Life Insurance Co., Des Moines, IA; *U.S. Private*, pg. 886

Ascher, Neil, Sr. V.P. & Grp. Media Dir.--DMB&B New York, New York, NY; *U.S. Private*, pg. 302

Ascolese, Mark, Sr. V.P.--Worldwide Services Group, Raleigh, NC; *Int'l*, pg. 126

Ascolese, Mark A., Sr. V.P. & Gen. Mgr.-Americas Grp.--Exide Electronics Group, Inc., Raleigh, NC; *Int'l*, pg. 126

Ash, Margy, Sr. V.P.-Opers.--Commercial Federal Corporation, Omaha, NE; *U.S. Public*, pg. 411

Ash, Sam M., Sr. V.P.--Sam Ash Music Corp., Hicksville, NY; *U.S. Private*, pg. 88

Ashakul, Teera, Dr., Sr. V.P.--The Industrial Finance Corporation of Thailand, Bangkok, Thailand; *Int'l*, pg. 677

Ashbaugh, H.S., Sr. V.P.-Sls. & Mktg.--Allvac, Monroe, NC; *U.S. Public*, pg. 43

Ashby, Charles G., Sr. V.P. & Copywriter--McKinney & Silver, Raleigh, NC; *U.S. Private*, pg. 723

Ashe, Robert G., Sr. V.P.-Application Devel. Tools--Cognos Inc., Ottawa, Canada; *Int'l*, pg. 305

Asheim, Petter, Sr. V.P.-Cash Mgmnt.--Christiania Bank og Kreditkasse ASA, Oslo, Norway; *Int'l*, pg. 289

Ashenberg, Wayne R., Chief Fin. Officer, Sr. V.P. & Treas.--Sentry Insurance, A Mutual Company, Stevens Point, WI; *U.S. Private*, pg. 985

Asher, Darryl, Sr. V.P. & Gen. Mgr.--Asher/Gould Advertising, Inc., Los Angeles, CA; *U.S. Private*, pg. 88

Ashiba, Yoshiro, Mng. Dir. & Sr. V.P.--Japan Airlines Company, Ltd., Tokyo, Japan; *Int'l*, pg. 699

Ashley, Barbara J., Sr. V.P.-Retail Svcs.--Taubman Centers, Inc., Bloomfield Hills, MI; *U.S. Public*, pg. 1561

Ashwill, Nancy, Sr. V.P.--National Bank of Alaska, Anchorage, AK; *U.S. Public*, pg. 1153

Askwyth, Diane, Chief Oper. Officer & Sr. V.P.--Willis Corroon Marine & Energy, New York, NY; *Int'l*, pg. 1508

Aspegren, Carl, Sr. V.P. & Sec.--Trelleborg AB, Trelleborg, Sweden; *Int'l*, pg. 1419

Assad, Shay D., Sr. V.P.-Contracts--Raytheon Company, Lexington, MA; *U.S. Public*, pg. 1364

Assicurato, C.P., Sr. V.P.-Opers.--Beiersdorf, Inc., Norwalk, CT; *Int'l*, pg. 182

Assour, Jacques, Dr., Sr. V.P.-Opers.--Centennial Technologies, Inc., Wilmington. MA; *U.S. Public*, pg. 322

Astar, David R., Sr. V.P.--Employers Health Insurance Company, Green Bay, WI; *U.S. Public*, pg. 847

Asteljoki, Jussi, Sr. V.P.-Res. & Devel.--Outokumpu Oyj, Espoo, Finland; *Int'l*, pg. 1015

Astrom, Hakan, Sr. V.P.-Strategic Plng. & Investor Rels.--Pharmacia & Upjohn, Inc., Windsor, United Kingdom; *Int'l*, pg. 1047

Ater, William C., Chief Admin. Officer, Sr. V.P. & Sec.--Anacomp, Inc., Indianapolis, IN; *U.S. Public*, pg. 106

Athens, Zack G., Chief Fin. Officer, Sr. V.P. & Treas.--Columbia Universal Life Insurance Company, Austin, TX; *U.S. Public*, pg. 79

Athos, Gus J., Sr. V.P., Gen. Counsel & Sec.--Eagle Industries, Inc., Chicago, IL; *U.S. Private*, pg. 473

Atkin, Mary, Sr. V.P. & Mgr.-Corp. Communications--A.G. Edwards, Inc., Saint Louis, MO; *U.S. Public*, pg. 565

Atkins-Pattenson, Wendy, Sr. V.P. & Human Resources Dir.--Ketchum Advertising/San Francisco, San Francisco, CA; *U.S. Private*, pg. 616

Atkins, A., Sr. V.P.--MEPC American Properties, Dallas, TX; *U.S. Private*, pg. 686

Atkinson, Darlene, Sr. V.P. & Mngmt. Representative--EvansGroup, Dallas, TX; *U.S. Private*, pg. 385

Atkinson, Ian, Sr. V.P.-Exploration--Battle Mountain Gold Company, Houston, TX; *U.S. Public*, pg. 193

Atkinson, Jerome, Sr. V.P., Gen. Counsel & Sec.--Fortis, Inc., New York, NY; *Int'l*, pg. 499

Atkinson, Jerome A., Sr. V.P., Gen. Counsel & Sec.--American Security Group, Atlanta, GA; *Int'l*, pg. 499

Atnip, Michael G., Sr. V.P.-Opers. Support--American General Corporation, Houston, TX; *U.S. Public*, pg. 76

Atteterry, E. Wayne, Sr. V.P.-Grp. Insurance--Standard Insurance Co., Portland, OR; *U.S. Private*, pg. 1031

Attig, Ron, Sr. V.P.-Heavy Division--M.A. Mortenson Company, Minneapolis, MN; *U.S. Private*, pg. 763

Attiyeh, Robert S., Chief Fin. Officer & Sr. V.P.-Fin. & Corp. Devel.--Amgen Inc., Thousand Oaks, CA; *U.S. Public*, pg. 100

Atwood, J. Richard, Sr. V.P.--First Pacific Advisors, Inc., Los Angeles, CA; *U.S. Public*, pg. 1673

Atwood, Perry, Chief Sls. Officer & Corp. Sr. V.P.--Brenton Banks, Inc., Des Moines, IA; *U.S. Public*, pg. 251

Au Yeong, Hoh Koon, Chief Fin. Officer & Sr. V.P.--Club Med Sales, Inc., New York, NY; *Int'l*, pg. 298

Au, Gregory A., Sr. V.P.-Far East & Hawaii--Mauna Loa Macadamia Nut Corporation, Hilo, HI; *U.S. Private*, pg. 190

Auchinleck, R.H., Sr. V.P.-Intl. & Mktg.--Gulf Canada Resources Ltd., Calgary, Canada; *Int'l*, pg. 577

Auckerman, Raymond, Sr. V.P.--GAB Robins North America, Inc., Parsippany, NJ; *Int'l*, pg. 1153

Audet, Paul, Sr. V.P.-Fin. Services--PNC Bank Corp., Pittsburgh, PA; *U.S. Public*, pg. 1242

Auer, Mike, Sr. V.P.-Gen. Sls. Mgr.--Fruit of the Loom, Inc., Chicago, IL; *U.S. Public*, pg. 685

Auer, Ronald, Sr. V.P.--Investment Research Company, Rancho Santa Fe, CA; *U.S. Public*, pg. 1673

Auerbuch, Boris J., Sr. V.P.-Engrng. & Chief Tech. Officer--Premisys Communications, Inc., Fremont, CA; *U.S. Public*, pg. 1323

August, Art, Sr. V.P.--Helen of Troy Corporation, El Paso, TX; *U.S. Public*, pg. 807

August, John W., Sr. V.P.-Bus. Devel.--Monro Muffler/Brake, Inc., Rochester, NY; *U.S. Public*, pg. 1124

August, Robert W., Sr. V.P. & Sec.--Monro Muffler/Brake, Inc., Rochester, NY; *U.S. Public*, pg. 1124

Auletta, Patrick V., Sr. V.P.--Keycorp, Cleveland, OH; *U.S. Public*, pg. 954

Austell, Barbara, Sr. V.P.-Fin. & Treas.--Aramark Corp., Philadelphia, PA; *U.S. Private*, pg. 78

Austin, Frank E., Sr. V.P., Gen. Counsel & Corp. Sec.--Glenborough Realty Trust Incorporated, San Mateo, CA; *U.S. Public*, pg. 747

Austin, Gary, Sr. V.P. & Dir.-Publications--Haas Publishing Companies, Inc., Norcross, GA; *U.S. Public*, pg. 1327

Austin, Glenn T., Jr., Sr. V.P.-Southeastern Reg.--Federal National Mortgage Association (Fannie Mae), Washington, DC; *U.S. Public*, pg. 615

Austin, Norm, Sr. V.P.-Audit--Security Pacific Financial Services Inc., San Diego, CA; *U.S. Public*, pg. 181

Austin, William, Chief Fin. Officer & Sr. V.P.--BMC Software, Inc., Houston, TX; *U.S. Public*, pg. 162

Auteri, Enrico, Sr. V.P.-H.R.--Fiat Auto SpA, Turin, Italy; *Int'l*, pg. 480

Auton, J. Paul, Sr. V.P.--Arthur D. Little, Inc., Cambridge, MA; *U.S. Private*, pg. 670

Avant, Thomas G., Sr. V.P.-Fin.--Albemarle Corporation, Richmond, VA; *U.S. Public*, pg. 37

Avedovech, Thomas S., Sr. V.P. & Mgr.-Trust Support Svcs. Div.--First Security Bank of Utah, N.A., Salt Lake City, UT; *U.S. Public*, pg. 637

Avellino, Ann Marie, Sr. V.P. & Controller--Stackig Advertising and Public Relations, Mc Lean, VA; *U.S. Private*, pg. 1028

Averett, Devron, Sr. V.P.-Res. & Devel.--ICN Pharmaceuticals, Inc., Costa Mesa, CA; *U.S. Public*, pg. 853

Avery, James P., Sr. V.P.--Louisiana Gas Service Co., Harvey, LA; *U.S. Public*, pg. 380

Avery, John, Sr. V.P. & Copy Dir.--Robert A. Becker, New York, NY; *Int'l*, pg. 601

Avery, Kelley, Sr. V.P.-Retail Mktg.--Buena Vista Home Video, Burbank, CA; *U.S. Public*, pg. 513

Avery, Lorraine, Sr. V.P. & Mgr.-Customer & Acct. Services--First Financial Bank, FSB, Stevens Point, WI; *U.S. Public*, pg. 140

Avery, Paul, Sr. V.P.-Opers.--Outback Steakhouse Inc., Tampa, FL; *U.S. Public*, pg. 1235

Avis, Joe, Sr. V.P.--Riggs National Corporation, Washington, DC; *U.S. Public*, pg. 1389

Ayerlee, Don, Sr. V.P.--Frank B. Ross Co. Inc., Jersey City, NJ; *U.S. Private*, pg. 946

Ayers, D. Tom, Sr. V.P.--MBT Architecture, San Francisco, CA; *U.S. Private*, pg. 686

Ayers, Steve, Sr. V.P.-Contracts & Procurement--Science Applications International Corp., San Diego, CA; *U.S. Private*, pg. 975

Ayers, W. Ben, Sr. V.P.-Credit--Reliable Stores, Inc., Columbia, MD; *U.S. Private*, pg. 920

Aylesworth, William A., Chief Fin. Officer, Sr. V.P. & Treas.--Texas Instruments Incorporated, Dallas, TX; *U.S. Public*, pg. 1585

Aylsworth, Jack, Sr. V.P.--BVK/McDonald, Cape Coral, FL; *U.S. Private*, pg. 108

Azar, James R., Sr. V.P.--Alfa Corporation, Montgomery, AL; *U.S. Public*, pg. 40

Aziz, Javaid, Sr. V.P.-European Field Opers.--Silicon Graphics, Inc., Mountain View, CA; *U.S. Public*, pg. 1473

Aziz, Javaid K., Sr. V.P.--Silicon Graphics S.A. Intl., Geneva, Switzerland; *U.S. Public*, pg. 1474

Azumi, Yasuharu, Assoc. Dir.-Gen. Affairs--Asahi Breweries Ltd., Tokyo, Japan; *Int'l*, pg. 83

Azzam, Atef A., Sr. V.P.--Shannon & Wilson, Inc., Seattle, WA; *U.S. Private*, pg. 989

Azzara, Cynthia O., Chief Fin. Officer, Sr. V.P. & Treas.--CRIIMI MAE, Rockville, MD; *U.S. Public*, pg. 459

Baackes, John, Sr. V.P.--Kaiser Permanente, Northeast Division, Farmington, CT; *U.S. Private*, pg. 605

Baarcke, Charles F., Jr., Sr. V.P.--First Financial Holdings, Inc., Charleston, SC; *U.S. Public*, pg. 634

Baasch, Don, Sr. V.P. & Dir.-Mktg. & Franchise Sls.--AVC/Nu-Vision, Inc., Flint, MI; *U.S. Private*, pg. 9

Baba, Yukihiko, Assoc. Sr. V.P.--NEC Corporation, Tokyo, Japan; *Int'l*, pg. 899

Babb, Douglas J., Sr. V.P.-Mdse. Bus. Unit--Burlington Northern Santa Fe Corporation, Fort Worth, TX; *U.S. Public*, pg. 268

Babchick, Donald, Sr. V.P. & Dir.-Training--Weatherby Health Care, Norwalk, CT; *U.S. Private*, pg. 1155

Babcock, Dennis, Sr. V.P.--ADI (Ademco Distribution, Inc.), Syosset, NY; *U.S. Public*, pg. 1306

Babcock, Elaine H., Sr. V.P.--ITC Learning Corp., Herndon, VA; *U.S. Public*, pg. 859

Babian, Walter, Sr. V.P.--Eli's Cheese Cake Company, Chicago, IL; *U.S. Private*, pg. 371

Babjak, Robert J., Sr. V.P.--ContiFinancial Corporation, New York, NY; *U.S. Public*, pg. 439

Babjak, Robert J., Chief Credit Officer & Sr. V.P.--ContiMortgage Corporation, Horsham, PA; *U.S. Public*, pg. 439

Baccei, Louis J., Dr., Pres.-Res. & Devel.--Loctite Corporation, Rocky Hill, CT; *Int'l*, pg. 611

Bachand, Charles J., Chief Fin. Officer & Sr. V.P.--Highlands Insurance Co., Houston, TX; *U.S. Public*, pg. 826

Bachman, Brian R., Sr. V.P.-Semiconductor & Specialty Systems--Eaton Corporation, Cleveland, OH; *U.S. Public*, pg. 555

Bachman, Jay S., Sr. V.P., Treas. & Mgr.-Corp. Devel.--First Security Corporation, Salt Lake City, UT; *U.S. Public*, pg. 637

Bachman, Pete, Sr. V.P.-Opers.--Stimson Lane Ltd., Woodinville, WA; *U.S. Public*, pg. 661

Bacigalupo, Charles A., Sr. V.P. & Sec.--Legg Mason, Inc., Baltimore, MD; *U.S. Public*, pg. 984

Back, John, Sr. V.P.-H.R.--Fingerhut Corp., Minnetonka, MN; *U.S. Public*, pg. 623

Back, Ragnar, Sr. V.P.-Bus. Networks--Telefonaktiebolaget LM Ericsson, Stockholm, Sweden; *Int'l*, pg. 1363

Backes, Robert J., Sr. V.P.-H.R.--United HealthCare Corporation, Minnetonka, MN; *U.S. Public*, pg. 1677

Bacon, Kenneth J., Sr. V.P.-Northeastern Reg.--Federal National Mortgage Association (Fannie Mae), Washington, DC; *U.S. Public*, pg. 615

Bacon, Larry S., Sr. V.P.-H.R.--Berg Electronics, Saint Louis, MO; *U.S. Public*, pg. 212

Bacon, Michel J., Sr. V.P.-Canada & Pacific--Albany International Corp., Albany, NY; *U.S. Public*, pg. 36

Bacon, Nancy M., Sr. V.P.--Energy Conversion Devices, Inc., Troy, MI; *U.S. Public*, pg. 581

Bacon, Richard A., Sr. V.P. & Gen. Counsel--John Wieland Homes Inc., Atlanta, GA; *U.S. Private*, pg. 1175

Bader, Mark, Sr. V.P.--Shapell Industries, Inc., Beverly Hills, CA; *U.S. Private*, pg. 990

Badillo, Nicolas, Sr. V.P.-Info. Sys.--Firstbank Puerto Rico, Santurce, PR; *U.S. Public*, pg. 644

Badyna, Barbara, Sr. V.P. & Casting Dir.--Young & Rubicam New York, New York, NY; *U.S. Private*, pg. 1198

Baer, Amy, Sr. V.P.-Production--TriStar Pictures, Culver City, CA; *Int'l*, pg. 1283

Baez, Frank, Sr. V.P.--The Equitable Companies Incorporated, New York, NY; *U.S. Public*, pg. 588

Baez, Manuel A., Sr. V.P. & Pres.-Analytical Instruments--The Perkin-Elmer Corporation, Norwalk, CT; *U.S. Public*, pg. 1279

Bagby, S. Richard, Chief Credit Officer & Sr. V.P.--MainStreet BankGroup Incorporated, Martinsville, VA; *U.S. Public*, pg. 1038

Bahadurian, Armen, Sr. V.P.-Mdsg.--Kay-Bee Toy & Hobby Shops, Inc., Pittsfield, MA; *U.S. Public*, pg. 437

Baham, Susan E., Chief Fin. Officer & Sr. V.P.--First Financial Holdings, Inc., Charleston, SC; *U.S. Public*, pg. 634

Baham, Susan E., Chief Fin. Officer & Sr. V.P.--First Federal Savings & Loan Association of Charleston, Charleston, SC; *U.S. Public*, pg. 634

Bahar, Moshe, Sr. V.P.-Generation--The Israel Electric Corporation Ltd., Haifa, Israel; *Int'l*, pg. 690

Bahler, S.M., Sr. V.P.-Media--Brown Marketing Communications, Chicago, IL; *U.S. Private*, pg. 174

Bahlman, Robert S., Chief Fin. Officer, Sr. V.P. & Treas.--Midwest Express Holdings, Inc., Oak Creek, WI; *U.S. Public*, pg. 1111

Bahlmann, Jerome R., Sr. V.P. & Gen. Counsel--Battelle Memorial Institute, Columbus, OH; *U.S. Private*, pg. 123

Bahniuk, Frank T., Sr. V.P.-Energy Mngmt.--NUI Corporation, Bedminster, NJ; *U.S. Public*, pg. 1147

Bailey, Dustin L., Chief Exec. Officer & Sr. V.P.-Special Services Div.--Diversco, Inc., Spartanburg, SC; *U.S. Private*, pg. 336

Bailey, Glenn, Sr. V.P.-Plng. & Admin.--Thomas Nelson Inc., Nashville, TN; *U.S. Public*, pg. 1167

Bailey, Leon, Sr. V.P. & Dir.-Store Opers.--AVC/Nu-Vision, Inc., Flint, MI; *U.S. Private*, pg. 9

Bailey, Mark W., Sr. V.P.-Bus. Devel.--Symantec Corporation, Cupertino, CA; *U.S. Public*, pg. 1545

Bailey, Michael J., Chief Fin. Officer & Sr. V.P.-Admin. & Fin.--Standard Motor Products Inc., Long Island City, NY; *U.S. Public*, pg. 1503

Bailey, Mike, Sr. V.P.--Biederman, Kelly & Shaffer, Inc., New York, NY; *U.S. Private*, pg. 142

Bailey, Robert J., Sr. V.P.-Quality Assurance & Admin.--The Hertz Corporation, Park Ridge, NJ; *U.S. Public*, pg. 664

Bailey, Steve R., Sr. V.P. & Customer Contact--Countrywide Funding Corporation, Pasadena, CA; *U.S. Public*, pg. 453

Bailey, William G., V.P.-System Opers.--TCA Management Company, Tyler, TX; *U.S. Public*, pg. 1553

Bain, Donald R., Chief Fin. Officer & Sr. V.P.--Diversco, Inc., Spartanburg, SC; *U.S. Private*, pg. 336

Baines, Bruce, Sr. V.P. & Treas.--Starbanc Corporation, Cincinnati, OH; *U.S. Public*, pg. 1510

Baird, Bruce M., Sr. V.P. & Mgr.-Salt Lake Div.--First Security Bank of Utah, N.A., Salt Lake City, UT; *U.S. Public*, pg. 637

Baird, Scott, Sr. V.P.--Mrs. Baird's Bakeries, Inc., Fort Worth, TX; *U.S. Private*, pg. 765

Baird, William, Sr. V.P. & Dir.-Life & Employee Benefits Div.--Willis Corroon Corp. of Nashville, Nashville, TN; *Int'l*, pg. 1506

Baireuther, James, Chief Fin. Officer & Sr. V.P.--The Bon Ton Stores, Inc., York, PA; *U.S. Public*, pg. 244

Baisley, James M., Sr. V.P., Gen. Counsel & Sec.--W.W. Grainger, Inc., Lincolnshire, IL; *U.S. Public*, pg. 758

Baitler, Jay, Sr. V.P.-Contract Sls.--Staples, Inc., Westborough, MA; *U.S. Public*, pg. 1509

Baittinger, Ken, Sr. V.P.-Client Relations--Automotive Rentals, Inc. (ARI), Mount Laurel, NJ; *U.S. Private*, pg. 535
Bajon, Roger D., Sr. V.P.-Specialized Industries--Hibernia Corporation, New Orleans, LA; *U.S. Public*, pg. 825
Baker, A.B., Corp Sec.--Riggs National Corporation, Washington, DC; *U.S. Public*, pg. 1389
Baker, Ann Marie, Sr. V.P. & Branch Mgr.--United Missouri Bank of Springfield, Springfield, MO; *U.S. Public*, pg. 1655
Baker, David W., Sr. V.P.-Opers.--Proffitt's, Inc., Alcoa, TN; *U.S. Public*, pg. 1333
Baker, Diane Price, Chief Fin. Officer & Sr. V.P.--The New York Times Company, New York, NY; *U.S. Public*, pg. 1173
Baker, John M., Sr. V.P. & Pres.-ADC Wireless Sys. Grp.--ADC Telecommunications, Inc., Minnetonka, MN; *U.S. Public*, pg. 4
Baker, Joshua S., Ph.D., Sr. V.P.-Opers.--Pharmaceutical Product Development, Inc., Wilmington, NC; *U.S. Public*, pg. 1285
Baker, Lynne, Sr. V.P. & Mng. Dir.--Western International Media Corporation, Atlanta, GA; *U.S. Private*, pg. 1167
Baker, Mari J., Sr. V.P.-Consumer Fin.--Intuit, Inc., Mountain View, CA; *U.S. Public*, pg. 911
Baker, Paul, Sr. V.P.--Weatherford National Bank, Weatherford, TX; *U.S. Public*, pg. 633
Baker, Paul T., Chief Oper. Officer & Sr. V.P.--Indiana Gas Company, Inc., Indianapolis, IN; *U.S. Public*, pg. 875
Baker, Raymond R., Sr. V.P.--PCC Flow Technologies, Inc., Houston, TX; *U.S. Public*, pg. 1320
Balasco, Vincent, Sr. V.P.-Banking Services--Citizens Savings Bank, Providence, RI; *Int'l*, pg. 1132
Balasco, Vincent, Sr. V.P.-Banking Services--Citizens Trust Company, Providence, RI; *Int'l*, pg. 1132
Balazs, Csaba S., Sr. V.P.-Architecture--L. Robert Kimball & Associates, Ebensburg, PA; *U.S. Private*, pg. 619
Baldini, Bob, Sr. V.P.-Reg. Opers.--Ruby Tuesday, Inc., Mobile, AL; *U.S. Public*, pg. 1411
Baldwin, D.D., Sr. V.P.-Resources Div.--Imperial Oil Limited, Toronto, Canada; *U.S. Public*, pg. 602
Baldwin, David, Sr. V.P. & Exec. Creative Dir.--McKinney & Silver, Raleigh, NC; *U.S. Private*, pg. 723
Baldwin, Ralph, Sr. V.P.-Consumer Lending--Wilmington Savings Fund Society (FSB), Wilmington, DE; *U.S. Public*, pg. 1729
Baldwin, Robert D., Sr. V.P.-Sls. & Mktg.--Forest Products & Recycled Paperboard Div., Montvale, NJ; *U.S. Public*, pg. 903
Baldwin, William D., Sr. V.P. & Chief Mktg. Officer--The Life Insurance Co. of Virginia, Richmond, VA; *U.S. Public*, pg. 712
Bale, Chris, Sr. V.P.--McKnight Medical Communications Company, Northfield, IL; *U.S. Public*, pg. 1601
Baley, Charles P., Sr. V.P.-Info. Svcs.--National Western Life Insurance Company, Austin, TX; *U.S. Public*, pg. 1161
Ball, Brad A., Sr. V.P.-U.S. Mktg.--McDonald's Corporation, Oak Brook, IL; *U.S. Public*, pg. 1068
Ball, Damon H., Sr. V.P.--Desai Capital Management Incorporated, New York, NY; *U.S. Private*, pg. 326
Ball, David A., Pres.-Public Carrier Networks & Sr. V.P.--Northern Telecom Limited, Brampton, Canada; *Int'l*, pg. 968
Ball, Fred, Sr. V.P.-Loan Origination--Zions First National Bank, Salt Lake City, UT; *U.S. Public*, pg. 1793
Ball, James A., Sr. V.P.-Corp. Communications--Dr Pepper/ Seven Up No. America, Dallas, TX; *Int'l*, pg. 248
Ball, James A., Sr. V.P.-Corp. Communications--Dr. Pepper Co., Dallas, TX; *Int'l*, pg. 248
Ball, John A., Sr. V.P.--Champion International Corp., Stamford, CT; *U.S. Public*, pg. 333
Ball, Keith, V.P. & Dir.-Editorial--Paisano Publications, Inc., Agoura, CA; *U.S. Private*, pg. 834
Ball, Margaret A., Sr. V.P.-Underwriting--EMC Insurance Group, Inc., Des Moines, IA; *U.S. Public*, pg. 545
Ball, Peter, Sr. V.P. & Treas.--Topa Insurance Company, Los Angeles, CA; *U.S. Private*, pg. 1091
Ball, Steve, Sr. V.P.--ATHOL Corporation, Butner, NC; *U.S. Private*, pg. 94
Ball, Steven S., Chief Oper. Officer & Sr. V.P.--Williams Pipe Line Co., Tulsa, OK; *U.S. Public*, pg. 1769
Ballard, Calvin A., Sr. V.P.-Human Resources--Citizens Savings Bank, Providence, RI; *Int'l*, pg. 1132
Ballard, Max, Sr. V.P.--Good Humor/Breyers Ice Cream, Green Bay, WI; *Int'l*, pg. 1435
Ballow, Michael, Sr. V.P.-Devel.--Crown American Realty Trust, Johnstown, PA; *U.S. Public*, pg. 461
Balman, Loron, Sr. V.P. Mktg./Artist Development--Word, Incorporated, Dallas, TX; *U.S. Public*, pg. 704
Balsamo, Vincent, Sr. V.P.--Citizens Mortgage Corporation, Atlanta, GA; *Int'l*, pg. 1132
Baltis, Pam, Sr. V.P.--Security Pacific Financial Services Inc., San Diego, CA; *U.S. Public*, pg. 181
Baltzell, R. Eric, Sr. V.P.-Stores--Fred Meyer Stores, Portland, OR; *U.S. Public*, pg. 1103
Balzarini, Francis A., Sr. V.P.--Emigrant Savings Bank, New York, NY; *U.S. Private*, pg. 373
Bamber, Mary Ann, Sr. V.P.-Retail Banking--Associated Banc-Corp, Green Bay, WI; *U.S. Public*, pg. 140
Bamberger, Ivor, Chief Fin. Officer & Sr. V.P.--Beber & Silverstein & Partners, Inc., Miami, FL; *U.S. Private*, pg. 128
Band, Sheila, Sr. V.P. & Media Dir.--Pedone & Partners Adv., Inc., New York, NY; *U.S. Private*, pg. 846
Bane, Daniel T., Chief Fin. Officer & Sr. V.P.-Fin. & Admin.--Certified Grocers of California, Los Angeles, CA; *U.S. Private*, pg. 226
Bankers, Eugene E., Sr. V.P.-Mktg.--Ames Department Stores, Inc., Rocky Hill, CT; *U.S. Public*, pg. 99
Banks, Arthur, Sr. V.P.-H.R.--Blue Cross and Blue Shield of Massachusetts, Boston, MA; *U.S. Private*, pg. 151
Banks, Ralph A., Jr., Sr. V.P.--Trinity Industries Inc., Dallas, TX; *U.S. Public*, pg. 1638
Banpotjit, Pongsak, Sr. V.P.-Support Grp.--Nakornthon Bank Public Company Limited, Bangkok, Thailand; *Int'l*, pg. 904
Bantit, Stuart, Sr. V.P.-Gen. Mdse.--Pic'n Pay Stores, Inc., Matthews, NC; *U.S. Private*, pg. 864
Banu, A. John, Sr. V.P.--ContiFinancial Corporation, New York, NY; *U.S. Public*, pg. 439
Bar-Shavit, Ptachia, Sr. V.P.-Economics--Bank Hapoalim, Tel Aviv, Israel; *Int'l*, pg. 149
Baranski, Scott M., Sr. V.P. & Mgr.-Intl. Banking--American National Bank & Trust Co. of Chicago, Chicago, IL; *U.S. Public*, pg. 628
Barash, Anthony H., Sr. V.P.-Corp. Affairs & Gen. Counsel--Bowater Incorporated, Greenville, SC; *U.S. Public*, pg. 247
Barba, L. Douglas, Sr. V.P. & Gen. Mgr.--Catamount Energy Corporation, Rutland, VT; *U.S. Public*, pg. 328
Barbara, Vito, Sr. V.P.-Media & Opers.--Western International Media Corporation, New York, NY; *U.S. Private*, pg. 1166
Barbeau, David C., Sr. V.P.-Distr. Opers.--APS Holding Corporation, Houston, TX; *U.S. Public*, pg. 10
Barber, Donald G., Chief Fin. Officer & Sr. V.P.--Santa Fe International Corporation, Dallas, TX; *Int'l*, pg. 765
Barber, Fred, Sr. V.P.-TV--Capitol Broadcasting Co., Inc., Raleigh, NC; *U.S. Private*, pg. 206
Barber, Kenneth R., Sr. V.P.-Fin.--Tandem Computers Inc., Cupertino, CA; *U.S. Public*, pg. 417
Barberis, Rex A., Sr. V.P.--Hartford Europe, Inc., Hartford, CT; *U.S. Public*, pg. 795
Barbre, John H., Sr. V.P.-Individual Div.--American United Life Insurance Company, Indianapolis, IN; *U.S. Private*, pg. 64
Barcena, Valentin Valderrabano, Sr. V.P.--Banco Santander Puerto Rico, Hato Rey, PR; *Int'l*, pg. 143
Bardeen, William L., Sr. V.P. & Grp. Exec.-Consumer Energy Services--PECO Energy Company, Philadelphia, PA; *U.S. Public*, pg. 1268
Bardenheier, George, Jr., Sr. V.P.-Corp. Devel.--May & Speh, Inc., Downers Grove, IL; *U.S. Public*, pg. 1063
Bardon, Pierre, Sr. V.P.-Chilled & Frozen Ready-to-Serve Dishes--Danone Group, Paris, France; *Int'l*, pg. 379
Bare, James A., Chief Fin. Officer & Sr. V.P.--Consumer Finance Group, Tampa, FL; *U.S. Public*, pg. 1741
Barkan, Lee, Sr. V.P, Sec. & Gen. Counsel--AVC/Nu-Vision, Inc., Flint, MI; *U.S. Private*, pg. 9
Barker, Jerry, Sr. V.P.-Mktg.--Tom's Foods, Inc., Columbus, GA; *U.S. Private*, pg. 1090
Barker, John, Sr. V.P., Grp. Mngmt. Supvr. & Creative Dir.--Grey Entertainment Inc., New York, NY; *U.S. Public*, pg. 764
Barker, Steve, Sr. V.P. & Controller--Deposit Guaranty Corp., Jackson, MS; *U.S. Public*, pg. 500
Barkley, Barry R., Sr. V.P. & Controller--Great Western Financial Corporation, Chatsworth, CA; *U.S. Public*, pg. 1741
Barkley, Kenneth R., Chief Fin. Officer, Sr. V.P.-Fin. & Treas.--Cagle's Farms Inc., Dalton, GA; *U.S. Public*, pg. 292
Barkofske, Francis L., Chief Fin. Officer & Sr. V.P.--Zeigler Coal Holding Company, Fairview Heights, IL; *U.S. Public*, *pg. 1790*
Barksdale, C. Bruce, Sr. V.P.--TII Industries, Inc., Copiague, NY; *U.S. Public*, pg. 1556
Barksdale, Robin, Sr. V.P.-Opers.--Hospital Affiliates Development Corporation, Nashville, TN; *U.S. Private*, pg. 540
Barnaby, Alan, Sr. V.P.-Store Opers.--The Home Depot, Inc., Atlanta, GA; *U.S. Public*, pg. 831
Barnard, Glen, Sr. V.P. & Reg. Gen. Mgr.--Kaufman and Broad Home Corporation, Los Angeles, CA; *U.S. Public*, pg. 944
Barnard, Lee A., Sr. V.P. & Gen. Mgr.-Fabrics--Fabri-Centers of America, Inc., Hudson, OH; *U.S. Public*, pg. 609
Barnes, Deborah, Sr. V.P.--NatCity Investments, Inc., Cleveland, OH; *U.S. Public*, pg. 1154
Barnes, Don, Sr. V.P.-Sls. & Mktg.--Presidential Life Corporation, Nyack, NY; *U.S. Public*, pg. 1323
Barnes, Hugh, Sr. V.P.-Portable PC Div.--COMPAQ Computer Corporation, Houston, TX; *U.S. Public*, pg. 417
Barnes, John L., Jr., Chief Fin. Officer & Sr. V.P.--Triarc Companies, Inc., New York, NY; *U.S. Public*, pg. 1634
Barnes, John P., Sr. V.P.-Loan Review--Chittenden Corporation, Burlington, VT; *U.S. Public*, pg. 350
Barnes, Lee, Sr. V.P.-Sls. & Mktg.--Spectrulite Consortium, Inc., Madison, IL; *U.S. Private*, pg. 1024
Barnes, Margery, Sr. V.P. & Acct. Plng. Dir.-Insights Grp.--Young & Rubicam New York, New York, NY; *U.S. Private*, pg. 1198
Barnes, Margo L., Sr. V.P.-Corp. Communications--Bayer Corporation, Pittsburgh, PA; *Int'l*, pg. 172
Barnes, Michael H., Chief Fin. Officer, Sr. V.P. & Corp. Sec.--Intellicall, Inc., Carrollton, TX; *U.S. Public*, pg. 887
Barnes, Randall C., Sr. V.P. & Treas.--PepsiCo, Inc., Purchase, NY; *U.S. Public*, pg. 1276
Barnes, Ray, Sr. V.P.--Reed Business Information (USA), New York, NY; *Int'l*, pg. 1094
Barnes, Ronald L., Sr. V.P.--Total System Services, Inc., Columbus, GA; *U.S. Public*, pg. 1550
Barnes, Thomas O., Chm. Bd. & Sr. V.P.-Admin.--Barnes Group Inc., Bristol, CT; *U.S. Public*, pg. 189
Barnes, W. Michael, Chief Fin. Officer & Sr. V.P.-Fin. & Plng.--Rockwell International Corporation, Costa Mesa, CA; *U.S. Public*, pg. 1397
Barnes, William, Sr. V.P.--Keycorp, Cleveland, OH; *U.S. Public*, pg. 954
Barnett, Bill M., Sr. V.P.--Harcourt Brace & Company - Elementary Div., Orlando, FL; *U.S. Public*, pg. 783
Barnett, Steven B., Chief Fin. Officer, Sr. V.P. & Treas.--Rag Shops, Inc., Hawthorne, NJ; *U.S. Public*, pg. 1358
Barnhart, Dale A., Sr. V.P.-Mktg. & Sls.--Wolverine Tube Inc., Huntsville, AL; *U.S. Public*, pg. 1774
Barnhill, Carl, Sr. V.P.-Sls.--Adolph Coors Company, Golden, CO; *U.S. Public*, pg. 445
Barnhill, Carl L., Sr. V.P.-Sls.--Coors Brewing Company, Golden, CO; *U.S. Public*, pg. 445
Barnhill, Charles L., Sr. V.P.-Regional Mgr.--Santa Fe Drilling Co., Alhambra, CA; *Int'l*, pg. 765
Barnhill, Jeff, Sr. V.P.-Health Svc.--Hospital Staffing Services, Inc., Fort Lauderdale, FL; *U.S. Public*, pg. 840
Barnickol, Karl R., Sr. V.P., Gen. Counsel & Sec.--Solutia Inc., Saint Louis, MO; *U.S. Public*, pg. 1483
Baron, Dan, Sr. V.P.-Retail Sls.--Nakano Foods Inc., Arlington Heights, IL; *Int'l*, pg. 883
Baron, Diana, Sr. V.P.-Publicity--A&M Records, Hollywood, CA; *Int'l*, pg. 1052
Baron, Steven R., Sr. V.P.-Mktg. & Leasing/CBD Office--Prime Group Realty Trust, Chicago, IL; *U.S. Public*, pg. 1326
Baroni, Ron, V.P.--F.T. Reynolds Company, Glendive, MT; *U.S. Private*, pg. 926
Barquero, Francisco Alario, Sr. V.P.--Banco Santander Puerto Rico, Hato Rey, PR; *Int'l*, pg. 143
Barr, Donald, Sr. V.P.--Epstein Construction Inc., Chicago, IL; *U.S. Private*, pg. 379
Barr, Jay, Sr. V.P.-Retail--Riggs Bank N.A., Washington, DC; *U.S. Public*, pg. 1390
Barr, Michael J., Sr. V.P.-Estimating--J.E. Dunn Construction Co., Kansas City, MO; *U.S. Private*, pg. 347
Barr, Pamela S., Sr. V.P.--Watt, Roop & Co., Cleveland, OH; *U.S. Private*, pg. 1154
Barr, William P., Sr. V.P. & Gen. Counsel--GTE Corporation, Stamford, CT; *U.S. Public*, pg. 696
Barrett, Deborah, Chief Fin. Officer & Sr. V.P.--Harrowston Corporation, Toronto, Canada; *Int'l*, pg. 599
Barrett, Don W. Jr., Sr. V.P.--Acxiom Corporation, Conway, AR; *U.S. Public*, pg. 18
Barrett, Edward L., Sr. V.P. & Dir.-Sls.--Marquette Coppersmithing Co., Inc., Philadelphia, PA; *U.S. Private*, pg. 706
Barrett, Edward V., Sr. V.P.-Law--Citizens Savings Bank, Providence, RI; *Int'l*, pg. 1132
Barrett, Jennifer T., Sr. V.P.--Acxiom Corporation, Conway, AR; *U.S. Public*, pg. 18
Barrett, Kent E., Sr. V.P., Controller & Treas.--American General Life & Accident Insurance Co., Nashville, TN; *U.S. Public*, pg. 76
Barrett, Paul, Chief Fin. Officer, & Sr. V.P.-Fin.--Bill's Dollar Stores, Inc., Ridgeland, MS; *U.S. Private*, pg. 144
Barrett, Pete, Sr. V.P.-Affil. Mktg. & Stragic Plng.--ABC Television Network Group, New York, NY; *U.S. Public*, pg. 511
Barrett, Stephen W., Sr. V.P.--Rollins Burdick Hunter Co. (Bermuda) Ltd., Hamilton, Bermuda; *U.S. Public*, pg. 119
Barrett, Susan C., Sr. V.P.-Loan Servicing--Washington Mutual Inc., Seattle, WA; *U.S. Public*, pg. 1741
Barrett, William, Sr. V.P. & Client Services Dir.--SFM Media Corporation, New York, NY; *U.S. Private*, pg. 956
Barriero, Vincent, Chief Information Officer & Sr. V.P.-MIS--The Sharper Image, San Francisco, CA; *U.S. Public*, pg. 1464
Barrilleaux, Katy, Sr. V.P. & Mngmt. Representative--EvansGroup, Dallas, TX; *U.S. Private*, pg. 385
Barringer, Thomas, Sr. V.P.-Mass Mktg.--Fieldcrest Cannon, Inc., Kannapolis, NC; *U.S. Public*, pg. 1296
Barrios, Richard, Sr. V.P.-Investments--Banco Popular de Puerto Rico, San Juan, PR; *U.S. Public*, pg. 175
Barron, Arnold S., Sr. V.P. & Grp. Exec.--The TJX Companies, Inc., Framingham, MA; *U.S. Public*, pg. 1556
Barron, Harold S., Sr. V.P., Gen. Counsel & Sec.--Unisys Corporation, Blue Bell, PA; *U.S. Public*, pg. 1671
Barron, Jeffrey, Sr. V.P.--Levy Real Estate Partners, Chicago, IL; *U.S. Private*, pg. 664
Barrow, M.J., Sr. V.P.-Fin. & Admin., Treas., Sec. & Dir.--M.S. Carriers, Inc., Memphis, TN; *U.S. Public*, pg. 1027
Barrows, Craig, Sr. V.P., Gen. Counsel & Corp. Sec.--M/A-COM Inc., Lowell, MA; *U.S. Public*, pg. 8
Barry, Donald J., Sr. V.P.-Law--Citizens Bank of Massachusetts, Fairhaven, MA; *Int'l*, pg. 1132
Barry, Thomas M., Sr. V.P.-Federal Rels.--Southwestern Bell Telephone Co., Saint Louis, MO; *U.S. Public*, pg. 1416
Barsema, Dennis, Sr. V.P.-Worldwide Sls.--Centigram Communications Corporation, San Jose, CA; *U.S. Public*, *pg. 323*
Barshay, Stanley F., Sr. V.P.--American Home Products Corporation, Madison, NJ; *U.S. Public*, pg. 79
Bartels, William, Sr. V.P.-Underwriting--Western Indemnity Insurance Company, Houston, TX; *U.S. Public*, pg. 685
Barth, David S., Sr. V.P.-Western Sls.--VWR Scientific Products, West Chester, PA; *U.S. Public*, pg. 1703
Bartholdson, John, Chief Fin. Officer & Sr. V.P.--Triumph Group, Inc., Wayne, PA; *U.S. Public*, pg. 1640
Bartholin, Christian, Sr. V.P.--Bank of America NT&SA, Paris, France; *U.S. Public*, pg. 182
Bartlett, Carl, Sr. V.P. & Sec.--Jim Wilson & Associates, Inc., Montgomery, AL; *U.S. Private*, pg. 1181
Bartlett, John B., Chief Fin. Officer & Sr. V.P.--UniFirst Corporation, Wilmington, MA; *U.S. Public*, pg. 1665
Bartlett, Phil, Sr. V.P.-Sls. & Mktg.--Russell-Stanley Corporation, Red Bank, NJ; *U.S. Private*, pg. 953
Bartley, David, Sr. V.P.--HK Systems, Inc., New Berlin, WI; *U.S. Private*, pg. 491
Bartoli, Henry E., Sr. V.P.--Foster Wheeler Corporation, Clinton, NJ; *U.S. Public*, pg. 676
Barton, John K., Sr. V.P.-Engnrg., Construction & Support Services--Staples, Inc., Westborough, MA; *U.S. Public*, pg. 1509
Barton, Nancy E., Sr. V.P., Gen. Counsel & Sec.--General Electric Capital Services, Inc., Stamford, CT; *U.S. Public*, *pg. 711*
Barton, Sharon, Sr. V.P.--R.T.M. Winners, Atlanta, GA; *U.S. Private*, pg. 906
Barton, William J., Sr. V.P.-Pacific Century Trust Investment Admin.--Bank of Hawaii, Honolulu, HI; *U.S. Public*, pg. 1248

Bartow, Jerome E., Sr. V.P. & Dir.-Admin.--Hartford Fire Insurance Co., Hartford, CT; *U.S. Public*, pg. 794

Bartsocas, Gus, Sr. V.P.-Intl. & Non-Traditional Devel.--Miami Subs Corporation, Fort Lauderdale, FL; *U.S. Public*, pg. 1103

Basch, Saul, Chief Fin. Officer, Sr. V.P. & Treas.--The Hartford Steam Boiler Inspection & Insurance Co., Hartford, CT; *U.S. Public*, pg. 795

Basco, Don, Sr. V.P.-Credit Admin.--First Security Bank of New Mexico, Albuquerque, NM; *U.S. Public*, pg. 637

Baseler, Theodor, Sr. V.P.--International Wine & Spirits Ltd., Greenwich, CT; *U.S. Public*, pg. 1661

Basham, Wylie D., Sr. V.P.-Prod. Grp. Opers.--DSC Communications Corporation, Plano, TX; *U.S. Public*, pg. 475

Bashoff, K.H., Sr. V.P.-Gen. Counsel & Sec.--Fidelity Mutual Life Insurance Co., Radnor, PA; *U.S. Private*, pg. 403

Bashore, Ronald, Sr. V.P.-Commercial Lending--National Penn Bank, Boyertown, PA; *U.S. Public*, pg. 1159

Basinger, George W., Sr. V.P.-Power Opers.--LG & E Energy Corp., Louisville, KY; *U.S. Public*, pg. 970

Baskett, Forest, Ph.D., Chief Tech. Officer & Sr. V.P.-Res. & Devel.--Silicon Graphics, Inc., Mountain View, CA; *U.S. Public*, pg. 1473

Bass, Ira, Sr. V.P.-Media Services--Rockett, Burkhead, Lewis & Winslow, Raleigh, NC; *U.S. Private*, pg. 938

Bass, Paul M., Sr. V.P.-Food--BJ's Wholesale Club, Inc., Natick, MA; *U.S. Public*, pg. 162

Bastien, Michel, Sr. V.P.-Foreign Equities--Montrusco Associates, Inc., Montreal, Canada; *Int'l*, pg. 888

Bateman, John A., Sr. V.P.--Electronic Data Systems Corporation, Plano, TX; *U.S. Public*, pg. 569

Batenic, Mark K., Sr. V.P.-Retail Sls. & Mktg.--Fleming Companies, Inc., Oklahoma City, OK; *U.S. Public*, pg. 652

Bates, Richard B., Sr. V.P.--Sonat Inc., Birmingham, AL; *U.S. Public*, pg. 1484

Bates, Robert M., Sr. V.P.--Southwest Marine, Inc., San Diego, CA; *U.S. Private*, pg. 213

Batesole, Jon, Sr. V.P.--General Growth Properties Inc., Chicago, IL; *U.S. Public*, pg. 715

Batkie, Ellen L., Sr. V.P.-Investor Rels.--Charter One Financial, Inc., Cleveland, OH; *U.S. Public*, pg. 336

Batres, Roberto, Sr. V.P.--Arthur D. Little, Inc., Cambridge, MA; *U.S. Private*, pg. 670

Batson, Catherine W., Sr. V.P. & Controller--Carolina First Corporation, Greenville, SC; *U.S. Public*, pg. 306

Battaglia, John A., Sr. V.P.--Citizens Mortgage Corporation, Atlanta, GA; *Int'l*, pg. 1132

Battani, Larry, Sr. V.P.-Mktg.--American Republic Insurance Co., Des Moines, IA; *U.S. Private*, pg. 61

Battey, Brenda, Sr. V.P. & Controller--FirstFed Financial Corp., Santa Monica, CA; *U.S. Public*, pg. 645

Battin, Jim, Sr. V.P.-Interactive & Mktg. Dir.--Partners & Shevack, Inc., New York, NY; *U.S. Private*, pg. 842

Battin, John, Sr. V.P. & Gen. Mgr.-Multimedia Grp.--Motorola, Inc., Schaumburg, IL; *U.S. Public*, pg. 1136

Batting, Douglas A., Sr. V.P.--Chubb & Son, Inc., Warren, NJ; *U.S. Public*, pg. 355

Battista, Bernie, Sr. V.P.-Mktg.-Americas Group--Dow Jones Telerate Holdings, Inc., Jersey City, NJ; *U.S. Public*, pg. 525

Battista, Mark E., Sr. V.P. & Chief Medical Dir.--UNUM Life Insurance Company of America, Portland, ME; *U.S. Public*, pg. 1699

Battle, Thomas P., Sr. V.P., Gen. Counsel & Sec.--Mitchell Energy & Development Corp., Spring, TX; *U.S. Public*, pg. 1117

Baucom, Earl W., Sr. V.P. & Chief Fin. Officer--The Franklin Life Insurance Company, Springfield, IL; *U.S. Public*, pg. 76

Baudoin, Jean, Sr. V.P.-H.R.--Credit Commercial de France, Paris, France; *Int'l*, pg. 341

Bauer, James A., Sr. V.P.-Communications & Admin.--The Antec Corporation, Rolling Meadows, IL; *U.S. Public*, pg. 116

Bauerlein, Dudley L., Jr., Chief Fin. Officer & Sr. V.P.--Fortune Brands, Inc., Old Greenwich, CT; *U.S. Public*, pg. 674

Baugh, Gene A., Sr. V.P. & Treas.--ITT Educational Services, Inc., Indianapolis, IN; *U.S. Public*, pg. 1512

Baum, Clemens, Dr., Sr. V.P. & Controller--Deutz AG, Cologne, Germany; *Int'l*, pg. 407

Baum, James H., Sr. V.P.-Grp. Dept.--American Heritage Life Insurance Co., Jacksonville, FL; *U.S. Public*, pg. 79

Bauman, James R., Sr. V.P.-Bus. Devel.--Apache Corporation, Houston, TX; *U.S. Public*, pg. 119

Baumann, Manfred Jurgen, Sr. V.P.--Bayerische Landesbank Girozentrale - Berlin Branch, Berlin, Germany; *Int'l*, pg. 176

Baumgarten, Herbert J., Sr. V.P., Gen. Counsel & Sec.--Unilever United States Inc., New York, NY; *Int'l*, pg. 1435

Baumgartner, M.A., Sr. V.P.--Ziegler Securities Division, Chicago, IL; *U.S. Public*, pg. 1792

Bausmann, Bruce, Sr. V.P.-Real Estate--Musicland Group Inc., Minnetonka, MN; *U.S. Public*, pg. 1142

Baustert, Alain, Sr. V.P.--Landesbank Rheinland Pfalz International S.A., Luxembourg, Luxembourg; *Int'l*, pg. 799

Bautista, Jaimie J., Chief Fin. Officer & Sr. V.P.-Fin.--Philippine Airlines, Inc., Manila, Philippines; *Int'l*, pg. 1050

Bautista, Steve, Sr. V.P. & Creative Dir.--Ingalls, Boston, MA; *U.S. Private*, pg. 562

Baxter, Lyn H., Sr. V.P.-Opers.--MGM Grand Hotel, Inc., Las Vegas, NV; *U.S. Public*, pg. 1027

Baxter, Waldo, Sr. V.P.--Hereford State Bank, Hereford, TX; *U.S. Public*, pg. 633

Bayless, Laurie, Sr. V.P.- Corp. Relations--Transamerica Life Companies, Los Angeles, CA; *U.S. Public*, pg. 1630

Baylis, Joseph J., Sr. V.P.-Corp. Devel.--Battle Mountain Gold Company, Houston, TX; *U.S. Public*, pg. 193

Bays, F. Barry, Chief Oper. Officer & Sr. V.P.-Opers.--Xomed Surgical Products, Jacksonville, FL; *U.S. Public*, pg. 253

Bazlen, James, Sr. V.P.--The Trump Group, Miami, FL; *U.S. Private*, pg. 1107

Beach, Mary Anne, Sr. V.P.-Customer Information & Mktg.--First American Corporation, Nashville, TN; *U.S. Public*, pg. 624

Beacom, Vincent E., V.P.-Minnesota Electric--Northern States Power Company, Minneapolis, MN; *U.S. Public*, pg. 1195

Beadle, Robert S., Sr. V.P.-Corp. Devel.--Ultramar Diamond Shamrock Corporation, San Antonio, TX; *U.S. Public*, pg. 1663

Beale, R. Michelle, Sr. V.P.-H.R., Pub. Affairs & Admin. Svcs.--The Minute Maid Company, Houston, TX; *U.S. Public*, pg. 392

Beam, Bryan H., Sr. V.P.-Distr. & Transportation--Heilig-Meyers Company, Richmond, VA; *U.S. Public*, pg. 804

Beamer, Kenneth W., Sr. V.P. & Div. Mgr.--Henkels & McCoy, Inc., Blue Bell, PA; *U.S. Private*, pg. 522

Bean, F. Terry, Sr. V.P.-Comml. Bus.--Office Depot Inc., Delray Beach, FL; *U.S. Public*, pg. 1212

Bean, Gregory R., Sr. V.P. & Sr. Trust Officer--FirstMerit Corporation, Akron, OH; *U.S. Public*, pg. 646

Beane, Brenda L., Sr. V.P. & Mgr.-Admin.--Willis Corroon Corp. of Portland, Portland, OR; *Int'l*, pg. 1507

Bear, James W., Sr. V.P. & Treas.--Consolidated Products, Inc., Indianapolis, IN; *U.S. Public*, pg. 436

Bear, James W., Sr. V.P. & Treas.--SNS Investment Company, Indianapolis, IN; *U.S. Public*, pg. 436

Bear, James W., Chief Fin. Officer, Sr. V.P. & Treas.--Steak 'n Shake, Inc., Indianapolis, IN; *U.S. Public*, pg. 437

Beard, David R., Sr. V.P.--RTKL Associates Inc., Baltimore, MD; *U.S. Private*, pg. 906

Beard, Thomas, Chief Fin. Officer, Sr. V.P. & Treas.--Petroleum Inc., Wichita, KS; *U.S. Private*, pg. 858

Beardi, James J., Sr. V.P.--Manufacturers & Traders Trust Company, Buffalo, NY; *U.S. Public*, pg. 631

Beardsley, Diane, Sr. V.P.-Fin. & Treas.--Leiner Health Products, Inc., Carson, CA; *U.S. Private*, pg. 659

Beardsley, James R., Sr. V.P.--Willis Corroon Corp. of Maryland, Hunt Valley, MD; *Int'l*, pg. 1506

Bearse, Richard, Sr. V.P.-Plng. & Devel.--United Dominion Industries, Ltd., Charlotte, NC; *U.S. Public*, pg. 1675

Bearzatto, D.L., Sr. V.P.--AEGON Levensverzekering NV, Hague, Netherlands; *Int'l*, pg. 25

Beasley, John H., Sr. V.P.-Personnel & Admin.--The Pepper Companies, Inc., Chicago, IL; *U.S. Private*, pg. 851

Beasley, Lynn J., Sr. V.P.-Winston/Camel Bus. Unit--R.J. Reynolds Tobacco Company, Winston Salem, NC; *U.S. Public*, pg. 1355

Beasley, Marvin, Sr. V.P.-Mdsg.--Helzberg's Diamond Shops, Inc., Kansas City, MO; *U.S. Public*, pg. 220

Beason, J.I., Sr. V.P.--Mojave Pipeline Company, Bakersfield, CA; *U.S. Public*, pg. 567

Beatson, David I., Sr. V.P.--CNF Transportation Inc., Palo Alto, CA; *U.S. Public*, pg. 281

Beattie, David, Sr. V.P.-Sls. & Mktg.--McNaughton-McKay Electric Co., Madison Heights, MI; *U.S. Private*, pg. 724

Beattie, Douglas, Sr. V.P.-Sls. & Mktg.--Liquid Controls LLC, Lake Bluff, IL; *U.S. Private*, pg. 669

Beaty, Michael, Sr. V.P.-Bakery Opers./Flowers Bakeries, Inc.--Flowers Industries, Inc., Thomasville, GA; *U.S. Public*, pg. 656

Beauchamp, Bob, Sr. V.P.-Res. & Devel.--BMC Software, Inc., Houston, TX; *U.S. Public*, pg. 162

Beaud, Roland, Sr. V.P. & Legal Advisor--Ferrier Lullin & Cie SA, Geneva, Switzerland; *Int'l*, pg. 480

Beaudin, Timothy, Sr. V.P.-Property Opers. & Indus. Devel.--Catellus Development Corporation, San Francisco, CA; *U.S. Public*, pg. 314

Beaudouin, Mark T., 1st Sr. V.P. & Gen. Counsel--J. Baker, Inc., Canton, MA; *U.S. Public*, pg. 167

Beaudouin, Mark T., Sr. V.P., Gen. Counsel & Asst. Sec.--Morse Shoe, Inc., Canton, MA; *U.S. Public*, pg. 168

Beaudouin, Mark T., 1st Sr. V.P., Gen. Counsel & Asst. Sec.--Casual Male, Inc., Hyde Park, MA; *U.S. Public*, pg. 168

Beaulieu, Louis J., Sr. V.P.-Trust Devel.--Chittenden Corporation, Burlington, VT; *U.S. Public*, pg. 350

Beaulieu, Michel, Sr. V.P.--The Equitable Companies Incorporated, New York, NY; *U.S. Public*, pg. 588

Beaumont, Steve, Sr. V.P. & Creative Dir.--Dailey & Associates, West Hollywood, CA; *U.S. Public*, pg. 909

Beaver, Jeffrey T., Sr. V.P.--IBJ Schroder Bank & Trust Company, New York, NY; *Int'l*, pg. 674

Beavers, Robert M., Jr., Sr. V.P. & Zone Mgr.--McDonald's Corporation, Oak Brook, IL; *U.S. Public*, pg. 1068

Beberman, Richard A., Sr. V.P.-Corp. Fin.--Rothschild North America Inc., New York, NY; *U.S. Private*, pg. 947

Bechard, Yvon, First Exec. V.P. & Asst. Sec.--The Jean Coutu Group (PJC) Inc., Longueuil, Canada; *Int'l*, pg. 340

Becherer, Joseph L., Sr. V.P.-Cutler-Hammer--Eaton Corporation, Cleveland, OH; *U.S. Public*, pg. 555

Bechet, Paul R., Chief Fin. Officer & Sr. V.P.--Brookline Savings Bank, Brookline, MA; *U.S. Public*, pg. 171

Beck, Dan, Sr. V.P.-Mktg./Artist Devel.--Sony Music Entertainment, Inc., New York, NY; *Int'l*, pg. 1281

Beck, David A., Sr. V.P.--Clark Grave Vault Co., Columbus, OH; *U.S. Private*, pg. 243

Beck, Deborah A., Sr. V.P.-Insurance Opers.--Northwestern Mutual Life Insurance Co., Milwaukee, WI; *U.S. Private*, pg. 807

Beck, Douglas J., Sr. V.P.-Bus. Devel.--ICF Kaiser International Inc., Fairfax, VA; *U.S. Public*, pg. 852

Beck, Joel, Sr. V.P.-Opers.--EMC Corporation, Hopkinton, MA; *U.S. Public*, pg. 545

Beck, Kim, Sr. V.P.--Ruiz Food Products, Inc., Dinuba, CA; *U.S. Private*, pg. 951

Beck, Michael, Sr. V.P.-Fin.--Westat Inc., Rockville, MD; *U.S. Private*, pg. 1163

Beck, Philip D., Sr. V.P.--Summit Bank, Bethlehem, PA; *U.S. Public*, pg. 1528

Beck, Robert N., Sr. V.P.-Corp. Human Resources--Gateway 2000, North Sioux City, SD; *U.S. Public*, pg. 703

Becker, Christian, Chief Fin. Officer, Sr. V.P. & Treas.--Comdial Corporation, Charlottesville, VA; *U.S. Public*, pg. 407

Becker, Deborah L., Sr. V.P.-Personal Insurance Opers.--American Bankers Insurance Co. of Florida, Miami, FL; *U.S. Public*, pg. 67

Becker, Deborah L., Sr. V.P.-Personal Insurance Opers.--American Bankers Life Assurance Co. of Florida, Miami, FL; *U.S. Public*, pg. 67

Becker, James, Sr. V.P.-Trust Admin.--Nevada State Bank, Las Vegas, NV; *U.S. Public*, pg. 1793

Becker, Mark, Sr. V.P. & Assoc. Gen Counsel--Showtime Networks Inc., New York, NY; *U.S. Private*, pg. 779

Becker, Patrick J., Sr. V.P.-Sls. & Mktg.--NxTrend Technology, Inc., Colorado Springs, CO; *U.S. Private*, pg. 809

Becker, Richard E., Sr. V.P.-Sls./Major Accts.--Nutmeg Mills Inc., Tampa, FL; *U.S. Public*, pg. 1702

Beckerlegge, Bernard R., Sr. V.P. & Gen. Counsel--Keyport Life Insurance Company, Boston, MA; *U.S. Private*, pg. 666

Beckert, Richard N., Sr. V.P.-Admin.--Bristol Hotels & Resorts, Dallas, TX; *U.S. Public*, pg. 253

Beckert, William J., Sr. V.P.-Corp. Plng. & Economics--Citgo Petroleum Corporation, Tulsa, OK; *Int'l*, pg. 1045

Beckman, Erik, Sr. V.P.-Human Resources--Nykredit, Copenhagen, Denmark; *Int'l*, pg. 993

Beckwith, Dean, Sr. V.P.-Global Service Strategy--Siemens Business Communication Systems, Inc., Santa Clara, CA; *Int'l*, pg. 1245

Beckwith, Gerald L., Sr. V.P. & Pres.-Commun. Sys. Division--QUALCOMM, San Diego, CA; *U.S. Public*, pg. 1348

Bedbury, Scott, Sr. V.P.-Mktg.--Starbucks Coffee Company, Seattle, WA; *U.S. Public*, pg. 1510

Bede, Jessica I., Sr. V.P.-Medical Products--Capintec Inc., Ramsey, NJ; *U.S. Private*, pg. 205

Bedewi, Elizabeth M., Sr. V.P., Sec. & Treas.--New Mexico & Arizona Land Co., Phoenix, AZ; *U.S. Public*, pg. 1172

Bedosky, J.J., Sr. V.P.--The F.A. Bartlett Tree Expert Co., Stamford, CT; *U.S. Private*, pg. 119

Bedwell, Steven, Sr. V.P.-Customer Service--Home Shopping Network, Inc., Saint Petersburg, FL; *U.S. Public*, pg. 1685

Beer, Donald C., Sr. V.P.--First National Bank of Southwestern Ohio, Hamilton, OH; *U.S. Public*, pg. 633

Beers, Bob, Sr. V.P.-Mktg. & Bus. Devel.--KTI, Orange, CA; *U.S. Public*, pg. 939

Beery, L. Merl, Sr. V.P.-Pur. & Tech. Services--Bob Evans Farms, Inc., Columbus, OH; *U.S. Public*, pg. 596

Beery, R. Earl, Sr. V.P.-Opers.--Bob Evans Farms, Inc., Columbus, OH; *U.S. Public*, pg. 596

Beevers, Edward A., Sr. V.P.-Gen. Mdse.--BJ's Wholesale Club, Inc., Natick, MA; *U.S. Public*, pg. 162

Behm, Frank J., Sr. V.P.--The Equitable Companies Incorporated, New York, NY; *U.S. Public*, pg. 588

Behne, Noel D., Sr. V.P.-Institutional & Intl. Banking--First Security Bank of New Mexico, Albuquerque, NM; *U.S. Public*, pg. 637

Behnke, William, Sr. V.P.-Sls. & Mktg.--General Communication, Inc., Anchorage, AK; *U.S. Public*, pg. 708

Beier, Thomas E., Chief Fin. Officer & Sr. V.P.--IVAX Corporation, Miami, FL; *U.S. Public*, pg. 914

Beining, Michael J., Sr. V.P.-Sls. & Mktg.--BAX Global, Irvine, CA; *U.S. Public*, pg. 1305

Beisler, Gary, Sr. V.P.-Opers.--Rally's Hamburgers, Inc., Louisville, KY; *U.S. Public*, pg. 1359

Beisner, Edward F., Sr. V.P.-Acctng. & Admin.--World Financial Properties, Inc., New York, NY; *Int'l*, pg. 1004

Beittel, T. Brooks, Sr. V.P., Sec. & Treas.--Duff & Phelps Utilities Income Inc., Chicago, IL; *U.S. Public*, pg. 534

Belcher, Randy, Sr. V.P.-Fin.--Buster Brown Apparel, Inc., Chattanooga, TN; *U.S. Private*, pg. 189

Beldon, Sanford, Sr. V.P.--Rodale Press, Inc., Emmaus, PA; *U.S. Private*, pg. 939

Beldotti, D.M., Sr. V.P.-ABB Lummus Global Americas--ABB Lummus Global Inc., Bloomfield, NJ; *Int'l*, pg. 4

Belfrage, Jan, Sr. V.P.-Fin.--AGA AB, Lidingo, Sweden; *Int'l*, pg. 12

Belich, Mel F., Sr. V.P., Gen. Counsel & Sec.--IPL Energy Inc., Calgary, Canada; *Int'l*, pg. 651

Belk, Johnny, Sr. V.P.-Sys. & Control--Belk Stores Services Inc., Charlotte, NC; *U.S. Private*, pg. 131

Belknap, Jerry T., Sr. V.P.-Comml. Lending--Rurban Financial Corp., Defiance, OH; *U.S. Public*, pg. 1412

Belknap, John, Chief Fin. Officer & Sr. V.P.--Richfood Holdings, Inc., Glen Allen, VA; *U.S. Public*, pg. 1388

Bell, Albert J., Sr. V.P., Gen. Counsel & Sec.--Consolidated Stores Corp., Columbus, OH; *U.S. Public*, pg. 437

Bell, Allen W., Sr. V.P.-H.R.--The Toronto Dominion Bank, Toronto, Canada; *Int'l*, pg. 1401

Bell, David C., Sr. V.P.-Sls.--J. Gibson McIlvain Co., White Marsh, MD; *U.S. Private*, pg. 722

Bell, Edward, Jr., Sr. V.P.--The Lane Company, Inc., Altavista, VA; *U.S. Public*, pg. 688

Bell, Gary C., Sr. V.P.--Health Management Associates, Inc., Naples, FL; *U.S. Public*, pg. 802

Bell, Graham P., Sr. V.P.-Opers.--Greenwich Air Services, Miami, FL; *U.S. Public*, pg. 710

Bell, James R., Sr. V.P.-Input Technologies Div.--CalComp Technology, Inc., Anaheim, CA; *U.S. Public*, pg. 1007

Bell, Morton C., Sr. V.P.-Underwriting & Admin.--Kentucky Medical Insurance Company (KMIC), Louisville, KY; *U.S. Private*, pg. 741

Bell, William M., Sr. V.P.-Trust--Liberty Bancorp, Inc., Oklahoma City, OK; *U.S. Public*, pg. 174

Bellestri, Jack, Sr. V.P.--TCF Financial Corp., Minneapolis, MN; *U.S. Public*, pg. 1554

Bellisario, Earl J., Chief Fin. Officer & Sr. V.P.--Dravo Corporation, Pittsburgh, PA; *U.S. Public*, pg. 527

Bellon, Nolan X., Sr. V.P. & Controller--Zions First National Bank, Salt Lake City, UT; *U.S. Public*, pg. 1793
Bellotti, L. F., Sr. V.P.-Opers.--U.S. Borax Inc., Valencia, CA; *Int'l*, pg. 1119
Belsky, Joel, Sr. V.P. & Controller--Federated Department Stores, Inc., Cincinnati, OH; *U.S. Public*, pg. 617
Belstock, Richard, Sr. V.P.--Sierra West Bancorp, Truckee, CA; *U.S. Public*, pg. 1470
Belt, Don, Sr. V.P.-Mktg. & Strategic Devel.--TruServ Corporation, Chicago, IL; *U.S. Private*, pg. 1108
Belt, Marie B., Sr. V.P. & Sec.--Artistic Greetings, Inc., Elmira, NY; *U.S. Public*, pg. 136
Beltz, Gerald, Ph.D, Sr. V.P.-Res. & Devel.--Aquila Biopharmaceuticals, Inc., Worcester, MA; *U.S. Public*, pg. 126
Ben-Arie, Yigel, Sr. V.P.-Jerusalem District--The Israel Electric Corporation Ltd., Haifa, Israel; *Int'l*, pg. 690
Benavides, Roland, Sr. V.P.-Sls.--The Stiffel Company, Chicago, IL; *U.S. Private*, pg. 1043
Bendelius, Ronald A., Sr. V.P. & Comptroller--Arnhold and S. Bleichroeder, Inc., New York, NY; *U.S. Private*, pg. 83
Bender, Brian W., Sr. V.P., Controller & Asst. Treas.--Younkers, Inc., Des Moines, IA; *U.S. Public*, pg. 1334
Bender, John C., Sr. V.P.--Erie Family Life Insurance Company, Erie, PA; *U.S. Public*, pg. 590
Bender, Robert, Sr. V.P. & Gen. Mdse. Mgr.-Soft, Decorative Home, Smallware, Furn--Carson Pirie Scott & Co., Milwaukee, WI; *U.S. Public*, pg. 309
Benefield, Randy, Sr. V.P. & Dir.-MIS--AmeriCredit Corp., Fort Worth, TX; *U.S. Public*, pg. 96
Benenati, Robert W., Sr. V.P.-Opers.--Bradlees Inc., Braintree, MA; *U.S. Public*, pg. 249
Benet, Jay S., Sr. V.P.-Annuities--The Travelers Life & Annuity Co., Hartford, CT; *U.S. Public*, pg. 1633
Benford, Steven, Sr. V.P.-Risk--National Trust Company, Stratford, Canada; *Int'l*, pg. 910
Benger, Scott C., Sr. V.P.-Fin., Treas. & Sec.--Analytical Surveys, Inc., Colorado Springs, CO; *U.S. Public*, pg. 110
Benham, Doug, Sr. V.P.-Fin.--Mrs. Winner's Chicken & Biscuit Restaurants, Atlanta, GA; *U.S. Private*, pg. 766
Benidt, Bruce, Sr. V.P.--Shandwick Minneapolis, Minneapolis, MN; *Int'l*, pg. 1227
Benito, Mariano, Sr. V.P.-Data Processing Center--Banco Santander, Madrid, Spain; *Int'l*, pg. 143
Benjamin, Gerry, Sr. V.P.-H.R. & Admin.--Henry Schein, Inc., Melville, NY; *U.S. Public*, pg. 1437
Benjamin, Michael S., Sr. V.P., Gen. Counsel & Sec.--Meditrust Corporation, Needham, MA; *U.S. Public*, pg. 1081
Bennen, Frank L., Sr. V.P.- Opers.--Delchamps, Inc., Mobile, AL; *U.S. Private*, pg. 588
Bennerdt, Staffan, Sr. V.P.-Fin.--NCC AB, Solna, Sweden; *Int'l*, pg. 898
Benners, Morris C., Jr., Sr. V.P.-Treas. Mngmt.--SouthTrust Corporation, Birmingham, AL; *U.S. Public*, pg. 1491
Bennett, Carl L., Sr. V.P.-Admin. & Sls.--Quad/Graphics, Inc., Pewaukee, WI; *U.S. Private*, pg. 897
Bennett, Craig, Sr. V.P.-Sls. & Mktg.--Utility Trailer Manufacturing Co., City of Industry, CA; *U.S. Private*, pg. 1130
Bennett, Dale, Sr. V.P.--Fasco Industries, Inc., Southfield, MI; *Int'l*, pg. 125
Bennett, Howard, Sr. V.P.--Coast Savings Financial, Inc., Los Angeles, CA; *U.S. Public*, pg. 388
Bennett, John F., Sr. V.P.--JSB Financial, Lynbrook, NY; *U.S. Public*, pg. 919
Bennett, Larry, Sr. V.P. & Assoc. Creative Dir.--McKinney & Silver, Raleigh, NC; *U.S. Private*, pg. 723
Bennett, R. Gerald, Sr. V.P.--Equitable Resources, Inc., Pittsburgh, PA; *U.S. Public*, pg. 589
Bennett, R.L., Sr. V.P.--Sofamor Danek Group, Inc., Memphis, TN; *U.S. Public*, pg. 1482
Bennett, Robert, Sr. V.P.--Willis Corroon Administrative Services Corporation, Nashville, TN; *Int'l*, pg. 1505
Bennett, Walter L., Chief Admin. Officer, Sr. V.P.-Fin. & Sec.--Thor Industries, Inc., Jackson Center, OH; *U.S. Public*, pg. 1602
Benninger, Brian D., Sr. V.P.--Harvard Industries, Inc., Tampa, FL; *U.S. Public*, pg. 796
Bennink, Jan, Sr. V.P.-Dairy Products Europe--Danone Group, Paris, France; *Int'l*, pg. 379
Bennyhoff, George R., Sr. V.P.-Human Resources & Pub. Affairs--The West Company, Incorporated, Lionville, PA; *U.S. Public*, pg. 1755
Benoliel, Joel, Sr. V.P.-Real Estate & Law, Gen. Counsel & Corp. Sec.--Costco Wholesale, Issaquah, WA; *U.S. Public*, pg. 451
Bensabat, Mark P., Sr. V.P.--City National Bank of Baton Rouge, Baton Rouge, LA; *U.S. Public*, pg. 629
Bensdorp, W.L., Sr. Dir.-Strategy & Bus. Devel.--Koninklijke Hoogovens N.V., Ijmuiden, Netherlands; *Int'l*, pg. 753
Bensinger, Steven, Sr. V.P.--Hudson Insurance Company, New York, NY; *Int'l*, pg. 1258
Benson, Robert A., Sr. V.P.--Fay, Spofford & Thorndike, Inc., Burlington, MA; *U.S. Private*, pg. 397
Benson, Stan M., Sr. V.P.-Sls. & Mktg.--Amgen Inc., Thousand Oaks, CA; *U.S. Public*, pg. 100
Benson, W. Arthur, Sr. V.P.--Metallgesellschaft Corp., New York, NY; *Int'l*, pg. 861
Benstein, Craig, Sr. V.P.-Prod. Devel.--Kohl's Corporation, Menomonee Falls, WI; *U.S. Public*, pg. 965
Benstock, Peter, Sr. V.P.--Superior Surgical Mfg. Co., Inc., Seminole, FL; *U.S. Public*, pg. 1539
Bensyl, William, Sr. V.P.-Personnel--PepsiCo, Inc., Purchase, NY; *U.S. Public*, pg. 1276
Bentley, Jeanette, Sr. V.P.-Lending Law--Hibernia Corporation, New Orleans, LA; *U.S. Public*, pg. 825
Bentley, Julia A., Sr. V.P.-Plng. & Inv. Rels. & Sec.--Proffitt's, Inc., Alcoa, TN; *U.S. Public*, pg. 1333
Bentley, Roger, Sr. V.P. & Creative Dir.--Hill, Holliday/Altschiller, New York, NY; *U.S. Private*, pg. 529
Benton, J.E., III, Sr. V.P.--ABM Industries, San Francisco, CA; *U.S. Public*, pg. 2
Benton, Lura, Sr. V.P.--The William Cook Agency, Inc., Jacksonville, FL; *U.S. Private*, pg. 273
Bentzinger, Susan E., Partner & Sr. V.P.--Media That Works, Cincinnati, OH; *U.S. Private*, pg. 727
Benyas, Donald A., Sr. V.P.--Acordia Northeast, Boston, MA; *Int'l*, pg. 671
Benz, Harry R., Chief Fin. Officer & Sr. V.P.-Fin.--Hoechst Marion Roussel, Inc., Bridgewater, NJ; *Int'l*, pg. 624
Berard, Joseph, Sr. V.P.-Mktg.--Empire Blue Cross & Blue Shield, New York, NY; *U.S. Private*, pg. 374
Berard, Raymond A., Sr. V.P.-Tech.--Interface Research Corporation, Kennesaw, GA; *U.S. Public*, pg. 889
Berardi, Louis, Sr. V.P.-New Bus. Devel. & Strategic Plng.--Roberts Pharmaceutical Corporation, Eatontown, NJ; *U.S. Public*, pg. 1393
Bercu, Donald F., Sr. V.P.--Acordia Northeast, Boston, MA; *Int'l*, pg. 671
Berding, John B., Sr. V.P.-Investments--American Annuity Group, Cincinnati, OH; *U.S. Public*, pg. 74
Berdusco, Roger, Sr. V.P.-Mktg.--Frito-Lay Company, Plano, TX; *U.S. Public*, pg. 1277
Berendt, Ph.D., Michael J., Sr. V.P.-Res. Pharmaceutical Division--Bayer Corporation, Pittsburgh, PA; *Int'l*, pg. 172
Berenzweig, Evan, Sr. V.P.--Rag Shops, Inc., Hawthorne, NJ; *U.S. Public*, pg. 1358
Beresford, P., Sr. V.P.--McDonald's Restaurants of Canada Ltd., Toronto, Canada; *U.S. Public*, pg. 1069
Berey, Mark H., Chief Fin. Officer, Sr. V.P.-Fin. & Treas.--Giant Food Inc., Landover, MD; *U.S. Public*, pg. 741
Berg, Mark S., Sr. V.P. & Gen. Counsel--American General Corporation, Houston, TX; *U.S. Public*, pg. 76
Berg, Richard C., Sr. V.P.--CitFed Mortgage Corporation of America, Dayton, OH; *U.S. Public*, pg. 376
Berg, Suzanne, Sr. V.P.-Promo.--GRP Records, New York, NY; *Int'l*, pg. 1215
Bergeman, Richard P., Sr. V.P.-Human Resources--Bestfoods, Englewood Cliffs, NJ; *U.S. Public*, pg. 223
Bergemann, Fred W., Chief Lending Officer & Sr. V.P.--Pacific One Bank, Portland, OR; *U.S. Public*, pg. 635
Bergen, Jack, Sr. V.P.-Corp. Rels.--CBS, New York, NY; *U.S. Public*, pg. 273
Bergen, John D., Sr. V.P.-Corp. Rels.--CBS Corporation, Pittsburgh, PA; *U.S. Public*, pg. 273
Berger, Ernie, Sr. V.P.-Small Bus. Services Mktg.--American Express Travel Related Services Co., Inc., New York, NY; *U.S. Public*, pg. 73
Berger, Joyce M., Sr. V.P.-California Oper. (North)--Kaiser Permanente, Oakland, CA; *U.S. Private*, pg. 605
Berger, Nol, Sr. V.P.-Legal Affairs & Corp. Sec.--Koninklijke Ahold NV, Zaandam, Netherlands; *Int'l*, pg. 749
Berger, Robert J., Chief Fin. Officer, Sr. V.P. & Treas.--ONBANCorp, Inc., Syracuse, NY; *U.S. Public*, pg. 631
Bergeron, Kaye, Sr. V.P.--Hibernia Corporation, New Orleans, LA; *U.S. Public*, pg. 825
Bergeron, Keith, Sr. V.P.--Hibernia Corporation, New Orleans, LA; *U.S. Public*, pg. 825
Bergeron, Paul D., Sr. V.P. & Dir.-Human Resources--Whitney Holding Corporation, New Orleans, LA; *U.S. Public*, pg. 1766
Berges, Orlando, Sr. V.P. & Controller--Banco Popular de Puerto Rico, San Juan, PR; *U.S. Public*, pg. 175
Bergeson, Scott, Sr. V.P.-Human Resources--American Stores Company, Salt Lake City, UT; *U.S. Public*, pg. 92
Bergholtz-Widell, Curt, Sr. V.P.-Human Resources & Security--Vattenfall AB, Stockholm, Sweden; *Int'l*, pg. 1452
Bergin, Maggie, Sr. V.P. & Mngmt. Dir.--Cliff Freeman & Partners, New York, NY; *U.S. Public*, pg. 1422
Berglass, Judith R., Sr. V.P. & Sec.--Dep Corporation, Rancho Dominguez, CA; *U.S. Public*, pg. 500
Berglund, Jon, Sr. V.P., Dir.-Claims & Asst. Sec.--Federated Mutual Insurance Company, Owatonna, MN; *U.S. Private*, pg. 399
Bergmann, Horst A., Sr. V.P.--The Times Mirror Company, Los Angeles, CA; *U.S. Public*, pg. 1615
Bergner, William H., Sr. V.P.--Firstar Corporation, Milwaukee, WI; *U.S. Public*, pg. 642
Bergstedt, Lennart, Sr. V.P.-Personnel--Trelleborg AB, Trelleborg, Sweden; *Int'l*, pg. 1419
Bergstrom, John, Sr. V.P. & Chief Mktg. Officer--Berkshire Life Insurance Company, Pittsfield, MA; *U.S. Private*, pg. 136
Bergstrom, Rolf, Sr. V.P.--Perstorp AB, Perstorp, Sweden; *Int'l*, pg. 1036
Berk, Alan, Sr. V.P. & Corp. Controller--A. Epstein and Sons, Intl., Inc., Chicago, IL; *U.S. Private*, pg. 379
Berk, Howard, Sr. V.P.--Millicom International Cellular SA, Bertrange, Luxembourg; *Int'l*, pg. 867
Berk, Howard, Sr. V.P.--MIC-USA Inc., New York, NY; *Int'l*, pg. 867
Berkenbile, Terry, Sr. V.P.-Sls. & Mktg.--Pilgrim's Pride Corporation, Pittsburg, TX; *U.S. Public*, pg. 1296
Berkley, Suzan, Sr. V.P.-ATM--Brink's, Inc., Darien, CT; *U.S. Public*, pg. 1305
Berkowitz, Martin A., Sr. V.P. & Comptroller--The Prudential Insurance Company of America, Newark, NJ; *U.S. Private*, pg. 892
Berkowitz, Paul, Sr. V.P.--Marie Brizard Wines & Spirits USA, North Miami, FL; *U.S. Private*, pg. 702
Berlin, Joel, Sr. V.P.--Empire Insurance Group, New York, NY; *U.S. Public*, pg. 990
Berlin, Joel M., Sr. V.P.--Allcity Insurance Co., New York, NY; *U.S. Public*, pg. 990
Berlin, Roger, Ph.D., Sr. V.P.-Scientific Affairs Worldwide--Whitehall-Robins Healthcare, Madison, NJ; *U.S. Public*, pg. 80
Berlin, Steven R., Chief Fin. Officer & Sr. V.P.-Fin.--Citgo Petroleum Corporation, Tulsa, OK; *Int'l*, pg. 1045
Berlin, Terry, Sr. V.P. & Media Dir.--The Summit Media Group, New York, NY; *U.S. Private*, pg. 1050
Berlow, Myer, Sr. V.P.-Interactive Mktg.--America Online Incorporated, Dulles, VA; *U.S. Public*, pg. 66
Berman, David, Sr. V.P.-Mktg. & Bus. Devel.--PHP Healthcare Corporation, Reston, VA; *U.S. Public*, pg. 1241
Berman, Gene, Sr. V.P. & Mngmt. Rep.--Grey Advertising Inc., San Francisco, CA; *U.S. Public*, pg. 764
Berman, R., Sr. V.P.--Senior Engineering Company-USA, City of Commerce, CA; *Int'l*, pg. 1222
Berman, Steve, Sr. V.P.-Creative Affairs--Columbia TriStar Television, Culver City, CA; *Int'l*, pg. 1282
Bern, Nancy F., Sr. V.P.-Long Term Care--John Hancock Mutual Life Insurance Company, Boston, MA; *U.S. Private*, pg. 589
Bernacki, Claire, Sr. V.P. & Brdcst. Production Dir.--DMB&B Detroit, Troy, MI; *U.S. Private*, pg. 302
Bernal, Ronald, Sr. V.P.-Scalable & Network Servers--Silicon Graphics, Inc., Mountain View, CA; *U.S. Public*, pg. 1473
Bernard, David, Sr. V.P.-Information Services--Quantum Plus, New York, NY; *U.S. Public*, pg. 1224
Bernard, Marcel, Sr. V.P.-Ontario Div.--St. Lawrence Cement Inc., Montreal, Canada; *Int'l*, pg. 628
Bernard, Thomas J., Sr. V.P. & Gen. Mgr.-Infrastructure Prods. Division--QUALCOMM, San Diego, CA; *U.S. Public*, pg. 1348
Bernardo, Thomas, Sr. V.P.-Franchise Sls.--Days Inns of America, Inc., Parsippany, NJ; *U.S. Public*, pg. 321
Bernardy, Raymond L., Sr. V.P.-Fin.--Bankers Systems Incorporated, Saint Cloud, MN; *U.S. Private*, pg. 114
Bernauer, David W., Chief Information Officer & Sr. V.P.--Walgreen Co., Deerfield, IL; *U.S. Public*, pg. 1733
Berner, Richard B., Exec. V.P.-Economics & Chief Economist--Mellon Bank Corporation, Pittsburgh, PA; *U.S. Public*, pg. 1084
Bernhart, James A., Sr. V.P.-Consumer Business Office--Motorola, Inc., Schaumburg, IL; *U.S. Public*, pg. 1136
Bernier, Segundo, Sr. V.P.-Opers.--Banco Popular de Puerto Rico, San Juan, PR; *U.S. Public*, pg. 175
Bernstein, A.A., Sr. V.P.--Amerada Hess Corporation, New York, NY; *U.S. Public*, pg. 65
Bernstein, Steven, Sr. V.P.--Health-Chem Corporation, New York, NY; *U.S. Public*, pg. 802
Bernstein, Steven, Sr. V.P.--Herculite Products, Inc., York, PA; *U.S. Public*, pg. 802
Berntsen, Bjarne T., Sr. V.P.-Franchise Div.--Marriott Hotels, Resorts, and Suites, Washington, DC; *U.S. Public*, pg. 1048
Berrien, James S., Sr. V.P. & Grp. Publisher--American Express Publishing Corporation, New York, NY; *U.S. Public*, pg. 74
Berrios, Filiberto, Sr. V.P. & Pres.-Blockbuster Div.--Pueblo Xtra International, Inc., Pompano Beach, FL; *U.S. Private*, pg. 894
Berry, Amy, Sr. V.P. & Grp. Media Dir.--Young & Rubicam New York, New York, NY; *U.S. Private*, pg. 1198
Berry, Daniel H., Sr. V.P.-Sls., Service & Mktg.--Ultratech Stepper, Inc., San Jose, CA; *U.S. Public*, pg. 1663
Berry, George, Sr. V.P.--Cousins Properties Incorporated, Atlanta, GA; *U.S. Public*, pg. 453
Berry, Jon M., Sr. V.P. & Treas.--Jacor Communications, Inc., Covington, KY; *U.S. Public*, pg. 922
Berry, Rudy A., Sr. V.P.--Southeastern Steel Company, Florence, SC; *U.S. Private*, pg. 1015
Berry, William S., Sr. V.P.--Rayonier Forest Resources, Stamford, CT; *U.S. Public*, pg. 1363
Bersch, Neil R., Sr. V.P.--Roll International Corporation, Los Angeles, CA; *U.S. Private*, pg. 941
Bersoff, Marilyn, Sr. V.P.-Admin. & Sec.--BTG, Inc., Fairfax, VA; *U.S. Public*, pg. 164
Bert, Paul A., Sr. V.P.-Mktg. Consumer Svcs.--The ServiceMaster Company, Downers Grove, IL; *U.S. Public*, pg. 1461
Bert, Paul A., Sr. V.P.-Mktg.--ServiceMaster Consumer Services Company, Memphis, TN; *U.S. Public*, pg. 1461
Bertelsen, Annette, Sr. V.P.--Colle & McVoy Marketing Communications, Minneapolis, MN; *U.S. Private*, pg. 252
Berthels, L. Frans, Sr. V.P.--Raychem Corporation, Menlo Park, CA; *U.S. Public*, pg. 1362
Berto, L. Rogerio, Chief Fin. Officer & Sr. V.P.--TVX Gold Inc., Toronto, Canada; *Int'l*, pg. 1345
Bertolino, Robert E., Sr. V.P.--Fay, Spofford & Thorndike, Inc., Burlington, MA; *U.S. Private*, pg. 397
Bertolucci, Michael D., Sr. V.P.--Interface Inc., Atlanta, GA; *U.S. Public*, pg. 889
Bertorp, Michael, Sr. V.P. & Gen. Counsel--Svenska Cellulosa Aktiebolaget (SCA), Stockholm, Sweden; *Int'l*, pg. 1326
Bertrand, Mario, Sr. V.P.--Steinberg Inc., Montreal, Canada; *Int'l*, pg. 1272
Bertsch, Douglas, Sr. V.P.-Mdsg.--Associated Merchandising Corp. (AMC), New York, NY; *U.S. Private*, pg. 91
Berube, Jacques B., Pres.-Nortel Europe & Sr. V.P.-Special Projects--Northern Telecom Limited, Brampton, Canada; *Int'l*, pg. 968
Berumen, Michael, Sr. V.P.--PM Group Life Insurance Company, Fountain Valley, CA; *U.S. Private*, pg. 831
Bescoby, Janet, Sr. V.P. & Grp. Plng. Dir.--Western International Media Corporation, Los Angeles, CA; *U.S. Private*, pg. 1165
Beseler, Chris, Sr. V.P.-Mktg. & Sls.--Waccamaw Corporation, Myrtle Beach, SC; *U.S. Private*, pg. 1145
Beskow, Craig, Sr. V.P. & Cashier--First National Bank in Cleburne, Cleburne, TX; *U.S. Public*, pg. 633
Besosa, Jorge J., Sr. V.P.-Individual Lending--Banco Popular de Puerto Rico, San Juan, PR; *U.S. Public*, pg. 175
Bessant, Thomas A., Jr., Chief Fin. Officer, Sr. V.P. & Treas.--Cash America International, Inc., Fort Worth, TX; *U.S. Public*, pg. 312
Besse, Robert, Sr. V.P.--Coleman Powermate Compressors, Springfield, MN; *U.S. Private*, pg. 691
Best, Alex B., Sr. V.P.-Engrng.--Cox Communications, Inc., Atlanta, GA; *U.S. Public*, pg. 454

Best, Robert O., Sr. V.P. & Chief Information Officer--Provident Companies, Inc., Chattanooga, TN; *U.S. Public*, pg. 1337
Beste, William B., Sr. V.P.-Fin.--Vantage Companies, Dallas, TX; *U.S. Private*, pg. 1134
Bethell, Benjamin L., Sr. V.P.-Human Resources--The Procter & Gamble Company, Cincinnati, OH; *U.S. Public*, pg. 1330
Betin, Pierre, Sr. V.P.-Tech. Strategy--SNECMA - Societe Nationale d'Etude et de Construction de Moteurs d'Aviation, Paris, France; *Int'l*, pg. 1165
Betker, Rick G., Sr. V.P.-Interactive Technologies--Ross Roy Communications, Inc., Bloomfield Hills, MI; *U.S. Private*, pg. 946
Betley, John, Sr. V.P. & Dir.-DMB&B Fin. Opers.-USA--DMB&B Communications, New York, NY; *U.S. Private*, pg. 302
Betts, Gene M., Sr. V.P.-Corp. Fin.--Sprint Corporation, Westwood, KS; *U.S. Public*, pg. 1500
Beuls, Marc, Sr. V.P.-Fin.--Millicom International Cellular SA, Bertrange, Luxembourg; *Int'l*, pg. 867
Beusse, Carlton G., Sr. V.P., Mng. Dir.-RMS, Exec. V.P. & Chief Oper. Officer-CRRUX--Willis Corroon Corp. of Wisconsin, Milwaukee, WI; *Int'l*, pg. 1507
Beutner, Roger E., Sr. V.P.-Opers.--Amway Corporation, Ada, MI; *U.S. Private*, pg. 69
Bevilacqua, Michael P., V.P.-Inflammation & Medicinal Chemistry--Amgen Inc., Thousand Oaks, CA; *U.S. Public*, pg. 100
Bevis, Harold, Sr. V.P.-Product Mngmt.--General Cable Corporation, Highland Heights, KY; *Int'l*, pg. 1486
Bewley, Peter D., Sr. V.P., Gen. Counsel & Sec.--NovaCare Inc., King of Prussia, PA; *U.S. Public*, pg. 1203
Bexon, R., Sr. V.P.-Mktg. Sls.--Brown & Williamson Tobacco Corp., Louisville, KY; *Int'l*, pg. 111
Beyer, Michael K., Sr. V.P., Gen. Counsel & Sec.--Robert Mondavi Winery, Inc., Oakville, CA; *U.S. Public*, pg. 1393
Beyman, Jonathan E., Chief Info. Officer & Sr. V.P.--CUC International, Inc., Stamford, CT; *U.S. Public*, pg. 320
Bezik, Cynthia B., Sr. V.P.-Fin.--Cleveland-Cliffs Inc, Cleveland, OH; *U.S. Public*, pg. 386
Bhardwaj, Sunil, V.P.-Admin. & Plng.--Consolidated Freightways Corp., Menlo Park, CA; *U.S. Public*, pg. 435
Bianchi, Marco B., Sr. V.P.--Amerada Hess Corporation, New York, NY; *U.S. Public*, pg. 65
Bianco, Joseph R., Sr. V.P.--Somerset Savings Bank, Somerville, MA; *U.S. Public*, pg. 1484
Biasucci, Sam B., Sr. V.P., Sec. & Cashier--First Western Bank, National Association, New Castle, PA; *U.S. Public*, pg. 642
Biasuzzi, John M., Sr. V.P. & Treas.--Citizens Savings Bank, Providence, RI; *Int'l*, pg. 1132
Biasuzzi, John M., Sr. V.P. & Treas.--Citizens Trust Company, Providence, RI; *Int'l*, pg. 1132
Bibby, Douglas M., Sr. V.P.-Human Resources--Federal National Mortgage Association (Fannie Mae), Washington, DC; *U.S. Public*, pg. 615
Bichai, Joseph, Sr. V.P.-Mfr.--Genfoot Inc., Montreal, Canada; *Int'l*, pg. 549
Bickers, Gary, Sr. V.P.-Western Area--Arrow/Schweber Electronics, Carrollton, TX; *U.S. Public*, pg. 134
Bickford, Andrew T., Sr. V.P.--Independent Publications, Inc., Bryn Mawr, PA; *U.S. Private*, pg. 559
Bickford, Michael, Sr. V.P.-Derivative Securities Mktg.--The American Stock Exchange, New York, NY; *U.S. Private*, pg. 62
Bicknell, Bob, Sr. V.P.-Mktg. & Sls.--Campbell Hausfeld Division of Scott Fetzer, Harrison, OH; *U.S. Public*, pg. 217
Biehl, George C., Chief Fin. Officer, Sr. V.P. & Sec.--Southwest Gas Corporation, Las Vegas, NV; *U.S. Public*, pg. 1493
Biehl, George C., Chief Fin. Officer & Sr. V.P.--Carson Water Co., Las Vegas, NV; *U.S. Public*, pg. 1493
Biehl, John C., Sr. V.P.-Admin.--Valvoline Company, Lexington, KY; *U.S. Public*, pg. 139
Biehl, Peter, Sr. V.P.--Agripac Inc., Salem, OR; *U.S. Private*, pg. 26
Biel, Howard S., Sr. V.P. & Mng. Dir.-Devel.--Federal Realty Investment Trust, Rockville, MD; *U.S. Public*, pg. 616
Bielen, Richard J., Sr. V.P.-Investments--Protective Life Corporation, Birmingham, AL; *U.S. Public*, pg. 1336
Bielsky, Hyman, Sr. V.P. & Gen. Counsel--Safety-Kleen Corp., Elgin, IL; *U.S. Public*, pg. 1425
Bielun, John A., Chief Fin. Officer, Sr. V.P. & Treas.--Alta Gold Co., Henderson, NV; *U.S. Public*, pg. 58
Biemeck, Bruce J., Chief Fin. Officer & Sr. V.P.--Great Lakes Dredge & Dock Co., Oak Brook, IL; *U.S. Private*, pg. 474
Bien, Timothy E., Sr. V.P.-Professional Services & Pur.--Omnicare, Inc., Covington, KY; *U.S. Public*, pg. 1223
Biggar, Jeffrey M., Sr. V.P.-Private Client Grp.--National City Corporation, Cleveland, OH; *U.S. Public*, pg. 1154
Biggerstaff, Don B., Sr. V.P.-Fin. & Admin.--Drexel Heritage Furnishings Inc., Drexel, NC; *U.S. Private*, pg. 432
Biggs, Michael W., Sr. V.P.-Asset Mngmnt.--Camden Property Trust, Houston, TX; *U.S. Public*, pg. 298
Biggs, R.G., Sr. V.P. & Dir.-H.R.--Fedco, Inc., Santa Fe Springs, CA; *U.S. Private*, pg. 398
Bigler, Robert J., Chief Fin. Officer & Sr. V.P.--Estee Lauder Companies Inc., New York, NY; *U.S. Public*, pg. 594
Bilger, Mark, Sr. V.P.-Prod. Devel.--Hyperion Software, Stamford, CT; *U.S. Public*, pg. 851
Bilhartz, H.L., Sr. V.P.-ARCO Explorations Tech.--Atlantic Richfield Company, Los Angeles, CA; *U.S. Public*, pg. 144
Biller, Joel, Sr. V.P. & Gen. Counsel--Manpower Inc., Milwaukee, WI; *U.S. Public*, pg. 1042
Billet, Kevin, Sr. V.P.-Bus. & Legal Affairs--Niagara Frontier Hockey, L.P., Buffalo, NY; *U.S. Private*, pg. 798
Billia, Darlene, Sr. V.P. & Acct. Plng. Dir.-Insights Grp.--Young & Rubicam New York, New York, NY; *U.S. Private*, pg. 1198
Billick, Steven M., Chief Fin. Officer, Sr. V.P. & Treas.--Signature Brands USA, Inc., Solon, OH; *U.S. Public*, pg. 1472
Billings, David A., Sr. V.P.-Info. & Tech. Sys.--Airborne Freight Corporation, Seattle, WA; *U.S. Public*, pg. 32
Bills, Gregory S., Sr. V.P.-Lending--Republic Security Bank, West Palm Beach, FL; *U.S. Public*, pg. 1382
Bilodeau, Gerard L., Sr. V.P. & Sec.--Arrow Financial Corporation, Glens Falls, NY; *U.S. Public*, pg. 135
Biltz, Jim, Sr. V.P.-Texas Reg.--Tenet Healthcare Corporation, Santa Barbara, CA; *U.S. Public*, pg. 1576
Bina, Pete, Sr. V.P.--M & I Thunderbird Bank, Phoenix, AZ; *U.S. Public*, pg. 1050
Bingaman, Anne, Sr. V.P.--LCI International, Inc., Dublin, OH; *U.S. Public*, pg. 969
Bingham, Gordon J., Sr. V.P.-Mktg.--Olsten Corporation, Melville, NY; *U.S. Public*, pg. 1220
Bingham, Paul M., Sr. V.P.-Fin.--Fleetwood Enterprises, Inc., Riverside, CA; *U.S. Public*, pg. 650
Binkley, Chris, Pres.-Southeast Division & Sr. V.P.--Kaiser Permanente, Oakland, CA; *U.S. Private*, pg. 605
Biondollilo, Michael A., Sr. V.P.-H.R.--The Penn Mutual Life Insurance Company, Philadelphia, PA; *U.S. Private*, pg. 849
Birch, Drew, Sr. V.P. & Mgr.-P&C--Willis Corroon Corp. of Orange County, Santa Ana, CA; *Int'l*, pg. 1506
Bird, Anat, Sr. V.P.--Norwest Corporation, Minneapolis, MN; *U.S. Public*, pg. 1201
Birdsall, John, Sr. V.P. & Exec. Chef--Koo Koo Roo, Inc., Los Angeles, CA; *U.S. Public*, pg. 966
Birk, David R., Sr. V.P., Gen. Counsel & Sec.--Avnet, Inc., Great Neck, NY; *U.S. Public*, pg. 155
Birkhahn, Jonathan, Sr. V.P.-Bus. Affairs & Gen. Counsel--King World Productions, Inc., New York, NY; *U.S. Public*, pg. 961
Birkhauser, Dave, Sr. V.P.-Sls.-Grove Crane--Grove WorldWide, Shady Grove, PA; *Int'l*, pg. 593
Birmingham, Joseph K., Sr. V.P.-Property Devel.--The TJX Companies, Inc., Framingham, MA; *U.S. Public*, pg. 1556
Birn, S.R., Sr. V.P. & Assoc. Gen. Counsel--Auto-Owners Insurance, Lansing, MI; *U.S. Private*, pg. 100
Birnbaum, Joel S., Sr. V.P.-Res. & Devel. & Dir.-HP Laboratories--Hewlett-Packard Company, Palo Alto, CA; *U.S. Public*, pg. 813
Biro, Jon C., Sr. V.P. & Treas.--ICO, Inc., Houston, TX; *U.S.* Public, pg. 853
Bisaro, Paul, Sr. V.P., Gen. Counsel & Sec.--Barr Laboratories Inc., Pomona, NY; *U.S. Public*, pg. 191
Bishop, Cam, Sr. V.P.--Intertec Publishing, Overland Park, KS; *U.S. Public*, pg. 1327
Bishop, Derry E., Sr. V.P.--The Equitable Companies Incorporated, New York, NY; *U.S. Public*, pg. 588
Bishop, John J., Sr. V.P. & Asst. Sec.--Motorists Mutual Insurance Co., Columbus, OH; *U.S. Private*, pg. 764
Bishop, Larry, Sr. V.P.--Conklin Instrument Corporation, Pleasant Valley, NY; *U.S. Private*, pg. 263
Bishop, Laura M., Chief Fin. Officer & Sr. V.P.--Luby's Cafeterias, Inc., San Antonio, TX; *U.S. Public*, pg. 1017
Bishop, Mark L., Sr. V.P.--Boykin Lodging Co., Cleveland, OH; *U.S. Public*, pg. 249
Bishop, T. Hal, Sr. V.P.--NationsBank of Tennessee, Nashville, TN; *U.S. Public*, pg. 1163
Bishop, Virgil, Sr. V.P.--American Consumers, Inc., Fort Oglethorpe, GA; *U.S. Public*, pg. 70
Bishopric, Bob, Sr. V.P. & Acct. Mngmt. Supvr.--Tinsley Advertising, Miami, FL; *U.S. Private*, pg. 1088
Bismante, Antomio A., Sr. V.P.--TrizecHahn Properties Inc., Chicago, IL; *Int'l*, pg. 1425
Bismuth, J., Sr. V.P.-Media, Studies--Danone Group, Paris, France; *Int'l*, pg. 379
Bissel, Brent, Sr. V.P. & Direct Response Dir.--Colle & McVoy Marketing Communications, Minneapolis, MN; *U.S. Private*, pg. 252
Bissell, Brent J., Sr. V.P., Integrated Response Grp. Mgr. & Acct. Exec.--Colle & McVoy, Inc., Minneapolis, MN; *U.S. Private*, pg. 252
Bistrom, Helena, Sr. V.P. & Controller--Metra Corporation, Helsinki, Finland; *Int'l*, pg. 862
Bitar, Javier, Sr. V.P.-Fin.--Maguire Partners, Los Angeles, CA; *U.S. Private*, pg. 696
Bitar, Khalil, Chief Fin. Officer & Exec. V.P.--Intermarkets Advertising, Beirut, Lebanon; *Int'l*, pg. 680
Bitler, Harold P., Sr. V.P.--SunTrust Banks, Inc., Atlanta, GA; *U.S. Public*, pg. 1537
Bittner, Daniel P., Sr. V.P.-Fin. & Corp. Svcs.--Wisconsin Public Service Corporation, Green Bay, WI; *U.S. Public*, pg. 1728
Biundo, Emmanual, Sr. V.P.-Fin. & Opers.--Hiram Walker, Southfield, MI; *Int'l*, pg. 63
Bivolcic, David J., Sr. V.P.--AMATI Communications Corp., San Jose, CA; *U.S. Public*, pg. 1585
Bivona, Frank J., Chief Fin. Officer, Sr. V.P. & Treas.--AMBAC Financial Group, Inc., New York, NY; *U.S. Public*, pg. 62
Bizzack, Jeffrey M., Sr. V.P.-Sls.--ProBusiness Services, Inc., Pleasanton, CA; *U.S. Public*, pg. 1330
Bjerke, Lars T., Sr. V.P.-Exploration & Evaluation Div.--Saga Petroleum ASA, Sandvika, Norway; *Int'l*, pg. 1169
Bjorkman, Lincoln, Sr. V.P. & Grp. Creative Dir.-Concepts--Wunderman Cato Johnson, New York, NY; *U.S. Private*, pg. 1197
Bjornsson, Steinn Logi, Sr. V.P.--Icelandair, Reykjavik, Iceland; *Int'l*, pg. 658
Blachman, Rochel, Sr. V.P.-Bus. Affairs & Acquisitions--Paramount Pictures Corporation, Los Angeles, CA; *U.S. Private*, pg. 776
Black, C. Robert, Sr. V.P.--Texaco Inc., White Plains, NY; *U.S. Public*, pg. 1582
Black, David, Sr. V.P.-Sls.--Camco International Inc., Houston, TX; *U.S. Public*, pg. 297
Black, David R., Sr. V.P.-Fin.--Jitney-Jungle Stores of America, Inc., Jackson, MS; *U.S. Private*, pg. 588
Black, Donald V., Sr. V.P.-Mktg. & Airline Fin.--McDonnell Aircraft & Missile Systems Div., Berkeley, MO; *U.S. Public*, pg. 241
Black, James E.C., Sr. V.P.-Engrng.--Boole & Babbage, Inc., San Jose, CA; *U.S. Public*, pg. 244
Black, Neal, Sr. V.P.-Prod. Devel. & Hardlines Mdse. Mngmt.--Venture Stores, Inc., O Fallon, MO; *U.S. Public*, pg. 1716
Black, Peter D., Sr. V.P.-Mktg.--BPA International, New York, NY; *U.S. Private*, pg. 107
Blackburn, Jack, Sr. V.P.-Mktg.--Country Life Insurance Company, Bloomington, IL; *U.S. Private*, pg. 278
Blackburn, John, Sr. V.P.-Mktg.--CC Services, Bloomington, IL; *U.S. Private*, pg. 279
Blackin, Jack, Sr. V.P. & Asst. Sec.--Valley National Bancorp, Wayne, NJ; *U.S. Public*, pg. 1705
Blackman, Joyce, Sr. V.P.-Admin. Support--Memphis Light, Gas & Water, Memphis, TN; *U.S. Private*, pg. 731
Blackmon, Charles, Sr. V.P.--North Carolina Mutual Life Insurance Co., Durham, NC; *U.S. Private*, pg. 804
Blackwell, Richard M., Sr. V.P.--Metropolitan Life Insurance Co., New York, NY; *U.S. Private*, pg. 737
Blackwell, Robert J., Sr. V.P.-Mktg.--OHM Remediation Services Corp., Findlay, OH; *U.S. Public*, pg. 1208
Blair, Ken, Sr. V.P.--Century Business Credit Corporation, New York, NY; *U.S. Private*, pg. 225
Blair, Robert J., Sr. V.P.-Corp. Investor Rels.--Western Digital Corporation, Irvine, CA; *U.S. Public*, pg. 1758
Blair, Stephen L., Sr. V.P.--The Time Inc. Book Company, New York, NY; *U.S. Public*, pg. 1613
Blake, Gerald K., Chief Investment Officer, Sr. V.P. & Corp. Sec.--National Travelers Life Co., West Des Moines, IA; *U.S. Private*, pg. 787
Blake, John, Sr. V.P.-Properties & Facilities--The Hertz Corporation, Park Ridge, NJ; *U.S. Public*, pg. 664
Blake, John T., Sr. V.P.--Keycorp, Cleveland, OH; *U.S. Public*, pg. 954
Blanchard, Larry H., Sr. V.P.-Commun. & Pub. Rels.--CUNA Mutual Insurance Society, Madison, WI; *U.S. Private*, pg. 296
Blandford, Jack, Sr. V.P. & Brdcst. Production Dir.--North Castle Partners Advertising, Inc., Stamford, CT; *U.S. Private*, pg. 804
Blankinship, Bill, Sr. V.P.--Willis Corroon Corp. of Georgia, Atlanta, GA; *Int'l*, pg. 1506
Blankstein, Roger, Sr. V.P.-Trade Mktg.--Fruit of the Loom, Inc., Chicago, IL; *U.S. Public*, pg. 685
Blanton, Ray, Sr. V.P.-Mdsg.--Shonac Corporation, Columbus, OH; *U.S. Private*, pg. 996
Blasius, Larry, Sr. V.P. & Dir.-NBU--National Broadcast Unit, New York, NY; *U.S. Public*, pg. 1641
Blattmachr, Doug, Sr. V.P. & Trust Officer--TrustCorp., Great Falls, MT; *U.S. Private*, pg. 314
Blay, Abby, Sr. V.P.-Trng.--Ross Roy Communications, Inc., Bloomfield Hills, MI; *U.S. Private*, pg. 946
Bleier, Michael E., Sr. V.P. & Gen. Counsel--Mellon Bank Corporation, Pittsburgh, PA; *U.S. Public*, pg. 1084
Blem, Donald D., Sr. V.P.-Opers.--ATL Ultrasound, Inc., Bothell, WA; *U.S. Public*, pg. 11
Bliss, Clinton, Sr. V.P.--Imperial Bank, Inglewood, CA; *U.S. Public*, pg. 871
Blitz, David, Sr. V.P.--Imperial Bank, Inglewood, CA; *U.S. Public*, pg. 871
Block, Charles K., Sr. V.P.-Loan Review--Liberty Bancorp, Inc., Oklahoma City, OK; *U.S. Public*, pg. 174
Block, Philip W., Sr. V.P.-H.R.--Ashland, Inc., Russell, KY; *U.S. Public*, pg. 138
Block, Richard H., Sr. V.P.-Fertilizer Opers.--Freeport-McMoRan Resource Partners, Ltd., New Orleans, LA; *U.S. Public*, pg. 681
Blohowiak, Bruce, Chief Oper. Officer, Sr. V.P. & Gen. Counsel--Metropolitan Mortgage & Securities Co., Inc., Spokane, WA; *U.S. Private*, pg. 738
Blonigen, Joseph P., Sr. V.P. & Mgr.-Residential Mortgage Loans--First Financial Bank, FSB, Stevens Point, WI; *U.S. Public*, pg. 140
Bloom, Alan, Sr. V.P., Gen. Counsel & Sec.--Maxicare Health Plans, Inc., Los Angeles, CA; *U.S. Public*, pg. 1061
Bloom, E., Sr. V.P.-Opers.--Metal Improvement Co., Paramus, NJ; *U.S. Public*, pg. 469
Bloom, Marvin, Sr. V.P.--URS Greiner, New York, NY; *U.S. Public*, pg. 1659
Bloom, Philip M., Sr. V.P.--TCF Financial Corp., Minneapolis, MN; *U.S. Public*, pg. 1554
Blossom, Charles C., Jr., Sr. V.P.-Mktg.--Action Performance Companies, Inc., Phoenix, AZ; *U.S. Public*, pg. 17
Blossom, Rick L., Chief Lending Officer & Sr. V.P.--First Financial Bancorp, Hamilton, OH; *U.S. Public*, pg. 632
Blotky, Randolph, Sr. V.P.--Warner Bros. Consumer Products, Burbank, CA; *U.S. Public*, pg. 1610
Blount, Daniel J., Sr. V.P.-Fin.--Montgomery KONE Inc., Moline, IL; *Int'l*, pg. 746
Blowers, Carl, Sr. V.P.-Mfg./Tech.--Jostens, Minneapolis, MN; *U.S. Public*, pg. 934
Blubaugh, John S., Sr. V.P.--Citizens National Bank of Southern Pennsylvania, Greencastle, PA; *U.S. Public*, pg. 1542
Blue, Karen S., Sr. V.P.--Keycorp, Cleveland, OH; *U.S. Public*, pg. 954
Blue, Linden S., Vice Chm. & Sr. V.P.--General Atomics, San Diego, CA; *U.S. Private*, pg. 443
Bluestein, David, Sr. V.P. & Pres.-IFF Flavors--International Flavors & Fragrances, Inc., New York, NY; *U.S. Public*, pg. 898
Blum, Jonathan D., Sr. V.P.-Pub. Affairs--Tricon Global Restaurants, Inc., Louisville, KY; *U.S. Public*, pg. 1636
Blum, Richard, Sr. V.P.-Intl.--Swank, Inc., Attleboro, MA; *U.S. Public*, pg. 1543
Blum, Stephen D., Sr. V.P.-Corp. Commun.--Quaker State Corporation, Irving, TX; *U.S. Public*, pg. 1348
Blumberg, Michael, Sr., Sr. V.P.-Pur. & Sec.--Sound Advice, Inc., Dania, FL; *U.S. Public*, pg. 1488

Blume, Dennis A., Sr. V.P.--Lincoln National Realty Corporation, Fort Wayne, IN; *U.S. Public*, pg. 998
Blumenstein, Lisa, Sr. V.P. & Acct. Dir.--Young & Rubicam New York, New York, NY; *U.S. Private*, pg. 1198
Blumenthal, David, Chief Oper. Officer & Sr. V.P.--Lion Brand Yarn Co., New York, NY; *U.S. Private*, pg. 669
Blumenthal, Randall, Sr. V.P.--The Penn Companies, Philadelphia, PA; *U.S. Private*, pg. 849
Blumenthal, Richard A., Sr. V.P., Gen. Counsel & Sec.--Systems & Computer Technology Corporation, Malvern, PA; *U.S. Public*, pg. 1552
Blyth, Myrna, Sr. V.P., Editor-in-Chief & Dir.-Publ.--Ladies' Home Journal, New York, NY; *U.S. Public*, pg. 1094
Boas, Hilda H., Sr. V.P. & Dir.-Human Resources & Corp. Admin.--Municipal Bond Investors Assurance Corporation, Armonk, NY; *U.S. Public*, pg. 1023
Bobeff, Peter A., Sr. V.P.-Corp. Affairs--Foster's Brewing Group Limited, Southbank, Australia; *Int'l*, pg. 500
Bober, Joanne L., Sr. V.P., Gen. Counsel & Sec.--General Signal Corporation, Stamford, CT; *U.S. Public*, pg. 726
Boch, William J., Sr. V.P.--Arnold Communications, Inc., Boston, MA; *U.S. Private*, pg. 83
Bock, Paul, Sr. V.P.-Bus. Devel.--Rainbow Technologies, Inc., Irvine, CA; *U.S. Public*, pg. 1359
Bockman, Dan, Sr. V.P. & Creative Dir.--EvansGroup Technology, Seattle, WA; *U.S. Private*, pg. 385
Bockus, Douglas L., Sr. V.P.--Centris Group Inc., Costa Mesa, CA; *U.S. Public*, pg. 328
Bocola, Marty, Sr. V.P.-Stores--Builders Square, Inc., San Antonio, TX; *U.S. Private*, pg. 477
Bodager, Brian R., Sr. V.P., Gen. Counsel & Sec.--Associated Banc-Corp, Green Bay, WI; *U.S. Public*, pg. 140
Bodenmann, Allison, Sr. V.P. & Brdcst. Dir.--Jordan, McGrath, Case & Taylor Inc., New York, NY; *U.S. Private*, pg. 598
Bodge, Rick, Sr. V.P.-Client Services--Jordan, McGrath, Case & Taylor Inc., New York, NY; *U.S. Private*, pg. 598
Bodine, Norman R., Sr. V.P.--United Technologies Corporation, Hartford, CT; *U.S. Public*, pg. 1689
Bodine, William E., Chief Fin. Officer & Sr. V.P.--Bodine Assembly and Test Systems, Bridgeport, CT; *U.S. Private*, pg. 154
Bodor, Paul W., Sr. V.P. & Dir.-Compliance & Risk Mngmt.--Jefferies & Company, Inc., Los Angeles, CA; *U.S. Public, pg. 925*
Bodor, Paul W., Chief Oper. Officer, Sr. V.P. & Treas.--W & D Securities, Inc., Jersey City, NJ; *U.S. Public*, pg. 925
Boeck, Phil, Sr. V.P.--Block Distributing Company, San Antonio, TX; *U.S. Private*, pg. 149
Boede, David C., Sr. V.P. & Worldwide Acct. Dir.--EURO RSCG Dahlin Smith White, LLC, Salt Lake City, UT; *U.S.* Private, pg. 384
Boehnen, David L., Sr. V.P.-Law & External Rels.--SuperValu, Inc., Eden Prairie, MN; *U.S. Public*, pg. 1540
Boenning, Dickson G., Sr. V.P.-Private Banking--Citizens Trust Company, Providence, RI; *Int'l*, pg. 1132
Boer, Cor J.H., Sr. V.P.-Tax--AEGON N.V., Hague, Netherlands; *Int'l*, pg. 25
Boerner, Thomas R., Sr. V.P.--Equitable Savings & Loan Association, Wauwatosa, WI; *U.S. Private*, pg. 380
Boerner, Thomas R., Sr. V.P.--The Equitable Bank, Hales Corners, WI; *U.S. Private*, pg. 380
Boggs, Timothy A., Sr. V.P.-Public Policy--Time Warner Inc., New York, NY; *U.S. Public*, pg. 1610
Bohannon, Nancy C., Sr. V.P. & Dir.-Mktg.--First Farmers & Merchants National Bank, Columbia, TN; *U.S. Private*, pg. 407
Bohlig, James W., Chief Oper. Officer & Sr. V.P.--Casella Waste Systems, Inc., Rutland, VT; *U.S. Public*, pg. 312
Bohling, John A., Sr. V.P.--PacifiCorp, Portland, OR; *U.S. Public*, pg. 1251
Bohmrich, Roger, Sr. V.P. & Dir.-Fine Wines--Frederick Wildman & Sons Ltd., New York, NY; *U.S. Private*, pg. 1176
Bohner, Richard, Sr. V.P.-Tech. Opers.--Sandoz Pharmaceuticals Corp., East Hanover, NJ; *Int'l*, pg. 974
Bohrofen, Judy, Sr. V.P. & Dir.-H.R.--Brenton Banks, Inc., Des Moines, IA; *U.S. Public*, pg. 251
Boike, James, Sr. V.P.-Retail--Williams-Sonoma, Inc., San Francisco, CA; *U.S. Public*, pg. 1770
Boisture, William W., Jr., Sr. V.P.--Gulfstream Aerospace Corporation, Savannah, GA; *U.S. Private*, pg. 419
Boivin, Daniel W., Sr. V.P.--Nova Corporation, Calgary, Canada; *Int'l*, pg. 971
Bol, Gerrit J., Sr. V.P.--Harcourt Brace & Company - Elementary Div., Orlando, FL; *U.S. Public*, pg. 783
Bolanos, Jorge Walter, Chief Fin. Officer, Sr. V.P. & Treas.--H.B. Fuller Company, Saint Paul, MN; *U.S. Public*, pg. 686
Boldischar, Paul J., Jr., Sr. V.P.--ITT Hartford Life & Annuity Insurance Corporation, Minneapolis, MN; *U.S. Public*, pg. 795
Boldt-Christmas, Bjorn, Sr. V.P.-Info. Sys. Div.--Scandinavian Airlines System (SAS), Solna, Sweden; *Int'l*, pg. 1201
Bolduc, Leonard J., Sr. V.P.-Consumer Lending--D & N Bank, Hancock, MI; *U.S. Public*, pg. 472
Bolen, Dave, Sr. V.P. & Gen. Mgr.--Fabri-Centers of America, Inc., Hudson, OH; *U.S. Public*, pg. 609
Boles, Doug, Sr. V.P.-Human Resources--Armstrong World Industries, Inc., Lancaster, PA; *U.S. Public*, pg. 131
Boley, E. Harry, Sr. V.P.--Willis Corroon Corp. of Utah, Salt Lake City, UT; *Int'l*, pg. 1507
Bolger, Pat, Chief Fin. Officer & Sr. V.P.--The Bon Marche, Inc., Seattle, WA; *U.S. Public*, pg. 617
Bolger, Susan R., Sr. V.P.-Human Resources--Starwood Hotels & Resorts, Phoenix, AZ; *U.S. Public*, pg. 1512
Bolger, T.M., Sr. V.P.--Marshall & Ilsley Corporation, Milwaukee, WI; *U.S. Public*, pg. 1049
Bolivar, Octavio, Sr. V.P.--Andover Bancorp, Inc., Andover, MA; *U.S. Public*, pg. 111
Bolivar, Octavio, Sr. V.P.--Andover Bank, Andover, MA; *U.S.* Public, pg. 112
Bolle, Elaine D., Sr. V.P. & Gen. Mgr.-Consumer Money Transfer Services--Western Union Financial Services, Inc., Paramus, NJ; *U.S. Public*, pg. 631
Bollimpalli, Rao G., Sr. V.P.-Engrng.--JLG Industries, Inc., McConnellsburg, PA; *U.S. Public*, pg. 918
Bollinger, Dell K., Sr. V.P.-Admin.--Bollinger Industries Inc., Grand Prairie, TX; *U.S. Public*, pg. 243
Bollington, John R., Sr. V.P., Gen. Counsel & Sec.--20th Century Industries, Woodland Hills, CA; *U.S. Public*, pg. 1646
Bolokofsky, Eric, Sr. V.P.-Mdsg.--Arbor Drugs, Inc., Troy, MI; *U.S. Public*, pg. 126
Bolotin, Irving, Sr. V.P.--Lennar Corporation, Miami, FL; *U.S.* Public, pg. 987
Bolotin, Irving, Sr. V.P.--Lennar Homes Inc., Miami, FL; *U.S.* Public, pg. 988
Bolton, G. Thomas, Sr. V.P.-Claims Admin.--Acceptance Insurance Co., Inc., Omaha, NE; *U.S. Public*, pg. 14
Bolton, James E., Sr. V.P.--Chemical Bank Bay Area, Bay City, MI; *U.S. Public*, pg. 345
Bolton, James R., Sr. V.P.-Mktg.-Networking/Data Commun.--Wyle Electronics, Irvine, CA; *Int'l*, pg. 1457
Bolton, John, Sr. V.P.--American Enterprise Institute for Public Policy Research, Washington, DC; *U.S. Private*, pg. 53
Bolton, Roger, Sr. V.P.-Corp. Communications--Aetna Inc., Hartford, CT; *U.S. Public*, pg. 26
Bonach, Edward J., Sr. V.P. & Chief Fin. Officer--Allianz Life Insurance Company of North America, Minneapolis, MN; *Int'l*, pg. 58
Bond, Elroy, Sr. V.P.-Insurance Admin.--Golden State Mutual Life Insurance Company, Los Angeles, CA; *U.S. Private*, pg. 461
Bond, Jonathan, Sr. V.P.--Columbia/H.C.A., Dallas, TX; *U.S.* Public, pg. 404
Bond, Larry R., Sr. V.P.-Retail Fin. Services--Washington Mutual Inc., Seattle, WA; *U.S. Public*, pg. 1741
Bond, Ritchie L., Chief Fin. Officer & Sr. V.P.--Florimex Worldwide, Inc., Danville, VA; *U.S. Public*, pg. 510
Bonds, Andrew, Sr. V.P.-Sls.--DeLeuw, Cather & Company, Washington, DC; *U.S. Private*, pg. 841
Bonds, Andrew, Sr. V.P.--DeLeuw, Cather International Ltd., Abu Dhabi, United Arab Emirates; *U.S. Private*, pg. 842
Bonds, Gary, Sr. V.P. & Controller--Bancorp South Inc., Tupelo, MS; *U.S. Public*, pg. 176
Bondurri, Araldo, Sr. V.P.--RNBNY Branch Office-Milan, Milan, Italy; *U.S. Public*, pg. 1381
Bondy, Richard, Sr. V.P., Mngmt. Supvr. & Acct. Exec.--Doremus & Company, New York, NY; *U.S. Public*, pg. 1223
Bonham, Mike, Sr. V.P.-Sls. & Mktg.--Cerprobe Corporation, Gilbert, AZ; *U.S. Public*, pg. 332
Bonicatto, L.P., Sr. V.P.--Champion, Inc., Iron Mountain, MI; *U.S. Private*, pg. 228
Bonifay, Cam, Sr. V.P. & Gen. Mgr.--Pittsburgh Pirates, Pittsburgh, PA; *U.S. Private*, pg. 867
Bonita, Joseph C., Sr. V.P. & Chief Underwriting Counsel--Chicago Title Insurance Co., Chicago, IL; *U.S. Public*, pg. 42
Bonk, Christopher, Sr. V.P.--MENDIK Management Co., Inc., New York, NY; *U.S. Private*, pg. 731
Bonnecaze, Earl C., Sr. V.P.-Store Opers.--Mac Frugal's Bargains Close-Outs Inc., Rancho Dominguez, CA; *U.S. Public*, pg. 437
Bonner, Stephen B., Sr. V.P.-Income Markets--Keyport Life Insurance Company, Boston, MA; *U.S. Private*, pg. 666
Bonnet, Emmanuel, Sr. V.P.-Latin America--SGS Societe Generale de Surveillance Holding S.A., Geneva, Switzerland; *Int'l*, pg. 1153
Bonnet, Michel, Sr. V.P.-Mktg. & Public Affairs--Elf Aquitane, Paris, France; *Int'l*, pg. 444
Bonno, Anthony J., Sr. V.P.-H.R.--Pacific Life Insurance Company, Newport Beach, CA; *U.S. Private*, pg. 831
Bonnville, John W., Sr. V.P.--Wilbur Smith Associates, Columbia, SC; *U.S. Private*, pg. 1009
Bonny, Paul A., Sr. V.P.-Intl. Opers.--Transatlantic Holdings Inc., New York, NY; *U.S. Public*, pg. 84
Bono, F. Wayne, Sr. V.P.-Admin. Services--United Companies Financial Corporation, Baton Rouge, LA; *U.S. Public*, pg. 1675
Bonomo, Joseph F., Jr., Sr. V.P.--C.S. McKee & Company, Inc., Pittsburgh, PA; *U.S. Public*, pg. 1673
Bonton, Bruce, Sr. V.P.-Systems & Services--Intermetrics, Inc., Burlington, MA; *U.S. Private*, pg. 567
Boone, R.E., Sr. V.P.--Versa Services Ltd., Etobicoke, Canada; *U.S. Private*, pg. 79
Boorstein, Joan, Sr. V.P.-Creative Affairs--Showtime Networks Inc., New York, NY; *U.S. Private*, pg. 779
Booth, Peter, Sr. V.P.-Strategy & Devel.--Corning Incorporated, Corning, NY; *U.S. Public*, pg. 448
Booth, Russell, Sr. V.P. & Grp. Media Dir.--Grey Advertising Inc., New York, NY; *U.S. Public*, pg. 764
Boots, Thomas E., V.P.-Product Devel.--Continental Western Insurance Company, Urbandale, IA; *U.S. Public, pg. 215*
Borba, Mary P., Sr. V.P.-Human Resources--News America Marketing, Norwalk, CT; *Int'l*, pg. 925
Bordeaux, Phillip, Sr. V.P.-Mktg. & Customer Service--Intermountain Gas Co., Boise, ID; *U.S. Private*, pg. 568
Bordeaux, Susan, Sr. V.P. & Retail Admin.--FirstFed Financial Corp., Santa Monica, CA; *U.S. Public*, pg. 645
Borelli, Frank J., Chief Fin. Officer & Sr. V.P.--Marsh & McLennan Companies, Inc., New York, NY; *U.S. Public*, pg. 1048
Boren, Robert P., C.P.A., Chief Fin. Officer & Sr. V.P.-Fin.--State Volunteer Mutual Insurance Co., Brentwood, TN; *U.S. Private*, pg. 1037
Borg, Rune, Sr. V.P.-Corp. Communications--Pharmacia & Upjohn, Inc., Windsor, United Kingdom; *Int'l*, pg. 1047
Borgardt, Bryon, Sr. V.P.--James Hardie USA, Mission Viejo, CA; *Int'l*, pg. 597
Borges, Lynne M., Sr. V.P.-H.R.--London Fog Industries, Inc., New York, NY; *U.S. Private*, pg. 673
Borgeson, Steven E., Sr. V.P., Gen. Counsel, Sec., Treas. & Clerk--ChemDesign Corporation, Fitchburg, MA; *Int'l*, pg. 173
Borgman, Dean C., Sr. V.P.-McDonnell Douglas Helicoper Systems--McDonnell Aircraft & Missile Systems Div., Berkeley, MO; *U.S. Public*, pg. 241
Borgman, Dean C., Sr. V.P. & Gen. Mgr.--Boeing Helicopter Division, Mesa, AZ; *U.S. Public*, pg. 241
Borman, Kimberly, Sr. V.P. & Grp. Acct. Dir.--Wickersham Hunt Schwantner, Boston, MA; *U.S. Private*, pg. 84
Borocz, Michael S., Sr. V.P. & Controller--PNC Bank, Camp Hill, PA; *U.S. Public*, pg. 1243
Borsen, Theodora, Sr. V.P. & Creative Dir.--Jerry & Ketchum, New York, NY; *U.S. Private*, pg. 616
Borseso, Donna, Sr. V.P. & Human Resources Dir.--McCann-Erickson Worldwide, New York, NY; *U.S. Public, pg. 909*
Borseth, John D., Sr. V.P.-Sls. & Mktg.--Newcor, Inc., Bloomfield Hills, MI; *U.S. Public*, pg. 1176
Borshell, David, Sr. V.P.-Sls. & Mktg.--Image Entertainment, Inc., Chatsworth, CA; *U.S. Public*, pg. 870
Boscamp, James W., Sr. V.P.--Genesco Inc., Nashville, TN; *U.S. Public*, pg. 728
Bosco, Rose Ann, Sr. V.P.-Human Resources--Michael Anthony Jewelers, Inc., Mount Vernon, NY; *U.S. Public*, pg. 1103
Boselli, Colleen, Sr. V.P. & Client Services Dir.--Arnold Communications, Inc., Boston, MA; *U.S. Private*, pg. 83
Boshoven, Stephen, Sr. V.P.--Foremost Corporation of America, Caledonia, MI; *U.S. Public*, pg. 667
Boshoven, Stephen J., Sr. V.P.--Foremost Insurance Co., Caledonia, MI; *U.S. Public*, pg. 667
Bossa, George S., Jr., Sr. V.P.--Indian Rocks National Bank, Largo, FL; *U.S. Public*, pg. 608
Bostic, James E., Jr., Sr. V.P.-Environment, Govt. Affairs & Communications--Georgia-Pacific Corporation, Atlanta, GA; *U.S. Public*, pg. 735
Bostick, Gerri Feemster, Sr. V.P.-Human Resources--AnnTaylor, Inc., New York, NY; *U.S. Public*, pg. 116
Boston, Wallace E., Jr., Sr. V.P.-Acquisitions--Manor Care, Inc., Gaithersburg, MD; *U.S. Public*, pg. 1041
Boswell, Edward F., Sr. V.P.-Pulp & Paper--George Weston Limited, Toronto, Canada; *Int'l*, pg. 1494
Bosworth, Harold, Sr. V.P. & Gen. Mgr.--Talbots, Inc., Hingham, MA; *Int'l*, pg. 28
Bott, Robert L., Sr. V.P.-Opers.--Quick & Reilly, Inc., New York, NY; *U.S. Public*, pg. 650
Bouchard, J. Thomas, Sr. V.P.-Human Resources--International Business Machines Corporation, Armonk, NY; *U.S. Public*, pg. 895
Bouchard, Michel, Sr. V.P. & Gen. Mgr.--Allergan France S.A., Lingolsheim, France; *U.S. Public*, pg. 46
Bouchard, Ron, Sr. V.P.-Quality Assurance--Mitsubishi Silicon America, Salem, OR; *Int'l*, pg. 875
Bouchaud, Joel, Sr. V.P.-Middle East, Asia & Latin America--Elf Aquitane, Paris, France; *Int'l*, pg. 444
Boucher, David, Sr. V.P.-Fin.--Chemical Leaman Tank Lines, Inc., Exton, PA; *U.S. Private*, pg. 233
Boucher, Rodney M., Sr. V.P.--Calpine Corporation, San Jose, CA; *U.S. Public*, pg. 296
Boudreau, David, Chief Fin. Officer & Sr. V.P.--Jan Bell Marketing Inc., Sunrise, FL; *U.S. Public*, pg. 207
Boudreau, John, Sr. V.P.-Opers.--First Independence National Bank, Detroit, MI; *U.S. Public*, pg. 635
Boudreau, Paul J., Sr. V.P.-Chicago Service Center--Combined Insurance Company of America, Chicago, IL; *U.S. Public*, pg. 118
Boudreau, Tom, Sr. V.P. & Gen. Counsel--Express Scripts, Inc., Maryland Heights, MO; *U.S. Public*, pg. 600
Boudreault, Andre, Sr. V.P.-Forest Prods. Grp.--Tembec Inc., Montreal, Canada; *Int'l*, pg. 1374
Bouffard, Gaston, Sr. V.P./Sls. & Mktg./Paper & Bus. Devel.--Donohue Inc., Quebec, Canada; *Int'l*, pg. 1075
Boulanger, Pierre, Sr. V.P.-Credit & Grp. Risk Mgmnt.--The Toronto Dominion Bank, Toronto, Canada; *Int'l*, pg. 1401
Boulette, E. Thomas, Sr. V.P.-Nuclear Opers.--Boston Edison Company, Boston, MA; *U.S. Public*, pg. 247
Bounds, Linda K., Chief Fin. Officer & Sr. V.P.--Bell Sports Corp., San Jose, CA; *U.S. Public*, pg. 207
Bounds, Vincent, Sr. V.P.-Deepwater Opers.--Marine Drilling Companies, Inc., Sugar Land, TX; *U.S. Public*, pg. 1044
Bourgeois, Wayne J., Sr. V.P.--Halter Marine Group, Inc., Gulfport, MS; *U.S. Public*, pg. 778
Bourgoin, John, Sr. V.P. & Pres.-MIPS Grp.--Silicon Graphics, Inc., Mountain View, CA; *U.S. Public*, pg. 1473
Bourgon, George M., Jr., Sr. V.P. & Dir.-Personnel--First Federal of Michigan, Detroit, MI; *U.S. Public*, pg. 336
Bourke, Diana M., Sr. V.P.-Systems & Quality--A.C. Nielsen, Stamford, CT; *U.S. Public*, pg. 1183
Bourns, Richard T., Sr. V.P.-Imaging Opers.--Eastman Kodak Company, Rochester, NY; *U.S. Public*, pg. 550
Boushy, John M., Sr. V.P.-Information Tech. & Corp. Mktg. Services--Harrah's Entertainment, Inc., Memphis, TN; *U.S. Public*, pg. 790
Boutin, Bob, Chief Fin. Officer & Sr. V.P.--Computer City, Fort Worth, TX; *U.S. Public*, pg. 1560
Boutin, Frederick W., Sr. V.P.--TransMontaigne Oil Company, Denver, CO; *U.S. Public*, pg. 1631
Bouverie, William M., Sr. V.P.-Engrng.--Datamax International Corporation, Orlando, FL; *U.S. Private*, pg. 313
Bouverot, Georges, Sr. V.P.-Corp. Human Resources--Renault, Boulogne-Billancourt, France; *Int'l*, pg. 1102
Bovalino, Michael J., Sr. V.P.-Mktg.--Rochester Gas And Electric Corporation, Rochester, NY; *U.S. Public*, pg. 1395
Bover, J. Michael, Sr. V.P.-Giftware Div. Sls.--Crystal Clear Industries, Ridgefield Park, NJ; *U.S. Private*, pg. 293
Bovis, George S., Sr. V.P.-Devel. & Growth Plng.--White Hen Pantry, Inc., Elmhurst, IL; *U.S. Private*, pg. 1172
Bowden, David L., Sr. V.P.-Timber--Longview Fibre Company, Longview, WA; *U.S. Public*, pg. 1013
Bowden, Gary A., Sr. V.P.--RTKL Associates Inc., Baltimore, MD; *U.S. Private*, pg. 906

Bowden, James A., Chief Fin. Officer & Sr. V.P.--J.A. Jones, Inc., Charlotte, NC; *Int'l*, pg. 633

Bowen, James C., Jr., Sr. V.P.-Mktg.--ReliaStar Mortgage Company, West Des Moines, IA; *U.S. Public*, pg. 1376

Bowen, Robert, Sr. V.P.-MIS--American Pad and Paper Company, Dallas, TX; *U.S. Public*, pg. 88

Bowen, Robert, Sr. V.P.-Fin. & Admin.--A.W. Chesterton Company, Stoneham, MA; *U.S. Private*, pg. 234

Bowen, Robert, Sr. V.P.--National Computer Systems, Eden Prairie, MN; *U.S. Public*, pg. 1155

Bowen, Robert A., Sr. V.P.-Information Systems--The Life Insurance Co. of Virginia, Richmond, VA; *U.S. Public*, pg. 712

Bower, Art, Sr. Exec. V.P.--Black Rogers Sullivan Goodnight, Inc., Houston, TX; *U.S. Private*, pg. 147

Bower, Bob, Sr. V.P.--Rosendin Electric, Inc., San Jose, CA; *U.S. Private*, pg. 945

Bower, Curtis A., Chief Fin. Officer, Sr. V.P. & Treas.--Parsons Corporation, Pasadena, CA; *U.S. Private*, pg. 841

Bower, Kevin D., Chief Fin. Officer & Sr. V.P.--Alltrista Corporation, Muncie, IN; *U.S. Public*, pg. 56

Bower, Paul, Sr. V.P.-Mngmt. Svcs. Dept.--Allen & Ohara, Inc., Memphis, TN; *U.S. Private*, pg. 36

Bower, Robert R., Sr. V.P.--S.T. Research, Newington, VA; *U.S. Private*, pg. 958

Bower, Scott, Sr. V.P.-Sls. & Mktg.--AST Research Inc., Irvine, CA; *Int'l*, pg. 1181

Bowerman, Laurel L., Sr. V.P.-Commercial Real Estate--Citizens Savings Bank, Providence, RI; *Int'l*, pg. 1132

Bowerman, Laurel L., Sr. V.P.-Commerical Real Estate--Citizens Trust Company, Providence, RI; *Int'l*, pg. 1132

Bowerman, Toni, Sr. V.P. & Creative Dir.--Cipriani Kremer Design, Boston, MA; *U.S. Private*, pg. 84

Bowers, Christopher D., Sr. V.P.-Intl.--UAL Corporation, Elk Grove Village, IL; *U.S. Public*, pg. 1652

Bowers, Christopher D., Sr. V.P.-Intl.--United Air Lines, Inc., Elk Grove Village, IL; *U.S. Public*, pg. 1653

Bowers, R. Todd, Chief Fin. Officer & Sr. V.P.--SunTrust, Orlando, FL; *U.S. Public*, pg. 1537

Bowers, W.P., Sr. V.P.-Mktg.--Georgia Power Co., Atlanta, GA; *U.S. Public*, pg. 1490

Bowler, E. Joseph, Sr. V.P. & Treas.--Westamerica Bancorporation, Fairfield, CA; *U.S. Public*, pg. 1756

Bowling, Gene H., V.P.-Corp. & Mgr.-Intl. Sls.--Alkota Cleaning Systems, Inc., Alcester, SD; *U.S. Private*, pg. 34

Bowman, David W., Sr. V.P., Gen. Counsel & Sec.--Mapco Inc., Tulsa, OK; *U.S. Public*, pg. 1042

Bowman, Dennis J., Chief Information Officer & Sr. V.P.--Circuit City Stores, Inc., Richmond, VA; *U.S. Public*, pg. 374

Bowman, Patricia, Sr. V.P.-Res. & Devel.--The Dial Corporation, Phoenix, AZ; *U.S. Public*, pg. 505

Bowman, Paul, Sr. V.P.-Client Services--Quantum Plus, New York, NY; *U.S. Public*, pg. 1224

Bowman, Richard, Sr. V.P. & Station Mgr.--WTTW (Channel 11), Chicago, IL; *U.S. Private*, pg. 1145

Bowman, Richard F., Chief Fin. Officer, Sr. V.P. & Treas.--First Virginia Banks, Inc., Falls Church, VA; *U.S. Public*, pg. 641

Bowman, Rod, Sr. V.P.-Human Resource--White Consolidated Industries, Inc., Cleveland, OH; *Int'l*, pg. 439

Bowron, John B., Sr. V.P.--Landstar Holding, Shelton, CT; *U.S. Public*, pg. 978

Box, Barbara, Sr. V.P.--Golin/Harris Communications, Inc., Chicago, IL; *Int'l*, pg. 1226

Boxer, Shelly M., Sr. V.P.--Sid Tool Co. Inc., Plainview, NY; *U.S. Private*, pg. 998

Boyce, Jefferson C., Sr. V.P.-Asset Mngmt.--New York Life Insurance Company, New York, NY; *U.S. Private*, pg. 794

Boyce, Ronald E., Chief Info. Officer & Sr. V.P.--National Penn Bank, Boyertown, PA; *U.S. Public*, pg. 1159

Boyd, Ed, Sr. V.P. & Acct. Services Dir.--Don Coleman Advertising, Inc., Southfield, MI; *U.S. Private*, pg. 251

Boyd, James R., Sr. V.P. & Grp. Oper. Officer-Arch Mineral Corp.--Ashland, Inc., Russell, KY; *U.S. Public*, pg. 138

Boyd, Larry, Sr. V.P.--Tri-State Armature & Electric Works, Memphis, TN; *U.S. Private*, pg. 1100

Boyd, Margaret, Sr. V.P.-Sls. & Mktg.--First Tennessee National Corporation, Memphis, TN; *U.S. Public*, pg. 638

Boyd, Michael A., Sr. V.P. & Gen. Counsel--Donaldson, Lufkin, & Jenrette, Inc., New York, NY; *U.S. Public*, pg. 589

Boyd, R.B., Sr. V.P.-CN West--Canadian National Railway Company, Montreal, Canada; *Int'l*, pg. 258

Boyd, Ron, Sr. V.P. & Client Services Dir.--DMB&B Los Angeles, Los Angeles, CA; *U.S. Private*, pg. 303

Boyd, Stan, Sr. V.P.-Sls. & Mktg.--The Fairmont Hotels, San Francisco, CA; *U.S. Private*, pg. 391

Boyd, Thomas B., Sr. V.P.--Laserscope Surgical Systems, San Jose, CA; *U.S. Public*, pg. 979

Boyer, Jim, Sr. V.P.-Portland Brdcst. & Gen. Mgr.--Fisher Broadcasting Inc., Seattle, WA; *U.S. Public*, pg. 648

Boyle, James, Sr. V.P., Controller & Treas.--Broad National Bancorporation, Newark, NJ; *U.S. Public*, pg. 257

Boyle, James, Sr. V.P. & Comptroller--Broad National Bank, Newark, NJ; *U.S. Public*, pg. 257

Boyle, James A., Sr. V.P.-Medical & Regulatory Affairs--The Liposome Company, Inc., Princeton, NJ; *U.S. Public*, pg. 1000

Boyle, Jan, Sr. V.P., Grp. Dir.--Ammirati, Puris & Lintas, Inc., New York, NY; *U.S. Private*, pg. 66

Boyle, Kevin, Sr. V.P.-Comml. Real Estate--Citizens Bank of Massachusetts, Fairhaven, MA; *Int'l*, pg. 1132

Boyle, Matthew A., Sr. V.P.-Corp. Counsel--Dassault Falcon Jet Corp., South Hackensack, NJ; *Int'l*, pg. 383

Boyle, Patrick, Sr. V.P.-Pension--New York Life Insurance Company, New York, NY; *U.S. Private*, pg. 794

Boynton, Peter G., Sr. V.P.-Gaming & Pres. & CEO-Caesars World, Inc.--ITT Corporation, New York, NY; *U.S. Public*, pg. 1512

Boyt, Hugh L., Sr. V.P.-Production--Santa Fe Energy Resources, Inc., Houston, TX; *U.S. Public*, pg. 1431

Bozarth, Glenn, Sr. V.P.-Corp. Commun.--Mattel, Inc., El Segundo, CA; *U.S. Public*, pg. 1057

Bozlinski, Thomas J., Sr. V.P.-Info. Svcs.--Fingerhut Corp., Minnetonka, MN; *U.S. Public*, pg. 623

Bozzo, Ernest, Sr. V.P.--Valley National Bank, Parsippany, NJ; *U.S. Public*, pg. 1705

Braasch, Steve, Sr. V.P.--GSD&M, Austin, TX; *U.S. Private*, pg. 436

Bracas, William C., Sr. V.P. & Gen. Mgr.-Little Rock--Dassault Falcon Jet Corp., South Hackensack, NJ; *Int'l*, pg. 383

Bracken, Gary, Sr. V.P. & Controller--TCI Communications, Inc., Englewood, CO; *U.S. Public*, pg. 1554

Bradbury, R. Douglas, Chief Fin. Officer & Sr. V.P.--MFS WorldCom, Inc., Omaha, NE; *U.S. Public*, pg. 1779

Braddock, Marvin T., Sr. V.P.-Design & Construction--Brinker International, Inc., Dallas, TX; *U.S. Public*, pg. 253

Braden, G.F., Sr. V.P.--Central Allied Enterprises, Canton, OH; *U.S. Private*, pg. 222

Bradfield, William S., Pres. & Sr. V.P.--Sathers Inc., Round Lake, MN; *U.S. Private*, pg. 397

Bradford, David, Sr. V.P., Gen. Counsel & Corp. Sec.--Novell, Inc., Orem, UT; *U.S. Public*, pg. 1203

Bradley, Bernie J., Sr. V.P.--AEC Pipelines, Calgary, Canada; *Int'l*, pg. 48

Bradley, David R., Sr. V.P.--Hartford Fire Insurance Co., Hartford, CT; *U.S. Public*, pg. 794

Bradley, Gary M., Sr. V.P.--BT Financial Corporation, Johnstown, PA; *U.S. Public*, pg. 163

Bradley, John R., Sr. V.P.-Comml. Banking--NBT Bancorp Inc., Norwich, NY; *U.S. Public*, pg. 1144

Bradley, Robert J., Sr. V.P. & Treas.--Cramer-Krasselt, Milwaukee, WI; *U.S. Private*, pg. 285

Bradley, William L., Sr. V.P.-Central States Reg.--Tenet Healthcare Corporation, Santa Barbara, CA; *U.S. Public*, pg. 1576

Bradshaw, Joanna, Sr. V.P.-Mdsg.--Dansk International Designs Ltd., White Plains, NY; *U.S. Public*, pg. 261

Brady, Don, Sr. V.P.-Sls. & Mktg.--Bruning Paint Company, Baltimore, MD; *U.S. Private*, pg. 176

Brady, Francis P., Pres. & Sr. V.P.-Television Division--Viacom Broadcasting Inc., New York, NY; *U.S. Private*, pg. 778

Brady, Frank, Sr. V.P.-Contract Services & Intl. Sls.--Pandrol Jackson, Inc., Ludington, MI; *Int'l*, pg. 280

Brady, John T., Sr. V.P.--Spelling Television, Los Angeles, CA; *U.S. Private*, pg. 776

Brady, Walter M., Sr. V.P.-Agency--New York Life Insurance Company, New York, NY; *U.S. Private*, pg. 794

Brakken, William P., Chief Fin. Officer, Sr. V.P., Treas. & Sec.--Lanoga Corporation, Redmond, WA; *U.S. Private*, pg. 650

Bralower, Steve, Sr. V.P.-Leasing--Carr Real Estate Services, Washington, DC; *U.S. Public*, pg. 309

Bralower, Steven N., Sr. V.P.-Leasing--CarrAmerica Realty, Washington, DC; *U.S. Public*, pg. 308

Bram, Stephen B., Sr. V.P.--Consolidated Edison Company of New York, Inc., New York, NY; *U.S. Public*, pg. 434

Brambani, Karen, Sr. V.P. & Print/Trade Services Dir.--Active International, Pearl River, NY; *U.S. Private*, pg. 15

Brame, Kenneth, Chief Info. Officer & Sr. V.P.-Info. Tech.--Service Merchandise Company, Inc., Brentwood, TN; *U.S. Public*, pg. 1461

Brams, Leonard A., Chief Fin. Officer, Sr. V.P.-Fin. & Sec.--Handleman Company, Troy, MI; *U.S. Public*, pg. 779

Branch, Debbie J., Sr. V.P.--Southwestern Energy Pipeline Company, Fayetteville, AR; *U.S. Public*, pg. 1494

Branch, John D., Chief Fin. Officer & Sr. V.P.-Fin.--Earl Scheib, Inc., Beverly Hills, CA; *U.S. Public*, pg. 1437

Brandaleone, Sara H., Sr. V.P.--Rothschild/Pell, Rudman & Co., Inc., Baltimore, MD; *U.S. Public*, pg. 1674

Brander, Tom, Sr. V.P.-Systems & Programming--Compass Bank, Birmingham, AL; *U.S. Public*, pg. 418

Brandes, R.D., Sr. V.P.--Hughes Electronics Corporation, Westchester, CA; *U.S. Public*, pg. 720

Brandewie, Richard T., Chief Fin. Officer & Sr. V.P.--MTL Inc., Plant City, FL; *U.S. Public*, pg. 1028

Brandon, B.M., Sr. V.P.--Longs Drug Stores California, Inc., Walnut Creek, CA; *U.S. Public*, pg. 1013

Brandon, Bill M., Sr. V.P.--Longs Drug Stores Corporation, Walnut Creek, CA; *U.S. Public*, pg. 1013

Brandon, Joseph P., Chief Fin. Officer & Sr. V.P.--General Re Corporation, Stamford, CT; *U.S. Public*, pg. 725

Brandon, Joseph P., Sr. V.P.--General Reinsurance Corp., Stamford, CT; *U.S. Public*, pg. 725

Brandt, Donald E., Sr. V.P.-Fin.--Ameren Corporation, Saint Louis, MO; *U.S. Public*, pg. 65

Brandt, Donald E., Sr. V.P.-Fin. & Corp. Services--AmerenUE, Saint Louis, MO; *U.S. Public*, pg. 66

Brandt, Gerard R., Sr. V.P.-Human Resources--Georgia-Pacific Corporation, Atlanta, GA; *U.S. Public*, pg. 735

Brandt, Roden A., Sr. V.P.-Plng. & Mktg.--Trans World Airlines, Inc., Saint Louis, MO; *U.S. Public*, pg. 1629

Branigan, Mark W., Sr. V.P.-Residential Asset Mgmt.--Continental Mortgage and Equity Trust, Dallas, TX; *U.S. Public*, pg. 441

Branigan, Mark W., Sr. V.P.-Residential Asset Mngmt.--Transcontinental Realty Investors, Inc., Dallas, TX; *U.S. Public*, pg. 1630

Branman, M. Jeffrey, Sr. V.P.-Corp. Devel.--Woolworth Corporation, New York, NY; *U.S. Public*, pg. 1777

Branscomb, Kc, Sr. V.P.-Bus. Devel.--Lotus Development Corporation, Cambridge, MA; *U.S. Public*, pg. 896

Branscome, James, Sr. V.P.-Equity Information Services--McGraw-Hill Financial Information Services Group, New York, NY; *U.S. Public*, pg. 1071

Brant, Robert W., Sr. V.P.-Comml. Real Estate Loan Division--Bank of Hawaii, Honolulu, HI; *U.S. Public*, pg. 1248

Brantley, Ernest, Sr. V.P.-Opers.--Old Dominion Freight Line, Inc., High Point, NC; *U.S. Public*, pg. 1216

Brashears, David F., Sr. V.P.-Tech.--Gencor Industries, Inc., Orlando, FL; *U.S. Public*, pg. 705

Brasser, Bob, Sr. V.P.-Consumer Prods.--Riddell Sports, Inc., New York, NY; *U.S. Public*, pg. 1389

Bratcher, Claudia, Sr. V.P.--Superior Federal Bank, Fort Smith, AR; *U.S. Private*, pg. 1054

Bratton, Robert O., Chief Oper. Officer, Chief Fin. Officer & Exec. V.P.--First Charter Corporation, Concord, NC; *U.S. Public*, pg. 627

Brauer, C. Andrew, Sr. V.P.-Merger & Acquisition--New York Life Insurance Company, New York, NY; *U.S. Private*, pg. 794

Brauer, Jeffrey, Sr. V.P.--Republic Entertainment, Inc., Los Angeles, CA; *U.S. Private*, pg. 776

Brauer, William C., Sr. V.P.--PacifiCorp, Portland, OR; *U.S. Public*, pg. 1251

Braun, William V., Sr. V.P. & Dir.-Corp. Res. & Devel.--Motorola, Inc., Schaumburg, IL; *U.S. Public*, pg. 1136

Brauninger, Andrew W., Sr. V.P.--Hvide Marine Incorporated, Fort Lauderdale, FL; *U.S. Public*, pg. 851

Bravman, Richard, Sr. V.P. & Gen. Mgr.-Mobile & Wireless Systems Division--Symbol Technologies, Inc., Holtsville, NY; *U.S. Public*, pg. 1546

Bray, Karen, Sr. V.P.-Sls.--Baltimore Stationery Co./Total Office, Baltimore, MD; *U.S. Private*, pg. 113

Bray, Michael E., Sr. V.P.-Electric Bus. Unit--Long Island Lighting Company, Hicksville, NY; *U.S. Public*, pg. 1013

Braybrooks, Colin S., Sr. V.P., Gen. Counsel & Sec.--United Family Life Insurance Co., Atlanta, GA; *Int'l*, pg. 499

Breazeale, Joyce, Sr. V.P. & Div. Dir.--Underwriters Management Associates, Inc., Nashville, TN; *Int'l*, pg. 1508

Brechtel, William J., Chief Fin. Officer & Sr. V.P.--ReliaStar Mortgage Company, West Des Moines, IA; *U.S. Public*, pg. 1376

Breda, Michael A., Sr. V.P. & Grp. Acct. Dir.--Ingalls Moranville Advertising/Seattle, Bainbridge Island, WA; *U.S. Private*, pg. 316

Bredehoft, Susan U., Sr. V.P. & Dir.-Compliance--Summit Bancorp, Princeton, NJ; *U.S. Public*, pg. 1527

Bredwell, Jo, Sr. V.P. & Corp. Mktg. Comm. Dir.--Bernard Hodes Group, New York, NY; *U.S. Public*, pg. 1224

Breech, Stephen V., Sr. V.P. & Pres.-Big Bear Div.--The Penn Traffic Company, Syracuse, NY; *U.S. Public*, pg. 1270

Breen, Donald, Jr., Sr. V.P.-Sls. & Mktg.--John Morrell & Co., Cincinnati, OH; *U.S. Public*, pg. 1479

Breen, Frank, Jr., Sr. V.P.-No. Region--The Grand Union Company, Wayne, NJ; *U.S. Public*, pg. 758

Breen, Kevin C., Sr. V.P.-Opers.--PriceSmart Inc., San Diego, CA; *U.S. Public*, pg. 1324

Breffeilh, Angela, Sr. V.P. & Treas.--Hibernia Corporation, New Orleans, LA; *U.S. Public*, pg. 825

Breindel, Eric, Sr. V.P.--The News Corporation Limited, Sydney, Australia; *Int'l*, pg. 925

Breitnauer, Paul J., Sr. V.P. & Treas.--Capitol Indemnity Corporation, Madison, WI; *U.S. Public*, pg. 302

Breitnauer, Paul J., Sr. V.P. & Treas.--Capitol Specialty Insurance Corporation, Madison, WI; *U.S. Public*, pg. 302

Bremer, John M., Sr. V.P., Gen. Counsel & Sec.--Northwestern Mutual Life Insurance Co., Milwaukee, WI; *U.S. Private*, pg. 807

Bremer, Thomas R., Sr. V.P. & Gen. Counsel--U.S. Surgical Corp., Norwalk, CT; *U.S. Public*, pg. 1687

Brendzel, Ronald I., Chief Fin. Officer , Sr. V.P. & Sec.--Safeguard Health Enterprises, Inc., Anaheim, CA; *U.S. Public*, pg. 1424

Brennan, Allen, Sr. V.P.-Fin.--Hughes Family Markets, Inc., Irwindale, CA; *U.S. Public*, pg. 1349

Brennan, Andy, Sr. V.P.--Labatt U.S.A., Darien, CT; *Int'l*, pg. 679

Brennan, Joseph T., Sr. V.P.--Quaker City Motor Parts Company, Middletown, DE; *U.S. Private*, pg. 898

Brennan, Michael K., Sr. V.P. & Mgr.-Gen. Mdsg.--Office Depot Inc., Delray Beach, FL; *U.S. Public*, pg. 1212

Brennan, Terry, Chief Fin. Officer & Sr. V.P.--Western Industries, Inc., Milwaukee, WI; *U.S. Private*, pg. 1165

Brennard, Jim, Sr. V.P.-Handlines Mdsg.--Service Merchandise Company, Inc., Brentwood, TN; *U.S. Public, pg. 1461*

Brenner, David, Sr. V.P.- Special Projects--Universal Studios TV, Universal City, CA; *Int'l*, pg. 1215

Brenner, David H., Sr. V.P.-Mktg. Devel.--Amway Corporation, Ada, MI; *U.S. Private*, pg. 69

Brent, Gary G., Sr. V.P.-Investment Mngmt.--CT Financial Services, Inc., Toronto, Canada; *Int'l*, pg. 112

Brenton, Woodward G., Chief Comml. Banking Officer & Corp. Sr. V.P.--Brenton Banks, Inc., Des Moines, IA; *U.S.* Public, pg. 251

Brereton, Peter E., Sr. V.P.--Keycorp, Cleveland, OH; *U.S. Public*, pg. 954

Breseman, Rick, Sr. V.P.-Mktg.--Sealaska Timber Corporation, Ketchikan, AK; *U.S. Private*, pg. 978

Brett, Barbara S., Sr. V.P. & Treas.--Norwest Bank Minnesota N.A., Minneapolis, MN; *U.S. Public*, pg. 1202

Brett, J.A., Sr. V.P.--MidCon Gas Services Corp., Houston, TX; *U.S. Public*, pg. 1210

Brevers, Bernard, Sr. V.P. & Gen. Mgr.-Mdse.--The Bon Ton Stores, Inc., York, PA; *U.S. Public*, pg. 244

Brewer, Brian, Sr. V.P.-Bus. Mktg.--MCI Communications Corp., Atlanta, GA; *U.S. Public*, pg. 1023

Brewer, R. Michael, Chief Fin. Officer & Sr. V.P.-Fin.--Boca Research Inc., Boca Raton, FL; *U.S. Public*, pg. 239

Brewi, Michael, Sr. V.P. & Grp. Dir.--Ryan Drossman & Partners, New York, NY; *U.S. Private*, pg. 953

Brewster. James, Sr. V.P.-Fin.--Newport News, Inc., New York, NY; *U.S. Public*, pg. 1499

Breyer, Allan D., Sr. V.P. & Mgr.-Mngmt. Information Systems--First Federal of Michigan, Detroit, MI; *U.S. Public*, pg. 336

Breyer, Karl J., Sr. V.P.-Corp. Affairs & Gen. Counsel--American Express Financial Advisor, Minneapolis, MN; *U.S. Public*, pg. 73

Brick, Pamela, Sr. V.P.-Science & Bus. Devel.-Phase V--Grey Healthcare Group, New York, NY; *U.S. Public*, pg. 765

Brickman, Laurence M., Ph.D., Sr. V.P.--Ecology and Environment, Inc., Lancaster, NY; *U.S. Public*, pg. 562

Bridendall, John P., Sr. V.P.-Corp. Devel.--Brown-Forman Corporation, Louisville, KY; *U.S. Public*, pg. 261

Bridgeford, Gregory, Sr. V.P. & Gen. Mdse. Mgr.--Lowe's Companies, Inc., North Wilkesboro, NC; *U.S. Public*, pg. 1015

Bridger, Robert N., Sr. V.P.-Engrng. Svcs. & Construction--Koger Equity Inc., Jacksonville, FL; *U.S. Public*, pg. 965

Bridges, Maurice, Sr. V.P.-Diversity Affairs--Hardee's Food Systems, Inc., Rocky Mount, NC; *U.S. Public*, pg. 278

Bridwell, Jerry L., Sr. V.P.-Exploration & Land--Santa Fe Energy Resources, Inc., Houston, TX; *U.S. Public*, pg. 1431

Briedenbach, Rainer, Sr. V.P.-Sls. & Mktg.--Deutz AG, Cologne, Germany; *Int'l*, pg. 407

Briganti, Michael, Chief Fin. Officer & Sr. V.P.--SGS North America Inc., New York, NY; *Int'l*, pg. 1153

Briggs, Mark R., Sr. V.P.--Intelligent Electronics, Inc., Exton, PA; *U.S. Public*, pg. 887

Briggs, Paul A., Sr. V.P.-Middle Market Banking--Mellon Bank Corporation, Pittsburgh, PA; *U.S. Public*, pg. 1084

Brigham, S.T. Jack, III, Sr. V.P.-Corp. Affairs & Gen. Counsel--Hewlett-Packard Company, Palo Alto, CA; *U.S. Public*, pg. 813

Brighton, Steve, Sr. V.P.--Acxiom Corporation, Conway, AR; *U.S. Public*, pg. 18

Brinberg, Simeon, Sr. V.P. & Sec.--Georgetown Partners, Inc., Great Neck, NY; *U.S. Private*, pg. 466

Brindle, Winn F., Sr. V.P.--Wards Cove Packing Company, Seattle, WA; *U.S. Private*, pg. 1149

Brindley, Robert P., Exec. V.P.--Input/Output, Inc., Stafford, TX; *U.S. Public*, pg. 880

Brine, Kevin R., Sr. V.P.--Sanford C. Bernstein & Co., Inc., New York, NY; *U.S. Private*, pg. 137

Briner, Kurt, Sr. V.P.-Pharmaceuticals--Elf Aquitane, Paris, France; *Int'l*, pg. 444

Brinker, Lynne, Sr. V.P. & Grp. Acct. Dir.--DMB&B St. Louis, Saint Louis, MO; *U.S. Private*, pg. 303

Brinkerhoff, James, Sr. V.P.-Real Estate--Fortis Advisers, Inc., New York, NY; *Int'l*, pg. 499

Brinkerhoff, John, Sr. V.P. & Creative Dir.--Lord, Sullivan & Yoder Inc. Marketing Communications, Columbus, OH; *U.S. Private*, pg. 676

Brinsford, Michael W., Sr. V.P.--CSC Financial Services Group, Austin, TX; *U.S. Public*, pg. 422

Brintle, Kelly, Sr. V.P.--Ventura Foods LLC, City of Industry, CA; *Int'l*, pg. 879

Brisco, Robert N., Sr. V.P.-Mktg. & New Bus. Devel.--Los Angeles Times, Los Angeles, CA; *U.S. Public*, pg. 1616

Briskey, Charles E., Sr. V.P.-Opers.--Interactive Technologies, Inc., Saint Paul, MN; *U.S. Public*, pg. 888

Briskman, Louis J., Sr. V.P. & Gen. Counsel--CBS Corporation, Pittsburgh, PA; *U.S. Public*, pg. 273

Britt, William R., Sr. V.P.--Old National Bancorp, Evansville, IN; *U.S. Public*, pg. 1217

Brittain, John S., Jr., Sr. V.P. & Treas.--Sotheby's Holdings Inc., New York, NY; *U.S. Public*, pg. 1487

Broad, Alan S., Sr. V.P.--DSP Technology Inc., Fremont, CA; *U.S. Public*, pg. 475

Broatch, Robert E., Sr. V.P.-Fin.--Aetna Inc., Hartford, CT; *U.S. Public*, pg. 26

Broatch, Robert E., Chief Fin. Officer & Sr. V.P.-Fin.--UNUM Corporation, Portland, ME; *U.S. Public*, pg. 1699

Broatch, Robert E., Chief Fin. Officer & Sr. V.P.--UNUM Holding Company, Portland, ME; *U.S. Public*, pg. 1699

Broatch, Robert E., Sr. V.P.--UNUM Life Insurance Company of America, Portland, ME; *U.S. Public*, pg. 1699

Broce, Alan, Sr. V.P.-Mktg.--MTV: Music Television, New York, NY; *U.S. Private*, pg. 779

Brochhausen, Jim, Sr. V.P.-Sls.--Pinnacle Brands, Inc., Dallas, TX; *U.S. Private*, pg. 866

Brock, Stephen P., Sr. V.P.-Sls. & Mktg.--Baldwin Piano & Organ Company, Loveland, OH; *U.S. Public*, pg. 169

Brockett, Susan P., Sr. V.P.--Keycorp, Cleveland, OH; *U.S. Public*, pg. 954

Brockhaus, Ronald E., Sr. V.P.-Metalforming Opers.--Wozniak Industries, Inc., Oak Brook Terrace, IL; *U.S. Private*, pg. 1192

Brockman, Daniel L., Sr. V.P.-Fin.--PriceSmart Inc., San Diego, CA; *U.S. Public*, pg. 1324

Broder, Samuel, Sr. V.P.-Res. & Devel. & Chief Scientific Officer--IVAX Corporation, Miami, FL; *U.S. Public*, pg. 914

Broderick, Dennis J., Sr. V.P., Gen. Counsel & Sec.--Federated Department Stores, Inc., Cincinnati, OH; *U.S. Public*, pg. 617

Broderick, John E., Sr. V.P.--Zenith Insurance Company, Woodland Hills, CA; *U.S. Public*, pg. 1791

Broderick, Timothy W., V.P.--The El-Bee Chargit Corp., Dayton, OH; *U.S. Private*, pg. 367

Brodie, Bruce B., Sr. V.P.-Information Tech.--CNA Insurance Companies, Chicago, IL; *U.S. Public*, pg. 1010

Brodin, Ulf, Sr. V.P.-After Sls.--BT Industries AB, Mjolby, Sweden; *Int'l*, pg. 123

Brody, Jon, Sr. V.P. & Grp. Acct. Dir.--Cliff Freeman & Partners, New York, NY; *U.S. Public*, pg. 1422

Brody, Steven R., Sr. V.P.-Real Estate--Lincoln Investment Management Inc., Fort Wayne, IN; *U.S. Public*, pg. 998

Broedling, Laurie A., Sr. V.P.-Human Resources & Quality--McDonnell Aircraft & Missile Systems Div., Berkeley, MO; *U.S. Public*, pg. 241

Brofft, Jerome V., Sr. V.P.-Pur. & Logistics--World Color Press, Inc., Greenwich, CT; *U.S. Public*, pg. 1778

Broich, L.D., Sr. V.P.--Westfield Companies, Westfield Center, OH; *U.S. Private*, pg. 1169

Brolick, Emil J., Sr. V.P.-Strategic Plng. & Res.--Wendy's International Inc., Dublin, OH; *U.S. Public*, pg. 1754

Broman, Donald E., Sr. V.P.-Mfg. & Tech.--Snap-On Tools Corporation, Kenosha, WI; *U.S. Public*, pg. 1480

Bromley-Williams, Barbara, Sr. V.P.-Professional Services--Salick Health Care, Inc., Los Angeles, CA; *Int'l*, pg. 1524

Bronczek, David J., Sr. V.P.-Europe, Africa & Mediterranean--FDX Corporation, Memphis, TN; *U.S. Public*, pg. 603

Brondyke, Robert E., Sr. V.P.--ServiceMaster Food Management Services, Downers Grove, IL; *U.S. Public*, pg. 1462

Bronkoski, Robert J., Chief Information Officer & Sr. V.P.--Standard Federal Bank, Troy, MI; *Int'l*, pg. 10

Bronson, David, Chief Fin. Officer, Sr. V.P.-Fin. & Sec.--VWR Scientific Products, West Chester, PA; *U.S. Public*, pg. 1703

Brooks, Craig C., Sr. V.P.--Keycorp, Cleveland, OH; *U.S. Public*, pg. 954

Brooks, Douglas H., Sr. V.P.-Chili's Grill & Bar--Brinker International, Inc., Dallas, TX; *U.S. Public*, pg. 253

Brooks, Elizabeth, Sr. V.P.-Acct. Services--Western International Media Corporation, New York, NY; *U.S. Private*, pg. 1166

Brooks, Harvey L., Sr. V.P.-Ontario & Western Canada--National Bank of Canada, Montreal, Canada; *Int'l*, pg. 907

Brooks, Joan, Sr. V.P. & Admin. Dir.--Jerry & Ketchum, New York, NY; *U.S. Private*, pg. 616

Brooks, M., Sr. V.P.--Jelrus International, Hicksville, NY; *U.S. Private*, pg. 28

Brooks, Mark, Sr. V.P.--Air Techniques, Inc., Hicksville, NY; *U.S. Private*, pg. 28

Brooks, Martha, Sr. V.P. & Creative Dir.--Grey Advertising Inc., New York, NY; *U.S. Public*, pg. 764

Brooks, Paul W., Sr. V.P.-Corp. & Mngmt. Devel.--Koch Industries, Incorporated, Wichita, KS; *U.S. Private*, pg. 628

Brooks, Peter M., Sr. Zone V.P.--Gap Stores Division, San Bruno, CA; *U.S. Public*, pg. 702

Brooks, Wallis, Chief Fin. Officer & Sr. V.P.--Authentic Fitness Corp., Los Angeles, CA; *U.S. Public*, pg. 147

Brookstein, Steven M., Sr. V.P.-East/West Reg.--Comcast Cable Communications, Inc., Philadelphia, PA; *U.S. Public*, pg. 407

Brophy, Margaret M., Sr. V.P.-Strategic Plng. & Res. Dir.--Young & Rubicam Detroit, Detroit, MI; *U.S. Private*, pg. 1198

Brophy, Mary, Sr. V.P. & Pub. Rels. Dir.--Grant/Jacoby, Inc., Chicago, IL; *U.S. Private*, pg. 470

Brophy, Mary Alice, Sr. V.P.-Compliance--Dain Rauscher Corporation, Minneapolis, MN; *U.S. Public*, pg. 476

Brosh, Amnon, Sr. V.P.--Kulite Semiconductor Products, Inc., Leonia, NJ; *U.S. Private*, pg. 636

Brother, Thomas E., Sr. V.P.-Distribution--Albertson's, Inc., Boise, ID; *U.S. Public*, pg. 38

Brothers, Carl W., Sr. V.P.-Intl. Rice & Partnership--Riceland Foods, Inc., Stuttgart, AR; *U.S. Private*, pg. 928

Brotman, Joel A., Sr. V.P. & Residential Mortgage--Bank of the Hudson, Poughkeepsie, NY; *U.S. Public*, pg. 1319

Brotter, Art, Sr. V.P.--Fremont Indemnity Corp., Santa Monica, CA; *U.S. Public*, pg. 681

Browers, Jerry D., V.P.-System Opers.--TCA Management Company, Tyler, TX; *U.S. Public*, pg. 1553

Browing, Nicole, Sr. V.P.-Affil. Sls.--MTV Networks, New York, NY; *U.S. Private*, pg. 779

Brown, Barry, Sr. V.P.--CB Commercial Real Estate Group Eastern Division, Stamford, CT; *U.S. Public*, pg. 272

Brown, Brett, Sr. V.P.--Security Pacific Financial Services Inc., San Diego, CA; *U.S. Public*, pg. 181

Brown, Carol M., Sr. V.P.-Health Services--Wackenhut Corrections Corporation, Palm Beach Gardens, FL; *U.S. Public*, pg. 1731

Brown, Charles A., Sr. V.P.-Rocky Mountains--Snyder Oil Corporation, Fort Worth, TX; *U.S. Public*, pg. 1481

Brown, Charles S., Sr. V.P.--Phelps Dodge Sales Company, New York, NY; *U.S. Public*, pg. 1287

Brown, Craig J., Chief Fin. Officer, Sr. V.P.-Admin. & Treas.--The Standard Register Company, Dayton, OH; *U.S. Public*, pg. 1505

Brown, D.A., Chief Fin. Officer & Sr. V.P.-Admin.--Glaxo Wellcome Inc., Mississauga, Canada; *Int'l*, pg. 553

Brown, Daniel, Sr. V.P.-Sls. & Mktg.--J.H. Heafner Co. Inc., Lincolnton, NC; *U.S. Private*, pg. 514

Brown, Dave, Sr. V.P.-Bus. Plng. & Admin.--The William Carter Company, Morrow, GA; *U.S. Private*, pg. 217

Brown, Dennis M., Sr. V.P.-Northern Reg.--Tenet Healthcare Corporation, Santa Barbara, CA; *U.S. Public*, pg. 1576

Brown, Donald O., Sr. V.P.-Pharmaceutical Opers.--U.S. Bioscience, Inc., Conshohocken, PA; *U.S. Public*, pg. 1681

Brown, Donald R., Sr. V.P.-Southeast Reg.--TDS Telecommunications Corporation, Madison, WI; *U.S. Public*, pg. 1570

Brown, Doug, Chief Oper. Officer & Sr. V.P.--Willis Corroon Corp. of Birmingham, Birmingham, AL; *Int'l*, pg. 1505

Brown, Gregory A., Sr. V.P.-Sls.--Gibson Greetings, Inc., Cincinnati, OH; *U.S. Public*, pg. 742

Brown, Jack D., Sr. V.P.--Standard Federal Bank, Troy, MI; *Int'l*, pg. 10

Brown, James, Sr. V.P.-Opers.--Four Seasons Hotels Inc., Don Mills, Canada; *Int'l*, pg. 502

Brown, James L., Sr. V.P. & Gen. Mgr.-Casino Aztar Evansville--Aztar Corporation, Phoenix, AZ; *U.S. Public*, pg. 158

Brown, James P., Sr. V.P.--Policy Management Systems Corporation, Blythewood, SC; *U.S. Public*, pg. 1314

Brown, James R., Sr. V.P.-Lending--The Norwich Savings Society, Norwich, CT; *U.S. Public*, pg. 1203

Brown, Jeremy, Partner & Exec. V.P.--Yesawich, Pepperdine & Brown, Orlando, FL; *U.S. Private*, pg. 1195

Brown, Joann, Sr. V.P.-Print Production--McKinney & Silver, Raleigh, NC; *U.S. Private*, pg. 723

Brown, John, Sr. V.P. & Mng. Dir.--State Street Australia Ltd., Sydney, Australia; *U.S. Public*, pg. 1513

Brown, John A., Sr. V.P.-Sls./Fin. Services--The Great-West Life Assurance Company, Winnipeg, Canada; *Int'l*, pg. 557

Brown, John K., Sr. V.P.--Associates Commercial Corporation, Dallas, TX; *U.S. Public*, pg. 663

Brown, John R., Sr. V.P.-Distr. & Logics--Walgreen Co., Deerfield, IL; *U.S. Public*, pg. 1733

Brown, Kenneth R., Sr. V.P.-Investments & Sec.--Liberty Bancorp, Inc., Oklahoma City, OK; *U.S. Public*, pg. 174

Brown, L. Don, Sr. V.P.-Opers. & Tech.--Coors Brewing Company, Golden, CO; *U.S. Public*, pg. 445

Brown, Larry, V.P.-Prod. Assurance--Analog Devices, Santa Clara, CA; *U.S. Public*, pg. 108

Brown, Lynn T., Sr. V.P.--Wachovia Corporation, Winston Salem, NC; *U.S. Public*, pg. 1730

Brown, Mark E., Sr. V.P.--Howard Hughes Corporation, Las Vegas, NV; *U.S. Public*, pg. 1407

Brown, Mark R., Chief Info. Officer & Sr. V.P.--Viking Office Products, Torrance, CA; *U.S. Public*, pg. 1720

Brown, Max, Sr. V.P. & Pres.-Diamond Park Div.--Zale Corporation, Irving, TX; *U.S. Public*, pg. 1789

Brown, Michael L., Sr. V.P.--Summit Bank, Bethlehem, PA; *U.S. Public*, pg. 1528

Brown, Mike, Sr. V.P. & Asst. Oper.-Sls. & Mktg.--Alvey Systems, Inc, Saint Louis, MO; *U.S. Private*, pg. 47

Brown, Paul, Dir.-UK Retail Banking--Lloyds TSB Group PLC, London, United Kingdom; *Int'l*, pg. 812

Brown, R. Scott, Sr. V.P.-Worldwide Sls.--Xilinx, Inc., San Jose, CA; *U.S. Public*, pg. 1786

Brown, Randi, Sr. V.P.-Creative Adv.--Metro-Goldwyn-Mayer Inc., Santa Monica, CA; *U.S. Public*, pg. 1101

Brown, Ray, Sr. V.P.--Superior Industries International, Inc., Van Nuys, CA; *U.S. Public*, pg. 1539

Brown, Richard G., Sr. V.P.--Trinity Industries Inc., Dallas, TX; *U.S. Public*, pg. 1638

Brown, Robert J., Sr. V.P.--Foremost Insurance Co., Caledonia, MI; *U.S. Public*, pg. 667

Brown, Robert M., Chief Admin. Officer & Sr. V.P.--Uno Restaurant Corporation, West Roxbury, MA; *U.S. Public*, pg. 1698

Brown, Roger A., Sr. V.P., Sec. & Gen. Counsel--Harleysville Group, Harleysville, PA; *U.S. Public*, pg. 786

Brown, Scott M., Sr. V.P., Gen. Counsel & Sec.--Tenet Healthcare Corporation, Santa Barbara, CA; *U.S. Public*, pg. 1576

Brown, Sharon S., Sr. V.P.-Sls. & Service Div.--First Hawaiian Bank, Honolulu, HI; *U.S. Public*, pg. 634

Brown, Stephen F., Sr. V.P.-Treasury & Tax.--Cineplex Odeon Corporation, Toronto, Canada; *Int'l*, pg. 292

Brown, Stephen F., Chief Info. Officer & Sr. V.P.--Tenet Healthcare Corporation, Santa Barbara, CA; *U.S. Public*, pg. 1576

Brown, Steve, Sr. V.P.--First American Title Insurance Co. of Oregon, Portland, OR; *U.S. Public*, pg. 626

Brown, Thomas, Sr. V.P.-Engrng. & Estimating--Heavy Civil Construction, Boise, ID; *U.S. Public*, pg. 1134

Brown, Tracy, Sr. V.P. & Editor-in-Chief--Book of the Month Club, New York, NY; *U.S. Public*, pg. 1612

Browne, Fred, Sr. V.P.-Sls.--Zee Medical, Inc., Irvine, CA; *U.S. Public*, pg. 1073

Browne, Peter, Sr. V.P.--First Union Corporation, Charlotte, NC; *U.S. Public*, pg. 639

Browne, Wayne, Sr. V.P.--SAFECO Property & Casualty Insurance Companies, Seattle, WA; *U.S. Public*, pg. 1423

Brownell, David P., Sr. V.P.--Tyco International Ltd., Exeter, NH; *U.S. Public*, pg. 1647

Brownfield, Debbie, Chief Fin. Officer, Sr. V.P. & Sec.--Lamonts Apparel, Inc., Kirkland, WA; *U.S. Public*, pg. 975

Browning, Kenneth W., Jr., Sr. V.P.-Hide Div.--IBP, Inc., Dakota City, NE; *U.S. Public*, pg. 852

Browning, Scot R., Sr. V.P.--Century Bancshares, Inc., Washington, DC; *U.S. Public*, pg. 328

Browning, Toni, Sr. V.P.-Store Opers.--Younkers, Inc., Des Moines, IA; *U.S. Public*, pg. 1334

Brownjohn, Barry, Sr. V.P. & Country Mgr.--Bank of America NT&SA, Sydney, Australia; *U.S. Public*, pg. 182

Brownlee, Gary T., Sr. V.P.--Pinnacle Bank, Valparaiso, IN; *U.S. Public*, pg. 1297

Brownlee, Neil, Sr. V.P. & Copy Chief--Lois/EJL New York, New York, NY; *U.S. Public*, pg. 1011

Brownlee, Wayne R., Sr. V.P.-Expansion & Devel.--Potash Corporation of Saskatchewan Inc., Saskatoon, Canada; *Int'l*, pg. 1064

Brownley, John F., Sr. V.P. & Treas.--Wendy's International Inc., Dublin, OH; *U.S. Public*, pg. 1754

Brownlie, David, Sr. V.P.-Fin.--Whistler Mountain Holdings, Limited, Whistler, Canada; *Int'l*, pg. 685

Brownlie, William R., Sr. V.P.-Environmental Systems--Tetra Tech, Inc., Pasadena, CA; *U.S. Public*, pg. 1582

Brownridge, Kent, Sr. V.P.--Wenner Media, New York, NY; *U.S. Private*, pg. 1162

Brownstein, Martin, Sr. V.P.--Uniflex, Inc., Hicksville, NY; *U.S. Public*, pg. 1665

Brucato, Linda, Sr. V.P.-Opers.--Republic Security Bank, West Palm Beach, FL; *U.S. Public*, pg. 1382

Bruckheimer, Allen J., Sr. V.P. & Assoc. Treas.--Mutual of America Life Insurance Company, New York, NY; *U.S. Private*, pg. 769

Bruckman, Carol, Sr. V.P. & Mktg. Res. Dir.--Cramer-Krasselt, Chicago, IL; *U.S. Private*, pg. 285

Bruder, George A., Jr., Chief Oper. Officer & Sr. V.P.--DBT Online, Inc., Las Vegas, NV; *U.S. Public*, pg. 472

Bruder, John, Sr. V.P.-Fin. Svcs. Div.--The Minnesota Mutual Life Insurance Company, Saint Paul, MN; *U.S. Private*, pg. 750

Brueggen, David V., Sr. V.P.-Fin.--Anson Industries, Inc., Melrose Park, IL; *U.S. Private*, pg. 76

Bruehl, Thomas, Sr. V.P.-Video Opers.--Paramount Pictures Corporation, Los Angeles, CA; *U.S. Private*, pg. 776

Bruggeman, Mike, Sr. V.P.-H.R.--Commercial Federal Corporation, Omaha, NE; *U.S. Public*, pg. 411

Bruggmann, Hinrich, Sr. V.P.-Admin.--Hako-Werke GmbH & Co., Bad Oldesloe, Germany; *Int'l*, pg. 587
Bruheuhuis, Andre, Sr. V.P.-Fin.--Koninklijke Ahold NV, Zaandam, Netherlands; *Int'l*, pg. 749
Brumleve, David, Sr. V.P., Treas. & Sec.--Siemer Milling Company, Teutopolis, IL; *U.S. Private*, pg. 998
Brumm, P. Michael, Chief Fin. Officer & Sr. V.P.--The Fifth Third Bank, Cincinnati, OH; *U.S. Public*, pg. 621
Brun, Bernard, Chief of Staff & Sr. V.P.--Electricite de France, Paris, France; *Int'l*, pg. 437
Brunini, Frank, Sr. V.P.--Warrens Waller Press, Inc., South San Francisco, CA; *U.S. Private*, pg. 1151
Brunius, Robert E., Sr. V.P.-Engrng.--Interactive Technologies, Inc., Saint Paul, MN; *U.S. Public*, pg. 888
Brunner, Thomas, Sr. V.P.--Aceto Corporation, Lake Success, NY; *U.S. Public*, pg. 15
Bruno, John, Sr. V.P.-Sls. & Mktg.--Cagle's Inc., Atlanta, GA; *U.S. Public*, pg. 291
Brunt, Bill, Sr. V.P.--Hill, Holliday/Altschiller, New York, NY; *U.S. Private*, pg. 529
Brush, Bo, Sr. V.P.--First National Bank of Ohio, Akron, OH; *U.S. Public*, pg. 646
Brust, Robert, Chief Fin. Officer, Sr. V.P. & Controller--Unisys Corporation, Blue Bell, PA; *U.S. Public*, pg. 1671
Bruster, Hal, Sr. V.P. & Creative Dir.--Rainoldi, Kerzner & Radcliffe, San Francisco, CA; *U.S. Public*, pg. 1224
Bryan, A. Bradford, Jr., Sr. V.P.-Architecture & Construction--Marriott International, Inc., Washington, DC; *U.S. Public*, pg. 1047
Bryan, G. Robert, Sr. V.P.-Transmission--Lone Star Gas Co., Dallas, TX; *U.S. Public*, pg. 1587
Bryan, George W., Sr. V.P.--Sara Lee Corporation, Chicago, IL; *U.S. Public*, pg. 1432
Bryan, James L., Sr. V.P.-Opers.--Dresser Industries, Inc., Dallas, TX; *U.S. Public*, pg. 528
Bryant, D.L., Sr. V.P., Acct. Plng. Dir. & Acct. Planner--Howard, Merrell & Partners, Inc., Raleigh, NC; *U.S. Private*, pg. 542
Bryant, James E., Jr., Sr. V.P.--Acxiom Corporation, Conway, AR; *U.S. Public*, pg. 18
Bryant, Randolph W., Sr. V.P., Gen. Counsel & Sec.--Group Maintenance America Corp., Houston, TX; *U.S. Public*, pg. 766
Bryman, David, Sr. V.P.-Acct. Services--Western International Media Corporation, Los Angeles, CA; *U.S. Private*, pg. 1165
Bryson, Brent, Sr. V.P.-Reg. Opers.--Ramsay Health Care, Inc., Coral Gables, FL; *U.S. Public*, pg. 1360
Bryson, Garff, Sr. V.P.-Sls. & Mktg.--Tropical Sportswear International, Tampa, FL; *U.S. Private*, pg. 1105
Bryson, Michael A., Sr. V.P.-Strategic Plng.--Mellon Bank Corporation, Pittsburgh, PA; *U.S. Public*, pg. 1084
Bryson, Polly, Sr. V.P.-Mktg.--Spaulding & Slye, Boston, MA; *U.S. Private*, pg. 1021
Bubendorff, Jean G., Sr. V.P.-Sls./Quebec--Mackenzie Financial Corporation, Toronto, Canada; *Int'l*, pg. 828
Bubenzer, Joe A., Sr. V.P.--Dura Automotive Systems, Inc., Minneapolis, MN; *U.S. Public*, pg. 537
Bucalo, Jack P., Sr. V.P.-Corp. Human Resources--Fiserv, Inc., Brookfield, WI; *U.S. Public*, pg. 647
Bucchi, Richard A., Sr. V.P.-Sls. & Mktg.--Moore Medical Corp., New Britain, CT; *U.S. Public*, pg. 1128
Bucek, Dennis C., Sr. V.P., Treas. & Asst. Sec.--Coherent, Inc., Santa Clara, CA; *U.S. Public*, pg. 395
Buchanan, John D., Sr. V.P.-Legal--SouthTrust Corporation, Birmingham, AL; *U.S. Public*, pg. 1491
Buchanan, Patrick, Sr. V.P. & Grp. Acct. Dir.--Cohn & Wells, San Francisco, CA; *Int'l*, pg. 601
Buchanan, Paul W., Sr. V.P. & Controller--Hovnanian Enterprises, Inc., Red Bank, NJ; *U.S. Public*, pg. 843
Buchen, Michael, Sr. V.P.-Store Opers.--Payless Cashways, Inc., Kansas City, MO; *U.S. Public*, pg. 1267
Buchholz, William E., Chief Fin. Officer & Sr. V.P.--Nalco Chemical Company, Naperville, IL; *U.S. Public*, pg. 1150
Buchmann, Heinrich-Alfred, Dipl. Ing, Sr. V.P.--Ruhrgas AG, Essen, Germany; *Int'l*, pg. 1149
Buchwald, Lee E., Sr. V.P.--Rothschild Inc., New York, NY; *U.S. Private*, pg. 947
Buck, Paul C., Jr., Sr. V.P.--Manufacturers & Traders Trust Company, Buffalo, NY; *U.S. Public*, pg. 631
Buck, Robert, Chief Fin. Officer & Sr. V.P.--Bremer Financial Corporation, Saint Paul, MN; *U.S. Private*, pg. 167
Buck, Robert R., Sr. V.P.--Cintas Corporation, Mason, OH; *U.S. Public*, pg. 370
Buck, Rodney, Chief Investment Officer & Sr. V.P.--National Life Insurance Company, Montpelier, VT; *U.S. Private*, pg. 785
Buckelew, Alan, Sr. V.P.-Corp. Services--Princess Cruise Lines, Los Angeles, CA; *Int'l*, pg. 1035
Buckler, Robert J., Sr. V.P.--DTE Energy Company, Detroit, MI; *U.S. Public*, pg. 475
Buckley, Mike, Sr. V.P.-Mktg.--American General Life & Accident Insurance Co., Nashville, TN; *U.S. Public*, pg. 76
Buckley, Susan, Partner & Sr. V.P.--Media That Works, Cincinnati, OH; *U.S. Private*, pg. 727
Buckley, W.P., Sr. V.P.-Energy Prods.--Shaw Industries Ltd., Etobicoke, Canada; *Int'l*, pg. 1231
Bucknall, William L. Jr., Sr. V.P.-Human Resources & Organization--United Technologies Corporation, Hartford, CT; *U.S. Public*, pg. 1689
Buckner, Chuck, Sr. V.P.-Sls.--Gelco Information Network, Inc., Eden Prairie, MN; *U.S. Private*, pg. 442
Buda, T.J., Sr. V.P., Sec. & Gen. Counsel--Auto-Owners Insurance, Lansing, MI; *U.S. Private*, pg. 100
Budd, J. Richard, 111, Sr. V.P.--Metallurg, Inc., New York, NY; *U.S. Private*, pg. 735
Budd, Mike, Sr. V.P.-Sls--Overhead Door Corporation, Dallas, TX; *U.S. Private*, pg. 822
Budd, William B., Sr. V.P.--United Asset Management Corporation, Boston, MA; *U.S. Public*, pg. 1672
Budde, Kenneth C., Chief Acctg. Officer, Sr. V.P.-Fin., Treas. & Sec.--Stewart Enterprises, Inc., Metairie, LA; *U.S. Public*, pg. 1518
Budge, Scott, Sr. V.P.--SEI Investments, Oaks, PA; *U.S. Public*, pg. 1417
Budhraja, Vikram S., Sr. V.P.-Power Grid Bus. Unit--Southern California Edison Company, Rosemead, CA; *U.S. Public*, pg. 564
Buechner, Barry L., Sr. V.P.-Bus. Plng. & Systems--Day & Zimmermann, Inc., Philadelphia, PA; *U.S. Private*, pg. 316
Buedel, Carl W., Sr. V.P.--Meridian Insurance Group, Inc., Indianapolis, IN; *U.S. Public*, pg. 1095
Buehler, Philip, Sr. V.P.-Resources & Info Services--Wunderman Cato Johnson, New York, NY; *U.S. Private*, pg. 1197
Buehrer, David, Sr. V.P.-Fin. & Admin. Services--WTTW (Channel 11), Chicago, IL; *U.S. Private*, pg. 1145
Bueno, Olavo Franco, Jr., Sr. V.P.-Fin.--Banco Itau S.A., Sao Paulo, Brazil; *Int'l*, pg. 142
Buettner, Bob, Sr. V.P. & Corp. Counsel--Alabama Power Co., Birmingham, AL; *U.S. Public*, pg. 1489
Bugbee, Robert, Sr. V.P.--OMI Corp., New York, NY; *U.S. Public*, pg. 1208
Buie, W. G., Sr. V.P.--Allen & Hoshall, Inc., Memphis, TN; *U.S. Private*, pg. 36
Buisson, Jean-Rene, Sr. V.P.-H.R.--Danone Group, Paris, France; *Int'l*, pg. 379
Bukovinsky, Edward F., Sr. V.P.-Mktg. & Tech. Services--Willis Corroon Corp. of Seattle, Seattle, WA; *Int'l*, pg. 1507
Buldak, Gerald E., Sr. V.P.-Pub. Affairs--First Chicago NBD Corporation, Chicago, IL; *U.S. Public*, pg. 627
Bulen, E.H., Sr. V.P. & Gen. Mgr.-Mdse.--Lamonts Apparel, Inc., Kirkland, WA; *U.S. Public*, pg. 975
Buler, David, Sr. V.P.-Mktg.--The Israel Electric Corporation Ltd., Haifa, Israel; *Int'l*, pg. 690
Bulle, Ralph, Sr. V.P.-Human Resources--Hanover Direct, Inc., Weehawken, NJ; *U.S. Public*, pg. 782
Bullinger, Roy D., Sr. V.P.-Bus. Mngmnt. & Mktg.--Safety-Kleen Corp., Elgin, IL; *U.S. Public*, pg. 1425
Bullock, Don, Sr. V.P.--The Dunlap Company, Fort Worth, TX; *U.S. Private*, pg. 346
Bullock, Jerry D., Sr. V.P.-Exploration & Production--The Coastal Corporation, Houston, TX; *U.S. Public*, pg. 389
Bullwinkel, George J., Jr., Sr. V.P.-Retail Electric--South Carolina Electric & Gas Co. (SCE&G), Columbia, SC; *U.S. Public*, pg. 1436
Bumgardner, Clifton Y., Chief Tech. Officer & Sr. V.P.--BTG, Inc., Fairfax, VA; *U.S. Public*, pg. 164
Bumroongvidya, Pratheep, Sr. V.P.--Bangkok Rubber Public Co., Ltd., Bangkok, Thailand; *Int'l*, pg. 146
Bumstead, R. Glenn, Sr. V.P. & Gen. Counsel--The Toronto Dominion Bank, Toronto, Canada; *Int'l*, pg. 1401
Bunce, Leonard, Sr. V.P.-Fin. & Treas.--Schmidt Baking Co., Inc., Baltimore, MD; *U.S. Private*, pg. 970
Bunch, Doyle, Sr. V.P.-Corp. Plng. & Devel.--New Century Energies, Inc., Denver, CO; *U.S. Public*, pg. 1170
Buntel, John, Sr. V.P.-Engrng. Services--Hasbro, Inc., Pawtucket, RI; *U.S. Public*, pg. 797
Buntin, Nancy C., Sr. V.P.-Community Affairs--Synovus Financial Corp., Columbus, GA; *U.S. Public*, pg. 1548
Buntin, William, Sr. V.P.-Auto Div.--Kingston-Warren Corporation, Newfields, NH; *U.S. Public*, pg. 796
Bunting, Clark W., Sr. V.P.-Programming--Discovery Networks, Inc., Bethesda, MD; *U.S. Private*, pg. 334
Bunting, David, Sr. V.P.--Riggs National Corporation, Washington, DC; *U.S. Public*, pg. 1389
Burak Melchione, Janet, Sr. V.P., Gen. Counsel & Sec.--Everest Reinsurance Holdings, Liberty Corner, NJ; *U.S. Public*, pg. 597
Burak Melchione, Janet, Sr. V.P. & Gen. Counsel--Everest Reinsurance Co., Liberty Corner, NJ; *U.S. Public*, pg. 597
Burch, Cary G., Sr. V.P.-Mortgage Conduit Services--Advanta Mortgage Corp. USA, Fort Washington, PA; *U.S. Public*, pg. 22
Burch, Dennis, Sr. V.P.--First National Bank of Warsaw, Warsaw, IN; *U.S. Public*, pg. 674
Burch, Howe, Sr. V.P.-Adv. & Communications--Fila USA, Sparks, MD; *Int'l*, pg. 484
Burch, Stephen A., Sr. V.P.-Mid-Atlantic Reg.--Comcast Cable Communications, Inc., Philadelphia, PA; *U.S. Public*, pg. 407
Burchett, Chet, Sr. V.P.--Edelman Public Relations Worldwide, Chicago, IL; *U.S. Private*, pg. 362
Burd, Larry W., Sr. V.P.-Mfg.--Kreonite, Inc., Wichita, KS; *U.S. Private*, pg. 635
Burdeau, Steven, Sr. V.P.--UST Leasing Corporation, Boston, MA; *U.S. Public*, pg. 1660
Burdette, Steve, Sr. V.P.-Corp. Devel. & Acting Sr. V.P.-Opers.--MobileComm, Ridgefield Park, NJ; *U.S. Public*, pg. 1120
Burell, Nadine, Sr. V.P.-Retail Opers.--Supercuts, Inc., San Francisco, CA; *U.S. Public*, pg. 1373
Burge, Gary L., Sr. V.P.-Engrng. & Network Opers.--360 Degrees Communications Company, Chicago, IL; *U.S. Public*, pg. 1607
Burgess, Debbie, Sr. V.P. & Quality Control Dir.--Western International Media Corporation, Los Angeles, CA; *U.S. Private*, pg. 1165
Burgetz, Bruce, Sr. V.P.-Information Tech.--Shoppers Drug Mart, Ltd., Toronto, Canada; *Int'l*, pg. 112
Burggraf, Bonnie, Sr. V.P. & Mngmt. Supvr.--DMB&B New York, New York, NY; *U.S. Private*, pg. 302
Burgos, Fred J., Sr. V.P. & Assoc. Creative Dir.--Arnold Advertising, Mc Lean, VA; *U.S. Private*, pg. 84
Burian, Robert J., Sr. V.P.-H.R.--Safety-Kleen Corp., Elgin, IL; *U.S. Public*, pg. 1425
Burkart, James S., Sr. V.P.--Willis Corroon Corp. of Birmingham, Montgomery, AL; *Int'l*, pg. 1505
Burkart, Thomas D., Sr. V.P.-Vehicle Seating--Flexsteel Industries, Inc., Dubuque, IA; *U.S. Public*, pg. 653
Burke, Bob, Sr. V.P.-Sls.--Banyan Systems Inc., Westborough, MA; *U.S. Public*, pg. 189
Burke, Brian T., Chief Acctg. Officer, Sr. V.P. & Controller--Symbol Technologies, Inc., Holtsville, NY; *U.S. Public*, pg. 1546
Burke, George, Sr. V.P.-Mktg.--Globe Life And Accident Insurance Co., Oklahoma City, OK; *U.S. Public*, pg. 1622
Burke, James A., Sr., Sr. V.P.-Opers.--Rapid Industries, Inc., Louisville, KY; *U.S. Private*, pg. 910
Burke, James R., Sr. V.P.--Weatherford Enterra Incorporated, Houston, TX; *U.S. Public*, pg. 1749
Burke, James R., Sr. V.P.--Weatherford U.S., Inc., Houston, TX; *U.S. Public*, pg. 1749
Burke, Robert J., Sr. V.P.--American Appraisal Associates, Inc., Milwaukee, WI; *U.S. Private*, pg. 49
Burke, Robert P., Sr. V.P.-Mktg.--Luby's Cafeterias, Inc., San Antonio, TX; *U.S. Public*, pg. 1017
Burke, Therese, Sr. V.P.-Sls. & Mktg. Devel.--HarperCollins Publishers, New York, NY; *Int'l*, pg. 926
Burkeen, June, Sr. V.P. & Reg. Dir.--Arnold Advertising, Milwaukee, WI; *U.S. Private*, pg. 84
Burkett, Johnny, Sr. V.P.-Opers.--Cagle's Inc., Atlanta, GA; *U.S. Public*, pg. 291
Burkett, Larry, Sr. V.P.-Corp. & Member Rels.--Ag Processing Inc., A Cooperative, Omaha, NE; *U.S. Private*, pg. 26
Burkey, J. Brent, Sr. V.P., Gen. Counsel & Sec.--Matria Healthcare, Inc., Marietta, GA; *U.S. Public*, pg. 1057
Burkhardt, Greg, Sr. V.P.-Direct Mktg.--Ross Roy Communications, Inc., Bloomfield Hills, MI; *U.S. Private*, pg. 946
Burkhart, Glenda K., Sr. V.P.-Strategic Plng. & H.R.--The Reader's Digest Association, Inc., Pleasantville, NY; *U.S. Public*, pg. 1367
Burlingame, John, Sr. V.P.-Devel.--Hyatt Corporation, Chicago, IL; *U.S. Private*, pg. 551
Burlingthon, Brett, Sr. V.P.-Strategic Devel.--Excite, Inc., Redwood City, CA; *U.S. Public*, pg. 599
Burmeister, James T., Chief Fin. Officer & Sr. V.P.--Tapemark, Saint Paul, MN; *U.S. Private*, pg. 1068
Burne, Thomas C., Chief Fin. Officer & Sr. V.P.--Phillips Publishing International, Inc., Potomac, MD; *U.S. Private*, pg. 862
Burnett, Charles V., Sr. V.P.-Pharmacy--Costco Wholesale, Issaquah, WA; *U.S. Public*, pg. 451
Burnett, Iris, Sr. V.P.-Corp. Communications & Pub. Affairs--USA Networks, New York, NY; *U.S. Public*, pg. 1686
Burnison, Gary D., Sr. V.P. & Dir.-Bus. Analysis & Plng.--Jefferies & Company, Inc., Los Angeles, CA; *U.S. Public*, pg. 925
Burns, B. Bernard, Jr., Sr. V.P., Gen. Counsel & Sec.--United Dominion Industries, Ltd., Charlotte, NC; *U.S. Public*, pg. 1675
Burns, Charles, Sr. V.P.-Adv.--Minyard Food Stores, Inc., Coppell, TX; *U.S. Private*, pg. 752
Burns, Daniel T., Sr. V.P. & Gen. Counsel--TruServ Corporation, Chicago, IL; *U.S. Private*, pg. 1108
Burns, John F., Chief Fin. Officer & Sr. V.P.--Arthur D. Little, Inc., Cambridge, MA; *U.S. Private*, pg. 670
Burns, Ken, Sr. V.P. & Bond Mgr.--Willis Corroon Corp. of Birmingham, Birmingham, AL; *Int'l*, pg. 1505
Burns, Ralph, Sr. V.P.-Mfg. & Res./Devel.--Peerless Carpet Corporation, Acton Vale, Canada; *Int'l*, pg. 1032
Burns, Richard, Sr. V.P.-Sls.--GT Interactive Software Corp., New York, NY; *U.S. Public*, pg. 696
Burns, Sylvia H., Sr. V.P.--Rapides Bank & Trust Company of Alexandria, Alexandria, LA; *U.S. Public*, pg. 630
Burns, Thomas J., Sr. V.P.- Info. Sys.--D & N Financial Corporation, Hancock, MI; *U.S. Public*, pg. 472
Burns, Thomas L., Sr. V.P.--Summit Bank, Bethlehem, PA; *U.S. Public*, pg. 1528
Burnside, Jerry, Sr. V.P.-Mktg.--Longs Drug Stores California, Inc., Walnut Creek, CA; *U.S. Public*, pg. 1013
Burrell, Richard L., Sr. V.P.-Fin., Treas. & Sec.--R.G. Barry Corporation, Pickerington, OH; *U.S. Public*, pg. 192
Burrow, Ray, Sr. V.P.-Quality Process & Fin.--National Computer Print, Inc., Birmingham, AL; *U.S. Private*, pg. 780
Burt, James A., Jr., Sr. V.P. & Gen. Mgr.--Meldrum & Fewsmith Retail Services Group, Cleveland, OH; *U.S. Private*, pg. 730
Burt, Steven R., Sr. V.P.-Field Opers.--Daw Technologies, Inc., Salt Lake City, UT; *U.S. Public*, pg. 489
Burton, Edwin T., Sr. V.P.--Rothschild Inc., New York, NY; *U.S. Private*, pg. 947
Burton, Malcolm B., Sr. V.P.--Chubb & Son, Inc., Warren, NJ; *U.S. Public*, pg. 355
Burton, Richard A., Sr. V.P.-Taxes--Host Marriott Corporation, Bethesda, MD; *U.S. Public*, pg. 841
Burton, Robert A., Chief Fin. Officer & Sr. V.P.--Krause's Furniture Inc., Brea, CA; *U.S. Public*, pg. 967
Busam, S. James, Sr. V.P.-Bus. Devel.--ADP Marshall Contractors Inc., Rumford, RI; *U.S. Public*, pg. 660
Busby, Robert L., III, Chief Fin. & Admin. Officer, Sr. V.P. & Treas.--National Western Life Insurance Company, Austin, TX; *U.S. Public*, pg. 1161
Busceme, Charles, Sr. V.P.-Wedco USA--Wedco Technology, Bloomsbury, NJ; *U.S. Public*, pg. 854
Buscho, Shannon, Sr. V.P.-Stores--Mervyn's California, Hayward, CA; *U.S. Public*, pg. 489
Bush, Donald, Sr. V.P. & Gen. Labor Counsel--Quebecor Printing (USA) Corp., Boston, MA; *Int'l*, pg. 1076
Bush, Donald P., Jr., Sr. V.P.--Chubb & Son, Inc., Warren, NJ; *U.S. Public*, pg. 355
Bush, Nathan W., Sr. V.P.--Hibernia Corporation, New Orleans, LA; *U.S. Public*, pg. 825
Bushell, Dan, Chief Fin. Officer & Exec. V.P.--United Stationers Inc., Des Plaines, IL; *U.S. Public*, pg. 1689
Bushey, Craig S., Sr. V.P. & Pres.-Hardee's--Advantica Restaurant Group, Inc., Spartanburg, SC; *U.S. Public*, pg. 22
Bushey, Richard K., V.P. & Controller--Southern California Edison Company, Rosemead, CA; *U.S. Public*, pg. 564

Bushkin, Nancy, V.P.-Corp. Commun.--Spelling Entertainment Group, Inc., Los Angeles, CA; *U.S. Private*, pg. 776

Busik, William A., Sr. V.P.--The Annapolis Banking & Trust Co., Annapolis, MD; *U.S. Public*, pg. 1088

Buss, Gene, Sr. V.P. & Treas.--Sangamon Industries, Taylorville, IL; *U.S. Private*, pg. 965

Busse, Paul A., Sr. V.P.-Fin. & Admin.--Resound Corporation, Redwood City, CA; *U.S. Public*, pg. 1382

Busse, Wolf-Dieter, Ph.D., Sr. V.P.-Biotechnology Pharmaceutical Div.--Bayer Corporation, Pittsburgh, PA; *Int'l*, pg. 172

Butensky, Irwin S., Sr. V.P.-Res. & Devel.--Playtex Products Inc., Westport, CT; *U.S. Public*, pg. 1310

Butkovich, John, Sr. V.P.-Media Adv.--Columbia Pictures, Culver City, CA; *Int'l*, pg. 1281

Butler, Albert A., Sr. V.P.-Opers.--QMS, Inc., Mobile, AL; *U.S. Public*, pg. 1346

Butler, Dean, Sr. V.P.-Misc. Pur.--Reinalt-Thomas Corp., Ann Arbor, MI; *U.S. Private*, pg. 919

Butler, Gary L., Sr. V.P.--United Missouri Bank Northwest, Saint Joseph, MO; *U.S. Public*, pg. 1654

Butler, Jerry, Sr. V.P.--Brite Voice Systems, Canton, MA; *U.S. Public*, pg. 257

Butler, L. Daniel, Sr. V.P.-Customer Service--EMC Corporation, Hopkinton, MA; *U.S. Public*, pg. 545

Butler, Mike, Sr. V.P. & Mngmt. Supvr.--Miller Meester Advertising Inc., Minneapolis, MN; *U.S. Private*, pg. 747

Butler, Peggy, Sr. V.P.--Grey Advertising Inc., New York, NY; *U.S. Public*, pg. 764

Butler, R.W., Sr. V.P.--Sverdrup Corporation, Maryland Heights, MO; *U.S. Private*, pg. 1057

Butler, Van H., Sr. V.P.-Div. Mdse.--Toys "R" Us, Inc., Paramus, NJ; *U.S. Public*, pg. 1626

Butler, Van H., Sr. V.P.-Mktg. & Div. Mdse. Mgr.--Toys "R" Us United States, Paramus, NJ; *U.S. Public*, pg. 1626

Buto, Joan, Sr. V.P.-Production--Dugan Valva Contess Inc., Morristown, NJ; *U.S. Private*, pg. 345

Butters, Kim D., Sr. V.P.-Retail Credit--Zions First National Bank, Salt Lake City, UT; *U.S. Public*, pg. 1793

Butters, Norm, Sr. V.P.-Sls. & Mktg.--Norpac Foods, Inc., Stayton, OR; *U.S. Private*, pg. 802

Button, Graham, Sr. V.P. & Creative Dir.--Grey Advertising Inc., New York, NY; *U.S. Public*, pg. 764

Butts, David W., Sr. V.P.--Illinois Power Company, Decatur, IL; *U.S. Public*, pg. 869

Butts, Edward A., V.P.-Gen. Counsel & Sec.--Ameritech, Chicago, IL; *U.S. Public*, pg. 97

Butts, Wayne K., Sr. V.P. & Dir.-Reg. Opers.--Safeguard Health Enterprises, Inc., Anaheim, CA; *U.S. Public*, pg. 1424

Butzine, Craig, Sr. V.P. & Mngmt. Supvr.--The St. George Group, Inc., Pittsburgh, PA; *U.S. Private*, pg. 960

Buxton, Sarah L., Sr. V.P. & Dir.-Field & Div. Underwriting--Federated Mutual Insurance Company, Owatonna, MN; *U.S. Private*, pg. 399

Buzby, Russell C., Sr. V.P.--Brown-Forman Corporation, Louisville, KY; *U.S. Public*, pg. 261

Byerlein, Julie, Sr. V.P.-Mktg.--Mrs. Fields' Original Cookies, Inc., Salt Lake City, UT; *U.S. Private*, pg. 688

Byfuglin, Max, Sr. V.P.-Bakery Opers.--Cheesecake Factory Incorporated, Calabasas Hills, CA; *U.S. Public*, pg. 343

Bylin, Bob, Chief Fin. Officer & Sr. V.P.-Fin.--Storage Dimensions, Inc., Milpitas, CA; *U.S. Public*, pg. 1522

Bynum, Bryant P., Sr. V.P.-Fin.--Foodbrands America, Inc., Oklahoma City, OK; *U.S. Public*, pg. 852

Bynum, Lanny P., Sr. V.P.-Fin. & Opers.--Rockett, Burkhead, Lewis & Winslow, Raleigh, NC; *U.S. Private*, pg. 938

Byram, Robert G., Sr. V.P.-Nuclear--Pennsylvania Power & Light Company-Lehigh Div., Allentown, PA; *U.S. Public*, pg. 1244

Byrd, Bernard C., Sr. V.P.-Opers.--NovaCare Employee Services, Inc., Norristown, PA; *U.S. Public*, pg. 1203

Byrd, Marion E., Sr. V.P.-Human Resources--Government Employees Insurance Co. (GEICO), Washington, DC; *U.S. Public*, pg. 220

Byrne, Daniel G., Chief Fin. Officer & Sr. V.P.--Sterling Financial Corporation, Spokane, WA; *U.S. Public*, pg. 1516

Byrne, Tim, Chief Fin. Officer & Sr. V.P.--Corson Lime Company, Plymouth Meeting, PA; *U.S. Public*, pg. 1685

Byrne, Timothy, Chief Fin. Officer & Sr. V.P.--Arkansas Lime Co., Batesville, AR; *U.S. Public*, pg. 1685

Byrne, Timothy, Chief Fin. Officer & Sr. V.P.--Texas Lime Co., Cleburne, TX; *U.S. Public*, pg. 1685

Byrne, Timothy W., Chief Fin. Officer, Sr. V.P. & Sec.--United States Lime & Minerals, Dallas, TX; *U.S. Public*, pg. 1684

Byrnes, J.T., Sr. V.P.--Marshall & Ilsley Corporation, Milwaukee, WI; *U.S. Public*, pg. 1049

Byrnes, Ralph R., Sr. V.P.-Automotive Resource Dir.--Consumers Financial Corporation, Camp Hill, PA; *U.S. Public*, pg. 437

Byrnes, Richard, Jr., Sr. V.P.-Opers.--Swank, Inc., Attleboro, MA; *U.S. Public*, pg. 1543

Byrnes, Robert M., Sr. V.P.-Human Resources--International Paper Company, Purchase, NY; *U.S. Public*, pg. 901

Cabanes, Pierre, Sr. V.P. & Corp. Sec.--Thomson-CSF S.A., Paris, France; *Int'l*, pg. 1383

Cabaniss, Wyman, Sr. V.P.-Underwriting--Alfa Corporation, Montgomery, AL; *U.S. Public*, pg. 40

Cabello, David, Sr. V.P., Gen. Counsel & Sec.--COMPAQ Computer Corporation, Houston, TX; *U.S. Public*, pg. 417

Cabrera, Luis, Sr. V.P.-Treas. & Investments--Firstbank Puerto Rico, Santurce, PR; *U.S. Public*, pg. 644

Caccini, Gian Paolo, Sr. V.P.--Saint-Gobain, Courbevoie, France; *Int'l*, pg. 1170

Cadden, Thomas W., Sr. V.P. & Gen. Mgr.--Industrial & Retail Packaging Div., Chicago, IL; *U.S. Public*, pg. 1521

Cadigan, Robert, Sr. V.P.-QVC Programming--QVC, Inc., West Chester, PA; *U.S. Private*, pg. 897

Caetano, William, Sr. V.P.--Imperial Bank, Inglewood, CA; *U.S. Public*, pg. 871

Caferro, Jay, Sr. V.P.-Underwritting--Metropolitan Mortgage & Securities Co., Inc., Spokane, WA; *U.S. Private*, pg. 738

Caffey, Bill R., Sr. V.P.-Transportation & Opers. Services--Koch Industries, Incorporated, Wichita, KS; *U.S. Private*, pg. 628

Caffrey, Tom, Sr. V.P.-Bus. Devel.--Jordan Industries, Inc., Deerfield, IL; *U.S. Private*, pg. 598

Caggia, Andrew M., Sr. V.P.-Fin.--General Semiconductor, Inc., Melville, NY; *U.S. Public*, pg. 726

Cahill, Gerald, Chief Fin. Officer & Sr. V.P.-Fin.--Carnival Corporation, Miami, FL; *U.S. Public*, pg. 306

Cahill, John, Sr. V.P.-Fin., Chief Fin. Officer & Treas.--Kentucky Fried Chicken Corporation (KFC), Louisville, KY; *U.S. Public*, pg. 1636

Cahoon, R.L., Sr. V.P.-Sls.--Dunlop Tire Corporation, Buffalo, NY; *Int'l*, pg. 1317

Cain, David P., Sr. V.P., Gen. Counsel & Sec.--International Comfort Products, Franklin, TN; *U.S. Public*, pg. 898

Cain, Harry P., II, Sr. V.P.-Federal Programs--Blue Cross and Blue Shield Association, Chicago, IL; *U.S. Private*, pg. 151

Cain, Kelly, Sr. V.P.-Prod. Devel. & Mdsg.--Stanley Furniture Co. Inc., Stanleytown, VA; *U.S. Public*, pg. 1508

Caine, Robert, Sr. V.P. & Pres.-Bath & Floor Fashions--Peerless Carpet Corporation, Acton Vale, Canada; *Int'l*, pg. 1032

Cairns, Patrick J., Sr. V.P.--EnerMark Income Fund, Calgary, Canada; *Int'l*, pg. 454

Calabrese, Julia J., Sr. V.P.-Property Mngmt.--The Kaempfer Company, Investment Builders, Washington, DC; *U.S. Private*, pg. 604

Calabretta, Victor V., Sr. V.P. & Mgr.-Northeast Opers.--Maguire Group Inc., Foxboro, MA; *U.S. Private*, pg. 696

Calabria, Carl C., Sr. V.P.-Engrng.--Truevision, Inc., Santa Clara, CA; *U.S. Public*, pg. 1642

Calafati, Peter G., V.P.--Frank Briscoe Co. Inc., Kenilworth, NJ; *U.S. Private*, pg. 169

Calafell, Robert C., Sr. V.P.-Plng. & Devel.--GTE Corporation, Stamford, CT; *U.S. Public*, pg. 696

Calaiaro, Kerry K., Sr. V.P.--Summit Bancorp, Princeton, NJ; *U.S. Public*, pg. 1527

Calasibetta, John, Sr. V.P.--Bergen Brunswig Corporation, Orange, CA; *U.S. Public*, pg. 213

Calbert, Michael M., Sr. V.P.-Corp. Devel.--Randalls Food Markets, Inc., Houston, TX; *U.S. Private*, pg. 909

Calcano, Frank, Sr. V.P.--Imperia Bros., Inc., Pelham Manor, NY; *U.S. Private*, pg. 558

Caldentey, Juan M., Deputy Mng. Dir. & Sr. V.P.-Devel. City Div. Europe--Sol Melia, Palma de Mallorca, Spain; *Int'l*, pg. 1277

Calder, Steve, Sr. V.P. & Media Dir.--Citron Haligman Bedecarre, San Francisco, CA; *U.S. Private*, pg. 241

Calderin, Roberto, Sr. V.P. & Field Mktg. Dir.--DMB&B New York, New York, NY; *U.S. Private*, pg. 302

Calderon, Alvin A., Sr. V.P.--Manufacturers & Traders Trust Company, Buffalo, NY; *U.S. Public*, pg. 631

Calderon, Zayra F., Sr. V.P.-Strategic Prod. Devel.--Cigna Healthcare, Inc., Bloomfield, CT; *U.S. Public*, pg. 359

Calderoni, Robert M., Chief Fin. Officer & Sr. V.P.-Fin.--Avery Dennison Corporation, Pasadena, CA; *U.S. Public*, pg. 152

Caldon, Daniel, Chief Fin. Officer & Sr. V.P.--Bissell Inc., Grand Rapids, MI; *U.S. Private*, pg. 145

Caldwell, Bruce, Chief Fin. Officer & Sr. V.P.--Great Western Consumer Finance Group, Tampa, FL; *U.S. Public*, pg. 1741

Caldwell, Eugene, Chief Fin. Officer, Sr. V.P. & Treas.--Venture Stores, Inc., O Fallon, MO; *U.S. Public*, pg. 1716

Caldwell, Peggy K., Sr. V.P.-Mktg.--Tech Data Corporation, Clearwater, FL; *U.S. Public*, pg. 1562

Calek, Terry A., Sr. V.P.-Pub. Affairs--Mutual of Omaha Insurance Company, Omaha, NE; *U.S. Private*, pg. 769

Caley, Susan A., Sr. V.P. & Human Resources Dir.--Creswell, Munsell, Fultz & Zirbel, L.P., Cedar Rapids, IA; *U.S. Private*, pg. 1197

Calhoon, Donald, Sr. V.P.-Corp. Mktg.--Wendy's International Inc., Dublin, OH; *U.S. Public*, pg. 1754

Calhoun, Craig, Sr. V.P.--Jim Walter Homes, Inc., Tampa, FL; *U.S. Public*, pg. 1737

Calhoun, Jay, Sr. V.P. & Treas.--New York Life Insurance Company, New York, NY; *U.S. Private*, pg. 794

Cali, Phil, Sr. V.P.-Opers.--Northern Illinois Gas Company, Naperville, IL; *U.S. Public*, pg. 1183

Caliendo, G.D., Sr. V.P., Gen. Counsel & Sec.--Orange and Rockland Utilities, Inc., Pearl River, NY; *U.S. Public*, pg. 1229

Caliri, Rich, Sr. V.P.-Mktg.--Envoy Corporation, Nashville, TN; *U.S. Public*, pg. 587

Calise, William J., Jr., Sr. V.P., Gen. Counsel & Sec.--Rockwell International Corporation, Costa Mesa, CA; *U.S. Public*, pg. 1397

Call, John, Chief Fin. Officer & Sr. V.P.--Ross Stores, Inc., Newark, CA; *U.S. Public*, pg. 1405

Call, Lawrence M., Chief Fin. Officer & Sr. V.P.--Amway Corporation, Ada, MI; *U.S. Private*, pg. 69

Callahan, Bob, Sr. V.P.-Sls., Mktg. & Oper.--U.S. Tsubaki, Inc., Wheeling, IL; *Int'l*, pg. 1425

Callahan, D.W., Sr. V.P.--Chevron Chemical Co., San Ramon, CA; *U.S. Public*, pg. 348

Callahan, J. Sean, Chief Fin. Officer & Sr. V.P.-Fin. & Admin.--Preston Trucking Company, Inc., Preston, MD; *U.S. Public*, pg. 1788

Callahan, John D., Sr. V.P.--PSC Inc., Webster, NY; *U.S. Public*, pg. 1245

Callahan, Michael L., Sr. V.P.-Corp. Compliance--New York Life Insurance Company, New York, NY; *U.S. Private*, pg. 794

Callahan, T.E., Chief Fin. Officer & Sr. V.P.-Fin.--Welch Foods Inc., A Cooperative, Concord, MA; *U.S. Private*, pg. 784

Callas, Ariadne, Sr. V.P.--Grey Advertising Inc., New York, NY; *U.S. Public*, pg. 764

Callas, Christopher, Sr. V.P. & Acct. Dir.--Young & Rubicam New York, New York, NY; *U.S. Private*, pg. 1198

Calle, Craig R.L., Sr. V.P.-Fin. & Treas.--Crown Cork & Seal Company, Inc., Philadelphia, PA; *U.S. Public*, pg. 462

Calleja, Francisco, Sr. V.P.--Banco Santander, Madrid, Spain; *Int'l*, pg. 143

Callender, DeLisle, Chief Fin. Officer & Sr. V.P.--The Chisholm-Mingo Group, New York, NY; *U.S. Private*, pg. 237

Calvaruso, Joseph, Sr. V.P.--Shoreline Financial Corp., Benton Harbor, MI; *U.S. Public*, pg. 1467

Calvaruso, Joseph S., Sr. V.P.-Loan Admin.--Shoreline Bank, Benton Harbor, MI; *U.S. Public*, pg. 1468

Camacho, Don, Sr. V.P. & Controller--Converse Inc., North Reading, MA; *U.S. Public*, pg. 441

Camba, Jose A., Chief Oper. Officer & Sr. V.P.--Banco Santander Puerto Rico, Hato Rey, PR; *Int'l*, pg. 143

Cambridge, Daniel A., Sr. V.P. & Creative Dir.--Creswell, Munsell, Fultz & Zirbel, L.P., Cedar Rapids, IA; *U.S. Private*, pg. 1197

Cambridge, Michael, Sr. V.P.--Rockefeller Center Management Corporation, New York, NY; *Int'l*, pg. 873

Camens, Bernard, Sr. V.P.-Sls.-Lighting Div.--Crystal Clear Industries, Ridgefield Park, NJ; *U.S. Private*, pg. 293

Cameron, Eric, Sr. V.P. & Chief Info. Officer--Nycomed Amersham, Oslo, Norway; *Int'l*, pg. 993

Camilleri, Louis C., Chief Fin. Officer & Sr. V.P.--Philip Morris Companies Inc., New York, NY; *U.S. Public*, pg. 1287

Camiro Vazquez, Ruben, Chief Fin. Officer & Sr. V.P.--Grupo Casa Autrey, Mexico, Mexico; *Int'l*, pg. 573

Camosy, John P., Sr. V.P.--Camosy, Inc., Russell, IL; *U.S. Private*, pg. 203

Campbell, A.A., Sr. V.P.-Sls. & Mktg.--Celotex Corporation, Tampa, FL; *U.S. Private*, pg. 221

Campbell, Allan R., Sr. V.P. & Gen. Counsel--Unitrode Corporation, Merrimack, NH; *U.S. Public*, pg. 1694

Campbell, Andrew, Chief Fin. Officer & Sr. V.P.--Safety-Kleen Corp., Elgin, IL; *U.S. Public*, pg. 1425

Campbell, Bill, Sr. V.P.-Mktg.--United Farm Family Life Insurance Co., Indianapolis, IN; *U.S. Private*, pg. 1122

Campbell, Gerald D., Sr. V.P.-Midwest Reg.--Comcast Cable Communications, Inc., Philadelphia, PA; *U.S. Public*, pg. 407

Campbell, J.A., Chief Fin. Officer & Sr. V.P.-Fin.--ATCO Group Co., Calgary, Canada; *Int'l*, pg. 95

Campbell, J.R., Sr. V.P.-Imports--Wal-Mart Stores, Inc., Bentonville, AR; *U.S. Public*, pg. 1732

Campbell, James C., Sr. V.P.--Peabody COALSALES Company, Saint Louis, MO; *Int'l*, pg. 594

Campbell, John J., Sr. V.P.--Elbeco Incorporated, Reading, PA; *U.S. Private*, pg. 367

Campbell, Judith E., Chief Info. Officer & Sr. V.P.--New York Life Insurance Company, New York, NY; *U.S. Private*, pg. 794

Campbell, Michael H., Sr. V.P.-H.R.--Continental Airlines, Houston, TX; *U.S. Public*, pg. 439

Campbell, Nick, Sr. V.P.-Mktg.--The Penn Traffic Company, Syracuse, NY; *U.S. Public*, pg. 1270

Campbell, Paul, Sr. V.P.-Plng.--M.A. Mortenson Company, Minneapolis, MN; *U.S. Private*, pg. 763

Campbell, Robin A., Sr. V.P. & Gen. Counsel--TrizecHahn Corporation, Toronto, Canada; *Int'l*, pg. 1424

Campbell, Robyn, Sr. V.P. & Mng. Dir.--Western International Media Corporation, Minneapolis, MN; *U.S. Private*, pg. 1167

Campbell, Roger A., Sr. V.P. & Gen. Mgr.-Eastern Div.--Costco Wholesale, Issaquah, WA; *U.S. Public*, pg. 451

Campbell, Shelly, Sr. V.P.--Edelman Worldwide, Inc., New York, NY; *U.S. Private*, pg. 362

Campbell, Tom, Sr. V.P.-Pur.--Brinker International, Inc., Dallas, TX; *U.S. Public*, pg. 253

Campbell, Victor L., Sr. V.P.--Columbia/HCA Healthcare Corporation, Nashville, TN; *U.S. Public*, pg. 403

Campeau, Cliff, Sr. V.P.-Mktg.--Venture Stores, Inc., O Fallon, MO; *U.S. Public*, pg. 1716

Campion, Donald, Chief Fin. Officer & Sr. V.P.--Delco Electronics Corporation, Kokomo, IN; *U.S. Public*, pg. 720

Campion, Donald C., Chief Fin. Officer & Sr. V.P.--Oxford Automotive, Inc., Troy, MI; *U.S. Private*, pg. 825

Campion, Frank, Sr. V.P. & Creative Dir.--Long Haymes Carr, Inc., Winston Salem, NC; *U.S. Public*, pg. 909

Campo, Fred S., Sr. V.P.-Risk Mngmt.--Broad National Bancorporation, Newark, NJ; *U.S. Public*, pg. 257

Campos, Jorge Planos, Sr. V.P.-Hearst Magazines Intl.--Hearst Magazines Division, New York, NY; *U.S. Private*, pg. 516

Canavera, David L., Sr. V.P.-Towel & Tissue--Wausau-Mosinee Paper Corporation, Mosinee, WI; *U.S. Public*, pg. 1747

Canavera, David L., Sr. V.P.-Towel & Tissue--Bay West Paper Corporation, Harrodsburg, KY; *U.S. Public*, pg. 1747

Cancell, Leonard, Sr. V.P.-Opers.--New Plan Realty Trust, New York, NY; *U.S. Public*, pg. 1172

Cancio, Leopoldo V., Sr. V.P.-P.P.D.--Clopay Corporation, Cincinnati, OH; *U.S. Public*, pg. 766

Canete, Antonio V., Sr. V.P.-New Business Ventures--Atlas Consolidated Mining & Development Corporation, Manila, Philippines; *Int'l*, pg. 95

Canevera, David L., Sr. V.P.-Towel & Tissue--Bay West Paper Corp. Towel & Tissue Div., Middletown, OH; *U.S. Public*, pg. 1747

Canfield, Alan B., Sr. V.P.--Select Canfield, Chicago, IL; *U.S. Private*, pg. 982

Cannada, Charles T., Sr. V.P.-Corp. Devel., Investor Rels. & Real Estate Devel.--WorldCom, Inc., Jackson, MS; *U.S. Public*, pg. 1779

Cannada, Charles T., Sr. V.P.-Corp. Devel., Investor Rels. & Real Estate--LDDS WorldCom Inc., East Rutherford, NJ; *U.S. Public*, pg. 1779

Cannada, Charles T., Sr. V.P.-Corp. Devel.--LDDS/ WorldCom Communications, Revere, MA; *U.S. Public*, pg. 1779
Cannata, Mike, Sr. V.P.-Fin.--ADI (Ademco Distribution, Inc.), Syosset, NY; *U.S. Public*, pg. 1306
Cannata, Mike, Sr. V.P.--ADI Mexico, Colonia, Mexico; *U.S. Public*, pg. 1307
Cannata, Mike, Sr. V.P.--ADI Puerto Rico, San Juan, PR; *U.S. Public*, pg. 1307
Cannelli, John, Sr. V.P.-Music & Talent--MTV: Music Television, New York, NY; *U.S. Private*, pg. 779
Cannington, John T., Jr., Sr. V.P.-Field Opers.--Manugistics Group, Inc., Rockville, MD; *U.S. Public*, pg. 1042
Cannizzo, Michael, Sr. V.P.-Admin.--NVR Homes, Inc., Gaithersburg, MD; *U.S. Public*, pg. 1148
Cannon, Aimen, Sr. V.P. & Brdcst. Dir.--Partners & Shevack, Inc., New York, NY; *U.S. Private*, pg. 842
Cannon, John R., Exec. V.P.--DataMate Products Group, Chicago, IL; *U.S. Public*, pg. 1101
Cannon, W. Stephen, Sr. V.P. & Gen. Counsel--Circuit City Stores, Inc., Richmond, VA; *U.S. Public*, pg. 374
Canny, Yolanda, Sr. V.P.-Global Mktg.--Pilkington Barnes Hind (PBH), San Diego, CA; *U.S. Private*, pg. 111
Canright, Mark W., Sr. V.P.-Worldwide Sls.--Exabyte Corporation, Boulder, CO; *U.S. Public*, pg. 597
Cantilina, Hilary, Sr. V.P.-Creative Services--Burrell/DFA Advertising, New York, NY; *U.S. Private*, pg. 188
Caparelli, William D., Sr. V.P.-Worldwide Sls.--Cirrus Logic, Inc., Fremont, CA; *U.S. Public*, pg. 375
Capell, Robert L., III, Sr. V.P.-Advanced Data Networks--BellSouth Corporation, Atlanta, GA; *U.S. Public*, pg. 207
Capellupo, Vic, Exec. V.P. & Insights Grp. Mgr.--Young & Rubicam New York, New York, NY; *U.S. Private*, pg. 1198
Capezzuti, Nancy M., Sr. V.P.- Human Resources--Southern Union Company, Austin, TX; *U.S. Public*, pg. 1491
Caplan, Bernie, Jr., Sr. V.P.-Industrial Prods. Div.--Brother International Corporation, Somerset, NJ; *Int'l*, pg. 229
Caplan, Mitchell, Sr. V.P.--Media Resources International, New York, NY; *U.S. Private*, pg. 727
Caporale, Charles, Chief Fin. Officer, Sr. V.P. & Treas.--Centris Group Inc., Costa Mesa, CA; *U.S. Public*, pg. 328
Caporale, Michael, Sr. V.P. & Gen. Mgr.--Great Lakes Window, Inc., Toledo, OH; *U.S. Public*, pg. 1193
Capp, Ray, Sr. V.P.-Opers.--Thomas Nelson Inc., Nashville, TN; *U.S. Public*, pg. 1167
Cappelletti, Joe, Sr. V.P.-Sls.--ADI (Ademco Distribution, Inc.), Syosset, NY; *U.S. Public*, pg. 1306
Cappellucci, David, Sr. V.P. & Mgr.-Bus.--Simon & Schuster Elementary Division, Parsippany, NJ; *U.S. Private*, pg. 778
Cappleman, Charles, Sr. V.P.-West Coast Opers. & Engrng.--CBS, New York, NY; *U.S. Public*, pg. 273
Cappo, Joe, Sr. V.P.-Intl.--Advertising Age, Chicago, IL; *U.S. Private*, pg. 284
Cappo, Joseph C., Sr. V.P. & Grp. Publisher--Crain Communications, Inc., Chicago, IL; *U.S. Private*, pg. 284
Capps, Robert, Sr. V.P. & Gen. Sls. Mgr.--TriStar Pictures, Culver City, CA; *Int'l*, pg. 1283
Capps, Roger, Chief Oper. Officer & Sr. V.P.--Prairie Farms Dairy, Inc., Carlinville, IL; *U.S. Private*, pg. 878
Capria, Ernest, Sr. V.P. & Dir.-Mktg.--Carillon Importers, Ltd., Fort Lee, NJ; *Int'l*, pg. 409
Caputo, Art, Sr. V.P.-Sls. & Mktg.--Waters Corporation, Milford, MA; *U.S. Public*, pg. 1745
Caradonna, Ross S., Chief Info. Officer & Sr. V.P.--Scott's Restaurants Inc., Markham, Canada; *Int'l*, pg. 1213
Cardamon, James M., Sr. V.P.--First National Bank of Pennsylvania, Hermitage, PA; *U.S. Public*, pg. 607
Cardinal, Lawrence, Jr., Sr. V.P. & Controller--First National Bank of Ohio, Akron, OH; *U.S. Public*, pg. 646
Cardner, Larry, Sr. V.P.--1st Source Corporation, South Bend, IN; *U.S. Public*, pg. 638
Carella, Patrick, Sr. V.P. & Assoc. Creative Dir.--Moss/ Dragoti, New York, NY; *Int'l*, pg. 117
Carey, Christopher J., Sr. V.P. & Controller--CoreStates Financial Corp., Philadelphia, PA; *U.S. Public*, pg. 446
Carey, H. Augustus, Sr. V.P. & Mng. Dir.--W.P. Carey & Co., Inc., New York, NY; *U.S. Private*, pg. 209
Carey, Mike, Sr. V.P.-New Media--The Weather Channel, Atlanta, GA; *U.S. Private*, pg. 647
Carinalli, Charles P., Sr. V.P. & Chief Tech. Officer--National Semiconductor Corporation, Santa Clara, CA; *U.S. Public*, pg. 1159
Carlin, Don, Sr. V.P., Grp. Acct. Dir. & Mngmt. Supvr.--Ingalls, Boston, MA; *U.S. Private*, pg. 562
Carlin, Raymond G., Sr. V.P.-The Americas Region--NCR Corporation, Dayton, OH; *U.S. Public*, pg. 1146
Carlisle, Todd, Exec. V.P.-Sls.--Croft Metals, Inc., McComb, MS; *U.S. Private*, pg. 290
Carlock, Roger E., Sr. V.P.--Massachusetts Financial Services Company (MFS), Boston, MA; *Int'l*, pg. 1319
Carlow, Russell, Sr. V.P.--The Chestertown Bank of Maryland, Chestertown, MD; *U.S. Public*, pg. 1088
Carlsen, Sigurd, Sr. V.P.-Investor Rels.--Christiania Bank og Kreditkasse ASA, Oslo, Norway; *Int'l*, pg. 289
Carlson, Andrew, Sr. V.P.-Quality & Safety--Jacobs Engineering Group Inc., Pasadena, CA; *U.S. Public*, pg. 921
Carlson, Carl, Sr. V.P.--Kraus-Anderson Mortgage Company, Minneapolis, MN; *U.S. Private*, pg. 635
Carlson, D.A., Jr., Sr. V.P.--B.C. Ziegler & Co., West Bend, WI; *U.S. Public*, pg. 1792
Carlson, D.B., Sr. V.P.-Equity Portfolios--General Electric Investment Corp., Stamford, CT; *U.S. Public*, pg. 712
Carlson, David M., Chief Tech. Officer & Sr. V.P.--Ingram Micro Inc., Santa Ana, CA; *U.S. Public*, pg. 878
Carlson, Edgar T., Sr. V.P.-California Oper. (South)--Kaiser Permanente, Oakland, CA; *U.S. Private*, pg. 605
Carlson, Gary L., Sr. V.P.-Strategic Devel.--Avatar Holdings Inc., Coral Gables, FL; *U.S. Public*, pg. 151
Carlson, Gary L., Sr. V.P.-Strategic Devel.--Avatar Properties Inc., Miami, FL; *U.S. Public*, pg. 151
Carlson, Gerald K., Sr. V.P.-Corp. Devel.--Ecolab Inc., Saint Paul, MN; *U.S. Public*, pg. 562
Carlson, Hans, Sr. V.P.-Human Resources--Pharmacia & Upjohn, Inc., Windsor, United Kingdom; *Int'l*, pg. 1047
Carlson, Jeffrey R., Sr. V.P.-Asset/Based Lending--Citizens Trust Company, Providence, RI; *Int'l*, pg. 1132
Carlson, Jennie P., Sr. V.P., Deputy Gen. Counsel & Asst. Sec.--Starbanc Corporation, Cincinnati, OH; *U.S. Public*, pg. 1510
Carlson, Kelly, Sr. V.P.-Distr. Plng.--Phoenix Home Life Mutual Insurance Company, Hartford, CT; *U.S. Private*, pg. 863
Carlson, Lars T., Sr. V.P.-Admin.--H.B. Fuller Company, Saint Paul, MN; *U.S. Public*, pg. 686
Carlson, Samuel L., Sr. V.P.-Admin. & Sec.--Pancho's Mexican Buffet, Inc., Fort Worth, TX; *U.S. Public*, pg. 1255
Carlson, Stanley A., Sr. V.P., Gen. Counsel & Corp. Sec.--Seafirst Corporation, Seattle, WA; *U.S. Public*, pg. 181
Carlson, Stuart R., Sr. V.P.-Specialty Papers--Wausau-Mosinee Paper Corporation, Mosinee, WI; *U.S. Public*, pg. 1747
Carlson, Stuart R., Sr. V.P.-Specialty Papers--The Sorg Paper Co., Middletown, OH; *U.S. Public*, pg. 1747
Carlson, Terry, Sr. V.P.-Mktg.--Vermont American Tool Corp., Louisville, KY; *U.S. Public*, pg. 575
Carlson, William E., Sr. V.P.-Prods. & Technology--Intermetrics, Inc., Burlington, MA; *U.S. Private*, pg. 567
Carlson, William J., Sr. V.P.--Atkinson, San Bruno, CA; *U.S. Public*, pg. 143
Carlsson, Richard I., Sr. V.P.-Underwriting--Argonaut Co., Menlo Park, CA; *U.S. Public*, pg. 129
Carlucci, John F., Sr. V.P.--Carrafiello, Diehl & Associates, Inc., Irvington, NY; *U.S. Private*, pg. 215
Carman, Trent J., Sr. V.P. & Treas.--United Artists Theatre Circuits Incorporated, Englewood, CO; *U.S. Private*, pg. 1120
Carmany, Catherine M., Sr. V.P. & Trust Officer--The Old Phoenix National Bank of Medina, Medina, OH; *U.S. Public*, pg. 646
Carmichael, Alan, Sr. V.P.-Communications--Tennessee Valley Authority, Knoxville, TN; *U.S. Public*, pg. 1580
Carmichael, David R., Sr. V.P. & Gen. Counsel--Pacific Life Insurance Company, Newport Beach, CA; *U.S. Private*, pg. 831
Carnahan, Douglas K., Sr. V.P. & Gen. Mgr.-Meas. Sys. Org.--Hewlett-Packard Company, Palo Alto, CA; *U.S. Public*, pg. 813
Carneal, Drew St. J., Sr. V.P., Corp. Counsel & Sec.--Owens & Minor Inc., Glen Allen, VA; *U.S. Public*, pg. 1236
Carnella, Frank T., Sr. V.P.-Tech.--Texas Commerce Bank, Houston, TX; *U.S. Public*, pg. 339
Carnovale, Raymond J., Sr. V.P.-Engrng. & Opers.--Baton Broadcasting Incorporated, Scarborough, Canada; *Int'l*, pg. 170
Carollo, Susan, Sr. V.P. & Media Dir.--Cline, Davis & Mann, Inc., New York, NY; *U.S. Private*, pg. 246
Caron, J. Raymond, Sr. V.P.-Management Info. Services--Cigna Corp., Philadelphia, PA; *U.S. Public*, pg. 356
Caron, Michael A., Sr. V.P. & Pres.-Armor All Intl.--Armor All Products Group, Oakland, CA; *U.S. Public*, pg. 387
Carosi, Al, Sr. V.P.--Parker Brothers, Beverly, MA; *U.S. Public*, pg. 797
Carpenter, Bob R., Chief Admin. Officer, V.P. & Gen. Counsel--Dollar General Corporation, Nashville, TN; *U.S. Public*, pg. 515
Carpenter, Chadwick H., Jr., Sr. V.P.-Corp. Devel.--Progress Software Corporation, Bedford, MA; *U.S. Public*, pg. 1334
Carpenter, James A., Sr. V.P.--First National Bank of Ohio, Akron, OH; *U.S. Public*, pg. 646
Carpenter, Jan, Sr. V.P., Fin. Dir. & Opers. Dir.--Hal Riney & Partners, Inc., San Francisco, CA; *U.S. Private*, pg. 931
Carpenter, Lewis H., Sr. V.P.-Intl.--FileNet Corporation, Costa Mesa, CA; *U.S. Public*, pg. 622
Carpenter, Robert C., Sr. V.P.--Policy Management Systems Corporation, Blythewood, SC; *U.S. Public*, pg. 1314
Carpenter, Robert L., Jr., Sr. V.P. & Controller--First Maryland Bancorp, Baltimore, MD; *Int'l*, pg. 64
Carpenter, Scott R., V.P.-Sls.--Bachman Company, Reading, PA; *U.S. Private*, pg. 109
Carr, David, Chief Fin. Officer, Sr. V.P. & Sec.--Latshaw Enterprises, Inc., Wichita, KS; *U.S. Public*, pg. 979
Carr, Ed, Sr. V.P.-Admin.--Steelcase Inc., Grand Rapids, MI; *U.S. Private*, pg. 1038
Carr, Jerome H., Chief Fin. Officer & Sr. V.P.--Reliance Insurance Company, Philadelphia, PA; *U.S. Public*, pg. 1374
Carr, Joseph J., Sr. V.P.--American Home Products Corporation, Madison, NJ; *U.S. Public*, pg. 79
Carr, Linda, Sr. V.P.-Property Opers.--Berkshire Realty Company, Inc., Boston, MA; *U.S. Public*, pg. 221
Carr, Robin, Sr. V.P. & Brand Mktg. Partner--DMB&B Detroit, Troy, MI; *U.S. Private*, pg. 302
Carr, Tom, Sr. V.P.-Brand Opers.--Harrah's Entertainment, Inc., Memphis, TN; *U.S. Public*, pg. 790
Carrabba, Lori, Sr. V.P. & Production Dir.--Girgenti, Hughes, Butler & McDowell, New York, NY; *U.S. Private*, pg. 455
Carrey, Mark, Chief Fin. Officer & Sr. V.P.-Fin.--Signature Inns, Inc., Indianapolis, IN; *U.S. Public*, pg. 1473
Carrico, David E., Sr. V.P.-Sls.--Churchill Downs, Inc., Louisville, KY; *U.S. Public*, pg. 356
Carrier, Jean-Jacques, Chief Fin. Officer & Sr. V.P.-Fin.--Mitel Corporation, Kanata, Canada; *Int'l*, pg. 870
Carriere, Michelle A., Sr. V.P.--Hibernia Corporation, New Orleans, LA; *U.S. Public*, pg. 825
Carrigan, Ralph, Sr. V.P. & Dir.-Loan Admin.--Barclays American/Mortgage Corp., Charlotte, NC; *Int'l*, pg. 165
Carrizosa, Fernando, Sr. V.P.--The Wackenhut Corporation, Palm Beach Gardens, FL; *U.S. Public*, pg. 1731
Carroll, Angus J., Sr. V.P.--Medicus Systems Corporation, Evanston, IL; *U.S. Public*, pg. 1080
Carroll, Anthony J., Chief Fin. Officer & Sr. V.P.--Au Bon Pain Co., Inc., Boston, MA; *U.S. Public*, pg. 146
Carroll, Dennis C., Chief Fin. Officer & Sr. V.P.-Fin. & Admin.--The Good Guys, Inc., Brisbane, CA; *U.S. Public*, pg. 750
Carroll, Gerard P., Sr. V.P.-Mfg. & Engrng.--National Gypsum Company, Charlotte, NC; *Int'l*, pg. 790
Carroll, J. Martin, Sr. V.P.-Managed Care--Merck Human Health Division (U.S. Human Health), West Point, PA; *U.S. Public*, pg. 1091
Carroll, John S., Sr. V.P. & Editor--The Baltimore Sun Newspapers, Baltimore, MD; *U.S. Public*, pg. 1616
Carroll, Kenneth P., Sr. V.P. & Gen. Counsel--United Retail Group, Inc., Rochelle Park, NJ; *U.S. Public*, pg. 1679
Carroll, Ron, Sr. V.P. & Acct. Dir.--Young & Rubicam New York, New York, NY; *U.S. Private*, pg. 1198
Carrothers, P.C., Sr. V.P.-Opers.--Imperial Holly Corporation, Sugar Land, TX; *U.S. Public*, pg. 872
Carrubba, Sc.D., Sr. V.P.--Calgon Carbon Corporation, Pittsburgh, PA; *U.S. Public*, pg. 292
Carson, Charles, Sr. V.P.-Mktg. & Sls.--Genesee Corporation, Rochester, NY; *U.S. Public*, pg. 728
Carson, Tom, Chief Fin. Officer & Sr. V.P.--Spelling Television, Los Angeles, CA; *U.S. Private*, pg. 776
Carson, William K., Sr. V.P.--NationsBank West, Saint Louis, MO; *U.S. Public*, pg. 1164
Carter, David L., Sr. V.P.--Roberts & Schaefer Company-Salt Lake City, Salt Lake City, UT; *U.S. Private*, pg. 371
Carter, Frederick R., Sr. V.P.-Taxes & Insurance--Citizens Savings Bank, Providence, RI; *Int'l*, pg. 1132
Carter, Jerry N, Sr. V.P.-Human Resources--Union Camp Corporation, Wayne, NJ; *U.S. Public*, pg. 1665
Carter, Joe M., Jr., Sr. V.P. & Dir.-Interim Loan Admin.--Barclays American/Mortgage Corp., Charlotte, NC; *Int'l*, pg. 165
Carter, Kimball G., Sr. V.P. & Creative Dir.--EURO RSCG Dahlin Smith White, LLC, Salt Lake City, UT; *U.S. Private*, pg. 384
Carter, Mark, Sr. V.P.-Mktg.--American Express Financial Advisor, Minneapolis, MN; *U.S. Public*, pg. 73
Carter, Ray, Sr. V.P.--M & I Thunderbird Bank, Phoenix, AZ; *U.S. Public*, pg. 1050
Carter, Richard, Sr. V.P.-Res. & Prod. Mngmt.--National Bank of Canada, Montreal, Canada; *Int'l*, pg. 907
Carter, Robert D., Sr. V.P. & Asst. Sec.--Regency Finance Company, Hermitage, PA; *U.S. Public*, pg. 607
Carteris, George, Chief Fin. Officer & Sr. V.P.--Lowe McAdams Healthcare, New York, NY; *U.S. Private*, pg. 678
Carton, Bernard, Chief Fin. Officer & Sr. V.P.--Sodexho S.A., Montigny-le-Bretonneux, France; *Int'l*, pg. 1274
Cartwright, William C., Sr. V.P.-BankCard Div.--First Security Service Company, Salt Lake City, UT; *U.S. Public*, pg. 638
Carty, Douglas A., Chief Fin. Officer & Sr. V.P.-Fin.--Canadian Airlines Corporation, Calgary, Canada; *Int'l*, pg. 255
Carty, Douglas A., Chief Fin. Officer & Sr. V.P.--Canadian Airlines International Ltd., Calgary, Canada; *Int'l*, pg. 256
Carty, Michael A., Sr. V.P.--Terre Haute First National Bank, Terre Haute, IN; *U.S. Public*, pg. 634
Caruso, Carl, Sr. V.P.--Aeroflex Laboratories Inc., Plainview, NY; *U.S. Public*, pg. 24
Caruso, Dominic J., Chief Fin. Officer & Sr. V.P.--Centocor, Inc., Malvern, PA; *U.S. Public*, pg. 323
Carvalho, Jean, Sr. V.P. & Corp. Sec.--BankAtlantic Bancorp, Inc., Fort Lauderdale, FL; *U.S. Public*, pg. 183
Cary, Walter L., Sr. V.P. & Trust Officer--Security Bank & Trust Co., Vincennes, IN; *U.S. Public*, pg. 1217
Casadesus, Penelope, Sr. V.P. & Grp. Media Dir.--Grey Advertising Inc., New York, NY; *U.S. Public*, pg. 764
Casale, Michael J., Sr. V.P.-Direct Mktg.--American Bankers Life Assurance Co. of Florida, Miami, FL; *U.S. Public*, pg. 67
Casciani, William, Sr. V.P.-Opers. & Admin.--Arnhold and S. Bleichroeder, Inc., New York, NY; *U.S. Private*, pg. 83
Cascio, William M., Sr. V.P. & Dir.-Global Franchise Wine Grp.--Brown-Forman Beverages Worldwide, Louisville, KY; *U.S. Public*, pg. 261
Case, Daniel H., Sr. V.P. & Gen. Mgr.-Voice Messaging Div.--Glenayre Electronics, Inc., Quincy, IL; *U.S. Public*, pg. 747
Case, Janice, Sr. V.P.-Energy Solutions--Florida Power Corporation, Saint Petersburg, FL; *U.S. Public*, pg. 655
Case, Jeanne, Sr. V.P. & Mngmt. Supvr.--Dailey & Associates, West Hollywood, CA; *U.S. Public*, pg. 909
Case, Paul, Chief Info. Officer & Sr. V.P.--ADVO, Inc., Windsor, CT; *U.S. Public*, pg. 23
Casebolt, Victor A., Sr. V.P.-Indus. Pkgng.--International Paper Company, Purchase, NY; *U.S. Public*, pg. 901
Casey, Michael, Chief Fin. Officer & Sr. V.P.--Starbucks Coffee Company, Seattle, WA; *U.S. Public*, pg. 1510
Casey, Mike, Chief Fin. Officer & Sr. V.P.--The William Carter Company, Morrow, GA; *U.S. Private*, pg. 217
Casey, Neil P., Sr. V.P. & Creative Dir.--Cramer-Krasselt, Milwaukee, WI; *U.S. Private*, pg. 286
Cash, Charles R., Sr. V.P. & Reg. Exec. Officer--First Virginia Banks, Inc., Falls Church, VA; *U.S. Public*, pg. 641
Casper, Wayne, Exec. V.P.-Mktg.--Sargento Foods Inc., Plymouth, WI; *U.S. Private*, pg. 966
Caspers, Warner, Sr. V.P.--THP United Enterprises, Waukesha, WI; *Int'l*, pg. 1061
Caspersen, Dan, Sr. V.P.-Community Rels.--Mervyn's California, Hayward, CA; *U.S. Public*, pg. 489
Cassel, Calvin L., Jr., Sr. V.P.-Opers. Grp.--Lebanon Valley Farmers Bank, Lebanon, PA; *U.S. Public*, pg. 688
Cassel, Michael E., Chief Admin. Officer & Sr. V.P.--Willis Corroon Corp. of California, San Francisco, CA; *Int'l*, pg. 1505
Cassidy, Charles T., Sr. V.P.-Mktg. & Prod. Devel.--State Street Bank & Trust Co., Boston, MA; *U.S. Public*, pg. 1513

Cassidy, Charles T., Sr. V.P. & Mng. Dir.--State Street Bank & Trust Co., London, London, United Kingdom; *U.S. Public*, pg. 1513

Cassidy, John, Sr. V.P.-Opers.--Yaffe & Company, Southfield, MI; *U.S. Private*, pg. 1195

Cassidy, Michael P., Sr. V.P. & Gen. Mgr.-Computer Telephony Prod. Grp.--Artisoft, Inc., Tucson, AZ; *U.S. Public*, pg. 136

Cassidy, Rick, V.P.-Military & Aerospace--National Semiconductor Corporation, Santa Clara, CA; *U.S. Public*, pg. 1159

Castagnola, Dennis, Sr. V.P.-Proprietary Prods.--The Coast Distribution System, San Jose, CA; *U.S. Public*, pg. 388

Castaldi, Alexander, Chief Fin. Officer & Sr. V.P.--Kendall Healthcare Products Company, Mansfield, MA; *U.S. Public*, pg. 1647

Castell, J. Ronald, Sr. V.P.-Investor Rels. & Communications--Florida Panthers Holdings, Inc., Fort Lauderdale, FL; *U.S. Public*, pg. 654

Castell, J. Ronald, Sr. V.P.-Commun. Strategy & Svc.--Republic Industries, Inc., Fort Lauderdale, FL; *U.S. Public*, pg. 1378

Castellana, Angelo D., Sr. V.P.--EG & G, Inc., Wellesley, MA; *U.S. Public*, pg. 542

Castellana, Michael, Sr. V.P.-Retail Opers.--Western Beef, Inc., Ridgewood, NY; *U.S. Public*, pg. 1758

Castellano, Michael J., Sr. V.P. & Controller--Merrill Lynch & Co., Inc., New York, NY; *U.S. Public*, pg. 1097

Castilla, Craig K., Sr. V.P.--Rothschild Inc., New York, NY; *U.S. Private*, pg. 947

Castillon, Pierre, Sr. V.P.-Res., Tech. & Environment--Elf Aquitane, Paris, France; *Int'l*, pg. 444

Castle, Donald M., Sr. V.P.--California State Bank, West Covina, CA; *U.S. Public*, pg. 294

Casullo, D.T., Sr. V.P. & Gen. Mgr.-Conroc--Burrows Paper Corporation, Little Falls, NY; *U.S. Private*, pg. 188

Caswell, Hollis, Chief Oper. Officer-Advanced Energy Industry, Fort Collins, CO; *U.S. Public*, pg. 20

Catalano, Joe, Sr. V.P.-Sls./Fortis Long Term Care--Time Insurance, Milwaukee, WI; *Int'l*, pg. 499

Catalano, Joe, Sr. V.P.-Mdsg. & Opers.--Strauss Discount Auto, South River, NJ; *U.S. Private*, pg. 1046

Cataldo, Jerome, Sr. V.P.-Fin. & Sys.--Hostmark Management Group, Rolling Meadows, IL; *U.S. Private*, pg. 541

Catchpole, Sherry, Sr. V.P.-Opers.--Western Interactive Media, Los Angeles, CA; *U.S. Private*, pg. 1166

Catlin, John N., Sr. V.P.-Comml. Banking--The Provident Bank, Cincinnati, OH; *U.S. Public*, pg. 1338

Catron, William G., Chief Admin. Officer, Exec. V.P. & Gen. Counsel--Galoob Toys, Inc., South San Francisco, CA; *U.S. Public*, pg. 698

Catto, W. Martin, Chief Fin. Officer & Sr. V.P.-Fin.--Harlequin Enterprises Ltd., Don Mills, Canada; *Int'l*, pg. 1402

Cattreuw, Bernard, Sr. V.P.-Support--Airbus Industrie, Blagnac, France; *Int'l*, pg. 39

Caudle, Jerry W., Sr. V.P.-West--Waste Management, Inc., Oak Brook, IL; *U.S. Public*, pg. 1744

Caufield, William E., Sr. V.P.--John Hancock Mutual Life Insurance Company, Boston, MA; *U.S. Private*, pg. 589

Cauley, Bruce, Sr. V.P.-Devel.--The Dyson-Kissner-Moran Corporation, New York, NY; *U.S. Private*, pg. 351

Causey, Alan, Sr. V.P., Social Analysis & Forecasts Dir.--Ammirati, Puris & Lintas, Inc., New York, NY; *U.S. Private*, pg. 66

Causey, J.P., Jr., Sr. V.P., Gen. Counsel & Sec.--Chesapeake Corporation, Richmond, VA; *U.S. Public*, pg. 346

Cavalle, Bill, Chief Fin. Officer & Sr. V.P.-Fin.--Chief Auto Parts, Dallas, TX; *U.S. Private*, pg. 236

Cavanagh, Jan, Sr. V.P. & Local Brdcst. Dir.--Media Partnership Corporation, Norwalk, CT; *U.S. Private*, pg. 1168

Cavanaugh, Andrew J., Sr. V.P.-H.R.--Estee Lauder Companies Inc., New York, NY; *U.S. Public*, pg. 594

Cavanaugh, Terrence W., Sr. V.P.--Chubb & Son, Inc., Warren, NJ; *U.S. Public*, pg. 355

Cavanaugh, Valerie, Sr. V.P.-Business & Legal Affairs--UPN-United Paramount Network, Los Angeles, CA; *U.S. Public*, pg. 352

Cavanaugh, Valerie, Sr. V.P.-Business & Legal Affairs--UPN-United Paramount Network, Los Angeles, CA; *U.S. Private*, pg. 777

Cavanaugh, W. Scott, Sr. V.P.--Citizens Mortgage Corporation, Atlanta, GA; *Int'l*, pg. 1132

Cave, Jack, Sr. V.P.-Production Services--ICO, Inc., Houston, TX; *U.S. Public*, pg. 853

Cavin, Wylie D., III, Sr. V.P.--Rapides Bank & Trust Company of Alexandria, Alexandria, LA; *U.S. Public*, pg. 630

Cawen, Klaus, Sr. V.P.-Acquisions & Gen. Counsel--Kone Corporation, Helsinki, Finland; *Int'l*, pg. 746

Cawley, Jim, Sr. V.P.-Mktg. & Sls.--GRP Records, New York, NY; *Int'l*, pg. 1215

Cawley, John M., Sr. V.P.-Engrng.--TII Industries, Inc., Copiague, NY; *U.S. Public*, pg. 1556

Cazenave, Ira Paul, Sr. V.P.--Hibernia Corporation, New Orleans, LA; *U.S. Public*, pg. 825

Cearlock, Dennis B., Dr., Sr. V.P.--Battelle Memorial Institute, Columbus, OH; *U.S. Private*, pg. 123

Cecere, Domenico, Chief Fin. Officer & Sr. V.P.--Owens Corning, Toledo, OH; *U.S. Public*, pg. 1236

Ceconi, Roberto G., Sr. V.P.-Corp. Engrng.--Phillips Petroleum Company, Bartlesville, OK; *U.S. Public*, pg. 1290

Cefalo, Romeo R., Sr. V.P. & Gen. Mgr.--Lucky Stores Southern California Division, Buena Park, CA; *U.S. Public*, pg. 93

Cellers, Pat, Sr. V.P. & Mgr.-Admin.--Willis Corroon Corp. of Eugene, Eugene, OR; *Int'l*, pg. 1505

Cenatiempo, John, Sr. V.P.-Creative Services--Biederman, Kelly & Shaffer, Inc., New York, NY; *U.S. Private*, pg. 142

Cephus, Will, Sr. V.P.-Sls. & Mktg.--The Arnold Palmer Golf Company, Ooltewah, TN; *U.S. Public*, pg. 132

Cerf, Vinton G., Sr. V.P.-Internet Engrng.--MCI Communications Corp., Atlanta, GA; *U.S. Public*, pg. 1023

Cerminaro, Gail, Sr. V.P. & Mngmt. Supvr.--The Sawtooth Group, Woodbridge, NJ; *U.S. Private*, pg. 969

Cerniglia, John, Sr. V.P., Acct. Services Dir. & Mngmt. Supvr.--Kovel Kresser & Partners, Santa Monica, CA; *U.S. Private*, pg. 634

Cernugel, William J., Sr. V.P.-Fin. & Controller--Alberto-Culver Company, Melrose Park, IL; *U.S. Public*, pg. 37

Cerra, Enzo, Sr. V.P.-Mdsg.--Eckerd Corporation, Largo, FL; *U.S. Public*, pg. 917

Cerrato, John, Sr. V.P.-Corp. Svcs.--Mutual of America Life Insurance Company, New York, NY; *U.S. Private*, pg. 769

Cezauru, Nat, Sr. V.P.-Sls. & Mktg.--4C Foods Corporation, Brooklyn, NY; *U.S. Private*, pg. 421

Chabot, Claude, Sr. V.P.-Popcorn Communications--Cineplex Odeon Corporation, Toronto, Canada; *Int'l*, pg. 292

Chabre, Jean R., Sr. V.P.--Merck Human Health Division, Rahway, NJ; *U.S. Public*, pg. 1090

Chadburn, Carl T., Sr. V.P.-Human Resources--Phoenix Home Life Mutual Insurance Co., Hartford, CT; *U.S. Private*, pg. 863

Chaddock, H.W., Sr. V.P.--Columbia Gas System Service Corp., Wilmington, DE; *U.S. Public*, pg. 403

Chaffee, John C., Jr., Sr. V.P. & Pres.-Television Div.--Malrite Communications Group, Inc., Cleveland, OH; *U.S. Private*, pg. 698

Chahil, Satjiv S., Sr. V.P.-Worldwide Corp. Mktg.--Apple Computer, Inc., Cupertino, CA; *U.S. Public*, pg. 121

Chalermtiaranakul, Somnuk, Sr. V.P.--Siam City Credit Finance & Securities Co., Ltd., Bangkok, Thailand; *Int'l*, pg. 1239

Chalfin, Marc, Sr. V.P.--New York Life Insurance Company, New York, NY; *U.S. Private*, pg. 794

Chalifoux, Michael T., Chief Fin. Officer, Sr. V.P. & Sec.--Circuit City Stores, Inc., Richmond, VA; *U.S. Public*, pg. 374

Challis, Georgina, Sr. V.P.-Corp. Communications & Legal Counsel--BPI Communications Inc., New York, NY; *Int'l*, pg. 1446

Chamberlain, George M., Jr., Sr. V.P. & Sec.--Delaware Management Holdings, Inc., Philadelphia, PA; *U.S. Public*, pg. 997

Chamberlain, Michael, Sr. V.P.--Norwest Mortgage, Inc., Des Moines, IA; *U.S. Public*, pg. 1202

Chamberlain, Michael D., Sr. V.P. & Pres.-SCT Software Group--Systems & Computer Technology Corporation, Malvern, PA; *U.S. Public*, pg. 1552

Chambers, Donald C., Sr. V.P. & Chief Medical Officer--Lincoln National Reinsurance Company (Bermuda) Limited, Fort Wayne, IN; *U.S. Public*, pg. 998

Chambers, Donald C., M.D., Sr. V.P. & Chief Medical Dir.--The Lincoln National Life Insurance Co., Fort Wayne, IN; *U.S. Public*, pg. 998

Chambers, Donald C., M.D., Sr. V.P.--Lincoln National Health & Casualty Insurance Co., Fort Wayne, IN; *U.S. Public*, pg. 998

Chambers, Donald C., M.D., Sr. V.P. & Chief Medical Dir.--Lincoln National Reinsurance Company (Barbados) Limited, Fort Wayne, IN; *U.S. Public*, pg. 998

Chambers, Ed, Chief Fin. Officer & Sr. V.P.--Wawa, Inc., Media, PA; *U.S. Private*, pg. 1155

Chambers, J.V., Sr. V.P.--TNP Enterprises, Inc., Fort Worth, TX; *U.S. Public*, pg. 1557

Chambers, Jack V., Sr. V.P. & Chief Customer Officer--Texas-New Mexico Power Co., Fort Worth, TX; *U.S. Public*, pg. 1557

Chambers, William S., Sr. V.P.-Engrng. & Sec.--Kingsbury, Inc., Philadelphia, PA; *U.S. Private*, pg. 622

Chambolle, Thierry, Sr. V.P.-Strategy & Tech--Lyonnaise des Eaux S.A., Nanterre, France; *Int'l*, pg. 822

Champagne, George R., Chief Fin. Officer & Sr. V.P.--Service Corporation International, Houston, TX; *U.S. Public*, pg. 1460

Champagne, Rene, Sr. V.P.--ITT Information Services, Inc., New York, NY; *U.S. Public*, pg. 1512

Champion, Geoffrey, Sr. V.P.--Dataquest Incorporated, San Jose, CA; *U.S. Public*, pg. 535

Champley, Michael E., Sr. V.P.-Customer Energy Solutions--DTE Energy Company, Detroit, MI; *U.S. Public*, pg. 475

Champvillard, Pierre-Denis, Grp. Sr. V.P.--SCOR, Paris, France; *Int'l*, pg. 1152

Chan, Agnes, Sr. V.P.-Shareholder Services--Mackenzie Financial Corporation, Toronto, Canada; *Int'l*, pg. 828

Chan, Ricky, Exec. V.P.-Far East Opers. & Sr. V.P.-Prod. Devel.--Russ Berrie and Company, Inc., Oakland, NJ; *U.S. Public*, pg. 222

Chandler, Howard, J., Sr. V.P. & Chief Admin. Officer--LucasVarity Inc., Buffalo, NY; *Int'l*, pg. 820

Chandler, John F., Sr. V.P.-Mktg. & Pipelines--Western Gas Resources, Inc., Denver, CO; *U.S. Public*, pg. 1758

Chandler, William E., Chief Fin. Officer, Sr. V.P.-Fin. & Sec.--Hunt Corporation, Philadelphia, PA; *U.S. Public*, pg. 848

Chandonnet, Noel A., Sr. V.P.--Government Employees Insurance Co. (GEICO), Washington, DC; *U.S. Public*, pg. 220

Chandran, Clarence J., Pres.-Northern Telecom CALA & Sr. V.P.--Northern Telecom Limited, Brampton, Canada; *Int'l*, pg. 968

Chang, David J.W., Sr. V.P. & Mgr.-Info. Svcs.--Central Pacific Bank, Honolulu, HI; *U.S. Public*, pg. 283

Chang, Erf-Hsun, Sr. V.P. & Gen. Mgr.-Far East--Logitech International SA, Morges, Switzerland; *Int'l*, pg. 815

Chang, Gareth C.C., Sr. V.P.-Mktg.--Hughes Electronics Corporation, Westchester, CA; *U.S. Public*, pg. 720

Chang, Yeong-Ho, Sr. V.P. & Country Mgr.--Bank of America NT&SA, Seoul, Korea; *U.S. Public*, pg. 182

Chang, Ying-Ying, Sr. V.P. & Gen. Mgr.-Data Processing & Information Dept.--The International Commercial Bank of China, Taipei, Taiwan; *Int'l*, pg. 683

Chant, Phil, Sr. V.P.-Media Dir. (CCL)--Maritime Telegraph & Telephone Company, Ltd., Halifax, Canada; *Int'l*, pg. 116

Chapel, Burdette, Sr. V.P.--Capital Development Co., Lacey, WA; *U.S. Private*, pg. 205

Chapman, Curtis, Sr. V.P.-Flowers Bakeries, Inc.--Flowers Industries, Inc., Thomasville, GA; *U.S. Public*, pg. 656

Chapman, Donald, Sr. V.P.--SAFECO Property & Casualty Insurance Companies, Seattle, WA; *U.S. Public*, pg. 1423

Chapman, John G., Sr. V.P.-Cashier--SouthTrust Bank of Charleston, Charleston, SC; *U.S. Public*, pg. 1492

Chapman, Laurence A., Chief Fin. Officer & Sr. V.P.--Rohr, Inc., Chula Vista, CA; *U.S. Public*, pg. 751

Chapman, Richard E., Chief Info. Officer & Sr. V.P.--Vencor, Inc., Louisville, KY; *U.S. Public*, pg. 1711

Chapman, Wayne P., Sr. V.P.-Investment Svcs.--The Bank of Bermuda Limited, Hamilton, Bermuda; *Int'l*, pg. 150

Chapple, Thomas L., Sr. V.P., Gen. Counsel & Sec.--Gannett Company, Inc., Arlington, VA; *U.S. Public*, pg. 698

Charbanic, Diane, Sr. V.P.-Coop Adv.--New Line Cinema Corporation, New York, NY; *U.S. Public*, pg. 1614

Charbonnet, Michael D., Sr. V.P. & Comptroller--Whitney Holding Corporation, New Orleans, LA; *U.S. Public*, pg. 1766

Chardawoyne, David C., Sr. V.P.--United Water Management & Services, Harrington Park, NJ; *U.S. Public*, pg. 1692

Charette, Albert E., Sr. V.P.-Mdsg.--Encore Shoe Corporation, Rochester, NH; *U.S. Private*, pg. 375

Charlesworth, Tom G., Sr. V.P.--Cousins Properties Incorporated, Atlanta, GA; *U.S. Public*, pg. 453

Charlton, Samuel H., III, Sr. V.P.--American Oil & Gas Corporation, Houston, TX; *U.S. Public*, pg. 937

Charpiot, Frederic H., Sr. V.P.-Credit Admin.--San Jose National Bank, San Jose, CA; *U.S. Public*, pg. 1418

Chartron, M., Sr. V.P.-Servive Bus.--Kone Corporation, Helsinki, Finland; *Int'l*, pg. 746

Chase, Andrew, Sr. V.P. & Mng. Dir.-Dir. Mail--Western International Media Corporation, Los Angeles, CA; *U.S. Private*, pg. 1165

Chase, Doug, Sr. V.P.-Entertainment--Western International Media Corporation, Burbank, CA; *U.S. Private*, pg. 1166

Chase, G.C., Sr. V.P.-Business Devel.--Ranger Oil Limited, Calgary, Canada; *Int'l*, pg. 1086

Chastain, Judy, Sr. V.P.-Media Services--Turner Broadcasting System Inc., Atlanta, GA; *U.S. Public*, pg. 1614

Chatelain, R. Blake, Sr. V.P.--Rapides Bank & Trust Company of Alexandria, Alexandria, LA; *U.S. Public*, pg. 630

Chattaway, D.N., Sr. V.P.-Acquistions--Hinckley & Schmitt, Inc., Chicago, IL; *Int'l*, pg. 1322

Chauncey, Paula E., Sr. V.P.-Loan Review--BayBanks, Inc., Boston, MA; *U.S. Public*, pg. 184

Chavez, Art, Sr. V.P. & Grp. Acct. Supvr.-GHG--Grey Healthcare Group, New York, NY; *U.S. Public*, pg. 765

Chavez, Richard C., Chief Oper. Officer & Sr. V.P.-Asia--Costco Wholesale, Issaquah, WA; *U.S. Public*, pg. 451

Chavez, Susan, Chief Fin. Officer & Sr. V.P.--Mendoza, Dillon & Asociados, Inc., Newport Beach, CA; *Int'l*, pg. 1483

Cheatham, John B., Sr. V.P.--Atlantic Richfield Company, Los Angeles, CA; *U.S. Public*, pg. 144

Checchia, John, Sr. V.P. & Gen. Mgr.--Media Printing Corporation, Pompano Beach, FL; *U.S. Private*, pg. 726

Chee, Felix, Sr. V.P. & Treas.--Manulife Financial (The Manufacturers Life Insurance Company), Toronto, Canada; *Int'l*, pg. 840

Cheema, Manjit S., Chief Fin. Officer & Sr. V.P.--TNP Enterprises, Inc., Fort Worth, TX; *U.S. Public*, pg. 1557

Cheesbrough, Peter H., Chief Fin. Officer & Sr. V.P.-Fin.--Echo Bay Mines Ltd., Englewood, CO; *U.S. Public*, pg. 561

Chen, Ching-Lo, Sr. V.P. & Gen. Mgr.--The International Commercial Bank of China, Vancouver, Canada; *Int'l*, pg. 684

Chen, Heng W., Sr. V.P.-Fin. & Controller--City National Corporation, Beverly Hills, CA; *U.S. Public*, pg. 380

Chen, Terry, Chief Fin. Officer & Sr. V.P.--Allright Corporation, Houston, TX; *U.S. Private*, pg. 42

Cheney, Jeff, Sr. V.P., & Gen. Counsel--Atari Games Corporation, Milpitas, CA; *U.S. Public*, pg. 1727

Cheng, Eng Hwee, Sr. V.P.-Corp. Affairs--Superior Metal Printing Limited, Singapore, Singapore; *Int'l*, pg. 1322

Cheng, Sheng-Shan, Sr. V.P. & Superintendent--The International Commercial Bank of China, Taipei, Taiwan; *Int'l*, pg. 683

Cheon, Hee Kyoon, Sr. V.P.-Engrng.--Korean Airlines Co., Ltd., Seoul, Korea; *Int'l*, pg. 758

Cheong, Ng Cheng, Sr. V.P.-Supply & Transportation--Singapore Petroleum Company Ltd., Singapore, Singapore; *U.S. Public*, pg. 102

Chernock, Maria, Sr. V.P. & Mngmt. Supvr.--Thomas G. Ferguson Associates, Inc., Parsippany, NJ; *Int'l*, pg. 1483

Chervony, Anne, Sr. V.P.-Risk Mngmt.--BankAtlantic Bancorp, Inc., Fort Lauderdale, FL; *U.S. Public*, pg. 183

Cheskis, Herbert L., Sr. V.P.-Northeastern Agencies--New York Life Insurance Company, New York, NY; *U.S. Private*, pg. 794

Chesler, Randall M., Sr. V.P.-Member Rels.--Visa U.S.A. Inc., San Francisco, CA; *U.S. Private*, pg. 1141

Chester, Arthur N., Sr. V.P.--Hughes Electronics Corporation, Westchester, CA; *U.S. Public*, pg. 720

Chester, Kenneth A., Sr. V.P.-Circulation--Women's Magazines Group, New York, NY; *Int'l*, pg. 190

Chestnut, James E., Chief Fin. Officer & Sr. V.P.--The Coca-Cola Company, Atlanta, GA; *U.S. Public*, pg. 392

Chestnut, Kathie T., Sr. V.P.-Res. & Devel., Quality Assurance & Pur.--Wendy's International Inc., Dublin, OH; *U.S. Public*, pg. 1754

Chevalier, Joseph, Sr. V.P.-Intl.--LaSalle National Bank, Chicago, IL; *Int'l*, pg. 10

Chewens, Michael J., Sr. V.P.-Control Grp.--NBT Bancorp Inc., Norwich, NY; *U.S. Public*, pg. 1144

Cheyne, Robert S., Sr. V.P. & Grp. Acct. Dir.--Hill, Holliday, Connors, Cosmopulos, Inc., Boston, MA; *U.S. Private*, pg. 529

Chianciola, Trudy, Sr. V.P.-Store Opers.--Hit or Miss, Inc., Stoughton, MA; *U.S. Private*, pg. 531

Chiappetta, Carmen M., Sr. V.P. & Mgr.-Electrical Dept.--Sargent & Lundy, Chicago, IL; *U.S. Private*, pg. 965

Chiarella, Philip V., Sr. V.P.--Bauer Sports Inc., Montreal, Canada; *U.S. Public*, pg. 1184

Chiarello, Richard, Sr. V.P.-Sls.--Computer Associates International, Inc., Islandia, NY; *U.S. Public*, pg. 420

Chiavelli, Dennis, Sr. V.P.-Opers.--Smart & Final, Vernon, CA; *Int'l*, pg. 563

Chiba, Masato, Sr. V.P.--NEC Corporation, Tokyo, Japan; *Int'l*, pg. 899

Chicco, Louis, Sr. V.P.--Heritage Air Systems, Inc., Deer Park, NY; *U.S. Public*, pg. 572

Chicoine, Jerry, Chief Fin. Officer & Sr. V.P.--Pioneer Hi-Bred International, Inc., Des Moines, IA; *U.S. Public*, pg. 1298

Chicoine, Michelle L., Chief Fin. Officer, Sr. V.P. & Treas.--EnergyNorth, Inc., Manchester, NH; *U.S. Public*, pg. 581

Chihaya, Akira, Sr. V.P.--Nippon Steel Corporation, Tokyo, Japan; *Int'l*, pg. 939

Chik, Alex, Sr. V.P. & Acct. Dir.--Media Partnership Corporation, Norwalk, CT; *U.S. Private*, pg. 1168

Chikamoto, Alwyn, Sr. V.P. & Mgr.-Corp. Banking Div.--Central Pacific Bank, Honolulu, HI; *U.S. Public*, pg. 283

Child, Betsy L., Sr. V.P.-Economic Devel.--Tennessee Valley Authority, Knoxville, TN; *U.S. Public*, pg. 1580

Childers, Mark V., Sr. V.P.-Organizational Devel. & Human Resources--Champion International Corp., Stamford, CT; *U.S. Public*, pg. 333

Childs, Bill W., Sr. V.P.-Product Mngmt.--HBO & Company/Cycare Business Group, Scottsdale, AZ; *U.S. Public*, pg. 770

Childs, Frank L., Sr. V.P.--EnergyNorth, Inc., Manchester, NH; *U.S. Public*, pg. 581

Chiles, James, Sr.-V.P.-Prod.--Early Times Distillers Co., Louisville, KY; *U.S. Public*, pg. 261

Chiles, James, Sr. V.P.-Production--Clintock Limited, Dublin, Ireland; *U.S. Public*, pg. 262

Chiles, James B., Sr. V.P.-Brown-Forman Distillery Co.--Brown-Forman Beverages Worldwide, Louisville, KY; *U.S. Public*, pg. 261

Chilibeck, Peter, Sr. V.P.-Legal Affairs--Imax Corporation, Mississauga, Canada; *Int'l*, pg. 661

Chilton, John B., Sr. V.P.-Global Opers.--Estee Lauder Companies Inc., New York, NY; *U.S. Public*, pg. 594

Chin, Frederick, Sr. V.P. & Country Mgr.--Bank of America Malaysia Berhad, Kuala Lumpur, Malaysia; *U.S. Public*, pg. 182

Chin, Kai J., Sr. V.P.-East Asia Division--Bank of Hawaii, Honolulu, HI; *U.S. Public*, pg. 1248

Ching, Alan, Sr. V.P., Media Plng. & Res. Dir.--Hal Riney & Partners, Inc., San Francisco, CA; *U.S. Private*, pg. 931

Ching, David, Chief Information Officer & Sr. V.P.--Safeway Inc., Pleasanton, CA; *U.S. Public*, pg. 1426

Ching, Patrick D., Sr. V.P. & Treas.--Servco Pacific Inc., Honolulu, HI; *U.S. Private*, pg. 986

Chiono, Pat, Sr. V.P. & Creative Dir.--DMB&B New York, New York, NY; *U.S. Private*, pg. 302

Chipego, Albert J., Sr. V.P.--Commonwealth Relocation Services, Inc., Philadelphia, PA; *U.S. Public*, pg. 1374

Chirico, Carl F., Pres.-Southern Region--BNY Holdings (New Jersey) Corp., West Paterson, NJ; *U.S. Public*, pg. 178

Chisholm, John R., Sr. V.P.--Acadian Asset Management, Boston, MA; *U.S. Public*, pg. 1672

Chitwood, Frank W., Sr. V.P. & Asst. Sec.--Dewberry Design Group, Oklahoma City, OK; *U.S. Private*, pg. 329

Chitwood, James L., Dr., Sr. V.P.--Eastman Chemical Company, Kingsport, TN; *U.S. Public*, pg. 550

Chizick, Jerry, Sr. V.P.--Corporate Foods Ltd., Etobicoke, Canada; *Int'l*, pg. 841

Chmiel, Mark, Sr. V.P. & Acct. Dir.--Young & Rubicam New York, New York, NY; *U.S. Private*, pg. 1198

Chmura, John A., Sr. V.P.-Sls.--Aerovox Inc., New Bedford, MA; *U.S. Public*, pg. 25

Cho, Young-Han, Sr. V.P.-Fin., Acct. & Auditing--Korean Airlines Co., Ltd., Seoul, Korea; *Int'l*, pg. 758

Choat, James E., Sr. V.P.-Field Mngmt.--American Express Financial Advisor, Minneapolis, MN; *U.S. Public*, pg. 73

Choate, Chris A., Sr. V.P., Gen. Counsel & Sec.--AmeriCredit Corp., Fort Worth, TX; *U.S. Public*, pg. 96

Cholnoky, I. John, Sr. V.P.--General Reinsurance Corp., Stamford, CT; *U.S. Public*, pg. 725

Chomakos, James, Sr. V.P. & Mgr.-Mktg. Admin.--First Federal of Michigan, Detroit, MI; *U.S. Public*, pg. 336

Choquette, William H., Sr. V.P.--Gilbane Building Company, Providence, RI; *U.S. Private*, pg. 452

Chorney, Alvan F., Sr. V.P.-Sls. & Mktg.--Ferrofluidics Corporation, Nashua, NH; *U.S. Public*, pg. 620

Chouinard, John J., Chief Fin. Officer & Sr. V.P.--Geraghty & Miller, Inc., Denver, CO; *Int'l*, pg. 607

Chouraqui, Michael, Sr. V.P.-Spencer Gifts, Inc. & Gen. Mgr.-DAPY Div.--Spencer Gifts, Inc., Egg Harbor Township, NJ; *Int'l*, pg. 1216

Chow, Shirley, Sr. V.P.-Admin. & Fin. & Corp. Sec.--Bachmann Industries, Inc., Philadelphia, PA; *U.S. Private*, pg. 109

Choy, Benedict, Sr. V.P. & Sec.--Supertex, Inc., Sunnyvale, CA; *U.S. Public*, pg. 1539

Chrisanthopoulos, Peter, Exec. V.P.-Research, Mktg. & Promotion--ABC Television Network, New York, NY; *U.S.* Public, pg. 511

Chrisman, Valerie A., Sr. V.P.-Customer & Employee Services--Horace Mann Educators Corporation, Springfield, IL; *U.S. Public*, pg. 835

Christ, William F., Chief Fin. Officer & Sr. V.P.--Hershey Foods Corporation, Hershey, PA; *U.S. Public*, pg. 811

Christen, Karl, Chief Tech. Officer & Sr. V.P.--Compuware Corporation, Farmington Hills, MI; *U.S. Public*, pg. 423

Christenbury, Edward S., Sr. V.P. & Gen. Counsel--Tennessee Valley Authority, Knoxville, TN; *U.S. Public*, pg. 1580

Christensen, Blayne, Sr. V.P. & Mgr.-Mortgage Loan Div.--First Security Bank of Utah, N.A., Salt Lake City, UT; *U.S. Public*, pg. 637

Christensen, Boyd A., Sr. V.P.--Imagery & Information Systems, San Diego, CA; *U.S. Public*, pg. 1627

Christensen, Carsten, Sr. V.P.-Information Tech.--Nykredit, Copenhagen, Denmark; *Int'l*, pg. 993

Christensen, Janis Strong, Sr. V.P.--MBIA Inc., Armonk, NY; *U.S. Public*, pg. 1023

Christensen, Janis Strong, Sr. V.P. & Dir.-Underwriting Policy & Review--Municipal Bond Investors Assurance Corporation, Armonk, NY; *U.S. Public*, pg. 1023

Christensen, Joel, Sr. V.P.-Personal Lines--Union Insurance Company, Lincoln, NE; *U.S. Public*, pg. 216

Christensen, Marc D., Sr. V.P.-Customer Service & Pub. Affairs--Public Service Company of New Mexico, Albuquerque, NM; *U.S. Public*, pg. 1339

Christensen, Thomas A., Sr. V.P.--NationsBank/Miami, Miami, FL; *U.S. Public*, pg. 1162

Christensen, Torben C., Sr. V.P.-Hematology Diagnostics/Diagnostics Div.--Bayer Corporation, Pittsburgh, PA; *Int'l*, pg. 172

Christensen, Wayne L., Sr. V.P. & Mgr.-Mortgage Loan Div.--First Security Bank of Idaho, N.A., Boise, ID; *U.S. Public*, pg. 637

Christenson, Eric F., Sr. V.P.--Chubb & Son, Inc., Warren, NJ; *U.S. Public*, pg. 355

Christian, Dennis W., Sr. V.P.-Acq. & Opers.--Callon Petroleum Company, Natchez, MS; *U.S. Public*, pg. 295

Christian, George, Sr. V.P.--BancTec, Inc., Dallas, TX; *U.S. Public*, pg. 176

Christiansen, Mark, Sr. V.P.-MGM/UA Dist. Co.--MGM/UA Distribution Co., Santa Monica, CA; *U.S. Public*, pg. 1102

Christie, Carole, Sr. V.P. & Grp. Creative Dir.--DMB&B St. Louis, Saint Louis, MO; *U.S. Private*, pg. 303

Christie, William G., Sr. V.P.-Mngmt. Information Systems--Caldor, Inc., Norwalk, CT; *U.S. Public*, pg. 292

Christopher, David, Sr. V.P.-Passenger Svcs.--Costa Cruise Lines, N.V., Miami, FL; *U.S. Private*, pg. 278

Chronis, John, Chief Fin. Officer & Sr. V.P.--Western Indemnity Insurance Company, Houston, TX; *U.S. Public*, pg. 685

Chu, Lee P., Sr. V.P.-INS--Genicom Corporation, Chantilly, VA; *U.S. Public*, pg. 729

Chua, Andrew, Sr. V.P.-Corp. Banking--DBS Bank Ltd., Singapore, Singapore; *Int'l*, pg. 350

Chumney, Jim C., Sr. V.P.-Engrng.--Inter-Tel, Incorporated, Phoenix, AZ; *U.S. Public*, pg. 888

Chumney, Jimmy C., Sr. V.P.-Engrng.--Inter-Tel Integrated Systems, Inc., Chandler, AZ; *U.S. Public*, pg. 888

Chun, Joanne L., Sr. V.P.-Credit Svcs. Division--Bank of Hawaii, Honolulu, HI; *U.S. Public*, pg. 1248

Churak, Joseph, Sr. V.P.--Babcock Lumber Company, Pittsburgh, PA; *U.S. Private*, pg. 108

Church, Douglas M. Jr., Sr. V.P. & Reg. Exec. Officer--First Virginia Banks, Inc., Falls Church, VA; *U.S. Public*, pg. 641

Church, Steven C., Sr. V.P.--Avnet, Inc., Great Neck, NY; *U.S. Public*, pg. 155

Churchman, William, Sr. V.P.-Admin. & Fin.--Imperial Pools, Inc., Latham, NY; *U.S. Private*, pg. 558

Chuvalas, Curt, Sr. V.P. & Exec. Art. Dir.--EvansGroup, Indianapolis, IN; *U.S. Private*, pg. 385

Chynsky, Ira, Sr. V.P. & Creative Services Dir.--Young & Rubicam New York, New York, NY; *U.S. Private*, pg. 1198

Cichon, Joe, Sr. V.P.-Mfg.--INX International, Milwaukee, WI; *Int'l*, pg. 1311

Cihiy, Kenneth, Sr. V.P.-Claim--United States Fidelity & Guaranty Company, Baltimore, MD; *U.S. Public*, pg. 1659

Cikacz, Michael, Chief Oper. Officer & Sr. V.P.--Healthcare Staffing Solutions, Inc., Lowell, MA; *U.S. Public*, pg. 1373

Cilfone, Nicholas J., Sr. V.P.--Citizens Banking Corporation, Flint, MI; *U.S. Public*, pg. 379

Cincere, Henry P., Sr. V.P.--Comdata Corporation, Brentwood, TN; *U.S. Public*, pg. 331

Cintron, Luis, Sr. V.P.-Trust--Banco Popular de Puerto Rico, San Juan, PR; *U.S. Public*, pg. 175

Cipolla, Barbara, Sr. V.P. & Media Services Dir.--Ingalls, Boston, MA; *U.S. Private*, pg. 562

Citron, John, Chief Fin. Officer & Sr. V.P.--SFM Media Corporation, New York, NY; *U.S. Private*, pg. 956

Civgin, Donald, Sr. V.P.-Fin.--Montgomery Ward & Co., Inc., Chicago, IL; *U.S. Private*, pg. 758

Claassen, James G., Sr. V.P.-Sls. & Sls. Services--Montgomery KONE Inc., Moline, IL; *Int'l*, pg. 746

Clabby, Joseph S., Sr. V.P.-Insurance Co. Services--Willis Corroon Financial Services Corp., New York, NY; *Int'l*, pg. 1507

Claflin, Bruce L., Sr. V.P.-Sls. & Mktg.--Digital Equipment Corporation, Maynard, MA; *U.S. Public*, pg. 507

Clancy, Robert G., Sr. V.P.--Bankers Life & Casualty Company, Chicago, IL; *U.S. Public*, pg. 433

Clancy, William J., Jr., Sr. V.P. & Dir.-Admin.--CACI International Inc, Arlington, VA; *U.S. Public*, pg. 272

Clandy, Tom, Sr. V.P.-Human Resources--QVC, Inc., West Chester, PA; *U.S. Private*, pg. 897

Clanin, Robert J., Chief Fin. Officer, Sr. V.P. & Treas.--United Parcel Service of America, Inc., Atlanta, GA; *U.S.* Private, pg. 1123

Clanton, Stephen L., Chief Fin. Officer, Sr. V.P. & Treas.--International Comfort Products, Franklin, TN; *U.S. Public*, pg. 898

Clapp, David W., Chief Oper. Officer & Sr. V.P.--TrizecHahn Properties Inc., Chicago, IL; *Int'l*, pg. 1425

Clapp, Richard, Sr. V.P.-Personnel--Gannett Company, Inc., Arlington, VA; *U.S. Public*, pg. 698

Clark, Candace, Chief Legal Officer, Sr. V.P. & Sec.--Kaman Corporation, Bloomfield, CT; *U.S. Public*, pg. 941

Clark, Carolyn, Sr. V.P. & Strategic Plng. Dir.--Ingalls, Boston, MA; *U.S. Private*, pg. 562

Clark, Chuck, Sr. V.P. & Gen. Mgr.-Drives & Metals Div.--ABB Industrial Systems, Inc., Columbus, OH; *Int'l*, pg. 4

Clark, F.L., Sr. V.P.--Amerada Hess Corporation, New York, NY; *U.S. Public*, pg. 65

Clark, G. Edmond, Sr. V.P.-Opers. Support & Engrng.--FDX Corporation, Memphis, TN; *U.S. Public*, pg. 603

Clark, Harry, Mng. Partner--Clark & Weinstock, New York, NY; *U.S. Public*, pg. 1223

Clark, J. Coley, Sr. V.P.--Electronic Data Systems Corporation, Plano, TX; *U.S. Public*, pg. 569

Clark, John E., Sr. V.P.-Bus. Opers.--Day & Zimmermann LLC, Philadelphia, PA; *U.S. Private*, pg. 317

Clark, John F., Sr. V.P.--Mark Lipman Div., Memphis, TN; *U.S. Private*, pg. 486

Clark, John F., Sr. V.P.-Acctg.--Sumitomo Bank Capital Markets, Inc., New York, NY; *Int'l*, pg. 1308

Clark, John F., Jr., Sr. V.P.--Guardsmark, Inc., Memphis, TN; *U.S. Private*, pg. 486

Clark, Karen A., Sr. V.P.--USTrust, Boston, MA; *U.S. Public*, pg. 1660

Clark, Kenneth J., Sr. V.P.--The Lincoln National Life Insurance Co., Fort Wayne, IN; *U.S. Public*, pg. 998

Clark, Laurie A., Sr. V.P.-Mdsg.--Staples, Inc., Westborough, MA; *U.S. Public*, pg. 1509

Clark, Mariel, Sr. V.P.--Au Bon Pain Co., Inc., Boston, MA; *U.S. Public*, pg. 146

Clark, Michael, Chief Oper. Officer & Sr. V.P.--Pegasus Gold Corporation, Spokane, WA; *U.S. Public*, pg. 1269

Clark, Mike, Sr. V.P.-Fin.--Evergreen International Aviation, Inc., McMinnville, OR; *U.S. Private*, pg. 386

Clark, Mitchell J., Sr. V.P.-Sls.--Robert Mondavi Winery, Inc., Oakville, CA; *U.S. Public*, pg. 1393

Clark, Paul N., Sr. V.P.-Pharmaceutical Opers.--Abbott Laboratories, Abbott Park, IL; *U.S. Public*, pg. 12

Clark, Robert J., Sr. V.P.--Thomasville Energy Corporation, Fort Worth, TX; *U.S. Public*, pg. 1482

Clark, Sean, Sr. V.P. & Media Dir.--Evans, Hardy & Young, Inc., Santa Barbara, CA; *U.S. Private*, pg. 384

Clark, Stanley, Sr. V.P.--Simplex Time Recorder Co., Gardner, MA; *U.S. Private*, pg. 1002

Clark, Steven R., Sr. V.P.-Human Resources--The Cato Corporation, Charlotte, NC; *U.S. Public*, pg. 318

Clark, Susanne G., Sr. V.P.-Investor Rels.--State Street Corporation, Boston, MA; *U.S. Public*, pg. 1513

Clarke, Eugene B., Sr. V.P.-Quality Mngmt.--Beverly Enterprises, Inc., Fort Smith, AR; *U.S. Public*, pg. 227

Clarke, George T., Sr. V.P. & Controller--UST Corporation, Boston, MA; *U.S. Public*, pg. 1660

Clarke, George T., Sr. V.P. & Controller--USTrust, Boston, MA; *U.S. Public*, pg. 1660

Clarke, Graeme, Sr. V.P.-AAA Products & Services--American Automobile Association, Heathrow, FL; *U.S. Private*, pg. 50

Clarke, Hubert P., Sr. V.P.--UJB Discount Brokerage, Ridgefield Park, NJ; *U.S. Public*, pg. 1528

Clarke, John G., Sr. V.P.-Mktg.--Dr. Pepper Co., Dallas, TX; *Int'l*, pg. 248

Clarke, John U., Chief Fin. Officer & Sr. V.P.--NGC Corporation, Houston, TX; *U.S. Public*, pg. 1146

Clarke, Vaughn A., Sr. V.P. & Treas.--Viacom Inc., New York, NY; *U.S. Private*, pg. 775

Clarkson, Lawrence W., Sr. V.P.-Plng. & Intl. Devel.--The Boeing Company, Seattle, WA; *U.S. Public*, pg. 239

Clarkson, Lawrence W., Sr. V.P.--Boeing Commercial Airplane Group, Renton, WA; *U.S. Public*, pg. 240

Clasen, Robert B., Sr. V.P. & Pres.-Comcast International--Comcast Corporation, Philadelphia, PA; *U.S. Public*, pg. 406

Claudon, Jean-Gerard, Sr. V.P.--Saint-Gobain, Courbevoie, France; *Int'l*, pg. 1170

Clausen, Robert A., Chief Fin. Officer & Sr. V.P.--Solutia Inc., Saint Louis, MO; *U.S. Public*, pg. 1483

Clauser, Barry, Sr. V.P.-Mdse.--Piercing Pagoda, Inc., Bethlehem, PA; *U.S. Public*, pg. 1296

Claussen, W. Henry, Sr. V.P. & Mgr.-Loan Admin.--Stockton Savings Bank, Stockton, CA; *U.S. Public*, pg. 1575

Clay, Philip G., Sr. V.P.--General Reinsurance Corp., Stamford, CT; *U.S. Public*, pg. 725

Claypool, Larry, Sr. V.P.- Res. & Quality--Mid-America Dairymen, Inc., Springfield, MO; *U.S. Private*, pg. 743

Clayton, Jim, Sr. V.P.-Bus. Affairs & Fin.--Home & Garden Television, Knoxville, TN; *U.S. Public*, pg. 1447

Clayton, Thomas F., Sr. V.P.-Opers.--Old National Bancorp, Evansville, IN; *U.S. Public*, pg. 1217

Cleary, Steve, Sr. V.P.-Opers.--Rogers N.K. Seed Co., Boise, ID; *Int'l*, pg. 974

Clegg, Tom, Sr. V.P.-Brand Mktg.--Sargento Foods Inc., Plymouth, WI; *U.S. Private*, pg. 966

Clem, Toni, Sr. V.P.-Media--Creative Alliance, Inc., Louisville, KY; *U.S. Private*, pg. 287

Clement, Dale E., Sr. V.P.-Fin.--Black Hills Corporation, Rapid City, SD; *U.S. Public*, pg. 235

Clement, Paul, Sr. V.P.--American Television Time, Inc., Austin, TX; *U.S. Private*, pg. 63

Clements, Bob, Sr. V.P.-Natl. Sls.--Farley Candy Company, Chicago, IL; *U.S. Private*, pg. 397

Clements, George B., Sr. V.P. & Dir.--The Robinson-Humphrey Company, Inc., Atlanta, GA; *U.S. Public*, pg. 1633

Clements, James F., Sr. V.P.--George Rice & Sons, Los Angeles, CA; *U.S. Public*, pg. 1779

Clendenning, Rick, Sr. V.P.-Intl. Opers.--INX International, Milwaukee, WI; *Int'l*, pg. 1311

Cless, Gerard, Exec. V.P.-Engrng. & Tech.--Zebra Technologies Corporation, Vernon Hills, IL; *U.S. Public*, pg. 1790

Clevenger, Jeffrey G., Sr. V.P.-Copper--Cyprus Amax Minerals Company, Englewood, CO; *U.S. Public*, pg. 470

Clevenstine, Walter M., Sr. V.P.-Specialty Prods./Indus. Chemicals Div.--Bayer Corporation, Pittsburgh, PA; *Int'l*, pg. 172

Clifford, Don, Sr. V.P.-Technology--MarketSource Corporation, Cranbury, NJ; *U.S. Private*, pg. 705

Clifford, James F., Sr. V.P.--Firstar Bank of Minnesota, Bloomington, MN; *U.S. Public*, pg. 643

Clifford, Patrick A., Sr. V.P.--The Times Mirror Company, Los Angeles, CA; *U.S. Public*, pg. 1615

Clifford, Peter, Chief Acctg. Officer, Sr. V.P.-Fin. & Controller--John Wiley & Sons, Inc., New York, NY; *U.S. Public*, pg. 1768

Clifton, Paul H., Jr., Sr. V.P.-Sls. & Mktg.--Colonial Companies, Inc., Columbia, SC; *U.S. Public*, pg. 1699

Cline, George, Sr. V.P. & Acct. Mngmt. Dir.--Fahlgren, Dublin, OH; *U.S. Private*, pg. 391

Cline, Randy, Sr. V.P.-Mktg.--Regence BlueCross BlueShield of Oregon, Portland, OR; *U.S. Private*, pg. 917

Cline, Robert N., Sr. V.P. & Acct. Grp. Dir.--Creswell, Munsell, Fultz & Zirbel, L.P., Cedar Rapids, IA; *U.S. Private*, pg. 1197

Clinton, Chris W., Sr. V.P.-Asset Mngmt.--Tarragon Realty Investors, Dallas, TX; *U.S. Public*, pg. 1561

Clinton, Stephen P., Chief Oper. Officer & Sr. V.P.--Hayes, Seay, Mattern & Mattern, Inc., Roanoke, VA; *U.S. Private*, pg. 513

Clongo, David, Sr. V.P.--Lady Marlene Sales Corp., New York, NY; *U.S. Private*, pg. 642

Closs, Willie, Sr. V.P. & Controller--North Carolina Mutual Life Insurance Co., Durham, NC; *U.S. Private*, pg. 804

Clough, Arlo, Sr. V.P.-Tech. Svcs.--Mesa Air Group, Las Vegas, NV; *U.S. Public*, pg. 1098

Clough, Arlo, Sr. V.P.-Tech. Svcs.--Mesa Airlines, Inc., Farmington, NM; *U.S. Public*, pg. 1099

Clouser, Christopher E., Sr. V.P.-Admin.--Northwest Airlines Corp., Saint Paul, MN; *U.S. Public*, pg. 1199

Clucas, George L., Sr. V.P.--The Union Central Life Insurance Co., Cincinnati, OH; *U.S. Private*, pg. 1118

Cluett, Geoff, Sr. V.P.-Field Opers./Europe, Middle East & Africa--Comshare, Incorporated, Ann Arbor, MI; *U.S. Public*, pg. 425

Cluett, Geoff, Sr. V.P.-Field Opers.--Comshare Ltd., London, United Kingdom; *U.S. Public*, pg. 425

Cluff, John, Sr. V.P.-Heavy Division--Sundt Corp., Tucson, AZ; *U.S. Private*, pg. 1051

Coad, P. Turner, Sr. V.P.--Attorneys' Title Insurance Fund, Orlando, FL; *U.S. Private*, pg. 98

Coakley, James F., Sr. V.P. & Grp. Mngmt. Supvr.--Pedone & Partners Adv., Inc., New York, NY; *U.S. Private*, pg. 846

Coates, Doug, Sr. V.P.-Natl. Accts.--The Gibson-Homans Company, Twinsburg, OH; *U.S. Private*, pg. 451

Coatney, Michael, Sr. V.P. & Gen. Mgr.--Acme Truck Line, Inc., Harvey, LA; *U.S. Private*, pg. 14

Cobb, J.E., Sr. V.P. & Grp. Bus. Dir.--Howard, Merrell & Partners, Inc., Raleigh, NC; *U.S. Private*, pg. 542

Cobb, Michael M., Sr. V.P.--Hunt Oil Company, Dallas, TX; *U.S. Private*, pg. 548

Cobb, Patricia A., Esq., Sr. V.P.--Pioneer American Holding Company, Carbondale, PA; *U.S. Public*, pg. 1298

Coble, Diane F., Sr. V.P.--Keycorp, Cleveland, OH; *U.S. Public*, pg. 954

Cobuzzi, Robert J., Chief Fin. Officer, Sr. V.P. & Treas.--Kollmorgen Corporation, Waltham, MA; *U.S. Public*, pg. 965

Cocce, John, Sr. V.P.-Mfg.--American Media, Inc., Lake Worth, FL; *U.S. Public*, pg. 87

Cochran, Bob, Sr. V.P.--ICF Kaiser International Inc., Fairfax, VA; *U.S. Public*, pg. 852

Cochran, Robert, Sr. V.P.-Office Leasing--Lat Purser & Associates, Charlotte, NC; *U.S. Private*, pg. 896

Cochran, Robert P., Sr. V.P.-Mngmnt. Information Systems--QVC, Inc., West Chester, PA; *U.S. Private*, pg. 897

Cocke, James E., Sr. V.P.-Fin. & Admin.--Raytheon Systems Co., Kirkwood, NY; *U.S. Public*, pg. 1364

Cocke, Norman A., Chief Fin. Officer, Sr. V.P. & Sec.--Chronimed Inc., Minnetonka, MN; *U.S. Public*, pg. 352

Cocker, Gail, Sr. V.P.--Bank of Montreal - Winnipeg, Winnipeg, Canada; *Int'l*, pg. 153

Cocoros, Lela, Sr. V.P.-Commun.--TCI Communications, Inc., Englewood, CO; *U.S. Public*, pg. 1554

Codispoti, Lisa S., Sr. V.P.--Keycorp, Cleveland, OH; *U.S. Public*, pg. 954

Coen, Steven M., Sr. V.P.--Manufacturers & Traders Trust Company, Buffalo, NY; *U.S. Public*, pg. 631

Coffee, Paul B., Sr. V.P. & Western Regl. Mgr.--A.G. Edwards & Sons, Inc., Saint Louis, MO; *U.S. Public*, pg. 565

Coffin, J. Robert, Sr. V.P.-Tech.--American States Insurance Companies, Indianapolis, IN; *U.S. Public*, pg. 997

Coffman, Franklin E., Sr. V.P.-DOE Programs & Corp. Bus. Devel.--International Technology Corporation, Monroeville, PA; *U.S. Public*, pg. 907

Coffman, John, Sr. V.P.-Strategic Decision Services--May & Speh, Inc., Downers Grove, IL; *U.S. Public*, pg. 1063

Cohane, Timothy F., Sr. V.P.--Amphenol Corporation, Wallingford, CT; *U.S. Private*, pg. 629

Cohen, Burton D., Sr. V.P.--McDonald's Corporation, Oak Brook, IL; *U.S. Public*, pg. 1068

Cohen, Carol, Sr. V.P.--Levy Restaurants, Chicago, IL; *U.S. Private*, pg. 664

Cohen, Charles, Sr. V.P.-Financial Plng. & Analysis--Metro-Goldwyn-Mayer Inc., Santa Monica, CA; *U.S. Public*, pg. 1101

Cohen, Colin M., Chief Fin. Officer & Sr. V.P.--The Fairchild Corporation, Chantilly, VA; *U.S. Public*, pg. 610

Cohen, Daniel, Sr. V.P.-Adv.--The New York Times Company, New York, NY; *U.S. Public*, pg. 1173

Cohen, Daniel, Sr. V.P.-Adv.--The New York Times, New York, NY; *U.S. Public*, pg. 1174

Cohen, David, Sr. V.P.-Acq. & Investments--Dole Food Company, Inc., Westlake Village, CA; *U.S. Public*, pg. 515

Cohen, Gerald, Sr. V.P.-Personnel & Admin.--SLM Holding Corp., Washington, DC; *U.S. Public*, pg. 1419

Cohen, Hank, Sr. V.P.-Devel.--MGM Worldwide Television, Group., Santa Monica, CA; *U.S. Public*, pg. 1102

Cohen, Herbert L., Sr. V.P.--Imperial Bank, Inglewood, CA; *U.S. Public*, pg. 871

Cohen, Isaac, Sr. V.P.-Mdsg.--Jan Bell Marketing Inc., Sunrise, FL; *U.S. Public*, pg. 207

Cohen, Leonard, Sr. V.P. & Dir.--Ketchum Directory Advertising/Kansas City, Overland Park, KS; *U.S. Private*, pg. 616

Cohen, Michael, Sr. V.P. & Music Dir.--Grey Advertising Inc., New York, NY; *U.S. Public*, pg. 764

Cohen, Michael S., Sr. V.P.-Opers.--Aloha Airgroup, Inc., Honolulu, HI; *U.S. Private*, pg. 44

Cohen, Patti, Sr. V.P.-Pub. Rels.--Donna Karan, New York, NY; *U.S. Public*, pg. 517

Cohen, Pinya, Ph.D., Sr. V.P.-Quality Assurance & Regulatory Affairs--Nabi, Boca Raton, FL; *U.S. Public*, pg. 1148

Cohen, Stan, Sr. V.P.--The Hotsy Corporation, Englewood, CO; *U.S. Private*, pg. 500

Cohen, Valerie A., Sr. V.P. & Asst. Gen. Counsel--The Walt Disney Company, Burbank, CA; *U.S. Public*, pg. 511

Cohn, Derek, Sr. V.P.-Mktg. & Sls.--International Plastics Company, New York, NY; *U.S. Private*, pg. 571

Cohn, Donald L., Sr. V.P.--Acxiom Corporation, Conway, AR; *U.S. Public*, pg. 18

Coin, Kerry W., Sr. V.P. & Gen. Mgr.-Boston Pacific--Carl Karcher Enterprises, Inc., Anaheim, CA; *U.S. Public*, pg. 278

Coit, Lynde H., Sr. V.P. & Gen. Counsel--Ogden Corporation, New York, NY; *U.S. Public*, pg. 1213

Cojuangco, Miguel O., Sr. V.P.-Customer Svcs.--Philippine Long Distance Telephone Company, Manila, Philippines; *Int'l*, pg. 1051

Colabraro, Tony, Chief Fin. Officer & Sr. V.P.--Worldvision Enterprises, New York, NY; *U.S. Private*, pg. 776

Colalillo, Claudia, Sr. V.P.-Organizational Devel.--May & Speh, Inc., Downers Grove, IL; *U.S. Public*, pg. 1063

Colalucci, Francis M., Chief Fin. Officer, Sr. V.P. & Treas.--Empire Insurance Group, New York, NY; *U.S. Public*, pg. 990

Colalucci, Francis M., Chief Fin. Officer, Sr. V.P. & Treas.--Allcity Insurance Co., New York, NY; *U.S. Public*, pg. 990

Colamussi, Karen, Sr. V.P.-Mktg.--Atlantic Recording Corporation, New York, NY; *U.S. Public*, pg. 1611

Colando, Greg, Sr. V.P.-Sls. & Mktg.--Interface Flooring Systems Inc., La Grange, GA; *U.S. Public*, pg. 889

Colantoni, Alfred, Sr. V.P. & Treas.--Press Communications, LLC, Wall, NJ; *U.S. Private*, pg. 882

Colao, Anthony F., Sr. V.P.--Old Republic International Corporation, Chicago, IL; *U.S. Public*, pg. 1218

Colbert, Virgis W., Sr. V.P.-Opers.--Miller Brewing Company, Milwaukee, WI; *U.S. Public*, pg. 1289

Colby, Sandy S., Sr. V.P. & Gen. Mgr.-Mdse.--Bradlees Inc., Braintree, MA; *U.S. Public*, pg. 249

Cole, Anne, Sr. V.P.--Cole of California, Los Angeles, CA; *U.S. Public*, pg. 148

Cole, J. Weldon, Sr. V.P.-Admin. & Devel.--Albany International Corp., Albany, NY; *U.S. Public*, pg. 36

Cole, Jon W., Sr. V.P.--Transocean Offshore, Inc., Houston, TX; *U.S. Public*, pg. 1631

Cole, Les, Sr. V.P.-Opers.--Superior Coffee and Foods, Bensenville, IL; *U.S. Public*, pg. 1434

Cole, Lloyd, Chief Information Officer & Sr. V.P.--Heitman Financial Ltd., Chicago, IL; *U.S. Public*, pg. 1673

Cole, Michael J., Sr. V.P.-Central--Waste Management, Inc., Oak Brook, IL; *U.S. Public*, pg. 1744

Cole, Patricia, Chief Fin. Officer & Sr. V.P.--Fair, Isaac and Company, Inc., San Rafael, CA; *U.S. Public*, pg. 609

Coleman, Gerald F., Sr. V.P.-Investments--Mackenzie Financial Corporation, Toronto, Canada; *Int'l*, pg. 828

Coleman, Herbert H., Sr. V.P.--Trustmark National Bank, Jackson, MS; *U.S. Public*, pg. 1643

Coleman, James, Sr. V.P.-Loans--Westpac Banking Corporation, Sydney, Australia; *Int'l*, pg. 1495

Coleman, James C., Sr. V.P.-Human Resources--Premark International, Inc., Deerfield, IL; *U.S. Public*, pg. 1321

Coleman, James W., Jr., Sr. V.P.-Strategic Bus. Units--Selective Insurance Group, Inc, Branchville, NJ; *U.S. Public*, pg. 1455

Coleman, James W., Jr., Sr. V.P.-Strategic Bus. Units--Selective Insurance Company of America, Branchville, NJ; *U.S. Public*, pg. 1455

Coleman, John M., Sr. V.P.-Law & Pub. Affairs--Campbell Soup Company, Camden, NJ; *U.S. Public*, pg. 298

Coleman, Kenneth L., Sr. V.P.-Customer & Prof. Svcs.--Silicon Graphics, Inc., Mountain View, CA; *U.S. Public*, pg. 1473

Coleman, Kim F., Sr. V.P.--Philadelphia Reserve Supply Company, Croydon, PA; *U.S. Private*, pg. 861

Coleman, T.W., Sr. V.P.-Opers.--Kerr-McGee Chemical Corp., Oklahoma City, OK; *U.S. Public*, pg. 952

Coleman, William R., Sr. V.P.-Fin. & Controller--Cincinnati Bell Information Systems Inc., Cincinnati, OH; *U.S. Public*, pg. 367

Coles, Richard, Sr. V.P. & Gen. Mgr.-Investments--Manulife Financial (The Manufacturers Life Insurance Company), Toronto, Canada; *Int'l*, pg. 840

Colgate, Jessie M., Sr. V.P.-Govt. Affairs--New York Life Insurance Company, New York, NY; *U.S. Private*, pg. 794

Colin, Dan, Sr. V.P.-Bus. Devel.--Cerberus Pyrotronics Inc., Cedar Knolls, NJ; *Int'l*, pg. 1246

Collas, James, Sr. V.P.-Global Prods.--Gateway 2000, North Sioux City, SD; *U.S. Public*, pg. 703

Colley, Gerald, Sr. V.P.-Intl. Exploration & Prod.--Seagull Energy Corporation, Houston, TX; *U.S. Public*, pg. 1450

Collier, L. Michael, Sr. V.P.-Northeast--Waste Management, Inc., Oak Brook, IL; *U.S. Public*, pg. 1744

Collier, R., Sr. V.P.-Govt. Services--SGS Societe Generale de Surveillance Holding S.A., Geneva, Switzerland; *Int'l*, pg. 1153

Collin, George, Sr. V.P.-Fin. & Admin.--Dexter Electronic Materials Division, City of Industry, CA; *U.S. Public*, pg. 504

Collins, Bruce, Sr. V.P. & Mngmt. Supvr.--Dailey & Associates, West Hollywood, CA; *U.S. Public*, pg. 909

Collins, Daniel F., Sr. V.P.--The Coastal Corporation, Houston, TX; *U.S. Public*, pg. 389

Collins, Jill, Sr. V.P.--Edelman Public Relations Worldwide, Chicago, IL; *U.S. Private*, pg. 362

Collins, John H., Sr. V.P.--Bellemead Development Corp., Roseland, NJ; *U.S. Public*, pg. 355

Collins, Kenneth K., Sr. V.P.-San Diego Area--Kaiser Permanente, Oakland, CA; *U.S. Private*, pg. 605

Collins, Maunty C., Sr. V.P. & Dir.-Opers./Central Reg.--Boyd Gaming Corporation, Las Vegas, NV; *U.S. Public*, pg. 249

Collins, Richard, Sr. V.P.-Sls. & Mktg.--Golden Books Family Entertainment Inc., New York, NY; *U.S. Public*, pg. 749

Collins, Richard G., Sr. V.P. & Acct. Grp. Dir.--Creswell, Munsell, Fultz & Zirbel, L.P., Cedar Rapids, IA; *U.S. Private*, pg. 1197

Collupy, Ed, Sr. V.P.--The Pantry, Inc., Sanford, NC; *U.S. Private*, pg. 837

Colmer, Buddy, Sr. V.P.--Brookshire Bros., Ltd., Lufkin, TX; *U.S. Private*, pg. 172

Colraine, Tom, Chief Fin. Officer & Sr. V.P.--Willis Corroon Americas, Nashville, TN; *Int'l*, pg. 1505

Colton, Edward, Sr. V.P. & Gen. Counsel--Alpha Therapeutic Corp., Los Angeles, CA; *Int'l*, pg. 558

Colville, William W., Sr. V.P., Gen. Counsel & Acting Sec.--Owens Corning, Toledo, OH; *U.S. Public*, pg. 1236

Colvin, Clark T., Sr. V.P.-External Affairs--Cajun Electric Power Co-op, Baton Rouge, LA; *U.S. Private*, pg. 199

Comerford, Vince, Sr. V.P.-Global Sls.--Noville, South Hackensack, NJ; *U.S. Private*, pg. 808

Comiskey, James, Sr. V.P. & Publisher--Glencoe/Mc-Graw Hill, Westerville, OH; *U.S. Public*, pg. 1070

Comment, Denis, Sr. V.P. & Head-Mdsg.--Little Switzerland, Inc., Charlotte Amalie, VI; *U.S. Public*, pg. 1001

Compitello, Yvonne, Sr. V.P.-Real Estate--MBL Life Assurance Corporation, Newark, NJ; *U.S. Private*, pg. 685

Compo, Lawrence J., Sr. V.P.--Associates Relocation Management Company, Inc., Dallas, TX; *U.S. Public*, pg. 663

Compton, Gregory A., Sr. V.P., Sec. & Gen. Counsel--NTS Development Company, Louisville, KY; *U.S. Private*, pg. 772

Conaway, J. Michael, Chief Fin. Officer & Sr. V.P.--Fluor Corporation, Irvine, CA; *U.S. Public*, pg. 659

Concepcion, Antonio V., Sr. V.P. & Chief Mktg. Officer--La Tondena Distillers, Inc., Manila, Philippines; *Int'l*, pg. 785

Condit, Richard, Sr. V.P.-Personnel--Sundt Corp., Tucson, AZ; *U.S. Private*, pg. 1051

Condon, William P., Sr. V.P. & Dir.-Health Care, Special Revenue & Corp. Util. Prods.--Municipal Bond Investors Assurance Corporation, Armonk, NY; *U.S. Public*, pg. 1023

Condrin, J. Paul, III, Chief Fin. Officer & Sr. V.P.--Liberty Mutual Insurance Co., Boston, MA; *U.S. Private*, pg. 666

Congdon, George, Sr. V.P.-Opers.--Jackpot Enterprises, Inc., Las Vegas, NV; *U.S. Public*, pg. 920

Conger, Kenneth W., Sr. V.P.-H.R.--Kohler Company, Kohler, WI; *U.S. Private*, pg. 630

Coniglio, Nicholas, Sr. V.P., Fin. Dir. & Bus. Mgr.-NY--DMB&B New York, New York, NY; *U.S. Private*, pg. 302

Conine, Jim, Sr. V.P.-Real Estate--Minyard Food Stores, Inc., Coppell, TX; *U.S. Private*, pg. 752

Conine, Jim, Sr. V.P.-Real Estate--Minyard Properties, Inc., Coppell, TX; *U.S. Private*, pg. 752

Conine, William T., Sr. V.P.-Info. Svcs.--Farm Family Casualty Insurance Co., Glenmont, NY; *U.S. Private*, pg. 394

Conklin, Thomas J., Sr. V.P. & Corp. Sec.--The Mutual Life Insurance Company of New York, New York, NY; *U.S. Private*, pg. 769

Conklyn, Elizabeth D., Sr. V.P.-Human Resources--General Signal Corporation, Stamford, CT; *U.S. Public*, pg. 726

Conlee, Michael, Sr. V.P.--Banexi International Financial Services (North America) Corp., New York, NY; *Int'l*, pg. 163

Conley, Forrest M., Jr., Sr. V.P. Intl. Groy Wolf, Inc., Houston, TX; *U.S. Public*, pg. 765

Conley, Michael, Sr. V.P.--McDonald's Corporation, Oak Brook, IL; *U.S. Public*, pg. 1068

Conley, R. Michael, Sr. V.P.-Employee Benefits Div.--ReliaStar Financial Corp., Minneapolis, MN; *U.S. Public*, pg. 1375

Conliffe, Roy R., Sr. V.P.-Labor Rels.--George Weston Limited, Toronto, Canada; *Int'l*, pg. 1494

Conly, Michael J., Sr. V.P.--Harte-Hanks Communications, Inc., San Antonio, TX; *U.S. Public*, pg. 793

Connell, Eugene C., Sr. V.P.--Erie Family Life Insurance Company, Erie, PA; *U.S. Public*, pg. 590

Connell, Gordon E., Sr. V.P.--Standard Federal Bank, Troy, MI; *Int'l*, pg. 10

Connelly, Elizabeth K., Sr. V.P., Corp. Sec., Human Resources & Office Mngmt.--Adler Boschetto Peebles & Partners, Inc., New York, NY; *U.S. Private*, pg. 17

Connelly, Jim, Sr. V.P.--National Football League Properties, Inc., New York, NY; *U.S. Private*, pg. 783

Connolly, Michael, Sr. V.P.--Edelman Worldwide, Inc., Washington, DC; *U.S. Private*, pg. 362

Connor, Brandt D., Sr. V.P. & Relationship Mktg. Dir.--Long Haymes Carr, Inc., Winston Salem, NC; *U.S. Public*, pg. 909

Connor, Gene, Sr. V.P.-Opers.--Advanced Micro Devices, Inc., Sunnyvale, CA; *U.S. Public*, pg. 21

Connor, Susan J., Sr. V.P. & Gen. Mgr.-ERP Customer Service & PRISM--Marcam Solutions, Inc., Newton, MA; *U.S. Public*, pg. 1042

Connor, Vernon J., Sr. V.P.-Mktg.--Voyager Group, Inc., Jacksonville, FL; *U.S. Public*, pg. 68

Connor, Vernon J., Sr. V.P.-Mktg.--Voyager Indemnity Insurance Company, Fort Worth, TX; *U.S. Public*, pg. 68

Connors, Dennis M., Chief Information Officer & Sr. V.P.--The Gap, Inc., San Francisco, CA; *U.S. Public*, pg. 702

Connors, George W., Sr. V.P.--Century Bancshares, Inc., Washington, DC; *U.S. Public*, pg. 328

Connors, Jack, Sr. V.P.--JSB Financial, Lynbrook, NY; *U.S. Public*, pg. 919

Connors, Mary Jean, Sr. V.P.-H.R.--Knight-Ridder, Inc., Miami, FL; *U.S. Public*, pg. 963

Connors, Richard, Sr. V.P.-Mktg.--The Mutual Life Insurance Company of New York, New York, NY; *U.S. Private*, pg. 769

Conrey, Robert, Sr. V.P.-Mktg.--American Eagle Group, Inc., Dallas, TX; *U.S. Public*, pg. 71

Conroy, Catherine M., Sr. V.P. & Dir.-Corp. Communications--Donaldson, Lufkin, & Jenrette, Inc., New York, NY; *U.S. Public*, pg. 589

Conroy, David, Sr. V.P.--First National Bank of Ohio, Akron, OH; *U.S. Public*, pg. 646

Conroy, James T., Sr. V.P.-Corp. Affairs--MacAndrews & Forbes Holdings Inc., New York, NY; *U.S. Private*, pg. 689

Conroy, James T., Sr. V.P.-Pub. Affairs--Andrews Group, Incorporated, New York, NY; *U.S. Private*, pg. 689

Conroy, John J., Sr. V.P.--JSB Financial, Lynbrook, NY; *U.S. Public*, pg. 919

Conroy, John L., Sr. V.P. & Fin. Controller--Jefferies & Company, Inc., Los Angeles, CA; *U.S. Public*, pg. 925

Constantini, Ben, Exec. V.P.-Sls.--Wavetek Corporation, San Diego, CA; *U.S. Private*, pg. 1154

Constien, Robert W., Sr. V.P.--Rurban Financial Corp., Defiance, OH; *U.S. Public*, pg. 1412

Conti, Barbara, Sr. V.P.--Andover Bank, Andover, MA; *U.S. Public*, pg. 112

Conti, Barbara J., Sr. V.P.--Andover Bancorp, Inc., Andover, MA; *U.S. Public*, pg. 111

Conti, Joe, Sr. V.P.-Sls.--Johnny Carson Apparel, Inc., Buffalo, NY; *U.S. Public*, pg. 796

Conti, Joseph, Sr. V.P.-Sls.--Intercontinental Branded Apparel, Buffalo, NY; *U.S. Public*, pg. 796

Contino, Michael D., Chief Information Officer & Sr. V.P.--Hanover Direct, Inc., Weehawken, NJ; *U.S. Public*, pg. 782

Conto, James A., Sr. V.P.-Mergers & Acquisitions--United HealthCare Corporation, Minnetonka, MN; *U.S. Public*, pg. 1677

Contois, Leo L., Sr. V.P.-Human Resources--Syntex, Palo Alto, CA; *Int'l*, pg. 1120

Contos, Gayaneh, Sr. V.P.--Versar Inc., Springfield, VA; *U.S. Public*, pg. 1717

Conway, Daniel J., Sr. V.P.-External Affairs--The Chubb Corporation, Warren, NJ; *U.S. Public*, pg. 354

Conway, Heather, Sr. V.P.-Pub. Rels. & Corp. Commun.--The Toronto Dominion Bank, Toronto, Canada; *Int'l*, pg. 1401

Conway, Michael A., Sr. V.P. & Sr. Investment Officer--AON Corporation, Chicago, IL; *U.S. Public*, pg. 117

Conway, Peter P., Jr., Sr. V.P.--Continental Assurance Company, Chicago, IL; *U.S. Private*, pg. 267

Conway, Ronald J., Chief Oper. Officer & Sr. V.P.-Opers.--Conrail, Inc., Philadelphia, PA; *U.S. Public*, pg. 431

Conway, Vernon D., Sr. V.P.--MBC Realty, Inc., Baltimore, MD; *U.S. Public*, pg. 1089

Conwell, Michael R., Sr. V.P.-Intl. Dept. Mgr.--Hibernia Corporation, New Orleans, LA; *U.S. Public*, pg. 825

Conza, Joseph A., Sr. V.P.-Equipment & Design Services--Blimpie International, Inc., Atlanta, GA; *U.S. Public*, pg. 236

Coogan, Michael, Sr. V.P.-Dir. Mktg/Dir. Response--Genfoot Inc., Montreal, Canada; *Int'l*, pg. 549

Coogan, William, Sr. V.P.--Expeditors International Ocean, Inc., Seattle, WA; *U.S. Public*, pg. 600

Coogan, William J., Sr. V.P.-Ocean--Expeditors International of Washington, Inc., Seattle, WA; *U.S. Public*, pg. 600

Cook, Cary, Chief Fin. Officer & Sr. V.P.--AMCORE Bank N.A., Northwest, Woodstock, IL; *U.S. Public*, pg. 64

Cook, Charlyn, Sr. V.P.-Opers.--Commemorative Brands, Inc., Austin, TX; *U.S. Private*, pg. 258

Cook, Gerald A., Sr. V.P.-Store Opers.--The Bombay Company, Inc., Fort Worth, TX; *U.S. Public*, pg. 244

Cook, James S., Sr. V.P.-Opers.--Playtex Products Inc., Westport, CT; *U.S. Public*, pg. 1310

Cook, James W., Sr. V.P.--CMS Energy Corporation, Dearborn, MI; *U.S. Public*, pg. 279

Cook, Jerry, Sr. V.P.-Store Opers.--The Bombay Company, Fort Worth, TX; *U.S. Public*, pg. 244

Cook, John, Sr. V.P.-Communications--Nationwide Insurance Enterprise, Columbus, OH; *U.S. Private*, pg. 788

Cook, John F., Sr. V.P.--Manufacturers & Traders Trust Company, Buffalo, NY; *U.S. Public*, pg. 631

Cook, John G., Sr. V.P.-Energy Supply Business Group--Illinois Power Company, Decatur, IL; *U.S. Public*, pg. 869

Cook, John R., Chief Fin. Officer & Sr. V.P.--Harcourt General, Inc., Chestnut Hill, MA; *U.S. Public*, pg. 782

Cook, Laura, Sr. V.P.-Bus. Affairs & Legal--20th Century Fox Home Entertainment, Los Angeles, CA; *U.S. Public*, pg. 275

Cook, Laura, Sr. V.P.-Bus. Affairs & Legal--20th Century Fox Home Entertainment, Los Angeles, CA; *Int'l*, pg. 926

Cook, Matthew, Sr. V.P. & Branch Mgr.--Willis Corroon Melling Inc., Ottawa, Canada; *Int'l*, pg. 1509

Cook, Norman, Sr. V.P.-Mktg.--Universal Life Insurance Company, Memphis, TN; *U.S. Private*, pg. 1127

Cook, Randall, Sr. V.P.-Property & Casualty & Mgr.-N. Div.--Willis Corroon Administrative Services Corporation, Louisville, KY; *Int'l*, pg. 1504

Cook, Richard C., Sr. V.P. & Gen. Mgr.-MAPICS Bus. Grp.--Marcam Solutions, Inc., Newton, MA; *U.S. Public*, pg. 1042

Cook, Robyn Shreiber, Sr. V.P.-West--J & J Snack Foods Corporation, Pennsauken, NJ; *U.S. Public*, pg. 916

Cook, Sid, Sr. V.P. & Dir.-Mktg.--Bank One, Indiana, N.A., Indianapolis, IN; *U.S. Public*, pg. 173

Cook, Stephen E., Sr. V.P.--Citizens First State Bank, Hartford City, IN; *U.S. Public*, pg. 632

Cook, Terry, Sr. V.P., Gen. Counsel & Sec.--Kaiser Ventures, Inc., Ontario, CA; *U.S. Public*, pg. 941

Cook, Tim, Sr. V.P.--Intelligent Electronics, Inc., Exton, PA; *U.S. Public*, pg. 887

Cook, William M., Sr. V.P.-Comml. & Indus.--Donaldson Company, Inc., Minneapolis, MN; *U.S. Public*, pg. 517

Cooke, John D., Sr. V.P.--McDonald's Corporation, Oak Brook, IL; *U.S. Public*, pg. 1068

Cooke, Peter H., Pres.-Eastern Cement Region & Sr. V.P.--Lafarge Corporation, Reston, VA; *Int'l*, pg. 788

Cooke, Roger, Sr. V.P., Gen. Counsel & Sec.--Smith's Food & Drug Centers, Inc., Salt Lake City, UT; *U.S. Public*, pg. 1103

Cooke, Roger A., Sr. V.P., Gen. Counsel & Sec.--Fred Meyer Incorporated, Portland, OR; *U.S. Public*, pg. 1103

Cooke, Stephen D., Sr. V.P., Gen. Counsel & Sec.-AMBAC Assurance Corp.--AMBAC Financial Group, Inc., New York, NY; *U.S. Public*, pg. 62

Cool, Judd R., Sr. V.P.-H.R.--Allegheny Teledyne Incorporated, Pittsburgh, PA; *U.S. Public*, pg. 43

Cooler, Charles, Sr. V.P. & Gen. Mgr.--BASES International Research Division, Westport, CT; *U.S. Private*, pg. 120

Cooley, Jesse G., V.P. & Claims Mgr.--Firemen's Insurance Company of Washington, D.C., Bethesda, MD; *U.S. Public*, pg. 215

Cooley, Kevin, Sr. V.P.-Personnel Trng. & Devel.--The PBS&J Corporation, Miami, FL; *U.S. Private*, pg. 825

Coomes, R.E., Sr. V.P. & Controller--Dorr-Oliver Incorporated, Milford, CT; *Int'l*, pg. 839

Cooney, Ed, Sr. V.P.-Personnel--The Bon Marche, Inc., Seattle, WA; *U.S. Public*, pg. 617

Cooney, Edward, Chief Fin. Officer, Sr. V.P. & Treas.--Amtrol Inc., West Warwick, RI; *U.S. Private*, pg. 300

Cooney, Michael B., Sr. V.P.-Law & Admin. & Sec.--A.P. Green Industries, Inc., Mexico, MO; *U.S. Public*, pg. 761

Cooper, Brian G., Sr. V.P.--Cox Newspapers, Inc., Atlanta, GA; *U.S. Private*, pg. 281

Cooper, C. Donald, Chief Strategy Officer & Sr. V.P.-Bus. Devel. & Quality Control--Plantronics Inc., Santa Cruz, CA; *U.S. Public*, pg. 1308

Cooper, C. Martin, Sr. V.P. & Dir.-Mfg.--ITT Fluid Technology Corporation, Midland Park, NJ; *U.S. Public*, pg. 860

Cooper, Charles A., Sr. V.P.--American Arbitration Association, New York, NY; *U.S. Private*, pg. 50

Cooper, Dennis E., Sr. V.P.--R.T.M. Winners, Atlanta, GA; *U.S. Private*, pg. 906

Cooper, Douglas, Sr. V.P.-New Bus. Devel.--Western International Media Corporation, New York, NY; *U.S. Private*, pg. 1166

Cooper, James M., Jr., Sr. V.P.--Selective Insurance Group, Inc, Branchville, NJ; *U.S. Public*, pg. 1455

Cooper, John S., Sr. V.P. & Grp. Exec.-Railroad Grp.--Portec, Inc., Lake Forest, IL; *U.S. Public*, pg. 1317

Cooper, Marvin, Sr. V.P. & Dir.-Stores--Brooks Brothers, New York, NY; *Int'l*, pg. 843

Cooper, Matthew J., Sr. V.P.--Capital One Financial Corporation, Falls Church, VA; *U.S. Public*, pg. 302

Cooper, Robert, Sr. V.P.-HBO Pictures--Home Box Office, Inc., New York, NY; *U.S. Public*, pg. 1612

Cooper, Russell L., Sr. V.P.-Franchising & Devel.--Shoney's, Inc., Nashville, TN; *U.S. Public*, pg. 1467

Cooper, Sally, Sr. V.P.-C&E Group--Wholesale Electronic Supply, Dallas, TX; *U.S. Private*, pg. 1174

Coos, Per-Erik, Sr. V.P.-Private Markets Div.--Trygg-Hansa, Stockholm, Sweden; *Int'l*, pg. 1425

Coots, Gary F., Sr. V.P.-Comml. Lending--Security Bank & Trust Co., Vincennes, IN; *U.S. Public*, pg. 1217

Cope, Peter, Sr. V.P.--Pall Corporation, Greenvale, NY; *U.S. Public*, pg. 1253

Coppinger, William G., Sr. V.P.--Southland Industries, Long Beach, CA; *U.S. Private*, pg. 1018

Coppock, Paul C., Chief Admin. Officer, Sr. V.P., Gen. Counsel & Sec.--Harsco Corporation, Camp Hill, PA; *U.S. Public*, pg. 792

Coppola, Sebastian, Sr. V.P. & Treas.--MCN Energy Group, Inc., Detroit, MI; *U.S. Public*, pg. 1024

Coppola, Sebastian, Sr. V.P. & Treas.--MCN Investment, Detroit, MI; *U.S. Public*, pg. 1025

Copps, Stephen L., Sr. V.P.-Corp. Mktg.-Govt.--Intermetrics, Inc., Burlington, MA; *U.S. Private*, pg. 567

Coraci-McCann, Catherine, Sr. V.P. & Human Resources Dir.--Young & Rubicam Detroit, Detroit, MI; *U.S. Private*, pg. 1198

Corak, Randy W., Sr. V.P.-Residential Opers.--TJ International, Inc., Boise, ID; *U.S. Public*, pg. 1556

Corbett, Dave, V.P.-Sls. & Mktg.--Crane Manufacturing, Cudahy, WI; *U.S. Private*, pg. 286

Corbett, Jeff, Sr. V.P.-Sls. & Mktg.--DHL Worldwide Express, Redwood City, CA; *U.S. Private*, pg. 301

Corbett, Jeff, Sr. V.P.-Mktg. & Sls.--DHL Airways, Inc., Redwood City, CA; *U.S. Private*, pg. 302

Corbett, John C., Sr. V.P.-Exploration & Production--Giant Exploration & Production Co., Farmington, NM; *U.S. Public*, pg. 742

Corbett, Lawrence, Sr. V.P.--Applied Innovation Inc., Dublin, OH; *U.S. Public*, pg. 123

Corbi, Lana, Sr. V.P.-Network Distribution--Fox Broadcasting Company (FBC), Beverly Hills, CA; *Int'l*, pg. 926

Corbin, Karen C., Sr. V.P.-Programming & Devel.--Tribune Entertainment Company, Los Angeles, CA; *U.S. Public*, pg. 1636

Corbin, Richard L., Chief Fin. Officer & Sr. V.P.--Thiokol Corporation, Ogden, UT; *U.S. Public*, pg. 1596

Corbitt, J. Larry, Chief Fin. Officer & Sr. V.P.--United Family Life Insurance Co., Atlanta, GA; *Int'l*, pg. 499

Cordial, Michelle, Sr. V.P.-Acct. Services--Western International Media Corporation, Los Angeles, CA; *U.S. Private*, pg. 1165

Corica, Vincent C., Sr. V.P.-East, Bus. Sls. & Service--MCI Communications Corp., Atlanta, GA; *U.S. Public*, pg. 1023

Corigliano, Cosmo, Chief Fin. Officer & Sr. V.P.--Cendant Corporation, Stamford, CT; *U.S. Public*, pg. 320

Corigliano, Cosmo, Chief Fin. Officer & Sr. V.P.--CUC International, Inc., Stamford, CT; *U.S. Public*, pg. 320

Cormack, David A., Sr. V.P.-Sls.--IQ Software Corporation, Norcross, GA; *U.S. Public*, pg. 858

Corn, Allan, Chief Fin. Officer & Sr. V.P.--Michael Anthony Jewelers, Inc., Mount Vernon, NY; *U.S. Public*, pg. 1103

Cornelison, Lee T., Sr. V.P.--Peabody COALSALES Company, Saint Louis, MO; *Int'l*, pg. 594

Cornell, G.L., Sr. V.P.-Acctg., Real Estate & Treas.--Auto-Owners Insurance, Lansing, MI; *U.S. Private*, pg. 100

Cornely, Joseph H., III, 1st Sr. V.P., Dir.-Store Plng. & Mgr.-Real Estate--J. Baker, Inc., Canton, MA; *U.S. Public*, pg. 167

Cornett, Arlen C., Sr. V.P.--CR Minerals Corporation, Golden, CO; *U.S. Public*, pg. 302

Cornett, Ernestine, Sr. V.P.-Gray KY Television, Gen. Mgr. & Station Mgr.--WYMT-TV, Hazard, KY; *U.S. Public*, pg. 759

Corrao, Peter A., Sr. V.P.-Strategic Ntl. Accts.--ADVO, Inc., Windsor, CT; *U.S. Public*, pg. 23

Correia, Armand, Chief Fin. Officer & Sr. V.P.--The Dress Barn, Inc., Suffern, NY; *U.S. Public*, pg. 528

Corrigall, Stephen S., Sr. V.P.--New Hampshire Insurance Group, New York, NY; *U.S. Public*, pg. 84

Corrigan-Davis, Mary Ann, Sr. V.P.-Intl.--American Greetings Corporation, Cleveland, OH; *U.S. Public*, pg. 77

Corrigan, John M., Sr. V.P.-Global Info. Sys.--Estee Lauder Companies Inc., New York, NY; *U.S. Public*, pg. 594

Corrigan, Kim, Sr. V.P. & Acct. Mng. Dir.--Young & Rubicam New York, New York, NY; *U.S. Private*, pg. 1198

Corrini, Christopher P., Sr. V.P.-Fin.--Brink's, Inc., Darien, CT; *U.S. Public*, pg. 1305

Cors, Allan D., Sr. V.P.-Govt. Affairs--Corning Incorporated, Corning, NY; *U.S. Public*, pg. 448

Corsi, Emerick, Sr. V.P.-Leasing--Forest City Commercial Construction Company, Inc., Cleveland, OH; *U.S. Public*, pg. 668

Corsi, Pietro, Sr. V.P.-Hotel Services--Princess Cruise Lines, Los Angeles, CA; *Int'l*, pg. 1035

Corson, Nancy R., Sr. V.P.-Commercial Lending--National Penn Bank, Boyertown, PA; *U.S. Public*, pg. 1159

Corson, Tom, Sr. V.P.-Mktg.--Sony Music Entertainment, Inc., New York, NY; *Int'l*, pg. 1281

Corvino, Claude, Sr. V.P.--Harding Lawson Associates Group, Inc., Novato, CA; *U.S. Public*, pg. 785

Corwin, Steve, Sr. V.P. & Mngmt. Supvr.--Robert A. Becker, New York, NY; *Int'l*, pg. 601

Coslov, Alan, Sr. V.P.-Opers.--Tube City Inc., Glassport, PA; *U.S. Private*, pg. 1108

Cosner, Alan, V.P., Treas. & Sec.--Lady Baltimore Foods, Inc., Kansas City, KS; *U.S. Public*, pg. 975

Cosse, Steven A., Sr. V.P. & Gen. Counsel--Murphy Oil Corporation, El Dorado, AR; *U.S. Public*, pg. 1141

Cosser, Julie R., Sr. V.P.-Mdsg.--Eddie Bauer, Inc., Redmond, WA; *U.S. Public*, pg. 1499

Cossette, Paul, Sr. V.P.-Washington District--M.A. Mortenson Company, Minneapolis, MN; *U.S. Private*, pg. 763

Costantini, William P., Sr. V.P. & Gen. Counsel--Olsten Corporation, Melville, NY; *U.S. Public*, pg. 1220

Costanza, Robert, Sr. V.P.-Opers.--Del Mar Avionics, Irvine, CA; *U.S. Private*, pg. 321

Costanzo, Patrick M., Sr. V.P. & Mgr.-Heavy Construction Div.--Granite Construction Incorporated, Watsonville, CA; *U.S. Public*, pg. 759

Costas, Stephen J., Sr. V.P.--Associates Commercial Corporation, Dallas, TX; *U.S. Public*, pg. 663

Costello, Joanne, Sr. V.P. & Brdcst. Dir.--Grey Direct, New York, NY; *U.S. Public*, pg. 764

Costello, Mark E., Sr. V.P.-Correspondent Lending--Aames Financial Corporation, Los Angeles, CA; *U.S. Public*, pg. 12

Costello, Thomas E., Sr. V.P.-Distr. Bus.--International Paper Company, Purchase, NY; *U.S. Public*, pg. 901

Coster, Malcom, Sr. V.P.-Strategic Bus. Devel.--Unisys Corporation, Blue Bell, PA; *U.S. Public*, pg. 1671

Costigan, John M., Sr. V.P., Gen. Counsel & Sec.--Premark International, Inc., Deerfield, IL; *U.S. Public*, pg. 1321

Costlow, Curtis C., Sr. V.P.-Property Management--Crown American Realty Trust, Johnstown, PA; *U.S. Public*, pg. 461

Coston, Larry B., Sr. V.P.-Mktg.--Precision Drilling Corporation, Calgary, Canada; *Int'l*, pg. 1066

Cote, Arthur, Sr. V.P.-Opers. Grp. & Chief Engr.--National Fire Protection Association, Quincy, MA; *U.S. Private*, pg. 782

Cothran, Larry, Sr. V.P.-Plng.--Huitt-Zollars, Inc., Dallas, TX; *U.S. Private*, pg. 547

Cotran, Ralph, Sr. V.P.--Willis Corroon International/ Americas, Glendale, CA; *Int'l*, pg. 1507

Cotshott, Gary J., Sr. V.P.-Worldwide Customer Svcs.--NCR Corporation, Dayton, OH; *U.S. Public*, pg. 1146

Cottam, Barbara S., Sr. V.P.-Pub. Affairs--Citizens Savings Bank, Providence, RI; *Int'l*, pg. 1132

Cotter, John, Sr. V.P.-Bus. Devel.--Paul Arpin Vanlines, Inc., West Warwick, RI; *U.S. Private*, pg. 85

Cotter, Richard, Sr. V.P.-Mktg.--Bentley Mills, Inc., City of Industry, CA; *U.S. Public*, pg. 889

Cotter, Robert F., Sr. V.P. & Dir.-Opers.-Europe--ITT Sheraton Corporation, Boston, MA; *U.S. Public*, pg. 1512

Cotton, Gary D., Sr. V.P.-Customer Opers.--San Diego Gas & Electric Company, San Diego, CA; *U.S. Public*, pg. 584

Cotton, Susan, Sr. V.P. & Dir.-Mktg. Info. & Analysis--BankAmerica Corporation, San Francisco, CA; *U.S. Public*, pg. 179
Cotton, Vicki, Sr. V.P.-Pur.--Ingram Micro Inc., Santa Ana, CA; *U.S. Public*, pg. 878
Cottrell, G. Walton, Chief Fin. Officer & Sr. V.P.-Fin.--Carpenter Technology Corporation, Reading, PA; *U.S. Public*, pg. 307
Couch, Frank, Sr. V.P.-Thomas Nelson Bibles--Thomas Nelson Inc., Nashville, TN; *U.S. Public*, pg. 1167
Couch, Michael J., Sr. V.P.--Fina, Inc., Dallas, TX; *Int'l*, pg. 1044
Cougher, Harry F., Chief Oper. Officer-Mining & Sr. V.P.--Sunshine Mining And Refining Company, Boise, ID; *U.S. Public*, pg. 1536
Coughlin, Karen A., Sr. V.P.--Humana Health Chicago, Inc., Chicago, IL; *U.S. Public*, pg. 847
Coughlin, Karen A., Sr. V.P.--Employers Health Insurance Company, Green Bay, WI; *U.S. Public*, pg. 847
Coughlin, Karen A., Sr. V.P.--Humana Health Plan of Texas, Inc., San Antonio, TX; *U.S. Public*, pg. 848
Coughlin, Karen A., Sr. V.P.--Humana Health Plan of Alabama, Inc., Montgomery, AL; *U.S. Public*, pg. 848
Coughlin, Karen A., Sr. V.P.--Humana Wisconsin Health Organization Insurance Corporation, Milwaukee, WI; *U.S. Public*, pg. 848
Coughlin, Karen A., Sr. V.P.--Network EPO, Inc., Milwaukee, WI; *U.S. Public*, pg. 848
Couillard, Richard, Sr. V.P.-Explorations & Prod.--Numac Energy Inc., Calgary, Canada; *Int'l*, pg. 990
Couk, Marty D., Sr. V.P.-Pizza Hut Opers.--Pizza Hut Division, Pittsburg, KS; *U.S. Public*, pg. 1147
Coulter, Chail, Sr. V.P. & Gen. Counsel--National Life Insurance Company, Montpelier, VT; *U.S. Private*, pg. 785
Countryman, Dean C., Sr. V.P. & Sr. Fixed Income Mgr.--AMCORE Capital Management, Inc., Rockford, IL; *U.S. Public*, pg. 64
Couper, Gavin J., Sr. V.P.--Transcanada Pipelines Limited, Calgary, Canada; *Int'l*, pg. 1416
Courtney, Sally A., Sr. V.P. & Gen. Mgr.-Mdse.-Hechinger Stores--Hechinger Company Investors II, L.P., Largo, MD; *U.S. Private*, pg. 477
Cousineau, Charles, Sr. V.P.-Mktg.--Environetx, Itasca, IL; *U.S. Private*, pg. 378
Coutinho, Artur A.V., Sr. V.P.-Prod.--Embraer-Empresa Brasileira de Aeronautica S.A., Sao Jose dos Campos, Brazil; *Int'l*, pg. 452
Couto, Arnaldo Soto, Sr. V.P.-Construction Loans--Banco Popular de Puerto Rico, San Juan, PR; *U.S. Public*, pg. 175
Couto, Terry, Chief Fin. Officer & Sr. V.P.--Citizens Mortgage Corporation, Atlanta, GA; *Int'l*, pg. 1132
Coutts, Thomas M., Sr. V.P. & Gen. Mgr.-European Div.--Life Technologies, Inc., Rockville, MD; *U.S. Public*, pg. 504
Couture, Becky R., Sr. V.P.--TCF Bank Minnesota FSB, Minneapolis, MN; *U.S. Public*, pg. 1554
Covington, Christopher, Sr. V.P. & Gen. Counsel--Vanstar Corporation, Pleasanton, CA; *U.S. Public*, pg. 1708
Cowdrey, Bill, Sr. V.P.--Kenwood USA, Long Beach, CA; *Int'l*, pg. 730
Cowen, Jeffrey, Sr. V.P.-Production--Big Dog Holdings Inc., Santa Barbara, CA; *U.S. Public*, pg. 227
Cowen, Robert N., Sr. V.P. & Sec.--Overseas Shipholding Group, Inc., New York, NY; *U.S. Public*, pg. 1236
Cox, Beverley, Sr. V.P.-H.R.--Glenayre Technologies, Inc., Charlotte, NC; *U.S. Public*, pg. 746
Cox, Douglas, Chief Fin. Officer & Sr. V.P.-Fin.--Elf Atochem North America, Inc., Philadelphia, PA; *Int'l*, pg. 445
Cox, Garvin, Sr. V.P.--Texas Refinery Corp., Fort Worth, TX; *U.S. Private*, pg. 1078
Cox, J. William, Sr. V.P.-Opers. & Admin.--The Dallas Morning News, Inc., Dallas, TX; *U.S. Public*, pg. 209
Cox, James Dan, Sr. V.P. & Gen. Mgr.-Southern Opers.--Altec Industries, Inc., Birmingham, AL; *U.S. Private*, pg. 47
Cox, Jennifer, Sr. V.P.-Acctg. Div.--First of America Bank Corporation, Kalamazoo, MI; *U.S. Public*, pg. 636
Cox, R.M., Jr., Sr. V.P.--Emerson Electric Co., Saint Louis, MO; *U.S. Public*, pg. 572
Cox, Warren D., Sr. V.P.- Distr.--The Vons Companies, Inc., Arcadia, CA; *U.S. Public*, pg. 1426
Cox, William J., Sr. V.P.--The M&T Company, King of Prussia, PA; *U.S. Public*, pg. 277
Coyle, James E., III, Sr. V.P.-Mdsg. & Sls.--DeCorp, Carrollton, TX; *U.S. Public*, pg. 048
Coyne, William E., Sr. V.P.-Res. & Devel.--3M, Saint Paul, MN; *U.S. Public*, pg. 1604
Cozadd, Bruce, Chief Fin. Officer & Sr. V.P.--Alza Corporation, Palo Alto, CA; *U.S. Public*, pg. 62
Crabtree, Dennis, Sr. V.P.-Opers.--Midwest Express Airlines, Inc., Oak Creek, WI; *U.S. Public*, pg. 1111
Crabtree, Dennis J., Sr. V.P.-Opers.--Midwest Express Holdings, Inc., Oak Creek, WI; *U.S. Public*, pg. 1111
Crabtree, Donald, Sr. V.P.--Willis Corroon Marine & Energy, Houston, TX; *Int'l*, pg. 1508
Crabtree, Larry L., Sr. V.P.-Asia Grp.--United States Filter Corporation, Palm Desert, CA; *U.S. Public*, pg. 1681
Craft, Daniel L., Sr. V.P.-Human Resources--1st Source Bank Consolidated, South Bend, IN; *U.S. Public*, pg. 638
Crager, Bruce, Sr. V.P.-Oceaneering Prod. Systems--Oceaneering International, Inc., Houston, TX; *U.S. Public*, pg. 1211
Crager, Bruce L., Sr. V.P.--Oceaneering Production Systems, Houston, TX; *U.S. Public*, pg. 1211
Craig, Barton J., Sr. V.P. & Gen. Counsel--Morgan's Foods, Inc., Beachwood, OH; *U.S. Public*, pg. 1133
Craig, Bruce, Sr. V.P.-Retail Field Opers.--Starbucks Coffee Company, Seattle, WA; *U.S. Public*, pg. 1510
Craig, Ian A., Pres.-Broadband Network & Sr. V.P.--Northern Telecom Limited, Brampton, Canada; *Int'l*, pg. 968
Craig, Maureen, Sr. V.P. & Strategic Plng. Dir.--DMB&B Los Angeles, Los Angeles, CA; *U.S. Private*, pg. 303
Craig, Paul W., Jr., Sr. V.P.--Hibernia Corporation, New Orleans, LA; *U.S. Public*, pg. 825
Craig, Peter, Sr. V.P. & Mngmt. Supvr.--Fahlgren, Cincinnati, OH; *U.S. Private*, pg. 391
Craig, Tom, Sr. V.P.-Sls. & Mktg.--Golden Flake Snack Foods, Inc., Birmingham, AL; *U.S. Public*, pg. 750
Craigs, Anne F., Sr. V.P.--Androscoggin Savings Bank, Lewiston, ME; *U.S. Private*, pg. 74
Cramer, Jeffrey R., Sr. V.P. & Gen. Mgr.-Tech. Svcs. Cluster--Anacomp, Inc., Indianapolis, IN; *U.S. Public*, pg. 106
Cramer, Neal P., Sr. V.P.--Western Atlas International, Inc., Houston, TX; *U.S. Public*, pg. 1757
Cramm, Gene F., Sr. V.P. & Dir.-Games & Concept Devel.--ShowBiz Pizza Time, Inc., Irving, TX; *U.S. Public*, pg. 1468
Crandall, Peter, Sr. V.P.--National Bank of Alaska, Anchorage, AK; *U.S. Public*, pg. 1153
Crandell, Donnie, Sr. V.P.-Corp. Devel. & Pres.-MP/Real Estate Holdings--Minnesota Power, Duluth, MN; *U.S. Public*, pg. 1116
Crane, Michael R., Sr. V.P.-N. American Grp.--Dentsply International Inc., York, PA; *U.S. Public*, pg. 498
Crane, Robert M., Sr. V.P.-Interdivisional Svcs.--Kaiser Permanente, Oakland, CA; *U.S. Private*, pg. 605
Crane, Russell L., Sr. V.P.-Human Resources & Admin.--PPG Industries, Inc., Pittsburgh, PA; *U.S. Public*, pg. 1245
Crane, Therese, Sr. V.P.-Strategic Market Segments--Apple Computer, Inc., Cupertino, CA; *U.S. Public*, pg. 121
Cranois, Nicole, Sr. V.P.-Corp. Communications--Elf Aquitane, Paris, France; *Int'l*, pg. 444
Cranor, Timothy W., Sr. V.P.-Pur.--Interstate Bakeries Corporation, Kansas City, MO; *U.S. Public*, pg. 909
Crantz, Robert, Sr. V.P. & Creative Dir.--DCA Advertising, Inc., New York, NY; *Int'l*, pg. 393
Craugh, Joseph P., Jr., Sr. V.P. & Govt. Affairs Counsel--Harleysville Group, Harleysville, PA; *U.S. Public*, pg. 786
Craven, Patrick, Sr. V.P.-Opers. & Branch Mgr.--W & D Securities, Inc., Jersey City, NJ; *U.S. Public*, pg. 925
Craves, Robert E., Sr. V.P.-Membership & Mktg.--Costco Wholesale, Issaquah, WA; *U.S. Public*, pg. 451
Crawford, David, Sr. V.P.--Sundt Corp., Tucson, AZ; *U.S. Private*, pg. 1051
Crawford, John, Sr. V.P.-Opers.--L3 Communications Narda-Microwave Div., Hauppauge, NY; *U.S. Private*, pg. 638
Crawford, John T., Sr. V.P.-Information Mngmt.--The Hartford Financial Services Group Inc., Hartford, CT; *U.S. Public*, pg. 794
Crawford, Kathleen, Sr. V.P. & Treas.--Admiral Insurance Company, Cherry Hill, NJ; *U.S. Public*, pg. 216
Crawford, S., Sr. V.P. & Creative Dir.--Howard, Merrell & Partners, Inc., Raleigh, NC; *U.S. Private*, pg. 542
Creany, Cathleen A., Sr. V.P.--KOTV Inc., Tulsa, OK; *U.S. Public*, pg. 209
Creany, Cathy, Sr. V.P.-Television Grp.--A.H. Belo Corporation, Dallas, TX; *U.S. Public*, pg. 209
Crecca, A., Sr. V.P.-Sls./Cosmed Div.--Beiersdorf, Inc., Norwalk, CT; *Int'l*, pg. 182
Creel, Brady W., Sr. V.P. & Chief Mktg. Officer--The Franklin Life Insurance Company, Springfield, IL; *U.S. Public*, pg. 76
Creel, L. Anderson, Chief Fin. Officer, Sr. V.P., Treas. & Sec.--Prime Bancshares Inc., Houston, TX; *U.S. Public*, pg. 1326
Cregg, Brian M., Sr. V.P.--First Maryland Bancorp, Baltimore, MD; *Int'l*, pg. 64
Cress, Fred, Sr. V.P.-Airport Svcs.--Cara Operations Limited, Toronto, Canada; *Int'l*, pg. 266
Cress, Steven A., Sr. V.P.--Chronimed Inc., Minnetonka, MN; *U.S. Public*, pg. 352
Cresta, Ron, Sr. V.P.-Opers.--Lenox Collections, Langhorne, PA; *U.S. Public*, pg. 261
Creveling, Allen C., Sr. V.P.-Human Resources--Symbol Technologies, Inc., Holtsville, NY; *U.S. Public*, pg. 1546
Creviston, Robert L., Sr. V.P.-Human Resources--Kellogg Company, Battle Creek, MI; *U.S. Public*, pg. 947
Crews, Steve, Sr. V.P.--Golin/Harris Communications, Inc., Chicago, IL; *Int'l*, pg. 1226
Cribari, J. Matt, Sr. V.P.-North American Aftermarket--Tenneco Automotive, Deerfield, IL; *U.S. Public*, pg. 1577
Crilly, James, Sr. V.P.-Sls./Arm & Hammer Div.--Church & Dwight Co., Inc., Princeton, NJ; *U.S. Public*, pg. 355
Cristofoli, Nino M., Sr. V.P.-Sls. & Mktg., Nestle Refigerated Food Co.--Nestle Frozen/Refrigerated Food Co., Solon, OH; *Int'l*, pg. 918
Critchlow, Paul, Sr. V.P.-Mktg. & Communications--Merrill Lynch & Co., Inc., New York, NY; *U.S. Public*, pg. 1097
Crivelli, Mark, Sr. V.P.-Secondary Mktg.--Kaufman and Broad Mortgage Co., Woodland Hills, CA; *U.S. Public*, pg. 945
Crivolio, James J., Sr. V.P.--American Security Group, Atlanta, GA; *Int'l*, pg. 499
Crocitto, Peter, First Sr. V.P.--Valley National Bank, Parsippany, NJ; *U.S. Public*, pg. 1705
Crockett, Joan M., Sr. V.P.-Human Resources--The Allstate Corporation, Northbrook, IL; *U.S. Public*, pg. 55
Crockford, Clifford J., Jr., Sr. V.P.--Associated Banc-Corp, Green Bay, WI; *U.S. Public*, pg. 140
Croft, Jerry L., Sr. V.P.-Adv. & Publr.--Century Publishing Company, Evanston, IL; *U.S. Private*, pg. 226
Croisier, J.P.L., Sr. V.P. & Treas.--Essex International, Inc., Fort Wayne, IN; *U.S. Public*, pg. 593
Croll, Ian, Sr. V.P. & Media Services Dir.--Gray Kirk/VanSant Advertising, Inc., Baltimore, MD; *U.S. Private*, pg. 472
Crombie, William J., Sr. V.P.--Pulte Corporation, Bloomfield Hills, MI; *U.S. Public*, pg. 1344
Cromer, Jenny, Sr. V.P.--First Commerce Corporation, New Orleans, LA; *U.S. Public*, pg. 629
Cromwell, Joan, Sr. V.P. & Sr. Auditor--First Commerce Bancshares, Inc., Lincoln, NE; *U.S. Public*, pg. 629
Cronan, James E., Chief Fin. Officer & Sr. V.P.--Harvey Industries, Inc., Waltham, MA; *U.S. Private*, pg. 508
Cronin, Dick, Sr. V.P.--Provident Mutual Life Insurance Co., Berwyn, PA; *U.S. Private*, pg. 891
Cronin, Richard J., III, Chief Fin. Officer & Sr. V.P.--Sithe Energies, Inc., New York, NY; *U.S. Private*, pg. 1004
Cronin, Robert J., Sr. V.P.-Fin.--SHL Systemhouse, Ottawa, Canada; *Int'l*, pg. 1154
Cronk, Robert T., Sr. V.P.--Mapco Natural Gas Liquids Inc., Tulsa, OK; *U.S. Public*, pg. 1042
Crook, Dennis, Sr. V.P.-Admin. & Gasoline--The Pantry, Inc., Sanford, NC; *U.S. Private*, pg. 837
Crooke, Stephen V., Sr. V.P.--Republic National Bank of New York (U.K.), London, United Kingdom; *U.S. Public*, pg. 1381
Crosby, Robert C., Sr. V.P. & Pres. ATH--Beverly Enterprises, Inc., Fort Smith, AR; *U.S. Public*, pg. 227
Croskey, Carl, Sr. V.P.-Reg. Opers.--MichCon, Detroit, MI; *U.S. Public*, pg. 1025
Cross, C. Allen, Sr. V.P.-Human Resources--First American Federal Savings Bank, Bristol, VA; *U.S. Public*, pg. 624
Cross, Michael, Sr. V.P. & Gen. Mgr.-Opers.--Universal Studios Japan, Ltd., Tokyo, Japan; *Int'l*, pg. 1216
Crossland, James, Sr. V.P. & Dir.--GPC Government Policy Consultants (Federal), Ottawa, Canada; *U.S. Public*, pg. 1225
Crosswhite, Randal, Chief Fin. Officer & Sr. V.P.--Independent Bankshares, Inc., Abilene, TX; *U.S. Public*, pg. 874
Crotts, B.A., Exec. V.P.--U.S. Pipeline, Inc., Houston, TX; *Int'l*, pg. 31
Crotty, Gerald C., Sr. V.P. & Pres.-ITT Information Services, Inc.--ITT Corporation, New York, NY; *U.S. Public*, pg. 1512
Crouch, C.H., Sr. V.P.-Investor Rels.--SouthTrust Corporation, Birmingham, AL; *U.S. Public*, pg. 1491
Crouch, Keith M., Sr. V.P. & Gen. Counsel--Patina Oil & Gas Corp., Denver, CO; *U.S. Public*, pg. 1264
Crouch, Kenneth, Sr. V.P.-Exploration & Production--Kerr-McGee Corporation, Oklahoma City, OK; *U.S. Public*, pg. 952
Crouch, Kenneth W., Sr. V.P.-N. America & Intl. Exploration--Kerr-McGee Petroleum Exploration & Production Division, Oklahoma City, OK; *U.S. Public*, pg. 952
Crouch, Robert D., Sr. V.P.-Sls. & Mktg.--Respironics, Inc., Pittsburgh, PA; *U.S. Public*, pg. 1383
Crouch, Taylor J., Sr. V.P.-Worldwide Client Rels. & Mktg.--PAREXEL International Corporation, Waltham, MA; *U.S. Public*, pg. 1257
Crowder, Otis P., Sr. V.P.--Crowder Construction Co., Charlotte, NC; *U.S. Private*, pg. 291
Crowder, Richard T., Sr. V.P.-Intl.--Dekalb Genetics Corporation, De Kalb, IL; *U.S. Public*, pg. 493
Crowell, Robert I., Sr. V.P.-Investments Division--Bank of Hawaii, Honolulu, HI; *U.S. Public*, pg. 1248
Crowl, Richard R., Sr. V.P. & Gen. Counsel--ReliaStar Financial Corp., Minneapolis, MN; *U.S. Public*, pg. 1375
Crowley, Francis E., Chief Fin. Officer & Sr. V.P.--Cargill Salt Inc., Minneapolis, MN; *Int'l*, pg. 48
Crudele, Anthony, Chief Fin. Officer & Sr. V.P.--The Sports Authority Inc., Fort Lauderdale, FL; *U.S. Public*, pg. 1499
Cruickshank, D.J., Chief Fin. Officer & Sr. V.P.--Flexible Products Company, Marietta, GA; *U.S. Private*, pg. 412
Cruikshank, Bruce A., Sr. V.P.--Sealed Air Corporation, Saddle Brook, NJ; *U.S. Public*, pg. 1450
Cruikshank, Kirk, Sr. V.P.-Mktg.--Arbor Software Corporation, Sunnyvale, CA; *U.S. Public*, pg. 127
Crumbine, Dennis, Sr. V.P.-Fin.--The Perrier Group of America, Greenwich, CT; *Int'l*, pg. 919
Crumley, Dale C., Sr. V.P.--Global Power Company, Waverly, TN; *Int'l*, pg. 74
Crumley, Robert W., Sr. V.P.-Personnel--Boddie-Noell Enterprises Inc., Rocky Mount, NC; *U.S. Private*, pg. 154
Cuccia, F. Paul, Chief Info. Officer & Sr. V.P.--Sotheby's Holdings Inc., New York, NY; *U.S. Public*, pg. 1487
Cuddy, Steve, Sr. V.P.-Bus.-to-Bus. & Acct. Exec.--Colle & McVoy, Inc., Minneapolis, MN; *U.S. Private*, pg. 252
Cuddy, Steve, Sr. V.P.-Bus.-to-Bus.--Colle & McVoy Marketing Communications, Minneapolis, MN; *U.S. Private*, pg. 252
Cuellar, John, Sr. V.P. & Gen. Counsel--El Chico Restaurants, Inc., Dallas, TX; *U.S. Private*, pg. 283
Cuff, Dennis, Sr. V.P.-Human Resources--Eckerd Corporation, Largo, FL; *U.S. Public*, pg. 917
Culbertson, Michael A., Sr. V.P.--The Seibels Bruce Group, Inc., Columbia, SC; *U.S. Public*, pg. 1453
Cullen, Brian D., Sr. V.P.--Raytheon E-Systems, Greenville, TX; *U.S. Public*, pg. 1365
Culligan, Elizabeth, Sr. V.P.-Biscuit Mktg.--Nabisco Inc., Parsippany, NJ; *U.S. Public*, pg. 1355
Cullison, Rod, Sr. V.P. & Mgr.--First Security Processing Services, Inc., Salt Lake City, UT; *U.S. Public*, pg. 638
Cullison, Rodney, Sr. V.P.-Electronic Services Div.--First Security Service Company, Salt Lake City, UT; *U.S. Public*, pg. 638
Culwell, Mark, Sr. V.P.-Asset Mngmt.--Lexford Residential Trust, Columbus, OH; *U.S. Public*, pg. 991
Cuming, David B., Sr. V.P.--Alleghany Corporation, New York, NY; *U.S. Public*, pg. 42
Cummin, I.R., Exec. Gen. Mgr.-Human Resources--Southcorp Holdings Ltd., Adelaide, Australia; *Int'l*, pg. 1287
Cummings, Robert J., Sr. V.P.-Corp. & Commercial Fin. Services--CT Financial Services, Inc., Toronto, Canada; *Int'l*, pg. 112
Cummins, Mark R., Sr. V.P., Chief Investment Officer & Treas.--Harleysville Group, Harleysville, PA; *U.S. Public*, pg. 786
Cuneo, Ronald E., Sr. V.P.--Wang Laboratories, Inc., Billerica, MA; *U.S. Public*, pg. 1787
Cunliffe, Ken, Sr. V.P.--Willis Corroon Melling Inc., Toronto, Canada; *Int'l*, pg. 1509

Cunnignham, James P., Sr. V.P.-Offshore Sourcing--The Gap, Inc., San Francisco, CA; *U.S. Public,* pg. 702

Cunningham, Bob, Sr. V.P.-Sls. & Mktg.--Pico Products, Inc., Lake View Terrace, CA; *U.S. Public,* pg. 1294

Cunningham, Dale, Sr. V.P. & Gen. Counsel--Sunkist Growers, Inc., Sherman Oaks, CA; *U.S. Private,* pg. 1052

Cunningham, G.K., Exec. Gen. Mgr.-Corp. Affairs--Southcorp Holdings Ltd., Adelaide, Australia; *Int'l,* pg. 1287

Cunningham, M.W., Exec. V.P.--ING North America Insurance Company, Atlanta, GA; *Int'l,* pg. 648

Cunningham, Michael H., Sr. V.P.--Glen Falls National Bank & Trust Company, Glens Falls, NY; *U.S. Public,* pg. 135

Cunningham, William J., Sr. V.P.-Mfg. & Prod. Devl.--Data General Corporation, Westborough, MA; *U.S. Public,* pg. 485

Curado, Frederico P.F., Exec. V.P.-Plng. & Devel.--Embraer-Empresa Brasileira de Aeronautica S.A., Sao Jose dos Campos, Brazil; *Int'l,* pg. 452

Curless, Michael A., Sr. V.P. & Tech. & Trng. Dir.--Creswell, Munsell, Fultz & Zirbel, L.P., Cedar Rapids, IA; *U.S. Private,* pg. 1197

Curley, Denis M., Chief Fin. Officer, Sr. V.P., Treas. & Sec.--The Ackerley Group, Seattle, WA; *U.S. Public,* pg. 15

Curley, Robert M., Sr. V.P.--Keycorp, Cleveland, OH; *U.S. Public,* pg. 954

Curling, David, Sr. V.P.--The William Cook Agency, Inc., Jacksonville, FL; *U.S. Private,* pg. 273

Curran, Kevin J., Sr. V.P., Gen. Counsel & Sec.--Parsons Brinckerhoff Inc., New York, NY; *U.S. Private,* pg. 841

Curran, Timothy J., Sr. V.P.-Sls.--Tech Data Corporation, Clearwater, FL; *U.S. Public,* pg. 1562

Currat, Claude, Sr. V.P.-Logistics--Bobst S.A., Lausanne, Switzerland; *Int'l,* pg. 198

Current, Jim, Jr., Pres.-NCG Global Energy Svcs. & Sr. V.P.--NGC Corporation, Houston, TX; *U.S. Public,* pg. 1146

Currey, Russell M., Sr. V.P.-Mktg. & Plng.--Rock-Tenn Company, Norcross, GA; *U.S. Public,* pg. 1396

Currie, Peter, Chief Fin. Officer, Chief Admin. Officer & Exec. V.P.--Netscape Communications Corp., Mountain View, CA; *U.S. Public,* pg. 1168

Currie, Peter W., Chief Fin. Officer & Sr. V.P.--Northern Telecom Limited, Brampton, Canada; *Int'l,* pg. 968

Currie, Philip R., Sr. V.P.-Newspaper Division--Gannett Company, Inc., Arlington, VA; *U.S. Public,* pg. 698

Currier, James L., Asst. V.P.-Claims--Willis Corroon Corp. of Seattle, Seattle, WA; *Int'l,* pg. 1507

Curry, John F., Sr. V.P.-Facilities--Bob Evans Farms, Inc., Columbus, OH; *U.S. Public,* pg. 596

Curson, R. John, Chief Fin. Officer, Sr. V.P.-Fin. & Sec.--Truevision, Inc., Santa Clara, CA; *U.S. Public,* pg. 1642

Curtin, John, Sr. V.P.-Production & Logistics--The Stroh Brewery Company, Detroit, MI; *U.S. Private,* pg. 1047

Curtis, Ann B., Sr. V.P.--Calpine Corporation, San Jose, CA; *U.S. Public,* pg. 296

Curtis, Harold R., Chief Fin. Officer, Sr. V.P., Treas. & Sec.--The M/A/R/C Group, Irving, TX; *U.S. Public,* pg. 1022

Curtis, Kathleen M., Sr. V.P.--Century Bancshares, Inc., Washington, DC; *U.S. Public,* pg. 328

Curtiss, Jeff, Chief Fin. Officer & Sr. V.P.--Browning-Ferris Industries, Inc., Houston, TX; *U.S. Public,* pg. 262

Cusato, Richard, Sr. V.P.-Acct. Mngmt.--Grey Advertising Inc., New York, NY; *U.S. Public,* pg. 764

Cush, H. Terry, Sr. V.P. & Dir.--Bank of America NT&SA, Grand Cayman, Cayman Islands; *U.S. Public,* pg. 182

Cushing, Robert T., Chief Fin. Officer & Sr. V.P.--Trustco Bank, N.A., Schenectady, NY; *U.S. Public,* pg. 1643

Cushman, Paul M., Sr. V.P.-Intl.--Riggs Bank N.A., Washington, DC; *U.S. Public,* pg. 1390

Cusson, Craig V., Sr. V.P.-Customer Svcs.--Berkshire Life Insurance Company, Pittsfield, MA; *U.S. Private,* pg. 136

Cutchins, Clifford A., IV, Sr. V.P. & Gen. Counsel--Fort James Corporation, Richmond, VA; *U.S. Public,* pg. 670

Cutilleta, Thomas, Sr. V.P. & Controller--Stone Container Corporation, Chicago, IL; *U.S. Public,* pg. 1520

Cutler, Bruce, Sr. V.P.--SEIKO Canada Inc., Markham, Canada; *Int'l,* pg. 1218

Cutler, Katie, Sr. V.P.-Corp. Commun.--Crown Vantage Inc., Oakland, CA; *U.S. Public,* pg. 465

Cutter, Edward A., Sr. V.P., Gen. Counsel & Sec.--The Clorox Company, Oakland, CA; *U.S. Public,* pg. 386

Cutwright, Brenda F., Chief Fin. Officer, Sr. V.P.-Fin. & Treas.--Aloha Airgroup, Inc., Honolulu, HI; *U.S. Private,* pg. 44

Cutwright, Brenda F., Chief Fin. Officer & Sr. V.P.-Fin. & Plng.--Island Air, Honolulu, HI; *U.S. Private,* pg. 44

Cuzzopoli, Joe, Sr. V.P.--American Pacific Corporation, Las Vegas, NV; *U.S. Public,* pg. 88

Cvijanovic, Vince, Sr. V.P.-Mktg.--Fournier Furniture, Saint Paul, VA; *U.S. Private,* pg. 422

Cybulski, John, Sr. V.P.-Aerospace--Coltec Holdings Inc, Charlotte, NC; *U.S. Public,* pg. 401

Cygan, Henry, Sr. V.P.-Bus. Devel.--Raytheon Infrastructure Incorporated, New York, NY; *U.S. Public,* pg. 1366

Cypress, Ellyn, Sr. V.P. & Dir.-Sls. & Svc.--Beverly Bancorporation Inc., Chicago, IL; *U.S. Public,* pg. 227

Cyranoski, Dave, Sr. V.P., Controller & Sec.--Northern Illinois Gas Company, Naperville, IL; *U.S. Public,* pg. 1183

Cyranoski, David L., Sr. V.P., Controller & Sec.--NICOR Inc., Naperville, IL; *U.S. Public,* pg. 1182

Cyrus, Kenneth M., Sr. V.P., Gen. Counsel & Sec.--Pharmacia & Upjohn, Inc., Windsor, United Kingdom; *Int'l,* pg. 1047

Czerwinski, Gregory D., Sr. V.P.--TCF Bank Minnesota FSB, Minneapolis, MN; *U.S. Public,* pg. 1554

Czubay, Ken, Sr. V.P.-JM Family & Southeast Toyota & Asst. Gen. Mgr.--JM Family Enterprises Inc., Deerfield Beach, FL; *U.S. Private,* pg. 577

Czura, Antony, Sr. Exec. V.P.--SGS Societe Generale de Surveillance Holding S.A., Geneva, Switzerland; *Int'l,* pg. 1153

Czwornog, Michael, Sr. V.P.--Comdata Corporation, Brentwood, TN; *U.S. Public,* pg. 331

D'Alessandro, Robert T., Sr. V.P. & Controller--UST Inc., Greenwich, CT; *U.S. Public,* pg. 1660

D'Alusio, John V., Sr. V.P.--Zenith Insurance Company, Woodland Hills, CA; *U.S. Public,* pg. 1791

D'Amaro, Lou, Sr. V.P.-Sls.--Esselte Corporation, Garden City, NY; *Int'l,* pg. 459

D'Amico, Catherine, Chief Fin. Officer, Sr. V.P.-Fin. & Treas.--Monro Muffler/Brake, Inc., Rochester, NY; *U.S. Public,* pg. 1124

D'Amico, Richard, Sr. V.P. & Mngmt. Supvr.--Greenstone Roberts Advertising, Melville, NY; *U.S. Public,* pg. 763

D'Amore, F. Paul, Chief Admin. Officer & Sr. V.P.--Kemper Reinsurance Co., Long Grove, IL; *U.S. Private,* pg. 614

D'Annibale, Anthony, Sr. V.P.-Mdsg.--Loehmann's, Inc., Bronx, NY; *U.S. Public,* pg. 1010

D'Antoni, David J., Sr. V.P.--Ashland, Inc., Russell, KY; *U.S.* Public, pg. 138

D'Antonio, Richard H., Chief Info. Officer & Sr. V.P.--Dixon Ticonderoga Company, Heathrow, FL; *U.S. Public,* pg. 514

D'Arcy, Paul, Sr. V.P.--Sanyo Fisher Company, Chatsworth, CA; *Int'l,* pg. 1191

D'Elia, Vivian, Sr. V.P.-Human Resources--Movado Group, Inc., Lyndhurst, NJ; *U.S. Public,* pg. 1140

d'Estaing, Henri Giscard, Sr. V.P.-Mineral Water Div.--Danone Group, Paris, France; *Int'l,* pg. 379

d'Hautefeuille, Eric, Sr. V.P.--Saint-Gobain, Courbevoie, France; *Int'l,* pg. 1170

Dabarno, Susan F., Sr. V.P.-Insurance Services--CT Financial Services, Inc., Toronto, Canada; *Int'l,* pg. 112

Dabrowski, Michael, Sr. V.P. & Acct. Dir.--Young & Rubicam New York, New York, NY; *U.S. Private,* pg. 1198

Dack, Jerilyn, Sr. V.P., Media Dir. & Consumer Plng. Dir.--Hill, Holliday/Altschiller, New York, NY; *U.S. Private,* pg. 529

Dagenais, Scott E., Sr. V.P.--Manufacturers & Traders Trust Company, Buffalo, NY; *U.S. Public,* pg. 631

Dagnon, Jim, Sr. V.P.--The Boeing Company, Seattle, WA; *U.S. Public,* pg. 239

Dahan, Andre, Sr. V.P.-Worldwide Field Opers.--Sequent Computer Systems, Inc., Beaverton, OR; *U.S. Public,* pg. 1459

Dahan, Asher, Sr. V.P.-Quality--The Israel Electric Corporation Ltd., Haifa, Israel; *Int'l,* pg. 690

Dahl, Ed, Sr. V.P. & Exec. Art Dir.--Grant Marketing Communications, Ardmore, PA; *U.S. Private,* pg. 470

Dahl, Ed, Sr. V.P. & Exec. Art Dir.--Kingswood Advertising, Inc., Ardmore, PA; *U.S. Private,* pg. 622

Dahlberg, Christer, Sr. V.P.-Pur.--Svedala Industri AB, Malmo, Sweden; *Int'l,* pg. 1323

Dahlen, Tom, Sr. V.P.-Mktg.--Ralphs Grocery Company, Compton, CA; *U.S. Private,* pg. 1202

Dahlka, Ed, Grp. Sr. V.P.-LaSalle Chicago Leasing Corp.--LaSalle National Bank, Chicago, IL; *Int'l,* pg. 10

Dahlke, Wayne T., Sr. V.P.-Power Delivery--Georgia Power Co., Atlanta, GA; *U.S. Public,* pg. 1490

Daichendt, Gary J., Sr. V.P.-Worldwide Opers.--Cisco Systems, Inc., San Jose, CA; *U.S. Public,* pg. 375

Dailey, Bill, Chief Fin. Officer--Heckethorn Mfg. Company, Inc., Dyersburg, TN; *U.S. Private,* pg. 519

Daily, Don, Sr. V.P.-GSI Steel Opers.--GS Industries, Inc., Charlotte, NC; *U.S. Private,* pg. 435

Dajani, Ashraf T., Sr. V.P.--Edison Capital, Irvine, CA; *U.S. Public,* pg. 564

Dakin, Robert, Sr. V.P. & Dir.-Stores--AnnTaylor, Inc., New York, NY; *U.S. Public,* pg. 116

Dalbeck, Betsey, Sr. V.P. & Creative Services Dir.--Hill, Holliday, Connors, Cosmopulos, Inc., Boston, MA; *U.S. Private,* pg. 529

Dalbey, Steve, Sr. V.P.--GSD&M, Austin, TX; *U.S. Private,* pg. 436

Daley, William, Sr. V.P.--The Medical Protective Company, Fort Wayne, IN; *U.S. Private,* pg. 728

Dalgleish, Terrence, Sr. V.P.-Law--Transalta Corporation, Calgary, Canada; *Int'l,* pg. 1416

Dalinger, Trudy, Chief Fin. Officer & Sr. V.P.--TSC Shannock Corporation, Burnaby, Canada; *Int'l,* pg. 1343

Dallas, Terry G., Sr. V.P. & Treas.--Atlantic Richfield Company, Los Angeles, CA; *U.S. Public,* pg. 144

Dalrymple, Edwin A., Sr. V.P.--Interstate/Johnson Lane, Inc., Charlotte, NC; *U.S. Public,* pg. 909

Dalton, H.E., Chief Acctg. Officer & Sr. V.P.--The St. Paul Companies, Inc., Saint Paul, MN; *U.S. Public,* pg. 1429

Dalton, Robb, Sr. V.P.-Bus. & Program Devel.--CBS Enterprises Division, New York, NY; *U.S. Public,* pg. 274

Dalton, Robert A., Sr. V.P. & Mgr.-Northern Div.--First Security Bank of Utah, N.A., Salt Lake City, UT; *U.S. Public,* pg. 637

Dalton, Ronald, Sr. V.P., Treas. & Sec.--Huron Valley Steel Corp., Belleville, MI; *U.S. Private,* pg. 549

Dalvi, Ajit M., Sr. V.P.-Mktg. & Programming--Cox Communications, Inc., Atlanta, GA; *U.S. Public,* pg. 454

Daly, Gene, Sr. V.P. & Bus. Devel. Dir.-U.S.A.--Ketchum Directory Advertising/Chicago, Chicago, IL; *U.S. Private,* pg. 616

Daly, J., Sr. V.P.-Mktg.--Metal Improvement Co., Paramus, NJ; *U.S. Public,* pg. 469

Daly, James G., Sr. V.P.-Energy Resources--Unitil Corporation, Hampton, NH; *U.S. Public,* pg. 1692

Daly, James G., Sr. V.P.--UNITIL Service Corporation, Hampton, NH; *U.S. Public,* pg. 1693

Daly, Keith, Sr. V.P.--FootAction USA, Irving, TX; *U.S. Public,* pg. 661

Daly, Thomas H., Sr. V.P.--The Insurance Corp. of New York, New York, NY; *U.S. Public,* pg. 336

Daly, Thomas M., Sr. V.P.--Chartwell Re Corporation, Stamford, CT; *U.S. Public,* pg. 336

Damiano, V. Jay, Sr. V.P.-Sls.--General Datacomm Industries, Inc., Middlebury, CT; *U.S. Public,* pg. 708

Damonte, John J., Jr., Sr. V.P.--MBT Architecture, San Francisco, CA; *U.S. Private,* pg. 686

Dan, Avi, Sr. V.P.-Dir. Brand Equity--Ryan Drossman & Partners, New York, NY; *U.S. Private,* pg. 953

Dana, Lewis, Sr. V.P. & Grp. Creative Dir.--Wunderman Cato Johnson, New York, NY; *U.S. Private,* pg. 1197

Dana, Nicholas, Sr. V.P.--Douglas Elliman, New York, NY; *U.S. Private,* pg. 341

Danderidge, M., Sr. V.P. & Gen. Mgr.--Electronics & Systems Integration Division, Melbourne, FL; *U.S. Public, pg. 1198*

Dandy, Bill, Sr. V.P.-Mktg.--Famous Footwear, Madison, WI; *U.S. Public,* pg. 262

Dane, Peter, Sr. V.P.--Allright Corporation, Houston, TX; *U.S. Private,* pg. 42

Dane, Richard, Sr. V.P.--Allright Corporation, Houston, TX; *U.S. Private,* pg. 42

Danes, Mark, Sr. V.P.--Edelman Worldwide, Inc., New York, NY; *U.S. Private,* pg. 362

Daniel, James R., Chief Fin. Officer & Sr. V.P.--MicroAge, Inc., Tempe, AZ; *U.S. Public,* pg. 1104

Daniel, John, Chief Credit Officer & Sr. V.P.--CNB Bancshares, Inc., Evansville, IN; *U.S. Public,* pg. 280

Daniel, Patrick D., Sr. V.P.--IPL Energy Inc., Calgary, Canada; *Int'l,* pg. 651

Daniel, Sam, Jr., Sr. V.P.-Reg. Opers.--W.R. Berkley Corporation, Greenwich, CT; *U.S. Public,* pg. 215

Daniels, Douglas, Sr. V.P.-Packaging--Domtar Inc., Montreal, Canada; *Int'l,* pg. 416

Daniels, Frank N., Sr. V.P.--Trans-Lux Corporation, Norwalk, CT; *U.S. Public,* pg. 1628

Daniels, John, Sr. V.P. & Acct. Exec.--Doremus & Company, New York, NY; *U.S. Public,* pg. 1223

Daniels, Richard A., Sr. V.P.-Sls.--Periphonics Corp., Bohemia, NY; *U.S. Public,* pg. 1278

Daniels, Thomas, Sr. V.P.-Stores--The Bon Ton Stores, Inc., York, PA; *U.S. Public,* pg. 244

Danielson, Robert E., Chief Information Officer & Sr. V.P.--Pioneer-Standard Electronics, Inc., Cleveland, OH; *U.S. Public,* pg. 1300

Dankmeyer, T. R., Sr. V.P. & Gen. Counsel--New Business Development, San Francisco, CA; *Int'l,* pg. 224

Dann, L. Kevin, Sr. V.P.--Jefferies & Company, Inc., Los Angeles, CA; *U.S. Public,* pg. 925

Danner, E.L., Chief Fin. Officer & Sr. V.P.--MidCon Corp., Lombard, IL; *U.S. Public,* pg. 1210

Danse, Edward H., Sr. V.P.-North East Asia Region--Allergan, Inc., Irvine, CA; *U.S. Public,* pg. 46

Danski, Jon F., Sr. V.P. & Controller--ITT Corporation, New York, NY; *U.S. Public,* pg. 1512

Dantzler, Larry W., Chief Fin. Officer & Sr. V.P.--International Family Entertainment, Inc., Virginia Beach, VA; *Int'l,* pg. 927

Daoust, Jacques, Sr. V.P.-General Trust of Canada--National Bank of Canada, Montreal, Canada; *Int'l,* pg. 907

Dapres, Paule, M.D., Sr. V.P.-Res. Opers./Europe--PAREXEL International Corporation, Waltham, MA; *U.S. Public,* pg. 1257

Darby, Jonathan, Sr. V.P.-Production--TriStar Pictures, Culver City, CA; *Int'l,* pg. 1283

Darcy, Randy G., Sr. V.P.-Opers.--General Mills, Inc., Minneapolis, MN; *U.S. Public,* pg. 717

Darden, J., Chief Fin. Officer & Sr. V.P.--GAB Robins North America, Inc., Parsippany, NJ; *Int'l,* pg. 1153

Dardess, Margaret, Sr. V.P.-Corp. Affairs--Glaxo Wellcome Inc., Research Triangle Park, NC; *Int'l,* pg. 552

Dare, B.R., Sr. V.P.--Dare Foods Limited, Kitchener, Canada; *Int'l,* pg. 383

Darlington, R.W., Sr. V.P.--STV Architects, Douglassville, PA; *U.S. Public,* pg. 1421

Darmstaeder, William, II, Sr. V.P.--NationsBank of St. Louis, Saint Louis, MO; *U.S. Public,* pg. 1164

Darnell, Thomas F., Sr. V.P.--Trustmark National Bank, Jackson, MS; *U.S. Public,* pg. 1643

Darr, James E., Jr., Sr. V.P., Gen. Counsel & Sec.--Dillard's, Inc., Little Rock, AR; *U.S. Public,* pg. 509

Darragh, Kent, Sr. V.P.-Shoes & Rubber--M.A. Hanna Company, Cleveland, OH; *U.S. Public,* pg. 780

Darragh, Robert J., Sr. V.P.-Mktg. & Sls.--Copes-Vulcan Inc., Lake City, PA; *U.S. Private,* pg. 274

Darricarrere, Yves-Louis, Sr. V.P.-Fin.--Elf Aquitane, Paris, France; *Int'l,* pg. 444

Darrow, Chris, Chief Fin. Officer & Sr. V.P.--Western Beef, Inc., Ridgewood, NY; *U.S. Public,* pg. 1758

Darrow, Katharine P., Sr. V.P.-Brdcst., Corp. Devel. & H.R.--The New York Times Company, New York, NY; *U.S. Public,* pg. 1173

Darwin, David A., Sr. V.P.-State Regulatory Affairs--TDS Telecommunications Corporation, Madison, WI; *U.S. Public,* pg. 1570

Dashnaw, Richard L., Sr. V.P.-Grp. Opers.--Coltec Holdings Inc, Charlotte, NC; *U.S. Public,* pg. 401

Dashner, Ronald E., Sr. V.P.-Opers.--Patina Oil & Gas Corp., Denver, CO; *U.S. Public,* pg. 1264

Dasse, Kurt, Dr., Sr. V.P.--Thermo Cardiosystems Inc., Woburn, MA; *U.S. Public,* pg. 1592

Dassonville, Georges, Sr. V.P.-Europe--SGS Societe Generale de Surveillance Holding S.A., Geneva, Switzerland; *Int'l,* pg. 1153

Dathe, Robert F., Chief Fin. Officer, Sr. V.P.-Fin., & Corp. Sec.--Marotta Scientific Controls, Inc., Montville, NJ; *U.S.* Private, pg. 706

Datoo, Bashir, Dr., Sr. V.P.-Strategic Mktg. Services--Total Research Corporation, Princeton, NJ; *U.S. Public,* pg. 1625

Dattilo, David A., Sr. V.P.-Sls. & Service--Safety-Kleen Corp., Elgin, IL; *U.S. Public,* pg. 1425

Daub, Kenneth E., Sr. V.P.--LTX Corporation, Westwood, MA; *U.S. Public,* pg. 972

Dauer, Stephen J., Sr. V.P.-Sls.--Dyersburg Corporation, Dyersburg, TN; *U.S. Public,* pg. 538

Daugherty, J.R., Sr. V.P.-Sls. & Mktg.--The Chas. H. Lilly Co., Portland, OR; *U.S. Private,* pg. 667

Daugherty, Michael J., Sr. V.P.-Space Systems Grp.--Aerospace Corporation, El Segundo, CA; *U.S. Private*, pg. 24
Daum, Gary C., Sr. V.P. & Gen. Mgr.--Quebecor Printing Fairfield Inc., Fairfield, PA; *Int'l*, pg. 1076
Daum, Gary C., Sr. V.P. & Gen. Mgr.--Quebecor Printing Martinsburg, Martinsburg, WV; *Int'l*, pg. 1076
Dauphinee, Jim, Sr. V.P.-Programming & Devel.--CBS Enterprises Division, New York, NY; *U.S. Public*, pg. 274
Davant, Jack, Sr. V.P.--Financial Aims Corporation, Great Falls, MT; *U.S. Private*, pg. 314
Dave, Bharat, Sr. V.P.-Mktg. & Field Support--Siemens Business Communication Systems, Inc., Santa Clara, CA; *Int'l*, pg. 1245
Davey, R.K., Sr. V.P.--Kennecott Holdings Corporation, Magna, UT; *Int'l*, pg. 1119
David, Daryl D., Sr. V.P.-Human Resources & Admin.--MagneTek, Inc., Nashville, TN; *U.S. Public*, pg. 1037
David, Glen, Sr. V.P.--HK Systems, Inc., New Berlin, WI; *U.S. Private*, pg. 491
Davids, Hollace, V.P.-Publicity & Special Projects--TriStar Pictures, Culver City, CA; *Int'l*, pg. 1283
Davidson, Gene, Sr. V.P.--NationsBank of Tennessee, Nashville, TN; *U.S. Public*, pg. 1163
Davidson, James L., Exec. V.P.--DFM/TATHAM, Chicago, IL; *Int'l*, pg. 601
Davidson, Megan, Sr. V.P.-Mortgage Banking--FirstFed Financial Corp., Santa Monica, CA; *U.S. Public*, pg. 645
Davidson, Stephen A., Sr. V.P.-Org. Devel.--GTECH Corporation, West Greenwich, RI; *U.S. Public*, pg. 767
Davie, Edward, Sr. V.P. & Pres.-Asia Pacific Div.--ITT Sheraton Corporation, Boston, MA; *U.S. Public*, pg. 1512
Davieau, Robert, Sr. V.P. & Mng. Dir.--The Corporate Communications Group, Whippany, NJ; *U.S. Private*, pg. 276
Davies, Bob, Chief Fin. Officer & Sr. V.P.--Favorite Brands International, Inc., Lincolnshire, IL; *U.S. Private*, pg. 397
Davies, C.J. David, Chief Fin. Officer & Sr. V.P.-Fin.--Hawaiian Airlines, Inc., Honolulu, HI; *U.S. Public*, pg. 799
Davies, C.J. David, Chief Fin. Officer, Sr. V.P.-Fin.--Hawaiian Airlines, Inc., Honolulu, HI; *U.S. Public*, pg. 799
Davies, G. Basil, Sr. V.P.-Sls. & Mktg.--Copperweld Fayetteville Division, Fayetteville, TN; *Int'l*, pg. 662
Davies, G. Basil, Sr. V.P.-Sls. & Mktg.--Copperweld Chicago Division, Chicago, IL; *Int'l*, pg. 662
Davies, J. Derek M., Sr. V.P.-Corp. Strategy--BCE Inc., Montreal, Canada; *Int'l*, pg. 114
Davies, Jonathan, Sr. V.P.-Intl. Client Services--Grey Europe/London, London, United Kingdom; *U.S. Public*, pg. 765
Davis, Allen S., Sr. V.P.-Mktg. & Mdsg. Services--White Hen Pantry, Inc., Elmhurst, IL; *U.S. Private*, pg. 1172
Davis, Ben, Sr. V.P.--Advance Seed Co., Fulton, KY; *Int'l*, pg. 566
Davis, Bruce K., Sr. V.P. & Acct. Grp. Dir.--Creswell, Munsell, Fultz & Zirbel, L.P., Cedar Rapids, IA; *U.S. Private*, pg. 1197
Davis, Carlisle R., Sr. V.P.-Opers.--Outboard Marine Corporation, Waukegan, IL; *U.S. Private*, pg. 478
Davis, Christine, Sr. V.P.--Raytheon Systems Company, Arlington, VA; *U.S. Public*, pg. 1364
Davis, Cindy, Sr. V.P.-Bus. Devel.--The Arnold Palmer Golf Company, Ooltewah, TN; *U.S. Public*, pg. 132
Davis, Darwin N., Sr. V.P.--The Equitable Companies Incorporated, New York, NY; *U.S. Public*, pg. 588
Davis, David J., Sr. V.P.-Opers.--Tab Products Co., Palo Alto, CA; *U.S. Public*, pg. 1559
Davis, Gary L., Sr. V.P.-Admin. & Personnel--JC Penney Company, Inc., Plano, TX; *U.S. Public*, pg. 916
Davis, Gary W., Sr. V.P.-Engrng. & Prod.--Western Gas Resources, Inc., Denver, CO; *U.S. Public*, pg. 1758
Davis, George E., Sr. V.P.-Human Resources--Lincoln National Corporation, Fort Wayne, IN; *U.S. Public*, pg. 997
Davis, J. Brad, Sr. V.P.-Mktg. & Corp. Rels.--Washington Mutual Inc., Seattle, WA; *U.S. Public*, pg. 1741
Davis, J. Kennerly, Jr., Sr. V.P., Treas. & Corp. Sec.--Virginia Electric and Power Company, Richmond, VA; *U.S. Public*, pg. 516
Davis, James C., Sr. V.P.-Integrated Svcs.--PG&E Energy Services, San Francisco, CA; *U.S. Public*, pg. 1241
Davis, James K., Sr. V.P.-Corp. Rels.--Georgia Power Co., Atlanta, GA; *U.S. Public*, pg. 1490
Davis, James M., Sr. V.P.-Mktg. & Adv.--Quality Stores Inc., Muskegon, MI; *U.S. Private*, pg. 899
Davis, James M., Jr., Sr. V.P.-Power Opers.--Carolina Power & Light Company, Raleigh, NC; *U.S. Public*, pg. 300
Davis, Janine, Sr. V.P. & Acct. Plng. Dir.--Ketchum Advertising/Pittsburgh, Pittsburgh, PA; *U.S. Private*, pg. 616
Davis, Jim H., Sr. V.P.--Willis Corroon Melling Inc., Toronto, Canada; *Int'l*, pg. 1509
Davis, Joe, Chief Info. Officer & Sr. V.P.--Express Scripts, Inc., Maryland Heights, MO; *U.S. Public*, pg. 600
Davis, Joel P., Sr. V.P.-Plng. & Devel.--The Gillette Company, Boston, MA; *U.S. Public*, pg. 743
Davis, John K., Chief Information Officer & Sr. V.P.--Trans Financial, Inc., Bowling Green, KY; *U.S. Public*, pg. 1628
Davis, Jr., C. Bruce, Sr. V.P.--Policy Management Systems Corporation, Blythewood, SC; *U.S. Public*, pg. 1314
Davis, Kim A., Sr. V.P. & Pres.-Gelman Sciences, Inc.--Pall Corporation, Greenvale, NY; *U.S. Public*, pg. 1253
Davis, Kristi A., Sr. V.P.-Information Services--Signet Star Reinsurance Company, Florham Park, NJ; *U.S. Public*, pg. 216
Davis, Lynn J., Sr. V.P. & Pres.-Broadband Connectivity Grp.--ADC Telecommunications, Inc., Minnetonka, MN; *U.S. Public*, pg. 4
Davis, Michael H., Sr. V.P.-Information Services--Tennessee Valley Authority, Knoxville, TN; *U.S. Public*, pg. 1580
Davis, Mitch, Sr. V.P.-People Affairs--C & S Wholesale Grocery Inc., Brattleboro, VT; *U.S. Private*, pg. 192
Davis, Nathaniel, Sr. V.P.-Fin. & Local Markets--MCI Communications Corp., Atlanta, GA; *U.S. Public*, pg. 1023
Davis, Parke, Sr. V.P.-Retail--Commemorative Brands, Inc., Austin, TX; *U.S. Private*, pg. 258
Davis, Paul R., Sr. V.P.--Hagler, Mastrovita & Hewitt, Inc., Boston, MA; *U.S. Public*, pg. 1673
Davis, Richard A., Chief Fin. Officer & Sr. V.P.-Fin.--PharmHouse, Inc., New York, NY; *U.S. Public*, pg. 1286
Davis, Rick, Sr. V.P.-Activewear--Fruit of the Loom, Inc., Chicago, IL; *U.S. Public*, pg. 685
Davis, Robert, Sr. V.P. & Exec. Creative Dir.-Ingalls One-to-One Marketing--Ingalls, Boston, MA; *U.S. Private*, pg. 562
Davis, Robert A., Sr. V.P.-Global Quality--NCR Corporation, Dayton, OH; *U.S. Public*, pg. 1146
Davis, Stephen, Sr. V.P. & Art Dir.--McKinney & Silver, Raleigh, NC; *U.S. Private*, pg. 723
Davis, Thomas C., Exec. V.P.--The Ward Machinery Company, Hunt Valley, MD; *U.S. Private*, pg. 1149
Davis, William W., Chief Fin. Officer & Sr. V.P.--Sunshine Precious Metals, Inc., Kellogg, ID; *U.S. Public*, pg. 1536
Davloor, Raghunath, Sr. V.P.-Investments--O&Y Properties Corporation, Toronto, Canada; *Int'l*, pg. 993
Dawahare, Anne G., Sr. V.P.-Fin.--Synovus Financial Corp., Columbus, GA; *U.S. Public*, pg. 1548
Dawson, Channing, Sr. V.P.-New Media--Home & Garden Television, Knoxville, TN; *U.S. Public*, pg. 1447
Dawson, G. Steven, Chief Fin. Officer, Sr. V.P.-Fin. & Treas.--Camden Property Trust, Houston, TX; *U.S. Public*, pg. 298
Dawson, Richard, Sr. V.P.-Law & Admin., Gen. Counsel & Sec.--Harvard Industries, Inc., Tampa, FL; *U.S. Public*, pg. 796
Day, Bernie, Sr. V.P.-Lumber--TruServ Corporation, Chicago, IL; *U.S. Private*, pg. 1108
Day, Courtney, Sr. V.P. & Grp. Acct. Dir.--DMB&B New York, New York, NY; *U.S. Private*, pg. 302
Day, Eric, Sr. V.P.--Zieman Manufacturing Company, Whittier, CA; *U.S. Private*, pg. 1205
Day, Fred N., Sr. V.P.-Energy Delivery--Carolina Power & Light Company, Raleigh, NC; *U.S. Public*, pg. 306
Day, Larry, Sr. V.P. & Gen. Counsel--Forecast Group, Rancho Cucamonga, CA; *U.S. Private*, pg. 418
Day, Steven R., Sr. V.P.-Opers.--Geo-Con, Inc., Denver, CO; *U.S. Public*, pg. 1657
Day, Timothy A., Sr. V.P.-Private Banking--National Penn Bank, Boyertown, PA; *U.S. Public*, pg. 1159
Daya, Jackie, Chief Fin. Officer & Sr. V.P.--Reed Elsevier Business Information, Newton, MA; *Int'l*, pg. 1095
Dayoob, Edward A., Sr. V.P.--Fred Meyer Stores, Portland, OR; *U.S. Public*, pg. 1103
Dayton, Peter E., Sr. V.P.-Natl. Sls.--Recoton Corporation, Lake Mary, FL; *U.S. Public*, pg. 1369
De Armas, Eloy R., Sr. V.P.--Business Mens Insurance Corporation, Coral Gables, FL; *U.S. Private*, pg. 189
De Balmann, Yves C., Sr. V.P.--Bankers Trust New York Corporation, New York, NY; *U.S. Public*, pg. 185
De Blasio, Michael P., Chief Fin. Officer & Sr. V.P.--Loral Space & Communications, New York, NY; *U.S. Public*, pg. 1014
de Bruyne, Eric, Corp. V.P.-Wire Intl.--N.V. Bekaert S.A., Kortrijk, Belgium; *Int'l*, pg. 183
De Caprio, Vincent, Chief Tech. Officer & Sr. V.P.--Becton Dickinson & Company, Franklin Lakes, NJ; *U.S. Public*, pg. 199
de Combret, Bernard, Exec V.P.-Refinig, Mktg. & Trading--Elf Aquitane, Paris, France; *Int'l*, pg. 444
de Freitas, Sergio Silva, Sr. V.P.-Corp. Banking--Banco Itau S.A., Sao Paulo, Brazil; *Int'l*, pg. 142
De Guzman, Aurelio M., Sr. V.P.--AGP Industrial Corporation, Manila, Philippines; *Int'l*, pg. 14
De Herder, Richard G., Sr. V.P. & Gen. Mgr.-Sls. & Mktg. Support--Mattel, Inc., El Segundo, CA; *U.S. Public*, pg. 1057
de Kervenoael, Maurice, Sr. V.P.-Beer Div.--Danone Group, Paris, France; *Int'l*, pg. 379
de Lasa, Jose M., Sr. V.P., Gen. Counsel & Sec.--Abbott Laboratories, Abbott Park, IL; *U.S. Public*, pg. 12
de Lasa, Jose M., Sr. V.P., Sec. & Gen. Counsel--Abbott Laboratories, Abbott Park, IL; *U.S. Public*, pg. 13
de Latour, Grace, Sr. V.P.-Employee Rels.--TCI Communications, Inc., Englewood, CO; *U.S. Public*, pg. 1554
De Leevin, Walter J., Sr. V.P. & Gen. Mgr.--Raytheon Environmental Services Company, Houston, TX; *U.S. Public*, pg. 1366
de Luna Valdez, Carlos, Sr. V.P.-Fin.--Grupo Acerero del Norte S.A. de C.V. (GAN), Mexico, Mexico; *Int'l*, pg. 572
De Micco, Frank J., Sr. V.P.--United Water Management & Services, Harrington Park, NJ; *U.S. Public*, pg. 1692
de Preux, Philippe, Sr. V.P.-Sls. & Mktg.--Bobst S.A., Lausanne, Switzerland; *Int'l*, pg. 198
De Rios, Tere Loubriel, Sr. V.P.-Total Quality--Banco Popular de Puerto Rico, San Juan, PR; *U.S. Public*, pg. 175
de Roux, Vincent, Vice Pres.--BCI Mer Rouge, Djibouti, Djibouti; *Int'l*, pg. 163
de Septfontaines, Thierry de Baynast, Sr. V.P.--Banque Internationale a Luxembourg S.A., Luxembourg, Luxembourg; *Int'l*, pg. 162
de Sostoa, Vincent, Chief Fin. Officer, Sr. V.P.& Treas.--OMI Corp., New York, NY; *U.S. Public*, pg. 1208
de Virville, Michel, Sr. V.P. & Corp. Sec.--Renault, Boulogne-Billancourt, France; *Int'l*, pg. 1102
de Vries, William L.J., Sr. V.P.--Universal Leaf Tobacco Company, Inc., Richmond, VA; *U.S. Public*, pg. 1694
de Wissocq, Francois, Sr. V.P.--Elf Aquitane, Paris, France; *Int'l*, pg. 444
De'Ath, Nick, M.B.E., Sr. V.P.-Opers.--Triton Energy Limited, Dallas, TX; *U.S. Public*, pg. 1640
Dea, Peter A., Sr. V.P.-Exploration--Barrett Resources Corporation, Denver, CO; *U.S. Public*, pg. 191
Deaderick, Jimmy R., Sr. V.P.--Chubb & Son, Inc., Warren, NJ; *U.S. Public*, pg. 355
Deamer, Hans A., Sr. V.P.--Windmoeller & Hoelscher Corp., Lincoln, RI; *Int'l*, pg. 1511
Dean, Jay, Exec. V.P., Strategic Planning Dir. & Digital Branding Dir.--Young & Rubicam San Francisco, San Francisco, CA; *U.S. Private*, pg. 1198
Dean, Robert W., Sr. V.P.-Admin. & Advanced Bus. Devel.--Ball Systems Engineering Operations, San Diego, CA; *U.S. Public*, pg. 171
DeAngelis, Art, Sr. V.P.-Grady's American Grill--Brinker International, Inc., Dallas, TX; *U.S. Public*, pg. 253
DeAngelis, Louis W., Sr. V.P.--Associates Communications Div., Dallas, TX; *U.S. Public*, pg. 663
Dearborn, Stephen L., Sr. V.P.-Strategic Plng. & Opers.--Grow Group, Inc., Cleveland, OH; *Int'l*, pg. 663
Deardorff, Steven L., Sr. V.P.--CTX Mortgage Co., Inc., Dallas, TX; *U.S. Public*, pg. 323
DeArmas, Celeste, Sr. V.P.-Mktg., Nestle Refrigerated Foods--Nestle Frozen, Refrigerated, and Ice Cream Companies, Solon, OH; *Int'l*, pg. 918
Deaton, Scott, Sr. V.P.-Mktg.--Follett College Stores Corp., Elmhurst, IL; *U.S. Private*, pg. 417
DeBarr, Harold J., Sr. V.P.-Mfg. & Engrng.--Oneida Silversmiths Div., Oneida, NY; *U.S. Public*, pg. 1226
Deblieux, Karen S., Sr. V.P.--Hibernia Corporation, New Orleans, LA; *U.S. Public*, pg. 825
DeBoer, Jerry, Sr. V.P. & Gen. Mgr.-Mdsg., Ladies Apparel & Accessories--Venture Stores, Inc., O Fallon, MO; *U.S. Public*, pg. 1716
Debord, Connie Snapp, Sr. V.P. & Strategic Mktg. Dir.--Russ Reid Company, Inc., Pasadena, CA; *U.S. Private*, pg. 952
Debreceny, Peter, Sr. V.P.--Edelman Public Relations Worldwide, Chicago, IL; *U.S. Private*, pg. 362
Debrecht, Donald R., Sr. V.P., Treas. & Controller--Hill-Behan Lumber Company, Saint Louis, MO; *U.S. Private*, pg. 529
Debrosse, Gayle, Sr. V.P.-Pub. Rels.--El Torito Restaurants Inc., Irvine, CA; *U.S. Private*, pg. 393
DeCabia, Thomas, Sr. V.P. & Acct. Supvr.--Paul Schulman Co., New York, NY; *Int'l*, pg. 117
DeCamello, Sarah, Sr. V.P.-Creative Services--Jordan, McGrath, Case & Taylor Inc., New York, NY; *U.S. Private*, pg. 598
DeCius, Dennis A., Chief Fin. Officer & Sr. V.P.--First National Bank of Central California, Salinas, CA; *U.S. Public*, pg. 1248
Decker, Brian, Sr. V.P. & Media Services Dir.--Eisner & Associates, Inc., Baltimore, MD; *U.S. Private*, pg. 366
Decker, Robert, Chief Fin. Officer & Sr. V.P.-Fin. & Devel.--Churchill Downs, Inc., Louisville, KY; *U.S. Public*, pg. 356
DeCrona, Bruce, Chief Fin. Officer & Sr. V.P.--Exchange Bank, Santa Rosa, CA; *U.S. Public*, pg. 599
Dedmon, Judith, Sr. V.P.-Southwestern Reg.--Federal National Mortgage Association (Fannie Mae), Washington, DC; *U.S. Public*, pg. 615
Dedmon, R. Scott, Sr. V.P.--Dewberry Design Group, Oklahoma City, OK; *U.S. Private*, pg. 329
Dedrick, Kenneth C., Sr. V.P.-Claims--Utica Mutual Insurance Company, New Hartford, NY; *U.S. Private*, pg. 1129
Dee, Marti, Sr. V.P.--Edelman Public Relations Worldwide, Chicago, IL; *U.S. Private*, pg. 362
Dee, Marti, Sr. V.P.--Edelman Worldwide, Inc., Atlanta, GA; *U.S. Private*, pg. 362
Deem, Peter, Sr. V.P.-Mktg.--Holnam Inc. (West Division), Lakewood, CO; *Int'l*, pg. 628
Deen, Craig, Sr. V.P.--Deen Wholesale Meat Company, Inc., Fort Worth, TX; *U.S. Private*, pg. 320
Deer, David W., Sr. V.P.--Hibernia Corporation, New Orleans, LA; *U.S. Public*, pg. 825
Defelice, Nicholas A., Sr. V.P.--First Maryland Bancorp, Baltimore, MD; *Int'l*, pg. 64
DeFelice, Rita, Sr. V.P.--Willis Corroon Corp. of Penn., Radnor, PA; *Int'l*, pg. 1507
DeFerrari, Diana, Sr. V.P. & Sec.--Plasma-Therm, Inc., Saint Petersburg, FL; *U.S. Public*, pg. 1308
Defonte, Robert G., Sr. V.P.-Mdsg. & Sec.--E & B Marine Incorporated, Edison, NJ; *U.S. Public*, pg. 1756
DeForest, Walter E., Sr. V.P. & Pres.-Leidy Hub, Inc.--National Fuel Gas Company, Buffalo, NY; *U.S. Public*, pg. 1156
DeForest, Walter E., Sr. V.P.--National Fuel Gas Distribution Corp., Buffalo, NY; *U.S. Public*, pg. 1156
Defrancesco, Camillo, Chief Fin. Officer & Sr. V.P.--Witco Corporation, Greenwich, CT; *U.S. Public*, pg. 1773
DeGeorge, Sal, Sr. V.P.-Sls. & Mktg.--Bridgford Foods Corporation, Anaheim, CA; *U.S. Public*, pg. 252
DeGiso, Patrick J., V.P. & Gen Mgr.--George W. Prescott Publishing Co., Quincy, MA; *U.S. Private*, pg. 882
Degnan, John J., Vice Chm. & Gen. Counsel--Chubb & Son, Inc., Warren, NJ; *U.S. Public*, pg. 355
DeGregorio, Louis W., Sr. V.P.-Sls.--Paul-Son Gaming Corporation, Las Vegas, NV; *U.S. Public*, pg. 1265
DeHart, Pete, Sr. V.P.-Sls. & Mktg.--Alpha Therapeutic Corp., Los Angeles, CA; *Int'l*, pg. 558
Dehondt, Carolyn B., Sr. V.P.--Hibernia Corporation, New Orleans, LA; *U.S. Public*, pg. 825
Deisinger, Robert, Chief Fin. Officer & Sr. V.P.--American Technical Publishers, Inc., Homewood, IL; *U.S. Private*, pg. 63
Deitch, Marc W., Sr. V.P. & Medical Dir.--American Home Products Corporation, Madison, NJ; *U.S. Public*, pg. 79
Deitch, Mark, Sr. V.P.--Edelman Worldwide, Inc., New York, NY; *U.S. Private*, pg. 362
Deitcher, Herbert, Sr. V.P. & Treas.--Raytheon Company, Lexington, MA; *U.S. Public*, pg. 1364
DeJesus, David, Chief Fin. Officer & Sr. V.P.--Media General Cable of Fairfax County Inc., Chantilly, VA; *U.S. Public*, pg. 1078
Dekanich, Ron, Sr. V.P. & Mgr.-Prod.--Willis Corroon Melling Ltd., Vancouver, Canada; *Int'l*, pg. 1509

Del Belso, Richard, Sr. V.P.-Worldwide Adv. & Mktg. Res.--Warner Bros. Studios, Inc., Burbank, CA; *U.S. Public*, pg. 1611
Del Priore, Michael J., Sr. V.P. & Mng. Dir.--J. & W. Seligman & Co., New York, NY; *U.S. Private*, pg. 982
Del Sontro, Rick, Sr. V.P.-Franchise Sls. & Devel.--Century 21 Real Estate Corp., Parsippany, NJ; *U.S. Public*, pg. 321
Delaforge, Gerard, Sr. Officer--Banque Indosuez, Geneva, Switzerland; *Int'l*, pg. 314
Delahunt, Robert M., Sr. V.P.-New Bus.Grp.--Polaroid Corporation, Cambridge, MA; *U.S. Public*, pg. 1313
Delalo, Armand M., Sr. V.P. & Chief Actuary--The Guardian Life Insurance Company of America, New York, NY; *U.S. Private*, pg. 486
Delamatte, David, Sr. V.P.--Durham Transportation, Inc., Austin, TX; *U.S. Private*, pg. 348
Delaney, Marnie, Sr. V.P. & Dir.-Adv. & Mktg. Communcaitons--BankAmerica Corporation, San Francisco, CA; *U.S. Public*, pg. 179
Delaney, Richard M., Sr. V.P. & Dir.-Mktg.--UMB Financial Corporation, Kansas City, MO; *U.S. Public*, pg. 1653
Delaney, Timothy, Sr. V.P. & Creative Dir.--Hal Riney & Partners Heartland, Chicago, IL; *U.S. Private*, pg. 931
DeLang, J.R., Sr. V.P.--The Todd-AO Corporation, Hollywood, CA; *U.S. Public*, pg. 1619
Delatte, Jerry A., Sr. V.P.-Domestic Food Sls.--Riceland Foods, Inc., Stuttgart, AR; *U.S. Private*, pg. 928
Deleuze, Rene, Sr. V.P.-Chemicals--Elf Aquitane, Paris, France; *Int'l*, pg. 444
Delfs, James, Chief Fin. Officer & Sr. V.P.-Fin.--Stein Mart, Inc., Jacksonville, FL; *U.S. Public*, pg. 1514
Delgadillo, J.L., Sr. V.P.--Marshall & Ilsley Corporation, Milwaukee, WI; *U.S. Public*, pg. 1049
Delker, Steven J., Sr. V.P.--Farmers Bank & Trust Co., Henderson, KY; *U.S. Public*, pg. 1217
Della Femina, Joe, Sr. V.P.-Copy--Jerry & Ketchum, New York, NY; *U.S. Private*, pg. 616
Dellamaria, Tom, Sr. V.P.-Production & Mfg.--Reed Elsevier Business Information, Newton, MA; *Int'l*, pg. 1095
Dellinger, Caroline K., Sr. V.P. & Chief Fin. Officer--Barclays American/Mortgage Corp., Charlotte, NC; *Int'l*, pg. 165
Dellinger, J. Ben, III, Sr. V.P.-Fin.--Rodgers Builders, Inc., Charlotte, NC; *U.S. Private*, pg. 939
Dellio, Clarence L., Sr. V.P.-Opers.--XOMA Corporation, Berkeley, CA; *U.S. Public*, pg. 1786
Delman, David, Chief Fin. Officer & Sr. V.P.--Key Risk Management Services, Inc., Greensboro, NC; *U.S. Public*, pg. 216
Delmotte, Andrew D., Sr. V.P.--Cape Coral National Bank, Cape Coral, FL; *U.S. Public*, pg. 607
DeLoach, Thomas C., Jr., Chief Fin. Officer & Sr. V.P.--Mobil Oil Corporation, Fairfax, VA; *U.S. Public*, pg. 1118
Delorme, Jean-Paul, Sr. V.P.--Air Liquide S.A., Paris, France; *Int'l*, pg. 37
Deltino, Louis, Sr. V.P.--Medieval Times Dinner & Tournament, Inc., Buena Park, CA; *U.S. Private*, pg. 728
DelTufo, Anthony J., Chief Fin. Officer, Sr. V.P. & Treas.--W.R. Berkley Corporation, Greenwich, CT; *U.S. Public*, pg. 215
DeLuca, Anthony T., Chief Info. Officer & Sr. V.P.--Avnet, Inc., Great Neck, NY; *U.S. Public*, pg. 155
Delucca, John J., Sr. V.P. & Treas.--RJR Nabisco Holdings Corp., New York, NY; *U.S. Public*, pg. 1354
DeLuccio, Jerome, Sr. V.P.-Supply Chain Mngmt.--Canandaigua Wine Co., Canandaigua, NY; *U.S. Public*, pg. 300
DeMain, Dominic P., Sr. V.P. -Mktg.--Combe Incorporated, White Plains, NY; *U.S. Private*, pg. 257
Demaio, Ellen, Sr. V.P. & Gen. Mgr.-Mdsg.--United Retail Group, Inc., Rochelle Park, NJ; *U.S. Public*, pg. 1679
DeMarco, Eric, Chief Fin. Officer & Sr. V.P.--The Titan Corporation, San Diego, CA; *U.S. Public*, pg. 1618
Demarest, David, Sr. V.P. & Dir.-Corp. Communications--BankAmerica Corporation, San Francisco, CA; *U.S. Public*, pg. 179
DeMarino, Louis T., Sr. V.P.-Sls. & Mktg.--The Jaydor Corporation, Millburn, NJ; *U.S. Private*, pg. 584
Demars, P., Sr. V.P.-Corp. Tech. Services--Lafarge Canada Inc., Montreal, Canada; *Int'l*, pg. 789
Demars, Patrick, Sr. V.P.-Corp. Technical Services--Lafarge Corporation, Reston, VA; *Int'l*, pg. 788
DeMartino, Jerry A., Sr. V.P.-Global Strategy--MCI Communications Corp., Atlanta, GA; *U.S. Public*, pg. 1023
DeMartino, Tony, Sr. V.P.--Edelman Worldwide, Inc., New York, NY; *U.S. Private*, pg. 362
Demarty, Jacques, Sr. V.P.-Containers Div.--Danone Group, Paris, France; *Int'l*, pg. 379
Dembowski, David M., Sr. V.P. & Sec.--ONBANCorp, Inc., Syracuse, NY; *U.S. Public*, pg. 631
Dembsky, Maurice, Chief Fin. Officer & Sr. V.P.--Bergdorf Goodman, New York, NY; *U.S. Public*, pg. 785
DeMelle, Arthur W., Chief Fin. Officer & Sr. V.P.--Data General Corporation, Westborough, MA; *U.S. Public*, pg. 485
Demirdjian, Paul B., Sr. V.P.--Davel Communications Group, Inc., Jacksonville, IL; *U.S. Public*, pg. 488
DeMory, Chuck, Sr. V.P.-Sls.--Comdisco, Inc., Rosemont, IL; *U.S. Public*, pg. 407
DeMoura, Brian L., Sr. V.P.--Interface Inc., Atlanta, GA; *U.S. Public*, pg. 889
DeMovick, Harvey C., Jr., Sr. V.P.-Medical & Govt. Programs--Coventry Corporation, Nashville, TN; *U.S. Public*, pg. 454
Dempsey, Christine P., Sr. V.P.-Fin.--FirstFed Financial Corp., Santa Monica, CA; *U.S. Public*, pg. 645
Dempsey, David, Sr. V.P.-Fin.--Quorum Health Resources, Inc., Brentwood, TN; *U.S. Public*, pg. 1354
Dempsey, Don, Chief Fin. Officer & Sr. V.P.--Promus Hotel Corporation, Memphis, TN; *U.S. Public*, pg. 1335
Dempsey, Paul, Sr. V.P.-Mktg.--Pioneer New Media Technologies, Long Beach, CA; *U.S. Private*, pg. 866
Denaro, Larry, Sr. V.P.-Brand Solutions--EvansGroup, Seattle, WA; *U.S. Private*, pg. 385
Denaro, Larry, Sr. V.P.--BrandSolutions, Seattle, WA; *U.S. Private*, pg. 385
Denecker, Paul, Corp. V.P.-Tech.--N.V. Bekaert S.A., Kortrijk, Belgium; *Int'l*, pg. 183
Deneka, Charles W., Sr. V.P.-Science & Tech.--Corning Incorporated, Corning, NY; *U.S. Public*, pg. 448
Denison, Floyd G., Sr. V.P.-Investments--American Bankers Insurance Co. of Florida, Miami, FL; *U.S. Public*, pg. 67
Denman, Owen S., Sr. V.P.-Opers.--Energy Absorption Systems, Inc., Chicago, IL; *U.S. Public*, pg. 1353
Denne, Donald R., Sr. V.P. & Pres.-Healthcare--Alba-Waldensian, Inc., Valdese, NC; *U.S. Public*, pg. 35
Dennig, Louis, Sr. V.P.-Programming--Worldvision Enterprises, New York, NY; *U.S. Private*, pg. 776
Dennis, Cynthia S., Sr. V.P. & Mgr.-Gen. Mdse.--Gymboree Corporation, Burlingame, CA; *U.S. Public*, pg. 770
Dennis, Shari, Sr. V.P. & Mngmt. Supvr.--The Buntin Group, Nashville, TN; *U.S. Private*, pg. 181
Dennison, Tim, Sr. V.P.--Cramer-Krasselt, Chicago, IL; *U.S. Private*, pg. 285
Denny, D.C., Sr. V.P.--Miller Freeman Inc., San Francisco, CA; *Int'l*, pg. 1443
DeNovellis, Donato A., Chief Fin. Officer & Sr. V.P.--Ekco Housewares, Inc., Franklin Park, IL; *U.S. Public*, pg. 566
Dent, Dirk A., Sr. V.P.--CDI Engineering Group, Inc., Kingsport, TN; *U.S. Public*, pg. 277
Denton, Donald H., Jr., Sr. V.P. & Chief Plng. Officer--Duke Energy Corporation, Charlotte, NC; *U.S. Public*, pg. 534
Denton, Norman, Sr. V.P.-Sls. & Mktg.--Rainbow Technologies, Inc., Irvine, CA; *U.S. Public*, pg. 1359
Dentz, Jeffrey, Sr. V.P.-Human Resources--Horace Small Apparel Company, Nashville, TN; *Int'l*, pg. 635
Denvir, S., Sr. V.P.--BBDO Canada, Toronto, Canada; *U.S. Private*, pg. 104
DeParis, Lawrence, Chief Fin. Officer & Sr. V.P.--Calvin Klein, Inc., New York, NY; *U.S. Private*, pg. 202
DePaul, John A., Sr. V.P.-Admin.--RSR Corporation, Dallas, TX; *U.S. Private*, pg. 900
DePinto, David, Sr. V.P. & Pub. Rels. Dir.--Ketchum Public Relations, Los Angeles, CA; *U.S. Private*, pg. 617
Deppen, Douglas D., Chief Fin. Officer & Sr. V.P.--First American Federal Savings Bank, Bristol, VA; *U.S. Public*, pg. 624
Der Marderosian, Armen, Sr. V.P.-Tech. & Systems--GTE Corporation, Stamford, CT; *U.S. Public*, pg. 696
Derbick, J. G., Sr. V.P. & Acct. Dir.--Brown Marketing Communications, Chicago, IL; *U.S. Private*, pg. 174
Derksen, Paul W., Chief Fin. Officer & Sr. V.P.--CT Financial Services, Inc., Toronto, Canada; *Int'l*, pg. 112
Derlin, Gerald, Sr. V.P.-Americas--AST Research Inc., Irvine, CA; *Int'l*, pg. 1181
Deroo, Herman, Sr. V.P.-Social Affairs--Sidmar N.V., Gent, Belgium; *Int'l*, pg. 79
Derosa, Dominick A., Sr. V.P.-Sls.--HBOC, Atlanta, GA; *U.S. Public*, pg. 770
Derrah, Robert E., Sr. V.P.--UNUM Life Insurance Company of America, Portland, ME; *U.S. Public*, pg. 1699
Derry, R. Michael, Sr. V.P.-Human Resources & Admin.--HON Industries Inc., Muscatine, IA; *U.S. Public*, pg. 772
des Deserts, Henri, Sr. V.P.-Intl. Opers.--Credit Commercial de France, Paris, France; *Int'l*, pg. 341
Desai, Mukesh, Sr. V.P.-Tech,/Semiconductor Group--SpeedFan International, Inc., Chandler, AZ; *U.S. Public*, pg. 1497
DeSantis, Donald A., Chief Fin. Officer, Sr. V.P. & Treas.--First Brands Corporation, Danbury, CT; *U.S. Public*, pg. 626
DeSantis, Michael, Sr. V.P.-Sls.--Chancellor Corporation, Boston, MA; *U.S. Public*, pg. 335
Desautels, Robert O., Chief Fin. Officer, Sr. V.P. & Treas.--Domco Inc., Farnham, Canada; *Int'l*, pg. 415
Desbiens, Pierre, Sr. V.P.-Insurance--National Bank of Canada, Montreal, Canada; *Int'l*, pg. 907
Descombes, Daniel, Sr. V.P.--Banque Cantonale Vaudoise, Lausanne, Switzerland; *Int'l*, pg. 160
Deshaw, Lawrence W., Sr. V.P.-Chittenden Home Mortgage--Chittenden Corporation, Burlington, VT; *U.S. Public*, pg. 350
Desimone, Matt, Sr. V.P.-Acct. Mngmt.--Grey Advertising Inc., New York, NY; *U.S. Public*, pg. 764
DeSimone, Richard D., Sr. V.P.--Atlantic Mutual Companies, New York, NY; *U.S. Private*, pg. 95
Desmond, Mark L., Chief Fin. Officer & Sr. V.P.--Nationwide Health Properties Inc., Newport Beach, CA; *U.S. Public*, pg. 1166
DeSosota, Vincent, Sr. V.P.--OMI Bulk Management Co., New York, NY; *U.S. Public*, pg. 1208
Desrochers, Gisele, Sr. V.P.-Human Resources & Admin.--National Bank of Canada, Montreal, Canada; *Int'l*, pg. 907
Desronier, Jim, Sr. V.P.-Mktg.--Excite, Inc., Redwood City, CA; *U.S. Public*, pg. 599
DeStefano, John J., Sr. V.P.-Bus. Devel.--Kansas City Power & Light Company, Kansas City, MO; *U.S. Public*, pg. 943
Dethlefson, Walter, Sr. V.P.--Network Services Company, Mount Prospect, IL; *U.S. Private*, pg. 791
Detjen, Larry L., Sr. V.P.-U.S. Prods.--Valvoline Company, Lexington, KY; *U.S. Public*, pg. 139
Detourbet, Gerard, Sr. V.P.-Mechanical Engrng. & Mfg.--Renault, Boulogne-Billancourt, France; *Int'l*, pg. 1102
Detter, Gerald L., Sr. V.P.--CNF Transportation Inc., Palo Alto, CA; *U.S. Public*, pg. 281
Deujcre, Malques, Sr. V.P.-Engr.--Sidmar N.V., Gent, Belgium; *Int'l*, pg. 79
Deull, Charles B., Sr. V.P.-Legal & Bus. Affairs & Sec.--Scholastic Corporation, New York, NY; *U.S. Public*, pg. 1440
Devers, T.F., Sr. V.P.--Columbia Gas Distribution Companies, Columbus, OH; *U.S. Public*, pg. 402
Devine, Thomas G., Sr. V.P.--F&G Re, Inc., Morristown, NJ; *U.S. Public*, pg. 1659
DeVino, Frank, Sr. V.P.-Graphics--General Media International Inc., New York, NY; *U.S. Private*, pg. 444
DeVino, Frank, Sr. V.P. & Graphics Dir.--Omni Publications International Ltd., New York, NY; *U.S. Private*, pg. 444
Devito, Jerry, Sr. V.P.--Westcorp, Irvine, CA; *U.S. Public*, pg. 1756
Devitre, Dinyar, Sr. V.P.-Corp. Plng.--Philip Morris Companies Inc., New York, NY; *U.S. Public*, pg. 1287
Devlin, Gail E., Sr. V.P.-Fin. & Dir.-Investor Rels.--The Chubb Corporation, Warren, NJ; *U.S. Public*, pg. 354
Devlin, R., Sr. V.P.-Devel.--Hilton International Co., Coral Gables, FL; *Int'l*, pg. 787
Devos, Denis, Sr. V.P.-Individual Canadian Opers.--The Great-West Life Assurance Company, Winnipeg, Canada; *Int'l*, pg. 557
Devos, Doug, Sr. V.P. & Mng. Dir.-Amway N. America--Amway Corporation, Ada, MI; *U.S. Private*, pg. 69
DeVoto, Terry, Sr. V.P. & Acct. Services Dir.--Western International Media Corporation, San Francisco, CA; *U.S. Private*, pg. 1167
DeWald, James E., Sr. V.P.-Actuary--MMI Companies, Inc., Deerfield, IL; *U.S. Public*, pg. 1027
Dewey, David W., Sr. V.P.-Overseas Opers.--Department 56 Inc., Eden Prairie, MN; *U.S. Public*, pg. 500
Dewey, R. Bruce, Sr. V.P. & Gen. Counsel--Mestek, Inc., Westfield, MA; *U.S. Public*, pg. 1099
DeWolf, John E., III, Sr. V.P.-Real Estate--Woolworth Corporation, New York, NY; *U.S. Public*, pg. 1777
Dexter, Bonnie, Sr. V.P.-Mdsg.--Loehmann's, Inc., Bronx, NY; *U.S. Public*, pg. 1010
Di Bono, Paul, Jr., Sr. V.P. & Gen. Mgr.-Midrange Div.--American Software, Inc., Atlanta, GA; *U.S. Public*, pg. 91
Di Santo, Carol, Sr. V.P.-Audio/Video--Cline, Davis & Mann, Inc., New York, NY; *U.S. Private*, pg. 246
Dial, Michael C., Chief Fin. Officer & Sr. V.P.--Cooper Communities, Inc., Bella Vista, AR; *U.S. Private*, pg. 273
Diamond, J. Edward, Sr. V.P.-Investment Services Exec.--The Dime Savings Bank of New York, New York, NY; *U.S. Public*, pg. 509
Diamond, Ronald T., Sr. V.P.-Consumer Appliances & Toiletries Div.--Conair Corporation, Stamford, CT; *U.S. Private*, pg. 261
Diaz, Ariel, Sr. V.P.-Research--Columbia Pictures, Culver City, CA; *Int'l*, pg. 1281
Diaz, Cass F., Sr. V.P.-Worldwide Sls. & Mktg.--ATL Ultrasound, Inc., Bothell, WA; *U.S. Public*, pg. 11
Diaz, Jim, Sr. V.P. & Gen. Mgr.--Star Tribune, Minneapolis-St. Paul, Minneapolis, MN; *U.S. Private*, pg. 281
DiBenedetto, Fernando, Sr. V.P.-Opers.--Hudson General Corporation, Great Neck, NY; *U.S. Public*, pg. 845
DiBiagio, A.J. Joseph, Sr. V.P.-Bus. Devel.--Starcraft Corporation, Goshen, IN; *U.S. Public*, pg. 1510
DiBrita, Anthony J., Sr. V.P.--Brooklyn Union, Brooklyn, NY; *U.S. Public*, pg. 259
DiCanio, Gerard, Sr. V.P.-Fin.--Viacom Productions Inc., Universal City, CA; *U.S. Private*, pg. 779
Dicasali, Ray L., Chief Tech. Officer & Sr. V.P.--Anacomp, Inc., Indianapolis, IN; *U.S. Public*, pg. 106
DiCecco, John A., Sr. V.P.-Logistics & Mfg.--General Nutrition, Inc., Pittsburgh, PA; *U.S. Public*, pg. 725
DiCenso, Robert E., Sr. V.P.-Personnel & Admin.--The Gillette Company, Boston, MA; *U.S. Public*, pg. 743
DiCiccio, John M., Sr. V.P.--John Hancock Mutual Life Insurance Company, Boston, MA; *U.S. Private*, pg. 589
DiCiuccio, David M., PE, Sr. V.P.--Giffels Hoyem Basso, Inc., Troy, MI; *U.S. Private*, pg. 452
Dick, Kenneth P., Sr. V.P.-Sls.--TBC Corporation, Memphis, TN; *U.S. Public*, pg. 1553
Dick, Lee, Sr. V.P. & Grp. Dir.--DavisElen Advertising, Inc., Los Angeles, CA; *U.S. Private*, pg. 316
Dickerson, Larry, Chief Fin. Officer & Sr. V.P.--Diamond Offshore Drilling, Inc., Houston, TX; *U.S. Public*, pg. 1011
Dickey, Lee D., Sr. V.P.-Credit Policy--Lawrence Savings Bank, North Andover, MA; *U.S. Public*, pg. 980
Dickinson, Harry L., Sr. V.P.-Sls.--S3 Incorporated, Santa Clara, CA; *U.S. Public*, pg. 1415
Dickson, Bruce E., Sr. V.P.--Scotia Discount Brokerage Inc., Toronto, Canada; *Int'l*, pg. 155
Dickson, Howard C., Sr. V.P.-Information Tech.--National Trustco Inc., Toronto, Canada; *Int'l*, pg. 909
Dickson, James G., Jr., Sr. V.P.--Prime Bancshares Inc., Houston, TX; *U.S. Public*, pg. 1326
Dickson, Rush S., III, Sr. V.P.--Harris Teeter, Inc., Charlotte, NC; *U.S. Public*, pg. 1412
Dickson, William D., Sr. V.P. & Treas.--Noble Affiliates, Inc., Ardmore, OK; *U.S. Public*, pg. 1186
DiDonna, Dominick W., Sr. V.P. & Gen. Mgr.--Hercules Incorporated, Wilmington, DE; *U.S. Public*, pg. 809
Diederick, Dale R., Sr. V.P.-Loan Admin.--First National Bank of Central California, Salinas, CA; *U.S. Public*, pg. 1248
Diehl, Thomas R., Exec. V.P.--Citizens National Bank of Southern Pennsylvania, Greencastle, PA; *U.S. Public*, pg. 1542
Diener, Gunter, Sr. V.P.--Deutsche Girozentrale-Deutsche Kommunalbank, Frankfurt/Main, Germany; *Int'l*, pg. 406
Dierckman, Thomas E., Sr. V.P.-Valencia Co.--The Newhall Land And Farming Company, Valencia, CA; *U.S. Public*, pg. 1178
Dieter, William J., Chief Acctg. Officer & Sr. V.P.--Heilig-Meyers Company, Richmond, VA; *U.S. Public*, pg. 804
Dieterle, Robert, Sr. V.P. & Gen. Mgr.--Cerner Corporation, Kansas City, MO; *U.S. Public*, pg. 331
Dietrich, Alan D., Sr. V.P. & Mktg. Oper. Officer--Cerner Corporation, Kansas City, MO; *U.S. Public*, pg. 331
Dietrich, Martin A., Sr. V.P.-Retail Banking--NBT Bancorp Inc., Norwich, NY; *U.S. Public*, pg. 1144
Dietz, George R., Sr. V.P.--Isomedix Inc., Whippany, NJ; *U.S. Public*, pg. 1515
Dietz, Mark, Sr. V.P.--Club Corporation International, Dallas, TX; *U.S. Private*, pg. 247

DiFazio, Louis T., Sr. V.P.-Worldwide Pharmaceuticals Grp.--Bristol-Myers Squibb Company, New York, NY; *U.S. Public*, pg. 253
DiForio, Richard J., Sr. V.P.-Environment--Champion International Corp., Stamford, CT; *U.S. Public*, pg. 333
Diggs, James C., Sr. V.P. & Gen. Counsel--PPG Industries, Inc., Pittsburgh, PA; *U.S. Public*, pg. 1245
DiGiovanni, Rico, Sr. V.P. & Mng. Dir.--IMPACT/FCB, Toronto, Canada; *U.S. Private*, pg. 389
Digney, James B., Sr. V.P.-Real Estate--Metropolitan Life Insurance Co., New York, NY; *U.S. Private*, pg. 737
Dileo, James J., Sr. V.P. & Information Services Dir.--DMB&B Central And Regional IT Services, Troy, MI; *U.S. Private*, pg. 302
Dillingham, Hugh J., Sr. V.P.-Post Collection--Browning-Ferris Industries, Inc., Houston, TX; *U.S. Public*, pg. 262
Dillon, Mike, Sr. V.P.--Asher/Gould Advertising, Inc., Los Angeles, CA; *U.S. Private*, pg. 88
Dillon, Paul E., Sr. V.P. & Treas.--Mid Atlantic Medical Services, Inc., Rockville, MD; *U.S. Public*, pg. 1109
Dills, Dennis B., Sr. V.P.-Trust Opers.--SunTrust Banks, Inc., Atlanta, GA; *U.S. Public*, pg. 1537
DiLorenzo, Barbara, Sr. V.P.-Creative Services--Jordan, McGrath, Case & Taylor Inc., New York, NY; *U.S. Private*, pg. 598
Dimaggio, Dennis, Sr. V.P.--American Bankers Insurance Group, Inc., Miami, FL; *U.S. Public*, pg. 67
DiMaggio, Dennis, Sr. V.P.-Legal, Govt. Affairs & Compliance--American Bankers Life Assurance Co. of Florida, Miami, FL; *U.S. Public*, pg. 67
DiMarco, James F., Sr. V.P.-Worldwide Consumer Products, Research, Devel. & Engrng.--S.C. Johnson & Son, Inc., Racine, WI; *U.S. Private*, pg. 592
DiMarco, Michael A., Sr. V.P.-Natl. Accts. Div.--Paging Network, Inc., Plano, TX; *U.S. Public*, pg. 1252
DiMatteo, Carmen, Sr. V.P.-Services & Sls.--Semco Industries Inc., Stoughton, MA; *U.S. Private*, pg. 983
DiMatteo, Carmen, Sr. V.P.--Spaulding Company, Inc., Stoughton, MA; *U.S. Private*, pg. 983
DiMichele, Sam, Sr. V.P.-Real Estate Devel.--Cineplex Odeon Corporation, Toronto, Canada; *Int'l*, pg. 292
Dimick, Alison, Sr. V.P.-Acq.--Camden Property Trust, Houston, TX; *U.S. Public*, pg. 298
Dimit, Gregory S., Sr. V.P.--United Asset Management Corporation, Boston, MA; *U.S. Public*, pg. 1672
Dimond, Michael J., Sr. V.P.-Mktg.--Gaylord Entertainment Co., Nashville, TN; *U.S. Public*, pg. 704
DiMuccio, Rob A., Sr. V.P. & Treas.--Amica Mutual Insurance Co., Lincoln, RI; *U.S. Private*, pg. 66
Dinardi, Peter L., Sr. V.P.-Fin.--UAM Retirement Plan Services, Inc., New York, NY; *U.S. Public*, pg. 1674
Dingman, C.E., Sr. V.P.-Human Resources--National Trustco Inc., Toronto, Canada; *Int'l*, pg. 909
Dingman, Robert J., Sr. V.P.-Custom Opers.--Trus Joist MacMillan, Boise, ID; *Int'l*, pg. 829
Dingman, Robert J., Sr. V.P.-Custom Opers.--TJ International, Inc., Boise, ID; *U.S. Public*, pg. 1556
Dingman, Robert J., Sr. V.P.-Custom Opers.--Trus Joist MacMillan, Boise, ID; *U.S. Public*, pg. 1556
DiNicola, Patrick, Chief Fin. Officer & Sr. V.P.-Fin. & Admin.--Trico Products Corporation, Buffalo, NY; *Int'l*, pg. 1397
Dinnocenzo, Debra, Sr. V.P.-Mktg.--Learning International, Stamford, CT; *U.S. Public*, pg. 1617
Dinsmore, Anne L., Sr. V.P.--UNUM Life Insurance Company of America, Portland, ME; *U.S. Public*, pg. 1699
Dinsmore, Gerald K., Sr. V.P.-Fin. & Plng., Telephone Opers.--GTE Corporation, Stamford, CT; *U.S. Public*, pg. 696
Dinsmore, Gerald K., Sr. V.P.-Fin. & Plng.--GTE North Incorporated, Irving, TX; *U.S. Public*, pg. 696
Dinsmore, Gerald K., Sr. V.P.-Fin. & Plng.--GTE South Incorporated, Irving, TX; *U.S. Public*, pg. 697
Dion, Ronald, Sr. V.P.-Fin.--Altec Lansing Technologies, Inc., Milford, PA; *U.S. Private*, pg. 479
Dionne, Michael L., Sr. V.P. & Gen. Mgr.-AppleAssist--Apple Computer, Inc., Cupertino, CA; *U.S. Public*, pg. 121
DiPaolo, Anthony M., Chief Fin. Officer & Sr. V.P.--Capital Associates, Inc., Lakewood, CO; *U.S. Public*, pg. 302
Diren, Daniel D., Sr. V.P.-Admin. & Controller--R.G. Barry Corporation, Pickerington, OH; *U.S. Public*, pg. 192
Dirig, Tim, Sr. V.P.--The Medical Protective Company, Fort Wayne, IN; *U.S. Private*, pg. 728
Dirkes, Mark, Sr. V.P.-Mktg.--Interstate Bakeries Corporation, Kansas City, MO; *U.S. Public*, pg. 909
Dirks, Robert E., Sr. V.P.-Mktg.--Hilton Hotels Corporation, Beverly Hills, CA; *U.S. Public*, pg. 828
Dirks, Robert E., Sr. V.P.-Mktg.--Hilton Hotels Div., Beverly Hills, CA; *U.S. Public*, pg. 829
Dirks, Tricia, Sr. V.P.-Human Resources--The Department Store Division of Dayton Hudson Corporation, Minneapolis, MN; *U.S. Public*, pg. 489
Dirrim, Julie, Chief Fin. Officer & Sr. V.P.--Valley Bank & Trust, Brighton, CO; *U.S. Private*, pg. 1132
Dirth, G. Randolph, Sr. V.P.-Williams-Sonoma Retail Mdsg.--Williams-Sonoma, Inc., San Francisco, CA; *U.S. Public*, pg. 1770
DiSalvatore, Joseph A., Sr. V.P.--American Appraisal Associates, Inc., Milwaukee, WI; *U.S. Private*, pg. 49
DiSanto, Salvatore C., Sr. V.P.-Trust Investment--Citizens Savings Bank, Providence, RI; *Int'l*, pg. 1132
DiSanto, Salvatore C., Sr. V.P.-Trust InvestmentMngmt.--Citizens Trust Company, Providence, RI; *Int'l*, pg. 1132
Disbrow, Clifford, Sr. V.P.-Technical Opers.--Glaxo Wellcome Inc., Research Triangle Park, NC; *Int'l*, pg. 552
DiSciullo, William J., Sr. V.P.-Security & Oper. Risk--Citizens Savings Bank, Providence, RI; *Int'l*, pg. 1132
Diskin, Joe, Sr. V.P.-Sls.--Johnny Carson Apparel, Inc., Buffalo, NY; *U.S. Public*, pg. 796
Disque, Don R., Sr. V.P.-Sls. & Mktg.--Phelps Dodge Magnet Wire Co., Fort Wayne, IN; *U.S. Public*, pg. 1286
Dissinger, Anthony, Sr. V.P.-Supply Chain Mngmt. & Logistics--Fabri-Centers of America, Inc., Hudson, OH; *U.S. Public*, pg. 609
DiStefano, Tony F., Sr. V.P.-Corp. Devel.--PG&E Corporation San Francisco, CA; *U.S. Public*, pg. 1240
Ditka, Ashton L., Sr. V.P.--United Refining Company, Warren, PA; *U.S. Private*, pg. 915
Ditto, Jeffrey E., Sr. V.P.-Engrng.--Binkley Company, Warrenton, MO; *U.S. Private*, pg. 534
Dix, Ron, Sr. V.P.-Mktg. & Sls.--Bush Brothers & Company, Knoxville, TN; *U.S. Private*, pg. 189
Dixon, James M., Sr. V.P.--AT&T Wireless Services, Kirkland, WA; *U.S. Public*, pg. 11
Dixon, William J., Sr. V.P.-Opers.--Paging Network, Inc., Plano, TX; *U.S. Public*, pg. 1252
Dmiszewicki, Steven, Chief Fin. Officer & Sr. V.P.-Fin.--Seer Technologies, Inc., Cary, NC; *U.S. Public*, pg. 1453
Doan, Christopher, Sr. V.P.-Maintenance--US Airways Group, Inc., Arlington, VA; *U.S. Public*, pg. 1680
Doan, Christopher, Sr. V.P.-Maintenance--US Airways, Inc., Arlington, VA; *U.S. Public*, pg. 1680
Dobel, Steve, Sr. V.P.-Sls.--WorldCom, Inc., Jackson, MS; *U.S. Public*, pg. 1779
Dobra, John A., Sr. V.P.-Risk Mngmt. & Compliance--USTrust, Boston, MA; *U.S. Public*, pg. 1660
Dobson, John R., Sr. V.P.-Sls.--Owen Industries, Inc., Carter Lake, IA; *U.S. Private*, pg. 824
Dobson, Rich, Sr. V.P.-Adv.--Milwaukee Journal Sentinel, Milwaukee, WI; *U.S. Private*, pg. 601
Docken, Donald L., Sr. V.P.-Mdse. Presentation--Montgomery Ward & Co., Inc., Chicago, IL; *U.S. Private*, pg. 758
Dockery, J. Glenn, Sr. V.P.--Willis Corroon Financial Services Corp., Atlanta, GA; *Int'l*, pg. 1507
Dodd, Martin H., Sr. V.P., Gen. Counsel & Sec.--TRC Companies, Inc., Windsor, CT; *U.S. Public*, pg. 1557
Dodd, Michael, Sr. V.P. & Dir.-Reg. Opers.--State Automobile Mutual Insurance Co., Columbus, OH; *U.S. Private*, pg. 1036
Dodd, Val, Sr. V.P.--InterAmerican-Star Group, Los Angeles, CA; *Int'l*, pg. 1529
Dodge, Peter A., Sr. V.P.--F&G Re, Inc., Morristown, NJ; *U.S. Public*, pg. 1659
Dodson, Don, V.P.-Opers.--Furr's/Bishops, Inc., Lubbock, TX; *U.S. Public*, pg. 689
Dodson, Larry S., Chief Fin. Officer & Sr. V.P.--Zimmerman Holdings, Inc., San Marino, CA; *U.S. Private*, pg. 1206
Dodson, Mark, Sr. V.P.-Gaming Opers.--Hilton Hotels, Gaming Div., Las Vegas, NV; *U.S. Public*, pg. 829
Doelger, Frank W., Sr. V.P.--Douglas Elliman, New York, NY; *U.S. Private*, pg. 341
Doescher, William F., Sr. V.P.--The Dun & Bradstreet Corporation, Murray Hill, NJ; *U.S. Public*, pg. 535
Doetzel, Elizabeth T., Sr. V.P.-Deposit & Comml. Banking--Citizens Savings Bank, Providence, RI; *Int'l*, pg. 1132
Doggett, John V., Sr. V.P.--UAM Investment Services, Inc., Boston, MA; *U.S. Public*, pg. 1674
Dogon, Gerald, Chief Fin. Officer & Sr. V.P.--DSP Communications Inc., Cupertino, CA; *U.S. Public*, pg. 475
Doherty, Edward D., Sr. V.P.--Kaneb Services, Inc., Richardson, TX; *U.S. Public*, pg. 942
Dolan, Arnold, Sr. V.P., Publisher-Plume--Penguin Putnam Inc., New York, NY; *Int'l*, pg. 1027
Dolan, Jeff, Sr. V.P.-Sls. & Mktg.--Selfix, Inc., Chicago, IL; *U.S. Public*, pg. 832
Dolan, Jeffrey R., Sr. V.P.-Sls. & Mktg.-Selfix--Home Products International, Inc., Chicago, IL; *U.S. Public*, pg. 832
Dolan, Regina, Chief Fin. Officer & Sr. V.P.--PaineWebber Group Incorporated, New York, NY; *U.S. Public*, pg. 1252
Dolan, Richard, Sr. V.P.-Legal Affairs & Gen. Counsel--SNC-Lavalin Group Inc., Montreal, Canada; *Int'l*, pg. 1161
Dolara, Peter J., Sr. V.P.-Miami, Carribean & Latin America--American Airlines, Inc., Fort Worth, TX; *U.S. Public*, pg. 9
Dolci, Louis, Sr. V.P.--Torcon, Inc., Westfield, NJ; *U.S. Private*, pg. 1092
Dolezan, Gary A., Sr. V.P.--Shoreline Financial Corp., Benton Harbor, MI; *U.S. Public*, pg. 1467
Dolezan, Gary A., Sr. V.P.-Mortgage Lending--Shoreline Bank, Benton Harbor, MI; *U.S. Public*, pg. 1468
Dolin, Lisa M., Sr. V.P.-Specialty Companies--Cardinal Health Inc., Dublin, OH; *U.S. Public*, pg. 304
Doll, Mark G., Sr. V.P. & Treas.--Northwestern Mutual Life Insurance Co., Milwaukee, WI; *U.S. Private*, pg. 807
Doman, Alan J., Sr. V.P.-Opers.--Washington Mutual Inc., Seattle, WA; *U.S. Public*, pg. 1741
Domanico, Robert A., Sr. V.P.--General Reinsurance Corp., Stamford, CT; *U.S. Public*, pg. 725
Dombroski, Raymond E., Sr. V.P.-Engrng. & New Tech.--Comcast Cellular Communications, Inc., Wayne, PA; *U.S. Public*, pg. 407
Dombrovick, Ken, Sr. V.P.--ABN AMRO Chicago Corporation, Chicago, IL; *Int'l*, pg. 10
Donabedian, David L., Sr. V.P.--Rothschild/Pell, Rudman & Co., Inc., Baltimore, MD; *U.S. Public*, pg. 1674
Donahee, Gary Richard, Pres.-Nortel CALA & Sr. V.P.--Northern Telecom Limited, Brampton, Canada; *Int'l*, pg. 968
Donaher, Paul, Sr. V.P. & Dir.-Strategic Plng.--Sotheby's Holdings Inc., New York, NY; *U.S. Public*, pg. 1487
Donahey, Kenneth C., Sr. V.P. & Controller--Columbia/HCA Healthcare Corporation, Nashville, TN; *U.S. Public*, pg. 403
Donahue-Dalton, Ellen I., Sr. V.P.-Mktg. & Pres.-GameScape, Inc.--GTECH Corporation, West Greenwich, RI; *U.S. Public*, pg. 767
Donahue, Jeffrey H., Chief Fin. Officer & Sr. V.P.--The Rouse Company, Columbia, MD; *U.S. Public*, pg. 1407
Donahue, John F., Sr. V.P.--Hartford Fire Insurance Co., Hartford, CT; *U.S. Public*, pg. 794
Donahue, Timothy J., Sr. V.P. & Controller--Crown Cork & Seal Company, Inc., Philadelphia, PA; *U.S. Public*, pg. 462
Donahue, Timothy M., Sr. V.P.--AT&T Wireless Services, Kirkland, WA; *U.S. Public*, pg. 11
Donaldson, John, Sr. V.P.--Capital Development Co., Lacey, WA; *U.S. Private*, pg. 205
Donaldson, John, Chief Fin. Officer & Sr. V.P.--Fremont Indemnity Corp., Santa Monica, CA; *U.S. Public*, pg. 681
Doneson, Lin, Sr. V.P.-Mdsg.--Jan Bell Marketing Inc., Sunrise, FL; *U.S. Public*, pg. 207
Donlin, Bill, Sr. V.P.-Strategic Devel.--Dugan Valva Contess Inc., Morristown, NJ; *U.S. Private*, pg. 345
Donlin, Dennis, Sr. V.P. & Media Services Dir.--DMB&B Detroit, Troy, MI; *U.S. Private*, pg. 302
Donly, Stephen M., Sr. V.P.-Mktg./Ryder Transportation Svcs.--Ryder System, Inc., Miami, FL; *U.S. Public*, pg. 1413
Donnaruma, Tom, Sr. V.P.-Sls.--Sony Music Entertainment, Inc., New York, NY; *Int'l*, pg. 1281
Donnelly, John F., Sr. V.P.-Corp. Bus. Devel. & Mktg.--Donnelly Corporation, Holland, MI; *U.S. Public*, pg. 519
Donnelly, Timothy J., Chief Fin. Officer & Sr. V.P.--District Petroleum Products, Inc., Sandusky, OH; *U.S. Private*, pg. 336
Donnici, Jim, Sr. V.P.-Creative Svcs. & New Bus.--Chicago Creative Partnership, Chicago, IL; *U.S. Private*, pg. 234
Donnon, Simon, Sr. V.P.-Creative Services--Barneys Inc., New York, NY; *U.S. Private*, pg. 116
Donofrio, Nicholas M., Sr. V.P. & Grp. Exec.-Res., Mfg. & Procurement--International Business Machines Corporation, Armonk, NY; *U.S. Public*, pg. 895
Donoghue, John, Sr. V.P.-Consumer Mktg.--MCI Communications Corp., Atlanta, GA; *U.S. Public*, pg. 1023
Donoghue, John, Sr. V.P.-Consumer Mktg.--MCI Telecommunications Corp., Washington, DC; *U.S. Public*, pg. 1024
Donoghue, Laurence J., Sr. V.P. & Mgr.-Gen. Mdse.--McRae's, Inc., Jackson, MS; *U.S. Public*, pg. 1333
Donohue, Frank, Sr. V.P.-Construction--Sithe Energies, Inc., New York, NY; *U.S. Private*, pg. 1004
Donohue, Jeffrey, Sr. V.P.--Washington Homes, Inc., Landover, MD; *U.S. Public*, pg. 1741
Donohue, Jeffrey, Sr. V.P.--Homebuyer's Mortgage, Inc., Landover, MD; *U.S. Public*, pg. 1741
Donohue, Jim, Chief Fin. Officer & Sr. V.P.--Vail Resorts, Inc., Vail, CO; *U.S. Public*, pg. 1704
Donohue, Raymond J., Chief Fin. Officer & Sr. V.P.--Matson Navigation Company, Inc., San Francisco, CA; *U.S. Public*, pg. 39
Donoughue, Kevin R., Sr. V.P.-Acct. Mngmnt.--Qualex Inc., Durham, NC; *U.S. Public*, pg. 551
Donovan, John, Sr. V.P.-Leasing--Carr Real Estate Services, Washington, DC; *U.S. Public*, pg. 309
Donovan, John J., Jr., Sr. V.P.-Leasing--CarrAmerica Realty, Washington, DC; *U.S. Public*, pg. 308
Donovan, Mary, Sr. V.P.-Publicity--New Line Cinema Corporation, New York, NY; *U.S. Public*, pg. 1614
Donovan, Michael P., Sr. V.P.-Bus. Devel.--PHP Healthcare Corporation, Reston, VA; *U.S. Public*, pg. 1241
Donovan, Robert G., Sr. V.P. & Dir.-Opers.--Legg Mason, Inc., Baltimore, MD; *U.S. Public*, pg. 984
Donovan, Robert H., Sr. V.P.-Fin. & Treas.--Devon Group, Inc., Stamford, CT; *U.S. Public*, pg. 503
Dooley, C. Terry, Sr. V.P.--Morley Builders, Santa Monica, CA; *U.S. Private*, pg. 761
Dooley, J. Gregory, Sr. V.P.-Audit--Provident Financial Group, Inc., Cincinnati, OH; *U.S. Public*, pg. 1338
Dooley, Robert, Sr. V.P.-Worldwide Computer Sls. & Mktg.--Global Direct Mail Corp, Port Washington, NY; *U.S. Public*, pg. 747
Doolittle, John C., Chief Fin. Officer & Sr. V.P.--Shandwick Americas, New York, NY; *Int'l*, pg. 1226
Doomany, Charles G., Chief Fin. Officer & Sr. V.P.--Harrison & Star, Inc., New York, NY; *U.S. Private*, pg. 506
Dor, Christian, Chief Fin. Officer & Sr. V.P.--Renault, Boulogne-Billancourt, France; *Int'l*, pg. 1102
Dorais, Richard N., Sr. V.P.--Turner Construction Co., San Francisco, CA; *U.S. Public*, pg. 1645
Doran, Carl, Sr. V.P.-Export--Ford Meter Box Company, Wabash, IN; *U.S. Private*, pg. 418
Dorey, William G., Sr. V.P. & Mgr.-Branch Div.--Granite Construction Incorporated, Watsonville, CA; *U.S. Public*, pg. 759
Dorff, Gordon, Sr. V.P.-Human Resources--Ag Processing Inc., A Cooperative, Omaha, NE; *U.S. Private*, pg. 26
Dorfman, Robert M., Sr. V.P.-Mktg. & Bus. Devel.--Marriott Distribution Services (MDS), Washington, DC; *U.S. Public*, pg. 1048
Dorier, Philippe, Chief Fin. Officer & Sr. V.P.--BGF Industries Inc., Greensboro, NC; *U.S. Private*, pg. 106
Doris-Smith, Mary, Sr. V.P.-Customer Relationship Mktg.--Ross Roy Communications, Inc., Bloomfield Hills, MI; *U.S. Private*, pg. 946
Dorn, Forest D., Sr. V.P.-Gulf Coast Region--Forest Oil Corporation, Denver, CO; *U.S. Public*, pg. 670
Dorsen, Hariette, Sr. V.P., Sec. & Gen. Counsel--Bantam Doubleday Dell Publishing Group, Inc., New York, NY; *Int'l*, pg. 191
Dorsett, C. Powers, Sr. V.P., Gen. Counsel & Sec.--Springs Industries, Inc., Fort Mill, SC; *U.S. Public*, pg. 1499
Dorsey, James R., Sr. V.P. & Dir.-Corp. Affairs--Citizens Financial Group, Inc., Providence, RI; *Int'l*, pg. 1132
Dorsey, Patrick B., Sr. V.P., Gen. Counsel & Sec.--Tiffany & Co., New York, NY; *U.S. Public*, pg. 1608
Dorsman, Peter A., Sr. V.P. & Gen. Mgr.--The Standard Register Company, Dayton, OH; *U.S. Public*, pg. 1505
Dosher, John R., Sr. V.P.--The Pace Consultants, Inc., Houston, TX; *U.S. Public*, pg. 921
Dotson, Donald L., Sr. V.P.-Labor & Employment--Beverly Enterprises, Inc., Fort Smith, AR; *U.S. Public*, pg. 227

Dotterer, Herbert T., Chief Fin. Officer, Sr. V.P.-Fin. & Admin. & Sec.--Eagle Food Centers, Inc., Milan, IL; *U.S. Public*, pg. 547
Doubleday, M., Sr. V.P.-Manpower, United Kingdom--SGS Societe Generale de Surveillance Holding S.A., Geneva, Switzerland; *Int'l*, pg. 1153
Doubrava, C.E., Sr. V.P.--Natural Gas Pipeline Co. America, Lombard, IL; *U.S. Public*, pg. 1210
Doubrava, C.E., Sr. V.P.--MidCon Texas Pipeline Operator, Inc., Houston, TX; *U.S. Public*, pg. 1210
Doucette, Paul F., Sr. V.P.--Bell Industries, Inc., El Segundo, CA; *U.S. Public*, pg. 204
Dougherty, Clyde J.B., Sr. V.P.--Standard Federal Bank, Troy, MI; *Int'l*, pg. 10
Dougherty, James T., Sr. V.P., Gen. Counsel & Sec.--Lone Star Technologies, Inc., Dallas, TX; *U.S. Public*, pg. 1012
Dougherty, Patrick, Sr. V.P.--Advanced Marine Enterprises, Inc., Arlington, VA; *U.S. Public*, pg. 1182
Douglas, Dianne, Sr. V.P.-Investor Rels.--Associates First Capital Corporation, Dallas, TX; *U.S. Public*, pg. 662
Douglas, Murray, Sr. V.P.--Brunschwig & Fils, Inc., White Plains, NY; *U.S. Private*, pg. 176
Douglas, W. Leslie, Sr. V.P.--Folger Nolan Fleming Douglas, Washington, DC; *U.S. Private*, pg. 416
Douville, Richard A., Chief Fin. Officer & Sr. V.P.--U.S. Surgical Corp., Norwalk, CT; *U.S. Public*, pg. 1687
Dow, John A.S., Sr. V.P.-Exploration--Newmont Mining Corporation, Denver, CO; *U.S. Public*, pg. 1178
Dow, John A.S., Sr. V.P.-Exploration--Newmont Gold Company, Denver, CO; *U.S. Public*, pg. 1179
Dowd, Edward P., Sr. V.P.-Real Estate--John Hancock Mutual Life Insurance Company, Boston, MA; *U.S. Private*, pg. 589
Dowd, Gerard, Sr. V.P.-Foodservice Sls. & Mktg.--Tyson Foods, Inc., Springdale, AR; *U.S. Public*, pg. 1652
Dowey, Mark, Sr. V.P.--Sealright Company, Inc., De Soto, KS; *U.S. Public*, pg. 1451
Dowling, Richard P., Sr. V.P.-Corp. Devel.--General Communication, Inc., Anchorage, AK; *U.S. Public*, pg. 708
Dowling, Stephen E., Sr. V.P.-Sls. & Mktg.--Lincoln Foodservice Products, Inc., Fort Wayne, IN; *Int'l*, pg. 188
Downes, David K., Chief Fin. Officer, Chief Admin. Officer, Sr. V.P. & Treas.--Delaware Management Holdings, Inc., Philadelphia, PA; *U.S. Public*, pg. 997
Downing, Donald S., Sr. V.P.-Mortgage Services--SunTrust Banks, Inc., Atlanta, GA; *U.S. Public*, pg. 1537
Downing, Kathryn M., Sr. V.P.--The Times Mirror Company, Los Angeles, CA; *U.S. Public*, pg. 1615
Downing, Margaret Ryan, Sr. V.P.--UNUM Life Insurance Company of America, Portland, ME; *U.S. Public*, pg. 1699
Downing, Robert B., Sr. V.P.--Oxford Realty Financial Group, Bethesda, MD; *U.S. Private*, pg. 825
Downs, Christopher Y., Sr. V.P.-Consumer Fin.--Citizens Savings Bank, Providence, RI; *Int'l*, pg. 1132
Downs, Michael L., Sr. V.P.--The Hartford Steam Boiler Inspection & Insurance Co., Hartford, CT; *U.S. Public*, pg. 795
Doyle, Gary D., Sr. V.P.-Asset Mngmt.--Taubman Centers, Inc., Bloomfield Hills, MI; *U.S. Public*, pg. 1561
Doyle, J.F., Sr. V.P.--Pennsylvania General Insurance Company, Philadelphia, PA; *Int'l*, pg. 543
Doyle, James M., Sr. V.P.-Mfg.--King Milling Company, Lowell, MI; *U.S. Private*, pg. 621
Doyle, John, Sr. V.P.-Professional & Programs Div.--National Union Fire Ins. Co. of Pittsburgh, Pa., New York, NY; *U.S. Public*, pg. 84
Doyle, John F., Sr. V.P.-Mktg.--The Camden Fire Insurance Assn., Philadelphia, PA; *Int'l*, pg. 543
Doyle, John F., Sr. V.P.-Mktg. & Field Admin.--General Accident Insurance, Philadelphia, PA; *Int'l*, pg. 543
Doyle, M.P., Sr. V.P.-Retail Opers.--B.C. Ziegler & Co., West Bend, WI; *U.S. Public*, pg. 1792
Doyle, Michael A., Sr. V.P.-Northeast Reg.--Comcast Cable Communications, Inc., Philadelphia, PA; *U.S. Public*, pg. 407
Doyle, Robert E., Sr. V.P.--K2 Inc., Los Angeles, CA; *U.S. Public*, pg. 940
Doyle, William H.W., Sr. V.P.-Devel.--TrizecHahn Centers Inc., San Diego, CA; *Int'l*, pg. 1425
Drader, Kelly I., Chief Fin. Officer, Sr. V.P. & Corp. Sec.--EnerMark Income Fund, Calgary, Canada; *Int'l*, pg. 454
Draeger, D.M., Sr. V.P.-Specialty Alloys Opers.--Carpenter Specialty Alloys Operations, Reading, PA; *U.S. Public*, pg. 307
Draeger, D.M., Sr. V.P.-Specialty Alloys Opers.--Carpenter Steel Div., Orangeburg, SC; *U.S. Public*, pg. 307
Draeger, D.M., Sr. V.P.-Specialty Alloys--Green Bay Supply Co., Inc., Hatfield, PA; *U.S. Public*, pg. 307
Draeger, D.M., Sr. V.P.-Specialty Alloys Opers.--Carpenter Technology Corp. (Taiwan) Ltd., Taipei, Taiwan; *U.S. Public*, pg. 308
Draeger, Dennis M., Sr. V.P.-Specialty Alloys Opers.--Carpenter Technology Corporation, Reading, PA; *U.S. Public*, pg. 307
Draganosky, Joyce, Sr. V.P.--Edelman Worldwide, Inc., New York, NY; *U.S. Private*, pg. 362
Draper, John M., Sr. V.P. & Gen. Counsel--Liberty Media Corporation, Englewood, CO; *U.S. Public*, pg. 1555
Draper, S.M., Sr. V.P.--SGS North America Inc., New York, NY; *Int'l*, pg. 1153
Draznin, Michael, Sr. V.P. & Corp. Communications Dir.--Lowe & Partners/SMS, New York, NY; *U.S. Private*, pg. 678
Drennan, Thomas W., Sr. V.P.-Mortgage Services--Astoria Financial Corporation, Lake Success, NY; *U.S. Public*, pg. 141
Drewliner, Peter G., Sr. V.P.-Electronic Banking Division--Bank of Hawaii, Honolulu, HI; *U.S. Public*, pg. 1248
Drewry, June E., Sr. V.P. & Tech. Officer--Lincoln National Corporation, Fort Wayne, IN; *U.S. Public*, pg. 997
Drews, Jurgen, Sr. V.P.-Hoffmann LaRoche Inc. & Pres.-Intl. Research--Hoffmann-La Roche Inc., Nutley, NJ; *Int'l*, pg. 1120
Drexel, Carolyn, Sr. V.P.-Branch Admin.--North Fork Bancorporation, Inc., Melville, NY; *U.S. Public*, pg. 1194
Dreyer, Brian F., Sr. V.P.-Commercial Banking--People's Bank, Bridgeport, CT; *U.S. Public*, pg. 1274
Driansky, Harvey, Sr. V.P.-Mktg.--Movado Group, Inc., Lyndhurst, NJ; *U.S. Public*, pg. 1140
Drinkwater, Gary W., Sr. V.P. & Gen. Mgr.-Project Svcs.--McDermott International, Inc., New Orleans, LA; *U.S. Public*, pg. 1067
Driscoll, D.L., Sr. V.P.--Telecredit Marketing Services, Tampa, FL; *U.S. Public*, pg. 588
Driscoll, David M., Sr. V.P.--Hellman, Jordan Management Company, Inc., Boston, MA; *U.S. Public*, pg. 1673
Driscoll, Gerald M., Sr. V.P. & Chief Credit Officer--Farmers and Merchants Bank and Trust, Hagerstown, MD; *U.S. Public*, pg. 1542
Droher, Paul F., Sr. V.P. & Dir.-P & C Home Office Underwriting--Federated Mutual Insurance Company, Owatonna, MN; *U.S. Private*, pg. 399
Drought, David W., Sr. V.P.-Fin.--First Financial Bank, FSB, Stevens Point, WI; *U.S. Public*, pg. 140
Drugg, Barry L., Sr. V.P.-Human Resources--Swisher International Group, Inc., Darien, CT; *U.S. Public*, pg. 1543
Drumgoole, Michael J., Sr. V.P.-Sls. & Mktg.--Medical Resources Inc., Hackensack, NJ; *U.S. Public*, pg. 1080
Dryburgh, Douglas T., Sr. V.P.-Sls. & Mktg.--Starter Corp., New Haven, CT; *U.S. Public*, pg. 1511
Dryburgh, James T., Chief Fin. Officer & Sr. V.P.--Mackenzie Financial Corporation, Toronto, Canada; *Int'l*, pg. 828
Duarte da Silveira, Jose C., Sr. V.P.--ITT Information Services, Inc., New York, NY; *U.S. Public*, pg. 1512
Dubach, Marcel, Sr. V.P.--Jelmoli AG, Zurich, Switzerland; *Int'l*, pg. 705
Dube, Jean-Louis, Sr. V.P.-Opers.--SITQ Immobilier, Montreal, Canada; *Int'l*, pg. 249
Dubin, Stephen V., Sr. V.P., Gen. Counsel & Sec.--CSS Industries, Inc., Philadelphia, PA; *U.S. Public*, pg. 283
Dubois-Dumee, Alain, Sr. V.P.-Corp. Commun.--Renault, Boulogne-Billancourt, France; *Int'l*, pg. 1102
Dubois, Richard, Sr. V.P.-Fin. & Admin.--Reed MIDEM Organisation S.A., Paris, France; *Int'l*, pg. 1097
DuBose, Pamela, Sr. V.P. & Acct. Mng. Dir.--Young & Rubicam New York, New York, NY; *U.S. Private*, pg. 1198
DuBow, Myron, Sr. V.P.-Bus. & Legal Affairs--Playboy Entertainment Group, Inc., Beverly Hills, CA; *U.S. Public*, pg. 1310
DuBow, Myron, Sr. V.P.--Alta Loma Productions, Inc., Beverly Hills, CA; *U.S. Public*, pg. 1310
Ducey, Bud, Sr. V.P.-MIS--Nationwide Credit Inc., Marietta, GA; *U.S. Private*, pg. 788
Duchardt, Karl H., Ph.D., Sr. V.P.-Production & Engrng./Biological Prods.--Bayer Corporation, Pittsburgh, PA; *Int'l*, pg. 172
Ducich, Dan, Chief Fin. Officer & Sr. V.P.--Recreational Equipment, Inc., Kent, WA; *U.S. Private*, pg. 914
Duckett, Paul, Sr. V.P.-Distribution & Retail Store Opers.--Swank, Inc., Attleboro, MA; *U.S. Public*, pg. 1543
Duda, Matthew, Sr. V.P.-Program Acquisition & Plng.--Showtime Networks Inc., New York, NY; *U.S. Private*, pg. 779
Duda, Ronald P., Sr. V.P.--Market Facts, Inc., Arlington Heights, IL; *U.S. Public*, pg. 1046
Duddles, Charles W., Chief Fin. Officer & Exec. V.P.--Foodmaker, Inc., San Diego, CA; *U.S. Public*, pg. 661
Duddy, John, Sr. V.P. & Gen. Mgr.-Directory Services Grp.--Liggett-Stashower, Inc., Cleveland, OH; *U.S. Private*, pg. 667
Duddy, John, Sr. V.P. & Gen. Mgr.--Directory Services Group, Cleveland, OH; *U.S. Private*, pg. 667
Duddy, Thomas J., Sr. V.P.--The Equitable Companies Incorporated, New York, NY; *U.S. Public*, pg. 588
Dudley, Connie C., Sr. V.P.--Total System Services, Inc., Columbus, GA; *U.S. Public*, pg. 1550
Duehming, Doug, Sr. V.P.-Fin.--Ocean Beauty Seafoods, Inc., Seattle, WA; *U.S. Private*, pg. 810
Duerk, Barry S., Sr. V.P.--Summit Bancorp, Princeton, NJ; *U.S. Public*, pg. 1527
Duey, George A., Sr. V.P.--Longs Drug Stores Corporation, Walnut Creek, CA; *U.S. Public*, pg. 1013
Duff, Gill, Sr. V.P. & Acct. Dir.--Young & Rubicam New York, New York, NY; *U.S. Private*, pg. 1198
Duff, James I., Sr. V.P.--Continental Western Insurance Company, Urbandale, IA; *U.S. Public*, pg. 215
Duffield, Albert W., Sr. V.P.-Sls.--PeopleSoft, Inc., Pleasanton, CA; *U.S. Public*, pg. 1276
Duffield, Michael O., Sr. V.P.-Opers.--Wallace Computer Services, Inc., Lisle, IL; *U.S. Public*, pg. 1735
Duffy, Charles R., Jr., Sr. V.P.-Opers.--Kansas City Life Insurance Co., Kansas City, MO; *U.S. Public*, pg. 942
Duffy, David L., Sr. V.P.-Corp. Commun.--The Chubb Corporation, Warren, NJ; *U.S. Public*, pg. 354
Duffy, David L., Sr. V.P.--Chubb & Son, Inc., Warren, NJ; *U.S. Public*, pg. 355
Duffy, Dennis J., Sr. V.P.-Customer Service Plng. & Delivery--Union Pacific Railroad Company, Omaha, NE; *U.S. Public*, pg. 1668
Duffy, E. Patrick, Sr. V.P. & Pres.-Coated Paper & Pulp Div.--Bowater Incorporated, Greenville, SC; *U.S. Public*, pg. 247
Duffy, Lou, Sr. V.P.-Industry Rels.--Martindale-Hubbell, New Providence, NJ; *Int'l*, pg. 1096
Duffy, William, Sr. V.P. & Gen. Mgr.-Emerging Mkts.--Epsilon, Burlington, MA; *U.S. Public*, pg. 74
Dufour, Jacques-Henry, Sr. V.P.-Fin.--SNECMA - Societe Nationale d'Etude et de Construction de Moteurs d'Aviation, Paris, France; *Int'l*, pg. 1165
Dufresne, D. Raymond, Chief Fin. Officer & Sr. V.P.--Mohawk Paper Mills, Inc., Cohoes, NY; *U.S. Private*, pg. 755
Dufresne, M., Sr. V.P.-Quebec & Atlantic--HongKong Bank of Canada, Vancouver, Canada; *Int'l*, pg. 583
Dugan, Allan E., Sr. V.P.-Corp. Strategic Services--Xerox Corporation, Stamford, CT; *U.S. Public*, pg. 1783
Dugan, Daniel R., Sr. V.P.-Worldwide Sls., Service & Mktg.--Acuson Corporation, Mountain View, CA; *U.S. Public*, pg. 18
Dugan, Dennis, Sr. V.P.-Sls. & Mktg.--Burns & Roe Enterprises, Inc., Oradell, NJ; *U.S. Private*, pg. 187
Dugan, Joel H., Sr. V.P.-Admin.--Heilig-Meyers Company, Richmond, VA; *U.S. Public*, pg. 804
Dugan, Joel H., Sr. V.P.-Fin. & Admin., & Sec.--Rhodes, Inc., Atlanta, GA; *U.S. Public*, pg. 805
Dugan, Joseph M., Sr. V.P.-Info. Svcs.--United Farm Family Life Insurance Co., Indianapolis, IN; *U.S. Private*, pg. 1122
Duggal, Arun, Sr. V.P. & Country Mgr.--Bank of America NT&SA, Tokyo, Japan; *U.S. Public*, pg. 182
Duggan, Larry, Sr. V.P.--Swinerton Inc., San Francisco, CA; *U.S. Private*, pg. 1059
Duguay, Robert F., Sr. V.P. & Trust Officer--Penn Security Bank and Trust Co., Scranton, PA; *U.S. Public*, pg. 1270
Duke, Ron, Sr. V.P. & Chief Fin. Officer--St. Clair Paint and Wallpaper Corporation, Toronto, Canada; *Int'l*, pg. 1170
Dukes, Terry, Sr. V.P. & Acct. Mng. Dir.--Young & Rubicam New York, New York, NY; *U.S. Private*, pg. 1198
Dumas, Jocelyn, Chief Fin. Officer & Sr. V.P.-Fin.--Fast Food Merchandisers Inc., Rocky Mount, NC; *U.S. Public*, pg. 278
Dumeny, Marcel J., Sr. V.P., Chief Gen. Counsel & Corp. Sec.--Fairfield Communities, Inc., Little Rock, AR; *U.S. Public*, pg. 610
Dumler, Denny D., Sr. V.P.-Consumer Banking--Colorado National Bankshares, Inc., Denver, CO; *U.S. Public*, pg. 1680
Dummigan, J. Patrick, Sr. V.P. & Gen. Mgr.--Ball Telecommunication Products Division, Broomfield, CO; *U.S. Public*, pg. 171
Dunaway, David F., Sr. V.P. & Gen. Mgr.--Speedy Car-X, Inc., Chicago, IL; *U.S. Public*, pg. 1578
Duncan, Delbert, Sr. V.P.-Admin.--Minyard Food Stores, Inc., Coppell, TX; *U.S. Private*, pg. 752
Duncan, Lloyd A., Sr. V.P. & Mgr.-Southwest Div.--First Security Bank of Idaho, N.A., Boise, ID; *U.S. Public*, pg. 637
Duncan, Milne J., Sr. V.P.--First Federal Capital Corp., La Crosse, WI; *U.S. Public*, pg. 632
Duncan, O. Wayne, Sr. V.P.-Opers.--Sysco Corporation, Houston, TX; *U.S. Public*, pg. 1550
Duncheon, Charles S., Sr. V.P.-Mktg. & Sls.--Adept Technology, Inc., San Jose, CA; *U.S. Public*, pg. 19
Dundas, Ray, Sr. V.P.-Network Neg.--SFM Media Corporation, New York, NY; *U.S. Private*, pg. 956
Dunham, Archie W., Sr. V.P.-Polymers--Du Pont (E.I. Du Pont De Nemours & Co.), Wilmington, DE; *U.S. Public*, pg. 530
Dunham, Mark, Sr. V.P.-Corporation--General Electric Investment Corp., Stamford, CT; *U.S. Public*, pg. 712
Dunivant, Noel, Dr., Sr. V.P.-Res. & Strategic Plng.--FGI Inc., Chapel Hill, NC; *U.S. Private*, pg. 389
Dunlap, Ira G., Sr. V.P.--The Dunlap Company, Fort Worth, TX; *U.S. Private*, pg. 346
Dunlap, Pamela L., Chief Fin. Officer & Sr. V.P.--ATL Ultrasound, Inc., Bothell, WA; *U.S. Public*, pg. 11
Dunlop, Edward, Sr. V.P.--The Chubb Corporation, Warren, NJ; *U.S. Public*, pg. 354
Dunn, Bob, Sr. V.P.--General Nutrition Centers, Pittsburgh, PA; *U.S. Public*, pg. 725
Dunn, Bryan C., Chief Mktg. Officer & Sr. V.P.--The Western and Southern Life Insurance Company, Cincinnati, OH; *U.S. Private*, pg. 1164
Dunn, Eric C.W., Chief Tech. Officer & Sr. V.P.-New Bus. & Intl.--Intuit, Inc., Mountain View, CA; *U.S. Public*, pg. 911
Dunn, Leslie, Sr. V.P., Gen. Counsel & Sec.--Cole National Corporation, Cleveland, OH; *U.S. Public*, pg. 396
Dunn, Marianne, Sr. V.P.--Bradley Real Estate, Inc., Northbrook, IL; *U.S. Public*, pg. 250
Dunn, Michael, Sr. V.P.-Mktg.--20th Century Fox Home Entertainment, Los Angeles, CA; *U.S. Public*, pg. 275
Dunn, Michael, Sr. V.P.-Mktg.--20th Century Fox Home Entertainment, Los Angeles, CA; *Int'l*, pg. 926
Dunn, Robert J., Sr. V.P. & Dir.-Bus. Devel.--Willis Corroon Melling Inc., Montreal, Canada; *Int'l*, pg. 1509
Dunn, Robert V., Sr. V.P.-Law & Admin.--General Nutrition, Inc., Pittsburgh, PA; *U.S. Public*, pg. 725
Dunn, Roger D., Sr. V.P.--AEC Oil & Gas, Calgary, Canada; *Int'l*, pg. 48
Dunning, Judith, Sr. V.P.-Plng. & Allocation--Bradlees Inc., Braintree, MA; *U.S. Public*, pg. 249
Dunphy, Kevin, Sr. V.P.--The Bank of New York Company, Inc., New York, NY; *U.S. Public*, pg. 178
Dunphy, Thomas E., Sr. V.P.--Bankers Life & Casualty Company, Chicago, IL; *U.S. Public*, pg. 433
Dunstan, Ericson M., Sr. V.P.-Corp. Engrng. & Sec.--Micropolis Corporation, Chatsworth, CA; *U.S. Private*, pg. 742
Duplain, Robert, Chief Fin. Officer & Sr. V.P.--The Buschman Co., Cincinnati, OH; *U.S. Private*, pg. 188
Dupps, Kirkwood, Sr. V.P.-Food & Commodities--Sam's Clubs Div., Bentonville, AR; *U.S. Public*, pg. 1733
Durant-des Aulnois, Jean Pierre, Sr. V.P.--Gemini Consulting, Morristown, NJ; *Int'l*, pg. 264
Durant, Martin A., III, Sr. V.P.-Corp. Services--AFLAC Incorporated, Columbus, GA; *U.S. Public*, pg. 28
Durast, Harold, Sr. V.P.-Fin. & Admin.--McCain Foods Inc., Oak Brook, IL; *Int'l*, pg. 850
Durbin, Ed, Sr. V.P.--Kaiser Aerospace & Electronics Corp., Foster City, CA; *U.S. Private*, pg. 605
Durden, M. Frances, Sr. V.P., Gen. Counsel & Sec.--Michael Anthony Jewelers, Inc., Mount Vernon, NY; *U.S.* Public, pg. 1103

Durels, Lisa, Sr. V.P. & Acct. Dir.--Young & Rubicam New York, New York, NY; *U.S. Private*, pg. 1198

Durham, James W., Sr. V.P.-Legal & Gen. Counsel--PECO Energy Company, Philadelphia, PA; *U.S. Public*, pg. 1268

Durkee, M.C., Sr. V.P.-Fin.--Perry Equipment Corporation, Mineral Wells, TX; *U.S. Private*, pg. 855

Durocher, Joseph, Chief Info. Officer & Sr. V.P.--Hilton Hotels Corporation, Beverly Hills, CA; *U.S. Public*, pg. 828

Dusonchet, Yves-Pascal, Sr. V.P.-Africa/Middle East--SGS Societe Generale de Surveillance Holding S.A., Geneva, Switzerland; *Int'l*, pg. 1153

Dussek, Steven, Chief Oper. Officer & Sr. V.P.--Paging Network, Inc., Plano, TX; *U.S. Public*, pg. 1252

Dussing, Donald I., Jr., Sr. V.P.--Manufacturers & Traders Trust Company, Buffalo, NY; *U.S. Public*, pg. 631

Dusto, Bradley P., Sr. V.P.-Engrng.--Comcast Cable Communications, Inc., Philadelphia, PA; *U.S. Public*, pg. 407

Dutta, Rono, Sr. V.P.-Plng.--United Air Lines, Inc., Elk Grove Village, IL; *U.S. Public*, pg. 1653

Dutta, Rono J., Sr. V.P.-Plng.--UAL Corporation, Elk Grove Village, IL; *U.S. Public*, pg. 1652

Duva, Philip, Sr. V.P. & Gen. Mgr.--Simon & Schuster Consumer Group, New York, NY; *U.S. Private*, pg. 777

Duval, James P., Sr. V.P. & Reg. Mgr.--McDonald's Corporation, Oak Brook, IL; *U.S. Public*, pg. 1068

Duvall, William R., Sr. V.P.-Opers.--LoJack Corporation, Dedham, MA; *U.S. Public*, pg. 1012

Duzan, Jean-Batiste, Sr. V.P.-Pur.--Renault, Boulogne-Billancourt, France; *Int'l*, pg. 1102

Dvir, Joseph, Sr. V.P.-Fin. & Econ.--The Israel Electric Corporation Ltd., Haifa, Israel; *Int'l*, pg. 690

Dvorchak, Thomas, Sr. V.P.--Bandag, Incorporated, Muscatine, IA; *U.S. Public*, pg. 177

Dwiggins, Michael, Sr. V.P.--Amtrade International Bank, Miami, FL; *U.S. Private*, pg. 68

Dwight, John E., Sr. V.P.--Blonder-Tongue Laboratories, Inc., Old Bridge, NJ; *U.S. Public*, pg. 237

Dwyer, Gregg A., Sr. V.P., Gen. Counsel & Sec.--Duracell International Inc., Bethel, CT; *U.S. Public*, pg. 743

Dwyer, James E., Jr., Sr. V.P.-Mktg.--Tropicana Dole Beverages North America, Bradenton, FL; *Int'l*, pg. 1217

Dwyer, John, Chief Fin. Officer, Sr. V.P. & Treas.--Bally Total Fitness Holdings Corporation, Chicago, IL; *U.S. Public*, pg. 171

Dwyer, John, Chief Fin. Officer & Sr. V.P.--Bally Total Fitness Corporation, Chicago, IL; *U.S. Public*, pg. 171

Dwyer, Joseph, Chief Fin. Officer & Sr. V.P.--Winstar Global Products, Inc., Fairfield, NJ; *U.S. Public*, pg. 1772

Dwyer, Kate, Sr. V.P.-H.R.--City National Corporation, Beverly Hills, CA; *U.S. Public*, pg. 380

Dwyer, Kathy, Sr. Exec. V.P.--Revlon, Inc., New York, NY; *U.S. Private*, pg. 689

Dwyer, Matthew P., Sr. V.P.-Sls./Leasing, NE--Spaulding & Slye, Boston, MA; *U.S. Private*, pg. 1021

Dwyer, Timothy P., Sr. V.P.-Unit Train & Auto Svcs. Grp.--Conrail, Inc., Philadelphia, PA; *U.S. Public*, pg. 431

Dwyer, William F., Sr. V.P. & Chief Investment Officer--Citizens Savings Bank, Providence, RI; *Int'l*, pg. 1132

Dybvad, Larry E., Sr. V.P.-PPGA Mktg.--American Mutual Life Holding Co., Des Moines, IA; *U.S. Private*, pg. 59

Dye, Cecil, Sr. V.P.-Worldwide Sls.--Network Computing Devices, Inc., Mountain View, CA; *U.S. Public*, pg. 1168

Dye, Laburn R., Sr. V.P.--Power & Telephone Supply Company, Memphis, TN; *U.S. Private*, pg. 877

Dyen, Randall, Sr. V.P., Gen. Counsel & Sec.--General Accident Insurance, Philadelphia, PA; *Int'l*, pg. 543

Dyer, Daniel P., Chief Fin. Officer & Sr. V.P.--Advanta Business Services, Voorhees, NJ; *U.S. Public*, pg. 22

Dyer, John R., Sr. V.P.-Managed Health Care--American Stores Company, Salt Lake City, UT; *U.S. Public*, pg. 92

Dyer, Robert, Sr. V.P.--Forest City Land Group, Cleveland, OH; *U.S. Public*, pg. 668

Dziurzynski, Bogdan, Sr. V.P.-Regulatory Affairs & Quality Assurance--MedImmune, Inc., Gaithersburg, MD; *U.S. Public*, pg. 1081

Dzuricky, David J., Sr. V.P.-Fin.--Piedmont Natural Gas Co., Inc., Charlotte, NC; *U.S. Public*, pg. 1295

Eades, Vincent, Sr. V.P.-Specialty Sls. & Mktg.--Starbucks Coffee Company, Seattle, WA; *U.S. Public*, pg. 1510

Eads, Emanuel, Sr. V.P.-Intl. Sports Devel.--Central Parking Corp., Nashville, TN; *U.S. Public*, pg. 326

Eagan, Edward, Sr. V.P.-Mktg.--Universal Pictures, Universal City, CA; *Int'l*, pg. 1216

Eagan, James, Chief Fin. Officer & Sr. V.P.--Riverwood International Corporation, Atlanta, GA; *U.S. Public*, pg. 1391

Eagen, Jack, Sr. V.P.--Moore & Taber Grouting Services, Anaheim, CA; *Int'l*, pg. 31

Eager, William E., Sr. V.P.-Opers.--First National Bank of Ohio, Akron, OH; *U.S. Public*, pg. 646

Eagles, M.E., Sr. V.P.--Weatherford Enterra Incorporated, Houston, TX; *U.S. Public*, pg. 1749

Earle, Michael J., Sr. V.P.--Southwest National Bank of Pennsylvania, Greensburg, PA; *U.S. Public*, pg. 1493

Earley, Robert K., Sr. V.P.-Distr.--Williams-Sonoma, Inc., San Francisco, CA; *U.S. Public*, pg. 1770

Early, William B., Sr. V.P.--Jeld-Wen, Inc., Klamath Falls, OR; *U.S. Private*, pg. 585

Earnshaw, Antonia, Sr. V.P. & Acct. Plng. Dir.-Insights Grp.--Young & Rubicam New York, New York, NY; *U.S. Private*, pg. 1198

Easley, Robert, Sr. V.P. & Grp. Acct. Dir.--DMB&B New York, New York, NY; *U.S. Private*, pg. 302

Easley, William K., Sr. V.P.--Springs Industries, Inc., Fort Mill, SC; *U.S. Public*, pg. 1499

Easley, William K., Sr. V.P. & Pres.-Textile Mfg.--Home Furnishings Segment, Fort Mill, SC; *U.S. Public*, pg. 1500

Eason, William E., Jr., Sr. V.P., Gen. Counsel & Sec.--Scientific-Atlanta, Inc., Norcross, GA; *U.S. Public*, pg. 1443

Eastin, Carol, Sr. V.P.-MIS--Starbucks Coffee Company, Seattle, WA; *U.S. Public*, pg. 1510

Eastman, Kent, Sr. V.P. & Sr. Credit Officer--Hibernia Corporation, New Orleans, LA; *U.S. Public*, pg. 825

Eastment, George T., III, Sr. V.P.--The Long & Foster Companies, Inc., Fairfax, VA; *U.S. Private*, pg. 674

Eastment, George T., III, Sr. V.P.--The Long & Foster Real Estate, Inc., Fairfax, VA; *U.S. Private*, pg. 674

Eaton, Charles, Sr. V.P.-Sls.--Shorewood Packaging Corporation, New York, NY; *U.S. Public*, pg. 1468

Eaton, Dick, Chief Fin. Officer & Sr. V.P.--Highway One Communications, Integrated Marketing Services, San Francisco, CA; *U.S. Private*, pg. 303

Eaton, Scott M., Sr. V.P.-Legal--SHL Systemhouse, Ottawa, Canada; *Int'l*, pg. 1154

Ebensteiner, JoAnne, Sr. V.P. & Creative Dir.--Campbell Mithun Esty, Minneapolis, MN; *U.S. Private*, pg. 204

Eberly, Larry H., Sr. V.P.-Trust Svcs.--Lebanon Valley Farmers Bank, Lebanon, PA; *U.S. Public*, pg. 688

Ebetino, Charles A., Jr., Sr. V.P.-Fuel Supply--American Electric Power Service Corp., Columbus, OH; *U.S. Public*, pg. 72

Ebling, Thomas D., Sr. V.P.-Protean Devel.--Marcam Solutions, Inc., Newton, MA; *U.S. Public*, pg. 1042

Ebner, Stanley, Sr. V.P.-Washington Opers.--McDonnell Aircraft & Missile Systems Div., Berkeley, MO; *U.S. Public*, pg. 241

Ebsen, Greg, Sr. V.P.-Sls. & Mktg.--J.R. Simplot Company Food Group, Boise, ID; *U.S. Private*, pg. 1002

Eby, C. Leonard, Jr., Sr. V.P.-Lending--Omega Bank, N.A., State College, PA; *U.S. Public*, pg. 1222

Echeverria, Matt J., Sr. V.P. & Acting Chief Exec. Officer--Tejon Ranch Company, Lebec, CA; *U.S. Public*, pg. 1566

Eckard, Dalthard, Sr. V.P.-Sls. & Mktg.--The Berkline Corporation, Morristown, TN; *U.S. Private*, pg. 432

Eckberg, Edwin, Sr. V.P.--Keystone Financial Service Group, Inc., Altoona, PA; *U.S. Public*, pg. 956

Eckel, James A., Sr. V.P.-Personnel--Cullen/Frost Bankers, Inc., San Antonio, TX; *U.S. Public*, pg. 467

Eckenrode, W.J., Chief Fin. Officer & Sr. V.P.--Berwind Corporation, Philadelphia, PA; *U.S. Private*, pg. 138

Ecker, H. Allen, Ph.D., Chief Oper. Officer & Sr. V.P.-Tech. Opers.--Scientific-Atlanta, Inc., Norcross, GA; *U.S. Public*, pg. 1443

Ecker, Michael, Sr. V.P.--Andover Bank, Andover, MA; *U.S. Public*, pg. 112

Ecker, Michael J., Sr. V.P.--Andover Bancorp, Inc., Andover, MA; *U.S. Public*, pg. 111

Eckerman, Bjorn, Sr. V.P.-Corp. Internal Audit--Telia AB, Farsta, Sweden; *Int'l*, pg. 1373

Eckhaus, Barry, Sr. V.P.-Far East--Bestform Foundations, Inc., Long Island City, NY; *U.S. Private*, pg. 140

Ecklin, Robert L., Sr. V.P.-Environmental Prods.--Corning Incorporated, Corning, NY; *U.S. Public*, pg. 448

Eckstaedt, James R., Chief Fin. Officer & Sr. V.P.--The Cerplex Group, Inc., Tustin, CA; *U.S. Public*, pg. 332

Economos, George, Sr. V.P. & Dir.-Mktg.--The Dartnell Corporation, Chicago, IL; *U.S. Private*, pg. 312

Eddy, Brenda, Sr. V.P.-Adv.--Choice Hotels International, Inc., Silver Spring, MD; *U.S. Public*, pg. 351

Eddy, Larry A., Sr. V.P.-Corp. Devel.--CCL Industries, Inc., Willowdale, Canada; *Int'l*, pg. 238

Edelman, Renee, Sr. V.P.--Edelman Worldwide, Inc., New York, NY; *U.S. Private*, pg. 362

Edels, Howard, Sr. V.P.-Mngmnt. Information Services--CVS Corp., Woonsocket, RI; *U.S. Public*, pg. 287

Edelstein, Michael, Sr. V.P. & Creative Dir.--Gillespie, Lawrenceville, NJ; *U.S. Private*, pg. 453

Edens, Charles G., Sr. V.P.--Willis Faber North America, Inc.-North Carolina, Greensboro, NC; *Int'l*, pg. 1503

Eder, Steven E., Sr. V.P.-Asset Mngmt. Fin. Svcs.--Taubman Centers, Inc., Bloomfield Hills, MI; *U.S. Public*, pg. 1561

Edern, Yves, Sr. V.P.-Fin./Refining & Mktg.--Elf Aquitane, Paris, France; *Int'l*, pg. 444

Edgar, Roger S., Sr. V.P.-Information Systems--American Express Financial Advisor, Minneapolis, MN; *U.S. Public*, pg. 73

Edgson, George A., Sr. V.P.-Opers.--Slocan Forest Products Ltd., Richmond, Canada; *Int'l*, pg. 1263

Edinger, Gary A., Sr. V.P.-Energy Delivery--New Jersey Natural Gas Co., Wall, NJ; *U.S. Public*, pg. 1172

Edison, E. Charles, III, Sr. V.P.-Sls.--Asymetrix Learning Systems, Inc., Bellevue, WA; *U.S. Private*, pg. 93

Edkins, William D., Sr. V.P.-Strategic Plng.--The May Department Stores Company, Saint Louis, MO; *U.S. Public*, pg. 1063

Edmonds, Lynn, Sr. V.P. & Gen. Mgr.-Fundraising & Membership Services--Epsilon, Burlington, MA; *U.S. Public*, pg. 74

Edmonds, Scott, Sr. V.P.-Opers.--Chico's Fas Inc, Fort Myers, FL; *U.S. Public*, pg. 349

Edmondson, Dave, Sr. V.P.-Adv. & Mktg.--RadioShack, Fort Worth, TX; *U.S. Public*, pg. 1560

Edmondson, O.G., Sr. V.P.-Fin. & Admin.--Alberta Power Limited, Edmonton, Canada; *Int'l*, pg. 95

Edney, John, Sr. V.P.--Durham Transportation, Inc., Austin, TX; *U.S. Private*, pg. 348

Edson, Richard L., Sr. V.P.-Client Access/New Bus. Initiatives--3Com Corporation, Santa Clara, CA; *U.S. Public*, pg. 1603

Edwards, Diane, Sr. V.P. & Pub. Rels. Dir.--Mintz & Hoke Inc., Avon, CT; *U.S. Private*, pg. 751

Edwards, Greg, Sr. V.P. & Controller--The Irvine Company, Newport Beach, CA; *U.S. Private*, pg. 575

Edwards, John, Sr. V.P.-Corp. Rels.--Texas-New Mexico Power Co., Fort Worth, TX; *U.S. Public*, pg. 1557

Edwards, John D., Sr. V.P.-Combat Systems--Logicon Syscon Corporation, Falls Church, VA; *U.S. Public*, pg. 1199

Edwards, John F., Sr. V.P.--Grey Advertising Inc., New York, NY; *U.S. Public*, pg. 764

Edwards, John P., Sr. V.P.--TNP Enterprises, Inc., Fort Worth, TX; *U.S. Public*, pg. 1557

Edwards, Julie H., Chief Fin. Officer & Sr. V.P.-Fin.--Wainoco Oil Corporation, Houston, TX; *U.S. Public*, pg. 1732

Edwards, Larry, Sr. V.P.--Jason Incorporated, Milwaukee, WI; *U.S. Public*, pg. 923

Edwards, Michael J., Sr. V.P.-Gen. Mdsg.--CompUSA, Dallas, TX; *U.S. Public*, pg. 420

Edwards, Richard M., Sr. V.P.-Intl. Mktg.--National Western Life Insurance Company, Austin, TX; *U.S. Public*, pg. 1161

Edwards, Robert D., Sr. V.P.-Cash Mngmt.--PNC Bank Corp., Pittsburgh, PA; *U.S. Public*, pg. 1242

Edwards, Warren, Sr. V.P.--Affiliated Computer Services, Inc., Dallas, TX; *U.S. Public*, pg. 27

Edwards, Wesley B., Sr. V.P.-Opers.--Jabil Circuit, Inc., Saint Petersburg, FL; *U.S. Public*, pg. 919

Edwards, Wiliam, Sr. V.P.--QEI, Inc., Springfield, NJ; *U.S. Private*, pg. 897

Edwards, William F., Chief Fin. Officer & Sr. V.P.--Niagara Mohawk Power Corporation, Syracuse, NY; *U.S. Public*, pg. 1181

Edwards, William S., Sr. V.P.-Opers.--Physician Computer Network, Inc., Morris Plains, NJ; *U.S. Public*, pg. 1293

Eells, Gwen J., Sr. V.P. & Asst. Gen. Counsel--Countrywide Funding Corporation, Pasadena, CA; *U.S. Public*, pg. 453

Eells, Gwen J., Sr. V.P. & Gen. Counsel-Secondary Mktg.--INMC Mortgage Holdings, Inc., Pasadena, CA; *U.S. Public*, pg. 857

Effinger, William L., III, Sr. V.P. & Dir.--The Robinson-Humphrey Company, Inc., Atlanta, GA; *U.S. Public*, pg. 1633

Egami, Jerry, Sr. V.P.--Isemoto Contracting Co. Ltd., Hilo, HI; *U.S. Private*, pg. 575

Egan, Daniel J., Sr. V.P.--ContiFinancial Corporation, New York, NY; *U.S. Public*, pg. 439

Egan, Daniel J., Chief Fin. Officer, Sr. V.P. & Treas.--ContiMortgage Corporation, Horsham, PA; *U.S. Public*, pg. 439

Egan, Edward, Sr. V.P.-Mktg.--TriStar Pictures, Culver City, CA; *Int'l*, pg. 1283

Egan, Thomas F., Sr. V.P.--Suprema Specialties Northeast, Inc., Ogdensburg, NY; *U.S. Public*, pg. 1541

Egan, Thomas J., Sr. V.P. & Sr. Admin. Deputy--Freeport-McMoRan Inc., New Orleans, LA; *U.S. Public*, pg. 680

Egg, William C., Jr., Sr. V.P.--Plains Resources Inc., Houston, TX; *U.S. Public*, pg. 1307

Eggenberger, Hans, Sr. V.P.-Res. & Devel.--Bobst S.A., Lausanne, Switzerland; *Int'l*, pg. 198

Eggleston, Alan P., Sr. V.P. & Gen. Counsel--Astoria Financial Corporation, Lake Success, NY; *U.S. Public*, pg. 141

Egnot, John W., Sr. V.P.--Laurel Bånk, Johnstown, PA; *U.S. Public*, pg. 164

Eguchi, Takashi, Sr. V.P.--Softbank Corporation, Tokyo, Japan; *Int'l*, pg. 1276

Ehlen, John M., Sr. V.P.-Refining & Engrng.--Koch Industries, Incorporated, Wichita, KS; *U.S. Private*, pg. 628

Ehlinger, Peter, Sr. V.P.-Human Resources--Intercontinental Branded Apparel, Buffalo, NY; *U.S. Public*, pg. 796

Ehner, William J., Sr. V.P.-Strategic Plng.--Johns Manville Corporation, Denver, CO; *U.S. Public*, pg. 927

Ehrenstrom, James E., Sr. V.P.--Northwestern Mutual Life Insurance Co., Milwaukee, WI; *U.S. Private*, pg. 807

Ehresman, William, Sr. V.P. & Sec.--Gannett Fleming Affiliates, Inc., Camp Hill, PA; *U.S. Private*, pg. 439

Ehret, Bob, Sr. V.P.-H.R. & Commun.--Adolph Coors Company, Golden, CO; *U.S. Public*, pg. 445

Ehret, Robert W., Sr. V.P.-Human Resources--Coors Brewing Company, Golden, CO; *U.S. Public*, pg. 445

Ehrhorn, William G., Sr. V.P.-Mortgage Opers.--Federal National Mortgage Association (Fannie Mae), Washington, DC; *U.S. Public*, pg. 615

Ehringer, George D., Sr. V.P.--Michael Baker, Jr., Inc., Beaver, PA; *U.S. Public*, pg. 168

Ehrlichman, John, Sr. V.P.--Law Companies Group, Atlanta, GA; *U.S. Private*, pg. 653

Eichler, Richard S., Sr. V.P.--SAFECO Properties, Inc., Seattle, WA; *U.S. Public*, pg. 1423

Eid, Gordon L., Sr. V.P. & Deputy Gen. Counsel--American Express Financial Advisor, Minneapolis, MN; *U.S. Public*, pg. 73

Eidson, Julian, Sr. V.P. & Controller--Scientific-Atlanta, Inc., Norcross, GA; *U.S. Public*, pg. 1443

Eikelboom, S. D., Sr. V.P.-Strategy & Devel.--Royal Pakhoed NV, Rotterdam, Netherlands; *Int'l*, pg. 1147

Eilert, Norman E., Chief Fin. Officer & Exec. V.P.--A. Teichert & Son, Inc., Sacramento, CA; *U.S. Private*, pg. 1072

Einarson, Gudmundur, Sr. V.P.-Silicon Div.--Elkem ASA, Oslo, Norway; *Int'l*, pg. 446

Eino, Moni, Dr., Pres.-Ingredients Div. & Sr. V.P.-Opers.--Parmalat Canada Ltd., Etobicoke, Canada; *Int'l*, pg. 1023

Eiriksson, Petur, Sr. V.P.-Mktg.--IceLandAir, Columbia, MD; *Int'l*, pg. 658

Eiriksson, Petur J., Sr. V.P.--Icelandair, Reykjavik, Iceland; *Int'l*, pg. 658

Eisele, Anne E., Chief Fin. Officer & Sr. V.P.--Geotek Communications, Montvale, NJ; *U.S. Public*, pg. 739

Eisemann, Joel M., Sr. V.P.-Lodging Devel.-Asia/Pacific--Marriott International, Inc., Washington, DC; *U.S. Public*, pg. 1047

Eisen, Audrey D., Sr. V.P. & Mngmt. Supvr.--Fahlgren, Atlanta, GA; *U.S. Private*, pg. 391

Eisen, Elaine, Sr. V.P.-Acct. Mngmt.--Corbett HealthConnect, A Frank J. Corbett, Inc., Company, Chicago, IL; *U.S. Public*, pg. 1223

Eisen, Harvey P., Sr. V.P.-Investments--Travelers Group, New York, NY; *U.S. Public*, pg. 1632

Eisenberg, Bruce, Sr. V.P.-Real Estate--Trans World Entertainment Corporation, Albany, NY; *U.S. Public*, pg. 1629

Eisenberg, Glenn A., Chief Fin. Officer & Sr. V.P.--United Dominion Industries, Ltd., Charlotte, NC; *U.S. Public*, pg. 1675

Eisenberg, Phillip, Sr. V.P. & Chief Actuary--The Mutual Life Insurance Company of New York, New York, NY; *U.S. Private*, pg. 769

Eisenman, Marc, Sr. V.P. & Design Dir.--EvansGroup, Los Angeles, CA; *U.S. Private*, pg. 385

Eisenman, William J., Sr. V.P.-Computer Sys. Grp.--NCR Corporation, Dayton, OH; *U.S. Public*, pg. 1146

Eisenstadt, Samuel, Sr. V.P. & Res. Chm.--Value Line, Inc., New York, NY; *U.S. Private*, pg. 137

Eisenstein, Les, Sr. V.P.-Mdse. Sls.--Active International, Pearl River, NY; *U.S. Private*, pg. 15

Eisman, W. Paul, Sr. V.P.-Refining--Ultramar Diamond Shamrock Corporation, San Antonio, TX; *U.S. Public*, pg. 1663

Eisner, Sara, Sr. V.P. & Mngmt. Supvr.--Eisner & Associates, Inc., Baltimore, MD; *U.S. Private*, pg. 366

Ek, Dave, Sr. V.P.--Wells/Bloomfield, Verdi, NV; *U.S. Public*, *pg. 1497*

Eklund, Gosta, Sr. V.P.--W. Rosenlew Ltd., Helsinki, Finland; *Int'l*, pg. 1428

El Shami, Said, Chief Scientific Officer & Sr. V.P.-Res. & Devel.--Diagnostic Products Corporation, Los Angeles, CA; *U.S. Public*, pg. 505

El-Hillow, Michael, Chief Fin. Officer & Sr. V.P.--Helix Technology Corp., Mansfield, MA; *U.S. Public*, pg. 808

Elbaum, Mark E., Sr. V.P.-Fin.--Aames Financial Corporation, Los Angeles, CA; *U.S. Public*, pg. 12

Elberg, Dale, Sr. V.P.-Sls. & Mktg.--Royal Oak Enterprises, Inc., Atlanta, GA; *U.S. Private*, pg. 948

Elchynski, Ted, Chief Fin. Officer & Sr. V.P.--Cincinnati Financial Corp., Fairfield, OH; *U.S. Public*, pg. 368

Elders, Robert K., Sr. V.P.--PCC Flow Technologies, Inc., Houston, TX; *U.S. Public*, pg. 1320

Eldridge, George Thomas, Sr. V.P.-Corp. Services--American Mutual Life Holding Co., Des Moines, IA; *U.S. Private*, pg. 59

Elek, Gary J., Sr. V.P.--FirstMerit Corporation, Akron, OH; *U.S. Public*, pg. 646

Elenbaas, Marvin, Sr. V.P. & Controller--Comerica Incorporated, Detroit, MI; *U.S. Public*, pg. 408

Elias, Antonio L., Sr. V.P.-Advanced Programs--Orbital Sciences Corporation, Dulles, VA; *U.S. Public*, pg. 1229

Elias, Jeffrey A., Sr. V.P.-H.R. & Admin.--RemedyTemp, Inc., San Juan Capistrano, CA; *U.S. Public*, pg. 1376

Elias, Lawrence, Sr. V.P.-MIS--Pueblo Xtra International, Inc., Pompano Beach, FL; *U.S. Private*, pg. 894

Elisiario, Joao M., Sr. V.P.-Mktg.--Banco Espirito Santo e Comercial de Lisboa SA, Lisbon, Portugal; *Int'l*, pg. 142

Elkins, Ken J., Sr. V.P.-Broadcasting Opers.--Pulitzer Publishing Company, Saint Louis, MO; *U.S. Public*, pg. 1343

Ellard, Denis, Sr. V.P.--Canadian Utilities Limited, Calgary, Canada; *Int'l*, pg. 95

Ellberger, Larry, Chief Fin. Officer & Sr. V.P.-Strategic Plng. & Devel.--W.R. Grace & Co., Boca Raton, FL; *U.S. Public*, pg. 754

Elledge, Richard D., Chief Acctg. Officer, Sr. V.P. & Asst. Sec.--Lowe's Companies, Inc., North Wilkesboro, NC; *U.S. Public*, pg. 1015

Ellgass, Leory, Sr. V.P.-Fin.--Hess Engineering Inc., Niles, MI; *U.S. Private*, pg. 524

Ellington, Robert N., Jr., Sr. V.P.--Willis Faber North America, Inc.-North Carolina, Greensboro, NC; *Int'l*, pg. 1503

Elliot, Geoffrey, Sr. V.P.-Corp. Affairs & Govt.--Air Canada, Saint-Laurent, Canada; *Int'l*, pg. 36

Elliot, William, Sr. V.P., Gen. Counsel & Asst. Sec.--Gateway 2000, North Sioux City, SD; *U.S. Public*, pg. 703

Elliott, Daniel R., Jr., Sr. V.P., Gen. Counsel & Sec.--White Consolidated Industries, Inc., Cleveland, OH; *Int'l*, pg. 439

Elliott, Daryl, Sr. V.P. & Acct. Dir.--Young & Rubicam New York, New York, NY; *U.S. Private*, pg. 1198

Elliott, H. Jay, Chief Fin. Officer, Sr. V.P. & Treas.--The Lincoln Electric Company, Cleveland, OH; *U.S. Public*, pg. 996

Elliott, James J., Sr. V.P.-Opers.--Santa Fe Minerals Inc., Dallas, TX; *Int'l*, pg. 765

Elliott, James V., Sr. V.P., Gen. Counsel & Sec.--AEGON USA, Inc., Louisville, KY; *Int'l*, pg. 26

Elliott, Jay A., Sr. V.P.-Natl. Sls.--Jackson National Life Insurance Company, Lansing, MI; *Int'l*, pg. 1073

Elliott, John W., Sr. V.P. & Trust Officer--First National Bank of Warsaw, Warsaw, IN; *U.S. Public*, pg. 674

Elliott, Sharon, Sr. V.P.-Human Resources--Starbucks Coffee Company, Seattle, WA; *U.S. Public*, pg. 1510

Ellis, Barry W., Sr. V.P.-Devel., Real Estate & Environment--Cooper Communities, Inc., Bella Vista, AR; *U.S. Private*, pg. 273

Ellis, C. Lee, Sr. V.P.-Investments--Alfa Corporation, Montgomery, AL; *U.S. Public*, pg. 40

Ellis, C. Lee, Sr. V.P.-Investments--Alfa Investment Corp. & Builders Inc., Montgomery, AL; *U.S. Public*, pg. 40

Ellis, D. Michael, Sr. V.P. & Dir.-Central Loan Prod. Oper.--Barclays American/Mortgage Corp., Charlotte, NC; *Int'l*, pg. 165

Ellis, Ellwood, Sr. V.P. & Publisher--Glencoe/Mc-Graw Hill, Westerville, OH; *U.S. Public*, pg. 1070

Ellis, Evan, Sr. V.P.-Markets--Silicon Graphics, Inc., Mountain View, CA; *U.S. Public*, pg. 1473

Ellis, Gary, Sr. V.P. & Chief Fin. Officer--Consolidated Cigar Corp., Fort Lauderdale, FL; *U.S. Private*, pg. 690

Ellis, James A., Sr. V.P.-Sls. & Service Div.--CVB Financial Corp., Ontario, CA; *U.S. Public*, pg. 286

Ellis, Jerry C.D., Sr. V.P.--Acxiom Corporation, Conway, AR; *U.S. Public*, pg. 18

Ellis, Larry W., Sr. V.P.-Power Opers. & Plng.--Virginia Electric and Power Company, Richmond, VA; *U.S. Public*, pg. 516

Ellis, Lewis, Sr. V.P.-Engrng.--Kirby Building Systems, Inc., Portland, TN; *Int'l*, pg. 699

Ellison, Lee, Sr. V.P.-Intl. Opers.--Glenayre Technologies, Inc., Charlotte, NC; *U.S. Public*, pg. 746

Elmore, E. Whitehead, Sr. V.P., Gen. Counsel & Sec.--Albemarle Corporation, Richmond, VA; *U.S. Public*, pg. 37

Elop, Stephen, Sr. V.P.-Information Systems--Boston Chicken, Inc., Golden, CO; *U.S. Public*, pg. 247

Else, Tom, Sr. V.P. & Acct. Dir.--Hal Riney & Partners, Inc., San Francisco, CA; *U.S. Private*, pg. 931

Elsley, John E., Sr. V.P.-Plants & Bulbs--George W. Park Seed Co., Inc., Greenwood, SC; *U.S. Private*, pg. 839

Elyea, Thomas E., Sr. V.P.--Fort Wayne National Corporation, Fort Wayne, IN; *U.S. Public*, pg. 673

Embree, Steven S., Sr. V.P. & Mgr.-Gen. Mdsg.--Office Depot Inc., Delray Beach, FL; *U.S. Public*, pg. 1212

Emens, John A., Sr. V.P.--First Maryland Bancorp, Baltimore, MD; *Int'l*, pg. 64

Emery, J. D., Sr. V.P.-Res.--Brown Marketing Communications, Chicago, IL; *U.S. Private*, pg. 174

Emery, Phillip, Sr. V.P. & Div. Mgr.-Fine Papers--Westvaco Corporation, New York, NY; *U.S. Public*, pg. 1762

Emmerson, Peter, Sr. V.P.-Intl.--Coach, New York, NY; *U.S. Public*, pg. 1433

Emmert, John C., Jr., Chief Fin. Officer, Sr. V.P. & Treas.--American Arbitration Association, New York, NY; *U.S. Private*, pg. 50

Emmick, Gary K., Sr. V.P.-Employee Rels.--Corning Incorporated, Corning, NY; *U.S. Public*, pg. 448

Emmons, William H., Sr. V.P. & Reg. Mgr.--Albertson's, Inc., Boise, ID; *U.S. Public*, pg. 38

Empey, Steven, Sr. V.P.--Imperial Bank, Inglewood, CA; *U.S. Public*, pg. 871

Empson, Jon R., Sr. V.P.-Legislative, Regulatory & Environmental Services--UtiliCorp United Inc., Kansas City, MO; *U.S. Public*, pg. 1700

Ende, Eric S., Sr. V.P.--First Pacific Advisors, Inc., Los Angeles, CA; *U.S. Public*, pg. 1673

Endemann, Carlton, Jr., Sr. V.P.--Pepsi-Cola Albany Bottling Co., Inc., Latham, NY; *U.S. Private*, pg. 852

Endres, William S., Sr. V.P.-Mktg.--The Rival Company, Kansas City, MO; *U.S. Public*, pg. 1391

Eng, David, Sr. V.P.-Worldwide Sls.--C-COR Electronics, Inc., State College, PA; *U.S. Public*, pg. 272

Engberg, John, Sr. V.P.--Imperial Bank, Inglewood, CA; *U.S. Public*, pg. 871

Engel, David R., Sr. V.P.--Southwest Marine, Inc., San Diego, CA; *U.S. Private*, pg. 213

Engel, Debra J., Sr. V.P.-Corp. Svcs.--3Com Corporation, Santa Clara, CA; *U.S. Public*, pg. 1603

Engel, Leslie J., Sr. V.P. & Human Resources Dir.-NY--DMB&B New York, New York, NY; *U.S. Private*, pg. 302

Engel, Robert A., Jr., Sr. V.P.-Film & Adv.--Regal Cinemas Inc., Knoxville, TN; *U.S. Public*, pg. 1371

Engel, Roger K., Dr., Sr. V.P.-Bus. Devel.--California Microwave, Inc.-Government Grp., Sunnyvale, CA; *U.S. Public*, pg. 293

Engelberg, Steven L., Sr. V.P.--Monsanto Company, Saint Louis, MO; *U.S. Public*, pg. 1124

Engelhardt, Aggie, Sr. V.P.-Acctg. & MIS--Keyes Martin, East Hanover, NJ; *U.S. Private*, pg. 618

Engelman, Wayne, Sr. V.P., Treas. & Sec.--Colle & McVoy, Inc., Minneapolis, MN; *U.S. Private*, pg. 252

Engelman, Wayne, Chief Fin. Officer & Sr. V.P.--Colle & McVoy Marketing Communications, Minneapolis, MN; *U.S. Private*, pg. 252

Engelmann, Les, Sr. V.P.--Ames Co., Inc., Woodland, CA; *U.S. Public*, pg. 1746

Engels, Robert, Sr. V.P.-European Opers.--Cognos Inc., Ottawa, Canada; *Int'l*, pg. 305

Engi, Leonhard, Sr. V.P.--Westdeutsche Landesbank (Schweiz) AG, Zurich, Switzerland; *Int'l*, pg. 799

England, Garry L., Sr. V.P.-Warsaw Opers.--Biomet, Inc., Warsaw, IN; *U.S. Public*, pg. 231

England, Joseph W., Sr. V.P.-Worldwide Parts Div. & Corp. Admin.--Deere & Company, Moline, IL; *U.S. Public*, pg. 491

Englander, Jeffrey A., Sr. V.P.--Trenwick America Reinsurance Corporation, Stamford, CT; *U.S. Public*, pg. 1634

Englander, Ken, Sr. V.P.-Mktg.--Central Lewmar, Newark, NJ; *U.S. Private*, pg. 223

Englar, John D., Sr. V.P.-Corp. Devel. & Law--Burlington Industries, Inc., Greensboro, NC; *U.S. Public*, pg. 268

Engler, Richard, Sr. V.P. & Mgr.-W. Region--Heery International, Inc., Atlanta, GA; *U.S. Private*, pg. 519

Engles, Charles R., Sr. V.P.-Corp. Devel.--Johns Manville Corporation, Denver, CO; *U.S. Public*, pg. 927

Englestad, Robert J., Sr. V.P.-Mortgage & Lender Standards--Federal National Mortgage Association (Fannie Mae), Washington, DC; *U.S. Public*, pg. 615

English, Jim, Sr. V.P. & Gen. Mgr.-Pay Television--Playboy Entertainment Group, Inc., Beverly Hills, CA; *U.S. Public*, *pg. 1310*

English, Joel, Sr. V.P.--BVK/McDonald, Milwaukee, WI; *U.S. Private*, pg. 108

English, Lawrence W., Sr. V.P.-Admin.--American International Group, Inc., New York, NY; *U.S. Public*, pg. 83

English, Paul, Sr. V.P.-Prod. Devel.--Interleaf, Inc., Waltham, MA; *U.S. Public*, pg. 893

English, Roderick, Sr. V.P.-Human Resources & Communications--Delco Remy America, Inc., Anderson, IN; *U.S. Public*, pg. 495

English, William F., Sr. V.P.-Opers.--Jevic Transportation, Inc., Delanco, NJ; *U.S. Public*, pg. 927

Engmark-Nauser, Deborah, Sr. V.P.--The Mercury Group, Alexandria, VA; *U.S. Private*, pg. 13

Engwall, K. Wyatt, Sr. V.P.-Fin. & Asst. Sec.--Morrison Health Care Inc., Smyrna, GA; *U.S. Public*, pg. 1133

Enneking, Daniel J., Sr. V.P.-Systemedia Grp.--NCR Corporation, Dayton, OH; *U.S. Public*, pg. 1146

Ennen, Dennis W., Sr. V.P. & Trust Officer--The Bradford National Bank of Greenville, Greenville, IL; *U.S. Private*, pg. 164

Ennis, Martin D., Sr. V.P.-Insurance Opers.--Medical Assurance, Inc., Birmingham, AL; *U.S. Public*, pg. 1079

Eno, Rex B., Sr. V.P.-Agency Grp.--AEGON USA, Inc., Baltimore, MD; *Int'l*, pg. 26

Eno, Woodrow E., Sr. V.P.-Law & Govt. Rels., Sec. & Gen. Counsel--Aid Association for Lutherans, Appleton, WI; *U.S. Private*, pg. 27

Enright, Vincent D., Chief Fin. Officer & Sr. V.P.--Brooklyn Union, Brooklyn, NY; *U.S. Public*, pg. 259

Ensley, Ronnie L., Sr. V.P.-Mfg.--American & Efird, Inc., Mount Holly, NC; *U.S. Public*, pg. 1412

Enstice, Keith, Sr. V.P.-Personal Systems--Manugistics Group, Inc., Rockville, MD; *U.S. Public*, pg. 1042

Entzinger, J.J.T., Sr. V.P. & Gen. Sec.--KLM Royal Dutch Airlines, Amstelveen, Netherlands; *Int'l*, pg. 719

Epp, A. Jake, Sr. V.P.--Transcanada Pipelines Limited, Calgary, Canada; *Int'l*, pg. 1416

Epperly, Michael P., Sr. V.P.-Opers.--Buckeye Partners, L.P., Allentown, PA; *U.S. Public*, pg. 266

Epstein, David, Sr. V.P.-Fin.--Forecast Group, Rancho Cucamonga, CA; *U.S. Private*, pg. 418

Epstein, Henry P., Sr. V.P.-Opers.--Staples, Inc., Westborough, MA; *U.S. Public*, pg. 1509

Epstein, Jeffrey E., Sr. V.P. & Gen. Mgr.-Auto--CUC International, Inc., Stamford, CT; *U.S. Public*, pg. 320

Epstein, Lisa, Sr. V.P. & Acct. Dir.--Young & Rubicam New York, New York, NY; *U.S. Private*, pg. 1198

Erb, Bruce R., Sr. V.P.-Trust Services--Hollidaysburg Trust Company, Hollidaysburg, PA; *U.S. Public*, pg. 1222

Erdmann, Rainer, Sr. V.P.--Westdeutsche Landesbank (Schweiz) AG, Zurich, Switzerland; *Int'l*, pg. 799

Erdmann, Richard, Sr. V.P.-Human Resources--Serigraph, Inc., West Bend, WI; *U.S. Private*, pg. 985

Ereckson, Stanley, Jr., Sr. V.P., Gen. Counsel & Sec.--Vicorp Restaurants, Inc., Denver, CO; *U.S. Public*, pg. 1719

Eresman, Randall K., Sr. V.P.--Alberta Energy Company, Ltd., Calgary, Canada; *Int'l*, pg. 48

Erickson, Bill, Sr. V.P. & Pres.-Americas--Medtronic, Inc., Minneapolis, MN; *U.S. Public*, pg. 1082

Erickson, Diane, Chief Fin. Officer & Sr. V.P.--Diversified Dynamics Corporation, Minneapolis, MN; *U.S. Private*, pg. 336

Erickson, Kim, Sr. V.P.-Fin.--SuperValu, Inc., Eden Prairie, MN; *U.S. Public*, pg. 1540

Ericsson, Alice, Sr. V.P. & Grp. Creative Dir.--Grey Advertising Inc., New York, NY; *U.S. Public*, pg. 764

Eriks, Timothy J., Sr. V.P. & Chief Credit Officer--Bank of Homewood, Homewood, IL; *U.S. Private*, pg. 474

Eriksson, Bengt-Ake, Sr. V.P.-Data Processing--Nordbanken AB, Stockholm, Sweden; *Int'l*, pg. 957

Ernst, David, Sr. V.P. & Dir.--Worldwide Media Research, New York, NY; *U.S. Public*, pg. 1641

Ernst, Didier, Sr. V.P.-Biscuits Europe--Danone Group, Paris, France; *Int'l*, pg. 379

Ernsting, Kenneth W., Sr. V.P.-Sls. & Mktg.--Physician Computer Network, Inc., Morris Plains, NJ; *U.S. Public*, pg. 1293

Erston, Daniel A., Sr. V.P.--J.E. Dunn Construction Co., Kansas City, MO; *U.S. Private*, pg. 347

Ervin, Jon D., Sr. V.P.--Enron Acess, Dublin, OH; *U.S. Public*, pg. 584

Erwin, Mark A., Sr. V.P.-Field Svcs.--Continental Airlines, Houston, TX; *U.S. Public*, pg. 439

Erwin, Tom, Chief Fin. Officer & Sr. V.P.-Fin.--Stant Corporation, Denver, CO; *Int'l*, pg. 1396

Erxleben, William, Pres. & Chief Exec. Officer--Data I/O Corporation, Redmond, WA; *U.S. Public*, pg. 486

Escalante, Michael J., Sr. V.P.--TrizecHahn Properties Inc., Chicago, IL; *Int'l*, pg. 1425

Escriba, Antonio, Sr. V.P. & Sec.--Firstbank Puerto Rico, Santurce, PR; *U.S. Public*, pg. 644

Eskenasi, Peggy, Sr. V.P.-Private Label & Brand Devel.--Proffitt's, Inc., Alcoa, TN; *U.S. Public*, pg. 1333

Eskow, Alan D., Sr. V.P.-Fin. Admin. & Sec.--Valley National Bancorp, Wayne, NJ; *U.S. Public*, pg. 1705

Eslinger, Robert M., Sr. V.P.--Fredericktown Bank & Trust Co., Frederick, MD; *U.S. Public*, pg. 1089

Espino, Alberto N., Sr. V.P.--Coastal Fuel Terminals, Inc., Miami, FL; *U.S. Public*, pg. 390

Esposito, John, Sr. V.P.-Sls.--Schieffelin & Somerset Co., New York, NY; *Int'l*, pg. 412

Esslinger, Perry J., Sr. V.P.--J.S. Alberici Construction Co., Inc., Saint Louis, MO; *U.S. Private*, pg. 32

Esson, Robert L., Sr. V.P.-Mfg. & Distr.--BeautiControl Cosmetics, Inc., Carrollton, TX; *U.S. Public*, pg. 198

Esstman, Edward H., Sr. V.P. & Chief Credit Officer--AmeriCredit Corp., Fort Worth, TX; *U.S. Public*, pg. 96

Estepa, Romeo B., Sr. V.P.--First Hawaiian Creditcorp, Inc., Honolulu, HI; *U.S. Public*, pg. 635

Estival, Juan, Sr. V.P.-Opers. Div.--Grupo Synkro, S.A. de C.V., Mexico, Mexico; *Int'l*, pg. 576

Estrada, Mike, Sr. V.P.-Sls.--The Rockport Company, Marlborough, MA; *U.S. Public*, pg. 1370

Ethridge, Joseph A., Chief Fin. Officer & Sr. V.P.--Sammons Enterprises, Inc., Dallas, TX; *U.S. Private*, pg. 963

Etiel, Yoav, Sr. V.P.-Mktg.--Bentley Systems, Inc., Exton, PA; *U.S. Private*, pg. 134

Etter, Thomas, Sr. V.P.-Bus. Devel.--Ogden Entertainment, Inc., New York, NY; *U.S. Public*, pg. 1213

Ettestad, Peggy, Sr. V.P.-Opers.--Fortis Financial Group, Woodbury, MN; *Int'l*, pg. 499

Etzel, L.A., Sr. V.P.-Industrial--Sundt Corp., Tucson, AZ; *U.S. Private*, pg. 1051

Etzweiler, William D., Corp. Sr. V.P. & Chief Oper. Officer--Heckett MultiServ, Butler, PA; *U.S. Public*, pg. 793

Eustis, Ernest L., III, Sr. V.P.-Exec. & Professional Banking--Hibernia Corporation, New Orleans, LA; *U.S. Public*, pg. 825

Evangelist, Frank E., Sr. V.P.-Fin. & Sec.--Regis Corporation, Minneapolis, MN; *U.S. Public*, pg. 1373

Evans, Al, Sr. V.P.--Partners & Shevack, Inc., New York, NY; *U.S. Private*, pg. 842
Evans, Andrew J., Chief Fin. Officer & Sr. V.P.--Harrison Paint Corp., Canton, OH; *U.S. Private*, pg. 506
Evans, Barton, Jr., Sr. V.P.--Dionex Corporation, Sunnyvale, CA; *U.S. Public*, pg. 510
Evans, David V., Sr. V.P. & Dir.-Plng. & Information Systems--JC Penney Company, Inc., Plano, TX; *U.S. Public*, pg. 916
Evans, Gary R., Sr. V.P.--First Indiana Corporation, Indianapolis, IN; *U.S. Public*, pg. 1484
Evans, H. Stephen, Sr. V.P.-Real Estate, Legal & Govt. Affairs--The Bon Ton Stores, Inc., York, PA; *U.S. Public*, pg. 244
Evans, Henry, Sr. V.P.-Opers.--ADVO, Inc., Windsor, CT; *U.S. Public*, pg. 23
Evans, I.J., Sr. V.P.--Emerson Electric Co., Saint Louis, MO; *U.S. Public*, pg. 572
Evans, James E., Sr. V.P. & Gen. Counsel--American Financial Group, Cincinnati, OH; *U.S. Public*, pg. 74
Evans, Jayne, Sr. V.P. & Acct. Mng. Dir.--Young & Rubicam New York, New York, NY; *U.S. Private*, pg. 1198
Evans, John, Sr. V.P.-Production--General Media International Inc., New York, NY; *U.S. Private*, pg. 444
Evans, John, Sr. V.P. & Pub. Rels. Dir.--Al Paul Lefton Co., Inc., Philadelphia, PA; *U.S. Private*, pg. 658
Evans, Lucy, Sr. V.P.-Fin. & Bus. Devel.--Swift Textiles, Inc., Atlanta, GA; *Int'l*, pg. 415
Evans, Noel, Sr. V.P. & Grp. Mngmt. Supvr.--Dailey & Associates, West Hollywood, CA; *U.S. Public*, pg. 909
Evans, Philip, Sr. V.P. & Pres.-Betterware Company--Avon Products, Inc., New York, NY; *U.S. Public*, pg. 155
Evans, Richard H., Chief Strategy Officer & Sr. V.P.-Global Human Resources--NCR Corporation, Dayton, OH; *U.S. Public*, pg. 1146
Evans, Robert B., Sr. V.P.-Income--First Union Corporation, Charlotte, NC; *U.S. Public*, pg. 639
Evans, Steven C., Sr. V.P. & Benefits/Employment Attorney--Synovus Financial Corp., Columbus, GA; *U.S. Public*, pg. 1548
Evans, Wayne, Sr. V.P.-Paving--Hubbard Construction Co., Winter Park, FL; *U.S. Private*, pg. 544
Evanson, Michael J., Sr. V.P.-Bank Admin.--Mercantile Bank of Iowa, Des Moines, IA; *U.S. Public*, pg. 1087
Even, James A., Sr. V.P.--Hartford Fire Insurance Co., Hartford, CT; *U.S. Public*, pg. 794
Everbach, O. George, Sr. V.P.-Law & Govt. Affairs--Kimberly-Clark Corporation, Dallas, TX; *U.S. Public*, pg. 958
Everett, G. Carl, Jr., Sr. V.P. & Gen. Mgr.-Microprocessor Prods. Grp.--Intel Corporation, Santa Clara, CA; *U.S. Public*, pg. 886
Everett, Lila, Sr. V.P.-Mktg.--Home & Garden Television, Knoxville, TN; *U.S. Public*, pg. 1447
Evergates-Price, Anthy, Sr. V.P.-Media & Co-op Adv.--Universal Pictures, Universal City, CA; *Int'l*, pg. 1216
Everitt, Charles P., Sr. V.P.--Trustmark National Bank, Jackson, MS; *U.S. Public*, pg. 1643
Everson, Murry, Mgr.-Opers.--Sonic Couriers of Arizona, Inc., Scottsdale, AZ; *U.S. Private*, pg. 1123
Everton, Mitchell W., Sr. V.P.-Tax & Opers.--ProBusiness Services, Inc., Pleasanton, CA; *U.S. Public*, pg. 1330
Ewald, Greg D., Sr. V.P.-Underwriting--Acceptance Insurance Co., Inc., Omaha, NE; *U.S. Public*, pg. 14
Ewalt, Alan R., Sr. V.P.-H.R.--Tenet Healthcare Corporation, Santa Barbara, CA; *U.S. Public*, pg. 1576
Ewert, Paul F., Sr. V.P.-Mdsg.--CompUSA, Dallas, TX; *U.S. Public*, pg. 420
Exnicios, Donna Lee, Sr. V.P.--Hibernia Corporation, New Orleans, LA; *U.S. Public*, pg. 825
Eza, John, FLMI, Chief Information Officer & Sr. V.P.--Vision Financial Corporation, Keene, NH; *U.S. Private*, pg. 1141
Ezekiel, Sam, Sr. V.P.-Mktg.--Network Equipment Technologies, Inc., Redwood City, CA; *U.S. Public*, pg. 1168
Ezell, Mark, Sr. V.P.-Sls. & Mktg.--Purity Dairies Inc., Nashville, TN; *U.S. Private*, pg. 895
Faas, Andrew J., Sr. V.P.-Human Resources--George Weston Limited, Toronto, Canada; *Int'l*, pg. 1494
Faber, Karl Heinz, Sr. V.P.-Prod. Compliance, Service & Parts--Mercedes-Benz of North America, Inc., Montvale, NJ; *Int'l*, pg. 368
Fabian, David L., Sr. V.P.-Corp. Services--Capital Associates, Inc., Lakewood, CO; *U.S. Public*, pg. 302
Fabrizi, Michele S., Sr. V.P. & Client Services Dir.--MARC, Pittsburgh, PA; *U.S. Private*, pg. 701
Facey, Paul D., Sr. V.P. & Chief Actuary--National Western Life Insurance Company, Austin, TX; *U.S. Public*, pg. 1161
Fadool, George J., Sr. V.P.--Alex J. Etkin, Inc., Farmington, MI; *U.S. Private*, pg. 384
Fagan, James S., Chief Fin. Officer & Sr. V.P.--Herbert Malarkey Roofing Company, Portland, OR; *U.S. Private*, pg. 698
Fagerlund, Mats, Sr. V.P. & Gen. Counsel--Vattenfall AB, Stockholm, Sweden; *Int'l*, pg. 1452
Fagon, R., Sr. V.P.-Fin. Publications--Medical Economics Company Inc., Montvale, NJ; *U.S. Public*, pg. 1601
Fahlen, Lars, Sr. V.P.-H.R.--Incentive AB, Stockholm, Sweden; *Int'l*, pg. 666
Faigle, Shelley R., Sr. V.P.--PacifiCorp, Portland, OR; *U.S. Public*, pg. 1251
Failla, Ronald J., Sr. V.P.--General Accident Insurance, Philadelphia, PA; *Int'l*, pg. 543
Fain, John W., Sr. V.P.-Mktg. & Sls.--Overnite Transportation Co., Richmond, VA; *U.S. Public*, pg. 1668
Faircloth, Phillip, Chief Fin. Officer, Sr. V.P., Treas.--Warehouse Home Furnishings Distributor, Dublin, GA; *U.S. Private*, pg. 1150
Faletti, Richard P., Pres.-Multimedia Communication Systems & Sr. V.P.--Northern Telecom Limited, Brampton, Canada; *Int'l*, pg. 968
Falkowski, Anthony J., Sr. V.P.--Executive Risk, Inc., Simsbury, CT; *U.S. Public*, pg. 599
Fall, David, Sr. V.P.-Sls.--Eversharp Pen Co., Franklin Park, IL; *U.S. Private*, pg. 386
Falla, Enrique C., Sr. V.P.--The Dow Chemical Company, Midland, MI; *U.S. Public*, pg. 522
Falla, Gabe, Sr. V.P.--Intertek Testing Services, Andover, MA; *Int'l*, pg. 672
Falotti, Pier Carlo, Sr. V.P.-Europe, Middle East & Africa--Oracle Corporation, Redwood City, CA; *U.S. Public*, pg. 1227
Falterman, Darrell J., Sr. V.P.-Federal Warranty--American Bankers Life Assurance Co. of Florida, Miami, FL; *U.S. Public*, pg. 67
Falzareno, Cathryn, Sr. V.P.-Human Resources--Builders Square, Inc., San Antonio, TX; *U.S. Private*, pg. 477
Fankhauser, Andre, Sr. V.P.-Opers. & Admin.--Ferrier Lullin & Cie SA, Geneva, Switzerland; *Int'l*, pg. 480
Fanning, Thomas A., Chief Information Officer & Sr. V.P.--Georgia Power Co., Atlanta, GA; *U.S. Public*, pg. 1490
Fano, Anthony E., Sr. V.P.-Retail Sys. Grp.--NCR Corporation, Dayton, OH; *U.S. Public*, pg. 1146
Fansler, Alan L., Chief Oper. Officer & Exec. V.P.--Quality Stores Inc., Muskegon, MI; *U.S. Private*, pg. 899
Fant, Jim, Sr. V.P.--MEPC American Properties, Dallas, TX; *U.S. Private*, pg. 686
Fanta, David E., Sr. V.P.-Central Grp.--Philip Industrial Services Group, Houston, TX; *Int'l*, pg. 1050
Fanti, R. Timothy, Sr. V.P.-Fin. & Admin.--Beiersdorf, Inc., Norwalk, CT; *Int'l*, pg. 182
Farady, John T., Sr. V.P. & Treas.--John Hancock Mutual Life Insurance Company, Boston, MA; *U.S. Private*, pg. 589
Farb, Rosalyn S., Sr. V.P.--Wendy's International Inc., Dublin, OH; *U.S. Public*, pg. 1754
Farber, Bernard, Sr. V.P.-Sls. & Mdsg.--West Mill Clothes, Inc., Woodside, NY; *U.S. Private*, pg. 1163
Farbo, Rebecca, Sr. V.P. & Grp. Dir.--Wolf Mansfield Bolling Advertising Inc., Buffalo, NY; *U.S. Private*, pg. 1185
Farell, H.D., Sr. V.P. & Controller--TU Electric, Dallas, TX; *U.S. Public*, pg. 1588
Farella, Steven, Sr. V.P. & Dir.-North America Media Opers.--DMB&B Communications, New York, NY; *U.S. Private*, pg. 302
Faria, J., Sr. V.P.--Becker Milk Co. Ltd., Scarborough, Canada; *Int'l*, pg. 182
Farias, Brandt G., Sr. V.P.-Mktg. Communications Div.--First Hawaiian Bank, Honolulu, HI; *U.S. Public*, pg. 634
Farid, Khalid, Sr. V.P.-Tech. Businesses--ABB Lummus Global Inc., Bloomfield, NJ; *Int'l*, pg. 4
Faris, Mark E., Sr. V.P.--Norwest Mortgage, Inc., Des Moines, IA; *U.S. Public*, pg. 1202
Farmer, Bryce E., Sr. V.P.-Admin.--ACCEL International Corporation, Dublin, OH; *U.S. Public*, pg. 14
Farmer, H. Randolph, Sr. V.P.-Corp. Commun. & Investor Rels.--Lawyers Title Insurance Corporation, Richmond, VA; *U.S. Public*, pg. 981
Farmer, Ralph L., Sr. V.P. & Mgr.-Natl. Sls.--Arandell Corporation, Menomonee Falls, WI; *U.S. Private*, pg. 79
Farnon, Robert J., Sr. V.P.--Valley National Bank, Parsippany, NJ; *U.S. Public*, pg. 1705
Farr, Kevin M., Sr. V.P. & Controller--Mattel, Inc., El Segundo, CA; *U.S. Public*, pg. 1057
Farr, Pam, Sr. V.P.-Human Resources--Fairfield Inn, Washington, DC; *U.S. Public*, pg. 1048
Farr, Richard D., Sr. V.P. & Chief Fin. Officer--Tompkins County Trust Company, Ithaca, NY; *U.S. Public*, pg. 1621
Farrar, Eileen C., Sr. V.P.-Human Resources--UNUM Corporation, Portland, ME; *U.S. Public*, pg. 1699
Farrar, Eileen C., Sr. V.P.--UNUM Life Insurance Company of America, Portland, ME; *U.S. Public*, pg. 1699
Farrell, Jim, Sr. V.P.-H.R.--The M/A/R/C Group, Irving, TX; *U.S. Public*, pg. 1022
Farrell, Moira, Sr. V.P.-Corp. Res. & Sls. Mktg.--King World Productions, Inc., New York, NY; *U.S. Public*, pg. 961
Farrell, Moira, Sr. V.P.-Corp. Res. & Sls. Mktg.--King World Productions, Los Angeles, CA; *U.S. Public*, pg. 961
Farrell, Robert E., First Sr. V.P.--Valley National Bank, Parsippany, NJ; *U.S. Public*, pg. 1705
Farrell, Robert L., Sr. V.P.-Bus. Devel.--Medical Resources Inc., Hackensack, NJ; *U.S. Public*, pg. 1080
Farrell, Scott, Sr. V.P.--Golin/Harris Communications, Inc., Chicago, IL; *Int'l*, pg. 1226
Farrell, Thomas F., II, Sr. V.P.-Corp. Affairs--Dominion Resources, Inc., Richmond, VA; *U.S. Public*, pg. 516
Farrenkopf, Kevin R., Sr. V.P.-Retail Banking--Westcorp, Irvine, CA; *U.S. Public*, pg. 1756
Farrenkopf, Kevin R., Sr. V.P.-Retail Banking--Western Financial Bank, Irvine, CA; *U.S. Public*, pg. 1757
Fasano, William, Sr. V.P.-Mktg. & Opers.--News America Marketing, Norwalk, CT; *Int'l*, pg. 925
Fasbender, David J., Sr. V.P.-Sls.--Smead Manufacturing Company, Hastings, MN; *U.S. Private*, pg. 1006
Fasching, Leslie, Sr. V.P. & Acct. Mngmt. Dir.--Fahlgren, Parkersburg, WV; *U.S. Private*, pg. 391
Fasick, Ross W., Sr. V.P.-Automotive Prods.--Du Pont (E.I. Du Pont De Nemours & Co.), Wilmington, DE; *U.S. Public*, pg. 530
Fass, Harold, Sr. V.P.-Acct. Mngmt.--Grey Advertising Inc., New York, NY; *U.S. Public*, pg. 764
Fass, Peter H., M.D., Sr. V.P.--Keycorp, Cleveland, OH; *U.S. Public*, pg. 954
Fassati, Ariberto, Sr. Officer--Banque Indosuez, Milan, Italy; *Int'l*, pg. 314
Fassio, James S., Sr. V.P.-Property Devel.--Ross Stores, Inc., Newark, CA; *U.S. Public*, pg. 1405
Fassnacht, Debra Kerr, Sr. V.P.-Mktg. & Pub. Affairs--John G. Shedd Aquarium, Chicago, IL; *U.S. Private*, pg. 991
Fasulo, Edward, Sr. V.P. & Asst. Sec.--Elsinore Corporation, Las Vegas, NV; *U.S. Public*, pg. 570
Faulkenberry, Lowell, Sr. V.P.-Risk Mngmt.--BOK Financial Corp., Tulsa, OK; *U.S. Public*, pg. 163
Faulkner, Michael, Sr. V.P. & Creative Dir.--Dailey & Associates, West Hollywood, CA; *U.S. Public*, pg. 909
Fausher, Duane, Sr. V.P.-H.R.--Marvin Lumber & Cedar Company, Warroad, MN; *U.S. Private*, pg. 710
Faust, Richard M., Sr. V.P. & Auditor--First Tennessee Bank National Association, Memphis, TN; *U.S. Public*, pg. 639
Faust, Richard W., Sr. V.P. & Auditor--First Tennessee National Corporation, Memphis, TN; *U.S. Public*, pg. 638
Faver, Gary, Sr. V.P. & Media Plng. Dir.--Partners & Shevack, Inc., New York, NY; *U.S. Private*, pg. 842
Favit, Luigi L., Sr. V.P. & Controller--TrizecHahn Corporation, Toronto, Canada; *Int'l*, pg. 1424
Fawcett, Scott, Sr. V.P.-Sls. & Mktg.--Springs Window Fashions Division, Middleton, WI; *U.S. Public*, pg. 1500
Fay, George R., Sr. V.P.--Chubb & Son, Inc., Warren, NJ; *U.S. Public*, pg. 355
Fay, Sarah, Sr. V.P. & New Bus. Contact--Freeman Associates, Inc., Wellesley, MA; *U.S. Private*, pg. 425
Fazzari, Anthony, Sr. V.P.-Retail Mktg. & Sls.--Chock Full O' Nuts Corporation, New York, NY; *U.S. Public*, pg. 351
Feagin, Alan W., Sr. V.P.-Sls.--United Family Life Insurance Co., Atlanta, GA; *Int'l*, pg. 499
Fearing, Judy, Sr. V.P.-Mktg.--ESPN, Inc., Bristol, CT; *U.S. Public*, pg. 512
Feather, William L., Sr. V.P., Gen. Counsel & Sec.--Allegiance Healthcare Corp., McGaw Park, IL; *U.S. Public*, pg. 44
Feazell, Thomas L., Sr. V.P., Gen. Counsel & Sec.--Ashland, Inc., Russell, KY; *U.S. Public*, pg. 138
Feck, Luke M., Sr. V.P.-Corp. Communications--American Electric Power Service Corp., Columbus, OH; *U.S. Public*, pg. 72
Fedchyshyn, J. Roman, Sr. V.P.--Manulife Bank of Canada, Waterloo, Canada; *Int'l*, pg. 840
Feddersen, Rolf, Sr. V.P.-Indus. & Programmes--Airbus Industrie, Blagnac, France; *Int'l*, pg. 39
Federico, Rick, Sr. V.P.-Italian Concept--Brinker International, Inc., Dallas, TX; *U.S. Public*, pg. 253
Feemster, Phillip, Sr. V.P. & Exec. Creative Dir.--Highway One Communications, Integrated Marketing Services, San Francisco, CA; *U.S. Private*, pg. 303
Feidelson, Marc, Sr. V.P. & Media Dir.--Dailey & Associates, West Hollywood, CA; *U.S. Public*, pg. 909
Feil, Kim, Sr. V.P.-Mktg--Cadbury Beverages, Stamford, CT; *Int'l*, pg. 248
Fein, Harold, Sr. V.P.-Special Products--Sony Music Entertainment, Inc., New York, NY; *Int'l*, pg. 1281
Fein, Norman B., Sr. V.P.-Regional News Services--Rainbow Programming Holdings, Inc., Woodbury, NY; *U.S. Public*, pg. 288
Feintuck, Lester, Sr. V.P.--Grey Advertising Inc., New York, NY; *U.S. Public*, pg. 764
Feipel, Larry, Sr. V.P.-Telemarketing & Incentives--Ross Roy Communications, Inc., Bloomfield Hills, MI; *U.S. Private*, pg. 946
Feirstein, Michael, Sr. V.P. & Chief Legal Counsel--Reed Elsevier Business Information, Newton, MA; *Int'l*, pg. 1095
Feiwel, Jean L., Sr. V.P. & Publisher-Children's Book Publishing--Scholastic Corporation, New York, NY; *U.S. Public*, pg. 1440
Fejes, William T., Sr. V.P.--Pacific Scientific Company, Newport Beach, CA; *U.S. Public*, pg. 1250
Feldman, Janet, Sr. V.P.--Jack Schwartz Shoes, Inc., New York, NY; *U.S. Private*, pg. 974
Feldman, Paul, Sr. V.P.-Sls.--Duro Bag Manufacturing Co., Ludlow, KY; *U.S. Private*, pg. 348
Feldman, Rubin, Sr. V.P.--American Greetings Corporation, Cleveland, OH; *U.S. Public*, pg. 77
Feldman, Susan, Sr. V.P.-Corp. Commun.--Counsel Corporation, Toronto, Canada; *Int'l*, pg. 338
Feldt, Richard E., Sr. V.P. & Gen. Mgr.-Opers.--Symbol Technologies, Inc., Holtsville, NY; *U.S. Public*, pg. 1546
Felix, Charles R., Sr. V.P.-Devel.--Universal Forest Products, Inc., Grand Rapids, MI; *U.S. Public*, pg. 1696
Feller, Harriet Burns, Sr. V.P., Gen. Counsel & Sec.--Western Financial Bank, Irvine, CA; *U.S. Public*, pg. 1757
Fellows, Dave, Sr. V.P.-Therapeutics--Allergan, Inc., Irvine, CA; *U.S. Public*, pg. 46
Felmet, Mark H., Sr. V.P.-Retail Loan Div.--First Hawaiian Bank, Honolulu, HI; *U.S. Public*, pg. 634
Felsenthal, Robert M., Sr. V.P.-Bus. Devel.--IMC Global, Bannockburn, IL; *U.S. Public*, pg. 856
Feltenstein, George, Sr. V.P.-Worldwide Mktg., Classics--MGM/UA Home Entertainment, Inc., Santa Monica, CA; *U.S. Public*, pg. 1102
Felter, Timothy, Sr. V.P.-Mortgage Lending--Lawrence Savings Bank, North Andover, MA; *U.S. Public*, pg. 980
Felton, Dean P., Sr. V.P.-Bus. Devel.--Willis Corroon Financial Services Corp., New York, NY; *Int'l*, pg. 1507
Fender, Susan, Sr. V.P. & Creative Dir.--Lowe McAdams Healthcare, New York, NY; *U.S. Private*, pg. 678
Fenimore, George W., Sr. V.P.-Pub. Affairs--Peck Jones Construction, Los Angeles, CA; *U.S. Private*, pg. 846
Fenlason, John, Sr. V.P.--SAFECO Life and Health Insurance Companies, Redmond, WA; *U.S. Public*, pg. 1423
Fenton, Charles E., Sr. V.P. & Gen. Counsel--The Black & Decker Corporation, Towson, MD; *U.S. Public*, pg. 233
Fenton, Dennis M., Sr. V.P.-Opers.--Amgen Inc., Thousand Oaks, CA; *U.S. Public*, pg. 100
Fenton, Gary B., Sr. V.P.-Coated Paper Opers.--Repap New Brunswick Inc., Montreal, Canada; *Int'l*, pg. 1104
Fenton, Steve, Sr. V.P. & DMB&B Dir.-Worldwide Creative Services--DMB&B Communications, New York, NY; *U.S. Private*, pg. 302
Fenyves, Steve, Sr. V.P.--Andover Togs, Inc., New York, NY; *U.S. Public*, pg. 112
Feraro, Anthony, Sr. V.P.-Zions Small Bus. Fin.--Zions First National Bank, Salt Lake City, UT; *U.S. Public*, pg. 1793
Feraudo, William K., Sr. V.P.--Brooklyn Union, Brooklyn, NY; *U.S. Public*, pg. 259

Ferguson, Bear, Sr. V.P., Mngmt. Supvr.--EJL Advertising/Houston, Houston, TX; *U.S. Private*, pg. 673

Ferguson, Bob, Sr. V.P.-Mktg. & Sls. Promo.--Younkers, Inc., Des Moines, IA; *U.S. Public*, pg. 1334

Ferguson, Charles L., Sr. V.P.--Granite State Manufacturing Co., Manchester, NH; *U.S. Private*, pg. 36

Ferguson, Curtis, Sr. V.P.--Manhattan Construction Company, Tulsa, OK; *U.S. Private*, pg. 943

Ferguson, Fay, Sr. V.P. & Client Svcs. Dir.--Burrell Communications Group Inc., Chicago, IL; *U.S. Private*, pg. 188

Ferguson, Ian, Chief Oper. Officer & Sr. V.P.--Parmalat Canada Ltd., Etobicoke, Canada; *Int'l*, pg. 1023

Ferguson, Jack, Sr. V.P.-Distribution--Doubletree Corporation, Memphis, TN; *U.S. Public*, pg. 1335

Ferguson, Jerry, Sr. V.P.--Biomet, Inc., Warsaw, IN; *U.S. Public*, pg. 231

Ferguson, Lewis, Sr. V.P.-Merger & Acq.--Wright Medical Technology, Arlington, TN; *U.S. Private*, pg. 1192

Ferguson, Robert A., Sr. V.P.--Bankers Trust New York Corporation, New York, NY; *U.S. Public*, pg. 185

Fernandes, Fred, Sr. V.P.--Media Resources International, New York, NY; *U.S. Private*, pg. 727

Fernandes, Richard J., Sr. V.P.-Interactive Services--CUC International, Inc., Stamford, CT; *U.S. Public*, pg. 320

Fernandez, Aurelio E., Sr. V.P.-Worldwide Sls.--EXAR Corporation, Fremont, CA; *U.S. Public*, pg. 597

Fernandez, Claude, Chief Fin. Officer, Exec. V.P., Sr. V.P. & Mng. Dir.--W.P. Carey & Co., Inc., New York, NY; *U.S. Private*, pg. 209

Fernandez, Greg, Pres.-Labor & Mngmt. Partnerships--Kaiser Permanente, Oakland, CA; *U.S. Private*, pg. 605

Fernstrom, Petri, Sr. V.P. & Gen. Counsel--Outokumpu Oyj, Espoo, Finland; *Int'l*, pg. 1015

Ferra, Dennis J., Chief Fin. Officer & Sr. V.P.--ALLTEL Corporation, Little Rock, AR; *U.S. Public*, pg. 55

Ferrara, Roger C., Sr. V.P.-Investment Advisory Svcs.--Mutual of America Life Insurance Company, New York, NY; *U.S. Private*, pg. 769

Ferrari, Claudio, Sr. V.P.--Foster Wheeler Corporation, Clinton, NJ; *U.S. Public*, pg. 676

Ferrari, Debra L., Sr. V.P.-H.R.--360 Degrees Communications Company, Chicago, IL; *U.S. Public*, pg. 1607

Ferree, James, Sr. V.P. & Gen. Mgr.-Mdse.--Lamonts Apparel, Inc., Kirkland, WA; *U.S. Public*, pg. 975

Ferreer, Michael J., Sr. V.P.--Hampshire Chemical Corp., Lexington, MA; *U.S. Private*, pg. 498

Ferrucci, Richard F., Sr. V.P.--AON Corporation, Chicago, IL; *U.S. Public*, pg. 117

Ferry, William L., Sr. V.P. & Pres.-North America--Wang Laboratories, Inc., Billerica, MA; *U.S. Public*, pg. 1737

Ferstl, Eberhard, Sr. V.P.-Treas.--Bayerische Landesbank, Munich, Germany; *Int'l*, pg. 176

Ferverda, Mike, Sr. V.P.-Flight Opers.--Mesa Airlines, Inc., Farmington, NM; *U.S. Public*, pg. 1099

Fesperman, John E., Sr. V.P. & Dir.-Support--JC Penney Company, Inc., Plano, TX; *U.S. Public*, pg. 916

Fess, John, Sr. V.P.-Database Mktg.--Cohn & Wells, San Francisco, CA; *Int'l*, pg. 601

Fetterman, Robert, Sr. V.P.-Fin.--Canandaigua Wine Co., Canandaigua, NY; *U.S. Public*, pg. 300

Fetterolf, J.J., Sr. V.P.--STV Construction Services, Douglassville, PA; *U.S. Public*, pg. 1421

Fetters, Thomas, Sr. V.P-Exploration--National Energy Group, Inc., Dallas, TX; *U.S. Public*, pg. 1156

Field, Culver, Sr. V.P.-Corp. Plng. & Devel.--Morgan Foods, Inc., Austin, IN; *U.S. Private*, pg. 761

Field, George G., Sr. V.P.-Prod. Support--McDonnell Aircraft & Missile Systems Div., Berkeley, MO; *U.S. Public*, pg. 241

Field, John D., Jr., Sr. V.P.-Hawaii Banking Division--Bank of Hawaii, Honolulu, HI; *U.S. Public*, pg. 1248

Field, Stephen H., Sr. V.P.-Real Estate Banking--Texas Commerce Bank, Houston, TX; *U.S. Public*, pg. 339

Field, William, Sr. V.P. & Acct. Service Dir.--Mintz & Hoke Inc., Avon, CT; *U.S. Private*, pg. 751

Fielder, Joann, Sr. V.P.-Design--AnnTaylor, Inc., New York, NY; *U.S. Public*, pg. 116

Fields, D. Stan, III, Sr. V.P. & Acct. Dir.--DMB&B Detroit, Troy, MI; *U.S. Private*, pg. 302

Fields, Gary I., Sr. V.P. & Gen. Counsel--Medical Resources Inc., Hackensack, NJ; *U.S. Public*, pg. 1080

Fields, Marvin G., Chief Oper. Officer & Sr. V.P.--Frisch's Restaurants, Inc., Cincinnati, OH; *U.S. Public*, pg. 682

Fields, Sara, Sr. V.P.-Onboard Services--United Air Lines, Inc., Elk Grove Village, IL; *U.S. Public*, pg. 1653

Fields, Sara A., Sr. V.P.-Onboard Service--UAL Corporation, Elk Grove Village, IL; *U.S. Public*, pg. 1652

Fife, Lorin M., Sr. V.P. & Gen. Counsel--SunAmerica Inc., Los Angeles, CA; *U.S. Public*, pg. 1532

Figenshu, William R., Pres. & Sr. V.P.-Radio Division--Viacom Broadcasting Inc., New York, NY; *U.S. Private*, pg. 778

Fight, Kevan A., Chief Fin. Officer & Exec. V.P.--Malrite Communications Group, Inc., Cleveland, OH; *U.S. Private*, pg. 698

Figley, Brad, Sr. V.P.--Quanterra Environmental Services, Englewood, CO; *U.S. Private*, pg. 899

Figueredo, Jorge L., Sr. V.P.-H.R.--Liz Claiborne, Inc., New York, NY; *U.S. Public*, pg. 1005

Filer, Fred, Sr. V.P.--Lebhar-Friedman, Inc., New York, NY; *U.S. Private*, pg. 656

Filipelli, Tony, Sr. V.P.-Mktg. Svcs.--Rhea & Kaiser Marketing Communications, Naperville, IL; *U.S. Private*, pg. 927

Fillenwarth, Al, Sr. V.P. & Fin. Services Dir.--DMB&B St. Louis, Saint Louis, MO; *U.S. Private*, pg. 303

Fillingham, Robin A., Chief Fin. Officer & Sr. V.P.-Admin.--Baton Broadcasting Incorporated, Scarborough, Canada; *Int'l*, pg. 170

Filppu, Len, Sr. V.P.-Pub. Rels.--Karakas, Vansickle, Ouellette Advertising & Public Relations, Mountain View, CA; *U.S. Private*, pg. 607

Fina, Frank, Jr., Sr. V.P.-Bus. Devel.--General Cigar Company, Inc., Bloomfield, CT; *U.S. Public*, pg. 708

Finacana, Ann, Sr. V.P.-Corp. Mktg.--Fleet National Bank, Providence, RI; *U.S. Public*, pg. 649

Finacana, Ann, Sr. V.P.-Corp. Mktg., Fleet Fin. Grp.--Fleet Bank-NH, Nashua, NH; *U.S. Public*, pg. 649

Finch, Bill, Sr. V.P.-Mfg. & Distr.--Thomas Nelson Inc., Nashville, TN; *U.S. Public*, pg. 1167

Finci, Joseph, Sr. V.P.-Commercial Opers.--Pacific Crest Capital, Inc., Agoura Hills, CA; *U.S. Public*, pg. 1248

Findel, David, Sr. V.P. & Acct. Dir.--Young & Rubicam New York, New York, NY; *U.S. Private*, pg. 1198

Findlay, Konstance J.K., Sr. V.P.-Bus. Devel. & Sec.--Conso Products Company, Union, SC; *U.S. Public*, pg. 434

Findlay, Marsha A., Sr. V.P. & Mgr.-Retail Banking--Brenton Banks, Inc., Des Moines, IA; *U.S. Public*, pg. 251

Findley, Norman P., Sr. V.P.-Intl. Mktg. & Pres.-European Grp.--Coca-Cola Enterprises Inc., Atlanta, GA; *U.S. Public*, pg. 393

Fine, Edward L., Sr. V.P. & Exec. Creative Dir.--MARC, Pittsburgh, PA; *U.S. Private*, pg. 701

Fine, Jay, Sr. V.P. & Gen. Mgr.-East Coast Brdcst. Opers.--CBS, New York, NY; *U.S. Public*, pg. 273

Fine, Karen, Sr. V.P.-Human Resources--Primerica Financial Services, Duluth, GA; *U.S. Public*, pg. 1633

Finger, Jennifer J., Sr. V.P.--Starbanc Corporation, Cincinnati, OH; *U.S. Public*, pg. 1510

Finger, Larry E., Chief Fin. Officer & Sr. V.P.--Washington Real Estate Investment Trust, Kensington, MD; *U.S. Public*, pg. 1743

Fink, Jeff, Sr. V.P.-Sls.--LIVE Entertainment Inc., Van Nuys, CA; *U.S. Private*, pg. 671

Fink, Jeffrey, Sr. V.P.-Sls.--LIVE Film & Mediaworks, Van Nuys, CA; *U.S. Private*, pg. 671

Fink, Kevin J., Sr. V.P.--TCF Financial Corp., Minneapolis, MN; *U.S. Public*, pg. 1554

Fink, Richard A., Sr. Exec. V.P. & Chief Credit Officer--Glendale Federal Bank, F.S.B., Glendale, CA; *U.S. Public*, pg. 747

Fink, Richard H., Sr. V.P.-Govt. & Pub. Affairs--Koch Industries, Incorporated, Wichita, KS; *U.S. Private*, pg. 628

Finke, Robbie, Sr. V.P. & Acct. Dir.--Korey, Kay & Partners, New York, NY; *U.S. Private*, pg. 632

Finkel, Jeff, Sr. V.P.--RTG Furniture Corp., Seffner, FL; *U.S. Private*, pg. 905

Finkelman, David, Sr. V.P.-Corp. Commun.--BankAtlantic Bancorp, Inc., Fort Lauderdale, FL; *U.S. Public*, pg. 183

Finkelstein, William S., Chief Fin. Officer & Sr. V.P.--Warnaco Inc., New York, NY; *U.S. Public*, pg. 1738

Finkenheller, John, Sr. V.P. & Controller--RehabCare Group, Inc., Saint Louis, MO; *U.S. Public*, pg. 1373

Finley, David, Sr. V.P.-Human Resources--Ingram Micro Inc., Santa Ana, CA; *U.S. Public*, pg. 878

Finley, G. Stephen, Chief Admin. Officer & Sr. V.P.--Baker Hughes Incorporated, Houston, TX; *U.S. Public*, pg. 165

Finley, Jon L., Sr. V.P.--General Mills, Inc., Minneapolis, MN; *U.S. Public*, pg. 717

Finley, Peter S., Sr. V.P.--Harbour Group Ltd., Saint Louis, MO; *U.S. Private*, pg. 500

Finley, Wayne, Sr. V.P. & Dir.-Devel.--TrizecHahn Centers Inc., San Diego, CA; *Int'l*, pg. 1425

Finn, Tim, Sr. V.P.-Foot Locker Int'l.--Foot Locker, New York, NY; *U.S. Public*, pg. 1777

Finneran, John G., Jr., Sr. V.P., Gen. Counsel & Sec.--Capital One Financial Corporation, Falls Church, VA; *U.S. Public*, pg. 302

Finucane, Anne, Sr. V.P.--Fleet Financial Group, Inc., Boston, MA; *U.S. Public*, pg. 648

Fiola, Janet S., Sr. V.P.-Human Resources--Medtronic, Inc., Minneapolis, MN; *U.S. Public*, pg. 1082

Fiore, N.F., Sr. V.P.-Engineered Products Group--Carpenter Special Products Corp., El Cajon, CA; *U.S. Public*, pg. 307

Fiore, N.F., Sr. V.P.-Engineered Products Group--Crafts Technology, Inc., Elk Grove Village, IL; *U.S. Public*, pg. 307

Fiore, Nicholas F., Sr. V.P.-Engineered Prods. Grp.--Carpenter Technology Corporation, Reading, PA; *U.S. Public*, pg. 307

Fiorelli, Bob, Sr. V.P.-Mdsg.--CVS Corp., Woonsocket, RI; *U.S. Public*, pg. 287

Fiorivanti, Domenick, Sr. V.P.-Intl. Networks--Discovery Networks, Inc., Bethesda, MD; *U.S. Private*, pg. 334

Firestine, Michael H., Sr. V.P.-Agricultural Banking--Lebanon Valley Farmers Bank, Lebanon, PA; *U.S. Public*, pg. 688

Firlotte, Charles V., Chief Oper. Officer & Sr. V.P.--BHC Company, Bridgeport, CT; *U.S. Public*, pg. 126

Firmenich, Heinz-Werner, Sr. V.P.--Landesbank Rheinland-Pfalz, Mainz, Germany; *Int'l*, pg. 799

Fischer, B.J., Sr. V.P.-Prods. & Chemical Div.--Imperial Oil Limited, Toronto, Canada; *U.S. Public*, pg. 602

Fischer, David, Sr. V.P.--Zions Mortgage Company, Salt Lake City, UT; *U.S. Public*, pg. 1793

Fischer, George, Sr. V.P. -H.R.--Ameron International Corporation, Pasadena, CA; *U.S. Public*, pg. 98

Fischer, Hans, Sr. Exec. V.P.--SGS Societe Generale de Surveillance Holding S.A., Geneva, Switzerland; *Int'l*, pg. 1153

Fischer, John J., Jr., Chief Info. Officer & Sr. V.P.--The CIT Group Holdings, Inc., New York, NY; *Int'l*, pg. 360

Fischer, Ron, Sr. V.P.--Gemini Consulting, Morristown, NJ; *Int'l*, pg. 264

Fischer, Scott, Sr. V.P. & Dir.-Community Newspapers-West--Freedom Communication Inc., Irvine, CA; *U.S. Private*, pg. 425

Fiser, Phyllis S., Sr. V.P.--Clyde Savings Bank Company, Clyde, OH; *U.S. Public*, pg. 632

Fish, Steven, Sr. V.P.-Fin. Svcs.--Grey Directory Marketing Inc., Chicago, IL; *U.S. Public*, pg. 764

Fishelson-Holstine, Hollis, Sr. V.P.-North American Markets--Fair, Isaac and Company, Inc., San Rafael, CA; *U.S. Public*, pg. 609

Fisher, Alice, Sr. V.P.-Public Rels.--Greenstone Roberts Public Relations, Coconut Creek, FL; *U.S. Public*, pg. 763

Fisher, Bruce A., Chief Fin. Officer, Sr. V.P. & Sec.--PCA International, Inc., Matthews, NC; *U.S. Public*, pg. 1240

Fisher, Dean, Sr. V.P.-Corp. Affairs--Bell Sports Corp., San Jose, CA; *U.S. Public*, pg. 207

Fisher, Deborah L., Sr. V.P. & Chief Auditor--USTrust, Boston, MA; *U.S. Public*, pg. 1660

Fisher, Elizabeth, Sr. V.P. & Client Service Dir.-GHG--Grey Healthcare Group, New York, NY; *U.S. Public*, pg. 765

Fisher, Joseph F., Chief Fin. Officer & Sr. V.P.--Royal Insurance, Charlotte, NC; *Int'l*, pg. 1130

Fisher, Lawrence N., Sr. V.P.-Law & Sec.--Fluor Corporation, Irvine, CA; *U.S. Public*, pg. 659

Fisher, Russell S., Sr. V.P.--General Reinsurance Corp., Stamford, CT; *U.S. Public*, pg. 725

Fisher, Sara B., Sr. V.P. & Dir.-Mktg.--NBSC Corporation, Columbia, SC; *U.S. Public*, pg. 1549

Fisher, Will G., Sr. V.P. & Mgr.-Intl. & Natl. Dept.--Regions Financial Corporation, Birmingham, AL; *U.S. Public*, pg. 1371

Fishkin, Nathan P., Sr. V.P.-Real Estate--Federal Realty Investment Trust, Rockville, MD; *U.S. Public*, pg. 616

Fitzgerald, John, Sr. V.P.-Allocations & Distr.--Pic'n Pay Stores, Inc., Matthews, NC; *U.S. Private*, pg. 864

Fitzgerald, Kathy, Sr. V.P.-Pub. Rels. & Investor Rels.--Lucent Technologies Inc., Murray Hill, NJ; *U.S. Public*, pg. 1017

Fitzgerald, Margaret, Sr. V.P. & Community Rels. Dir.--Hill, Holliday, Connors, Cosmopulos, Inc., Boston, MA; *U.S. Private*, pg. 529

Fitzgerald, Richard E., Sr. V.P.-Employee Benefits--Willis Corroon Corp. of Seattle, Seattle, WA; *Int'l*, pg. 1507

Fitzgerald, Stephen, Sr. V.P. & Publisher--Professional Book Group, New York, NY; *U.S. Public*, pg. 1071

Fitzgerald, William, Sr. V.P.--TCI Communications, Inc., Englewood, CO; *U.S. Public*, pg. 1554

Fitzgibbon, Pierre, Chief Fin. Officer & Sr. V.P.-Fin.--Domtar Inc., Montreal, Canada; *Int'l*, pg. 416

Fitzmaurice, Robert, Sr. V.P.-Mktg.--UST Inc., Greenwich, CT; *U.S. Public*, pg. 1660

Fitzpatrick, Charles R., Chief Fin. Officer & First Sr. V.P.--Commercial Union Insurance Company, Boston, MA; *Int'l*, pg. 308

Fitzpatrick, Pat, Sr. V.P.-California Region--United States Cold Storage, Inc., Cherry Hill, NJ; *U.S. Private*, pg. 1124

FitzPatrick, Patrick C., Chief Fin. Officer, Sr. V.P. & Treas.--DynCorp, Reston, VA; *U.S. Private*, pg. 351

Fitzpatrik, Brian J., Chief Fin. Officer & Sr. V.P.-Fin.--Jevic Transportation, Inc., Delanco, NJ; *U.S. Public*, pg. 927

FitzRoy, Forrest S., Sr. V.P. & Gen. Counsel--NationsBank West, Saint Louis, MO; *U.S. Public*, pg. 1164

Fitzsimmons, C. Victor, Sr. V.P.-Worldwide Mfg.--Printronix, Inc., Irvine, CA; *U.S. Public*, pg. 1329

Fitzsimmons, Jack, Sr. V.P.-Admin.--Circuit City Stores, Inc., Richmond, VA; *U.S. Public*, pg. 374

Fitzsimmons, Robert J., Sr. V.P.-Treas.--The FINOVA Group Inc., Phoenix, AZ; *U.S. Public*, pg. 624

Fitzsimmons, Thomas D., Sr. V.P.--First Maryland Bancorp, Baltimore, MD; *Int'l*, pg. 64

Fixter, D.G., Sr. V.P.-Org. & Bus. Devel.--GSW Inc., Guelph, Canada,; *Int'l*, pg. 538

Fjelstul, Dean M., Chief Fin. Officer & Sr. V.P.--Walter Industries, Inc., Tampa, FL; *U.S. Public*, pg. 1736

Flaherty, Joseph, Sr. V.P.-Technology/CBS Opers. & Admin.--CBS, New York, NY; *U.S. Public*, pg. 273

Flaherty, Walter J., Chief Fin. Officer & Sr. V.P.--Eastern Enterprises, Weston, MA; *U.S. Public*, pg. 548

Flaherty, William H., Sr. V.P.-Devel. & Leasing--Maguire Partners, Los Angeles, CA; *U.S. Private*, pg. 696

Flam, Donald, Sr. V.P.-Sls. Promo.--Genfoot Inc., Montreal, Canada; *Int'l*, pg. 549

Flanagan, Edward, Sr. V.P. & Grp. Creative Dir.--Wunderman Cato Johnson, New York, NY; *U.S. Private*, pg. 1197

Flanagan, Martin L., Chief Fin. Officer & Sr. V.P.--Franklin Resources, Inc., San Mateo, CA; *U.S. Public*, pg. 679

Flanagan, Terry M., Sr. V.P.--Jaymark, Inc., San Diego, CA; *U.S. Private*, pg. 584

Flaster, S.R., Sr. V.P.-Sls.--Ingram Book Company, La Vergne, TN; *U.S. Private*, pg. 563

Flatley, James L., Sr. V.P.-Franchise Opers.--Gingiss International, Addison, IL; *U.S. Private*, pg. 455

Flavin, James E., Sr. V.P.-Fin. & Controller--Staples, Inc., Westborough, MA; *U.S. Public*, pg. 1509

Flavin, Robert M., Chief Fin. Officer & Sr. V.P.--Basis Petroleum, Inc., Houston, TX; *U.S. Public*, pg. 1704

Flaws, James B., Chief Fin. Officer, Sr. V.P. & Treas.--Corning Incorporated, Corning, NY; *U.S. Public*, pg. 448

Flax, Edward J., Sr. V.P.--Martin/F. Weber Company, Philadelphia, PA; *U.S. Private*, pg. 710

Fleischer, Joyce S., Sr. V.P.-Mktg.--Citizens Savings Bank, Providence, RI; *Int'l*, pg. 1132

Fleischer, Joyce S., Sr. V.P.-Mktg.--Citizens Trust Company, Providence, RI; *Int'l*, pg. 1132

Fleischer, Stuart, Sr. V.P.--Communications Diversified, New York, NY; *U.S. Private*, pg. 259

Fleishman, Ernest B., Sr. V.P.-Education & Corp. Rels.--Scholastic Corporation, New York, NY; *U.S. Public*, pg. 1440

Fleming, David D., Sr. V.P. & Pres.-Diagnostic Prods.--Genzyme Corporation, Cambridge, MA; *U.S. Public*, pg. 733

Fleming, Frederick D., Sr. V.P. & Chief Lending Officer--First National Bank of Huntington, Huntington, IN; *U.S. Public*, pg. 674

Fleming, Richard H., Chief Fin. Officer & Sr. V.P.--USG Corporation, Chicago, IL; *U.S. Public*, pg. 1660

Flemming, Ned, Sr. V.P.--The William Cook Agency, Inc., Jacksonville, FL; *U.S. Private*, pg. 273

Flesh, Robert T., Sr. V.P.--Thrifty Oil Co., Santa Fe Springs, CA; *U.S. Private*, pg. 1084

Fletcher, Keith, Sr. V.P.-Bus. Devel.--J.R. Simplot Company Food Group, Boise, ID; *U.S. Private*, pg. 1002

Fletcher, Len, Sr. V.P. & Gen. Mgr.--Central Transport, Archdale, NC; *U.S. Private*, pg. 225

Fletcher, William D., Sr. V.P.-Tech. & Bus. Devel.--Rockwell International Corporation, Costa Mesa, CA; *U.S. Public*, pg. 1397

Flieck, Henry, Sr. V.P.-Real Estate--Staples, Inc., Westborough, MA; *U.S. Public*, pg. 1509

Flint, Bill, Sr. V.P.--Flambeau Corporation, Baraboo, WI; *U.S. Private*, pg. 409

Floegel, John, Sr. V.P. & Acct. Services Grp. Head--Arnold Advertising, New York, NY; *U.S. Private*, pg. 84

Floen, Keith, Sr. V.P.-Card Svcs.--CUNA Service Group, Inc., Madison, WI; *U.S. Private*, pg. 288

Floerchinger, Tom, Chief Fin. Officer & Sr. V.P.-Fin.--L. Luria & Son, Inc., Medley, FL; *U.S. Public*, pg. 1020

Floisand, John, Sr. V.P.-Worldwide Sls.--Apple Computer, Inc., Cupertino, CA; *U.S. Public*, pg. 121

Flood, Bob, Sr. V.P.-Natl. Brdcst.--DeWitt Media, Inc., New York, NY; *U.S. Private*, pg. 329

Flood, James P., Sr. V.P.--Continental Assurance Company, Chicago, IL; *U.S. Private*, pg. 267

Flood, Roy M., Sr. V.P. & Pres.-P&C Div.--The Penn Traffic Company, Syracuse, NY; *U.S. Public*, pg. 1270

Flora, H.B., Sr. V.P.-Travel & Tourism--Southern Progress Corporation, Birmingham, AL; *U.S. Public*, pg. 1612

Florance, Stanley H., Sr. V.P.-Fin.--Owen Health Care, Inc., Houston, TX; *U.S. Public*, pg. 304

Flores, Armando B., Sr. V.P.-Human Resources & Corp. Services--APS, Phoenix, AZ; *U.S. Public*, pg. 1297

Flores, William, Chief Fin. Officer & Sr. V.P.--Western Atlas Inc., Houston, TX; *U.S. Public*, pg. 1757

Florian, Claudia, Sr. V.P. & Mgr.-Jewelery Dept.--Phillips Fine Art Auctioneers, New York, NY; *U.S. Private*, pg. 861

Flott, Andrew F., Sr. V.P.--Potomac Valley Bank, Gaithersburg, MD; *U.S. Public*, pg. 1089

Flourney, Selwyn L., Jr., Chief Fin. Officer & Sr. V.P.--The Life Insurance Co. of Virginia, Richmond, VA; *U.S. Public*, pg. 712

Flowers, Robert J., Sr. V.P.-Commercial Lending Opers.--Washington Mutual Inc., Seattle, WA; *U.S. Public*, pg. 1741

Fluker, E. Michael, Sr. V.P.-Admin.--MediaNews Group Inc., Denver, CO; *U.S. Private*, pg. 727

Fluker, E. Michael, Sr. V.P.-Admin.--Garden State Newspapers, Inc., Denver, CO; *U.S. Private*, pg. 727

Flyg, Bill, Chief Fin. Officer & Sr. V.P.--The Pantry, Inc., Sanford, NC; *U.S. Private*, pg. 837

Flynn, Charles R., Ph.D.,, Sr. V.P. & Dir.-Market Sector & Federal Programs--EA Engineering, Science & Technology, Inc., Hunt Valley, MD; *U.S. Public*, pg. 540

Flynn, James E., Sr. V.P.--Mission Management Systems, San Diego, CA; *U.S. Public*, pg. 1627

Flynn, Lucy A., Sr. V.P.-Corp. Mktg. & Commun.--Wang Laboratories, Inc., Billerica, MA; *U.S. Public*, pg. 1737

Flynn, R.J., Sr. V.P.-Electric Services--Public Service Company of New Mexico, Albuquerque, NM; *U.S. Public*, *pg. 1339*

Fockler, Douglas D., Sr. V.P.-Opers.--John Crane North America, Morton Grove, IL; *Int'l*, pg. 1339

Foertch, Ron, Sr. V.P.--Monico Alloys, Inc., Los Angeles, CA; *U.S. Private*, pg. 757

Fogelman, Martin, V.P. & Div. Mdse. Mgr.--Toys "R" Us United States, Paramus, NJ; *U.S. Public*, pg. 1626

Fogelman, Yvonne, Sr. V.P.-Information Technologies--Western International Media Corporation, Los Angeles, CA; *U.S. Private*, pg. 1165

Fogelson, Steph, Exec. V.P.-Perry Ellis Sportswear--Salant Corporation, New York, NY; *U.S. Public*, pg. 1429

Fogle, Thomas W., Sr. V.P.-Opers.--Allied Security, Inc., Pittsburgh, PA; *U.S. Private*, pg. 40

Fogwell, Douglas, Sr. V.P.-Mktg.--Diners Club Inc., Chicago, IL; *U.S. Public*, pg. 377

Folco, Fred A., Sr. V.P.--The Equitable Companies Incorporated, New York, NY; *U.S. Public*, pg. 588

Foley, Ann W., Sr. V.P.-Programming & Creative Opers.--Showtime Networks Inc., New York, NY; *U.S. Private*, pg. 779

Foley, Jerome P., Sr. V.P.--Valley National Bank, Parsippany, NJ; *U.S. Public*, pg. 1705

Foley, Joseph R., Sr. V.P.--UNUM Life Insurance Company of America, Portland, ME; *U.S. Public*, pg. 1699

Foley, Michael, Sr. V.P.-Energy Delivery--Florida Power Corporation, Saint Petersburg, FL; *U.S. Public*, pg. 655

Foley, Richard J., Sr. V.P.-Contracts--Raytheon Systems Company, Arlington, VA; *U.S. Public*, pg. 1364

Follick, Wayne, Sr. V.P.--NW Transport Service, Inc., Denver, CO; *U.S. Private*, pg. 772

Follman, John P., Chief Fin. Officer & Sr. V.P.--Day & Zimmermann, Inc., Philadelphia, PA; *U.S. Private*, pg. 316

Folta, Carl D., Sr. V.P.-Corp. Rels.--Viacom Inc., New York, NY; *U.S. Private*, pg. 775

Foltz, Gary F., Sr. V.P.--UMB Financial Corporation, Kansas City, MO; *U.S. Public*, pg. 1653

Fong, Dave J., Sr. V.P.-Pharmacy--Longs Drug Stores Corporation, Walnut Creek, CA; *U.S. Public*, pg. 1013

Font, Louis E., Sr. V.P.--Columbia Gas System Service Corp., Wilmington, DE; *U.S. Public*, pg. 403

Fontana, John, Sr. V.P.-Food Services & Industrial--Novartis Nutrition Corporation, Saint Louis Park, MN; *Int'l*, pg. 974

Fontana, John A., Sr. V.P.-Sls.--National Insurance Group, South San Francisco, CA; *U.S. Public*, pg. 1157

Fontana, John A., Sr. V.P.-Sls.--Pinnacle Data Corporation, San Bruno, CA; *U.S. Public*, pg. 1158

Fontana, John A., Sr. V.P.-Sls.--FASTRAC Systems, Inc.-Insurance Agent & Broker, South San Francisco, CA; *U.S. Public*, pg. 1158

Fontanes, A. Alexander, Chief Investment Officer & Sr. V.P.--Liberty Mutual Insurance Co., Boston, MA; *U.S. Private*, pg. 666

Foote, Emerson L., Sr. V.P.-Mfg. & Tech. Support/Agricultural Div.--Bayer Corporation, Pittsburgh, PA; *Int'l*, pg. 172

Fooutkusune, Worachote, Sr. V.P.-Info. Svcs.--Pan-American Life Insurance Company, New Orleans, LA; *U.S. Private*, pg. 836

Forberg, Steiner, Sr. V.P.-Fin.--A/S Ivaran Rederi, Lysaker, Norway; *Int'l*, pg. 696

Forbush, James S., Sr. V.P.-Catalog Sls. & Mktg.--Staples, Inc., Westborough, MA; *U.S. Public*, pg. 1509

Force, Jill L., Sr. V.P., Gen. Counsel & Sec.--Vencor, Inc., Louisville, KY; *U.S. Public*, pg. 1711

Ford, Brendan A., Sr. V.P.-Corp. Devel.--Cardinal Health Inc., Dublin, OH; *U.S. Public*, pg. 304

Ford, James T., Sr. V.P. & Mgr.-Closed-End Consumer Loans--First Financial Bank, FSB, Stevens Point, WI; *U.S. Public*, pg. 140

Ford, John, Sr. V.P.-Mktg. & Sls.--UDL Laboratories, Inc., Rockford, IL; *U.S. Public*, pg. 1143

Ford, P.M., Chief Fin. Officer & Sr. V.P.--ESCO Electronics Corporation, Saint Louis, MO; *U.S. Public*, pg. 546

Ford, Richard, Sr. V.P.--Porsche Cars North America, Inc., Reno, NV; *Int'l*, pg. 1063

Foreman, Jay, Sr. V.P.--Galoob Toys, Inc., South San Francisco, CA; *U.S. Public*, pg. 698

Forest, Diane, Chief Info. Officer & Sr. V.P.--Henry Schein, Inc., Melville, NY; *U.S. Public*, pg. 1437

Forester, William C., Sr. V.P.-Mfg./Polymers Div.--Bayer Corporation, Pittsburgh, PA; *Int'l*, pg. 172

Forgotson, Jay M., Sr. V.P.-Commerical Banking & Chief Credit Policy Officer--People's Bank, Bridgeport, CT; *U.S.* Public, pg. 1274

Forman, Brett, Sr. V.P. & Chief Admin. Officer--County Seat Stores, Inc., Dallas, TX; *U.S. Private*, pg. 279

Fornaro, Robert L., Sr. V.P.-Planning--US Airways, Inc., Arlington, VA; *U.S. Public*, pg. 1680

Fornasieri, Jean, Sr. V.P.-Mng. Dir.--Hachette Filipacchi Magazines Inc., New York, NY; *Int'l*, pg. 794

Fornetti, Louis C., Chief Fin. Officer & Sr. V.P.--American Express Financial Advisor, Minneapolis, MN; *U.S. Public*, *pg. 73*

Forney, Paul, Sr. V.P.-Sls.--Beverage Canners International Corp., Miami, FL; *U.S. Private*, pg. 106

Forsblad, Peter, Chief Information Officer & Sr. V.P.--Nordbanken AB, Stockholm, Sweden; *Int'l*, pg. 957

Forseth, Doug, Sr. V.P.-Opers.--Whistler Mountain Holdings, Limited, Whistler, Canada; *Int'l*, pg. 685

Forssman, Peter, Sr. V.P.-Public Relations & Gov. Affairs--Scandinavian Airlines System (SAS), Solna, Sweden; *Int'l*, pg. 1201

Forster, Frank L., Chief Oper. Officer & Sr. V.P.--Hawaiian Airlines, Inc., Honolulu, HI; *U.S. Public*, pg. 799

Forster, Michael H., Sr. V.P.-Worldwide Field Opers.--Sybase, Inc., Emeryville, CA; *U.S. Public*, pg. 1544

Forte, Mary, Sr. V.P. & Pres.-Gordon's Div.--Zale Corporation, Irving, TX; *U.S. Public*, pg. 1789

Fortenberry, S. Rawls, Sr. V.P.-Florida Regl. Mgr.--A.G. Edwards & Sons, Inc., Saint Louis, MO; *U.S. Public*, pg. 565

Forterre, Bernard, Sr. V.P.--Compagnie Generale Des Eaux, Paris, France; *Int'l*, pg. 321

Fortier, Camille, Sr. V.P.-Fin., Human Resources & Tech.--Assurance vie Desjardins-Laurentienne, Levis, Canada; *Int'l*, pg. 396

Fortis, Jerry, Sr. V.P. & Dir.-Mktg.--RAM Golf Corporation, Melrose Park, IL; *U.S. Private*, pg. 908

Fortunato, Joe, Sr. V.P. & Fin. Dir.--Bernard Hodes Group, New York, NY; *U.S. Public*, pg. 1224

Fortune, Patrick J., Sr. V.P. & Gen. Mgr.-Aluminum & Plastic Pkgng.--Tenneco Packaging, Evanston, IL; *U.S. Public*, pg. 1579

Fortune, Raymond, Sr. V.P.-Intl. Sls.--EMC Corporation, Hopkinton, MA; *U.S. Public*, pg. 545

Forys, Michael, Sr. V.P.-Admin.--Scripto-Tokai Corp., Fontana, CA; *U.S. Private*, pg. 977

Fosnaugh, Charles B., Sr. V.P.-Bus. Devel. & Fin. Officer--Spartan Stores Inc., Grand Rapids, MI; *U.S. Private*, pg. 1021

Foss, Deb, Sr. V.P.-Human Resources--Fortis Financial Group, Woodbury, MN; *Int'l*, pg. 499

Foss, Gary, Sr. V.P.--Office Depot Inc., Delray Beach, FL; *U.S. Public*, pg. 1212

Foster, David J., Sr. V.P. & Gen. Mgr.-Collagen Technologies Grp.--Collagen Corporation, Palo Alto, CA; *U.S. Public*, pg. 399

Foster, Geraldine U., Sr. V.P.-Investor Rels. & Corp. Communications--Schering-Plough Corporation, Madison, NJ; *U.S. Public*, pg. 1438

Foster, Greg, Sr. V.P.-Production--Metro-Goldwyn-Mayer Pictures, Inc., Santa Monica, CA; *U.S. Public*, pg. 1102

Foster, Henry L., Sr. V.P.--Bausch & Lomb Incorporated, Rochester, NY; *U.S. Public*, pg. 194

Foster, Marvin L., Sr. V.P. & Sec.--Nationwide Homes, Inc., Martinsville, VA; *U.S. Private*, pg. 788

Foster, Phillip B., Chief Oper. Officer & Sr. V.P.--Erving Paper Mills, Inc., Erving, MA; *U.S. Private*, pg. 382

Foster, Robert, Sr. V.P.-Pub. Affairs--Edison International, Rosemead, CA; *U.S. Public*, pg. 564

Foster, Robert B., Sr. V.P.-Sulphur Opers.--Freeport-McMoRan Resource Partners, Ltd., New Orleans, LA; *U.S. Public*, pg. 681

Foster, Robert G., Sr V.P.-Pub. Affairs--Southern California Edison Company, Rosemead, CA; *U.S. Public*, pg. 564

Foster, Sara E., Sr. V.P.-H.R.--Commerce Bancshares, Inc., Kansas City, MO; *U.S. Public*, pg. 409

Foster, Walter, Sr. V.P.--The Stellar Group Inc., Jacksonville, FL; *U.S. Private*, pg. 1040

Fotiades, George L., Sr. V.P. & Gen. Mgr.--Clairol, Inc., Stamford, CT; *U.S. Public*, pg. 254

Foulkes, Mike, Sr. V.P. & Gen. Mgr.--Fogarty Klein & Partners, San Antonio, TX; *U.S. Private*, pg. 416

Fourniadis, Robert A., Sr. V.P., Gen. Counsel & Sec.--Calton, Inc., Manalapan, NJ; *U.S. Public*, pg. 296

Fournie, Daniel, Sr. V.P.-Exploration--Elf Aquitane, Paris, France; *Int'l*, pg. 444

Fouts, Ronnie L., Chief Oper. Officer & Sr. V.P.--Willis Corroon Corp. of Chattanooga, Chattanooga, TN; *Int'l*, pg. 1505

Fouts, Terry, M.D., Sr. V.P.-Medical Affairs--Qual-Med, Inc., Pueblo, CO; *U.S. Public*, pg. 678

Foutz, Terry, Sr. V.P. & Mngmt. Rep.--Grey Advertising Inc., San Francisco, CA; *U.S. Public*, pg. 764

Fower, David S., Exec. V.P.--Chubb & Son, Inc., Warren, NJ; *U.S. Public*, pg. 355

Fowkes, Richard, Sr. V.P.-Business Affairs--Paramount Pictures Corporation, Los Angeles, CA; *U.S. Private*, pg. 776

Fowler, Bonnie, Sr. V.P. & Trust Officer--Stephenville Bank & Trust Co., Stephenville, TX; *U.S. Public*, pg. 633

Fowler, C. Thomas, Sr. V.P.-Mktg.--Motion Industries, Inc., Irondale, AL; *U.S. Public*, pg. 732

Fowler, David S., Chief Admin. Officer & Sr. V.P.--The Chubb Corporation, Warren, NJ; *U.S. Public*, pg. 354

Fowler, Harry V., Sr. V.P.--Metric Systems Corp., Fort Walton Beach, FL; *U.S. Public*, pg. 1563

Fowler, Paul L., Sr. V.P.-Midwest Reg.--BP Oil Co., Cleveland, OH; *Int'l*, pg. 220

Fox, Alan, Sr. V.P.-Pur.--Uno Restaurant Corporation, West Roxbury, MA; *U.S. Public*, pg. 1698

Fox, Diann, Sr. V.P.--Scott & Stringfellow, Inc., Richmond, VA; *U.S. Public*, pg. 1445

Fox, Diann D., Sr. V.P.--Scott & Stringfellow Financial, Inc., Richmond, VA; *U.S. Public*, pg. 1445

Fox, Dianne F., Sr. V.P.-Admin. & Sec.--Hilb, Rogal and Hamilton Company, Glen Allen, VA; *U.S. Public*, pg. 826

Fox, J. Eugene, Ph.D., Sr. V.P., Chief Scientist & New Tech.--Mallinckrodt Inc., Saint Louis, MO; *U.S. Public*, pg. 1039

Fox, James L., Chief Fin. Officer & Sr. V.P.--Investors Services Group, Boston, MA; *U.S. Public*, pg. 631

Fox, Mary Lou, Sr. V.P.-Professional Services--Manugistics Group, Inc., Rockville, MD; *U.S. Public*, pg. 1042

Fox, Mary Lou, Sr. V.P.-Mktg.--Omnicare, Inc., Covington, KY; *U.S. Public*, pg. 1223

Fox, Mike, Sr. V.P. & Grp. Acct. Dir.--Long Haymes Carr, Inc., Winston Salem, NC; *U.S. Public*, pg. 909

Fox, Piers G.D., Sr. V.P.--CSC Financial Services Group, Austin, TX; *U.S. Public*, pg. 422

Foxworthy, James C., Sr. V.P.-Human Resources--Inland Container Corporation, Indianapolis, IN; *U.S. Public*, pg. 1575

Foy, Lesley T., Sr. V.P.--Jay Advertising, Inc.-Tampa, Tampa, FL; *U.S. Private*, pg. 583

Fraback, Alan, Sr. V.P. & Mng. Dir.--Western International Media Corporation, Seattle, WA; *U.S. Private*, pg. 1167

Fracassi, Philip, Chief Oper. Officer & Sr. V.P.--Philip Services Corp., Hamilton, Canada; *Int'l*, pg. 1050

Fradin, Russell P., Sr. Corp. V.P.--Automatic Data Processing, Inc., Roseland, NJ; *U.S. Public*, pg. 150

Frady, David Patrick, Sr. V.P.--Hibernia Corporation, New Orleans, LA; *U.S. Public*, pg. 825

Fragnito, M., Sr. V.P.-Production--Penguin Putnam Inc., New York, NY; *Int'l*, pg. 1027

Fraine, Bill, Sr. V.P.-Worldwide Sls.--FDX Corporation, Memphis, TN; *U.S. Public*, pg. 603

Fraizer, Michael, Sr. V.P., Controller & Treas.--American Mutual Life Holding Co., Des Moines, IA; *U.S. Private*, pg. 59

Fraizer, Michael D., Sr. V.P. & Gen. Mgr.--G.E. Capital Commercial Real Estate Financing, Stamford, CT; *U.S. Public*, pg. 712

Fraleigh, John E., Sr. V.P.-Tobacco Procurement--Swisher International Group, Inc., Darien, CT; *U.S. Public*, pg. 1543

Frame, Larry A., Sr. V.P. & Grp. Exec.-Navigation, Guidance & Control Sys.--Litton Industries, Inc., Woodland Hills, CA; *U.S. Public*, pg. 1002

Francht, Joseph E., Jr., Sr. V.P.-Fin. & Treas.--Northwest Airlines Corp., Saint Paul, MN; *U.S. Public*, pg. 1199

Francht, Joseph E., Jr., Sr. V.P.-Fin. & Treas.--Northwest Airlines, Inc., Saint Paul, MN; *U.S. Public*, pg. 1200

Francis, George E., Chief Fin. Officer, Sr. V.P. & Sec.--First Commonwealth Corporation, Springfield, IL; *U.S. Private*, *pg. 406*

Francis, Robert D., Sr. V.P.-Underwriting & Corp. Sec.--Medical Assurance, Inc., Birmingham, AL; *U.S. Public*, pg. 1079

Francisco, David, Sr. V.P.-Intl. Opers.--Newmont Mining Corporation, Denver, CO; *U.S. Public*, pg. 1178

Franciscovich, George, Sr. V.P.-Legal Affairs--Cable Television Division, New Canaan, CT; *U.S. Public*, pg. 329

Franck, Donald G., Sr. V.P & Mgr.-Commercial Real Estate Loans--First Federal of Michigan, Detroit, MI; *U.S. Public*, *pg. 336*

Franco, Felipe, Sr. V.P.-Mortgage Loans--Banco Popular de Puerto Rico, San Juan, PR; *U.S. Public*, pg. 175

Franco, Harry, Sr. V.P.--SDI Technologies Inc., Rahway, NJ; *U.S. Private*, pg. 956

Franco, Jorge Ballesteros, Sr. V.P.--Grupo Synkro, S.A. de C.V., Mexico, Mexico; *Int'l*, pg. 576

Francois, Emile, Sr. V.P.--Saint-Gobain, Courbevoie, France; *Int'l*, pg. 1170

Frangos, John E., Sr. V.P.--C.R. Daniels, Inc., Ellicott City, MD; *U.S. Private*, pg. 310

Frank, Alan, Sr. V.P. & Gen. Counsel--Olympia & York Developments Ltd., Toronto, Canada; *Int'l*, pg. 1004

Frank, Michael, Sr. V.P. & Mng. Dir.-Ag Div./Europe, Africa & Middle East--Deere & Company, Moline, IL; *U.S. Public*, pg. 491

Frank, Michael R., Sr. V.P.--MFS WorldCom, Inc., Omaha, NE; *U.S. Public*, pg. 1779

Frank, Peter, Sr. V.P.-Opers.--Starbanc Corporation, Cincinnati, OH; *U.S. Public*, pg. 1510

Frank, Richard W., Sr. V.P.-Consumer Care Div.--Bayer Corporation, Pittsburgh, PA; *Int'l*, pg. 172

Frankel, Randolph B., Sr. V.P.-Therapeutic Economics--MEDCO Containment Services, Inc., Montvale, NJ; *U.S. Public*, pg. 1091
Frankel, S. Leroy, Sr. V.P.--R & R Marketing, West Caldwell, NJ; *U.S. Private*, pg. 902
Frankel, S. Leroy, Sr. V.P.--Royal Division, West Caldwell, NJ; *U.S. Private*, pg. 902
Frankel, S. Leroy, Sr. V.P.--Reitman Division, West Caldwell, NJ; *U.S. Private*, pg. 902
Frankel, S. Leroy, Sr. V.P.--Spectrum Division, West Caldwell, NJ; *U.S. Private*, pg. 902
Frankel, S. Leroy, Sr. V.P.--Raritan Display Division, West Caldwell, NJ; *U.S. Private*, pg. 902
Frankfort, Lew, Sr. V.P.--Sara Lee Corporation, Chicago, IL; *U.S. Public*, pg. 1432
Franklin, Churchill G., Sr. V.P.--Acadian Asset Management, Boston, MA; *U.S. Public*, pg. 1672
Franklin, George, Sr. V.P.--International Research & Evaluation, Eagan, MN; *U.S. Private*, pg. 571
Franklin, Ken, Sr. V.P.-Sls.--Metz Baking Company, Deerfield, IL; *U.S. Private*, pg. 1022
Franklin, Marc S., Sr. V.P.-Strategic Plng. & Devel.--Pacific Life Insurance Company, Newport Beach, CA; *U.S. Private*, pg. 831
Franklin, Nick, Sr. V.P.--PacifiCare Health Systems, Inc., Cypress, CA; *U.S. Public*, pg. 1250
Franks, John R., Chief Oper. Officer & Sr. V.P.--Penn Central National Bank, Huntingdon, PA; *U.S. Public*, pg. 1222
Franks, Martin D., Sr. V.P. & Pres.-CBS Foundation--CBS, New York, NY; *U.S. Public*, pg. 273
Frantisak, Frank, Dr., Sr. V.P.-Environmental--Noranda Inc., Toronto, Canada; *Int'l*, pg. 433
Frantz, Francis X., Sr. V.P.-External Affairs, Gen Counsel & Sec.--ALLTEL Corporation, Little Rock, AR; *U.S. Public*, pg. 55
Franz, G. Andrew, Chief Oper. Officer & Sr. V.P.-Opers./Pharmaceuticals--Jones Medical Industries Inc., Saint Louis, MO; *U.S. Public*, pg. 933
Franza, Thomas A., Sr. V.P.--Comarco, Inc., Yorba Linda, CA; *U.S. Public*, pg. 406
Franzoni, Catherine D., V.P. & Treas.--Pulse Bancorp, Inc., South River, NJ; *U.S. Public*, pg. 1344
Fraser, Bruce D., Chief Fin. Officer & Sr. V.P.--Grease Monkey International Inc., Denver, CO; *U.S. Public*, pg. 759
Fratangelo, James R., Sr. V.P.-Secondary Mktg.--Ryland Mortgage Co., Columbia, MD; *U.S. Public*, pg. 1414
Frauenknecht, Willy, Sr. V.P.-Dealing--Liechtenstein Global Trust Limited, Vaduz, Liechtenstein; *Int'l*, pg. 809
Frautzen, Douglas J., Sr. V.P.--UNUM Life Insurance Company of America, Portland, ME; *U.S. Public*, pg. 1699
Frazier, Russ, Sr. V.P.-Opers.--Video Products Distributors, Inc., Sacramento, CA; *U.S. Private*, pg. 1139
Frease, Belden A., Sr. V.P. & Sec.--Computer Associates International, Inc., Islandia, NY; *U.S. Public*, pg. 420
Frechette, Robert M., Sr. V.P.-Merchant Acceptance--Mastercard International, Inc., Purchase, NY; *U.S. Private*, pg. 714
Frecon, Leslie M., Sr. V.P.-Corp. Fin.--General Mills, Inc., Minneapolis, MN; *U.S. Public*, pg. 717
Frederick, Stephen, Sr. V.P. & Creative Dir.-Art--Girgenti, Hughes, Butler & McDowell, New York, NY; *U.S. Private*, pg. 455
Fredinburg, Wes, Sr. V.P. & Gen. Counsel--National Car Rental System, Inc., Minneapolis, MN; *U.S. Public*, pg. 1379
Fredrickson, Dennis R., Sr. V.P.--Firstar Corporation, Milwaukee, WI; *U.S. Public*, pg. 642
Fredrickson, Dennis R., Sr. V.P.--Firstar Milwaukee Bank, N.A., Milwaukee, WI; *U.S. Public*, pg. 643
Freece, Robert A., Sr. V.P.--Vishay Intertechnology, Inc., Malvern, PA; *U.S. Public*, pg. 1721
Freed, Vicki, Sr. V.P.-Sls. & Mktg.--Carnival Corporation, Miami, FL; *U.S. Public*, pg. 306
Freedman, Larry S., Sr. V.P., Gen. Counsel & Sec.--Platinum Technology, Inc., Oak Brook Terrace, IL; *U.S. Public*, pg. 1309
Freehill, Michael H., Sr. V.P.--Market Facts, Inc., Arlington Heights, IL; *U.S. Public*, pg. 1046
Freeman, Douglas L., Sr. V.P.-Opers. Support, Lending--United Companies Financial Corporation, Baton Rouge, LA; *U.S. Public*, pg. 1675
Freeman, James I., Chief Fin. Officer & Sr. V.P.--Dillard's, Inc., Little Rock, AR; *U.S. Public*, pg. 509
Freeman, Jeff E., Sr. V.P.-Fin., Sec. & Treas.--Havatampa, Inc., Tampa, FL; *U.S. Private*, pg. 510
Freeze, Walter E., Chief Fin. Officer & Sr. V.P.--Doubleday Publishing Company, New York, NY; *Int'l*, pg. 191
Fregonara, Zanotti, Sr. V.P. & Gen. Mgr.--Cariplo New York, New York, NY; *Int'l*, pg. 275
Freiberg, Lowell C., Chief Fin. Officer & Sr. V.P.--Reliance Group Holdings, Inc., New York, NY; *U.S. Public*, pg. 1374
Freiborg, A., Sr. V.P.--Marquette Bank Rochester, Rochester, MN; *U.S. Private*, pg. 706
Freidenberg, Charles, Sr. V.P.-Mdsg.--Consolidated Stores Corp., Columbus, OH; *U.S. Public*, pg. 437
Freilich, Joan S., Chief Fin. Officer & Sr. V.P.--Consolidated Edison Company of New York, Inc., New York, NY; *U.S. Public*, pg. 434
Freimark, Jeffrey P., Chief Fin. Officer, Sr. V.P. & Sec.--The Grand Union Company, Wayne, NJ; *U.S. Public*, pg. 758
Freimuth, Steven J., Sr. V.P.-Residential Lending Opers.--Washington Mutual Inc., Seattle, WA; *U.S. Public*, pg. 1741
Fremont, Carl, Sr. V.P. & Media Plng. Dir.--Wunderman Cato Johnson, New York, NY; *U.S. Private*, pg. 1197
French, B.J., Sr. V.P.-Corp. Communications--Dain Rauscher Corporation, Minneapolis, MN; *U.S. Public*, pg. 476
Frenz, Dean A., Sr. V.P.-Rail--L.B. Foster Company, Pittsburgh, PA; *U.S. Public*, pg. 675
Fresca, Victor A., Sr. V.P.-Sys. Engrng. Division--Bank of Hawaii, Honolulu, HI; *U.S. Public*, pg. 1248
Fresquez, Luis, Chief Info. Officer & Sr. V.P.--American Automobile Association, Heathrow, FL; *U.S. Private*, pg. 50
Fretz, Deborah M., Sr. V.P.-Logistics--Sun Company, Inc., Philadelphia, PA; *U.S. Public*, pg. 1530
Fretz, Deborah M., Sr. V.P.-Logistics--Sun Refining & Marketing Co. Operations Div., Philadelphia, PA; *U.S. Public*, pg. 1530
Freudmann, Axel I., Sr. V.P.-Human Resources--American International Group, Inc., New York, NY; *U.S. Public*, pg. 83
Freund, Otto, Sr. V.P.-Latin American Reg.--Valmet Chile Ltda., Santiago, Chile; *Int'l*, pg. 1448
Frey, Jeffrey, Sr. V.P. & Creative Dir.--DMB&B New York, New York, NY; *U.S. Private*, pg. 302
Frey, Ronald L., Sr. V.P. & Sr. CRA Officer--Farmers and Merchants Bank and Trust, Hagerstown, MD; *U.S. Public*, pg. 1542
Freytag, Michael, Sr. V.P.-Engrng.--Bayer Corporation, Pittsburgh, PA; *Int'l*, pg. 172
Friberg, Peter A., Sr. V.P.-Memorial Sls. & Dir.-Sls. & Mktg.--Rock of Ages Corporation, Graniteville, VT; *U.S. Public*, pg. 1396
Fricas, Victor J., Sr. V.P.-Continuity Svcs.--Comdisco, Inc., Rosemont, IL; *U.S. Public*, pg. 407
Fricas, Victor J., Sr. V.P.--Comdisco Continuity Services, Rosemont, IL; *U.S. Public*, pg. 408
Fricke, John W., Sr. V.P.-Community Banks--NationsBank West, Saint Louis, MO; *U.S. Public*, pg. 1164
Fricklas, Michael D., Sr. V.P.-Legal & Deputy Gen. Counsel--Viacom Inc., New York, NY; *U.S. Private*, pg. 775
Fridman, Josef J., Sr. V.P.-Law, Corp. Services & Sec.--BCE Inc., Montreal, Canada; *Int'l*, pg. 114
Fried, Robert, Sr. V.P.-Mktg.--Signature Eyewear, Inc., Inglewood, CA; *U.S. Public*, pg. 1473
Friedewald, William T., MD, Sr. V.P. & Chief Medical Dir.--Metropolitan Life Insurance Co., New York, NY; *U.S. Private*, pg. 737
Friedl, Robert R., Chief Fin. Officer & Sr. V.P.--The Manitowoc Company, Inc., Manitowoc, WI; *U.S. Public*, pg. 1040
Friedlander, Gary, Sr. V.P.--Rice Food Markets Inc., Houston, TX; *U.S. Private*, pg. 927
Friedlander, Lindy J., Sr. V.P.-Res. & Prod. Devel.--Washington Mutual Inc., Seattle, WA; *U.S. Public*, pg. 1741
Friedlander, Tom, Sr. V.P.--Rice Food Markets Inc., Houston, TX; *U.S. Private*, pg. 927
Friedman, Alan, Sr. V.P. & Dir.-H.R.--Arthur D. Little, Inc., Cambridge, MA; *U.S. Private*, pg. 670
Friedman, Clifford H., Sr. V.P.-Universal New Media Grp.--Universal Studios, Inc., Universal City, CA; *Int'l*, pg. 1215
Friedman, Daniel, Sr. V.P.--AMREP Corporation, New York, NY; *U.S. Public*, pg. 104
Friedman, Frank, Sr. V.P.-Health, Environment & Safety--Elf Atochem North America, Inc., Philadelphia, PA; *Int'l*, pg. 445
Friedman, George H., Sr. V.P.--American Arbitration Association, New York, NY; *U.S. Private*, pg. 50
Friedman, Harvey, Sr. V.P.--Gibraltar Corp. of America, New York, NY; *U.S. Public*, pg. 1528
Friedman, Herbert J., Sr. V.P.-Mdsg.--Krause's Furniture Inc., Brea, CA; *U.S. Public*, pg. 967
Friedman, Ira, Sr. V.P.-Law--Metropolitan Life Insurance Co., New York, NY; *U.S. Private*, pg. 737
Friedman, Joel, Sr. V.P.--Rowe International, Inc., Grand Rapids, MI; *U.S. Private*, pg. 904
Friedman, Joel S., Sr. V.P.-Opers.--General Signal Corporation, Stamford, CT; *U.S. Public*, pg. 726
Friedman, Mark, Sr. V.P. & Assoc. Creative Dir.--Cline, Davis & Mann, Inc., New York, NY; *U.S. Private*, pg. 246
Friedrich, Kurt, Sr. V.P. & Gen. Mgr.-Systems Devel.Grp.--Tandem Computers Inc., Cupertino, CA; *U.S. Public*, pg. 417
Friel, John P., Sr. V.P. & Gen. Mgr.--Medrad, Inc., Indianola, PA; *Int'l*, pg. 1204
Friel, William D., Sr. V.P. & Chief Information Officer--The Prudential Insurance Company of America, Newark, NJ; *U.S. Private*, pg. 892
Friend, Ross D., Sr. V.P., Gen. Counsel & Sec.--The Franklin Life Insurance Company, Springfield, IL; *U.S. Public*, pg. 76
Friesen, Walter, Sr. V.P.--Westower Corporation, Vancouver, WA; *U.S. Public*, pg. 1762
Friis-Hansen, Klaus, Sr. V.P.--Danisco A/S, Copenhagen, Denmark; *Int'l*, pg. 378
Friley, C.B., Sr. V.P.--Phillips Alaska Natural Gas Corporation, Bellaire, TX; *U.S. Public*, pg. 1291
Friou, Jack, Sr. V.P. & Dir.-Govt. Rels.--AFLAC Incorporated, Columbus, GA; *U.S. Public*, pg. 28
Frisbie, F. Richard, Sr. V.P.-Deepwater Tech.--Oceaneering International, Inc., Houston, TX; *U.S. Public*, pg. 1211
Frisbie, F. Richard, Sr. V.P.-Deepwater Tech.--Oilfield Marine Services-Americas Region, Morgan City, LA; *U.S. Public*, pg. 1211
Frisch, Judith A., Sr. V.P.--Cliggott Publishing, Greenwich, CT; *U.S. Private*, pg. 246
Frissora, Mark P., Sr. V.P.-North American Original Equipment--Tenneco Automotive, Deerfield, IL; *U.S. Public*, pg. 1577
Frithiof, Ulla, Sr. V.P.-Information Services--Svedala Industri AB, Malmo, Sweden; *Int'l*, pg. 1323
Fritz, Eric R., Sr. V.P.--Huron Valley Steel Corp., Belleville, MI; *U.S. Private*, pg. 549
Fritzson, Paul, Sr. V.P.-Mktg., Mdsg. & Distrib.--Hannaford Bros. Co., Scarborough, ME; *U.S. Public*, pg. 781
Froberg, James, Sr. V.P. & Gen. Counsel--LINC Capital Group, Chicago, IL; *U.S. Public*, pg. 996
Froesel, David W., Jr., Chief Fin. Officer & Sr. V.P.--Omnicare, Inc., Covington, KY; *U.S. Public*, pg. 1223
Frolich, Kenneth R., Chief Actuarial Officer & Sr. V.P.--Reliance Insurance Company, Philadelphia, PA; *U.S. Public*, pg. 1374
Fromm, Jeff, Sr. V.P.--Barkley & Evergreen Advertising, Inc., Kansas City, MO; *U.S. Private*, pg. 116
Frost, Thomas E., Sr. V.P. & Gen. Counsel--The Mills Corporation, Arlington, VA; *U.S. Public*, pg. 1113
Frulla, Roberto, Sr. V.P.-Environmental Technologies Grp.--Tetra Tech NUS, Inc., Gaithersburg, MD; *U.S. Public*, pg. 1582
Fry, Pat, Sr. V.P.--Sutter Health, Sacramento, CA; *U.S. Private*, pg. 1057
Frye, John W., Chief Fin. Officer, Sr. V.P.-Fin. & Treas.--Old Dominion Freight Line, Inc., High Point, NC; *U.S. Public*, pg. 1216
Fudold, Wallace A., Sr. V.P.--TCF Bank Minnesota FSB, Minneapolis, MN; *U.S. Public*, pg. 1554
Fuehrer, George E., Sr. V.P.--EnviroSource, Inc., Horsham, PA; *U.S. Public*, pg. 587
Fuentes Lignan, Ramon Pablo, Sr. V.P.--Bufete Industrial S.A. de C.V., Mexico, Mexico; *Int'l*, pg. 232
Fuentevilla, Ramon, Sr. V.P.-Sls.--Mattel, Inc., El Segundo, CA; *U.S. Public*, pg. 1057
Fuerbringer, N.L., Sr. V.P.-Admin.--B.C. Ziegler & Co., West Bend, WI; *U.S. Public*, pg. 1792
Fuerst, Randall C., Sr. V.P.--BTG, Inc., Fairfax, VA; *U.S. Public*, pg. 164
Fuette, Kenneth R., Sr. V.P.--Foamex International Inc., Linwood, PA; *U.S. Private*, pg. 1094
Fuhriman, David H., Sr. V.P.-Branch Sls. & Svc.--Zions First National Bank, Salt Lake City, UT; *U.S. Public*, pg. 1793
Fujii, K., Sr. V.P. & Asst. Treas.--Mitsubishi International Corporation, New York, NY; *Int'l*, pg. 871
Fujii, Keiichi, Sr. V.P.--Nippon Credit Trust Company, New York, NY; *Int'l*, pg. 933
Fujikawa, Clifford F., Sr. V.P. & Mgr.-Real Estate--Central Pacific Bank, Honolulu, HI; *U.S. Public*, pg. 283
Fujinaga, Genichi, Sr. V.P.--Infrastructure Leasing & Financial Services Limited, Mumbai, India; *Int'l*, pg. 1009
Fujisawa, Yoshiyuki, Deputy Pres.--The Industrial Bank of Japan, Limited, Tokyo, Japan; *Int'l*, pg. 674
Fujitani, Gary Y., Sr. V.P.-Bus. Services Div.--First Hawaiian Bank, Honolulu, HI; *U.S. Public*, pg. 634
Fukui, Toshiaki, Sr. V.P.--Nippon Telegraph and Telephone Corporation, Tokyo, Japan; *Int'l*, pg. 940
Fukuyama, Hiroomi, Sr. V.P.--Fanuc Ltd., Yamanashi, Japan; *Int'l*, pg. 477
Fulford, John H., III, Sr. V.P.-Mktg.--Federal National Mortgage Association (Fannie Mae), Washington, DC; *U.S. Public*, pg. 615
Fuller, Amy, Sr. V.P. & Grp. Acct. Dir.--The Lord Group, New York, NY; *U.S. Private*, pg. 325
Fuller, Arthur D., Sr. V.P. & Pres.-Newsprint Div.--Bowater Incorporated, Greenville, SC; *U.S. Public*, pg. 247
Fuller, Dennis, Sr. V.P.-Global Devel.--Blimpie International, Inc., Atlanta, GA; *U.S. Public*, pg. 236
Fuller, Janith P., Sr. V.P.--Market Facts, Inc., Arlington Heights, IL; *U.S. Public*, pg. 1046
Fuller, Scott, Sr. V.P.-Commercial Adv.--Texas Commerce Bank, Houston, TX; *U.S. Public*, pg. 339
Fuller, W. John, Sr. V.P.--Keycorp, Cleveland, OH; *U.S. Public*, pg. 954
Fullerton, Charles A., Sr. V.P.--ServiceMaster Residential/Commercial Services Co., Memphis, TN; *U.S. Public*, pg. 1461
Fullinwider, Stuart, Sr. V.P.-Fin. & Systems--Boston Chicken, Inc., Golden, CO; *U.S. Public*, pg. 247
Fullmer, John H., Chief Mktg. Officer & Sr. V.P.--CUC International, Inc., Stamford, CT; *U.S. Public*, pg. 320
Fulscher, Gary, Dr., Sr. V.P.-Opers.--Alza Corporation, Palo Alto, CA; *U.S. Public*, pg. 62
Fultz, Larry L., Sr. V.P.-Bus. Devel.--LEXIS-NEXIS, Miamisburg, OH; *Int'l*, pg. 1096
Fumagalli, Douglas A., Sr. V.P.-Human Resources--SHL Systemhouse, Ottawa, Canada; *Int'l*, pg. 1154
Fumiatti, John P., Sr. V.P.-Prod. Design--Gap Stores Division, San Bruno, CA; *U.S. Public*, pg. 702
Fumiiri, Hidetoshi, Sr. V.P. & Dir.--Kodansha Ltd., Tokyo, Japan; *Int'l*, pg. 742
Funk, Charles N., Chief Investment Officer, Corp. Sr. V.P. & Pres.-Des Moines--Brenton Banks, Inc., Des Moines, IA; *U.S. Public*, pg. 251
Funkhouser, Elmer N., III, Sr. V.P.--Sealed Air Corporation, Saddle Brook, NJ; *U.S. Public*, pg. 1450
Furlow, Brenda, Sr. V.P. & Gen. Counsel--Credit Union National Association, Madison, WI; *U.S. Private*, pg. 288
Furnad, Bob, Sr. V.P. & Sr. Exec. Producer--CNN (Cable News Network), Atlanta, GA; *U.S. Public*, pg. 1614
Furnas, Walt, Sr. V.P.-Human Resources--Red Roof Inns, Inc., Hilliard, OH; *U.S. Public*, pg. 1369
Furst, Ditlef, Sr. V.P.-Mktg.--BT Industries AB, Mjolby, Sweden; *Int'l*, pg. 123
Furu, Niels Christian, Chief Oper. Officer & Exec. V.P.--Olicom A/S, Lyngby, Denmark; *Int'l*, pg. 1001
Fury, Jerry, Sr. V.P.-Creative--Clarity Coverdale Fury Advertising, Minneapolis, MN; *U.S. Private*, pg. 242
Fusto, John, Sr. V.P. & Controller--Audiovox Corporation, Hauppauge, NY; *U.S. Public*, pg. 147
Gaan, Cary A., Sr. V.P. & Gen. Counsel--Bally Total Fitness Holdings Corporation, Chicago, IL; *U.S. Public*, pg. 171
Gaan, Cary A., Sr. V.P. & Gen. Counsel--Bally Total Fitness Corporation, Chicago, IL; *U.S. Public*, pg. 171
Gaard, Tom, Sr. V.P.--Principal Mutual Life Insurance Co., Des Moines, IA; *U.S. Private*, pg. 886
Gabbert, William E., Exec. V.P. & Mgr.-Prod.--Willis Corroon Corp. of Arizona, Phoenix, AZ; *Int'l*, pg. 1505
Gabor, Karen, Sr. V.P. & Assoc. Media Dir.-USA--Active International, Pearl River, NY; *U.S. Private*, pg. 15
Gabriel, Antoinette S., Chief Admin. Officer & Sr. V.P.--Crown Vantage Inc., Oakland, CA; *U.S. Public*, pg. 465
Gabriel, Clarence "Gabe", Sr. V.P.-Installers' Service Warehouse--APS Holding Corporation, Houston, TX; *U.S. Public*, pg. 10

Gabrysch, Raymond C., Sr. V.P.-Opers.--Luby's Cafeterias, Inc., San Antonio, TX; *U.S. Public*, pg. 1017
Gaddy, Errol, Sr. V.P.--Willis Corroon Corp. of Georgia, Atlanta, GA; *Int'l*, pg. 1506
Gadra, David M., Chief Information Officer & Sr. V.P.--Ikon Office Solutions, Inc., Malvern, PA; *U.S. Public*, pg. 862
Gaeddert, Jim, Sr. V.P.-Commercial Opers.-Europe--New Holland Ltd., Brentford, United Kingdom; *Int'l*, pg. 484
Gaff, Bill, Sr. V.P. & Gen. Mgr.--Vactor Mfg. Inc., Streator, IL; *U.S. Public*, pg. 617
Gaffney, Barbara L., Sr. V.P.-Worldwide Customer Services--Sequent Computer Systems, Inc., Beaverton, OR; *U.S. Public*, pg. 1459
Gaffney, Patrick, Sr. V.P.--Inman Construction Corporation, Memphis, TN; *U.S. Private*, pg. 564
Gagen, James, Sr. V.P. & Media Svcs. Dir.--Liggett-Stashower, Inc., Cleveland, OH; *U.S. Private*, pg. 667
Gagnon, Richard, Sr. V.P. & Mgr.-Natl. Sls.--White Cap Industries, Inc., Costa Mesa, CA; *U.S. Public*, pg. 1765
Gail, Brian, Sr. V.P.-Corp. Communications--Aramark Corporation, Philadelphia, PA; *U.S. Private*, pg. 79
Gailey, Ward H., Sr. V.P.-Cash Mngmt. Services--SunTrust Banks, Inc., Atlanta, GA; *U.S. Public*, pg. 1537
Gaines, Gene, Sr. V.P.--Fidelity & Guaranty Life Insurance Co., Baltimore, MD; *U.S. Public*, pg. 1659
Gaither, Michael, Sr. V.P. & Gen. Counsel--J.H. Heafner Co. Inc., Lincolnton, NC; *U.S. Private*, pg. 514
Gajanandana, Kitti, Sr. V.P.--Siam City Bank Public Company Limited, Bangkok, Thailand; *Int'l*, pg. 1239
Galanti, Lisa, Sr. V.P. & Mngmt. Supvr.--Fitzgerald & Co., Atlanta, GA; *U.S. Private*, pg. 409
Galbraith, John, Sr. V.P. & Mngmt. Supvr.--Hoffman/Lewis, San Francisco, CA; *U.S. Private*, pg. 532
Gale, James C., Chief Fin. Officer & Sr. V.P.-Fin.--Genicom Corporation, Chantilly, VA; *U.S. Public*, pg. 729
Galenza, L., Sr. V.P. & Gen. Mgr.--Barber Industries Inc., Calgary, Canada; *Int'l*, pg. 164
Galetto, Charles, Sr. V.P.-Fin. & Treas.--PMR Corporation, San Diego, CA; *U.S. Public*, pg. 1242
Galla, Ronald M., Chief Information Officer & Sr. V.P.--Kaman Corporation, Bloomfield, CT; *U.S. Public*, pg. 941
Gallagher, Gerard A., Jr., Sr. V.P.-Special Projects--Ecology and Environment, Inc., Lancaster, NY; *U.S. Public*, pg. 562
Gallagher, J.M., Sr. V.P.-Environmental Division--Davy International, San Francisco, San Ramon, CA; *Int'l*, pg. 774
Gallagher, Kevin C., Sr. V.P., Gen. Counsel & Sec.--360 Degrees Communications Company, Chicago, IL; *U.S. Public*, pg. 1607
Gallagher, Patrick J., Sr. V.P.--San Francisco Giants Baseball Club, San Francisco, CA; *U.S. Private*, pg. 964
Gallagher, Shay, Sr. V.P. & Gen. Mgr.-Mktg.--Bradford Exchange Ltd., Niles, IL; *U.S. Private*, pg. 163
Gallagher, Steven G., Sr. V.P.--American Arbitration Association, New York, NY; *U.S. Private*, pg. 50
Gallagher, Thomas W., Sr. V.P., Gen. Counsel & Sec.--Citizens Banking Corporation, Flint, MI; *U.S. Public*, pg. 379
Galli, Charles J., Sr. V.P.-Home Regl. Mgr.--A.G. Edwards & Sons, Inc., Saint Louis, MO; *U.S. Public*, pg. 565
Galligan, Peter, Sr. V.P.-Comml. Banking Services--Citizens Bank of Massachusetts, Fairhaven, MA; *Int'l*, pg. 1132
Gallion, Steve, Sr. V.P.-Sls.--Reed Travel Publishing-Los Angeles, Los Angeles, CA; *Int'l*, pg. 1097
Gallo, John, Sr. V.P.-Opers.--Domco Inc., Farnham, Canada; *Int'l*, pg. 415
Gallo, Michael, Sr. V.P.-N.E. Agencies--New York Life Insurance Company, New York, NY; *U.S. Private*, pg. 794
Gallo, Michael W., Sr. V.P.-Fin./Western Division--Tenet Healthcare Corporation, Santa Barbara, CA; *U.S. Public*, pg. 1576
Galloway, William R., Sr. V.P.--Hibernia Corporation, New Orleans, LA; *U.S. Public*, pg. 825
Galluccio, Joseph, Sr. V.P.-Sls.--P.F. Collier LP, New York, NY; *Int'l*, pg. 433
Galotti, Donna Kalajian, Sr. V.P. & Publr.--Cosmopolitan, New York, NY; *U.S. Private*, pg. 517
Galvez, Jan Gerard, Sr. V.P.-Intl. Opers.--BancTec, Inc., Dallas, TX; *U.S. Public*, pg. 176
Galvin, W.J., Chief Fin. Officer & Sr. V.P.-Fin.--Emerson Electric Co., Saint Louis, MO; *U.S. Public*, pg. 572
Gamazo, Asis, Sr. Officer--Banque Indosuez Espana S.A., Madrid, Spain; *Int'l*, pg. 315
Gamba, John F., Sr. V.P.-Corp. Resources & Performance Assurance--Bell Atlantic Corporation, New York, NY; *U.S. Public*, pg. 201
Gamba, Philippe, Sr. V.P.-Europe Mkt.--Renault, Boulogne-Billancourt, France; *Int'l*, pg. 1102
Gamber, Brice R., Sr. V.P.--Chubb & Son, Inc., Warren, NJ; *U.S. Public*, pg. 355
Gambero, Darrell J., Sr. V.P.-Voyager--American Bankers Life Assurance Co. of Florida, Miami, FL; *U.S. Public*, pg. 67
Gambill, Gene, Sr. V.P.--Tiernay Metals, Redondo Beach, CA; *U.S. Private*, pg. 1085
Gameson, Ray, Sr. V.P.-Human Resources--Pilgrim's Pride Corporation, Pittsburg, TX; *U.S. Public*, pg. 1296
Gamner, Bengt, Sr. V.P.-Tech.--Celsius AB, Stockholm, Sweden; *Int'l*, pg. 276
Gamsin, Marc H., Sr. V.P.--SunAmerica Inc., Los Angeles, CA; *U.S. Public*, pg. 1532
Gan, K.C., Sr. V.P. & Country Mgr.--Bank of America NT&SA, Jakarta, Indonesia; *U.S. Public*, pg. 182
Gander, Robert, Sr. V.P.--Champion Laboratories, Inc., Albion, IL; *U.S. Private*, pg. 178
Ganey, M.J., Sr. V.P. & Grp. Bus. Dir.--Howard, Merrell & Partners, Inc., Raleigh, NC; *U.S. Private*, pg. 542
Gangone, Joe, Sr. V.P.-Adv.--Madison Square Garden Network, New York, NY; *U.S. Public*, pg. 288
Ganley, Barry S., Chief Information Officer & Sr. V.P.--Beverly Enterprises, Inc., Fort Smith, AR; *U.S. Public*, pg. 227
Gannon, J. Timothy, Sr. V.P.--Outback Steakhouse Inc., Tampa, FL; *U.S. Public*, pg. 1235
Gannon, Michael J., Chief Fin. Officer & Sr. V.P.--Flint Ink Corp., Detroit, MI; *U.S. Private*, pg. 413
Gano, Michael B., Sr. V.P., Prod. Mgr. & Reg. Construction Mng. Dir.--Willis Corroon Corp. of Portland, Portland, OR; *Int'l*, pg. 1507
Gans, Bruce M., Sr. V.P.-Rehab & Post-Acute Care--The Detroit Medical Center, Detroit, MI; *U.S. Private*, pg. 328
Gantes, Michael, Sr. V.P. & Dir.-Mdsg.--Fedco, Inc., Santa Fe Springs, CA; *U.S. Private*, pg. 398
Gantner, Robert, Sr. V.P.-Mktg.--Magna Group, Inc., Saint Louis, MO; *U.S. Public*, pg. 1037
Gantz, George R., Sr. V.P.-Commun. & Regulation--Unitil Corporation, Hampton, NH; *U.S. Public*, pg. 1692
Gantz, George R., Sr. V.P.--UNITIL Service Corporation, Hampton, NH; *U.S. Public*, pg. 1693
Ganz, Kenneth, Sr. V.P.-Distr.--Liz Claiborne, Inc., New York, NY; *U.S. Public*, pg. 1005
Ganzak, Dennis, Sr. V.P.-Fin.--CBS Television Network, New York, NY; *U.S. Public*, pg. 274
Ganzi, Victor F., Sr. V.P. & Group Head--Hearst Books/Business Publishing Group, New York, NY; *U.S. Private*, pg. 515
Gapp, Gary, Sr. V.P.-Franchise Opers.--Supercuts, Inc., San Francisco, CA; *U.S. Public*, pg. 1373
Garahi, Masood, Chief Tech. Officer & Sr. V.P.--Mobile Telecommunications Technologies Corp., Jackson, MS; *U.S. Public*, pg. 1120
Garand, Christopher P., Sr. V.P.--General Reinsurance Corp., Stamford, CT; *U.S. Public*, pg. 725
Garavaglia, James, Sr. V.P.-Pub. Affairs--Comerica Incorporated, Detroit, MI; *U.S. Public*, pg. 408
Garb, Monica, Sr. V.P. & Assoc. Creative Dir.--Girgenti, Hughes, Butler & McDowell, New York, NY; *U.S. Private*, pg. 455
Garbarino, Joe, Sr. V.P.-Corp. Sls. Promo.--Belk Stores Services Inc., Charlotte, NC; *U.S. Private*, pg. 131
Garbeaux, Jean-Marie, Sr. V.P.-Corp. Communications--Elf Aquitane, Paris, France; *Int'l*, pg. 444
Garber, Josie, Sr. V.P. & Database Mktg. Dir.--Wunderman Cato Johnson, New York, NY; *U.S. Private*, pg. 1197
Garber, Richard P., First Sr. V.P.--Valley National Bank, Parsippany, NJ; *U.S. Public*, pg. 1705
Garcia, Alejandro M., Sr. V.P. & Regional Dir.-N. America--Banca Serfin, S.A., New York Agency, New York, NY; *Int'l*, pg. 137
Garcia, Alex, Sr. V.P.-Sls.--BankAtlantic Bancorp, Inc., Fort Lauderdale, FL; *U.S. Public*, pg. 183
Garcia, E.R. (Ted), Sr. V.P.-Supply Chain Opers.--Starbucks Coffee Company, Seattle, WA; *U.S. Public*, pg. 1510
Garcia, Leonardo F., Sr. V.P.-Investments--American Bankers Insurance Co. of Florida, Miami, FL; *U.S. Public*, pg. 67
Garcia, Leonardo F., Sr. V.P.-Investments--American Bankers Life Assurance Co. of Florida, Miami, FL; *U.S. Public*, pg. 67
Garcia, Philip A., Sr. V.P. & Controller--Erie Family Life Insurance Company, Erie, PA; *U.S. Public*, pg. 590
Gardiner, Ralph J., Sr. V.P.-Application Systems Mngmt.--Strategic Technology Services, Cerritos, CA; *Int'l*, pg. 1154
Gardiol, Olivier, Sr. V.P.-Prod.--Bobst S.A., Lausanne, Switzerland; *Int'l*, pg. 198
Gardner, Allan, Sr. V.P.--True North Diversified Companies, New York, NY; *U.S. Public*, pg. 1642
Gardner, Andrew J., Sr. V.P. & Controller--CommNet Cellular Inc., Englewood, CO; *U.S. Public*, pg. 414
Gardner, David, Sr. V.P.--Hill, Holliday, Connors, Cosmopulos, Inc., Boston, MA; *U.S. Private*, pg. 529
Gardner, Donald R., Chief Fin. Officer, Sr. V.P. & Sec.--Rigel Energy Corporation, Calgary, Canada; *Int'l*, pg. 1117
Gardner, James L., Sr. V.P. & Gen. Counsel--A.T. Massey Coal Company, Inc., Richmond, VA; *U.S. Public*, pg. 660
Gardner, Jay K., Chief Oper. Officer & Sr. V.P.--Fort Wayne National Corporation, Fort Wayne, IN; *U.S. Public*, pg. 673
Gardner, Jeffery, Sr. V.P.-Fin.--360 Degrees Communications Company, Chicago, IL; *U.S. Public*, pg. 1607
Gardner, Larry A., Sr. V.P.-Opers. & Admin. Services--1st Source Bank Consolidated, South Bend, IN; *U.S. Public*, pg. 638
Gardner, P. Frank, Sr. V.P.-Brdcst. Television--The E.W. Scripps Company, Cincinnati, OH; *U.S. Public*, pg. 1447
Gardner, Richard P., Sr. V.P.-Worldwide Sls. & Mktg.--BMC Software, Inc., Houston, TX; *U.S. Public*, pg. 162
Garel, John R., Sr. V.P.-Mktg. & Sls.--America West Airlines, Inc., Phoenix, AZ; *U.S. Public*, pg. 67
Garguilo, L., Sr. V.P.--Daher Golden Eagle - New York, Jamaica, NY; *U.S. Public*, pg. 749
Garin, Carolos E., Sr. V.P.-Corp. & Reg. Head-Latin America--Corporate & Institutional Financial Services - Montreal, Toronto, Canada; *Int'l*, pg. 153
Garland, Jerry, Sr. V.P.-Kansas City Division--Associated Wholesale Grocers, Inc., Kansas City, KS; *U.S. Private*, pg. 93
Garman, Roy A., Sr. V.P. & Controller--Donaldson, Lufkin, & Jenrette, Inc., New York, NY; *U.S. Public*, pg. 589
Garner, Michael C., Sr. V.P.--Continental Assurance Company, Chicago, IL; *U.S. Private*, pg. 267
Garner, Richard, Sr. V.P.-Human Resources--Pic'n Pay Stores, Inc., Matthews, NC; *U.S. Private*, pg. 864
Garnick, Terri, Chief Acctg. Officer & Sr. V.P.--Glenborough Realty Trust Incorporated, San Mateo, CA; *U.S. Public*, pg. 747
Garofalo, Diane M., Sr. V.P.--UNUM Life Insurance Company of America, Portland, ME; *U.S. Public*, pg. 1699
Garred, Albert E., Sr. V.P.--Stone & Webster Engineering & Constructors Corp., Boston, MA; *U.S. Public*, pg. 1519
Garrett, C.L., Chief Fin. Officer & Sr. V.P.-Fin.--SENCORP, Newport, KY; *U.S. Private*, pg. 983
Garrett, Edward E., Sr. V.P. & Mgr.-Prod.--Willis Corroon Corp. of Missouri, Saint Louis, MO; *Int'l*, pg. 1506
Garrett, James, Sr. V.P. & Pres.-Fin. Markets Div.--John H. Harland Company, Decatur, GA; *U.S. Public*, pg. 785
Garrett, Marvin J., V.P.-Regulatory Affairs--XOMA Corporation, Berkeley, CA; *U.S. Public*, pg. 1786
Garrett, Mike, Sr. V.P.-External Affairs--Alabama Power Co., Birmingham, AL; *U.S. Public*, pg. 1489
Garrett, Robert, Sr. V.P.-Mktg. & Adv.--Warehouse Home Furnishings Distributor, Dublin, GA; *U.S. Private*, pg. 1150
Garrett, Steve, Sr. V.P.--American Fidelity Corp., Oklahoma City, OK; *U.S. Private*, pg. 54
Garrett, Todd, Chief Info. Officer & Sr. V.P.--The Procter & Gamble Company, Cincinnati, OH; *U.S. Public*, pg. 1330
Garrison, Bob, Sr. V.P. & Media Dir.--N.W. Ayer & Partners Chicago, Chicago, IL; *U.S. Private*, pg. 104
Garrison, John, Sr. V.P.-Sls. & Mktg./Consumer Electronics--Samsung Electronics America, Inc., Ridgefield Park, NJ; *Int'l*, pg. 1183
Garrow, Robert E., Sr. V.P.-Special Assets--Citizens Trust Company, Providence, RI; *Int'l*, pg. 1132
Garske, Chris, Sr. V.P.-Publ.--GT Interactive Software Corp., New York, NY; *U.S. Public*, pg. 696
Garson, Gary, V.P., Deputy Gen. Counsel & Asst. Sec.--Loews Corporation, New York, NY; *U.S. Public*, pg. 1010
Garten, Wayne P., Chief Fin. Officer & Sr. V.P.--Micro Warehouse, Inc., Norwalk, CT; *U.S. Public*, pg. 1104
Garthwaite, Stephen J., Sr. V.P.-Innovation & Tech.--General Mills, Inc., Minneapolis, MN; *U.S. Public*, pg. 717
Gartin, Robert E., Chief Fin. Officer & Sr. V.P.--Manheim Auctions, Inc., Atlanta, GA; *U.S. Private*, pg. 282
Gartland, Timothy C., Sr. V.P.-Human Resources--Provident Companies, Inc., Chattanooga, TN; *U.S. Public*, pg. 1337
Gartner, Elliot, Sr. V.P.--Vantage Global Advisors, Inc., New York, NY; *U.S. Public*, pg. 998
Gartzke, David G., Chief Fin. Officer & Sr. V.P.-Fin.--Minnesota Power, Duluth, MN; *U.S. Public*, pg. 1116
Garvey, John, Sr. V.P.--Parade Publications Inc., New York, NY; *U.S. Private*, pg. 20
Garvin, Richard W., Sr. V.P. & Mgr.-Eastern Div.--First Security Bank of Idaho, N.A., Boise, ID; *U.S. Public*, pg. 637
Garwood, Paul, Sr. V.P.-Fabrics--Lever Brothers Co., New York, NY; *Int'l*, pg. 1435
Gary J. Sekulski, Sr. V.P.-Cient Analysis & Consulting--MEDCO Containment Services, Inc., Montvale, NJ; *U.S. Public*, pg. 1091
Gasca Neri, Enrique, Sr. V.P.-Mktg. & Quality--Grupo Acerero del Norte S.A. de C.V. (GAN), Mexico, Mexico; *Int'l*, pg. 572
Gaskin, George C., Sr. V.P. & Gen. Counsel--Anacomp, Inc., Indianapolis, IN; *U.S. Public*, pg. 106
Gass, Peter A., Sr. V.P.--J.S. Alberici Construction Co., Inc., Saint Louis, MO; *U.S. Private*, pg. 32
Gaston, John, Chief Fin. Officer & Sr. V.P.-Corp. Svcs.--SF Services, North Little Rock, AR; *U.S. Private*, pg. 956
Gaston, Roger C., Sr. V.P.-Human Resources--Toys "R" Us, Inc., Paramus, NJ; *U.S. Public*, pg. 1626
Gaston, S. Albert, Chief Fin. Officer & Sr. V.P.--Tom's Foods, Inc., Columbus, GA; *U.S. Private*, pg. 1090
Gaswhala, Sid A., Sr. V.P.--Knight Architects Engineers Planners, Inc., Chicago, IL; *U.S. Private*, pg. 626
Gately, Arthur T., Jr., Sr. V.P.-Admin.--Swank, Inc., Attleboro, MA; *U.S. Public*, pg. 1543
Gately, James A., Sr. V.P.--Manufacturers & Traders Trust Company, Buffalo, NY; *U.S. Public*, pg. 631
Gately, James H., Sr. V.P.-Institutional--The Vanguard Group, Inc., Valley Forge, PA; *U.S. Private*, pg. 1133
Gatepithaya, Anant, Sr. Exec. V.P.--SCF Finance & Securities Co., Ltd., Bangkok, Thailand; *Int'l*, pg. 1239
Gates, Richard D., Sr. V.P.-Investor Rels. & Bus. Devel.--Rubbermaid Incorporated, Wooster, OH; *U.S. Public*, pg. 1411
Gathers, Thomas W., Sr. V.P.-H.R.--Uno Restaurant Corporation, West Roxbury, MA; *U.S. Public*, pg. 1698
Gatsch, Mary E., Chief Fin. Officer & Sr. V.P.--Peterson's Guides, Inc., Princeton, NJ; *U.S. Private*, pg. 858
Gatti, Robert, Exec. V.P.-Mfg.--Rieter Automotive North America Inc, Farmington Hills, MI; *Int'l*, pg. 1117
Gattinella, Wayne, Sr. V.P.-Mktg.--MEDCO Containment Services, Inc., Montvale, NJ; *U.S. Public*, pg. 1091
Gattis, J. Michael, Sr. V.P.-Sls.--Bindley Western Drug Company, Indianapolis, IN; *U.S. Public*, pg. 228
Gatto, David F., Sr. V.P.-Intl.--L.A. Gear, Inc., Santa Monica, CA; *U.S. Public*, pg. 969
Gatto, Jeanette, Sr. V.P. & Corp. Local Brdcst. Buying Dir.--Hal Riney & Partners, Inc., San Francisco, CA; *U.S. Private*, pg. 931
Gatzek, Deborah R., Sr. V.P., Gen. Counsel & Asst. Sec.--Franklin Resources, Inc., San Mateo, CA; *U.S. Public*, pg. 679
Gaubert, Daniel R., Chief Fin. Officer, Sr. V.P.-Fin. & Controller--McDermott International, Inc., New Orleans, LA; *U.S. Public*, pg. 1067
Gaubier, Alain, Sr. V.P.--Dumez-GTM, Singapore, Singapore; *Int'l*, pg. 823
Gaudie, H. Alan, Sr. V.P.-Fin. & Treas.--Galoob Toys, Inc., South San Francisco, CA; *U.S. Public*, pg. 698
Gaudy, Richard A., Sr. V.P. & Mgr.-Retail Loan Sls.--Glendale Federal Bank, F.S.B., Glendale, CA; *U.S. Public*, pg. 747
Gauer, Donald L., Sr. V.P. & Chief Actuary--Sun Life Assurance Company of Canada, Toronto, Canada; *Int'l*, pg. 1318
Gauthier, Efrain Rivera, Sr. V.P.-Puerto Rico--Heilig-Meyers Company, Richmond, VA; *U.S. Public*, pg. 804
Gauthier, Philippe J., Sr. V.P.-Animal Health/Agriculture Div.--Bayer Corporation, Pittsburgh, PA; *Int'l*, pg. 172
Gauvry, Belle, Sr. V.P. & Media Rels. Dir.--Harrison & Star, Inc., New York, NY; *U.S. Private*, pg. 506
Gavalda, Jean-Francois, Sr. V.P.-African Opers.--Elf Aquitane, Paris, France; *Int'l*, pg. 444

Gavin, Moira, Sr. V.P.-Sls.-Lenox Brands--Lenox, Incorporated, Lawrenceville, NJ; *U.S. Public*, pg. 261
Gawelek, Randolph A., Exec. V.P.& Sec.--The Kitchen Collection Inc., Chillicothe, OH; *U.S. Public*, pg. 1149
Gawlak, Kathryn, Sr. V.P.-Stores--Strawberries Inc., Milford, MA; *U.S. Private*, pg. 1046
Gay, Alvin, Sr. V.P. & Exec. Creative Dir.--Uniworld Group, Inc., New York, NY; *U.S. Private*, pg. 1128
Gay, David, Sr. V.P.-Opers.--The Apparel Group, Ltd., Louisville, KY; *U.S. Private*, pg. 78
Gay, Lawrence W., Sr. V.P.-Sls. & Bus. Devel.--GTECH Corporation, West Greenwich, RI; *U.S. Public*, pg. 767
Gay, Louis Benton, Sr. V.P.--Hibernia Corporation, New Orleans, LA; *U.S. Public*, pg. 825
Gay, R. Norwood, III, Sr. V.P., Gen. Counsel & Sec.--Attorneys' Title Insurance Fund, Orlando, FL; *U.S. Private*, pg. 98
Gazzo, John J., Sr. V.P.-OSS Div.--Porta Systems Corp., Syosset, NY; *U.S. Public*, pg. 1317
Gdula, James M., Sr. V.P.-Natl. Accts.--The Mills Corporation, Arlington, VA; *U.S. Public*, pg. 1113
Gearing, Margaret, Sr. V.P. & Client Services Dir.--Austin Kelley Advertising, Inc., Atlanta, GA; *U.S. Private*, pg. 100
Geary, Thomas, Sr. V.P.--S L C Graphics, LP, Pittston, PA; *U.S. Private*, pg. 955
Gebhardt, Scott W., Sr. V.P.--PG&E Corporation, San Francisco, CA; *U.S. Public*, pg. 1240
Gee, Gregory W., Sr. V.P., Gen. Counsel & Sec.--Sun Life Assurance Company of Canada, Toronto, Canada; *Int'l*, pg. 1318
Gefen, Sharon, Sr. V.P.-Corp. Intl. Commun. & Pub. Rels.--Bank Hapoalim, Tel Aviv, Israel; *Int'l*, pg. 149
Gehring, Roger, Sr. V.P.--WGM Safety Corporation, Reading, PA; *Int'l*, pg. 462
Gehrke, Robbin, Sr. V.P. & Exec. Creative Dir.--Russ Reid Company, Inc., Pasadena, CA; *U.S. Private*, pg. 952
Geib, Dennis M., Sr. V.P.--Erie Family Life Insurance Company, Erie, PA; *U.S. Public*, pg. 590
Geider, Gregg, Sr. V.P. & Mngmt. Supvr.--Harrison & Star, Inc., New York, NY; *U.S. Private*, pg. 506
Geier, B. Gwen, Sr. V.P.-Employee Svcs.--Attorneys' Title Insurance Fund, Orlando, FL; *U.S. Private*, pg. 98
Geiger, Paul K., Chief Fin. Officer & Sr. V.P.--Kelly Services, Inc., Troy, MI; *U.S. Public*, pg. 949
Geiges, Lukas A., Sr. V.P.-Intl. Devel.--Checkpoint Systems Inc., Thorofare, NJ; *U.S. Public*, pg. 343
Geist, Herbert, Dr., Sr. V.P.--Landesbank Rheinland-Pfalz, Mainz, Germany; *Int'l*, pg. 799
Gekler, Brooks, Sr. V.P.-Mktg.--General Mills Canada Inc., Etobicoke, Canada; *U.S. Public*, pg. 718
Gelb, Mike, Sr. V.P.-Dept. Store Sls.--Crystal Clear Industries, Ridgefield Park, NJ; *U.S. Private*, pg. 293
Geller, Rachel, Sr. V.P. & Intl. Strategic Plng. Dir.--Saatchi & Saatchi Kid Connection, New York, NY; *U.S. Public*, pg. 1422
Gellerman, David, Sr. V.P.-Opers.--Jaydon Incorporated, Rock Island, IL; *U.S. Private*, pg. 584
Gellis, Andrew, Sr. V.P.-Film--Imax Corporation, Mississauga, Canada; *Int'l*, pg. 661
Gelman, Steven, Sr. V.P.--Wilshire Oil Co. of Texas, Jersey City, NJ; *U.S. Public*, pg. 1770
Gemignani, Gino, Sr. V.P.-Mktg. Bus. Devel.--The Whiting-Turner Contracting Co., Baltimore, MD; *U.S. Private*, pg. 1174
Genoway, Karen A., Sr. V.P.--EnerMark Income Fund, Calgary, Canada; *Int'l*, pg. 454
Gentile, Patrick E., Sr. V.P. & Acct. Exec.--Odyssey Reinsurance Corporation, New York, NY; *Int'l*, pg. 1258
Gentner, Craig, Chief Fin. Officer, Sr. V.P.-Fin. & Admin. & Sec.--Network Equipment Technologies, Inc., Redwood City, CA, *U.S. Public*, pg. 1168
Gentry, Allen M., Sr. V.P.-Central Div.--Chicago Title Insurance Co., Chicago, IL; *U.S. Public*, pg. 42
Gentry, Mary M., Sr. V.P. & Treas.--Carolina First Corporation, Greenville, SC; *U.S. Public*, pg. 306
Gentz, Jim, Sr. V.P.-Sls. & Mktg.--Yamaha Motor Corp., U.S.A., Cypress, CA; *Int'l*, pg. 1516
Gentz, Robert J., Sr. V.P.-Franchising & Devel.--DenAmerica Corp., Scottsdale, AZ; *U.S. Public*, pg. 498
Geoghegan, Andrew P., Sr. V.P., Gen. Counsel & Sec.--Hannaford Bros. Co., Scarborough, ME; *U.S. Public*, pg. 781
George, Christian R., Sr. V.P.--Hibernia Corporation, New Orleans, LA; *U.S. Public*, pg. 825
George, D.L., Sr. V.P.--Pennzoil Products Co., Houston, TX; *U.S. Public*, pg. 1272
George, Doug, Sr. V.P.--Weaver Construction, LLC, Greensboro, NC; *U.S. Private*, pg. 1156
George, Thomas A., Chief Fin. Officer & Sr. V.P.--Remec, Inc., San Diego, CA; *U.S. Public*, pg. 1376
Georges, Charles, Sr. V.P.--Banque Internationale a Luxembourg S.A., Luxembourg, Luxembourg; *Int'l*, pg. 162
Geraldino, Pedro, Gen. Mgr. & Sr. V.P.--Chilton Research Services, Radnor, PA; *Int'l*, pg. 1096
Gerber, Catharine, Sr. V.P.-Strategic, Interactive & Media Plng.--Hal Riney & Partners Heartland, Chicago, IL; *U.S. Private*, pg. 931
Gerber, Dylan, Sr. V.P.-Adv. & Mktg.--UPN-United Paramount Network, Los Angeles, CA; *U.S. Public*, pg. 352
Gerber, Dylan, Sr. V.P.-Adv. & Mktg.--UPN-United Paramount Network, Los Angeles, CA; *U.S. Private*, pg. 777
Gerber, Robert, Chief Acctg. Officer, Sr. V.P. & Controller--Fabri-Centers of America, Inc., Hudson, OH; *U.S. Public*, *pg. 609*
Gerbino, John, Sr. V.P.-Product & Service Devel.--Fair, Isaac and Company, Inc., San Rafael, CA; *U.S. Public*, pg. 609
Gereaue, Michael, Sr. V.P.-Pensions--Pan-American Life Insurance Company, New Orleans, LA; *U.S. Private*, pg. 836
Gerhard, Gilbert C., Chief Fin. Officer, Sr. V.P.-Fin. & Admin. & Treas.--Arbor Drugs, Inc., Troy, MI; *U.S. Public*, *pg. 126*
Gerhardt, Hans Peter, Sr. V.P.--General Re Corporation, Stamford, CT; *U.S. Public*, pg. 725
Gerhardy, Louis P., Sr. V.P.--Swinerton Inc., San Francisco, CA; *U.S. Private*, pg. 1059
Gerharter, Tom, Sr. V.P.-Opers.--Horizon Air Industries, Seattle, WA; *U.S. Public*, pg. 35
Gerlach, Duane L., Sr. V.P. & Chief Lending Officer--Firstbank of Illinois Co., Springfield, IL; *U.S. Public*, pg. 643
Gerlich, Gary, Sr. V.P.-Post Production--Metro-Goldwyn-Mayer Pictures, Inc., Santa Monica, CA; *U.S. Public*, pg. 1102
Germaise, Vicky, Sr. V.P.-Product Devel.--Atlantic Recording Corporation, New York, NY; *U.S. Public*, pg. 1611
German, Gary E., Chief Oper. Officer & Sr. V.P.--TVX Gold Inc., Toronto, Canada; *Int'l*, pg. 1345
Germer, R. E., Sr. V.P.--Flying J. Inc., Brigham City, UT; *U.S. Private*, pg. 415
Gerritsen, W.J.H., Sr. V.P.--AEGON Levensverzekering NV, Hague, Netherlands; *Int'l*, pg. 25
Gerritsen, W.J.H., Sr. V.P.--AEGON Schadeverzekering N.V., Hague, Netherlands; *Int'l*, pg. 26
Gershberg, Jay, Sr. V.P. & Pres.-Travel Nurse Grp.--Hospital Staffing Services, Inc., Fort Lauderdale, FL; *U.S. Public*, pg. 840
Gershel, George F., Jr., Sr. V.P.-Tobacco--Consolidated Cigar Corporation, Fort Lauderdale, FL; *U.S. Private*, pg. 690
Gershel, Seth, Sr. V.P. & Publisher--Simon & Schuster Audio, New York, NY; *U.S. Private*, pg. 778
Gersie, Mike, Chief Fin. Officer, Chief Info. Officer & Sr. V.P.--The Principal Financial Group, Des Moines, IA; *U.S.* Private, pg. 885
Gersie, Mike, Chief Fin. Officer & Sr. V.P.--Principal Mutual Life Insurance Co., Des Moines, IA; *U.S. Private*, pg. 886
Gerson, Elliot S., Sr. V.P. & Asst. Chief Legal Counsel--Rite Aid Corporation, Camp Hill, PA; *U.S. Public*, pg. 1390
Gerstner, Kenneth W., Chief Fin. Officer & Sr. V.P.--Farr Company, El Segundo, CA; *U.S. Public*, pg. 613
Gertz, William, Sr. V.P.-Mktg.--American Institute for Foreign Study, Greenwich, CT; *U.S. Private*, pg. 56
Geschwind, Richard D., Sr. V.P.--Bank of Pontiac, Pontiac, IL; *U.S. Public*, pg. 1316
Gesmar-Larsen, Jan, Sr. V.P.-Apple Europe--Apple Computer, Inc., Cupertino, CA; *U.S. Public*, pg. 121
Gessner, Lee, Sr. V.P.-Sls.--Word, Incorporated, Dallas, TX; *U.S. Public*, pg. 704
Gessner, Lee, Sr. V.P. & Deputy Publr.-Word Publishing--Thomas Nelson Inc., Nashville, TN; *U.S. Public*, pg. 1167
Gestman, Peter, Sr. V.P. & Gen. Counsel--Robson Communities, Sun Lakes, AZ; *U.S. Private*, pg. 937
Gethin, John, Sr. V.P.-Opers.--Standard Motor Products Inc., Long Island City, NY; *U.S. Public*, pg. 1503
Getson, Lisa M., Sr. V.P-Mktg.--Apria Healthcare Group Inc., Costa Mesa, CA; *U.S. Public*, pg. 125
Getter, Ruth, Sr. V.P. & Chief Economist--The Toronto Dominion Bank, Toronto, Canada; *Int'l*, pg. 1401
Gettins, R. Barry, Ph.D., Sr. V.P.-Opers. & Tech. Devel.--The Dexter Corporation, Windsor Locks, CT; *U.S. Public*, *pg. 504*
Gettlefinger, Jim, Sr. V.P.--Superior Label Systems, Inc., Mason, OH; *U.S. Private*, pg. 1055
Getz, Herbert, Sr. V.P., Gen. Counsel & Sec.--Waste Management, Inc., Oak Brook, IL; *U.S. Public*, pg. 1744
Geyer, Fred, Sr. V.P.-Strategy Devel.--Texas Instruments Incorporated, Dallas, TX; *U.S. Public*, pg. 1585
Gezundhajt, B., Sr. V.P.-Mktg. & Sls.--Zim-American Israeli Shipping Co., New York, NY; *U.S. Private*, pg. 1206
Ghelson, J. Tyrone, Sr. V.P.-Cash Protection, Securities & Services--Federal Reserve Bank of Dallas, Dallas, TX; *U.S. Private*, pg. 399
Gherardi, Mark, Sr. V.P.-Mfg.--Rock of Ages Canada, Inc., Beebe, Canada; *U.S. Public*, pg. 1396
Gherardi, Mark A., Sr. V.P.-Mfg. Opers./Barre & Canada--Rock of Ages Corporation, Graniteville, VT; *U.S. Public*, pg. 1396
Ghiloni, Peter, Sr. V.P.-Mktg.--Swisher International Group, Inc., Darien, CT; *U.S. Public*, pg. 1543
Ghose, Dev, Sr. V.P.-Fin. & Treas.--Health Care Property Investors, Inc., Newport Beach, CA; *U.S. Public*, pg. 801
Giacomino, Robert, Sr. V.P. & Media Mgr.--Grey Advertising Inc., New York, NY; *U.S. Public*, pg. 764
Giambrone, Andrea, Sr. V.P. & Creative Dir.--Lois/EJL Los Angeles, Los Angeles, CA; *U.S. Public*, pg. 1011
Giambrone, Andrea, Sr. V.P.--Year 2K Communications, Los Angeles, CA; *U.S. Public*, pg. 1011
Giangiulio, Joseph, Sr. V.P.-Bus. Devel.--Southwest National Bank of Pennsylvania, Greensburg, PA; *U.S. Public*, pg. 1493
Giangiulio, Randall C., Sr. V.P.--Phoenix Home Life Mutual Insurance Co., Hartford, CT; *U.S. Private*, pg. 863
Giangiulo, Randall C., Sr. V.P.-Grp. Sls.--Phoenix Home Life Mutual Insurance Company, Hartford, CT; *U.S. Private*, pg. 863
Giannola, Ralph, Sr. V.P.-Consumer Mktg.--Marriott Hotels, Resorts, and Suites, Washington, DC; *U.S. Public*, pg. 1048
Giannone, Dot, Sr. V.P.-Acct. Support--Young & Rubicam New York, New York, NY; *U.S. Private*, pg. 1198
Gibbon, Michael A., Sr. V.P.-Tech.--Imax Corporation, Mississauga, Canada; *Int'l*, pg. 661
Gibbons, Tom, Sr. V.P. & Treas.--Del Monte Foods, San Francisco, CA; *U.S. Private*, pg. 321
Gibbs, Ed, Sr. V.P.--Columbian Advertising Inc., Chicago, IL; *U.S. Private*, pg. 256
Gibbs, Marcus C., Sr. V.P.-Customer Services--American General Life & Accident Insurance Co., Nashville, TN; *U.S. Public*, pg. 76
Gibbs, Ron, Sr. V.P.--Edelman Public Relations Worldwide, Chicago, IL; *U.S. Private*, pg. 362
Gibbs, William H., Sr. V.P.--Apollo Group, Inc., Phoenix, AZ; *U.S. Public*, pg. 120
Giblin, John, Sr. V.P. & Controller--Crawford & Company, Atlanta, GA; *U.S. Public*, pg. 458
Gibney, Charles W., Chief Fin. Officer & Sr. V.P.--Macromedia Incorporated, Hackensack, NJ; *U.S. Private*, *pg. 693*
Gibson, Bruce, Sr. V.P.-Govt. Affairs--Houston Industries Incorporated, Houston, TX; *U.S. Public*, pg. 842
Gibson, Gary, Sr. V.P.-Small Bus. Lending--Nevada State Bank, Las Vegas, NV; *U.S. Public*, pg. 1793
Gibson, John, Sr. V.P.-Acq. & Devel.--Merry Land & Investment Company, Inc., Augusta, GA; *U.S. Public*, pg. 1098
Gibson, Marie-France, Sr. V.P.-Mdsg. & Procurement--Loeb Inc., Ottawa, Canada; *Int'l*, pg. 1073
Gibson, Rodney C., Dr., Sr. V.P.-Sys. Plng. & Engrng.--Aerospace Corporation, El Segundo, CA; *U.S. Private*, pg. 24
Gibson, William D., Sr. V.P.-Credit & Loan Admin.--Citizens Savings Bank, Providence, RI; *Int'l*, pg. 1132
Gibson, William D., Sr. V.P.-Credit & Loan Admin.--Citizens Trust Company, Providence, RI; *Int'l*, pg. 1132
Gieck, Dennis R., Sr. V.P.--EnerMark Income Fund, Calgary, Canada; *Int'l*, pg. 454
Gienko, Glenn A., Sr. V.P. & Dir.-Human Resources--Motorola, Inc., Schaumburg, IL; *U.S. Public*, pg. 1136
Giering, John L., Chief Fin. Officer & Sr. V.P.-Fin. & Admin.--NCR Corporation, Dayton, OH; *U.S. Public*, pg. 1146
Giertz, James R., Chief Fin. Officer & Sr. V.P.--Donaldson Company, Inc., Minneapolis, MN; *U.S. Public*, pg. 517
Gietzen, Kenneth A., Sr. V.P.--Chelsea State Bank, Chelsea, MI; *U.S. Private*, pg. 231
Giffin, Kenneth N., Sr. V.P.-Govt. Rels. & Real Estate--IWC Resources Corporation, Indianapolis, IN; *U.S. Public*, pg. 1185
Giffin, Kenneth N., Sr. V.P.-Govt. Rels.--Indianapolis Water Company, Indianapolis, IN; *U.S. Public*, pg. 1185
Giglio, Martin, Sr. V.P.--The St. George Group, Inc., Pittsburgh, PA; *U.S. Private*, pg. 960
Gil, Bianco, Chief Fin. Officer & Sr. V.P.--Agis Industries Ltd., Bnei-Brak, Israel; *Int'l*, pg. 30
Gilbert. Kathy, Sr. V.P. & Mngmt. Supvr.--Biederman, Kelly & Shaffer, Inc., New York, NY; *U.S. Private*, pg. 142
Gilbert, Chris, Sr. V.P.-Sls.--Altec Lansing Technologies, Inc., Milford, PA; *U.S. Private*, pg. 479
Gilbert, John M., Sr. V.P.--State Volunteer Mutual Insurance Co., Brentwood, TN; *U.S. Private*, pg. 1037
Gilbert, Ken W., Sr. V.P.-Mktg. (Mistic & Snapple)--Triarc Companies, Inc., New York, NY; *U.S. Public*, pg. 1634
Gilbert, Ken W., Sr. V.P.-Mktg./Mistic & Snapple--Triarc Beverage Group, White Plains, NY; *U.S. Public*, pg. 1635
Gilbert, Ken W., Sr. V.P.-Mktg.--Snapple Beverage Company, White Plains, NY; *U.S. Public*, pg. 1635
Gilbert, Steve, Sr. V.P. & Cashier--Hereford State Bank, Hereford, TX; *U.S. Public*, pg. 633
Giles, Douglas J., Sr. V.P.-Human Resources--The May Department Stores Company, Saint Louis, MO; *U.S. Public*, pg. 1063
Giles, J. LaMar, Sr. V.P. & Mgr.-Credit Div.--First Security Bank of Idaho, N.A., Boise, ID; *U.S. Public*, pg. 637
Giles, Olin S., Sr. V.P. & Chief Tech. Officer--Sensormatic Electronics Corporation, Boca Raton, FL; *U.S. Public*, pg. 1457
Gill, A. Malcolm, Sr. V.P.-Corp. Affairs--Thyssen Inc., Detroit, MI; *Int'l*, pg. 1389
Gill, Ed, Sr. V.P.-Sls. Admin.--Jockey International, Inc., Kenosha, WI; *U.S. Private*, pg. 588
Gill, Frank C., Sr. V.P.-Small Bus. Networking--Intel Corporation, Santa Clara, CA; *U.S. Public*, pg. 886
Gill, Glenn, Sr. V.P. & Creative Dir.--Trone Advertising, Inc., Greensboro, NC; *U.S. Private*, pg. 1104
Gill, Libby, Sr. V.P.-Media Rels.--Universal Studios TV, Universal City, CA; *Int'l*, pg. 1215
Gill, Linda, Sr. V.P. & Mngmt. Supvr.--Girgenti, Hughes, Butler & McDowell, New York, NY; *U.S. Private*, pg. 455
Gill, Margaret, Sr. V.P.-Legal & External Affairs & Corp. Sec.--AirTouch Communications, Inc., San Francisco, CA; *U.S. Public*, pg. 34
Gille, Lori-Jean, J.D., Sr. V.P., Gen. Counsel & Sec.--MGI PHARMA INC., Minneapolis, MN; *U.S. Public*, pg. 1026
Gillen, James R., Sr. V.P. & Gen. Counsel--The Prudential Insurance Company of America, Newark, NJ; *U.S. Private*, pg. 892
Gillen, James R., Sr. V.P. & Gen. Counsel--The Prudential Investment Corp., Newark, NJ; *U.S. Private*, pg. 892
Gillen, Michael T., Sr. V.P.--Canandaigua Wine Company, Inc., Canandaigua, NY; *U.S. Public*, pg. 300
Gillenwater, James H., Jr., Sr. V.P.-Plng. & Devel.--Vencor, Inc., Louisville, KY; *U.S. Public*, pg. 1711
Gillespee, Maureen, Sr. V.P.--Edelman Worldwide, Inc., New York, NY; *U.S. Private*, pg. 362
Gillespie, Edward, Sr. V.P. & Client Services Dir.--Burrell/DFA Advertising, New York, NY; *U.S. Private*, pg. 188
Gillespie, Jerry, Sr. V.P.-Opers.--Hutch Sports USA, Inc., Hebron, KY; *U.S. Public*, pg. 1354
Gillespie, John B., Sr. V.P.--John Wieland Homes Inc., Atlanta, GA; *U.S. Private*, pg. 1175
Gillespie, John F., Sr. V.P.-Human Resources--Woolworth Corporation, New York, NY; *U.S. Public*, pg. 1777
Gillespie, John H., Sr. V.P.--Chubb & Son, Inc., Warren, NJ; *U.S. Public*, pg. 355
Gillespie, William A., MD, Pres.-Southwest Division & Sr. V.P.--Kaiser Permanente, Oakland, CA; *U.S. Private*, pg. 605
Gillette, Thomas, Sr. V.P.-Devel.--Atlantic Gulf Communities Corporation, Miami, FL; *U.S. Public*, pg. 144
Gilliam, Doyle, V.P.-Sls.--E.C. Barton & Company, Jonesboro, AR; *U.S. Private*, pg. 119
Gillies, James E., Sr. V.P.-Canadian Mkt. Devel.--Newell Co., Freeport, IL; *U.S. Public*, pg. 1176
Gilligan, Fernanda K., Sr. V.P.-Pub. Rels.--Tiffany & Co., New York, NY; *U.S. Public*, pg. 1608

Gillin, John J., Sr. V.P.--The Coca-Cola Company, Atlanta, GA; *U.S. Public*, pg. 392
Gilliss, Archie, Sr. V.P.-Opers.--New Brunswick Power Corporation, Fredericton, Canada; *Int'l*, pg. 923
Gillman, James W., Sr. V.P. & Dir.-Patents, Trademarks & Licensing--Motorola, Inc., Schaumburg, IL; *U.S. Public*, pg. 1136
Gillooly, Edward F., Sr. V.P.-Mktg.--BJ's Wholesale Club, Inc., Natick, MA; *U.S. Public*, pg. 162
Gilman, John, Sr. V.P. & Mgr.-Natl. Sls.--Allyn & Bacon, Needham, MA; *U.S. Private*, pg. 778
Gilman, Richard H., Sr. V.P.-Opers.--The New York Times Company, New York, NY; *U.S. Public*, pg. 1173
Gilmer, Lawrence W., Sr. V.P.--Keycorp, Cleveland, OH; *U.S. Public*, pg. 954
Gilmore, James A., Sr. V.P.-Banking Svcs.--Federal Home Loan Bank of New York, New York, NY; *U.S. Private*, pg. 399
Gilrane, James J., Sr. V.P. & Treas.--ITT Information Services, Inc., New York, NY; *U.S. Public*, pg. 1512
Gimple, Ron, Sr. V.P. & Gen. Counsel--CBL & Associates Properties, Inc., Chattanooga, TN; *U.S. Public*, pg. 273
Gimson, Curtis S., Sr. V.P. & Gen. Counsel--Triarc Restaurant Group, Fort Lauderdale, FL; *U.S. Public*, pg. 1635
Gindin, Peter J., Sr. V.P. & Litigation Counsel--Summit Bancorp, Princeton, NJ; *U.S. Public*, pg. 1527
Ginet, Francois, Sr. V.P.-Govt. Services--SGS Societe Generale de Surveillance Holding S.A., Geneva, Switzerland; *Int'l*, pg. 1153
Gingerich, James G., Chief Fin. Officer & Sr. V.P.--InterTAN Inc., Fort Worth, TX; *U.S. Public*, pg. 910
Gingold, Chuck, Sr. V.P.-Programming--Discovery Networks, Inc., Bethesda, MD; *U.S. Private*, pg. 334
Ginibre, Jean-Louis, Sr. V.P.--Hachette Filipacchi USA, New York, NY; *Int'l*, pg. 794
Ginnetti, John P., Sr. V.P.--Hartford Life & Accident Insurance Company, Hartford, CT; *U.S. Public*, pg. 795
Ginns, Susan M., Sr. V.P. & Treas.--Brookline Savings Bank, Brookline, MA; *U.S. Private*, pg. 171
Ginocchio, Peter L., Sr. V.P.-Customer Support--Dassault Falcon Jet Corp., South Hackensack, NJ; *Int'l*, pg. 383
Ginsky, Marvin H., Sr. V.P. & Gen. Counsel--Champion International Corp., Stamford, CT; *U.S. Public*, pg. 333
Giordano, James A., Sr. V.P.--The Insurance Corp. of New York, New York, NY; *U.S. Public*, pg. 336
Gipson, Douglas R., Sr. V.P.--DTE Energy Company, Detroit, MI; *U.S. Public*, pg. 475
Gipson, Kelly, Sr. V.P. & Mngmt. Supvr.--Adler Boschetto Peebles & Partners, Inc., New York, NY; *U.S. Private*, pg. 17
Girard, Fernand-Guy, Sr. V.P.-Woodlands & Sawmills--Donohue Inc., Quebec, Canada; *Int'l*, pg. 1075
Girndt, Rick, Sr. V.P.-Exploration Services--ICO, Inc., Houston, TX; *U.S. Public*, pg. 853
Girvan, Daniel J., Sr. V.P.-H.R. & Admin.--Fort James Corporation, Richmond, VA; *U.S. Public*, pg. 670
Gisi, John J., Sr. V.P.-Arizona Admin.--Zions Bancorporation, Salt Lake City, UT; *U.S. Public*, pg. 1792
Gisiger, Michel, Sr. Exec. V.P.--SGS Societe Generale de Surveillance Holding S.A., Geneva, Switzerland; *Int'l*, pg. 1153
Giuliano, James R., III, Chief Fin. Officer & Sr. V.P.--The Edward J. DeBartolo Corporation, Youngstown, OH; *U.S.* Private, pg. 319
Giuliano, Vincent, Sr. V.P.-Govt. Rels.--ADVO, Inc., Windsor, CT; *U.S. Public*, pg. 23
Givan, Boyd E., Chief Fin. Officer & Sr. V.P.--The Boeing Company, Seattle, WA; *U.S. Public*, pg. 239
Gladden, Joseph R., Jr., Sr. V.P. & Gen. Counsel--The Coca-Cola Company, Atlanta, GA; *U.S. Public*, pg. 392
Gladden, Roger D., Sr. V.P. & Pres.-Commercial Fixtures & Displays Group--Leggett & Platt, Incorporated, Carthage, MO; *U.S. Public*, pg. 985
Glader, Douglas J., Sr. V.P.-Mfg. Opers.--Digi International Inc., Minnetonka, MN; *U.S. Public*, pg. 506
Glakas, Nicholas J., Sr. V.P.-Govt. Affairs--ITT Corporation, New York, NY; *U.S. Public*, pg. 1512
Glankler, Frank, III, Chief Oper. Officer & Sr. V.P.--Forecast Group, Rancho Cucamonga, CA; *U.S. Private*, pg. 418
Glascott, John W., Sr. V.P.-Hearst Magazines Intl. & V.P. & Dir. of Brand Devel.--Hearst Magazines Division, New York, NY; *U.S. Private*, pg. 516
Glasier, Richard J., Chief Fin. Officer & Sr. V.P.--Royal Caribbean Cruises Ltd., Miami, FL; *U.S. Public*, pg. 1410
Glass, Donnis R., Chief Fin. Officer, Sr. V.P. & Treas.--Jefferson-Pilot Corporation, Greensboro, NC; *U.S. Public*, *pg. 925*
Glass, John M., Sr. V.P.-Tech. Imaging Systems--Bayer Corporation, Pittsburgh, PA; *Int'l*, pg. 172
Glass, Robert, Chief Fin. Officer & Sr. V.P.--Loehmann's, Inc., Bronx, NY; *U.S. Public*, pg. 1010
Glass, Robert W., Sr. V.P.-Corp. Devel.--Robert Half International Inc., Menlo Park, CA; *U.S. Public*, pg. 774
Glass, Sandra D., Sr. V.P.--Scott & Stringfellow Financial, Inc., Richmond, VA; *U.S. Public*, pg. 1445
Glass, Sandra D., Sr. V.P.--Scott & Stringfellow, Inc., Richmond, VA; *U.S. Public*, pg. 1445
Glass, William, Chief Fin. Officer & Sr. V.P.--Quebecor Printing (USA) Corp., Boston, MA; *Int'l*, pg. 1076
Glasser, Frederick E., Sr. V.P.--Panalpina, Inc., Jersey City, NJ; *Int'l*, pg. 1022
Glassett, Tim, Sr. V.P. & Sec.--H.F. Ahmanson & Co., Irwindale, CA; *U.S. Public*, pg. 29
Glassman, Stuart, Sr. V.P.--Arocom Marketing Group, Inc., Cleveland, OH; *U.S. Private*, pg. 730
Glatfelter, G.H., II, Sr. V.P.--P.H. Glatfelter Company, Spring Grove, PA; *U.S. Public*, pg. 746
Glatzau, Sandy, Sr. V.P.-Mktg. & Sls.--Browning-Ferris Industries, Inc., Houston, TX; *U.S. Public*, pg. 262
Glave, Jans-Gunnar, Sr. V.P.-Civil Engineering--Skanska AB, Danderyd, Sweden; *Int'l*, pg. 1260
Glaz, Bernice, Sr. V.P.--JSB Financial, Lynbrook, NY; *U.S. Public*, pg. 919
Gleason, John H., Sr. V.P.-Project Plng. & Devel.--Del Webb Corporation, Phoenix, AZ; *U.S. Public*, pg. 494
Gleason, John S., Exec. V.P.-North America Opers.--Hussmann Corp., Bridgeton, MO; *U.S. Public*, pg. 1766
Gleeson, Kerry J., Sr. V.P.-Bus. Mngmt.--Oral-B Laboratories, Belmont, CA; *U.S. Public*, pg. 743
Gleeson, Timothy P., Sr. V.P.-Investments--Mackenzie Financial Corporation, Toronto, Canada; *Int'l*, pg. 828
Gleicher, Alan A., Sr. V.P.-Sls.--Intuit, Inc., Mountain View, CA; *U.S. Public*, pg. 911
Gleiner, Richard, Sr. V.P. & Gen. Counsel--Marcus Cable Company, L.P., Dallas, TX; *U.S. Private*, pg. 702
Glen, Douglas, Sr. V.P.-Bus. Devel. & Strategic Plng.--Mattel, Inc., El Segundo, CA; *U.S. Public*, pg. 1057
Glendening, R. Bradley, Sr. V.P., Sec. & Gen. Counsel--Mary Kay Corporation, Dallas, TX; *U.S. Private*, pg. 710
Glenewinkel, Gary W., Sr. V.P.--Centex-Rooney Construction Co., Inc., Fort Lauderdale, FL; *U.S. Public*, pg. 322
Glenn, Alan, Sr. V.P.--Drug Guild Div., Secaucus, NJ; *U.S. Public*, pg. 1169
Glenn, T. Michael, Sr. V.P.-Worldwide Mktg., Customer Service & Corp. Communications--FDX Corporation, Memphis, TN; *U.S. Public*, pg. 603
Glenn, W. Brown, Sr. V.P.--Eastbridge Capital Inc., New York, NY; *Int'l*, pg. 933
Gleysteen, Nicholas, Sr. V.P.--Hellman, Jordan Management Company, Inc., Boston, MA; *U.S. Public*, pg. 1673
Glick, C.S., Chief Fin. Officer, Sr. V.P. & Sec.--Gulf Canada Resources Ltd., Calgary, Canada; *Int'l*, pg. 577
Glick, David E., Sr. V.P. & Gen. Mgr.-Central Grp.--Treasure Chest Advertising Co., Inc., Glendora, CA; *U.S. Public*, pg. 228
Globensky, Jerry, Sr. V.P.-Comml. Loans--Shoreline Financial Corp., Benton Harbor, MI; *U.S. Public*, pg. 1467
Globensky, Jerry, Sr. V.P.-Commercial Lending--Shoreline Bank, Benton Harbor, MI; *U.S. Public*, pg. 1468
Glore, Jodie K., Sr. V.P. & Pres.-Rockwell Automation--Rockwell International Corporation, Costa Mesa, CA; *U.S. Public*, pg. 1397
Glosser, Paul L., Sr. V.P.--G B Stores, Columbus, OH; *U.S. Private*, pg. 972
Glover, William J., Jr., Sr. V.P. & Clerk--Fay, Spofford & Thorndike, Inc., Burlington, MA; *U.S. Private*, pg. 397
Gluck, Barry S., Sr. V.P. & Gen. Mgr.-Mdsg.--Ross Stores, Inc., Newark, CA; *U.S. Public*, pg. 1405
Glytas, Valentine J., Sr. V.P. & Mgr.-Open-End Consumer Loans--First Financial Bank, FSB, Stevens Point, WI; *U.S. Public*, pg. 140
Gmur, Beat, Sr. V.P.-Personnel--Liechtenstein Global Trust Limited, Vaduz, Liechtenstein; *Int'l*, pg. 809
Gnatz, Bill, Sr. V.P.-Agribusiness--Colle & McVoy Marketing Communications, Minneapolis, MN; *U.S. Private*, pg. 252
Goalen, Stephen L., Sr. V.P. & Mgr.-Commercial Banking Div.--First Security Bank of Utah, N.A., Salt Lake City, UT; *U.S. Public*, pg. 637
Goard, Tom, Sr. V.P.--The Principal Financial Group, Des Moines, IA; *U.S. Private*, pg. 885
Gochenaur, Jack A., Sr. V.P.-Client Services--Time Insurance, Milwaukee, WI; *Int'l*, pg. 499
Godde, Gerard, Sr. V.P.--Pride International, Inc., Houston, TX; *U.S. Public*, pg. 1324
Godemont, J., Sr. V.P.-Consumer Prods./Industry--SGS Societe Generale de Surveillance Holding S.A., Geneva, Switzerland; *Int'l*, pg. 1153
Godfrey, Arrel E., Sr. V.P.--Potomac Valley Bank, Gaithersburg, MD; *U.S. Public*, pg. 1089
Godfrey, Cullen M., Sr. V.P., Gen. Counsel & Sec.--Fina, Inc., Dallas, TX; *Int'l*, pg. 1044
Godfrey, Ralph, Sr. V.P.-Client Access/America Sls.--3Com Corporation, Santa Clara, CA; *U.S. Public*, pg. 1603
Godiner, Donald L., Sr. V.P., Gen. Counsel & Sec.--Laclede Gas Company, Saint Louis, MO; *U.S. Public*, pg. 973
Godley, Nigel, Sr. V.P.--Arthur D. Little, Inc., Cambridge, MA; *U.S. Private*, pg. 670
Godoy, Wendy, Sr. V.P.-Fin.--TrizecHahn Centers Inc., San Diego, CA; *Int'l*, pg. 1425
Godwin, Robert W., Sr. V.P.-Taxation--NationsBank West, Saint Louis, MO; *U.S. Public*, pg. 1164
Goebel, Andrew E., Chief Fin. Officer, Sr. V.P. & Sec.--SIGCORP, Inc., Evansville, IN; *U.S. Public*, pg. 1471
Goebel, Andrew E., Chief Fin. Officer, Sr. V.P. & Treas.--Southern Indiana Gas & Electric Co., Evansville, IN; *U.S. Public*, pg. 1471
Goebel, Chick, Sr. V.P.--Harris, Baio & McCullough Inc., Philadelphia, PA; *U.S. Private*, pg. 504
Goebert, Robert J., Sr. V.P.--The Bank of New York, New York, NY; *U.S. Public*, pg. 178
Goehring, Ralph J., Chief Fin. Officer & Sr. V.P.--Berry Petroleum Company, Taft, CA; *U.S. Public*, pg. 223
Goetz, William R., Jr., Sr. V.P.-Southeast Reg.--Comcast Cable Communications, Inc., Philadelphia, PA; *U.S. Public*, pg. 407
Goff, Neal, Chief Oper. Officer & Sr. V.P.--R.R. Bowker, New Providence, NJ; *Int'l*, pg. 1096
Goff, Raymond E., Sr. V.P.-Asia-Pacific--Anheuser-Busch Companies, Inc., Saint Louis, MO; *U.S. Public*, pg. 113
Gofus, Nancy B., Sr. V.P.-Concert Communications Services--MCI Communications Corp., Atlanta, GA; *U.S. Public*, pg. 1023
Goggiano, Stephen, Sr. V.P.-Mfg.--Silicon Graphics, Inc., Mountain View, CA; *U.S. Public*, pg. 1473
Goguel-Nyegaard, Denis, Sr. V.P.-Europe & U.S.--Elf Aquitane, Paris, France; *Int'l*, pg. 444
Goh, Janice, Sr. V.P.-Retail Banking--DBS Bank Ltd., Singapore, Singapore; *Int'l*, pg. 350
Goines, Mark R., Sr. V.P.-Intl.--Intuit, Inc., Mountain View, CA; *U.S. Public*, pg. 911
Gold, Bruce, Sr. V.P.--Mullen Advertising, Inc., Wenham, MA; *U.S. Private*, pg. 766
Gold, Daniel E., Sr. V.P. & Pres.-Century Cable Division--Century Communications Corp., New Canaan, CT; *U.S. Public*, pg. 329
Gold, Edward M., Sr. V.P.-H.R.--The Ryland Group, Inc., Columbia, MD; *U.S. Public*, pg. 1414
Gold, Isaac, Sr. V.P.-Sls. & Procurement Fresh Pork--Thorn Apple Valley, Inc., Southfield, MI; *U.S. Public*, pg. 1602
Gold, Jeff, Sr. V.P.-Creative Services--Warner Bros. Records, Inc., Burbank, CA; *U.S. Public*, pg. 1611
Gold, Michael, Sr. V.P.-Corp. Commun. & Adv.--Packard Bell NEC, Sacramento, CA; *U.S. Private*, pg. 833
Goldberg, Andy, Sr. V.P.--Publishers Clearing House, Port Washington, NY; *U.S. Private*, pg. 893
Goldberg, Arthur, Sr. V.P. & Grp. Acct. Supvr.--BGM Health Communications, Inc., Los Angeles, CA; *U.S. Public*, pg. 1223
Goldberg, Bruce, Sr. V.P.-Mktg.--Brink's Home Security, Inc., Irving, TX; *U.S. Public*, pg. 1305
Goldberg, Jon, Sr. V.P.--Edelman Worldwide, Inc., New York, NY; *U.S. Private*, pg. 362
Goldberg, Lena G., Sr. V.P. & Gen. Counsel--Fidelity Investments (FMR Corp.), Boston, MA; *U.S. Private*, pg. 402
Goldberg, Lewis, Sr. V.P.--K-Swiss Inc., Chatsworth, CA; *U.S. Public*, pg. 937
Goldberg, Louis S., Sr. V.P.-Human Resources--GAF Corporation, Wayne, NJ; *U.S. Private*, pg. 433
Goldberg, Marc S., Sr. V.P.-Worldwide Opers. & Tech.--Philip Morris Companies Inc., New York, NY; *U.S. Public*, *pg. 1287*
Goldberg, Norm, Sr. V.P. & Gen. Mgr.-Network Products Div.--UB Networks, Santa Clara, CA; *Int'l*, pg. 924
Goldberg, Sanford, Sr. V.P.--A&W Restaurants, Inc.-Carousel Div., Minneapolis, MN; *U.S. Private*, pg. 2
Golden, David J., Sr. V.P.--The Tranzonic Companies, Pepper Pike, OH; *U.S. Public*, pg. 1632
Golden, Jim, Chief Fin. Officer & Sr. V.P.--Lillie Rubin Fashions Inc., Miami, FL; *U.S. Private*, pg. 667
Goldenberg, Melvin, Sr. V.P.--Aspen Systems Corp., Rockville, MD; *Int'l*, pg. 1513
Goldfeder, Melvin, Sr. V.P.-Special Markets--Swank, Inc., Attleboro, MA; *U.S. Public*, pg. 1543
Goldfinger, Sam, Sr. V.P.-Individual Life--New York Life Insurance Company, New York, NY; *U.S. Private*, pg. 794
Goldklank, Mitchell, Sr. V.P.-Sls. & Mktg.--LCS Industries, Inc., Clifton, NJ; *U.S. Public*, pg. 970
Goldman, Allan, Sr. V.P.-Mktg.--The Cosmetic Center Inc., Columbia, MD; *U.S. Private*, pg. 689
Goldman, Gerald, Sr. V.P.-Fin. & Production--Paramount Pictures Corporation, Los Angeles, CA; *U.S. Private*, pg. 776
Goldman, Glenn S., Sr. V.P.--ContiFinancial Corporation, New York, NY; *U.S. Public*, pg. 439
Goldman, Steven R., Sr. V.P. & Dir.-Acquisitions--Starwood Hotels & Resorts, Phoenix, AZ; *U.S. Public*, pg. 1512
Goldner, Leonard H., Sr. V.P. & Gen. Counsel--Symbol Technologies, Inc., Holtsville, NY; *U.S. Public*, pg. 1546
Goldschmidt, Mark E., Sr. V.P.-Adv. & Mktg.--Hearst Magazines Division, New York, NY; *U.S. Private*, pg. 516
Goldsmith, Phillip R., Sr. V.P.-Consumer Lending--PNC Bank Corp., Pittsburgh, PA; *U.S. Public*, pg. 1242
Goldstein, Adam, Sr. V.P.-Mktg.--Royal Caribbean Cruises Ltd., Miami, FL; *U.S. Public*, pg. 1410
Goldstein, Faith P., Sr. V.P.--Summit Bancorp, Princeton, NJ; *U.S. Public*, pg. 1527
Goldstein, Frann, Sr. V.P.- Worldwide Media--Quantum Media International, Inc., New York, NY; *U.S. Private*, pg. 899
Goldstein, George, Sr. V.P.--The Ivaco Group, Montreal, Canada; *Int'l*, pg. 695
Goldstein, Jill S., Sr. V.P.-Actuary--The New England, Boston, MA; *U.S. Private*, pg. 737
Goldstein, Laurie, Sr. V.P.-Production Mngmt.--MTV Networks, New York, NY; *U.S. Private*, pg. 779
Goldstein, Ned, Sr. V.P. & Gen. Counsel--Ticketmaster Corporation, West Hollywood, CA; *U.S. Private*, pg. 1084
Goldstine, Josh, Sr. V.P.-Creative Adv.--Columbia Pictures, Culver City, CA; *Int'l*, pg. 1281
Goldston, Nancy Jane, Sr. V.P.-Mktg. & Mdsg.--Spencer Gifts, Inc., Egg Harbor Township, NJ; *Int'l*, pg. 1216
Golik, Donald E., Chief Fin. Officer, Sr. V.P. & Sec.--Paul Mueller Company, Springfield, MO; *U.S. Public*, pg. 1141
Golinveaux, James E., Sr. V.P.-Tech. Service--Central Sprinkler Company, Lansdale, PA; *U.S. Public*, pg. 327
Gollnick, Jerry F., Sr. V.P. & Gen. Mgr.-Bus. Devel.--Williams Field Services, Tulsa, OK; *U.S. Public*, pg. 1769
Goluch, Chester, Sr. V.P. (CCL) & Creative Dir.--Maritime Telegraph & Telephone Company, Ltd., Halifax, Canada; *Int'l*, pg. 116
Goman, Stan, Sr. V.P. Retail Opers.--MTS, Inc., West Sacramento, CA; *U.S. Private*, pg. 688
Gomes, Tony, Sr. V.P., Assoc. Creative Dir.--Ammirati, Puris & Lintas, Inc., New York, NY; *U.S. Private*, pg. 66
Gomez, Consuelo A., Sr. V.P., Grp. Mngmt. Supvr.--EJL Advertising/Los Angeles, Los Angeles, CA; *U.S. Private*, pg. 673
Gomez, Edward H., Chief Fin. Officer & Sr. V.P.--The Bank of Bermuda Limited, Hamilton, Bermuda; *Int'l*, pg. 150
Gomez, Manuel, Sr. V.P.-Intl. Opers.--Renault, Boulogne-Billancourt, France; *Int'l*, pg. 1102
Gomez, Marco A., Sr. V.P. & Country Mgr.--Bank of America NT&SA, Santiago, Chile; *U.S. Public*, pg. 182
Gongas, John C., Sr. V.P.--Equitable Resources, Inc., Pittsburgh, PA; *U.S. Public*, pg. 589
Gonzales, Charles H., Sr. V.P.-Subsidiary Opers.--Horizon/CMS Healthcare Corporation, Albuquerque, NM; *U.S. Public*, pg. 836
Gonzales, Dick W., Sr. V.P.- Human Resources--The Vons Companies, Inc., Arcadia, CA; *U.S. Public*, pg. 1426
Gonzalez-Urien, Eliseo, Sr. V.P.-Exploration--Placer Dome Inc., Vancouver, Canada; *Int'l*, pg. 1060
Gonzalez, E., Sr. V.P.-Creative--Brown Marketing Communications, Chicago, IL; *U.S. Private*, pg. 174

Gonzalez, Jamie, Sr. V.P. & Gen. Mgr.-Mexico--Costco Wholesale, Issaquah, WA; *U.S. Public*, pg. 451
Gonzalez, Norberto, Sr. V.P.-Credit Admin.--PonceBank, F.S.B., Ponce, PR; *U.S. Public*, pg. 1316
Good, Kenneth R., Sr. V.P.--Pogo Producing Company, Houston, TX; *U.S. Public*, pg. 1312
Good, Laurence, Sr. V.P.-Insurance Opers.--Bankers Life & Casualty Company, Chicago, IL; *U.S. Public*, pg. 433
Goode, Richard L., Sr. V.P.--Searle Laboratories, Skokie, IL; *U.S. Public*, pg. 1125
Goodlett, O.M., Chief Fin. Officer & Sr. V.P.-Fin. & Admin.--KU Energy, Lexington, KY; *U.S. Public*, pg. 940
Goodman, Bruce, Sr. V.P.-Global Media, Investor Rels. & Bus. Affairs--National Media Corporation, Philadelphia, PA; *U.S. Public*, pg. 1158
Goodman, Chris, Sr. V.P. & Acct. Dir.--Young & Rubicam New York, New York, NY; *U.S. Private*, pg. 1198
Goodman, Debra, Sr. V.P. & Media Dir.--Carrafiello, Diehl & Associates, Inc., Irvington, NY; *U.S. Private*, pg. 215
Goodman, Harlan, Sr. V.P.-Music--Paramount Pictures Corporation, Los Angeles, CA; *U.S. Private*, pg. 776
Goodman, John M., Chief Exec. Officer & Sr. V.P.--Lewis Homes Management Corp., Upland, CA; *U.S. Private*, pg. 665
Goodman, Shira, Sr. V.P.-Merger Integration--Staples, Inc., Westborough, MA; *U.S. Public*, pg. 1509
Goodnight, Cecil L., Chief Admin. Officer & Sr. V.P.-Admin. Svcs.--Carolina Power & Light Company, Raleigh, NC; *U.S. Public*, pg. 306
Goodpasture, John W., Sr. V.P.--Seagull Energy Corporation, Houston, TX; *U.S. Public*, pg. 1450
Goodrich, Douglas P., Sr. V.P.--PLM International, Inc., San Francisco, CA; *U.S. Public*, pg. 1241
Goodrich, Douglas P., Sr. V.P.--PLM Financial Services, Inc., San Francisco, CA; *U.S. Public*, pg. 1241
Goodrich, Douglas P., Sr. V.P.--Transportation Equipment Corporation, San Francisco, CA; *U.S. Public*, pg. 1241
Goodrich, Philip, Sr. V.P.-Corp. Devel.--AMETEK, Inc., Paoli, PA; *U.S. Public*, pg. 99
Goodwin, James E., Sr. V.P.-N. America--UAL Corporation, Elk Grove Village, IL; *U.S. Public*, pg. 1652
Goodwin, James E., Sr. V.P.-North America--United Air Lines, Inc., Elk Grove Village, IL; *U.S. Public*, pg. 1653
Goodwin, Richard G., Sr. V.P.-H.R.--Airborne Freight Corporation, Seattle, WA; *U.S. Public*, pg. 32
Goodwyn, Debbie, Sr. V.P. & Opers. Dir.--The Buntin Group, Nashville, TN; *U.S. Private*, pg. 181
Goolrick, Robert, Sr. V.P. & Grp. Creative Dir.--Grey Advertising Inc., New York, NY; *U.S. Public*, pg. 764
Goolsby, O.B., Jr., Sr. V.P.-Prepared Foods--Pilgrim's Pride Corporation, Pittsburg, TX; *U.S. Public*, pg. 1296
Gorda, Ronald B., Sr. V.P. & Pres.-Linkabit--The Titan Corporation, San Diego, CA; *U.S. Public*, pg. 1618
Gorday, Virginia, Sr. V.P.-Opers.--AMC, Inc., Atlanta, GA; *U.S. Private*, pg. 6
Gordon, Cindy, Sr. V.P.--Golin/Harris Communications, Inc., Chicago, IL; *Int'l*, pg. 1226
Gordon, Howard, Sr. V.P.-Bus. Devel. & New Ventures--Cheesecake Factory Incorporated, Calabasas Hills, CA; *U.S. Public*, pg. 343
Gordon, John M., Sr. V.P. & Mng. Dir.-Valvoline International--Valvoline Company, Lexington, KY; *U.S. Public*, pg. 139
Gordon, Mitch, Sr. V.P. & Creative Dir.--Hal Riney & Partners Heartland, Chicago, IL; *U.S. Private*, pg. 931
Gordon, Rick, Sr. V.P.-Sls.--All American Semiconductor, Inc., Miami, FL; *U.S. Public*, pg. 41
Gordon, Steven, Sr. V.P.-Devel./Drama--Viacom Productions Inc., Universal City, CA; *U.S. Private*, pg. 779
Gordon, Warren H., Sr. V.P. & Gen. Mgr.-Cliggott Communications--Cliggott Publishing, Greenwich, CT; *U.S. Private*, pg. 246
Gordon, William G., Sr. V.P.--Indiana Lawrence Bank, North Manchester, IN; *U.S. Public*, pg. 633
Gorham, David L., Deputy Chief Oper. Officer & Sr. V.P.--The New York Times Company, New York, NY; *U.S. Public*, pg. 1173
Gorkuscha, Mischa, Chief Fin. Officer & Sr. V.P.--Liberty Bancorp, Inc., Oklahoma City, OK; *U.S. Public*, pg. 174
Gorman, Jeffrey S., Sr. V.P.--The Gorman-Rupp Company, Mansfield, OH; *U.S. Public*, pg. 754
Gorman, Robert M., Sr. V.P.--Analysis & Technology, Inc., North Stonington, CT; *U.S. Public*, pg. 109
Gorman, Robert R., Ph.D., Sr. V.P.--Pharmacia & Upjohn, Inc., Windsor, United Kingdom; *Int'l*, pg. 1047
Gorman, Timothy C., Sr. V.P.-Opers--Pinnacle Data Corporation, San Bruno, CA; *U.S. Public*, pg. 1158
Gorman, Timothy C., Sr. V.P.-Opers.--FASTRAC Systems, Inc.-Insurance Agent & Broker, South San Francisco, CA; *U.S. Public*, pg. 1158
Gormley, Pamela D., Sr. V.P.--Keycorp, Cleveland, OH; *U.S. Public*, pg. 954
Gormly, John, Sr. V.P.--Oltmans Construction Company, Whittier, CA; *U.S. Private*, pg. 815
Gornet, Michel, Sr. V.P.-Mfg.--Renault, Boulogne-Billancourt, France; *Int'l*, pg. 1102
Gorzalski, Edward, Sr. V.P.-Plng., Market Res. & Media Services--Thomas G. Ferguson Associates, Inc., Parsippany, NJ; *Int'l*, pg. 1483
Goslee, Dwight J., Chief Info. Officer, Sr. V.P.-Bus. Systems & Devel.--ConAgra, Inc., Omaha, NE; *U.S. Public*, pg. 425
Goss, David R., Sr. V.P.-Opers.--LSB Industries, Inc., Oklahoma City, OK; *U.S. Public*, pg. 970
Goss, Lawrence A., Sr. V.P.-Bus. Devel.--California Microwave, Inc.-Wireless Products Grp., Sunnyvale, CA; *U.S. Public*, pg. 293
Gosselin, Robert G., Sr. V.P.-UKI Quality Control--Dyersburg Corporation, Dyersburg, TN; *U.S. Public*, pg. 538
Gosselin, Robert G., Sr. V.P.-Quality Control--United Knitting, Inc., Cleveland, TN; *U.S. Public*, pg. 538
Gostkowski, Jeffrey, Sr. V.P.--Pulse Bancorp, Inc., South River, NJ; *U.S. Public*, pg. 1344
Gotcher, Alan J., Sr. V.P.--Avery Dennison Corporation, Pasadena, CA; *U.S. Public*, pg. 152
Gothe, Stig, Sr. V.P.-Bus. & Strategic Devel.--Vattenfall AB, Stockholm, Sweden; *Int'l*, pg. 1452
Gotoh, M., Sr. V.P.--Mitsubishi International Corporation, New York, NY; *Int'l*, pg. 871
Gottesman, Joel, Sr. V.P, Gen. Counsel & Sec.--Green Tree Financial Corporation, Saint Paul, MN; *U.S. Public*, pg. 761
Gotthelf, Michael, Dr., Sr. V.P.--Metallgesellschaft Corp., New York, NY; *Int'l*, pg. 861
Gould, Jay D., Sr. V.P. & Chief Mktg. Officer--The Minute Maid Company, Houston, TX; *U.S. Public*, pg. 392
Gould, Matthew J., Sr. V.P.--Georgetown Partners, Inc., Great Neck, NY; *U.S. Private*, pg. 466
Gould, Richard, Sr. V.P.--Apogee Enterprises, Inc., Minneapolis, MN; *U.S. Public*, pg. 120
Goulden, David I., Sr. V.P.-Software Prods. Div.--Wang Laboratories, Inc., Billerica, MA; *U.S. Public*, pg. 1737
Goulson, George, Sr. V.P.-Franchise Devel.--A&W Restaurants, Inc., Livonia, MI; *U.S. Private*, pg. 1
Gourde, Rejean, Sr. V.P.-Guiana Shield--Cambior Inc., Montreal, Canada; *Int'l*, pg. 253
Gourlay, George, Sr. V.P.--The Coca-Cola Company, Atlanta, GA; *U.S. Public*, pg. 392
Gouth, David, Sr. V.P.--National Programs Division, Tampa, FL; *U.S. Public*, pg. 1312
Govaere, Ben, Sr. V.P.--Cattleman's, Inc., Detroit, MI; *U.S. Public*, pg. 318
Gove, Sue, Sr. V.P.-Plng. & Analysis--Zale Corporation, Irving, TX; *U.S. Public*, pg. 1789
Governali, Gloria, Sr. V.P. & Grp. Acct. Supvr.-Phase V--Grey Healthcare Group, New York, NY; *U.S. Public*, pg. 765
Gow, Tom, Sr. V.P. & Grp. Creative Dir.--DMB&B St. Louis, Saint Louis, MO; *U.S. Private*, pg. 303
Gowaty, Nina L., Sr. V.P.-Human Resources--B.M.J. Financial Corp., Bordentown, NJ; *U.S. Public*, pg. 1528
Gowaty, Nina L., Sr. V.P.-Pub. Rels.--The Bank of Mid-Jersey, Bordentown, NJ; *U.S. Public*, pg. 1528
Goya, Donna, Sr. V.P.-H.R.--Levi Strauss & Co., San Francisco, CA; *U.S. Private*, pg. 662
Goyer, Jacques V., Sr. V.P.-Investments--Assurance vie Desjardins-Laurentienne, Levis, Canada; *Int'l*, pg. 396
Gozalo, Roman, Chief Admin. Officer & Sr. V.P.--Elf Aquitane, Paris, France; *Int'l*, pg. 444
Grabe, Lennard, Sr. V.P.-Corp. Bus. Deve.--Telefonaktiebolaget LM Ericsson, Stockholm, Sweden; *Int'l*, pg. 1363
Grabel, William G., Chief Fin. Officer & Sr. V.P.-Fin., Human Resources & Admin.--TDS Telecommunications Corporation, Madison, WI; *U.S. Public*, pg. 1570
Grabell, Neil S., Sr. V.P., Gen. Counsel & Sec.--QVC, Inc., West Chester, PA; *U.S. Private*, pg. 897
Grace, Jerry L., Sr. V.P. & Treas.--Provident Financial Group, Inc., Cincinnati, OH; *U.S. Public*, pg. 1338
Grace, Jerry L., Sr. V.P.-Investment & Liability Mngmt., V.P. & Treas.--The Provident Bank, Cincinnati, OH; *U.S. Public*, pg. 1338
Grace, Richard C., Sr. V.P.-Human Resources--PNC Bank Corp., Pittsburgh, PA; *U.S. Public*, pg. 1242
Grady, Patrick E., Sr. V.P. & Treas.--Western National Corporation, Houston, TX; *U.S. Public*, pg. 76
Graeve, Heiko, Sr. V.P.--Jagenberg AG, Neuss, Germany; *Int'l*, pg. 1108
Graf, Mark G., Sr. V.P. & Acct. Dir.--Meldrum & Fewsmith Communications Inc., Cleveland, OH; *U.S. Private*, pg. 730
Graf, Michael A., Sr. V.P. & Controller--Norwest Corporation, Minneapolis, MN; *U.S. Public*, pg. 1201
Graf, Tom, Sr. V.P.--The Principal Financial Group, Des Moines, IA; *U.S. Private*, pg. 885
Graf, Tom, Sr. V.P.--Principal Mutual Life Insurance Co., Des Moines, IA; *U.S. Private*, pg. 886
Gragg, Gary S., Sr. V.P.--First Financial Bankshares, Inc., Abilene, TX; *U.S. Public*, pg. 633
Graham, Allan J., Sr. V.P.-Continuity Svcs.--Comdisco, Inc., Rosemont, IL; *U.S. Public*, pg. 407
Graham, Allan J., Sr. V.P.--Comdisco Continuity Services, Rosemont, IL; *U.S. Public*, pg. 408
Graham, Barbara, Chief Fin. Officer & Sr. V.P.--Atlantic Electric Co., Pleasantville, NJ; *U.S. Public*, pg. 430
Graham, Barbara S., Chief Fin. Officer & Sr. V.P.--Conectiv, Wilmington, DE; *U.S. Public*, pg. 430
Graham, Barbara S., Chief Fin. Officer & Sr. V.P.--Delmarva Power & Light Company, Wilmington, DE; *U.S. Public*, pg. 430
Graham, Baxter J., Sr. V.P.-H.R.--The Chubb Corporation, Warren, NJ; *U.S. Public*, pg. 354
Graham, Baxter W., Sr. V.P.--Chubb & Son, Inc., Warren, NJ; *U.S. Public*, pg. 355
Graham, Douglas W., Sr. V.P. & Dir.-Corp. Personnel--Regions Financial Corporation, Birmingham, AL; *U.S. Public*, pg. 1371
Graham, Edward J., Sr. V.P.-Gas Supply--South Jersey Gas Co., Folsom, NJ; *U.S. Public*, pg. 1488
Graham, Eunice, Sr. V.P.--NationsBank Virginia, Richmond, VA; *U.S. Public*, pg. 1163
Graham, Jim, Sr. V.P.-Corp. Sls. & Mktg.--Time Inc., New York, NY; *U.S. Public*, pg. 1612
Graham, John G., Chief Fin. Officer & Sr. V.P.--GPU, Inc., Morristown, NJ; *U.S. Public*, pg. 695
Graham, Lawrence F., Sr. V.P.-Mngmt.--World Financial Properties, Inc., New York, NY; *Int'l*, pg. 1004
Graham, R.W., Sr. V.P.--Jefferson Smurfit Corporation, Saint Louis, MO; *Int'l*, pg. 1271
Graham, Roy, Sr. V.P.-Sls. & Mktg.--Wyse Technology Inc., San Jose, CA; *U.S. Private*, pg. 1194
Graham, Steven, Chief Information Officer & Sr. V.P.-Information Tech.--Daisytek International Corporation, Plano, TX; *U.S. Public*, pg. 477
Graham, Steven, Chief Information Officer & Sr. V.P.--Daisytek Incorporated, Plano, TX; *U.S. Public*, pg. 477
Graham, Steven, Chief Information Officer & Sr. V.P.--Daisytek (Canada) Inc., Toronto, Canada; *U.S. Public*, pg. 477
Graham, Steven, Chief Information Officer & Sr. V.P.--Daisytek Latin America, Miami, FL; *U.S. Public*, pg. 477
Graham, Steven, Chief Information Officer & Sr. V.P.--Daisytek De Mexico S.A. de C.V., Mexico, Mexico; *U.S. Public*, pg. 477
Graham, Steven, Chief Information Officer & Sr. V.P.--Priority Fulfillment Services, Inc., Plano, TX; *U.S. Public*, pg. 477
Graham, Steven, Chief Information Officer & Sr. V.P.--Daisytek Australia Pty. Ltd., Alexandria, Australia; *U.S. Public*, pg. 477
Grahn, Gary, Chief Fin. Officer & Sr. V.P.-Fin. & Admin.--Mail Boxes Etc. USA, San Diego, CA; *U.S. Public*, pg. 1687
Gralnick, Helene, Sr. V.P.-Design & Concept--Chico's Fas Inc, Fort Myers, FL; *U.S. Public*, pg. 349
Grammatica, Robert, Sr. V.P. & Mng. Dir.--The Chapman Agency, New York, NY; *U.S. Private*, pg. 1197
Granath, Herbert A., Pres.-ABC Cable & Intl. Broadcast Grp. & Sr. V.P.--ABC, Inc, New York, NY; *U.S. Public*, pg. 511
Grandstaff, Linda A., Sr. V.P.--Keycorp, Cleveland, OH; *U.S. Public*, pg. 954
Granier, James, Chief Information Officer & Sr. V.P.-Data Processing--First Commerce Corporation, New Orleans, LA; *U.S. Public*, pg. 629
Granlund, Leland R., Chief Fin. Officer, Sr. V.P & Treas.--Western Petroleum Company, Eden Prairie, MN; *U.S. Private*, pg. 1168
Grant-Chakiry, Karen, Sr. V.P. & Assoc. Creative Dir.--Partners & Shevack, Inc., New York, NY; *U.S. Private*, pg. 842
Grant, Carl, Sr. V.P.-Communications--Nation's Business, Washington, DC; *U.S. Private*, pg. 788
Grant, Chris, Sr. V.P.-Mngmt. Svcs.--The ServiceMaster Company, Downers Grove, IL; *U.S. Public*, pg. 1461
Grant, Edward L., Sr. V.P.--MasTec, Inc., Miami, FL; *U.S. Public*, pg. 1055
Grant, Howard C., Sr. V.P. & Creative Dir.--Grant Marketing Communications, Ardmore, PA; *U.S. Private*, pg. 470
Grant, Howard C., Sr. V.P. & Creative Dir.--Kingswood Advertising, Inc., Ardmore, PA; *U.S. Private*, pg. 622
Grant, J. A., Sr. V.P.-Admin.--Brown Marketing Communications, Chicago, IL; *U.S. Private*, pg. 174
Grant, James R., Sr. V.P.-Grp.--The Great-West Life Assurance Company, Winnipeg, Canada; *Int'l*, pg. 557
Grant, Lawrence, Sr. V.P.--Chubb & Son, Inc., Warren, NJ; *U.S. Public*, pg. 355
Grant, Stephen, Sr. V.P.-Compliance--Louisiana Pacific Corporation, Portland, OR; *U.S. Public*, pg. 1015
Grant, Stephen W., Sr. V.P. & Mgr.-Construction--Willis Corroon Corp. of Massachusetts, Boston, MA; *Int'l*, pg. 1506
Grant, William E., Jr., Sr. V.P.--Willis Corroon Corp. of Seattle, Seattle, WA; *Int'l*, pg. 1507
Granucci, Leo, Sr. V.P.-Mktg. & Sls.--Core-Mark International, South San Francisco, CA; *U.S. Private*, pg. 275
Granzow, Paul H., Sr. V.P.--Weston Paper & Manufacturing Co., Terre Haute, IN; *U.S. Private*, pg. 1169
Grasse, John, Sr. V.P.-Pur. & Quality Control--Serigraph, Inc., West Bend, WI; *U.S. Private*, pg. 985
Grau, Charles C., Sr. V.P.--Southwest Banks, Inc., Naples, FL; *U.S. Public*, pg. 607
Graveline, Kathleen M., Sr. V.P.-Direct Distrib.--John Hancock Mutual Life Insurance Company, Boston, MA; *U.S. Private*, pg. 589
Graves, James W., Sr. V.P.--Acadian Asset Management, Boston, MA; *U.S. Public*, pg. 1672
Graves, Kenny M., Sr. V.P.--Andersen 2000 Inc., Peachtree City, GA; *U.S. Public*, pg. 462
Graves, Richard, Sr. V.P.-Mktg.--Lexington Furniture Industries, Lexington, NC; *U.S. Private*, pg. 432
Gravino, Richard, Sr. V.P.-Consumer Fin.--Provident Financial Group, Inc., Cincinnati, OH; *U.S. Public*, pg. 1338
Grawe, John D., Sr. V.P.-Opers.--Public Service Company of North Carolina, Inc., Gastonia, NC; *U.S. Public*, pg. 1340
Gray, Alex, Sr. V.P.-Corp. Opers.--Octel Messaging Division, Milpitas, CA; *U.S. Public*, pg. 1017
Gray, Anthony R., Sr. V.P.-Investment Mngmt.--SunTrust Banks, Inc., Atlanta, GA; *U.S. Public*, pg. 1537
Gray, Cynthia J., Sr. V.P.-Mktg.--Norwest Corporation, Minneapolis, MN; *U.S. Public*, pg. 1201
Gray, David L., Chief Fin. Officer, Sr. V.P. & Treas.--First Indiana Corporation, Indianapolis, IN; *U.S. Public*, pg. 1484
Gray, Derek K., Sr. V.P.--Adobe Systems Incorporated, San Jose, CA; *U.S. Public*, pg. 20
Gray, Gardner, Jr., Chief Fin. Officer & Sr. V.P.--CSE Insurance Group, San Francisco, CA; *U.S. Private*, pg. 197
Gray, J.H., Sr. V.P.-Mfg. & Engrng.--Dunlop Tire Corporation, Buffalo, NY; *Int'l*, pg. 1317
Gray, Jimmie L., Chief Fin. Officer, Sr. V.P. & Treas.--Universal Fidelity Life Insurance Company, Duncan, OK; *U.S. Private*, pg. 1127
Gray, John, Sr. V.P.-Corp. Communications--R.T.M. Winners, Atlanta, GA; *U.S. Private*, pg. 906
Gray, L. Rainey, Sr. V.P.--NationsBank of St. Louis, Saint Louis, MO; *U.S. Public*, pg. 1164
Gray, Logan B., Sr. V.P.--SouthTrust Corporation, Birmingham, AL; *U.S. Public*, pg. 1491
Gray, Richard E., Sr. V.P.--GAI Consultants, Inc., Monroeville, PA; *U.S. Private*, pg. 433
Gray, Roger J., Sr. V.P.--Ecology and Environment, Inc., Lancaster, NY; *U.S. Public*, pg. 562
Gray, William J., Sr. V.P.-Mktg. & Supply--Holly Corporation, Dallas, TX; *U.S. Public*, pg. 830

Gray, William J., Sr. V.P.--Navajo Refining Co., Artesia, NM; *U.S. Public*, pg. 830
Graziano, Frank, Sr. V.P.-Tech.--Material Sciences Corporation, Elk Grove Village, IL; *U.S. Public*, pg. 1056
Greaves, Kristin, Sr. V.P. & H.R./Devel. Dir.--Deutsch, Inc., New York, NY; *U.S. Private*, pg. 328
Greaves, Kristin, Sr. V.P. & H.R./Devel. Dir.--Deutsch LA, Santa Monica, CA; *U.S. Private*, pg. 328
Greco, Edward M., Sr. V.P. & Pres.-EA International, Inc.--EA Engineering, Science & Technology, Inc., Hunt Valley, MD; *U.S. Public*, pg. 540
Greed, John, Sr. V.P. & Treas.--American Life Insurance Company of New York, New York, NY; *U.S. Private*, pg. 769
Greeley, Michael A., Sr. V.P.--GCC Investments, Inc., Chestnut Hill, MA; *U.S. Public*, pg. 693
Green-Taylor, Robyn, Sr. V.P. & Media Dir.--Keyes Martin, East Hanover, NJ; *U.S. Private*, pg. 618
Green, Jack, Sr. V.P. & Gen. Counsel--Converse Inc., North Reading, MA; *U.S. Public*, pg. 441
Green, Kaj, Sr. V.P.-Bus. Devel. & Information Tech.--Celsius AB, Stockholm, Sweden; *Int'l*, pg. 276
Green, Kelly E., Sr. V.P.-New Bus. Devel.--CUC International, Inc., Stamford, CT; *U.S. Public*, pg. 320
Green, Laura, Sr. V.P.-Los Angeles County Corp. Banking--Southern California Bank, Newport Beach, CA; *U.S. Public*, pg. 1758
Green, Michael, Sr. V.P.-Mktg.--Parisian, Inc., Birmingham, AL; *U.S. Public*, pg. 1333
Green, Nancy H., Sr. V.P.-Corp. Rels.--The Equitable Companies Incorporated, New York, NY; *U.S. Public*, pg. 588
Green, Royce, Sr. V.P.--Affiliated Computer Services, Inc., Dallas, TX; *U.S. Public*, pg. 27
Green, Sterling, Sr. V.P. & Acct. Dir.--Don Coleman Advertising, Inc., Southfield, MI; *U.S. Private*, pg. 251
Green, Sylvester, Sr. V.P.--Chubb & Son, Inc., Warren, NJ; *U.S. Public*, pg. 355
Green, William G., Esq., Sr. V.P., Gen. Counsel & Sec.--Chiron Corporation, Emeryville, CA; *U.S. Public*, pg. 349
Green, William J., Sr. V.P.--The Equitable Companies Incorporated, New York, NY; *U.S. Public*, pg. 588
Greenberg, Arnold K., Sr. V.P.-Consumer Services--Astoria Financial Corporation, Lake Success, NY; *U.S. Public*, pg. 141
Greenberg, Jerome, Sr. V.P. & Grp. Dir.--Grey Advertising Inc., New York, NY; *U.S. Public*, pg. 764
Greenberg, Susan, Sr. V.P.-H.R.--New York Life Insurance Company, New York, NY; *U.S. Private*, pg. 794
Greenblatt, Alfred A., Pres.-Apparel/Home/Industrial Fabrics & Sr. V.P.--Guilford Mills, Inc., Greensboro, NC; *U.S. Public*, pg. 768
Greene, Carl W., Sr. V.P.-Fin. & Regulatory Matters--Consolidated Edison Company of New York, Inc., New York, NY; *U.S. Public*, pg. 434
Greene, Ed, Sr. V.P.-Pur.--Bennigan's, Dallas, TX; *U.S. Private*, pg. 736
Greene, Harold, Sr. V.P.-Sls.--Forever Living Products International, Inc., Scottsdale, AZ; *U.S. Private*, pg. 418
Greenfield, Rachel, Sr. V.P.--Ziff-Davis Publishing Company, New York, NY; *Int'l*, pg. 1276
Greenfield, Rick, Sr. V.P. & Mktg. Res. Dir.--Colle & McVoy, Inc., Minneapolis, MN; *U.S. Private*, pg. 252
Greenfield, Robert, Sr. V.P.-Bus. Admin.--Viacom Productions Inc., Universal City, CA; *U.S. Private*, pg. 779
Greenholtz, Wayne M., Sr. V.P.--Government Employees Financial Corporation, Washington, DC; *U.S. Public*, pg. 220
Greening, John T., Sr. V.P. & Grp. Acct. Dir.--DMB&B Detroit, Troy, MI; *U.S. Private*, pg. 302
Greenlee, Daniel D., Sr. V.P. & Controller--D & N Financial Corporation, Hancock, MI; *U.S. Public*, pg. 472
Greenlee, Daniel D., Sr. V.P. & Controller--D & N Bank, Hancock, MI; *U.S. Public*, pg. 472
Greenlee, Patt, Sr. V.P.--First Commercial Mortgage Co., Little Rock, AR; *U.S. Public*, pg. 630
Greeno, J. Ladd, Sr. V.P.-Environmental Resources--Arthur D. Little, Inc., Cambridge, MA; *U.S. Private*, pg. 670
Greensmith, Peter L., Sr. V.P.--Market Facts, Inc., Arlington Heights, IL; *U.S. Public*, pg. 1046
Greenspan, Stephan B., Sr. V.P.-Quality & Customer Service--Seagate Technology Inc., Scotts Valley, CA; *U.S. Public*, pg. 1449
Greenwood, Bruce A., Sr. V.P. & Gen. Mgr.-Los Angeles Region--Costco Wholesale, Issaquah, WA; *U.S. Public*, pg. 451
Greenwood, Donald J., Sr. V.P. & Dir.-Res. & Devel.--Monarch Avalon, Inc., Baltimore, MD; *U.S. Public*, pg. 1123
Greenwood, Gary R., Sr. V.P.-Fin. & Acctg.--Peter Pan Seafoods, Inc., Seattle, WA; *Int'l*, pg. 928
Greer, Homer L., Sr. V.P.--FootAction USA, Irving, TX; *U.S. Public*, pg. 661
Greer, Jana Waring, Pres.-SunAmerica Mktg. Inc. & Sr. V.P. SunAmerica, Inc. Affairs--SunAmerica Inc., Los Angeles, CA; *U.S. Public*, pg. 1532
Greer, Wilbur C., Sr. V.P.--Law Engineering, Inc., Atlanta, GA; *U.S. Private*, pg. 653
Gregg, Kirk P., Sr. V.P.-Admin.--Corning Incorporated, Corning, NY; *U.S. Public*, pg. 448
Gregg, Michael W., Sr. V.P.-Acctg. & Controller--Illinois Tool Works Inc., Glenview, IL; *U.S. Public*, pg. 865
Gregg, Paul P., Chief Fin. Officer & Sr. V.P.-Fin.--CNG Producing Co., New Orleans, LA; *U.S. Public*, pg. 435
Gregor, Andrew, Chief Fin. Officer & Sr. V.P.-Fin. & Admin.--GT Interactive Software Corp., New York, NY; *U.S. Public*, pg. 696
Gregory, John M.M., III, Sr. V.P.--Universal Leaf Tobacco Company, Inc., Richmond, VA; *U.S. Public*, pg. 1694
Gregory, Kathleen, Sr. V.P. & Dir.-Local Broadcast--Lois/EJL Chicago, Chicago, IL; *U.S. Public*, pg. 1011
Greiner, C.H., Jr., Sr. V.P.--Union Camp Corporation, Wayne, NJ; *U.S. Public*, pg. 1665
Greiner, Julie, Sr. V.P.-GMM Home-Domestics/Furniture--Bloomingdale's, New York, NY; *U.S. Public*, pg. 617
Greinor, Robert, Sr. V.P.-CATV Sls.--Pico Products, Inc., Lake View Terrace, CA; *U.S. Public*, pg. 1294
Grelle, John K., Chief Fin. Officer & Sr. V.P.--ULLICO Inc., Washington, DC; *U.S. Private*, pg. 1115
Gremaud, Laurent, Chief Information Officer & Sr. V.P.-Mktg.--UMS Swiss Metalworks Holding Ltd, Dornach, Switzerland; *Int'l*, pg. 1427
Grenell, Dennis W., Sr. V.P.--Laurel Bank, Johnstown, PA; *U.S. Public*, pg. 164
Grenesko, Donald C., Sr. V.P.-Fin. & Admin.--Tribune Company, Chicago, IL; *U.S. Public*, pg. 1635
Grenier, Donald J., Sr. V.P.-Information Systems--News America Marketing, Norwalk, CT; *Int'l*, pg. 925
Greninger, Rich, Sr. V.P.-Property Mngmnt.--CarrAmerica Realty, Washington, DC; *U.S. Public*, pg. 308
Greninger, Richard, Sr. V.P.-Property Mngmt.--Carr Real Estate Services, Washington, DC; *U.S. Public*, pg. 309
Greskovich, Charles F., Sr. V.P.--Zenith Insurance Company, Woodland Hills, CA; *U.S. Public*, pg. 1791
Greve, Jan M., Sr. V.P. & Gen. Counsel--Kvaerner a.s.a., Lysaker, Norway; *Int'l*, pg. 766
Greves, Larry A., Sr. V.P.--Firstar Corporation, Milwaukee, WI; *U.S. Public*, pg. 642
Grey, Bob, Sr. V.P.-Sls.--Tyco Toys, Inc., Mount Laurel, NJ; *U.S. Public*, pg. 1058
Grey, Robert J., Sr. V.P., Gen. Counsel & Sec.--PP&L Resources, Allentown, PA; *U.S. Public*, pg. 1244
Grey, Robert J., Sr. V.P., Gen. Counsel & Sec.--Pennsylvania Power & Light Company-Lehigh Div., Allentown, PA; *U.S. Public*, pg. 1244
Gribbin, Ed, Sr. V.P.-Hospitality Sls.--Angelica Image Apparel, Saint Louis, MO; *U.S. Public*, pg. 113
Grice, Jeff, Sr. V.P. & Grp. Acct. Dir.-Corp. Trng.--Ross Roy Communications, Inc., Bloomfield Hills, MI; *U.S. Private*, pg. 946
Griesing, Sharon, Sr. V.P. & Media Dir.--Berry-Brown Advertising, Inc., Dallas, TX; *U.S. Private*, pg. 137
Grieve, Allen, Sr. V.P.-Cash Mngmt.--Magna Group, Inc., Saint Louis, MO; *U.S. Public*, pg. 1037
Griffen, Donald K., Sr. V.P.--INTEGRATEC, Atlanta, GA; *U.S. Public*, pg. 588
Griffey, Marvin, Sr. V.P.-Quality Assurance--Fike Corporation, Blue Springs, MO; *U.S. Private*, pg. 404
Griffin, Debra C., Chief Fin. Officer & Sr. V.P.--Tierney & Partners, Philadelphia, PA; *U.S. Public*, pg. 1641
Griffin, George D., Sr. V.P. & Auditor--FirstMerit Corporation, Akron, OH; *U.S. Public*, pg. 646
Griffin, J. Timothy, Sr. V.P.-Market Plng. & Sys.--Northwest Airlines Corp., Saint Paul, MN; *U.S. Public*, pg. 1199
Griffin, James, Sr. V.P.--Smart & Final, Vernon, CA; *Int'l*, pg. 563
Griffin, Jesse O., Sr. V.P. & Controller--United Companies Financial Corporation, Baton Rouge, LA; *U.S. Public*, pg. 1675
Griffin, Michael J., Sr. V.P.--Pinnacle Bank, Valparaiso, IN; *U.S. Public*, pg. 1297
Griffin, R.E., Sr. V.P.--Sivalls, Inc., Odessa, TX; *U.S. Private*, pg. 1004
Griffin, Ron, Chief Info. Officer & Sr. V.P.-Information Services--The Home Depot, Inc., Atlanta, GA; *U.S. Public*, pg. 831
Griffin, Thomas P., Sr. V.P.-Sls. & Opers.--Williams Telecommunications Systems, Inc., Houston, TX; *U.S. Public*, pg. 1769
Griffin, Timothy, Sr. V.P.-Market Plng. & Sys.--Northwest Airlines, Inc., Saint Paul, MN; *U.S. Public*, pg. 1200
Griffith, Glen, Chief Oper. & Information Officer & Sr. V.P.--Trammell Crow Company, Dallas, TX; *U.S. Public*, pg. 1628
Griffith, James M., Sr. V.P.-Investor Rels. & Corp. Communication--Beverly Enterprises, Inc., Fort Smith, AR; *U.S. Public*, pg. 227
Griffith, John G., Sr. V.P.-Intl.--VWR Scientific Products, West Chester, PA; *U.S. Public*, pg. 1703
Griffith, Robert, Sr. V.P.-Leasing--Crown American Realty Trust, Johnstown, PA; *U.S. Public*, pg. 461
Griffith, Ronald L., Sr., Chief Fin. Officer, Sr. V.P.-Fin., Treas. & Sec.--Burnham, Lancaster, PA; *U.S. Public*, pg. 270
Grigaliunas, Ben, Ph.D., Sr. V.P.-H.R.--Advocate Health Care, Oak Brook, IL; *U.S. Private*, pg. 23
Grigg, James L., Sr. V.P.-Supply Chain Mngmt.--Owens & Minor Inc., Glen Allen, VA; *U.S. Public*, pg. 1236
Grill, Jeffrey, Sr. V.P. & Sr. Partner--N.W. Ayer & Partners New York, New York, NY; *U.S. Private*, pg. 104
Grillo, Frank, Sr. V.P.-Mktg.--WorldCom, Inc., Jackson, MS; *U.S. Public*, pg. 1779
Grimes, Thomas A., Sr. V.P.-West Pacific Division--Bank of Hawaii, Honolulu, HI; *U.S. Public*, pg. 1248
Grimm, Clyde L., Sr. V.P.-U.S. Sls., Mktg. & Service & Gen. Mgr.--Bayer Corporation, Pittsburgh, PA; *Int'l*, pg. 172
Grinbaum, Jacob, Sr. V.P.-Treasury--Nordbanken AB, Stockholm, Sweden; *Int'l*, pg. 957
Gring, Clayton, Sr., Chief Oper. Officer & Sr. V.P.--Fairfield Communities, Inc., Little Rock, AR; *U.S. Public*, pg. 610
Gringolo, Alberto, Ph.D., Sr. V.P. & Gen. Mgr.-Worldwide Regulatory Affairs--PAREXEL International Corporation, Waltham, MA; *U.S. Public*, pg. 1257
Grinstead, Mary Jane, Sr. V.P. & Gen. Mgr.-North America West--Anacomp, Inc., Indianapolis, IN; *U.S. Public*, pg. 106
Grippa, Vincent V., Sr. V.P. & Mng. Dir.--State Street Canada, Inc., Toronto, Canada; *U.S. Public*, pg. 1513
Grise, Cheryl, Sr. V.P.--Northeast Utilities, Berlin, CT; *U.S. Public*, pg. 1194
Grise, Cheryl W., Sr. V.P.--The Connecticut Light & Power Co., Berlin, CT; *U.S. Public*, pg. 1194
Griswold, Paul J., Sr. V.P.-Intl. Opers.--Tenneco Packaging, Evanston, IL; *U.S. Public*, pg. 1579
Gritton, Gregory C., Sr. V.P. & Chief Fin. Officer--Creswell, Munsell, Fultz & Zirbel, L.P., Cedar Rapids, IA; *U.S. Private*, pg. 1197
Grizzle, J. David, Sr. V.P.-Alliance Devel.--Continental Airlines, Houston, TX; *U.S. Public*, pg. 439
Groackie, Kirt, Sr. V.P.--Monterey's Acquisition Corporation, Houston, TX; *U.S. Private*, pg. 758
Grob, Timothy J., Chief Fin. Officer, Chief Admin. Officer & Sr. V.P.--Grant/Jacoby, Inc., Chicago, IL; *U.S. Private*, pg. 470
Groberg, James J., Sr. V.P.--Volt Information Sciences, Inc., New York, NY; *U.S. Public*, pg. 1724
Groce, A. Ben, Sr. V.P.-Mfg., Paper Div.--Boise Cascade Corporation, Boise, ID; *U.S. Public*, pg. 242
Grochoski, Gregory, Sr. V.P.-Res. & Devel.--Amway Corporation, Ada, MI; *U.S. Private*, pg. 69
Groefsema, Bruce, Sr. V.P.-Sls.--Calcot, Ltd., Bakersfield, CA; *U.S. Private*, pg. 200
Groessl, David, Sr. V.P.--Wisconsin Label Corporation, Algoma, WI; *U.S. Private*, pg. 1184
Groff, James R., Sr. V.P. & Gen. Mgr.-Info. Appliance Prods. Div.--Apple Computer, Inc., Cupertino, CA; *U.S. Public*, pg. 121
Grohowski, Frank, Sr. V.P.-Opers.--Scholastic Corporation, New York, NY; *U.S. Public*, pg. 1440
Gronningsaeter, Marius H., Sr. V.P.-Legal, Gen. Counsel & Sec.--Elkem ASA, Oslo, Norway; *Int'l*, pg. 446
Groom, Brian E., Sr. V.P.-Global Treas.--Bank of Hawaii, Honolulu, HI; *U.S. Public*, pg. 1248
Groom, Bruce M., Sr. V.P. & Sr. Trust Officer--Chemical Bank & Trust Company, Midland, MI; *U.S. Public*, pg. 345
Gros, Robert, Sr. V.P.-Production, CBS Productions--CBS Entertainment, Los Angeles, CA; *U.S. Public*, pg. 274
Grose, S.L., Sr. V.P.-Appalachia--Lomak Petroleum Inc., Fort Worth, TX; *U.S. Public*, pg. 1012
Gross, Arnold, Sr. V.P.-Intl. & Pres.-Handleman Intl.--Handleman Company, Troy, MI; *U.S. Public*, pg. 779
Gross, Bert M., Sr. V.P. & Gen. Counsel--Regis Corporation, Minneapolis, MN; *U.S. Public*, pg. 1373
Gross, Murray, Sr. V.P., Gen. Counsel & Clerk--EG & G, Inc., Wellesley, MA; *U.S. Public*, pg. 542
Gross, Neil G., Sr. V.P.--Acme Mills Co. Inc., Detroit, MI; *U.S. Private*, pg. 13
Gross, Richard B., Sr. V.P., Gen. Counsel & Sec.--AMBAC Financial Group, Inc., New York, NY; *U.S. Public*, pg. 62
Gross, Richard W., Sr. V.P.--Interpool, Inc., Princeton, NJ; *U.S. Public*, pg. 908
Gross, Steve, Sr. V.P.-Mktg.--MobileComm, Ridgefield Park, NJ; *U.S. Public*, pg. 1120
Grossbard, Elliott B., M.D., Sr. V.P.-Devel.--Scios Inc., Mountain View, CA; *U.S. Public*, pg. 1444
Grossestreuer, Joseph, Sr. V.P.-Sls./Outsourcing--May & Speh, Inc., Downers Grove, IL; *U.S. Public*, pg. 1063
Grossestreuer, Joseph C., Sr. V.P.--SHL Systemhouse, Ottawa, Canada; *Int'l*, pg. 1154
Grossi, Mark D., Sr. V.P.--Charter One Financial, Inc., Cleveland, OH; *U.S. Public*, pg. 336
Grossman, Barbara, Sr. V.P., Publisher-Viking--Penguin Putnam Inc., New York, NY; *Int'l*, pg. 1027
Grossman, Judy, Sr. V.P.--Edelman Worldwide, Inc., New York, NY; *U.S. Private*, pg. 362
Grossman, Marc A., Sr. V.P.-Corp. Affairs.--Hilton Hotels Corporation, Beverly Hills, CA; *U.S. Public*, pg. 828
Grosso, Anthony J., Sr. V.P.-Mktg.--PMA Reinsurance Corporation, Philadelphia, PA; *U.S. Public*, pg. 1272
Grote, Robert D., Sr. V.P. & Mgr.-Central Iowa Comml. Division--Brenton Banks, Inc., Des Moines, IA; *U.S. Public*, pg. 251
Grottum, Tore, Sr. V.P. & Head-Group Acctng.--Christiania Bank og Kreditkasse ASA, Oslo, Norway; *Int'l*, pg. 289
Grove, Ronald C., Sr. V.P.-Logistics Plng.--PETsMART, Inc., Phoenix, AZ; *U.S. Public*, pg. 1281
Grove, Timberlee T., Sr. V.P.--Markel Service, Inc., Glen Allen, VA; *U.S. Public*, pg. 1046
Grove, Timberlee T., Sr. V.P.--Markel American Insurance Co., Glen Allen, VA; *U.S. Public*, pg. 1046
Groven, Darrol N., Sr. V.P.--Morrison Knudsen Corporation, Boise, ID; *U.S. Public*, pg. 1133
Grover, William G., Sr. V.P.-Sls. & Mktg.--Comdial Corporation, Charlottesville, VA; *U.S. Public*, pg. 407
Grozman, Desiderio M., Sr. V.P.-Mfg.--La Tondena Distillers, Inc., Manila, Philippines; *Int'l*, pg. 785
Grube, T., Sr. V.P., Gen Counsel & Sec.--Mack Trucks, Inc., Allentown, PA; *Int'l*, pg. 1102
Gruber, Thomas A., Sr. V.P.--Blockbuster Entertainment Group, Dallas, TX; *U.S. Private*, pg. 775
Gruen, Marlon T., Sr. V.P.--Medicus Systems Corporation, Evanston, IL; *U.S. Public*, pg. 1080
Gruen, Rob, Sr. V.P.-Retail Bus. Devel.--Warner Bros. Consumer Products, Burbank, CA; *U.S. Public*, pg. 1610
Gruenewald, C.W., II, Chief Fin. Officer, Sr. V.P. & Treas.--United Foods, Inc., Bells, TN; *U.S. Public*, pg. 1677
Grunyk, Stephen N., Sr. V.P. & Exec. Creative Dir.-Des Moines--Creswell, Munsell, Fultz & Zirbel, L.P., Cedar Rapids, IA; *U.S. Private*, pg. 1197
Grupp, Karl R., Sr. V.P.-Opers.--Amlings Flowerland, Hinsdale, IL; *U.S. Private*, pg. 66
Grush, John T., Sr. V.P.--Centris Group Inc., Costa Mesa, CA; *U.S. Public*, pg. 328
Grutsch, R.J., Sr. V.P. Opers.--Sithe Energies, Inc., New York, NY; *U.S. Private*, pg. 1004
Gsell, Thomas C., Dr., Sr. V.P.--Pall Corporation, Greenvale, NY; *U.S. Public*, pg. 1253
Guarino, Carl A., Sr. V.P.--SEI Investments, Oaks, PA; *U.S. Public*, pg. 1417
Gubernick, Joseph, Sr. V.P.-Res. & Devel.--Estee Lauder Companies Inc., New York, NY; *U.S. Public*, pg. 594
Guelich, Bob, Sr. V.P.-Mdsg.--Target Stores, Minneapolis, MN; *U.S. Public*, pg. 489
Guenther, John S., Sr. V.P.--Ball Horticultural Company, West Chicago, IL; *U.S. Private*, pg. 112
Guequierre, John P., Sr. V.P.-Admin.--Marlette Homes, Inc., Middlebury, IN; *U.S. Public*, pg. 1442
Guerard, John B., Sr. V.P.--Vantage Global Advisors, Inc., New York, NY; *U.S. Public*, pg. 998

Guerico, Vincent M., Sr. V.P.-Worldwide Sls. & Mktg.--General Semiconductor, Inc., Melville, NY; *U.S. Public*, pg. 726

Guernsey, William A., Sr. V.P.-Corp. Devel.--BMC Industries, Inc., Minneapolis, MN; *U.S. Public*, pg. 162

Guerrero, Juan, Sr. V.P.-Investment & Fin. Services--Banco Popular de Puerto Rico, San Juan, PR; *U.S. Public*, pg. 175

Guerrette, Armand, Sr. V.P. & Branch Mgr.--Willis Corroon Melling Ltd., Edmonton, Canada; *Int'l*, pg. 1509

Guest, John, Sr. V.P.-Sls.--Salomon-North America Inc., Georgetown, MA; *Int'l*, pg. 1181

Gugulyn, Sr. V.P.-Admin.--Potash Corporation of Saskatchewan Inc., Saskatoon, Canada; *Int'l*, pg. 1064

Guha, Richard, Sr. V.P.-Mktg.--MediaOne, Boston, MA; *U.S. Public*, pg. 1688

Guiliano, Louis J., Sr. V.P.--ITT Industries, Inc., White Plains, NY; *U.S. Public*, pg. 859

Guillory, Winston, Sr. V.P.-Sls., Mktg. & Field Opers.--Amtech Systems Corporation, Dallas, TX; *U.S. Public*, pg. 105

Guimont-Hall, Ann, Sr. V.P. & Reg. Dir.--Outdoor Services, Seattle, WA; *U.S. Private*, pg. 1166

Guinn, Chet G., Sr. V.P.-Sls.--Longview Fibre Co. Western Div., Seattle, WA; *U.S. Public*, pg. 1014

Guion, James F., Sr. V.P.-Prod. & Opers.--Kerr-McGee Corporation, Oklahoma City, OK; *U.S. Public*, pg. 952

Gulick, Henry G., Sr. V.P. & Sec.--Chubb & Son, Inc., Warren, NJ; *U.S. Public*, pg. 355

Gulley, Joan L., Sr. V.P.-Strategic Plng.--PNC Bank Corp., Pittsburgh, PA; *U.S. Public*, pg. 1242

Gulling, Douglas R., Sr. V.P. & Corp. Controller--Brenton Banks, Inc., Des Moines, IA; *U.S. Public*, pg. 251

Gulmi, James S., Chief Fin. Officer, Sr. V.P.-Fin. & Treas.--Genesco Inc., Nashville, TN; *U.S. Public*, pg. 728

Guloien, Donald, Sr. V.P.-Bus. Devel.--Manulife Financial (The Manufacturers Life Insurance Company), Toronto, Canada; *Int'l*, pg. 840

Gumbiner, Burke, Sr. V.P.-Insurance--Pacificare Health Systems, Santa Ana, CA; *U.S. Public*, pg. 1251

Gundell, James, Sr. V.P.-GMM FA & IA--Bloomingdale's, New York, NY; *U.S. Public*, pg. 617

Gunkler, Andrew C., Sr. V.P.--Houlihan's Restaurant Group, Kansas City, MO; *U.S. Public*, pg. 841

Gunn, G. Tom, Sr. V.P.-Capital Funds & Chief Fin. Officer--CT Financial Services, Inc., Toronto, Canada; *Int'l*, pg. 112

Gunn, George C., III, Sr. V.P.--Trustmark National Bank, Jackson, MS; *U.S. Public*, pg. 1643

Gunn, Thomas M., Sr. V.P.-Bus. Devel.--McDonnell Aircraft & Missile Systems Div., Berkeley, MO; *U.S. Public*, pg. 241

Gunter, Hubert, Sr. V.P.-Fund Mngmt. & Res.--Liechtenstein Global Trust Limited, Vaduz, Liechtenstein; *Int'l*, pg. 809

Gunter, Joe T., Sr. V.P. & Special Counsel--Fairfield Communities, Inc., Little Rock, AR; *U.S. Public*, pg. 610

Gunter, Mary Jo, Sr. V.P.-Banking Svc.--Pinnacle Bank, Jasper, AL; *U.S. Public*, pg. 1297

Gunter, William F., Sr. V.P. & Dir.-Fin. Prods./Svcs.--Scott & Stringfellow Financial, Inc., Richmond, VA; *U.S. Public*, pg. 1445

Gunter, William F., Sr. V.P.--Scott & Stringfellow, Inc., Richmond, VA; *U.S. Public*, pg. 1445

Gurdy, Mike, Sr. V.P.-Bus. Devel.--Associates Financial Services Corporation, Dallas, TX; *U.S. Public*, pg. 663

Gurnick, Larisa, Sr. V.P.-Strategic Plng.--FirstFed Financial Corp., Santa Monica, CA; *U.S. Public*, pg. 645

Gust, Anne B. ., Sr. V.P. & Gen. Counsel--The Gap, Inc., San Francisco, CA; *U.S. Public*, pg. 702

Gustafson, Albert W., Sr. V.P. & Portfolio Mgr.--Fiduciary Management Associates, Inc., Chicago, IL; *U.S. Public*, pg. 1673

Gustafson, Bengt, Sr. V.P. & Chief Legal Counsel--Svedala Industri AB, Malmo, Sweden; *Int'l*, pg. 1323

Gustafson, Claes, Sr. V.P.-Building--Skanska AB, Danderyd, Sweden; *Int'l*, pg. 1260

Gustafson, James M., Sr. V.P. & Mgr.-Real Estate Mngmt.--FirstMerit Corporation, Akron, OH; *U.S. Public*, pg. 646

Gustafson, Robert, Sr. V.P.--UNC Accessory Services, Annapolis, MD; *U.S. Public*, pg. 710

Gustafsson, Goran, Sr. V.P.-Pur.--Skanska AB, Danderyd, Sweden; *Int'l*, pg. 1260

Gustin, Carl E., Jr., Sr. V.P. & Chief Mktg. Officer--Eastman Kodak Company, Rochester, NY; *U.S. Public*, pg. 550

Guthlein, William J., Chief Fin. Officer, V.P. & Treas.--Chancellor Corporation, Boston, MA; *U.S. Public*, pg. 335

Guthrie, Alan S., Sr. V.P.--Horizon Paper Co., Inc., New York, NY; *U.S. Private*, pg. 539

Guthrie, James, Sr. V.P.-Sls. & Mktg.--Petersen Publishing Company, L.L.C., Los Angeles, CA; *U.S. Private*, pg. 856

Guthrie, Roy A., Sr. V.P.-U.S.--Associates International Management Company, Dallas, TX; *U.S. Public*, pg. 663

Gutman, Harvey, Sr. V.P.-Real Estate & Res. & Devel.--Pathmark Stores Incorporated, Woodbridge, NJ; *U.S. Private*, pg. 843

Gutterman, Allen, Sr. V.P.-Mktg.--New York City Off-Track Betting Corp., New York, NY; *U.S. Private*, pg. 794

Guy, Geoff I., Sr. V.P.-Fin. & Chief Actuary--Manulife Financial (The Manufacturers Life Insurance Company), Toronto, Canada; *Int'l*, pg. 840

Guy, Thomas D., Sr. V.P.-Opers.--U.S. Surgical Corp., Norwalk, CT; *U.S. Public*, pg. 1687

Guyardo, Paul, Exec. V.P.-Mktg.--Home Shopping Network, Inc., Saint Petersburg, FL; *U.S. Public*, pg. 1685

Guzzo, Walter B., Sr. V.P.--Chubb & Son Inc., Warren, NJ; *U.S. Public*, pg. 355

Gwartney, Stephen W., Sr. V.P.-Loan Admin.--UMB Financial Corporation, Kansas City, MO; *U.S. Public*, pg. 1653

Gwinn, D. Byrd, Sr. V.P.--Chubb & Son, Inc., Warren, NJ; *U.S. Public*, pg. 355

Gwizdala, Lori A., Chief Fin. Officer, Sr. V.P. & Treas.--Chemical Financial Corporation, Midland, MI; *U.S. Public*, pg. 345

Gyouda, Haruhiko, Sr. V.P., Gen. Mgr. & Dir.--Tokio Marine Management Inc. - Western Regional Office, Pasadena, CA; *Int'l*, pg. 1392

Gyrulf, Svante, Sr. V.P.-Comml. Insurance Div.--Trygg-Hansa, Stockholm, Sweden; *Int'l*, pg. 1425

Haan, Phillip, Sr. V.P.-Intl.--Northwest Airlines, Inc., Saint Paul, MN; *U.S. Public*, pg. 1200

Haan, Phillip C., Sr. V.P.-Intl.--Northwest Airlines Corp., Saint Paul, MN; *U.S. Public*, pg. 1199

Haas, Frederick C., Sr. V.P.--Westvaco Corporation, New York, NY; *U.S. Public*, pg. 1762

Haas, Kelley, Chief Oper. Officer & Sr. V.P.--MRA, An Integrated Marketing Communications Agency, Overland Park, KS; *U.S. Private*, pg. 687

Haas, Leo G., Sr. V.P.--NationsBank West, Saint Louis, MO; *U.S. Public*, pg. 1164

Haas, Roby, Sr. V.P.--Landesbank Rheinland Pfalz International S.A., Luxembourg, Luxembourg; *Int'l*, pg. 799

Haase, Barbara S., Sr. V.P.-H.R.--General Alum & Chemical, Holland, OH; *U.S. Private*, pg. 443

Haase, Daniel, Sr. V.P. & Mng. Dir.--BankAmerica Trust & Banking Corp. (Cayman) Ltd., Georgetown, Cayman Islands; *U.S. Public*, pg. 183

Haavardtun, Arne, Sr. V.P.--Det Norske Veritas, Hovik, Norway; *Int'l*, pg. 396

Habegger, Ronald J., Sr. V.P.-N. American Opers.--Phelps Dodge Magnet Wire Co., Fort Wayne, IN; *U.S. Public*, pg. 1286

Haber, Barry, Sr. V.P.-Consumer Electronics & Cuisinart--Conair Corporation, Stamford, CT; *U.S. Private*, pg. 261

Haber, Thomas R., Sr. V.P.-Fin.--Glaxo Wellcome Inc., Research Triangle Park, NC; *Int'l*, pg. 552

Haberman, Richard C., Sr. V.P.-Fidelity Mngmt. & Res. Company--Fidelity Investments (FMR Corp.), Boston, MA; *U.S. Private*, pg. 402

Habicht, F. Henry, II, Sr. V.P.-Corp. Devel. & Environment--Safety-Kleen Corp., Elgin, IL; *U.S. Public*, pg. 1425

Haboush, Louis, Sr. V.P. & Mgr.-Natl. Sls./Comdisco Healthcare Group, Inc.--Comdisco, Inc., Rosemont, IL; *U.S. Public*, pg. 407

Hacker, Douglas A., Chief Fin. Officer & Sr. V.P.-Fin.--UAL Corporation, Elk Grove Village, IL; *U.S. Public*, pg. 1652

Hackman, Dodd, Sr. V.P.--Grizzard, Atlanta, GA; *U.S. Private*, pg. 482

Hackman, Dodd, Sr. V.P.-Sls. & Mktg.--TABS Direct (Operating Div.), Stafford, TX; *U.S. Private*, pg. 482

Hadelman, Lewis E., Sr. V.P. & Dir.-Business Systems--SRA International Inc., Arlington, VA; *U.S. Private*, pg. 957

Hadley, Bret R, Sr. V.P.-Mktg.-Boys Line--Aviva Sport, Inc., El Segundo, CA; *U.S. Public*, pg. 1058

Hadley, Bret R., Sr. V.P.-Mktg.-Boys Line--Mattel, Inc., El Segundo, CA; *U.S. Public*, pg. 1057

Haeck, James F., Sr. V.P.-Comml.--The LTV Corporation, Cleveland, OH; *U.S. Public*, pg. 971

Haefele, Raymond J., Sr. V.P. & Pres.-Continental Deli Foods--Foodbrands America, Inc., Oklahoma City, OK; *U.S. Public*, pg. 852

Haefling, Karen R., Sr. V.P.--Keycorp, Cleveland, OH; *U.S. Public*, pg. 954

Haeg, Lawrence P., Sr. V.P.-Corp. Communications--Norwest Corporation, Minneapolis, MN; *U.S. Public*, pg. 1201

Haemers, Guy, Corp. V.P.-Advanced Materials--N.V. Bekaert S.A., Kortrijk, Belgium; *Int'l*, pg. 183

Haesche, Stephen W., Sr. V.P. & Grp. Creative Head--Mullen Advertising, Inc., Wenham, MA; *U.S. Private*, pg. 766

Haesele, Kathleen, Sr. V.P. & Exec. Dir.--Advanswers Media/Programming, Saint Louis, MO; *Int'l*, pg. 117

Hafer, Thomas F., Sr. V.P., Gen. Counsel & Sec.--Salient 3 Communications, Inc., Reading, PA; *U.S. Public*, pg. 1429

Hafling, David N., Sr. V.P. & Actuary--American States Insurance Companies, Indianapolis, IN; *U.S. Public*, pg. 997

Hafner, Kenneth O., Sr. V.P.--Johnson Bros. Corporation, Litchfield, MN; *U.S. Private*, pg. 590

Hafner, Volker W., Sr. V.P.-Engrng.--Acorn Engineering Company, City of Industry, CA; *U.S. Private*, pg. 14

Hafnor, Ole-Andreas, Sr. V.P.--Det Norske Veritas, Hovik, Norway; *Int'l*, pg. 396

Hagan, Henry J., Chief Mktg. Officer & Sr. V.P.--Monumental Life Insurance Company, Baltimore, MD; *Int'l*, pg. 27

Hagan, Thomas M., Sr. V.P.-External Affairs--Central and South West Corporation, Dallas, TX; *U.S. Public*, pg. 324

Hagelauer, Alain, Sr. V.P.-Fin.--Thomson-CSF S.A., Paris, France; *Int'l*, pg. 1383

Hageman, Douglas L., Sr. V.P. & Gen. Counsel--TrizecHahn Centers Inc., San Diego, CA; *Int'l*, pg. 1425

Hageman, John A., Sr. V.P. & Gen. Counsel--Metals USA, Inc., Houston, TX; *U.S. Public*, pg. 1100

Hageman, John A., Sr. V.P.-Legal Affairs, Gen. Counsel & Sec.--Physician Corporation of America, Miami, FL; *U.S. Public*, pg. 1293

Hagen, Allen O., Sr. V.P.-Sls.--Bluewater, Mora, MN; *U.S. Private*, pg. 153

Hagen, Barbara, Sr. V.P.--The McClure Group, Wayne, PA; *U.S. Private*, pg. 719

Hagen, E. Sven, Ph.D., Sr. V.P.-Exploration & Production--Benton Oil & Gas Company, Carpinteria, CA; *U.S. Public*, pg. 212

Hagen, G. Thomas, III, Sr. V.P.-East Oahu Reg.--Bank of Hawaii, Honolulu, HI; *U.S. Public*, pg. 1248

Hager, George V., Jr., Chief Fin. Officer & Sr. V.P.--Genesis Health Ventures, Inc., Kennett Square, PA; *U.S. Public*, pg. 728

Hager, George V., Jr., Chief Fin. Officer & Sr. V.P.--Genesis ElderCare, Philadelphia, PA; *U.S. Public*, pg. 728

Hagerman, John, Sr. V.P.-Mktg.--Maxtor Corporation, Milpitas, CA; *Int'l*, pg. 641

Hagerty, James J., Sr. V.P.--United Services Life Insurance Co., Arlington, VA; *U.S. Public*, pg. 1376

Haggard, Rick, Sr. V.P.-Comml. Loans--Federal Savings Bank, Fort Smith, AR; *U.S. Private*, pg. 614

Hagge, Patrick J., Sr. V.P.--First Commercial Bank, N.A., Little Rock, AR; *U.S. Public*, pg. 630

Haggen, Arthur W., Sr. V.P. & Sec.--American Bankers Insurance Co. of Florida, Miami, FL; *U.S. Public*, pg. 67

Haggerty, John R., Sr. Exec. V.P.--Summit Bank, Chatham, NJ; *U.S. Public*, pg. 1528

Haggerty, Robert, Sr. V.P.-Human Resources & Training--Grossman's, Inc., Stoughton, MA; *U.S. Private*, pg. 585

Hagood, Bo, Sr. V.P.-Opers.--Signature Inns, Inc., Indianapolis, IN; *U.S. Public*, pg. 1473

Hahl, Neil M., Sr. V.P.--American Financial Group, Cincinnati, OH; *U.S. Public*, pg. 75

Hahn, Alan C., Sr. V.P.-Deal Direct Mktg.--Jackson National Life Insurance Company, Lansing, MI; *Int'l*, pg. 1073

Hahn, David, Sr. V.P., Gen. Counsel & Sec.--The Titan Corporation, San Diego, CA; *U.S. Public*, pg. 1618

Hahs, Dwain L., Sr. V.P.-Intl.--Bausch & Lomb Inc., Rochester, NY; *U.S. Public*, pg. 194

Haidar, Steve A., Sr. V.P.-Fin. & Admin.--Western Atlas Logging Services, Houston, TX; *U.S. Public*, pg. 1757

Hain, Charles R., Chief Fin. Officer & Sr. V.P.-Fin.--Klein Tools Inc., Skokie, IL; *U.S. Private*, pg. 625

Haines, Albert E., Sr. V.P.-Admin.--American General Corporation, Houston, TX; *U.S. Public*, pg. 76

Haines, Charles, Sr. V.P. & Exec.Dir--Advanswers Media/Programming, Saint Louis, MO; *Int'l*, pg. 117

Hair, Dan H., Sr. V.P.--Zenith Insurance Company, Woodland Hills, CA; *U.S. Public*, pg. 1791

Hairston, Peyton T., Sr. V.P.-Labor Relations & Safety--Tennessee Valley Authority, Knoxville, TN; *U.S. Public*, pg. 1580

Haist, Jim, Sr. V.P. & Grp. Acct. Supvr.--Rhea & Kaiser Marketing Communications, Naperville, IL; *U.S. Private*, pg. 927

Hake, William, Sr. V.P.-Coal Opers.--Kerr-McGee Corporation, Oklahoma City, OK; *U.S. Public*, pg. 952

Hake, William D., Sr. V.P.-Coal--Kerr-McGee Coal Corp., Oklahoma City, OK; *U.S. Public*, pg. 952

Halamandans, Harry, Sr. V.P.--Amecom Div., College Park, MD; *U.S. Public*, pg. 1002

Halamandaris, Harry, Sr. V.P. & Grp. Exec.-Electronic Warfare Sys.--Litton Industries, Inc., Woodland Hills, CA; *U.S. Public*, pg. 1002

Hale, Bruce H., Sr. V.P.--National Fuel Gas Distribution Corp., Buffalo, NY; *U.S. Public*, pg. 1156

Hale, Bruce H., Sr. V.P.--National Fuel Gas Supply Corp., Erie, PA; *U.S. Public*, pg. 1156

Hale, James T., Sr. V.P., Gen. Counsel & Sec.--Dayton Hudson Corporation, Minneapolis, MN; *U.S. Public*, pg. 489

Hale, Joseph E., Sr. V.P.-Mktg.--Aloha Airgroup, Inc., Honolulu, HI; *U.S. Private*, pg. 44

Hale, Judson D., Sr., Vice Chm. & Sr. V.P.--Yankee Publishing Incorporated, Dublin, NH; *U.S. Private*, pg. 1195

Hale, Keri, Sr. V.P. & Exec. Dir.-Agency Services--Grey Healthcare Group, New York, NY; *U.S. Public*, pg. 765

Hale, Mark, Sr. V.P.-Opers.--Home & Garden Television, Knoxville, TN; *U.S. Public*, pg. 1447

Haley, David, Sr. V.P.-Natl. Promo.--MCA Records, Inc., Universal City, CA; *Int'l*, pg. 1215

Haley, Eugene T., Sr. V.P.-Customer Satisfaction--Qualex Inc., Durham, NC; *U.S. Public*, pg. 551

Haley, Steve, Sr. V.P.-Resource Devel.--Woodward-Clyde Group, Inc., Denver, CO; *U.S. Public*, pg. 1655

Halfacre, William E., Sr. V.P.-Retail & Pur.--Regis Corporation, Minneapolis, MN; *U.S. Public*, pg. 1373

Halford, David D., Sr. V.P.--First Wisconsin Asset Management, Inc., Madison, WI; *U.S. Public*, pg. 643

Hall, B. D., Sr. V.P. & Mktg. Analysis Dir.--Howard, Merrell & Partners, Inc., Raleigh, NC; *U.S. Private*, pg. 542

Hall, Bruce C., Sr. V.P.-Reg. Opers.--Toys "R" Us, Inc., Paramus, NJ; *U.S. Public*, pg. 1626

Hall, Bruce C., Sr. V.P.-Reg. Opers.--Toys "R" Us United States, Paramus, NJ; *U.S. Public*, pg. 1626

Hall, David A., Sr. V.P. & Chief Investment Officer--Hartford Life & Accident Insurance Company, Hartford, CT; *U.S. Public*, pg. 795

Hall, Gary F., Chief Fin. Officer & Sr. V.P.--Cajun Electric Power Co-op, Baton Rouge, LA; *U.S. Private*, pg. 199

Hall, J. Robert, Sr. V.P.-Strategic Plng.--Nabisco Inc., Parsippany, NJ; *U.S. Public*, pg. 1355

Hall, John B., Sr. V.P. & Sec.--Norbest, Inc., Midvale, UT; *U.S. Private*, pg. 801

Hall, Joseph C., Chief Oper. Officer & Sr. V.P.--Food Lion, Inc., Salisbury, NC; *Int'l*, pg. 463

Hall, Kevin, Sr. V.P.-Special Projects--American Business Information, Inc., Omaha, NE; *U.S. Public*, pg. 69

Hall, Lindsay, Sr. V.P. & Creative Dir.--Stackig Advertising and Public Relations, Mc Lean, VA; *U.S. Private*, pg. 1028

Hall, Paul, Sr. V.P.--Shandwick Detroit, Southfield, MI; *Int'l*, pg. 1227

Hall, R.A., Sr. V.P.--Vilter Manufacturing Corporation, Cudahy, WI; *U.S. Private*, pg. 1140

Hall, Robert, Sr. V.P.-Credit--Fleet Capital Corporation, Glastonbury, CT; *U.S. Public*, pg. 649

Hall, Stephen J., Sr. V.P.--The Mutual Life Insurance Company of New York, New York, NY; *U.S. Private*, pg. 769

Hall, Steven V., Sr. V.P. & Dir- Opers.--Barclays American/Mortgage Corp., Charlotte, NC; *Int'l*, pg. 165

Hall, Terry, Sr. V.P.-Worldwide Sls.--Cognos Inc., Ottawa, Canada; *Int'l*, pg. 305

Hall, Terry, Chief Fin. Officer & Sr. V.P.--US Airways Group, Inc., Arlington, VA; *U.S. Public*, pg. 1680

Hall, William W., Sr. V.P.-Electronic Delivery--Zions First National Bank, Salt Lake City, UT; *U.S. Public*, pg. 1793

Hallacy, Eugene, Sr. V.P. & Media Dir.--Price/McNabb, Inc., Charlotte, NC; *U.S. Private*, pg. 883
Hallagan, Kevin, Sr. V.P. & Corp. Counsel--Bank of America Illinois, Chicago, IL; *U.S. Public*, pg. 180
Hallberg, John, Sr. V.P.-Worldwide Mktg.--Encyclopaedia Britannica, Inc., Chicago, IL; *U.S. Private*, pg. 375
Hallberg, Nancy, Sr. V.P. & Acct. Plng. Dir.-Insights Grp.--Young & Rubicam New York, New York, NY; *U.S. Private*, pg. 1198
Haller, Tom C., Sr. V.P.--Bituminous Roadways, Inc., Inver Grove Heights, MN; *U.S. Private*, pg. 146
Hallett, F.N., Chief Fin. Officer & Sr. V.P.--National Steel & Shipbuilding Company, San Diego, CA; *U.S. Private*, pg. 787
Hallett, R.A., Sr. V.P.-Human Resources--Shoppers Drug Mart, Ltd., Toronto, Canada; *Int'l*, pg. 112
Halliday, James B., Chief Fin. Officer & Sr. V.P.--Argonaut Co., Menlo Park, CA; *U.S. Public*, pg. 129
Hallinan, William J., Sr. V.P., Gen. Counsel & Sec.--The FINOVA Group Inc., Phoenix, AZ; *U.S. Public*, pg. 624
Hallman, Russel, Sr. V.P.-Mktg. & Sls.--Electronic Data Magnetics, Inc., High Point, NC; *U.S. Private*, pg. 370
Hallowell, Chris, Sr. V.P. & Mng. Dir.--The Program Exchange, New York, NY; *U.S. Public*, pg. 1422
Hallsey, James, Sr. V.P.--Smith's Food & Drug Centers, Inc., Salt Lake City, UT; *U.S. Public*, pg. 1103
Halluska, Richard, Sr. V.P.--OMI Corp., New York, NY; *U.S. Public*, pg. 1208
Hallworth, Bruce J., Sr. V.P.-Corp. Lending--Citizens Savings Bank, Providence, RI; *Int'l*, pg. 1132
Hallworth, Bruce J., Sr. V.P.-Corp. Lending--Citizens Trust Company, Providence, RI; *Int'l*, pg. 1132
Halmrast, Dave, Sr. V.P.-Corp. Plng.--AFLAC Incorporated, Columbus, GA; *U.S. Public*, pg. 28
Halper, Lynn M., Sr. V.P.--Trenwick America Reinsurance Corporation, Stamford, CT; *U.S. Public*, pg. 1634
Halperin, Richard E., Sr. V.P.--MacAndrews & Forbes Holdings Inc., New York, NY; *U.S. Private*, pg. 689
Halpin, Denise, Partner & Sr. V.P.--Media That Works, Cincinnati, OH; *U.S. Private*, pg. 727
Halpin, Julie, Sr. V.P. & Gen. Mgr.--Saatchi & Saatchi Kid Connection, New York, NY; *U.S. Public*, pg. 1422
Halrorsen, William T., Sr. V.P.-Western Div.--Chicago Title Insurance Co., Chicago, IL; *U.S. Public*, pg. 42
Halse, Bengt, Sr. V.P.-Microwave Systems--Telefonaktiebolaget LM Ericsson, Stockholm, Sweden; *Int'l*, pg. 1363
Halstead, Burnett A., Jr., Sr. V.P.--First Penn-Pacific Life Insurance Co., Oak Brook Terrace, IL; *U.S. Public*, pg. 998
Halversen, David, Sr. V.P.-Bus. Devel. & Commun.--Tupperware Corporation, Orlando, FL; *U.S. Public*, pg. 1644
Halverson, Steve, Sr. V.P.-Bus. Devel.--M.A. Mortenson Company, Minneapolis, MN; *U.S. Private*, pg. 763
Hamann, Curtis, Dr., Sr. V.P. & Medical Dir.--Tactyl Technologies, Inc., Vista, CA; *U.S. Public*, pg. 1425
Hamann, Dennis, Chief Fin. Officer & Sr. V.P.--Young's Holdings Inc., Orange, CA; *U.S. Private*, pg. 1202
Hamburg, Ed, Chief Fin. Officer & Sr. V.P.--SPSS Inc., Chicago, IL; *U.S. Public*, pg. 1420
Hamburger, Alan, Sr. V.P. & Sr. Creative Dir.--Rubin Ehrenthal & Associates, New York, NY; *U.S. Private*, pg. 949
Hamel, Dave, Sr. V.P.--Cramer-Krasselt, Chicago, IL; *U.S. Private*, pg. 285
Hames, Cedar, Sr. V.P.-St. Petersburg--Yesawich, Pepperdine & Brown, Orlando, FL; *U.S. Private*, pg. 1195
Hames, Ronald, Chief Fin. Officer & Sr. V.P.--Harbor Financial Mortgage Corp., Houston, TX; *U.S. Public*, pg. 644
Hamill, Randy A., Sr. V.P.-Mfg. & Resources--Square Two Golf Incorporated, Fairfield, NJ; *U.S. Public*, pg. 1501
Hamilton, Gary L., Sr. V.P.--Intercool Energy Corporation, Latham, NY; *U.S. Public*, pg. 894
Hamilton, J. Chad, Sr. V.P.-Trust Dept.--Zions First National Bank, Salt Lake City, UT; *U.S. Public*, pg. 1793
Hamilton, James P., Sr. V.P.--General Reinsurance Corp., Stamford, CT; *U.S. Public*, pg. 725
Hamilton, John, Sr. V.P.-Fin.--Parmalat Canada Ltd., Etobicoke, Canada; *Int'l*, pg. 1023
Hamilton, John M., Sr. V.P.-Opers.--Heilig-Meyers Company, Richmond, VA; *U.S. Public*, pg. 804
Hamilton, Lawrence W., Sr. V.P.-Human Resources--Tech Data Corporation, Clearwater, FL; *U.S. Public*, pg. 1562
Hamilton, Marianne, Sr. V.P.-Organization Devel. & Mgmt. Resources--Atlas Copco AB, Stockholm, Sweden; *Int'l*, pg. 95
Hamilton, Michael, Sr. V.P.-Personnel Training & Dev.--First Citizens Banc Shares, Inc., Raleigh, NC; *U.S. Public*, pg. 628
Hamilton, Pamela J., Sr. V.P.-Human Resources, Environment, Health & Safety--W.R. Grace & Co., Boca Raton, FL; *U.S. Public*, pg. 754
Hamilton, Peter B., Chief Fin. Officer, Sr. V.P. & Sec.--Brunswick Corporation, Lake Forest, IL; *U.S. Public*, pg. 265
Hamilton, Richard J.M., Sr. V.P. & Controller--ITT Industries, Inc., White Plains, NY; *U.S. Public*, pg. 859
Hamilton, Stephen G., Sr. V.P., Gen. Counsel & Sec.--Computer Sales International Inc., Saint Louis, MO; *U.S. Private*, pg. 260
Hamilton, Stephen W., Sr. V.P.-Intl.--Comdisco, Inc., Rosemont, IL; *U.S. Public*, pg. 407
Hamlin, Hatti, Sr. V.P. & Gen. Mgr.-Pub. Rels.--EvansGroup, San Francisco, CA; *U.S. Private*, pg. 385
Hamlin, Paul J., Sr. V.P.-Consumer Admin.--Chittenden Corporation, Burlington, VT; *U.S. Public*, pg. 350
Hamlin, William, Chief Fin. Officer & Sr. V.P.--C & S Wholesale Grocery Inc., Brattleboro, VT; *U.S. Private*, pg. 192
Hamline, Steven T., Sr. V.P.--J.E. Dunn Construction Co., Kansas City, MO; *U.S. Private*, pg. 347
Hamm, Alexander J., Sr. V.P.--Bioproducts, Inc., Fairlawn, OH; *U.S. Private*, pg. 145
Hammer, Carol A., Sr. V.P.--La Petite Academy Inc., Overland Park, KS; *U.S. Private*, pg. 640
Hammer, Steven G., Sr. V.P.--Indiana Lawrence Bank, North Manchester, IN; *U.S. Public*, pg. 633
Hammer, Thomas L., Sr. V.P.-Buying & Mdsg.--PriceSmart Inc., San Diego, CA; *U.S. Public*, pg. 1324
Hammett, Craig M., Chief Fin. Officer & Sr. V.P.--CalEnergy Co., Omaha, NE; *U.S. Public*, pg. 292
Hammett, Ric, Sr. V.P.-Sls.--Baltimore Stationery Co./Total Office, Baltimore, MD; *U.S. Private*, pg. 113
Hammic, David, Sr. V.P.--Competitive Media Reporting, New York, NY; *Int'l*, pg. 1447
Hammill, Dick, Sr. V.P.-Adv. & Mktg.--The Home Depot, Inc., Atlanta, GA; *U.S. Public*, pg. 831
Hammond, Dwain, Sr. V.P.-Engrng.--InterVoice, Inc., Dallas, TX; *U.S. Public*, pg. 910
Hammond, J., Sr. V.P.--Del Mar Avionics, Irvine, CA; *U.S. Private*, pg. 321
Hammond, Jack A., Sr. V.P.--Westvaco Corporation, New York, NY; *U.S. Public*, pg. 1762
Hammond, Michael R., Sr. V.P.-Mkt. Svcs.--Attorneys' Title Insurance Fund, Orlando, FL; *U.S. Private*, pg. 98
Hammond, Stella M., Sr. V.P.--Acadian Asset Management, Boston, MA; *U.S. Public*, pg. 1672
Hammons, Ron L., Sr. V.P.-Human Resources & Pur.--Johns Manville Corporation, Denver, CO; *U.S. Public*, pg. 927
Hampel, William F., Sr. V.P.-Res. & Devel.--Credit Union National Association, Madison, WI; *U.S. Private*, pg. 288
Hampson, Jim, Sr. V.P.-Mktg.--Great Western Consumer Finance Group, Tampa, FL; *U.S. Public*, pg. 1741
Hampton, Cynthia, Sr. V.P. & Acct. Mng. Dir.--Young & Rubicam New York, New York, NY; *U.S. Private*, pg. 1198
Hampton, Dennis E., Sr. V.P.-Trust--Omega Bank, N.A., State College, PA; *U.S. Public*, pg. 1222
Hampton, John L.M., Sr. V.P., Gen. Counsel & Sec.--Potash Corporation of Saskatchewan Inc., Saskatoon, Canada; *Int'l*, pg. 1064
Hampton, John W., Sr. V.P. - Fin.--NTS Development Company, Louisville, KY; *U.S. Private*, pg. 772
Hamwey, Emile J., Sr. V.P. & Treas.--Fay, Spofford & Thorndike, Inc., Burlington, MA; *U.S. Private*, pg. 397
Hamza, Ezzeldin A., Sr. V.P.-Res. & Devel.--Barr Laboratories Inc., Pomona, NY; *U.S. Public*, pg. 191
Hanawa, Akihiko, Sr. Mng. Dir.-Gen. Mdsg.--Ito-Yokado Co., Ltd., Tokyo, Japan; *Int'l*, pg. 693
Hance, Charles E., Sr. V.P. & Gen. Counsel--Beneficial Management Corporation, Peapack, NJ; *U.S. Public*, pg. 211
Hance, Charles E., Sr. V.P. & Gen. Counsel--Beneficial Management Corporation of America & Affiliated Corps., Wilmington, DE; *U.S. Public*, pg. 211
Hancock, John W., Sr. V.P. & Treas.--Atlantic American Corporation, Atlanta, GA; *U.S. Public*, pg. 143
Hancock, Joyce K., Sr. V.P. & Controller--First Federal of Michigan, Detroit, MI; *U.S. Public*, pg. 336
Hancock, Norman L., Chief Compliance Officer & Sr. V.P.--Scott & Stringfellow Financial, Inc., Richmond, VA; *U.S. Public*, pg. 1445
Hancock, Norman L., Sr. V.P.--Scott & Stringfellow, Inc., Richmond, VA; *U.S. Public*, pg. 1445
Hancock, Scott, Sr. V.P.-Mktg. & Sls.--Unapix Entertainment Inc., New York, NY; *U.S. Public*, pg. 1664
Handa, Nar, Sr. V.P.--Plastek Group, Erie, PA; *U.S. Private*, pg. 870
Handelsman, Harold, Sr. V.P. & Gen. Counsel--Hyatt Corporation, Chicago, IL; *U.S. Private*, pg. 551
Handley, John M., Sr. V.P.-Mktg. & Sls.--Industrial Acoustics Company, Inc., Bronx, NY; *U.S. Public*, pg. 875
Handley, Richard L., Sr. V.P. & Gen. Counsel--Florida Panthers Holdings, Inc., Fort Lauderdale, FL; *U.S. Public*, pg. 654
Handley, Richard L., Sr. V.P., Gen. Counsel & Sec.--Republic Industries, Inc., Fort Lauderdale, FL; *U.S. Public*, pg. 1378
Handy, Edard O., III, Sr. V.P.-Comml. Real Estate Lending--Citizens Savings Bank, Providence, RI; *Int'l*, pg. 1132
Haneda, Katsuo, Sr. V.P.--Japan Airlines Company, Ltd., Tokyo, Japan; *Int'l*, pg. 699
Haney, R.H., Sr. V.P.-Electrical Bus.--Graybar Electric Company, Inc., Clayton, MO; *U.S. Private*, pg. 472
Haney, R.L., Chief Fin. Officer & Sr. V.P.--Orange and Rockland Utilities, Inc., Pearl River, NY; *U.S. Public*, pg. 1229
Haney, Robert W., Sr. V.P.-Claims--Acceptance Insurance Co., Inc., Omaha, NE; *U.S. Public*, pg. 14
Hankins, Robert D., Sr. V.P.-Banking Supervision, Discount, Credit & Fin. Indus.--Federal Reserve Bank of Dallas, Dallas, TX; *U.S. Private*, pg. 399
Hankins, Steven, Sr. V.P.-Fin. Plng. & Shared Services--Tyson Foods, Inc., Springdale, AR; *U.S. Public*, pg. 1652
Hanks, Douglas R., Sr. V.P.-Mktg.--CNB Bancshares, Inc., Evansville, IN; *U.S. Public*, pg. 280
Hanks, Ken, Sr. V.P.-Sls.--Ranir Corporation/DCP, Grand Rapids, MI; *U.S. Private*, pg. 909
Hanley, Brian, Sr. V.P. & Grp. Media Dir.--Young & Rubicam New York, New York, NY; *U.S. Private*, pg. 1198
Hanley, Joseph P., Sr. V.P.-Asset Quality Review Exec.--The Dime Savings Bank of New York, New York, NY; *U.S. Public*, pg. 509
Hanley, Patrick D., Chief Fin. Officer & Sr. V.P.--Overnite Transportation Co., Richmond, VA; *U.S. Public*, pg. 1668
Hanley, Philip M., Sr. V.P. & Chief Fin. Officer--American General Finance, Inc., Evansville, IN; *U.S. Public*, pg. 76
Hanna, John A., Chief Fin. Officer, Sr. V.P.-Fin. & Admin.--Westburne Inc., Montreal, Canada; *Int'l*, pg. 1491
Hannah, Thomas A., Sr. V.P.-Opers.--The Good Guys, Inc., Brisbane, CA; *U.S. Public*, pg. 750
Hannibal, Ed, Sr. V.P. & Grp. Creative Dir.--Grey Advertising Inc., New York, NY; *U.S. Public*, pg. 764
Hanning, Franz, Sr. V.P.-Corp. Sls.--Fairfield Communities, Inc., Little Rock, AR; *U.S. Public*, pg. 610
Hanno, Marshall W., Sr. V.P.-Sls.--LCI International, Inc., Dublin, OH; *U.S. Public*, pg. 969
Hannon, Kevin P., Sr. V.P. & Sec.--Admiral Insurance Company, Cherry Hill, NJ; *U.S. Public*, pg. 216
Hanover, Jerome A., Sr. V.P.--Belz Enterprises, Memphis, TN; *U.S. Private*, pg. 132
Hanrahan, Timothy J., Sr. V.P.--Meridian Insurance Group, Inc., Indianapolis, IN; *U.S. Public*, pg. 1095
Hans, Allen, Sr. V.P. & Gen. Counsel--Minolta Corporation, Ramsey, NJ; *Int'l*, pg. 869
Hans, Robert, Sr. V.P.-Info. Sys. Admin.--Federal Home Loan Bank of New York, New York, NY; *U.S. Private*, pg. 399
Hansberry, Thomas J., Sr. V.P.--Huntington National Bank, Morgantown, WV; *U.S. Public*, pg. 850
Hansbrough, John R., Sr. V.P.-Mngmt. Info. Sys.--Jitney-Jungle Stores of America, Inc., Jackson, MS; *U.S. Private*, pg. 588
Hanscom, S. Wayne, Sr. V.P.--McCain Citrus Inc., Oak Brook, IL; *Int'l*, pg. 850
Hansen, Dave, Sr. V.P.-Store Opers.--Ralphs Grocery Company, Compton, CA; *U.S. Private*, pg. 1202
Hansen, Dennis R., Sr. V.P. & Controller--Westamerica Bancorporation, Fairfield, CA; *U.S. Public*, pg. 1756
Hansen, Frank J., Chief Oper. Officer & Sr. V.P.-Opers.--IDEX Corporation, Northbrook, IL; *U.S. Public*, pg. 862
Hansen, Glenn J., Sr. V.P.-Auditing--BPA International, New York, NY; *U.S. Private*, pg. 107
Hansen, H.F., Sr. V.P.--Central Gulf Lines, Inc., New Orleans, LA; *U.S. Public*, pg. 907
Hansen, Jorgen H., Sr. V.P.-Eastern Reg.--Hilton Hotels Div., Beverly Hills, CA; *U.S. Public*, pg. 829
Hansen, Kent E., Sr. V.P. & Sec.--Fedders Corp., Liberty Corner, NJ; *U.S. Public*, pg. 614
Hansen, Larry, Chief Fin. Officer & Sr. V.P.--Signet Star Holdings, Inc., Stamford, CT; *U.S. Public*, pg. 216
Hansen, Raymond A., Sr. V.P.-Opers.--ADVO, Inc., Windsor, CT; *U.S. Public*, pg. 23
Hansen, Richard A., Sr. V.P.--New York Life Insurance Company, New York, NY; *U.S. Private*, pg. 794
Hansen, Stephen, Chief Fin. Officer& Sr. V.P.--Universal Studios Recreation Services Group, Universal City, CA; *Int'l*, pg. 1216
Hansen, Thomas E., Sr. V.P. & Reg. Mgr.--Community First Bankshares, Inc., Fargo, ND; *U.S. Public*, pg. 416
Hanson, Breck, Grp. Sr. V.P.-Real Estate--LaSalle National Bank, Chicago, IL; *Int'l*, pg. 10
Hanson, Dave, Sr. V.P.-Opers.-Wisconsin--Marcus Cable Company, L.P., Dallas, TX; *U.S. Private*, pg. 702
Hanson, Lawrence W., Sr. V.P.--Canadian Western Bank, Edmonton, Canada; *Int'l*, pg. 259
Hanson, Marcia S., Sr. V.P.--Firstar Corporation-Iowa, Des Moines, IA; *U.S. Public*, pg. 643
Hanson, Richard, Sr. V.P.-Sls.--Northland Aluminum Products, Inc., Minneapolis, MN; *U.S. Private*, pg. 805
Hara, Sadao, Sr. V.P.--Japan Airlines Company, Ltd., Tokyo, Japan; *Int'l*, pg. 699
Harada, Tadakazu, Sr. V.P.-Tire Devel.--Bridgestone Corporation, Tokyo, Japan; *Int'l*, pg. 213
Harada, Yuki, Sr. V.P.--Sanwa Bank California, Los Angeles, CA; *Int'l*, pg. 1189
Haraway, James E., Sr. V.P.-Eastern Reg.--Wyle Electronics, Irvine, CA; *Int'l*, pg. 1457
Harbeck, Tom, Sr. V.P.-Nickelodean Mktg. & On-Air Promo. & Creative Dir.--Nickelodeon/Nick At Nite, New York, NY; *U.S. Private*, pg. 779
Harber, H.F., Sr. V.P.-Corp. Services--Atmos Energy Corporation, Dallas, TX; *U.S. Public*, pg. 145
Harbin, Roger F., Sr. V.P.--SAFECO Life and Health Insurance Companies, Redmond, WA; *U.S. Public*, pg. 1423
Harde, Karl, Sr. V.P.-Benelux/Scandinavia & Source Plasma Europe--Haemonetics Corporation, Braintree, MA; *U.S. Public*, pg. 773
Harden, David R., Sr. V.P. & Pres.-West Penn/CDT--Cable Design Technologies Corporation, Pittsburgh, PA; *U.S. Public*, pg. 287
Harden, Oleta J., Sr. V.P., Gen. Counsel & Corp. Sec.--New Jersey Resources Corporation, Wall, NJ; *U.S. Public*, pg. 1172
Harding, Lester L., Sr. V.P.--United Southwest Bank, Washington, IN; *U.S. Public*, pg. 1217
Harding, Steve, Chief Fin. Officer & Sr. V.P.--Neiman Marcus Co., Dallas, TX; *U.S. Public*, pg. 785
Hardt, Laurel K., Chief Info. Officer & Sr. V.P.--Fred Meyer Stores, Portland, OR; *U.S. Public*, pg. 1103
Hare, Dan, Sr. V.P.--EJL Advertising/Chicago, Chicago, IL; *U.S. Private*, pg. 673
Haren, H. Joseph, Chief Info. Officer & Sr. V.P.--FirstMerit Corporation, Akron, OH; *U.S. Public*, pg. 646
Hargadine, Richard C., Sr. V.P.--United Missouri Bank of Boonville, Boonville, MO; *U.S. Public*, pg. 1654
Hargraves, Ann D., Sr. V.P.--Fleet Bank NH, Hooksett, NH; *U.S. Public*, pg. 649
Harkey, Robert S., Sr. V.P., Gen. Counsel & Sec.--Delta Air Lines, Inc., Atlanta, GA; *U.S. Public*, pg. 497
Harkness, Brian, Sr. V.P. & New Bus. Dir.--SBC Advertising, Columbus, OH; *U.S. Private*, pg. 955
Harling, Cal C., Sr. V.P.--GATX Capital Corporation, San Francisco, CA; *U.S. Public*, pg. 690
Harlow, John, Sr. V.P.-Opers.--Genovese Drug Stores, Inc., Melville, NY; *U.S. Public*, pg. 730
Harlow, Robert D., Sr. V.P. & Gen. Mgr.-Mills & Molded Fibre--Tenneco Packaging, Evanston, IL; *U.S. Public*, pg. 1579
Harmon, Barry L., Chief Fin. Officer & Sr. V.P.--Electro Scientific Industries, Inc., Portland, OR; *U.S. Public*, pg. 568
Harmon, Samuel W., Sr. V.P.-H.R.--GenCorp Inc., Fairlawn, OH; *U.S. Public*, pg. 705
Harmon, Thomas F., Sr. V.P.--Chicago Asset Management Company, Chicago, IL; *U.S. Public*, pg. 1672

Harner, James F., Sr. V.P.-Customer Service & Opers.--The May Department Stores Company, Saint Louis, MO; *U.S. Public*, pg. 1063
Harnett, Ralph, Sr. V.P.--Raychem Corporation, Menlo Park, CA; *U.S. Public*, pg. 1362
Harnett, Susan, Sr. V.P. & Mng. Dir.-Opers.--Citibank, Federal Savings Bank (Illinois), Chicago, IL; *U.S. Public*, pg. 378
Harper, Benny, Sr. V.P.-Fin., Treas. & Sec.--Friedman Industries, Inc., Houston, TX; *U.S. Public*, pg. 682
Harper, I.D., Sr. V.P.-British Columbia--HongKong Bank of Canada, Vancouver, Canada; *Int'l*, pg. 583
Harper, John W., Chief Fin. Officer & Sr. V.P.-Fin.--US Airways, Inc., Arlington, VA; *U.S. Public*, pg. 1680
Harper, S.R., Sr. V.P.--Chemetics International Company Ltd Vancouver Operations, Vancouver, Canada; *Int'l*, pg. 774
Harper, Victor L., Sr. V.P.--Scott & Stringfellow, Inc., Richmond, VA; *U.S. Public*, pg. 1445
Harper, William B., Jr., Sr. V.P.-Life Opers.--Alfa Corporation, Montgomery, AL; *U.S. Public*, pg. 40
Harpur, John J., Sr. V.P. & Media Dir.--MARC, Pittsburgh, PA; *U.S. Private*, pg. 701
Harr, Lucy, Sr. V.P.-Credit Union Devel.--Credit Union National Association, Madison, WI; *U.S. Private*, pg. 288
Harreld, J. Bruce, Sr. V.P.-Strategy--International Business Machines Corporation, Armonk, NY; *U.S. Public*, pg. 895
Harrell, Francis C., Sr. V.P.-USA Sls.--International Comfort Products, Franklin, TN; *U.S. Public*, pg. 898
Harrell, Samuel A., Ph.D., Sr. V.P.--KLA Tencor Corporation, San Jose, CA; *U.S. Public*, pg. 939
Harrelson, Harvey D., Sr. V.P.--Interstate/Johnson Lane, Inc., Charlotte, NC; *U.S. Public*, pg. 909
Harrey, Jack, Sr. V.P.-SkyTel Opers.--Mobile Telecommunications Technologies Corp., Jackson, MS; *U.S. Public*, pg. 1120
Harrill, Donald L., Sr. V.P.-Vacation Ownership Opers.--Hilton Hotels Corporation, Beverly Hills, CA; *U.S. Public*, pg. 828
Harrington, Brian K., Chief Fin. Officer, Sr. V.P. & Treas.--Kirby Corporation, Houston, TX; *U.S. Public*, pg. 961
Harrington, John P., Sr. V.P.-Gas Supply & Asst. Pres.--Colonial Gas Company, Lowell, MA; *U.S. Public*, pg. 400
Harris, Charles, Sr. V.P.--Comdata Corporation, Brentwood, TN; *U.S. Public*, pg. 331
Harris, David, Chief Fin. Officer, Sr. V.P. & Dir.-Human Resources--Whitin Roberts Co., Sanford, NC; *U.S. Private*, pg. 309
Harris, E.G., Sr. V.P.-Equity Portfolios--General Electric Investment Corp., Stamford, CT; *U.S. Public*, pg. 712
Harris, Henry C., Sr. V.P.-Strategic Plng. & Alliance--Zitel Corporation, Fremont, CA; *U.S. Public*, pg. 1793
Harris, Lee A., Sr. V.P., Gen. Counsel & Sec.--IRT Property Company, Atlanta, GA; *U.S. Public*, pg. 858
Harris, Marva H., Sr. V.P.--PNC Bank Corp., Pittsburgh, PA; *U.S. Public*, pg. 1242
Harris, Michael G., Sr. V.P.-Engrng.--Century Communications Corp., New Canaan, CT; *U.S. Public*, pg. 329
Harris, Patrick B., Sr. V.P.-Sls. & Retail--News America Marketing, Norwalk, CT; *Int'l*, pg. 925
Harris, Paul, Sr. V.P. & Gen. Mgr.--British Aerospace Holdings Inc., Chantilly, VA; *Int'l*, pg. 218
Harris, R., Sr. V.P. & Broadcast Production Dir.--BBDO Canada, Toronto, Canada; *U.S. Private*, pg. 104
Harris, Susan, Sr. V.P. & Media Dir.--CSI International Corporation, New York, NY; *U.S. Private*, pg. 197
Harris, Susan L., Sr. V.P., Gen. Counsel & Sec.--SunAmerica Inc., Los Angeles, CA; *U.S. Public*, pg. 1532
Harrison, Barry, Sr. V.P.-RE Lending--Nevada State Bank, Las Vegas, NV; *U.S. Public*, pg. 1793
Harrison, David H., Sr. V.P.--Manheim Auctions, Inc., Atlanta, GA; *U.S. Private*, pg. 282
Harrison, F. Alison, Sr. V.P.--Mosby-Year Book, Inc., Saint Louis, MO; *U.S. Public*, pg. 1616
Harrison, James F., Sr. V.P.-Sls. & Mktg.--Muzak Limited Partnership, Seattle, WA; *U.S. Private*, pg. 222
Harrison, Lloyd B., Sr. V.P.--The National Bank of Fredericksburg, Fredericksburg, VA; *U.S. Public*, pg. 1089
Harrison, Robert E., Chief Fin. Officer & Sr. V.P.--Standard Commercial Tobacco Co., Inc., Wilson, NC; *U.S. Public*, pg. 1502
Harrison, Sam, Sr. V.P. Creative Dir.--The Check Store, Lakewood, CO; *U.S. Public*, pg. 785
Harrison, Thomas, Sr. V.P.--K-Swiss Inc., Chatsworth, CA; *U.S. Public*, pg. 937
Harriton, Lorraine, Sr. V.P.-Mktg. & Bus. Devel.--Network Computing Devices, Inc., Mountain View, CA; *U.S. Public*, pg. 1168
Harrold, Tim, Exec. V.P.-Classical Music--Polygram N.V., Baarn, Netherlands; *Int'l*, pg. 1051
Harslem, Eric F., Sr. V.P.-Prod. & Tech. Strategy--Dell Computer Corporation, Round Rock, TX; *U.S. Public*, pg. 495
Hart, Cynthia L., Sr. V.P. & Dir.-Sls. & Banking Opers.--Bay View Capital Corporation, San Mateo, CA; *U.S. Public*, pg. 197
Hart, David L., V.P. & Asst to Pres.--Ohio Valley Electric Corporation, Piketon, OH; *U.S. Private*, pg. 813
Hart, John H., Chief Tech. Officer & Sr. V.P.--3Com Corporation, Santa Clara, CA; *U.S. Public*, pg. 1603
Hart, Peter, Sr. V.P.-Mngmt. Information Systems--Ross Stores, Inc., Newark, CA; *U.S. Public*, pg. 1405
Hart, Robert M., Sr. V.P., Gen. Counsel & Sec.--Alleghany Corporation, New York, NY; *U.S. Public*, pg. 42
Hart, Stanley V., Sr. V.P.--Terre Haute First National Bank, Terre Haute, IN; *U.S. Public*, pg. 634
Harte, Mary, Sr. V.P. & Mngmt. Supvr.--FerrellCalvillo Communications, Inc., New York, NY; *U.S. Private*, pg. 401
Harter, James M., Sr. V.P.-Newhall Ranch Co.--The Newhall Land And Farming Company, Valencia, CA; *U.S. Public*, pg. 1178
Harter, Robert J., Jr., Sr. V.P.-Admin. & Gen. Counsel--Rykoff-Sexton, Inc., Wilkes-Barre, PA; *U.S. Public*, pg. 918
Hartigan, Edward G., Sr. V.P.--ITT Educational Services, Inc., Indianapolis, IN; *U.S. Public*, pg. 1512
Hartlage, James A., Sr. V.P.-Tech. & Opers.--Stepan Company, Northfield, IL; *U.S. Public*, pg. 1514
Hartman, Brent, Sr. V.P.-Opers.--Meridian Insurance Group, Inc., Indianapolis, IN; *U.S. Public*, pg. 1095
Hartman, Donn A., Sr. V.P.--Cloud Corporation, Des Plaines, IL; *U.S. Private*, pg. 247
Hartman, Gerald W., Sr. V.P.-Opers.--MasTec, Inc., Miami, FL; *U.S. Public*, pg. 1055
Hartmann, Chris, Sr. V.P.--Grey Advertising Inc., New York, NY; *U.S. Public*, pg. 764
Hartrich, James E., Sr. V.P.--Mullen Advertising, Inc., Wenham, MA; *U.S. Private*, pg. 766
Hartwall, Jerker, Sr. V.P.--Perstorp AB, Perstorp, Sweden; *Int'l*, pg. 1036
Hartwig, Eugene L., Sr. V.P., Gen. Counsel & Sec.--Kelly Services, Inc., Troy, MI; *U.S. Public*, pg. 949
Harvey, F.L. Mike, Sr. V.P. & Grp. Pres.--Sterling Software, Inc., Dallas, TX; *U.S. Public*, pg. 1516
Harvey, Kent M., Chief Fin. Officer, Sr. V.P. & Treas.--Pacific Gas & Electric Company, San Francisco, CA; *U.S. Public*, pg. 1241
Harvey, William D., Sr. V.P.--South Beloit Water, Gas & Electric Co., South Beloit, IL; *U.S. Public*, pg. 1728
Harwood, Brent, Sr. V.P.--Arnold Communications, Inc., Boston, MA; *U.S. Private*, pg. 83
Harwood, George L., Chief Fin. Officer, Sr. V.P-Information Systems & Sec.--Printronix, Inc., Irvine, CA; *U.S. Public*, pg. 1329
Hasbrouck, John C., Sr. V.P.--Zenith Insurance Company, Woodland Hills, CA; *U.S. Public*, pg. 1791
Haschke, Lynda, Sr. V.P.--Ackerman McQueen, Inc., Tulsa, OK; *U.S. Private*, pg. 13
Hashem, Ghazi J., Sr. V.P.-Tech. Opers.--EVI, Inc., Houston, TX; *U.S. Public*, pg. 547
Hashiguchi, Ryuji, Sr. Mng. Dir.--Namco Ltd., Tokyo, Japan; *Int'l*, pg. 905
Hashimoto, Goro, Sr. V.P.--Softbank Corporation, Tokyo, Japan; *Int'l*, pg. 1276
Haskell, Charles L., Sr. Exec. V.P.--Lettuce Entertain You Enterprises, Inc., Chicago, IL; *U.S. Private*, pg. 661
Haskell, Eric, Chief Fin. Officer, Sr. V.P.-Fin. & Admin., & Treas.--Systems & Computer Technology Corporation, Malvern, PA; *U.S. Public*, pg. 1552
Haskell, Robert G., Sr. V.P.-Public Affairs--Pacific Life Insurance Company, Newport Beach, CA; *U.S. Private*, pg. 831
Hasken, Walter, Sr. V.P. & Mgr.-Life & Employee Benefits Div.--Willis Corroon Corp. of Nashville, Nashville, TN; *Int'l*, pg. 1506
Hasley, Michael A., Sr. V.P.-Fin.--Sun Life Assurance Company of Canada, Toronto, Canada; *Int'l*, pg. 1318
Hason, Hugh W., Sr. V.P.--First Commerce Bancshares, Inc., Lincoln, NE; *U.S. Public*, pg. 629
Hassberger, Richard L., Sr. V.P.-Mortgage--American Bankers Life Assurance Co. of Florida, Miami, FL; *U.S. Public*, pg. 67
Hasselbusch, Stan L., Sr. V.P.-Construction & Tubular Prods.--L.B. Foster Company, Pittsburgh, PA; *U.S. Public*, pg. 675
Hasskleson, Pierre, Sr. V.P.-Opers.--ATAPCO Office Products Group, Saint Louis, MO; *U.S. Private*, pg. 64
Hasslinger, Nikolaus, Dr., Sr. V.P.-Project Fin. & Syndicated Loans--Deutsche Girozentrale-Deutsche Kommunalbank, Frankfurt/Main, Germany; *Int'l*, pg. 406
Hasson, Arthur, Sr. V.P.-Eastern Sls.--Universal Studios TV, Universal City, CA; *Int'l*, pg. 1215
Hasson, Eibert, Sr. V.P.-Human Resources--Perstorp AB, Perstorp, Sweden; *Int'l*, pg. 1036
Hastings, Donald M., Sr. V.P. & Exec. V.P.-West Penn/CDT--Cable Design Technologies Corporation, Pittsburgh, PA; *U.S. Public*, pg. 287
Hatch, J.E., Jr., Sr. V.P.-Mktg.--The Hite Company, Altoona, PA; *U.S. Private*, pg. 531
Hatch, Ronald, Sr. V.P.-Dealer Banking--Zions First National Bank, Salt Lake City, UT; *U.S. Public*, pg. 1793
Hatcher, David A., Sr. V.P.-Exploration--Santa Fe Minerals Inc., Dallas, TX; *Int'l*, pg. 765
Hatcher, Robert V., III, Sr. V.P.--Willis Faber North America, Inc.-Pennsylvania, Radnor, PA; *Int'l*, pg. 1504
Hatenbach, Brian V., Sr. V.P.--First National Bank of Naples, Naples, FL; *U.S. Public*, pg. 607
Hatfield, Bennett K., Chief Admin. Officer & Sr. V.P.--A.T. Massey Coal Company, Inc., Richmond, VA; *U.S. Public*, pg. 660
Hatfield, M.A., Sr. V.P. & Sec.--Marshall & Ilsley Corporation, Milwaukee, WI; *U.S. Public*, pg. 1049
Hathaway, Lee, Sr. V.P. & Print Production Dir.--Hill, Holliday, Connors, Cosmopulos, Inc., Boston, MA; *U.S. Private*, pg. 529
Hathaway, P.J., Sr. V.P.-Equity Portfolios--General Electric Investment Corp., Stamford, CT; *U.S. Public*, pg. 712
Haubein, Robert H., Sr. V.P.-Fossil & Hydro Power--Georgia Power Co., Atlanta, GA; *U.S. Public*, pg. 1490
Hauck, Donald F., Sr. V.P.--Bush Industries Inc., Jamestown, NY; *U.S. Public*, pg. 270
Haug, Richard L., Sr. V.P. & Gen. Auditor--Old Kent Financial Corporation, Grand Rapids, MI; *U.S. Public*, pg. 1216
Haugen, Baard, Chief Fin. Officer & Sr. V.P.--Elkem ASA, Oslo, Norway; *Int'l*, pg. 446
Haught, Melvin, Sr. V.P.-Opers.--Pella Corporation, Pella, IA; *U.S. Private*, pg. 848
Haunschild, Robert L., Chief Fin. Officer & Sr. V.P.--PNC Bank Corp., Pittsburgh, PA; *U.S. Public*, pg. 1242
Haupert, Carolyn, Sr. V.P.-Prods. & Service--CyData, Inc., Scottsdale, AZ; *U.S. Public*, pg. 770
Hauser, Cindy, Sr. V.P.-Print Adv.--Fox Broadcasting Company (FBC), Beverly Hills, CA; *Int'l*, pg. 926
Hauser, Fred P., Sr. V.P. & Controller--Metropolitan Life Insurance Co., New York, NY; *U.S. Private*, pg. 737
Haussener, Albert, Sr. V.P.--ITT Information Services, Inc., New York, NY; *U.S. Public*, pg. 1512
Havel, Rick, Sr. V.P.--Petty Company, Inc., Effingham, IL; *U.S. Private*, pg. 860
Havens, Christopher, Sr. V.P.-Retail Mktg.--Ultramar Diamond Shamrock Corporation, San Antonio, TX; *U.S. Public*, pg. 1663
Haver, Kenneth W., Chief Fin. Officer & Sr. V.P.--Telxon Corporation, Akron, OH; *U.S. Public*, pg. 1573
Hawes, Aubrey, Sr. V.P.-Corp. Mktg. Resources--The Chase Manhattan Bank, New York, NY; *U.S. Public*, pg. 338
Hawes, John R., Sr. V.P.--M & I Bank of Racine, Racine, WI; *U.S. Public*, pg. 1050
Hawes, Peter B., Sr. V.P.--Orion Capital Corporation, New York, NY; *U.S. Public*, pg. 1231
Hawk, Jim, Sr. V.P.--Rosendin Electric, Inc., San Jose, CA; *U.S. Private*, pg. 945
Hawkes, John, Sr. V.P. & Chief Mktg. Officer--McDonald's Hamburgers Limited, London, United Kingdom; *U.S. Public*, pg. 1069
Hawkes, Phil, Sr. V.P.-Sls. & Mktg.--Abco Markets, Inc., Phoenix, AZ; *U.S. Private*, pg. 10
Hawkey, L.W., Jr., Sr. V.P.-Devel. & Acq.--Hostmark Management Group, Rolling Meadows, IL; *U.S. Private*, pg. 541
Hawkins, D. Hunt, Sr. V.P.-Human Resources--Stein Mart, Inc., Jacksonville, FL; *U.S. Public*, pg. 1514
Hawkins, Jonathan A., Chief Fin. Officer & Sr. V.P.--Southern States Cooperative, Inc., Richmond, VA; *U.S. Private*, pg. 1017
Hawkins, Lawrence, Sr. V.P. & Pres.-Investors Trust, Inc.--Stewart Enterprises, Inc., Metairie, LA; *U.S. Public*, pg. 1518
Hawkins, Philip E., Sr. V.P.- Stores--The Vons Companies, Inc., Arcadia, CA; *U.S. Public*, pg. 1426
Hawkins, Thomas W., Sr. V.P., Gen. Counsel & Sec.--Blockbuster Entertainment Group, Dallas, TX; *U.S. Private*, pg. 775
Hawkins, Thomas W., Sr. V.P.-Corp. Devel.--Republic Industries, Inc., Fort Lauderdale, FL; *U.S. Public*, pg. 1378
Hawks, Tammeria K., Sr. V.P.--Norwest Financial, Inc., Des Moines, IA; *U.S. Public*, pg. 1202
Hawley, Edmund, Chief Exec. Officer & Sr. V.P.--Skyway Freight Systems, Inc., Watsonville, CA; *U.S. Private*, pg. 1005
Hawley, Phillip W., Sr. V.P.--Arthur D. Little, Inc., Cambridge, MA; *U.S. Private*, pg. 670
Hawn, Eric, Sr. V.P.-Stores--The Dress Barn, Inc., Suffern, NY; *U.S. Public*, pg. 528
Haworth, Jim H., Sr. V.P.-Opers.--Sam's Clubs Div., Bentonville, AR; *U.S. Public*, pg. 1733
Haworth, Leslie W., Chief Fin. Officer & Sr. V.P.--Laidlaw Inc., Burlington, Canada; *Int'l*, pg. 259
Hay, Frederick D., Sr. V.P.-Transportation--Snap-On Tools Corporation, Kenosha, WI; *U.S. Public*, pg. 1480
Hay, Lewis, III, Chief Fin. Officer & Sr. V.P.--JP Foodservice, Inc., Columbia, MD; *U.S. Public*, pg. 918
Hay, Lewis, III, Chief Fin. Officer & Sr. V.P.--JP Foodservice Distributors, Inc., Columbia, MD; *U.S. Public*, pg. 918
Hay, Maureene, Sr. V.P. & Acct. Grp. Dir.--Western International Media Corporation, Los Angeles, CA; *U.S. Private*, pg. 1165
Hayashi, Hiromi, Assoc. Sr. V.P.--NEC Corporation, Tokyo, Japan; *Int'l*, pg. 899
Haydamack, William J., Sr. V.P. & Gen. Mgr.-Design Software--Data I/O Corporation, Redmond, WA; *U.S. Public*, pg. 486
Hayden, Anne E., Sr. V.P.-Corp. H.R.--Metropolitan Life Insurance Co., New York, NY; *U.S. Private*, pg. 737
Hayden, Donald J., Jr., Sr. V.P.-Bus. Devel., Worldwide Pharmaceuticals Grp.--Bristol-Myers Squibb Company, New York, NY; *U.S. Public*, pg. 253
Hayden, Edmund M., III, Sr. V.P.-Credit Admin.--Banknorth Group Inc., Burlington, VT; *U.S. Public*, pg. 186
Hayden, Gerard M., Jr., Chief Fin. Officer, Sr. V.P. & Treas.--Allied Clinical Laboratories, Inc., Nashville, TN; *U.S. Public*, pg. 973
Hayden, John W., Sr. Exec. V.P.--American Modern Home Insurance Group, Amelia, OH; *U.S. Public*, pg. 1110
Hayden, Laura, Sr. V.P.-H.R.--Bruno's Inc., Birmingham, AL; *U.S. Public*, pg. 265
Hayden, Thomas, Sr. V.P.-Bus. Plng. & Communications--Showtime Networks Inc., New York, NY; *U.S. Private*, pg. 779
Haydon, Ted, Sr. V.P.-Sls. & Mktg.--Rock of Ages Canada, Inc., Beebe, Canada; *U.S. Public*, pg. 1396
Hayes, David M., Sr. V.P., Gen. Counsel & Sec.--Agway, Inc., De Witt, NY; *U.S. Private*, pg. 27
Hayes, Gregory A., Sr. V.P. & Controller--Shoney's, Inc., Nashville, TN; *U.S. Public*, pg. 1467
Hayes, J. Thomas Jr., Sr. V.P.-Opers.--Enviroq, Birmingham, AL; *U.S. Public*, pg. 881
Hayes, Jack D., Sr. V.P.-Mktg.--Kansas City Life Insurance Co., Kansas City, MO; *U.S. Public*, pg. 942
Hayes, Jimmy W., Chief Fin. Officer & Sr. V.P.-Fin.--Cox Communications, Inc., Atlanta, GA; *U.S. Public*, pg. 454
Hayes, John R., Sr. V.P.-Midwestern Reg.--Federal National Mortgage Association (Fannie Mae), Washington, DC; *U.S. Public*, pg. 615
Hayes, Peter J., Sr. V.P. & Gen. Mgr.--Chem-Trend Incorporated, Howell, MI; *Int'l*, pg. 235
Hayes, William J., Sr. V.P.--Fidelity Investments (FMR Corp.), Boston, MA; *U.S. Private*, pg. 402
Haylon, Michael E., Sr. V.P.-Pub. Bonds--Phoenix Home Life Mutual Insurance Company, Hartford, CT; *U.S. Private*, pg. 863
Haynie, John H., Sr. V.P.--Interstate/Johnson Lane, Inc., Charlotte, NC; *U.S. Public*, pg. 909
Hays, Clyde C., III, Sr. V.P.-Opers.--Luby's Cafeterias, Inc., San Antonio, TX; *U.S. Public*, pg. 1017

Hayward, Cynthia, Sr. V.P.--Chi Systems Division, Ann Arbor, MI; *U.S. Public*, pg. 1539

Hazell, Bernice, Sr. V.P.-Client Service--TMP Worldwide, Inc., New York, NY; *U.S. Private*, pg. 1064

Hazelwood, Mark L., Sr. V.P.-External Affairs--Atlantic Richfield Company, Los Angeles, CA; *U.S. Public*, pg. 144

Head, Andrea L., Sr. V.P.--BWC Financial Corp., Walnut Creek, CA; *U.S. Private*, pg. 108

Head, Joe, Sr. V.P. & Co-Founder--ODS Networks, Inc., Richardson, TX; *U.S. Public*, pg. 1206

Head, Malcolm, Sr. V.P. & Sec.--TIG Holdings, Inc., New York, NY; *U.S. Public*, pg. 1555

Heald, J.T., Sr. V.P.-Converting--Union Camp Corporation, Wayne, NJ; *U.S. Public*, pg. 1665

Healey, Dennis, Chief Fin. Officer, Sr. V.P. & Treas.--Medicore Inc., Hialeah, FL; *U.S. Public*, pg. 1080

Healey, Dennis, Sr. V.P.-Mnmgt. Information Systems--Toys "R" Us, Inc., Paramus, NJ; *U.S. Public*, pg. 1626

Healey, Paul F., Sr. V.P.--UAM Investment Services, Inc., Boston, MA; *U.S. Public*, pg. 1674

Healy, John, Sr. V.P.-Infrastructure Services--Raytheon Infrastructure Incorporated, New York, NY; *U.S. Public*, pg. 1366

Healy, Robert E., Jr., Chief Fin. Officer & Sr. V.P.-Fin. & Admin.--NovaCare Inc., King of Prussia, PA; *U.S. Public*, pg. 1203

Heaphy, Janis, Sr. V.P.-Adv.--Los Angeles Times, Los Angeles, CA; *U.S. Public*, pg. 1616

Heard, Grayson, Sr. V.P.-Mining--Consolidation Coal Co.-Mid-Continent Region, Saint Louis, MO; *U.S. Public*, pg. 531

Hearn, David A., Sr. V.P.--Willis Faber North America, Inc.-Pennslyvania, Radnor, PA; *Int'l*, pg. 1504

Hearn, Peter C., Sr. V.P. & Resident Mgr.--Willis Faber North America, Inc.-Pennslyvania, Radnor, PA; *Int'l*, pg. 1504

Hearn, William J., Jr., Sr. V.P.-Trust Mktg.--SunTrust Banks, Inc., Atlanta, GA; *U.S. Public*, pg. 1537

Hearne, Timothy C., Sr. V.P.-Fin. & Admin. Svcs.--New Jersey Natural Gas Co., Wall, NJ; *U.S. Public*, pg. 1172

Heartsell, Gordon L., Sr. V.P.--Russell Petroleum Corporation, Montgomery, AL; *U.S. Private*, pg. 953

Heath, J.B., Sr. V.P.-Construction--John Brown E & C Corporate Offices (U.S.), Houston, TX; *Int'l*, pg. 774

Heath, Jim, Chief Oper. Officer & Sr. V.P.-Construction--Gulf States, Inc., Freeport, TX; *U.S. Private*, pg. 487

Heath, Malcolm T., Sr. V.P.-U.S. Intl.--BAX Global, Irvine, CA; *U.S. Public*, pg. 1305

Heath, Rob, Sr. V.P.--CareerTrack Inc., Boulder, CO; *U.S. Public*, pg. 1555

Heath, Robert S., Sr. V.P.-Sls.--BeautiControl Cosmetics, Inc., Carrollton, TX; *U.S. Public*, pg. 198

Hebb, Walter M., Sr. V.P.-Mktg. & Prod. Devel.--General Binding Corporation, Northbrook, IL; *U.S. Public*, pg. 707

Hebble, Thomas B., Sr. V.P.--First National Bank of Pennsylvania, Hermitage, PA; *U.S. Public*, pg. 607

Heberle, Richard A., Sr. V.P.--BetzDearborn Inc., Trevose, PA; *U.S. Public*, pg. 226

Hebert, Edward M., Chief Fin. Officer, Sr. V.P. & Treas.--Rymer Foods Inc., Chicago, IL; *U.S. Public*, pg. 1414

Hecht, John R., Chief Fin. Officer & Sr. V.P.--Amcore Financial, Inc., Rockford, IL; *U.S. Public*, pg. 64

Hecht, John R., Chief Fin. Officer & Sr. V.P.--AMCORE Bank N.A., Rockford, Rockford, IL; *U.S. Public*, pg. 64

Hecht, Stephen, Sr. V.P.-Sls & Mktg.--Centimark Corporation, Canonsburg, PA; *U.S. Private*, pg. 222

Hechtman, George, Sr. V.P.-Store Opers. Western Div.--OfficeMax, Shaker Heights, OH; *U.S. Public*, pg. 1212

Heck, John, Sr. V.P.--The Scoular Company, Omaha, NE; *U.S. Private*, pg. 977

Heckel, Gary, Sr. V.P.-Opers.--Bahama Breeze, Orlando, FL; *U.S. Public*, pg. 484

Hecker, David, Sr. V.P., Sec. & Gen. Counsel--S.C. Johnson & Son, Inc., Racine, WI; *U.S. Private*, pg. 592

Hedberg, David J., Sr. V.P.-Strategic Svcs.--National Rural Utilities Cooperative Finance Corporation, Herndon, VA; *U.S. Private*, pg. 786

Hedge, Larry F., Sr. V.P.--Advanta Mortgage Corp. USA, Fort Washington, PA; *U.S. Public*, pg. 22

Hedges, Brian, Chief Fin. Officer & Sr. V.P.-Fin.--Russel Metals Inc., Mississauga, Canada; *Int'l*, pg. 1149

Hedges, Robert, Jr., Sr. V.P.--Fleet Financial Group, Inc., Boston, MA; *U.S. Public*, pg. 648

Hedlund, Karen J., Sr. V.P. & Gen. Counsel--SunAmerica Inc., Los Angeles, CA; *U.S. Public*, pg. 1532

Heeger, James J., Sr. V.P.-Small Bus.--Intuit, Inc., Mountain View, CA; *U.S. Public*, pg. 911

Heekin, W. Michael, Sr. V.P., Gen. Counsel & Sec.--American Heritage Life Investment Corp., Jacksonville, FL; *U.S. Public*, pg. 78

Heep, Don, Sr. V.P.--Tesoro Alaska Petroleum Co., Anchorage, AK; *U.S. Public*, pg. 1582

Heer, E. LeRoy, Sr. V.P. & Chief Corp. Actuary--W.R. Berkley Corporation, Greenwich, CT; *U.S. Public*, pg. 215

Heerwagen, John, Sr. V.P.--Andover Bank, Andover, MA; *U.S. Public*, pg. 112

Heerwagen, John R., Sr. V.P.--Andover Bancorp, Inc., Andover, MA; *U.S. Public*, pg. 111

Heether, Ernest, Sr. V.P.-Mdse. Opers., Plng. & Devel.--Kmart Corporation, Troy, MI; *U.S. Public*, pg. 963

Heffernan, Gerard E., Sr. V.P.--Stratton Management Company, Plymouth Meeting, PA; *U.S. Private*, pg. 1046

Heffernan, John V., Sr. V.P.--Genzyme Corporation, Cambridge, MA; *U.S. Public*, pg. 733

Heffner, Randy R., Sr. V.P.-Client Access/Opers.--3Com Corporation, Santa Clara, CA; *U.S. Public*, pg. 1603

Heffron, Brent F., Sr. V.P. & Pres.-Southern Div.--Stewart Enterprises, Inc., Metairie, LA; *U.S. Public*, pg. 1518

Hegarty, Kevin P., Sr. V.P. & Controller--Associates First Capital Corporation, Dallas, TX; *U.S. Public*, pg. 662

Hegarty, R. Cort, Sr. V.P.--United Missouri Bank Northwest, Saint Joseph, MO; *U.S. Public*, pg. 1654

Hegeman, John, Sr. V.P.-Mktg. & Distr.--MGM/UA Distribution Co., Santa Monica, CA; *U.S. Public*, pg. 1102

Heggen, Arthur W., Sr. V.P. & Sec.--American Bankers Life Assurance Co. of Florida, Miami, FL; *U.S. Public*, pg. 67

Heggie, Betty-Ann, Sr. V.P.-Corp. Rels.--Potash Corporation of Saskatchewan Inc., Saskatoon, Canada; *Int'l*, pg. 1064

Heggland, Roy T., Sr. V.P., Gen. Counsel & Sec.--Cincinnati Bell Information Systems Inc., Cincinnati, OH; *U.S. Public*, pg. 367

Heidenthal, Tom, Chief Fin. Officer & Sr. V.P.--Doane Products Co., Joplin, MO; *U.S. Private*, pg. 337

Heidenthal, Tom, Chief Fin. Officer & Sr. V.P.--Doane Products Co., Branded Sales Div., Joplin, MO; *U.S. Private*, pg. 337

Heidinger, G. F., Sr. V.P.-Fin.--Grove WorldWide, Shady Grove, PA; *Int'l*, pg. 593

Heidt, W. Daniel, Sr. V.P.-Airplane Components--Boeing Commercial Airplane Group, Renton, WA; *U.S. Public*, pg. 240

Heikinheimo, Jaakko, Sr. V.P.--Rauma Ltd., Helsinki, Finland; *Int'l*, pg. 1428

Heil, Michael, Sr. V.P.-World-Wide Consumer Business--COMPAQ Computer Corporation, Houston, TX; *U.S. Public*, pg. 417

Heil, Terry W., Sr. V.P.--Raytheon Systems Company, Arlington, VA; *U.S. Public*, pg. 1364

Heil, Terry W., Sr. V.P.--Raytheon E-Systems, Greenville, TX; *U.S. Public*, pg. 1365

Heil, William W., Jr., Sr. V.P. & Gen. Mgr.-Nonstop Software-Tandem Computers Inc., Cupertino, CA; *U.S. Public*, pg. 417

Heilman, David, Sr. V.P.-Sls. & Mktg.--Photronics, Inc., Brookfield, CT; *U.S. Public*, pg. 1293

Heim, Jim, Sr. V.P.--American Safety Razor Company, Verona, VA; *U.S. Private*, pg. 597

Heimers, Edward F., Sr. V.P.-Natl. Bus. Opers. Rx.--Sandoz Pharmaceuticals Corp., East Hanover, NJ; *Int'l*, pg. 974

Heinemann, Henry, Sr. V.P.--Keycorp, Cleveland, OH; *U.S. Public*, pg. 954

Heiner, Clyde M., Sr. V.P.--Questar Corporation, Salt Lake City, UT; *U.S. Public*, pg. 1352

Heinicka, Jeffrey R., Chief Fin. Officer & Sr. V.P.--Florida Progress Corporation, Saint Petersburg, FL; *U.S. Public*, pg. 655

Heininger, Dan, Sr. V.P. & Gen. Counsel--Renaissance International Hotels, Cleveland, OH; *U.S. Public*, pg. 1048

Heinle, Herman J., Sr. V.P. & Gen. Mgr.-Mdsg.--Jacobson Stores Inc., Jackson, MI; *U.S. Public*, pg. 922

Heinz, James J., Exec. V.P., Consumer Div. Mgr. & Acct. Exec.--Colle & McVoy, Inc., Minneapolis, MN; *U.S. Private*, pg. 252

Heipt, J. Dennis, Sr. V.P.-Admin. & Sec.--Science Applications International Corp., San Diego, CA; *U.S. Private*, pg. 975

Heise, Arthur G., Sr. V.P. & Auditor--Mercantile Bancorporation Inc., Saint Louis, MO; *U.S. Public*, pg. 1087

Heise, Arthur G., Sr. V.P. & Auditor--Mercantile Bank of St. Louis N.A., Saint Louis, MO; *U.S. Public*, pg. 1087

Heistad, John R., Chief Credit Officer & Sr. V.P.--Firstar Corporation, Milwaukee, WI; *U.S. Public*, pg. 642

Heitz, Bill, Sr. V.P. & Mgr.-E. Region--Heery International, Inc., Atlanta, GA; *U.S. Private*, pg. 519

Held, Bryan H., Chief Fin. Officer & Sr. V.P.--Derlan Industries Limited, Toronto, Canada; *Int'l*, pg. 395

Held, George F., Sr. V.P. & Dir.-CARITRAK--Creswell, Munsell, Fultz & Zirbel, L.P., Cedar Rapids, IA; *U.S. Private*, pg. 1197

Held, Gerald, Sr. V.P.-Server Tech.--Oracle Corporation, Redwood City, CA; *U.S. Public*, pg. 1227

Held, Molly, Sr. V.P.-Admin. & Treas.--Lundy Packing Co., Clinton, NC; *U.S. Private*, pg. 681

Heldman, Barbara, Sr. V.P.-Fin. & Admin.--Northlich Stolley LaWarre, Cincinnati, OH; *U.S. Private*, pg. 806

Heldman, Paul W., Sr. V.P., Gen. Counsel & Sec.--The Kroger Co., Cincinnati, OH; *U.S. Public*, pg. 967

Helio, Robert, Sr. V.P.--ENI, Rochester, NY; *U.S. Private*, pg. 354

Hellberg, S.W., Sr. V.P.-Mktg. & Sls.--Creative Productions, Pittsburgh, PA; *U.S. Private*, pg. 288

Heller, John L., Sr. V.P. & Gen. Mgr.-Contractor Equipment Div.--Graco Inc., Golden Valley, MN; *U.S. Public*, pg. 756

Heller, K.L., Sr. V.P.-CN East--Canadian National Railway Company, Montreal, Canada; *Int'l*, pg. 258

Heller, Noble, Sr. V.P. & Dir.-Store Plng.--Kohl's Corporation, Menomonee Falls, WI; *U.S. Public*, pg. 965

Heller, Richard, Sr. V.P.-Comedy Devel. Columbia TriStar Television, Culver City, CA; *Int'l*, pg. 1282

Heller, William J., Sr. V.P.-Strategic Plng. & New Bus. Deve.--Edison International, Rosemead, CA; *U.S. Public*, pg. 564

Hellment, Brian A., Sr. V.P.--Northern Capital Management, Inc., Madison, WI; *U.S. Public*, pg. 1673

Hellriegel, Jack, Sr. V.P.-Opers.--A&W Restaurants, Inc., Livonia, MI; *U.S. Private*, pg. 1

Hellriegel, Michael C., Chief Fin. Officer & Sr. V.P.-Fin.--Butler International, Inc., Montvale, NJ; *U.S. Public*, pg. 270

Hellrung, Stephen A., Sr. V.P. & Gen. Counsel--The Pillsbury Company, Minneapolis, MN; *Int'l*, pg. 411

Helms, Ann, Sr. V.P. & Mngmt. Representative--EvansGroup, Dallas, TX; *U.S. Private*, pg. 385

Helms, William E., Sr. V.P.-Corp. Expansion--Heilig-Meyers Company, Richmond, VA; *U.S. Public*, pg. 804

Helter, Diana K., Sr. V.P.--First National Bank of Naples, Naples, FL; *U.S. Public*, pg. 607

Helzen, Berndt-Olof, Sr. V.P.-Electricity Network--Vattenfall AB, Stockholm, Sweden; *Int'l*, pg. 1452

Hemp, J. Michael, Sr. V.P.--Lincoln Financial Group, Inc., Fort Wayne, IN; *U.S. Public*, pg. 997

Hemp, John Michael, Sr. V.P.-Sls.--The Lincoln National Life Insurance Co., Fort Wayne, IN; *U.S. Public*, pg. 998

Hemphill, Neil D., Sr. V.P.-Human Resources & Admin.--Columbia/HCA Healthcare Corporation, Nashville, TN; *U.S. Public*, pg. 403

Hemphill, Teresa G., Sr. V.P.--Trustmark National Bank, Jackson, MS; *U.S. Public*, pg. 1643

Hemstead, George H., III, Sr. V.P.-Law & Admin.--Millennium Chemicals Inc., Iselin, NJ; *U.S. Public*, pg. 1111

Henaut, Michel, Sr. V.P.-EDP & Logistics--Banque Internationale a Luxembourg S.A., Luxembourg, Luxembourg; *Int'l*, pg. 162

Henderson, Barbara, Sr. V.P. & Mng. Dir.-Pub. Rels.--Ingalls, Boston, MA; *U.S. Private*, pg. 562

Henderson, Byron, Sr. V.P. & Gen. Mgr.--Capitol City Steel Co., Buda, TX; *U.S. Public*, pg. 413

Henderson, Doug, Chief Fin. Officer & Sr. V.P.--Publicis/Bloom Inc., New York, NY; *Int'l*, pg. 470

Henderson, Frank E., Sr. V.P.--Plant City Steel Co., Plant City, FL; *U.S. Public*, pg. 793

Henderson, Gary, Sr. V.P.-Bus. Devel. & Scientific Affairs--Del Laboratories, Inc., Farmingdale, NY; *U.S. Public*, pg. 494

Henderson, Harold L., Sr. V.P. & Gen. Counsel--Eastman Chemical Company, Kingsport, TN; *U.S. Public*, pg. 550

Henderson, Jon L., Sr. V.P.-Investment Banking--Magna Group, Inc., Saint Louis, MO; *U.S. Public*, pg. 1037

Hendra, Tom, Sr. V.P.-Mdsg.--ShopKo Stores, Inc., Green Bay, WI; *U.S. Public*, pg. 1467

Hendren, Michael, Sr. V.P.-N. American Sls.--Ascend Communications, Inc., Alameda, CA; *U.S. Public*, pg. 138

Hendrick, Richard M., Sr. V.P.-Mining & Preparation--A.T. Massey Coal Company, Inc., Richmond, VA; *U.S. Public*, *pg. 660*

Hendricks, John, Sr. V.P.--Moyer Packing Company, Souderton, PA; *U.S. Private*, pg. 765

Hendricksen, Donald G., Sr. V.P.-Stores--Pamida, Inc., Omaha, NE; *U.S. Public*, pg. 1255

Hendrickson, Charles J., Sr. V.P. & Treas.--Donaldson, Lufkin, & Jenrette, Inc., New York, NY; *U.S. Public*, pg. 589

Hendrickson, Eddie, Sr. V.P.--Safecare Company, Seattle, WA; *U.S. Public*, pg. 1423

Hendrickson, Marshall D., Sr. V.P.-Admin.--UMB Financial Corporation, Kansas City, MO; *U.S. Public*, pg. 1653

Hendrickson, Warren J., Sr. V.P.--Knight Architects Engineers Planners, Inc., Chicago, IL; *U.S. Private*, pg. 626

Hendrie, Richard, Sr. V.P.-Mktg.--Unique Casual Restaurants, inc., Danvers, MA; *Int'l*, pg. 324

Hendriks, J., Sr. V.P.--AEGON Schadeverzekering N.V., Hague, Netherlands; *Int'l*, pg. 26

Hendrix, Daniel T., Chief Fin. Officer, Sr. V.P. & Treas.--Interface Inc., Atlanta, GA; *U.S. Public*, pg. 889

Hendrix, John L., Chief Fin. Officer & Sr. V.P.--APS Holding Corporation, Houston, TX; *U.S. Public*, pg. 10

Hendry, Gregory L., Chief Acctg. Officer & Sr. V.P.--Glendale Federal Bank, F.S.B., Glendale, CA; *U.S. Public*, pg. 747

Heneghan, Michael R., Sr. V.P.--Illinova Generating Co., Decatur, IL; *U.S. Public*, pg. 870

Hengesbaugh, Bernard L., Sr. V.P.--Continental Assurance Company, Chicago, IL; *U.S. Private*, pg. 267

Henke, Theodore R., Sr. V.P.--Atlantic Mutual Companies, New York, NY; *U.S. Private*, pg. 95

Henley, Terry E., Sr. V.P.-H.R.--Provident Financial Group, Inc., Cincinnati, OH; *U.S. Public*, pg. 1338

Henley, William Curtis, Chief Fin. Officer & Sr. V.P.--The Bionetics Corporation, Newport News, VA; *U.S. Private*, pg. 145

Henmi, Toshie, Sr. Mng. Dir.-Mngmt. Devel.--Ito-Yokado Co., Ltd., Tokyo, Japan; *Int'l*, pg. 693

Henn, Michael, Chief Fin. Officer & Sr. V.P.--Kaufman and Broad Home Corporation, Los Angeles, CA; *U.S. Public*, pg. 944

Henneman, Bob, Sr. V.P.--York Wallcoverings Inc., York, PA; *U.S. Private*, pg. 1196

Hennessy, John T., Sr. V.P.-Commercial Lending--Prime Bank, Philadelphia, PA; *U.S. Public*, pg. 1326

Hennessy, Paul V., Sr. V.P.--Chubb Insurance Company of Europe, Brussels, Belgium; *U.S. Public*, pg. 355

Hennigan, George R., Sr. V.P.--Kerr-McGee Corporation, Oklahoma City, OK; *U.S. Public*, pg. 952

Henning, Edward J., Sr. V.P., Gen. Counsel & Sec.--Health Care Property Investors, Inc., Newport Beach, CA; *U.S. Public*, pg. 801

Henning, Fred L., Jr., Sr. V.P.--Fidelity Investments (FMR Corp.), Boston, MA; *U.S. Private*, pg. 402

Henning, Kevin M., Sr. V.P.-Supply & Transportation--Marathon Ashland Petroleum LLC, Findlay, OH; *U.S. Public*, pg. 139

Henning, William W., Sr. V.P.-Sls.--Toter Incorporated, Statesville, NC; *U.S. Private*, pg. 1092

Henninger, Robert J., Jr., Sr. V.P.--Republic Industries, Inc., Fort Lauderdale, FL; *U.S. Public*, pg. 1378

Henningsen, Robert C., Sr. V.P.-H.R. & Admin.--International Comfort Products, Franklin, TN; *U.S. Public*, *pg. 898*

Henricsson, Wiking, Sr. V.P.--Perstorp AB, Perstorp, Sweden; *Int'l*, pg. 1036

Henrion, Romain, Sr. V.P.-Iron & Steel Making, Long Prods.--Arbed S.A., Luxembourg, Luxembourg; *Int'l*, pg. 78

Henry, A. Shafer, Sr. V.P.--E.P. Henry Corporation, Woodbury, NJ; *U.S. Private*, pg. 522

Henry, Garth, Sr. V.P.-Intl. Opers.--M.A. Hanna Company, Cleveland, OH; *U.S. Public*, pg. 780

Henry, James R., Sr. V.P.--Bank of the West, Walnut Creek, CA; *Int'l*, pg. 163

Henry, John T., Sr. V.P.--UJB Investor Services Company, Paramus, NJ; *U.S. Public*, pg. 1528

Henry, John W., Sr. V.P.--Jack Henry & Associates, Inc., Monett, MO; *U.S. Public*, pg. 808

Henry, Maurice, Sr. V.P.-Springfield Division--Associated Wholesale Grocers, Inc., Kansas City, KS; *U.S. Private*, pg. 93

Henry, Nancy L., Sr. V.P. & Gen. Counsel--The Dun & Bradstreet Corporation, Murray Hill, NJ; *U.S. Public*, pg. 535

Henry, Robert C., Sr. V.P.-U.S. Field Opers.--Silicon Graphics, Inc., Mountain View, CA; *U.S. Public*, pg. 1473

Henry, Sam L., Chief Fin. Officer, Sr. V.P. & Sec.--Helen of Troy Corporation, El Paso, TX; *U.S. Public*, pg. 807

Hensel, C.L., Sr. V.P. & Pres.-Titan Systems--The Titan Corporation, San Diego, CA; *U.S. Public*, pg. 1618

Hensel, Fritz H., Sr. V.P.-Fin.--Akzo Nobel N.V., Arnhem, Netherlands; *Int'l*, pg. 42

Hensely, David, Sr. V.P.-Store Opers.--Eckerd Corporation, Largo, FL; *U.S. Public*, pg. 917

Henske, Robert C., Sr. V.P.--Arthur D. Little, Inc., Cambridge, MA; *U.S. Private*, pg. 670

Hensler, Thomas P., III, Sr. V.P.-Finance--The Minute Maid Company, Houston, TX; *U.S. Public*, pg. 392

Hensley, Robert, Sr. V.P.-Human Resources--Venture Stores, Inc., O Fallon, MO; *U.S. Public*, pg. 1716

Hensley, Ron, Sr. V.P.-Ins.--John Burnham & Co., San Diego, CA; *U.S. Private*, pg. 186

Henson, Jim L., Sr. V.P. & Chief Mktg. Officer--Shenandoah Life Insurance Company, Roanoke, VA; *U.S. Private*, pg. 992

Henson, Ron, Sr. V.P.-Sls.--S&D Coffee Inc., Concord, NC; *U.S. Private*, pg. 954

Henwood, Bill, Sr. V.P.-Sls. & Mktg.--Nicklaus Golf Company, L.C., West Palm Beach, FL; *U.S. Private*, pg. 799

Hepler, Merrilee, Sr. V.P.-H.R.--MMI Companies, Inc., Deerfield, IL; *U.S. Public*, pg. 1027

Heppe, Jan, Sr. V.P. & Dir.-Stores--Loehmann's, Inc., Bronx, NY; *U.S. Public*, pg. 1010

Herbst, George, Sr. V.P.-Mfg.--Ball Metal Beverage Container Corp., Westminster, CO; *U.S. Public*, pg. 171

Hercules, Duane, Sr. V.P. & Treas.--Safety National Casualty Corp., Saint Louis, MO; *U.S. Public*, pg. 496

Herdman, Michael, Sr. V.P.-Beverage Cans, Europe--American National Can Company, Chicago, IL; *Int'l*, pg. 1029

Heredia, Raoul, Chief Fin. Officer & Sr. V.P.-Fin.--Peerless Carpet Corporation, Acton Vale, Canada; *Int'l*, pg. 1032

Herling, Michael, Sr. V.P.--The Ivaco Group, Montreal, Canada; *Int'l*, pg. 695

Herman, Cheri, Sr. V.P. & Acct. Supvr.--EvansGroup, Los Angeles, CA; *U.S. Private*, pg. 385

Herman, David, Sr. V.P.- & Gen. Mgr.-Dansk & Lenox Retail--Lenox Retail, Lawrenceville, NJ; *U.S. Public*, pg. 261

Herman, Joan E., Sr. V.P.--Phoenix Home Life Mutual Insurance Company, Hartford, CT; *U.S. Private*, pg. 863

Herman, Robert, Sr. V.P.-Res. & Devel.--Data Transmission Network Corporation, Omaha, NE; *U.S. Public*, pg. 486

Herman, Robin A., Sr. V.P., Gen. Counsel & Sec.--Western Staff Services, Walnut Creek, CA; *U.S. Public*, pg. 1760

Herman, Scott, Sr. V.P.--CBS Radio, New York, NY; *U.S. Public*, pg. 274

Hernandez-Beneyto, Jose M., Sr. V.P.--Banco Santander, Madrid, Spain; *Int'l*, pg. 143

Hernandez, Pablo Pardo, Sr. V.P.--Banco Santander Puerto Rico, Hato Rey, PR; *Int'l*, pg. 143

Hernandez, Robert, Sr. V.P.-Corp. Information Services--The TJX Companies, Inc., Framingham, MA; *U.S. Public*, *pg. 1556*

Hernandez, William H., Sr. V.P.-Fin.--PPG Industries, Inc., Pittsburgh, PA; *U.S. Public*, pg. 1245

Herndon, Wanda, Sr. V.P.-Communications & Pub. Affairs--Starbucks Coffee Company, Seattle, WA; *U.S. Public*, pg. 1510

Herne, Mary, Sr. V.P. & Gen. Mgr.-Intl. Distribution--Playboy Entertainment Group, Inc., Beverly Hills, CA; *U.S. Public*, *pg. 1310*

Herne, Mary, Sr. V.P.--After Dark Video, Inc., Beverly Hills, CA; *U.S. Public*, pg. 1310

Heroman, Donald T., Sr. V.P. & Treas.--SunTrust Banks, Inc., Atlanta, GA; *U.S. Public*, pg. 1537

Heroux, Paul B., Sr. V.P.-Fin. Opers.--Federal Home Loan Bank of New York, New York, NY; *U.S. Private*, pg. 399

Herrell, R.E., Sr. V.P.-Mfg.--Celotex Corporation, Tampa, FL; *U.S. Private*, pg. 221

Herrick, Glenn W., Sr. V.P.-Tech. Services--Comptek Federal Systems, Inc., Buffalo, NY; *U.S. Public*, pg. 419

Herriman, M. Davis, Jr., Sr. V.P.-Grocery, Pharmacy & Bakery Opers.--Giant Food Inc., Landover, MD; *U.S. Public*, pg. 741

Herring, Jerome, Sr. V.P. & Sec.--BB&T Corporation, Winston Salem, NC; *U.S. Public*, pg. 159

Herring, Lee, II, Sr. V.P.-Logistics--Lowe's Companies, Inc., North Wilkesboro, NC; *U.S. Public*, pg. 1015

Herringshaw, Douglas H., Exec. V.P.--Chemical Bank Bay Area, Bay City, MI; *U.S. Public*, pg. 345

Herrington, William P., Sr. V.P.--Hibernia Corporation, New Orleans, LA; *U.S. Public*, pg. 825

Herron, W.B.G., Sr. V.P.-Services Grp.--Precision Drilling Corporation, Calgary, Canada; *Int'l*, pg. 1066

Hershey, Darrel J., Sr. V.P.-Investments--Cambiar Investors, Inc., Englewood, CO; *U.S. Public*, pg. 1672

Hertlein, Rudolph L., Sr. V.P.-Corp. Devel.--Viacom Inc., New York, NY; *U.S. Private*, pg. 775

Hertz, Benny, Sr. V.P. & Mgr.--Bank Leumi le-Israel B.M., Chicago, IL; *Int'l*, pg. 150

Hertzberg, Andy, Sr. V.P. & Mngmt. Supvr.--Eisner & Associates, Inc., Baltimore, MD; *U.S. Private*, pg. 366

Hervey, George A., Chief Fin. Officer & Sr. V.P.-Fin.--S3 Incorporated, Santa Clara, CA; *U.S. Public*, pg. 1415

Herzog, Douglas, Sr. V.P.-Programming--MTV: Music Television, New York, NY; *U.S. Private*, pg. 779

Hess, E.J., Sr. V.P.--Exxon Corporation, Irving, TX; *U.S. Public*, pg. 601

Hess, H.E., Sr. V.P. & Reg. Dir.--Winn-Dixie Stores, Inc., Jacksonville, FL; *U.S. Public*, pg. 1771

Hess, James W., Sr. V.P. & Controller--Farmers and Merchants Bank and Trust, Hagerstown, MD; *U.S. Public*, pg. 1542

Hessamfar, Elahe, Chief Info. Officer & Sr. V.P.--The Dun & Bradstreet Corporation, Murray Hill, NJ; *U.S. Public*, pg. 535

Hester, John T., Sr. V.P.--National Programs Division, Tampa, FL; *U.S. Public*, pg. 1312

Hester, Troy, Sr. V.P.--Hibernia Corporation, New Orleans, LA; *U.S. Public*, pg. 825

Hestwood, Robert M., Sr. V.P.-Broking--Willis Faber North America, Inc.-New York, New York, NY; *Int'l*, pg. 1503

Hete, Joseph, Chief Oper. Officer & Sr. V.P.-Admin.--ABX Air, Inc., Wilmington, OH; *U.S. Public*, pg. 33

Hetherwick, Gilbert, Sr. V.P.-Intl. Mktg., Sony Classical--Sony Music Entertainment, Inc., New York, NY; *Int'l*, pg. 1281

Hettich, James, Sr. V.P. & Grp. Dir.--Wolf Mansfield Bolling Advertising Inc., Buffalo, NY; *U.S. Private*, pg. 1185

Heuer, Brian W., Sr. V.P.-Admin. Services Exec.--The Dime Savings Bank of New York, New York, NY; *U.S. Public*, pg. 509

Heugly, Mark, Sr. V.P.-Investments--Zions First National Bank, Salt Lake City, UT; *U.S. Public*, pg. 1793

Hewes, Philip A., Sr. V.P. & Sec.--Comdisco, Inc., Rosemont, IL; *U.S. Public*, pg. 407

Hewett, Robert M., Sr. V.P.-Customer Opers. & Mktg.--Kentucky Utilities Company, Lexington, KY; *U.S. Public*, pg. 941

Hewitt, Steven J., Chief Fin. Officer & Sr. V.P.--Commercial Intertech Corp., Youngstown, OH; *U.S. Public*, pg. 411

Heyboer, Judy, Sr. V.P.-Human Resources--Genentech, Inc., South San Francisco, CA; *Int'l*, pg. 1120

Heyerdahl, Timothy S., Sr. V.P.-Fin, Treasury & Acctg.--HBOC, Atlanta, GA; *U.S. Public*, pg. 770

Heying, Gregory C., Sr. V.P.-Distr.--SuperValu, Inc., Eden Prairie, MN; *U.S. Public*, pg. 1540

Heys, Thomas B., Jr., Sr. V.P.-Risk Mngmt.--Provident Companies, Inc., Chattanooga, TN; *U.S. Public*, pg. 1337

Heysse, Bruce A., Sr. V.P.-Acquisitions--Community First Bankshares, Inc., Fargo, ND; *U.S. Public*, pg. 416

Heyward, Westley M., Sr. V.P.--Zenith National Insurance Corp., Woodland Hills, CA; *U.S. Public*, pg. 1790

Hibner, Geoffrey J., Chief Fin. Officer & Sr. V.P.-Fin. & Admin.--Timberland GmbH c/o The Timberland Company, Stratham, NH; *U.S. Public*, pg. 1609

Hickey, John D., Sr. V.P.--General Reinsurance Corp., Stamford, CT; *U.S. Public*, pg. 725

Hickey, Scott S., Sr. V.P.--Firstar Bank of Minnesota, Bloomington, MN; *U.S. Public*, pg. 643

Hickman, Brett M., Chief Fin. Officer & Sr. V.P.--National Infusion Services, Inc., Indianapolis, IN; *U.S. Public*, pg. 229

Hickman, R. N., Sr. V.P.- & Grp. Gen. Mgr.--The BHP Copper Group, San Francisco, CA; *Int'l*, pg. 224

Hickman, Robert N., Sr. V.P. & Grp. Gen. Mgr.--New Business Development, San Francisco, CA; *Int'l*, pg. 224

Hickman, Winston E., Chief Fin. Officer, Sr. V.P. & Sec.--Pacific Scientific Company, Newport Beach, CA; *U.S. Public*, pg. 1250

Hicks, Henry Howard, Jr., Sr. V.P. & Reg. Exec. Officer--First Virginia Banks, Inc., Falls Church, VA; *U.S. Public*, pg. 641

Hicks, Jack, Sr. V.P.--Chubb & Son, Inc., Warren, NJ; *U.S. Public*, pg. 355

Hicks, Jim R., Sr. V.P.-Customer Opers.--Duke Energy Corporation, Charlotte, NC; *U.S. Public*, pg. 534

Hicok, Robert D., Sr. V.P. & Gen. Mgr.-San Diego Region--Costco Wholesale, Issaquah, WA; *U.S. Public*, pg. 451

Hiett, John M., Sr. V.P.-Customer Service--MTI Technology Corporation, Anaheim, CA; *U.S. Public*, pg. 1028

Higashiura, Akira, Sr. V.P. & Dir.--Kodansha Ltd., Tokyo, Japan; *Int'l*, pg. 742

Higginbotham, Stephen, Sr. V.P.-Comml. Lending--Citizens Savings Bank, Providence, RI; *Int'l*, pg. 1132

Higgins, Andrew L., Sr. V.P.-Corp. Services--Barnett Banks, Inc., Jacksonville, FL; *U.S. Public*, pg. 1162

Higgins, Dennis P., Sr. V.P.-Publicity--Columbia Pictures, Culver City, CA; *Int'l*, pg. 1281

Higgins, Kathie E., Sr. V.P. & Dir.-H.R.--Nevada State Bank, Las Vegas, NV; *U.S. Public*, pg. 1793

Higgins, Michael J., Sr. V.P.-Federal Programs--Jacobs Engineering Group Inc., Pasadena, CA; *U.S. Public*, pg. 921

Higgins, Stephen T., Sr. V.P.--Phelps Dodge Sales Company, New York, NY; *U.S. Public*, pg. 1287

Higgins, Steve, Sr. V.P.-Mdse.--L. Luria & Son, Inc., Medley, FL; *U.S. Public*, pg. 1020

Higgs, Richard A., Sr. V.P. & Gen. Auditor--Compass Bank, Birmingham, AL; *U.S. Public*, pg. 418

High, Thomas W., Sr. V.P.-Admin. & External Affairs--PG&E Corporation, San Francisco, CA; *U.S. Public*, pg. 1240

Higham, Paul H., Sr. V.P.-Mktg. & Sls. Promo.--Wal-Mart Stores, Inc., Bentonville, AR; *U.S. Public*, pg. 1732

Hight, Kenneth C., Sr. V.P.-Inst. Equities--The Toronto Dominion Bank, Toronto, Canada; *Int'l*, pg. 1401

Hightower, Jack, Sr. V.P.-Field Opers.--Jan Bell Marketing Inc., Sunrise, FL; *U.S. Public*, pg. 207

Hignett, Kenneth L., Chief Fin. Officer, Sr. V.P. & Sec.--Morgan's Foods, Inc., Beachwood, OH; *U.S. Public*, pg. 1133

Hildebrand, Janet, Sr. V.P.-Human Resources--Richfood Holdings, Inc., Glen Allen, VA; *U.S. Public*, pg. 1388

Hildebrandt, David A., Sr. V.P.-Intl. Sls.--Starcraft Automotive Group, Inc., Goshen, IN; *U.S. Public*, pg. 1511

Hiles, Roy L., Sr. V.P.-Comml. Banking--The Provident Bank, Cincinnati, OH; *U.S. Public*, pg. 1338

Hilk, Clifford L., Sr. V.P. & Sr. Loan Officer--St. Michaels Bank, Saint Michaels, MD; *U.S. Public*, pg. 1089

Hilker, Louis M., Sr. V.P.-Coord. Scheduling--J.E. Dunn Construction Co., Kansas City, MO; *U.S. Private*, pg. 347

Hill, Colin, Sr. V.P.-Casting Grp.--Esco Corporation, Portland, OR; *U.S. Private*, pg. 382

Hill, Dan J., Sr. V.P.-Terminaling & Mktg.--The Coastal Corporation, Houston, TX; *U.S. Public*, pg. 389

Hill, Dan J., Sr. V.P.--Coastal Refining & Marketing, Wichita, KS; *U.S. Public*, pg. 390

Hill, Daryl D., Sr. V.P.-Quality & Compliance--Amgen Inc., Thousand Oaks, CA; *U.S. Public*, pg. 100

Hill, David F., Sr. V.P.--Liberty Life Insurance Company, Greenville, SC; *U.S. Public*, pg. 992

Hill, David F., Sr. V.P.-Strategic Mktg.--Northwestern National Life Insurance Co., Minneapolis, MN; *U.S. Public*, pg. 1375

Hill, George E., Sr. V.P.--Golden State Mutual Life Insurance Company, Los Angeles, CA; *U.S. Private*, pg. 461

Hill, George R., Sr. V.P.-Bus. Devel.--The Lubrizol Corporation, Wickliffe, OH; *U.S. Public*, pg. 1016

Hill, Herbert W., Jr., Chief Acctg. Officer & Sr. V.P.--Clear Channel Communications, Inc., San Antonio, TX; *U.S. Public*, pg. 383

Hill, James, Dr., Sr. V.P. & Dir.-Corp. Affairs--SmithKline Beecham plc, Brentford, United Kingdom; *Int'l*, pg. 1264

Hill, John P., Jr., Chief Fin. Officer & Sr. V.P.--Heery International, Inc., Atlanta, GA; *U.S. Private*, pg. 519

Hill, John S., Sr. V.P.-Fin. & Treas.--Carolina Casualty Insurance Company, Jacksonville, FL; *U.S. Public*, pg. 216

Hill, Kevin, Sr. V.P. & Grp. Media Dir.--The Lord Group, New York, NY; *U.S. Private*, pg. 325

Hill, Larry, Sr. V.P. & Dir.-Stores/NY--Saks Fifth Avenue, New York, NY; *U.S. Public*, pg. 1429

Hill, Norman J., Sr. V.P.-Human Resources--Cracker Barrel Old Country Store, Inc., Lebanon, TN; *U.S. Public*, pg. 455

Hill, R. F., Sr. V.P.-Commercial Opers.--Virginia Electric and Power Company, Richmond, VA; *U.S. Public*, pg. 516

Hill, Rick, Sr. V.P.-Information Systems--National Health Enhancement Systems, Inc., Phoenix, AZ; *U.S. Public*, pg. 1157

Hill, Robert F., Sr. V.P.-Acctg.--American Bankers Life Assurance Co. of Florida, Miami, FL; *U.S. Public*, pg. 67

Hill, Ronald E., Sr. V.P.-Fin.--PP&L Resources, Allentown, PA; *U.S. Public*, pg. 1244

Hill, Ronald E., Sr. V.P.-Fin.--Pennsylvania Power & Light Company-Lehigh Div., Allentown, PA; *U.S. Public*, pg. 1244

Hill, Steven D., Sr. V.P.--MediaOne, Boston, MA; *U.S. Public*, pg. 1688

Hill, Steven H., Sr. V.P. & Sec.--Southern Container Corporation, Hauppauge, NY; *U.S. Private*, pg. 1016

Hill, Ted, Chief Oper. Officer & Sr. V.P.--KTI, Inc., Guttenberg, NJ; *U.S. Public*, pg. 939

Hill, Vada, Sr. V.P.-Mktg.--Taco Bell Corp., Irvine, CA; *U.S. Public*, pg. 1637

Hillan, Kathleen M., Sr. V.P.-Fin.--Price Enterprises, Inc., San Diego, CA; *U.S. Public*, pg. 1324

Hillard, David D., Chief Fin. Officer & Sr. V.P.--Fisher Companies Inc., Seattle, WA; *U.S. Public*, pg. 647

Hillback, Elliott, Jr., Sr. V.P. & Pres. & Chief Exec. Officer-IG Laboratories--Genzyme Corporation, Cambridge, MA; *U.S. Public*, pg. 733

Hiller, David D., Sr. V.P.-Devel.--Tribune Company, Chicago, IL; *U.S. Public*, pg. 1635

Hillers, Kim, Sr. V.P. & Acct. Dir.--Young & Rubicam New York, New York, NY; *U.S. Private*, pg. 1198

Hilliard, Lester E., Sr. V.P.-Fin. Plng.--Starbanc Corporation, Cincinnati, OH; *U.S. Public*, pg. 1510

Hilliard, Robert E., Sr. V.P.--American Modern Home Insurance Group, Amelia, OH; *U.S. Public*, pg. 1110

Hillin, W.K., Sr. V.P., Gen. Counsel & Sec.--Reading & Bates Corporation, Houston, TX; *U.S. Public*, pg. 1354

Hillis, John C., Sr. V.P.--Comarco, Inc., Yorba Linda, CA; *U.S. Public*, pg. 406

Hillman, Anna E., Sr. V.P.-Fin. & Admin.--Comcast Cellular Communications, Inc., Wayne, PA; *U.S. Public*, pg. 407

Hillman, John, Sr. V.P.-Opers.--Bay State Milling Co., Quincy, MA; *U.S. Private*, pg. 124

Hillman, S.M., Sr. V.P.--MC2 Inc., Lombard, IL; *U.S. Public*, pg. 1210

Hilt, Thomas A., Sr. V.P.-Opers. & Admin.--Community First Bankshares, Inc., Fargo, ND; *U.S. Public*, pg. 416

Hilton, Ray, Sr. V.P. & Client Svcs.--Lois/EJL New York, New York, NY; *U.S. Public*, pg. 1011

Hilty, Wayne, Chief Fin. Officer & Sr. V.P.--Copart, Inc., Benicia, CA; *U.S. Public*, pg. 446

Hilzinger, Kurt J., Chief Fin. Officer & Sr. V.P.--AmeriSource Health Corp., Malvern, PA; *U.S. Public*, pg. 96

Himes, Norman, Sr. V.P. & Chief Info. Officer--FCA International Ltd., Westmount, Canada; *Int'l*, pg. 470

Himes, Richard H., Jr., Sr. V.P.-Title Insurance--United Companies Financial Corporation, Baton Rouge, LA; *U.S. Public*, pg. 1675

Himmer, Robert G., Sr. V.P.--Atlantic Mutual Companies, New York, NY; *U.S. Private*, pg. 95

Hinchliff, James T., Sr. V.P. & Gen. Counsel--Peoples Energy Corporation, Chicago, IL; *U.S. Public*, pg. 1274

Hinchliff, James T., Sr. V.P. & Gen. Counsel--Peoples District Energy Corporation, Chicago, IL; *U.S. Public*, pg. 1275

Hinchliff, James T., Sr. V.P. & Gen. Counsel--Peoples Energy Services Corporation, Chicago, IL; *U.S. Public*, pg. 1275

Hinchliff, James T., Sr. V.P. & Gen. Counsel--Peoples NGV Corp., Chicago, IL; *U.S. Public*, pg. 1275

Hinckley, Greg, Chief Oper. Officer, Chief Fin. Officer & Sr. V.P.--Mentor Graphics Corporation, Wilsonville, OR; *U.S. Public*, pg. 1086

Hinderhofer, Kathryn M., Sr. V.P.-Acquisition Conversion--Citizens Savings Bank, Providence, RI; *Int'l*, pg. 1132

Hindert, Thomas M., Sr. V.P.-Real Estate--The Mills Corporation, Arlington, VA; *U.S. Public*, pg. 1113

Hines, John, Chief Fin. Officer & Sr. V.P.-Admin.--HK Systems, Inc., New Berlin, WI; *U.S. Private*, pg. 491

Hinfray, Francois, Sr. V.P.-France Mkt. Area--Renault, Boulogne-Billancourt, France; *Int'l*, pg. 1102

Hingiss, Mark H., Sr. V.P.-Mktg.--Honeymead Products Co., Mankato, MN; *U.S. Private*, pg. 537
Hinrichs, Horst, Sr. V.P.-Automotive Prods.--American Standard Inc., Piscataway, NJ; *U.S. Public*, pg. 91
Hinrichs, Horst, Sr. V.P.-Automotive Products--WABCO Automotive Poducts Group, Hannover, Germany; *U.S. Public*, pg. 92
Hinson, Richard E., Sr. V.P.-Worldwide Franchise Mngmt. & Pharmaceuticals Grp.--Bristol-Myers Squibb Company, New York, NY; *U.S. Public*, pg. 253
Hinton, Donald E., Sr. V.P.--Imperial Bank, Inglewood, CA; *U.S. Public*, pg. 871
Hinton, Hud, Sr. V.P.-Opers.--Westin Hotels & Resorts, Seattle, WA; *U.S. Public*, pg. 1512
Hinton, James, Sr. V.P.-Devel.--Camden Property Trust, Houston, TX; *U.S. Public*, pg. 298
Hinton, John R., Chief Fin. Officer, Sr. V.P.-Admin.--Kellogg Company, Battle Creek, MI; *U.S. Public*, pg. 947
Hiotaky, William, Sr. V.P.-Plng. & Design--Taubman Centers, Inc., Bloomfield Hills, MI; *U.S. Public*, pg. 1561
Hippensteel, William R., Sr. V.P. & Mgr.-Corp. Mktg.--AMCORE Bank N.A., Rockford, Rockford, IL; *U.S. Public*, pg. 64
Hippensteel, William T., Sr. V.P. & Mgr.-Corp. Mktg.--Amcore Financial, Inc., Rockford, IL; *U.S. Public*, pg. 64
Hipple, Richard J., Sr. V.P.-Pur., Engrng. & Strategic Plng.--The LTV Corporation, Cleveland, OH; *U.S. Public*, pg. 971
Hippler, James W., Sr. V.P.-Admin.--Boyd Gaming Corporation, Las Vegas, NV; *U.S. Public*, pg. 249
Hipps, Jeff, Sr. V.P.-Mktg.--Inkel USA Corporation, La Mirada, CA; *U.S. Private*, pg. 563
Hipwell, Arthur P., Sr. V.P. & Gen. Counsel--Humana Inc., Louisville, KY; *U.S. Public*, pg. 847
Hipwell, Roger, Sr. V.P.-Sls. & Mktg.--Bay State Milling Co., Quincy, MA; *U.S. Private*, pg. 124
Hirano, Satoshi, Mng. Dir. & Sr. V.P.--Japan Airlines Company, Ltd., Tokyo, Japan; *Int'l*, pg. 699
Hirata, Dean K., Sr. V.P. & Controller--First Hawaiian, Inc., Honolulu, HI; *U.S. Public*, pg. 634
Hirata, Dean K., Sr. V.P. & Controller--First Hawaiian Bank, Honolulu, HI; *U.S. Public*, pg. 634
Hire, Nancy P., Sr. V.P.--First National Bank of Naples, Naples, FL; *U.S. Public*, pg. 607
Hirko, Joseph M., Chief Fin. Officer, Sr. V.P. & Treas.--Portland General Electric Co., Portland, OR; *U.S. Public*, pg. 584
Hirooka, Yoshihiko, Sr. Mng. Dir.-Petrochemicals & Plastics Sector--Sumitomo Chemical Company, Ltd., Tokyo, Japan; *Int'l*, pg. 1310
Hirota, Iwao, Sr. V.P.--Yokogawa Electric Corporation, Tokyo, Japan; *Int'l*, pg. 1520
Hirsch, Barry, Sr. V.P., Gen. Counsel & Sec.--Loews Corporation, New York, NY; *U.S. Public*, pg. 1010
Hirsch, Gary A., Sr. V.P.-Bus. Affairs--TriStar Pictures, Culver City, CA; *Int'l*, pg. 1283
Hirschauer, Karl P., Sr. V.P.--Trans-Lux Corporation, Norwalk, CT; *U.S. Public*, pg. 1628
Hirschfeld, Ron, Exec. V.P.-Intl. Sls. & Mktg.--Galoob Toys, Inc., South San Francisco, CA; *U.S. Public*, pg. 698
Hirschman, Susan C., Sr. V.P. & Editor-in Chief-Greenwillow Books--William Morrow & Co., Inc., New York, NY; *U.S. Private*, pg. 515
Hirst, Richard B., Sr. V.P.-Corp. Affairs--Northwest Airlines Corp., Saint Paul, MN; *U.S. Public*, pg. 1199
Hirst, William J., Sr. V.P. & Intl. Fin. Dir.--Grey Advertising Inc., New York, NY; *U.S. Public*, pg. 764
Hiser, Dennis, Sr. V.P.-Sls. & Mktg.--World Color-Chicago Div., Elk Grove Village, IL; *U.S. Public*, pg. 1778
Hisiger, Rinda, Sr. V.P.-Stores--County Seat Stores, Inc., Dallas, TX; *U.S. Private*, pg. 279
Hislip, Daniel, Sr. V.P. & Legal Counsel--Cerberus Pyrotronics Inc., Cedar Knolls, NJ; *Int'l*, pg. 1246
Hissey, Ted, Sr. V.P.-Spirits--Heublein, Inc., Hartford, CT; *Int'l*, pg. 410
Hitchcock, Jack, Sr. V.P.-Lending--First National Bank of Central California, Salinas, CA; *U.S. Public*, pg. 1248
Hitt, Travis, Sr. V.P.-Retail Innovations--Bell Sports Corp., San Jose, CA; *U.S. Public*, pg. 207
Hjelm, Thomas B., Sr. V.P.-Acctg. & Control--Axel Johnson AB, Stockholm, Sweden; *Int'l*, pg. 707
Hnatek, Richard, Sr. V.P.-Sls. Officer--Falcon Products, Inc., Saint Louis, MO; *U.S. Public*, pg. 611
Hoak, Jonathon S., Sr. V.P. & Gen. Counsel--NCR Corporation, Dayton, OH; *U.S. Public*, pg. 1146
Hobbs, John, Sr. V.P.--Leon Shaffer Golnick Advertising, Inc., Fort Lauderdale, FL; *U.S. Private*, pg. 463
Hobbs, Lewis Ray, Sr. V.P.-Mdsg.--Wal-Mart Stores, Inc., Bentonville, AR; *U.S. Public*, pg. 1732
Hobgood, William P., Sr. V.P.-People--UAL Corporation, Elk Grove Village, IL; *U.S. Public*, pg. 1652
Hobgood, William P., Sr. V.P.-People--United Air Lines, Inc., Elk Grove Village, IL; *U.S. Public*, pg. 1653
Hobson, Harry E., Sr. V.P. & Graphic Production Dir.--Liggett-Stashower, Inc., Cleveland, OH; *U.S. Private*, pg. 667
Hochfelder, Thomas G., Sr. V.P.--Beldoch Industries, West Hempstead, NY; *U.S. Public*, pg. 519
Hock, Gerald C., Sr. V.P.-Admin. & Plng.--Green Bay Packaging Inc., Green Bay, WI; *U.S. Private*, pg. 476
Hockaday, Peter S., Sr. V.P.--MBT Architecture, San Francisco, CA; *U.S. Private*, pg. 686
Hockensmith, James T., Sr. V.P.-Environ. Svcs.--L. Robert Kimball & Associates, Ebensburg, PA; *U.S. Private*, pg. 619
Hodapp, John, Sr. V.P.-Mktg.--Florists' Mutual Insurance Co., Edwardsville, IL; *U.S. Private*, pg. 415
Hodge, Ronald C., Sr. V.P.-Retail Opers./Northeast--Hannaford Bros. Co., Scarborough, ME; *U.S. Public*, pg. 781
Hodges, Alex, Sr. V.P.-Universal Concerts--Universal Studios, Inc., Universal City, CA; *Int'l*, pg. 1215
Hodges, Bobby, Sr. V.P.-Mfg.--Stanley Furniture Co. Inc., Stanleytown, VA; *U.S. Public*, pg. 1508
Hodges, Cheryl D., Sr. V.P., Sec. & Dir. Inv. Rels.--Omnicare, Inc., Covington, KY; *U.S. Public*, pg. 1223
Hodges, H. Gaylord, Sr. V.P.-Admin.--The Life Insurance Co. of Virginia, Richmond, VA; *U.S. Public*, pg. 712
Hodgins, John A., Chief Oper. Officer & Sr. V.P.--Rigel Energy Corporation, Calgary, Canada; *Int'l*, pg. 1117
Hodgins, Robert B., Chief Fin. Officer & Sr. V.P.--Transcanada Pipelines Limited, Calgary, Canada; *Int'l*, pg. 1416
Hodnett, Bill M., Sr. V.P.-Cash Mngmt./U.S.--Brink's, Inc., Darien, CT; *U.S. Public*, pg. 1305
Hodson, Thomas, Sr. V.P.-Mktg. Sls.--Ford Meter Box Company, Wabash, IN; *U.S. Private*, pg. 418
Hodson, Thomas W., Chief Fin. Officer & Sr. V.P.--Caremark International Inc, Northbrook, IL; *U.S. Public*, pg. 1082
Hoechester, Stephen, Sr. V.P.--Edelman Worldwide, Inc., New York, NY; *U.S. Private*, pg. 362
Hoelscher, Douglas R., Sr. V.P.--Tennant Company, Minneapolis, MN; *U.S. Public*, pg. 1577
Hofer, J. Gerald, Sr. V.P.-Admin. Services--Laclede Gas Company, Saint Louis, MO; *U.S. Public*, pg. 973
Hoffa, Lucius W., Jr., Sr. V.P.-Info. Svcs.--Rubbermaid Incorporated, Wooster, OH; *U.S. Public*, pg. 1411
Hoffer, Philip A., Sr. V.P.-Real Estate Opers.--Prime Group Realty Trust, Chicago, IL; *U.S. Public*, pg. 1326
Hoffernan, Patrick T., Sr. V.P.-Liquid Coating Resins--McWhorter Technologies, Inc., Carpentersville, IL; *U.S. Public*, pg. 1074
Hoffhines, William A., Sr. V.P. & Mgr. Grand Rapids Div.--First Federal of Michigan, Detroit, MI; *U.S. Public*, pg. 336
Hoffman, Allison, Partner & Sr. V.P.--Media That Works, Cincinnati, OH; *U.S. Private*, pg. 727
Hoffman, C. Steven, Sr. V.P.--IMC Global, Bannockburn, IL; *U.S. Public*, pg. 856
Hoffman, Don, Sr. V.P.--Axiom Inc., Moorestown, NJ; *U.S. Public*, pg. 157
Hoffman, Edward N., Sr. V.P.--Miller Advertising Agency Inc., New York, NY; *U.S. Private*, pg. 746
Hoffman, John R., Sr. V.P.-External Affairs--Sprint Corporation, Westwood, KS; *U.S. Public*, pg. 1500
Hoffman, Judy, Sr. V.P.-Sls. & Mktg.--Lionel LLC, Chesterfield, MI; *U.S. Private*, pg. 669
Hoffman, Keith J., Sr. V.P.-Wholesale Lending--United Companies Financial Corporation, Baton Rouge, LA; *U.S. Public*, pg. 1675
Hoffman, Marc, Sr. V.P.-Fin. Mkts.--Banque Internationale a Luxembourg S.A., Luxembourg, Luxembourg; *Int'l*, pg. 162
Hoffman, Paul, Publisher & Sr. V.P.--Encyclopaedia Britannica, Inc., Chicago, IL; *U.S. Private*, pg. 375
Hoffman, Robert B., Chief Fin. Officer & Sr. V.P.--Monsanto Company, Saint Louis, MO; *U.S. Public*, pg. 1124
Hoffman, Stuart G., Sr. V.P. & Chief Economist--PNC Bank Corp., Pittsburgh, PA; *U.S. Public*, pg. 1242
Hoffman, Thomas, Sr. V.P.--Performance Food Group Company, Richmond, VA; *U.S. Public*, pg. 1278
Hofmann, George B., III, Sr. V.P.-Nevada Admin.--Zions Bancorporation, Salt Lake City, UT; *U.S. Public*, pg. 1792
Hofmann, Herbert C., Sr. V.P.--Loews Corporation, New York, NY; *U.S. Public*, pg. 1010
Hofmann, Rob, Sr. V.P.-Adv. & Mktg.--Chittenden Corporation, Burlington, VT; *U.S. Public*, pg. 350
Hogan, Eleanor L., Sr. V.P.-Comml. Lending--People's Bank & Trust Co., Mount Vernon, IN; *U.S. Public*, pg. 1217
Hogan, James D., Sr. V.P. & Controller--Starbanc Corporation, Cincinnati, OH; *U.S. Public*, pg. 1510
Hogan, James J., Sr. V.P.-Corp. Mktg. & Commun.--Wang Laboratories, Inc., Billerica, MA; *U.S. Public*, pg. 1737
Hogan, John E., Sr. V.P.-Radio Div.--Jacor Communications, Inc., Covington, KY; *U.S. Public*, pg. 922
Hogan, Kenneth W., Chief Fin. Officer, Sr. V.P. & Sec.--Valley Resources, Inc., Cumberland, RI; *U.S. Public*, pg. 1706
Hogan, Kenneth W., Chief Fin. Officer, Sr. V.P. & Sec.--Bristol & Warren Gas Company, Bristol, RI; *U.S. Public*, pg. 1706
Hogg, Jack B., Sr. V.P.--Better Brands Of Atlanta, Inc., Atlanta, GA; *U.S. Private*, pg. 141
Hoglund, Mats, Sr. V.P.-Grp. Insurance--Trygg-Hansa, Stockholm, Sweden; *Int'l*, pg. 1425
Hohmann, Errol G., Sr. V.P.--Firstar Corporation, Milwaukee, WI; *U.S. Public*, pg. 642
Hohn, Richard G., Sr. V.P., Sec. & Counsel--USLIFE Corporation, New York, NY; *U.S. Public*, pg. 77
Hok, Gan Tjoen, Sr. V.P.--Republic National Bank of New York (Singapore) Ltd., Singapore, Singapore; *U.S. Public*, pg. 1381
Hokin, William J., Sr. V.P.--Century America Corporation, Chicago, IL; *U.S. Private*, pg. 225
Holaas, A., Sr. V.P.--Elkem Mangan, Oslo, Norway; *Int'l*, pg. 447
Holaday, G.S., Sr. V.P.--A & B-Hawaii, Inc., Honolulu, HI; *U.S. Public*, pg. 39
Holas, Arnfinn, Sr. V.P.-Manganese/Chrome & Shared Functions--Elkem ASA, Oslo, Norway; *Int'l*, pg. 446
Holborn, Donald C., Sr. V.P.-Natl. Sls. Plng.--FMR Corp., Boston, MA; *U.S. Private*, pg. 403
Holbrook, Jerry, Sr. V.P. & Controller--Wilmington Savings Fund Society (FSB), Wilmington, DE; *U.S. Public*, pg. 1729
Holbrook, Lisa J., Sr. V.P.-Fin., Treas. & Sec.--Longview Fibre Company, Longview, WA; *U.S. Public*, pg. 1013
Holcombe, Robert S., Sr. V.P.,Gen. Counsel & Sec.--Apria Healthcare Group Inc., Costa Mesa, CA; *U.S. Public*, pg. 125
Holden, James H., Sr. V.P.--Keeney Manufacturing Co., Newington, CT; *U.S. Private*, pg. 611
Holder, Jeff, Sr. V.P.-Animation Devel.--Hanna-Barbera Productions, Inc., Hollywood, CA; *U.S. Public*, pg. 1614
Holder, Patrick M., Sr. V.P.-Best Practices--Lexford Residential Trust, Columbus, OH; *U.S. Public*, pg. 991
Holen, Helge, Sr. V.P.-Matls. & Bus. Devel.--Elkem ASA, Oslo, Norway; *Int'l*, pg. 446
Holen, Helge, Sr. V.P.--Elkem ASA Ferrosilicon Division, Oslo, Norway; *Int'l*, pg. 448
Holinski, Stephan A., Sr. V.P. & Chief Fin. Officer--Moore Document Solutions, Lake Forest, IL; *Int'l*, pg. 890
Holinski, Stephen A., Chief Fin. Officer & Sr. V.P.--Moore Corporation Limited, Toronto, Canada; *Int'l*, pg. 888
Holland, Al, Chief Fin. Officer & Sr. V.P.--Trinity Industries Inc., Dallas, TX; *U.S. Public*, pg. 1638
Holland, Alan W., Sr. V.P.--Acxiom Corporation, Conway, AR; *U.S. Public*, pg. 18
Holland, E.J., Jr., Sr. V.P.-H.R. & Sec.--Payless Cashways, Inc., Kansas City, MO; *U.S. Public*, pg. 1267
Holland, J. Floyd, Sr. V.P.-Opers.--Greyhound Lines, Inc., Dallas, TX; *U.S. Public*, pg. 765
Holland, James M., Sr. V.P. & Sec.--Atwood Oceanics, Inc., Houston, TX; *U.S. Public*, pg. 146
Holland, John L., Sr. V.P.--BetzDearborn Inc., Trevose, PA; *U.S. Public*, pg. 226
Holland, Martyn, Sr. V.P.-MIS--Jan Bell Marketing Inc., Sunrise, FL; *U.S. Public*, pg. 207
Holland, Michael C., Sr. V.P.--El Paso Natural Gas Co., Houston, TX; *U.S. Public*, pg. 567
Holland, Robert B., III, Sr. V.P., Gen. Counsel & Sec.--Triton Energy Limited, Dallas, TX; *U.S. Public*, pg. 1640
Hollander, Gail, Sr. V.P. & Grp. Acct. Dir.--DMB&B New York, New York, NY; *U.S. Private*, pg. 302
Hollars, James A., Sr. V.P. & Pres.-BMW Div.--Lear Corporation, Southfield, MI; *U.S. Public*, pg. 981
Hollatz, James A., Sr. V.P.--Stanley Consultants, Inc., Muscatine, IA; *U.S. Private*, pg. 1033
Holleis, Guenter, Sr. V.P.--Voest-Alpine Industries, Inc., New York, NY; *Int'l*, pg. 1470
Holleran, John W., Sr. V.P. & Gen. Counsel--Boise Cascade Corporation, Boise, ID; *U.S. Public*, pg. 242
Holliday, Ralph K., Sr. V.P.--Keycorp, Cleveland, OH; *U.S. Public*, pg. 954
Holliday, Susan J., Sr. V.P. & Gen. Counsel--CBS, New York, NY; *U.S. Public*, pg. 273
Hollingsworth, Schuyler, Sr. V.P. & Treas.--Beverly Enterprises, Inc., Fort Smith, AR; *U.S. Public*, pg. 227
Hollis, Betty, Chief Admin. Officer & Sr. V.P.--Willis Corroon Corp. of Birmingham, Birmingham, AL; *Int'l*, pg. 1505
Hollis, Mark, Sr. V.P.-Sls. & Mktg.--Inverness Corp., Fair Lawn, NJ; *U.S. Private*, pg. 574
Hollonbeck, Stephen, V.P.-Gas Energy Delivery--MidAmerican Energy Holdings, Des Moines, IA; *U.S. Public*, pg. 1109
Holloway, Arnold, Sr., Sr. V.P.-Benefit Services--Regence BlueCross BlueShield of Oregon, Portland, OR; *U.S. Private*, pg. 917
Holloway, Douglas, Sr. V.P.-Affiliate Rels.--USA Networks, New York, NY; *U.S. Public*, pg. 1686
Holloway, Richard A., Sr. V.P.--SCI Systems, Inc., Huntsville, AL; *U.S. Public*, pg. 1416
Holloway, Ronald M., Sr. V.P.-Lending Svcs.--Ameriana Bancorp, New Castle, IN; *U.S. Public*, pg. 66
Hollowell, Gary, Sr. V.P.-Natl. Acct.--Aladdin Mills, Dalton, GA; *U.S. Public*, pg. 1121
Holm, George L., Sr. V.P.-Opers.--Sysco Corporation, Houston, TX; *U.S. Public*, pg. 1550
Holm, Soren, Sr. V.P. & Treas.--Nykredit, Copenhagen, Denmark; *Int'l*, pg. 993
Holmes, J.W., Sr. V.P.-Oil & Gas--ABB Lummus Global Inc., Bloomfield, NJ; *Int'l*, pg. 4
Holmes, Kate, Sr. V.P. & Media Dir.--Long Haymes Carr, Inc., Winston Salem, NC; *U.S. Public*, pg. 909
Holmes, Terry J., Sr. V.P.--American Telecasting, Inc., Colorado Springs, CO; *U.S. Public*, pg. 93
Holmstrom-Lindgren, Inger, Sr. V.P.-Corp. Rels. & Communications--Vattenfall AB, Stockholm, Sweden; *Int'l*, pg. 1452
Holquist, Daniel R., Sr. V.P.--First National Bank of Pennsylvania, Hermitage, PA; *U.S. Public*, pg. 607
Holroyd, Charles T., Jr., Sr. V.P.-Fin. Modeling--Countrywide Funding Corporation, Pasadena, CA; *U.S. Public*, pg. 453
Holschuh, Laurel A., Sr. V.P., Asst. Gen. Counsel & Sec.--Norwest Corporation, Minneapolis, MN; *U.S. Public*, pg. 1201
Holson, Philip L., Chief Fin. Officer & Sr. V.P.--Associated Industrial Supply, Inc., Columbia, SC; *U.S. Private*, pg. 91
Holt, Barry, Sr. V.P.-Communications--A.C. Nielsen, Stamford, CT; *U.S. Public*, pg. 1183
Holt, Donald F., Sr. V.P. & Controller--Keystone Financial Inc., Harrisburg, PA; *U.S. Public*, pg. 956
Holt, Jim, Sr. V.P.-Global Mktg.--Telxon Corporation, Akron, OH; *U.S. Public*, pg. 1573
Holt, Richard B., Sr. V.P. & Controller--Hasbro, Inc., Pawtucket, RI; *U.S. Public*, pg. 797
Holt, Scott, Sr. V.P.-Worldwide Sls.--Diamond Multimedia Systems, Inc., San Jose, CA; *U.S. Public*, pg. 505
Holtta, Pekka, Sr. V.P. & Treas.--Valmet Corporation, Helsinki, Finland; *Int'l*, pg. 1447
Holtz, A, Sr. V.P.-Sls.--Penguin Putnam Inc., New York, NY; *Int'l*, pg. 1027
Holtz, Diane, Sr. V.P. & Mgr.-Gen. Mdse.--AnnTaylor Stores Corporation, New York, NY; *U.S. Public*, pg. 116
Holub, Greg, Sr. V.P.--Mars Advertising Co., Southfield, MI; *U.S. Private*, pg. 706
Holub, Mark C., Sr. V.P.-Visual Mdsg. & Store Plng.--Younkers, Inc., Des Moines, IA; *U.S. Public*, pg. 1334
Holvoet, Marc, Corp. V.P.-Procurement--N.V. Bekaert S.A., Kortrijk, Belgium; *Int'l*, pg. 183
Homfray, Christopher, Partner & Sr. V.P.--Scotchbrook Communications Ltd., Wan Chai, Hong Kong; *U.S. Private*, pg. 411
Honeycutt, Conrad, Sr. V.P.-Sls.--Gelco Information Network, Inc., Eden Prairie, MN; *U.S. Private*, pg. 442
Hong, Cheo Chai, Sr. V.P.-Corp. Banking--DBS Bank Ltd., Singapore, Singapore; *Int'l*, pg. 350
Honig, Joni, Sr. V.P. & Client Services Dir.--Lally, McFarland & Pantello Inc., New York, NY; *Int'l*, pg. 601

Honour, D.M., Sr. V.P.--Jannock Steel Fabricating, Inc., Danville, KY; *Int'l*, pg. 699

Hood, Robin, Sr. V.P. & Gen. Mgr.-AG Div.--SGI Integrated Graphic Systems, Houston, TX; *U.S. Public*, pg. 971

Hoogerwerf, David J., Chief Fin. Officer-N. America & Sr. V.P.--Gerber Products Company, Fremont, MI; *Int'l*, pg. 973

Hooker, E.O., Sr. V.P. & Grp. Exec.-Govt. Grp.--McDermott International, Inc., New Orleans, LA; *U.S. Public*, pg. 1067

Hookstratten, Jon, Sr. V.P.-Bus. Affairs--CBS Enterprises Division, New York, NY; *U.S. Public*, pg. 274

Hooper, C.D., Sr. V.P. & Grp. Bus. Dir.--Howard, Merrell & Partners, Inc., Raleigh, NC; *U.S. Private*, pg. 542

Hooten, Doug, Sr. V.P.--Carpenter Co., Richmond, VA; *U.S. Private*, pg. 214

Hoover, Annette, Sr. V.P.-Property Opers.--Lexford Residential Trust, Columbus, OH; *U.S. Public*, pg. 991

Hoover, Dennis A., Sr. V.P. & Gen. Mgr.-N. California Region--Costco Wholesale, Issaquah, WA; *U.S. Public*, pg. 451

Hoover, George, Sr. V.P.-Veg. Oils--Ag Processing Inc., A Cooperative, Omaha, NE; *U.S. Private*, pg. 26

Hoover, Mary N., Sr. V.P.--First National Bank of Ohio, Akron, OH; *U.S. Public*, pg. 646

Hopeman, Jean, Sr. V.P. & Sr. Loan Officer--Sonoma Valley Bank, Sonoma, CA; *U.S. Public*, pg. 1487

Hopkins, Alma, Sr. V.P. & Exec. Creative Dir.--Burrell Communications Group Inc., Chicago, IL; *U.S. Private*, pg. 188

Hopkins, John D., Sr. V.P. & Gen. Counsel--Jefferson-Pilot Corporation, Greensboro, NC; *U.S. Public*, pg. 925

Hopkins, Kenneth R., Sr. V.P.--Berkley Risk Services, Inc., Minneapolis, MN; *U.S. Public*, pg. 215

Hopkins, R. Howard, Sr. V.P., Gen. Counsel & Sec.--SGS North America Inc., New York, NY; *Int'l*, pg. 1153

Hopkins, Tracy, Sr. V.P. & Mngmt. Representative--EvansGroup, Dallas, TX; *U.S. Private*, pg. 385

Hopp, James A., Sr. V.P. & Gen. Mdsg. Mgr.-Women's Apparel--Elder-Beerman Stores Div., Dayton, OH; *U.S. Private*, pg. 367

Hoppe, Francine, Sr. V.P.-Fin. Institutions--Bank Hapoalim, Tel Aviv, Israel; *Int'l*, pg. 149

Hoppe, Mark, Grp. Sr. V.P.-Institutional Banking--ABN/LaSalle North America Inc., Chicago, IL; *Int'l*, pg. 11

Hoppe, Sebastian M., Sr. V.P.--Imperial Credit Commercial Mortgage Investment Corp., Los Angeles, CA; *U.S. Public*, pg. 872

Hopper, Charles C., Sr. V.P.--ONEOK Inc., Tulsa, OK; *U.S. Public*, pg. 1226

Hopper, David A., Sr. V.P.-Individual Markets--Lincoln National Reinsurance Company (Bermuda) Limited, Fort Wayne, IN; *U.S. Public*, pg. 998

Hopper, Mike, Chief Fin. Officer & Sr. V.P.--Ozark Motor Lines, Memphis, TN; *U.S. Private*, pg. 825

Hopper, Preston D., Sr. V.P.-Plng. & Acctg. & Controller--CMS Energy Corporation, Dearborn, MI; *U.S. Public*, pg. 279

Hopping, Andrew B., Sr. V.P.-Fin.--Jackson National Life Insurance Company, Lansing, MI; *Int'l*, pg. 1073

Hopwood, Howard H., III, Sr. V.P. & Gen. Counsel--Firstar Corporation, Milwaukee, WI; *U.S. Public*, pg. 642

Horan, Anthony J., Sr. V.P. & Sec.--The Chase Manhattan Corporation, New York, NY; *U.S. Public*, pg. 337

Horan, Douglas S., Sr. V.P. & Gen. Counsel--Boston Edison Company, Boston, MA; *U.S. Public*, pg. 247

Horan, Thomas W., Chief Fin. Officer, Sr. V.P.-Fin. & Sec.--Great Dane Trailers, Inc., Savannah, GA; *U.S. Private*, pg. 1030

Horein, James R., Sr. V.P.--Lincoln National Administrative Services Corp., Fort Wayne, IN; *U.S. Public*, pg. 998

Horein, James R., Sr. V.P.--Lincoln National Health & Casualty Insurance Co., Fort Wayne, IN; *U.S. Public*, pg. 998

Horein, James R., Sr. V.P.-Intl.--Lincoln National Reinsurance Company (Barbados) Limited, Fort Wayne, IN; *U.S. Public*, pg. 998

Horein, James R., Sr. V.P.--Old Fort Insurance Co., Ltd. (Bermuda), Hamilton, Bermuda; *U.S. Public*, pg. 998

Horejsi, J.R., Sr. V.P.-Canadian Opers.--Ranger Oil Limited, Calgary, Canada; *Int'l*, pg. 1086

Horgan, Sam, Chief Fin. Officer & Sr. V.P.--OAO Technology Solutions, Inc., Greenbelt, MD; *U.S. Public*, pg. 1425

Horigan, John, Sr. V.P.--Morton Automotive Coatings, Lansing, IL; *U.S. Public*, pg. 1135

Horikoshi, Walter, Sr. V.P. & Mgr.-Legal Dept.--Central Pacific Bank, Honolulu, HI; *U.S. Public*, pg. 283

Horler, Clifford J., Sr. V.P.-Design & Construction--The Great Atlantic & Pacific Tea Company, Inc., Montvale, NJ; *Int'l*, pg. 1375

Horn, David D., Sr. V.P. & Gen. Mgr.--Sun Life Assurance Company of Canada (U.S.), Wellesley Hills, MA; *Int'l*, pg. 1319

Horn, Greg, Sr. V.P.-Sls.--General Nutrition Centers, Pittsburgh, PA; *U.S. Public*, pg. 725

Horn, Gregory T., Sr. V.P.-Retail Sls. & Mktg.--General Nutrition, Inc., Pittsburgh, PA; *U.S. Public*, pg. 725

Horn, Guy R., Sr. V.P.-Energy Supply--Nebraska Public Power District, Columbus, NE; *U.S. Private*, pg. 789

Horn, Paul M., Sr. V.P.-Research--International Business Machines Corporation, Armonk, NY; *U.S. Public*, pg. 895

Horne, Ander, Sr. V.P.-Sls. & Mktg.--Ridgeview, Inc., Newton, NC; *U.S. Private*, pg. 930

Horne, William, Sr. V.P.-MIS--Cash America International, Inc., Fort Worth, TX; *U.S. Public*, pg. 312

Horner, Robert W., III, Sr. V.P., Gen. Counsel & Sec.--Vitalink Pharmacy Services, Inc., Naperville, IL; *U.S. Public*, pg. 1041

Horner, Russell G., Jr., Sr. V.P., Gen. Counsel & Sec.--Kerr-McGee Corporation, Oklahoma City, OK; *U.S. Public*, pg. 952

Horner, Tom, Sr. V.P. & Grp. Media Dir.--DMB&B New York, New York, NY; *U.S. Private*, pg. 302

Horoschak, John, Sr. V.P.--Rolock, Inc., Fairfield, CT; *U.S. Private*, pg. 942

Horowitz, Edward D., Sr. V.P.-Tech. & Chm.-Viacom New Media--National Amusements, Inc., Dedham, MA; *U.S. Private*, pg. 775

Horowitz, Edward D., Sr. V.P.-Tech. & Chm.-Viacom Interactive Media--Viacom Inc., New York, NY; *U.S. Private*, pg. 775

Horowitz, Irving, Sr. V.P.--Amerbelle Corporation, Rockville, CT; *U.S. Private*, pg. 48

Horowitz, Jeffrey R., Sr. V.P., Gen. Counsel & Sec.--Ogden Energy Group, Inc., Fairfield, NJ; *U.S. Public*, pg. 1213

Horrigan, Chris, Sr. V.P.-Intl. Opers.--Liggett Group Inc., Durham, NC; *U.S. Public*, pg. 259

Horris, Christina D., Esq., Sr. V.P.-Regulatory Affairs & Compliance--NovaCare Employee Services, Inc., Norristown, PA; *U.S. Public*, pg. 1203

Horsley, Sherel, Sr. V.P.-Digital Printing Systems--Texas Instruments Incorporated, Dallas, TX; *U.S. Public*, pg. 1585

Horstmann, Dennis, Sr. V.P. & Gen. Mgr.-Mdse. (Contemporary Div.)--Petrie Retail, Inc., Secaucus, NJ; *U.S. Private*, pg. 858

Horton, Alan M., Sr. V.P.-Publishing--The E.W. Scripps Company, Cincinnati, OH; *U.S. Public*, pg. 1447

Horton, Gerald W., Sr. V.P. & Gen. Mgr.--Burns & Wilcox Ltd., Farmington, MI; *U.S. Private*, pg. 609

Hortum, Leslie, Sr. V.P.-Federation Devel.--Nation's Business, Washington, DC; *U.S. Private*, pg. 788

Horvath, Linda, Sr. V.P.-Capital Markets--Federal National Mortgage Association (Fannie Mae), Washington, DC; *U.S. Public*, pg. 615

Hoscheit, Donald, Sr. V.P.-Managed Health Care--Osco Drug, Salt Lake City, UT; *U.S. Public*, pg. 93

Hoskin, Daniel W., Sr. V.P.-Sls. & Mktg.--Kenney Manufacturing Company, Warwick, RI; *U.S. Private*, pg. 615

Hosono, T., Sr. V.P.--Mitsubishi International Corporation, New York, NY; *Int'l*, pg. 871

Hotchner, Ursula, Sr. V.P.--Newman's Own, Inc., Westport, CT; *U.S. Private*, pg. 797

Hotta, Hiroyuki, Assoc. Dir.-Intl. Bus. Devel.--Asahi Breweries Ltd., Tokyo, Japan; *Int'l*, pg. 83

Houde, Jean, Sr. V.P.-Banking--National Bank of Canada, Montreal, Canada; *Int'l*, pg. 907

Hougaard, Henrik, Sr. V.P.-Communications--Nykredit, Copenhagen, Denmark; *Int'l*, pg. 993

Houghtlin, David C., Sr. V.P.--Citizens Mortgage Corporation, Atlanta, GA; *Int'l*, pg. 1132

Houghton, Kenneth R., Sr. V.P.-Investment Securities--SunTrust Banks, Inc., Atlanta, GA; *U.S. Public*, pg. 1537

Hourihan, Edward P., Sr. V.P.-Information Systems--Phoenix Home Life Mutual Insurance Co., Hartford, CT; *U.S. Private*, pg. 863

Hourihau, Edward, Sr. V.P.-Info. Sys.--Phoenix Home Life Mutual Insurance Company, Hartford, CT; *U.S. Private*, pg. 863

Houry, Jean Michel, Sr. V.P. & Pres.-Sensormatic Europe Retail Opers.--Sensormatic Electronics Corporation, Boca Raton, FL; *U.S. Public*, pg. 1457

House, David L., Sr. V.P. & Dir.-Corp. Strategy--Intel Corporation, Santa Clara, CA; *U.S. Public*, pg. 886

Houser, Charles, Sr. V.P.--LCI International, Inc., Dublin, OH; *U.S. Public*, pg. 969

Houser, Frank M., Dr., Sr. V.P.-Quality & Medical Dir.--Columbia/HCA Healthcare Corporation, Nashville, TN; *U.S. Public*, pg. 403

Houseworth, Lucile, Sr. V.P. & Dir.-Mktg.--SunTrust Banks of Tennessee, Inc., Nashville, TN; *U.S. Public*, pg. 1538

Housh, E. William, Sr. V.P.-Alliance Development--HON Industries Inc., Muscatine, IA; *U.S. Public*, pg. 772

Houston, John, Sr. V.P. & Gen. Mgr.-North American Bus. Unit--Pulse Engineering, Inc., San Diego, CA; *U.S. Public*, pg. 1564

Houston, Randy, Sr. V.P.--W.L. Hailey & Company, Inc., Nashville, TN; *U.S. Private*, pg. 494

Hovland, Finn, Sr. V.P.--Du Pont Canada Inc., Mississauga, Canada; *U.S. Public*, pg. 532

Howald, Jeff, Sr. V.P.--Nine West Group, Inc., Stamford, CT; *U.S. Public*, pg. 1185

Howard, Chandler, Sr. V.P.-Hartford Reg.--People's Bank, Bridgeport, CT; *U.S. Public*, pg. 1274

Howard, Don, Sr. V.P.--bd Systems, Inc, Torrance, CA; *U.S. Private*, pg. 106

Howard, Donald J., Sr. V.P.-Real Estate & Construction--The Vons Companies, Inc., Arcadia, CA; *U.S. Public*, pg. 1426

Howard, Fred R., Sr. V.P.-Bus. Resources--Boeing Commercial Airplane Group, Renton, WA; *U.S. Public*, pg. 240

Howard, James D., Sr. V.P.-Lending--Penn Central National Bank, Huntingdon, PA; *U.S. Public*, pg. 1222

Howard, Larry, Sr. V.P.-HMO & Insurance Opers.--Sierra Health Services, Inc., Las Vegas, NV; *U.S. Public*, pg. 1469

Howard, Michael T., Chief Fin. Officer. & Sr. V.P.--Medrad, Inc., Indianola, PA; *Int'l*, pg. 1204

Howard, Robert W., Sr. V.P.-Fin. & Treas.--Barrett Resources Corporation, Denver, CO; *U.S. Public*, pg. 191

Howard, Will, Sr. V.P. & Mng. Dir.--Western International Media Corporation, Chicago, IL; *U.S. Private*, pg. 1167

Howard, William R., Sr. V.P.-Corp. Opers.--Crown Cork & Seal Company, Inc., Philadelphia, PA; *U.S. Public*, pg. 462

Howe, J.L., Sr. V.P.-Chemicals & Plastics--Phillips Petroleum Company, Bartlesville, OK; *U.S. Public*, pg. 1290

Howe, James, Sr. V.P.--Freeman Decorating Co., Dallas, TX; *U.S. Private*, pg. 426

Howe, Michael, Sr. V.P.-Franchise Support--Triarc Restaurant Group, Fort Lauderdale, FL; *U.S. Public*, pg. 1635

Howe, Rick, Sr. V.P.--Security Pacific Financial Services Inc., San Diego, CA; *U.S. Public*, pg. 181

Howell-Saxton, Delight, Chief Fin. Officer, Sr. V.P. & Sec.--McGrath RentCorp, Livermore, CA; *U.S. Public*, pg. 1069

Howell, Doug, Chief Fin. Officer, Sr. V.P. & Treas.--Preferred Risk Mutual Insurance, West Des Moines, IA; *U.S. Private*, pg. 880

Howell, Joseph, Chief Fin. Officer & Sr. V.P.--Merix Corporation, Forest Grove, OR; *U.S. Public*, pg. 1096

Howell, Josh, Sr. V.P.-Corp. Mktg.--MFS WorldCom, Inc., Omaha, NE; *U.S. Public*, pg. 1779

Howell, Richard P., Sr. V.P.-Admn.--Countrywide Funding Corporation, Pasadena, CA; *U.S. Public*, pg. 453

Howell, Robert, Sr. V.P.-Corp. Devel.--UtiliCorp United Inc., Kansas City, MO; *U.S. Public*, pg. 1700

Howells, Jeffery P., Chief Fin. Officer & Sr. V.P.-Fin.--Tech Data Corporation, Clearwater, FL; *U.S. Public*, pg. 1562

Howeth, Robert W., Chief Fin. Officer & Sr. V.P.--Fairfield Communities, Inc., Little Rock, AR; *U.S. Public*, pg. 610

Howoll, Gary L., Sr. V.P. & Creative Dir.--DMB&B Detroit, Troy, MI; *U.S. Private*, pg. 302

Howsam, Robert, Sr. V.P. & Mngmt. Supvr.--Ackerman McQueen, Inc., Colorado Springs, CO; *U.S. Private*, pg. 13

Hoxton, Jerome, Sr. V.P.-Sls. & Mktg.--Renaissance Publishing Co., Inc., Auburn, IN; *Int'l*, pg. 185

Hoyes, Louis W., Sr. V.P.-Multifamily Lending & Investment--Federal National Mortgage Association (Fannie Mae), Washington, DC; *U.S. Public*, pg. 615

Hoysradt, Jean E., Sr. V.P.-Investment--New York Life Insurance Company, New York, NY; *U.S. Private*, pg. 794

Hoyt, Thomas B., Sr. V.P.--Hibernia Corporation, New Orleans, LA; *U.S. Public*, pg. 825

Hrabe, Jon F., Sr. V.P.-Real Estate--Younkers, Inc., Des Moines, IA; *U.S. Public*, pg. 1334

Hricik, Kathleen, Sr. V.P.-Intl. Program Sls.--Nickelodeon/Nick At Nite, New York, NY; *U.S. Private*, pg. 779

Hsia, James C., Ph.D., Sr. V.P.-Research--Candela Corporation, Wayland, MA; *U.S. Public*, pg. 300

Hsiu, Wen-Bin, Sr. V.P.--Bangkok Rubber Public Co., Ltd., Bangkok, Thailand; *Int'l*, pg. 146

Hu, Jackson K.C., Sr. V.P.-Engrng. & Opers.--S3 Incorporated, Santa Clara, CA; *U.S. Public*, pg. 1415

Hu, Joseph K.M., Sr. V.P.-Insurance--Servco Pacific Inc., Honolulu, HI; *U.S. Private*, pg. 986

Huang, George, Sr. V.P. & Gen. Controller--Acer Incorporated, Taipei, Taiwan; *Int'l*, pg. 22

Hubbard, Bob M., Sr. V.P.-Pur. & Engrng.--TBC Corporation, Memphis, TN; *U.S. Public*, pg. 1553

Hubbard, Fred N., Sr. V.P.-Commercial Govt. & Bus.--Bell Helicopter Textron, Hurst, TX; *U.S. Public*, pg. 1588

Hubbard, Mike, Sr. V.P.-Sls.--Allen Canning Company, Siloam Springs, AR; *U.S. Private*, pg. 36

Huber, Michael S., Chief Fin. Officer, Sr. V.P. & Treas.--Andal Corp., New York, NY; *U.S. Public*, pg. 111

Hucko, Daniel, Sr. V.P. & New Media Dir.--Hutchins/Young & Rubicam, Rochester, NY; *U.S. Private*, pg. 1197

Hucks, Terry L., Sr. V.P.-Info. Services--Heilig-Meyers Company, Richmond, VA; *U.S. Public*, pg. 804

Hudis, Martin, Sr. V.P.-Tech. Devel.--Aerovox Inc., New Bedford, MA; *U.S. Public*, pg. 25

Hudnut, Stewart S., Sr. V.P., Sec. & Gen. Counsel--Illinois Tool Works Inc., Glenview, IL; *U.S. Public*, pg. 865

Hudson, Douglas K., Sr. V.P.--Poe & Brown, Inc., Daytona Beach, FL; *U.S. Public*, pg. 1312

Hudson, Douglas K., Sr. V.P.--National Programs Division, Tampa, FL; *U.S. Public*, pg. 1312

Hudson, Michael, Sr. V.P.-Mktg.--Tidel Engineering, Inc., Carrollton, TX; *U.S. Public*, pg. 1608

Hudson, P.E., Dr., Sr. Exec. V.P.--Radian International LLC, Austin, TX; *U.S. Public*, pg. 522

Hudspeth, Robert, J., Sr. V.P--NationsBank of St. Louis, Saint Louis, MO; *U.S. Public*, pg. 1164

Hueber, Paul J., Sr. V.P.-Opers.--Kmart Corporation, Troy, MI; *U.S. Public*, pg. 963

Huebner, Bryan J., Sr. V.P.-Hartford Region & Human Resources--People's Bank, Bridgeport, CT; *U.S. Public*, pg. 1274

Huey, J.H., Chief Information Officer & Sr. V.P.--Motorists Mutual Insurance Co., Columbus, OH; *U.S. Private*, pg. 764

Huezey, Peter F., Sr. V.P. & Dir.-Internal Audit--Republic National Bank of New York, New York, NY; *U.S. Public*, pg. 1380

Huff, Bruce N., Chief Fin. Officer & Sr. V.P.--Harken Energy Corporation, Irving, TX; *U.S. Public*, pg. 785

Hufnager, Joseph, Sr. V.P.--Imperial Schrade Corp., Ellenville, NY; *U.S. Private*, pg. 559

Hufstedler, E.K., III, Sr. V.P.--First National Bank in Cleburne, Cleburne, TX; *U.S. Public*, pg. 633

Huge, Art, Chief Fin. Officer & Sr. V.P.--The LTV Corporation, Cleveland, OH; *U.S. Public*, pg. 971

Huggins, Kenneth L., Sr. V.P.--Unifi Inc., Greensboro, NC; *U.S. Public*, pg. 1665

Hughes, Brian, Sr. V.P. & Media Dir.-Burger King--DMB&B New York, New York, NY; *U.S. Private*, pg. 302

Hughes, Dwain H., Chief Fin. Officer & Sr. V.P.--Tandy Corporation, Fort Worth, TX; *U.S. Public*, pg. 1560

Hughes, Ed, Sr. V.P. & Grp. Media Dir.--Young & Rubicam New York, New York, NY; *U.S. Private*, pg. 1198

Hughes, Eugene L., Sr. V.P.--Nature's Sunshine Products, Inc., Provo, UT; *U.S. Public*, pg. 1166

Hughes, Jack, Chief Fin. Officer & Sr. V.P.--BTG, Inc., Fairfax, VA; *U.S. Public*, pg. 164

Hughes, James G., Sr. V.P.-Personal Services--Investors Trust Company, Wyomissing, PA; *U.S. Public*, pg. 1159

Hughes, John G., Sr. V.P.-Worldwide Claims--American International Group, Inc., New York, NY; *U.S. Public*, pg. 83

Hughes, John T., Sr. V.P. & Chief Investment Officer--The Great-West Life Assurance Company, Winnipeg, Canada; *Int'l*, pg. 557

Hughes, Larry, Sr. V.P.-Field Services & Customer Service--DHL Airways, Inc., Redwood City, CA; *U.S. Private*, pg. 302
Hughes, Patrick, Sr. V.P.-Mktg. & Sls.--Blue Cross and Blue Shield of Massachusetts, Boston, MA; *U.S. Private*, pg. 151
Hughes, Stephen C., Chief Fin. Officer & Sr. V.P.--SRA International Inc., Arlington, VA; *U.S. Private*, pg. 957
Hughes, Timothy W., Sr. V.P.-Admin.--Cox Enterprises, Inc., Atlanta, GA; *U.S. Private*, pg. 281
Hughes, Valarie, Sr. V.P.-Acct. Services--Towne, Silverstein, Rotter Inc., New York, NY; *U.S. Private*, pg. 1093
Huh, Hyung Hwe, Chief Tech. Officer & Sr. V.P.--Diamond Multimedia Systems, Inc., San Jose, CA; *U.S. Public*, pg. 505
Hukatsu, Shunzo, Sr. V.P.--Meiji Seika Kaisha, Ltd., Tokyo, Japan; *Int'l*, pg. 855
Hulbert, Larry, Sr. V.P.-Sls. & Svc.--Alcatel Telecom, Richardson, TX; *Int'l*, pg. 55
Hulick, R.S., Sr. V.P.--TTX Co., Chicago, IL; *U.S. Private*, pg. 1066
Hull, Craig W., Sr. V.P.-Corp. Services--Occidental Chemical Corporation, Dallas, TX; *U.S. Public*, pg. 1210
Hull, Robert W., Sr. V.P.--Harbour Group Ltd., Saint Louis, MO; *U.S. Private*, pg. 500
Hull, Steve, Sr. V.P.--National Journal Group, Washington, DC; *U.S. Private*, pg. 785
Humber, Steve, Sr. V.P.-Data Processing--Total System Services, Inc., Columbus, GA; *U.S. Public*, pg. 1550
Hume, D. William, Sr. V.P. & Asst. Sec.--Penn Security Bank and Trust Co., Scranton, PA; *U.S. Public*, pg. 1270
Humenesky, Greg, Sr. V.P.-Human Resources--Zale Corporation, Irving, TX; *U.S. Public*, pg. 1789
Huml, Donald S., Chief Fin. Officer & Sr. V.P.-Fin.--Snap-On Tools Corporation, Kenosha, WI; *U.S. Public*, pg. 1480
Hummel, Joseph W., Sr. V.P.-Los Angeles Area.--Kaiser Permanente, Oakland, CA; *U.S. Private*, pg. 605
Humphrey, David R., Sr. V.P.-Investor Relations & Strategic Plng.--International Family Entertainment, Inc., Virginia Beach, VA; *Int'l*, pg. 927
Humphreys, Barry E., Sr. V.P.-Fin. & Treas.--Potash Corporation of Saskatchewan Inc., Saskatoon, Canada; *Int'l*, pg. 1064
Humphreys, Paul R., Chief Fin. Officer & Sr. V.P.-Fin.--Laidlaw Environmental Services, Inc., Columbia, SC; *U.S. Public*, pg. 975
Humphries, Lynn W., Sr. V.P.-Commercial Asset Mgmnt.--Continental Mortgage and Equity Trust, Dallas, TX; *U.S. Public*, pg. 441
Humphries, Lynn W., Sr. V.P.-Comml. Asset Mngmt.--Transcontinental Realty Investors, Inc., Dallas, TX; *U.S. Public*, pg. 1630
Hundahl, Blair L., Sr. V.P.-Fin.--Salick Health Care, Inc., Los Angeles, CA; *Int'l*, pg. 1524
Huneke, Wayne R., Chief Fin. Officer, Sr. V.P. & Treas.--ReliaStar Financial Corp., Minneapolis, MN; *U.S. Public*, pg. 1375
Huneke, Wayne R., Sr. V.P.--Northwestern National Life Insurance Co., Minneapolis, MN; *U.S. Public*, pg. 1375
Hungelman, Jim, Sr. V.P.-Intl.--J.R. Simplot Company Food Group, Boise, ID; *U.S. Private*, pg. 1002
Hungler, Chuck, Sr. V.P.--Jac Pac Foods, Ltd., Manchester, NH; *U.S. Private*, pg. 579
Hunnell, Matthew, Sr. V.P.-Mdsg.--Consolidated Stores Corp., Columbus, OH; *U.S. Public*, pg. 437
Hunnicut, John, Sr. V.P.-Pub. Rels.--American Institute of C.P.A.'s Inc., New York, NY; *U.S. Private*, pg. 57
Hunt, Bill, Sr. V.P.-Client Relations--Total System Services, Inc., Columbus, GA; *U.S. Public*, pg. 1550
Hunt, C.H., Chief Oper. Officer & Sr. V.P.- Co. Mngd. Htls. U.S.--Holiday Inn Worldwide, Atlanta, GA; *Int'l*, pg. 170
Hunt, James K., Sr. V.P.-SunAmerica Investments--SunAmerica Inc., Los Angeles, CA; *U.S. Public*, pg. 1532
Hunt, Philip R., Sr. V.P.--Zenith Insurance Company, Woodland Hills, CA; *U.S. Public*, pg. 1791
Hunt, Ronald L., Sr. V.P.--CDI Marine Company, Jacksonville, FL; *U.S. Public*, pg. 277
Hunt, William, Sr. V.P.--State Street Trust & Banking Company, Ltd., Tokyo, Japan; *U.S. Public*, pg. 1513
Hunter, Barry, Sr. V.P.--Keywell Corporation, Chicago, IL; *U.S. Private*, pg. 619
Hunter, Gerald F., Sr. V.P.--Associates International Management Company, Dallas, TX; *U.S. Public*, pg. 663
Hunter, John, Sr. V.P.-Mfg. & Engrng. Plastic Div.--Russell-Stanley Corporation, Red Bank, NJ; *U.S. Private*, pg. 953
Hunter, Nelson C., Chief Fin. Officer & Sr. V.P.--Greenstone Roberts Advertising, Melville, NY; *U.S. Public*, pg. 763
Hunter, Raymond L., Jr., Chief Information Officer & Sr. V.P.--Blue Cross & Blue Shield of Texas, Inc., Richardson, TX; *U.S. Private*, pg. 152
Hunter, Richard, Sr. V.P.-Intl. Opers. & Devel.--Williams-Sonoma, Inc., San Francisco, CA; *U.S. Public* pg. 1770
Hunter, Richard W., Dr., Sr. V.P. & Deputy Dir.-Integrated Business Systems--SRA International Inc., Arlington, VA; *U.S. Private*, pg. 957
Hunter, Stephanie Y., Sr. V.P. & Deputy Gen. Counsel--Synovus Financial Corp., Columbus, GA; *U.S. Public*, pg. 1548
Huntley, Max, Sr. V.P.-Mfg.--Parkdale Mills, Gastonia, NC; *U.S. Private*, pg. 840
Huntzinger, Judith, Sr. V.P. & Controller--BDM International, Inc., Mc Lean, VA; *U.S. Public*, pg. 1558
Hurcomb, Thomas J., Sr. V.P.--Smart Energy Services, Inc., Rutland, VT; *U.S. Public*, pg. 328
Huret, Jerome P., Sr. V.P.-Nortel World Trade--Northern Telecom Limited, Brampton, Canada; *Int'l*, pg. 968
Hurlbut, John, Sr. V.P. & Mngmt. Supvr.--Ingalls, Boston, MA; *U.S. Private*, pg. 562
Hurley, D. Brent, Sr. V.P.--Baltimore Trust Company, Selbyville, DE; *U.S. Public*, pg. 1088
Hurley, J.T., Sr. V.P.-Mktg.--Consolidated Papers, Inc., Wisconsin Rapids, WI; *U.S. Public*, pg. 436
Hurley, James, Chief Fin. Officer & Sr. V.P.-Fin./MIS--Quality Stores Inc., Muskegon, MI; *U.S. Private*, pg. 899
Hurley, Melissa M., Sr. V.P., Gen. Counsel & Sec.--Northstar Investment Management Corporation, Greenwich, CT; *U.S. Public*, pg. 1375
Hurley, Terri, Sr. V.P. & Dep. Gen. Mgr.-Consumer--Edelman Public Relations Worldwide, Chicago, IL; *U.S. Private*, pg. 362
Hurley, Thomas A., Sr. V.P.-Programming--Comcast Cable Communications, Inc., Philadelphia, PA; *U.S. Public*, pg. 407
Hurst, Frank, Sr. V.P.--Carpenter Co., Richmond, VA; *U.S. Private*, pg. 214
Hurst, Gordon S., Sr. V.P.-Sls.--Waukesha Cherry-Burrell, Delavan, WI; *U.S. Public*, pg. 1677
Hurst, J. Gordon, Sr. V.P. & Gen. Mgr.-Opers.--SIGCORP, Inc., Evansville, IN; *U.S. Public*, pg. 1471
Hurst, J. Gordon, Sr. V.P. & Gen. Mgr.-Opers.--Southern Indiana Gas & Electric Co., Evansville, IN; *U.S. Public*, pg. 1471
Hurt, Douglas, Chief Fin. Officer & Sr. V.P.--Glaxo Wellcome Inc., Research Triangle Park, NC; *Int'l*, pg. 552
Hurtubise, Ken, Sr. V.P.-Sls. & Mktg.--ECRM, Tewksbury, MA; *U.S. Private*, pg. 353
Hurwitz, Steven L., Sr. V.P.-Mktg.--Rhodes, Inc., Atlanta, GA; *U.S. Public*, pg. 805
Husby, Philip G., Chief Fin. Officer & Sr. V.P.--Ogden Corporation, New York, NY; *U.S. Public*, pg. 1213
Huse, Mike, Chief Oper. Officer & Sr. V.P.--Quality Food Centers, Inc., Bellevue, WA; *U.S. Public*, pg. 1349
Husinger, Rich, Sr. V.P.--WinCup, Phoenix, AZ; *U.S. Private*, pg. 1182
Hutaserani, Krisda, Sr. V.P.--Siam City Bank Public Company Limited, Bangkok, Thailand; *Int'l*, pg. 1239
Hutchinson, Carroll R., Chief Actuary & Sr. V.P.--The Western and Southern Life Insurance Company, Cincinnati, OH; *U.S. Private*, pg. 1164
Hutchinson, James, Sr. V.P.-Pur.--Fast Food Merchandisers Inc., Rocky Mount, NC; *U.S. Public*, pg. 278
Hutchison, J.H., Sr. V.P.--Serigraph, Inc., West Bend, WI; *U.S. Private*, pg. 985
Hutchison, P.A., Sr. V.P.-H.R. & Admin.--ESCO Electronics Corporation, Saint Louis, MO; *U.S. Public*, pg. 546
Hutchison, Peter S., Sr. V.P.-Corp. Tax--Manulife Financial (The Manufacturers Life Insurance Company), Toronto, Canada; *Int'l*, pg. 840
Hutchison, Robert, Sr. V.P.--First Bank N.A., Milwaukee, WI; *U.S. Public*, pg. 1680
Huwitt, Jim, Sr. V.P.-Admin.--Qualex Inc., Durham, NC; *U.S. Public*, pg. 551
Hwa, Roy Tsou Chen, Sr. V.P.-Mktg.--Singapore Petroleum Company Ltd., Singapore, Singapore; *U.S. Public*, pg. 102
Hyatt, Lawrence E., Sr. V.P.-Fin. & Plng., Marriott Mngmt. Services--Marriott International, Inc., Washington, DC; *U.S. Public*, pg. 1047
Hyde, Dee A., Sr. V.P.-Loan Info. Mgmt.--Zions First National Bank, Salt Lake City, UT; *U.S. Public*, pg. 1793
Hyde, James R., Sr. V.P. & Pres.-Grace Div.--W.R. Grace & Co., Boca Raton, FL; *U.S. Public*, pg. 754
Hyde, Thomas D., Sr. V.P. & Gen. Counsel--Raytheon Company, Lexington, MA; *U.S. Public*, pg. 1364
Hyder, C.D., Sr. V.P.-Tech. Svcs.--Varco-Pruden Buildings, Memphis, TN; *U.S. Public*, pg. 1677
Hyland, Dennis M., Sr. V.P.-Commercial Lines Underwriting--Harleysville Group, Harleysville, PA; *U.S. Public*, pg. 786
Hyliuski, Thomas, Sr. V.P.-Residential Lending--People's Bank, Bridgeport, CT; *U.S. Public*, pg. 1274
Hymers, Glenn S., Sr. V.P.-Personal Trust Services--National Trust Company, Stratford, Canada; *Int'l*, pg. 910
Hymes, William W., Sr. V.P.--Sterling Commerce, Inc., Dublin, OH; *U.S. Public*, pg. 1515
Iaco, James V., Jr., Chief Fin. Officer & Sr. V.P.--Edison Mission Energy, Irvine, CA; *U.S. Public*, pg. 564
Ianello, Angelo, Sr. V.P.-Fin. & Treas.--Contract Freighters, Inc., Joplin, MO; *U.S. Private*, pg. 270
Iauco, David N., Sr. V.P.-Worldwide Bus. Devel.--R.J. Reynolds Tobacco Company, Winston Salem, NC; *U.S. Public*, pg. 1355
Ibarbia, Ezequiel P., Chief Fin. Officer & Sr. V.P.--P.L. Porter Co., Woodland Hills, CA; *U.S. Private*, pg. 876
Ichikawa, Mamoru, Sr. V.P.--Japan Airlines Company, Ltd., Tokyo, Japan; *Int'l*, pg. 699
Ichinosawa, Takeshi, Sr. V.P.-Hokkaido, Sapporo--Japan Airlines Company, Ltd., Tokyo, Japan; *Int'l*, pg. 699
Ide, Isao, Sr. Mng. Dir.-Labor Rels.--Ito-Yokado Co., Ltd., Tokyo, Japan; *Int'l*, pg. 693
Ide, R. William, III, Sr. V.P., Gen. Counsel & Sec.--Monsanto Company, Saint Louis, MO; *U.S. Public*, pg. 1124
Idell, J.B., Sr. V.P.-Corp. Devel.--Science Applications International Corp., San Diego, CA; *U.S. Private*, pg. 975
Idoni, William, Sr. V.P.--Chemical Bank & Trust Company, Midland, MI; *U.S. Public*, pg. 345
Igarashi, Osamu, Sr. V.P. -Corp. Plng. & Sr. Mng. Dir.--Japan Airlines Company, Ltd., Tokyo, Japan; *Int'l*, pg. 699
Iglesias, Fernando, Sr. V.P.-Special Loans--Firstbank Puerto Rico, Santurce, PR; *U.S. Public*, pg. 644
Ihlenfeld, Brad, Chief Fin. Officer & Sr. V.P.--Meridian Technology Leasing Services, Deerfield, IL; *U.S. Private*, pg. 732
Iki, Gary K., Sr. V.P.-Corp. Banking Hawaii Division--Bank of Hawaii, Honolulu, HI; *U.S. Public*, pg. 1248
Iles, T. Randall, Sr. V.P.-Mktg. & Sls.--Pella Corporation, Pella, IA; *U.S. Private*, pg. 848
Illana, Jose, Sr. V.P.--Banco Santander, Madrid, Spain; *Int'l*, pg. 143
Imamura, Austin Y., Sr. V.P. & Sec.--CPB Properties, Inc., Honolulu, HI; *U.S. Public*, pg. 283
Imanaka, Marie M., Sr. V.P.-Mortgage Banking Division--Bank of Hawaii, Honolulu, HI; *U.S. Public*, pg. 1248
Imayoshi, Masatoshi, Sr. V.P.--G-Net Corporation, Osaka, Japan; *Int'l*, pg. 531
Imazeki, Ryoji, Sr. V.P.--Fanuc Ltd., Yamanashi, Japan; *Int'l*, pg. 477
Imbler, Stephen, Chief Fin. Officer & Sr. V.P.--Arbor Software Corporation, Sunnyvale, CA; *U.S. Public*, pg. 127
Imel, Robert, Chief Fin. Officer & Sr. V.P.--National Energy Group, Inc., Dallas, TX; *U.S. Public*, pg. 1156
Immelt, Mark W., Sr. V.P.-Trust Svcs.--First Financial Bancorp, Hamilton, OH; *U.S. Public*, pg. 632
Immelt, Mark W., Sr. V.P.--First National Bank of Southwestern Ohio, Hamilton, OH; *U.S. Public*, pg. 633
Impey, Bill, Sr. V.P.-Mktg. & Prod. Devel.--Oregon Freeze Dry, Inc., Albany, OR; *U.S. Private*, pg. 819
Imse, Robert A., Sr. V.P.--Hartford Fire Insurance Co., Hartford, CT; *U.S. Public*, pg. 794
Inazumi, Toshiki, Assoc. Sr. V.P.--NEC Corporation, Tokyo, Japan; *Int'l*, pg. 899
Inbar, Abraham, Sr. V.P.--Vishay Intertechnology, Inc., Malvern, PA; *U.S. Public*, pg. 1721
Inbar, Doron, Chief Fin. Officer & Sr. V.P.--ECI Telecom Ltd., Petah Tiqwa, Israel; *Int'l*, pg. 643
Indart, Geri, Sr. V.P. & Local TV Brdcst. Dir.--The Media Edge, New York, NY; *U.S. Private*, pg. 1079
Infanger, Walter, Chm. Bd. & Sr. V.P.--Ferrier Lullin & Cie SA, Geneva, Switzerland; *Int'l*, pg. 480
Ingebrand, Richard, Sr. V.P. & Gen. Mgr.-Northcentral Region-Denver--Showtime Networks Inc., New York, NY; *U.S. Private*, pg. 779
Ingelmark, Lars, Sr. V.P.--Pharmacia & Upjohn, Inc., Windsor, United Kingdom; *Int'l*, pg. 1047
Ingle, Don, Sr. V.P. & Pub. Rels. Dir.--Rockett, Burkhead, Lewis & Winslow, Raleigh, NC; *U.S. Private*, pg. 938
Ingram, Benny K., Sr. V.P.--Trustmark National Bank, Jackson, MS; *U.S. Public*, pg. 1643
Ingram, John C., Sr. V.P.-Securities--Jefferson-Pilot Life Insurance Co., Greensboro, NC; *U.S. Public*, pg. 926
Ingrassia, John, Sr. V.P.-Columbia Records Group--Sony Music Entertainment, Inc., New York, NY; *Int'l*, pg. 1281
Inkel, H. Albert, Sr. V.P.-Assoc. Rels. & Communication--Horace Mann Educators Corporation, Springfield, IL; *U.S. Public*, pg. 835
Innes, Debbie, Sr. V.P. & Natl. Brdcst. Dir.--Media Partnership Corporation, Norwalk, CT; *U.S. Private*, pg. 1168
Inoue, K., Sr. V.P.--Mitsubishi International Corporation, New York, NY; *Int'l*, pg. 871
Inoue, Makoto, Sr. V.P.--Meitsu Inc., Tokyo, Japan; *Int'l*, pg. 856
Inoue, Makoto, Sr. V.P.--ORIX USA Corporation-Los Angeles, Los Angeles, CA; *Int'l*, pg. 1009
Inouye, Glenn K., Sr. V.P.-Corp. Control Opers.--Servco Pacific Inc., Honolulu, HI; *U.S. Private*, pg. 986
Inouye, Wayne R., Sr. V.P.-Mktg./Computers & Home Office--Best Buy Co., Inc., Eden Prairie, MN; *U.S. Public*, pg. 223
Insalaco, J., Sr. V.P.-Mktg.--California Products Corp., Cambridge, MA; *U.S. Private*, pg. 201
Interlandi, Daniel G., Sr. V.P. & Gen. Mgr.-Leisure & Entertainment Prods.--Micros Systems Inc., Beltsville, MD; *U.S. Public*, pg. 1106
Iocco, Robert, Sr. V.P.--National Programs Division, Tampa, FL; *U.S. Public*, pg. 1312
Iorillo, Anthony J., Sr. V.P.--Hughes Electronics Corporation, Westchester, CA; *U.S. Public*, pg. 720
Irani, Ronnie K., Exec. V.P.-Engrng. & Exploration--Louis Dreyfus Natural Gas Corp., Oklahoma City, OK; *U.S. Private*, pg. 342
Iraola, Manuel J., Sr. V.P.--Phelps Dodge Corporation, Phoenix, AZ; *U.S. Public*, pg. 1286
Irons, Ed, Sr. V.P. & Media Dir.--Mars Advertising Co., Southfield, MI; *U.S. Private*, pg. 706
Irons, William L., Sr. V.P.-MIS--Lowe's Companies, Inc., North Wilkesboro, NC; *U.S. Public*, pg. 1015
Irvin, Thomas W., V.P. & Fin. Services Dir.--The Buntin Group, Nashville, TN; *U.S. Private*, pg. 181
Irving, Richard H., III, Sr. V.P. & Gen. Counsel--Blount International, Inc., Montgomery, AL; *U.S. Public*, pg. 237
Irving, Richard H., III, Sr. V.P. & Gen. Counsel--Blount, Inc., Montgomery, AL; *U.S. Public*, pg. 238
Irwin, A. Scott, Sr. V.P.-Mktg.--Irwin Toy Ltd., Toronto, Canada; *Int'l*, pg. 688
Irwin, Carol, Sr. V.P. & Acct. Dir.--Berry-Brown Advertising, Inc., Dallas, TX; *U.S. Private*, pg. 137
Irwin, Rick, Sr. V.P.-Sls. & Gen. Mgr.-Publication Papers Div.--Gould Paper Corporation, New York, NY; *U.S. Private*, pg. 466
Irwin, Susan N., Sr. V.P.--Willis Corroon Melling Inc., Toronto, Canada; *Int'l*, pg. 1509
Irwin, T. Bryan, Sr. V.P.-Sls.--Irwin Toy Ltd., Toronto, Canada; *Int'l*, pg. 688
Isaac, R.M., Sr. V.P.--McJunkin Corporation, Charleston, WV; *U.S. Private*, pg. 722
Isacke, John F., Chief Fin. Officer & Sr. V.P.--Consumers Water Company, Portland, ME; *U.S. Public*, pg. 438
Isakoff, Louis A., Sr. V.P., Gen. Counsel & Sec.--International Family Entertainment, Inc., Virginia Beach, VA; *Int'l*, pg. 927
Isenberg, Debra, Sr. V.P.-Mktg.--Dow Jones Markets, Jersey City, NJ; *U.S. Public*, pg. 525
Isenhart, John, Sr. V.P.-Tech.--EMC Insurance Group, Inc., Des Moines, IA; *U.S. Public*, pg. 545
Isenhart, John D., Sr. V.P.-Tech.--EMC Insurance Companies, Des Moines, IA; *U.S. Public*, pg. 545
Isenstein, Joe, Sr. V.P.-Employee Rels.--Bertelsmann Music Group, Wilmington, DE; *Int'l*, pg. 191
Isham, Rick, Sr. V.P.--D.L. Blair Inc., Garden City, NY; *U.S. Private*, pg. 148
Ishee, Jimmie F., Sr. V.P.--Trustmark National Bank, Jackson, MS; *U.S. Public*, pg. 1643
Ishibashi, Kensuke, Sr. V.P.--ORIX Commercial Alliance Corporation, Secaucus, NJ; *Int'l*, pg. 1009
Ishiguro, Tatsuo, Assoc. Sr. V.P.--NEC Corporation, Tokyo, Japan; *Int'l*, pg. 899

Ishihara, Wayne T., Sr. V.P.-Branch Admin.--American Savings Bank, F.S.B., Honolulu, HI; *U.S. Public*, pg. 800
Ishikawa, Norikazu, Sr. V.P.--Softbank Corporation, Tokyo, Japan; *Int'l*, pg. 1276
Isinger, William R., Sr. V.P.-Fin.--Los Angeles Times, Los Angeles, CA; *U.S. Public*, pg. 1616
Isler, Peter, Sr. V.P.-Res. & Devel.--UMS Swiss Metalworks Holding Ltd, Dornach, Switzerland; *Int'l*, pg. 1427
Islinger, Bob, Sr. V.P.-Mktg.--Payless Cashways, Inc., Kansas City, MO; *U.S. Public*, pg. 1267
Isobe, Asahiko, Sr. Exec. Mng. Dir.--Hitachi, Ltd., Tokyo, Japan; *Int'l*, pg. 621
Isoherranen, Seppo, Sr. V.P.-Comml. Affairs--Outokumpu Oyj, Espoo, Finland; *Int'l*, pg. 1015
Isono, Denis K., Sr. V.P. & Controller--Pacific Century Financial Corporation, Honolulu, HI; *U.S. Public*, pg. 1248
Israel, Jason J., Exec. V.P.-Admin.--American Bankers Insurance Co. of Florida, Miami, FL; *U.S. Public*, pg. 67
Israel, Simon, Sr. V.P.-Asia-Pacific Div.--Danone Group, Paris, France; *Int'l*, pg. 379
Itavuori, Jussi, Sr. V.P.-H.R.--Kone Corporation, Helsinki, Finland; *Int'l*, pg. 746
Itkin, Myles R., Chief Fin. Officer, Sr. V.P. & Treas.--Overseas Shipholding Group, Inc., New York, NY; *U.S. Public*, pg. 1236
Ito, Yasuhisa, Sr. Mng. Dir.-Store Opers.--Ito-Yokado Co., Ltd., Tokyo, Japan; *Int'l*, pg. 693
Itokazu, John, Sr. V.P.-Retail Oper.--Zions First National Bank, Salt Lake City, UT; *U.S. Public*, pg. 1793
Itomine, I., V.P.-Indiana Office--Fujitsu Ten Corp. of America, Torrance, CA; *Int'l*, pg. 526
Itzkovitch, Irwin J., Dr., Sr. V.P.-Tech.--Noranda Inc., Toronto, Canada; *Int'l*, pg. 433
Ivanier, Sydney, Sr. V.P.--The Ivaco Group, Montreal, Canada; *Int'l*, pg. 695
Iversen, Leif, Sr. V.P.--Det Norske Veritas, Hovik, Norway; *Int'l*, pg. 396
Iversen, Soren, Sr. V.P.--F.L. Smith & Co. A/S, Copenhagen, Denmark; *Int'l*, pg. 475
Ivy, Leslie, Sr. Principal & Exec. Dir.-Creative Svcs.--Publicis Public Relations, Dallas, TX; *Int'l*, pg. 470
Iwamura, H., Sr. V.P.--Mitsubishi International Corporation, New York, NY; *Int'l*, pg. 871
Iwao, Yoshio, Sr. Mng. Dir. & Sr. V.P.-Flight Opers. Div.--Japan Airlines Company, Ltd., Tokyo, Japan; *Int'l*, pg. 699
Izawa, Tatsuo, Sr. V.P.--Nippon Telegraph and Telephone Corporation, Tokyo, Japan; *Int'l*, pg. 940
Jablin, Burton, Sr. V.P.-Programming--Home & Garden Television, Knoxville, TN; *U.S. Public*, pg. 1447
Jablonski, Carl L., Sr. V.P.-Opers.--Acme Markets, Malvern, PA; *U.S. Public*, pg. 93
Jack, H. Patrick, Sr. V.P.--Fina, Inc., Dallas, TX; *Int'l*, pg. 1044
Jackied, Walt, Sr. V.P.--St. Louis National Baseball Club L.P., Saint Louis, MO; *U.S. Private*, pg. 961
Jackson, David, Sr. V.P.--Hill, Holliday, Connors, Cosmopulos, Inc., Boston, MA; *U.S. Private*, pg. 529
Jackson, David, Sr. V.P.-Opers.--Wal-Mart Stores, Inc., Bentonville, AR; *U.S. Public*, pg. 1732
Jackson, Jack J., Sr. V.P.--Pharmacia & Upjohn, Inc., Windsor, United Kingdom; *Int'l*, pg. 1047
Jackson, Jack J., Sr. V.P.-Intl. Pharmaceutical Oper.--Pharmacia & Upjohn, Kalamazoo, MI; *Int'l*, pg. 1048
Jackson, James E., Sr. V.P.--Pioneer American Holding Company, Carbondale, PA; *U.S. Public*, pg. 1298
Jackson, James S., Sr. V.P.-Funds Mngmt.--1st Source Bank Consolidated, South Bend, IN; *U.S. Public*, pg. 638
Jackson, John D., Sr. V.P. & Sec.--The Fairchild Corporation, Chantilly, VA; *U.S. Public*, pg. 610
Jackson, John E., Sr. V.P.--Nordson Corporation, Westlake, OH; *U.S. Public*, pg. 1188
Jackson, John E., Sr. V.P.--Nordson North American Div., Duluth, GA; *U.S. Public*, pg. 1188
Jackson, Lawrence V., Sr. V.P.--PepsiCo, Inc., Purchase, NY; *U.S. Public*, pg. 1276
Jackson, Mark A., Chief Fin. Officer & Sr. V.P.--Snyder Oil Corporation, Fort Worth, TX; *U.S. Public*, pg. 1481
Jackson, Marshall, Sr. V.P.-Mktg.--AVX Corporation, Myrtle Beach, SC; *Int'l*, pg. 775
Jackson, Michael, Sr. V.P.--Petrie Retail, Inc., Secaucus, NJ; *U.S. Private*, pg. 858
Jackson, Parker, Sr. V.P.--Harbor Financial/New America, Walnut Creek, CA; *U.S. Public*, pg. 644
Jackson, Robert T., Chief Fin. Officer & Sr. V.P.--American Century Investments, Kansas City, MO; *U.S. Private*, pg. 52
Jackson, Roderick P., Sr. V.P.--Mylan Laboratories, Inc., Pittsburgh, PA; *U.S. Public*, pg. 1143
Jackson, Roger A., Sr. V.P.-Human Resources & Corp. Rels.--Lear Corporation, Southfield, MI; *U.S. Public*, pg. 981
Jackson, Roland W., Sr. V.P.--F&G Re, Inc., Morristown, NJ; *U.S. Public*, pg. 1659
Jackson, Stanley H., Chief Oper. Officer & Sr. V.P.-Indus. Div.--Diversco, Inc., Spartanburg, SC; *U.S. Private*, pg. 336
Jackson, Steven H., Chief Credit Officer & Sr. V.P.--Prime Bancshares Inc., Houston, TX; *U.S. Public*, pg. 1326
Jackson, V. Charles, Sr. V.P.--Mellon Financial Services, Los Angeles, CA; *U.S. Public*, pg. 1085
Jaco, Ron, Sr. V.P. & Media Dir.-Seattle & Dir.--EvansGroup, Salt Lake City, UT; *U.S. Private*, pg. 385
Jaco, Ron, Sr. V.P. & Media Dir.--EvansGroup, Seattle, WA; *U.S. Private*, pg. 385
Jacob, Stacy Leyendecker, Sr. V.P. & Corp. Resources Dir.--Black Rogers Sullivan Goodnight, Inc., Houston, TX; *U.S. Private*, pg. 147
Jacobi, Moshe, Sr. V.P.--Kulicke & Soffa Industries, Inc., Willow Grove, PA; *U.S. Public*, pg. 968
Jacobs, Andrew F., Sr. V.P.-Control, Treas. & Sec.--Capstead Mortgage Corporation, Dallas, TX; *U.S. Public*, *pg. 303*
Jacobs, Curtis M., Sr. V.P., Chief Counsel & Sec.--National City Bank, Kentucky, Louisville, KY; *U.S. Public*, pg. 1154
Jacobs, James, Sr. V.P.-Store Opers.--Ross Stores, Inc., Newark, CA; *U.S. Public*, pg. 1405
Jacobs, Jay, Sr. V.P.-Mdsg.--Pier 1 Imports, Inc., Fort Worth, TX; *U.S. Public*, pg. 1295
Jacobs, Matthew S., Sr. V.P.--Total System Services, Inc., Columbus, GA; *U.S. Public*, pg. 1550
Jacobs, Paul E., Sr. V.P. & Pres.-Subscriber Prods.--QUALCOMM, San Diego, CA; *U.S. Public*, pg. 1348
Jacobs, Phil S., Sr. V.P.-Managed Network Solutions & Pres.-BellSouth BSE, Inc.--BellSouth Corporation, Atlanta, GA; *U.S. Public*, pg. 207
Jacobs, Rick, Sr. V.P.-Talent & Casting--Columbia TriStar Television, Culver City, CA; *Int'l*, pg. 1282
Jacobs, Seth, Sr. V.P. & Gen. Counsel--Blue Shield of California, San Francisco, CA; *U.S. Private*, pg. 153
Jacobsen, Lowell P., Sr. V.P.-Corp. Affairs--Medtronic, Inc., Minneapolis, MN; *U.S. Public*, pg. 1082
Jacobsen, Pat, Sr. V.P.-Human Resources & Corp. Services--Manulife Financial, Toronto, Canada; *Int'l*, pg. 840
Jacobsen, Raymond W., Sr. V.P.--Orion Capital Corporation, New York, NY; *U.S. Public*, pg. 1231
Jacobsen, Steven J., Sr. V.P.-Devel.--The Mills Corporation, Arlington, VA; *U.S. Public*, pg. 1113
Jacobsen, William K., Sr. V.P. & Dir.-Retail Opers.--Schultz Sav-O Stores, Inc., Sheboygan, WI; *U.S. Public*, pg. 1442
Jacobson, Gary L., Sr. V.P.--ReliaStar Investment Research, Inc., Minneapolis, MN; *U.S. Public*, pg. 1376
Jacobson, Howard, Sr. V.P.-Customer Bus. Centers--Canandaigua Wine Co., Canandaigua, NY; *U.S. Public*, pg. 300
Jacobson, Jake, Sr. V.P.-Bus. Affairs--Paramount Pictures Corporation, Los Angeles, CA; *U.S. Private*, pg. 776
Jacobson, Larry, Sr. V.P.--Ventura Foods LLC, City of Industry, CA; *Int'l*, pg. 879
Jacobson, Larry, Sr. V.P.-Fin.--Fox, Inc., Los Angeles, CA; *Int'l*, pg. 926
Jacobson, Michael W., Sr. V.P.--Zenith National Insurance Corp., Woodland Hills, CA; *U.S. Public*, pg. 1790
Jacobson, Michael W., Sr. V.P.--CalFarm Insurance Company, Sacramento, CA; *U.S. Public*, pg. 1791
Jacobson, Michael W., Sr. V.P.--Zenith Insurance Company, Woodland Hills, CA; *U.S. Public*, pg. 1791
Jacobson, Robert P., Chief Fin. Officer, Sr. V.P. & Treas.--Everest Reinsurance Holdings, Liberty Corner, NJ; *U.S. Public*, pg. 597
Jacobson, Sibyl, Sr. V.P.-External Rel.--Metropolitan Life Insurance Co., New York, NY; *U.S. Private*, pg. 737
Jacobson, Susie, Sr. V.P. & Mngmt. Dir.--Grant/Jacoby, Inc., Chicago, IL; *U.S. Private*, pg. 470
Jacoby, Frederic J., Sr. V.P.--Arinc Inc. (Consolidated), Annapolis, MD; *U.S. Private*, pg. 81
Jacques, Jerome C., Chief Fin. Officer, Sr. V.P. & Treas.--Guardsmark, Inc., Memphis, TN; *U.S. Private*, pg. 486
Jadelis, Tom, Sr. V.P.--Advanced Risk Management Services, New York, NY; *Int'l*, pg. 1505
Jaeger, Jo-Anne C., Sr. V.P.-Mdsg. & Intl. Devel.--BeautiControl Cosmetics, Inc., Carrollton, TX; *U.S. Public*, pg. 198
Jaeger, Michael, Sr. V.P.-Mktg.--Sutter Home Winery, Inc., Saint Helena, CA; *U.S. Private*, pg. 1057
Jaeger, Robert J., Sr. V.P.-Fin., Controller & Treas.--Westmoreland Coal Co., Colorado Springs, CO; *U.S. Public*, pg. 1761
Jaeggi, Kenneth G., Chief Fin. Officer & Sr. V.P.--Symbol Technologies, Inc., Holtsville, NY; *U.S. Public*, pg. 1546
Jaffe, Arlene, Sr. V.P. & Creative Dir.--DMB&B New York, New York, NY; *U.S. Private*, pg. 302
Jaffe, Elise, Sr. V.P.--The Dress Barn, Inc., Suffern, NY; *U.S. Public*, pg. 528
Jaffe, Tony, Sr. V.P. & Creative Dir.--MARC, Pittsburgh, PA; *U.S. Private*, pg. 701
Jahn, Joseph A., Jr., Sr. V.P.-Admin. & Opers.--Sumitomo Bank of New York Trust Company, New York, NY; *Int'l*, pg. 1309
Jaisson, J., Sr. V.P. & Sec.--Elf Atochem S.A., Paris, France; *Int'l*, pg. 445
Jaisson, Jacques, Sr. V.P./Chemicals--Elf Aquitane, Paris, France; *Int'l*, pg. 444
Jakab, Paul, Sr. V.P.-International--Mindscape, Inc., Novato, CA; *Int'l*, pg. 1026
James, Donald E., Sr. V.P.-Public Affairs--Atmos Energy Corporation, Dallas, TX; *U.S. Public*, pg. 145
James, George, Chief Fin. Officer & Sr. V.P.--Levi Strauss & Co., San Francisco, CA; *U.S. Private*, pg. 662
James, John, Sr. V.P.--Pioneer Hi-Bred International, Inc., Des Moines, IA; *U.S. Public*, pg. 1298
James, Phyllis P., Sr. V.P.-Mdsg.--Buster Brown Apparel, Inc., Chattanooga, TN; *U.S. Private*, pg. 189
James, Ross N., Sr. V.P. & Grp. Gen. Mgr.--The BHP Copper Group, San Francisco, CA; *Int'l*, pg. 224
James, W. Jack, Jr., Sr. V.P.-Credit Admin. & Review Div.--Compass Bank, Birmingham, AL; *U.S. Public*, pg. 418
Jamieson, Irene A., Sr. V.P. & Gen. Mgr.-Mdsg.--Ross Stores, Inc., Newark, CA; *U.S. Public*, pg. 1405
Jamieson, Jeanette, Sr. V.P.-Mdsg./Staples Contract & Comml.--Staples, Inc., Westborough, MA; *U.S. Public*, pg. 1509
Jamis, Mary, Ph.D., Sr. V.P.-Plng.--Long Haymes Carr, Inc., Winston Salem, NC; *U.S. Public*, pg. 909
Jamison, Lawrence, Sr. V.P.-Admin.--ADP Marshall Contractors Inc., Rumford, RI; *U.S. Public*, pg. 660
Jammet, Bernard, Sr. V.P.-Intl. Dealers--Micros Systems Inc., Beltsville, MD; *U.S. Public*, pg. 1106
Janas, Paul, Sr. V.P. & Creative Dir.--Hal Riney & Partners Heartland, Chicago, IL; *U.S. Private*, pg. 931
Janavey, Harry, Chief Fin. Officer & Sr. V.P.--The Chapman Agency, New York, NY; *U.S. Private*, pg. 1197
Janckila, Darrel D., Sr. V.P.--Scicom Data Services, Ltd., Minnetonka, MN; *U.S. Private*, pg. 975
Janey, T. Michael, Chief Fin. Officer, Sr. V.P. & Treas.--Datamax International Corporation, Orlando, FL; *U.S. Private*, pg. 313
Janke, Kenneth S., Jr., Sr. V.P.-Investor Rels.--AFLAC Incorporated, Columbus, GA; *U.S. Public*, pg. 28
Jansen Kraemer, Harry M., Jr., Pres., Chief Fin. Officer & Sr. V.P.--Baxter International Inc., Deerfield, IL; *U.S. Public*, pg. 196
Janssen, Kathy, Chief Fin. Officer & Sr. V.P.--Contract Interiors Inc., Taylor, MI; *U.S. Private*, pg. 270
Jansson, Hakan, Sr. V.P.-Corp. Tech.--Telefonaktiebolaget LM Ericsson, Stockholm, Sweden; *Int'l*, pg. 1363
Jansson, Ingrid, Sr. V.P.-Mktg.--Trygg-Hansa, Stockholm, Sweden; *Int'l*, pg. 1425
Janz, James F., Sr. V.P.--Zilber, Ltd., Milwaukee, WI; *U.S. Private*, pg. 1206
Jarc, Lyn, Partner & Sr. V.P.--Media That Works, Cincinnati, OH; *U.S. Private*, pg. 727
Jarc, Richard, Sr. V.P. & Grp. Dir.--DavisElen Advertising, Inc., Los Angeles, CA; *U.S. Private*, pg. 316
Jarecki, Robert, Sr. V.P.-Information Tech.--Wendy's International Inc., Dublin, OH; *U.S. Public*, pg. 1754
Jartz, John G., Sr. V.P.-Law & Bus. Devel./Corp. Sec.--The Quaker Oats Company, Chicago, IL; *U.S. Public*, pg. 1347
Jarvi, K.T., Sr. V.P. & Gen. Counsel--MidCon Corp., Lombard, IL; *U.S. Public*, pg. 1210
Jarvis, Burney K., Sr. V.P. & Dir.-Branch Sls. & Admin.--Barclays American/Mortgage Corp., Charlotte, NC; *Int'l*, pg. 165
Jarvis, David, Sr. V.P.--Key Bank Life Insurance, Ltd., Cleveland, OH; *U.S. Public*, pg. 954
Jarvis, John, Sr. V.P.-Europe & Mng. Dir.-John Wiley & Sons, Ltd.--John Wiley & Sons, Inc., New York, NY; *U.S. Public*, pg. 1768
Jarvis, John, Sr. V.P.-Europe & Mng. Dir.-Wiley Europe Ltd.--Wiley Europe Limited, Chichester, United Kingdom; *U.S.* Public, pg. 1768
Jarvis, Mark E., Chief Fin. Officer & Sr. V.P.--Tuesday Morning Corporation, Dallas, TX; *U.S. Public*, pg. 1644
Javosky, Rudolph V., Sr. V.P.-Design & Construction--Federated Department Stores, Inc., Cincinnati, OH; *U.S. Public*, pg. 617
Jay, Lonny J., Sr. V.P.-Plng. & Reporting--The May Department Stores Company, Saint Louis, MO; *U.S. Public*, pg. 1063
Jaycox, William, Sr. V.P.-Human Resources--Tyson Foods, Inc., Springdale, AR; *U.S. Public*, pg. 1652
Jaye, Steven A., Sr. V.P., Gen. Counsel & Corp. Sec.--Sunrise Medical, Inc., Carlsbad, CA; *U.S. Public*, pg. 1535
Jazwiec, John, Chief Info. Officer & Sr. V.P.--May & Speh, Inc., Downers Grove, IL; *U.S. Public*, pg. 1063
Jean, Ronald W., Sr. V.P.-Actuarial--EMC Insurance Group, Inc., Des Moines, IA; *U.S. Public*, pg. 545
Jeanes, William, Sr. V.P. & Grp. Publr.-Automotive Grp.-Car & Driver/Road & Track--Hachette Filipacchi Magazines Inc., New York, NY; *Int'l*, pg. 794
Jeannin, Gerard, Sr. Officer--Banque Indosuez, New York, NY; *Int'l*, pg. 313
Jeanonougin, David, Sr. V.P. & Sec.--Cintas Corporation, Mason, OH; *U.S. Public*, pg. 370
Jefferies, Robert A., Jr., Sr. V.P.-Mergers, Acquisitions & Strategic Plng.--Leggett & Platt, Incorporated, Carthage, MO; *U.S. Public*, pg. 985
Jehle, Kathryn A., Chief Fin. Officer & Sr. V.P.--Comshare, Incorporated, Ann Arbor, MI; *U.S. Public*, pg. 425
Jembelis, Thomas, Sr. V.P.--Nozaki America, Inc., New York, NY; *Int'l*, pg. 990
Jen, Chih, Sr. V.P. & Gen. Mgr.-Asian Opers.--Atmel Corporation, San Jose, CA; *U.S. Public*, pg. 145
Jenest, Jeffrey, Sr. V.P. & Gen. Mgr.-Home Video--Playboy Entertainment Group, Inc., Beverly Hills, CA; *U.S. Public*, *pg. 1310*
Jenest, Jeffrey, Sr. V.P.--After Dark Video, Inc., Beverly Hills, CA; *U.S. Public*, pg. 1310
Jenkin, Thomas, Sr. V.P. & Gen. Mgr.--Harrah's Laughlin, Inc., Laughlin, NV; *U.S. Public*, pg. 790
Jenkins-Stark, Jack F., Sr. V.P.--PG&E Corporation, San Francisco, CA; *U.S. Public*, pg. 1240
Jenkins, B. Larry, Sr. V.P.-Home Services Grp.--AEGON USA, Inc., Baltimore, MD; *Int'l*, pg. 26
Jenkins, Charles J., Sr. V.P.--American Modern Home Insurance Group, Amelia, OH; *U.S. Public*, pg. 1110
Jenkins, Christopher D., Sr. V.P.--The Todd-AO Corporation, Hollywood, CA; *U.S. Public*, pg. 1619
Jenkins, David F., Sr. V.P.--SCI Systems, Inc., Huntsville, AL; *U.S. Public*, pg. 1416
Jenkins, Dick, Sr. V.P.-Fin.--D.P. Fitness, Opelika, AL; *U.S. Public*, pg. 1354
Jenkins, J.D., Sr. V.P.--MidCon Texas Pipeline Operator, Inc., Houston, TX; *U.S. Public*, pg. 1210
Jenkins, J.D., Sr. V.P.--MidCon Gas Products Corp., Houston, TX; *U.S. Public*, pg. 1210
Jenkins, Jeffrey A., Sr. V.P.-Integrated Mngmt. Services--Willis Corroon Corp. of South Carolina, Greenville, SC; *U.S. Private*, pg. 1507
Jenkins, Jerry W., Sr. V.P.--Thompson, Siegel & Walmsley, Inc., Richmond, VA; *U.S. Public*, pg. 1674
Jenkins, Peter, Sr. V.P.-Mktg. & Sls.--Hawaiian Airlines, Inc., Honolulu, HI; *U.S. Public*, pg. 799
Jenkins, Peter W., Sr. V.P.-Mktg. & Sls.--Hawaiian Airlines, Inc., Honolulu, HI; *U.S. Public*, pg. 799
Jenkins, William B., Chief Info. Officer & Sr. V.P.--General Accident Insurance, Philadelphia, PA; *Int'l*, pg. 543
Jenkins, William B., Sr. V.P.--General Accident Insurance, Philadelphia, PA; *Int'l*, pg. 543
Jenks, Karen, Sr. V.P.-H.R.--George W. Park Seed Co., Inc., Greenwood, SC; *U.S. Private*, pg. 839
Jennett, Thomas R., Sr. V.P. & Gen. Mgr.-Aftermarket Div.--Delco Remy America, Inc., Anderson, IN; *U.S. Public*, pg. 495
Jennette, Walton C., Jr., Sr. V.P. & Trust Officer--Bank of the West, Walnut Creek, CA; *Int'l*, pg. 163

Jennings, Charles W., Jr., Sr. V.P.-Human Resources--Old Kent Financial Corporation, Grand Rapids, MI; *U.S. Public*, pg. 1216
Jennings, Karen P., Sr. V.P.-Mktg.--George W. Park Seed Co., Inc., Greenwood, SC; *U.S. Private*, pg. 839
Jennings, Michael E., Sr. V.P.--NationsBank West, Saint Louis, MO; *U.S. Public*, pg. 1164
Jennings, Reynold J., Sr. V.P.-Gulf States Reg.--Tenet Healthcare Corporation, Santa Barbara, CA; *U.S. Public*, pg. 1576
Jennings, Richard V., Sr. V.P.-Admin.--Abco Markets, Inc., Phoenix, AZ; *U.S. Private*, pg. 10
Jennings, Suzie, Sr. V.P. & Creative Dir.--Fogarty Klein & Partners, Houston, TX; *U.S. Private*, pg. 415
Jennings, Thomas P., Sr. V.P., Gen. Counsel & Sec.--First Virginia Banks, Inc., Falls Church, VA; *U.S. Public*, pg. 641
Jenschke, Melvin R., Sr. V.P.-Engrng.--TCA Management Company, Tyler, TX; *U.S. Public*, pg. 1553
Jensen, Bill G., Sr. V.P.--Arthur J. Gallagher & Co., Itasca, IL; *U.S. Public*, pg. 698
Jensen, Darrel, Sr. V.P.--Harmon City, Inc., Salt Lake City, UT; *U.S. Private*, pg. 503
Jensen, Ernest W., Sr. V.P. & Chief Credit Officer--Bremer Financial Corporation, Saint Paul, MN; *U.S. Private*, pg. 167
Jensen, Ernest W., Sr. V.P.-Credit--Bremer Financial Services, Inc., Saint Paul, MN; *U.S. Private*, pg. 167
Jensen, Karen M., Sr. V.P. & Treas.--QST Environmental Inc., Peoria, IL; *U.S. Public*, pg. 367
Jensen, Kenneth L., Sr. V.P.-Corp. Devel. & Investor Rels.--Johns Manville Corporation, Denver, CO; *U.S. Public*, pg. 927
Jensen, Lance, Sr. V.P.--Arnold Communications, Inc., Boston, MA; *U.S. Private*, pg. 83
Jenson, Warren C., Sr. V.P.-Fin.--National Broadcasting Co., Inc., New York, NY; *U.S. Public*, pg. 712
Jeppson, Sam, Sr. V.P. & Mgr.-Credit Div.--First Security Bank of Utah, N.A., Salt Lake City, UT; *U.S. Public*, pg. 637
Jernigan, Jeff, Exec. V.P.--Pinkerton & Laws Inc., Atlanta, GA; *U.S. Private*, pg. 865
Jerritts, Stephen G., Sr. V.P.--Wang Laboratories, Inc., Billerica, MA; *U.S. Public*, pg. 1737
Jerumanis, Aivars L., Chief Information Officer & Sr. V.P.-Mngmt. Information--Maxicare Health Plans, Inc., Los Angeles, CA; *U.S. Public*, pg. 1061
Jeske, Robert, Sr. V.P.-Specialized Transportation Grp.--Atlas Specialized Transportation, Evansville, IN; *U.S. Private*, pg. 97
Jespersen, C. Kent, Sr. V.P.--Nova Corporation, Calgary, Canada; *Int'l*, pg. 971
Jespersen, Randall L., Sr. V.P.-Gas Supply--BC Gas Utility, Vancouver, Canada; *Int'l*, pg. 114
Jessick, Dave, Chief Fin. Officer & Sr. V.P.--Smith's Food & Drug Centers, Inc., Salt Lake City, UT; *U.S. Public*, pg. 1103
Jessick, David R., Chief Fin. Officer & Sr. V.P.-Fin.--Fred Meyer Stores, Portland, OR; *U.S. Public*, pg. 1103
Jett, Michelle D., Sr. V.P. & Cashier--California State Bank, West Covina, CA; *U.S. Public*, pg. 294
Jeub, Michael L., Chief Fin. Officer, Sr. V.P. & Treas.--Jenny Craig, Inc., La Jolla, CA; *U.S. Public*, pg. 926
Jewell, J.N., Sr. V.P.-Opers.--Brown & Williamson Tobacco Corp., Louisville, KY; *Int'l*, pg. 111
Job, Lyndsay, Sr. V.P.--Hibernia Corporation, New Orleans, LA; *U.S. Public*, pg. 825
Joeckel, Helmut G., Sr. V.P.--Deutsch-Sudamerikanische Bank AG, Miami Agency, Miami, FL; *Int'l*, pg. 418
Joerres, Jeffrey A., Sr. V.P.-Mktg. & Major Accts.--Manpower Inc., Milwaukee, WI; *U.S. Public*, pg. 1042
Jogan, Tsuneo, Sr. V.P.--Yokogawa Electric Corporation, Tokyo, Japan; *Int'l*, pg. 1520
Johansen, Carol, Sr. V.P.-Human Resources--Beverly Enterprises, Inc., Fort Smith, AR; *U.S. Public*, pg. 227
Johansson, Jan, Sr. V.P.-Electricity Sls.--Vattenfall AB, Stockholm, Sweden; *Int'l*, pg. 1452
Johansson, Kurt J., Sr. V.P.--Mark IV Industries Inc., Amherst, NY; *U.S. Public*, pg. 1044
Johansson, Lars-Eric, Chief Fin. Officer & Sr. V.P.--Falconbridge Limited, Toronto, Canada; *Int'l*, pg. 433
Johansson, Lennart, Sr. V.P.-Acctg. & Auditing & Controller--Atlas Copco AB, Stockholm, Sweden; *Int'l*, pg. 95
Johansson, Nils A., Chief Fin. Officer & Sr. V.P.--Bell & Howell Holdings, Skokie, IL; *U.S. Public*, pg. 201
Johenning, Sue, Sr. V.P. & Special Projects Dir.--Western International Media Corporation, Los Angeles, CA; *U.S. Private*, pg. 1165
John, David, Sr. V.P.--The McClure Group, Wayne, PA; *U.S. Private*, pg. 719
John, Frederick E., Sr. V.P.--Pacific Enterprises, Los Angeles, CA; *U.S. Public*, pg. 1249
John, T. Grant, Sr. V.P.-Plng.--Lukens Inc., Coatesville, PA; *U.S. Public*, pg. 1019
Johns, Adrienne M., Sr. V.P.-Human Resources--The Gap, Inc., San Francisco, CA; *U.S. Public*, pg. 702
Johns, Marietta L., Sr. V.P.-Field Mngmt.--American Express Financial Advisor, Minneapolis, MN; *U.S. Public*, pg. 73
Johns, William J., Sr. V.P. & Chief Acctg. Officer--PNC Bank Corp., Pittsburgh, PA; *U.S. Public*, pg. 1242
Johnson Morris, Rule, Sr. V.P., MIS Dir.--Ammirati, Puris & Lintas, Inc., New York, NY; *U.S. Private*, pg. 66
Johnson, Alan B., Sr. V.P. & Media Services Dir.--Mullen Advertising, Inc., Wenham, MA; *U.S. Private*, pg. 766
Johnson, Andrew V., Sr. V.P.-Mktg.--Fingerhut Corp., Minnetonka, MN; *U.S. Public*, pg. 623
Johnson, B. Kristine, Sr. V.P. & Pres.-Vascular Business--Medtronic, Inc., Minneapolis, MN; *U.S. Public*, pg. 1082
Johnson, Barbara P., Sr. V.P.-New Haven Region--People's Bank, Bridgeport, CT; *U.S. Public*, pg. 1274
Johnson, Brad, Partner & Sr. V.P.--Media That Works, Cincinnati, OH; *U.S. Private*, pg. 727
Johnson, Bradley K., Chief Fin. Officer, Chief Admin. Officer & Sr. V.P.--Lands' End, Inc., Dodgeville, WI; *U.S. Public*, pg. 977
Johnson, Bruce D., Sr. V.P.-Design & Construction--Regis Corporation, Minneapolis, MN; *U.S. Public*, pg. 1373
Johnson, Camille, Sr. V.P. & Media Dir.--Goldberg Moser O'Neill, San Francisco, CA; *U.S. Private*, pg. 459
Johnson, Charles E., Sr. V.P.--Franklin Resources, Inc., San Mateo, CA; *U.S. Public*, pg. 679
Johnson, Craig A., Sr. V.P.-Sls.--Philip Morris U.S.A., New York, NY; *U.S. Public*, pg. 1289
Johnson, Craig M., Sr. V.P.-Community Devel.--U.S. Home Corporation, Houston, TX; *U.S. Public*, pg. 1682
Johnson, Curt, Sr. V.P.-Construction--Hubbard Construction Co., Winter Park, FL; *U.S. Private*, pg. 544
Johnson, D., Sr. V.P.-Fivetrac--Del Mar Avionics, Irvine, CA; *U.S. Private*, pg. 321
Johnson, Dale D., Sr. V.P.--The Union Central Life Insurance Co., Cincinnati, OH; *U.S. Private*, pg. 1118
Johnson, Daniel R., Sr. V.P., Gen. Counsel & Sec.--Combe Incorporated, White Plains, NY; *U.S. Private*, pg. 257
Johnson, Donald G., Sr. V.P.--Arnold Industries, Inc., Lebanon, PA; *U.S. Public*, pg. 132
Johnson, E. Peter, Sr. V.P. & Gen. Counsel--Sundt Corp., Tucson, AZ; *U.S. Private*, pg. 1051
Johnson, Edward G., Sr. V.P. & Resident Mgr.--Willis Faber North America, Inc.-Georgia, Atlanta, GA; *Int'l*, pg. 1503
Johnson, Edwin D., Chief Fin. Officer & Sr. V.P.--MasTec, Inc., Miami, FL; *U.S. Public*, pg. 1055
Johnson, Elizabeth A., Sr. V.P. & Cashier--United Missouri Bank N.A., Brookfield, MO; *U.S. Public*, pg. 1654
Johnson, Elizabeth Pringle, Sr. V.P., Gen. Counsel & Sec.--Camden Property Trust, Houston, TX; *U.S. Public*, pg. 298
Johnson, Fred, Sr. V.P. & Dir.-Newspaper Rels.--Parade Publications Inc., New York, NY; *U.S. Private*, pg. 20
Johnson, Gary J., Sr. V.P.-Multimedia & Mobile Prods.--S3 Incorporated, Santa Clara, CA; *U.S. Public*, pg. 1415
Johnson, George W., Sr. V.P.--SAFECO Property & Casualty Insurance Companies, Seattle, WA; *U.S. Public*, pg. 1423
Johnson, Glen R., M.D., Sr. V.P.-Medical Affairs--Physician Corporation of America, Miami, FL; *U.S. Public*, pg. 1293
Johnson, Grant F., Sr. V.P.-Canadian Individual Distr.--The Great-West Life Assurance Company, Winnipeg, Canada; *Int'l*, pg. 557
Johnson, Grant W., Chief Fin. Officer & Sr. V.P.--Dep Corporation, Rancho Dominguez, CA; *U.S. Public*, pg. 500
Johnson, Greg, Sr. V.P.-UMEG--Time Insurance, Milwaukee, WI; *Int'l*, pg. 499
Johnson, Harold O., Sr. V.P.-Contact Lens Div.--Bausch & Lomb Incorporated, Rochester, NY; *U.S. Public*, pg. 194
Johnson, Harold R., Sr. V.P.-Bus. Devel.--The Fairchild Corporation, Chantilly, VA; *U.S. Public*, pg. 610
Johnson, Herb, Sr. V.P.-Logistics--CVS Corp., Woonsocket, RI; *U.S. Public*, pg. 287
Johnson, J. Brooke, Jr., Sr. V.P. & Gen. Counsel--Medpartners Inc., Birmingham, AL; *U.S. Public*, pg. 1082
Johnson, J.B., Jr., Sr. V.P.--Birdsong Corporation, Suffolk, VA; *U.S. Private*, pg. 145
Johnson, James E., Sr. V.P.-Group Ins.--The Minnesota Mutual Life Insurance Company, Saint Paul, MN; *U.S. Private*, pg. 750
Johnson, James J., Sr. V.P. & Gen. Counsel--The Procter & Gamble Company, Cincinnati, OH; *U.S. Public*, pg. 1330
Johnson, Jeff W., Sr. V.P.-Integrated Energy Mngmt.--CNG Energy Services Corporation, Pittsburgh, PA; *U.S. Public*, pg. 435
Johnson, Jerry L., Sr. V.P.-Opers.--Safeguard Scientifics, Inc., Wayne, PA; *U.S. Public*, pg. 1424
Johnson, Jim, Sr. V.P. & Acct. Mngmt. Supvr.--Tinsley Advertising, Miami, FL; *U.S. Private*, pg. 1088
Johnson, John R., Sr. V.P.-Programs, Tech. & Quality Assurance--Rohr, Inc., Chula Vista, CA; *U.S. Public*, pg. 751
Johnson, John T., Sr. V.P.-Bus. Devel.--Oilfield Marine Services-Americas Region, Morgan City, LA; *U.S. Public*, pg. 1211
Johnson, Jon, Sr. V.P.--Willis Corroon Corp. of Georgia, Atlanta, GA; *Int'l*, pg. 1506
Johnson, Julia F., Sr. V.P.--Banc One Corporation, Columbus, OH; *U.S. Public*, pg. 172
Johnson, K.O., Sr. V.P.-Special Projects--The Coastal Corporation, Houston, TX; *U.S. Public*, pg. 389
Johnson, Kenneth D., Sr. V.P.-Claims--Signet Star Reinsurance Company, Florham Park, NJ; *U.S. Public*, pg. 216
Johnson, Kenneth O., Sr. V.P.--Coastal States Trading, Inc., Houston, TX; *U.S. Public*, pg. 390
Johnson, Larry, Sr. V.P.-Sls.--Grindmaster Corporation, Louisville, KY; *U.S. Private*, pg. 482
Johnson, LeRoy, Sr. V.P.-Admin. & H.R.--Pioneer Aluminum, Inc., Los Angeles, CA; *U.S. Private*, pg. 866
Johnson, Leslie A., Sr. V.P.-Client Services--ProBusiness Services, Inc., Pleasanton, CA; *U.S. Public*, pg. 1330
Johnson, Lucy, Sr. V.P.-Daytime/Children's Programs & Special Projects--CBS Entertainment, Los Angeles, CA; *U.S. Public*, pg. 274
Johnson, Martin, Chief Fin. Officer & Sr. V.P.--Technology Solutions Company (TSC), Chicago, IL; *U.S. Public*, pg. 1564
Johnson, Martin C., Sr. V.P.-Mktg.--Robert Mondavi Winery, Inc., Oakville, CA; *U.S. Public*, pg. 1393
Johnson, Mike, Sr. V.P.-Opers.--Evenflo Company, Inc., Piqua, OH; *U.S. Private*, pg. 629
Johnson, P.J., Dir-Pub. Rels. & Adv.--Nomura Securities International, Inc., New York, NY; *Int'l*, pg. 956
Johnson, Philip, Sr. V.P.-Human Resources--Entex Information Services, Rye Brook, NY; *U.S. Private*, pg. 378
Johnson, R.W., Sr. V.P.--The Turner Corporation, New York, NY; *U.S. Public*, pg. 1645
Johnson, Ralph, Sr. V.P.-Power Resources--Texas-New Mexico Power Co., Fort Worth, TX; *U.S. Public*, pg. 1557
Johnson, Ralph S., Sr. V.P.-Power Resources--TNP Enterprises, Inc., Fort Worth, TX; *U.S. Public*, pg. 1557
Johnson, Reid, Chief Fin. Officer & Sr. V.P.--Woolworth Corporation, New York, NY; *U.S. Public*, pg. 1777
Johnson, Richard, Sr. V.P.-Trust--Banknorth Group Inc., Burlington, VT; *U.S. Public*, pg. 186
Johnson, Robert, Sr. V.P. & Dir.-Client Services--Goldberg Moser O'Neill, San Francisco, CA; *U.S. Private*, pg. 459
Johnson, Robert, Sr. V.P. & Ketchum Interactive Dir.--Ketchum Advertising/San Francisco, San Francisco, CA; *U.S. Private*, pg. 616
Johnson, Robert H., Jr., Sr. V.P. & Asst. Sec.--Franklin/Templeton Distributors, Inc., San Mateo, CA; *U.S. Public*, pg. 680
Johnson, Robert W., Sr. V.P.--Mercantile Bankshares Corporation, Baltimore, MD; *U.S. Public*, pg. 1088
Johnson, Robin, Sr. V.P.-Corp. Devel.--Time Inc., New York, NY; *U.S. Public*, pg. 1612
Johnson, Roger, Exec. V.P.--Aid Association for Lutherans, Appleton, WI; *U.S. Private*, pg. 27
Johnson, S. Clark, Sr. V.P.-Refining Opers.--Wainoco Oil Corporation, Houston, TX; *U.S. Public*, pg. 1732
Johnson, Scurry, Sr. V.P.--Haas, Wheat & Partners, Dallas, TX; *U.S. Private*, pg. 492
Johnson, Stephen L., Sr. V.P.-Legal Affairs--America West Holdings Corporation, Phoenix, AZ; *U.S. Public*, pg. 66
Johnson, Stephen L., Sr. V.P.-Legal Affairs & Gen. Counsel--America West Airlines, Inc., Phoenix, AZ; *U.S. Public*, pg. 67
Johnson, Susan L., Sr. V.P.--Hibernia Corporation, New Orleans, LA; *U.S. Public*, pg. 825
Johnson, Theodore C., Sr. V.P.-Human Resources--The Bon Ton Stores, Inc., York, PA; *U.S. Public*, pg. 244
Johnson, Timothy L., Sr. V.P. & Dir.-Mktg.--MetLife Capital Holdings, Inc., Bellevue, WA; *U.S. Private*, pg. 737
Johnson, Tina, Sr. V.P.--Publix Supermarkets Inc., Lakeland, FL; *U.S. Private*, pg. 893
Johnson, Tom, Sr. V.P.-Intl. Franchising--Ruby Tuesday, Inc., Mobile, AL; *U.S. Public*, pg. 1411
Johnson, Victor L., Sr. V.P.--Great Dane Trailers, Inc., Savannah, GA; *U.S. Private*, pg. 1030
Johnson, Victor R., Jr., Sr. V.P.--Harding Lawson Associates Group, Inc., Novato, CA; *U.S. Public*, pg. 785
Johnson, William R., Sr. V.P.-Motor Grp.--Reliance Electric, Cleveland, OH; *U.S. Public*, pg. 1397
Johnson, William R., Sr. V.P.--Motor Group, Euclid, OH; *U.S. Public*, pg. 1398
Johnston, Barry, Sr. V.P.-Credit Admin.--Nevada State Bank, Las Vegas, NV; *U.S. Public*, pg. 1793
Johnston, Carmon, Sr. V.P. & Exec. Producer--Uniworld Group, Inc., New York, NY; *U.S. Private*, pg. 1128
Johnston, Dale L., Sr. V.P.--Policy Management Systems Corporation, Blythewood, SC; *U.S. Public*, pg. 1314
Johnston, David, Sr. V.P. & Acct. Grp. Dir.--McKinney & Silver, Raleigh, NC; *U.S. Private*, pg. 723
Johnston, Jim, Sr. V.P.-Acct. Services--Western International Media Corporation, Las Vegas, NV; *U.S. Private*, pg. 1167
Johnston, Ken, Sr. V.P.-Franchise Devel.--Triarc Restaurant Group, Fort Lauderdale, FL; *U.S. Public*, pg. 1635
Johnston, Rodney, Sr. V.P.--Willis Corroon, Fort Worth, TX; *Int'l*, pg. 1504
Johnston, Stephen E., Sr. V.P.-H.R.--Analysis & Technology, Inc., North Stonington, CT; *U.S. Public*, pg. 109
Johnston, Summerfield K., III, Sr. V.P. & Pres.-Eastern Grp.--Coca-Cola Enterprises Inc., Atlanta, GA; *U.S. Public*, pg. 393
Johnston, Thomas W., Sr. V.P.-Mfg.--Zinc Corporation of America, Monaca, PA; *U.S. Private*, pg. 540
Joinnides, Art, Sr. V.P.-Publisher--Butterick Company, Inc., New York, NY; *U.S. Private*, pg. 190
Jokiel, Peter, Chief Fin. Officer & Sr. V.P.--CNA Insurance Companies, Chicago, IL; *U.S. Public*, pg. 1010
Jokiel, Peter E., Sr. V.P.--Continental Assurance Company, Chicago, IL; *U.S. Private*, pg. 267
Joli-Caeur, Claude, Sr. V.P.-Legal & Intl. Affairs--Coscient Group Inc., Montreal, Canada; *Int'l*, pg. 335
Jolles, Ira H., Sr. V.P. & Gen. Counsel--GPU, Inc., Morristown, NJ; *U.S. Public*, pg. 695
Jolly, Al, Sr. V.P.-Human Resources--CVS Corp., Woonsocket, RI; *U.S. Public*, pg. 287
Jonas, Nelson J., Sr. V.P.-Construction Opers.--Bartlett Cocke, Inc., San Antonio, TX; *U.S. Private*, pg. 249
Jones Kane, M'Liss, Sr. V.P., Gen. Counsel & Corp. Sec.--Fidelity National Financial, Inc., Irvine, CA; *U.S. Public*, pg. 620
Jones, Alan E., Sr. V.P. & Dir.-Store Opers., The Casual Male--J. Baker, Inc., Canton, MA; *U.S. Public*, pg. 167
Jones, Arthur L., Sr. V.P.-Retail Devel. & Sls.--Associated Grocers, Inc., Seattle, WA; *U.S. Private*, pg. 90
Jones, Ben F., Sr. V.P.--Young Electric Sign Company, Salt Lake City, UT; *U.S. Private*, pg. 1201
Jones, Brian R., Sr. V.P.--AirTouch Communications, Inc., San Francisco, CA; *U.S. Public*, pg. 34
Jones, Charles L., Chief Fin. Officer & Sr. V.P.--Country Life Insurance Company, Bloomington, IL; *U.S. Private*, pg. 278
Jones, Charles L., Chief Fin. Officer & Sr. V.P.--Country Mutual Insurance Company, Bloomington, IL; *U.S. Private*, pg. 279
Jones, Charles L., Chief Fin. Officer& Sr. V.P.--CC Services, Bloomington, IL; *U.S. Private*, pg. 279
Jones, D.R., Sr. V.P.--Marshall & Ilsley Corporation, Milwaukee, WI; *U.S. Public*, pg. 1049
Jones, Dennis H., Chief Info. Officer & Sr. V.P.--FDX Corporation, Memphis, TN; *U.S. Public*, pg. 603
Jones, Dereck M., Sr. V.P. & Gen. Counsel--Bank of Montreal, Toronto, Canada; *Int'l*, pg. 153
Jones, Donald B., Sr. V.P.-Information Services--Citizens Trust Company, Providence, RI; *Int'l*, pg. 1132

Jones, Donald M., Sr. V.P.-Pur.--Owen Health Care, Inc., Houston, TX; *U.S. Public*, pg. 304

Jones, G. Jeffrey, Sr. V.P.--Hibernia Corporation, New Orleans, LA; *U.S. Public*, pg. 825

Jones, Gary L., Sr. V.P.-Republic Pictures Home Video--Republic Entertainment, Inc., Los Angeles, CA; *U.S. Private*, pg. 776

Jones, Glenn C., Chief Fin. Officer & Sr. V.P.--Sierra Semiconductor, San Jose, CA; *U.S. Public*, pg. 1470

Jones, Gordon, Sr. V.P. & Mng. Dir.--Allergan Limited, High Wycombe, United Kingdom; *U.S. Public*, pg. 46

Jones, Howard, Sr. V.P.-Tech. Services--Curative Health Services, East Setauket, NY; *U.S. Public*, pg. 469

Jones, Jerry D., Sr. V.P.-U.S. Opers.--The Minute Maid Company, Houston, TX; *U.S. Public*, pg. 392

Jones, Jerry L., Sr. V.P.-Retail Opers.--Jitney-Jungle Stores of America, Inc., Jackson, MS; *U.S. Private*, pg. 588

Jones, Jimmy R., Chief Fin. Officer, Sr. V.P. & Treas.--Attorneys' Title Insurance Fund, Orlando, FL; *U.S. Private*, pg. 98

Jones, John R., III, Sr. V.P.-Fossil/Hydro Production--American Electric Power Service Corp., Columbus, OH; *U.S. Public*, pg. 72

Jones, Kevin, Sr. V.P.-Production--Columbia Pictures, Culver City, CA; *Int'l*, pg. 1281

Jones, Michael D., Sr. V.P.-Research & Devel.--Jefferson-Pilot Data Services, Inc., Memphis, TN; *U.S. Public*, pg. 925

Jones, Morris E., Jr., Chief Tech. Officer & Sr. V.P.--Chips and Technologies, Inc., San Jose, CA; *U.S. Public*, pg. 349

Jones, P.D., Sr. V.P.-Tech.--Dunlop Tire Corporation, Buffalo, NY; *Int'l*, pg. 1317

Jones, Patricia, Sr. V.P. & Dir.-HR--AmeriCredit Corp., Fort Worth, TX; *U.S. Public*, pg. 96

Jones, Ralph E., III, Sr. V.P.--Chubb & Son, Inc., Warren, NJ; *U.S. Public*, pg. 355

Jones, Raymond E., Exec. V.P. & Sec.--Shelter Mutual Insurance Company, Columbia, MO; *U.S. Private*, pg. 992

Jones, Rena, Sr. V.P.--Grizzard, Atlanta, GA; *U.S. Private*, pg. 482

Jones, Richard G., Sr. V.P. & Acct. Dir.--Young & Rubicam New York, New York, NY; *U.S. Private*, pg. 1198

Jones, Richard H., Sr. V.P.--Coventry Corporation, Nashville, TN; *U.S. Public*, pg. 454

Jones, Rick, Chief Oper. Officer, Sr. V.P. & Gen. Mgr.-Mdse.--Tops Appliance City, Edison, NJ; *U.S. Public*, pg. 1622

Jones, Robert E., Sr. V.P.--TCF Bank Illinois, Oak Brook, IL; *U.S. Public*, pg. 1554

Jones, Robert G., Sr. V.P.--Keycorp, Cleveland, OH; *U.S. Public*, pg. 954

Jones, Sandy, Sr. V.P. & Creative Dir.--Kovel Kresser & Partners, Santa Monica, CA; *U.S. Private*, pg. 634

Jones, Scott T., Sr. V.P.-Ventures--Rothschild Inc., New York, NY; *U.S. Private*, pg. 947

Jones, Scott W., Sr. V.P. & Sls. Mgr.-Midwest--Jefferies & Company, Inc., Los Angeles, CA; *U.S. Public*, pg. 925

Jones, W. Scott, Sr. V.P. & Dir.-Whlsl. Loan Prod.--Barclays American/Mortgage Corp., Charlotte, NC; *Int'l*, pg. 165

Jones, William, Sr. V.P.-Opers.--National Energy Group, Inc., Dallas, TX; *U.S. Public*, pg. 1156

Jones, William C., Sr. V.P.--Omaha Public Power District, Omaha, NE; *U.S. Private*, pg. 815

Jonglez, Antoine, Sr. V.P.-Business Devel.--Elf Aquitane, Paris, France; *Int'l*, pg. 444

Jonson, Dan L., Sr. V.P.-Stragetic Systems Devel.--Avemco Corporation, Frederick, MD; *U.S. Public*, pg. 151

Jonsson, Helge, Sr. V.P.-EU Office--Vattenfall AB, Stockholm, Sweden; *Int'l*, pg. 1452

Joost, Hobart, Jr., Sr. V.P.--Walter Dickinson Inc., Jacksonville, FL; *U.S. Private*, pg. 331

Jordan, Albert, Sr. V.P.--First State Bank N.A., Abilene, Abilene, TX; *U.S. Public*, pg. 874

Jordan, Amilcar, Sr. V.P.-Comptroller--Banco Popular de Puerto Rico, San Juan, PR; *U.S. Public*, pg. 175

Jordan, Amilcar L., Esq., Sr. V.P.--BanPonce Corporation, Hato Rey, PR; *U.S. Public*, pg. 176

Jordan, David A., Sr. V.P.-Bus. Devel.--Shoney's, Inc., Nashville, TN; *U.S. Public*, pg. 1467

Jordan, Henry, Chief Fin. Officer & Sr. V.P.--The Foothill Group, Inc., Los Angeles, CA; *U.S. Public*, pg. 1201

Jordan, Jim, Sr. V.P.--First State Bank N.A., Abilene, Abilene, TX; *U.S. Public*, pg. 874

Jordan, John A., Jr., Sr. V.P.-Admin.--Bethlehem Steel Corporation, Bethlehem, PA; *U.S. Public*, pg. 226

Jordan, Joseph W., Sr. V.P.--Metropolitan Life Insurance Co., New York, NY; *U.S. Private*, pg. 737

Jordan, Patrick R., Sr. V.P.--Willis Corroon Financial Services Corp., New York, NY; *Int'l*, pg. 1507

Jordan, Rodney W., Sr. V.P.-Human Resources--Jostens, Minneapolis, MN; *U.S. Public*, pg. 934

Jordan, Russell W., III, Sr. V.P., Gen. Counsel & Sec.--Lawyers Title Insurance Corporation, Richmond, VA; *U.S. Public*, pg. 981

Jordan, Veronica G.H., Ph.D., Sr. V.P.-Client Rels.--PAREXEL International Corporation, Waltham, MA; *U.S. Public*, pg. 1257

Jordnou, Andreas, Sr. V.P. & Mgr.-Fiji Country--Bank of Hawaii, Honolulu, HI; *U.S. Public*, pg. 1248

Jordon, Charles, Exec. V.P. & Publr.-World Trade Publishing--Word, Incorporated, Dallas, TX; *U.S. Public*, pg. 704

Jorg, Christian H., Sr. V.P.-Bus. Affairs & Bus. Devel.--Imax Corporation, Mississauga, Canada; *Int'l*, pg. 661

Jorgensen, Marty, Sr. V.P.-Pur. & Adv.--Video Products Distributors, Inc., Sacramento, CA; *U.S. Private*, pg. 1139

Jorgensen, T. Dennis, Sr. V.P.-Admin.--Tenet Healthcare Corporation, Santa Barbara, CA; *U.S. Public*, pg. 1576

Jorgenson, Gorden, Sr. V.P.--Imperial Bank, Inglewood, CA; *U.S. Public*, pg. 871

Jose, Fran U., Sr. V.P.-Mktg. & Visual--Proffitt's, Inc., Alcoa, TN; *U.S. Public*, pg. 1333

Josefowicz, Gregory P., Sr. V.P. & Gen. Mgr.--Jewel-Osco, Melrose Park, IL; *U.S. Public*, pg. 93

Joseph, George A., Sr. V.P.-Distr.--The Gap, Inc., San Francisco, CA; *U.S. Public*, pg. 702

Joseph, Meril, Sr. V.P.-Mktg. & Communications--Fortis, Inc., New York, NY; *Int'l*, pg. 499

Josephson, Lee, Ph.D., Sr. V.P.-Res.--Advanced Magnetics, Inc., Cambridge, MA; *U.S. Public*, pg. 20

Joslin, Dick, Sr. V.P. & Creative Dir.--The Sawtooth Group, Woodbridge, NJ; *U.S. Private*, pg. 969

Joslin, Roger, Sr. V.P. & Treas.--State Farm Mutual Automobile Insurance Company, Bloomington, IL; *U.S. Private*, pg. 1036

Joutsen, R.P., Sr. V.P.-New Elevator Bus.--Kone Corporation, Helsinki, Finland; *Int'l*, pg. 746

Joy, Carl, Sr. V.P.-Casting--Entertainment Partners, Burbank, CA; *U.S. Private*, pg. 554

Joyal, Robert E., Sr. V.P.--Massmutual Corporate Investors, Springfield, MA; *U.S. Public*, pg. 1055

Joyce, R. J., Sr. V.P.--Westfield Companies, Westfield Center, OH; *U.S. Private*, pg. 1169

Joyce, Richard, Sr. V.P.-Client Access/Remote Access Prods. Div.--3Com Corporation, Santa Clara, CA; *U.S. Public*, pg. 1603

Joyce, Stephen F., Sr. V.P.-Human Resources--Ross Stores, Inc., Newark, CA; *U.S. Public*, pg. 1405

Joyner, Ronnie L., Sr. V.P.--Foremost Insurance Co., Caledonia, MI; *U.S. Public*, pg. 667

Judd, Gary S., Sr. V.P.-Colorado Admin.--Zions Bancorporation, Salt Lake City, UT; *U.S. Public*, pg. 1792

Judd, Steven W., Sr. V.P. & Dir.-Acturial Svcs.--Federated Mutual Insurance Company, Owatonna, MN; *U.S. Private*, pg. 399

Judge, Frederick L., Sr. V.P. & Pres.-Titan Information Systems--The Titan Corporation, San Diego, CA; *U.S. Public*, pg. 1618

Judge, James J., Sr. V.P. & Treas.--Boston Edison Company, Boston, MA; *U.S. Public*, pg. 247

Juetten, George H., Chief Fin. Officer & Sr. V.P.--Dresser Industries, Inc., Dallas, TX; *U.S. Public*, pg. 528

Juillus, Kenneth J., Sr. V.P.-Sls.--George Uhe Co., Inc., Paramus, NJ; *U.S. Private*, pg. 1115

Julian, John, Sr. V.P.-Worldwide Mktg.--ICN Pharmaceuticals, Inc., Costa Mesa, CA; *U.S. Public*, pg. 853

Jund, Daniel E., Pres.-Transamerica Assurance Co. & Sr. V.P.--Transamerica Life Companies, Los Angeles, CA; *U.S. Public*, pg. 1630

Jungwirth, Philip R., Sr. V.P.-Admin.--Brown & Bigelow, Inc., Saint Paul, MN; *U.S. Private*, pg. 172

Jurgens, Richard, Chief Admin. Officer & Sr. V.P.--Hy-Vee Food Stores Incorporated, West Des Moines, IA; *U.S. Private*, pg. 550

Jurick, Martin H., Sr. V.P.--Silicon Systems, Inc., Tustin, CA; *U.S. Public*, pg. 1585

Jurik, James J., Sr. V.P. & Chief Credit Officer--First National Bank of Blue Island, Blue Island, IL; *U.S. Private*, pg. 474

Juselius, Jussi, Sr. V.P.-Logistic & Personnel Devel.--Metsa-Serla Corporation, Espoo, Finland; *Int'l*, pg. 863

Just, Donna, Sr. V.P. & Mngmt. Supvr.--Girgenti, Hughes, Butler & McDowell, New York, NY; *U.S. Private*, pg. 455

Justesen, Joan, Sr. Exec. Partner--MeritCare Health System, Fargo, ND; *U.S. Private*, pg. 733

Justiliano, P.R., Sr. V.P. & Controller--Marshall & Ilsley Corporation, Milwaukee, WI; *U.S. Public*, pg. 1049

Kaback, Deborah, Sr. V.P.--OppenheimerFunds Distributor, Inc., New York, NY; *U.S. Private*, pg. 818

Kabak, Scott, Sr. V.P.-Opers. & Multimedia--Times Mirror Magazines, Inc., New York, NY; *U.S. Public*, pg. 1616

Kabele, Thomas G., Sr. V.P.-Taxes & Reinsurance Pools--The Guardian Life Insurance Company of America, New York, NY; *U.S. Private*, pg. 486

Kaczon, Donald W., Sr. V.P.--Fleetwood Credit Corp., Yorba Linda, CA; *U.S. Public*, pg. 663

Kadota, James M., Sr. V.P.-Admin. Svcs.--American Savings Bank, F.S.B., Honolulu, HI; *U.S. Public*, pg. 800

Kaelin, R.R., Sr. V.P.-Municipal Bonds--General Electric Investment Corp., Stamford, CT; *U.S. Public*, pg. 712

Kaenzig, J. Gary, Jr., Sr. V.P. & Pres.-Grace Packaging--W.R. Grace & Co., Boca Raton, FL; *U.S. Public*, pg. 754

Kahan, James S., Sr. V.P.-Corp. Devel.--SBC Communications Inc., San Antonio, TX; *U.S. Public*, pg. 1415

Kahane, Benjamin B., Sr. V.P.-Labor Rels.--Metro-Goldwyn-Mayer Inc., Santa Monica, CA; *U.S. Public*, pg. 1101

Kahler, Harry, Sr. V.P.--RMS Techs, Inc., Lanham, MD; *U.S. Private*, pg. 905

Kahmann, Mike, Sr. V.P.-Mktg.--The CIT Group/Capital Finance Inc., New York, NY; *Int'l*, pg. 360

Kahme, Heidi, Sr. V.P.-Children's Media--Active Entertainment, Pearl River, NY; *U.S. Private*, pg. 15

Kahn, David, Sr. V.P.--Sceptre Hospitality Resources, Inc., Englewood, CO; *U.S. Private*, pg. 929

Kain, George, Sr. V.P.--Valero Marketing & Supply Company, San Antonio, TX; *U.S. Public*, pg. 1704

Kain, George E., Sr. V.P.--Valero Refining Company, San Antonio, TX; *U.S. Public*, pg. 1704

Kaiser, Mark P., Sr. V.P.-Sls., Mktg. & Procurement--JP Foodservice, Inc., Columbia, MD; *U.S. Public*, pg. 918

Kaiser, Robert J., Sr. V.P.-Sls.--Emkay, Inc., Itasca, IL; *U.S. Private*, pg. 374

Kajiwara, Yasushi, Sr. Mng. Dir.--Tosoh Corporation, Tokyo, Japan; *Int'l*, pg. 1407

Kajiyama, Edmund H., Sr. V.P.-Branch Support Div.--First Hawaiian Bank, Honolulu, HI; *U.S. Public*, pg. 634

Kalajian Galotti, Donna, Sr. V.P.--Hearst Magazines Division, New York, NY; *U.S. Private*, pg. 516

Kalasky, Mike, Sr. V.P. & Dir.-Mktg./Intl. RMS--Willis Corroon Corp. of Nashville, Nashville, TN; *Int'l*, pg. 1506

Kalb, Allan J., Sr. V.P.-Systems--A.G. Edwards & Sons, Inc., Saint Louis, MO; *U.S. Public*, pg. 565

Kalec, John J., Chief Fin. Officer, Sr. V.P. & Sec.--Clayton Homes, Inc., Knoxville, TN; *U.S. Public*, pg. 382

Kalelkar, Ashok S., Sr. V.P. & Grp. Officer--Arthur D. Little, Inc., Cambridge, MA; *U.S. Private*, pg. 670

Kalff, D.J.A., Sr. V.P.-Corp. Devel.--KLM Royal Dutch Airlines, Amstelveen, Netherlands; *Int'l*, pg. 719

Kalhorn, Gene, Sr. V.P.--Watlow Electric Manufacturing Company, Saint Louis, MO; *U.S. Private*, pg. 1153

Kalin, Jeffrey M., Sr. V.P.--Kalin Enterprises, Inc., Sarasota, FL; *U.S. Private*, pg. 606

Kallenborn, John J., III, Sr. V.P.--Hibernia Corporation, New Orleans, LA; *U.S. Public*, pg. 825

Kallio, Gordon, Sr. V.P. & Gen. Mgr.--EvansGroup Technology, Boise, ID; *U.S. Private*, pg. 385

Kalmbach, Lisa, Sr. V.P. & Reg. Gen. Mgr.--Kaufman and Broad Home Corporation, Los Angeles, CA; *U.S. Public*, pg. 944

Kamba, Robert L., Sr. V.P.-Network Opers.--MCI Communications Corp., Atlanta, GA; *U.S. Public*, pg. 1023

Kambanis, Steve, Sr. V.P.-Creative Services--Jordan, McGrath, Case & Taylor Inc., New York, NY; *U.S. Private*, pg. 598

Kambe, Hisashi, Sr. V.P. & Acct. Dir.--Meitsu Inc., Tokyo, Japan; *Int'l*, pg. 856

Kamber, Martin, Sr. V.P.-Corp. Devel.--ITT Industries, Inc., White Plains, NY; *U.S. Public*, pg. 859

Kamer, Joel Y., Sr. V.P.-Retail Distr. Fin. Services--John Hancock Mutual Life Insurance Company, Boston, MA; *U.S. Private*, pg. 589

Kametches, Chris L., Sr. V.P.--Fieldcrest/Cannon Bed Fashions Division, New York, NY; *U.S. Public*, pg. 1296

Kamine, Ilene, Sr. V.P.--Liggett-Stashower, Inc., Cleveland, OH; *U.S. Private*, pg. 667

Kaminski, Thomas W., Sr. V.P.-Comml. Real Estate Loans--Magna Group, Inc., Saint Louis, MO; *U.S. Public*, pg. 1037

Kammerer, Michael J., Sr. V.P. & Pres.-Engineered Equipment & Systems Group--Dresser Industries, Inc., Dallas, TX; *U.S. Public*, pg. 528

Kampanartsanyakorn, Bunlue, V.P.--The Siam Cement Public Company Limited, Bangkok, Thailand; *Int'l*, pg. 1237

Kanaley, James E., Sr. V.P.-Personal Products Div.--Bausch & Lomb Incorporated, Rochester, NY; *U.S. Public*, pg. 194

Kanarek, Arnold W., Sr. V.P. & Sec.--Industrial Acoustics Company, Inc., Bronx, NY; *U.S. Public*, pg. 875

Kanari, Yoshiaki, Chief Fin. Officer & Sr. V.P.--Gould Electronics Inc., Eastlake, OH; *U.S. Public*, pg. 1591

Kanasugi, Akinobu, Assoc. Sr. V.P.--NEC Corporation, Tokyo, Japan; *Int'l*, pg. 899

Kane, James P., Sr. V.P.-Opers.--Southwest Gas Corporation, Las Vegas, NV; *U.S. Public*, pg. 1493

Kane, John C., Sr. V.P.-Ross Prods.--Abbott Laboratories, Abbott Park, IL; *U.S. Public*, pg. 13

Kane, Jonathan, Sr. V.P.--Millicom International Cellular SA, Bertrange, Luxembourg; *Int'l*, pg. 867

Kane, Jonathan, Sr. V.P.--MIC-USA Inc., New York, NY; *Int'l*, pg. 867

Kane, Kathleen G., Sr. V.P.-Head Counsel--World Financial Properties, Inc., New York, NY; *Int'l*, pg. 1004

Kane, Michael, Sr. V.P. & Exec. Creative Dir.--Miller Meester Advertising Inc., Minneapolis, MN; *U.S. Private*, pg. 747

Kane, Phillip M., Sr. V.P.-Fin.--La Petite Academy Inc., Overland Park, KS; *U.S. Private*, pg. 640

Kane, Richard C., Sr. V.P. & Mgr.-San Francisco Sls.--Jefferies & Company, Inc., Los Angeles, CA; *U.S. Public*, *pg. 925*

Kane, Robert J., Sr. V.P.--Medusa Corporation, Cleveland, OH; *U.S. Public*, pg. 1084

Kaneko, Isao, Mng. Dir. & Sr. V.P.-Industrial Rels. & Medical Svcs.--Japan Airlines Company, Ltd., Tokyo, Japan; *Int'l*, pg. 699

Kaner, Joan, Sr. V.P. & Dir.-Fashion--Neiman Marcus Co., Dallas, TX; *U.S. Public*, pg. 785

Kanesada, Yoshio, Sr. V.P.--Ryobi Ltd., Tokyo, Japan; *Int'l*, pg. 1151

Kannappan, S. Kenneth, Sr. V.P.--Plantronics Inc., Santa Cruz, CA; *U.S. Public*, pg. 1308

Kanou, Kazuhiko, Sr. V.P.--NEC Corporation, Tokyo, Japan; *Int'l*, pg. 899

Kantor, Jonathan, Sr. V.P., Gen. Counsel & Sec.--Continental Assurance Company, Chicago, IL; *U.S. Private*, pg. 267

Kantor, Susan, Sr. V.P.-Adv. & Promo.-Worldwide TV Distrb.--Universal Studios TV, Universal City, CA; *Int'l*, pg. 1215

Kaplan, Andrew P., Chief Fin. Officer & Sr. V.P.--Treasure Chest Advertising Co., Inc., Glendora, CA; *U.S. Public*, pg. 228

Kaplan, Arnold H., Sr. V.P.-Fin.--Air Products and Chemicals, Inc., Allentown, PA; *U.S. Public*, pg. 30

Kaplan, Gerald, Sr. V.P. & Tax Counsel--New York Life Insurance Company, New York, NY; *U.S. Private*, pg. 794

Kaplan, Ira, Chief Fin. Officer & Sr. V.P.--Claire's Boutiques, Inc., Pembroke Pines, FL; *U.S. Public*, pg. 381

Kaplan, Ira D., Chief Fin. Officer & Sr. V.P.--Claire's Stores Inc., Pembroke Pines, FL; *U.S. Public*, pg. 381

Kaplan, Jay M., Chief Fin. Officer & Sr. V.P.--MEDIQ/PRN Life Support Services, Inc., Pennsauken, NJ; *U.S. Public*, *pg. 1081*

Kaplan, Kalman R., Sr. V.P.--Associates Insurance Group, Inc., Dallas, TX; *U.S. Public*, pg. 663

Kaplan, Leslie, Sr. V.P. & Mng. Partner-Direct--Hill, Holliday, Connors, Cosmopulos, Inc., Boston, MA; *U.S. Private*, pg. 529

Kaplan, Martin, Sr. V.P.-Mktg.--New York Life Insurance Company, New York, NY; *U.S. Private*, pg. 794

Kaplan, Matthew, Sr. V.P. & Gen. Mgr.-Corrugated Container Div.--Stone Container Corporation, Chicago, IL; *U.S. Public*, pg. 1520

Kaplan, Nadia, Sr. V.P. & Grp. Acct. Supvr.--Lowe McAdams Healthcare, New York, NY; *U.S. Private*, pg. 678

Kaplan, Noel, Sr. V.P.-Alliance Rels. & Zone Mgr.--McDonald's Corporation, Oak Brook, IL; *U.S. Public*, pg. 1068

Kaplan, Stanley A., Sr. V.P.-Res. & Devel.--U.S. Pharmaceuticals, Baltimore, MD; *U.S. Public*, pg. 58

Kaplan, Theodore S., Sr. V.P. & Gen. Counsel--Legg Mason, Inc., Baltimore, MD; *U.S. Public*, pg. 984

Kaplin, Jim, Sr. V.P.--Freeman Decorating Co., Dallas, TX; *U.S. Private*, pg. 426

Kaputa, Catherine, Sr. V.P. & Dir.-Adv. & Community Affairs--Salomon Smith Barney Holdings, Inc., New York, NY; *U.S. Public*, pg. 1633

Kara, Alan, Sr. V.P.-Adv.--Calvin Klein, Inc., New York, NY; *U.S. Private*, pg. 202

Karalis, John P., Sr. V.P.-Corp. Devel. & Sec.--Tektronix, Inc., Wilsonville, OR; *U.S. Public*, pg. 1567

Karas, Richard, Sr. V.P.-Sls. & Fin. Svcs.--Nationwide Life Insurance Co., Columbus, OH; *U.S. Private*, pg. 789

Karas, Rick, Sr. V.P.-Sls.-Financial Services--Nationwide Insurance Enterprise, Columbus, OH; *U.S. Private*, pg. 788

Karch, William D., Sr. V.P.-Lending--Omega Bank, N.A., State College, PA; *U.S. Public*, pg. 1222

Kardon, Brian, Sr. V.P.-Corp. Mktg.--Reed Elsevier Business Information, Newton, MA; *Int'l*, pg. 1095

Kark, Jan-Ake, Sr. V.P.-Microwave Systems--Telefonaktiebolaget LM Ericsson, Stockholm, Sweden; *Int'l*, pg. 1363

Karlsson, Anders C., Sr. V.P.-Tech. & Industrial Co.--Skanska AB, Danderyd, Sweden; *Int'l*, pg. 1260

Karlsson, Hans-Olof, Sr. V.P.-Corp. Communications--NCC AB, Solna, Sweden; *Int'l*, pg. 898

Karlsson, Markku, Sr. V.P.-Tech.--Valmet Corporation, Helsinki, Finland; *Int'l*, pg. 1447

Karlsson, Sven, Sr. V.P.-Personnel--Nordbanken AB, Stockholm, Sweden; *Int'l*, pg. 957

Karlsson, Werner, Sr. V.P.-Organization--Saga Petroleum ASA, Sandvika, Norway; *Int'l*, pg. 1169

Karow, Alann, Sr. V.P.-Fin. & Admin.--Sargent & Greenleaf, Inc., Nicholasville, KY; *U.S. Private*, pg. 965

Karpan, John, Sr. V.P.-Human Resources--Illinois Tool Works Inc., Glenview, IL; *U.S. Public*, pg. 865

Karsh, Mark, Chief Fin. Officer & Sr. V.P.--Tseng Labs, Norristown, PA; *U.S. Public*, pg. 1643

Karsner, Michael S., Chief Fin. Officer & Sr. V.P.--Republic Industries, Inc., Fort Lauderdale, FL; *U.S. Public*, pg. 1378

Karst, Darren, Chief Fin. Officer & Sr. V.P.--Dominick's Finer Foods, Northlake, IL; *U.S. Private*, pg. 1202

Karube, Norio, Dr., Sr. V.P.--Fanuc Ltd., Yamanashi, Japan; *Int'l*, pg. 477

Karvelis, Gary P., Sr. V.P. & Dir.-Secondary Mkt. Prods.--Municipal Bond Investors Assurance Corporation, Armonk, NY; *U.S. Public*, pg. 1023

Kasahara, Masaaki, Sr. V.P.--Nippon Telegraph and Telephone Corporation, Tokyo, Japan; *Int'l*, pg. 940

Kasamatsu, Shigeyasu, Sr. V.P.--Tokyo-Mitsubishi Derivative Products (USA), Inc., New York, NY; *Int'l*, pg. 157

Kasbar, Michael, Sr. V.P.-Marine Fueling--International Recovery Corp., Miami Springs, FL; *U.S. Public*, pg. 906

Kaschub, William J., Sr. V.P.-Human Resources--PECO Energy Company, Philadelphia, PA; *U.S. Public*, pg. 1268

Kasdagly, Dino G., Sr. V.P.-Devel.--Digi International Inc., Minnetonka, MN; *U.S. Public*, pg. 506

Kashida, Yoshinobu, Sr. Mng. Dir.--Tosoh Corporation, Tokyo, Japan; *Int'l*, pg. 1407

Kasindorf, Matt, Sr. V.P.--Partners & Shevack, Inc., New York, NY; *U.S. Private*, pg. 842

Kasman, Joseph D., Chief Fin. Officer & Sr. V.P.--Tower Realty Trust, Inc., New York, NY; *U.S. Public*, pg. 1625

Kasper, Bob, Sr. V.P. & Chief Creative Officer--Redgate Communications Corp., Vero Beach, FL; *U.S. Public*, pg. 66

Kasper, Karen M., Chief Fin. Officer, Sr. V.P & Treas.--Fort Wayne National Corporation, Fort Wayne, IN; *U.S. Public*, pg. 673

Kasper, Karen M., Chief Fin. Officer & Sr. V.P.--Fort Wayne National Bank, Fort Wayne, IN; *U.S. Public*, pg. 674

Kasper, Ron, Sr. V.P.--Zee Medical, Inc., Irvine, CA; *U.S. Public*, pg. 1073

Kass, Deborah, Sr. V.P.-H.R.--Yellow Corporation, Overland Park, KS; *U.S. Public*, pg. 1788

Kass, Deborah, Sr. V.P.-H.R.--Yellow Freight System, Inc., Overland Park, KS; *U.S. Public*, pg. 1788

Kassab, Albert A., Chief Fin. Officer & Sr. V.P.--The Ivaco Group, Montreal, Canada; *Int'l*, pg. 695

Kassab, Albert A., Sr. V.P.--The Ivaco Group, Montreal, Canada; *Int'l*, pg. 695

Kassolis, Duke S., Sr. V.P. & Dir.-Office & Mixed-Use Opers.--The Rouse Company, Columbia, MD; *U.S. Public*, pg. 1407

Kassolis, Duke S., Sr. V.P. & Dir.-Office & Mixed-Use Opers.--Rouse Office & Community Development Div., Columbia, MD; *U.S. Public*, pg. 1407

Kastan, David, Sr. V.P. & Mgr.-Pur. Dept.--Mitsui Foods, Inc., Norwood, NJ; *Int'l*, pg. 879

Kastory, Bernard H., Sr. V.P.-Fin. & Admin.--Bestfoods, Englewood Cliffs, NJ; *U.S. Public*, pg. 223

Kataoka, Katsutaro, Sr. Mngmt. Dir.--Alps Electric Co., Ltd., Tokyo, Japan; *Int'l*, pg. 65

Katatski, Laurie, Sr. V.P.-Mktg.--Chi-Chi's Inc., Louisville, KY; *U.S. Private*, pg. 393

Kato, Kunihiro, Sr. V.P.--Nippon Telegraph and Telephone Corporation, Tokyo, Japan; *Int'l*, pg. 940

Kato, Norman, Sr. V.P.-Opers.--Nob Hill General Store, Inc., Gilroy, CA; *U.S. Private*, pg. 799

Kato, Takeo, Assoc. Dir.-Fin.--Asahi Breweries Ltd., Tokyo, Japan; *Int'l*, pg. 83

Katsumata, Matt, Sr. V.P.-Engrng. & Tech. Support--Pioneer New Media Technologies, Long Beach, CA; *U.S. Private, pg. 866*

Katsumata, Yasuo, Sr. V.P.--Mutual Trading Co., Inc., Los Angeles, CA; *U.S. Private*, pg. 770

Katz, Burton, Sr. V.P.--Avnet, Inc., Great Neck, NY; *U.S. Public*, pg. 155

Katz, Charles, Sr. V.P.-Mktg.-Universal Studios Home Video--Universal Pictures, Universal City, CA; *Int'l*, pg. 1216

Katz, Enid, Sr. V.P. & Comml. Production Dir.--Young & Rubicam Chicago, Chicago, IL; *U.S. Private*, pg. 1198

Katz, Lily, Sr. V.P. & Acct. Grp. Dir.--Western International Media Corporation, Los Angeles, CA; *U.S. Private*, pg. 1165

Katz, Martin, Sr. V.P.-Bus. Plng. & Mktg.--WSFS Financial Corporation, Wilmington, DE; *U.S. Public*, pg. 1728

Katzman, Howard, Dr., Sr. V.P. & Sec.--Bowl America, Incorporated, Alexandria, VA; *U.S. Public*, pg. 248

Kauffman, Jacques, Sr. V.P.--Banque Internationale a Luxembourg S.A., Luxembourg, Luxembourg; *Int'l*, pg. 162

Kauffman, Will, Chief Oper. Officer & Sr. V.P.--Komag, Incorporated, San Jose, CA; *U.S. Public*, pg. 966

Kaufman, Gary C., Chief Fin. Officer & Sr. V.P.-Fin. & Admin.--Micros Systems Inc., Beltsville, MD; *U.S. Public*, pg. 1106

Kaufman, Howard M., Sr. V.P., Treas. & Sec.--Lynch & Mayer, Inc, New York, NY; *U.S. Public*, pg. 998

Kaufman, Neal B., Sr. V.P.--Aura Systems, Inc., El Segundo, CA; *U.S. Public*, pg. 147

Kaufman, Tina, Sr. V.P.-Fin.--Jones Medical Industries Inc., Saint Louis, MO; *U.S. Public*, pg. 933

Kauser, Nicholas, Sr. V.P.--AT&T Wireless Services, Kirkland, WA; *U.S. Public*, pg. 11

Kavanagh, Robert E., Sr. V.P.-Sls. & Employee Benefits--The Great-West Life Assurance Company, Winnipeg, Canada; *Int'l*, pg. 557

Kavanaugh, David D., Sr. V.P.-RMS Casualty--Willis Corroon Corp. of Western Michigan, Grand Rapids, MI; *Int'l*, pg. 1507

Kawakami, Kunio, Sr. Mng. Dir.--Namco Ltd., Tokyo, Japan; *Int'l*, pg. 905

Kawamura, Toshiro, Assoc. Sr. V.P.--NEC Corporation, Tokyo, Japan; *Int'l*, pg. 899

Kawamura, Yasushi, Sr. Mng. Dir.--The Daishi Bank, Ltd., Niigata, Japan; *Int'l*, pg. 372

Kawate, Shiro, Sr. Exec. Mng. Dir.--Hitachi, Ltd., Tokyo, Japan; *Int'l*, pg. 621

Kawazoe, Shinichiro, Sr. V.P.--Marubeni America Corporation, New York, NY; *Int'l*, pg. 844

Kay, Michelle, Sr. V.P. & Mngmt. Rep.--Grey Advertising Inc., New York, NY; *U.S. Public*, pg. 764

Kay, Steven R., Chief Fin. Officer & Sr. V.P.--Amwest Insurance Group, Inc., Calabasas, CA; *U.S. Public*, pg. 106

Kay, Walter A., Sr. V.P. & Treas.--Vance Publishing Corporation, Lincolnshire, IL; *U.S. Private*, pg. 1133

Kaye, Aimee, Sr. V.P.-Human Resources--Madison Square Garden Corporation, New York, NY; *U.S. Public*, pg. 288

Kaye, Alan, Sr. V.P.-H.R. & Admin.--Mattel, Inc., El Segundo, CA; *U.S. Public*, pg. 1057

Kaye, Gordon H., Sr. V.P.-Sls.--Fair, Isaac and Company, Inc., San Rafael, CA; *U.S. Public*, pg. 609

Kazlo, Ronald, Sr. V.P.-Fin. & Asst. Sec.--ACCO Brands, Inc., Wheeling, IL; *U.S. Public*, pg. 674

Kean, John S., Sr. V.P.--Cintas Corporation, Mason, OH; *U.S. Public*, pg. 370

Keane, Dennis M., Sr. V.P.-Fin. & Info. Sys.--Novartis Pharmaceuticals, East Hanover, NJ; *Int'l*, pg. 973

Keane, John K., Jr., Sr. V.P. & Gen. Counsel--Washington Gas Light Co., Springfield, VA; *U.S. Public*, pg. 1740

Keane, Michael E., Chief Fin. Officer & Sr. V.P.--UNOVA, Inc., Beverly Hills, CA; *U.S. Public*, pg. 1698

Kearney, John F., Sr. V.P.-Underwriting--Executive Risk, Inc., Simsbury, CT; *U.S. Public*, pg. 599

Kearney, Joseph P., Sr. V.P.--PG&E Corporation, San Francisco, CA; *U.S. Public*, pg. 1240

Kearney, Pat, Sr. V.P.-Direct Div.--Inacom Corp., Omaha, NE; *U.S. Public*, pg. 873

Kearney, Thomas, Sr. V.P. & Corp. Auditor--WSFS Financial Corporation, Wilmington, DE; *U.S. Public*, pg. 1728

Kearney, Thomas B., Sr. V.P.--General Reinsurance Corp., Stamford, CT; *U.S. Public*, pg. 725

Kearns, Dale, Chief Fin. Officer & Sr. V.P.-Fin.--O&Y Properties Corporation, Toronto, Canada; *Int'l*, pg. 993

Kearns, Irene M., Sr. V.P.-Corp. Banking--Citizens Bank Of Connecticut, New London, CT; *Int'l*, pg. 1132

Keaster, James C., Sr. V.P. & Cashier--The Bradford National Bank of Greenville, Greenville, IL; *U.S. Private*, pg. 164

Keat, Law Peng, Sr. V.P.--GATX Terminals (Pte.) Ltd., Singapore, Singapore; *U.S. Public*, pg. 693

Keating, Roger B., Sr. V.P.-On Line Communications--Comcast Cable Communications, Inc., Philadelphia, PA; *U.S. Public*, pg. 407

Kee, Chow Kok, Sr. V.P.-Correspondent Banking--DBS Bank Ltd., Singapore, Singapore; *Int'l*, pg. 350

Keefer, R. Scott, Chief Fin. Officer & Sr. V.P.--Calgon Carbon Corporation, Pittsburgh, PA; *U.S. Public*, pg. 292

Keegan, Brendan M., Sr. V.P.-Human Resources--Marriott International, Inc., Washington, DC; *U.S. Public*, pg. 1047

Keegan, Robert J., Pres.-Consumer Imaging & Sr. V.P.--Eastman Kodak Company, Rochester, NY; *U.S. Public*, pg. 550

Keele, Richard V., Sr. V.P. & Gen. Mgr.-CDS Cluster--Anacomp, Inc., Indianapolis, IN; *U.S. Public*, pg. 106

Keeling, William S., Sr. V.P.-Opers.--Gateway Press, Inc., Louisville, KY; *U.S. Private*, pg. 441

Keely, William J., Sr. V.P.-Area West--Hapag-Lloyd (America), Inc., Piscataway, NJ; *Int'l*, pg. 596

Keen, James F., Sr. V.P. & Controller--First Tennessee Bank National Association, Memphis, TN; *U.S. Public*, pg. 639

Keenan, John P., Chief Oper. Officer & Sr. V.P.--Bankers American Life Assurance Company, Pearl River, NY; *U.S. Public*, pg. 68

Keenan, Stephen, Sr. V.P.--Willis Corroon Marine & Energy, Houston, TX; *Int'l*, pg. 1508

Keeney, Karen, Sr. V.P.-Information Systems--National Insurance Group, South San Francisco, CA; *U.S. Public*, pg. 1157

Keeney, Richard H., Sr. V.P.-Category Advisory Services--Fleming Companies, Inc., Oklahoma City, OK; *U.S. Public*, pg. 652

Keeshan, Harry, Sr. V.P. & Natl. Brdcst. Dir.--Wells BDDP, Inc., New York, NY; *Int'l*, pg. 117

Kegelman, Thomas G., Sr. V.P.--Brown-Forman Beverages Worldwide, Louisville, KY; *U.S. Public*, pg. 261

Keil, Jim, Sr. V.P.-Direct Mktg.--Rockett, Burkhead, Lewis & Winslow, Raleigh, NC; *U.S. Private*, pg. 938

Keilman, Robert E., Sr. V.P.--The Bank of New York, New York, NY; *U.S. Public*, pg. 178

Keir, Gerald J., Sr. V.P.-Corp. Communications Div.--First Hawaiian Bank, Honolulu, HI; *U.S. Public*, pg. 634

Keith, Alan, Chief Fin. Officer & Sr. V.P.--Hanna-Barbera Productions, Inc., Hollywood, CA; *U.S. Public*, pg. 1614

Keler, Marianne M., Sr. V.P. & Gen. Counsel--SLM Holding Corp., Washington, DC; *U.S. Public*, pg. 1419

Kelleher, Robert X., Sr. V.P.-Human Resources--Long Island Lighting Company, Hicksville, NY; *U.S. Public*, pg. 1013

Kelleher, Timothy J., Sr. V.P.-Labor Rels.--Detroit Newspapers, Detroit, MI; *U.S. Public*, pg. 965

Keller, Joseph J., Jr., Sr. V.P.-Admin. & Opers.--PharmHouse, Inc., New York, NY; *U.S. Public*, pg. 1286

Kelley, Jack, Sr. V.P.--Preferred Risk Mutual Insurance, West Des Moines, IA; *U.S. Private*, pg. 880

Kelley, James F., Sr. V.P.-Law & Gen. Counsel--Georgia-Pacific Corporation, Atlanta, GA; *U.S. Public*, pg. 735

Kelley, James M., Sr. V.P.--Savannah Foods & Industries, Inc., Savannah, GA; *U.S. Public*, pg. 872

Kelley, John J., Sr. V.P.--The Hartford Steam Boiler Inspection & Insurance Co., Hartford, CT; *U.S. Public*, pg. 795

Kelley, Kevin, Sr. V.P.-External Affairs--QUALCOMM, San Diego, CA; *U.S. Public*, pg. 1348

Kelley, Larry, Sr. V.P.-Media & Res.--Fogarty Klein & Partners, Houston, TX; *U.S. Private*, pg. 415

Kelley, Robert L., Sr. V.P. & Gen. Counsel--Insituform Technologies, Inc., Chesterfield, MO; *U.S. Public*, pg. 881

Kelliher, James, Sr. V.P.-Fin.--Parametric Technology Corporation, Waltham, MA; *U.S. Public*, pg. 1257

Kellner, Lawrence W., Chief Fin. Officer & Exec. V.P.--Continental Airlines, Houston, TX; *U.S. Public*, pg. 439

Kellstrom, William H., Sr. V.P.-Strategic Planning--NorAm Energy Corp., Houston, TX; *U.S. Public*, pg. 843

Kelly-Ennis, Debra, Sr. V.P.-Mktg.--Gerber Products Company, Fremont, MI; *Int'l*, pg. 973

Kelly, Anastasia D., Sr. V.P. & Deputy Gen. Counsel--Federal National Mortgage Association (Fannie Mae), Washington, DC; *U.S. Public*, pg. 615

Kelly, Brian T., Sr. V.P.-Global Mktg. & Sls.--Occidental Chemical Corporation, Dallas, TX; *U.S. Public*, pg. 1210

Kelly, Colin P., Sr. V.P.-Human Resources--Household International, Inc., Prospect Heights, IL; *U.S. Public*, pg. 842

Kelly, Colleen, Sr. V.P. & Media Plng. Dir.--Deutsch LA, Santa Monica, CA; *U.S. Private*, pg. 328

Kelly, Edward J., Sr. V.P.-Corp. Devel.--CalMat Co., Los Angeles, CA; *U.S. Public*, pg. 295

Kelly, J. M., Sr. V.P. & Media Mgr.--Brown Marketing Communications, Chicago, IL; *U.S. Private*, pg. 174

Kelly, J. Michael, Chief Fin. Officer & Sr. V.P.-Fin.--GTE Corporation, Stamford, CT; *U.S. Public*, pg. 696

Kelly, J. Patrick, V.P. & Sr. V.P.-Disease Mngmt./U.S. Pharmaceuticals Grp.--Pfizer Inc., New York, NY; *U.S. Public*, pg. 1281

Kelly, Jack, Chief Oper. Officer & Sr. V.P.--Producto Machine Co. Ring Division, Jamestown, NY; *U.S. Private, pg. 889*

Kelly, James E., Sr. V.P. & Controller--Midlantic Bank, N.A., Philadelphia, PA; *U.S. Public*, pg. 1242

Kelly, Janet Langford, Sr. V.P., Gen. Counsel & Sec.--Sara Lee Corporation, Chicago, IL; *U.S. Public*, pg. 1432

Kelly, John A., Chief Oper. Officer & Sr. V.P.--The Producto Machine Co., Bridgeport, CT; *U.S. Private*, pg. 889

Kelly, John H., Sr. V.P.-H.R.--Atlantic Richfield Company, Los Angeles, CA; *U.S. Public*, pg. 144

Kelly, Margaret, Sr. V.P.--RE/MAX International, Inc., Englewood, CO; *U.S. Private*, pg. 912

Kelly, Michael N., Sr. V.P.-Opers.--Baxter Research Medical, Inc., Midvale, UT; *U.S. Public*, pg. 196

Kelly, Paul L., Sr. V.P.--Rowan Companies, Inc., Houston, TX; *U.S. Public*, pg. 1409

Kelly, Pete, Sr. V.P.-Sls.-Hasbro Toy Grp.--Hasbro, Inc., Pawtucket, RI; *U.S. Public*, pg. 797

Kelly, Susan, Sr. V.P. & Sec.--Albert M. Greenfield & Company, Philadelphia, PA; *U.S. Private*, pg. 477

Kelly, Wally C., Sr. V.P.--Outdoor Systems, Inc., Phoenix, AZ; *U.S. Public*, pg. 1235

Kelly, William H., Sr. V.P.-Plng. & Devel.--NorAm Energy Corp., Houston, TX; *U.S. Public*, pg. 843

Kelly, William M., Chief Fin. Officer & Sr. V.P.-Corp. Opers.--Silicon Graphics, Inc., Mountain View, CA; *U.S. Public*, pg. 1473

Kelman, J. Brent, Pres.-Truscan Realty Ltd. & Sr. V.P.--CT Financial Services, Inc., Toronto, Canada; *Int'l*, pg. 112

Kelsky, Steven E., Sr. V.P.-Strategic Plng. & Devel.--Physician Computer Network, Inc., Morris Plains, NJ; *U.S. Public*, pg. 1293

Kelso, Joyce M., Chief Oper. Officer & Sr. V.P.--Concord EFS, Inc., Memphis, TN; *U.S. Public*, pg. 429

Kelty, Mike P., Sr. V.P. & Gen. Mgr.-Professional Bus. Grp.--The Scotts Company, Marysville, OH; *U.S. Public*, pg. 1446

Kemp, Judith W., Sr. V.P.--Market Facts, Inc., Arlington Heights, IL; *U.S. Public*, pg. 1046

Kempin, Joachim, Sr. V.P.-OEM Sls.--Microsoft Corporation, Redmond, WA; *U.S. Public*, pg. 1107

Kemppainen, Pekka, Sr. V.P.-Tech.--Kone Corporation, Helsinki, Finland; *Int'l*, pg. 746
Kenety, Cindy, Sr. V.P.--Partners & Shevack, Inc., New York, NY; *U.S. Private*, pg. 842
Kenmore, Charles R., Sr. V.P.-Intl. Sls.--ADC Telecommunications, Inc., Minnetonka, MN; *U.S. Public*, pg. 4
Kenmore, Charles R., Sr. V.P. & Gen. Mgr.-Intl.--Boca Research Inc., Boca Raton, FL; *U.S. Public*, pg. 239
Kennard, Janice, Sr. V.P. & Chief of Staff--The Bionetics Corporation, Newport News, VA; *U.S. Private*, pg. 145
Kennard, John V.O., Sr. V.P. Mktg.-Louisville--Brown-Forman Corporation, Louisville, KY; *U.S. Public*, pg. 261
Kennard, John V.O., Sr. V.P.-Spirits Brands Co.--Brown-Forman Beverages Worldwide, Louisville, KY; *U.S. Public*, pg. 261
Kennast, Mike, Sr. V.P.-Natl. Acct. Sls.--The Spring Air Company, Des Plaines, IL; *U.S. Private*, pg. 1027
Kenneally, William, Sr. V.P., Gen. Counsel & Sec.--Golub Corporation, Schenectady, NY; *U.S. Private*, pg. 463
Kennedy, Clint M., Sr. V.P.-Pulp, Bleached Board & Logistics--Georgia-Pacific Corporation, Atlanta, GA; *U.S. Public*, pg. 735
Kennedy, Colin, Sr. V.P.--Air Liquide S.A., Paris, France; *Int'l*, pg. 37
Kennedy, David, Sr. V.P.-Mktg.--SunGard Employee Benefits Systems, Birmingham, AL; *U.S. Public*, pg. 1534
Kennedy, David O., Sr. V.P.--Lester B. Knight Facilities Management, Inc., Chicago, IL; *U.S. Private*, pg. 627
Kennedy, Jim, Sr. V.P.-Professional Risks--Willis Corroon Corp. of New York, New York, NY; *Int'l*, pg. 1506
Kennedy, John, Chief Fin. Officer, Sr. V.P. & Treas.--Smith International, Inc., Houston, TX; *U.S. Public*, pg. 1478
Kennedy, Jon, Sr. V.P.-Admin.--Eagle USA Airfreight, Houston, TX; *U.S. Public*, pg. 547
Kennedy, Kitty S., Sr. V.P.-Insurance & Chief Actuary--United Companies Financial Corporation, Baton Rouge, LA; *U.S. Public*, pg. 1675
Kennedy, Mark, Chief Fin. Officer & Sr. V.P.--Department 56 Inc., Eden Prairie, MN; *U.S. Public*, pg. 500
Kennedy, Michael, Sr. V.P.-Film/Canada--Cineplex Odeon Corporation, Toronto, Canada; *Int'l*, pg. 292
Kennedy, Mike, Sr. V.P.-IS--Westin Hotels & Resorts, Seattle, WA; *U.S. Public*, pg. 1512
Kennedy, Ruth A., Sr. V.P., Gen. Counsel & Sec.--Electronic Arts, San Mateo, CA; *U.S. Public*, pg. 569
Kennedy, Tom, Sr. V.P.-Creative Adv.--Metro-Goldwyn-Mayer Inc., Santa Monica, CA; *U.S. Public*, pg. 1101
Kennedy, W.T., Sr. V.P. & Chief Oper. Officer-New Holland Inc.--New Holland Ltd., Brentford, United Kingdom; *Int'l*, pg. 484
Kenney, J.R., Sr. V.P.-Asset Accumulation Grp.--AEGON USA, Inc., Baltimore, MD; *Int'l*, pg. 26
Kenney, R.J., Chief Fin. Officer & Sr. V.P.-Fin.--Consolidated Papers, Inc., Wisconsin Rapids, WI; *U.S. Public*, pg. 436
Kennig, Michael, Sr. V.P.--Holder Corporation, Atlanta, GA; *U.S. Private*, pg. 533
Kenny, Mary Ellen, Sr. V.P. & Acct. Mng. Dir.--Young & Rubicam New York, New York, NY; *U.S. Private*, pg. 1198
Kenny, Peter, Sr. V.P.-Lending--Broad National Bancorporation, Newark, NJ; *U.S. Public*, pg. 257
Kenny, Richard, Sr. V.P.-New Bus. Mgr.--Citibank, Federal Savings Bank (Illinois), Chicago, IL; *U.S. Public*, pg. 378
Kenshol, David R., Sr. V.P.-Mktg. & Adv.--HomeBase, Inc., Irvine, CA; *U.S. Public*, pg. 832
Kent, Jeffrey, Sr. V.P.-Fin., Theaters & MIS--Cineplex Odeon Corporation, Toronto, Canada; *Int'l*, pg. 292
Kentra, Edward J., Sr. V.P.--Central Steel & Wire Company, Chicago, IL; *U.S. Public*, pg. 327
Keogh, Christopher J., Sr. V.P.-Industrial Components--Wajax Limited, Delta, Canada; *Int'l*, pg. 1484
Keone, L. Michael, Sr. V.P.-Pacific Agencies--New York Life Insurance Company, New York, NY; *U.S. Private*, pg. 794
Keough, William H., Chief Fin. Officer, Sr. V.P. & Treas.--The Pioneer Group, Inc., Boston, MA; *U.S. Public*, pg. 1298
Kepra, Donald, Sr. V.P.-Opers.--Lucky Stores Northern California Division, San Leandro, CA; *U.S. Public*, pg. 93
Kerbis, Elliott J., Sr. V.P. & Gen. Mgr.-Mdse.--Caldor, Inc., Norwalk, CT; *U.S. Public*, pg. 292
Kerby, Lynn A., Sr. V.P.--Calpine Corporation, San Jose, CA; *U.S. Public*, pg. 296
Kerchenko, Richard, Sr. V.P.--Hardee's Food Systems, Inc., Rocky Mount, NC; *U.S. Public*, pg. 278
Kerckhove, George H., Sr. V.P.-Plumbing Prods.--American Standard Inc., Piscataway, NJ; *U.S. Public*, pg. 91
Kerckhove, Goerge H., Sr. V.P.-Plumbing Prods.--American Standard Plumbing Products, Piscataway, NJ; *U.S. Public*, pg. 92
Keresman, Michael, III, Chief Fin. Officer & Sr. V.P.--Steris Corporation, Mentor, OH; *U.S. Public*, pg. 1515
Kern, E.F., Jr., Sr. V.P.-Service & Customer Satisfaction--American Isuzu Motors Inc., Whittier, CA; *Int'l*, pg. 692
Kern, Michael, Sr. V.P.-Mktg.--Long John Silver's, Inc., Lexington, KY; *U.S. Private*, pg. 674
Kern, Peter M., Sr. V.P.-Strategic Devel. & Corp. Fin.--Home Shopping Network, Inc., Saint Petersburg, FL; *U.S. Public*, pg. 1685
Kern, Ronald C., Sr. V.P. & Agent--Banca Serfin, S.A., New York Agency, New York, NY; *Int'l*, pg. 137
Kern, William J., Jr., Sr. V.P.-Sls.--The Pepper Companies, Inc., Chicago, IL; *U.S. Private*, pg. 851
Kerns, Larry, Sr. V.P.--GSC Enterprises, Inc., Sulphur Springs, TX; *U.S. Private*, pg. 436
Kerr, Aven A., Sr. V.P.-H.R.--NovaCare Inc., King of Prussia, PA; *U.S. Public*, pg. 1203
Kerr, Darlene, Sr. V.P.-Energy Distr.--Niagara Mohawk Power Corporation, Syracuse, NY; *U.S. Public*, pg. 1181
Kerr, Irene, Sr. V.P.-Quality Assurance & Tech. Service/Diagnostics Div.--Bayer Corporation, Pittsburgh, PA; *Int'l*, *pg. 172*
Kerr, Margaret G., Sr. V.P.-Environ., Ethics & Quality--Northern Telecom Limited, Brampton, Canada; *Int'l*, pg. 968
Kerr, Robert A., Sr. V.P.--General Accident Insurance, Philadelphia, PA; *Int'l*, pg. 543
Kerr, William A., Sr. V.P.--The Hartford Steam Boiler Inspection & Insurance Co., Hartford, CT; *U.S. Public*, pg. 795
Kerr, William D., Chief Info. Officer& Sr. V.P.--MainStreet BankGroup Incorporated, Martinsville, VA; *U.S. Public*, pg. 1038
Kerry, William, Sr. V.P.-Licenses--American Business Information, Inc., Omaha, NE; *U.S. Public*, pg. 69
Kershaw, Alan, Sr. V.P. & Mgr.-Treasury--The Bank of Bermuda Limited, Hamilton, Bermuda; *Int'l*, pg. 150
Kershner, Rodger A., Sr. V.P. & Gen. Counsel--CMS Energy Corporation, Dearborn, MI; *U.S. Public*, pg. 279
Kersten, Keith, Sr. V.P.-Opers.--Lund Food Holdings, Inc., Edina, MN; *U.S. Private*, pg. 680
Kersting, Jerome L., Sr. V.P.-Radio Div.--Jacor Communications, Inc., Covington, KY; *U.S. Public*, pg. 922
Kerth, Alfred H., Sr. Partner & Sr. V.P.--Fleishman-Hillard Inc., Saint Louis, MO; *U.S. Private*, pg. 411
Kerwin, Ralph E., Sr. V.P.-Deposit Svcs.--Ameriana Bancorp, New Castle, IN; *U.S. Public*, pg. 66
Kerwin, Ralph E., Sr. V.P.-Deposit Svcs.--Ameriana Bank, New Castle, IN; *U.S. Public*, pg. 66
Keschel, Mark L., Sr. V.P.-Real Estate--OfficeMax, Shaker Heights, OH; *U.S. Public*, pg. 1212
Keshner, Fred, Sr. V.P.--Glenoit Mills, Inc., Tarboro, NC; *U.S. Private*, pg. 456
Kesner, Harvey J., Esq., Sr. V.P., Gen. Counsel & Sec.--American Banknote Corp., New York, NY; *U.S. Public*, pg. 68
Kessel, Roger H., Sr. V.P., Gen. Counsel & Sec.--TECO Energy, Inc., Tampa, FL; *U.S. Public*, pg. 1565
Kessel, Silvia, Chief Fin. Officer, Exec. V.P. & Treas.--Metromedia International Group, Inc., East Rutherford, NJ; *U.S. Public*, pg. 1102
Kessel, William B., Sr. V.P.--Independent Bank, Ionia, MI; *U.S. Public*, pg. 874
Kessler, Alan J., Sr. V.P.-Global Sls./Enterprise Sys.--3Com Corporation, Santa Clara, CA; *U.S. Public*, pg. 1603
Kessler, John, Sr. V.P.--Fike Corporation, Blue Springs, MO; *U.S. Private*, pg. 404
Kessler, Leonard, Sr. V.P. & Gen. Counsel--Morse Diesel International, Inc., New York, NY; *U.S. Private*, pg. 762
Kesson, Mary F., Sr. V.P.--Citizens Financial Group, Inc., Providence, RI; *Int'l*, pg. 1132
Kest, Theodore M., Sr. V.P.--UJB Discount Brokerage, Ridgefield Park, NJ; *U.S. Public*, pg. 1528
Kester, Dennis, Sr. V.P.-Plastic Packaging--American National Can Company, Chicago, IL; *Int'l*, pg. 1029
Kester, Gary W., Sr. V.P.-Credit & Opers.--Advanta Business Services, Voorhees, NJ; *U.S. Public*, pg. 22
Ketcham, William P., Sr. V.P.-Mktg. & Pub. Affairs--QFC Holding Company, Stamford, CT; *U.S. Public*, pg. 1349
Ketive, Samuel G., Sr. V.P.--Bellemead Development Corp., Roseland, NJ; *U.S. Public*, pg. 355
Ketsuwan, Sobson, Sr. V.P.--The Siam Cement Public Company Limited, Bangkok, Thailand; *Int'l*, pg. 1237
Ketterhagen, James, Dr., Sr. V.P.-Medical Dir.--Time Insurance, Milwaukee, WI; *Int'l*, pg. 499
Kettler, Jack, Sr. V.P.--Continental Assurance Company, Chicago, IL; *U.S. Private*, pg. 267
Keyes, Cathleen J., Sr. V.P.-Mktg.--National Bank of Alaska, Anchorage, AK; *U.S. Public*, pg. 1153
Keyes, John A., Sr. V.P.-Opers.--Battle Mountain Gold Company, Houston, TX; *U.S. Public*, pg. 193
Keymer, Dietrich, Sr. V.P.-Payments--Bayerische Landesbank, Munich, Germany; *Int'l*, pg. 176
Keys, David N., Chief Fin. Officer, Sr. V.P. & Treas.--American Pacific Corporation, Las Vegas, NV; *U.S. Public*, pg. 88
Keyser, S.A., Chief Fin. Officer & Sr. V.P.--Burrows Paper Corporation, Little Falls, NY; *U.S. Private*, pg. 188
Kibler, Charles R., Sr. V.P.-Drugstore Opers.--Rite Aid Corporation, Camp Hill, PA; *U.S. Public*, pg. 1390
Kiel, Douglas G., Exec. V.P.--Journal Communications Inc., Milwaukee, WI; *U.S. Private*, pg. 601
Kiel, Roger, Sr. V.P.-Engrng.--Symbol Technologies, Inc., Holtsville, NY; *U.S. Public*, pg. 1546
Kienzle, Charles M., Sr. V.P.-Opers.--Aviall, Inc., Dallas, TX; *U.S. Public*, pg. 154
Kiernan, Donald E., Chief Fin. Officer, Sr. V.P. & Treas.--SBC Communications Inc., San Antonio, TX; *U.S. Public*, *pg. 1415*
Kiernan, Nick, Sr. V.P.-Affiliate Rels.--Westwood One, Inc., New York, NY; *U.S. Public*, pg. 1763
Kiernan, Tom, Sr. V.P.-Corp. Services--American Airlines, Inc., Fort Worth, TX; *U.S. Public*, pg. 9
Kiester, Charles E., Sr. V.P.-Engrng., Quality & Mfg. Svcs.--3M, Saint Paul, MN; *U.S. Public*, pg. 1604
Kikuta, Tokuji, Sr. V.P. & Deputy Gen. Mgr-Bus.--Japan Airlines Company, Ltd., Tokyo, Japan; *Int'l*, pg. 699
Kilfoy, Lawrence B., Sr. V.P.-Bus. Devel.--Service America Corporation, Stamford, CT; *U.S. Private*, pg. 986
Kilgore, Jack, Sr. V.P.--Rich SeaPak Corp., Saint Simons Island, GA; *U.S. Private*, pg. 928
Killebrew, John F., Sr. V.P. & Acct. Exec.--Willis Corroon Corp. of Chattanooga, Chattanooga, TN; *Int'l*, pg. 1505
Killeffer, Louis, Sr. V.P., Grp. Dir.--Ammirati, Puris & Lintas, Inc., New York, NY; *U.S. Private*, pg. 66
Killingsworth, Cleve L., Jr., Pres.-Central East Division & Sr. V.P.--Kaiser Permanente, Oakland, CA; *U.S. Private*, pg. 605
Killmer, Jonathon E., Chief Fin. Officer, Sr. V.P. & Treas.--Digi International Inc., Minnetonka, MN; *U.S. Public*, pg. 506
Killoran, Dermot E., Sr. Mng. Dir.--Bank of Ireland - Tokyo Representative Office, Tokyo, Japan; *Int'l*, pg. 153
Killoren, Jack K., Sr. V.P.-Mktg.--Sterling Electronics Corporation, Houston, TX; *U.S. Public*, pg. 1051
Killough, James, Sr. V.P.-Construction Svcs., Inc.--The PBS&J Corporation, Miami, FL; *U.S. Private*, pg. 825
Killough, Ray B., Sr. V.P.-Opers.--Piedmont Natural Gas Co., Inc., Charlotte, NC; *U.S. Public*, pg. 1295
Kiltie, Susan A., Sr. V.P. & Media Dir.--Young & Rubicam Detroit, Detroit, MI; *U.S. Private*, pg. 1198
Kim, Tae Jo, Sr. V.P. & Reg. Dir.--Korean Airlines Co., Ltd., Seoul, Korea; *Int'l*, pg. 758
Kimball, Brian, Sr. V.P.-Loans--First Independence National Bank, Detroit, MI; *U.S. Public*, pg. 635
Kimmel, Gregory G., Sr. V.P.-Corp. Devel.--Kevco, Inc., Fort Worth, TX; *U.S. Public*, pg. 952
Kimmel, Terry D., Sr. V.P.--Pinnacle Bank, Valparaiso, IN; *U.S. Public*, pg. 1297
Kimmons, W. Arnold, Sr. V.P.-Foodservice Div.--Oneida Ltd., Oneida, NY; *U.S. Public*, pg. 1225
Kimura, Itsuo, Sr. V.P.--Kanematsu Corporation, Tokyo, Japan; *Int'l*, pg. 722
Kiner, Tracee, Sr. V.P. & Dir.-Global Adv.--Hachette Filipacchi Magazines Inc., New York, NY; *Int'l*, pg. 794
King, Albert R., Sr. V.P. & Mgr.-Mortgage Opers.--First Federal of Michigan, Detroit, MI; *U.S. Public*, pg. 336
King, Ben F., Sr. V.P.-Fin./Eastern Division--Tenet Healthcare Corporation, Santa Barbara, CA; *U.S. Public*, pg. 1576
King, C. Gerald, Sr. V.P.-Boeing/McDonnell Douglas Transition Team Leader--The Boeing Company, Seattle, WA; *U.S. Public*, pg. 239
King, Carolyn, Sr. V.P.-Investment Prods.--Protective Life Corporation, Birmingham, AL; *U.S. Public*, pg. 1336
King, Christine, Sr. V.P.-Prod. Devel.--Brite Voice Systems, Inc., Heathrow, FL; *U.S. Public*, pg. 257
King, Daniel J., Sr. V.P.-Prod. Supply--The Dial Corporation, Phoenix, AZ; *U.S. Public*, pg. 505
King, David, Sr. V.P.-Prod. Devel.--Comshare, Incorporated, Ann Arbor, MI; *U.S. Public*, pg. 425
King, David A., Sr. V.P.-Investor's Service--John Hancock Mutual Life Insurance Company, Boston, MA; *U.S. Private*, pg. 589
King, David P., Sr. V.P. & Chief Actuary--United Family Life Insurance Co., Atlanta, GA; *Int'l*, pg. 499
King, Eddy, Sr. V.P.--Namanco LLC, Tulsa, OK; *U.S. Private*, pg. 773
King, Eugene J., Jr., Sr. V.P. & Asst. Treas.-Corp. Control--A.G. Edwards, Inc., Saint Louis, MO; *U.S. Public*, pg. 565
King, Eugene J., Jr., Sr. V.P., Asst. Treas. & Comptroller--A.G. Edwards & Sons, Inc., Saint Louis, MO; *U.S. Public*, *pg. 565*
King, G. Austin, Sr. V.P.--Transocean Offshore, Inc., Houston, TX; *U.S. Public*, pg. 1631
King, George J., Sr. V.P.--SCI Systems, Inc., Huntsville, AL; *U.S. Public*, pg. 1416
King, Gwendolyn S., Sr. V.P.-Corp. & Pub. Affairs--PECO Energy Company, Philadelphia, PA; *U.S. Public*, pg. 1268
King, James C., Sr. V.P. & Sec.--BHA Group Holdings Inc., Kansas City, MO; *U.S. Public*, pg. 161
King, James D., Sr. V.P.-Investment Services--Investors Trust Company, Wyomissing, PA; *U.S. Public*, pg. 1159
King, Justin R., Sr. V.P.-Exploration & Production--Sonat Exploration Company, Houston, TX; *U.S. Public*, pg. 1485
King, Kerman F., Sr. V.P.-Agency Grp.--Metropolitan Life Insurance Co., New York, NY; *U.S. Private*, pg. 737
King, Rachel, Sr. V.P.-Devel.--Fair, Isaac and Company, Inc., San Rafael, CA; *U.S. Public*, pg. 609
King, Robert, Sr. V.P.-Strategic Plng. & Acquisitions--King World Productions, Inc., New York, NY; *U.S. Public*, pg. 961
King, Robert M., Chief Fin. Officer & Sr. V.P.--Nuevo Energy Company, Houston, TX; *U.S. Public*, pg. 1206
King, Roger L., Sr. V.P. & Gen. Mgr.-Int'l Opers.--Graco Inc., Golden Valley, MN; *U.S. Public*, pg. 756
King, Shannon, Sr. V.P.-Mdsg.--The Sharper Image, San Francisco, CA; *U.S. Public*, pg. 1464
King, Timothy, Sr. V.P.-Plng. & Devel.--John Wiley & Sons, Inc., New York, NY; *U.S. Public*, pg. 1768
King, W. Russell, Sr. V.P.-Fed. Govt. Rels.--Freeport-McMoRan Inc., New Orleans, LA; *U.S. Public*, pg. 680
Kingbury, C.W., Sr. V.P.--General Dynamics Land Systems Div., Muskegon, MI; *U.S. Public*, pg. 709
Kingery, Thomas K., Sr. V.P. & Dir.-Stores--Elder-Beerman Stores Div., Dayton, OH; *U.S. Private*, pg. 367
Kinitsky, Larry, Sr. V.P. & Dir. Prod., Mngmt. & Research--The Dime Savings Bank of New York, New York, NY; *U.S. Public*, pg. 509
Kinney, Charles F., Sr. V.P.--Chemical Bank & Trust Company, Midland, MI; *U.S. Public*, pg. 345
Kinney, Jon C., Chief Fin. Officer & Sr. V.P.--Illinois Tool Works Inc., Glenview, IL; *U.S. Public*, pg. 865
Kinney, Larry, Chief Fin. Officer & Sr. V.P.--Chadwick's of Boston, West Bridgewater, MA; *U.S. Public*, pg. 996
Kinnier, Stephen R., Chief Fin. Officer & Sr. V.P.--Virginia First Savings Bank, F.S.B., Petersburg, VA; *U.S. Public*, pg. 1721
Kinoshita, Andrew, Sr. V.P.-Information Services--Parmalat Canada Ltd., Etobicoke, Canada; *Int'l*, pg. 1023
Kinser, David A., Sr. V.P.-Opers.--Intuit, Inc., Mountain View, CA; *U.S. Public*, pg. 911
Kinsey, Michael A., Sr. V.P.-Comml. Markets--SunTrust Banks, Inc., Atlanta, GA; *U.S. Public*, pg. 1537
Kinsley, Marnie J., Sr. V.P. & Chief Auditor--Bank of Montreal, Toronto, Canada; *Int'l*, pg. 153
Kintzinger, Douglas, Sr. V.P.--Jeld-Wen, Inc., Klamath Falls, OR; *U.S. Private*, pg. 585
Kinzer, Charles, Sr. V.P.-Opers.--Barton Brands of Georgia, Inc., Atlanta, GA; *U.S. Public*, pg. 300
Kinzer, Charles, Sr. V.P.-Opers.--Barton Brands of California, Inc., Carson, CA; *U.S. Public*, pg. 300
Kipp, Terry S., Sr. V.P. & Corp. Sec.--National Bancorp of Alaska, Inc., Anchorage, AK; *U.S. Public*, pg. 1153
Kipp, Terry S., Sr. V.P.--National Bank of Alaska, Anchorage, AK; *U.S. Public*, pg. 1153
Kippen, John, Sr. V.P.-Mktg.& Sls.--Plano Molding Co., Plano, IL; *U.S. Private*, pg. 869

Kirby, Kenneth E., Sr. V.P.--The Franklin Institute, Philadelphia, PA; *U.S. Private*, pg. 424

Kirby, Rick, Sr. V.P.--Hydro/Kirby Agri Service, Inc., Lancaster, PA; *U.S. Private*, pg. 552

Kirby, William J., Sr. V.P.--FMC Corporation, Chicago, IL; *U.S. Public*, pg. 604

Kirchner, William E., Sr. V.P.-Prod. Devel. & Adv.--Department 56 Inc., Eden Prairie, MN; *U.S. Public*, pg. 500

Kiremidjian, Fred, Sr. V.P. & Gen. Mgr.-Nuwave Grp.--Network Peripherals Inc., Milpitas, CA; *U.S. Public*, pg. 1169

Kirihara, Wayne, Sr. V.P.-Retail Banking--Central Pacific Bank, Honolulu, HI; *U.S. Public*, pg. 283

Kirk, Brad, Sr. V.P.-Mktg.--20th Century Fox Home Entertainment, Los Angeles, CA; *U.S. Public*, pg. 275

Kirk, Brad, Sr. V.P.-Mktg.--20th Century Fox Home Entertainment, Los Angeles, CA; *Int'l*, pg. 926

Kirk, Chuck, Chief Info. Officer & Sr. V.P.--Fruit of the Loom, Inc., Chicago, IL; *U.S. Public*, pg. 685

Kirk, Diana E., Sr. V.P.-Private Banking Dept.--Zions First National Bank, Salt Lake City, UT; *U.S. Public*, pg. 1793

Kirk, James R., Sr. V.P. & Pres.-Res. & Devel.--Campbell Soup Company, Camden, NJ; *U.S. Public*, pg. 298

Kirk, Larry, Sr. V.P.--First State Bank N.A., Abilene, Abilene, TX; *U.S. Public*, pg. 874

Kirk, Mark C., Sr. V.P.-Credit Mgmt. Dept.--Zions First National Bank, Salt Lake City, UT; *U.S. Public*, pg. 1793

Kirk, Michael A., Sr. V.P.-Production--Metropolitan Mortgage & Securities Co., Inc., Spokane, WA; *U.S. Private*, pg. 738

Kirk, Tom, Sr. V.P. & Grp. Acct. Dir.--Rubin Postaer & Associates, Santa Monica, CA; *U.S. Private*, pg. 949

Kirklin, Max F., Sr. V.P.--Allied Security, International, Spokane, WA; *U.S. Private*, pg. 41

Kirkner, Gary E., Sr. V.P.--UNUM Life Insurance Company of America, Portland, ME; *U.S. Public*, pg. 1699

Kirkpatrick, Robert, Sr. V.P. & Media Services Dir.--DMB&B St. Louis, Saint Louis, MO; *U.S. Private*, pg. 303

Kirkwood, Bud, Sr. V.P.-Adult Care/Fortis Long Term Care--Time Insurance, Milwaukee, WI; *Int'l*, pg. 499

Kirkwood, Merlyn C., Sr. V.P.--American Security Group, Atlanta, GA; *Int'l*, pg. 499

Kirman, Roger, Sr. V.P.-Business Affairs--Viacom Productions Inc., Universal City, CA; *U.S. Private*, pg. 779

Kirnbauer, Erwin A., Sr. V.P. & Dir.-Scientific & Laboratory Services--Pall Corporation, Greenvale, NY; *U.S. Public*, pg. 1253

Kirshner, Sandi, Sr. V.P. & Editorial Dir.--Allyn & Bacon, Needham, MA; *U.S. Private*, pg. 778

Kirtland, Fred G., Sr. V.P.-Agency--Security Mutual Life Insurance Co. of New York, Binghamton, NY; *U.S. Private*, pg. 981

Kirwan, James L., Sr. V.P.-Opers.--International Comfort Products, Franklin, TN; *U.S. Public*, pg. 898

Kiryluk, Carol, Sr. V.P.-H.R.--Tupperware Corporation, Orlando, FL; *U.S. Public*, pg. 1644

Kishi, Hajimu, Sr. V.P.--Fanuc Ltd., Yamanashi, Japan; *Int'l*, pg. 477

Kisler, Dennis B., Sr. V.P., Treas. & Sec.--Agronaut Great Central Insurance Co., Peoria, IL; *U.S. Public*, pg. 129

Kisner, Scott Gerald, Sr. V.P.--Hibernia Corporation, New Orleans, LA; *U.S. Public*, pg. 825

Kissinger, D.L., Sr. V.P.-Individual Insurance Opers.--People's Security Life Insurance, Durham, NC; *Int'l*, pg. 27

Kissko, Lawrence, Sr. V.P. & Dir.-Real Estate--Lincoln National Corporation, Fort Wayne, IN; *U.S. Public*, pg. 997

Kitabatake, Kazuaki, Sr. V.P. & Grp. Head--Fuji Bank, New York Branch, New York, NY; *Int'l*, pg. 519

Kitlas, Ron, Sr. V.P.-Opers.--Edison Parking Properties, LLC, Newark, NJ; *U.S. Private*, pg. 364

Kittaka, Jacqueline Y., Sr. V.P.-H.R.--FirstFed Financial Corp., Santa Monica, CA; *U.S. Public*, pg. 645

Kitterman, James M., Sr. V.P.-Opers.--Swift Energy Company, Houston, TX; *U.S. Public*, pg. 1543

Kittinger, Kenneth R., Sr. V.P.-Govt. Affairs--Doron Precision Systems, Inc., Binghamton, NY; *U.S. Private*, pg. 341

Kittner, Marc R., Sr. V.P. & Corp. Counsel--Washington Mutual Inc., Seattle, WA; *U.S. Public*, pg. 1741

Kivela, Pekka, Sr. V.P.-Grp. Communications Affairs--Metsa-Serla Corporation, Espoo, Finland; *Int'l*, pg. 863

Klag, Robert W., Sr. V.P., Controller & Treas.--National Insurance Group, South San Francisco, CA; *U.S. Public*, pg. 1157

Klaity, John D., Sr. V.P.--General Reinsurance Corp., Stamford, CT; *U.S. Public*, pg. 725

Klar, Henry, Sr. V.P.-Personnel--Riverside Manufacturing Co., Moultrie, GA; *U.S. Private*, pg. 934

Klatt, Roger J., Chief Fin. Officer, Sr. V.P., Treas. & Asst. Sec.--Gundle/SLT Environmental, Inc., Houston, TX; *U.S. Public*, pg. 769

Klausby, Jes, Sr. V.P.-Plng. & Devel.--Nykredit, Copenhagen, Denmark; *Int'l*, pg. 993

Klayko, Michael A., Sr. V.P.-Sls./North American--EMC Corporation, Hopkinton, MA; *U.S. Public*, pg. 545

Klebe, Donald F., Sr. V.P.--Stanley Consultants, Inc., Muscatine, IA; *U.S. Private*, pg. 1033

Klee, Marc H., Sr. V.P.--American Fund Advisors, Inc., Garden City, NY; *U.S. Private*, pg. 55

Klei, Steven E., Chief Fin. Officer, Sr. V.P.-Fin. & Sec.--ProBusiness Services, Inc., Pleasanton, CA; *U.S. Public*, pg. 1330

Klein, Carol, Sr. V.P.-Communications--Red Roof Inns, Inc., Hilliard, OH; *U.S. Public*, pg. 1369

Klein, David M., Sr. V.P.--Hartford Fire Insurance Co., Hartford, CT; *U.S. Public*, pg. 794

Klein, Douglas, Sr. V.P.-Tech.--Network Computing Devices, Inc., Mountain View, CA; *U.S. Public*, pg. 1168

Klein, Jason, Sr. V.P.-Outdoor Life, Field & Stream--Times Mirror Magazines, Inc., New York, NY; *U.S. Public*, pg. 1616

Klein, Jason, Sr. V.P.--Field & Stream, New York, NY; *U.S. Public*, pg. 1617

Klein, Jason, Sr. V.P.--Outdoor Life, New York, NY; *U.S. Public*, pg. 1617

Klein, Jeffrey S., Sr. V.P.-Mktg.--Los Angeles Times, Los Angeles, CA; *U.S. Public*, pg. 1616

Klein, Linda L., Sr. V.P.-Eastern Retail Div.--Countrywide Funding Corporation, Pasadena, CA; *U.S. Public*, pg. 453

Klein, Richard, Sr. V.P.-Dir. Mktg.--Vitt Media International, Inc., New York, NY; *U.S. Private*, pg. 1142

Klein, Richard B., Sr. V.P.-Investor Rels.--Corning Incorporated, Corning, NY; *U.S. Public*, pg. 448

Klein, William B., Sr. V.P.-Business Affairs--CBS Entertainment, Los Angeles, CA; *U.S. Public*, pg. 274

Kleinberg, Brian, Sr. V.P.-Mktg. & Business Devel.--American Express Company, New York, NY; *U.S. Public*, pg. 73

Kleinhenz, Karen R., Sr. V.P.--Keycorp, Cleveland, OH; *U.S. Public*, pg. 954

Klemme, Kenneth, Sr. V.P.--Demeter, Inc., Folwer, IN; *U.S. Public*, pg. 127

Klemz, Michael R., Sr. V.P.--TCF Bank Wisconsin, Milwaukee, WI; *U.S. Public*, pg. 1554

Klesius, Ralph E., Sr. V.P.--Delmarva Power & Light Company, Wilmington, DE; *U.S. Public*, pg. 430

Kline, Barry L., Chief Fin. Officer & Sr. V.P.--Penn National Insurance, Harrisburg, PA; *U.S. Private*, pg. 850

Kline, Bernie S., Sr. V.P.--Indian Rocks National Bank, Largo, FL; *U.S. Public*, pg. 608

Kline, Lowry F., Sr. V.P. & Gen. Counsel--Coca-Cola Enterprises Inc., Atlanta, GA; *U.S. Public*, pg. 393

Kline, Sam, Sr. V.P.-Prod. Factory--Brite Voice Systems, Inc., Heathrow, FL; *U.S. Public*, pg. 257

Kling, Herman V., Sr. V.P.-Mktg.--International Comfort Products, Franklin, TN; *U.S. Public*, pg. 898

Kling, Richard W., Sr. V.P.-Risk Mngmt. Prods.--American Express Financial Advisor, Minneapolis, MN; *U.S. Public*, pg. 73

Kling, Stephen, Sr. V.P.-Creative Services--Jordan, McGrath, Case & Taylor Inc., New York, NY; *U.S. Private*, pg. 598

Kling, Stephen, Sr. V.P.--Stawasz & Partners/Health Care Communications, New York, NY; *U.S. Private*, pg. 599

Klingberg, Robert, Chief Tech. Officer & Sr. V.P.--Reuter Manufacturing Inc., Hopkins, MN; *U.S. Public*, pg. 1383

Klinger, John, Sr. V.P. & Deputy Exec. Creative Dir.--DMB&B Detroit, Troy, MI; *U.S. Private*, pg. 302

Klipfell, John M., Sr. V.P.-Electronic Mktg.--American Greetings Corporation, Cleveland, OH; *U.S. Public*, pg. 77

Klitgaard, Thomas, Sr. V.P. & Gen. Counsel--Sega of America Inc., Redwood City, CA; *Int'l*, pg. 1218

Klocke, Delmar D., Sr. V.P.--Linder & Associates, Inc., Wichita, KS; *U.S. Private*, pg. 668

Klopfer, John, Sr. V.P.-Healthcare Corp. Accts.--Angelica Image Apparel, Saint Louis, MO; *U.S. Public*, pg. 113

Klops, Jeff, Sr. V.P. & Sec.--Security Capital Group Incorporated, Santa Fe, NM; *U.S. Private*, pg. 980

Klotz, Kevin, Sr. V.P.-Profits & Processing--American Bankers Insurance Co. of Florida, Miami, FL; *U.S. Public*, pg. 67

Klotz, R. Kevin, Sr. V.P.-Opers.--American Bankers Life Assurance Co. of Florida, Miami, FL; *U.S. Public*, pg. 67

Kluberdanz, Wallace, Sr. V.P.-Fin.--Marcel Dekker, Inc., New York, NY; *U.S. Private*, pg. 321

Kluempke, Patrick, Sr. V.P.-Corp. Plng. & Devel.--Harvest States Cooperatives, Saint Paul, MN; *U.S. Private*, pg. 508

Klug, Susan, Sr. V.P.-Mktg.--The Vons Companies, Inc., Arcadia, CA; *U.S. Public*, pg. 1426

Kluger, Barry, Sr. V.P.-Media & Network Talent Rels./VH-1--MTV Networks, New York, NY; *U.S. Private*, pg. 779

Kluger, Barry, Sr. V.P.-Media & Network Talent Rels.--VH-1/Video Hits One, New York, NY; *U.S. Private*, pg. 779

Klugman, Robert D., Sr. V.P.-Corp. Devel.--Coors Brewing Company, Golden, CO; *U.S. Public*, pg. 445

Klumpp, Brian, Sr. V.P.-H.R.--Brite Voice Systems, Inc., Heathrow, FL; *U.S. Public*, pg. 257

Klutch, Alan J., Sr. V.P.-Fin.--Cognizant Corporation, Westport, CT; *U.S. Public*, pg. 395

Kmiecik, Thomas T., Sr. V.P. & Treas.--First Union Real Estate Investments, Cleveland, OH; *U.S. Public*, pg. 640

Knapp, Arthur F., Jr., Chief Fin. Officer, Sr. V.P. & Sec.--Boole & Babbage, Inc., San Jose, CA; *U.S. Public*, pg. 244

Knapp, Gene, Sr. V.P.--Simon Marketing, Inc., Oak Brook Terrace, IL; *U.S. Private*, pg. 1001

Knapp, Patrick J., Sr. V.P. & Assoc. Creative Dir.--Cramer-Krasselt, Milwaukee, WI; *U.S. Private*, pg. 286

Knapp, W.A., Sr. V.P.--A.Y. McDonald Industries, Inc., Dubuque, IA; *U.S. Private*, pg. 721

Knauer, Erwin D., Sr. V.P.--Ramapo Financial Corporation, Wayne, NJ; *U.S. Public*, pg. 1360

Knechtges, Donald P., Sr. V.P.-Res. & Engrng.--The Geon Company, Avon Lake, OH; *U.S. Public*, pg. 733

Knedlik, Ronald, Chief Fin. Officer, Sr. V.P.-Fin., Treas. & Sec.--Alex Lee, Inc., Hickory, NC; *U.S. Private*, pg. 657

Kneip, Robert C., Sr. V.P.-Corp. Plng. & Devel.--The Wackenhut Corporation, Palm Beach Gardens, FL; *U.S. Public*, pg. 1731

Kneisel, Frank, Sr. V.P.-Fin.--Champion International Corp., Stamford, CT; *U.S. Public*, pg. 333

Kneissl, William L., Sr. V.P., Treas. & Sec.--The Troy Savings Bank, Troy, NY; *U.S. Private*, pg. 1106

Knepper, Peter, Chief Fin. Officer, Sr. V.P. & Treas.--Ticketmaster Corporation, West Hollywood, CA; *U.S. Private*, pg. 1084

Kniffen, Jan R., Sr. V.P. & Treas.--The May Department Stores Company, Saint Louis, MO; *U.S. Public*, pg. 1063

Knight, Gerald T., Chief Fin. Officer & Sr. V.P.--Fingerhut Corp., Minnetonka, MN; *U.S. Public*, pg. 623

Knight, Linda K., Sr. V.P. & Treas.--Federal National Mortgage Association (Fannie Mae), Washington, DC; *U.S. Public*, pg. 615

Knight, Mark D., Sr. V.P. & Sec.--The Thomson Corporation, Stamford, CT; *U.S. Public*, pg. 1599

Knight, Roger P., Sr. V.P.-North Asia Opers. & Pres.-China--CPC Asia Consumer Foods Division, Hong Kong, Hong Kong; *U.S. Public*, pg. 224

Knight, Sharon E., Sr. V.P.--Hibernia Corporation, New Orleans, LA; *U.S. Public*, pg. 825

Knipmeyer, Steve, Sr. V.P.-Software Devel.--Bentley Systems, Inc., Exton, PA; *U.S. Private*, pg. 134

Knister, James A., Sr. V.P.-Non-Automotive Bus.--Donnelly Corporation, Holland, MI; *U.S. Public*, pg. 519

Knobblock, Denise, Sr. V.P.-Pur., Facilities, Administration & Travel--Compuware Corporation, Farmington Hills, MI; *U.S. Public*, pg. 423

Knobloch, Kevin F., Sr. V.P.--City National Bank of Baton Rouge, Baton Rouge, LA; *U.S. Public*, pg. 629

Knoll, David E., Sr. V.P.-Corp. Devel.--Sun Company, Inc., Philadelphia, PA; *U.S. Public*, pg. 1530

Knopf, Robert J., Sr. V.P.-Devel.--Quadrangle Development Corporation, Washington, DC; *U.S. Private*, pg. 898

Knopke, Raymond C., Jr., Sr. V.P. & Pres.-Western Div.--Stewart Enterprises, Inc., Metairie, LA; *U.S. Public*, pg. 1518

Knopp, Maurice J., Sr. V.P.--Essex Chemical Corporation, Clifton, NJ; *U.S. Public*, pg. 523

Knowles, Tommy L., Sr. V.P.-Exploration & Production--Belden & Blake Corporation, Canton, OH; *U.S. Private*, pg. 1078

Knudson, Peter, Sr. V.P.--Imperial Bank, Inglewood, CA; *U.S. Public*, pg. 871

Knudtson, Lee G., Sr. V.P.-Exploration--Plains Petroleum Operating Co., Lakewood, CO; *U.S. Public*, pg. 191

Knutson, Gary A., Sr. V.P.-Acquisiton Integration--Community First Bankshares, Inc., Fargo, ND; *U.S. Public*, pg. 416

Kobayashi, Isao, Sr. Mng. Dir.-Gen. Store Devel.--Ito-Yokado Co., Ltd., Tokyo, Japan; *Int'l*, pg. 693

Kobayashi, Issaku, Sr. V.P.--Calpis Food Industry Co. Ltd., Tokyo, Japan; *Int'l*, pg. 252

Kobayashi, Kazuhiko, Assoc. Sr. V.P.--NEC Corporation, Tokyo, Japan; *Int'l*, pg. 899

Kobayashi, Masao, Sr. Mng. Dir.--Nippon Paper Industries Company Limited, Tokyo, Japan; *Int'l*, pg. 937

Kobayashi, Shigeru, Sr. V.P. & Gen. Mgr.--Nippon Life Insurance Company of America, New York, NY; *Int'l*, pg. 935

Kobayashi, Toshitada, Sr. V.P.--Softbank Corporation, Tokyo, Japan; *Int'l*, pg. 1276

Kobernus, John A., Sr. V.P.-Appliance & Electronics Distr.--Servco Pacific Inc., Honolulu, HI; *U.S. Private*, pg. 986

Kobeyashi, Etsuo, Sr. V.P.-Fin.--Ricoh Corporation, West Caldwell, NJ; *Int'l*, pg. 1114

Kobrynsky, George, Sr. V.P.-Fine Papers--Domtar Inc., Montreal, Canada; *Int'l*, pg. 416

Koch, E., Sr. Reg. V.P.--Geraghty & Miller, Inc., Denver, CO; *Int'l*, pg. 607

Koch, Garry D., Sr. V.P. & Chief Credit Officer--National Penn Bank, Boyertown, PA; *U.S. Public*, pg. 1159

Koch, Hans J., Sr. V.P.-Fin. & Admin.--ENSR, Acton, MA; *U.S. Private*, pg. 354

Koch, Harold O., Sr. V.P.-Bus. Devel.--Akorn, Inc., Lincolnshire, IL; *U.S. Public*, pg. 34

Koch, John D., Sr. V.P.--Charter One Financial, Inc., Cleveland, OH; *U.S. Public*, pg. 336

Koch, Richard J., V.P., Sec. & Gen. Counsel--American City Business Journals, Inc., Charlotte, NC; *U.S. Private*, pg. 19

Koch, Roland E., Sr. V.P.-Opers.--The Provident Bank, Cincinnati, OH; *U.S. Public*, pg. 1338

Koch, Susan, Sr. V.P. & Dir.-Mktg.--Whitney Holding Corporation, New Orleans, LA; *U.S. Public*, pg. 1766

Koch, Susan, Sr. V.P. & Dir.--Whitney National Bank, New Orleans, LA; *U.S. Public*, pg. 1766

Kochanski, Thaddeus M., V.P. & Controller--The Lehigh Press, Inc., Cherry Hill, NJ; *U.S. Private*, pg. 658

Koci, Dennis, Sr. V.P.-Opers. Support--Hilton Hotels Div., Beverly Hills, CA; *U.S. Public*, pg. 829

Kocurek, W. Neal, Sr. V.P.--Radian International LLC, Austin, TX; *U.S. Public*, pg. 522

Koenderman, Paul P., Sr. V.P. & Grp. Exec.-Power Generation Grp.--McDermott International, Inc., New Orleans, LA; *U.S. Public*, pg. 1067

Koenig, William C., FSA, Sr. V.P.-Chief Actuary--Northwestern Mutual Life Insurance Co., Milwaukee, WI; *U.S. Private*, pg. 807

Koepke, Jack E., Sr. V.P.--General Reinsurance Corp., Stamford, CT; *U.S. Public*, pg. 725

Koeppe, Alfred C., Sr. V.P.-Corp. Svcs. & External Affairs--Public Service Electric & Gas Co., Newark, NJ; *U.S. Public*, pg. 1340

Koerner, Scott F., Sr. V.P.--Creative Computers, Inc., Elk Grove Village, IL; *U.S. Public*, pg. 458

Koets, Ann, Sr. V.P.-Fin. Svcs.--TCI Communications, Inc., Englewood, CO; *U.S. Public*, pg. 1554

Koffman, Richard E., Sr. V.P.--Great American Industries, Inc., Vestal, NY; *U.S. Private*, pg. 473

Koga, H., Sr. V.P.--Mitsubishi International Corporation, New York, NY; *Int'l*, pg. 871

Kogan, Eric D., Sr. V.P.-Corp. Devel.--Triarc Companies, Inc., New York, NY; *U.S. Public*, pg. 1634

Kohl, David C., Sr. V.P.--Church & Church Inc., Auburn Hills, MI; *U.S. Private*, pg. 239

Kohlberger, Richard A., Sr. V.P.--UST Inc., Greenwich, CT; *U.S. Public*, pg. 1660

Kohlhepp, A.J., Sr. V.P.-Equities--General Electric Investment Corp., Stamford, CT; *U.S. Public*, pg. 712

Kohn, David, Sr. V.P.-Generation & Transmission--The Israel Electric Corporation Ltd., Haifa, Israel; *Int'l*, pg. 690

Kohn, Louis S., Sr. V.P.--Acordia Northeast, Boston, MA; *Int'l*, pg. 671

Kohn, Pam, Sr. V.P.-Mdsg.--Food Lion, Inc., Salisbury, NC; *Int'l*, pg. 463

Kohn, Paul, Sr. V.P.--Pall Corporation, Greenvale, NY; *U.S. Public*, pg. 1253

Koide, Kanji, Sr. V.P.--Nippon Telegraph and Telephone Corporation, Tokyo, Japan; *Int'l*, pg. 940

Kojalo, Jacob, Sr. V.P.-Comml. Lending & Bus. Devel.--Lawrence Savings Bank, North Andover, MA; *U.S. Public*, pg. 980

Kojima, Y., Sr. V.P.--Mitsubishi International Corporation, New York, NY; *Int'l*, pg. 871

Kok, Gan Kim, Sr. V.P.-Credit Admin. & Risk Mngmt.--DBS Bank Ltd., Singapore, Singapore; *Int'l*, pg. 350

Kokulis, George C., Sr. V.P.-Life & Long-Term Care Insurance--The Travelers Life & Annuity Co., Hartford, CT; *U.S. Public*, pg. 1633

Kolakawski, Stephen C., Chief Fin. Officer, Sr. V.P. & Treas.--Underwriters Reinsurance, Woodland Hills, CA; *U.S. Public*, pg. 42

Kolar, Susan, Sr. V.P. & Chief Fin. Officer--Viacom Entertainment, New York, NY; *U.S. Private*, pg. 779

Kolb, Paul, Sr. V.P.--Intertek Testing Services, Andover, MA; *Int'l*, pg. 672

Kolesar, Carolyn L., Sr. V.P.--Morrison Health Care Inc., Smyrna, GA; *U.S. Public*, pg. 1133

Kolhagen, Donald W., Sr. V.P. & Treas.--Pinnacle Financial Services Inc., Saint Joseph, MI; *U.S. Public*, pg. 1297

Koling, Barry, Sr. V.P.-Corp. Commun.--Crestar Financial Corporation, Richmond, VA; *U.S. Public*, pg. 458

Koll, Leslie A., Sr. V.P.-Mktg.--Jenny Craig, Inc., La Jolla, CA; *U.S. Public*, pg. 926

Kolle, Peter O., Sr. V.P.--Vereinsbank Capital Corporation, New York, NY; *Int'l*, pg. 180

Koller, Gerald, Sr. V.P.--Banque Cantonale Vaudoise, Lausanne, Switzerland; *Int'l*, pg. 160

Kollmeyer, Kenneth S., Sr. V.P.-Opers.--Moore Medical Corp., New Britain, CT; *U.S. Public*, pg. 1128

Koltochnik, Zvi, Sr. V.P.-Northern District--The Israel Electric Corporation Ltd., Haifa, Israel; *Int'l*, pg. 690

Komejan, Maryam, Sr. V.P.-Corp. Admin. & Corp. Sec.--Donnelly Corporation, Holland, MI; *U.S. Public*, pg. 519

Komives, M., Sr. V.P. & Consulting Dir.--Howard, Merrell & Partners, Inc., Raleigh, NC; *U.S. Private*, pg. 542

Konczakowski, Peter, Sr. V.P.-Mktg.--National City Bank, Pennsylvania, Pittsburgh, PA; *U.S. Public*, pg. 1154

Kondo, Shinji, Sr. V.P. & Dir.--Kodansha Ltd., Tokyo, Japan; *Int'l*, pg. 742

Konecnik, Kenneth, Sr. V.P.-Creative Services--Creative Marketing International Corp., West Chicago, IL; *U.S. Private*, pg. 287

Konen, Mark E., Sr. V.P. & Corp. Actuary--Jefferson-Pilot Corporation, Greensboro, NC; *U.S. Public*, pg. 925

Koning, E.W., Sr. V.P.-Investments--AEGON Nederland N.V., Hague, Netherlands; *Int'l*, pg. 26

Konishi, H., Sr. V.P.--Mitsubishi International Corporation, New York, NY; *Int'l*, pg. 871

Konkol, Janice R., Sr. V.P.--TCF Bank Wisconsin, Milwaukee, WI; *U.S. Public*, pg. 1554

Konney, Paul E., Sr. V.P., Gen. Counsel & Sec.--Quaker State Corporation, Irving, TX; *U.S. Public*, pg. 1348

Kono, Peggy, Sr. V.P. & Mngmt. Supvr.--Dailey & Associates, West Hollywood, CA; *U.S. Public*, pg. 909

Konopka, John S., Sr. V.P.-Construction--Spaulding & Slye, Boston, MA; *U.S. Private*, pg. 1021

Konowitz, Thomas J., Sr. V.P.-Mktg.--New Jersey Natural Gas Co., Wall, NJ; *U.S. Public*, pg. 1172

Konrad, Max, Dr., Sr. V.P.-Domestic Commercial Banking, Cashiers--Liechtenstein Global Trust Limited, Vaduz, Liechtenstein; *Int'l*, pg. 809

Konradt, Joseph, Sr. V.P.-Sls.--First Federal Capital Corp., La Crosse, WI; *U.S. Public*, pg. 632

Konstantin, Peter, Dr., Sr. V.P.-Res. & Devel.--Gelman Sciences, Inc., Ann Arbor, MI; *U.S. Public*, pg. 1253

Kontomerkos, Andrew, Sr. V.P.-Hardware Engnrng. & Production--Executone Information Systems, Inc., Milford, CT; *U.S. Public*, pg. 599

Kontos, Mark W., Chief Fin. Officer, Sr. V.P. & Treas.--Battelle Memorial Institute, Columbus, OH; *U.S. Private*, pg. 123

Konviser, Arthur, Sr. V.P.-Pub. Affairs--Shoppers Drug Mart, Ltd., Toronto, Canada; *Int'l*, pg. 112

Kooluris, George, Sr. V.P.-Corp. Devel.--Bristol-Myers Squibb Company, New York, NY; *U.S. Public*, pg. 253

Koon, Jerry, Sr. V.P.-Fin.--Physicians Mutual Insurance Co., Omaha, NE; *U.S. Private*, pg. 864

Koonce, Paul D., Sr. V.P.--Sonat Energy Services Company, Birmingham, AL; *U.S. Public*, pg. 1485

Kooyman, S.P.; Sr. V.P. & Gen. Mgr.--VNU USA, Inc., New York, NY; *Int'l*, pg. 1447

Kopchinsky, John, Sr. Partner-Fin.--J. Walter Thompson Company, New York, NY; *Int'l*, pg. 1483

Kopec, Chet, Chief Fin. Officer, Sr. V.P. & Treas.--Michigan Wheel Corporation, Grand Rapids, MI; *U.S. Private*, pg. 741

Kopec, Frank, Sr. V.P., Media Dir.--EJL Advertising/Houston, Houston, TX; *U.S. Private*, pg. 673

Kopf, Claire M., Sr. V.P.--Manufacturers & Traders Trust Company, Buffalo, NY; *U.S. Public*, pg. 631

Koponen, Matti, Sr. V.P.-Environ. Affairs--Outokumpu Oyj, Espoo, Finland; *Int'l*, pg. 1015

Kopp, Marvin J., Sr. V.P.-Human Resources--Hardee's Food Systems, Inc., Rocky Mount, NC; *U.S. Public*, pg. 278

Kopycinski, Walter L., Sr. V.P.--Prime Bancshares Inc., Houston, TX; *U.S. Public*, pg. 1326

Korn, Joel, Sr. V.P. & Area Gen. Mgr.--Bank of America NT&SA, Sao Paulo, Brazil; *U.S. Public*, pg. 182

Kornblau, Barry M., Sr. V.P.-Opers.--United Dominion Realty Trust, Inc., Richmond, VA; *U.S. Public*, pg. 1677

Kornich, H., Sr. V.P.-Escalator Bus.--Kone Corporation, Helsinki, Finland; *Int'l*, pg. 746

Korpisaari, Hannu, Sr. V.P. & Controller--Valmet Corporation, Helsinki, Finland; *Int'l*, pg. 1447

Korstange, Jason E., Sr. V.P.--TCF Bank Minnesota FSB, Minneapolis, MN; *U.S. Public*, pg. 1554

Korte, Clifford S., Sr. V.P.-Underwriting--Fortis Benefits Insurance Company, Kansas City, MO; *Int'l*, pg. 499

Kosche, Peter C., Sr. V.P.-Corp. Affairs--Olin Corporation, Norwalk, CT; *U.S. Public*, pg. 1218

Koskinen, Erkki, Sr. V.P.--W. Rosenlew Ltd., Helsinki, Finland; *Int'l*, pg. 1428

Koskinen, Jouko, Sr. V.P.--Rauma Ltd., Helsinki, Finland; *Int'l*, pg. 1428

Kossler, Hans, Sr. V.P.-Opers.--Stevens International, Inc., Fort Worth, TX; *U.S. Public*, pg. 1517

Kosten, Bart J., Sr. V.P.-Fortis Long Term Care--Time Insurance, Milwaukee, WI; *Int'l*, pg. 499

Koster, Elaine, Sr. V.P., Publisher-Dutton/Signet--Penguin Putnam Inc., New York, NY; *Int'l*, pg. 1027

Kosterman, Gayle P., Sr. V.P.-Worldwide H.R.--S.C. Johnson & Son, Inc., Racine, WI; *U.S. Private*, pg. 592

Kotsonis, James N., Chief Fin. Officer, Sr. V.P. & Chief Actuary--Manhattan Life Insurance Company, Cincinnati, OH; *U.S. Private*, pg. 1118

Kottler, Bob, Sr. V.P.--Hibernia Corporation, New Orleans, LA; *U.S. Public*, pg. 825

Kottonen, Hannu, Sr. V.P.-Fin.--Huhtamaki Oy, Espoo, Finland; *Int'l*, pg. 638

Kotz, Richard P., Sr. V.P.-Acct. Mngmt.--Grey Advertising Inc., New York, NY; *U.S. Public*, pg. 764

Koumantzelis, Arthur G., Chief Fin. Officer & Sr. V.P.--Cumberland Farms, Inc., Canton, MA; *U.S. Private*, pg. 295

Kounelias, Christina, Sr. V.P.-Publicity & Promotions--New Line Cinema Corporation, New York, NY; *U.S. Public*, pg. 1614

Kovach, Gerald J., Sr. V.P.-Govt. Rels.--MCI Communications Corp., Atlanta, GA; *U.S. Public*, pg. 1023

Koval, Donita R., Sr. V.P.-Credit Admin.--Omega Financial Corporation, State College, PA; *U.S. Public*, pg. 1222

Koval, Donita R., Sr. V.P.--Omega Bank, N.A., State College, PA; *U.S. Public*, pg. 1222

Kowalczyk, Barbara S., Sr. V.P. & Dir.-Corp. Plng. & Devel.--Lincoln National Corporation, Fort Wayne, IN; *U.S. Public*, pg. 997

Kowalczyk, Barbara S., Sr. V.P.--Lincoln National (China) Inc., Fort Wayne, IN; *U.S. Public*, pg. 998

Koziol, Chris, Sr. V.P.-Sls.--MicroAge, Inc., Tempe, AZ; *U.S. Public*, pg. 1104

Kozlowski, Don R., Sr. V.P.-Transport Aircraft--McDonnell Aircraft & Missile Systems Div., Berkeley, MO; *U.S. Public*, pg. 241

Kozuki, Tsuneo, Sr. V.P.--Kintetsu World Express, Inc., Tokyo, Japan; *Int'l*, pg. 734

Kraft, Burnell D., Sr. V.P.--Archer Daniels Midland Company (ADM), Decatur, IL; *U.S. Public*, pg. 127

Krain, Dick, Sr. V.P.-Acct. Mngmt.--Grey Advertising Inc., New York, NY; *U.S. Public*, pg. 764

Krakoff, Reed, Sr. V.P. & Chief Mktg. Officer--Coach, New York, NY; *U.S. Public*, pg. 1433

Krakowsky, Philippe, Sr. V.P. & Corp. Communications Dir.--Young & Rubicam Inc., New York, NY; *U.S. Private*, pg. 1196

Krall, Brad M., Sr. V.P.-Centralized Opers.--GTE South Incorporated, Irving, TX; *U.S. Public*, pg. 697

Kramberg, Bernie, Sr. V.P. & Reg. Dir.--Arnold Communications, Inc., Boston, MA; *U.S. Private*, pg. 83

Kramer, Jack, Sr. V.P.-Adv. & Corp. Communications--CVS Corp., Woonsocket, RI; *U.S. Public*, pg. 287

Kramer, Mindy, Sr. V.P.--Edelman Worldwide, Inc., New York, NY; *U.S. Private*, pg. 362

Kramer, Phillip D., Chief Fin. Officer, Sr. V.P. & Treas.--Plains Resources Inc., Houston, TX; *U.S. Public*, pg. 1307

Kranstuber, T. L., Sr. V.P.--Westfield Companies, Westfield Center, OH; *U.S. Private*, pg. 1169

Krant, Robert, Sr. V.P.-Intl. Fin.--City National Corporation, Beverly Hills, CA; *U.S. Public*, pg. 380

Kranzow, Ron, Sr. V.P. & Legal Counsel--Frito-Lay Company, Plano, TX; *U.S. Public*, pg. 1277

Krassenksy, Ron, Sr. V.P.-Sls. & Mktg.--Air Conditioning Co., Inc., Glendale, CA; *U.S. Private*, pg. 28

Krat, Gary W., Sr. V.P.--SunAmerica Inc., Los Angeles, CA; *U.S. Public*, pg. 1532

Kratovil, Edward D., Sr. V.P.--UST Inc., Greenwich, CT; *U.S. Public*, pg. 1660

Kraus, Joseph K., IV, Sr. V.P.-Bus. Devel. & Founder--Excite, Inc., Redwood City, CA; *U.S. Public*, pg. 599

Kraus, Larry, Sr. V.P.-Admin.--Nation's Business, Washington, DC; *U.S. Private*, pg. 788

Kraus, Peter, Ph.D., Sr. V.P.-Res. & Devel./Crop Protection--Bayer Corporation, Pittsburgh, PA; *Int'l*, pg. 172

Krause, Donald L., Sr. V.P. & Controller--Newell Co., Freeport, IL; *U.S. Public*, pg. 1176

Krause, Michael S., Sr. V.P.-Global Opers.--Tambrands Inc., Cincinnati, OH; *U.S. Public*, pg. 1331

Krauss, Axel, Sr. V.P. & Pres.-Best Food Div.--Bestfoods, Englewood Cliffs, NJ; *U.S. Public*, pg. 223

Krauss, Robert A., Sr. V.P.--Gary Steel Co., Inc., Long Beach, CA; *U.S. Private*, pg. 884

Kravets, Alan R., Sr. V.P.--Sheldon Good & Co., Chicago, IL; *U.S. Private*, pg. 463

Kraynick, John A., Sr. V.P.--Engle Homes, Inc., Boca Raton, FL; *U.S. Public*, pg. 583

Kreig, James J., Sr. V.P.--Summit Bancorp, Princeton, NJ; *U.S. Public*, pg. 1527

Kreikemeier, K.G., Sr. V.P.--Sverdrup Corporation, Maryland Heights, MO; *U.S. Private*, pg. 1057

Kreindler, Peter M., Sr. V.P., Gen. Counsel & Sec.--AlliedSignal Inc., Morristown, NJ; *U.S. Public*, pg. 49

Kreissman, Robert, Sr. V.P.--Combe Incorporated, White Plains, NY; *U.S. Private*, pg. 257

Kreitzer, J. Karl, Sr. V.P.--SAFECO Property & Casualty Insurance Companies, Seattle, WA; *U.S. Public*, pg. 1423

Krem, Guy, Sr. V.P. & Branch Mgr.-Frase Valley--Willis Corroon Melling Ltd., White Rock, Canada; *Int'l*, pg. 1509

Kremers, Chuck, Sr. V.P.-Mktg.--Service Merchandise Company, Inc., Brentwood, TN; *U.S. Public*, pg. 1461

Kress, Ricke A., Sr. V.P.-Oper.--Seneca Foods Corporation, Pittsford, NY; *U.S. Public*, pg. 1456

Kreuger, James A., Sr. V.P.-Matls. Mngmt.--Corning Incorporated, Corning, NY; *U.S. Public*, pg. 448

Kreutzjans, Michael J., Sr. V.P.-Systems Devel.--PC Quote, Inc., Chicago, IL; *U.S. Public*, pg. 1240

Krevans, Sarah, Sr. V.P.-Sacramento Valley--Kaiser Permanente, Oakland, CA; *U.S. Private*, pg. 605

Krieble, Jeffrey R., Sr. V.P. & Trust Officer--Merchants National Bank, Terre Haute, IN; *U.S. Public*, pg. 1217

Krieg, Kenneth J., Sr. V.P.--Florists' Mutual Insurance Co., Edwardsville, IL; *U.S. Private*, pg. 415

Krieger, James F., Sr. V.P.--Standard Medical Imaging, Inc., Columbia, MD; *U.S. Private*, pg. 1032

Kriegshauser, Patrick A., Chief Fin. Officer, Sr. V.P. & Treas.--Arch Coal, Inc., Saint Louis, MO; *U.S. Public*, pg. 139

Krill, David G., Sr. V.P. & Mgr.-Comml. Real Estate Loans--First Financial Bank, FSB, Stevens Point, WI; *U.S. Public*, pg. 140

Krill, Katherine Lawther, Sr. V.P. & Gen. Mgr.-Mdse./Ann Taylor Loft--AnnTaylor, Inc., New York, NY; *U.S. Public*, pg. 116

Kring, Gail, Sr. V.P.--Plains Co-op Oil Mill, Lubbock, TX; *U.S. Private*, pg. 868

Kring, Maurice W., Sr. V.P.-Container Board & Packaging--Georgia-Pacific Corporation, Atlanta, GA; *U.S. Public*, pg. 735

Kringel, John G., Sr. V.P.-Hospital Prods.--Abbott Laboratories, Abbott Park, IL; *U.S. Public*, pg. 12

Kringstad, Knut, Sr. V.P.-Res. & Devel.--Norske Skogindustrier A.S, Skogn, Norway; *Int'l*, pg. 965

Krips, W.M., Sr. V.P.-Exploration & Production--Union Texas Petroleum Holdings, Houston, TX; *U.S. Public*, pg. 1669

Krisak, Edward G., Sr. V.P.--Zenith Insurance Company, Woodland Hills, CA; *U.S. Public*, pg. 1791

Krissoff, Robert, Sr. V.P.-Food Store Div.--Murry's, Inc., Upper Marlboro, MD; *U.S. Private*, pg. 768

Kroener, Bix, Sr. V.P.-Mktg. & Sls.--Adaptive Information Systems, Mission Viejo, CA; *Int'l*, pg. 946

Kroneberger, Greg, Sr. V.P.-Sls.--Baltimore Stationery Co./Total Office, Baltimore, MD; *U.S. Private*, pg. 113

Kronfeld, Gary H., Sr. V.P.--Spirite Industries, Inc., Englewood, NJ; *U.S. Private*, pg. 1026

Kroske, Douglas W., Sr. V.P.--Liberty Investment Group, Inc., Greenville, SC; *U.S. Public*, pg. 992

Kruasin, Warawudh, Sr. V.P.--Siam City Bank Public Company Limited, Bangkok, Thailand; *Int'l*, pg. 1239

Krueger, Bob, Sr. V.P.-Engrng.--Centigram Communications Corporation, San Jose, CA; *U.S. Public*, pg. 323

Kruk, Brian, Sr. V.P.--MWCA, Rexburg, ID; *U.S. Public*, pg. 804

Krul, Joseph, Chief Fin. Officer & Sr. V.P.--Standard Federal Bank, Troy, MI; *Int'l*, pg. 10

Krumwiede, Adam, Sr. V.P. & Media Dir.--North Castle Partners Advertising, Inc., Stamford, CT; *U.S. Private*, pg. 804

Krupka, Robert J., Sr. V.P.-Comml. Lending--D & N Financial Corporation, Hancock, MI; *U.S. Public*, pg. 472

Krupka, Robert J., Sr. V.P.-Comml. Lending--D & N Bank, Hancock, MI; *U.S. Public*, pg. 472

Kruse, Ronald, Sr. V.P.--First National Bank of Ohio, Akron, OH; *U.S. Public*, pg. 646

Kuchler, Jacques-Andre, Sr. V.P.-Fin.--SGS Societe Generale de Surveillance Holding S.A., Geneva, Switzerland; *Int'l*, pg. 1153

Kuckro, Lee G., Sr. V.P., Gen. Counsel & Sec.--The Advest Group, Inc., Hartford, CT; *U.S. Public*, pg. 23

Kudo, Hironaka, Sr. Mng. Dir.-Gen. Affairs--Ito-Yokado Co., Ltd., Tokyo, Japan; *Int'l*, pg. 693

Kuechenmeister, Joseph P., Sr. V.P. & Dir.-Mktg.--AFLAC Incorporated, Columbus, GA; *U.S. Public*, pg. 28

Kuechenmeister, Karl, Sr. V.P.-One World Entertainment--MTV Networks, New York, NY; *U.S. Private*, pg. 779

Kuelbs, John T., Sr. V.P.-Legal--Raytheon Systems Company, Arlington, VA; *U.S. Public*, pg. 1364

Kuenstler, Walt, Sr. V.P.-Acct. Mngmt.--Grant Marketing Communications, Ardmore, PA; *U.S. Private*, pg. 470

Kuenstler, Walt, Sr. V.P.-Acct. Grp. Mngmt.--Kingswood Interactive, Ardmore, PA; *U.S. Private*, pg. 622

Kuenstler, Walt C., Sr. V.P.-Acct. Mngmt.--Kingswood Advertising, Inc., Ardmore, PA; *U.S. Private*, pg. 622

Kugler, Adam C., Sr. V.P.--Manufacturers & Traders Trust Company, Buffalo, NY; *U.S. Public*, pg. 631

Kuhlmann, F. Mark, Sr. V.P.-Admin. & Gen. Counsel--McDonnell Aircraft & Missile Systems Div., Berkeley, MO; *U.S. Public*, pg. 241

Kuhn, Frank, Sr. V.P.-Sls.--INX International, Milwaukee, WI; *Int'l*, pg. 1311

Kuhn, Kelly L., Chief Oper. Officer & Sr. V.P.--Arrington Travel Center Inc., Chicago, IL; *U.S. Private*, pg. 85

Kuhn, Michael, Sr. V.P.-Media Div.--Polygram N.V., Baarn, Netherlands; *Int'l*, pg. 1051

Kuhn, Tom, Sr. V.P. & Mngmt. Supvr.--Lois/EJL New York, New York, NY; *U.S. Public*, pg. 1011

Kuhr, Dennis, Sr. V.P. & Creative Dir.--Dailey & Associates, West Hollywood, CA; *U.S. Public*, pg. 909

Kuk, Kenneth U., Sr. V.P.-Strategic Mktg.--ReliaStar Financial Corp., Minneapolis, MN; *U.S. Public*, pg. 1375

Kuller, Alan S., Sr. V.P.-Real Estate--Caldor, Inc., Norwalk, CT; *U.S. Public*, pg. 292

Kumagai, Steven C., Sr. V.P.-Field Mngmt. & Bus. Systems--American Express Financial Advisor, Minneapolis, MN; *U.S. Public*, pg. 73

Kumar, Alex, Sr. V.P.-Intl. Opers.--Bausch & Lomb Incorporated, Rochester, NY; *U.S. Public*, pg. 194

Kumiega, Kim, Sr. V.P.--Edelman Public Relations Worldwide, Chicago, IL; *U.S. Private*, pg. 362

Kumpf, Michael S., Sr. V.P.--Transact Technologies Incorporated, Wallingford, CT; *U.S. Public*, pg. 1629

Kunkel, Bill, Sr. V.P.-Intl. Media Sls.--CBS Enterprises Division, New York, NY; *U.S. Public*, pg. 274

Kunkel, David, Sr. V.P.-Mfg.--Ford Meter Box Company, Wabash, IN; *U.S. Private*, pg. 418

Kunkel, O., Sr. V.P.-Fin.--SGS Societe Generale de Surveillance Holding S.A., Geneva, Switzerland; *Int'l*, pg. 1153
Kuntzendorf, Robert, Sr. V.P.-Opers.--Vanstar Corporation, Pleasanton, CA; *U.S. Public*, pg. 1708
Kunz, Gerry J., Sr. V.P.-Intl., Large Accts. & Ocean Marine--Willis Corroon Corp. of South Carolina, Greenville, SC; *Int'l*, pg. 1507
Kunz, Heidi, Chief Fin. Officer & Sr. V.P.--ITT Industries, Inc., White Plains, NY; *U.S. Public*, pg. 859
Kuoni, Charles, Chief Fin. Officer & Sr. V.P.--Coastal Physician Group, Inc., Durham, NC; *U.S. Public*, pg. 391
Kupper, Randy, Sr. V.P.-MIS--Interval International Inc., Miami, FL; *U.S. Public*, pg. 320
Kurai, Tomio, Sr. V.P.--Nissan Mutual Life Insurance Company, Tokyo, Japan; *Int'l*, pg. 945
Kurakake, Mistuo, Sr. V.P.--Fanuc Ltd., Yamanashi, Japan; *Int'l*, pg. 477
Kurcz, Lottie A., Sr. V.P.-Risk Prods.--First Health Group Corp., Downers Grove, IL; *U.S. Public*, pg. 635
Kurgan, G. John, Sr. V.P.--Michael Baker, Jr., Inc., Beaver, PA; *U.S. Public*, pg. 168
Kurgan, Ira, Sr. V.P.-Bus. Affairs--Fox Broadcasting Company (FBC), Beverly Hills, CA; *Int'l*, pg. 926
Kurlander, Craig M., Sr. V.P.-Stores--L. Luria & Son, Inc., Medley, FL; *U.S. Public*, pg. 1020
Kurlander, Lawrence T., Chief Admin. Officer & Sr. V.P.--Newmont Mining Corporation, Denver, CO; *U.S. Public*, pg. 1178
Kuroki, Sharon, Sr. V.P.-Music Club. Mktg.--Columbia House Music Club, New York, NY; *Int'l*, pg. 1281
Kurosu, Raymond, Sr. V.P. & Mgr.-Opers. Div.--Central Pacific Bank, Honolulu, HI; *U.S. Public*, pg. 283
Kurowski, Bettina, Sr. V.P.-Managed Care--Salick Health Care, Inc., Los Angeles, CA; *Int'l*, pg. 1524
Kurpis, Joseph J., Sr. V.P.-Indus. & Intl. Sls.--Stearns Manufacturing Company, Sauk Rapids, MN; *U.S. Public*, pg. 940
Kurz, Rick, Chief Mktg. Officer & Sr. V.P.-Mktg.--ADVO, Inc., Windsor, CT; *U.S. Public*, pg. 23
Kurzweil, Larry, Sr. V.P. & Gen. Mgr.-Universal City Walk--Universal Studios Recreation Services Group, Universal City, CA; *Int'l*, pg. 1216
Kustasayanon, Bhisip, Sr. V.P.--Thai Airways International Ltd., Bangkok, Thailand; *Int'l*, pg. 1381
Kuta, David L., Sr. V.P.--Harvard Industries, Inc., Tampa, FL; *U.S. Public*, pg. 796
Kutsche, Ron A., Sr. V.P.--BetzDearborn Inc., Trevose, PA; *U.S. Public*, pg. 226
Kuwano, Fumio, Mng. Dir. & Sr. V.P.-Information Sys.--Japan Airlines Company, Ltd., Tokyo, Japan; *Int'l*, pg. 699
Kux, Johannes, Sr. V.P. & Mgr.--DG Bank-New York, New York, NY; *Int'l*, pg. 352
Kuzma, David R., Chief Fin. Officer, Sr. V.P. & Treas.--Enova Corp, San Diego, CA; *U.S. Public*, pg. 583
Kuzma, David R., Chief Fin. Officer, Sr. V.P. & Treas.--San Diego Gas & Electric Company, San Diego, CA; *U.S. Public*, pg. 584
Kvarnback, Bengt, Sr. Exec. V.P.--Atlas Copco AB, Stockholm, Sweden; *Int'l*, pg. 95
Kwitoski, Stephen A., Sr. V.P.-Loan & Mktg. Admin.--Santa Monica Bank, Santa Monica, CA; *U.S. Public*, pg. 1757
Kyger, Frank T., Sr. V.P.--Anderson Electric, Inc., Springfield, IL; *U.S. Private*, pg. 72
Kyle, Terrence W., Sr. V.P., Treas. & Asst. Sec.--Shared Medical Systems Corporation, Malvern, PA; *U.S. Public*, pg. 1463
Kynard, Colleen W., Sr. V.P.--Total System Services, Inc., Columbus, GA; *U.S. Public*, pg. 1550
Kyogoku, Tetsuo, Sr. V.P.--Sumitomo Sitix Corporation, Amagasaki, Japan; *Int'l*, pg. 1317
La Duc, John T., Sr. V.P.--Maxxam Inc., Houston, TX; *U.S. Public*, pg. 1062
La Forgia, Robert, Sr. V.P. & Controller--Hilton Hotels Corporation, Beverly Hills, CA; *U.S. Public*, pg. 828
La Monte, Steve, Sr. V.P.-Mktg.--Schering-Plough Healthcare Products Inc., Liberty Corner, NJ; *U.S. Public*, *pg. 1438*
Labash, Lawrence W., Sr. V.P.--Market Facts, Inc., Arlington Heights, IL; *U.S. Public*, pg. 1046
LaBau, Melissa, Sr. V.P.-Plng. & Allocation--AnnTaylor, Inc., New York, NY; *U.S. Public*, pg. 116
Labona, Bruce, Chief Tech. Officer & Sr. V.P.--Crawford & Company, Atlanta, GA; *U.S. Public*, pg. 458
Labonte, Michel, Sr. V.P.-Fin.--National Bank of Canada, Montreal, Canada; *Int'l*, pg. 907
Labourer, Marlene M., Sr. V.P.--Hibernia Corporation, New Orleans, LA; *U.S. Public*, pg. 825
Labrecque, Richard J., Sr. V.P.--ITT Industries, Inc., White Plains, NY; *U.S. Public*, pg. 859
Lacey, L.A., Jr., Sr. V.P.--Ingram Distribution Group Inc., La Vergne, TN; *U.S. Private*, pg. 563
Lach, Michael L., Sr. V.P.-Information Systems--Allergan, Inc., Irvine, CA; *U.S. Public*, pg. 46
Lachapelle, A.D., Sr. V.P.-Mktg. & Sls.--Reed & Barton Corporation, Taunton, MA; *U.S. Private*, pg. 916
Lackey, E. Hugh, Sr. V.P.-Opers.--Town & Country Fine Jewelry Group, Inc., Chelsea, MA; *U.S. Public*, pg. 1625
Lacombe, Michel, Sr. V.P. & Pres.-Microsoft Europe--Microsoft Corporation, Redmond, WA; *U.S. Public*, pg. 1107
Lacy, Ken, Sr. V.P.-Info. Svcs.--United Parcel Service of America, Inc., Atlanta, GA; *U.S. Private*, pg. 1123
Ladd, David, Sr. V.P.-Production--Metro-Goldwyn-Mayer Pictures, Inc., Santa Monica, CA; *U.S. Public*, pg. 1102
Ladd, William, Sr. V.P.-Bus. Devel.--Sithe Energies, Inc., New York, NY; *U.S. Private*, pg. 1004
Ladnier, Cheryl Jan, Sr. V.P.-Mktg. & Corp. Communication--The Bon Ton Stores, Inc., York, PA; *U.S. Public*, pg. 244
Laeng, Peter, Reg. Mgr.-Europe/Africa--Sika Finanz AG, Baar, Switzerland; *Int'l*, pg. 1248
Laferriere, Roland A., Sr. V.P.-Info. Svcs.--BJ's Wholesale Club, Inc., Natick, MA; *U.S. Public*, pg. 162
Lafferty, James F., Sr. V.P.--Henkels & McCoy, Inc., Blue Bell, PA; *U.S. Private*, pg. 522
Lagamarsino, Louis, Sr. V.P.--Huitt-Zollars, Inc., Dallas, TX; *U.S. Private*, pg. 547
Lagarhus, Otto, Sr. V.P.-Prod. Div.--Scandinavian Airlines System (SAS), Solna, Sweden; *Int'l*, pg. 1201
Lager, Esa, Sr. V.P. & Treas.--Outokumpu Oyj, Espoo, Finland; *Int'l*, pg. 1015
Lagergren, Bo, Sr. V.P.-H.R.--Trygg-Hansa, Stockholm, Sweden; *Int'l*, pg. 1425
LaGrone, F. Scott, Sr. V.P.--Radian International LLC, Austin, TX; *U.S. Public*, pg. 522
Lahey, Edward V., Jr., Sr. V.P., Gen. Counsel & Sec.--PepsiCo, Inc., Purchase, NY; *U.S. Public*, pg. 1276
Lahey, Joseph P., Sr. V.P.--Kaneb Services, Inc., Richardson, TX; *U.S. Public*, pg. 942
LaHood, Steve, Sr. V.P.-Opers.--Henry Schein, Inc., Melville, NY; *U.S. Public*, pg. 1437
Lai, Jeffrey R., Sr. V.P.-Bus. & Legal Affairs--Playboy Entertainment Group, Inc., Beverly Hills, CA; *U.S. Public*, *pg. 1310*
Lai, N.C. Joseph, Ph.D., Vice Chm. & Sr. V.P.--Criticare Systems, Inc., Waukesha, WI; *U.S. Public*, pg. 459
Lai, Shiow-Shyong, Sr. V.P. & Gen. Mgr.--The International Commercial Bank of China, Tokyo, Japan; *Int'l*, pg. 683
Lail, Charlie J., Sr. V.P.-Opers./AGL--AGL Resources, Atlanta, GA; *U.S. Public*, pg. 6
Lailey, D.J., Sr. V.P.-Pipeline & Tubular Prods.--Shaw Industries Ltd., Etobicoke, Canada; *Int'l*, pg. 1231
Laing, Earl D., Sr. V.P.-Southeaster Regl. Mgr.--A.G. Edwards & Sons, Inc., Saint Louis, MO; *U.S. Public*, pg. 565
Laird, E.T., Sr. V.P. & Mgr.-Atlanta Sls.--Jefferies & Company, Inc., Los Angeles, CA; *U.S. Public*, pg. 925
Laita, Luis, Sr. V.P.--Banco Santander, Madrid, Spain; *Int'l*, pg. 143
Lake, Ralph B., Sr. V.P., Gen. Counsel & Sec.--Promus Hotel Corporation, Memphis, TN; *U.S. Public*, pg. 1335
Lalik, Sharron, Sr. V.P. & Local Media Plng. Dir.-Coca Cola--DMB&B New York, New York, NY; *U.S. Private*, pg. 302
Lam, Carol K., Sr. V.P.-Properties--Servco Pacific Inc., Honolulu, HI; *U.S. Private*, pg. 986
Lam, Rick, Sr. V.P. & Dir.-Prod. & Services--Columbine JDS Systems, Inc., Denver, CO; *U.S. Public*, pg. 228
Lam, Ron, Chief Fin. Officer & Sr. V.P.--Universal Studios Hollywood, Universal City, CA; *Int'l*, pg. 1216
LaMacchia, Anthony, Sr. V.P.-Oper.--Salick Health Care, Inc., Los Angeles, CA; *Int'l*, pg. 1524
Lamadrid, Carlos, Chief Fin. Officer, Sr. V.P. & Sec.--Pope & Talbot, Inc., Portland, OR; *U.S. Public*, pg. 1316
Lamb, Ed, Chief Fin. Officer & Sr. V.P.--Fremont Financial Corporation, Santa Monica, CA; *U.S. Public*, pg. 681
Lamb, Kent W., Sr. V.P. & Controller--Western National Life Insurance Co., Houston, TX; *U.S. Public*, pg. 76
Lamb, William G., Sr. V.P. & Sr. Lending Officer--Elyria Savings & Trust National Bank, Elyria, OH; *U.S. Public*, pg. 646
Lambert, James, Sr. V.P.-Opers. & Total Quality--GenCorp Inc., Fairlawn, OH; *U.S. Public*, pg. 705
Lambert, Keith M., Sr. V.P.-Strategy & Devel.--Foster's Brewing Group Limited, Southbank, Australia; *Int'l*, pg. 500
Lambert, Mark, Sr. V.P.-Sls. & Mktg.--Freightliner Corp., Portland, OR; *Int'l*, pg. 368
Lambert, Michael D., Sr. V.P.-Server Grp.--Dell Computer Corporation, Round Rock, TX; *U.S. Public*, pg. 495
Lamborn, Earle, Sr. V.P.-Drilling--Unit Corporation, Tulsa, OK; *U.S. Public*, pg. 1672
Lamborn, Earle, Sr. V.P.--Unit Drilling Company, Tulsa, OK; *U.S. Public*, pg. 1672
Lamendola, Robert, Sr. V.P.-Fidelity/Surety--United States Fidelity & Guaranty Company, Baltimore, MD; *U.S. Public*, pg. 1659
Lamer, Allan J., Exec. V.P.-Sls. & Mktg.--Marine Travelift, Inc., Sturgeon Bay, WI; *U.S. Private*, pg. 703
Lamere, David F., Sr. V.P.-Investment Mngmt. & Trust--Mellon Bank Corporation, Pittsburgh, PA; *U.S. Public*, pg. 1084
Lamm, Douglas, Sr. V.P. & Gen. Mgr.-Mdse.--The Bon Ton Stores, Inc., York, PA; *U.S. Public*, pg. 244
Lamm, Elaine A., Sr. V.P.--Erie Family Life Insurance Company, Erie, PA; *U.S. Public*, pg. 590
Lamm, Kenneth R., Sr. V.P.--Cramer-Krasselt, Milwaukee, WI; *U.S. Private*, pg. 286
Lamm, Lloyd H., Sr. V.P., Chief Oper. Officer & Sec.--The Metropolitan Savings Bank of Ohio, Youngstown, OH; *U.S. Public*, pg. 608
Lammert, Richard A., Sr. V.P., Gen. Counsel & Sec.--First Empire State Corporation, Buffalo, NY; *U.S. Public*, pg. 631
Lammert, Richard A., Sr. V.P.--Manufacturers & Traders Trust Company, Buffalo, NY; *U.S. Public*, pg. 631
Lammi, Edward, Sr. V.P.-Tape Production--Columbia TriStar Television, Culver City, CA; *Int'l*, pg. 1282
Land, Ron, Sr. V.P.-Mass Market Book & Bible Sls.--Thomas Nelson Inc., Nashville, TN; *U.S. Public*, pg. 1167
Land, Thomas K., Chief Fin. Officer, Sr. V.P. & Asst. Sec.--Santa Fe Gaming Corporation, Las Vegas, NV; *U.S. Public*, pg. 1432
Landau, Yair, Sr. V.P.-Corp. Devel. & Strategic Plng.--Sony Pictures Entertainment, Culver City, CA; *Int'l*, pg. 1281
Lande, Sabra, Sr. V.P.-Retail Stores & Licensing--Giorgio Beverly Hills, Santa Monica, CA; *U.S. Public*, pg. 1331
Landers, Thomas A., Sr. V.P. & Dir.-Market Res.--Municipal Bond Investors Assurance Corporation, Armonk, NY; *U.S. Public*, pg. 1023
Landew, Barry S., Sr. V.P. & Dir.-Corp. Devel.--SRA International Inc., Arlington, VA; *U.S. Private*, pg. 957
Landgraf, John W., Sr. V.P.-Commercial Real Estate Div. & Japan Bus. Devel.--First Hawaiian Bank, Honolulu, HI; *U.S. Public*, pg. 634
Landin, Bo, Sr. V.P.-Asia--Telefonaktiebolaget LM Ericsson, Stockholm, Sweden; *Int'l*, pg. 1363
Landis, Dirk B., Sr. V.P.-Corp. Banking--Mellon Bank Corporation, Pittsburgh, PA; *U.S. Public*, pg. 1084
Landry, Gregory J., Sr. V.P.-Opers.--Jacobs Engineering Group Inc., Pasadena, CA; *U.S. Public*, pg. 921
Landsberg, George, Sr. V.P.-European Opers.--Medex Inc., Hilliard, OH; *U.S. Public*, pg. 689
Landskron, Jerry, Sr. V.P.-Admin.--Pioneer New Media Technologies, Long Beach, CA; *U.S. Private*, pg. 866
Landy, Richard, Chief Admin. Officer & Sr. V.P.--Entergy Corporation, New Orleans, LA; *U.S. Public*, pg. 585
Lane, Bill, Pres.-Systems Grp. & Sr. V.P.--Stackig Advertising and Public Relations, Mc Lean, VA; *U.S. Private*, pg. 1028
Lane, Jeffrey H., Sr. V.P., Gen. Counsel & Sec.--MGIC Investment Corporation, Milwaukee, WI; *U.S. Public*, pg. 1026
Lane, Jeffrey H., Sr. V.P., Gen. Counsel & Sec.--Mortgage Guaranty Insurance Corporation, Milwaukee, WI; *U.S. Public*, pg. 1026
Lane, John S., Sr. V.P.-Investments--Sun Life Assurance Company of Canada, Toronto, Canada; *Int'l*, pg. 1318
Lane, Laurence F., Sr. V.P.-Regulatory Affairs--NovaCare Inc., King of Prussia, PA; *U.S. Public*, pg. 1203
Lane, Molly, Sr. V.P.--Cline, Davis & Mann, Inc., New York, NY; *U.S. Private*, pg. 246
Lane, Robert M., Sr. V.P.-Trust--PNC Bank, Camp Hill, PA; *U.S. Public*, pg. 1243
Lane, Robert W., Chief Fin. Officer & Sr. V.P.-Fin./Tax/Acctg.--Deere & Company, Moline, IL; *U.S. Public*, pg. 491
Laney, Chris, Sr. V.P.-PSO--Vanstar Corporation, Pleasanton, CA; *U.S. Public*, pg. 1708
Laney, Sandra E., Chief Admin. Officer & Sr. V.P.--Chemed Corporation, Cincinnati, OH; *U.S. Public*, pg. 343
Lang, Edward J., Sr. V.P.-Mfg. Opers.--R.J. Reynolds Tobacco Intl., Inc., Geneva, Switzerland; *U.S. Public*, pg. 1355
Lang, Eugene A., Jr., Sr. V.P. & Gen. Counsel--Barrett Resources Corporation, Denver, CO; *U.S. Public*, pg. 191
Lang, Laurie, Sr. V.P.-Strategic Mktg.--The Walt Disney Company, Burbank, CA; *U.S. Public*, pg. 511
Lang, Paul L., Sr. V.P.-Customer Service Business Group--Illinois Power Company, Decatur, IL; *U.S. Public*, pg. 869
Lang, Roger M., Sr. V.P.-Preconstruction--The Turner Corporation, New York, NY; *U.S. Public*, pg. 1645
Lang, Rudolph E., Jr., Chief Fin. Officer & Sr. V.P.--Litton Industries, Inc., Woodland Hills, CA; *U.S. Public*, pg. 1002
Langer, David, Sr. V.P.--City Gas Company of Florida, Hialeah, FL; *U.S. Public*, pg. 1147
Langer, Hart, Sr. V.P.-Flight Opers.--United Air Lines, Inc., Elk Grove Village, IL; *U.S. Public*, pg. 1653
Langer, Hart A., Sr. V.P.-Flight Opers.--UAL Corporation, Elk Grove Village, IL; *U.S. Public*, pg. 1652
Langer, Ralph, Sr. V.P.-Exec. Editor--The Dallas Morning News, Inc., Dallas, TX; *U.S. Public*, pg. 209
Langford, Stephen J., Sr. V.P.-Mdsg.--Shoppers Drug Mart, Ltd., Toronto, Canada; *Int'l*, pg. 112
Langford, Travis, Sr. V.P.-Upholstery--Bassett Furniture Industries, Incorporated, Bassett, VA; *U.S. Public*, pg. 193
Langlais, Arthur R., Sr. V.P.-Acctg.--Citizens Trust Company, Providence, RI; *Int'l*, pg. 1132
Langley, Glenn C., Sr. V.P.-H.R.--American National Insurance Company, Galveston, TX; *U.S. Public*, pg. 87
Langman, Allen, Sr. V.P. & Treas.--Arnhold and S. Bleichroeder, Inc., New York, NY; *U.S. Private*, pg. 83
Langner, David, Sr. V.P.--Republic National Bank of New York (U.K.), London, United Kingdom; *U.S. Public*, pg. 1381
Langston-Carter, Brian, Sr. V.P.-Entertainment--Princess Cruise Lines, Los Angeles, CA; *Int'l*, pg. 1035
Langston, N. Mitchell, Sr. V.P.-Data Processing--North Fork Bancorporation, Inc., Melville, NY; *U.S. Public*, pg. 1194
Lankford, H. Raymond, Jr., Sr. V.P.-Alternative Mkts. Opers.--W.R. Berkley Corporation, Greenwich, CT; *U.S. Public*, pg. 215
Lankford, Thomas E., Sr. V.P.-Opers.--Sysco Corporation, Houston, TX; *U.S. Public*, pg. 1550
Lannie, P. Anthony, Sr. V.P., Gen. Counsel & Sec.--Tejas Gas Corporation, Houston, TX; *Int'l*, pg. 1136
Lanza, Shelley B., Sr. V.P.-Law & Corp. Affairs & Gen. Counsel--Starbucks Coffee Company, Seattle, WA; *U.S. Public*, pg. 1510
Lapassat, Guy, Sr. V.P.-Info. Tech.--Credit Commercial de France, Paris, France; *Int'l*, pg. 341
Lapiejko, Kenneth J., Chief Fin. Officer & Sr. V.P.--R.J. Reynolds Tobacco Company, Winston Salem, NC; *U.S. Public*, pg. 1355
Lapin, Jeff, Sr. V.P.-Magazine Div., V.P. & Gen. Mgr.-Magazine & Educational--F & W Publications, Inc., Cincinnati, OH; *U.S. Private*, pg. 388
Lapine, Jay M., Sr. V.P., Gen. Counel & Asst. Sec.--HBOC, Atlanta, GA; *U.S. Public*, pg. 770
LaPointe, Gary, Sr. V.P. & Midwest Media Dir.--Fahlgren, Dublin, OH; *U.S. Private*, pg. 391
LaPointe, Paul R., Sr. V.P.-Procurement--Tennessee Valley Authority, Knoxville, TN; *U.S. Public*, pg. 1580
LaPorta, Scott A., Sr. V.P. & Treas.--Hilton Hotels Corporation, Beverly Hills, CA; *U.S. Public*, pg. 828
Lappala, Eric G., Sr. V.P.--Harding Lawson Associates Group, Inc., Novato, CA; *U.S. Public*, pg. 785
Laraocque, Ghislaine, Sr. V.P.-Quebec Gas Distrib.--Gaz Metropolitain & Company, Montreal, Canada; *Int'l*, pg. 541
Laraya, Rogelio G., Sr. V.P.-Fin. & Treas.--Benguet Corporation, Manila, Philippines; *Int'l*, pg. 186
Largent, William H., Chief Fin. Officer & Sr. V.P.--Applied Innovation Inc., Dublin, OH; *U.S. Public*, pg. 123
Larinto, Vincent, Sr. V.P.-Sls.--20th Century Fox Home Entertainment, Los Angeles, CA; *U.S. Public*, pg. 275

Larinto, Vincent, Sr. V.P.-Sls.--20th Century Fox Home Entertainment, Los Angeles, CA; *Int'l*, pg. 926

Larkin, A. C., Sr. V.P.-Fin. & Investor Rels.--Foster's Brewing Group Limited, Southbank, Australia; *Int'l*, pg. 500

Larkin, Jay, Sr. V.P.-Sports & Events--Showtime Networks Inc., New York, NY; *U.S. Private*, pg. 779

Larkin, Mary Ellen, Sr. V.P.-Compliance--Central Reserve Life Corporation, Strongsville, OH; *U.S. Public*, pg. 326

Larkins, Thomas F., Sr. V.P., Gen. Counsel & Sec.--L.A. Gear, Inc., Santa Monica, CA; *U.S. Public*, pg. 969

Larmer, Felice L., Sr. V.P.-Investment & Insurance Services--FirstMerit Corporation, Akron, OH; *U.S. Public*, pg. 646

LaRock, Marta, Sr. V.P. & Acct. Plng. Dir.-Insights Grp.--Young & Rubicam New York, New York, NY; *U.S. Private*, pg. 1198

Laron, Moshe, Sr. V.P.-Organization & Logistics--The Israel Electric Corporation Ltd., Haifa, Israel; *Int'l*, pg. 690

Larroucau, Enrique M., Chief Fin. Officer & Sr. V.P.--Destec Energy, Inc., Houston, TX; *U.S. Public*, pg. 1146

Larsen, James T., Sr. V.P. & Cashier--M & I Community State Bank, Eau Claire, WI; *U.S. Public*, pg. 1050

Larsen, Kris, Sr. V.P. & Mng. Dir.--Interbrand Schechter, Chicago, IL; *U.S. Public*, pg. 1224

Larsen, Tom, Sr. V.P.--Desai Capital Management Incorporated, New York, NY; *U.S. Private*, pg. 326

Larsen, Tryave Roed, Sr. V.P.--Det Norske Veritas, Hovik, Norway; *Int'l*, pg. 396

Larsh, Ivan, Sr. V.P.-Opers.--Waukesha Cherry-Burrell, Delavan, WI; *U.S. Public*, pg. 1677

Larson, Eric J., Sr. V.P. & Dir.-Investor Rels.--General Mills, Inc., Minneapolis, MN; *U.S. Public*, pg. 717

Larson, Lloyd J., Sr. V.P.--Stanley Consultants, Inc., Muscatine, IA; *U.S. Private*, pg. 1033

Larson, Mark, Sr. V.P.-Finance & Treas.--Heublein, Inc., Hartford, CT; *Int'l*, pg. 410

Larson, Max J., Sr. V.P.--Firstar Corporation-Iowa, Des Moines, IA; *U.S. Public*, pg. 643

Larsson, Kent A., Sr. V.P.-Mktg. & Sls. Promo.--Consolidated Stores Corp., Columbus, OH; *U.S. Public*, pg. 437

Lartigau, Maurice, Sr. V.P.-Metro New York--Seagram Chateau & Estate Wines Co., New York, NY; *Int'l*, pg. 1215

Lartigue, Henry, Sr. V.P.-Investment Banking--Texas Commerce Bank, Houston, TX; *U.S. Public*, pg. 339

Lartigue, Jean-Bernard, Sr. V.P.-Chemicals--Elf Aquitane, Paris, France; *Int'l*, pg. 444

LaRusso, Anthony C., Sr. V.P.-Elkem North America--Elkem ASA, Oslo, Norway; *Int'l*, pg. 446

LaRusso, David V., Chief Fin. Officer, Sr. V.P.-Fin. & Treas.--ROHN Industries, Inc., Peoria, IL; *U.S. Public*, pg. 1404

Lasalandra, Peter, Sr. V.P.-Fin.--American Institute for Foreign Study, Greenwich, CT; *U.S. Private*, pg. 56

LaSalle, Peter J., Sr. V.P.--Market Facts, Inc., Arlington Heights, IL; *U.S. Public*, pg. 1046

Lasche, Gary, Sr. V.P. & Asst. Treas.--UMB Financial Corporation, Kansas City, MO; *U.S. Public*, pg. 1653

Lash, Fred, Chief Fin. Officer, Sr. V.P. & Treas.--Hooper Holmes Corporation, Basking Ridge, NJ; *U.S. Public*, pg. 835

Lashley, Curtis R., M.D., Sr. V.P.-Client Services--Jefferson-Pilot Life Insurance Co., Greensboro, NC; *U.S. Public*, pg. 926

Lasiter, Paul B., Sr. V.P. & Controller--Imperial Credit Industries, Inc., Torrance, CA; *U.S. Public*, pg. 872

Lasker, Mark F., Sr. V.P.--Howmet Corporation, Greenwich, CT; *U.S. Private*, pg. 213

Lasker, Mark F., Sr. V.P.--Howmet Corporation, Greenwich, CT; *U.S. Public*, pg. 1597

Lasowski, Cathy, Sr. V.P. & Acct. Mng. Dir.--Young & Rubicam New York, New York, NY; *U.S. Private*, pg. 1198

Lasser, Sherman H., Sr. V.P. & Mgr.-Sls.--Brown Group, Inc., Saint Louis, MO; *U.S. Public*, pg. 262

Lassila, Kari, Sr. V.P. & Controller--Outokumpu Oyj, Espoo, Finland; *Int'l*, pg. 1015

Lassman, Franklin J., Sr. V.P.-Eastern Hemisphere Opers.--QMS, Inc., Mobile, AL; *U.S. Public*, pg. 1346

Lassman, Ira, Sr. V.P. & Exec. Producer--DMB&B New York, New York, NY; *U.S. Private*, pg. 302

Lastihenos, Jerry, Sr. V.P.--Hazen & Sawyer, New York, NY; *U.S. Private*, pg. 514

Latch, Mark S., Sr. V.P.--BT Financial Corporation, Johnstown, PA; *U.S. Public*, pg. 163

Latek, Robert, Sr. V.P. & Controller--Energy Absorption Systems, Inc., Chicago, IL; *U.S. Public*, pg. 1353

Lathe, Timothy J., Sr. V.P. & Mgr.-Multinational Div.--National City Bancorp, Minneapolis, MN; *U.S. Public*, pg. 1153

Latimer, R. Garry, Sr. V.P.-Opers.--Allied Clinical Laboratories, Inc., Nashville, TN; *U.S. Public*, pg. 973

Latorre, Rafael Blanco, Sr. V.P.--Banco Santander Puerto Rico, Hato Rey, PR; *Int'l*, pg. 143

Latrenta, Nicholas D., Sr. V.P.-Bus. Devel.--Metropolitan Life Insurance Co., New York, NY; *U.S. Private*, pg. 737

Latta, Paul I., Sr. V.P. & Dir.-Retail Opers.--Rouse Operating Properties Div., Columbia, MD; *U.S. Public*, pg. 1407

Latta, Paul I., Jr., Sr. V.P. & Dir.-Retail Opers.--The Rouse Company, Columbia, MD; *U.S. Public*, pg. 1407

Latz, Jeanie Sell, Chief Legal Officer & Sr. V.P.-Corp. Services--Kansas City Power & Light Company, Kansas City, MO; *U.S. Public*, pg. 943

Latzer, Richard N., Sr. V.P. & Chief Investment Officer--Transamerica Corporation, San Francisco, CA; *U.S. Public*, pg. 1629

Lau, Joseph, Chief Oper. Officer & Sr. V.P.--IWI Holding Limited, Westmont, IL; *U.S. Public*, pg. 861

Laub, Steven A., Chief Oper. Officer & Sr. V.P.--Lattice Semiconductor Corporation, Hillsboro, OR; *U.S. Public*, pg. 979

Laubenstein, Jerome H., Sr. V.P.-Delivering Member Services--Aid Association for Lutherans, Appleton, WI; *U.S. Private*, pg. 27

Laud, Paul J., Sr. V.P.--CIT Group/Equity Investments, Livingston, NJ; *Int'l*, pg. 360

Laudadio, Mario, Sr. V.P.--SNC-Lavalin Group Inc., Montreal, Canada; *Int'l*, pg. 1161

Lauder, Evelyn H., Sr. V.P.--Estee Lauder Companies Inc., New York, NY; *U.S. Public*, pg. 594

Lauer, Thomas H., Chief Fin. Officer & Sr. V.P.--Advent International, Boston, MA; *U.S. Private*, pg. 22

Lauer, Thomas W., Sr. V.P.--ITT Educational Services, Inc., Indianapolis, IN; *U.S. Public*, pg. 1512

Laufgraben, Allan, Sr. V.P.-Mdsg.--Deb Shops, Inc., Philadelphia, PA; *U.S. Public*, pg. 491

Laughlin, Philip M., Sr. V.P. & Pres.-Cardiac Surgery Bus.--Medtronic, Inc., Minneapolis, MN; *U.S. Public*, pg. 1082

Launer, Leland C., Jr., Sr. V.P.-Fixed-Income Investments--Metropolitan Life Insurance Co., New York, NY; *U.S. Private*, pg. 737

Lauren, Jerry, Sr. V.P.-Mens Design--Polo/Ralph Lauren Corporation, New York, NY; *U.S. Private*, pg. 874

Lause, Dennis C., Sr. V.P.-World--Bourns, Inc., Riverside, CA; *U.S. Private*, pg. 161

Lautenbach, Ned C., Sr. V.P. & Grp. Exec.--International Business Machines Corporation, Armonk, NY; *U.S. Public*, pg. 895

Lautensack Jr., Robert G., Sr. V.P.-Individual Fin.--Phoenix Home Life Mutual Insurance Company, Hartford, CT; *U.S. Private*, pg. 863

Lauterbach, Dennis, Sr. V.P.-Branch Oper.--Montgomery KONE Inc., Moline, IL; *Int'l*, pg. 746

Lauver, E. Eugene, Sr. V.P., Gen. Counsel & Sec.--A.P.S., Inc., Houston, TX; *U.S. Public*, pg. 10

LaVacca, John, Sr. V.P.-Fin. & Admin.--Macmillan/McGraw-Hill School Publishing Company, New York, NY; *U.S. Public*, pg. 1070

Laval, Larry, V.P.-Carpets--William M. Bird & Co., Inc., Charleston, SC; *U.S. Private*, pg. 145

LaValle, John W., Chief Fin. Officer, Sr. V.P. & Sec.--Trikon Technologies Inc., Chatsworth, CA; *U.S. Public*, pg. 1638

LaVecchia, Jean M., Sr. V.P.-Organization Devel.--Southern New England Telecommunications Corporation, New Haven, CT; *U.S. Public*, pg. 1490

Lavelle, Francis W., Sr. V.P.--Shared Medical Systems Corporation, Malvern, PA; *U.S. Public*, pg. 1463

Lavelle, Timothy E., Sr. V.P. & Mng. Dir.--Trident Financial Corporation, Raleigh, NC; *U.S. Private*, pg. 1103

Lavely, Anthony, Sr. V.P.-Sls. & Mktg.--Rally's Hamburgers, Inc., Louisville, KY; *U.S. Public*, pg. 1359

Lavers, Julian P., Sr. V.P.-Sls. & Field Opers.--Wechsler Coffee Corp., Moonachie, NJ; *U.S. Private*, pg. 1158

Lavine, Gary J., Sr. V.P.-Legal & Corp. Rels.--Niagara Mohawk Power Corporation, Syracuse, NY; *U.S. Public*, pg. 1181

Laviolette, Rene, Sr. V.P.-Prod. Devel.--Manufacturers Technologies, Inc., West Springfield, MA; *U.S. Private*, pg. 701

Lavoie, James R., Sr. V.P.--Analysis & Technology, Inc., North Stonington, CT; *U.S. Public*, pg. 109

Lavut, Cipora Kurtzman, Sr. V.P.-Corp. Communications--Aura Systems, Inc., El Segundo, CA; *U.S. Public*, pg. 147

Law, L. William, Jr., Sr. V.P., Gen. Counsel & Sec.--Eastern Enterprises, Weston, MA; *U.S. Public*, pg. 548

Lawler, Donald M., Sr. Grp. V.P.-W. Canada--Westburne Inc., Montreal, Canada; *Int'l*, pg. 1491

Lawler, Thomas A., Sr. V.P.-Portfolio Mngmt.--Federal National Mortgage Association (Fannie Mae), Washington, DC; *U.S. Public*, pg. 615

Lawler, Thomas J., Sr. V.P. & Corp. Counsel--Duro-Last Roofing, Inc., Saginaw, MI; *U.S. Private*, pg. 349

Lawlor, Thomas J., Jr., Chief Fin. Officer & Sr. V.P.--Boeing Realty Corporation, Long Beach, CA; *U.S. Public*, pg. 241

Lawrence, Dan, Sr. V.P.-Multinational Sourcing--The Bombay Company, Fort Worth, TX; *U.S. Public*, pg. 244

Lawrence, Daniel L., Sr. V.P.-Multinational Sourcing--The Bombay Company, Inc., Fort Worth, TX; *U.S. Public*, pg. 244

Lawrence, J. Rodney, Sr. V.P.-Legal Affairs & Corp. Sec.--Pier 1 Imports, Inc., Fort Worth, TX; *U.S. Public*, pg. 1295

Lawrence, Jane, Sr. V.P.-Acct. Services--Western International Media Corporation, Chicago, IL; *U.S. Private*, pg. 1167

Lawrence, Jim, Chief Fin. Officer & Exec. V.P.--Northwest Airlines, Inc., Saint Paul, MN; *U.S. Public*, pg. 1200

Lawrence, Randall L., Chief Fin. Officer & Sr. V.P.--Detroit Diesel Corp., Detroit, MI; *U.S. Private*, pg. 850

Lawrence, Robert A., Sr. V.P.-Equity--Fidelity Investments (FMR Corp.), Boston, MA; *U.S. Private*, pg. 402

Lawrence, Robert H., Jr., Sr. V.P.--UST Inc., Greenwich, CT; *U.S. Public*, pg. 1660

Lawrence, Ron, Sr. V.P. & Media Dir.--DMB&B Los Angeles, Los Angeles, CA; *U.S. Private*, pg. 303

Lawrence, Ted, Sr. V.P. & Grp. Dir.--Ryan Drossman & Partners, New York, NY; *U.S. Private*, pg. 953

Lawrence, Thomas W., Sr. V.P.--PNMR Securities, Seattle, WA; *U.S. Public*, pg. 1423

Lawrence, William, Chief Fin. Officer & Sr. V.P.--Jay Jacobs, Inc., Seattle, WA; *U.S. Public*, pg. 922

Lawrence, William S., Chief Fin. Officer & Sr. V.P.-Fin.--General Datacomm Industries, Inc., Middlebury, CT; *U.S. Public*, pg. 708

Lawshe, Jeff, Sr. V.P. & Gen. Mgr.--The Corporate Communications Group, Whippany, NJ; *U.S. Private*, pg. 276

Lawson, John K., Sr. V.P.-Engrng., Tech. & H.R.--Deere & Company, Moline, IL; *U.S. Public*, pg. 491

Lawson, Linda K., Sr. V.P. & Gen. Mgr.-Global Access--The Williams Companies, Inc., Tulsa, OK; *U.S. Public*, pg. 1769

Lawson, Louis L., Sr. V.P.-Strategic Sls.--United Family Life Insurance Co., Atlanta, GA; *Int'l*, pg. 499

Lawson, Peter, Sr. V.P. & Gen. Counsel--Motorola, Inc., Schaumburg, IL; *U.S. Public*, pg. 1136

Lawson, Ron, Sr. V.P.-Sls. & Customer Service--Howmedica, Inc., Rutherford, NJ; *U.S. Public*, pg. 1282

Lawson, William M., Jr., Sr. V.P.-Corp. Dev. & Intl. Opers.--Fleming Companies, Inc., Oklahoma City, OK; *U.S. Public*, pg. 652

Laxell, Pekka, Sr. V.P.--Rauma Ltd., Helsinki, Finland; *Int'l*, pg. 1428

Lay, Roger, Sr. V.P.-Internal Audit--Firstbank Puerto Rico, Santurce, PR; *U.S. Public*, pg. 644

Lay, Sherry, Sr. V.P.-Mdsg. & Mktg.--Sunglass Hut International, Coral Gables, FL; *U.S. Public*, pg. 1535

Layden, D.W., Jr., Sr. V.P.--Marshall & Ilsley Corporation, Milwaukee, WI; *U.S. Public*, pg. 1049

Layefsky, Jerry, Sr. V.P. & Strategic Plng. Dir.--DMB&B New York, New York, NY; *U.S. Private*, pg. 302

Layfield, Debbi, Sr. V.P.--Grizzard, Atlanta, GA; *U.S. Private*, pg. 482

Laymon, Eileen C., Sr. V.P.-Mktg.--GAB Robins North America, Inc., Parsippany, NJ; *Int'l*, pg. 1153

Layton, Mel, Sr. V.P.--Republic Entertainment, Inc., Los Angeles, CA; *U.S. Private*, pg. 776

Lazear, Scott, Sr. V.P.-Sls.--National Card Control, Inc., Crozier, VA; *U.S. Public*, pg. 321

Le Count, Samuel, Sr. V.P.--Scicom Data Services, Ltd., Minnetonka, MN; *U.S. Private*, pg. 975

Le Gouis, Claude, Sr. V.P.-Americas, Africa, Pacific--Danone Group, Paris, France; *Int'l*, pg. 379

Le Quement, Patrick, Sr. V.P.-Quality & Corp. Design--Renault, Boulogne-Billancourt, France; *Int'l*, pg. 1102

Le, Luu, Sr. V.P. & Country Mgr.--Bank of America NT&SA, Hanoi, Vietnam; *U.S. Public*, pg. 182

Leach, M. Robert, Sr. V.P.-Consulting--Cadence Design Systems, Inc., San Jose, CA; *U.S. Public*, pg. 290

Leader, Lennert, Chief Fin. Officer, Sr. V.P. & Treas.--America Online Incorporated, Dulles, VA; *U.S. Public*, pg. 66

Leadingham, Deanna R., V.P.--The El-Bee Chargit Corp., Dayton, OH; *U.S. Private*, pg. 367

Leaf, Greg, Sr. V.P.-Pub. Rels.--Miller Meester Advertising Inc., Minneapolis, MN; *U.S. Private*, pg. 747

Leahy, John, Sr. V.P.-Intl. Corp. Sls.--Playtex Beauty Care, Inc., Westport, CT; *U.S. Public*, pg. 1311

Leahy, John D., Sr. V.P.-Intl. Corp. Sls.--Playtex Products Inc., Westport, CT; *U.S. Public*, pg. 1310

Leahy, John J., Sr. V.P.-Comml.--Airbus Industrie, Blagnac, France; *Int'l*, pg. 39

Leahy, Robert B., Sr. V.P.-Sls. & Mktg.--Folger Nolan Fleming Douglas, Washington, DC; *U.S. Private*, pg. 416

Leak, Peggy E., Sr. V.P.--Atlantic Mutual Companies, New York, NY; *U.S. Private*, pg. 95

Leal, Fernando A., Sr. V.P.--Pharmacia & Upjohn, Inc., Windsor, United Kingdom; *Int'l*, pg. 1047

Leal, Fernando A., Sr. V.P.-Strategic Planning & Business Devel.--Pharmacia & Upjohn, Kalamazoo, MI; *Int'l*, pg. 1048

Leatherman, Michael T., Chief Info. Officer & Sr. V.P.--Wallace Computer Services, Inc., Lisle, IL; *U.S. Public*, pg. 1735

Leavesley, James C., Sr. V.P.-Construction & Maintenance--JE Merit Constructors, Inc., Houston, TX; *U.S. Public*, pg. 921

Leavitt, Thomas, Sr. V.P.-Opers.--United Asset Management Corporation, Boston, MA; *U.S. Public*, pg. 1672

Leavitt, Victoria, Sr. V.P. & Bus. Devel. Dir.--Campbell Mithun Esty, Minneapolis, MN; *U.S. Private*, pg. 204

LeBeau, William M., Sr. V.P.-Loan & Asset Review--ONBANCorp, Inc., Syracuse, NY; *U.S. Public*, pg. 631

LeBlanc, Annette T., Sr. V.P.--Hibernia Corporation, New Orleans, LA; *U.S. Public*, pg. 825

LeBlanc, Eddie M., Chief Fin. Officer & Sr. V.P.--Coho Energy, Inc., Dallas, TX; *U.S. Public*, pg. 396

Lebovitz, James A., Sr. V.P., Gen. Counsel & Sec.--FPA Medical Management, Inc., San Diego, CA; *U.S. Public*, pg. 608

Lebovitz, Stephen D., Sr. V.P.--CBL & Associates Properties, Inc., Waltham, MA; *U.S. Public*, pg. 273

Lebreton, Joel, Sr. V.P.-Contracts & Sls. Fin.--Avions de Transport Regional - ATR, Blagnac, France; *Int'l*, pg. 654

LeBright, R.P., Sr. V.P.-ABB Lummus Global Europe--ABB Lummus Global Inc., Bloomfield, NJ; *Int'l*, pg. 4

Lecaldare, Mario, Sr. V.P.-Corp. Banking, Canada--National Bank of Canada, Montreal, Canada; *Int'l*, pg. 907

Leckie, John L., Sr. V.P.-Main Street Banking--The Toronto Dominion Bank, Toronto, Canada; *Int'l*, pg. 1401

LeCroy, Edwin P., Jr., Sr. V.P.--Durham Transportation, Inc., Austin, TX; *U.S. Private*, pg. 348

Leddy, Kevin, Sr. V.P.-Mktg.--Time Warner Cable, Stamford, CT; *U.S. Public*, pg. 1610

Lederer, Ann E., Sr. V.P., Gen. Counsel & Sec.--FirstFed Financial Corp., Santa Monica, CA; *U.S. Public*, pg. 645

Lederer, Klaus, Dr., Sr. V.P.--ITT Automotive, Inc., Auburn Hills, MI; *U.S. Public*, pg. 859

Lederman, Frank L., Sr. V.P. & Dir.-Res.--Noranda Inc., Toronto, Canada; *Int'l*, pg. 433

Lederman, Ira S., Sr. V.P., Asst. Gen. Counsel & Asst. Sec.--W.R. Berkley Corporation, Greenwich, CT; *U.S. Public*, pg. 215

Ledgett, Ronald A., Sr. V.P.-Fossil Div.--Boston Edison Company, Boston, MA; *U.S. Public*, pg. 247

Ledman, William J., Sr. V.P.-Info. Systems & Svcs.--Federal Home Loan Mortgage Corporation, Mc Lean, VA; *U.S. Public*, pg. 615

Ledwin, William F., Chief Investmenbt Officer & Sr. V.P.--The Western and Southern Life Insurance Company, Cincinnati, OH; *U.S. Private*, pg. 1164

Lee, Christopher, Sr. V.P.-Production--TriStar Pictures, Culver City, CA; *Int'l*, pg. 1283

Lee, Curtis D., Sr. V.P.-Auto General Opers.--Servco Pacific Inc., Honolulu, HI; *U.S. Private*, pg. 986

Lee, Dan, Sr. V.P.--Isolyser Company, Inc., Norcross, GA; *U.S. Public*, pg. 914
Lee, Daniel R., Chief Fin. Officer, Sr. V.P.-Fin. & Devel. & Treas.--Mirage Resorts Incorporated, Las Vegas, NV; *U.S. Public*, pg. 1116
Lee, Dann R., Sr. V.P.-Retail Banking--Compass Bank Houston, Houston, TX; *U.S. Public*, pg. 419
Lee, David A., Sr. V.P. & Reg. Mgr.--Community First Bankshares, Inc., Fargo, ND; *U.S. Public*, pg. 416
Lee, Howard, Sr. V.P. & Gen. Mgr.-Servers & Alternate Platform Prods. Div.--Apple Computer, Inc., Cupertino, CA; *U.S. Public*, pg. 121
Lee, Jack R., Sr. V.P.-Mktg.--Domco Inc., Farnham, Canada; *Int'l*, pg. 415
Lee, Jesse, Chief Fin. Officer, Sr. V.P. & Sec.--The IDI Group Companies, Arlington, VA; *U.S. Private*, pg. 554
Lee, Kathy, Sr. V.P.--RNBNY Branch Office-Hong Kong, Central, Hong Kong; *U.S. Public*, pg. 1381
Lee, Soo Bu, Sr. V.P.-Kimhae Area Admin.--Korean Airlines Co., Ltd., Seoul, Korea; *Int'l*, pg. 758
Lee, Sue, Sr. V.P.-Human Resources & Communications--Suncor Inc., Calgary, Canada; *Int'l*, pg. 1320
Lee, Terry, Sr. V.P. & Mgr.-Corp. Commun.--First Tennessee National Corporation, Memphis, TN; *U.S. Public*, pg. 638
Lee, Terry, Sr. V.P. & Mgr.-Corp. Communications--First Tennessee Bank National Association, Memphis, TN; *U.S. Public*, pg. 639
Lee, Wanda, Sr. V.P.-H.R.--PacifiCare Health Systems, Inc., Cypress, CA; *U.S. Public*, pg. 1250
Lee, Won Young, Sr. V.P.-Cargo & Adv.--Korean Airlines Co., Ltd., Seoul, Korea; *Int'l*, pg. 758
Leech, Robert E., Sr. V.P.-Trust Services--Keystone Financial Inc., Harrisburg, PA; *U.S. Public*, pg. 956
Leeper, Dwight, Sr. V.P.--Grey Advertising Inc., New York, NY; *U.S. Public*, pg. 764
Leese, Daniel T., Sr. V.P. & Gen. Mgr.-Fetzer Brands--Brown-Forman Beverages Worldwide, Louisville, KY; *U.S. Public*, pg. 261
LeFauve, Richard G., Sr. V.P.-Global Leadership Devel. & H.R.--General Motors Corporation, Detroit, MI; *U.S. Public*, pg. 718
LeFevre, John H., Sr. V.P. & Sec.--Deluxe Corporation, Shoreview, MN; *U.S. Public*, pg. 498
LeFevre, Robert M., Sr. V.P.-Mktg. & Sls.--The United States Playing Card Company, Cincinnati, OH; *U.S. Private*, pg. 1125
Legault, G.J., Chief. Fin. Officer & Sr. V.P.-Fin. & Admin.--AGRA Monenco, Oakville, Canada; *Int'l*, pg. 30
Legget, Malcolm H., First Sr. V.P.--Commercial Union Corporation, Boston, MA; *Int'l*, pg. 308
Legget, Malcolm H., First Sr. V.P.--Commercial Union Insurance Company, Boston, MA; *Int'l*, pg. 308
Lehman, Alice, Sr. V.P. & Mng. Dir.-Corp. Rels.--First Union Corporation, Charlotte, NC; *U.S. Public*, pg. 639
Lehman, Schuyler, Sr. V.P.--Ketchum, Inc., Pittsburgh, PA; *U.S. Private*, pg. 617
Lehmbeck, Barney, Sr. V.P.--Liberty Bank & Trust Company of Oklahoma City, Oklahoma City, OK; *U.S. Public*, pg. 174
Lehnhard, Mary Nell, Sr. V.P.-Policy & Representation--Blue Cross and Blue Shield Association, Chicago, IL; *U.S. Private*, pg. 151
Lehr, Harry, Sr. V.P.-Fin.--Alaska Air Group, Inc., Seattle, WA; *U.S. Public*, pg. 35
Lehr, Harry G., Sr. V.P.-Fin.--Alaska Airlines, Inc., Seattle, WA; *U.S. Public*, pg. 35
Lehr, Tom, Sr. V.P. & Grp. Mngmt. Supvr.--Dailey & Associates, West Hollywood, CA; *U.S. Public*, pg. 909
Leibee, Beverly, Sr. V.P.-Acct. Services--Western International Media Corporation, Chicago, IL; *U.S. Private*, pg. 1167
Leibman, Lee, Sr. V.P.--Asher/Gould Advertising, Inc., Los Angeles, CA; *U.S. Private*, pg. 88
Leibowitz, George, Sr. V.P.-Fin. & Corp. Devel.--Petroleum Heat & Power Co., Stamford, CT; *U.S. Public*, pg. 1281
Leichsering, Volker, Sr. V.P.-Corp. Commun.--ABB Asea Brown Boveri (Holding) Ltd., Zurich, Switzerland; *Int'l*, pg. 1
Leichter, Pamela, Sr. V.P. & Media Dir.--Ryan Drossman & Partners, New York, NY; *U.S. Private*, pg. 953
Leick, Frederick, Sr. V.P.-Opers.--ADVO, Inc., Windsor, CT; *U.S. Public*, pg. 23
Leidner, J.H., Chief Fin. Officer & Sr. V.P.--Fuller Company, Bethlehem, PA; *Int'l*, pg. 475
Leiferman, Ronald, Chief Fin. Officer & Sr. V.P.--Leo A. Daly Company, Omaha, NE; *U.S. Private*, pg. 309
Leigh, Robert, Sr. V.P. & Group Dir. Of Stores--The Bon Marche, Inc., Seattle, WA; *U.S. Public*, pg. 617
Leijdekker, Hans, Sr. V.P.--ADM Cocoa, Inc., Stamford, CT; *U.S. Public*, pg. 127
Leininger, Peter A., Sr. V.P.-Medical, Education & Training--Kinetic Concepts, Inc., San Antonio, TX; *U.S. Private*, pg. 620
Leisten, Arthur G., Sr. V.P. & Gen. Counsel--USG Corporation, Chicago, IL; *U.S. Public*, pg. 1660
Leitner, Howard M., Chief Fin. Officer & Sr. V.P.--Chock Full O' Nuts Corporation, New York, NY; *U.S. Public*, pg. 351
Leivo, Eero, Sr. V.P.-Admin.--Valmet Corporation, Helsinki, Finland; *Int'l*, pg. 1447
Lekkerkerker, E.C., Sr. V.P.--AEGON Levensverzekering NV, Hague, Netherlands; *Int'l*, pg. 25
Lekkerkerker, E.C., Sr. V.P.--AEGON Schadeverzekering N.V., Hague, Netherlands; *Int'l*, pg. 26
LeMarier, John, Sr. V.P.-Legal--International Plastics Company, New York, NY; *U.S. Private*, pg. 571
Lemasters, S. Craig, Sr. V.P.-Bank--American Bankers Life Assurance Co. of Florida, Miami, FL; *U.S. Public*, pg. 67
Lemay, Nicole, Sr. V.P.-Human Resources--SNC-Lavalin Group Inc., Montreal, Canada; *Int'l*, pg. 1161
Lemberg, Thomas M., Sr. V.P., Gen. Counsel & Sec.--Polaroid Corporation, Cambridge, MA; *U.S. Public*, pg. 1313
Lemberger, Mark, Sr. V.P.-Sls. & Mktg.--Western States Envelope Co., Milwaukee, WI; *U.S. Private*, pg. 1168
Lemery, Francis P., Sr. V.P. & Actuary--Kansas City Life Insurance Co., Kansas City, MO; *U.S. Public*, pg. 942
Lemmer, Peter L., Sr. V.P. & Gen. Counsel--D & N Financial Corporation, Hancock, MI; *U.S. Public*, pg. 472
LeMoine, Laurie L., Sr. V.P.--Hibernia Corporation, New Orleans, LA; *U.S. Public*, pg. 825
Lemons, Richard M., Sr. V.P.--Knight Architects Engineers Planners, Inc., Chicago, IL; *U.S. Private*, pg. 626
Lemons, Robert K., Sr. V.P.-Property/Asset Mngmt.--Spaulding & Slye, Boston, MA; *U.S. Private*, pg. 1021
LeMonte, Lamar, Sr. V.P. & Grp. Acct. Dir.--Hill, Holliday/Altschiller, New York, NY; *U.S. Private*, pg. 529
Lempereus, Fred, Sr. V.P.-Packaging--Grace Packaging, Duncan, SC; *U.S. Public*, pg. 755
Lempke, R. Michael, Sr. V.P. & Treas.--Fort James Corporation, Richmond, VA; *U.S. Public*, pg. 670
Lenandowski, Thomas, Sr. V.P.-Mktg.--Jones Medical Industries Inc., Saint Louis, MO; *U.S. Public*, pg. 933
Lenderin, Gary B., Sr. V.P.-Grp. Insurance--The Guardian Life Insurance Company of America, New York, NY; *U.S. Private*, pg. 486
Lennartson, Kris, Sr. V.P.-Sports & Entertainment--Haworth Group Inc., Minneapolis, MN; *U.S. Private*, pg. 511
Lennartson, Kris, Sr. V.P.-Sports & Entertainment--The Haworth Group, Inc., Los Angeles, CA; *U.S. Private*, pg. 511
Lentz, John M., Sr. V.P.--Hardee's Food Systems, Inc., Rocky Mount, NC; *U.S. Public*, pg. 278
Lentzsch, Kathi, Sr. V.P.-Pottery Barn Mdsg.--Williams-Sonoma, Inc., San Francisco, CA; *U.S. Public*, pg. 1770
Leon, Jean-Paul, Sr. V.P.-Fin. & Admin.--Elf Aquitane, Paris, France; *Int'l*, pg. 444
Leon, Luis, Chief Fin. Officer, Sr. V.P. & Treas.--GS Industries, Inc., Charlotte, NC; *U.S. Private*, pg. 435
Leonard, Charles H., Chief Fin. Officer & Sr. V.P.--TEPPCO Partners L.P., Houston, TX; *U.S. Public*, pg. 534
Leonard, Charles H., Sr. V.P. & Chief Fin. Officer--Texas Eastern Products Pipeline Company, L.P., Houston, TX; *U.S. Public*, pg. 535
Leonard, Earl T., Sr. V.P.-Corp. Affairs--The Coca-Cola Company, Atlanta, GA; *U.S. Public*, pg. 392
Leonard, Paul, Sr. V.P. & Pres.-Guild Div.--Zale Corporation, Irving, TX; *U.S. Public*, pg. 1789
Leonard, Stephen P., Sr. V.P. & Treas.--Vesta Insurance Group, Inc., Birmingham, AL; *U.S. Public*, pg. 1718
Leonardo, Antone, Sr. V.P.-Tech. Infrastructure--Citizens Savings Bank, Providence, RI; *Int'l*, pg. 1132
Leone, Michael J., Sr. V.P.-Bridgeport Region--People's Bank, Bridgeport, CT; *U.S. Public*, pg. 1274
Leong, Charles, Sr. V.P.-Americas--Singapore Tourist Promotion Board - Los Angeles, Beverly Hills, CA; *Int'l*, pg. 1254
Leonoff, Lawrence, Sr. V.P., Gen. Counsel & Sec.--Ontario Hydro, Toronto, Canada; *Int'l*, pg. 1007
Lepere, F. V., Sr. V.P.-Fin.--Hapag-Lloyd (America), Inc., Piscataway, NJ; *Int'l*, pg. 596
LePlae, Robert, Sr. V.P. & Grp. Acct. Exec.--Rubin Postaer & Associates, Santa Monica, CA; *U.S. Private*, pg. 949
Lepola, Ismo, Sr. V.P.--United Paper Mills Ltd., Valkeakoski, Finland; *Int'l*, pg. 1429
Lepore, Donald A., Sr. V.P. & Grp. Exec.-Electronic Components & Matls.--Litton Industries, Inc., Woodland Hills, CA; *U.S. Public*, pg. 1002
LePore, Philip t., Sr. V.P.--Raytheon Systems Company, Arlington, VA; *U.S. Public*, pg. 1364
Leppert, Tom, Sr. V.P.-Sls. & Mktg.--Sargent & Greenleaf, Inc., Nicholasville, KY; *U.S. Private*, pg. 965
Lerner, Linda J., Sr. V.P.-Human Resources--UST Corporation, Boston, MA; *U.S. Public*, pg. 1660
Lerner, Linda J., Sr. V.P.-Human Resources--USTrust, Boston, MA; *U.S. Public*, pg. 1660
LeRoy, Spencer, III, Sr. V.P., Gen. Counsel & Sec.--Old Republic International Corporation, Chicago, IL; *U.S. Public*, pg. 1218
LeRoy, Stephen B., Sr. V.P.-Intl. & Real Estate--The Southland Corporation, Dallas, TX; *Int'l*, pg. 693
Lescoe, Daniel, Sr. V.P.-Mdsg.--Big Y Foods Inc., Springfield, MA; *U.S. Private*, pg. 143
Leshay, Jeff, Sr. V.P.--Golin/Harris Communications, Inc., Chicago, IL; *Int'l*, pg. 1226
Leshinski, Bruce A., Sr. V.P.-Sls. & Mktg.--Newly Weds Foods Inc., Chicago, IL; *U.S. Private*, pg. 796
Leshner, Zane, Sr. V.P.-Opers.--Taco Bell Corp., Irvine, CA; *U.S. Public*, pg. 1637
Leshtz, Barry, Sr. V.P. & Gen. Mgr.-Home Video--Playboy Entertainment Group, Inc., Beverly Hills, CA; *U.S. Public*, *pg. 1310*
Lesko, John, Sr. V.P.-MIS & Continuous Improvement--Eckerd Corporation, Largo, FL; *U.S. Public*, pg. 917
Lesley, Siobhan, Sr. V.P. & Client Services Dir.--Valentine Radford, Inc., Kansas City, MO; *U.S. Private*, pg. 1131
Leslie, David, Sr. V.P. & Gen. Mgr.--Eastalco Aluminum Company, Frederick, MD; *U.S. Public*, pg. 60
Leslie, James, Sr. V.P.-Sustainable Devel.--Transalta Corporation, Calgary, Canada; *Int'l*, pg. 1416
Lesman, Howard, Sr. V.P., Grp. Dir.--Ammirati, Puris & Lintas, Inc., New York, NY; *U.S. Private*, pg. 66
Lestelle, James F., Sr. V.P.-Corp. Commun.--Hibernia Corporation, New Orleans, LA; *U.S. Public*, pg. 825
Lester, David W., Chief Oper. Officer & Sr. V.P.--Kentucky Medical Insurance Company (KMIC), Louisville, KY; *U.S. Private*, pg. 741
Letendre, Gary, Sr. V.P.-Sourcing--Starter Corp., New Haven, CT; *U.S. Public*, pg. 1511
Letham, Dennis J., Chief Fin. Officer & Sr. V.P.-Fin.--Anixter International, Chicago, IL; *U.S. Public*, pg. 115
Letofsky, Alan R., Sr. V.P.--U.S. Healthcare, Inc., Blue Bell, PA; *U.S. Public*, pg. 26
Leuchten, William E., Sr. V.P.--Essex Chemical Corporation, Clifton, NJ; *U.S. Public*, pg. 523
Leuliette, Timothy D., Sr. V.P.--ITT Industries, Inc., White Plains, NY; *U.S. Public*, pg. 859
Leung, Robert, Sr. V.P. & Assoc. Creative Dir.--Carrafiello, Diehl & Associates, Inc., Irvington, NY; *U.S. Private*, pg. 215
Leunis, William G., III, Chief Fin. Officer, Sr. V.P.-Fin., Treas. & Sec.--Ultratech Stepper, Inc., San Jose, CA; *U.S. Public*, pg. 1663
LeVasseur, Richard, Sr. V.P.--Elsinore Corporation, Las Vegas, NV; *U.S. Public*, pg. 570
Levenson, Al, Sr. V.P.--Ostrow Textile Co., Inc., Rock Hill, SC; *U.S. Private*, pg. 821
Leventhal, Ted, Sr. V.P. & Mgr.-Claims--Willis Corroon Corp. of Orange County, Santa Ana, CA; *Int'l*, pg. 1506
Lever, James, Sr. V.P. & Dir.-MIS--Arnhold and S. Bleichroeder, Inc., New York, NY; *U.S. Private*, pg. 83
Levergood, John H., Sr. V.P.-Corp. Operating Committee--Scientific-Atlanta, Inc., Norcross, GA; *U.S. Public*, pg. 1443
Levesque, Mark J., Sr. V.P.-Information Systems & Mngmt. Services--National Life Insurance Company, Montpelier, VT; *U.S. Private*, pg. 785
Levey, Gerald S., Sr. V.P.-Medical & Scientific Affairs--Merck Human Health Division, Rahway, NJ; *U.S. Public*, pg. 1090
Levi-Garza, Jalaane, Sr. V.P. & Dir.-Adv.--Mediatex Communications Corporation, Austin, TX; *U.S. Private*, pg. 727
Levin, Fred J., Sr. V.P.-Intl.--Movado Group, Inc., Lyndhurst, NJ; *U.S. Public*, pg. 1140
Levin, Harvey, Sr. V.P.-Human Resources--American Greetings Corporation, Cleveland, OH; *U.S. Public*, pg. 77
Levin, Kenneth, Sr. V.P.--Simon Marketing, Inc., Oak Brook Terrace, IL; *U.S. Private*, pg. 1001
Levin, Larry, Sr. V.P.--New World Entertainment, Inc., Los Angeles, CA; *Int'l*, pg. 926
Levin, Lawrence R., Sr. V.P.--Market Facts, Inc., Arlington Heights, IL; *U.S. Public*, pg. 1046
Levin, Michael D., Sr. V.P., Gen. Counsel & Sec.--Sears, Roebuck and Co., Hoffman Estates, IL; *U.S. Public*, pg. 1452
Levine, Adam, Sr. V.P. & Interactive Client Svcs. Dir.--Interactive Deutsch, New York, NY; *U.S. Private*, pg. 329
Levine, Gary M., Sr. V.P.-Mktg.--Medicine Shoppe International, Inc., Saint Louis, MO; *U.S. Public*, pg. 304
Levine, Harlan, M.D., Sr. V.P.-Physician & Program Devel.--Salick Health Care, Inc., Los Angeles, CA; *Int'l*, pg. 1524
Levine, James M., Sr. V.P.-Nuclear Generation--APS, Phoenix, AZ; *U.S. Public*, pg. 1297
Levine, Janet, Sr. V.P.-Personal Care--Herbalife International of America, Inc., Century City, CA; *U.S. Public*, pg. 809
Levine, Jeff, Sr. V.P.-Acct. Mngmt.--Grey Advertising Inc., New York, NY; *U.S. Public*, pg. 764
LeVine, Joan, Sr. V.P.--Concord Assets Group, Boca Raton, FL; *U.S. Private*, pg. 261
Levine, Martin D., Sr. V.P.-Low & Moderate Income Housing--Federal National Mortgage Association (Fannie Mae), Washington, DC; *U.S. Public*, pg. 615
Levine, Robert R., Sr. V.P.-Servicing--SLM Holding Corp., Washington, DC; *U.S. Public*, pg. 1419
Levins, Peter, V.P. & Sr. Local Brdcst. Negotiator--Media Partnership Corporation, Norwalk, CT; *U.S. Private*, pg. 1168
Levinson, Randy, Sr. V.P.-Creative Affairs--Universal Studios TV, Universal City, CA; *Int'l*, pg. 1215
Levitan, Jeff, Sr. V.P.-Strategic Plng. & Bus. Devel.--Staples, Inc., Westborough, MA; *U.S. Public*, pg. 1509
Levitetz, Howard, Sr. V.P.--Marketing Support, Incorporated, Chicago, IL; *U.S. Private*, pg. 705
Levitt, David, Sr. V.P. & DMB&B Worldwide Dir.-Training & Devel.--DMB&B Communications, New York, NY; *U.S. Private*, pg. 302
Levitt, Kevin, Sr. V.P.-Fin. & Admin.--The New York Times Magazine Company Group, Trumbull, CT; *U.S. Public*, pg. 1174
Levran, Alexander, Ph.D., Sr. V.P.-Tech.--MagneTek, Inc., Nashville, TN; *U.S. Public*, pg. 1037
Levy, Barbara, Sr. V.P. & Gen. Mgr.-Mdsg.--Ross Stores, Inc., Newark, CA; *U.S. Public*, pg. 1405
Levy, Carolyn J., Sr. V.P.-Mktg. & Sls. Information--Philip Morris U.S.A., New York, NY; *U.S. Public*, pg. 1289
Levy, David, Sr. V.P.-Tech. & Customer Service--MidAmerican Energy Holdings, Des Moines, IA; *U.S. Public*, pg. 1109
Levy, Fredric R., Sr. V.P.--Heritage Sportswear, Marion, SC; *U.S. Public*, pg. 1472
Levy, Jordan, Sr. V.P. & Plng. Dir.--Focus Media, Santa Monica, CA; *U.S. Private*, pg. 415
Levy, Rich, Sr. V.P. & Mng. Dir.--Western International Media Corporation, Hollywood, FL; *U.S. Private*, pg. 1167
Levy, Richard, Sr. V.P. & Controller--New York Life Insurance Company, New York, NY; *U.S. Private*, pg. 794
Levy, Richard C., Sr. V.P.-Corp. Svcs.--Berkshire Life Insurance Company, Pittsfield, MA; *U.S. Private*, pg. 136
Lewent, Judy C., Chief Fin. Officer & Sr. V.P.--Merck & Co., Inc., Whitehouse Station, NJ; *U.S. Public*, pg. 1090
Lewin, Dennis, V.P.--ABC Sports, Inc., New York, NY; *U.S. Public*, pg. 511
Lewin, Margareta, Sr. V.P.-Human Resources--Esselte AB, Solna, Sweden; *Int'l*, pg. 459
Lewis, Blake, Sr. V.P.--Edelman Worldwide, Inc., Dallas, TX; *U.S. Private*, pg. 362
Lewis, Caroline A., Sr. V.P.-Pub. Rels. Div.--Serino Coyne Public Relations, Potomac, MD; *U.S. Private*, pg. 985
Lewis, Diane B., Sr. V.P. & Media Dir.--Arnold Advertising, Mc Lean, VA; *U.S. Private*, pg. 84
Lewis, Dick, Sr. V.P.-Mktg. & Sls.--Fortis Financial Group, Woodbury, MN; *Int'l*, pg. 499
Lewis, Gerard, Sr. V.P.-Res. & Devel.--Boston Chicken, Inc., Golden, CO; *U.S. Public*, pg. 247

Lewis, H. Nelson, Sr. V.P.-Human Resources--The Great Atlantic & Pacific Tea Company, Inc., Montvale, NJ; *Int'l, pg. 1375*
Lewis, Jeanne, Sr. V.P.-Retail & Small Bus. Mktg.--Staples, Inc., Westborough, MA; *U.S. Public*, pg. 1509
Lewis, Jeff, Chief Fin. Officer & Sr. V.P.--The Hunt Corporation, Indianapolis, IN; *U.S. Private*, pg. 548
Lewis, Jeff, Sr. V.P.-Sls. & Opers.--Lafarge Construction Materials, Canfield, OH; *Int'l*, pg. 788
Lewis, John, Sr. V.P.-Sls.--MicroAge, Inc., Tempe, AZ; *U.S. Public*, pg. 1104
Lewis, John R., Sr. V.P.-Exploration & Prod.--CNG Producing Co., New Orleans, LA; *U.S. Public*, pg. 435
Lewis, Joseph E., Chief Oper. Officer & Sr. V.P.--Silcorp Limited, Scarborough, Canada; *Int'l*, pg. 1249
Lewis, Robert A., Dr., Pres.-Syntex Discovery Res. & Sr. V.P.--Syntex, Palo Alto, CA; *Int'l*, pg. 1120
Lewis, Russell D., Chief Information Officer & Sr. V.P.--Jefferies & Company, Inc., Los Angeles, CA; *U.S. Public, pg. 925*
Lewis, Stanley R., Sr. V.P.--Dewberry Design Group, Oklahoma City, OK; *U.S. Private*, pg. 329
Lewis, Stephen H., Sr. V.P.-Product Mgnmt.--The Lincoln National Life Insurance Co., Fort Wayne, IN; *U.S. Public, pg. 998*
Lewis, Thomas, Jr., Sr. V.P.-Information Systems--United States Fidelity & Guaranty Company, Baltimore, MD; *U.S. Public*, pg. 1659
Leyden, Paul J., Sr. V.P.-Pub. Rels.--The Bank of New York Company, Inc., New York, NY; *U.S. Public*, pg. 178
Li, Stephanie, Partner & Sr. V.P.--Scotchbrook Communications Ltd., Wan Chai, Hong Kong; *U.S. Private*, pg. 411
Lian, Ho Fong, Sr. V.P.-Data Resources--DBS Bank Ltd., Singapore, Singapore; *Int'l*, pg. 350
Libby, Hank, Sr. V.P.--Rule Industries, Inc., Gloucester, MA; *U.S. Public*, pg. 950
Libby, Henry G., Sr. V.P.-Consumer--Greenfield Industries Inc., Evans, GA; *U.S. Public*, pg. 950
Libera, Heidi, Sr. V.P.-PROSPERA Design--Shandwick Minneapolis, Minneapolis, MN; *Int'l*, pg. 1227
Libkin, Kenneth, Sr. V.P.--Imperial Bank, Inglewood, CA; *U.S. Public*, pg. 871
Librizzi, Joseph A., Sr. V.P.-Mktg. & Sls.--Jevic Transportation, Inc., Delanco, NJ; *U.S. Public*, pg. 927
Liburdi, Richard J., Sr. V.P.--The Penn Mutual Life Insurance Company, Philadelphia, PA; *U.S. Private*, pg. 849
Licursi, Richard A., Sr. V.P.-Telecommunications--SHL Systemhouse, Ottawa, Canada; *Int'l*, pg. 1154
Liduena, Gilbert, Exec. V.P.--Lafarge Ciments, Saint Cloud, France; *Int'l*, pg. 788
Lieberman-Martucci, Debbie, Sr. V.P.--Media That Works, Cincinnati, OH; *U.S. Private*, pg. 727
Lieberman, Bonnie, Sr. V.P. & Gen. Mgr.-College Div.--Educational Publishing, New York, NY; *U.S. Public*, pg. 1768
Liebman, Lisa, Sr. V.P. & Mngmt. Supvr.--DMB&B New York, New York, NY; *U.S. Private*, pg. 302
Liebner, Mark, Chief Fin. Officer & Sr. V.P.--Rural Metro Corporation, Scottsdale, AZ; *U.S. Public*, pg. 1412
Liegel, R.D., Sr. V.P.-Tech.--Hein-Werner Corporation, Waukesha, WI; *U.S. Public*, pg. 805
Lienenbrugger, Herbert Gene, Sr. V.P.-Fin.--Pella Corporation, Pella, IA; *U.S. Private*, pg. 848
Lies, James E., Chief Fin. Officer & Sr. V.P.--D.O.C. Optics Corporation, Southfield, MI; *U.S. Private*, pg. 305
Lietz, Cordell A., Sr. V.P.-Acq. & Institutional Capital--Taubman Centers, Inc., Bloomfield Hills, MI; *U.S. Public*, pg. 1561
Lietz, Marsha, Sr. V.P.-Cost. Mngmt.--Citibank, Federal Savings Bank (Illinois), Chicago, IL; *U.S. Public*, pg. 378
Liever, Damon, Sr. V.P.-Mktg. & Bus. Devel.--Uno Restaurant Corporation, West Roxbury, MA; *U.S. Public*, pg. 1698
Light, Michelle, Sr. V.P.-Sls. & Mktg.--Michael Anthony Jewelers, Inc., Mount Vernon, NY; *U.S. Public*, pg. 1103
Lightbourne, Michael R., Sr. V.P.-Mktg.--Rentrak Corporation, Portland, OR; *U.S. Public*, pg. 1377
Lightstone, Stephen, Chief Fin. Officer, Sr. V.P.-Fin. & Treas.--Payless Cashways, Inc., Kansas City, MO; *U.S. Public*, pg. 1267
Ligon, Austin, Sr. V.P.-Automotive--Circuit City Stores, Inc., Richmond, VA; *U.S. Public*, pg. 374
Lilienthal, Martin M., Chief Fin. Officer & Sr. V.P.--The Advest Group, Inc., Hartford, CT; *U.S. Public*, pg. 23
Lilja, Sven Ingvar, Sr. V.P.--Det Norske Veritas, Hovik, Norway; *Int'l*, pg. 396
Liljedahl, Arne, Sr. V.P. & Controller--Nordbanken AB, Stockholm, Sweden; *Int'l*, pg. 957
Liljstrom, Gunnar, Sr. V.P.-Admin. & Head-Legal Affairs & Personnel--NCC AB, Solna, Sweden; *Int'l*, pg. 898
Lilly, Lynn K., Sr. V.P. & Creative Dir.--Liggett-Stashower, Inc., Cleveland, OH; *U.S. Private*, pg. 667
Lilly, Maria, Sr. V.P.--Edelman Worldwide, Inc., New York, NY; *U.S. Private*, pg. 362
Lilly, Steven L., Chief Fin. Officer & Sr. V.P.--National Rural Utilities Cooperative Finance Corporation, Herndon, VA; *U.S. Private*, pg. 786
Lin, Wen-Long, Sr. V.P. & Gen. Mgr.--The International Commercial Bank of China, New York, NY; *Int'l*, pg. 683
Linakis, John S., Sr. V.P.-Transportation--American Institute for Foreign Study, Greenwich, CT; *U.S. Private*, pg. 56
Linard, Jay M., Sr. V.P.--Alumax Inc., Atlanta, GA; *U.S. Public*, pg. 59
Linard, Jay M., Sr. V.P.--Alumax Mill Products, Inc., Morris, IL; *U.S. Public*, pg. 59
Lindaman, Christine, Sr. V.P.--Raymond James Financial, Inc., Saint Petersburg, FL; *U.S. Public*, pg. 923
Lindauer, Alfred, Sr. V.P.-Foreign Exchange--Deutsche Girozentrale-Deutsche Kommunalbank, Frankfurt/Main, Germany; *Int'l*, pg. 406
Lindblom, Paul, Sr. V.P. & Gen. Mgr.-Mdse.--The Bon Ton Stores, Inc., York, PA; *U.S. Public*, pg. 244
Linde-Neidermeyer, Pat, Sr. V.P.-Print Production--Gianettino & Meredith Advertising, Short Hills, NJ; *U.S. Private*, pg. 450
Lindegren, Lars, Sr. V.P.-Corp. Projects--Pharmacia & Upjohn, Inc., Windsor, United Kingdom; *Int'l*, pg. 1047
Lindemood, Patricia J., Sr. V.P. & Cashier--United Missouri Bank of Carthage, Carthage, MO; *U.S. Public*, pg. 1654
Linden, Richard A., Sr. V.P.--MMI Companies, Inc., Deerfield, IL; *U.S. Public*, pg. 1027
Lindenau, Kenneth R., Sr. V.P. & Gen. Mgr.-Arocom Direct--Arocom Marketing Group, Inc., Cleveland, OH; *U.S. Private*, pg. 730
Lindenauer, Charles, Chief Fin. Officer & Sr. V.P.-Fin.--Randa Corp., Kinston, NC; *U.S. Private*, pg. 909
Lindenmann, Walter, Dr., Sr. V.P. & Res. Dir.--Ketchum Public Relations Worldwide, New York, NY; *U.S. Private, pg. 617*
Linder, Mariana Burenstam, Sr. V.P.-Info. Tech.--Trygg-Hansa, Stockholm, Sweden; *Int'l*, pg. 1425
Linder, Mary Carroll, Sr. V.P.-Global Commun.--Estee Lauder Companies Inc., New York, NY; *U.S. Public*, pg. 594
Linderman, Leeanne B., Sr. V.P.-Banking Centers.--Zions First National Bank, Salt Lake City, UT; *U.S. Public*, pg. 1793
Lindholm, Sten, Sr. V.P.-Corp. Communication--Svenska Cellulosa Aktiebolaget (SCA), Stockholm, Sweden; *Int'l*, pg. 1326
Lindner, Phil, Chief Fin. Officer & Sr. V.P.--MidAmerican Energy Holdings, Des Moines, IA; *U.S. Public*, pg. 1109
Lindquist, Bob, Sr. V.P.-Estimating--Hubbard Construction Co., Winter Park, FL; *U.S. Private*, pg. 544
Lindsey, David A., Sr. V.P.--First Indiana Corporation, Indianapolis, IN; *U.S. Public*, pg. 1484
Lindsey, Francis, Sr. V.P.-World Mktg.--Conair Corporation, Stamford, CT; *U.S. Private*, pg. 261
Lindskog, Carl W., Sr. V.P.--New Haven Savings Bank, New Haven, CT; *U.S. Private*, pg. 793
Lineback, Charles D., Sr. V.P.-Reinsurance Div.--American United Life Insurance Company, Indianapolis, IN; *U.S. Private*, pg. 64
Lineberry, Gary E., Sr. V.P.--Metropolitan Life Insurance Co., New York, NY; *U.S. Private*, pg. 737
Lingen, Charles, Chief Fin. Officer & Sr. V.P.--The Sportsman's Guide, Inc., Saint Paul, MN; *U.S. Public*, pg. 1499
Lingg, Kathy, Sr. V.P.-Drama Series Devel. & Strategic Plng.--Paramount Pictures Corporation, Los Angeles, CA; *U.S. Private*, pg. 776
Link, Richard A., Chief Acctg. Officer & Sr. V.P.-Acctg.--Maxicare Health Plans, Inc., Los Angeles, CA; *U.S. Public*, pg. 1061
Link, Steven J., Sr. V.P.--Midwest Employer's Casualty Company, Maryland Heights, MO; *U.S. Public*, pg. 215
Linnat, Terrence G., Sr. V.P. & Gen. Counsel--The B.F. Goodrich Company, Richfield, OH; *U.S. Public*, pg. 751
Linpinsk, Larry, Sr. V.P.--HK Systems, Inc., New Berlin, WI; *U.S. Private*, pg. 491
Linsky, Barry R., Sr. V.P.-Plng. & Bus. Devel.--The Interpublic Group of Companies, Inc., New York, NY; *U.S. Public*, pg. 908
Lintner, Richard P., Sr. V.P.--Weaver Popcorn Company, Inc., Van Buren, IN; *U.S. Private*, pg. 1156
Lintz, L.P., Sr. V.P.--Halstead Industries, Inc., Greensboro, NC; *U.S. Private*, pg. 496
Lipe, Rodney, Sr. V.P. & Mngmt. Supvr.--Ackerman McQueen, Inc., Oklahoma City, OK; *U.S. Private*, pg. 12
Lipham, James B., Chief Fin. Officer & Sr. V.P.--Total System Services, Inc., Columbus, GA; *U.S. Public*, pg. 1550
Lipiro, Frank, Sr. V.P.-Licensing--Starter Corp., New Haven, CT; *U.S. Public*, pg. 1511
Lipkowitz, John, Sr. V.P. & Gen. Mgr.--Rio Hotel & Casino Inc., Las Vegas, NV; *U.S. Public*, pg. 1390
Lippart, Thomas E., Sr. V.P.-Fin. & Admin. & Gen. Counsel--Tube City Inc., Glassport, PA; *U.S. Private*, pg. 1108
Lippman, William J., Sr. V.P.--Franklin Resources, Inc., San Mateo, CA; *U.S. Public*, pg. 679
Lipschultz, Claire M., Sr. V.P.--First Health Group Corp., Downers Grove, IL; *U.S. Public*, pg. 635
Lipscomb, James L., Sr. V.P.-Real Estate Investments--Metropolitan Life Insurance Co., New York, NY; *U.S. Private*, pg. 737
Lipson, Dave, Sr. V.P. & Creative Dir.--Ackerman McQueen, Inc., Irving, TX; *U.S. Private*, pg. 13
Lipton, Steven D., Sr. V.P.--The Elder-Beerman Stores Corp., Dayton, OH; *U.S. Private*, pg. 367
Lisko, John, Sr. V.P. & Media Services Dir.--Wyse Advertising/Cleveland, Cleveland, OH; *U.S. Private*, pg. 1194
Lisman, Philip, Sr. V.P.-Tax--H.F. Ahmanson & Co., Irwindale, CA; *U.S. Public*, pg. 29
Lisnow, Mark, Sr. V.P.-Mdsg.--Designs, Inc., Needham, MA; *U.S. Public*, pg. 501
Lissy, David H., Sr. V.P., Gen. Counsel & Corp. Sec.--Ames Department Stores, Inc., Rocky Hill, CT; *U.S. Public*, pg. 99
List, John J., Sr. V.P.-Member Svcs.--National Rural Utilities Cooperative Finance Corporation, Herndon, VA; *U.S. Private*, pg. 786
Lister, Harry J., Sr. V.P.--Johnston, Lemon & Co. Inc., Washington, DC; *U.S. Private*, pg. 595
Listwin, Donald J., Sr. V.P.-Cisco IOS Devel. & Mktg.--Cisco Systems, Inc., San Jose, CA; *U.S. Public*, pg. 375
Litnack, Sanford M., Sr. Exec. V.P.-Corp. Opers.--Disneyland, Anaheim, CA; *U.S. Public*, pg. 511
Litt, Stuart P., Sr. V.P.-Opers.--American Technical Ceramics Corp., Huntington Station, NY; *U.S. Public*, pg. 93
Little, Bradley A., Chief Fin. Officer, Sr. V.P.-Fin. & Treas.--Calton, Inc., Manalapan, NJ; *U.S. Public*, pg. 296
Little, Richard K., Sr. V.P. & Treas.--Rosser International, Inc., Atlanta, GA; *U.S. Private*, pg. 946
Little, S.W., Sr. V.P.-Book Prod. Group--Ingram Book Company, La Vergne, TN; *U.S. Private*, pg. 563
Littley, Jack, Sr. V.P.-Plng. & Devel--BTG, Inc., Fairfax, VA; *U.S. Public*, pg. 164
Litwin, Alisa, Sr. V.P.-Creative Services--Jordan, McGrath, Case & Taylor Inc., New York, NY; *U.S. Private*, pg. 598
Litzen, Ulla, Sr. V.P.--Investor AB, Stockholm, Sweden; *Int'l, pg. 686*
Liu, Donald, Dr., Sr. V.P.-Tech.--American Bureau of Shipping, New York, NY; *U.S. Private*, pg. 51
Liu, George H., Exec. V.P.--American Appraisal Associates, Inc., Milwaukee, WI; *U.S. Private*, pg. 49
Liu, Ruey-Jen, Sr. V.P. & Gen. Mgr.--The International Commercial Bank of China, Bangkok, Thailand; *Int'l*, pg. 683
Livermore, Jeanne M., Sr. V.P.--John Hancock Mutual Life Insurance Company, Boston, MA; *U.S. Private*, pg. 589
Livesey, William D., Sr. V.P.--Metropolitan Life Insurance Co., New York, NY; *U.S. Private*, pg. 737
Livingston , Jonas, Sr. V.P.-Creative Affairs--MCA Records, Inc., Universal City, CA; *Int'l*, pg. 1215
Livingston, David H., Sr. V.P.-Opers.--Delco Remy America, Inc., Anderson, IN; *U.S. Public*, pg. 495
Livingston, Philip B., Chief Fin. Officer & Sr. V.P.--Catalina Marketing Corporation, Saint Petersburg, FL; *U.S. Public, pg. 314*
Livingston, Stuart, Sr. V.P.-Opers. & Bus. Affairs--Telemundo Group, Inc., Hialeah, FL; *U.S. Public*, pg. 1570
Livorsi, Joseph M., Sr. V.P.-Sls. & Mdsg.--Buttrey Food & Drug Company, Great Falls, MT; *U.S. Public*, pg. 271
Lliteras, Mark W., Sr. V.P. & Mgr.-Commercial Banking Div.--First Security Bank of Idaho, N.A., Boise, ID; *U.S. Public*, pg. 637
Lloyd, Chris, Sr. V.P. & Mngmt. Supvr.--McKinney & Silver, Raleigh, NC; *U.S. Private*, pg. 723
Lloyd, David G., Chief Fin. Officer & Sr. V.P.--Taco Cabana, San Antonio, TX; *U.S. Public*, pg. 1559
Lloyd, Frank, Sr. V.P. & Gen. Mgr.-Information Systems Grp.--Motorola, Inc., Schaumburg, IL; *U.S. Public*, pg. 1136
Lloyd, Peter F., Sr. V.P. & Mngmt. Supvr.--Fahlgren, Charlotte, NC; *U.S. Private*, pg. 391
Loadman, David, Sr. V.P.-Global Prod. & Systems Devel.--Telxon Corporation, Akron, OH; *U.S. Public*, pg. 1573
Loarie, John A., V.P.-RV & Marine--Shurflo Pump Manufacturing Co., Santa Ana, CA; *U.S. Public*, pg. 1767
Lobben, Thor, Sr. V.P.-Resources--Norske Skogindustrier A.S, Skogn, Norway; *Int'l*, pg. 965
Lobinsky, Jim, Sr. V.P.--Publix Supermarkets Inc., Lakeland, FL; *U.S. Private*, pg. 893
Lobo, Joe, Sr. V.P.--Willis Corroon Melling Inc., Toronto, Canada; *Int'l*, pg. 1509
Lochman, William H., Jr., Sr. V.P.-Human Resources--PNC Bank, Camp Hill, PA; *U.S. Public*, pg. 1243
Lochner, Philip R. Jr., Sr. V.P.--Time Warner Inc., New York, NY; *U.S. Public*, pg. 1610
Locibento, Arthur T., Jr., Sr. V.P.-H.R.--NovaCare Employee Services, Inc., Norristown, PA; *U.S. Public*, pg. 1203
Lock, Terry R., Sr. V.P.-Intl.--Boise Cascade Corporation, Boise, ID; *U.S. Public*, pg. 242
Locke, Melvin W., Jr., Sr. V.P. & Dir.-People Services--Jefferies & Company, Inc., Los Angeles, CA; *U.S. Public, pg. 925*
Lockhart, Debi, Sr. V.P., Human Resources Dir. & Office Facilities Dir.--Publicis/Bloom Inc., New York, NY; *Int'l*, pg. 470
Lockhart, Robert W., Sr. V.P.-Asset Mngmt.--Tarragon Realty Investors, Dallas, TX; *U.S. Public*, pg. 1561
Lockhart, William, Sr. V.P.-Asset Mngmt.--National Income Realty Trust, New York, NY; *U.S. Public*, pg. 1157
Lockridge, B. Russell, Sr. V.P.-H.R.--IMC Global, Bannockburn, IL; *U.S. Public*, pg. 856
Lockwood, Francis J., Jr., Sr. V.P.--Trenwick America Reinsurance Corporation, Stamford, CT; *U.S. Public*, pg. 1634
Lockwood, Gerald A., Sr. V.P.--The Union Central Life Insurance Co., Cincinnati, OH; *U.S. Private*, pg. 1118
Lockwood, Glenn C., Chief Fin. Officer & Sr. V.P.--New Jersey Resources Corporation, Wall, NJ; *U.S. Public*, pg. 1172
Lockwood, Robert J., Sr. V.P.-Claims--Harleysville Group, Harleysville, PA; *U.S. Public*, pg. 786
Loebig, David, Sr. V.P.-Information Services--Owen Health Care, Inc., Houston, TX; *U.S. Public*, pg. 304
Loebig, Gary L., Sr. V.P.-Market & Prod. Devel.--Stuart Entertainment Inc., Council Bluffs, IA; *U.S. Public*, pg. 1526
Loebl, Richard M., Sr. V.P.-Jewelry Mdsg.--L. Luria & Son, Inc., Medley, FL; *U.S. Public*, pg. 1020
Loeser, David, Sr. V.P.-H.R.--Quaker State Corporation, Irving, TX; *U.S. Public*, pg. 1348
Loez, Bernard, Sr. V.P.--Dumez-GTM Chine, Beijing, China; *Int'l*, pg. 823
Loez, Bernard, Sr. V.P.--Dumez-GTM Hong Kong, Hong Kong, Hong Kong; *Int'l*, pg. 823
Lofquist, Peter A., Sr. V.P.--Mellon Bank Corporation, Pittsburgh, PA; *U.S. Public*, pg. 1084
Loftus, Tom, Sr. V.P. & Gen. Mgr.--Lord Corporation, Mechanical Products Division, Erie, PA; *U.S. Private*, pg. 676
Logan, H.V., Sr. V.P.-Fleet Mngmt.--TTX Co., Chicago, IL; *U.S. Private*, pg. 1066
Logan, James, Sr. V.P.-Real Estate--Fortis, Inc., New York, NY; *Int'l*, pg. 499
Logan, James, Sr. V.P.-Mortgages--Fortis Advisers, Inc., New York, NY; *Int'l*, pg. 499
Logan, James M., Chief Info. Officer & Sr. V.P.--Metropolitan Life Insurance Co., New York, NY; *U.S. Private*, pg. 737
Logan, Ray E., Sr. V.P.--Manufacturers & Traders Trust Company, Buffalo, NY; *U.S. Public*, pg. 631

Logan, Robert, Sr. V.P.-European Sls. & Mktg.--R.R. Donnelley & Sons Company, Chicago, IL; *U.S. Public,* pg. 517
Logsdon, Linda, Sr. V.P.-Health Mktg. Svcs.--Express Scripts, Inc., Maryland Heights, MO; *U.S. Public,* pg. 600
Logue, George A., Sr. V.P.-School Publ.--Houghton Mifflin Company, Boston, MA; *U.S. Public,* pg. 841
Loiseau, Denis, Sr. V.P.-Commercial Risk Mngmt.--Willis Corroon Corp. of California, San Francisco, CA; *Int'l,* pg. 1505
Lok, Christopher, Sr. V.P.--RNBNY Branch Office-Hong Kong, Central, Hong Kong; *U.S. Public,* pg. 1381
Loken, Michael E., Sr. V.P.-MIS--Lutheran Brotherhood, Minneapolis, MN; *U.S. Private,* pg. 681
Loker, Susan J., Sr. V.P.-Human Resources--Cambridge Technology Partners, Cambridge, MA; *U.S. Public,* pg. 1424
Lokosh, John L., Sr. V.P.-Intl.--Willis Corroon Corp. of Seattle, Seattle, WA; *Int'l,* pg. 1507
Lombard, Gilberte, Sr. V.P.-Investor Rels.--Credit Commercial de France, Paris, France; *Int'l,* pg. 341
Lombardo, Judith, Sr. V.P.--Rag Shops, Inc., Hawthorne, NJ; *U.S. Public,* pg. 1358
Lombardo, Salvatore A., Sr. V.P. & Co-Creative Dir.--JMCT/ Direct, New York, NY; *U.S. Private,* pg. 599
Lombardozzi, Micahel E., Sr. V.P. & Gen. Counsel--Signet Star Reinsurance Company, Florham Park, NJ; *U.S. Public,* pg. 216
Lomita, Sol, Sr. V.P.-Post Production--TriStar Pictures, Culver City, CA; *Int'l,* pg. 1283
London, Fredric S., Sr. V.P., Gen. Counsel & Sec.--OMI Corp., New York, NY; *U.S. Public,* pg. 1208
London, Mark, Sr. V.P.--General Growth Properties Inc., Chicago, IL; *U.S. Public,* pg. 715
London, Robby, Sr. V.P.-Creative Affairs--DIC Entertainment, Burbank, CA; *U.S. Public,* pg. 513
Lonergan, Kevin M., Sr. V.P. & Dir.-Stores & Opers.--Old Navy Stores, San Francisco, CA; *U.S. Public,* pg. 703
Long, Catherine, Sr. V.P.-Acctg.--Franchise Finance Corp. of America, Scottsdale, AZ; *U.S. Public,* pg. 679
Long, Charles, Chief Fin. Officer, Sr. V.P. & Treas.--Highmark Inc., Pittsburgh, PA; *U.S. Private,* pg. 528
Long, Deborah J., Sr. V.P. & Gen. Counsel--Protective Life Corporation, Birmingham, AL; *U.S. Public,* pg. 1336
Long, Haney A., Sr. V.P.-Pur. & Distr.--Shoney's, Inc., Nashville, TN; *U.S. Public,* pg. 1467
Long, Lucinda P., Sr. V.P. & Gen. Counsel--Valley National Bank, Parsippany, NJ; *U.S. Public,* pg. 1705
Long, Robert L., Chief Fin. Officer & Sr. V.P.--Transocean Offshore, Inc., Houston, TX; *U.S. Public,* pg. 1631
Long, W. Audie, Sr., Sr. V.P., Gen. Counsel & Sec.--USLD Communications Corp., San Antonio, TX; *U.S. Public,* pg. 969
Longaberger, Rachel, Sr. V.P.--The Longaberger Company, Dresden, OH; *U.S. Private,* pg. 675
Longo, Edward, Sr. V.P.-ISO--Keane, Inc., Boston, MA; *U.S.* Public, pg. 946
Longo, Edward, Sr. V.P.-Info. Svcs. Div.--Information Services Division, Boston, MA; *U.S. Public,* pg. 946
Longwell, H.J., Sr. V.P.--Exxon Corporation, Irving, TX; *U.S. Public,* pg. 601
Longwell, John D., Sr. V.P.-Opers.--Prima Energy Corporation, Denver, CO; *U.S. Public,* pg. 1325
Longworth, T.J., Sr. V.P.-Strategic Business Devel.--Canfor Corporation, Vancouver, Canada; *Int'l,* pg. 260
Lonnborg, Lars, Sr. V.P.-Health/Welfare Div. & Baltic Opers.--Trygg-Hansa, Stockholm, Sweden; *Int'l,* pg. 1425
Lonnebotn, Trygve, Sr. V.P.-Opers.--RAYOVAC Corporation, Madison, WI; *U.S. Private,* pg. 912
Loof, Per-Olof, Sr. V.P.-Fin. Sys. Grp.--NCR Corporation, Dayton, OH; *U.S. Public,* pg. 1146
Loomis, Richard C., Sr. V.P.--Comarco, Inc., Yorba Linda, CA; *U.S. Public,* pg. 406
Looyenga, R.L., Sr. V.P.-Mktg.--Auto-Owners Insurance, Lansing, MI; *U.S. Private,* pg. 100
Loper, William, Sr. V.P.-Creative Adv.--Universal Pictures, Universal City, CA; *Int'l,* pg. 1216
Loper, William, Sr. V.P.-Creative Adv.--TriStar Pictures, Culver City, CA; *Int'l,* pg. 1283
Lopez de Amely, Maria V., Sr. V.P. & Gen. Mgr.-Money Express--Firstbank Puerto Rico, Santurce, PR; *U.S. Public,* pg. 644
Lopez, David B., Sr. V.P-Legal Counsel--Clopay Corporation, Cincinnati, OH; *U.S. Public,* pg. 766
Lopez, Filomon, Sr. V.P.-Adv. Sls.--Comcast Cable Communications, Inc., Philadelphia, PA; *U.S. Public,* pg. 407
Lopez, Santos, Sr. V.P. & Studio Mgr.--Carrafiello, Diehl & Associates, Inc., Irvington, NY; *U.S. Private,* pg. 215
Lopiano, John A., Sr. V.P. & Pres.-Production Systems Group--Xerox Corporation, Stamford, CT; *U.S. Public,* pg. 1783
Lopuch, George Z., Sr. V.P.-Strategic Plng. & Res.--SuperValu, Inc., Eden Prairie, MN; *U.S. Public,* pg. 1540
Lopushansky, Mark E., Sr. V.P.-Funds Mngmt.--Southwest National Corporation, Greensburg, PA; *U.S. Public,* pg. 1493
Lopushansky, Mark E., Sr. V.P.-Funds Mngmt.--Southwest National Bank of Pennsylvania, Greensburg, PA; *U.S. Public,* pg. 1493
Lordi, Michael J., Sr. V.P.-Electric Trading--CNG Energy Services Corporation, Pittsburgh, PA; *U.S. Public,* pg. 435
Lorenz, Gary, Sr. V.P. & Gen. Mgr.--Griffin Technology Inc., Amsec Div., Rancho Dominguez, CA; *U.S. Public,* pg. 506
Lorenz, Nancy J., Sr. V.P.-H.R., Mngmt. & Org. Devel.--Magna Group, Inc., Saint Louis, MO; *U.S. Public,* pg. 1037
Lorenzen, Niels Erik, Sr. V.P.--F.L. Smidth & Co. A/S, Copenhagen, Denmark; *Int'l,* pg. 475
Lorenzini, Paul G., Sr. V.P.--PacifiCorp, Portland, OR; *U.S. Public,* pg. 1251
Loring, Denis W., Sr. V.P.-Reinsurance--The Equitable Companies Incorporated, New York, NY; *U.S. Public,* pg. 588
Lorio, Thomas D., Sr. V.P.--Hibernia Corporation, New Orleans, LA; *U.S. Public,* pg. 825
Lorraine, Richard A., Sr. V.P.--ITT Automotive, Inc., Auburn Hills, MI; *U.S. Public,* pg. 859
Losee, Tom, Sr. V.P. & Publishing Dir.--Architectural Digest, Los Angeles, CA; *U.S. Private,* pg. 20
Losier, John, Sr. V.P. & Gen. Mgr.-Worldwide Sls. & Mktg.--Tandem Computers Inc., Cupertino, CA; *U.S. Public,* pg. 417
Losito, David J., Sr. V.P.--Jefferies & Company, Inc., Los Angeles, CA; *U.S. Public,* pg. 925
Lottes, Ronald L., Sr. V.P.--Norwest Financial, Inc., Des Moines, IA; *U.S. Public,* pg. 1202
Loudermilk, Joey M., Sr. V.P., Gen. Counsel, & Corp. Sec.--AFLAC Incorporated, Columbus, GA; *U.S. Public,* pg. 28
Loughlin, John P., Sr. V.P. & Grp. Publisher--Women's Magazines Group, New York, NY; *Int'l,* pg. 190
Loughran, Judy, Sr. V.P.--Da-Lite Screen Company, Inc., Warsaw, IN; *U.S. Private,* pg. 306
Loughrey, Robert G., Sr. V.P.-Mellon Bus. Credit--Mellon Bank Corporation, Pittsburgh, PA; *U.S. Public,* pg. 1084
Lousteau, Stephen M., Sr. V.P.--Hibernia Corporation, New Orleans, LA; *U.S. Public,* pg. 825
Louttit, Gordon J., Sr. V.P., Gen. Counsel & Sec.--Aerospace Corporation, El Segundo, CA; *U.S. Private,* pg. 24
Loux, P. Ogden, Chief Fin. Officer & Sr. V.P.--W.W. Grainger, Inc., Lincolnshire, IL; *U.S. Public,* pg. 758
Love, Jimmy, Sr. V.P. & Sec.--T.L. James & Company, Ruston, LA; *U.S. Private,* pg. 580
Lovecchio, Nicholas M., Sr. V.P. & Dir.-RMS--Willis Corroon Corp. of Penn., Radnor, PA; *Int'l,* pg. 1507
Lovelady, Ron E., Sr. V.P.-Human Resources--Longs Drug Stores Corporation, Walnut Creek, CA; *U.S. Public,* pg. 1013
Lovell, Mary S., Sr. V.P.-Utility Services--Atmos Energy Corporation, Dallas, TX; *U.S. Public,* pg. 145
Loveridge, Gary, Sr. V.P.-Admin. Services & Gen. Counsel--Sutter Health, Sacramento, CA; *U.S. Private,* pg. 1057
Lovett, Jeffrey A., Sr. V.P.--AMCORE Bank, Rock River Valley, Dixon, IL; *U.S. Public,* pg. 64
Lovett, Keith, Sr. V.P.-Human Resources--Fred Meyer Stores, Portland, OR; *U.S. Public,* pg. 1103
Lovett, M.F., Chief Fin. Officer & Sr. V.P.--Ingram Book Company, La Vergne, TN; *U.S. Private,* pg. 563
Lovett, Rosalee, Chief Fin. Officer & Sr. V.P.--BPI Communications Inc., New York, NY; *Int'l,* pg. 1446
Low, Coby, Sr. V.P. & Media Resources Dir.--Rubin Postaer & Associates, Santa Monica, CA; *U.S. Private,* pg. 949
Low, Fowler H., Sr. V.P.--Genesco Inc., Nashville, TN; *U.S. Public,* pg. 728
Low, Reginald G., Sr. V.P.--Products, San Diego, CA; *U.S. Public,* pg. 1627
Lowber, John M., Chief Fin. Officer, Sr. V.P., Treas. & Sec.--General Communication, Inc., Anchorage, AK; *U.S. Public,* pg. 708
Lowe, Challis, Sr. V.P.-H.R.--Beneficial Corporation, Wilmington, DE; *U.S. Public,* pg. 211
Lowe, Challis, Sr. V.P.-H.R., Admin. & Special Projects--Beneficial Management Corporation, Peapack, NJ; *U.S. Public,* pg. 211
Lowe, Michael B., Sr. V.P.-H.R.--Corporate & Institutional Financial Services - Montreal, Toronto, Canada; *Int'l,* pg. 153
Lowenberg, David A., Sr. V.P. & Dir.-Site Opers.--Express Scripts, Inc., Maryland Heights, MO; *U.S. Public,* pg. 600
Lowenfels, Fred M., Sr. V.P. & Gen. Counsel--Transammonia Inc., New York, NY; *U.S. Private,* pg. 1096
Lowery, Joseph M., Sr. V.P.-Asset Liability Mngmt.--Synovus Financial Corp., Columbus, GA; *U.S. Public,* pg. 1548
Lowman, James F., Sr. V.P.-Central Arizona Div.--Southwest Gas Corporation, Las Vegas, NV; *U.S. Public, pg. 1493*
Lowry, Donald M., Sr. V.P., Gen. Counsel & Sec.--Continental Assurance Company, Chicago, IL; *U.S. Private,* pg. 267
Lowry, Raymond, Sr. V.P.-Comml. Loans--Magna Group, Inc., Saint Louis, MO; *U.S. Public,* pg. 1037
Loy, Rob, Sr. V.P.-Fin.--Kauffman Products, Inc., Carmel, IN; *U.S. Private,* pg. 609
Lozier, Mark, Sr. V.P.--Keywell Corporation, Chicago, IL; *U.S. Private,* pg. 619
Lubarsky, Paul, Sr. V.P.-Fin. & Admin.--Deutsch, Inc., New York, NY; *U.S. Private,* pg. 328
Lubin, Myron L., Sr. V.P.-Sls.--ADVO, Inc., Windsor, CT; *U.S. Public,* pg. 23
Lucado, William E., Sr. V.P.--Concord EFS, Inc., Memphis, TN; *U.S. Public,* pg. 429
Lucas, Barbara B., Sr. V.P.-Pub. Affairs & Corp. Sec.--The Black & Decker Corporation, Towson, MD; *U.S. Public,* pg. 233
Lucas, Dennis C., Sr. V.P. & Reg. Mgr.--Albertson's, Inc., Boise, ID; *U.S. Public,* pg. 38
Lucas, Peter, Chief Fin. Officer & Sr. V.P.--Westower Corporation, Vancouver, WA; *U.S. Public,* pg. 1762
Lucas, Raymond D., Chief Strategic Officer & Sr. V.P.-Strategic Opers.--Scientific-Atlanta, Inc., Norcross, GA; *U.S. Public,* pg. 1443
Lucas, Wayne T., Sr. V.P.-Energy Supply--Kentucky Utilities Company, Lexington, KY; *U.S. Public,* pg. 941
Lucenta, Dominic, Sr. V.P.-H.R.--Essex International, Inc., Fort Wayne, IN; *U.S. Public,* pg. 593
Lucey, Douglas M., Sr. V.P.-Asset Mngmt.--Taubman Centers, Inc., Bloomfield Hills, MI; *U.S. Public,* pg. 1561
Lucey, Richard E., Chief Fin. Officer & Sr. V.P.-Edison Capital--Edison Capital, Irvine, CA; *U.S. Public,* pg. 564
Luchs, Kenneth, Sr. V.P.-Mktg., Sls. & Adv.--Reliable Stores, Inc., Columbia, MD; *U.S. Private,* pg. 920
Luck, Linda C., Sr. V.P.--Peoples Savings Bank of Ashtabula, Ashtabula, OH; *U.S. Public,* pg. 647
Lucore, George R., Sr. V.P.--Erie Family Life Insurance Company, Erie, PA; *U.S. Public,* pg. 590
Ludh, William, Sr. V.P.-Mktg.--The Sportsman's Guide, Inc., Saint Paul, MN; *U.S. Public,* pg. 1499
Ludrof, Jeffrey A., Sr. V.P.--Erie Family Life Insurance Company, Erie, PA; *U.S. Public,* pg. 590
Ludwig, Douglas L., Chief Fin. Officer, Sr. V.P. & Treas.--Four Seasons Hotels Inc., Don Mills, Canada; *Int'l,* pg. 502
Ludwig, Edward J., Chief Fin. Officer & Sr. V.P.-Fin.--Becton Dickinson & Company, Franklin Lakes, NJ; *U.S. Public,* pg. 199
Ludwig, Kenneth M., Sr. V.P.-H.R.--Culp, Inc., High Point, NC; *U.S. Public,* pg. 467
Lue, Larry, Sr. V.P. & Grp. Acct. Dir.--The Lord Group, New York, NY; *U.S. Private,* pg. 325
Luebrecht, Donald E., Sr. V.P.--Crown Equipment Corporation, New Bremen, OH; *U.S. Private,* pg. 292
Lueck, Fred E., Sr. V.P.-Mine Facilities--Environmental/ Government Group, Boise, ID; *U.S. Public,* pg. 1134
Luedke, Jerry, Sr. V.P. & Fin. Dir.--Citron Haligman Bedecarre, San Francisco, CA; *U.S. Private,* pg. 241
Luft, Eric P., Sr. V.P.-Men's Div.--Swank, Inc., Attleboro, MA; *U.S. Public,* pg. 1543
Luhr, Alfred F., III, Sr. V.P.--Manufacturers & Traders Trust Company, Buffalo, NY; *U.S. Public,* pg. 631
Luhtanen, Andrea, Sr. V.P.-Mktg. Svcs.--Haworth Group Inc., Minneapolis, MN; *U.S. Private,* pg. 511
Luino, Ronald F., Sr. V.P.-Fin. & Admin.--SEIKO Corporation of America, Mahwah, NJ; *Int'l,* pg. 1218
Luke, Edwin E., Sr. V.P.-Michigan Regl. Mgr.--A.G. Edwards & Sons, Inc., Saint Louis, MO; *U.S. Public,* pg. 565
Luke, Paul B., Chief Fin. Officer, Sr. V.P., Treas. & Sec.--T&W Financial Corporation, Tacoma, WA; *U.S. Public,* pg. 1552
Lukens, John J., Sr. V.P.--Raritan Bancorp Inc., Bridgewater, NJ; *U.S. Public,* pg. 1361
Luker, Ken L., Sr. V.P.--Stephenville Bank & Trust Co., Stephenville, TX; *U.S. Public,* pg. 633
Lukkari, Jorma, Sr. V.P.--Engineering Division, Oulu, Finland; *Int'l,* pg. 1088
Lukman, John C., Sr. V.P. & Sec.--Stanchem Inc., East Berlin, CT; *U.S. Private,* pg. 1030
Lula, George, Sr. V.P.-Corp. Credit Policy--PNC Bank Corp., Pittsburgh, PA; *U.S. Public,* pg. 1242
Lum, Raymond S., Sr. V.P.--Servco Pacific Inc., Honolulu, HI; *U.S. Private,* pg. 986
Lumley, David R., Sr. V.P.-Sls. & Mktg.--Outboard Marine Corporation, Waukegan, IL; *U.S. Private,* pg. 478
Lummis, P. Bradley, Sr. V.P., Treas. & Sec.--Mrs. Baird's Bakeries, Inc., Fort Worth, TX; *U.S. Private,* pg. 765
Lumpkin, Steven K., Sr. V.P.-Admin.--Applebee's International, Inc., Overland Park, KS; *U.S. Public,* pg. 122
Lumsden, George H., Sr. V.P. & Gen. Auditor--First Hawaiian Bank, Honolulu, HI; *U.S. Public,* pg. 634
Lund, Alan H., Chief Fin. Officer, Sr. V.P., Treas.--International Lease Finance Corporation, Los Angeles, CA; *U.S. Public,* pg. 85
Lund, James, Sr. V.P.--National Bank of Alaska, Anchorage, AK; *U.S. Public,* pg. 1153
Lund, Mark R., Sr. V.P., Controller & Asst. Treas.--TCF Financial Corp., Minneapolis, MN; *U.S. Public,* pg. 1554
Lund, Mark R., Sr. V.P., Contoller & Asst. Treas.--TCF Bank Minnesota FSB, Minneapolis, MN; *U.S. Public,* pg. 1554
Lundborg, Jay R., Sr. V.P. & Dir.-Tax--First Midwest Bancorp, Inc., Itasca, IL; *U.S. Public,* pg. 636
Lundeen, Stephen P., Sr. V.P.-Human Resources--Eddie Bauer, Inc., Redmond, WA; *U.S. Public,* pg. 1499
Lundin, Nils Ingvar, Sr. V.P.--Investor AB, Stockholm, Sweden; *Int'l,* pg. 686
Lundquist, Lars, Sr. V.P.-Investment & Life Div.--Trygg-Hansa, Stockholm, Sweden; *Int'l,* pg. 1425
Lunetta, Lawerence, Sr. V.P.-Sls. & Service--Caere Corporation, Los Gatos, CA; *U.S. Public,* pg. 291
Lunt, Jack R., Sr. V.P., Asst. Gen. Counsel & Sec.--American Stores Company, Salt Lake City, UT; *U.S. Public,* pg. 92
Lunt, Wayne E., Sr. V.P.-Assoc. Pipelines & Chemicals--Transcanada Pipelines Limited, Calgary, Canada; *Int'l,* pg. 1416
Lupien, Jack, Sr. V.P.-Ins.--John Burnham & Co., San Diego, CA; *U.S. Private,* pg. 186
Lupinski, Thomas M., Chief Fin. Officer & Sr. V.P.--Swiss Army Brands, Inc., Shelton, CT; *U.S. Public,* pg. 1544
Lupo, John, Sr. V.P.-Mdsg.--Wal-Mart Stores, Inc., Bentonville, AR; *U.S. Public,* pg. 1732
Luppert, David R., Sr. V.P.-Fin. & Admin.--F & W Publications, Inc., Cincinnati, OH; *U.S. Private,* pg. 300
Luppi, Mark J., Sr. V.P.-Retail Bankin, Boston Reg.--Citizens Bank of Massachusetts, Fairhaven, MA; *Int'l,* pg. 1132
Lushefski, John E., Chief Fin. Officer & Sr. V.P.--Millennium Chemicals Inc., Iselin, NJ; *U.S. Public,* pg. 1111
Lusk, Alice H., Sr. V.P.-Bus. Solutions Grp.--NCR Corporation, Dayton, OH; *U.S. Public,* pg. 1146
Lusk, William C., Jr., Sr. V.P. & Treas.--Shaw Industries, Inc., Dalton, GA; *U.S. Public,* pg. 1464
Luskin, Kevin, Sr. V.P.--Luskin's, Inc., Columbia, MD; *U.S. Private,* pg. 681
Lust, Kenneth E., Chief Oper. Officer & Sr. V.P.--MainStreet BankGroup Incorporated, Martinsville, VA; *U.S. Public,* pg. 1038
Lustenader, Jim, Sr. V.P.-Mktg. Svcs.--Dugan Valva Contess Inc., Morristown, NJ; *U.S. Private,* pg. 345
Lustig, Paul J., Sr. V.P.--Sara Lee Corporation, Chicago, IL; *U.S. Public,* pg. 1432
Luter, Joseph W., IV, Sr. V.P.-Mktg. & Sls./Fresh Pork--The Smithfield Packing Co., Inc., Smithfield, VA; *U.S. Public,* pg. 1479
Luterman, Gerald, Chief Fin. Officer & Sr. V.P.--Arrow Electronics, Inc., Melville, NY; *U.S. Public,* pg. 133

Lutes, Bill, Chief Fin. Officer & Sr. V.P.--Pyramid Mouldings, Jacksonville, FL; *Int'l*, pg. 1335

Lutes, Ian G., Sr. V.P.--Foster Wheeler Energy International, Inc., Clinton, NJ; *U.S. Public*, pg. 676

Luthman, Carl R., Sr. V.P. & Dir.-Admin. Services--Selective Insurance Group, Inc, Branchville, NJ; *U.S. Public*, pg. 1455

Luthman, Carl R., Sr. V.P.--Selective Insurance Company of America, Branchville, NJ; *U.S. Public*, pg. 1455

Luthman, Carl R., Sr. V.P.--Selective Way Insurance Company, Branchville, NJ; *U.S. Public*, pg. 1456

Lutsch, James R., Chief Info. Officer & Sr. V.P.--St. Paul Bancorp, Inc., Chicago, IL; *U.S. Public*, pg. 1428

Lutsch, James R., Chief Info. Officer & Sr. V.P.--St. Paul Federal Bank for Savings, Chicago, IL; *U.S. Public*, pg. 1428

Lutter, A.W. Jr., Sr. V.P.-Mktg. & Bus. Affairs--National Steel & Shipbuilding Company, San Diego, CA; *U.S. Private*, pg. 787

Luttrell, Robert S., Sr. V.P.-Trust Div.--Farmers First Bank, Lititz, PA; *U.S. Public*, pg. 1542

Lutz, L.H., Sr. V.P.-Tech.--Bliss-Salem, Inc., Salem, OH; *U.S. Private*, pg. 149

Luzier, Patricia, Sr. V.P.-H.R.--Vicorp Restaurants, Inc., Denver, CO; *U.S. Public*, pg. 1719

Lybeck, Katarina, Sr. V.P.-Corp. Commun.--Outokumpu Oyj, Espoo, Finland; *Int'l*, pg. 1015

Lyden, Jerry J., Sr. V.P.-Sls.--Apria Healthcare Group Inc., Costa Mesa, CA; *U.S. Public*, pg. 125

Lyman, Roger, Sr. V.P.-Health Care Delivery--Regence BlueCross BlueShield of Oregon, Portland, OR; *U.S. Private*, pg. 917

Lynam, Niall, Chief Tech. Officer & Sr. V.P.-Res. & Devel.--Donnelly Corporation, Holland, MI; *U.S. Public*, pg. 519

Lynch, Chuck, Chief Fin. Officer & Sr. V.P.--Mervyn's California, Hayward, CA; *U.S. Public*, pg. 489

Lynch, Donald T., Sr. V.P.-Fin. Opers.--MCI Communications Corp., Atlanta, GA; *U.S. Public*, pg. 1023

Lynch, Michael R., Sr. V.P.-Stores--Caldor, Inc., Norwalk, CT; *U.S. Public*, pg. 292

Lynch, Patrick J., Chief Fin. Officer & Sr. V.P.--Texaco Inc., White Plains, NY; *U.S. Public*, pg. 1582

Lynch, Peter, Sr. V.P.--People's Choice TV Corp., Shelton, CT; *U.S. Public*, pg. 1274

Lynch, Richard J., Sr. V.P.--Fairchild Publications, New York, NY; *U.S. Public*, pg. 513

Lynch, Thomas C., Sr. V.P.--Safeguard Scientifics, Inc., Wayne, PA; *U.S. Public*, pg. 1424

Lyndon, Leslie, Sr. V.P.-Creative & Dir.-Mktg.--Fox Broadcasting Company (FBC), Beverly Hills, CA; *Int'l*, pg. 926

Lyngaas, Michael E., Sr. V.P.--General Reinsurance Corp., Stamford, CT; *U.S. Public*, pg. 725

Lyngsie, K., Sr. V.P.--Fuller Company, Bethlehem, PA; *Int'l*, pg. 475

Lynn, Michael, Sr. V.P. & Central Region Plng. Dir.--Western International Media Corporation, Chicago, IL; *U.S. Private*, pg. 1167

Lynn, Wayne, Sr. V.P. & Gen. Mgr.-Eastern Grp.--Treasure Chest Advertising Co., Inc., Glendora, CA; *U.S. Public*, pg. 228

Lynyak, Robert M., Sr. V.P.--Chubb & Son, Inc., Warren, NJ; *U.S. Public*, pg. 355

Lyon-Caen, Yves, Sr. V.P.--Air Liquide S.A., Paris, France; *Int'l*, pg. 37

Lyon, Arthur S., Jr., Chief Mktg. Officer & Sr. V.P.--Integon Corporation, Winston Salem, NC; *U.S. Public*, pg. 719

Lyons, Daniel M., Sr. V.P.-Personnel--Darden Restaurants, Inc., Orlando, FL; *U.S. Public*, pg. 483

Lyons, Janis, Sr. V.P.-Corp. Acctg.--National City Corporation, Cleveland, OH; *U.S. Public*, pg. 1154

Lyons, John, Sr. V.P.-Sls. & Mktg.--Entex Information Services, Rye Brook, NY; *U.S. Private*, pg. 378

Lyons, Martin J., V.P.-Fin.--Moog Automotive, Inc., Saint Louis, MO; *U.S. Public*, pg. 443

Lyons, Michael H., II, Sr. V.P.-Maui Reg.--Bank of Hawaii, Honolulu, HI; *U.S. Public*, pg. 1248

Lyons, Norbert, Sr. V.P.-Sls.--Syroco Inc., Peabody, MA; *Int'l*, pg. 844

Lyons, Robert E., III, Sr. V.P.--Drug Emporium, Inc., Powell, OH; *U.S. Public*, pg. 530

Lytwynec, Brian P., Sr. V.P.-Mktg.--Utica Mutual Insurance Company, New Hartford, NY; *U.S. Private*, pg. 1129

Maas, Ronald B., Sr. V.P.-Pipeline Opers. & Engrng.--Westcoast Energy Inc., Vancouver, Canada; *Int'l*, pg. 1492

Mabee, William H., Sr. V.P.--Manufacturers & Traders Trust Company, Buffalo, NY; *U.S. Public*, pg. 631

Mac Donald, Ron, Sr. V.P.-Pricing & Mktg.--Manufacturers Consolidation Service, Inc., Memphis, TN; *U.S. Private*, pg. 700

Macaulay, Andrew, Sr. V.P. & Strategic Plng. Dir.--Roche Macaulay & Partners, Toronto, Canada; *U.S. Private*, pg. 678

Maccarrone, Franz A., Sr. V.P.-Opers.--Farah U.S.A., Inc., El Paso, TX; *U.S. Public*, pg. 613

MacClelland, Ken, Sr. V.P.--Willis Corroon Inspace, Inc., Bethesda, MD; *Int'l*, pg. 1507

MacConnell, George A., Sr. V.P.-Distr. & Millwork--Georgia-Pacific Corporation, Atlanta, GA; *U.S. Public*, pg. 735

MacCrum, John M., Sr. V.P.--Calgon Carbon Corporation, Pittsburgh, PA; *U.S. Public*, pg. 292

MacDonald, Arthur A., Sr. V.P.--Northern Telecom Limited, Brampton, Canada; *Int'l*, pg. 968

MacDonald, David J., Sr. V.P.--Hartford Life & Accident Insurance Company, Hartford, CT; *U.S. Public*, pg. 795

MacDonald, John, Sr. V.P.-Opers.--McNaughton-McKay Electric Co., Madison Heights, MI; *U.S. Private*, pg. 724

MacDonald, Sherri, Sr. V.P.-Opers.--UDL Laboratories, Inc., Rockford, IL; *U.S. Public*, pg. 1143

MacDougald, Suzanne M., Sr. V.P. & Sec.--ABR Information Services, Inc., Palm Harbor, FL; *U.S. Public*, pg. 2

MacDougall, R.A., Sr. V.P.-Fixed Incomes--General Electric Investment Corp., Stamford, CT; *U.S. Public*, pg. 712

Macekonis, Gerda, Sr. V.P.-Mktg.--Gilette Food Flavorings, Inc., Union, NJ; *U.S. Private*, pg. 453

Macey, Jonathan, Sr. V.P. & Controller--Beneficial Corporation, Wilmington, DE; *U.S. Public*, pg. 211

MacFadyen, C.R., Sr. V.P.--AGRA Earth & Environmental, Inc., Anaheim, CA; *Int'l*, pg. 31

MacFarlane, David C., Sr. V.P.--DeVry Institutes, Oak Brook Terrace, IL; *U.S. Public*, pg. 503

Macfarlane, S. Scott, Sr. V.P.-Folding Carton/Boxboard Mill--Jefferson Smurfit Corporation, Saint Louis, MO; *Int'l*, pg. 1269

MacGinnitie, W. James, Chief Fin. Officer & Sr. V.P.--Continental Assurance Company, Chicago, IL; *U.S. Private*, pg. 267

Machado, Edward J., Chief Fin. Officer & Sr. V.P.--Shenandoah Life Insurance Company, Roanoke, VA; *U.S. Private*, pg. 992

Machen, Robert J., Sr. V.P. & Gen. Mgr.-McDermott Mktg. Services--McDermott International, Inc., New Orleans, LA; *U.S. Public*, pg. 1067

Machenberg, Donald E., Sr. V.P. & Dir.-Bus. Devel. & Mkltg.--ITT Fluid Technology Corporation, Midland Park, NJ; *U.S. Public*, pg. 860

Machi, Vito A., Sr. V.P., Sr. Loan Admin., Asst. Sec. & Asst. Treas.--The Metropolitan Savings Bank of Ohio, Youngstown, OH; *U.S. Public*, pg. 608

Machida, Chiaki, Assoc. Dir.-Pkg. Devel.--Asahi Breweries Ltd., Tokyo, Japan; *Int'l*, pg. 83

Macias, E. James, Sr. V.P. & Gen. Mgr.-Generation, Transmission & Supply Bus. Unit--Pacific Gas & Electric Company, San Francisco, CA; *U.S. Public*, pg. 1241

MacIlwraith, Ian, Sr. V.P.-Opers.--Prism Integrated Sanitation Management, Inc., Miami, FL; *U.S. Private*, pg. 592

Macina, Frank A., Sr. V.P. & Acct. Service Grp. Head--Arnold Advertising, Mc Lean, VA; *U.S. Private*, pg. 84

Mack, John E., Sr. V.P. & Treas.--NationsBank Corporation, Charlotte, NC; *U.S. Public*, pg. 1162

MacKay, Donald R., Sr. V.P.--Dana Canada Inc., Saint Catharines, Canada; *U.S. Public*, pg. 480

Mackay, J. Cliff, Sr. V.P.--Spar Space Systems, Brampton, Canada; *Int'l*, pg. 1288

MacKay, John G., Sr. V.P. & Exec. V.P.-Europe--United Dominion Industries, Ltd., Charlotte, NC; *U.S. Public*, pg. 1675

Mackedanz, LeRoy H., Sr. V.P.--SCI Systems, Inc., Huntsville, AL; *U.S. Public*, pg. 1416

Macken, Clare, Sr. V.P. & Mngmt. Supvr.--Girgenti, Hughes, Butler & McDowell, New York, NY; *U.S. Private*, pg. 455

MacKenzie, George, Chief Fin. Officer & Sr. V.P.--Hercules Incorporated, Wilmington, DE; *U.S. Public*, pg. 809

Mackenzie, Gordon S., Sr. V.P.-Opers.--Overnite Transportation Co., Richmond, VA; *U.S. Public*, pg. 1668

MacKenzie, Tod, Sr. V.P.-Pub. Affairs--Frito-Lay Company, Plano, TX; *U.S. Public*, pg. 1277

Mackey, Judy, Sr. V.P.--Edelman Worldwide, Inc., New York, NY; *U.S. Private*, pg. 362

MacKinnon, Ian A., Sr. V.P.-Fixed Income Grp.--The Vanguard Group, Inc., Valley Forge, PA; *U.S. Private*, pg. 1133

MacKinnon, Larry D., Sr. V.P.-Credit Dept.--Chittenden Corporation, Burlington, VT; *U.S. Public*, pg. 350

Macklin, Ruth E., Sr. V.P. & Treas.--Bowl America, Incorporated, Alexandria, VA; *U.S. Public*, pg. 248

Mackoul, Sabry J., Sr. Exec. V.P.--Summit Bank, Chatham, NJ; *U.S. Public*, pg. 1528

MacLachlan, Neil T., Sr. V.P.-Asia Opers.--Barrick Power Gold Corporation of China Limited, Beijing, China; *Int'l*, pg. 169

MacLean, George H., Sr. V.P., Gen. Counsel & Sec.--U.S. Industries, Inc., Iselin, NJ; *U.S. Public*, pg. 1683

MacLeod, James S., Sr. V.P.-Sls.--Mortgage Guaranty Insurance Corporation, Milwaukee, WI; *U.S. Public*, pg. 1026

MacMillan, Michael, Sr. V.P.-Fin., Systems & Distr.--Winners Apparel Ltd., Toronto, Canada; *U.S. Public*, pg. 1557

Macnee, Peter, Sr. V.P.-Opers./Asia--Millicom International Cellular SA, Bertrange, Luxembourg; *Int'l*, pg. 867

Macomber, Scott, Sr. V.P. & Treas.--Vitalink Pharmacy Services, Inc., Naperville, IL; *U.S. Public*, pg. 1041

Macomber, Scott, Chief Fin. Officer, Sr. V.P. & Treas.--Vitalink Pharmacy Services, Inc., Atlanta, GA; *U.S. Public*, pg. 1042

MacPhail, Paul, Sr. V.P.-Opers.--Uno Restaurant Corporation, West Roxbury, MA; *U.S. Public*, pg. 1698

Macrini, Edward L., Sr. V.P.-Finance & Admin.--BPA International, New York, NY; *U.S. Private*, pg. 107

Madan, Robert, Sr. V.P.--GAB Robins North America, Inc., Parsippany, NJ; *Int'l*, pg. 1153

Madara, John M., Jr., Sr. V.P. & Grp. Exec.-Power Generation Grp.--PECO Energy Company, Philadelphia, PA; *U.S. Public*, pg. 1268

Madden, Chris, Sr. V.P. & Acct. Dir.--Wunderman Cato Johnson, New York, NY; *U.S. Private*, pg. 1197

Madden, Robert V., Sr. V.P.-Admin.--King World Productions, Inc., New York, NY; *U.S. Public*, pg. 961

Madden, Steve, Sr. V.P.-Cash Mngmt.--First Citizens Banc Shares, Inc., Raleigh, NC; *U.S. Public*, pg. 628

Maddock, Barbara M., Sr. V.P.-Human Resources--The McGraw-Hill Companies, New York, NY; *U.S. Public*, pg. 1069

Maddock, John P., Sr. V.P.-Mktg.--The Ailing & Cory Company, Rochester, NY; *U.S. Public*, pg. 1666

Maddox, Elton, Sr. V.P. & Gen. Mgr.--Poultry Div., Gainesville, GA; *U.S. Private*, pg. 268

Maddox, Lyn E., Sr. V.P.--PG&E Corporation, San Francisco, CA; *U.S. Public*, pg. 1240

Maddox, Richard, Sr. V.P.-Sls. & Mktg.--Bachmann Industries, Inc., Philadelphia, PA; *U.S. Private*, pg. 109

Maddox, Thomas E., Sr. V.P. & Deputy Gen. Counsel--American Stores Company, Salt Lake City, UT; *U.S. Public*, pg. 92

Madec, Alan, Exec. V.P. & Dir.-Strategy & Fin.--Total S.A., Paris, France; *Int'l*, pg. 1408

Madeja, Peter C., Sr. V.P.--Provident Companies, Inc., Chattanooga, TN; *U.S. Public*, pg. 1337

Madia, William J., Dr., Sr. V.P.--Battelle Memorial Institute, Columbus, OH; *U.S. Private*, pg. 123

Madison, John, Sr. V.P.-Sls.--Polygram Records, Inc., New York, NY; *Int'l*, pg. 1052

Madler, Mike, Chief Oper. Officer & Sr. V.P.--Prime Medical Services, Inc., Austin, TX; *U.S. Public*, pg. 1327

Madoff, Steven, Sr. V.P.-Bus. Affairs & Legal--Paramount Pictures Corporation, Los Angeles, CA; *U.S. Private*, pg. 776

Madsen, Adam M., Sr. V.P.-Corp. & Strategic Plng.--Long Island Lighting Company, Hicksville, NY; *U.S. Public*, pg. 1013

Maduri, John D., Chief Fin. Officer & Sr. V.P.-Fin.--Rogers Cantel Mobile Communications Inc., Saint-Laurent, Canada; *Int'l*, pg. 1122

Maehl, Doug, Sr. V.P.-Mfg., Pur. & Distr.--Safelite AutoGlass, Columbus, OH; *U.S. Private*, pg. 960

Maekawa, Shunji, Sr. V.P.--Marubeni America Corporation, New York, NY; *Int'l*, pg. 844

Maerki, Max H., Chief Fin. Officer & Sr. V.P.--Public Service Company of New Mexico, Albuquerque, NM; *U.S. Public*, pg. 1339

Maffeo, Vincent A., Sr. V.P. & Gen. Counsel--ITT Industries, Inc., White Plains, NY; *U.S. Public*, pg. 859

Maffucci, David G., Chief Fin. Officer & Sr. V.P.--Bowater Incorporated, Greenville, SC; *U.S. Public*, pg. 247

Magary, Richard, Sr. V.P.-Admin. & Asst. Sec.--American Shared Hospital Services, San Francisco, CA; *U.S. Public*, pg. 91

Magda, Robert, Sr. V.P.--Lawn Doctor Inc., Holmdel, NJ; *U.S. Private*, pg. 653

Magee, Bruce J., Chief Fin. Officer & Sr. V.P.--Harleysville Group, Harleysville, PA; *U.S. Public*, pg. 786

Magee, Mark E., Sr. V.P., Gen. Counsel & Sec.--Provident Financial Group, Inc., Cincinnati, OH; *U.S. Public*, pg. 1338

Magid, Karen, Sr. V.P.-Legal Affairs--Paramount Pictures Corporation, Los Angeles, CA; *U.S. Private*, pg. 776

MaGill, Mike, Chief Fin. Officer & Sr. V.P.--Safeguard Business Systems, Inc., Fort Washington, PA; *U.S. Private*, pg. 960

Magley, Philip L., Sr. V.P.--Columbia Gas System Service Corp., Wilmington, DE; *U.S. Public*, pg. 403

Magna, Larry, Sr. V.P.-Info. & Tech.--CSE Insurance Group, San Francisco, CA; *U.S. Private*, pg. 197

Magnani, Joseph, Chief Fin. Officer & Sr. V.P.--New York City Off-Track Betting Corp., New York, NY; *U.S. Private*, pg. 794

Magnemi, Joe, Sr. V.P. & Controller--Cline, Davis & Mann, Inc., New York, NY; *U.S. Private*, pg. 246

Magner, William F., Sr. V.P.-Sls./Leasing, DC--Spaulding & Slye, Boston, MA; *U.S. Private*, pg. 1021

Magnesen, Larry, Sr. V.P.--Old Kent Bank, Grand Rapids, MI; *U.S. Public*, pg. 1216

Magnus-Jackson, Judy, Sr. V.P. & Human Resources Dir.--Wunderman Cato Johnson, New York, NY; *U.S. Private*, pg. 1197

Magnuson, Brent, Sr. V.P.-Mdsg.--The Bombay Company, Fort Worth, TX; *U.S. Public*, pg. 244

Magnuson, Brent A., Sr. V.P.-Mdse. & Mktg. (Interim)--The Bombay Company, Inc., Fort Worth, TX; *U.S. Public*, pg. 244

Magnusson, Leifur, Sr. V.P.--Icelandair, Reykjavik, Iceland; *Int'l*, pg. 658

Maguire, Dennis, Sr. V.P.-Sls.--Buena Vista Home Video, Burbank, CA; *U.S. Public*, pg. 513

Maguire, Tom, Chief Info. Officer & Sr. V.P.--JM Family Enterprises Inc., Deerfield Beach, FL; *U.S. Private*, pg. 577

Mahady, Joseph, Sr. V.P.-Natl. Business--Wyeth-Ayerst Laboratories, Inc., Philadelphia, PA; *U.S. Public*, pg. 80

Mahar, Michael C., Sr. V.P.--The Troy Savings Bank, Troy, NY; *U.S. Private*, pg. 1106

Maher, Michael R., Sr. V.P. & Controller--Standard Federal Bank, Troy, MI; *Int'l*, pg. 10

Mahin, Elizabeth A., Sr. V.P. & Chief Acctg. Officer--American Heritage Life Insurance Co., Jacksonville, FL; *U.S. Public*, pg. 79

Mahoney, Frank G., Sr. V.P.-Annuity & Investment Products--Jefferson-Pilot Life Insurance Co., Greensboro, NC; *U.S. Public*, pg. 926

Mahoney, James R., Sr. V.P.-Consulting, Ventures & Corp. Devel.--International Technology Corporation, Monroeville, PA; *U.S. Public*, pg. 907

Mahoney, Thomas F., Sr. V.P.-Sls.--Trans-Lux Corporation, Norwalk, CT; *U.S. Public*, pg. 1628

Mahood, Willard S., Sr. V.P.-Acquisitions--Urstadt Biddle Properties, Inc., Greenwich, CT; *U.S. Public*, pg. 1700

Mai, Chao C., Dr., Sr. V.P.-Wafer Fabrication & Tech. Devel.--Dallas Semiconductor Corporation, Dallas, TX; *U.S. Public*, pg. 478

Maibach, George R., Sr. V.P.-Opers.--Bentley Mills, Inc., City of Industry, CA; *U.S. Public*, pg. 889

Maiden, Benjamin G., Dr., Sr. V.P.--Battelle Memorial Institute, Columbus, OH; *U.S. Private*, pg. 123

Maier, F., Sr. V.P.-Devel.--Enserch Development Inc., Florham Park, NJ; *U.S. Public*, pg. 1587

Maier, Richard, Sr. V.P.-Fin.--LaSalle National Bank, Chicago, IL; *Int'l*, pg. 10

Mailer, Dee Jay, Sr. V.P. & Reg. Mgr.-Hawaii--Kaiser Permanente, Oakland, CA; *U.S. Private*, pg. 605

Maillar, Barbara B., Sr. V.P. & Mgr.-Claims--Willis Corroon Corp. of Massachusetts, Boston, MA; *Int'l*, pg. 1506

Main, Alan, Sr. V.P.-Research--Novartis Pharmaceuticals, East Hanover, NJ; *Int'l*, pg. 973

Main, Timothy L., Sr. V.P.-Bus. Devel.--Jabil Circuit, Inc., Saint Petersburg, FL; *U.S. Public*, pg. 919

Mainthia, Nik, Sr. V.P. & Media Dir.--Fitzgerald & Co., Atlanta, GA; *U.S. Private*, pg. 409

Maintz, John J., Sr. V.P.-Credit Admin.--BOK Financial Corp., Tulsa, OK; *U.S. Public*, pg. 163
Mainzer, Bruce, Sr. V.P.-Mktg.--Vail Resorts, Inc., Vail, CO; *U.S. Public*, pg. 1704
Mainzer, Bruce, Sr. V.P.-Mkts.--Vail Associates, Inc., Vail, CO; *U.S. Public*, pg. 1704
Maio, Douglas, Sr. V.P.--Dataquest Incorporated, San Jose, CA; *U.S. Public*, pg. 535
Maio, Thomas A., Sr. V.P.--American Appraisal Associates, Inc., Milwaukee, WI; *U.S. Private*, pg. 49
Majewicz, Ronald J., Sr. V.P. & Controller--Federal Home Loan Mortgage Corporation, Mc Lean, VA; *U.S. Public*, pg. 615
Majewski, Andrea S., Sr. V.P.--Chicago Asset Management Company, Chicago, IL; *U.S. Public*, pg. 1672
Majka, Lawrence J., Sr. V.P.-Fin. & Treas.--Advocate Health Care, Oak Brook, IL; *U.S. Private*, pg. 23
Major, Tom, Sr. V.P. & Gen. Mgr.--Six Flags Great Adventure Theme Park & Wild Safari Animal Park, Jackson, NJ; *U.S. Public*, pg. 1611
Majors, Robert F., Sr. V.P.--Willis Corroon Corp. of Missouri, Saint Louis, MO; *Int'l*, pg. 1506
Makabe, Mark, Sr. V.P.-Entertainment Sls. & Mktg.--Pioneer New Media Technologies, Long Beach, CA; *U.S. Private*, *pg. 866*
Makela, Ron D., Sr. V.P.-Opers. & Admin.--Santa Monica Bank, Santa Monica, CA; *U.S. Public*, pg. 1757
Makino, Shoichi, Sr. V.P.--Nippon Telegraph and Telephone Corporation, Tokyo, Japan; *Int'l*, pg. 940
Makowski, James D., Sr. V.P. & Lender--Valley Bank & Trust, Brighton, CO; *U.S. Private*, pg. 1132
Makris, Tony, Sr. V.P.--The Mercury Group, Alexandria, VA; *U.S. Private*, pg. 13
Maland, Timothy, Chief Fin. Officer & Sr. V.P.--Caesars Palace, Las Vegas, NV; *U.S. Public*, pg. 1512
Malanga, Michael E., Sr. V.P.-Devel.--Family Restaurants, Inc., Irvine, CA; *U.S. Private*, pg. 393
Malango, Tom, Sr. V.P.-Fin. & Admin--MGM Worldwide Television, Group., Santa Monica, CA; *U.S. Public*, pg. 1102
Malanowsky, Edgar J., Sr. V.P.--Southwest National Bank of Pennsylvania, Greensburg, PA; *U.S. Public*, pg. 1493
Malaspina, Alex, Sr. V.P.--The Coca-Cola Company, Atlanta, GA; *U.S. Public*, pg. 392
Malcolm, J. Parke, Sr. V.P. & Gen. Mgr.-Serials--UMI, Ann Arbor, MI; *U.S. Public*, pg. 201
Malcolm, Karen M., Sr. V.P.-Private Client Svcs.--The Bank of Bermuda Limited, Hamilton, Bermuda; *Int'l*, pg. 150
Malcolm, Steven J., Sr. V.P. & Gen. Mgr.-Gathering & Processing--Williams Field Services, Tulsa, OK; *U.S. Public*, pg. 1769
Maldari, Maureen, Sr. V.P.--Grey Advertising Inc., New York, NY; *U.S. Public*, pg. 764
Malena, Richard J., Sr. V.P., Branch Admin.--Bank of the Hudson, Poughkeepsie, NY; *U.S. Public*, pg. 1319
Malenfant, Matt, Sr. V.P.--VWR Scientific Products, West Chester, PA; *U.S. Public*, pg. 1703
Malerba, Jim, Sr. V.P. & Corp. Acctg.--Keycorp, Cleveland, OH; *U.S. Public*, pg. 954
Maleu, Gordon, Sr. V.P.--Ventura Foods, City of Industry, CA; *U.S. Private*, pg. 508
Malhouitre, Guy, Sr. V.P.--Gaz de France, Paris, France; *Int'l*, pg. 541
Malik, Shahid A., Sr. V.P. & Mng. Dir.--Ferrellgas Houston, Houston, TX; *U.S. Public*, pg. 618
Malinoski, Frank J., Sr. V.P.-Medical & Clinical Affairs--Nabi, Boca Raton, FL; *U.S. Public*, pg. 1148
Malinowitz, Michael, Sr. V.P.--D.L. Blair Inc., Garden City, NY; *U.S. Private*, pg. 148
Malkin, Roy K., Sr. V.P.--Steris Corporation, Mentor, OH; *U.S. Public*, pg. 1515
Malko, Robert, Sr. V.P. & Acct. Dir.--Wyse Advertising/Cleveland, Cleveland, OH; *U.S. Private*, pg. 1194
Mallabon, Brian, Sr. V.P.--Intelligent Controls Inc., Lynnwood, WA; *U.S. Private*, pg. 566
Mallardi, Michael P., Pres.-Broadcast Grp. & Sr. V.P.--ABC, Inc, New York, NY; *U.S. Public*, pg. 511
Mallea, Dan, Sr. V.P.-Fin. & Treas.--Regence BlueCross BlueShield of Oregon, Portland, OR; *U.S. Private*, pg. 917
Mallen, David J., Sr. V.P.-Fin--The Wilder Companies, Boston, MA; *U.S. Private*, pg. 1176
Mallett, Jeff, Sr. V.P.-Bus. Opers.--Yahoo!, Inc., Santa Clara, CA; *U.S. Public*, pg. 1787
Malley, Robert J., Sr. V.P. & Gen. Counsel--State Street Corporation, Boston, MA; *U.S. Public*, pg. 1513
Mallin, Ed, Sr. V.P.-Natl. Sls.--Database America Companies, Montvale, NJ; *U.S. Private*, pg. 312
Mallon, James A., Sr. V.P.--ITT Hartford Life & Annuity Insurance Corporation, Minneapolis, MN; *U.S. Public*, pg. 795
Mallory, Kevin E., Sr. V.P. & Hotel Bus. Devel.--Starwood Hotels & Resorts, Phoenix, AZ; *U.S. Public*, pg. 1512
Malloy, John R., Sr. V.P.--Du Pont De Nemours & Co.), Wilmington, DE; *U.S. Public*, pg. 530
Malloy, Michael, Sr. V.P.-Mktg.--Fair, Isaac and Company, Inc., San Rafael, CA; *U.S. Public*, pg. 609
Malmuth, David L., Sr. V.P.-Devel.--TrizecHahn Centers Inc., San Diego, CA; *Int'l*, pg. 1425
Malo, Kare O., Sr. V.P.-Pur.--Dahl International AB, Stockholm, Sweden; *Int'l*, pg. 359
Malone, James C., Sr. V.P.-Fin. & Controller--Cognizant Corporation, Westport, CT; *U.S. Public*, pg. 395
Malone, James M., Sr. V.P. & Gen. Mgr.-Paper--Burrows Paper Corporation, Little Falls, NY; *U.S. Private*, pg. 188
Malone, Jerry J., Sr. V.P.--The M&T Company, King of Prussia, PA; *U.S. Public*, pg. 277
Malone, Joe N., Chief Oper. Officer & Sr. V.P.--Blockbuster Music, Dallas, TX; *U.S. Private*, pg. 776
Maloney, James F., Sr. V.P.--ITT Information Services, Inc., New York, NY; *U.S. Public*, pg. 1512
Maloney, Mark, Sr. V.P.-Sls.--Trust Fund Advisors, Inc., Washington, DC; *U.S. Private*, pg. 1116
Maloney, William, Sr. V.P.-College--Barnes & Noble Inc., New York, NY; *U.S. Public*, pg. 189
Maloni, William R., Sr. V.P.-Govt. & Industry Rels.--Federal National Mortgage Association (Fannie Mae), Washington, DC; *U.S. Public*, pg. 615
Maloof, George E., Sr. V.P.--Bindley Western Industries, Inc., Indianapolis, IN; *U.S. Public*, pg. 228
Maloy, Terry E., Sr. V.P.-Mktg. & Plng.--American Drug Stores Inc., Oak Brook, IL; *U.S. Public*, pg. 93
Maltby, Sandra M., Sr. V.P.--Keycorp, Cleveland, OH; *U.S. Public*, pg. 954
Maltzman, Marvin S., Sr. V.P.-Admin., Sec. & Gen. Counsel--House of Fabrics, Inc., Sherman Oaks, CA; *U.S. Public*, pg. 842
Malys, Gerald J., Chief Fin. Officer & Sr. V.P.--Cyprus Amax Minerals Company, Englewood, CO; *U.S. Public*, pg. 470
Mamada, Yasuya, Sr. V.P.--Marubeni America Corporation, New York, NY; *Int'l*, pg. 844
Mancuso, John H., Sr. V.P. & Deputy Gen. Counsel--Keycorp, Cleveland, OH; *U.S. Public*, pg. 954
Mancuso, Lauren, Sr. V.P. & Reg. Dir.--Arnold Advertising, Albany, NY; *U.S. Private*, pg. 84
Mancuso, Lauren, Sr. V.P. & Reg. Dir.--Arnold Advertising, Rochester, NY; *U.S. Private*, pg. 84
Mancuso, Michael J., Chief Fin. Officer & Sr. V.P.--General Dynamics Corporation, Falls Church, VA; *U.S. Public*, pg. 708
Manczak, John E., Sr. V.P.-Retails Sls. & Svcs.--Carolina Power & Light Company, Raleigh, NC; *U.S. Public*, pg. 306
Mandart, Tracy J., Sr. V.P.--Hibernia Corporation, New Orleans, LA; *U.S. Public*, pg. 825
Mandel, Jonathan, Sr. V.P. & Natl. Brdcst. Dir.--Grey Advertising Inc., New York, NY; *U.S. Public*, pg. 764
Mandell, Andrew, Chief Fin. Officer & Sr. V.P.--ITT Sheraton Corporation, Boston, MA; *U.S. Public*, pg. 1512
Mandell, Michele, Sr. V.P.-Stores--Talbots, Inc., Hingham, MA; *Int'l*, pg. 28
Manenti, Thomas J., Sr. V.P.-Mktg. & Sls.--MiTek, Inc., Chesterfield, MO; *Int'l*, pg. 1106
Maney, William J., Chief Fin. Officer, Sr. V.P. & Treas.--American Annuity Group, Cincinnati, OH; *U.S. Public*, pg. 74
Manfredi, Robert R., Sr. V.P.--RTKL Associates Inc., Baltimore, MD; *U.S. Private*, pg. 906
Mangan, Daryl K., Sr. V.P.--SAFECO Properties, Inc., Seattle, WA; *U.S. Public*, pg. 1423
Mangan, Frank, Sr. V.P. & Acct. Grp. Dir.--Arnold Advertising, Mc Lean, VA; *U.S. Private*, pg. 84
Mangini, Ron, Sr. V.P.-Sls.--Jacques Moret, Inc., New York, NY; *U.S. Private*, pg. 580
Mangold, Ed, Sr. V.P.-Mktg--Applied Communications, Inc., Omaha, NE; *U.S. Public*, pg. 1629
Mangold, Edward H., Sr. V.P.-Americas Region--Transaction Systems Architects, Inc., Omaha, NE; *U.S. Public*, pg. 1629
Mangrem, Larry, Sr. V.P. & Cashier--Weatherford National Bank, Weatherford, TX; *U.S. Public*, pg. 633
Mangum, Stephen F., Chief Fin. Officer & Sr. V.P.--Pier 1 Imports, Inc., Fort Worth, TX; *U.S. Public*, pg. 1295
Manheim, Glen E., Chief Oper. Officer & Sr. V.P.--Empire Life Insurance Company, Seattle, WA; *U.S. Public*, pg. 1742
Manibusan, Dennis A., Sr. V.P.-Aircraft Maintenance--ABX Air, Inc., Wilmington, OH; *U.S. Public*, pg. 33
Manion, F. William, Sr. V.P. & Mgr.-Branch Opers.--First Federal of Michigan, Detroit, MI; *U.S. Public*, pg. 336
Manire, Ross W., Sr. V.P.-Carrier Sys.--3Com Corporation, Santa Clara, CA; *U.S. Public*, pg. 1603
Maniyar, Prabhav V., Chief Fin. Officer, Sr. V.P. & Sec.--Startec Global Communications Corporation, Bethesda, MD; *U.S. Public*, pg. 1511
Manjan, Thomas, Sr. V.P.-Sls. & Mktg.--Microlog Corporation, Germantown, MD; *U.S. Public*, pg. 1105
Manji, Anil, Sr. V.P.-Actuary--West Coast Life Insurance Co., San Francisco, CA; *U.S. Public*, pg. 1336
Mank, Darrell A., Sr. V.P.-Design Services--Cadence Design Systems, Inc., San Jose, CA; *U.S. Public*, pg. 290
Manley, Charles G., Sr. V.P.-Admin.--Anadarko Petroleum Corporation, Houston, TX; *U.S. Public*, pg. 107
Mann, Donald C., Sr. V.P.-Human Resources--The Prudential Investment Corp., Newark, NJ; *U.S. Private*, pg. 892
Mannes, Barry L., Sr. V.P.-H.R.--Travelers Group, New York, NY; *U.S. Public*, pg. 1632
Mannes, Scott M., Sr. V.P.--ContiFinancial Corporation, New York, NY; *U.S. Public*, pg. 439
Manning, Clark, Sr. V.P. & Chief Actuary--Jackson National Life Insurance Company, Lansing, MI; *Int'l*, pg. 1073
Manning, Clark P., Jr., Sr. V.P.--SunAmerica Inc., Los Angeles, CA; *U.S. Public*, pg. 1532
Manning, Dennis J., Chief Mktg. Officer & Sr. V.P.--The Guardian Life Insurance Company of America, New York, NY; *U.S. Private*, pg. 486
Manning, Martha E., Sr. V.P., Gen. Counsel & Sec.--U.S. Bioscience, Inc., Conshohocken, PA; *U.S. Public*, pg. 1681
Manning, Mary, Sr. V.P.-Mktg. & Devel.--Coty Inc., New York, NY; *Int'l*, pg. 185
Mansell, Thomas S., Sr. V.P., Legal Counsel & Asst. Sec.--First Western Bancorp, Inc., New Castle, PA; *U.S. Public*, pg. 642
Mansfield, Christopher C., Sr. V.P. & Gen. Counsel--Liberty Mutual Insurance Co., Boston, MA; *U.S. Private*, pg. 666
Mansfield, William G., Sr. V.P. & Mng. Dir.--National Distributing Co., Inc., Jacksonville, FL; *U.S. Private*, pg. 781
Manshouri, Ahmad, Sr. V.P.-Corp. Opers.--Vanstar Corporation, Pleasanton, CA; *U.S. Public*, pg. 1708
Manske, Juergen, Sr. V.P.-Area South--Hapag-Lloyd (America), Inc., Piscataway, NJ; *Int'l*, pg. 596
Manske, Stephen C., Sr. V.P.-COFI Cluster--Anacomp, Inc., Indianapolis, IN; *U.S. Public*, pg. 106
Manson, Anthony, Sr. V.P. & New Tech. Mgr.--Y&R New Technologies, New York, NY; *U.S. Private*, pg. 1198
Manson, Robert, Sr. V.P.-Information Systems--The Stop & Shop Companies, Inc., Quincy, MA; *Int'l*, pg. 750
Mansor, Dato'Mohamed Idris, Dr., Sr. V.P.--Petroliam Nasional Berhad (Petronas), Kuala Lumpur, Malaysia; *Int'l*, pg. 1046
Mantle, Philip, Sr. V.P.-Sls.--Vertel, Woodland Hills, CA; *U.S. Public*, pg. 1717
Manto, Gwen, Sr. V.P. & Gen. Mgr.-Mdsg.--Kids "R" Us, Paramus, NJ; *U.S. Public*, pg. 1626
Manwaring, Keith J., Sr. V.P. & Gen. Mgr.-Intl. Grp.--Integrity Incorporated, Mobile, AL; *U.S. Public*, pg. 886
Manzella, Ernest V., Jr., Sr. V.P.-Publ. Services--Aspen Publishers, Inc., Gaithersburg, MD; *Int'l*, pg. 1513
Manziano, Frederic, Sr. V.P.--Liberty Mutual Insurance Co., Boston, MA; *U.S. Private*, pg. 666
Mapelli, Roland L., Sr. V.P.--ConAgra Red Meat Companies, Greeley, CO; *U.S. Public*, pg. 427
Marasco, Fran, Pres.-Pharmacy Benefit Mngmt. & Mail Service Pharmacy & Sr. V.P.--Eckerd Corporation, Largo, FL; *U.S. Public*, pg. 917
Marber, Susan, Sr. V.P.-Acct. Mngmt.--Grey Advertising Inc., New York, NY; *U.S. Public*, pg. 764
MarcAurele, Joseph J., Sr. V.P.-Corp. Lending--Citizens Savings Bank, Providence, RI; *Int'l*, pg. 1132
MarcAurele, Joseph J., Sr. V.P.-Corp. Lending--Citizens Trust Company, Providence, RI; *Int'l*, pg. 1132
Marchetti, Mike, Sr. V.P.-Store Opers.--Finish Line, Inc., Indianapolis, IN; *U.S. Public*, pg. 623
Marchildren, Christine, Sr. V.P.-Corp. Services--Federation des caisses populaires Desjardins, Montreal, Canada; *Int'l*, pg. 479
Marchioli, Nelson J., Sr. V.P.--Advantica Restaurant Group, Inc., Spartanburg, SC; *U.S. Public*, pg. 22
Marchioli, Nelson J., Pres. & Sr. V.P.--El Pollo Loco, Irvine, CA; *U.S. Public*, pg. 23
Marcionetti, Harry, Sr. V.P.-Opers.--Igloo Products Corporation, Houston, TX; *U.S. Public*, pg. 265
Marcus, Julius L., Sr. V.P.-Strategic Relationships--Xerox Corporation, Stamford, CT; *U.S. Public*, pg. 1783
Marcusson, Reese, Sr. V.P.-Corp. Plng. & Communications--WTTW (Channel 11), Chicago, IL; *U.S. Private*, pg. 1145
Mardirossian, Olga, Sr. V.P. & Controller--Western International Media Corporation, Los Angeles, CA; *U.S. Private*, pg. 1165
Mare, Robert V., Sr. V.P.-Corp. Devel.--Ponderosa Steakhouse, Dallas, TX; *U.S. Private*, pg. 736
Marella, Philip, Sr. V.P.-Legal & Bus. Affairs--Worldvision Enterprises, New York, NY; *U.S. Private*, pg. 776
Marengi, Joseph A., Sr. V.P.--Dell Computer Corporation, Round Rock, TX; *U.S. Public*, pg. 495
Maresca, Anthony R., Chief Fin. Officer, Sr. V.P., Treas. & Sec.--ACR Group, Houston, TX; *U.S. Public*, pg. 3
Margolis, Bruce, Sr. V.P. & Dir.-Human Services/The Marmaxx Grp.--The TJX Companies, Inc., Framingham, MA; *U.S. Public*, pg. 1556
Mariangeli, Dan, Sr. V.P.-Fin. Div.--The Toronto Dominion Bank, Toronto, Canada; *Int'l*, pg. 1401
Marini, Vincent, Sr. V.P.-Direct Production Services--Gillespie, Lawrenceville, NJ; *U.S. Private*, pg. 453
Marino, Joseph M., Sr. V.P.--Analysis & Technology, Inc., North Stonington, CT; *U.S. Public*, pg. 109
Marino, Nancy, Sr. V.P.-Intl. Opers.--Associated Merchandising Corp. (AMC), New York, NY; *U.S. Private*, *pg. 91*
Marino, Richard J., Sr. V.P.--The Sherwood Group, Inc., Jersey City, NJ; *U.S. Public*, pg. 1466
Marino, Vincent J., Sr. V.P.--Nippon Credit Trust Company, New York, NY; *Int'l*, pg. 933
Marino, Vincenzo, Sr. V.P. & Dir.-Mktg.--Frederick Wildman & Sons Ltd., New York, NY; *U.S. Private*, pg. 1176
Marion, Benjamin N., Sr. V.P. & Creative Dir.--Creswell, Munsell, Fultz & Zirbel, L.P., Cedar Rapids, IA; *U.S. Private*, pg. 1197
Mariucci, Anne L., Sr. V.P. & Pres. & Gen. Mgr.-Terravita Corp.--Del Webb Corporation, Phoenix, AZ; *U.S. Public*, pg. 494
Markey, Arthur, Chief Fin. Officer, Sr. V.P. & Treas.--Carpenter Co., Richmond, VA; *U.S. Private*, pg. 214
Markl, Thomas L., Sr. V.P.--UTILX Corporation, Kent, WA; *U.S. Public*, pg. 1701
Markman, Ken, Sr. V.P.-Consumer--International Family Entertainment, Inc., Virginia Beach, VA; *Int'l*, pg. 927
Markman, Ken, Sr. V.P.-Promo. & Communications--MTM Enterprises, Inc., Studio City, CA; *Int'l*, pg. 927
Markovitz, Philip D., Sr. V.P.-Store Devel.--Rite Aid Corporation, Camp Hill, PA; *U.S. Public*, pg. 1390
Markow, Richard E., Sr. V.P. & Trust Mgr.--United Missouri Bank of St. Louis, Saint Louis, MO; *U.S. Public*, pg. 1655
Markowski, Joseph, Sr. V.P.-Mktg.--Coty Inc., New York, NY; *Int'l*, pg. 185
Marks, Amy P., Sr. V.P.-Human Resources--USF&G Corporation, Baltimore, MD; *U.S. Public*, pg. 1659
Marks, Bill, Sr. V.P. & Acct. Mngmt.--Hal Riney & Partners Heartland, Chicago, IL; *U.S. Private*, pg. 931
Marks, Eugene, Jr., Sr. V.P.--Metropolitan Life Insurance Co., New York, NY; *U.S. Private*, pg. 737
Marks, George V., Sr. V.P.-Transportation--Huitt-Zollars, Inc., Dallas, TX; *U.S. Private*, pg. 547
Marks, Robert, Sr. V.P. & Acct. Services Dir.--Berenter Greenhouse & Webster, Inc., New York, NY; *U.S. Private*, pg. 135
Marks, Roberta, Sr. V.P.--Edelman Worldwide, Inc., New York, NY; *U.S. Private*, pg. 362
Marks, Ron, Sr. V.P.-Res. & Devel.--Applebee's International, Inc., Overland Park, KS; *U.S. Public*, pg. 122
Marks, Ronald D., Sr. V.P. & Treas.--Comerica Incorporated, Detroit, MI; *U.S. Public*, pg. 408
Markwell, Warren, Sr. V.P.-Fin.--S-B Power Tool Company, Chicago, IL; *Int'l*, pg. 205
Marlatt, M. Andy, Sr. V.P.-Corp. Services--Owen Health Care, Inc., Houston, TX; *U.S. Public*, pg. 304

Marlinski, Mary Jane, Sr. V.P. & Gen. Mgr.-Crafts--Fabri-Centers of America, Inc., Hudson, OH; *U.S. Public*, pg. 609
Marquaire, Jean-Francois, Sr. V.P.-Legal & Human Resources--Compagnie Generale de Geophysique, Massy, France; *Int'l*, pg. 241
Marquardt, Timothy A., Chief Fin. Officer & Sr. V.P.--NationsBank Sunwest, Inc., Albuquerque, NM; *U.S. Public*, pg. 1165
Marquiss, James J., Sr. V.P. & Co-Pres.-Ag. Svcs.--Data Transmission Network Corporation, Omaha, NE; *U.S. Public*, pg. 486
Marra, Anthony F., Sr. V.P. & Deputy Gen. Counsel--Federal National Mortgage Association (Fannie Mae), Washington, DC; *U.S. Public*, pg. 615
Marranzino, Michael A., Sr. V.P. & Chief Intl. Officer--Coors Brewing Company, Golden, CO; *U.S. Public*, pg. 445
Marre, Roger, Sr. V.P.-Personnel & Safety--Compagnie Generale de Geophysique, Massy, France; *Int'l*, pg. 241
Marren, Harry T., Sr. V.P.--Federal Data Corporation, Bethesda, MD; *U.S. Private*, pg. 398
Marrero, Manuel, Chief Fin. Officer, Sr. V.P.-Admin., Treas. & Sec.--Autologic Information International, Inc., Thousand Oaks, CA; *U.S. Public*, pg. 1724
Marriman, James I., Sr. V.P.--Collins Electric Company, Inc., Chicopee, MA; *U.S. Private*, pg. 253
Marrinan, Patrick, Sr. V.P. & Acct. Dir.--Young & Rubicam New York, New York, NY; *U.S. Private*, pg. 1198
Marriott, Walter, III, Sr. V.P.-West--Gannett Fleming Affiliates, Inc., Camp Hill, PA; *U.S. Private*, pg. 439
Marron, George, Sr. V.P.-Sls.--Opp Micolas Mills Inc., Opp, AL; *U.S. Public*, pg. 933
Mars, Lisa, Sr. V.P.-People Div.--Computer Associates International, Inc., Islandia, NY; *U.S. Public*, pg. 420
Marsh, C. Alan, Vice Chm. & Sr. V.P.-Corp. Devel.--Marsh Supermarkets, Inc., Indianapolis, IN; *U.S. Public*, pg. 1049
Marsh, D.P., Sr. V.P.-Life Opers.--Auto-Owners Insurance, Lansing, MI; *U.S. Private*, pg. 100
Marsh, Pamela, Sr. V.P. & Dir.-H.R.--INMC Mortgage Holdings, Inc., Pasadena, CA; *U.S. Public*, pg. 857
Marsh, Stephen P., Chief Fin. Officer, Sr V.P. & Cashier--Community National Bank, Derby, VT; *U.S. Public*, pg. 416
Marshall, Betty, Sr. V.P.-Corp. Communications & Community Rels.--Shoney's, Inc., Nashville, TN; *U.S. Public*, pg. 1467
Marshall, Dick, Sr. V.P.-Devel.--Lat Purser & Associates, Charlotte, NC; *U.S. Private*, pg. 896
Marshall, Ed, Sr. V.P.-Corp. Communications & Pub. Rels.--First Commerce Corporation, New Orleans, LA; *U.S. Public*, pg. 629
Marshall, Gregory K., Sr. V.P. & Chm. & Chief Exec. Officer-The SYGMA Network--Sysco Corporation, Houston, TX; *U.S. Public*, pg. 1550
Marshall, Howard B., Sr. V.P.-Opers.--Raytheon Systems Co., Kirkwood, NY; *U.S. Public*, pg. 1364
Marshall, John F., Jr., Sr. V.P.--Hibernia Corporation, New Orleans, LA; *U.S. Public*, pg. 825
Marshall, Ken, Sr. V.P.-Mfg., Res., Design & Devel.--The Rockport Company, Marlborough, MA; *U.S. Public*, pg. 1370
Marshall, Quintin G., Sr. V.P.-Corp. Devel.--Ogden Corporation, New York, NY; *U.S. Public*, pg. 1213
Marshall, Siri S., Sr. V.P. & Gen. Counsel--General Mills, Inc., Minneapolis, MN; *U.S. Public*, pg. 717
Marshburn, Joe D., Sr. V.P.--Citrus World Inc., Lake Wales, FL; *U.S. Private*, pg. 241
Marsiglio, Ronald L., Sr. V.P. & Gen. Mgr.-Color T.V.--Philips Consumer Electronics, Knoxville, TN; *Int'l*, pg. 1054
Marston, James S., Chief Information Officer & Sr. V.P.--APL Limited, Oakland, CA; *Int'l*, pg. 912
Martell, Dorn, Sr. V.P. & Creative Grp. Head--Tinsley Advertising, Miami, FL; *U.S. Private*, pg. 1088
Martin, Brian, Sr. V.P.-Corp. Communications--Avon Products, Inc., New York, NY; *U.S. Public*, pg. 155
Martin, Brian J., Sr. V.P.-Human Resources & Gen. Counsel--Proffitt's, Inc., Alcoa, TN; *U.S. Public*, pg. 1333
Martin, C. Keith, Sr. V.P.--Hibernia Corporation, New Orleans, LA; *U.S. Public*, pg. 825
Martin, Craig, Pres.-CRSS Architects Inc. & Sr. V.P.-Opers.--CRSS Inc., Houston, TX; *Int'l*, pg. 1415
Martin, Craig L., Sr. V.P.-Gen. Sls. & Mktg.--Jacobs Engineering Group Inc., Pasadena, CA; *U.S. Public*, pg. 921
Martin, Gary T., Sr. V.P.-Product Supply--The Procter & Gamble Company, Cincinnati, OH; *U.S. Public*, pg. 1330
Martin, Geoffrey T., Sr. V.P.-Worldwide Converting, Graphic Systems & Specialty Tapes--Avery Dennison Corporation, Pasadena, CA; *U.S. Public*, pg. 152
Martin, Glenda, Sr. V.P. & Media Dir.--Valentine Radford, Inc., Kansas City, MO; *U.S. Private*, pg. 1131
Martin, James R., Sr. V.P.--Huntington National Bank, Morgantown, WV; *U.S. Public*, pg. 850
Martin, JoAnn M., Chief Fin. Officer, Sr. V.P. & Controller--Ameritas Life Insurance Corp., Lincoln, NE; *U.S. Private*, pg. 65
Martin, Joseph G., Sr. V.P.-Engrng.--Starcraft Automotive Group, Inc., Goshen, IN; *U.S. Public*, pg. 1511
Martin, Kathleen A., Sr. V.P.-Modernization Dir.--Synovus Financial Corp., Columbus, GA; *U.S. Public*, pg. 1548
Martin, Kent, Sr. V.P.--Servo Corporation of America, Westbury, NY; *U.S. Private*, pg. 987
Martin, Leticia, Sr. V.P. & Chief Creative Officer--DKB & Partners, Inc., Morristown, NJ; *U.S. Private*, pg. 302
Martin, M. Lamar, Chief Fin. Officer, Sr. V.P. & Treas.--Centex Construction Company, Dallas, TX; *U.S. Public*, pg. 322
Martin, Marie L., Sr. V.P.-Client Service--UAM Retirement Plan Services, Inc., New York, NY; *U.S. Public*, pg. 1674
Martin, Michael D., Sr. V.P. & Complex Mgr.--Pilgrim's Pride Corporation, Pittsburg, TX; *U.S. Public*, pg. 1296
Martin, Michael S., Sr. V.P.-Mktg.--The Equitable Companies Incorporated, New York, NY; *U.S. Public*, pg. 588
Martin, Patrick, Sr. V.P.--The Richard Leahy Corporation, Fort Wayne, IN; *U.S. Public*, pg. 997
Martin, Richard A., Sr. V.P.--MYR Group Inc., Rolling Meadows, IL; *U.S. Public*, pg. 1029
Martin, Stephen E., Sr. V.P.-Estimating--Baker Concrete Construction, Inc., Monroe, OH; *U.S. Private*, pg. 111
Martin, Steve, Sr. V.P. & Exec. Creative Dir.--SicolaMartin Inc., Austin, TX; *U.S. Private*, pg. 998
Martin, Thomas D., Sr. V.P.-Mdsg.--PriceSmart Inc., San Diego, CA; *U.S. Public*, pg. 1324
Martin, Varick D., Sr. V.P.--Manufacturers & Traders Trust Company, Buffalo, NY; *U.S. Public*, pg. 631
Martin, Von, Chief Acctg. Officer & Sr. V.P.--Lund Food Holdings, Inc., Edina, MN; *U.S. Private*, pg. 680
Martin, Webb F., Sr. V.P.-Pacific Century Trust--Bank of Hawaii, Honolulu, HI; *U.S. Public*, pg. 1248
Martin, William A., Chief Fin. Officer, Sr. V.P. & Asst. Sec.--Insituform Technologies, Inc., Chesterfield, MO; *U.S. Public*, pg. 881
Martin, William L., III, Sr. V.P. & Pres.-Bus. Broadband Grp.--ADC Telecommunications, Inc., Minnetonka, MN; *U.S. Public*, pg. 4
Martincic, Joseph, Sr. V.P.-Admin. Services--Regence BlueCross BlueShield of Oregon, Portland, OR; *U.S. Private*, pg. 917
Martindale, Kenneth A., Sr. V.P.-Sls. & Procurement--Smith's Food & Drug Centers, Inc., Salt Lake City, UT; *U.S. Public*, pg. 1103
Martinelli, Edward C., Sr. V.P.-Comml.--The Geon Company, Avon Lake, OH; *U.S. Public*, pg. 733
Martinez, Gary W., Sr. V.P.--Phoenix American Incorporated, San Rafael, CA; *U.S. Private*, pg. 862
Martinez, Walfrido A., Chief Fin. Officer, Sr. V.P. & Controller--E & B Marine Incorporated, Edison, NJ; *U.S. Public*, pg. 1756
Martino, Barbara, Sr. V.P.--Grey Advertising Inc., New York, NY; *U.S. Public*, pg. 764
Martonen, Ari, Chief Fin. Officer & Sr. V.P.--Metsa-Serla Corporation, Espoo, Finland, *Int'l*, pg. 863
Martovano, Charles, Sr. V.P.--Imperial Bank, Inglewood, CA; *U.S. Public*, pg. 871
Marty, Wayne A., Sr. V.P.--TCF Bank Minnesota FSB, Minneapolis, MN; *U.S. Public*, pg. 1554
Marvin, Susan I., Sr. V.P.- Sls. & Mktg.--Marvin Lumber & Cedar Company, Warroad, MN; *U.S. Private*, pg. 710
Marxer, Ewald, Sr. V.P.-Investment Counselling & Securities Admin.--Liechtenstein Global Trust Limited, Vaduz, Liechtenstein; *Int'l*, pg. 809
Marzella, Dennis, Sr. V.P.-Res. & Devel.--Yesawich, Pepperdine & Brown, Orlando, FL; *U.S. Private*, pg. 1195
Marziano, Peter, Sr. V.P.--H. Freeman & Son, Inc., Philadelphia, PA; *U.S. Private*, pg. 426
Marzocchi, Robert A., Sr. V.P.--Chubb & Son, Inc., Warren, NJ; *U.S. Public*, pg. 355
Marzol, Adolfo, Sr. V.P.-Capital Markets--Federal National Mortgage Association (Fannie Mae), Washington, DC; *U.S. Public*, pg. 615
Marzoli, Jane, Sr. V.P.-Audit--North Fork Bancorporation, Inc., Melville, NY; *U.S. Public*, pg. 1194
Masago, Yukio, Sr. Mng. Dir.--Shoko Chukin Bank, Tokyo, Japan; *Int'l*, pg. 1236
Mascari, Dave, Sr. V.P.-Asset Recovery & Retail Collections--First Financial Bank, FSB, Stevens Point, WI; *U.S. Public*, pg. 140
Mascheroni, Eleanor, Sr. V.P.-Pub. Rels.--Scudder Kemper Investments, Inc., New York, NY; *Int'l*, pg. 1530
Maschio, Joseph, Sr. V.P.-Mktg.--Newspapers First, New York, NY; *U.S. Public*, pg. 964
Masci, Thomas A., Jr., Sr. V.P. & Treas.--U.S. Quality Algorithms, Inc., Blue Bell, PA; *U.S. Public*, pg. 27
Maselli, Alfredo, Sr. V.P. & Gen. Mgr.-Intl. Div.--Kelly Services, Inc., Troy, MI; *U.S. Public*, pg. 949
Masket, Steven N., Sr. V.P. & Gen. Counsel--Maidenform Worldwide, New York, NY; *U.S. Private*, pg. 697
Mason, Chris, V.P.-Fin. & Admin.--Kelly (UK) Services Ltd., Kingston upon Thames, United Kingdom; *U.S. Public*, pg. 949
Mason, Fred, Sr. V.P.--J.B. Rodgers Mechanical Contractors, Phoenix, AZ; *U.S. Private*, pg. 939
Mason, Glenn M., Sr. V.P.-CompuSafe--Brink's, Inc., Darien, CT; *U.S. Public*, pg. 1305
Mason, Paul, Sr. V.P.-Productions--Viacom Productions Inc., Universal City, CA; *U.S. Private*, pg. 779
Mason, William R., Sr. V.P. & Gen. Mgr.-Sls.--American Greetings Corporation, Cleveland, OH; *U.S. Public*, pg. 77
Mason, William R., Sr. V.P. & Gen. Mgr.-Sls.--American Greetings U.S. Greeting Card Division, Cleveland, OH; *U.S. Public*, pg. 78
Masquelier, Xavier, Sr. V.P.--W. Rosenlew Ltd., Helsinki, Finland; *Int'l*, pg. 1428
Mass, Harvey, Sr. V.P.-Sls. & Mktg.--First Central Financial Corporation, Lynbrook, NY; *U.S. Private*, pg. 406
Mass, Nathaniel J., Sr. V.P.-Strategic Growth--GenCorp Inc., Fairlawn, OH; *U.S. Public*, pg. 705
Massa. Barbara K., Sr. V.P.-Corp. Communications--First Union Corporation, Charlotte, NC; *U.S. Public*, pg. 639
Massanelli, Stephen C., Sr. V.P. & Treas.--Zale Corporation, Irving, TX; *U.S. Public*, pg. 1789
Masselli, Michael, Sr. V.P.-Sls. & Mktg.--Jordan's Meats, Portland, ME; *U.S. Private*, pg. 599
Massengill, Matt, Sr. V.P. & Gen. Mgr.--Western Digital Corporation, Irvine, CA; *U.S. Public*, pg. 1758
Massey, Glenn, Sr. V.P. & Mng. Dir.--Western International Media Corporation, Dallas, TX; *U.S. Private*, pg. 1167
Massey, W. Mark, Sr. V.P.-Mfg.--Forest Products & Recycled Paperboard Div., Montvale, NJ; *U.S. Public*, pg. 903
Massicotte, Francis R., Sr. V.P. & Sec.--Potomac Valley Bank, Gaithersburg, MD; *U.S. Public*, pg. 1089
Massimini, Dante J., Sr. V.P. & Treas.--Pennsylvania Real Estate Investment Trust, Fort Washington, PA; *U.S. Public*, pg. 1272
Massung, Thomas, Sr. V.P.--First Empire State Corporation, Buffalo, NY; *U.S. Public*, pg. 631
Massung, Thomas J., Sr. V.P.--Manufacturers & Traders Trust Company, Buffalo, NY; *U.S. Public*, pg. 631
Masters, Stan, Sr. V.P.-Sls.--USLD Communications Corp., San Antonio, TX; *U.S. Public*, pg. 969
Mastrogiovanni, Ronald D., Chief Information Officer & Sr. V.P.--Avon Products, Inc., New York, NY; *U.S. Public*, pg. 155
Masuda, Raymond K., Sr. V.P.-Service & Opers. Division--Bank of Hawaii, Honolulu, HI; *U.S. Public*, pg. 1248
Masuda, Y., Sr. V.P.--Mitsubishi International Corporation, New York, NY; *Int'l*, pg. 871
Masuhr, Mark J., Sr. V.P.--Firstar Milwaukee Bank, N.A., Milwaukee, WI; *U.S. Public*, pg. 643
Mater, Maud, Sr. V.P., Gen. Counsel & Sec.--Federal Home Loan Mortgage Corporation, Mc Lean, VA; *U.S. Public*, pg. 615
Mateus, Lois, Sr. V.P.--Brown-Forman Corporation, Louisville, KY; *U.S. Public*, pg. 261
Mathews, Curtis, Sr. V.P.-Corp. Devel.--ICO, Inc., Houston, TX; *U.S. Public*, pg. 853
Mathews, Michael P., Sr. V.P.-Quality Assurance & Solutions Devel.--Haemonetics Corporation, Braintree, MA; *U.S. Public*, pg. 773
Mathews, Stuart I., Sr. V.P.--Metapoint Partners, Peabody, MA; *U.S. Private*, pg. 735
Mathewson, R., Sr. V.P. & Pres.-Building Prods.--Johns Manville Corporation, Denver, CO; *U.S. Public*, pg. 927
Mathias, Robert, Sr. V.P.--NationsBank of St. Louis, Saint Louis, MO; *U.S. Public*, pg. 1164
Mathiasen, Raymond L., Chief Acctg. Officer & Sr. V.P.--Tenet Healthcare Corporation, Santa Barbara, CA; *U.S. Public*, pg. 1576
Mathieu, Glenn D., Sr. V.P.--Meldisco, Mahwah, NJ; *U.S. Public*, pg. 661
Mathison, Robert J., Sr. V.P.-Information Systems--Washington Mutual Inc., Seattle, WA; *U.S. Public*, pg. 1741
Matsil, Paul, Sr. V.P.--Host for Her, New York, NY; *U.S. Private*, pg. 540
Matsuda, Matt, Chief Fin. Officer & Sr. V.P.--Clarion Corporation of America, Gardena, CA; *Int'l*, pg. 296
Matsui, Hideyoshi, Sr. Mngmt. Dir.--Alps Electric Co., Ltd., Tokyo, Japan; *Int'l*, pg. 65
Matsumoto, Morio, Exec. V.P.--Asahi Glass Co., Ltd., Tokyo, Japan; *Int'l*, pg. 84
Matsumoto, Shigeo, Sr. V.P.--NEC Corporation, Tokyo, Japan; *Int'l*, pg. 899
Matsuo, N., Sr. V.P.--Mitsubishi International Corporation, New York, NY; *Int'l*, pg. 871
Matsuura, Yoshinori, Sr. V.P.--Marubeni America Corporation, New York, NY; *Int'l*, pg. 844
Mattei, Peter, Sr. V.P.-Prod. & Vineyards--Robert Mondavi Winery, Inc., Oakville, CA; *U.S. Public*, pg. 1393
Matter, Gary L., Sr. V.P., Controller & Sec.--Commercial Federal Corporation, Omaha, NE; *U.S. Public*, pg. 411
Matteson, E. David, Sr. V.P.--Seneca Falls Technology Group, Seneca Falls, NY; *U.S. Private*, pg. 984
Matthews, Bill, Sr. V.P.--First Commercial Bank, N.A., Little Rock, AR; *U.S. Public*, pg. 630
Matthews, David J., Sr. V.P.-Pur. & Gen. Mdse.--Hill-Behan Lumber Company, Saint Louis, MO; *U.S. Private*, pg. 529
Matthews, Harold, Sr. V.P.--Allright Corporation, Houston, TX; *U.S. Private*, pg. 42
Matthews, Jerry, Chief Fin. Officer & Sr. V.P.--D & W Food Centers, Inc., Grand Rapids, MI; *U.S. Private*, pg. 300
Matthews, John, Sr. V.P.-Human Resources & Risk Mngmt.--Costco Wholesale, Issaquah, WA; *U.S. Public*, pg. 451
Matthews, Kelly K., Dr., Sr. V.P. & Chief Economist--First Security Corporation, Salt Lake City, UT; *U.S. Public*, pg. 637
Matthews, Terry, Sr. V.P.-Sls. & Mktg.--J.B. Hunt Transport Services, Inc., Lowell, AR; *U.S. Public*, pg. 849
Matthews, Thomas J., Sr. V.P.-Admin.--Southern Pacific Rail Corporation, San Francisco, CA; *U.S. Public*, pg. 1668
Matthys, Paul, Sr. V.P.-Trading, Stainless Steel/Brazil--Arbed S.A., Luxembourg, Luxembourg; *Int'l*, pg. 78
Mattimore, John, Sr. V.P.-Natl. Brdcst.--Zenith Media Services, Inc., New York, NY; *U.S. Private*, pg. 1204
Mattson, Eric L., Chief Fin. Officer & Sr. V.P.--Baker Hughes Incorporated, Houston, TX; *U.S. Public*, pg. 165
Mattson, Todd, Sr. V.P.--EvansGroup, San Francisco, CA; *U.S. Private*, pg. 385
Matz, George, Sr. V.P.-World Sls.--Comverse Network Systems, Wakefield, MA; *U.S. Public*, pg. 425
Matz, R. Kevin, Sr. V.P. & Treas.--EMCOR Group, Inc., Norwalk, CT; *U.S. Public*, pg. 571
Mauck, Fred A., Sr. V.P.--Berkley Risk Services, Inc., Minneapolis, MN; *U.S. Public*, pg. 215
Maude, Harold E., Sr. V.P.-Independence Fin. Network--The Penn Mutual Life Insurance Company, Philadelphia, PA; *U.S. Private*, pg. 849
Mauer, Aloys, Sr. V.P.-Opers.--Deutz AG, Cologne, Germany; *Int'l*, pg. 407
Mauk, Kevin R., Sr. V.P.-MIS--Mid Atlantic Medical Services, Inc., Rockville, MD; *U.S. Public*, pg. 1109
Maul, Richard A., Sr. V.P. & Gen. Mgr.-Northeast Region--Showtime Networks Inc., New York, NY; *U.S. Private*, pg. 779
Maulbetsch, Stephen, Sr. V.P.-Property & Acquisitions--Health Care Property Investors, Inc., Newport Beach, CA; *U.S. Public*, pg. 801
Maupin, Patrick, Sr. V.P.-Sls. & Mktg.--Jaydon Incorporated, Rock Island, IL; *U.S. Private*, pg. 584
Maurer, Christopher, Sr. V.P.--First National Bank of Ohio, Akron, OH; *U.S. Public*, pg. 646
Maurer, Henry, Sr. V.P.-Design & Product Devel.--Voyager Emblems, Inc., Sanborn, NY; *U.S. Private*, pg. 1143

McMillen, Glenn G., Sr. V.P.-Opers.--Service Corporation International, Houston, TX; *U.S. Public*, pg. 1460
McMillin, Tom, Chief Fin. Officer & Sr. V.P.-Fin.--Marcus Cable Company, L.P., Dallas, TX; *U.S. Private*, pg. 702
McMinn, JoAnn N., Sr. V.P. & Controller--Omega Financial Corporation, State College, PA; *U.S. Public*, pg. 1222
McMullen, Dennis, Sr. V.P.-Real Estate--CVS Corp., Woonsocket, RI; *U.S. Public*, pg. 287
McMullen, W. Rodney, Chief Fin. Officer & Sr. V.P.--The Kroger Co., Cincinnati, OH; *U.S. Public*, pg. 967
McMullin, J. Ross, Sr. V.P.-Fin.--Oral-B Laboratories, Belmont, CA; *U.S. Public*, pg. 743
McMurtry, Bruce, Sr. V.P.-Federal Gov't. Rels.--Aetna Inc., Hartford, CT; *U.S. Public*, pg. 26
McNally, Michael, Sr. V.P.-Corp. & Human Resources--Rogers Group Inc., Nashville, TN; *U.S. Private*, pg. 939
McNally, Michael F., Sr. V.P.--ADP Marshall Contractors Inc., Rumford, RI; *U.S. Public*, pg. 660
McNally, Thomas M., Sr. V.P.-Agricultural Prods.--Abbott Laboratories, Abbott Park, IL; *U.S. Public*, pg. 13
McNamara, Dennis, Sr. V.P. & Gen. Counsel--Plaid Clothing Company, New York, NY; *U.S. Public*, pg. 796
McNaughton, Cameron, Sr. V.P. & Mngmt. Supvr.--McKinney & Silver, Raleigh, NC; *U.S. Private*, pg. 723
McNease, D.F., Sr. V.P.--Rowan Companies, Inc., Houston, TX; *U.S. Public*, pg. 1409
McNeely, Milinda, Sr. V.P.-Legal--Paramount Pictures Corporation, Los Angeles, CA; *U.S. Private*, pg. 776
McNeely, Perry R., Sr. V.P.-Logistics--Pier 1 Imports, Inc., Fort Worth, TX; *U.S. Public*, pg. 1295
McNeil, Donald E., Sr. V.P.-Lending Svcs.--Ameriana Bank, New Castle, IN; *U.S. Public*, pg. 66
McNeil, Donald G., Sr. V.P. & Pres.-Great Northern Paper, Inc.--Bowater Incorporated, Greenville, SC; *U.S. Public*, pg. 247
McNeil, Gary L., Chief Oper. Officer & Sr. V.P.--ASCG, Inc., Anchorage, AK; *U.S. Private*, pg. 80
McNeive, Gerald T., Jr., Chief Fin. Officer & Sr. V.P.--Laclede Gas Company, Saint Louis, MO; *U.S. Public*, pg. 973
McNelis, Michael F., Sr. V.P.--The Equitable Companies Incorporated, New York, NY; *U.S. Public*, pg. 588
McNiel, Bruce A., Sr. V.P.--Mark IV Industries Inc., Amherst, NY; *U.S. Public*, pg. 1044
McNulty, John, Sr. V.P.-Sls. & Mktg.--Brunswick Bicyles Div., Bannockburn, IL; *U.S. Public*, pg. 265
McNutly, David, Sr. V.P. & Sec.--First Bank National Association, Chicago, IL; *U.S. Public*, pg. 1681
McPherson, Allister J., Sr. V.P.-Treasury & Opers.--Canadian Western Bank, Edmonton, Canada; *Int'l*, pg. 259
McPherson, David L., Sr. V.P.--Raytheon Company, Lexington, MA; *U.S. Public*, pg. 1364
McQuillan, Tom, Exec. V.P.--Select Robinson Inc., Portland, ME; *Int'l*, pg. 274
McReynolds, Frank B., Sr. V.P.--United Missouri Bank of Joplin, Joplin, MO; *U.S. Public*, pg. 1655
McShane, Michael, Chief Fin. Officer & Sr. V.P.-Fin.--BJ Services Company, Houston, TX; *U.S. Public*, pg. 161
McSherry, John, Sr. Partner & Media Resources Dir.--BJK&E Media Group, New York, NY; *U.S. Public*, pg. 1642
McShulkis, Joseph, Sr. V.P.--Atlantic Aviation Corp., New Castle, DE; *U.S. Private*, pg. 94
McTaggart, K. James, Sr. V.P.-Opers.--Krause's Furniture Inc., Brea, CA; *U.S. Public*, pg. 967
McVicker, James M., Chief Fin. Officer & Sr. V.P.--Mercantile Stores Company, Inc., Fairfield, OH; *U.S. Public*, pg. 1089
McVicker, Robert, Sr. V.P.-Tech. Grp. & Kraft Food Ingredients Corp.--Kraft Foods, Inc., Northfield, IL; *U.S. Public*, pg. 1287
McWhinney, Bruce D., Sr. V.P.-Pharmacy Practice & Quality Assurance--Cardinal Health Inc., Dublin, OH; *U.S. Public, pg. 304*
McWhorter, Robert J., Sr. V.P.-Generating Plant & Transmission Opers.--FirstEnergy Corp., Akron, OH; *U.S.* Public, pg. 644
McWilliams, D. Bradley, Chief Fin. Officer & Sr. V.P.-Fin.--Cooper Industries, Inc., Houston, TX; *U.S. Public*, pg. 442
McWilliams, Larry S., Sr. V.P.-Sls. U.S. Future Consumption--The Minute Maid Company, Houston, TX; *U.S. Public*, pg. 392
Mead, Ray W., Sr. V.P.--UJB Discount Brokerage, Ridgefield Park, NJ; *U.S. Public*, pg. 1528
Mead, Sarah, Sr. V.P.-H.R.--Durham Transportation, Inc., Austin, TX; *U.S. Private*, pg. 348
Meade, Michael G., Sr. V.P.-Information Services--Mortgage Guaranty Insurance Corporation, Milwaukee, WI, *U.S. Public*, pg. 1026
Meade, Robert E., Sr. V.P.--American Arbitration Association, New York, NY; *U.S. Private*, pg. 50
Meads, Mindy C., Sr. V.P. & Mgr.-Gen. Mdse.--Gymboree Corporation, Burlingame, CA; *U.S. Public*, pg. 770
Meadvin, Michael, Sr. V.P. & Gen. Counsel--Castle Oil Corporation, Harrison, NY; *U.S. Private*, pg. 219
Meagher, Janice, Sr. V.P.-Mktg.-Universal Studios Hollywood & Univ. City Walk--Universal Studios Hollywood, Universal City, CA; *Int'l*, pg. 1216
Meahl, Stephen K., Sr. V.P.--UNUM Life Insurance Company of America, Portland, ME; *U.S. Public*, pg. 1699
Mean, J.P., Sr. V.P.-Legal--SGS Societe Generale de Surveillance Holding S.A., Geneva, Switzerland; *Int'l*, pg. 1153
Mears, James, Sr. V.P.--Mears Transportation Group, Orlando, FL; *U.S. Private*, pg. 726
Mechanic, Carol, Sr. V.P. & Gen. Mgr.--Showtime Networks Inc., New York, NY; *U.S. Private*, pg. 779
Mechura, Frank J., Sr. V.P.--Crown Cork & Seal, Americas Division, Philadelphia, PA; *U.S. Public*, pg. 463
Medenica, Gordon, Sr. V.P. & Grp. Publr.--The New York Times Company, New York, NY; *U.S. Public*, pg. 1173
Medenica, Gordon, Sr. V.P.-Grp. Publr.--The New York Times Magazine Company Group, Trumbull, CT; *U.S. Public*, pg. 1174
Medland, Richard H., Chief Admin. Officer & Sr. V.P.--Outboard Marine Corporation, Waukegan, IL; *U.S. Private*, pg. 478
Medlin, George, Sr. V.P.-Internal Audit--Mutual of America Life Insurance Company, New York, NY; *U.S. Private*, pg. 769
Medlin, George, Sr. V.P.-Internal Audit--American Life Insurance Company of New York, New York, NY; *U.S. Private*, pg. 769
Mee, Michael F., Chief Fin. Officer & Sr. V.P.--Bristol-Myers Squibb Company, New York, NY; *U.S. Public*, pg. 253
Meek, Phillip J., Pres.-Publishing Grp. & Sr. V.P.--ABC, Inc, New York, NY; *U.S. Public*, pg. 511
Meeks, James E., Chief Oper. Officer & Sr. V.P.--Copart, Inc., Benicia, CA; *U.S. Public*, pg. 446
Meenan, Hubert V., Sr. V.P. & Mng. Dir.--Price/McNabb, Inc., Charlotte, NC; *U.S. Private*, pg. 883
Mehmet, Robert, Sr. V.P.--Philadelphia Sign Company, Palmyra, NJ; *U.S. Private*, pg. 861
Mehrtens, Leslie R., Sr. V.P.-H.R.--Magna Group, Inc., Saint Louis, MO; *U.S. Public*, pg. 1037
Meiers, Ronald L., Sr. V.P.-Shopping Centre Group--Cambridge Shopping Centres Limited, Toronto, Canada; *Int'l*, pg. 253
Meiland, Nico J., Sr. V.P.-Worldwide Mfg. & Procurement--S.C. Johnson & Son, Inc., Racine, WI; *U.S. Private*, pg. 592
Meilen, Robert, Sr. V.P.-Information Services--AnnTaylor, Inc., New York, NY; *U.S. Public*, pg. 116
Meiling, Gerald S., Sr. V.P.-Strategy, Science & Tech.--Corning Incorporated, Corning, NY; *U.S. Public*, pg. 448
Meils, Frederick S., Sr. V.P.-Corp. Devel.--QFC Holding Company, Stamford, CT; *U.S. Public*, pg. 1349
Meisler, Joanne, Sr. V.P., Gen. Counsel & Sec.--Bellemead Development Corp., Roseland, NJ; *U.S. Public*, pg. 355
Meisner, Joseph M., Sr. V.P.-Construction--Tridel Enterprises Inc., Downsview, Canada; *Int'l*, pg. 1423
Meister, Paul M., Vice Chm., Chief Fin. Officer & Sr. V.P.--Fisher Scientific International, Hampton, NH; *U.S. Private*, pg. 658
Melamed, John, Sr. V.P.--Cramer-Krasselt, Milwaukee, WI; *U.S. Private*, pg. 286
Melchor, Pierre S., Sr. V.P. & Treas.--ITEQ, Inc., Houston, TX; *U.S. Public*, pg. 914
Meldon, Ronald J., Sr. V.P.-Sls.--Planes Moving And Storage, Inc., Cincinnati, OH; *U.S. Private*, pg. 869
Mele, Mary Ann, Sr. V.P.--R&R Advertising, Las Vegas, NV; *U.S. Private*, pg. 902
Melia, Jr., James E., Sr. V.P.-Retail Credit & Servicing--Citizens Trust Company, Providence, RI; *Int'l*, pg. 1132
Mellegers, Jan, Sr. V.P.--UAM Investment Services, Inc., Boston, MA; *U.S. Public*, pg. 1674
Mellett, John R., Chief Fin. Officer & Sr. V.P.--Zurn Industries, Inc., Erie, PA; *U.S. Public*, pg. 1794
Melli, Patrick J., Sr. V.P.-Inventory Mngmt. & Information Services--E & B Marine Incorporated, Edison, NJ; *U.S. Public*, pg. 1756
Melliger, Rene H., Sr. V.P.-Acctg. & Controller--Liechtenstein Global Trust Limited, Vaduz, Liechtenstein; *Int'l*, pg. 809
Mellin, Randall J., Sr. V.P.-Information Svcs.--Argonaut Co., Menlo Park, CA; *U.S. Public*, pg. 129
Mello, Carlos R., Sr. V.P. & Controller--People's Bank, Bridgeport, CT; *U.S. Public*, pg. 1274
Melnick, Rene, Sr. V.P.-Art/DDB Needham--The Bank of New York Company, Inc., New York, NY; *U.S. Public*, pg. 178
Melton, Arthur F., Sr. V.P.--Amwest Insurance Group, Inc., Calabasas, CA; *U.S. Public*, pg. 106
Meltzer, Jay H., Sr. V.P., Gen. Counsel & Sec.--The TJX Companies, Inc., Framingham, MA; *U.S. Public*, pg. 1556
Meltzer, Ronni, Sr. V.P. & Controller--Morse Diesel International, Inc., New York, NY; *U.S. Private*, pg. 762
Melvin, William, Sr. V.P.-Opers.--Crabar Business Systems, Dayton, OH; *U.S. Private*, pg. 283
Memon, Imdad Ali, Sr. V.P. & Gen. Mgr.--Habib Bank Ltd., Ruwi, Oman; *Int'l*, pg. 584
Menaker, Frank H., Jr., Sr. V.P. & Gen. Counsel--Lockheed Martin Corporation, Bethesda, MD; *U.S. Public*, pg. 1006
Menard, Luc-Alexandre, Sr. V.P.-Mercosur Unit--Renault, Boulogne-Billancourt, France; *Int'l*, pg. 1102
Mencier, Bernard, Sr. V.P.--Credit Commercial de France, Paris, France; *Int'l*, pg. 341
Mendelsohn, H. Jake, Sr. V.P.--PETsMART, Inc., Phoenix, AZ; *U.S. Public*, pg. 1281
Mendelson, Stuart, Sr. V.P.-Sales Div.--Murry's, Inc., Upper Marlboro, MD; *U.S. Private*, pg. 768
Mendelson, Vicki, Sr. V.P. & Acct. Dir.--DeWitt Media, Inc., New York, NY; *U.S. Private*, pg. 329
Mendenhall, Candice, Sr. V.P.-H.R.--Federal Home Loan Mortgage Corporation, Mc Lean, VA; *U.S. Public*, pg. 615
Mendenhall, Steven C., Chief Admin. Officer & Sr. V.P.--Fortune Brands, Inc., Old Greenwich, CT; *U.S. Public*, pg. 674
Mendez, Serafin, Sr. V.P.--Banco Santander, Madrid, Spain; *Int'l*, pg. 143
Mendola, Annette, Sr. V.P.-Spot Brdcst.--SFM Media Corporation, New York, NY; *U.S. Private*, pg. 956
Menefee, Steven W., Sr. V.P.--Arrow Electronics, Inc., Melville, NY; *U.S. Public*, pg. 133
Menerey, Robert J., Sr. V.P. & Pres.-Drilling & Production Group--Dresser Industries, Inc., Dallas, TX; *U.S. Public*, pg. 528
Mensik, Frank, Sr. V.P.--Reed Tool Company, Houston, TX; *U.S. Public*, pg. 298
Mercer, D. Scott, Sr. V.P.-Desktop Bus. Unit--Dell Computer Corporation, Round Rock, TX; *U.S. Public*, pg. 495
Mercer, Laura, Sr. V.P. & Mng. Dir.--Price/McNabb, Inc., Charlotte, NC; *U.S. Private*, pg. 883
Merchant, David M., Sr. V.P.-Trust Services--Citizens Savings Bank, Providence, RI; *Int'l*, pg. 1132
Merchant, David M., Sr. V.P.-Trust Services--Citizens Trust Company, Providence, RI; *Int'l*, pg. 1132
Merclean, David B., Chief Fin. Officer & Sr. V.P.--Selective Insurance Group, Inc, Branchville, NJ; *U.S. Public*, pg. 1455
Mercurio, John, Chief Fin. Officer & Sr. V.P.--Lowe Direct, New York, NY; *U.S. Private*, pg. 678
Mercurio, P.A., Sr. V.P.-Retirement Services--General Electric Investment Corp., Stamford, CT; *U.S. Public*, pg. 712
Meredith, Gary E., Sr. V.P.--Evans & Sutherland Computer Corporation, Salt Lake City, UT; *U.S. Public*, pg. 595
Meredith, Glenn, Sr. V.P.-Bus. Affairs--TriStar Pictures, Culver City, CA; *Int'l*, pg. 1283
Meredith, Thomas J., Chief Fin. Officer & Sr. V.P.-Fin. & MIS--Dell Computer Corporation, Round Rock, TX; *U.S. Public*, pg. 495
Mergen, Donald E., Sr. V.P.--Chubb & Son, Inc., Warren, NJ; *U.S. Public*, pg. 355
Mericle, William, Sr. V.P. & Creative Dir.--Hal Riney & Partners Heartland, Chicago, IL; *U.S. Private*, pg. 931
Meringer, Patricia C., Sr. V.P., Corp. Counsel & Sec.--Hibernia Corporation, New Orleans, LA; *U.S. Public*, pg. 825
Meriwether, J. Bruce, Sr. V.P.--Mercantile Bank of Iowa, Des Moines, IA; *U.S. Public*, pg. 1087
Merkley, Clark, Sr. V.P.-Health Alliances--Time Insurance, Milwaukee, WI; *Int'l*, pg. 499
Merland, J., Exec. V.P.-Innovation, Res. & Industrialization--Compagnie Generale de Geophysique, Massy, France; *Int'l*, pg. 241
Merlo, Larry, Sr. V.P.-Stores--CVS Corp., Woonsocket, RI; *U.S. Public*, pg. 287
Merlo, Saverio, Sr. V.P.-Corp. Mktg.--Boole & Babbage, Inc., San Jose, CA; *U.S. Public*, pg. 244
Merrick, Harold A., Sr. V.P.--CSW Leasing, Inc., Dallas, TX; *U.S. Public*, pg. 324
Merrill, Robert L., Sr. V.P.-Mktg. & Sls.--Fraser Papers, Inc., Stamford, CT; *Int'l*, pg. 434
Merriman, Mark, Sr. V.P. & Grp. Acct. Dir.--Lowe Direct, New York, NY; *U.S. Private*, pg. 678
Merritt, Robert S., Chief Fin. Officer, Sr. V.P.-Fin. & Treas.--Outback Steakhouse Inc., Tampa, FL; *U.S. Public*, pg. 1235
Merritt, Sara P., Sr. V.P. & Dir.-H.R.--Chittenden Corporation, Burlington, VT; *U.S. Public*, pg. 350
Merritt, William E., Jr., Sr. V.P.-Claims--ACCEL International Corporation, Dublin, OH; *U.S. Public*, pg. 14
Merson, Barbara, Chief Fin. Officer & Sr. V.P.--Castle Oil Corporation, Harrison, NY; *U.S. Private*, pg. 219
Merwarth, Mike, Exec. V.P.--Global Software, Inc., Raleigh, NC; *U.S. Private*, pg. 457
Merwise, Norm, Sr. V.P.-Sls. & Mktg.--Scripto-Tokai Corp., Fontana, CA; *U.S. Private*, pg. 977
Meschery, Ann, Sr. V.P., Media Dir.--Campbell Media Alliance, New York, NY; *U.S. Public*, pg. 1641
Mesker, David W., Sr. V.P. & Dir.-Staff--A.G. Edwards & Sons, Inc., Saint Louis, MO; *U.S. Public*, pg. 565
Meskill, James F., Sr. V.P.-Sls.--Kay Home Products, Inc., Cleveland, OH; *U.S. Public*, pg. 1258
Meslow, John A., Sr. V.P. & Pres.-Neurological Bus.--Medtronic, Inc., Minneapolis, MN; *U.S. Public*, pg. 1082
Messana, Steve, Sr. V.P.-Human Resources--The Home Depot, Inc., Atlanta, GA; *U.S. Public*, pg. 831
Messey, R.J., Chief Fin. Officer & Sr. V.P.--Sverdrup Corporation, Maryland Heights, MO; *U.S. Private*, pg. 1057
Messinger, Martin P., Sr. V.P. & Gen. Counsel--CBS, New York, NY; *U.S. Public*, pg. 273
Metcalf, John, Chief Fin. Officer & Sr. V.P.-Fin.--Mitsubishi Silicon America, Salem, OR; *Int'l*, pg. 875
Metevier, James F., Sr. V.P.-Corp. Counseling--Associates Financial Services Corporation, Dallas, TX; *U.S. Public*, pg. 663
Meti, Tony P., Sr. V.P.-Banking--National Bank of Canada, Montreal, Canada; *Int'l*, pg. 907
Metropoulos, Jim, M.D., Sr. V.P. & Chief Strategic Officer--Lowe McAdams Healthcare, New York, NY; *U.S. Private, pg. 678*
Mettee, Richard W., Sr. V.P.--Stanley Consultants, Inc., Muscatine, IA; *U.S. Private*, pg. 1033
Mettemeyer, Richard A., Sr. V.P.-Fin.--Penn-Daniels, Inc., Quincy, IL; *U.S. Public*, pg. 1467
Metz, Dorothea C., Sr. V.P.--Pioneer American Holding Company, Carbondale, PA; *U.S. Public*, pg. 1290
Metz, Lawrence A., Sr. V.P. & Deputy Gen. Counsel--American Stores Company, Salt Lake City, UT; *U.S. Public*, pg. 92
Metz, Norman, Sr. V.P.-Opers.--DeVry Institutes, Oak Brook Terrace, IL; *U.S. Public*, pg. 503
Meuller, Hans, Sr. V.P.-Global Bus. Devel.--American Home Products Corporation, Madison, NJ; *U.S. Public*, pg. 79
Meyer, Carl E., Sr. V.P.-Corp. Services--Central Hudson Gas & Electric Corporation, Poughkeepsie, NY; *U.S. Public*, pg. 324
Meyer, James W., Sr. V.P., Chief Technical Officer & Dir.-Res./Devel.--Eastman Kodak Company, Rochester, NY; *U.S. Public*, pg. 550
Meyer, Jim, Sr. V.P. & Exec. Grp. Acct. Dir.--DMB&B New York, New York, NY; *U.S. Private*, pg. 302
Meyer, John P., Sr. V.P. & Controller--Sprint Corporation, Westwood, KS; *U.S. Public*, pg. 1500
Meyer, Lee, Sr. V.P. & Gen. Mgr.--Variform, Inc., Kearney, MO; *U.S. Public*, pg. 1193
Meyer, Stephen P., Sr. V.P.--The Titan Corporation, San Diego, CA; *U.S. Public*, pg. 1618
Meyer, William A., Sr. V.P.--Great Lakes Lithograph Co., Cleveland, OH; *U.S. Private*, pg. 474
Meyer, William S., Chief Fin. Officer, Sr. V.P. & Controller--American Greetings Corporation, Cleveland, OH; *U.S. Public*, pg. 77

Meyercord, Wade, Sr. V.P.-MIS & Continuous Improvement--Diamond Multimedia Systems, Inc., San Jose, CA; *U.S. Public*, pg. 505
Meyers, Charles E., Chief Fin. Officer & Sr. V.P.--Chartwell Re Corporation, Stamford, CT; *U.S. Public*, pg. 336
Meyers, Hans W., Sr. V.P. & Gen. Mgr.--DG Bank-New York, New York, NY; *Int'l*, pg. 352
Meyers, James E., Sr. V.P.-Credit--Fleet Capital Corporation, Glastonbury, CT; *U.S. Public*, pg. 649
Meyers, Kevin, Chief Fin. Officer & Sr. V.P.-Loan Admin.--Countrywide Funding Corporation, Pasadena, CA; *U.S. Public*, pg. 453
Meyers, Raymond G., Chief Admin. Officer & Sr. V.P.--Fremont General Corporation, Santa Monica, CA; *U.S. Public*, pg. 681
Meyers, Robert G., Sr. V.P.--Defender Services, Inc., Columbia, SC; *U.S. Private*, pg. 320
Meyerson, Aaron, Sr. V.P.-Motion Pictures--DIC Entertainment, Burbank, CA; *U.S. Public*, pg. 513
Meynard, John, Chief Fin. Officer & Sr. V.P.--Royal LePage Limited, Don Mills, Canada; *Int'l*, pg. 1143
Mezey, Philip C., Sr. V.P.-System Svcs.--GPU Service Corp., Parsippany, NJ; *U.S. Public*, pg. 695
Mezger, Dieter J., Sr. V.P.-VLSI Tech. Inc., Pres.-COMPASS Design Automation, Inc.--VLSI Technology, Inc., San Jose, CA; *U.S. Public*, pg. 1703
Miars, Bob, Sr. V.P.-Design, Construction & Engrng.--Bristol Hotels & Resorts, Dallas, TX; *U.S. Public*, pg. 253
Micallef, Joseph C., Sr. V.P.-Fin. & Opers.--Educational & Professional Publishing Group, New York, NY; *U.S. Public*, pg. 1070
Micallef, Leonard J., Sr. V.P.--Greyvest Capitol Inc., Toronto, Canada; *Int'l*, pg. 559
Michael, C. Kim, Sr. V.P.-H.R.--Southwest National Corporation, Greensburg, PA; *U.S. Public*, pg. 1493
Michael, C. Kim, Sr. V.P.--Southwest National Bank of Pennsylvania, Greensburg, PA; *U.S. Public*, pg. 1493
Michael, Lanny H., Sr. V.P. & Treas.--Airborne Freight Corporation, Seattle, WA; *U.S. Public*, pg. 32
Michael, Mark D., Sr. V.P., Gen. Counsel & Sec.--3Com Corporation, Santa Clara, CA; *U.S. Public*, pg. 1603
Michael, Robert W., Sr. V.P. & Grp. Exec.--Walter Industries, Inc., Tampa, FL; *U.S. Public*, pg. 1736
Michaelis, Dana, Sr. V.P.-Affiliate Sls.--The Weather Channel, Atlanta, GA; *U.S. Private*, pg. 647
Michaels, Brent, Sr. V.P.-Opers. Services & Training--Hardee's Food Systems, Inc., Rocky Mount, NC; *U.S. Public*, pg. 278
Michaelsen, Alfred L., Sr. V.P.-Patent Opers.--Corning Incorporated, Corning, NY; *U.S. Public*, pg. 448
Michaud, Richard O., Sr. V.P.--Acadian Asset Management, Boston, MA; *U.S. Public*, pg. 1672
Michel, Gregory A., Sr. V.P. & Acct. Grp. Dir.--Creswell, Munsell, Fultz & Zirbel, L.P., Cedar Rapids, IA; *U.S. Private*, pg. 1197
Michels, Frances G., Sr. V.P.-Support Svcs.--Morrison Health Care Inc., Smyrna, GA; *U.S. Public*, pg. 1133
Michelson, Arne G., Sr. V.P.-Trading Analysis--The American Stock Exchange, New York, NY; *U.S. Private*, pg. 62
Michlin, Irv, Sr. V.P.--Transkrit Corporation, Roanoke, VA; *U.S. Private*, pg. 782
Michon, D., Sr. V.P.-Tech. Res.--Compagnie Generale de Geophysique, Massy, France; *Int'l*, pg. 241
Middendorf, Richard, Sr. V.P. & Co.-Creative Dir.--The Lord Group, New York, NY; *U.S. Private*, pg. 325
Middlebrooks, Bob M., Sr. V.P.--Allied Products Corporation, Chicago, IL; *U.S. Public*, pg. 48
Middlebrooks, Bobby, Corp. Sr. V.P.--Bush Hog Division, Selma, AL; *U.S. Public*, pg. 48
Middleton, Lee, Sr. Dir.-Public Affairs--American Express Bank Ltd., New York, NY; *U.S. Public*, pg. 73
Middleton, Ted, Sr. V.P.-Devel. Fin.--Hilton Hotels Corporation, Beverly Hills, CA; *U.S. Public*, pg. 828
Miears, James L., Exec. V.P. & Gen. Mgr.-Cedar Point--Cedar Fair, L.P., Sandusky, OH; *U.S. Public*, pg. 319
Mielke, Donald, Sr. V.P.-Stores--Venture Stores, Inc., O Fallon, MO; *U.S. Public*, pg. 1716
Mifune, Tsuyoshi, Sr. V.P.--Ryobi Ltd., Tokyo, Japan; *Int'l*, pg. 1151
Migel, Christopher J., Sr. V.P.--General Reinsurance Corp., Stamford, CT; *U.S. Public*, pg. 725
Migura, Marvin J., Chief Fin. Officer & Sr. V.P.--Oceaneering International, Inc., Houston, TX; *U.S. Public*, pg. 1211
Migura, Marvin J., Chief Fin. Officer & Sr. V.P.--Oceaneering International, Inc., Morgan City, LA; *U.S. Public*, pg. 1211
Mihaichuk, Garry P., Sr. V.P.--Transcanada Pipelines Limited, Calgary, Canada; *Int'l*, pg. 1416
Mihm, J.C., Sr. V.P.-Corp. Tech.--Phillips Petroleum Company, Bartlesville, OK; *U.S. Public*, pg. 1290
Mihulka, Charles R., Sr. V.P.-Internal Audit--Federal Home Loan Bank of New York, New York, NY; *U.S. Private*, pg. 399
Mikami, Toru, Sr. V.P.--NEC Corporation, Tokyo, Japan; *Int'l*, pg. 899
Mikelonis, David A., Sr. V.P. & Gen. Counsel-Consumers--CMS Energy Corporation, Dearborn, MI; *U.S. Public*, pg. 279
Mikhail, Roosevelt, Sr. V.P. Engrng. & Tech. Oper.--Time Warner Cable of New York City, New York, NY; *U.S. Public*, pg. 1611
Miksis-Zivic, Rosemarie, Sr. V.P. & Assoc. Creative Dir.--Towne, Silverstein, Rotter Inc., New York, NY; *U.S. Private*, pg. 1093
Mikulay, Robert L., Sr. V.P.-Mktg.--Philip Morris U.S.A., New York, NY; *U.S. Public*, pg. 1289
Milam, Christopher, Sr. V.P.-European Opers.--Golub & Co., Chicago, IL; *U.S. Private*, pg. 463
Milano, Joanne, Sr. V.P. & Media Res. Dir.--Jordan, McGrath, Case & Taylor Inc., New York, NY; *U.S. Private*, pg. 598
Milano, Kathryn, Sr. V.P. & Acct. Mng. Dir.--Young & Rubicam New York, New York, NY; *U.S. Private*, pg. 1198
Milasius, Alan R., Sr. V.P., Sec. & Dir.-Internal Audit--First Midwest Bancorp, Inc., Itasca, IL; *U.S. Public*, pg. 636
Milbank, Patrick, Sr. V.P.--Imperial Bank, Inglewood, CA; *U.S. Public*, pg. 871
Mildren, Kevin W., Sr. V.P.--Laurel Bank, Johnstown, PA; *U.S. Public*, pg. 164
Miles, L. William, Sr. V.P.--Call Interactive, Omaha, NE; *U.S. Public*, pg. 631
Miles, Michael W., Chief Fin. Officer & Sr. V.P.--Safeguard Scientifics, Inc., Wayne, PA; *U.S. Public*, pg. 1424
Mileusnic, George, Chief Fin. Officer & Sr. V.P.--The Coleman Company, Inc., Golden, CO; *U.S. Private*, pg. 690
Milich, Miguel, Sr. V.P.-Sls. & Mgr.-Natl. Sls.--Amcel Corp., Watertown, MA; *U.S. Private*, pg. 48
Millan, Augusto H., Sr. V.P. & Gen. Mgr.-Intl. Sls.--International Comfort Products, Franklin, TN; *U.S. Public*, pg. 898
Millard, J., Sr. V.P.-Opers./Traffic--Zim-American Israeli Shipping Co., New York, NY; *U.S. Private*, pg. 1206
Millenbruch, Gary L., Chief Fin. Officer, Exec. V.P. & Treas.--Bethlehem Steel Corporation, Bethlehem, PA; *U.S. Public*, pg. 226
Miller, Alan E., Sr. V.P. & Gen. Mgr.-Mdsg.--Younkers, Inc., Des Moines, IA; *U.S. Public*, pg. 1334
Miller, Barbara, Sr. V.P. & Dir.-H.R.--Bremer Financial Services, Inc., Saint Paul, MN; *U.S. Private*, pg. 167
Miller, Barbara E., Sr. V.P. & Dir.-Human Resources--Bremer Financial Corporation, Saint Paul, MN; *U.S. Private*, pg. 167
Miller, Bennett, Sr. V.P. & Creative Dir.--Grey Advertising Inc., San Francisco, CA; *U.S. Public*, pg. 764
Miller, Bruce, Sr. V.P.-Corp. Plng. & Devel.--Northwestern Mutual Life Insurance Co., Milwaukee, WI; *U.S. Private*, pg. 807
Miller, C. Doyle, Sr. V.P. & Pres.-Hercules Chemical Specialties Co.--Hercules Incorporated, Wilmington, DE; *U.S. Public*, pg. 809
Miller, Charles W., Sr. V.P.-Opers.--HBOC, Atlanta, GA; *U.S. Public*, pg. 770
Miller, Charlotte L., Sr. V.P., Gen. Counsel & Sec.--Summit Family Restaurants, Inc., Salt Lake City, UT; *U.S. Public*, pg. 278
Miller, Clayton W., Chief Acctg. Officer & Sr. V.P.--Washington Homes, Inc., Landover, MD; *U.S. Public*, pg. 1741
Miller, D.W., Chief Fin. Officer & Sr. V.P.--Russell-Stanley Corporation, Red Bank, NJ; *U.S. Private*, pg. 953
Miller, Darren B., Chief Fin. Officer & Sr. V.P.--Group Maintenance America Corp., Houston, TX; *U.S. Public*, pg. 766
Miller, David B., Sr. V.P.--Erie Family Life Insurance Company, Erie, PA; *U.S. Public*, pg. 590
Miller, Donald E., Sr. V.P., Gen. Counsel & Sec.--The Fairchild Corporation, Chantilly, VA; *U.S. Public*, pg. 610
Miller, Edward J., Sr. V.P.--Standard Federal Bank, Troy, MI; *Int'l*, pg. 10
Miller, Ellen, Sr. V.P. & Grp. Res. Dir.--Jordan, McGrath, Case & Taylor Inc., New York, NY; *U.S. Private*, pg. 598
Miller, Fred D., Sr. V.P.-Public Policy--Portland General Electric Co., Portland, OR; *U.S. Public*, pg. 584
Miller, Gary H., Chief Fin. Officer & Sr. V.P.--FirstCity Financial Corporation, Waco, TX; *U.S. Public*, pg. 644
Miller, Gary S., Sr. V.P.-Design & Devel.--Herman Miller, Inc., Zeeland, MI; *U.S. Public*, pg. 1111
Miller, George, Sr. V.P.-Admin.--CD Products, Inc., New Providence, NJ; *U.S. Public*, pg. 276
Miller, George D., Sr. V.P.-Mdse.--Central Tractor Farm & Country, Inc., Des Moines, IA; *U.S. Private*, pg. 237
Miller, Glenn, V.P.-Opers.--Active Tool & Manufacturing Co., Inc., Roseville, MI; *U.S. Private*, pg. 16
Miller, Gregg P., V.P.-Human Resources--Dwyer Instruments Inc., Michigan City, IN; *U.S. Private*, pg. 350
Miller, H.R., Sr. V.P.--National Yarn Crafts, New York, NY; *U.S. Private*, pg. 787
Miller, Harold A., Sr. V.P.-Opers.--Sam's Clubs Div., Bentonville, AR; *U.S. Public*, pg. 1733
Miller, Heidi G., Chief Fin. Officer & Sr. V.P.--Travelers Group, New York, NY; *U.S. Public*, pg. 1632
Miller, Henry, Sr. V.P.--Houlihan's Restaurant Group, Kansas City, MO; *U.S. Public*, pg. 841
Miller, J.J., Sr. V.P.-Corp. Devel.--The Western and Southern Life Insurance Company, Cincinnati, OH; *U.S. Private*, pg. 1164
Miller, James G., Sr. V.P.-Energy Delivery--UtiliCorp United Inc., Kansas City, MO; *U.S. Public*, pg. 1700
Miller, James R., Sr. V.P.--J.E. Dunn Construction Co., Kansas City, MO; *U.S. Private*, pg. 347
Miller, Janet M., Sr. V.P.--Sparks State Bank, Sparks, MD; *U.S. Public*, pg. 1089
Miller, Jay, Sr. V.P.-Fin., Treas. & Sec.--Perfection Bakeries Inc., Fort Wayne, IN; *U.S. Private*, pg. 852
Miller, Jim, Chief Underwriting Officer & Sr. V.P.--Kemper Reinsurance Co., Long Grove, IL; *U.S. Private*, pg. 614
Miller, John, Sr. V.P.--General Growth Management, Inc., Chicago, IL; *U.S. Public*, pg. 715
Miller, John, Sr. V.P. & Grp. Media Dir.-OOH--Young & Rubicam New York, New York, NY; *U.S. Private*, pg. 1198
Miller, John, Sr. V.P. & Dir.-Process Equipment Devel.--Pall Corporation, Greenvale, NY; *U.S. Public*, pg. 1253
Miller, John C., Sr. V.P.-New Concept Devel.--Brinker International, Inc., Dallas, TX; *U.S. Public*, pg. 253
Miller, John L., Sr. V.P.-N. America Sls.--American & Efird, Inc., Mount Holly, NC; *U.S. Public*, pg. 1412
Miller, John T., Chief Fin. Officer & Sr. V.P.-Fin.--E-Z Serve Corp., Houston, TX; *U.S. Public*, pg. 540
Miller, Joseph, Sr. V.P.-Prod. Devel.--Sega of America Inc., Redwood City, CA; *Int'l*, pg. 1218
Miller, Ken, Sr. V.P.-Corrosion Control Services--ICO, Inc., Houston, TX; *U.S. Public*, pg. 853
Miller, Kirk, Sr. V.P., Sec. & Gen. Counsel--Kaiser Permanente, Oakland, CA; *U.S. Private*, pg. 605
Miller, Lanneau, Sr. V.P. & Mgr.-P&C--Willis Corroon Corp. of Orange County, Santa Ana, CA; *Int'l*, pg. 1506
Miller, Lawrence B., Sr. V.P.--Imperial Bank, Inglewood, CA; *U.S. Public*, pg. 871
Miller, Michael, Chief Fin. Officer & Sr. V.P.-Fin.--Fender Musical Instruments, Scottsdale, AZ; *U.S. Private*, pg. 400
Miller, Michael E., Chief Admin. Officer & Sr. V.P.--Solutia Inc., Saint Louis, MO; *U.S. Public*, pg. 1483
Miller, Michael P., Sr. V.P.-Worldwide Oil & Gas Mktg.--Occidental Oil & Gas Corporation, Bakersfield, CA; *U.S. Public*, pg. 1210
Miller, Michael P., Sr. V.P.-Real Estate--Toys "R" Us, Inc., Paramus, NJ; *U.S. Public*, pg. 1626
Miller, Michael T., Sr. V.P. & Chief Credit Officer--AmeriCredit Corp., Fort Worth, TX; *U.S. Public*, pg. 96
Miller, Paul S., Sr. V.P. & Gen. Counsel--Pfizer Inc., New York, NY; *U.S. Public*, pg. 1281
Miller, Phebe C., Sr. V.P. & Chief Legal Officer--The Bank of New York, New York, NY; *U.S. Public*, pg. 178
Miller, Preston A., Sr. V.P. & Treas.--AmeriCredit Corp., Fort Worth, TX; *U.S. Public*, pg. 96
Miller, Richard, Sr. V.P. & Mng. Dir.-Pub. Rels.--Northlich Stolley LaWarre Public Relations, Cincinnati, OH; *U.S. Private*, pg. 806
Miller, Richard, Sr. V.P.--Harlan Electric Co., Rochester Hills, MI; *U.S. Public*, pg. 1029
Miller, Richard D., Sr. V.P.--Imperial Bank, Inglewood, CA; *U.S. Public*, pg. 871
Miller, Robert A., Sr. V.P.--Willis Corroon Corp. of Missouri, Saint Louis, MO; *Int'l*, pg. 1506
Miller, Robert C., Sr. V.P.-Admin. Svcs.--Kansas City Life Insurance Co., Kansas City, MO; *U.S. Public*, pg. 942
Miller, Ronald, Sr. V.P.-Distr.--Rite Aid Corporation, Camp Hill, PA; *U.S. Public*, pg. 1390
Miller, Samuel M., Chief Fin. Officer & Sr. V.P.-Fin.--Liz Claiborne, Inc., New York, NY; *U.S. Public*, pg. 1005
Miller, Scott, Sr. V.P., Gen. Counsel & Asst. Sec.--Coherent, Inc., Santa Clara, CA; *U.S. Public*, pg. 395
Miller, Ted, Sr. V.P.-Opers.--Aerovox Inc., New Bedford, MA; *U.S. Public*, pg. 25
Miller, Theresa, Sr. V.P. & Media Dir.--Mendoza, Dillon & Asociados, Inc., Newport Beach, CA; *Int'l*, pg. 1483
Miller, Tish, Sr. V.P.-Acct. Services--Western International Media Corporation, Los Angeles, CA; *U.S. Private*, pg. 1165
Miller, W. Walter, Jr., Sr. V.P.--Total System Services, Inc., Columbus, GA; *U.S. Public*, pg. 1550
Miller, Walter M., Sr. V.P.-Strategy & Devel.--Becton Dickinson & Company, Franklin Lakes, NJ; *U.S. Public*, pg. 199
Miller, Ward M., Jr., Sr. V.P., Gen. Counsel & Sec.--Avon Products, Inc., New York, NY; *U.S. Public*, pg. 155
Miller, Wendy, Sr. V.P.-Madison Design--Young & Rubicam New York, New York, NY; *U.S. Private*, pg. 1198
Miller, William G., Sr. V.P.-Mid-South Refining & Mktg.--Mapco Petroleum Inc., Tulsa, OK; *U.S. Public*, pg. 1042
Millerick, John J., Chief Fin. Officer & Sr. V.P.--CalComp Technology, Inc., Anaheim, CA; *U.S. Public*, pg. 1007
Milliaressis, Renee, Sr. V.P. & Media Dir.-DMB&B/NY--DMB&B New York, New York, NY; *U.S. Private*, pg. 302
Milligan, Lawrence D., Sr. V.P.-Customer Bus. Devel.--The Procter & Gamble Company, Cincinnati, OH; *U.S. Public*, pg. 1330
Milliken, Chris, Sr. V.P.--Boise Cascade Office Products Corporation, Itasca, IL; *U.S. Public*, pg. 243
Milliken, George, Sr. V.P. & Strategic Services Dir.--DavisElen Advertising, Inc., Los Angeles, CA; *U.S. Private*, pg. 316
Milliou, Andre, Sr. V.P.-Hotel Opers.--Atlantic City Showboat, Atlantic City, NJ; *U.S. Public*, pg. 1469
Mills, Jack, Sr. V.P.-Sls.--Bob Evans Farms, Inc., Columbus, OH; *U.S. Public*, pg. 596
Mills, Rita Johnson, Chief Oper. Officer & Sr. V.P.--D.C. Chartered Health Plan, Washington, DC; *U.S. Public*, pg. 1241
Millsap, James M., Sr. V.P.-Corp. Devel.--IVAX Corporation, Miami, FL; *U.S. Public*, pg. 914
Millstein, David J., Sr. V.P.--Millstein Industries, Youngwood, PA; *U.S. Private*, pg. 749
Milne, John, Vice Chm., Chief Acq. Officer, Sr. V.P., Treas. & Sec.--United Waste Systems, Inc., Houston, TX; *U.S. Public*, pg. 1691
Milne, Malcolm R., Sr. V.P. & Treas.--First Federal of Michigan, Detroit, MI; *U.S. Public*, pg. 336
Milner, R.C., Sr. V.P.--Nova Corporation, Calgary, Canada; *Int'l*, pg. 971
Milos, Charles D., Jr., Sr. V.P. & Investment Analyst--National Western Life Insurance Company, Austin, TX; *U.S. Public*, pg. 1161
Mimiaga, Paul, Sr. V.P. & Creative Dir.--Hal Riney & Partners, Inc., San Francisco, CA; *U.S. Private*, pg. 931
Mindrup, Larry A., Chief Banking Officer & Corp. Sr. V.P.--Brenton Banks, Inc., Des Moines, IA; *U.S. Public*, pg. 251
Miner, James J., Sr. V.P.-Farm Production--Pilgrim's Pride Corporation, Pittsburg, TX; *U.S. Public*, pg. 1296
Mines, Raymond C., Jr., Sr. V.P.-Franchisee Rels.--McDonald's Corporation, Oak Brook, IL; *U.S. Public*, pg. 1068
Ming, Jenny J., Sr. V.P.-Mdsg.--Old Navy Stores, San Francisco, CA; *U.S. Public*, pg. 703
Minich, Clay B., Sr. V.P. & Dir.-Loan Mktg.--Barclays American/Mortgage Corp., Charlotte, NC; *Int'l*, pg. 165
Minick, Carl, Sr. V.P.-D.P.--Fort Wayne National Corporation, Fort Wayne, IN; *U.S. Public*, pg. 673
Mink, Robert S., Sr. V.P. & Mgr.-Northern Div.--First Security Bank of Idaho, N.A., Boise, ID; *U.S. Public*, pg. 637
Minneti, Alice, Sr. V.P. & Brdcst. Dir.--Wunderman Cato Johnson, New York, NY; *U.S. Private*, pg. 1197
Minnich, Donna L., Sr. V.P.--Chicago Asset Management Company, Chicago, IL; *U.S. Public*, pg. 1672

Minnig, Rebecca L., Sr. V.P.-Opers.--The Commercial Bank, Delphos, OH; *U.S. Public*, pg. 410
Minor, Joe C., Chief Fin. Officer, Sr. V.P. & Treas.--NBT Bancorp Inc., Norwich, NY; *U.S. Public*, pg. 1144
Minor, Robert O., Dr., Sr. V.P.-Education--Sylvan Learning Systems Inc., Baltimore, MD; *U.S. Public*, pg. 1545
Minor, Todd C., Sr. V.P.-Mortgage Servicing & Fin.--National Income Realty Trust, New York, NY; *U.S. Public*, pg. 1157
Minor, Todd C., Sr. V.P.-Mortgage Services & Fin.--Tarragon Realty Investors, Dallas, TX; *U.S. Public*, pg. 1561
Minsky, Carla, Sr. V.P. & Mngmt. Supvr.--Laughlin/Constable, Inc., Milwaukee, WI; *U.S. Private*, pg. 653
Minsky, Mark E., Sr. V.P. & Gen. Mgr.-Mdse.--Caldor, Inc., Norwalk, CT; *U.S. Public*, pg. 292
Minton, Frank A., Sr. V.P.-Sls. Centers--American Bankers Life Assurance Co. of Florida, Miami, FL; *U.S. Public*, pg. 67
Minton, Keith, Sr. V.P.-N.A. Opers.--Hoover Company, Canton, OH; *U.S. Public*, pg. 1065
Minton, Peter, Sr. V.P.--General Reinsurance Corp., Stamford, CT; *U.S. Public*, pg. 725
Mintz, Alan, Sr. V.P.-Corp. Devel.--ServiCenter USA, Deerfield Beach, FL; *U.S. Public*, pg. 1201
Mintz, Charles E., Sr. V.P. & Dir.-Retail Mkts.--Scott & Stringfellow Financial, Inc., Richmond, VA; *U.S. Public*, pg. 1445
Mintz, Charles E., Sr. V.P.--Scott & Stringfellow, Inc., Richmond, VA; *U.S. Public*, pg. 1445
Minutoli, Robert, Sr. V.P.-New Bus.--The Rouse Company, Columbia, MD; *U.S. Public*, pg. 1407
Minutoli, Robert, Sr. V.P.-New Bus.--New Business, Columbia, MD; *U.S. Public*, pg. 1407
Miodunski, Robert L., Sr. V.P.--Alliance Gaming Corporation, Las Vegas, NV; *U.S. Public*, pg. 46
Mirabella, Anthony C., Sr. V.P.-District Heating & Cooling--Energy Networks, Inc. (ENI), Hartford, CT; *U.S. Public*, pg. 285
Miraben, George, Sr. V.P.-Policy & H.R.--Tucson Electric Power Company, Tucson, AZ; *U.S. Public*, pg. 1670
Miramonti, Robert C., Sr. V.P.--Associates Commercial Equipment Div., Dallas, TX; *U.S. Public*, pg. 663
Miraselli, Anthony, Sr. V.P.-Mktg. & Sls.--Cobra Electronics Corporation, Chicago, IL; *U.S. Public*, pg. 391
Mirlisena, John R., Jr., Sr. V.P.-Cleveland Region--The Provident Bank, Cincinnati, OH; *U.S. Public*, pg. 1338
Miron, Randi, Sr. V.P.--Edelman Public Relations Worldwide, Chicago, IL; *U.S. Private*, pg. 362
Misaki, Alan T., Sr. V.P.-Residential Lending--American Savings Bank, F.S.B., Honolulu, HI; *U.S. Public*, pg. 800
Misakian, Jeffrey D., Sr. V.P. & Dir.-Corp. Rels.--Glendale Federal Bank, F.S.B., Glendale, CA; *U.S. Public*, pg. 747
Mischell, Thomas E., Sr. V.P.-Taxation--American Financial Group, Cincinnati, OH; *U.S. Public*, pg. 74
Mischler, Terrence W., Ph.D., Sr. V.P.-Govt. & Intl. Affairs--Pharmaceutical Product Development, Inc., Wilmington, NC; *U.S. Public*, pg. 1285
Misener, James, Sr. V.P. & Gen. Mgr.--Newcourt Financial USA, Inc., Indianapolis, IN; *Int'l*, pg. 924
Misher, Kevin, Sr. V.P.-Production--TriStar Pictures, Culver City, CA; *Int'l*, pg. 1283
Mita, Kiyoshi, Sr. V.P.--Nippon Telegraph and Telephone Corporation, Tokyo, Japan; *Int'l*, pg. 940
Mita, Y., Sr. V.P.--Mitsubishi International Corporation, New York, NY; *Int'l*, pg. 871
Mitchell, Beverly L., Sr. V.P. & Chief Market Mgr.--MainStreet BankGroup Incorporated, Martinsville, VA; *U.S. Public*, pg. 1038
Mitchell, Clarence, Sr. V.P.--Oglethorpe Power Corp., Tucker, GA; *U.S. Private*, pg. 812
Mitchell, Lori, Sr. V.P.--Hibernia Corporation, New Orleans, LA; *U.S. Public*, pg. 825
Mitchell, Patrick, Sr. V.P. & Treas.--National Financial Insurance Company, Fort Worth, TX; *U.S. Private*, pg. 782
Mitchell, Peter, Sr. V.P. & Acct. Dir.--Berry-Brown Advertising, Inc., Dallas, TX; *U.S. Private*, pg. 137
Mitchell, Richard, Sr. V.P.--Analysis & Technology, Inc., North Stonington, CT; *U.S. Public*, pg. 109
Mitchell, Robert, Sr. V.P.--Imperial Bank, Inglewood, CA; *U.S. Public*, pg. 871
Mitchell, Steve A., Sr. V.P.--Laurel Bank, Johnstown, PA; *U.S. Public*, pg. 164
Mitchell, Susan, Sr. V.P.--The CIT Group Holdings, Inc., New York, NY; *Int'l*, pg. 360
Mitchell, Tandy, Sr. V.P.--Cinemark USA, Inc., Dallas, TX; *U.S. Private*, pg. 240
Mitchell, William F., Sr. V.P.--Chubb & Son, Inc., Warren, NJ; *U.S. Public*, pg. 355
Mitford-Burgess, David, Sr. Mgr.-Pest Control--W.A. Flick & Co. Pty. Limited, Lane Cove, Australia; *Int'l*, pg. 495
Mitgang, Steve, Sr. V.P.--Jostens Learning Corporation, San Diego, CA; *U.S. Private*, pg. 601
Mitsch, Steve, Sr. V.P. & Assoc. Creative Dir.--Hill, Holliday/Altschiller, New York, NY; *U.S. Private*, pg. 529
Mitsdarfer, Richard J., Sr. V.P. & Asst. Sec.--Citizens Banking Corporation, Flint, MI; *U.S. Public*, pg. 379
Mittakarin, Duangchai, Sr. V.P.-Acctg.--The Industrial Finance Corporation of Thailand, Bangkok, Thailand; *Int'l*, pg. 677
Miura, Satoshi, Sr. V.P.--Nippon Telegraph and Telephone Corporation, Tokyo, Japan; *Int'l*, pg. 940
Mixon, James P., Sr. V.P.-Distribution & Transportation--Best Buy Co., Inc., Eden Prairie, MN; *U.S. Public*, pg. 223
Miyao, Stanley K., Sr.V.P.--CalFarm Insurance Company, Sacramento, CA; *U.S. Public*, pg. 1791
Miyata, Junjiro, Dir.-Raw Materials--Asahi Breweries Ltd., Tokyo, Japan; *Int'l*, pg. 83
Miyauchi, Ken, Sr. V.P.--Softbank Corporation, Tokyo, Japan; *Int'l*, pg. 1276
Miyazaki, Hidekazu, Sr. V.P.--Marubeni America Corporation, New York, NY; *Int'l*, pg. 844
Mizell, Sidney C., Sr. V.P.-Sls. & Mktg.--Halter Marine Group, Inc., Gulfport, MS; *U.S. Public*, pg. 778
Mizoguchi, Fumio, Sr. V.P.--Yokogawa Electric Corporation, Tokyo, Japan; *Int'l*, pg. 1520
Mizugai, Takehiko, Sr. Mng. Dir.--Mitsubishi Materials Corp., Tokyo, Japan; *Int'l*, pg. 874
Mlekush, Kenneth C., Sr. V.P.--Jefferson-Pilot Corporation, Greensboro, NC; *U.S. Public*, pg. 925
Moates, Kathleen, Sr. V.P. & Deputy Gen. Counsel--Synovus Financial Corp., Columbus, GA; *U.S. Public*, pg. 1548
Moberg, David, Sr. V.P. & Publr.-Bible & Reference--Word, Incorporated, Dallas, TX; *U.S. Public*, pg. 704
Moberg, David, Sr. V.P.-Author Devel. Word Publishing--Thomas Nelson Inc., Nashville, TN; *U.S. Public*, pg. 1167
Moberg, Roger W., Sr. V.P.-Admin.--North American Van Lines, Inc., Fort Wayne, IN; *U.S. Public*, pg. 1191
Mobley, Stacey J., Sr. V.P.-External Affairs--Du Pont (E.I. Du Pont De Nemours & Co.), Wilmington, DE; *U.S. Public*, pg. 530
Mock, C.A., Chief Fin. Officer, Sr. V.P. & Sec.--Consolidated Pipe & Supply Company, Birmingham, AL; *U.S. Private*, pg. 266
Mockli, Hanspeter, Sr. V.P.-Fin.--Bobst S.A., Lausanne, Switzerland; *Int'l*, pg. 198
Modak, James M., Sr. V.P.--Total System Services, Inc., Columbus, GA; *U.S. Public*, pg. 1550
Modeen, Rolf, Sr. V.P.--Rauma Ltd., Helsinki, Finland; *Int'l*, pg. 1428
Modeer, Bengt, Sr. V.P.-Corp. Communications--Incentive AB, Stockholm, Sweden; *Int'l*, pg. 666
Modzelewski, Mike, Sr. V.P.-Acquisitions & Strategic Plng.--Melitta U.S.A., Inc., Clearwater, FL; *Int'l*, pg. 857
Moeckel, Alfred J., Sr. V.P.-Mfg.--American Trouser, Inc., Columbus, MS; *U.S. Private*, pg. 64
Moehl, Robert, Sr. V.P. & Grp. Creative Dir.--DMB&B New York, New York, NY; *U.S. Private*, pg. 302
Moeller, Wolfgang, Sr. V.P.-Acctg. & Taxes--Commerzbank AG, Frankfurt, Germany; *Int'l*, pg. 308
Moerdyk, Carol B., Chief Fin. Officer & Sr. V.P.--Boise Cascade Office Products Corporation, Itasca, IL; *U.S. Public*, pg. 243
Mogensen, Dennis, Chief Fin. Officer & Sr. V.P.--J.R. Simplot Company, Boise, ID; *U.S. Private*, pg. 1002
Moghadam, Hossein M., Dr., Sr. V.P. & Chief Tech. Officer-Data Storage Prods.--Seagate Technology Inc., Scotts Valley, CA; *U.S. Public*, pg. 1449
Mogle, David B., Sr. V.P. & Sec.--First National Bank of Pennsylvania, Hermitage, PA; *U.S. Public*, pg. 607
Mohapatra, Surya N., Dr., Sr. V.P. & Gen. Mgr.-Magnetic Resonance--Picker International, Inc., Cleveland, OH; *Int'l*, pg. 545
Mohrman, Gary F., Sr. V.P. & Chief Lending Officer--Security Bank & Trust Co., Mount Carmel, IL; *U.S. Public*, pg. 1217
Moles, Robert L., Sr. V.P.-Stores--Jacobson Stores Inc., Jackson, MI; *U.S. Public*, pg. 922
Moley, Kevin E., Sr. V.P.-Prod. & Bus. Devel.--PCS Health Systems, Inc., Scottsdale, AZ; *U.S. Public*, pg. 993
Molinelli, John J., Chief Fin. Officer & Sr. V.P.--AMETEK, Inc., Paoli, PA; *U.S. Public*, pg. 99
Molitor, Michael R., Sr. V.P.-Mdse. Plng. & Analysis--Proffitt's, Inc., Alcoa, TN; *U.S. Public*, pg. 1333
Molle, Jason, Sr. V.P.-North America--The Dialog Corporation plc, London, United Kingdom; *Int'l*, pg. 412
Moller, Wolf-Peter, Sr. V.P.--Jagenberg AG, Neuss, Germany; *Int'l*, pg. 1108
Molluso, D. Anthony, Sr. Grp. V.P.-E. Canada--Westburne Inc., Montreal, Canada; *Int'l*, pg. 1491
Molnar, Andrew J., Sr. V.P. & Creative Dir.--DMB&B Detroit, Troy, MI; *U.S. Private*, pg. 302
Moloney, Herbert W., Sr. V.P.-Mktg. & Sls.--Treasure Chest Advertising Co., Inc., Glendora, CA; *U.S. Public*, pg. 228
Molter, Robert, Sr. V.P.-Consumer Lending--The Provident Bank, Cincinnati, OH; *U.S. Public*, pg. 1338
Molyneux, Richard E., Sr. V.P.-Tech.--Mattel, Inc., El Segundo, CA; *U.S. Public*, pg. 1057
Mombert, Jean, Sr. V.P.-Direct Mail--Brooks Brothers, New York, NY; *Int'l*, pg. 843
Momomoto, Atsuhiro, Sr. V.P.--Kintetsu World Express, Inc., Tokyo, Japan; *Int'l*, pg. 734
Monaco, Carmen, Sr. V.P.-Mktg. & Adv.--Goody's Family Clothing, Inc., Knoxville, TN; *U.S. Public*, pg. 753
Monda, Keith D., Sr. V.P.-Opers.--Timberland GmbH c/o The Timberland Company, Stratham, NH; *U.S. Public*, pg. 1609
Mongan, Tod V., Sr. V.P., Gen. Counsel, & Sec.--BancTec, Inc., Dallas, TX; *U.S. Public*, pg. 176
Mongrain, Andre C., Sr. Grp. V.P.-U.S. Pacific--Westburne Inc., Montreal, Canada; *Int'l*, pg. 1491
Monrad, Elizabeth A., Sr. V.P. & Treas.--General Reinsurance Corp., Stamford, CT; *U.S. Public*, pg. 725
Monson, John, Sr. V.P.--Intuit, Inc., Mountain View, CA; *U.S. Public*, pg. 911
Monson, Pauline, Sr. V.P. & Mng. Art Dir.--The McClure Group, Wayne, PA; *U.S. Private*, pg. 719
Monsorno, Richard, Sr. V.P.-Tech.--American Technical Ceramics Corp., Huntington Station, NY; *U.S. Public*, pg. 93
Montanaro, Carl, Sr. V.P.-Sls. & Mdsg.--Foodarama Supermarkets, Inc., Freehold, NJ; *U.S. Public*, pg. 661
Montanez, Marisol Flores, Sr. V.P.--Caribbean American Life Assurance Company, Hato Rey, PR; *U.S. Public*, pg. 67
Montano, Jill, Sr. V.P.--Media Partnership Corporation, Norwalk, CT; *U.S. Private*, pg. 1168
Montanus, Gary G., Sr. V.P.-Worldwide Mktg.--Worldvision Enterprises, New York, NY; *U.S. Private*, pg. 776
Montaperto, Stephen, Sr. V.P.-Fin.--Hanover Direct, Inc., Weehawken, NJ; *U.S. Public*, pg. 782
Monte, Joan, Sr. V.P.--Media Partnership Corporation, Norwalk, CT; *U.S. Private*, pg. 1168
Monte, Thomas J., Sr. V.P.--Chubb & Son, Inc., Warren, NJ; *U.S. Public*, pg. 355
Montemurro, Michael F., Sr. V.P.-Fin.--Snap-On Tools Corporation, Kenosha, WI; *U.S. Public*, pg. 1480
Montgomery, B.J., Sr. V.P.-Res. & Devel. & Bus. Mngmt.--Kerr-McGee Chemical Corp., Oklahoma City, OK; *U.S. Public*, pg. 952
Montgomery, George G., Sr., Sr. V.P.-Mergers & Acq.--Hambrecht & Quist LLC., San Francisco, CA; *U.S. Public*, pg. 778
Montgomery, Michael P., Sr. V.P.-Opers.--PC Service Source, Inc., Dallas, TX; *U.S. Public*, pg. 1240
Montgomery, Mike, Sr. V.P.--Law Companies Group, Atlanta, GA; *U.S. Private*, pg. 653
Montoya, Sergio, Sr. V.P.--Willis Faber North America, Inc.-Florida, Miami, FL; *Int'l*, pg. 1503
Montross, Franklin, IV, Sr. V.P.--General Re Corporation, Stamford, CT; *U.S. Public*, pg. 725
Montross, Franklin, IV, Sr. V.P.--General Reinsurance Corp., Stamford, CT; *U.S. Public*, pg. 725
Montry, Gerald F., Chief Fin. Officer & Sr. V.P.--DSC Communications Corporation, Plano, TX; *U.S. Public*, pg. 475
Moody, Christopher, Sr. V.P.--Helix Technology Corp., Mansfield, MA; *U.S. Public*, pg. 808
Mook, Gilbert D., Sr. V.P.-Air Opers.--FDX Corporation, Memphis, TN; *U.S. Public*, pg. 603
Moon, Franklin, Sr. V.P.--Bernard Johnson Young Inc., Houston, TX; *U.S. Private*, pg. 136
Moon, R. Kent, Sr. V.P.-Small Bus. Dept.--Zions First National Bank, Salt Lake City, UT; *U.S. Public*, pg. 1793
Mooney, Mark, Sr. V.P. & Chief Tech. Officer--Houghton Mifflin Company, Boston, MA; *U.S. Public*, pg. 841
Mooney, Robert J., Chief Fin. Officer & Sr. V.P.--Ethyl Corporation, Richmond, VA; *U.S. Public*, pg. 595
Moore, Andy, Sr. V.P. & Creative Art Dir.--Robert A. Becker, New York, NY; *Int'l*, pg. 601
Moore, Bradley, Sr. V.P.-Systems--Munck Automation Technology, Newport News, VA; *U.S. Private*, pg. 767
Moore, Bruce E., Chief Fin. Officer & Sr. V.P.--J.E. Dunn Construction Co., Kansas City, MO; *U.S. Private*, pg. 347
Moore, Charles, Sr. V.P.-Intl. & Diversified Markets--Thomas Nelson Inc., Nashville, TN; *U.S. Public*, pg. 1167
Moore, Cindy A., Chief Fin. Officer, Sr. V.P. & Controller--ACCEL International Corporation, Dublin, OH; *U.S. Public*, pg. 14
Moore, Dana, Sr. V.P.-Health Care Concepts--Willis Corroon Corp. of Texas, Dallas, TX; *Int'l*, pg. 1507
Moore, Daniel D., Chief Fin. Officer & Sr. V.P.--GATX Logistics, Inc., Jacksonville, FL; *U.S. Public*, pg. 691
Moore, Daryl D., Chief Credit Officer & Sr. V.P.--Old National Bancorp, Evansville, IN; *U.S. Public*, pg. 1217
Moore, Daryl D., Sr. V.P. & Chief Credit Officer--Merchants National Bank, Terre Haute, IN; *U.S. Public*, pg. 1217
Moore, Derek, Sr. V.P. & Creative Dir.--CM Partners, Inc., Rolling Meadows, IL; *U.S. Private*, pg. 195
Moore, Donald, Chief Fin. Officer & Sr. V.P.--Unique Casual Restaurants, inc., Danvers, MA; *Int'l*, pg. 324
Moore, Donnie M., Chief Fin. Officer & Sr. V.P.-Fin. & Admin.--Cognos Inc., Ottawa, Canada; *Int'l*, pg. 305
Moore, Gary B., Sr. V.P.--Electronic Data Systems Corporation, Plano, TX; *U.S. Public*, pg. 569
Moore, Gary R., Sr. V.P.--Willis Corroon Marine & Energy, Glendale, CA; *Int'l*, pg. 1508
Moore, Gary S., Sr. V.P.--Paccar Inc., Bellevue, WA; *U.S. Public*, pg. 1246
Moore, Geoffrey, Sr. V.P.-Strategic Communications--Dow Jones Markets, Jersey City, NJ; *U.S. Public*, pg. 525
Moore, George C., Exec. V.P.--Moore Company, Westerly, RI; *U.S. Private*, pg. 759
Moore, James, Sr. V.P.--Edelman Worldwide, Inc., New York, NY; *U.S. Private*, pg. 362
Moore, James R., Sr. V.P.-CNG, Energy & Gas Services--Lone Star Gas Co., Dallas, TX; *U.S. Public*, pg. 1587
Moore, Julie A., Sr. V.P.-Asset & Liability Mngmt.--Capstead Mortgage Corporation, Dallas, TX; *U.S. Public*, pg. 303
Moore, Kathy, Sr. V.P.-Human Resources--Caesars World, Inc., Las Vegas, NV; *U.S. Public*, pg. 1512
Moore, Larry, Sr. V.P.-Loan Admin.--Deposit Guaranty Mortgage Co., Jackson, MS; *U.S. Public*, pg. 501
Moore, Michael F., Chief Info. Officer & Sr. V.P.-Info. Svcs.--American Electric Power Service Corp., Columbus, OH; *U.S. Public*, pg. 72
Moore, Michael J., Chief Info. Officer & Sr. V.P.--Vanstar Corporation, Pleasanton, CA; *U.S. Public*, pg. 1708
Moore, Mike, Sr. V.P.-Sls.--Shelby Williams Industries, Inc., Morristown, TN; *U.S. Public*, pg. 1464
Moore, Pattye, Sr. V.P.-Mktg.--Sonic Corporation, Oklahoma City, OK; *U.S. Public*, pg. 1485
Moore, Paul D., Sr. V.P.--Manufacturers & Traders Trust Company, Buffalo, NY; *U.S. Public*, pg. 631
Moore, Ron, Sr. V.P. & Mgr.-Employee Benefits--Willis Corroon, Fort Worth, TX; *Int'l*, pg. 1504
Moore, Rosella, Sr. V.P.--Trader Joe's Co., South Pasadena, CA; *U.S. Private*, pg. 1067
Moore, Sarah H., Sr. V.P.--The Colonial BancGroup, Inc., Montgomery, AL; *U.S. Public*, pg. 400
Moore, Steve, Sr. V.P.--Flexible Products Company, Marietta, GA; *U.S. Private*, pg. 412
Moore, Terry D., Sr. V.P.--Zenith Insurance Company, Woodland Hills, CA; *U.S. Public*, pg. 1791
Moore, William S., Sr. V.P.-Sls. & Mktg.--Rocky Shoes & Boots, Inc., Nelsonville, OH; *U.S. Public*, pg. 1402
Moosmuller, Martin, Sr. Exec. V.P.-Securities Div.--Bayerische Landesbank, Munich, Germany; *Int'l*, pg. 176
Morabito, Joseph M., Sr. V.P.-Banking Opers./Western Canada--CT Financial Services, Inc., Toronto, Canada; *Int'l*, pg. 112
Morales, Alberto J., Sr. V.P.-Admin.--Provident Companies, Inc., Chattanooga, TN; *U.S. Public*, pg. 1337
Morales, Antonino, Sr. V.P.-Employee Devel.--Security Pacific Financial Services Inc., San Diego, CA; *U.S. Public*, pg. 181

Moran, Glenn, Sr. V.P., Gen. Counsel & Sec.--The LTV Corporation, Cleveland, OH; *U.S. Public*, pg. 971
Moran, James D., Sr. V.P.--Crown Equipment Corporation, New Bremen, OH; *U.S. Private*, pg. 292
Moran, James G., Sr. V.P.-Corp. Admin.--Regal Ware, Inc., Kewaskum, WI; *U.S. Private*, pg. 917
Moran, John J., Sr. V.P. & Controller--Anchor Financial Corporation, Myrtle Beach, SC; *U.S. Public*, pg. 111
Moran, Raymond E., Sr. V.P.--American Appraisal Associates, Inc., Milwaukee, WI; *U.S. Private*, pg. 49
Morat, Arthur, Sr. V.P. & Creative Services Dir.--DMB&B Detroit, Troy, MI; *U.S. Private*, pg. 302
Morawski, David M., Sr. V.P. & Acct. Plng. Dir.--Meldrum & Fewsmith Communications Inc., Cleveland, OH; *U.S. Private*, pg. 730
Morchison, Gloria, Sr. V.P.-Personnel--Auto-Owners Insurance, Lansing, MI; *U.S. Private*, pg. 100
Morden, Larry, Sr. V.P.-H.R. & Corp. Affairs--Parmalat Canada Ltd., Etobicoke, Canada; *Int'l*, pg. 1023
Morden, Ronald P., Sr. V.P. & Treas.--American Republic Insurance Co., Des Moines, IA; *U.S. Private*, pg. 61
Morehead, C. Richard, Sr. V.P. & Treas.--First Colonial Insurance Company, Jacksonville, FL; *U.S. Public*, pg. 79
Morehead, Robert, Sr. V.P.--Union Planters Corporation, Cordova, TN; *U.S. Public*, pg. 1668
Morehouse, T.K., Sr. V.P.-Mktg.--Central Freight Lines, Inc., Waco, TX; *U.S. Private*, pg. 223
Moreillon, Olivier, Sr. V.P.--Ferrier Lullin & Cie SA, Geneva, Switzerland; *Int'l*, pg. 480
Morel, Ernie, Sr. V.P.-Plng. & Projects--Bank of Montreal - Winnipeg, Winnipeg, Canada; *Int'l*, pg. 153
Moreland, Jeffrey R., Sr. V.P.-Law & Gen. Counsel--Burlington Northern Santa Fe Corporation, Fort Worth, TX; *U.S. Public*, pg. 268
Morenes, Guillermo Luis, Sr. V.P.--Banco Santander, Madrid, Spain; *Int'l*, pg. 143
Moreno, Albert, Sr. V.P. & Gen. Counsel--Levi Strauss & Co., San Francisco, CA; *U.S. Private*, pg. 662
Moreno, X., Sr. V.P.--Compagnie de Suez, Paris, France; *Int'l*, pg. 313
Morgan-Silvester, Sarah, Sr. V.P.-British Columbia--HongKong Bank of Canada, Vancouver, Canada; *Int'l*, pg. 583
Morgan, Barbara, Sr. V.P. & Editor-in-Chief-Books & Home Entertainment Prods.--The Reader's Digest Association, Inc., Pleasantville, NY; *U.S. Public*, pg. 1367
Morgan, Billy M., Sr. V.P.-Mdsg.--Hancock Fabrics, Inc., Tupelo, MS; *U.S. Public*, pg. 779
Morgan, Denny, Sr. V.P. & Chief Engineer--Remec, Inc., San Diego, CA; *U.S. Public*, pg. 1376
Morgan, Donald, Sr. V.P. & Grp. Mngmt. Supvr.--Lowe McAdams Healthcare, New York, NY; *U.S. Private*, pg. 678
Morgan, Donald S., Sr. V.P.-Bus. Devel.--WestWayne, Inc., Atlanta, GA; *U.S. Private*, pg. 1170
Morgan, Edward L., Jr., Sr. V.P.-Corp. Rels. & Govt. Affairs--The Hartford Financial Services Group Inc., Hartford, CT; *U.S. Public*, pg. 794
Morgan, Edwin W., Jr., Sr. V.P.-N. American Grp.--Brown-Forman Beverages Worldwide, Louisville, KY; *U.S. Public*, pg. 261
Morgan, Eugene P., Sr. V.P.-Fin. & Acctg.--Ball Aerospace & Technologies Corp., Broomfield, CO; *U.S. Public*, pg. 171
Morgan, James A., Sr. V.P., Gen. Counsel & Sec.--Rubbermaid Incorporated, Wooster, OH; *U.S. Public*, pg. 1411
Morgan, Larry J., Sr. V.P.-Orient Opers.--Mattel, Inc., El Segundo, CA; *U.S. Public*, pg. 1057
Morgan, Louis W., Sr. V.P.--First Commercial Bank, N.A., Little Rock, AR; *U.S. Public*, pg. 630
Morgan, Nathan J., Sr. V.P.-Investment Dept.--Zions First National Bank, Salt Lake City, UT; *U.S. Public*, pg. 1793
Morgan, Robert P., Sr. V.P.-N. Central Div.--Interstate Brands Corporation, Kansas City, MO; *U.S. Public*, pg. 909
Morgano, Anthony F., Sr. V.P.--American Express Publishing Corporation, New York, NY; *U.S. Public*, pg. 74
Morgenfeld, Robert J., Sr. V.P.-Flight Opers.--ABX Air, Inc., Wilmington, OH; *U.S. Public*, pg. 33
Mori, Gertrude M., Sr. V.P.-GMS Control Grp.--Servco Pacific Inc., Honolulu, HI; *U.S. Private*, pg. 986
Moriarity, Patricia J., Sr. V.P.--Firstar Milwaukee Bank, N.A., Milwaukee, WI; *U.S. Public*, pg. 643
Moriarty, Brian D., Sr. V.P.-Human Resources--First Financial Bancorp, Hamilton, OH; *U.S. Public*, pg. 632
Moriarty, Brian D., Sr. V.P.--First National Bank of Southwestern Ohio, Hamilton, OH; *U.S. Public*, pg. 633
Morikami, Melvin T., Sr. V.P.-Visitor Indus.--Bank of Hawaii, Honolulu, HI; *U.S. Public*, pg. 1248
Morin, Bruno, Sr. V.P.-Network--Federation des caisses populaires Desjardins, Montreal, Canada; *Int'l*, pg. 479
Morin, Rudolph, Sr. V.P.-Fin. & Admin.--Memorex Telex Corp., Irving, TX; *Int'l*, pg. 857
Morin, Rudolph G., Sr. V.P.-Fin. & Admin.--Memorex Telex N.V., Amsterdam, Netherlands; *Int'l*, pg. 857
Morisato, Susan C., Sr. V.P.--Bankers Life & Casualty Company, Chicago, IL; *U.S. Public*, pg. 433
Morketter, Ronald C., Chief Engrng. & Tech. Officer--Harley Ellington Design, Southfield, MI; *U.S. Private*, pg. 503
Morkin, Thomas E., Sr. V.P.--First National Bank of Pennsylvania, Hermitage, PA; *U.S. Public*, pg. 607
Morkved, Lorents, Sr. V.P.-Newsprint--Norske Skogindustrier A.S, Skogn, Norway; *Int'l*, pg. 965
Morlat, Francois, Sr. V.P.--Credit Commercial de France, Paris, France; *Int'l*, pg. 341
Morley, Michael P., Sr. V.P. & Dir.-Human Resources--Eastman Kodak Company, Rochester, NY; *U.S. Public*, pg. 550
Moroz, Michael, Sr. V.P.-Mktg. Prods. & Svcs.--Damark International, Inc., Minneapolis, MN; *U.S. Public*, pg. 478
Morphis, Gene, Chief Fin. Officer & Sr. V.P.-Fin.--Stream International Holdings Inc., Canton, MA; *U.S. Public*, pg. 518
Morral, William G., Sr. V.P.-Fin. & Treas.--Moyer Packing Company, Souderton, PA; *U.S. Private*, pg. 765
Morrell, Michael P., Chief Fin. Officer & Sr. V.P.--Allegheny Power System, Inc., Hagerstown, MD; *U.S. Public*, pg. 42
Morris, Anthony, Sr. V.P.--Long Island Bancorp, Inc., Melville, NY; *U.S. Public*, pg. 1013
Morris, C. Wayne, Sr. V.P.-Prof. Prods.--Signature Brands USA, Inc., Solon, OH; *U.S. Public*, pg. 1472
Morris, C.R., Sr. V.P.--McCain Foods Limited, Florenceville, Canada; *Int'l*, pg. 850
Morris, Edward J., Sr. V.P.--Rothschild Inc., New York, NY; *U.S. Private*, pg. 947
Morris, George S., Sr. V.P.-Prod.--Willis Corroon Corp. of Northern Ohio, Cleveland, OH; *Int'l*, pg. 1506
Morris, James V., Sr. V.P.--Security Industrial Insurance Co., Inc., Donaldsonville, LA; *Int'l*, pg. 814
Morris, Jefferson, Sr. V.P.-New Media & Tech.--Showtime Networks Inc., New York, NY; *U.S. Private*, pg. 779
Morris, John, Sr. V.P.-European Opers.--Monmouth Pharmaceutical, Ltd., Guildford, United Kingdom; *U.S. Public*, pg. 1394
Morris, Roberta J., Chief Fin. Officer &Treas.--Big Dog Holdings Inc., Santa Barbara, CA; *U.S. Public*, pg. 227
Morris, Shawn D., Sr. V.P.-Mktg.--National General Insurance Co., Earth City, MO; *U.S. Public*, pg. 721
Morris, T.C., Chief Fin. Officer & Sr. V.P.--Phillips Petroleum Company, Bartlesville, OK; *U.S. Public*, pg. 1290
Morrison, David E., Sr. V.P. & Actuary--The Great-West Life Assurance Company, Winnipeg, Canada; *Int'l*, pg. 557
Morrison, Donald J., Sr. V.P.--Market Facts, Inc., Arlington Heights, IL; *U.S. Public*, pg. 1046
Morrison, Norman G., Sr. V.P.--TCF Financial Corp., Minneapolis, MN; *U.S. Public*, pg. 1554
Morrison, Richard F., Chief Info. Officer & Sr. V.P.--Travelers Group, New York, NY; *U.S. Public*, pg. 1632
Morrison, Stewart R., Sr. V.P.-Investments--Keyport Life Insurance Company, Boston, MA; *U.S. Private*, pg. 666
Morrison, Sylvia, Sr. V.P. & Gen. Mgr.-Direct Mktg.--Liggett-Stashower, Inc., Cleveland, OH; *U.S. Private*, pg. 667
Morrisroe, Frank, Sr. V.P.--Resort Condominiums International, Indianapolis, IN; *U.S. Public*, pg. 322
Morrissey, Steve, Sr. V.P. & Acct. Dir.--Hal Riney & Partners, Inc., San Francisco, CA; *U.S. Private*, pg. 931
Morrisson, A.S., Sr. V.P., Gen. Counsel & Sec.--Sverdrup Corporation, Maryland Heights, MO; *U.S. Private*, pg. 1057
Morrow, John C., Sr. V.P. & Controller--BOK Financial Corp., Tulsa, OK; *U.S. Public*, pg. 163
Morrow, John C., Sr. V.P. & Controller--Bank of Oklahoma, N.A., Tulsa, OK; *U.S. Public*, pg. 163
Morrow, Mary Jane, Chief Fin. Officer--Federal Realty Investment Trust, Rockville, MD; *U.S. Public*, pg. 616
Morse, F.A., Sr. V.P.--Riggs National Corporation, Washington, DC; *U.S. Public*, pg. 1389
Morse, Valerie, Sr. V.P.-Govt. Rels.--Beneficial Management Corporation, Peapack, NJ; *U.S. Public*, pg. 211
Mortellaro, Robert, Sr. V.P. & Sec.--Louis P. Ciminelli Construction Co. Inc., Buffalo, NY; *U.S. Private*, pg. 239
Mortensen, Douglas L., Sr. V.P.-Tech. & Worksite Programs--Successful Money Management Seminars, Inc., Tualatin, OR; *U.S. Public*, pg. 1376
Morton, B. Carole, Sr. V.P. & Pres.-Info. Mngmt. Div.--Sterling Software, Inc., Dallas, TX; *U.S. Public*, pg. 1516
Morton, Ciaran, Sr. V.P.-Europe, Middle East & Africa--The Dialog Corporation plc, London, United Kingdom; *Int'l*, pg. 412
Morton, John, Sr. V.P.- Strategic Mktg. Services--Total Research Corporation, Princeton, NJ; *U.S. Public*, pg. 1625
Morton, Leo E., Sr. V.P.-Human Resources & Opers. Support--UtiliCorp United Inc., Kansas City, MO; *U.S. Public*, pg. 1700
Morton, Marshall N., Chief Fin. Officer & Sr. V.P.--Media General, Inc., Richmond, VA; *U.S. Public*, pg. 1077
Morton, T. Ronald, Sr. V.P.--Paccar Inc., Bellevue, WA; *U.S. Public*, pg. 1246
Mosallem, Mitch, Sr. V.P. & Graphic Svcs. Dir.--Grey Advertising Inc., New York, NY; *U.S. Public*, pg. 764
Mosby, Marty, Sr. V.P.-Strategic Plng. & Investor Rels.--First Tennessee National Corporation, Memphis, TN; *U.S. Public*, pg. 638
Moscone, M.M., Sr. V.P.--Long Manufacturing, Ltd., Oakville, Canada; *Int'l*, pg. 815
Moseley, Chris, Sr. V.P.-Adv. & Promo.--Discovery Communications, Inc., Bethesda, MD; *U.S. Private*, pg. 334
Moseley, Chris, Sr. V.P.-Adv. & Promo.--Discovery Networks, Inc., Bethesda, MD; *U.S. Private*, pg. 334
Moseley, Roger L., Sr. V.P.-Opers.--Argonaut Co., Menlo Park, CA; *U.S. Public*, pg. 129
Moser, Alan, Mng. Partner & Sr. V.P.--HMS Partners-Columbus, Columbus, OH; *U.S. Private*, pg. 492
Moser, Franz Xaver, Sr. V.P.-Res. & Devel.--Deutz AG, Cologne, Germany; *Int'l*, pg. 407
Moser, Greg, Sr. V.P.-Admin.--Credit Union National Association, Madison, WI; *U.S. Private*, pg. 288
Moses, Neil, Chief Fin. Officer & Sr. V.P.--Bradlees Inc., Braintree, MA; *U.S. Public*, pg. 249
Mosher, R.F., Sr. V.P.--AEGON International B.V., Hague, Netherlands; *Int'l*, pg. 25
Mosier, Steve, Sr. V.P. & Mgr.-P&C--Willis Corroon Corp. of Orange County, Santa Ana, CA; *Int'l*, pg. 1506
Mosley, Karyn, Sr. V.P.--The Colonial BancGroup, Inc., Montgomery, AL; *U.S. Public*, pg. 400
Moss, Chet, Sr. V.P. & Creative Dir.--The Sawtooth Group, Woodbridge, NJ; *U.S. Private*, pg. 969
Mossburg, Kelley, Sr. V.P.-H.R.--Long John Silver's, Inc., Lexington, KY; *U.S. Private*, pg. 674
Mossler, Helen, Sr. V.P.-Talent & Casting--Paramount Pictures Corporation, Los Angeles, CA; *U.S. Private*, pg. 776
Mossman, Mike, Sr. V.P.--Rena-Ware Distributors Inc., Redmond, WA; *U.S. Private*, pg. 922
Most, Nathan, Sr. V.P.--The American Stock Exchange, New York, NY; *U.S. Private*, pg. 62
Mosteller, Richard G., Chief Fin. Officer & Sr. V.P.--Masco Corporation, Taylor, MI; *U.S. Public*, pg. 1052
Motamed, Thomas F., Sr. V.P.--Chubb & Son, Inc., Warren, NJ; *U.S. Public*, pg. 355
Mote, Kevin, Sr. V.P. & Exec. Creative Dir.--EvansGroup, Dallas, TX; *U.S. Private*, pg. 385
Mothershed, J. Russell, Chief Fin. Officer & Sr. V.P.-Fin.--Ruby Tuesday, Inc., Mobile, AL; *U.S. Public*, pg. 1411
Mottier, Bradley D., Sr. V.P.--Unison Industries, Jacksonville, FL; *U.S. Private*, pg. 1120
Motz, James D., Sr. V.P.-Opers. & Employee Benefits--The Great-West Life Assurance Company, Winnipeg, Canada; *Int'l*, pg. 557
Moulds, John J., Chief Science Officer & Sr. V.P.--Gamma Biologicals Inc., Houston, TX; *U.S. Public*, pg. 698
Moullet, Barry, Sr. V.P.-Pur.--Darden Restaurants, Inc., Orlando, FL; *U.S. Public*, pg. 483
Moulton, Paul, Sr. V.P.-MIS--Costco Wholesale, Issaquah, WA; *U.S. Public*, pg. 451
Mounsey, J.B., Sr. V.P.-Investments--Manulife International Investment Office, London, United Kingdom; *Int'l*, pg. 841
Mounsey, Joseph B., Sr. V.P.-Investments--Manulife Financial (The Manufacturers Life Insurance Company), Toronto, Canada; *Int'l*, pg. 840
Mow, Barney, Sr. V.P.-Opers.--Bugle Boy Industries, Inc., Simi Valley, CA; *U.S. Private*, pg. 179
Mow, Genevieve, Sr. V.P.-Mktg.--Bugle Boy Industries, Inc., Simi Valley, CA; *U.S. Private*, pg. 179
Mowell, R.W., Sr. V.P.--Reading & Bates Development Co., Houston, TX; *U.S. Public*, pg. 1354
Moylan, James E., Jr., Chief Fin. Officer & Sr. V.P. & Pres.-Sonat Services Inc.--Sonat Inc., Birmingham, AL; *U.S. Public*, pg. 1484
Moyn, John A., Sr. V.P.-Opers.--Atlantic Aviation Corp., New Castle, DE; *U.S. Private*, pg. 94
Moynihan, Peter J., Sr. V.P.-Investments--UNUM Corporation, Portland, ME; *U.S. Public*, pg. 1699
Mozilo, Ralph S., Exec. V.P. & Chief Underwiting Officer--Countrywide Funding Corporation, Pasadena, CA; *U.S. Public*, pg. 453
Mucci, Robert V., Sr. V.P. & Actuary--Transatlantic Holdings Inc., New York, NY; *U.S. Public*, pg. 84
Mucciolo, Michael R., Chief Fin. Officer & Sr. V.P.--Beverage America, Inc., Holland, MI; *U.S. Private*, pg. 141
Muehlhausen, Richard W., Sr. V.P.-Corp. Svcs.--Otter Tail Power Company, Fergus Falls, MN; *U.S. Public*, pg. 1234
Mueller, Edward A., Sr. V.P.--Southwestern Bell Telephone Co., Saint Louis, MO; *U.S. Public*, pg. 1416
Mueller, G.L., Sr. V.P.-Customer Service & Opers.--Canadian Airlines International Ltd., Calgary, Canada; *Int'l*, pg. 256
Mueller, Gary, Sr. V.P. & Creative Dir.--BVK/McDonald, Milwaukee, WI; *U.S. Private*, pg. 108
Mueller, Hans, Ph.D., Sr. V.P.-Bus. Devel.--Wyeth-Ayerst Laboratories, Inc., Philadelphia, PA; *U.S. Public*, pg. 80
Mueller, Ken, Sr. V.P. & Controller--Platinum Technology, Inc., Oak Brook Terrace, IL; *U.S. Public*, pg. 1309
Mueller, Michael P., Sr. V.P.--Toronto Dominion Securities (U.S.A.) Inc., New York, NY; *Int'l*, pg. 1401
Mueller, Peter R., Ph.D., Sr. V.P.-Plastics/Polymers Division--Bayer Corporation, Pittsburgh, PA; *Int'l*, pg. 172
Mueller, Willaim A., Sr., Sr. V.P.--Freeman Decorating Co., Dallas, TX; *U.S. Private*, pg. 426
Muff, Walter, Sr. V.P. & Treas.--Norfoods, Inc., Overland Park, KS; *U.S. Private*, pg. 802
Muir, Douglas R., Sr. V.P., Treas. & Sec.--Oakwood Homes Corporation, Greensboro, NC; *U.S. Public*, pg. 1209
Muir, Ron, Sr. V.P.-Latin America--Brink's, Inc., Darien, CT; *U.S. Public*, pg. 1305
Mujica, M. Christine, Sr. V.P. & Fin. Admin.--Dugan/Farley Communications, Upper Saddle River, NJ; *U.S. Public*, pg. 1642
Mukumoto, H., Sr. V.P.--Mitsubishi International Corporation, New York, NY; *Int'l*, pg. 871
Mulally, Alan R., Sr. V.P. & Pres.-Boeing Defense & Space Grp.--The Boeing Company, Seattle, WA; *U.S. Public*, pg. 239
Muldoon, Patricia, Sr. V.P.-Commercial Services--Wilmington Savings Fund Society (FSB), Wilmington, DE; *U.S. Public*, pg. 1729
Mulet, Harold, Sr. V.P.-Stores--Service Merchandise Company, Inc., Brentwood, TN; *U.S. Public*, pg. 1461
Mulhern, Brian W., Sr. V.P. & Grp. Acct. Dir.--Cliff Freeman & Partners, New York, NY; *U.S. Public*, pg. 1422
Mull, Kathy A., Sr. V.P.-Corp. Devel.--United Family Life Insurance Co., Atlanta, GA; *Int'l*, pg. 499
Mullen, George J., Jr., Sr. V.P.--Fiduciary Trust Company International, New York, NY; *U.S. Public*, pg. 621
Muller, Frank M., Sr. V.P.--Coastal States Management Corp., Houston, TX; *U.S. Public*, pg. 390
Muller, Heinz, Sr. V.P.--Voest-Alpine Industries, Inc., New York, NY; *Int'l*, pg. 1470
Muller, Michael, Sr. V.P.-Govt. Services--SGS Societe Generale de Surveillance Holding S.A., Geneva, Switzerland; *Int'l*, pg. 1153
Mulligan, M. Isabelle, Sr. V.P.-Investor Rels.--Barrick Gold Corporation, Toronto, Canada; *Int'l*, pg. 168
Mulligan, Robert J., Sr. V.P.--Valley National Bank, Parsippany, NJ; *U.S. Public*, pg. 1705
Mullin, W. James, Sr. V.P. & Gen. Mgr.--Newmont Gold Company, Denver, CO; *U.S. Public*, pg. 1179
Mullins, Butch, Sr. V.P. & Gen. Mgr.-Mdsg.--Neiman Marcus Co., Dallas, TX; *U.S. Public*, pg. 785

Mullock, Paul S., Sr. V.P.-Sls.--Alliance America, Norcross, GA; *U.S. Private*, pg. 37

Mumm, Michael, Chief Fin. Officer, Sr. V.P. & Treas.--Petty Company, Inc., Effingham, IL; *U.S. Private*, pg. 860

Munczinski, R.E., Sr. V.P.-Corp. Plng. & Budgeting--American Electric Power Service Corp., Columbus, OH; *U.S. Public*, pg. 72

Munder, Barbara A., Sr. V.P.-Public Affairs--The McGraw-Hill Companies, New York, NY; *U.S. Public*, pg. 1069

Mundie, Craig, Sr. V.P.-Consumer Platforms Div.--Microsoft Corporation, Redmond, WA; *U.S. Public*, pg. 1107

Mundy, Donna T., Sr. V.P.-External Affairs--UNUM Corporation, Portland, ME; *U.S. Public*, pg. 1699

Mundy, Donna T., Sr. V.P.--UNUM Life Insurance Company of America, Portland, ME; *U.S. Public*, pg. 1699

Munkley, Ronald D., Sr. V.P.--IPL Energy Inc., Calgary, Canada; *Int'l*, pg. 651

Munns, David, Sr. V.P.--PolyGram International Ltd., London, United Kingdom; *Int'l*, pg. 1053

Munro, Laurie J., Sr. V.P.-Mktg.--Mackenzie Financial Corporation, Toronto, Canada; *Int'l*, pg. 828

Munro, Peter G., Sr. V.P. & Chief Investment Officer--The Great-West Life Assurance Company, Winnipeg, Canada; *Int'l*, pg. 557

Munson, Alden V., Jr., Sr. V.P. & Grp. Exec.-Info. Sys.--Litton Industries, Inc., Woodland Hills, CA; *U.S. Public*, pg. 1002

Murata, K., Sr. V.P.--Mitsubishi International Corporation, New York, NY; *Int'l*, pg. 871

Murata, Yoshihiko, Mng. Dir. & Sr. V.P.-Engrng., Res. & Devel.--Japan Airlines Company, Ltd., Tokyo, Japan; *Int'l*, pg. 699

Murdoch, David, Sr. V.P.-Business Support--Blue Cross and Blue Shield Association, Chicago, IL; *U.S. Private*, pg. 151

Murin, Kathryn J., Sr. V.P.--C.S. McKee & Company, Inc., Pittsburgh, PA; *U.S. Public*, pg. 1673

Murphey, Cynthia Kiser, Sr. V.P.-Human Resources & Admin.--MGM Grand Hotel, Inc., Las Vegas, NV; *U.S. Public*, pg. 1027

Murphy, Barry J., Sr. V.P.-Client Service--American Express Financial Advisor, Minneapolis, MN; *U.S. Public*, pg. 73

Murphy, Brian J., Sr. V.P.-H.R.--Brink's, Inc., Darien, CT; *U.S. Public*, pg. 1305

Murphy, Bruce D., Sr. V.P.--Keycorp, Cleveland, OH; *U.S. Public*, pg. 954

Murphy, Bud, Sr. V.P. & Gen. Mgr.-Office Prods. Div.--Minolta Corporation, Ramsey, NJ; *Int'l*, pg. 869

Murphy, David D., Sr. V.P. & Pres.-Intl. Foods--General Mills, Inc., Minneapolis, MN; *U.S. Public*, pg. 717

Murphy, David G., Sr. V.P.-Corp. Credit--Washington Mutual Inc., Seattle, WA; *U.S. Public*, pg. 1741

Murphy, Des, Sr. V.P.--Willis Corroon Aerospace of Canada Ltd., Montreal, Canada; *Int'l*, pg. 1509

Murphy, Edwin J., Sr. V.P.-Equity & Investor Services--McGraw-Hill Financial Information Services Group, New York, NY; *U.S. Public*, pg. 1071

Murphy, Glenn E., Jr., Sr. V.P.--Pell, Rudman & Company, Boston, MA; *U.S. Public*, pg. 1673

Murphy, Gregory E., Chief Fin. Officer & Sr. V.P.-Fin.--Selective Insurance Company of America, Branchville, NJ; *U.S. Public*, pg. 1455

Murphy, Gregory E., Sr. V.P.-Fin.--Selective Way Insurance Company, Branchville, NJ; *U.S. Public*, pg. 1456

Murphy, Harry V., Sr. V.P.-Devel.--Taubman Centers, Inc., Bloomfield Hills, MI; *U.S. Public*, pg. 1561

Murphy, James, Sr. V.P.-Custom Bus. Units--Read-Rite Corporation, Milpitas, CA; *U.S. Public*, pg. 1366

Murphy, James P., Sr. V.P.-Europe--Costco Wholesale, Issaquah, WA; *U.S. Public*, pg. 451

Murphy, James T., Sr. V.P.-New Prod. Devel.--Magellan Health Services, Inc., Atlanta, GA; *U.S. Public*, pg. 1033

Murphy, James W., Sr. V.P.-Corp. Fin.--American United Life Insurance Company, Indianapolis, IN; *U.S. Private*, pg. 64

Murphy, Jeffrey J., Sr. V.P.-Law & Human Resources, Sec. & Gen. Counsel--Aviall, Inc., Dallas, TX; *U.S. Public*, pg. 154

Murphy, Jill, Sr. V.P.-Grp. Client Svcs.--Shandwick Americas, New York, NY; *Int'l*, pg. 1226

Murphy, John L., Sr. V.P.--Cousins Properties Incorporated, Atlanta, GA; *U.S. Public*, pg. 453

Murphy, John P., Chief Fin. Officer & Sr. V.P.--Johns Manville Corporation, Denver, CO; *U.S. Public*, pg. 927

Murphy, K.C., Sr. V.P.-Corp. Strategy--Cadence Design Systems, Inc., San Jose, CA; *U.S. Public*, pg. 290

Murphy, Martha, Sr. V.P.-Mktg.--Helen of Troy Corporation, El Paso, TX; *U.S. Public*, pg. 807

Murphy, Michael A., Sr. V.P. & Mng. Dir.--Trident Financial Corporation, Raleigh, NC; *U.S. Private*, pg. 1103

Murphy, Michael A., Sr. V.P.-Construction & Surety--Willis Corroon Corp. of Seattle, Seattle, WA; *Int'l*, pg. 1507

Murphy, Peter E., Chief Fin. Officer & Sr. V.P.--ABC Inc., Los Angeles, CA; *U.S. Public*, pg. 511

Murphy, Raymond G., Sr. V.P.-Fin. & Treas.--Marriott International, Inc., Washington, DC; *U.S. Public*, pg. 1047

Murphy, Richard E., Sr. V.P.--Sea-Land Service, Inc., Charlotte, NC; *U.S. Public*, pg. 284

Murphy, Richard J., Sr. V.P.--Hoffmann-La Roche Inc., Nutley, NJ; *Int'l*, pg. 1120

Murphy, Robert, Sr. V.P. & Gen. Counsel--Sun Healthcare Group Inc., Albuquerque, NM; *U.S. Public*, pg. 1530

Murphy, Robert H., Sr. V.P.-Organization & Human Resources--Rockwell International Corporation, Costa Mesa, CA; *U.S. Public*, pg. 1397

Murphy, S. Wayne, Sr. V.P., Gen. Counsel & Sec.--McDermott International, Inc., New Orleans, LA; *U.S. Public*, pg. 1067

Murphy, Susan, Sr. V.P. & Gen. Mgr.--Ramada Express, Laughlin, NV; *U.S. Public*, pg. 158

Murphy, William, Sr. V.P. & Assoc. Creative Dir.--Hill, Holliday, Connors, Cosmopulos, Inc., Boston, MA; *U.S. Private*, pg. 529

Murrah, Judy, Sr. V.P.-Mktg. Communicaitons--Symbol Technologies, Inc., Holtsville, NY; *U.S. Public*, pg. 1546

Murrah, Lance, Sr. V.P. & Gen. Mgr.--Standard Microsystems Corp., Hauppauge, NY; *U.S. Public*, pg. 1502

Murray, Douglas L., Sr. V.P.-Mktg. & Security Officer--First American Federal Savings Bank, Bristol, VA; *U.S. Public*, pg. 624

Murray, E. Carlton, Sr. V.P.--Hibernia Corporation, New Orleans, LA; *U.S. Public*, pg. 825

Murray, George, Chief Human Resources Officer & Sr. V.P.--Canandaigua Wine Company, Inc., Canandaigua, NY; *U.S. Public*, pg. 300

Murray, J. Mikell, Chief Oper. Officer & Sr. V.P.--Utilities Construction Co., Inc. Of South Carolina, Charleston, SC; *U.S. Private*, pg. 1130

Murray, Joe, Sr. V.P.-Sls. & Mktg.--Frank Industries, Inc., Brown City, MI; *U.S. Private*, pg. 423

Murray, Lee J., Sr. V.P.-Corp. Quality--The American Stock Exchange, New York, NY; *U.S. Private*, pg. 62

Murray, Patrick M., Sr. V.P. & Pres.-Strategic Intiative Technology--Dresser Industries, Inc., Dallas, TX; *U.S. Public*, pg. 528

Murray, R.W., Chief Fin. Officer, Sr. V.P., Treas., Controller & Sec.--Webb, Murray & Associates, Houston, TX; *U.S. Private*, pg. 1157

Murray, Rick, Sr. V.P.--Golin/Harris Communications, Inc., Chicago, IL; *Int'l*, pg. 1226

Murray, Sean, Sr. V.P.-Mktg.--U.S. Borax Inc., Valencia, CA; *Int'l*, pg. 1119

Murray, William J., Sr. V.P.--American Home Products Corporation, Madison, NJ; *U.S. Public*, pg. 79

Murray, William M., Sr. V.P.-Arizona Reg.--Tenet Healthcare Corporation, Santa Barbara, CA; *U.S. Public*, pg. 1576

Murtaugh, Hunter, Sr. V.P. & Music/Radio Dir.--Young & Rubicam New York, New York, NY; *U.S. Private*, pg. 1198

Mustilli, Joseph M., Chief Fin. Officer, Sr. V.P. & Opers. Dir.--The McClure Group, Wayne, PA; *U.S. Private*, pg. 719

Mustoe, Jack S., Sr. V.P., Gen. Counsel & Eniron. Officer--Nova Corporation, Calgary, Canada; *Int'l*, pg. 971

Mut, Stephen R., Sr. V.P. & Pres.-ARCO Global Energy Ventures--Atlantic Richfield Company, Los Angeles, CA; *U.S. Public*, pg. 144

Muther, Stephen C., Sr. V.P.-Admin., Gen. Counsel & Sec.--Buckeye Partners, L.P., Allentown, PA; *U.S. Public*, pg. 266

Mutterperl, William C., Sr. V.P., Gen. Counsel & Sec.--Fleet Financial Group, Inc., Boston, MA; *U.S. Public*, pg. 648

Mybry, Seth, Sr. V.P.-Radio Div.--Telemobitel, Haninge, Sweden; *Int'l*, pg. 1373

Myer, Dale, V.P., Treas. & Sec.--Signet Star Holdings, Inc., Stamford, CT; *U.S. Public*, pg. 216

Myer, Dale A., Sr. V.P., Treas. & Sec.--Signet Star Reinsurance Company, Florham Park, NJ; *U.S. Public*, pg. 216

Myers, Carol, Sr. V.P.--Advanta Insurance Companies, Horsham, PA; *U.S. Public*, pg. 22

Myers, Dan, M.D., Sr. V.P.--Prime Medical Services, Inc., Austin, TX; *U.S. Public*, pg. 1327

Myers, Jerry K., Sr. V.P.--Oklahoma Natural Gas Company, Tulsa, OK; *U.S. Public*, pg. 1226

Myers, Larry F., Chief Fin. Officer, Sr. V.P., Treas. & Sec.--Mitre Corporation, Bedford, MA; *U.S. Private*, pg. 753

Myers, Louis J., Sr. V.P.-Consumer Banking--PNC Bank Corp., Pittsburgh, PA; *U.S. Public*, pg. 1242

Myers, Mark B., Sr. V.P.-Corp. Res. & Tech.--Xerox Corporation, Stamford, CT; *U.S. Public*, pg. 1783

Myers, Mike, Sr. V.P.-Opers.--Boston Whaler, Inc., Edgewater, FL; *U.S. Private*, pg. 689

Myers, Priscilla A., Sr. V.P. & Auditor--The Prudential Insurance Company of America, Newark, NJ; *U.S. Private*, pg. 892

Myers, Richard C., Sr. V.P.--American Security Group, Atlanta, GA; *Int'l*, pg. 499

Myers, Robert, Sr. V.P.-Teleservices Div.--Integrated Marketing Services, Omaha, NE; *U.S. Public*, pg. 631

Myers, Terry D., Sr. V.P.-Dental--American Dental Technologies, Southfield, MI; *U.S. Public*, pg. 70

Myers, Truman, Sr. V.P.-Pub. Rels.--Yesawich, Pepperdine & Brown, Orlando, FL; *U.S. Private*, pg. 1195

Myerscough, David R., Sr. V.P.-Corp. Business Strategy--Xerox Corporation, Stamford, CT; *U.S. Public*, pg. 1783

Myoda, Vicki, Sr. V.P.-H.R.--WSFS Financial Corporation, Wilmington, DE; *U.S. Public*, pg. 1728

Myoi, Tadashi, Sr. V.P.--Nippon Paint Company Ltd., Osaka, Japan; *Int'l*, pg. 937

Myskowski, Stephen, Chief Fin. Officer & Sr. V.P.--Recon/Optical, Inc., Barrington, IL; *U.S. Private*, pg. 914

Myster, Jay D., Sr. V.P.-Govt. & Legal & Sec.--Otter Tail Power Company, Fergus Falls, MN; *U.S. Public*, pg. 1234

Nabholz, David, Sr. V.P.--Nabholz Construction Corp., Conway, AR; *U.S. Private*, pg. 772

Nacata, S., Sr. V.P.-SRL Admin.--Dunlop Tire Corporation, Buffalo, NY; *Int'l*, pg. 1317

Nacht, Sergio, Ph.D., Sr. V.P.-Science & Tech.--Advanced Polymer Systems, Redwood City, CA; *U.S. Public*, pg. 22

Nadeau, Michel, Sr. V.P. & Asst. Gen. Mgr.--Caisse de depot et placement du Quebec, Montreal, Canada; *Int'l*, pg. 249

Nadelberg, Stephen, Sr. V.P. & Pres.-North Coast Entertainment--Handleman Company, Troy, MI; *U.S. Public*, pg. 779

Naeini, Ray, Sr. V.P.-Network Prods.--Brite Voice Systems, Inc., Heathrow, FL; *U.S. Public*, pg. 257

Nagao, Wayne K., Sr. V.P. & Dir.-Facilities--Jefferies & Company, Inc., Los Angeles, CA; *U.S. Public*, pg. 925

Nagelberg, Howard, Chief Fin. Officer-GHG & Sr. V.P.--Grey Healthcare Group, New York, NY; *U.S. Public*, pg. 765

Naggar, Avner, Sr. V.P.-Plng. & Design--Taubman Centers, Inc., Bloomfield Hills, MI; *U.S. Public*, pg. 1561

Naggiar, Caroline, V.P.-Mktg. Communications--Tiffany & Co., New York, NY; *U.S. Public*, pg. 1608

Nagle, Arlington, Jr., Sr. V.P. & Treas.--CDI Corp., Philadelphia, PA; *U.S. Public*, pg. 276

Nagle, Rita M., Sr. V.P.-Gas Trading--CNG Energy Services Corporation, Pittsburgh, PA; *U.S. Public*, pg. 435

Nagy, Ed, Sr. V.P.-Store Plng.--Wal-Mart Stores, Inc., Bentonville, AR; *U.S. Public*, pg. 1732

Nahl, M.C., Chief Fin. Officer & Sr. V.P.--Albany International Corp., Albany, NY; *U.S. Public*, pg. 36

Naimark, Richard, Sr. V.P.--American Arbitration Association, New York, NY; *U.S. Private*, pg. 50

Nakagawa, Ken, Chief Fin. Officer, Sr. V.P.-Treasury--Alpha Therapeutic Corp., Los Angeles, CA; *Int'l*, pg. 558

Nakagawa, Kenshi, Sr. V.P.-Legal & Sec.--DIC Trading (USA) Inc., Fort Lee, NJ; *Int'l*, pg. 369

Nakagawa, Osamu, Sr. V.P.--Willis Corroon International/Americas, Glendale, CA; *Int'l*, pg. 1507

Nakamura, David H., Sr. V.P. & Client Services Dir.--Gerbig, Snell/Weisheimer & Assoc., Inc., Columbus, OH; *U.S. Private*, pg. 449

Nakamura, Katsu, Sr. V.P.-Plng.--SEIKO Corporation of America, Mahwah, NJ; *Int'l*, pg. 1218

Nakamura, Kirk, Sr. V.P.-Corp. Plng.--Pioneer New Media Technologies, Long Beach, CA; *U.S. Private*, pg. 866

Nakamura, Norio, Sr. V.P.--Yokogawa Electric Corporation, Tokyo, Japan; *Int'l*, pg. 1520

Nakamura, Shigeichi, Sr. Mng. Dir.--Namco Ltd., Tokyo, Japan; *Int'l*, pg. 905

Nakano, Andrew S., Sr. V.P.-Automotive Opers.--Servco Pacific Inc., Honolulu, HI; *U.S. Private*, pg. 986

Nakkonen, Kari, Sr. V.P.--United Paper Mills Ltd., Valkeakoski, Finland; *Int'l*, pg. 1429

Nalston, Terry Read, Sr. V.P.--First National Bank of Naples, Naples, FL; *U.S. Public*, pg. 607

Namacher, William E., Sr. V.P.--Chubb Insurance Company of Europe, Brussels, Belgium; *U.S. Public*, pg. 355

Namchaisiri, Julaporn, Sr. Exec. V.P.--SCF Finance & Securities Co., Ltd., Bangkok, Thailand; *Int'l*, pg. 1239

Nanavati, Amit M., Sr. V.P.--United Asset Management Corporation, Boston, MA; *U.S. Public*, pg. 1672

Nance, Peter M., Sr. V.P.--General Reinsurance Corp., Stamford, CT; *U.S. Public*, pg. 725

Nanula, Richard D., Chief Fin. Officer & Sr. Exec. V.P.--The Walt Disney Company, Burbank, CA; *U.S. Public*, pg. 511

Napier, Richard H., Sr. V.P.--General Reinsurance Corp., Stamford, CT; *U.S. Public*, pg. 725

Napoles, George, Chief Information Officer & Sr. V.P.--Jackson National Life Insurance Company, Lansing, MI; *Int'l*, pg. 1073

Napua, Josh, Jr., Sr. V.P.-Computer Prods. Mktg.--Wyle Electronics, Irvine, CA; *Int'l*, pg. 1457

Narber, Gregg, Sr. V.P. & Gen. Counsel--The Principal Financial Group, Des Moines, IA; *U.S. Private*, pg. 885

Narber, Gregg, Sr. V.P. & Gen. Counsel--Principal Mutual Life Insurance Co., Des Moines, IA; *U.S. Private*, pg. 886

Narciso, Anthony, Sr. V.P. & Controller--Odyssey Reinsurance Corporation, New York, NY; *Int'l*, pg. 1258

Nardecchia, Vince, Sr. V.P.-Mfg.--Quebecor Printing Clarksville, Clarksville, TN; *Int'l*, pg. 1076

Nardi, Tom, Sr. V.P.-Bus. Devel.--Northern Illinois Gas Company, Naperville, IL; *U.S. Public*, pg. 1183

Narowetz, Todd N., Sr. V.P.--Northern Capital Management, Inc., Madison, WI; *U.S. Public*, pg. 1673

Narzisi, Joy J., Sr. V.P., Treas. & Asst. Sec.--Commercial Federal Corporation, Omaha, NE; *U.S. Public*, pg. 411

Nash, Lee, Sr. V.P. & Co-Creative Dir.--Cipriani Kremer Design, Boston, MA; *U.S. Private*, pg. 84

Nash, Ronald M., Sr. V.P.-Corp. Svcs.--Trigon Blue Cross & Blue Shield, Richmond, VA; *U.S. Public*, pg. 1637

Nasman, Lars, Sr. V.P.--Rauma Ltd., Helsinki, Finland; *Int'l*, pg. 1428

Naso, Robert B., Sr. V.P.-Res. & Devel.--Nabi, Boca Raton, FL; *U.S. Public*, pg. 1148

Nass, Howard, Sr. V.P., Exec. Dir.-Brdcst. Devel.--TN Entertainment, New York, NY; *U.S. Public*, pg. 1641

Nass, Howard, Sr. V.P. & Corp. Dir.-Spot Brdcst.--Spot Broadcasting Unit, New York, NY; *U.S. Public*, pg. 1641

Nass, Kevin, Sr. V.P. & Treas.--Farmers and Traders Life Insurance Co., Syracuse, NY; *U.S. Private*, pg. 394

Nassif, Robert, Sr. V.P.-Audit Services--Keystone Financial Inc., Harrisburg, PA; *U.S. Public*, pg. 956

Natathanapat, Chutima, Sr. V.P.-Policy & Plng.--The Industrial Finance Corporation of Thailand, Bangkok, Thailand; *Int'l*, pg. 677

Natathanapat, Supat, Sr. V.P.-Admin. Svcs.--The Industrial Finance Corporation of Thailand, Bangkok, Thailand; *Int'l*, pg. 677

Natcher, Stephen, Sr. V.P.-Admin., Gen. Counsel, & Sec.--Wyle Electronics, Irvine, CA; *Int'l*, pg. 1457

Naughton, J.J., Sr. V.P.--Potomac Insurance Co. of Illinois, Philadelphia, PA; *Int'l*, pg. 543

Naughton, Nancy, Sr. V.P. & Dir.--Ketchum Directory Advertising/Louisville, Louisville, KY; *U.S. Private*, pg. 616

Navamuel, Francisco, Sr. V.P.--Banco Santander, Madrid, Spain; *Int'l*, pg. 143

Nawrot, Richard, Sr. V.P.-Info. Sys. & Svcs.--Payless Cashways, Inc., Kansas City, MO; *U.S. Public*, pg. 1267

Nayden, Denis, Sr. V.P.--General Electric Company, Fairfield, CT; *U.S. Public*, pg. 709

Naylor, Alan F., Sr. V.P.--Firstar Bank of Minnesota, Bloomington, MN; *U.S. Public*, pg. 643

Naylor, Michael E., Sr. V.P.-Opers.--Rubbermaid Incorporated, Wooster, OH; *U.S. Public*, pg. 1411

Nazarathy, Moshe, Sr. V.P.--Harmonic Lightwaves, Sunnyvale, CA; *U.S. Public*, pg. 788

Nazem, Farzad, Sr. V.P.-Prod Devel. & Site Opers.--Yahoo!, Inc., Santa Clara, CA; *U.S. Public*, pg. 1787

Neal, Amy, Sr. V.P. & Acct. Dir.--Wunderman Cato Johnson, New York, NY; *U.S. Private*, pg. 1197

Neal, Jane, Sr. V.P.-H.R.--NBT Bancorp Inc., Norwich, NY; *U.S. Public*, pg. 1144

Neal, Mark, Sr. V.P.-Corp. Plng.--Coast Savings Financial, Inc., Los Angeles, CA; *U.S. Public*, pg. 388

Neally, David, Sr. V.P.-Opers.--American Shared Hospital Services, San Francisco, CA; *U.S. Public*, pg. 91

Nederlof, Gerhard B., Sr. V.P.-Mktg., Bus. Devel. & Svcs.--C-COR Electronics, Inc., State College, PA; *U.S. Public*, pg. 272

Nedjib, Chantal, Sr. V.P.-Corp. Commun.--Credit Commercial de France, Paris, France; *Int'l*, pg. 341

Needham, Thomas A., Exec. V.P.-Credit Admin.--First Security Bank of Nevada, Las Vegas, NV; *U.S. Public*, pg. 637

Needleman, Philip, Ph.D., Sr. V.P.--Monsanto Company, Saint Louis, MO; *U.S. Public*, pg. 1124

Needleman, Stuart M., Sr. V.P. & Pres.-CompUSA Direct--CompUSA, Dallas, TX; *U.S. Public*, pg. 420

Needler, Glenn, Sr. V.P.-Eastern Canada--Laidlaw Transit Limited, Burlington, Canada; *Int'l*, pg. 259

Neel, Curt, Sr. V.P.-Logistics--Eckerd Corporation, Largo, FL; *U.S. Public*, pg. 917

Neely, Karla, Sr. Principal & Exec. Dir.-Media Svcs.--Publicis Public Relations, Dallas, TX; *Int'l*, pg. 470

Nehrig, Ralph, Sr. V.P.--NESCO, Inc., Cleveland, OH; *U.S. Private*, pg. 791

Neil, G., Sr. V.P.--Asahi Glass America, Inc., New York, NY; *Int'l*, pg. 84

Neilson, Robert D., Sr. V.P.-Strategy & Bus. Devel.--Itron Inc., Spokane, WA; *U.S. Public*, pg. 914

Neiman, John C., Sr. V.P.-National Industries--Compass Bank, Birmingham, AL; *U.S. Public*, pg. 418

Neises, Kenneth J., Sr. V.P.-Gas Supply--Laclede Gas Company, Saint Louis, MO; *U.S. Public*, pg. 973

Nellis, James, Sr. V.P.-Pub. Rels.--The St. George Group, Inc., Pittsburgh, PA; *U.S. Private*, pg. 960

Nellis, James F., Sr. V.P.--First National Bank of Pennsylvania, Hermitage, PA; *U.S. Public*, pg. 607

Nelson, Alicia, Sr. V.P.-Acct. Services--Western International Media Corporation, Los Angeles, CA; *U.S. Private*, pg. 1165

Nelson, Bill, Chief Fin. Officer & Sr. V.P.--Home Box Office, Inc., New York, NY; *U.S. Public*, pg. 1612

Nelson, C.J., Sr. V.P.-Fin. Services Grp.--Koch Industries, Incorporated, Wichita, KS; *U.S. Private*, pg. 628

Nelson, Craig, Sr. V.P.-Fin.--Morrison Restaurants, Inc., Atlanta, GA; *U.S. Public*, pg. 1134

Nelson, Erik G., Chief Fin. Officer & Sr. V.P.--The Procter & Gamble Company, Cincinnati, OH; *U.S. Public*, pg. 1330

Nelson, Georgia R., Sr. V.P.-Opers.--Edison Mission Energy, Irvine, CA; *U.S. Public*, pg. 564

Nelson, Gerald, Sr. V.P.-Southern Region--United States Cold Storage, Inc., Cherry Hill, NJ; *U.S. Private*, pg. 1124

Nelson, Gordon, Sr. V.P.-Fashion & Education--Regis Corporation, Minneapolis, MN; *U.S. Public*, pg. 1373

Nelson, John, Sr. V.P.-Res. & Devel.--Waters Corporation, Milford, MA; *U.S. Public*, pg. 1745

Nelson, John O., Sr. V.P.--UAM Investment Services, Inc., Boston, MA; *U.S. Public*, pg. 1674

Nelson, Joseph J., Sr. V.P. & Dir.-Special Acctg. & Tax Policy--PNC Bank Corp., Pittsburgh, PA; *U.S. Public*, pg. 1242

Nelson, Mark B., Sr. V.P.--AT&T Wireless Services, Kirkland, WA; *U.S. Public*, pg. 11

Nelson, Michael W., Sr. V.P. & Mgr.-Heat Treat Opers.--Lindberg Corporation, Rosemont, IL; *U.S. Public*, pg. 999

Nelson, O.D., Sr. V.P.-Intl.--Fair, Isaac and Company, Inc., San Rafael, CA; *U.S. Public*, pg. 609

Nelson, P., Sr. V.P.--Horsehead Resource Development Company, Inc., Palmerton, PA; *U.S. Private*, pg. 540

Nelson, Ralph S., Sr. V.P., Gen. Counsel & Sec.--Burlington Motor Holdings Inc., Daleville, IN; *U.S. Private*, pg. 183

Nelson, Robert D., Sr. V.P.--Tellus, Inc., Bellevue, WA; *U.S. Public*, pg. 1342

Nelson, Robert S., Sr. V.P.-Community Lending--Citizens Savings Bank, Providence, RI; *Int'l*, pg. 1132

Nelson, Robert S., Sr. V.P.-Community Lending--Citizens Trust Company, Providence, RI; *Int'l*, pg. 1132

Nelson, Roger A., Sr. V.P.--UDC Homes, Inc., Scottsdale, AZ; *U.S. Private*, pg. 5

Nelson, Ted, Sr. V.P. & Plng. Dir.--Mullen Advertising, Inc., Wenham, MA; *U.S. Private*, pg. 766

Nelson, Terry D., Sr. V.P.-Systems Grp.--Reliance Electric, Cleveland, OH; *U.S. Public*, pg. 1397

Nelson, Terry D., Sr. V.P.--Systems Group, Milwaukee, WI; *U.S. Public*, pg. 1398

Nelson, Thomas E., Jr., Sr. V.P.-Field Svcs./Area II--Airborne Freight Corporation, Seattle, WA; *U.S. Public*, pg. 32

Nelson, Tom, Sr. V.P.-Sls.--Converse Inc., North Reading, MA; *U.S. Public*, pg. 441

Nelson, W. John, Sr. V.P.-Worldwide Opers.--General Semiconductor, Inc., Melville, NY; *U.S. Public*, pg. 726

Nemeth, Denny, Sr. V.P.-Opers.--Favorite Brands International, Inc., Lincolnshire, IL; *U.S. Private*, pg. 397

Nemeth, Ralph, Sr. V.P.-Company Stores--A.P.S., Inc., Houston, TX; *U.S. Public*, pg. 10

Nemeth, Ralph D., Sr. V.P.-Company Stores--APS Holding Corporation, Houston, TX; *U.S. Public*, pg. 10

Nemling, Ingomar, Sr. V.P.--Voest-Alpine Steel Corp., New York, NY; *Int'l*, pg. 1471

Nemmers, Sherry, Sr. V.P. & Creative Dir.--DMB&B New York, New York, NY; *U.S. Private*, pg. 302

Nenninger, John, Sr. V.P. & Dir.-Mktg.--Starbanc Corporation, Cincinnati, OH; *U.S. Public*, pg. 1510

Nesbit, Frankie C., Sr. V.P.--Hibernia Corporation, New Orleans, LA; *U.S. Public*, pg. 825

Nesbitt, Jeffery L., Sr. V.P.--SCI Systems, Inc., Huntsville, AL; *U.S. Public*, pg. 1416

Neshner, Giora, Sr. V.P.-Transmission & Substation Div.--The Israel Electric Corporation Ltd., Haifa, Israel; *Int'l*, pg. 690

Ness, Ben, Sr. V.P.-Strategic Plng. & Credit Services--AnnTaylor, Inc., New York, NY; *U.S. Public*, pg. 116

Ness, Tony, Sr. V.P.-Devel.--Taubman Centers, Inc., Bloomfield Hills, MI; *U.S. Public*, pg. 1561

Nessim, Lucien, Sr. V.P.--Sara Lee Corporation, Chicago, IL; *U.S. Public*, pg. 1432

Neth, Jerry, Sr. V.P.-Publishing Opers.--Reed Elsevier Business Information, Newton, MA; *Int'l*, pg. 1095

Nethery, Tom O., Sr. V.P.--Eastman Chemical Company, Kingsport, TN; *U.S. Public*, pg. 550

Netter, Donald T., Sr. V.P.-Investments--Independence Holding Company, Stamford, CT; *U.S. Private*, pg. 446

Neu, Margaret, Sr. V.P.-Acct. Mngmt.--Grey Advertising Inc., New York, NY; *U.S. Public*, pg. 764

Neubarth, Sandy, Sr. V.P. & Chief Actuary--American Bankers Insurance Co. of Florida, Miami, FL; *U.S. Public*, pg. 67

Neubarth, Sanford L., Sr. V.P.-Actuarial--American Bankers Life Assurance Co. of Florida, Miami, FL; *U.S. Public*, pg. 67

Neuberger, Joseph J., Sr. V.P.--The Richard Leahy Corporation, Fort Wayne, IN; *U.S. Public*, pg. 997

Neuger, Win J., Sr. V.P. & Chief Investment Officer--American International Group, Inc., New York, NY; *U.S. Public*, pg. 83

Neuhauser, Charles W., Sr. V.P.--Investment Counselors of Maryland, Inc., Baltimore, MD; *U.S. Public*, pg. 1673

Neukom, William H., Sr. V.P.-Law & Corp. Affairs & Sec.--Microsoft Corporation, Redmond, WA; *U.S. Public*, pg. 1107

Neuman, Eric W., Sr. V.P.-Fin.--Chancellor Radio Broadcasting Co., Dallas, TX; *U.S. Public*, pg. 335

Neuman, Norm, Sr. V.P.-Mktg.--Comshare, Incorporated, Ann Arbor, MI; *U.S. Public*, pg. 425

Neumann, Dan, Chief Oper. Officer & Sr. V.P.--Onyx Technologies Ltd., Tel Aviv, Israel; *Int'l*, pg. 1007

Neumann, Karen, Sr. V.P.-Client Svcs.--Western International Media Corporation, Boston, MA; *U.S. Private*, pg. 1167

Neun, Carl W., Chief Fin. Officer & Sr. V.P.--Tektronix, Inc., Wilsonville, OR; *U.S. Public*, pg. 1567

Nevers, Leon, Sr. V.P.--Kingston-Warren Corporation, Newfields, NH; *U.S. Public*, pg. 796

Neville, Richard S., Sr. V.P.-Mktg.--Western Petroleum Company, Eden Prairie, MN; *U.S. Private*, pg. 1168

Nevins, Bruce, Sr. V.P.-Intl.--Reebok International Ltd., Stoughton, MA; *U.S. Public*, pg. 1369

Newall, Fred, Sr. V.P.-Worldwide Sls.--Dun & Bradstreet Software Services, Atlanta, GA; *Int'l*, pg. 532

Newberry, Brian, Sr. V.P. & Acct. Dir.--Meldrum & Fewsmith Communications Inc., Cleveland, OH; *U.S. Private*, pg. 730

Newberry, Courtland L., Sr. V.P.-Mdsg., Food Service, Bus. Delivery & Special Projects--Costco Wholesale, Issaquah, WA; *U.S. Public*, pg. 451

Newcomer, R.P., Chief Fin. Officer & Sr. V.P.--P.H. Glatfelter Company, Spring Grove, PA; *U.S. Public*, pg. 746

Newcomer, Randy M., Sr. V.P-Alaska Refining & Mktg.--Mapco Petroleum Inc., Tulsa, OK; *U.S. Public*, pg. 1042

Newell, Matthew, Sr. V.P. & Controller--Allied Advertising Agency, Public Relations, Boston, MA; *U.S. Private*, pg. 38

Newell, Michael L., Sr. V.P.-Consumer Fin. Div.--Green Tree Financial Corporation, Saint Paul, MN; *U.S. Public*, pg. 761

Newhouse, Wayne M., Interim Chief Exec. Officer & Sr. V.P.-Intl.--Norcen Energy Resources Limited, Calgary, Canada; *Int'l*, pg. 434

Newkirk, Howard W., Sr. V.P.-Client/Server Systems--Compuware Corporation, Farmington Hills, MI; *U.S. Public*, pg. 423

Newman, Steve, Sr. V.P.-Adv. Sls.--Home & Garden Television, Knoxville, TN; *U.S. Public*, pg. 1447

Newman, Terry G., Chief Oper. Officer & Sr. V.P.--Co-Steel Inc., Toronto, Canada; *Int'l*, pg. 298

Newsome, Larry J., Chief Fin. Officer, Sr. V.P., Treas. & Sec.--Echelon International Corporation, Saint Petersburg, FL; *U.S. Public*, pg. 560

Newton, C. Lee, Sr. V.P.-Opers.--IMCO Recycling Inc., Irving, TX; *U.S. Public*, pg. 870

Newton, Gary, V.P.-Consumer Loans--Federal Savings Bank, Fort Smith, AR; *U.S. Private*, pg. 614

Newton, Gregory D., Sr. V.P.-Portfolio Mngmt.--Washington Mutual Inc., Seattle, WA; *U.S. Public*, pg. 1741

Newton, John, Sr. V.P.--Arnold Communications, Inc., Boston, MA; *U.S. Private*, pg. 83

Newton, Paul, Sr. V.P.-Intl. Bus. Devel.--International Family Entertainment, Inc., Virginia Beach, VA; *Int'l*, pg. 927

Neylon, James, Chief Admin. Officer & Sr. V.P.--Willis Corroon Americas, Nashville, TN; *Int'l*, pg. 1505

Ng, Elson Keng Kwan, Sr. V.P.-Southeast Asia Reg.--Bank of Hawaii, Honolulu, HI; *U.S. Public*, pg. 1248

Ng, James, Sr. V.P. & Dir. of Bus. Devel/Asia Pacific--Dentsu Young & Rubicam Partnerships, New York, NY; *U.S. Private*, pg. 325

Ng, Stephen T., Sr. V.P. & Chief Matls. Officer--Solectron Corporation, Milpitas, CA; *U.S. Public*, pg. 1483

Nguyen, Khoa D., Sr. V.P. & Chief Technology Officer-Grp. Sys. Div.--PictureTel, Andover, MA; *U.S. Public*, pg. 1294

Nicholas, Michael J., Sr. V.P.--Facultative Resources, Inc., Stamford, CT; *U.S. Public*, pg. 215

Nicholas, Ronald J., Sr. V.P.--Keycorp, Cleveland, OH; *U.S. Public*, pg. 954

Nichols, Daniel A., Sr. V.P.-Taxes--Schering-Plough Corporation, Madison, NJ; *U.S. Public*, pg. 1438

Nichols, David K., Sr. V.P.--The Bank of New York Company, Inc., New York, NY; *U.S. Public*, pg. 178

Nichols, Frank H., Sr. V.P.-Organizational Performance--Conrail, Inc., Philadelphia, PA; *U.S. Public*, pg. 431

Nichols, M.L., Sr. V.P. & Acct. Dir.--North Castle Partners Advertising, Inc., Stamford, CT; *U.S. Private*, pg. 804

Nichols, Marylisa "M.L.", Sr. V.P. & Acct. Dir.--North Castle Partners Advertising, Boston, MA; *U.S. Private*, pg. 804

Nichols, Peter, Sr. V.P. & Assoc. Creative Dir.--Houston Herstek Favat, Boston, MA; *U.S. Private*, pg. 542

Nichols, Roy J., Sr. V.P.--Nichols Research Corporation, Huntsville, AL; *U.S. Public*, pg. 1182

Nicholson, David C., Chief Fin. Officer & Sr. V.P.--Rock-Tenn Company, Norcross, GA; *U.S. Public*, pg. 1396

Nicholson, Earl, Sr. V.P.--NCH Corporation, Irving, TX; *U.S. Public*, pg. 1145

Nicholson, Faithe, Sr. V.P. & Chief Acctg. Officer--Levenson & Hill, Inc., Dallas, TX; *U.S. Private*, pg. 662

Nicholson, Glenn D., Chief Mktg. Officer & Sr. V.P.--Manhattan Life Insurance Company, Cincinnati, OH; *U.S. Private*, pg. 1118

Nicholson, James A., Chief Fin. Officer & Sr. V.P.--PAULA Financial, Pasadena, CA; *U.S. Public*, pg. 1266

Nicholson, Jon, Sr. V.P.-Custom Solutions Group--Fortis Financial Group, Woodbury, MN; *Int'l*, pg. 499

Nicholson, Lori, Sr. V.P. & Client Acctg. Dir.--Young & Rubicam New York, New York, NY; *U.S. Private*, pg. 1198

Nicholson, Peter J.M., Sr. V.P.-Corp. Strategy--BCE Inc., Montreal, Canada; *Int'l*, pg. 114

Nicholson, Stuart C., Chief Fin. Officer & Sr. V.P.--D.A. Davidson & Co., Great Falls, MT; *U.S. Private*, pg. 314

Nichter, Harrold, Sr. V.P.-Customer Fulfillment--VWR Scientific Products, West Chester, PA; *U.S. Public*, pg. 1703

Nickel, Daryl A., Sr. V.P.-Lodging Devel.--Marriott International, Inc., Washington, DC; *U.S. Public*, pg. 1047

Nicolaisen, Jennifer, Sr. V.P. & Acct. Grp. Dir.--Western International Media Corporation, Los Angeles, CA; *U.S. Private*, pg. 1165

Nicolosi, Roy S., Sr. V.P.-Tech.--GTECH Corporation, West Greenwich, RI; *U.S. Public*, pg. 767

Niebler, Carol H. Delino, Sr. V.P.--Hibernia Corporation, New Orleans, LA; *U.S. Public*, pg. 825

Niederman, Diane, Sr. V.P. & Dir.-Chicago--Ketchum Directory Advertising/Chicago, Chicago, IL; *U.S. Private*, pg. 616

Niederman, Ted A., Sr. V.P.--RTKL Associates Inc., Baltimore, MD; *U.S. Private*, pg. 906

Nielsen, Steve, Chief Oper. Officer & Sr. V.P.--Agripac Inc., Salem, OR; *U.S. Private*, pg. 26

Niemiec, Edward W., Sr. V.P.-Opers. & Info. Tech.--American Institute of C.P.A.'s Inc., New York, NY; *U.S. Private*, pg. 57

Niemier, Charles, Sr. V.P.-Intl. Opers.--Biomet, Inc., Warsaw, IN; *U.S. Public*, pg. 231

Nieporent, Herb, Sr. V.P.--Zotos International, Darien, CT; *Int'l*, pg. 1236

Niese, William A., Sr. V.P.-Law & Human Resources--Los Angeles Times, Los Angeles, CA; *U.S. Public*, pg. 1616

Nietschmann, William J., Sr. V.P.--Acordia Northeast, Boston, MA; *Int'l*, pg. 671

Nieuwenhuis, Garret G., Sr. V.P.--Valley National Bank, Parsippany, NJ; *U.S. Public*, pg. 1705

Nikornpun, Singha, Sr. V.P.-Treas.--Nakornthon Bank Public Company Limited, Bangkok, Thailand; *Int'l*, pg. 904

Nikunen, Harri, Sr. V.P.--W. Rosenlew Ltd., Helsinki, Finland; *Int'l*, pg. 1428

Niles, Robert K., Sr. V.P.--Helene Curtis Industries, Inc., Chicago, IL; *Int'l*, pg. 1434

Nilsson, Thomas, Sr. V.P.--Investor AB, Stockholm, Sweden; *Int'l*, pg. 686

Ninemire, Stanley, Chief Fin. Officer & Sr. V.P.--Tandy Brands Accessories, Inc., Arlington, TX; *U.S. Public*, pg. 1560

Ninomiya, Ichiro, Sr. V.P.-Int'l. Legal & Aerospace--Japan Aviation Electronics Industry, Ltd., Tokyo, Japan; *Int'l*, pg. 701

Ninsananda, Bunyaraks, Sr. V.P. & Gen. Mgr.--Bangkok Bank Public Company Limited, Bangkok, Thailand; *Int'l*, pg. 146

Nisbett, Janet S., Chief Fin. Officer & Sr. V.P.--Old Kent Bank, Grand Rapids, MI; *U.S. Public*, pg. 1216

Nishiguchi, Yasuo, Sr. Mng. Dir.--Kyocera Corporation, Kyoto, Japan; *Int'l*, pg. 775

Nishijo, Atsushi, Exec. V.P.--Sumitomo Corporation of America, New York, NY; *Int'l*, pg. 1312

Nishikawa, Sugao, Assoc. Dir.-Pub. Rels.--Asahi Breweries Ltd., Tokyo, Japan; *Int'l*, pg. 83

Nishimura, Kazuyuki, Sr. V.P. & Grp. Head--Fuji Bank, New York Branch, New York, NY; *Int'l*, pg. 519

Nishimura, Leslie T., Sr. V.P. & Pres.-Solectron Washington, Inc.--Solectron Corporation, Milpitas, CA; *U.S. Public*, pg. 1483

Nisita, Maurizio, Sr. V.P.-Global Opers.--Ecolab Inc., Saint Paul, MN; *U.S. Public*, pg. 562

Nissim, Zvi, Sr. V.P.-Liquidity Mgmnt.--Bank Hapoalim, Tel Aviv, Israel; *Int'l*, pg. 149

Nitibhon, Chaktip, Sr. Officer--Banque Indosuez, Bangkok, Thailand; *Int'l*, pg. 314

Nixdorf, D. Udo, Sr. V.P.--Chubb Insurance Co. of Canada, Toronto, Canada; *U.S. Public*, pg. 355

Nixon, Daniel E., Jr., Sr. V.P. & Dir.-Retail--First Union Management, Inc., Cleveland, OH; *U.S. Public*, pg. 641

Noakes, Douglas T., Sr. V.P.-Homebuilding Opers.--Avatar Holdings Inc., Coral Gables, FL; *U.S. Public*, pg. 151

Noakes, Douglas T., Sr. V.P.-Home Building Opers.--Avatar Properties Inc., Miami, FL; *U.S. Public*, pg. 151

Noble, Craig, Sr. V.P.-Opers./Canada--FCA International Ltd., Westmount, Canada; *Int'l*, pg. 470

Noble, Jerry F., Sr. V.P.--Apollo Group, Inc., Phoenix, AZ; *U.S. Public*, pg. 120

Noble, Larry M., Sr. V.P.--Chemical Bank & Trust Company, Midland, MI; *U.S. Public*, pg. 345

Noble, Scott C., Sr. V.P.-Real Estate Investments--Phoenix Home Life Mutual Insurance Company, Hartford, CT; *U.S. Private*, pg. 863

Noble, Stephanie B., Sr. V.P.-Mdsg.--DM Management Company, Hingham, MA; *U.S. Public*, pg. 473

Nobles, C.S., Sr. V.P.-Refining & Chemical Grp.--Koch Industries, Incorporated, Wichita, KS; *U.S. Private*, pg. 628

Nobles, Chuck, Sr. V.P.-Adv.--Karakas, VanSickle, Ouellette Advertising & Public Relations, Portland, OR; *U.S. Private*, pg. 607

Nocco, Brian W., Sr. V.P.--The Chubb Corporation, Warren, NJ; *U.S. Public*, pg. 354
Nocco, Brian W., Sr. V.P.--Chubb & Son, Inc., Warren, NJ; *U.S. Public*, pg. 355
Nocero, Rinzy J., Sr. V.P.-Restaurant Opers.--Bob Evans Farms, Inc., Columbus, OH; *U.S. Public*, pg. 596
Noel, Alfred C., Sr. V.P.-H.R.--Sentry Insurance, A Mutual Company, Stevens Point, WI; *U.S. Private*, pg. 984
Noelle, G.L., Sr. V.P. & Dir.-Grp. Insurance--American National Insurance Company, Galveston, TX; *U.S. Public*, pg. 87
Noes, Don, Sr. V.P.-Sls. & Mktg.--Provident Music Group, Brentwood, TN; *Int'l*, pg. 1529
Noes, Don, Sr. V.P.-Sls. & Mktg.--Provident Music Distribution, Nashville, TN; *Int'l*, pg. 1529
Noeth, Rick, Sr. V.P.-Bakery & Produce Opers.--Gerland Corp., Houston, TX; *U.S. Private*, pg. 449
Nogle, Jane A., Sr. V.P.-Permanent Loan Production--Washington Federal Savings, Seattle, WA; *U.S. Public*, pg. 1740
Noguchi, Morikazu, Sr. V.P. & Gen. Mgr.--Chicago Branch Office, Chicago, IL; *Int'l*, pg. 935
Noguchi, Norio, Sr. Mng. Dir.--Amada Co., Ltd., Kanagawa, Japan; *Int'l*, pg. 70
Nolan, J. Michael, Sr. V.P., Sec. & Gen. Counsel--Argonaut Co., Menlo Park, CA; *U.S. Public*, pg. 129
Nolan, Patrick J., Chief Fin. Officer & Sr. V.P.-Fin.--Levitz Furniture Incorporated, Boca Raton, FL; *U.S. Public*, pg. 990
Nolan, Peter F., Sr. V.P. & Gen. Counsel--Walt Disney Consumer Products, Burbank, CA; *U.S. Public*, pg. 511
Nolen, George, Sr. V.P.-Sls. & Svc.--Siemens Business Communication Systems, Inc., Santa Clara, CA; *Int'l*, pg. 1245
Nolen, Norman W., Sr. V.P. & Treas.--Weatherford U.S., Inc., Houston, TX; *U.S. Public*, pg. 1749
Nolen, Sara, Sr. V.P. & Chief Admin. Officer--First Security Investor Services, Inc., Salt Lake City, UT; *U.S. Public*, pg. 638
Nomoto, Masao, Sr. V.P.--Kintetsu World Express, Inc., Tokyo, Japan; *Int'l*, pg. 734
Nomura, Takamichi, Sr. Mng. Dir.--The Kyoei Mutual Fire & Marine Insurance Company, Tokyo, Japan; *Int'l*, pg. 777
Nonouchi, Takashi, Sr. Exec. Mng. Dir.--Hitachi, Ltd., Tokyo, Japan; *Int'l*, pg. 621
Noon, Margaret, Sr. V.P. & Creative Dir.--Lowe McAdams Healthcare, New York, NY; *U.S. Private*, pg. 678
Noonan, James F., Chief Investment Officer & Sr. V.P.--Royal Insurance, Charlotte, NC; *Int'l*, pg. 1130
Noonan, James F., Sr. V.P.-Corp. Communications--Warner Music Group, Inc., New York, NY; *U.S. Public*, pg. 1612
Nooyi, Indra K., Sr. V.P.-Strategic Planning--PepsiCo, Inc., Purchase, NY; *U.S. Public*, pg. 1276
Nordgren, Bradley J., Chief Fin. Officer, Sr. V.P. & Dir.--EvansGroup, Salt Lake City, UT; *U.S. Private*, pg. 385
Nordh, Nils G., Sr. V.P.-Marine Opers.--Royal Caribbean Cruises Ltd., Miami, FL; *U.S. Public*, pg. 1410
Nordholm, Edwin B., Sr. V.P.--Brookfield Properties Corporation, Toronto, Canada; *Int'l*, pg. 228
Nordin, Staffan, Sr. V.P.-Electricity Generation--Vattenfall AB, Stockholm, Sweden; *Int'l*, pg. 1452
Nordloh, Mary, Sr. V.P. & Creative Dir.--Lands' End, Inc., Dodgeville, WI; *U.S. Public*, pg. 977
Norman, Donald E., Chief Information Officer & Sr. V.P.--Kmart Corporation, Troy, MI; *U.S. Public*, pg. 963
Norman, Gary E., Sr. V.P.-Bus. Devel.--Elkins Constructors, Inc., Jacksonville, FL; *U.S. Private*, pg. 372
Norman, T. Neil, Sr. V.P.--Trustmark National Bank, Jackson, MS; *U.S. Public*, pg. 1643
Normile, Michael T., Sr. V.P.-Fin. & Controller--Mercantile Bancorporation Inc., Saint Louis, MO; *U.S. Public*, pg. 1087
Norris, Alan, Chief Fin. Officer, Sr. V.P. & Sec.--Consolidated Carma Corporation, Calgary, Canada; *Int'l*, pg. 229
Norris, David L., Chief Fin. Officer & Sr. V.P.--American Eco Corporation, Toronto, Canada; *Int'l*, pg. 73
Norris, James, Sr. V.P.--Newsday, Melville, NY; *U.S. Public*, pg. 1616
Norris, James R., Sr. V.P.--Sterling Capital Management Company, Charlotte, NC; *U.S. Public*, pg. 1674
Norris, Michael, Sr. V.P., Gen. Counsel & Sec.--National Financial Insurance Company, Fort Worth, TX; *U.S. Private*, pg. 782
Norris, Robert, Sr. V.P.-Fin. & Admin.--Calcot, Ltd., Bakersfield, CA; *U.S. Private*, pg. 200
North, Gary J., Sr. V.P.-Opers.--Matson Navigation Company, Inc., San Francisco, CA; *U.S. Public*, pg. 39
Northey, Randy, Sr. V.P., Gen. Counsel & Sec.--O&Y Properties Corporation, Toronto, Canada; *Int'l*, pg. 993
Northrop, Bruce A., Sr. V.P. & Mgr.-Loss Control--Willis Corroon Corp. of Massachusetts, Boston, MA; *Int'l*, pg. 1506
Northup, James, Sr. V.P.-North American Opers.--Photronics, Inc., Brookfield, CT; *U.S. Public*, pg. 1293
Norton, Dave, Sr. V.P.-Retail--Eagle Food Centers, Inc., Milan, IL; *U.S. Public*, pg. 547
Norton, Margaret, Sr. V.P.-VIS--Octel Messaging Division, Milpitas, CA; *U.S. Public*, pg. 1017
Norton, Patrick H., Sr. V.P.-Sls. & Mktg.--La-Z-Boy Incorporated, Monroe, MI; *U.S. Public*, pg. 972
Norton, Richard G., Sr. V.P.--FirstMerit Corporation, Akron, OH; *U.S. Public*, pg. 646
Norton, Robert, Sr. V.P. & Gen. Counsel--Mastercard International, Inc., Purchase, NY; *U.S. Private*, pg. 714
Norton, Stan, Sr. V.P. & Exec. Creative Dir.--The William Cook Agency, Inc., Jacksonville, FL; *U.S. Private*, pg. 273
Norwak, Ronald A., Sr. V.P.--CSC Financial Services Group, Austin, TX; *U.S. Public*, pg. 422
Norwood, Ellyn M., Sr. V.P.-Human Resources--The Foothill Group, Inc., Los Angeles, CA; *U.S. Public*, pg. 1201
Norz, C.H., Sr. V.P.--Amerada Hess Corporation, New York, NY; *U.S. Public*, pg. 65
Notaro, Pat, Sr. V.P. & Gen. Mgr.-Domestic Distr.--Sony Pictures Studios, Culver City, CA; *Int'l*, pg. 1283
Notestein, David, Sr. V.P.--Transport Insurance Co., Dallas, TX; *U.S. Public*, pg. 75
Notini, Albert A., Sr. V.P., Gen. Counsel & Sec.--Wang Laboratories, Inc., Billerica, MA; *U.S. Public*, pg. 1737
Noto, Blaise J., Sr. V.P.-Natl. Publicity--Paramount Pictures Corporation, Los Angeles, CA; *U.S. Private*, pg. 776
Nottingham, R. Kendall, Sr. V.P.-Life Insurance--American International Group, Inc., New York, NY; *U.S. Public*, pg. 83
Nova, Jamie Gonzalez, Sr. V.P.--Controladora Comercial Mexicana, S.A. de C.V., Mexico, Mexico; *Int'l*, pg. 328
Novak, Louis R., Chief Oper. Officer & Exec. V.P.--Galoob Toys, Inc., South San Francisco, CA; *U.S. Public*, pg. 698
Novello, Leonard P., Sr. V.P. & Gen. Counsel--Long Island Lighting Company, Hicksville, NY; *U.S. Public*, pg. 1013
Novick, Randy, Sr. V.P. & Media Dir.--Greenstone Roberts Advertising, Melville, NY; *U.S. Public*, pg. 763
Novick, Sanford, Sr. V.P.--Mississippi Valley Gas Co., Jackson, MS; *U.S. Private*, pg. 753
Novinger, Cathy B., Sr. V.P.-Admin., Govt. & Pub. Affairs--SCANA Corporation, Columbia, SC; *U.S. Public*, pg. 1436
Nowak, Edward J., Sr. V.P. & Asst. Gen. Counsel--The Walt Disney Company, Burbank, CA; *U.S. Public*, pg. 511
Nowak, James, Sr. V.P.-Fin.--AmSouth Bank, Tampa, FL; *U.S. Public*, pg. 105
Nowak, Tom, Sr. V.P.-MIS--Golub Corporation, Schenectady, NY; *U.S. Private*, pg. 463
Nowell, Ralph P., Sr. V.P.-Opers. Support--Yellow Freight System, Inc., Overland Park, KS; *U.S. Public*, pg. 1788
Nozzolillo, Anthony, Chief Fin. Officer & Sr. V.P.-Fin.--Long Island Lighting Company, Hicksville, NY; *U.S. Public*, pg. 1013
Nuckols, James, Sr. V.P.--Times Mirror Magazines, Inc., New York, NY; *U.S. Public*, pg. 1616
Nudelman, Phillip A., Pres.-Northwest Division & Sr. V.P.--Kaiser Permanente, Oakland, CA; *U.S. Private*, pg. 605
Nugent, John O.C., Sr. V.P.-Consumer Products Grp.--Chesebrough-Pond's, Trumbull, CT; *Int'l*, pg. 1436
Nuhn, Adriaan, Sr. V.P.--Sara Lee Corporation, Chicago, IL; *U.S. Public*, pg. 1432
Nunes, Geoffrey, Sr. V.P.--Millipore Corporation, Bedford, MA; *U.S. Public*, pg. 1112
Nunes, Melbourne, Sr. V.P., Dep. Counsel & Sec.--New York Life Insurance Company, New York, NY; *U.S. Private*, pg. 794
Nunez, Tony, Sr. V.P.-Mfg.--The Spring Air Company, Des Plaines, IL; *U.S. Private*, pg. 1027
Nunn, Charles E., Jr., Sr. V.P.--United National Bancorp, Bridgewater, NJ; *U.S. Public*, pg. 1679
Nunotani, Ryuji, Sr. V.P.--Nippon Telegraph and Telephone Corporation, Tokyo, Japan; *Int'l*, pg. 940
Nuortila, Olli, Sr. V.P. & Gen. Counsel--Metsa-Serla Corporation, Espoo, Finland; *Int'l*, pg. 863
Nussbaum, D.E., Sr. V.P.--Miller Freeman Inc., San Francisco, CA; *Int'l*, pg. 1443
Nussbaum, Jay H., Sr. V.P. & Gen. Mgr.-Oracle Federal Div.--Oracle Corporation, Redwood City, CA; *U.S. Public*, pg. 1227
Nussbaum, Marc H., Sr. V.P.-Engrng./Personal Storage Div.--Western Digital Corporation, Irvine, CA; *U.S. Public*, pg. 1758
Nute, Lee F., Sr. V.P., Gen. Counsel & Sec.--Bayer Corporation, Pittsburgh, PA; *Int'l*, pg. 172
Nyberg, Hans, Sr. V.P.-Internal Audit--Trelleborg AB, Trelleborg, Sweden; *Int'l*, pg. 1419
Nye, Bruce, Sr. V.P.-Corp. Devel.--The Cerplex Group, Inc., Tustin, CA; *U.S. Public*, pg. 332
Nye, Cynthia, Sr. V.P.-Corp. Support Services--Staff Builders Inc., Lake Success, NY; *U.S. Public*, pg. 1501
Nyman, Sven, Sr. V.P.--Investor AB, Stockholm, Sweden; *Int'l*, pg. 686
Nyren, Anders, Sr. V.P.-Trading--Nordbanken AB, Stockholm, Sweden; *Int'l*, pg. 957
Nysten, Thomas, Sr. V.P.-Mktg. Grp.--Metsa-Serla Corporation, Espoo, Finland; *Int'l*, pg. 863
O'bleness, Denise, Sr. V.P. & Creative Dir.--Grey Advertising Inc., New York, NY; *U.S. Public*, pg. 764
O'Boyle, Thomas, Sr. V.P.-Truck Components Opers.--Eaton Corporation, Cleveland, OH; *U.S. Public*, pg. 555
O'Brien, Bill, Sr. V.P. & Chief Oper. Officer--Reed Elsevier Business Information, Newton, MA; *Int'l*, pg. 1095
O'Brien, Danny H., Sr. V.P. & Gen. Mgr.-North--Chittenden Corporation, Burlington, VT; *U.S. Public*, pg. 350
O'Brien, Dennis, Sr. V.P.-Mktg.--Armstrong World Industries, Inc., Lancaster, PA; *U.S. Public*, pg. 131
O'Brien, Edward J., Sr. V.P. & Treas.--Hanover Direct, Inc., Weehawken, NJ; *U.S. Public*, pg. 782
O'Brien, Gordon, Sr. V.P.-Human Resources--Schering-Plough Corporation, Madison, NJ; *U.S. Public*, pg. 1438
O'Brien, James J., Sr. V.P.--Ashland, Inc., Russell, KY; *U.S. Public*, pg. 138
O'Brien, John, Sr. V.P. & Acct. Dir.--Young & Rubicam New York, New York, NY; *U.S. Private*, pg. 1198
O'Brien, John D., Sr. V.P.--Borg-Warner Security Corporation, Chicago, IL; *U.S. Public*, pg. 245
O'Brien, Mark, Chief Fin. Officer & Sr. V.P.--Griffin Bacal Inc., New York, NY; *U.S. Private*, pg. 480
O'Brien, Michael A., Sr. V.P.-Pacific Century Trust--Bank of Hawaii, Honolulu, HI; *U.S. Public*, pg. 1248
O'Brien, Michael A., Sr. V.P.-Human Resources--Pulte Corporation, Bloomfield Hills, MI; *U.S. Public*, pg. 1344
O'Brien, Ray, Sr. V.P.-Sls. & Mktg.-SkyTel--Mobile Telecommunications Technologies Corp., Jackson, MS; *U.S. Public*, pg. 1120
O'Brien, Richard T., Chief Fin. Officer & Sr. V.P.--PacifiCorp, Portland, OR; *U.S. Public*, pg. 1251
O'Brien, Richard T., Sr. V.P.--Utah Power & Light, Salt Lake City, UT; *U.S. Public*, pg. 1251
O'Brien, Sheila, Sr. V.P.-H.R.--Nova Corporation, Calgary, Canada; *Int'l*, pg. 971
O'Brien, Thomas, Sr. V.P.-Client Services--Grey Europe/Brussels, Brussels, Belgium; *U.S. Public*, pg. 765
O'Brien, Thomas R., Sr. V.P. & Gen. Counsel--Foster Wheeler Corporation, Clinton, NJ; *U.S. Public*, pg. 676
O'Brien, Tony, Chief Fin. Officer & Sr. V.P.--Atlantic Recording Corporation, New York, NY; *U.S. Public*, pg. 1611
O'Bryan, Kevin M., Sr. V.P. & Asst. Sec.--The Troy Savings Bank, Troy, NY; *U.S. Private*, pg. 1106
O'Callaghan, Michael J., Sr. V.P.-Utility Sys.--Itron Inc., Spokane, WA; *U.S. Public*, pg. 914
O'Connell, John, Jr., Sr. V.P.--Freeman Decorating Co., Dallas, TX; *U.S. Private*, pg. 426
O'Connell, Joseph M., Chief Information Officer & Sr. V.P.--John H. Harland Company, Decatur, GA; *U.S. Public*, pg. 785
O'Connell, Robert J., Sr. V.P.--Air Express International Corporation, Darien, CT; *U.S. Public*, pg. 30
O'Connell, Robert T., Sr. V.P.--EMC Corporation, Hopkinton, MA; *U.S. Public*, pg. 545
O'Connor, Austin J., Sr. V.P.-Europe--The Bank of Bermuda Limited, Hamilton, Bermuda; *Int'l*, pg. 150
O'Connor, James E., Sr. V.P.-Southeast--Waste Management, Inc., Oak Brook, IL; *U.S. Public*, pg. 1744
O'Connor, John, Sr. V.P.--Media That Works, Cincinnati, OH; *U.S. Private*, pg. 727
O'Connor, John, Chief Fin. Officer, Sr. V.P. & Treas.--Woman's Day, New York, NY; *Int'l*, pg. 795
O'Connor, John J., Pres.-Worldwide Exploration & Exec. V.P.--Texaco Inc., White Plains, NY; *U.S. Public*, pg. 1582
O'Dea, Marita, Sr. V.P.-Human Resources--Neiman Marcus Co., Dallas, TX; *U.S. Public*, pg. 785
O'Dell, Basil F., Sr. V.P.--Independent Bank, Ionia, MI; *U.S. Public*, pg. 874
O'Dell, Kenneth, Chief Fin. Officer & Sr. V.P.-Fin.--Kolmar Laboratories, Inc., Port Jervis, NY; *Int'l*, pg. 239
O'Dell, Michael, Sr. V.P.-Prod. Devel.--VTEL Corporation, Austin, TX; *U.S. Public*, pg. 1703
O'Dell, Michael R., Chief Fin. Officer, Sr. V.P. & Sec.--First Financial Bancorp, Hamilton, OH; *U.S. Public*, pg. 632
O'Dell, Michael R., Chief Fin. Officer & Sr. V.P.--First National Bank of Southwestern Ohio, Hamilton, OH; *U.S. Public*, pg. 633
O'Dell, Theodore, Sr. V.P. & Controller--Mutual of America Life Insurance Company, New York, NY; *U.S. Private*, pg. 769
O'Dell, Theodore, Sr. V.P. & Controller--American Life Insurance Company of New York, New York, NY; *U.S. Private*, pg. 769
O'Donnell, James P., Chief Fin. Officer & Sr. V.P.--ConAgra, Inc., Omaha, NE; *U.S. Public*, pg. 425
O'Donnell, Michael, Chief Fin. Officer & Sr. V.P.--ChemDesign Corporation, Fitchburg, MA; *Int'l*, pg. 173
O'Donnell, Michael W., Chief Fin. Officer & Sr. V.P.--Columbia Energy Group, Reston, VA; *U.S. Public*, pg. 402
O'Donnell, Michael W., Chief Fin. Officer & Sr. V.P.--Columbia Gas System Service Corp., Wilmington, DE; *U.S. Public*, pg. 403
O'Donnell, Robert F., Sr. V.P. & Bus. Mgr.-Intl. Publishing--Playboy Enterprises, Inc., Chicago, IL; *U.S. Public*, pg. 1309
O'Driscoll, John P., Sr. V.P.--Mellon Europe-London, London, United Kingdom; *U.S. Public*, pg. 1086
O'Drobinak, James, Chief Fin. Officer, Sr. V.P. & Controller--ABR Information Services, Inc., Palm Harbor, FL; *U.S. Public*, pg. 2
O'Flynn, Terry, Sr. V.P.-OEM Sls.--Recoton Corporation, Lake Mary, FL; *U.S. Public*, pg. 1369
O'Gorman, Anne Marie, Sr. V.P.-Corp. Devel. & Sec.--Coho Energy, Inc., Dallas, TX; *U.S. Public*, pg. 396
O'Grady, John P., Sr. V.P.-Admin.--Rayonier Inc., Stamford, CT; *U.S. Public*, pg. 1363
O'Hanlon, James P., Sr. V.P.-Nuclear Opers.--Virginia Electric and Power Company, Richmond, VA; *U.S. Public*, pg. 516
O'Hara, Charles, Sr. V.P.--Imperial Bank, Inglewood, CA; *U.S. Public*, pg. 871
O'Hara, Jack, Sr. V.P. & Exec. Creative Dir.--EvansGroup, Indianapolis, IN; *U.S. Private*, pg. 385
O'Hara, Michael J., Sr. V.P.-Franchise Sls.--Knights Franchise Systems, Inc., Parsippany, NJ; *U.S. Public*, pg. 321
O'Hare, Dave, Sr. V.P. & Exec. Creative Dir.--Hal Riney & Partners, Inc., San Francisco, CA; *U.S. Private*, pg. 931
O'Hare, James P., Sr. V.P. & Gen. Counsel--Cambridge Technology Partners, Cambridge, MA; *U.S. Public*, pg. 1424
O'Harra, Daniel C., Sr. V.P.-Opers.--Caldor, Inc., Norwalk, CT; *U.S. Public*, pg. 292
O'Hearn, Dennis, Sr. V.P.-Client Services--Jordan, McGrath, Case & Taylor Inc., New York, NY; *U.S. Private*, pg. 598
O'Hern, Thomas E., Chief Fin. Officer, Chief Acctg. Officer & Sr. V.P.--The Macerich Company, Santa Monica, CA; *U.S. Public*, pg. 1030
O'Keefe, Carole, Sr. V.P. & Publisher--Glencoe/Mc-Graw Hill, Westerville, OH; *U.S. Public*, pg. 1070
O'Keefe, Ed, Sr. V.P. & Media Services Dir.--The Weightman Group, Philadelphia, PA; *U.S. Private*, pg. 1159
O'Keefe, Scott, Chief Fin. Officer & Sr. V.P.--Grey Wolf, Inc., Houston, TX; *U.S. Public*, pg. 765
O'Kelly, William B., Sr. V.P.--Valley National Bank, Parsippany, NJ; *U.S. Public*, pg. 1705
O'Leary, Bob, Chief Fin. Officer & Sr. V.P.--Cox Enterprises, Inc., Atlanta, GA; *U.S. Private*, pg. 281
O'Leary, Robert C., Sr. V.P.-Opers.--Cox Communications, Inc., Atlanta, GA; *U.S. Public*, pg. 454
O'Meara, S.C., Sr. V.P. & Gen. Counsel--The Ziegler Companies, Inc., West Bend, WI; *U.S. Public*, pg. 1791
O'Neal, Frederic K., Sr. V.P. & Treas.--Computer Sales International Inc., Saint Louis, MO; *U.S. Private*, pg. 260

O'Neil, A.F., Sr. V.P.--O'Neil Industries Inc., Chicago, IL; *U.S. Private*, pg. 817
O'Neil, Edward W., Sr. V.P. & Grp. Actuary--Jefferson-Pilot Life Insurance Co., Greensboro, NC; *U.S. Public*, pg. 926
O'Neil, Frank B., Sr. V.P.-Corp. Commun.--Medical Assurance, Inc., Birmingham, AL; *U.S. Public*, pg. 1079
O'Neil, James, Sr. V.P.--Intertek Testing Services, Andover, MA; *Int'l*, pg. 672
O'Neil, Sean, Sr. V.P. & Chief Information Systems Officer--ITT Sheraton Corporation, Boston, MA; *U.S. Public*, pg. 1512
O'Neill, James J., Sr. V.P.--Rothschild Inc., New York, NY; *U.S. Private*, pg. 947
O'Neill, Jim, Sr. V.P.-Sls. & Mktg.--Alpine Electronics of America, Inc., Torrance, CA; *Int'l*, pg. 65
O'Neill, John M., Sr. V.P.--First National Bank of Southwestern Ohio, Hamilton, OH; *U.S. Public*, pg. 633
O'Neill, Kevin M., Sr. V.P.-Bus. Devel. & Strategy--Anacomp, Inc., Indianapolis, IN; *U.S. Public*, pg. 106
O'Neill, Michael J., Sr. V.P.-Public Affairs & Communications--American Express Travel Related Services Co., Inc., New York, NY; *U.S. Public*, pg. 73
O'Neill, Peter, Sr. V.P.-Worldwide Field Opers.--Sequent Computer Systems, Inc., Beaverton, OR; *U.S. Public*, pg. 1459
O'Neill, Peter J., Sr. V.P.-Fin., Controller & Treas.--Agway, Inc., De Witt, NY; *U.S. Private*, pg. 27
O'Neill, Thomas P., Chief Fin. Officer & Sr. V.P.--Tupperware Corporation, Orlando, FL; *U.S. Public*, pg. 1644
O'Neill, Timothy J., Sr. V.P.--First Indiana Corporation, Indianapolis, IN; *U.S. Public*, pg. 1484
O'Ray, Patrick, Sr. V.P. & Pres.-Specialty Brands Div.--Foodbrands America, Inc., Oklahoma City, OK; *U.S. Public*, pg. 852
O'Reilly, Ellen, Sr. V.P. & Gen. Mgr.-Yellow Pages--Hutchins/Young & Rubicam, Rochester, NY; *U.S. Private*, pg. 1197
O'Reilly, John J., Chief Fin. Officer & Sr. V.P.--Esselte Corporation, Garden City, NY; *Int'l*, pg. 459
O'Reilly, Michael, Sr. V.P.-Equity Investments--The Chubb Corporation, Warren, NJ; *U.S. Public*, pg. 354
O'Reilly, Michael, Sr. V.P.--Chubb & Son, Inc., Warren, NJ; *U.S. Public*, pg. 355
O'Reilly, Richard D., Sr. V.P.-Human Resources--DIMON, Incorporated, Danville, VA; *U.S. Public*, pg. 509
O'Rourke, Betsy, Sr. V.P.-Adv.--Choice Hotels International, Inc., Silver Spring, MD; *U.S. Public*, pg. 351
O'Rourke, Dennis, Chief Fin. Officer & Sr. V.P.--Goldberg Moser O'Neill, San Francisco, CA; *U.S. Private*, pg. 459
O'Rourke, Jerry, Chief Fin. Officer, Sr. V.P. & Treas.--Wackenhut Corrections Corporation, Palm Beach Gardens, FL; *U.S. Public*, pg. 1731
O'Rourke, Kevin C. C., Sr. V.P. & Gen. Counsel--Matson Navigation Company, Inc., San Francisco, CA; *U.S. Public*, pg. 39
O'Shea, Paul C., Sr. V.P. & Dir.-Corp. Communications--Municipal Bond Investors Assurance Corporation, Armonk, NY; *U.S. Public*, pg. 1023
O'Shea, Peter J., Jr., Sr. V.P. & Gen. Counsel--Consolidated Edison Company of New York, Inc., New York, NY; *U.S. Public*, pg. 434
O'Toole, A.M., Sr. V.P. & Sec.--The Coastal Corporation, Houston, TX; *U.S. Public*, pg. 389
O'Toole, Michael B., Sr. V.P.-Retail Sls. Practises--John Hancock Mutual Life Insurance Company, Boston, MA; *U.S. Private*, pg. 589
O'Toole, Timothy T., Sr. V.P.-Law & Govt. Affairs--Conrail, Inc., Philadelphia, PA; *U.S. Public*, pg. 431
Oak, Alan D., Chief Fin. Officer, Sr. V.P.-Fin. & Treas.--TECO Energy, Inc., Tampa, FL; *U.S. Public*, pg. 1565
Oak, Michael, Chief Info. Officer & Sr. V.P.-True North Communications Inc.--True North Communications Inc., Chicago, IL; *U.S. Public*, pg. 1641
Oakes, John, Sr. V.P.--Union Planters Corporation, Cordova, TN; *U.S. Public*, pg. 1668
Oakley, Andrew C., Sr. V.P. & Dir.-Engrng.--Huitt-Zollars, Inc., Dallas, TX; *U.S. Private*, pg. 547
Oakley, Ed, Sr. V.P.--McDonald's Hamburgers Limited, London, United Kingdom; *U.S. Public*, pg. 1069
Oakley, Robert A., Chief Fin. Officer & Sr. V.P.--Nationwide Insurance Enterprise, Columbus, OH; *U.S. Private*, pg. 788
Oaks, Robert C., Sr. V.P.-Opers.--US Airways, Inc., Arlington, VA; *U.S. Public*, pg. 1680
Oatman, James E., Sr. V.P. & Chief Actuary--Time Insurance, Milwaukee, WI; *Int'l*, pg. 499
Oberdorfer, Eugene II, Sr. V.P.--Acordia Northeast, Boston, MA; *Int'l*, pg. 671
Oberg, Kathy, Sr. V.P.-Acct. Services--SSD&W Integrated Marketing Communications, Montville, NJ; *U.S. Private*, pg. 958
Oberg, Leif, Sr. V.P.-Information Svcs.--Trelleborg AB, Trelleborg, Sweden; *Int'l*, pg. 1419
Oberlink, William B., Sr. V.P.--AT&T Wireless Services, Kirkland, WA; *U.S. Public*, pg. 11
Obermeyer, James R., Sr. V.P. Pres.-Contruction Services--Woodward-Constructors, Denver, CO; *U.S. Public*, pg. 1657
Obers, Gary P., Sr. V.P.-Corp. Svcs.--National City Corporation, Cleveland, OH; *U.S. Public*, pg. 1154
Obey, David, Sr. V.P. & Dir.-Consumer Mktg.--Weider Publications, Inc., Woodland Hills, CA; *U.S. Private*, pg. 1159
Obourn, Jeff T., Sr. V.P.-Opers.--Tipperary Corporation, Denver, CO; *U.S. Public*, pg. 1618
Obreiter, William, Vice Pres.--Chicopee Inc., Dayton, NJ; *Int'l*, pg. 113
Ocampo, Antonio V., Sr. V.P., Gen. Counsel & Sec.--Philippine Airlines, Inc., Manila, Philippines; *Int'l*, pg. 1050
Ocampo, Raymond L., Jr., Sr. V.P., Gen Counsel & Sec.--Oracle Corporation, Redwood City, CA; *U.S. Public*, pg. 1227
Ocasek, Ronald W., Chief Fin. Officer, Sr. V.P. & Treas.--Riser Foods, Inc., Bedford, OH; *U.S. Private*, pg. 450
Occelli, Daniel J., Sr. V.P.--Imperial Credit Commercial Mortgage Investment Corp., Los Angeles, CA; *U.S. Public*, pg. 872
Ochi, Gene, Sr. V.P.-Mktg.--Union-Transport Corporation, Rancho Dominguez, CA; *U.S. Private*, pg. 1119
Ochiltree, Jamie, Sr. V.P.-Branch Opers.--Selective Way Insurance Company, Branchville, NJ; *U.S. Public*, pg. 1456
Ochiltree, Jamie, III, Sr. V.P.-Branch Opers.--Selective Insurance Group, Inc, Branchville, NJ; *U.S. Public*, pg. 1455
Ochotta, Martin, Sr. V.P.-Fin.--BOMAG, Boppard, Germany; *U.S. Public*, pg. 1677
Oda, Beverley J., Sr. V.P.-Programming--Baton Broadcasting Incorporated, Scarborough, Canada; *Int'l*, pg. 170
Odelberg, Carl, Sr. V.P.-Legal Affairs & Sec.--Esselte AB, Solna, Sweden; *Int'l*, pg. 459
Odell, R. Thomas, Sr. V.P.-Bus. Process Improvement--National Semiconductor Corporation, Santa Clara, CA; *U.S. Public*, pg. 1159
Odom, Michael E., Sr. V.P.-Hub & Air Opers.--BAX Global, Irvine, CA; *U.S. Public*, pg. 1305
Oelman, Bradford C., Sr. V.P.-Govt. & Pub. Affairs--Owens Corning, Toledo, OH; *U.S. Public*, pg. 1236
Oesch, Kurt, Sr. V.P.--Banque Cantonale Vaudoise, Lausanne, Switzerland; *Int'l*, pg. 160
Offredi, Paul, Sr. V.P.-Prod. Opers.--IKOS Systems, Inc., Cupertino, CA; *U.S. Public*, pg. 864
Offutt, James A., Exec. V.P.--Shelter Mutual Insurance Company, Columbia, MO; *U.S. Private*, pg. 992
Ofner, C.R., Sr. V.P.--Reading & Bates Drilling Co., Houston, TX; *U.S. Public*, pg. 1354
Ogaard, Thomas D., Sr. V.P.--TCF Bank Wisconsin, Milwaukee, WI; *U.S. Public*, pg. 1554
Ogawa, T., Sr. V.P. & Asst. Treas.--Mitsubishi International Corporation, New York, NY; *Int'l*, pg. 871
Ogden, R.W., Sr. V.P.-Natl. Acct. Partnerships--Time Insurance, Milwaukee, WI; *Int'l*, pg. 499
Ogee, JoAnn, Sr. V.P.-Women's Shoes--Payless ShoeSource, Inc., Topeka, KS; *U.S. Public*, pg. 1268
Ogle, Sandy S., Chief Admin. Officer & Sr. V.P.--Willis Corroon Corp. of Northern Ohio, Dublin, OH; *Int'l*, pg. 1506
Oglesby, C., Sr. V.P.--Houston Industries Incorporated, Houston, TX; *U.S. Public*, pg. 842
Ogren, Eldon L., Sr. V.P.--APAC Holdings, Inc., Atlanta, GA; *U.S. Public*, pg. 139
Ogura, Yasuo, Sr. Mng. Dir.--Asahi Breweries Ltd., Tokyo, Japan; *Int'l*, pg. 83
Ohanian, Michael, Sr. V.P.--UNOVA, Inc., Beverly Hills, CA; *U.S. Public*, pg. 1698
Ohlde, Frederick A., Sr. V.P.-Creating Helping Opportuniies for Members--Aid Association for Lutherans, Appleton, WI; *U.S. Private*, pg. 27
Ohly, Jeffrey W., Sr. V.P., Treas. & Sec.--World Acceptance Corporation, Greenville, SC; *U.S. Public*, pg. 1778
Ohtsuka, Kouichi, Assoc. Sr. V.P.--NEC Corporation, Tokyo, Japan; *Int'l*, pg. 899
Okazaki, Toshiki, Sr. V.P.-Eastern Japan--Japan Airlines Company, Ltd., Tokyo, Japan; *Int'l*, pg. 699
Oki, Katsutoshi, Sr. V.P. & Gen. Mgr.--Los Angeles Branch Office, Los Angeles, CA; *Int'l*, pg. 935
Okimi, Katsuya, Sr. V.P.--Nippon Telegraph and Telephone Corporation, Tokyo, Japan; *Int'l*, pg. 940
Okochi, Akira, Chief Oper. Officer & Sr. V.P.--Haseko (New York) Inc., New York, NY; *Int'l*, pg. 600
Okon, Joseph, Sr. V.P.-Natl. Adv.--Fairfield Inn, Washington, DC; *U.S. Public*, pg. 1048
Okonow, Dale, Chief Fin. Officer & Sr. V.P.--H M K Enterprises, Inc., Waltham, MA; *U.S. Private*, pg. 489
Oksendahl, Douglas C., Chief Fin. Officer, Exec. V.P.-Fin. & Treas.--Pioneer Mutual Life Insurance Company, Fargo, ND; *U.S. Private*, pg. 866
Older, Pam, Sr. V.P. & Dir.-Production--The New Yorker Magazine, New York, NY; *U.S. Private*, pg. 795
Oldham, Mike, Sr. V.P. & Dir.-Sls. & Mktg.--Columbine JDS Systems, Inc., Denver, CO; *U.S. Public*, pg. 228
Olen, Jim, Sr. V.P. & Grp. Creative Dir.--Partners & Shevack, Inc., New York, NY; *U.S. Private*, pg. 842
Oler, Debbie, Sr. V.P. & Gen. Mgr.--Alliant Foodservice, Bensenville, IL; *U.S. Private*, pg. 244
Oleson, Ken, Sr. V.P.-Special Projects--H.B. Zachry, San Antonio, TX; *U.S. Private*, pg. 1203
Olevson, Ken, Gen. Mgr.--Sermatech Klock, Manchester, CT; *U.S. Public*, pg. 1570
Olewinski, Dave, Sr. V.P.--Leslie Metal Arts Co., Inc., Grand Rapids, MI; *U.S. Private*, pg. 660
Olinger, Donald, Sr. V.P. & Controller--Host Marriott Corporation, Bethesda, MD; *U.S. Public*, pg. 841
Olingy, Jeffrey F., Sr. V.P.-Sls. & Mktg.--Provident Companies, Inc., Chattanooga, TN; *U.S. Public*, pg. 1337
Olinotos, Frank, Sr. V.P.--Genzyme Corporation, Cambridge, MA; *U.S. Public*, pg. 733
Olivares, Alejandro Sada, Grp. V.P.--Grupo Televisa, S.A. de C.V., Mexico, Mexico; *Int'l*, pg. 576
Oliver, David, Sr. V.P.-Risk Mngmt. Services--Willis Corroon Corp. of Georgia, Atlanta, GA; *Int'l*, pg. 1506
Oliver, Walter M., Sr. V.P.-Human Resources--Ameritech Corp., Chicago, IL; *U.S. Public*, pg. 98
Oliveria, Milton, Sr. V.P.-Opers.--Delta Rubber Company, Danielson, CT; *U.S. Private*, pg. 323
Olivier, David M., Sr. V.P.--American Home Products Corporation, Madison, NJ; *U.S. Public*, pg. 79
Olivier, Maurice J., Sr. V.P.--Arthur D. Little, Inc., Cambridge, MA; *U.S. Private*, pg. 670
Olivier, Paul, Sr. V.P. & Cashier--Frost National Bank, San Antonio, TX; *U.S. Public*, pg. 467
Olivieri, Oliviero, Sr. V.P.--Bauer Sports Inc., Montreal, Canada; *U.S. Public*, pg. 1184
Ollari, Frank J., Sr. V.P.-Mortgage Finance--New York Life Insurance Company, New York, NY; *U.S. Private*, pg. 794
Olney, David, Sr. V.P.-Acquisitions--Berkshire Realty Company, Inc., Boston, MA; *U.S. Public*, pg. 221
Olschan, Brian S., Sr. V.P.-Mktg. & Sls.--Acme United Corporation, Fairfield, CT; *U.S. Public*, pg. 17
Olsen, Al, Sr. V.P.-Adv.--Reinalt-Thomas Corp., Ann Arbor, MI; *U.S. Private*, pg. 919
Olsen, David M., Sr. V.P.-Coffee--Starbucks Coffee Company, Seattle, WA; *U.S. Public*, pg. 1510
Olsen, Geoffrey G., Sr. V.P.-Legal--Coast Savings Financial, Inc., Los Angeles, CA; *U.S. Public*, pg. 388
Olsen, Ib, Sr. V.P.-Mfg.--Sudamtex de Uruguay, S.A., Montevideo, Uruguay; *Int'l*, pg. 1304
Olsen, John F., Sr. V.P.-Worldwide Sls.--Cadence Design Systems, Inc., San Jose, CA; *U.S. Public*, pg. 290
Olsen, M.D., Sr. V.P. & Chief Admin. Officer--Valtek International, Springville, UT; *U.S. Public*, pg. 658
Olsen, Richard B., Chief Fin. Officer & Sr. V.P.--ISP Chemicals Inc., Calvert City, KY; *U.S. Public*, pg. 858
Olsen, Richard B., Sr. V.P. & Chief Fin. Officer--ISP Technologies Inc., Texas City, TX; *U.S. Public*, pg. 859
Olsen, Richard J., Sr. V.P. & Asst. Sec.--Candela Corporation, Wayland, MA; *U.S. Public*, pg. 300
Olsen, William S., Sr. V.P.--General Reinsurance Corp., Stamford, CT; *U.S. Public*, pg. 725
Olson, A. Craig, Chief Fin. Officer & Sr. V.P.-Fin.--Albertson's, Inc., Boise, ID; *U.S. Public*, pg. 38
Olson, Barry D., Sr. V.P.--Computer Horizons Corp., Mountain Lakes, NJ; *U.S. Public*, pg. 421
Olson, James R., Sr. V.P.-External Affairs--Toyota Motor Sales, U.S.A., Inc., Torrance, CA; *Int'l*, pg. 1412
Olson, Kurt, Sr. V.P.-Sls.--Advance Machine Company, Plymouth, MN; *Int'l*, pg. 932
Olson, Michael C., Sr. V.P.-Branch Opers. & Mktg. Svcs.--Ameriana Bank, New Castle, IN; *U.S. Public*, pg. 66
Olson, Paul L.H., Sr. V.P.--Sterling Commerce, Inc., Dublin, OH; *U.S. Public*, pg. 1515
Olson, Robert W., Sr. V.P., Gen. Counsel & Sec.--American Financial Group, Cincinnati, OH; *U.S. Public*, pg. 75
Olson, Rodney E., Chief Fin. Officer & Sr. V.P.-Fin. & Corp. Devel.--Sabreliner Corporation, Saint Louis, MO; *U.S. Private*, pg. 959
Olson, Willard P., Sr. V.P.-Space & Defense Systems--McDonnell Aircraft & Missile Systems Div., Berkeley, MO; *U.S. Public*, pg. 241
Oltman, Lou, Sr. V.P.-Sls--Simplicity Holdings Inc., New York, NY; *U.S. Private*, pg. 1002
Oman, Larry M., Sr. V.P.-Automotive Components--Eaton Corporation, Cleveland, OH; *U.S. Public*, pg. 555
Oman, Philip, Sr. V.P.-Retail Store Opers.--RadioShack, Fort Worth, TX; *U.S. Public*, pg. 1560
Omori, Vernon T., Sr. V.P.-Residential Real Estate Div.--First Hawaiian Bank, Honolulu, HI; *U.S. Public*, pg. 634
Omorio, Yoshio, Sr. V.P.--NEC Corporation, Tokyo, Japan; *Int'l*, pg. 899
Omtvedt, Craig P., Chief Acctg. Officer & Sr. V.P.--Fortune Brands, Inc., Old Greenwich, CT; *U.S. Public*, pg. 674
Ondatje, Elmo F., Sr. V.P.-Intl. Banking--California State Bank, West Covina, CA; *U.S. Public*, pg. 294
Onikoyi, Abbey, Sr. V.P. & Creative Dir.--Don Coleman Advertising, Inc., Southfield, MI; *U.S. Private*, pg. 251
Ono, B.T., Sr. V.P.--Mitsubishi International Corporation, New York, NY; *Int'l*, pg. 871
Ono, Masatoshi, Sr. V.P.--Bridgestone Corporation, Tokyo, Japan; *Int'l*, pg. 213
Ono, Shigeki, Sr. V.P. & Treas.--ITOCHU International Inc., New York, NY; *Int'l*, pg. 694
Oomen, Faye I., Sr. V.P.-Devel. & Leasing/Suburban Office--Prime Group Realty Trust, Chicago, IL; *U.S. Public*, pg. 1326
Ootani, Yukio, Mng. Dir. & Sr. V.P.-The Americas--Japan Airlines Company, Ltd., Tokyo, Japan; *Int'l*, pg. 699
Oquet, George, Sr. V.P.--Republic National Bank of New York (Canada), Montreal, Canada; *U.S. Public*, pg. 1381
Orchow, W., Sr. V.P.--Kennecott Holdings Corporation, Magna, UT; *Int'l*, pg. 1119
Orcutt, W.P., Sr. V.P.--Consolidated Papers, Inc., Wisconsin Rapids, WI; *U.S. Public*, pg. 436
Ord, Kenneth S., Chief Fin. Officer & Sr. V.P.--Pacificare Health Systems, Santa Ana, CA; *U.S. Public*, pg. 1251
Ord, Kent, Sr. V.P. & Mng. Dir.--FUTUREWORKS, Seattle, WA; *U.S. Private*, pg. 385
Ord, W. Michael, Sr. V.P.-South Pacific Division--Bank of Hawaii, Honolulu, HI; *U.S. Public*, pg. 1248
Ordelheide, Gerd, Sr. V.P.-Sls.-European Opers.--BMC Software, Inc., Houston, TX; *U.S. Public*, pg. 162
Ordway, Linda, Sr. V.P.--National Programs Division, Tampa, FL; *U.S. Public*, pg. 1312
Orenstein, Bonnie, Sr. V.P. & Mgr.-Adv.--PaineWebber Group Incorporated, New York, NY; *U.S. Public*, pg. 1252
Orenstein, Bonnie, Sr. V.P. & Mgr.-Adv.--PaineWebber Incorporated, New York, NY; *U.S. Public*, pg. 1252
Orfao, David, Sr. V.P.-Worldwide Sls.--SQA, Inc., Burlington, MA; *U.S. Public*, pg. 1361
Ori, Geno, Sr. V.P. & Dir.-Environmental Affairs--Motorola, Inc., Schaumburg, IL; *U.S. Public*, pg. 1136
Orlando, Philip J., Chief Investment Officer-Value Line Asset Mngmt.--Value Line, Inc., New York, NY; *U.S. Private*, pg. 137
Orlick, Robin, Sr. V.P.-Licensing--Calvin Klein, Inc., New York, NY; *U.S. Private*, pg. 202
Orloff, Michael A., Sr. V.P.-Sls. & Mktg.--Roman, Inc., Roselle, IL; *U.S. Private*, pg. 942
Orme, Jed, Sr. V.P. & Gen. Counsel--DHL Worldwide Express, Redwood City, CA; *U.S. Private*, pg. 301
Orr, David, Sr. V.P.-Industrial Svcs.--Lat Purser & Associates, Charlotte, NC; *U.S. Private*, pg. 896
Orr, Sean, Sr. V.P. & Controller--PepsiCo, Inc., Purchase, NY; *U.S. Public*, pg. 1276
Orser, James S., Sr. V.P.--UNUM Life Insurance Company of America, Portland, ME; *U.S. Public*, pg. 1699

Orsi, Dennis R., Sr. V.P.--Eastbridge Capital Inc., New York, NY; *Int'l*, pg. 933
Ort, Richard H., Sr. V.P.--Chubb & Son, Inc., Warren, NJ; *U.S. Public*, pg. 355
Ortiz, Patrick T., Sr. V.P., Gen. Counsel & Sec.--Public Service Company of New Mexico, Albuquerque, NM; *U.S. Public*, pg. 1339
Ortman, Kenneth J., Sr. V.P.-Grp. Opers.--Nortek, Inc., Providence, RI; *U.S. Public*, pg. 1192
Orton, David E., Sr. V.P.-Visual Sys.--Silicon Graphics, Inc., Mountain View, CA; *U.S. Public*, pg. 1473
Orvieto, Roberto, Sr. V.P. & Gen. Mgr.--Banca Monte dei Paschi di Siena S.p.A., Siena, Italy; *Int'l*, pg. 136
Orwin, Jeffrey, Chief Fin. Officer & Sr. V.P.--Gilmore Bros., Inc., Kalamazoo, MI; *U.S. Private*, pg. 454
Ory, Valerie S., Sr. V.P.--Hibernia Corporation, New Orleans, LA; *U.S. Public*, pg. 825
Osborn, Mike, Sr. V.P.-Mktg.--Robson Communities, Sun Lakes, AZ; *U.S. Private*, pg. 937
Osborn, Richard J., Chief Fin. Officer & Sr. V.P.--Duke Energy Corporation, Charlotte, NC; *U.S. Public*, pg. 534
Osborne, Jerome K., Sr. V.P.--First National Bank of Pennsylvania, Hermitage, PA; *U.S. Public*, pg. 607
Osborne, Michael A., Sr. V.P.-North America--Pennzoil Exploration & Production Co., Houston, TX; *U.S. Public*, pg. 1272
Osborne, Terry, Sr. V.P.-Human Resources--SunTrust, Orlando, FL; *U.S. Public*, pg. 1537
Oshrey, Elliott S., Sr. V.P.--Ketchum, Inc., Pittsburgh, PA; *U.S. Private*, pg. 617
Osman, Dewaine L., Sr. V.P.--Unisys Corporation, Blue Bell, PA; *U.S. Public*, pg. 1671
Osowski, Richard J., Sr. V.P.-Fin. & Asst. Sec.--Criticare Systems, Inc., Waukesha, WI; *U.S. Public*, pg. 459
Ossolinski, John, Sr. V.P.-H.R.--Kolmar Laboratories, Inc., Port Jervis, NY; *Int'l*, pg. 239
Osteen, Debra K., Sr. V.P.-Behavioral Health--Universal Health Services, Inc., King of Prussia, PA; *U.S. Public*, pg. 1696
Osten, Judd, Sr. V.P., Gen. Counsel & Sec.--Crawford & Company, Atlanta, GA; *U.S. Public*, pg. 458
Oster, Kalman, Sr. V.P.-Acctg. & Econ.--The Israel Electric Corporation Ltd., Haifa, Israel; *Int'l*, pg. 690
Oster, Richard, Chief Fin. Officer & Sr. V.P.-Fin.--Crowley Maritime Corporation, Oakland, CA; *U.S. Private*, pg. 292
Oster, Wolfgang, M.D., Sr. V.P.-Worldwide Clinical Res.--U.S. Bioscience, Inc., Conshohocken, PA; *U.S. Public*, pg. 1681
Ostergaard, Ian, Sr. V.P.-Human Resources--Citibank, Federal Savings Bank (Illinois), Chicago, IL; *U.S. Public*, pg. 378
Ostrander, Robert G., Sr. V.P.--UNUM Life Insurance Company of America, Portland, ME; *U.S. Public*, pg. 1699
Ostroff, Jonathan, Sr. V.P.--Central Lewmar, Newark, NJ; *U.S. Private*, pg. 223
Ostrov, Rob, Sr. V.P.-H.R.--TruServ Corporation, Chicago, IL; *U.S. Private*, pg. 1108
Otaguro, Curt T., Sr. V.P.-Opers. Res. & Devel. Div.--First Hawaiian Bank, Honolulu, HI; *U.S. Public*, pg. 634
Otake, Ruby T., Sr. V.P.-Main Branch--Bank of Hawaii, Honolulu, HI; *U.S. Public*, pg. 1248
Otamura-Kester, Judith K., Sr. V.P., Asst. Gen. Counsel & Asst. Sec.--Jefferies & Company, Inc., Los Angeles, CA; *U.S. Public*, pg. 925
Otellini, Paul S., Sr. V.P. & Gen. Mgr.-Microprocessor Products Group--Intel Corporation, Santa Clara, CA; *U.S.* Public, pg. 886
Otis, Clarence, Jr., Sr. V.P.-Investor Rels. & Treas.--Darden Restaurants, Inc., Orlando, FL; *U.S. Public*, pg. 483
Otis, Samuel A., Sr. V.P.--Independence Investment Associates, Inc., Boston, MA; *U.S. Private*, pg. 589
Otras, George, Sr. V.P.-Trading--Active International, Pearl River, NY; *U.S. Private*, pg. 15
Ott, John, Chief Fin. Officer & Sr. V.P.--The Fairmont Hotels, San Francisco, CA; *U.S. Private*, pg. 391
Ott, John L., Jr., Sr. V.P.--First Financial Holdings, Inc., Charleston, SC; *U.S. Public*, pg. 634
Ott, Rene B., Sr. V.P.-External Relations--Liechtenstein Global Trust Limited, Vaduz, Liechtenstein; *Int'l*, pg. 809
Ottaway, James, Sr. V.P.--Barron's The Dow Jones Business & Financial Weekly, New York, NY; *U.S. Public*, pg. 524
Ottaway, James H. Jr., Sr. V.P. & Chm.-Ottaway Newspapers, Inc.--Dow Jones & Company, Inc., New York, NY; *U.S. Public*, pg. 524
Otte, R. Adrian, M.D., Sr. V.P.-Res. Opers./N. America--PAREXEL International Corporation, Waltham, MA; *U.S. Public*, pg. 1257
Otten, Douglas B., Sr. V.P.--Canadian Occidental Petroleum Ltd., Calgary, Canada; *U.S. Public*, pg. 1210
Otto, Albert J., Chief Fin. Officer & Sr. V.P.--Branford Savings Bank, Branford, CT; *U.S. Public*, pg. 250
Otto, Charlotte R., Sr. V.P.-Pub. Affairs--The Procter & Gamble Company, Cincinnati, OH; *U.S. Public*, pg. 1330
Otto, Joseph, Sr. V.P.--Concord Assets Group, Boca Raton, FL; *U.S. Private*, pg. 261
Otto, Kenneth W., Sr. V.P.--Domino Sugar Corporation, New York, NY; *Int'l*, pg. 1356
Otto, Myron L., Sr. V.P. & Trust Officer--Bank of Pontiac, Pontiac, IL; *U.S. Public*, pg. 1316
Oubre, Richard, Jr., Sr. V.P.--Hibernia Corporation, New Orleans, LA; *U.S. Public*, pg. 825
Ouf, Hazem, Pres., Chief Exec. Officer & Sr. V.P.--Lyon's Restaurants, Inc., Foster City, CA; *U.S. Private*, pg. 684
Ounsworth, James A., Sr. V.P., Gen. Counsel & Sec.--Safeguard Scientifics, Inc., Wayne, PA; *U.S. Public*, pg. 1424
Overall, James, Sr. V.P. & Assoc. Creative Dir.--Hill, Holliday, Connors, Cosmopulos, Inc., Boston, MA; *U.S. Private*, pg. 529
Overend, Jim, Sr. V.P. & Client Svcs. Dir.--Grybauskas Beatrice, New York, NY; *U.S. Private*, pg. 485
Overend, Mark G., Chief Fin. Officer & Sr. V.P.--SLM Holding Corp., Washington, DC; *U.S. Public*, pg. 1419
Overton, Russell G., Sr. V.P.-Bus. Devel.--HBOC, Atlanta, GA; *U.S. Public*, pg. 770
Overton, Samuel, Sr. V.P. & Treas.--Mattison Technologies, Inc., Rockford, IL; *U.S. Private*, pg. 714
Owcar, Gary J., Sr. V.P.--Chubb & Son, Inc., Warren, NJ; *U.S. Public*, pg. 355
Owen, Peggy, Sr. V.P. & Media Dir.--The Buntin Group, Nashville, TN; *U.S. Private*, pg. 181
Owens, Carroll W., Jr., Sr. V.P.--Johnston, Lemon & Co. Inc., Washington, DC; *U.S. Private*, pg. 595
Owens, David C., Sr. V.P.-Corp. Health, Environment & Safety--Bayer Corporation, Pittsburgh, PA; *Int'l*, pg. 172
Owens, Davud, Sr. V.P.--EvansGroup, Seattle, WA; *U.S. Private*, pg. 385
Owens, Jane, Sr. V.P. & Gen. Counsel--The Dial Corporation, Phoenix, AZ; *U.S. Public*, pg. 505
Owens, Michael L., Chief Oper. Officer, Sr. V.P. & Treas.--Monumental General Insurance Company, Baltimore, MD; *Int'l*, pg. 27
Owens, Tom, Sr. V.P.-Programming--Jacor Communications, Inc., Covington, KY; *U.S. Public*, pg. 922
Owerstrom, Dan M., Sr. V.P.-Corp. Law & Sec.--Trygg-Hansa, Stockholm, Sweden; *Int'l*, pg. 1425
Owett, Adam, Sr. V.P. & Grp. Creative Dir.--Partners & Shevack, Inc., New York, NY; *U.S. Private*, pg. 842
Oxman, Michael, Sr. V.P. & Brand Mktg. Partner--DMB&B Detroit, Troy, MI; *U.S. Private*, pg. 302
Oxnard, Benjamin A., Jr., Sr. V.P.-Raw Sugar--Savannah Foods & Industries, Inc., Savannah, GA; *U.S. Public*, pg. 872
Oyler, G. Atlee, Sr. V.P.--Bright National Bank, Flora, IN; *U.S. Public*, pg. 633
Paalanne, Pekka, Chief Fin. Officer & Sr. V.P.--Amer Group Ltd., Helsinki, Finland; *Int'l*, pg. 72
Pace, Grant, Sr. V.P. & Creative Dir.--Long Haymes Carr, Inc., Winston Salem, NC; *U.S. Public*, pg. 909
Pace, Michael, Sr. V.P.-Sls.--ERO Industries, Inc., Mount Prospect, IL; *U.S. Private*, pg. 526
Pace, Simone J., Chief Information Officer & Sr. V.P.--GEICO Corporation, Washington, DC; *U.S. Public*, pg. 219
Pachino, Barton P., Sr. V.P. & Gen. Counsel--Kaufman and Broad Home Corporation, Los Angeles, CA; *U.S. Public*, pg. 944
Pacholder, Robin E., Sr. V.P. & Gen. Counsel--ICO, Inc., Houston, TX; *U.S. Public*, pg. 853
Pack, Sterling, Sr. V.P.-Investor Rels.--The Coastal Corporation, Houston, TX; *U.S. Public*, pg. 389
Packard, Ralph K., Chief Fin. Officer & Sr. V.P.--The Vanguard Group, Inc., Valley Forge, PA; *U.S. Private*, pg. 1133
Packer, Kathy, Sr. V.P.-Adv.--Entertainment Publications, Inc., Troy, MI; *U.S. Public*, pg. 320
Packer, Kathy, Sr. V.P.-Adv.--Welcome Wagon-Intl., Inc., Trumbull, CT; *U.S. Public*, pg. 321
Padden, Preston, Sr. V.P.-Affiliates--Fox Broadcasting Company (FBC), Beverly Hills, CA; *Int'l*, pg. 926
Paddock, Jim, Sr. V.P. & Creative Dir.--Fitzgerald & Co., Atlanta, GA; *U.S. Private*, pg. 409
Padewer, Harvey J., Sr. V.P.-Energy Resources & Power Services--UtiliCorp United Inc., Kansas City, MO; *U.S. Public*, pg. 1700
Padilla, Steve, Sr. V.P.-D.P. & Engrng.--Hunter Contracting Company, Gilbert, AZ; *U.S. Private*, pg. 549
Padukone, Nina, Sr. V.P. & Creative Dir.--Lowe McAdams Healthcare, New York, NY; *U.S. Private*, pg. 678
Pagano, James, Chief Fin. Officer & Sr. V.P.--Cogentrix Incorporated, Charlotte, NC; *U.S. Private*, pg. 249
Page, Allan R., Sr. V.P.-Customer Servies--Central Hudson Gas & Electric Corporation, Poughkeepsie, NY; *U.S. Public*, pg. 324
Page, Mark L., Sr. V.P.-Store Opers.--The Pep Boys-Manny, Moe & Jack, Philadelphia, PA; *U.S. Public*, pg. 1276
Page, Martin R., Sr. V.P.-Worldwide Regulatory Affairs & Quality Assurance--Centocor, Inc., Malvern, PA; *U.S. Public*, pg. 323
Paglia, Louis J., Sr. V.P. & Treas.--TIG Holdings, Inc., New York, NY; *U.S. Public*, pg. 1555
Pahud, Serge, Sr. Exec. V.P. & Dir.-Fin.--SGS Societe Generale de Surveillance Holding S.A., Geneva, Switzerland; *Int'l*, pg. 1153
Paiement, Ray, Sr. V.P.-Construction--Willis Corroon Corp. of Eugene, Eugene, OR; *Int'l*, pg. 1505
Paige, Michael R., Ph.D., Sr. V.P.-Electronic Prepress Systems--Bayer Corporation, Pittsburgh, PA; *Int'l*, pg. 172
Painter, Richard O., Sr. V.P.-Southeastern Agencies--New York Life Insurance Company, New York, NY; *U.S. Private*, pg. 794
Paisley, Christopher B., Chief Fin. Officer & Sr. V.P.-Fin.--3Com Corporation, Santa Clara, CA; *U.S. Public*, pg. 1603
Paisley, Thomas E., III, Sr. V.P.--PNC Bank Corp., Pittsburgh, PA; *U.S. Public*, pg. 1242
Pajot, Gilles, Sr. V.P.--Pharmacia & Upjohn, Inc., Windsor, United Kingdom; *Int'l*, pg. 1047
Paladino, Steven, Chief Fin. Officer & Sr. V.P.--Henry Schein, Inc., Melville, NY; *U.S. Public*, pg. 1437
Palamara, J. Francis, Sr. V.P.--Jefferies & Company, Inc., Los Angeles, CA; *U.S. Public*, pg. 925
Palin, Nick, Sr. V.P.-Sls. & Mktg.--Rexall Sundown Inc., Boca Raton, FL; *U.S. Public*, pg. 1384
Palker, Jeffrey, Sr. V.P. & Chief Lending Officer--The Old Phoenix National Bank of Medina, Medina, OH; *U.S. Public*, pg. 646
Pall, Brian, Sr. V.P.-Devel.--The Great Atlantic & Pacific Tea Company, Inc., Montvale, NJ; *Int'l*, pg. 1375
Palladino, Wayne, Chief Fin. Officer & Sr. V.P.--Transworld Home Healthcare, Inc., New York, NY; *U.S. Public*, pg. 1632
Palm, Robert N., Sr. V.P. & Complex Mgr.--Pilgrim's Pride Corporation, Pittsburg, TX; *U.S. Public*, pg. 1296
Palmer, Bob, Sr. V.P.-Grocery Procurement--C & S Wholesale Grocery Inc., Brattleboro, VT; *U.S. Private*, pg. 192
Palmer, Donald H., Sr. V.P.--WWF Paper Corporation, Bala Cynwyd, PA; *U.S. Private*, pg. 1145
Palmer, George E., Sr. V.P.-Tech./IMS & NMR--Cognizant Corporation, Westport, CT; *U.S. Public*, pg. 395
Palmer, Howell M., III, Sr. V.P. & Actuary--Berkshire Life Insurance Company, Pittsfield, MA; *U.S. Private*, pg. 136
Palmer, James A., Sr. V.P.-Opers.--VeriFone, Inc., Redwood City, CA; *U.S. Public*, pg. 815
Palmer, John A.B., Sr. V.P.-Fin. & Admin.-Bed Fashions--Home Furnishings Segment, Fort Mill, SC; *U.S. Public*, pg. 1500
Palmer, John J., Sr. V.P.-Prod. Mngmt.--The Life Insurance Co. of Virginia, Richmond, VA; *U.S. Public*, pg. 712
Palmer, Kenneth A., Sr. V.P.-Info. Svcs.--The Western and Southern Life Insurance Company, Cincinnati, OH; *U.S. Private*, pg. 1164
Palmer, Keri, Chief Fin. Officer & Sr. V.P.--Austin Kelley Advertising, Inc., Atlanta, GA; *U.S. Private*, pg. 100
Palmer, Mack, Sr. V.P.--Ocean Beauty Seafoods, Inc., Seattle, WA; *U.S. Private*, pg. 810
Palmer, Richard, Chief Fin. Officer & Sr. V.P.--Western Financial Bank, Irvine, CA; *U.S. Public*, pg. 1757
Palmer, Roger, Sr. V.P. & Pres.-CETCO--AMCOL International Corp., Arlington Heights, IL; *U.S. Public*, pg. 63
Palmer, Ronald J., Sr. V.P. & Gen. Counsel--Standard Federal Bank, Troy, MI; *Int'l*, pg. 10
Palmieri, Robert J., Sr. V.P.--Computer Horizons Corp., Mountain Lakes, NJ; *U.S. Public*, pg. 421
Palmisano, Robert J., Sr. V.P.-Eyewear Div.--Bausch & Lomb Incorporated, Rochester, NY; *U.S. Public*, pg. 194
Palsson, Gudmundur, Sr. V.P.--Icelandair, Reykjavik, Iceland; *Int'l*, pg. 658
Paneyko, Stephen H., Sr. Exec. V.P.--Summit Bank, Chatham, NJ; *U.S. Public*, pg. 1528
Panfil, Robert J., Sr. V.P.-Fin.--Stenograph Corporation, Mount Prospect, IL; *U.S. Private*, pg. 860
Pang, Gerald M., Chief Credit Officer & Sr. V.P.--First Hawaiian, Inc., Honolulu, HI; *U.S. Public*, pg. 634
Panglinan, Pastor C., Sr. V.P.-Svc. Support Grp.--Philippine Airlines, Inc., Manila, Philippines; *Int'l*, pg. 1050
Panjawatanakul, Sompoch, Sr. V.P.-Investment Banking--Nakornthon Bank Public Company Limited, Bangkok, Thailand; *Int'l*, pg. 904
Pankratz, Frank D., Sr. V.P. & Gen. Mgr.-Sun City Summerlin & MacDonald Ranch--Del Webb Corporation, Phoenix, AZ; *U.S. Public*, pg. 494
Pannell, Michael, Sr. V.P. & Controller--Riggs National Corporation, Washington, DC; *U.S. Public*, pg. 1389
Pannier, Loren C., Sr. V.P.-Investor Relations--CKE Restaurants Inc., Anaheim, CA; *U.S. Public*, pg. 278
Pannier, Loren C., Chief Fin. Officer & Sr. V.P.--Carl Karcher Enterprises, Inc., Anaheim, CA; *U.S. Public*, pg. 278
Pantlin, David, Sr. V.P.--Banque Internationale a Luxembourg S.A., Luxembourg, Luxembourg; *Int'l*, pg. 162
Pantuso, Bill, Sr. V.P.-Mktg.--Chief Auto Parts, Dallas, TX; *U.S. Private*, pg. 236
Paolercio, Michael Anthony, Sr. V.P. & Treas.--Michael Anthony Jewelers, Inc., Mount Vernon, NY; *U.S. Public*, pg. 1103
Papa, Vincent, Sr. V.P. & Sec.--Metallgesellschaft Corp., New York, NY; *Int'l*, pg. 861
Papadados, Mike, Sr. V.P.-Western--HongKong Bank of Canada, Vancouver, Canada; *Int'l*, pg. 583
Papandrea, Gina R., Sr. V.P.-Fin.--Genstar Development Company, San Diego, CA; *Int'l*, pg. 112
Papazian, Gerald S., Sr. V.P.-Admin.--Aura Systems, Inc., El Segundo, CA; *U.S. Public*, pg. 147
Pape, Gregory, Sr. V.P.-Sls. & Mktg.--American Shared Hospital Services, San Francisco, CA; *U.S. Public*, pg. 91
Pape, William R., Chief Information Officer & Sr. V.P.-Smart-Fone Systems Div.--VeriFone, Inc., Redwood City, CA; *U.S. Public*, pg. 815
Papesh, Patricia A., Sr. V.P.-Mktg.--American Greetings Corporation, Cleveland, OH; *U.S. Public*, pg. 77
Papesh, Patricia A., Sr. V.P.-Prod. Devel.--American Greetings U.S. Greeting Card Division, Cleveland, OH; *U.S. Public*, pg. 78
Pappas, James P., Sr. V.P.--UAM Investment Services, Inc., Boston, MA; *U.S. Public*, pg. 1674
Parchman, R. Wayne, Sr. V.P.-Special Mkts.--Lenox, Incorporated, Lawrenceville, NJ; *U.S. Public*, pg. 261
Pardey, William, Sr. V.P.--CSW Leasing, Inc., Dallas, TX; *U.S. Public*, pg. 324
Parent, Henri, Sr. V.P.-Equity Research & Investment--Compagnie de Suez, Paris, France; *Int'l*, pg. 313
Parent, Kenneth R., Chief Fin. Officer & Sr. V.P.--The Mills Corporation, Arlington, VA; *U.S. Public*, pg. 1113
Paretti, Mike, Sr. V.P.-Food Services--Agripac Inc., Salem, OR; *U.S. Private*, pg. 26
Parfet, Donald R., Sr. V.P.-Affiliated Businesses--Pharmacia & Upjohn, Inc., Windsor, United Kingdom; *Int'l*, pg. 1047
Parise, Joseph R., Sr. V.P. & Mng. Dir.--Imperial Credit Commercial Mortgage Investment Corp., Los Angeles, CA; *U.S. Public*, pg. 872
Parish, Rhonda J., Sr. V.P., Gen. Counsel & Sec.--Advantica Restaurant Group, Inc., Spartanburg, SC; *U.S.* Public, pg. 22
Parizino, Mike, Sr. V.P. & Mgr.-Surety--Willis Corroon Corp. of Orange County, Santa Ana, CA; *Int'l*, pg. 1506
Park, Bill, Chief Oper. Officer & Sr. V.P.--Curtis Mathes Holding Corp., Dallas, TX; *U.S. Public*, pg. 1057
Park, Hyo Sung, Sr. V.P.-Passenger Sls., Mktg. & Traffic--Korean Airlines Co., Ltd., Seoul, Korea; *Int'l*, pg. 758
Park, Jerry, Sr. V.P.-CBA Sls., Nelson Word Publishing--Thomas Nelson Inc., Nashville, TN; *U.S. Public*, pg. 1167

Park, John J., Sr. V.P.-Fin., Asst. Treas. & Dir.-Res.--W.P. Carey & Co., Inc., New York, NY; *U.S. Private*, pg. 209

Parke, James A., Sr. V.P.-Fin.--General Electric Capital Services, Inc., Stamford, CT; *U.S. Public*, pg. 711

Parke, Robert N., Chief Fin. Officer & Sr. V.P.-Fin.--St. Paul Bancorp, Inc., Chicago, IL; *U.S. Public*, pg. 1428

Parker-Wingate, Beatrice, Sr. V.P. & Admin. Services Dir.--Arnold Advertising, Mc Lean, VA; *U.S. Private*, pg. 84

Parker, A. Joseph, Sr. V.P.-Retail Bus. Line Mngmt.--National City Corporation, Cleveland, OH; *U.S. Public*, pg. 1154

Parker, B.Z., Sr. V.P.-Refining, Mktg. & Transportation--Phillips Petroleum Company, Bartlesville, OK; *U.S. Public*, pg. 1290

Parker, Bill, Sr. V.P. & Creative Dir.--Bensimon Byrne DMB&B Toronto, Toronto, Canada; *U.S. Private*, pg. 303

Parker, Brian, Chief Fin. Officer & Sr. V.P.--Grubb & Ellis Company, Northbrook, IL; *U.S. Public*, pg. 767

Parker, Brian, Chief Fin. Officer & Sr. V.P.--Grubb & Ellis Management Services, Inc., Northbrook, IL; *U.S. Public*, pg. 767

Parker, Bruce D., Chief Info. Officer & Sr. V.P.--UAL Corporation, Elk Grove Village, IL; *U.S. Public*, pg. 1652

Parker, Chris, Sr. V.P.-Sls. & Bus.--A.P.S., Memphis, TN; *U.S. Public*, pg. 10

Parker, F. Dennis, Sr. V.P.--Peninsula Bank, Princess Anne, MD; *U.S. Public*, pg. 1089

Parker, George M., Sr. V.P. & Print Production Dir.--Long Haymes Carr, Inc., Winston Salem, NC; *U.S. Public*, pg. 909

Parker, Harvey W., Sr. V.P.--Shannon & Wilson, Inc., Seattle, WA; *U.S. Private*, pg. 989

Parker, Howard E., Chief Fin. Officer & Sr. V.P.-Fin. & Admin.--Atlas World Group, Inc., Evansville, IN; *U.S. Private*, pg. 97

Parker, John, Sr. V.P. & Gen. Mgr.--Lifetouch, Portrait Studios, Eden Prairie, MN; *U.S. Private*, pg. 667

Parker, Keith L., Sr. V.P.--Mercury General Corporation, Los Angeles, CA; *U.S. Public*, pg. 1093

Parker, Lawrence, Sr. V.P. & Gen. Mgr.-Quality--Delco Remy America, Inc., Anderson, IN; *U.S. Public*, pg. 495

Parker, Michael R., Sr. V.P.--Willis Faber North America, Inc.-Connecticut, Stamford, CT; *Int'l*, pg. 1503

Parker, Richard J., Sr. V.P. & Mgr.-Mill & Production--Longview Fibre Company, Longview, WA; *U.S. Public*, pg. 1013

Parker, S. Victoria, Sr. V.P.--John Wieland Homes Inc., Atlanta, GA; *U.S. Private*, pg. 1175

Parker, Steven, Sr. V.P.-Mktg. & Sls.--Red Roof Inns, Inc., Hilliard, OH; *U.S. Public*, pg. 1369

Parker, W. Douglas, Chief Fin. Officer & Sr. V.P.--America West Holdings Corporation, Phoenix, AZ; *U.S. Public*, pg. 66

Parker, W. Douglas, Chief Fin. Officer & Sr. V.P.--America West Airlines, Inc., Phoenix, AZ; *U.S. Public*, pg. 67

Parker, Wallace P., Jr., Sr. V.P.--Brooklyn Union, Brooklyn, NY; *U.S. Public*, pg. 259

Parker, William H., Sr. V.P.-Mdsg.--Payless Cashways, Inc., Kansas City, MO; *U.S. Public*, pg. 1267

Parkerson, Danny L., Sr. V.P. & Gen. Mgr.--Churchill Downs, Inc., Louisville, KY; *U.S. Public*, pg. 356

Parkin, Roger, Sr. V.P. & Gen. Mgr.-Chemicals, Oil & Gas Div.--ABB Industrial Systems, Inc., Columbus, OH; *Int'l*, pg. 4

Parkinson, Robert L., Jr., Sr. V.P.-Intl. Opers.--Abbott Laboratories, Abbott Park, IL; *U.S. Public*, pg. 12

Parks, Bruce, Sr. V.P. & Creative Dir.--Ackerman McQueen, Inc., Tulsa, OK; *U.S. Private*, pg. 13

Parks, Charles N., Sr. V.P.--SCI Systems, Inc., Huntsville, AL; *U.S. Public*, pg. 1416

Parks, Peter, Sr. V.P. & Mngmt. Supvr.--Thomas G. Ferguson Associates, Inc., Parsippany, NJ; *Int'l*, pg. 1483

Parks, Richard E., Sr. V.P.-Recreational Vehicle Grp.--Fleetwood Enterprises, Inc., Riverside, CA; *U.S. Public*, pg. 650

Parks, Walter J., Chief Fin. Officer & Sr. V.P.--AnnTaylor Stores Corporation, New York, NY; *U.S. Public*, pg. 116

Parks, Walter J., Chief Fin. Officer, Sr. V.P. & Treas.--AnnTaylor, Inc., New York, NY; *U.S. Public*, pg. 116

Parlongo, Joseph B., Sr. V.P.-Services--Brown & Root Inc., Alhambra, CA; *U.S. Public*, pg. 775

Parra, Mario A., Sr. V.P.--Associates Commercial Equipment Div., Dallas, TX; *U.S. Public*, pg. 663

Parrillo, Gillian M., Sr. V.P. & Grp. Pres.--Sterling Software, Inc., Dallas, TX; *U.S. Public*, pg. 1516

Parrin, David J., Sr. V.P. & Controller--U.S. Bancorp, Minneapolis, MN; *U.S. Public*, pg. 1680

Parris, Gail, Chief Fin. Officer & Sr. V.P.--Yellow Freight System, Inc., Overland Park, KS; *U.S. Public*, pg. 1788

Parrish, Richard B., Sr. V.P.-Building Products--Boise Cascade Timber & Wood Products Division, Boise, ID; *U.S. Public*, pg. 243

Parrish, Robert R., Sr. V.P.--Boise Cascade Building Materials Distribution Div., Boise, ID; *U.S. Public*, pg. 243

Parrish, Steven C., Sr. V.P.-Corp. Affairs--Philip Morris Companies Inc., New York, NY; *U.S. Public*, pg. 1287

Parros, James G., Sr. V.P.-Stores & Distribution Center Opers./Kid "R" Us--Toys "R" Us, Inc., Paramus, NJ; *U.S. Public*, pg. 1626

Parros, James G., Sr. V.P.-Stores & Distr. Center Opers.--Kids "R" Us, Paramus, NJ; *U.S. Public*, pg. 1626

Parros, John T., Sr. V.P. & Gen. Mgr.-Mdsg.--Younkers, Inc., Des Moines, IA; *U.S. Public*, pg. 1334

Parrott, Anita N., Chief Fin. Officer & Sr. V.P.--St. Michaels Bank, Saint Michaels, MD; *U.S. Public*, pg. 1089

Parrs, Marianne M., Chief Fin. Officer & Sr. V.P.--International Paper Company, Purchase, NY; *U.S. Public*, pg. 901

Parsinen, Peter H., Sr. V.P.-Customer & Mktg. Support--Bell Helicopter Textron, Hurst, TX; *U.S. Public*, pg. 1588

Parsons, Craig A., Sr. V.P.-Corp. Commun. & Investor Rels.--Metro-Goldwyn-Mayer Inc., Santa Monica, CA; *U.S. Public*, pg. 1101

Parsons, Don L., Sr. V.P.-Fin. & Admin.--Curtis-Toledo, Inc., Saint Louis, MO; *U.S. Private*, pg. 298

Parsons, Earl, Sr. V.P.-Fossil Generation--Alabama Power Co., Birmingham, AL; *U.S. Public*, pg. 1489

Parsons, Jeff, Chief Fin. Officer & Sr. V.P.--Redgate Communications Corp., Vero Beach, FL; *U.S. Public*, pg. 66

Parsons, John R., Sr.V.P.-Engrng. & Tech.--Aerospace Corporation, El Segundo, CA; *U.S. Private*, pg. 24

Parten, Jeanette, Sr. V.P.-Northern Wholesale Div.--Countrywide Funding Corporation, Pasadena, CA; *U.S. Public*, pg. 453

Partington, Donald E., Sr. V.P. & Gen. Counsel--Fidelity National Title Insurance Company, Irvine, CA; *U.S. Public*, pg. 620

Parunak, H. John, Sr. V.P.-Telephone Services & Sls.--Citizens Savings Bank, Providence, RI; *Int'l*, pg. 1132

Paskett, Leslie F., Sr. V.P. & Tax Officer--First Security Corporation, Salt Lake City, UT; *U.S. Public*, pg. 637

Pasquale, Anthony C., Sr. V.P.-Investments--The Equitable Companies Incorporated, New York, NY; *U.S. Public*, pg. 588

Passarello, Steven A., Sr. V.P.-Intl. Div.--Arbor Acres Farm, Inc., Glastonbury, CT; *Int'l*, pg. 202

Passarello, Tony, Sr. V.P.--TCBY Systems, Inc., Little Rock, AR; *U.S. Public*, pg. 1554

Passman, S. David, III, Chief Fin. Officer & Sr. V.P.--John H. Harland Company, Decatur, GA; *U.S. Public*, pg. 785

Passman, S. David, III, Chief Fin. Officer & Sr. V.P.--The Check Store, Lakewood, CO; *U.S. Public*, pg. 785

Patanio, Salvatore P., Sr. V.P.--Rothschild Inc., New York, NY; *U.S. Private*, pg. 947

Pate, Ronald O., Sr. V.P.-Sls. & Mktg.--Horace Small Apparel Company, Nashville, TN; *Int'l*, pg. 635

Patent, Patrick H., Chief Oper. Officer & Sr. V.P.--Megapulse, Inc., Bedford, MA; *U.S. Private*, pg. 729

Paterson, Brian D., Sr. V.P.-Pur. & Mktg.--Southern Electronics Corporation, Tucker, GA; *U.S. Public*, pg. 1490

Paterson, Douglas J., Sr. V.P.-Comml. Surety--Amwest Surety Insurance Company, Calabasas, CA; *U.S. Public*, pg. 106

Paterson, William A., Sr. V.P. & Controller--Fort James Corporation, Richmond, VA; *U.S. Public*, pg. 670

Patino, Santiago, Sr. V.P.--UJB Discount Brokerage, Ridgefield Park, NJ; *U.S. Public*, pg. 1528

Patlove, Abram E., Sr. V.P.-Plng. & Devel./Intl.--Comcast Corporation, Philadelphia, PA; *U.S. Public*, pg. 406

Patnaude, Jude T., Sr. V.P. & Trust Officer--Chemical Bank & Trust Company, Midland, MI; *U.S. Public*, pg. 345

Patrick, Ray, Sr. V.P.-Dist. Opers.--Mary Kay, Inc., Dallas, TX; *U.S. Private*, pg. 711

Patrone, Anthony J., Sr. V.P.-Opers.--Symbol Technologies, Inc., Holtsville, NY; *U.S. Public*, pg. 1546

Patrylo, Robert J., Sr. V.P. & Grp. Exec.-Gas Services--PECO Energy Company, Philadelphia, PA; *U.S. Public*, pg. 1268

Patsko, Carl, Sr. V.P.-Credit Admin.--Sunwest Bank, Tustin, CA; *U.S. Public*, pg. 1755

Patterson-Huag, Deborah G., Sr. V.P.-Private Banking & Investments--Bank of Hawaii, Honolulu, HI; *U.S. Public*, pg. 1248

Patterson, Angela, Sr. V.P.-Visual Display--Bergdorf Goodman, New York, NY; *U.S. Public*, pg. 785

Patterson, David B., Sr. V.P. & Acct. Grp. Dir.--Creswell, Munsell, Fultz & Zirbel, L.P., Cedar Rapids, IA; *U.S. Private*, pg. 1197

Patterson, Michael, Sr. V.P.--Petty Company, Inc., Effingham, IL; *U.S. Private*, pg. 860

Patterson, W. R., Sr. V.P.--First Commercial Bank, N.A., Little Rock, AR; *U.S. Public*, pg. 630

Patterson, Wayne S., Sr. V.P.--Toll Brothers, Inc., Huntingdon Valley, PA; *U.S. Public*, pg. 1620

Patton, Bob, Sr. V.P.-Sls.--The Genie Company, Alliance, OH; *U.S. Private*, pg. 823

Patton, T. C., Sr. V.P.--Kennecott Holdings Corporation, Magna, UT; *Int'l*, pg. 1119

Patton, Terry E., Sr. V.P. & Sec.--FirstMerit Corporation, Akron, OH; *U.S. Public*, pg. 646

Patton, William B. Jr., Sr. V.P.--Unisys Corporation, Blue Bell, PA; *U.S. Public*, pg. 1671

Paul, Gary S., Sr. V.P.--First Empire State Corporation, Buffalo, NY; *U.S. Public*, pg. 631

Paul, Gary S., Sr. V.P.--Manufacturers & Traders Trust Company, Buffalo, NY; *U.S. Public*, pg. 631

Paul, Kathryn, Sr. V.P. & Reg. Mgr.--Kaiser Permanente, Rocky Mountain Division, Denver, CO; *U.S. Private*, pg. 605

Paul, Kathryn A., Pres.-Rocky Mountain Division & Sr. V.P.--Kaiser Permanente, Oakland, CA; *U.S. Private*, pg. 605

Paul, Pat, Sr. V.P.--Imperial Bank, Inglewood, CA; *U.S. Public*, pg. 871

Paul, Ray M., Jr., Sr. V.P.--Universal Leaf Tobacco Company, Inc., Richmond, VA; *U.S. Public*, pg. 1694

Paul, Richard S., Sr. V.P. & Gen. Counsel--Xerox Corporation, Stamford, CT; *U.S. Public*, pg. 1783

Paul, Robert, Sr. V.P.-H.R.--NVR, Inc., Mc Lean, VA; *U.S. Public*, pg. 1148

Paul, Robert A., Sr. V.P.-Corp. Plng.--Commonwealth Energy System, Cambridge, MA; *U.S. Public*, pg. 414

Paulin, Kenneth W., Sr. V.P.--Manufacturers & Traders Trust Company, Buffalo, NY; *U.S. Public*, pg. 631

Pauline, Kenneth, Jr., Sr. V.P.--First Empire State Corporation, Buffalo, NY; *U.S. Public*, pg. 631

Paull, Jim, Sr. V.P.-Sls. & Mktg.--Competitive Media Reporting, New York, NY; *Int'l*, pg. 1447

Paulson, Mary, Sr. V.P.-Client Svcs.--Grey Directory Marketing Inc., Chicago, IL; *U.S. Public*, pg. 764

Pauly, Jay W., Chief Oper. Officer & Sr. V.P.--BRE Properties, Inc., San Francisco, CA; *U.S. Public*, pg. 163

Paupe, Christian M., Chief Fin. Officer & Sr. V.P.--Southam Inc., Don Mills, Canada; *Int'l*, pg. 631

Pausig, Ralph W., Sr. V.P.-Human Resources--ITT Corporation, New York, NY; *U.S. Public*, pg. 1512

Pavey, Michael A., Chief Fin. Officer & Sr. V.P.--Transalta Corporation, Calgary, Canada; *Int'l*, pg. 1416

Pavlicek, Stephen E., Sr. V.P. & Controller--American National Insurance Company, Galveston, TX; *U.S. Public*, pg. 87

Pavlick, W.E., Sr. V.P., Gen. Counsel & Sec.--Modine Manufacturing Company, Racine, WI; *U.S. Public*, pg. 1121

Paxton, C. William, Sr. V.P.-Engr. Prods.--Bliss-Salem, Inc., Salem, OH; *U.S. Private*, pg. 149

Payen, Gerard, Sr. V.P.--Lyonnaise des Eaux S.A., Nanterre, France; *Int'l*, pg. 822

Payne, Bruce, Sr. V.P. & Grp. Acct. Dir.--Bensimon Byrne DMB&B Toronto, Toronto, Canada; *U.S. Private*, pg. 303

Payne, D.P., Sr. V.P.--Waste Management, Inc., Oak Brook, IL; *U.S. Public*, pg. 1744

Payne, Dan, Sr. V.P.-Gen Mdse. Mgr--The Bon Marche, Inc., Seattle, WA; *U.S. Public*, pg. 617

Payne, Douglas, Sr. V.P.-Fin. & Admin.--Stanley Furniture Co. Inc., Stanleytown, VA; *U.S. Public*, pg. 1508

Payne, Jim C., Sr. V.P.-Branch Lending--National Bank of Alaska, Anchorage, AK; *U.S. Public*, pg. 1153

Payne, Maureen, Sr. V.P.--GPC Communications (Calgary), Calgary, Canada; *U.S. Public*, pg. 1225

Paynting, Richard J., Sr. V.P.--Helix Technology Corp., Mansfield, MA; *U.S. Public*, pg. 808

Payton, Jerry, Chief Oper. Officer & Sr. V.P.--Old America Stores, Howe, TX; *U.S. Public*, pg. 1215

Payzant, J.S., Sr. V.P.-Trust Investments & Treas.--National Trustco Inc., Toronto, Canada; *Int'l*, pg. 909

Pazos, Javier, Sr. V.P.--Banco Santander, Madrid, Spain; *Int'l*, pg. 143

Peabody, A.W., Sr. V.P.-Exploration & Production--Union Texas Petroleum Holdings, Houston, TX; *U.S. Public*, pg. 1669

Peabody, Ron, Sr. V.P. & Grp. Acct. Supvr.--Rhea & Kaiser Marketing Communications, Naperville, IL; *U.S. Private*, pg. 927

Peacock, Oren, Sr. V.P.--Eckerd Drug Co., Garland, TX; *U.S. Public*, pg. 917

Pearl, Carleton D., Sr. V.P. & Treas.--McDonald's Corporation, Oak Brook, IL; *U.S. Public*, pg. 1068

Pearlman, M., Sr. V.P. & Media Dir.--BBDO Canada, Toronto, Canada; *U.S. Private*, pg. 104

Pearson, Bryan, Sr. V.P.-Telecommunications--Millicom International Cellular SA, Bertrange, Luxembourg; *Int'l*, pg. 867

Pearson, Dudley G., Sr. V.P.--Interstate/Johnson Lane Corporation, Charlotte, NC; *U.S. Public*, pg. 910

Pearson, J. Thomas, Sr. V.P.-Tax--RJR Nabisco Holdings Corp., New York, NY; *U.S. Public*, pg. 1354

Pearson, John, Sr. V.P.-Mdsg.--Tractor Supply Co., Nashville, TN; *U.S. Public*, pg. 1627

Pearson, Ronald L., Sr. V.P.--The National Bank of Fredericksburg, Fredericksburg, VA; *U.S. Public*, pg. 1089

Peary, Stephen, Sr. V.P., Sec. & Gen. Counsel--PLM International, Inc., San Francisco, CA; *U.S. Public*, pg. 1241

Peck, Chuck, Sr. V.P.-Mktg., Prods., Organization & Devel.--American Institute of C.P.A.'s Inc., New York, NY; *U.S. Private*, pg. 57

Peck, Diane, Sr. V.P.-Human Resources--Safeway Inc., Pleasanton, CA; *U.S. Public*, pg. 1426

Peck, George, Sr. V.P.-Engrng.--Mylex Corporation, Fremont, CA; *U.S. Public*, pg. 1143

Peck, Thomas A., Sr. V.P.-Mfg.--Starcraft Automotive Group, Inc., Goshen, IN; *U.S. Public*, pg. 1511

Peckham, Barry, Sr. V.P.-Information Systems--A.H. Belo Corporation, Dallas, TX; *U.S. Public*, pg. 209

Pecori, Sergio A., Sr. V.P.--Hanson Engineers Inc., Springfield, IL; *U.S. Private*, pg. 500

Peddicord, Herschel, Sr. V.P.-Mktg., Sls. & Engrng.--Criticare Systems, Inc., Waukesha, WI; *U.S. Public*, pg. 459

Pedersen, Ray, Sr. V.P. & Pres.-Princess Tours--Princess Cruise Lines, Los Angeles, CA; *Int'l*, pg. 1035

Pedersen, Zaid, Chief Fin. Officer & Sr. V.P.--Trygg-Hansa, Stockholm, Sweden; *Int'l*, pg. 1425

Pedrick, James E., Sr. V.P.--ContiFinancial Corporation, New York, NY; *U.S. Public*, pg. 439

Peek, Ron, Sr. V.P.-Opers.--Ingram Merchandising Service Inc., La Vergne, TN; *U.S. Private*, pg. 563

Peel, Michael A., Sr. V.P.-Personnel--General Mills, Inc., Minneapolis, MN; *U.S. Public*, pg. 717

Peelen, Jan, Chm.-Foods Exec. & Dir.-U.S. Foods Business--Unilever Plc, London, United Kingdom; *Int'l*, pg. 1433

Peeler, David, Sr. V.P.--Competitive Media Reporting, New York, NY; *Int'l*, pg. 1447

Peery, Pat, Sr. V.P. & Dir.-Real Estate--Kohl's Corporation, Menomonee Falls, WI; *U.S. Public*, pg. 965

Pefanis, Harry N., Sr. V.P.--Plains Resources Inc., Houston, TX; *U.S. Public*, pg. 1307

Pegg, Daniel O., Sr. V.P.-Pub. Affairs--QUALCOMM, San Diego, CA; *U.S. Public*, pg. 1348

Pegher, R. William, Sr. V.P.--National Marine, Inc., New Orleans, LA; *U.S. Private*, pg. 1135

Pehrson, Gary, Sr. V.P.-Opers.--In Focus Systems, Inc., Wilsonville, OR; *U.S. Public*, pg. 873

Pei, Edward Y.W., Sr. V.P.-Electronic Banking Div.--First Hawaiian Bank, Honolulu, HI; *U.S. Public*, pg. 634

Peirce, Greg, Sr. V.P. & Mgr.-S.E. Region--Heery International, Inc., Atlanta, GA; *U.S. Private*, pg. 519

Peitler, Michael A., Sr. V.P.-Worldwide Sls.--Emulex Corporation, Costa Mesa, CA; *U.S. Public*, pg. 579

Pelagalli, James A., Sr. V.P.--Central Reserve Life Corporation, Strongsville, OH; *U.S. Public*, pg. 326

Pelagalli, James A., Dr., Sr. V.P. & Medical Dir.--Central Reserve Life of North America Insurance Co., Strongsville, OH; *U.S. Public*, pg. 326

Pellegrino, Frank, Sr. V.P.--Grey Entertainment Inc., New York, NY; *U.S. Public*, pg. 764

Pellenaars, P.A.M., Sr. V.P.-Fin. & Admin.--Royal Pakhoed NV, Rotterdam, Netherlands; *Int'l*, pg. 1147

Pelletier, J.L., Sr. V.P.--MidCon Corp., Lombard, IL; *U.S. Public*, pg. 1210

Pelletier, Neville, Sr. V.P.-Consumer--Novartis Nutrition Corporation, Saint Louis Park, MN; *Int'l*, pg. 974

Pena, Kathleen, Sr. V.P.-Financial Svcs.--CIS Technologies, Inc., Tulsa, OK; *U.S. Public*, pg. 1155

Pena, Mardella, Sr. V.P.-H.R.--ADVO, Inc., Windsor, CT; *U.S. Public*, pg. 23

Penchansky, Alan, Sr. V.P.--Edelman Worldwide, Inc., New York, NY; *U.S. Private*, pg. 362

Penczak, Bill, Sr. V.P.-Acct. Mngmt.--Fogarty Klein & Partners, Houston, TX; *U.S. Private*, pg. 415

Pendegast, Michael, Chief Oper. Officer-Florida Office & Sr. V.P.--Weatherby Health Care, Norwalk, CT; *U.S. Private*, pg. 1155

Pendergraft, Jeffrey R., Chief Admin. Officer & Sr. V.P.--Lyondell Petrochemical Company, Houston, TX; *U.S. Public*, pg. 1022

Pendexter, Harold E., Jr., Chief Admin. Officer & Sr. V.P.--USG Corporation, Chicago, IL; *U.S. Public*, pg. 1660

Pendleton, T., Sr. V.P.-Sls. & Mktg.--Corner Brook Pulp & Paper Limited, Corner Brook, Canada; *Int'l*, pg. 761

Pendleton, T.N., Sr. V.P.-Sls. & Mktg./Paper Prods.--Kruger Inc., Montreal, Canada; *Int'l*, pg. 761

Pendleton, T.N., Sr. V.P.-Sls. & Mktg./Paper Prods.--Bromptonville Mill, Bromptonville, Canada; *Int'l*, pg. 761

Pendleton, T.N., Sr. V.P.-Sls. & Mktg.--Kruger Inc., Montreal, Canada; *Int'l*, pg. 761

Pendleton, Terry, Sr. V.P.-Sls.--Trois-Rivieres Mill, Trois-Rivieres, Canada; *Int'l*, pg. 761

Pendrey, J.C., Jr., Chief Fin. Officer, Sr. V.P., Treas. & Sec.--Holder Corporation, Atlanta, GA; *U.S. Private*, pg. 533

Penglase, Frank D., Sr. V.P. & Treas.--The McGraw-Hill Companies, New York, NY; *U.S. Public*, pg. 1069

Peninger, Michael J., Chief Fin. Officer & Sr. V.P.--Fortis Benefits Insurance Company, Kansas City, MO; *Int'l*, pg. 499

Penn, Steve, Sr. V.P.--Colle & McVoy Marketing Communications, Minneapolis, MN; *U.S. Private*, pg. 252

Pennell, G. Clifton, Sr. V.P.-Brands--R.J. Reynolds Tobacco Company, Winston Salem, NC; *U.S. Public*, pg. 1355

Pennella, Frank, Sr. V.P.-Residential Mortgage--Wilmington Savings Fund Society (FSB), Wilmington, DE; *U.S. Public*, pg. 1729

Penniman, Nicholas G., IV, Sr. V.P.-Newspaper Opers.--Pulitzer Publishing Company, Saint Louis, MO; *U.S. Public*, pg. 1343

Pennington, Carl W., Exec. V.P.-Corp. Mdsg.--Albertson's, Inc., Boise, ID; *U.S. Public*, pg. 38

Pennino, Lara, Sr. V.P. & Gen. Mgr.--Edelman Worldwide, Inc., Houston, TX; *U.S. Private*, pg. 362

Penrod, Jack, Sr. V.P. & Grp. Head--Fuji Bank, New York Branch, New York, NY; *Int'l*, pg. 519

Penruddocke, Charles B., Sr. V.P.--F&G Re, Inc., Morristown, NJ; *U.S. Public*, pg. 1659

Pepe, Francis, Chief Fin. Officer & Sr. V.P.--JWK International Corp., Annandale, VA; *U.S. Private*, pg. 579

Pepin, Denis, Sr. V.P.-Sls. & Brokerage--Meridian Technology Leasing Services, Deerfield, IL; *U.S. Private*, pg. 732

Peppard, JoAnne, Sr. V.P. & Creative Dir.--Lowe McAdams Healthcare, New York, NY; *U.S. Private*, pg. 678

Pepper, Douglas S., Sr. V.P. & Treas.--Carboline Co., Saint Louis, MO; *U.S. Public*, pg. 1357

Pepperdine, James, Chief Oper. Officer & Exec. V.P.--Yesawich, Pepperdine & Brown, Orlando, FL; *U.S. Private*, pg. 1195

Pepples, Jr., E.C., Sr. V.P.- Govt. Affairs--Brown & Williamson Tobacco Corp., Louisville, KY; *Int'l*, pg. 111

Percenti, Don, Sr. V.P.-Sls. & Mktg./Balfour--Commemorative Brands, Inc., Austin, TX; *U.S. Private*, pg. 258

Percenti, Don, Sr. V.P.-Sls. & Mktg.--L.G. Balfour Co., Inc., Austin, TX; *U.S. Private*, pg. 258

Percoco, Susan, Sr. V.P.--New Hampshire Insurance Group, New York, NY; *U.S. Public*, pg. 84

Perdue, David, Sr. V.P.-Intl. Affairs--Haggar Corporation, Dallas, TX; *U.S. Public*, pg. 774

Perdue, Sharon, Sr. V.P.-Fin.--Tropical Sportswear International, Tampa, FL; *U.S. Private*, pg. 1105

Perdue, T. Ramon, Sr. V.P.--Disability Operations, Chattanooga, TN; *U.S. Public*, pg. 1338

Pereira, Douglas L., Chief Fin. Officer & Sr. V.P.--Clothestime Stores, Inc., Anaheim, CA; *U.S. Public*, pg. 387

Perelson, Jerome M., Chief Fin. Officer & Sr. V.P.--ContiFinancial Corporation, New York, NY; *U.S. Public*, pg. 439

Perely, Bill, Sr. V.P. & Gen. Mgr.--Dr Pepper/Seven-Up Fountain Foodservice, Dallas, TX; *Int'l*, pg. 248

Perera, Ismael, Sr. V.P.-Oper.--MasTec, Inc., Miami, FL; *U.S. Public*, pg. 1055

Perez, Carl A., Chief Fin. Officer & Sr. V.P.--Perez Trading Co. Inc., Miami, FL; *U.S. Private*, pg. 852

Perez, Michael G., Sr. V.P.--Stainless Incorporated, Deerfield Beach, FL; *U.S. Private*, pg. 1029

Perier, Francois, Sr. V.P.-Chemicals--Elf Aquitane, Paris, France; *Int'l*, pg. 444

Perkins, Bruce D., Sr. V.P.-Provider Affairs & Reengineering--Humana Inc., Louisville, KY; *U.S. Public*, pg. 847

Perkins, James A., Chief Personnel Officer & Sr. V.P.--FDX Corporation, Memphis, TN; *U.S. Public*, pg. 603

Perkins, Paul, Sr. V.P.-Australia--UtiliCorp United Inc., Kansas City, MO; *U.S. Public*, pg. 1700

Perkins, Stephen R., Sr. V.P.--Sterling Commerce, Inc., Dublin, OH; *U.S. Public*, pg. 1515

Perlberg, Mark, Sr. V.P., Pres., Fin. Sls. Mktg. Division--The Check Store, Lakewood, CO; *U.S. Public*, pg. 785

Perlberg, Mark C., Sr. V.P. & Pres.-Fin. Mkt. Div.--John H. Harland Company, Decatur, GA; *U.S. Public*, pg. 785

Perlman, Raymond, Sr. V.P.-Jewelry--Jewelcor Companies, Wilkes-Barre, PA; *U.S. Private*, pg. 587

Perona, Dale F., Sr. V.P. & Sec.-True North Communications Inc.--True North Communications Inc., Chicago, IL; *U.S. Public*, pg. 1641

Perpich, William M., Sr. V.P.--STS Consultants, Inc., Deerfield, IL; *U.S. Private*, pg. 959

Perratzi, Michel, Sr. V.P.-Chemicals--Elf Aquitane, Paris, France; *Int'l*, pg. 444

Perreault, Fernand, Sr. V.P.-Caisse Real Estate Grp.--Caisse de depot et placement du Quebec, Montreal, Canada; *Int'l*, pg. 249

Perreault, Mark S.P., Sr. V.P.-H.R.--The Bank of Bermuda Limited, Hamilton, Bermuda; *Int'l*, pg. 150

Perri, David F., Sr. V.P.--Shared Medical Systems Corporation, Malvern, PA; *U.S. Public*, pg. 1463

Perriello, James J., Sr. V.P.-Subsidiaries--Logicon Syscon Corporation, Falls Church, VA; *U.S. Public*, pg. 1199

Perrier, Louis E., Sr. V.P.--Coastal Refining & Marketing, Wichita, KS; *U.S. Public*, pg. 390

Perrine, Don E., Sr. V.P.--United Missouri Bank Northeast, Monroe City, MO; *U.S. Public*, pg. 1654

Perry, Diane, Sr. V.P.--Edelman Worldwide, Inc., New York, NY; *U.S. Private*, pg. 362

Perry, John W., Sr. V.P.--Terre Haute First National Bank, Terre Haute, IN; *U.S. Public*, pg. 634

Perry, Michael D., Chief Fin. Officer & Sr. Corp. V.P.--A.H. Belo Corporation, Dallas, TX; *U.S. Public*, pg. 209

Perry, Newton A., Sr. V.P.-Refinery Chemicals--Ethyl Corporation, Richmond, VA; *U.S. Public*, pg. 595

Perry, Paul A., Sr. V.P.--Northern Capital Management, Inc., Madison, WI; *U.S. Public*, pg. 1673

Perry, Stephen, Sr. V.P.-Fin.--Care Free Aluminum Products, Inc., Charlotte, MI; *U.S. Private*, pg. 194

Persante, Patricia, Sr. V.P.-Contract Compliance--Wackenhut Corrections Corporation, Palm Beach Gardens, FL; *U.S. Public*, pg. 1731

Persavich, Warren D., Chief Fin. Officer & Sr. V.P.--Banner Aerospace, Inc., Washington, DC; *U.S. Public*, pg. 187

Persson, Ulf, Sr. V.P. & Gen. Auditor--Svedala Industri AB, Malmo, Sweden; *Int'l*, pg. 1323

Peru, Ramiro G., Sr. V.P.-Org. Devel. & Info. Tech.--Phelps Dodge Corporation, Phoenix, AZ; *U.S. Public*, pg. 1286

Perusse, Gary, Sr. V.P.-Risk Mngmt.--Ogden Corporation, New York, NY; *U.S. Public*, pg. 1213

Perz, Joe, Sr. V.P. & Creative Dir.--Beber & Silverstein & Partners, Inc., Miami, FL; *U.S. Private*, pg. 128

Pesch, Jorg, Sr. V.P.--Jagenberg AG, Neuss, Germany; *Int'l*, pg. 1108

Pester, Jack C., Sr. V.P.-Intl. Refining & Mktg.--The Coastal Corporation, Houston, TX; *U.S. Public*, pg. 389

Pester, Jack C., Sr. V.P.--Cosbel Petroleum Corp., Houston, TX; *U.S. Public*, pg. 390

Peterka, John, Sr. V.P.-Fin.--Rittenhouse Inc., Park Ridge, IL; *U.S. Private*, pg. 933

Peterman, Donna C., Sr. V.P. & Dir.-Corp. Communications--PaineWebber Group Incorporated, New York, NY; *U.S. Public*, pg. 1252

Peterman, Donna C., Sr. V.P. & Dir. Corp. Communications--PaineWebber Incorporated, New York, NY; *U.S. Public*, pg. 1252

Peterman, Tom, Sr. V.P. & Gen. Counsel--MGM Grand Hotel, Inc., Las Vegas, NV; *U.S. Public*, pg. 1027

Peternell, Ben C., Sr. V.P.-Human Resources & Corp. Rels.--Harrah's Entertainment, Inc., Memphis, TN; *U.S. Public*, pg. 790

Peters, Arthur W., Sr. V.P. & Gen. Mgr.-Energy--Union Pacific Railroad Company, Omaha, NE; *U.S. Public*, pg. 1668

Peters, Charles E., Jr., Chief Fin. Officer & Sr. V.P.--Burlington Industries, Inc., Greensboro, NC; *U.S. Public*, pg. 268

Peters, Heuricus A., Exec. V.P. & Gen. Mgr.--Osram Sylvania Inc., Malvern, PA; *Int'l*, pg. 1245

Peters, Janet J., Sr. V.P.-Intimate Apparel Prod. Design--VF Corporation, Wyomissing, PA; *U.S. Public*, pg. 1702

Peters, Jeanette, Chief Fin. Officer & Sr. V.P.--Rose's Stores, Inc., Henderson, NC; *U.S. Public*, pg. 1405

Peters, John, Sr. V.P.--TLC Group, Inc., Zeeland, MI; *U.S. Public*, pg. 352

Peters, John E., Sr. V.P., Gen. Counsel & Sec.--Block Drug Company, Inc., Jersey City, NJ; *U.S. Public*, pg. 236

Peters, John S., Sr. V.P.-Opers.--Waxman Industries, Inc., Bedford, OH; *U.S. Public*, pg. 1748

Peters, John S., Sr. V.P.-Opers.--WOC Inc., Bedford, OH; *U.S. Public*, pg. 1748

Peters, John S., Sr. V.P.-Opers.--Waxman USA Inc., Bedford, OH; *U.S. Public*, pg. 1749

Peters, Paul, Sr. V.P.--Hibernia Corporation, New Orleans, LA; *U.S. Public*, pg. 825

Petersen, Wally, Sr. V.P.-Corp. Affairs Worldwide--Leo Burnett Company, Inc., Chicago, IL; *U.S. Private*, pg. 183

Peterson, Brent, Sr. V.P.-Bus. Systems--Green Tree Financial Corporation, Saint Paul, MN; *U.S. Public*, pg. 761

Peterson, C.T., Sr. V.P.--DOALL Company, Des Plaines, IL; *U.S. Private*, pg. 337

Peterson, Coleman, Sr. V.P.-Human Resources--Wal-Mart Stores, Inc., Bentonville, AR; *U.S. Public*, pg. 1732

Peterson, David, Sr. V.P. & Sec.--Rockford Products Corp., Rockford, IL; *U.S. Private*, pg. 938

Peterson, Erick, Grp. Sr. V.P.-Cash Mngmt.--LaSalle National Bank, Chicago, IL; *Int'l*, pg. 10

Peterson, Florence M., Sr. V.P.--American Arbitration Association, New York, NY; *U.S. Private*, pg. 50

Peterson, George, III, Sr. V.P.--OppenheimerFunds Distributor, Inc., New York, NY; *U.S. Private*, pg. 818

Peterson, Jeffrey H., Sr. V.P.-Mktg.--John Deere Industrial Equipment Company, Moline, IL; *U.S. Public*, pg. 492

Peterson, Jerry, Chief Lending Officer & Sr. V.P.--Somerset Savings Bank, Somerville, MA; *U.S. Public*, pg. 1484

Peterson, Kim, Sr. V.P.-Human Resources--C. Brewer & Company, Limited, Honolulu, HI; *U.S. Private*, pg. 190

Peterson, Larry, Chief Fin. Officer & Sr. V.P.-Fin.--Sunglass Hut International, Coral Gables, FL; *U.S. Public*, pg. 1535

Peterson, M. Robert, Chief Fin. Officer & Sr. V.P.-Fin.--Air Canada, Saint-Laurent, Canada; *Int'l*, pg. 36

Peterson, Paul R., Sr. V.P., Gen. Counsel & Sec.--Technology Solutions Company (TSC), Chicago, IL; *U.S. Public*, pg. 1564

Peterson, Paul T., Sr. V.P.-Servicer Div.--Federal Home Loan Mortgage Corporation, Mc Lean, VA; *U.S. Public*, pg. 615

Peterson, Pete, Sr. V.P.--Ploof Truck Lines, Inc., Jacksonville, FL; *U.S. Private*, pg. 872

Peterson, Robert H., Chief Oper. Officer-Metallurgical & Sr. V.P.--Sunshine Mining And Refining Company, Boise, ID; *U.S. Public*, pg. 1536

Peterson, Stacy, Sr. V.P.--Western Marketing-Los Angeles Region, Sherman Oaks, CA; *U.S. Public*, pg. 650

Peterson, Wayne S., Chief Fin. Officer, Sr. V.P. & Sec.--Buttrey Food & Drug Company, Great Falls, MT; *U.S. Public*, pg. 271

Peterson, William E., Sr. V.P. & Gen. Counsel--Sierra Pacific Resources, Reno, NV; *U.S. Public*, pg. 1470

Petit, Geoffrey, Chief Fin. Officer, V.P. & Treas.--Fina, Inc., Dallas, TX; *Int'l*, pg. 1044

Petit, Mary E., Sr. V.P.-Opers.--Barr Laboratories Inc., Pomona, NY; *U.S. Public*, pg. 191

Petitclerc, Jean-Charles, Sr. V.P.-Systems & Support Services--Montreal Trustco, Montreal, Canada; *Int'l*, pg. 155

Petitti, Tony, Sr. V.P.-Bus. Affairs & Programming--CBS Sports Div., New York, NY; *U.S. Public*, pg. 274

Petkus, Donald A., Sr. V.P.--Unicom Corporation, Chicago, IL; *U.S. Public*, pg. 1664

Petkus, Donald A., Pres.-Unicom Thermal Tech. & Sr. V.P.--ComEd, Chicago, IL; *U.S. Public*, pg. 1664

Petmecky, William M., Sr. V.P. & Sec.--Seneca Resources Corp., Houston, TX; *U.S. Public*, pg. 1156

Petrie, Michael J., Sr. V.P.--Commerce Bancshares, Inc., Kansas City, MO; *U.S. Public*, pg. 409

Petrillo, Alfred B., Jr., Sr. V.P.-Store Plng.--Ames Department Stores, Inc., Rocky Hill, CT; *U.S. Public*, pg. 99

Petrillo, Nancy, Sr. V.P.-Fin.--Edelman Public Relations Worldwide, Chicago, IL; *U.S. Private*, pg. 362

Petrini, David J., Chief Fin. Officer & Sr. V.P.--Providian Financial Corporation, San Francisco, CA; *U.S. Public*, pg. 1338

Petrocelli, Philip V., Sr. V.P.-Western Opers.--OHM Remediation Services Corp., Findlay, OH; *U.S. Public*, pg. 1208

Petrosino, Gary C., Sr. V.P.--Chubb & Son, Inc., Warren, NJ; *U.S. Public*, pg. 355

Petrovich, Michael J., Sr. V.P.-Special Projects--New York Life Insurance Company, New York, NY; *U.S. Private*, pg. 794

Petrula, Stephen, Sr. V.P.--The Bank of New York Company, Inc., New York, NY; *U.S. Public*, pg. 178

Petterson, David S., Sr. V.P. & Corp. Controller--Costco Wholesale, Issaquah, WA; *U.S. Public*, pg. 451

Petterson, John S., Sr. V.P.-Corp. Sls.--Tiffany & Co., New York, NY; *U.S. Public*, pg. 1608

Pettersson, Ake, Sr. V.P.-Corp. Audit & Security--Telefonaktiebolaget LM Ericsson, Stockholm, Sweden; *Int'l*, pg. 1363

Pettersson, Mats, Sr. V.P.-Bus. Devel.--Pharmacia & Upjohn, Inc., Windsor, United Kingdom; *Int'l*, pg. 1047

Pettinella, Nicholas A., Chief Fin. Officer, Sr. V.P., Treas. & Asst. Sec.--Intermetrics, Inc., Burlington, MA; *U.S. Private*, pg. 567

Pettingill, Richard R., Sr. V.P.-San Francisco Area--Kaiser Permanente, Oakland, CA; *U.S. Private*, pg. 605

Pettis, Chuck, Sr. V.P.-Brand Solutions--EvansGroup, Seattle, WA; *U.S. Private*, pg. 385

Pettis, Chuck, Sr. V.P.--BrandSolutions, Seattle, WA; *U.S. Private*, pg. 385

Peverell, Ed, Sr. V.P.-Sls. & Support--Network Equipment Technologies, Inc., Redwood City, CA; *U.S. Public*, pg. 1166

Peyton, Dean L., Sr. V.P. & Comml. Banker--Brenton Banks, Inc., Des Moines, IA; *U.S. Public*, pg. 251

Pfautsch, George E., Chief Fin. Officer & Sr. V.P.--Potlatch Corporation, Spokane, WA; *U.S. Public*, pg. 1318

Pfeiffer, Gary L., Sr. V.P.-Fin. & Commercial Svcs.--Marathon Ashland Petroleum LLC, Findlay, OH; *U.S. Public*, pg. 139

Pfeiffer, Paul A., Sr. V.P.- Production Services--Jepson-Murray Advertising, Lansing, MI; *U.S. Private*, pg. 586

Pfeiffer, Robert N., Sr. V.P.-H.R. & Customer Opers.--St. Paul Bancorp, Inc., Chicago, IL; *U.S. Public*, pg. 1428

Pfeiffer, Robert N., Sr. V.P.--St. Paul Federal Bank for Savings, Chicago, IL; *U.S. Public*, pg. 1428

Pflimlin, Tom, Sr. V.P.-Acct. Services--Western International Media Corporation, Los Angeles, CA; *U.S. Private*, pg. 1165

Pharand, Gilles, Sr. V.P.-Corp. Affairs, Gen. Counsel & Sec.--Domtar Inc., Montreal, Canada; *Int'l*, pg. 416

Pharr, Linda, Sr. V.P. & Acct. Mng. Dir.--Young & Rubicam New York, New York, NY; *U.S. Private*, pg. 1198

Phelan, William S., Sr. V.P.--The Euclid Chemical Company, Cleveland, OH; *U.S. Public*, pg. 1358

Philip, Craig, Chief Oper. Officer & Sr. V.P.--Ingram Barge Company, Nashville, TN; *U.S. Private*, pg. 563

Philipps, Jeffry, Sr. V.P.-Retail Div.--Carr Gottstein Foods, Anchorage, AK; *U.S. Public*, pg. 308

Phillion, Joseph P., Sr. V.P.--Somerset Savings Bank, Somerville, MA; *U.S. Public*, pg. 1484

Phillips, B. Frank, Sr. V.P.--Weatherby Locums Inc., Fort Lauderdale, FL; *U.S. Private*, pg. 1155

Phillips, Benny J., Sr. V.P.-Intl.--IPL Energy Inc., Calgary, Canada; *Int'l*, pg. 651

Phillips, Bill, Sr. V.P.-Sls.--The Coleman Company, Inc., Golden, CO; *U.S. Private*, pg. 690

Phillips, Douglas M., Chief Fin. Officer & Sr. V.P.-Fin.--MDS Inc., Etobicoke, Canada; *Int'l*, pg. 826
Phillips, Gary, Sr. V.P.--Electro Rent Corporation, Van Nuys, CA; *U.S. Public*, pg. 568
Phillips, Joe, Sr. V.P.-Mktg.--Champion Products Inc., Winston Salem, NC; *U.S. Public*, pg. 1433
Phillips, John P., Sr. V.P.-Worldwide Technology--General Semiconductor, Inc., Melville, NY; *U.S. Public*, pg. 726
Phillips, John, Jr., V.P.-Mktg. & Sls.--McKee Foods Corporation, Collegedale, TN; *U.S. Private*, pg. 723
Phillips, Kevin, Sr. V.P.-Stores--Office Depot Inc., Delray Beach, FL; *U.S. Public*, pg. 1212
Phillips, M. A., Sr. V.P. & Controller--Brown Marketing Communications, Chicago, IL; *U.S. Private*, pg. 174
Phillips, Peggy, Sr. V.P. & Dir.-Pharmaceutical Devel.--Immunex Corporation, Seattle, WA; *U.S. Public*, pg. 871
Phillips, Richard B., Sr. V.P.-Tech.--International Paper Company, Purchase, NY; *U.S. Public*, pg. 901
Phillips, Robert L., Sr. V.P.--Huitt-Zollars, Inc., Dallas, TX; *U.S. Private*, pg. 547
Phillips, Tony, Sr. V.P.--Willis Faber North America, Inc.-Florida, Miami, FL; *Int'l*, pg. 1503
Phillips, William, Sr. V.P.-Law & Gen. Counsel--GenCorp Inc., Fairlawn, OH; *U.S. Public*, pg. 705
Philmon, Carolyn, Sr. V.P.-Loan Services--Coast Savings Financial, Inc., Los Angeles, CA; *U.S. Public*, pg. 388
Philpott, Ted, Sr. V.P.-Sls.--Lexington Furniture Industries, Lexington, NC; *U.S. Private*, pg. 432
Phinney, John, Sr. V.P.-Surety Bond Div.--National Union Fire Ins. Co. of Pittsburgh, Pa., New York, NY; *U.S. Public*, pg. 84
Phippen, John T., Chief Info. Officer & Sr. V.P.-Info. Sys.--Mattel, Inc., El Segundo, CA; *U.S. Public*, pg. 1057
Phipps, Leland, Sr. V.P.--BTG, Inc., Fairfax, VA; *U.S. Public*, *pg. 164*
Piasetzky, Joshua, Chief Tech. Officer & Sr. V.P.--ECI Telecom Ltd., Petah Tiqwa, Israel; *Int'l*, pg. 643
Piccinninni, Michael, Sr. V.P.- Corp. Fin.--Quantum Media International, Inc., New York, NY; *U.S. Private*, pg. 899
Picco, Ronald C., Sr. V.P.-Opers.--Western Staff Services, Walnut Creek, CA; *U.S. Public*, pg. 1760
Picillo, Phil, Sr. V.P.--UST Corporation, Boston, MA; *U.S. Public*, pg. 1660
Pickering, Arthur W., Sr. V.P.-Domestic Mktg.--National Western Life Insurance Company, Austin, TX; *U.S. Public*, pg. 1161
Pickert, Richard W., Chief Fin. Officer & Sr. V.P.--American Media, Inc., Lake Worth, FL; *U.S. Public*, pg. 87
Pickler, W.H., III, Sr. V.P.-Mngmt. Information Systems--Ingram Book Company, La Vergne, TN; *U.S. Private*, pg. 563
Picknelly, Paul, Sr. V.P.--Peter Pan Bus Lines, Inc., Springfield, MA; *U.S. Private*, pg. 856
Pickryl, W. Jeffrey, Sr. V.P.-Commercial Lending--Liberty Bancorp, Inc., Oklahoma City, OK; *U.S. Public*, pg. 174
Picot, Claude, Pres.-Containers Div. & Sr. V.P.--Saint-Gobain, Courbevoie, France; *Int'l*, pg. 1170
Picquet, W.R., Sr. V.P.-North America--Gulf Canada Resources Ltd., Calgary, Canada; *Int'l*, pg. 577
Pictaggi, Phil, Sr. V.P.-Opers. & Bus. Devel.-Universal Studios Home Video--Universal Pictures, Universal City, CA; *Int'l*, pg. 1216
Pidgeon, Ralph A., Sr. V.P.--Trustco Bank, N.A., Schenectady, NY; *U.S. Public*, pg. 1643
Piell, Katherine, Sr. V.P.--Summit Bancorp, Princeton, NJ; *U.S. Public*, pg. 1527
Piepenburg, Sheldon, Sr. V.P.-Surveying & Mapping--L. Robert Kimball & Associates, Ebensburg, PA; *U.S. Private*, pg. 619
Pieper, Roel, Sr. V.P. & Gen. Mgr.-Worldwide Sls. & Mktg.--Tandem Computers Inc., Cupertino, CA; *U.S. Public*, pg. 417
Pierce, Garrett E., Sr. V.P. & Chief Fin. Officer--Sensormatic Electronics Corporation, Boca Raton, FL; *U.S. Public*, pg. 1457
Pierce, John S., Jr., Sr. V.P. & Mgr.-Commercial Accts.--Willis Corroon Corp. of Massachusetts, Boston, MA; *Int'l*, *pg. 1506*
Pierce, Matthew V., Sr. V.P.--Acadian Asset Management, Boston, MA; *U.S. Public*, pg. 1672
Pierce, Michael C., Sr. V.P.-Gen. Services--Coast Savings Financial, Inc., Los Angeles, CA; *U.S. Public*, pg. 388
Pierce, R. E., Sr. V.P.--Kennecott Holdings Corporation, Magna, UT; *Int'l*, pg. 1119
Pierce, William L., Sr. V.P.--Trenwick America Reinsurance Corporation, Stamford, CT; *U.S. Public*, pg. 1634
Pierce, William M., Chief Fin. Officer & Sr. V.P.--Florida Panthers Holdings, Inc., Fort Lauderdale, FL; *U.S. Public*, *pg. 654*
Pierson, Rodney, Chief Fin. Officer, Sr. V.P. & Sec.--SAFECO Corporation, Seattle, WA; *U.S. Public*, pg. 1423
Pieters, H.G.J., Sr. V.P.-Information Systems--AEGON Nederland N.V., Hague, Netherlands; *Int'l*, pg. 26
Pietrangelo, James E., Sr. V.P.--Charter One Financial, Inc., Cleveland, OH; *U.S. Public*, pg. 336
Pietropoli, Vittorio, Sr. V.P.--Orthofix International N.V., Curacao, Netherlands Antilles; *Int'l*, pg. 1011
Pietroski, Joseph J., Sr. V.P. & Gen. Counsel--Manulife Financial, Toronto, Canada; *Int'l*, pg. 840
Pietrowski, Philip E., Sr. V.P.-North American Opers.--The Cerplex Group, Inc., Tustin, CA; *U.S. Public*, pg. 332
Pifer, Jay S., Sr. V.P.--Allegheny Power System, Inc., Hagerstown, MD; *U.S. Public*, pg. 42
Pignatelli, James N., Chief Oper. Officer & Sr. V.P.-Bus. Devel.--Tucson Electric Power Company, Tucson, AZ; *U.S. Public*, pg. 1670
Pignatellis, James S., Chief Oper. Officer & Sr. V.P.--UniSource Energy Corporation, Tucson, AZ; *U.S. Public*, pg. 1670
Pijanowski, Brian, V.P.-Buying & Mdsg.--Shaw's Supermarkets, Inc., East Bridgewater, MA; *Int'l*, pg. 1170
Pike, Bob, Sr. V.P.-Mtel H.R.--Mobile Telecommunications Technologies Corp., Jackson, MS; *U.S. Public*, pg. 1120
Pike, Tyrone, Sr. V.P. & Chief Technology Officer--UB Networks, Santa Clara, CA; *Int'l*, pg. 924
Pil, Geo, Corp. V.P.--N.V. Bekaert S.A., Kortrijk, Belgium; *Int'l*, pg. 183
Pile, Susan, Sr. V.P.-Worldwide Publicity & Field Promo.--Metro-Goldwyn-Mayer Inc., Santa Monica, CA; *U.S. Public*, pg. 1101
Pilgrim, Dale, Sr. V.P.-Engrng.--SyQuest Technology, Inc., Fremont, CA; *U.S. Public*, pg. 1550
Pillings-Rinker, Laurie, Sr. V.P. & Client Svcs. Dir.--Promotion House, San Francisco, CA; *U.S. Private*, pg. 1166
Pilliter, Charles J., Pres. & Sr. V.P.-Northern California--Certified Grocers of California, Los Angeles, CA; *U.S. Private*, pg. 226
Pilon, Lawrence J., Sr. V.P.-Human Resources--Whitman Corporation, Rolling Meadows, IL; *U.S. Public*, pg. 1766
Pineda, Prudencio, Sr. V.P.-Distr.--Minyard Food Stores, Inc., Coppell, TX; *U.S. Private*, pg. 752
Pines, Ellis, Sr. V.P.--Stackig Advertising and Public Relations, Mc Lean, VA; *U.S. Private*, pg. 1028
Pinion, Joe D., Sr. V.P.--Health Management Associates, Inc., Naples, FL; *U.S. Public*, pg. 802
Pintsov, David, Dr., Sr. V.P.--Mitek Systems, Inc., San Diego, CA; *U.S. Public*, pg. 1117
Pionke, Edward J., Chief Fin. Officer & Sr. V.P.-Fin., Admin. & Intl. Fin.--Nelson Westerberg, Inc., Elk Grove Village, IL; *U.S. Private*, pg. 1163
Pionke, Edward J., Chief Fin. Officer & V.P.-Fin.--Nelson Westerberg Atlas, Mableton, GA; *U.S. Private*, pg. 1164
Pionke, Edward J., Chief Fin. Officer & Sr. V.P.-Fin.--Nelson Westerberg of Illinois, Elk Grove Village, IL; *U.S. Private*, *pg. 1164*
Pionke, Edward J., Chief Fin. Officer & Sr. V.P.-Fin.--Nelson Westerberg Atlas, Carrollton, TX; *U.S. Private*, pg. 1164
Pionke, Edward J., Chief Fin. Officer & Sr. V.P.-Fin.--Nelson Westerberg International Inc., Elk Grove Village, IL; *U.S. Private*, pg. 1164
Pipes, Keith B., Chief Fin. Officer & Sr. V.P.--Sierra Capital Management, Northridge, CA; *U.S. Public*, pg. 1742
Pipitone, Joseph F., Sr. V.P. & Sec.--The Citizens National Bank, Laurel, MD; *U.S. Public*, pg. 1089
Pirnie, Douglas D., Jr., Sr. V.P.-Sls. & Mktg.--IMG, New York, NY; *U.S. Private*, pg. 555
Piro, Lawrence D., M.D., Sr. V.P.-Professional Affairs--Salick Health Care, Inc., Los Angeles, CA; *Int'l*, pg. 1524
Pirrie, David, Dir.-Inter. Banking & Private Banking & Fin. Services--Lloyds TSB Group PLC, London, United Kingdom; *Int'l*, pg. 812
Pirtle, W.N., Sr. V.P.-Oklahoma City--Oklahoma Natural Gas Company, Tulsa, OK; *U.S. Public*, pg. 1226
Pirtle, William B., Sr. V.P.-Mktg. & Sls.--Barclay Furniture Company, Sherman, MS; *U.S. Public*, pg. 974
Piske, Thomas, Sr. V.P.-Private Banking--Liechtenstein Global Trust Limited, Vaduz, Liechtenstein; *Int'l*, pg. 809
Piskin, Joe, Sr. V.P.-Sls.--Intercontinental Branded Apparel, Buffalo, NY; *U.S. Public*, pg. 796
Pitcher, Max G., Sr. V.P.--Du Pont (E.I. Du Pont De Nemours & Co.), Wilmington, DE; *U.S. Public*, pg. 530
Pitcherella, Tom, Sr. V.P.--The McClure Group, Wayne, PA; *U.S. Private*, pg. 719
Pitkowsky, Murray, Chief Fin. Officer, Sr. V.P. & Treas.--Datascope Corp., Montvale, NJ; *U.S. Public*, pg. 487
Pitkowsky, Murray, Sr. V.P.--Datascope Corp., Montvale, NJ; *U.S. Public*, pg. 487
Pitluck, Morris, Sr. V.P. & Res. Dir.--Bernstein-Rein Advertising, Inc., Kansas City, MO; *U.S. Private*, pg. 137
Pitlyk, Paul, Sr. V.P.--NationsBank of St. Louis, Saint Louis, MO; *U.S. Public*, pg. 1164
Pitman Schmidt, Robert, Sr. V.P.--Harold M. Pitman Co., Inc., Totowa, NJ; *U.S. Private*, pg. 867
Pittroff, Pete, Sr. V.P.-Sls.--Duron, Inc., Beltsville, MD; *U.S. Private*, pg. 349
Pitts, Bob, Sr. V.P. & Div. Dir.--PENCO-Ohio, Worthington, OH; *Int'l*, pg. 1508
Pitts, L. Ray, Jr., Sr. V.P.-Construction--Willis Corroon Corp. of Texas, Dallas, TX; *Int'l*, pg. 1507
Pitts, Virginia M., 1st Sr. V.P. & Dir.-Human Resources--J. Baker, Inc., Canton, MA; *U.S. Public*, pg. 167
Pittsman, Santo J., Chief Fin. Officer & Sr. V.P.--MobileComm, Ridgefield Park, NJ; *U.S. Public*, pg. 1120
Pitzel, Bernie, Sr. V.P. & Exec. Creative Dir.--Grant/Jacoby, Inc., Chicago, IL; *U.S. Private*, pg. 470
Piza, Stanley J., Sr. V.P.--Alloy Products Corp, Waukesha, WI; *U.S. Private*, pg. 42
Plaisance, Melissa, Sr. V.P.-Fin. & Pub. Affairs--Safeway Inc., Pleasanton, CA; *U.S. Public*, pg. 1426
Plangere, Jules L., III, Sr. V.P.--Press Communications, LLC, Wall, NJ; *U.S. Private*, pg. 882
Plante, Arnold, Sr. V.P.--Keywell Corporation, Chicago, IL; *U.S. Private*, pg. 619
Platt, Donald H., Chief Fin. Officer & Sr. V.P.--U.S. Office Products Company, Washington, DC; *U.S. Public*, pg. 1686
Platt, Jim, Sr. V.P.-Corp. Affairs--News America Publishing Inc., New York, NY; *Int'l*, pg. 925
Platt, Ron, Sr. V.P.-Sls.--Hutch Sports USA, Inc., Hebron, KY; *U.S. Public*, pg. 1354
Plattner, Jim, Chief Fin. Officer & Sr. V.P.--J. Brown/LMC Group, Stamford, CT; *U.S. Public*, pg. 764
Plaxe, Jack R., Chief Fin. Officer & Sr. V.P.--PAXAR Corporation, White Plains, NY; *U.S. Public*, pg. 1266
Plazonja, Jonathan, Sr. V.P. & Assoc. Creative Dir.--Hill, Holliday, Connors, Cosmopulos, Inc., Boston, MA; *U.S. Private*, pg. 529
Plepler, Richard L., Sr. V.P.-Corp. Communication--Home Box Office, Inc., New York, NY; *U.S. Public*, pg. 1612
Plesnicher, Carl J., Jr., Sr. V.P.-Human Resources--Cooper Industries, Inc., Houston, TX; *U.S. Public*, pg. 442
Pless, Judith, Sr. V.P.-Intl. Bus. Devel.--Showtime Networks Inc., New York, NY; *U.S. Private*, pg. 779
Plimpton, Rodney B., Sr. V.P.-H.R.--American Electric Power Service Corp., Columbus, OH; *U.S. Public*, pg. 72
Plimpton, Thomas E., Sr. V.P.--Paccar Inc., Bellevue, WA; *U.S. Public*, pg. 1246
Ploor, E.A., Sr. V.P.-Data Services--Auto-Owners Insurance, Lansing, MI; *U.S. Private*, pg. 100
Plott, Cody, Sr. V.P.-Bus. Devel.--Airport Group International, Inc., Glendale, CA; *U.S. Public*, pg. 1009
Plum, Dave, Sr. V.P.-Bus. Opers.--Tapemark, Saint Paul, MN; *U.S. Private*, pg. 1068
Plummer, Jerry L., Sr. V.P.-Human Resources & Corp. Support--American United Life Insurance Company, Indianapolis, IN; *U.S. Private*, pg. 64
Plunk, Stephen D., Sr. V.P.-Opers. & Credit--Liberty Bancorp, Inc., Oklahoma City, OK; *U.S. Public*, pg. 174
Pluss, Werner, Sr. V.P.-Petroleum & Petrochemicals--SGS Societe Generale de Surveillance Holding S.A., Geneva, Switzerland; *Int'l*, pg. 1153
Poad, William J., Sr. V.P.--Lester B. Knight & Associates, Inc., Chicago, IL; *U.S. Private*, pg. 626
Poad, William J., Sr. V.P.--Knight Architects Engineers Planners, Inc., Chicago, IL; *U.S. Private*, pg. 626
Pode, John S., Sr. V.P. & Pres.- Comet Rice Div.--American Rice Inc., Houston, TX; *U.S. Public*, pg. 591
Poehler, Patricia A., Sr. V.P.-Admin.--United Farm Family Life Insurance Co., Indianapolis, IN; *U.S. Private*, pg. 1122
Poehlmann, Kevin C., Sr. V.P.-New Bus. Devel.--George Uhe Co., Inc., Paramus, NJ; *U.S. Private*, pg. 1115
Poeschel, Gordon P., Ph.D., Sr. V.P.-Mktg./Crop Protection Agriculture Div.--Bayer Corporation, Pittsburgh, PA; *Int'l*, pg. 172
Pogge, Kirk H., V.P.-Admin--Grassland Equipment & Irrigation Corp., Blasdell, NY; *U.S. Private*, pg. 471
Pohlman, James J., Sr. V.P.-Fin. & Admin.--American Home Products Corporation, Madison, NJ; *U.S. Public*, pg. 79
Poho, Juhani, Chief Fin. Officer & Sr. V.P.--Tamrock Corp., Tampere, Finland; *Int'l*, pg. 1352
Poindexter, Randy, Sr. V.P.-Mktg.--Bojangles' Restaraunts, Inc., Charlotte, NC; *U.S. Private*, pg. 154
Poissant, Gerald R., Sr. V.P.-Taxes & Fin. Plng.--Taubman Centers, Inc., Bloomfield Hills, MI; *U.S. Public*, pg. 1561
Pokorny, Gerold, Corp. V.P. & Grp. Exec.--Electronic Devices and Materials, San Carlos, CA; *U.S. Public*, pg. 1003
Pol, Anne, Sr. V.P.-H.R.--Trex Medical Corporation, Danbury, CT; *U.S. Public*, pg. 1595
Polacheck, Jerry, Exec. V.P.-Sls.--Reliable Knitting Works, Milwaukee, WI; *U.S. Private*, pg. 920
Polack, Valerie, Sr. V.P.--Acme Poultry Company, Inc., Renton, WA; *U.S. Private*, pg. 13
Poland, Jeffrey, Sr. V.P.-Fin. & Acctg.--MATRIXX Marketing Inc., Cincinnati, OH; *U.S. Public*, pg. 368
Polark, Roger L., Chief Fin. Officer & Sr. V.P.--Walgreen Co., Deerfield, IL; *U.S. Public*, pg. 1733
Polich, Michael L., Sr. V.P.--Harvard Industries, Inc., Tampa, FL; *U.S. Public*, pg. 796
Polito, Ronald, Sr. V.P.-Info. Svcs.--Grey Directory Marketing Inc., Chicago, IL; *U.S. Public*, pg. 764
Polizzi, John A., Sr. V.P.-MIS--Horace Small Apparel Company, Nashville, TN; *Int'l*, pg. 635
Pollack, Gerald D., Chief Fin. Officer & Sr. V.P.--Rayonier Inc., Stamford, CT; *U.S. Public*, pg. 1363
Pollack, Marv, Sr. V.P. & Strategy Devel. Dir.--Grant/Jacoby, Inc., Chicago, IL; *U.S. Private*, pg. 470
Pollard, Frank W., Chief Information Officer & Sr. V.P.--The Allstate Corporation, Northbrook, IL; *U.S. Public*, pg. 55
Pollard, James T., Chief Information Officer & Sr. V.P.--Tech Data Corporation, Clearwater, FL; *U.S. Public*, pg. 1562
Pollini, Jacqueline, Sr. V.P--Cline, Davis & Mann, Inc., New York, NY; *U.S. Private*, pg. 246
Pollnow, C., Chief Fin. Officer & Sr. V.P.--Simpson Investment Co., Seattle, WA; *U.S. Private*, pg. 1003
Polsivelli, Perry, Sr. V.P.-Tech. Svcs.--Mobile Technology Inc., Los Angeles, CA; *U.S. Private*, pg. 754
Polsky, Barbara S., Sr. V.P. & Gen. Counsel--Aames Financial Corporation, Los Angeles, CA; *U.S. Public*, pg. 12
Pomerantz, Saul, Chief Fin. Officer, Sr. V.P. & Sec.--Movie Star, Inc., New York, NY; *U.S. Public*, pg. 1140
Pompe, Raymond J., Sr. V.P.-Engrng. & Construction Grp.--International Technology Corporation, Monroeville, PA; *U.S. Public*, pg. 907
Pond, Dale C., Sr. V.P.-Mktg.--Lowe's Companies, Inc., North Wilkesboro, NC; *U.S. Public*, pg. 1015
Pond, Fred, Sr. V.P.-Mktg.--Ridge Tool Co., Elyria, OH; *U.S. Public*, pg. 574
Pong, Walter, Sr. V.P.-MIS--C & S Wholesale Grocery Inc., Brattleboro, VT; *U.S. Private*, pg. 192
Pongress, Andrew J., Sr. V.P.--Marketing Support, Incorporated, Chicago, IL; *U.S. Private*, pg. 705
Pongsuwan, Sornchai, Sr. V.P.--The Industrial Finance Corporation of Thailand, Bangkok, Thailand; *Int'l*, pg. 677
Pont, Neil F., Sr. V.P.-Sls.--Amwest Insurance Group, Inc., Calabasas, CA; *U.S. Public*, pg. 106
Ponton, Ellis E., Sr. V.P. & Gen. Mgr.-SemiConductor Group--SpeedFan International, Inc., Chandler, AZ; *U.S. Public*, pg. 1497
Poole, Charles, Sr. V.P.--Mason & Hanger Corporation, Inc., Lexington, KY; *U.S. Private*, pg. 711
Poole, Gary, Sr. V.P. & Res. Dir.--Lois/EJL New York, New York, NY; *U.S. Public*, pg. 1011
Poole, Larry, Sr. V.P.--Policy Management Systems Corporation, Blythewood, SC; *U.S. Public*, pg. 1314
Pope, Lydia, Sr. V.P. & Acct. Plng. Dir.-Insights Grp.--Young & Rubicam New York, New York, NY; *U.S. Private*, pg. 1198
Popky, Dan, Sr. V.P.-Fin.--Allied Holdings, Inc., Decatur, GA; *U.S. Public*, pg. 48
Popky, Dan, Sr. V.P.-Fin.--Allied Automotive Group, Decatur, GA; *U.S. Public*, pg. 48
Porio, Sal, Sr. V.P.-Burlington House Catlin Farish--Burlington House Fabrics Group, New York, NY; *U.S. Public*, pg. 268

Porkert, Helmut F., Ph.D., Sr. V.P.-Matls. Mngmt.--Bayer Corporation, Pittsburgh, PA; *Int'l*, pg. 172

Porter, Abel, Sr. V.P.-Intermountain Reg.--Smith's Food & Drug Centers, Inc., Salt Lake City, UT; *U.S. Public*, pg. 1103

Porter, Carl W., Chief Oper. Officer & Sr. V.P.--Southeastern Michigan Gas Enterprises, Inc., Port Huron, MI; *U.S. Public*, pg. 1489

Porter, Clyde, Sr. V.P.-Construction--Allen & Ohara, Inc., Memphis, TN; *U.S. Private*, pg. 36

Porter, Daniel, Sr. V.P.-Global Opers.--Telxon Corporation, Akron, OH; *U.S. Public*, pg. 1573

Porter, David, Sr. V.P.--Wisconsin Energy Corporation, Milwaukee, WI; *U.S. Public*, pg. 1773

Porter, David K., Sr. V.P.--Wisconsin Electric Power Company, Milwaukee, WI; *U.S. Public*, pg. 1773

Porter, David W., Sr. V.P.--Zenith Insurance Company, Woodland Hills, CA; *U.S. Public*, pg. 1791

Porter, Marjorie, Sr. V.P. & Grp. Acct. Dir.--DMB&B New York, New York, NY; *U.S. Private*, pg. 302

Porter, Robert W., Sr. V.P.-Mktg./North America--Deere & Company, Moline, IL; *U.S. Public*, pg. 491

Porter, William G., Sr. V.P.--Hayes, Seay, Mattern & Mattern, Inc., Roanoke, VA; *U.S. Private*, pg. 513

Portes, Paulo, Sr. V.P.-Fin.--Cervejarias Kaiser Brasil Ltda., Campinas, Brazil; *Int'l*, pg. 279

Porth, Susan E., Chief Fin. Officer & Sr. V.P.-Corp. Svcs.--Kaiser Permanente, Oakland, CA; *U.S. Private*, pg. 605

Porto, Bryan D., Sr. V.P.--MPSI Systems Inc., Tulsa, OK; *U.S. Public*, pg. 1027

Posa, Sandy, Sr. V.P.-Bus. Devel.--Kraft Foods, Inc., Northfield, IL; *U.S. Public*, pg. 1287

Posluszny, Joseph, Sr. V.P.--Erisco, Inc., New York, NY; *U.S. Public*, pg. 395

Posner, Jackie, Sr. V.P. & Acct. Plng. Dir.-Insights Grp.--Young & Rubicam New York, New York, NY; *U.S. Private*, pg. 1198

Posner, Ken, Sr. V.P.-Fin.--Hyatt Corporation, Chicago, IL; *U.S. Private*, pg. 551

Posner, Lawrence E., M.D., Sr. V.P.-Pharmaceutical Devel./Pharaceutical Div.--Bayer Corporation, Pittsburgh, PA; *Int'l*, pg. 172

Posner, Lawrence E., MD, Sr. V.P.-Fin.--Bayer Corporation/Pharmaceutical Division, West Haven, CT; *Int'l*, pg. 173

Poss, G.A., Sr. V.P.--Miller Freeman Inc., San Francisco, CA; *Int'l*, pg. 1443

Poss, Richard L., Sr. V.P.-Organization & Mngmt. Devel.--National Computer Systems, Eden Prairie, MN; *U.S. Public*, pg. 1155

Post, David P., Sr. V.P.-Steel Commercial--Bethlehem Steel Corporation, Bethlehem, PA; *U.S. Public*, pg. 226

Post, Tony, Sr. V.P.-Mktg. & Gen. Mgr.--The Rockport Company, Marlborough, MA; *U.S. Public*, pg. 1370

Potchen, Peter K., Sr. V.P. & Gen. Auditor--Keycorp, Cleveland, OH; *U.S. Public*, pg. 954

Pottash, Bruce, Sr. V.P.-Business Affairs & Legal--Paramount Pictures Corporation, Los Angeles, CA; *U.S. Private*, pg. 776

Potter, David B., Sr. V.P.-Procurement--American Italian Pasta Company, Excelsior Springs, MO; *U.S. Public*, pg. 85

Potter, Duane W., Sr. V.P. & Pres.-Foam Components Grp.--Leggett & Platt, Incorporated, Carthage, MO; *U.S. Public*, pg. 985

Potter, James, Sr. V.P.-Bus. Units--International Specialty Products, Inc., Wayne, NJ; *U.S. Public*, pg. 858

Potter, James E., Sr. V.P.-Opers. Support--Inter-Continental Hotels & Resorts Corporation, New York, NY; *Int'l*, pg. 1178

Potter, Michael J., Chief Fin. Officer & Sr. V.P.--Consolidated Stores Corp., Columbus, OH; *U.S. Public*, pg. 437

Potts, Charles F., Sr. V.P.--Ashland, Inc., Russell, KY; *U.S. Public*, pg. 138

Potts, Jeff, Sr. V.P.--TLC Group, Inc., Zeeland, MI; *U.S. Public*, pg. 352

Potts, Robert S., V.P. & Gen. Mgr.-Yearbooks--Herff Jones Inc., Indianapolis, IN; *U.S. Private*, pg. 523

Potts, Willis J., Jr., Sr. V.P.--Union Camp Corporation, Wayne, NJ; *U.S. Public*, pg. 1665

Poulter, Brian, Sr. V.P.-Engrng.--Interstate Bakeries Corporation, Kansas City, MO; *U.S. Public*, pg. 909

Povich, Ilissa, Sr. V.P. & Gen. Counsel--Interactive Data Corporation, Lexington, MA; *Int'l*, pg. 1025

Powell, Catherine C., Sr. V.P.-Employee Svcs.--Central Louisiana Electric Company, Inc., Pineville, LA; *U.S. Public*, pg. 325

Powell, James R., Sr. V.P.-Sls. & Mktg.--Daisytek International Corporation, Plano, TX; *U.S. Public*, pg. 477

Powell, James R., Sr. V.P.-Sls. & Mktg.--Daisytek Incorporated, Plano, TX; *U.S. Public*, pg. 477

Powell, James R., Sr. V.P.-Sls. & Mktg.--Daisytek (Canada) Inc., Toronto, Canada; *U.S. Public*, pg. 477

Powell, James R., Sr. V.P.-Sls. & Mktg.--Daisytek Latin America, Miami, FL; *U.S. Public*, pg. 477

Powell, James R., Sr. V.P.-Sls. & Mktg.--Daisytek De Mexico S.A. de C.V., Mexico, Mexico; *U.S. Public*, pg. 477

Powell, James R., Sr. V.P.-Sls. & Mktg.--Priority Fulfillment Services, Inc., Plano, TX; *U.S. Public*, pg. 477

Powell, James R., Sr. V.P.-Sls. & Mktg.--Daisytek Australia Pty. Ltd., Alexandria, Australia; *U.S. Public*, pg. 477

Powell, Larry E., Sr. V.P.-Pipeline Customer Services--Southern Natural Gas Company, Birmingham, AL; *U.S. Public*, pg. 1485

Powell, Marilyn, Sr. V.P.-Mktg.--Atlantic Electric Co., Pleasantville, NJ; *U.S. Public*, pg. 430

Powell, Michael W., Sr. V.P. & Chief Admin. Officer--Markel Insurance Co., Glen Allen, VA; *U.S. Public*, pg. 1046

Powell, Ronnie L., Sr. V.P.--Chemical Bank Michigan, Clare, MI; *U.S. Public*, pg. 345

Powell, Scott D, Sr. Grp. V.P.-Emergency Medicine--Weatherby Health Care, Norwalk, CT; *U.S. Private*, pg. 1155

Powers, John W., Sr. V.P.--Selective Way Insurance Company, Branchville, NJ; *U.S. Public*, pg. 1456

Powers, Richard P., Chief Fin. Officer & Sr. V.P.--Syntex, Palo Alto, CA; *Int'l*, pg. 1120

Powers, Ronald S., Sr. V.P.-Sr. Loan Officer--SouthTrust Bank of Charleston, Charleston, SC; *U.S. Public*, pg. 1492

Powers, Terri, Sr. V.P.-Leasing--TrizecHahn Centers Inc., San Diego, CA; *Int'l*, pg. 1425

Poynter, Thomas W., Sr. V.P.-Ground Opers.--ABX Air, Inc., Wilmington, OH; *U.S. Public*, pg. 33

Poythress, H.C., Sr. V.P.-Adv.--Heilig-Meyers Company, Richmond, VA; *U.S. Public*, pg. 804

Pozos, Anthony M., Sr. V.P.-Human Resources & Corp. Services--Amdahl Corporation, Sunnyvale, CA; *Int'l*, pg. 527

Prades, Bernard, Sr. V.P.--Lyonnaise des Eaux S.A., Nanterre, France; *Int'l*, pg. 822

Pradetto, Richard V., Sr. V.P.-Mktg.--Cincinnati Incorporated, Harrison, OH; *U.S. Private*, pg. 240

Prado, Marta, Chief Oper. Officer & Sr. V.P.-MedPartners Govt. Svcs.--Medpartners Inc., Birmingham, AL; *U.S. Public*, pg. 1082

Prager, Michael J., Sr. V.P. & Sr. Fin. Officer--PennCorp Financial Group, Inc., New York, NY; *U.S. Public*, pg. 1271

Prairie, Patti, Sr. V.P.-Tech.--Beneficial Management Corporation, Peapack, NJ; *U.S. Public*, pg. 211

Prange, John, Sr. V.P.-Prof. Rels.--Alpo Pet Foods, Inc., Allentown, PA; *Int'l*, pg. 917

Prange, William, Sr. V.P. & Gen. Mdse. Mgr.--Brauns Fashions Corporation, Plymouth, MN; *U.S. Public*, pg. 251

Praske, Dennis D., Sr. V.P.-Worldwide Opers.--Diamond Multimedia Systems, Inc., San Jose, CA; *U.S. Public*, pg. 505

Prater, William L., Sr. V.P.-Acctg.--SouthTrust Corporation, Birmingham, AL; *U.S. Public*, pg. 1491

Prather, Rick, Sr. V.P. & Asst. Gen. Mgr.--Jostens Sportswear, Overland Park, KS; *U.S. Public*, pg. 686

Prather, Susan, Sr. V.P. & Pub. Rels. Dir.--Cramer-Krasselt, Chicago, IL; *U.S. Private*, pg. 285

Pratt, Michael, Sr. V.P.--Republic National Bank of New York (U.K.), London, United Kingdom; *U.S. Public*, pg. 1381

Pratt, Warren C., Ph.D., Sr. V.P.-Silicon Interactive Grp.--Silicon Graphics, Inc., Mountain View, CA; *U.S. Public*, pg. 1473

Pratte, Gary S., Sr. V.P.-Loan Admin.--NationsBank West, Saint Louis, MO; *U.S. Public*, pg. 1164

Praw, Albert Z., Sr. V.P. & Reg. Gen. Mgr.--Kaufman and Broad Home Corporation, Los Angeles, CA; *U.S. Public*, pg. 944

Prebil, Jim, Sr. V.P.--Gelco Information Network, Inc., Eden Prairie, MN; *U.S. Private*, pg. 442

Prendergast, Sean, Sr. V.P.--Baker/OTS International Ltd., Harrow, United Kingdom; *U.S. Public*, pg. 168

Prentice, F. Sheldon, Sr. V.P., Gen. Counsel & Sec.--Chittenden Corporation, Burlington, VT; *U.S. Public*, pg. 350

Prescott, Dana C., Sr. V.P.-Mktg.--Sunrise Leasing Corporation, Golden Valley, MN; *U.S. Public*, pg. 1535

Prescott, Pamela W., Sr. V.P.-Branch Opers.--Citizens Savings Bank, Providence, RI; *Int'l*, pg. 1132

Presley, Clay, Sr. V.P.-Sls.--C.R. Gibson Co., Norwalk, CT; *U.S. Public*, pg. 1168

Presley, Karen, Sr. V.P.-Capital Corp.--USAA (United Services Automobile Association), San Antonio, TX; *U.S. Private*, pg. 1114

Presley, W. Clay, Sr. V.P.-Sls.-Gift Prods.--Thomas Nelson Inc., Nashville, TN; *U.S. Public*, pg. 1167

Press, James E., Sr. V.P.--Toyota Motor Sales, U.S.A., Inc., Torrance, CA; *Int'l*, pg. 1412

Pressler, Paul, Sr. V.P.-Disney Licensing--Walt Disney Consumer Products, Burbank, CA; *U.S. Public*, pg. 511

Preston, Carr T., Sr. V.P.--Allied Capital Financial Corporation, Washington, DC; *U.S. Public*, pg. 48

Preston, John E., Sr. V.P. & Gen. Counsel--Litton Industries, Inc., Woodland Hills, CA; *U.S. Public*, pg. 1002

Preston, Michael L., Sr. V.P.-Sls. & Mktg.--APS Holding Corporation, Houston, TX; *U.S. Public*, pg. 10

Preston, Mike, Sr. V.P.--A.P.S., Memphis, TN; *U.S. Public*, pg. 10

Preston, Steven, Chief Fin. Officer. & Sr. V.P.--The ServiceMaster Company, Downers Grove, IL; *U.S. Public*, pg. 1461

Pretzsch, Timothy E., Sr. V.P. & Acct. Mng. Dir.--Young & Rubicam Chicago, Chicago, IL; *U.S. Private*, pg. 1198

Prewitt-Wood, Ken, Sr. V.P.Mktg.--Blue Shield of California, San Francisco, CA; *U.S. Private*, pg. 153

Prezzano, Domnick A., Sr. V.P.-Corp. Property Mngmnt.--Metropolitan Life Insurance Co., New York, NY; *U.S. Private*, pg. 737

Priadka, Nickolas, Sr. V.P.-OE Engine--Donaldson Company, Inc., Minneapolis, MN; *U.S. Public*, pg. 517

Price, David, Sr. V.P.--Burns & Wilcox Ltd., Farmington, MI; *U.S. Private*, pg. 609

Price, I. Edward, Sr. V.P. & Actuary-Individual Insurance Grp.--The Prudential Insurance Company of America, Newark, NJ; *U.S. Private*, pg. 892

Price, J. Donald, Sr. V.P.-Fin.--Alfa Insurance Corp., Montgomery, AL; *U.S. Public*, pg. 40

Price, James E., Sr. V.P.--Chubb & Son, Inc., Warren, NJ; *U.S. Public*, pg. 355

Price, Kenneth, Sr. V.P.-Sls. & Mktg.--Toymax International Inc., Plainview, NY; *U.S. Public*, pg. 1626

Price, Mark, Sr. V.P.-New Bus. Devel.--Sterling Healthcare Group, Inc., Miami, FL; *U.S. Public*, pg. 608

Price, R. Kevin, Sr. V.P. & Sec.--The Hartford Steam Boiler Inspection & Insurance Co., Hartford, CT; *U.S. Public*, pg. 795

Price, Randy J., Sr. V.P.--First National Bank of Pennsylvania, Hermitage, PA; *U.S. Public*, pg. 607

Price, Ronald D., Chief Fin. Officer, Sr. V.P. & Sec.--Slocan Forest Products Ltd., Richmond, Canada; *Int'l*, pg. 1263

Price, Scott, Sr. V.P.-Marine, Aviation & Intl. Div.--Willis Faber North America, Inc.-New York, New York, NY; *Int'l*, pg. 1503

Price, Terry W., Pres.-Commercial/Indus. Worldwide Opers. & Sr. V.P.--Sensormatic Electronics Corporation, Boca Raton, FL; *U.S. Public*, pg. 1457

Price, Vincent, Sr. V.P.--Willis Corroon Administrative Services Corporation, Nashville, TN; *Int'l*, pg. 1505

Prickett, F. Daniel, Sr. V.P. & Head-Priv. Banking--First Union Corporation, Charlotte, NC; *U.S. Public*, pg. 639

Pridgen, Eugen, Sr. V.P. & Gen. Counsel--Glenayre Technologies, Inc., Charlotte, NC; *U.S. Public*, pg. 746

Priestap, Linda, Sr. V.P.-Mktg.--First Data Corporation, Englewood, CO; *U.S. Public*, pg. 631

Priestnell, Ian, Sr. V.P.--BetzDearborn Inc., Trevose, PA; *U.S. Public*, pg. 226

Prijatel, Donald, Sr. V.P.-Adv. & Promo.--King World Productions, Inc., New York, NY; *U.S. Public*, pg. 961

Prijatel, Donald, Sr. V.P.-Adv. & Promo.--King World Productions, Los Angeles, CA; *U.S. Public*, pg. 961

Prilick, Gustavo, Sr. V.P.-Opers./Latin America--Millicom International Cellular SA, Bertrange, Luxembourg; *Int'l*, pg. 867

Prillman, Bob M., Sr. V.P.--Caraustar Industries, Inc., Austell, GA; *U.S. Public*, pg. 303

Prince, John, Sr. V.P.--First National Bank in Cleburne, Cleburne, TX; *U.S. Public*, pg. 633

Prince, Nancy L., Sr. V.P.-Corp. Plng.--BayBanks, Inc., Boston, MA; *U.S. Public*, pg. 184

Priode, A. Len, Sr. V.P.-Distr. & Information Services--Rose's Stores, Inc., Henderson, NC; *U.S. Public*, pg. 1405

Prior, John C., Chief Fin. Officer, Sr. V.P.-Fin. & Sec.--Curative Health Services, East Setauket, NY; *U.S. Public*, pg. 469

Pritchard, Marianne, Chief Fin. Officer & Sr. V.P.--Berkshire Realty Company, Inc., Boston, MA; *U.S. Public*, pg. 221

Privateer, Pete, Sr. V.P.-Opers.--Axent Technologies, Rockville, MD; *U.S. Public*, pg. 157

Probst, Lawrence E., Sr. V.P.-Opers.--Comptek Federal Systems, Inc., Buffalo, NY; *U.S. Public*, pg. 419

Prochaska, Bob, Sr. V.P.-Opers.--Kayser-Roth Corporation, Inc., Greensboro, NC; *Int'l*, pg. 576

Proctor, David F., Sr. V.P. & Country Mgr.--Bank of America NT&SA, Bangkok, Thailand; *U.S. Public*, pg. 182

Proctor, Morris, Sr. V.P.--Union Planters Corporation, Cordova, TN; *U.S. Public*, pg. 1668

Proctor, Timothy D., Sr. V.P., Gen. Counsel & Sec.--Glaxo Wellcome Inc., Research Triangle Park, NC; *Int'l*, pg. 552

Proffitt, Randall S., Sr. V.P.--Meldisco, Mahwah, NJ; *U.S. Public*, pg. 661

Prol, John H., Sr. V.P.--Valley National Bank, Parsippany, NJ; *U.S. Public*, pg. 1705

Propp, Gail, Chief Info. Officer & Sr. V.P.--Slim-Fast Foods Company, West Palm Beach, FL; *U.S. Private*, pg. 1006

Prosser, John W., Jr., Sr. V.P.-Fin. & Admin. & Treas.--Jacobs Engineering Group Inc., Pasadena, CA; *U.S. Public*, pg. 921

Protsch, Eliot G., Sr. V.P.--Wisconsin Power & Light Company, Madison, WI; *U.S. Public*, pg. 1728

Protto, Frank W., Sr. V.P.--Canadian Occidental Petroleum Ltd., Calgary, Canada; *U.S. Public*, pg. 1210

Proulx, Daniel, Sr. V.P.-Fin. & Admin.--Coscient Group Inc., Montreal, Canada; *Int'l*, pg. 335

Prounis, Charlene, Sr. V.P. & Mktg. Dir.-New Bus.--Grey Healthcare Group, New York, NY; *U.S. Public*, pg. 765

Prowse, W. James, Sr. V.P.-Human Resources & Recruiting--Compuware Corporation, Farmington Hills, MI; *U.S. Public*, pg. 423

Pruet, Ronald B., Jr., Sr. V.P. & Treas.--Sonat Exploration Company, Houston, TX; *U.S. Public*, pg. 1485

Pryor, Vikki, Sr. V.P.-Opers. & Sys.--Blue Cross and Blue Shield of Massachusetts, Boston, MA; *U.S. Private*, pg. 151

Psilos, Anthony P., Sr. V.P.--Hibernia Corporation, New Orleans, LA; *U.S. Public*, pg. 825

Ptashek, Harvey I., Sr. V.P.--Rowe Furniture Corp., Mc Lean, VA; *U.S. Public*, pg. 1410

Puckett, Bill, Sr. V.P. & Creative Dir.--Long Haymes Carr, Inc., Winston Salem, NC; *U.S. Public*, pg. 909

Pudlin, Helen P., Sr. V.P. & Gen. Counsel--PNC Bank Corp., Pittsburgh, PA; *U.S. Public*, pg. 1242

Pugel, Joe, Sr. V.P.--The Vernon Company, Newton, IA; *U.S. Private*, pg. 1137

Pugh, David, Sr. V.P.--Industrial Control Group, Milwaukee, WI; *U.S. Public*, pg. 1397

Pugh, Michael D., Sr. V.P.--Foundation Health Systems, Inc., Pueblo, CO; *U.S. Public*, pg. 678

Pugh, Richard, Sr. V.P. & Gen. Counsel--Fremont Financial Corporation, Santa Monica, CA; *U.S. Public*, pg. 681

Pugiello, Peter, Chief Fin. Officer, Sr. V.P., Treas. & Asst. Sec.--Blonder-Tongue Laboratories, Inc., Old Bridge, NJ; *U.S. Public*, pg. 237

Pugliese, Tony, Sr. V.P. & Grp. Creative Dir.--Grey Advertising Inc., New York, NY; *U.S. Public*, pg. 764

Puglisi, Anthony J., Chief Fin. Officer, Sr. V.P. & Treas.--Olsten Corporation, Melville, NY; *U.S. Public*, pg. 1220

Pujalet, Marc, Sr. V.P.--Westin Hotels & Resorts, Seattle, WA; *U.S. Public*, pg. 1512

Puleo, Lenore F., Sr. V.P.--Brooklyn Union, Brooklyn, NY; *U.S. Public*, pg. 259

Pulk, David R., Sr. V.P.-Sls. & Mktg.--Golden Eagle Group, Inc., Humble, TX; *U.S. Public*, pg. 749

Pulkrabek, Larry A., Sr. V.P., Sec. & Gen. Counsel--Armstrong World Industries, Inc., Lancaster, PA; *U.S. Public*, pg. 131

Pulse, M. Lester, Jr., Sr. V.P.-Tax--Marriott International, Inc., Washington, DC; *U.S. Public*, pg. 1047

Pump, Juergen, Sr. V.P.-Area East/Midwest--Hapag-Lloyd (America), Inc., Piscataway, NJ; *Int'l*, pg. 596

Purcell, Eileen, Sr. V.P. & Mng. Dir.--The Chapman Agency, New York, NY; *U.S. Private*, pg. 1197

Purcell, Tom, Sr. V.P.-Sls.--Fedders Corp., Liberty Corner, NJ; *U.S. Public*, pg. 614

Purcell, Tom, Sr. V.P.-Sls.--Fedders North America, Inc., Whitehouse, NJ; *U.S. Public*, pg. 614

Purdy, Alan M., Chief Fin. Officer & Sr. V.P.--RemedyTemp, Inc., San Juan Capistrano, CA; *U.S. Public*, pg. 1376

Purdy, John, Sr. V.P.-Brand Devel.--Clarity Coverdale Fury Advertising, Minneapolis, MN; *U.S. Private*, pg. 242

Puri, Ajai, Sr. V.P.--The Minute Maid Company, Houston, TX; *U.S. Public*, pg. 392

Purkis, Len, Chief Fin. Officer, Sr. V.P.-Fin. & Treas.--Iomega Corporation, Roy, UT; *U.S. Public*, pg. 912

Purtell, Lawrence R., Sr. V.P., Gen. Counsel & Sec.--McDermott International, Inc., New Orleans, LA; *U.S. Public*, pg. 1067

Push-Leak, Jackie, Sr. V.P. & Creative Dir.--DMB&B New York, New York, NY; *U.S. Private*, pg. 302

Putman, Gerald E., Sr. V.P.--New York State Electric & Gas Corporation, Binghamton, NY; *U.S. Public*, pg. 1173

Putman, Gerald H., Sr. V.P.-H.R.--Raytheon Systems Company, Arlington, VA; *U.S. Public*, pg. 1364

Pyles, David, Sr. V.P.-Sls.--Bentley Mills, Inc., City of Industry, CA; *U.S. Public*, pg. 889

Quails, Robert, Sr. V.P., Corp. Treas. & Asst Sec.--Haggar Corporation, Dallas, TX; *U.S. Public*, pg. 774

Qualey, Allen R., Sr. V.P.-Trans. & Equip. Fin. Grp.--1st Source Bank Consolidated, South Bend, IN; *U.S. Public*, pg. 638

Qualls, Stephen A., Sr. V.P.-Retail Svcs.--Nevada State Bank, Las Vegas, NV; *U.S. Public*, pg. 1793

Qualters, Irene M., Sr. V.P.-Tech. Computing & Pres.-Cray Research--Silicon Graphics, Inc., Mountain View, CA; *U.S. Public*, pg. 1473

Quarles, Steve, Sr. V.P. & Mngmt. Supvr.--The Buntin Group, Nashville, TN; *U.S. Private*, pg. 181

Quaterman, Ch., Sr. V.P.-Information Systems & Telecommunications--SGS Societe Generale de Surveillance Holding S.A., Geneva, Switzerland; *Int'l*, pg. 1153

Queen, Gary, Sr. V.P.-Capital Management Grp.--The Provident Bank, Cincinnati, OH; *U.S. Public*, pg. 1338

Quehl, Stephen R., Sr. V.P.-North America Field Opers.--Wang Laboratories, Inc., Billerica, MA; *U.S. Public*, pg. 1737

Quereau, James Van Dyke, Sr. V.P.--Stratton Management Company, Plymouth Meeting, PA; *U.S. Private*, pg. 1046

Quick, B. Dale, Sr. V.P.-Servicing, Lending--United Companies Financial Corporation, Baton Rouge, LA; *U.S. Public*, pg. 1675

Quicksall, D.E., Chief Fin. Officer, Sr. V.P. & Treas.--Central Freight Lines, Inc., Waco, TX; *U.S. Private*, pg. 223

Quigley, James E., III, Sr. V.P.--Rothschild Inc., New York, NY; *U.S. Private*, pg. 947

Quimby, Edward D., Sr. V.P.-Sls. & Mktg.--The Turner Corporation, New York, NY; *U.S. Public*, pg. 1645

Quimby, Edward D., Sr. V.P.-Sls. & Mktg.--Turner Construction Company, New York, NY; *U.S. Public*, pg. 1645

Quin, J. Marvin, Chief Fin. Officer & Sr. V.P.--Ashland, Inc., Russell, KY; *U.S. Public*, pg. 138

Quiner, Paul, Sr. V.P. & Gen. Counsel--Coram Healthcare Corporation, Denver, CO; *U.S. Public*, pg. 446

Quinlan, Mark D., Sr. V.P.-MIS--Starbanc Corporation, Cincinnati, OH; *U.S. Public*, pg. 1510

Quinn, Christopher J., Sr. V.P.-Grp. Mktg. & Service & Gen. Mgr./Diagnostics Div.--Bayer Corporation, Pittsburgh, PA; *Int'l*, pg. 172

Quinn, Jeffry N., Sr. V.P.-Law & Human Resources, Gen. Counsel & Sec.--Arch Coal, Inc., Saint Louis, MO; *U.S. Public*, pg. 139

Quinn, John A., Sr. V.P.-Regional Opers.--Ramsay Health Care, Inc., Coral Gables, FL; *U.S. Public*, pg. 1360

Quinn, Kathleen, Sr. V.P.-Brdcst. Bus.--Partners & Shevack, Inc., New York, NY; *U.S. Private*, pg. 842

Quinn, Michael A., Sr. V.P.-Credit Loss Mngmt.--Federal National Mortgage Association (Fannie Mae), Washington, DC; *U.S. Public*, pg. 615

Quinn, Robert, Sr. V.P.-Legal--LaSalle National Bank, Chicago, IL; *Int'l*, pg. 10

Quinn, Smita Patel, Sr. V.P. & Dir.-Prod. Plng. & Systems--Barclays American/Mortgage Corp., Charlotte, NC; *Int'l*, pg. 165

Quinn, Terry C., Sr. V.P.--Computer Horizons Corp., Mountain Lakes, NJ; *U.S. Public*, pg. 421

Quinones, Charles, Sr. V.P.-Opers.--Worldvision Enterprises, New York, NY; *U.S. Private*, pg. 776

Quiroga, Dario, Sr. V.P.-Cashier--Santa Monica Bank, Santa Monica, CA; *U.S. Public*, pg. 1757

Raab, Paul, Sr. V.P.--Golin/Harris Communications, Inc., Chicago, IL; *Int'l*, pg. 1226

Rabinoff, Robert J., Sr. V.P. & Controller--Quick & Reilly, Inc., New York, NY; *U.S. Public*, pg. 650

Rabur, Ch., Sr. V.P.-Banking--Compagnie de Suez, Paris, France; *Int'l*, pg. 313

Race, Mark, Sr. V.P.-Store Plng.--OfficeMax, Shaker Heights, OH; *U.S. Public*, pg. 1212

Racine, Robert, Sr. V.P.-Pub. Affairs & Investor Rels.--SNC-Lavalin Group Inc., Montreal, Canada; *Int'l*, pg. 1161

Rack, Janet Olson, Sr. V.P.--Hibernia Corporation, New Orleans, LA; *U.S. Public*, pg. 825

Radam, Janice, Sr. V.P. & Media Dir.--Lowe McAdams Healthcare, New York, NY; *U.S. Private*, pg. 678

Radano, Robert M., Chief Oper. Officer & Sr. V.P.--J & J Snack Foods Corporation, Pennsauken, NJ; *U.S. Public*, pg. 916

Radbill, Geoffrey, Sr. V.P.-Agency Admin.--The Equitable Companies Incorporated, New York, NY; *U.S. Public*, pg. 588

Radcliffe, Jim, Sr. V.P.--The William Cook Agency, Inc., Jacksonville, FL; *U.S. Private*, pg. 273

Raddi, William J., Chief Tech. Officer, Sr. V.P. & Gen. Mgr.--Small Systems Group, Raleigh, NC; *Int'l*, pg. 126

Rademacher, Kent D., Sr. V.P.-Dental Office Opers., Sls & Mktg.--Safeguard Health Enterprises, Inc., Anaheim, CA; *U.S. Public*, pg. 1424

Rademacher, Randy D., Chief Fin. Officer & Sr. V.P.--Comair Holdings, Inc., Erlanger, KY; *U.S. Public*, pg. 406

Rado, Eugene J., Sr. V.P. & Gen. Mgr.--VSM, Inc., New York, NY; *U.S. Private*, pg. 1130

Rados, Stephen S., Sr. V.P.--The Rados Companies, Santa Ana, CA; *U.S. Private*, pg. 907

Rados, Walter S., Sr. V.P.--The Rados Companies, Santa Ana, CA; *U.S. Private*, pg. 907

Rafaniello, Ralph R., Sr. V.P.-Sls.--The American Stock Exchange, New York, NY; *U.S. Private*, pg. 62

Rafferty, Sherwood J., Chief Fin. Officer & Sr. V.P.--New York State Electric & Gas Corporation, Binghamton, NY; *U.S. Public*, pg. 1173

Ragan, Rod, Sr. V.P.--Parsons Power Group, Inc., Reading, PA; *U.S. Private*, pg. 841

Raggio, Stanley P., Sr. V.P.-Sourcing & Logistics--The Gap, Inc., San Francisco, CA; *U.S. Public*, pg. 702

Raghavan, Asuri, Sr. V.P. & Pres.-Equipment Div.--Kulicke & Soffa Industries, Inc., Willow Grove, PA; *U.S. Public*, pg. 968

Ragland, Ronald M., Sr. V.P.-Human Resources & Trng.--Heilig-Meyers Company, Richmond, VA; *U.S. Public*, pg. 804

Ragsdale, Perry A., Sr. V.P.-Design & Construction--Chick-fil-A, Inc., Atlanta, GA; *U.S. Private*, pg. 236

Ragus, W.D., Sr. V.P.--Miller Freeman Inc., San Francisco, CA; *Int'l*, pg. 1443

Rahbar, Sherry, Sr. V.P.-Fin.--DavisElen Advertising, Inc., Los Angeles, CA; *U.S. Private*, pg. 316

Raimondi, Thomas P., Jr., Sr. V.P. & Gen. Mgr.--MTI Technology Corporation, Anaheim, CA; *U.S. Public*, pg. 1028

Rain, Burton J., Sr. V.P.-Natl. Agency--Chicago Title Insurance Co., Chicago, IL; *U.S. Public*, pg. 42

Rainey, R., Sr. V.P.-Treas.--Bituminous Casualty Corp., Rock Island, IL; *U.S. Public*, pg. 1218

Rains, Douglas J., Sr. V.P.-Natl. Sls.--Wm. E. Wright Limited Partnership, West Warren, MA; *U.S. Private*, pg. 1192

Rainville, William A., Sr. V.P.--Thermo Electron Corporation, Waltham, MA; *U.S. Public*, pg. 1591

Raj, Anil, Sr. V.P.--Halter Marine Group, Inc., Gulfport, MS; *U.S. Public*, pg. 778

Rajahalme, Aimo, Sr. V.P.-Fin. & Treas.--Kone Corporation, Helsinki, Finland; *Int'l*, pg. 746

Rajaji, Raj, Chief Fin. Officer & Sr. V.P.--BancTec, Inc., Dallas, TX; *U.S. Public*, pg. 176

Rajappa, Sampath, Sr. V.P. & Controller--Federal National Mortgage Association (Fannie Mae), Washington, DC; *U.S. Public*, pg. 615

Rajendra, Ajita, Sr. V.P.-Industrial Prods. Grp.--Greenfield Industries Inc., Evans, GA; *U.S. Public*, pg. 950

Rajfer, Sol I., Sr. V.P.-Clinical Res. & Devel.--Bristol-Myers Squibb Company, New York, NY; *U.S. Public*, pg. 253

Rakestraw, John, Sr. V.P. & Gen. Mgr.--Cattle Feeding Div., Boulder, CO; *U.S. Private*, pg. 268

Rakow, May T., Sr. V.P.-Personnel & Sec.--IHC Group, Inc., South Elgin, IL; *U.S. Private*, pg. 555

Raleigh, Robert E., Sr. V.P.-Domestic Sls.--Worldvision Enterprises, New York, NY; *U.S. Private*, pg. 776

Rallo, Ron, Sr. V.P.-Mdsg. & Procurement--Pathmark Stores Incorporated, Woodbridge, NJ; *U.S. Private*, pg. 843

Ralston, David A., Sr. V.P.-Bus. Devel. & Plng.--Environmental/Government Group, Boise, ID; *U.S. Public*, pg. 1134

Ralston, Douglas J., Sr. V.P.-H.R.--The Quaker Oats Company, Chicago, IL; *U.S. Public*, pg. 1347

Ramas, Guillermo N., Sr., Sr. V.P. & Pres.-SMS Intl.--Shared Medical Systems Corporation, Malvern, PA; *U.S. Public*, pg. 1463

Rambaud, P., Sr. V.P.-Mktg. & Strategic Devel.--Danone Group, Paris, France; *Int'l*, pg. 379

Ramey, Thomas, Exec. V.P.--Liberty Mutual Insurance Co., Boston, MA; *U.S. Private*, pg. 666

Ramirez, Armando, Sr. V.P.-Strategic Plng. & Mergers & Acq.--National City Corporation, Cleveland, OH; *U.S. Public*, pg. 1154

Ramirez, Jose A., Sr. V.P.-Opers. Admin.--Farah U.S.A., Inc., El Paso, TX; *U.S. Public*, pg. 613

Ramirez, Michael, Sr. V.P.-Fin.--Philip Industrial Services Group, Houston, TX; *Int'l*, pg. 1050

Ramirez, Suzette, Sr. V.P. & Human Resources Dir.--DMB&B Detroit, Troy, MI; *U.S. Private*, pg. 302

Rammelt, Anthony W.E., Sr. V.P. & Intl. Mng. Dir.-Europe--Regis Corporation, Minneapolis, MN; *U.S. Public*, pg. 1373

Ramrath, Joseph R., Sr. V.P. & Gen. Counsel--United Asset Management Corporation, Boston, MA; *U.S. Public*, pg. 1672

Ramsdal, Kjell, Sr. V.P.--Elkem ASA Manganese/Chrome Division, Oslo, Norway; *Int'l*, pg. 447

Ramsey, David W., Sr. V.P., Dir.-Admin. & Asst. Sec.--Federated Mutual Insurance Company, Owatonna, MN; *U.S. Private*, pg. 399

Ramsey, Steven C., Chief Fin. Officer & Sr. V.P.--Buckeye Partners, L.P., Allentown, PA; *U.S. Public*, pg. 266

Ramsey, Steven C., Chief Fin. Officer & Sr. V.P.-Fin.--Buckeye Pipe Line Company, L.P., Allentown, PA; *U.S. Public*, pg. 266

Ramyarupa, Apichart, Sr. V.P. & Gen. Mgr.--Bangkok Bank Public Company Limited, Bangkok, Thailand; *Int'l*, pg. 146

Rand, Mike, Sr. V.P.-Kansas City Division--Associated Wholesale Grocers, Inc., Kansas City, KS; *U.S. Private*, pg. 93

Randall, Karen, Sr. V.P. & Gen. Counsel--Universal Studios, Inc., Universal City, CA; *Int'l*, pg. 1215

Randolph, James K., Sr. V.P. & Gen. Mgr.-Distr. & Customer Service Bus. Unit--Pacific Gas & Electric Company, San Francisco, CA; *U.S. Public*, pg. 1241

Randolph, Kenneth, Sr. V.P. & Gen. Counsel--NGC Corporation, Houston, TX; *U.S. Public*, pg. 1146

Raney, Dennis R., Chief Fin. Officer & Sr. V.P.-Fin. & Admin.--QAD Inc, Carpinteria, CA; *U.S. Public*, pg. 1345

Rangel, John J., Sr. V.P.-Fin.--K2 Inc., Los Angeles, CA; *U.S. Public*, pg. 940

Ranieri, Robert, Sr. V.P. & Creative Dir.--Lowe McAdams Healthcare, New York, NY; *U.S. Private*, pg. 678

Rank, Robert P., Chief Investment Officer & Sr. V.P.--Selective Insurance Group, Inc, Branchville, NJ; *U.S. Public*, pg. 1455

Rank, Robert P., Chief Investment Officer & Sr. V.P.--Selective Insurance Company of America, Branchville, NJ; *U.S. Public*, pg. 1455

Rank, Robert P., Sr. V.P. & Chief Investment Officer--Selective Way Insurance Company, Branchville, NJ; *U.S.* Public, pg. 1456

Rankin, Larry V., Sr. V.P.--BetzDearborn Inc., Trevose, PA; *U.S. Public*, pg. 226

Rankin, Lorna, Sr. V.P. & Creative Dir.--The Chapman Agency, New York, NY; *U.S. Private*, pg. 1197

Rankin, R.A., Jr., Sr. V.P.-Corp. Relations--Fairfield Inn, Washington, DC; *U.S. Public*, pg. 1048

Rano, John, Sr. V.P.-Mktg.--General Cigar Company, Inc., Bloomfield, CT; *U.S. Public*, pg. 708

Ransom, Mal, Sr. V.P.-Mktg.--Packard Bell NEC, Sacramento, CA; *U.S. Private*, pg. 833

Rapp, Charles R., Sr. V.P.--International Wine & Spirits Ltd., Greenwich, CT; *U.S. Public*, pg. 1661

Rapp, Kenneth M., Sr. V.P.--Fair, Isaac and Company, Inc., San Rafael, CA; *U.S. Public*, pg. 609

Rapp, Kenneth R., Sr. Zone V.P.--Gap Stores Division, San Bruno, CA; *U.S. Public*, pg. 702

Rapp, Nemmart, Chief Fin. Officer & Sr. V.P.--Spectra-Physics AB, Stockholm, Sweden; *Int'l*, pg. 1288

Rappeneau, Gilles, Sr. V.P.-Exploration & Production Tech.--Elf Aquitane, Paris, France; *Int'l*, pg. 444

Rash, John, Sr. V.P. & Brdcst. Negotiations Dir.--Campbell Mithun Esty, Minneapolis, MN; *U.S. Private*, pg. 204

Rashidn, Zafar Kerry, Chief Fin. Officer & Sr. V.P.--Fortis, Inc., New York, NY; *Int'l*, pg. 499

Rasmussen, Dale L., Sr. V.P. & Sec.--AirSensors, Inc., Seattle, WA; *U.S. Public*, pg. 33

Rasmussen, James W., Sr. V.P.-Credit Card Services--SunTrust Banks, Inc., Atlanta, GA; *U.S. Public*, pg. 1537

Rasmussen, John, Sr. V.P. & Gen. Counsel--MidAmerican Energy Holdings, Des Moines, IA; *U.S. Public*, pg. 1109

Rasmussen, Nicholas R., Sr. V.P.-Corp. Dev.--American General Corporation, Houston, TX; *U.S. Public*, pg. 76

Rasor, John F., Sr. V.P.-Forest Resources--Georgia-Pacific Corporation, Atlanta, GA; *U.S. Public*, pg. 735

Raspino, Louis A., Jr., Chief Fin. Officer & Sr. V.P.--The Louisiana Land and Exploration Company, New Orleans, LA; *U.S. Public*, pg. 269

Rassman, Joel H., Chief Fin. Officer, Sr. V.P., Treas. & Asst. Sec.--Toll Brothers, Inc., Huntingdon Valley, PA; *U.S. Public*, pg. 1620

Ratanachaichan, Nutta, Sr. V.P.-Fin.--The Industrial Finance Corporation of Thailand, Bangkok, Thailand; *Int'l*, pg. 677

Ratcliffe, Martyn R., Sr. V.P. & Gen. Mgr.-Europe--Dell Computer Corporation, Round Rock, TX; *U.S. Public*, pg. 495

Rateliff, Charles, Sr. V.P.-Benefits Admin.--Wal-Mart Stores, Inc., Bentonville, AR; *U.S. Public*, pg. 1732

Rathberger, John F., Sr. V.P.--F&G Re, Inc., Morristown, NJ; *U.S. Public*, pg. 1659

Rathmann, Jerry, Sr. V.P.--Foster & Gallagher, Inc., Peoria, IL; *U.S. Private*, pg. 420

Ratkovic, Richard D., Sr. V.P. & Trust Mgr.--Santa Monica Bank, Santa Monica, CA; *U.S. Public*, pg. 1757

Ratkus, Ted, Sr. V.P.-Sls.--Shorewood Packaging Corporation of Virginia-Williamsburg Operations, Newport News, VA; *U.S. Public*, pg. 1468

Ratkus, Theodore S., Sr. V.P.-Sls. & Mktg.--Shorewood Packaging Corporation, New York, NY; *U.S. Public*, pg. 1468

Ratnathicam, Chutta, Chief Fin. Officer & Sr. V.P.--CNF Transportation Inc., Palo Alto, CA; *U.S. Public*, pg. 281

Ratner, Brian J., Sr. V.P.-Devel.--Forest City Enterprises, Inc., Cleveland, OH; *U.S. Public*, pg. 667

Rattray, Timothy S., Sr. V.P.--Bankers Trust New York Corporation, New York, NY; *U.S. Public*, pg. 185

Ratz, E. Wayne, Chief Info. Officer & Sr. V.P.--Harleysville Group, Harleysville, PA; *U.S. Public*, pg. 786

Rauch, Michael, Sr. V.P.-Production--Showtime Networks Inc., New York, NY; *U.S. Private*, pg. 779

Rauch, Ray, Sr. V.P.-Mktg.--Kraus-Anderson Construction Company, Minneapolis, MN; *U.S. Private*, pg. 635

Rauscher, Robert, Sr. V.P.--Commerce Bancshares, Inc., Kansas City, MO; *U.S. Public*, pg. 409

Rauwerdink, David A., Sr. V.P.--Firstar Corporation, Milwaukee, WI; *U.S. Public*, pg. 642

Ravasio, Robert, Chief Oper. Officer & Sr. V.P.--Ketchum Advertising/San Francisco, San Francisco, CA; *U.S. Private*, pg. 616

Ravencroft, Thomas, Sr. V.P. & Pres.-Dairy Div.--Dean Foods Company, Franklin Park, IL; *U.S. Public*, pg. 489

Ravilly, Claude, Chief Fin. Officer & Sr. Exec. V.P.--Club Mediterranee SA, Paris, France; *Int'l*, pg. 298

Rawlings, James W., Sr. V.P. & Dir.-Human Resources--UMB Financial Corporation, Kansas City, MO; *U.S. Public*, pg. 1653

Rawlings, John, Sr. V.P.-Editorial--The Sporting News Publishing Company, Saint Louis, MO; *U.S. Public*, pg. 1616

Rawls, Brian, Sr. V.P.-S. Zone Domestic Mfg.--Haggar Corporation, Dallas, TX; *U.S. Public*, pg. 774

Rawson, Joel P., Sr. V.P. & Exec. Editor--Providence Journal-Bulletin, Providence, RI; *U.S. Public*, pg. 209

Rawson, Rich, Sr. V.P. & Gen. Counsel--Lucent Technologies Inc., Murray Hill, NJ; *U.S. Public*, pg. 1017

Ray, Donald R., Sr. V.P.--Transocean Offshore, Inc., Houston, TX; *U.S. Public*, pg. 1631

Ray, Gary A., Sr. V.P.-H.R.--Kaufman and Broad Home Corporation, Los Angeles, CA; *U.S. Public*, pg. 944

Ray, John T., Jr., Sr. V.P.-Adhesives, Sealants & Coatings--H.B. Fuller Company, Saint Paul, MN; *U.S. Public*, pg. 686
Ray, Robert F., Sr. V.P.--First Maryland Bancorp, Baltimore, MD; *Int'l*, pg. 64
Ray, Stephen M., Chief Fin. Officer & Sr. V.P.--Health Management Associates, Inc., Naples, FL; *U.S. Public*, pg. 802
Ray, Stephen M., Sr. V.P.--Health Management Associates, Inc., Naples, FL; *U.S. Public*, pg. 802
Raye, Stephen P., Sr. V.P.--General Re Services Corp., Stamford, CT; *U.S. Public*, pg. 725
Raymond, Judy, Sr. V.P.--Simplicity Holdings Inc., New York, NY; *U.S. Private*, pg. 1002
Raymond, Real, Sr. V.P.-Treas. & Fin. Markets--National Bank of Canada, Montreal, Canada; *Int'l*, pg. 907
Raymond, Ronald T., Sr. V.P.-Asset Protection--Bradlees Inc., Braintree, MA; *U.S. Public*, pg. 249
Raymond, Scott D., Sr. V.P. & Cashier--Independent Bank, Ionia, MI; *U.S. Public*, pg. 874
Raynaud, Alain-Pierre, Sr. V.P. & Controller--Renault, Boulogne-Billancourt, France; *Int'l*, pg. 1102
Raynor, Stephen K., Sr. V.P.-Urban Group--Cambridge Shopping Centres Limited, Toronto, Canada; *Int'l*, pg. 253
Raza, Syed Ali, Sr. V.P. & Country Mgr.--Bank of America NT&SA, Karachi, Pakistan; *U.S. Public*, pg. 182
Reach, Francois, Grp. Sr. V.P.--SCOR, Paris, France; *Int'l*, pg. 1152
Read, Randolph C., Chief Fin. Officer-Fin. & Plng. & Sr. V.P.--Stone Container Corporation, Chicago, IL; *U.S. Public*, pg. 1520
Real, William J., Sr. V.P.-Gas Opers.--Public Service Company of New Mexico, Albuquerque, NM; *U.S. Public, pg. 1339*
Reale, Michael A., Sr. V.P.-Mfg.--Boca Research Inc., Boca Raton, FL; *U.S. Public*, pg. 239
Reali, Joseph A., Sr. V.P.-Bank Fin. Svcs.--Metropolitan Life Insurance Co., New York, NY; *U.S. Private*, pg. 737
Reals, Janice A., Sr. V.P.--AMBAC Financial Group, Inc., New York, NY; *U.S. Public*, pg. 62
Ream, Charles S., Sr. V.P.-Fin.--Raytheon Systems Company, Arlington, VA; *U.S. Public*, pg. 1364
Reardon, Frank, Sr. V.P.-Admin. Services--Compass Bank, Birmingham, AL; *U.S. Public*, pg. 418
Reardon, N.A., Sr. V.P.-H.R. & Corp. Affairs--Borden, Inc., Columbus, OH; *U.S. Private*, pg. 157
Reaugh, O.H., Sr. V.P. & Asst. Sec.--States, Inc., Breckenridge, TX; *U.S. Private*, pg. 1037
Reaves, Mike, Sr. V.P.-Drivers Services--M.S. Carriers, Inc., Memphis, TN; *U.S. Public*, pg. 1027
Rebata, Virginia, Sr. V.P.-Human Resources--Fortis, Inc., New York, NY; *Int'l*, pg. 499
Rebholz, David F., Sr. V.P.-Americas & Canada--FDX Corporation, Memphis, TN; *U.S. Public*, pg. 603
Rebmann, Joel G., Sr. V.P.-Credit--The May Department Stores Company, Saint Louis, MO; *U.S. Public*, pg. 1063
Reck, Larry J., Sr. V.P.-Check Collection & Data Services--Federal Reserve Bank of Dallas, Dallas, TX; *U.S. Private*, pg. 399
Recker, David H., Sr. V.P.-Intl. Opers.--Inland Container Corporation, Indianapolis, IN; *U.S. Public*, pg. 1575
Reckford, Jonathan, Sr. V.P.-Plng. & Communications--Circuit City Stores, Inc., Richmond, VA; *U.S. Public*, pg. 374
Rectanus, Peg, Sr. V.P.-Credit Union Prods. & Svcs.--CUNA Service Group, Inc., Madison, WI; *U.S. Private*, pg. 288
Rector, Del, Sr. V.P.--NTH Consultants, Ltd., Farmington, MI; *U.S. Private*, pg. 772
Rector, Harry, Sr. V.P.-Sls. & Mktg.--Southern Bag Corporation, Madison, MS; *U.S. Private*, pg. 1015
Redden, David M., Sr. V.P.-Human Resources--Marsh Supermarkets, Inc., Indianapolis, IN; *U.S. Public*, pg. 1049
Redditt, Bruce, Sr. V.P.-Corp. Communications & Pub. Affairs--Sony Pictures Entertainment, Culver City, CA; *Int'l*, pg. 1281
Reddy, C.N., Sr. V.P.-Engrng. & Opers. & Sec.--Alliance Semiconductor Corp., San Jose, CA; *U.S. Public*, pg. 47
Redepenning, Charles W., Jr., Sr. V.P., Gen. Counsel & Sec.--Unique Casual Restaurants, inc., Danvers, MA; *Int'l*, pg. 324
Redlinger, Donald J., Sr. V.P.-Human Resources & Communications--AlliedSignal Inc., Morristown, NJ; *U.S. Public*, pg. 49
Redman, Charles B., Sr. V.P.--Hibernia Corporation, New Orleans, LA; *U.S. Public*, pg. 825
Redman, Dennis, Sr. V.P.-Education Div.--Wholesale Electronic Supply, Dallas, TX; *U.S. Private*, pg. 1174
Redman, James D., Sr. V.P.--Rapides Bank & Trust Company of Alexandria, Alexandria, LA; *U.S. Public*, pg. 630
Redman, Monte N., Chief Fin. Officer, Sr. V.P. & Treas.--Astoria Financial Corporation, Lake Success, NY; *U.S. Public*, pg. 141
Redmond, John, Sr. V.P.--MGM Grand Development, Inc., Las Vegas, NV; *U.S. Public*, pg. 1027
Redmond, Lee R., III, Sr. V.P.-Real Estate--Kaiser Ventures, Inc., Ontario, CA; *U.S. Public*, pg. 941
Redo, D.L., Sr. V.P. & Mng. Dir.--The Fremont Group, San Francisco, CA; *U.S. Private*, pg. 427
Reece, Paris G., III, Chief Fin. Officer & Sr. V.P.--M.D.C. Holdings, Inc., Denver, CO; *U.S. Public*, pg. 1025
Reed, Catherine I., Sr. V.P. & Dir.-Mktg.--Brenton Banks, Inc., Des Moines, IA; *U.S. Public*, pg. 251
Reed, Cynthia S., Sr. V.P. & Gen. Counsel--Hasbro, Inc., Pawtucket, RI; *U.S. Public*, pg. 797
Reed, Debra L., Sr. V.P.-Energy Distr. Services--Southern California Gas Co., Los Angeles, CA; *U.S. Public*, pg. 1249
Reed, Gareth L., Sr. V.P. & Grp. V.P.-Camshafts--Weyburn Bartel, Inc., Grand Haven, MI; *Int'l*, pg. 1334
Reed, Howard W., Sr. V.P.-Human Resources--Bayer Corporation, Pittsburgh, PA; *Int'l*, pg. 172
Reed, Mark E., Sr. V.P.-Sls. & Mktg. Service--In Focus Systems, Inc., Wilsonville, OR; *U.S. Public*, pg. 873
Reed, Robert, Sr. V.P. & Gen. Mgr.-Semiconductor Products Group--Intel Corporation, Santa Clara, CA; *U.S. Public*, pg. 886
Reed, William, Sr. V.P. & Sr. Credit Officer--FirstMerit Corporation, Akron, OH; *U.S. Public*, pg. 646
Reeedy, Edward R., Sr. V.P.-Opers.--Golden Eagle Group, Inc., Humble, TX; *U.S. Public*, pg. 749
Reenan, Thomas, Sr. V.P. & Gen. Mgr.--Avon Workshop Ficks Reed, Cincinnati, OH; *U.S. Private*, pg. 102
Rees, William, Sr. V.P.--Huron Valley Steel Corp., Belleville, MI; *U.S. Private*, pg. 549
Reese, Larry, Chief Fin. Officer & Sr. V.P.--ADT Automotive, Inc., Nashville, TN; *U.S. Public*, pg. 1648
Reese, Roger C., Sr. V.P.--Zions Mortgage Company, Salt Lake City, UT; *U.S. Public*, pg. 1793
Reeves, Jerry D., M.D., Chief Medical Officer & Sr. V.P.--Humana Inc., Louisville, KY; *U.S. Public*, pg. 847
Reeves, Jerry D., M.D., Sr. V.P.--Humana Health Insurance of Nevada, Inc., Las Vegas, NV; *U.S. Public*, pg. 847
Reeves, Jerry D., M.D., Sr. V.P.--Employers Health Insurance Company, Green Bay, WI; *U.S. Public*, pg. 847
Reeves, Jerry D., M.D., Sr. V.P.--Humana Insurance Company, Kansas City, MO; *U.S. Public*, pg. 848
Reeves, Jerry D., M.D., Sr. V.P.--Network EPO, Inc., Milwaukee, WI; *U.S. Public*, pg. 848
Reeves, John, Exec. V.P.--The Wheatley Group, Inc., Stamford, CT; *U.S. Public*, pg. 152
Reeves, Ketherine, Sr. V.P. & Cashier--San Angelo National Bank, San Angelo, TX; *U.S. Public*, pg. 633
Reeves, Michael W., Sr. V.P.-Western Agencies--New York Life Insurance Company, New York, NY; *U.S. Private*, pg. 794
Reeves, Robert S., Sr. V.P.-Sls.--Kerr Group, Inc., Lancaster, PA; *U.S. Public*, pg. 952
Regan, John R., Jr., Sr. V.P.-Real Estate Investment Grp.--Fleet Financial Group, Inc., Boston, MA; *U.S. Public*, pg. 648
Regan, Joseph, Sr. V.P.-Sls. & Mktg.--Solectron Corporation, Milpitas, CA; *U.S. Public*, pg. 1483
Regent, Aaron W., Sr. V.P.-Corp. Devel.--EdperBrascan Corporation, Toronto, Canada; *Int'l*, pg. 433
Regis, Jannine, Sr. V.P.-New Bus.--Jordan, McGrath, Case & Taylor Inc., New York, NY; *U.S. Private*, pg. 598
Reglin, David C., Sr. V.P. & Cashier--Independent Bank-West Michigan, Rockford, MI; *U.S. Public*, pg. 874
Rego, Charles A., Sr. V.P.-Produce Opers.--Riser Foods, Inc., Bedford, OH; *U.S. Private*, pg. 450
Rego, Thomas A., Sr. V.P.-Store Devel. & Sec.--Riser Foods, Inc., Bedford, OH; *U.S. Private*, pg. 450
Rehkatch, A.F., Chief Fin. Officer & Sr. V.P.--A&W Food Services of Canada Inc., North Vancouver, Canada; *Int'l, pg. 1*
Rehling, Louise, Sr. V.P.-Devel.--SPSS Inc., Chicago, IL; *U.S. Public*, pg. 1420
Reich, Michael, Chief Information Officer & Sr. V.P.--Presidential Life Corporation, Nyack, NY; *U.S. Public*, pg. 1323
Reichbach, Joseph, Sr. V.P.-Sls. & Mktg.--Merix Corporation, Forest Grove, OR; *U.S. Public*, pg. 1096
Reid, Donald G., Chief Fin. Officer & Sr. V.P.--George Weston Limited, Toronto, Canada; *Int'l*, pg. 1494
Reid, Gerald, Sr. V.P.-Customer Service--Zenith Electronics Corp., Glenview, IL; *U.S. Public*, pg. 1790
Reid, Greg, Sr. V.P.-Mktg.--Yellow Corporation, Overland Park, KS; *U.S. Public*, pg. 1788
Reid, Greg, Sr. V.P.-Mktg.--Yellow Freight System, Inc., Overland Park, KS; *U.S. Public*, pg. 1788
Reid, Robert J., Sr. V.P.--Transcanada Pipelines Limited, Calgary, Canada; *Int'l*, pg. 1416
Reigard, Alan K., Sr. V.P. & Grp. Acct. Dir.--EURO RSCG Dahlin Smith White, LLC, Salt Lake City, UT; *U.S. Private*, pg. 384
Reiland, David P., Chief Fin. Officer & Sr. V.P.--MagneTek, Inc., Nashville, TN; *U.S. Public*, pg. 1037
Reilly, Frank R., Chief Fin. Officer & Sr. V.P.--U.S. Industries, Inc., Iselin, NJ; *U.S. Public*, pg. 1683
Reilly, Richard M., Sr. V.P.--American Arbitration Association, New York, NY; *U.S. Private*, pg. 50
Reilly, William J., Jr., Sr. V.P.--Checkpoint Systems Inc., Thorofare, NJ; *U.S. Public*, pg. 343
Reimers, John, Sr. V.P.-Admin.--Teledyne Ryan Aeronautical, San Diego, CA; *U.S. Public*, pg. 43
Reimers, T., Sr. V.P.--Assurity Life Inc., Lincoln, NE; *U.S. Private*, pg. 1187
Reimers, Todd, Sr. V.P. & Dir.-Agencies--Woodmen Accident & Life Co., Lincoln, NE; *U.S. Private*, pg. 1187
Reinard, Gaston, Sr. V.P.--Banque Internationale a Luxembourg S.A., Luxembourg, Luxembourg; *Int'l*, pg. 162
Reinebach, Thomas J., Chief Info. Officer & Sr. V.P.--Toys "R" Us, Inc., Paramus, NJ; *U.S. Public*, pg. 1626
Reinebach, Thomas J., Sr. V.P.-Distr. & Support Services--Toys "R" Us United States, Paramus, NJ; *U.S. Public*, pg. 1626
Reiner, Gary M., Chief Information Officer & Sr. V.P.--General Electric Company, Fairfield, CT; *U.S. Public*, pg. 709
Reines, Lewis, Sr. V.P.--Harcourt Brace & Company - Elementary Div., Orlando, FL; *U.S. Public*, pg. 783
Reinhard, Michael, Sr. V.P.-Fin.--National Penn Bank, Boyertown, PA; *U.S. Public*, pg. 1159
Reinhardt, P.C., Sr. V.P.-Equities Portfolios--General Electric Investment Corp., Stamford, CT; *U.S. Public*, pg. 712
Reinhart, Francis E., Sr. V.P.-Information Services--Keyport Life Insurance Company, Boston, MA; *U.S. Private*, pg. 666
Reinhart, Peter, Chief Info. Officer & Sr. V.P.--Keyport Life Insurance Company, Boston, MA; *U.S. Private*, pg. 666
Reinhart, Peter S., Sr. V.P. & Gen. Counsel--Hovnanian Enterprises, Inc., Red Bank, NJ; *U.S. Public*, pg. 843
Reinhart, Thomas R., Sr. V.P.--Production Operators, Inc., Houston, TX; *U.S. Public*, pg. 298
Reinking, John, Sr. V.P. & Plng. & Res. Dir.--Dailey & Associates, West Hollywood, CA; *U.S. Public*, pg. 909
Reischauer, Bennett D., Sr. V.P.--Stanley Consultants, Inc., Muscatine, IA; *U.S. Private*, pg. 1033
Reiser, Don, Sr. V.P.-Engrng.--S.T. Research, Newington, VA; *U.S. Private*, pg. 958
Reising, Richard P., Sr. V.P.--Archer Daniels Midland Company (ADM), Decatur, IL; *U.S. Public*, pg. 127
Reisman, Garry, Sr. V.P. & Integrated Dir.--The Lord Group, New York, NY; *U.S. Private*, pg. 325
Reiss, Judy, Sr. V.P. & Acct. Dir.--Young & Rubicam New York, New York, NY; *U.S. Private*, pg. 1198
Reiss, Les, V.P. & Acct. Supvr.--Paul Schulman Co., New York, NY; *Int'l*, pg. 117
Reiss, Robert C., Sr. V.P.--Chubb & Son, Inc., Warren, NJ; *U.S. Public*, pg. 355
Reitan, Bernt, Sr. V.P.-Aluminum Div.--Elkem ASA, Oslo, Norway; *Int'l*, pg. 446
Reitan, Bernt, Sr. V.P.--Elkem Aluminium ANS, Oslo, Norway; *Int'l*, pg. 446
Reiter, Douglas, Sr. V.P.-Sls. & Mktg., Dallas--Safeguard Business Systems, Inc., Fort Washington, PA; *U.S. Private*, pg. 960
Reiter, Robin, Sr. V.P.-BankAtlantic Foundation--BankAtlantic Bancorp, Inc., Fort Lauderdale, FL; *U.S. Public*, pg. 183
Reitman, Jeff, Sr. V.P.-Human Resources--Texas Commerce Bank, Houston, TX; *U.S. Public*, pg. 339
Reitz, Bonnie, Sr. V.P.-Mktg. & Sls. Distr.--Continental Airlines, Houston, TX; *U.S. Public*, pg. 439
Rekrutiak, Kenneth E., Sr. V.P.--Westcoast Energy Inc., Vancouver, Canada; *Int'l*, pg. 1492
Rem, Bemgt A., Sr. V.P.-Corp. Fin. Reporting--Aker Raj Asa, Oslo, Norway; *Int'l*, pg. 41
Remillard, Serge, Sr. V.P.-Admin. & Fin.--Caisse de depot et placement du Quebec, Montreal, Canada; *Int'l*, pg. 249
Rempe, James H., Sr. V.P., Gen. Counsel & Sec.--Manor Care, Inc., Gaithersburg, MD; *U.S. Public*, pg. 1041
Remsen, Michael, Sr. V.P.-Mdsg.--Stein Mart, Inc., Jacksonville, FL; *U.S. Public*, pg. 1514
Remus, Frank, Sr. V.P.-Sls.--Dixon Ticonderoga Company, Heathrow, FL; *U.S. Public*, pg. 514
Renda, Larree M., Sr. V.P.-Corp. Retail Opers.--Safeway Inc., Pleasanton, CA; *U.S. Public*, pg. 1426
Renehan, Patrick L., Sr. V.P.--Kaman Diversified Technologies Corp., Bloomfield, CT; *U.S. Public*, pg. 942
Renkwitz, Linda, Sr. V.P. & Corp. Sec.--Robert Fleming, Inc., New York, NY; *Int'l*, pg. 493
Renn, Robin, Sr. V.P.-Strategic Plng.--American Express Travel Related Services Co., Inc., New York, NY; *U.S. Public*, pg. 73
Renninger, Barry, Exec. V.P. & Chief Oper. Officer--American Foodservice Corp., King of Prussia, PA; *U.S. Private*, pg. 54
Rescoe, Michael E., Chief Fin. Officer, Sr. V.P. & Treas.--PG&E Corporation, San Francisco, CA; *U.S. Public*, pg. 1240
Resinger, Scott, Sr. V.P.-Devel.--Leiner Health Products, Inc., Carson, CA; *U.S. Private*, pg. 659
Resnikoff, Bruce, Sr. V.P.-Special Markets & Prods.--MCA Records, Inc., Universal City, CA; *Int'l*, pg. 1215
Ressler, Azarya, Sr. V.P. & Mgr.--Bank Hapoalim (Chicago), Chicago, IL; *Int'l*, pg. 149
Resweber, Lou, Sr. V.P.--Network Long Distance, Inc., Baton Rouge, LA; *U.S. Public*, pg. 1169
Resweber, Louis J., Sr. V.P.-Investor Relations--United Companies Financial Corporation, Baton Rouge, LA; *U.S. Public*, pg. 1675
Retherford, John C., Chief Fin. Officer & Sr. V.P.-Fin.--Ag-Chem Equipment Co., Inc., Minnetonka, MN; *U.S. Public, pg. 6*
Reuling, Michael F., Exec. V.P.-Store Devel.--Albertson's, Inc., Boise, ID; *U.S. Public*, pg. 38
Reuschle, Robert, Sr. V.P. & Media Dir.--N.W. Ayer & Partners Detroit, Detroit, MI; *U.S. Private*, pg. 104
Reusing, Vincent P., Sr. V.P.-External Relations--Metropolitan Life Insurance Co., New York, NY; *U.S. Private*, pg. 737
Reuss, Daniel J., Sr. V.P., Controller & Treas.--Dain Rauscher Corporation, Minneapolis, MN; *U.S. Public*, pg. 476
Reuther, David, Sr. V.P. & Editor-in-Chief-Morrow Jr. Books--William Morrow & Co., Inc., New York, NY; *U.S. Private, pg. 515*
Revach, Moritz, Sr. V.P.-Southern District--The Israel Electric Corporation Ltd., Haifa, Israel; *Int'l*, pg. 690
Reveman, Lars, Sr. V.P.-Personnel--Svedala Industri AB, Malmo, Sweden; *Int'l*, pg. 1323
Revie, Charles, Sr. V.P.-RMS Unit--Willis Corroon Corp. of Wisconsin, Milwaukee, WI; *Int'l*, pg. 1507
Rexford, John, Sr. V.P.-Corp. Devel.--Affiliated Computer Services, Inc., Dallas, TX; *U.S. Public*, pg. 27
Reymond, Kevin L., Chief Fin. Officer & Sr. V.P.--Viacom Broadcasting Inc., New York, NY; *U.S. Private*, pg. 778
Reynolds, Barbara, Sr. V.P.--Realty One, Cleveland, OH; *U.S. Private*, pg. 914
Reynolds, David W., Sr. V.P.-Admin.--Georgia-Pacific Corporation, Atlanta, GA; *U.S. Public*, pg. 735
Reynolds, Edwin J., Sr. V.P.-Intl.--Cardinal Health Inc., Dublin, OH; *U.S. Public*, pg. 304
Reynolds, Joe, Chief Fin. Officer & Sr. V.P.--RE/MAX International, Inc., Englewood, CO; *U.S. Private*, pg. 912
Reynolds, R.A., Sr. V.P.-Comm/Data Bus.--Graybar Electric Company, Inc., Clayton, MO; *U.S. Private*, pg. 472
Reynolds, Robert D., Pres.-Sls. Grp. & Sr. V.P.--Newsprint South, Inc., Jackson, MS; *U.S. Private*, pg. 797
Reynolds, Terrence E., Sr. V.P.-U.S. Opers.--Midas-International Corp., Chicago, IL; *U.S. Public*, pg. 1766
Reynolds, William D., Sr. V.P.-Mfg.--Varco-Pruden Buildings, Memphis, TN; *U.S. Public*, pg. 1677
Reypert, Neil P., Sr. V.P.--RNBNY Branch Office-Hong Kong, Central, Hong Kong; *U.S. Public*, pg. 1381
Rezende, Ubiratan Simoes, Sr. V.P.-Intl. Opers.--MasTec, Inc., Miami, FL; *U.S. Public*, pg. 1055

Rheault, Janet, Sr. V.P.-Opers.--Jenny Craig, Inc., La Jolla, CA; *U.S. Public*, pg. 926

Rhoads, Gary L., Sr. V.P., Controller & Cashier--National Penn Bank, Boyertown, PA; *U.S. Public*, pg. 1159

Rhoads, R. Darren, Sr. V.P.--Independent Bank, Ionia, MI; *U.S. Public*, pg. 874

Rhoads, Robert K., Sr. V.P., Gen. Counsel & Sec.--Wal-Mart Stores, Inc., Bentonville, AR; *U.S. Public*, pg. 1732

Rhoads, S. Keating, Sr. V.P.-Opers.--Los Angeles Times, Los Angeles, CA; *U.S. Public*, pg. 1616

Rhodes, David L., Jr., Sr. V.P.-Sls. & Mktg.--Unisource Worldwide, Inc., Berwyn, PA; *U.S. Public*, pg. 1670

Rhodes, Stanley, Sr. V.P.--Standard Federal Bank, Troy, MI; *Int'l*, pg. 10

Rhorbacker, Dennis, Sr. V.P.--Creditcorp Div., Los Angeles, CA; *U.S. Public*, pg. 871

Ricahardson, Jerry W., Sr. V.P.-Engrng.--Public Service Company of North Carolina, Inc., Gastonia, NC; *U.S. Public*, pg. 1340

Riccardi, Ralph, Sr. V.P.-Technology/Applications--CIS Technologies, Inc., Tulsa, OK; *U.S. Public*, pg. 1155

Ricciardi, Lawrence R., Sr. V.P. & Gen. Counsel--International Business Machines Corporation, Armonk, NY; *U.S. Public*, pg. 895

Riccio, Bruce, Sr. V.P.-Sls.--Milton Bradley Company, East Longmeadow, MA; *U.S. Public*, pg. 797

Riccitiello, John S., Sr. V.P.--Sara Lee Corporation, Chicago, IL; *U.S. Public*, pg. 1432

Rice, Andrew, Sr. V.P.-Corp. Devel.--Jordan Industries, Inc., Deerfield, IL; *U.S. Private*, pg. 598

Rice, Beverly A., Sr. V.P.-Fashion & Mdsg. Strategy--Jacobson Stores Inc., Jackson, MI; *U.S. Public*, pg. 922

Rice, Dennis, Sr. V.P.-Mktg.--Buena Vista Home Video, Burbank, CA; *U.S. Public*, pg. 513

Rice, James, Sr V.P. & Controller--Essex International, Inc., Fort Wayne, IN; *U.S. Public*, pg. 593

Rice, John, Sr. V.P. & Gen. Mgr.-Personnel--Lever Brothers Co., New York, NY; *Int'l*, pg. 1435

Rice, Ronald R., Sr. V.P.-Mfg.--The Kroger Co., Cincinnati, OH; *U.S. Public*, pg. 967

Rice, Sue, Sr. V.P.-Human Resources--Reed Elsevier Business Information, Newton, MA; *Int'l*, pg. 1095

Rice, William D., Sr. V.P.-Strategic Devel.--Curtice Burns Foods, Rochester, NY; *U.S. Private*, pg. 887

Rich, G. Andrew, Sr. V.P.-Human Resources--Williams-Sonoma, Inc., San Francisco, CA; *U.S. Public*, pg. 1770

Rich, Gary S., Sr. V.P.-Global Human Resources--A.C. Nielsen, Stamford, CT; *U.S. Public*, pg. 1183

Rich, Gerald I., Sr. V.P., Controller & Treas.--Coast Savings Financial, Inc., Los Angeles, CA; *U.S. Public*, pg. 388

Rich, Michael J., Sr. V.P.-Underwriting--The Equitable Companies Incorporated, New York, NY; *U.S. Public*, pg. 588

Rich, Norman, Sr. V.P.-Interactive/Direct Response Grp.--Arnold Advertising, Mc Lean, VA; *U.S. Private*, pg. 84

Richard, Daniel D., Jr., Sr. V.P.-Govt. & Regulatory Rels.--Pacific Gas & Electric Company, San Francisco, CA; *U.S. Public*, pg. 1241

Richard, Greg, Sr. V.P.-Rehability Grp.--American Rehability Services, Inc., Brentwood, TN; *U.S. Public*, pg. 1257

Richard, Peter, Exec. V.P.--P.C. Richard & Son, Farmingdale, NY; *U.S. Private*, pg. 928

Richards, Craig, Sr. V.P.-Sls. & Mktg.--Proteon, Inc., Westborough, MA; *U.S. Public*, pg. 1336

Richards, David, Sr. V.P.-Mktg.--Lenscrafters, Cincinnati, OH; *Int'l*, pg. 822

Richards, George, Sr. V.P.-Mktg. Customers & Clients--Damark International, Inc., Minneapolis, MN; *U.S. Public*, *pg. 478*

Richards, Kip, Sr. V.P.--Sooner Pipe & Supply Corp., Tulsa, OK; *U.S. Private*, pg. 1014

Richards, Sandra, Sr. V.P.--Pac Rim Holding Corporation, Woodland Hills, CA; *U.S. Public*, pg. 1246

Richards, Sandra, Sr. V.P.--The Pacific Rim Assurance Company, Woodland Hills, CA; *U.S. Public*, pg. 1246

Richards, Stanley, Sr. V.P. & Gen. Counsel--General Growth Properties Inc., Chicago, IL; *U.S. Public*, pg. 715

Richards, Stephen D., Sr. V.P. & Gen. Counsel--Consolidated Freightways Corp., Menlo Park, CA; *U.S. Public*, pg. 435

Richards, Steven A., Sr. V.P.--Nabors Drilling USA, Inc., Houston, TX; *U.S. Public*, pg. 1149

Richardson, Alan F., Sr. V.P.--The Bank of Bermuda Limited, Hamilton, Bermuda; *Int'l*, pg. 150

Richardson, Alison S., Sr. V.P.-Admin. & Fin.--Integrity Incorporated, Mobile, AL; *U.S. Public*, pg. 886

Richardson, Betsy, Sr. V.P.-Direct Corp. Mktg.--Fleet Financial Group, Inc., Boston, MA; *U.S. Public*, pg. 648

Richardson, Cantey, Sr. V.P.-Sls & Mktg.--Diversco, Inc., Spartanburg, SC; *U.S. Private*, pg. 336

Richardson, Gregory J., Sr. V.P.--F&G Re, Inc., Morristown, NJ; *U.S. Public*, pg. 1659

Richardson, James R., Sr. V.P.-Mktg.--Flexsteel Industries, Inc., Dubuque, IA; *U.S. Public*, pg. 653

Richardson, Joe, Sr. V.P.--Jim Walter Homes, Inc., Tampa, FL; *U.S. Public*, pg. 1737

Richardson, John D., Sr. V.P. & Gen. Mgr.-U.S. Opers.--Manulife Financial (The Manufacturers Life Insurance Company), Toronto, Canada; *Int'l*, pg. 840

Richardson, Lee, Sr. V.P.-Mktg.--Rich's/Lazarus/Goldsmith's, Atlanta, GA; *U.S. Public*, pg. 618

Richardson, Lindy B., Sr. V.P.-Mktg. & Public Affairs--Columbia/HCA Healthcare Corporation, Nashville, TN; *U.S. Public*, pg. 403

Richardson, Randall, Sr. V.P.--GGP/Homart, Inc., Chicago, IL; *U.S. Public*, pg. 715

Richardson, Roland, Sr. V.P.-Acquisitions--Quorum Health Group, Inc., Brentwood, TN; *U.S. Public*, pg. 1353

Richardson, Valerie, Sr. V.P.-Real Estate--AnnTaylor, Inc., New York, NY; *U.S. Public*, pg. 116

Richey, Joseph B., II, Sr. V.P.-Total Quality Mngmt. & Pres.-Invacare Technologies--Invacare Corporation, Elyria, OH; *U.S. Public*, pg. 911

Richman, Karen, Sr. V.P. & Local Brdcst. Dir.--Grey Advertising Inc., New York, NY; *U.S. Public*, pg. 764

Richman, Larry, Grp. Sr. V.P.-Chicago Commercial Banking--ABN/LaSalle North America Inc., Chicago, IL; *Int'l*, pg. 11

Richmond, John A., Sr. V.P. & Gen. Mgr.-Beet Sugar Opers.--Holly Sugar Corporation, Sugar Land, TX; *U.S. Public*, pg. 872

Richter, Sid, V.P.--Voltelcon, Rancho Cucamonga, CA; *U.S. Public*, pg. 1724

Richter, Steve, Sr. V.P. & Treas.--Weingarten Realty Investors, Houston, TX; *U.S. Public*, pg. 1751

Rickard, David B., Chief Fin. Officer & Sr. V.P.--RJR Nabisco Holdings Corp., New York, NY; *U.S. Public*, pg. 1354

Rickard, Lisa A., Sr. V.P.-Govt. Affairs--Ryder System, Inc., Miami, FL; *U.S. Public*, pg. 1413

Ricketts, Barrie, Chief Fin. Officer & Sr. V.P.--Ball Horticultural Company, West Chicago, IL; *U.S. Private*, pg. 112

Ricottilli, John, Jr., Sr. V.P.--Taco Incorporated, Cranston, RI; *U.S. Private*, pg. 1066

Riddick, Frank A., III, Chief Fin. Officer & Sr. V.P.--Armstrong World Industries, Inc., Lancaster, PA; *U.S. Public*, pg. 131

Rider, R.P. Field, Sr. V.P.--Androscoggin Savings Bank, Lewiston, ME; *U.S. Private*, pg. 74

Ridgeway, R.B., Sr. V.P.-Energy Services--Public Service Company of New Mexico, Albuquerque, NM; *U.S. Public*, *pg. 1339*

Ridgway, Ronald H., Sr. V.P.-Fin.--Pulitzer Publishing Company, Saint Louis, MO; *U.S. Public*, pg. 1343

Ridlehuber, Ronald H., Sr. V.P.-Independent Mktg.--Jefferson-Pilot Life Insurance Co., Greensboro, NC; *U.S. Public*, pg. 926

Ridley, R.S., Sr. V.P.--Miller Freeman Inc., San Francisco, CA; *Int'l*, pg. 1443

Ridley, Scott A., Sr. V.P.--Hibernia Corporation, New Orleans, LA; *U.S. Public*, pg. 825

Rieck, Kim A., Sr. V.P., Gen. Counsel & Sec.--The Edward J. DeBartolo Corporation, Youngstown, OH; *U.S. Private*, *pg. 319*

Ried, Gerald C., Sr. V.P.--Firstar Information Services Corporation, Milwaukee, WI; *U.S. Public*, pg. 643

Rieder, Raymond J., Chief Mktg. Officer & Sr. V.P.--Hudson General Corporation, Great Neck, NY; *U.S. Public*, pg. 845

Riedhammer, Thomas M., Ph.D., Sr. V.P.-Pharmaceuticals, Surgical & Hearing Aids Prods.--Bausch & Lomb Incorporated, Rochester, NY; *U.S. Public*, pg. 194

Riedy, Robert D., Sr. V.P. & Dir.-Retail Leasing--The Rouse Company, Columbia, MD; *U.S. Public*, pg. 1407

Rief, James, Sr. V.P.-Tech. & Admin.--Philip Industrial Services Group, Houston, TX; *Int'l*, pg. 1050

Rieger, Glenn T., Sr. V.P.--Safeguard Scientifics, Inc., Wayne, PA; *U.S. Public*, pg. 1424

Rieger, James, Chief Fin. Officer & Sr. V.P.--Ponderosa Steakhouse, Dallas, TX; *U.S. Private*, pg. 736

Riemer, W. John, Sr. V.P.-Engrng.--Replogle Globes, Inc., Broadview, IL; *U.S. Private*, pg. 923

Rieschel, Gary, Sr. V.P.--Softbank Holdings Inc., Newton, MA; *Int'l*, pg. 1276

Riese, Arthur C., Sr. V.P.--Harding Lawson Associates Group, Inc., Novato, CA; *U.S. Public*, pg. 785

Riffel, Connie, Sr. V.P.-New Bus.--National Health Enhancement Systems, Inc., Phoenix, AZ; *U.S. Public*, pg. 1157

Riffle, Don, Sr. V.P.-Sls. & Mktg.--Sea Watch International, Ltd., Easton, MD; *Int'l*, pg. 928

Riffner, Linda, Sr. V.P.-Mktg.--Commercial Federal Corporation, Omaha, NE; *U.S. Public*, pg. 411

Rifkin, Sue, Sr. V.P. & Media Dir.--Grey Advertising Inc., Western Div., Los Angeles, CA; *U.S. Public*, pg. 764

Rigas, Denny A., Sr. V.P.-Mktg., Tech. & Sls.--Innovative Valve Technology, Inc., Houston, TX; *U.S. Public*, pg. 880

Righini, Giovanna, Sr. V.P.--Tokyo-Mitsubishi Derivative Products (USA), Inc., New York, NY; *Int'l*, pg. 157

Rigsbee, Walter Z., Sr. V.P.-Loan Servicing--Ryland Mortgage Co., Columbia, MD; *U.S. Public*, pg. 1414

Rigsby, Robert E., Sr. V.P.-Fin. & Controller--Virginia Electric and Power Company, Richmond, VA; *U.S. Public*, pg. 516

Rikardsen, Bernhard, Sr. V.P.-Human Resources--Scandinavian Airlines System (SAS), Solna, Sweden; *Int'l*, pg. 1201

Riklin, Matt, Sr. V.P.-Program Enterprises & Distr.--Showtime Networks Inc., New York, NY; *U.S. Private*, pg. 779

Riley, Darren, Sr. V.P.-Intl. Media--Active International, Pearl River, NY; *U.S. Private*, pg. 15

Riley, Kevin P., Sr. V.P.--Keycorp, Cleveland, OH; *U.S. Public*, pg. 954

Riley, Lester W., Sr. V.P. & Pres.-Dermatology & Skin Care--Advanced Polymer Systems, Redwood City, CA; *U.S. Public*, pg. 22

Riley, Michael T., Sr. V.P.-Mktg., Infosvcs. & Opers.--First Financial Bancorp, Hamilton, OH; *U.S. Public*, pg. 632

Rinehart, Charles, Sr. V.P.-New Bus. Devel.--Dayton Newspapers, Inc., Dayton, OH; *U.S. Private*, pg. 281

Rinella, Thomas J., Sr. V.P. & Dir.-Community Lending--St. Paul Bancorp, Inc., Chicago, IL; *U.S. Public*, pg. 1428

Rinella, Thomas J., Sr. V.P.--St. Paul Federal Bank for Savings, Chicago, IL; *U.S. Public*, pg. 1428

Rinella, Thomas J., Sr. V.P.--Community Finance Corporation, Chicago, IL; *U.S. Public*, pg. 1428

Ringel, Barbara A., Ph.D., Sr. V.P. & Strategic Plng. Dir.--Pedone & Partners Adv., Inc., New York, NY; *U.S. Private*, pg. 846

Ringel, Jordan, Sr. V.P.-Bus. Affairs--SFM Media Corporation, New York, NY; *U.S. Private*, pg. 956

Ringler, William, Sr. V.P. & Mgr.-Info. Sys.--Regions Financial Corporation, Birmingham, AL; *U.S. Public*, pg. 1371

Rinke, Douglas H., Sr. V.P.-Human Resources--Mapco Inc., Tulsa, OK; *U.S. Public*, pg. 1042

Riopel, Louis M., Sr. V.P.-Devel.--Societe Generale de Financement du Quebec, Montreal, Canada; *Int'l*, pg. 1274

Ripp, Peter, Chief Fin. Officer & Sr. V.P.--Northville Industries Corp., Melville, NY; *U.S. Private*, pg. 806

Rippy, James B., Sr. V.P.-Mfg. Opers.--Continental General Tire, Inc., Charlotte, NC; *Int'l*, pg. 327

Rishell, Paul, Sr. V.P.-Opers.--Interval International Inc., Miami, FL; *U.S. Public*, pg. 320

Rising, Lowell, Sr. V.P.--Champion Pneumatic Machinery Co., Inc., Princeton, IL; *U.S. Private*, pg. 228

Risinger, James A., Sr. V.P.--Old National Bancorp, Evansville, IN; *U.S. Public*, pg. 1217

Rislakki, Jaakko, Sr. V.P.--United Paper Mills Ltd., Valkeakoski, Finland; *Int'l*, pg. 1429

Ritchie, John, Sr. V.P.-Sls. & Mktg.--KLLM Transport Services, Inc., Jackson, MS; *U.S. Public*, pg. 939

Ritchie, Kim, Sr. V.P.-Technology--AVX Corporation, Myrtle Beach, SC; *Int'l*, pg. 775

Ritgert, Frank, Sr. V.P.-Opers.--American Pad and Paper Company, Dallas, TX; *U.S. Public*, pg. 88

Rittenhouse, Vivian M., Sr. V.P.-Hospital Alliance--Kaiser Permanente, Oakland, CA; *U.S. Private*, pg. 605

Ritter, Barry C., Sr. V.P.-Info. Svcs.--Ameritas Life Insurance Corp., Lincoln, NE; *U.S. Private*, pg. 65

Ritter, Henry L., Chief Oper. Officer & Sr. V.P.--Albert Kahn Associates, Inc., Detroit, MI; *U.S. Private*, pg. 604

Ritter, P.C., Sr. V.P.-Sls.--Mack Trucks, Inc., Allentown, PA; *Int'l*, pg. 1102

Rivera-Soto, Roberto, Sr. V.P. & Gen. Counsel--Caesars World, Inc., Las Vegas, NV; *U.S. Public*, pg. 1512

Rivera, Haydee, Sr. V.P.-Branch Banking Opers.--Firstbank Puerto Rico, Santurce, PR; *U.S. Public*, pg. 644

Rivera, Petronio Y., Sr. V.P.--Benguet Corporation, Manila, Philippines; *Int'l*, pg. 186

Rivers, Al, Sr. V.P.-Comml. Loans--Magna Group, Inc., Saint Louis, MO; *U.S. Public*, pg. 1037

Rivers, Deborah A., Sr. V.P.-Acct. Mngmt.--Towne, Silverstein, Rotter Inc., New York, NY; *U.S. Private*, pg. 1093

Rivers, Tom, Sr. V.P. & Branch Mgr.--Willis Corroon Melling Ltd., Vancouver, Canada; *Int'l*, pg. 1509

Rives, James C., Sr. V.P.--Seitel, Inc., Houston, TX; *U.S. Public*, pg. 1454

Riviere, Charles J., Sr. V.P. & Dir. Gen.-SRA Europe--SRA International Inc., Arlington, VA; *U.S. Private*, pg. 957

Rizer, E. Lloyd, Sr. V.P.-Fin.--The Hotsy Corporation, Englewood, CO; *U.S. Private*, pg. 500

Rizzardi, Dennis, Sr. V.P.--Wilcox Electric, Inc., Kansas City, MO; *Int'l*, pg. 1384

Rizzo, G.A., Sr. V.P.--Exxon Chemical Company, Houston, TX; *U.S. Public*, pg. 601

Rizzo, Louis J., Sr. V.P.-Store Opers. & Devel.--Buttrey Food & Drug Company, Great Falls, MT; *U.S. Public*, pg. 271

Roach, Charles T., Sr. V.P. & Gen. Mgr.-Sun City West & Sun City Grand--Del Webb Corporation, Phoenix, AZ; *U.S. Public*, pg. 494

Roach, Robin L., Sr. V.P.-Corp. Fin.--Franchise Finance Corp. of America, Scottsdale, AZ; *U.S. Public*, pg. 679

Roales, Judith, Exec. V.P. & Publr.--The Times Publishing Co., Saint Petersburg, FL; *U.S. Private*, pg. 1087

Robason, Jim, Sr. V.P.-Opers.--Allen Canning Company, Siloam Springs, AR; *U.S. Private*, pg. 36

Robbin, Bruce B., Sr. V.P.-Multinational--PNC Bank, N.A., Pittsburgh, PA; *U.S. Public*, pg. 1243

Robbins, Barry D., Sr. V.P.-Strategic Plng.--TBC Corporation, Memphis, TN; *U.S. Public*, pg. 1553

Robbins, Carol, Sr. V.P.-Mktg.--Prudential Securities Inc., New York, NY; *U.S. Private*, pg. 892

Robbins, Charles, III, Sr. V.P. & Reg. Exec. Officer--First Virginia Banks, Inc., Falls Church, VA; *U.S. Public*, pg. 641

Robbins, Donald M., Sr. V.P., Gen. Counsel & Sec.--Hasbro, Inc., Pawtucket, RI; *U.S. Public*, pg. 797

Robbins, Joseph H., Sr. V.P.--Robbins Manufacturing Company, Tampa, FL; *U.S. Private*, pg. 935

Robbins, Michael, Sr. V.P.-Worldwide Opers.--Trivoli Systems, Indianapolis, IN; *U.S. Public*, pg. 896

Robbins, Robert W., Sr. V.P.-Sls.--Synovus Financial Corp., Columbus, GA; *U.S. Public*, pg. 1548

Robbins, Thomas M., Sr. V.P.-Eastern Zone--Apria Healthcare Group Inc., Costa Mesa, CA; *U.S. Public*, pg. 125

Robbins, Tom, Sr. V.P.-Mktg.--Delchamps, Inc., Mobile, AL; *U.S. Private*, pg. 588

Roberson, Dennis A., Chief Tech. Officer & Sr. V.P.--NCR Corporation, Dayton, OH; *U.S. Public*, pg. 1146

Roberts, Gary, Chief Fin. Officer, Sr. V.P.-Admin. & Sec.--Sierracin Corporation, Sylmar, CA; *U.S. Private*, pg. 999

Roberts, Hugh, Sr. V.P.-Strategy--Kraft Foods, Inc., Northfield, IL; *U.S. Public*, pg. 1287

Roberts, J.L., Sr. V.P.--Marshall & Ilsley Corporation, Milwaukee, WI; *U.S. Public*, pg. 1049

Roberts, James C., Sr. V.P.-Admin.--South Trust Bank of Georgia, Atlanta, GA; *U.S. Public*, pg. 1492

Roberts, Janice M., Sr. V.P.-Mktg. & Bus. Devel.--3Com Corporation, Santa Clara, CA; *U.S. Public*, pg. 1603

Roberts, Jerry, Sr. V.P.-Network Bus. Devel.--BBDO Worldwide Inc., New York, NY; *U.S. Public*, pg. 1223

Roberts, John D., Chief Trust Officer & Sr. V.P.--NBT Bancorp Inc., Norwich, NY; *U.S. Public*, pg. 1144

Roberts, John S., Sr. V.P.--UNUM Life Insurance Company of America, Portland, ME; *U.S. Public*, pg. 1699

Roberts, Keith C., Sr. V.P., Exec. V.P.-Riedel Environmental Services Inc.--Smith Technologies Corp., Portland, OR; *U.S. Public*, pg. 1478

Roberts, Michael, Sr. V.P.--Jim Walter Homes, Inc., Tampa, FL; *U.S. Public*, pg. 1737

Roberts, Norman L., Sr. V.P. & Gen. Counsel--Western Atlas Inc., Houston, TX; *U.S. Public*, pg. 1757

Roberts, Ralph L., II, Exec. V.P.-Opers.--Gator Freightways, Inc., Wilmington, OH; *U.S. Private*, pg. 441
Roberts, Richard S., Pres.-Fibers & Sr. V.P.--Guilford Mills, Inc., Greensboro, NC; *U.S. Public*, pg. 768
Roberts, Skip, Sr. V.P.--N.W. Ayer & Partners Detroit, Detroit, MI; *U.S. Private*, pg. 104
Roberts, Stephen, Sr. V.P.-Asia-Pacific--Lehman Brothers Holdings Inc., New York, NY; *U.S. Public*, pg. 987
Roberts, Wm. Juan, Sr. V.P. & Creative Dir.--Don Coleman Advertising, Inc., Southfield, MI; *U.S. Private*, pg. 251
Robertson, David, Sr. V.P. & Gen. Mgr.-U.S.A.--Royal Bank of Canada, New York, NY; *Int'l*, pg. 1131
Robertson, David L., Sr. V.P.-H.R.--Rubbermaid Incorporated, Wooster, OH; *U.S. Public*, pg. 1411
Robertson, J Michael, Sr. V.P.--Tighe Industries, Inc., York, PA; *U.S. Private*, pg. 1086
Robertson, Jim, Sr. V.P.-Cash & Carry--Provigo Distribution, Montreal, Canada; *Int'l*, pg. 1073
Robertson, K.N., Sr. V.P.--Exxon Chemical Company, Houston, TX; *U.S. Public*, pg. 601
Robertson, Lowell L., Sr. V.P. & Controller--The Dial Corporation, Phoenix, AZ; *U.S. Public*, pg. 505
Robertson, Mary Jane, Chief Fin. Officer & Sr. V.P.--Capsure Holdings Corp., Chicago, IL; *U.S. Public*, pg. 303
Robertson, Monroe W., Sr. V.P. & Sec.--Key Production Company, Inc., Denver, CO; *U.S. Public*, pg. 953
Robertson, P.J., Sr. V.P.-Alberta Div.--Bank of Montreal - Calgary, Calgary, Canada; *Int'l*, pg. 153
Robertson, Paul W., Sr. V.P.-Mktg.--Baton Broadcasting Incorporated, Scarborough, Canada; *Int'l*, pg. 170
Robertson, Walter, Sr. V.P.-Commercial--GS Industries, Inc., Charlotte, NC; *U.S. Private*, pg. 435
Robertson, William J., Chief Oper. Officer & Sr. V.P.--Cominco, Ltd., Vancouver, Canada; *Int'l*, pg. 307
Robey, Randall, Chief Fin. Officer & Sr. V.P.--The Annapolis Banking & Trust Co., Annapolis, MD; *U.S. Public*, pg. 1088
Robidoux, Roy, Sr. V.P.-Mktg. & Sls.--The Cerplex Group, Inc., Tustin, CA; *U.S. Public*, pg. 332
Robie, Calvin, Sr. V.P.--BWC Financial Corp., Walnut Creek, CA; *U.S. Private*, pg. 108
Robie, Richard S., III, Sr. V.P.--United Asset Management Corporation, Boston, MA; *U.S. Public*, pg. 1672
Robillard, Don, Sr. V.P.-Fin.--Hunt Oil Company, Dallas, TX; *U.S. Private*, pg. 548
Robin, Kenneth, Sr. V.P. & Gen. Counsel--Household International, Inc., Prospect Heights, IL; *U.S. Public*, pg. 842
Robins, Irwin B., Sr. V.P.--Volt Information Sciences, Inc., New York, NY; *U.S. Public*, pg. 1724
Robins, W. Randolph, Sr. V.P.--Universal Leaf Tobacco Company, Inc., Richmond, VA; *U.S. Public*, pg. 1694
Robinson, Caren, Sr. V.P. & Dir.-Mktg.--City National Corporation, Beverly Hills, CA; *U.S. Public*, pg. 380
Robinson, Connie, Sr. V.P. & Grp. Plng. Dir.--Western International Media Corporation, Los Angeles, CA; *U.S. Private*, pg. 1165
Robinson, Douglas, Sr. V.P.-Investor Rels.--Computer Associates International, Inc., Islandia, NY; *U.S. Public*, pg. 420
Robinson, Earl J., Sr. V.P.-Product Devel.--Fairchild Aerospace Corporation, San Antonio, TX; *U.S. Private*, pg. 391
Robinson, Ed, Sr. V.P. & Gen. Counsel--Harrah's Entertainment, Inc., Memphis, TN; *U.S. Public*, pg. 790
Robinson, James, Sr. V.P.-Counsellor To The Pres.--Nation's Business, Washington, DC; *U.S. Private*, pg. 788
Robinson, Jeffrey F., Sr. V.P.-Insurance--Fair, Isaac and Company, Inc., San Rafael, CA; *U.S. Public*, pg. 609
Robinson, John R., Sr. V.P., Controller & Treas.--Purity Dairies Inc., Nashville, TN; *U.S. Private*, pg. 895
Robinson, Joseph A., Chief Fin. Officer, Sr. V.P., Treas. & Sec.--Excel Industries, Inc., Elkhart, IN; *U.S. Public*, pg. 598
Robinson, Mark, Sr. V.P. & Creative Dir.--Austin Kelley Advertising, Inc., Atlanta, GA; *U.S. Private*, pg. 100
Robinson, Neal E., Sr. V.P.-Fin. & Acctg.--Banknorth Group Inc., Burlington, VT; *U.S. Public*, pg. 186
Robinson, Peter, Sr. V.P.--Hazen & Sawyer, New York, NY; *U.S. Private*, pg. 514
Robinson, Richard L., Sr. V.P.--Associates Financial Services Corporation, Dallas, TX; *U.S. Public*, pg. 663
Robinson, Robert L., Sr. V.P.--Cigna Corp., Philadelphia, PA; *U.S. Public*, pg. 356
Robinson, Stephen D., Sr. V.P.-Gen. Mdse.--Pamida, Inc., Omaha, NE; *U.S. Public*, pg. 1255
Robinson, Steven A., Sr. V.P.-Mktg.--Chick-fil-A, Inc., Atlanta, GA; *U.S. Private*, pg. 236
Robinson, Tom, Sr. V.P.--MGM Grand Development, Inc., Las Vegas, NV; *U.S. Public*, pg. 1027
Robinson, W., Sr. V.P.--GS Industries, Inc., Charlotte, NC; *U.S. Private*, pg. 435
Robinson, William B., Sr. V.P.-Mktg.--United Family Life Insurance Co., Atlanta, GA; *Int'l*, pg. 499
Robison, Shane, Sr. V.P.-Engrng.--Cadence Design Systems, Inc., San Jose, CA; *U.S. Public*, pg. 290
Robison, William J., Sr. V.P.-Employee Resources--Pfizer Inc., New York, NY; *U.S. Public*, pg. 1281
Robson, Peter, Sr. V.P.--Kraft Jacobs Suchard AG, Zurich, Switzerland; *U.S. Public*, pg. 1288
Robuste, Fidias, Exec. V.P. & Mng. Dir.--Molinos Nacionales, C.A. (Venezuela), Caracas, Venezuela; *U.S. Public*, pg. 901
Rocca, Michael A., Chief Fin. Officer & Sr. V.P.--Mallinckrodt Inc., Saint Louis, MO; *U.S. Public*, pg. 1039
Rocco, James V., Sr. V.P.-Opers.--Valvoline Company, Lexington, KY; *U.S. Public*, pg. 139
Roche, David H., Sr. V.P.--Savannah Foods & Industries, Inc., Savannah, GA; *U.S. Public*, pg. 872
Roche, John J., Sr. V.P.--The Flatley Company, Braintree, MA; *U.S. Private*, pg. 410
Roche, Susan, Sr. V.P. & Human Resources Dir.--Arnold Communications, Inc., Boston, MA; *U.S. Private*, pg. 83
Rochester, Ralph G., Sr. V.P.-Sls. & Mktg.--Comcast Cable Communications, Inc., Philadelphia, PA; *U.S. Public*, pg. 407
Rock, Robert D., Sr. V.P.-Individual Annuity--New York Life Insurance Company, New York, NY; *U.S. Private*, pg. 794
Rockwell, Lloyd, Sr. V.P.-Opers./Wine Div.--Canandaigua Wine Company, Inc., Canandaigua, NY; *U.S. Public*, pg. 300
Rodby, Craig R., Sr. V.P.--Northwestern National Life Insurance Co., Minneapolis, MN; *U.S. Public*, pg. 1375
Rodefeld, James A., Sr. V.P.-Mktg.--Jacobson Stores Inc., Jackson, MI; *U.S. Public*, pg. 922
Rodelli, Gerald N., Sr. V.P.--Stonecutter Mills Corp., Spindale, NC; *U.S. Private*, pg. 1044
Roder, Ronald E., Sr. V.P.--Firstar Milwaukee Bank, N.A., Milwaukee, WI; *U.S. Public*, pg. 643
Rodgers, Franklin H., Sr. V.P.-Admin. Opers.--Western National Corporation, Houston, TX; *U.S. Public*, pg. 76
Rodgers, Franklin H., Sr. V.P.-Admin.--Western National Life Insurance Co., Houston, TX; *U.S. Public*, pg. 76
Rodgers, John A., Sr. V.P.-New Bus. Devel.--Starbucks Coffee Company, Seattle, WA; *U.S. Public*, pg. 1510
Rodler, John, Chief Fin. Officer, Sr. V.P., Treas. & Sec.--Folger Nolan Fleming Douglas, Washington, DC; *U.S. Private*, pg. 416
Rodriguez, Eduardo A., Sr. V.P.-Customer & Corp. Svcs.--El Paso Electric Company, El Paso, TX; *U.S. Public*, pg. 567
Rodriguez, Jose H., Sr. V.P.-Branch Banking Opers.--Firstbank Puerto Rico, Santurce, PR; *U.S. Public*, pg. 644
Rodriguez, Luis Fernando, Sr. V.P.-Mktg.--Banco Popular de Puerto Rico, San Juan, PR; *U.S. Public*, pg. 175
Rodriguez, Plinio, Sr. V.P.-Security--Banco Popular de Puerto Rico, San Juan, PR; *U.S. Public*, pg. 175
Rodriguez, Robert A., Dr., Sr. V.P. & Exec. Dir.-Special Projects--La Petite Academy Inc., Overland Park, KS; *U.S. Private*, pg. 640
Roe, Christian, Sr. V.P.-Fin.--Reinalt-Thomas Corp., Ann Arbor, MI; *U.S. Private*, pg. 919
Roe, Harwood S., Jr., Sr. V.P.-Opers.--Sun Company, Inc., Philadelphia, PA; *U.S. Public*, pg. 1530
Roe, Paula S., Sr. V.P.-Compensation Benefits--Norwest Corporation, Minneapolis, MN; *U.S. Public*, pg. 1201
Roe, Robert L., Dr., Pres.-Syntex Devel. Res. & Sr. V.P.--Syntex, Palo Alto, CA; *Int'l*, pg. 1120
Roeck, Thomas J., Jr., Chief Fin. Officer & Sr. V.P.-Fin.--Delta Air Lines, Inc., Atlanta, GA; *U.S. Public*, pg. 497
Roehlk, Thomas, Sr. V.P., Gen. Counsel & Sec.--Tupperware Corporation, Orlando, FL; *U.S. Public*, pg. 1644
Roehm, James R., Sr. V.P.--Erie Family Life Insurance Company, Erie, PA; *U.S. Public*, pg. 590
Roentgen, Konrad, Dr., Sr. V.P.-Info. Tech.--Commerzbank AG, Frankfurt, Germany; *Int'l*, pg. 308
Rogenstein, Janet, Sr. V.P.-Corp. Svcs.--The American Stock Exchange, New York, NY; *U.S. Private*, pg. 62
Rogers, J. Artie, Sr. V.P.-Fin. & Sec.--Empire of Carolina, Inc., Delray Beach, FL; *U.S. Public*, pg. 579
Rogers, James, Sr. V.P.--General Electric Company, Fairfield, CT; *U.S. Public*, pg. 709
Rogers, James, Sr. V.P. & Treas.--MidCoast Mortgage Corporation, Lake Worth, FL; *U.S. Private*, pg. 744
Rogers, James P., Chief Fin. Officer & Sr. V.P.--GAF Corporation, Wayne, NJ; *U.S. Private*, pg. 433
Rogers, James P., Chief Fin. Officer & Sr. V.P.--G Industries Corporation, Wilmington, DE; *U.S. Private*, pg. 433
Rogers, James P., Chief Fin. Officer & Sr. V.P.--GAF Materials Corporation, Wayne, NJ; *U.S. Private*, pg. 433
Rogers, James P., Chief Fin. Officer & Sr. V.P.--Building Materials Corporation of America, Wayne, NJ; *U.S. Private*, pg. 433
Rogers, James P., Chief Fin. Officer & Sr. V.P.--ISP Holdings, Inc., Wayne, NJ; *U.S. Public*, pg. 858
Rogers, James P., Sr. V.P.-Fin. & Treas.--International Specialty Products, Inc., Wayne, NJ; *U.S. Public*, pg. 858
Rogers, Jeff, Sr. V.P.-Investor Rels.--The Money Store, Sacramento, CA; *U.S. Public*, pg. 1124
Rogers, Jim, Sr. V.P. & Gen. Mgr.--Harrah's Reno Holding Company, Carson City, NV; *U.S. Public*, pg. 791
Rogers, John, Sr. V.P.-Minerals--SGS Societe Generale de Surveillance Holding S.A., Geneva, Switzerland; *Int'l*, pg. 1153
Rogers, Mark C., Dr., Chief Tech. Officer & Sr. V.P.-Corp. Devel.--The Perkin-Elmer Corporation, Norwalk, CT; *U.S. Public*, pg. 1279
Rogers, Nancy A., Sr. V.P.-Mktg. Svcs. & Sec.--Ameriana Bancorp, New Castle, IN; *U.S. Public*, pg. 66
Rogers, Randall K., Sr. V.P.-Opers.--TCA Cable TV, Inc., Tyler, TX; *U.S. Public*, pg. 1553
Rogers, Shelby R., Sr. V.P. & Gen. Counsel--Texas Commerce Bank, Houston, TX; *U.S. Public*, pg. 339
Rogers, Thomas W., Sr. V.P.-Sls. & Mktg.--IMCO Recycling Inc., Irving, TX; *U.S. Public*, pg. 870
Rogers, Todd, Sr. V.P.-Fin. & Admin.--DocuCorp International, Dallas, TX; *U.S. Public*, pg. 1425
Rogliano, Gary R., Chief Fin. Officer & Sr. V.P.--The Pittston Company, Glen Allen, VA; *U.S. Public*, pg. 1305
Rogna, Lawrence G., Sr. V.P.--Gaylord Container Corporation, Deerfield, IL; *U.S. Public*, pg. 704
Rognerud, D.M., Sr. V.P.--Ziegler Securities Division, Chicago, IL; *U.S. Public*, pg. 1792
Rogoff, Ellen K., Sr. V.P.-Human Resources--Broad National Bancorporation, Newark, NJ; *U.S. Public*, pg. 257
Rohde, Mark R., Sr. V.P.-Sls. & Mktg.--Cincinnati Bell Information Systems Inc., Cincinnati, OH; *U.S. Public*, pg. 367
Rohde, Mark W., Sr. V.P.--TCF Bank Illinois, Oak Brook, IL; *U.S. Public*, pg. 1554
Rohling, Edward J., Sr. V.P.-Corp. Devel.--Bristol Hotels & Resorts, Dallas, TX; *U.S. Public*, pg. 253
Rohloff, Winfried, Sr. V.P.-Worldwide Sls., Mktg. & Services--CalComp Technology, Inc., Anaheim, CA; *U.S. Public*, pg. 1007
Rohrbach, Kate, Sr. V.P.-Corp. Commun.--The Charles Schwab Corporation, San Francisco, CA; *U.S. Public*, pg. 1442
Rohrer, Doug, Sr. V.P.-Adv. Sls.-MTV & VH1--MTV Networks, New York, NY; *U.S. Private*, pg. 779
Roland, Mark C., Sr. V.P.-Eastern Div.--World Acceptance Corporation, Greenville, SC; *U.S. Public*, pg. 1778
Rollans, James O., Chief Admin. Officer & Sr. V.P.--Fluor Corporation, Irvine, CA; *U.S. Public*, pg. 659
Rollins, Kevin B., Sr. V.P. & Gen. Mgr.-Americas--Dell Computer Corporation, Round Rock, TX; *U.S. Public*, pg. 495
Roloff, Kirk D., Chief Fin. Officer & Sr. V.P.--Monticello Management Co., San Diego, CA; *U.S. Private*, pg. 759
Rolston, Bill, Sr. V.P.--ElectroCom Automation L.P., Arlington, TX; *Int'l*, pg. 1244
Roman, Geoff, Sr. V.P.-Sls. & Support--Broadband Networks Group, Hatboro, PA; *U.S. Public*, pg. 716
Roman, Spencer M., Sr. V.P.-Home Office Opers.--Harleysville Group, Harleysville, PA; *U.S. Public*, pg. 786
Romandetti, John A., Sr. V.P.--Advantica Restaurant Group, Inc., Spartanburg, SC; *U.S. Public*, pg. 22
Romano, Anthony, Sr. V.P.-Logistics--AnnTaylor, Inc., New York, NY; *U.S. Public*, pg. 116
Romano, James, Sr. V.P.--The Sherwood Group, Inc., Jersey City, NJ; *U.S. Public*, pg. 1466
Romanov, Edward B., Jr., Sr. V.P.-Devel.--Genesis Health Ventures, Inc., Kennett Square, PA; *U.S. Public*, pg. 728
Romberg, Bert, Sr. V.P.--Commercial Metals Company, Dallas, TX; *U.S. Public*, pg. 411
Romer, Gordon, Sr. V.P.--Physician Computer Network, Inc., Morris Plains, NJ; *U.S. Public*, pg. 1293
Romero, James, Sr. V.P.--Sun TV & Appliances, Inc., Groveport, OH; *U.S. Public*, pg. 1532
Romick, Steven T., Sr. V.P.--First Pacific Advisors, Inc., Los Angeles, CA; *U.S. Public*, pg. 1673
Romieu, Michel, Sr. V.P.-Natural Gas--Elf Aquitane, Paris, France; *Int'l*, pg. 444
Romita, Louis, Sr. V.P.--Castle Oil Corporation, Harrison, NY; *U.S. Private*, pg. 219
Romm, Marcy A., Sr. V.P. & Dir.-H.R.--ICF Kaiser International Inc., Fairfax, VA; *U.S. Public*, pg. 852
Romo, Larry, Sr. V.P. & Dir.-Lending--First Federal FSB, Hutchinson, MN; *U.S. Public*, pg. 608
Ronan, Tim, Sr. V.P. & Grp. Acct. Dir.--Long Haymes Carr, Inc., Winston Salem, NC; *U.S. Public*, pg. 909
Roney, Michelle, Sr. V.P.--Mars Advertising Co., Southfield, MI; *U.S. Private*, pg. 706
Roof, Donald L., Chief Fin. Officer & Sr. V.P.-Finance--J.H. Heafner Co. Inc., Lincolnton, NC; *U.S. Private*, pg. 514
Roolf, James M., Sr. V.P. & Dir.-Corp. Communications--First Midwest Bancorp, Inc., Itasca, IL; *U.S. Public*, pg. 636
Rooney, Gerry, Sr. V.P.-Opers.--Joy Mining Machinery, Warrendale, PA; *U.S. Public*, pg. 790
Rooney, John, Sr. V.P.-Natl. Sls.--Carillon Importers, Ltd., Fort Lee, NJ; *Int'l*, pg. 409
Root, C. William, Sr. V.P.--First National Bank of Naples, Naples, FL; *U.S. Public*, pg. 607
Root, Gordon C., Sr. V.P.-Sls. & Distr. Strategy--Successful Money Management Seminars, Inc., Tualatin, OR; *U.S. Public*, pg. 1376
Roper, William W., III, Sr. V.P.--Chubb & Son, Inc., Warren, NJ; *U.S. Public*, pg. 355
Ropers, Stefan W., Sr. V.P.--Bayerische Landesbank Girozentrale - Frankfurt Branch, Frankfurt, Germany; *Int'l*, pg. 176
Roren, Eivald M.Q., Sr. V.P.--Det Norske Veritas, Hovik, Norway; *Int'l*, pg. 396
Rorie, Albert S., Sr. V.P.-Data Processing--Family Dollar Stores, Inc., Matthews, NC; *U.S. Public*, pg. 612
Rose, Anthony D., Jr., Sr. V.P.-Adv.--AutoZone, Inc., Memphis, TN; *U.S. Public*, pg. 150
Rose, Carolyn, Sr. V.P. & Gen. Mgr.--Novell, Inc., Orem, UT; *U.S. Public*, pg. 1203
Rose, Clark, Sr. V.P.-Opers./Oil Recovery & Envirosystems--Safety-Kleen Corp., Elgin, IL; *U.S. Public*, pg. 1425
Rose, James, Sr. V.P.-Taxes & Govt. Affairs--Tupperware Corporation, Orlando, FL; *U.S. Public*, pg. 1644
Rose, John T., Sr. V.P.-Enterprise Computing--COMPAQ Computer Corporation, Houston, TX; *U.S. Public*, pg. 417
Rose, M. Robert, Sr. V.P.-Credit Policy--BayBanks, Inc., Boston, MA; *U.S. Public*, pg. 184
Rose, Matthew K., Chief Oper. Officer & Sr. V.P.--Burlington Northern Santa Fe Corporation, Fort Worth, TX; *U.S. Public*, pg. 268
Rose, Michael C., Sr. V.P.--Marketing Communications, Lenexa, KS; *U.S. Public*, pg. 794
Rose, Michael E., Chief Fin. Officer & Sr. V.P.-Fin.--Anadarko Petroleum Corporation, Houston, TX; *U.S. Public*, pg. 107
Rose, Timothy L., Sr. V.P.-Mdsg., Foods, Sundries & Fresh Foods--Costco Wholesale, Issaquah, WA; *U.S. Public*, pg. 451
Roselin, Phillip D., Sr. V.P. & Mng. Dir.-Proworx--Cline, Davis & Mann, Inc., New York, NY; *U.S. Private*, pg. 246
Rosello, Jossiane, Sr. V.P.-Mktg. & Pub. Rels.--Firstbank Puerto Rico, Santurce, PR; *U.S. Public*, pg. 644
Rosen, Andrea S., Sr. V.P.-Investment Banking, CIBG--The Toronto Dominion Bank, Toronto, Canada; *Int'l*, pg. 1401
Rosen, Carl E., Sr. V.P.--Bulova Corporation, Woodside, NY; *U.S. Public*, pg. 1010
Rosen, Deborah, Sr. V.P.-Corp. Communications & Pub. Affairs--Universal Studios, Inc., Universal City, CA; *Int'l*, pg. 1215
Rosen, Fredric K., Sr. V.P.--Gerber Scientific, Inc., South Windsor, CT; *U.S. Public*, pg. 740
Rosen, Hy, Sr. V.P. & Grp. Creative Dir.--Grey Advertising Inc., New York, NY; *U.S. Public*, pg. 764

Rosen, Shelley, Sr. V.P.--Simon Marketing, Inc., Oak Brook Terrace, IL; *U.S. Private*, pg. 1001

Rosenast, Hilmar A., Sr. V.P.-Western Reg.--Hilton Hotels Div., Beverly Hills, CA; *U.S. Public*, pg. 829

Rosenberg, Andrew, Sr. V.P.-Mktg.--General Textiles, San Diego, CA; *U.S. Private*, pg. 445

Rosenberg, Barnett, Sr. V.P., Gen. Counsel & Sec.--Mattel, Inc., El Segundo, CA; *U.S. Public*, pg. 1057

Rosenberg, Frank B., Sr. V.P.-Mktg.--Crown Central Petroleum Corporation, Baltimore, MD; *U.S. Public*, pg. 462

Rosenberg, George-Ann, Sr. V.P.--Edelman Worldwide, Inc., Washington, DC; *U.S. Private*, pg. 362

Rosenberg, Gerald B., Sr. V.P.-Pharmaceutical Div.--Bayer Corporation, Pittsburgh, PA; *Int'l*, pg. 172

Rosenberg, Gerald B., Sr. V.P.-Mktg. & Sls.--Bayer Corporation/Pharmaceutical Division, West Haven, CT; *Int'l*, pg. 173

Rosenberg, Leon E., Sr. V.P.-Scientific Affairs--Bristol-Myers Squibb Company, New York, NY; *U.S. Public*, pg. 253

Rosenberg, Marc, Sr. V.P.-Sls. & Prod. Distr.--Air Canada, Saint-Laurent, Canada; *Int'l*, pg. 36

Rosenberg, Marvin B., Sr. V.P. & Gen. Counsel--Terex Corporation, Westport, CT; *U.S. Public*, pg. 1581

Rosenberg, Michael, Sr. V.P.--Keywell Corporation, Chicago, IL; *U.S. Private*, pg. 619

Rosenberg, Michael, Sr. V.P.--Metallgesellschaft Corp., New York, NY; *Int'l*, pg. 861

Rosenberg, Philip G., 1st Sr. V.P., Treas., Controller & Asst. Sec.--Morse Shoe, Inc., Canton, MA; *U.S. Public*, pg. 168

Rosenberg, Robert C., Sr. V.P.--Starrett HRH, New York, NY; *U.S. Private*, pg. 1035

Rosenberg, Zach, Sr. V.P. & Acct. Grp. Dir.--Western International Media Corporation, Los Angeles, CA; *U.S. Private*, pg. 1165

Rosenblatt, Charlotte, Sr. V.P. & Creative Production Resources Dir.--DMB&B New York, New York, NY; *U.S. Private*, pg. 302

Rosenbloom, Harvey, Sr. V.P. & Dir.-Stores/W. Region--Saks Fifth Avenue, New York, NY; *U.S. Public*, pg. 1429

Rosenblum, Harvey, Sr. V.P.-Res. & Statistics & Dir.-Res.--Federal Reserve Bank of Dallas, Dallas, TX; *U.S. Private*, pg. 399

Rosenblum, Kenneth, Sr. V.P.-Sls./Home Entertainment--Shorewood Packaging Corporation, New York, NY; *U.S. Public*, pg. 1468

Rosenblum, William F., Sr. V.P., Deputy Gen. Counsel & Corp. Sec.--Republic New York Corporation, New York, NY; *U.S. Public*, pg. 1380

Rosenburgh, Carleton F., Sr. V.P.-Gannett Newspaper Div.--Gannett Company, Inc., Arlington, VA; *U.S. Public*, pg. 698

Rosencrantz, Fredrik, Sr. V.P.-Indus. & Marine Insurance--Trygg-Hansa, Stockholm, Sweden; *Int'l*, pg. 1425

Rosendahl, William, Sr. V.P.--Cable Television Division, New Canaan, CT; *U.S. Public*, pg. 329

Rosenfield, Ruth, Sr. V.P. & Creative Dir.--Hal Riney & Partners, Inc., San Francisco, CA; *U.S. Private*, pg. 931

Rosengard, Andrew, Sr. V.P. & Controller--Cablevision Systems Corporation, Woodbury, NY; *U.S. Public*, pg. 288

Rosengren, William R., Sr. V.P.-Law & Gen. Counsel--Ecolab Inc., Saint Paul, MN; *U.S. Public*, pg. 562

Rosenkoetter, Glenn N., Sr. V.P.-Payor Solutions Grp. & HBOC U.K. Ltd.--HBOC, Atlanta, GA; *U.S. Public*, pg. 770

Rosenkranz, Eric, Sr. V.P. & Client Services Dir.--Grey Advertising, New York, NY; *U.S. Public*, pg. 764

Rosenstein, Stuart B., Chief Fin. Officer, Sr. V.P. & Treas.--Pricellular Corporation, White Plains, NY; *U.S. Public*, pg. 1324

Rosenthal, Ilene, Sr. V.P. & Acct. Dir.--Young & Rubicam New York, New York, NY; *U.S. Private*, pg. 1198

Rosenthal, William E., Sr. V.P. & Pres.-KPR Foods Div.--Foodbrands America, Inc., Oklahoma City, OK; *U.S. Public*, pg. 852

Rosentraub, Michael C., Sr. V.P.--Associates Insurance Group, Inc., Dallas, TX; *U.S. Public*, pg. 663

Rosenzweig, Israel, Sr. V.P.--Georgetown Partners, Inc., Great Neck, NY; *U.S. Private*, pg. 466

Rosenzweig, Joachim, Sr. V.P.--Landesbank Rheinland-Pfalz, Mainz, Germany; *Int'l*, pg. 799

Rosholt, Robert A., Chief Fin. Officer & Exec. V.P.--First Chicago NBD Corporation, Chicago, IL; *U.S. Public*, pg. 627

Rosica, Gabriel A., Sr. V.P.--Keithley Instruments, Inc., Cleveland, OH; *U.S. Public*, pg. 946

Rosilier, Glenn D., Chief Fin. Officer & Sr. V.P.--Central and South West Corporation, Dallas, TX; *U.S. Public*, pg. 324

Rosilier, Glenn D., Chief Fin. Officer & Sr. V.P.--Central and South West Services, Inc., Dallas, TX; *U.S. Public*, pg. 324

Rosoff, William L., Sr. V.P. & Gen. Counsel--RJR Nabisco Holdings Corp., New York, NY; *U.S. Public*, pg. 1354

Ross, A.J. Eddie, Sr. V.P.-Forestry Prods.--Domtar Inc., Montreal, Canada; *Int'l*, pg. 416

Ross, Donald G., Sr. V.P.--St. Paul Federal Bank for Savings, Chicago, IL; *U.S. Public*, pg. 1428

Ross, David E., Sr. V.P.--SCS Engineers, Long Beach, CA; *U.S. Private*, pg. 955

Ross, Donald G, Sr. V.P.-Retail Banking--St. Paul Bancorp, Inc., Chicago, IL; *U.S. Public*, pg. 1428

Ross, George C., Chief Credit Officer & Sr. V.P.--Travelers Group, New York, NY; *U.S. Public*, pg. 1632

Ross, Glenn, Sr. V.P.--Republic Entertainment, Inc., Los Angeles, CA; *U.S. Private*, pg. 776

Ross, Jack, Sr. V.P. & Gen. Mgr.-Pulp & Paper Div.--ABB Industrial Systems, Inc., Columbus, OH; *Int'l*, pg. 4

Ross, James P., Sr. V.P.--Zenith National Insurance Corp., Woodland Hills, CA; *U.S. Public*, pg. 1790

Ross, Joe, Sr. V.P. & Acct. Grp. Dir.--Kragie/Newell, Des Moines, IA; *U.S. Private*, pg. 634

Ross, John H. III, Sr. V.P. & Gen. Counsel--Ash Grove Cement Company, Shawnee Mission, KS; *U.S. Private*, pg. 87

Ross, Maggie, Sr. V.P. & Local Brdcst. & Network Radio Dir.--Young & Rubicam New York, New York, NY; *U.S. Private*, pg. 1198

Ross, Marshall, Sr. V.P. & Creative Dir.--Cramer-Krasselt, Chicago, IL; *U.S. Private*, pg. 285

Ross, Mason G., Sr. V.P.-Real Estate--Northwestern Mutual Life Insurance Co., Milwaukee, WI; *U.S. Private*, pg. 807

Ross, Michael C., Sr. V.P., Gen. Counsel & Sec.--Safeway Inc., Pleasanton, CA; *U.S. Public*, pg. 1426

Ross, Peter, Sr. V.P.-H.R.--The Dun & Bradstreet Corporation, Murray Hill, NJ; *U.S. Public*, pg. 535

Ross, Stephen M., Sr. V.P.-Pur.--Hillsdale Tool & Mfg. Co., Hillsdale, MI; *U.S. Private*, pg. 355

Ross, Stephen M., Sr. V.P.-GMM Apparel & Soft Home--Kmart Corporation, Troy, MI; *U.S. Public*, pg. 963

Ross, Steve, Sr. V.P.-Worldwide Promotions--Twentieth Century Fox Film Corp., Los Angeles, CA; *Int'l*, pg. 926

Ross, Terry, Sr. V.P.-Transportation--Ag Processing Inc., A Cooperative, Omaha, NE; *U.S. Private*, pg. 26

Ross, Thomas, Sr. V.P.-Adv. & Creative Services--Oneida Ltd., Oneida, NY; *U.S. Public*, pg. 1225

Rossbach, Walt, Pres.-Aerospace/Defense Grp. & Sr. V.P.--Stackig Advertising and Public Relations, Mc Lean, VA; *U.S. Private*, pg. 1028

Rosseau, Robert H., Sr. V.P.--Deluxe Corporation, Shoreview, MN; *U.S. Public*, pg. 498

Rossi-Espagnet, Gian, Sr. V.P.-Intl.--SunTrust Banks, Inc., Atlanta, GA; *U.S. Public*, pg. 1537

Rosskamm, Betty, Sr. V.P. & Sec.--Fabri-Centers of America, Inc., Hudson, OH; *U.S. Public*, pg. 609

Rossman, Jim, Sr. V.P. & Client Services Dir.--The Chapman Agency, New York, NY; *U.S. Private*, pg. 1197

Rosso, Lizzie, Sr. V.P.-Alternative Delivery Channels--Banco Popular de Puerto Rico, San Juan, PR; *U.S. Public*, pg. 175

Rost, Jordan, Sr. V.P.-Mktg.--Warner Music Group, Inc., New York, NY; *U.S. Public*, pg. 1612

Rostvold, Mark C., Sr. V.P.-Worldwide Commercial & Consumer Equipment Div.--Deere & Company, Moline, IL; *U.S. Public*, pg. 491

Rotchstein, Janice, Sr. V.P.--Edelman Worldwide, Inc., New York, NY; *U.S. Private*, pg. 362

Roth, Gary M., Sr. V.P. & Gen. Mgr.-Magnetics Cluster--Anacomp, Inc., Indianapolis, IN; *U.S. Public*, pg. 106

Roth, Hal, Chief Fin. Officer & Sr. V.P.--NW Transport Service, Inc., Denver, CO; *U.S. Private*, pg. 772

Rothman, Joan, Sr. V.P.-Strategic Res. & Plng.--The Dun & Bradstreet Corporation, Murray Hill, NJ; *U.S. Public*, pg. 535

Rothnie, James B., Sr. V.P.-Mktg.--EMC Corporation, Hopkinton, MA; *U.S. Public*, pg. 545

Rothon, Simon J., Sr. V.P.-Consumer Prods. Div.--Van den Bergh Foods Company, Lisle, IL; *Int'l*, pg. 1436

Rothstein, Al, Sr. V.P. & Mgr.-Southern Reg.--Paramount Pictures Corporation, Los Angeles, CA; *U.S. Private*, pg. 776

Rothstein, Ellen, Sr. V.P.--Partners & Shevack, Inc., New York, NY; *U.S. Private*, pg. 842

Rothwell, Allan, Chief Fin. Officer & Sr. V.P.--Eastman Chemical Company, Kingsport, TN; *U.S. Public*, pg. 550

Rothwell, John D., Sr. V.P. & Mgr.-Natl. Sls.--Mackenzie Financial Corporation, Toronto, Canada; *Int'l*, pg. 828

Rotkowitz, Irving P., Sr. V.P.--OppenheimerFunds Distributor, Inc., New York, NY; *U.S. Private*, pg. 818

Rotsch, Jeffrey R., Sr. V.P.-Sls. & Distr.--General Mills, Inc., Minneapolis, MN; *U.S. Public*, pg. 717

Rottenberg, Alan, Sr. V.P.-Bus. Intelligence Tools--Cognos Inc., Ottawa, Canada; *Int'l*, pg. 305

Roub, Bryan R., Chief Fin. Officer & Sr. V.P.--Harris Corporation, Melbourne, FL; *U.S. Public*, pg. 791

Rounds, Joanne M., Sr. V.P.-Info. Tech. & SSD--Blue Cross & Blue Shield of Illinois, Chicago, IL; *U.S. Private*, pg. 151

Rounds, Timothy Q., Sr. V.P.--Market Facts, Inc., Arlington Heights, IL; *U.S. Public*, pg. 1046

Rourke, Glenn R., Grp. Head-Central & Eatern Canada & Sr. V.P.--Bank of Montreal - Montreal, Montreal, Canada; *Int'l*, pg. 153

Rourke, James G., Sr. V.P.--Fay, Spofford & Thorndike, Inc., Burlington, MA; *U.S. Private*, pg. 397

Rourke, Michael J., Sr. V.P.-Communications & Corp. Affairs--The Great Atlantic & Pacific Tea Company, Inc., Montvale, NJ; *Int'l*, pg. 1375

Rouse, John A., Sr. V.P.--Ghent Manufacturing, Inc., Lebanon, OH; *U.S. Private*, pg. 450

Rousseau, Joseph B., Sr. V.P. & Exec. Dir.--Advanswers Media/Programming, Saint Louis, MO; *Int'l*, pg. 117

Rovira, Lourdes M., Sr. V.P.-Admin. & Treas.--Caribbean American Life Assurance Company, Hato Rey, PR; *U.S. Public*, pg. 67

Rowan, James W., Sr. V.P.--SunAmerica Inc., Los Angeles, CA; *U.S. Public*, pg. 1532

Rowe, Allan D., Chief Fin. Officer & Sr. V.P.-Fin.--Empire Company Limited, Stellarton, Canada; *Int'l*, pg. 453

Rowe, Robert C., Sr. V.P. & Sec.--Golden West Financial Corporation, Oakland, CA; *U.S. Public*, pg. 750

Rowe, Rosemary M., Sr. V.P. & Opers. Officer--Community National Bank, Derby, VT; *U.S. Public*, pg. 416

Rowe, Tracy W., Sr. V.P.--PNC Bank Corp., Pittsburgh, PA; *U.S. Public*, pg. 1242

Rowland, Lawrence T., Sr. V.P.--Lincoln National Health & Casualty Insurance Co., Fort Wayne, IN; *U.S. Public*, pg. 998

Rowland, Lawrence T., Sr. V.P.-Individual Mkts.--Lincoln National Reinsurance Company (Barbados) Limited, Fort Wayne, IN; *U.S. Public*, pg. 998

Rowley, Peter, Sr. V.P.--People's Choice TV Corp., Shelton, CT; *U.S. Public*, pg. 1274

Roy, Carol, Chief Fin. Officer & Sr. V.P.--Biggs Gilmore Communications, Kalamazoo, MI; *U.S. Private*, pg. 143

Roy, Henry A., Chief Fin. Officer & Sr. V.P.-Admin. & Fin.--Cambior Inc., Montreal, Canada; *Int'l*, pg. 253

Rozek, Thomas M., Sr. V.P.-Women's & Children's Svcs.--The Detroit Medical Center, Detroit, MI; *U.S. Private*, pg. 328

Rozelle, Daniel, Sr. V.P. & Corp. Mktg. Dir.--Fort Wayne National Corporation, Fort Wayne, IN; *U.S. Public*, pg. 673

Ruane, Thomas G., Chief Fin. Officer & Sr. V.P.--PerSeptive Biosystems, Inc., Framingham, MA; *U.S. Public*, pg. 1279

Ruark, Jerry, Sr. V.P.--Morganfield National Bank, Morganfield, KY; *U.S. Public*, pg. 1217

Rubenovitch, Peter H., Sr. V.P. & Controller--Manulife Financial (The Manufacturers Life Insurance Company), Toronto, Canada; *Int'l*, pg. 840

Rubens, Stuart R., Sr. V.P.-Federal Systems--SRA International Inc., Arlington, VA; *U.S. Private*, pg. 957

Rubenstein, Amy, Sr. V.P. & Acct. Dir.--Wunderman Cato Johnson, New York, NY; *U.S. Private*, pg. 1197

Rubenstein, Marke, Sr. V.P. & Pub. Rels. Dir.--North Castle Partners Advertising, Inc., Stamford, CT; *U.S. Private*, pg. 804

Rubin, Bernie, Sr. V.P.--YKK (U.S.A.), Marietta, GA; *Int'l*, pg. 1515

Rubin, Donald S., Sr. V.P.-Inv. Rels.--The McGraw-Hill Companies, New York, NY; *U.S. Public*, pg. 1069

Rubin, Eric, Sr. V.P.-Res. & Analysis--New York Life Insurance Company, New York, NY; *U.S. Private*, pg. 794

Rubin, Rob, Sr. V.P. & Chief Tech. Officer--Reed Elsevier Business Information, Newton, MA; *Int'l*, pg. 1095

Rubin, William F., Sr. V.P.-Reg. Sls./Atlanta--Swank, Inc., Attleboro, MA; *U.S. Public*, pg. 1543

Rubinfeld, Arthur I., Sr. V.P.-Store Devel.--Starbucks Coffee Company, Seattle, WA; *U.S. Public*, pg. 1510

Rubino, John A., Sr. V.P.-Human Resources--Walgreen Co., Deerfield, IL; *U.S. Public*, pg. 1733

Rubinstein, Marc, Sr. V.P. & Gen. Counsel--Caesars Palace, Las Vegas, NV; *U.S. Public*, pg. 1512

Ruch, Charles E., Sr. V.P.--The Annapolis Banking & Trust Co., Annapolis, MD; *U.S. Public*, pg. 1088

Ruch, Michael K., Sr. V.P.--The Auburn State Bank, Auburn, IN; *U.S. Public*, pg. 674

Rucker, Ronald L., Sr. V.P.--First National Bank of Naples, Naples, FL; *U.S. Public*, pg. 607

Ruddy, James, Sr. V.P. & Gen. Counsel--SAFECO Corporation, Seattle, WA; *U.S. Public*, pg. 1423

Rudge, Howard J., Sr. V.P. & Gen. Counsel--Du Pont (E.I. Du Pont De Nemours & Co.), Wilmington, DE; *U.S. Public*, pg. 530

Rudgers, James J., Sr. V.P.-Corp. Lending--Citizens Trust Company, Providence, RI; *Int'l*, pg. 1132

Rudgers, James T., Sr. V.P.-Corp. Lending--Citizens Savings Bank, Providence, RI; *Int'l*, pg. 1132

Rudick, Richard S., Sr. V.P. & Gen. Counsel--John Wiley & Sons, Inc., New York, NY; *U.S. Public*, pg. 1768

Rudin, Gary L., Sr. V.P.--Electronic Data Systems Corporation, Plano, TX; *U.S. Public*, pg. 569

Rudis, David, Grp. Sr. V.P.-Chicago Comml. Banking--ABN/LaSalle North America Inc., Chicago, IL; *Int'l*, pg. 11

Rudnick, Harold, Sr. V.P.-Retail Pur.--The Vons Companies, Inc., Arcadia, CA; *U.S. Public*, pg. 1426

Rudolfo, Cheri, Sr. V.P.-Corp. Mktg.--Time Insurance, Milwaukee, WI; *Int'l*, pg. 499

Rudolfsson, Torsten, Sr. V.P.--NCC Eskilstuna, Eskilstuna, Sweden; *Int'l*, pg. 899

Rudy, Ronald, Sr. V.P.-Opers.--International Aluminum Corporation, Monterey Park, CA; *U.S. Public*, pg. 894

Rudzik, John A., Chief Fin. Officer, Sr. V.P.-Fin. & Treas.--Centimark Corporation, Canonsburg, PA; *U.S. Private*, pg. 222

Rudzin, Ronald E., Sr. V.P.-Retail Stores--Jennifer Convertibles Inc., Woodbury, NY; *U.S. Public*, pg. 926

Rue, Richard, Chief Fin. Officer & Sr. V.P.--ITA Group Inc., West Des Moines, IA; *U.S. Private*, pg. 555

Rueger, Gregory M., Sr. V.P. & Gen. Mgr.-Nuclear Power Generation Bus. Unit--Pacific Gas & Electric Company, San Francisco, CA; *U.S. Public*, pg. 1241

Ruel, Peter E., Sr. V.P. & Syndicate Mgr.--Jefferies & Company, Inc., Los Angeles, CA; *U.S. Public*, pg. 925

Ruesch, James, Sr. V.P.-Engrng.--Liquid Controls LLC, Lake Bluff, IL; *U.S. Private*, pg. 669

Ruest, Ron E., Sr. V.P.-Real Estate--The Toronto Dominion Bank, Toronto, Canada; *Int'l*, pg. 1401

Ruffer, Herbert L., Sr. V.P.-Underwriting Svcs.--Admiral Insurance Company, Cherry Hill, NJ; *U.S. Public*, pg. 216

Ruffer, Michael R., Sr. V.P.-New Ventures--Marriott International, Inc., Washington, DC; *U.S. Public*, pg. 1047

Rufi, Richard E., Sr. V.P.--First National Bank of Fort Myers, Fort Myers, FL; *U.S. Public*, pg. 608

Rugg, Peter, Chief Fin. Officer & Sr. V.P.--Triton Energy Limited, Dallas, TX; *U.S. Public*, pg. 1640

Ruggiero, Anthony W., Chief Fin. Officer & Sr. V.P.--Olin Corporation, Norwalk, CT; *U.S. Public*, pg. 1218

Ruggles, Gordon, Sr. V.P.--Hazen & Sawyer, New York, NY; *U.S. Private*, pg. 514

Rugotzke, Tom, Sr. V.P.-Opers.--Bush Brothers & Company, Knoxville, TN; *U.S. Private*, pg. 189

Ruhl, Douglas L., Sr. V.P.-Retail Banking--Liberty Bancorp, Inc., Oklahoma City, OK; *U.S. Public*, pg. 174

Ruhnke, Kirk, Sr. V.P.--Laughlin/Constable, Inc., Milwaukee, WI; *U.S. Private*, pg. 653

Ruiz, Lucio San Pedro, Dir.-Service Stations--Repsol Comercial de Productos Petroliferos, S.A., Madrid, Spain; *Int'l*, pg. 1104

Rulevich, Robert, Sr. V.P.--The Advest Group, Inc., Hartford, CT; *U.S. Public*, pg. 23

Rulli, John, Sr. V.P.-H.R. & Corp. Opers.--Simon DeBartolo Group, Inc., Indianapolis, IN; *U.S. Public*, pg. 1474

Rullo, Stephen, Sr. V.P.-ARCO Prods. Co.--Atlantic Richfield Company, Los Angeles, CA; *U.S. Public*, pg. 144

Rullo, Steve, Sr. V.P.-Mktg.--ARCO Products Co., Los Angeles, CA; *U.S. Public*, pg. 144

Rumke, M.J., Sr. V.P.-H.R.--Holiday Inn Worldwide, Atlanta, GA; *Int'l*, pg. 170
Rumowicz, Nancy, Sr. V.P. & Mngmt. Supvr.--Tausche Martin Lonsdorf, Atlanta, GA; *U.S. Private*, pg. 1069
Rumpf, Francois, Sr. V.P.--Ferrier Lullin & Cie SA, Geneva, Switzerland; *Int'l*, pg. 480
Rumph, Stephanie C., Sr. V.P.--Associates Insurance Group, Inc., Dallas, TX; *U.S. Public*, pg. 663
Rumsey, E. Christine, Sr. V.P.-H.R.--HBOC, Atlanta, GA; *U.S. Public*, pg. 770
Runk, Fred J., Sr. V.P. & Treas.--American Financial Group, Cincinnati, OH; *U.S. Public*, pg. 74
Runtagh, Hellene S., Sr. V.P.--Universal Studios, Inc., Universal City, CA; *Int'l*, pg. 1215
Runyan, John S., Sr. V.P.-Retail Concepts--Fleming Companies, Inc., Oklahoma City, OK; *U.S. Public*, pg. 652
Runyon, Marvin T., III, Sr. V.P.-Corp. Fin.--Associates First Capital Corporation, Dallas, TX; *U.S. Public*, pg. 662
Ruppert, Raymond L., Sr. V.P.- Client Services--Jepson-Murray Advertising, Lansing, MI; *U.S. Private*, pg. 586
Rus, William, Sr. V.P.-Creative Adv.--Paramount Pictures Corporation, Los Angeles, CA; *U.S. Private*, pg. 776
Rusak, William K., Chief Admin. Officer & Sr. V.P.--Dominion Textile Inc., Montreal, Canada; *Int'l*, pg. 415
Rusch, Richard R., Sr. V.P.--First Security Bank of Oregon, Salem, OR; *U.S. Public*, pg. 637
Rusden, R., Sr. V.P.--Kennecott Holdings Corporation, Magna, UT; *Int'l*, pg. 1119
Rush, Bill, Grp. V.P.-Reg. Stores--Marshall Field, Chicago, IL; *U.S. Public*, pg. 489
Rusine, James, Sr. V.P.--Vision Financial Corporation, Keene, NH; *U.S. Private*, pg. 1141
Rusis, Robert, Sr. V.P. & Gen. Counsel--The Chubb Corporation, Warren, NJ; *U.S. Public*, pg. 354
Rusis, Robert, Sr. V.P.--Chubb & Son, Inc., Warren, NJ; *U.S. Public*, pg. 355
Russel, Joyce, Chief Fin. Officer, Sr. V.P. & Controller--Jostens Learning Corporation, San Diego, CA; *U.S. Private*, pg. 601
Russel, Terry, Sr. V.P.--John Wieland Homes Inc., Atlanta, GA; *U.S. Private*, pg. 1175
Russell, Dave, Sr. V.P.--Applied Communications, Inc., Omaha, NE; *U.S. Public*, pg. 1629
Russell, David C., Sr. V.P. & Dir.--Transaction Systems Architects, Inc., Omaha, NE; *U.S. Public*, pg. 1629
Russell, Don E., Sr. V.P.--Interface Inc., Atlanta, GA; *U.S. Public*, pg. 889
Russell, Edward, Sr. V.P.-Publicity, Promo. & Field Opers.--TriStar Pictures, Culver City, CA; *Int'l*, pg. 1283
Russell, George A., Sr. V.P.-Govt. Affairs--State Street Corporation, Boston, MA; *U.S. Public*, pg. 1513
Russell, James, Sr. V.P.-Natl. Sls.--The Wine Alliance, Healdsburg, CA; *Int'l*, pg. 63
Russell, Joyce M., Sr. V.P. & Gen. Counsel--Fruit of the Loom, Inc., Chicago, IL; *U.S. Public*, pg. 685
Russell, L.G., Sr. V.P.-Opers.--Ingram Book Company, La Vergne, TN; *U.S. Private*, pg. 563
Russell, Michael, Sr. V.P.--The William Cook Agency, Inc., Jacksonville, FL; *U.S. Private*, pg. 273
Russell, Richard G., Sr. V.P. & Controller--RJR Nabisco Holdings Corp., New York, NY; *U.S. Public*, pg. 1354
Russell, Robert, Sr. V.P.--RNBNY Branch Office-Tokyo, Tokyo, Japan; *U.S. Public*, pg. 1381
Russell, Robert M., Sr. V.P. & Gen. Mgr.--Sweet's Div., New York, NY; *U.S. Public*, pg. 1070
Russey, C. Keith, Sr. V.P.-Contracts & Bus. Devel.--Mooney Aircraft Corporation, Kerrville, TX; *U.S. Private*, pg. 759
Rutherford, Jeffrey, Sr. V.P.-Fin.--OfficeMax, Shaker Heights, OH; *U.S. Public*, pg. 1212
Ruthven, Hugh, Sr. V.P. & Client Svcs. Dir.--Palmer Jarvis Communications, Vancouver, Canada; *Int'l*, pg. 1022
Rutledge, Robert K., Sr. V.P.--J.S. Alberici Construction Co., Inc., Saint Louis, MO; *U.S. Private*, pg. 32
Rutledge, Scott, Sr. V.P.--Farmers Mutual Hail Insurance Co. of Iowa, Des Moines, IA; *U.S. Private*, pg. 395
Rutledge, Steve, Sr. V.P.--Farmers Mutual Hail Insurance Co. of Iowa, Des Moines, IA; *U.S. Private*, pg. 395
Rutman, Charles, Sr. V.P. & Media Dir.-Coca Cola--DMB&B New York, New York, NY; *U.S. Private*, pg. 302
Ruzicka, Raymond C., Sr. V.P. & Exec. Dir.--Advanswers Media/Programming, Saint Louis, MO; *Int'l*, pg. 117
Rwelle, Mark, Chief Fin. Officer & Sr. V.P.--Sierra Pacific Resources, Reno, NV; *U.S. Public*, pg. 1470
Ryan, Bill, Sr. V.P.-Cellular--Price Communications Corporation, New York, NY; *U.S. Public*, pg. 1324
Ryan, Bob, Sr. V.P. & Treas.--CM Partners, Inc., Rolling Meadows, IL; *U.S. Private*, pg. 195
Ryan, Bruce A., Sr. V.P.--Wang Laboratories, Inc., Billerica, MA; *U.S. Public*, pg. 1737
Ryan, Conall E., Sr. V.P.-Houghton Interactive Corp.--Houghton Mifflin Company, Boston, MA; *U.S. Public*, pg. 841
Ryan, Daniel B., III, Sr. V.P.--Willis Faber North America, Inc.-Illinois, Chicago, IL; *Int'l*, pg. 1503
Ryan, Denny, Sr. V.P.-Mdsg.--The Home Depot, Inc., Atlanta, GA; *U.S. Public*, pg. 831
Ryan, Edward J., Sr. V.P.--Thompson Steel Co., Inc., Canton, MA; *U.S. Private*, pg. 1083
Ryan, Ellen, Sr. V.P. & Telemedia Dir.--Wunderman Cato Johnson, New York, NY; *U.S. Private*, pg. 1197
Ryan, Frederick J., Jr., Vice Chm. & Sr. V.P.--Allbritton Communications Company, Washington, DC; *U.S. Private*, pg. 854
Ryan, Frederick J., Jr., Sr. V.P.--Allbritton Communications Company, Washington, DC; *U.S. Private*, pg. 854
Ryan, Gary L., Sr. V.P. & Corp. Counsel--Hibernia Corporation, New Orleans, LA; *U.S. Public*, pg. 825
Ryan, J. Thomas, III, Exec. V.P.--Swisher International Group, Inc., Darien, CT; *U.S. Public*, pg. 1543
Ryan, James F., Sr. V.P.-Dealer Rels.--Canadian Tire Corporation Limited, Toronto, Canada; *Int'l*, pg. 259
Ryan, John M., Sr. V.P.--Keycorp, Cleveland, OH; *U.S. Public*, pg. 954
Ryan, Lynn, Sr. V.P. & Data Processing--Sanwa Bank California, Los Angeles, CA; *Int'l*, pg. 1189
Ryan, Mark, Sr. V.P. & Creative Dir.--Greenstone Roberts Advertising, Melville, NY; *U.S. Public*, pg. 763
Ryan, Mary L., Chief Fin. Officer & Sr. V.P.--Thompson Steel Co., Inc., Canton, MA; *U.S. Private*, pg. 1083
Ryan, Mary Pat, Sr. V.P.-Mktg.--United States Satellite Broadcasting, Co., Saint Paul, MN; *U.S. Private*, pg. 544
Ryan, Robert L., Chief Fin. Officer & Sr. V.P.--Medtronic, Inc., Minneapolis, MN; *U.S. Public*, pg. 1082
Ryan, Thomas, Sr. V.P.-Bus. Devel.--Long John Silver's, Inc., Lexington, KY; *U.S. Private*, pg. 674
Ryan, Thomas D., Sr. V.P.-Consumer Credit--Magna Group, Inc., Saint Louis, MO; *U.S. Public*, pg. 1037
Ryanczak, Anthony J., Sr. V.P.-Sls. & Mktg.--Griffin Technology Incorporated, Farmington, NY; *U.S. Public*, pg. 506
Rychlik, Andy, Sr. V.P. & Mngmt. Supvr.--Laughlin/Constable, Inc., Milwaukee, WI; *U.S. Private*, pg. 653
Rycroft, Donald C., Sr. V.P. & Treas.--Continental Assurance Company, Chicago, IL; *U.S. Private*, pg. 267
Rydant, Jeffrey J., Sr. V.P. & Dir.-Information Mngmt. & Tech.--SRA International Inc., Arlington, VA; *U.S. Private*, pg. 957
Ryder, Larry, Sr. V.P.-Fin. & Admin.--Hooker Furniture Corporation, Martinsville, VA; *U.S. Private*, pg. 538
Rygiel, Edward K., Sr. V.P.-Corp. Devel. & Pres.-MDS Capital Corp.--MDS Inc., Etobicoke, Canada; *Int'l*, pg. 826
Rygor, Stanley, Sr. V.P. & Acct. Exec.--Doremus & Company, New York, NY; *U.S. Public*, pg. 1223
Ryland, Joyce, Sr. V.P.& Exec. Sec.--Leiner Health Products, Inc., Carson, CA; *U.S. Private*, pg. 659
Rysa, Mikko, Sr. V.P.--Rauma Ltd., Helsinki, Finland; *Int'l*, pg. 1428
Saake, William J., Sr. V.P.--Zenith Insurance Company, Woodland Hills, CA; *U.S. Public*, pg. 1791
Sabala, James A., Chief Fin. Officer & Sr. V.P.-Fin.--Coeur D'Alene Mines Corporation, Coeur D'Alene, ID; *U.S. Public*, pg. 394
Sabatacakis, Petros K., Sr. V.P.-Fin. Services--American International Group, Inc., New York, NY; *U.S. Public*, pg. 83
Saber, Rommel C., Sr. V.P.-Air Export--Expeditors International of Washington, Inc., Seattle, WA; *U.S. Public*, pg. 600
Sabia, Michael, Chief Fin. Officer & Sr. V.P.--Canadian National Railway Company, Montreal, Canada; *Int'l*, pg. 258
Sable, Robert M., Jr., Chief Fin. Officer & Sr. V.P.--CNG Energy Services Corporation, Pittsburgh, PA; *U.S. Public*, pg. 435
Sable, Ronald K., Sr. V.P.-Corp. Devel.--Aerospace Corporation, El Segundo, CA; *U.S. Private*, pg. 24
Sabo, Dennis R., Sr. V.P.-Urine Chemistry/Diagnostics Div.--Bayer Corporation, Pittsburgh, PA; *Int'l*, pg. 172
Saby, Nadine, Sr. V.P.--GPC Communications (Ontario), Toronto, Canada; *U.S. Public*, pg. 1225
Saccento, James, Sr. V.P. & Creative Services Dir.--Grey Healthcare Group, New York, NY; *U.S. Public*, pg. 765
Sachs, William J., Sr. V.P., Dir.-G.D.D.--Clopay Corporation, Cincinnati, OH; *U.S. Public*, pg. 766
Sackett, Richard, Sr. V.P.--LeGrand Johnson Construction Co., Logan, UT; *U.S. Private*, pg. 591
Sacris, Eduardo M., Sr. V.P.-Opers./Masinloc Chromite--Benguet Corporation, Manila, Philippines; *Int'l*, pg. 186
Saddington, Richard W., Sr. V.P-Real Estate--Corporate & Institutional Financial Services - Montreal, Toronto, Canada; *Int'l*, pg. 153
Sadler, John, Sr. V.P.-Corp. Affairs--Newcourt Credit Group Inc., Toronto, Canada; *Int'l*, pg. 924
Sadler, Martin F., Sr. V.P.-Fin.--Hoffmann-La Roche Inc., Nutley, NJ; *Int'l*, pg. 1120
Sadler, Terrell L., Sr. V.P.-Domestic--Grey Wolf, Inc., Houston, TX; *U.S. Public*, pg. 765
Sadowsk, Stephen, Sr. V.P.--HK Systems, Inc., New Berlin, WI; *U.S. Private*, pg. 491
Sadowski, Raymond, Chief Fin. Officer, Sr. V.P. & Asst. Sec.--Avnet, Inc., Great Neck, NY; *U.S. Public*, pg. 155
Saeng-Xuto, Chaisak, Sr. V.P.--The Siam Cement Public Company Limited, Bangkok, Thailand; *Int'l*, pg. 1237
Saengaroon, Pornchai, Sr. V.P.--The Industrial Finance Corporation of Thailand, Bangkok, Thailand; *Int'l*, pg. 677
Safford, Bob, Sr. V.P. & Gen. Mgr.-Integrated Services--Campbell Mithun Esty, Minneapolis, MN; *U.S. Private*, pg. 204
Saganski, Moira, Sr. V.P. & Pres.-M.R.S. Trust Company--Mackenzie Financial Corporation, Toronto, Canada; *Int'l*, pg. 828
Sagara, Jiro, Mng. Dir. & Sr. V.P.-Acctg.--Japan Airlines Company, Ltd., Tokyo, Japan; *Int'l*, pg. 699
Sagebien, R.L., Sr. V.P.--Amerada Hess Corporation, New York, NY; *U.S. Public*, pg. 65
Sager, Harry C., Sr. V.P.--Du Pont (E.I. Du Pont De Nemours & Co.), Wilmington, DE; *U.S. Public*, pg. 530
Said, Mohand Sidi, V.P., Sr. V.P.-Pfizer Pharm. Grp. & Area Pres.-Asia/Africa/Mid. E--Pfizer Inc., New York, NY; *U.S.* Public, pg. 1281
Sailer, Joseph R., Sr. V.P.--First Hawaiian Creditcorp, Inc., Honolulu, HI; *U.S. Public*, pg. 635
Saito, Gerald H., Sr. V.P.-District Mgr.--Longs Drug Stores Corporation, Walnut Creek, CA; *U.S. Public*, pg. 1013
Saito, Gerald H., Sr. V.P.--Longs Drug Stores California, Inc., Walnut Creek, CA; *U.S. Public*, pg. 1013
Saito, Kenneth O., Sr. V.P.-Fin. & Admin.--Blount, Inc. Oregon Cutting Systems Division, Portland, OR; *U.S. Public*, pg. 238
Saito, Norio, Assoc. Sr. V.P.--NEC Corporation, Tokyo, Japan; *Int'l*, pg. 899
Sakamato, Kazuhiko, Chief Fin. & Admin. Officer & Sr. V.P.--Marubeni America Corporation, New York, NY; *Int'l*, pg. 844
Sakamoto, Alvin N., Chief Fin. Officer & Sr. V.P.--American Savings Bank, F.S.B., Honolulu, HI; *U.S. Public*, pg. 800
Sakamoto, Norio, Sr. V.P.--Mitsui Fudosan (USA), Inc., New York, NY; *Int'l*, pg. 882
Sakamoto, Yasushi, Sr. V.P.--Advantest Corporation, Tokyo, Japan; *Int'l*, pg. 25
Sakata, Kathy, Sr. V.P.-Acct. Services--Western International Media Corporation, Chicago, IL; *U.S. Private*, pg. 1167
Sakolsky, Chuck, V.P.-Sls., USA--Irwin Toy Ltd., Toronto, Canada; *Int'l*, pg. 688
Sakornratanakul, Sirichai, Sr. Exec. V.P.--The Industrial Finance Corporation of Thailand, Bangkok, Thailand; *Int'l*, pg. 677
Sakowski, Ray, Sr. V.P.-Mktg.--Voyager Service Warranties, Inc., Fort Worth, TX; *U.S. Public*, pg. 68
Saks, Samuel R., Sr. V.P.-Medical Affairs--Alza Corporation, Palo Alto, CA; *U.S. Public*, pg. 62
Sakuma, Sadayuki, Sr. V.P.--Terumo Corporation, Tokyo, Japan; *Int'l*, pg. 1375
Sakurada, Yutaka, Sr. V.P. & Pres.-Haemonetics Japan--Haemonetics Corporation, Braintree, MA; *U.S. Public*, pg. 773
Salato, S.M., Sr. V.P.--MidCon Gas Services Corp., Houston, TX; *U.S. Public*, pg. 1210
Salazar, Susan, Sr. V.P.--Westin Hotels & Resorts, Seattle, WA; *U.S. Public*, pg. 1512
Salcedo, Rick, Sr. V.P.-Mktg. & Creative Services--CNN (Cable News Network), Atlanta, GA; *U.S. Public*, pg. 1614
Sale, Richard H., Sr. V.P. & Sec.--Commercial National Bank, Shreveport, LA; *U.S. Public*, pg. 500
Salehi, Sean, Chief Info. Officer & Sr. V.P.--Fair, Isaac and Company, Inc., San Rafael, CA; *U.S. Public*, pg. 609
Salerno, Diane, Sr. V.P.-Natl. Promo.--Columbia Pictures, Culver City, CA; *Int'l*, pg. 1281
Salipante, Robert C., Sr. V.P.-Personal Fin. Services--ReliaStar Financial Corp., Minneapolis, MN; *U.S. Public*, pg. 1375
Salipante, Robert C., Chief Fin. Officer & Sr. V.P.--Northwestern National Life Insurance Co., Minneapolis, MN; *U.S. Public*, pg. 1375
Salipante, Robert C., Sr. V.P.--Northwestern National Life Insurance Co., Minneapolis, MN; *U.S. Public*, pg. 1375
Salisbury, Randy, Sr. V.P. & Mngmt. Supvr.--Fitzgerald & Co., Atlanta, GA; *U.S. Private*, pg. 409
Sall, John P., Co-Founder & Sr. V.P.--SAS Institute Inc., Cary, NC; *U.S. Private*, pg. 966
Salmon, J., Sr. V.P.--Serigraph, Inc., West Bend, WI; *U.S. Private*, pg. 985
Salmon, Jeff, Sr. V.P.--Dick Clark Corporate Productions, Inc., Burbank, CA; *U.S. Public*, pg. 382
Salo, Ralph, Chief Fin. Officer & Sr. V.P.--Target Stores, Minneapolis, MN; *U.S. Public*, pg. 489
Salomon, Lars, Sr. V.P. & Controller--AGA AB, Lidingo, Sweden; *Int'l*, pg. 12
Salony, John, III, Sr. V.P.--Reistertown Federal Savings Bank, Baltimore, MD; *U.S. Public*, pg. 1543
Salop, John P., Sr. V.P.--First Virginia Banks, Inc., Falls Church, VA; *U.S. Public*, pg. 641
Salpeter, Allyn, Sr. V.P.-Fin. & Admin.--Ziccardi & Partners, Inc., New York, NY; *U.S. Private*, pg. 1205
Salter, Kevin, Sr. V.P.-N.J. Opers.--Willis Corroon Corp. of New Jersey, Morris Plains, NJ; *Int'l*, pg. 1506
Saltzman, Ellin, Sr. V.P. & Fashion Dir.--Bergdorf Goodman, New York, NY; *U.S. Public*, pg. 785
Saltzman, Lee S., Sr. V.P.--Rockefeller Center Development Corporation, New York, NY; *Int'l*, pg. 873
Salvagni, Carlos, Sr. V.P.-Tech. Opers.--Pharmacia & Upjohn, Inc., Windsor, United Kingdom; *Int'l*, pg. 1047
Salvagni, Carlos A., Sr. V.P.-Worldwide Mfg. & Engrng.--Pharmacia & Upjohn, Kalamazoo, MI; *Int'l*, pg. 1048
Salvatore, Tony, Sr. V.P.--Willis Corroon Corp. of Georgia, Atlanta, GA; *Int'l*, pg. 1506
Salver, Henry A., Sr. V.P.--GAI Consultants, Inc., Monroeville, PA; *U.S. Private*, pg. 433
Sammis, Robert J., Sr. V.P.-Corp. Devel.--GATX Capital Corporation, San Francisco, CA; *U.S. Public*, pg. 690
Sammon, John P., Sr. V.P.-CORE Service Grp.--Conrail, Inc., Philadelphia, PA; *U.S. Public*, pg. 431
Sammons, Mary, Sr. V.P.-Gen. Grp.--Fred Meyer Stores, Portland, OR; *U.S. Public*, pg. 1103
Sample, Thomas A., Sr. V.P.-MIS--Haggar Corporation, Dallas, TX; *U.S. Public*, pg. 774
Sampson, Ronald, Sr. V.P.-Corp. Devel.--Burrell Communications Group Inc., Chicago, IL; *U.S. Private*, pg. 188
Samsel, Erven A., Sr. V.P.-Field Mngmt.--American Express Financial Advisor, Minneapolis, MN; *U.S. Public*, pg. 73
Samsing, Robert, Sr. V.P.-Sls. & Mktg.--Briggs Industries, Inc., Tampa, FL; *U.S. Private*, pg. 168
Samson, Antonio R., Sr. V.P.-Corp. Services--Philippine Long Distance Telephone Company, Manila, Philippines; *Int'l*, pg. 1051
Samson, Roger, Sr. V.P.-Mktg. & Devel.--Sico Inc., Longueuil, Canada; *Int'l*, pg. 1239
Sanborn, Grant C., Sr. V.P.-Store Opers.--Ames Department Stores, Inc., Rocky Hill, CT; *U.S. Public*, pg. 99
Sanders, A. Brian, Chief Mktg. Officer & Sr. V.P.--ADVO, Inc., Windsor, CT; *U.S. Public*, pg. 23
Sanders, Alma, Sr. V.P.-Fin. & Admin.--CNN (Cable News Network), Atlanta, GA; *U.S. Public*, pg. 1614
Sanders, Bernard, Sr. V.P. & Corp. Sec.--Farmland Industries, Inc., Kansas City, MO; *U.S. Private*, pg. 395
Sanders, D. Faye, Sr. V.P. & Dir.-Community Rels. & Govt. Affairs--Citizens Financial Group, Inc., Providence, RI; *Int'l*, pg. 1132
Sanders, D. Faye, Sr. V.P.-Community Relations--Citizens Trust Company, Providence, RI; *Int'l*, pg. 1132
Sanders, Darrel M., Sr. V.P.-Opers.--The Rival Company, Kansas City, MO; *U.S. Public*, pg. 1391
Sanders, Gerald, V.P.--Queens Group, Inc., Long Island City, NY; *U.S. Private*, pg. 900

Sanders, John W., Sr. V.P.-Intl.--Cleveland-Cliffs Inc, Cleveland, OH; *U.S. Public*, pg. 386

Sanders, Kenneth W., Chief Fin. Officer, Sr. V.P.-Fin., Treas. & Asst. Sec.--Paging Network, Inc., Plano, TX; *U.S. Public*, pg. 1252

Sanders, Molly P., Sr. V.P.--Trenwick America Reinsurance Corporation, Stamford, CT; *U.S. Public*, pg. 1634

Sanders, Neal, Chief Information Officer & Sr. V.P.--Microdyne Corporation, Alexandria, VA; *U.S. Public*, pg. 1105

Sanders, Tom, Sr. V.P.-Mktg.--Information & Engineering Technology, Fairfax, VA; *U.S. Private*, pg. 351

Sanders, Vonda, Sr. V.P.--San Angelo National Bank, San Angelo, TX; *U.S. Public*, pg. 633

Sanders, W. Robert, Sr. V.P. & Zone Mgr.--McDonald's Corporation, Oak Brook, IL; *U.S. Public*, pg. 1068

Sandford, Debra, Sr. V.P.-Orange County Corp. Banking--Southern California Bank, Newport Beach, CA; *U.S. Public*, pg. 1758

Sandie, Robert A., Sr. V.P.-Corp. Matls.--Seagate Technology Inc., Scotts Valley, CA; *U.S. Public*, pg. 1449

Sandler, Robert M., Sr. V.P. & Controller--The Cato Corporation, Charlotte, NC; *U.S. Public*, pg. 318

Sandman, Paul, Sr. V.P., Gen. Counsel & Sec.--Boston Scientific Corp., Natick, MA; *U.S. Public*, pg. 247

Sando, Arthur R., Sr. V.P.-Corp. Communications--King World Productions, Inc., New York, NY; *U.S. Public*, pg. 961

Sandoe, Timothy L., Sr. V.P.-Community Banking--Lebanon Valley Farmers Bank, Lebanon, PA; *U.S. Public*, pg. 688

Sands, James A., Sr. V.P.--Standard Federal Bank, Troy, MI; *Int'l*, pg. 10

Sands, Pamela A., Sr. V.P. & Res. Loan Opers.--Barclays American/Mortgage Corp., Charlotte, NC; *Int'l*, pg. 165

Sanford, Curtis, Sr. V.P.-Intl. Sls. & Gen. Mgr.-Intl. Opers.--Ascend Communications, Inc., Alameda, CA; *U.S. Public*, pg. 138

Sanford, Philip H., Sr. V.P.-Fin. & Admin.--Coca-Cola Enterprises Inc., Atlanta, GA; *U.S. Public*, pg. 393

Sanford, Sharon A., Sr. V.P.--Market Data Retrieval, Shelton, CT; *U.S. Public*, pg. 536

Sangster, R. Hugh B., Sr. V.P.-Corp. Devel.--IPL Energy Inc., Calgary, Canada; *Int'l*, pg. 651

Sanguinetti, Pat, Sr. V.P.--Blue Anchor, Inc., Dinuba, CA; *U.S. Private*, pg. 150

Sansolo, Jack, Sr. V.P.-Global Brand Direction--Eddie Bauer, Inc., Redmond, WA; *U.S. Public*, pg. 1499

Santangelo, Steven J., Sr. V.P.-Strategic Mktg. & Res. Consultation--Tierney & Partners, Philadelphia, PA; *U.S. Public*, pg. 1641

Santillana, Ignacio, Sr. V.P.-Intl. Bus. Devel.--GTE Corporation, Stamford, CT; *U.S. Public*, pg. 696

Santo, James M., Exec. V.P.-Admin.--Eckerd Corporation, Largo, FL; *U.S. Public*, pg. 917

Santoro, David S., P.E., L.S., Sr. V.P.-Project Risk Mngmt.--EA Engineering, Science & Technology, Inc., Hunt Valley, MD; *U.S. Public*, pg. 540

Santoro, M.R., Sr. V.P.--STV International, New York, NY; *U.S. Public*, pg. 1421

Santry, Jim, Sr. V.P.--Bituminous Casualty Corp., Rock Island, IL; *U.S. Public*, pg. 1218

Saperstein, Steven A., Sr. V.P.--USLIFE Equity Sales Corp., New York, NY; *U.S. Public*, pg. 77

Saphier, David J., Sr. V.P. & Gen. Mgr.-Remote Communications Prod. Grp.--Artisoft, Inc., Tucson, AZ; *U.S. Public*, pg. 136

Sapienza, Robert, Sr. V.P.-Sls.--Wittnauer International, Inc., New Rochelle, NY; *U.S. Public*, pg. 273

Sapp, G. David, Sr. V.P.-Investments--American United Life Insurance Company, Indianapolis, IN; *U.S. Private*, pg. 64

Sara, Heikki, Sr. V.P.-Resources--UPM-Kymmene Corporation, Helsinki, Finland; *Int'l*, pg. 1427

Sara, Heikki, Sr. V.P.--United Paper Mills Ltd., Valkeakoski, Finland; *Int'l*, pg. 1429

Sarcone, Anthony, Sr. V.P.--Century Business Credit Corporation, New York, NY; *U.S. Private*, pg. 225

Sardelli, Richard, Sr. V.P.--Fidelity Investments (FMR Corp.), Boston, MA; *U.S. Private*, pg. 402

Sariego, Jose M., Sr. V.P. & Gen. Counsel--MasTec, Inc., Miami, FL; *U.S. Public*, pg. 1055

Sarnoff, Bret, Sr. V.P.-Fin.--Carsey-Werner Company, LLC, Studio City, CA; *U.S. Private*, pg. 216

Sarto, John F., Sr. V.P. & Gen Mgr.-OmniTRACS Div.--QUALCOMM, San Diego, CA; *U.S. Public*, pg. 1348

Sarver, Terry, Sr. V.P.--Bawden Corporation, Eldridge, IA; *U.S. Private*, pg. 124

Sarver, Terry, Sr. V.P.-Mfg.--Bawden Printing, Inc., Eldridge, IA; *U.S. Private*, pg. 124

Sasaki, Robert K., Sr. V.P.--A & B Properties, Inc., Honolulu, HI; *U.S. Public*, pg. 39

Sasaki, Tomohiko, Sr. V.P.--Toshiba Corporation, Tokyo, Japan; *Int'l*, pg. 1402

Sasloff, Alan, Sr. V.P.--Century Business Credit Corporation, New York, NY; *U.S. Private*, pg. 225

Sassano, Carl E., Sr. V.P.-Various Divs.--Bausch & Lomb Incorporated, Rochester, NY; *U.S. Public*, pg. 194

Sasser, Bob L., Sr. V.P.-Mdsg. & Mktg.--Rose's Stores, Inc., Henderson, NC; *U.S. Public*, pg. 1405

Sasson, David, Sr. V.P.--RNBNY Branch Office-Hong Kong, Central, Hong Kong; *U.S. Public*, pg. 1381

Satake, Akio, Sr. V.P.--Pall Corporation, Greenvale, NY; *U.S. Public*, pg. 1253

Saterbo, Bryan, Sr. V.P. & Treas.--Colorado Boxed Beef Co., Auburndale, FL; *U.S. Private*, pg. 254

Saterbo, John, Sr. V.P. & Sec.--Colorado Boxed Beef Co., Auburndale, FL; *U.S. Private*, pg. 254

Saterbo, Stephen, Sr. V.P.-Fin. & Mktg.--Colorado Boxed Beef Co., Auburndale, FL; *U.S. Private*, pg. 254

Sato, Kotaro, Sr. V.P.-Pub. Rels.--Japan Airlines Company, Ltd., Tokyo, Japan; *Int'l*, pg. 699

Sato, Tata, Sr. V.P. & Acct. Plng. Dir.-Insights Grp.--Young & Rubicam New York, New York, NY; *U.S. Private*, pg. 1198

Sato, Toshikazu, Sr. V.P. & Dir.--Kodansha Ltd., Tokyo, Japan; *Int'l*, pg. 742

Satola, Robert, Sr. V.P.--Domino Sugar Corporation, New York, NY; *Int'l*, pg. 1356

Sattabudsutthi, Visut, Sr. V.P.-Treasury Dept.--The Industrial Finance Corporation of Thailand, Bangkok, Thailand; *Int'l*, pg. 677

Sattler, Ryan J., Sr. V.P.-Opers.--The Bon Ton Stores, Inc., York, PA; *U.S. Public*, pg. 244

Sauerlaender, J. Friedrich, Sr. V.P.-Corp. Communications & Investor Rels.--SGS Societe Generale de Surveillance Holding S.A., Geneva, Switzerland; *Int'l*, pg. 1153

Saul, Alan, Sr. V.P.--Willis Corroon Corp. of Georgia, Atlanta, GA; *Int'l*, pg. 1506

Saul, Jeff, Sr. V.P. & Assoc. Creative Dir.-Retail Div.--Gianettino & Meredith Advertising, Short Hills, NJ; *U.S. Private*, pg. 450

Saulic, Donald B., Sr. V.P.-Global Chief Information Officer--BAX Global, Irvine, CA; *U.S. Public*, pg. 1305

Saunders, Greg W., Sr. V.P.-Hotel Opers.--MGM Grand Hotel, Inc., Las Vegas, NV; *U.S. Public*, pg. 1027

Saunders, John H., Sr. V.P. & Reg. Mgr.-Africa--Standard Commercial Tobacco Co., Inc., Wilson, NC; *U.S. Public*, pg. 1502

Saunders, Nancy, Sr. V.P.--Texas Commerce Bank, Houston, TX; *U.S. Public*, pg. 339

Saunders, R. Reed, Sr. V.P.-Corp. Strategy & Devel.--American Express Financial Advisor, Minneapolis, MN; *U.S. Public*, pg. 73

Saunders, R.G., Sr. V.P.--InterDigital Communications Corp., King of Prussia, PA; *U.S. Public*, pg. 889

Saunders, Robert H., Jr., Sr. V.P.-Fin.--Kaman Corporation, Bloomfield, CT; *U.S. Public*, pg. 941

Saunders, Stuart D., Sr. V.P. & Gen. Counsel--Prime Bancshares Inc., Houston, TX; *U.S. Public*, pg. 1326

Sauvageau, JoAnn R., Sr. V.P. & Gen. Mgr.-Mdsg.--Younkers, Inc., Des Moines, IA; *U.S. Public*, pg. 1334

Savage, Larry, Sr. V.P. & Chief Underwritter--Empire Blue Cross & Blue Shield, New York, NY; *U.S. Private*, pg. 374

Savage, Roger P., Sr. V.P.-Bus. Banking--Republic Security Financial Corporation, West Palm Beach, FL; *U.S. Public*, pg. 1381

Savage, Roger P., Sr. V.P.-Commercial & Consumer Loan Mgr.--Republic Security Bank, West Palm Beach, FL; *U.S. Public*, pg. 1382

Savage, Steven A., Sr. V.P.-Mfg.--Terra Nitrogen Company, L.P., Tulsa, OK; *U.S. Public*, pg. 1581

Savard, Donald D., Sr. V.P-Corp. Services--Interprovincial Pipe Line Inc., Edmonton, Canada; *Int'l*, pg. 652

Savela, Mary, Sr. V.P. & Grp. Media Dir.--DMB&B New York, New York, NY; *U.S. Private*, pg. 302

Saville, Paul, Chief Fin. Officer & Sr. V.P.--NVR, Inc., Mc Lean, VA; *U.S. Public*, pg. 1148

Sawada, Susumu, Sr. V.P.-Tech. Equip.--Anritsu Corporation, Tokyo, Japan; *Int'l*, pg. 77

Sawaya, William J., Ph.D., Sr. V.P.-Mfg.--Daw Technologies, Inc., Salt Lake City, UT; *U.S. Public*, pg. 489

Saxon, Franklin N., Chief Fin. Officer, Sr. V.P., Treas. & Sec.--Culp, Inc., High Point, NC; *U.S. Public*, pg. 467

Saxton, Robert L., Sr. V.P.-Casino Opers.--Alliance Gaming Corporation, Las Vegas, NV; *U.S. Public*, pg. 46

Saxton, Tom, Sr. V.P.--Hayes-Dana Service Parts Div., Beamsville, Canada; *U.S. Public*, pg. 480

Sayatovic, Wayne P., Chief Fin. Officer & Sr. V.P.-Fin.--IDEX Corporation, Northbrook, IL; *U.S. Public*, pg. 862

Saydun, Yuda, Sr. V.P. & Gen. Mgr.-Latin America--Tech Data Corporation, Clearwater, FL; *U.S. Public*, pg. 1562

Sayles, Helen, Sr. V.P. & Mgr.-H.R.--Liberty Mutual Insurance Co., Boston, MA; *U.S. Private*, pg. 666

Scager, Robert, Sr. V.P.-Sls. & Mktg.--Comdisco Canada Ltd., Toronto, Canada; *U.S. Public*, pg. 408

Scalera, Ron, Sr. V.P. & Creative Dir.-Adv. & Promo.--CBS Television Network, New York, NY; *U.S. Public*, pg. 274

Scales, Leon, Sr. V.P.-Interest Rate Risk Mngmt.--Coast Savings Financial, Inc., Los Angeles, CA; *U.S. Public*, pg. 388

Scalet, J. Chris, V.P.-Information Systems--Mapco Inc., Tulsa, OK; *U.S. Public*, pg. 1042

Scalise, George M., Chief Admin. Officer & Sr. V.P.--National Semiconductor Corporation, Santa Clara, CA; *U.S. Public*, pg. 1159

Scallon, Jim, Sr. V.P. & Gen. Councel--Citibank, Federal Savings Bank (Illinois), Chicago, IL; *U.S. Public*, pg. 378

Scanlon, Jack R., Jr., Sr. V.P.--First Health Group Corp., Downers Grove, IL; *U.S. Public*, pg. 635

Scannell, Timothy M., Sr. V.P.--Pinnacle Bank, Valparaiso, IN; *U.S. Public*, pg. 1297

Scarangella, Frank, Sr. V.P.--The Bank of New York Company, Inc., New York, NY; *U.S. Public*, pg. 178

Scarborough, C. Kermit, Sr. V.P.-Labor Rels.--Yellow Freight System, Inc., Overland Park, KS; *U.S. Public*, pg. 1788

Scarpati, Steve, Sr. V.P.-Fin. Mngmt. & Controller--The Guardian Life Insurance Company of America, New York, NY; *U.S. Private*, pg. 486

Scarpetta, Paul, Sr. V.P.-Shareholder Rels.--Federal Home Loan Mortgage Corporation, Mc Lean, VA; *U.S. Public*, pg. 615

Scartezina, Stan, Sr. V.P.-Human Resources--Kennecott Holdings Corporation, Magna, UT; *Int'l*, pg. 1119

Scatergood, James E., Sr. V.P.-Admin.--B.M.J. Financial Corp., Bordentown, NJ; *U.S. Public*, pg. 1528

Scavo, Alton J., Sr. V.P. & Dir.-Community Devel., Gen. Mgr.-Columbia--The Rouse Company, Columbia, MD; *U.S. Public*, pg. 1407

Scavo, Alton J., Sr. V.P., Gen. Mgr.-Columbia & Dir.-Community Devel.--Rouse Office & Community Development Div., Columbia, MD; *U.S. Public*, pg. 1407

Schaapveld, Larry, Sr. V.P.--Grain Processing Corp., Muscatine, IA; *U.S. Private*, pg. 1134

Schackelford, Daniel O., Sr. V.P.--Investment Counselors of Maryland, Inc., Baltimore, MD; *U.S. Public*, pg. 1673

Schaecher, Frances P., Sr. V.P.-Opers.--Lands' End, Inc., Dodgeville, WI; *U.S. Public*, pg. 977

Schaechterle, Gordon E., Jr., V.P., Controller & Tax Counsel--Mapco Inc., Tulsa, OK; *U.S. Public*, pg. 1042

Schaeffer, Mark, Sr. V.P., Client Services Dir. & New Bus. Contact--Bromley, Aguilar & Associates, San Antonio, TX; *U.S. Private*, pg. 692

Schaeffer, Scott F., Sr. V.P.-Real Estate & Pres.-Resource Properties, Inc.--Resource America, Inc., Philadelphia, PA; *U.S. Public*, pg. 1382

Schafer, David, Sr. V.P.-Worldwide Sls.--Western Digital Corporation, Irvine, CA; *U.S. Public*, pg. 1758

Schafer, Timothy J., Sr. V.P.-Fin. & Taxation--Reinalt-Thomas Corp., Ann Arbor, MI; *U.S. Private*, pg. 919

Schaffer, Donald J., Chief Fin. Officer & Sr. V.P.-Fin.--General American Transportation Corporation, Chicago, IL; *U.S. Public*, pg. 692

Schaler, Linda, Sr. V.P.-Client Services--Jordan, McGrath, Case & Taylor Inc., New York, NY; *U.S. Private*, pg. 598

Schankland, Joe, Sr. V.P.-Sls. & Mktg.--Select Beverages, Inc., Darien, IL; *U.S. Private*, pg. 982

Scharp, Robert C., Sr. V.P.-Oil & Gas Opers.--Kerr-McGee Corporation, Oklahoma City, OK; *U.S. Public*, pg. 952

Scheckner, Barry D., Chief Fin. Officer & Sr. V.P.--Finlay Enterprises, Inc., New York, NY; *U.S. Public*, pg. 623

Schecter, William H., Sr. V.P.-Merchant Banking--National City Corporation, Cleveland, OH; *U.S. Public*, pg. 1154

Scheff, Debbie, Sr. V.P. & Chief Oper. Officer-Managed Care--PHP Healthcare Corporation, Reston, VA; *U.S. Public*, pg. 1241

Scheffler, Barbara I., Sr. V.P.-Corp. & Scientific Affairs--U.S. Bioscience, Inc., Conshohocken, PA; *U.S. Public*, pg. 1681

Scheffler, Peter M., Sr. V.P.--SCI Systems, Inc., Huntsville, AL; *U.S. Public*, pg. 1416

Scheich, Don, Sr. V.P.-Mopar--Ross Roy Communications, Inc., Bloomfield Hills, MI; *U.S. Private*, pg. 946

Scheihing, Betty Jane, Sr. V.P.--Arrow Electronics, Inc., Melville, NY; *U.S. Public*, pg. 133

Scheiner, Jay M., 1st Sr. V.P. & Chief Information Officer--J. Baker, Inc., Canton, MA; *U.S. Public*, pg. 167

Scheiner, Jay M., Chief Information Officer & 1st Sr. V.P.--Morse Shoe, Inc., Canton, MA; *U.S. Public*, pg. 168

Scheiner, Jay M., Chief Information Officer & 1st Sr. V.P.--Casual Male, Inc., Hyde Park, MA; *U.S. Public*, pg. 168

Schell, Theodore H., Sr. V.P.-Strategic Plng. & Corp. Devel.--Sprint Corporation, Westwood, KS; *U.S. Public*, pg. 1500

Schenfeld, Larry, Sr. V.P.--U.S. Yellow Pages, San Francisco, CA; *U.S. Private*, pg. 1168

Schenk, Alice F., Sr. V.P.--Great Western Bank, Chatsworth, CA; *U.S. Public*, pg. 1741

Schenk, Eric, Sr. V.P.--Hill, Holliday, Connors, Cosmopulos, Inc., Boston, MA; *U.S. Private*, pg. 529

Schenker, Leo, Sr. Exec. V.P.--Central National-Gottesman Inc., Purchase, NY; *U.S. Private*, pg. 224

Schepis, Joseph M., Sr., Chief Oper. Officer & Sr. V.P.--Washington Gas Light Co., Springfield, VA; *U.S. Public*, pg. 1740

Scherb, Jeff R., Chief Tech. Officer & Sr. V.P.--Tribune Company, Chicago, IL; *U.S. Public*, pg. 1635

Scherer, Donn, Sr. V.P.-Real Estate--Osco Drug, Salt Lake City, UT; *U.S. Public*, pg. 93

Scherer, J. Peter, Sr. V.P.-Legal Svcs.--Taubman Centers, Inc., Bloomfield Hills, MI; *U.S. Public*, pg. 1561

Scherer, Richard P., Sr. V.P.-Mktg. & Bus. Devel.--Laser Power Corporation, San Diego, CA; *U.S. Private*, pg. 652

Scherer, Thomas O., Sr. V.P. & Dir.-Portfolio Surveillance & Reporting--Municipal Bond Investors Assurance Corporation, Armonk, NY; *U.S. Public*, pg. 1023

Scherer, Thomas W., Chief Fin. Officer & Sr. V.P.--ServiceMaster Consumer Services Company, Memphis, TN; *U.S. Public*, pg. 1461

Scherr, Allan L., Sr. V.P.--EMC Corporation, Hopkinton, MA; *U.S. Public*, pg. 545

Scherrer, William H., Jr., Chief Oper. Officer & Sr. V.P.--Emery Customs Brokers, Cleveland, OH; *U.S. Public*, pg. 281

Scheuer, Patricia L., Chief Investment Officer & Sr. V.P.--National Western Life Insurance Company, Austin, TX; *U.S. Public*, pg. 1161

Schexnaydre, Ronald J., Sr. V.P.--Hilb, Rogal and Hamilton Company, Glen Allen, VA; *U.S. Public*, pg. 826

Schierbaum, Wayne D., Sr. V.P.-Fin. & Controller--White Consolidated Industries, Inc., Cleveland, OH; *Int'l*, pg. 439

Schieren, George A., Sr. V.P. & Gen. Counsel--Merrill Lynch, Pierce, Fenner & Smith, Inc., New York, NY; *U.S.* Public, pg. 1098

Schievelbein, Karen, Chief Fin. Officer & Sr. V.P.--Blue Shield of California, San Francisco, CA; *U.S. Private*, pg. 153

Schiff, Morton I., Sr. V.P.-Special Prod.--Industrial Acoustics Company, Inc., Bronx, NY; *U.S. Public*, pg. 875

Schiffer, Daniel L., Sr. V.P., Gen. Counsel & Sec.--MCN Energy Group, Inc., Detroit, MI; *U.S. Public*, pg. 1024

Schiffmacher, William G., Sr. V.P.-Customer Rels., Information Systems & Tech.--Long Island Lighting Company, Hicksville, NY; *U.S. Public*, pg. 1013

Schifrin, Kevin, Exec. V.P.-Sls. & Mktg.--Stegner Food Products Co., Cincinnati, OH; *U.S. Private*, pg. 1039

Schifrin, Mark E., Sr. V.P.--Oxford Realty Financial Group, Bethesda, MD; *U.S. Private*, pg. 825

Schillig, Janice, Sr. V.P. & Mngmt. Supvr.--Adler Boschetto Peebles & Partners, Inc., New York, NY; *U.S. Private*, pg. 17

Schilling, Ernest, Sr. V.P.-Midwest & West--Powell Electronics Inc., Philadelphia, PA; *U.S. Private*, pg. 877

Schilling, Lee, Sr. V.P.-Sls. & Mktg.--Collins & Aikman Floorcoverings, Inc., Dalton, GA; *U.S. Private*, pg. 192

Schimelman, Joan K., Sr. V.P.-H.R. & Mktg./Adv.--Republic Security Financial Corporation, West Palm Beach, FL; *U.S. Public*, pg. 1381

Schindele, Wendel, Dr., Sr. V.P.--ITT Automotive, Inc., Auburn Hills, MI; *U.S. Public*, pg. 859

Schinner, E., Sr. V.P.--Baltimore Aircoil Company, Jessup, MD; *U.S. Private*, pg. 68

Schirripa, Felix, Sr. V.P.-Prod. Devel. & Mngmt.--Metropolitan Life Insurance Co., New York, NY; *U.S. Private*, pg. 737

Schlegel, Patrick, Sr. V.P.--Ferrier Lullin & Cie SA, Geneva, Switzerland; *Int'l*, pg. 480

Schlichting, Duane, Sr. Partner & Brdcst. Production Mgr.--TN Services Inc., Omaha, NE; *U.S. Public*, pg. 1642

Schloss, Marcel, Sr. V.P.-Fin. & Admin.--Parade Publications Inc., New York, NY; *U.S. Private*, pg. 20

Schlosser, D.A., Sr. V.P.--B.C. Ziegler & Co., West Bend, WI; *U.S. Public*, pg. 1792

Schlough, Harry W., Sr. V.P.-Strategy & Markets--SHL Systemhouse, Ottawa, Canada; *Int'l*, pg. 1154

Schmeler, Frank R., Sr. V.P.-U.S. & Latin America--Albany International Corp., Albany, NY; *U.S. Public*, pg. 36

Schmidt, Carl G., Chief Fin. Officer, Sr. V.P., Treas. & Sec.--Johnson Worldwide Associates, Inc., Sturtevant, WI; *U.S.* Public, pg. 932

Schmidt, Dennis, Sr. V.P.-Fin.--Regal Ware, Inc., Kewaskum, WI; *U.S. Private*, pg. 917

Schmidt, Dwight C., Sr. V.P.-Specialty Opers.--Inland Container-Container Division, Indianapolis, IN; *U.S. Public*, pg. 1575

Schmidt, Fred L., Sr. V.P.-Human Resources--Public Service Company of North Carolina, Inc., Gastonia, NC; *U.S. Public*, pg. 1340

Schmidt, Helmut, Sr. V.P.-Accounts--Bayerische Landesbank, Munich, Germany; *Int'l*, pg. 176

Schmidt, Janet L., Sr. V.P.-H.R.--The Acacia Group - Acacia Life Insurance Co., Bethesda, MD; *U.S. Private*, pg. 10

Schmidt, Mark, Sr. V.P.-Supercenter Division--Wal-Mart Stores, Inc., Bentonville, AR; *U.S. Public*, pg. 1732

Schmidt, Marvin L., Sr. V.P.-Corp. Devel.--Copart, Inc., Benicia, CA; *U.S. Public*, pg. 446

Schmidt, Michael, Sr. V.P. & Dir.-Stores--Gottschalks Inc., Fresno, CA; *U.S. Public*, pg. 754

Schmidt, R. John, Jr., Sr. V.P. & Controller--Office Depot Inc., Delray Beach, FL; *U.S. Public*, pg. 1212

Schmidt, Randy F., Sr. V.P.--AMBAC Financial Group, Inc., New York, NY; *U.S. Public*, pg. 62

Schmidt, Richard, Sr. V.P.-Sls. & Mktg.--Federal Process Corp., Cleveland, OH; *U.S. Private*, pg. 399

Schmidt, Sanford V., Chief Admin. Officer & Sr. V.P.--American Trading and Production Corporation, Baltimore, MD; *U.S. Private*, pg. 63

Schmidt, Tracy G., Sr. V.P.-Air Ground Terminal & Transportation--FDX Corporation, Memphis, TN; *U.S. Public*, pg. 603

Schmitt, David L., Sr. V.P.-Admin., Gen. Counsel & Sec.--Bradlees Inc., Braintree, MA; *U.S. Public*, pg. 249

Schmitt, Hans-Georg, Ph.D., Sr. V.P.-Organics/Fibers, Organics & Rubber Div.--Bayer Corporation, Pittsburgh, PA; *Int'l*, pg. 172

Schmitt, Robert E., Sr. V.P.--Industrial Acoustics Company, Inc., Bronx, NY; *U.S. Public*, pg. 875

Schmittbetz, Klaus, Sr. V.P.-Prod.--Deutz AG, Cologne, Germany; *Int'l*, pg. 407

Schmoeller, Joseph, Sr. V.P.--Carpenter Co., Richmond, VA; *U.S. Private*, pg. 214

Schmoller, Eberhard G.H., Sr. V.P., Gen. Counsel & Sec.--CNF Transportation Inc., Palo Alto, CA; *U.S. Public*, pg. 281

Schnabel, Jay H., Sr. V.P.-Diagnostics--Snap-On Tools Corporation, Kenosha, WI; *U.S. Public*, pg. 1480

Schnack, Uwe, Sr. V.P. & Gen. Mgr.--TSC Shannock Corporation, Burnaby, Canada; *Int'l*, pg. 1343

Schnatter, Charles W., Sr. V.P. & Sec.--Papa John's International Inc., Louisville, KY; *U.S. Public*, pg. 1255

Schneider, Forrest M., Chief Fin. Officer & Sr. V.P.--Lane Industries, Inc., Northbrook, IL; *U.S. Private*, pg. 649

Schneider, Jon, Sr. V.P. & Acct. Dir.--Wunderman Cato Johnson, New York, NY; *U.S. Private*, pg. 1197

Schneider, Paul L., Chief Fin. Officer & Sr. V.P.--The Acacia Group - Acacia Life Insurance Co., Bethesda, MD; *U.S. Private*, pg. 10

Schneider, Paul L., Chief Fin. Officer & Sr. V.P.--Acacia Financial Corporation, Bethesda, MD; *U.S. Private*, pg. 11

Schneider, Robert E., Sr. V.P.-Res. & Devel.--ProBusiness Services, Inc., Pleasanton, CA; *U.S. Public*, pg. 1330

Schneider, Scott N., Chief Fin. Officer, Sr. V.P. & Treas.--Century Communications Corp., New Canaan, CT; *U.S. Public*, pg. 329

Schneider, Steven L., Sr. V.P.-Sls. & Mktg.--Eagle Electronics, Catoosa, OK; *U.S. Public*, pg. 1016

Schneider, Steven L., Sr. V.P.-Sls. & Mktg.--Lowrance Avionics, Tulsa, OK; *U.S. Public*, pg. 1016

Schnieders, Richard J., Sr. V.P.-Mdsg. & Multi-Unit Sls.--Sysco Corporation, Houston, TX; *U.S. Public*, pg. 1550

Schnomeier, Theodore, Sr. V.P.--Jeld-Wen, Inc., Klamath Falls, OR; *U.S. Private*, pg. 585

Schnug, Tony, Sr. Grp. V.P.-Support OPS--Ralphs Grocery Company, Compton, CA; *U.S. Private*, pg. 1202

Schnur, Alan E., Sr. V.P.-H.R.--Robert Mondavi Winery, Inc., Oakville, CA; *U.S. Public*, pg. 1393

Schnur, Daniel R., Sr. V.P., Gen. Counsel & Sec.--Richfood Holdings, Inc., Glen Allen, VA; *U.S. Public*, pg. 1388

Schnurr, Kenneth E., Sr. V.P.-Field Opers.--Eby Corporation, Wichita, KS; *U.S. Private*, pg. 359

Schober, G. Stephen, Sr. V.P.-Fin. Plng. & Investments--TCG International Inc., Burnaby, Canada; *Int'l*, pg. 1336

Schoeffler, Michael H., Sr. V.P.-Fin.--Starcraft Automotive Group, Inc., Goshen, IN; *U.S. Public*, pg. 1511

Schoel, William, Jr., Sr. V.P.-Human Resources Devel.--SouthTrust Corporation, Birmingham, AL; *U.S. Public*, pg. 1491

Schoenberg, Lester L., Sr. V.P.-Individual Policy Services--New York Life Insurance Company, New York, NY; *U.S. Private*, pg. 794

Schoenecker, Larry, Sr. V.P.--Schoeneckers, Inc., Minneapolis, MN; *U.S. Private*, pg. 971

Schoenfeld, Barry, Sr. V.P. & Strategic Plng. Dir.--Asher/Gould Advertising, Inc., Los Angeles, CA; *U.S. Private*, pg. 88

Schoenfeld, Joel M., Sr. V.P. & General Counsel--Bertelsmann Music Group, Wilmington, DE; *Int'l*, pg. 191

Schoenfeld, Peter, Sr. V.P.-Television Bus. Devel.-Universal Studios Pay TV--Universal Studios TV, Universal City, CA; *Int'l*, pg. 1215

Schoenholz, David A., Chief Fin. Officer & Sr. V.P.--Household International, Inc., Prospect Heights, IL; *U.S. Public*, pg. 842

Schoeny, Don, Sr. V.P.-Sls. Worldwide & Service Support--PerSeptive Biosystems, Inc., Framingham, MA; *U.S. Public*, pg. 1279

Schoewe, Thomas M., Chief Fin. Officer & Sr. V.P.--The Black & Decker Corporation, Towson, MD; *U.S. Public*, pg. 233

Schofield, Ernest A., Chief Fin. Officer & Sr. V.P.--Horizon/CMS Healthcare Corporation, Albuquerque, NM; *U.S. Public*, pg. 836

Schofield, Mark, Sr. V.P.-Acct. Services--McKinney & Silver, Raleigh, NC; *U.S. Private*, pg. 723

Scholtes, Rusty, Sr. V.P. & Grp. Acct. Dir.--Bernstein-Rein Advertising, Inc., Kansas City, MO; *U.S. Private*, pg. 137

Scholton, Richard A., Sr. V.P.-Lending--Hollidaysburg Trust Company, Hollidaysburg, PA; *U.S. Public*, pg. 1222

Schon, Cecilia, Sr. V.P.-Corp. Commun.--Trygg-Hansa, Stockholm, Sweden; *Int'l*, pg. 1425

Schoonover, Philip J., Sr. V.P.-Mktg./Consumer Electronics & Appliances--Best Buy Co., Inc., Eden Prairie, MN; *U.S.* Public, pg. 223

Schorb, Robert B., Sr. V.P.--Associates Insurance Group, Inc., Dallas, TX; *U.S. Public*, pg. 663

Schotters, Bernard W., Sr. V.P.-Fin.--TCI Communications, Inc., Englewood, CO; *U.S. Public*, pg. 1554

Schrader, James, Sr. V.P.--Pacific Combining Corp., Los Angeles, CA; *U.S. Public*, pg. 802

Schrader, William, Sr. V.P. & Loan Officer--Exchange Bank, Santa Rosa, CA; *U.S. Public*, pg. 599

Schram, Henry B., Chief Acctg. Officer & Sr. V.P.--The Chubb Corporation, Warren, NJ; *U.S. Public*, pg. 354

Schrank, Doug, Sr. V.P.-Pediatrics Americas--M.A. Hanna Company, Cleveland, OH; *U.S. Public*, pg. 780

Schreck, Wayne A., Sr. V.P.--Riverside Group, Inc., Jacksonville, FL; *U.S. Public*, pg. 1391

Schreger, Ira A., Sr. V.P. & Sec.--Sequa Corporation, New York, NY; *U.S. Public*, pg. 1458

Schreiber, Caron, Sr. V.P. & Dir.--EVEREN Securities, Inc., Chicago, IL; *U.S. Public*, pg. 597

Schreiber, Elliot S., Sr. V.P.-Corp. Commun.--Northern Telecom Limited, Brampton, Canada; *Int'l*, pg. 968

Schreibman, Joel, Sr. V.P. & Gen. Mgr.-Mdse., The Casual Male--J. Baker, Inc., Canton, MA; *U.S. Public*, pg. 167

Schreibman, Robert, Sr. V.P. & Dir.-Internal Audit--Countrywide Funding Corporation, Pasadena, CA; *U.S. Public*, pg. 453

Schreier, Lois R., Sr. V.P.-Intl. Banking--Citizens Bank of Massachusetts, Fairhaven, MA; *Int'l*, pg. 1132

Schrider, Leo A., Sr. V.P.-Tech. Devel.--Belden & Blake Corporation, Canton, OH; *U.S. Private*, pg. 1078

Schroeder, Gary P., Sr. V.P. & Pres.-Western Grp.--Coca-Cola Enterprises Inc., Atlanta, GA; *U.S. Public*, pg. 393

Schroeder, James, Chief Oper. Officer & Exec. V.P.--Sid Tool Co. Inc., Plainview, NY; *U.S. Private*, pg. 998

Schroeder, John M., Sr. V.P. & Advisor to the Chm.--S.C. Johnson & Son, Inc., Racine, WI; *U.S. Private*, pg. 592

Schruth, Peter, Sr. V.P.-Affiliate Rels. Div.--CBS Broadcast Group, New York, NY; *U.S. Public*, pg. 274

Schruth, Peter K., Sr. V.P. & Gen. Mgr.-Affiliate Rels.--CBS Television Network, New York, NY; *U.S. Public*, pg. 274

Schub, Craig, Sr. V.P.--PacifiCare Health Systems, Inc., Cypress, CA; *U.S. Public*, pg. 1250

Schubert, Thomas D., Chief Fin. & Acctg. Officer & Sr. V.P.--NovaCare Employee Services, Inc., Norristown, PA; *U.S.* Public, pg. 1203

Schuchart, Wayne L., Sr. V.P.-Info. Sys.--Oakwood Homes Corporation, Greensboro, NC; *U.S. Public*, pg. 1209

Schugart, Charles F., Chief Fin. Officer & Sr. V.P.--Innovative Valve Technology, Inc., Houston, TX; *U.S. Public*, pg. 880

Schukai, Charles J., Sr. V.P.-Customer Svcs.--AmerenUE, Saint Louis, MO; *U.S. Public*, pg. 66

Schulaner, Felice, Sr. V.P.-Human Resources--Salant Corporation, New York, NY; *U.S. Public*, pg. 1429

Schuldt, John C., Sr. V.P. & Gen. Mgr.-Pkgng.--Burrows Paper Corporation, Little Falls, NY; *U.S. Private*, pg. 188

Schuler, Mark, Chief Fin. Officer & Sr. V.P.--IIT Research Institute, Chicago, IL; *U.S. Private*, pg. 555

Schuler, Steven T., Chief Fin. Officer, Corp. Sr. V.P., Treas. & Sec.--Brenton Banks, Inc., Des Moines, IA; *U.S. Public*, pg. 251

Schulhof, Pierre, Sr. V.P.--Compagnie Generale Des Eaux, Paris, France; *Int'l*, pg. 321

Schulman, Lynn, Sr. V.P.--Edelman Worldwide, Inc., New York, NY; *U.S. Private*, pg. 362

Schulman, Nancy, Sr. V.P. & Grp. Acct. Dir.--Ketchum Advertising/San Francisco, San Francisco, CA; *U.S. Private*, pg. 616

Schulman, Robert P., Sr. V.P. & Gen. Counsel--Kimco Realty Corporation, New Hyde Park, NY; *U.S. Public*, pg. 960

Schulthies, Ronald A., Sr. V.P. & Mgr.-Fin. Services Div.--First Security Bank of Utah, N.A., Salt Lake City, UT; *U.S. Public*, pg. 637

Schultz, Bradford C., Sr. V.P.-Sls. & Mktg.--Accuride Corp., Henderson, KY; *U.S. Public*, pg. 1286

Schultz, Charles L., Sr. V.P.-Intermodal & Automotive Bus. Unit--Burlington Northern Santa Fe Corporation, Fort Worth, TX; *U.S. Public*, pg. 268

Schultz, Dan, Chief Fin. Officer & Sr. V.P.--Grey Entertainment Inc., New York, NY; *U.S. Public*, pg. 764

Schultz, James D., Chief Fin. Officer, Sr. V.P., Treas. & Sec.--Old America Stores, Howe, TX; *U.S. Public*, pg. 1215

Schultz, Lisa A., Sr. V.P.-Design--Gap Stores Division, San Bruno, CA; *U.S. Public*, pg. 702

Schultz, Ronald E., Chief Oper. Officer & Sr. V.P.--MATRIXX Marketing Inc., Cincinnati, OH; *U.S. Public*, pg. 368

Schultz, Steven A., Sr. V.P.-Fin. Institutions--Protective Life Corporation, Birmingham, AL; *U.S. Public*, pg. 1336

Schulz, William J., Sr. V.P. & Sec.--Firstar Corporation, Milwaukee, WI; *U.S. Public*, pg. 642

Schulze, Donald W., Sr. V.P.-H.R.--D & N Financial Corporation, Hancock, MI; *U.S. Public*, pg. 472

Schulze, Donald W., Sr. V.P.-H.R.--D & N Bank, Hancock, MI; *U.S. Public*, pg. 472

Schulze, Jurgen H., Sr. V.P.-Pur.--Deutz AG, Cologne, Germany; *Int'l*, pg. 407

Schulzezur Wiersch, Ulrich, Sr. V.P. & Mng. Dir.--Pharm-Allergan GmbH, Ettlingen, Germany; *U.S. Public*, pg. 46

Schumacher, Bill, Chief Fin. Officer & Sr. V.P.--Select Beverages, Inc., Darien, IL; *U.S. Private*, pg. 982

Schumacher, Diane Kosmach, Sr. V.P., Gen. Counsel & Sec.--Cooper Industries, Inc., Houston, TX; *U.S. Public*, pg. 442

Schuman, Barry R., Sr. V.P.-Human Resources--Tenneco Inc., Greenwich, CT; *U.S. Public*, pg. 1577

Schumann, Paul D., Chief Oper. Officer & Sr. V.P.--Consumers Water Company, Portland, ME; *U.S. Public*, pg. 438

Schumann, William F., Sr. V.P. & Pres-Old Republic Insured Credit Services, Inc.--Old Republic International Corporation, Chicago, IL; *U.S. Public*, pg. 1218

Schumer, William, Sr. V.P. & Dir.-Mktg.--Bank One, Cincinnati, Cincinnati, OH; *U.S. Public*, pg. 173

Schun, Arsene, Sr. V.P.-Chemicals--Elf Aquitane, Paris, France; *Int'l*, pg. 444

Schuneman, Norman D., Chief Credit Officer & Corp. Sr. V.P.--Brenton Banks, Inc., Des Moines, IA; *U.S. Public*, pg. 251

Schurz, James M., Sr. V.P.-Newspapers--Schurz Communications, Inc., South Bend, IN; *U.S. Private*, pg. 973

Schuster, James E., Sr. V.P.-Opers.--MagneTek, Inc., Nashville, TN; *U.S. Public*, pg. 1037

Schutt, Douglas W., Sr. V.P.-Mdsg. & Non-Foods--Costco Wholesale, Issaquah, WA; *U.S. Public*, pg. 451

Schutte, Kenneth E., Sr. V.P. & Treas.--Mercantile Bancorporation Inc., Saint Louis, MO; *U.S. Public*, pg. 1087

Schutz, Lindy, Sr. V.P., Reg. Mgr. & Mgr.-Key Accts.--BASES Worldwide, Covington, KY; *U.S. Private*, pg. 120

Schwab, Bill, Sr. V.P., Assoc. Creative Dir.--Ammirati, Puris & Lintas, Inc., New York, NY; *U.S. Private*, pg. 66

Schwab, Lowell F., Sr. V.P.-Opers.--Donaldson Company, Inc., Minneapolis, MN; *U.S. Public*, pg. 517

Schwalbe, William, Sr. V.P., Editorial Dir.-Adult Books--William Morrow & Co., Inc., New York, NY; *U.S. Private*, pg. 515

Schwan, Joseph V., Sr. V.P. & Gen. Mgr.-Forms Div.--The Standard Register Company, Dayton, OH; *U.S. Public*, pg. 1505

Schwartz, Chuck, Chief Fin. Officer & Sr. V.P.--People's Choice TV Corp., Shelton, CT; *U.S. Public*, pg. 1274

Schwartz, David E., Sr. V.P.--Tokyo-Mitsubishi Derivative Products (USA), Inc., New York, NY; *Int'l*, pg. 157

Schwartz, Dean, Sr. V.P.-Client Services--Jordan, McGrath, Case & Taylor Inc., New York, NY; *U.S. Private*, pg. 598

Schwartz, Gil, Sr. V.P.-Communications--CBS, New York, NY; *U.S. Public*, pg. 273

Schwartz, Gil, Sr. V.P.-Communications--CBS Broadcast Group, New York, NY; *U.S. Public*, pg. 274

Schwartz, H.G., Jr., Sr. V.P.--Sverdrup Corporation, Maryland Heights, MO; *U.S. Private*, pg. 1057

Schwartz, Harold A., Sr. V.P. & Treas.--FerrellCalvillo Communications, Inc., New York, NY; *U.S. Private*, pg. 401

Schwartz, Helene, Sr. V.P.-H.R.--The American Stock Exchange, New York, NY; *U.S. Private*, pg. 62

Schwartz, Ira, Sr. V.P. & Exec. Grp. Acct. Dir.--DMB&B New York, New York, NY; *U.S. Private*, pg. 302

Schwartz, Joel, Sr. V.P.-Worldwide Sls.--Data General Corporation, Westborough, MA; *U.S. Public*, pg. 485

Schwartz, Larry, Sr. V.P.--Friendship Dairies, Inc., Jericho, NY; *U.S. Private*, pg. 429

Schwartz, Lloyd, Sr. V.P.--Southwest Marine, Inc., San Diego, CA; *U.S. Private*, pg. 213

Schwartz, Peter A., Chief Fin. Officer & Sr. V.P.--Computer Associates International, Inc., Islandia, NY; *U.S. Public*, pg. 420

Schwartz, Rhonda, Sr. V.P.-Law--Fortis Financial Group, Woodbury, MN; *Int'l*, pg. 499

Schwartz, Roy R., Sr. V.P.--Imasco Limited, Montreal, Canada; *Int'l*, pg. 112

Schwarz, Ronald E., Sr. V.P.-Retail Banking--Broad National Bancorporation, Newark, NJ; *U.S. Public*, pg. 257

Schweitzer, John, Sr. V.P.-Opers.--Tractor Supply Co., Nashville, TN; *U.S. Public*, pg. 1627

Schwenk, Reinhold, Sr. V.P.-Creative Services--Jordan, McGrath, Case & Taylor Inc., New York, NY; *U.S. Private*, pg. 598

Schwer, W.F., Sr. V.P., Gen. Counsel & Sec.--Imperial Holly Corporation, Sugar Land, TX; *U.S. Public*, pg. 872

Schwindt, Kendall, Sr. V.P.-Opers.--Wal-Mart Stores, Inc., Bentonville, AR; *U.S. Public*, pg. 1732

Schwinn, Doug, Chief Information Officer & Sr. V.P.--OfficeMax, Shaker Heights, OH; *U.S. Public*, pg. 1212

Schwob, Robert, Sr. V.P.-Acct. Svcs.--Yesawich, Pepperdine & Brown, Orlando, FL; *U.S. Private*, pg. 1195

Schwolsky, Peter M., Chief Legal Officer & Sr. V.P.--Columbia Energy Group, Reston, VA; *U.S. Public*, pg. 402

Scicinger, Bernard, Sr. V.P.--Genome Therapeutics Corporation, Waltham, MA; *U.S. Public*, pg. 730

Sciortino, Tom, Sr. V.P.-Admin. & Human Resources--Congoleum Corporation, Mercerville, NJ; *U.S. Public*, pg. 69

Sciuto, Joseph F., Sr. V.P.-Bus. Devel.--Comptek Federal Systems, Inc., Buffalo, NY; *U.S. Public*, pg. 419
Scoder, Mark, Sr. V.P.-Bus. Devel. & Commun.--John Alden Financial Corporation, Miami, FL; *U.S. Public*, pg. 39
Scoffield, Jim, Sr. V.P. & Mngmt. Representative--EvansGroup, Dallas, TX; *U.S. Private*, pg. 385
Scoggins, R.D., Sr. V.P.--Kaneb Pipe Line Partners, L.P., Richardson, TX; *U.S. Public*, pg. 942
Scolnick, Edward M., M.D., Exec. V.P. & Pres.-Merck Res. Laboratories--Merck & Co., Inc., Whitehouse Station, NJ; *U.S. Public*, pg. 1090
Scopellito, Tony, Sr. V.P. & Mngmt. Supvr.--DMB&B New York, New York, NY; *U.S. Private*, pg. 302
Scott, A. Brock, Sr. V.P.--Associates Commercial Equipment Div., Dallas, TX; *U.S. Public*, pg. 663
Scott, Bob, Sr. V.P. & Acct. Supvr.--Western International Media Corporation, Atlanta, GA; *U.S. Private*, pg. 1167
Scott, Carl E., Sr. V.P.-Prod. Mngmt. & Natl. Adv.--Mutual of Omaha Insurance Company, Omaha, NE; *U.S. Private*, pg. 769
Scott, Carl E., Exec. V.P.--United World Life Insurance Company, Omaha, NE; *U.S. Private*, pg. 770
Scott, D.E., Sr. V.P. & Gen. Counsel--Science Applications International Corp., San Diego, CA; *U.S. Private*, pg. 975
Scott, Daniel H., Chief Fin. Officer & Sr. V.P.--MGM Grand Hotel, Inc., Las Vegas, NV; *U.S. Public*, pg. 1027
Scott, David A., Sr. V.P.-South Central Reg.--Comcast Cable Communications, Inc., Philadelphia, PA; *U.S. Public*, pg. 407
Scott, Diana, Sr. V.P. & Mng. Dir.-Ingalls One-to-One Marketing--Ingalls, Boston, MA; *U.S. Private*, pg. 562
Scott, F. Andrerw, Sr. V.P.-Corp. Devel.--The Loewen Group, Inc., Burnaby, Canada; *Int'l*, pg. 814
Scott, Gary M., Sr. V.P.-European Opers.--MTI Technology Corporation, Anaheim, CA; *U.S. Public*, pg. 1028
Scott, Gerald, Sr. V.P.-Claims--Safety National Casualty Corp., Saint Louis, MO; *U.S. Public*, pg. 496
Scott, Gerald L., Sr. V.P.-Opers.--H.B. Fuller Company, Saint Paul, MN; *U.S. Public*, pg. 686
Scott, H. Lee, Jr., Sr. V.P.-Distr. & Transportation--Wal-Mart Stores, Inc., Bentonville, AR; *U.S. Public*, pg. 1732
Scott, Mark, Sr. V.P. & Client Service Dir.--EvansGroup, Seattle, WA; *U.S. Private*, pg. 385
Scott, Paul, Sr. V.P.--Octel Messaging Division, Milpitas, CA; *U.S. Public*, pg. 1017
Scott, Peter F., Chief Fin. Officer & Sr. V.P.-Fin. & Opers.--Beringer Wine Estates Holdings, Inc., Saint Helena, CA; *U.S. Private*, pg. 1078
Scott, Sidney A., Chief Fin. Officer & Sr. V.P.-Fin. & Admin.--Daubert Industries, Inc., Westchester, IL; *U.S. Private*, pg. 313
Scott, William J., Sr., Sr. V.P.--Joy Mining Machinery, Warrendale, PA; *U.S. Public*, pg. 789
Scovanner, Doug, Chief Fin. Officer & Sr. V.P.--Dayton Hudson Corporation, Minneapolis, MN; *U.S. Public*, pg. 489
Scowsill, D., Sr. V.P.-Sls. & Mktg.--Hilton International Co., Coral Gables, FL; *Int'l*, pg. 787
Scribner, Raymond, Sr. V.P.--Telescope Casual Furniture, Inc., Granville, NY; *U.S. Private*, pg. 1074
Scro, Jerome, Chief Fin. Officer & Sr. V.P.--Showtime Networks Inc., New York, NY; *U.S. Private*, pg. 779
Sculfort, Ray, Sr. V.P.-Mktg.--Better Homes and Gardens Real Estate Service, Des Moines, IA; *U.S. Public*, pg. 1094
Scullin, Hugh J., Sr. V.P.-Opers.--Linens 'n Things, Inc., Clifton, NJ; *U.S. Private*, pg. 668
Scully, Jim, Sr. V.P.-Sls.--Sony Music Entertainment, Inc., New York, NY; *Int'l*, pg. 1281
Scully, John, Sr. V.P.-Human Resources--LaSalle National Bank, Chicago, IL; *Int'l*, pg. 10
Scully, Richard W., Sr. V.P.-Foster's Intl.--Foster's Brewing Group Limited, Southbank, Australia; *Int'l*, pg. 500
Sculti, Leon, Sr. V.P.--Torcon, Inc., Westfield, NJ; *U.S. Private*, pg. 1092
Seals, Lindsay C., Sr. V.P.-Mktg., Insurance--United Companies Financial Corporation, Baton Rouge, LA; *U.S. Public*, pg. 1675
Searer, Rick, V.P. & Gen. Mgr.--Oscar Mayer Foods Corp., Madison, WI; *U.S. Public*, pg. 1288
Searle, Stewart A., III, Sr. V.P.-Plng. & Devel.--National Service Industries, Inc., Atlanta, GA; *U.S. Public*, pg. 1160
Sease, Gary, Sr. V.P.-Logistics--Service Merchandise Company, Inc., Brentwood, TN; *U.S. Public*, pg. 1461
Seaton, Charles E., Sr. V.P.--The Vigoro Corporation, Chicago, IL; *U.S. Public*, pg. 856
Seaton, John, Sr. V.P. & Brdcst. Production Dir.--DMB&B St. Louis, Saint Louis, MO; *U.S. Private*, pg. 303
Seawell, William L., II, Sr. V.P.-Ordinary Mktg.--Jefferson-Pilot Life Insurance Co., Greensboro, NC; *U.S. Public*, pg. 926
Seay, Doug, Sr. V.P. & Brdcst. Program Dir.--Hal Riney & Partners, Inc., San Francisco, CA; *U.S. Private*, pg. 931
Seay, Robert S., Sr. V.P.-Opers./Western Div.--CompUSA, Dallas, TX; *U.S. Public*, pg. 420
Sedel, Arnold, Sr. V.P.-Store Opers.--The Sports Authority Inc., Fort Lauderdale, FL; *U.S. Public*, pg. 1499
Sedwick, Lindsay M., Chief Fin. Officer & Sr. V.P.--Standex International Corporation, Salem, NH; *U.S. Public*, pg. 1505
Seedman, Michael S., Sr. V.P.-Client Access/Personal Commun. Div.--3Com Corporation, Santa Clara, CA; *U.S. Public*, pg. 1603
Seelig, Karen, Sr. V.P.-Human Resources--North Fork Bancorporation, Inc., Melville, NY; *U.S. Public*, pg. 1194
Seeman, Leslie C., Sr. V.P. & Gen. Counsel--Orbital Sciences Corporation, Dulles, VA; *U.S. Public*, pg. 1229
Seery, Robert P., Chief Fin. Officer & Sr. V.P.--Sumitomo Bank Securities, Inc., New York, NY; *Int'l*, pg. 1309
Seff, Laura, Sr. V.P.-Corp Quality & Sec.--Sterling Healthcare Group, Inc., Miami, FL; *U.S. Public*, pg. 608
Segal, Jon, Sr. V.P. & Dir.-Community Newspapers-East--Freedom Communication Inc., Irvine, CA; *U.S. Private*, pg. 425
Sege, Ronald A., Sr. V.P.-Global Prods./Enterprise Sys.--3Com Corporation, Santa Clara, CA; *U.S. Public*, pg. 1603
Segerblom, Bjoern, Sr. V.P.-Asia--SGS Societe Generale de Surveillance Holding S.A., Geneva, Switzerland; *Int'l*, pg. 1153
Segerstolpe, Lars, Sr. V.P.-Corp. Acctg.--Vattenfall AB, Stockholm, Sweden; *Int'l*, pg. 1452
Segner, Kevin A., Sr. V.P.-Admin.--The Dometic Corporation, Elkhart, IN; *Int'l*, pg. 440
Seibert, Dane, Sr. V.P.-Sls. & Mktg.--Glacier Water Services Inc., Carlsbad, CA; *U.S. Public*, pg. 745
Seibert, Gregg A., Sr. V.P.-Corp. Fin.--Franchise Finance Corp. of America, Scottsdale, AZ; *U.S. Public*, pg. 679
Seibert, Kurt, Sr. V.P.-Strategic Plng.--Computer Associates International, Inc., Islandia, NY; *U.S. Public*, pg. 420
Seidman, Allan, Sr. V.P.-Pub. Rels.--Almay, Inc., New York, NY; *U.S. Private*, pg. 689
Seidman, Allyn, Sr. V.P.-Corp. Communications--Revlon, Inc., New York, NY; *U.S. Private*, pg. 689
Seidman, Allyn, Sr. V.P.-Pub. Rels.--Revlon-Realistic Professional Products, Inc., New York, NY; *U.S. Private*, pg. 690
Seifert, Norbert M., Sr. V.P.--Imperial Credit Commercial Mortgage Investment Corp., Los Angeles, CA; *U.S. Public*, pg. 872
Seifert, Shelley J., Sr. V.P.-H.R.--National City Corporation, Cleveland, OH; *U.S. Public*, pg. 1154
Seiki, Kunio, Deputy Pres.--The Industrial Bank of Japan, Limited, Tokyo, Japan; *Int'l*, pg. 674
Seils, William G., Sr. V.P., Gen. Counsel & Corp. Sec.--Richardson Electronics, Ltd., Lafox, IL; *U.S. Public*, pg. 1387
Seitz, Nicholas, Sr. V.P. & Editor in Chief--Sports/Leisure Magazines Group, Trumbull, CT; *U.S. Public*, pg. 1174
Seitz, Nicholas J., Sr. V.P. & Editor-in-Chief--The New York Times Magazine Company Group, Trumbull, CT; *U.S. Public*, pg. 1174
Sekimoto, Teruyasu, Sr. V.P.-East Asian Field Opers.--Silicon Graphics, Inc., Mountain View, CA; *U.S. Public*, pg. 1473
Sekine, Tatsuhiro, Sr. Mng. Dir.-Fin.--Ito-Yokado Co., Ltd., Tokyo, Japan; *Int'l*, pg. 693
Self, Nancy, Sr. V.P. & Creative Dir.--Fogarty Klein & Partners, Houston, TX; *U.S. Private*, pg. 415
Selid, Paul, Sr. V.P.-Acq.--Lexford Residential Trust, Columbus, OH; *U.S. Public*, pg. 991
Sella, Tony, Sr. V.P.-Creative Adv.--Twentieth Century Fox Film Corp., Los Angeles, CA; *Int'l*, pg. 926
Sells, James E., Chief Info. Service & Sr. V.P.-Photo Service--First American Federal Savings Bank, Bristol, VA; *U.S. Public*, pg. 624
Sells, James E., Sr. V.P.-Information Svcs.--First American Federal Savings Bank, Bristol, VA; *U.S. Public*, pg. 624
Sellyn, Laurence G., Chief Fin. Officer & Sr. V.P.-Fin. & Corp. Devel.--Wajax Limited, Delta, Canada; *Int'l*, pg. 1484
Selman, Susan E., Sr. V.P.-Load Production Admin.--Deposit Guaranty Mortgage Co., Jackson, MS; *U.S. Public*, pg. 501
Selner, Joseph B., Chief Fin. Officer & Sr. V.P.--Associated Banc-Corp, Green Bay, WI; *U.S. Public*, pg. 140
Selzer, Jim, Chief Fin. Officer, Sr. V.P.-Fin. & Asst. Corp. Sec.--Pico Products, Inc., Lake View Terrace, CA; *U.S. Public*, pg. 1294
Semanie, George, Sr. V.P.-Perishable Procurement--C & S Wholesale Grocery Inc., Brattleboro, VT; *U.S. Private*, pg. 192
Semple, Frank H., Sr. V.P. & Gen. Mgr.--Williams Natural Gas Company, Tulsa, OK; *U.S. Public*, pg. 1769
Senay, David T., Sr. Partner & Sr. V.P.--Fleishman-Hillard Inc., Saint Louis, MO; *U.S. Private*, pg. 411
Senior, David, Sr. V.P.-Real Estate--Texas Commerce Bank, Houston, TX; *U.S. Public*, pg. 339
Senn, Rolf, Sr. V.P.--Bank of Yokohama (Schwiez) AG, Zurich, Switzerland; *Int'l*, pg. 159
Sensor, Edward E., Sr. V.P.-Retail Loan Prods.--Banknorth Group Inc., Burlington, VT; *U.S. Public*, pg. 186
Sentillo, Carl, Chief Fin. Officer & Sr. V.P.--American General Corporation, Houston, TX; *U.S. Public*, pg. 76
Sentman, David K., Chief Fin. Officer, Sr. V.P. & Treas.--American Telecasting, Inc., Colorado Springs, CO; *U.S. Public*, pg. 93
Sentner, Timothy, Sr. V.P.--Colonial Penn Group, Inc., Wilmington, DE; *U.S. Public*, pg. 990
Senuk, Raymond E., Chief Information Officer & Sr. V.P.--NationsBank West, Saint Louis, MO; *U.S. Public*, pg. 1164
Seper, Robert, Sr. V.P. & H.R. Dir.--Campbell Mithun Esty, Minneapolis, MN; *U.S. Private*, pg. 204
Septer, Charles, Sr. V.P.-Jewelry Mdsg.--Service Merchandise Company, Inc., Brentwood, TN; *U.S. Public*, *pg. 1461*
Sepulveda, Lisa, Sr. V.P.--Edelman Worldwide, Inc., New York, NY; *U.S. Private*, pg. 362
Serff, Paul, Sr. V.P.-Human Resources--Tom's Foods, Inc., Columbus, GA; *U.S. Private*, pg. 1090
Sergel, Richard P., Sr. V.P.--New England Electric System, Westborough, MA; *U.S. Public*, pg. 1171
Sernelin, Tommy, Sr. V.P.-Tech.--Skanska AB, Danderyd, Sweden; *Int'l*, pg. 1260
Serrano, Rosa, Sr. V.P.--Western Multicultural Group, Los Angeles, CA; *U.S. Private*, pg. 1167
Servais, Michael G., Sr. V.P. & Pres.-Acute Care--Universal Health Services, Inc., King of Prussia, PA; *U.S. Public*, pg. 1696
Servetnick, Randi, Sr. V.P. & Reg. Dir.--Arnold Advertising, Wayne, PA; *U.S. Private*, pg. 84
Serwin, Bradley K., Sr. V.P., Gen. Counsel & Sec.--PAULA Financial, Pasadena, CA; *U.S. Public*, pg. 1266
Sessman, Bernie, Sr. V.P.-Sls. & Mktg.--L&R Manufacturing Co., Kearny, NJ; *U.S. Private*, pg. 638
Seta, Atsuyuki, Sr. V.P.--Anritsu Corporation, Tokyo, Japan; *Int'l*, pg. 77
Seta, Joji, Sr. V.P.-Japan Market--Bank of Hawaii, Honolulu, HI; *U.S. Public*, pg. 1248
Setasuvarna, Vallobh, Sr. V.P.-Credit Admin.--Nakornthon Bank Public Company Limited, Bangkok, Thailand; *Int'l*, pg. 904
Sethi, Vinay, Sr. V.P.--Hibernia Corporation, New Orleans, LA; *U.S. Public*, pg. 825
Setton, Murry, Sr. V.P.-Admin.--A&E Stores, Inc., Teterboro, NJ; *U.S. Private*, pg. 1
Setz, Bruno, Sr. V.P.-Montreal--LEP International Inc., Etobicoke, Canada; *U.S. Private*, pg. 571
Setzer, Lewis F., Sr. V.P.--Hickory Printing Group, Inc., Conover, NC; *U.S. Private*, pg. 525
Severson, Allan W., Sr. V.P.-California Admin.--Zions Bancorporation, Salt Lake City, UT; *U.S. Public*, pg. 1792
Severson, Howard A., Chief Real Estate Officer & Sr. V.P.--The Cato Corporation, Charlotte, NC; *U.S. Public*, pg. 318
Severson, Sid, Chief Fin. Officer & Sr. V.P.--Sunflower Electric Power Corporation, Hays, KS; *U.S. Private*, pg. 1052
Sevin, R.A., Sr. V.P.--Winn-Dixie Stores, Inc., Jacksonville, FL; *U.S. Public*, pg. 1771
Seward, John E., Sr., Sr. V.P.--The Paty Company, Piney Flats, TN; *U.S. Private*, pg. 844
Sexton, Clarence D., Sr. V.P.--Republic Contracting Corp., Columbia, SC; *U.S. Private*, pg. 923
Sexton, Kevin, Sr. V.P.-Fin--Foss Manufacturing Company Incorporated, Hampton, NH; *U.S. Private*, pg. 420
Seymour, Allen, Sr. V.P.-Sls.--Evenflo Company, Inc., Piqua, OH; *U.S. Private*, pg. 629
Seymour, Leo R., Sr. V.P.--Trustmark National Bank, Jackson, MS; *U.S. Public*, pg. 1643
Seymour, William E., III, Sr. V.P.--Market Facts, Inc., Arlington Heights, IL; *U.S. Public*, pg. 1046
Seywert, Jean, Sr. V.P.-H.R.--Banque Internationale a Luxembourg S.A., Luxembourg, Luxembourg; *Int'l*, pg. 162
Shack, Timothy G., Sr. V.P.-Opers. & Data Processing--PNC Bank Corp., Pittsburgh, PA; *U.S. Public*, pg. 1242
Shackleford, Robert M., Sr. V.P.--Gulf Lumber Company, Inc., Mobile, AL; *U.S. Private*, pg. 487
Shadle, Mark, Sr. V.P.--Edelman Public Relations Worldwide, Chicago, IL; *U.S. Private*, pg. 362
Shaffer, Adam, Sr. V.P.-Prod. & Mktg.--Micro Warehouse, Inc., Norwalk, CT; *U.S. Public*, pg. 1104
Shahabi, Donna K., Sr. V.P. & Dir.-Opers.--Jefferies & Company, Inc., Los Angeles, CA; *U.S. Public*, pg. 925
Shahid, J.A., Sr. V.P. & Gen. Mgr.--Habib Bank Ltd., Dhaka, Bangladesh; *Int'l*, pg. 584
Shaio, Alberto, Sr. V.P. & Gen. Mgr.-Plastics Machinery Grp.--Farrel Corporation, Ansonia, CT; *U.S. Public*, pg. 614
Shalack, Theodore J., Sr. V.P. & Chief Compliance Officer--The Mutual Life Insurance Company of New York, New York, NY; *U.S. Private*, pg. 769
Shalders, Alan, Sr. V.P.-Engrng.--Universal Builders Supply, Inc., Mount Vernon, NY; *U.S. Private*, pg. 1126
Shalibo, Donald, Sr. V.P.--Barton Malow Enterprises, Inc., Southfield, MI; *U.S. Private*, pg. 120
Shamilzadeh, David, Chief Fin. Officer & Sr. V.P.-Fin.--Allou Health & Beauty Care, Inc., Brentwood, NY; *U.S. Public*, pg. 55
Shane, William R., Chief Fin. Officer-Cemetery & Combination Div. & Sr. V.P.--The Loewen Group, Inc., Burnaby, Canada; *Int'l*, pg. 814
Shanesy, Steve, Sr. V.P. & Gen Mgr.-Batteries--RAYOVAC Corporation, Madison, WI; *U.S. Private*, pg. 912
Shank, Daniel R., Sr. V.P.--First Security Bank of Oregon, Salem, OR; *U.S. Public*, pg. 637
Shanks, Donald, Sr. V.P.--IDS Property Casualty Insurance Company, Minneapolis, MN; *U.S. Public*, pg. 73
Shanley, Gerald, Sr. V.P.-Opers.--Azon Corporation, Johnson City, NY; *U.S. Private*, pg. 104
Shannon, James, Sr. V.P.-Admin. & Gen. Counsel--National Fire Protection Association, Quincy, MA; *U.S. Private*, pg. 782
Shannon, R. Patrick, Sr. V.P.-Loan Review--NationsBank West, Saint Louis, MO; *U.S. Public*, pg. 1164
Shao, Shiu, Chief Fin. Officer & Sr. V.P.--Oroamerica, Inc., Burbank, CA; *U.S. Public*, pg. 1232
Shapiro, Amy M., Sr. V.P., Gen. Counsel & Sec.--CommNet Cellular Inc., Englewood, CO; *U.S. Public*, pg. 414
Shapiro, Bob, Sr. V.P.-Corp. Opers.--County Seat Stores, Inc., Dallas, TX; *U.S. Private*, pg. 279
Shapiro, Dan, Sr. V.P.-Mktg.--George Weston Limited, Toronto, Canada; *Int'l*, pg. 1494
Shapiro, Gary H., Sr. V.P.--American Credit Indemnity, Baltimore, MD; *Int'l*, pg. 464
Shapiro, Ron, Sr. V.P. & Gen. Mgr.--Atlantic Recording Corporation, New York, NY; *U.S. Public*, pg. 1611
Shapland, Dave, Sr. V.P.--Bush Brothers & Company, Knoxville, TN; *U.S. Private*, pg. 189
Sharkey, Phillip J., Sr. V.P.-Human Resources--American Bankers Life Assurance Co. of Florida, Miami, FL; *U.S. Public*, pg. 67
Sharkey, William, Sr. V.P.-Mktg.--CNA Insurance Companies, Chicago, IL; *U.S. Public*, pg. 1010
Sharkey, William H., Jr., Sr. V.P. & Chief Mktg. Officer--Continental Assurance Company, Chicago, IL; *U.S. Private*, pg. 267
Sharkley, Philip J., Sr. V.P.-Human Resources--American Bankers Insurance Co. of Florida, Miami, FL; *U.S. Public*, *pg. 67*
Sharma, Satya, Sr. V.P.-Quality & Training--Symbol Technologies, Inc., Holtsville, NY; *U.S. Public*, pg. 1546
Sharp, Dave, Sr. V.P. & Acct. Grp. Dir.--CF2GS, Seattle, WA; *U.S. Private*, pg. 194
Sharp, J. Brad, Sr. V.P.--Sterling Commerce, Inc., Dublin, OH; *U.S. Public*, pg. 1515

Sharp, Jack, Chief Fin. Officer & Sr. V.P.--Aladdin Mills, Dalton, GA; *U.S. Public*, pg. 1121
Sharp, Patricia, Sr. V.P.-Human Resources--Apple Computer, Inc., Cupertino, CA; *U.S. Public*, pg. 121
Sharpless, Andrew, Sr. V.P.-Interactive Media, Discovery Enterprises Worldwide--Discovery Communications, Inc., Bethesda, MD; *U.S. Private*, pg. 334
Sharretts, David K., Sr. V.P.--David A. Bramble, Inc., Chestertown, MD; *U.S. Private*, pg. 165
Shassian, D.R., Chief Fin. Officer & Sr. V.P.--The Southern New England Telephone Company, New Haven, CT; *U.S. Public*, pg. 1491
Shassian, Donald R., Chief Fin. Officer & Sr. V.P.--Southern New England Telecommunications Corporation, New Haven, CT; *U.S. Public*, pg. 1490
Shatley, William, Chief Fin. Officer, Sr. V.P. & Treas.--Polyphase Corporation, Dallas, TX; *U.S. Public*, pg. 1315
Shattuck, George H., Sr. V.P.--Foremost Insurance Co., Caledonia, MI; *U.S. Public*, pg. 667
Shaver, Mary Louise, Sr. V.P.--BVK/McDonald, Milwaukee, WI; *U.S. Private*, pg. 108
Shaw, Christine, Sr. V.P. & New Bus. Contact--Freeman Associates, Inc., Wellesley, MA; *U.S. Private*, pg. 425
Shaw, Henry D., Sr. V.P.-Individual Insurance Prods.--John Hancock Mutual Life Insurance Company, Boston, MA; *U.S. Private*, pg. 589
Shaw, James, Chief Fin. Officer & Sr. V.P.--Newsday, Melville, NY; *U.S. Public*, pg. 1616
Shaw, Jerome, Exec. V.P. & Sec.--Volt Information Sciences, Inc., New York, NY; *U.S. Public*, pg. 1724
Shaw, Maurice K., Corp. Affairs Officer & Sr. V.P.--Brooklyn Union, Brooklyn, NY; *U.S. Public*, pg. 259
Shaw, Patrick W., Sr. V.P.--Hibernia Corporation, New Orleans, LA; *U.S. Public*, pg. 825
Shaw, Richard C., Sr. V.P.-Intl. & Corp. Devel.--Phoenix Home Life Mutual Insurance Company, Hartford, CT; *U.S. Private*, pg. 863
Shaw, Robert, Sr. V.P.-Services--Oracle Corporation, Redwood City, CA; *U.S. Public*, pg. 1227
Shaw, Robert B., Sr. V.P.--Great Western Bank, Chatsworth, CA; *U.S. Public*, pg. 1741
Shaw, Ruth G., Chief Admin. Officer & Sr. V.P.-Corp. Resources--Duke Energy Corporation, Charlotte, NC; *U.S. Public*, pg. 534
Shaye, Lewis, Sr. V.P.-Restaurant Devel.--Papa Gino's Inc., Dedham, MA; *U.S. Private*, pg. 837
Shea, John, Sr. V.P.-Music & Talent--MTV: Music Television, New York, NY; *U.S. Private*, pg. 779
Shea, Martin M., Sr. V.P.-Corp. Commun.--Triarc Companies, Inc., New York, NY; *U.S. Public*, pg. 1634
Shea, Michael, Sr. V.P.-Sls. & Mktg.--Daw Technologies, Inc., Salt Lake City, UT; *U.S. Public*, pg. 489
Shea, Thomas G., Sr. V.P.--Carrafiello, Diehl & Associates, Inc., Irvington, NY; *U.S. Private*, pg. 215
Shearing, John, Chief Fin. Officer WH & Sr. V.P.--Hilti Inc., Tulsa, OK; *Int'l*, pg. 620
Shecter, Janet W., Sr. V.P. & Media Dir.--Towne, Silverstein, Rotter Inc., New York, NY; *U.S. Private*, pg. 1093
Shediac, Rawy R., Sr. V.P.-Production--Fair, Isaac and Company, Inc., San Rafael, CA; *U.S. Public*, pg. 609
Shedlarz, David L., Chief Fin. Officer & Sr. V.P.--Pfizer Inc., New York, NY; *U.S. Public*, pg. 1281
Sheehan, Bill, Sr. V.P.-Natl. Brdcst.--Zenith Media Services, Inc., New York, NY; *U.S. Private*, pg. 1204
Sheehan, John, Sr. V.P.-Opers.--Pathmark Stores Incorporated, Woodbridge, NJ; *U.S. Private*, pg. 843
Sheerin, William K., Sr. V.P.-Admin. & Gen. Services & Corp. Sec.--Astoria Financial Corporation, Lake Success, NY; *U.S. Public*, pg. 141
Sheetz, Ralph, Sr. V.P.--Carlos R. Leffler Inc., Richland, PA; *U.S. Private*, pg. 658
Shelby, Tony M., Chief Fin. Officer & Sr. V.P.--LSB Industries, Inc., Oklahoma City, OK; *U.S. Public*, pg. 970
Sheldon, Curtiss S., Sr. V.P. & Chief Actuary--American Heritage Life Insurance Co., Jacksonville, FL; *U.S. Public*, pg. 79
Shelger, James M., Sr. V.P., Gen. Counsel & Sec.--Service Corporation International, Houston, TX; *U.S. Public*, pg. 1460
Shelley, Tully, III, Sr. V.P.--MBT Architecture, San Francisco, CA; *U.S. Private*, pg. 686
Shelton, Daniel, Sr. V.P.--Liberty Bank & Trust Company of Oklahoma City, Oklahoma City, OK; *U.S. Public*, pg. 174
Shelton, David E., Sr. V.P.-Real Estate/Engrng. & Construction--Lowe's Companies, Inc., North Wilkesboro, NC; *U.S. Public*, pg. 1015
Shelton, E. Ray, Sr. V.P.--Independence Investment Associates, Inc., Boston, MA; *U.S. Private*, pg. 589
Shelton, Jack, Sr. V.P.-Mktg.--Fender Musical Instruments, Scottsdale, AZ; *U.S. Private*, pg. 400
Shelton, Paul G., Chief Fin. Officer, Sr. V.P. & Pres.-Americo Carriers--AMCOL International Corp., Arlington Heights, IL; *U.S. Public*, pg. 63
Shelton, Stanley W., Sr. V.P. & Gen. Mgr.--State Street Bank-London Branch, London, United Kingdom; *U.S. Public*, pg. 1513
Shelton, Stephen, Sr. V.P.-Electronic Distrib.--MidAmerican Energy Holdings, Des Moines, IA; *U.S. Public*, pg. 1109
Shemin, Barry L., Sr. V.P. & Corp. Actuary-Corp. Actuarial Services--John Hancock Mutual Life Insurance Company, Boston, MA; *U.S. Private*, pg. 589
Shencavitz, Gerald, Sr. V.P.-Opers. & Tech.--Banknorth Group Inc., Burlington, VT; *U.S. Public*, pg. 186
Shendow, Harry S., Sr. V.P.--S & K Famous Brands, Inc., Glen Allen, VA; *U.S. Public*, pg. 1414
Shenk, Dale M., Sr. V.P.--Titleist & Foot-Joy Worldwide, Fairhaven, MA; *U.S. Public*, pg. 675
Shepard, Stephen E., Sr. V.P.-Special Projects--Huitt-Zollars, Inc., Dallas, TX; *U.S. Private*, pg. 547
Shephard, James B., Sr. V.P.-Corp. Bus. Devel.--Landstar Holding, Shelton, CT; *U.S. Public*, pg. 978
Shepherd, Carl, Sr. V.P.-Life Co.--United Farm Family Life Insurance Co., Indianapolis, IN; *U.S. Private*, pg. 1122
Shepherd, Jill Z., Sr. V.P. & Gen. Auditor--Hibernia Corporation, New Orleans, LA; *U.S. Public*, pg. 825
Sheplee, Michael L., Sr. V.P.--ReliaStar Investment Research, Inc., Minneapolis, MN; *U.S. Public*, pg. 1376
Sheridan, Dave, Sr. V.P.-Environ.--Gannett Fleming Affiliates, Inc., Camp Hill, PA; *U.S. Private*, pg. 439
Sheridan, William S., Chief Fin. Officer & Sr. V.P.--Sotheby's Holdings Inc., New York, NY; *U.S. Public*, pg. 1487
Sherif, Osama, Sr. V.P.--Dynacare, Inc., Toronto, Canada; *Int'l*, pg. 425
Sherlock, Karen, Sr. V.P. & Product Mgr.--Motown Record Company, J.P., New York, NY; *Int'l*, pg. 1052
Sherlock, Michael, Sr. V.P.-Canada & Casualwear--Fruit of the Loom, Inc., Chicago, IL; *U.S. Public*, pg. 685
Sherlock, Mike, Sr. V.P. & Gen. Mgr.--Gitano Fashions Ltd., Bowling Green, KY; *U.S. Public*, pg. 686
Sherman, Albert, Sr. V.P.--Arthur D. Little, Inc., Cambridge, MA; *U.S. Private*, pg. 670
Sherman, Barry M., M.D., Sr. V.P. & Chief Medical Officer--Genentech, Inc., South San Francisco, CA; *Int'l*, pg. 1120
Sherman, Bill, Sr. V.P.-Institutional Prod.--Riddell Sports, Inc., New York, NY; *U.S. Public*, pg. 1389
Sherman, Earl, Sr. V.P.-Bus. Devel.--Aerovox Inc., New Bedford, MA; *U.S. Public*, pg. 25
Sherman, Ginger, Sr. V.P.--Prudential Real Estate Affiliates Inc., Costa Mesa, CA; *U.S. Private*, pg. 892
Sherman, Ivan, Sr. V.P.-Creative Services--Jordan, McGrath, Case & Taylor Inc., New York, NY; *U.S. Private*, pg. 598
Sherman, James, Sr. V.P. & Dir.-Corp. Communications--LaSalle Cragin Bank, Chicago, IL; *Int'l*, pg. 10
Sherman, L.J., Sr. V.P.-Corp. Finance--A.Y. McDonald Industries, Inc., Dubuque, IA; *U.S. Private*, pg. 721
Sherman, Lawrence L., Sr. VP.-SEMCO Energy Services--Southeastern Michigan Gas Enterprises, Inc., Port Huron, MI; *U.S. Public*, pg. 1489
Sherman, Leigh I., Sr. V.P.--Marshall & Ilsley Corporation, Milwaukee, WI; *U.S. Public*, pg. 1049
Sherman, Michael, Sr. V.P.-Bus. Devel., Gen. Counsel & Sec.--Fingerhut Corp., Minnetonka, MN; *U.S. Public*, pg. 623
Sherman, Peter M., Chief Investment Officer & Sr. V.P.--The Penn Mutual Life Insurance Company, Philadelphia, PA; *U.S. Private*, pg. 849
Sherman, Philip S., Sr. V.P. & Grp. Controller--Reliance Group Holdings, Inc., New York, NY; *U.S. Public*, pg. 1374
Sherringham, Philip, Sr. V.P. & Controller--Sanwa Bank California, Los Angeles, CA; *Int'l*, pg. 1189
Sherry, Thomas J., Sr. V.P.-Customer Care--Owens & Minor Inc., Glen Allen, VA; *U.S. Public*, pg. 1236
Sherwood, Craig R., Sr. V.P.-Affiliate Relations--International Family Entertainment, Inc., Virginia Beach, VA; *Int'l*, pg. 927
Sherwood, Kent, Sr. V.P.--Sutter Health, Sacramento, CA; *U.S. Private*, pg. 1057
Shevillo, Jack, Sr. V.P.-Professional Service Div.--Compuware Corporation, Farmington Hills, MI; *U.S. Public*, pg. 423
Shevrin, Scott, Sr. V.P. & Mngmt. Supvr.--Harrison & Star, Inc., New York, NY; *U.S. Private*, pg. 506
Shia, David, Sr. V.P.-Scientific Affairs--Watson Laboratories, Inc., Corona, CA; *U.S. Public*, pg. 1746
Shiba, Hiroshi, Sr. V.P.--NEC Corporation, Tokyo, Japan; *Int'l*, pg. 899
Shibao, Masahiro, Sr. V.P.--Nippon Telegraph and Telephone Corporation, Tokyo, Japan; *Int'l*, pg. 940
Shibuya, Naotaka, Sr. V.P.--Japan Airlines Company, Ltd., Tokyo, Japan; *Int'l*, pg. 699
Shiel, James G., Sr. V.P.-Investments--W.R. Berkley Corporation, Greenwich, CT; *U.S. Public*, pg. 215
Shields, Joseph P., Sr. V.P.-Energy Svcs.--New Jersey Natural Gas Co., Wall, NJ; *U.S. Public*, pg. 1172
Shiflet, Steven P., Chief Fin. Officer & Sr. V.P.--Sterling Commerce, Inc., Dublin, OH; *U.S. Public*, pg. 1515
Shigeta, Toyo, Sr. V.P. & Grp. Acct. Dir.--DCA Advertising, Inc., New York, NY; *Int'l*, pg. 393
Shih, Elizabeth, Sr. V.P.-System Integration--Sutter Health, Sacramento, CA; *U.S. Private*, pg. 1057
Shillet, Maureen, Sr. V.P. & New Bus. Dir.-Worldwide--FCB, New York, NY; *U.S. Private*, pg. 389
Shima, Atsushi, Sr. V.P.--Fanuc Ltd., Yamanashi, Japan; *Int'l*, pg. 477
Shimada, Hirofumi, Sr. V.P.--Nippon Telegraph and Telephone Corporation, Tokyo, Japan; *Int'l*, pg. 940
Shimakura, Keiichi, Assoc. Sr. V.P.--NEC Corporation, Tokyo, Japan; *Int'l*, pg. 899
Shimizu, Mary, Sr. V.P.-Project Office--Bank of Hawaii, Honolulu, HI; *U.S. Public*, pg. 1248
Shimizu, Yutaka, Sr. Mngmt. Dir.--Alps Electric Co., Ltd., Tokyo, Japan; *Int'l*, pg. 65
Shimomura, Chiaki, Sr. V.P.--Marubeni America Corporation, New York, NY; *Int'l*, pg. 844
Shimomura, Naohisa, Sr. V.P.--Toshiba Corporation, Tokyo, Japan; *Int'l*, pg. 1402
Shimomura, Tokihiko, Sr. V.P.--Oki America Inc., Hackensack, NJ; *Int'l*, pg. 1000
Shinbrood, Mark, Sr. V.P.-Bus. Devel.--Axent Technologies, Rockville, MD; *U.S. Public*, pg. 157
Shindler, Steven M., Chief Fin. Officer & Sr. V.P.--Nextel Communications, Mc Lean, VA; *U.S. Public*, pg. 1180
Shinmachi, Koji, Mng. Dir. & Sr. V.P.-Airport Opers.--Japan Airlines Company, Ltd., Tokyo, Japan; *Int'l*, pg. 699
Shinoda, Hiroshi, Sr. V.P.-Sls. & Mktg.--Pentel of America, Ltd., Torrance, CA; *Int'l*, pg. 1035
Shinohara, Iwao, Assoc. Sr. V.P.--NEC Corporation, Tokyo, Japan; *Int'l*, pg. 899
Shinohara, Tadahiko, Sr. Exec. Mng. Dir.--Hitachi, Ltd., Tokyo, Japan; *Int'l*, pg. 621
Shiota, Toshio, Sr. V.P. & Reg. Mgr.-Fukuoka--Japan Airlines Company, Ltd., Tokyo, Japan; *Int'l*, pg. 699
Shipley, Ed, Sr. V.P.-Construction--W.M. Grace Development, Phoenix, AZ; *U.S. Private*, pg. 468
Shipley, Patricia, Sr. V.P.-Opers.--National Bank of Alaska, Anchorage, AK; *U.S. Public*, pg. 1153
Shipley, Robert, Sr. V.P.--Huitt-Zollars, Inc., Dallas, TX; *U.S. Private*, pg. 547
Shipley, Roderick, Sr. V.P.-Trust--National Bank of Alaska, Anchorage, AK; *U.S. Public*, pg. 1153
Shipley, Sheila, Sr. V.P. & Gen. Mgr.--Decca Records--Universal Studios, Inc., Universal City, CA; *Int'l*, pg. 1215
Shipman, Mark L., Sr. V.P.--Advantica Restaurant Group, Inc., Spartanburg, SC; *U.S. Public*, pg. 22
Shippee, James H., Sr. V.P.--Litchfield Financial Corporation, Williamstown, MA; *U.S. Public*, pg. 1001
Shippee, Thomas P., Sr. V.P.--Norwest Financial, Inc., Des Moines, IA; *U.S. Public*, pg. 1202
Shipper, Gary, Sr. V.P. & Acct. Dir.--DMB&B St. Louis, Saint Louis, MO; *U.S. Private*, pg. 303
Shirk, Guy L., Sr. V.P. & Acct. Dir.--Meldrum & Fewsmith Communications Inc., Cleveland, OH; *U.S. Private*, pg. 730
Shirley, Dennis A., Sr. V.P. & Dir.-Mktg.--Great Western Financial Corporation, Chatsworth, CA; *U.S. Public*, pg. 1741
Shirreff, Bruce M., Sr. V.P.-Mortgages--The Toronto Dominion Bank, Toronto, Canada; *Int'l*, pg. 1401
Shive, Dunia A., Sr. V.P.-Corp. Opers.--A.H. Belo Corporation, Dallas, TX; *U.S. Public*, pg. 209
Shively, Art., Chief Fin. Officer & Sr. V.P.--Glencoe/Mc-Graw Hill, Westerville, OH; *U.S. Public*, pg. 1070
Shively, Arthur C., Chief Fin. Officer & Sr. V.P.--SRA McGraw Hill, Worthington, OH; *U.S. Public*, pg. 1070
Shivers, Gary R., Sr. V.P.-Sls.--Advanta Business Services, Voorhees, NJ; *U.S. Public*, pg. 22
Shmaruk, J., Sr. V.P.-Opers.--Penguin Putnam Inc., New York, NY; *Int'l*, pg. 1027
Shneider, Jerry, Chief Fin. Officer & Sr. V.P.--Kelly, Scott And Madison, Inc., Chicago, IL; *U.S. Private*, pg. 613
Shockley, Leila M., Sr. V.P. & Mgr.-Construction Div.--Willis Corroon Corp. of California, San Francisco, CA; *Int'l*, pg. 1505
Sholl, Jack, Sr. V.P.-H.R.--ICN Pharmaceuticals, Inc., Costa Mesa, CA; *U.S. Public*, pg. 853
Shomper, Michael L., Chief Fin. Officer & Sr. VP.--Fairfax Savings Bank, Baltimore, MD; *U.S. Public*, pg. 1543
Shonka, Jeffrey A., Sr. V.P.-New Prods.--Amwest Surety Insurance Company, Calabasas, CA; *U.S. Public*, pg. 106
Shontell, Jayne J., Sr. V.P.-Investor Rels.--Federal National Mortgage Association (Fannie Mae), Washington, DC; *U.S. Public*, pg. 615
Shook, Carl D., Sr. V.P.-Refining Grp. Opers.--Giant Industries Arizona, Inc., Scottsdale, AZ; *U.S. Public*, pg. 742
Shook, Gregory R., Sr. V.P.-Admin. & Sec.--Branford Savings Bank, Branford, CT; *U.S. Public*, pg. 250
Shook, James E., Sr. V.P.--Bank of Southern Maryland, La Plata, MD; *U.S. Public*, pg. 1088
Shook, Mark, Sr.-V.P.-Intl.--The Dial Corporation, Phoenix, AZ; *U.S. Public*, pg. 505
Shoop, Edward C., Sr. V.P. & Actuary--Zenith Insurance Company, Woodland Hills, CA; *U.S. Public*, pg. 1791
Shopoff, Bruce, Sr. V.P.-Reg. Sls./Los Angeles--Swank, Inc., Attleboro, MA; *U.S. Public*, pg. 1543
Short, H. Drexel, Sr. V.P.-Grp. Opers.--A.T. Massey Coal Company, Inc., Richmond, VA; *U.S. Public*, pg. 660
Short, Len, Sr. V.P.-Adv.--Charles Schwab & Co. Inc., San Francisco, CA; *U.S. Public*, pg. 1443
Short, Leonard, Sr. V.P.-Adv. & Brand Mngmt.--The Charles Schwab Corporation, San Francisco, CA; *U.S. Public*, pg. 1442
Short, Michael E., Sr. V.P.-Opers.--Blount, Inc. Forestry & Industrial Equipment Division, Zebulon, NC; *U.S. Public*, pg. 238
Short, Richard D., Sr. V.P.--National Technical Systems, Inc., Calabasas, CA; *U.S. Public*, pg. 1161
Shouse, Thelma, Sr. V.P.-Mngmt. Info. Systems--Coast Savings Financial, Inc., Los Angeles, CA; *U.S. Public*, pg. 388
Showalter, Joan, Sr. V.P.-Human Resources--CBS, New York, NY; *U.S. Public*, pg. 273
Shreiner, Jay W., Chief Information Officer & Sr. V.P.--Kellogg Company, Battle Creek, MI; *U.S. Public*, pg. 947
Shrem, Henry, Sr. V.P.--Commonwealth Metal, Englewood Cliffs, NJ; *U.S. Public*, pg. 412
Shriver, Debra, Sr. V.P.-Mktg. Communications--Hearst Magazines Division, New York, NY; *U.S. Private*, pg. 516
Shroff, Avanti C., Sr. V.P.--Iffland Kavanagh Waterbury, PLLC, New York, NY; *U.S. Private*, pg. 364
Shuey, David E., Sr. V.P., Mgr.-Commercial Brokerage & E. Div. Dir.--Willis Corroon Corp. of Penn., Radnor, PA; *Int'l*, pg. 1507
Shufeldt, R. Charles, Sr. V.P.-Capital Markets--SunTrust Banks, Inc., Atlanta, GA; *U.S. Public*, pg. 1537
Shulman, Dean F., Sr. V.P.--Brother International Corporation, Somerset, NJ; *Int'l*, pg. 229
Shumacher, Norbert, Sr. V.P.-Publication Services--Modern Plastics, New York, NY; *U.S. Public*, pg. 1071
Shumaker, James E., Jr., Sr. V.P.--Trustmark National Bank, Jackson, MS; *U.S. Public*, pg. 1643
Shumate, McKinley, Jr., Sr. V.P.-Underwriting/ANIC--ACCEL International Corporation, Dublin, OH; *U.S. Public*, pg. 14
Shur, Shlomo, Sr. V.P.-Advanced Tech.--Executone Information Systems, Inc., Milford, CT; *U.S. Public*, pg. 599
Shurtleff, Douglas, Chief Fin. Officer & Sr. V.P.-Fin.--USCS International, Inc., Rancho Cordova, CA; *U.S. Public*, pg. 1659
Shutts, Kenneth R., Sr. V.P., Gen. Counsel & Sec.--Penn National Insurance, Harrisburg, PA; *U.S. Private*, pg. 850
Shwytzen, Yoma, Sr. V.P.-Engrng.--The Israel Electric Corporation Ltd., Haifa, Israel; *Int'l*, pg. 690
Sibbick, Bill, Sr. V.P.-Sls.--Stanley Furniture Co. Inc., Stanleytown, VA; *U.S. Public*, pg. 1508

Sibold, Stephen P., Sr. V.P., Gen. Counsel & Corp. Sec.--Canadian Airlines Corporation, Calgary, Canada; *Int'l*, pg. 255

Siciliano, John C., Sr. V.P. & Dir.-Western United States--Dresdner Bank AG, Los Angeles, CA; *Int'l*, pg. 418

Sickler, John J., Sr. V.P. & Pres.-TFX Equites--Teleflex Incorporated, Plymouth Meeting, PA; *U.S. Public*, pg. 1569

Sidlow, Kenneth D., Sr. V.P. & Sr. Copywriter--DMB&B Detroit, Troy, MI; *U.S. Private*, pg. 302

Sieber, John D., Sr. V.P. & C.N.O.--Duquesne Light Company, Pittsburgh, PA; *U.S. Public*, pg. 474

Siegal, Patricia, Sr. V.P.-Inland Empire Area--Kaiser Permanente, Oakland, CA; *U.S. Private*, pg. 605

Siegel, Barby, Sr. V.P.--Edelman Worldwide, Inc., New York, NY; *U.S. Private*, pg. 362

Siegel, Daniel L., Sr. V.P. & Dir.-Midwest Reg.--Willis Faber North America, Inc.-Illinois, Chicago, IL; *Int'l*, pg. 1503

Siegel, Gary M., Sr. V.P.--Montgomery Watson, Cleveland, OH; *U.S. Private*, pg. 759

Siegel, James, Sr. V.P. & Acct. Dir.--Young & Rubicam New York, New York, NY; *U.S. Private*, pg. 1198

Siegel, John C., Sr. V.P.--Chris-Craft Industries, Inc., New York, NY; *U.S. Public*, pg. 351

Siegel, John C., Sr. V.P.--BHC Communications, Inc., New York, NY; *U.S. Public*, pg. 352

Siegel, Kenneth S., Sr. V.P., Gen. Counsel & Corp. Sec.--Cognizant Corporation, Westport, CT; *U.S. Public*, pg. 395

Siegel, William D., Sr. V.P.--Chris-Craft Industries, Inc., New York, NY; *U.S. Public*, pg. 351

Siegfried, Debbie, Sr. V.P.-Pub. Affairs--Texas Commerce Bank, Houston, TX; *U.S. Public*, pg. 339

Siemborski, Steven L., Chief Fin. Officer & Sr. V.P.--Figgie International Inc., Cleveland, OH; *U.S. Public*, pg. 622

Sierk, James E., Sr. V.P.-Quality & Productivity--AlliedSignal Inc., Morristown, NJ; *U.S. Public*, pg. 49

Sievers, Mark S., Chief Admin. Officer & Sr. V.P.--Long John Silver's, Inc., Lexington, KY; *U.S. Private*, pg. 674

Sievers, Phil, Sr. V.P. & Acct. Exec.--Doremus & Company, New York, NY; *U.S. Public*, pg. 1223

Siewert, James A., Sr. V.P.--Chicago Asset Management Company, Chicago, IL; *U.S. Public*, pg. 1672

Sifton, Jennifer, Sr. V.P.--Edelman Public Relations Worldwide, Chicago, IL; *U.S. Private*, pg. 362

Signorelli, James, Sr. V.P.--Lois/EJL Chicago, Chicago, IL; *U.S. Public*, pg. 1011

Sigurdsson, Einar, Sr. V.P.--Icelandair, Reykjavik, Iceland; *Int'l*, pg. 658

Sigurthorsson, Gudmundur, Sr. V.P.--Det Norske Veritas, Hovik, Norway; *Int'l*, pg. 396

Siiteri, Mikko, Sr. V.P.-Res. & Devel.--Valmet Corporation, Helsinki, Finland; *Int'l*, pg. 1447

Silberman, Ira, Sr. V.P.--D.P. Fitness, Opelika, AL; *U.S. Public*, pg. 1354

Silberman, Michael, Sr. V.P.-Theatrical Sls.--October Films, Inc., New York, NY; *Int'l*, pg. 1216

Silberman, Robert S., Sr. V.P.-Mktg. & Implement Action--CalEnergy Co., Omaha, NE; *U.S. Public*, pg. 292

Silk, Betram, Sr. V.P.-Industry Rels.--Canandaigua Wine Co., Canandaigua, NY; *U.S. Public*, pg. 300

Sillers, Coby, Sr. V.P.-Sls. & Mktg.--Oki Telecom Group, Suwanee, GA; *Int'l*, pg. 1000

Sillis, Leonard, Sr. V.P.-Opers.--Blount, Inc. Oregon Cutting Systems Division, Portland, OR; *U.S. Public*, pg. 238

Silva, Brian D., Sr. V.P.--Linens 'n Things, Inc., Clifton, NJ; *U.S. Private*, pg. 668

Silva, Kevin D., Sr. V.P & Dir.-Human Resources--MBIA Inc., Armonk, NY; *U.S. Public*, pg. 1023

Silver, Lawrence A., Sr. V.P.-Investor Rels.--Raymond James Financial, Inc., Saint Petersburg, FL; *U.S. Public*, pg. 923

Silver, Louis, Sr. V.P.-Branch Opers.--Fremont Investment & Loan, Anaheim, CA; *U.S. Public*, pg. 681

Silver, Robert C., Sr. V.P. & Dir.-H.R.--Sierra West Bancorp, Truckee, CA; *U.S. Public*, pg. 1470

Silverberg, Brad A., Sr. V.P.-Applications & Internet Client Grp.--Microsoft Corporation, Redmond, WA; *U.S. Public*, pg. 1107

Silverberg, Edward L., Sr. V.P.--Keystone Foods Corporation, Bala Cynwyd, PA; *U.S. Private*, pg. 619

Silverberg, Michael, Sr. V.P.--Moyer Packing Company, Souderton, PA; *U.S. Private*, pg. 765

Silverman, Gerrald B., Sr. V.P.-Sls. The Keds Corporation--The Stride Rite Corporation, Lexington, MA; *U.S. Public*, pg. 1524

Silverman, Nat, Sr. V.P.-Opers.--C & S Wholesale Grocery Inc., Brattleboro, VT; *U.S. Private*, pg. 192

Silverman, Scott D., Sr. V.P., Gen. Counsel & Sec.--PennCorp Financial Group, Inc., New York, NY; *U.S. Public*, pg. 1271

Silvernail, Robert F., Sr. V.P.--Norwest Financial, Inc., Des Moines, IA; *U.S. Public*, pg. 1202

Silvers, Robert, Sr. V.P., Exec. Publr. & Sec.--Benjamin Franklin Literary & Medical Society, Inc., Indianapolis, IN; *U.S. Private*, pg. 133

Silverstein, Barry, Sr. V.P.-Client Services--Jordan, McGrath, Case & Taylor Inc., New York, NY; *U.S. Private*, pg. 598

Silverstein, Steven B., Sr. V.P. & Gen. Mgr.-Mdse.--Linens 'n Things, Inc., Clifton, NJ; *U.S. Private*, pg. 668

Silvey, Gary L., Sr. V.P.--Associates Insurance Group, Inc., Dallas, TX; *U.S. Public*, pg. 663

Simaga, Richard C., Sr. V.P.--Pinnacle Bank, Valparaiso, IN; *U.S. Public*, pg. 1297

Simeroth, Hal H., Sr. V.P.-Digital Imaging Systems Div.--CalComp Technology, Inc., Anaheim, CA; *U.S. Public*, pg. 1007

Simkins, Robert, Sr. V.P.--Pall Corporation, Greenvale, NY; *U.S. Public*, pg. 1253

Simmons, Janet, Sr. V.P.-Pur.--Del Taco, Inc., Laguna Hills, CA; *U.S. Private*, pg. 321

Simmons, Jay B., Sr. V.P., Gen. Counsel & Sec.--Trans Financial, Inc., Bowling Green, KY; *U.S. Public*, pg. 1628

Simmons, John, Sr. V.P.--First Commercial Mortgage Co., Little Rock, AR; *U.S. Public*, pg. 630

Simmons, T. Randy, Sr. V.P. & Gen. Mgr.-CED Cluster--Anacomp, Inc., Indianapolis, IN; *U.S. Public*, pg. 106

Simms, Robert B., Sr. V.P.--National Geographic Magazine, Paris, France; *U.S. Private*, pg. 784

Simon, Andrea, Sr. V.P. & Deputy Gen. Counsel--Showtime Networks Inc., New York, NY; *U.S. Private*, pg. 779

Simon, Anthony, Sr. V.P.-Bus. Devel.--CPC Europe Consumer Foods Division, Brussels, Belgium; *U.S. Public*, pg. 224

Simon, Barry P., Sr. V.P.-Intl.--Continental Airlines, Houston, TX; *U.S. Public*, pg. 439

Simon, Brian A., Sr. V.P.--U.S. Manufacturing Corp., Fraser, MI; *U.S. Private*, pg. 1125

Simon, James H., Sr. V.P.--Hibernia Corporation, New Orleans, LA; *U.S. Public*, pg. 825

Simon, Jayne, Sr. V.P.-Sls.--MCA Records, Inc., Universal City, CA; *Int'l*, pg. 1215

Simon, John L., Sr. V.P.-Devel.--Taubman Centers, Inc., Bloomfield Hills, MI; *U.S. Public*, pg. 1561

Simon, Joseph A., Sr. V.P.--U.S. Manufacturing Corp., Fraser, MI; *U.S. Private*, pg. 1125

Simon, Laurence B., Sr. V.P. & Corp. Sec.--Health Management Systems, Inc., New York, NY; *U.S. Public*, pg. 802

Simon, Lawrence, Sr. V.P.-Fin.--Riddell Sports, Inc., New York, NY; *U.S. Public*, pg. 1389

Simon, Lawrence F., Sr. V.P. & Treas.--Riddell Sports, Inc., Chicago, IL; *U.S. Public*, pg. 1389

Simon, Martin S., Sr. V.P.--Connell Co., Westfield, NJ; *U.S. Private*, pg. 264

Simon, Owen, Sr. V.P.-Creative Services--CBS Enterprises Division, New York, NY; *U.S. Public*, pg. 274

Simon, Robert J., Sr. V.P.--Seitel, Inc., Houston, TX; *U.S. Public*, pg. 1454

Simon, William A., Chief Fin. Officer & Sr. V.P.-Admin.--Advantage Companies, Inc., Wichita, KS; *U.S. Private*, pg. 22

Simone, Ginny, Sr. V.P. & Mng. Dir.--The Mercury Group, Alexandria, VA; *U.S. Private*, pg. 13

Simonis, Dennis J., Chief Fin. Officer & Sr. V.P.--Mauna Loa Macadamia Nut Corporation, Hilo, HI; *U.S. Private*, pg. 190

Simons, Robert R., Sr. V.P.--Harcourt Brace & Company - Elementary Div., Orlando, FL; *U.S. Public*, pg. 783

Simonsen, Eric A., Chief Fin. Officer & Sr. V.P.--First Allmerica Financial Life Insurance Company, Worcester, MA; *U.S. Public*, pg. 54

Simonsen, Sandra L., Sr. V.P.-IS--Equis Financial Group, Boston, MA; *U.S. Private*, pg. 379

Simonson, David G., Sr. V.P. & Reg. Mgr.--Albertson's, Inc., Boise, ID; *U.S. Public*, pg. 38

Simonson, Eric, Sr. V.P.-Investments--John Hancock Mutual Life Insurance Company, Boston, MA; *U.S. Private*, pg. 589

Simonson, John A., Sr. V.P. & Treas.--Keycorp, Cleveland, OH; *U.S. Public*, pg. 954

Simonson, Robert, Sr. V.P.-Promo.--MARC, Pittsburgh, PA; *U.S. Private*, pg. 701

Simpson, Bruce W., Sr. V.P.--Nova Corporation, Calgary, Canada; *Int'l*, pg. 971

Simpson, Dixon E., Sr. V.P.-Retail Services--Fleming Companies, Inc., Oklahoma City, OK; *U.S. Public*, pg. 652

Simpson, Harry R., Sr. V.P.-Life Company--American States Insurance Companies, Indianapolis, IN; *U.S. Public*, pg. 997

Simpson, Harry R., Sr. V.P.-Life Company--American States Life Insurance Co., Indianapolis, IN; *U.S. Public*, pg. 997

Simpson, Hugh A., Sr. V.P., Gen. Counsel & Sec.--Cash America International, Inc., Fort Worth, TX; *U.S. Public*, pg. 312

Simpson, J. Kirk, Chief Fin. Officer--Call Interactive, Omaha, NE; *U.S. Public*, pg. 631

Simpson, James R., Sr. V.P.-Human Resources--The Times Mirror Company, Los Angeles, CA; *U.S. Public*, pg. 1615

Simpson, Larry, Sr. V.P.-Human Resources--Svenska Cellulosa Aktiebolaget (SCA), Stockholm, Sweden; *Int'l*, pg. 1326

Simpson, S., Sr. V.P. & Mng. Dir.--BBDO Canada, Toronto, Canada; *U.S. Private*, pg. 104

Simpson, William, Sr. V.P.-Field Svcs./Area I--Airborne Freight Corporation, Seattle, WA; *U.S. Public*, pg. 32

Simpson, William A., Sr. V.P.-Mortgage Guaranty & Pres.-Republic Mortgage Ins. Co.--Old Republic International Corporation, Chicago, IL; *U.S. Public*, pg. 1218

Sims, Barry D., Chief Fin. Officer & Sr. V.P.--Taco John's International, Inc., Cheyenne, WY; *U.S. Private*, pg. 1066

Sims, Jon C., Sr. V.P. & New Bus. Devel. Dir.--Long Haymes Carr, Inc., Winston Salem, NC; *U.S. Public*, pg. 909

Sims, Raymond J., Chief Fin. Officer & Sr. V.P.--Raychem Corporation, Menlo Park, CA; *U.S. Public*, pg. 1362

Sims, Richard R., Sr. V.P.--The Tranzonic Companies, Pepper Pike, OH; *U.S. Public*, pg. 1632

Sims, Richard G., Sr. V.P.--Software Spectrum, Inc., Garland, TX; *U.S. Public*, pg. 1483

Sims, Robert, Sr. V.P.--National Geographic Society, Washington, DC; *U.S. Private*, pg. 783

Sims, Stewart C., Sr. V.P.-Mktg--Tiger Electronics, Inc., Vernon Hills, IL; *U.S. Private*, pg. 1086

Sims, William, Sr. V.P.-Admin.--Midland National Life Insurance Co., Sioux Falls, SD; *U.S. Private*, pg. 963

Sinclair, Mel, Sr. V.P. & Dir.-Human Resources--Carolina First Corporation, Greenville, SC; *U.S. Public*, pg. 306

Sinclair, Wayne, Sr. V.P., Gen. Counsel & Sec.--MMI Companies, Inc., Deerfield, IL; *U.S. Public*, pg. 1027

Sindelar, David M., Chief Fin. Officer & Sr. V.P.--Berg Electronics, Saint Louis, MO; *U.S. Public*, pg. 212

Singer, Jack, Sr. V.P.--Imperial Bank, Inglewood, CA; *U.S. Public*, pg. 871

Singer, laura, Sr. V.P.--The Sherwood Group, Inc., Jersey City, NJ; *U.S. Public*, pg. 1466

Singleton, Raun V., Chief Fin. Officer & Sr. V.P.--Four-S Baking Company, Los Angeles, CA; *U.S. Private*, pg. 422

Singleton, Richard R., Sr. V.P.--Oxford Realty Financial Group, Bethesda, MD; *U.S. Private*, pg. 825

Sinner, Stephen W., Sr. V.P.--TCF Bank Wisconsin, Milwaukee, WI; *U.S. Public*, pg. 1554

Sinnett, James M., Sr. V.P.-Advanced Sys. & Tech.--McDonnell Aircraft & Missile Systems Div., Berkeley, MO; *U.S. Public*, pg. 241

Sipes, Sherrill F., Jr., Sr. V.P.--ABM Industries, San Francisco, CA; *U.S. Public*, pg. 2

Sirasudhi, Manusan, Sr. V.P.-Audit Office--Nakornthon Bank Public Company Limited, Bangkok, Thailand; *Int'l*, pg. 904

Siriwadhana, Anchalee, Sr. V.P.-Acctg.--Nakornthon Bank Public Company Limited, Bangkok, Thailand; *Int'l*, pg. 904

Sislak, Elizabeth L., Sr. V.P.--Dix & Eaton Incorporated, Cleveland, OH; *U.S. Private*, pg. 336

Sisodia, Jag, Sr. V.P.--Intertek Testing Services, Andover, MA; *Int'l*, pg. 672

Sisson, Jaci, Sr. V.P. & Creative Dir.--Dailey & Associates, West Hollywood, CA; *U.S. Public*, pg. 909

Sisson, Jack, Sr. V.P. & Mgr.-Bus.--Dow Jones Markets, Jersey City, NJ; *U.S. Public*, pg. 525

Sivayathorn, Kulathida, Sr. V.P. & Gen. Mgr.--Bangkok Bank Public Company Limited, Bangkok, Thailand; *Int'l*, pg. 146

Sizemore, Dennis, Sr. V.P. & Controller--Howard Hughes Corporation, Las Vegas, NV; *U.S. Public*, pg. 1407

Sjogren, Lennart, Sr. V.P.--W. Rosenlew Ltd., Helsinki, Finland; *Int'l*, pg. 1428

Skaggs, Joseph, Sr. V.P.-Opers.--Follett College Stores Corp., Elmhurst, IL; *U.S. Private*, pg. 417

Skaggs, Rick, Chief Fin. Officer & Sr. V.P.--MRA, An Integrated Marketing Communications Agency, Overland Park, KS; *U.S. Private*, pg. 687

Skaggs, Stephen, Chief Fin. Officer & Sr. V.P.--Lattice Semiconductor Corporation, Hillsboro, OR; *U.S. Public*, pg. 979

Skains, Thomas E., Sr. V.P.-Gas Supply & Svcs.--Piedmont Natural Gas Co., Inc., Charlotte, NC; *U.S. Public*, pg. 1295

Skalicky, Steven S., Sr. V.P. & Controller--Transatlantic Holdings Inc., New York, NY; *U.S. Public*, pg. 84

Skara, Susan, Sr. V.P.-H.R.--Apria Healthcare Group Inc., Costa Mesa, CA; *U.S. Public*, pg. 125

Skarupa, Emery E., Sr. V.P.-Mfg. & Matls.--Anacomp, Inc., Indianapolis, IN; *U.S. Public*, pg. 106

Skatoff, Lawrence B., Chief Fin. Officer & Sr. V.P.--Premark International, Inc., Deerfield, IL; *U.S. Public*, pg. 1321

Skebba, Bill, Jr., Sr. V.P.-Sls. & Mktg.--M.W. Kasch Company, Mequon, WI; *U.S. Private*, pg. 608

Skelton, Brenda, Sr. V.P.-Mktg. & Customer Svc.--Midwest Express Airlines, Inc., Oak Creek, WI; *U.S. Public*, pg. 1111

Skelton, Brenda F., Sr. V.P.-Mktg. & Customer Svcs.--Midwest Express Holdings, Inc., Oak Creek, WI; *U.S. Public*, pg. 1111

Skelton, Don, Sr. V.P.-Mktg. & Sls.--Illinois Central Corporation, Chicago, IL; *U.S. Public*, pg. 864

Skemp, Randy, Sr. V.P.-Sls.--HBO & Company/Cycare Business Group, Scottsdale, AZ; *U.S. Public*, pg. 770

Skeoch, Don, Sr. V.P.-Mktg.--Baskin-Robbins Incorporated, Glendale, CA; *Int'l*, pg. 63

Skerl, Damir S., Sr. V.P.--Western Atlas Inc., Houston, TX; *U.S. Public*, pg. 1757

Skerl, Damir S., Sr. V.P.--Western Atlas International, Inc., Houston, TX; *U.S. Public*, pg. 1757

Skidmore, Dennis W., Sr. V.P.-U.S. Div.--St. Lawrence Cement Inc., Montreal, Canada; *Int'l*, pg. 628

Skinner, James A., Sr. V.P. & Zone Mgr.--McDonald's Corporation, Oak Brook, IL; *U.S. Public*, pg. 1068

Skinner, James P., Sr. V.P.-Parts & Supply Grp.--Coachmen Industries, Inc., Elkhart, IN; *U.S. Public*, pg. 387

Skinner, Peter G., Sr. V.P., Gen. Counsel, Sec. & Pres.-Television--Dow Jones & Company, Inc., New York, NY; *U.S. Public*, pg. 524

Skinner, Robert H., Sr. V.P.-Sls.--Best Software, Inc., Reston, VA; *U.S. Public*, pg. 223

Skinner, William L., Sr. V.P.-Admin. & Corp. Devel.--Alltrista Corporation, Muncie, IN; *U.S. Public*, pg. 56

Sklar, Bob, Sr. V.P.-Sls.--Interactive Telecard Services, Inc. (ITS), Miami, FL; *U.S. Private*, pg. 566

Skrgic, Peter J., Sr. V.P.--Allegheny Power System, Inc., Hagerstown, MD; *U.S. Public*, pg. 42

Skubiak, O. John, Sr. V.P.--DeVry Institutes, Oak Brook Terrace, IL; *U.S. Public*, pg. 503

Skurnick, David, Sr. V.P.--F&G Re, Inc., Morristown, NJ; *U.S. Public*, pg. 1659

Skutt, Jay B., Sr. V.P.--Deluxe Corporation, Shoreview, MN; *U.S. Public*, pg. 498

Slabas, Stanley F., Chief Fin. Officer & Sr. V.P.--S & C Electric Company, Chicago, IL; *U.S. Private*, pg. 954

Slack, Paul, Sr. V.P. & Controller--Mullen Advertising, Inc., Wenham, MA; *U.S. Private*, pg. 766

Sladnick, Clifford, Sr. V.P., Gen. Counsel & Sec.--St. Paul Bancorp, Inc., Chicago, IL; *U.S. Public*, pg. 1428

Slamad, Donald G., Chief Fin. Officer & Sr. V.P.--Turner Construction Company, New York, NY; *U.S. Public*, pg. 1645

Slangen, Louis F.J., Sr. V.P.-Sls. & Mktg.--Invacare Corporation, Elyria, OH; *U.S. Public*, pg. 911

Slater, John E., Sr. V.P. & Publisher--Electrical World, New York, NY; *U.S. Public*, pg. 1071

Slater, John J., Sr. V.P. & Publisher--Power, New York, NY; *U.S. Public*, pg. 1071

Slater, Lucy, Sr. V.P.-Prod. Devel.--E-Z Bowz, Inc., Sevierville, TN; *U.S. Private*, pg. 352

Slattery, Anne M., Sr. V.P.--Fleet Financial Group, Inc., Boston, MA; *U.S. Public*, pg. 648

Slattery, William H., Sr. V.P. & Gen. Counsel--Republic National Bank of New York, New York, NY; *U.S. Public*, pg. 1380

Slaughter, George, Sr. V.P.-Intl. Opers.--Hunt Oil Company, Dallas, TX; *U.S. Private*, pg. 548

Slavitt, Andrew M., Chief Oper. Officer & Sr. V.P.--PAULA Financial, Pasadena, CA; *U.S. Public*, pg. 1266

Sleeman, Donald G., Chief Fin. Officer, Sr. V.P., Controller & Treas.--The Turner Corporation, New York, NY; *U.S. Public*, pg. 1645

Sloan, Dale R., Chief Fin. Officer & Sr. V.P.--Rochester Midland Corporation, Rochester, NY; *U.S. Private*, pg. 937

Sloan, Lee, Sr. V.P. & Creative Dir.--Fahlgren, Dublin, OH; *U.S. Private*, pg. 391

Sloan, Stephen, Sr. V.P. & Gen. Mgr.-Mdse.--The Bon Ton Stores, Inc., York, PA; *U.S. Public*, pg. 244

Slobodien, David J., Sr. V.P. & Gen. Counsel--Dun & Bradstreet, Murray Hill, NJ; *U.S. Public*, pg. 535

Slobodin, Fred W., Sr. V.P. & Brdcst. Production Dir.--Wunderman Cato Johnson, New York, NY; *U.S. Private*, pg. 1197

Slocum, Terry, Sr. V.P.-Corp. Devel.--Western Staff Services, Walnut Creek, CA; *U.S. Public*, pg. 1760

Slotkin, Todd J., Sr. V.P.--MacAndrews & Forbes Holdings Inc., New York, NY; *U.S. Private*, pg. 689

Slusher, Carroll, Dir.-N. American Rehab.--Insituform Technologies, Inc., Chesterfield, MO; *U.S. Public*, pg. 881

Slusser, Daniel E., V.P., Sr. V.P. & Gen. Mgr.-Universal City--Universal Studios, Inc., Universal City, CA; *Int'l*, pg. 1215

Small, John G., Sr. V.P.-Client Services--The New England, Boston, MA; *U.S. Private*, pg. 737

Small, Philip W., Sr. V.P.-Fin.--Beverly Enterprises, Inc., Fort Smith, AR; *U.S. Public*, pg. 227

Smallen, Lawrence H., Chief Fin. Officer, Sr. V.P.-Fin. & Treas.--Apria Healthcare Group Inc., Costa Mesa, CA; *U.S. Public*, pg. 125

Smallenberger, James Andrew, Sr. V.P. & Sec.--American Mutual Life Holding Co., Des Moines, IA; *U.S. Private*, pg. 59

Smalley, Jerome D., Sr. V.P. & Dir.-Commercial & Office Devel.--The Rouse Company, Columbia, MD; *U.S. Public*, *pg. 1407*

Smalley, Kathleen, Sr. V.P., Gen. Counsel & Sec.--Catellus Development Corporation, San Francisco, CA; *U.S. Public*, pg. 314

Smalley, Wayne H., Sr. V.P.--Hibernia Corporation, New Orleans, LA; *U.S. Public*, pg. 825

Smart, John, Sr. V.P. & Mng. Dir.--Interbrand Schechter, San Francisco, CA; *U.S. Public*, pg. 1224

Smartt, Bill, Chief Fin. Officer & Sr. V.P.-Fin.--DHL Worldwide Express, Redwood City, CA; *U.S. Private*, pg. 301

Smeester, Charles A., Sr. V.P.-Opers.--Old Kent Bank, Grand Rapids, MI; *U.S. Public*, pg. 1216

Smerz, Susan M., Sr. V.P., Controller & Asst. Sec.--First Midwest Bancorp, Inc., Itasca, IL; *U.S. Public*, pg. 636

Smialowski, Joe, Chief Info. Officer & Sr. V.P.--Sears, Roebuck and Co., Hoffman Estates, IL; *U.S. Public*, pg. 1452

Smith III, Valentine W. R., Sr. V.P.--Gaylord Entertainment Co., Nashville, TN; *U.S. Public*, pg. 704

Smith-Jensen, Kimberly, Sr. V.P.--The Atlantic Monthly Magazine, Boston, MA; *U.S. Private*, pg. 95

Smith, A. Gary, Sr. V.P.--United States Tobacco Company, Greenwich, CT; *U.S. Public*, pg. 1661

Smith, Alan E., Sr. V.P.--Keller & Gannon, San Francisco, CA; *U.S. Private*, pg. 626

Smith, Alan F., Sr. V.P.-Fabricated Prods. Grp.--Wolverine Tube Inc., Huntsville, AL; *U.S. Public*, pg. 1774

Smith, Andrew P., Sr. V.P.--Eastbridge Asset Management Inc., New York, NY; *Int'l*, pg. 933

Smith, Brian, Sr. V.P.-Sls.--Vail Resorts, Inc., Vail, CO; *U.S. Public*, pg. 1704

Smith, Brian L., Sr. V.P.-Mngmt. Liability, Claims Consulting & Prod. Devel.--Willis Corroon Financial Services Corp., New York, NY; *Int'l*, pg. 1507

Smith, Bruce D., Chief Fin. Officer & Sr. V.P.--Hancock Fabrics, Inc., Tupelo, MS; *U.S. Public*, pg. 779

Smith, C.W., Sr. V.P.-Equities--General Electric Investment Corp., Stamford, CT; *U.S. Public*, pg. 712

Smith, Carla J., Sr. V.P., Gen. Counsel & Sec.--Dain Rauscher Corporation, Minneapolis, MN; *U.S. Public*, pg. 476

Smith, Claire M., Sr. V.P.-Retail Banking--Citizens Savings Bank, Providence, RI; *Int'l*, pg. 1132

Smith, Dan, Chief Info. Officer & Sr. V.P.--Saks Fifth Avenue, New York, NY; *U.S. Public*, pg. 1429

Smith, Daniel C., Sr. V.P.-Information Services--Younkers, Inc., Des Moines, IA; *U.S. Public*, pg. 1334

Smith, David, Sr. V.P. & Grp. Acct. Dir.--Bensimon Byrne DMB&B Toronto, Toronto, Canada; *U.S. Private*, pg. 303

Smith, David J., Chief Admin. Officer & Sr. V.P.--The Turner Corporation, New York, NY; *U.S. Public*, pg. 1645

Smith, David R., Sr. V.P.--Jefferies & Company, Inc., Los Angeles, CA; *U.S. Public*, pg. 925

Smith, David T., Sr. V.P.-Corp. Trust--The Bank of Bermuda Limited, Hamilton, Bermuda; *Int'l*, pg. 150

Smith, David W., Sr. V.P. & Gen. Counsel--Transatlantic Holdings Inc., New York, NY; *U.S. Public*, pg. 84

Smith, Deborah, Sr. V.P. & Media Buying Dir.--North Castle Partners Advertising, Inc., Stamford, CT; *U.S. Private*, pg. 804

Smith, Deborah K., Sr. V.P.-Human Resources--Merck & Co., Inc., Whitehouse Station, NJ; *U.S. Public*, pg. 1090

Smith, Dennis H., Sr. V.P.-Mktg.--Fiduciary Management Associates, Inc., Chicago, IL; *U.S. Public*, pg. 1673

Smith, Dickinson M., Sr. V.P. & Chief Nuclear Officer-Nuclear Generation Grp.--PECO Energy Company, Philadelphia, PA; *U.S. Public*, pg. 1268

Smith, Dudley R., Sr. V.P.--Chubb & Son, Inc., Warren, NJ; *U.S. Public*, pg. 355

Smith, E. Berry, Sr. V.P.-Broadcasting--Schurz Communications, Inc., South Bend, IN; *U.S. Private*, pg. 973

Smith, Ernest, Sr. V.P.--The Advest Group, Inc., Hartford, CT; *U.S. Public*, pg. 23

Smith, Frank E., Chief Fin. Officer, Sr. V.P. & Sec.--West Coast Bancorp, Newport Beach, CA; *U.S. Public*, pg. 1755

Smith, Frank E., Chief Fin. Officer & Sr. V. P.--Sunwest Bank, Tustin, CA; *U.S. Public*, pg. 1755

Smith, Frederick J., Sr. V.P.-Opers.--Lukens Inc., Coatesville, PA; *U.S. Public*, pg. 1019

Smith, G. Patricia, Sr. V.P. & Auditor--Wilmington Savings Fund Society (FSB), Wilmington, DE; *U.S. Public*, pg. 1729

Smith, Gary, Sr. V.P. & Dir.-Mktg.--Safeway Inc., Pleasanton, CA; *U.S. Public*, pg. 1426

Smith, Gary, Sr. V.P.-Sls.--UST Inc., Greenwich, CT; *U.S. Public*, pg. 1660

Smith, Gary A., Sr. V.P.-Distr. & Opers.--Parisian, Inc., Birmingham, AL; *U.S. Public*, pg. 1333

Smith, George S., Sr. V.P. & Chief Fin. Officer--Viacom International Inc., New York, NY; *U.S. Private*, pg. 778

Smith, Gerard, Sr. V.P. & Plng. Dir.-North America--DMB&B Communications, New York, NY; *U.S. Private*, pg. 302

Smith, Gordon, Sr. V.P.-Human Resources--Olsten Health Services, Melville, NY; *U.S. Public*, pg. 1221

Smith, Greg, Sr. V.P.-Sls.--InterVoice, Inc., Dallas, TX; *U.S. Public*, pg. 910

Smith, Gregory E., Sr. V.P.-Content--Dow Jones Markets, Jersey City, NJ; *U.S. Public*, pg. 525

Smith, H.S., III, Sr. V.P.-Information Services--SuperValu, Inc., Eden Prairie, MN; *U.S. Public*, pg. 1540

Smith, Harold J., Sr. V.P. & Sec.--Tradehome Shoe Stores, Inc., Saint Paul, MN; *U.S. Private*, pg. 1095

Smith, J.G., Sr. V.P.--CIBC Mortgage Corporation, Toronto, Canada; *Int'l*, pg. 256

Smith, Jack S., Sr. V.P.-Domestic Mfg.--Haggar Corporation, Dallas, TX; *U.S. Public*, pg. 774

Smith, James, Sr. V.P.--Bromar Inc., Newport Beach, CA; *U.S. Private*, pg. 171

Smith, James A., Sr. V.P.--First Maryland Bancorp, Baltimore, MD; *Int'l*, pg. 64

Smith, James D., Sr. V.P.-Opers.--Clear Channel Metroplex, Tulsa, OK; *U.S. Public*, pg. 383

Smith, James P., Jr., Sr. V.P.-Human Resources--ITT Industries, Inc., White Plains, NY; *U.S. Public*, pg. 859

Smith, Jane S., Sr. V.P.--Policy Management Systems Corporation, Blythewood, SC; *U.S. Public*, pg. 1314

Smith, Jeffrey K., Sr. V.P.--New York State Electric & Gas Corporation, Binghamton, NY; *U.S. Public*, pg. 1173

Smith, Jeffrey K., Sr. V.P. & Dir.--Kluwer Academic Publishers, Norwell, MA; *Int'l*, pg. 1513

Smith, Jeffrey M., Sr. V.P.-Plng. & Devel.--Churchill Downs, Inc., Louisville, KY; *U.S. Public*, pg. 356

Smith, Jennifer H., Sr. V.P.-H.R.--Lutheran Brotherhood, Minneapolis, MN; *U.S. Private*, pg. 681

Smith, John B., Sr. V.P., Gen. Counsel & Sec.--Interim Services Inc., Fort Lauderdale, FL; *U.S. Public*, pg. 892

Smith, John J., Sr. V.P.--UJB Discount Brokerage, Ridgefield Park, NJ; *U.S. Public*, pg. 1528

Smith, Joseph W., Jr., Sr. V.P. & Chief Investment Officer--AFLAC Incorporated, Columbus, GA; *U.S. Public*, pg. 28

Smith, Kenneth, Sr. V.P.-Opers.--Marotta Scientific Controls, Inc., Montville, NJ; *U.S. Private*, pg. 706

Smith, Kenneth, Sr. V.P.--Hibernia Corporation, New Orleans, LA; *U.S. Public*, pg. 825

Smith, Kevin M., Sr. V.P.-Reg. Admin.--Fidelity Investments (FMR Corp.), Boston, MA; *U.S. Private*, pg. 402

Smith, L. Craig, Chief Fin. Officer & Sr. V.P.--Wyle Laboratories, Inc., El Segundo, CA; *U.S. Private*, pg. 1193

Smith, Lachlan M., Chief Fin. Officer, Sr. V.P. & Treas.--National City Bank, Kentucky, Louisville, KY; *U.S. Public*, *pg. 1154*

Smith, Lawrence W., Sr. V.P.-Sls. & Mktg./N. America--FCA International Ltd., Westmount, Canada; *Int'l*, pg. 470

Smith, Linda, Sr. V.P. & Mngmt. Supvr.--RBT/Strum, Cherry Hill, NJ; *U.S. Private*, pg. 902

Smith, M., Sr. V.P. & Assoc. Creative Dir.--BBDO Canada, Toronto, Canada; *U.S. Private*, pg. 104

Smith, M. Garrett, Chief Fin. Officer, Sr. V.P. & Treas.--Pioneer Natural Resources Co., Irving, TX; *U.S. Public*, pg. 1299

Smith, M. Lazane, Chief Fin. Officer & Sr. V.P.-Fin.--CompuCom Systems, Inc., Dallas, TX; *U.S. Public*, pg. 1424

Smith, Mallory S., Sr. V.P.-Housing Grp.--Fleetwood Enterprises, Inc., Riverside, CA; *U.S. Public*, pg. 650

Smith, Marcus H., Jr., Sr. V.P.-Real Estate--Goody's Family Clothing, Inc., Knoxville, TN; *U.S. Public*, pg. 753

Smith, Marschall I., Sr. V.P., Gen. Counsel & Asst. Sec.--IMC Global, Bannockburn, IL; *U.S. Public*, pg. 856

Smith, Marvin W., Sr. V.P.-Opers. Admin.--NationsBank West, Saint Louis, MO; *U.S. Public*, pg. 1164

Smith, Matthew J., Sr. V.P.-Info. Sys. & Logistics--Oneida Ltd., Oneida, NY; *U.S. Public*, pg. 1225

Smith, Merrill, Sr. V.P.-Tech.--Congoleum Corporation, Mercerville, NJ; *U.S. Public*, pg. 69

Smith, Michael, Chief Info. Officer & Sr. V.P.--Builders Square, Inc., San Antonio, TX; *U.S. Private*, pg. 477

Smith, Michael B., Sr. V.P.--Turner Construction Co., Miami, FL; *U.S. Public*, pg. 1645

Smith, Michael J., Sr. V.P. & Chief Acctg. Officer--Countrywide Funding Corporation, Pasadena, CA; *U.S. Public*, pg. 453

Smith, Michael J., Sr. V.P. & Creative Dir.--Creswell, Munsell, Fultz & Zirbel, L.P., Cedar Rapids, IA; *U.S. Private*, pg. 1197

Smith, Milo A., Chief Fin. Officer & Sr. V.P.--Dominion Textile Inc., Montreal, Canada; *Int'l*, pg. 415

Smith, Ned A., Pres. & Chief Exec. Officer--American Steamship Company, Williamsville, NY; *U.S. Public*, pg. 690

Smith, Patrick D., Sr. V.P.-Mfg. Opers.--TJ International, Inc., Boise, ID; *U.S. Public*, pg. 1556

Smith, Patrick N., Sr. V.P. & Tech. Officer--Strategic Technology Services, Cerritos, CA; *Int'l*, pg. 1154

Smith, Paul D., Sr. V.P.-Opers & Bus. Affairs--TriStar Pictures, Culver City, CA; *Int'l*, pg. 1283

Smith, Philip N., Sr. V.P. & Gen. Counsel--Trace International Holdings, Inc., New York, NY; *U.S. Private*, pg. 1094

Smith, Philip S., Chief Fin. Officer, Sr. V.P. & Pres.-Admin.--Mitchell Energy & Development Corp., Spring, TX; *U.S. Public*, pg. 1117

Smith, Randolph J., Sr. V.P.--Atlantic Mutual Companies, New York, NY; *U.S. Private*, pg. 95

Smith, Raymond, Sr. V.P.--Andover Bank, Andover, MA; *U.S. Public*, pg. 112

Smith, Raymond P., Sr. V.P.--Andover Bancorp, Inc., Andover, MA; *U.S. Public*, pg. 111

Smith, Richard C., Jr., Sr. V.P.-Quality Devel. & Pub. Rels.--Sprint Corporation, Westwood, KS; *U.S. Public*, pg. 1500

Smith, Richard H., Sr. V.P., Gen. Counsel & Sec.--Cooper Communities, Inc., Bella Vista, AR; *U.S. Private*, pg. 273

Smith, Robert E., Sr. V.P.-Res.--Nabisco Inc., Parsippany, NJ; *U.S. Public*, pg. 1355

Smith, Robert E., Sr. V.P.-Energy Opers.--Rochester Gas And Electric Corporation, Rochester, NY; *U.S. Public*, pg. 1395

Smith, Robert W., Sr. V.P.-Store Devel. & Plng.--Fleming Companies, Inc., Oklahoma City, OK; *U.S. Public*, pg. 652

Smith, Ronald G., Sr. V.P.--Commercial National Bank, Shreveport, LA; *U.S. Public*, pg. 500

Smith, S.A., Sr. V.P. & Controller--Loblaw Companies Limited, North York, Canada; *Int'l*, pg. 1495

Smith, Sheri, Sr. V.P. & Pub. Rels. Dir.--EvansGroup, Dallas, TX; *U.S. Private*, pg. 385

Smith, Stephen, Sr. V.P.-Intl. Devel.--John Wiley & Sons, Inc., New York, NY; *U.S. Public*, pg. 1768

Smith, Steve, Sr. V.P.-Opers.--NationsCredit Commercial Corporation, Cleveland, OH; *U.S. Public*, pg. 1165

Smith, T. Richard, Sr. V.P.--Trustmark National Bank, Jackson, MS; *U.S. Public*, pg. 1643

Smith, Terence L., Sr. V.P. & Gen. Mgr.-Imports--The Home Depot, Inc., Atlanta, GA; *U.S. Public*, pg. 831

Smith, Thomas B., Sr. V.P. & Creative Dir.--Wyse Advertising/Cleveland, Cleveland, OH; *U.S. Private*, pg. 1194

Smith, Thomas G., Chief Fin. Officer, Sr. V.P. & Sec.--Forest City Enterprises, Inc., Cleveland, OH; *U.S. Public*, *pg. 667*

Smith, Thomas J., Sr. V.P.--Peoples Savings Bank of Ashtabula, Ashtabula, OH; *U.S. Public*, pg. 647

Smith, Thomas J., Sr. V.P.-Credit Services--Tompkins County Trust Company, Ithaca, NY; *U.S. Public*, pg. 1621

Smith, Victor N., Sr. V.P. & Mgr.-Private Banking--First Security Bank of Idaho, N.A., Boise, ID; *U.S. Public*, pg. 637

Smith, Walter, Sr. V.P. & Mngmt. Supvr.--Hal Riney & Partners, Inc., San Francisco, CA; *U.S. Private*, pg. 931

Smith, Wayne R., Sr. V.P.--Continental Assurance Company, Chicago, IL; *U.S. Private*, pg. 267

Smith, William J., Sr. V.P.-Sls. & Mktg.--Premisys Communications, Inc., Fremont, CA; *U.S. Public*, pg. 1323

Smith, Winifred S., Sr. V.P.--ReliaStar Investment Research, Inc., Minneapolis, MN; *U.S. Public*, pg. 1376

Smithers, Wayne D., Sr. V.P.--Valero Marketing & Supply Company, San Antonio, TX; *U.S. Public*, pg. 1704

Smithers, Wayne D., Sr. V.P.--Valero Refining Company, San Antonio, TX; *U.S. Public*, pg. 1704

Smoak, Neil A., Sr. V.P.--Fina, Inc., Dallas, TX; *Int'l*, pg. 1044

Smock, Roger P., Sr. V.P.-United States--National Bank of Canada, Montreal, Canada; *Int'l*, pg. 907

Smodilla, Timothy, Sr. V.P.-Company Opers.--Gingiss International, Addison, IL; *U.S. Private*, pg. 455

Smolik, T. James, Sr. V.P.-Project Devel.--Placer Dome Inc., Vancouver, Canada; *Int'l*, pg. 1060

Smorada, Joseph F., Chief Fin. Officer & Sr. V.P.--Axel Johnson Inc., Stamford, CT; *Int'l*, pg. 709

Smothers, William D., Sr. V.P.-Real Estate--Hancock Fabrics, Inc., Tupelo, MS; *U.S. Public*, pg. 779

Smrke, John R., Sr. V.P.--Royal Oak Mines Inc., Kirkland, WA; *U.S. Public*, pg. 1410

Smull, Ned, Sr. V.P.-Loans--Bank of Agriculture & Commerce, Stockton, CA; *U.S. Private*, pg. 114

Smyth, George C., Pres.-Bell Northern Res. & Sr. V.P.--Northern Telecom Limited, Brampton, Canada; *Int'l*, pg. 968

Sneed, Paula A., Sr. V.P.-Mktg. Services--Kraft Foods, Inc., Northfield, IL; *U.S. Public*, pg. 1287

Snelling, William, Sr. V.P.-Adv.--Cineplex Odeon Corporation, Toronto, Canada; *Int'l*, pg. 292

Snetzler, Carol J., Sr. V.P. & Print Production Dir.--Creswell, Munsell, Fultz & Zirbel, L.P., Cedar Rapids, IA; *U.S. Private*, pg. 1197

Snider, Carol, Sr. V.P.-Atlantic Provinces Div.--Bank of Montreal - Halifax, Halifax, Canada; *Int'l*, pg. 153

Snider, Meldon H., Sr. V.P.-Fin. & Admin.--CCL Industries, Inc., Willowdale, Canada; *Int'l*, pg. 238

Snider, Stephen A., Sr. V.P.--Tidewater Inc., New Orleans, LA; *U.S. Public*, pg. 1608

Sniffin, John H., Sr. V.P.-Govt. Rels.--Heilig-Meyers Company, Richmond, VA; *U.S. Public*, pg. 804

Snijders, Ludo, Sr. V.P.-Middle East--Maison Mathieu, S.A., Antwerp, Belgium; *Int'l*, pg. 846

Snodgrass, Richard W., Sr. V.P.--First National Bank of Warsaw, Warsaw, IN; *U.S. Public*, pg. 674

Snowden, Diana E., Sr. V.P.-Local Exchange Company Opers.--Pacific Telecom Cellular, Inc., Vancouver, WA; *U.S. Public*, pg. 1252

Sny, Sharon, Pres.-Plastic Pkgng. & Sr. V.P.--Duro-Last Roofing, Inc., Saginaw, MI; *U.S. Private*, pg. 349

Snyder, Allison Weirtheim, Sr. V.P.--Edelman Worldwide, Inc., San Francisco, CA; *U.S. Private*, pg. 362

Snyder, Dale E., Sr. V.P.-Tech. Svcs.--Kohler Company, Kohler, WI; *U.S. Private*, pg. 630

Snyder, Elizabeth A., Sr. V.P.-Western Reg.--Federal National Mortgage Association (Fannie Mae), Washington, DC; *U.S. Public*, pg. 615

Snyder, Eric, Sr. V.P. & Dir.-Corp. Leasing--CBL & Associates Properties, Inc., Chattanooga, TN; *U.S. Public*, pg. 273

Snyder, Fred, Sr. V.P.-Collection--Browning-Ferris Industries, Inc., Houston, TX; *U.S. Public*, pg. 262

Snyder, John H., Sr. V.P. & Dir. -Stores--Elder-Beerman Stores Div., Dayton, OH; *U.S. Private*, pg. 367

Snyder, Lauren, Sr. V.P.--Edelman Worldwide, Inc., New York, NY; *U.S. Private*, pg. 362

Snyder, Paul H., Chief Fin. Officer & Sr. V.P.--Salient 3 Communications, Inc., Reading, PA; *U.S. Public*, pg. 1429

Snyder, R. Kent, Sr. V.P.-Comml. Affairs--Agouron Pharmaceuticals, Inc., La Jolla, CA; *U.S. Public*, pg. 28

Snyder, Richard V., Sr. V.P.-Fleet Services--Enterprise Rent-A-Car Company, Saint Louis, MO; *U.S. Private*, pg. 377

Snyder, Ross B., Pres.-Grp. Life & Health & Sr. V.P.--Blue Cross & Blue Shield of Texas, Inc., Richardson, TX; *U.S. Private*, pg. 152

Snyder, S.I., Chief Fin. Officer, Sr. V.P.-Fin., Treas. & Sec.--Kaufman Footwear, Kitchener, Canada; *Int'l*, pg. 725

Snyder, William W., Sr. V.P.-MIS--Enterprise Rent-A-Car Company, Saint Louis, MO; *U.S. Private*, pg. 377

Sobel, Beth, Sr. V.P.-Sls.--Ranir Corporation/DCP, Grand Rapids, MI; *U.S. Private*, pg. 909

Sobo, William T., Jr., Chief Fin. Officer, Sr. V.P. & Treas.--PAREXEL International Corporation, Waltham, MA; *U.S. Public*, pg. 1257

Soderberg, Olle, Sr. V.P.-Adv.--Skandinaviska Enskilda Banken, Stockholm, Sweden; *Int'l*, pg. 1258

Soderberg, Steven R., Sr. V.P.-Info. Sys.--Robert Mondavi Winery, Inc., Oakville, CA; *U.S. Public*, pg. 1393

Soefje, Shannon A., Sr. V.P.-Corp. Commun. & Sec.--HD Vest Financial Services, Irving, TX; *U.S. Public*, pg. 770

Sogel, Yona, Sr. V.P.-Developmental Strategy--Bank Leumi le-Israel B.M., Tel Aviv, Israel; *Int'l*, pg. 150

Sojakka, Antti, Sr. V.P.-Pkgng.--Metsa-Serla Corporation, Espoo, Finland; *Int'l*, pg. 863

Sokal, Steve, Sr. V.P.-Opers.--Hyatt Corporation, Chicago, IL; *U.S. Private*, pg. 551

Sokolowski, George, Sr. V.P.-Corp. Mktg.--The TJX Companies, Inc., Framingham, MA; *U.S. Public*, pg. 1556

Solana, Lorenzo, Sr. V.P.--Banco Santander, Madrid, Spain; *Int'l*, pg. 143

Solganik, David, Sr. V.P.-Retail Leasing--Lat Purser & Associates, Charlotte, NC; *U.S. Private*, pg. 896

Solheim, Bjoern F., Sr. V.P.-Tech. & Devel.--Saga Petroleum ASA, Sandvika, Norway; *Int'l*, pg. 1169

Sollitt, David, Sr. V.P. & Acct. Mng. Dir.--Young & Rubicam New York, New York, NY; *U.S. Private*, pg. 1198

Sollmann, Robert E., Jr., Sr. V.P.-Grp. Natl. Accounts--Metropolitan Life Insurance Co., New York, NY; *U.S. Private*, pg. 737

Solomon, James E., Sr. V.P. & Principal Technologist--Cadence Design Systems, Inc., San Jose, CA; *U.S. Public*, pg. 290

Solomon, James R., Sr. V.P.--TrizecHahn Properties Inc., Chicago, IL; *Int'l*, pg. 1425

Solomon, Paul F., Sr. V.P. & Gen. Counsel--Jacor Communications, Inc., Covington, KY; *U.S. Public*, pg. 922

Solt, Russell E., Chief Fin. Officer, Sr. V.P.-Fin. & Sec.--Williams-Sonoma, Inc., San Francisco, CA; *U.S. Public*, pg. 1770

Somekh, Sasson, Sr. V.P.-Worldwide Prod. Oper.--Applied Materials, Inc., Santa Clara, CA; *U.S. Public*, pg. 123

Somerdyk, Harry, Sr. V.P.-Mktg. & Brand Devel.--Business Week, New York, NY; *U.S. Public*, pg. 1069

Somers, John W., Sr. V.P. & Branch Mgr.--DG Bank-Atlanta Branch, Atlanta, GA; *Int'l*, pg. 352

Somerville, Penelope F., Sr. V.P. & Corp. Controller--Bank of Montreal, Toronto, Canada; *Int'l*, pg. 153

Sommer, Regina, Chief Fin. Officer & Sr. V.P.--Open Market, Inc., Burlington, MA; *U.S. Public*, pg. 1226

Sommer, Zandra, Sr. V.P. & Exec. Media Dir.--WestWayne, Inc., Atlanta, GA; *U.S. Private*, pg. 1170

Sommerlatte, W. Tom, Sr. V.P.--Arthur D. Little, Inc., Cambridge, MA; *U.S. Private*, pg. 670

Sompolski, Timothy A., Sr. V.P.-Human Resources & Admin.--Philip Morris Companies Inc., New York, NY; *U.S. Public*, pg. 1287

Sondeno, Dudley J., Chief Tech. & Knowledge Officer & Sr. V.P.--Southwest Gas Corporation, Las Vegas, NV; *U.S. Public*, pg. 1493

Sondereker, John W., Sr. V.P.--Norwest Financial, Inc., Des Moines, IA; *U.S. Public*, pg. 1202

Sondey, Edward J., Sr. V.P.--Brooklyn Union, Brooklyn, NY; *U.S. Public*, pg. 259

Sondles, R.D., Sr. V.P.--Westfield Companies, Westfield Center, OH; *U.S. Private*, pg. 1169

Sone, Y., Sr. V.P.--Mitsubishi International Corporation, New York, NY; *Int'l*, pg. 871

Sonnabend, Stephen, Sr. V.P.--Sonesta International Hotels Corporation, Boston, MA; *U.S. Public*, pg. 1485

Sonneman, Ronald D., Sr. V.P. & Trust Officer--Shoreline Financial Corp., Benton Harbor, MI; *U.S. Public*, pg. 1467

Sonneman, Ronald D., Sr. V.P. & Trust Officer--Shoreline Bank, Benton Harbor, MI; *U.S. Public*, pg. 1468

Sonntag, Willi, Sr. V.P.-Adv. & Pub. Rels.--Commerzbank AG, Frankfurt, Germany; *Int'l*, pg. 308

Soper, Thomas, III, Sr. V.P.-Human Resources--Tambrands Inc., Cincinnati, OH; *U.S. Public*, pg. 1331

Sorensen, Robert, Sr. V.P.-Asset Mngmt.--TrizecHahn Centers Inc., San Diego, CA; *Int'l*, pg. 1425

Sorensen, Vagn, Sr. V.P.-Bus. Sys. Div.--Scandinavian Airlines System (SAS), Solna, Sweden; *Int'l*, pg. 1201

Sorenson, Arne M., Sr. V.P.-Bus. Devel. Marriott Lodging--Marriott International, Inc., Washington, DC; *U.S. Public*, pg. 1047

Sorenson, Max E., Sr. V.P-Engrng., Mfg. & Tech.--Geneva Steel, Vineyard, UT; *U.S. Public*, pg. 729

Soricelli, A., Sr. V.P.-Intl.--International Home Foods Inc., Parsippany, NJ; *U.S. Private*, pg. 526

Sorkenn, S.J., Sr. V.P.--Medical Economics Company Inc., Montvale, NJ; *U.S. Public*, pg. 1601

Sormani, Charles R., Sr. V.P.--Unioncare, Inc., Washington, DC; *U.S. Private*, pg. 1116

Sorsby, J. Larry, Chief Fin. Officer, Sr. V.P. & Treas.--Hovnanian Enterprises, Inc., Red Bank, NJ; *U.S. Public*, pg. 843

Sosson, George, Sr. V.P.-Opers.--Clear Channel Radio, Inc., Hamden, CT; *U.S. Public*, pg. 383

Sotir, Mark, Sr. V.P.-Mktg.--Budget Rent A Car Corporation, Lisle, IL; *U.S. Private*, pg. 178

Souder, Robert, Sr. V.P.-Labor Rels.--Rite Aid Corporation, Camp Hill, PA; *U.S. Public*, pg. 1390

Souders, Ronald L., Sr. V.P.--Advanta Insurance Companies, Horsham, PA; *U.S. Public*, pg. 22

Souquet, Jacques, Sr. V.P.-Prod. Generation--ATL Ultrasound, Inc., Bothell, WA; *U.S. Public*, pg. 11

Sourdiff, Gerald, Chief Fin. Officer & Sr. V.P.--Lutheran Brotherhood, Minneapolis, MN; *U.S. Private*, pg. 681

Sourdiff, Jerald, Sr. V.P. & Controller--Lutheran Brotherhood, Minneapolis, MN; *U.S. Private*, pg. 681

South, Hamilton, Sr. V.P.-Worldwide Commun. & New Projects--Polo/Ralph Lauren Corporation, New York, NY; *U.S. Private*, pg. 874

Southam, Arthur M., Sr. V.P.--Foundation Health Systems, Inc., Pueblo, CO; *U.S. Public*, pg. 678

Southam, Ted, Sr. V.P. & Gen. Mgr.-Entertainment Division--Shorewood Packaging Corporation of Canada, Ltd., Scarborough, Canada; *U.S. Public*, pg. 1468

Southern, Douglas G., Chief Fin. Officer & Sr. V.P.--Immunex Corporation, Seattle, WA; *U.S. Public*, pg. 871

Southern, Raymond C., Sr. V.P.--Centex-Rooney Construction Co., Inc., Fort Lauderdale, FL; *U.S. Public*, pg. 322

Southerst, Mark, Sr. V.P., Gen. Counsel & Sec.--Greyhound Lines, Inc., Dallas, TX; *U.S. Public*, pg. 765

Souza, Lawrence M., Sr. V.P.-Res.--Amgen Inc., Thousand Oaks, CA; *U.S. Public*, pg. 100

Sowden, Alfred F., Sr. V.P.-Acct. Mngmt.--Fair, Isaac and Company, Inc., San Rafael, CA; *U.S. Public*, pg. 609

Sowers, Brad, Sr. V.P.-Opers.--Memorex Telex Corp., Irving, TX; *Int'l*, pg. 857

Sowers, C. Martin, Sr. V.P.-Fin.--Family Dollar Stores, Inc., Matthews, NC; *U.S. Public*, pg. 612

Sowiak, Michael C., Sr. V.P.-Info. & Communication Services--First Financial Bank, FSB, Stevens Point, WI; *U.S. Public*, pg. 140

Sowinski, Frank, Chief Fin. Officer & Sr. V.P.--The Dun & Bradstreet Corporation, Murray Hill, NJ; *U.S. Public*, pg. 535

Spackman, Randall P., Sr. V.P. & Gen. Counsel--Opal Concepts, Inc., Anaheim, CA; *U.S. Private*, pg. 817

Spaeth, Sandy, Sr. V.P.-Mktg.--Parade Publications Inc., New York, NY; *U.S. Private*, pg. 20

Spahr, Parry E., Sr. V.P.-Stamford Region--People's Bank, Bridgeport, CT; *U.S. Public*, pg. 1274

Spain, William, Sr. V.P.-Res., Govt. Affairs & Indus. Rels.--Del Monte Foods, San Francisco, CA; *U.S. Private*, pg. 321

Spalding, Daniel L., Sr. V.P.--PacifiCorp, Portland, OR; *U.S. Public*, pg. 1251

Spalding, Jan, Sr. V.P. & Dir.-Mktg.--Harcourt Brace & Company - Elementary Div., Orlando, FL; *U.S. Public*, pg. 783

Spangler, John M., Sr. V.P.-Northeast Opers.--The JPM Company, Lewisburg, PA; *U.S. Public*, pg. 919

Spanne, Ingvar, Sr. V.P.-Engrng.--Vattenfall AB, Stockholm, Sweden; *Int'l*, pg. 1452

Spanninga, D.A., Sr. V.P.-Pre Production Svcs.--National Steel & Shipbuilding Company, San Diego, CA; *U.S. Private*, pg. 787

Sparkman, Steve, Sr. V.P.-Tech.--EvansGroup, Seattle, WA; *U.S. Private*, pg. 385

Sparkman, Steve, Sr. V.P.--EvansGroup Technology, Seattle, WA; *U.S. Private*, pg. 385

Sparks, James C., Sr. V.P. & Gen. Mgr.-Mdse.--Bradlees Inc., Braintree, MA; *U.S. Public*, pg. 249

Spaul, Michael, Sr. V.P. & Gen. Mgr.-Communicolor Div.--The Standard Register Company, Dayton, OH; *U.S. Public*, pg. 1505

Spayd, Sandra L., Sr. V.P. & Corp. Sec.--National Penn Bank, Boyertown, PA; *U.S. Public*, pg. 1159

Speaker, Joseph, Sr. V.P.-Fin. & Admin.--Rite Aid Corporation, Camp Hill, PA; *U.S. Public*, pg. 1390

Spears, R.N., Sr. V.P.--The Ziegler Companies, Inc., West Bend, WI; *U.S. Public*, pg. 1791

Spears, Robert, Sr. V.P.-Americas Group--Gateway 2000, North Sioux City, SD; *U.S. Public*, pg. 703

Spears, Stanhope S., Sr. V.P.-Bonds--Willis Corroon Corp. of South Carolina, Columbia, SC; *Int'l*, pg. 1507

Speck, Robert A., Sr. V.P.-Strategic Plng.--Shoney's, Inc., Nashville, TN; *U.S. Public*, pg. 1467

Spector, David, Sr. V.P.-Secondary Mktg./Loan Sales--Countrywide Funding Corporation, Pasadena, CA; *U.S. Public*, pg. 453

Spector, Elisabeth N., Sr. V.P.--Legg Mason, Inc., Baltimore, MD; *U.S. Public*, pg. 984

Spector, Howard B., Sr. V.P.-Govt. Affairs & Communications--Guardsmark, Inc., Memphis, TN; *U.S. Private*, pg. 486

Spector, James A., Sr. V.P.-Human Resources--Catherines Stores Corporation, Memphis, TN; *U.S. Public*, pg. 317

Spector, Paul, Chief Fin. Officer, Sr. V.P., Treas. & Sec.--Aris Industries, Inc., New York, NY; *U.S. Public*, pg. 129

Speed, James, Sr. V.P. & Controller--Hardee's Food Systems, Inc., Rocky Mount, NC; *U.S. Public*, pg. 278

Speirs, Jim, Chief Tech. Officer & Sr. V.P.-Network Opers.--USLD Communications Corp., San Antonio, TX; *U.S. Public*, pg. 969

Spell, Randy, Sr. V.P.-Sls.--Lorillard Tobacco Company, Greensboro, NC; *U.S. Public*, pg. 1011

Spellman, Richard A., Sr. V.P., Gen. Counsel & Sec.--Guarantee Life Insurance Co., Omaha, NE; *U.S. Public*, pg. 768

Spence, N. David, Sr. V.P. & Gen. Mgr.- Paper Div.--Boise Cascade Corporation, Boise, ID; *U.S. Public*, pg. 242

Spencer, Douglas C., Sr. V.P.-Branch Admin.--California State Bank, West Covina, CA; *U.S. Public*, pg. 294

Spencer, Gregory R., Chief Admin. Officer & Sr. V.P.--Equitable Resources, Inc., Pittsburgh, PA; *U.S. Public*, pg. 589

Spencer, J. Greg, Sr. V.P., Treas. & Asst. Sec.--American Stores Company, Salt Lake City, UT; *U.S. Public*, pg. 92

Spencer, James F., Sr. V.P.--Pell, Rudman & Company, Boston, MA; *U.S. Public*, pg. 1673

Spencer, John, Sr. V.P.--Cullen/Frost Bankers, Inc., San Antonio, TX; *U.S. Public*, pg. 467

Spencer, John A., Chief Fin. Officer & Sr. V.P.-Fin.--Del Webb Corporation, Phoenix, AZ; *U.S. Public*, pg. 494

Spencer, Kathelen, Sr. V.P. & Dir.-Corp. Communications--AFLAC Incorporated, Columbus, GA; *U.S. Public*, pg. 28

Spencer, Leroy, Chief Fin. Officer & Sr. V.P.--Jerell, Inc., Dallas, TX; *U.S. Private*, pg. 586

Spencer, R. Michael, Sr. V.P. & Treas.--PCA International, Inc., Matthews, NC; *U.S. Public*, pg. 1240

Spencer, Russell P., Sr. V.P.-Electronic Prepress Field Service--Bayer Corporation, Pittsburgh, PA; *Int'l*, pg. 172

Spendley, Christopher, Chief Fin. Officer & Sr. V.P.--Washington Homes, Inc., Landover, MD; *U.S. Public*, pg. 1741

Spengler, Tim, Sr. V.P. & Deputy Dir.--Western International Media Corporation, Los Angeles, CA; *U.S. Private*, pg. 1165

Spenser, Tom R., Sr. V.P.-Risk Mngmt.--The Toronto Dominion Bank, Toronto, Canada; *Int'l*, pg. 1401

Speranza, Ernest V., Sr. V.P.-Adv./Mktg.--Toys "R" Us United States, Paramus, NJ; *U.S. Public*, pg. 1626

Sperco, John J., Sr. V.P.-Consumer Sls. & Service--MCI Communications Corp., Atlanta, GA; *U.S. Public*, pg. 1023

Sperry, A.R., Sr. V.P. & Sec.--Royal Oak Enterprises, Inc., Atlanta, GA; *U.S. Private*, pg. 948

Spicer, Lloyd J., Sr. V.P. & Portfolio Mgr.--Fiduciary Management Associates, Inc., Chicago, IL; *U.S. Public*, pg. 1673

Spiegel-Solovay, Susan, Sr. V.P. & Grp. Creative Dir.--Grey Advertising Inc., New York, NY; *U.S. Public*, pg. 764

Spiegel, Edwin J., Sr. V.P. & Gen. Mgr.-MRT Energy Marketing Co.--Mississippi River Transmission, Saint Louis, MO; *U.S. Public*, pg. 843

Spiegelman, Jayne, Sr. V.P.-Mdsg.--The Good Guys, Inc., Brisbane, CA; *U.S. Public*, pg. 750

Spielberger, Ronald C., Sr. V.P.--JSB Financial, Lynbrook, NY; *U.S. Public*, pg. 919

Spies, Robert J., Sr. V.P.--Berol Corporation, Brentwood, TN; *U.S. Public*, pg. 1178

Spillane, Jim, Sr. V.P.-Sls.--Bell Sports Corp., San Jose, CA; *U.S. Public*, pg. 207

Spillard, Ernest J., Sr. V.P.-Fin.--Pool Energy Services Co., Houston, TX; *U.S. Public*, pg. 1316

Spina, John, Sr. V.P. & Controller--Sudler & Hennessey, New York, NY; *U.S. Private*, pg. 1197

Spindler, Garold R., Sr. V.P.--Cyprus Amax Minerals Company, Englewood, CO; *U.S. Public*, pg. 470

Spindler, George S., Sr. V.P.-Law & Corp. Affairs & Gen. Counsel--Amoco Corporation, Chicago, IL; *U.S. Public*, pg. 101

Spindler, Manfred, Sr. V.P.-Refining--Marathon Ashland Petroleum LLC, Findlay, OH; *U.S. Public*, pg. 139

Spinner, Robert, Sr. V.P.-Worldwide Sls.--Clarify Inc., San Jose, CA; *U.S. Public*, pg. 382

Spinney, Tracy, Sr. V.P.-Creative Services--Jordan, McGrath, Case & Taylor Inc., New York, NY; *U.S. Private*, pg. 598

Spires, Richard A., Sr. V.P. & Dir.-IBM Strategic Partnership--SRA International Inc., Arlington, VA; *U.S. Private*, pg. 957

Spitler, Michael C., Sr. V.P.--TCF Bank Illinois, Oak Brook, IL; *U.S. Public*, pg. 1554

Spittel, Steven, Sr. V.P. & Grp. Mngmt. Supvr.--Lowe McAdams Healthcare, New York, NY; *U.S. Private*, pg. 678

Splawnyk, Peter, Sr. V.P.-Energy Pricing & Regulatory Svcs.--American Electric Power Service Corp., Columbus, OH; *U.S. Public*, pg. 72

Spooler, John, Sr. V.P. & Dir. of Agencies--Academy Insurance Group, Inc., Alpharetta, GA; *Int'l*, pg. 27

Sprague, Clifford G., Chief Fin. Officer & Sr. V.P.--Kulicke & Soffa Industries, Inc., Willow Grove, PA; *U.S. Public*, pg. 968

Spraque, Jan, Sr. V.P.--Riggs National Corporation, Washington, DC; *U.S. Public*, pg. 1389

Spratlin, Rebecca W., Sr. V.P.--Foremost Insurance Co., Caledonia, MI; *U.S. Public*, pg. 667

Sprecher, Greg, Chief Fin. Officer & Sr. V.P.--Mauna Loa Resources Inc., Honolulu, HI; *U.S. Private*, pg. 191

Sprecher, Gregory A., Chief Fin. Officer & Sr. V.P.--Mauna Loa Macadamia Partners, L.P., Honolulu, HI; *U.S. Public*, pg. 1060

Spriesser, John R., Chief Fin. Officer, Sr. V.P. & Sec.--IDC Services, Inc., Chicago, IL; *U.S. Private*, pg. 554

Spriesser, Judith A., Chief Fin. Officer & Sr. V.P.--Sara Lee Corporation, Chicago, IL; *U.S. Public*, pg. 1432

Spring, Robert G., Sr. V.P.--Trustmark National Bank, Jackson, MS; *U.S. Public*, pg. 1643

Spring, Tony, Sr. V.P.-Mktg.--Bloomingdale's, New York, NY; *U.S. Public*, pg. 617

Springer, Anna Marie, Sr. V.P.-Retail Lending--American Savings Bank, F.S.B., Honolulu, HI; *U.S. Public*, pg. 800

Springer, Denis E., Chief Fin. Officer & Sr. V.P.--Burlington Northern Santa Fe Corporation, Fort Worth, TX; *U.S. Public*, pg. 268
Springer, Gordon, Sr. V.P.--Imperial Bank, Inglewood, CA; *U.S. Public*, pg. 871
Springer, Paul, Sr. V.P. & Asst. Gen. Counsel--Paramount Pictures Corporation, Los Angeles, CA; *U.S. Private*, pg. 776
Springs, Leonard F., Sr. V.P.--First Union Corporation, Charlotte, NC; *U.S. Public*, pg. 639
Sproule, Martha S., Sr. V.P.--Rothschild Inc., New York, NY; *U.S. Private*, pg. 947
Sprowl, David C., Sr. V.P. & Southwestern Regl. Mgr.--A.G. Edwards & Sons, Inc., Saint Louis, MO; *U.S. Public*, pg. 565
Sprowls, Robert J., Chief Fin. Officer & Sr. V.P.--QST Enterprises Inc., Peoria, IL; *U.S. Public*, pg. 367
Spruell, Jim, Sr. V.P. & Exec. Creative Dir.--Austin Kelley Advertising, Inc., Atlanta, GA; *U.S. Private*, pg. 100
Sprung, Raymond W., Sr. V.P.--Hibernia Corporation, New Orleans, LA; *U.S. Public*, pg. 825
Spurlock, Rick L., Sr. V.P.-Human Resources & Admin. Services--NorAm Energy Corp., Houston, TX; *U.S. Public*, pg. 843
Spurlock, Ted L., Sr. V.P. & Dir.-Fin. Services & Govt. Rels.--JC Penney Company, Inc., Plano, TX; *U.S. Public*, pg. 916
Squires, Vernon T., Sr. V.P. & Gen. Counsel--The ServiceMaster Company, Downers Grove, IL; *U.S. Public*, pg. 1461
Srisukphun, Hatta, Sr. V.P.--Siam City Bank Public Company Limited, Bangkok, Thailand; *Int'l*, pg. 1239
Srsic, Edward P., Jr., Sr. V.P.-Private Label--Farah U.S.A., Inc., El Paso, TX; *U.S. Public*, pg. 613
St. Clair, Richard G., Sr. V.P.--BT Financial Corporation, Johnstown, PA; *U.S. Public*, pg. 163
St. Clair, Thomas M., Chief Fin. Officer & Sr. V.P.--Phelps Dodge Corporation, Phoenix, AZ; *U.S. Public*, pg. 1286
St. Clare, Mark S., Chief Fin. Officer, Sr. V.P.-Fin. & Sec.--FileNet Corporation, Costa Mesa, CA; *U.S. Public*, pg. 622
St. Germain, Thomas A., Chief Fin. Officer & Sr. V.P.--Summa Four, Inc., Manchester, NH; *U.S. Public*, pg. 1527
St. Jean, David, Sr. V.P.--Jefferies & Company, Inc., Los Angeles, CA; *U.S. Public*, pg. 925
St. John, Cheryl L., Sr. V.P.-Credit Bureau & Solicitation--Fair, Isaac and Company, Inc., San Rafael, CA; *U.S. Public*, pg. 609
St. John, Julie, Sr. V.P.-Transaction, Processing & Mngmt. Systems--Federal National Mortgage Association (Fannie Mae), Washington, DC; *U.S. Public*, pg. 615
St. John, N. Kay, Sr. V.P.-Natl., Intl. & Correspondent Banking--Hibernia Corporation, New Orleans, LA; *U.S. Public*, pg. 825
St. Pe, Gerald J., Sr. V.P. & Pres.-Ingalls Shipbuilding--Litton Industries, Inc., Woodland Hills, CA; *U.S. Public*, pg. 1002
Staack, Craig F., Sr. V.P.-Mktg.--Heilig-Meyers Company, Richmond, VA; *U.S. Public*, pg. 804
Stablein, Larry, Sr. V.P.-Mktg.--Jewel-Osco, Melrose Park, IL; *U.S. Public*, pg. 93
Stacey, Gary, Sr. V.P.-Res. & Devel. & Tech. Assessment--Haemonetics Corporation, Braintree, MA; *U.S. Public*, pg. 773
Stacey, Steve, Sr. V.P.--Century Business Credit Corporation, New York, NY; *U.S. Private*, pg. 225
Staciokas, Leon J., Sr. V.P.-Opers. & Chief Internal Oper. Officer--Iomega Corporation, Roy, UT; *U.S. Public*, pg. 912
Stack, Pat, Sr. V.P.-Mktg.--BTI Americas, Inc., Northbrook, IL; *U.S. Private*, pg. 108
Stackpole, Earle, Sr. V.P.--New York Carpet World, Dalton, GA; *U.S. Public*, pg. 1464
Stade, Yngve, Sr. V.P.-Res. & Devel.--Stora Kopparbergs Bergslags AB, Falun, Sweden; *Int'l*, pg. 1302
Stadlen, Diane E., Sr. V.P. & Mktg. Analysis & Media Services Dir.--Creswell, Munsell, Fultz & Zirbel, L.P., Cedar Rapids, IA; *U.S. Private*, pg. 1197
Staggs, Thomas O., Sr. V.P-Strategic Plng.--The Walt Disney Company, Burbank, CA; *U.S. Public*, pg. 511
Stahl, Francis, Sr. V.P.-Light Comml. Vehicles Div.--Renault, Boulogne-Billancourt, France; *Int'l*, pg. 1102
Stahle, Phyllis, Sr. V.P.-Adv.--BayBanks, Inc., Boston, MA; *U.S. Public*, pg. 184
Stahlin, Paul V., Sr. V.P.--Summit Bancorp, Princeton, NJ; *U.S. Public*, pg. 1527
Staines, Michael L., Sr. V.P. & Sec.--Resource America, Inc., Philadelphia, PA; *U.S. Public*, pg. 1382
Stait-Gardner, Zane, Sr. V.P. & Gen. Mgr.-Reinsurance Opers.--Manulife Financial (The Manufacturers Life Insurance Company), Toronto, Canada; *Int'l*, pg. 840
Staker, Thomas, Sr. V.P.-Opers.--Big O Tires Incorporated, Englewood, CO; *U.S. Public*, pg. 1553
Stalberg, Lars A., Sr. V.P.-Corp. Rels.--Telefonaktiebolaget LM Ericsson, Stockholm, Sweden; *Int'l*, pg. 1363
Stalder, Dennis, Sr. V.P.-Wholesale Opers.--Associated Grocers, Inc., Seattle, WA; *U.S. Private*, pg. 90
Staley, Craig, Sr. V.P. & Grp. Acct. Dir.--Wickersham Hunt Schwantner, Boston, MA; *U.S. Private*, pg. 84
Staley, Douglas G., Sr. V.P.--Hibernia Corporation, New Orleans, LA; *U.S. Public*, pg. 825
Staluppi, Joseph, Sr. V.P. & Sr. Art Dir.--DMB&B New York, New York, NY; *U.S. Private*, pg. 302
Stalzer, Robert J., Sr. V.P.-Admin., Fin., Treas. & Asst. Sec.--Servo Corporation of America, Westbury, NY; *U.S. Private*, pg. 987
Stamatis, Jim, Sr. V.P.-Devel.--W.M. Grace Development, Phoenix, AZ; *U.S. Private*, pg. 468
Stampone, Frederick A., Chief Admin. Officer, Sr. V.P. & Sec.--The Pep Boys-Manny, Moe & Jack, Philadelphia, PA; *U.S. Public*, pg. 1276
Stamy, Lloyd F., Jr., Sr. V.P.--C.S. McKee & Company, Inc., Pittsburgh, PA; *U.S. Public*, pg. 1673
Standen, Craig C., Sr. V.P.-Corp. Devel.--The E.W. Scripps Company, Cincinnati, OH; *U.S. Public*, pg. 1447
Stander, Joe W., Sr. V.P. & Controller--Colorado National Bankshares, Inc., Denver, CO; *U.S. Public*, pg. 1680
Standish, Myles E., Sr. V.P. & Gen. Counsel--Oakwood Homes Corporation, Greensboro, NC; *U.S. Public*, pg. 1209
Standish, T., Sr. V.P.-Distr. Opers.--Houston Lighting & Power Company, Houston, TX; *U.S. Public*, pg. 843
Standler, Stephen F., Sr. V.P.-Law--National Broadcasting Co., Inc., New York, NY; *U.S. Public*, pg. 712
Standley, John, Chief Fin. Officer & Sr. V.P.--Ralphs Grocery Company, Compton, CA; *U.S. Private*, pg. 1202
Staneisce, Keith, Sr. V.P.--Barr & Barr, Inc., New York, NY; *U.S. Private*, pg. 117
Stanek, John G., Chief Fin. Officer & Sr. V.P.--Burrell Communications Group Inc., Chicago, IL; *U.S. Private*, pg. 188
Stanford, Donald L., Sr. V.P.-Tech.--GTECH Corporation, West Greenwich, RI; *U.S. Public*, pg. 767
Stang, Sandy, Sr. V.P.-Opers.--National Card Control, Inc., Crozier, VA; *U.S. Public*, pg. 321
Stange, R., Sr. V.P.--Yamaha Corporation of America, Buena Park, CA; *Int'l*, pg. 1516
Stangel, Michael, Sr. V.P.-Professional Div.--Alberto-Culver Company, Melrose Park, IL; *U.S. Public*, pg. 37
Staniar, Linda B., Sr. V.P.-Corp. Communications, Adv. & Video Systems--New York Life Insurance Company, New York, NY; *U.S. Private*, pg. 794
Stanley, A. Jack, Sr. V.P. & Pres.-Engrg. & Construction Group--Dresser Industries, Inc., Dallas, TX; *U.S. Public*, pg. 528
Stanley, Curt, Sr. V.P.-Distributor Rels.--Zee Medical, Inc., Irvine, CA; *U.S. Public*, pg. 1073
Stanley, G. Brent, Sr. V.P.-H.R.--PG&E Corporation, San Francisco, CA; *U.S. Public*, pg. 1240
Stanley, J. Ronald, Sr. V.P.-Data Processing--Amvestors Financial Corporation, Topeka, KS; *U.S. Private*, pg. 59
Stanley, James R., Sr. V.P.--Howmet Corporation, Greenwich, CT; *U.S. Private*, pg. 213
Stanley, James R., Sr. V.P.--Howmet Corporation, Greenwich, CT; *U.S. Public*, pg. 1597
Stanley, Joe, Sr. V.P. & Brdcst. Production Dir.--Dailey & Associates, West Hollywood, CA; *U.S. Public*, pg. 909
Stanley, Neal A., Sr. V.P.-Western Region--Forest Oil Corporation, Denver, CO; *U.S. Public*, pg. 670
Stanley, Richard L., Sr. V.P. & Gen. Mgr.-Automotive Systems--Delco Remy America, Inc., Anderson, IN; *U.S. Public*, pg. 495
Stanley, Ron, Sr. V.P. & Gen. Mgr.--Royal Bank of Canada, London, United Kingdom; *Int'l*, pg. 1131
Stannard, Charles I., Sr. V.P. & Plng. Dir.--DMB&B Detroit, Troy, MI; *U.S. Private*, pg. 302
Stanner, H. Kent, Sr. V.P.--IMG, Cleveland, OH; *U.S. Private*, pg. 555
Stansifer, William E., Chief Credit Policy Officer & Sr. V.P.--FirstMerit Corporation, Akron, OH; *U.S. Public*, pg. 646
Stanziale, Ronald C., Chief Fin. Officer & Sr. V.P.--Willis Faber North America, Inc.-New York, New York, NY; *Int'l*, pg. 1503
Staple, Peter, Sr. V.P. & Gen. Counsel--Alza Corporation, Palo Alto, CA; *U.S. Public*, pg. 62
Staples, Chris, Sr. V.P. & Sr. Creative Dir.--Palmer Jarvis Communications, Vancouver, Canada; *Int'l*, pg. 1022
Staples, Patricia J., Sr. V.P.-Mktg.--Community First Bankshares, Inc., Fargo, ND; *U.S. Public*, pg. 416
Stapleton, Ray, Sr. V.P. & Gen. Mgr.-Enterprising Service Solutions Div.--Genicom Corporation, Chantilly, VA; *U.S. Public*, pg. 729
Stapleton, Thomas L., Sr. V.P. & Tax Dir.--Metropolitan Life Insurance Co., New York, NY; *U.S. Private*, pg. 737
Stark, Eliot R., Sr. V.P.-Mergers & Acquistions & Strategic & Corp. Plng.--Compuware Corporation, Farmington Hills, MI; *U.S. Public*, pg. 423
Stark, Joel, Sr. V.P.-Mktg. & Devel.--Providence Journal-Bulletin, Providence, RI; *U.S. Public*, pg. 209
Stark, Leslie J., Sr. V.P. & Exec. Producer--DMB&B New York, New York, NY; *U.S. Private*, pg. 302
Stark, Linda S., Sr. V.P.-Deposit Opers.--National Penn Bank, Boyertown, PA; *U.S. Public*, pg. 1159
Stark, W., Sr. V.P., Gen. Counsel & Sec.--ESCO Electronics Corporation, Saint Louis, MO; *U.S. Public*, pg. 546
Starkey, James H., III, Sr. V.P.--Universal Leaf Tobacco Company, Inc., Richmond, VA; *U.S. Public*, pg. 1694
Starkman, Ronald P., Sr. V.P. & Treas.--Borden, Inc., Columbus, OH; *U.S. Private*, pg. 157
Starks, Richard, Sr. V.P.-Sls. & Mktg.--The Dallas Morning News, Inc., Dallas, TX; *U.S. Public*, pg. 209
Starr, Denny, Sr. V.P.-Fin.--Central Tractor Farm & Country, Inc., Des Moines, IA; *U.S. Private*, pg. 237
Starr, James L., Chief Fin. Officer, Sr. V.P. & Treas.--Sierra Health Services, Inc., Las Vegas, NV; *U.S. Public*, pg. 1469
Startari, Edward, Sr. V.P.-Opers.--Bacharach Inc., Pittsburgh, PA; *U.S. Private*, pg. 109
Stashower, Sara E., Sr. V.P. & Gen. Mgr.-Consulting--Liggett-Stashower, Inc., Cleveland, OH; *U.S. Private*, pg. 667
Statham, Peter B., Sr. V.P.-Corp. Devel.--The Flood Company, Hudson, OH; *U.S. Private*, pg. 414
Stathers, Richard N., Sr. V.P.-Sls. & Mktg.--Centennial Technologies, Inc., Wilmington, MA; *U.S. Public*, pg. 322
Statler, Benjamin, Sr. V.P.--Consolidated Coal Co., Moundsville, WV; *U.S. Public*, pg. 531
Statler, Benjamin, Sr. V.P.-Mining--Consolidation Coal Co.-Eastern Region, Washington, PA; *U.S. Public*, pg. 531
Stattin-Jellheden, Birgit A., Sr. V.P.-Worldwide Prod. Devel.--Pharmacia & Upjohn, Inc., Windsor, United Kingdom; *Int'l*, pg. 1047
Staubitz, Arthur, Sr. V.P. & Gen. Counsel--Baxter International Inc., Deerfield, IL; *U.S. Public*, pg. 196
Stauder, Michael, Sr. V.P.-Fin. Institutions--Bayerische Landesbank, Munich, Germany; *Int'l*, pg. 176
Stavro, William, Sr. V.P. & Treas.--Mattel, Inc., El Segundo, CA; *U.S. Public*, pg. 1057
Stawarz, Raymond R., Sr. V.P., Dir.-Corp. Acctg. & Asst. Treas. & Asst. Sec.--Federated Mutual Insurance Company, Owatonna, MN; *U.S. Private*, pg. 399
Stebbins, Byron H., Sr. V.P.-Market Devel.--Newell Co., Freeport, IL; *U.S. Public*, pg. 1176
Stebbins, Paul, Sr. V.P.--International Recovery Corp., Miami Springs, FL; *U.S. Public*, pg. 906
Stec, John, Sr. V.P.-Real Estate--Fabri-Centers of America, Inc., Hudson, OH; *U.S. Public*, pg. 609
Steckiel, Richard E., Sr. V.P.-Trust--Citizens Savings Bank, Providence, RI; *Int'l*, pg. 1132
Steed, Michael R., Sr. V.P.-Investments--ULLICO Inc., Washington, DC; *U.S. Private*, pg. 1115
Steel, Gordon M., Chief Fin. Officer & Sr. V.P.-Fin.--Xilinx, Inc., San Jose, CA; *U.S. Public*, pg. 1786
Steele, Christine, Sr. V.P.--Asher/Gould Advertising, Inc., Los Angeles, CA; *U.S. Private*, pg. 88
Steele, Donald F., Sr. V.P.-Employee Rels.--The Hertz Corporation, Park Ridge, NJ; *U.S. Public*, pg. 664
Steele, Frank C., Sr. V.P.-Sls.--Airborne Freight Corporation, Seattle, WA; *U.S. Public*, pg. 32
Steele, George, Sr. V.P.-Mktg.--Rollerblade, Inc., Minnetonka, MN; *U.S. Private*, pg. 941
Steele, Michael A., Sr. V.P. & Gen. Mgr.--Destination Products International, Inc., Toronto, Canada; *Int'l*, pg. 338
Steele, Richard A., Sr. V.P.-Sls. & Mktg.--Printronix, Inc., Irvine, CA; *U.S. Public*, pg. 1329
Steenbergen, Leo, Chief Fin. Officer & Corp V.P.-Fin. & Admin.--N.V. Bekaert S.A., Kortrijk, Belgium; *Int'l*, pg. 183
Steenblick, R. James, Sr. V.P. & Mgr.-Personal Trust Div.--First Security Bank of Utah, N.A., Salt Lake City, UT; *U.S. Public*, pg. 637
Steeneck, Lee R., Sr. V.P.--General Reinsurance Corp., Stamford, CT; *U.S. Public*, pg. 725
Steenland, Douglas, Sr. V.P. & Gen. Counsel--Northwest Airlines Corp., Saint Paul, MN; *U.S. Public*, pg. 1199
Steep, John D., Sr. V.P.-Banking Opers./Metro Toronto & Eastern Canada--CT Financial Services, Inc., Toronto, Canada; *Int'l*, pg. 112
Steeves, Sheldon B., Sr. V.P.-Exploration--Renaissance Energy Ltd., Calgary, Canada; *Int'l*, pg. 1102
Stefanski, Stan, Sr. V.P. & Bus. Affairs & Admin. Dir.--Young & Rubicam New York, New York, NY; *U.S. Private*, pg. 1198
Steffel, Robert C., Sr. V.P.--Medicus Systems Corporation, Evanston, IL; *U.S. Public*, pg. 1080
Steffey, Stewart H., Jr., Sr. V.P.--Liberty Mutual Insurance Co., Boston, MA; *U.S. Private*, pg. 666
Stegemoller, David C., Sr. V.P.--Harvard Industries, Inc., Tampa, FL; *U.S. Public*, pg. 796
Steger, Robert B., Sr. V.P.-Gas Bus. Unit--Long Island Lighting Company, Hicksville, NY; *U.S. Public*, pg. 1013
Steigman, Don S., Sr. V.P.-Florida Reg.--Tenet Healthcare Corporation, Santa Barbara, CA; *U.S. Public*, pg. 1576
Stein, C.L., Sr. V.P.--Palm Beach Div.-Florida Public Utilites, West Palm Beach, FL; *U.S. Public*, pg. 655
Stein, Charles L., Sr. V.P.--Florida Public Utilities Company, West Palm Beach, FL; *U.S. Public*, pg. 655
Stein, Jay A., Sr. V.P. & Dir.-Technical--Hologic, Inc., Waltham, MA; *U.S. Public*, pg. 831
Stein, Jean B., Sr. V.P.--CSW Leasing, Inc., Dallas, TX; *U.S. Public*, pg. 324
Stein, Stan, Sr. V.P. & Mng. Dir.--DMB&B Public Relations, Troy, MI; *U.S. Private*, pg. 303
Steinbeck, Gary, Sr. V.P. & Fin. Dir.--Active International, Pearl River, NY; *U.S. Private*, pg. 15
Steinberg, Dennis P., Sr. V.P.--PacifiCorp, Portland, OR; *U.S. Public*, pg. 1251
Steinberg, Howard E., Sr. V.P., Sec. & Gen. Counsel--Reliance Group Holdings, Inc., New York, NY; *U.S. Public*, pg. 1374
Steinberg, Robert, Sr. V.P.--Summit Bancorp, Princeton, NJ; *U.S. Public*, pg. 1527
Steinberg, Selwyn, Sr. V.P.-Adv.--Slant/Fin Corporation, Greenvale, NY; *U.S. Private*, pg. 1005
Steiner, Eric I., Sr. V.P.--Banner Aerospace, Inc., Washington, DC; *U.S. Public*, pg. 187
Steiner, H., Sr. V.P.-Quality Certification, United Kingdom--SGS Societe Generale de Surveillance Holding S.A., Geneva, Switzerland; *Int'l*, pg. 1153
Steinig, Stephen N., Sr. V.P. & Chief Actuary--New York Life Insurance Company, New York, NY; *U.S. Private*, pg. 794
Steinman, Mark C., Chief Fin Officer & Sr. V.P.--Spar Aerospace Limited, Toronto, Canada; *Int'l*, pg. 1287
Steinmeyer, Jim, Sr. V.P.-Mktg.--Oakwood Homes Corporation, Greensboro, NC; *U.S. Public*, pg. 1209
Stejskal, William R., Sr. V.P.-Buntin Marketing Services--The Buntin Group, Nashville, TN; *U.S. Private*, pg. 181
Stelmach, Orest B., Sr. V.P. & Chief Investment Officer--TIG Holdings, Inc., New York, NY; *U.S. Public*, pg. 1555
Stenson, James F., Sr. V.P.-Facilities & Svcs.--Metropolitan Life Insurance Co., New York, NY; *U.S. Private*, pg. 737
Stepenson, Todd R., Chief Fin. Officer, Sr. V.P. & Treas.--American States Insurance Companies, Indianapolis, IN; *U.S. Public*, pg. 997
Stephan, John, Sr. V.P. & Mgr.-Sls. & Svc.--Great Western Financial Corporation, Chatsworth, CA; *U.S. Public*, pg. 1741
Stephan, Richard W., Chief Info. Officer & Sr. V.P.--Westcorp, Irvine, CA; *U.S. Public*, pg. 1756
Stephas, Gus, Sr. V.P. & Controller--CBL & Associates Properties, Inc., Chattanooga, TN; *U.S. Public*, pg. 273
Stephen, Michael A., Sr. V.P.--Aetna Inc., Hartford, CT; *U.S. Public*, pg. 26
Stephens, Chad, Sr. V.P.-Mid Continent--Lomak Petroleum Inc., Fort Worth, TX; *U.S. Public*, pg. 1012
Stephens, G. Martin, Sr. V.P.--Golden Gem Growers Inc., Umatilla, FL; *U.S. Private*, pg. 460

Stephens, Joseph M., Chief Fin. Officer, Sr. V.P. & Treas.--Centex-Rodgers Construction Company, Nashville, TN; *U.S. Public*, pg. 322

Stephens, Philip, Chief Oper. Officer-Surety & Sr. V.P.--SAFECO Property & Casualty Insurance Companies, Seattle, WA; *U.S. Public*, pg. 1423

Stephens, Suzann M., Sr. V.P.--Reistertown Federal Savings Bank, Baltimore, MD; *U.S. Public*, pg. 1543

Stephenson, Bob, Sr. V.P.-Opers.--PACCAR Automotive Inc., Renton, WA; *U.S. Public*, pg. 1247

Stephenson, R.L., Sr. V.P.-Sls. & Mktg.--Resco Products, Inc., Conshohocken, PA; *U.S. Private*, pg. 924

Stephenson, Robert, Grp. Pres.-Mainframes & Computer Chips, Grp. Exec. & Sr. V.P.--International Business Machines Corporation, Armonk, NY; *U.S. Public*, pg. 895

Stephenson, Roger T., Sr. V.P.--M & I First National Bank, West Bend, WI; *U.S. Public*, pg. 1050

Stephenson, Vivian M., Chief Information Officer & Sr. V.P.--Dayton Hudson Corporation, Minneapolis, MN; *U.S. Public*, pg. 489

Sterling, Charlotte B., Sr. V.P.-Corp. Rels.--Marriott International, Inc., Washington, DC; *U.S. Public*, pg. 1047

Sterling, Michael W., Sr. V.P. & Chief Technology Officer--Cimlinc Incorporated, Itasca, IL; *U.S. Private*, pg. 239

Stern, Brian E., Sr. V.P. & Pres.-Office Documents Product Group--Xerox Corporation, Stamford, CT; *U.S. Public*, pg. 1783

Stern, Frederick H., Sr. V.P.-Corp. Communications--Associates First Capital Corporation, Dallas, TX; *U.S. Public*, pg. 662

Stern, Neal M., Sr. V.P.-Acctg.--USLIFE Corporation, New York, NY; *U.S. Public*, pg. 77

Sternheimer, Ross, Chief Fin. Officer & Sr. V.P.--Sternheimer Brothers Inc., Sandston, VA; *U.S. Private*, pg. 1042

Sterns, J.B., Sr. V.P. & Natl. Dir.-Health Care Fin.--Ziegler Securities Division, Chicago, IL; *U.S. Public*, pg. 1792

Sterstein, David, Sr. V.P.--Edelman Worldwide, Inc., New York, NY; *U.S. Private*, pg. 362

Stertz, John, Sr. V.P. & Creative Dir.--Fahlgren, Tampa, FL; *U.S. Private*, pg. 391

Steuber, Frederick G., Sr. V.P., Gen. Counsel & Sec.--The Lincoln Electric Company, Cleveland, OH; *U.S. Public*, pg. 996

Steuert, D. Michael, Chief Fin. Officer & Sr. V.P.--GenCorp Inc., Fairlawn, OH; *U.S. Public*, pg. 705

Stevens, David C., Sr. V.P.-Insured Portfolio Mngmt. Dept.--Municipal Bond Investors Assurance Corporation, Armonk, NY; *U.S. Public*, pg. 1023

Stevens, David W., Sr. V.P.-Opers.--Southern Union Company, Austin, TX; *U.S. Public*, pg. 1491

Stevens, M. Brent, Sr. V.P.--Jefferies & Company, Inc., Los Angeles, CA; *U.S. Public*, pg. 925

Stevens, Michael, Sr. V.P.-Leasing--Forest City Commercial Construction Company, Inc., Cleveland, OH; *U.S. Public*, pg. 668

Stevens, Paul E., Sr. V.P.-Mktg.--Matson Navigation Company, Inc., San Francisco, CA; *U.S. Public*, pg. 39

Stevens, Sandra K., Sr. V.P.-Human Resources--Haggar Corporation, Dallas, TX; *U.S. Public*, pg. 774

Stevens, Vince, Sr. V.P.--Orkin Exterminating Co., Inc., Atlanta, GA; *U.S. Public*, pg. 1404

Stevenson, Allan J., Chief Fin. Officer, Sr. V.P. & Controller--Parsons Brinckerhoff Inc., New York, NY; *U.S. Private*, pg. 841

Stevenson, R.H., Sr. V.P.-Sls. & Mktg.--North State Pyrophyllite, Greensboro, NC; *U.S. Private*, pg. 924

Stever, Bernard G., Sr. V.P.-Global Devel.--The Middleby Corporation, Rolling Meadows, IL; *U.S. Public*, pg. 1109

Steves, Susan S., Sr. V.P. & Mgr.-Securities Grp.--ABN-AMRO North America Inc., Chicago, Chicago, IL; *Int'l*, pg. 10

Stewart, Charles R., Sr. V.P.-Intl. Bus. & Tech. Devel.--Ball Packaging Holdings Corp., Westminster, CO; *U.S. Public*, pg. 171

Stewart, Donald S., Sr. V.P.-Trust & Investment Services--Tompkins County Trust Company, Ithaca, NY; *U.S. Public*, pg. 1621

Stewart, Glen L., Sr. V.P.-Trans Pacific--Hawaiian Airlines, Inc., Honolulu, HI; *U.S. Public*, pg. 799

Stewart, Gordon, Sr. V.P.--Construction Specialties, Inc., Cranford, NJ; *U.S. Private*, pg. 266

Stewart, H. Malcolm, Sr. V.P.-Construcion--Camden Property Trust, Houston, TX; *U.S. Public*, pg. 298

Stewart, Hugh, Sr. V.P.-Bus. Opers.--Bliss-Salem, Inc., Salem, OH; *U.S. Private*, pg. 149

Stewart, John M., Sr. V.P.--Brookfield Homes California Inc., Santa Ana, CA; *Int'l*, pg. 228

Stewart, Lee M., Sr. V.P.-Energy Transportation Services--Southern California Gas Co., Los Angeles, CA; *U.S. Public*, pg. 1249

Stewart, Mary M., Sr. V.P.--Total System Services, Inc., Columbus, GA; *U.S. Public*, pg. 1550

Stewman, Paul H., Sr. V.P.--Chubb & Son, Inc., Warren, NJ; *U.S. Public*, pg. 355

Sthika, Ellen, Sr. V.P.-Mdsg. & Designing--Kleinert's, Inc., of Alabama, Elba, AL; *U.S. Private*, pg. 625

Stibich, Donald C., Sr. V.P.-Paper Sls.--Longview Fibre Company, Longview, WA; *U.S. Public*, pg. 1013

Stickelmaier, Chuck, Sr. V.P.-Mfg.--Prince Golf International, Bordentown, NJ; *U.S. Private*, pg. 884

Stidham, Reese M., III, Sr. V.P. & Dir.--The Robinson-Humphrey Company, Inc., Atlanta, GA; *U.S. Public*, pg. 1633

Stigi, Peter, Sr. V.P.-Sls. & Mktg.--Tuscan/Lehigh Dairies LP, Union, NJ; *U.S. Public*, pg. 1110

Stigler, David M., Sr. V.P.-Legal & Pub. Affairs, Gen. Counsel & Sec.--ADVO, Inc., Windsor, CT; *U.S. Public*, pg. 23

Stiglitz, Joseph E., Sr. V.P. & Chief Economist--The World Bank, Washington, DC; *U.S. Private*, pg. 1188

Still, John T., III, Sr. V.P.-Corp. Devel.--Jefferson-Pilot Corporation, Greensboro, NC; *U.S. Public*, pg. 925

Stillings, John, Chief Lending Officer & Sr. V.P.--Nevada State Bank, Las Vegas, NV; *U.S. Public*, pg. 1793

Stillo, John F., Sr. V.P.-Corp. Fin.--Associates First Capital Corporation, Dallas, TX; *U.S. Public*, pg. 662

Stillo, John F., Sr. V.P.--Associates Commercial Corporation, Dallas, TX; *U.S. Public*, pg. 663

Stimpert, Michael A., Sr. V.P.-Plng. & Admin.--Gold Kist, Inc., Atlanta, GA; *U.S. Private*, pg. 459

Stimpson, William Sandy, Chief Fin. Officer & Sr. V.P.--Gulf Lumber Company, Inc., Mobile, AL; *U.S. Private*, pg. 487

Stinnett, Wayne D., Jr., Chief Fin. Officer & Sr. V.P.--Entex, Houston, TX; *U.S. Public*, pg. 843

Stinson, Greg, Sr. V.P.-Mktg.--Ruppman Marketing Technologies, Inc., Peoria, IL; *U.S. Private*, pg. 951

Stirling, Karon, Sr. V.P. & Client Svcs. Dir.--Promotion House, San Francisco, CA; *U.S. Private*, pg. 1166

Stith, Andrew W., Sr. V.P.-Sls. & Mktg.--NovaCare Employee Services, Inc., Norristown, PA; *U.S. Public*, pg. 1203

Stockdale, William, Sr. V.P.--The Hartford Steam Boiler Inspection & Insurance Co., Hartford, CT; *U.S. Public*, pg. 795

Stocker, Jeff, Sr. V.P. & Creative Dir.--Mars Advertising Co., Southfield, MI; *U.S. Private*, pg. 706

Stockman, David E., Sr. V.P.-Opers.--Lawry's Restaurants, Inc., Pasadena, CA; *U.S. Private*, pg. 654

Stockton, Bryan, V.P. & Gen. Mgr.--Oscar Mayer Foods Corp., Madison, WI; *U.S. Public*, pg. 1288

Stoddard-Smith, Janis E., Sr. V.P.-Claims--American States Insurance Companies, Indianapolis, IN; *U.S. Public*, pg. 997

Stodder, John, Sr. V.P.--Edelman Worldwide, Inc., Los Angeles, CA; *U.S. Private*, pg. 362

Stoeckel, Howard, Sr. V.P.-Mktg.--Wawa, Inc., Media, PA; *U.S. Private*, pg. 1155

Stoecker, M., Sr. V.P.--Serigraph, Inc., West Bend, WI; *U.S. Private*, pg. 985

Stoehr, Charles M., Chief Fin. Officer & Sr. V.P.--Audiovox Corporation, Hauppauge, NY; *U.S. Public*, pg. 147

Stoelk, Thomas W., Chief Fin. Officer & Sr. V.P.-Fin. & Admin.--Lomak Petroleum Inc., Fort Worth, TX; *U.S. Public*, pg. 1012

Stoffel, George F., Sr. V.P. & Mgr.-Casualty Clash/High Excess--NAC Reinsurance Corporation, Greenwich, CT; *U.S. Public*, pg. 1144

Stoffel, George F., Sr. V.P.--Greenwich Insurance Company, Greenwich, CT; *U.S. Public*, pg. 1144

Stoffel, George F., Sr. V.P.--Indian Harbor Insurance Company, Greenwich, CT; *U.S. Public*, pg. 1144

Stohler, Robert, Sr. V.P.-Intl. Grp.--The Scotts Company, Marysville, OH; *U.S. Public*, pg. 1446

Stokes, Burt, Chief Fin. Officer & Sr. V.P.-Corp. Services--Rochester Gas And Electric Corporation, Rochester, NY; *U.S. Public*, pg. 1395

Stokes, George Ann, Sr. V.P. & Gen. Counsel--The Minute Maid Company, Houston, TX; *U.S. Public*, pg. 392

Stokes, Joseph C., Jr., Chief Fin. Officer & Sr. V.P.--Life Technologies, Inc., Rockville, MD; *U.S. Public*, pg. 504

Stokes, T. Andrew, Sr. V.P.-Corp. Devel.--Nationwide Health Properties Inc., Newport Beach, CA; *U.S. Public*, pg. 1166

Stolarz, Michael, Sr. V.P.-Sls.--The Great Atlantic & Pacific Tea Company, Inc., Montvale, NJ; *Int'l*, pg. 1375

Stolberg, Phil, Sr. V.P.--Grizzard, Atlanta, GA; *U.S. Private*, pg. 482

Stolberg, Phil, Sr. V.P.--Grizzard/Los Angeles, Los Angeles, CA; *U.S. Private*, pg. 482

Stoll, William F., Sr. V.P. & Gen. Counsel--Borden, Inc., Columbus, OH; *U.S. Private*, pg. 157

Stoltz, Jon T., Sr. V.P.-Plng. & Rates--Cascade Natural Gas Corporation, Seattle, WA; *U.S. Public*, pg. 311

Stoltz, Scott L., Sr. V.P.-SunAmerica Financial--SunAmerica Inc., Los Angeles, CA; *U.S. Public*, pg. 1532

Stolz, Scott L., Sr. V.P.-Admin.--Jackson National Life Insurance Company, Lansing, MI; *Int'l*, pg. 1073

Stolzer, Julie, Sr. V.P. & Acct. Dir.--Wyse Advertising/Cleveland, Cleveland, OH; *U.S. Private*, pg. 1194

Stone, Barry N., Sr. V.P.--Camtronics Ltd., Hartland, WI; *U.S. Public*, pg. 109

Stone, David D., Sr. V.P.--UNUM Life Insurance Company of America, Portland, ME; *U.S. Public*, pg. 1699

Stone, David K., Sr. V.P. & Dir.-Opers.--Fiduciary Trust Company International, New York, NY; *U.S. Public*, pg. 621

Stone, Gary L., Sr. V.P., Gen. Counsel & Sec.--Parsons Corporation, Pasadena, CA; *U.S. Private*, pg. 841

Stone, Ira N., Sr. V.P.-Mktg., Communications & Pub. Affairs--Stone Container Corporation, Chicago, IL; *U.S. Public*, pg. 1520

Stone, James H., Sr. V.P.--NCH Corporation, Irving, TX; *U.S. Public*, pg. 1145

Stone, Monty, Sr. V.P.--Allright Corporation, Houston, TX; *U.S. Private*, pg. 42

Stone, Rick, Sr. V.P. & Chief Fin. Officer--Sea Ray, Knoxville, TN; *U.S. Public*, pg. 266

Stone, Teresa M., Sr. V.P.--Jefferson-Pilot Corporation, Greensboro, NC; *U.S. Public*, pg. 925

Stonehocker, Keith, Sr. V.P.--Christianity Today, Inc., Carol Stream, IL; *U.S. Private*, pg. 238

Stonehouse, Stephen G., Sr. V.P.--Chubb & Son, Inc., Warren, NJ; *U.S. Public*, pg. 355

Stoner, Jack L., Sr. V.P.-Admin.--Service Corporation International, Houston, TX; *U.S. Public*, pg. 1460

Stoner, John D., Sr. V.P.-Cashiers--PNC Bank, Camp Hill, PA; *U.S. Public*, pg. 1243

Stonner, Richard, Sr. V.P.-Opers.--Pic'n Pay Stores, Inc., Matthews, NC; *U.S. Private*, pg. 864

Stoops, W.G., Sr. V.P.-Sls., East--Emkay, Inc., Itasca, IL; *U.S. Private*, pg. 374

Storch, Gerald L., Sr. V.P.-Strategic Plng.--Dayton Hudson Corporation, Minneapolis, MN; *U.S. Public*, pg. 489

Stordahl, Ann, Sr. V.P. & Gen. Mgr.-Mdsg.--Neiman Marcus Co., Dallas, TX; *U.S. Public*, pg. 785

Storin, Phillip J., Chief Fin. Officer & Sr. V.P.--USLD Communications Corp., San Antonio, TX; *U.S. Public*, pg. 969

Storms, Clifford B., Sr. V.P. & Gen. Counsel--Bestfoods, Englewood Cliffs, NJ; *U.S. Public*, pg. 223

Storrs, Val B., Sr. V.P.-Opers.--The Bartell Drug Company, Seattle, WA; *U.S. Private*, pg. 118

Stote, Robert, Sr. V.P.--Bentley Pharmaceuticals, Inc., Tampa, FL; *U.S. Public*, pg. 212

Stottlemyer, Todd A., V.P.-Corp. & Investor Rels.--BDM International, Inc., Mc Lean, VA; *U.S. Public*, pg. 1558

Stout, Karen L., Sr. V.P.-Opers.--Harris Teeter, Inc., Charlotte, NC; *U.S. Public*, pg. 1412

Stoveken, James E., Jr., Chief Fin. Officer & Sr. V.P.--Westvaco Corporation, New York, NY; *U.S. Public*, pg. 1762

Stover, Craig G., Sr. V.P.-Fin.--American & Efird, Inc., Mount Holly, NC; *U.S. Public*, pg. 1412

Stoves, Lorelei G., Sr. V.P.-Construction & Land Loans--Washington Federal Savings, Seattle, WA; *U.S. Public*, pg. 1740

Strain, Hugh W., Sr. V.P.-Canadian Drilling--Precision Drilling Corporation, Calgary, Canada; *Int'l*, pg. 1066

Strain, Laura, Sr. V.P.-Mktg. & Communications--First Bank N.A., Milwaukee, WI; *U.S. Public*, pg. 1680

Straka, Michael, Sr. V.P.-Mfg.--Tropical Sportswear International, Tampa, FL; *U.S. Private*, pg. 1105

Stranger, John, Sr. V.P. & Mngmt. Supvr.--Dailey & Associates, West Hollywood, CA; *U.S. Public*, pg. 909

Stratter, William, Sr. V.P.-Mfg.--Electronic Data Magnetics, Inc., High Point, NC; *U.S. Private*, pg. 370

Strauss, Art, Sr. V.P.-A/V--Young & Rubicam New York, New York, NY; *U.S. Private*, pg. 1198

Strauss, David, Sr. V.P. & Client Services Dir.--Western International Media Corporation, Atlanta, GA; *U.S. Private*, pg. 1167

Strauss, Les, Sr. V.P.-Acct. Mngmt.--Grey Advertising Inc., New York, NY; *U.S. Public*, pg. 764

Strawbridge, Philip O., Chief Fin. Officer, Chief Admin. Officer & Sr. V.P.--OHM Remediation Services Corp., Findlay, OH; *U.S. Public*, pg. 1208

Strecker, Al M., Sr. V.P.-Fin. & Admin.--OGE Energy Corp., Oklahoma City, OK; *U.S. Public*, pg. 1207

Street, James E., Sr. V.P.-Human Resources--Tejas Gas Corporation, Houston, TX; *Int'l*, pg. 1136

Strelioff, Susan J., Sr. V.P. Corp. Governance & Sec.--National Trustco Inc., Toronto, Canada; *Int'l*, pg. 909

Strelow, G.D., Sr. V.P.--Marshall & Ilsley Corporation, Milwaukee, WI; *U.S. Public*, pg. 1049

Strickland, Danny L., Sr. V.P.-Res. & Devel.--General Mills, Inc., Minneapolis, MN; *U.S. Public*, pg. 717

Stricklin, John, Sr. V.P.--National Income Realty Trust, New York, NY; *U.S. Public*, pg. 1157

Stringfellow, Charles A., Sr. V.P.-Employees Health--New York Life Insurance Company, New York, NY; *U.S. Private*, pg. 794

Strohl, Bruce E., Chief Exec. Officer & Sr. V.P.-Fin.--The Cosmetic Center Inc., Columbia, MD; *U.S. Private*, pg. 689

Strohl, Dale S., Sr. V.P.-Opers.--Tiffany & Co., New York, NY; *U.S. Public*, pg. 1608

Strom, Barb, Sr. V.P.-Mktg. Strategy & Mdsg.--Things Remembered, Inc., Highland Heights, OH; *U.S. Public*, pg. 397

Strom, Leonard A., Sr. V.P.-H.R.--The Black & Decker Corporation, Towson, MD; *U.S. Public*, pg. 233

Stromberg, Gordon, Sr. V.P.-Adv.--Shoppers Drug Mart, Ltd., Toronto, Canada; *Int'l*, pg. 112

Stromberg, LeRoy J., Sr. V.P.--J.S. Alberici Construction Co., Inc., Saint Louis, MO; *U.S. Private*, pg. 32

Strome, William F., Sr. V.P. & Deputy Gen. Counsel--PNC Bank Corp., Pittsburgh, PA; *U.S. Public*, pg. 1242

Strong, Robert T., Sr. V.P.-Residential Lending--Prime Bank, Philadelphia, PA; *U.S. Public*, pg. 1326

Strunk, Steven A., Sr. V.P.-Credit Risk--NationsBank Sunwest, Inc., Albuquerque, NM; *U.S. Public*, pg. 1165

Strupp, James J., Sr. V.P.-Human Resources--International Specialty Products, Inc., Wayne, NJ; *U.S. Public*, pg. 858

Strutt, A. J., Sr. V.P.--The Standard Bank of South Africa, New York, NY; *Int'l*, pg. 1293

Stryjewski, Frank T., Sr. V.P.-Opers.--General Cinema Theatres, Inc., Chestnut Hill, MA; *U.S. Public*, pg. 693

Stuart, Andy, Sr. V.P.-Passenger Svcs.--Norwegian Cruise Line, Miami, FL; *U.S. Private*, pg. 808

Stuart, Ben R., Sr. V.P.-Opers.--Dresser Industries, Inc., Dallas, TX; *U.S. Public*, pg. 528

Stuart, Robert M., Jr., Sr. V.P.--Hibernia Corporation, New Orleans, LA; *U.S. Public*, pg. 825

Stuart, Thomas J., Sr. V.P.--R.P. Scherer Corporation, Troy, MI; *U.S. Public*, pg. 1437

Stubblefield, John K., Jr., Chief Fin. Officer & Sr. V.P.--Sysco Corporation, Houston, TX; *U.S. Public*, pg. 1550

Stucki, Ronald, Sr. V.P.-Opers.--Westmoreland Coal Co., Colorado Springs, CO; *U.S. Public*, pg. 1761

Studer, J.A., Sr. V.P.-Equities--General Electric Investment Corp., Stamford, CT; *U.S. Public*, pg. 712

Stuebing, Bradley F., Sr. V.P.-Intl. Mktg.--Pennzoil Products Co., Houston, TX; *U.S. Public*, pg. 1272

Stuelpnagel, Berthold, Sr. V.P. & Mgr.--Bayerische Landesbank - New York Branch, New York, NY; *Int'l*, pg. 176

Stuenkel, Wayne E., Sr. V.P. & Chief Actuary--Protective Life Insurance Co., Birmingham, AL; *U.S. Public*, pg. 1336

Stuhmiller, James H., Sr. V.P.--Jaymark, Inc., San Diego, CA; *U.S. Private*, pg. 584

Stuhr, Hans-Erik, Sr. V.P.-Station Svcs. Div.--Scandinavian Airlines System (SAS), Solna, Sweden; *Int'l*, pg. 1201

Stumhiller, James H., Ph.D., Sr. V.P.--Jacor, Inc., San Diego, CA; *U.S. Private*, pg. 584

Sturgeon, Karen A., Sr. V.P.-Sls. & Mdse.--Lucky Stores Northern California Division, San Leandro, CA; *U.S. Public*, pg. 93

Sturgeon, Roy, Sr. V.P.-Quality Assurance & Technical Svcs.--American Home Products Corporation, Madison, NJ; *U.S. Public*, pg. 79

Sturm, Cheryl L., Sr. V.P. & Acct. Grp. Dir.--Creswell, Munsell, Fultz & Zirbel, L.P., Cedar Rapids, IA; *U.S. Private*, pg. 1197

Sturm, F. Peter, Sr. V.P. & Gen. Auditor--Seafirst Corporation, Seattle, WA; *U.S. Public*, pg. 181

Sturm, Frederick H.S., Sr. V.P.-Investments--Mackenzie Financial Corporation, Toronto, Canada; *Int'l*, pg. 828

Sturm, Leslie, Sr. V.P. & Natl. Radio Dir.--The Media Edge, New York, NY; *U.S. Private*, pg. 1079

Sturm, Richard, Sr. V.P.-Mktg. & Entertainment--MGM Grand Hotel, Inc., Las Vegas, NV; *U.S. Public*, pg. 1027

Sturzinger, Walter H., Sr. V.P.-Internal Audit--Union Bank of Switzerland, Zurich, Switzerland; *Int'l*, pg. 1439

Stutrud, Donald M., Sr. V.P.-Store Opers.--Arbor Drugs, Inc., Troy, MI; *U.S. Public*, pg. 126

Styer, Paul A., Sr. V.P., Gen. Counsel & Sec.--Copart, Inc., Benicia, CA; *U.S. Public*, pg. 446

Suarez, Angel, Sr. V.P.-Auto Fin. & Opers.--Firstbank Puerto Rico, Santurce, PR; *U.S. Public*, pg. 644

Suarez, Dennis, Sr. V.P.-Devel.--Berkshire Realty Company, Inc., Boston, MA; *U.S. Public*, pg. 221

Subin, Robert, Sr. V.P.-Global Sourcing & Engrng.--Campbell Soup Company, Camden, NJ; *U.S. Public*, pg. 298

Sucaldito, Enrique L., Sr. V.P. & Gen. Mgr.-Machinery Div.--EEI Corporation, Manila, Philippines; *Int'l*, pg. 425

Suckow, Paul E., Sr. V.P. & Chief Investment Officer-Fixed Income--Delaware Management Holdings, Inc., Philadelphia, PA; *U.S. Public*, pg. 997

Suda, Hideaki, Sr. Mng. Dir.-Tech. & Research Mngmt.--Sumitomo Chemical Company, Ltd., Tokyo, Japan; *Int'l*, pg. 1310

Suduiraut, Hubert de, Sr. V.P. & Gen. Mgr.-Western Canada Region--Costco Wholesale, Issaquah, WA; *U.S. Public*, pg. 451

Suehiro, Rokuro, Sr. V.P.--Nippon Steel Corporation, Tokyo, Japan; *Int'l*, pg. 939

Suffoletto, Matthew V., Sr. V.P.-Sls.--Primavera Systems, Inc., Bala Cynwyd, PA; *U.S. Private*, pg. 884

Sugalski, Thomas A., Sr. V.P.-Chemicals--Canadian Occidental Petroleum Ltd., Calgary, Canada; *U.S. Public*, pg. 1210

Sugarman, Ronald H., Sr. V.P. & Center for Adv. Services Dir.--The Interpublic Group of Companies, Inc., New York, NY; *U.S. Public*, pg. 908

Sugihara, Kanji, Assoc. Sr. V.P.--NEC Corporation, Tokyo, Japan; *Int'l*, pg. 899

Sugishita, David M., Chief Fin. Officer & Sr. V.P.-Fin.--Synopsys, Inc., Mountain View, CA; *U.S. Public*, pg. 1548

Sugiyama, Mineo, Sr. V.P.--NEC Corporation, Tokyo, Japan; *Int'l*, pg. 899

Sukemune, Yoshiyuki, Sr. V.P.--Nippon Telegraph and Telephone Corporation, Tokyo, Japan; *Int'l*, pg. 940

Sulerzyski, Charles, Sr. V.P.-Retail--Provident Financial Group, Inc., Cincinnati, OH; *U.S. Public*, pg. 1338

Sullentrup, Greg, Sr. V.P. & Grp. Creative Dir.--DMB&B St. Louis, Saint Louis, MO; *U.S. Private*, pg. 303

Sullivan, Austin P., Jr., Sr. V.P.-Corp. Rels.--General Mills, Inc., Minneapolis, MN; *U.S. Public*, pg. 717

Sullivan, Beth, Sr. V.P. & Dir. Mkt. Res.--Arnold Communications, Inc., Boston, MA; *U.S. Private*, pg. 83

Sullivan, Coleman, Sr. V.P.--Hardee's Food Systems, Inc., Rocky Mount, NC; *U.S. Public*, pg. 278

Sullivan, Daniel J., Sr. V.P.-Lending--First Federal Savings, East Hartford, CT; *U.S. Public*, pg. 632

Sullivan, Daniel L., Sr. V.P.-H.R.--QUALCOMM, San Diego, CA; *U.S. Public*, pg. 1348

Sullivan, Francis, Sr. V.P. & Creative Dir.--Arnold Advertising, Mc Lean, VA; *U.S. Private*, pg. 84

Sullivan, Frank B., Sr. V.P.-Sls. & Mktg.--Square D Company, Palatine, IL; *Int'l*, pg. 1208

Sullivan, George, Sr. V.P.-Mktg.--Genmar Holdings, Inc., Minneapolis, MN; *U.S. Private*, pg. 447

Sullivan, Jere, Sr. V.P.--Edelman Worldwide, Inc., Washington, DC; *U.S. Private*, pg. 362

Sullivan, Jim, Sr. V.P.--Liberty Bank & Trust Company of Oklahoma City, Oklahoma City, OK; *U.S. Public*, pg. 174

Sullivan, John, Chief Fin. Officer , Sr. V.P.-Fin. & Treas.--Trans World Entertainment Corporation, Albany, NY; *U.S. Public*, pg. 1629

Sullivan, John F., Sr. V.P.-Intl. Div.--CUNA Mutual Insurance Society, Madison, WI; *U.S. Private*, pg. 296

Sullivan, Joseph R., Sr. V.P.--Associates Financial Services Corporation, Dallas, TX; *U.S. Public*, pg. 663

Sullivan, Joseph T., Sr. V.P.--Ciba Specialty Chemicals, Tarrytown, NY; *Int'l*, pg. 291

Sullivan, Kenneth, Sr. V.P.--UST Corporation, Boston, MA; *U.S. Public*, pg. 1660

Sullivan, Margie, Sr. V.P. & Creative Services Dir.--Arnold Communications, Inc., Boston, MA; *U.S. Private*, pg. 83

Sullivan, Martin J., Sr. V.P.-Foreign Gen. Insurance--American International Group, Inc., New York, NY; *U.S. Public*, pg. 83

Sullivan, Maureen O., Sr. V.P. & Gen. Counsel--Halter Marine Group, Inc., Gulfport, MS; *U.S. Public*, pg. 778

Sullivan, Nanci, Sr. V.P. & Chief Appraiser--Bay View Capital Corporation, San Mateo, CA; *U.S. Public*, pg. 197

Sullivan, Richard, Sr. V.P.-Adv.--The Home Depot, Inc., Atlanta, GA; *U.S. Public*, pg. 831

Sullivan, Robert J., Sr. V.P.-Asset-Based Lending--Southern California Bank, Newport Beach, CA; *U.S. Public*, pg. 1758

Sullivan, Stephen G., Sr. V.P. & Mgr.-Commun. Svcs.--Liberty Mutual Insurance Co., Boston, MA; *U.S. Private*, pg. 666

Sullivan, Stephen W., Sr. V.P.--Harte-Hanks Communications, Inc., San Antonio, TX; *U.S. Public*, pg. 793

Sullivan, Terrence M., Sr. V.P.-Individual Ins.--The Minnesota Mutual Life Insurance Company, Saint Paul, MN; *U.S. Private*, pg. 750

Sullivan, Tim, Partner & Sr. V.P.--Media That Works, Cincinnati, OH; *U.S. Private*, pg. 727

Sullivan, Timothy J., Chief Fin. Officer, Chief Admin. Officer, Sr. V.P., Treas. & Sec.--Market Facts, Inc., Arlington Heights, IL; *U.S. Public*, pg. 1046

Sullivan, Tony, Sr. V.P.--Willis Corroon Corp. of Western Michigan, Grand Rapids, MI; *Int'l*, pg. 1507

Sultenfuss, John H., Sr. V.P.-Mktg. & Sls.--CF Industries, Inc., Long Grove, IL; *U.S. Private*, pg. 193

Sulzbach, Christi R., Sr. V.P.-Pub. Affairs & Assoc. Gen. Counsel--Tenet Healthcare Corporation, Santa Barbara, CA; *U.S. Public*, pg. 1576

Summer, Thomas, Chief Fin. Officer & Sr. V.P.--Canandaigua Wine Company, Inc., Canandaigua, NY; *U.S. Public*, pg. 300

Summers, C. Richard, Sr. V.P.-Plng. & Devel.--Texas Commerce Bank, Houston, TX; *U.S. Public*, pg. 339

Summers, Miles J., Sr. V.P. & Gen. Mgr.-Travel Division--Scott's Restaurants Inc., Markham, Canada; *Int'l*, pg. 1213

Summers, Miles J., Sr. V.P. & Gen. Mgr.--Scott's Management Services Inc., Markham, Canada; *Int'l*, pg. 1213

Sunderland, Ronald B., Exec. V.P.-Business Affairs & Contracts--ABC Inc., Los Angeles, CA; *U.S. Public*, pg. 511

Sundsbo, Svein, Sr. V.P.-Corp. Communications & Energy--Elkem ASA, Oslo, Norway; *Int'l*, pg. 446

Sung-Lee, Moo, Sr. V.P.-Fin.--Korean Airlines Co., Ltd., Seoul, Korea; *Int'l*, pg. 758

Suozzo, Diane, Sr. V.P. & Client Services Dir.--Burrell/DFA Advertising, New York, NY; *U.S. Private*, pg. 188

Supron, Nicholas R., Sr. V.P.-Worldwide Opers.--GTECH Corporation, West Greenwich, RI; *U.S. Public*, pg. 767

Surace, Lee, Sr. V.P.-Fin.--L.L. Bean, Inc., Freeport, ME; *U.S. Private*, pg. 639

Surane, James, Sr. V.P.-Sls.--Vermont American Tool Corp., Louisville, KY; *U.S. Public*, pg. 575

Suranyi, John B., Sr. V.P.--American Telecasting, Inc., Colorado Springs, CO; *U.S. Public*, pg. 93

Surerus, William E., Sr. V.P. & Controller--Mesirow Financial, Chicago, IL; *U.S. Private*, pg. 733

Surin, Arthur A., Sr. V.P. & Mng. Dir.-NY Hilton--Hilton Hotels Div., Beverly Hills, CA; *U.S. Public*, pg. 829

Surma, John P., Sr. V.P.-Fin. & Acctg. & Controller--Marathon Oil Company, Houston, TX; *U.S. Public*, pg. 1661

Surmanek, Jim, Sr. V.P. & Gen. Mgr.--Carat ICG, Chicago, IL; *U.S. Private*, pg. 207

Susareey Anel, Arturo, Sr. V.P.--Bufete Industrial S.A. de C.V., Mexico, Mexico; *Int'l*, pg. 232

Susick, Greg, Sr. V.P.--Central Parking Corp., Nashville, TN; *U.S. Public*, pg. 326

Susnara, Gary, Sr. V.P.--Sutter Health, Sacramento, CA; *U.S. Private*, pg. 1057

Susor, Robert J., Sr. V.P.-Mkt. Devel.--Genuine Parts Company, Atlanta, GA; *U.S. Public*, pg. 732

Sussberg, L., Sr. V.P-Sls.--SEIKO Corporation of America, Mahwah, NJ; *Int'l*, pg. 1218

Susskind, Emily H., Sr. V.P.-Tech.--Dow Jones & Company, Inc., New York, NY; *U.S. Public*, pg. 524

Sussman, Bernard M., Sr. V.P.--Spectrum Asset Management, Inc., Stamford, CT; *U.S. Public*, pg. 1674

Sussman, Dennis, Sr. V.P.-Sls.-Lighting Div.--Crystal Clear Industries, Ridgefield Park, NJ; *U.S. Private*, pg. 293

Sussman, Ph.D., Joseph L., Sr. V.P.-Mfg./Diagnostics Div.--Bayer Corporation, Pittsburgh, PA; *Int'l*, pg. 172

Sutherland Fuchs, Anne, Sr. V.P. & Grp. Publ. Dir.--Hearst Magazines Division, New York, NY; *U.S. Private*, pg. 516

Sutherland, Allan, Sr. V.P.-Fin.--Henry Lee Company, Miami, FL; *U.S. Private*, pg. 657

Sutherland, Allan C., Sr. V.P.-Leasing & Investments--Illinois Tool Works Inc., Glenview, IL; *U.S. Public*, pg. 865

Sutherland, Jeffrey, Sr. V.P.--IDX Systems Corporation, Burlington, VT; *U.S. Public*, pg. 854

Sutivong, Pramon, Sr. V.P.--The Siam Cement Public Company Limited, Bangkok, Thailand; *Int'l*, pg. 1237

Sutliffe, Ralph, Sr. V.P.-Compliance--Security Pacific Financial Services Inc., San Diego, CA; *U.S. Public*, pg. 181

Suto, Shinzo, Sr. Mng. Dir. & Sr. V.P.-Intl. Passenger Mktg. Div.--Japan Airlines Company, Ltd., Tokyo, Japan; *Int'l*, pg. 699

Sutphen, John C., Sr. V.P.-Intl. Bus. Devel.--American Express Travel Related Services Co., Inc., New York, NY; *U.S. Public*, pg. 73

Sutter, Suzanne, Sr. V.P.--Cole Gift Centers, Inc., Cleveland, OH; *U.S. Public*, pg. 396

Sutton, Neal, Sr. V.P., Gen. Counsel & Sec.--Smith International, Inc., Houston, TX; *U.S. Public*, pg. 1478

Suzuki, Kaneo, Assoc. Sr. V.P.--NEC Corporation, Tokyo, Japan; *Int'l*, pg. 899

Svenson, Ulrik, Sr. V.P.-Fin. Control--Millicom International Cellular SA, Bertrange, Luxembourg; *Int'l*, pg. 867

Svensson, Karl N., Sr. V.P.-Opers.--Farrel Corporation, Ansonia, CT; *U.S. Public*, pg. 614

Svoboda, Larry J., Chief Fin. Officer & Sr. V.P.--Hanover Direct, Inc., Weehawken, NJ; *U.S. Public*, pg. 782

Swaffer, Keith M., Sr. V.P.--NTH Consultants, Ltd., Farmington, MI; *U.S. Private*, pg. 772

Swafford, John, Sr. V.P.--Mueller Sports Medicine, Inc., Prairie Du Sac, WI; *U.S. Private*, pg. 766

Swain, Jonathan, Sr. V.P.-Opers.--Tropicana Resort & Casino, Las Vegas, NV; *U.S. Public*, pg. 159

Swan, George R., Sr. V.P.-Private Client Services--The Trust Company of Bank of Montreal, Toronto, Canada; *Int'l*, pg. 153

Swanick, Patrick J., Sr. V.P.--Keycorp, Cleveland, OH; *U.S. Public*, pg. 954

Swank, Gary, Sr. V.P.-Opers.--Haggar Corporation, Dallas, TX; *U.S. Public*, pg. 774

Swanlund, Larry, Sr. V.P.--BVK/McDonald, Milwaukee, WI; *U.S. Private*, pg. 108

Swanson, Donald, Sr. V.P.-Pension--ReliaStar Financial Corp., Minneapolis, MN; *U.S. Public*, pg. 1375

Swanson, Eric A., Sr. V.P. & Gen. Mgr.-Scientific, Tech. & Medical Pub. Div.--John Wiley & Sons, Inc., New York, NY; *U.S. Public*, pg. 1768

Swanson, John, Sr. V.P.--The Levy Organization, Chicago, IL; *U.S. Private*, pg. 664

Swanson, John, Sr. V.P.--Levy Restaurants, Chicago, IL; *U.S. Private*, pg. 664

Swanson, R.E., Sr. V.P.-Mfg.--Consolidated Papers, Inc., Wisconsin Rapids, WI; *U.S. Public*, pg. 436

Swanson, Richard, Sr. V.P.--Mullen Advertising, Inc., Wenham, MA; *U.S. Private*, pg. 766

Swanson, Robert O., Sr. V.P.--Mobil Oil Corporation, Fairfax, VA; *U.S. Public*, pg. 1118

Swart, Louis, Sr. V.P.-Managed Opers.--Genesis Health Ventures, Inc., Kennett Square, PA; *U.S. Public*, pg. 728

Swartley, John S., Sr. V.P.-Corp. Devel.--United States Filter Corporation, Palm Desert, CA; *U.S. Public*, pg. 1681

Swartz, Michael, Sr. V.P.-Mktg.--JLG Industries, Inc., McConnellsburg, PA; *U.S. Public*, pg. 918

Swartz, Steve, Sr. V.P. & Dir.-Investor Rels.--H.F. Ahmanson & Co., Irwindale, CA; *U.S. Public*, pg. 29

Swartz, Ted, Sr. V.P. & Mng. Dir.-Bus.-to-Bus. Grp.--Grant/Jacoby, Inc., Chicago, IL; *U.S. Private*, pg. 470

Swaurt, Duane, Sr. V.P.-Corp. Services--Motorists Mutual Insurance Co., Columbus, OH; *U.S. Private*, pg. 764

Sweatt, Millard E., Sr. V.P.-Opers. Analysis, Pur. & Legal & Gen. Counsel--Federal Reserve Bank of Dallas, Dallas, TX; *U.S. Private*, pg. 399

Swedin, Ronald, Sr. V.P.-Stores--One Price Clothing Stores, Inc., Duncan, SC; *U.S. Public*, pg. 1225

Swedlow, David B., MD, Sr. V.P.-Medical Affairs/Tech. Devel.--Nellcor Puritan Bennett Incorporated, Pleasanton, CA; *U.S. Public*, pg. 1039

Sweed, Phyllis, Sr. V.P.--Geyer-McAllister Publications, Inc., New York, NY; *U.S. Private*, pg. 450

Sweeney, John, Sr. V.P. & Chief Information Officer--USF&G Corporation, Baltimore, MD; *U.S. Public*, pg. 1659

Sweeney, John, Sr. V.P.-Investments--United States Fidelity & Guaranty Company, Baltimore, MD; *U.S. Public*, pg. 1659

Sweeney, Kathleen, Sr. V.P. & Mgr.-Corp. Fin.--The Hokkaido Takushoku Bank, Ltd., New York Branch, New York, NY; *Int'l*, pg. 626

Sweeney, P.R., Sr. V.P. & Cashier--Security Bank & Trust Co., Vincennes, IN; *U.S. Public*, pg. 1217

Sweet, Frederic H., Sr. V.P.-Govt. Relations--Northwestern Mutual Life Insurance Co., Milwaukee, WI; *U.S. Private*, pg. 807

Sweet, Lawrence L., Sr. V.P.-Information Systems--Associates Financial Services Corporation, Dallas, TX; *U.S. Public*, pg. 663

Swegel, Thomas C., Sr. V.P.-Commercial Banking--Zions First National Bank, Salt Lake City, UT; *U.S. Public*, pg. 1793

Sweigart, Donald E., Sr. V.P.--Burnham, Lancaster, PA; *U.S. Public*, pg. 270

Sweitzer, Steve, Sr. V.P. & Exec. Creative Dir.--Hal Riney & Partners, Inc., San Francisco, CA; *U.S. Private*, pg. 931

Swenka, Arthur J., Sr. V.P.-Opers.--Sysco Corporation, Houston, TX; *U.S. Public*, pg. 1550

Swenson, David, Sr. V.P.-Grain & Agra-Services--Harvest States Cooperatives, Saint Paul, MN; *U.S. Private*, pg. 508

Swenson, Edward J., Sr. V.P.--Electro Scientific Industries, Inc., Portland, OR; *U.S. Public*, pg. 568

Swenson, Kathy, Sr. V.P.-Sls., Mktg. & Commun.--Kaiser Permanente, Oakland, CA; *U.S. Private*, pg. 605

Swerdlick, Dorothy, Sr. V.P.-Local Brdcst. & Opers. Mgr.--Zenith Media Services, Inc., New York, NY; *U.S. Private*, pg. 1204

Swett, John P., Sr. V.P.-Sls., Mktg. & Tech. Services/Rubber Div.--Bayer Corporation, Pittsburgh, PA; *Int'l*, pg. 172

Swick, Norman H., Sr. V.P. & Gen. Auditor--Washington Mutual Inc., Seattle, WA; *U.S. Public*, pg. 1741

Swienton, Gregory T., Sr. V.P.-Coal & Agricultural Commodities Bus. Unit--Burlington Northern Santa Fe Corporation, Fort Worth, TX; *U.S. Public*, pg. 268

Swift, Henry W., Jr., Sr. V.P. & Dir.--The Robinson-Humphrey Company, Inc., Atlanta, GA; *U.S. Public*, pg. 1633

Swiskow, Jonathan D, Sr. V.P.-Sls. & Mktg.--Hickory Specialties, Inc., Brentwood, TN; *U.S. Public*, pg. 596

Switz, Robert E., Chief Fin. Officer & Sr. V.P.--ADC Telecommunications, Inc., Minnetonka, MN; *U.S. Public*, pg. 4

Switzer, Thomas W., Sr. V.P.-Mngmt. Information Systems--UMB Financial Corporation, Kansas City, MO; *U.S. Public*, pg. 1653

Swope, Melvin, Sr. V.P.-Production (TV)--MGM Worldwide Television, Group., Santa Monica, CA; *U.S. Public*, pg. 1102

Sword, Ian, Sr. Exec. V.P.--SGS Societe Generale de Surveillance Holding S.A., Geneva, Switzerland; *Int'l*, pg. 1153

Sych, John, Sr. V.P.-Mdsg.--Ross Roy Communications, Inc., Bloomfield Hills, MI; *U.S. Private*, pg. 946

Sychowski, Jerry, Chief Information Officer & Sr. V.P.--Equitable of Iowa Companies, Des Moines, IA; *Int'l*, pg. 647

Sylla, Casey J., Sr. V.P. & Chief Investment Officer--The Allstate Corporation, Northbrook, IL; *U.S. Public*, pg. 55

Sylvester, Jim, Sr. V.P.-Lancaster Colony Automotive Grp. Opers.--Lancaster Colony Automotive Group, Dublin, OH; *U.S. Public*, pg. 977

Sylvester, Ron, Sr. V.P.--Edelman Worldwide, Inc., New York, NY; *U.S. Private*, pg. 362

Sylvia, Kenneth A., Sr. V.P., Grp. Publr. & Publr. Consultant--Cliggott Publishing, Greenwich, CT; *U.S. Private*, pg. 246
Symens, Raymond D., Sr. V.P.--Tetra Technologies, Woodlands, TX; *U.S. Public*, pg. 1582
Symes, Douglas L., Sr. V.P.--Zenith Insurance Company, Woodland Hills, CA; *U.S. Public*, pg. 1791
Synott, Lee, Sr. V.P.--Ingram Distribution Group Inc., La Vergne, TN; *U.S. Private*, pg. 563
Sytsma, James A., Sr. V.P.-Mktg. & New Prod. Devel.--Altec Industries, Inc., Birmingham, AL; *U.S. Private*, pg. 47
Szczepanski, Thomas, Sr. V.P. & Acct. Dir.-Jeep/Eagle--Ross Roy Communications, Inc., Bloomfield Hills, MI; *U.S. Private*, pg. 946
Szerlong, Timothy J., Sr. V.P.--Chubb & Son, Inc., Warren, NJ; *U.S. Public*, pg. 355
Szescila, Andrew J., Sr. V.P. & Pres.-Hughes Christensen Co.--Baker Hughes Incorporated, Houston, TX; *U.S. Public*, pg. 165
Szmadzinski, Joseph, Sr. V.P.-Tech.--Handleman Company, Troy, MI; *U.S. Public*, pg. 779
Szomjassy, Michael A., Sr. V.P.-Eastern Opers.--OHM Remediation Services Corp., Findlay, OH; *U.S. Public*, pg. 1208
Szostak, M. Anne, Sr. V.P.--Fleet Financial Group, Inc., Boston, MA; *U.S. Public*, pg. 648
Szwack, Tom, Sr. V.P.-Sls.--Republic Entertainment, Inc., Los Angeles, CA; *U.S. Private*, pg. 776
Szymonik, Richard J., Sr. V.P.--Associates Commercial Corporation, Dallas, TX; *U.S. Public*, pg. 663
Taake, Janice, Sr. V.P. & Dir.-MIS--FirstFed Financial Corp., Santa Monica, CA; *U.S. Public*, pg. 645
Tabar, Klaus, Sr. V.P.-Devel., Store Plng. & Construction--Krause's Furniture Inc., Brea, CA; *U.S. Public*, pg. 967
Tabinsky, William J., Sr. V.P.--Chubb & Son, Inc., Warren, NJ; *U.S. Public*, pg. 355
Tabor, Joanne, Sr. V.P.--Imperial Bank, Inglewood, CA; *U.S. Public*, pg. 871
Tackett, Bill D., Sr. V.P.-Central & Eastern Region--United States Cold Storage, Inc., Cherry Hill, NJ; *U.S. Private*, pg. 1124
Tadlock, Bill, Sr. V.P.-Special Projects--J.B. Hunt Transport Services, Inc., Lowell, AR; *U.S. Public*, pg. 849
Tagawa, Craig K., Chief Fin. Officer & Sr. V.P.--American Shared Hospital Services, San Francisco, CA; *U.S. Public*, pg. 91
Taggart, David, Sr. V.P. & Sec.--Montgomery Watson, Pasadena, CA; *U.S. Private*, pg. 759
Tait, William P., Sr. V.P.-Fin.--American Eagles Outfitters Inc., Warrendale, PA; *U.S. Private*, pg. 53
Takada, Yoichiro, Sr. V.P. & Deputy Gen. Mgr.-Engrng. & Maintenance Div.--Japan Airlines Company, Ltd., Tokyo, Japan; *Int'l*, pg. 699
Takahashi, Hideaki, Sr. V.P.-Asia/Pacific Reg.--NCR Corporation, Dayton, OH; *U.S. Public*, pg. 1146
Takahashi, Kazuo, Sr. Mng. Dir.--Asahi Breweries Ltd., Tokyo, Japan; *Int'l*, pg. 83
Takahashi, Koichi, Sr. V.P.--Mikimoto (America) Co. Ltd., New York, NY; *Int'l*, pg. 866
Takahashi, Tim, Sr. V.P.-Bus. Devel.--Pioneer New Media Technologies, Long Beach, CA; *U.S. Private*, pg. 866
Takashima, Seiji, Sr. V.P.--Nippon Telegraph and Telephone Corporation, Tokyo, Japan; *Int'l*, pg. 940
Takayama, Yoshi, Sr. V.P.--NEC Corporation, Tokyo, Japan; *Int'l*, pg. 899
Takeda, Yasahiro, Sr. Mngmt. Dir.--Alps Electric Co., Ltd., Tokyo, Japan; *Int'l*, pg. 65
Takeda, Yasutsugu, Sr. Exec. Mng. Dir.--Hitachi, Ltd., Tokyo, Japan; *Int'l*, pg. 621
Takei, Tadashi, Sr. V.P. & Joint Gen. Mgr.--Bank of Yokohama New York, New York, NY; *Int'l*, pg. 159
Taker, B.S., Sr. V.P.-Human Resources--Hilton International Co., Coral Gables, FL; *Int'l*, pg. 787
Takeuchi, Michio, Sr. V.P.--Nippon Telegraph and Telephone Corporation, Tokyo, Japan; *Int'l*, pg. 940
Talbi, Stanley J., Sr. V.P.-Fin. & Acturial--Metropolitan Life Insurance Co., New York, NY; *U.S. Private*, pg. 737
Talbott. O. James, II, Sr. V.P. Mercantile Bankshares Corporation, Baltimore, MD; *U.S. Public*, pg. 1088
Talent, Richard L., Sr. V.P.-Customer Service--Tennessee Valley Authority, Knoxville, TN; *U.S. Public*, pg. 1580
Taljaard, D.L.M., Sr. V.P.-Real Estate--Hilton International Co., Coral Gables, FL; *Int'l*, pg. 787
Talkington, Dorothy, Sr. V.P.- Strategic Resources--Ketchum Directory Advertising/Pittsburgh, Pittsburgh, PA; *U.S. Private*, pg. 616
Talkington, Jack A., Sr. V.P.-Lending, Controller--United Companies Financial Corporation, Baton Rouge, LA; *U.S. Public*, pg. 1675
Tallent, Michael S., Sr. V.P.-Acctg. & Admin.--Comcast Cable Communications, Inc., Philadelphia, PA; *U.S. Public*, pg. 407
Tallent, Tom, Sr. V.P.-Fin. & H.R.--Gemtron Corporation, Sweetwater, TN; *Int'l*, pg. 1523
Tallett, W.K., Sr. V.P.-Real Estate/Corp. Devel.--C. Brewer & Company, Limited, Honolulu, HI; *U.S. Private*, pg. 190
Talley, James L., Sr. V.P.--Chubb & Son, Inc., Warren, NJ; *U.S. Public*, pg. 355
Talovich, Michael, Sr. V.P. & Brand Mktg. Partner--DMB&B Detroit, Troy, MI; *U.S. Private*, pg. 302
Talton, James M., Sr. V.P.-Human Resources--Rite Aid Corporation, Camp Hill, PA; *U.S. Public*, pg. 1390
Talz, Frank J., Sr. V.P.-Organizational Devel.--ADVO, Inc., Windsor, CT; *U.S. Public*, pg. 23
Tam, Gilbert K.T., Sr. V.P.-Mkt. & Community Svcs. Division--Bank of Hawaii, Honolulu, HI; *U.S. Public*, pg. 1248
Tamburo, Vincent A., Sr. V.P., Gen. Counsel & Sec.--1st Source Bank Consolidated, South Bend, IN; *U.S. Public*, pg. 638
Tamcsin, Dennis, Sr. V.P.-Agencies--Northwestern Mutual Life Insurance Co., Milwaukee, WI; *U.S. Private*, pg. 807
Tamcsin, Todd, Sr. V.P.--BVK/McDonald, Fort Lauderdale, FL; *U.S. Private*, pg. 108
Tamminen, Sakari, Sr. V.P.--Rauma Ltd., Helsinki, Finland; *Int'l*, pg. 1428
Tamsburg, William T., Sr. V.P.--Cameron & Barkley Company, Charleston, SC; *U.S. Private*, pg. 203
Tan, Simon Y., Sr. V.P.-Individual Mkt. Devel. & Prod.--Phoenix Home Life Mutual Insurance Company, Hartford, CT; *U.S. Private*, pg. 863
Tan, Simon Y., Sr. V.P.-Individual Mkt. Devel.--Phoenix Home Life Mutual Insurance Co., Hartford, CT; *U.S. Private*, pg. 863
Tanahira, T., Sr. V.P. & Treas.--Mazda Motor of America, Inc., Irvine, CA; *Int'l*, pg. 849
Tanaka, Fori, Sr. V.P.-Domestic Passenger Mktg.--Japan Airlines Company, Ltd., Tokyo, Japan; *Int'l*, pg. 699
Tanaka, Hitoshi, Sr. V.P.--Designatronics, Inc., New Hyde Park, NY; *U.S. Private*, pg. 327
Tandon, Sanjiv, Sr. V.P.--Bank of Montreal - New York, New York, NY; *Int'l*, pg. 154
Tang, Henry, Sr. V.P. & Dir.-Investment Services--Jefferies & Company, Inc., Los Angeles, CA; *U.S. Public*, pg. 925
Tanks, Wallace T., Sr. V.P.-H.R.--Tennessee Valley Authority, Knoxville, TN; *U.S. Public*, pg. 1580
Tannehill, Kevin, Sr. V.P.-Network Distrib.--UPN-United Paramount Network, Los Angeles, CA; *U.S. Public*, pg. 352
Tannehill, Kevin, Sr. V.P.-Network Distrib.--UPN-United Paramount Network, Los Angeles, CA; *U.S. Private*, pg. 777
Tansey, James R., Chief Fin. Officer & Sr. V.P.--Jaydon Incorporated, Rock Island, IL; *U.S. Private*, pg. 584
Tansou, Youichi, Sr. V.P.--Nissan Mutual Life Insurance Company, Tokyo, Japan; *Int'l*, pg. 945
Tapling, Mark E., Sr. V.P.-Field Opers./Americas--Comshare, Incorporated, Ann Arbor, MI; *U.S. Public*, pg. 425
Tapper, Mayer S., Sr. V.P.--TCF Bank Minnesota FSB, Minneapolis, MN; *U.S. Public*, pg. 1554
Tarantik, Gerhard, Sr. V.P.--Westpac Banking Corporation, Sydney, Australia; *Int'l*, pg. 1495
Taratus, Kenneth S., Sr. V.P.--Jefferies & Company, Inc., Los Angeles, CA; *U.S. Public*, pg. 925
Tarbet, Ted N., Chief Fin. Officer & Sr. V.P.--Sunrise Medical, Inc., Carlsbad, CA; *U.S. Public*, pg. 1535
Tarbutton, Allen J., Jr., Sr. V.P. & Pres.-Gas Services Div.--Mitchell Energy & Development Corp., Spring, TX; *U.S. Public*, pg. 1117
Tardieu, J., Sr. V.P.-Agriculture--SGS Societe Generale de Surveillance Holding S.A., Geneva, Switzerland; *Int'l*, pg. 1153
Tarello, John A., Sr. V.P. & Treas.--Analogic Corporation, Peabody, MA; *U.S. Public*, pg. 109
Tarney, Wayne, Sr. V.P.-Customer Svcs.--New Jersey Natural Gas Co., Wall, NJ; *U.S. Public*, pg. 1172
Tarnoff, Jeffrey, Sr. V.P.--OppenheimerFunds Distributor, Inc., New York, NY; *U.S. Private*, pg. 818
Tarpey, Michael T., Sr. V.P.-Pub. Rels.--NCR Corporation, Dayton, OH; *U.S. Public*, pg. 1146
Tarpley, Gray, Sr. V.P.--First Commercial Bank, N.A., Little Rock, AR; *U.S. Public*, pg. 630
Tarpley, Joe, Sr. V.P.--J.L. Todd Auction Co., Rome, GA; *U.S. Private*, pg. 1090
Tarrant, Johnny, Sr. V.P.--Quik Print Inc., Wichita, KS; *U.S. Private*, pg. 421
Tarrero, Emilio, Sr. V.P.--Banco Santander, Madrid, Spain; *Int'l*, pg. 143
Tartikoff, Peter A., Chief Fin. Officer & Sr. V.P.--Cousins Properties Incorporated, Atlanta, GA; *U.S. Public*, pg. 453
Tartre, Richard R., Sr. V.P.--Metropolitan Life Insurance Co., New York, NY; *U.S. Private*, pg. 737
Tarver, Joe, Sr. V.P.-Pur.--Minyard Food Stores, Inc., Coppell, TX; *U.S. Private*, pg. 752
Tarver, Larry R., Sr. V.P.--El Paso Natural Gas Co., Houston, TX; *U.S. Public*, pg. 567
Tassaro, Jeanne, Sr. V.P. & Print Services Dir.--Young & Rubicam New York, New York, NY; *U.S. Private*, pg. 1198
Tatalias, Marilee, Sr. V.P.-Sls. & Oper. Support--DSC Logistics, Inc., Des Plaines, IL; *U.S. Private*, pg. 306
Tate, Jeffrey S., Sr. V.P.--American Annuity Group, Cincinnati, OH; *U.S. Public*, pg. 74
Tate, Richard L., Sr. V.P.-Mdsg.--Fingerhut Corp., Minnetonka, MN; *U.S. Public*, pg. 623
Tateishi, Katsumi, Sr. Mng. Dir.--Itoham Foods Inc., Tokyo, Japan; *Int'l*, pg. 695
Tatum, T.W., Sr. V.P.-Human Resources--Lafarge Canada Inc., Montreal, Canada; *Int'l*, pg. 789
Tatum, Thomas W., Sr. V.P.-Human Resources--Lafarge Corporation, Reston, VA; *Int'l*, pg. 788
Taunton-Rigby, Alison, Sr. V.P. Bio-Therapeutics--Genzyme Corporation, Cambridge, MA; *U.S. Public*, pg. 733
Tayler, H. David, Sr. V.P. & Gen. Mgr.--International Comfort Products, Franklin, TN; *U.S. Public*, pg. 898
Tayler, H.D., Sr. V.P. & Gen. Mgr.--Keeprite Inc, Brantford, Canada; *U.S. Public*, pg. 898
Taylor Hines, Charlee, Sr. V.P. & Acct. Plng. Dir.-Insights Grp.--Young & Rubicam New York, New York, NY; *U.S. Private*, pg. 1198
Taylor, Barry, Sr. Mgr.--W.A. Flick & Co. Pty. Limited, Lane Cove, Australia; *Int'l*, pg. 495
Taylor, Bing, Sr. V.P.--International Div., New York, NY; *U.S. Public*, pg. 1440
Taylor, Carl N., Sr. V.P.-Trans.--CSX Transportation, Inc., Jacksonville, FL; *U.S. Public*, pg. 284
Taylor, Collette, Sr. V.P.--Golin/Harris Communications, Inc., Chicago, IL; *Int'l*, pg. 1226
Taylor, Douglas H., Sr. V.P.--Superior Consultant Company, Inc., Southfield, MI; *U.S. Public*, pg. 1539
Taylor, Gerald F., Chief Fin. Officer & Sr. V.P.--Applied Materials, Inc., Santa Clara, CA; *U.S. Public*, pg. 123
Taylor, Gretchen, Sr. V.P., Dir.--Ketchum Directory Advertising/San Francisco, San Francisco, CA; *U.S. Private*, pg. 617
Taylor, J.L., Sr. V.P.--Ingram Distribution Group Inc., La Vergne, TN; *U.S. Private*, pg. 563
Taylor, James A., Sr. V.P.-Global Mktg.--Gateway 2000, North Sioux City, SD; *U.S. Public*, pg. 703
Taylor, Jimmie F., Chief Fin. Officer, Sr. V.P. & Treas.--TCA Management Company, Tyler, TX; *U.S. Public*, pg. 1553
Taylor, Jo D., Sr. V.P.--Farmers Bank & Trust Co., Henderson, KY; *U.S. Public*, pg. 1217
Taylor, John, Sr. V.P.-Opers.--Tropical Sportswear International, Tampa, FL; *U.S. Private*, pg. 1105
Taylor, Jon K., Sr. V.P.-Asset Mngmt.--Franchise Finance Corp. of America, Scottsdale, AZ; *U.S. Public*, pg. 679
Taylor, Karl, Sr. V.P.-Strategic & Mdse. Plng.--Montgomery Ward & Co., Inc., Chicago, IL; *U.S. Private*, pg. 758
Taylor, Kathleen, Sr. V.P. & Gen. Counsel--Four Seasons Hotels Inc., Don Mills, Canada; *Int'l*, pg. 502
Taylor, Keith D., Sr. V.P. & Treas.--Washington Federal Savings, Seattle, WA; *U.S. Public*, pg. 1740
Taylor, Ken, Sr. V.P.-Fin.--First Travelcorp Inc., Raleigh, NC; *U.S. Private*, pg. 408
Taylor, Lonnie, Sr. V.P.-Congressional Rels.--Nation's Business, Washington, DC; *U.S. Private*, pg. 788
Taylor, Malcolm, Sr. V.P. & Mng. Dir.-European Opers.--Bridgeport Machines, Inc., Bridgeport, CT; *U.S. Public*, pg. 251
Taylor, Mark, Sr. V.P.-Preliminary Design--Galoob Toys, Inc., South San Francisco, CA; *U.S. Public*, pg. 698
Taylor, Meredith, Sr. V.P.-Fin. & Mktg.--Stuart Anderson's Black Angus/Cattle Company Restaurants, Los Altos, CA; *U.S. Private*, pg. 61
Taylor, Robert, Sr. V.P. & Chief Acctg. Officer--LaSalle Cragin Bank, Chicago, IL; *Int'l*, pg. 10
Taylor, Robert C., Sr. V.P.--SAFECO Property & Casualty Insurance Companies, Seattle, WA; *U.S. Public*, pg. 1423
Taylor, Roni, Sr. V.P. & Acct. Grp. Dir.--Arnold Advertising, Mc Lean, VA; *U.S. Private*, pg. 84
Taylor, S. Tucker, Sr. V.P.--Columbia/H.C.A., Dallas, TX; *U.S. Public*, pg. 404
Taylor, S.R., Sr. V.P.-Distribution--Ingram Book Company, La Vergne, TN; *U.S. Private*, pg. 563
Taylor, Steve, Sr. V.P.-Consulgting--Quantum Plus, New York, NY; *U.S. Public*, pg. 1224
Taylor, Thomas E., Sr. V.P. & Gen. Counsel--Cincinnati Bell Telephone Company, Cincinnati, OH; *U.S. Public*, pg. 367
Taylor, Tim, Sr. V.P.-Fin.--Pursell Industries, Sylacauga, AL; *U.S. Private*, pg. 896
Teague, Henry H., Sr. V.P.--Rosser International, Inc., Atlanta, GA; *U.S. Private*, pg. 946
Teale, Michael J., Sr. V.P.-Worldwide Opers. & Technology--Kellogg Company, Battle Creek, MI; *U.S. Public*, pg. 947
Tebo, Joseph J., Sr. V.P.-Intl. Bus.--PriceSmart Inc., San Diego, CA; *U.S. Public*, pg. 1324
Techamontrikul, Anothai, Sr. Exec. V.P.--The Industrial Finance Corporation of Thailand, Bangkok, Thailand; *Int'l*, pg. 677
Teck, See Leong, Sr. V.P. & Gen. Mgr.--Singapore Technologies Shipbuilding & Engineering Limited, Singapore, Singapore; *Int'l*, pg. 1253
Tedder, D.R., Sr. V.P.-Leaf & Support Services--Lorillard Tobacco Company, Greensboro, NC; *U.S. Public*, pg. 1011
Teder, Ando, Sr. V.P.-Opers.--Dick Clark Restaurants, Inc., Burbank, CA; *U.S. Public*, pg. 382
Tedesco, Ralph R., Sr. V.P.--New York State Electric & Gas Corporation, Binghamton, NY; *U.S. Public*, pg. 1173
Teel, Lauren, Sr. V.P.-Investments--Kleinwort Benson Investment Management Americas Inc., New York, NY; *Int'l*, pg. 420
Teele, Gerald A., Chief Fin. Officer, Sr. V.P. & Treas.--North Carolina Natural Gas Corporation, Fayetteville, NC; *U.S. Public*, pg. 1194
Teeters, Bruce W., Sr. V.P.-Fin. & Treas.--Consolidated-Tomoka Land Co., Daytona Beach, FL; *U.S. Public*, pg. 437
Teixeira, Appollo, Sr. V.P.-Hess Sundwig Grp.--Hess Engineering Inc., Niles, MI; *U.S. Private*, pg. 524
Teixera, Edward, Sr. V.P.-Franchising--Staff Builders Inc., Lake Success, NY; *U.S. Public*, pg. 1501
Tell, William K., Jr., Sr. V.P.--Texaco Inc., White Plains, NY; *U.S. Public*, pg. 1582
Telljohan, Eric P., Sr. V.P.-Fin.--NationsCredit Commercial Corporation, Cleveland, OH; *U.S. Public*, pg. 1165
Tempesta, John, Sr. V.P.-Distribution & Logistics--Caldor, Inc., Norwalk, CT; *U.S. Public*, pg. 292
Temple, J. Keith, Sr. V.P.--Texas National Bank, Southlake, TX; *U.S. Public*, pg. 633
Templer, Jeffrey A., Chief Fin. Officer & Sr. V.P.--Aerovox Inc., New Bedford, MA; *U.S. Public*, pg. 25
Templeton, James M., Sr. V.P.-Real Estate & Franchising--WSMP, Inc., Claremont, NC; *U.S. Public*, pg. 1729
Tennis, Mike, Sr. V.P.-Fin.--INX International, Milwaukee, WI; *Int'l*, pg. 1311
Tennyson, Christopher J., Sr. V.P.-Corp. Affairs--Taubman Centers, Inc., Bloomfield Hills, MI; *U.S. Public*, pg. 1561
Tensho, Yasutoshi, Sr. V.P.-Fin.--Scripto-Tokai Corp., Fontana, CA; *U.S. Private*, pg. 977
Tepper, Mike, Sr. V.P.-Intl.--LSB Industries, Inc., Oklahoma City, OK; *U.S. Public*, pg. 970
Teraji, Alan R., Sr. V.P.--Manufacturers & Traders Trust Company, Buffalo, NY; *U.S. Public*, pg. 631
Teramura, Yasuhiko, Sr. V.P. & Joint Gen. Mgr.--Bank of Yokohama New York, New York, NY; *Int'l*, pg. 159
Teran, Tim, Sr. V.P.--Grey Advertising Inc., New York, NY; *U.S. Public*, pg. 764
Terho, Helena, Sr. V.P.-Quality--Kone Corporation, Helsinki, Finland; *Int'l*, pg. 746
Termain, A. Cole, Sr. V.P.-Indus. Rels. & Pub. Affairs--The LTV Corporation, Cleveland, OH; *U.S. Public*, pg. 971
Terrenzi, John T., Sr. V.P.-Grp.--Security Mutual Life Insurance Co. of New York, Binghamton, NY; *U.S. Private*, pg. 981

Terreri, Peter, Sr. V.P.-Fin.--Teva USA - Biocraft, Fair Lawn, NJ; *Int'l*, pg. 1381
Terrone, Michael R., Sr. V.P.--Indiana Lawrence Bank, North Manchester, IN; *U.S. Public*, pg. 633
Terry, Charles P., Sr. V.P.-Fin. & Treas.--Reed & Barton Corporation, Taunton, MA; *U.S. Private*, pg. 916
Terry, Ronald L., Sr. V.P.-Wheel & Rim Tech.--Hess Engineering Inc., Niles, MI; *U.S. Private*, pg. 524
Terwilliger, Patrick, Sr. V.P.-Architecture & Construction--Hilton Hotels Corporation, Beverly Hills, CA; *U.S. Public*, pg. 828
Tessier, Yvon, Sr. V.P.-Inv. & Asset Mgmnt.--SITQ Immobilier, Montreal, Canada; *Int'l*, pg. 249
Tessman, Tom, Sr. V.P. & Promotional Mktg. Dir.--Campbell Mithun Esty, Minneapolis, MN; *U.S. Private*, pg. 204
Testa, Francis P., Sr. V.P.--Summit Bank, Bethlehem, PA; *U.S. Public*, pg. 1528
Teurfs, Roger, Sr. V.P. & Compliance Officer--Long Island Bancorp, Inc., Melville, NY; *U.S. Public*, pg. 1013
Tevis, G. Phillip, Sr. V.P. & Pres.-Global Marketing Group--Dresser Industries, Inc., Dallas, TX; *U.S. Public*, pg. 528
Teytaud, Cecile, Sr. V.P.-Legal & Tax Affairs--Credit Commercial de France, Paris, France; *Int'l*, pg. 341
Thaicham, Sunantha, Sr. V.P.--Siam City Bank Public Company Limited, Bangkok, Thailand; *Int'l*, pg. 1239
Thanas, Peter H., Sr. V.P. & Treas.--Fall River Gas Company, Fall River, MA; *U.S. Public*, pg. 611
Tharp, Charles G., Sr. V.P.-Human Resources--Bristol-Myers Squibb Company, New York, NY; *U.S. Public*, pg. 253
Thatcher, G.D., Sr. V.P. & Treas.--All America Insurance Company, Van Wert, OH; *U.S. Private*, pg. 224
Thatcher, Gerald D., Chief Fin. Officer, Sr. V.P. & Treas.--Central Mutual Insurance Co., Van Wert, OH; *U.S. Private*, pg. 223
Thatcher, R., Sr. V.P.--Staff Builders Inc., Lake Success, NY; *U.S. Public*, pg. 1501
Thawerbhoy, Nazim G., Sr. V.P. & Controller--Jacobs Engineering Group Inc., Pasadena, CA; *U.S. Public*, pg. 921
Thebault, Andre, Sr. V.P.-Production--Elf Aquitane, Paris, France; *Int'l*, pg. 444
Theilken, Mark S., Sr. V.P.--Acxiom Corporation, Conway, AR; *U.S. Public*, pg. 18
Thelan, John D., Sr. V.P.-Depots--Costco Wholesale, Issaquah, WA; *U.S. Public*, pg. 451
Thiel, David N., Sr. V.P. & Sec.--Omega Financial Corporation, State College, PA; *U.S. Public*, pg. 1222
Thiel, David N., Sr. V.P. & Sec.--Omega Bank, N.A., State College, PA; *U.S. Public*, pg. 1222
Thiele, E.E., Sr. V.P. & Treas.--Rowan Companies, Inc., Houston, TX; *U.S. Public*, pg. 1409
Thieme, Hans R., Sr. V.P.-Photo Imaging Systems--Bayer Corporation, Pittsburgh, PA; *Int'l*, pg. 172
Tholey, James M., Sr. V.P.-Audio/Video--Peirce-Phelps, Inc., Philadelphia, PA; *U.S. Private*, pg. 847
Thom, Ronald F., Sr. V.P.-Automotive Grp.--TCG International Inc., Burnaby, Canada; *Int'l*, pg. 1336
Thoma, Edward W., Sr. V.P.-Fin.--Oneida Ltd., Oneida, NY; *U.S. Public*, pg. 1225
Thoma, Michael, Sr. V.P.-Worldwide Mktg.--Brightware, Inc., Novato, CA; *U.S. Private*, pg. 168
Thoman, G. Richard, Chief Fin. Officer & Sr. V.P.--International Business Machines Corporation, Armonk, NY; *U.S. Public*, pg. 895
Thomas, A. Robert, Sr. V.P.-Fin.--Data Documents, Inc., Omaha, NE; *U.S. Public*, pg. 449
Thomas, Alan R., Chief Fin. Officer, Sr. V.P. & Treas.--Noranda Inc., Toronto, Canada; *Int'l*, pg. 433
Thomas, Barbara, Sr. V.P.--Tribble & Stephens Co., Houston, TX; *U.S. Private*, pg. 1102
Thomas, Brantley D., Jr., Sr. V.P.--Westvaco Corporation, New York, NY; *U.S. Public*, pg. 1762
Thomas, Bruce V., Chief Fin. Officer, Sr. V.P. & Gen. Counsel--Cadmus Communications Corporation, Richmond, VA; *U.S. Public*, pg. 290
Thomas, Buddy, Sr. V.P.-Export--Southwestern Petroleum Corporation, Fort Worth, TX; *U.S. Private*, pg. 1019
Thomas, Carole, Sr. V.P. & Media Dir.--Lois/EJL New York, New York, NY; *U.S. Public*, pg. 1011
Thomas, Dalen D., Sr. V.P.-Sls., Mktg. & Strategic Plng.--Amtran, Inc., Indianapolis, IN; *U.S. Public*, pg. 106
Thomas, David A., Sr. V.P.-Natl. Opers.--Wall Street Deli, Inc., Birmingham, AL; *U.S. Public*, pg. 1734
Thomas, Edward A., Sr. V.P.-Specialty Opers.--W.R. Berkley Corporation, Greenwich, CT; *U.S. Public*, pg. 215
Thomas, Elbert L., Jr., Sr. V.P. & Treas.--First Tennessee Bank National Association, Memphis, TN; *U.S. Public*, pg. 639
Thomas, Grady G., Jr., Sr. V.P.--Interstate/Johnson Lane Corporation, Charlotte, NC; *U.S. Public*, pg. 910
Thomas, H. Suzanne, Sr. V.P., Gen. Counsel & Sec.--Weatherford Enterra Incorporated, Houston, TX; *U.S. Public*, pg. 1749
Thomas, H. Suzanne, Sr. V.P. & Sec.--Weatherford U.S., Inc., Houston, TX; *U.S. Public*, pg. 1749
Thomas, Jeff, Sr. V.P.-Mdsg.--Farm Fresh, Inc., Norfolk, VA; *U.S. Public*, pg. 1388
Thomas, Jerry F., Sr. V.P.--SCI Systems, Inc., Huntsville, AL; *U.S. Public*, pg. 1416
Thomas, John E., Sr. V.P.-Mktg. & Creative Services--Mutual of Omaha Insurance Company, Omaha, NE; *U.S.* Private, pg. 769
Thomas, John R., Sr. V.P.-Information & Technology--American Express Financial Advisor, Minneapolis, MN; *U.S. Public*, pg. 73
Thomas, Judy, Sr. V.P. & Natl. Brdcst. Dir.--Focus Media, Santa Monica, CA; *U.S. Private*, pg. 415
Thomas, Kenneth A., Sr. V.P.--Scott & Stringfellow Financial, Inc., Richmond, VA; *U.S. Public*, pg. 1445
Thomas, Kenneth A., Sr. V.P.--Scott & Stringfellow, Inc., Richmond, VA; *U.S. Public*, pg. 1445
Thomas, Kenneth A., Chief Fin. Officer & Sr. V.P.--Triarc Restaurant Group, Fort Lauderdale, FL; *U.S. Public*, pg. 1635
Thomas, Kerry A., Sr. V.P.-Integration Methods--Strategic Technology Services, Cerritos, CA; *Int'l*, pg. 1154
Thomas, Larry, Sr. V.P.-Corp. Communications--The Irvine Company, Newport Beach, CA; *U.S. Private*, pg. 575
Thomas, Lee M., Sr. V.P.-Paper--Georgia-Pacific Corporation, Atlanta, GA; *U.S. Public*, pg. 735
Thomas, Louis, Chief Fin. Officer & Sr. V.P.-Fin.--Associated Grocers of Florida, Inc., Miami, FL; *U.S. Private*, pg. 91
Thomas, Matthew W., Sr. V.P.-Commerical Lending--National Penn Bank, Boyertown, PA; *U.S. Public*, pg. 1159
Thomas, Ralph, Sr. V.P.-Matls.--Fender Musical Instruments, Scottsdale, AZ; *U.S. Private*, pg. 400
Thomas, Stewart, Sr. V.P. & Gen. Mgr.--Newsprint South, Inc., Jackson, MS; *U.S. Private*, pg. 797
Thomas, Thomas L., Chief Info. Officer & Sr. V.P.-Global Info. Sys.--3Com Corporation, Santa Clara, CA; *U.S. Public*, pg. 1603
Thomas, William E., Sr. V.P.--SAFECO Property & Casualty Insurance Companies, Seattle, WA; *U.S. Public*, pg. 1423
Thomason, Joel D., Sr. V.P. & Controller--The Pepper Companies, Inc., Chicago, IL; *U.S. Private*, pg. 851
Thomason, Robert S., Chief Fin. Officer & Sr. V.P.-Fin.--The Quaker Oats Company, Chicago, IL; *U.S. Public*, pg. 1347
Thomason, William P., Sr. V.P.--Policy Management Systems Europe, Ltd., Thames Ditton, United Kingdom; *U.S. Public*, pg. 1315
Thome, Kenneth L., Sr. V.P.-Fin. Opers.--General Mills, Inc., Minneapolis, MN; *U.S. Public*, pg. 717
Thompson, Bruce, V., Sr. V.P.-Admin. Mktg. & Gen. Counsel--Forest Oil Corporation, Denver, CO; *U.S. Public*, pg. 670
Thompson, C.J., Sr. V.P.-Opers.--OshKosh B'Gosh, Inc., Oshkosh, WI; *U.S. Public*, pg. 1232
Thompson, Christopher, Sr. V.P. & Gen. Mgr.--Fleishman-Hillard France, Paris, France; *U.S. Private*, pg. 411
Thompson, Darrell C., Sr. V.P. & Sr. Equity Mgr.--AMCORE Capital Management, Inc., Rockford, IL; *U.S. Public*, pg. 64
Thompson, David A., Sr. V.P.-Diagnostic Opers.--Abbott Laboratories, Abbott Park, IL; *U.S. Public*, pg. 13
Thompson, David K., Sr. V.P. & Asst. Gen. Counsel--The Walt Disney Company, Burbank, CA; *U.S. Public*, pg. 511
Thompson, Dean, Sr. V.P. & Mngmt. Supvr.--Dailey & Associates, West Hollywood, CA; *U.S. Public*, pg. 909
Thompson, Emerson L., Sr. V.P. & Dir.-Financial Services--SRA International Inc., Arlington, VA; *U.S. Private*, pg. 957
Thompson, Garry D., Sr. V.P.-Plumbing--Westburne Inc., Montreal, Canada; *Int'l*, pg. 1491
Thompson, Gerald W., Sr. V.P.-Sls.--Town & Country Fine Jewelry Group, Inc., Chelsea, MA; *U.S. Public*, pg. 1625
Thompson, Jennifer, Sr. V.P.--Midland Walwyn Inc., Toronto, Canada; *Int'l*, pg. 865
Thompson, Jim, Sr. V.P.--Broadway & Seymour, Inc., Charlotte, NC; *U.S. Public*, pg. 258
Thompson, John D., Sr. V.P.-Strategic & Bus. Devel.--The Dexter Corporation, Windsor Locks, CT; *U.S. Public*, pg. 504
Thompson, John M., Sr. V.P. & Grp. Exec.--International Business Machines Corporation, Armonk, NY; *U.S. Public*, pg. 895
Thompson, Kenneth J., Sr. V.P.--Atlantic Richfield Company, Los Angeles, CA; *U.S. Public*, pg. 144
Thompson, Kenton A., Sr. V.P.--Keycorp, Cleveland, OH; *U.S. Public*, pg. 954
Thompson, Kevin T., Sr. V.P. & Controller--First of America Bank Corporation, Kalamazoo, MI; *U.S. Public*, pg. 636
Thompson, Marissa, Sr. V.P. & Acct. Mgr.--Jerry & Ketchum, New York, NY; *U.S. Private*, pg. 616
Thompson, Michael, Sr. V.P. & Dir.-H.R.--CVB Financial Corp., Ontario, CA; *U.S. Public*, pg. 286
Thompson, Michael G., Sr. V.P., Gen. Counsel & Sec.--Entergy Corporation, New Orleans, LA; *U.S. Public*, pg. 585
Thompson, Olin W., Jr., Sr. V.P.-Process Bus. Grp.--Marcam Solutions, Inc., Newton, MA; *U.S. Public*, pg. 1042
Thompson, Phillip W., Sr. V.P.-Store Opers.--Family Dollar Stores, Inc., Matthews, NC; *U.S. Public*, pg. 612
Thompson, R. Duff, Sr. V.P.-Corp. Devel.--Novell, Inc., Orem, UT; *U.S. Public*, pg. 1203
Thompson, R. Keith, Sr. V.P.-Real Estate & Devel. & Asst. Sec.--Regal Cinemas Inc., Knoxville, TN; *U.S. Public*, pg. 1371
Thompson, Rosalind, Sr. V.P.-Human Resources--Fabri-Centers of America, Inc., Hudson, OH; *U.S. Public*, pg. 609
Thompson, Scott L., Chief Fin. Officer, Sr. V.P. & Treas.--Group 1 Automotive, Inc., Houston, TX; *U.S. Public*, pg. 767
Thompson, Sheldon L., Chief Admin. Officer & Sr. V.P.--Sun Company, Inc., Philadelphia, PA; *U.S. Public*, pg. 1530
Thompson, Terrie J., Sr. V.P.--AmClyde Engineered Products Co., Inc., Saint Paul, MN; *U.S. Public*, pg. 778
Thompson, Thomas, Sr. V.P.-Sls. & Mktg.--Friedman Industries, Inc., Houston, TX; *U.S. Public*, pg. 682
Thompson, Tim, Sr. V.P.--OppenheimerFunds Distributor, Inc., New York, NY; *U.S. Private*, pg. 818
Thompson, Tommy D., Sr. V.P.-San Diego County Corp. Banking--Southern California Bank, Newport Beach, CA; *U.S. Public*, pg. 1758
Thomsen, Jim, Sr. V.P.-Sls.--JanSport, Appleton, WI; *U.S. Public*, pg. 1702
Thomson, Gregory M., Sr. V.P.-H.R.--Owens Corning, Toledo, OH; *U.S. Public*, pg. 1236
Thomson, John A., Chief Fin. Officer, Sr. V.P. & Sec.--Renaissance Energy Ltd., Calgary, Canada; *Int'l*, pg. 1102
Thomson, William H., Sr. V.P. & Sr. Trust Officer--First National Bank of Blue Island, Blue Island, IL; *U.S. Private*, pg. 474
Thorell, Algot F., Jr., Sr. V.P. & Pres.-Chestnut Hill National Bank Div.--National Penn Bank, Boyertown, PA; *U.S. Public*, pg. 1159
Thorne, James R., Sr. V.P.--The Kroger Co., Cincinnati, OH; *U.S. Public*, pg. 967
Thorne, Richard, Sr. V.P.-Airline Business--Reed Travel Publishing, Dunstable, United Kingdom; *Int'l*, pg. 1097
Thorngren, Bertil, Sr. V.P.-Corp. Strategy--Telia AB, Farsta, Sweden; *Int'l*, pg. 1373
Thornton, Barbara, Sr. V.P.-Strategic Decision Services--May & Speh, Inc., Downers Grove, IL; *U.S. Public*, pg. 1063
Thornton, Daniel P., Sr. V.P.-Sls. & Mktg.--Progress Printing Company, Lynchburg, VA; *U.S. Private*, pg. 890
Thornton, Donald W., Sr. V.P. & Sec.--Vesta Insurance Group, Inc., Birmingham, AL; *U.S. Public*, pg. 1718
Thornton, Joseph, M., Sr. V.P.--Capitol Construction Group, Inc., Wheeling, IL; *U.S. Private*, pg. 206
Thornton, Wilmer F., Sr. V.P.--SouthTrust Corporation, Birmingham, AL; *U.S. Public*, pg. 1491
Thrasher, Scott, Sr. V.P.-Sls. & Mktg.--Toastmaster, Inc., Columbia, MO; *U.S. Public*, pg. 1619
Thrift, Bill, Sr. V.P.--Hawthorne Corp., Charleston, SC; *U.S. Private*, pg. 512
Throdahl, Mark C., Sr. V.P.-Global Opers.--Becton Dickinson & Company, Franklin Lakes, NJ; *U.S. Public*, pg. 199
Thune, Nelson F., Sr. V.P.-Opers. & Plng.--Hycor Biomedical, Inc., Irvine, CA; *U.S. Public*, pg. 851
Thurman, Donald W., Sr. V.P. & Gen. Mgr.-North America East--Anacomp, Inc., Indianapolis, IN; *U.S. Public*, pg. 106
Tibert, Alfred, Sr. V.P.--Barr & Barr, Inc., New York, NY; *U.S. Private*, pg. 117
Tickner, John J., Sr. V.P. & Sec.--Zenith National Insurance Corp., Woodland Hills, CA; *U.S. Public*, pg. 1790
Tidball, Robert N., Sr. V.P.--PLM Trailer Leasing, San Francisco, CA; *U.S. Public*, pg. 1241
Tiemeier, Gregory J., Sr. V.P.-Opers. & Tech.--RLI Corp., Peoria, IL; *U.S. Public*, pg. 1356
Tierjen, James R., Sr. V.P. & Gen. Auditor--Comerica Incorporated, Detroit, MI; *U.S. Public*, pg. 408
Tierney, David S., MD, Sr. V.P.-Medical & Regulatory Affairs--Roberts Pharmaceutical Corporation, Eatontown, NJ; *U.S. Public*, pg. 1393
Tierney, Fred, Sr. V.P.--Outdoor Services, New York, NY; *U.S. Private*, pg. 1166
Tierney, Kevin J., Sr. V.P., Gen. Counsel & Sec.--UNUM Corporation, Portland, ME; *U.S. Public*, pg. 1699
Tighe, Gary, Chief Fin. Officer & Sr. V.P.--Staff Builders Inc., Lake Success, NY; *U.S. Public*, pg. 1501
Tighe, Michael R., Sr. V.P.-Worldwide Concrete--Corrpro Companies, Inc., Medina, OH; *U.S. Public*, pg. 451
Tighe, Steven, Sr. V.P.-Human Resources--Time Insurance, Milwaukee, WI; *Int'l*, pg. 499
Tikhman, Anatoly, Sr. V.P.--Quarterdeck Corp., Marina Del Rey, CA; *U.S. Public*, pg. 1350
Tiles, Wendy, Sr. V.P. & Acct. Mng. Dir.--Young & Rubicam New York, New York, NY; *U.S. Private*, pg. 1198
Tilghman, Richard H., Pres.-Pepper Environ. Tech.& Sr. V.P.--The Pepper Companies, Inc., Chicago, IL; *U.S. Private*, pg. 851
Tillett, Wesley, Sr. V.P. & Dir.-Store Opers.-Licensed Div.--J. Baker, Inc., Canton, MA; *U.S. Public*, pg. 167
Tilly, Duncan F., Sr. V.P.-Exec. Resources--CT Financial Services, Inc., Toronto, Canada; *Int'l*, pg. 112
Tilney, Elizabeth A., Sr. V.P.-Corp. Mktg.--Enron Corp., Houston, TX; *U.S. Public*, pg. 584
Tilton, Glenn F., Pres.-Global Bus. & Sr. V.P.--Texaco Inc., White Plains, NY; *U.S. Public*, pg. 1582
Timinski, Bob, Sr. V.P. & Gen. Mgr.-Mdsg.--The Sports Authority Inc., Fort Lauderdale, FL; *U.S. Public*, pg. 1499
Timm, Marcia Marrs, Sr. V.P. & Controller--First Security Bank of Idaho, N.A., Boise, ID; *U.S. Public*, pg. 637
Timmerman, Jose, Sr. V.P.-Opers.--Tupperware Corporation, Orlando, FL; *U.S. Public*, pg. 1644
Timmons, Shirley A., Sr. V.P. & Mgr.-Mktg.--Willis Corroon Corp. of Kansas, Wichita, KS; *Int'l*, pg. 1506
Tindall, Dana, Sr. V.P.-Legal & Regulatory Affairs--General Communication, Inc., Anchorage, AK; *U.S. Public*, pg. 708
Tindall, William L., Sr. V.P.-Pension Div.--American United Life Insurance Company, Indianapolis, IN; *U.S. Private*, pg. 64
Tinebra, Vince, Sr. V.P.-Sls.--Vanstar Corporation, Pleasanton, CA; *U.S. Public*, pg. 1708
Tinmouth, WilliamW., Sr. V.P.-Corp. Affairs & Law--Cambridge Shopping Centres Limited, Toronto, Canada; *Int'l*, pg. 253
Tinstman, Thomas, Sr. V.P.--Cerner Corporation, Kansas City, MO; *U.S. Public*, pg. 331
Tipton, James W., Sr. V.P.-Nonregulated Activities--KU Energy, Lexington, KY; *U.S. Public*, pg. 940
Tipton, James W., Sr. V.P.-Nonutility Activities--KU Capital Corporation, Lexington, KY; *U.S. Public*, pg. 941
Tirado del Pozzo, Jorge Antonio, Sr. V.P.-Beverages Div.--Grupo Continental S.A., Tampico, Mexico; *Int'l*, pg. 573
Tischler, Ben R., Sr. V.P.-Managed Care--D & K Healthcare Resources, Inc., Saint Louis, MO; *U.S. Public*, pg. 471
Tishkoff, Stuart M., Sr. V.P. & Gen. Mgr.-Mdse., Shoe Corp. of America--J. Baker, Inc., Canton, MA; *U.S. Public*, pg. 167
Titz, Wolfgang, Dr., Sr. V.P.--Landesbank Rheinland-Pfalz, Mainz, Germany; *Int'l*, pg. 799
Tobin, Thomas M., Sr. V.P., Gen. Counsel & Corp. Sec.--Odyssey Reinsurance Corporation, New York, NY; *Int'l*, pg. 1258
Tocheff, Helen, Sr. V.P.-Natl. Brdcst.--Zenith Media Services, Inc., New York, NY; *U.S. Private*, pg. 1204
Tochteman, David, Sr. V.P.-Creative Affairs--Carsey-Werner Company, LLC, Studio City, CA; *U.S. Private*, pg. 216

Tocklin, Adrian M., Sr. V.P.--Continental Assurance Company, Chicago, IL; *U.S. Private*, pg. 267
Tocklin, Adrian M., Sr. V.P.-Diversified Opers.--CNA Insurance Companies, Chicago, IL; *U.S. Public*, pg. 1010
Toerres, Claude, Sr. V.P.-Fin.--Systra-Sofretu-Sofrerail, Paris, France; *Int'l*, pg. 1165
Toffler, Van, Sr. V.P.-Entertainment & Bus. Devel. & Gen. Mgr.--MTV: Music Television, New York, NY; *U.S. Private*, pg. 779
Tokuhisa, Roy T., Sr. V.P.-Direct Sls. Opers.--Servco Pacific Inc., Honolulu, HI; *U.S. Private*, pg. 986
Tokumitsu, Yoshito, Sr. V.P. & Asst. to Chief Exec.--National Steel Corporation, Mishawaka, IN; *Int'l*, pg. 902
Tokushima, Takayoshi, Sr. V.P. & Dir.--Kodansha Ltd., Tokyo, Japan; *Int'l*, pg. 742
Tolis, Gust, Chief Fin. Officer & Sr. V.P.--Chicago Title & Trust Co., Chicago, IL; *U.S. Public*, pg. 42
Tolis, Gust J., Chief Fin. Officer & Sr. V.P.--Chicago Title Insurance Co., Chicago, IL; *U.S. Public*, pg. 42
Tollefson, Dean R., Sr. V.P.--Firstar Bank of Minnesota, Bloomington, MN; *U.S. Public*, pg. 643
Tolliver, Norris L., Sr. V.P.-Personal Markets--SunTrust Banks, Inc., Atlanta, GA; *U.S. Public*, pg. 1537
Tolonen, Jim, Chief Fin. Officer & Sr. V.P.--Novell Inc., San Jose, CA; *U.S. Public*, pg. 1203
Tomack, John K., Sr. V.P.-Mktg. Communications--First National Bank of Chicago, Chicago, IL; *U.S. Public*, pg. 627
Tomain, Michael J., Sr. V.P.--General Reinsurance Corp., Stamford, CT; *U.S. Public*, pg. 725
Tomblinson, Ted, Grp. Sr. V.P. & Dir.-MIS--Golden West Financial Corporation, Oakland, CA; *U.S. Public*, pg. 750
Tomechko, Edward, Sr. V.P. & Treas.--County Seat Stores, Inc., Dallas, TX; *U.S. Private*, pg. 279
Tomko, Carole W., Sr. V.P.-Human Resources--Cardinal Health Inc., Dublin, OH; *U.S. Public*, pg. 304
Tomlin, Melodye Mayes, Sr. V.P. & Gen. Auditor--First Virginia Banks, Inc., Falls Church, VA; *U.S. Public*, pg. 641
Tomlinson, Janice M., Sr. V.P.--Chubb & Son, Inc., Warren, NJ; *U.S. Public*, pg. 355
Tomlinson, Mack, Sr. V.P.-Sls. & Mktg.--Carfel, Inc., Miami, FL; *U.S. Private*, pg. 210
Tompkins, Jack I., Chief Information, Admin. & Acctg. Officer & Sr. V.P.--Enron Corp., Houston, TX; *U.S. Public*, pg. 584
Tompkins, Jeffrey, Sr. V.P.--Edelman Worldwide, Inc., New York, NY; *U.S. Private*, pg. 362
Tompkins, Wayne, Sr. V.P.-Opers.--Eagle USA Airfreight, Houston, TX; *U.S. Public*, pg. 547
Tonani, Ronald, Sr. V.P.--Pac Rim Holding Corporation, Woodland Hills, CA; *U.S. Public*, pg. 1246
Tonani, Ronald, Sr. V.P.--The Pacific Rim Assurance Company, Woodland Hills, CA; *U.S. Public*, pg. 1246
Tong, Bryant J., Sr. V.P.--Phoenix American Incorporated, San Rafael, CA; *U.S. Private*, pg. 862
Tonkko, Maija, Sr. V.P.-Fin. & Control--Oy Nokia Ab/Nokia Group, Helsinki, Finland; *Int'l*, pg. 951
Toole, Lawrence J., Sr. V.P.-Human Resources--General Electric Capital Services, Inc., Stamford, CT; *U.S. Public*, pg. 711
Toolen, John T., Sr. V.P.-Sls.--WestPoint Stevens Inc., West Point, GA; *U.S. Public*, pg. 1762
Toomey, Kevin, Sr. V.P. & Gen. Mgr.-Sls.--Kayser-Roth Corporation, Inc., Greensboro, NC; *Int'l*, pg. 576
Toomey, Rodger, Sr. V.P.-Mktg. & Bus. Devel.--Food Services of America, Seattle, WA; *U.S. Private*, pg. 987
Toothaker, Barry C., Sr. V.P.-Retail Delivery Grp.--Citizens Trust Company, Providence, RI; *Int'l*, pg. 1132
Topham, Verl R., Sr. V.P. & Gen. Counsel--PacifiCorp, Portland, OR; *U.S. Public*, pg. 1251
Toppi, Angela, Chief Fin. Officer, Sr. V.P., Treas. & Sec.--Trans-Lux Corporation, Norwalk, CT; *U.S. Public*, pg. 1628
Torgerson, William T., Sr. V.P.-External Affairs & Gen. Counsel--Potomac Electric Power Company, Washington, DC; *U.S. Public*, pg. 1318
Torii, Takashi, Assoc. Sr. V.P.--NEC Corporation, Tokyo, Japan; *Int'l*, pg. 899
Torkar, Bob, Sr. V.P.-Fin., Treas. & Chief Acctg. Officer--Jackpot Enterprises, Inc., Las Vegas, NV; *U.S. Public*, pg. 920
Tornowski, S. Joseph, Sr. V.P.-Tech. Opers.--CellPro, Incorporated, Bothell, WA; *U.S. Public*, pg. 320
Toro, Cynthia, Sr. V.P.-Commercial Loans--Banco Popular de Puerto Rico, San Juan, PR; *U.S. Public*, pg. 175
Toro, Ricardo, Sr. V.P.-Corp. Banking--Banco Popular de Puerto Rico, San Juan, PR; *U.S. Public*, pg. 175
Torrence, Corey, Sr. V.P. & Gen. Mgr.--Logica, Inc., Lexington, MA; *Int'l*, pg. 814
Torrence, Samuel L., Sr. V.P.--Westvaco Corporation, New York, NY; *U.S. Public*, pg. 1762
Torres, Angel, Sr. V.P. & Gen. Mgr.--Bacardi-Martini Caribbean Corporation, Catano, PR; *Int'l*, pg. 132
Torres, Javier, Sr. V.P.--Banco Santander, Madrid, Spain; *Int'l*, pg. 143
Tortelli, Ronald C., Sr. V.P.-Human Resources--SuperValu, Inc., Eden Prairie, MN; *U.S. Public*, pg. 1540
Tortorella, Albert J., Sr. V.P.-Communications--UST Inc., Greenwich, CT; *U.S. Public*, pg. 1660
Tosaka, Kaoru, Assoc. Sr. V.P.--NEC Corporation, Tokyo, Japan; *Int'l*, pg. 899
Toth, Steve, Sr. V.P.--RehabCare Group, Inc., Saint Louis, MO; *U.S. Public*, pg. 1373
Toto, Joseph P., Sr. V.P. & Treas.--Karnak Corporation, Clark, NJ; *U.S. Private*, pg. 607
Totter, Donald H., Sr. V.P.--J.J. Kenny Co., Inc., New York, NY; *U.S. Public*, pg. 1070
Touanen, P., Sr. V.P.--P.R. Newswire Association Inc., New York, NY; *Int'l*, pg. 1443
Toucher, Brenda, Sr. V.P. & Exec. Producer--DMB&B New York, New York, NY; *U.S. Private*, pg. 302
Touhill, C. Joseph, Exec. V.P.--EG & G Environmental, Inc., Pittsburgh, PA; *U.S. Public*, pg. 543
Toulot, J., Sr. V.P.-Equity Investments--Compagnie de Suez, Paris, France; *Int'l*, pg. 313
Touma, Gaby, Sr. V.P.-Intl.--National Bank of Canada, Montreal, Canada; *Int'l*, pg. 907
Toups, Leonard, Jr., Sr. V.P.--Hibernia Corporation, New Orleans, LA; *U.S. Public*, pg. 825
Toura, Toshio, Exec. V.P.--Chori Co., Ltd., Osaka, Japan; *Int'l*, pg. 288
Tow, Claire L., Sr. V.P.--Century Communications Corp., New Canaan, CT; *U.S. Public*, pg. 329
Tow, Frank, V.P. & Sr. V.P.-Broadband Networks--Century Communications Corp., New Canaan, CT; *U.S. Public*, pg. 329
Towers, John R., Sr. V.P., Gen. Counsel & Sec.--State Street Bank & Trust Co., Boston, MA; *U.S. Public*, pg. 1513
Towler, Robert A., Sr. V.P.-Bus. Devel.--Alberta Energy Company, Ltd., Calgary, Canada; *Int'l*, pg. 48
Townley, Matthew B., Sr. V.P.--Shared Medical Systems Corporation, Malvern, PA; *U.S. Public*, pg. 1463
Townsend, Christopher G., Sr. V.P. & Gen. Counsel--Host Marriott Corporation, Bethesda, MD; *U.S. Public*, pg. 841
Townsend, James W., Jr., Sr. V.P. & Sec.--First Charter Corporation, Concord, NC; *U.S. Public*, pg. 627
Townsend, Linda W., Sr. V.P.--Century Bancshares, Inc., Washington, DC; *U.S. Public*, pg. 328
Tozun, Orhan, Sr. V.P.-Engrng.--International Microcircuits, Inc., Milpitas, CA; *U.S. Private*, pg. 571
Trace, Ronald B., Sr. V.P.--CT Financial Services, Inc., Toronto, Canada; *Int'l*, pg. 112
Tracey, Doug, Sr. V.P.-Natl. Distr. & Managing Dir.-On Cue--Musicland Group Inc., Minnetonka, MN; *U.S. Public*, pg. 1142
Tracey, Doug, Sr. V.P., Mng. Dir.-On Cue & Natl. Distr.--On Cue, Inc., Minnetonka, MN; *U.S. Public*, pg. 1142
Tracey, Timothy, Sr. V.P.-Credit Policy--Summit Bancorp, Princeton, NJ; *U.S. Public*, pg. 1527
Tracey, Vinnie, Sr. V.P.--RE/MAX International, Inc., Englewood, CO; *U.S. Private*, pg. 912
Traff, Tim L., Sr. V.P.--United States Filter Corporation, Palm Desert, CA; *U.S. Public*, pg. 1681
Tramontina, Al, Sr. V.P. & Acct. Grp. Dir.--Kragie/Newell, Des Moines, IA; *U.S. Private*, pg. 634
Tran, Khanh T., Chief Fin. Officer & Sr. V.P.--Pacific Life Insurance Company, Newport Beach, CA; *U.S. Private*, pg. 831
Transier, William L., Chief Fin. Officer & Sr. V.P.--Seagull Energy Corporation, Houston, TX; *U.S. Public*, pg. 1450
Trapnell, Britt, Sr. V.P. & Dir.-Mktg.--Caribbean American Life Assurance Company, Hato Rey, PR; *U.S. Public*, pg. 67
Trapnell, Joan P., Sr. V.P.--UAM Investment Services, Inc., Boston, MA; *U.S. Public*, pg. 1674
Trapp, Tim, Sr. V.P.-Design--Rock Bottom Restaurants, Louisville, CO; *U.S. Public*, pg. 1396
Trastek, Victor F., Sr. V.P.--The Metal Ware Corp., Two Rivers, WI; *U.S. Private*, pg. 734
Traver, William, Sr. V.P.-Mfg.--World Color-Chicago Div., Elk Grove Village, IL; *U.S. Public*, pg. 1778
Travers, Gilbert Anthony, Sr. V.P. & Country Mgr.--Bank of America NT&SA, Manila, Philippines; *U.S. Public*, pg. 182
Travis, Bruce, Sr. V.P.-Sls.--Duracell International Inc., Bethel, CT; *U.S. Public*, pg. 743
Traw, William L., Sr. V.P.--National Technical Systems, Inc., Calabasas, CA; *U.S. Public*, pg. 1161
Traynor, Francis M., Jr., Sr. V.P.-Investments & Dir.--The Robinson-Humphrey Company, Inc., Atlanta, GA; *U.S. Public*, pg. 1633
Trebek, Elaine, Sr. V.P.-Mktg.--Arcade Inc., Chattanooga, TN; *U.S. Private*, pg. 79
Treder, Bill, Sr. V.P.-Central Region--Durham Transportation, Inc., Austin, TX; *U.S. Private*, pg. 348
Treinen, David C., Sr. V.P.-Fin. & Sec.--International Aluminum Corporation, Monterey Park, CA; *U.S. Public*, pg. 894
Tremayne, John C., Chief Fin. Officer & Sr. V.P.--EdperBrascan Corporation, Toronto, Canada; *Int'l*, pg. 433
Tremblay, Dale E., Chief Fin. Officer & Sr. V.P.--Precision Drilling Corporation, Calgary, Canada; *Int'l*, pg. 1066
Treml, Raymond F., Sr. V.P.-Mfg.--JLG Industries, Inc., McConnellsburg, PA; *U.S. Public*, pg. 918
Tremse, John J., Sr. V.P.-Information Systems--Bayer Corporation, Pittsburgh, PA; *Int'l*, pg. 172
Trepant, Philippe, Sr. V.P.-Intl.--Elf Aquitane, Paris, France; *Int'l*, pg. 444
Treschon, Lotta, Sr. V.P.-Investor Rels.--Skandinaviska Enskilda Banken, Stockholm, Sweden; *Int'l*, pg. 1258
Tretowicz, Richard A., FSA, Sr. V.P.-Chief Actuary--Farmers and Traders Life Insurance Co., Syracuse, NY; *U.S. Private*, pg. 394
Trible, Clayton J., Jr., Sr. V.P. & Treas.--Standard Federal Bank, Troy, MI; *Int'l*, pg. 10
Tribone, Thomas A., Sr. V.P.--AES Corporation, Arlington, VA; *U.S. Public*, pg. 5
Tridico, Louis, Sr. V.P. & Creative Dir.--Levenson & Hill, Inc., Dallas, TX; *U.S. Private*, pg. 662
Triefus, Robert, Sr. V.P.-Global Communications & Promo.--Calvin Klein, Inc., New York, NY; *U.S. Private*, pg. 202
Trigardi, John, Sr. V.P.-Corp. Affairs & Franchise Opers.--TCG International Inc., Burnaby, Canada; *Int'l*, pg. 1336
Trigg, Donald C., Sr. V.P.-Sec. & Gen. Counsel--Anthem, Inc., Indianapolis, IN; *U.S. Private*, pg. 76
Trimble, James M., Sr. V.P.-Exploration & Production--Cabot Oil & Gas Corporation, Houston, TX; *U.S. Public*, pg. 289
Tringale, Steven, Sr. V.P.-External Affairs--Blue Cross and Blue Shield of Massachusetts, Boston, MA; *U.S. Private*, pg. 151
Tripp, Kevin H., Sr. V.P.-Pharmacy Sls. & Opers.--American Drug Stores Inc., Oak Brook, IL; *U.S. Public*, pg. 93
Tristani, Dennis C., Sr. V.P.-Credit Review--Banco Popular de Puerto Rico, San Juan, PR; *U.S. Public*, pg. 175
Troeften, Jon, Sr. V.P.-Information--Orkla A.S.A., Oslo, Norway; *Int'l*, pg. 1010
Troia, S.A., Sr. V.P.--Marshall & Ilsley Corporation, Milwaukee, WI; *U.S. Public*, pg. 1049
Trost, Bruce, Sr. V.P.-Property & Casualty Co., Claims Div.--United Farm Family Life Insurance Co., Indianapolis, IN; *U.S. Private*, pg. 1122
Trost, Robert A., Sr. V.P.-Rates & Accouting--Mississippi River Transmission, Saint Louis, MO; *U.S. Public*, pg. 843
Trotman, Keith E., Sr. V.P.--Zenith Insurance Company, Woodland Hills, CA; *U.S. Public*, pg. 1791
Trout, Terry, Sr. V.P. & Cashier--Stephenville Bank & Trust Co., Stephenville, TX; *U.S. Public*, pg. 633
Troutman, Edward L., Sr. V.P.--Foremost Insurance Co., Caledonia, MI; *U.S. Public*, pg. 667
Truax, C. Barry, Sr. V.P. & Grp. Supvr.-Acct. Services--Gray Kirk/VanSant Advertising, Inc., Baltimore, MD; *U.S. Private*, pg. 472
Trubeck, William L., Chief Fin. Officer & Sr. V.P.--International Multifoods Corporation, Minneapolis, MN; *U.S. Public*, pg. 900
Trudeau, Paul, Sr. V.P.-Bus. Devel./Royal Crown--Triarc Beverage Group, White Plains, NY; *U.S. Public*, pg. 1635
Truitt, Roger, Sr. V.P.--Atlantic Richfield Company, Los Angeles, CA; *U.S. Public*, pg. 144
Trukenbrod, William S., Exec. V.P.-Credit Policy--Northern Trust Corporation, Chicago, IL; *U.S. Public*, pg. 1195
Trumbo, Kirby, Sr. V.P.-Mktg. & Product Mngmt.--First American Corporation, Nashville, TN; *U.S. Public*, pg. 624
Trumbore, John, Sr. V.P.--Harris, Baio & McCullough Inc., Philadelphia, PA; *U.S. Private*, pg. 504
Trunk, Russell J., Sr. V.P.-Opers.--Stokely USA, Inc., Oconomowoc, WI; *U.S. Public*, pg. 1518
Trupiano, Teresa, Sr. V.P.--Champion Aluminum Window Corporation, Syosset, NY; *U.S. Private*, pg. 227
Truswell, Derek P., Chief Fin. Officer & Sr. V.P.--IPL Energy Inc., Calgary, Canada; *Int'l*, pg. 651
Truswell, Derek P., Chief Fin. Officer & Sr. V.P.--Interprovincial Pipe Line Inc., Edmonton, Canada; *Int'l*, pg. 652
Tsai, Ken, Sr. V.P. & Pres.-Solectron Asia--Solectron Corporation, Milpitas, CA; *U.S. Public*, pg. 1483
Tschantz, Ralph F., Sr. V.P.--Illinova Energy Partners, Inc., Oak Brook, IL; *U.S. Public*, pg. 870
Tschirhart, Paul M., Sr. V.P., Gen. Counsel & Sec.--The Hertz Corporation, Park Ridge, NJ; *U.S. Public*, pg. 664
Tse, Stephen Y.N., Sr. V.P.--American International Group, Inc., New York, NY; *U.S. Public*, pg. 83
Tsubouchi, Daniel T., Sr. V.P.-Corp. Affairs & Fin. & Sec.--Mark Resources Inc., Calgary, Canada; *Int'l*, pg. 842
Tsuchiya, Ikuo, Sr. Mng. Dir.--Juki Corporation, Tokyo, Japan; *Int'l*, pg. 716
Tsukada, Akira, Sr. V.P.--Mitsubishi International Corporation, New York, NY; *Int'l*, pg. 871
Tsuruta, Kuniaki, Sr. V.P.-Pur.--Continental Airlines, Houston, TX; *U.S. Public*, pg. 439
Tsusaka, Jun, Sr. V.P.-Merger/Acquisition--Millicom International Cellular SA, Bertrange, Luxembourg; *Int'l*, pg. 867
Tsuura, Takashi, Sr. Mng. Dir.-Iron & Steel Grp.--Sumitomo Corporation, Tokyo, Japan; *Int'l*, pg. 1312
Tubbs, Robert J., Exec. V.P., Gen. Counsel & Sec.--Coltec Holdings Inc, Charlotte, NC; *U.S. Public*, pg. 401
Tubbs, Robert J., Sr. V.P. & Gen. Counsel--Coltec Industries Inc., Charlotte, NC; *U.S. Public*, pg. 401
Tubito, Vincent, Sr. V.P.-HR--Jan Bell Marketing Inc., Sunrise, FL; *U.S. Public*, pg. 207
Tucker, C.E., Sr. V.P.--Crowder Construction Co., Charlotte, NC; *U.S. Private*, pg. 291
Tucker, M. Douglas, Chief Fin. & Acctg. Officer, Sr. V.P.-Fin. & Sec.--BeautiControl Cosmetics, Inc., Carrollton, TX; *U.S. Public*, pg. 198
Tucker, Mike, Sr. V.P.-H.R.--Baxter International Inc., Deerfield, IL; *U.S. Public*, pg. 196
Tuckman, Michael S., Sr. V.P.-Nuclear Generation--Duke Energy Corporation, Charlotte, NC; *U.S. Public*, pg. 534
Tudanger, Edward, Sr. V.P.-Southeast Reg.--Tenet Healthcare Corporation, Santa Barbara, CA; *U.S. Public*, pg. 1576
Tull, Richard M., Sr. V.P.-Construction Lending--Prime Bank, Philadelphia, PA; *U.S. Public*, pg. 1326
Tully, William P., Sr. V.P.--Chubb & Son, Inc., Warren, NJ; *U.S. Public*, pg. 355
Tumber, William T., Sr. V.P.--C.R. Bard, Inc., Murray Hill, NJ; *U.S. Public*, pg. 189
Tung, Theodore H., Sr. V.P. & Economist--National City Corporation, Cleveland, OH; *U.S. Public*, pg. 1154
Tuominen, F. William, Sr. V.P. & Chief Tech. & Environ. Officer--Ecolab Inc., Saint Paul, MN; *U.S. Public*, pg. 562
Turchi, Kenneth L., Sr. V.P.--First Indiana Corporation, Indianapolis, IN; *U.S. Public*, pg. 1484
Turcotte, Jeffrey, Sr. V.P.--Intertek Testing Services, Andover, MA; *Int'l*, pg. 672
Turek, Anthony J., Sr. V.P.--DVI, Inc., Doylestown, PA; *U.S. Public*, pg. 476
Turek, Jan P., Sr. V.P.-Biological Prods./Pharmaceutical Div.--Bayer Corporation, Pittsburgh, PA; *Int'l*, pg. 172
Turgeon, Guy, Chief Fin. Officer & Sr. V.P.--St. Lawrence Cement Inc., Montreal, Canada; *Int'l*, pg. 628
Turkish, Gary, Sr. V.P.--Century Business Credit Corporation, New York, NY; *U.S. Private*, pg. 225
Turmes, Joseph, Sr. V.P.-Opers.--Horizon/CMS Healthcare Corporation, Albuquerque, NM; *U.S. Public*, pg. 836
Turnbaugh, Charles W., Sr. V.P. & Gen. Counsel--Riggs National Corporation, Washington, DC; *U.S. Public*, pg. 1389
Turnbull, A.M. Gordon, Chief Fin. Officer & Sr. V.P.-Fin.--Hawker Siddeley Canada Inc., Mississauga, Canada; *Int'l*, pg. 604
Turnbull, Alexander W., Chief Fin. Officer & Sr. V.P.--Ocean Spray Cranberries, Inc., Middleboro, MA; *U.S. Private*, pg. 811

Turnbull, Gene, Sr. V.P.-Sls.--Genuine Parts Company, Atlanta, GA; *U.S. Public*, pg. 732
Turnbull, Mike, Sr. V.P.-Mktg.--AMC, Inc., Atlanta, GA; *U.S. Private*, pg. 6
Turner, A.E., Sr. V.P.-Opers.--Triton Energy Limited, Dallas, TX; *U.S. Public*, pg. 1640
Turner, Byron, Sr. V.P.-S. Central Reg.--Sterling Electronics Corporation, Houston, TX; *U.S. Public*, pg. 1051
Turner, Charles H., Sr. V.P.-Stores--Pier 1 Imports, Inc., Fort Worth, TX; *U.S. Public*, pg. 1295
Turner, Clay, Sr. V.P. & Creative Dir.--Ackerman McQueen, Inc., Colorado Springs, CO; *U.S. Private*, pg. 13
Turner, Curtis L., Sr. V.P.-Mktg. & Devel.--Mapco Natural Gas Liquids Inc., Tulsa, OK; *U.S. Public*, pg. 1042
Turner, Daniel L., Sr. V.P.-Fin.--UMB Financial Corporation, Kansas City, MO; *U.S. Public*, pg. 1653
Turner, George P., Sr. V.P.-Merger Transition--Conrail, Inc., Philadelphia, PA; *U.S. Public*, pg. 431
Turner, Harold W., Sr. V.P.--Hibernia Corporation, New Orleans, LA; *U.S. Public*, pg. 825
Turner, J. Timothy, Sr. V.P.-Sls. & Mktg.--Old Dominion Freight Line, Inc., High Point, NC; *U.S. Public*, pg. 1216
Turner, James G., Sr. V.P.-Tech.--R.R. Donnelley & Sons Company, Chicago, IL; *U.S. Public*, pg. 517
Turner, John, Sr. V.P. & Grp. Dir.--DavisElen Advertising, Inc., Los Angeles, CA; *U.S. Private*, pg. 316
Turner, John B., Sr. V.P.-Education, Training & Diversity--Tennessee Valley Authority, Knoxville, TN; *U.S. Public*, pg. 1580
Turner, John T., Sr. V.P.-Corp. Devel.--Group 1 Automotive, Inc., Houston, TX; *U.S. Public*, pg. 767
Turner, Joseph L. Jr., Sr. V.P.-Major Accts.--NIPSCO Industries, Inc., Hammond, IN; *U.S. Public*, pg. 1185
Turner, Joseph L., Jr., Sr. V.P.-Major Accounts--Northern Indiana Public Service Company, Hammond, IN; *U.S. Public*, pg. 1185
Turner, M. Caroline, Sr. V.P., Gen. Counsel & Asst. Sec.--Adolph Coors Company, Golden, CO; *U.S. Public*, pg. 445
Turner, M. Caroline, Sr. V.P., Gen. Counsel & Asst. Sec.--Coors Brewing Company, Golden, CO; *U.S. Public*, pg. 445
Turner, Marj, Sr. V.P.-Gen Mdse. Mgr.--The Bon Marche, Inc., Seattle, WA; *U.S. Public*, pg. 617
Turner, Mark, Sr. V.P. & Controller--WSFS Financial Corporation, Wilmington, DE; *U.S. Public*, pg. 1728
Turner, Ritay, Sr. V.P.-Mktg.--NationsBank of Texas, N.A., Dallas, TX; *U.S. Public*, pg. 1163
Turner, Robert, Sr. V.P.--Jeld-Wen, Inc., Klamath Falls, OR; *U.S. Private*, pg. 585
Turner, Roger J., Sr. V.P.-Commercial Loans--Huntington National Bank, Morgantown, WV; *U.S. Public*, pg. 850
Turner, Ron L., Sr. V.P.--Kurtz Bros., Inc., Clearfield, PA; *U.S. Private*, pg. 637
Turner, Sherri, Sr. V.P.--Tonka Corporation, Pawtucket, RI; *U.S. Public*, pg. 797
Turney, Sharon, Sr. V.P. & Gen. Mgr.-Mdsg.--Neiman Marcus Co., Dallas, TX; *U.S. Public*, pg. 785
Turny, Julie, Sr. V.P., Chief Mktg. Officer-Bus.-to-Bus. & Dir.--Noble & Associates Promotion Group, Springfield, MO; *U.S. Private*, pg. 800
Turpin, Jayne A., Sr. V.P.-Opers.--Inverness Corp., Fair Lawn, NJ; *U.S. Private*, pg. 574
Turunen, Eero, Sr. V.P.-Sls. & Mktg.--Valmet Corporation, Helsinki, Finland; *Int'l*, pg. 1447
Turunen, Seppo, Sr. V.P.-H.R.--Outokumpu Oyj, Espoo, Finland; *Int'l*, pg. 1015
Tusa, Bob, Sr. V.P.--Hibernia Corporation, New Orleans, LA; *U.S. Public*, pg. 825
Tusa, David P., Chief Fin. Officer & Sr. V.P.--Tyler Corporation, Dallas, TX; *U.S. Public*, pg. 1651
Tuszynski, R.J., Sr. V.P.--B.C. Ziegler & Co., West Bend, WI; *U.S. Public*, pg. 1792
Tuters, Peter V., Sr. V.P.-Investments--American General Corporation, Houston, TX; *U.S. Public*, pg. 76
Tuttle, Elizabeth A., Sr. V.P. & Treas.--ITT Corporation, New York, NY; *U.S. Public*, pg. 1512
Twoby, John, Sr. V.P.-Mktg.--Interval International Inc., Miami, FL; *U.S. Public*, pg. 320
Twong, Donald H., Sr. V.P.--Collins Electric Company, Inc., Chicopee, MA; *U.S. Private*, pg. 253
Twonig, Steve, Chief Fin. Officer & Sr. V.P.--The Donohoe Companies, Inc., Washington, DC; *U.S. Private*, pg. 340
Twyble, William J., Sr. V.P.-Res. & Devel. Mktg. & Customer Satisfaction--The Lincoln Electric Company, Cleveland, OH; *U.S. Public*, pg. 996
Twyver, David A., Pres.-Wireless Systems & Sr. V.P.--Northern Telecom Limited, Brampton, Canada; *Int'l*, pg. 968
Tyler, Robert L., Chief Fin. Officer & Sr. V.P.--Aliant Communications Inc., Lincoln, NE; *U.S. Public*, pg. 40
Tyler, Tee W., Sr. V.P.--Zions Mortgage Company, Salt Lake City, UT; *U.S. Public*, pg. 1793
Tyler, William K., Sr. V.P. & Asst. Treas.--The Lincoln National Life Insurance Co., Fort Wayne, IN; *U.S. Public, pg. 998*
Tyler, William K., Sr. V.P.--Underwriters & Management Services Inc., Indianapolis, IN; *U.S. Public*, pg. 998
Typermass, Arthur G., Sr. V.P. & Treas.--Metropolitan Life Insurance Co., New York, NY; *U.S. Private*, pg. 737
Tyree, David L., Sr. V.P.--Associates Commercial Equipment Div., Dallas, TX; *U.S. Public*, pg. 663
Tyson, Andrew R., Sr. V.P.-Corp. Devel.--Keycorp, Cleveland, OH; *U.S. Public*, pg. 954
Tyson, Bernard J., Sr. V.P.-East Bay Area.--Kaiser Permanente, Oakland, CA; *U.S. Private*, pg. 605
Tytel, Bud, Sr. V.P.-Intl.--Mattel, Inc., El Segundo, CA; *U.S. Public*, pg. 1057
Uberstine, Mitchell, Sr. V.P. & Mgr.-Gen. Svcs.--FirstFed Financial Corp., Santa Monica, CA; *U.S. Public*, pg. 645
Uchida, Isao, Sr. V.P.--Yokogawa Electric Corporation, Tokyo, Japan; *Int'l*, pg. 1520
Uchida, Michio, Sr. V.P.-Freight & Mail Dept.--Japan Airlines Company, Ltd., Tokyo, Japan; *Int'l*, pg. 699
Uchtman, Edwin, Jr., Sr. V.P., Gen. Mgr.-Mdsg.-Men's, Children's & Sporting Goods--Venture Stores, Inc., O Fallon, MO; *U.S. Public*, pg. 1716
Ucles, Jose Ignacio, Sr. V.P. & Legal Counsel--Banco Santander, Madrid, Spain; *Int'l*, pg. 143
Uda, Yoshinori, Sr. V.P.--Nippon Telegraph and Telephone Corporation, Tokyo, Japan; *Int'l*, pg. 940
Ueba, Joichi, Sr. V.P.--Yokogawa Electric Corporation, Tokyo, Japan; *Int'l*, pg. 1520
Uehlein, James L., Sr. V.P.--Deerfield Manufacturing Co., Inc., Mason, OH; *U.S. Private*, pg. 1044
Ueno, Michitomo, Sr. V.P.--Nippon Telegraph and Telephone Corporation, Tokyo, Japan; *Int'l*, pg. 940
Ueno, Toru, Sr. V.P. & Grp. Head--Fuji Bank, New York Branch, New York, NY; *Int'l*, pg. 519
Ughetta, William C., Sr. V.P. & Gen. Counsel--Corning Incorporated, Corning, NY; *U.S. Public*, pg. 448
Ugol, Marc, Sr. V.P.-H.R.--Platinum Technology, Inc., Oak Brook Terrace, IL; *U.S. Public*, pg. 1309
Uhlig, Tom, Sr. V.P.-GM Sys. Division--Ferrofluidics Corporation, Nashua, NH; *U.S. Public*, pg. 620
Uhlman, Tom, Sr. V.P.-Corp. Strategy, Devel. & Pub. Affairs--Lucent Technologies Inc., Murray Hill, NJ; *U.S. Public*, pg. 1017
Uicker, Joseph B., Sr. V.P.--SmithGroup, Inc., Detroit, MI; *U.S. Private*, pg. 1010
Ukkestad, Donald C., Sr. V.P.--Bird Products Corporation, Palm Springs, CA; *U.S. Public*, pg. 1591
Ulman, John, Sr. V.P.-Brdcst. Fin.--Fisher Broadcasting Inc., Seattle, WA; *U.S. Public*, pg. 648
Ulrich, Keith, Sr. V.P. & Brand Mktg. Partner--DMB&B Detroit, Troy, MI; *U.S. Private*, pg. 302
Ulrich, Robert G., Sr. V.P. & Gen. Counsel--The Great Atlantic & Pacific Tea Company, Inc., Montvale, NJ; *Int'l, pg. 1375*
Ulstad, Richard C., Sr. V.P.-Consumable Div.--The Lincoln Electric Company, Cleveland, OH; *U.S. Public*, pg. 996
Umamoto, Calvin H., Sr. V.P.--First Hawaiian Creditcorp, Inc., Honolulu, HI; *U.S. Public*, pg. 635
Umbach, John, Sr. V.P. & V.P.--Joseph Victori Wines, Inc., New Rochelle, NY; *U.S. Private*, pg. 1139
Umezawa, Jyo, Sr. V.P.--MPSI Systems Inc., Tulsa, OK; *U.S. Public*, pg. 1027
Underhill, James F., Sr. V.P. & Controller--McJunkin Corporation, Charleston, WV; *U.S. Private*, pg. 722
Underhill, Jerry D., Sr. V.P.-Sls. & Mktg.--Morrison Health Care Inc., Smyrna, GA; *U.S. Public*, pg. 1133
Underhill, Robert A., Sr. V.P.-Res. & Devel.fficer--Kimberly-Clark Corporation, Dallas, TX; *U.S. Public*, pg. 958
Underhill, Robert L., Chief Oper. Officer & Exec. V.P.--Channing L. Bete Co., Inc., South Deerfield, MA; *U.S. Private*, pg. 140
Unger, Tom, Sr. V.P.--Horsehead Resource Development Company, Inc., Palmerton, PA; *U.S. Private*, pg. 540
Unneberg, Arild, Sr. V.P.-Opers.--Saga Petroleum ASA, Sandvika, Norway; *Int'l*, pg. 1169
Unrine, Thomas, Sr. V.P.-Mdsg.--One Price Clothing Stores, Inc., Duncan, SC; *U.S. Public*, pg. 1225
Unruh, David G., Sr. V.P.-Law & Sec.--Westcoast Energy Inc., Vancouver, Canada; *Int'l*, pg. 1492
Unruh, Richard G., Jr., Sr. V.P.--Delaware Management Holdings, Inc., Philadelphia, PA; *U.S. Public*, pg. 997
Unterman, Thomas, Chief Fin. Officer & Sr. V.P.--The Times Mirror Company, Los Angeles, CA; *U.S. Public*, pg. 1615
Unterreiner, Bernard C., Sr. V.P. & Sec.--Voyager Service Warranties, Inc., Fort Worth, TX; *U.S. Public*, pg. 68
Unton, T.F., Sr. V.P.-Fin. & treas.--MACtac Morgan Adhesive Company, Stow, OH; *U.S. Public*, pg. 210
Unverzagt, Philip, Chief Fin. Officer & Sr. V.P.--Oregon Freeze Dry, Inc., Albany, OR; *U.S. Private*, pg. 819
Upton, John, Sr. V.P. & Acct. Dir.--RP alpha, Santa Monica, CA; *U.S. Private*, pg. 950
Upton, Mark R., Sr. V.P.--UDC Homes, Inc., Scottsdale, AZ; *U.S. Private*, pg. 5
Upton, Richard, Sr. V.P. & Grp. Mgmt. Supvr.--The Martin Agency, Richmond, VA; *U.S. Private*, pg. 678
Urankar, John, Sr. V.P.-Claims--Transport Insurance Co., Dallas, TX; *U.S. Public*, pg. 75
Urbach, Michael G., Sr. V.P.-Ambulatory Surgery Centers--Universal Health Services, Inc., King of Prussia, PA; *U.S.* Public, pg. 1696
Urbanovsky, Marty, Sr. V.P.-Fin.--GSD&M, Austin, TX; *U.S. Private*, pg. 436
Urey, Joe, Sr. V.P.--Price/McNabb, Inc., Charlotte, NC; *U.S.* Private, pg. 883
Urquhart, Ronald T., Sr. V.P.-Consumer Banking--People's Bank, Bridgeport, CT; *U.S. Public*, pg. 1274
Ursu, John J., Sr. V.P.-Legal Affairs & Gen. Counsel--3M, Saint Paul, MN; *U.S. Public*, pg. 1604
Uselton, Chris L., Sr. V.P.--Zenith Insurance Company, Woodland Hills, CA; *U.S. Public*, pg. 1791
Usher, F. Barrie, Sr. V.P.-Canada--New York Life Insurance Company, New York, NY; *U.S. Private*, pg. 794
Usher, F. Barrie, Sr. V.P.-Canadian Individual Insurance Opers.--Manulife Financial (The Manufacturers Life Insurance Company), Toronto, Canada; *Int'l*, pg. 840
Usher, Thomas, Sr. V.P.--M.F. Bank Restoration Co., Duluth, GA; *U.S. Private*, pg. 114
Utecht, Andrea, Sr. V.P., Gen. Counsel & Sec.--Elf Atochem North America, Inc., Philadelphia, PA; *Int'l*, pg. 445
Utley, John E., Sr. V.P.-Strategic Mktg.--LucasVarity Inc., Buffalo, NY; *Int'l*, pg. 820
Utley, John E., Sr. V.P.-Strategic Mktg.--Varity Kelsey Hayes, Livonia, MI; *Int'l*, pg. 820
Utton, Nicholas A., Sr. V.P.-Mktg.--Mastercard International, Inc., Purchase, NY; *U.S. Private*, pg. 714
Vaaraniemi, Markku, Sr. V.P. & Bus. Unit Exec.--Valmet Automation Kajaani Ltd., Kajaani, Finland; *Int'l*, pg. 1449
Vacek, Richard, Chief Fin. Officer & Sr. V.P.--Horace Small Apparel Company, Nashville, TN; *Int'l*, pg. 635
Vachani, Mohan, Chief Fin. Officer & Sr. V.P.--AMREP Corporation, New York, NY; *U.S. Public*, pg. 104
Vacher, P.B.E., Sr. V.P. & Controller--AEGON Nederland N.V., Hague, Netherlands; *Int'l*, pg. 26
Vadasz, Leslie L., Sr. V.P. & Dir.-Corp. Bus. Devel.--Intel Corporation, Santa Clara, CA; *U.S. Public*, pg. 886
Vahue, Howard B., Sr. V.P.--Manufacturers & Traders Trust Company, Buffalo, NY; *U.S. Public*, pg. 631
Vail, James, Sr. V.P., Media Dir.--R.J. Palmer, Inc., New York, NY; *U.S. Private*, pg. 835
Vaillancourt, Paul, Sr. V.P.-Pur.--DHP Limited Partnership, Chicopee, MA; *U.S. Private*, pg. 302
Vainio, Mainio, Sr. V.P.--United Paper Mills Ltd., Valkeakoski, Finland; *Int'l*, pg. 1429
Valade, Raymond D., Jr., Sr. V.P.-Retail Banking--First Federal Savings, East Hartford, CT; *U.S. Public*, pg. 632
Valan, Sherry B., Sr. V.P.-Adv. Standards & Bus. Affairs--DMB&B New York, New York, NY; *U.S. Private*, pg. 302
Valdalma, Ray, Sr. V.P.--Imperial Bank, Inglewood, CA; *U.S.* Public, pg. 871
Valdes Govea, Carlos, Sr. V.P.-Beverages Div.--Grupo Continental S.A., Tampico, Mexico; *Int'l*, pg. 573
Valdes, Carlos A., Sr. V.P.-Fin.--MasTec, Inc., Miami, FL; *U.S. Public*, pg. 1055
Valeika, Ray, Sr. V.P.-Tech. Opers.--Delta Air Lines, Inc., Atlanta, GA; *U.S. Public*, pg. 497
Valencia, Oscar, Exec. Sr. V.P.--Etienne Aigner, New York, NY; *U.S. Private*, pg. 384
Valenti, Carl M., Sr. V.P.-Tech. & Affiliates--Dow Jones & Company, Inc., New York, NY; *U.S. Public*, pg. 524
Valentine, Bryan, Sr. V.P.-Human Resources--Structural Dynamics Research Corp., Milford, OH; *U.S. Public*, pg. 1525
Valentine, Chuck, Sr. V.P. & Grp. Acct. Dir.--Rubin Postaer & Associates, Santa Monica, CA; *U.S. Private*, pg. 950
Valentine, Stephen W., Sr. V.P.-Systems, Tech. & Support--AutoZone, Inc., Memphis, TN; *U.S. Public*, pg. 150
Valentino, James A., Sr. V.P.-Corp. Mktg.--Metropolitan Life Insurance Co., New York, NY; *U.S. Private*, pg. 737
Valenzuela, Gary, Chief Fin. Officer & Sr. V.P.-Fin. & Admin.--Yahoo!, Inc., Santa Clara, CA; *U.S. Public*, pg. 1787
Valinski, Sandi, Sr. V.P.-Sls.--Thompson Nutritional Products, Boca Raton, FL; *U.S. Public*, pg. 1384
Valk, G. Lindsay, Sr. V.P. & Dir. of Circulation Mktg.--Hearst Magazines Division, New York, NY; *U.S. Private*, pg. 516
Vallee, B. A., Sr. V.P. & Acct. Dir.--Brown Marketing Communications, Chicago, IL; *U.S. Private*, pg. 174
Valli, Louis A., Sr. V.P.-Employee Rels.--USX Corporation, Pittsburgh, PA; *U.S. Public*, pg. 1661
Vallin, Gunnar, Sr. V.P.-Intl. Mkts.--Vattenfall AB, Stockholm, Sweden; *Int'l*, pg. 1452
Vallner, Joseph, Ph.D., Sr. V.P.-Res. & Devel.--Sequus Pharmaceuticals, Inc., Menlo Park, CA; *U.S. Public*, pg. 1460
Vamos, James E., Sr. V.P.-Real Estate--McGean-Rohco, Inc., Cleveland, OH; *U.S. Private*, pg. 721
Vamos, Steven, Sr. V.P.-Apple Asia Pacific--Apple Computer, Inc., Cupertino, CA; *U.S. Public*, pg. 121
Van Aken, John, Sr. V.P.-H.R.--Visa U.S.A. Inc., San Francisco, CA; *U.S. Private*, pg. 1141
Van Akker, Richard J., Sr. V.P.--Chemical Bank Bay Area, Bay City, MI; *U.S. Public*, pg. 345
Van Arsdale, James R., Sr. V.P.-Opers.--American Greetings Corporation, Cleveland, OH; *U.S. Public*, pg. 77
Van Auken, Bradley A., Sr. V.P., Gen. Counsel & Sec.--Lexford Residential Trust, Columbus, OH; *U.S. Public*, pg. 991
Van Berken, J. Thomas, Chief Human Resources Officer & Sr. V.P.--ADVO, Inc., Windsor, CT; *U.S. Public*, pg. 23
Van Damme, Etienne, Sr. V.P.-Sls. & Mktg./Electronic Prepress Systems--Bayer Corporation, Pittsburgh, PA; *Int'l*, pg. 172
Van de Cater, Pat, Sr. V.P.-Local Brdcst.--DeWitt Media, Inc., New York, NY; *U.S. Private*, pg. 329
van de Starre, Jaap, Sr. V.P.-Actuarial--AEGON N.V., Hague, Netherlands; *Int'l*, pg. 25
van den Berg, R.A., Sr. V.P.-Fin.--AEGON N.V., Hague, Netherlands; *Int'l*, pg. 25
van der Luft, Robert, Sr. V.P.-Chemicals & Pigments--Du Pont (E.I. Du Pont De Nemours & Co.), Wilmington, DE; *U.S. Public*, pg. 530
Van Dijk, Jacques A.N., Sr. V.P.--Sara Lee Corporation, Chicago, IL; *U.S. Public*, pg. 1432
Van Dorn, Joe, Sr. V.P.--Marubeni America Corporation, New York, NY; *Int'l*, pg. 844
Van Dyke, John, Chief Fin. Officer & Sr. V.P.--American Optical Corporation, Greenwich, CT; *U.S. Private*, pg. 60
Van Dyke, Paul, Sr. V.P.--Forever Living Products International, Inc., Scottsdale, AZ; *U.S. Private*, pg. 418
Van Erp, Dirk, Sr. V.P.--Knight Architects Engineers Planners, Inc., Chicago, IL; *U.S. Private*, pg. 626
van Evoenewoud, R., Sr. V.P.-Engrng. & Maintenance--KLM Royal Dutch Airlines, Amstelveen, Netherlands; *Int'l*, pg. 719
Van Gels, John J., Sr. V.P.-Opers.--McDonnell Aircraft & Missile Systems Div., Berkeley, MO; *U.S. Public*, pg. 241
Van Gieson, Robert T., Sr. V.P.--Chubb & Son, Inc., Warren, NJ; *U.S. Public*, pg. 355
Van Graafeiland, Gary P., Sr. V.P. & Gen. Counsel--Eastman Kodak Company, Rochester, NY; *U.S. Public*, pg. 550
Van Grinsven, Mark J., Jr., Sr. V.P.--The Northern Trust Co., London, United Kingdom; *U.S. Public*, pg. 1197
Van Hettinga, Gary, V.P.-Fin.--Tropicana Casino & Resort, Atlantic City, NJ; *U.S. Public*, pg. 159
Van Himbergen, Thomas W., Chief Fin. Officer & Sr. V.P.--Deluxe Corporation, Shoreview, MN; *U.S. Public*, pg. 498
Van Hooser, David G., Sr. V.P. & Dir.-Corp. Strategy--Owens-Illinois, Inc., Toledo, OH; *U.S. Public*, pg. 1238
Van Hooser, Russell E., Sr. V.P.--MGIC Investment Corporation, Milwaukee, WI; *U.S. Public*, pg. 1026
Van Hooser, Russell E., Sr. V.P.-Regulatory Rels.--Mortgage Guaranty Insurance Corporation, Milwaukee, WI; *U.S. Public*, pg. 1026
Van Horn, L.R., Sr. V.P.- Fin.--The Ziegler Companies, Inc., West Bend, WI; *U.S. Public*, pg. 1791

Van Horn, L.R., Sr. V.P.-Fin.--B.C. Ziegler & Co., West Bend, WI; *U.S. Public*, pg. 1792
Van Houten, G. David, Jr., Sr. V.P. & Pres.-Central Grp.--Coca-Cola Enterprises Inc., Atlanta, GA; *U.S. Public*, pg. 393
Van Hove, Scott J., Chief Admin. Officer & Sr. V.P.--Manor Care, Inc., Gaithersburg, MD; *U.S. Public*, pg. 1041
Van Lanen, James L., Sr. V.P.-Coal, Chemicals & Power--The Coastal Corporation, Houston, TX; *U.S. Public*, pg. 389
Van Lenten, Liz, Sr. V.P.--Golin/Harris Communications, Inc., Chicago, IL; *Int'l*, pg. 1226
Van Meevwen, Alexander, Sr. V.P.-Graphic Systems--Bayer Corporation, Pittsburgh, PA; *Int'l*, pg. 172
van Roden, John C., Jr., Chief Fin. Officer, Sr. V.P. & Treas.--Lukens Inc., Coatesville, PA; *U.S. Public*, pg. 1019
Van Saun, Richard W., Sr. V.P. & Gen. Mgr.-Service Tools Div.--Fluke Corporation, Everett, WA; *U.S. Public*, pg. 659
Van Schaick, Anthony G., Chief Fin. Officer & Sr. V.P.--John Wieland Homes Inc., Atlanta, GA; *U.S. Private*, pg. 1175
Van Schandevijl, Jean-Paul, Sr. V.P.-Europe, Africa & Middle East Regions--T.D. Williamson, Inc., Tulsa, OK; *U.S. Private*, pg. 1179
van Schoonenberg, Robert G., Sr. V.P., Gen. Counsel & Sec.--Avery Dennison Corporation, Pasadena, CA; *U.S. Public*, pg. 152
Van Stedum, Edward J., Sr. V.P.-Human Resources--Genuine Parts Company, Atlanta, GA; *U.S. Public*, pg. 732
Van Syckle, William, Sr. V.P.--General Reinsurance Corp., Stamford, CT; *U.S. Public*, pg. 725
Van Valkenburgh, Deborah, Sr. V.P.-Sls. & Mktg.--First Maryland Bancorp, Baltimore, MD; *Int'l*, pg. 64
van Vliet, N.W., Sr. V.P.-Legal--AEGON N.V., Hague, Netherlands; *Int'l*, pg. 25
Van Vooren, V.C., Sr. V.P., Treas. & Asst. Sec.--The Ziegler Companies, Inc., West Bend, WI; *U.S. Public*, pg. 1791
van Wijk, Deo, Sr. V.P.--Metallgesellschaft Corp., New York, NY; *Int'l*, pg. 861
Van Wooten, Richard A., Chief Oper. Officer & Sr. V.P.--Walk, Haydel & Associates, Inc., New Orleans, LA; *Int'l*, pg. 624
Vanaria, Robert, Chief Fin. Officer & Sr. V.P.-Admin.--Greenwich Air Services, Miami, FL; *U.S. Public*, pg. 710
Vance, Gary R., Sr. V.P. & Comptroller--First Security Corporation, Salt Lake City, UT; *U.S. Public*, pg. 637
Vande Noorde, Edwin L., Sr. V.P. & Gen. Mgr.--Ball Aerospace Systems Division, Boulder, CO; *U.S. Public*, pg. 171
Vandeman, George A., Sr. V.P., Gen. Counsel & Sec.--Amgen Inc., Thousand Oaks, CA; *U.S. Public*, pg. 100
Vander Haar, R. William, Sr. V.P.-Res. & Devel./Consumer Care Div.--Bayer Corporation, Pittsburgh, PA; *Int'l*, pg. 172
Vander Hoek, Arlie, Sr. V.P.--Vermeer Manufacturing Company, Pella, IA; *U.S. Private*, pg. 1137
Vander Zwaag, Donald D., Sr. V.P. & Treas.--Bradford Company, Holland, MI; *U.S. Private*, pg. 163
Vanderberg, Bruce, Sr. V.P.--Imperial Bank, Inglewood, CA; *U.S. Public*, pg. 871
Vanderfin, Bernard, Sr. V.P.-Admin. Intl.--Columbia Tri-Star International Releasing Corp., Culver City, CA; *Int'l*, pg. 1281
Vanderheiden, George A., Sr. V.P.--Fidelity Investments (FMR Corp.), Boston, MA; *U.S. Private*, pg. 402
VanderLind, Merwyn R., Dr., Sr. V.P.--Battelle Memorial Institute, Columbus, OH; *U.S. Private*, pg. 123
Vanderwal, Richard B., Chief Fin. Officer & Sr. V.P.-Fin.--Gingiss International, Addison, IL; *U.S. Private*, pg. 455
VanderWeele, Julie, Sr. V.P.-Mktg.--Mesirow Financial, Chicago, IL; *U.S. Private*, pg. 733
VanLeeuwen, John C., Sr. V.P.-Loan Review--Arrow Financial Corporation, Glens Falls, NY; *U.S. Public*, pg. 135
Vann, Kyle D., Sr. V.P.-Supply, Trading & Transportation Grp.--Koch Industries, Incorporated, Wichita, KS; *U.S. Private*, pg. 628
Vannick, Carroll, Sr. V.P.-Sls./East Coast--Freeman Cosmetic Corp., Los Angeles, CA; *U.S. Private*, pg. 426
VanNoy, James E., Sr. V.P.-Mngmt. Information Systems--Proffitt's, Inc., Alcoa, TN; *U.S. Public*, pg. 1333
Vanos, Russ, Sr. V.P.-Utility Sls.--Itron Inc., Spokane, WA; *U.S. Public*, pg. 914
VanRamshorst, Lee B., Sr. V.P.-Bus. Devel.--Plains Petroleum Operating Co., Lakewood, CO; *U.S. Public*, pg. 191
Vanthournout, Jeffrey A., Sr. V.P.-Equipment Fin. Div.--Green Tree Financial Corporation, Saint Paul, MN; *U.S. Public*, pg. 761
VantLeven, Karen L., Sr. V.P.-Employee Benefits--Willis Corroon Corp. of Seattle, Seattle, WA; *Int'l*, pg. 1507
VanWormer, Greg, Sr. V.P.--The Timberland Company, Stratham, NH; *U.S. Public*, pg. 1609
Vardman, Lorna, Sr. V.P.-Mdse.--Penn-Daniels, Inc., Quincy, IL; *U.S. Public*, pg. 1467
Varela, Manuel, Sr. V.P.--Banco Santander, Madrid, Spain; *Int'l*, pg. 143
Varhol, James A., Sr. V.P.-Asset Protection--Ames Department Stores, Inc., Rocky Hill, CT; *U.S. Public*, pg. 99
Varley, Andrew P., Sr. V.P.-Energy Pricing & Regulatory Services--American Electric Power Service Corp., Columbus, OH; *U.S. Public*, pg. 72
Varvi, John, Sr. V.P. & Creative Dir.--Friedland Jacobs Communications, Burbank, CA; *U.S. Private*, pg. 428
Vasko, Anthony J., Sr. V.P.--Triad International Maintenance Corporation, Greensboro, NC; *U.S. Public*, pg. 1325
Vaspasiano, John, Sr. V.P.--New Haven Savings Bank, New Haven, CT; *U.S. Private*, pg. 793
Vassos, James, Sr. V.P.-Business Affairs & Planning--Cineplex Odeon Corporation, Toronto, Canada; *Int'l*, pg. 292
Vasta, Salvatore, Sr. V.P. & Gen. Mdse. MGr.--Kay-Bee Toy & Hobby Shops, Inc., Pittsfield, MA; *U.S. Public*, pg. 437
Vasto, Salvatore J., Chief Fin. Officer, Sr. V.P. & Treas.--American Security Group, Atlanta, GA; *Int'l*, pg. 499
Vaswani, Richard N., Chief Fin. Officer & Sr. V.P.--Clark Construction Group, Inc., Bethesda, MD; *U.S. Private*, pg. 242
Vaterlaus, Alan J., Sr. V.P. & Mgr.-Consumer Loan Div.--First Security Bank of Idaho, N.A., Boise, ID; *U.S. Public*, pg. 637
Vaughan, Bernard, Sr. V.P. & Gen. Counsel--Flexi-Van Leasing, Inc., Kenilworth, NJ; *U.S. Private*, pg. 413
Vaughan, James, Jr., Sr. V.P.-Energy Grp.--Tetra Tech NUS, Inc., Gaithersburg, MD; *U.S. Public*, pg. 1582
Vaughn, Don S., Sr. V.P.--Freeman Decorating Co., Dallas, TX; *U.S. Private*, pg. 426
Vaughn, John M., Sr. V.P.-Engrng. & Tech.--Inland Container Corporation, Indianapolis, IN; *U.S. Public*, pg. 1575
Vaughn, Louie, Sr. V.P.-Fin.--Gulf South Medical Supply, Inc., Ridgeland, MS; *U.S. Public*, pg. 1294
Vaughn, Ronald E., Jr., Sr. V.P. & Chief Lending Officer--Pulse Bancorp, Inc., South River, NJ; *U.S. Public*, pg. 1344
Vaupen, Hy, Chief Fin. Officer, Exec. V.P. & Sec.--BCI Holding Corporation, Miami, FL; *U.S. Private*, pg. 106
Vaux, Robert G., Sr. V.P.-Fin. & Corp. Devel.--Labatt Brewing Company Limited, Toronto, Canada; *Int'l*, pg. 679
Vavra, John, Sr. V.P.-Sls. & Mktg.--Ascom Hasler Mailing Systems, Inc., Shelton, CT; *Int'l*, pg. 86
Veal, Murray, Sr. V.P.--Farmers Bank & Trust Co., Henderson, KY; *U.S. Public*, pg. 1217
Veasey, Samuel, Chief Fin. Officer & Sr. V.P.--Liggett Group Inc., Durham, NC; *U.S. Public*, pg. 259
Vecilla, Nancy, Sr. V.P. & Creative Dir.--The Chapman Agency, New York, NY; *U.S. Private*, pg. 1197
Veeder, Betty A., Sr. V.P.--Hibernia Corporation, New Orleans, LA; *U.S. Public*, pg. 825
Veen, Steven C., Chief Fin. Officer & Sr. V.P.--Aura Systems, Inc., El Segundo, CA; *U.S. Public*, pg. 147
Veitch, Richard A., Sr. V.P.-Flat Rolled Opers.--The LTV Corporation, Cleveland, OH; *U.S. Public*, pg. 971
Velasco, Jose A., Sr. V.P., Gen. Counsel & Sec.--Centris Group Inc., Costa Mesa, CA; *U.S. Public*, pg. 328
Vels, M.H., Sr. V.P.-Fin.--Maple Leaf Foods Inc., Toronto, Canada; *Int'l*, pg. 841
Venema, John, Sr. V.P.-Mktg. & Mktg. Devel.--Overhead Door Corporation, Dallas, TX; *U.S. Private*, pg. 822
Veniard, Kenneth M., Sr. V.P.-Credit Quality--Barnett Banks, Inc., Jacksonville, FL; *U.S. Public*, pg. 1162
Venkateswaran, Ambi, Sr. V.P. & Country Mgr.--Bank of America NT&SA, New Delhi, India; *U.S. Public*, pg. 182
Ventosa, Martinet H., Sr. V.P. & Media Dir.--Hemisphere-Leo Burnett, Inc., Manila, Philippines; *U.S. Private*, pg. 184
Ventre, Philippe, Sr. V.P.-Vehicle Engrng.--Renault, Boulogne-Billancourt, France; *Int'l*, pg. 1102
Verba, Stephen M., Chief Info. Officer & Sr. V.P.--Realty One, Cleveland, OH; *U.S. Private*, pg. 914
Verbout, Peter G., Sr. V.P.--Valley National Bank, Parsippany, NJ; *U.S. Public*, pg. 1705
Verciglio, Joseph D., Sr. V.P.--SouthTrust Corporation, Birmingham, AL; *U.S. Public*, pg. 1491
Verdon, William, Sr. V.P. & Gen. Counsel--Crowley Maritime Corporation, Oakland, CA; *U.S. Private*, pg. 292
Verdugo Orozco, Ernesto, Sr. V.P.--Bufete Industrial S.A. de C.V., Mexico, Mexico; *Int'l*, pg. 232
Verduin, Roger, Sr. V.P.-Mngmt. Information Systems--Bernard Hodes Group, New York, NY; *U.S. Public*, pg. 1224
Verga, Joseph, Sr. V.P., Treas. & Sec.--Techdyne, Inc., Hialeah, FL; *U.S. Public*, pg. 1080
Vergne, Jean-Luc, Sr. V.P.-Human Resources/Elf--Elf Aquitane, Paris, France; *Int'l*, pg. 444
Vergnes, Bernard P., Sr. V.P. & Chm. Bd.-Microsoft Europe--Microsoft Corporation, Redmond, WA; *U.S. Public*, pg. 1107
Verhenne, Jan, Corp. V.P.-H.R. Mgmnt.--N.V. Bekaert S.A., Kortrijk, Belgium; *Int'l*, pg. 183
Verhey, James F., Chief Fin. Officer & Sr. V.P.-Fin.--Kaiser Ventures, Inc., Ontario, CA; *U.S. Public*, pg. 941
Verlander, Chris A., Sr. V.P. & Sec.--First Colonial Insurance Company, Jacksonville, FL; *U.S. Public*, pg. 79
Verlinich, Ray, Sr. V.P.-Fin. & Admin.--Season-All Industries, Inc., Indiana, PA; *Int'l*, pg. 267
Vernier, Allen, Sr. V.P. & Grp. Acct. Dir.-Intl.--Ross Roy Communications, Inc., Bloomfield Hills, MI; *U.S. Private*, pg. 946
Vernon, T. J., Sr. V.P. & Acct. Dir.--Brown Marketing Communications, Chicago, IL; *U.S. Private*, pg. 174
Vesci, Dennis J., Sr. V.P.-Opers.--Inland Container-Container Division, Indianapolis, IN; *U.S. Public*, pg. 1575
Vescuso, Michael A., Sr. V.P.-Human Resources--America West Airlines, Inc., Phoenix, AZ; *U.S. Public*, pg. 67
Vest, Carla K., Sr. V.P.-H.R.--Indianapolis Life Insurance Co., Indianapolis, IN; *U.S. Private*, pg. 560
Veucelli, Lodi, Sr. V.P.--Distributed Systems Division, Lisle, IL; *U.S. Public*, pg. 1522
Veysey, Michael C., Sr. V.P. & Gen. Counsel--Gould Electronics Inc., Eastlake, OH; *U.S. Public*, pg. 1591
Vezina, Raynald, Sr. V.P.-Canada--Cambior Inc., Montreal, Canada; *Int'l*, pg. 253
Vialard, Diane, Sr. V.P. & Brdcst. Dir.--The Lord Group, New York, NY; *U.S. Private*, pg. 325
Vibber, Bradly E., Sr. V.P.--Chemical Bank & Trust Company, Midland, MI; *U.S. Public*, pg. 345
Vice, Preston, Sr. V.P.-Publishing Services--Penton Publishing, Inc., Cleveland, OH; *U.S. Public*, pg. 1306
Vichitranondha, Suthanyah, Sr. V.P. & Gen. Mgr.--Bangkok Bank Public Company Limited, Bangkok, Thailand; *Int'l*, pg. 146
Vickers, John, III, Sr. V.P.-Opers.--American Dental Technologies, Southfield, MI; *U.S. Public*, pg. 70
Vickery, David M., Sr. V.P.-Advisory Services--Spaulding & Slye, Boston, MA; *U.S. Private*, pg. 1021
Vickery, Robert, Sr. V.P.-Mktg.--Colonial Penn Group, Inc., Wilmington, DE; *U.S. Public*, pg. 990
Viebranz, Curt, Sr. V.P.-Intl.--Time-Life, Inc., Alexandria, VA; *U.S. Public*, pg. 1613
Vierig, Bradley M., Sr. V.P. & Controller--American Stores Company, Salt Lake City, UT; *U.S. Public*, pg. 92
Viger, Pierre, Sr. V.P.-Quebec & The Maritimes Div.--St. Lawrence Cement Inc., Montreal, Canada; *Int'l*, pg. 628
Vigna, John A., Sr. V.P.-Fin. & Admin.--The West Company, Incorporated, Lionville, PA; *U.S. Public*, pg. 1755
Vignola, Nancy, Sr. V.P.-Home Collection Design--Polo/Ralph Lauren Corporation, New York, NY; *U.S. Private*, pg. 874
Viig, Hans, Sr. V.P.--Det Norske Veritas, Hovik, Norway; *Int'l*, pg. 396
Vilhjalmsson, Halldor, Sr. V.P.--Icelandair, Reykjavik, Iceland; *Int'l*, pg. 658
Vilhjalmsson, Halldor, Sr. V.P.-Fin.--IceLandAir, Columbia, MD; *Int'l*, pg. 658
Villamil, Felix, Sr. V.P. & Auditor--Banco Popular de Puerto Rico, San Juan, PR; *U.S. Public*, pg. 175
Villamil, Felix, Sr. V.P.--BanPonce Corporation, Hato Rey, PR; *U.S. Public*, pg. 176
Villarino, Laura, Sr. V.P. & Controller--Firstbank Puerto Rico, Santurce, PR; *U.S. Public*, pg. 644
Vincent, James W., Sr. V.P.-Loans & Sec.--The Commercial Bank, Delphos, OH; *U.S. Public*, pg. 410
Vincent, Robert M., Chief Fin. Officer & Sr. V.P.-Fin. & Treas.--Uno Restaurant Corporation, West Roxbury, MA; *U.S. Public*, pg. 1698
Viner, Anthony P., Sr. V.P.-Broadcasting--Rogers Communications, Inc., Toronto, Canada; *Int'l*, pg. 1122
Vines, Jim, Sr. V.P.--San Angelo National Bank, San Angelo, TX; *U.S. Public*, pg. 633
Vines, Michael, Sr. V.P.-Creative Services--Jordan, McGrath, Case & Taylor Inc., New York, NY; *U.S. Private*, pg. 598
Vining, Paul H., Sr. V.P.--Peabody COALSALES Company, Saint Louis, MO; *Int'l*, pg. 594
Vinnedge, Sydney, Sr. Exec. V.P.--All American Communications, Inc., Santa Monica, CA; *U.S. Public*, pg. 41
Vinson, Harold W., Sr. V.P.-Property Mngmt.--Franchise Finance Corp. of America, Scottsdale, AZ; *U.S. Public*, pg. 679
Vipond, David, Sr. V.P.-Acct. Services--Towne, Silverstein, Rotter Inc., New York, NY; *U.S. Private*, pg. 1093
Virag, Lou, Sr. V.P.-Gen. Mdse. Mgr.--The Bon Marche, Inc., Seattle, WA; *U.S. Public*, pg. 617
Virag, Louis, Sr. V.P.--Ross Stores, Inc., Newark, CA; *U.S. Public*, pg. 1405
Virata, Nestor Luis A., Sr. V.P.-Interconnection--Philippine Long Distance Telephone Company, Manila, Philippines; *Int'l*, pg. 1051
Virmani, Prem, V.P.-Technical Services--Cott Corporation, Pointe-Claire, Canada; *Int'l*, pg. 337
Virtanen, Pekka, Sr. V.P.-Personnel--Metra Corporation, Helsinki, Finland; *Int'l*, pg. 862
Visconti, Frank P., Sr. V.P.-Retail Opers.--Mirage Resorts Incorporated, Las Vegas, NV; *U.S. Public*, pg. 1116
Visentin, Robert, Chief Fin. Officer & Sr. V.P.--Brookfield Homes, Del Mar, CA; *Int'l*, pg. 228
Visentine, Robert, Chief Fin. Officer & Sr. V.P.--Brookfield Homes Ltd., Toronto, Canada; *Int'l*, pg. 228
Viskin, Ilan, Sr. V.P.-Trading Room--Bank Hapoalim, Tel Aviv, Israel; *Int'l*, pg. 149
Visscher, H.B.H., Sr. V.P.--AEGON International B.V., Hague, Netherlands; *Int'l*, pg. 25
Visscher, Herbert B.H., Sr. V.P.-Grp. Bus. Devel.--AEGON N.V., Hague, Netherlands; *Int'l*, pg. 25
Vitale, Joseph M., Sr. V.P., Gen. Counsel & Sec.--Belden & Blake Corporation, Canton, OH; *U.S. Private*, pg. 1078
Vitkus, Richard F., Sr. V.P., Gen. Counsel & Sec.--Zenith Electronics Corp., Glenview, IL; *U.S. Public*, pg. 1790
Vitulli, Clark, Sr. V.P. & Pres.-OMC Boat Group--Outboard Marine Corporation, Waukegan, IL; *U.S. Private*, pg. 478
Vitzthum, Anton F., Sr. V.P.-Mfg.--Material Sciences Corporation, Elk Grove Village, IL; *U.S. Public*, pg. 1056
Voegtle, D. E., Sr. V.P.-Creative--Brown Marketing Communications, Chicago, IL; *U.S. Private*, pg. 174
Voelte, Donald R., Sr. V.P.-Plng.--Atlantic Richfield Company, Los Angeles, CA; *U.S. Public*, pg. 144
Vogel, Allen, Sr. V.P.-New Business Accounts Receivable Financing--Century Business Credit Corporation, New York, NY; *U.S. Private*, pg. 225
Vogt, Andy, Chief Fin. Officer & Sr. V.P.--Galles Chevrolet, Albuquerque, NM; *U.S. Private*, pg. 438
Vogt, Carl, 1st Sr. V.P. & Dir.-Mdse. Plng. & Distr., Licensed Discount Div.--J. Baker, Inc., Canton, MA; *U.S. Public*, pg. 167
Vogt, Fred K., Sr. V.P.-Specialty Chemicals--Tetra Technologies, Woodlands, TX; *U.S. Public*, pg. 1582
Voigts, Keith L., Sr. V.P.-Fin.--Halter Marine Group, Inc., Gulfport, MS; *U.S. Public*, pg. 778
Volleneider, Emmett, Sr. V.P.--Bank One, Louisiana, Baton Rouge, LA; *U.S. Public*, pg. 173
Vollenweider, Heinz, Sr. V.P.--PartnerRe Ltd., Pembroke, Bermuda; *Int'l*, pg. 1024
Vollmuth, George, Chief Fin. Officer & Sr. V.P.--Time Inc., New York, NY; *U.S. Public*, pg. 1612
Volovelsky, Mordechai, Sr. V.P.-Commercial Aviation, Industrial & Marine--Greenwich Air Services, Miami, FL; *U.S. Public*, pg. 710
Volpe, Thomas J., Sr. V.P.-Fin. & Opers.--The Interpublic Group of Companies, Inc., New York, NY; *U.S. Public*, pg. 908

Von Deylen, Larry, Sr. V.P.-Mfg.--Oregon Freeze Dry, Inc., Albany, OR; *U.S. Private*, pg. 819
Von Glahn, William G., Sr. V.P. & Gen. Counsel--The Williams Companies, Inc., Tulsa, OK; *U.S. Public*, pg. 1769
von Maack, Wolfgang, Sr. V.P.-Health Services--Manor Care, Inc., Gaithersburg, MD; *U.S. Public*, pg. 1041
von Maack, Wolfgang, Sr. V.P.-Health Services--Manor Healthcare Corp., Gaithersburg, MD; *U.S. Public*, pg. 1041
Von Neumann, Johnny, Chief Info. Officer & Sr. V.P.-IS--International Plastics Company, New York, NY; *U.S. Private*, pg. 571
von Post, Claes, Sr. V.P.--Investor AB, Stockholm, Sweden; *Int'l*, pg. 686
Von Seggern, Walter, Sr. V.P.-Mktg.--Kulicke & Soffa Industries, Inc., Willow Grove, PA; *U.S. Public*, pg. 968
Von Wald, Richard B., Sr. V.P., Gen. Counsel & Sec.--Johns Manville Corporation, Denver, CO; *U.S. Public*, pg. 927
Vonnegut, Mary G., Sr. V.P.-Mktg.--Hanover Direct, Inc., Weehawken, NJ; *U.S. Public*, pg. 782
vonRosen, John E., Sr. V.P.-Process Devel.--MichCon, Detroit, MI; *U.S. Public*, pg. 1025
Voorhees, Steven C., Sr. V.P.--Sonat Energy Services Company, Birmingham, AL; *U.S. Public*, pg. 1485
Vorce, Betsy, Sr. V.P.-Pub. Rels.--Viacom Entertainment, New York, NY; *U.S. Private*, pg. 779
Vorhoff, Stephanie, Sr. V.P.--HMS/Cincinnati, Cincinnati, OH; *U.S. Private*, pg. 492
Vorhoff, Stephanie, Sr. V.P.--HMS Direct, Cincinnati, OH; *U.S. Private*, pg. 492
Vos, Jochen, Sr. V.P.--Fried. Krupp AG, Essen, Germany; *Int'l*, pg. 507
Vosloo, Paul M., Sr. V.P.--Porter Novelli International, New York, NY; *U.S. Public*, pg. 1224
Voss-Grumish, James A., Sr. V.P. & Gen. Mgr.-Creative Services--Campbell Mithun Esty, Minneapolis, MN; *U.S. Private*, pg. 204
Voss, Dietmar, Sr. V.P.-Sls. & Mktg. Worldwide--Columbian Chemicals Company, Atlanta, GA; *U.S. Public*, pg. 1286
Voss, John, Sr. V.P.--Huntington Bancshares Inc., Columbus, OH; *U.S. Public*, pg. 849
Voss, Stephen C., Sr. V.P.--Harken Energy Corporation, Irving, TX; *U.S. Public*, pg. 785
Voswinckel, Richard, Sr. V.P. & Gen. Mgr.--Deutsch-Sudamerikanische Bank AG, Miami Agency, Miami, FL; *Int'l*, pg. 418
Vradenburg, George, Sr. V.P. & Gen. Counsel--America Online Incorporated, Dulles, VA; *U.S. Public*, pg. 66
Vrba, John, Sr. V.P. & Mng. Dir.--Western International Media Corporation, Newport Beach, CA; *U.S. Private*, pg. 1167
Vuagniaux, John T., Sr. V.P.-Opers.--Glacier Water Services Inc., Carlsbad, CA; *U.S. Public*, pg. 745
Vuorio, Timo, Sr. V.P.-Grp. Admin.--Partek Corporation, Helsinki, Finland; *Int'l*, pg. 1024
Wachtel, Betsy, Sr. V.P. & Information Services Dir.--Hill, Holliday, Connors, Cosmopulos, Inc., Boston, MA; *U.S. Private*, pg. 529
Wachtel, Jeff, Sr. V.P.-Drama--Columbia TriStar Television, Culver City, CA; *Int'l*, pg. 1282
Wachtel, Kenneth, Sr. V.P.-Adv.--Excite, Inc., Redwood City, CA; *U.S. Public*, pg. 599
Wacker, J.C., Sr. V.P.-Production & Sls., Western & Central Container Div.--Longview Fibre Company, Longview, WA; *U.S. Public*, pg. 1013
Waclawik, James J., Chief Fin. Officer, Sr. V.P. & Sec.--Material Sciences Corporation, Elk Grove Village, IL; *U.S. Public*, pg. 1056
Wada, Chris, Sr. V.P.-Govt. Rels.--Sony Electronics, Park Ridge, NJ; *Int'l*, pg. 1281
Wada, Kenichi, Sr. V.P.--Nippon Paint Company Ltd., Osaka, Japan; *Int'l*, pg. 937
Waddell, Alexander P., IV, Sr. V.P.--First American Corporation, Nashville, TN; *U.S. Public*, pg. 624
Waddell, M. Keith, Chief Fin. Officer, Sr. V.P. & Treas.--Robert Half International Inc., Menlo Park, CA; *U.S. Public*, pg. 774
Waddle, Allan C., Sr. V.P.-Pub. Affairs--National City Corporation, Cleveland, OH; *U.S. Public*, pg. 1154
Wade, Byron, Chief Legal Officer & Sr. V.P.--The Pacific Lumber Company, Scotia, CA; *U.S. Public*, pg. 1062
Wade, Byron L., Chief Legal Officer & Sr. V.P.--Maxxam Inc., Houston, TX; *U.S. Public*, pg. 1062
Wade, Byron L., Chief Legal Officer & Sr. V.P.--MAXXAM Property Company, Houston, TX; *U.S. Public*, pg. 1062
Wade, Janis M., Sr. V.P.-H.R. & Corp. Commun.--CCL Industries, Inc., Willowdale, Canada; *Int'l*, pg. 238
Wade, Thomas M., Sr. V.P.--Coastal Refining & Marketing, Wichita, KS; *U.S. Public*, pg. 390
Wadhams, Andrew W., Sr. V.P.-Retail--Big Dog Holdings Inc., Santa Barbara, CA; *U.S. Public*, pg. 227
Wadler, Ame, Sr. V.P.--Edelman Worldwide, Inc., New York, NY; *U.S. Private*, pg. 362
Wadler, Arnold, Sr. V.P., Gen. Counsel & Sec.--Metromedia Company, East Rutherford, NJ; *U.S. Private*, pg. 736
Wadler, Arnold L., Sr. V.P., Gen. Counsel & Sec.--Metromedia International Group, Inc., East Rutherford, NJ; *U.S. Public*, pg. 1102
Wadsworth, John T., Sr. V.P.-Head Corp. Tax--Bankers Trust New York Corporation, New York, NY; *U.S. Public*, pg. 185
Wagener, Frank N., Sr. V.P.-Universal Banking--Banque Internationale a Luxembourg S.A., Luxembourg, Luxembourg; *Int'l*, pg. 162
Waggoner, Donald, Sr. V.P.-Corp. Devel.--Leupold & Stevens, Inc., Beaverton, OR; *U.S. Private*, pg. 662
Waggoner, Stuart F., Sr. V.P.-Opers.--Applebee's International, Inc., Overland Park, KS; *U.S. Public*, pg. 122
Wagler, Paul, Chief Fin. Officer & Sr. V.P.-Fin.--The Loewen Group, Inc., Burnaby, Canada; *Int'l*, pg. 814
Wagner, Fred, Sr. V.P.--Banque Internationale a Luxembourg S.A., Luxembourg, Luxembourg; *Int'l*, pg. 162
Wagner, Gerald, Ph.D., Sr. V.P.-Immunodiagnostics & Clinical Chemistry--Bayer Corporation, Pittsburgh, PA; *Int'l*, pg. 172
Wagner, Harvey A., Chief Fin. Officer, Sr. V.P.-Fin. & Treas.--Scientific-Atlanta, Inc., Norcross, GA; *U.S. Public*, pg. 1443
Wagner, Henry A., Sr. V.P.-Data Processing--The May Department Stores Company, Saint Louis, MO; *U.S. Public*, pg. 1063
Wagner, Jack E., Sr. V.P. & Gen. Mgr.-Calspan Opers.--Calspan SRL Corporation, Washington, DC; *U.S. Private*, pg. 1136
Wagner, Jim, Sr. V.P.-Adv. & Mdsg.--Warner Bros. Records, Inc., Burbank, CA; *U.S. Public*, pg. 1611
Wagner, Larry A., Sr. V.P.-Human Resources--Fleming Companies, Inc., Oklahoma City, OK; *U.S. Public*, pg. 652
Wagner, Sylvia, Sr. V.P.-Human Resources--Fortis Benefits Insurance Company, Kansas City, MO; *Int'l*, pg. 499
Wagstaff, John, Sr. V.P.-DSD--Coach, New York, NY; *U.S. Public*, pg. 1433
Wahrsager, Stewart H., Sr. V.P., Gen. Counsel & Sec.--The Alpine Group, Inc., New York, NY; *U.S. Public*, pg. 58
Wai, Gilbert C., Sr. V.P.-Prod. Devel.--Legato Systems, Inc., Palo Alto, CA; *U.S. Public*, pg. 984
Waisanen, Larry, Chief Fin. Officer & Sr. V.P.--Lafarge Canada Inc., Montreal, Canada; *Int'l*, pg. 789
Waisanen, Larry J., Chief Fin. Officer & Sr. V.P.--Lafarge Corporation, Reston, VA; *Int'l*, pg. 788
Waite, Brad A., Sr. V.P.-Human Resources--Consolidated Stores Corp., Columbus, OH; *U.S. Public*, pg. 437
Wakayama, Masa, Sr. V.P.--Mazda Motor of America, Inc., Irvine, CA; *Int'l*, pg. 849
Wakefield, Mary Lou, Sr. V.P.-Human Resources--Ralphs Grocery Company, Compton, CA; *U.S. Private*, pg. 1202
Waldeck, James, Sr. V.P.-Branch Opers.--Poland Spring Corporation, Greenwich, CT; *Int'l*, pg. 919
Waldek, Jim, Sr. V.P.- Route Div.--The Perrier Group of America, Greenwich, CT; *Int'l*, pg. 919
Waldman, Robert A., Sr. V.P. & Gen. Counsel--Continental Mortgage and Equity Trust, Dallas, TX; *U.S. Public*, pg. 441
Waldron, Francis J., Sr. V.P.-Intl.--The Mutual Life Insurance Company of New York, New York, NY; *U.S. Private*, pg. 769
Waldrop, Robert, Sr. V.P.-Commun.--Houston Industries Incorporated, Houston, TX; *U.S. Public*, pg. 842
Walduck, Kenneth C., Sr. V.P.-Actuarial, Reinsurance Engrng. & Tech. Services & Marine--Royal Insurance Company of Canada, Toronto, Canada; *Int'l*, pg. 1131
Waldvogel, Lynn, Sr. V.P. & Mgr.-Mktg.--PaineWebber Group Incorporated, New York, NY; *U.S. Public*, pg. 1252
Waldvogel, Lynn, Sr. V.P. & Mgr.-Mktg.--PaineWebber Incorporated, New York, NY; *U.S. Public*, pg. 1252
Waligora Jr., Adalbert J., Sr. V.P.--BT Financial Corporation, Johnstown, PA; *U.S. Public*, pg. 163
Walk, Paul W., Jr., Sr. V.P.--Virginia First Savings Bank, F.S.B., Petersburg, VA; *U.S. Public*, pg. 1721
Walker, Catherine, Sr. V.P. & Gen. Counsel--Westin Hotels & Resorts, Seattle, WA; *U.S. Public*, pg. 1512
Walker, Craig, Sr. V.P.-Mktg.--Pic'n Pay Stores, Inc., Matthews, NC; *U.S. Private*, pg. 864
Walker, Daniel W., Sr. V.P.--Kokosing Construction Company, Inc., Fredericktown, OH; *U.S. Private*, pg. 631
Walker, Darcy, Sr. V.P.-Credit--Citibank, Federal Savings Bank (Illinois), Chicago, IL; *U.S. Public*, pg. 378
Walker, Diane E., Sr. V.P., Gen. Counsel & Sec.--CT Financial Services, Inc., Toronto, Canada; *Int'l*, pg. 112
Walker, Dixon R., Sr. V.P.-Roofing, Bldg. Insulation & Info. Tech.--Johns Manville Corporation, Denver, CO; *U.S. Public*, pg. 927
Walker, E. Dow, Sr. V.P.-Healthcare Concerpts--Willis Faber North America, Inc.-Tennessee, Nashville, TN; *Int'l*, pg. 1504
Walker, F.B., Sr. V.P.-Refining & Mktg.--Amerada Hess Corporation, New York, NY; *U.S. Public*, pg. 65
Walker, Gerald T., Sr. V.P.-Grp., Life & Health Div.--American United Life Insurance Company, Indianapolis, IN; *U.S. Private*, pg. 64
Walker, J. Philip, Sr. V.P.-Sls. & Mktg.--Interface Europe B.V., Scherpenzeel, Netherlands; *U.S. Public*, pg. 889
Walker, James A., Jr., Sr. V.P. & Controller--Wal-Mart Stores, Inc., Bentonville, AR; *U.S. Public*, pg. 1732
Walker, James M., Chief Fin. Officer & Sr. V.P.--Diamond Multimedia Systems, Inc., San Jose, CA; *U.S. Public*, pg. 505
Walker, Joan, Sr. V.P.-Corp. Communications--Ameritech Corporation, Chicago, IL; *U.S. Public*, pg. 97
Walker, Joan, Sr. V.P.-Corp. Communications--Ameritech Corp., Chicago, IL; *U.S. Public*, pg. 98
Walker, John C., Sr. V.P.--Longview Fibre Co. Central Container Div., Milwaukee, WI; *U.S. Public*, pg. 1014
Walker, John H., Sr. V.P.--Interface Inc., Atlanta, GA; *U.S. Public*, pg. 889
Walker, Joseph C., Sr. V.P.-Real Estate--National Penn Bank, Boyertown, PA; *U.S. Public*, pg. 1159
Walker, Marty, Sr. V.P.-Sls. & Mktg.--Iams Company, Dayton, OH; *U.S. Private*, pg. 556
Walker, Mauro J., Sr. V.P. & Dir.-Mfg.--Motorola, Inc., Schaumburg, IL; *U.S. Public*, pg. 1136
Walker, Nancy, Sr. V.P.-Bus. Innovation--Times Mirror Magazines, Inc., New York, NY; *U.S. Public*, pg. 1616
Walker, Robert C., Sr. V.P. & Gen. Counsel--The Hartford Steam Boiler Inspection & Insurance Co., Hartford, CT; *U.S. Public*, pg. 795
Walker, Robert L., Chief Fin. Officer & Sr. V.P.-Fin.--AEGON USA, Inc., Louisville, KY; *Int'l*, pg. 26
Walker, Scott, Chief Tech. Officer & Sr. V.P.--Delco Electronics Corporation, Kokomo, IN; *U.S. Public*, pg. 720
Walker, T.P., Vice Chm. & Sec.--Stonecutter Mills Corp., Spindale, NC; *U.S. Private*, pg. 1044
Walker, Thomas B., Jr., Sr. V.P.--Acxiom Corporation, Conway, AR; *U.S. Public*, pg. 18
Walker, Thomas H., Jr., Sr. V.P.-Investor Rels.--American Re Corporation, Princeton, NJ; *Int'l*, pg. 897
Walker, Thomas K., Sr. V.P.-Construction, Pur. & Depots--Costco Wholesale, Issaquah, WA; *U.S. Public*, pg. 451
Walker, Thomas K., Sr. V.P.--ITT Automotive, Inc., Auburn Hills, MI; *U.S. Public*, pg. 859
Walker, W. Bryce, Sr. V.P.-Canadian Grp. Benefits--Manulife Financial (The Manufacturers Life Insurance Company), Toronto, Canada; *Int'l*, pg. 840
Walker, W.S., Sr. V.P.--Hughes Electronics Corporation, Westchester, CA; *U.S. Public*, pg. 720
Walker, Walter P., Exec. V.P.-Opers.--Hibernia Corporation, New Orleans, LA; *U.S. Public*, pg. 825
Walklet, Judith C., Sr. V.P.-Sls.--Quebecor Printing (USA) Corp., Greenwich, CT; *Int'l*, pg. 1078
Wall, James, Sr. V.P. & Pres.-AMREP Southwest, Inc.--AMREP Corporation, New York, NY; *U.S. Public*, pg. 104
Wall, John, Sr. V.P.-Sls. & Mktg.--Owsley & Sons, Inc., Fort Mill, SC; *U.S. Private*, pg. 824
Wall, Ron, Sr. V.P.--Intertec Publishing, Overland Park, KS; *U.S. Public*, pg. 1327
Wallace, John A., Sr. V.P.-Methane--Taurus Exploration, Inc., Birmingham, AL; *U.S. Public*, pg. 581
Wallace, Lee, Sr. V.P.-Reg. Opers.--Ruby Tuesday, Inc., Mobile, AL; *U.S. Public*, pg. 1411
Wallace, Michael J., Sr. V.P.--ComEd, Chicago, IL; *U.S. Public*, pg. 1664
Wallace, Robert M., Sr. V.P.--First National Bank of Pennsylvania, Hermitage, PA; *U.S. Public*, pg. 607
Wallace, Roger, Sr. V.P. & Co-Pres.-Ag. Svcs.--Data Transmission Network Corporation, Omaha, NE; *U.S. Public*, pg. 486
Wallace, Stephen P., Chief Fin. Officer & Sr. V.P.--Catellus Development Corporation, San Francisco, CA; *U.S. Public*, pg. 314
Wallack, Howard, Sr. V.P.--Laidlaw Transit, Inc, Van Nuys, CA; *Int'l*, pg. 259
Wallenberg, Lars, Sr. V.P.-Grp. Counsel--Trelleborg AB, Trelleborg, Sweden; *Int'l*, pg. 1419
Waller, Stephen L., Sr. V.P.-Network Transportation--DHL Worldwide Express, Redwood City, CA; *U.S. Private*, pg. 301
Waller, William A., Sr. V.P., Gen. Counsel & Sec.--Petty Company, Inc., Effingham, IL; *U.S. Private*, pg. 860
Wallin, Bjorn, Sr. V.P.-Corp. Gen. Staff--Telia AB, Farsta, Sweden; *Int'l*, pg. 1373
Wallinger, R. Scott, Sr. V.P.--Westvaco Corporation, New York, NY; *U.S. Public*, pg. 1762
Wallingford, Logan W., Sr. V.P.--Columbia Gas System Service Corp., Wilmington, DE; *U.S. Public*, pg. 403
Wallingford, Rufus, Sr. V.P. & Gen. Counsel--Browning-Ferris Industries, Inc., Houston, TX; *U.S. Public*, pg. 262
Wallis, W. Budge, Sr. V.P. & Gen. Mgr.-Book Div.--F & W Publications, Inc., Cincinnati, OH; *U.S. Private*, pg. 388
Wallock, Terrence, Sr. V.P., Sec. & Gen. Counsel--Ralphs Grocery Company, Compton, CA; *U.S. Private*, pg. 1202
Walner, Robert, Sr. V.P. & Sec.--Grubb & Ellis Management Services, Inc., Northbrook, IL; *U.S. Public*, pg. 767
Walner, Robert J., Sr. V.P., Gen. Counsel & Corp. Sec.--Grubb & Ellis Company, Northbrook, IL; *U.S. Public*, pg. 767
Walpert, Harvey B., Sr. V.P.-Corp. Affairs--Halter Marine Group, Inc., Gulfport, MS; *U.S. Public*, pg. 778
Walrath, Brett, Sr. V.P.--Edelman Worldwide, Inc., New York, NY; *U.S. Private*, pg. 362
Walsh, David J., Sr. V.P.-Intl. Opers.--Scholastic Corporation, New York, NY; *U.S. Public*, pg. 1440
Walsh, Dennis E., Sr. V.P.-Western Zone--Apria Healthcare Group Inc., Costa Mesa, CA; *U.S. Public*, pg. 125
Walsh, James F., Sr. V.P.-Direct Mkts.--Blue Cross & Blue Shield of Illinois, Chicago, IL; *U.S. Private*, pg. 151
Walsh, Jane Carluccio, Sr. V.P. & Grp. Creative Dir.--Wunderman Cato Johnson, New York, NY; *U.S. Private*, pg. 1197
Walsh, Mary, Sr. V.P. & Grp. Media Dir.--Young & Rubicam New York, New York, NY; *U.S. Private*, pg. 1198
Walsh, Mike, Sr. V.P., Fin. Dir. & Opers. Dir.--Ketchum Advertising/Pittsburgh, Pittsburgh, PA; *U.S. Private*, pg. 616
Walsh, Peter, Sr. V.P.-Retail Banking--Citizens Bank Of Connecticut, New London, CT; *Int'l*, pg. 1132
Walsh, Richard F., Sr. V.P.-Human Resources--ABB Inc., Norwalk, CT; *Int'l*, pg. 3
Walsh, Sam, Sr. V.P. & Brdcst. Production Dir.--Hal Riney & Partners, Inc., San Francisco, CA; *U.S. Private*, pg. 931
Walsh, Stan, Exec. V.P.-Mdsg. & Mktg.--Builders Square, Inc., San Antonio, TX; *U.S. Private*, pg. 477
Walsh, Terry J., Chief Fin. Officer & Sr. V.P.--Scott's Restaurants Inc., Markham, Canada; *Int'l*, pg. 1213
Walsh, William P., Sr. V.P.--Trenwick America Reinsurance Corporation, Stamford, CT; *U.S. Public*, pg. 1634
Walston, Terry Read, Sr. V.P.--Southwest Banks, Inc., Naples, FL; *U.S. Public*, pg. 607
Walter, John, Sr. V.P.--Lincoln Property Company, Dallas, TX; *U.S. Private*, pg. 668
Walter, Joseph C., Jr., Sr. V.P.-Commercial Lending--National Penn Bank, Boyertown, PA; *U.S. Public*, pg. 1159
Walter, Michael D., Sr. V.P.-Trading & Procurement--ConAgra, Inc., Omaha, NE; *U.S. Public*, pg. 425
Walter, R. Blane, Sr. V.P.-Bus. Devel.--Gerbig, Snell/Weisheimer & Assoc., Inc., Columbus, OH; *U.S. Private*, pg. 449
Walters, Bruce, Chief Devel. Officer & Sr. V.P.--KinderCare Learning Centers, Inc., Portland, OR; *U.S. Public*, pg. 961
Walters, Carole, Sr. V.P. & Media Dir.--Northlich Stolley LaWarre, Cincinnati, OH; *U.S. Private*, pg. 806
Walters, E.T., Sr. V.P. & Reg. Dir.--Winn-Dixie Stores, Inc., Jacksonville, FL; *U.S. Public*, pg. 1771

Walters, Glen R., Sr. V.P.--Firstar Bank of Minnesota, Bloomington, MN; *U.S. Public*, pg. 643

Walters, John C., Sr. V.P. & Gen. Counsel--John H. Harland Company, Decatur, GA; *U.S. Public*, pg. 785

Walters, Kirk, Chief Fin. Officer, Sr. V.P. & Treas.--Chittenden Corporation, Burlington, VT; *U.S. Public*, pg. 350

Walters, Kirk, Sr. V.P.-Treas. & Fin. Div.--Union Planters Bank, Memphis, TN; *U.S. Public*, pg. 1669

Walters, M.K., Chief Acctg. Officer, Sr. V.P. & Treas.--Union Planters Corporation, Cordova, TN; *U.S. Public*, pg. 1668

Walters, Robert F., Sr. V.P.--John Hancock Mutual Life Insurance Company, Boston, MA; *U.S. Private*, pg. 589

Waltman, Gerald, Sr. V.P.-Govt. Programs--Greenwich Air Services, Miami, FL; *U.S. Public*, pg. 710

Walton, Brian R., Jr., Sr. V.P.--Sterling Capital Management Company, Charlotte, NC; *U.S. Public*, pg. 1674

Walton, Jim, Sr. V.P.-Sports--CNN (Cable News Network), Atlanta, GA; *U.S. Public*, pg. 1614

Walton, Jon D., Sr. V.P., Gen. Counsel & Sec.--Allegheny Teledyne Incorporated, Pittsburgh, PA; *U.S. Public*, pg. 43

Walton, R. Edwin, Sr. V.P.--First Commercial Bank, N.A., Little Rock, AR; *U.S. Public*, pg. 630

Walton, Wyche H., Sr. V.P.--Haas, Wheat & Partners, Dallas, TX; *U.S. Private*, pg. 492

Walvoord, Ellen M., Sr. V.P.-Human Resources--Abbott Laboratories, Abbott Park, IL; *U.S. Public*, pg. 12

Wambach, Thomas, Sr. V.P.-Creative Services--Jordan, McGrath, Case & Taylor Inc., New York, NY; *U.S. Private*, pg. 598

Wander-Perna, Lucy, Sr. V.P.--Sony Pictures Entertainment, Culver City, CA; *Int'l*, pg. 1281

Wanek, Stephen J., Sr. V.P.--Interactive Technologies, Inc., Saint Paul, MN; *U.S. Public*, pg. 888

Wang, Andrew, Sr. V.P.--Foundation Health Systems, Inc., Pueblo, CO; *U.S. Public*, pg. 678

Wang, David N.K., Sr. V.P.--Applied Materials, Inc., Santa Clara, CA; *U.S. Public*, pg. 123

Wang, Heh-song, Sr. V.P. & Chief Economist--The International Commercial Bank of China, Taipei, Taiwan; *Int'l*, pg. 683

Wang, Ming, Sr. V.P. & Dir.-Res.--Investment Research Company, Rancho Santa Fe, CA; *U.S. Public*, pg. 1673

Wang, Shue-sheng, Sr. V.P. & Gen. Mgr.-Credit Admin.--The International Commercial Bank of China, Taipei, Taiwan; *Int'l*, pg. 683

Wang, Stanley L., Sr. V.P., Gen. Counsel & Sec.--Comcast Corporation, Philadelphia, PA; *U.S. Public*, pg. 406

Wang, Susan S., Chief Fin. Officer, Sr. V.P. & Sec.--Solectron Corporation, Milpitas, CA; *U.S. Public*, pg. 1483

Wangaard, Frederick f., Sr. V.P.-Corp. Banking--Colorado National Bankshares, Inc., Denver, CO; *U.S. Public*, pg. 1680

Wann, Raymond, Sr. V.P.--Executive Risk, Inc., Simsbury, CT; *U.S. Public*, pg. 599

Wantula, Peter, Sr. V.P.-Strategic Plng & New Bus.--Optima Direct, Inc., Vienna, VA; *U.S. Public*, pg. 1224

Ward, Bill, Sr. V.P., Gen. Counsel & Sec.--NW Transport Service, Inc., Denver, CO; *U.S. Private*, pg. 772

Ward, David, Sr. V.P. & Media Dir.--Hill, Holliday, Connors, Cosmopulos, Inc., Boston, MA; *U.S. Private*, pg. 529

Ward, John, Sr. V.P.-Sls. & Mktg.--Boston Whaler, Inc., Edgewater, FL; *U.S. Private*, pg. 689

Ward, Michael, Sr. V.P. & Deputy Gen. Counsel--Showtime Networks Inc., New York, NY; *U.S. Private*, pg. 779

Ward, R. Noel, Sr. V.P.--Nationwide Homes, Inc., Martinsville, VA; *U.S. Private*, pg. 788

Ward, Richard, Sr. V.P.--Avnet, Inc., Great Neck, NY; *U.S. Public*, pg. 155

Ward, Robert S., Sr. V.P.-Container Div.--Sea Containers Ltd., Hamilton, Bermuda; *Int'l*, pg. 1213

Ward, Sydney, Sr. V.P. & Acct. Plng. Dir.-Insights Grp.--Young & Rubicam New York, New York, NY; *U.S. Private*, pg. 1198

Wardinski, Bruce D., Sr. V.P. & Treas.--Host Marriott Corporation, Bethesda, MD; *U.S. Public*, pg. 841

Wardlaw, William H., Sr. V.P.--Trustmark National Bank, Jackson, MS; *U.S. Public*, pg. 1643

Ware, Adam, Sr. V.P.-Network Distribution--Fox Broadcasting Company (FBC), Beverly Hills, CA; *Int'l*, pg. 926

Ware, Warren, Sr. V.P.-Sls.--Ridge Tool Co., Elyria, OH; *U.S. Public*, pg. 574

Warehime, Steve, Sr. V.P. & Dir.-Real Estate--Bob Evans Farms, Inc., Columbus, OH; *U.S. Public*, pg. 596

Warf, Alben W., Sr. V.P.-Electronic Systems Devel.--Diebold, Incorporated, Canton, OH; *U.S. Public*, pg. 506

Warfel, John C., Sr. V.P.-Admin. & Fin.--Starter Corp., New Haven, CT; *U.S. Public*, pg. 1511

Warfield, Charles, Jr., Sr. V.P. & Gen. Mgr.-Uptown/Universal Records--Universal Studios, Inc., Universal City, CA; *Int'l*, pg. 1215

Warfield, Michael J., Sr. V.P.--Chartwell Re Corporation, Stamford, CT; *U.S. Public*, pg. 336

Warga, Thomas J., Sr. V.P. & Gen. Auditor--New York Life Insurance Company, New York, NY; *U.S. Private*, pg. 794

Waring, Thomas, Sr. V.P.-Opers.--MTA Long Island Rail Road, Jamaica, NY; *U.S. Private*, pg. 739

Warinini, Oliver N., Sr. V.P.-Exploration--New Business Development, San Francisco, CA; *Int'l*, pg. 224

Warner, Jamie, Sr. V.P.--Edelman Worldwide, Inc., Sacramento, CA; *U.S. Private*, pg. 362

Warner, John D., Sr. V.P.--The Boeing Company, Seattle, WA; *U.S. Public*, pg. 239

Warnock, John J., Jr., Chief Fin. Officer & Sr. V.P.--FTP Software Inc., Andover, MA; *U.S. Public*, pg. 609

Warr, A. Joe, Sr. V.P.--Gary-Williams Energy Corporation, Denver, CO; *U.S. Private*, pg. 440

Warr, Charles J., Sr. V.P.--W. Rosenlew Ltd., Helsinki, Finland; *Int'l*, pg. 1428

Warren, Bill, Sr. V.P.-Sls.--Tyco Toys, Inc., Mount Laurel, NJ; *U.S. Public*, pg. 1058

Warren, Bob, Sr. V.P. & Creative Dir.--Sawyer Riley Compton Inc., Atlanta, GA; *U.S. Private*, pg. 969

Warren, Doug, Sr. V.P.-Risk Mngmt.--Banknorth Group Inc., Burlington, VT; *U.S. Public*, pg. 186

Warren, Linda, Sr. V.P.-Mktg.--Walt Disney Attractions-Walt Disney World, Lake Buena Vista, FL; *U.S. Public*, pg. 513

Warren, Louis, Sr. V.P. & Deputy Dir.-Brdcst. Production--Grey Advertising Inc., New York, NY; *U.S. Public*, pg. 764

Warren, William M., Sr. V.P., Gen. Counsel & Asst. Sec.--Forest City Enterprises, Inc., Cleveland, OH; *U.S. Public*, pg. 667

Warrener, Richard C., Chief Fin. Officer & Sr. V.P.--Rurban Financial Corp., Defiance, OH; *U.S. Public*, pg. 1412

Warrington, Gary L., Sr. V.P.-Insurance--United Companies Financial Corporation, Baton Rouge, LA; *U.S. Public*, pg. 1675

Warschuorr, Bonnie, Sr. V.P.--Edelman Worldwide, Inc., New York, NY; *U.S. Private*, pg. 362

Washington, Alvin, Sr. V.P.-Corp. Human Resources--The McGraw-Hill Companies, New York, NY; *U.S. Public*, pg. 1069

Washington, Earl S., Sr. V.P.-Communications--Rockwell International Corporation, Costa Mesa, CA; *U.S. Public*, pg. 1397

Wasiak, Cristina, Sr. V.P.--Keycorp, Cleveland, OH; *U.S. Public*, pg. 954

Wasikowski, Ronald R., Sr. V.P.-Mktg. & Sls.--World Airways, Inc., Herndon, VA; *U.S. Public*, pg. 1780

Wasserman, Phyllis, Sr. V.P.-Adv. & Commun.--Staples, Inc., Westborough, MA; *U.S. Public*, pg. 1509

Watanabe, Noritsugu, Sr. V.P.--Marubeni America Corporation, New York, NY; *Int'l*, pg. 844

Watanabe, Tadashi, Sr. Mng. Dir.--Kansai Paint Co., Ltd., Osaka, Japan; *Int'l*, pg. 723

Watchorn, C.L.F., Sr. V.P. & Gen. Mgr.--Sun Life of Canada, Toronto, Canada; *Int'l*, pg. 1319

Waterman, Joseph F., Chief Fin. Officer & Sr. V.P.--Sanchez Computer Associates, Malvern, PA; *U.S. Public*, pg. 1425

Waterman, Richard S., Sr. Grp. V.P.-Ontario--Westburne Inc., Montreal, Canada; *Int'l*, pg. 1491

Waters, Richard, Sr. V.P.-Casino Opers.--Caesars Palace, Las Vegas, NV; *U.S. Public*, pg. 1512

Waterson, David, Sr. V.P.-Res. & Devel. & Mktg.--Icon Health & Fitness, Inc., Logan, UT; *U.S. Private*, pg. 556

Watkins, Barry, Sr. V.P.-Pub. Rels.--Madison Square Garden Corporation, New York, NY; *U.S. Public*, pg. 288

Watkins, David H., Sr. V.P.-Exploration--Cyprus Amax Minerals Company, Englewood, CO; *U.S. Public*, pg. 470

Watkins, Jim, Sr. V.P.-Worldwide Mktg.--Burger King Corporation, Miami, FL; *Int'l*, pg. 411

Watnabe, Tadayoshi, Sr. V.P.--Marubeni America Corporation, New York, NY; *Int'l*, pg. 844

Watson, C. David, Sr. V.P.-Admin. & Gen. Counsel--National Propane Corp., Cedar Rapids, IA; *U.S. Public*, pg. 1635

Watson, David N., Sr. V.P. & Pres.-Comcast Cellular Communications--Comcast Corporation, Philadelphia, PA; *U.S. Public*, pg. 406

Watson, David R., Sr. V.P.-Customer Support & Bus. Devel.--Rohr, Inc., Chula Vista, CA; *U.S. Public*, pg. 751

Watson, I. Benjamin, Sr. V.P.-H.R.--Sprint Corporation, Westwood, KS; *U.S. Public*, pg. 1500

Watson, John, Sr. V.P.-Strategic Mktg.--Reebok International Ltd., Stoughton, MA; *U.S. Public*, pg. 1369

Watson, Roger, Sr. V.P.-Comml. Real Estate--Starbanc Corporation, Cincinnati, OH; *U.S. Public*, pg. 1510

Watson, Scott, Exec. V.P.--J.E. Higgins Lumber Co., Concord, CA; *U.S. Private*, pg. 527

Watson, Stuart, Sr. V.P.-MCA Intl.-London--MCA Records, Inc., Universal City, CA; *Int'l*, pg. 1215

Watson, Stuart, Ph.D., Sr. V.P.-Res. & Devel.--Carpenter Co., Richmond, VA; *U.S. Private*, pg. 214

Watson, Susan B., Chief Fin. Officer & Sr. V.P.--Equitable Life Insurance Company of Iowa, Des Moines, IA; *Int'l*, pg. 647

Watson, Thomas G., Sr. V.P. & Controller--Shoreline Financial Corp., Benton Harbor, MI; *U.S. Public*, pg. 1467

Watson, Thomas G., Sr. V.P. & Controller--Shoreline Bank, Benton Harbor, MI; *U.S. Public*, pg. 1468

Watson, Timothy J., Sr. V.P.-Devel.--NxTrend Technology, Inc., Colorado Springs, CO; *U.S. Private*, pg. 809

Watt, Amy, Sr. V.P.--Mullen Advertising, Inc., Wenham, MA; *U.S. Private*, pg. 766

Watt, Thomas J., Sr. V.P.-Multifamily Housing--Federal Home Loan Mortgage Corporation, Mc Lean, VA; *U.S. Public*, pg. 615

Watt, William F., Sr. V.P.-Portfolio Mktg.--Countrywide Funding Corporation, Pasadena, CA; *U.S. Public*, pg. 453

Watts, Robert F., Sr. V.P.--John Hancock Mutual Life Insurance Company, Boston, MA; *U.S. Private*, pg. 589

Watts, Robert Z., Sr. V.P.-Corp. Res. & Devel.--International Game Technology, Reno, NV; *U.S. Public*, pg. 900

Watts, Thomas L., Sr. V.P.-Labor Rels. & Merger Implementation--Union Pacific Railroad Company, Omaha, NE; *U.S. Public*, pg. 1668

Waugh, James, Sr. V.P.--Hibernia Corporation, New Orleans, LA; *U.S. Public*, pg. 825

Waxenberg, Alan, Sr. V.P. & Publisher--Hearst Magazines Division, New York, NY; *U.S. Private*, pg. 516

Waxenberg, Alan M., Sr. V.P. & Publisher--Good Housekeeping, New York, NY; *U.S. Private*, pg. 517

Waxman, Laurance, Sr. V.P. & Pres.-Waxman Consumer Prods.--WOC Inc., Bedford, OH; *U.S. Public*, pg. 1748

Waxman, Laurance, Sr. V.P. & Pres.-Waxman Consumer Prods.--Waxman USA Inc., Bedford, OH; *U.S. Public*, pg. 1749

Wayman, James M., Sr. V.P.-Bank Properties Div.--First Hawaiian Bank, Honolulu, HI; *U.S. Public*, pg. 634

Wayman, Reva, Sr. V.P. & Mng. Dir.-Pub. Rels.--Harrison & Star, Inc., New York, NY; *U.S. Private*, pg. 506

Weadock, Daniel P., Sr. V.P.-Hotels & Pres.-ITT Sheraton Corporation--ITT Corporation, New York, NY; *U.S. Public*, pg. 1512

Weatherly, E. Mitchell, Sr. V.P.-Human Resources--Pier 1 Imports, Inc., Fort Worth, TX; *U.S. Public*, pg. 1295

Weaver, Dorenda K., Sr. V.P.--Total System Services, Inc., Columbus, GA; *U.S. Public*, pg. 1550

Weaver, Gary D., Sr. V.P.-Worldwide Mfg. Opers.--AST Research Inc., Irvine, CA; *Int'l*, pg. 1181

Weaver, J.C., Sr. V.P.--Hughes Electronics Corporation, Westchester, CA; *U.S. Public*, pg. 720

Weaver, Jerry, Sr. V.P.-Comml. Lending--National Bank of Alaska, Anchorage, AK; *U.S. Public*, pg. 1153

Weaver, Norman, Jr., Sr. V.P.-Field Mngmt.--American Express Financial Advisor, Minneapolis, MN; *U.S. Public*, pg. 73

Weaver, Sharon L., Sr. V.P.-Human Resources & Branch Admin.--National Penn Bank, Boyertown, PA; *U.S. Public*, pg. 1159

Weaver, William C., Sr. V.P.--Oak Industries Inc., Waltham, MA; *U.S. Public*, pg. 1209

Webb, Gregory C., Sr. V.P.--Varsity Spirit Corporation, Memphis, TN; *U.S. Public*, pg. 1389

Webb, James C., Sr. V.P.-Real Estate--House of Fabrics, Inc., Sherman Oaks, CA; *U.S. Public*, pg. 842

Webb, Max, Sr. V.P.--Shapell Industries, Inc., Beverly Hills, CA; *U.S. Private*, pg. 990

Webb, Michael G., Sr. V.P.-Plng. & Devel.--Kerr-McGee Corporation, Oklahoma City, OK; *U.S. Public*, pg. 952

Webb, Perry, Sr. V.P.--Ketchum, Inc., Pittsburgh, PA; *U.S. Private*, pg. 617

Webb, Robert D., Sr. V.P. & Treas.--Knight Architects Engineers Planners, Inc., Chicago, IL; *U.S. Private*, pg. 626

Webb, Scott, Sr. V.P.-Nickelodean & Nick at Nite On-Line Network--Nickelodeon/Nick At Nite, New York, NY; *U.S. Private*, pg. 779

Webb, Stan, Sr. V.P.-Opers.--Clear Channel Radio, Inc., Austin, TX; *U.S. Public*, pg. 383

Webber, Frederick W., Jr., Sr. V.P. & Exec. Dir.--Advanswers Media/Programming, Saint Louis, MO; *Int'l*, pg. 117

Webber, W. Scott, Sr. V.P.-Mktg.--Trivoli Systems, Indianapolis, IN; *U.S. Public*, pg. 896

Weber, C.R., Chief Fin. Officer & Sr. V.P.--OMNI Superstores, Northlake, IL; *U.S. Private*, pg. 1202

Weber, Daryl Ann, Sr. V.P.--First Pacific Advisors, Inc., Los Angeles, CA; *U.S. Public*, pg. 1673

Weber, Dave, Sr. V.P. & Acct. Dir.--G2 Advertising, Huntington Beach, CA; *U.S. Public*, pg. 764

Weber, Don, Sr. V.P.--Cramer-Krasselt, Chicago, IL; *U.S. Private*, pg. 285

Weber, Douglas, Sr. V.P.-Adv.--Journal of Commerce, Inc., New York, NY; *Int'l*, pg. 1026

Weber, Kathy, Sr. V.P.--Golin/Harris Communications, Inc., Chicago, IL; *Int'l*, pg. 1226

Weber, Mark, Sr. V.P.-Bus. Devel.--Reed Exhibition Companies-North America, Norwalk, CT; *Int'l*, pg. 1096

Weber, Max, Sr. V.P.-Foreign Exchange & Money Market Opers.--Banque Cantonale Vaudoise, Lausanne, Switzerland; *Int'l*, pg. 160

Weber, R. Christopher, Chief Fin. Officer & Sr. V.P.--Jacor Communications, Inc., Covington, KY; *U.S. Public*, pg. 922

Weber, Stanley G., Chief Fin. Officer, Sr. V.P.-Fin. & Sec.--Sceptre Resources Limited, Calgary, Canada; *Int'l*, pg. 1203

Weber, Stephen J., Sr. V.P.--Market Facts, Inc., Arlington Heights, IL; *U.S. Public*, pg. 1046

Weber, Steven A., Sr. V.P.-Developing Member Solutions--Aid Association for Lutherans, Appleton, WI; *U.S. Private*, pg. 27

Weber, Vin, Mng. Partner--Clark & Weinstock, Washington, DC; *U.S. Public*, pg. 1223

Webster, David S., Sr. V.P.-Natl. Accts.--Willis Corroon Corp. of Mobile, Mobile, AL; *Int'l*, pg. 1506

Webster, Ronald B., Sr. V.P.--Gerber Scientific, Inc., South Windsor, CT; *U.S. Public*, pg. 740

Wechsler, Alfred E., Sr. V.P. & Chief Professional Officer--Arthur D. Little, Inc., Cambridge, MA; *U.S. Private*, pg. 670

Wecker, Irwin, Sr. V.P.-H.R.--Morse Diesel International, Inc., New York, NY; *U.S. Private*, pg. 762

Weed, Clayton, Sr. V.P.--Weatherby Health Care, Norwalk, CT; *U.S. Private*, pg. 1155

Weed, Mike, Sr. V.P. & Grp. Creative Dir.--The Buntin Group, Nashville, TN; *U.S. Private*, pg. 181

Weeden, Jeffrey B., Chief Fin. Officer, Sr. V.P., & Treas.--Firstar Corporation-Iowa, Des Moines, IA; *U.S. Public*, pg. 643

Weeks, Jerry E., Sr. V.P.--Great Western Bank, Chatsworth, CA; *U.S. Public*, pg. 1741

Weeks, Paul, II, Sr. V.P., Gen. Counsel & Sec.--ICF Kaiser International Inc., Fairfax, VA; *U.S. Public*, pg. 852

Weger, Kris, Sr. V.P. & Gen Mgr.--Unistrut Corporation, Wayne, MI; *U.S. Public*, pg. 1651

Wegner, Frank W., Sr. V.P.--Associates Communications Div., Dallas, TX; *U.S. Public*, pg. 663

Wegrzyn, Patricia E., Sr. V.P.-Fin.--Citizens Savings Bank, Providence, RI; *Int'l*, pg. 1132

Wehling, Robert, Sr. V.P.-Mktg. Research & Govt. Rels.--Richardson-Vicks, Inc., Health Care Products, Cincinnati, OH; *U.S. Public*, pg. 1331

Wehling, Robert L., Sr. V.P.-Adv., Market Res. & Govt. Rels.--The Procter & Gamble Company, Cincinnati, OH; *U.S. Public*, pg. 1330

Wehrle, Michael H., Chief Fin. Officer & Sr. V.P.--McJunkin Corporation, Charleston, WV; *U.S. Private*, pg. 722

Weicht, Richard A., Sr. V.P.--Adolfson & Peterson, Inc., Minneapolis, MN; *U.S. Private*, pg. 17

Weidemeyer, Thomas H., Sr. V.P.-Air Opers.--United Parcel Service of America, Inc., Atlanta, GA; *U.S. Private*, pg. 1123

Weiden, Jeff, Sr. V.P.-Fin. & Treas.--Firstar Corporation, Milwaukee, WI; *U.S. Public*, pg. 642

Weidenmuller, Manfred, Sr. V.P.-Service--Deutz AG, Cologne, Germany; *Int'l*, pg. 407

Weidler, Jay B., Sr. V.P.--Brown & Root Energy Services, London, United Kingdom; *U.S. Public*, pg. 775

Weidner, Ronald L., Sr. V.P.-Commercial Lending--National Penn Bank, Boyertown, PA; *U.S. Public*, pg. 1159

Weigand, Alvin J., Sr. V.P. & Grp. Exec.- Bulk Power Enterprises Group--PECO Energy Company, Philadelphia, PA; *U.S. Public*, pg. 1268

Weigand, George W., Chief Fin. Officer & Sr. V.P.--Rubbermaid Incorporated, Wooster, OH; *U.S. Public*, pg. 1411

Weigel, Kent, Sr. V.P.-Corp. Property Services--Washington Mutual Inc., Seattle, WA; *U.S. Public*, pg. 1741

Weihs, Kurt, Sr. V.P. & Grp. Creative Dir.--Lois/EJL New York, New York, NY; *U.S. Public*, pg. 1011

Weiland, James R., Sr., Sr. V.P.--STS Services Inc., Nashville, TN; *U.S. Public*, pg. 277

Weiler, Robert K., Sr. V.P.-N. American Bus. Grp.--Lotus Development Corporation, Cambridge, MA; *U.S. Public*, pg. 896

Weiler, Robert K., Sr. V.P. & Pres.-Software--Wang Laboratories, Inc., Billerica, MA; *U.S. Public*, pg. 1737

Weill, Bob, Sr. V.P.--Gould Paper Corporation, New York, NY; *U.S. Private*, pg. 466

Weill, Marc P., Chief Investment Officer & Sr. V.P.--Travelers Group, New York, NY; *U.S. Public*, pg. 1632

Weiman, S.G., Sr. V.P.--Natural Gas Pipeline Co. America, Lombard, IL; *U.S. Public*, pg. 1210

Weimann, Denise, Sr. V.P. & Brdcst., Prog. & Pur. Grp. Supvr.--Young & Rubicam New York, New York, NY; *U.S. Private*, pg. 1198

Weinberg, Richard G., Sr. V.P., Gen. Counsel & Sec.--GAF Corporation, Wayne, NJ; *U.S. Private*, pg. 433

Weinberg, Robert, Sr. V.P.-Mdsg.--Toys "R" Us, Inc., Paramus, NJ; *U.S. Public*, pg. 1626

Weinberg, Robert J., Sr. V.P. & Div. Mgr.-Mdse.--Toys "R" Us United States, Paramus, NJ; *U.S. Public*, pg. 1626

Weiner, David M., Sr. V.P.--Advance Mechanical Systems, Inc., Mount Prospect, IL; *U.S. Private*, pg. 18

Weiner, Gilbert, Sr. V.P.--Pall Corporation, Greenvale, NY; *U.S. Public*, pg. 1253

Weiner, Paul, Chief Fin. Officer, Sr. V.P. & Treas.--McCrory Corporation, New York, NY; *U.S. Private*, pg. 720

Weiner, Susan, Sr. V.P.-Brand Mngmt.--Pearle Vision Express, Dallas, TX; *U.S. Public*, pg. 397

Weinfeld, Lewis, Chief Fin. Officer & Sr. V.P.--HRH Construction Corp., New York, NY; *U.S. Private*, pg. 1035

Weinholzer, Charles, Sr. V.P. & Reg. Mgr.--INX International, Milwaukee, WI; *Int'l*, pg. 1311

Weinmann, Richard, Sr. V.P.-Admin.--Hehr International Inc., Los Angeles, CA; *U.S. Private*, pg. 519

Weinstein, Alan A., Chief Fin. Officer & Sr. V.P.--Gottschalks Inc., Fresno, CA; *U.S. Public*, pg. 754

Weinstein, Allen, Sr. V.P.-Mdse.--Catherines Stores Corporation, Memphis, TN; *U.S. Public*, pg. 317

Weinstein, Dina, Sr. V.P.-Acct. Services--Western International Media Corporation, Los Angeles, CA; *U.S. Private*, pg. 1165

Weinstein, Mark M., Sr. V.P.-Govt. Affairs--Viacom Inc., New York, NY; *U.S. Private*, pg. 775

Weinstein, Martin, Sr. V.P.-Chromalloy Gas Turbine Opers.--Sequa Corporation, New York, NY; *U.S. Public*, pg. 1458

Weinstock, Davis, Mng. Partner--Clark & Weinstock, New York, NY; *U.S. Public*, pg. 1223

Weinstock, Michael, Sr. V.P. & Gen. Counsel--Pacificare Health Systems, Santa Ana, CA; *U.S. Public*, pg. 1251

Weintraub, Stephen, Sr. V.P. & Sec.--Counsel Corporation, Toronto, Canada; *Int'l*, pg. 338

Weintraub, William H., Sr. V.P.-Mktg.--Coors Brewing Company, Golden, CO; *U.S. Public*, pg. 445

Weir, Ron J., Sr. V.P.-Technology Center--R.R. Donnelley & Sons Company, Chicago, IL; *U.S. Public*, pg. 517

Weis, Gretchen, Sr. V.P.--Edelman Worldwide, Inc., Houston, TX; *U.S. Private*, pg. 362

Weisbarth, James, Sr. V.P., Treas. & Asst. Sec.--Central Reserve Life Corporation, Strongsville, OH; *U.S. Public*, pg. 326

Weisbarth, James A., Sr. V.P. & Controller--Central Reserve Life of North America Insurance Co., Strongsville, OH; *U.S. Public*, pg. 326

Weisberger, Edward, Sr. V.P.-Fin.--HomeBase, Inc., Irvine, CA; *U.S. Public*, pg. 832

Weisbruch, W. Douglas, Sr. V.P.-Distribution--Lone Star Gas Co., Dallas, TX; *U.S. Public*, pg. 1587

Weiser, Ann, Sr. V.P.-Human Resources--R.R. Donnelley & Sons Company, Chicago, IL; *U.S. Public*, pg. 517

Weiser, David H., Sr. V.P.-Legal & Human Resources--Department 56 Inc., Eden Prairie, MN; *U.S. Public*, pg. 500

Weiser, Edie, Sr. V.P. & Assoc. Creative Dir.--Carrafiello, Diehl & Associates, Inc., Irvington, NY; *U.S. Private*, pg. 215

Weisman, Susan, Sr. V.P. & Controller--BankAtlantic Bancorp, Inc., Fort Lauderdale, FL; *U.S. Public*, pg. 183

Weisner, B.A., Sr. V.P. & Chief Oper. Officer-Service Centres--Fedmet International Inc., Mississauga, Canada; *Int'l*, pg. 1150

Weiss, Andrew D., Sr. V.P.-Advanced Bus. & Tech. Engrng.--Federal National Mortgage Association (Fannie Mae), Washington, DC; *U.S. Public*, pg. 615

Weiss, Anthony A., Sr. V.P.-Direct Sls.--CompUSA, Dallas, TX; *U.S. Public*, pg. 420

Weiss, Erwin, Sr. V.P.-Consumer Prods.--American Greetings Corporation, Cleveland, OH; *U.S. Public*, pg. 77

Weiss, Jane, Sr. V.P. & Acct. Plng. Dir.-Insights Grp.--Young & Rubicam New York, New York, NY; *U.S. Private*, pg. 1198

Weiss, Jeff, Sr. V.P.-Distribution--Jan Bell Marketing Inc., Sunrise, FL; *U.S. Public*, pg. 207

Weiss, Jim, Sr. V.P.--Rentrak Corporation, Portland, OR; *U.S. Public*, pg. 1377

Weiss, Judy E., Sr. V.P.-MetLife Small Bus. Ctr.--Metropolitan Life Insurance Co., New York, NY; *U.S. Private*, pg. 737

Weiss, Martin, Sr. Exec. V.P.-Sls.--Lily of France, Inc., New York, NY; *U.S. Private*, pg. 140

Weiss, Stephen I., Sr. V.P.-Fin.--Lyons Lavey Nickel Swift, Inc., New York, NY; *U.S. Public*, pg. 1224

Weiss, Steven, Sr. V.P. & Gen. Counsel--Sanwa Bank California, Los Angeles, CA; *Int'l*, pg. 1189

Weiss, Steven L., Sr. V.P. & Innovatiion & Strategic Plng. Dir.--The Interpublic Group of Companies, Inc., New York, NY; *U.S. Public*, pg. 908

Weisshaar, Kenneth R., Sr. V.P.-Worldwide Consumer Prods./Diabetes Care--Becton Dickinson & Company, Franklin Lakes, NJ; *U.S. Public*, pg. 199

Weiswasser, Stephen A., Pres.-Capital Cities/ABC Media Grp., Sr. V.P. & Gen. Counsel--ABC, Inc, New York, NY; *U.S. Public*, pg. 511

Wejman, Janet, Chief Info. Officer & Sr. V.P.--Continental Airlines, Houston, TX; *U.S. Public*, pg. 439

Welch, Charles, Sr. V.P. & Dir.--North Carolina Mutual Life Insurance Co., Durham, NC; *U.S. Private*, pg. 804

Welch, Edward A., Sr. V.P. & Asst. Treas.--Fay, Spofford & Thorndike, Inc., Burlington, MA; *U.S. Private*, pg. 397

Welch, M.D., Sr. V.P.-Opers.--Elkins Constructors, Inc., Jacksonville, FL; *U.S. Private*, pg. 372

Welch, Martin E., III, Chief Fin. Officer & Sr. V.P.--Kmart Corporation, Troy, MI; *U.S. Public*, pg. 963

Welch, William E., Sr. V.P.-D.P.--Magna Group, Inc., Saint Louis, MO; *U.S. Public*, pg. 1037

Welcome, Richard, Sr. V.P.-Devel.--TrizecHahn Centers Inc., San Diego, CA; *Int'l*, pg. 1425

Wellborn, William C., Chief Fin. Officer & Sr. V.P.--Lenox, Incorporated, Lawrenceville, NJ; *U.S. Public*, pg. 261

Welle, Bernie, Sr. V.P.-Human Resources--The Dial Corporation, Phoenix, AZ; *U.S. Public*, pg. 505

Wellen, Randy L., Sr. V.P.--Great Western Bank, Chatsworth, CA; *U.S. Public*, pg. 1741

Wellendorf, Donald R., V.P., Treas. & Investor Rels.--Mapco Inc., Tulsa, OK; *U.S. Public*, pg. 1042

Welling, Richard, Sr. V.P. & Treas.--Ameriana Bancorp, New Castle, IN; *U.S. Public*, pg. 66

Welliver, Byron L., Sr. V.P.-Fin., Controller & Treas.--Noble Drilling Corporation, Houston, TX; *U.S. Public*, pg. 1186

Welliver, Byron L., Sr. V.P.-Fin. & Treas.--Noble Offshore Corporation, Houston, TX; *U.S. Public*, pg. 1186

Wellman, F. Selby, Sr. V.P.-Bus. Units--Cisco Systems, Inc., San Jose, CA; *U.S. Public*, pg. 375

Wells, Henry, Sr. V.P.-H.R.--Brach & Brock Confections, Inc., Chicago, IL; *U.S. Private*, pg. 163

Wells, Jeffrey, Sr. V.P.-Human Resources--Circuit City Stores, Inc., Richmond, VA; *U.S. Public*, pg. 374

Wells, Mark C., Sr. V.P.-Franchise Svcs.--Promus Hotel Corporation, Memphis, TN; *U.S. Public*, pg. 1335

Wells, R. Murray, Sr. V.P.--Radian International LLC, Austin, TX; *U.S. Public*, pg. 522

Wells, Richard A., Sr. V.P.-Fin.--Kohler Company, Kohler, WI; *U.S. Private*, pg. 630

Welp, David, Pres.-Raytheon TI Systems & Sr. V.P.--Raytheon TI Systems, Lewisville, TX; *U.S. Public*, pg. 1365

Welsh, Benton, Sr. V.P.-TMI Grp.--American Rehability Services, Inc., Brentwood, TN; *U.S. Public*, pg. 1257

Welsh, Dennie M., Sr. V.P. & Grp. Exec.-Computer Services--International Business Machines Corporation, Armonk, NY; *U.S. Public*, pg. 895

Welshimer, Rosanne, Sr. V.P.--The Bank of New York Company, Inc., New York, NY; *U.S. Public*, pg. 178

Wendland, Dennis, Sr. V.P.-Grain & Agra-Services--Harvest States Cooperatives, Saint Paul, MN; *U.S. Private*, pg. 508

Wendling, Louise, Sr. V.P. & Gen. Mgr.-Eastern Canada Region--Costco Wholesale, Issaquah, WA; *U.S. Public*, pg. 451

Wenich, Ozzie, Chief Fin. Officer, Sr. V.P. & Treas.--H & R Block, Inc., Kansas City, MO; *U.S. Public*, pg. 770

Wennett, Robert, Sr. V.P.-Acquisitions--Federal Realty Investment Trust, Rockville, MD; *U.S. Public*, pg. 616

Wennlund, Lloyd, Sr. V.P.-Mktg. & Personal Fin. Services--Northern Trust Corporation, Chicago, IL; *U.S. Public*, pg. 1195

Wentraub, Bill, Sr. V.P.-Mktg.--Adolph Coors Company, Golden, CO; *U.S. Public*, pg. 445

Wentworth, Bob, Chief Fin. Officer & Sr. V.P.--Pilot Software, Cambridge, MA; *U.S. Private*, pg. 872

Wentworth, Clare G., Sr. V.P.-Pur.--Thor Industries, Inc., Jackson Center, OH; *U.S. Public*, pg. 1602

Wentworth, Francis M., Jr., Sr. V.P., Sec. & General Counsel--Gaylord Entertainment Co., Nashville, TN; *U.S. Public*, pg. 704

Wentworth, John A., Sr. V.P.-Media Rels.--Paramount Pictures Corporation, Los Angeles, CA; *U.S. Private*, pg. 776

Wenzel, Frank, Ph.D., Sr. V.P. & Controller--Bayer Corporation, Pittsburgh, PA; *Int'l*, pg. 172

Wenzler, Joseph P., Chief Fin. Officer, Sr. V.P. & Treas.--WICOR, Inc., Milwaukee, WI; *U.S. Public*, pg. 1767

Wergeland, Jens Henrik, Sr. V.P.--Det Norske Veritas, Hovik, Norway; *Int'l*, pg. 396

Werner, Douglas, Sr. V.P.-Strategic Plng. & Bus. Devel.--Foundation Health Systems, Inc., Pueblo, CO; *U.S. Public*, pg. 678

Werner, George, Sr. V.P. & Gen. Mgr.--Higher Education Division, Upper Saddle River, NJ; *U.S. Private*, pg. 778

Werner, Jeffrey S., Sr. V.P.--G.E. Capital Commercial Real Estate Financing, Stamford, CT; *U.S. Public*, pg. 712

Werner, Olle, Sr. V.P.-H.R.--Akzo Nobel N.V., Arnhem, Netherlands; *Int'l*, pg. 42

Wert, John H., Jr., Chief Fin. Officer & Sr. V.P.-Fin.--Owosso Corporation, King of Prussia, PA; *U.S. Public*, pg. 1238

Wertz, John C., Chief Oper. Officer, Sr. V.P. & Treas.--Banner Aerospace, Inc., Washington, DC; *U.S. Public*, pg. 187

Wesner, Patricia A., Sr. V.P.--Firstar Milwaukee Bank, N.A., Milwaukee, WI; *U.S. Public*, pg. 643

Wesselink, David, Chief Fin. Officer & Sr. V.P.--Advanta Corp., Spring House, PA; *U.S. Public*, pg. 22

Wesselmann, Lee A., Chief Fin. Officer & Sr. V.P.--Owens-Illinois, Inc., Toledo, OH; *U.S. Public*, pg. 1238

Wessels, Jerry, Sr. V.P. & Gen. Mgr.--Italia Advertising, Dallas, TX; *U.S. Private*, pg. 576

Wessling, Gregory J., Sr. V.P. & Gen. Mgr.-Mdse.--Lowe's Companies, Inc., North Wilkesboro, NC; *U.S. Public*, pg. 1015

Wesstrom, Olof, Sr. V.P.-Listed Stocks Portfolio--AB Industrivarden, Stockholm, Sweden; *Int'l*, pg. 678

West, A. Stanley, Sr. V.P.-Sls.--Cleveland-Cliffs Inc, Cleveland, OH; *U.S. Public*, pg. 386

West, A.S., Sr. V.P.-Sls.--The Cleveland-Cliffs Iron Company, Cleveland, OH; *U.S. Public*, pg. 386

West, David M., Sr. V.P. & Sec.-Fin. & Gen. Group--Toyota Motor Sales, U.S.A., Inc., Torrance, CA; *Int'l*, pg. 1412

West, J. Thomas, Sr. V.P.-Advanced Devel.--Data General Corporation, Westborough, MA; *U.S. Public*, pg. 485

West, Jacque, Sr. V.P.-Consumer Svcs.--Comdata Corporation, Brentwood, TN; *U.S. Public*, pg. 331

West, Judy H., Sr. V.P. & Treas.--Corbett HealthConnect, A Frank J. Corbett, Inc., Company, Chicago, IL; *U.S. Public*, pg. 1223

West, Richard E., Sr. V.P.-Residential Lending--D & N Bank, Hancock, MI; *U.S. Public*, pg. 472

West, Robert R., M.D., Chief Tech. Officer & Sr. V.P.--Allied Clinical Laboratories, Inc., Nashville, TN; *U.S. Public*, pg. 973

West, Stephen A., Sr. V.P. & Gen. Counsel--Fairfield Inn, Washington, DC; *U.S. Public*, pg. 1048

West, William W., Sr. V.P. & Chief Lending Officer--Potomac Valley Bank, Gaithersburg, MD; *U.S. Public*, pg. 1089

Westadt, Wendy, Sr. V.P. & Print Production Dir.--Laughlin/Constable, Inc., Milwaukee, WI; *U.S. Private*, pg. 653

Westberg, Bjorn, Sr. V.P.--Nordbanken AB, Stockholm, Sweden; *Int'l*, pg. 957

Westbrook, C. Hunter, Sr. V.P.--TCF Bank Illinois, Oak Brook, IL; *U.S. Public*, pg. 1554

Westen, B. Curtis, Sr. V.P., Gen. Counsel & Sec.--Foundation Health Systems, Inc., Pueblo, CO; *U.S. Public*, pg. 678

Westerbeck, David F., Sr. V.P., Gen. Counsel & Sec.--The Union Central Life Insurance Co., Cincinnati, OH; *U.S. Private*, pg. 1118

Westerberg, Rick, Sr. V.P.--Cody Energy, Inc., Denver, CO; *U.S. Private*, pg. 249

Westerlund, David A., Sr. V.P.-Admin.--Ball Corporation, Muncie, IN; *U.S. Public*, pg. 170

Westerman, T.G., Sr. V.P.--Hughes Electronics Corporation, Westchester, CA; *U.S. Public*, pg. 720

Westervelt, James J., Sr. V.P. & Grp. Controller--The Hartford Financial Services Group Inc., Hartford, CT; *U.S. Public*, pg. 794

Westfall, David M., Chief Fin. Officer & Sr. V.P.--Consolidated Natural Gas Company, Pittsburgh, PA; *U.S. Public*, pg. 435

Westhoff, William N., Sr. V.P.-Fixed Income Mngmt.--American Express Financial Advisor, Minneapolis, MN; *U.S. Public*, pg. 73

Westin, David, Pres.-Prod., ABC Television Network Grp. & Sr. V.P.--ABC, Inc, New York, NY; *U.S. Public*, pg. 511

Westin, Eric A., Sr. V.P.--Gaylord Entertainment Co., Nashville, TN; *U.S. Public*, pg. 704

Weston, Stephen W., Sr. V.P.-Donor Mngmt.--Nabi, Boca Raton, FL; *U.S. Public*, pg. 1148

Weston, W. William, Sr. V.P.-European Grp.--Dentsply International Inc., York, PA; *U.S. Public*, pg. 498

Westover, Frank T., Sr. V.P. & Controller--Whitman Corporation, Rolling Meadows, IL; *U.S. Public*, pg. 1766

Wetheim, Moshe, Sr. V.P.-Engnrg.--Olympia & York Developments Ltd., Toronto, Canada; *Int'l*, pg. 1004

Wetzler, Graydon A., Sr. V.P.-Opers.--Rohr, Inc., Chula Vista, CA; *U.S. Public*, pg. 751

Weverka, Dennis, Sr. V.P.--National Financial Insurance Company, Fort Worth, TX; *U.S. Private*, pg. 782

Wexler, Paul R., Sr. V.P.-Procurement & Distr.--Advantica Restaurant Group, Inc., Spartanburg, SC; *U.S. Public*, pg. 22

Weymuller, Bruno, Chief Fin. Officer& Sr. V.P.--Elf Aquitane, Paris, France; *Int'l*, pg. 444

Weyner, David, Sr. V.P. & Gen. Mgr., Sony Classical USA--Sony Music Entertainment, Inc., New York, NY; *Int'l*, pg. 1281

Whalen, Thomas, Sr. V.P. & Treas.--Advance Mechanical Systems, Inc., Mount Prospect, IL; *U.S. Private*, pg. 18

Whaley, Billy, Sr. V.P.-H.R.--Greenwood Mills, Inc., Greenwood, SC; *U.S. Private*, pg. 479

Whatcott, Lee A., Chief Fin. Officer & Sr. V.P.--Westcorp, Irvine, CA; *U.S. Public*, pg. 1756

Wheatley, Bruce C., Sr. V.P.-Admin.--Commercial Intertech Corp., Youngstown, OH; *U.S. Public*, pg. 411

Wheaton, Robert, Sr. V.P.-Sls.--Wind River Systems, Inc., Alameda, CA; *U.S. Public*, pg. 1770

Wheeler, William J., Sr. V.P.-Fin. Opers.--Metropolitan Life Insurance Co., New York, NY; *U.S. Private*, pg. 737

Wheeling, Joe, Sr. V.P.-Opers. Support--Motel 6 Operating L.P., Dallas, TX; *Int'l*, pg. 21

Wherry, Dennis P., Sr. V.P.-Opers.--Recoton Corporation, Lake Mary, FL; *U.S. Public*, pg. 1369

Wherry, Ken A., Sr. V.P.-Customer Satisfaction & Sls.--Eddie Bauer, Inc., Redmond, WA; *U.S. Public*, pg. 1499

Whipkey, James M., Chief Fin. Officer & Sr. V.P.--Benton Oil & Gas Company, Carpinteria, CA; *U.S. Public*, pg. 212

Whisenant, J. Douglas, Sr. V.P. & Gen. Mgr.--Northwest Pipeline Corp., Salt Lake City, UT; *U.S. Public*, pg. 1769

Whitacre, Huntley R., Sr. V.P.-Investor Rels.--RJR Nabisco Holdings Corp., New York, NY; *U.S. Public*, pg. 1354

Whitaker, Mark, Sr. V.P.-Central Tax Services--H & R Block, Inc., Kansas City, MO; *U.S. Public*, pg. 770

Whitcomb, Stanley R., Sr. V.P.-Information Tech.--American Stores Company, Salt Lake City, UT; *U.S. Public*, pg. 92

Whitcome, James P., Sr. V.P.-Capital Svcs.--The Mills Corporation, Arlington, VA; *U.S. Public*, pg. 1113

White-Lee, Jennifer, Sr. V.P. & Acct. Plng. Dir.--CPM, Inc., Chicago, IL; *U.S. Private*, pg. 196

White, Bill, Sr. V.P.-Govt. Rels.--Cash America International, Inc., Fort Worth, TX; *U.S. Public*, pg. 312

White, Charles D., Sr. V.P. & Treas.--Norwest Corporation, Minneapolis, MN; *U.S. Public*, pg. 1201

White, David, Sr. V.P.--Banco Santander, Madrid, Spain; *Int'l*, pg. 143

White, David A., Jr., Sr. V.P.-Corp. Plng. & Devel.--Cooper Industries, Inc., Houston, TX; *U.S. Public*, pg. 442

White, Gary, Sr. V.P.--Commercial Federal Corporation, Omaha, NE; *U.S. Public*, pg. 411

White, J. Spratt, Sr. V.P.-Growth & Devel. & Human Resources--Springs Industries, Inc., Fort Mill, SC; *U.S. Public*, pg. 1499

White, James D., Sr. V.P.-Worldwide Indus. Equip.--Deere & Company, Moline, IL; *U.S. Public*, pg. 491

White, James D., Sr. V.P.-Mfg.--John Deere Industrial Equipment Company, Moline, IL; *U.S. Public*, pg. 492

White, John J., Sr. V.P.-Profit Improvement & Special Projects--Proffitt's, Inc., Alcoa, TN; *U.S. Public*, pg. 1333

White, Judy, Sr. V.P.-TV Production--Jordan, McGrath, Case & Taylor Inc., New York, NY; *U.S. Private*, pg. 598

White, Kathy Brittain, Chief Info. Officer & Sr. V.P.--Allegiance Healthcare Corp., McGaw Park, IL; *U.S. Public*, pg. 44

White, Kevin R., Exec. V.P.-Corp. Devel. & Strategic Plng.--Louis Dreyfus Natural Gas Corp., Oklahoma City, OK; *U.S. Private*, pg. 342

White, Martin A., Sr. V.P.-Corp. Devel.--MDU Resources Group, Inc., Bismarck, ND; *U.S. Public*, pg. 1025

White, Miles, Sr. V.P.-Diagnostic Opers.--Abbott Laboratories, Abbott Park, IL; *U.S. Public*, pg. 12

White, Peter, Sr. V.P. & Exec. Creative Dir.--The Chapman Agency, New York, NY; *U.S. Private*, pg. 1197

White, Richard, Sr. V.P.--The Richard Leahy Corporation, Fort Wayne, IN; *U.S. Public*, pg. 997

White, Richard E., Sr. V.P.-Mktg.--Marathon Ashland Petroleum LLC, Findlay, OH; *U.S. Public*, pg. 139

White, Thomas W., Sr. V.P.--Federal National Mortgage Association (Fannie Mae), Washington, DC; *U.S. Public*, pg. 615

Whitehill, Clifford L., Sr. V.P. & Gen. Counsel--Darden Restaurants, Inc., Orlando, FL; *U.S. Public*, pg. 483

Whiteley, Amy G., Sr. V.P.--Sparks State Bank, Sparks, MD; *U.S. Public*, pg. 1089

Whitener, Gordon D., Sr. V.P.--Interface Inc., Atlanta, GA; *U.S. Public*, pg. 889

Whitfield, Charles, Sr. V.P.-Human Resources--SouthTrust Corporation, Birmingham, AL; *U.S. Public*, pg. 1491

Whiting, Kent L., Sr. V.P.-Information Services--Rite Aid Corporation, Camp Hill, PA; *U.S. Public*, pg. 1390

Whiting, Lawson, Sr. V.P.-Sls.--Asko, Inc, Homestead, PA; *U.S. Private*, pg. 89

Whiting, Thomas L., Sr. V.P.-Pacific Rim & Latin America--Dentsply International Inc., York, PA; *U.S. Public*, pg. 498

Whitlock, Orion, Sr. V.P.-Claims--American Bankers Insurance Co. of Florida, Miami, FL; *U.S. Public*, pg. 67

Whitlock, Orion, Sr. V.P.-Claims--American Bankers Life Assurance Co. of Florida, Miami, FL; *U.S. Public*, pg. 67

Whitlock, Robert G., Jr., Sr. V.P. & Actuary--Harleysville Group, Harleysville, PA; *U.S. Public*, pg. 786

Whitmeyer, Angelyn, Sr. V.P. & Controller--Trone Advertising, Inc., Greensboro, NC; *U.S. Private*, pg. 1104

Whitmore, Bruce G., Sr. V.P., Gen. Counsel & Sec.--Atlantic Richfield Company, Los Angeles, CA; *U.S. Public*, pg. 144

Whitmoyer, Ellen M., Sr. V.P.-Mktg.--Lebanon Valley Farmers Bank, Lebanon, PA; *U.S. Public*, pg. 688

Whitney, Jon R., Sr. V.P.--CIG Exploration, Inc., Houston, TX; *U.S. Public*, pg. 390

Whitt, Greg, Sr. V.P.-Opers.--Briggs Industries, Inc., Tampa, FL; *U.S. Private*, pg. 168

Whitt, John R., Sr. V.P.-Mktg., Sls. & Sec.--Sherman & Reilly, Inc., Chattanooga, TN; *U.S. Private*, pg. 993

Whittaker, Richard, Sr. V.P.-Strategic Devel. & Mktg. Opers.--Schering-Plough Healthcare Products Inc., Liberty Corner, NJ; *U.S. Public*, pg. 1438

Whittier, Ronald J., Sr. V.P. & Gen. Mgr.-Architecture & Software Technology Group--Intel Corporation, Santa Clara, CA; *U.S. Public*, pg. 886

Whitworth, J. Bryan, Sr. V.P. & Gen. Counsel--Phillips Petroleum Company, Bartlesville, OK; *U.S. Public*, pg. 1290

Whyte, Ralph, Sr. V.P.--Willis Corroon Aerospace of Canada Ltd., Vancouver, Canada; *Int'l*, pg. 1509

Wichard, Neal, Sr. V.P.-Real Estate--Buffets, Inc., Eden Prairie, MN; *U.S. Public*, pg. 267

Wickens, Wayne R., Sr. V.P.--Eagle-Picher Industries, Inc., Cincinnati, OH; *U.S. Private*, pg. 355

Wicker, William M., Sr. V.P.-Corp. Devel.--Texaco Inc., White Plains, NY; *U.S. Public*, pg. 1582

Wickham, Robert B., Sr. V.P. & Treas.--TrizecHahn Corporation, Toronto, Canada; *Int'l*, pg. 1424

Wickstrom, Kathy, Grp. V.P.-Reg. Stores--Marshall Field, Chicago, IL; *U.S. Public*, pg. 489

Wickus, James D., Sr. V.P.-Opers.--Sysco Corporation, Houston, TX; *U.S. Public*, pg. 1550

Widler, Niki, Sr. V.P.-Mktg.--Acceptance Insurance Co., Inc., Omaha, NE; *U.S. Public*, pg. 14

Widler, Niki, Sr. V.P.-Mktg.--Acceptance Insurance Companies, Inc., Omaha, NE; *U.S. Public*, pg. 15

Widman, Philip, Chief Fin. Officer & Sr. V.P.--ABB Inc., Norwalk, CT; *Int'l*, pg. 3

Widmann, Nancy, Sr. V.P.-Mkt. Devel.--CBS Enterprises Division, New York, NY; *U.S. Public*, pg. 274

Widmer, Peter, Sr. V.P.-Intl. Commercial Banking--Liechtenstein Global Trust Limited, Vaduz, Liechtenstein; *Int'l*, pg. 809

Wiedenbeck, Ulrich, Sr. V.P.-South America Sls.--K-Tron America, Inc., Pitman, NJ; *U.S. Public*, pg. 938

Wiedenfeld, William, Sr. V.P.--San Angelo National Bank, San Angelo, TX; *U.S. Public*, pg. 633

Wiedenhoft, Charles, Sr. V.P.-Mfg.--Ash Grove Cement Company, Shawnee Mission, KS; *U.S. Private*, pg. 87

Wiehe, Bill, Sr. V.P.-Adv. Sls.--The Weather Channel, Atlanta, GA; *U.S. Private*, pg. 647

Wiela, Fred, Sr. V.P.-Sls. & Mktg.--Komag, Incorporated, San Jose, CA; *U.S. Public*, pg. 966

Wieland, Rich, Chief Fin. Officer & Sr. V.P.--Fujisawa U.S.A., Deerfield, IL; *Int'l*, pg. 525

Wiele, Andreas, Sr. V.P. & Gen. Mgr.--Gruner + Jahr USA Publishing, Inc., New York, NY; *Int'l*, pg. 190

Wiele, Robin, Sr. V.P.--Cline, Davis & Mann, Inc., New York, NY; *U.S. Private*, pg. 246

Wienke, Robert O., Sr. V.P.-Law & Gen. Counsel--The Loewen Group, Inc., Burnaby, Canada; *Int'l*, pg. 814

Wiersbe, Dale E., Sr. V.P.--Inland Steel Industries, Inc., Chicago, IL; *U.S. Public*, pg. 879

Wiese, James R., Sr. V.P. & Gen. Mgr.-Residential Prods. Grp.--International Comfort Products, Franklin, TN; *U.S. Public*, pg. 898

Wieser, Raymond C., Sr. V.P.-Americas--Molex Incorporated, Lisle, IL; *U.S. Public*, pg. 1121

Wiggenhorn, A. William, Sr. V.P. & Pres.-Motorola University--Motorola, Inc., Schaumburg, IL; *U.S. Public*, pg. 1136

Wiggins, Morty, Sr. V.P.-Mktg.--A&M Records, Hollywood, CA; *Int'l*, pg. 1052

Wiggins, Richard A., Sr. V.P.-Fin. & Admin.--QMS, Inc., Mobile, AL; *U.S. Public*, pg. 1346

Wiggonton, Adam, Sr. V.P.-Mktg.--OAG, Oak Brook, IL; *Int'l*, pg. 1097

Wight, G. Earle, Sr. V.P.--Hooper Holmes Corporation, Basking Ridge, NJ; *U.S. Public*, pg. 835

Wigler, Aizig, Sr. V.P.-Construction--The Israel Electric Corporation Ltd., Haifa, Israel; *Int'l*, pg. 690

Wiglesworth, Michael, Sr. V.P. & Acct. Services--Cohn & Wells, New York, NY; *Int'l*, pg. 601

Wignall, David A., Sr. V.P. & Database Mktg. Grp. Dir.--Creswell, Munsell, Fultz & Zirbel, L.P., Cedar Rapids, IA; *U.S. Private*, pg. 1197

Wigton, Nancy H., Sr. V.P.-Mktg.--Cambiar Investors, Inc., Englewood, CO; *U.S. Public*, pg. 1672

Wikander, Bengt, Sr. V.P.-Corp. Communications--Esselte AB, Solna, Sweden; *Int'l*, pg. 459

Wiksten, Barry F., Sr. V.P.--Cigna Corp., Philadelphia, PA; *U.S. Public*, pg. 356

Wilcox, Gregory G., Sr. V.P.-Investor Rels.--The Equitable Companies Incorporated, New York, NY; *U.S. Public*, pg. 588

Wilcox, Jann Ozzello, Chief Fin. Officer & Sr. V.P.--Marquette Bancshares Inc., Minneapolis, MN; *U.S. Private*, pg. 706

Wilcox, Robert K., Sr. V.P.-Mfg.--American Banknote Corp., New York, NY; *U.S. Public*, pg. 68

Wilcox, Tina, Sr. V.P. & Creative Dir.--FAME, Minneapolis, MN; *U.S. Private*, pg. 710

Wilder, Michael S., Sr. V.P. & Gen. Counsel--The Hartford Financial Services Group Inc., Hartford, CT; *U.S. Public*, pg. 794

Wilder, Thomas, Sr. V.P.--The Wilder Companies, Boston, MA; *U.S. Private*, pg. 1176

Wilder, William, Sr. V.P.--Washington Homes, Inc., Landover, MD; *U.S. Public*, pg. 1741

Wilderman, Kathleen M., Sr. V.P.-Personnel/Human Resources--First Financial Bank, FSB, Stevens Point, WI; *U.S. Public*, pg. 140

Wildman, Peter W., Sr. V.P. & Chief Actuary--Chartwell Re Corporation, Stamford, CT; *U.S. Public*, pg. 336

Wildman, Peter W., Sr. V.P. & Chief Actuary--The Insurance Corp. of New York, New York, NY; *U.S. Public*, pg. 336

Wiley, Deborah E., Sr. V.P.-Corp. Commun.--John Wiley & Sons, Inc., New York, NY; *U.S. Public*, pg. 1768

Wiley, Linda R, Sr. V.P.--First National Bank of Pennsylvania, Hermitage, PA; *U.S. Public*, pg. 607

Wiley, Max R., Sr. V.P.-Sub. Admin.--Colorado National Bank, Denver, CO; *U.S. Public*, pg. 1680

Wilhelm, Bob, Sr. V.P.-Sls. & Mktg.--Unitog Company, Kansas City, MO; *U.S. Public*, pg. 1693

Wilhelm, Mark, Sr. V.P.-Underwriting--Safety National Casualty Corp., Saint Louis, MO; *U.S. Public*, pg. 496

Wilhelm, R.E., Sr. V.P.--Exxon Corporation, Irving, TX; *U.S. Public*, pg. 601

Wilhelmsen, Wilhelm, Chm. Bd.--Det Norske Veritas, Hovik, Norway; *Int'l*, pg. 396

Wilhite, David J., Sr. V.P.-Mdsg.--AutoZone, Inc., Memphis, TN; *U.S. Public*, pg. 150

Wilk, Gerald M., Sr. V.P.--Safeguard Scientifics, Inc., Wayne, PA; *U.S. Public*, pg. 1424

Wilk, James J., Sr. V.P.-Human Resources--Foundation Health Systems, Inc., Pueblo, CO; *U.S. Public*, pg. 678

Wilker, Harry R., Sr. V.P.& Gen. Mgr.-Print Shop--Broderbund Software, Inc., Novato, CA; *U.S. Public*, pg. 258

Wilkerson, M. Tony, Sr. V.P.-Mktg.--Haverty Furniture Companies, Inc., Atlanta, GA; *U.S. Public*, pg. 799

Wilkes, David, Exec. V.P. & Dir.-Adv.--Meadow Steel Products, Tampa, FL; *Int'l*, pg. 593

Wilkes, James C., II, Sr. V.P.-Carrier Sls.--MCI Communications Corp., Atlanta, GA; *U.S. Public*, pg. 1023

Wilkie, Ian C., Sr. V.P.-Strategic Devel., Gen. Counsel & Sec.--Cara Operations Limited, Toronto, Canada; *Int'l*, pg. 266

Wilkinson, William J., Sr. V.P.-Human Resources--The Walt Disney Company, Burbank, CA; *U.S. Public*, pg. 511

Wilkirchen, R., Sr. V.P.--Serigraph, Inc., West Bend, WI; *U.S. Private*, pg. 985

Willcox, Christopher P., Sr. V.P. & Worldwide Editor-in-Chief-Reader's Digest Magazine--The Reader's Digest Association, Inc., Pleasantville, NY; *U.S. Public*, pg. 1367

Willcox, Riley R., Chief Fin. Officer, Sr. V.P.-Fin. & Admin.--Premisys Communications, Inc., Fremont, CA; *U.S. Public*, pg. 1323

Wille, Rod, Sr. V.P.-Regional Madages--Turner Construction Co., Chicago, IL; *U.S. Public*, pg. 1645

Willensky, David R., Sr. V.P.-Corp. Plng. & Devel.--ConAgra, Inc., Omaha, NE; *U.S. Public*, pg. 425

Willersdorf, R. Graeme, Sr. V.P.-Pub. Affairs--Foster's Brewing Group Limited, Southbank, Australia; *Int'l*, pg. 500

Willi, Ernst, Dr., Sr. V.P.-Admin. & Opers. & Sec.--Georg Fischer Ltd., Schaffhausen, Switzerland; *Int'l*, pg. 488

Williams, Alan, Sr. V.P.--MBT Architecture, San Francisco, CA; *U.S. Private*, pg. 686

Williams, Ava C., Sr. V.P.--UAM Investment Services, Inc., Boston, MA; *U.S. Public*, pg. 1674

Williams, Boyd B., Sr. V.P.-Internal Audit & Security--Coast Savings Financial, Inc., Los Angeles, CA; *U.S. Public*, pg. 388

Williams, C.G., Sr. V.P.-Corp. Mktg.--AGRA Monenco, Oakville, Canada; *Int'l*, pg. 30

Williams, Clayton A., Sr. V.P.--UNOVA, Inc., Beverly Hills, CA; *U.S. Public*, pg. 1698

Williams, Darryl K., Sr. V.P.--Eastman Chemical Company, Kingsport, TN; *U.S. Public*, pg. 550

Williams, Dave, Sr. V.P.--W.A. Adams, Inc., Wilson, NC; *U.S. Public*, pg. 1502

Williams, David E., Chief Fin. Officer, Sr. V.P., Sec. & Treas.--Ethika Corporation, Hilton Head Island, SC; *U.S. Public*, pg. 595

Williams, Dennis A., Sr. V.P.--Summit Bancorp, Princeton, NJ; *U.S. Public*, pg. 1527

Williams, Donald E., Sr. V.P.--Selective Insurance Group, Inc, Branchville, NJ; *U.S. Public*, pg. 1455

Williams, Donald E., Sr. V.P.--Selective Insurance Company of America, Branchville, NJ; *U.S. Public*, pg. 1455

Williams, Donald E., Sr. V.P.--Selective Way Insurance Company, Branchville, NJ; *U.S. Public*, pg. 1456

Williams, Douglas, Sr. V.P. & Dir.-Discovery--Immunex Corporation, Seattle, WA; *U.S. Public*, pg. 871

Williams, Duston, Chief Fin. Officer & Sr. V.P.--Western Digital Corporation, Irvine, CA; *U.S. Public*, pg. 1758

Williams, Ed, Sr. V.P.-Mktg.--Aladdin Mills, Dalton, GA; *U.S. Public*, pg. 1121

Williams, Fred D., Sr. V.P.-Wholesale Mkts.--Georgia Power Co., Atlanta, GA; *U.S. Public*, pg. 1490

Williams, George, Sr. V.P.-Sls.--Hayward Industries, Inc., Elizabeth, NJ; *U.S. Private*, pg. 513

Williams, Glenn, Sr. V.P.-Mktg.--Globe Life And Accident Insurance Co., Oklahoma City, OK; *U.S. Public*, pg. 1622

Williams, Glenn, Sr. V.P. & Dir.-Mktg.--United American Insurance Co., Dallas, TX; *U.S. Public*, pg. 1623

Williams, Gross T., Sr. V.P.--Hibernia Corporation, New Orleans, LA; *U.S. Public*, pg. 825

Williams, Gwyn E., Sr. V.P.-Banking Opers./Central Ontario-CT Financial Services, Inc., Toronto, Canada; *Int'l*, pg. 112

Williams, J. Don, Chief Fin. Officer & Sr. V.P.-Corp. Support Grp.--Altec Industries, Inc., Birmingham, AL; *U.S. Private*, pg. 47

Williams, J. M., Sr. V.P.--P.R. Newswire Association Inc., New York, NY; *Int'l*, pg. 1443

Williams, Jacquelyn C., Chief Fin. Officer & Sr. V.P.--Nevada State Bank, Las Vegas, NV; *U.S. Public*, pg. 1793

Williams, James, Sr. V.P.-Strategic Devel. & H.R.--Kaiser Permanente, Oakland, CA; *U.S. Private*, pg. 605

Williams, James B., Sr. V.P.-Commercial Programs--Environmental/Government Group, Boise, ID; *U.S. Public*, pg. 1134

Williams, Jim, Sr. V.P.-Info. Sys.--PacifiCare Health Systems, Inc., Cypress, CA; *U.S. Public*, pg. 1250

Williams, John, Sr. V.P.-Fin.--Country Fresh, Inc., Grand Rapids, MI; *U.S. Public*, pg. 1526

Williams, John A., Sr. V.P.-Exploration & Production--The Louisiana Land and Exploration Company, New Orleans, LA; *U.S. Public*, pg. 269

Williams, John B., Sr. V.P.--Firstar Milwaukee Bank, N.A., Milwaukee, WI; *U.S. Public*, pg. 643

Williams, John L., Sr. V.P.-Lodging Devel. North America--Marriott International, Inc., Washington, DC; *U.S. Public*, pg. 1047

Williams, Jon, Sr. V.P.-Loan Admin.--Republic Security Financial Corporation, West Palm Beach, FL; *U.S. Public*, pg. 1381

Williams, Keith, Sr. V.P.--Avnet, Inc., Great Neck, NY; *U.S. Public*, pg. 155

Williams, Kenneth L., Sr. V.P.--CSC Financial Services Group, Austin, TX; *U.S. Public*, pg. 422

Williams, Larry E., Sr. V.P.-Opers.--Wal-Mart Stores, Inc., Bentonville, AR; *U.S. Public*, pg. 1732

Williams, Lonnie, Sr. V.P.--Nabholz Construction Corp., Conway, AR; *U.S. Private*, pg. 772

Williams, Lougene, Sr. V.P.--Hudson, RCI, Temecula, CA; *U.S. Private*, pg. 546

Williams, M.P., Sr. V.P.-Tech.--Welch Foods Inc., A Cooperative, Concord, MA; *U.S. Private*, pg. 784

Williams, Mary, Sr. V.P. & Asst. Sec.--American Reliable Insurance Company, Scottsdale, AZ; *U.S. Public*, pg. 67

Williams, McGhee, Sr. V.P. & Gen. Mgr.--Burrell Communications Group, Inc., Atlanta, GA; *U.S. Private*, pg. 188

Williams, Michael J., Sr. V.P.- Customer Applications & Tech. Intergration--Federal National Mortgage Association (Fannie Mae), Washington, DC; *U.S. Public*, pg. 615

Williams, Michael L., Sr. V.P.-Personal Lines Underwriting--Harleysville Group, Harleysville, PA; *U.S. Public*, pg. 786

Williams, Noel, Sr. V.P.-Info. Sys.--Columbia/HCA Healthcare Corporation, Nashville, TN; *U.S. Public*, pg. 403

Williams, Peter, Sr. V.P. & Gen. Mgr.-Intl. Grp.--Anacomp, Inc., Indianapolis, IN; *U.S. Public*, pg. 106

Williams, Randy, Sr. V.P.-Ins.--John Burnham & Co., San Diego, CA; *U.S. Private*, pg. 186

Williams, Robert, Sr. V.P. & Mgr.-Natl. Sls.--Waddell & Reed, Inc., Shawnee Mission, KS; *U.S. Public*, pg. 1623

Williams, Roger J., Sr. V.P. & Mgr.-Southern Div.--First Security Bank of Utah, N.A., Salt Lake City, UT; *U.S. Public*, pg. 637

Williams, S. Linn, Sr. V.P. & Gen. Counsel--Edison Mission Energy, Irvine, CA; *U.S. Public*, pg. 564

Williams, Serena, Sr. V.P. & Client Service Dir.--Fahlgren, Toledo, OH; *U.S. Private*, pg. 391

Williams, Sharron, Sr. V.P. & Gen. Mgr.-Corp. Mdsg.--Proffitt's, Inc., Alcoa, TN; *U.S. Public*, pg. 1333

Williams, Shirley, Sr. V.P. & Grp. Acct. Dir.-Dodge--Ross Roy Communications, Inc., Bloomfield Hills, MI; *U.S. Private*, pg. 946

Williams, Stephen E., Sr. V.P. & Gen. Counsel--Consolidated Natural Gas Company, Pittsburgh, PA; *U.S.* Public, pg. 435

Williams, Wade, Sr. V.P.-Corp. Devel.--Smith's Food & Drug Centers, Inc., Salt Lake City, UT; *U.S. Public*, pg. 1103

Williamson, Anthony J., Sr., Sr. V.P.-Investments--Metropolitan Life Insurance Co., New York, NY; *U.S. Private*, pg. 737

Williamson, Billie I., Sr. V.P.-Fin. & Controller--Marriott International, Inc., Washington, DC; *U.S. Public*, pg. 1047

Williamson, Jeff, Sr. V.P. & Grp. Creative Dir.--Partners & Shevack, Inc., New York, NY; *U.S. Private*, pg. 842

Williamson, Mark C., Sr. V.P.-Energy Services--Madison Gas and Electric Company, Madison, WI; *U.S. Public*, pg. 1032

Williamson, Robert W., Sr. V.P.-Credit--Merrill Lynch & Co., Inc., New York, NY; *U.S. Public*, pg. 1097

Williamson, Scott, Sr. V.P.--First Cash, Inc., Arlington, TX; *U.S. Public*, pg. 627

Williamson, Thomas A., Sr. V.P.--Harcourt Brace & Company - Elementary Div., Orlando, FL; *U.S. Public*, pg. 783

Willis, Donald E., Jr., Chief Information Officer & Sr. V.P.--Rykoff-Sexton, Inc., Wilkes-Barre, PA; *U.S. Public*, pg. 918

Willis, Mark, Sr. V.P.--Watt, Roop & Co., Cleveland, OH; *U.S. Private*, pg. 1154

Willkie, Wendell L., II, Sr. V.P. & Gen. Counsel--Westvaco Corporation, New York, NY; *U.S. Public*, pg. 1762

Willman, George L., Sr. V.P. & Gen. Mgr.-United Kingdom--Confederation Life Insurance Company, Toronto, Canada; *Int'l*, pg. 325

Willmschen, Robert W., Chief Fin. Officer, Sr. V.P. & Sec.--ABC Rail Products Corp., Chicago, IL; *U.S. Public*, pg. 2

Wills, Cathy, Sr. V.P.-Mktg.--Maybelline, Inc., New York, NY; *Int'l*, pg. 819

Wilmes, Jody, Sr. V.P.-Pur.--Metz Baking Company, Deerfield, IL; *U.S. Private*, pg. 1022

Wilmes, Pierre, Sr. V.P.-Fin.--Sidmar N.V., Gent, Belgium; *Int'l*, pg. 79

Wilmot, Robert J., Sr. V.P.-Leasing--Wilmorite, Inc., Rochester, NY; *U.S. Private*, pg. 1180

Wilock, Robert, Sr. V.P.-Client Services--Jordan, McGrath, Case & Taylor Inc., New York, NY; *U.S. Private*, pg. 598

Wilock, Robert, Sr. V.P.--Stawasz & Partners/Health Care Communications, New York, NY; *U.S. Private*, pg. 599

Wilson, Alan R., Sr. V.P.-Mdsg.--Strawberries Inc., Milford, MA; *U.S. Private*, pg. 1046

Wilson, B.A., Sr. V.P.-Opers.--Brierley & Partners, Dallas, TX; *U.S. Private*, pg. 168

Wilson, B.E., Chief Fin. Officer & Sr. V.P.--National Trustco Inc., Toronto, Canada; *Int'l*, pg. 909

Wilson, Barbara, Sr. V.P. & Acct. Grp. Dir.-Detroit--Kragie/Newell, Des Moines, IA; *U.S. Private*, pg. 634

Wilson, C. Kenneth, Sr. V.P. & Mng. Dir.-B.F. Wine Brands--Brown-Forman Beverages Worldwide, Louisville, KY; *U.S. Public*, pg. 261

Wilson, D.H., Sr. V.P. & Treas.--Marshall & Ilsley Corporation, Milwaukee, WI; *U.S. Public*, pg. 1049

Wilson, Delbert H., Sr. V.P. & Zone Mgr.--McDonald's Corporation, Oak Brook, IL; *U.S. Public*, pg. 1068

Wilson, Ed, Sr. V.P.-Syndication--Columbia Tri-Star Television Distribution, Burbank, CA; *Int'l*, pg. 1282

Wilson, Harold A., Sr. V.P.-Distr. & Transportation Services--Consolidated Stores Corp., Columbus, OH; *U.S. Public*, pg. 437

Wilson, James D., Sr. V.P.--Lenox, Incorporated, Lawrenceville, NJ; *U.S. Public*, pg. 261

Wilson, Judy, Sr. V.P.-Guaranteed Investment Contracts--Protective Life Corporation, Birmingham, AL; *U.S. Public*, *pg. 1336*

Wilson, Paul, Sr. V.P.--Biggs Gilmore Communications, Kalamazoo, MI; *U.S. Private*, pg. 143

Wilson, Phil, Sr. V.P.-Human Resources--Oracle Corporation, Redwood City, CA; *U.S. Public*, pg. 1227

Wilson, Rich A., Chief Oper. Officer & Sr. V.P.--Ensco International Incorporated (ENSCO), Dallas, TX; *U.S. Public*, pg. 585

Wilson, Rita P., Sr. V.P.-Corp. Rels.--The Allstate Corporation, Northbrook, IL; *U.S. Public*, pg. 55

Wilson, Roy, Sr. V.P.-H.R.--BMC Software, Inc., Houston, TX; *U.S. Public*, pg. 162

Wilson, Thomas J., Sr. V.P.-Sls. & Mktg.--California & Hawaiian Sugar Company Inc., Crockett, CA; *U.S. Public*, *pg. 39*

Wilson, Thomas J., Chief Fin. Officer & Sr. V.P.--The Allstate Corporation, Northbrook, IL; *U.S. Public*, pg. 55

Wilson, Vernon R., Sr. V.P.-Compliance--Regions Financial Corporation, Birmingham, AL; *U.S. Public*, pg. 1371

Wilson, Walter W., Sr. V.P. & Pres.-Solectron Americas--Solectron Corporation, Milpitas, CA; *U.S. Public*, pg. 1483

Wilson, William L., Sr. V.P.-Mktg.--Data General Corporation, Westborough, MA; *U.S. Public*, pg. 485

Wilton, W. Gary, Sr. V.P.-Retirement & Investment Services--The Great-West Life Assurance Company, Winnipeg, Canada; *Int'l*, pg. 557

Wimbush, Frank A., Sr. V.P.-Mktg. & Branch Opers.--Noland Company, Newport News, VA; *U.S. Public*, pg. 1187

Winchester, Bill, Sr. V.P.--Colle & McVoy Marketing Communications, Minneapolis, MN; *U.S. Private*, pg. 252

Winchlecter, David, Sr. V.P. & Dir.-DMB&B Corp. Fin.--DMB&B Communications, New York, NY; *U.S. Private*, pg. 302

Winder, Edwin C., Sr. V.P.-Sls.--Active Software, Inc., Santa Clara, CA; *U.S. Private*, pg. 15

Winebarger, Paige, Sr. V.P. & Gen. Counsel--Marquette Bancshares Inc., Minneapolis, MN; *U.S. Private*, pg. 706

Wineburgh, Joel, Sr. V.P.--Cometals, New York, NY; *U.S. Public*, pg. 412

Winfield, David J.S., Sr. V.P.-Govt. Rels.--Northern Telecom Limited, Brampton, Canada; *Int'l*, pg. 968

Wing, Alan A., Sr. V.P. & Sr. Loan Officer--Community National Bank, Derby, VT; *U.S. Public*, pg. 416

Wing, Dennis R., Sr. V.P.--First Marathon Securities Limited, Toronto, Canada; *Int'l*, pg. 486

Winge, C.E., Sr. V.P. & Reg. Dir.--Winn-Dixie Stores, Inc., Jacksonville, FL; *U.S. Public*, pg. 1771

Winger, Dennis L., Chief Fin. Officer, Sr. V.P. & Treas.--The Perkin-Elmer Corporation, Norwalk, CT; *U.S. Public*, pg. 1279

Winget, A. Kncx, III, Sr. V.P.-Mktg.--American & Efird, Inc., Mount Holly, NC; *U.S. Public*, pg. 1412

Winiecki, Alexander, Sr. V.P.-Store Opers.--Brookstone Company, Inc., Nashua, NH; *U.S. Public*, pg. 259

Winkel, Judy K., Sr. V.P.-Govt. Affairs--Associates First Capital Corporation, Dallas, TX; *U.S. Public*, pg. 662

Winkel, Judy K., Sr. V.P.-Govt. Affairs--Associates Financial Services Corporation, Dallas, TX; *U.S. Public*, pg. 663

Winkler, Michael, Sr. V.P. & Grp. Gen. Mgr.-PC Prods. Grp.--COMPAQ Computer Corporation, Houston, TX; *U.S. Public*, pg. 417

Winn, Jerry, Sr. V.P. & Mgr.-Inspection Department--Geo. H. Lehleitner & Co., Inc., Kenner, LA; *U.S. Private*, pg. 659

Winsky, Gregory J., Sr. V.P.--Franklin Electronic Publishers, Inc., Burlington, NJ; *U.S. Public*, pg. 679

Winslow, Michael, Sr. V.P. & Exec. Creative Dir.--Rockett, Burkhead, Lewis & Winslow, Raleigh, NC; *U.S. Private*, pg. 938

Winter, Lon, Sr. V.P. & Copy Chief--Greenstone Roberts/Florida, Orlando, FL; *U.S. Public*, pg. 763

Winterbottom, Warren, Sr. V.P.-Sls.-Americas--Bentley Systems, Inc., Exton, PA; *U.S. Private*, pg. 134

Winterer, Tim R., Sr. V.P. & Grp. Gen. Mgr.--BHP World Minerals, San Francisco, CA; *Int'l*, pg. 224

Wintermans, Jos, Sr. V.P.-Diversified Businesses--Canadian Tire Corporation Limited, Toronto, Canada; *Int'l*, pg. 259

Winvick, Stanley, Sr. V.P.-Human Resources--Advanced Micro Devices, Inc., Sunnyvale, CA; *U.S. Public*, pg. 21

Winzig, Peter, Sr. V.P. & Acct. Dir.--Wyse Advertising/Cleveland, Cleveland, OH; *U.S. Private*, pg. 1194

Wisdorf, Douglas G., Sr. V.P. & Controller--Washington Mutual Inc., Seattle, WA; *U.S. Public*, pg. 1741

Wise, Doug, Sr. V.P.-Mktg.--Players International, Inc., Atlantic City, NJ; *U.S. Public*, pg. 1310

Wise, Richard, Sr. V.P. & Strategic Plng. Dir.--Mezzina/Brown Inc., New York, NY; *U.S. Private*, pg. 739

Wise, Stephen C., Sr. V.P.-Fin.--Novell, Inc., Orem, UT; *U.S.* Public, pg. 1203

Wise, Steven M., Chief Info. Officer & Sr. V.P.-MIS--NovaCare Inc., King of Prussia, PA; *U.S. Public*, pg. 1203

Wise, Timothy B., Sr. V.P.--J.S. Alberici Construction Co., Inc., Saint Louis, MO; *U.S. Private*, pg. 32

Wiseman, Donald C., Sr. V.P.-Gas Supply--Alabama Gas Corporation, Birmingham, AL; *U.S. Public*, pg. 581

Wishart, Steven W., Sr. V.P. & Chief Investment Officer--ReliaStar Financial Corp., Minneapolis, MN; *U.S. Public*, pg. 1375

Wishart, Steven W., Chief Information Officer & Sr. V.P.--Northwestern National Life Insurance Co., Minneapolis, MN; *U.S. Public*, pg. 1375

Wishart, Steven W., Sr. V.P.--Northwestern National Life Insurance Co., Minneapolis, MN; *U.S. Public*, pg. 1375

Wishart, Warren T., Chief Fin. Officer & Sr. V.P.--The Leslie Fay Companies, Inc., New York, NY; *U.S. Public*, pg. 989

Wishengrad, Marti, Sr. V.P. & Agency/Client Rels. Mgr.--Zenith Media Services, Inc., Los Angeles, CA; *U.S. Private*, pg. 1204

Wishnafski, Diane L., Sr. V.P.--New Haven Savings Bank, New Haven, CT; *U.S. Private*, pg. 793

Wiskur, Jim, Sr. V.P.-Corp. Sls.--Manufacturers Consolidation Service, Inc., Memphis, TN; *U.S. Private*, pg. 700

Wisniewski, Henry G., Sr. V.P.-Fin.--Tuthill Corporation, Hinsdale, IL; *U.S. Private*, pg. 1110

Wissinger, Peter J., Sr. V.P.--Norwest Mortgage, Inc., Des Moines, IA; *U.S. Public*, pg. 1202

Withell, Guy, Sr. V.P.--SGS Control Services Inc., Edison, NJ; *Int'l*, pg. 1153

Withem, Jeffrey S., Sr. V.P.-Commun.--Anacomp, Inc., Indianapolis, IN; *U.S. Public*, pg. 106

Withers, F. Wayne, Chief Fin. Officer & Sr. V.P.--Aurora Electronics, Inc., Irvine, CA; *U.S. Public*, pg. 147

Withers, W.W., Sr. V.P., Gen. Counsel & Sec.--Emerson Electric Co., Saint Louis, MO; *U.S. Public*, pg. 572

Withrow, Charles, Sr. V.P. & Creative Dir.--Wyse Advertising/Cleveland, Cleveland, OH; *U.S. Private*, pg. 1194

Witinig, Silvia, Sr. V.P.-Engrng. Projects--The Israel Electric Corporation Ltd., Haifa, Israel; *Int'l*, pg. 690

Witkowski, Chris, Sr. V.P. & Controller--Hubco, Inc., Mahwah, NJ; *U.S. Public*, pg. 845

Witmer, John H., Jr., Sr. V.P., Gen. Counsel & Sec.--Dekalb Genetics Corporation, De Kalb, IL; *U.S. Public*, pg. 493

Witte, P. P., Sr. V.P.-Human Resources--Royal Pakhoed NV, Rotterdam, Netherlands; *Int'l*, pg. 1147

Witthoeft, Ross, Sr. V.P.-Intl.--Century Business Credit Corporation, New York, NY; *U.S. Private*, pg. 225

Witthuhn, Tom, Sr. V.P.-B.D. Baggies--The Apparel Group, Ltd., Louisville, KY; *U.S. Private*, pg. 78

Wittkowske, Fred, Jr., Sr. V.P. & Gen. Auditor--Firstar Corporation, Milwaukee, WI; *U.S. Public*, pg. 642

Wittlich, Jae L., Sr. V.P.--Continental Assurance Company, Chicago, IL; *U.S. Private*, pg. 267

Wnorowski, A.K., Sr. V.P.-Admin. & Gen. Counsel.--Comverse Network Systems, Wakefield, MA; *U.S. Public*, *pg. 425*

Woda, Jerry W., Chief Fin. Officer, Sr. V.P. & Treas.--Miami Subs Corporation, Fort Lauderdale, FL; *U.S. Public*, pg. 1103

Wodack, Howard, Sr. V.P Information Services--Automotive Rentals, Inc. (ARI), Mount Laurel, NJ; *U.S. Private*, pg. 535

Woeller, Mike D., Sr. V.P.-Information Services--CT Financial Services, Inc., Toronto, Canada; *Int'l*, pg. 112

Wohl, Linda, Sr. V.P.-Music Legal Affairs--Paramount Pictures Corporation, Los Angeles, CA; *U.S. Private*, pg. 776

Wohl, Ron, Sr. V.P.-Applications Div.--Oracle Corporation, Redwood City, CA; *U.S. Public*, pg. 1227

Wohleber, Robert M., Chief Fin. Officer & Sr. V.P.--Freeport-McMoRan Inc., New Orleans, LA; *U.S. Public*, pg. 680

Wohlers, Robert L., Sr. V.P. & Chief Technical Officer--Datamax International Corporation, Orlando, FL; *U.S. Private*, pg. 313

Wohlschlaeger, Frederick G., Sr. V.P. & Gen. Counsel--Hartmarx Corporation, Chicago, IL; *U.S. Public*, pg. 795

Woit, Erik P., Sr. V.P.-North America--Sea Containers Ltd., Hamilton, Bermuda; *Int'l*, pg. 1213

Wojcik, Walt J., Sr. V.P.-Info. Systems--Northwestern Mutual Life Insurance Co., Milwaukee, WI; *U.S. Private*, pg. 807

Wolahan, Brian K., Sr. V.P.--Acadian Asset Management, Boston, MA; *U.S. Public*, pg. 1672

Wolak, Robert M., Sr. V.P.--Chemical Bank Bay Area, Bay City, MI; *U.S. Public*, pg. 345

Wolanski, Rich, Sr. V.P.--Huron Valley Steel Corp., Belleville, MI; *U.S. Private*, pg. 549

Wolf, Boyd, Sr. V.P.--National Programs Division, Tampa, FL; *U.S. Public*, pg. 1312

Wolf, Christopher F., Chief Fin. Officer, Sr. V.P., Treas. & Sec.--Swank, Inc., Attleboro, MA; *U.S. Public*, pg. 1543

Wolf, Dale B., Chief Fin. Officer, Sr. V.P. & Treas.--Coventry Corporation, Nashville, TN; *U.S. Public*, pg. 454

Wolf, Dennis, Chief Fin. Officer & Sr. V.P.-Opers. & Admin.--Centigram Communications Corporation, San Jose, CA; *U.S. Public*, pg. 323

Wolf, Irvin, III, Sr. V.P.-Jacksonville, FL--All American Agency Facilities, Inc., Redmond, WA; *U.S. Public*, pg. 216

Wolf, Jeff, Sr. V.P.--Central Parking Corp., Nashville, TN; *U.S. Public*, pg. 326

Wolf, Kurt, Sr. V.P.-Intl. Opers., Europe--K2 Ski-Sport & Mode GmbH, Puchheim, Germany; *U.S. Public*, pg. 940

Wolf, Mark C., Sr. V.P. & Creative Dir.--Creswell, Munsell, Fultz & Zirbel, L.P., Cedar Rapids, IA; *U.S. Private*, pg. 1197

Wolf, Martin D., Sr. V.P. & Pres.-Merisel FAB, Inc.--Merisel, Inc., El Segundo, CA; *U.S. Public*, pg. 1095

Wolf, Mary Jean, Sr. V.P.-Org. Svcs.--La Petite Academy Inc., Overland Park, KS; *U.S. Private*, pg. 640

Wolf, Philip C., Sr. V.P., Gen. Counsel & Sec.--Cyprus Amax Minerals Company, Englewood, CO; *U.S. Public*, pg. 470

Wolf, Robert P., Sr. V.P. & Gen. Counsel--Alumax Inc., Atlanta, GA; *U.S. Public*, pg. 59

Wolf, Timothy V., Chief Fin. Officer & Sr. V.P.--Adolph Coors Company, Golden, CO; *U.S. Public*, pg. 445

Wolf, Timothy V., Chief Fin. Officer, Sr. V.P. & Treas.--Coors Brewing Company, Golden, CO; *U.S. Public*, pg. 445

Wolf, Timothy V., Sr. V.P.-Plng. & Human Resources--Hyatt Hotels Corporation, Chicago, IL; *U.S. Private*, pg. 551

Wolfe, Fred, Sr. V.P.--Acapulco Restaurants, Long Beach, CA; *U.S. Private*, pg. 925

Wolfe, Harry F., Jr., Sr. V.P.--Sterling Capital Management Company, Charlotte, NC; *U.S. Public*, pg. 1674

Wolfe, Jane, Exec. V.P. & Chief Lending Officer--Downey Savings & Loan Association, F.A., Newport Beach, CA; *U.S. Public*, pg. 526

Wolfe, Larry J., Sr. V.P.-Tax Prods.--Intuit, Inc., Mountain View, CA; *U.S. Public*, pg. 911

Wolfe, Ralph, Sr. V.P.--Panasonic Consumer Electric Co., Secaucus, NJ; *Int'l*, pg. 847

Wolfe, Russ, Sr. V.P.-Perishables--Topco Associates, Inc., Skokie, IL; *U.S. Private*, pg. 1091

Wolfe, Ted, Sr. V.P.-Sls.--Butler Manufacturing Company, Kansas City, MO; *U.S. Public*, pg. 271

Wolfer, Ernest, Sr. V.P.-Mfg.--Marcal Paper Mills, Inc., Elmwood Park, NJ; *U.S. Private*, pg. 701

Wolff, Frederick A., Sr. V.P. & Cashier--United Missouri Bank of Warrensburg, Warrensburg, MO; *U.S. Public*, pg. 1655

Wolff, Herbert E., Sr. V.P. & Sec.--First Hawaiian, Inc., Honolulu, HI; *U.S. Public*, pg. 634

Wolff, Herbert E., Sr. V.P. & Sec.--First Hawaiian Bank, Honolulu, HI; *U.S. Public*, pg. 634

Wolff, Sherman M., Sr. V.P.-Fin.--Blue Cross & Blue Shield of Illinois, Chicago, IL; *U.S. Private*, pg. 151

Wolff, Suzanne G., Sr. V.P.--Mercantile Bankshares Corporation, Baltimore, MD; *U.S. Public*, pg. 1088

Wolfsheimer, R., Sr. V.P. & Controller--Calvert Group, Ltd., Bethesda, MD; *U.S. Private*, pg. 11

Wolfson, Alan D., Sr. v.P.-Market Intelligence--Canada Trustco Mortgage Company, London, Canada; *Int'l*, pg. 112

Wolfson, George, Sr. V.P.-Opers., Radio Division--Viacom Broadcasting Inc., New York, NY; *U.S. Private*, pg. 778

Wolfson, Martin, Chief Fin. Officer & Sr. V.P.--Concord Fabrics Inc., New York, NY; *U.S. Public*, pg. 429

Wolkenmuth, Ed, Sr. V.P. & Gen. Mgr.-Vantis Intl.--BASES Worldwide, Covington, KY; *U.S. Private*, pg. 120

Wolter, Gary J., Sr. V.P.-Admin. & Sec.--Madison Gas and Electric Company, Madison, WI; *U.S. Public*, pg. 1032

Wolthausen, Reed, Chief Fin. Officer & Sr. V.P.--Burke Industries, Inc., San Jose, CA; *U.S. Private*, pg. 183

Woltil, Robert D., Chief Fin. Officer & Sr. V.P.-Fin.--Sun Healthcare Group Inc., Albuquerque, NM; *U.S. Public*, pg. 1530

Womack, E. Allen, Jr., Chief Tech. Officer, Sr. V.P. & Grp. Exec.--McDermott International, Inc., New Orleans, LA; *U.S. Public*, pg. 1067

Womack, E. Allen, Jr., Chief Tech. Officer, Sr. V.P. & Grp. Exec.-Indus. Grp.--Babcock & Wilcox Co., Barberton, OH; *U.S. Public*, pg. 1068

Womack, William L., Sr. V.P.--Perini Building Co., Inc. U.S. Heavy Division, Framingham, MA; *U.S. Public*, pg. 1278

Wondrasch, Paul, Sr. V.P.-Intl.--AT&T Corporation, Basking Ridge, NJ; *U.S. Public*, pg. 10

Wong, Kenneth, Sr. V.P. & Gen. Mgr.--Daiwa Bank-United Centre Branch, Hong Kong, Hong Kong; *Int'l*, pg. 374

Wong, Roger, Sr. V.P. Opers.--Papa Gino's Inc., Dedham, MA; *U.S. Private*, pg. 837

Wong, Timothy, Sr. V.P. & Dir.-Risk Audit--Bay View Capital Corporation, San Mateo, CA; *U.S. Public*, pg. 197

Wong, William G., Sr. V.P.-Claims--Argonaut Co., Menlo Park, CA; *U.S. Public*, pg. 129

Woo-Nelson, Yeanna, Sr. V.P.-Mktg./Men's--Jay Jacobs, Inc., Seattle, WA; *U.S. Public*, pg. 922

Wood, Barbara S., Sr. V.P.-Fin. & Treas.--Hornor, Townsend & Kent, Philadelphia, PA; *U.S. Private*, pg. 849

Wood, C. Martin, III, Chief Fin. Officer & Sr. V.P.--Flowers Industries, Inc., Thomasville, GA; *U.S. Public*, pg. 656

Wood, Charles R., Sr. V.P. & Pres.-Fin. Svcs.--Data Transmission Network Corporation, Omaha, NE; *U.S. Public*, pg. 486

Wood, Donald, Chief Fin. Officer & Sr. V.P.--Caesars World, Inc., Las Vegas, NV; *U.S. Public*, pg. 1512

Wood, Glenn, Sr. V.P.--Chemical Bank Montcalm, Stanton, MI; *U.S. Public*, pg. 345

Wood, John W., Jr., Sr. V.P.--Thermo Electron Corporation, Waltham, MA; *U.S. Public*, pg. 1591

Wood, Raymond B., Sr. V.P.-Govt. Opers.--Technology Research Corporation, Clearwater, FL; *U.S. Public*, pg. 1564

Wood, Stephen W., Sr. V.P.-H.R. & Corp. Affairs--Advantica Restaurant Group, Inc., Spartanburg, SC; *U.S. Public*, pg. 22

Wood, Thomas, Sr. V.P.--Hibernia Corporation, New Orleans, LA; *U.S. Public*, pg. 825

Woodall, Tony, Sr. V.P.-Admin.--Kellwood Sportswear, Rutherford, TN; *U.S. Public*, pg. 948

Woodard, Michael R., Sr. V.P.-Field Mngmt.--American Express Financial Advisor, Minneapolis, MN; *U.S. Public, pg. 73*

Woodard, Ronald B., Sr. V.P. & Pres.-Boeing Comml. Airplane Grp.--The Boeing Company, Seattle, WA; *U.S. Public*, pg. 239

Woodbury, Brian, Sr. V.P.-East Region--Mobile Technology Inc., Los Angeles, CA; *U.S. Private*, pg. 754

Woodbury, Kimball D., Sr. V.P.-Devel.--Atlantic Gulf Communities Corporation, Miami, FL; *U.S. Public*, pg. 144

Woodcock, Kenneth R., Sr. V.P.--AES Corporation, Arlington, VA; *U.S. Public*, pg. 5

Woodcock, Tracey, Sr. V.P. & Opers. Officer--Frankfurt Balkind Partners, New York, NY; *U.S. Private*, pg. 424

Woodfield, Marion, Sr. V.P.-Acctg. Services--EvansGroup, Salt Lake City, UT; *U.S. Private*, pg. 385

Woodhead, Michael L., Sr. V.P.--ProEquities, Inc., Birmingham, AL; *U.S. Public*, pg. 1336

Woodhouse, Michael A., Chief Fin. Officer & Sr. V.P.--Cracker Barrel Old Country Store, Inc., Lebanon, TN; *U.S. Public*, pg. 455

Woodhull, Tim, Sr. V.P.-Construction--Willis Corroon Corp. of New York, New York, NY; *Int'l*, pg. 1506

Woodley, Michael, Sr. V.P.-Architecture--Kaufman and Broad Home Corporation, Los Angeles, CA; *U.S. Public*, pg. 944

Woodlock, Maren, Sr. V.P. & Mng. Dir.--Quantum Media International, Inc., Chicago, IL; *U.S. Private*, pg. 899

Woodrow, David M., Sr. V.P.-Broadband Services--Cox Communications, Inc., Atlanta, GA; *U.S. Public*, pg. 454

Woodruff, Lawrence W., Sr. V.P.--Hicks & Associates Inc., Mc Lean, VA; *U.S. Private*, pg. 976

Woods, B. Kabe, Chief Info. Officer & Sr. V.P.--ADVO, Inc., Windsor, CT; *U.S. Public*, pg. 23

Woods, Jack F., Sr. V.P., Grp. Acct. Dir. & People Services Dir.--Young & Rubicam Chicago, Chicago, IL; *U.S. Private*, pg. 1198

Woods, Kevin J., Sr. V.P.--Newberg Perini, Chicago, IL; *U.S.* Public, pg. 1278

Woods, Theodore E., Sr. V.P.--Syntron, Inc., Houston, TX; *U.S. Public*, pg. 1563

Woodward, Donald M., Sr. V.P.-Insurance--United Companies Financial Corporation, Baton Rouge, LA; *U.S. Public*, pg. 1675

Woodward, Patricia, Sr. V.P. & Acct. Dir.--Young & Rubicam New York, New York, NY; *U.S. Private*, pg. 1198

Woodward, Sam, Sr. V.P.-Opers. & Plng.--Yellow Corporation, Overland Park, KS; *U.S. Public*, pg. 1788

Woodward, W.P., Sr. V.P.-Mktg.--Kerr-McGee Chemical Corp., Oklahoma City, OK; *U.S. Public*, pg. 952

Woodworth, Gerald C., Sr. V.P.--Andover Bancorp, Inc., Andover, MA; *U.S. Public*, pg. 111

Wooley, Jeffrey J., Sr. V.P.--Schlotzsky's, Inc., Austin, TX; *U.S. Public*, pg. 1439

Woolf, Brian, Sr. V.P. & Gen. Mgr.-Mdse.--Caldor, Inc., Norwalk, CT; *U.S. Public*, pg. 292

Woolf, Mark, V.P. & Gen. Mgr.-Drug. Div.--Smith's Food & Drug Centers, Inc., Salt Lake City, UT; *U.S. Public*, pg. 1103

Woolf, Steven, Sr. V.P.-Fin.--President Baking Company, Atlanta, GA; *Int'l*, pg. 1069

Wooten, William D., Sr. V.P.-Human Resources--MCI Communications Corp., Atlanta, GA; *U.S. Public*, pg. 1023

Wooton, Edward J., Sr. V.P.-Subsidiaries--Ameriana Bancorp, New Castle, IN; *U.S. Public*, pg. 66

Worcester, Theodore E., Sr. V.P.-Law & Admin. & Gen. Counsel--Westmoreland Coal Co., Colorado Springs, CO; *U.S. Public*, pg. 1761

Worcester, Tim, Sr. V.P.-Mktg.--Bradlees Inc., Braintree, MA; *U.S. Public*, pg. 249

Work, David E., Sr. V.P.--Amoco Corporation, Chicago, IL; *U.S. Public*, pg. 101

Worley, Dana, Chief Fin. Officer & Sr. V.P.--Black Rogers Sullivan Goodnight, Inc., Houston, TX; *U.S. Private*, pg. 147

Wormington, Stephen, Sr. V.P. & Corp. Audit Dir.--Metallgesellschaft Corp., New York, NY; *Int'l*, pg. 861

Wormwood, Dale, Sr. V.P.--Sealed Air Corporation, Saddle Brook, NJ; *U.S. Public*, pg. 1450

Wormwood, Ronadl, Sr. V.P.--Hancock Lumber, Inc., Casco, ME; *U.S. Private*, pg. 498

Worrell, Douglas C., Chief Fin. Officer, Sr. V.P. & Cashier--Texas National Bank, Southlake, TX; *U.S. Public*, pg. 633

Worrell, John K., Sr. V.P.-Sls.--Igloo Products Corporation, Houston, TX; *U.S. Public*, pg. 265

Wortham, Samuel T., Sr. V.P.--Pall Biomedical Products Corp., Greenvale, NY; *U.S. Public*, pg. 1254

Worthing, Marcia L., Sr. V.P.-Human Resources & Corp. Affairs--Avon Products, Inc., New York, NY; *U.S. Public*, pg. 155

Worthington, Brookes, Sr. V.P.--Weatherford National Bank, Weatherford, TX; *U.S. Public*, pg. 633

Worthington, Bruce R., Sr. V.P. & Gen. Counsel--PG&E Corporation, San Francisco, CA; *U.S. Public*, pg. 1240

Worthington, Jack, Sr. V.P.-Western Region--Durham Transportation, Inc., Austin, TX; *U.S. Private*, pg. 348

Worthington, Wendy J., Sr. V.P.--Keycorp, Cleveland, OH; *U.S. Public*, pg. 954

Worthley, Donald S., Sr. V.P.--General Reinsurance Corp., Stamford, CT; *U.S. Public*, pg. 725

Worthy, W. Craig, Chief Fin. Officer & Sr. V.P.--Boddie-Noell Enterprises Inc., Rocky Mount, NC; *U.S. Private*, pg. 154

Wozniak, Dennis, Sr. V.P.-Pur. & Mktg.--Arbor Drugs, Inc., Troy, MI; *U.S. Public*, pg. 126

Wozniak, Greg, Sr. V.P. & Fin. Services Dir.--DMB&B Detroit, Troy, MI; *U.S. Private*, pg. 302

Wraase, Dennis R., Chief Fin. Officer & Sr. V.P.--Potomac Electric Power Company, Washington, DC; *U.S. Public*, pg. 1318

Wraback, Thomas F., Chief Fin. Officer & Sr. V.P.--Physician Computer Network, Inc., Morris Plains, NJ; *U.S. Public*, pg. 1293

Wratschko, B., Sr. V.P.--Daher Golden Eagle - Los Angeles, El Segundo, CA; *U.S. Public*, pg. 749

Wray, R. Logan, Chief Fin. Officer & Sr. V.P.--Sterling Software, Inc., Dallas, TX; *U.S. Public*, pg. 1516

Wray, William K., Sr. V.P.-Credit Policy--Citizens Savings Bank, Providence, RI; *Int'l*, pg. 1132

Wredberg, Conrad, Sr. V.P.--Scientific-Atlanta, Inc., Norcross, GA; *U.S. Public*, pg. 1443

Wrench, Gary D., Chief Fin. Officer & Sr. V.P.--BEI Technologies, Inc., San Francisco, CA; *U.S. Public*, pg. 160

Wrenn, Susan, Sr. V.P. & Dir.-Media--Paramount Pictures Corporation, Los Angeles, CA; *U.S. Private*, pg. 776

Wright, Alan M., Chief Fin. Officer, Sr. V.P. & Treas.--CMS Energy Corporation, Dearborn, MI; *U.S. Public*, pg. 279

Wright, Benford E., Jr., Sr. V.P.--Laurel Bank, Johnstown, PA; *U.S. Public*, pg. 164

Wright, Daniel P., Chief Fin. Officer & Sr. V.P.--Electrohome Ltd., Kitchener, Canada; *Int'l*, pg. 438

Wright, Donald, Sr. V.P.-Real Estate & Engrng.--Safeway Inc., Pleasanton, CA; *U.S. Public*, pg. 1426

Wright, Donald E., Sr. V.P.-Fin. & Acctg.--Proffitt's, Inc., Alcoa, TN; *U.S. Public*, pg. 1333

Wright, Donald F., Sr. V.P.-Eastern Newspapers--The Times Mirror Company, Los Angeles, CA; *U.S. Public*, pg. 1615

Wright, Elease, Sr. V.P.-Human Resources--Aetna Inc., Hartford, CT; *U.S. Public*, pg. 26

Wright, Elizabeth B., Sr. V.P.-Strategic Plng. & Mktg.--National Trust Company, Stratford, Canada; *Int'l*, pg. 910

Wright, Frances, Sr. V.P.-Retirement Plans--Mutual of Omaha Insurance Company, Omaha, NE; *U.S. Private*, pg. 769

Wright, Harold D., Sr. V.P. & Gen. Mgr.-N. American Paperboard--Stone Container Corporation, Chicago, IL; *U.S. Public*, pg. 1520

Wright, Jan F., Sr. V.P.-Branch Opers.--Ameriana Bancorp, New Castle, IN; *U.S. Public*, pg. 66

Wright, Jason H., Sr. V.P.-Worldwide Communications--RJR Nabisco Holdings Corp., New York, NY; *U.S. Public*, pg. 1354

Wright, John, Sr. V.P.--Harbor Financial Mortgage Corp., Houston, TX; *U.S. Public*, pg. 644

Wright, Michael L., Sr. V.P.-Tech.--Lincoln National Corporation, Fort Wayne, IN; *U.S. Public*, pg. 997

Wright, Michael L., Sr. V.P. & Chief Info. Officer--The Lincoln National Life Insurance Co., Fort Wayne, IN; *U.S.* Public, pg. 998

Wright, Monroe M., CPA, Sr. V.P. & Treas.--Dixie National Life Insurance Company, Richland, MS; *U.S. Public*, pg. 1502

Wright, Stephen R., Sr. V.P.-Agriculture & Gen. Mgr.-Pro-Fac Coop.--Curtice Burns Foods, Rochester, NY; *U.S. Private*, pg. 887

Wright, Thomas G., Sr. V.P.--Elf Aquitaine, Inc., New York, NY; *Int'l*, pg. 445

Wright, Virgil W., Sr. V.P.--McArdle Printing Co., Inc., Upper Marlboro, MD; *U.S. Private*, pg. 182

Wrightson, Robert E., Sr. V.P. & Controller--Consolidated Freightways Corp., Menlo Park, CA; *U.S. Public*, pg. 435

Wrobel, Bruce, Sr. V.P.--Sithe Energies, Inc., New York, NY; *U.S. Private*, pg. 1004

Wroe, David W., Sr. V.P. & Chief Tech. Officer--Continental Assurance Company, Chicago, IL; *U.S. Private*, pg. 267

Wryn, JoLene, Sr. V.P. & Dir.-H.R.--Downey Savings & Loan Association, F.A., Newport Beach, CA; *U.S. Public*, pg. 526

Wu, Herbert B.D., Sr. V.P. & Gen. Mgr.-Human Resources--The International Commercial Bank of China, Taipei, Taiwan; *Int'l*, pg. 683

Wummer, Michael L., Sr. V.P.-Residential Mortgage & Retail Lending--National Penn Bank, Boyertown, PA; *U.S. Public*, pg. 1159

Wunderink, R.C.J., Sr. V.P.-Pub. Rels.--KLM Royal Dutch Airlines, Amstelveen, Netherlands; *Int'l*, pg. 719

Wunderlich, James B., Sr. V.P.-Information Systems--National Insurance Group, South San Francisco, CA; *U.S. Public*, pg. 1157

Wunderlich, James B., Sr. V.P.-Info. Systems--Pinnacle Data Corporation, San Bruno, CA; *U.S. Public*, pg. 1158

Wunderlich, James B., Sr. V.P.-Info. Systems--FASTRAC Systems, Inc.-Insurance Agent & Broker, South San Francisco, CA; *U.S. Public*, pg. 1158

Wunner, S. Bruce, Sr. V.P.--McDonald's Corporation, Oak Brook, IL; *U.S. Public*, pg. 1068

Wurster, Gale E., Sr. V.P.--First National Bank of Pennsylvania, Hermitage, PA; *U.S. Public*, pg. 607

Wurth, Michael, Sr. V.P.-Fin.--Arbed S.A., Luxembourg, Luxembourg; *Int'l*, pg. 78

Wyckoff, Thomas C., Sr. V.P., Gen. Counsel & Asst. Sec.--Artistic Greetings, Inc., Elmira, NY; *U.S. Public*, pg. 136

Wyker, Kenneth, Sr. V.P.-Legal Affairs--Clear Channel Communications, Inc., San Antonio, TX; *U.S. Public*, pg. 383

Wyman, Dell, Sr. V.P.-Mktg.--Farm Family Casualty Insurance Co., Glenmont, NY; *U.S. Private*, pg. 394

Wyman, Georgina, Sr. V.P.-Corp. Svcs.--Manulife Financial (The Manufacturers Life Insurance Company), Toronto, Canada; *Int'l*, pg. 840

Wynandts, A.R., Sr. V.P.--AEGON International B.V., Hague, Netherlands; *Int'l*, pg. 25

Wyne, Jon R., Sr. V.P. & Treas.--Bayer Corporation, Pittsburgh, PA; *Int'l*, pg. 172

Wynne, Cyndy, Sr. V.P., Corp. Trade--Vitt Media International, Inc., New York, NY; *U.S. Private*, pg. 1142

Wynne, Diana S., Sr. V.P.- Internal Audit--Ponderosa Steakhouse, Dallas, TX; *U.S. Private*, pg. 736

Wynne, Michael W., Sr. V.P.-Intl. Plng. & Devel.--General Dynamics Corporation, Falls Church, VA; *U.S. Public*, pg. 708

Wyshynski, Mel, Chief Oper. Officer & Sr. V.P.--P.T. International Nickel Indonesia, Jakarta, Indonesia; *Int'l*, pg. 947

Yabe, Takayuki, Sr. V.P.--Softbank Corporation, Tokyo, Japan; *Int'l*, pg. 1276

Yacullo, Dave, Sr. V.P. & Reg. Dir.--Outdoor Services, Sherman Oaks, CA; *U.S. Private*, pg. 1166

Yaeger, Riff, Sr. V.P. & Pub. Rels. Dir.--Colle & McVoy Marketing Communications, Minneapolis, MN; *U.S. Private*, pg. 252

Yaffa, Glen D., Sr. V.P.-Sls.--Stimson Lane Ltd., Woodinville, WA; *U.S. Public*, pg. 1661

Yager, Earl L., Chief Fin. Officer, Sr. V.P. & Sec.--Chad Therapeutics, Chatsworth, CA; *U.S. Public*, pg. 332

Yakupcin, Ronald J., Sr. V.P.-Technical Svcs.--Kolmar Laboratories, Inc., Port Jervis, NY; *Int'l*, pg. 239

Yakura, Toshiaki, Sr. V.P. & Grp. Head--Fuji Bank, New York Branch, New York, NY; *Int'l*, pg. 519

Yakush, Arlene L., Sr. V.P.--New Haven Savings Bank, New Haven, CT; *U.S. Private*, pg. 793

Yamada, Kunio, Chief Oper. Officer & Exec. V.P.--Rohto Pharmaceutical Co., Osaka, Japan; *Int'l*, pg. 1126

Yamaga, Noriyuki, Sr. Mng. Dir.--Kawasho Corporation, Tokyo, Japan; *Int'l*, pg. 726

Yamaguchi, Yoshinobu, Sr. V.P.--Marubeni America Corporation, New York, NY; *Int'l*, pg. 844

Yamamoto, Michihisa, Sr. Mng. Dir.--Kyocera Corporation, Kyoto, Japan; *Int'l*, pg. 775

Yamamoto, Sadao, Sr. Mng. Dir.--Kyocera Corporation, Kyoto, Japan; *Int'l*, pg. 775

Yamamura, Yuzo, Sr. Mng. Dir.--Kyocera Corporation, Kyoto, Japan; *Int'l*, pg. 775

Yamashita, Hidetoshi, Sr. V.P.--Bank of Tokyo-Mitsubishi (Switzerland) Ltd., Zurich, Switzerland; *Int'l*, pg. 158

Yanagi, Rintaro, Sr. V.P.-Europe, Middle East & Africa & London--Japan Airlines Company, Ltd., Tokyo, Japan; *Int'l*, pg. 699

Yancy, Larry, Sr. V.P.--Shamrock Foods Company, Phoenix, AZ; *U.S. Private*, pg. 989

Yandall, Roger, Sr. V.P.--Huitt-Zollars, Inc., Dallas, TX; *U.S. Private*, pg. 547

Yandell, Jerry P., Sr. V.P.-Opers.--TCA Management Company, Tyler, TX; *U.S. Public*, pg. 1553

Yang, Brett, Sr. V.P. & Dir.-Corp. Commun.--J. & W. Seligman & Co., New York, NY; *U.S. Private*, pg. 982

Yang, Edward V., Sr. V.P.--Electronic Data Systems Corporation, Plano, TX; *U.S. Public*, pg. 569

Yang, Felix, Sr. V.P. & Controller--Partners & Shevack, Inc., New York, NY; *U.S. Private*, pg. 842

Yang, Kenneth T., Dr., Sr. V.P.--ThermoTrex, San Diego, CA; *U.S. Public*, pg. 1595

Yang, Won S., Acting Chief Fin. Officer & Sr. V.P.--AST Research Inc., Irvine, CA; *Int'l*, pg. 1181

Yaniko, David, Sr. V.P.--Avnet, Inc., Great Neck, NY; *U.S. Public*, pg. 155

Yanke, Ron, Sr. V.P.--Imperial Bank, Inglewood, CA; *U.S. Public*, pg. 871
Yano, Kaori, Assoc. Sr. V.P.--NEC Corporation, Tokyo, Japan; *Int'l*, pg. 899
Yanotta, Patrick P., Sr. V.P.-Fin.--Conair Corporation, Stamford, CT; *U.S. Private*, pg. 261
Yanowitch, Marilyn, Sr. V.P. & Creative Dir.--Lowe McAdams Healthcare, New York, NY; *U.S. Private*, pg. 678
Yanowitz, Harry, Sr. V.P.-Pur.--Chapters Inc., Etobicoke, Canada; *Int'l*, pg. 280
Yara, Ronald T., Sr. V.P.-Strategic Mktg. & Sec.--S3 Incorporated, Santa Clara, CA; *U.S. Public*, pg. 1415
Yarborough, David, Sr. V.P.-Mining Prod.--GS Industries, Inc., Charlotte, NC; *U.S. Private*, pg. 435
Yarbro, Alan D., Sr. V.P. & Sec.--Mercantile Bankshares Corporation, Baltimore, MD; *U.S. Public*, pg. 1088
Yarbrough, Jon, Sr. V.P. & Creative Dir.--RP alpha, Santa Monica, CA; *U.S. Private*, pg. 950
Yared, Paul D., Sr. V.P., Gen. Counsel & Sec.--Foremost Corporation of America, Caledonia, MI; *U.S. Public*, pg. 667
Yarossi, Paul A., Chief Oper. Officer& Sr. V.P.--HNTB Corporation, Kansas City, MO; *U.S. Private*, pg. 492
Yartz, Deanne, Chief Fin. Officer & Sr. V.P.--Wallpapers-To-Go, Houston, TX; *U.S. Private*, pg. 1175
Yarvela, Yuha, Sr. V.P.--Metform Division, Hameenlinna, Finland; *Int'l*, pg. 1088
Yassin, Roberta M., Sr. V.P.--Great Western Bank, Chatsworth, CA; *U.S. Public*, pg. 1741
Yates, Christopher, Sr. V.P.-Bus. Devel.--Daisytek International Corporation, Plano, TX; *U.S. Public*, pg. 477
Yates, Christopher, Sr. V.P.-Bus. Devel.--Daisytek Incorporated, Plano, TX; *U.S. Public*, pg. 477
Yates, Christopher, Sr. V.P.-Bus. Devel.--Daisytek (Canada) Inc., Toronto, Canada; *U.S. Public*, pg. 477
Yates, Christopher, Sr. V.P.-Bus. Devel.--Daisytek Latin America, Miami, FL; *U.S. Public*, pg. 477
Yates, Christopher, Sr. V.P.-Bus. Devel.--Daisytek De Mexico S.A. de C.V., Mexico, Mexico; *U.S. Public*, pg. 477
Yates, Christopher, Sr. V.P.-Bus. Devel.--Priority Fulfillment Services, Inc., Plano, TX; *U.S. Public*, pg. 477
Yates, Christopher, Sr. V.P.-Bus. Devel.--Daisytek Australia Pty. Ltd., Alexandria, Australia; *U.S. Public*, pg. 477
Yates, Guy W., Sr. V.P.-Supply & Mktg.--Giant Industries Arizona, Inc., Scottsdale, AZ; *U.S. Public*, pg. 742
Yates, Herbert S., Chief Fin. Officer & Sr. V.P.-Fin.--Camco International Inc., Houston, TX; *U.S. Public*, pg. 298
Yates, Jerry G., Sr. V.P.--SRA International Inc., Arlington, VA; *U.S. Private*, pg. 957
Yates, P. Martin, Sr. V.P.-Leasing--Taubman Centers, Inc., Bloomfield Hills, MI; *U.S. Public*, pg. 1561
Yaw, William R., Jr., Sr. V.P.--Standard Federal Bank, Troy, MI; *Int'l*, pg. 10
Yawata, Keisuke, Sr. V.P.--Applied Materials, Inc., Santa Clara, CA; *U.S. Public*, pg. 123
Yeager, Jim, Sr. V.P.-Publicity & Pub. Rels.--Universal Studios Recreation Services Group, Universal City, CA; *Int'l*, pg. 1216
Yeager, Riff, Sr. V.P. & Pub. Rels. Dir.--Colle & McVoy, Inc., Minneapolis, MN; *U.S. Private*, pg. 252
Yeary, Robert C., Sr. V.P.--Imperial Bank, Inglewood, CA; *U.S. Public*, pg. 871
Yeates, Rick, Sr. V.P.-Sls.--Steelcase Inc., Grand Rapids, MI; *U.S. Private*, pg. 1038
Yednock, Kenneth, Sr. V.P. & Acct. Services Dir.--Gray Kirk/VanSant Advertising, Inc., Baltimore, MD; *U.S. Private*, pg. 472
Yee, Robert, Sr. V.P.--MBT Architecture, San Francisco, CA; *U.S. Private*, pg. 686
Yellin, Ira, Sr. V.P.-Southern California Devel.--Catellus Development Corporation, San Francisco, CA; *U.S. Public*, pg. 314
Yelton, E. Jay, Sr. V.P.--Jefferson-Pilot Corporation, Greensboro, NC; *U.S. Public*, pg. 925
Yiatchos, Gary, Sr. V.P.-Mktg. & Sls. Promo.--The Bon Marche, Inc., Seattle, WA; *U.S. Public*, pg. 617
Yin, Patrick, Sr. V.P.-Engrng.--Aspec Technology, Inc., Sunnyvale, CA; *U.S. Private*, pg. 89
Yoakum, James R., Sr. V.P.-Information & Reservation Systems--Choice Hotels International, Inc., Silver Spring, MD; *U.S. Public*, pg. 351
Yoder, Patricia D., Sr. V.P.-Corp. Affairs--Avis Rent A Car System, Inc., Garden City, NY; *U.S. Public*, pg. 321
Yoder, Patti B., Sr. V.P. & Dir.-Human Resources--Riggs National Corporation, Washington, DC; *U.S. Public*, pg. 1389
Yoffe, Stuart A., Sr. V.P.-Law--John Hancock Mutual Life Insurance Company, Boston, MA; *U.S. Private*, pg. 589
Yohe, Michael C., Sr. V.P.-Small Bus. Banking--Hibernia Corporation, New Orleans, LA; *U.S. Public*, pg. 825
Yoho, Franklin H., Sr. V.P.-Mktg. & Gas Supply--Public Service Company of North Carolina, Inc., Gastonia, NC; *U.S. Public*, pg. 1340
Yoho, Mendal L., Sr. V.P.--CNG Transmission Corporation, Clarksburg, WV; *U.S. Public*, pg. 435
Yokley, Arlen G., Sr. V.P.-Corp. Compliance & Sec.--BellSouth Corporation, Atlanta, GA; *U.S. Public*, pg. 207
Yokota, Tad, Sr. V.P. & Gen. Mgr.-Bus. Systems Div.--Minolta Corporation, Ramsey, NJ; *Int'l*, pg. 869
Yokoyama, Zenta, Sr. V.P. & Reg. Mgr.-Osaka--Japan Airlines Company, Ltd., Tokyo, Japan; *Int'l*, pg. 699
Yonekura, Shuji, Sr. V.P.-Sls. & Mktg.--Sanden International (U.S.A.), Inc., Wylie, TX; *Int'l*, pg. 1184
Yoon, John, Sr. V.P. & Acct. Services Dir.--DCA Advertising, Inc., New York, NY; *Int'l*, pg. 393
York, Steve M., Chief Fin. Officer, Sr. V.P. & Treas.--Amtech Corporation, Dallas, TX; *U.S. Public*, pg. 105
Yoshihiro, Seiya, Sr. V.P.--Dentsu USA-Atlanta Office, Atlanta, GA; *Int'l*, pg. 393
Yoshikawa, Eiichi, Sr. V.P.--NEC Corporation, Tokyo, Japan; *Int'l*, pg. 899
Yoshimatsu, Takashi, Sr. V.P.--Eastbridge Capital Inc., New York, NY; *Int'l*, pg. 933
Yoshimitsu, Kiyoshi, Sr. V.P.--Marubeni America Corporation, New York, NY; *Int'l*, pg. 844
Youell, Gerald W., Sr. V.P.-E & P--Chieftain International (U.S.) Inc., Edmonton, Canada; *Int'l*, pg. 284
Young, Allan N., Sr. V.P.-Tech. Claims--Argonaut Co., Menlo Park, CA; *U.S. Public*, pg. 129
Young, Barry H., Sr. V.P.-Specialty Leasing--The Mills Corporation, Arlington, VA; *U.S. Public*, pg. 1113
Young, Carl, Sr. V.P. & Gen. Counsel--Anchor Glass Container Corporation, Tampa, FL; *Int'l*, pg. 327
Young, Dennis E., Sr. V.P. & Treas.--Norwest Financial, Inc., Des Moines, IA; *U.S. Public*, pg. 1202
Young, Donald W., Sr. V.P.-Mktg.--Willis Corroon Corp. of Northern Ohio, Cleveland, OH; *Int'l*, pg. 1506
Young, H. Peter, Sr. V.P.-Logistics--Williams-Sonoma, Inc., San Francisco, CA; *U.S. Public*, pg. 1770
Young, J. Morgan, Sr. V.P.-Fin. & Admin.--Dassault Falcon Jet Corp., South Hackensack, NJ; *Int'l*, pg. 383
Young, J.H., Jr., Sr. V.P.--MPX Systems, Inc., Cayce, SC; *U.S. Public*, pg. 1436
Young, James F., Ph.D., Sr. V.P.-Res. & Devel.--MedImmune, Inc., Gaithersburg, MD; *U.S. Public*, pg. 1081
Young, Jim, Sr. V.P.-Commercial Devel.--Alza Corporation, Palo Alto, CA; *U.S. Public*, pg. 62
Young, Judy, Sr. V.P. & Media Dir.--Ketchum Advertising/San Francisco, San Francisco, CA; *U.S. Private*, pg. 616
Young, Katherine C., Sr. V.P.- Worldwide Materials--Maxtor Corporation, Milpitas, CA; *Int'l*, pg. 641
Young, Michael, Sr. V.P.--Sermatech International, Inc., Limerick, PA; *U.S. Public*, pg. 1569
Young, Paul, Sr. V.P.--Curtis C. Gunn, Inc., San Antonio, TX; *U.S. Private*, pg. 488
Young, Phil, Sr. V.P.--The Medical Protective Company, Fort Wayne, IN; *U.S. Private*, pg. 728
Young, Richard, Chief Information Officer & Sr. V.P.--The Strober Organization, Inc., Brooklyn, NY; *U.S. Private*, pg. 403
Young, Rick, Sr. V.P.--Security Pacific Financial Services Inc., San Diego, CA; *U.S. Public*, pg. 181
Young, Rob, Sr. V.P.-Plng. & Res.--Harrison, Young, Pesonen & Newell Inc., Toronto, Canada; *Int'l*, pg. 598
Young, Robert, Sr. V.P.--People's Choice TV Corp., Shelton, CT; *U.S. Public*, pg. 1274
Young, Robert A.M., Sr. V.P.-Law--Transcanada Pipelines Limited, Calgary, Canada; *Int'l*, pg. 1416
Young, Ronald K., Sr. V.P.-Product Mgmt.--American States Insurance Companies, Indianapolis, IN; *U.S. Public*, pg. 997
Young, Susan D., Sr. V.P.--Odyssey Reinsurance Corporation, New York, NY; *Int'l*, pg. 1258
Young, William, Sr. V.P. & Chief Admin. Officer--Lowe McAdams Healthcare, New York, NY; *U.S. Private*, pg. 678
Young, William D., Exec. V.P.--Genentech, Inc., South San Francisco, CA; *Int'l*, pg. 1120
Younger, Laurie, Sr. V.P.-Network Television--Walt Disney Network Television, Burbank, CA; *U.S. Public*, pg. 511
Younggren, David, Sr. V.P.--Gary-Williams Energy Corporation, Denver, CO; *U.S. Private*, pg. 440
Younghanz, Terry L., Sr. V.P.-Underwriting--RLI Corp., Peoria, IL; *U.S. Public*, pg. 1356
Youngling, Edward J., Sr. V.P.-Engrng. & Construction--Long Island Lighting Company, Hicksville, NY; *U.S. Public*, pg. 1013
Younkin, Timothy D., Sr. V.P. & Chief Mktg. Officer--Brown-Forman Beverages Worldwide, Louisville, KY; *U.S. Public*, pg. 261
Younkman, Dan, Sr. V.P.-Opers.--Jumbo Sports Inc., Tampa, FL; *U.S. Public*, pg. 935
Younts, Rosemary, Sr. V.P.-Commun.--GenCorp Inc., Fairlawn, OH; *U.S. Public*, pg. 705
Yow, Lawson S., Sr. V.P.-Investments & Dir.--The Robinson-Humphrey Company, Inc., Atlanta, GA; *U.S. Public*, pg. 1633
Yu, Albert Y. C., Sr. V.P. & Gen. Mgr.-Microproccessor Products Group--Intel Corporation, Santa Clara, CA; *U.S. Public*, pg. 886
Yu, Henry H.H., Sr. V.P.-China Market--Bank of Hawaii, Honolulu, HI; *U.S. Public*, pg. 1248
Yuasa, Yasushi, Sr. V.P. & Dept. Gen. Mgr.-Flight Opers.--Japan Airlines Company, Ltd., Tokyo, Japan; *Int'l*, pg. 699
Yukevich, Stanley, Sr. V.P.--Carpenter Co., Richmond, VA; *U.S. Private*, pg. 214
Yungmann, George L., Sr. V.P. & Controller--The Rouse Company, Columbia, MD; *U.S. Public*, pg. 1407
Yuracko, Ellen, Sr. V.P.-Mktg. & Sec.--Gerber Life Insurance Co., White Plains, NY; *Int'l*, pg. 973
Yusa, Mitsuru, Sr. V.P. & Head-Info. Sys.--Fuji Bank, New York Branch, New York, NY; *Int'l*, pg. 519
Yusko, Gary J., Sr. V.P.-Fin.--Westwood One, Inc., New York, NY; *U.S. Public*, pg. 1763
Yuspeh, Alan, Sr. V.P.-Ethics, Compliance & Corp. Responsibility--Columbia/HCA Healthcare Corporation, Nashville, TN; *U.S. Public*, pg. 403
Yvan, Jo, V.P.-Sls. & Mktg.--Pride Products, Inc., Elizabeth, NJ; *U.S. Private*, pg. 883
Zabel, Brad, Sr. V.P. & Grp. Acct. Dir.--Long Haymes Carr, Inc., Winston Salem, NC; *U.S. Public*, pg. 909
Zachau, John H., Jr., Sr. V.P. & Auditor--First Empire State Corporation, Buffalo, NY; *U.S. Public*, pg. 631
Zachau, John H., Jr., Sr. V.P. & Auditor--Manufacturers & Traders Trust Company, Buffalo, NY; *U.S. Public*, pg. 631
Zachem, Harry M., Sr. V.P.-Pub. Affairs--Ashland, Inc., Russell, KY; *U.S. Public*, pg. 138
Zack, Michael, Sr. V.P.-Intl.--Henry Schein, Inc., Melville, NY; *U.S. Public*, pg. 1437
Zaffaroni, Paul, Sr. V.P.--Acxiom Corporation, Conway, AR; *U.S. Public*, pg. 18
Zaffos, Lou, Sr. V.P. & Art Dir.--Carrafiello, Diehl & Associates, Inc., Irvington, NY; *U.S. Private*, pg. 215
Zagin, Tim, Sr. V.P. & Intl. Media Mgr.--International Media, New York, NY; *U.S. Public*, pg. 1641
Zahn, Ron, Sr. V.P.-Leasing--AMI Leasing Corporation, Worcester, MA; *U.S. Private*, pg. 7
Zahrn, James F., Chief Fin. Officer & Sr. V.P.--Springs Industries, Inc., Fort Mill, SC; *U.S. Public*, pg. 1499
Zainey, Michael Scott, Sr. V.P.-H.R.--Hibernia Corporation, New Orleans, LA; *U.S. Public*, pg. 825
Zakaria, Adel A., Sr. V.P.-Worldwide Engrng. & Mfg.--Deere & Company, Moline, IL; *U.S. Public*, pg. 491
Zalzneck, Robert J., Sr. V.P.--Universal Leaf Tobacco Company, Inc., Richmond, VA; *U.S. Public*, pg. 1694
Zamarbide, Guillermo, Sr. V.P.-Mfg.--Sudamtex de Uruguay, S.A., Montevideo, Uruguay; *Int'l*, pg. 1304
Zambelli, Thomas, Chief Fin. Officer & Sr. V.P.--Tops Appliance City, Edison, NJ; *U.S. Public*, pg. 1622
Zambri, Robert R., Sr. V.P., Gen. Counsel & Sec.--Fortis Benefits Insurance Company, Kansas City, MO; *Int'l*, pg. 499
Zampini, Dino G., Sr. V.P.-Opers.--Datamax International Corporation, Orlando, FL; *U.S. Private*, pg. 313
Zanchelli, Robert, V.P.-Sls.--General Binding Corporation, Northbrook, IL; *U.S. Public*, pg. 707
Zander, Don, Sr. V.P. & Controller--Benson Motors Corporation, Metairie, LA; *U.S. Private*, pg. 134
Zane, Robert J., Sr. V.P.-Mfg. & Sourcing--Liz Claiborne, Inc., New York, NY; *U.S. Public*, pg. 1005
Zanellis, William G., Sr. V.P.--NationsCredit Commercial Corporation, Cleveland, OH; *U.S. Public*, pg. 1165
Zanitsch, Jerry, Sr. V.P.-Mktg.--New World Entertainment, Inc., Los Angeles, CA; *Int'l*, pg. 926
Zanotti, Judith A., Sr. V.P.-Human Resources--Public Service Company of New Mexico, Albuquerque, NM; *U.S. Public*, pg. 1339
Zantop, Duane G., Sr. V.P.--Zantop International Airlines, Inc., Ypsilanti, MI; *U.S. Private*, pg. 1204
Zapanta, Avelino L., Sr. V.P.-Sls. & Svcs.--Philippine Airlines, Inc., Manila, Philippines; *Int'l*, pg. 1050
Zapico, Mark C., Sr. V.P. & Grp. Creative Dir.--DMB&B Detroit, Troy, MI; *U.S. Private*, pg. 302
Zapisek, John R., Chief Fin. Officer, Sr. V.P. & Treas.--Utica Mutual Insurance Company, New Hartford, NY; *U.S. Private*, pg. 1129
Zarges, Thomas H., Sr. V.P.-Opers.--Morrison Knudsen Corporation, Boise, ID; *U.S. Public*, pg. 1133
Zarick, Robert S., Sr. V.P.-Human Resources--Central Reserve Life of North America Insurance Co., Strongsville, OH; *U.S. Public*, pg. 326
Zaricki, Thomas L., Sr. V.P.-Retail Opers.--Fleming Companies, Inc., Oklahoma City, OK; *U.S. Public*, pg. 652
Zarrow, Scott, Sr. V.P.--Sooner Pipe & Supply Corp., Tulsa, OK; *U.S. Private*, pg. 1014
Zatkin, Steven R., Sr. V.P.-Govt. Rels.--Kaiser Permanente, Oakland, CA; *U.S. Private*, pg. 605
Zawadke, Gunther, Exec. V.P.-Accounts--Bayerische Landesbank, Munich, Germany; *Int'l*, pg. 176
Zeh, Herbert J., Jr., Sr. V.P.-Legal Supply--Reichhold Chemicals, Inc., Durham, NC; *Int'l*, pg. 370
Zeifman, Sue, Sr. V.P. & Gen. Mgr.-RPM--Young & Rubicam San Francisco, San Francisco, CA; *U.S. Private*, pg. 1198
Zeiger, Thomas, Sr. V.P.--Shapell Industries, Inc., Beverly Hills, CA; *U.S. Private*, pg. 990
Zelencik, Stephen, Chief Mktg. Exec. & Sr. V.P.--Advanced Micro Devices, Inc., Sunnyvale, CA; *U.S. Public*, pg. 21
Zeller, Lyle, Sr. V.P.-Home Improvement Div. --Green Tree Financial Corporation, Saint Paul, MN; *U.S. Public*, pg. 761
Zellner, Lou T., Sr. V.P.-Corp. Plng.--Mortgage Guaranty Insurance Corporation, Milwaukee, WI; *U.S. Public*, pg. 1026
Zelniker, Marvin H., Sr. V.P. & Print Production Dir.--Carrafiello, Diehl & Associates, Inc., Irvington, NY; *U.S. Private*, pg. 215
Zeltman, Gail, Sr. V.P. & Exec. Producer--DMB&B New York, New York, NY; *U.S. Private*, pg. 302
Zemach, Yehoshua, Sr. V.P.-Logistics & Real Estate--The Israel Electric Corporation Ltd., Haifa, Israel; *Int'l*, pg. 690
Zemelman, David, Sr. V.P.-Human Resources--CBS Corporation, Pittsburgh, PA; *U.S. Public*, pg. 273
Zemmelman, David, Sr. V.P.-Human Resources--CBS, New York, NY; *U.S. Public*, pg. 273
Zepnick, Glen R., Sr. V.P.--Zenith Insurance Company, Woodland Hills, CA; *U.S. Public*, pg. 1791
Zercher, Jack, Sr. V.P.-MIS & Opers.--First Western Bancorp, Inc., New Castle, PA; *U.S. Public*, pg. 642
Zerrer, Jeff, Sr. V.P.-Mktg.--American Finance Group, Inc., Boston, MA; *U.S. Public*, pg. 1241
Zick, John, Sr. V.P. & Gen. Mgr.--North American Grain Div., Chicago, IL; *U.S. Private*, pg. 268
Zickuhr, Keith, Sr. V.P.-Mktg.--Magna Group, Inc., Saint Louis, MO; *U.S. Public*, pg. 1037
Ziegler, Charles, Sr. V.P.-External Affairs--Ciba Specialty Chemicals, Tarrytown, NY; *Int'l*, pg. 291
Ziegler, Donald E., Chief Fin. Officer & Sr. V.P.--Hadron, Inc., Alexandria, VA; *U.S. Public*, pg. 773
Ziegler, Douglas F., Chief Investment Officer, Sr. V.P. & Treas.--Erie Family Life Insurance Company, Erie, PA; *U.S. Public*, pg. 590
Ziegler, Kurt, Sr. V.P.--Republic National Bank of New York (U.K.), London, United Kingdom; *U.S. Public*, pg. 1381
Ziegler, P.D., Sr. V.P.--Ziegler Asset Management, Inc., West Bend, WI; *U.S. Public*, pg. 1792
Ziesing, Peter R., Sr. V.P.--Trenwick America Reinsurance Corporation, Stamford, CT; *U.S. Public*, pg. 1634
Zietz, Allen M., Sr. V.P. & Gen. Mgr.--Lucky Stores Northern California Division, San Leandro, CA; *U.S. Public*, pg. 93

Zigas, Barry, Sr. V.P. & Exec. Dir.-Natl. Housing Impact--Federal National Mortgage Association (Fannie Mae), Washington, DC; *U.S. Public*, pg. 615
Zilinskas, M.J., Chief Fin. Officer & Sr. V.P.--The Dyson-Kissner-Moran Corporation, New York, NY; *U.S. Private*, pg. 351
Zimmer, Thomas, Sr. V.P. & Gen. Mgr.-Western Grp.--Treasure Chest Advertising Co., Inc., Glendora, CA; *U.S. Public*, pg. 228
Zimmerman, Alma, Sr. V.P.--Fabri-Centers of America, Inc., Hudson, OH; *U.S. Public*, pg. 609
Zimmerman, Derk, Sr. V.P.-New Ventures & Bus. Devel.--CBS, New York, NY; *U.S. Public*, pg. 273
Zimmerman, J. Conrad, Jr., Sr. V.P. & Dir.--The Robinson-Humphrey Company, Inc., Atlanta, GA; *U.S. Public*, pg. 1633
Zimmerman, Jennifer, Sr. V.P. & Bus. Devel. Dir.--The Chapman Agency, New York, NY; *U.S. Private*, pg. 1197
Zimmerman, Justin, Sr. V.P. & Asst. Sec.--Fabri-Centers of America, Inc., Hudson, OH; *U.S. Public*, pg. 609
Zimmerman, Ron, Sr. V.P.-Mktg. & Bus. Devel.--Leach International, Buena Park, CA; *U.S. Private*, pg. 655
Zimmerman, S. LaNette, Sr. V.P. & Dir.-Human Resources--Chicago Title & Trust Co., Chicago, IL; *U.S. Public*, pg. 42
Zimmermann, Charles, Sr. V.P.-Opers.--Triarc Beverage Group, White Plains, NY; *U.S. Public*, pg. 1635
Zingale, Anthony, Sr. V.P.-Worlwide Mktg.--Cadence Design Systems, Inc., San Jose, CA; *U.S. Public*, pg. 290
Zinger, Doron, Chief Oper. Officer & Sr. V.P.--ECI Telecom Ltd., Petah Tiqwa, Israel; *Int'l*, pg. 643
Zinn, James M., Chief Fin. Officer & Sr. V.P.--Capital One Financial Corporation, Falls Church, VA; *U.S. Public*, pg. 302
Zinsou, Lionel, Sr. V.P.-Pasta & Ready-to-Serve Dishes Div.--Danone Group, Paris, France; *Int'l*, pg. 379
Zion, R. Scott, Sr. V.P. & Gen. Mgr.-Ophthalmic Div.--Akorn, Inc., Lincolnshire, IL; *U.S. Public*, pg. 34
Zion, W. Earl, Sr. V.P.-Admin.--The Fifth Third Bank of Kentucky, Louisville, Louisville, KY; *U.S. Public*, pg. 621
Zipser, Michael A., Sr. V.P.-Store Opers. Eastern Div.--OfficeMax, Shaker Heights, OH; *U.S. Public*, pg. 1212
Zitoun, Olivier, Sr. V.P. & Gen. Mgr.-Networking Prod. Grp.--Artisoft, Inc., Tucson, AZ; *U.S. Public*, pg. 136
Zitter, Robert M., Sr. V.P.-Technology Opers.--Home Box Office, Inc., New York, NY; *U.S. Public*, pg. 1612
Zivelonghi, Larry, Sr. V.P.-Agribusiness Dept.--CVB Financial Corp., Ontario, CA; *U.S. Public*, pg. 286
Zock, George J., Sr. V.P.-Insurance Opers.--Horace Mann Educators Corporation, Springfield, IL; *U.S. Public*, pg. 835
Zoghbi, Sami, Sr. V.P. & Pres.-Africa & Middle East--ITT Sheraton Corporation, Boston, MA; *U.S. Public*, pg. 1512
Zohouri, Saeed, Ph.D., Sr. V.P., Chief Tech. Officer & Pres.-Solectron California Corp.--Solectron Corporation, Milpitas, CA; *U.S. Public*, pg. 1483
Zoley, George C., Vice Chm., Chief Exec. Officer & Sr. V.P.-Wackenhut Corrections--The Wackenhut Corporation, Palm Beach Gardens, FL; *U.S. Public*, pg. 1731
Zolot, Stuart M., Chief Fin. Officer & Sr. V.P.--MARC, Pittsburgh, PA; *U.S. Private*, pg. 701
Zondag, Sharon Jones, Sr. V.P.-Field Opers.--Piercing Pagoda, Inc., Bethlehem, PA; *U.S. Public*, pg. 1296
Zonis, Irwin S., Sr. V.P.--Essex Chemical Corporation, Clifton, NJ; *U.S. Public*, pg. 523
Zonis, Meshulam, Sr. V.P.-Opers./Carnival Cruise Lines--Carnival Corporation, Miami, FL; *U.S. Public*, pg. 306
Zorio, John W., Sr. V.P.-No. Central Agencies--New York Life Insurance Company, New York, NY; *U.S. Private*, pg. 794
Zorkers, Walter S., Sr. V.P.-Devel.--Hvide Marine Incorporated, Fort Lauderdale, FL; *U.S. Public*, pg. 851
Zott, John C., Chief Fin. Officer & Sr. V.P.-Fin.--West Marine, Inc., Watsonville, CA; *U.S. Public*, pg. 1756
Zoukis, Paul, Sr. V.P.-Mktg. & Sls.--Hogan Systems, Inc., Dallas, TX; *U.S. Public*, pg. 422
Zub, Edward S., Sr. V.P.-Regulations & Prod. Pricing--Southwest Gas Corporation, Las Vegas, NV; *U.S. Public*, pg. 1493
Zucco, Donato B., Ph.D, Chief Admin. Officer & Sr. V.P.--Crown American Realty Trust, Johnstown, PA; *U.S. Public*, pg. 461
Zucht, Earle, Sr. V.P.-Semiconductor Mktg.--Wyle Electronics, Irvine, CA; *Int'l*, pg. 1457
Zucker, Hans, Sr. V.P. & Mktg. Services Dir.--Korey, Kay & Partners, New York, NY; *U.S. Private*, pg. 632
Zucker, Mark L., Sr. V.P.-Admin. & Opers.--Columbia Pictures, Culver City, CA; *Int'l*, pg. 1281
Zucker, Michael, Sr. V.P.-Creative Services--Universal Studios TV, Universal City, CA; *Int'l*, pg. 1215
Zuill, Cummings V., Sr. V.P.-Exec. Mngmt.--The Bank of Bermuda Limited, Hamilton, Bermuda; *Int'l*, pg. 150
Zules, Tony, Sr. V.P. & Assoc. Creative Dir.--Carrafiello, Diehl & Associates, Inc., Irvington, NY; *U.S. Private*, pg. 215
Zunk, Charles R., Sr. V.P.-Opers.--The United States Playing Card Company, Cincinnati, OH; *U.S. Private*, pg. 1125
Zunker, Arthur R., Chief Fin. Officer, Sr. V.P.-Fin. & Treas.--Centex Construction Products, Inc., Dallas, TX; *U.S. Public*, pg. 322
Zurn, James A., Sr. V.P.--Zurn Industries, Inc., Erie, PA; *U.S. Public*, pg. 1794
Zwicky, Elisabeth, Sr. V.P.-Legal Affairs & Special Projects--Liechtenstein Global Trust Limited, Vaduz, Liechtenstein; *Int'l*, pg. 809
Zyboyovsky, James F., Sr. V.P.--Kearney-National, Inc., White Plains, NY; *U.S. Private*, pg. 351
Zych, Leonard A., Sr. V.P.--Chase Financial Management Corp., Cleveland, OH; *U.S. Public*, pg. 358
Zyma, Roger, Sr. V.P.-STV Inc.--STV Group, Inc., Douglassville, PA; *U.S. Public*, pg. 1421
Zyma, Roger, Sr. V.P.--STV Environmental, Douglassville, PA; *U.S. Public*, pg. 1421
Zyman, Sergio, Chief Mktg. Officer & Sr. V.P.--The Coca-Cola Company, Atlanta, GA; *U.S. Public*, pg. 392

TREASURER

Aamoth, William L., Asst. Treas.-Intl.--TRW Inc., Cleveland, OH; *U.S. Public*, pg. 1558
Aanenson, Vernon O., Pres. & Treas.--Old Dutch Foods, Inc., Roseville, MN; *U.S. Private*, pg. 814
Aaron, Marcus, II, Pres. & Treas.--The Homer Laughlin China Company, Newell, WV; *U.S. Private*, pg. 653
Aaron, Marcus, II, Pres. & Treas.--The Newell Company, Newell, WV; *U.S. Private*, pg. 653
Aaron, Marcus, II, Pres. & Treas.--Newell Bridge & Railway Company, Newell, WV; *U.S. Private*, pg. 653
Abair, Daniel, Treas. & Sec.--Park Motor Sales Company, Detroit, MI; *U.S. Private*, pg. 840
Abatamarco, Vincent, Treas.--The Stroh Brewery Company, Detroit, MI; *U.S. Private*, pg. 1047
Abbey, Richard, Treas.--Automotive Moulding Company, Warren, MI; *U.S. Private*, pg. 485
Abbot, Patricia, Treas. & Sec.--Metro Label Corp., Garland, TX; *U.S. Private*, pg. 736
Abbott, John C., Treas.--Inter-Tel, Incorporated, Phoenix, AZ; *U.S. Public*, pg. 888
Abbott, R. William, Chief Fin. Officer & Exec. V.P.--WSFS Financial Corporation, Wilmington, DE; *U.S. Public*, pg. 1728
Abdalla Black, Barbara, V.P. & Treas.--Abdalla's Lafayette, Inc., Lafayette, LA; *U.S. Private*, pg. 10
Abdela, Angelo, V.P.-Strategic & Capital Investments--Bestfoods, Englewood Cliffs, NJ; *U.S. Public*, pg. 223
Aberant, John A., V.P. & Treas.--AmeriSource Health Corp., Malvern, PA; *U.S. Public*, pg. 96
Abercrombie, Jack, V.P.-Fin. & Admin. & Treas.--Doman Industries Limited, Duncan, Canada; *Int'l*, pg. 414
Abernathy, James, Treas.--Associated Electric Co-op Inc., Springfield, MO; *U.S. Private*, pg. 89
Ables, Thomas, Treas.--The W.W. Williams Company, Columbus, OH; *U.S. Private*, pg. 1178
Abram, Albert, V.P. & Treas.--Consorcio G. Grupo Dina, S.A. de C.V., Mexico, Mexico; *Int'l*, pg. 326
Abrams, Gary N., Chief Fin. Officer, Sr. V.P. & Treas.--Somerset Savings Bank, Somerville, MA; *U.S. Public*, pg. 1484
Abrams, Jerry, Chief Fin. Officer & Treas.--Hoogovens Aluminium Corp., Secaucus, NJ; *Int'l*, pg. 755
Abramson, Stephen, Sr. V.P. & Treas.--New Line Cinema Corporation, New York, NY; *U.S. Public*, pg. 1614
Abshire, Richard B., V.P.-Fin. & Treas.--Adams Resources & Energy, Inc., Houston, TX; *U.S. Public*, pg. 18
Accardo, Jack P., Chief Fin. Officer, V.P., Treas. & Sec.--Kasper Machine Company, Madison Heights, MI; *U.S. Private*, pg. 608
Acey, Thomas M., Treas. & Sec.--Conmed Corporation, Utica, NY; *U.S. Public*, pg. 431
Achorn, Edward H., Asst. Treas. & Dir.-Cash Mngmt.--Hershey Foods Corporation, Hershey, PA; *U.S. Public*, pg. 811
Ackerman, Patricia K., Asst. Treas.--A.O. Smith Corporation, Milwaukee, WI; *U.S. Public*, pg. 1476
Ackermans, W.W.M., Treas.--KPN Koninklyke PTT Nederland NV, Groningen, Netherlands; *Int'l*, pg. 720
Acri, Robert, Controller & Treas.--Tribune Review Publishing Co., Greensburg, PA; *U.S. Private*, pg. 1102
Adam, Brian, Treas.--Amtrak-National Railroad Passenger Corp., Washington, DC; *U.S. Private*, pg. 68
Adamo, James, Treas. & Sec.--Burnside Construction Co., Downers Grove, IL; *U.S. Private*, pg. 187
Adams, James E., Chief Fin. Officer, Exec. V.P. & Treas.--MainStreet BankGroup Incorporated, Martinsville, VA; *U.S. Public*, pg. 1038
Adams, Joe, Exec. V.P. & Treas.--Creative Alliance, Inc., Louisville, KY; *U.S. Private*, pg. 287
Adams, John B., Chief Fin. Officer, Exec. V.P.-Fin., Sec. & Treas.--Big O Tires Incorporated, Englewood, CO; *U.S. Public*, pg. 1553
Adams, John S., V.P. & Treas.--Hatzel & Buehler, Inc., Wilmington, DE; *U.S. Private*, pg. 266
Adams, Kenneth, Treas.--Subway Franchise Advertising Fund Trust, Milford, CT; *U.S. Private*, pg. 1048
Adams, Mark, Sr. V.P., Treas. & Sec.--Hechinger Company Investors II, L.P., Largo, MD; *U.S. Private*, pg. 477
Adams, Mel J., Treas.--Avondale Industries, Inc., Avondale, LA; *U.S. Public*, pg. 156
Adams, Paul D., Chief Fin. Officer, Sr. V.P. & Treas.--Old Republic International Corporation, Chicago, IL; *U.S. Public*, pg. 1218
Adams, Peter S., Pres. & Treas.--UNUM Sales Corp., Portland, ME; *U.S. Public*, pg. 1700
Adams, Richard B., Pres., Chief Exec. Officer & Treas.--R.P. Adams Company, Inc., Tonawanda, NY; *U.S. Public*, pg. 19
Adams, Robin J., V.P. & Treas.--Borg Warner Automotive, Inc., Chicago, IL; *U.S. Public*, pg. 245
Adcock, Edward, Chief Fin. Officer, Treas. & Sec.--General Processors, Inc., Oxford, NC; *U.S. Public*, pg. 1502
Addesso, Dominic J., Pres. & Treas.--Exchange Insurance Company, Buffalo, NY; *U.S. Public*, pg. 1455
Adik, Stephen P., Chief Fin. Officer, Sr. V.P. & Treas.--NIPSCO Industries, Inc., Hammond, IN; *U.S. Public*, pg. 1185
Aglinsky, William E., V.P. & Treas.--Management Recruiters International, Inc., Cleveland, OH; *U.S. Public*, pg. 277
Agnihotri, Rashmi, Asst. Treas. & Cash Mgr.--The Andersons Incorporated, Maumee, OH; *U.S. Public*, pg. 111
Agresti, Michael L., V.P.-Fin., Treas. & Sec.--Lee Pharmaceuticals, South El Monte, CA; *U.S. Public*, pg. 984
Ahart, J.F., Chief Fin. Officer, V.P., Treas. & Sec.--Powell Industries, Inc., Houston, TX; *U.S. Public*, pg. 1319
Ahearn, Michael J., Controller & Treas.--C.R. Daniels, Inc., Ellicott City, MD; *U.S. Private*, pg. 310
Ahting, Frank, V.P.-Fin.--Athey Products Corporation, Wake Forest, NC; *U.S. Public*, pg. 142
Ailes, Bruce, Mgr.-Treasury--CompPair LeRoi, Sidney, OH; *Int'l*, pg. 1242
Aina, Olusegun, Treas.--Cadbury Nigeria PLC, Ikeja, Nigeria; *Int'l*, pg. 248
Aizawa, Hiroshi, Chief Fin. Officer & Div. Mgr.--Sumitomo Bank of California, San Francisco, CA; *Int'l*, pg. 1309
Ajer, Randolph E., Chief Fin. Officer, Exec. V.P., Treas. & Sec.--Mercury Air Group Inc., Los Angeles, CA; *U.S. Public*, pg. 1092
Akin, Richard L., V.P. & Treas.--Golf Hosts, Inc., Palm Harbor, FL; *U.S. Private*, pg. 1036
Alafita, Carlos G., Treas.--Sandusky International Inc., Sandusky, OH; *U.S. Private*, pg. 964
Alberghini, Dolores, Dir.-H.R. & Asst. Treas.--Cains Foods, L.P., Ayer, MA; *U.S. Private*, pg. 199
Alberici, Gabriel J., Chm. Bd. & Treas.--J.S. Alberici Construction Co., Inc., Saint Louis, MO; *U.S. Private*, pg. 32
Albert, Rachel F., Treas.--The Harodite Finishing Company Inc., North Dighton, MA; *U.S. Private*, pg. 503
Alberts, Robert J., Treas. & Sec.--Templeton, Kenly & Co., Inc., Broadview, IL; *U.S. Private*, pg. 1075
Albo, Richard G., Treas.--CPI Corp., Saint Louis, MO; *U.S. Public*, pg. 283
Albrecht, Fred, Exec. V.P.-Fin.--First Worthing Company, Dallas, TX; *U.S. Private*, pg. 408
Alchin, John R., Sr. V.P. & Treas.--Comcast Corporation, Philadelphia, PA; *U.S. Public*, pg. 406
Alderton, Susan, V.P. & Treas.--NL Industries, Inc., Houston, TX; *U.S. Private*, pg. 270
Aldrich, David J., V.P. & Treas.--Alpha Industries, Inc., Woburn, MA; *U.S. Public*, pg. 57
Alegria, A., Treas.--International Columbia Resources Corporation, Bogota, Colombia; *U.S. Public*, pg. 602
Alem, Nancy, Sec. & Treas.--Compar, New York, NY; *Int'l*, pg. 1073
Alesia, Patrick L., V.P. & Treas.--Griffon Corp., Jericho, NY; *U.S. Public*, pg. 766
Alessi, Laurie, Treas.--Interstate Commodities Inc., Troy, NY; *U.S. Private*, pg. 573
Alexander, Bill, Chief Fin. Officer, V.P. & Treas.--Purcell Co., Inc., Diamondhead, MS; *U.S. Private*, pg. 895
Alexander, Forbes I.J., Treas.--Jabil Circuit, Inc., Saint Petersburg, FL; *U.S. Public*, pg. 919
Alexander, R.M., Treas. & Asst. Sec.--Gulf Canada Resources Ltd., Calgary, Canada; *Int'l*, pg. 577
Alexander, Ronald, Chief Fin. Officer & Treas.--GRC International, Inc., Vienna, VA; *U.S. Public*, pg. 695
Alflen, J., Treas. & Sec.--Torrance Nissan, Inc., Torrance, CA; *U.S. Public*, pg. 1380
Alford, M.L., Chief Fin. Officer & Treas.--Staple Cotton Cooperative Association, Greenwood, MS; *U.S. Private*, pg. 1033
Allbritton, Roxane C., V.P. & Treas.--Granite Construction Incorporated, Watsonville, CA; *U.S. Public*, pg. 759
Allchin, Steven J., Asst. Treas.--Stanley Design-Build, Inc., Muscatine, IA; *U.S. Private*, pg. 1033
Allchin, Steven J., Asst.Treas.--Stanley Enviromental, Inc., Coralville, IA; *U.S. Private*, pg. 1033
Allen, Clinton G., Treas. & Sec.--Bill Heard Oldsmobile Company, Columbus, GA; *U.S. Private*, pg. 515
Allen, David H., Treas.--Komag, Incorporated, San Jose, CA; *U.S. Public*, pg. 966
Allen, Gary, Treas.--United Dairymen of Arizona, Tempe, AZ; *U.S. Private*, pg. 1121
Allen, Joseph, Exec. V.P., Treas. & Sec.--Brant Allen Industries, Inc., Greenwich, CT; *U.S. Private*, pg. 165
Allen, Kenneth R., V.P. & Treas.--Texas Industries, Inc., Dallas, TX; *U.S. Public*, pg. 1585
Allen, L. Nash, Jr., Chief Fin. Officer & Treas.--Bancorp South Inc., Tupelo, MS; *U.S. Public*, pg. 176
Allen, Robert A., Controller & Treas.--Skeena Cellulose Inc., Vancouver, Canada; *Int'l*, pg. 1261
Allen, Suzanne S., Treas.--Nash Finch Company, Edina, MN; *U.S. Public*, pg. 1151
Alles, Charles, Treas. & Sec.--Windemuller Electric Inc., Wayland, MI; *U.S. Private*, pg. 1182
Alley, J. Ken, Treas.--Suncor Inc., Calgary, Canada; *Int'l*, pg. 1320
Alley, Ralph L., Sr. V.P., Controller & Treas.--CNB Bancshares, Inc., Evansville, IN; *U.S. Public*, pg. 280
Allgyer, James D., Controller--Masland, Carlisle, PA; *U.S. Public*, pg. 981
Allmendinger, Bruno, Deputy Treas. & Controller--Sulzer Ltd., Winterthur, Switzerland; *Int'l*, pg. 1305
Allred, Gary L., Treas. & Sec.--AC Corporation, Greensboro, NC; *U.S. Private*, pg. 3
Allsup, Barbara J., V.P., Sec. & Treas.--Allsups Convenience Stores Inc., Clovis, NM; *U.S. Private*, pg. 44
Almquist, Stephan, Sr. V.P. & Corp. Treas.--Telefonaktiebolaget LM Ericsson, Stockholm, Sweden; *Int'l*, pg. 1363
Alongi, Linda, Treas. & Sec.--American Furniture Company, Albuquerque, NM; *U.S. Private*, pg. 55
Alosa, Joseph R., Pres. & Treas.--Patsy's, Inc., Concord, NH; *U.S. Private*, pg. 843
Alperson, Lonnie, Treas. & Sec.--Rolled Steel Products Corporation, Los Angeles, CA; *U.S. Private*, pg. 941
Alslen, Joseph C., Treas. & Sec.--Southern California Auto Group, Torrance, CA; *U.S. Private*, pg. 1016
Altenbaumer, Larry F., Chief Fin. Officer, Controller & Treas.--Illinova Inc., Decatur, IL; *U.S. Public*, pg. 869
Alteslaben, Robert, V.P. & Treas.--Bosch Packaging Machinery Division, South Plainfield, NJ; *Int'l*, pg. 204
Althof, Timothy D., Treas. & Sec.--New England Business Service, Inc., Groton, MA; *U.S. Public*, pg. 1170
Altieri, Edward J., Chief Fin. Officer & Treas.--Construction Specialties, Inc., Cranford, NJ; *U.S. Private*, pg. 266

Altmaier, Chris, Controller & Treas.--Southern Belle Dairy Company, Somerset, KY; *U.S. Private*, pg. 1015
Alton, John W., Pres.--Mineralac Co., Addison, IL; *U.S. Private*, pg. 750
Alvarez, Jose Antonio, Treas.--CODELCO Chile (Corporacion Nacional Del Cobre De Chile), Santiago, Chile; *Int'l*, pg. 302
Ambrose, Nadine, Treas.--Bellamy Brothers, Inc., Ellenwood, GA; *U.S. Private*, pg. 132
Ambrose, William A., Exec. V.P. & Treas.--Worsley Companies Inc., Wilmington, NC; *U.S. Private*, pg. 1191
Ames, J.W., V.P.-Fin., Treas. & Sec.--Milwaukee Electric Tool Corp., Brookfield, WI; *Int'l*, pg. 96
Amini, Rex, Exec. V.P. & Treas.--Sage Energy Company, San Antonio, TX; *U.S. Public*, pg. 1426
Ammann, William R., V.P.-Admin. & Treas.--Aeroquip-Vickers, Inc., Maumee, OH; *U.S. Public*, pg. 24
Amyot, R., V.P. & Treas.--Rothmans Inc., North York, Canada; *Int'l*, pg. 1129
Anathan, James M., III, Treas.--Filene's Basement, Inc., Wellesley, MA; *U.S. Public*, pg. 622
Ancona, Edgar, V.P. & Treas.--Household International, Inc., Prospect Heights, IL; *U.S. Public*, pg. 842
Andersen, Joseph G., V.P.-Fin., Treas. & Sec.--Continental Circuits Corp., Phoenix, AZ; *U.S. Public*, pg. 440
Anderskow, David, Chief Fin. Officer, Controller & Treas.--Power Contracting & Engineering Corp., Schaumburg, IL; *U.S. Private*, pg. 877
Anderson, Al, V.P.-Fin.--Dreis & Krump Manufacturing Company, Chicago, IL; *U.S. Private*, pg. 342
Anderson, Andrew E., V.P.-Fin. & Treas.--Otter Tail Power Company, Fergus Falls, MN; *U.S. Public*, pg. 1234
Anderson, Anne-Drue, Exec. V.P. & Treas.--H.F. Ahmanson & Co., Irwindale, CA; *U.S. Public*, pg. 29
Anderson, Basil L., Chief Fin. Officer, Exec. V.P. & Treas.--Campbell Soup Company, Camden, NJ; *U.S. Public*, pg. 298
Anderson, Carroll, Treas.--Iowa Paint Mfg. Company, Inc., Des Moines, IA; *U.S. Private*, pg. 575
Anderson, David G., V.P.-Fin. & Asst. Treas.--Columbia/HCA Healthcare Corporation, Nashville, TN; *U.S. Public*, pg. 403
Anderson, Eric, Exec. V.P. & Treas.--The Conde Nast Publications Inc., New York, NY; *U.S. Private*, pg. 20
Anderson, Eugene K., V.P. & Asst. Treas.--Valhi, Inc., Dallas, TX; *U.S. Private*, pg. 270
Anderson, George R., Chief Fin. Officer, V.P.-Fin. & Admin. & Treas.--Rock of Ages Corporation, Graniteville, VT; *U.S. Public*, pg. 1396
Anderson, Gregory, Chief Fin. Officer--Electrovert, Grand Prairie, TX; *Int'l*, pg. 328
Anderson, J. David, Asst. Treas. & Asst. Sec.--Roanoke Gas Company, Roanoke, VA; *U.S. Public*, pg. 1392
Anderson, John K., Chief Fin. Officer, Exec. V.P. & Treas.--American Heritage Life Insurance Co., Jacksonville, FL; *U.S. Public*, pg. 79
Anderson, John K., Jr., Chief Fin. Officer, Exec. V.P. & Treas.--American Heritage Life Investment Corp., Jacksonville, FL; *U.S. Public*, pg. 78
Anderson, Kelly, Asst. Treas.--Allied Capital Corporation, Washington, DC; *U.S. Public*, pg. 47
Anderson, Lyn D., V.P.-Fin., Treas. & Sec.--Tom's Foods, Inc., Columbus, GA; *U.S. Private*, pg. 1090
Anderson, Margaret A., Chief Fin. Officer, Sr. V.P.-Admin. & Treas.--Aerospace Corporation, El Segundo, CA; *U.S. Private*, pg. 24
Anderson, Mark A., Chief Fin. Officer, Sec. & Treas.--Community First Bankshares, Inc., Fargo, ND; *U.S. Public*, pg. 416
Anderson, Michael O., Treas.--Delco Electronics Corporation, Kokomo, IN; *U.S. Public*, pg. 720
Anderson, Reid, Treas.--Grand Prairie Co-op, Inc., Tolono, IL; *U.S. Private*, pg. 468
Anderson, Robert M., Treas.--Dairyland Power Cooperative, La Crosse, WI; *U.S. Private*, pg. 307
Anderson, Robert W., Controller, Treas. & Sec.--Superior Oil Co. Inc., Indianapolis, IN; *U.S. Private*, pg. 1055
Anderson, Ronald A., Sec. & Asst. Treas.--St. Joe Corp., Jacksonville, FL; *U.S. Public*, pg. 1426
Anderson, Sandra M., Treas.--Bestolife Corp., Dallas, TX; *U.S. Private*, pg. 900
Anderson, Sandra M., V.P., Controller & Treas.--Quemetco, Inc., Dallas, TX; *U.S. Private*, pg. 900
Anderson, Sandra M., V.P. & Treas.--Quemetco Realty, Inc., Dallas, TX; *U.S. Private*, pg. 900
Anderson, Sandra M., Treas.--Riteway Trucking, Dallas, TX; *U.S. Private*, pg. 900
Anderson, Sandra M., V.P. & Treas.--Environmental Service Insurance Co., Dallas, TX; *U.S. Private*, pg. 900
Anderson, Sandra M., V.P. & Treas.--West Morris Properties, Inc., Dallas, TX; *U.S. Private*, pg. 901
Anderson, Suzanne, Treas.--Core-Mark International, South San Francisco, CA; *U.S. Private*, pg. 275
Anderson, William, V.P. & Treas.--Wilsey Bennett Co., San Francisco, CA; *U.S. Private*, pg. 1180
Andersson, Nil-Ove, Exec. V.P.-Fin. & Treas.--Celsius AB, Stockholm, Sweden; *Int'l*, pg. 276
Ando, Tetsuo, Chief Fin. Officer, Exec. V.P. & Treas.--Bridgestone/Firestone, Inc., Nashville, TN; *Int'l*, pg. 213
Andonian, Hratch K., Co-Chm., Exec. V.P., Treas. & Sec.--A K H Company, Inc., City of Commerce, CA; *U.S. Private*, *pg. 2*
Andre, Wayne, Treas. & Sec.--Roseville Chrysler Plymouth Jeep Inc., Roseville, MI; *U.S. Private*, pg. 946
Andrepont, Kevin, Chief Fin. Officer, V.P. & Treas.--Baton Rouge Water Works Company, Baton Rouge, LA; *U.S. Private*, pg. 122
Andrepont, Kevin, Sr. V.P. & Treas.--Parish Water Company, Inc., Baton Rouge, LA; *U.S. Private*, pg. 123
Andres, P.J., V.P. & Treas.--U.S. Can Company, Oak Brook, IL; *U.S. Public*, pg. 1681
Andretta, Vincent J., Pres., Chief Exec. Officer & Treas.--Colony Liquor Distributors, Inc., Kingston, NY; *U.S. Private*, pg. 254
Andrew, Frederick, V.P. & Treas.--BCE Inc., Montreal, Canada; *Int'l*, pg. 114
Andrews, Donald L., Treas.--SRI International, Menlo Park, CA; *U.S. Private*, pg. 958
Andrews, Glenn C., Treas.--Glaxo Wellcome PLC, Research Triangle Park, NC; *Int'l*, pg. 553
Andritsakis, Helen, Treas. & Dir.-Fin.--Ferry-Morse Seed Company, Modesto, CA; *Int'l*, pg. 566
Angermeier, Kurt A., Treas. & Sec.--Battle Creek Gas Company, Battle Creek, MI; *U.S. Public*, pg. 1489
Anguish, J. Edward, V.P. & Treas.--John Hancock Networking Insurance Agency, Boston, MA; *U.S. Private*, *pg. 590*
Ankeney, Daniel, Treas.--Menasha Corporation, Neenah, WI; *U.S. Private*, pg. 731
Annett, Michelle, Controller & Treas.--Peters Construction Corp., Waterloo, IA; *U.S. Private*, pg. 856
Ansted, James P., Chief Fin. Officer, Treas., & Sec.--Plastic Suppliers, Inc., Columbus, OH; *U.S. Private*, pg. 871
Antebi, Joseph, Chief Fin. Officer & Treas.--Simpson Gumpertz & Heger Inc., Arlington, MA; *U.S. Private*, pg. 1002
Antenberg, Bruce F., Sr. V.P. & Treas.--Great Western Financial Corporation, Chatsworth, CA; *U.S. Public*, pg. 1741
Antes, Richard, Chief Fin. Office & V.P.-Fin.--Tetko, Inc., Briarcliff Manor, NY; *U.S. Private*, pg. 1078
Anthony, Aubra, Jr., Gen. Counsel, Treas. & Sec.--Anthony Forest Products Co., Inc., El Dorado, AR; *U.S. Private*, pg. 76
Anthony, Steven M., Treas. & Sec.--Bearden Lumber Company, Inc., Bearden, AR; *U.S. Private*, pg. 127
Anton, Charles T., Treas. & Sec.--Lift-All Co., Inc., Manheim, PA; *U.S. Private*, pg. 667
Antonopoulou, X., Treas.--Geo-Young & Rubicam, Athens, Greece; *U.S. Private*, pg. 1199
Antwine, Danny, Treas. & Sec.--Choctaw Electric Co-Op, Hugo, OK; *U.S. Private*, pg. 238
Aoki, T., Treas.--Honda Motor Co., Ltd., Tokyo, Japan; *Int'l*, pg. 634
Apeseche, Frank, Treas.--Berkshire Realty Company, Inc., Boston, MA; *U.S. Public*, pg. 221
Apgar, Phillip E., CPA, Chief Fin. Officer, V.P. & Treas.--American Indemnity Financial Corp., Galveston, TX; *U.S.* Public, pg. 83
Appelbaum, Michael, Treas.--Essex Chemical Corporation, Clifton, NJ; *U.S. Public*, pg. 523
Appelwick, Karen K., Treas. & Sec.--New Apple Lines, Inc., Madison, SD; *U.S. Private*, pg. 792
Applebaum, David, V.P.-Mfg. & Treas.--Triangle Marketing Corp., New York, NY; *U.S. Private*, pg. 1102
Arakelian, Dorothy J., Treas. & Sec.--Standard Manufacturing Co., Inc., Troy, NY; *U.S. Private*, pg. 1031
Arana, Cheryl, Treas. & Sec.--Chase Chevrolet Co., Inc., Stockton, CA; *U.S. Private*, pg. 230
Arana, Perla, Treas.--Sarmiento Rappan Industries, Manila, Philippines; *Int'l*, pg. 1194
Aranow, Peter J., Exec. V.P., Treas. & Sec.--Players International, Inc., Atlantic City, NJ; *U.S. Public*, pg. 1310
Arborio, Peter, Controller & Asst. Treas.--Dutchess Quarry & Supply Co. Inc., Pleasant Valley, NY; *U.S. Private*, pg. 350
Arbuckle, James E., Chief Fin. Officer, Exec. V.P. & Treas.--Besser Company, Alpena, MI; *U.S. Private*, pg. 139
Arcadi, Vincent, Treas. & Sec.--Depew Development Inc., Lancaster, NY; *U.S. Private*, pg. 326
Arcari, John J., Chief Fin. Officer--Robotic Vision Systems, Inc., Hauppauge, NY; *U.S. Public*, pg. 1395
Arceneaux, Darin, Chief Fin. Officer & Treas.--Associated Grocers, Inc., Baton Rouge, LA; *U.S. Private*, pg. 90
Archambault, Mike, V.P. & Treas.--Entex Information Services, Rye Brook, NY; *U.S. Private*, pg. 378
Archer, Charles P., Treas.--Archer Daniels Midland Company (ADM), Decatur, IL; *U.S. Public*, pg. 127
Archibald, Andrew M., Treas. & Sec.--International Container Systems, Tampa, FL; *Int'l*, pg. 685
Arcieri, Elizabeth, V.P.-Fin. & Admin. & Treas.--Bird Incorporated, Norwood, MA; *Int'l*, pg. 1170
Ardila, Jaime, Treas.--General Motors de Mexico, S.A. de C.V., Mexico, Mexico; *U.S. Public*, pg. 722
Arditte, Edward C., V.P. & Treas.--Textron Inc., Providence, RI; *U.S. Public*, pg. 1588
Ardrey, J. Kelly, Treas.--ProEquities, Inc., Birmingham, AL; *U.S. Public*, pg. 1336
Arena, Daniel E., Treas. & Asst. Sec.--General Microwave Corporation, Amityville, NY; *U.S. Public*, pg. 717
Arena, M. S., V.P. & Treas.--Alcon Laboratories, Inc., Fort Worth, TX; *Int'l*, pg. 916
Arena, Nick F., Exec. V.P. & Treas.--The Flood Company, Hudson, OH; *U.S. Private*, pg. 414
Arenoibia, Marta, Treas.--Northwestern Meats Inc., Miami, FL; *U.S. Private*, pg. 807
Arfmann, Bruce L., Chief Fin. Officer, Treas. & Sec.--Colorado MEDtech, Inc., Boulder, CO; *U.S. Public*, pg. 401
Argudin, Bernard, Chief Fin. Officer & Treas.--Republic National Bank of Miami, Miami, FL; *U.S. Private*, pg. 924
Arjaluoto, Ilkka, V.P.-Fin. & Legal Admin.--Rautaruukki Oy, Helsinki, Finland; *Int'l*, pg. 1088
Armbrister, Gary, Asst. Treas. & Asst. Sec.--Stanley Furniture Co. Inc., Stanleytown, VA; *U.S. Public*, pg. 1508
Armstrong, Richard V., Asst. Treas.--Mauna Kea Agribusiness Co., Inc., Papaikou, HI; *U.S. Private*, pg. 190
Armstrong, William J., V.P. & Treas.--Ingersoll-Rand Company, Woodcliff Lake, NJ; *U.S. Public*, pg. 876
Arna, Nick F., V.P. & Treas.--ALLTEL Service Corporation, Hudson, OH; *U.S. Public*, pg. 56
Arnheim, Walter R., V.P. & Treas.--Mobil Oil Corporation, Fairfax, VA; *U.S. Public*, pg. 1118
Arnold, Barbara M., Treas.--Petroleum Products Corp., Middletown, PA; *U.S. Private*, pg. 859
Arnold, William, Chief Fin. Officer & Treas.--McCoy Group Inc., Shullsburg, WI; *U.S. Private*, pg. 720
Arns, Joy R., Asst. Treas.--Consolidated Freightways Corp., Menlo Park, CA; *U.S. Public*, pg. 435
Aronson, Robert C., Asst. Treas.--Northeast Utilities, Berlin, CT; *U.S. Public*, pg. 1194
Aronstan, Peter J., Asst. Treas.--Northern Telecom Limited, Brampton, Canada; *Int'l*, pg. 968
Arrigo, Joseph F., Chief Fin. Officer, Exec. V.P. & Treas.--UIS, Inc., Jersey City, NJ; *U.S. Private*, pg. 1113
Arriola, Dennis V., V.P. & Treas.--Pacific Enterprises, Los Angeles, CA; *U.S. Public*, pg. 1249
Arriola, Dennis V., V.P. & Treas.--Southern California Gas Co., Los Angeles, CA; *U.S. Public*, pg. 1249
Arth, Jerry, V.P.-Fin. & Admin., Controller & Treas.--Malco Products, Inc., Barberton, OH; *U.S. Private*, pg. 698
Arthur, James, Asst. Treas.--Norcal Waste Systems, San Francisco, CA; *U.S. Public*, pg. 1188
Artz, Frederick A., Treas.--Spang & Company, Butler, PA; *U.S. Private*, pg. 1020
Arvantinos, S.C., Sr. V.P. & Treas.--Hope's Architectural Products Inc., Jamestown, NY; *U.S. Private*, pg. 538
Asami, Tadahiro, Treas.--Asian Development Bank, Manila, Philippines; *Int'l*, pg. 88
Asch, David, Exec. V.P.-Treas. & Sec.--Twincraft, Inc., Winooski, VT; *U.S. Private*, pg. 1111
Asch, Michael A., Pres., Chief Oper. Officer, Chief Fin. Officer & Treas.--Rexx Environmental Corp., New York, NY; *U.S. Public*, pg. 1384
Asche, Ronald D., V.P.-Bus. Support, Controller & Treas.--Nebraska Public Power District, Columbus, NE; *U.S. Private*, pg. 789
Aschelman, Steven J., Treas.--Pharmacia & Upjohn, Kalamazoo, MI; *Int'l*, pg. 1048
Aschinger, Carl J., Jr., Chm. Bd., Pres. & Chief Exec. Officer--Columbus Show Case Company, Columbus, OH; *U.S. Private*, pg. 257
Aselage, Susan Seabury, V.P., Asst. Treas. & Sec.--Sabreliner Corporation, Saint Louis, MO; *U.S. Private*, pg. 959
Ash, Bernice, Treas.--Sam Ash Music Corp., Hicksville, NY; *U.S. Private*, pg. 88
Ashby, Michael, Chief Fin. Officer, V.P.-Fin./Admin. & Treas.--Bytex Corporation, Westborough, MA; *U.S. Public*, pg. 1522
Ashby, Scott, Asst. Treas.--McCall Oil & Chemical Corp., Portland, OR; *U.S. Private*, pg. 719
Ashenberg, Wayne R., Chief Fin. Officer, Sr. V.P. & Treas.--Sentry Insurance, A Mutual Company, Stevens Point, WI; *U.S. Private*, pg. 985
Ashley, Ken, Treas. & Sec.--CCH Incorporated, Riverwoods, IL; *Int'l*, pg. 1513
Ashley, Ken, V.P. & Treas.-True North Communications Inc.--True North Communications Inc., Chicago, IL; *U.S. Public*, pg. 1641
Ashley, Kenneth, Chief Fin. Officer & Sec.--National R.V., Inc., Perris, CA; *U.S. Public*, pg. 1159
Askegaard, Paul, Treas.--Aetrium Inc., Saint Paul, MN; *U.S. Public*, pg. 27
Askey, Darrel F., Chief Fin. Officer, V.P.-Fin., Treas. & Sec.--Celestial Seasonings, Boulder, CO; *U.S. Public*, pg. 319
Astle, Frederic C., V.P.-Fin. & Treas.--A-P-A Transport Corp., North Bergen, NJ; *U.S. Private*, pg. 2
Astrup, Dan, Treas. & Sec.--Astrup Drugs, Inc., Austin, MN; *U.S. Private*, pg. 93
Athens, Zack G., Chief Fin. Officer, Sr. V.P. & Treas.--Columbia Universal Life Insurance Company, Austin, TX; *U.S. Public*, pg. 79
Atieh, Michael G., Treas.--Merck & Co., Inc., Whitehouse Station, NJ; *U.S. Public*, pg. 1090
Atkin, J.G. (Tom), Treas.--Alcoa of Australia Limited, Melbourne, Australia; *U.S. Public*, pg. 62
Atkins, Deborah J., Asst. Treas.--ALLTEL Corporation, Little Rock, AR; *U.S. Public*, pg. 55
Atkins, William, V.P. & Treas.--Relm Communications, Inc., Indianapolis, IN; *U.S. Public*, pg. 1376
Atkinson, A. Kelley, Pres., Chief Exec. Officer & Treas.--United HealthCare of Georgia, Inc., Atlanta, GA; *U.S. Public*, pg. 1678
Attardi, Charles, Jr., Sec. & Treas.--North Carolina Equipment Co., Raleigh, NC; *U.S. Private*, pg. 804
Attebury, Ronald L., Chief Fin. Officer & Treas.--Norbest, Inc., Midvale, UT; *U.S. Private*, pg. 801
Attwood, Anthony R., Treas.--Minorco, Luxembourg, Luxembourg; *Int'l*, pg. 77
Atwater, Peter J., Treas.--Banc One Corporation, Columbus, OH; *U.S. Public*, pg. 172
Atwater, Peter W., Exec. V.P. & Treas.--First USA, Inc., Dallas, TX; *U.S. Public*, pg. 174
Atwood, Charles, V.P. & Treas.--Harrah's Entertainment, Inc., Memphis, TN; *U.S. Public*, pg. 790
Aubin, Denis, V.P. & Treas.--Cambior Inc., Montreal, Canada; *Int'l*, pg. 253
Aubrey, Richard, Treas.--Bank of the West, Walnut Creek, CA; *Int'l*, pg. 163
Auguste, Macdonald, Treas.--Rayonier Inc., Stamford, CT; *U.S. Public*, pg. 1363
Auray, Delbert L., Pres. & Treas.--Bridgeport Fittings, Inc., Stratford, CT; *U.S. Private*, pg. 168
Auriemmo, Frank J., V.P. & Treas.--USLIFE Corporation, New York, NY; *U.S. Public*, pg. 77
Aurnou, Michael W., Chief Fin. Officer & Treas.--Yenkin-Majestic Paint Corporation, Columbus, OH; *U.S. Private*, pg. 1195
Ausburn, Kevin R., Chief Fin. Officer, Treas. & Sec.--Southern Missouri Containers Inc., Springfield, MO; *U.S. Private*, pg. 1017
Austell, Barbara, Sr. V.P.-Fin. & Treas.--Aramark Corp., Philadelphia, PA; *U.S. Private*, pg. 78
Austin, Joan D., Exec. V.P. & Treas.--A-Dec, Inc., Newberg, OR; *U.S. Private*, pg. 2
Austin, Lawrence, V.P.-Fin., Sec. & Treas.--Miniature Precision Components, Walworth, WI; *U.S. Private*, pg. 750

Austin, Michael D., Treas.--CILCORP Inc., Peoria, IL; *U.S. Public*, pg. 367

Austin, Michael D., Treas.--CILCORP Investment Management Inc., Peoria, IL; *U.S. Public*, pg. 367

Austin, Michael D., Treas.--CILCORP Ventures Inc., Peoria, IL; *U.S. Public*, pg. 367

Austin, William, Treas.--Credit Union National Association, Madison, WI; *U.S. Private*, pg. 288

Austin, William M., Treas.--Boeing Services, Inc., Khamis Mushayt, Saudi Arabia; *U.S. Public*, pg. 242

Austin, William M., Treas.--Construcciones Aeronauticas, SA, Madrid, Spain; *U.S. Public*, pg. 242

Avallone, Lynda M., Treas.--Augat, Inc., Mansfield, MA; *U.S.* Public, pg. 1597

Avatlone, Michael N., Treas.--Boston Energy Technology Group, Inc., Boston, MA; *U.S. Public*, pg. 247

Avery, James, Treas. & Sec.--Schumacher-Dugan Construction, West Chester, OH; *U.S. Private*, pg. 973

Avery, O. Keith, Treas. & Sec.--Presto Food Stores, Inc., Plant City, FL; *U.S. Private*, pg. 882

Avril, Mary J., V.P. & Treas.--Sakrete, Inc., Cincinnati, OH; *U.S. Private*, pg. 961

Avril, Vicki L., Treas.--Inland Steel Industries, Inc., Chicago, IL; *U.S. Public*, pg. 879

Ayers, Larry G., Chief Fin. Officer, V.P.-Fin., Treas. & Sec.--Southern Electronics Corporation, Tucker, GA; *U.S. Public*, pg. 1490

Ayers, Larry G., Chief Fin. Officer, V.P.-Fin., Sec. & Treas.--Southern Electronics Distributors International, Tucker, GA; *U.S. Public*, pg. 1490

Aylesworth, William A., Chief Fin. Officer, Sr. V.P. & Treas.--Texas Instruments Incorporated, Dallas, TX; *U.S. Public*, pg. 1585

Aymar, Mary M., Asst. Treas. & Branch Mgr.--Valley National Bank, Dover, NJ; *U.S. Public*, pg. 1706

Azzara, Cynthia O., Chief Fin. Officer, Sr. V.P. & Treas.--CRIIMI MAE, Rockville, MD; *U.S. Public*, pg. 459

Babcock, Theodore A., V.P., Treas. & Asst. Sec.--Long Island Lighting Company, Hicksville, NY; *U.S. Public*, pg. 1013

Babich, George, Jr., V.P.-Finance & Treas.--The Pep Boys-Manny, Moe & Jack, Philadelphia, PA; *U.S. Public*, pg. 1276

Bacciocco, James S., Treas.--The Kendall Company, Mansfield, MA; *U.S. Public*, pg. 1647

Bach, Harold H., Jr., Chief Fin. Officer, Chief Acctg. Officer, Treas.& V.P.-Fin.--WMS Industries Inc., Chicago, IL; *U.S.* Public, pg. 1727

Bachman, Jay S., Sr. V.P., Treas. & Mgr.-Corp. Devel.--First Security Corporation, Salt Lake City, UT; *U.S. Public*, pg. 637

Bachman, Lee W., V.P.-Fin. & Treas.--Bachman's, Inc., Minneapolis, MN; *U.S. Private*, pg. 109

Bachmann, Rolf C., Treas.--Alusuisse-Lonza America Inc., New York, NY; *Int'l*, pg. 67

Bachmeier, Ronald M., Chief Fin. Officer, V.P.-Fin. & Treas.--Xerxes Corporation, Minneapolis, MN; *U.S. Private*, pg. 1194

Bacigalupo, John W., Treas. & Sec.--Kelly-Moore Paint Company, Inc., San Carlos, CA; *U.S. Private*, pg. 613

Back, Phillipa Foster, Treas.--EMI Group plc, London, United Kingdom; *Int'l*, pg. 426

Backes, Wilfried, Chief Fin. Officer, Exec. V.P. & Treas.--Osram Sylvania Inc., Malvern, PA; *Int'l*, pg. 1245

Backstrom, John W., Treas.--LaSalle-Talman Bank, Chicago, IL; *Int'l*, pg. 11

Bacon, Carol L., Controller & Treas.--Town & Country Homes, Fort Worth, TX; *U.S. Public*, pg. 319

Bacon, Neil F., Chief Fin. Officer, Treas. & Controller--Homasote Company, Trenton, NJ; *U.S. Public*, pg. 831

Baden, Marvin, V.P.-Mktg. & Sls., Treas. & Sec.--Producers Rice Mill Inc., Stuttgart, AR; *U.S. Private*, pg. 888

Badlato, Charles, Treas.--Aeroflex Incorporated, Plainview, NY; *U.S. Public*, pg. 23

Baehni, Heinz, Treas.--Alusuisse-Lonza Holding Ltd., Zurich, Switzerland; *Int'l*, pg. 66

Baer, Kenneth A., V.P. & Treas.--Dixon Ticonderoga Company, Heathrow, FL; *U.S. Public*, pg. 514

Baer, Suzanne V., V.P. & Treas.--The Louisiana Land and Exploration Company, New Orleans, LA; *U.S. Public*, pg. 269

Baeten, Ralph G., Treas.--WPS Resources Corp., Green Bay, WI; *U.S. Public*, pg. 1728

Baeten, Ralph G., V.P. & Treas.--Wisconsin Public Service Corporation, Green Bay, WI; *U.S. Public*, pg. 1728

Baeten, Ralph G., Treas.--WPS Energy Services, Inc., Green Bay, WI; *U.S. Public*, pg. 1728

Baeten, Ralph G., Treas.--WPS Power Development, Inc., Green Bay, WI; *U.S. Public*, pg. 1728

Baeten, Ralph G., Treas.--WPS Leasing, Inc., Green Bay, WI; *U.S. Public*, pg. 1728

Bagley, Patrick J., V.P.-Fin. & Treas.--Matlack Systems, Inc., Wilmington, DE; *U.S. Public*, pg. 1057

Bagley, Patrick J., Chief Fin. Officer, V.P.-Fin. & Treas.--Rollins Truck Leasing Corp., Wilmington, DE; *U.S. Public*, *pg. 1405*

Bagwell, Leonard, Treas.--Greenwood Mills, Inc., Greenwood, SC; *U.S. Private*, pg. 479

Baham, Susan E., Chief Fin. Officer & Sr. V.P.--First Financial Holdings, Inc., Charleston, SC; *U.S. Public*, pg. 634

Bahlman, Robert, Chief Fin. Officer, V.P. & Treas.--Midwest Express Airlines, Inc., Oak Creek, WI; *U.S. Public*, pg. 1111

Bahlman, Robert S., Chief Fin. Officer, Sr. V.P. & Treas.--Midwest Express Holdings, Inc., Oak Creek, WI; *U.S. Public*, pg. 1111

Bailey, Alan, Sr. V.P. & Treas.--Paramount Pictures Corporation, Los Angeles, CA; *U.S. Private*, pg. 776

Bailey, Bob E., Treas.--E-Z Serve Corp., Houston, TX; *U.S. Public*, pg. 540

Bailey, Jack, Treas.--Smith-Lee Co., Inc., Oneida, NY; *U.S. Private*, pg. 1009

Bailey, John, Chm. Bd., Pres., Chief Exec. & Fin. Officer & Treas.--Cal Emblem Labels, Inc., Fresno, CA; *U.S. Private*, pg. 199

Bailey, Steven T., Chief Fin. Officer & Treas.--PIMCO Advisors, Stamford, CT; *U.S. Public*, pg. 1296

Bailey, Ted, Chief Oper. Officer, V.P. & Treas.--Heavy Machines, Inc., Memphis, TN; *U.S. Private*, pg. 518

Bailie, John, Treas.--Grassland Equipment & Irrigation Corp., Blasdell, NY; *U.S. Private*, pg. 471

Bain, D.W., Treas. & Controller--Cyanamid Canada Inc., Markham, Canada; *U.S. Public*, pg. 80

Baines, Bruce, Sr. V.P. & Treas.--Starbanc Corporation, Cincinnati, OH; *U.S. Public*, pg. 1510

Baines, Richard, Grp. Treas.--Bayer UK Ltd., Newbury, United Kingdom; *Int'l*, pg. 175

Baioni, Louis, Exec. V.P. & Treas.--Dunavant Enterprises, Inc., Memphis, TN; *U.S. Private*, pg. 346

Baird, Donn, Treas.--Kalamazoo Holdings, Inc., Kalamazoo, MI; *U.S. Private*, pg. 606

Baird, Thomas P., Chief Fin. Officer, V.P. & Treas.--Comarco, Inc., Yorba Linda, CA; *U.S. Public*, pg. 406

Bajalia, George A., Chief Fin. Officer & Treas.--Wickes Inc., Vernon Hills, IL; *U.S. Public*, pg. 1391

Bakehorn, Peggy, Treas. & Sec.--American Stationery Co., Inc., Peru, IN; *U.S. Private*, pg. 62

Baker, Calvin A., Treas.--Badger Service Co., Milwaukee, WI; *U.S. Public*, pg. 1773

Baker, Calvin A., Chief Fin. Officer & Teas.--Wisconsin Michigan Investment Corp., Milwaukee, WI; *U.S. Public*, pg. 1773

Baker, Calvin H., Chief Fin. Officer & Treas.--Wispark Corporation, Milwaukee, WI; *U.S. Public*, pg. 1773

Baker, Calvin H., Chief Fin. Officer & Treas.--Wisvest Corporation, Milwaukee, WI; *U.S. Public*, pg. 1773

Baker, Calvin H., Chief Fin. Officer & Treas.--Witech Corporation, Milwaukee, WI; *U.S. Public*, pg. 1773

Baker, Calvin H., Treas.--Syndesis Development Corp., Milwaukee, WI; *U.S. Public*, pg. 1773

Baker, Dave, Asst. Treas.--Material Sciences Corporation, Elk Grove Village, IL; *U.S. Public*, pg. 1056

Baker, Dave, Asst. Treas.--The Middleby Corporation, Rolling Meadows, IL; *U.S. Public*, pg. 1109

Baker, Dennis W., Treas.--CF Industries, Inc., Long Grove, IL; *U.S. Private*, pg. 193

Baker, James E., Chief Fin. Officer, V.P.-Fin. & Treas.--Guy Gannett Communications, Portland, ME; *U.S. Private*, pg. 439

Baker, Kent G., Treas.--Addison Insurance Company, Lombard, IL; *U.S. Public*, pg. 1677

Baker, Kent G., Treas.--Insurance Brokers & Managers, Inc., New Orleans, LA; *U.S. Public*, pg. 1677

Baker, Kent G., Treas.--Addison Insurance Agency, Lombard, IL; *U.S. Public*, pg. 1677

Baker, Kent G., Treas.--Crabtree Premium Finance, Lombard, IL; *U.S. Public*, pg. 1677

Baker, Mark J., V.P.-Fin. & Treas.--Roppe Corp., Fostoria, OH; *U.S. Private*, pg. 944

Baker, Newton D., Exec. V.P. & Treas.--Access Corporation, Cincinnati, OH; *Int'l*, pg. 994

Baker, T.F., Chief Fin. Officer, Grp. V.P.-Fin. & Treas.--Harvest States Cooperatives, Saint Paul, MN; *U.S. Private*, pg. 508

Baker, Wayne, Sec. & Asst. Treas.--Athey Products Corporation, Wake Forest, NC; *U.S. Public*, pg. 142

Baker, William D., Chief Fin. Officer & Treas.--The JPM Company, Lewisburg, PA; *U.S. Public*, pg. 919

Bakst, Bernard, V.P. & Treas.--Philips Components-Discrete Products Division, Slatersville, RI; *Int'l*, pg. 1054

Balardi, Patrick E., Chief Fin. Officer, V.P. & Treas.--The Lion Brewery, Inc., Wilkes-Barre, PA; *U.S. Public*, pg. 1000

Balcer, Brian, Treas. & Controller--Lyman Lumber Company, Excelsior, MN; *U.S. Private*, pg. 683

Baldwin, Daniel, Treas.--Science Applications International Corp., San Diego, CA; *U.S. Private*, pg. 975

Baldwin, Sandra Kaye, Pres. & Treas.--H & H Distributing Company, Inc., West Union, IA; *U.S. Private*, pg. 489

Balgenorth, Richard V., Chief Fin. Officer & Treas.--Noble International Ltd., Bloomfield Hills, MI; *U.S. Public*, pg. 1187

Ball-Miller, Paris M., Sec., Controller & Treas.--Troyer Foods, Inc., Goshen, IN; *Int'l*, pg. 619

Ball, Alice, Treas. & Sec.--Air Power, Inc., High Point, NC; *U.S. Private*, pg. 28

Ball, George L., V.P. & Treas.--Parsons Power Group, Inc., Reading, PA; *U.S. Private*, pg. 841

Ball, Peter, Sr. V.P. & Treas.--Topa Insurance Company, Los Angeles, CA; *U.S. Private*, pg. 1091

Ballance, T.S., V.P.-Fin. & Treas.--Somerset Refinery Inc., Somerset, KY; *U.S. Private*, pg. 1013

Ballarini, Roberto, Treas.--Merloni Elettrodomestici S.P.A., Fabriano, Italy; *Int'l*, pg. 860

Ballew, Jeffery A., Sr. V.P., Treas. & Sec.--Crystal Oil Company, Shreveport, LA; *U.S. Public*, pg. 466

Balsano, Bruce, V.P. & Treas.--Allied Van Lines, Inc., Naperville, IL; *Int'l*, pg. 901

Banbury, J. Hunter, Treas.--Cone-Blanchard Machine Company, Windsor, VT; *U.S. Private*, pg. 262

Bancaleiro, Louise, Treas.--Groupe Limagrain, Chappes, France; *Int'l*, pg. 566

Bancroft, Peter J., Controller & Asst. Treas.--Connecticut Water Service, Inc., Clinton, CT; *U.S. Public*, pg. 431

Banks, Michael, V.P. & Treas.--Atlantic Mutual Companies, New York, NY; *U.S. Private*, pg. 95

Banquer, C.S., Controller & Treas.--Acme Refrigeration Of Baton Rouge Inc., Baton Rouge, LA; *U.S. Private*, pg. 13

Barbee, Tom, Controller & Treas.--Feed Service Corp., Ohiowa, NE; *U.S. Private*, pg. 399

Barber, Alice, Controller & Treas.--Frequency and Time Systems, Inc., Beverly, MA; *U.S. Public*, pg. 488

Barber, Dan, V.P.-Fin., Treas. & Sec.--Barnett Millworks, Inc., Theodore, AL; *U.S. Private*, pg. 116

Barber, Donald G., Chief Fin. Officer & Sr. V.P.--Santa Fe International Corporation, Dallas, TX; *Int'l*, pg. 765

Barber, George W., Jr., Chm. Bd.--Barber Dairies, Inc., Birmingham, AL; *U.S. Private*, pg. 115

Barber, Kay A., Chief Fin. Officer, V.P. & Treas.--Merrill Corporation, Saint Paul, MN; *U.S. Public*, pg. 1097

Barberia, Anthony, Exec. V.P. & Treas.--Amloid Corporation, Saddle Brook, NJ; *U.S. Private*, pg. 66

Bardach, Neil M., Chief Fin. Officer & V.P.--The Genlyte Group Incorporated, Union, NJ; *U.S. Public*, pg. 729

Bares, Roger, Controller & Dir.-Fin.--Northland Aluminum Products, Inc., Minneapolis, MN; *U.S. Private*, pg. 805

Barg, David W., V.P. & Treas.--Finger Furniture Company, Inc., Houston, TX; *U.S. Private*, pg. 405

Barger, Donald G., Chief Fin. Officer, V.P. & Treas.--Worthington Industries, Inc., Columbus, OH; *U.S. Public*, pg. 1780

Bariletti, Robert P., Asst. Treas. & Asst. Sec.--Puget Energy Inc., Bothell, WA; *U.S. Public*, pg. 1342

Barker, B.G., Grp. Treas.--Ladbroke Group Plc, London, United Kingdom; *Int'l*, pg. 787

Barker, D.W., Chief Fin. Officer, Treas. & Sec.--Maescher Industries, Inc., Cincinnati, OH; *U.S. Private*, pg. 694

Barker, Joseph F., Chief Fin. Officer & V.P.-Fin.--Haynes International, Inc., Kokomo, IN; *U.S. Public*, pg. 801

Barker, Roger, Chief Fin. Officer, V.P. & Treas.--Buffalo Rock Company, Birmingham, AL; *U.S. Private*, pg. 179

Barker, Thomas W., Jr., Treas.--Sonat Energy Services Company, Birmingham, AL; *U.S. Public*, pg. 1485

Barkhurst, Kenneth, Asst. Treas.--Cherry Electrical Products Corporation, Waukegan, IL; *U.S. Public*, pg. 346

Barkley, Kenneth R., Chief Fin. Officer, Sr. V.P.-Fin. & Treas.--Cagle's Inc., Atlanta, GA; *U.S. Public*, pg. 291

Barkley, Kenneth R., Chief Fin. Officer, Sr. V.P.-Fin. & Treas.--Cagle's Farms Inc., Dalton, GA; *U.S. Public*, pg. 292

Barlow, Carol Ann, Treas. & Sec.--Macristy Industries, Inc., New Britain, CT; *U.S. Private*, pg. 693

Barlow, Charles, V.P.-Fin. & Treas.--Sinclair Oil Corp., Salt Lake City, UT; *U.S. Private*, pg. 1003

Barlow, James, Controller & Treas.--Wynn's International, Inc., Orange, CA; *U.S. Public*, pg. 1782

Barna, Peter, Treas. & Principal Acctg. Officer--Crompton & Knowles Corporation, Stamford, CT; *U.S. Public*, pg. 459

Barnard, Aubrey D., Sec., Treas. & Controller--SouthTrust Corporation, Birmingham, AL; *U.S. Public*, pg. 1491

Barnes, James, Chief Fin. Officer, V.P. & Treas.--Wohlert Corp., Lansing, MI; *U.S. Private*, pg. 1185

Barnes, Randall C., Sr. V.P. & Treas.--PepsiCo, Inc., Purchase, NY; *U.S. Public*, pg. 1276

Barnett, Carol A., V.P.-Corp. Plng. & Treas.--Jockey International, Inc., Kenosha, WI; *U.S. Private*, pg. 588

Barnett, David R., Treas.--Bender Shipbuilding & Repair Company, Inc., Mobile, AL; *U.S. Private*, pg. 132

Barnett, Steven B., Chief Fin. Officer, Sr. V.P. & Treas.--Rag Shops, Inc., Hawthorne, NJ; *U.S. Public*, pg. 1358

Barney, D.W., V.P. & Treas.--Union Camp Corporation, Wayne, NJ; *U.S. Public*, pg. 1665

Barney, Nancy, Treas. & Sec.--Simonds-Shields-Theis Grain Co., Kansas City, MO; *U.S. Private*, pg. 1001

Barnish, Steven, V.P.-Fin.--Duferco Steel Inc., Laurence Harbor, NJ; *U.S. Private*, pg. 345

Barocas, Leon, V.P., Treas. & Sec.--Santee Print Works, Inc., New York, NY; *U.S. Private*, pg. 965

Baron, Stanley, Treas.--Cortec Group, New York, NY; *U.S. Private*, pg. 277

Barone, Anthony, Chief Fin. Officer, V.P. & Treas.--Tower Automotive, Inc., Grand Rapids, MI; *U.S. Public*, pg. 1625

Barone, Elaine, Pres. & Treas.--Coken Company, Inc., Providence, RI; *U.S. Private*, pg. 250

Baroue, Daren, Treas. & Sec.--Watkins Contracting, Inc., San Diego, CA; *U.S. Public*, pg. 1384

Barr, Michael, Pres. & Treas.--Barr Electric Corporation, Wheeling, IL; *U.S. Private*, pg. 117

Barr, Thomas D., Treas.--Barr & Barr, Inc., New York, NY; *U.S. Private*, pg. 117

Barravecchia, John R., Chief Fin. Officer & Exec. V.P.--Franchise Finance Corp. of America, Scottsdale, AZ; *U.S. Public*, pg. 679

Barrett, Dennis, V.P.-Fin. & Treas.--Minnesota Brewing Company, Saint Paul, MN; *U.S. Public*, pg. 1115

Barrett, Emmett F., V.P. & Treas.--Lubriplate Div. of Fiske Bros. Refining Co., Newark, NJ; *U.S. Private*, pg. 409

Barrett, JoAnn, V.P.-Opers., Treas. & Sec.--Samuel Bingham Co, Bloomingdale, IL; *U.S. Private*, pg. 144

Barrett, John R., Treas.--Instron Corporation, Canton, MA; *U.S. Public*, pg. 882

Barrett, Kent E., Sr. V.P., Controller & Treas.--American General Life & Accident Insurance Co., Nashville, TN; *U.S. Public*, pg. 76

Barrett, Paul, Chief Fin. Officer, & Sr. V.P.-Fin.--Bill's Dollar Stores, Inc., Ridgeland, MS; *U.S. Private*, pg. 144

Barrett, William J., Sec. & Asst. Treas.--Supreme Industries, Inc., Goshen, IN; *U.S. Public*, pg. 1541

Barrette, Raymond, Exec. V.P., Chief Fin. Officer & Treas.--American Automobile Insurance Co., Creve Coeur, MO; *Int'l*, pg. 59

Barrocas, Alberto, Pres. & Treas.--Injection Footwear Corp., Miami, FL; *U.S. Private*, pg. 563

Barroso, Marjorie, Comptroller & Treas.--Maryland & Virginia Milk Producers Cooperative Association, Inc., Reston, VA; *U.S. Private*, pg. 711

Barrow, M.J., Sr. V.P.-Fin. & Admin., Treas., Sec. & Dir.--M.S. Carriers, Inc., Memphis, TN; *U.S. Public*, pg. 1027

Barry, Debby, Controller & Treas.--Vance Industries, Inc., Chicago, IL; *U.S. Private*, pg. 1133

Barry, James A., Chief Fin. Officer, V.P. & Treas.--American Vanguard Corporation, Newport Beach, CA; *U.S. Public*, pg. 94

Barry, Ralph, Chief Fin. Officer, V.P., Treas. & Sec.--Imaging Technologies Corp., San Diego, CA; *U.S. Public*, *pg. 870*

Bart, Todd, Chief Fin. Officer, Treas. & Sec.--Panaco, Inc., Kansas City, MO; *U.S. Public*, pg. 1255

Bartell, Gilbert G., Chief Fin. Officer & V.P.-Fin.--Conso Products Company, Union, SC; *U.S. Public,* pg. 434

Bartels, Michael G., V.P., Sec. & Treas.--The East Ohio Gas Co., Cleveland, OH; *U.S. Public,* pg. 435

Bartenstein, Jeff C., Controller, Treas. & Sec.--Alaska Industrial Hardware Inc., Anchorage, AK; *U.S. Private,* pg. 31

Bartholomeusz, Michael, Treas.--Signet Group plc, London, United Kingdom; *Int'l,* pg. 1248

Bartine, Allen, Treas. & Sec.--O'Bryan Brothers Inc., Chicago, IL; *U.S. Private,* pg. 810

Bartles, Gwen, Treas.--TWC of Florida, Incorporated, Saint Petersburg, FL; *U.S. Public,* pg. 1755

Bartlett, Noel, Treas.--Helena Laboratories Corporation, Beaumont, TX; *U.S. Private,* pg. 519

Barwick, John O., Chief Fin. Officer, V.P.-Fin. & Treas.--Carmike Cinemas, Inc., Columbus, GA; *U.S. Public,* pg. 305

Basch, Saul, Chief Fin. Officer, Sr. V.P. & Treas.--The Hartford Steam Boiler Inspection & Insurance Co., Hartford, CT; *U.S. Public,* pg. 795

Basham, Roxann R., Treas. & Corp. Sec.--Black Hills Corporation, Rapid City, SD; *U.S. Public,* pg. 235

Basler, William L., Chm. Bd., Chief Exec. Officer & Treas.--Basler Electric Company, Highland, IL; *U.S. Private,* pg. 121

Bass, Norma, Treas. & Sec.--The Parman Corporation, Nashville, TN; *U.S. Private,* pg. 840

Bast, Brian, Pres. & Treas.--Bast Chevrolet Inc., Seaford, NY; *U.S. Private,* pg. 122

Bast, Ralph, Mgr.-Treas./Portfolio Mngmt.--European Investment Bank, Luxembourg, Luxembourg; *Int'l,* pg. 465

Bastianen, Ben C.M., Treas.--Johnson Controls, Inc., Milwaukee, WI; *U.S. Public,* pg. 932

Bateman, Daniel, Chief Fin. Officer & Treas.--Bateman Brothers Lumber Co., Inc., New Britain, PA; *U.S. Private, pg. 122*

Batkin, Sanford L., Chm. Bd, Chief Exec. Officer & Treas.--Universal Folding Box Company, Inc., Hoboken, NJ; *U.S.* Private, pg. 1127

Battaglia, Dena M., Asst. V.P.-Fin. & Treas.--Sevenson Environmental Services, Inc., Niagara Falls, NY; *U.S. Public,* pg. 1462

Battaglia, Thomas S., V.P. & Treas.--American Standard Inc., Piscataway, NJ; *U.S. Public,* pg. 91

Battan, Thomas A., Comptroller & Treas.--W.L. Hailey & Company, Inc., Nashville, TN; *U.S. Private,* pg. 494

Batteast, Robert V., Chm. Bd., Pres. & Treas.--Batteast Construction Company, Inc., South Bend, IN; *U.S. Private,* pg. 123

Batten, James R., Chief Fin. Officer & V.P.-Fin.--O'Reilly Automotive Inc., Springfield, MO; *U.S. Public,* pg. 1230

Batty, John C., V.P. & Treas.--VLSI Technology, Inc., San Jose, CA; *U.S. Public,* pg. 1703

Bauer, James P., V.P.-Fin. & Treas.--Small Parts, Inc., Logansport, IN; *U.S. Private,* pg. 1006

Bauer, Mimi, Treas. & Sec.--Basic Food International Inc., Fort Lauderdale, FL; *U.S. Private,* pg. 121

Bauer, Ruth, Treas.--Hutchinson Technology Inc., Hutchinson, MN; *U.S. Public,* pg. 850

Bauerle, Robert, Chief Fin. Officer, Sr. V.P. & Treas.--American Bureau of Shipping, New York, NY; *U.S. Private,* pg. 51

Baugh, Gene A., Sr. V.P. & Treas.--ITT Educational Services, Inc., Indianapolis, IN; *U.S. Public,* pg. 1512

Baugher, John O., Pres. & Treas.--Baugher Chevrolet-Buick Inc., Waynesboro, VA; *U.S. Private,* pg. 123

Baughman, George, Vice Chm. & Treas.--Plastomer Corp., Livonia, MI; *U.S. Private,* pg. 872

Baulig, George L., Treas. & Sec.--South Jersey Industries, Inc., Folsom, NJ; *U.S. Public,* pg. 1488

Baulig, George L., Sec. & Asst. Treas.--South Jersey Gas Co., Folsom, NJ; *U.S. Public,* pg. 1488

Baum, W.A., III, Sec. & Treas.--W.A. Baum Company, Inc., Copiague, NY; *U.S. Private,* pg. 124

Bauman, John, Treas.--Semtech Corporation, Newbury Park, CA; *U.S. Public,* pg. 1456

Bauman, W.A., Pres. & Treas.--Enger-Kress Company, West Bend, WI; *U.S. Private,* pg. 376

Baumann, Henry J., Treas.--The Testor Corporation, Rockford, IL; *U.S. Public,* pg. 1358

Baumgardner, Roger L., V.P., Treas. & Sec.--Roanoke Gas Company, Roanoke, VA; *U.S. Public,* pg. 1392

Baumgardner, Vicki L., V.P.-Fin. & Treas.--Churchill Downs, Inc., Louisville, KY; *U.S. Public,* pg. 356

Baumgarte, Virginia, Sec. & Treas.--The Wiegmann Company, Freeburg, IL; *U.S. Public,* pg. 845

Bausch, Thomas P., Treas.--Battle Mountain Gold Company, Houston, TX; *U.S. Public,* pg. 193

Baveis, Edward, Sec. & Treas.--Bell Atlantic Paging, Parsippany, NJ; *U.S. Public,* pg. 203

Baxter, Mary Beth, Treas. & Asst. Sec.--Lynch Telephone Corporation, Greenwich, CT; *U.S. Public,* pg. 1022

Baxter, Randy P., Sec. & Treas.-Fin. Information Officer--Armada Corporation, Detroit, MI; *U.S. Private,* pg. 82

Baxter, Randy P., Treas. & Sec.--Hoskins Mfg. Co., Detroit, MI; *U.S. Private,* pg. 83

Bayley, Joanne, Treas. & Sec.--Robert E. Bayley Construction, Seattle, WA; *U.S. Private,* pg. 125

Bazaire, Keith, Treas.--Grocers Baking Co., Grand Rapids, MI; *U.S. Private,* pg. 482

Beach, Juanita, Sec. & Treas.--Beach Mold & Tool Inc., New Albany, IN; *U.S. Private,* pg. 125

Beagle, Gary J., Treas.--Canadian Occidental Petroleum Ltd., Calgary, Canada; *U.S. Public,* pg. 1210

Beak, Susan, Asst. Treas. & Cash Mngmt.--Bank of the Hudson, Poughkeepsie, NY; *U.S. Public,* pg. 1319

Beal, Karen, Sec. & Treas.--E.R. Probyn Ltd., New Westminster, Canada; *Int'l,* pg. 1071

Beal, Karen, Sec. & Treas.--Cedartone Specialties, Kent, WA; *Int'l,* pg. 1071

Beall, Pamela K.M., V.P., Treas., & Asst. Sec.--OHM Corporation, Findlay, OH; *U.S. Public,* pg. 1207

Beall, Pamela K.M., V.P., Treas. & Asst. Sec.--OHM Remediation Services Corp., Findlay, OH; *U.S. Public,* pg. 1208

Beall, Pamela K.M., Treas. & Asst. Sec.--OHM International, Inc., Findlay, OH; *U.S. Public,* pg. 1208

Bean, Delcie D., Pres., Chief Exec. Officer & Treas.--D.D. Bean & Sons Co., Jaffrey, NH; *U.S. Private,* pg. 126

Beans, Patrick E., Chief Fin. Officer, V.P., Treas. & Sec.--National Research Corporation, Lincoln, NE; *U.S. Public, pg. 1159*

Bear, James W., Sr. V.P. & Treas.--Consolidated Products, Inc., Indianapolis, IN; *U.S. Public,* pg. 436

Bear, James W., Sr. V.P. & Treas.--SNS Investment Company, Indianapolis, IN; *U.S. Public,* pg. 436

Bear, James W., Chief Fin. Officer, Sr. V.P. & Treas.--Steak 'n Shake, Inc., Indianapolis, IN; *U.S. Public,* pg. 437

Beard, Peggy, Chief Fin. Officer, V.P.-Fin. & Treas.--Schwab Corp., Lafayette, IN; *U.S. Private,* pg. 974

Beard, Thomas, Chief Fin. Officer, Sr. V.P. & Treas.--Petroleum Inc., Wichita, KS; *U.S. Private,* pg. 858

Beardsley, Diane, Sr. V.P.-Fin. & Treas.--Leiner Health Products, Inc., Carson, CA; *U.S. Private,* pg. 659

Beary, Michelle, Treas. & Sec.--Marsh Company, Belleville, IL; *U.S. Private,* pg. 707

Beatty, Ellen, V.P.-Fin. & Treas.--Quaker State Corporation, Irving, TX; *U.S. Public,* pg. 1348

Beatty, Stephen E., Chief Fin. Officer & Treas.--The Dwyer Group, Inc., Waco, TX; *U.S. Public,* pg. 537

Beauch, S.R., Treas. & Dir.-Fin.--Veda Incorporated, Alexandria, VA; *U.S. Private,* pg. 1136

Beauchamp, Patrick L., Chm. Bd., Pres. & Treas.--Beauchamp Distributing Company, Compton, CA; *U.S. Private,* pg. 127

Beaudoin, Marc, Treas. & Sec.--Hancock Lumber, Inc., Casco, ME; *U.S. Private,* pg. 498

Beaulieu, J.P., Treas.--Canadian National Railway Company, Montreal, Canada; *Int'l,* pg. 258

Beaulieu, Jon C., Treas. & Sec.--Anderson Trucking Service Inc., Saint Cloud, MN; *U.S. Private,* pg. 72

Beaver, William S., V.P. & Treas.--Westvaco Corporation, New York, NY; *U.S. Public,* pg. 1762

Becht, Sue A., Treas.--Duke Energy Corporation, Charlotte, NC; *U.S. Public,* pg. 534

Beck, Jeffrey D., V.P. & Treas.--Advanta Corp., Spring House, PA; *U.S. Public,* pg. 22

Beck, Mark A., Gen. Mgr. & Treas.--Clark Grave Vault Co., Columbus, OH; *U.S. Private,* pg. 243

Beck, Stuart J., Pres., Sec., Treas. & Dir.--Granite Broadcasting Corporation, New York, NY; *U.S. Public,* pg. 759

Beck, Thomas E., V.P. & Treas.--Bitrek Corporation, Waynesboro, PA; *U.S. Private,* pg. 145

Beck, Thomas E., V.P. & Treas.--Beck Manufacturing, Inc., Waynesboro, PA; *U.S. Private,* pg. 146

Beck, Wendy A., V.P.-Fin. & Treas.--Checkers Drive-In Restaurants, Inc., Clearwater, FL; *U.S. Public,* pg. 342

Becker, C. R., Treas.--South African Breweries, Ltd., Johannesburg, South Africa; *Int'l,* pg. 1286

Becker, Christian, Chief Fin. Officer, Sr. V.P. & Treas.--Comdial Corporation, Charlottesville, VA; *U.S. Public,* pg. 407

Becker, James, Treas.--Red Wing Publishing Company, Red Wing, MN; *U.S. Private,* pg. 915

Becker, Jerome, Chief Fin. Officer, Controller & Treas.--Masters, Inc., Westbury, NY; *U.S. Private,* pg. 714

Becker, Michael, Corp. V.P.-Fin. & Treas.--National Car Rental System, Inc., Minneapolis, MN; *U.S. Public,* pg. 1379

Becker, Paul, V.P., Treas., Gen. Counsel & Sec.--Cosco Industries, Spring Valley, NY; *U.S. Private,* pg. 277

Becker, Stephen, V.P. & Treas.--Southern Wine & Spirits of America Inc., Miami, FL; *U.S. Private,* pg. 1017

Becker, Wolf Dieter, Sec. & Treas.--Traub-Hermle Corporation, Menomonee Falls, WI; *Int'l,* pg. 1419

Beckman, Martin, V.P. & Treas.--Hauenstein & Burmeister, Inc., Minneapolis, MN; *U.S. Private,* pg. 510

Bedard, Mark D., Chief Fin. Officer & Treas.--The Smithfield Companies, Inc., Portsmouth, VA; *U.S. Public,* pg. 1479

Bedenbaugh, James R., V.P., Treas. & Asst. Sec.--Magellan Health Services, Inc., Atlanta, GA; *U.S. Public,* pg. 1033

Bedewi, Elizabeth M., Sr. V.P, Sec. & Treas.--New Mexico & Arizona Land Co., Phoenix, AZ; *U.S. Public,* pg. 1172

Bedford, Henry, V.P. & Treas.--Southwestern/Great American Inc., Nashville, TN; *U.S. Private,* pg. 1018

Bedford, Norman C., Treas.--Beckwith Elevator Co., Boston, MA; *U.S. Private,* pg. 128

Bednarz, Richard, Controller, Treas. & Sec.--Loga Athletic/Headwear Inc., Mattapoisett, MA; *U.S. Public,* pg. 1644

Beebe, Barbara J., Treas.--Sommer Metalcraft Corporation, Crawfordsville, IN; *U.S. Private,* pg. 1013

Beebe, Cheryl K., Treas.--Corn Products International, Inc., Bedford Park, IL; *U.S. Public,* pg. 447

Begnaud, James, Chief Acctg. Officer & Treas.--Allegiant Physician Services, Atlanta, GA; *U.S. Public,* pg. 45

Begue, John S., Comptroller & Treas.--Everlast World Boxing Corp., Bronx, NY; *U.S. Private,* pg. 386

Begue, John S., Comptroller & Treas.--Everlast Sports Manufacturing Corp., Bronx, NY; *U.S. Private,* pg. 386

Behler, Mary G., Treas. & Sec.--Blue Ridge Pressure Castings, Inc., Lehighton, PA; *U.S. Private,* pg. 153

Behrakis, George D., Pres., Chief Exec. Officer & Treas.--Muro Pharmaceutical, Inc., Tewksbury, MA; *U.S. Private,* pg. 767

Behrens, George, V.P.-Fin. & Treas.--Birdsall, Inc., Riviera Beach, FL; *U.S. Public,* pg. 1182

Beich, Brian, Treas.--Upper Midwest Industries, Incorporated, Minneapolis, MN; *U.S. Private,* pg. 1129

Beierwaltes, Martin F., Asst. Treas.--Certified Life Insurance, Chicago, IL; *U.S. Public,* pg. 433

Beirne, Anthony, Treas.--Heller International, Chicago, IL; *U.S. Private,* pg. 520

Beittel, T. Brooks, Sr. V.P., Sec. & Treas.--Duff & Phelps Utilities Income Inc., Chicago, IL; *U.S. Public,* pg. 534

Bell, Bob, Controller & Asst. Treas.--Rose Packing Company, Barrington, IL; *U.S. Private,* pg. 945

Bell, Bradley J., Chief Fin. Officer, V.P. & Treas.--Rohm and Haas Company, Philadelphia, PA; *U.S. Public,* pg. 1403

Bell, Bradley J., V.P. & Treas.--Whirlpool Corporation, Benton Harbor, MI; *U.S. Public,* pg. 1764

Bell, David G., V.P. & Treas.--Canadian Airlines Corporation, Calgary, Canada; *Int'l,* pg. 255

Bell, Donald C., V.P. & Treas.--SENCORP, Newport, KY; *U.S. Private,* pg. 983

Bell, Kayden, V.P., Treas. & Sec.--Arnold Machinery Company, Salt Lake City, UT; *U.S. Private,* pg. 84

Bell, Robert, Treas.--American Foundry Group, Inc., Bixby, OK; *U.S. Private,* pg. 54

Bellande, Rolland, V.P.-Fin. & Investor Rels.--Chargeurs, Paris, France; *Int'l,* pg. 280

Beller, Laurence, Treas.--Amsco School Publications, Inc., New York, NY; *U.S. Private,* pg. 67

Bellgraph, Tom, V.P.-Fin.--Hastings Manufacturing Company, Hastings, MI; *U.S. Public,* pg. 798

Bellina, Gerald, Chm. Bd., V.P.-Engrng. & Treas.--DAQ Electronics Inc., Piscataway, NJ; *U.S. Private,* pg. 300

Bellino, Joseph P., Chief Fin. Officer & Treas.--Steel Technologies Inc., Louisville, KY; *U.S. Public,* pg. 1513

Bellis, William J., Chief Fin. Officer, V.P.-Fin., Controller & Treas.--AGR International, Inc., Butler, PA; *U.S. Private,* pg. 5

Belrahmi, Amal, Chief Fin. Officer & Treas.--Hachette Filipacchi USA, New York, NY; *Int'l,* pg. 794

Belskus, Jeff, Exec. V.P. & Treas.--Hulman & Company, Terre Haute, IN; *U.S. Private,* pg. 547

Belzer, Burton E., Chm. Bd., Chief Exec. Officer, Chief Fin. Officer & Treas.--TCI Aluminum, Gardena, CA; *U.S. Private,* pg. 1063

Belzer, Burton E., Chm. Bd., Chief Exec. Officer, Cheif Fin. Officer & Treas.--E-Z Lok, Gardena, CA; *U.S. Private,* pg. 1063

Belzile, Andre, V.P.-Fin. & Treas.--The Cascades Group, Kingsey Falls, Canada; *Int'l,* pg. 273

Benac, William P., V.P. & Treas.--Electronic Data Systems Corporation, Plano, TX; *U.S. Public,* pg. 569

Benchimol, Albert A., V.P. & Treas.--Reliance Group Holdings, Inc., New York, NY; *U.S. Public,* pg. 1374

Bender, Brian W., Sr. V.P., Controller & Asst. Treas.--Younkers, Inc., Des Moines, IA; *U.S. Public,* pg. 1334

Bender, Michael, Treas., Controller & Chief Accountant--Lewis Drug, Inc., Sioux Falls, SD; *U.S. Private,* pg. 665

Bender, Traci L., Mgr.-Fin. & Risk, Asst. Treas.--Nebraska Public Power District, Columbus, NE; *U.S. Private,* pg. 789

Bendert, Jerry, Treas.--Ring Screw Works, Madison Heights, MI; *U.S. Private,* pg. 931

Benedetti, Stephen J., V.P., Controller & Treas.--Resource Mortgage Capital, Inc., Glen Allen, VA; *U.S. Public,* pg. 1382

Benedict, Shirley, V.P.-Fin.--Winona Knits, Winona, MN; *U.S. Private,* pg. 1183

Benfield, James, V.P. & Treas.--Transammonia Inc., New York, NY; *U.S. Private,* pg. 1096

Bengard, Tom, Treas.--Ocean Mist Farms Corp., Castroville, CA; *U.S. Private,* pg. 811

Benger, Scott C., Sr. V.P.-Fin., Treas. & Sec.--Analytical Surveys, Inc., Colorado Springs, CO; *U.S. Public,* pg. 110

Benners, Morris C., Jr., Sr. V.P.-Treas. Mngmt.--SouthTrust Corporation, Birmingham, AL; *U.S. Public,* pg. 1491

Bennett, G. Kirk, Jr., V.P. & Treas.--Bennett Brothers, Inc., Chicago, IL; *U.S. Private,* pg. 133

Bennett, Gary K., Controller & Treas.--Gerber Scientific, Inc., South Windsor, CT; *U.S. Public,* pg. 740

Bennett, Joel, Treas.--HD Vest Financial Services, Irving, TX; *U.S. Public,* pg. 770

Bennett, Nancy, Treas.--Nature's Recipe Pet Foods, Corona, CA; *U.S. Private,* pg. 789

Bennett, Peter N., V.P & Treas.--SHL Systemhouse, Ottawa, Canada; *Int'l,* pg. 1154

Bennitt, Fred Y., Sec. & Treas.--Sylvan Inc., Saxonburg, PA; *U.S. Public,* pg. 1545

Benno, Eli, V.P., Treas. & Sec.--Trading Port, Inc., Albany, NY; *U.S. Private,* pg. 1095

Benoit, David C., V.P.-Fin. & Treas.--Connecticut Water Service, Inc., Clinton, CT; *U.S. Public,* pg. 431

Benschip, Gary J., Treas.--Curtiss-Wright Corp., Lyndhurst, NJ; *U.S. Public,* pg. 469

Benschip, Gary J., Treas.--Thomas & Betts/Amerace, Brooksville, FL; *U.S. Public,* pg. 1598

Benson, Betty, Treas. & Sec.--Delaware Electric Co-Op, Greenwood, DE; *U.S. Private,* pg. 321

Benson, Craig R., Chm. Bd. & Treas.--Cabletron Systems, Inc., Rochester, NH; *U.S. Public,* pg. 288

Benson, David F., Pres. & Treas.--Meditrust Corporation, Needham, MA; *U.S. Public,* pg. 1081

Bentley, Nancy S., Treas. & Sec.--Associated Administrators, Inc., Portland, OR; *U.S. Private,* pg. 918

Bentley, P., Grp. Treas.--Grand Metropolitan Plc, London, United Kingdom; *Int'l,* pg. 408

Bentley, Rita P., Controller & Treas.--Daniel F. Young, Inc., New York, NY; *U.S. Private,* pg. 1200

Benton, Murray, Treas. & Dir.-Personnel--Mid South Sales, Helena, AR; *U.S. Private,* pg. 744

Benz, Edward, Controller & Asst. Treas.--Wheaton Van Lines, Inc., Indianapolis, IN; *U.S. Private,* pg. 1171

Beran, Robin D., Asst. Treas.--Caterpillar Inc., Peoria, IL; *U.S. Public,* pg. 315

Berdass, Margo, Treas.--Bermo, Inc., Circle Pines, MN; *U.S. Private,* pg. 136

Bereford, Gerry, Treas.--Fishery Products International Ltd., Saint Johns, Canada; *Int'l,* pg. 492

Beren, Eugene J., Treas. & Asst. Sec.--Merchant Capital Group Ltd., Chicago, IL; *U.S. Private,* pg. 732

Berey, Mark H., Chief Fin. Officer, Sr. V.P.-Fin. & Treas.--Giant Food Inc., Landover, MD; *U.S. Public,* pg. 741

Berg, Jack H., Pres., Chief Exec. Officer & Treas.--Serfilco, Ltd., Northbrook, IL; *U.S. Private,* pg. 985

Bergan, John W., V.P. & Treas.--Morgan Construction Co., Worcester, MA; *U.S. Private*, pg. 761
Berger, Bryan, Sec. & Treas.--Smith Farms, Inc., Flatonia, TX; *U.S. Private*, pg. 1008
Berger, Ezra, Treas.--Shepaug Corporation, New York, NY; *U.S. Private*, pg. 993
Berger, Morris W., Chief Fin. Officer--Careers USA Inc., Philadelphia, PA; *U.S. Private*, pg. 209
Berger, Robert J., Chief Fin. Officer, Sr. V.P. & Treas.--ONBANCorp, Inc., Syracuse, NY; *U.S. Public*, pg. 631
Bergeron, John, Treas. & Dir.-Taxes--Ionics, Incorporated, Watertown, MA; *U.S. Public*, pg. 912
Bergethon, Ragnar, Treas.--Champion Enterprises, Inc., Auburn Hills, MI; *U.S. Public*, pg. 332
Bergin, Chris, Treas.--Waters Corporation, Milford, MA; *U.S. Public*, pg. 1745
Berglund, S.W., Treas.--Spectra-Physics USA, Inc., Blue Bell, PA; *Int'l*, pg. 1289
Bergman, David R., Pres. & Treas.--Processed Plastic Company, Montgomery, IL; *U.S. Private*, pg. 888
Bergonzi, John A., Controller & Asst. Treas.--Equitable Resources, Inc., Pittsburgh, PA; *U.S. Public*, pg. 589
Berkley, Herbert R., Treas. & Sec.--Berkliff Corporation, New York, NY; *U.S. Private*, pg. 135
Berkley, Richard L., Treas. & Sec.--Tension Envelope Corp., Kansas City, MO; *U.S. Private*, pg. 1077
Berkow, David W., Treas.--Mercury Finance Co., Lake Forest, IL; *U.S. Public*, pg. 1093
Berlin, Marvin, Treas. & Sec.--New York Carpet World, Dalton, GA; *U.S. Public*, pg. 1464
Berman, Milton I., Chm. Bd., Pres. & Treas.--Avibank Mfg., Inc., Burbank, CA; *U.S. Private*, pg. 101
Berman, Robert, Treas. & Sec.--Metpar Corp., Westbury, NY; *U.S. Private*, pg. 735
Berman, Steven L., Exec. V.P., Treas. & Sec.--R&B, Inc., Colmar, PA; *U.S. Public*, pg. 1354
Bermudez, George E., Treas.--Logicon, Inc., Torrance, CA; *U.S. Public*, pg. 1198
Bernard, Walter, Treas.--La Salle County Farm Supply, Ottawa, IL; *U.S. Private*, pg. 640
Bernhardt, Robert J., Treas.--Joseph J. Henderson & Son, Inc., Gurnee, IL; *U.S. Private*, pg. 521
Berns, Joseph, V.P.-Fin. & Treas.--Plymouth Rubber Company, Inc., Canton, MA; *U.S. Public*, pg. 1311
Bernstein, Emil S., Chief Fin. Officer, Exec. V.P. & Treas.--Chelsea Industries, Inc., Peabody, MA; *U.S. Private*, pg. 231
Berresford, D.A., Treas.--Clyde Petroleum plc, Ledbury, United Kingdom; *Int'l*, pg. 577
Berry, Allen W., Controller & Treas.--Wehco Media, Inc., Little Rock, AR; *U.S. Private*, pg. 1159
Berry, Anna, V.P. & Treas.--Southwire Company, Carrollton, GA; *U.S. Private*, pg. 1019
Berry, James, Treas.--Sachs Holding Company, Chesterfield, MO; *U.S. Private*, pg. 959
Berry, Jon M., Sr. V.P. & Treas.--Jacor Communications, Inc., Covington, KY; *U.S. Public*, pg. 922
Berry, Sylvia J., Treas.--Fisca Oil Co., Inc., Westwood, KS; *U.S. Private*, pg. 408
Bersoff, Marilyn, Sr. V.P.-Admin. & Sec.--BTG, Inc., Fairfax, VA; *U.S. Public*, pg. 164
Bertelsen, Jeff, Chief Fin. Officer, V.P.-Fin. & Treas.--Computer Network Technology Corporation, Minneapolis, MN; *U.S. Public*, pg. 421
Bertholome, Serge, Treas.--Banque Nationale de Belgique, Brussels, Belgium; *Int'l*, pg. 162
Bertrand, Robert N., Chief Fin. Officer, V.P.-Fin. & Treas.--Industrial Acoustics Company, Inc., Bronx, NY; *U.S. Public*, pg. 875
Bertsch, James L., V.P. & Treas.--Armco Inc., Pittsburgh, PA; *U.S. Public*, pg. 131
Bertsche, Dawn, V.P. & Treas.--Clopay Corporation, Cincinnati, OH; *U.S. Public*, pg. 766
Bertschy, Terri, Treas.--Wal-Mart Stores, Inc., Bentonville, AR; *U.S. Public*, pg. 1732
Besing, Christopher S., Chief Fin. Officer, V.P. & Treas.--Action Performance Companies, Inc., Phoenix, AZ; *U.S. Public*, pg. 17
Bessant, Thomas A., Jr., Chief Fin. Officer, Sr. V.P. & Treas.--Cash America International, Inc., Fort Worth, TX; *U.S. Public*, pg. 312
Besse, Melissa, Treas.--Northern Michigan Veneers, Inc., Gladstone, MI; *U.S. Private*, pg. 805
Besse, Robert, Sr. V.P.--Coleman Powermate Compressors, Springfield, MN; *U.S. Private*, pg. 691
Bethurum, Shirley A., Treas. & Sec.--Bethurum Research & Development, Inc., Texas City, TX; *U.S. Private*, pg. 141
Bethurun, Shirley A., V.P., Treas. & Sec.--Bushwhacker Associates, Inc., Texas City, TX; *U.S. Private*, pg. 141
Betlach, Douglas J., Chief Fin. Officer, V.P. & Treas.--Dycom Industries, Inc., Palm Beach Gardens, FL; *U.S. Public*, pg. 538
Beumer, Dale, V.P.-Treasury & Investor Rels.--Medtronic, Inc., Minneapolis, MN; *U.S. Public*, pg. 1082
Beutler, Tom, Sec., Treas. & Controller--Beutler Heating & Air Conditioning Inc., Sacramento, CA; *U.S. Private*, pg. 141
Beverage, Bill M., Chief Fin. Officer, Treas. & Sec.--Outdoor Systems, Inc., Phoenix, AZ; *U.S. Public*, pg. 1235
Beyer, Richard P., Chief Fin. Officer, V.P.-Fin. & Treas.--Barrister Information Systems Corporation, Buffalo, NY; *U.S. Public*, pg. 192
Bhandari, Narottam K., Treas.--The Dial Corporation, Phoenix, AZ; *U.S. Public*, pg. 505
Bialick, David W., Treas. & Asst. Sec.--Computer Horizons Corp., Mountain Lakes, NJ; *U.S. Public*, pg. 421
Biasuzzi, John M., Sr. V.P. & Treas.--Citizens Savings Bank, Providence, RI; *Int'l*, pg. 1132
Biasuzzi, John M., Sr. V.P. & Treas.--Citizens Trust Company, Providence, RI; *Int'l*, pg. 1132
Bibler, Laurie, Chief Fin. Officer, Treas. & Sec.--Bibler Brothers, Inc., Russellville, AR; *U.S. Private*, pg. 142
Bickelhaupt, Herbert E., Treas.--Curt G. Joa, Inc., Sheboygan Falls, WI; *U.S. Private*, pg. 588
Biederman, Tom, Controller, Treas. & Sec.--Coleman Cadillac Inc., Bethesda, MD; *U.S. Private*, pg. 251
Biehl, Michael F., Treas. & Dir.-Fin.--Oglebay Norton Company, Cleveland, OH; *U.S. Public*, pg. 1213
Bielsker, Andrea, Treas.--Kansas City Power & Light Company, Kansas City, MO; *U.S. Public*, pg. 943
Bielun, John A., Chief Fin. Officer, Sr. V.P. & Treas.--Alta Gold Co., Henderson, NV; *U.S. Public*, pg. 58
Bienhoff, Donald, Treas.--Lozier Corporation, Omaha, NE; *U.S. Private*, pg. 679
Bienvenu, Wayne, Treas. & Sec.--Turnbull Enterprises, Inc., Baltimore, MD; *U.S. Private*, pg. 1109
Biewenga, J.K., Treas.--Esso N.V./S.A., Maasmechelen, Belgium; *U.S. Public*, pg. 602
Biggar, John R., Treas.--Power Markets Development Company, Allentown, PA; *U.S. Public*, pg. 1244
Biggart, James H., Treas.--Hubbell Incorporated, Orange, CT; *U.S. Public*, pg. 844
Biggs, Ricky, Treas. & Sec.--Edmonson Wheat Growers, Inc., Edmonson, TX; *U.S. Private*, pg. 364
Bilek, George J., V.P.-Fin. & Treas.--Juno Lighting, Inc., Des Plaines, IL; *U.S. Public*, pg. 935
Bilenki, Walter R., Treas.--DoFasco, Inc., Hamilton, Canada; *Int'l*, pg. 414
Billick, Steven M., Chief Fin. Officer, Sr. V.P. & Treas.--Signature Brands USA, Inc., Solon, OH; *U.S. Public*, pg. 1472
Billingham, Stephen, Dr., Treas.--BICC plc, London, United Kingdom; *Int'l*, pg. 120
Billy, Jacques, Treas.--Fotolabo S.A., Lausanne, Switzerland; *Int'l*, pg. 501
Binder, M., Treas. & Reg. Comptroller--Hilton Canada Inc., Montreal, Canada; *Int'l*, pg. 788
Binder, Susan A., V.P. & Treas.--ICC Industries, Inc., New York, NY; *U.S. Private*, pg. 553
Binkley, Kevin C., V.P. & Treas.--Jacobson Stores Inc., Jackson, MI; *U.S. Public*, pg. 922
Binkley, Ruth, Controller & Treas.--Cummings Inc., Nashville, TN; *U.S. Private*, pg. 295
Bintzler, Juile, V.P. & Treas.--BTG, Inc., Fairfax, VA; *U.S. Public*, pg. 164
Birch, Paul, Chief Fin. Officer, Treas. & Exec. V.P.-Fin. & Admin.--PSDI, Bedford, MA; *U.S. Private*, pg. 828
Birdsong, Jerre E., Treas.--AmerenUE, Saint Louis, MO; *U.S. Public*, pg. 66
Birdsong, Randall G., Controller, Treas. & Sec.--Spencer Companies Inc., Huntsville, AL; *U.S. Private*, pg. 1024
Birkhold, Shelly, Controller--United Aircraft Products, Forest, OH; *U.S. Public*, pg. 1262
Birney, Kathleen, Asst. Treas.--Arbor Drugs, Inc., Troy, MI; *U.S. Public*, pg. 126
Biro, Jon C., Sr. V.P. & Treas.--ICO, Inc., Houston, TX; *U.S. Public*, pg. 853
Biro, Jon C., Controller & Treas.--Wedco Technology, Bloomsbury, NJ; *U.S. Public*, pg. 854
Bishop, Earl, Treas. & Sec.--Free Service Tire Company, Inc., Johnson City, TN; *U.S. Private*, pg. 425
Bishop, Janet M., V.P. & Treas.--White Rock Distilleries Inc., Lewiston, ME; *U.S. Private*, pg. 1173
Bishop, M., Treas. & Fin. Controller--Scholl Plc, Newton, United Kingdom; *Int'l*, pg. 1209
Bishop, Rodney L., V.P. & Treas.--Solutia Inc., Saint Louis, MO; *U.S. Public*, pg. 1483
Bittker, David, Treas.--National Lumber Co., Warren, MI; *U.S. Private*, pg. 785
Bivona, Frank J., Chief Fin. Officer, Sr. V.P. & Treas.--AMBAC Financial Group, Inc., New York, NY; *U.S. Public*, pg. 62
Bixler, C.K., Treas.--Ranch-Way Feed Inc., Fort Collins, CO; *U.S. Private*, pg. 908
Bixler, R. Jeffrey, V.P., Gen. Counsel & Sec.--Health Care & Retirement Corporation, Toledo, OH; *U.S. Public*, pg. 801
Bjerg, Nils, Treas.--Monrovia Nursery Co., Azusa, CA; *U.S. Private*, pg. 757
Black, Jeff, Pres. & Treas.--Black & Co., Decatur, IL; *U.S. Private*, pg. 146
Black, Kenneth A., Chief Fin. Officer, Grp. V.P.-Corp. Fin., Controller & Treas.--First Citizens Banc Shares, Inc., Raleigh, NC; *U.S. Public*, pg. 628
Blackwell, Don W., Chief Fin. Officer, V.P. & Treas.--VASA Brougher, Inc., Indianapolis, IN; *Int'l*, pg. 464
Blagge, Diane L., V.P. & Treas.--Blagge Enterprises, Rancho Cordova, CA; *U.S. Private*, pg. 148
Blair, Gary J., V.P.-Admin. & Treas.--Blade Communications, Inc., Toledo, OH; *U.S. Private*, pg. 147
Blair, Ian D., V.P. & Treas.--A.M. Todd Company, Kalamazoo, MI; *U.S. Private*, pg. 1089
Blake, William, V.P. & Treas.--White Castle System, Inc., Columbus, OH; *U.S. Private*, pg. 1171
Blake, William, V.P. & Treas.--White Castle International Company, Columbus, OH; *U.S. Private*, pg. 1172
Blalock, Vance, Treas.--Western Gas Resources, Inc., Denver, CO; *U.S. Public*, pg. 1758
Blancard, Ken, V.P. & Treas.--The Airolite Company, Marietta, OH; *U.S. Private*, pg. 29
Blanchard, Craig A., V.P.-Fin., Controller & Treas.--Sheldons' Inc., Antigo, WI; *U.S. Private*, pg. 992
Blanchard, Daniel G., Treas. & Dir.-Corp. Devel.--Forest Oil Corporation, Denver, CO; *U.S. Public*, pg. 670
Blanchard, William C., Treas. & Sec.--Wm. Blanchard Co., Springfield, NJ; *U.S. Private*, pg. 148
Blandford, Jeff, V.P. & Treas.--TLPartnership, Dallas, TX; *U.S. Public*, pg. 1224
Blanding, Donald C., Treas.--Helian Health Group, Inc., Monterey, CA; *U.S. Public*, pg. 1715
Blank, David M., Treas.--The Cleveland Electric Illuminating Company, Independence, OH; *U.S. Public*, pg. 645
Blank, David M., Treas.--The Toledo Edison Company, Toledo, OH; *U.S. Public*, pg. 645
Blank, Steve, V.P. & Treas.--Ultramar Diamond Shamrock Corporation, San Antonio, TX; *U.S. Public*, pg. 1663
Blatt, Mike, Controller & Treas.--Future Foam, Inc., Council Bluffs, IA; *U.S. Private*, pg. 433
Blattner, Stephen C., Chief Fin. Officer, Treas. & Sec.--D.H. Blattner & Sons, Inc., Avon, MN; *U.S. Private*, pg. 148
Blauer, Charles, Chm. Bd., Pres.,Chief Exec. Officer & Treas.--Blauer Manufacturing Co., Inc., Boston, MA; *U.S. Private*, pg. 149
Blazer, Dennis, Treas.--Plastic Moldings Corp., Cincinnati, OH; *U.S. Private*, pg. 871
Bleier, Frederick L., Treas. & Controller--IP Timberlands, Ltd., Purchase, NY; *U.S. Public*, pg. 904
Bleser, Howard, Treas.--Wellcraft Marine Corp., Sarasota, FL; *U.S. Private*, pg. 447
Blethen, William, Treas.--Seattle Times Company, Seattle, WA; *U.S. Private*, pg. 980
Blickens, Robert, V.P.-Fin., Treas. & Controller--Komline-Sanderson Engineering Corp., Peapack, NJ; *U.S. Private*, *pg. 631*
Block, Thomas R., Pres. & Treas.--Block Drug Company, Inc., Jersey City, NJ; *U.S. Public*, pg. 236
Blocksom, David, Treas. & Sec.--Ohio Machinery Co., Cleveland, OH; *U.S. Private*, pg. 812
Blommer, Joseph, Pres. & Treas.--Blommer Chocolate Co., Chicago, IL; *U.S. Private*, pg. 150
Blonder, Lloyd, Chief Fin. Officer, Sr. V.P. & Treas.--National Technical Systems, Inc., Calabasas, CA; *U.S. Public*, pg. 1161
Bloom, David B., Chief Fin. Officer & Treas.--Bloom Electric Services, Inc., Oklahoma City, OK; *U.S. Private*, pg. 150
Bloom, Larry L., Chief Fin. Officer & Treas.--Lee Enterprises, Incorporated, Davenport, IA; *U.S. Public*, pg. 983
Blum, Bernard, Treas.--Colin Service Systems, Inc., White Plains, NY; *U.S. Private*, pg. 252
Blum, Donald R., Treas. & Asst. Sec.--The Weitz Company, Inc., Des Moines, IA; *U.S. Private*, pg. 1160
Blumberg, Donald D., Chm. Bd. & Treas.--Blumberg Communications Inc., Minneapolis, MN; *U.S. Public*, pg. 305
Blumenschein, George, V.P.-Fin. & Treas.--Peerless Tube Company, Bloomfield, NJ; *U.S. Public*, pg. 1269
Blurton, Jerry H., V.P. & Treas.--Halliburton Company, Dallas, TX; *U.S. Public*, pg. 775
Blurton, Jerry H., V.P. & Treas.--Halliburton Energy Services, Inc., Dallas, TX; *U.S. Public*, pg. 776
Bluth, Thomas, V.P., Treas. & Sec.--Catalina Lighting, Inc., Miami, FL; *U.S. Public*, pg. 314
Bluvas, William J., Treas.--Mutual of Omaha Investor Services, Inc., Omaha, NE; *U.S. Private*, pg. 770
Blythe, P.J., Grp. Treas.--Christies International plc, London, United Kingdom; *Int'l*, pg. 289
Bobel, Mary, Chief Fin. Officer--Genus Inc., Sunnyvale, CA; *U.S. Public*, pg. 732
Bobo, John D., V.P. & Treas.--Blissfield Manufacturing Company, Blissfield, MI; *U.S. Private*, pg. 149
Bockart, Richard L., V.P., Treas. & Sec.--Oshman's Sporting Goods, Inc., Houston, TX; *U.S. Public*, pg. 1233
Bodanza, Joseph F., Sr. V.P.-Fin. & Treas.--Boston Gas Company, Boston, MA; *U.S. Public*, pg. 549
Bodiford, Lowell, Treas. & Sec.--Fort Worth Lumber Company, Fort Worth, TX; *U.S. Private*, pg. 419
Bodor, Paul W., Chief Oper. Officer, Sr. V.P. & Treas.--W & D Securities, Inc., Jersey City, NJ; *U.S. Public*, pg. 925
Boeckman, Steven L., V.P. & Corp. Treas.--ESELCO, Inc., Sault Sainte Marie, MI; *U.S. Public*, pg. 591
Boeckmann, F. Jane, Treas.--Galpin Motors, North Hills, CA; *U.S. Private*, pg. 438
Boegner, Dieter K., V.P.-Fin., Sec. & Treas.--Installation Products Div., Lancaster, PA; *U.S. Public*, pg. 132
Boehm, William J., Chm. Bd., Pres. & Chief Exec. Officer--Connector Manufacturing Company, Hamilton, OH; *U.S. Private*, pg. 264
Boehmler, E. William, V.P. & Treas.--International Paper Company, Purchase, NY; *U.S. Public*, pg. 901
Boeshart, Frank, V.P., Controller & Treas.--Terminal Grain Corp., Sioux City, IA; *U.S. Private*, pg. 1077
Boesinger, Richard M., V.P.-Opers.--Republic Automotive Parts, Inc., Brentwood, TN; *U.S. Public*, pg. 1377
Boettcher, Gerald, Exec. V.P. & Treas.--Kalmbach Publishing Co., Waukesha, WI; *U.S. Private*, pg. 606
Bogan, Robert, Treas.--Buquet & Le Blanc Inc., Baton Rouge, LA; *U.S. Private*, pg. 181
Bogden, John M., V.P., Treas. & Sec.--On Technology Corporation, Cambridge, MA; *U.S. Public*, pg. 1225
Boggess, Jerry W., Treas.--HCBeck, Dallas, TX; *U.S. Private*, pg. 490
Bognon, Pierre, Treas.--Marsh & McLennan Companies, Inc., New York, NY; *U.S. Public*, pg. 1048
Boh, Stephen H., Treas.--Boh Bros. Construction Co., LLC, New Orleans, LA; *U.S. Private*, pg. 154
Bohmann, James R., Sr. V.P. Corp. Devel. & Treas.--Payco American Corporation, Brookfield, WI; *U.S. Public*, pg. 1267
Bohn, Jim, Chief Fin. Officer, V.P.-Fin., Treas. & Sec.--Intermatic Inc., Spring Grove, IL; *U.S. Private*, pg. 567
Bohs, G. Lee, Chief Fin. Officer & Exec. V.P.--Right Management Consultants, Inc., Philadelphia, PA; *U.S. Public*, pg. 1390
Boillargeon, Marcel, Comptroller & Treas.--Telebec Ltee, Anjou, Canada; *Int'l*, pg. 116
Boisseree, Brian, Treas. & Mgr.-Investor Rels.--Integrated Device Technology, Inc., Santa Clara, CA; *U.S. Public*, pg. 884
Boland, Michael, Treas. & Sec.--David Boland, Inc., Titusville, FL; *U.S. Private*, pg. 154
Bolanos, Jorge Walter, Chief Fin. Officer, Sr. V.P. & Treas.--H.B. Fuller Company, Saint Paul, MN; *U.S. Public*, pg. 686
Boldt, James R., Chief Fin. Officer & V.P.--Computer Task Group, Inc. (CTG), Buffalo, NY; *U.S. Public*, pg. 423
Boldt, Jim, Chief Fin. Officer, Treas. & Mgr.-Fin.--Austin Powder Co., Cleveland, OH; *U.S. Private*, pg. 100
Bole, R. Mark, Asst. V.P. & Asst. Treas.--Atlantic Southeast Airlines Inc., Atlanta, GA; *U.S. Public*, pg. 144

Bolin, Susan C., Chief Fin. Officer, Exec. V.P., Treas. & Sec.--The O'Boise Corporation, Oak Brook, IL; *U.S. Private*, pg. 810
Bolka, B.Y., V.P. & Treas.--Heraeus/Kulzer, Inc. - Dental Products Div., South Bend, IN; *Int'l*, pg. 616
Bollinger, Philip, Treas.--Chemical Coatings, Inc., Hudson, NC; *U.S. Public*, pg. 1357
Bollinger, Tom, Treas. & Mgr.-Sls.--The John C. Groub Company Inc., Seymour, IN; *U.S. Private*, pg. 484
Bolt, C.S., Jr., Treas.--Dan River Inc., Danville, VA; *U.S. Public*, pg. 478
Bolt, John, Treas.--Kellogg Company, Battle Creek, MI; *U.S. Public*, pg. 947
Bomberger, D.L., Sr. V.P. & Treas.--Guarantee Life Insurance Co., Omaha, NE; *U.S. Public*, pg. 768
Bomes, Allen S., Asst. Treas.--ABC, Inc, New York, NY; *U.S. Public*, pg. 511
Bond, David M., Controller & Asst. Treas.--American Dairy Queen Corporation, Minneapolis, MN; *U.S. Public*, pg. 220
Bond, Rod C., Treas.--Manitoba Hydro, Winnipeg, Canada; *Int'l*, pg. 834
Bond, Rodney S., Chief Fin. Officer, Treas. & Sec.--VTEL Corporation, Austin, TX; *U.S. Public*, pg. 1703
Bondi, Allen, Treas.--Kelso-Burnett Company, Rolling Meadows, IL; *U.S. Private*, pg. 613
Bondy, Timothy J., Chief Fin. Officer & V.P.--Northwestern Steel & Wire Co., Sterling, IL; *U.S. Public*, pg. 1201
Bonebrake, Merrill, Treas.--M.A.B. Paints, Terre Haute, IN; *U.S. Private*, pg. 175
Boner, Jim, Treas.--Deardorff-Jackson Company, Oxnard, CA; *U.S. Private*, pg. 319
Boniello, Michael P., Controller--Vester Corporation, Newtown Square, PA; *U.S. Private*, pg. 86
Bonn, Allan, Treas. & Sec.--F.H. Bonn Company, Springfield, OH; *U.S. Private*, pg. 156
Bonney, Mark J., Chief Fin. Officer, V.P.-Fin. & Admin. & Treas.--Zygo Corporation, Middlefield, CT; *U.S. Public*, pg. 1795
Boo, Dennis, Treas.--Plasti-Kote Company Inc., Medina, OH; *U.S. Private*, pg. 870
Boone, William L., V.P.-Fin., Treas. & Sec.--Kenan Transport Company, Chapel Hill, NC; *U.S. Public*, pg. 949
Booraem, Jonathan W., Treas.--Central Vermont Public Service Corporation, Rutland, VT; *U.S. Public*, pg. 327
Booth, Barbara, Controller & Treas.--Space Master International, Atlanta, GA; *U.S. Private*, pg. 1019
Booth, Erich J., Chief Fin. Officer & Treas.--Apple South, Inc., Madison, GA; *U.S. Public*, pg. 121
Booth, John, Treas.--Truelove & Maclean Inc., Waterbury, CT; *U.S. Private*, pg. 1107
Bootle, J. Ian, V.P. & Treas.--TransAlta Fly Ash Ltd., Calgary, Canada; *Int'l*, pg. 1416
Boppe, Larry, Chief Fin. Officer & V.P.-Opers.--Toter Incorporated, Statesville, NC; *U.S. Private*, pg. 1092
Borak, Robert L., Treas., Controller & Sec.--McGraw-Hill Securities Trading, Inc., New York, NY; *U.S. Public*, pg. 1071
Borden, R. Lindsay, Asst. Treas.--Owens Country Sausage, Inc., Richardson, TX; *U.S. Public*, pg. 596
Borg, Sandra A., Vice Chm. & Treas.--Macromedia Incorporated, Hackensack, NJ; *U.S. Private*, pg. 693
Borges, Gregory, Treas.--Transmedia Network Inc., Miami, FL; *U.S. Public*, pg. 1631
Borgeson, Steven E., Sr. V.P., Gen. Counsel, Sec., Treas. & Clerk--ChemDesign Corporation, Fitchburg, MA; *Int'l*, pg. 173
Borgh, John N., V.P. & Treas.--IBP, Inc., Dakota City, NE; *U.S. Public*, pg. 852
Borgman, Jerry, Controller & Treas.--Lyon's Restaurants, Inc., Foster City, CA; *U.S. Private*, pg. 684
Born, J. Ivan, V.P., Treas. & Sec.--Beaudry Ford, Inc., Atlanta, GA; *U.S. Private*, pg. 127
Borst, Walter G., Treas.--Delco Chassis Overseas Corporation, Detroit, MI; *U.S. Public*, pg. 723
Borton, Ronald, Treas. & Sec.--Sauder Manufacturing Corporation, Archbold, OH; *U.S. Private*, pg. 967
Boruch, Daniel M., Treas. & Dir.-Fin.--The Associated Press, New York, NY; *U.S. Private*, pg. 92
Borum, James, Treas. & Mgr.-Risk Mngmt.--Airgas, Inc., Radnor, PA; *U.S. Public*, pg. 33
Bos, Pete, Treas.--Burnham, Atlanta, GA; *Int'l*, pg. 686
Bosch, Joel, Treas. & Sec.--Minot Builders Supply Association, Minot, ND; *U.S. Private*, pg. 751
Boschma, Gerald A., Chief Fin. Officer, V.P. & Treas.--Michigan Sugar Company, Saginaw, MI; *U.S. Public*, pg. 873
Boschma, Gerald A., Chief Fin. Officer, V.P. & Treas.--Great Lakes Sugar Company, Fremont, OH; *U.S. Public*, pg. 873
Bosher, David E., V.P. & Treas.--Cadmus Communications Corporation, Richmond, VA; *U.S. Public*, pg. 290
Bosi, Robert A., Mgr.-Treas.--Essex Chemical Corporation, Clifton, NJ; *U.S. Public*, pg. 523
Boslievac, Bill, Treas.--Garnac Grain Co., Inc., Overland Park, KS; *U.S. Private*, pg. 802
Bospflug, Lance F., Chief Fin. Officer, Exec. V.P. & Treas.--T.L. James & Company, Ruston, LA; *U.S. Private*, pg. 580
Bosselman, John, Asst. V.P. & Treas.--Allmerica Securities Trust, Worcester, MA; *U.S. Public*, pg. 54
Bosserman, David N., Chief Fin. Officer, Exec. V.P. & Treas.--Best Software, Inc., Reston, VA; *U.S. Public*, pg. 223
Bostwick, Tony, V.P. & Treas.--Braum Ice Cream Stores Inc., Oklahoma City, OK; *U.S. Private*, pg. 166
Botts, T.M., Treas.--Shell Oil Company, Houston, TX; *Int'l*, pg. 1136
Botvin, George B., Chm. Bd., Chief Exec. Officer & Treas.--ACS Industries, Inc., Woonsocket, RI; *U.S. Private*, pg. 3
Boucher, Andre A., Treas.--Burke Engineering Company, South El Monte, CA; *U.S. Private*, pg. 183
Boucher, David, Sr. V.P.-Fin. & Treas.--Chemical Leaman Corporation, Exton, PA; *U.S. Private*, pg. 233
Bouchillon, J. Dan, Treas.--Town & Country Ford Inc., Louisville, KY; *U.S. Private*, pg. 1093
Boudreau, J.L., Treas. & Asst. Corp. Sec.--The St. Paul Companies, Inc., Saint Paul, MN; *U.S. Public*, pg. 1429
Boughton, Sid, Treas. & Sec.--Jacobsen Manufacturing, Inc., Safety Harbor, FL; *U.S. Private*, pg. 580
Bouknight, John L., V.P.-Assets--The Climatic Corp., Columbia, SC; *U.S. Private*, pg. 246
Bousquet, Henri, Treas.--Total S.A., Paris, France; *Int'l*, pg. 1408
Boutwell, David, V.P. & Controller--Harbert Corporation, Birmingham, AL; *U.S. Private*, pg. 500
Boverizer, J.G.F., Exec. V.P. & Treas.--Lloyds Bank Plc., New York, NY; *Int'l*, pg. 813
Bowen, Barry, Treas.--Charms Company, Chicago, IL; *U.S. Public*, pg. 1621
Bowen, Barry P., Treas.--Tootsie Roll Industries, Inc., Chicago, IL; *U.S. Public*, pg. 1621
Bower, Curtis A., Chief Fin. Officer, Sr. V.P. & Treas.--Parsons Corporation, Pasadena, CA; *U.S. Private*, pg. 841
Bowers, Robert E., V.P.-Fin.--Watt Publishing Co., Mount Morris, IL; *U.S. Private*, pg. 1154
Bowland, Charlotte, Treas.--Petro-Hunt Corporation, Dallas, TX; *U.S. Private*, pg. 858
Bowler, E. Joseph, Sr. V.P. & Treas.--Westamerica Bancorporation, Fairfield, CA; *U.S. Public*, pg. 1756
Bowler, E. Joseph, Sr. V.P. & Treas.--Westamerica Bank, San Rafael, CA; *U.S. Public*, pg. 1756
Bowlus, Douglas, Treas.--ABM Industries, San Francisco, CA; *U.S. Public*, pg. 2
Bowman, Elizabeth, Exec. V.P.-Fin. & Treas.--Universal Forest Products, Inc., Grand Rapids, MI; *U.S. Public*, pg. 1696
Bowman, Kathy, Controller & Treas.--B & K Steel & Supply, Inc., Ogden, UT; *U.S. Private*, pg. 105
Bowman, Max P., Treas. & Mgr.-Risk Mngmnt.--ChemFirst Inc., Jackson, MS; *U.S. Public*, pg. 344
Bowman, Richard F., Chief Fin. Officer, Sr. V.P. & Treas.--First Virginia Banks, Inc., Falls Church, VA; *U.S. Public*, pg. 641
Bowmer, Chris, Treas.--Rexam PLC, London, United Kingdom; *Int'l*, pg. 1106
Bowne, Garret, V.P. & Treas.--Hannaford Bros. Co., Scarborough, ME; *U.S. Public*, pg. 781
Boyce, Sheena, Grp. Treas.--Kingfisher plc, London, United Kingdom; *Int'l*, pg. 733
Boyd, Edson, Treas.--Gendis Inc., Winnipeg, Canada; *Int'l*, pg. 542
Boyd, James G., Treas.--The Intertech Group Inc., Charleston, SC; *Int'l*, pg. 113
Boyd, Paul, Treas.--Clayton Homes, Inc., Knoxville, TN; *U.S. Public*, pg. 382
Boyer de la Giroday, Eric, Head-Treasury & Capital Markets--Bank Brussels Lambert, Brussels, Belgium; *Int'l*, pg. 146
Boyet, Charles, Controller & Treas.--Sigmund Cohn Corp., Mount Vernon, NY; *U.S. Private*, pg. 250
Boylan, John L., Treas. & Asst. Sec.--Lancaster Colony Corporation, Columbus, OH; *U.S. Public*, pg. 976
Boyle, Beatrice W., Sec.--Alico, Inc., La Belle, FL; *U.S. Public*, pg. 41
Boyle, James, Sr. V.P., Controller & Treas.--Broad National Bancorporation, Newark, NJ; *U.S. Public*, pg. 257
Boyle, William, Chief Fin. Officer & V.P.-Fin.--Cubic Corporation, San Diego, CA; *U.S. Public*, pg. 466
Bozard, Richard F., V.P. & Treas.--Owens & Minor Inc., Glen Allen, VA; *U.S. Public*, pg. 1236
Bozynski, David A., V.P. & Treas.--Federal-Mogul Corporation, Southfield, MI; *U.S. Public*, pg. 615
Bozzuto, Michael A., Pres., Chief Exec. Officer & Treas.--Bozzuto's Inc., Cheshire, CT; *U.S. Public*, pg. 249
Braam, James R., Chief Fin. Officer, V.P.-Fin., Treas. & Sec.--Virco Mfg. Corporation, Torrance, CA; *U.S. Public*, pg. 1721
Brace, James, Chief Fin. Officer, V.P. & Treas.--Littelfuse, Inc., Des Plaines, IL; *U.S. Public*, pg. 1001
Bracken, Charles H., Jr., Treas.--The Hillman Company, Pittsburgh, PA; *U.S. Private*, pg. 530
Bracken, George R., V.P. & Treas.--MasTec, Inc., Miami, FL; *U.S. Public*, pg. 1055
Bracken, George R., V.P. & Treas.--National Beverage Corp., Plantation, FL; *U.S. Public*, pg. 1153
Bradbury, David, Asst. Treas.-Tax--Cone Mills Corporation, Greensboro, NC; *U.S. Public*, pg. 430
Braddock, James L., Chm. Bd., Pres. & Treas.--Fastec Industrial, Elkhart, IN; *U.S. Private*, pg. 397
Bradley, Henry H., Chm. Bd. & Treas.--News-Press & Gazette Company, Saint Joseph, MO; *U.S. Private*, pg. 797
Bradley, Robert J., Sr. V.P. & Treas.--Cramer-Krasselt, Milwaukee, WI; *U.S. Private*, pg. 285
Bradley, Scott, Treas.--American Mail-Well Envelope, Englewood, CO; *U.S. Public*, pg. 1038
Bradly, Charles E., Controller & Treas.--Fabreeka International, Inc., Stoughton, MA; *U.S. Private*, pg. 390
Bradshaw, Russ, Chief Fin. Officer & Treas.--Brown & Brown Venture Group, LLC, Mesa, AZ; *U.S. Private*, pg. 172
Brady, Linda, Asst. Treas.--Bank of the Hudson, Poughkeepsie, NY; *U.S. Public*, pg. 1319
Brady, Lona, Treas. & Controller--Army Times Publishing Co., Springfield, VA; *U.S. Public*, pg. 699
Bragin, D.H., Treas.--Winn-Dixie Stores, Inc., Jacksonville, FL; *U.S. Public*, pg. 1771
Braithwaite, Garlan, V.P., Treas. & Sec.--Whitehall Corporation, Dallas, TX; *U.S. Public*, pg. 1765
Brajie, Wayne, Treas.--Baker & McKenzie, Attorneys At Law, Chicago, IL; *U.S. Private*, pg. 111
Brakken, William P., Chief Fin. Officer, Sr. V.P., Treas. & Sec.--Lanoga Corporation, Redmond, WA; *U.S. Private*, pg. 650
Branche, Francois, Treas. & Controller--Calberson, Paris, France; *Int'l*, pg. 1163
Brandin, D.U., Asst. Treas.--Emerson Electric Co., Saint Louis, MO; *U.S. Public*, pg. 572
Brandin, Seymour, Chief Fin. Officer & Treas.--Heyman Corporation, Niles, IL; *U.S. Private*, pg. 524
Brandl, Rainer, Dr., Treas.--Deutsche Post AG, Bonn, Germany; *Int'l*, pg. 407
Brandon, Lynda, Treas. & Sec.--John J. Campbell Co., Inc., Memphis, TN; *U.S. Private*, pg. 204
Brandon, Terry T., Asst. Treas. & Asst. Sec.--Longview Fibre Company, Longview, WA; *U.S. Public*, pg. 1013
Brandt, Richard, Treas.--Symtron Systems, Inc., Fair Lawn, NJ; *U.S. Public*, pg. 1679
Brandt, Sandra K., Div. V.P. & Treas.--Wallace Computer Services, Inc., Lisle, IL; *U.S. Public*, pg. 1735
Branget, Giselle S., Treas.--Labatt Brewing Company Limited, Toronto, Canada; *Int'l*, pg. 679
Brannan, Michael, V.P. & Treas.--Meridian Technology Leasing Services, Deerfield, IL; *U.S. Private*, pg. 732
Brannen, John T., Treas. & Sec.--Mid America International Trucks, Inc., Memphis, TN; *U.S. Private*, pg. 743
Brashaw, Gerald L., V.P., Controller & Treas.--Paragon Electric Co., Inc., Two Rivers, WI; *Int'l*, pg. 1243
Bratt, Janice, Treas.--Brad Foote Gear Works, Inc., Cicero, IL; *U.S. Private*, pg. 417
Braun, Donald L., Chief Oper. Officer, Exec. V.P. & Treas.--Hall Financial Group, Inc., Dallas, TX; *U.S. Private*, pg. 495
Braun, Leonard, Treas.--CGS Industries, Inc., Long Island City, NY; *U.S. Private*, pg. 194
Braunegg, William T., Chief Fin. Officer & Treas.--Dwight Asset Management Company, Burlington, VT; *U.S. Public*, pg. 1673
Brauns, Margaret, V.P. & Treas.--Informix Software, Menlo Park, CA; *U.S. Public*, pg. 876
Brausen, Anthony, V.P. & Treas.--International Multifoods Corporation, Minneapolis, MN; *U.S. Public*, pg. 900
Bray, David E., Treas.--Cone Mills Corporation, Greensboro, NC; *U.S. Public*, pg. 430
Bray, John, Asst. Treas.--Johnston Industries, Inc., Columbus, GA; *U.S. Public*, pg. 933
Breffeilh, Angela, Sr. V.P. & Treas.--Hibernia Corporation, New Orleans, LA; *U.S. Public*, pg. 825
Brehm, John R., V.P. & Treas.--Ipalco Enterprises, Inc., Indianapolis, IN; *U.S. Public*, pg. 912
Breitnauer, Paul J., V.P. & Treas.--Capitol Indemnity Corporation, Madison, WI; *U.S. Public*, pg. 302
Breitnauer, Paul J., Sr. V.P. & Treas.--Capitol Indemnity Corporation, Madison, WI; *U.S. Public*, pg. 302
Breitnauer, Paul J., Sr. V.P. & Treas.--Capitol Specialty Insurance Corporation, Madison, WI; *U.S. Public*, pg. 302
Breittholz, Leo, Treas.--Overseas Military Sales Corporation, Woodbury, NY; *U.S. Private*, pg. 823
Brennan, John M., Sr. V.P. & Treas.--Capitol Broadcasting Co., Inc., Raleigh, NC; *U.S. Private*, pg. 206
Brennan, John V., Chief Fin. Officer, Exec. V.P. & Treas.--Webster Financial Corporation, Waterbury, CT; *U.S. Public*, pg. 1751
Brennan, Peter D., Chief Fin. Officer, V.P. & Treas.--Altron Incorporated, Wilmington, MA; *U.S. Public*, pg. 59
Brennan, Walter, Sec. & Treas.--American Fabrics Company, New York, NY; *U.S. Private*, pg. 53
Brent, David, Grp. Treas.--British Aerospace p.l.c., Farnborough, United Kingdom; *Int'l*, pg. 217
Brenzia, John, Treas.--Elliott Company, Jeannette, PA; *U.S. Private*, pg. 373
Bressler, Bernard, Treas. & Sec.--Gradco Systems, Inc., Las Vegas, NV; *U.S. Public*, pg. 757
Brett, Barbara S., Sr. V.P. & Treas.--Norwest Bank Minnesota N.A., Minneapolis, MN; *U.S. Public*, pg. 1202
Bretza, Thomas, V.P.-Fin. & Treas.--Krier Foods, Inc., Brown Deer, WI; *U.S. Private*, pg. 636
Brewer, Brian, V.P. & Treas.--Xerox Canada Ltd., North York, Canada; *U.S. Public*, pg. 1785
Brewer, O. Gordon, Jr., V.P.-Fin. & Treas.--Ikon Office Solutions, Inc., Malvern, PA; *U.S. Public*, pg. 862
Brewer, Stanley, Treas. & Sec.--Brewer Oil Co., Artesia, NM; *U.S. Private*, pg. 167
Brewer, Stephen E., Asst. Treas.--Great Lakes Chemical Corporation, West Lafayette, IN; *U.S. Public*, pg. 760
Brewer, Tom E., Chief Fin. Officer, Sr. V.P. & Treas.--Hillenbrand Industries, Inc., Batesville, IN; *U.S. Public*, pg. 828
Brice, Joni, Chief Exec. Officer--Heil-Brice Retail Advertising, Newport Beach, CA; *U.S. Private*, pg. 519
Bricker, Marvin, Co-Pres. & Treas.--Hawkeye Steel Products, Inc., Houghton, IA; *U.S. Private*, pg. 511
Bridges, Laura, Treas. & Sec.--Stones, Inc., Bainbridge, GA; *U.S. Private*, pg. 1045
Bridges, P.L., Treas.--Texas-New Mexico Power Co., Fort Worth, TX; *U.S. Public*, pg. 1557
Bridges, Patrick L., Treas.--TNP Enterprises, Inc., Fort Worth, TX; *U.S. Public*, pg. 1557
Bridges, Paul, Pres. & Treas.--Bridges & Company, Inc., Pittsburgh, PA; *U.S. Private*, pg. 168
Bridle, Dale, Grp. Treas.--Burns, Philp & Company Limited, Sydney, Australia; *Int'l*, pg. 236
Brier, Robert M., Treas.--Hanson North America, Woodbridge, NJ; *Int'l*, pg. 593
Brier, Robert M., V.P.-Fin. & Treas.--U.S. Industries, Inc., Iselin, NJ; *U.S. Public*, pg. 1683
Briggs, K. Douglas, Pres. & Treas.--Quincy Mutual Fire Insurance Company, Quincy, MA; *U.S. Private*, pg. 901
Brigham, Thomas, V.P.-Fin. & Treas.--Oakhurst Dairy, Portland, ME; *U.S. Private*, pg. 809
Bright, Clifford J., Chief Fin. Officer & V.P.-Fin.--Interform Corporation, Bridgeville, PA; *U.S. Public*, pg. 333
Brightbill, William R., Pres. & Treas.--Ritter Bros., Inc., Harrisburg, PA; *U.S. Private*, pg. 933
Brighton, Cynthia Z., V.P.-Fin. Services & Treas.--Swisher International Group, Inc., Darien, CT; *U.S. Public*, pg. 1543

Brinek, Alfred, Asst. Treas., Controller--Voest-Alpine Industries, Inc., New York, NY; *Int'l*, pg. 1470
Brink, Steven L., Chief Fin. Officer, Treas. & Sec.--Quiksilver, Inc., Costa Mesa, CA; *U.S. Public*, pg. 1353
Brinkman, Stephen L., Treas.--Gilroy Energy Company, Gilroy, CA; *U.S. Public*, pg. 296
Brinton, G.W., Treas.--Label-Aire Inc., Fullerton, CA; *U.S. Private*, pg. 641
Bristol, Gerald A., V.P.-Fin., Controller & Treas.--Red Wing Shoe Co., Inc., Red Wing, MN; *U.S. Private*, pg. 915
Bristow, T.H., Dir. & Treas.--Moore Business Forms U.K. Ltd., London, United Kingdom; *Int'l*, pg. 889
Britt, Robert D., Chief Fin. Officer, Treas. & Sec.--Green Mountain Coffee Roasters, Inc., Waterbury, VT; *U.S. Public*, pg. 761
Brittain, John S., Jr., Sr. V.P. & Treas.--Sotheby's Holdings Inc., New York, NY; *U.S. Public*, pg. 1487
Brittelli, Brenda S., Chief Fin. Officer, Controller, Treas. & Sec.--Adams Wine Co., Atlanta, GA; *U.S. Private*, pg. 17
Broadbent, John H., Jr., V.P.-Fin. & Treas.--Arrow International, Inc., Reading, PA; *U.S. Public*, pg. 135
Brock, Tony, Exec. V.P. & Treas.--Beadles Lumber Company, Inc., Moultrie, GA; *U.S. Private*, pg. 126
Brockman, Keith W., V.P. & Treas.--Overhead Door Corporation, Dallas, TX; *U.S. Private*, pg. 822
Brocksher, Jean, Sec. & Asst. Treas.--Allright Corporation, Houston, TX; *U.S. Private*, pg. 42
Brocoff, Robert R., Sr. V.P.-Fin.--Kraco Enterprises, Inc., Compton, CA; *U.S. Private*, pg. 634
Brod, Spencer, Treas. & Sec.--Empire Diamond Corporation, New York, NY; *U.S. Private*, pg. 374
Brode, Michael, Pres. & Treas.--Broder Bros. Co., Plymouth, MI; *U.S. Private*, pg. 170
Broder, Jeff, Controller & Treas.--HLB Communications, Inc., Chicago, IL; *U.S. Private*, pg. 491
Brodsky, Bernard, V.P., Treas. & Sec.--Charming Shoppes, Inc., Bensalem, PA; *U.S. Public*, pg. 335
Brodt, John D., Treas. & Sec.--Ohio Valley Electric Corporation, Piketon, OH; *U.S. Private*, pg. 813
Brogan, Cynthia D., V.P. & Asst. Treas.--The Sherwin-Williams Company, Cleveland, OH; *U.S. Public*, pg. 1465
Bronchetti, Robert J., Pres., Chief Exec. Officer & Chief Oper. Officer--National Auto Credit Inc., Solon, OH; *U.S. Public*, pg. 1152
Brookes, H.M., Treas. & Sec--Powerscreen International Plc, Dungannon, United Kingdom; *Int'l*, pg. 1066
Brooks, Dale, Treas.--Harken Energy Corporation, Irving, TX; *U.S. Public*, pg. 785
Brooks, John, V.P. & Treas.--SGS International Certification Services, Inc., Rutherford, NJ; *Int'l*, pg. 1153
Brooks, William R., Chief Fin. Officer, V.P. & Treas--Speedway Motorsports, Inc., Concord, NC; *U.S. Public*, pg. 1498
Brooks, Winfrey, Treas.--General Services Corporation, Richmond, VA; *U.S. Private*, pg. 445
Broome, H. Cuy, Jr., Controller & Treas.--Harry Pepper & Associates, Jacksonville, FL; *U.S. Private*, pg. 851
Brophy, Melonie, Treas.--Maxtor Corporation, Milpitas, CA; *Int'l*, pg. 641
Brostowitz, James, V.P., Treas., Controller & Asst. Sec.--Harley-Davidson, Inc., Milwaukee, WI; *U.S. Public*, pg. 786
Broughton, John R., Treas.--Broughton Foods Company, Marietta, OH; *U.S. Public*, pg. 259
Brousseau, Marc, Treas.--F.X. Coughlin Co., Taylor, MI; *U.S. Private*, pg. 278
Brown, A., Treas.--James Hardie Industries Ltd., Sydney, Australia; *Int'l*, pg. 596
Brown, Anthony S., Exec. V.P., Treas. & Portfolio Mgr.--Pax World Fund Family, Portsmouth, NH; *U.S. Public*, pg. 1266
Brown, C. Merrill, Treas.--F.M. Brown Sons, Inc., Birdsboro, PA; *U.S. Private*, pg. 174
Brown, Chris, Treas. & Sec.--Bruce Foods Corp., Cade, LA; *U.S. Private*, pg. 175
Brown, Craig J., Chief Fin. Officer, Sr. V.P.-Admin. & Treas.--The Standard Register Company, Dayton, OH; *U.S. Public*, pg. 1505
Brown, David A., V.P. & Treas.--Government Employees Financial Corporation, Washington, DC; *U.S. Public*, pg. 220
Brown, Dennis, Chief Fin. Officer, V.P. & Treas.--Sybron International Corporation, Milwaukee, WI; *U.S. Public*, pg. 1544
Brown, Edward C., Pres. & Treas.--Bill Brown Ford Inc., Livonia, MI; *U.S. Private*, pg. 173
Brown, Ike, Treas.--The Upper Room, Nashville, TN; *U.S. Private*, pg. 1129
Brown, Jack R., Chief Fin. Officer, Treas. & Sec.--Florida Public Utilities Company, West Palm Beach, FL; *U.S. Public*, pg. 655
Brown, James C., Chief Fin. Officer, V.P.-Fin., Treas. & Sec.--Patterson Energy, Inc., Snyder, TX; *U.S. Public*, pg. 1265
Brown, Jay, V.P.-Fin. & Treas.--Didde Corporation, Overland Park, KS; *U.S. Private*, pg. 331
Brown, Kathy M., Treas.--Standard Locknut, Inc., Westfield, IN; *U.S. Private*, pg. 1031
Brown, L. Russell, Chm. Bd. & Treas.--Agsco, Inc., Grand Forks, ND; *U.S. Private*, pg. 27
Brown, Mary E., Asst. Treas. & Asst. Sec.--AmerenCIPS, Springfield, IL; *U.S. Public*, pg. 65
Brown, Nancy, Treas. & Sec.--Heintzelman's Truck Center Inc., Orlando, FL; *U.S. Private*, pg. 519
Brown, Nancy M., Asst. Treas. & Branch Mgr.--Valley National Bank, Hackettstown, NJ; *U.S. Public*, pg. 1706
Brown, Raynard J., Chief Fin. Officer--Galamba Metals, Inc., Kansas City, KS; *U.S. Private*, pg. 437
Brown, Robert A., Treas.--Air Conditioning Co., Inc., Glendale, CA; *U.S. Private*, pg. 28
Brown, Stephen F., Sr. V.P.-Treasury & Tax.--Cineplex Odeon Corporation, Toronto, Canada; *Int'l*, pg. 292
Brown, Thomas L., V.P. & Treas.--Anacomp, Inc., Indianapolis, IN; *U.S. Public*, pg. 106
Brown, Todd S., Chief Fin. Officer, V.P. & Treas.--DenAmerica Corp., Scottsdale, AZ; *U.S. Public*, pg. 498
Brown, William, Sec. & Treas.--CNL Financial Corp., Macon, GA; *U.S. Public*, pg. 281
Brown, William C., CPA, V.P.-Fin.--MGI PHARMA INC., Minneapolis, MN; *U.S. Public*, pg. 1026
Brown, Woods R., Pres., Chief Exec. Officer & Treas.--Kingsbury, Inc., Philadelphia, PA; *U.S. Private*, pg. 622
Browne, D., Treas.--Arnotts plc, Dublin, Ireland; *Int'l*, pg. 81
Brownell, David A., Controller & Treas.--Electro Metrics, Inc., Johnstown, NY; *U.S. Private*, pg. 369
Brownell, Joel, V.P.-Fin. & Treas.--Walsworth Publishing Company, Inc., Marceline, MO; *U.S. Private*, pg. 1148
Brownfield, Debbie, Chief Fin. Officer, Sr. V.P. & Sec.--Lamonts Apparel, Inc., Kirkland, WA; *U.S. Public*, pg. 975
Browning, George, Treas. & Sec.--Elk Supply Company, Clinton, OK; *U.S. Private*, pg. 371
Browning, Jean, Treas. & Sec.--Browning Chemical Corporation, White Plains, NY; *U.S. Private*, pg. 175
Brownley, John F., Sr. V.P. & Treas.--Wendy's International Inc., Dublin, OH; *U.S. Public*, pg. 1754
Brownlow, I.P., V.P., Chief Fin. Officer & Treas.--Hondo Oil & Gas Company, Roswell, NM; *Int'l*, pg. 818
Broz, James E., V.P.-Fin. & Admin., & Treas.--Office Electronics, Inc., Itasca, IL; *U.S. Private*, pg. 812
Brubaker, Ernie, Treas.--Gardner Publications, Inc., Cincinnati, OH; *U.S. Private*, pg. 440
Bruckheimer, Allen J., Sr. V.P. & Assoc. Treas.--Mutual of America Life Insurance Company, New York, NY; *U.S. Private*, pg. 769
Bruggeman, Douglas, V.P.-Fin. & Treas.--Rex Stores Corp., Dayton, OH; *U.S. Public*, pg. 1384
Brumby, Jane, Treas.--Pumpelly Oil, Inc., Westlake, LA; *U.S. Private*, pg. 895
Brumleve, David, Sr. V.P., Treas. & Sec.--Siemer Milling Company, Teutopolis, IL; *U.S. Private*, pg. 998
Brummond, Brad, Chief Fin. Officer & Treas.--Super 8 Motels, Inc., Aberdeen, SD; *U.S. Public*, pg. 322
Brune, Fred M., Sr. V.P., Treas. & Sec.--Lockwood Greene Engineers, Inc., Spartanburg, SC; *Int'l*, pg. 633
Brunetta, David C., District Controller, Asst. Sec. & Treas.--Ragnar Benson, Inc., Monroeville, PA; *U.S. Private*, pg. 99
Brunko, C.E., Asst. Treas. & Asst. Sec.--Otter Tail Power Company, Fergus Falls, MN; *U.S. Public*, pg. 1234
Bruno, Richard M., Treas. & Asst. Sec.--Sonoco Engraph, Inc., Atlanta, GA; *U.S. Public*, pg. 1486
Brustein, Lawrence, Chief Fin. Officer, Sec. & Treas.--Henry Modell & Company, Inc., New York, NY; *U.S. Private*, pg. 754
Brusven, Arland D., V.P.-Fin. & Treas.--Northern States Power Company, Minneapolis, MN; *U.S. Public*, pg. 1195
Bruwelheide, Dale A., Chief Fin. Officer, V.P. & Treas.--Orange-Co., Inc., Bartow, FL; *U.S. Public*, pg. 1229
Bryan, Charles R., V.P., Treas. & Sec.--AVA, Atlanta, GA; *U.S. Private*, pg. 8
Bryan, Glynis A., V.P. & Treas.--Ryder System, Inc., Miami, FL; *U.S. Public*, pg. 1413
Bryan, Timothy, Treas.--Jones Spacelink, Ltd., Englewood, CO; *U.S. Private*, pg. 597
Bryan, William A., V.P.-Fin., Treas. & Sec.--Pardee Construction Company, Los Angeles, CA; *U.S. Public*, pg. 1764
Bryant, Carleton F., III, Chief Oper. Officer, Exec. V.P., Treas. & Sec.--Westerbeke Corporation, Avon, MA; *U.S. Public*, pg. 1757
Bryant, Geraldine D., Treas. & Sec.--Lowell Packing Company, Fitzgerald, GA; *U.S. Private*, pg. 679
Bryant, Richard J., Treas. & Sec.--Bryant Electric Supply Company, Inc., Lowell, NC; *U.S. Private*, pg. 177
Bryne, Brian, Treas.--Bull HN Information Systems Inc., Billerica, MA; *Int'l*, pg. 316
Bucciarelli, Gary, V.P.-Human Resources & Treas.--Medrad, Inc., Indianola, PA; *Int'l*, pg. 1204
Bucciaretti, Gary W., Treas.--Medrad, Inc., Indianola, PA; *Int'l*, pg. 1204
Bucek, Dennis C., Sr. V.P., Treas. & Asst. Sec.--Coherent, Inc., Santa Clara, CA; *U.S. Public*, pg. 395
Buchanan, James H., Chief Fin. Officer, Treas. & Sec.--Excalibur Technologies Corporation, Vienna, VA; *U.S. Public*, pg. 598
Buchanan, Jeffrey D., Chief Fin. Officer, V.P.-Fin./Admin., Treas. & Sec.--Three-Five Systems, Tempe, AZ; *U.S. Public*, pg. 1604
Buchas, Charles M., Jr., V.P. & Treas.--FDX Corporation, Memphis, TN; *U.S. Public*, pg. 603
Buchwald, Maureen, V.P.-Admin. & Treas. & Corp. Sec.--Ariel Corporation, Mount Vernon, OH; *U.S. Private*, pg. 81
Buckelew, L. Nick, Treas.--Trico Electric Co-Op, Tucson, AZ; *U.S. Private*, pg. 1102
Buckey, Alan, Chief Fin. Officer, Treas. & Legal Officer--Pease Industries, Inc., Fairfield, OH; *U.S. Private*, pg. 845
Buckingham, Richard L., V.P. & Treas.--Wang Laboratories, Inc., Billerica, MA; *U.S. Public*, pg. 1737
Buckley, C.E., V.P. & Treas.--Trafalgar House Holdings Inc., West Warwick, RI; *Int'l*, pg. 774
Buckman Davis, Katherine, Sec. & Asst. Treas--Bulab Holdings, Inc., Memphis, TN; *U.S. Private*, pg. 180
Buckner, Clay H., Jr., Controller & Treas.--Krystal Company, Chattanooga, TN; *U.S. Private*, pg. 636
Budde, Kenneth C., Chief Acctg. Officer, Sr. V.P.-Fin., Treas. & Sec.--Stewart Enterprises, Inc., Metairie, LA; *U.S. Public*, pg. 1518
Buddig, John C., Treas.--Carl Buddig & Company, Homewood, IL; *U.S. Private*, pg. 178
Budge, David L., Treas.--The Amalgamated Sugar Company LLC, Ogden, UT; *U.S. Private*, pg. 48
Budig, George J., V.P., Treas. & Sec.--Budco Group Inc., Cincinnati, OH; *U.S. Private*, pg. 178
Budnick, David, Treas. & Sec.--Hatfield Quality Meats, Hatfield, PA; *U.S. Private*, pg. 510
Buehler, Robert, Treas.--Trinity Universal Insurance Co., Dallas, TX; *U.S. Public*, pg. 1694
Buening, Rebecca, V.P. & Treas.--The Scotts Company, Marysville, OH; *U.S. Public*, pg. 1446
Buffington, Douglas A., Pres., Chief Oper. & Fin. Officer & Treas.--Square Two Golf Incorporated, Fairfield, NJ; *U.S. Public*, pg. 1501
Buha, Robert, V.P., Sec. & Treas.--Great Lakes Peterbilt, GMC, Portage, IN; *U.S. Private*, pg. 475
Buhrer, Gerhard, Mgr.-Treasury--Georg Fischer Ltd., Schaffhausen, Switzerland; *Int'l*, pg. 488
Buiter, Michael R., V.P.-Fin. & Treas.--Dr Pepper/Seven Up No. America, Dallas, TX; *Int'l*, pg. 248
Buller, Allan R., Chm. & Treas.--Worthington Foods Inc., Worthington, OH; *U.S. Public*, pg. 1780
Bullig, Randall W., Chief Fin. Officer & Treas.--Midwest Employer's Casualty Company, Maryland Heights, MO; *U.S. Public*, pg. 215
Bulloch, William J., Jr., Treas.--Riceland Foods, Inc., Stuttgart, AR; *U.S. Private*, pg. 928
Bullock, James R., Jr., Pres. & Treas.--Environmental Air Systems, Inc., Greensboro, NC; *U.S. Private*, pg. 378
Bunce, Leonard, Sr. V.P.-Fin. & Treas.--Schmidt Baking Co., Inc., Baltimore, MD; *U.S. Private*, pg. 970
Bunday, Dennis E., Treas.--Pope & Talbot, Inc., Portland, OR; *U.S. Public*, pg. 1316
Bunt, James R., V.P. & Treas.--General Electric Company, Fairfield, CT; *U.S. Public*, pg. 709
Bunting, M., Treas.--The Boots Company PLC, Nottingham, United Kingdom; *Int'l*, pg. 202
Burcham, Kay, Treas. & Sec--Manufacturers Consolidation Service, Inc., Memphis, TN; *U.S. Private*, pg. 700
Burchill, Jeff, V.P. & Treas.--Protection Mutual Insurance Co., Park Ridge, IL; *U.S. Private*, pg. 891
Burdick, Charles J., V.P.-Fin. & Asst. Treas.--U S West DEX, Denver, CO; *U.S. Public*, pg. 1689
Burgart, Richard H., Chief Fin. Officer, Treas. & Sec.--FSF Financial Corp., Hutchinson, MN; *U.S. Public*, pg. 608
Burgess, Arthur W., Treas.--BG Plc, Reading, United Kingdom; *Int'l*, pg. 118
Burgoyne, Mary Louise, Treas. & Sec.--Burgoyne, Inc., Philadelphia, PA; *U.S. Private*, pg. 182
Burillo, A., Treas.--Grupo Video Visa S.A. de C.V., Mexico, Mexico; *Int'l*, pg. 577
Burke, Frank, Treas.--Magna International Inc., Markham, Canada; *Int'l*, pg. 829
Burke, Monica J., Chief. Fin. Officer, Treas. & Sec.--Valley Forge Corporation, San Rafael, CA; *U.S. Public*, pg. 1705
Burke, Raymond T., Sec. & Tres.--Equitable Holding Corporation, Secaucus, NJ; *U.S. Public*, pg. 589
Burke, Thomas A., Treas.--Millennium Petrochemicals, Inc., Cincinnati, OH; *Int'l*, pg. 594
Burke, Timothy L., Treas.--SIGCORP, Inc., Evansville, IN; *U.S. Public*, pg. 1471
Burke, William B., Chief Fin. Officer & Treas.--Wahl Clipper Corp., Sterling, IL; *U.S. Private*, pg. 1146
Burke, William J., Sec. & Treas.--Insulate LLC, Auburn, WA; *Int'l*, pg. 1171
Burke, William P., Treas.--Moog Incorporated, East Aurora, NY; *U.S. Public*, pg. 1127
Burkett, Marvin D., Chief Fin. Officer, Sr. V.P. & Treas.--Advanced Micro Devices, Inc., Sunnyvale, CA; *U.S. Public*, pg. 21
Burkey, Michelle, Controller & Treas.--The Tobin Corporation, North Ridgeville, OH; *U.S. Private*, pg. 102
Burkholder, P.W., Sec. & Treas.--AC & S Inc., Lancaster, PA; *U.S. Public*, pg. 913
Burkowski, Susan, Asst. Treas.--Willis Corroon Corp. of Michigan, Livonia, MI; *Int'l*, pg. 1506
Burks, Edward, Chief Fin. Officer, V.P. & Treas.--Fritz Industries Inc., Mesquite, TX; *U.S. Private*, pg. 429
Burlinson, Robert F., V.P. & Treas.--Handy & Harman, New York, NY; *U.S. Public*, pg. 780
Burman, Don, Asst. Treas.--Atmos Energy Corporation, Dallas, TX; *U.S. Public*, pg. 145
Burnham, E., Treas. & Mgr.-Mktg.--Meyer International PLC, London, United Kingdom; *Int'l*, pg. 864
Burnham, Jed J., Chief Fin. Officer & Treas.--ACX Technologies Inc., Golden, CO; *U.S. Public*, pg. 3
Burns, Jack, Dep. Treas.--NJ Transit, Newark, NJ; *U.S. Private*, pg. 794
Burns, Kathleen M., V.P. & Treas.--Unisource Worldwide, Inc., Berwyn, PA; *U.S. Public*, pg. 1670
Burns, Lee D., Treas. & Sec.--Servotronics, Inc., Elma, NY; *U.S. Public*, pg. 1462
Burns, Michael B., V.P.-Treas. Mngmt.--Crown Cork & Seal Company, Inc., Philadelphia, PA; *U.S. Public*, pg. 462
Buron, Paul, Treas.--Donohue Inc., Quebec, Canada; *Int'l*, pg. 1075
Burr, Michael, Treas.--Milwaukee Bucks, Inc., Milwaukee, WI; *U.S. Private*, pg. 749
Burrell, Richard L., Sr. V.P.-Fin., Treas. & Sec.--R.G. Barry Corporation, Pickerington, OH; *U.S. Public*, pg. 192
Burris, Wayne C., Chief Fin. Officer--Corange U.S. Holdings, Inc, Indianapolis, IN; *Int'l*, pg. 331
Burroughs, Robert, Treas.--Raybestos Products Co., Crawfordsville, IN; *U.S. Public*, pg. 1363
Burrows, Dennis A., Exec V.P., Treas. & Sec.--Roper Bros. Lumber Co., Inc., Petersburg, VA; *U.S. Private*, pg. 944
Burslem, William, III, Chief Fin. Officer, V.P. & Sec.--Travel Ports of America Inc., Rochester, NY; *U.S. Public*, pg. 1632
Burtness, Dave, V.P., Treas. & Asst. Sec.--Witcher Construction Company, Eden Prairie, MN; *U.S. Private*, pg. 347
Busby, Robert L., III, Chief Fin. & Admin. Officer, Sr. V.P. & Treas.--National Western Life Insurance Company, Austin, TX; *U.S. Public*, pg. 1161
Buselmeier, Bernard J., V.P. & Treas.--GMAC Insurance Holdings, Detroit, MI; *U.S. Public*, pg. 719
Bush, Wendy, Treas.--Dyke Industry, Inc., Little Rock, AR; *U.S. Private*, pg. 350

Bushmann, Stephen J., Chief Fin. Officer, V.P. & Treas.--Stifel Financial Corp., Saint Louis, MO; *U.S. Public*, pg. 1518
Buss, Cal, V.P., Treas. & Sec.--Vallet Food Serv Inc., Dubuque, IA; *U.S. Private*, pg. 1131
Buss, Gene, Sr. V.P. & Treas.--Sangamon Industries, Taylorville, IL; *U.S. Private*, pg. 965
Butala, James, Chief Fin. Officer & Treas.--Lucht, Inc., Bloomington, MN; *U.S. Public*, pg. 1201
Buten, Max, V.P.-Fin. & Treas.--Buten, Division of Duron, King of Prussia, PA; *U.S. Private*, pg. 349
Butler, J.C., Jr., Mgr.-Corp. Devel. & Treas.--NACCO Industries, Inc., Cleveland, OH; *U.S. Public*, pg. 1149
Butler, John M., Pres. & Treas.--John Hancock Leasing Corporation, Boston, MA; *U.S. Private*, pg. 590
Butterfield, Michael J., V.P.-Fin. & Treas.--Equis Financial Group, Boston, MA; *U.S. Private*, pg. 379
Button, G., Grp. Treas.--John Fairfax Holdings Limited, Sydney, Australia; *Int'l*, pg. 477
Button, Russ, Sec. & Treas.--Hastings, Inc., Barrie, Canada; *U.S. Public*, pg. 798
Buzen, Jeffrey, Dr., Sr. V.P. & Treas.--BGS Systems, Inc., Waltham, MA; *U.S. Public*, pg. 161
Buzzell, James R., V.P., Treas. & Sec.--ADT Automotive, Inc., Nashville, TN; *U.S. Public*, pg. 1648
Bwint, Derek S., Treas.--Alberta Energy Company, Ltd., Calgary, Canada; *Int'l*, pg. 48
Bybee, O. Lynn, Controller, Treas. & Sec.--Wick Building Systems, Mazomanie, WI; *U.S. Private*, pg. 1174
Bybel, Danielle, V.P. & Treas.--Vaughan & Sons, Inc., San Antonio, TX; *U.S. Private*, pg. 1134
Byer, Marian, Treas. & Sec.--Byer California, San Francisco, CA; *U.S. Private*, pg. 191
Byers, R.A., Chief Fin. Officer, V.P.-Fin. & Treas.--Pitt-Des Moines, Inc., Pittsburgh, PA; *U.S. Public*, pg. 1304
Byrne, Daniel G., Chief Fin. Officer & Sr. V.P.--Sterling Financial Corporation, Spokane, WA; *U.S. Public*, pg. 1516
Byrne, Kevin R., V.P. & Treas.--The Equitable Companies Incorporated, New York, NY; *U.S. Public*, pg. 588
Byrne, Michael C., Chief Fin. Officer & Treas.--Gerald H. Phipps, Inc., Denver, CO; *U.S. Private*, pg. 862
Byrne, Thomas M., Asst. Treas.--Teleflex Incorporated, Plymouth Meeting, PA; *U.S. Public*, pg. 1569
Byrnes, John T., Pres & Treas.--M & I Capital Markets Group, Inc., Milwaukee, WI; *U.S. Public*, pg. 1051
Cable, Dale A., V.P. & Treas.--American Greetings Corporation, Cleveland, OH; *U.S. Public*, pg. 77
Cabrera, Luis, Sr. V.P.-Treas. & Investments--Firstbank Puerto Rico, Santurce, PR; *U.S. Public*, pg. 644
Cahill, J. Michael, Exec. V.P. & Chief Info. Officer--Channing L. Bete Co., Inc., South Deerfield, MA; *U.S. Private*, pg. 140
Cahill, James, Chief Fin. Officer, Exec. V.P., Treas. & Sec.--Strattec Securities Corporation, Milwaukee, WI; *U.S. Public*, pg. 1523
Cahill, John, Sr. V.P.-Fin., Chief Fin. Officer & Treas.--Kentucky Fried Chicken Corporation (KFC), Louisville, KY; *U.S. Public*, pg. 1636
Cahill, Kirk, V.P.-Fin., Controller & Treas.--Chicago Extruded Metals Co., Cicero, IL; *U.S. Private*, pg. 234
Cahill, Larry, Pres. & Treas.--Larken Inc., Cedar Rapids, IA; *U.S. Private*, pg. 651
Cain, Allen, Treas.--Dorsey Trailers, Inc., Atlanta, GA; *U.S. Public*, pg. 520
Cain, Peter, V.P.-Fin. & Treas.--Ogden Corporation, New York, NY; *U.S. Public*, pg. 1213
Calafati, Gabriel R., Chm. Bd., Pres. & Treas.--Frank Briscoe Co. Inc., Kenilworth, NJ; *U.S. Private*, pg. 169
Calamari, John J., V.P.-Fin. & Treas.--Advanta Insurance Companies, Horsham, PA; *U.S. Public*, pg. 22
Caldwell, Brucea, V.P. & Treas.--Caldor, Inc., Norwalk, CT; *U.S. Public*, pg. 292
Caldwell, Eugene, Chief Fin. Officer, Sr. V.P. & Treas.--Venture Stores, Inc., O Fallon, MO; *U.S. Public*, pg. 1716
Calhoun, Jay, Sr. V.P. & Treas.--New York Life Insurance Company, New York, NY; *U.S. Private*, pg. 794
Callahan, Sandra W., Treas. & Asst. Sec.--TECO Energy, Inc., Tampa, FL; *U.S. Public*, pg. 1565
Callan, Richard T., Chief Fin. Officer, V.P. & Controller--Alliance Construction Solutions, Inc., Fort Collins, CO; *U.S. Private*, pg. 38
Callaway, Joe, Treas. & Sec.--Coda Energy, Inc., Dallas, TX; *U.S. Public*, pg. 584
Calle, Craig R.L., Sr. V.P.-Fin. & Treas.--Crown Cork & Seal Company, Inc., Philadelphia, PA; *U.S. Public*, pg. 462
Callegari, Don, V.P.-Fin. & Acting Treas.--R.J. Gallagher Co., Houston, TX; *U.S. Private*, pg. 438
Calvani, Margaret, Asst. Treas. & Branch Mgr.--Valley National Bank, Landing, NJ; *U.S. Public*, pg. 1706
Cameron, Beatrice, Sec.--Barger Builders, Saint Petersburg, FL; *U.S. Private*, pg. 116
Cameron, Ronald W., V.P.-Fin. & Treas.--Ropak Corporation, Fullerton, CA; *Int'l*, pg. 811
Camimer, Carol, Treas.--Efficient Engineering Co., Troy, MI; *U.S. Private*, pg. 365
Camp, Tom, V.P., Treas., Gen. Counsel & Sec.--The Apogee Companies, Inc., Lake Oswego, OR; *U.S. Private*, pg. 77
Camp, William C., Chief Fin. Officer, V.P. & Treas.--Science & Engineering Associates, Albuquerque, NM; *U.S. Private*, pg. 975
Campbell, Duane, V.P. & Treas.--Nationwide Insurance Enterprise, Columbus, OH; *U.S. Private*, pg. 788
Campbell, Joseph, V.P. & Treas.--Associated Wholesale Grocers, Inc., Kansas City, KS; *U.S. Private*, pg. 93
Campbell, Nancy J., Treas.--Monongahela Power Co., Fairmont, WV; *U.S. Public*, pg. 42
Campbell, Nancy L., V.P. & Treas.--Allegheny Power System, Inc., Hagerstown, MD; *U.S. Public*, pg. 42
Campbell, Nancy L., Treas.--Allegheny Generating Co., New York, NY; *U.S. Public*, pg. 42
Campbell, Nancy L., Treas.--The Potomac Edison Co., Hagerstown, MD; *U.S. Public*, pg. 42
Campbell, Nancy L., Treas.--West Penn Power Co., Greensburg, PA; *U.S. Public*, pg. 42
Campbell, Robert, Asst. Treas.--Playboy Entertainment Group, Inc., Beverly Hills, CA; *U.S. Public*, pg. 1310
Campbell, Robert D., Treas. & Asst. Sec.--Playboy Enterprises, Inc., Chicago, IL; *U.S. Public*, pg. 1309
Campney, Robert, V.P. & Treas.--Pacesetter Corporation, Omaha, NE; *U.S. Private*, pg. 830
Camuzzi, Gian, Treas.--The Gillette Company, Boston, MA; *U.S. Public*, pg. 743
Canale, Chris W., Treas.--D. Canale Food Services, Inc., Memphis, TN; *U.S. Private*, pg. 204
Cannon, Bruce A., Chief Fin. Officer, Sr. V.P., Treas. & Sec.--SpecTran Corporation, Sturbridge, MA; *U.S. Public*, pg. 1497
Cannon, Dana M., Asst. Treas.--Petroleum & Resources Corp., Baltimore, MD; *U.S. Public*, pg. 1280
Cannon, John H., V.P. & Treas.--Woolworth Corporation, New York, NY; *U.S. Public*, pg. 1777
Cannon, Mark, Treas.--SCANA Corporation, Columbia, SC; *U.S. Public*, pg. 1436
Cannon, Rose Marie C., Treas. & Sec.--Cannon Express Inc., Springdale, AR; *U.S. Public*, pg. 301
Canosa, Albert A., Chief Fin. Officer & Corp. V.P.-Admin.--Raytech Corporation, Shelton, CT; *U.S. Public*, pg. 1363
Cantelo, Alan E., Treas.--Smiths Industries plc, London, United Kingdom; *Int'l*, pg. 1266
Cantrell, C. Lamar, Treas.--Mead Packaging (Canada) Ltd., Ajax, Canada; *U.S. Public*, pg. 1076
Caparco, Steven A., V.P. & Treas.--Unitrode Corporation, Merrimack, NH; *U.S. Public*, pg. 1694
Caplan, James A., Chm. Bd., Pres., Treas., Prod. Mgr. & Chief Engr.--Capp, Inc., Clifton Heights, PA; *U.S. Private*, pg. 207
Capo, Thomas P., V.P. & Treas.--Chrysler Corporation, Auburn Hills, MI; *U.S. Public*, pg. 352
Caponigro, Ralph A., Chief Fin. Officer, Sr. V.P.-Fin. & Treas.--Compuware Corporation, Farmington Hills, MI; *U.S. Public*, pg. 423
Caporale, Charles, Chief Fin. Officer, Sr. V.P. & Treas.--Centris Group Inc., Costa Mesa, CA; *U.S. Public*, pg. 328
Cappon, Paul A., V.P. & Treas.--Camillus Cutlery Co., Camillus, NY; *U.S. Private*, pg. 203
Caputo, Carmen M., Chief Fin. Officer, V.P.-Fin. & Treas.--Tork, Inc., Mount Vernon, NY; *U.S. Private*, pg. 1092
Caputo, Vincent, V.P., Asst. Treas. & Asst. Sec.--Aris Industries, Inc., New York, NY; *U.S. Public*, pg. 129
Carchedi, Frank A., Chief Fin. Officer & Treas.--ITC Learning Corp., Herndon, VA; *U.S. Public*, pg. 859
Card, Wesley, Chief Fin. Officer & Treas.--Jones Apparel Group, Inc., Bristol, PA; *U.S. Public*, pg. 933
Carey, William P., Treas.--Scanforms, Inc., Bristol, PA; *U.S. Public*, pg. 228
Carlevato, Jeff, Controller & Treas.--QST Industries, Inc., Chicago, IL; *U.S. Private*, pg. 897
Carlino, Elio, Controller & Asst. Treas.--Milgray Electronics, Inc., Farmingdale, NY; *U.S. Public*, pg. 205
Carlos, Andrew C., Exec. V.P. & Treas.--National Distributing Co., Inc., Atlanta, GA; *U.S. Private*, pg. 781
Carlson, Bruce R., Treas. & Sec.--Park Construction Company, Minneapolis, MN; *U.S. Private*, pg. 839
Carlson, D.A., Jr., Pres., Chief Exec. Officer & Treas.--Ziegler Securities Division, Chicago, IL; *U.S. Public*, pg. 1792
Carlson, Jane, Treas. & Sec.--D.C. Taylor Co., Cedar Rapids, IA; *U.S. Private*, pg. 1070
Carlson, Lee R., Treas.--NRG Energy, Inc., Minneapolis, MN; *U.S. Public*, pg. 1195
Carlson, Roslyn D., Asst. Treas.--Central Vermont Public Service Corporation, Rutland, VT; *U.S. Public*, pg. 327
Carlton, Dorothy, Treas. & Sec.--Corrugated Metals, Inc., Bedford Park, IL; *U.S. Private*, pg. 277
Carmack, Clint, Controller & Treas.--New Horizons LLC, Cincinnati, OH; *U.S. Private*, pg. 794
Carman, Gerald, Treas.--Santa Fe Energy Resources, Inc., Houston, TX; *U.S. Public*, pg. 1431
Carman, Trent J., Sr. V.P. & Treas.--United Artists Theatre Circuits Incorporated, Englewood, CO; *U.S. Private*, pg. 1120
Carmany, David J., Chief Fin. Officer, V.P.-Fin., Treas. & Controller--Castleberry/Snow's Brands Inc., Augusta, GA; *U.S. Private*, pg. 219
Carnahan, Karen L., Treas.--Cintas Corporation, Mason, OH; *U.S. Public*, pg. 370
Carnes, Candace, Treas.--Badger Air Brush Company, Franklin Park, IL; *U.S. Private*, pg. 110
Carney, Dennis, Chief Fin. Officer, Treas. & Sec.--Midwest Mutual Insurance Co., West Des Moines, IA; *U.S. Private*, pg. 881
Carney, Dennis, Treas. & Sec.--Equity Fire & Casualty Insurance Company, West Des Moines, IA; *U.S. Private*, pg. 881
Carney, Dennis R., Treas.--Preferred Risk Mutual Insurance, West Des Moines, IA; *U.S. Private*, pg. 880
Carney, Dennis R., Treas.--Preferred Abstainers Insurance Compan, West Des Moines, IA; *U.S. Private*, pg. 880
Carney, Richard, Treas.--Chuck Hutton Chevrolet Company, Memphis, TN; *U.S. Private*, pg. 550
Caroll, Mike, Treas.--George W. Auch Co., Pontiac, MI; *U.S. Private*, pg. 98
Carolus, Paul R., Chief Fin. Officer, Treas. & Sec.--Westwood Corporation, Tulsa, OK; *U.S. Public*, pg. 1763
Carpenter, Robert L., Jr., Treas. & Controller--First Maryland Life Insurance Company, Baltimore, MD; *Int'l*, pg. 64
Carper, John T., Chief Fin. Officer--Sealright Company, Inc., De Soto, KS; *U.S. Public*, pg. 1451
Carr, Jack R., Treas.--Russell Stover Candies, Inc., Kansas City, MO; *U.S. Private*, pg. 953
Carr, William A., Treas.--Mercantile Stores Company, Inc., Fairfield, OH; *U.S. Public*, pg. 1089
Carradine, John M., V.P.-Fin. & Treas.--Intellicall, Inc., Carrollton, TX; *U.S. Public*, pg. 887
Carrico, F. Donald, Treas. & Sec.--Rapid Industries, Inc., Louisville, KY; *U.S. Private*, pg. 910
Carrico, Patrick, Treas. & Sec.--Holderness Supplies, Tucson, AZ; *U.S. Private*, pg. 534
Carrig, John A., V.P. & Treas.--Phillips Petroleum Company, Bartlesville, OK; *U.S. Public*, pg. 1290
Carroll, Dennis W., V.P. & Treas.--Colonial Gas Company, Lowell, MA; *U.S. Public*, pg. 400
Carroll, Michael L., Treas.--Homestake Mining Company, San Francisco, CA; *U.S. Public*, pg. 832
Carroll, Robert, Sr. V.P.-East--Powell Electronics Inc., Philadelphia, PA; *U.S. Private*, pg. 877
Carrus, Gerald, Treas.--CBS Radio, New York, NY; *U.S. Public*, pg. 274
Carse, Jimmie L., Treas. & Sec.--Carse Oil Co. Inc., Orlando, FL; *U.S. Private*, pg. 216
Carter, David R., Treas. & Sec.--Trustmark National Bank, Jackson, MS; *U.S. Public*, pg. 1643
Carter, George K., V.P. & Treas.--Chevron Corporation, San Francisco, CA; *U.S. Public*, pg. 347
Carter, James D., V.P.-Fin. & Treas.--Vertex Communications Corporation, Kilgore, TX; *U.S. Public*, pg. 1717
Carter, Sam R., Chief Fin. Officer & Treas.--Farmers Co-op Market Inc., Frisco City, AL; *U.S. Private*, pg. 395
Carter, Stephen P., Chief Fin. Officer, V.P. & Treas.--Woodward Governor Company, Rockford, IL; *U.S. Public*, pg. 1776
Carty, Michael A., Treas.--First Financial Corporation, Terre Haute, IN; *U.S. Public*, pg. 633
Carver, Lucille A., Treas.--Bandag, Incorporated, Muscatine, IA; *U.S. Public*, pg. 177
Carver, Richard D., V.P. & Treas.--NationsBank West, Saint Louis, MO; *U.S. Public*, pg. 1164
Cary, Harold, V.P. & Treas.--Harold Moore & Associates, Inc., Fayetteville, TN; *U.S. Private*, pg. 759
Caschette, Gerard, Pres. & Treas.--Genesee Metal Stampings, Inc., West Henrietta, NY; *U.S. Private*, pg. 446
Casciano, Ronald J., Chief Fin. Officer, V.P. & Treas.--PAR Technology Corporation, New Hartford, NY; *U.S. Public*, pg. 1256
Case, Andy, Treas.--Whatman plc, Maidstone, United Kingdom; *Int'l*, pg. 1498
Casella, James A., Treas.--BPA International, New York, NY; *U.S. Private*, pg. 107
Casey, Joseph, Treas.--A. Duda & Sons Inc., Oviedo, FL; *U.S. Private*, pg. 344
Casey, Joseph F., Chief Fin. Officer & Treas.--Andover Bancorp, Inc., Andover, MA; *U.S. Public*, pg. 111
Casey, Karen L., Sec. & Treas.--Libertyville Lincoln-Mercury Sales, Inc., Libertyville, IL; *U.S. Private*, pg. 666
Cashwell, Henry V., Treas. & Sec.--Tencarva Machinery Co., Inc., Greensboro, NC; *U.S. Private*, pg. 1075
Cass, Ronald A., Chm. Bd., Pres., Chief Exec. Officer & Treas.--Hospital Staffing Services, Inc., Fort Lauderdale, FL; *U.S. Public*, pg. 840
Cassells, Peter, Mgr.-Fin. & Treas.--ELSAG Bailey Process Automation N.V., Schiphol, Netherlands; *Int'l*, pg. 449
Casselman, David A., V.P.-Fin., Controller, Sec. & Treas.--General Time Corp., Norcross, GA; *U.S. Private*, pg. 445
Cassens, Kay, Treas. & Sec.--Cassens Transport Company, Edwardsville, IL; *U.S. Private*, pg. 219
Cassidy, Emmet P., Treas. & Sec.--Peoples Energy Corporation, Chicago, IL; *U.S. Public*, pg. 1274
Cassidy, R. Brian, Chief Fin. Officer, Treas. & Sec.--Krasdale Foods Inc., White Plains, NY; *U.S. Private*, pg. 635
Cassner, Jon H., Treas.--Rotary Forms Press, Inc., Hillsboro, OH; *U.S. Private*, pg. 947
Cassreino, Charles W., Treas.--MCC Group, L.L.C., Metairie, LA; *U.S. Private*, pg. 686
Castelo, Enrique L., V.P. & Treas.--American Bankers Insurance Co. of Florida, Miami, FL; *U.S. Public*, pg. 67
Castelo, Enrique L., V.P. & Treas.--American Bankers Life Assurance Co. of Florida, Miami, FL; *U.S. Public*, pg. 67
Castelo, Enrique L., Treas.--Voyager Service Warranties, Inc., Fort Worth, TX; *U.S. Public*, pg. 68
Casterline, Steven T., V.P. & Treas.--Pinnacle Bank, Valparaiso, IN; *U.S. Public*, pg. 1297
Castiglione, Philip, Treas. & Sec.--Ray Laethem Pontiac-Buick-GMC-Truck, Inc., Detroit, MI; *U.S. Private*, pg. 642
Castillo, Carlos Minreles, Treas.--Altos Hornos de Mexico, S.A., Monclova, Mexico; *Int'l*, pg. 66
Castro, Amparo, V.P., Controller & Asst. Treas.--PharmHouse, Inc., New York, NY; *U.S. Public*, pg. 1286
Catalano, Peter, V.P. & Treas.--The Biltrite Corporation, Waltham, MA; *U.S. Private*, pg. 144
Catanzaro, Joseph S., V.P.-Fin.--Berg Electronics, Saint Louis, MO; *U.S. Public*, pg. 212
Cathcart, Joseph, Chief Fin. Officer & Treas.--F.A. Wilhelm Construction Co., Inc., Indianapolis, IN; *U.S. Private*, pg. 1176
Catherwood, Charles E., Chief Exec. Officer, V.P. & Treas.--Independent Publications, Inc., Bryn Mawr, PA; *U.S. Private*, pg. 559
Caton, Andrew, Grp. Treas.--Yorkshire Building Society, Bradford, United Kingdom; *Int'l*, pg. 1522
Catsimatidis, John A., Chm., Chief Exec. Officer & Treas.--Sloan's Supermarkets, Inc., New York, NY; *U.S. Private*, pg. 915
Cauthen, Charles, Treas.--Castleton Beverage Corp., Jacksonville, FL; *Int'l*, pg. 132
Cavanaugh, M.J., V.P., Gen. Mgr., Controller & Treas.--Day-Glo Color Corp., Cleveland, OH; *U.S. Public*, pg. 1357
Cavanaugh, Robert B., V.P. & Treas.--JC Penney Company, Inc., Plano, TX; *U.S. Public*, pg. 916
Cavender, William, Treas. & Sec.--Hallidie Machinery Company, Inc., Seattle, WA; *U.S. Private*, pg. 495
Cavnar, Robert L., Chief Fin. Officer, Sr. V.P. & Treas.--Cornerstone Natural Gas, Inc., Dallas, TX; *U.S. Public*, pg. 567

Cawthon, Vernon, Chief Fin. Officer, Controller & Treas.--Strachan Shipping Co., Garden City, GA; *U.S. Private*, pg. 1045

Ceccarelli, Joe, Treas.--Barneys Inc., New York, NY; *U.S. Private*, pg. 116

Celentano, Doris, Treas. & Sec.--Celentano Bros. Inc., Verona, NJ; *U.S. Private*, pg. 221

Chadwick, Everett, Chief Fin. Officer & Treas.--Chase Corporation, Braintree, MA; *U.S. Public*, pg. 337

Chaffin, Michael P., Treas.--B&W Co-op, Inc., Breckenridge, MI; *U.S. Private*, pg. 105

Chai, Darryl, Treas.--Maui Land & Pineapple Co., Inc., Kahului, HI; *U.S. Public*, pg. 1060

Chalk, Bradford M., Chief Fin. Officer & Sr. V.P.--Betac International Corporation, Alexandria, VA; *U.S. Private*, pg. 140

Chalmers, David B., Chm. Bd., Pres., Chief Exec. Officer & Treas.--Coral Oil & Gas Inc., Houston, TX; *U.S. Private*, pg. 275

Chambers, Herb, Pres. & Treas.--Herb Chambers Cos., Somerville, MA; *U.S. Private*, pg. 227

Chan, Thomas, Treas. & Dir.--Meco Development Limited, Hong Kong, Hong Kong; *Int'l*, pg. 852

Chaney, Mary D., V.P., Sec. & Treas.--Sterling Capital Management Company, Charlotte, NC; *U.S. Public*, pg. 1674

Chang, Michael F.H., Asst. Treas.--Hawaii Electric Light Co., Inc., Hilo, HI; *U.S. Public*, pg. 800

Chang, Roger, Treas.--Mauna Loa Macadamia Partners, L.P., Honolulu, HI; *U.S. Public*, pg. 1060

Chang, Willie, Treas.--H. Salt of Southern California, Inc., Monterey Park, CA; *U.S. Private*, pg. 489

Chapko, Stephen J., Chief Fin. Officer, Exec. V.P., Treas. & Sec.--Kent Electronics Corp., Houston, TX; *U.S. Public*, pg. 951

Chaplin, C. Edward, V.P. & Treas.--The Prudential Insurance Company of America, Newark, NJ; *U.S. Private*, pg. 892

Chapman, Carl L., Asst. Treas.--Indiana Energy, Inc., Indianapolis, IN; *U.S. Public*, pg. 874

Chapman, Fred J., V.P. & Treas.--LucasVarity Inc., Buffalo, NY; *Int'l*, pg. 820

Chapman, Jeff C., Pres. & Treas.--Primesouth, Inc., Columbia, SC; *U.S. Public*, pg. 1436

Chapman, Robert H., III, Chm. Bd., Pres., Chief Exec. Officer & Treas.--Inman Mills, Inman, SC; *U.S. Private*, pg. 564

Charboneau, Pierre, V.P., Controller & Treas.--Culinar Inc., Montreal, Canada; *Int'l*, pg. 348

Charland, Fran, Chief Oper. Officer & Treas.--The F. Dohmen Company, Germantown, WI; *U.S. Private*, pg. 338

Charlton, J.M., Treas.--Imperial Chemical Industries PLC, London, United Kingdom; *Int'l*, pg. 662

Charpentier, Marti, Treas.--AIC-FSS Advertising, Minneapolis, MN; *U.S. Private*, pg. 5

Charpentier, Marti R., Controller & Asst. Treas.--Analysts International Corporation, Minneapolis, MN; *U.S. Public*, pg. 110

Charron, Carol, Controller, Treas. & Sec.--Art Moran Pontiac-GMC Inc., Southfield, MI; *U.S. Private*, pg. 760

Chase, Dee Anne, Controller, Treas., Sec. & Dir.-Employee Benefits--Regency Lincoln Mercury, Inc., Dallas, TX; *U.S.* Private, pg. 918

Chauvette, Claude, Sec. & Treas.--St. Lawrence Cement Inc., Montreal, Canada; *Int'l*, pg. 628

Chauvin, William P., Chief Admin. Officer & Treas.--Global Special Risks, Inc. Holdings, Metairie, LA; *Int'l*, pg. 1503

Cheatham, C.L., Treas. & Controller--Brierley & Partners, Dallas, TX; *U.S. Private*, pg. 168

Cheatham, Geoffrey D., V.P. & Treas.--Becton Dickinson & Company, Franklin Lakes, NJ; *U.S. Public*, pg. 199

Chee, Felix, Sr. V.P. & Treas.--Manulife Financial (The Manufacturers Life Insurance Company), Toronto, Canada; *Int'l*, pg. 840

Chehayl, Peter, V.P. & Treas.--360 Degrees Communications Company, Chicago, IL; *U.S. Public*, pg. 1607

Chelette, David, Asst. Treas.--J.B. Hunt Transport Services, Inc., Lowell, AR; *U.S. Public*, pg. 849

Chen, John, Treas. & Sec.--Tang Industries Inc., Las Vegas, NV; *U.S. Private*, pg. 1068

Chen, Lily C., Dr., Chief Fin. Officer, Exec. V.P. & Treas.--General Sciences Corp., Laurel, MD; *U.S. Private*, pg. 976

Cheney, Dave, Controller--Millstone Coffee, Inc., Everett, WA; *U.S. Public*, pg. 1331

Cheney, Jeffrey P., Treas.--Kohler Company, Kohler, WI; *U.S. Private*, pg. 630

Cherkasly, Ronald L., Chief Fin. Officer & Treas.--J.C. Higgins Corp., Stoughton, MA; *U.S. Public*, pg. 572

Chevalier, Steve, Treas.--Zilber, Ltd., Milwaukee, WI; *U.S. Private*, pg. 1206

Chiampa, Karen, Asst. Treas.--Goldman Financial Group, Boston, MA; *U.S. Private*, pg. 461

Chicheportiche, Bernard, Treas.--GEODIS, Paris, France; *Int'l*, pg. 549

Chicoine, Michelle L., Chief Fin. Officer, Sr. V.P. & Treas.--EnergyNorth, Inc., Manchester, NH; *U.S. Public*, pg. 581

Childers, James H., V.P., Sec. & Treas.--Medicalodges, Inc., Coffeyville, KS; *U.S. Private*, pg. 728

Chin, Terence P., Treas.--Lexmark International Group, Inc., Lexington, KY; *U.S. Public*, pg. 991

Chin, Terence P., Treas.--Lexmark International, Inc., Lexington, KY; *U.S. Public*, pg. 991

Ching, Patrick D., Sr. V.P. & Treas.--Servco Pacific Inc., Honolulu, HI; *U.S. Private*, pg. 986

Chinowsky, Paul, Treas.--Wellmade Industries, Incorporated, New York, NY; *U.S. Private*, pg. 1161

Chirpatris, Michel, Treas.--Alcatel N.V., Amsterdam, Netherlands; *Int'l*, pg. 55

Cho, S.H., Treas.--Sunkyong America, Inc., New York, NY; *Int'l*, pg. 1320

Chokel, Charles B., Chief Fin. Officer & Treas.--The Progressive Corporation, Cleveland, OH; *U.S. Public*, pg. 1334

Choksi, Umesh, Asst. Treas.--ACF Industries, Inc., Saint Charles, MO; *U.S. Private*, pg. 556

Chopra, Beera, V.P.-Opers. & Treas.--Family Inns of America, Inc., Pigeon Forge, TN; *U.S. Private*, pg. 392

Chouinard, John, V.P. & Treas.--Geraghty & Miller, Inc., Denver, CO; *Int'l*, pg. 607

Chow, Shirley, Sr. V.P.-Admin. & Fin. & Corp. Sec.--Bachmann Industries, Inc., Philadelphia, PA; *U.S. Private*, *pg. 109*

Christ, David R., Treas.--Reading Anthracite Co., Pottsville, PA; *U.S. Private*, pg. 913

Christel, Henry E., V.P. & Treas.--William H. Sadlier, Inc., New York, NY; *U.S. Public*, pg. 1422

Christenson, Clifford J., Chief Oper. Officer & Exec. V.P.--Wellman, Inc., Shrewsbury, NJ; *U.S. Public*, pg. 1752

Christiansen, Dan, Chief Fin. Officer & Treas.--AVX Corporation, Myrtle Beach, SC; *Int'l*, pg. 775

Christiansen, Rich, Treas.--STS Consultants, Inc., Deerfield, IL; *U.S. Private*, pg. 959

Christoff, William M., Asst. Treas.-Taxes & Asst. Sec.--Brush Wellman Inc., Cleveland, OH; *U.S. Public*, pg. 266

Christofil, Jim, V.P.-Fin., Treas. & Sec.--Republic Storage Systems Company Inc., Canton, OH; *U.S. Private*, pg. 924

Chu, Chorng-Yi, Controller & Asst. Treas.--Payless Car Rental System, Inc., Saint Petersburg, FL; *U.S. Private*, pg. 844

Chua, Ler Ching, Chief Fin. Officer, Treas. & Sec.--GB Holdings, Jurong, Singapore; *Int'l*, pg. 531

Chuba, Patricia A., Sec. & Asst. Treas.--AGR International, Inc., Butler, PA; *U.S. Private*, pg. 5

Chulumovich, Keith, Controller & Treas.--Cambridge Industries Inc., Madison Heights, MI; *U.S. Private*, pg. 202

Chung, Ray, Chief Fin. Officer, Exec. V.P. & Treas.--Dartford Partnership, San Francisco, CA; *U.S. Private*, pg. 312

Church, R.D., Treas. & Sec.--Erico International, Solon, OH; *U.S. Private*, pg. 381

Chused, Andrew, Treas. & Asst. Sec.--Hampton Industries, Inc., Kinston, NC; *U.S. Public*, pg. 779

Chynoweth, Robert, Treas. & Sec.--Wyoming Machinery Company, Casper, WY; *U.S. Private*, pg. 1193

Ciarfalia, Neil A., Treas.--Aztar Corporation, Phoenix, AZ; *U.S. Public*, pg. 158

Cicigoi, Cynthia A., V.P. & Treas.--The Euclid Chemical Company, Cleveland, OH; *U.S. Public*, pg. 1358

Cifor, Jerry S., Chief Fin. Officer, V.P. & Treas.--Casella Waste Systems, Inc., Rutland, VT; *U.S. Public*, pg. 312

Cimmino, Gerald J., V.P. & Treas.--Arch Communications Group, Inc., Westborough, MA; *U.S. Public*, pg. 127

Cioffi, John, Treas.--Consolidated Edison Company of New York, Inc., New York, NY; *U.S. Public*, pg. 434

Ciola, Marsha, Treas. & Sec.--National Health Products, Orlando, FL; *U.S. Private*, pg. 784

Cipollone, Floriana G., Controller & Treas.--Goldcorp Inc., Toronto, Canada; *Int'l*, pg. 243

Cipollone, Floriana G., Controller & Treas.--Wharf Resources Ltd., Lead, SD; *Int'l*, pg. 243

Cipollone, Floriana G., Controller & Treas.--Lexam Explorations Inc., Toronto, Canada; *Int'l*, pg. 243

Cistone, Daniel, Treas.--M & C Remco Tape Products Co., North Hollywood, CA; *U.S. Private*, pg. 684

Clancy, Paul G., Chief Fin. Officer, V.P. & Treas.--Diversified Communications, Portland, ME; *U.S. Private*, pg. 336

Clanin, Robert J., Chief Fin. Officer, Sr. V.P. & Treas.--United Parcel Service of America, Inc., Atlanta, GA; *U.S.* Private, pg. 1123

Clanton, Stephen L., Chief Fin. Officer, Sr. V.P. & Treas.--International Comfort Products, Franklin, TN; *U.S. Public*, *pg. 898*

Clariond Reyes, Santiago, V.P. & Treas.--Grupo IMSA S.A. de C.V., Garza Garcia, Mexico; *Int'l*, pg. 575

Clark, A. Bayard, Chief Fin. Officer, Exec. V.P. & Treas.--Commerce Bancshares, Inc., Kansas City, MO; *U.S. Public*, pg. 409

Clark, A.G., Grp. Dir.-Treas. & Corp. Fin.--United Biscuits (Holdings) Plc, West Drayton, United Kingdom; *Int'l*, pg. 1442

Clark, Ainsley C., Treas.--Bank of Boston Ltd, London, United Kingdom; *U.S. Public*, pg. 184

Clark, Elaine, Treas.--R.W. Beck, Inc., Seattle, WA; *U.S. Private*, pg. 128

Clark, George R., Jr., Treas.--Ross Technology Corp., Leola, PA; *U.S. Private*, pg. 946

Clark, Jacquel K., Asst. Treas. & Asst. Sec.--Hughes Supply, Inc., Orlando, FL; *U.S. Public*, pg. 846

Clark, Kevin, V.P. & Treas.--Fisher Scientific International, Hampton, NH; *U.S. Private*, pg. 658

Clark, Larry L., V.P., Controller & Asst. Treas.--Chaparral Steel Co., Midlothian, TX; *U.S. Public*, pg. 1585

Clark, Paul J., Treas.--Towers Perrin, New York, NY; *U.S. Private*, pg. 1093

Clark, Scott W., Treas. & Sec.--Construction Management Service, Wilmington, DE; *U.S. Private*, pg. 266

Clark, Susan, V.P., Treas. & Asst. Sec.--Dewberry Design Group, Oklahoma City, OK; *U.S. Private*, pg. 329

Clark, Tom, Treas. & Sec.--Big Horn Co-Op Marketing Association, Greybull, WY; *U.S. Private*, pg. 143

Clark, Virginia G., Treas.--Lehigh Utilities Inc., Apopka, FL; *U.S. Public*, pg. 1116

Clarke, Carolyn, Treas.--Viking Office Products, Torrance, CA; *U.S. Public*, pg. 1720

Clarke, Lois A., Treas.--Virginia Metal Industries, Inc., Orange, VA; *U.S. Private*, pg. 1141

Clarke, R.A., Chief Fin. Officer & Treas.--British Mohair Spinners Limited, Bradford, United Kingdom; *Int'l*, pg. 219

Clarke, Ted, Chief Fin. Officer & V.P.-Fin.--Hynes Industries Inc., Youngstown, OH; *U.S. Private*, pg. 552

Clarke, Vaughn A., Sr. V.P. & Treas.--Viacom Inc., New York, NY; *U.S. Private*, pg. 775

Claunch, Joe Howard, Treas. & Sec.--Somerset Refinery Inc., Somerset, KY; *U.S. Private*, pg. 1013

Clausen, John, Asst. Treas.--Steck-Vaughn Company, Austin, TX; *U.S. Public*, pg. 784

Clausen, John, Asst. Treas.--National Education Credit Corporation, Irvine, CA; *U.S. Public*, pg. 784

Clausen, John, Asst. Treas.--National Education Payroll Corp., Irvine, CA; *U.S. Public*, pg. 784

Clausen, John L., Asst. Treas.--Steck-Vaughn Publishing Corporation, Austin, TX; *U.S. Public*, pg. 784

Claussen, Ronn L., Asst. Treas.--Newell Co., Freeport, IL; *U.S. Public*, pg. 1176

Clay, David, Asst. Treas.--Cash America International, Inc., Fort Worth, TX; *U.S. Public*, pg. 312

Clayton, Charles W., Chief Fin. Officer, V.P. & Treas.--Hampshire Group, Ltd., Anderson, SC; *U.S. Public*, pg. 778

Clayton, J. Kerry, Exec. V.P. & Treas.--Fortis, Inc., New York, NY; *Int'l*, pg. 499

Clayton, K.B., V.P., Treas. & Asst. Sec.--Taylor Woodrow Homes Florida Inc., Sarasota, FL; *Int'l*, pg. 1359

Cleary, Francis, Treas.--Keane, Inc., Boston, MA; *U.S. Public*, pg. 946

Cleary, Robert T., Chief Exec. Officer, Treas. & Sec.--KineticSystems Corporation, Lockport, IL; *U.S. Private*, pg. 620

Cleeland, Kenneth K., Chief Fin. Officer & Treas.--Urban Outfitters, Inc., Philadelphia, PA; *U.S. Public*, pg. 1700

Cleland, John, Treas.--Western Dairymen Cooperative, Inc., Thornton, CO; *U.S. Private*, pg. 1165

Clemens, Peter J., IV, V.P.-Fin. & Treas.--Medpartners Inc., Birmingham, AL; *U.S. Public*, pg. 1082

Clement, Dallas S., Asst. Treas.--Cox Communications, Inc., Atlanta, GA; *U.S. Public*, pg. 454

Clements, Norman F., V.P., Sec. & Treas.--EAC Corporation, Saint Louis, MO; *U.S. Private*, pg. 353

Clerkin, Francis, Treas.--Cushman & Wakefield, Inc., New York, NY; *Int'l*, pg. 873

Clifton, Jean B., Chief Fin. Officer, Exec. V.P., Treas. & Sec.--Journal Register Company, Trenton, NJ; *U.S. Public*, pg. 934

Cline, Richard E., Treas.--Akrochem Corporation, Akron, OH; *U.S. Private*, pg. 30

Clinebell, Kenneth M., Chief Fin. Officer, Treas. & Sec.--Precision Systems, Inc., Saint Petersburg, FL; *U.S. Public*, pg. 1321

Clowe, Kevin, Asst. Treas.--American International Group, Inc., New York, NY; *U.S. Public*, pg. 83

Clutterbuck, Robert T., Treas.--McDonald & Company Investments, Inc., Cleveland, OH; *U.S. Public*, pg. 1068

Coasson, lawrence P., Treas. & Sec.--FieldBrook Farms, Inc., Dunkirk, NY; *U.S. Private*, pg. 403

Coates, G.J., Grp. Treas.--Johnson Matthey Public Limited Company, London, United Kingdom; *Int'l*, pg. 713

Coates, Paul C., Controller--BWI Plc, Altrincham, United Kingdom; *Int'l*, pg. 130

Coats, W. John, V.P.-Fin.--Nutri/System Inc., Horsham, PA; *U.S. Private*, pg. 859

Cobb, Eliot, Treas.--Wherehouse Entertainment, Inc., Torrance, CA; *U.S. Private*, pg. 1171

Coble, Ted C., V.P., Treas. & Asst. Sec.--Piedmont Natural Gas Co., Inc., Charlotte, NC; *U.S. Public*, pg. 1295

Cobuzzi, Robert J., Chief Fin. Officer, Sr. V.P. & Treas.--Kollmorgen Corporation, Waltham, MA; *U.S. Public*, pg. 965

Cocchia, Peter, Treas.--Keating Building Corp., Bala Cynwyd, PA; *U.S. Private*, pg. 610

Cocher, Felix, Treas.--Forbo Holding SA, Eglisau, Switzerland; *Int'l*, pg. 496

Cochran, Steve, Treas.--Sooner Pipe & Supply Corp., Tulsa, OK; *U.S. Private*, pg. 1014

Cochrane, John G., Asst. Treas.--Narragansett Energy Resources Company, Providence, RI; *U.S. Public*, pg. 1171

Cochrane, Lee E., Treas.--Courier Corporation, North Chelmsford, MA; *U.S. Public*, pg. 453

Cockrell, D. Michael, Chief Fin. Officer & Treas.--Sanderson Farms, Inc., Laurel, MS; *U.S. Public*, pg. 1430

Cockrell, Mel, Chief Fin. Officer, Controller & Treas.--Ben E. Keith Company, Fort Worth, TX; *U.S. Private*, pg. 611

Coddens, Terry, Asst. Treas.--Coachmen Industries, Inc., Elkhart, IN; *U.S. Public*, pg. 387

Coelho de Sousa, Manuel Sotto-Mayor, Sr. Mgr.-Treas.--Caixa Geral de Depositos, Lisbon, Portugal; *Int'l*, pg. 250

Cogdill, Rick, Chief Fin. Officer & Exec. V.P.--Pilgrim's Pride Corporation, Pittsburg, TX; *U.S. Public*, pg. 1296

Cohen, Amir, Treas.--Laser Industries Ltd., Tel Aviv, Israel; *Int'l*, pg. 429

Cohen, Irving, Chief Fin. Officer & Treas.--Acme Canvas Co., Inc., Malden, MA; *U.S. Private*, pg. 13

Cohen, Jay R., Exec. V.P. & Treas.--CRI Liquidating REIT, Inc., Rockville, MD; *U.S. Public*, pg. 459

Cohen, Jeff, Controller & Treas.--Wavetek Corporation, San Diego, CA; *U.S. Private*, pg. 1154

Cohen, Larry, Treas.--Service Packing Company-United Food Group, Los Angeles, CA; *U.S. Private*, pg. 986

Cohen, Lewis, Controller & Treas.--Kastle Systems LLC, Arlington, VA; *U.S. Private*, pg. 608

Cohen, Melvin, V.P.-Plng. & Devel. & Treas.--CC Industries, Inc., Chicago, IL; *U.S. Private*, pg. 192

Cohen, Richard, Vice Chm.--Norstan, Inc., Plymouth, MN; *U.S. Public*, pg. 1192

Cohen, Robert, Treas.--Acme Canvas Co., Inc., Malden, MA; *U.S. Private*, pg. 13

Cohen, Robert B., V.P. & Treas.--Federal Compress & Warehouse Company, Inc., Memphis, TN; *U.S. Private*, pg. 398

Cohen, Warren, V.P.-Fin. & Treas.--Unisystems, Inc., New York, NY; *U.S. Private*, pg. 1120

Cohn, Carol, Treas. & Sec.--Decorative Crafts, Inc., Greenwich, CT; *U.S. Private*, pg. 320

Cohrs, Dan J., V.P. & Treas.--GTE Corporation, Stamford, CT; *U.S. Public*, pg. 696

Coker, John, Treas.--nexAir, LLC, Memphis, TN; *U.S. Private*, pg. 797

Colalucci, Francis M., Chief Fin. Officer, Sr. V.P. & Treas.--Empire Insurance Group, New York, NY; *U.S. Public*, pg. 990

Colalucci, Francis M., Chief Fin. Officer, Sr. V.P. & Treas.--Allcity Insurance Co., New York, NY; *U.S. Public*, pg. 990

Colantoni, Alfred, Sr. V.P. & Treas.--Press Communications, LLC, Wall, NJ; *U.S. Private*, pg. 882

Colarusso, Frank, Asst. Treas.--The Dun & Bradstreet Corporation, Murray Hill, NJ; *U.S. Public*, pg. 535

Colberg, Rick, Chief Fin. Officer, V.P. & Treas.--First Northern Capital Corp., Green Bay, WI; *U.S. Public*, pg. 636

Colbow, Brian R., Treas.--A. Schulman, Inc., Akron, OH; *U.S. Public*, pg. 1441

Colby, Albert A., Jr., V.P.-Domestic Phosphate, Treas. & Sec.--International Chemical Company, Tulsa, OK; *U.S. Private*, pg. 568

Colby, David, Chief Fin. Officer & Treas.--Columbia/HCA Healthcare Corporation, Nashville, TN; *U.S. Public*, pg. 404

Cole, David O., Chief Fin. Officer, V.P., Controller, Treas. & Sec.--Lincoln Foodservice Products, Inc., Fort Wayne, IN; *Int'l*, pg. 188

Cole, Denise, Asst. Treas.-Intl.--Ingram Industries Inc., Nashville, TN; *U.S. Private*, pg. 562

Cole, Glenda, Treas.--Bankhead Enterprises Inc., Atlanta, GA; *U.S. Private*, pg. 114

Cole, John, Chief Fin. Officer, Treas. & Controller--Square Industries, Inc., Jersey City, NJ; *U.S. Public*, pg. 326

Cole, Madison F., Jr., Treas.--Norrell Corporation, Atlanta, GA; *U.S. Public*, pg. 1192

Coleman, Robert E., Treas. & Sec.--Coleman Oldsmobile, Inc., Baton Rouge, LA; *U.S. Private*, pg. 252

Collett, Kenneth L., Treas.--Keeney Manufacturing Co., Newington, CT; *U.S. Private*, pg. 611

Collett, William C., Treas.--Dreyer's Grand Ice Cream, Inc., Oakland, CA; *U.S. Public*, pg. 529

Collin, Mark H., Chief Fin. Officer, Treas. & Sec.--Unitil Corporation, Hampton, NH; *U.S. Public*, pg. 1692

Collin, Mark H., Treas.--Concord Electric Company, Hampton, NH; *U.S. Public*, pg. 1692

Collin, Mark H., Treas.--Exeter & Hampton Electric Co., Hampton, NH; *U.S. Public*, pg. 1692

Collin, Mark H., Treas.--UNITIL Power Corporation, Hampton, NH; *U.S. Public*, pg. 1692

Collin, Mark H., Treas.--UNITIL Realty Corporation, Hampton, NH; *U.S. Public*, pg. 1692

Collin, Mark H., Treas.--Fitchburg Gas and Electric Light Co., Fitchburg, MA; *U.S. Public*, pg. 1692

Collin, Mark H., Treas.--UNITIL Resources, Inc., Hampton, NH; *U.S. Public*, pg. 1692

Collin, Mark H., V.P. & Treas.--UNITIL Service Corporation, Hampton, NH; *U.S. Public*, pg. 1693

Colling, John P., Jr., V.P. & Treas.--MagneTek, Inc., Nashville, TN; *U.S. Public*, pg. 1037

Collings, Glenn M., Chief Fin. Officer, V.P.-Fin. & Treas.--Moore Tool Company, Inc., Bridgeport, CT; *U.S. Private*, pg. 889

Collins, Catherine L., Treas.--Whiting Corporation, Harvey, IL; *U.S. Private*, pg. 1173

Collins, Donald F., Treas. & Sec.--Collins Electric Company, Inc., Chicopee, MA; *U.S. Private*, pg. 253

Collins, Julie E., Chief Fin. Officer, Treas. & Sec.--Continental Homes Holding Corp., Scottsdale, AZ; *U.S. Public*, pg. 440

Collins, Robert E., V.P. & Treas.--Syntex, Palo Alto, CA; *Int'l*, pg. 1120

Collins, William K., Treas.--Bill Collins Ford Inc., Louisville, KY; *U.S. Private*, pg. 253

Collinsworth, William J., Chief Fin. Officer, V.P.-Fin., Treas. & Asst. Sec.--Optek Technology, Inc., Carrollton, TX; *U.S. Public*, pg. 1227

Collum, Hugh, Treas.--SmithKline Beecham Corporation, Philadelphia, PA; *Int'l*, pg. 1264

Colotti, Raymond L., Treas.--Automatic Data Processing, Inc., Roseland, NJ; *U.S. Public*, pg. 150

Colton, Leonard H., Treas.--Domestic Uniform Rental Co., Farmington Hills, MI; *U.S. Private*, pg. 338

Colton, W.M., Treas.--Esso Sekiyu Kabushiki Kaisha, Tokyo, Japan; *U.S. Public*, pg. 602

Colucci, Elena, Treas.--Laminaire Corporation, Rahway, NJ; *U.S. Public*, pg. 1596

Colville, D.H., Treas.--Pearson plc, London, United Kingdom; *Int'l*, pg. 1025

Colwell, Dennis J., First V.P.-Investments & Treasury--People's Bank, Bridgeport, CT; *U.S. Public*, pg. 1274

Comas, Leigh C., V.P.-Fin. & Asst. Treas.--Manor Care, Inc., Gaithersburg, MD; *U.S. Public*, pg. 1041

Comes, Anastasia M., V.P. & Treas.--Ace Doran Hauling & Rigging Company, Cincinnati, OH; *U.S. Private*, pg. 340

Comes, Anastasia M., V.P. & Treas.--Ace Doran Brokerage, Cincinnati, OH; *U.S. Private*, pg. 340

Comfort, Eugene C., V.P. & Treas.--Pacific Metal Company, Portland, OR; *U.S. Private*, pg. 832

Comoreia, Ann, Chief Fin. Officer, V.P. & Treas.--Syms Corporation, Secaucus, NJ; *U.S. Public*, pg. 1547

Conant, Howard R., Chm. Bd.--Interstate Steel Co. Inc., Des Plaines, IL; *Int'l*, pg. 572

Conaway, Kevin D., Chief Acctg. Officer & Treas.--Wall Street Deli, Inc., Birmingham, AL; *U.S. Public*, pg. 1734

Conder, Patrick, Treas.--Owensboro Grain Co., Inc., Owensboro, KY; *U.S. Private*, pg. 824

Condon, James E., V.P. & Treas.--Hartmarx Corporation, Chicago, IL; *U.S. Public*, pg. 795

Condon, Robert V., Chief Fin. Officer, V.P.-Fin., Treas. & Sec.--Merrimac Industries, Inc., West Caldwell, NJ; *U.S. Public*, pg. 1098

Condon, Ronald L., V.P. & Treas.--Canadian American Railroad Company, Bangor, ME; *U.S. Private*, pg. 575

Condon, Ronald L., V.P. & Treas.--Bangor & Aroostook Railroad Co., Bangor, ME; *U.S. Private*, pg. 575

Conklin, Walter J., Treas.--John Wiley & Sons, Inc., New York, NY; *U.S. Public*, pg. 1768

Conley, John, Treas. & Dir.-Investor Rels.--Biogen, Inc., Cambridge, MA; *U.S. Public*, pg. 230

Conley, Olga L., Chief Fin. Officer--DM Management Company, Hingham, MA; *U.S. Public*, pg. 473

Conn, Richard, Treas. & Sec.--Ervin Industries, Inc., Ann Arbor, MI; *U.S. Private*, pg. 382

Connaughton, Michael, Treas.--Dahlem Company, Inc., Louisville, KY; *U.S. Private*, pg. 306

Connell, Terry, Sr. V.P. & Treas.--Connell Co., Westfield, NJ; *U.S. Private*, pg. 264

Connolly, William, Treas.--Globe Newspaper Company, Boston, MA; *U.S. Public*, pg. 1175

Connor, John, Treas.--Polyvinyl Films, Inc., Sutton, MA; *U.S. Private*, pg. 875

Connor, John M., Controller & Treas.--Cives Corporation, Roswell, GA; *U.S. Private*, pg. 241

Connors, Joseph J., Treas. & Asst. Sec.--Kleinert's Inc. of Florida, Largo, FL; *U.S. Private*, pg. 625

Connors, Susan, Asst. Treas.--Magneco/Metrel, Inc., Addison, IL; *U.S. Private*, pg. 695

Conrad, Kim R., Controller, Treas. & Sec.--B & G Wholesalers, Inc., Nashville, TN; *U.S. Private*, pg. 105

Conrad, Nicholas, Asst. Treas.-Long-Term Debt & Mgr.-Lease--The Andersons Incorporated, Maumee, OH; *U.S. Public*, pg. 111

Conradt, Woody, Chief Fin. Officer, Treas. & Sec.--Telsco Industries, Garland, TX; *U.S. Private*, pg. 1074

Considine, Mary, Treas.--Baker & Taylor, Inc., Charlotte, NC; *U.S. Private*, pg. 111

Contadino, Joseph, Chm. Bd., Pres. & Treas.--Del Webb's Coventry Homes, Phoenix, AZ; *U.S. Public*, pg. 495

Conte, Richard R., V.P. & Treas.--International Technology Corporation, Monroeville, PA; *U.S. Public*, pg. 907

Conti, Dominic, Treas.--Rosenthal Automotive Organization, Arlington, VA; *U.S. Private*, pg. 946

Conti, Philip P., Asst. Treas.-Fin.--Equitable Resources, Inc., Pittsburgh, PA; *U.S. Public*, pg. 589

Contreras, Carlos, Head-Dealing Room--Caja de Madrid Group, Madrid, Spain; *Int'l*, pg. 251

Conway, Frederick F., Treas.--Thompson Steel Co., Inc., Canton, MA; *U.S. Private*, pg. 1083

Conway, Joan I., Treas.--Rayrock Yellowknife Resources Inc., Toronto, Canada; *Int'l*, pg. 1089

Conway, Robert D., Treas. & Sec.--Schneider National, Inc., Green Bay, WI; *U.S. Private*, pg. 971

Conzelmann, Gerd, Treas.--The Wella Corporation, Montvale, NJ; *Int'l*, pg. 1489

Cook, Debbie, Sec. & Treas.--Cook Manufacturing Corporation, Duncan, OK; *U.S. Private*, pg. 272

Cook, George, Treas.--Mid America Steel, Inc., Fargo, ND; *U.S. Private*, pg. 743

Cook, J.M., V.P. & Treas.--American Cast Iron Pipe Co., Birmingham, AL; *U.S. Private*, pg. 51

Cook, Linda S., V.P., Treas. & Sec.--Georgia Casualty & Surety Company, Atlanta, GA; *U.S. Public*, pg. 143

Cook, Mike, Treas. & Sec.--Collins Oldsmobile Inc., Indianapolis, IN; *U.S. Private*, pg. 253

Cook, Paul R., Chief Fin. Officer, Exec. V.P. & Treas.--American Consumers, Inc., Fort Oglethorpe, GA; *U.S. Public*, pg. 70

Cook, Richard, Chief Fin. Officer & Treasurer--Genfoot Inc., Montreal, Canada; *Int'l*, pg. 549

Cook, Richard A., Chief Fin. Officer, Treas. & Sec.--Johanna Foods Inc., Flemington, NJ; *U.S. Private*, pg. 589

Cook, Troy D., Chief Fin. Officer, V.P.-Fin. & Treas.--NPC International, Inc., Pittsburg, KS; *U.S. Public*, pg. 1146

Cooke, C. Hunt, Chief Accountant & Treas.--BPB Industries PLC, Slough, United Kingdom; *Int'l*, pg. 122

Cooke, Samuel A., Exec. V.P. & Treas.--Molokai Ranch Ltd., Honolulu, HI; *Int'l*, pg. 216

Cookson, John S., Chief Fin. Officer, V.P.-Fin., Treas. & Sec.--Kingsbury Corporation, Keene, NH; *U.S. Private*, pg. 621

Cooley, James A., V.P. & Treas.--DIMON, Incorporated, Danville, VA; *U.S. Public*, pg. 509

Coombe, V.A., Chm. Bd., Chief Exec. Officer & Treas.--The Wm. Powell Company, Cincinnati, OH; *U.S. Private*, pg. 877

Coombs, E.D., Jr., V.P. & Treas.--Anderson-Tully Co., Memphis, TN; *U.S. Private*, pg. 73

Cooney, Edward, Chief Fin. Officer, Sr. V.P. & Treas.--Amtrol Inc., West Warwick, RI; *U.S. Private*, pg. 300

Cooney, Julie A., Asst. Treas. & Compliance Officer--Washington Square Securities, Minneapolis, MN; *U.S. Public*, pg. 1376

Coopee, Tom, Treas.--Merriam-Webster, Inc., Springfield, MA; *U.S. Private*, pg. 375

Cooper, Brian S., Treas.--Borg-Warner Security Corporation, Chicago, IL; *U.S. Public*, pg. 245

Cooper, Janet K., V.P.-Treas. & Tax--The Quaker Oats Company, Chicago, IL; *U.S. Public*, pg. 1347

Cooper, Robert, Treas.--Whitbread PLC, London, United Kingdom; *Int'l*, pg. 1498

Cooper, Robert H., Treas. & Dir.-Fin.--Mesaba Holdings, Inc., Minneapolis, MN; *U.S. Public*, pg. 1099

Cooper, Steve, Treas.--Best Access Systems, Indianapolis, IN; *U.S. Public*, pg. 223

Cooperman, Michael, Chief Fin. Officer, V.P. & Treas.--ICM Holdings Inc., New York, NY; *U.S. Private*, pg. 554

Coopr, Jerome, Treas. & Sec.--Green Bus Lines, Inc., Jamaica, NY; *U.S. Private*, pg. 476

Copland, James R., III, Pres., Chief Exec. Officer & Treas.--Copland Fabrics, Inc., Burlington, NC; *U.S. Private*, pg. 274

Copland, Ronald G., Exec. V.P., Sec. & Asst. Treas.--Copland Fabrics, Inc., Burlington, NC; *U.S. Private*, pg. 274

Coppola, Sebastian, Sr. V.P. & Treas.--MCN Energy Group, Inc., Detroit, MI; *U.S. Public*, pg. 1024

Coppola, Sebastian, Sr. V.P. & Treas.--MCN Investment, Detroit, MI; *U.S. Public*, pg. 1025

Coppola, Sebastian, Treas.--Citizens Gas Fuel Company, Adrian, MI; *U.S. Public*, pg. 1025

Corbett, John, Treas. & Sec.--United Feeds, Inc., Sheridan, IN; *U.S. Private*, pg. 1122

Corbett, Keith, V.P. & Treas.--North Carolina Mutual Life Insurance Co., Durham, NC; *U.S. Private*, pg. 804

Corbin, R. F., Treas. & Sec.--Metal Trades, Inc., Hollywood, SC; *U.S. Private*, pg. 734

Corcoran, James P., Treas.--York International Corporation, York, PA; *U.S. Public*, pg. 1788

Cordaro, Ralph C., Treas.--LaRoche Industries Inc., Atlanta, GA; *U.S. Private*, pg. 651

Cordek, Lawrence D., Chief Fin. Officer & Corp. Sec.--G B Stores, Columbus, OH; *U.S. Private*, pg. 972

Cordier, Steven O., Treas.--Universal Foods Corporation, Milwaukee, WI; *U.S. Public*, pg. 1695

Corkery, Neil A., Treas.--Proudfoot USA Company, West Palm Beach, FL; *Int'l*, pg. 1072

Corn, Pauline G., Chief Info. Officer, Treas. & Sec.--Industrial Maintenance Overflow Corporation, Fletcher, NC; *U.S. Private*, pg. 561

Cornacchio, Mario, V.P. & Treas.--Welch Foods Inc., A Cooperative, Concord, MA; *U.S. Private*, pg. 784

Cornacchio, Mario J., Asst. Treas.--Cabot Corporation, Boston, MA; *U.S. Public*, pg. 288

Cornell, G.L., Sr. V.P.-Acctg., Real Estate & Treas.--Auto-Owners Insurance, Lansing, MI; *U.S. Private*, pg. 100

Cornell, Helen, V.P., Treas. & Sec.--Gardner Denver Machinery Inc., Quincy, IL; *U.S. Public*, pg. 703

Corner, David, Chief Fin. Officer, Treas.--Fleck Manufacturing Inc., Tillsonburg, Canada; *Int'l*, pg. 955

Cornish, Jeff, Chief Fin. Officer & V.P.--Pilot Corporation, Knoxville, TN; *U.S. Private*, pg. 865

Cornish, Jeffrey L., Treas. & Sec.--Pilot Corporation, Knoxville, TN; *U.S. Private*, pg. 865

Cornwell, A.D., V.P. & Treas.--Chevron Chemical Co., San Ramon, CA; *U.S. Public*, pg. 348

Corr, Deborah A., Treas. & Asst. Sec.--VWR Scientific Products, West Chester, PA; *U.S. Public*, pg. 1703

Corr, Robert R., Controller, Treas. & Sec.--BEI Technologies, Inc., San Francisco, CA; *U.S. Public*, pg. 160

Corsini, John M., Pres., Chief Exec. Officer & Treas.--Uncas Manufacturing Company, Providence, RI; *U.S. Private*, pg. 1116

Corwin, Daniel K., V.P., Treas. & Gen. Mgr.--Acme Electric Corporation, East Aurora, NY; *U.S. Public*, pg. 16

Corwin, Stanley, CPA, Treas.--CFX Mortgage, Inc., Keene, NH; *U.S. Public*, pg. 278

Corwin, Theresa P., Treas.--Plantronics Inc., Santa Cruz, CA; *U.S. Public*, pg. 1308

Corydon, G. Patrick, V.P.-Fin. & Treas.--Baldwin & Lyons, Inc., Indianapolis, IN; *U.S. Public*, pg. 169

Cosaert, John P., Chief Fin. Officer, Exec. V.P.-Intl. Fin., Treas. & Controller--Heartland Express, Inc., Coralville, IA; *U.S. Public*, pg. 803

Cosbey, J.R., V.P., Treas. & Sec.--Daubert Industries, Inc., Westchester, IL; *U.S. Private*, pg. 313

Cosner, Alan, V.P., Treas. & Sec.--Lady Baltimore Foods, Inc., Kansas City, KS; *U.S. Public*, pg. 975

Cossar, Michael A., Treas.--CAE Inc., Toronto, Canada; *Int'l*, pg. 237

Costa, Kevin, Treas.--H.B. Smith Co., Inc., Westfield, MA; *U.S. Private*, pg. 1008

Costales, Thomas M., Chief Fin. Officer & Treas.--AirSensors, Inc., Seattle, WA; *U.S. Public*, pg. 33

Costello, Jonathan, Treas.--Safeguard International Group, Wayne, PA; *U.S. Public*, pg. 1424

Costello, Paul M., V.P. & Treas.--Du Pont Canada Inc., Mississauga, Canada; *U.S. Public*, pg. 532

Cott, Burl G., Sr. V.P. & Treas.--Conwell Corp., Dallas, TX; *U.S. Public*, pg. 685

Cotton, Gary, Chief Fin. Officer, V.P.-Fin. & Treas.--Rexall Sundown Inc., Boca Raton, FL; *U.S. Public*, pg. 1384

Cotton, Owen L., V.P.-Fin. & Treas.--J.R. Norton Company, Phoenix, AZ; *U.S. Private*, pg. 807

Cottsting, Jim, Asst. Treas.--Ciminelli Development Company, Inc., Williamsville, NY; *U.S. Private*, pg. 239

Coughlin, John, V.P.-Fin. & Treas.--Caldwell Manufacturing Company, Rochester, NY; *U.S. Private*, pg. 200

Coulombe, Cecile J., Treas.--White Rock Distilleries Inc., Lewiston, ME; *U.S. Private*, pg. 1173

Coulombe, Cecile J., V.P. & Treas.--Nuyens Liquor Importing, Inc., Syosset, NY; *U.S. Private*, pg. 1173

Coulter, Tim, Asst. Treas.--Sierra Health Services, Inc., Las Vegas, NV; *U.S. Public*, pg. 1469

Countryman, Peter J., Chief Fin. Officer & Treas.--Sabin Robbins Paper Co., Cincinnati, OH; *U.S. Private*, pg. 959

Coupe, Bruce A., Treas. & Sec.--Peerless Tyre Co., Denver, CO; *U.S. Private*, pg. 847

Cousins, George A., Treas.--HDS Services, Farmington Hills, MI; *U.S. Private*, pg. 490

Covey, Harold D., Exec. V.P., Treas. & Chief Admin. Officer--State Farm Fire and Casualty Co., Bloomington, IL; *U.S. Private*, pg. 1036

Covey, Harold D., Exec. V.P., Treas. & Chief Admin. Officer--State Farm General Insurance Co., Bloomington, IL; *U.S. Private*, pg. 1036

Covey, Joy D., Chief Fin. Officer, V.P.-Fin., Treas. & Sec.--Amazon.com, Inc., Seattle, WA; *U.S. Public*, pg. 62

Covin, Elaine, Treas.--Choctaw, Inc., Memphis, TN; *U.S. Private*, pg. 238

Covington, Edward H., Pres. & Treas.--Harriss & Covington Hosiery Mills, High Point, NC; *U.S. Private*, pg. 506

Cowan, Richard, Chief Fin. Officer, Treas., Controller & Sec.--Wheeler Brothers Grain Co., Watonga, OK; *U.S. Private*, pg. 1171

Cowell, Steven S., Chief Fin. Officer & Corp. V.P.--Agouron Pharmaceuticals, Inc., La Jolla, CA; *U.S. Public*, pg. 28

Cowin, John J., Chm. Bd., Pres. & Treas.--Cowin & Company, Inc., Birmingham, AL; *U.S. Private*, pg. 280

Cowles, Alfred L., III, Chief Fin. Officer, Treas. & Controller--Bluff City Distributing Co., Inc., Memphis, TN; *U.S. Private*, pg. 153
Cox, Arthur, Treas. & Sec.--The Knapheide Mfg. Co., Quincy, IL; *U.S. Private*, pg. 626
Cox, Mark B., Treas.--Giant Industries Inc., Scottsdale, AZ; *U.S. Public*, pg. 741
Cox, Samuel J., V.P. & Treas.--Mars Super Markets, Inc., Baltimore, MD; *U.S. Private*, pg. 707
Cox, Steve, Treas.--The Lewis Bear Company, Pensacola, FL; *U.S. Private*, pg. 127
Cox, Thomas L., V.P. & Treas.--Federal Paper Board Company, Inc., Montvale, NJ; *U.S. Public*, pg. 903
Cox, Thomas L., V.P. & Treas.--Imperial Bondware Corp., Montvale, NJ; *U.S. Public*, pg. 903
Cox, Thomas P., Sr. V.P.-Fin., Sec. & Treas.--Timberline Software Corporation, Beaverton, OR; *U.S. Public*, pg. 1609
Coxson, Timothy C., Chief Fin. Officer, Treas. & Exec. V.P.-Fin.--American Waste Services, Inc., Warren, OH; *U.S. Public*, pg. 94
Coyle, Janet, Asst. Treas.--The Challenge Machinery Co., Grand Haven, MI; *U.S. Private*, pg. 227
Coyle, Juliana M., V.P. & Treas.--United Asset Management Corporation, Boston, MA; *U.S. Public*, pg. 1672
Crabtree, Richard, Treas. & Sec.--SCR, Inc., Tigard, OR; *U.S. Private*, pg. 955
Craig, Paul, Chief Fin. Officer, Exec. V.P. & Treas.--Pac Rim Holding Corporation, Woodland Hills, CA; *U.S. Public*, pg. 1246
Crain, Mary Kay, Treas.--Crain Communications, Inc., Chicago, IL; *U.S. Private*, pg. 284
Cramer, John, Treas.--Nobility Homes, Inc., Ocala, FL; *U.S. Public*, pg. 1186
Cramer, Lee H., V.P. & Treas.--Rockwell International Corporation, Costa Mesa, CA; *U.S. Public*, pg. 1397
Cramp, Lori, V.P. & Treas.--Host Marriott Services Corporation, Bethesda, MD; *U.S. Public*, pg. 841
Crandall, George T., V.P., Treas., Controller & Sec.--Tridex Corporation, Westport, CT; *U.S. Public*, pg. 1637
Crandall, L. Dale, Chief Fin. Officer, Exec. V.P. & Treas.--APL Limited, Oakland, CA; *Int'l*, pg. 912
Crathon, Don, Treas.--The Parman Corporation, Nashville, TN; *U.S. Private*, pg. 840
Craver, Ted, V.P. & Treas.--Edison International, Rosemead, CA; *U.S. Public*, pg. 564
Craver, Theodore F., Jr., V.P. & Treas.--Southern California Edison Company, Rosemead, CA; *U.S. Public*, pg. 564
Crawford, James, Treas.--J.R. Simplot Company, Boise, ID; *U.S. Private*, pg. 1002
Crawford, John K., Chief Fin. Officer, V.P. & Treas.--Phycor, Inc., Nashville, TN; *U.S. Public*, pg. 1293
Crawford, Kathleen, Sr. V.P. & Treas.--Admiral Insurance Company, Cherry Hill, NJ; *U.S. Public*, pg. 216
Crawford, Randy, Pres. & Treas.--Adair Feed & Grain Company, Adair, IA; *U.S. Private*, pg. 16
Creed, D.R., Treas.--Tate & Lyle PLC, London, United Kingdom; *Int'l*, pg. 1356
Creek, Wallace W., Treas.--Holden's Engine Products Overseas Corporation, Melbourne, Australia; *U.S. Public*, pg. 723
Creekmuir, William S., Chief Fin. Officer, Exec. V.P., Treas. & Sec.--Ladd Furniture, Inc., Greensboro, NC; *U.S. Public*, pg. 974
Creel, L. Anderson, Chief Fin. Officer, Sr. V.P., Treas. & Sec.--Prime Bancshares Inc., Houston, TX; *U.S. Public*, pg. 1326
Creel, Mike, V.P. & Treas.--NorAm Energy Corp., Houston, TX; *U.S. Public*, pg. 843
Cress, Sally, Treas. & Sec.--Bancinsurance Corp., Columbus, OH; *U.S. Public*, pg. 175
Crews, J. Russell, Chief Fin. Officer, Sr. V.P. & Treas.--Snelling Personnel Services, Dallas, TX; *U.S. Private*, pg. 1010
Cribbs, Francis J., Exec. V.P., Chief Fin. Officer & Treas.--Lloyd Properties, Los Angeles, CA; *U.S. Private*, pg. 672
Crifasi, Jan, Treas.--Hi Nabor Supermarket Inc., Baton Rouge, LA; *U.S. Private*, pg. 525
Cripe, Richard L., Treas.--Gohmann Asphalt & Construction Inc., Clarksville, IN; *U.S. Private*, pg. 459
Crisafulli, Robert, Jr., Treas. & Sec.--The Orioles, Inc., Baltimore, MD; *U.S. Private*, pg. 819
Crisanti, John, Treas.--The U.S. Baird Corporation, Stratford, CT; *U.S. Private*, pg. 1124
Crisanti, John, Treas.--The A.H. Nilson Machine Co., Stratford, CT; *U.S. Private*, pg. 1124
Crisp, Max, V.P.-Fin., Treas. & Sec.--Stewart Information Services Corporation, Houston, TX; *U.S. Public*, pg. 1518
Criste, Robert M., Chief Fin. Officer, V.P. & Treas.--Stephenson Equipment, Inc., Harrisburg, PA; *U.S. Private*, pg. 1040
Critser, Gary P., Sr. Exec. V.P., Treas. & Sec.--Kimball International, Inc., Jasper, IN; *U.S. Public*, pg. 956
Crivelli, Joseph, Asst. Treas.--Penn Engineering & Manufacturing Corp., Danboro, PA; *U.S. Public*, pg. 1269
Croatti, Cynthia C., Treas.--UniFirst Corporation, Wilmington, MA; *U.S. Public*, pg. 1665
Crocker, Derwood, Chief Fin. Officer, V.P.-Fin. & Treas.--ScanTron Corporation, Tustin, CA; *U.S. Public*, pg. 786
Crocker, Frederick G., Jr., Chief Fin. Officer, V.P., Treas. & Sec.--Springborn Testing & Research, Inc., Enfield, CT; *U.S. Private*, pg. 1027
Croisier, J.P.L., Sr. V.P. & Treas.--Essex International, Inc., Fort Wayne, IN; *U.S. Public*, pg. 593
Cromer, Vicki, Chief Fin. Officer & Treas.--Bayou State Oil Corporation, Shreveport, LA; *U.S. Private*, pg. 125
Cronen, Vincent, Treas. & Sec.--Whittaker, Clark & Daniels, Inc., South Plainfield, NJ; *U.S. Private*, pg. 1174
Cronin, David M., Exec. V.P. & Treas.--First Maryland Bancorp, Baltimore, MD; *Int'l*, pg. 64
Cronin, Patrick, V.P.-Fin.--Delta Consolidated Industries, Inc., Raleigh, NC; *U.S. Public*, pg. 481
Cronin, Patrick, Treas.--Delta Consolidated Industries, Inc. (Co. Headquarters), Jonesboro, AR; *U.S. Public*, pg. 481
Cronin, William J., V.P. & Treas.--Phibro Division of Salomon Inc., Westport, CT; *U.S. Public*, pg. 1633
Cronqvist, Erling, Mgr.-Treas./Back Office--European Investment Bank, Luxembourg, Luxembourg; *Int'l*, pg. 465
Crook, Kent W., Pres. & Treas.--The Burton Company, North Haven, CT; *U.S. Public*, pg. 826
Crookshank, George A., Chief Fin. Officer & V.P.-Fin.--Ocelot Energy Inc., Calgary, Canada; *Int'l*, pg. 996
Cross, Art, Asst. Treas.--SPX Corporation, Muskegon, MI; *U.S. Public*, pg. 1420
Cross, Richard, Treas.--Best Products Co., Inc., Richmond, VA; *U.S. Private*, pg. 990
Cross, Scott, Treas., Controller & Chief Accountant--Lewis Drug, Inc., Sioux Falls, SD; *U.S. Private*, pg. 665
Cross, Silas R., V.P. & Treas.--The Todd-AO Corporation, Hollywood, CA; *U.S. Public*, pg. 1619
Crosson, Tom, Treas.--Rolls-Royce plc, London, United Kingdom; *Int'l*, pg. 1126
Croteau, Clara, Treas. & Sec.--Spiegel Meats, Inc., Miami, FL; *U.S. Private*, pg. 1025
Crouch, George W., Jr., Treas. & Sec.--Tallapoosa River Electric Co-Op, Lafayette, AL; *U.S. Private*, pg. 1067
Crouthamel, Michael R., Chief Fin. Officer & Treas.--John Solomon, Inc., Somerville, MA; *U.S. Private*, pg. 1013
Crow, Lisa, Treas.--Jani King, Inc., Dallas, TX; *U.S. Private*, pg. 581
Crowell, Judy, Asst. Treas.--Food Lion, Inc., Salisbury, NC; *Int'l*, pg. 463
Crowell, Steven H., Pres., Chief Oper. Officer, Chief Exec. Officer & Treas.--East Coast Steel, Inc., Claremont, NH; *U.S. Private*, pg. 356
Crowley, Elaine D., V.P.-Fin. & Treas.--The Bombay Company, Inc., Fort Worth, TX; *U.S. Public*, pg. 244
Crown, Marc, Asst. Treas.--Alumax Inc., Atlanta, GA; *U.S. Public*, pg. 59
Crozier, David, Treas. & Sec.--Sharon Tube Company, Sharon, PA; *U.S. Private*, pg. 990
Crum, Mary M., Treas. & Sec.--Crum Electric Supply Co., Inc., Casper, WY; *U.S. Private*, pg. 293
Crumbine, Dennis, Sr. V.P., Sec. & Treas.--Poland Spring Corporation, Greenwich, CT; *Int'l*, pg. 919
Cruncleton, Barbara A., Treas. & Sec.--John S. Frey Enterprises, Los Angeles, CA; *U.S. Private*, pg. 428
Crunk, Rebecca B., V.P., Controller & Treas.--United Services Life Insurance Co., Arlington, VA; *U.S. Public*, pg. 1376
Crutcher, Shirley, Treas. & Sec.--Atrium Companies, Inc., Dallas, TX; *U.S. Private*, pg. 98
Crutcher, Shirley, Treas. & Sec.--Atrium Companies, Inc., Irving, TX; *U.S. Private*, pg. 98
Crvarich, Gene, Chief Fin. Officer, V.P., Treas. & Sec.--Al Larson Boat Shop, Inc., Terminal Island, CA; *U.S. Private*, pg. 652
Cryder, Jeffrey A., Chief Fin. Officer--Bliss-Salem, Inc., Salem, OH; *U.S. Private*, pg. 149
Csepella, John, Treas.--Color Arts, Inc., Racine, WI; *U.S. Private*, pg. 254
Cubberly, Walter A., Chm. Bd. & Treas.--Kalas Manufacturing, Inc., Denver, PA; *U.S. Private*, pg. 606
Cudney, Cori, Chief Fin. Officer, V.P.-Fin. & Treas.--A. Levy & J. Zentner Co., Sacramento, CA; *U.S. Private*, pg. 663
Cudzewicz, Alexander J., Dir.-Fin.--Sargent & Lundy, Chicago, IL; *U.S. Private*, pg. 965
Cuff, Harry, Treas.--Kampgrounds of America, Inc., Billings, MT; *U.S. Private*, pg. 603
Cuffey, Jayashri S., Asst. Treas.--W.P. Carey & Co., Inc., New York, NY; *U.S. Private*, pg. 209
Culhane, Maureen M., V.P.-Fin. & Treas.--Sara Lee Corporation, Chicago, IL; *U.S. Public*, pg. 1432
Cull, Mike, V.P. & Treas.--RGP Holding, Inc., Wilmington, DE; *U.S. Private*, pg. 903
Cullen, Martin J., V.P., Treas & Sec.--Chock Full O' Nuts Corporation, New York, NY; *U.S. Public*, pg. 351
Culligan, James M., Treas.--Pratt & Lambert United, Inc., Cleveland, OH; *U.S. Public*, pg. 1466
Cullinane, Michael P., Chief Fin. Officer, Exec. V.P. & Treas.--Platinum Technology, Inc., Oak Brook Terrace, IL; *U.S. Public*, pg. 1309
Culverwell, Ronald L., Treas. & Asst. Sec.--Zions Co-operative Mercantile Institution, Salt Lake City, UT; *U.S. Public*, pg. 1793
Cummings, Beverly A., Chief Fin. Officer & Treas.--PrimeEnergy Corporation, Stamford, CT; *U.S. Public*, pg. 1328
Cummings, M. Laurie, Controller & Asst. Treas.--Dartford Partnership, San Francisco, CA; *U.S. Private*, pg. 312
Cummins, Mark R., Sr. V.P., Chief Investment Officer & Treas.--Harleysville Group, Harleysville, PA; *U.S. Public*, pg. 786
Cunningham, J. Dawson, V.P.-Fin. & Admin. & Treas.--Roadway Express, Inc., Akron, OH; *U.S. Public*, pg. 1392
Cunningham, N.J., Treas. & Sec.--Atlantic Generation, Inc., Pleasantville, NJ; *U.S. Public*, pg. 430
Cunningham, N.J., Pres. & Sec.--Atlantic Energy Technology, Inc., Pleasantville, NJ; *U.S. Public*, pg. 430
Cunningham, Richard F., Treas.--Hearst Entertainment, New York, NY; *U.S. Private*, pg. 516
Cunningham, Thomas P., V.P. & Treas.--Allmerica Securities Trust, Worcester, MA; *U.S. Public*, pg. 54
Cupric, Harry, Treas.--Morrison Petroleums Ltd., Calgary, Canada; *Int'l*, pg. 895
Curci, John, Chief Fin. Officer & Treas.--Arrowhead Holding Corporation, Brecksville, OH; *U.S. Private*, pg. 86
Curci, John, Chief Fin. Officer & Treas.--Vesper Corporation, Brecksville, OH; *U.S. Private*, pg. 86
Curdy, Harold M., V.P.-Fin. & Treas.--Keystone Consolidated Industries, Inc., Dallas, TX; *U.S. Public*, pg. 955
Curley, Denis M., Chief Fin. Officer, Sr. V.P., Treas. & Sec.--The Ackerley Group, Seattle, WA; *U.S. Public*, pg. 15
Curley, Stephen C., V.P. & Treas.--Primex Technologies, Inc., Saint Petersburg, FL; *U.S. Public*, pg. 1329
Curran, Cathie E., Asst. Treas.--Gaylord Container Corporation, Deerfield, IL; *U.S. Public*, pg. 704
Currie, Gordon E., V.P. & Treas.--Emco Limited, London, Canada; *Int'l*, pg. 452
Currie, K.M., Treas.--Northern Rock PLC, Newcastle upon Tyne, United Kingdom; *Int'l*, pg. 968
Currier, Jackie A., V.P. & Treas.--Northern States Power Company, Minneapolis, MN; *U.S. Public*, pg. 1195
Currier, Ronald, Treas. & Sec.--Gilpatrick Construction Company, Inc, Riverton, WY; *U.S. Private*, pg. 454
Curry, James, Treas. & Project Mgr.--Underground Construction Co., Inc., Benicia, CA; *U.S. Private*, pg. 1116
Curtas, William W., Chief Exec., Chief Oper. & Chief Fin. Officer & Exec. V.P.--Steego Corporation, West Palm Beach, FL; *Int'l*, pg. 216
Curtis, Harold R., Chief Fin. Officer, Sr. V.P., Treas. & Sec.--The M/A/R/C Group, Irving, TX; *U.S. Public*, pg. 1022
Curtis, Paul F., Pres., Chief Oper. Officer & Treas.--L.N. Curtis & Sons, Oakland, CA; *U.S. Private*, pg. 297
Curtis, Stan, Controller, Asst Treas & Asst. Sec.--Continental Forge Company, Compton, CA; *U.S. Private*, pg. 268
Curwin, Ronald, Chief Fin. Officer & Treas.--Bed Bath & Beyond Inc., Union, NJ; *U.S. Public*, pg. 200
Cushing, Raymond L., Treas.--Nordson Corporation, Westlake, OH; *U.S. Public*, pg. 1188
Cusimono, Nancy U., Treas.--Black Cadillac Olds, Inc., Greensboro, NC; *U.S. Private*, pg. 146
Cuthbert, I.C., Treas.--London International Group plc, London, United Kingdom; *Int'l*, pg. 815
Cutwright, Brenda F., Chief Fin. Officer, Sr. V.P.-Fin. & Treas.--Aloha Airgroup, Inc., Honolulu, HI; *U.S. Private*, pg. 44
Cuzzolina, Michael J., Treas.--AmeriGas Partners, L.P., Valley Forge, PA; *U.S. Public*, pg. 1653
Cvelbar, Anthony, Treas.--Cohen Furniture Company, Peoria Heights, IL; *U.S. Private*, pg. 250
Cyphers, Stanley P., V.P.-Fin. & Treas.--The Uhlmann Co., Kansas City, MO; *U.S. Private*, pg. 1115
Cyrus, Suzanne, Treas. & Sec.--Adams Investment Company, Bartlesville, OK; *U.S. Private*, pg. 16
Czarnecki, Walter P., Exec. V.P.--Penske Corporation, Detroit, MI; *U.S. Private*, pg. 850
d'Alessio, John W., Treas.--Armor All Products Group, Oakland, CA; *U.S. Public*, pg. 387
D'Ambrosio, Charles, Treas. & Dir.-Human Resources--Intermetrics, Inc., Burlington, MA; *U.S. Private*, pg. 567
D'Ambrosio, Thomas, V.P. & Treas.--The Stephan Company, Fort Lauderdale, FL; *U.S. Public*, pg. 1514
D'Amico, Catherine, Chief Fin. Officer, Sr. V.P.-Fin. & Treas.--Monro Muffler/Brake, Inc., Rochester, NY; *U.S. Public*, pg. 1124
D'Amore, John D., V.P.-Fin. & Treas.--Halifax Corporation, Alexandria, VA; *U.S. Public*, pg. 775
D'Erasmo, Maria Cris, Treas.--Meridian Medical Technology, Inc., Columbia, MD; *U.S. Public*, pg. 1095
D'Haeze, T.M., V.P.-Fin. & Acctg., Treas. & Sec.--Dwyer Instruments Inc., Michigan City, IN; *U.S. Private*, pg. 350
Dabrowski, Edward, V.P. & Treas.--Brother International Corporation, Somerset, NJ; *Int'l*, pg. 229
Dacek, Kenneth J., Treas.--Chase Financial Management Corp., Cleveland, OH; *U.S. Public*, pg. 338
Dahl, Valerie J., V.P., Treas. & Asst. Sec.--Stearns Enterprises, Inc., Lexington, KY; *U.S. Private*, pg. 1037
Dahmen, David S., V.P. & Treas.--National Semiconductor Corporation, Santa Clara, CA; *U.S. Public*, pg. 1159
Dailey, Jan, Treas.--Seaman Timber Company, Inc., Montevallo, AL; *U.S. Private*, pg. 979
Dalbeck, Richard W., Exec. V.P., Chief Fin. Officer & Sec.--The Guber Peters Entertainment Company, Los Angeles, CA; *Int'l*, pg. 1283
Daley, C. Michael, Chm. & Chief Exec. Officer--LoJack Corporation, Dedham, MA; *U.S. Public*, pg. 1012
Daley, Clayton C., Jr., V.P. & Treas.--The Procter & Gamble Company, Cincinnati, OH; *U.S. Public*, pg. 1330
Daley, Leo J., V.P. & Treas.--Air Products and Chemicals, Inc., Allentown, PA; *U.S. Public*, pg. 30
Dalinger, Trudy, Chief Fin. Officer & Sr. V.P.--TSC Shannock Corporation, Burnaby, Canada; *Int'l*, pg. 1343
Dallacqua, John, Chief Fin. Officer, V.P.-Fin., Treas. & Sec.--Crowley, Milner & Company, Detroit, MI; *U.S. Public*, pg. 461
Dallas, Terry G., Sr. V.P. & Treas.--Atlantic Richfield Company, Los Angeles, CA; *U.S. Public*, pg. 144
Dalrymple, Eric G., Treas.--Ernst & Young, LLP, New York, NY; *U.S. Private*, pg. 381
Dalton, Ronald, Sr. V.P., Treas. & Sec.--Huron Valley Steel Corp., Belleville, MI; *U.S. Private*, pg. 549
Daly, Leo A., Chm. Bd., Pres. & Treas.--Leo A. Daly Company, Omaha, NE; *U.S. Private*, pg. 309
Daly, M. Lorraine, V.P. & Treas.--Rogers Communications, Inc., Toronto, Canada; *Int'l*, pg. 1122
Daly, M. Lorraine, V.P. & Treas.--Maclean Hunter Publishing Ltd., Toronto, Canada; *Int'l*, pg. 1123
Daly, Michael J., Treas.--Chessco Industries, Inc., Westport, CT; *U.S. Private*, pg. 234
Daman, Thomas E., Treas.--Southdown, Inc., Houston, TX; *U.S. Public*, pg. 1488
DaMour, Joseph H., Treas.--General Motors do Brasil Ltda., Sao Caetano do Sul, Brazil; *U.S. Public*, pg. 722
Dancy, Richard H., Jr., V.P. & Treas.--The John Johnson Co., Detroit, MI; *U.S. Private*, pg. 591
Dandurand, Don, V.P. & Treas.--The Jewell Electrical Instruments Co., Manchester, NH; *U.S. Private*, pg. 36
Dandurand, S.R., Treas.--Fostoria Industries, Inc., Fostoria, OH; *U.S. Private*, pg. 421
Danford, Philip C., V.P.-Investor Rels. & Treas.--The Dun & Bradstreet Corporation, Murray Hill, NJ; *U.S. Public*, pg. 535
Danford, Philip C., Treas.--A.C. Nielsen Company, Schaumburg, IL; *U.S. Public*, pg. 1183
Daniel, Carole J., V.P. & Controllers.--National Print Group, Inc., Chattanooga, TN; *U.S. Private*, pg. 785

Drinkwater, Jim, V.P. & Treas.--Telus Corporation, Edmonton, Canada; *Int'l*, pg. 1374

Driscoll, Edward C., Chm. Bd., Chief Exec. Officer & Treas.--L.F. Driscoll Co., Bala Cynwyd, PA; *U.S. Private*, pg. 343

Droege, Mark E., V.P.-Fin. Mngmt. & Treas.--BellSouth Corporation, Atlanta, GA; *U.S. Public*, pg. 207

Drucker, K.A., V.P. & Treas.--Sequa Corporation, New York, NY; *U.S. Public*, pg. 1458

Drucker, Myra R., Asst. Treas.-Domestic Pension & Savings Plan Assets--Xerox Corporation, Stamford, CT; *U.S. Public*, pg. 1783

Drucker, Nate, Chief Fin. Officer, Treas. & Sec.--Weber Marking Systems, Inc., Arlington Heights, IL; *U.S. Private*, pg. 1157

Druggish, Thomas R., V.P., Treas. & Sec.--ELXSI Corporation, Orlando, FL; *U.S. Public*, pg. 545

Drumm, Wesley C., Chm. Bd., Pres. & Treas.--The Metal Ware Corp., Two Rivers, WI; *U.S. Private*, pg. 734

Drury, Richard B., Treas. & Sec.--TJ International, Inc., Boise, ID; *U.S. Public*, pg. 1556

Dryer, Ned, Treas. & Sec.--National Brands, Inc., Phoenix, AZ; *U.S. Private*, pg. 780

Du, Carmela, Treas.--Flojet Corporation, Irvine, CA; *U.S. Private*, pg. 414

Duane, Dave, Chief Fin. Officer, Controller & Treas.--Heat Controller, Inc., Jackson, MI; *U.S. Private*, pg. 518

Duarte, Jose Candido, Treas.--Aracruz Celulose S.A., Rio de Janeiro, Brazil; *Int'l*, pg. 78

Dubbin, Kenneth, Treas.--Royal Caribbean Cruises Ltd., Miami, FL; *U.S. Public*, pg. 1410

Dubner, Miriam, Sec. & Treas.--Gerson & Gerson, Inc., New York, NY; *U.S. Private*, pg. 449

Dubois, Everett D., Treas.--Burlington Resources Inc., Houston, TX; *U.S. Public*, pg. 269

Duch, Gregory S., Chief Fin. Officer--Castle Convertible Fund, Inc., New York, NY; *U.S. Public*, pg. 313

Duchesneau, M.A., Controller & Treas.--Central Vermont Railway, Inc., Saint Albans, VT; *Int'l*, pg. 258

Ducken, Lynn K., Treas.--Southern Pacific Rail Corporation, San Francisco, CA; *U.S. Public*, pg. 1668

Duckworth, James, Exec. V.P.-Fin. & Treas.--Quaker City Motor Parts Company, Middletown, DE; *U.S. Private*, pg. 898

Dudley, Kenneth E., Treas.--The Gorman-Rupp Company, Mansfield, OH; *U.S. Public*, pg. 754

Dueffert, Gregory, Pres. & Treas.--Lincoln Industries, Inc., Boonville, IN; *U.S. Private*, pg. 1207

Duersch, Charles A., Treas. & Sec.--Western States Machine Company, Hamilton, OH; *U.S. Private*, pg. 1168

Duffin, Patricia A., Treas. & Asst. Sec.--CH Mortgage Company, Scottsdale, AZ; *U.S. Public*, pg. 441

Dufour, Luc, Asst. Treas.--Donohue Inc., Quebec, Canada; *Int'l*, pg. 1075

Dugan, Mary E., Chm. Bd., Treas. & Sec.--Dugan Production Corp., Farmington, NM; *U.S. Private*, pg. 345

Duguid, Hank, Treas.--M M M Sales, Inc., City of Industry, CA; *U.S. Private*, pg. 685

DuHamel, Mark N., V.P. & Treas. Officer--FirstMerit Corporation, Akron, OH; *U.S. Public*, pg. 646

Duhec, George B., Treas.--Zippo Manufacturing Company, Bradford, PA; *U.S. Private*, pg. 1207

Duke, Andy, Treas.--Talisman Energy Inc., Calgary, Canada; *Int'l*, pg. 1352

Duke, Jean E., V.P.-Treas.--Colonial Companies, Inc., Columbia, SC; *U.S. Public*, pg. 1699

Dula, C. Stephen, Chief Fin. Officer, Treas. & Sec.--Salem National Corporation, Winston Salem, NC; *U.S. Private*, pg. 962

Dulany, Charles R., Treas.--Ocean Spray Cranberries, Inc., Middleboro, MA; *U.S. Private*, pg. 811

Dull, Philip L., V.P. & Treas.--Huttig Sash & Door Co., Chesterfield, MO; *U.S. Public*, pg. 457

Duman, Gregory J., Chief Fin. Officer & Treas.--Transaction Systems Architects, Inc., Omaha, NE; *U.S. Public*, pg. 1629

Dumbacher, Robert J., V.P.-Fin. & Treas.--Racetrac Petroleum, Inc., Smyrna, GA; *U.S. Private*, pg. 906

Dunavant, Philip L., Chief Fin. Officer, V.P. & Treas.--Mark VII, Inc., Memphis, TN; *U.S. Public*, pg. 1046

Dunaway, Harold, V.P.-Fin., Treas. & Sec.--Motion Industries, Inc., Irondale, AL; *U.S. Public*, pg. 732

Duncan, Debbie, Corp. Treas.--The Chase Manhattan Corporation, New York, NY; *U.S. Public*, pg. 337

Duncan, Deborah L., Exec. V.P. & Treas.--The Chase Manhattan Corporation, New York, NY; *U.S. Public*, pg. 337

Duncan, Donald E., Treas.--Jefferson Mills, Inc., Pulaski, VA; *U.S. Private*, pg. 584

Duncan, Edward, Controller & Treas.--Master Craft Corp., Kalamazoo, MI; *Int'l*, pg. 267

Duncan, Gary H., Treas.--Nodak Mutual Insurance Company, Fargo, ND; *U.S. Private*, pg. 800

Duncan, Larry J., Asst. Treas.--IES Industries Inc., Cedar Rapids, IA; *U.S. Public*, pg. 855

Duncan, Willis P., Jr., V.P.-Fin. & Treas.--Thomas Built Buses, Inc., High Point, NC; *U.S. Private*, pg. 1082

Dundas, Anthony J., V.P.-Fin. & Treas.--Repap New Brunswick Inc., Montreal, Canada; *Int'l*, pg. 1104

Dundrea, Matthew W., V.P. & Treas.--Apache Corporation, Houston, TX; *U.S. Public*, pg. 119

Dune, Daniel, Chief Fin. Officer, V.P.-Fin.& Treas.--Clark Foodservice, Inc., Elk Grove Village, IL; *U.S. Private*, pg. 242

Dunican, John J., Treas.--Huls America Inc., Somerset, NJ; *Int'l*, pg. 1455

Dunlap, Jane, V.P. & Treas.--Delphi Financial Group, Inc., Wilmington, DE; *U.S. Public*, pg. 496

Dunleavy, Karen, Treas.--Gould Investors, L.P., Great Neck, NY; *U.S. Private*, pg. 466

Dunn, Jerry, Chief Oper. Officer, V.P. & Treas.--The Odom Corporation, Seattle, WA; *U.S. Private*, pg. 811

Dunn, Philip J., V.P., Controller & Treas.--Circuit City Stores, Inc., Richmond, VA; *U.S. Public*, pg. 374

Dunn, Stephen D., Exec. V.P. & Treas.--Dunn Industries Inc., Kansas City, MO; *U.S. Private*, pg. 347

Dunn, Stephen D., Pres., Chief Exec. Officer & Treas.--Dunn Realty, Inc., Kansas City, MO; *U.S. Private*, pg. 347

Duplessis, Guy, Treas.--Rolland Inc., Saint-Jerome, Canada; *Int'l*, pg. 273

DuPont, Marc J., Treas.--Syntron, Inc., Houston, TX; *U.S. Public*, pg. 1563

Dupps, David M., Treas. & Sec.--Dupps Company, Germantown, OH; *U.S. Private*, pg. 348

Dupuis, Lenore, Chief Exec. Officer & Treas.--Your Man Tours, Inc., Inglewood, CA; *U.S. Private*, pg. 1202

Durando, Paul, V.P.-Fin. & Treas.--Nu Horizons Electronics Corp., Melville, NY; *U.S. Public*, pg. 1205

Duret, Herve, Treas.--Rexel, S.A., Paris, France; *Int'l*, pg. 1107

Durfee, John, Chm. Bd., Pres. & Treas.--Bethel Mills, Inc., Bethel, VT; *U.S. Private*, pg. 141

Durnin, Jerry L., Treas. & Sec.--A.K. Durnin Chrysler Plymouth, Inc., Baton Rouge, LA; *U.S. Private*, pg. 348

Durstberger, B., V.P.-Mktg. & Fin.--Treibacher Schleifmittel Corp., Niagara Falls, NY; *U.S. Private*, pg. 1099

Dusin, Carla R., Asst. Treas.--Roche Constructors, Inc., Greeley, CO; *U.S. Private*, pg. 937

Dutro, Stephen L., Chief Fin. Officer & Treas.--KLLM Transport Services, Inc., Jackson, MS; *U.S. Public*, pg. 939

Dutta, P.S., Treas. & Chief Fin. Officer--Indian Aluminium Co. Ltd., Calcutta, India; *Int'l*, pg. 51

Duval, William D., V.P. & Treas.--Masters Inc., Gaithersburg, MD; *U.S. Private*, pg. 714

Duwe, John, Treas. & Sec.--United States Bakery, Portland, OR; *U.S. Private*, pg. 1124

Dwyer, Daniel P., Chief Fin. Officer, Exec. V.P.-Fin. & Treas.--CommNet Cellular Inc., Englewood, CO; *U.S. Public*, pg. 414

Dwyer, John, Chief Fin. Officer, Sr. V.P. & Treas.--Bally Total Fitness Holdings Corporation, Chicago, IL; *U.S. Public*, pg. 171

Dwyer, Joseph P., Treas. & Sec.--Asplundh Tree Expert Co., Willow Grove, PA; *U.S. Private*, pg. 89

Dykstra, Thomas M., V.P. & Treas.--Effective Management Systems, Milwaukee, WI; *U.S. Public*, pg. 565

Dynof, Joe, Treas.--Kervick Enterprises, Inc., Worcester, MA; *U.S. Private*, pg. 616

Dyson, Harry, Treas. & Sec.--Providence Journal-Bulletin, Providence, RI; *U.S. Public*, pg. 209

Dziadzio, John F., Exec. V.P., Treas. & Sec.--JL Media, Inc., Union, NJ; *U.S. Private*, pg. 577

Dziedzic, John, Treas.--Warren Equities Inc., Providence, RI; *U.S. Private*, pg. 1151

Dzubin, Donna, Asst. Treas.--Packard BioScience Company, Meriden, CT; *U.S. Private*, pg. 833

Eacott, James H., III, Pres. & Treas.--Bartlett Brainard Eacott, Inc., Bloomfield, CT; *U.S. Private*, pg. 118

Eagin, Mary, Treas.--Hoffer Plastics Corporation, South Elgin, IL; *U.S. Private*, pg. 532

Eagle, Marjorie J., Treas. & Sec.--Pipe Fabricating & Supply Company, Santa Fe Springs, CA; *U.S. Private*, pg. 867

Eanes, Jasper R., Chief Fin. Officer, Exec. V.P. & Treas.--BankAtlantic Bancorp, Inc., Fort Lauderdale, FL; *U.S. Public*, pg. 183

Earnhardt, Jim Babe, Treas. & Sec.--Earnhardt's Motor Companies, Gilbert, AZ; *U.S. Private*, pg. 356

East, S.J., Treas. & Dir.-Taxation--Redland PLC, Reigate, United Kingdom; *Int'l*, pg. 1090

Easterly, Clark, Jr., Treas.--Johnstown Knitting Mill Co., Johnstown, NY; *U.S. Private*, pg. 595

Easton, Robert J., Treas.--Providence and Worcester Railroad Company, Worcester, MA; *U.S. Public*, pg. 1336

Easton, Stewart, Controller & Asst. Treas.--Pacific Coast Producers, Lodi, CA; *U.S. Private*, pg. 830

Ebers, Kevin H., V.P.-Fin. Analysis & Treas.--Union Insurance Company, Lincoln, NE; *U.S. Public*, pg. 216

Ebersole, Richard W., Chief Fin. Officer & Treas.--Outdoor Communications, Inc., Corinth, MS; *U.S. Private*, pg. 822

Ebihara, Steve, V.P.--Sapporo U.S.A., Inc., New York, New York, NY; *Int'l*, pg. 1193

Ebrahimi, Mahnaz, Dir.-Treas. Opers.--Agouron Pharmaceuticals, Inc., La Jolla, CA; *U.S. Public*, pg. 28

Eckenrod, Jeannie, Treas. & Sec.--FKG Oil Company, Belleville, IL; *U.S. Private*, pg. 764

Ecker, Dory, Treas.--First District Association, Litchfield, MN; *U.S. Private*, pg. 406

Eckerling, Sanford, Pres. & Treas.--Universal Overall Company, Chicago, IL; *U.S. Private*, pg. 1127

Eckhardt, Manfred J., V.P. & Treas.--Smith Corona Corp., Cortland, NY; *U.S. Private*, pg. 1007

Eckhart, Nathan S., Treas. & Asst. Sec.--Allen Organ Company, Macungie, PA; *U.S. Public*, pg. 45

Eddy, David L., Sr. V.P. & Treas.--Northern Trust Corporation, Chicago, IL; *U.S. Public*, pg. 1195

Edelbrock, Nancy, Treas.--Edelbrock Corp., Torrance, CA; *U.S. Public*, pg. 563

Edelman, Mitchell, Treas.--Greater New York Box Co., Clifton, NJ; *U.S. Private*, pg. 476

Edelmann, Klaus, Chief Fin. Officer & Exec. V.P.--Deutz AG, Cologne, Germany; *Int'l*, pg. 407

Edenfield, James C., Pres., Chief Exec. Officer & Treas.--American Software, Inc., Atlanta, GA; *U.S. Public*, pg. 91

Edgerton, Charles N., V.P. & Treas.--Central Securities Corporation, New York, NY; *U.S. Public*, pg. 326

Edreich, Jack, Treas. & Sec.--Brittany Dyeing & Printing Corporation, New Bedford, MA; *U.S. Private*, pg. 170

Edwards, Chester, Asst. Treas.--Standard Motor Products Inc., Long Island City, NY; *U.S. Public*, pg. 1503

Edwards, David R., V.P. & Treas.--Weyerhaeuser Company, Federal Way, WA; *U.S. Public*, pg. 1764

Edwards, Drew A., Controller & Treas.--Tredegar Industries Inc., Richmond, VA; *U.S. Public*, pg. 1633

Edwards, Jeffrey L., V.P. & Treas.--Allergan, Inc., Irvine, CA; *U.S. Public*, pg. 46

Edwards, L. Ward, V.P.-Fin., Treas. & Sec.--Moore-Handley, Inc., Pelham, AL; *U.S. Public*, pg. 1128

Edwards, Larry, V.P & Treas.--Handleman Company, Troy, MI; *U.S. Public*, pg. 779

Edwards, Michael, Exec. V.P. & Treas.--Citizens Savings Bank, Providence, RI; *Int'l*, pg. 1132

Edwards, Michael, Exec. V.P. & Treas.--Citizens Trust Company, Providence, RI; *Int'l*, pg. 1132

Edwards, T.L., Treas. & Sec.--Coastal Wholesale, Inc., Kinston, NC; *U.S. Private*, pg. 248

Edwards, William, V.P., Treas. & Controller--Kyocera International, Inc., San Diego, CA; *Int'l*, pg. 775

Edwards, William F., Treas. & Sec.--Pilot Air Freight Corp., Lima, PA; *U.S. Private*, pg. 865

Eenhuis, Loretta, Controller & Treas.--Westin, Inc., Omaha, NE; *U.S. Private*, pg. 1169

Effstrom, Carroll E., Sec. & Treas.--Farmers Marine Copper Works, Galveston, TX; *U.S. Private*, pg. 422

Egan, Daniel J., Chief Fin. Officer, Sr. V.P. & Treas.--ContiMortgage Corporation, Horsham, PA; *U.S. Public*, pg. 439

Egan, Evelyn P., Treas.--Goldblatt's Department Stores, Chicago, IL; *U.S. Public*, pg. 917

Egan, Gerald, Treas. & Sec.--The Schebler Co., Bettendorf, IA; *U.S. Private*, pg. 366

Egan, Gerald F., Chief Fin. Officer, V.P.-Fin., Treas. & Sec.--Duty Free International, Inc., Ridgefield, CT; *Int'l*, pg. 103

Egan, Gerald L., Treas. & Sec.--Egan McKay Electrical Contractors, Minneapolis, MN; *U.S. Private*, pg. 366

Egan, Pam, Treas. & Asst. Sec.--JG Industries, Inc., Chicago, IL; *U.S. Public*, pg. 917

Eggert, Ulrich, Treas.--Kowalski Sausage Co., Inc., Hamtramck, MI; *U.S. Private*, pg. 634

Eguchi, Shunsuke, Treas.--Toshiba America Inc., New York, NY; *Int'l*, pg. 1405

Ehresman, Michael W., V.P. & Treas.--Western Staff Services, Walnut Creek, CA; *U.S. Public*, pg. 1760

Ehret, A.D., V.P., Treas. & Sec.--Dexter Company, Fairfield, IA; *U.S. Private*, pg. 329

Eidell, Ronald G., Sr. V.P. & Treas.--R.R. Donnelley & Sons Company, Chicago, IL; *U.S. Public*, pg. 517

Eikenbary, Eldon, Treas. & Asst. Sec.--Clarkson Construction Companies, Kansas City, MO; *U.S. Private*, pg. 244

Eisen, Leonard, Treas.--The Oshawa Group Limited, Etobicoke, Canada; *Int'l*, pg. 1012

Eisenberg, Craig, Chief Fin. Officer & Treas.--American Strip Steel Inc., Kearny, NJ; *U.S. Private*, pg. 62

Eisenberg, Donald, Treas.--Master Industries Corp., New York, NY; *U.S. Private*, pg. 713

Eisenmayer, Mildred F., Sec. & Asst. Treas.--Cullman Ventures, Inc., Norwalk, CT; *U.S. Private*, pg. 294

Eisenmayer, Mildred F., Sec. & Asst. Treas.--Cullman Ventures, Inc., New York, NY; *U.S. Private*, pg. 295

Eisenschenk, Mark, Exec. V.P.--Ringer Corporation, Bloomington, MN; *U.S. Public*, pg. 1390

Eisenstadt, Ruth, Treas. & Office Mgr.--Pike & Fischer, Bethesda, MD; *U.S. Private*, pg. 182

Eisenstein, Joshua J., Treas.--Central National-Gottesman Inc., Purchase, NY; *U.S. Private*, pg. 224

Eisner, Henry, V.P.-Fin. & Sec.--MultiQuip, Inc., Carson, CA; *Int'l*, pg. 695

Ekle, Tom, Chief Fin. Officer & Treas.--AMI Industries, Inc., Colorado Springs, CO; *U.S. Public*, pg. 401

Eklund, Louis, E., Jr., Chm. & Treas.--Fleet Engineers, Inc., Muskegon, MI; *U.S. Private*, pg. 410

Ekman, Matts P., Treas.--Electrolux, AB, Stockholm, Sweden; *Int'l*, pg. 438

Elder, Tony, Treas.--Troy Motors, Troy, MI; *U.S. Private*, pg. 1106

Elingburg, Wesley R., Chief Fin. Officer, Exec. V.P. & Treas.--Laboratory Corp. of America Holdings, Burlington, NC; *U.S. Public*, pg. 973

Elkes, Matthew O., Chief Fin. Officer & Treas.--Almo Corp., Philadelphia, PA; *U.S. Private*, pg. 44

Elkin, Michael, V.P., Chief Fin. Officer & Treas.--Med/Waste, Inc., Hialeah, FL; *U.S. Public*, pg. 1077

Ellington, Stanley E., Jr., Chief Fin. Officer, V.P.-Fin. & Treas.--Production Management Companies, Inc., Harvey, LA; *U.S. Private*, pg. 888

Elliott, H. Jay, Chief Fin. Officer, Sr. V.P. & Treas.--The Lincoln Electric Company, Cleveland, OH; *U.S. Public*, pg. 996

Elliott, Tara, Treas.--AutoZone, Inc., Memphis, TN; *U.S. Public*, pg. 150

Ellis, Edward H., Treas.--Gaylord Entertainment Co., Nashville, TN; *U.S. Public*, pg. 704

Ellis, Margaret E., Asst. Sec. & Treas.--SI Handling Systems, Inc., Easton, PA; *U.S. Public*, pg. 1418

Ellis, Michael H., Dir.-Banking & Savings--Halifax plc, Halifax, United Kingdom; *Int'l*, pg. 589

Elliston, Michael, V.P.-Fin & Treas.--Holly's Inc., Grand Rapids, MI; *U.S. Private*, pg. 535

Elmer, George, Treas.--Norwalk Furniture Corporation, Norwalk, OH; *U.S. Private*, pg. 807

Elmore, William B., V.P. & Treas.--Coca-Cola Bottling Co. Consolidated, Charlotte, NC; *U.S. Public*, pg. 391

Eloi, Fenel M., Chief Fin. Officer, V.P.-Fin. & Treas.--Genome Therapeutics Corporation, Waltham, MA; *U.S. Public*, pg. 730

Elsenhans, John W., V.P.-Fin. & Treas.--Pogo Producing Company, Houston, TX; *U.S. Public*, pg. 1312

Elstob, Ben, Treas.--American Television Time, Inc., Austin, TX; *U.S. Private*, pg. 63

Elston, Harold C., Jr., V.P. & Treas.--TRC Companies, Inc., Windsor, CT; *U.S. Public*, pg. 1557

Elyea, Mike, V.P.-Fin. & Treas.--Burk Royalty Co., Wichita Falls, TX; *U.S. Private*, pg. 182

Emerson, Robert E., Chief Acctg. Officer, V.P. & Treasurer--Dale Electronics, Inc., Columbus, NE; *U.S. Public*, pg. 1722

Emerson, Ronnie, Controller & Treas.--Riverchase Homes, Haleyville, AL; *U.S. Public*, pg. 319

Emmanuelli, Milton, Controller & Treas.--Crown Andersen Inc., Peachtree City, GA; *U.S. Public*, pg. 462
Emmert, John C., Jr., Chief Fin. Officer, Sr. V.P. & Treas.--American Arbitration Association, New York, NY; *U.S. Private*, pg. 50
Emmet, Robert, V.P.-Fin. Plng. & Treas.--Cleveland-Cliffs Inc, Cleveland, OH; *U.S. Public*, pg. 386
Emmett, Denis L., Treas.--Erving Industries, Inc., Erving, MA; *U.S. Private*, pg. 382
Ender, P., Asst. Treas.--SGS U.S. Testing Company, Inc., Fairfield, NJ; *Int'l*, pg. 1153
Ender, P., Treas.--SGS Industrial Services, Iselin, NJ; *Int'l*, pg. 1153
Ender, Peter, Asst. Treas.--SGS Control Services Inc., Edison, NJ; *Int'l*, pg. 1153
Endsley, Woody P., V.P. & Treas.--Tracor, Inc., Austin, TX; *U.S. Public*, pg. 1627
Eng, Martin D., Asst. Treas.--CNF Transportation Inc., Palo Alto, CA; *U.S. Public*, pg. 281
Eng, Richard, Treas.--Lifetouch, Portrait Studios, Eden Prairie, MN; *U.S. Private*, pg. 667
Engel, Willard E., Jr., V.P. & Treas.--May & Speh, Inc., Downers Grove, IL; *U.S. Public*, pg. 1063
Engelman, Wayne, Sr. V.P., Treas. & Sec.--Colle & McVoy, Inc., Minneapolis, MN; *U.S. Private*, pg. 252
Engels, Lawrence A., Chief Fin. Officer, V.P., & Treas.--Commercial Metals Company, Dallas, TX; *U.S. Public*, pg. 411
Engle, Clyde W., Chm. Bd., Pres. & Treas.--GSC Enterprises, Inc., Chicago, IL; *U.S. Private*, pg. 436
English, Chris, Chief Fin. Officer & Treas.--Webster Industries Inc., Tiffin, OH; *U.S. Private*, pg. 1157
English, Ernest C., Jr., Corp. Controller & Asst. Treas.--Gundle/SLT Environmental, Inc., Houston, TX; *U.S. Public*, pg. 769
English, Robert, Chief Fin. Officer & Treas.--Value Property Trust, New Brunswick, NJ; *U.S. Public*, pg. 1707
English, William M., Treas.--Bell Atlantic-MD, Baltimore, MD; *U.S. Public*, pg. 202
English, William N., Treas.--KU Energy, Lexington, KY; *U.S. Public*, pg. 940
English, William N., Treas.--KU Capital Corporation, Lexington, KY; *U.S. Public*, pg. 941
Enhagen, Ingrid, Asst. Treas.--Canadian Tire Corporation Limited, Toronto, Canada; *Int'l*, pg. 259
Enhagen, Ingrid, Asst. Treas.--Canadian Tire Acceptance Ltd., Welland, Canada; *Int'l*, pg. 259
Enis, Joseph, Treas.--Frontier Corporation, Rochester, NY; *U.S. Public*, pg. 683
Ennest, John W., Vice Chm., Chief Fin. Officer & Treas.--Citizens Banking Corporation, Flint, MI; *U.S. Public*, pg. 379
Ennis, Richard A., Exec. V.P. & Treas.--Associated Grocers of New England, Inc., Manchester, NH; *U.S. Private*, pg. 91
Enriquez, Jackie, Controller, Treas., Dir.-Investor Rels. & Internal Auditor--Supertex, Inc., Sunnyvale, CA; *U.S. Public*, pg. 1539
Ensinger, James, Treas. & Sec.--Rudel Machinery Company, Inc., Shelton, CT; *U.S. Private*, pg. 950
Ent, Margaret A., V.P., Sec. & Treas.--CD Products, Inc., New Providence, NJ; *U.S. Public*, pg. 276
Entrono, Joseph A., Treas.--H.J. Baker & Bro., Inc., Stamford, CT; *U.S. Private*, pg. 112
Epel, Joseph H., Treas.--Lynch Corporation, Greenwich, CT; *U.S. Public*, pg. 1021
Eppel, Barbara J., Treas.--The Valspar Corporation, Minneapolis, MN; *U.S. Public*, pg. 1707
Epperlein, Richard, Controller & Treas.--A. Zeregas Sons, Inc., Fair Lawn, NJ; *U.S. Private*, pg. 1204
Eppich, John L., Treas.--Brown & Sharpe Manufacturing Company, North Kingstown, RI; *U.S. Public*, pg. 260
Epprecht, John W., V.P., Treas. & Sec.--The Great Lakes Cheese Co., Newbury, OH; *U.S. Private*, pg. 473
Erani, Albert, Chief Oper. Officer, Treas. & Sec.--A&E Stores, Inc., Teterboro, NJ; *U.S. Private*, pg. 1
Erdman, Lee, V.P. Fin. & Treas.--YSI Incorporated, Yellow Springs, OH; *U.S. Private*, pg. 1195
Erera, Laurence E., V.P. & Treas.--American Fund Advisors, Inc., Garden City, NY; *U.S. Private*, pg. 55
Erickson, Dennis D., Chief Fin. Officer, Treas. & Exec. V.P.--Norwest Bank Colorado N.A., Denver, CO; *U.S. Public*, pg. 1202
Erickson, Frederick J., Chief Fin. Officer, V.P., Treas. & Asst. Sec.--Bull Run Corporation, Atlanta, GA; *U.S. Public*, pg. 267
Erickson, Gerald, Treas.--Fiskars Inc., Wausau, WI; *Int'l*, pg. 492
Erickson, Mike, Controller, Treas. & Sec.--Wagstaff Inc., Spokane, WA; *U.S. Private*, pg. 1146
Erickson, Robert M., Chief Fin. Officer & Treas.--Citation Insurance Group, San Jose, CA; *U.S. Public*, pg. 376
Erickson, S.K., Exec. V.P. & Treas.--Ziegler Inc., Minneapolis, MN; *U.S. Private*, pg. 1205
Erikson, Robert W., Pres., Chief Fin. Officer & Treas.--CERBCO, Inc., Landover, MD; *U.S. Public*, pg. 330
Ertel, Charles M., Asst. Treas.--Community Bank System, Inc., De Witt, NY; *U.S. Public*, pg. 416
Ervin, Robert E., V.P. & Treas.--Consumers Water Company, Portland, ME; *U.S. Public*, pg. 438
Eschenbach, Ralph, V.P. & Asst. Treas.--TNL Flight Services, Inc., Austin, TX; *U.S. Public*, pg. 1638
Eskilson, Thomas T., Pres., Treas. & Sec.--Dixie Dairy Company, Gary, IN; *U.S. Private*, pg. 337
Eskowitz, Sheldon, Treas. & Sec.--Plascal Corporation, Farmingdale, NY; *U.S. Private*, pg. 870
Esporrin, Gary P., V.P. & Treas.--Centex-Rooney Construction Co., Inc., Fort Lauderdale, FL; *U.S. Public*, pg. 322
Esposito, Thomas R., Treas.--High Industries, Inc., Lancaster, PA; *U.S. Private*, pg. 528
Essenburg, Kim, Treas.--The Brulin Corporation, Indianapolis, IN; *U.S. Private*, pg. 176
Estes, Robey W., Jr., Pres. & Treas.--Estes Express Lines, Inc., Richmond, VA; *U.S. Private*, pg. 384
Etter, Brian, V.P. & Treas.--White Cap Industries, Inc., Costa Mesa, CA; *U.S. Public*, pg. 1765
Ettinger, Jeffrey M., Asst. Treas.--Hormel Foods Corp., Austin, MN; *U.S. Public*, pg. 840
Ettridge, Timothy, Sec. & Treas.--Temps & Company, Washington, DC; *U.S. Private*, pg. 1075
Evangelista, Joao Vicente, Controller & Treas.--Henkel S/A. Industrias Quimicas, Sao Paulo, Brazil; *Int'l*, pg. 613
Evanger, Marc, Chief Fin. Officer, V.P., Treas. & Sec.--QFC Holding Company, Stamford, CT; *U.S. Public*, pg. 1349
Evans, George M., V.P. & Treas.--Rochester & Pittsburgh Coal Company, Indiana, PA; *U.S. Public*, pg. 1395
Evans, H. Malloy, Jr., Pres. & Treas.--Cheraw Yarn Mills, Inc., Cheraw, SC; *U.S. Private*, pg. 233
Evans, J., V.P.-Fin.--Princess Hotels International Inc., New York, NY; *Int'l*, pg. 818
Evans, Jody, Treas. & Sec.--Ray Bell Construction Co. Inc., Brentwood, TN; *U.S. Private*, pg. 131
Evans, Maureen M., Dir.-Fin., Treas. & Asst. Sec.--Cerner Corporation, Kansas City, MO; *U.S. Public*, pg. 331
Evans, Milo R., Treas. & Sec.--Copes-Vulcan Inc., Lake City, PA; *U.S. Private*, pg. 274
Evans, Richard L., Chief Oper. Officer, Chief Fin. Officer, Exec. V.P. & Treas.--Reunion Industries, Inc., Stamford, CT; *U.S. Public*, pg. 1383
Evans, Rosemary H., Treas.--TRM Copy Centers Corporation, Portland, OR; *U.S. Public*, pg. 1558
Evatt, Danny R., Chief Acctg. Officer, V.P. & Treas.--Key Energy Group Inc., East Brunswick, NJ; *U.S. Public*, pg. 953
Eveleigh, Robert J., Chief Fin. Officer, V.P-Fin. & Treas.--Metro Information Services, Virginia Beach, VA; *U.S. Public*, pg. 1102
Everson, William, V.P. & Treas.--Premier Farnell, Cleveland, OH; *Int'l*, pg. 1068
Ewens, James J., Treas.--Quad/Graphics, Inc., Pewaukee, WI; *U.S. Private*, pg. 897
Ewing, Elizabeth R., Asst. Treas.--Nalco Chemical Company, Naperville, IL; *U.S. Public*, pg. 1150
Ewing, William, III, Treas.--Reeves International, Spartanburg, SC; *U.S. Private*, pg. 507
Eylon, Roni, Treas.--Agis Industries Ltd., Bnei-Brak, Israel; *Int'l*, pg. 30
Ezerski, Ronald E., Chief Fin. Officer, Exec. V.P., Treas. & Sec.--Patterson Dental Company, Saint Paul, MN; *U.S. Public*, pg. 1265
Fadden, Jerome T., Chief Fin. Officer, V.P. & Treas.--NAC Re Corp., Greenwich, CT; *U.S. Public*, pg. 1144
Fadden, Jerome T., Chief Fin. Officer, Exec. V.P. & Treas.--NAC Reinsurance Corporation, Greenwich, CT; *U.S. Public*, pg. 1144
Fadden, Jerome T., Chief Fin. Officer, Exec. V.P. & Treas.--Greenwich Insurance Company, Greenwich, CT; *U.S. Public*, pg. 1144
Fadden, Jerome T., Chief Fin. Officer, Exec. V.P. & Treas.--Indian Harbor Insurance Company, Greenwich, CT; *U.S. Public*, pg. 1144
Fagan, Brad, V.P., Controller, Treas. & Asst. Sec.--Pancho's Mexican Buffet, Inc., Fort Worth, TX; *U.S. Public*, pg. 1255
Fagan, James F., Chief Fin. Officer, Exec. V.P. & Treas.--Arrow Automotive Industries, Inc., Framingham, MA; *U.S. Public*, pg. 133
Fagan, Richard J., Controller & Treas.--Quaker Chemical Corporation, Conshohocken, PA; *U.S. Public*, pg. 1346
Fagin, N. Toby, Treas.--United Family Life Insurance Co., Atlanta, GA; *Int'l*, pg. 499
Fagundes, Carlos, Treas.--Banco Chase Manhattan, S.A., Santo Amaro, Brazil; *U.S. Public*, pg. 339
Fahs, John C., Chm. Bd., Pres., Chief Exec. Officer & Treas.--California Panel & Veneer Company, Cerritos, CA; *U.S. Private*, pg. 201
Faiella, John, Treas.--Gilman Paper Co., Saint Marys, GA; *U.S. Private*, pg. 454
Faircloth, Phillip, Chief Fin. Officer, Sr. V.P., Treas.--Warehouse Home Furnishings Distributor, Dublin, GA; *U.S. Private*, pg. 1150
Falardeau, Andre, V.P. & Treas.--SNC-Lavalin Group Inc., Montreal, Canada; *Int'l*, pg. 1161
Falconi, Robert, Chief Fin. Officer, Treas. & Sec.--Planning Systems Inc., Mc Lean, VA; *U.S. Private*, pg. 869
Fallon, Thomas P, Treas.-The Americas--Bestfoods, Englewood Cliffs, NJ; *U.S. Public*, pg. 223
Fallon, Tom, Treas.--United Utilities plc, Warrington, United Kingdom; *Int'l*, pg. 1444
Fancher, Jan T., Chief Fin. Officer, Treas. & Sec.--Cadet Manufacturing Company, Vancouver, WA; *U.S. Private*, pg. 198
Fanchi, Joseph B., Chief Fin. Officer, V.P.-Fin. & Treas.--Skyline Corporation, Elkhart, IN; *U.S. Public*, pg. 1476
Fankhauser, James R., Chief Fin. Officer & Treas.--Fahlgren, Dublin, OH; *U.S. Private*, pg. 391
Farady, John T., Sr. V.P. & Treas.--John Hancock Mutual Life Insurance Company, Boston, MA; *U.S. Private*, pg. 589
Farley, Paul W., Asst. Treas & V.P.-Fin., Card Div.--Gibson Greetings, Inc., Cincinnati, OH; *U.S. Public*, pg. 742
Farnsworth, W.K., V.P.-Fin.--Jagenberg, Inc., Enfield, CT; *Int'l*, pg. 1108
Farr, David, Treas.--Stewart's Ice Cream Co., Inc., Saratoga Springs, NY; *U.S. Private*, pg. 1043
Farris, Vicki, V.P.-Fin. & Treas.--Brite Voice Systems, Inc., Heathrow, FL; *U.S. Public*, pg. 257
Fato, Martha, Treas. & Sec.--Par Enterprises, Inc., Wheeling, WV; *U.S. Private*, pg. 838
Faussemagne, Jack, Treas.--The Ritz-Carlton Hotel Company LLC, Atlanta, GA; *U.S. Private*, pg. 594
Favereau, J., V.P. & Treas.--F.W. Myers & Co., Inc., Rouses Point, NY; *U.S. Private*, pg. 770
Fawer, Martin S., Chief Fin. Officer & Treas.--Zing Technologies, Inc., Valhalla, NY; *U.S. Public*, pg. 1792
Feaster, Joyce, Asst. Treas.--Wisconsin Electric Power Company, Milwaukee, WI; *U.S. Public*, pg. 1773
Featherstone, Bob, Chief Fin. Officer & Treas.--XATA Corporation, Burnsville, MN; *U.S. Public*, pg. 1783
Federline, Terry, Treas.--nexAir, Memphis, TN; *U.S. Private*, pg. 797
Fedock, R.N., Treas. & Controller--Friendswood Development Company, Houston, TX; *U.S. Public*, pg. 988
Fee, Frank, Treas.--National Fire Protection Association, Quincy, MA; *U.S. Private*, pg. 782
Fee, Frank J., III, Pres. & Treas.--Reliable Automatic Sprinkler Co., Inc., Mount Vernon, NY; *U.S. Private*, pg. 920
Feeney, Gerald F., Chief Fin. Officer, V.P. & Treas.--California Water Service Co., San Jose, CA; *U.S. Public*, pg. 294
Feir, Brian W., Asst. Treas.--General Electric Canada Inc., Mississauga, Canada; *U.S. Public*, pg. 713
Feldman, Jerome I., Treas.--Interferon Sciences, Inc., New Brunswick, NJ; *U.S. Public*, pg. 694
Feldman, Leon D., Exec. V.P., Treas. & Sec.--P & F Industries, Inc., Farmingdale, NY; *U.S. Public*, pg. 1239
Feldman, Mark, Chief Fin. Officer & Treas.--Fresh Juice Company, Great Neck, NY; *U.S. Private*, pg. 427
Feldman, Michael, Treas.--Hano Document Printers, Inc., Springfield, MA; *U.S. Public*, pg. 1686
Feldman, Shirley, Sec. & Treas.--Isfel Company, Inc., Rahway, NJ; *U.S. Private*, pg. 576
Feldstein, Eric A., Treas.--General Motors Corporation, Detroit, MI; *U.S. Public*, pg. 718
Felices, Carlos, Treas. & Mgr.-Corp. Fin.--Y.P.F., S.A., Buenos Aires, Argentina; *Int'l*, pg. 1515
Felix, Robert F., Chief Fin. Officer, Exec. V.P. & Treas.--First Federal Savings, East Hartford, CT; *U.S. Public*, pg. 632
Felker, Nancy E., V.P. & Treas.--Pinnacle West Capital Corporation, Phoenix, AZ; *U.S. Public*, pg. 1297
Fellenstein, Mike, Controller, Treas. & Sec.--Biddulph Automotive Group, Glendale, AZ; *U.S. Private*, pg. 142
Feller, Alan, Chief Oper. Officer, Chief Fin. Officer, Treas. & Sec.--G-III Apparel Group, Ltd., New York, NY; *U.S. Public*, pg. 690
Fellerman, William, Chief Fin. Officer, Treas. & Sec.--Star Multi Care Services Inc., Hicksville, NY; *U.S. Public*, pg. 1510
Fellows, Linda, Treas. & Dir.-Investor Rels.--Intuit, Inc., Mountain View, CA; *U.S. Public*, pg. 911
Felsenthal, Daniel L., V.P.-Fin., Treas. & Asst. Sec.--Barry's Jewelers, Inc., Monrovia, CA; *U.S. Public*, pg. 192
Felsenthal, James, Exec. V.P. & Treas.--Earle Industries, Inc., Earle, AR; *U.S. Private*, pg. 356
Felsh, Nicholas, V.P. & Treas.--Frederick Trading Company, Frederick, MD; *U.S. Private*, pg. 335
Felsher, Steven G., Exec. V.P.-Fin./Worldwide, Treas. & Sec.--Grey Advertising Inc., New York, NY; *U.S. Public*, pg. 764
Fenendael, Lee F., Treas.--Condon Oil Company, Inc., Ripon, WI; *U.S. Private*, pg. 262
Fenner, Robert, Asst. Treas. & Asst. Controller--Mount Snow Resort, Mount Snow, VT; *U.S. Private*, pg. 61
Fennessy, William J., V.P.-Fin. & Treas.--LDI, Ltd., Indianapolis, IN; *U.S. Private*, pg. 639
Fenster, Fred A., Treas. & Sec.--Capucci Creations International, Inc., Beverly Hills, CA; *U.S. Private*, pg. 207
Fenton, Jim, Pres., Chief Exec. Officer & Treas.--Southeastern Steel Company, Florence, SC; *U.S. Private*, pg. 1015
Fenton, John W., Jr., Treas. & Sec.--National Computer Systems, Eden Prairie, MN; *U.S. Public*, pg. 1155
Ferdinandi, John, Treas.--Spirol International Corp., Danielson, CT; *U.S. Private*, pg. 1026
Ferenbach, Richard, Treas.--Leon-Ferenbach Inc., Hoboken, NJ; *U.S. Private*, pg. 660
Ferens, Rick, Treas. & Dir.-Taxation--Pinkerton's Inc., Encino, CA; *U.S. Public*, pg. 1296
Ferguson, Bruce, Chief Fin. Officer & Treas.--Macro Computer Products Inc., Rochester Hills, MI; *U.S. Private*, pg. 693
Ferguson, Gary L., Pres. & Treas.--Dearborn Capital Corporation, Dearborn, MI; *U.S. Public*, pg. 663
Ferguson, Jack R., Chief Fin. Officer, V.P.-Fin. & Treas.--Ingles Markets, Incorporated, Black Mountain, NC; *U.S. Public*, pg. 878
Ferguson, Richard R., V.P., Treas. & Asst. Sec.--Great Lakes Chemical Corporation, West Lafayette, IN; *U.S. Public*, pg. 760
Ferguson, Tommy, Treas.--Mobile Telecommunications Technologies Corp., Jackson, MS; *U.S. Public*, pg. 1120
Ferman, Martha S., Treas. & Sec.--Ferman Oldsmobile, Tampa, FL; *U.S. Private*, pg. 401
Fernandez, Frank, Asst Treas. & Sec.--Barr & Barr, Inc., New York, NY; *U.S. Private*, pg. 117
Fernandez, Luis, Treas.--Atlantic Sugar Association, Inc., Belle Glade, FL; *U.S. Private*, pg. 95
Ferrara, Albert E., Jr., Asst. Treas.-Corp. Fin.--USX Corporation, Pittsburgh, PA; *U.S. Public*, pg. 1661
Ferraro, Charles J., Chief Fin. Officer & Treas.--ANESCO, Kingston, PA; *U.S. Private*, pg. 74
Ferrera, Alfred, Asst. Treas.--James Ferrera & Sons, Inc., Canton, MA; *U.S. Private*, pg. 401
Ferrera, James J., Controller & Treas.--James Ferrera & Sons, Inc., Canton, MA; *U.S. Private*, pg. 401
Ferstl, Eberhard, Sr. V.P.-Treas.--Bayerische Landesbank, Munich, Germany; *Int'l*, pg. 176
Fergheli, Paul, V.P. & Treas.--GAB Robins North America, Inc., Parsippany, NJ; *Int'l*, pg. 1153
Fessenden, R., Chief Fin. Officer, V.P.-Fin. & Admin. Treas.--KDI Precision Products, Inc., Cincinnati, OH; *U.S. Private*, pg. 603
Fetch, Mary T., Asst. Treas.--Cincinnati Milacron Inc., Cincinnati, OH; *U.S. Public*, pg. 368

Fey, David L., Treas.--National Bulk Carriers, Inc., New York, NY; *U.S. Private*, pg. 780
Feye, Lyle J., Chief Fin. Officer, V.P.-Fin. & Treas.--AXIA Incorporated, Lombard, IL; *U.S. Private*, pg. 103
Field, Benjamin R., III, Chief Fin. Officer, Sr. V.P. & Treas.--Bemis Company, Inc., Minneapolis, MN; *U.S. Public*, pg. 210
Field, Diane, V.P. & Treas.--Continental Web Press, Inc., Itasca, IL; *U.S. Private*, pg. 269
Field, Norman M., Chief Fin. Officer, V.P.-Fin. & Treas.--First Capital Financial Corp., Troy, MI; *U.S. Private*, pg. 473
Fielding, Sharon, Treas. & Sec.--Southwestern Reprographics Inc., Las Vegas, NV; *U.S. Private*, pg. 1176
Fields, Brian, Chief Fin. Officer, V.P. & Treas.--CarrAmerica Realty, Washington, DC; *U.S. Public*, pg. 308
Fields, Brian, Treas.--Carr Real Estate Services, Washington, DC; *U.S. Public*, pg. 309
Fields, Gary C., Asst. Treas.--Westvaco Corporation, New York, NY; *U.S. Public*, pg. 1762
Fields, William O., Controller & Treas.--Buffalo Color Corporation, Parsippany, NJ; *U.S. Private*, pg. 178
Figueiredo, Maria Paula, Treas. & Gen. Mgr.--Banco Totta & Acores, Lisbon, Portugal; *Int'l*, pg. 144
Fikejs, John W., V.P.-Finance.--Plymouth Tube Company, Warrenville, IL; *U.S. Private*, pg. 873
Filter, Eunice M., V.P., Treas. & Sec.--Xerox Corporation, Stamford, CT; *U.S. Public*, pg. 1783
Finan, Dan, Chief Fin. Officer & Treas.--Peavey Electronics Corp., Meridian, MS; *U.S. Private*, pg. 845
Fineman, Bernard S., Pres. & Treas.--Caldwell Tanks, Inc., Louisville, KY; *U.S. Private*, pg. 200
Fingerle, Larry, Sec. & Treas.--Fingerle Lumber Co., Ann Arbor, MI; *U.S. Private*, pg. 405
Fink, John, Chief Fin. Officer & Treas.--C.J. Langenfelder & Son, Inc., Baltimore, MD; *U.S. Private*, pg. 650
Fink, Thomas A., Treas.--US Airways Group, Inc., Arlington, VA; *U.S. Public*, pg. 1680
Fink, Thomas A., Treas.--US Airways Leasing & Services, Inc., Arlington, VA; *U.S. Public*, pg. 1680
Fink, Thomas A., Treas.--US Airways Fuel Corporation, Arlington, VA; *U.S. Public*, pg. 1680
Finlayson, Frank S., V.P. & Treas.--Morrison Knudsen Corporation, Boise, ID; *U.S. Public*, pg. 1133
Finn, Larry, Treas.--Stark Candy Company, Pewaukee, WI; *U.S. Private*, pg. 1113
Finn, Lawrence J., Treas.--New England Confectionery Co., Cambridge, MA; *U.S. Private*, pg. 1113
Finn, Richard L., Treas.--Sunset Life Insurance Co. of America, Olympia, WA; *U.S. Public*, pg. 943
Finn, Richard L., Chief Fin. Officer, V.P. & Asst. Treas.--Old American Insurance Co., Kansas City, MO; *U.S. Public*, pg. 943
Finnegan, Laurence P. Jr., Chief Fin. Officer, Sr. V.P. & Treas.--Bailey, Fischer & Porter Company, Warminster, PA; *Int'l*, pg. 449
Finney, B. Lynne, Asst. Treas.--DIMON, Incorporated, Danville, VA; *U.S. Public*, pg. 509
Finney, Charles, Chief Fin. Officer & Treas.--Computer Methods Corporation, Livonia, MI; *U.S. Private*, pg. 260
Finney, Mike, Treas.--Baugh Construction Company, Seattle, WA; *U.S. Private*, pg. 123
Finnigan, G. Michael, V.P. & Treas.--Turf Paradise, Inc., Phoenix, AZ; *U.S. Public*, pg. 831
Fiore, Donald A., Treas. & Mgr.-Personnel--Palmer Manufacturing Company, Malden, MA; *U.S. Private*, pg. 835
Fiorenza, David A., V.P. & Treas.--Ethyl Corporation, Richmond, VA; *U.S. Public*, pg. 595
Fischer, Jerome, Treas. & Sec.--Buerkle Buick-Honda Co., Saint Paul, MN; *U.S. Private*, pg. 178
Fischer, John, V.P. & Treas.--Atlantic Gulf Communities Corporation, Miami, FL; *U.S. Public*, pg. 144
Fischer, Philip, Treas. & Sec.--Torcon, Inc., Westfield, NJ; *U.S. Private*, pg. 1092
Fish, Dale, Treas. & Sec.--Lil'Champ/Food Stores Inc., Jacksonville, FL; *U.S. Private*, pg. 837
Fish, James, V.P.-Fin. & Treas.--Arkwright, Inc, Fiskeville, RI; *Int'l*, pg. 994
Fishbein, Robert, Co-Pres. & Treas.--West Shore Envelope Company, Inc., New York, NY; *U.S. Private*, pg. 1163
Fisher, Harold, V.P. & Treas.--Hillerich & Bradsby Co., Louisville, KY; *U.S. Private*, pg. 530
Fisher, John J., Controller, Treas. & Sec.--Tarlton Corporation, Saint Louis, MO; *U.S. Private*, pg. 1069
Fisher, Martha, Controller & Asst. Treas.--Prudential Metal Supply Corp., East Dedham, MA; *U.S. Private*, pg. 893
Fisher, Paul, Asst. Treas.--Huffy Corporation, Miamisburg, OH; *U.S. Public*, pg. 846
Fiskew, Philip, Chief Investment Officer & Treas.--MMI Companies, Inc., Deerfield, IL; *U.S. Public*, pg. 1027
Fissasloo, Bill, Sec. , Treas. & Dir.-Pur.--Gress Foods Inc., Gainesville, GA; *U.S. Private*, pg. 480
Fitch, Thomas R., Treas.--Rugg Manufacturing Company, Greenfield, MA; *U.S. Private*, pg. 950
Fitzgerald, D.F., Pres. & Treas.--Son Chief Electrics, Inc., Winsted, CT; *U.S. Private*, pg. 1014
Fitzgerald, David, Chief Fin. Officer & Treas.--Carris Financial Group, Rutland, VT; *U.S. Private*, pg. 215
Fitzgerald, David, Chief Fin. Officer & Treas.--Carris Reels, Inc., Rutland, VT; *U.S. Private*, pg. 215
Fitzgerald, Marie, Asst. Treas.--The Genlyte Group Incorporated, Union, NJ; *U.S. Public*, pg. 729
Fitzgerald, Thomas C., V.P. & Treas.--Hershey Foods Corporation, Hershey, PA; *U.S. Public*, pg. 811
Fitzhugh, A. Chad, Chief Fin. Officer, Treas. & Sec.--O'Charley's Inc., Nashville, TN; *U.S. Public*, pg. 1211
Fitzpatrick, Gregory J., V.P. & Treas.--Fitzpatrick & Weller, Inc., Ellicottville, NY; *U.S. Private*, pg. 409
FitzPatrick, Patrick C., Chief Fin. Officer, Sr. V.P. & Treas.--DynCorp, Reston, VA; *U.S. Private*, pg. 351
Fitzsimmons, Robert J., Sr. V.P.-Treas.--The FINOVA Group Inc., Phoenix, AZ; *U.S. Public*, pg. 624
Fjelstul, Dean M., Pres. & Treas.--Jim Walter Computer Services, Inc., Tampa, FL; *U.S. Public*, pg. 1737
Flaherty, Richard, Treas.--Ames Safety Envelope Company, Inc., Somerville, MA; *U.S. Private*, pg. 66
Flanagan, Martin L., Chief Fin. Officer & Sr. V.P.--Franklin Resources, Inc., San Mateo, CA; *U.S. Public*, pg. 679
Flanagan, Patricia, Treas. & Asst. Sec.--Newmont Mining Corporation, Denver, CO; *U.S. Public*, pg. 1178
Flanders, Margie S., V.P. & Asst. Treas.--Paddock Publications, Inc., Arlington Heights, IL; *U.S. Private*, pg. 833
Flaws, James B., Chief Fin. Officer, Sr. V.P. & Treas.--Corning Incorporated, Corning, NY; *U.S. Public*, pg. 448
Flay, Paul, V.P. & Treas.--J.L. de Ball-Girmes of America, Inc., Montreal, Canada; *Int'l*, pg. 552
Flegenheimer, Roy A., Chief Oper. Officer, Treas. & Sec.--Employee Solutions, Inc., Phoenix, AZ; *U.S. Public*, pg. 579
Fleischman, Donald, Chief Fin. Officer, V.P.-Fin. & Treas.--Ampacet Corporation, Tarrytown, NY; *U.S. Private*, pg. 67
Fleishell, John R., Treas.--McArdle Printing Co., Inc., Upper Marlboro, MD; *U.S. Private*, pg. 182
Fleming, Gordon, Treas. & Sec.--Brach & Brock Confections Inc., Chattanooga, TN; *U.S. Private*, pg. 163
Fleming, M. Jack, Chm. Bd., Pres., Chief Exec. Officer & Treas.--Merchants Publishing Co., Kalamazoo, MI; *U.S. Private*, pg. 732
Fleming, William, Treas.--A.I. Root Company, Medina, OH; *U.S. Private*, pg. 944
Fletcher, Emory, V.P. & Treas.--Martin Sprocket & Gear, Inc., Arlington, TX; *U.S. Private*, pg. 709
Fletcher, Paul, V.P. & Treas.--Excel Communications, Inc., Dallas, TX; *U.S. Public*, pg. 598
Fletcher, Wallace E., Comptroller & Asst. Treas.--Fall River Gas Company, Fall River, MA; *U.S. Public*, pg. 611
Fleury, Thomas J., Treas. & Gen. Credit Mgr.--Beckwith Machinery Company, Murrysville, PA; *U.S. Private*, pg. 129
Floberg, Ron, Chief Fin. Officer--Electron Corp., Littleton, CO; *U.S. Private*, pg. 370
Flood, Thomas, Chief Fin. Officer, V.P.-Admin. & Fin. & Treas.--Tractor Supply Co., Nashville, TN; *U.S. Public*, pg. 1627
Florek, Anita, Chief Fin. Officer & Treas.--Bank of Smithtown, Smithtown, NY; *U.S. Private*, pg. 114
Florek, Anita M., Chief Fin. Officer & Treas.--Smithtown Bancorp, Inc., Smithtown, NY; *U.S. Public*, pg. 1479
Flori, Robert D., Chm. Bd. & Treas.--Flori Corp., Phoenix, AZ; *U.S. Private*, pg. 414
Florig, Edward, Pres. & Treas.--Florig Equipment Company, Inc., Conshohocken, PA; *U.S. Private*, pg. 415
Florness, Daniel L., Chief Fin. Officer, Chief Acctg. Officer & Treas.--Fastenal Company, Winona, MN; *U.S. Public*, pg. 614
Flowers, Genia, Treas. & Sec.--Hickory Construction Company, Hickory, NC; *U.S. Private*, pg. 525
Flowers, Steven J., Treas.--Oryx Energy, Dallas, TX; *U.S. Public*, pg. 1232
Floyd, Thomas A., Sr. V.P.-Fin., Treas. & Admin.--Martin Exploration Management Company, Alsip, IL; *U.S. Private*, pg. 709
Fluegeman, Raymond W., Chief Fin. Officer, Treas., Controller & Dir.-D.P.--Robbins, Inc., Cincinnati, OH; *U.S. Private*, pg. 934
Flynn, Gary, Exec. V.P. & Treas.--Rotary Multiforms, Inc., Warren, MI; *U.S. Private*, pg. 947
Foch, Wayne T., Treas.--EnerMark Income Fund, Calgary, Canada; *Int'l*, pg. 454
Foecking, Leland R., Treas. & Sec.--Joseph Behr & Sons Inc., Rockford, IL; *U.S. Private*, pg. 130
Fogg, David H., Treas.--General Dynamics Corporation, Falls Church, VA; *U.S. Public*, pg. 708
Fogg, Glenice D., Treas. & Sec.--Southeastern Medequip, Inc., Jacksonville Beach, FL; *U.S. Private*, pg. 1015
Foglia, Dennis A., Exec. V.P., Treas. & Sec.--Equitable Savings & Loan Association, Wauwatosa, WI; *U.S. Private*, pg. 380
Foglia, Dennis A., Exec. V.P., Sec. & Treas.--The Equitable Bank, Hales Corners, WI; *U.S. Private*, pg. 380
Folts, John B., Exec. V.P., Treas. & Sec.--Hargro Enterprises, Inc., Stamford, CT; *U.S. Private*, pg. 502
Folwell, Ronald L., Sr., Chief Fin. Officer & V.P.-Fin., Leasing, Plng/Devel. & Real Est.--GSC Enterprises, Inc., Sulphur Springs, TX; *U.S. Private*, pg. 436
Fong, Henry, Treas.--Hamilton Lamp Corp., North Kansas City, MO; *U.S. Public*, pg. 1354
Fong, Steve, V.P.-Fin. & Treas.--Cadence Design Systems, Inc., San Jose, CA; *U.S. Public*, pg. 290
Fonn, Torbjoern, Treas.--Kaldnes Heavy Lift Trucks, Tonsberg, Norway; *Int'l*, pg. 965
Fontana, Victor, Pres., Chief Exec. Officer & Treas.--Autranet, Inc., New York, NY; *U.S. Public*, pg. 589
Ford, Jess B., Treas.--Tokheim Investment Corp., Houston, TX; *U.S. Public*, pg. 1620
Ford, Stephen, Treas. & Sec.--Ford Meter Box Company, Wabash, IN; *U.S. Private*, pg. 418
Forest, Carol A., Chief Fin. Officer, V.P.-Fin. & Treas.--Connecticut Energy Corporation, Bridgeport, CT; *U.S. Public*, pg. 431
Forest, Carol A., Chief Fin. Officer, V.P.-Fin. & Treas.--The Southern Connecticut Gas Company, Bridgeport, CT; *U.S. Public*, pg. 431
Forman, Willis M., Pres., Chief Exec. Officer & Treas.--Paper Calmenson & Co., Saint Paul, MN; *U.S. Private*, pg. 837
Fornella, Norman G., Chief Fin. Officer, Exec. V.P., Treas. & Sec.--Morse Diesel International, Inc., New York, NY; *U.S. Private*, pg. 762
Forney, James L., Chief Fin. Officer & Treas.--Fone America, Inc., Portland, OR; *U.S. Public*, pg. 661
Forrest, B.H., Treas.--Email Limited, Waterloo, Australia; *Int'l*, pg. 450
Forsdick, D.L., Treas.--AT&T ISTEL Limited, Redditch, United Kingdom; *U.S. Public*, pg. 11
Forster, Alan M., V.P. & Treas.--The Interpublic Group of Companies, Inc., New York, NY; *U.S. Public*, pg. 908
Fortmuller, George A., Chief Fin. Officer, V.P., Treas. & Sec.--Edwin B. Stimpson Company, Inc., Bayport, NY; *U.S. Private*, pg. 1043
Fortney, David, Controller & Treas.--United States Lock & Hardware Co., Columbia, PA; *U.S. Private*, pg. 1196
Fortney, David J., Chief Fin. Officer, Controller & Treas.--York Barbell Co., Inc., York, PA; *U.S. Private*, pg. 1196
Fortney, Teresa, Treas.--Schneider Corp., Kitchener, Canada; *Int'l*, pg. 1207
Fortunoff, Helene, Treas. & Sec.--Fortunoff, Uniondale, NY; *U.S. Private*, pg. 420
Foss, John H., Chief Fin. Officer, V.P. & Treas.--Tecumseh Products Company, Tecumseh, MI; *U.S. Public*, pg. 1565
Foster, Jim, Treas.--Foster Pontiac, Inc., Milwaukee, WI; *U.S. Private*, pg. 421
Foster, John M., V.P. & Treas.--COMPAQ Computer Corporation, Houston, TX; *U.S. Public*, pg. 417
Foster, L. Dale, Treas. & Sec.--Aeronca, Inc., Middletown, OH; *Int'l*, pg. 829
Foster, Michael L., V.P.-Fin. Plng. & Treas.--California Microwave, Inc., Sunnyvale, CA; *U.S. Public*, pg. 293
Foster, Phillip W., Chief Fin. Officer & V.P.-Fin.--Remmele Engineering, Inc., New Brighton, MN; *U.S. Private*, pg. 921
Foster, Robert J., V.P.-Fin.--National Machinery, Tiffin, OH; *U.S. Private*, pg. 785
Foster, Stephen P., V.P. & Treas.--Edlund Company, Inc., Burlington, VT; *U.S. Private*, pg. 364
Foster, Thomas M., V.P. & Treas.--Phelps Dodge Corporation, Phoenix, AZ; *U.S. Public*, pg. 1286
Foudree, Charles M., Exec. V.P.-Fin., Treas. & Sec.--Harmon Industries, Inc., Blue Springs, MO; *U.S. Public*, pg. 788
Fowke, Ben G., III, Treas.--Young Gas Storage Company, Denver, CO; *U.S. Public*, pg. 1170
Fowler, Richard E., Asst. Treas.--Gulf Power Company, Pensacola, FL; *U.S. Public*, pg. 1490
Fowler, Richard M., V.P.-Fin. & Treas.--Chaparral Steel Co., Midlothian, TX; *U.S. Public*, pg. 1585
Fox, Lou, Treas.--Goodman Manufacturing, Houston, TX; *U.S. Private*, pg. 464
Fox, Marvin, Treas.--El Dorado Tire Co., Troy, MI; *Int'l*, pg. 1312
Fox, Randolph, V.P.-Fin., Treas. & Sec.--Metal Masters Foodservice Equipment, Clayton, DE; *U.S. Private*, pg. 734
Fox, Richard, Treas.--American Laubscher Corp., Farmingdale, NY; *U.S. Private*, pg. 58
Fox, Robert, Sr. V.P.-Fin. & Admin., Treas. & Sec.--Rocor Transportation Companies Inc., Oklahoma City, OK; *U.S.* Private, pg. 938
Foxcroft, Ken B., Exec. V.P. & Treas.--The Toronto Dominion Bank, Toronto, Canada; *Int'l*, pg. 1401
Foy, Thomas, Treas.--Novellus Systems, Inc., San Jose, CA; *U.S. Public*, pg. 1204
Fraedrich, David S., Chief Fin. Officer, Exec. V.P. & Treas.--Rocky Shoes & Boots, Inc., Nelsonville, OH; *U.S. Public*, *pg. 1402*
Fraiyer, Scott, Controller & Treas.--EVCON Industries, Wichita, KS; *U.S. Public*, pg. 1788
Fraiyer, Scott, Treas. & Controller--Evcon Industries, Inc., Wichita, KS; *U.S. Public*, pg. 1788
Fraizer, Michael, Sr. V.P., Controller & Treas.--American Mutual Life Holding Co., Des Moines, IA; *U.S. Private*, pg. 59
Frame, George J., V.P.-Fin., Admin. & Treas.--Jaguar Cars, Mahwah, NJ; *U.S. Public*, pg. 664
Francht, Joseph E., Jr., Sr. V.P.-Fin. & Treas.--Northwest Airlines Corp., Saint Paul, MN; *U.S. Public*, pg. 1199
Francht, Joseph E., Jr., Sr. V.P.-Fin. & Treas.--Northwest Airlines, Inc., Saint Paul, MN; *U.S. Public*, pg. 1200
Francis, Spencer L., V.P. & Treas.--NGL Holdings Inc., Madison, WI; *U.S. Private*, pg. 784
Francis, Spencer L., V.P. & Treas.--NGL Financial Services Inc., Madison, WI; *U.S. Private*, pg. 784
Francis, Spencer L., V.P. & Treas.--NGL Investment Services Inc., Madison, WI; *U.S. Private*, pg. 784
Franck, Erik, Gen. Mgr.-Treas. & Foreign Exchange Div.--Fokus Bank A/S, Trondheim, Norway; *Int'l*, pg. 496
Franco, Frank J., Controller & Treas.--Peckham Industries, Inc., White Plains, NY; *U.S. Private*, pg. 846
Franco, Joseph, Chief Fin. Officer & Treas.--Haydon Switch & Instrument, Inc., Waterbury, CT; *U.S. Private*, pg. 513
Franco, Richard A., Treas.--Rieth-Riley Construction Co. Inc., Goshen, IN; *U.S. Private*, pg. 930
Franke , Kenneth, V.P. & Treas.--Riemeier Lumber Company, Inc., Cincinnati, OH; *U.S. Private*, pg. 930
Franklin, E. Thomas, Chm., Pres & Treas.--Franklin Baking Co., Inc., Goldsboro, NC; *U.S. Private*, pg. 424
Franklin, Irving H., Chm. Bd. & Treas.--Franklin Sports, Inc., Stoughton, MA; *U.S. Private*, pg. 424
Franklin, V.J., Mgr.-Treas.--Cyanamid of Great Britain Ltd., Gosport, United Kingdom; *U.S. Public*, pg. 81
Franson, Herbert, Controller & Asst. Treas.--Hathaway Corporation, Littleton, CO; *U.S. Public*, pg. 798
Franzoni, Catherine D., V.P. & Treas.--Pulse Bancorp, Inc., South River, NJ; *U.S. Public*, pg. 1344
Fraser, David S., Chief Fin. Officer & Treas.--Graphic Industries, Inc., Atlanta, GA; *U.S. Public*, pg. 1735
Fraser, Gregory A., Ph.D., Chief Fin. Officer, Exec. V.P., Treas. & Sec.--FARO Technologies, Inc., Lake Mary, FL; *U.S. Public*, pg. 613
Frastaci, Barbara A., Asst. Treas.--The Cleveland Electric Illuminating Company, Independence, OH; *U.S. Public*, pg. 645
Frastaci, Barbara A., Asst. Treas.--The Toledo Edison Company, Toledo, OH; *U.S. Public*, pg. 645
Frawley, Patrick, Treas.--NationsBank South, Atlanta, GA; *U.S. Public*, pg. 1163

Frazen, Mary A., Exec. V.P., Sec. & Treas.--Ed Marling Stores, Inc., Topeka, KS; *U.S. Private*, pg. 705
Frazer, Lewis, III, Chief Fin. Officer, Exec. V.P. & Treas.--Regal Cinemas Inc., Knoxville, TN; *U.S. Public*, pg. 1371
Frederick, Neil A., Treas.--Bush Industries Inc., Jamestown, NY; *U.S. Public*, pg. 270
Freebourn, Harry J., Asst. Treas.--Montana Power Company, Butte, MT; *U.S. Public*, pg. 1126
Freedman, Martin B., V.P. & Treas.--FMS Management Systems, Inc., Miami, FL; *U.S. Private*, pg. 389
Freedman, Sigmund, Treas.--New Brunswick Scientific Co., Inc., Edison, NJ; *U.S. Public*, pg. 1169
Freeland, G.W., Treas.--First Brands (Canada) Corp., Scarborough, Canada; *U.S. Public*, pg. 627
Freeman, Jeff E., Sr. V.P.-Fin., Sec. & Treas.--Havatampa, Inc., Tampa, FL; *U.S. Private*, pg. 510
Freeman, John R., V.P.-Fin. & Treas.--QC Optics, Inc., Wilmington, MA; *U.S. Public*, pg. 1345
Freeman, Peter C., Treas.--Dillingham Construction Corporation, Pleasanton, CA; *U.S. Private*, pg. 333
Freeman, William, Chief Fin. Officer, V.P. & Treas.--Seymour of Sycamore, Inc., Sycamore, IL; *U.S. Private*, pg. 988
Freilich, Joseph, Treas. & Sec.--Icahn & Co., Inc., New York, NY; *U.S. Private*, pg. 556
Freischlag, Paul, V.P.-Treasury--Koninklijke Ahold NV, Zaandam, Netherlands; *Int'l*, pg. 749
French, Jerry, V.P., Controller & Treas.--Shelter Mutual Insurance Company, Columbia, MO; *U.S. Private*, pg. 992
French, Morton R., Jr., Pres., Chief Exec. Officer, Chief Fin. Officer & Treas.--Commercial Plastics & Supplies Corp., Richmond Hill, NY; *U.S. Private*, pg. 258
French, R.G., Controller & Treas.--Sunkist Growers, Inc., Sherman Oaks, CA; *U.S. Private*, pg. 1052
Frenette, Charles J., Treas. & Sec.--Mason Shoe Mfg. Co., Chippewa Falls, WI; *U.S. Private*, pg. 712
Frenette, Charles J., Treas. & Sec.--Wissota Trader Ltd., Chippewa Falls, WI; *U.S. Private*, pg. 712
Frey, Susanne, Controller & Treas.--The Habegger Corporation, Cincinnati, OH; *U.S. Private*, pg. 492
Freyman, Robert C., Treas.--Abbott Laboratories, Abbott Park, IL; *U.S. Public*, pg. 13
Freyman, Thomas C., V.P. & Treas.--Abbott Laboratories, Abbott Park, IL; *U.S. Public*, pg. 12
Friedman, Dean, Treas. & Sec.--Great Lakes Wholesale Drugs, Livonia, MI; *U.S. Private*, pg. 475
Friedman, Howard, Chief Fin. Officer & Treas.--Van Cleef & Arpels, Inc., New York, NY; *U.S. Private*, pg. 1132
Friedman, Jerry, Exec. V.P., Treas. & Sec.--Marvin Engineering Company, Inc., Inglewood, CA; *U.S. Private*, pg. 710
Friedman, Louis, Treas.--E. & J. Gallo Winery, Modesto, CA; *U.S. Private*, pg. 438
Friedrich, Calvin H., Treas. & Asst. Sec.--Seneca Resources Corp., Houston, TX; *U.S. Public*, pg. 1156
Friedrich, Debra, Asst. Treas.--Bank of the Hudson, Poughkeepsie, NY; *U.S. Public*, pg. 1319
Friedrichsen, B.T., Treas. & Sec.--Wagner Mills Inc., Schuyler, NE; *U.S. Private*, pg. 1146
Frier, Rick, V.P. & Treas.--Treasure Chest Advertising Co., Inc., Glendora, CA; *U.S. Public*, pg. 228
Friesen, Eugene K., Chief Fin. Officer, Sr. V.P. & Treas.--Howard B. Wolf, Inc., Dallas, TX; *U.S. Public*, pg. 1774
Frilegh, Michael R., V.P. & Treas.--Noranda Inc., Toronto, Canada; *Int'l*, pg. 433
Friman, Kaj, Treas.--Kemira Oy, Helsinki, Finland; *Int'l*, pg. 727
Frisch, Benjamin P., V.P., Treas. & Sec.--Beaver Street Fisheries, Inc., Jacksonville, FL; *U.S. Private*, pg. 128
Frisco, John D., V.P.-Fin. & Asst. Treas.--Yarway Corporation, Blue Bell, PA; *U.S. Public*, pg. 1650
Fritz, Mike, Chief Fin. Officer & Treas.--Collegeville Flag & Mfg. Company, Collegeville, PA; *U.S. Private*, pg. 252
Fritze, Steven L., V.P. & Treas.--Ecolab Inc., Saint Paul, MN; *U.S. Public*, pg. 562
Fritzinger, Peter, Chief Fin. Officer & Treas.--Louis Dreyfus Natural Gas Corp., Oklahoma City, OK; *U.S. Private*, pg. 342
Froelich, John M., Chief Fin. Officer, V.P. & Treas.--Chatwins Group, Inc., Pittsburgh, PA; *U.S. Private*, pg. 231
Froelich, Mark A., Treas.--Thompson Tractor Company, Birmingham, AL; *U.S. Private*, pg. 1083
Frome, Stephen D., V.P.-Opers., Treas. & Admin.--Stone & Thomas, Wheeling, WV; *U.S. Private*, pg. 1044
Frost, William J., V.P., Sec. & Treas.--EDO Western Corporation, Salt Lake City, UT; *U.S. Public*, pg. 542
Fruchtman, Arthur, V.P.-Legal & Sec.--Ingersoll-Dresser Pump Company, Liberty Corner, NJ; *U.S. Public*, pg. 529
Fruge, Sherry, Sec. & Treas.--Texas Metal Works, Inc., Beaumont, TX; *U.S. Private*, pg. 1078
Frustaci, Pat R., V.P.-Fin. & Treas.--LCS Industries, Inc., Clifton, NJ; *U.S. Public*, pg. 970
Fry, Michael W., Asst V.P., Controller & Asst. Treas.--Lincoln National Administrative Services Corp., Fort Wayne, IN; *U.S. Public*, pg. 998
Fry, Thomas W., V.P.-Fin. & Admin., Treas. & Sec.--BEI Medical Systems Company, Hackensack, NJ; *U.S. Private*, pg. 106
Fryar, Russell M., V.P. & Treas.--Flowers Industries, Inc., Thomasville, GA; *U.S. Public*, pg. 656
Frye, Dan, Asst. Treas.-Credit Opers.--Diamond Shamrock Credit Card Center, Amarillo, TX; *U.S. Public*, pg. 1663
Frye, John W., Chief Fin. Officer, Sr. V.P.-Fin. & Treas.--Old Dominion Freight Line, Inc., High Point, NC; *U.S. Public*, pg. 1216
Frye, Mickey F., Asst. Treas.--Ruddick Corporation, Charlotte, NC; *U.S. Public*, pg. 1412
Fryz, Michael W., Asst. V.P., Controller & Asst. Treas.--Lincoln National Risk Management, Inc., Fort Wayne, IN; *U.S. Public*, pg. 998
Fuchs, Lois, Asst. Treas.--Rhone-Poulenc Inc., Princeton, NJ; *Int'l*, pg. 1112
Fuerbach, W.F., Jr., Chm. Bd., Pres. & Treas.--S.M. Frank & Co., Inc., Peekskill, NY; *U.S. Private*, pg. 423
Fuertsch, Charles, V.P. & Treas.--Ralphs Grocery Company, Compton, CA; *U.S. Private*, pg. 1202
Fugate, J. Robert, Chief Fin. Officer, V.P.-Fin. & Treas.--Mobile Telecommunications Technologies Corp., Jackson, MS; *U.S. Public*, pg. 1120
Fujii, K., Sr. V.P. & Asst. Treas.--Mitsubishi International Corporation, New York, NY; *Int'l*, pg. 871
Fujiki, Yoichi, Treas.--Argo-Tech Corporation, Cleveland, OH; *U.S. Private*, pg. 81
Fujioka, Paul N., Asst. Treas.--Hawaii Electric Light Co., Inc., Hilo, HI; *U.S. Public*, pg. 800
Fukuyama, Dave, Chief Fin. Officer & Treas.--Suntory International Corp., New York, NY; *Int'l*, pg. 1321
Fukuyama, Yasuhiro, Treas.--Suntory International Corp., New York, NY; *Int'l*, pg. 1321
Fulk, Keith W., V.P., Controller & Asst. Treas.--Folger Nolan Fleming Douglas, Washington, DC; *U.S. Private*, pg. 416
Fuller, Alan B., Treas.--Galardi Group, Inc., Newport Beach, CA; *U.S. Private*, pg. 437
Fuller, Gary W., Pres. & Treas.--Jamieson Film Company, Inc., Dallas, TX; *U.S. Public*, pg. 551
Fuller, Julia P., Asst. Treas.--Texas Industries, Inc., Dallas, TX; *U.S. Public*, pg. 1585
Fuller, Rich, Asst. Treas.--Summit Tool Company, Akron, OH; *U.S. Private*, pg. 1050
Fullerton, J. Manus, Asst. Dir.-Treasury & Intl.--TSB Bank Scotland Plc, Edinburgh, United Kingdom; *Int'l*, pg. 813
Fullerton, Manus S., Asst. Gen. Mgr.-Treas. & Intl.--TSB Bank Scotland Plc, Edinburgh, United Kingdom; *Int'l*, pg. 813
Funk, Tommy, Jr., Treas.--Sebastian Cotton & Grain Corp., Sebastian, TX; *U.S. Private*, pg. 980
Funston, Mark D., Chief Fin. Officer, Exec. V.P. & Treas.--COMNET Corporation, Lanham, MD; *U.S. Public*, pg. 416
Furck, Klaus, Treas.--Deutsche Lufthansa AG, Cologne, Germany; *Int'l*, pg. 407
Furlong, Daniel R., Exec. V.P. & Treas.--Paradigm Communications, Tampa, FL; *U.S. Private*, pg. 838
Furman, William W., Jr., Treas. & Mgr.-Data Processing--Furman Foods, Inc., Northumberland, PA; *U.S. Private*, pg. 431
Furst, Rafael, Sr. V.P., Treas. & Sec.--The Elder-Beerman Stores Corp., Dayton, OH; *U.S. Private*, pg. 367
Furstein, Steve, Treas. & Sec.--Duro Dyne Corporation, Farmingdale, NY; *U.S. Private*, pg. 349
Fusz, Martha, Treas.--Lou Fusz Automotive Network, Saint Louis, MO; *U.S. Private*, pg. 432
Futter, Kenneth, Treas. & Sec.--Futter Lumber Corporation, Rockville Center, NY; *U.S. Private*, pg. 432
Fyfe, Anne, Treas.--Laura Ashley Holdings Plc, Maidenhead, United Kingdom; *Int'l*, pg. 804
Fylnn, E.D., Treas.--Manitowoc Western Company, Inc., La Mirada, CA; *U.S. Public*, pg. 1041
Gable, Corey, Chief Fin. Officer & Treas.--Eateries, Inc., Oklahoma City, OK; *U.S. Public*, pg. 555
Gable, Corey, Chief Fin. Officer & Treas.--Pepperoni Grill, Oklahoma City, OK; *U.S. Public*, pg. 555
Gabriel, Doug, V.P., Controller & Treas.--Apperson Business Forms, Inc., Los Angeles, CA; *U.S. Private*, pg. 78
Gabrielsen, Robert, Chief Fin. Officer, Exec. V.P. & Treas.--Pawling Savings Bank, Pawling, NY; *U.S. Public*, pg. 1334
Gabrielsen, Robert A., Chief Fin. Officer & Treas.--Progressive Bank, Inc., Fishkill, NY; *U.S. Public*, pg. 1334
Gace, James M., V.P., Treas. & Sec.--Financial Industries Corp., Austin, TX; *U.S. Public*, pg. 622
Gace, James M., V.P. & Treas.--InternContinental Life Corp., Austin, TX; *U.S. Public*, pg. 622.
Gaffney, Tim, V.P.-Fin. & Treas.--Hoffman Laces, Ltd., Cobleskill, NY; *U.S. Public*, pg. 769
Gagalis, Robert J., Chief Fin. Officer, Treas. & V.P.--Wheelabrator Technologies Inc., Hampton, NH; *U.S. Public*, pg. 1745
Gaglioti, Joseph, V.P. & Treas.--Cole National Corporation, Cleveland, OH; *U.S. Public*, pg. 396
Gaglioti, Joseph, V.P. & Treas.--Cole Vision Corporation, Cleveland, OH; *U.S. Public*, pg. 396
Gagnon, Benoit, Chief Fin. Officer & Treas.--Agropur, Granby, Canada; *Int'l*, pg. 31
Gahm, Walter D., Jr., V.P. & Treas.--Kitchen Kompact, Inc., Jeffersonville, IN; *U.S. Private*, pg. 624
Gaines, D.E., Treas.--Puget Sound Energy Co., Bellevue, WA; *U.S. Public*, pg. 1342
Gaines, Donald E., Treas.--Puget Sound Energy, Inc., Bellevue, WA; *U.S. Public*, pg. 1342
Galbraith, Leslie A., Chief Fin. Officer, Exec. V.P., Treas. & Sec.--First International Bancorp, Inc., Hartford, CT; *U.S. Public*, pg. 635
Galbraith, Tony, Treas.--British Airways PLC, London, United Kingdom; *Int'l*, pg. 218
Galetto, Charles, Sr. V.P.-Fin. & Treas.--PMR Corporation, San Diego, CA; *U.S. Public*, pg. 1242
Galgano, Victor J., Chief Fin. Officer & V.P.--Hi-Shear Industries Inc., New Hyde Park, NY; *U.S. Public*, pg. 824
Gallager, Thomas, V.P.-Fin. & Treas.--Chem-Trend Incorporated, Howell, MI; *Int'l*, pg. 235
Gallagher, Cindy, Treas. & Sec.--Jim Fresard Pontiac Buick, Inc., Royal Oak, MI; *U.S. Private*, pg. 427
Gallagher, H. James, Chief Fin. Officer, Exec. V.P.-Fin. & Acting Treas.--CalMat Co., Los Angeles, CA; *U.S. Public*, pg. 295
Gallagher, Jack, Treas.--Peterson Tractor Company, San Leandro, CA; *U.S. Private*, pg. 858
Gallagher, John, Treas.--Hinkley Lighting Inc., Cleveland, OH; *U.S. Private*, pg. 530
Gallagher, Paul J., V.P. & Treas.--Air Express International Corporation, Darien, CT; *U.S. Public*, pg. 30
Gallaher, Edward W., Sr., Pres., Chief Exec. Officer & Treas.--Phoenix Medical Technology, Inc., Andrews, SC; *U.S. Public*, pg. 1292
Gallant, Steve, Treas.--Markem Corporation, Keene, NH; *U.S. Private*, pg. 704
Gallatin, Albert E., V.P. & Treas.--ENSERCH Corporation, Dallas, TX; *U.S. Public*, pg. 1587
Gallivan, Karen, Treas.--Robert Bosch Corporation, Broadview, IL; *Int'l*, pg. 204
Galloway, Carl H., V.P. & Treas.--Lawson Mardon Packaging Inc., Mississauga, Canada; *Int'l*, pg. 68
Gallucci, Michael A., Jr., V.P. & Treas.--Glaxo Wellcome Inc., Research Triangle Park, NC; *Int'l*, pg. 552
Galow, Geoffrey G., Asst. Treas.--Entergy Gulf States, Inc., Beaumont, TX; *U.S. Public*, pg. 586
Galuten, Sandra L., Treas.--SGD International Corp., Riverdale, NY; *U.S. Private*, pg. 957
Galvin, Doris, V.P. & Treas.--CMS Energy Corporation, Dearborn, MI; *U.S. Public*, pg. 279
Galvin, Doris F., Treas.--Michigan Gas Storage Co., Jackson, MI; *U.S. Public*, pg. 280
Galvin, John E., V.P. & Treas.--IMC Global, Bannockburn, IL; *U.S. Public*, pg. 856
Galvin, R. Terrence, V.P. & Treas.--The Great Atlantic & Pacific Tea Company, Inc., Montvale, NJ; *Int'l*, pg. 1375
Gambrell, George B., Asst. Treas.--Springs Industries, Inc., Fort Mill, SC; *U.S. Public*, pg. 1499
Gamron, W. Anthony, V.P. & Treas.--Kimberly-Clark Corporation, Dallas, TX; *U.S. Public*, pg. 958
Gannon, Kathleen R., V.P. & Treas.--Whitman Corporation, Rolling Meadows, IL; *U.S. Public*, pg. 1766
Ganong, John, Treas.--Highland Industries Inc., Greensboro, NC; *U.S. Private*, pg. 528
Gant, Harry, Chief Fin. Officer, V.P., Treas. & Sec.--Young Radiator Company, Racine, WI; *U.S. Private*, pg. 1201
Gantt, G. Russell, V.P., Treas., & Asst. Sec.--Glen Raven Mills, Inc., Glen Raven, NC; *U.S. Private*, pg. 456
Gapinski, Michael J., Treas. & Asst. Sec.--The Reynolds and Reynolds Company, Dayton, OH; *U.S. Public*, pg. 1384
Garber, Craig, V.P. & Treas.--Lam Research Corporation, Fremont, CA; *U.S. Public*, pg. 975
Garber, John, Chief Fin. Officer, V.P.-Fin. & Treas.--Newcor, Inc., Bloomfield Hills, MI; *U.S. Public*, pg. 1176
Garber, Stanley, Treas.--The Arlen Corporation, New York, NY; *U.S. Public*, pg. 131
Garchik, Sandy, V.P. & Asst. Treas.--Clark Enterprises, Inc., Bethesda, MD; *U.S. Private*, pg. 242
Garcia, Ileana, Treas. & Sec.--International Recovery Corp., Miami Springs, FL; *U.S. Public*, pg. 906
Garcia, Leonardo F., V.P. & Treas.--American Bankers Insurance Group, Inc., Miami, FL; *U.S. Public*, pg. 67
Gardiner, William J., Chief Fin. Officer, Sr. V.P. & Treas.--CRSS Inc., Houston, TX; *Int'l*, pg. 1415
Gardner, Jack R., Treas.--Makino Inc., Mason, OH; *Int'l*, pg. 831
Gardner, James, Treas.--Northwestern Industrial Piping, Niles, IL; *U.S. Private*, pg. 806
Garefino, Anello C., Chief Fin. Officer, V.P.-Fin. & Treas.--Herley Industries, Inc., Lancaster, PA; *U.S. Public*, pg. 811
Garfinkle, David M., Controller & Treas.--Bradley Real Estate, Inc., Northbrook, IL; *U.S. Public*, pg. 250
Garnaat, G., Treas.--Koninklijke BolsWessanen nv, Amstelveen, Netherlands; *Int'l*, pg. 750
Garner, Jerol, Asst. Treas.--Iomega Corporation, Roy, UT; *U.S. Public*, pg. 912
Garofolo, David A., Treas.--Inmet Mining Corporation, Toronto, Canada; *Int'l*, pg. 678
Garratt, Paul R., V.P.-H.R.--Air Canada, Saint-Laurent, Canada; *Int'l*, pg. 36
Garrett, J. Richard, V.P. & Treas.--The Hartford Financial Services Group Inc., Hartford, CT; *U.S. Public*, pg. 794
Garrett, Melinda, Treas.--Abrams Properties, Inc., Atlanta, GA; *U.S. Public*, pg. 14
Garrett, Thomas L., Jr., Treas.--BHP Copper North America, Tucson, AZ; *Int'l*, pg. 224
Garrett, Thomas L., Jr., V.P. & Treas.--Service Merchandise Company, Inc., Brentwood, TN; *U.S. Public*, pg. 1461
Garretty, Joan, Treas.--Meijer, Inc., Grand Rapids, MI; *U.S. Private*, pg. 729
Garrison, Gary G., Chief Fin. Officer, V.P.-Fin. & Treas.--Global Industrial Technologies, Dallas, TX; *U.S. Public*, pg. 747
Garrison, James W., Chief Fin. Officer, V.P.-Fin. & Treas.--InterDigital Communications Corp., King of Prussia, PA; *U.S. Public*, pg. 889
Garrison, Tom, V.P., Treas. & Sec.--American Freightways Corporation, Harrison, AR; *U.S. Public*, pg. 75
Garrity, William E., Treas.--Capital Industries, Inc., Seattle, WA; *U.S. Private*, pg. 206
Garvey, Nancy A., V.P.-Investor Rels. & Treas.--AlliedSignal Inc., Morristown, NJ; *U.S. Public*, pg. 49
Garvin, Andrew P., Chm. Bd., Pres., Chief Exec. Officer & Treas.--Find/SVP, Inc., New York, NY; *U.S. Public*, pg. 623
Gary, Christian, Treas.--Accor S.A., Evry, France; *Int'l*, pg. 20
Gasca, Peter, Treas. & Corp. Sec.--Wards Cove Packing Company, Seattle, WA; *U.S. Private*, pg. 1149
Gasparelli, Adeline, Treas.--Wyse Advertising, Cleveland, OH; *U.S. Private*, pg. 1193
Gatch-Priest, Robyn, V.P.-Controller & Asst. Treas.--CompUSA, Dallas, TX; *U.S. Public*, pg. 420
Gately, James E., V.P. & Treas.--Daniels Printing Company, Everett, MA; *U.S. Private*, pg. 310
Gates, Jordan, Chief Fin. Officer & Treas.--Expeditors International of Washington, Inc., Seattle, WA; *U.S. Public*, pg. 600
Gatewood, Robert C., Sr. Exec. V.P.-Legal Affairs, Sec. & Treas.--Dairy Queen Corporate Store, Louisville, KY; *U.S. Public*, pg. 220
Gatta, Rosanne, Asst. V.P. & Treas.--Provident Mutual Life Insurance Co., Berwyn, PA; *U.S. Private*, pg. 891
Gau, Jack, Sec. & Treas.--G.R. Herberger's, Inc., Saint Cloud, MN; *U.S. Public*, pg. 1333

Gaudette, Bryant, Treas.--BeautiControl Cosmetics, Inc., Carrollton, TX; *U.S. Public*, pg. 198

Gaudie, H. Alan, Sr. V.P.-Fin. & Treas.--Galoob Toys, Inc., South San Francisco, CA; *U.S. Public*, pg. 698

Gaudiosi, Joseph A., Asst. Treas.--Bailey, Fischer & Porter Company, Warminster, PA; *Int'l*, pg. 449

Gauvreau, Paul R., V.P.-Fin. & Treas.--Pittway Corporation, Chicago, IL; *U.S. Public*, pg. 1305

Gauvreau, Pierre, Chief Fin. Officer & Treas.--Cooperative Federee de Quebec, Montreal, Canada; *Int'l*, pg. 330

Gavin, Jon D., Chief Fin. Officer, V.P., Sec. & Treas.--Frontier Oil Corporation, Englewood, CO; *U.S. Public*, pg. 1732

Gavin, Jon D., Chief Fin. Officer, V.P., Sec. & Treas.--Frontier Holdings Inc., Englewood, CO; *U.S. Public*, pg. 1732

Gavin, Mark A., CPA, Treas.--CFX Funding, L.L.C., Keene, NH; *U.S. Public*, pg. 278

Gavin, Pat, Chief Fin. Officer, Exec. V.P. & Treas.--General Media International Inc., New York, NY; *U.S. Private*, pg. 444

Gaw, L.T.L., Treas.--Exxon Trading Asia Pacific Private Limited, Singapore, Singapore; *U.S. Public*, pg. 602

Gaylord, Thomas M., Treas. & Sec.--Mack Molding Company Inc., Arlington, VT; *U.S. Private*, pg. 691

Gazarek, Celeste, V.P.-Fin. & Treas.--National Frozen Foods Corp., Seattle, WA; *U.S. Private*, pg. 783

Gazmarian, Michael C., Chief Fin. Officer & Treas.--Insteel Industries, Inc., Mount Airy, NC; *U.S. Public*, pg. 882

Gebo, L. Evelyn, Treas. & Sec.--Gebo Distributing Co., Inc., Plainview, TX; *U.S. Private*, pg. 442

Gee, Edward, Treas. & Sec.--Cloverhill Bakery, Chicago, IL; *U.S. Private*, pg. 247

Gegick, Mary Lourdes, Asst. Treas.--Equitable Resources, Inc., Pittsburgh, PA; *U.S. Public*, pg. 589

Gehman, Robin H., Treas.--Tultex Corporation, Martinsville, VA; *U.S. Public*, pg. 1644

Geiger, Eugene G., Pres. & Treas.--Geiger Brothers, Lewiston, ME; *U.S. Private*, pg. 442

Geiger, Paul E., V.P., Sec. & Treas.--CMS Nomeco, Jackson, MI; *U.S. Public*, pg. 280

Geiser, James, Chief Fin. Officer, Controller & Treas.--Kokosing Construction Company, Inc., Fredericktown, OH; *U.S. Private*, pg. 631

Geisselbrecht, Elvin, V.P., Treas. & Sec.--YRJ Corporation, Houston, TX; *U.S. Private*, pg. 1176

Geisselbrecht, Elvin R., Treas. & Sec.--Wilco Reprographic, Inc., Las Vegas, NV; *U.S. Private*, pg. 1176

Gelder, Robert, Pres. & Treas.--Barden & Robeson Corporation, Middleport, NY; *U.S. Private*, pg. 116

Geldmacher, Kenneth K., Controller & Treas.--Centrifugal & Mechanical Industries, Saint Louis, MO; *U.S. Private*, pg. 370

Geliebter, Joel A., Treas. & Mgr.-Pension Admin. & Risk Mngmt.--Henry Schein, Inc., Melville, NY; *U.S. Public*, pg. 1437

Genera, Ernesto, Treas.--Nuevo Federal S.A., Buenos Aires, Argentina; *Int'l*, pg. 990

Genor, Andrew C., Chief Fin. Officer, V.P. & Treas.--Wyman-Gordon, North Grafton, MA; *U.S. Public*, pg. 1782

Gentile, Thomas, Treas.--BP America Inc., Cleveland, OH; *Int'l*, pg. 220

Gentry, Boyd P., V.P.-Investor Rels. & Treas.--Paragon Health Network, Inc., Atlanta, GA; *U.S. Public*, pg. 1256

Gentry, John, Pres. & Treas.--Positronic Industries, Inc., Springfield, MO; *U.S. Private*, pg. 876

Gentry, Mary M., Sr. V.P. & Treas.--Carolina First Corporation, Greenville, SC; *U.S. Public*, pg. 306

Gentry, Pamela J., Treas. & Asst. Sec.--Signal Apparel Company, Inc., Chattanooga, TN; *U.S. Public*, pg. 1472

Genuardi, Dominic, Treas.--Genuardi Family Markets Inc., Norristown, PA; *U.S. Private*, pg. 447

George, Dan, Pres. & Treas.--Central United Life Insurance Co., Houston, TX; *U.S. Private*, pg. 225

George, J.G., Grp. Treas.--LASMO plc, London, United Kingdom; *Int'l*, pg. 803

George, John B., Treas.--Republic Engineered Steels, Inc., Massillon, OH; *U.S. Public*, pg. 1378

George, Leslie, Jr., Treas. & Sec.--King Group, Inc., Ann Arbor, MI; *U.S. Private*, pg. 620

George, Michael J., V.P.-Fin. & Treas.--Fleming Company, Waukesha, WI; *U.S. Public*, pg. 653

George, Robert D., Controller & Treas.--Esterline Technologies Corporation, Bellevue, WA; *U.S. Public*, pg. 594

George, Thomas A., Sec. & Treas.--Melody Foods, Inc., Farmington Hills, MI; *U.S. Private*, pg. 730

George, Thomas D., Treas.--Ferro Corporation, Cleveland, OH; *U.S. Public*, pg. 618

George, Tom, Treas.--Pioneer Snacks, Farmington Hills, MI; *U.S. Private*, pg. 730

Georgoulis, John S., Treas.--TIC United Corporation, Dallas, TX; *U.S. Private*, pg. 1063

Gerard, Bryan, Asst. Treas.--Boeing Realty Corporation, Long Beach, CA; *U.S. Public*, pg. 241

Gerard, Bryan, Asst. Treas.--The Boeing Travel Company, Irvine, CA; *U.S. Public*, pg. 241

Gerard, Bryan, Asst. Treas.--Boeing Services, Inc., Khamis Mushayt, Saudi Arabia; *U.S. Public*, pg. 242

Gerard, Stephen, Pres., Chief Exec. Officer & Treas.--Bolliger, Inc., Stamford, CT; *U.S. Private*, pg. 155

Gerber, C. Allen, V.P. & Treas.--UB Foods U.S., Inc., Elmhurst, IL; *Int'l*, pg. 1442

Gerber, Laurie, Chief Fin. Officer--Meditrust Corporation, Needham, MA; *U.S. Public*, pg. 1081

Gerding, Ralph A., Treas.--Knouse Foods Inc., Peach Glen, PA; *U.S. Private*, pg. 627

Geremski, Terrence E., Chief Fin. Officer, V.P. & Treas.--Guilford Mills, Inc., Greensboro, NC; *U.S. Public*, pg. 768

Geren, Tracey, Treas. & Sec.--Weldon, Williams & Lick, Inc., Fort Smith, AR; *U.S. Private*, pg. 1161

Gerhard, Gilbert C., Chief Fin. Officer, Sr. V.P.-Fin. & Admin. & Treas.--Arbor Drugs, Inc., Troy, MI; *U.S. Public*, pg. 126

Gerhart, Karl D., Chief Fin. Officer & Treas.--Sovereign Bancorp, Inc., Wyomissing, PA; *U.S. Public*, pg. 1494

Germeroth, Gary M., Controller & Treas.--QST Enterprises Inc., Peoria, IL; *U.S. Public*, pg. 367

Germeroth, Gary M., Controller & Treas.--QST Communications, Inc., Peoria, IL; *U.S. Public*, pg. 367

Gerrein, Carl, V.P. & Treas.--Midland Enterprises Inc., Cincinnati, OH; *U.S. Public*, pg. 549

Gershenson, Glenn, Asst. Treas.--Rite Aid Corporation, Camp Hill, PA; *U.S. Public*, pg. 1390

Gerst, Carl W., Jr., Vice Chm., Chief Tech. Officer & Treas.--Anaren Microwave Inc., East Syracuse, NY; *U.S. Public*, pg. 110

Gerstein, Mel, Treas. & Dir.-Mktg., Adv. & Pub. Rels.--Thermwell Products Co., Inc., Paterson, NJ; *U.S. Private*, pg. 1081

Gerstein, Mitchell, V.P., Controller & Treas.--Krantor Corporation, Syosset, NY; *U.S. Public*, pg. 966

Gerstman, Henry, Controller, Treas. & Sec.--Century Business Credit Corporation, New York, NY; *U.S. Private*, pg. 225

Gertry, Mary M., Treas.--CF Investment Company, Greenville, SC; *U.S. Public*, pg. 306

Gerughty, Robert, Treas.--Altera Corporation, San Jose, CA; *U.S. Public*, pg. 59

Geswein, G.T., Treas.--M-B Pulp Company, Dayton, OH; *U.S. Public*, pg. 1076

Geswein, G.T., Treas.--Forest Kraft Company, Dayton, OH; *U.S. Public*, pg. 1076

Gettlefinger, Andrew, Sec. & Treas.--Kelso Oil Company, Knoxville, TN; *U.S. Private*, pg. 613

Gettlegfinger, Herman E., Chief Fin. Officer, Treas. & Sec.--Pride Oil Co., Inc., Knoxville, TN; *U.S. Private*, pg. 613

Geyer, Troy, Controller, Treas. & Sec.--Antenna Products Corp., Mineral Wells, TX; *U.S. Public*, pg. 289

Ghantous, Fred G., Treasurer--Pratt & Whitney Canada Inc., Longueuil, Canada; *U.S. Public*, pg. 1690

Ghose, Dev, Sr. V.P.-Fin. & Treas.--Health Care Property Investors, Inc., Newport Beach, CA; *U.S. Public*, pg. 801

Giangrande, Vincent A., Treas.--Axsys Technologies, Inc., New York, NY; *U.S. Public*, pg. 157

Giarrusso, Raymond J., Treas. & Sec.--GAI Consultants, Inc., Monroeville, PA; *U.S. Private*, pg. 433

Gibb, Bradley, Treas. & Sec.--Robert Gibb & Sons, Inc., Fargo, ND; *U.S. Private*, pg. 451

Gibbes, A.H., Pres. & Treas.--SCANA, Columbia, SC; *U.S. Public*, pg. 1436

Gibbons, John D., Treas.--Valero Refining Company, San Antonio, TX; *U.S. Public*, pg. 1704

Gibbons, Paul F., V.P. & Treas.--Harcourt General, Inc., Chestnut Hill, MA; *U.S. Public*, pg. 782

Gibbons, Tom, Sr. V.P. & Treas.--Del Monte Foods, San Francisco, CA; *U.S. Private*, pg. 321

Gibbs, David H., Treas.--Owen-Ames-Kimball Co., Grand Rapids, MI; *U.S. Private*, pg. 823

Gibbs, Jason A., Treas. & Controller--Pulaski Furniture Corporation, Pulaski, VA; *U.S. Public*, pg. 1342

Gibelli, William, Treas.--The Foxboro Company, Foxboro, MA; *Int'l*, pg. 1243

Gibney, Charles W., Chief Fin. Officer, Exec. V.P. & Treas.--Bergen Record Corp., Hackensack, NJ; *U.S. Private*, pg. 693

Gibson, B. Baird, Sec. & Treas.--Patterson Pump Company, Toccoa, GA; *U.S. Public*, pg. 754

Gibson, Cynthia, Treas. & Sec.--Wolcott & Lincoln, Inc., Kansas City, MO; *U.S. Private*, pg. 1185

Gibson, M.L., Chief Fin. Officer, Exec. V.P. & Treas.--Hardings, Inc., Elmira, NY; *U.S. Private*, pg. 502

Gibson, N.M., Sec. & Treas.--Synergistics Chemicals, Inc., Mississauga, Canada; *U.S. Public*, pg. 734

Gibson, Ralph M., Pres. & Treas.--Durrett-Sheppard Steel Co., Inc., Baltimore, MD; *U.S. Private*, pg. 349

Gibson, Robert V., V.P.-Fin.& Treas.--Datron Incorporated, Windsor, CT; *U.S. Private*, pg. 313

Gibson, Russell G., Chief Fin. Officer, Exec. V.P., Treas. & Asst. Sec.--Farah Incorporated, El Paso, TX; *U.S. Public*, pg. 612

Gideon, Kyle J., Asst. Treas.--Stewart & Stevenson Services, Inc., Houston, TX; *U.S. Public*, pg. 1517

Giffen, Ian, V.P.-Fin., Treas. & Chief Fin. Officer--Alias Wavefront, Toronto, Canada; *U.S. Public*, pg. 1474

Gifford, Russell M., Chief Fin. Officer, V.P. & Treas.--Barnwell Industries, Inc., Honolulu, HI; *U.S. Public*, pg. 190

Gignac, Kenneth, Chm. Bd. & Pres.--Elgin Dairy Foods, Inc., Chicago, IL; *U.S. Private*, pg. 370

Gilbane, Joan A., Treas.--Gilbane Building Company, Providence, RI; *U.S. Private*, pg. 452

Gilbert, Benjamin J., Treas.--International Women's Apparel Group, Easton, PA; *U.S. Public*, pg. 796

Gilbert, R.W., Exec. V.P.-Sls. & Mktg. & Treas.--Shure Brothers Incorporated, Evanston, IL; *U.S. Private*, pg. 997

Gilbert, Richard D., Chief Fin. Officer, Treas. & Sec.--The Converse Professional Group, Inc., Monrovia, CA; *U.S. Private*, pg. 271

Gilbert, Walter, Treas.--Cora Texas Manufacturing Co., Inc., White Castle, LA; *U.S. Private*, pg. 275

Gilbert, Walter F., Chm. Bd., Pres., Chief Exec. Officer & Treas.--Semco Industries Inc., Stoughton, MA; *U.S. Private*, pg. 983

Gilbertson, Jay, Pres., Co-Chief Oper. Officer, Chief Fin. Officer, Treas. & Sec.--HBOC, Atlanta, GA; *U.S. Public*, pg. 770

Gill, Nicholas P., Chief Fin. Officer, V.P., Treas. & Sec.--The Union Corporation, Greenwich, CT; *U.S. Public*, pg. 1667

Gillheeney, Gary S., V.P.- Fin. & Information Services & Treas.--Providence Energy Corporation, Providence, RI; *U.S. Public*, pg. 1337

Gillheeney, Gary S., V.P. & Treas.--Providence Gas Co., Providence, RI; *U.S. Public*, pg. 1337

Gillheeney, Gary S., Asst. Treas.--Newport America Corporation, Providence, RI; *U.S. Public*, pg. 1337

Gilliland, Dale, Controller & Treas.--Buccaneer Homes, Inc., Hamilton, AL; *U.S. Public*, pg. 318

Gillis, Edwin J., Chief Fin. Officer, Exec. V.P. & Treas.--Parametric Technology Corporation, Waltham, MA; *U.S. Public*, pg. 1257

Gillis, Ruth Ann M., V.P. & Treas.--Unicom Corporation, Chicago, IL; *U.S. Public*, pg. 1664

Gilmour, James H., Chief Fin. Officer, V.P. & Treas.--The Dispatch Printing Company, Columbus, OH; *U.S. Private*, pg. 334

Gilrane, James J., Sr. V.P. & Treas.--ITT Information Services, Inc., New York, NY; *U.S. Public*, pg. 1512

Gilstrap, James J., Chief Fin. Officer, V.P. & Treas.--Florida Rock Industries, Inc., Jacksonville, FL; *U.S. Public*, pg. 655

Gimberline, Jackie, Controller & Treas.--MidAmerican Capital Company, Des Moines, IA; *U.S. Public*, pg. 1109

Gingridge, Ken, Treas.--Superior Tube Company, Collegeville, PA; *U.S. Private*, pg. 1056

Ginns, Susan M., Sr. V.P. & Treas.--Brookline Savings Bank, Brookline, MA; *U.S. Private*, pg. 171

Ginsberg, Michael, Sec. & Treas.--F.T. Publications Inc., New York, NY; *Int'l*, pg. 1026

Ginsburg, George B., V.P., Treas. & Sec.--Money Point Diamond Co., Chesapeake, VA; *U.S. Private*, pg. 757

Ginther, Gary, V.P.-Fin.--Smart & Final, Vernon, CA; *Int'l*, pg. 563

Giordano, Sebastian, Chief Fin. Officer--Sterling Vision, Inc., East Meadow, NY; *U.S. Public*, pg. 1516

Giorgio, Michael R., Chief Fin. Officer, Controller & Treas.--Suarez Corporation Industries, Canton, OH; *U.S. Private*, pg. 1048

Girard, Marc, Asst. Treas.--BCE Inc., Montreal, Canada; *Int'l*, pg. 114

Girot, Francis P. Jr., Treas.--Northern Indiana Public Service Company, Hammond, IN; *U.S. Public*, pg. 1185

Giroux, Dennis, Controller & Treas.--Schwarz Paper Company, Morton Grove, IL; *U.S. Private*, pg. 974

Girsky, Joel H., Chm. Bd., Pres. & Treas.--Jaco Electronics, Inc., Hauppauge, NY; *U.S. Public*, pg. 920

Gisi, R.B., Asst. Treas.--Phillips Petroleum Company, Bartlesville, OK; *U.S. Public*, pg. 1290

Gittelman, Milton, Chief Exec. Officer, V.P, Treas. & Sec.--Triumph Pet Industries, Inc., Warwick, NY; *U.S. Private*, pg. 1104

Gittleman, M. Jeffrey, Treas.--Andrew Corporation, Orland Park, IL; *U.S. Public*, pg. 112

Giuliani, John, Treas. & Sec.--Lodal, Inc., Kingsford, MI; *U.S. Private*, pg. 672

Givan, Gregory, V.P. & Treas.--Commonwealth Industries, Inc., Louisville, KY; *U.S. Public*, pg. 415

Gladysz, Martin, V.P. & Treas.--Eckerd Corporation, Largo, FL; *U.S. Public*, pg. 917

Glass, Dennis R., Chief Fin. Officer, Sr. V.P. & Treas.--Jefferson-Pilot Corporation, Greensboro, NC; *U.S. Public*, pg. 925

Glass, Dennis R., Chief Fin. Officer, Exec. V.P. & Treas.--Jefferson-Pilot Life Insurance Co., Greensboro, NC; *U.S. Public*, pg. 926

Glass, Henry W., Jr., Treas.--Berkshire Life Insurance Company, Pittsfield, MA; *U.S. Private*, pg. 136

Glasshoff, R., V.P.-Fin.--Rexam Inc., Charlotte, NC; *Int'l*, pg. 1106

Glauber, Michael A., Sr. V.P.-Fin. & Admin.--Leggett & Platt, Incorporated, Carthage, MO; *U.S. Public*, pg. 985

Gleason, E.M., Controller, Corp. Treas. & Sec.--Wisconsin Power & Light Company, Madison, WI; *U.S. Public*, pg. 1728

Gleason, Edward M., V.P., Treas. & Corp. Sec.--WPL Holdings, Inc., Madison, WI; *U.S. Public*, pg. 1727

Gleason, Edward M., V.P., Controller, Treas. & Corp. Sec.--South Beloit Water, Gas & Electric Co., South Beloit, IL; *U.S. Public*, pg. 1728

Gleason, Thomas L., Treas.--Alumax Inc., Atlanta, GA; *U.S. Public*, pg. 59

Gleaves, James L., V.P. & Treas.--American General Corporation, Houston, TX; *U.S. Public*, pg. 76

Gleich, Peter A., Chief Fin. Officer & Treas.--Sigma-Aldrich Corporation, Saint Louis, MO; *U.S. Public*, pg. 1471

Glenn, Clyde A., Jr., Pres. & Treas.--Potter-Shackelford Construction Co., Greenville, SC; *U.S. Private*, pg. 877

Glenn, G. Lee, Chief Fin. Officer, V.P. & Treas.--Kelley Bean Co., Inc., Morrill, NE; *U.S. Private*, pg. 612

Glenn, Jerry, V.P.-Fin. & Treas.--Consolidated Group, Inc., Charlotte, NC; *U.S. Private*, pg. 351

Glick, Marty, V.P. & Treas.--Genentech, Inc., South San Francisco, CA; *Int'l*, pg. 1120

Glickstein, Neil A., V.P.-Fin.--Binney & Smith Inc., Easton, PA; *U.S. Private*, pg. 496

Glidden, Robert D., Jr., V.P.-Fin. & Treas.--Robert James Sales Inc., Buffalo, NY; *U.S. Private*, pg. 935

Gluck, Robert S., V.P. & Treas.--Bestfoods, Englewood Cliffs, NJ; *U.S. Public*, pg. 223

Gluth, Robert C., Exec. V.P. & Treas.--The Marmon Group, Inc., Chicago, IL; *U.S. Private*, pg. 706

Glyer, Paul, Treas.--Beckman Instruments, Inc., Fullerton, CA; *U.S. Public*, pg. 199

Glynn, John J., Treas. & Sec.--Baird, Patrick & Co., Inc., New York, NY; *U.S. Private*, pg. 111

Glynn, Terry, Treas. & Sec.--Select Canfield, Chicago, IL; *U.S. Private*, pg. 982

Gobris, Joseph J., Asst. Sec. & Asst. Treas.--Voest-Alpine International Corporation, New York, NY; *Int'l*, pg. 1470

Godchaux, Leslie K., Asst. Treas.--Riviana Foods Inc., Houston, TX; *U.S. Public*, pg. 1392

Goddard, Larry, Chief Fin. Officer, Treas. & Sec.--P.A.M. Transport, Inc., Tontitown, AR; *U.S. Private*, pg. 825

Godfrey, Robert, Treas. & Sec.--Central States Enterprises, Inc., Heathrow, FL; *U.S. Private*, pg. 225

Godin, Gary, Chief Acctg. Officer & Controller--Media 100, Inc., Marlborough, MA; *U.S. Public*, pg. 1079

Godin, Marc, Treas.--Teleglobe, Inc., Montreal, Canada; *Int'l*, pg. 1373
Goebel, A.E., Treas. & Sec.--Energy Systems Group, Inc., Evansville, IN; *U.S. Public*, pg. 1471
Goebel, A.E., Treas. & Sec.--ComSource, Inc., Evansville, IN; *U.S. Public*, pg. 1471
Goebel, Andrew E., Chief Fin. Officer, Sr. V.P. & Treas.--Southern Indiana Gas & Electric Co., Evansville, IN; *U.S.* Public, pg. 1471
Goedecke, Otto E., Pres. & Treas.--Otto Goedecke, Inc., Houston, TX; *U.S. Private*, pg. 458
Goeke, Gerard, V.P.-Info. Svcs. & Treas.--The Donohoe Companies, Inc., Washington, DC; *U.S. Private*, pg. 340
Goers, Charles, Pres., Chief Exec. Officer & Treas.--T O Plastics, Inc., Minneapolis, MN; *U.S. Private*, pg. 1065
Goesling, John, Exec. V.P. & Treas.--Nordstrom, Inc., Seattle, WA; *U.S. Public*, pg. 1190
Goetsch, Douglas G., V.P. & Treas.--Republic Automotive Parts, Inc., Brentwood, TN; *U.S. Public*, pg. 1377
Goetz, Tim, Chief Fin. Officer, Treas. & Dir.-Mktg.--Robinson Helicopter Company, Torrance, CA; *U.S. Private*, pg. 936
Goforth, James, Treas.--Renosol Corp., Saline, MI; *U.S. Private*, pg. 922
Goforth, Rene, Pres., Treas. & Sec.--Hilb, Rogal and Hamilton Company of Victoria, Victoria, TX; *U.S. Public*, pg. 827
Goh, Jessie, Treas. & Corp. Fin.--Scotts Holdings Limited, Singapore, Singapore; *Int'l*, pg. 1212
Goheen, Michael B., Chief Fin. Officer & Treas.--Steuart Investment Company, Chevy Chase, MD; *U.S. Private*, pg. 1042
Goist, James L., Treas.--Belden & Blake Corporation, Canton, OH; *U.S. Private*, pg. 1078
Gold, William, Treas.--PEC Israel Economic Corporation, New York, NY; *Int'l*, pg. 644
Goldberg, Cindy, Treas. & Sec.--FDP Corp., Miami, FL; *U.S.* Public, pg. 603
Goldberg, Sanford, Sr. V.P.--A&W Restaurants, Inc.-Carousel Div., Minneapolis, MN; *U.S. Private*, pg. 2
Golden, David, Chief Fin. Officer, Treas. & Sec.--Stephen Gould Paper Co., Inc., Whippany, NJ; *U.S. Private*, pg. 467
Goldenberg, Victoria, Sec. & Treas.--Fashion Shop of Kentucky Inc., Louisville, KY; *U.S. Private*, pg. 397
Goldman, David, Pres. & Treas.--Goldman Financial Group, Boston, MA; *U.S. Private*, pg. 461
Goldman, Marilyn S., Exec. V.P., Treas. & Sec.--S.I. Goldman Co., Longwood, FL; *U.S. Private*, pg. 461
Goldschein, Steven, Chief Exec. Officer, V.P.-Admin., Treas. & Sec.--Lambda Electronics Inc., Melville, NY; *Int'l*, pg. 1241
Goldstein, Melvyn C., V.P.-Fin. & Treas.--Del Laboratories, Inc., Farmingdale, NY; *U.S. Public*, pg. 494
Goldstein, Norman R., V.P., Treas. & Asst. Sec.--Barton Incorporated, Chicago, IL; *U.S. Public*, pg. 300
Gollner, Richard, Treas.--Chicago Heights Steel, Chicago Heights, IL; *U.S. Private*, pg. 234
Gombert, Rod T., V.P.-Fin. & Treas.--Bondo/Mar-Hyde Corporation, Cleveland, OH; *U.S. Public*, pg. 1357
Gombert, Rod T., V.P. & Treas.--Paramount Technical Products, Inc., Spearfish, SD; *U.S. Public*, pg. 1357
Gonda, Robert, Treas.--Family Restaurants, Inc., Irvine, CA; *U.S. Private*, pg. 393
Gonsalves, C.B., V.P. & Treas.--Esso Standard Oil S.A. Limited, Nassau, Bahamas; *U.S. Public*, pg. 602
Gonzalez, Richard J., Chief Fin. Officer, V.P., Treas. & Sec.--Bayou Steel Corporation, La Place, LA; *U.S. Public*, pg. 197
Goodell, Brenda, Treas. & Sec.--Willard Grain & Feed, Inc., Celina, TX; *U.S. Private*, pg. 1177
Goodger, John V., V.P., Treas. & Asst. Sec.--Pioneer-Standard Electronics, Inc., Cleveland, OH; *U.S. Public*, pg. 1300
Goodman, David W., Asst. Treas.--DeVry Institutes, Oak Brook Terrace, IL; *U.S. Public*, pg. 503
Goodman, Murray, Pres. & Treas.--Goodmans, Inc., Phoenix, AZ; *U.S. Private*, pg. 464
Goodman, Philip, Treas.--Burtman Iron Works, Inc., Readville, MA; *U.S. Private*, pg. 188
Goodman, Tom, Treas.--Outboard Marine Corporation, Waukegan, IL; *U.S. Private*, pg. 478
Goodwin, Morris, V.P. & Treas.--IDS Certificate Company, Minneapolis, MN; *U.S. Public*, pg. 73
Goodwin, Morris, Pres. & Treas.--IDS Deposit Corp., Midvale, UT; *U.S. Public*, pg. 73
Goodwin, Morris, Jr., V.P. & Treas.--Deluxe Corporation, Shoreview, MN; *U.S. Public*, pg. 498
Goodyear, E.D., Treas. & Sec.--Dispatch Consumer Services, Westerville, OH; *U.S. Private*, pg. 335
Goossen, Isabelle, V.P. & Treas.--Premark International, Inc., Deerfield, IL; *U.S. Public*, pg. 1321
Gordon, Alan, V.P. & Treas.--International Specialty Products, Inc., Wayne, NJ; *U.S. Public*, pg. 858
Gordon, B. Diane, V.P.-Fin., Treas. & Sec.--Buckeye Corrugated Inc., Wooster, OH; *U.S. Private*, pg. 177
Gordon, Richard, Sec., Treas. & Controller--Vital Signs, Inc., Totowa, NJ; *U.S. Public*, pg. 1723
Gordon, S. Amber, Sec.--Hadron, Inc., Alexandria, VA; *U.S. Public*, pg. 773
Gordon, William T., Chief Fin. Officer, Exec. V.P.-Fin. & Treas.--Black Entertainment Television Holdings Inc., Washington, DC; *U.S. Public*, pg. 235
Gore, Genevieve W., Dr., Treas. & Sec.--W.L. Gore & Associates, Inc., Newark, DE; *U.S. Private*, pg. 465
Gorey, Daniel P., Chief Fin. Officer, V.P. & Treas.--Quixote Corporation, Chicago, IL; *U.S. Public*, pg. 1353
Gorey, Daniel P., V.P. & Treas.--Energy Absorption Systems, Inc., Chicago, IL; *U.S. Public*, pg. 1353
Gorland, Ronald, Treas.--GTECH Corporation, West Greenwich, RI; *U.S. Public*, pg. 767
Gormley, Charles, Controller & Treas.--Philadelphia Reserve Supply Company, Croydon, PA; *U.S. Private*, pg. 861
Gorrell, Pat, Treas.--Hoffman Corporation, Portland, OR; *U.S. Private*, pg. 532
Goshien, Gerald, Controller & Treas.-Sls. For Meats & Produce--The Mad Butcher, Inc., Pine Bluff, AR; *U.S. Private*, pg. 693
Goss, Howard S., Chm. Bd., Chief Exec. Officer & Treas.--Transco Inc., Chicago, IL; *U.S. Private*, pg. 1096
Goss, Michael F., V.P.-Corp. Devel. & Treas.--Oak Industries Inc., Waltham, MA; *U.S. Public*, pg. 1209
Gossett, Darrell, Exec. V.P., Sec. & Treas.--Ermco, Inc., Indianapolis, IN; *U.S. Private*, pg. 381
Gottfried, P. Gene, Chief Fin. Officer, Sr. V.P. & Treas.--Peoples Federal Savings Bank, Wooster, OH; *U.S. Public*, pg. 647
Gough, William R., Treas.--Albuquerque Capital Management, Inc., New York, NY; *U.S. Public*, pg. 337
Gould, H. Joshua, Treas.--Interplan, Denver, CO; *U.S. Private*, pg. 905
Govreau, Paul M., Asst. Treas.--Furniture Brands International Inc., Saint Louis, MO; *U.S. Public*, pg. 688
Gowen, Lawrence W., Treas.--Royal Insurance, Charlotte, NC; *Int'l*, pg. 1130
Gowey, David, Controller & Treas.--Pacific Trail Inc., Seattle, WA; *U.S. Private*, pg. 673
Grabow, Barry, Treas.--Oneida Ltd., Oneida, NY; *U.S. Public*, pg. 1225
Grabowski, Jerry W., Pres., Chief Exec. Officer, Chief Fin. Officer & Treas.--Waters Instruments, Inc., Rochester, MN; *U.S. Public*, pg. 1745
Grace, Jerry L., Sr. V.P. & Treas.--Provident Financial Group, Inc., Cincinnati, OH; *U.S. Public*, pg. 1338
Grace, Jerry L., Sr. V.P.-Investment & Liability Mngmt., V.P. & Treas.--The Provident Bank, Cincinnati, OH; *U.S. Public*, pg. 1338
Grady, Edward, V.P. & Treas.--Reagan Equipment Company, Inc., Gretna, LA; *U.S. Private*, pg. 913
Grady, Edward J., V.P., Controller & Asst. Treas.--Shared Medical Systems Corporation, Malvern, PA; *U.S. Public*, pg. 1463
Grady, Elaine, Treas. & Sec.--Howards TV & Appliances, Inc., La Habra, CA; *U.S. Private*, pg. 543
Grady, Patrick E., Sr. V.P. & Treas.--Western National Corporation, Houston, TX; *U.S. Public*, pg. 76
Grady, Patrick E., V.P.-Investor Rels. & Treas.--Western National Life Insurance Co., Houston, TX; *U.S. Public*, pg. 76
Grae, Gary, Treas. & Sec.--Parisi Inc./Royal Store Fixture, Philadelphia, PA; *U.S. Private*, pg. 839
Graeff, Rodney J., V.P.-Fin. & Treas.--Weaber, Inc, Lebanon, PA; *U.S. Private*, pg. 1155
Graff, M., Treas. & Sec.--Douglas Stephen Plastics, Inc., Paterson, NJ; *U.S. Private*, pg. 341
Graham, David M., Treas.--Pacific Dunlop Limited, Melbourne, Australia; *Int'l*, pg. 1021
Graham, Glenn, Treas.--Taco Incorporated, Cranston, RI; *U.S. Private*, pg. 1066
Graham, Michael P., Sr. V.P.-Fin. & Treas.--Philadelphia Suburban Corporation, Bryn Mawr, PA; *U.S. Public*, pg. 1287
Graham, Russell, Treas.--Standard Duplicating Machines Corp., Andover, MA; *U.S. Private*, pg. 1031
Gramke, Ronald L., Asst. Treas.--The Midland Company, Cincinnati, OH; *U.S. Public*, pg. 1110
Grammas, Wendy B., Treas.--UST Inc., Greenwich, CT; *U.S.* Public, pg. 1660
Grams, David F., V.P. & Treas.--Quorum Health Group, Inc., Brentwood, TN; *U.S. Public*, pg. 1353
Granat, David J., V.P. & Treas.--Tribune Company, Chicago, IL; *U.S. Public*, pg. 1635
Granicher, John W., Sr. V.P. & Sec. & Treas.--Keller & Gannon, San Francisco, CA; *U.S. Private*, pg. 626
Granlund, Leland R., Chief Fin. Officer, Sr. V.P & Treas.--Western Petroleum Company, Eden Prairie, MN; *U.S. Private*, pg. 1168
Grannis, Richard, Treas.--QUALCOMM, San Diego, CA; *U.S. Public*, pg. 1348
Grant, Clark C., Exec. V.P.-Fin. & Treas.--Buffets, Inc., Eden Prairie, MN; *U.S. Public*, pg. 267
Grant, Michael, Grp. Treas.--The Eurotunnel Group, London, United Kingdom; *Int'l*, pg. 466
Grant, William E., Jr., Treas.--TRAK Microwave Corp., Tampa, FL; *U.S. Public*, pg. 1563
Grantham, Linda, Treas.--Grantham Distributing Company, Inc., Orlando, FL; *U.S. Private*, pg. 470
Grasberger, Nicholas, Treas.--H.J. Heinz Company, Pittsburgh, PA; *U.S. Public*, pg. 805
Grasso, Frank, Treas.--Parsons & Whittemore, Inc., Rye Brook, NY; *U.S. Private*, pg. 840
Grathwohl, Joseph A., Treas.--Jake Sweeney Auto Leasing, Inc., Cincinnati, OH; *U.S. Private*, pg. 1058
Gray, David L., Chief Fin. Officer, Sr. V.P. & Treas.--First Indiana Corporation, Indianapolis, IN; *U.S. Public*, pg. 1484
Gray, Franklin N., Exec. V.P., Treas. & Sec.--James N. Gray Construction Co., Inc., Lexington, KY; *U.S. Private*, pg. 472
Gray, James H., Treas.--The American Bankers Association, Washington, DC; *U.S. Private*, pg. 51
Gray, Jimmie L., Chief Fin. Officer, Sr. V.P. & Treas.--Universal Fidelity Life Insurance Company, Duncan, OK; *U.S. Private*, pg. 1127
Gray, John, Controller & Asst. Sec.-Treas.--Sugar Cane Growers Cooperative of Florida, Belle Glade, FL; *U.S. Private*, pg. 1049
Gray, Rodney L., V.P.-Fin. & Treas.--Enron Corp., Houston, TX; *U.S. Public*, pg. 584
Gray, W. Todd, Asst. Treas.--The Midland Company, Cincinnati, OH; *U.S. Public*, pg. 1110
Grayson, Christine, V.P.-H.R. & Asst. Treas.--Folger Nolan Fleming Douglas, Washington, DC; *U.S. Private*, pg. 416
Greathouse, Dianne, Asst. Treas. & Banking--Wendy's International Inc., Dublin, OH; *U.S. Public*, pg. 1754
Grecco, Samuel G., V.P., Controller & Treas.--Remington Arms Company, Inc., Madison, NC; *U.S. Private*, pg. 921
Greco, Robert, Chief Tech. Officer, Treas. & Sec.--Active Voice Corporation, Seattle, WA; *U.S. Public*, pg. 17
Greed, John, Sr. V.P. & Treas.--American Life Insurance Company of New York, New York, NY; *U.S. Private*, pg. 769
Greed, John R., Exec. V.P. & Treas.--Mutual of America Life Insurance Company, New York, NY; *U.S. Private*, pg. 769
Green, Jay M., Chief Fin. Officer, Exec. V.P. & Treas.--General Cigar Holdings Inc, New York, NY; *U.S. Public*, pg. 707
Green, Jerry M., Treas.--ALLTEL Corporation, Little Rock, AR; *U.S. Public*, pg. 55
Green, John M., Jr., V.P. & Treas.--El Paso Natural Gas Co., Houston, TX; *U.S. Public*, pg. 567
Green, John R., Treas. & Sec.--John E. Green Co., Detroit, MI; *U.S. Private*, pg. 477
Green, Nancy, Asst. Treas. & Asst. Sec.--Tab Products Co., Palo Alto, CA; *U.S. Public*, pg. 1559
Green, Paul M., V.P. & Treas.--HSI Aviation, Inc., Springfield, MO; *U.S. Public*, pg. 849
Green, R.L., Treas.--Ancon Insurance Company, Inc., Irving, TX; *U.S. Public*, pg. 601
Green, S.K., Gen. Mgr. & Grp. Treas.--HSBC Holdings plc, London, United Kingdom; *Int'l*, pg. 579
Green, Velmar, Treas.--Michigan Milk Producers Association, Novi, MI; *U.S. Private*, pg. 741
Green, William T., Exec. V.P., Treas. & Sec.--Art's-Way Manufacturing Co., Inc., Armstrong, IA; *U.S. Public*, pg. 136
Greenberg, Linda G., Treas.--Helix Technology Corp., Mansfield, MA; *U.S. Public*, pg. 808
Greenberger, Raymond S., Treas. & Asst. Sec.--AFA Protective Systems, Inc., Syosset, NY; *U.S. Public*, pg. 5
Greenburg, Arthur A., Sr. V.P. & Treas.--Capsure Holdings Corp., Chicago, IL; *U.S. Public*, pg. 303
Greene, David I., Chief Fin. Officer, V.P. & Treas.--Pearson, Inc., New York, NY; *Int'l*, pg. 1026
Greene, Jerry W., Sec. & Treas.--Hanes Companies, Inc., Winston Salem, NC; *U.S. Public*, pg. 986
Greene, Jesse J., Jr., V.P. & Treas.--Eastman Kodak Company, Rochester, NY; *U.S. Public*, pg. 550
Greenfield, Albert M., III, Pres. & Treas.--Albert M. Greenfield & Company, Philadelphia, PA; *U.S. Private*, pg. 477
Greenfield, Barry, V.P., Treas. & Sec.--Opus South Corporation, Tampa, FL; *U.S. Private*, pg. 818
Greenlee, Elaine B., Treas. & Sec.--Circle Plastics Products, Inc., Circleville, OH; *U.S. Private*, pg. 240
Greenman, Stanley, Chm. Bd., Chief Exec. Officer & Treas.--Noodle Kidoodle Inc., Syosset, NY; *U.S. Public*, pg. 1188
Greenough, Martha, Asst. Treas.--The New York Times Company, New York, NY; *U.S. Public*, pg. 1173
Greenwald, Martin W., Chm. Bd., Pres. & Chief Exec. Officer--Image Entertainment, Inc., Chatsworth, CA; *U.S. Public*, pg. 870
Greenwood, R.J., Asst. Treas.--Algoma Steel Inc., Sault Sainte Marie, Canada; *Int'l*, pg. 56
Greer, Jack, Jr., V.P. & Treas.--Autry Greer & Sons, Inc., Prichard, AL; *U.S. Private*, pg. 479
Gregg, Dennis, V.P.-Fin.--Lindal Cedar Homes, Inc., Seattle, WA; *U.S. Public*, pg. 998
Gregg, P., Grp. Treas.--Qantas Airways Ltd., Mascot, Australia; *Int'l*, pg. 1074
Gregg, Paul P., V.P. & Treas.--CNG Coal Co., New Orleans, LA; *U.S. Public*, pg. 435
Gregory, Jon, V.P. & Asst. Treas.--Carolina Quarries, Inc., Salisbury, NC; *U.S. Public*, pg. 1396
Gregory, Russell, Chief Fin. Officer & Treas.--The Ruhlin Company, Sharon Center, OH; *U.S. Private*, pg. 951
Gregory, Steve, Treas. & Asst. Sec.--Binkley Company, Warrenton, MO; *U.S. Private*, pg. 534
Greiner, Charles L., Sec. & Treas.--Western Pioneer Life Insurance Co., Louisville, KY; *U.S. Public*, pg. 853
Grietzer, Roland, Controller & Treas.--Alcom Printing Group, Inc., Bethlehem, PA; *U.S. Private*, pg. 33
Griffin, Dennis, V.P. & Treas.--Southern Farm Bureau Casualty Insurance Company, Ridgeland, MS; *U.S. Private*, pg. 1016
Griffin, LaDeane, Chief Fin. Officer, Treas. Controller & Sec.--Jenkins & Associates, Shawnee Mission, KS; *U.S. Private*, pg. 585
Griffith, Robert, V.P., Treas. & Sec.--The Chas. H. Lilly Co., Portland, OR; *U.S. Private*, pg. 667
Griffith, Ronald L., Sr., Chief Fin. Officer, Sr. V.P.-Fin., Treas. & Sec.--Burnham, Lancaster, PA; *U.S. Public*, pg. 270
Griggs, David, Pres., Chief Exec. & Chief Fin. Officer & Treas.--Jack Griggs Inc., Exeter, CA; *U.S. Private*, pg. 482
Grill, Dave, V.P. & Asst. Treas.--Reliance Group Holdings, Inc., New York, NY; *U.S. Public*, pg. 1374
Grillo, Robert T., Exec. V.P., Treas. & Sec.--General Office Environments Inc., Rochelle Park, NJ; *U.S. Private*, pg. 445
Grimes, Thomas D., Pres. & Treas.--Puritan Bakery, Inc., Carson, CA; *U.S. Private*, pg. 895
Grimley, Robert, Treas. & Sec.--Duo-Fast Corporation, Huntley, IL; *U.S. Private*, pg. 347
Grimm, Jeffrey, V.P.-Fin. & Treas.--Portland Food Products Company, Forest Grove, OR; *U.S. Private*, pg. 876
Grimmer, Susan L., V.P. & Treas.--Grimmer Realty Co. Inc., Birmingham, AL; *U.S. Private*, pg. 482
Grinbaum, Jacob, Sr. V.P.-Treasury--Nordbanken AB, Stockholm, Sweden; *Int'l*, pg. 957
Grinsley, Janet T., Treas. & Sec.--Lynch Machinery, Inc., Bainbridge, GA; *U.S. Public*, pg. 1022
Grischow, K. Donald, Treas.--The Coteau Properties Co., Beulah, ND; *U.S. Public*, pg. 1149
Griswold, Richard, V.P. & Treas.--Loos & Co., Inc., Pomfret, CT; *U.S. Private*, pg. 675
Gritman, John, Treas.--Continental General Tire, Inc., Charlotte, NC; *Int'l*, pg. 327

Grizzard, Claude H., Sr., Treas.--Grizzard, Atlanta, GA; U.S. Private, pg. 482
Grose, David, V.P.-Fin. & Treas.--National Energy Group, Inc., Dallas, TX; U.S. Public, pg. 1156
Grose, J. David, Chief Fin. Officer & V.P.-Fin.--Basic Construction Company, Newport News, VA; U.S. Private, pg. 121
Grose, Richard L., Treas.--Research, Incorporated, Eden Prairie, MN; U.S. Public, pg. 1382
Gross, Donald, Treas. & Sec.--Dan's Supreme Super Markets Inc., Hempstead, NY; U.S. Private, pg. 310
Gross, Greg J., Asst. Treas.--Reptron Electronics, Inc., Tampa, FL; U.S. Public, pg. 1377
Gross, Peter, Treas.--Plan International USA, Inc., Warwick, RI; U.S. Private, pg. 869
Grosseibl, Eric H., Sr. V.P. & Treas.--Bellemead Development Corp., Roseland, NJ; U.S. Public, pg. 355
Grossman, Deborah C., Asst. Treas.--Boeing Realty Corporation, Long Beach, CA; U.S. Public, pg. 241
Grossman, Deborah C., Asst. Treas.--The Boeing Travel Company, Irvine, CA; U.S. Public, pg. 241
Grossman, Deborah C., Asst. Treas.--The Boeing Company, London, United Kingdom; U.S. Public, pg. 242
Grossman, Deborah C., Asst. Treas.--Boeing Services, Inc., Khamis Mushayt, Saudi Arabia; U.S. Public, pg. 242
Grossman, Edgar, Treas.--Massachusetts Envelope Co., Somerville, MA; U.S. Private, pg. 712
Grossman, Morton, Chief Fin. Officer & Treas.--Waring & LaRosa, Inc., New York, NY; U.S. Private, pg. 1150
Grossman, Richard D., Treas. & Sec.--Therm, Inc., Ithaca, NY; U.S. Private, pg. 1079
Grossnickle, Elizabeth M., V.P. & Treas.--Fredericktown Bank & Trust Co., Frederick, MD; U.S. Public, pg. 1089
Groth, John F., Treas.--Baker Concrete Construction, Inc., Monroe, OH; U.S. Private, pg. 111
Grotti, Erich, Treas.--Trayco of S.C., Inc., Florence, SC; U.S. Private, pg. 352
Grow, David R., Chief Oper. & Fin. Officer & Exec. V.P.--Daw Technologies, Inc., Salt Lake City, UT; U.S. Public, pg. 489
Grubb, Richard N., Chief Fin. Officer, V.P. & Treas.--Vishay Intertechnology, Inc., Malvern, PA; U.S. Public, pg. 1721
Grubbe, K.S., Chief Fin. Officer, Grp. V.P.-Fin. & Asst. Sec.--Ag Processing Inc., A Cooperative, Omaha, NE; U.S. Private, pg. 26
Gruenewald, C.W., II, Chief Fin. Officer, Sr. V.P. & Treas.--United Foods, Inc., Bells, TN; U.S. Public, pg. 1677
Grueter, Frank J., Chief Fin. Officer & V.P.--George W. Prescott Publishing Co., Quincy, MA; U.S. Private, pg. 882
Grunnah, Judith, Treas.--Reliance Elevator Company, Chicago, IL; U.S. Private, pg. 921
Grupka, Richard A., Treas. & Sec.--John W. Danforth Co., Buffalo, NY; U.S. Private, pg. 309
Gruttadaurrio, Elizabeth A., V.P. & Treas.--Liggett-Stashower, Inc., Cleveland, OH; U.S. Private, pg. 667
Gryn, Len, Exec. V.P. & Treas.--Weber-Stephen Products Co., Palatine, IL; U.S. Private, pg. 1157
Guarino, Ludwig, Treas.--Volt Information Sciences, Inc., New York, NY; U.S. Public, pg. 1724
Guarino, Ludwig, Asst. Treas.--Jefferson Adams Corp., New York, NY; U.S. Public, pg. 1724
Guarisco, John, Treas. & Sec.--Berwick Bay Oil Co. Inc., Morgan City, LA; U.S. Private, pg. 138
Guber, Alfred M., V.P.-Fin. & Admin.--John Dusenbery Co., Inc., Randolph, NJ; U.S. Private, pg. 349
Guccione, Anthony, Treas. & Sec.--General Media International Inc., New York, NY; U.S. Private, pg. 444
Gudman, Jeff, Treas.--Oregon Natural Gas Development Corp., Portland, OR; U.S. Public, pg. 1200
Guebert, D., Chief Fin. Officer & Treas.--Aircraft of Canada Ltd., Calgary, Canada; U.S. Public, pg. 1365
Guedry, Donald J., Jr., V.P. & Treas.--Grey Wolf, Inc., Houston, TX; U.S. Public, pg. 765
Guercio, Thomas R., Chief Fin. Officer, Exec. V.P. & Treas.--Reliable Stores, Inc., Columbia, MD; U.S. Private, pg. 920
Guerrero, Pablo Torres, Treas.--Grupo Televisa, S.A. de C.V., Mexico, Mexico; Int'l, pg. 576
Guest, Christine M., Treas.--Allens Of Hastings, Inc., Hastings, NE; U.S. Private, pg. 37
Guest, J. Rodney, Controller & Treas.--Header Products Inc., Romulus, MI; U.S. Private, pg. 514
Guest, Roger H., V.P.-Regional Treas.--Toronto-Dominion Bank (United Kingdom) Ltd., London, United Kingdom; Int'l, pg. 1401
Gugliotta, R., V.P.-Fin. & Treas.--Uniflex, Inc., Hicksville, NY; U.S. Public, pg. 1665
Guidry, Leroy, Treas.--Pride International, Inc., Houston, TX; U.S. Public, pg. 1324
Guiliaume, Ray, Asst. Treas.--The Titan Corporation, San Diego, CA; U.S. Public, pg. 1618
Gulbas, Jacqueline, Treas. & Sec.--National Restaurant Supply Company, El Paso, TX; U.S. Private, pg. 786
Gulmi, James S., Chief Fin. Officer, Sr. V.P.-Fin. & Treas.--Genesco Inc., Nashville, TN; U.S. Public, pg. 728
Guna, John S., Treas.--Aristech Chemical Corporation, Pittsburgh, PA; Int'l, pg. 872
Gundermann, Paul H., Chief Fin. Officer & Treas.--Apex Supply Co., Inc., Atlanta, GA; U.S. Private, pg. 77
Gunnarsson, Kristjan, Mgr.-Treas.--Landsvirkjun - The National Power Co., Reykjavik, Iceland; Int'l, pg. 801
Gunnerson, R.M., Treas.--Modine Manufacturing Company, Racine, WI; U.S. Public, pg. 1121
Gunther, Christian H., V.P. & Treas.--Banner Associates Inc., Laramie, WY; U.S. Private, pg. 114
Guriel, Florian, Asst. Sec. & Treas.--Whiting Equipment Canada, Inc., Welland, Canada; U.S. Private, pg. 1173
Guthlein, William J., Chief Fin. Officer, V.P. & Treas.--Chancellor Corporation, Boston, MA; U.S. Public, pg. 335
Guthrie, T.M., V.P.-Admin. & Treas.--Builders Transport, Incorporated, Camden, SC; U.S. Public, pg. 267
Gutierrez, Jess R., V.P. & Asst. Treas.--Citation Insurance Group, San Jose, CA; U.S. Public, pg. 376
Gutierrez, Jess R., V.P. & Asst. Treas.--Citation National Insurance Company, San Jose, CA; U.S. Public, pg. 376
Gutknecht, James, Treas. & Sec.--Wheaton Inc., Millville, NJ; Int'l, pg. 67
Gutt, Daniel, V.P. & Treas.--The Gleason Works, Rochester, NY; U.S. Public, pg. 746
Guy, Geoffrey, V.P. & Treas.--The Manufacturers Life Insurance Company of Michigan, Toronto, Canada; Int'l, pg. 840
Gwiazdowski, Peter, Treas.--FKI Industries. Inc., Fairfield, CT; Int'l, pg. 472
Gwizdala, Lori A., Chief Fin. Officer, Sr. V.P. & Treas.--Chemical Financial Corporation, Midland, MI; U.S. Public, pg. 345
Haag, Stephen, V.P. & Treas.--Swaner Hardwood Company, Inc., Burbank, CA; U.S. Private, pg. 1057
Haas, Bruce, Treas.--The Ryland Group, Inc., Columbia, MD; U.S. Public, pg. 1414
Haas, David, Exec. V.P. & Treas.--Keen Compressed Gas Co., Wilmington, DE; U.S. Private, pg. 611
Haas, Douglas, Treas.--Saab Cars USA, Inc., Norcross, GA; Int'l, pg. 687
Haberberger, Arthur A., Treas.--American Real Estate Investment & Development Co., Chicago, IL; Int'l, pg. 9
Haberer, Mona, V.P. & Treas.--Florists' Mutual Insurance Co., Edwardsville, IL; U.S. Private, pg. 415
Habing, L., Treas. & Controller--Wavin Bv, Zwolle, Netherlands; Int'l, pg. 1135
Hachiro, Tetsuo, Gen. Mgr.-Treas. Plng.--The Mitsubishi Trust and Banking Corporation, Tokyo, Japan; Int'l, pg. 876
Hackamack, Kent W., V.P.-Fin., Controller & Treas.--Titan International, Inc., Quincy, IL; U.S. Public, pg. 1618
Hackerman, Willard, Pres., Chief Exec. Officer & Treas.--The Whiting-Turner Contracting Co., Baltimore, MD; U.S. Private, pg. 1174
Hadalgo, Omar, Treasurer--Procter & Gamble Venezuela, C.A., Caracas, Venezuela; U.S. Public, pg. 1332
Haddad, James, Treas.--Rich Products Corp., Buffalo, NY; U.S. Private, pg. 928
Haddan, Laverne, Controller, Treas. & Sec.--Dick Bruhn Incorporated, Salinas, CA; U.S. Private, pg. 175
Haddix, David D., Treas. & Dir.-Plng.--Therma-Tru Corp., Maumee, OH; U.S. Private, pg. 1079
Haddrill, Richard M., Pres., Chief Exec. Officer & Treas.--Power House Technologies, Inc., Bozeman, MT; U.S. Public, pg. 1319
Hadjigeorge, Christine, Treas.--Henry I. Siegel Company, Inc., New York, NY; U.S. Private, pg. 998
Hadley, Gary L., Chief Fin. Officer & Treas.--World Aerospace Corporation, Maple Grove, MN; U.S. Private, pg. 1188
Haefliger, Robert, Mgr.-Treas. Services--Micropolis Corporation, Chatsworth, CA; U.S. Private, pg. 742
Haeger, M.D., Treas.--Abell-Howe Company, Forest Park, IL; U.S. Private, pg. 10
Haentjens, Kate, Controller & Treas.--Hazleton Pumps Inc., Hazleton, PA; Int'l, pg. 967
Haft, Julie, Sec. & Treas.--Haywin Textile Products, Inc., Brooklyn, NY; U.S. Private, pg. 514
Hagan, Christina W., Treas.--Dawson Geophysical Company, Midland, TX; U.S. Public, pg. 489
Hage, Richard, Treas. & Sec.--Walser Automotive Group, Bloomington, MN; U.S. Private, pg. 1148
Hagedorn, Charles K., Treas. & Controller--Distrigas Corp., Boston, MA; U.S. Public, pg. 289
Hagel, Philip A., V.P. & Treas.--American Financial Group, Cincinnati, OH; U.S. Public, pg. 75
Hagen, Doug, Chief Fin. Officer--American Foods Group, Inc., Green Bay, WI; U.S. Private, pg. 54
Hagen, Larry, V.P. & Treas.--Denver Wholesale Florists Company, Denver, CO; U.S. Private, pg. 326
Hagenau, Steve, Treas. & Sec.--Dayton Andrews Inc., Clearwater, FL; U.S. Private, pg. 74
Hager, Jean, Treas. & Sec.--Air Industries Corporation, Garden Grove, CA; U.S. Private, pg. 28
Haggard, Paul, V.P. & Treas.--Interim Services Inc., Fort Lauderdale, FL; U.S. Public, pg. 892
Haggard, Paul H., V.P. & Treas.--Interim Services (Canada) Ltd., Montreal, Canada; U.S. Public, pg. 892
Hagge, Stephen, Chief Fin. Officer, Exec. V.P., Treas. & Sec.--AptarGroup, Inc., Crystal Lake, IL; U.S. Public, pg. 125
Haggerty, Gretchen R., V.P. & Treas.--USX Corporation, Pittsburgh, PA; U.S. Public, pg. 1661
Hagler, Billie S., Treas.--GIW Industries, Inc., Grovetown, GA; Int'l, pg. 721
Hahn, Edward L., V.P.-Fin. & Treas.--Chieftain International, Inc., Edmonton, Canada; Int'l, pg. 284
Hahn, Elizabeth, Treas. & Sec.--Conestoga Wood Specialties Corp., East Earl, PA; U.S. Private, pg. 262
Haigh, Robert B., Chm. Bd., Chief Exec. Officer & Treas.--Chicago Tube & Iron Co., Chicago, IL; U.S. Private, pg. 235
Haines, A.L., V.P., Controller & Treas.--CHEMCENTRAL Corporation, Bedford Park, IL; U.S. Private, pg. 231
Haines, Stanley K., Asst. Treas.--Vanguard Cellular Systems, Inc., Greensboro, NC; U.S. Public, pg. 1707
Hale, Darrell, Treas. & Asst. Sec.--Dura-Line Corp., Middlesboro, KY; U.S. Private, pg. 598
Hale, James R., Treas.--Tetra Technologies, Woodlands, TX; U.S. Public, pg. 1582
Hale, Phil, Treas.--Servico, Inc., West Palm Beach, FL; U.S. Public, pg. 1462
Haley, C. James, Jr., Treas. & Sec.--Lufkin Industries, Inc., Lufkin, TX; U.S. Public, pg. 1019
Hall, Dennis R., V.P.-Fin. & Chief Fin. Officer--Electrolux Canada, Mississauga, Canada; U.S. Private, pg. 370
Hall, Ed, Dir.-Inv. Rels. & Asst. Treas.--Northern States Power Company, Minneapolis, MN; U.S. Public, pg. 1195
Hall, Edwin F., Treas.--Bell Atlantic-PA, Philadelphia, PA; U.S. Public, pg. 203
Hall, John F., V.P.-Fin., Sec. & Treas.--Delta Natural Gas Company, Inc., Winchester, KY; U.S. Public, pg. 497
Hall, R. Wayne, Treas.--Provident Bankshares Corporation, Baltimore, MD; U.S. Public, pg. 1337
Hall, Thomas D., Pres. & Treas.--Acme Design Technology, Co., Crozet, VA; U.S. Private, pg. 13
Hall, William T., Treas.--John Bouchard & Sons Company, Nashville, TN; U.S. Private, pg. 161
Haller, Carl B., Treas.--GE Hydro, Lachine, Canada; U.S. Public, pg. 713
Halliday, James B., V.P., Treas. & Sec.--Argonaut Group, Inc., Los Angeles, CA; U.S. Public, pg. 129
Halparin, Scott, Chm. Bd., Chief Exec. Officer & Treas.--Saratoga Brands, Inc., Lakewood, NJ; U.S. Public, pg. 1435
Halterman, Darlene F., Sec. & Asst. Treas.--First Mount Joy Corporation, Mount Joy, PA; U.S. Private, pg. 407
Halvorson, Lorraine, Treas. & Sec.--Prospect Motors, Inc., Jackson, CA; U.S. Private, pg. 891
Ham, Benson, Treas. & Sec.--National Rural Utilities Cooperative Finance Corporation, Herndon, VA; U.S. Private, pg. 786
Hamann, Howard R., Asst. Treas. & Dir.-Pension Asset Mgmt.--Hershey Foods Corporation, Hershey, PA; U.S. Public, pg. 811
Hamblen, Charles A., V.P.-Fin. & Treas.--Acadia Insurance Company, Westbrook, ME; U.S. Public, pg. 215
Hamburg, Marc D., V.P. & Treas.--Berkshire Hathaway Inc., Omaha, NE; U.S. Public, pg. 217
Hamelin, Ray, Chief Fin. Officer, Comptroller & Treas.--Northwestel Inc., Whitehorse, Canada; Int'l, pg. 115
Hamilton, D. Steven, Treas. & Sec.--Rish Equipment Company, Bluefield, WV; U.S. Private, pg. 932
Hamilton, W. Brooke, V.P. & Treas.--Mitchell Energy & Development Corp., Spring, TX; U.S. Public, pg. 1117
Hammes, Lynn F., Treas. & Sec.--Amvestors Financial Corporation, Topeka, KS; U.S. Private, pg. 59
Hammond, Darrell G., Controller & Treas.--The Danis Companies, Dayton, OH; U.S. Private, pg. 310
Hampel, Robert E., Chief Fin. Officer, Treas. & Sec.--Keller Crescent Co., Evansville, IN; U.S. Private, pg. 612
Hampton, Mark R., Asst. Treas.-Europe--Standex International Corporation, Salem, NH; U.S. Public, pg. 1505
Hampton, Stephen J.S., Treas.--Pentland Group PLC, London, United Kingdom; Int'l, pg. 1035
Hamrick, Grant L., Chief Fin. Officer, Sr. V.P. & Treas.--American City Business Journals, Inc., Charlotte, NC; U.S. Private, pg. 19
Hamrick, H.R., Sec., Treas. & Mgr.-Data Processing--Haines City Citrus Growers Association, Haines City, FL; U.S. Private, pg. 494
Hamwey, Emile J., Sr. V.P. & Treas.--Fay, Spofford & Thorndike, Inc., Burlington, MA; U.S. Private, pg. 397
Hancock, John W., Sr. V.P. & Treas.--Atlantic American Corporation, Atlanta, GA; U.S. Public, pg. 143
Hancock, Paul, Treas.--Lex Service PLC, Bourne, United Kingdom; Int'l, pg. 806
Handel, Nancy H., Treas.--Applied Materials, Inc., Santa Clara, CA; U.S. Public, pg. 123
Handelsman, Jeffrey, Treas.--Noma Industries Limited, North York, Canada; Int'l, pg. 954
Handlon, Carolyn B., V.P.-Fin. & Asst. Treas.--Marriott International, Inc., Washington, DC; U.S. Public, pg. 1047
Hanigan, Brian, Treas.--Farley, Inc., Chicago, IL; U.S. Private, pg. 394
Hanka, Erina, Pres.--Suspa, Inc., Grand Rapids, MI; Int'l, pg. 1322
Hanley, John E., V.P.-Fin. & Treas.--Lydall, Inc., Manchester, CT; U.S. Public, pg. 1020
Hanlon, Peter, Treas.--Woolwich Plc, Bexley, United Kingdom; Int'l, pg. 1514
Hanlon, T.P., Treas.--L.B. Smith, Inc., Camp Hill, PA; U.S. Private, pg. 1009
Hannah, David, Chief Fin. Officer & Treas.--Metalcenter, Inc., Santa Fe Springs, CA; U.S. Public, pg. 1375
Hannon, John C., Asst. Treas.--Wilbur-Ellis Company & Connell Brothers Company, San Francisco, CA; U.S. Private, pg. 1175
Hanono, Fanny, V.P. & Treas.--Carfel, Inc., Miami, FL; U.S. Private, pg. 210
Hanono, Fanny, Treas. & Sec.--Supreme International Corp., Miami, FL; U.S. Public, pg. 1542
Hanratty, Margaret J., V.P. & Treas.--Cabot Corporation, Boston, MA; U.S. Public, pg. 288
Hansen, E.G., Treas.--Nevada Bell, Reno, NV; U.S. Public, pg. 1416
Hansen, Janet M., Chief Fin. Officer, Exec. V.P. & Treas.--Aquarion Company, Bridgeport, CT; U.S. Public, pg. 126
Hansen, Janet M., Treas.--Hydrocorp, Inc., Bridgeport, CT; U.S. Public, pg. 126
Hansen, Janet M., V.P. & Treas.--Aquarion Management Services, Inc., Bridgeport, CT; U.S. Public, pg. 126
Hansen, Larry E., V.P. & Treas.--Knife River Coal Mining Company, Bismarck, ND; U.S. Public, pg. 1025
Hanson, Dale S., Chief Fin. Officer, V.P.-Fin. & Treas.--C.H. Robinson Co., Eden Prairie, MN; U.S. Public, pg. 1394
Hanson, Gail, Treas.--United Wisconsin Services, Inc., Milwaukee, WI; U.S. Public, pg. 1692
Hanson, P.A., V.P. & Treas.--Exxon Asset Management Company, Irving, TX; U.S. Public, pg. 601
Hanson, Robert R., Asst. Treas.--The Washington Water Power Company, Spokane, WA; U.S. Public, pg. 1744
Harada, Curtis V., Asst. Treas.--HEI Power Corp., Honolulu, HI; U.S. Public, pg. 800
Harada, Curtis Y., Asst. Treas.--Pacific Energy Conservation Services, Inc., Honolulu, HI; U.S. Public, pg. 800
Harbour, Steven E., V.P., Treas. & Sec.--Environmental Treatment & Technologies Corp., Findlay, OH; U.S. Public, pg. 1208
Harden, Oleta J., Sr. V.P., Gen. Counsel & Corp. Sec.--New Jersey Resources Corporation, Wall, NJ; U.S. Public, pg. 1172

Hardin, R. Evan, Treas.--Rock-Tenn Company, Norcross, GA; *U.S. Public*, pg. 1396
Harding, Glenn, Asst. Treas.--Sealright Company, Inc., De Soto, KS; *U.S. Public*, pg. 1451
Harding, John C., Treas.--Plasticrete Block & Supply Corp., North Haven, CT; *U.S. Private*, pg. 871
Harding, Keith, Dir.-Treas.--Rolls-Royce plc, London, United Kingdom; *Int'l*, pg. 1126
Hardy, Gene M., Treas. & Sec.--La-Z-Boy Incorporated, Monroe, MI; *U.S. Public*, pg. 972
Hardy, Pat, Treas.--SSD&W Integrated Marketing Communications, Montville, NJ; *U.S. Private*, pg. 958
Hare, Jeff, Treas. & Sec.--Road Machinery Company, Phoenix, AZ; *U.S. Private*, pg. 934
Hare, Richard, Treas.--Wolverine Tube Inc., Huntsville, AL; *U.S. Public*, pg. 1774
Haretakis, John, Treas. & Sec.--Spires Restaurants Inc., Orange, CA; *U.S. Private*, pg. 1026
Harger, R.D., V.P.-Fin. & Acctg. & Treas.--McLane Company, Inc., Temple, TX; *U.S. Public*, pg. 1733
Hargrave, Robert L., Chief Exec. & Fin. Officer & Treas.--Stewart & Stevenson Services, Inc., Houston, TX; *U.S. Public*, pg. 1517
Hargrave, Robert L., V.P. & Treas.--Stewart & Stevenson International, Inc., Houston, TX; *U.S. Public*, pg. 1517
Hargrave, Robert L., V.P. & Treas.--Machinery Acceptance Corporation, Houston, TX; *U.S. Public*, pg. 1517
Hargrave, Robert L., V.P. & Treas.--Cypress Acquisition, Inc., Houston, TX; *U.S. Public*, pg. 1517
Hargrave, Robert L., V.P. & Treas.--S & S (Dihall) Cogeneration, Inc., Houston, TX; *U.S. Public*, pg. 1517
Hargrave, Robert L., V.P. & Treas.--Stewart & Stevenson de las Americas, Inc., Houston, TX; *U.S. Public*, pg. 1517
Hargrave, Robert L., V.P. & Treas.--Stewart & Stevenson Vehicle Services, Inc., Houston, TX; *U.S. Public*, pg. 1518
Hargrave, Robert L., Pres. & Treas.--Takumei Kumiai Holdings, Inc., Houston, TX; *U.S. Public*, pg. 1518
Harkenreader, Karl S., Treas.--The Napier Co., Meriden, CT; *U.S. Private*, pg. 774
Harkey, Matthew, Treas.--Trend Line Corporation, Jackson, MS; *U.S. Private*, pg. 1099
Harkey, Matthew, Treas.--Valley Innovative Management Service, Jackson, MS; *U.S. Private*, pg. 1099
Harkins, James F., Jr., V.P. & Treas.--CertainTeed Corporation, Valley Forge, PA; *Int'l*, pg. 1170
Harkins, James F., Jr., V.P. & Treas.--Air Vent Inc., Peoria Heights, IL; *Int'l*, pg. 1170
Harkins, James F., Jr., V.P. & Treas.--Bayex Incorporated, Albion, NY; *Int'l*, pg. 1170
Harkins, James F., Jr., V.P. & Treas.--Bay Mills (Delaware), Inc., Wilmington, DE; *Int'l*, pg. 1170
Harkins, James F., Jr., Treas.--CertainTeed Foreign Sales Corp., Valley Forge, PA; *Int'l*, pg. 1171
Harkins, James F., Jr., Treas.--Ludowici Roof Tile, Inc., New Lexington, OH; *Int'l*, pg. 1171
Harkins, James F., Jr., Treas.--CertainTeed Corporation Foundation, Valley Forge, PA; *Int'l*, pg. 1171
Harkins, James F., Jr., Treas.--CertainTeed International, Inc., Valley Forge, PA; *Int'l*, pg. 1171
Harkins, James F., Jr., Treas.--Ecophon CertainTeed, Inc., Valley Forge, PA; *Int'l*, pg. 1171
Harkins, James F., Jr., V.P. & Treas.--CertainTeed Ventures, Inc., Valley Forge, PA; *Int'l*, pg. 1171
Harkins, James F., Jr., Treas.--Perma Glas-Mesh, Inc., Dover, OH; *Int'l*, pg. 1171
Harkins, James F., Jr., V.P. & Treas.--Vetrotex CertainTeed Corporation, Wichita Falls, TX; *Int'l*, pg. 1171
Harkins, James F., Jr., Treas.--CertainTeed Manatee Insulation Ltd., Montreal, Canada; *Int'l*, pg. 1176
Harlan, Michael W., Treas.--Sanifill, Inc., Houston, TX; *U.S. Public*, pg. 1686
Harma, L.E., Treas.--Senior Engineering, Lyman, SC; *Int'l*, pg. 1222
Harmon, Gary A., Treas.--The Dixie Group, Inc., Chattanooga, TN; *U.S. Public*, pg. 514
Harmon, Linda L., Chief Fin. Officer & Treas.--Progressive Driver Services, Inc., Jacksonville, FL; *U.S. Private*, pg. 890
Haroian, Gary, Chief Fin. Officer, V.P.-Fin. & Admin. & Treas.--Concord Communications, Inc., Marlborough, MA; *U.S. Public*, pg. 429
Harp, Paul L., Sec. & Treas.--Metric Systems Corp., Fort Walton Beach, FL; *U.S. Public*, pg. 1563
Harper, Anne M., Treas.--Harper Bros., Inc., Fort Myers, FL; *U.S. Private*, pg. 504
Harper, Benny, Sr. V.P.-Fin., Treas. & Sec.--Friedman Industries, Inc., Houston, TX; *U.S. Public*, pg. 682
Harper, Lee, Controller & Treas.--Affiliated Computer Services, Inc., Dallas, TX; *U.S. Public*, pg. 27
Harpin, Ellen, V.P.-Fin. & Admin. & Treas.--Media 100, Inc., Marlborough, MA; *U.S. Public*, pg. 1079
Harra, Robert V.A., Jr., Pres., Chief Oper. Officer & Treas.--Wilmington Trust Corporation, Wilmington, DE; *U.S. Public*, pg. 1770
Harrah, Glen, Treas.--Goodkind & O'Dea, Inc., Rutherford, NJ; *U.S. Private*, pg. 329
Harrell, Thomas L., V.P. & Treas.--Glenoit Mills, Inc., Tarboro, NC; *U.S. Private*, pg. 456
Harrington, Brian K., Chief Fin. Officer, Sr. V.P. & Treas.--Kirby Corporation, Houston, TX; *U.S. Public*, pg. 961
Harrington, Laurence P., Treas.--Amray, Inc., Bedford, MA; *U.S. Private*, pg. 67
Harrington, Roger, V.P., Treas. & Sec.--Midwest Industries, Inc., Ida Grove, IA; *U.S. Private*, pg. 744
Harris, Bret J., Chief Fin. Officer & Treas.--Martin Color-Fi, Edgefield, SC; *U.S. Public*, pg. 1052
Harris, Cecily, Treas. & Sec.--GFA Brands, Inc., Cresskill, NJ; *U.S. Private*, pg. 435
Harris, Daria, Treas.--Harris Steel Co., Cicero, IL; *U.S. Private*, pg. 506
Harris, Debra, V.P., Controller & Treas.--SBS Enterprises Inc., Waco, TX; *U.S. Private*, pg. 955
Harris, Debra, V.P. & Treas.--Spenco Medical Corporation, Waco, TX; *U.S. Private*, pg. 955
Harris, Marc F., V.P. & Treas.--CCC Conveyors, Inc., Dallas, TX; *U.S. Private*, pg. 351
Harris, Richard J., V.P. & Treas.--Nortek, Inc., Providence, RI; *U.S. Public*, pg. 1192
Harris, Robin R., Mgr.-Treasury Svcs.--Ekco Group, Inc., Nashua, NH; *U.S. Public*, pg. 566
Harrison, David D., Chief Fin. Officer, Exec. V.P.-Fin & Treas.--Coltec Holdings Inc, Charlotte, NC; *U.S. Public*, pg. 401
Harrison, Douglas M., Chief Fin. Officer, V.P.-Fin. & Treas.--L & D Group, Aurora, IL; *U.S. Private*, pg. 638
Harrison, J. Steven, Treas.--Columbia Pipe & Supply Company, Chicago, IL; *U.S. Private*, pg. 256
Harrison, James M., Chief Fin. Officer, Exec. V.P., Treas. & Sec.--C.R. Gibson Co., Norwalk, CT; *U.S. Public*, pg. 1168
Harrison, William B., Jr., Chm., Pres. & Treas.--Chatham Ventures, Inc., New York, NY; *U.S. Public*, pg. 338
Hart, Ronald D., Pres. & Treas.--Hart Crowser, Inc., Seattle, WA; *U.S. Private*, pg. 507
Hart, Thomas L., V.P. & Treas.--Champion International Corp., Stamford, CT; *U.S. Public*, pg. 333
Hartl, Michael J., Exec. V.P., Chief Fin. Officer & Treas.--Norwich Financial Corp., Norwich, CT; *U.S. Public*, pg. 1203
Hartman, Gregory D., V.P.-Fin. & Treas.--Biomet, Inc., Warsaw, IN; *U.S. Public*, pg. 231
Hartman, Peter A., Treas. & Sec.--Chemung Ford, Inc., Elmira, NY; *U.S. Private*, pg. 233
Hartmann, Richard J., Sec. & Treas.--ALLTEL Answering Service, Inc., Export, PA; *U.S. Public*, pg. 55
Hartmann, Richard J., Sec. & Treas.--Brookville Telephone Company, Brookville, PA; *U.S. Public*, pg. 56
Hartnett, Joseph F., Jr., Treas.--American Water Works Company, Inc., Voorhees, NJ; *U.S. Public*, pg. 95
Hartough, James B., V.P.-Fin. & Treas.--The Pittston Company, Glen Allen, VA; *U.S. Public*, pg. 1305
Hartsig, Harold, Treas.--Pennock, Philadelphia, PA; *U.S. Private*, pg. 850
Hartt, A. Douglas, Treas.--Maritime Telegraph & Telephone Company, Ltd., Halifax, Canada; *Int'l*, pg. 116
Hartwell, Margaret, Treas. & Sec.--Microlog Corporation, Germantown, MD; *U.S. Public*, pg. 1105
Hartwick, Adele, Treas.--Advanstar Communications, Cleveland, OH; *U.S. Private*, pg. 22
Harty, Linda S., Asst. Treas.--Kimberly-Clark Corporation, Dallas, TX; *U.S. Public*, pg. 958
Harvey, Edward D., Jr., Asst. Treas.--Columbia Energy Group, Reston, VA; *U.S. Public*, pg. 402
Harvey, Jeff, Treas.--Trans Leasing International Inc., Northbrook, IL; *U.S. Public*, pg. 1628
Harvey, Kent M., Chief Fin. Officer, Sr. V.P. & Treas.--Pacific Gas & Electric Company, San Francisco, CA; *U.S. Public*, pg. 1241
Harvey, Nancy J., Treas.--J.H. Harvey Company, Nashville, GA; *U.S. Private*, pg. 508
Harvey, William G., V.P. & Treas.--Avenor, Inc., Montreal, Canada; *Int'l*, pg. 101
Harwell, William J., Controller & Asst. Treas.--Motion Industries, Inc., Irondale, AL; *U.S. Public*, pg. 732
Hasel, Philip L., V.P.-Fin. & Treas.--Intesys Technologies, Gilbert, AZ; *U.S. Private*, pg. 574
Haskell, Charles L., Sr. Exec. V.P.--Lettuce Entertain You Enterprises, Inc., Chicago, IL; *U.S. Private*, pg. 661
Haskell, Eric, Chief Fin. Officer, Sr. V.P.-Fin. & Admin., & Treas.--Systems & Computer Technology Corporation, Malvern, PA; *U.S. Public*, pg. 1552
Haskins, John H., Chm. Bd., Pres. & Treas.--Arrow Tank & Engineering Co., Minneapolis, MN; *U.S. Private*, pg. 85
Hassinger, Douglas, Treas. & Sec.--Perkasie Industries Corporation, Perkasie, PA; *U.S. Private*, pg. 854
Hasson, Nathan, Vice Chm. & Treas.--Republic National Bank of New York, New York, NY; *U.S. Public*, pg. 1380
Hasson, Nathan, Treas.--Republic Bank for Savings, New York, NY; *U.S. Public*, pg. 1380
Hastings, James H., V.P. & Treas.--Essex County Gas Company, Amesbury, MA; *U.S. Public*, pg. 593
Hastings, James H., V.P. & Treas.--LNG Storage Inc., Amesbury, MA; *U.S. Public*, pg. 593
Hastings, Jerry, Supvr. Gen. Acctg. & Asst. Controller--Sacramento Municipal Utility District, Sacramento, CA; *U.S. Private*, pg. 959
Hastings, John J., Chief Fin. Officer, Exec. V.P., Treas. & Sec.--The Middleby Corporation, Rolling Meadows, IL; *U.S. Public*, pg. 1109
Hastings, Michael G., Asst. Treas.--C.R. Bard, Inc., Murray Hill, NJ; *U.S. Public*, pg. 189
Hasychak, Michael C., Treas. & Sec.--Brush Wellman Inc., Cleveland, OH; *U.S. Public*, pg. 266
Hatcher, Michael J., Treas.--Marathon Oil Company, Houston, TX; *U.S. Public*, pg. 1661
Hatfield, James R., V.P. & Treas.--OGE Energy Corp., Oklahoma City, OK; *U.S. Public*, pg. 1207
Hatlen, Joel, Controller & Treas.--Data I/O Corporation, Redmond, WA; *U.S. Public*, pg. 486
Hattara, J.J., Asst. Treas. & Dir.-Corp. Fin.--USG Corporation, Chicago, IL; *U.S. Public*, pg. 1660
Hattendorf, William C., V.P. & Treas.--Cooper Tire & Rubber Company, Findlay, OH; *U.S. Public*, pg. 445
Hauglund, Jorgen, V.P. & Corp. Treas.--ISS-International Service System A/S, Holte, Denmark; *Int'l*, pg. 656
Hauman, Richard W., V.P. & Treas.--The Goodyear Tire & Rubber Company, Akron, OH; *U.S. Public*, pg. 752
Hausberg, Mark, V.P. & Treas.--Fortune Brands, Inc., Old Greenwich, CT; *U.S. Public*, pg. 674
Hauseman, Susan G., Treas.--General Motors Acceptance Corporation (GMAC), Detroit, MI; *U.S. Public*, pg. 719
Hauser, F.J., Treas. & Sec.--Conley Frog/Switch & Forge Co., Memphis, TN; *U.S. Private*, pg. 263
Hausmann, Karyn, Asst. Treas.--The Vons Companies, Inc., Arcadia, CA; *U.S. Public*, pg. 1426
Hauss, Suesan, Treas. & Sec.--Jeffrey Buick-Nissan Inc., Roseville, MI; *U.S. Private*, pg. 585
Haussler, Len, Asst. Treas.--Cincinnati Bell Telephone, Cincinnati, OH; *U.S. Public*, pg. 367
Hauswald, Jeananne K., V.P. & Treas.--The Seagram Company Ltd., Montreal, Canada; *Int'l*, pg. 1214
Hauswald, Jeananne K., Treas.--Joseph E. Seagram & Sons, Inc., New York, NY; *Int'l*, pg. 1215
Hawbaker, Alan, Treas. & Sec.--Glenn O. Hawbaker, Inc., State College, PA; *U.S. Private*, pg. 511
Hawes, Michael S., V.P.-Fin. & Treas.--The Coleman Company, Inc., Golden, CO; *U.S. Private*, pg. 690
Hawkins, Barbara, Treas.--Tseng Labs, Norristown, PA; *U.S. Public*, pg. 1643
Hawkins, Cleve, Treas.--Miller & Co., Selma, AL; *U.S. Private*, pg. 746
Hawkins, Frank, Treas. & Sec.--World Publishing Company, Tulsa, OK; *U.S. Private*, pg. 1190
Hawkins, Howard M., V.P. & Treas.--Hawkins Chemical, Inc., Minneapolis, MN; *U.S. Public*, pg. 800
Hawkins, John, V.P. & Treas.--Dillard's, Inc., Little Rock, AR; *U.S. Public*, pg. 509
Hawkins, Steven B., Chief Fin. Officer, V.P.-Fin. & Admin., Treas. & Sec.--FFP Marketing Company, Inc., Fort Worth, TX; *U.S. Public*, pg. 604
Hawkins, Wayne B., Treas.--Roberds, Inc., Carrollton, OH; *U.S. Public*, pg. 1393
Hawthorne, Marnin A., Asst. Treas.--Hawaiian Electric Company, Inc., Honolulu, HI; *U.S. Public*, pg. 800
Hawthorne, Marvin A., Asst. Treas.--Hawaii Electric Light Co., Inc., Hilo, HI; *U.S. Public*, pg. 800
Hawthorne, Marvin A., Asst. Treas.--Maui Electric Co., Ltd., Kahului, HI; *U.S. Public*, pg. 800
Hay, James F., Chief Fin. Officer & V.P.--Valk Manufacturing Company, New Kingstown, PA; *U.S. Private*, pg. 1131
Hayashi, Diane T., Asst. Treas.--Maui Electric Co., Ltd., Kahului, HI; *U.S. Public*, pg. 800
Hayden, Gerard M., Jr., Chief Fin. Officer, Sr. V.P. & Treas.--Allied Clinical Laboratories, Inc., Nashville, TN; *U.S. Public*, pg. 973
Hayes, Kevin J., Chief Fin. Officer, V.P., Treas. & Asst. Sec.--Methode Electronics Inc., Chicago, IL; *U.S. Public*, pg. 1101
Hayes, Robert, Controller, Treas. & Dir.-Fin.--The Gates Corporation, Denver, CO; *Int'l*, pg. 1396
Hays, Don L., Chief Fin. Officer, V.P. & Treas.--Diemakers, Inc., Monroe City, MO; *U.S. Private*, pg. 332
Hayward-Surry, Jeremy, Pres., Chief Fin. Officer & Treas.--Pall Corporation, Greenvale, NY; *U.S. Public*, pg. 1253
Haywood, C.A., Sec. & Treas.--Commercial Interior Builders, Inc., Jessup, MD; *U.S. Public*, pg. 913
Hazelbaker, Steven R., Chief Fin. Officer, V.P. & Treas.--Meridian Insurance Group, Inc., Indianapolis, IN; *U.S. Public*, pg. 1095
Hazen, Edward, Treas.--Avid Technology, Inc., Tewksbury, MA; *U.S. Public*, pg. 154
Heacock, Richard, V.P.-Fin., Treas. & Sec.--Apache Hose & Belting Company, Inc., Cedar Rapids, IA; *U.S. Private*, pg. 76
Head, Jack, Treas. & Partner--Maxcor Manufacturing, Inc., Colorado Springs, CO; *U.S. Private*, pg. 716
Heagney, Larry, Treas. & Sec.--Milliken & Company, Spartanburg, SC; *U.S. Private*, pg. 748
Heal, Kenneth L., Treas. & Sec.--Elco Textron, Rockford, IL; *U.S. Public*, pg. 1590
Healey, Dennis, Chief Fin. Officer, Sr. V.P. & Treas.--Medicore Inc., Hialeah, FL; *U.S. Public*, pg. 1080
Heaney, Daniel T., Treas.--EG & G, Inc., Wellesley, MA; *U.S. Public*, pg. 542
Heaney, John J., V.P. & Treas.--M.D.C. Holdings, Inc., Denver, CO; *U.S. Public*, pg. 1025
Heath, Frederick G., V.P., Treas. & Sec.--Brown Wood Preserving Company, Louisville, KY; *U.S. Private*, pg. 174
Heath, Milton W., Jr., Owner, Chm. Bd. & Treas.--Heath Consultants Incorporated, Houston, TX; *U.S. Private*, pg. 518
Heatwole, Gerald, Treas.--Milk Marketing Inc., Strongsville, OH; *U.S. Private*, pg. 745
Heatwole, Milton W., Exec. V.P. & Treas.--Shenandoah Mfg. Co. Inc., Harrisonburg, VA; *U.S. Private*, pg. 992
Hebert, Clifford J., Jr., V.P.-Fin., Treas. & Sec.--Eastern Utilities Associates, Boston, MA; *U.S. Public*, pg. 549
Hebert, Clifford J., Jr., V.P.-Fin. & Treas.--EUA Service Corporation, West Bridgewater, MA; *U.S. Public*, pg. 549
Hebert, Edward M., Chief Fin. Officer, Sr. V.P. & Treas.--Rymer Foods Inc., Chicago, IL; *U.S. Public*, pg. 1414
Hebert, William L., Chief Fin. Officer, Treas. & Dir.-Investor Rels.--Louisiana Pacific Corporation, Portland, OR; *U.S. Public*, pg. 1015
Hecht, S.E. Melvin, Chief Fin. Officer & Treas.--Marisa Christina Inc., New Hyde Park, NY; *U.S. Public*, pg. 1044
Hecker, Daren, Treas.--Ocean Beauty Seafoods, Inc., Seattle, WA; *U.S. Private*, pg. 810
Hectourne, Patrick, Treas.--The Limited, Inc., Columbus, OH; *U.S. Public*, pg. 995
Hedley, Robert P., V.P. & Treas.--Elf Aquitaine, Inc., New York, NY; *Int'l*, pg. 445
Hedrick, Charles M., Asst. Treas. & Cash Mgr.--Ashland, Inc., Russell, KY; *U.S. Public*, pg. 138
Hedrick, Gary, Chief Fin. Officer, V.P. & Treas.--El Paso Electric Company, El Paso, TX; *U.S. Public*, pg. 567
Heery, Joseph, V.P. & Chief Fin. Officer--Cyborg Systems, Inc., Chicago, IL; *U.S. Private*, pg. 299
Heffernan, Thomas, V.P.-Fin. & Treas.--Ferrari North America, Inc., Englewood Cliffs, NJ; *Int'l*, pg. 483
Hegger, David C., V.P. & Treas.--Peabody Holding Company, Inc., Saint Louis, MO; *Int'l*, pg. 594
Hehir, Joseph P., Chief Fin. Officer & Treas.--GZA GeoEnvironmental Technologies, Inc., Newton, MA; *U.S. Public*, pg. 697
Hehir, Joseph P., Treas.--GZA GeoEnvironmental, Inc., Newton, MA; *U.S. Public*, pg. 697

Heidtke, Brian J., V.P.-Fin. & Treas.--Colgate-Palmolive Company, New York, NY; *U.S. Public*, pg. 397
Heil, M., Treas. & Sec.--American Excelsior Company, Arlington, TX; *U.S. Private*, pg. 53
Heilig, William W., V.P. & Treas.--Berwind Corporation, Philadelphia, PA; *U.S. Private*, pg. 138
Heiligman, D.C., V.P.-Fin. & Corp. Sec.--Rochester Gas And Electric Corporation, Rochester, NY; *U.S. Public*, pg. 1395
Heinman, Gregg J., V.P.-Opers., Treas. & Sec.--Conway Import Co. Inc., Franklin Park, IL; *U.S. Private*, pg. 272
Heintjes, Charlotte, V.P.-Fin. & Treas.--Roytex, Inc., New York, NY; *U.S. Private*, pg. 949
Heiser, James S., Chief Fin. Officer, V.P., Gen. Counsel, Sec. & Treas.--Ducommun Incorporated, Carson, CA; *U.S. Public*, pg. 533
Heist, Gary A., Controller & Treas.--Continental Machines, Inc., Savage, MN; *U.S. Private*, pg. 268
Heit, Stephen A., Chief Fin. Officer & Treas.--AM Cosmetics Inc., Nyack, NY; *U.S. Private*, pg. 6
Held, K. Lars, Treas. & Sec.--Overly Manufacturing Co., Greensburg, PA; *U.S. Private*, pg. 823
Held, Molly, Sr. V.P.-Admin. & Treas.--Lundy Packing Co., Clinton, NC; *U.S. Private*, pg. 681
Helders, G.P., Sec. & Treas.--Hartford Insurance Group of Canada, Willowdale, Canada; *U.S. Public*, pg. 794
Heller, C.M., Jr., Vice Chm. & Treas.--Marquette Coppersmithing Co., Inc., Philadelphia, PA; *U.S. Private*, pg. 706
Hellman, Murray, Chief Fin. Officer, Controller, Sec. & Treas.--Pressman Toy Corp., New York, NY; *U.S. Private*, pg. 882
Hellner, Gary L., Asst. Treas.--Quanex Corporation, Houston, TX; *U.S. Public*, pg. 1349
Helmick, Louis G., III, V.P. & Treas.--Helmick Corporation, Fairmont, WV; *U.S. Private*, pg. 520
Helser, Phil, Chief Fin. Officer & Treas.--Lord, Sullivan & Yoder Inc. Marketing Communications, Columbus, OH; *U.S. Private*, pg. 676
Helsings, Harmen M., Treas.--N.V. Deli-Universal, Rotterdam, Netherlands; *U.S. Public*, pg. 1695
Helwig, Curtis, Treas.--CFB Industries, Inc., Chicago, IL; *U.S. Private*, pg. 194
Hemmelgarn, Gerald A., Controller & Asst. Treas.--Kennedy Tank & Manufacturing Co., Inc., Indianapolis, IN; *U.S. Private*, pg. 614
Hemmer, David G., Chief Fin. Officer, V.P. & Treas.--Stuart Hall Co., Inc., Kansas City, MO; *U.S. Public*, pg. 1178
Hemmer, Donald M., Treas. & Sec.--Paul Hemmer Construction Company, Fort Mitchell, KY; *U.S. Private*, pg. 521
Hempt, Gerald L., Sec. & Treas.--Hempt Brothers, Inc., Camp Hill, PA; *U.S. Private*, pg. 521
Henderson, Billy B., V.P. & Treas.--Utility Engineering Corporation, Amarillo, TX; *U.S. Public*, pg. 1170
Henderson, J. Michael, Treas.--Horace Mann Educators Corporation, Springfield, IL; *U.S. Public*, pg. 835
Henderson, James R., Chief Fin. Officer, V.P. & Treas.--Aydin Corporation, Horsham, PA; *U.S. Public*, pg. 158
Henderson, Richard, Treas.--Johnson County Farm Bureau Co-op, Franklin, IN; *U.S. Private*, pg. 591
Henderson, Sharon, V.P. & Treas.--Blimpie International, Inc., Atlanta, GA; *U.S. Public*, pg. 236
Hendrick, Howard, Asst. Treas. & Investor Rels.--BCE Inc., Montreal, Canada; *Int'l*, pg. 114
Hendrickson, Charles J., Sr. V.P. & Treas.--Donaldson, Lufkin, & Jenrette, Inc., New York, NY; *U.S. Public*, pg. 589
Hendrickson, Neal, V.P. & Treas.--Motek Engineering & Manufacturing Company, Cambridge, MN; *U.S. Private*, pg. 764
Hendrickson, Thomas N., Chm. Bd. & Chief Exec. Officer--CPAC, Inc., Leicester, NY; *U.S. Public*, pg. 282
Hendrix, Daniel T., Chief Fin. Officer, Sr. V.P. & Treas.--Interface Inc., Atlanta, GA; *U.S. Public*, pg. 889
Hendrix, I.E., V.P. & Treas.--Parker Drilling Company, Tulsa, OK; *U.S. Public*, pg. 1259
Hendrix, Stephen C., Treas.--Armstrong World Industries, Inc., Lancaster, PA; *U.S. Public*, pg. 131
Hendry, William J., Chief Fin. Officer & Treas.--Citrus World Inc., Lake Wales, FL; *U.S. Private*, pg. 241
Heneghan, Michael R., Sr. V.P.--Illinova Generating Co., Decatur, IL; *U.S. Public*, pg. 870
Henigson, David T., V.P., Treas., Dir.-Compliance & Internal Auditor--Value Line, Inc., New York, NY; *U.S. Private*, pg. 137
Henn, Dale, Asst. Treas.--Gannett Company, Inc., Arlington, VA; *U.S. Public*, pg. 698
Hennessy, Joseph J., Asst. Treas. & Controller--JSB Financial, Lynbrook, NY; *U.S. Public*, pg. 919
Henning, Theodore W., V.P. & Treas.--Belmont Metals, Inc., Brooklyn, NY; *U.S. Private*, pg. 132
Hennrich, W., V.P. & Treas.--Hoffmann-La Roche Inc., Nutley, NJ; *Int'l*, pg. 1120
Henquinet, Wayne K., Sec. & Treas.--New Mech Companies, Inc., Saint Paul, MN; *U.S. Private*, pg. 794
Henriksson, Nils, Treas.--Skandia Insurance Company Limited, Stockholm, Sweden; *Int'l*, pg. 1256
Henry, Brian J., V.P.-Fin. & Treas.--Terex Corporation, Westport, CT; *U.S. Public*, pg. 1581
Henry, G., Treas.--Exxon Chemical Polymeres, SNC, Paris, France; *U.S. Public*, pg. 602
Henry, Gregory, Asst. Treas.--Harman International Industries, Inc., Woodbury, NY; *U.S. Public*, pg. 787
Henry, Joseph C., Chief Fin. Officer, V.P. & Treas.--The Hanover Insurance Company, Worcester, MA; *U.S. Public*, pg. 54
Hensley, J.L., V.P., Treas. & Controller--Exxon Yemen Inc., Houston, TX; *U.S. Public*, pg. 601
Henss, Laurence R., V.P., Controller & Treas.--Industrial Dielectrics, Inc., Noblesville, IN; *U.S. Private*, pg. 560
Hentges, Richard J., Treas.--Foley-PLP Company, Rochester, NY; *U.S. Private*, pg. 416
Herald, James, V.P.-Fin., Sec & Treas.--Morgan Foods, Inc., Austin, IN; *U.S. Private*, pg. 761
Herbert, Vincent, Mgr.-Treasury--Bank Brussels Lambert, New York Branch, New York, NY; *Int'l*, pg. 147
Hercules, Duane, Sr. V.P. & Treas.--Safety National Casualty Corp., Saint Louis, MO; *U.S. Public*, pg. 496
Herley, Virlyn, Treas.--Atlas Wire Corporation, Schiller Park, IL; *U.S. Private*, pg. 97
Herman, W.A., Treas. & Sec.--Stauffer Communications, Inc., Augusta, GA; *U.S. Private*, pg. 995
Herman, W.A., III, Treas. & Sec.--Shivers Trading & Operating Co., Augusta, GA; *U.S. Private*, pg. 994
Hermanutz, G.E., Asst. Treas.--Pembina Pipeline Corporation, Calgary, Canada; *Int'l*, pg. 1032
Hermesmann, Fred, Treas.--Van Waters & Rogers Ltd., Richmond, Canada; *Int'l*, pg. 1147
Hernandez, Gaudencio H., Jr., V.P.-Fin. & Treas.--EEI Corporation, Manila, Philippines; *Int'l*, pg. 425
Hernandez, Louis R., V.P., Treas. & Asst. Sec.--W.P. Carey & Co., Inc., New York, NY; *U.S. Private*, pg. 209
Heroman, Donald T., Sr. V.P. & Treas.--SunTrust Banks, Inc., Atlanta, GA; *U.S. Public*, pg. 1537
Herran, Jose, Treas.--Real Holding Management Corp., Miami, FL; *U.S. Private*, pg. 913
Hersh, Gene, Treas.--California Manufacturing Enterprises, Corona, CA; *U.S. Private*, pg. 201
Hershkowitz, Thomas, Chief Fin. Officer, V.P., Treas. & Sec.--American Journal of Nursing Company, New York, NY; *Int'l*, pg. 1513
Herzberg, Steven M., Treas. & Dir.-Fin. Processing--The Penn Mutual Life Insurance Company, Philadelphia, PA; *U.S. Private*, pg. 849
Heskamp, Edward J., Asst. Treas.--The Midland Company, Cincinnati, OH; *U.S. Public*, pg. 1110
Hesser, Gregory, Controller--J.S. Alberici Construction Co., Inc., Saint Louis, MO; *U.S. Private*, pg. 32
Hessler, David J., Treas. & Sec.--MTD Products Limited, Kitchener, Canada; *U.S. Private*, pg. 688
Heulitt, K.D., Treas.--Amoco Credit Corporation, Chicago, IL; *U.S. Public*, pg. 103
Heumann, Stephen M., Chief Fin. Officer, V.P. & Treas.--The West Company, Incorporated, Lionville, PA; *U.S. Public*, pg. 1755
Hewett, Jack A., Sr. V.P.-Admin., Chief Fin. Officer & Treas.--VASA North Atlantic Insurance Company, Indianapolis, IN; *Int'l*, pg. 464
Hewett, Steve, Chief Fin. Officer, V.P. & Treas.--Quorum Health Group, Inc., Brentwood, TN; *U.S. Public*, pg. 1353
Hewitt, Dennis E., Treas.--Omnicom Group Inc., New York, NY; *U.S. Public*, pg. 1223
Hewlett-Brown, Wanda, Treas. & Sec.--Heights Heating & Cooling, Auburn Hills, MI; *U.S. Private*, pg. 519
Hiatt, David A., V.P., Treas. & Sec.--The National Super Service Co., Toledo, OH; *U.S. Private*, pg. 787
Hickox, Robert, Treas.--Food Carrier, Inc., Port Wentworth, GA; *U.S. Public*, pg. 872
Hicks, Brian V., Second V.P. & Treas.--Allianz Life Insurance Company of North America, Minneapolis, MN; *Int'l*, pg. 58
Hicks, J.C., Treas. & Sec.--ECC International Inc., Atlanta, GA; *Int'l*, pg. 455
Hicks, Jeff, Treas. & Sec.--English China Clays, Inc., Atlanta, GA; *Int'l*, pg. 455
Hicks, Maude H., Treas. & Sec.--Horton Homes, Inc., Eatonton, GA; *U.S. Private*, pg. 540
Hicks, Michael, Treas.--GenCorp Inc., Fairlawn, OH; *U.S. Public*, pg. 705
Higdon, Susan S., Treas.--Leggett & Platt, Incorporated, Carthage, MO; *U.S. Public*, pg. 985
Higgens, Alvin G., Asst. Treas.--Longview Fibre Company, Longview, WA; *U.S. Public*, pg. 1013
Higgins, Erik, Treas.--The Newhall Land And Farming Company, Valencia, CA; *U.S. Public*, pg. 1178
Higgins, Howard N., Treas.--Pace Industries, Inc., Fayetteville, AR; *U.S. Public*, pg. 986
Higgins, Michael R., Treas.--Amcast Industrial Corporation, Dayton, OH; *U.S. Public*, pg. 63
Hildewig, Donald R., Dir.-Fin.--DEC International, Inc., Madison, WI; *U.S. Private*, pg. 301
Hill, Alan J., V.P. & Treas.--Cooper Industries, Inc., Houston, TX; *U.S. Public*, pg. 442
Hill, Charles W., Controller & Treas.--Computer Language Research, Inc., Carrollton, TX; *U.S. Public*, pg. 421
Hill, Harley, V.P. & Treas.--Telxon Corporation, Akron, OH; *U.S. Public*, pg. 1573
Hill, John S., Sr. V.P.-Fin. & Treas.--Carolina Casualty Insurance Company, Jacksonville, FL; *U.S. Public*, pg. 216
Hill, Joseph G., Chief Fin. Officer, V.P.-Fin., Treas. & Sec.--DMI Furniture Inc., Louisville, KY; *U.S. Public*, pg. 473
Hill, Linda K., V.P. & Treas.--Tyler Corporation, Dallas, TX; *U.S. Public*, pg. 1651
Hill, Paul, Treas.--Austin Industries, Inc., Dallas, TX; *U.S. Private*, pg. 99
Hilliard, John A., Treas.--Ameripride Service Company, Minneapolis, MN; *U.S. Private*, pg. 65
Hilliard, Robert, Treas.--Lake County Press, Waukegan, IL; *U.S. Private*, pg. 643
Hilterbrand, Patricia, Controller, Treas. & Sec.--Pinkerton & Laws Inc., Atlanta, GA; *U.S. Private*, pg. 865
Hinkle, Charles E., V.P. & Treas.--Jumping Jacks, Monett, MO; *U.S. Private*, pg. 767
Hinman, Kirk, Pres., Chief Exec. Officer, Chief Fin. Officer & Treas.--Rome Strip Steel Co., Inc., Rome, NY; *U.S. Private*, pg. 942
Hinrichs, Charles A., V.P. & Treas.--Jefferson Smurfit Corporation, Saint Louis, MO; *Int'l*, pg. 1269
Hinshaw, Juanita H., V.P. & Treas.--Monsanto Company, Saint Louis, MO; *U.S. Public*, pg. 1124
Hinson, Eric, Asst. Treas.--Amtran, Inc., Indianapolis, IN; *U.S. Public*, pg. 106
Hinson, Laura K., Chief Fin. Officer & Treas.--Republic Financial Services, Inc., Dallas, TX; *Int'l*, pg. 346
Hinson, Laura K., V.P. & Treas.--Republic Underwriters Insurance Co., Dallas, TX; *Int'l*, pg. 346
Hinson, Laura K., V.P. & Treas.--Republic-Vanguard Life Insurance Co., Dallas, TX; *Int'l*, pg. 346
Hinson, Laura K., V.P. & Treas.--Republic Diversified Services, Inc., Dallas, TX; *Int'l*, pg. 346
Hinson, Laura K., V.P. & Treas.--Southern County Mutual Insurance Company, Dallas, TX; *Int'l*, pg. 346
Hinson, Laura K., V.P. & Treas.--Southern Insurance Co., Dallas, TX; *Int'l*, pg. 346
Hinson, Laura K., V.P. & Treas.--Republic Financial Services, Inc., Dallas, TX; *Int'l*, pg. 346
Hinson, Laura K., V.P. & Treas.--Southern Underwriters Insurance Company, Dallas, TX; *Int'l*, pg. 346
Hinson, Laura K., V.P. & Treas.--Republic Fire & Casualty Insurance Company, Dallas, TX; *Int'l*, pg. 346
Hinson, Laura K., V.P. & Treas.--Republic Group No. Two, Dallas, TX; *Int'l*, pg. 346
Hinson, Laura K., V.P. & Treas.--Eagle General Agency, Dallas, TX; *Int'l*, pg. 346
Hinson, Laura K., V.P. & Treas.--Allied Premium Finance, Dallas, TX; *Int'l*, pg. 346
Hintz, Charles B., Treas.--Morgan Stanley Group Inc., New York, NY; *U.S. Public*, pg. 1132
Hinze, Reinhild D., V.P.-Opers. & Treas.--Napco International, Inc., Hopkins, MN; *U.S. Public*, pg. 1716
Hirai, Frank, Chief Fin. Officer & Treas.--Mutoh America Inc., Phoenix, AZ; *Int'l*, pg. 897
Hirata, Dean K., Asst. Treas.--Pacific One Dealer Center, Inc., Costa Mesa, CA; *U.S. Public*, pg. 635
Hirko, Joseph M., Chief Fin. Officer, Sr. V.P. & Treas.--Portland General Electric Co., Portland, OR; *U.S. Public*, pg. 584
Hirschfeld, David L., Pres., Chief Exec. Officer & Treas.--Hirschfeld, Inc., San Angelo, TX; *U.S. Private*, pg. 530
Hison, Joan, V.P.-Fin.--Sterling Inc., Akron, OH; *Int'l*, pg. 1248
Hitchcock, Cameron C., Treas.--Dean Foods Company, Franklin Park, IL; *U.S. Public*, pg. 489
Hitchcock, Pat, Treas. & Sec.--WRM, Incoporated, Mabscott, WV; *U.S. Private*, pg. 1144
Hitchcock, T.P., Exec. V.P. & Treas.--Northwestern Energy Corp., Huron, SD; *U.S. Public*, pg. 1201
Hite, David S., Treas & Sec.--McKinnon Bridge Co., Franklin, TN; *U.S. Private*, pg. 723
Hluchan, Stephen E., Treas.--Minerals Technologies, Inc., New York, NY; *U.S. Public*, pg. 1115
Hnatin, Catherine B., Treas.--Exide Corporation, Reading, PA; *U.S. Public*, pg. 600
Hoben, Michael F., Asst. Treas.--Union Carbide Corporation, Danbury, CT; *U.S. Public*, pg. 1666
Hockett, Galen R., Sec. & Treas.--Larrys, Inc., Gillette, WY; *U.S. Private*, pg. 652
Hockman, Ralph C., V.P., Gen. Mgr., Treas. & Sec.-Access Floors--Tate Access Floors, Inc., Jessup, MD; *U.S. Private*, pg. 1069
Hodge, Allan, Exec. V.P. & Treas.--Foster's Brewing Group, Toronto, Canada; *Int'l*, pg. 501
Hodge, S.M.G., Treas.--Royal Dutch/Shell Group of Companies, Hague, Netherlands; *Int'l*, pg. 1135
Hodges, Charles, Controller & Treas.--Colonial Oil Industries, Savannah, GA; *U.S. Private*, pg. 253
Hodges, June Jenkins, Asst. Treas.--SL Industries, Inc., Mount Laurel, NJ; *U.S. Public*, pg. 1418
Hodgkin, Phil, Chief Fin. Officer, Controller & Treas.--Minarik Corp, Glendale, CA; *U.S. Private*, pg. 749
Hoehner, Mark, Treas.--Cain's Coffee Co., Oklahoma City, OK; *U.S. Public*, pg. 351
Hoff, George H., Treas. & Sec.--Sargento Foods Inc.- Food Service Div., Plymouth, WI; *U.S. Private*, pg. 966
Hoffman, Gary, Sec. & Treas.--Superior Water, Light & Power Company, Superior, WI; *U.S. Public*, pg. 1116
Hoffman, Martin, Pres., Chief Exec. & Fin. Officer, Treas.--Designatronics, Inc., New Hyde Park, NY; *U.S. Private*, pg. 327
Hoffman, P. D., V.P. & Treas.--Black & Veatch, Kansas City, MO; *U.S. Private*, pg. 146
Hoffmann, Dave, V.P. & Treas.--ALZA International, Palo Alto, CA; *U.S. Public*, pg. 62
Hoffmann, David R., V.P. & Treas.--Alza Corporation, Palo Alto, CA; *U.S. Public*, pg. 62
Hoffmann, Richard L., V.P.-Taxes & Asst. Treas.--Essex Industries, New Haven, CT; *Int'l*, pg. 18
Hofford, Cletus, Gen. Mgr., Controller & Treas.--Paranatal Care of America, Inc., Edina, MN; *U.S. Private*, pg. 839
Hofman, Charles, Treas.--Shopsmith, Inc., Dayton, OH; *U.S. Public*, pg. 1467
Hogan, Kenneth W., Chief Fin. Officer, Sr. V.P. & Sec.--Valley Resources, Inc., Cumberland, RI; *U.S. Public*, pg. 1706
Hogg, G. Scott, Treas. & Sec.--Better Brands Of Atlanta, Inc., Atlanta, GA; *U.S. Private*, pg. 141
Hoggarth, Karen, Treas.--Jeld-Wen, Inc., Klamath Falls, OR; *U.S. Private*, pg. 585
Hoguet, Karen M., Chief Fin. Officer--Federated Department Stores, Inc., Cincinnati, OH; *U.S. Public*, pg. 617
Hoipkemier, Gary N., Treas.--CTS Corporation, Elkhart, IN; *U.S. Public*, pg. 285
Hoke, Michael, V.P. & Treas.--Argosy Electronics, Inc., Eden Prairie, MN; *U.S. Private*, pg. 81
Holbrook, Janet, Sec. & Treas.--Morgan Lumber Sales Co., Columbus, OH; *U.S. Private*, pg. 761
Holbrook, Lisa J., Sr. V.P.-Fin., Treas. & Sec.--Longview Fibre Company, Longview, WA; *U.S. Public*, pg. 1013
Holcomb, Beth Ann, Asst. Treas.--The Dexter Corporation, Windsor Locks, CT; *U.S. Public*, pg. 504
Holcomb, Daryl K., Chief Fin. Officer, V.P. & Treas.--Ronson Corporation, Somerset, NJ; *U.S. Public*, pg. 1405
Holcomb, Robert J., Treas. & Sec.--V.T. Inc., Merriam, KS; *U.S. Private*, pg. 1131
Holden, William H., Treas.--NewTel Enterprises Limited, Saint Johns, Canada; *Int'l*, pg. 115

Holden, William H., Treas.--NewTel Communications, Saint Johns, Canada; *Int'l*, pg. 115
Holder, Thomas M., V.P.-Sls. & Treas.--Hershey Creamery Company, Harrisburg, PA; *U.S. Private*, pg. 524
Holihen, Jennifer A., Chief Fin. Officer, Treas. & Sec.--Crossmann Communities, Inc., Indianapolis, IN; *U.S. Public*, pg. 461
Holl, David, Chief Fin. Officer & Treas.--Mary Kay, Inc., Dallas, TX; *U.S. Private*, pg. 711
Holland, Jim D., Chief Fin. Officer, Sr. V.P. & Treas.--CMI Corporation, Oklahoma City, OK; *U.S. Public*, pg. 278
Holland, R. Van Ness, Jr., Chief Fin. Officer, Exec. V.P.-Fin. & Treas.--Wyle Electronics, Irvine, CA; *Int'l*, pg. 1457
Holland, Susan, Treas. & Controller--El Chico Restaurants, Inc., Dallas, TX; *U.S. Private*, pg. 283
Holland, Wayne E., Dir.-Cash Mngmt. & Asst. Treas.--Public Service Company of North Carolina, Inc., Gastonia, NC; *U.S. Public*, pg. 1340
Hollander, Jules A., Chm. Bd. & Treas.--Hartford Distributors Inc., Manchester, CT; *U.S. Private*, pg. 507
Hollenbeck, Leo, Treas.--Alro Group, Jackson, MI; *U.S. Private*, pg. 45
Holler, W.E., V.P.-Fin. & Treas.--The Deutsch Company, Santa Monica, CA; *U.S. Private*, pg. 328
Holliday, K. Roger, Treas.--Russell Corporation, Alexander City, AL; *U.S. Public*, pg. 1413
Holliday, Mike, Treas., UK--Reed Elsevier plc, London, United Kingdom; *Int'l*, pg. 1093
Hollingsed, Margaret, Asst. Treas.--Inter-Tel, Incorporated, Phoenix, AZ; *U.S. Public*, pg. 888
Hollingsworth, Schuyler, Sr. V.P. & Treas.--Beverly Enterprises, Inc., Fort Smith, AR; *U.S. Public*, pg. 227
Holloway, Cynthia E., Asst. Treas.--Aluminum Company of America, Pittsburgh, PA; *U.S. Public*, pg. 60
Holloway, John, Dir.-Fin.--Cannon Rubber Ltd., London, United Kingdom; *Int'l*, pg. 261
Holm, Soren, Sr. V.P. & Treas.--Nykredit, Copenhagen, Denmark; *Int'l*, pg. 993
Holman, Bobby G., Chief Fin. Officer, Treas. & Asst. Sec.--WSMP, Inc., Claremont, NC; *U.S. Public*, pg. 1729
Holmes-Johnson, P., Treas.--Gestetner Holdings PLC, London, United Kingdom; *Int'l*, pg. 1114
Holmes, John, Exec. V.P., Mktg. Dir. & Sec.--Paradigm Communications, Tampa, FL; *U.S. Private*, pg. 838
Holmes, Mary B., Treas.--Chelsea Milling Co., Chelsea, MI; *U.S. Private*, pg. 231
Holmes, V.J.R., Treas.--Marley PLC, Sevenoaks, United Kingdom; *Int'l*, pg. 843
Holstein, Andy, Treas.--Superior Die Tool And Machine Company, Columbus, OH; *U.S. Private*, pg. 1054
Holt, Jon H., Controller & Asst. Treas.--Pulitzer Publishing Company, Saint Louis, MO; *U.S. Public*, pg. 1343
Holt, Jon H., Asst. Treas.--St. Louis Post-Dispatch, Saint Louis, MO; *U.S. Public*, pg. 1343
Holte, William T., Treas.--Road Machinery & Supplies Co., Savage, MN; *U.S. Private*, pg. 934
Holter, Peter, V.P. & Treas.--Peter Lumber Company, Pleasantville, NJ; *U.S. Private*, pg. 856
Holtta, Pekka, Sr. V.P. & Treas.--Valmet Corporation, Helsinki, Finland; *Int'l*, pg. 1447
Holtz, Robert, Treas.--Modern Group Ltd., Bristol, PA; *U.S. Private*, pg. 754
Holtzman, Jeffrey P., Corp. V.P. & Treas.--B/E Aerospace, Inc., Wellington, FL; *U.S. Public*, pg. 159
Holtzman, Morton, V.P., Sec. & Treas.--Harve Benard Ltd., Secaucus, NJ; *U.S. Private*, pg. 508
Holtzman, Morton, V.P., Treas. & Sec.--Harve Benard Ltd., New York, NY; *U.S. Private*, pg. 508
Holzhause, Don, V.P.-Finance--Spangler Candy Company, Bryan, OH; *U.S. Private*, pg. 1020
Homan, Robert W., Pres. & Treas.--Homan Lumber Mart, Inc., Elkhart, IN; *U.S. Private*, pg. 536
Homer, G., V.P.-Fin. & Treas.--Wyeth Ltd., North York, Canada; *U.S. Public*, pg. 82
Homes, W.G., Chm. Bd., Pres. & Treas.--Homes & Son Contractors, Inc., Phoenix, AZ; *U.S. Private*, pg. 537
Homrich, Christopher F., Treas.--Stryker Corporation, Kalamazoo, MI; *U.S. Public*, pg. 1525
Honbarrier, Louise B., Treas. & Sec.--Central Transport, Archdale, NC; *U.S. Private*, pg. 225
Hones, Frank W., Asst. Treas. & Asst. Sec.--Jacobson Stores Inc., Jackson, MI; *U.S. Public*, pg. 922
Honig, David, Treas. & Sec.--Jarchem Industries, Inc., Newark, NJ; *U.S. Private*, pg. 582
Hood, Cecil G., Treas. & Sec.--Batson-Cook Company, West Point, GA; *U.S. Private*, pg. 123
Hoogenboom, Dale D., Asst. Treas.--Bock Industries Inc., Elkhart, IN; *Int'l*, pg. 265
Hooker, Bruce, Chief Fin. Officer & Sr. V.P.--Amperif Corporation, Chatsworth, CA; *U.S. Public*, pg. 1523
Hooker, Steven L., Treas.--HMO Oregon, Salem, OR; *U.S. Private*, pg. 918
Hooper, Steven W., Sr. V.P. & Treas.--AT&T Wireless Services, Kirkland, WA; *U.S. Public*, pg. 11
Hootkin, Pamela N., V.P., Treas. & Sec.--Phillips-Van Heusen Corporation, New York, NY; *U.S. Public*, pg. 1291
Hoover, Gerald, Gen. Mgr. & Asst. Treas.--Cleveland Thermal Energy Corporation, Cleveland, OH; *U.S. Public*, pg. 913
Hoover, Gerald, Gen. Mgr. & Treas.--Cleveland District Cooling Corp., Cleveland, OH; *U.S. Public*, pg. 913
Hopkinson, Mark R., Chief Fin. Officer, Treas. & Asst. Sec.--Artistic Carton Company, Elgin, IL; *U.S. Private*, pg. 87
Horan, Dennis, Chief Fin. Officer, Treas. & Sec.--URM Stores, Inc., Spokane, WA; *U.S. Private*, pg. 1114
Horn, Karen L., Asst. Treas.--The Times Mirror Company, Los Angeles, CA; *U.S. Public*, pg. 1615
Horn, Richard, Pres. & Treas.--Mulberry Metal Products, Inc., Union, NJ; *U.S. Private*, pg. 766
Hornick, Gerald C., V.P. & Asst. Treas.--Essef Corporation, Chardon, OH; *U.S. Public*, pg. 592
Horowitz, Donald, Chief Fin. Officer, Treas. & Sec.--Aceto Corporation, Lake Success, NY; *U.S. Public*, pg. 15
Horowitz, Donald, Treas. & Sec.--VGF Corporation, Lake Success, NY; *U.S. Public*, pg. 15
Horstia, Heikki, Sr. V.P. & Treas.--Metra Corporation, Helsinki, Finland; *Int'l*, pg. 862
Horstmann, Peter, Head-Trading & Intl. Network--Bank Brussels Lambert, Brussels, Belgium; *Int'l*, pg. 146
Horton, Ann N., Treas. & Sec.--Penn Virginia Oil & Gas Company, Kingsport, TN; *U.S. Public*, pg. 1271
Horton, Gary B., Chief Fin. Officer & Treas.--Amerco, Reno, NV; *U.S. Private*, pg. 48
Horvat, Peter D., Chief Fin. Officer, V.P., Treas. & Sec.--Lenape Forge, Inc., West Chester, PA; *U.S. Private*, pg. 659
Horwitz, Alan, Treas.--Blumenthal Print Works, Inc., New Orleans, LA; *U.S. Private*, pg. 153
Hosel, Werner, Treas.--General Motors Nordiska AB, Haninge, Sweden; *U.S. Public*, pg. 722
Hoshikawa, Ken, V.P. & Treas.--Sony Electronics, Park Ridge, NJ; *Int'l*, pg. 1281
Hoshikawa, Kyoji, Treas.--Sony Trans Com Systems Inc., Costa Mesa, CA; *Int'l*, pg. 1281
Hosier, Jacl W., V.P.-Fin. & Asst. Treas.--Shurflo Pump Manufacturing Co., Santa Ana, CA; *U.S. Public*, pg. 1767
Hoskins, John M., V.P. & Treas.--Tennessee Valley Authority, Knoxville, TN; *U.S. Public*, pg. 1580
Host, Gerard R., Treas.--Trustmark Corporation, Jackson, MS; *U.S. Public*, pg. 1643
Hostetter, Drew K., Treas.--Susquehanna Bancshares, Inc., Lititz, PA; *U.S. Public*, pg. 1542
Hotchkin, H.F., Treas.--Inductotherm Industries, Inc., Rancocas, NJ; *U.S. Private*, pg. 560
Hotta, Tsuyoshi, Treas.--Maruzen International Co., Ltd., Weehawken, NJ; *Int'l*, pg. 846
Hottovy, Ronald J., Chief Fin. Officer, Exec. V.P., Treas. & Sec.--Scientific Software-Intercomp, Inc., Denver, CO; *U.S. Public*, pg. 1443
Hough, Thomas M., V.P. & Treas.--Navistar International Corporation, Chicago, IL; *U.S. Public*, pg. 1167
Houle, David A., Chief Fin. Officer, Exec. V.P. & Treas.--Pacific Century Financial Corporation, Honolulu, HI; *U.S. Public*, pg. 1248
Houle, David A., Chief Fin. Officer & Exec. V.P.-Treas. Admin.--Bank of Hawaii, Honolulu, HI; *U.S. Public*, pg. 1248
Houle, Patricia S., Sec. & Asst. Treas.--Bozzuto's Inc., Cheshire, CT; *U.S. Public*, pg. 249
Householder, Peter R., Treas. & Mgr.-D.P.--Quality Control Corporation, Chicago, IL; *U.S. Private*, pg. 898
Housen, Morris, Asst. Treas.--Erving Industries, Inc., Erving, MA; *U.S. Private*, pg. 382
Housman, Peter J., II, Chief Fin. Officer & Treas.--Telemundo Group, Inc., Hialeah, FL; *U.S. Public*, pg. 1570
Houston, Alfred D., V.P. & Treas.--Narragansett Electric Co., Providence, RI; *U.S. Public*, pg. 1171
Houston, Alfred D., V.P. & Treas.--Narragansett Energy Resources Company, Providence, RI; *U.S. Public*, pg. 1171
Hovanec, Robert M., V.P. & Treas.--T.W. Phillips Gas and Oil Co., Butler, PA; *U.S. Private*, pg. 862
Howard, Bill, Treas. & Sec.--Mercer Transportation Co., Louisville, KY; *U.S. Private*, pg. 732
Howard, Connie, Controller--Camalloy, Incorporated, Washington, PA; *U.S. Private*, pg. 202
Howard, David P., Chief Fin. Officer, V.P. & Treas.--Furniture Brands International Inc., Saint Louis, MO; *U.S.* Public, pg. 688
Howard, Frank M., V.P. & Treas.--Genuine Parts Company, Atlanta, GA; *U.S. Public*, pg. 732
Howard, Larry, Asst. Treas.--HMO Texas, L.C., Houston, TX; *U.S. Public*, pg. 1470
Howard, Robert W., Sr. V.P.-Fin. & Treas.--Barrett Resources Corporation, Denver, CO; *U.S. Public*, pg. 191
Howard, Rudy C., CPA, Chief Fin. Officer, V.P.-Fin., Treas. & Sec.--Pharmaceutical Product Development, Inc., Wilmington, NC; *U.S. Public*, pg. 1285
Howard, W.R., Pres. & Treas.--Saddlebag Lake Resorts, Inc., La Belle, FL; *U.S. Public*, pg. 41
Howe, Harold, Jr., Chm. Bd., Chief Exec. Officer & Treas.--Howe Furniture Corporation, Trumbull, CT; *U.S. Private*, pg. 543
Howe, Maureen E., Treas--BC Gas Inc., Vancouver, Canada; *Int'l*, pg. 114
Howe, Robert S., Treas.--Central Securities Corp., Augusta, ME; *U.S. Public*, pg. 325
Howell, Doug, Chief Fin. Officer, Sr. V.P. & Treas.--Preferred Risk Mutual Insurance, West Des Moines, IA; *U.S. Private*, pg. 880
Howson, Richard, Treas. & Sec.--Dover Corp. (Canada) Ltd., Mississauga, Canada; *U.S. Public*, pg. 522
Howson, Terrance G., V.P. & Treas.--GPU, Inc., Morristown, NJ; *U.S. Public*, pg. 695
Hoyas, Jeff, Treas.--Levitt Corporation, Boca Raton, FL; *U.S. Private*, pg. 1035
Hoyme, Larry, V.P.-Fin. & Treas.--Tri-State Insurance Company of Minnesota, Luverne, MN; *U.S. Public*, pg. 215
Hritzo, Robert, Treas.--American Kennel Club, Inc., New York, NY; *U.S. Private*, pg. 58
Hrotko, William, Asst. Treas.--Sumitomo Electric Automotive Inc., Plymouth, MI; *Int'l*, pg. 1313
Hrotko, William, Asst. Treas.--Safa, LLC, La Grange, GA; *Int'l*, pg. 1313
Hrotko, William, Asst. Treas.--Lucas SEI Electronics, LLC, Rushford, MN; *Int'l*, pg. 1313
Hruby, Sandy, Asst. Treas.--Mark IV Industries Inc., Amherst, NY; *U.S. Public*, pg. 1044
Hubbard, Jim, Treas.--Robson Communities, Sun Lakes, AZ; *U.S. Private*, pg. 937
Hubbard, Joyce, Treas.--Abrams Fixture Corporation, Atlanta, GA; *U.S. Public*, pg. 14
Hubbard, Reginald H., V.P. & Treas.--Darlington Veneer Company, Darlington, SC; *U.S. Private*, pg. 311
Huber, Judy, Exec. V.P., Treas. & Sec.--Time Systems, Inc., Phoenix, AZ; *U.S. Private*, pg. 1086
Huber, Linda S., V.P.-Fin. & Asst. Treas.--PepsiCo, Inc., Purchase, NY; *U.S. Public*, pg. 1276
Huber, Michael S., Chief Fin. Officer, Sr. V.P. & Treas.--Andal Corp., New York, NY; *U.S. Public*, pg. 111
Huber, Rudolph P., Asst. Treas.--Aluminum Company of America, Pittsburgh, PA; *U.S. Public*, pg. 60
Huber, Stephen, Chief Fin. Officer, Treas. & Sec.--Birdsong Corporation, Suffolk, VA; *U.S. Private*, pg. 145
Huber, William, Treas.--IMI Cash Valve, Inc., Cullman, AL; *Int'l*, pg. 646
Hudson, Dean, Sr. V.P. & Treas.--Federal Savings Bank, Fort Smith, AR; *U.S. Private*, pg. 614
Hudson, M.K., V.P.--Fisca Oil Co., Inc., Westwood, KS; *U.S.* Private, pg. 408
Hudson, Robert C., Jr., Pres. & Treas.--H.D. Hudson Manufacturing Company, Chicago, IL; *U.S. Private*, pg. 545
Huether, James, Treas.--International Flavors & Fragrances, Inc., New York, NY; *U.S. Public*, pg. 898
Huey, John, Treas.--Trimble Navigation Limited, Sunnyvale, CA; *U.S. Public*, pg. 1638
Huff, Craig D., Chief Fin. Officer, V.P.-Fin. & Treas.--Nature's Sunshine Products, Inc., Provo, UT; *U.S. Public*, pg. 1166
Huff, Danny W., V.P. & Treas.--Georgia-Pacific Corporation, Atlanta, GA; *U.S. Public*, pg. 735
Huff, Phil E., V.P. & Treas.--Amwest Insurance Group, Inc., Calabasas, CA; *U.S. Public*, pg. 106
Huff, Phillip E., V.P. & Treas.--Amwest Surety Insurance Company, Calabasas, CA; *U.S. Public*, pg. 106
Huffaker, Craig, Chief Fin. Officer & Treas.--TIE/Communications, Inc., Overland Park, KS; *U.S. Private*, pg. 1085
Huffman, Charles P., Chief Fin. Officer, V.P. & Treas.--Mobile Gas Service Corp., Mobile, AL; *U.S. Public*, pg. 1120
Huffman, Charles P., Treas.--MGS Energy Services, Inc., Mobile, AL; *U.S. Public*, pg. 1120
Hufford, Jack E., Treas.--American United Life Insurance Company, Indianapolis, IN; *U.S. Private*, pg. 64
Hughes, Christine, Asst. Treas.--Apex Oil Company, Inc., Saint Louis, MO; *U.S. Private*, pg. 77
Hughes, David, Treas.--Central Supply Co., Inc., Indianapolis, IN; *U.S. Private*, pg. 225
Hughes, John F., Exec. V.P. & Treas.--Associates First Capital Corporation, Dallas, TX; *U.S. Public*, pg. 662
Hughes, John F., Exec. V.P. & Treas.--Associates Financial Services Corporation, Dallas, TX; *U.S. Public*, pg. 663
Hughes, Joseph F., Chm. Bd., Pres., Chief Exec. Officer & Treas.--TSR Inc., Hauppauge, NY; *U.S. Public*, pg. 1559
Hughes, Nick, Chief Fin. Officer & Treas.--TV Host Inc., Harrisburg, PA; *U.S. Private*, pg. 1066
Hughes, W. Alan, Treas.--Fleischli Oil Company, Inc., Cheyenne, WY; *U.S. Private*, pg. 410
Huitt, E. Larry, Chm. Bd., Exec. V.P., Treas. & Sec.--Huitt-Zollars, Inc., Dallas, TX; *U.S. Private*, pg. 547
Hull, John T., Chief Fin. Officer & Treas.--Modern American Life Insurance Company, Springfield, MO; *U.S. Public*, pg. 853
Hull, Stephen F., V.P. & Treas.--Fluor Corporation, Irvine, CA; *U.S. Public*, pg. 659
Hultman, Jayne A., Treas.--Ameritech, Chicago, IL; *U.S. Public*, pg. 97
Humphreys, Barry E., Sr. V.P.-Fin. & Treas.--Potash Corporation of Saskatchewan Inc., Saskatoon, Canada; *Int'l*, pg. 1064
Humphreys, Robert K., Chief Fin. Officer, Treas. & Sec.--Valley Detroit Diesel Allison, City of Industry, CA; *U.S. Private*, pg. 1132
Hums, Scott J., Controller, Treas. & Mgr.-Financial Reporting--DSM Engineering Plastic Products, Reading, PA; *Int'l*, pg. 354
Huneke, Kurt S., V.P.-Fin. & Treas.--Enron Corp., Houston, TX; *U.S. Public*, pg. 584
Huneke, Wayne R., Chief Fin. Officer, Sr. V.P. & Treas.--ReliaStar Financial Corp., Minneapolis, MN; *U.S. Public*, pg. 1375
Hunger, John E., Chief Fin. Officer & Treas.--World Shipping, Inc., Rocky River, OH; *U.S. Private*, pg. 1190
Hunley, Jim, Chief Fin. Officer & Treas.--Plains Co-op Oil Mill, Lubbock, TX; *U.S. Private*, pg. 868
Hunt, James K., Chief Fin. Officer, Exec. V.P. & Treas.--UST Corporation, Boston, MA; *U.S. Public*, pg. 1660
Hunt, Lester J., V.P. & Treas.--National General Insurance Co., Earth City, MO; *U.S. Public*, pg. 721
Hunte, Alan L., Chief Fin. Officer, Exec. V.P. & Treas.--Trenwick America Reinsurance Corporation, Stamford, CT; *U.S. Public*, pg. 1634
Hunter, Colin, Treas.--Blue Circle Industries PLC, London, United Kingdom; *Int'l*, pg. 197
Hunter, Jim, Treas.--Rossignol Ski Co., Williston, VT; *Int'l*, pg. 1127
Hunter, Renee, Treas.--American Systems Engineering Corporation, Virginia Beach, VA; *U.S. Private*, pg. 976
Hunter, Walter R., Controller & Treas.--Virginia Natural Gas, Inc., Norfolk, VA; *U.S. Public*, pg. 436
Huntsman, Barry N., Chief Fin. Officer & Treas.--Ambar, Inc., Lafayette, LA; *U.S. Private*, pg. 126
Huntsman, Barry N., Treas. & Sec.--AMBAR Marine, Inc., Lafayette, LA; *U.S. Private*, pg. 126
Hupfer, C.J., V.P., Treas. & Corp. Sec.--Sonoco Products Company, Hartsville, SC; *U.S. Public*, pg. 1485
Hurley, James, Chief Fin. Officer & Sr. V.P.-Fin./MIS--Quality Stores Inc., Muskegon, MI; *U.S. Private*, pg. 899
Hursh, Alan, Treas. & Sec.--Acousti Engineering Co. of Florida, Orlando, FL; *U.S. Private*, pg. 14
Husain, Altaf, Treas., Sec. & Mgr.-Fin. & Plng.--National Refinery Limited, Karachi, Pakistan; *Int'l*, pg. 909
Husband, W.D., Sec. & Treas.--Canadian Timken Ltd., Saint Thomas, Canada; *U.S. Public*, pg. 1617
Hussey, Edward Joseph, V.P., Sec. & Asst. Treas.--Liberty Homes, Inc., Goshen, IN; *U.S. Public*, pg. 992

Hutchins, Gary, Treas. & Dir.-Tax--A.W. Chesterton Company, Stoneham, MA; *U.S. Private*, pg. 234
Hutchins, William B., III, Treas.--Southern Electric Generating Co., Birmingham, AL; *U.S. Public*, pg. 1490
Hutchinson, Angela, Treas.--Persingers, Inc., Charleston, WV; *U.S. Private*, pg. 855
Hutchison, Ronald B., V.P. & Treas.--Advantica Restaurant Group, Inc., Spartanburg, SC; *U.S. Public*, pg. 22
Huton, Barry, V.P. & Treas.--Consolidated Pipe & Supply Company, Birmingham, AL; *U.S. Private*, pg. 266
Hutter, Marilyn, Treas.--Industrial Metals of the South, New Orleans, LA; *U.S. Private*, pg. 561
Hutton, Nancy, Controller, Treas. & Sec.--Crustbuster, Inc., Dodge City, KS; *U.S. Private*, pg. 293
Hutton, Ron, Treas.--Bio-Rad Laboratories, Inc., Hercules, CA; *U.S. Public*, pg. 230
Huyberts, Frank, Treas.--CAMI Automotive, Inc., Ingersoll, Canada; *U.S. Public*, pg. 722
Hyland, John T., Sec. & Treas.--Intercom Systems, Inc., Copiague, NY; *U.S. Public*, pg. 1556
Hyland, John T. Jr., V.P.-Auditing & Treas.--TII Industries, Inc., Copiague, NY; *U.S. Public*, pg. 1556
Hyland, John T., Jr., Treas.--TII Electronics, Inc., Copiague, NY; *U.S. Public*, pg. 1556
Hyland, John T., Jr., Treas.--TII-Ditel, Hickory, NC; *U.S. Public*, pg. 1556
Hyland, Richard F., Treas.--The Vanguard Group, Inc., Valley Forge, PA; *U.S. Private*, pg. 1133
Hyland, Richard F., Treas.--Vanguard Real Estate Fund II, Valley Forge, PA; *U.S. Private*, pg. 1134
Hyland, Robert J., Chief Fin. Officer, V.P. & Treas.--Barclay White Incorporated, Berwyn, PA; *U.S. Private*, pg. 115
Hymas, Scott L., Treas.--R.C. Willey Home Furnishings, Salt Lake City, UT; *U.S. Public*, pg. 221
Hyzy, Brian, Controller--Hammacher, Schlemmer & Co., Inc., Chicago, IL; *U.S. Private*, pg. 497
Iacovelli, David, Treas. & Sec.--Italian Food Manufacturers, Inc., Vestal, NY; *U.S. Private*, pg. 576
Iacovetti, Benedict J., Treas.--American Travellers Corporation, Bensalem, PA; *U.S. Public*, pg. 433
Ianello, Angelo, Sr. V.P.-Fin. & Treas.--Contract Freighters, Inc., Joplin, MO; *U.S. Private*, pg. 270
Iapalucci, Samuel H., Chief Fin. Officer & Treas.--CH2M Hill, Inc., Greenwood Village, CO; *U.S. Private*, pg. 195
Ibe, Jun, Exec. V.P. & Treas.--Tonen Energy International Corp., New York, NY; *Int'l*, pg. 1399
Ibsen, Robert, Dr., Chm. Bd., Pres., Chief Exec. Officer & Treas.--Den-Mat Corporation, Santa Maria, CA; *U.S. Private*, pg. 324
Ichimura-Kiehm, Natalie, V.P.-Devel. & Asst. Treas.--Malama Pacific Corp., Honolulu, HI; *U.S. Public*, pg. 800
Ikeda, Deorna L., Asst. Treas.--Hawaii Electric Light Co., Inc., Hilo, HI; *U.S. Public*, pg. 800
Ikeda, Nario, V.P. & Treas.--Q & B Foods, Inc., Irwindale, CA; *Int'l*, pg. 1074
Ilardo, Samuel J., Treas.--Springs Industries, Inc., Fort Mill, SC; *U.S. Public*, pg. 1499
Ilitch, Marian, Sec. & Treas.--Little Caesar Enterprises, Inc., Detroit, MI; *U.S. Private*, pg. 671
Imperia, Joseph, Treas. & Sec.--Imperia Bros., Inc., Pelham Manor, NY; *U.S. Private*, pg. 558
Indelicato, Dorothy, Treas.--Delicato Vineyards, Manteca, CA; *U.S. Private*, pg. 322
Indralak, Padungdej, Treas.--The Siam Cement Public Company Limited, Bangkok, Thailand; *Int'l*, pg. 1237
Ingalls, Harold, Chief Fin. Officer, V.P. & Treas.--Rust International Inc., Birmingham, AL; *U.S. Public*, pg. 1366
Ingalls, Henry A., Chief Fin. Officer, V.P. & Treas.--AgriBioTech, Inc., Las Vegas, NV; *U.S. Public*, pg. 28
Ingberman, Israel, Sec. & Treas.--Continental Health Affiliates, Inc., Englewood Cliffs, NJ; *U.S. Public*, pg. 440
Ingham, Donald E., Treas.--Air Canada, Saint-Laurent, Canada; *Int'l*, pg. 36
Ingham, James W., Treas.--Mentholatum Company, Buffalo, NY; *Int'l*, pg. 1126
Inghilterra, Louis S., V.P. & Treas.--Fiduciary Trust Company International, New York, NY; *U.S. Public*, pg. 621
Ingram, Betty, Treas. & Sec.--B & B Homes Corporation, Casper, WY; *U.S. Private*, pg. 105
Ingram, Glenn, Treas.--Fieldale Corporation, Baldwin, GA; *U.S. Private*, pg. 403
Ingram, Richard S., Jr., Chief Fin. Officer, Treas. & Sec.--T.A. Loving Company, Goldsboro, NC; *U.S. Private*, pg. 677
Ingulsrud, Brian, Asst. Treas. & Asst. Sec.--American Crystal Sugar Company, Moorhead, MN; *U.S. Private*, pg. 52
Inserra, Richard M., Asst. Treas.--Union Carbide Corporation, Danbury, CT; *U.S. Public*, pg. 1666
Intino, Tony, Chief Fin. Officer & Treas.--Power Designs, Inc., Danbury, CT; *U.S. Private*, pg. 878
Iorillo, John R., Treas.--Radiometer America Inc., Westlake, OH; *Int'l*, pg. 1083
Ippolito, Robert S., Chief Fin. Officer, Treas. & Sec.--Penn National Gaming, Inc., Wyomissing, PA; *U.S. Public*, pg. 1270
Iqbal, I., V.P. & Treas.-Tax & Plng.--Murphy Eastern Oil Co., London, United Kingdom; *U.S. Public*, pg. 1142
Iqbal, I., Treas. & Mgr.-Tax & Plng.--Murco Petroleum Ltd., London, United Kingdom; *U.S. Public*, pg. 1142
Iqbal, I., Treas. & Mgr.-Tax & Plng.--Murphy Petroleum Ltd., London, United Kingdom; *U.S. Public*, pg. 1142
Irey, Scott, Treas.--Sybase, Inc., Emeryville, CA; *U.S. Public*, *pg. 1544*
Irish, Rebecca R., Sec. & Treas.--A - 1 Medical Equipment, Inc., Orlando, FL; *U.S. Public*, pg. 884
Irish, Rebecca R., Sec. & Treas.--American Medical Rentals, Inc., Orlando, FL; *U.S. Public*, pg. 884
Isaacson, James, V.P.-Fin., Treas. & Sec.--International Airline Support Group, Inc., Atlanta, GA; *U.S. Public*, pg. 894
Iseman, Robert D., V.P. & Treas.--Foster Wheeler Corporation, Clinton, NJ; *U.S. Public*, pg. 676
Isemoto, Leslie, Pres. & Treas.--Isemoto Contracting Co. Ltd., Hilo, HI; *U.S. Private*, pg. 575
Ishikawa, Masahiro, V.P., Gen. Mgr., Treas. & Acctg.--Sumitomo Corporation of America, New York, NY; *Int'l*, pg. 1312
Iskra, Kathleen H., Chief Fin. Officer, V.P. & Treas.--Nextlink Communications Inc., Bellevue, WA; *U.S. Public*, *pg. 1181*
Isom, Donna, Treas. & Sec.--Quality Foods Inc., Little Rock, AR; *U.S. Private*, pg. 898
Israel, G.J., Chief Fin. Officer, V.P.-Fin. & Treas.--Detrex Corporation, Southfield, MI; *U.S. Public*, pg. 501
Istre, Keith A., V.P.-Fin. & Treas.--Lamar Corporation, Baton Rouge, LA; *U.S. Private*, pg. 644
Itkin, Lawrence, Treas.--Furniture Consultants, New York, NY; *U.S. Public*, pg. 1686
Itkin, Myles R., Chief Fin. Officer, Sr. V.P. & Treas.--Overseas Shipholding Group, Inc., New York, NY; *U.S. Public*, pg. 1236
Iuanow, Nicholas J., Treas.--Thiokol Corporation, Ogden, UT; *U.S. Public*, pg. 1596
Ivey, James, Treas.--The Williams Companies, Inc., Tulsa, OK; *U.S. Public*, pg. 1769
Iwasaki, Cindy, Treasury Admin.--Ameron International Corporation, Pasadena, CA; *U.S. Public*, pg. 98
Iwatani, Jon T., Asst. Treas. & Asst. Sec.--Ka'u Agribusiness Co., Inc., Pahala, HI; *U.S. Private*, pg. 190
Iwatani, Jon T., Asst. Treas. & Asst. Sec.--Olokele Sugar Co., Limited, Kaunakakai, HI; *U.S. Private*, pg. 191
Izzo, Mario, Asst. Treas.--Gibbs Wire & Steel Company, Inc., Southington, CT; *U.S. Private*, pg. 451
Jabanoski, James R., Asst. Treas.--John Deere Capital Corporation, Reno, NV; *U.S. Public*, pg. 492
Jackels, Curtis R., Chief Fin. Officer--Photo Control Corporation, Minneapolis, MN; *U.S. Public*, pg. 1292
Jackson, Carter, Treas.--Holy Cross Electric Association, Inc., Glenwood Springs, CO; *U.S. Private*, pg. 536
Jackson, Mary Anne, Chm. Bd., Pres., Chief Oper. & Chief Exec. Officer--My Own Meals, Inc., Deerfield, IL; *U.S. Private*, pg. 770
Jackson, Nelson, Asst. Treas.--Rollins, Inc., Atlanta, GA; *U.S. Public*, pg. 1404
Jackson, W. Stephen, Chief Fin. Officer & Treas.--Mesa Air Group, Las Vegas, NV; *U.S. Public*, pg. 1098
Jacobs, Andrew F., Sr. V.P.-Control, Treas. & Sec.--Capstead Mortgage Corporation, Dallas, TX; *U.S. Public*, *pg. 303*
Jacobs, C. Jeffrey, Treas.--Teleflex Incorporated, Plymouth Meeting, PA; *U.S. Public*, pg. 1569
Jacobs, Douglas L., Treas.--Fleet Financial Group, Inc., Boston, MA; *U.S. Public*, pg. 648
Jacobs, Leonard, V.P., Sec., Controller & Treas.--Perry Machinery Corporation, Hainesport, NJ; *U.S. Private*, pg. 855
Jacobs, Malcolm, Treas.--Atlantic Plumbing Supply Company, Washington, DC; *U.S. Private*, pg. 95
Jacobs, Russell J., Treas.--Mizuno Golf Company, Norcross, GA; *Int'l*, pg. 885
Jacobson, Gregory D., Treas.--GTE North Incorporated, Irving, TX; *U.S. Public*, pg. 696
Jacobson, Gregory D., Treas.--GTE South Incorporated, Irving, TX; *U.S. Public*, pg. 697
Jacobson, Ken, Chief Fin. Officer, Treas. & Sec.--Idea Engineering & Fabricating, Detroit, MI; *U.S. Private*, pg. 557
Jacobson, Lois, Treas.--Glencraft Lingerie, Inc., New York, NY; *U.S. Private*, pg. 456
Jacobson, Richard J., Treas.--Cox Enterprises, Inc., Atlanta, GA; *U.S. Private*, pg. 281
Jacobson, Richard J., Treas.--Cox Communications, Inc., Atlanta, GA; *U.S. Public*, pg. 454
Jacobson, Robert P., Chief Fin. Officer, Sr. V.P. & Treas.--Everest Reinsurance Holdings, Liberty Corner, NJ; *U.S. Public*, pg. 597
Jacoby, Andrea, Chief Fin. Officer--MBT Architecture, San Francisco, CA; *U.S. Private*, pg. 686
Jacques, Jerome C., Chief Fin. Officer, Sr. V.P. & Treas.--Guardsmark, Inc., Memphis, TN; *U.S. Private*, pg. 486
Jacquette, R. Preston, Treas.--David A. Bramble, Inc., Chestertown, MD; *U.S. Private*, pg. 165
Jacquier, Robert, Treas.--Agri-Mark, Inc., Lawrence, MA; *U.S. Private*, pg. 26
Jaeger, David A., V.P. & Treas.--The Boeing Company, Seattle, WA; *U.S. Public*, pg. 239
Jaeger, Robert J., Sr. V.P.-Fin., Controller & Treas.--Westmoreland Coal Co., Colorado Springs, CO; *U.S. Public*, pg. 1761
Jaffe, Roslyn S., Treas. & Sec.--The Dress Barn, Inc., Suffern, NY; *U.S. Public*, pg. 528
Jafri, Syed S., Treas. & Controller--Sun City Industries, Inc., Fort Lauderdale, FL; *U.S. Public*, pg. 1529
Jaggers, Gene, V.P.-Fin. & Treas.--Crucible Materials Corp., Solvay, NY; *U.S. Private*, pg. 293
Jahnke, Mark W., Chief Fin. Officer--Lifetime Doors Inc., Farmington, MI; *U.S. Private*, pg. 666
Jakober, Esther, Asst. V.P.-Treas.--Groupe Bruxelles Lambert S.A., Brussels, Belgium; *Int'l*, pg. 561
Jakubowski, Kenneth J., V.P. & Treas.--Integon Corporation, Winston Salem, NC; *U.S. Public*, pg. 719
James, Alan D., Asst Treas.--Marietta Corporation, Cortland, NY; *U.S. Private*, pg. 702
James, David, Chief Fin. Officer & V.P.-Fin. & Treas.--Joe E. Woods, Inc., Mesa, AZ; *U.S. Private*, pg. 1187
James, David, Treas. & Sec.--WJW Constructors, LLC, Mesa, AZ; *U.S. Private*, pg. 1187
James, David R., V.P., Corp. Controller & Treas.--Marcam Solutions, Inc., Newton, MA; *U.S. Public*, pg. 1042
James, Douglas, Asst. Treas.--The Quaker Oats Company, Chicago, IL; *U.S. Public*, pg. 1347
James, Maurice D., V.P. & Treas.--Salient 3 Communications, Inc., Reading, PA; *U.S. Public*, pg. 1429
James, Richard, Asst. Treas.--Food Lion, Inc., Salisbury, NC; *Int'l*, pg. 463
James, Ron, Controller & Treas.--ISK BioSciences, Memphis, TN; *Int'l*, pg. 689
James, Tony, Chief Fin. Officer & Treas.--Eagle Iron Works, Des Moines, IA; *U.S. Private*, pg. 354
Jamet, Jane, Chief Oper. Officer & Treas.--Sexton Can Co., Inc., Cambridge, MA; *U.S. Private*, pg. 988
Jamin, G.A., Treas.--Amerada Hess Corporation, New York, NY; *U.S. Public*, pg. 65
Janda, Linda, Sr. V.P.-Fin.--Qual-Med, Inc., Pueblo, CO; *U.S. Public*, pg. 678
Janeczek, Edward J., Exec. V.P. & Treas.--R.O. Whitesell & Associates, Inc, Indianapolis, IN; *U.S. Private*, pg. 1173
Janes, Terry, Treas.--Lands' End, Inc., Dodgeville, WI; *U.S. Public*, pg. 977
Janey, T. Michael, Chief Fin. Officer, Sr. V.P. & Treas.--Datamax International Corporation, Orlando, FL; *U.S. Private*, pg. 313
Janikies, Margaret R., Treas.--Jan-Co., Inc., Cranston, RI; *U.S. Private*, pg. 581
Jannette, Donald D., Asst. Treas. & Asst. Sec.--Interstate Power Company, Dubuque, IA; *U.S. Public*, pg. 910
Jansen, James, V.P. & Treas.--John Fabick Tractor Company, Fenton, MO; *U.S. Private*, pg. 390
Janson, Kenneth R., Chief Fin. Officer, Exec. V.P.-Fin. & Treas.--D & N Financial Corporation, Hancock, MI; *U.S. Public*, pg. 472
Japha, Barbara, Chief Fin. Officer, V.P. & Treas.--U S West Inc., Englewood, CO; *U.S. Public*, pg. 1688
Jarchow, Edward R., V.P. & Treas.--Barton Malow Enterprises, Inc., Southfield, MI; *U.S. Private*, pg. 120
Jardine, Ian, Mng. Dir. & Treas.--American Express Bank Ltd., New York, NY; *U.S. Public*, pg. 73
Jardine, Thomas V., Treas.--Atlas Refinery, Newark, NJ; *U.S. Private*, pg. 96
Jardon, Stephen, Asst. Treas.--International Correspondence Schools Ltd., Glasgow, United Kingdom; *U.S. Public*, pg. 784
Jardon, Stephen, Asst. Treas.--The School of Accountancy, Glasgow, United Kingdom; *U.S. Public*, pg. 784
Jardon, Stephen, Asst. Treas.--National Education Credit Corporation, Irvine, CA; *U.S. Public*, pg. 784
Jardon, Stephen, Asst. Treas.--National Education Payroll Corp., Irvine, CA; *U.S. Public*, pg. 784
Jardon, Stephen, Asst. Treas.--Steck-Vaughn Publishing Corporation, Austin, TX; *U.S. Public*, pg. 784
Jardon, Stephen, Asst. Treas.--Steck-Vaughn Distribution Company, Austin, TX; *U.S. Public*, pg. 784
Jardon, Stephen H., Asst. Treas.--Steck-Vaughn Company, Austin, TX; *U.S. Public*, pg. 784
Jareske, Michael J., Treas.--Exclusive Healthcare, Inc., Omaha, NE; *U.S. Private*, pg. 770
Jarvis, Mark E., Chief Fin. Officer & Sr. V.P.--Tuesday Morning Corporation, Dallas, TX; *U.S. Public*, pg. 1644
Jaska, James M., Chief Fin. Officer & Treas.--Tetra Tech, Inc., Pasadena, CA; *U.S. Public*, pg. 1582
Jaster, Kyle M., Chief Fin. Officer, Treas. & Sec.--Mooney Aircraft Corporation, Kerrville, TX; *U.S. Private*, pg. 759
Javary, Manuel, V.P. & Treas.--CAP Gemini S.A., Paris, France; *Int'l*, pg. 263
Jeffrey, Dennis, V.P.-Fin. & Treas.--Idaho Forest Industry, Inc., Coeur D'Alene, ID; *U.S. Private*, pg. 556
Jeffries, B., Treas.--Mellon Corporation, New York, NY; *U.S.* Private, pg. 730
Jelicich, Ron, Asst. Treas.--Sacramento Municipal Utility District, Sacramento, CA; *U.S. Private*, pg. 959
Jellison, William R., V.P., Controller & Treas.--Donnelly Corporation, Holland, MI; *U.S. Public*, pg. 519
Jen, Enoch, Chief Fin. Officer, V.P.-Fin. & Treas.--Gentex Corporation, Zeeland, MI; *U.S. Public*, pg. 731
Jenc, John E., Treas.--The Bureau of National Affairs, Inc., Washington, DC; *U.S. Private*, pg. 181
Jencks, Hollis W., III, V.P.-Engrng. & Treas.--Detroit Coil Company, Ferndale, MI; *U.S. Private*, pg. 328
Jenkins, Alan B., Chm. Bd. & Treas.--Felton Brush Inc., Manchester, NH; *U.S. Private*, pg. 400
Jenkins, Don, Jr., Pres. & Treas.--Athens Paper Co. Inc., Nashville, TN; *U.S. Private*, pg. 94
Jenkins, Thomas M., Chief Fin. Officer, Grp. V.P. & Treas-DPL, Inc.--DPL Inc., Dayton, OH; *U.S. Public*, pg. 473
Jensen, Irving F., Jr., Chm. Bd., Treas. & Sec.--Irving F. Jensen Co., Inc., Sioux City, IA; *U.S. Private*, pg. 586
Jensen, Karen M., Sr. V.P. & Treas.--QST Environmental Inc., Peoria, IL; *U.S. Public*, pg. 367
Jensen, Kenneth R., Chief Fin. Officer, Sr. Exec. V.P. & Treas.--Fiserv, Inc., Brookfield, WI; *U.S. Public*, pg. 647
Jensen, Kent D., V.P. & Treas.--Holnam Inc., Dundee, MI; *Int'l*, pg. 628
Jensen, Linda A., V.P. & Treas.--HEC, Inc., Natick, MA; *U.S.* Public, pg. 1194
Jensen, Loren K., V.P. & Treas.--Tandy Corporation, Fort Worth, TX; *U.S. Public*, pg. 1560
Jensen, Mary F., Chief Fin. Officer & Treas.--Venturian Corp., Hopkins, MN; *U.S. Public*, pg. 1716
Jensen, Michael J., Treas. & Sec.--Keck Instruments, Inc., Williamston, MI; *U.S. Public*, pg. 367
Jensen, Owen, Controller & Treas.--M.A. Mortenson Company, Minneapolis, MN; *U.S. Private*, pg. 763
Jensen, Tim, V.P. & Treas.--Merisel, Inc., El Segundo, CA; *U.S. Public*, pg. 1095
Jersky, Stanley, Treas.--Faber, Coe & Gregg, Inc., Secaucus, NJ; *U.S. Private*, pg. 390
Jesanis, Michael E., V.P. & Treas.--New England Electric System, Westborough, MA; *U.S. Public*, pg. 1171
Jett, Donald E., Treas.--TST/Impreso, Inc., Coppell, TX; *U.S. Private*, pg. 1066
Jett, Marvin, V.P. & Treas.--Dualite Inc., Williamsburg, OH; *U.S. Private*, pg. 344
Jeub, Michael L., Chief Fin. Officer, Sr. V.P. & Treas.--Jenny Craig, Inc., La Jolla, CA; *U.S. Public*, pg. 926
Jewell, Everett G., Chm. Bd., Pres., Chief Exec. Officer & Treas.--Jewell Building Systems, Dallas, NC; *U.S. Private*, pg. 587
Jimenez, Lita K., V.P. & Treas.--Garvey International, Inc., Saint Charles, IL; *U.S. Private*, pg. 440

Jiminez, David, Treas.--Owen Pacific, Los Angeles, CA; *U.S. Private*, pg. 824
Joannidi, Harold A., Controller, Treas. & Sec.--EcoScience Corporation, East Brunswick, NJ; *U.S. Public*, pg. 563
Jobe, Warren Y., Chief Fin. Officer, Exec. V.P. & Treas.--Georgia Power Co., Atlanta, GA; *U.S. Public*, pg. 1490
Johann, John E., Treas.--S & C Electric Company, Chicago, IL; *U.S. Private*, pg. 954
Johannsen, Richard A., Treas.--Pool Energy Services Co., Houston, TX; *U.S. Public*, pg. 1316
Johansson, Lars, Treas.--Spectra-Physics AB, Stockholm, Sweden; *Int'l*, pg. 1288
Johns, Buddy, Treas.--Mulach Steel Corporation, Leetsdale, PA; *U.S. Private*, pg. 766
Johnsey, Walter F., Chief Fin. Officer, Sr. Exec. V.P. & Treas.--Drummond Company, Inc., Jasper, AL; *U.S. Private*, pg. 343
Johnson, A.L., V.P. & Treas.--Shelba D. Johnson Trucking, Thomasville, NC; *U.S. Private*, pg. 594
Johnson, Andrew H., Chief Acctg. Officer & Treas.--CTG Resources, Inc., Hartford, CT; *U.S. Public*, pg. 285
Johnson, Andrew H., Chief Acctg. Officer & Treas.--Connecticut Natural Gas Corporation, Hartford, CT; *U.S. Public*, pg. 285
Johnson, Craig A., V.P. & Treas.--Jefferies & Company, Inc., Los Angeles, CA; *U.S. Public*, pg. 925
Johnson, Delois B., Jr., Treas.--Energy Networks, Inc. (ENI), Hartford, CT; *U.S. Public*, pg. 285
Johnson, Dianne, Asst. Treas.--VTEL Corporation, Austin, TX; *U.S. Public*, pg. 1703
Johnson, Donnie, Chief Fin. Officer--Brookshire Bros., Ltd., Lufkin, TX; *U.S. Private*, pg. 172
Johnson, Eunice W., Treas. & Sec.--Johnson Publishing Company, Inc., Chicago, IL; *U.S. Private*, pg. 591
Johnson, Frank, Chief Fin. Officer, Exec. V.P. & Treas.--Today's Man, Inc., Moorestown, NJ; *U.S. Public*, pg. 1619
Johnson, Galen K., Treas.--Alliant Techsystems, Hopkins, MN; *U.S. Public*, pg. 47
Johnson, George D., V.P. & Treas.--APAC/Ballenger Paving Company, Inc., Taylors, SC; *U.S. Public*, pg. 139
Johnson, Greg A., Controller & Treas.--F.H. Stoltze Land & Lumber Company, Saint Paul, MN; *U.S. Private*, pg. 1044
Johnson, J. Fred, Chief Fin. Officer, Exec. V.P. & Treas.--Piccadilly Cafeterias, Inc., Baton Rouge, LA; *U.S. Public*, pg. 1294
Johnson, J. Peter, V.P.-Fin., Controller, Treas. & Asst. Sec.--Tellabs Operations, Inc., Lisle, IL; *U.S. Public*, pg. 1572
Johnson, James A., Treas.--Precision Castparts Corp., Portland, OR; *U.S. Public*, pg. 1320
Johnson, Jeff, Chief Fin. Officer, Treas. & Sec.--Evans Industries, Inc., Detroit, MI; *U.S. Private*, pg. 385
Johnson, John B., Pres., Treas. & Editor--Johnson Newspaper Corporation, Watertown, NY; *U.S. Private*, pg. 591
Johnson, Karen A., Asst. Treas.--Agway, Inc., De Witt, NY; *U.S. Private*, pg. 27
Johnson, Kenneth D., Pres. & Treas.--Signet Star Reinsurance Company, Florham Park, NJ; *U.S. Public*, pg. 216
Johnson, Kent, Chief Fin. Officer & Asst. Treas.--Paddock Publications, Inc., Arlington Heights, IL; *U.S. Private*, pg. 833
Johnson, Lawrence M., Chm. Bd. & Chief Exec. Officer--Pacific Century Financial Corporation, Honolulu, HI; *U.S. Public*, pg. 1248
Johnson, M.O., Chief Fin. Officer, V.P. & Treas.--Andersen Corporation, Bayport, MN; *U.S. Private*, pg. 71
Johnson, Mark E., Asst. Treas.--PHH Corporation, Hunt Valley, MD; *U.S. Public*, pg. 321
Johnson, Matthew N., Treas.--Genesco Inc., Nashville, TN; *U.S. Public*, pg. 728
Johnson, Minnie, Asst. Sec. & Asst. Treas.--Saddlebag Lake Resorts, Inc., La Belle, FL; *U.S. Public*, pg. 41
Johnson, Patricia M., Treas., Sec. & Dir.-Fin.--Tony Downs Foods Company, Saint James, MN; *U.S. Private*, pg. 342
Johnson, Paul, Asst. Treas.--Southwest Marine, Inc., San Diego, CA; *U.S. Private*, pg. 213
Johnson, Richard, Chief Fin. Officer & Treas.--WHG Resorts & Casinos, Carolina, PR; *U.S. Public*, pg. 1265
Johnson, Richard A., V.P.-Fin.--Illinois Auto Electric Co., Elmhurst, IL; *U.S. Private*, pg. 557
Johnson, Robert, Asst. Treas.--Collins & Aikman Corporation, Charlotte, NC; *U.S. Public*, pg. 399
Johnson, Robert T., Sec. & Treas.--Blu-Ray, Middletown, CT; *U.S. Private*, pg. 142
Johnson, Stanley, Treas. & Sec.--Mueller Sports Medicine, Inc., Prairie Du Sac, WI; *U.S. Private*, pg. 766
Johnson, Stephen T., Chief Fin. Officer, V.P. & Treas.--Acuson Corporation, Mountain View, CA; *U.S. Public*, pg. 18
Johnson, Steve, Controller & Treas.--Baxter Research Medical, Inc., Midvale, UT; *U.S. Public*, pg. 196
Johnson, Stuart C., Treas.--Bell Atlantic Directory Graphics, Inc., Valley Forge, PA; *U.S. Public*, pg. 203
Johnson, Terrence M., Dir.-Fin.--Anderson Brothers Construction Brainerd, Brainerd, MN; *U.S. Private*, pg. 72
Johnson, Theodore W., Treas.--Velcro Industries N.V., Willemstad, Netherlands Antilles; *Int'l*, pg. 1462
Johnson, Tina P., Treas.--Publix Supermarkets Inc., Lakeland, FL; *U.S. Private*, pg. 893
Johnson, Todd T., Treas. & Sec.--Industrial Construction, Inc., Idaho Falls, ID; *U.S. Private*, pg. 560
Johnson, V. Douglas, Treas.--Mity-Lite, Inc., Orem, UT; *U.S. Public*, pg. 1118
Johnson, William A., Jr., Chief Fin. Officer & Treas.--Toymax International Inc., Plainview, NY; *U.S. Public*, pg. 1626
Johnston, Colleen M., Treas.--The Bank of Nova Scotia Trust Company, Toronto, Canada; *Int'l*, pg. 155
Johnston, Dorothy, Treas.--J.R. Wood Inc., Atwater, CA; *U.S. Private*, pg. 1186
Johnston, Jack W., Treas.--Primus Inc., Dayton, OH; *U.S. Private*, pg. 884
Jolliff, Robert A., Treas.--McDermott International, Inc., New Orleans, LA; *U.S. Public*, pg. 1067
Jomier, V., Grp. Treas.--Arjo Wiggins Appleton plc, Basingstoke, United Kingdom; *Int'l*, pg. 567
Jones, Bob, Chief Fin. Officer & Sr. V.P.-Opers.--Koh-I-Noor, Inc., Bloomsbury, NJ; *U.S. Private*, pg. 629
Jones, Carolyn, Chief Fin. Officer & Treas.--Hilb, Rogal and Hamilton Company, Glen Allen, VA; *U.S. Public*, pg. 826
Jones, Charles J., Treas.--Metallurg, Inc., New York, NY; *U.S. Private*, pg. 735
Jones, Dayton A., Treas.--Research Products Corporation, Madison, WI; *U.S. Private*, pg. 924
Jones, Eric, First V.P. & Treas.--BFCE New York, New York, NY; *Int'l*, pg. 161
Jones, Fred R., V.P.-Fin. & Treas.--Thomas & Betts Corporation, Memphis, TN; *U.S. Public*, pg. 1597
Jones, Garry, Chief Fin. Officer, Exec. V.P. & Asst. Treas.--Espey Mfg. & Electronics Corp., Saratoga Springs, NY; *U.S. Public*, pg. 592
Jones, Gary, Treas. & Sec.--Rural Electric Co-op, Lindsay, OK; *U.S. Private*, pg. 952
Jones, Gary L., Treas.--Florida Crushed Stone Company, Leesburg, FL; *U.S. Private*, pg. 414
Jones, James H., Treas.--Fannie May Candy Shops, Inc., Chicago, IL; *U.S. Private*, pg. 598
Jones, Jim, V.P., Controller & Treas.--LSB Industries, Inc., Oklahoma City, OK; *U.S. Public*, pg. 970
Jones, Jimmy R., Chief Fin. Officer, Sr. V.P. & Treas.--Attorneys' Title Insurance Fund, Orlando, FL; *U.S. Private*, pg. 98
Jones, Larry, Exec. V.P. & Treas.--Patriot American Hospitality, Inc., Dallas, TX; *U.S. Public*, pg. 1265
Jones, Mark L., V.P.-Finance, Corp. Sec. & Treas.--Sunbelt Nursery Group Inc., Fort Worth, TX; *U.S. Public*, pg. 715
Jones, Maureen A., Treas.--Petroleum & Resources Corp., Baltimore, MD; *U.S. Public*, pg. 1280
Jones, Nathan J., V.P. & Treas.--Deere & Company, Moline, IL; *U.S. Public*, pg. 491
Jones, Nathan J., Asst. Treas.--John Deere Credit Company, Moline, IL; *U.S. Public*, pg. 492
Jones, Stanley H., V.P.-Fin. & Treas.--Keeneland Assoc., Inc., Lexington, KY; *U.S. Private*, pg. 611
Jones, Sydney T., III, Pres. & Treas.--Hudson Valley Paper Company, Albany, NY; *U.S. Private*, pg. 546
Jordan, Anthony, Treas. & Controller--Kleer-Vu Plastics Corp., Compton, CA; *U.S. Public*, pg. 962
Jordan, Arthur D., Asst. Sec.--The Boeing Travel Company, Irvine, CA; *U.S. Public*, pg. 241
Jordan, J.E., Jr., Asst. Treas.--Young Refining Corp., Douglasville, GA; *U.S. Private*, pg. 1202
Jordan, Leon, V.P. & Treas.--Harbor Financial Mortgage Corp., Houston, TX; *U.S. Public*, pg. 644
Jorgenson, Thomas R., V.P. & Treas.--Leslie Paper, Minneapolis, MN; *U.S. Public*, pg. 903
Joseph, Randy M., Chief Fin. Officer, V.P. & Treas.--Advance Ross Corporation, Chicago, IL; *U.S. Public*, pg. 320
Joseph, Roger D., V.P. & Treas.--Kellwood Company, Chesterfield, MO; *U.S. Public*, pg. 948
Joslin, Mark W., Chief Fin. Officer & Treas.--Lawter International, Inc., Kenosha, WI; *U.S. Public*, pg. 980
Joslin, Roger, Sr. V.P. & Treas.--State Farm Mutual Automobile Insurance Company, Bloomington, IL; *U.S. Private*, pg. 1036
Jossell, Keith, Asst. Treas.--Sonic Corporation, Oklahoma City, OK; *U.S. Public*, pg. 1485
Journigan, Joanne, Treas. & Asst. Sec.--Heater Utilities, Incorporated, Cary, NC; *U.S. Public*, pg. 1116
Joyce, Christopher P., V.P. & Treas.--Xtra Corporation, Boston, MA; *U.S. Public*, pg. 1786
Joyce, James A., Jr., Asst. Treas.--Fieldcrest Cannon, Inc., Kannapolis, NC; *U.S. Public*, pg. 1296
Joyce, John M., V.P. & Treas.--Delco Electronics Overseas Corporation, Detroit, MI; *U.S. Public*, pg. 721
Joyce, Leon, Chief Fin. Officer, V.P. & Treas.--Carolina Biological Supply Co., Burlington, NC; *U.S. Private*, pg. 213
Joyce, Thomas J., V.P. & Treas.--Meritor Automotive, Inc., Troy, MI; *U.S. Public*, pg. 1096
Joyner, John F., V.P.-Fin., Treas. & Sec.--The Dickerson Group, Inc., Monroe, NC; *U.S. Private*, pg. 331
Jubelirer, Steven W., Treas. & Sec.--John Reyer Company, Sharon, PA; *U.S. Private*, pg. 926
Judd, Norman L., V.P. & Asst. Treas.--Sterling Financial Corporation, Spokane, WA; *U.S. Public*, pg. 1516
Judge, James J., Sr. V.P. & Treas.--Boston Edison Company, Boston, MA; *U.S. Public*, pg. 247
Judt, Ed, V.P.-Fin. & Controller--Peters-Revington Corp., Delphi, IN; *U.S. Public*, pg. 352
Juliano, Richard, Chief Fin. Officer, Sec. & Treas.--A.H. Hoffman, Inc., Landisville, PA; *U.S. Private*, pg. 532
Jumonville, Francis, Treas. & Sec.--Airtrol, Inc., Baton Rouge, LA; *U.S. Private*, pg. 29
Junius, Daniel M., Chief Fin. Officer, V.P.-Fin. & Treas.--Nashua Corporation, Nashua, NH; *U.S. Public*, pg. 1152
Juraschek, Paul J., Treas.--Programart France Incorporated, Clichy, France; *U.S. Private*, pg. 890
Jurasek, Kris, Chief Fin. Officer, V.P. & Treas.--Miner Enterprises Inc., Geneva, IL; *U.S. Private*, pg. 749
Kabacinski, Mary, Chief Fin. Officer--Marquette Medical Systems, Inc., Milwaukee, WI; *U.S. Public*, pg. 1047
Kabot, Stan, Treas.--Daniel Green Co., Dolgeville, NY; *U.S. Private*, pg. 477
Kadish, Mark, Controller--Axiom Inc., Moorestown, NJ; *U.S. Public*, pg. 157
Kahant, Elaine, V.P. & Treas.--CV Reit, Inc., West Palm Beach, FL; *U.S. Public*, pg. 286
Kahlig, Sandra, Treas. & Sec.--North Park Lincoln Mercury Inc., San Antonio, TX; *U.S. Private*, pg. 805
Kahn, Henry, V.P. & Treas.--FMC Corporation, Chicago, IL; *U.S. Public*, pg. 604
Kahn, Joel, Exec. V.P. & Treas.--Liberty Paper & Bag Co., Auburn Hills, MI; *Int'l*, pg. 233
Kahn, Stanley, Vice Chm., Treas. & Sec.--Croscill, Inc., New York, NY; *U.S. Private*, pg. 290
Kaiser, Van, Exec. V.P., Treas. & Creative Dir.--Rhea & Kaiser Marketing Communications, Naperville, IL; *U.S. Private*, pg. 927
Kaiser, William, Exec. V.P. & Treas.--KTI, Inc., Guttenberg, NJ; *U.S. Public*, pg. 939
Kaitz, Miriam Collins, Treas. & Sec.--Palm Beach Beauty Products Co., Minneapolis, MN; *U.S. Private*, pg. 834
Kallen, Thomas E., Chm. Bd. & Treas.--Bake-Line Products, Inc., Des Plaines, IL; *U.S. Public*, pg. 657
Kallgren, Theodore R., V.P.-Fin. & Treas.--Pameco Corp., Norcross, GA; *U.S. Public*, pg. 1255
Kallmeyer, L.B., Treas. & Sec.--The Kirk & Blum Mfg. Co., Cincinnati, OH; *U.S. Private*, pg. 623
Kalman, Francis S., V.P. & Treas.--Yarway Corporation, Blue Bell, PA; *U.S. Public*, pg. 1650
Kalman, Francis S., V.P. & Treas.--Anderson, Greenwood & Co., Stafford, TX; *U.S. Public*, pg. 1650
Kalman, Francis S., V.P. & Treas.--Keystone International Holdings Corp., Houston, TX; *U.S. Public*, pg. 1650
Kalman, Francis S., V.P. & Treas.--Keystone Valvtron, Inc., Houston, TX; *U.S. Public*, pg. 1650
Kalnins, K.A., Controller & Treas.--Ziegler Medical Equipment Group, Inc., Omaha, NE; *U.S. Public*, pg. 1792
Kam, Michael E., Asst. Treas.--Maui Electric Co., Ltd., Kahului, HI; *U.S. Public*, pg. 800
Kam, Samuel, V.P. & Treas.--Farrar, Straus & Giroux, Inc., New York, NY; *Int'l*, pg. 1479
Kamerick, Anthony J., V.P. & Treas.--Potomac Electric Power Company, Washington, DC; *U.S. Public*, pg. 1318
Kaminsky, Richard, Treas.--Greenwich Air Services, Miami, FL; *U.S. Public*, pg. 710
Kamm, C.P., Mgr.-Pension Admin. & Risk Mngmt.--Electric Furnace Co., Salem, OH; *U.S. Private*, pg. 367
Kanaver, William, Treas.--Bromar Inc., Newport Beach, CA; *U.S. Private*, pg. 171
Kanbel, Robert L., Chief Fin. Officer, V.P. & Treas.--Robinson Nugent, Inc., New Albany, IN; *U.S. Public*, pg. 1394
Kanda, Neal, V.P. & Treas.--CPB Inc., Honolulu, HI; *U.S. Public*, pg. 282
Kandrysawtz, Beth, V.P., Treas. & Sec.--The Motorlease Corp., Farmington, CT; *U.S. Private*, pg. 764
Kane, Aranka, Treas.--Sam Kane Beef Processors, Inc., Corpus Christi, TX; *U.S. Private*, pg. 607
Kane, Francis J., V.P.-Investor Rels. & Treas.--Cyprus Amax Minerals Company, Englewood, CO; *U.S. Public*, pg. 470
Kane, John, Chief Fin. Officer, V.P. & Treas.--IDX Systems Corporation, Burlington, VT; *U.S. Public*, pg. 854
Kane, William, Chief Fin. Officer, V.P., Treas. & Sec.--Molded Fiber Glass Companies, Ashtabula, OH; *U.S. Private*, pg. 755
Kanim, Elvira, Treas. & Sec.--Vivian & Elliette, Inc., Vernon, CA; *U.S. Private*, pg. 1142
Kankel, Keith V., V.P.-Fin., Treas. & Sec.--Patrick Industries Inc., Elkhart, IN; *U.S. Public*, pg. 1264
Kanner, Robert H., Chm. Bd., Pres., Chief Exec./Fin. Officer & Treas.--Pubco Corporation, Cleveland, OH; *U.S. Public*, pg. 1339
Kaplan, Harold E., V.P. & Corp. Treas.--Costco Wholesale, Issaquah, WA; *U.S. Public*, pg. 451
Kaplan, Harvey, Treas. & Sec.--Drew Industries Incorporated, White Plains, NY; *U.S. Public*, pg. 529
Kaplan, Harvey T., Treas.--Leslie Building Products, Inc., White Plains, NY; *U.S. Public*, pg. 989
Kaplan, Ira D., Chief Fin. Officer & Sr. V.P.--Claire's Stores Inc., Pembroke Pines, FL; *U.S. Public*, pg. 381
Kaplan, Jay M., Chief Fin. Officer--MEDIQ Incorporated, Pennsauken, NJ; *U.S. Public*, pg. 1081
Kaplan, Kenneth P., Chief Fin. Officer & V.P.--Regal-Beloit Corporation, Beloit, WI; *U.S. Public*, pg. 1370
Kaplan, Leonard D., Chm. & Treas.--Prime Tanning Co., Inc., Rochester, NH; *U.S. Private*, pg. 884
Kaplan, Sam D., Chief Fin. Officer, Controller, Treas. & Sec.--The He-Ro Group, Ltd., New York, NY; *U.S. Public*, pg. 801
Kaplanek, Rosemary, Treas. & Sec.--Floral Glass & Mirror, Inc., Hauppauge, NY; *U.S. Private*, pg. 414
Karklins, George J., V.P. & Treas.--CoreStates Capital Corp., Philadelphia, PA; *U.S. Public*, pg. 446
Karlen, Gerald, Chief Fin. Officer, V.P. & Treas.--Automatic Equipment Mfg. Co., Pender, NE; *U.S. Private*, pg. 101
Karp, Kevin, Treas.--Best Provision Co., Inc., Newark, NJ; *U.S. Private*, pg. 140
Karp, Leonard, Chief Exec. Officer, V.P. & Treas.--Best Provision Co., Inc., Newark, NJ; *U.S. Private*, pg. 140
Karpinski, Marie, Asst. Treas.--Pacific American Income Shares, Inc., Pasadena, CA; *U.S. Public*, pg. 1247
Karplus, E.J., Treas. & Controller--General Sekiyu K.K., Tokyo, Japan; *U.S. Public*, pg. 602
Karr, Howard H., Exec. V.P. & Treas.--First Hawaiian, Inc., Honolulu, HI; *U.S. Public*, pg. 634
Karr, Howard H., V.P. & Treas.--First Hawaiian Leasing, Inc., Honolulu, HI; *U.S. Public*, pg. 635
Karr, Howard H., V.P. & Treas.--American Security Properties, Inc., Honolulu, HI; *U.S. Public*, pg. 635
Karr, John, Treas.--American Business Products, Inc., Atlanta, GA; *U.S. Public*, pg. 70
Karras, Peter W., Exec. V.P. & Treas.--First Colony Life Insurance Co., Lynchburg, VA; *U.S. Public*, pg. 711
Karsk, Bruce C., V.P.-Fin., Treas. & Sec.--Lindsay Manufacturing Company, Lindsay, NE; *U.S. Public*, pg. 999
Karsten, Robert W., Vice Chm. & Treas.--Panel Processing, Inc., Alpena, MI; *U.S. Private*, pg. 836
Karwacki, Thomas J., Treas. & Sec.--The Park Circle Motor Co., Baltimore, MD; *U.S. Private*, pg. 839
Kasch, Vincent L., V.P., Controller & Asst. Treas.--National Western Life Insurance Company, Austin, TX; *U.S. Public*, pg. 1161

Kashmanian, Mark, Chief Acctg. Officer & Treas.--C.H. Heist Corp., Clearwater, FL; *U.S. Public*, pg. 807
Kasih, Vincent L., V.P. & Treas.--NWL Financial, Inc., Austin, TX; *U.S. Public*, pg. 1161
Kasih, Vincent L., V.P. & Treas.--NWL Services, Inc., Austin, TX; *U.S. Public*, pg. 1161
Kasper, Karen M., Chief Fin. Officer, Sr. V.P & Treas.--Fort Wayne National Corporation, Fort Wayne, IN; *U.S. Public*, pg. 673
Kassab, Charles S., Chm. Bd., Pres., Chief Exec. Officer & Treas.--Huntington Bancshares Michigan, Inc., Troy, MI; *U.S. Public*, pg. 850
Kassel, Robert L., Chm. Bd., Pres., Chief Exec. Officer & Treas.--U.S. Home & Garden Inc., San Francisco, CA; *U.S. Public*, pg. 1682
Kassouf, James, Pres., Chief Exec. Officer & Treas.--Metropolitan Properties Systems, Cleveland, OH; *U.S. Private*, pg. 739
Kasting, Barbara Glenn, Asst. Treas.--Cincinnati Milacron Inc., Cincinnati, OH; *U.S. Public*, pg. 368
Kato, Keshi, Treas.--Steelox Systems Inc., Mason, OH; *U.S.* Private, pg. 1038
Katz, Lawrence, V.P.-Fin. & Treas.--Dancker, Sellew & Douglas, Inc., New York, NY; *U.S. Private*, pg. 309
Katz, Leslye G., V.P. & Treas.--Cognizant Corporation, Westport, CT; *U.S. Public*, pg. 395
Katz, Solomon, Treas. & Sec.--Manhattan Store Interiors, Inc., Brooklyn, NY; *U.S. Private*, pg. 699
Katzenstein, Joseph, Treas.--Philipp Brothers Chemicals, Inc., Fort Lee, NJ; *U.S. Private*, pg. 861
Katzman, Lawrence, Chm. Bd. & Chief Exec. Officer--Kaz, Inc., New York, NY; *U.S. Private*, pg. 610
Kauer, David A., V.P. & Treas.--Insilco Corporation, Dublin, OH; *U.S. Public*, pg. 881
Kauffman, Emma Jo, Asst. Treas.--AutoZone, Inc., Memphis, TN; *U.S. Public*, pg. 150
Kauffman, Jeffery R., Asst. Treas. & Asst. Sec.--Lift-All Co., Inc., Manheim, PA; *U.S. Private*, pg. 667
Kaufman, Alan J., Treas. & Gen. Counsel--H.W. Kaufman Financial Group, Inc., Farmington, MI; *U.S. Private*, pg. 609
Kaufman, Howard M., Sr. V.P., Treas. & Sec.--Lynch & Mayer, Inc, New York, NY; *U.S. Public*, pg. 998
Kaufman, Jack, Chief Fin. Officer--The Hain Food Group Inc., Uniondale, NY; *U.S. Public*, pg. 774
Kautzman, Edward J., Treas.--Meyer Broadcasting Company, Bismarck, ND; *U.S. Private*, pg. 739
Kawakami, Takahisa, Treas.--Chugai Boyeki Co., Ltd., Tokyo, Japan; *Int'l*, pg. 290
Kawalsky, Jeffrey T., Asst. Treas.--UAL Corporation, Elk Grove Village, IL; *U.S. Public*, pg. 1652
Kawamoto, Naoyuki, Sr. V.P.-Admin. & Treas.--Sumitomo Bank Capital Markets, Inc., New York, NY; *Int'l*, pg. 1308
Kawasaki, Roger, Treas.--Puna Plantation Hawaii Ltd., Hilo, HI; *U.S. Private*, pg. 895
Kay, George C., Chief Fin. Officer, V.P. & Treas.--A.T. Massey Coal Company, Inc., Richmond, VA; *U.S. Public, pg. 660*
Kay, Steven R., Chief Fin. Officer & Sr. V.P.--Amwest Insurance Group, Inc., Calabasas, CA; *U.S. Public*, pg. 106
Kay, Walter A., Sr. V.P. & Treas.--Vance Publishing Corporation, Lincolnshire, IL; *U.S. Private*, pg. 1133
Kazmar, Ronald V., Asst. Treas.--Central Steel & Wire Company, Chicago, IL; *U.S. Public*, pg. 327
Kazmierczak, Kenneth J., Controller, Treas. & Sec.--Schreier Malting Co., Sheboygan, WI; *U.S. Private*, pg. 972
Kaznowski, Stan, Treas.--Curtis Screw Co., Inc., Buffalo, NY; *U.S. Private*, pg. 298
Kean, James, Controller & Treas.--Henderson Electric Co., Inc., Louisville, KY; *U.S. Private*, pg. 521
Keane, David L., V.P.-Fin./Admin. & Treas.--Penobscot Shoe Company, Old Town, ME; *U.S. Public*, pg. 1273
Keane, John B., V.P. & Treas.--Northeast Utilities, Berlin, CT; *U.S. Public*, pg. 1194
Kearl, Greg, Chief Oper. Officer, Exec. V.P., Treas. & Sec.--Menley & James Laboratories, Inc., Horsham, PA; *U.S. Public*, pg. 1086
Kearney, Michael, V.P. & Treas.--A.P.S., Inc., Houston, TX; *U.S. Public*, pg. 10
Kearns, Vincent, Controller & Treas.--Electrocatalytic, Inc., Union, NJ; *U.S. Private*, pg. 369
Keating, JoAn C., Treas.--Magellan Petroleum Corporation, Madison, CT; *U.S. Public*, pg. 1036
Keating, John J., Pres. & Asst. Treas.--P.J. Keating Company, Lunenburg, MA; *U.S. Private*, pg. 610
Keating, Michael K., Treas.--Fountain Square Management Co., Cincinnati, OH; *U.S. Public*, pg. 622
Keating, Stephen D., Asst. Treas.--The Toro Company, Bloomington, MN; *U.S. Public*, pg. 1623
Keegan, Michael S., V.P. & Treas.--G.F. Wright Steel & Wire Company, Worcester, MA; *U.S. Private*, pg. 1192
Keegan, R.Y., Treas.--Tri-Chem, Inc., Harrison, NJ; *U.S. Private*, pg. 1100
Keeler, Alexander, Pres. & Treas.--Keeler Motor Car Company, Inc., Latham, NY; *U.S. Private*, pg. 611
Keeler, Philip, Asst. Treas. & Sec.--Hatfield Quality Meats, Hatfield, PA; *U.S. Private*, pg. 510
Keeler, Robert D., V.P.-Fin. & Treas.--Cuplex, Inc., Garland, TX; *U.S. Private*, pg. 297
Keeley, Donald, V.P.-Admin. & Treas.--Amurol Confections Co., Yorkville, IL; *U.S. Public*, pg. 1781
Keen, Cathy S., Asst. Treas.-Taxes--IDC Services, Inc., Chicago, IL; *U.S. Private*, pg. 554
Keen, J. Lamont, Chief Fin. Officer, V.P. & Treas.--Idaho Power Company, Boise, ID; *U.S. Public*, pg. 861
Keene, Robert A., Chm. Bd., Sec. & Treas.--John Roberts Company, Minneapolis, MN; *U.S. Private*, pg. 935
Keener, Philip D., Treas.--The Manitowoc Company, Inc., Manitowoc, WI; *U.S. Public*, pg. 1040
Keepes, David, Asst. Treas.--Michaels Stores, Inc., Irving, TX; *U.S. Public*, pg. 1104
Kees, Ray, Chief Fin. Officer, Corp. Sec. & Treas.--Gem-Dandy, Inc., Madison, NC; *U.S. Private*, pg. 442
Kehoe, Robert C., Second V.P. & Asst. Treas.--W.P. Carey & Co., Inc., New York, NY; *U.S. Private*, pg. 209
Keilman, David W., Exec. V.P. & Treas.--Comark, Bloomingdale, IL; *U.S. Private*, pg. 257
Keinert, Stefan, Treas.--Burda Holding GmbH & Co., KG, Munich, Germany; *Int'l*, pg. 233
Keitel, Chris, Chief Fin. Officer, V.P.-Fin., Treas. & Controller--Hobart Brothers Co., Troy, OH; *U.S. Public*, pg. 866
Keklak, Chris, Asst. Treas.--American Electric Power Company, Inc., Columbus, OH; *U.S. Public*, pg. 71
Keller, Barbara, Treas. & Sec.--Hotel Corporation of America, Maple Hill, KS; *U.S. Private*, pg. 541
Keller, Chris, Controller & Treasurer--Life-Like Products, Inc., Baltimore, MD; *U.S. Private*, pg. 666
Keller, David J., Chief Fin. Officer & Treas.--D.R. Horton, Inc., Arlington, TX; *U.S. Public*, pg. 840
Keller, James D., Treas.--T & N Industries, Inc., Ann Arbor, MI; *Int'l*, pg. 1334
Keller, James E., Treas. & Controller--Rapid Mounting & Finishing Co., Chicago, IL; *U.S. Private*, pg. 910
Keller, James W., Asst. Treas.--The Washington Post Company, Washington, DC; *U.S. Public*, pg. 1742
Keller, Jeff, Chief Fin. Officer & Treas.--D.C.I., Inc., Saint Cloud, MN; *U.S. Private*, pg. 301
Keller, John, Chm. Bd. & Treas.--Meadville Forging Co., Meadville, PA; *U.S. Private*, pg. 726
Keller, T.A., Treas.--Akzo Nobel Coatings Inc., Columbus, OH; *Int'l*, pg. 48
Keller, Thomas C., Treas. & Sec.--Lou Ana Foods, Inc., Opelousas, LA; *Int'l*, pg. 879
Kelley, Bruce G., Pres., Chief Exec. Officer & Treas.--EMC Insurance Group, Inc., Des Moines, IA; *U.S. Public*, pg. 545
Kelley, Don K., Chief Fin. Officer & Treas.--Kappler Safety Group, Inc., Guntersville, AL; *U.S. Private*, pg. 607
Kellhofer, Don, Treas. & Sec.--Efco Corporation, Monett, MO; *U.S. Private*, pg. 353
Kellogg, Charles T., Pres., Chief Exec. Officer & Treas.--Hubbard Hall Inc., Waterbury, CT; *U.S. Private*, pg. 544
Kellogg, Cynthia P., Chief Fin. Officer, V.P., Treas. & Sec.--Heartland Development Corporation, Madison, WI; *U.S. Public*, pg. 1728
Kelly, Charles, Treas.--Edgcomb Metals, Bensalem, PA; *Int'l*, pg. 572
Kelly, David A., V.P. & Treas.--Borden, Inc., Columbus, OH; *U.S. Private*, pg. 157
Kelly, Dennis P., Chief Fin. Officer & V.P.-Fin.--Oregon Metallurgical Corporation, Albany, OR; *U.S. Public*, pg. 43
Kelly, Edward J., V.P., Controller & Treas.--Emery Worldwide, Redwood City, CA; *U.S. Public*, pg. 281
Kelly, J.P., Treas.--Shell Pipe Line Corp., Houston, TX; *Int'l*, pg. 1136
Kelly, Joe, Jr., Chief Fin. Officer, V.P. & Treas.--Jim Walter Homes, Inc., Tampa, FL; *U.S. Public*, pg. 1737
Kelly, Joseph T., Chief Fin. Officer, Treas. & Sec.--Ewing Cole Cherry Brott, Philadelphia, PA; *U.S. Private*, pg. 387
Kelly, Marty, Treas.--Paris Accessories, New York, NY; *U.S.* Private, pg. 839
Kelly, Marty, Treas.--Baar & Beards, New York, NY; *U.S. Private*, pg. 839
Kelly, Paul, Chief Fin. Officer & Treas.--Quaker Fabric Corporation, Fall River, MA; *U.S. Public*, pg. 1347
Kelly, Ralph, Treas.--Charter Communications, Inc., Saint Louis, MO; *U.S. Private*, pg. 230
Kelly, Richard C., Chief Fin. Officer, Exec. V.P.-Fin. & Treas.--Public Service Company of Colorado, Denver, CO; *U.S. Public*, pg. 1170
Kelly, Richard F., Treas.--Alox Corporation, Niagara Falls, NY; *U.S. Public*, pg. 1357
Kelly, Richard F., V.P. & Treas.--Kop-Coat, Pittsburgh, PA; *U.S. Public*, pg. 1357
Kelly, William C., Jr., Chief Acctg. Officer & Treas.--NN Ball & Roller, Inc., Erwin, TN; *U.S. Public*, pg. 1146
Kemenczuk, Linda L., Asst. Treas.--Survey Research Associates, Baltimore, MD; *U.S. Private*, pg. 123
Kemp, K. Thomas, Exec. V.P. & Treas.--Fund American Enterprises Holdings, Inc., Hanover, NH; *U.S. Public*, pg. 688
Kendall, Cheryl L., Chief Fin. Officer, V.P., Treas. & Sec.--Acme United Corporation, Fairfield, CT; *U.S. Public*, pg. 17
Kendrick, Randy W., Treas.--Guaranty Corporation, Baton Rouge, LA; *U.S. Private*, pg. 485
Keniry, J.P., V.P. & Treas.--Rexam Inc., Charlotte, NC; *Int'l*, pg. 1106
Kennalley, Thomas R., Treas. & Controller--Advantage Companies, Inc., Wichita, KS; *U.S. Private*, pg. 22
Kenneally, Jennifer, Asst. Treas. & Dir.-Treas. Opers.--Golub Corporation, Schenectady, NY; *U.S. Private*, pg. 463
Kennedy, Brian A., V.P. & Treas.--Blue Cross & Blue Shield of Illinois, Chicago, IL; *U.S. Private*, pg. 151
Kennedy, Charles G., Chief Fin. Officer & Exec. V.P.-Finance--Henley Paper Company, Greensboro, NC; *U.S. Private*, pg. 522
Kennedy, Glenn J., Chief Fin. Officer, Treas. & Sec.--Alba-Waldensian, Inc., Valdese, NC; *U.S. Public*, pg. 35
Kennedy, James W., Asst. Treas.--Federal Paper Board Company, Inc., Montvale, NJ; *U.S. Public*, pg. 903
Kennedy, John, Chief Fin. Officer, Sr. V.P. & Treas.--Smith International, Inc., Houston, TX; *U.S. Public*, pg. 1478
Kennedy, Julie, Treas.--Taylor-Morley, Inc., Saint Louis, MO; *U.S. Private*, pg. 1071
Kennedy, Lee A., Treas.--Telecredit Marketing Services, Tampa, FL; *U.S. Public*, pg. 588
Kennedy, William E., Jr., Chm. Bd., Chief Exec. Officer & Treas.--Kennedy Tank & Manufacturing Co., Inc., Indianapolis, IN; *U.S. Private*, pg. 614
Kennell, Gerald, V.P. & Treas.--Avis Rent A Car System, Inc., Garden City, NY; *U.S. Public*, pg. 321
Kenney, Brian A., V.P. & Treas.--GATX Corporation, Chicago, IL; *U.S. Public*, pg. 690
Kenny, Earl, Treas.--Quebecor Printing Eusey Press Inc., Leominster, MA; *Int'l*, pg. 1078
Kenny, John, Treas.--Loews Corporation, New York, NY; *U.S. Public*, pg. 1010
Keogh, Mark, Treas.--Rochester Gas And Electric Corporation, Rochester, NY; *U.S. Public*, pg. 1395
Keong, L.F., Treas.--Esso Production Malaysia Inc., Kuala Lumpur, Malaysia; *U.S. Public*, pg. 602
Keough, William H., Chief Fin. Officer, Sr. V.P. & Treas.--The Pioneer Group, Inc., Boston, MA; *U.S. Public*, pg. 1298
Ker, Alan S., Chief Fin. Officer, Treas. & Sec.--Universal Standard Healthcare, Inc., Southfield, MI; *U.S. Public*, pg. 1697
Ker, Alan S., Chief Fin. Officer & Treas.--Universal Standard HealthCare of Ohio Inc., Southfield, MI; *U.S. Public*, pg. 1698
Kerley, Gregory D., V.P., Treas. & Sec.--Southwestern Energy Company, Fayetteville, AR; *U.S. Public*, pg. 1494
Kerley, Gregory D., V.P., Sec. & Treas.--Southwestern Energy Pipeline Company, Fayetteville, AR; *U.S. Public*, pg. 1494
Kerley, Gregory D., V.P., Sec. & Treas.--Arkansas Western Pipeline Company, Fayetteville, AR; *U.S. Public*, pg. 1494
Kerley, Marsha L., Treas. & Sec.--Peterson Builders, Inc., Sturgeon Bay, WI; *U.S. Private*, pg. 857
Kern, Edward B., Treas.--WGM Safety Corporation, Reading, PA; *Int'l*, pg. 462
Kernan, Richard T., Asst. Treas.-Intl.--Dresser Industries, Inc., Dallas, TX; *U.S. Public*, pg. 528
Kerner, David, Treas.--Standard Motor Products Inc., Long Island City, NY; *U.S. Public*, pg. 1503
Kerr, Robert M., Treas.--Nooter Corporation, Saint Louis, MO; *U.S. Private*, pg. 801
Kerr, Ross, Asst. Treas.--Hills Stores Co., Canton, MA; *U.S.* Public, pg. 828
Kerr, Trevor D., V.P. & Treas.--EdperBrascan Corporation, Toronto, Canada; *Int'l*, pg. 433
Kerr, William R., V.P. & Treas.--Northern Telecom Limited, Brampton, Canada; *Int'l*, pg. 968
Kessel, Silvia, Chief Fin. Officer, Exec. V.P. & Treas.--Metromedia International Group, Inc., East Rutherford, NJ; *U.S. Public*, pg. 1102
Keszler, Charles J., V.P.-Fin. & Corp. Rels. & Treas.--Lone Star Technologies, Inc., Dallas, TX; *U.S. Public*, pg. 1012
Ketcham, Geoffrey C., Chief Fin. Officer, Exec. V.P. & Treas.--Energen Corporation, Birmingham, AL; *U.S. Public*, pg. 581
Ketsdever, Matthew, Treas.--Service Assets Corp., Newport Beach, CA; *U.S. Private*, pg. 171
Kettell, Russell W., Pres. & Treas.--Golden West Financial Corporation, Oakland, CA; *U.S. Public*, pg. 750
Keuler, Lloyd J., Treas. & Sec.--Turner Supply Company, Mobile, AL; *U.S. Private*, pg. 1110
Keup, Gregory J., Asst. Treas.--International Multifoods Corporation, Minneapolis, MN; *U.S. Public*, pg. 900
Key, Robert F., Treas.--The Seibels Bruce Group, Inc., Columbia, SC; *U.S. Public*, pg. 1453
Key, Robert F., Treas.--South Carolina Insurance Company, Columbia, SC; *U.S. Public*, pg. 1453
Keyes, Bryan F., Treas., Sec. & Dir.-Legal & Fin.--STB Systems, Inc., Richardson, TX; *U.S. Public*, pg. 1421
Keys, David N., Chief Fin. Officer, Sr. V.P. & Treas.--American Pacific Corporation, Las Vegas, NV; *U.S. Public*, pg. 88
Keyser, Mark, V.P.-Fin. & Treas.--Old Guard Insurance Group, Lancaster, PA; *U.S. Public*, pg. 1216
Keyser, S.A., Chief Fin. Officer & Sr. V.P.--Burrows Paper Corporation, Little Falls, NY; *U.S. Private*, pg. 188
Khan, A., Tres.--Maple Leaf Foods Inc., Toronto, Canada; *Int'l*, pg. 841
Khetrapal, Shoba, V.P. & Treas.--Moore Corporation Limited, Toronto, Canada; *Int'l*, pg. 888
Khilnani, Vinod M., Chief Fin. Officer, V.P. & Treas.--Simpson Industries, Inc., Plymouth, MI; *U.S. Public*, pg. 1474
Khoury, E.R., Controller & Treas.--Morrison Textile Machinery Co., Fort Lawn, SC; *U.S. Private*, pg. 762
Khoury, Richel G., Vice Chm., Treas. & Sec.--Monticello Management Co., San Diego, CA; *U.S. Private*, pg. 759
Kibblehouse, John R., Treas. & Sec.--Haines Kibblehouse, Skippack, PA; *U.S. Private*, pg. 494
Kibbon, Larry J., Treas. & Sec.--Walsh Group, Chicago, IL; *U.S. Private*, pg. 1148
Kiefer, Carl O., V.P.-Fin., Treas. & Sec.--Don F. Williams Co., Rock Island, IL; *U.S. Private*, pg. 1177
Kieffer, D.A., V.P.-Fin., Treas. & Sec.--McCall Oil & Chemical Corp., Portland, OR; *U.S. Private*, pg. 719
Kiel, Steven, Chief Fin. Officer & Treas.--Ground Round Inc., Braintree, MA; *U.S. Public*, pg. 766
Kiener, Dan W., Treas.--PPG Industries, Inc., Pittsburgh, PA; *U.S. Public*, pg. 1245
Kiernan, Donald E., Chief Fin. Officer, Sr. V.P. & Treas.--SBC Communications Inc., San Antonio, TX; *U.S. Public, pg. 1415*
Kierzkowski, John P., V.P. & Treas.--PP&L Resources, Allentown, PA; *U.S. Public*, pg. 1244
Kieseman, John, Asst. Treas. & Asst. Sec.--Allied Mercantile Company, Philadelphia, PA; *U.S. Private*, pg. 39
Kikkawa, Takashi, Sec.--Colonial Beef Co., Philadelphia, PA; *U.S. Private*, pg. 253
Kilbride, Marc, Treas.--Houston Industries Incorporated, Houston, TX; *U.S. Public*, pg. 842
Kilduff, Eugene A., Asst. Treas.--Federal Paper Board Company, Inc., Montvale, NJ; *U.S. Public*, pg. 903
Kilgannon, Memma S., Treas. & Sec.--Amkor Electronics, Inc., West Chester, PA; *U.S. Private*, pg. 66
Killingsworth, Marti, Exec. V.P. & Treas.--Griffin Manufacturing Co., Muskogee, OK; *U.S. Private*, pg. 481

Killmer, Jonathon E., Chief Fin. Officer, Sr. V.P. & Treas.--Digi International Inc., Minnetonka, MN; *U.S. Public*, pg. 506

Kim, Jae Sung, Treas.--SangAm Communications Co., Ltd., Seoul, Korea; *U.S. Public*, pg. 765

Kim, Kenneth H., Chm., Pres., Chief Exec. Officer, Corp. Sec. & Treas.--Medieval Times Dinner & Tournament, Inc., Buena Park, CA; *U.S. Private*, pg. 728

Kimball, L. Robert, Chief Exec. Officer & Treas.--L. Robert Kimball & Associates, Ebensburg, PA; *U.S. Private*, pg. 619

Kimball, Robert M., Treas--Loctite Corporation, Rocky Hill, CT; *Int'l*, pg. 611

Kimmins, Jon W., V.P. & Treas.--Toys "R" Us, Inc., Paramus, NJ; *U.S. Public*, pg. 1626

Kimmins, William J., Treas.--Anheuser-Busch Companies, Inc., Saint Louis, MO; *U.S. Public*, pg. 113

Kincaid, Brian, Treas. & Dir.-Fin.--Foster-Miller, Inc., Waltham, MA; *U.S. Private*, pg. 421

Kindl, Nancy A., Chief Fin. Officer, Treas., Controller & Sec.--Portec, Inc., Lake Forest, IL; *U.S. Public*, pg. 1317

Kindlund, Joanne M., V.P.-Fin., Treas. & Sec.--Holiday RV Superstores, Inc., Orlando, FL; *U.S. Public*, pg. 829

King, C. Eric, Chief Fin. Officer & Treas.--Warner Press, Inc., Anderson, IN; *U.S. Private*, pg. 1150

King, Dan A., V.P.-Fin., Treas. & Sec.--Cherry Electrical Products Corporation, Waukegan, IL; *U.S. Public*, pg. 346

King, Dennis E., Pres. & Treas.--Dunlap & Co. Inc., Columbus, IN; *U.S. Private*, pg. 346

King, Eugene J., Jr., Sr. V.P. & Asst. Treas.-Corp. Control--A.G. Edwards, Inc., Saint Louis, MO; *U.S. Public*, pg. 565

King, Eugene J., Jr., Sr. V.P., Asst. Treas. & Comptroller--A.G. Edwards & Sons, Inc., Saint Louis, MO; *U.S. Public*, pg. 565

King, F., Sec. & Treas.--Bill Ray Nissan, Inc., Longwood, FL; *U.S. Private*, pg. 911

King, James, Treas.--Kulicke & Soffa Industries, Inc., Willow Grove, PA; *U.S. Public*, pg. 968

King, Jan, V.P. & Treas.--Hercules Incorporated, Wilmington, DE; *U.S. Public*, pg. 809

King, Jimmie R., Jr., Treas.--Long MFG. NC, Inc., Tarboro, NC; *U.S. Private*, pg. 674

King, Lawrence E., Treas.--King Fuels Inc., Troy, NY; *U.S. Private*, pg. 620

King, Paul L., Exec. V.P. & Treas.--American Family Mutual Insurance Co., Madison, WI; *U.S. Private*, pg. 53

King, Sharon, Treas.--International Research & Evaluation, Eagan, MN; *U.S. Private*, pg. 571

King, William G., Treas.--King Industries, Inc., Norwalk, CT; *U.S. Private*, pg. 620

Kingman, Robert F., Treas.--Joshua L. Baily Co., Inc., Hoboken, NJ; *U.S. Private*, pg. 110

Kingsbury, J., Treas.--Costain Group PLC, London, United Kingdom; *Int'l*, pg. 336

Kiniyalocts, G., V.P.-Fin. & Treas.--Contech Construction Products Inc., Middletown, OH; *U.S. Private*, pg. 267

Kinley, Donald D., V.P. & Treas.--First Commerce Bancshares, Inc., Lincoln, NE; *U.S. Public*, pg. 629

Kinnamon, Kathryn, Asst. V.P. & Treas.--KCS Energy Inc., Edison, NJ; *U.S. Public*, pg. 938

Kinnen, Michael R., V.P. & Treas.--Vicorp Restaurants, Inc., Denver, CO; *U.S. Public*, pg. 1719

Kinning, Rick L., Pres. & Treas.--RK Mechanical, Inc., Denver, CO; *U.S. Private*, pg. 904

Kinsella, Daniel, Chief Fin. Officer, V.P. & Treas.--Grist Mill Company, Lakeville, MN; *U.S. Public*, pg. 766

Kinsella, Karen, Treas.--Chroma Corporation, McHenry, IL; *U.S. Private*, pg. 238

Kinsinger, Freeman J., Controller, Asst. Treas. & Asst. Sec.--CIPSCO Investment Company, Springfield, IL; *U.S. Public*, pg. 66

Kinzer, Donald M., Treas.--Old Dominion Life Insurance Co., Roanoke, VA; *U.S. Private*, pg. 992

Kirbie, Ellis, V.P., Treas. & Asst. Sec.--Smith Environmental Technologies Corp., Plymouth Meeting, PA; *U.S. Public*, pg. 1477

Kirby, David, V.P.-Fin. & Treas.--The Arnold Palmer Golf Company, Ooltewah, TN; *U.S. Public*, pg. 132

Kirchhoefer, Robert G., Treas.--Albemarle Corporation, Richmond, VA; *U.S. Public*, pg. 37

Kirk, Carole A., V.P. & Treas.--Chartwell Re Corporation, Stamford, CT; *U.S. Public*, pg. 336

Kirk, J., Treas. & Sec.--Exact Equipment Corporation, Langhorne, PA; *U.S. Private*, pg. 387

Kirkendall, Robert E., Sec. & Asst. Treas.--The Gorman-Rupp Company, Mansfield, OH; *U.S. Public*, pg. 754

Kirkwood, I., Treas.--Pilkington Plc, Saint Helens, United Kingdom; *Int'l*, pg. 1056

Kirschner, Mark, V.P. & Treas.--Wheaton Van Lines, Inc., Indianapolis, IN; *U.S. Private*, pg. 1171

Kirshenbaum, William, V.P. & Treas.--New Plan Realty Trust, New York, NY; *U.S. Public*, pg. 1172

Kirwan, Michael J., Asst. Treas.--Cleveland-Cliffs Inc, Cleveland, OH; *U.S. Public*, pg. 386

Kisler, Dennis B., Sr. V.P., Treas. & Sec.--Agronaut Great Central Insurance Co., Peoria, IL; *U.S. Public*, pg. 129

Kita, John J., Treas. & Controller--A.O. Smith Corporation, Milwaukee, WI; *U.S. Public*, pg. 1476

Kittilsby, Tim, Treas. & Sec.--Miles Sand & Gravel Company, Auburn, WA; *U.S. Private*, pg. 745

Kittner, Paula W., Mgr.-Cash & Asst. Treas.--Chemed Corporation, Cincinnati, OH; *U.S. Public*, pg. 343

Kitz, Edward G., V.P., Treas. & Sec.--Roundy's, Inc., Pewaukee, WI; *U.S. Private*, pg. 948

Klag, Robert W., Sr. V.P., Controller & Treas.--National Insurance Group, South San Francisco, CA; *U.S. Public*, pg. 1157

Klajbor, Jerry, Chief Fin. Officer, V.P. & Sec.--Stanford Telecommunications, Sunnyvale, CA; *U.S. Public*, pg. 1508

Klaszky, Carl W., Treas. & Sec.--A.N. Deringer, Inc., Saint Albans, VT; *U.S. Private*, pg. 326

Klatt, Roger J., Chief Fin. Officer, Sr. V.P., Treas. & Asst. Sec.--Gundle/SLT Environmental, Inc., Houston, TX; *U.S. Public*, pg. 769

Klaus, Richard W., Treas.--Klaus Radio Inc., Peoria, IL; *U.S. Private*, pg. 625

Klawitter, Ronald F., Chief Fin. Officer, V.P.-Fin., Treas. & Sec.--Key Tronic Corporation, Spokane, WA; *U.S. Public*, pg. 953

Kleczka, John, Sr. V.P.-Fin. & Treas.--Bradley Corporation, Menomonee Falls, WI; *U.S. Private*, pg. 164

Klein, Douglas P., Chief Fin. Officer, V.P., Sec. & Treas.--Go-Video, Inc., Scottsdale, AZ; *U.S. Public*, pg. 748

Klein, Stan, Controller, Treas. & Sec.--Cormier Chevrolet Company, Inc., Carson, CA; *U.S. Private*, pg. 276

Kleman, Charles, Chief Fin. Officer, Sec. & Treas.--Chico's Fas Inc, Fort Myers, FL; *U.S. Public*, pg. 349

Klerk, Bill, Controller & Asst. Treas.--McNeel International Corp., Tampa, FL; *U.S. Private*, pg. 724

Kleyn, R.B., Treas.--Ballast Nedam NV, Amstelveen, Netherlands; *Int'l*, pg. 133

Kline, Frederic M., V.P. & Treas.--Washington Gas Light Co., Springfield, VA; *U.S. Public*, pg. 1740

Kline, Gary, Treas.--Colfax, Inc., Pawtucket, RI; *U.S. Private*, pg. 252

Kline, Rodger S., Chief Oper. Officer, Exec. V.P. & Treas.--Acxiom Corporation, Conway, AR; *U.S. Public*, pg. 18

Klingbeil, Mark, Dir.-Fin. & Asst. Treas.--Medusa Corporation, Cleveland, OH; *U.S. Public*, pg. 1084

Klitgaard, Bill, Treas.--Kenetech Corp., San Francisco, CA; *U.S. Public*, pg. 950

Klosterman, Scott, Chief Fin. Officer, V.P.-Fin. & Corp. Sec.--Chattanooga Group, Inc., Hixson, TN; *U.S. Private*, pg. 231

Kluttz, Richard S., Controller & Treas.--Brigadier Homes of North Carolina, Nashville, NC; *U.S. Public*, pg. 318

Klyce, Michael J., V.P. & Treas.--Torchmark Corporation, Birmingham, AL; *U.S. Public*, pg. 1622

Kmez, Jaime, V.P. & Treas.--Lane Industries, Inc., Northbrook, IL; *U.S. Private*, pg. 649

Kmiecik, Thomas T., Sr. V.P. & Treas.--First Union Real Estate Investments, Cleveland, OH; *U.S. Public*, pg. 640

Knaebel, Richard L., Treas.--Mid-Am Building Supply, Inc., Moberly, MO; *U.S. Private*, pg. 743

Knedlik, Ronald, Chief Fin. Officer, Sr. V.P.-Fin., Treas. & Sec.--Alex Lee, Inc., Hickory, NC; *U.S. Private*, pg. 657

Knedlik, Ronald, Treas.--Merchants Distributors, Inc., Hickory, NC; *U.S. Private*, pg. 657

Knedlik, Ronald, Chief Fin. Officer & Treas.--Capital Resources, Inc., Hickory, NC; *U.S. Private*, pg. 657

Knedlik, Ronald, Chief Fin. Officer & Treas.--Merchants Transport of Hickory, Hickory, NC; *U.S. Private*, pg. 657

Knedlik, Ronald, Chief Fin. Officer & Treas.--Institution Food House, Inc., Hickory, NC; *U.S. Private*, pg. 657

Knedlik, Ronald, Chief Fin. Officer & Treas.--MDI Management Inc., Hickory, NC; *U.S. Private*, pg. 657

Knedlik, Ronald W., Chief Fin. Officer & Treas.--Lowe's Food Stores, Inc., Winston Salem, NC; *U.S. Private*, pg. 657

Knee, Larry, Treas.--Monfort, Inc., Greeley, CO; *U.S. Public*, pg. 427

Kneip, Kurt R., Chief Fin. Officer, V.P., Sec. & Treas.--Southwest Telephone Systems, Inc., Phoenix, AZ; *U.S. Public*, pg. 888

Kneissl, William L., Sr. V.P., Treas. & Sec.--The Troy Savings Bank, Troy, NY; *U.S. Private*, pg. 1106

Knepper, Peter, Chief Fin. Officer, Sr. V.P. & Treas.--Ticketmaster Corporation, West Hollywood, CA; *U.S. Private*, pg. 1084

Knese, William F., V.P., Treas. & Controller--CLARCOR, Inc., Rockford, IL; *U.S. Public*, pg. 381

Kniffen, D.E., Treas.--The Budd Company, Troy, MI; *Int'l*, pg. 1388

Kniffen, Jan R., Sr. V.P. & Treas.--The May Department Stores Company, Saint Louis, MO; *U.S. Public*, pg. 1063

Knight, Dan, V.P.-Treasury--Information Resources, Inc., Chicago, IL; *U.S. Public*, pg. 875

Knight, Gail, Treas. & Sec.--Keller Building Products of Charlotte, Inc., Charlotte, NC; *U.S. Private*, pg. 612

Knight, Linda K., Sr. V.P. & Treas.--Federal National Mortgage Association (Fannie Mae), Washington, DC; *U.S. Public*, pg. 615

Knight, Phyllis A., V.P. & Treas.--Green Tree Financial Corporation, Saint Paul, MN; *U.S. Public*, pg. 761

Knight, Robert B., Sr. V.P.-Admin. & Treas.--White Hen Pantry, Inc., Elmhurst, IL; *U.S. Private*, pg. 1172

Knight, S., Treas.--UBS Australia Ltd., Sydney, Australia; *Int'l*, pg. 1440

Knipe, P.W., Sec. & Treas.--STV Construction Services, Douglassville, PA; *U.S. Public*, pg. 1421

Knipe, P.W., Sec. & Treas.--STV International, New York, NY; *U.S. Public*, pg. 1421

Knipe, Peter W., Treas. & Sec.--STV Group, Inc., Douglassville, PA; *U.S. Public*, pg. 1421

Knispel, Isabel, Treas. & Sec.--Arrow Fastener Co., Inc., Saddle Brook, NJ; *U.S. Private*, pg. 85

Knoepfel, Robert, Mgr.-Treasury & Risk Mngmt.--Oerlikon-Buhrle Holding AG, Zurich, Switzerland; *Int'l*, pg. 996

Knoss, Bernice B., Treas.--School Apparel, Inc., San Bruno, CA; *U.S. Private*, pg. 972

Knott, Tim J., Treas.--The Broken Hill Proprietary Company Limited, Melbourne, Australia; *Int'l*, pg. 223

Knowles, J., Treas.--Woodside Petroleum Ltd., Melbourne, Australia; *Int'l*, pg. 1137

Knowles, Robert E., Chief Fin. Officer & Exec. V.P.--S & K Famous Brands, Inc., Glen Allen, VA; *U.S. Public*, pg. 1414

Knowlton, Angela K., V.P. & Treas.--Alltrista Corporation, Muncie, IN; *U.S. Public*, pg. 56

Knox, Richard, Pres., Treas. & Sec.--Knox Oil of Texas Inc., Dallas, TX; *U.S. Private*, pg. 627

Knudsen, Don, Treas. & Sec.--Denny Menholt Frontier Chevrolet, Billings, MT; *U.S. Private*, pg. 324

Knueuen, Gerald R., Chief Fin. Officer, Exec. V.P. & Treas.--Harold M. Pitman Co., Inc., Totowa, NJ; *U.S. Private*, pg. 867

Knutson, Dan, V.P., Controller & Treas.--Land O'Lakes, Inc., Arden Hills, MN; *U.S. Private*, pg. 645

Knutson, Roger, Sr. V.P. & Treas.--Soil Teq, Inc., Minnetonka, MN; *U.S. Public*, pg. 6

Kobayashi, Etsuo, Treas.--Ricoh Corporation, West Caldwell, NJ; *Int'l*, pg. 1114

Koch, Bernhard M., Chief Fin. Officer & Treas.--Desjardins Laurentian Life Assurance, Wayne, PA; *Int'l*, pg. 396

Koch, Diane M., Asst. Treas. & Asst. Sec.--PP&L Resources, Allentown, PA; *U.S. Public*, pg. 1244

Koch, Elizabeth, Corp. Sec. & Asst. Treas.--Plywood Plastics Inc., Buffalo, NY; *U.S. Private*, pg. 873

Koch, G. Fred, Chm. Bd., Chief Exec. Officer & Treas.--Plywood Plastics Inc., Buffalo, NY; *U.S. Private*, pg. 873

Koch, Joseph, Treas.--Countrymark Cooperative, Inc., Indianapolis, IN; *U.S. Private*, pg. 279

Koch, Tim, Chief Fin. Officer, Exec. V.P. & Treas.--EBP Life Insurnace Co., Minneapolis, MN; *U.S. Public*, pg. 635

Kocher, Thomas M., Asst. Treas.--Exide Corporation, Reading, PA; *U.S. Public*, pg. 600

Kocourek, Edward J., V.P., Treas. & Sec--Egan Cos., Minneapolis, MN; *U.S. Private*, pg. 365

Kocourek, Patrick, Treas.--Al Johnson Construction Co., Bloomington, MN; *U.S. Private*, pg. 590

Kodak, Boris, Sr. Treasury Analyst--Cognos Inc., Ottawa, Canada; *Int'l*, pg. 305

Koebel, Wayne R., Chief Fin. Officer, Exec. V.P., Treas. & Sec.--Shoreline Financial Corp., Benton Harbor, MI; *U.S. Public*, pg. 1467

Koechley, L. Thomas, Chief Fin. Officer, V.P.-Fin. & Treas.--Kirkwood Industries, Inc., Cleveland, OH; *U.S. Private*, pg. 623

Koefer, Erich, Grp. Treas. & Controller--Mikron Holding AG, Biel, Switzerland; *Int'l*, pg. 866

Koehn, Donald L., Exec. V.P., Treas. & Sec.--Bradbury Company, Inc., Moundridge, KS; *U.S. Private*, pg. 163

Koenig, Jeffrey H., V.P.-Fin., Controller & Treas.--Executive Risk, Inc., Simsbury, CT; *U.S. Public*, pg. 599

Koenig, Joseph T., Treas. & Asst. Sec.--The Hallwood Group Incorporated, Dallas, TX; *U.S. Public*, pg. 777

Koenitzer, Joyce C., Treas.--Helwig Carbon Products, Inc., Milwaukee, WI; *U.S. Private*, pg. 521

Koepke, Allen C., V.P.-Bus. Devel. & Internal Audit--Regal Ware, Inc., Kewaskum, WI; *U.S. Private*, pg. 917

Koether, Henry, V.P. & Treas.--American Trading and Production Corporation, Baltimore, MD; *U.S. Private*, pg. 63

Kofer, Roland, Treas.--Landis & Staefa AG, Zug, Switzerland; *Int'l*, pg. 800

Koffman, Burton, Pres. & Treas.--Ben Arnold Co., Inc., Vestal, NY; *U.S. Private*, pg. 83

Kogen, Howard, V.P. & Treas.--JMB Realty Corporation, Chicago, IL; *U.S. Private*, pg. 577

Kogod, Marvin, Treas. & Sec.--Maurice Electric Supply Company, Washington, DC; *U.S. Private*, pg. 715

Kogovsek, Conrad J., Treas. & Sec.--Keystone Powdered Metal Company, Saint Marys, PA; *U.S. Private*, pg. 619

Koh, Linda, V.P., Treas. & Sec.--Jupiter Industries, Inc., Northbrook, IL; *U.S. Private*, pg. 602

Kohls, William R., Chief Fin. Officer & Exec. V.P.--Independent Bank Corporation, Ionia, MI; *U.S. Public*, pg. 874

Koike, Yoshio, V.P. & Treas.--Sanyo Energy (U.S.A.) Corporation, San Diego, CA; *Int'l*, pg. 1191

Kojima, Takashi, Exec. V.P. & Treas.--Canon U.S.A., Inc., Lake Success, NY; *Int'l*, pg. 262

Kojima, Tatsunari, Treas.--Yokohama Corporation of North America, Akron, OH; *Int'l*, pg. 1521

Kojima, Yoshiharu, Sr. Mng. Dir.-Admin. & Treas.--Sogei Inc., Tokyo, Japan; *Int'l*, pg. 1277

Kokubun, Sharon, Treas.--Collagen Corporation, Palo Alto, CA; *U.S. Public*, pg. 399

Kolakawski, Stephen C., Chief Fin. Officer, Sr. V.P. & Treas.--Underwriters Reinsurance, Woodland Hills, CA; *U.S. Public*, pg. 42

Kolhagen, Donald W., Sr. V.P. & Treas.--Pinnacle Financial Services Inc., Saint Joseph, MI; *U.S. Public*, pg. 1297

Kolikof, Robert A., Pres., Chief Exec. Officer & Treas.--Prudential Metal Supply Corp., East Dedham, MA; *U.S. Private*, pg. 893

Kolovson, Mark, V.P. & Treas.--Blue Bell/King Koil, Inc., Windsor, CT; *U.S. Private*, pg. 150

Koman, Douglas, Treas.--Illinois Central Corporation, Chicago, IL; *U.S. Public*, pg. 864

Kombarji, Tarek I., Asst. Treas.--Associates Financial Services Corporation, Dallas, TX; *U.S. Public*, pg. 663

Konditzer, Gerald R., V.P. & Treas.--Chiquita Brands International, Inc., Cincinnati, OH; *U.S. Public*, pg. 349

Kontich, Michael J., Chief Fin. Officer & Treas.--Leupold & Stevens, Inc., Beaverton, OR; *U.S. Private*, pg. 662

Kontos, Mark W., Chief Fin. Officer, Sr. V.P. & Treas.--Battelle Memorial Institute, Columbus, OH; *U.S. Private*, pg. 123

Koolstra, John, Treas.--Vermeer Manufacturing Company, Pella, IA; *U.S. Private*, pg. 1137

Kopatz, Margaret, Controller & Asst. Treas.--Valu Discount, Incorporated, Louisville, KY; *U.S. Private*, pg. 1132

Kopec, Chet, Chief Fin. Officer, Sr. V.P. & Treas.--Michigan Wheel Corporation, Grand Rapids, MI; *U.S. Private*, pg. 741

Kopp, Joseph T., Controller, Treas. & Sec.--Massman Construction Company, Kansas City, MO; *U.S. Private*, pg. 713

Koppe, David P., V.P. & Asst. Treas.--HealthWise of America, Nashville, TN; *U.S. Public*, pg. 1678

Koppe, David P., Treas.--United HealthCare of Florida, Inc., Coral Gables, FL; *U.S. Public*, pg. 1678

Koppe, David P., Exec. V.P. & Asst. Treas.--United HealthCare of North Carolina, Inc., Greensboro, NC; *U.S. Public*, pg. 1678

Koppe, David P., Exec. V.P. & Asst. Treas.--United HealthCare of Nevada, Inc., Las Vegas, NV; *U.S. Public, pg. 1678*

Koppe, David P., V.P. & Asst. Treas.--United HealthCare of Oregon, Inc., Minnetonka, MN; *U.S. Public*, pg. 1678

Koral, Lawrence C., Mgr.-Fin. Reporting & Plng.--Varlen Corporation, Naperville, IL; *U.S. Public*, pg. 1710

Korber, Jessica, Controller, Treas. & Sec.--J. Korber & Company, Albuquerque, NM; *U.S. Private*, pg. 632

Korman, Robert, Chief Fin. Officer & V.P.--BFX Hospitality Group, Inc., Fort Worth, TX; *U.S. Public*, pg. 160

Korman, Timothy J., V.P. & Treas.--Hilb, Rogal and Hamilton Company of Canada, Limited, Winnipeg, Canada; *U.S. Public*, pg. 828

Kormann, Hermut, Dr., Member-Bd. of Mngmt. & Treas.--J.M. Voith, GmbH, Heidenheim, Germany; *Int'l*, pg. 1472

Korom, Louis, Jr., Asst. Treas.--Abbott Laboratories, Abbott Park, IL; *U.S. Public*, pg. 12

Koroneos, Len, V.P. & Treas.--Extendicare Inc., Markham, Canada; *Int'l*, pg. 468

Korpela, Richard A., Exec. V.P., Treas. & Sec.--Lynden Incorporated, Seattle, WA; *U.S. Private*, pg. 683

Korvenpaa, Timo, Grp. Treas.--Oy Nokia Ab/Nokia Group, Helsinki, Finland; *Int'l*, pg. 951

Korylak, John R., V.P. & Treas.--Unicorp Canada Corporation, Toronto, Canada; *Int'l*, pg. 1433

Kos, Donald J., Controller & Treas.--Tradehome Shoe Stores, Inc., Saint Paul, MN; *U.S. Private*, pg. 1095

Koschmeder, Mark A., Asst. Treas.--Comarco, Inc., Yorba Linda, CA; *U.S. Public*, pg. 406

Koshiyama, Takeshi, Treas.--KYB Industries Inc., Franklin, IN; *Int'l*, pg. 727

Kosht, Jon A., Pres., Chief Oper. Officer, Sec. & Treas.--Michigan Gas Company, Three Rivers, MI; *U.S. Public*, pg. 1489

Kosowski, Barry, Chief Fin. Officer, Treas. & Sec.--Customedix Corporation, Wallingford, CT; *U.S. Private*, pg. 298

Kotani, H., Chief Fin. Officer--Nissan Forklift Corporation, North America, Marengo, IL; *Int'l*, pg. 944

Kotsatos, Andrew G., Chm. Bd., Chief Exec. Officer & Treas.--Boston Acoustics, Inc., Peabody, MA; *U.S. Public*, pg. 246

Kovacs, Stephen D., Asst. Treas.--Exide Corporation, Reading, PA; *U.S. Public*, pg. 600

Koval, Thomas J., V.P. & Treas.--Radiator Specialty Company, Charlotte, NC; *U.S. Private*, pg. 906

Koval, Thomas J., Controller & Asst. Treas.--Pennsylvania Enterprises Inc., Wilkes-Barre, PA; *U.S. Public*, pg. 1271

Koval, Thomas J., Controller & Asst. Treas.--PG Energy, Inc., Wilkes-Barre, PA; *U.S. Public*, pg. 1271

Kowaleski, David L., Treas.--American Baler Co., Bellevue, OH; *U.S. Private*, pg. 102

Kowalke, Stephen C., Treas.--Dayton Hudson Corporation, Minneapolis, MN; *U.S. Public*, pg. 489

Kozlowski, Edward C., Treas.--ACR Industries Inc., Macomb Township, MI; *U.S. Private*, pg. 3

Kozma, M.J., Treas.--Maxitrol Co., Southfield, MI; *U.S. Private*, pg. 716

Kraber, Richard, Chief Fin. Officer & Sec.--Wind River Systems, Inc., Alameda, CA; *U.S. Public*, pg. 1770

Kraff, Eric, V.P., Controller & Treas.--MediaOne, Boston, MA; *U.S. Public*, pg. 1688

Kraft, Charles C., Treas.--LincAm Properties, Inc., Chicago, IL; *U.S. Public*, pg. 997

Kraft, Joe, V.P. & Treas.--Sony Pictures Entertainment, Culver City, CA; *Int'l*, pg. 1281

Kraines, R. Guy, V.P. & Treas.--CNF Transportation Inc., Palo Alto, CA; *U.S. Public*, pg. 281

Krakaver, Leonard, Pres.--Pall Rai, Inc., Hauppauge, NY; *U.S. Public*, pg. 1254

Kramer, Michael P., V.P.-Fin. & Treas.--Cutco Industries, Inc., Syosset, NY; *U.S. Public*, pg. 470

Kramer, Phillip D., Chief Fin. Officer, Sr. V.P. & Treas.--Plains Resources Inc., Houston, TX; *U.S. Public*, pg. 1307

Kramer, Richard, V.P. & Treas.--Dataproducts Corporation, Simi Valley, CA; *Int'l*, pg. 620

Kramme, Richard G., V.P. & Treas.--Ace Glass Incorporated, Vineland, NJ; *U.S. Private*, pg. 12

Krantz, James A., Chief Fin. Officer, V.P. & Treas.--Mission American Insurance Company, Rancho Dominguez, CA; *U.S. Public*, pg. 483

Krantz, John F., Chief Exec. Officer & Treas.--Adventure Lands of America, Inc., Des Moines, IA; *U.S. Private*, pg. 22

Krantz, Marie G., Chm. Bd. & Treas.--Fair Grounds Corporation, New Orleans, LA; *U.S. Public*, pg. 609

Krapohl, James R., Treas. & Asst. Sec.--Wolohan Lumber Co., Saginaw, MI; *U.S. Public*, pg. 1774

Krasny, Michael P., Chm. Bd., Chief Exec. Officer, Treas. & Sec.--CDW Computer Centers, Inc., Vernon Hills, IL; *U.S. Public*, pg. 277

Krausart, Gerald S., Chief Fin. Officer & Treas.--Dickten & Masch Manufacturing Co., Nashotah, WI; *U.S. Private*, pg. 331

Krause, Peter, V.P. & Treas.--Carhartt, Inc., Dearborn, MI; *U.S. Private*, pg. 210

Krausz, K.J., Treas.--CHEMCENTRAL Corporation, Bedford Park, IL; *U.S. Private*, pg. 231

Krebs, Michael A., V.P. & Treas.--BCE Mobile Communications Inc., Saint-Laurent, Canada; *Int'l*, pg. 115

Krechel, Roger, Treas. & Sec.--Breckenridge Material Company, Saint Louis, MO; *U.S. Private*, pg. 166

Kreider, Robert A., Treas. & Controller--Banta Corporation, Menasha, WI; *U.S. Public*, pg. 187

Kreindel, William S., V.P. & Treas.--Wm. Zinsser & Co., Inc., Somerset, NJ; *U.S. Public*, pg. 1358

Kreiter, Ned, Chief Oper. Officer, Treas. & Gen. Mgr.--Castcraft Industries, Inc., Skokie, IL; *U.S. Private*, pg. 219

Kremin, Alan F., Treas.--The Inland Group, Inc., Oak Brook, IL; *U.S. Private*, pg. 564

Krempa, Robert W., V.P. & Treas.--John Hancock Networking Insurance Agency, Boston, MA; *U.S. Private*, pg. 590

Krenek, Wilfred, Chief Fin. Officer, V.P., Treas. & Sec.--Bettis Corporation, Waller, TX; *U.S. Public*, pg. 482

Kresl, Miles L., Jr., V.P.-Admin., Treas. & Corp. Sec.--Badger Paper Mills, Inc., Peshtigo, WI; *U.S. Public*, pg. 165

Krick, Robert W., Asst. Treas.--UGI Corporation, King of Prussia, PA; *U.S. Public*, pg. 1653

Kridler, Terry E., Treas.--HFS, Incorporated, Parsippany, NJ; *U.S. Public*, pg. 321

Kriegshauser, Patrick A., Chief Fin. Officer, Sr. V.P. & Treas.--Arch Coal, Inc., Saint Louis, MO; *U.S. Public*, pg. 139

Krietzberg, David, Treas. & Dir.-Fin.--Executone Information Systems, Inc., Milford, CT; *U.S. Public*, pg. 599

Krihak, Paul R., Chief Exec. Officer & Treas.--Holbrook Lumber Company, Albany, NY; *U.S. Private*, pg. 533

Krishnamara, Ayuth, Treas.--Bangkok Bank Public Company Limited, Bangkok, Thailand; *Int'l*, pg. 146

Kristal, Samuel, Treas.--Key Food Stores Co-operative, Inc., Brooklyn, NY; *U.S. Private*, pg. 617

Kroese, John S., III, Chief Fin. Officer, Treas. & Sec.--Gaffney-Kroese Electrical Supply Corp., Rahway, NJ; *U.S. Private*, pg. 437

Kroetch, Karen, Treas. & Sec.--Krofam Inc., Philip, SD; *U.S. Private*, pg. 636

Krofcheck, Daniel J., Treas.--Century Aluminum Company, Monterey, CA; *U.S. Public*, pg. 328

Kroll, Michael, V.P. & Treas.--Matec Corporation, Hopkinton, MA; *U.S. Public*, pg. 1056

Kroll, Wolfgang, Exec. V.P.-Bus. Admin. & Fin. & Treas.--Siemens Medical Systems, Inc., Iselin, NJ; *Int'l*, pg. 1246

Kromer, Dennis R., Chief Fin. Officer & Treas.--Dunn-Edwards Corporation, Los Angeles, CA; *U.S. Private*, pg. 347

Krone, Roger A., V.P. & Treas.--McDonnell Aircraft & Missile Systems Div., Berkeley, MO; *U.S. Public*, pg. 241

Krucks, Kenneth R., Sec. & Asst. Treas.--Rauland-Borg Corporation, Skokie, IL; *U.S. Private*, pg. 911

Krueger, Robert A., Pres., Chief Exec. Officer & Treas.--Tri-Mark Metal Corp., Shelby, MI; *U.S. Private*, pg. 1100

Krueger, Robin, Asst. V.P. & Treas.--Alaska Airlines, Inc., Seattle, WA; *U.S. Public*, pg. 35

Krueger, Robin L., Staff V.P.-Fin. & Treas.--Alaska Air Group, Inc., Seattle, WA; *U.S. Public*, pg. 35

Krug, Kenneth M., Treas.--RAND, Santa Monica, CA; *U.S. Private*, pg. 908

Krugman, Mark, Chief Fin. Officer & Treas.--Lee National Corporation, New York, NY; *U.S. Private*, pg. 658

Krugman, Mark, Chief Fin. Officer & Treas.--Great Universal Capital Corp., New York, NY; *U.S. Private*, pg. 658

Krull, Charles D., Treas.--Albert Trostel & Sons Co., Milwaukee, WI; *U.S. Private*, pg. 1105

Krupa, Alan M., Asst. Treas.--Applied Industrial Technologies, Cleveland, OH; *U.S. Public*, pg. 122

Krutzmann, Ronald L., Treas. & Asst. Sec.--Laclede Gas Company, Saint Louis, MO; *U.S. Public*, pg. 973

Krzemien, Gregory M., Chief Fin. Officer & Treas.--Eastern Environmental Services, Inc., Drums, PA; *U.S. Public*, pg. 549

Krzyminski, Richard, Chief Fin. Officer, Treas. & Sec.--Baxter Hodell Donnelly Preston Inc., Cincinnati, OH; *U.S. Private*, pg. 124

Kubala, Maureen, V.P. & Treas.--CTB/McGraw Hill, Monterey, CA; *U.S. Public*, pg. 1070

Kuban, William G., Pres., Chief Exec. Officer & Treas.--Kurt Manufacturing Co. Inc., Fridley, MN; *U.S. Private*, pg. 637

Kubilus, John, Chief Fin. Officer & Treas.--Bovis Inc., New York, NY; *Int'l*, pg. 1033

Kucharz, Scott, Treas.--Southwest Medical Associates, Inc., Las Vegas, NV; *U.S. Public*, pg. 1470

Kuchinski, Thaddeus G., Chief Fin. Officer & Treas.--Holstein Association USA, Inc., Brattleboro, VT; *U.S. Private*, pg. 536

Kuck, Carol, Treas.--Regal Marine Industries Inc., Orlando, FL; *U.S. Private*, pg. 917

Kuck, Timothy W., Chief Fin. Officer, Treas. & Sec.--G&K Services, Inc., Minnetonka, MN; *U.S. Public*, pg. 690

Kuhne, Alice, Treas.--Gulf Oil Limited Partnership, Chelsea, MA; *U.S. Private*, pg. 487

Kuhnell, Roy E., Pres. & Treas.--Dempsey & Siders Insurance Agency, Cincinnati, OH; *U.S. Public*, pg. 75

Kuhnle, Kenneth R., V.P. & Treas.--Genesis Health Ventures, Inc., Kennett Square, PA; *U.S. Public*, pg. 728

Kuhr, Leonard G., Corp. V.P. & Treas.--Allegiance Healthcare Corp., McGaw Park, IL; *U.S. Public*, pg. 44

Kuk, Tom, Treas.--Clayton, Williams & Sherwood, Inc., Newport Beach, CA; *U.S. Private*, pg. 245

Kula, Donald, V.P.-Sls. & Treas.--Bloch/New England, Inc., Worcester, MA; *U.S. Private*, pg. 149

Kullas, Robert H., V.P. & Treas.--Aetna Inc., Hartford, CT; *U.S. Public*, pg. 26

Kummer, Fred S., Chm., Pres., Chief Exec. Officer, Treas. & Founder--HBE Corporation/Design Build Divisions, Saint Louis, MO; *U.S. Private*, pg. 489

Kump, Robert D., Treas.--New York State Electric & Gas Corporation, Binghamton, NY; *U.S. Public*, pg. 1173

Kundert, Thomas G., Treas.--Anschutz Corporation, Denver, CO; *U.S. Private*, pg. 75

Kunihara, Oamu, Treas.--KYB Corporation of America, Lombard, IL; *Int'l*, pg. 727

Kunkel, Taryn, Chief Fin. Officer, V.P. & Treas.--Pharmakinetics Laboratories, Inc., Baltimore, MD; *U.S. Public*, pg. 1285

Kuntz, Daniel S., Treas.--NWNL Management Corp., Minneapolis, MN; *U.S. Public*, pg. 1375

Kuntz, Daniel S., Asst. Treas. & Sr. Variable Prod. Accountant--Washington Square Securities, Minneapolis, MN; *U.S. Public*, pg. 1376

Kunzmann, Bruce W., V.P., Sec. & Treas.--Berkley Risk Managers, Somerset, NJ; *U.S. Public*, pg. 215

Kuroda, Hitoshi, Gen. Mgr.--Toyo Tire & Rubber Co., Ltd., Osaka, Japan; *Int'l*, pg. 1411

Kurry, Joseph, Chief Fin. Officer, V.P. & Treas.--Essex Corporation, Columbia, MD; *U.S. Public*, pg. 593

Kursman, Daniel R., Chm. Bd. & Treas.--Jetronic Industries, Inc., Philadelphia, PA; *U.S. Public*, pg. 926

Kurtz, Stephen, Treas. & Sec.--Kulite Semiconductor Products, Inc., Leonia, NJ; *U.S. Private*, pg. 636

Kurtzman, Christopher J., V.P. & Treas.--McCormick & Company, Incorporated, Sparks, MD; *U.S. Public*, pg. 1066

Kurucz, Donald M., V.P. & Treas.--Walter Industries, Inc., Tampa, FL; *U.S. Public*, pg. 1736

Kushner, Mark, Treas.--The Lathrop Company, Toledo, OH; *U.S. Public*, pg. 1645

Kusiak, Phil, Treas. & Sec.--Marsh Furniture Company, High Point, NC; *U.S. Private*, pg. 708

Kuyers, David J., Exec. V.P., Treas. & Sec.--American Seating Company, Grand Rapids, MI; *U.S. Private*, pg. 61

Kuzma, David R., Chief Fin. Officer, Sr. V.P. & Treas.--Enova Corp, San Diego, CA; *U.S. Public*, pg. 583

Kuzma, David R., Chief Fin. Officer, Sr. V.P. & Treas.--San Diego Gas & Electric Company, San Diego, CA; *U.S. Public*, pg. 584

Kyle, J.F., V.P. & Treas.--Imperial Oil Limited, Toronto, Canada; *U.S. Public*, pg. 602

Kyle, Terrence W., Sr. V.P., Treas. & Asst. Sec.--Shared Medical Systems Corporation, Malvern, PA; *U.S. Public*, pg. 1463

L'Hommedieu, Marcial, Treas.--Continental Can Co., Norwalk, CT; *U.S. Public*, pg. 439

La Forte, Paul A., V.P. & Treas.--N E D Corp., Worcester, MA; *U.S. Private*, pg. 771

LaBarge, Paul C., Sec. & Treas.--Corel Corporation, Ottawa, Canada; *Int'l*, pg. 331

Labrador, Carlos, Treas.--Bank Brussels Lambert Sucursal en Espana, Madrid, Spain; *Int'l*, pg. 148

Labroie, Michael, Treas.--Zantop International Airlines, Inc., Ypsilanti, MI; *U.S. Private*, pg. 1204

Lacchin, Louise M., Treas.--George Weston Limited, Toronto, Canada; *Int'l*, pg. 1494

Lacey, Margaret E., V.P. & Corp. Treas.--ConAgra, Inc., Omaha, NE; *U.S. Public*, pg. 425

Lachey, G., V.P.-Admin., Treas. & Sec.--Neenah Foundry Company, Neenah, WI; *U.S. Private*, pg. 790

Lacy, Paul A., Chief Fin. Officer & V.P.-Fin.--Kronos Incorporated, Waltham, MA; *U.S. Public*, pg. 967

Ladner, Charles L., Chief Fin. Officer, Sr. V.P.-Fin. & Treas.--UGI Corporation, King of Prussia, PA; *U.S. Public*, pg. 1653

LaDue, Jack W., Pres. & Treas.--Gas Equipment Company, Inc., Dallas, TX; *U.S. Private*, pg. 440

Laehy, Timothy P., V.P.-Corp. Fin. & Treas.--Leasing Solutions, Inc., San Jose, CA; *U.S. Public*, pg. 982

Laflamme, Michael D., Mgr.-Treas. Svcs.--Eastern Utilities Associates, Boston, MA; *U.S. Public*, pg. 549

LaFleur, Thomas, Treas.--United States Trust Company, Boston, MA; *U.S. Public*, pg. 1660

Lafontaine, M., V.P. & Treas.--Kruger Inc., Montreal, Canada; *Int'l*, pg. 761

Laforge, Rejean, Controller & Treas.--TQM Pipeline Partnership, Montreal, Canada; *Int'l*, pg. 541

LaForte, Mario J., Chief Fin. Officer--Minyard Food Stores, Inc., Coppell, TX; *U.S. Private*, pg. 752

Lager, Esa, Sr. V.P. & Treas.--Outokumpu Oyj, Espoo, Finland; *Int'l*, pg. 1015

Lahti, Ken J., Asst. Treas.--The Molson Companies Limited, Toronto, Canada; *Int'l*, pg. 887

Lallande, Joseph G., Gen. Mgr. & Treas.--Maine Potato Growers, Inc., Presque Isle, ME; *U.S. Private*, pg. 697

Lalonde, Timothy, Exec. V.P.-Fin. & Treas.--Carrols Corporation, Syracuse, NY; *U.S. Private*, pg. 216

Lalor, Michael A., Chief Fin. Officer, V.P.-Fin. & Treas.--State Industries Inc., Ashland City, TN; *U.S. Private*, pg. 1036

LaMange, Ronald J., V.P. & Treas.--Clipper Belt Lacer Company, Grand Rapids, MI; *U.S. Private*, pg. 413

LaMarche, Gary D., Controller & Treas.--Welco Lumber Company, Marysville, WA; *U.S. Private*, pg. 1161

Lamb, Dwight, Jr., V.P., Treas. & Production Mgr.-Post--Benjamin Franklin Literary & Medical Society, Inc., Indianapolis, IN; *U.S. Private*, pg. 133

Lamb, Isabelle S., Chm. Bd., Pres. & Treas.--Enterprises International Inc., Hoquiam, WA; *U.S. Private*, pg. 377

Lamb, Isabelle S., Treas. & Sec.--Ovalstrapping Inc., Hoquiam, WA; *U.S. Private*, pg. 378

Lamb, Janice B., Treas. & Sec.--Lamb Engineering & Construction Co., Salt Lake City, UT; *U.S. Private*, pg. 644

Lambert, David W., Treas.--Plum Creek Timber Co., L.P., Seattle, WA; *U.S. Public*, pg. 1311

Lambert, Pat, Controller & Treas.--Homestead Homes, Cordele, GA; *U.S. Public*, pg. 318

Lambert, Valerie C., V.P. & Treas.--BC Gas Inc., Vancouver, Canada; *Int'l*, pg. 114

Lamers, Bradley K., Chief Fin. Officer, V.P., Treas. & Sec.--Alternative Resources Corporation, Lincolnshire, IL; *U.S. Public*, pg. 59

Lamers, William F., V.P. & Treas.--Centex Forcum-Lannom, Inc., Dyersburg, TN; *U.S. Public*, pg. 322

Lamoreaux, Dave, Treas. & Sec.--United Producers & Consumers Co-Op, Phoenix, AZ; *U.S. Private*, pg. 1123

Lampe, Patricia, Chief Fin. Officer & Treas.--Chyron Corp., Melville, NY; *Int'l*, pg. 1372

Lampe, Scott, Treas.--Royal Oak Mines Inc., Kirkland, WA; *U.S. Public*, pg. 1410

Lampe, William J., Jr., Treas.--National Publishing Co., Philadelphia, PA; *U.S. Public*, pg. 453

Lamphere, George, Pres. & Treas.--Chas. H. Tompkins Co., Washington, DC; *Int'l*, pg. 633

Lancaster, Steven W., V.P. & Treas.--CCL Industries, Inc., Willowdale, Canada; *Int'l*, pg. 238

Lancaster, Tom, Treas. & Sec.--Bell Gas, Inc., Roswell, NM; *U.S. Private*, pg. 131
Lancaster, Wallace, Controller, Treas. & Sec.--Crown Buick, Inc., Metairie, LA; *U.S. Private*, pg. 292
Lanctot, Claire, V.P. & Treas.--Southam Inc., Don Mills, Canada; *Int'l*, pg. 631
Landau, Ellis, Chief Fin. Officer, Exec. V.P. & Treas.--Boyd Gaming Corporation, Las Vegas, NV; *U.S. Public*, pg. 249
Landers, Marsha S., Treas.--Anderson Electric, Inc., Springfield, IL; *U.S. Private*, pg. 72
Landgraf, Jeanne, Asst. Treas.--Korman Services, L.P., Trevose, PA; *U.S. Private*, pg. 632
Landis, Dean, Treas. & Sec.--United Credit Corp. & Patroit Funding, New York, NY; *U.S. Private*, pg. 1121
Landis, Robert, Treas.--Maxicare Health Plans, Inc., Los Angeles, CA; *U.S. Public*, pg. 1061
Landrigan, Dan, V.P. & Treas.--The Medical Protective Company, Fort Wayne, IN; *U.S. Private*, pg. 728
Landry, Gregory, Treas.--Dairy Mart, Inc., Enfield, CT; *U.S. Public*, pg. 476
Lane, Barry, Treas.--Ultrak Inc., Lewisville, TX; *U.S. Public*, pg. 1663
Lane, Lynn L., V.P.-Investor Rels. & Treas.--Burlington Industries, Inc., Greensboro, NC; *U.S. Public*, pg. 268
Lane, Michael H., V.P.-Fin., Treas. & Sec.--Laclede Steel Company, Saint Louis, MO; *U.S. Public*, pg. 974
Lang, Edward A., III, V.P. & Treas.--Dole Food Company, Inc., Westlake Village, CA; *U.S. Public*, pg. 515
Lang, Gerald, Treas. & Sec.--Delta Power Co., Rockford, IL; *U.S. Private*, pg. 322
Lang, Jeffery R., Chief Fin. Officer & Treas.--Maxon Corporation, Muncie, IN; *U.S. Private*, pg. 716
Lang, Patrick, V.P. & Treas.--Scholls Inc., Arden Hills, MN; *U.S. Private*, pg. 972
Lang, Theresa, Sr. V.P. & Treas.--Merrill Lynch & Co., Inc., New York, NY; *U.S. Public*, pg. 1097
Lang, Vera, Treas., USA--Reed Elsevier plc, London, United Kingdom; *Int'l*, pg. 1093
Langan, P.R., Pres. & Treas.--CENTIN Corporation, Strongsville, OH; *U.S. Public*, pg. 913
Lange, Bruce M., Treas.--Oracle Corporation, Redwood City, CA; *U.S. Public*, pg. 1227
Lange, Heinrich, Exec. V.P. & Treas.--Stinnes Corporation, Tarrytown, NY; *Int'l*, pg. 1460
Lange, Reinhardt J., Jr., Treas.--Potomac Graphic Industries, Inc., New York, NY; *Int'l*, pg. 699
Lange, Terry L., Treas.--Thomas Industries Inc., Louisville, KY; *U.S. Public*, pg. 1598
Langelotti, James P., Asst. Treas.--Sequa Corporation, New York, NY; *U.S. Public*, pg. 1458
Langer, Carol B., Chief Fin. Officer, Treas. & Sec.--Comverse Network Systems, Wakefield, MA; *U.S. Public*, pg. 425
Langer, Carol B., Chief Fin. Officer, V.P.-Investor Rels. & Treas.--LTX Corporation, Westwood, MA; *U.S. Public*, pg. 972
Langford, Gary R., Treas.--Fieldcrest Cannon, Inc., Kannapolis, NC; *U.S. Public*, pg. 1296
Langille, David C., Treas.--TVX Gold Inc., Toronto, Canada; *Int'l*, pg. 1345
Langley, Edsel C., Jr., Treas.--Financial Security Assurance Holdings Ltd., New York, NY; *U.S. Public*, pg. 622
Langley, Richard L., Chief Fin. Officer & Treas.--Sparton Corporation, Jackson, MI; *U.S. Public*, pg. 1496
Langley, W.B., Treas.--Electric Power Equipment Co., Columbus, OH; *U.S. Private*, pg. 368
Langman, Allen, Sr. V.P. & Treas.--Arnhold and S. Bleichroeder, Inc., New York, NY; *U.S. Private*, pg. 83
Langsner, Scott, Treas. & Sec.--MGM Grand, Inc., Las Vegas, NV; *U.S. Public*, pg. 1026
Lanier, Thomas, Exec. V.P., Chief Fin. Officer & Sec.--Salem Carpet Mills, Inc., Winston Salem, NC; *U.S. Public*, pg. 1464
Lanning, Mark R., V.P. & Treas.--Hillenbrand Industries, Inc., Batesville, IN; *U.S. Public*, pg. 828
Lant, Steven V., Treas. & Asst. Sec.--Central Hudson Gas & Electric Corporation, Poughkeepsie, NY; *U.S. Public*, pg. 324
Lanterman, A., Kirk, Treas. & Sec.--Usibelli Coal Mine, Inc., Healy, AK; *U.S. Private*, pg. 1129
Lanthier, Kim, Asst. Treas.--Dun & Bradstreet Canada Ltd., Mississauga, Canada; *U.S. Public*, pg. 536
Lanthier, Serge, Treas. & Comptroller--Shirmax Leasing Ltd., Montreal, Canada; *Int'l*, pg. 1235
Lapkoff, Gregg, Treas.--Automatic Liquid Packaging, Inc., Woodstock, IL; *U.S. Private*, pg. 101
LaPlante, Larry E., V.P.-Fin. & Treas.--Maine Public Service Company, Presque Isle, ME; *U.S. Public*, pg. 1038
LaPointe, William J., Pres. & Chief Exec. Officer--Andover Controls, Andover, MA; *U.S. Private*, pg. 73
LaPorta, Scott A., Sr. V.P. & Treas.--Hilton Hotels Corporation, Beverly Hills, CA; *U.S. Public*, pg. 828
Laramee, Gilles, Treas.--SNC-Lavalin Inc., Montreal, Canada; *Int'l*, pg. 1162
Laramy, William, Chief Fin. Officer, Treas. & Controller--The Purdy Corporation, Manchester, CT; *U.S. Private*, pg. 895
Laraya, Rogelio G., Sr. V.P.-Fin. & Treas.--Benguet Corporation, Manila, Philippines; *Int'l*, pg. 186
Larey, Mike, Treas.--BancTec, Inc., Dallas, TX; *U.S. Public*, pg. 176
Larkin, Linda, Treas.--North Shore Movers, Northbrook, IL; *U.S. Private*, pg. 805
Larkin, Lyle N., Treas.--Fleetwood Enterprises, Inc., Riverside, CA; *U.S. Public*, pg. 650
LaRocca, John Steven, Treas. & Sec.--Roberts Foods, Inc., Springfield, IL; *U.S. Private*, pg. 935
LaRose, Robert C., V.P.-Fin. & Treas.--Landstar Holding, Shelton, CT; *U.S. Public*, pg. 978
Laroucau, Enrique M., Treas.--Destec Energy, Inc., Houston, TX; *U.S. Public*, pg. 1146
Larsen, Edwin, Chief Fin. Officer, V.P. & Treas.--Megapulse, Inc., Bedford, MA; *U.S. Private*, pg. 729
Larsen, J.B., Asst. Treas.--Union Pacific Corporation, Dallas, TX; *U.S. Public*, pg. 1667
Larsen, Lars, V.P. & Treas.--Raychem Corporation, Menlo Park, CA; *U.S. Public*, pg. 1362
Larsen, Tom, Treas. & Sec.--Todd & Sargent, Inc., Ames, IA; *U.S. Private*, pg. 1089
Larson, Al, V.P. & Treas.--Townsend Engineering Co., Des Moines, IA; *U.S. Private*, pg. 1094
Larson, Brian L., Chief Fin. Officer, V.P., Treas. & Sec.--Data Transmission Network Corporation, Omaha, NE; *U.S. Public*, pg. 486
Larson, Ken, Controller & Treas.--BRW, Inc., Minneapolis, MN; *U.S. Private*, pg. 107
Larson, Kevin P., Treas.--UniSource Energy Corporation, Tucson, AZ; *U.S. Public*, pg. 1670
Larson, Kevin P., V.P. & Treas.--Tucson Electric Power Company, Tucson, AZ; *U.S. Public*, pg. 1670
Larson, Larry, Chief Fin. Officer, Controller, Treas. & Sec.--Holmquist Grain & Lumber Co., Oakland, NE; *U.S. Private*, pg. 535
Larson, Mark, Sr. V.P.-Finance & Treas.--Heublein, Inc., Hartford, CT; *Int'l*, pg. 410
Larson, Patricia, Treas.--Larson Manufacturing Company, Brookings, SD; *U.S. Private*, pg. 652
LaRusso, David V., Chief Fin. Officer, Sr. V.P.-Fin. & Treas.--ROHN Industries, Inc., Peoria, IL; *U.S. Public*, pg. 1404
Lascoe, John, Controller & Asst. Treas.--Russell Stover Candies, Inc., Kansas City, MO; *U.S. Private*, pg. 953
Lascoe, John, Treas.--Whitman's Candies, Inc., Kansas City, MO; *U.S. Private*, pg. 953
Lash, Fred, Chief Fin. Officer, Sr. V.P. & Treas.--Hooper Holmes Corporation, Basking Ridge, NJ; *U.S. Public*, pg. 835
Lash, Steven M., Chief Fin. Officer, Exec. V.P. & Treas.--FPA Medical Management, Inc., San Diego, CA; *U.S. Public*, pg. 608
Lassen, Richard, Treas.--Nationwide Building Society, Swindon, United Kingdom; *Int'l*, pg. 912
Lathrop, James P., Chief Acctg. Officer & Asst. Treas.--IWC Resources Corporation, Indianapolis, IN; *U.S. Public*, pg. 1185
Lathrop, James P., V.P. & Asst. Treas.--Indianapolis Water Company, Indianapolis, IN; *U.S. Public*, pg. 1185
Lathte, Rainer, Treas.--Von Roll AG, Gerlafingen, Switzerland; *Int'l*, pg. 1480
Latta, W.J., Asst. Treas.-Cash Mngmt. & Intl. Fin.--Sun Company, Inc (R&M), Philadelphia, PA; *U.S. Public*, pg. 1530
Lau, Constance H., Treas.--Hawaiian Electric Industries, Inc., Honolulu, HI; *U.S. Public*, pg. 799
Lau, Constance H., Chief Fin. Officer & Treas.--HEI Power Corp., Honolulu, HI; *U.S. Public*, pg. 800
Laufen, Klaus M., Mgr.-Fin.--Spar Handels AG, Schenefeld, Germany; *Int'l*, pg. 1288
Laulhere, Larry, Treas. & Sec.--Lombardi Holdings Inc., Whittier, CA; *U.S. Private*, pg. 673
Laurent, Jean Marie, Chief Fin. Officer & V.P.-Fin.--Poliet, Courbevoie, France; *Int'l*, pg. 1177
Laures, Gerald M., V.P.-Fin., Sec. & Treas.--Cobra Electronics Corporation, Chicago, IL; *U.S. Public*, pg. 391
Lauricella, William J., Chief Fin. Officer, V.P. & Treas.--Baldwin Technology Company, Inc., Norwalk, CT; *U.S. Public*, pg. 169
Laut, M., Treas.--Intertec Presentations, Englewood, CO; *U.S. Public*, pg. 1328
Lav-Brunson, Nina, Treas.--Wind River Systems, Inc., Alameda, CA; *U.S. Public*, pg. 1770
LaVictor, Brad W., V.P. & Treas.--United Properties, Bay City, MI; *U.S. Private*, pg. 1123
Lavigne, Laurier J., Treas.--Finch, Pruyn & Co., Inc., Glens Falls, NY; *U.S. Private*, pg. 405
Lavin, Bernice E., Vice Chm., Treas. & Sec.--Alberto-Culver Company, Melrose Park, IL; *U.S. Public*, pg. 37
Lavine, Gilbert S., Treas. & Sec.--Tax Management, Inc., Washington, DC; *U.S. Private*, pg. 182
Lavoie, Normand, V.P.-Opers. & Treas.--QEI, Inc., Springfield, NJ; *U.S. Private*, pg. 897
Lavonen, Helga, Treas.--Kone Corporation, Helsinki, Finland; *Int'l*, pg. 746
LaVoy, Tom, Chief Fin. Officer--Supershuttle Inc., Phoenix, AZ; *U.S. Private*, pg. 1056
Law, Betty J., V.P., Treas. & Sec.--Broadcast Supply Worldwide, Inc., Tacoma, WA; *U.S. Private*, pg. 170
Lawi, David S., Sec. & Treas.--Helm Resources Inc., Greenwich, CT; *U.S. Public*, pg. 808
Lawi, David S., Treas. & Sec.--Unapix Entertainment Inc., New York, NY; *U.S. Public*, pg. 1664
Lawler, Jim, V.P. & Treas.--Converse Inc., North Reading, MA; *U.S. Public*, pg. 441
Lawlor, Thomas J., Jr., Treas.--The Boeing Travel Company, Irvine, CA; *U.S. Public*, pg. 241
Lawrence, David L., Treas. & Asst. Sec.--National-Standard Co., Niles, MI; *U.S. Public*, pg. 1160
Lawrence, Robert A., Treas. & Sec.--Sullivan & Cozart Inc., Louisville, KY; *U.S. Private*, pg. 1049
Lawson, Alfred B., Jr., Asst. Treas.--Connecticut Natural Gas Corporation, Hartford, CT; *U.S. Public*, pg. 285
Lawson, Herbert S., V.P. & Treas.--COBE Laboratories, Inc., Lakewood, CO; *Int'l*, pg. 667
Lay, F. Edwin, Jr., Chief Fin. Officer & Treas.--Lay's Fine Foods, Knoxville, TN; *U.S. Private*, pg. 655
Laybourne, Linda, Chief Fin. Officer & Treas.--Sues, Young & Brown Inc., Baldwin Park, CA; *U.S. Private*, pg. 1049
Lazard, Jacques C., V.P. & Treas.--America West Airlines, Inc., Phoenix, AZ; *U.S. Public*, pg. 67
Leadbeater, D., Treas. & Tax Mgr.--English China Clays Plc, Theale, United Kingdom; *Int'l*, pg. 455
Leader, Lennert, Chief Fin. Officer, Sr. V.P. & Treas.--America Online Incorporated, Dulles, VA; *U.S. Public*, pg. 66
Leano, Alberto M., Treas.--Benguet Ebara Real Estate Corp., Laguna, Philippines; *Int'l*, pg. 187
Leary, Dennis, Chief Fin. Officer & Treas.--Creative Marketing International Corp., West Chicago, IL; *U.S. Private*, pg. 287
Leasure, George, Pres., Chief Exec. Officer, Chief Fin. Officer & Treas.--Ghent Manufacturing, Inc., Lebanon, OH; *U.S. Private*, pg. 450
Leath, Scott, V.P.-Bus. Mgr. & Treas.--Richmond Newspapers, Inc., Richmond, VA; *U.S. Public*, pg. 1079
Leatherby, Dennis, V.P. & Treas.--Tyson Foods, Inc., Springdale, AR; *U.S. Public*, pg. 1652
Leathers, Susan C., Sr. Dir. & Asst. Treas.--The LTV Corporation, Cleveland, OH; *U.S. Public*, pg. 971
Lebens, Jeffrey K., Chief Fin. Officer, V.P. & Treas.--Intermountain Industries, Inc., Boise, ID; *U.S. Private*, pg. 568
LeBlanc, Charles, V.P., Controller, Sec., & Asst. Treas.--National Service Cleaning Corporation, South Windsor, CT; *U.S. Public*, pg. 1208
Leblanc, Maryanne, Controller & Treas.--Tano Automation, Inc., Harahan, LA; *U.S. Public*, pg. 1763
LeBlanc, Richard, Treas. & Dir.-Fin. & Investor Relations--Ensco International Incorporated (ENSCO), Dallas, TX; *U.S. Public*, pg. 585
Lebovitz, Stephen D., Exec. V.P. & Treas.--CBL & Associates Properties, Inc., Chattanooga, TN; *U.S. Public*, pg. 273
Lebson, Evan M., V.P. & Treas.--Genzyme Corporation, Cambridge, MA; *U.S. Public*, pg. 733
Lebson, Evan M., V.P. & Treas.--Genzyme Transgenics, Framingham, MA; *U.S. Public*, pg. 733
LeBuhn, David, Treas.--MedImmune, Inc., Gaithersburg, MD; *U.S. Public*, pg. 1081
Leclair, Daniel, V.P.-Fin. & Treas.--Hydro-Quebec, Montreal, Canada; *Int'l*, pg. 640
Ledella, Paul, Treas.--Hubbard Farms, Inc., Walpole, NH; *U.S. Public*, pg. 1092
Ledella, Paul, Treas.--Hubbard Farms, Inc., Walpole, NH; *Int'l*, pg. 1114
Leduc, Joe, Treas.--Michigan Blueberry Growers Assn., Grand Junction, MI; *U.S. Private*, pg. 740
Lee-Guard, D.R., Treas.--General Motors-Holden's Automotive Limited, Melbourne, Australia; *U.S. Public*, pg. 723
Lee, An, Treas.--Hardel Mutual Plywood Corporation, Olympia, WA; *U.S. Private*, pg. 501
Lee, Beong W., Treas.--Crown Confectionery Co., Ltd., Seoul, Korea; *Int'l*, pg. 348
Lee, Brenda, V.P., Treas. & Controller--Malama Pacific Corp., Honolulu, HI; *U.S. Public*, pg. 800
Lee, Jeanne Marie, Treas. & Sec.--Lakeside Industries, Issaquah, WA; *U.S. Private*, pg. 644
Lee, John, Jr., Pres. & Treas.--Ireland Coffee Tea, Inc., Pleasantville, NJ; *U.S. Public*, pg. 351
Lee, Linda, Treas. Analyst--Cole National Corporation, Cleveland, OH; *U.S. Public*, pg. 396
Lee, Myron, Mgr.-Treasury--Solectron Corporation, Milpitas, CA; *U.S. Public*, pg. 1483
Lee, Young W., Treas.--American Home Shield Corporation, Memphis, TN; *U.S. Public*, pg. 1461
Leeder, C.W., Treas.--Bespak plc, Norfolk, United Kingdom; *Int'l*, pg. 193
Leef, Ruth L., Treas.--Industrial Towel & Uniform, New Berlin, WI; *U.S. Private*, pg. 561
Lefeuvre, Francois, Treas.--Credit Mutuel, Paris, France; *Int'l*, pg. 344
Leffler, Darryl, Treas. & Asst. Sec.--National Cooperative Refinery Association, Mc Pherson, KS; *U.S. Private*, pg. 781
Leffler, Donald, Treas. & Sec.--Redburn Tire Company, Phoenix, AZ; *U.S. Private*, pg. 915
Leffler, Georgiana E., Treas.--Carlos R. Leffler Inc., Richland, PA; *U.S. Private*, pg. 658
Lefkovits, Bernard, Treas.--Roselle Paper Co., Inc., Roselle, NJ; *U.S. Private*, pg. 945
Legault, Francois, Sr. V.P.-Fin. & Treas.--BioChem Pharma Inc., Laval, Canada; *Int'l*, pg. 196
Legg, Robert W., Treas.--Hollinger Inc., Vancouver, Canada; *Int'l*, pg. 630
LeGrande, E. David, Mng. Dir.-Export Division & Treas.--Gudebrod, Inc., Pottstown, PA; *U.S. Private*, pg. 486
Lehan, Bradley D., Asst. Treas.--Houghton Mifflin Company, Boston, MA; *U.S. Public*, pg. 841
Lehman, Branden, Treas.--Piercing Pagoda, Inc., Bethlehem, PA; *U.S. Public*, pg. 1296
Lehman, Harold L., V.P. & Treas.--Chicago Holdings, Inc., Pittsburgh, PA; *U.S. Private*, pg. 234
Lehmann, Manfred R., V.P. & Treas.--Nestle Holdings, Inc., Stamford, CT; *Int'l*, pg. 916
Lehmann, Richard, Sr. V.P.-Fin. & Treas.--Rolex Watch U.S.A., Inc., New York, NY; *Int'l*, pg. 1126
Lehr, Donald A., Chm. Bd., Chief Exec. Officer, Treas. & Sec.--Cubix Corporation, Carson City, NV; *U.S. Private*, pg. 294
Lekach, Rachmil, Chief Exec. Officer--L. Luria & Son, Inc., Medley, FL; *U.S. Public*, pg. 1020
Leland, John M., Jr., Dir.-Investor & Banking Rels.--Lukens Inc., Coatesville, PA; *U.S. Public*, pg. 1019
LeLeur, Robert, V.P. & Treas.--National Insurance Group, South San Francisco, CA; *U.S. Public*, pg. 1157
Lemajeur, Jeffrey W., Chief Fin. Officer, V.P.-Fin. & Treas.--Binks Sames Corporation, Franklin Park, IL; *U.S. Public*, pg. 229
LeMarchand, Francois, V.P. & Treas.--Bombardier Inc., Montreal, Canada; *Int'l*, pg. 199
Lembke, Mark L., Asst. Treas. & Asst. Sec.--American Crystal Sugar Company, Moorhead, MN; *U.S. Private*, pg. 52
Lemen, Juanita, Treas. & Sec.--The Auchter Company, Jacksonville, FL; *U.S. Private*, pg. 98
Lemmer, Juergen, Mng. Dir.-Treas.--Commerzbank AG, Frankfurt, Germany; *Int'l*, pg. 308
Lemos, Robert A., Chief Fin. Officer, V.P.-Fin. & Treas.--Varian Associates, Inc., Palo Alto, CA; *U.S. Public*, pg. 1710

Lempke, R. Michael, Sr. V.P. & Treas.--Fort James Corporation, Richmond, VA; *U.S. Public*, pg. 670
Lenderman, Gaynell, Treas. & Sec.--Gay Johnson's Inc., Grand Junction, CO; *U.S. Private*, pg. 595
Lennox, Douglas C., Treas.--IDEX Corporation, Northbrook, IL; *U.S. Public*, pg. 862
Lenschow, William, Treas.--Dairy Farmers of America, Inc., Arlington, TX; *U.S. Private*, pg. 307
Lentych, Larry E., Chief Fin. Officer & Treas.--1st Source Corporation, South Bend, IN; *U.S. Public*, pg. 638
Lentych, Larry E., Treas.--1st Source Leasing, South Bend, IN; *U.S. Public*, pg. 638
Lentz, Thomas E., Treas.--Avemco Corporation, Frederick, MD; *U.S. Public*, pg. 151
Lenzmeier, Allen U., Chief Fin. Officer & Exec. V.P.--Best Buy Co., Inc., Eden Prairie, MN; *U.S. Public*, pg. 223
Lenzmeier, Michael G., V.P.-Opers., Treas. & Asst. Sec.--PrimeVest Financial Services, Inc., Saint Cloud, MN; *U.S.* Public, pg. 1376
Leon, Luis, Chief Fin. Officer, Sr. V.P. & Treas.--GS Industries, Inc., Charlotte, NC; *U.S. Private*, pg. 435
Leonard, H.B., V.P. & Treas.--Mount Vernon Mills, Inc., Greenville, SC; *U.S. Private*, pg. 835
Leonard, Stephen P., Sr. V.P. & Treas.--Vesta Insurance Group, Inc., Birmingham, AL; *U.S. Public*, pg. 1718
Leonard, Timothy M., Chief Fin. Officer, V.P.-Fin. & Treas.--DBT Online, Inc., Las Vegas, NV; *U.S. Public*, pg. 472
Leone, John A., Pres. & Chief Exec. Officer--Bonney Forge Corporation, Allentown, PA; *U.S. Private*, pg. 156
Leone, William, Sr. V.P. & Treas.--Topa Insurance Company, Los Angeles, CA; *U.S. Private*, pg. 1091
Leonhardt, Jearld D., Exec. V.P.-Fin. & Admin. & Treas.--CommScope, Inc., Hickory, NC; *U.S. Public*, pg. 415
Lepley, Steve, Treas.--Simons Palmer Denton Clemmow & Johnson Ltd., London, United Kingdom; *Int'l*, pg. 1252
LePorte, James L., III, V.P., Treas. & Controller--Allen Telecom, Inc., Beachwood, OH; *U.S. Public*, pg. 45
Lerner, Martin, Chm. Bd., Pres. & Treas.--American List Corporation, Mineola, NY; *U.S. Public*, pg. 1481
Lesh, Rodger L., Chief Fin. Officer, V.P. & Treas.--Lewis Brothers Bakeries, Inc., Evansville, IN; *U.S. Private*, pg. 665
Leslie, C.L., Asst. Treas & Asst. Sec.--Lafarge Canada Inc., Montreal, Canada; *Int'l*, pg. 789
Leslie, Laurence, Controller & Treas.--Fluke Corporation, Everett, WA; *U.S. Public*, pg. 659
Leslie, R.D., Asst. Treas.--Lufkin Industries, Inc., Lufkin, TX; *U.S. Public*, pg. 1019
Lesser, Robert A., Treas. & Sec.--Alba Forwarding Co., Inc., Jersey City, NJ; *U.S. Private*, pg. 32
Lester, Rick, Chief Fin. Officer, V.P. & Asst. Sec.--Domain Energy Corporation, Houston, TX; *U.S. Public*, pg. 515
Lester, Sandy, Treas. & Sec.--First Financial Bankshares, Inc., Abilene, TX; *U.S. Public*, pg. 633
Letica, Gudrun, Sec. & Treas.--Letica Corporation, Rochester, MI; *U.S. Private*, pg. 661
Leunis, William G., III, Chief Fin. Officer, Sr. V.P.-Fin., Treas. & Sec.--Ultratech Stepper, Inc., San Jose, CA; *U.S. Public*, pg. 1663
Level, Leon J., Chief Fin. Officer, V.P. & Treas.--Computer Sciences Corporation, El Segundo, CA; *U.S. Public*, pg. 422
Levesque, Donald, V.P. & Treas.--Irwin Toy Ltd., Toronto, Canada; *Int'l*, pg. 688
Levin-Hoverter, Mia, Treas. & Sec.--Sturgis Iron & Metal Company, Inc., Sturgis, MI; *U.S. Private*, pg. 1048
Levin, Alan G., V.P. & Treas.--Pfizer Inc., New York, NY; *U.S. Public*, pg. 1281
Levin, Gilbert V., Dr., Chm., Pres., Chief Exec. Officer & Treas.--Biospherics Incorporated, Beltsville, MD; *U.S. Public*, pg. 232
Levine, Arnold H., Chief Fin. Officer, V.P.-Fin., Treas. & Asst. Sec.--General Microwave Corporation, Amityville, NY; *U.S. Public*, pg. 717
Levine, David, Dir.-Cash Mngmt. & Asst. Treas.--Fleming Companies, Inc., Oklahoma City, OK; *U.S. Public*, pg. 652
Levine, Leon, Chm. Bd. & Treas.--Family Dollar Stores, Inc., Matthews, NC; *U.S. Public*, pg. 612
Levine, Paul, V.P.-Fin., Treas. & Sec.--Magnetic Analysis Corp., Mount Vernon, NY; *U.S. Private*, pg. 695
Levinson, Anthony, Chief Fin. Officer, V.P. & Treas.--Automobile Protection Corporation-APCO, Atlanta, GA; *U.S. Public*, pg. 150
Levy, Bret W., V.P.-Credit & Customer Service & Treas.--Gottschalks Inc., Fresno, CA; *U.S. Public*, pg. 754
Levy, Edward C., Jr., Pres. & Treas.--Edward C. Levy Co., Dearborn, MI; *U.S. Private*, pg. 664
Levy, James G., V.P. & Treas.--IRT Property Company, Atlanta, GA; *U.S. Public*, pg. 858
Levy, Sally, Treas. & Sec.--Jacob Levy & Bros., Inc., Louisville, KY; *U.S. Private*, pg. 664
Levy, Steven A., Exec. V.P. & Treas.--The Titan Industrial Corp., New York, NY; *U.S. Private*, pg. 1089
Levy, Stuart, Chief Fin. Officer, V.P., Treas. & Sec.--Donnkenny, Inc., New York, NY; *U.S. Public*, pg. 519
Levy, Todd, Treas.--Color Spot Nursery, Inc., Pleasant Hill, CA; *U.S. Private*, pg. 254
Lew, James W., Exec. V.P., Treas. & Sec.--Lodgistix, Inc., Phoenix, AZ; *U.S. Public*, pg. 1527
Lewandowski, Greg, Controller & Asst. Treas.--Dean Pickle & Specialty Products Co., Green Bay, WI; *U.S. Public*, pg. 490
Lewis, A.M., Treas.--The Thomson Corporation, Stamford, CT; *U.S. Public*, pg. 1599
Lewis, Edwin A., V.P. & Treas.--The Hearst Corporation, New York, NY; *U.S. Private*, pg. 515
Lewis, George R., V.P. & Treas.--Philip Morris Companies Inc., New York, NY; *U.S. Public*, pg. 1287
Lewis, Ila J., Treas. & Dir.-Dir. Mktg. & Dir. Response--Gerber Plumbing Fixtures Corporation, Chicago, IL; *U.S. Private*, pg. 449
Lewis, Ila J., Treas.--Kokomo Sanitary Pottery Corp., Kokomo, IN; *U.S. Private*, pg. 449
Lewis, J.A., Controller, Treas. & Sec.--Logo 7, Inc., Indianapolis, IN; *U.S. Public*, pg. 1644
Lewis, Jim, Chief Fin. Officer, V.P., Treas. & Sec.--Hale-Halsell Company, Tulsa, OK; *U.S. Private*, pg. 494
Lewis, Lloyd, Dir.-Fin. & Treas.--Fischer Imaging Corporation, Denver, CO; *U.S. Public*, pg. 647
Lewis, Paul, Asst. Treas.--Ford Motor Company, Dearborn, MI; *U.S. Public*, pg. 661
Lewis, R. Leon, V.P.-Admin., Treas. & Sec.--Old Dominion Box Co., Inc., Madison Heights, VA; *U.S. Private*, pg. 814
Lewis, Richard H., Chm. Bd., Pres., Chief Exec. & Fin. Officer & Treas.--Prima Energy Corporation, Denver, CO; *U.S. Public*, pg. 1325
Ley, Stephen R., Treas.--Robbins & Myers, Inc., Dayton, OH; *U.S. Public*, pg. 1393
Libbe, Allan J., Treas. & Sec.--Rudolph/Libbe, Inc., Walbridge, OH; *U.S. Private*, pg. 950
Lichtenstein, Jack, Sec. & Treas.--Auburn Hosiery Mills, Inc., Auburn, KY; *U.S. Private*, pg. 98
Lickert, W.R., Treas. & Sec.--Mason & Hanger Corporation, Inc., Lexington, KY; *U.S. Private*, pg. 711
Lieberg, Eric N., Pres., Chief Fin. Officer & Exec. V.P.--Rundel Products, Inc., Cincinnati, OH; *U.S. Private*, pg. 951
Lieble, Randy, Treas.--National Presto Industries, Inc., Eau Claire, WI; *U.S. Public*, pg. 1159
Lierman, P., Asst. Treas.--London & Leeds (USA) Corporation, New York, NY; *Int'l*, pg. 788
Lietzke, Richard E., Asst. Treas.--Magna Lomason Corp., Farmington Hills, MI; *Int'l*, pg. 830
Light, Daniel T., Treas. & Sec.--Belle Tire Distributor Inc., Allen Park, MI; *U.S. Private*, pg. 132
Lightstone, Stephen, Chief Fin. Officer, Sr. V.P.-Fin. & Treas.--Payless Cashways, Inc., Kansas City, MO; *U.S. Public*, pg. 1267
Liles, Jack D., Pres. & Treas.--TVESCO, Inc., Memphis, TN; *U.S. Private*, pg. 1066
Lim, Bernardo D., V.P. & Treas.--AGP Industrial Corporation, Manila, Philippines; *Int'l*, pg. 14
Lim, Stewart C., V.P. & Treas.--Philippine Airlines, Inc., Manila, Philippines; *Int'l*, pg. 1050
Lind, Kenneth H., V.P.-Fin. & Treas.--Franklin Electronic Publishers, Inc., Burlington, NJ; *U.S. Public*, pg. 679
Lindahl, Roger, Treas.--Sweetheart Cup Company Inc., Owings Mills, MD; *U.S. Private*, pg. 1058
Lindberg, William P., Treas. & Asst Sec.--Peoples Electric Contractor, Inc., Saint Paul, MN; *U.S. Private*, pg. 851
Lindbergh, Leif, Treas.--Avesta Sheffield AB, Stockholm, Sweden; *Int'l*, pg. 221
Linder, Donald O., Treas.--Minnesota Electric Supply Company, Willmar, MN; *U.S. Private*, pg. 750
Lindgerg, Dennis N., Treas.--OmniTRAX Inc., Chicago, IL; *U.S. Private*, pg. 171
Lindley, William G., Treas. & Sec.--T.H. Rogers Lumber Co., Edmond, OK; *U.S. Private*, pg. 940
Lindsay, James W., Asst. Treas.--Acuson Corporation, Mountain View, CA; *U.S. Public*, pg. 18
Lindstedt, Charlotte Zethraeus, Treas.--NCC AB, Solna, Sweden; *Int'l*, pg. 898
Linehan, James B., Chief Fin. Officer, V.P.-Fin., Treas. & Controller--Ruslander & Sons, Inc., Buffalo, NY; *U.S. Private*, pg. 952
Lineuberg, A., Treas.--Orbotech Ltd., Yavne, Israel; *Int'l*, pg. 1007
Ling, Dennis, V.P. & Treas.--Avon Products, Inc., New York, NY; *U.S. Public*, pg. 155
Ling, Robert M., Treas.--Grocers & Merchants Management Co., Covina, CA; *U.S. Private*, pg. 227
Ling, Robert M., Jr., Treas.--Grocers Specialty Co., Los Angeles, CA; *U.S. Private*, pg. 227
Ling, Robert M., Jr., Treas.--Preferred Public Storage Co., Los Angeles, CA; *U.S. Private*, pg. 227
Lingen, Charles, Chief Fin. Officer & Sr. V.P.--The Sportsman's Guide, Inc., Saint Paul, MN; *U.S. Public*, pg. 1499
Link, J.F., Treas.--Texaco Inc., White Plains, NY; *U.S. Public*, pg. 1582
Linkous, Clare, Treas. & Sec.--Linkous Construction Company, Inc., Memphis, TN; *U.S. Private*, pg. 669
Linton, Myreel, Treas. & Sec.--Landa, Inc., Portland, OR; *U.S. Private*, pg. 646
Linton, Richard A., Controller & Treas.--Consolidated Midwest, Inc., La Crosse, WI; *U.S. Private*, pg. 265
Lipoff, Lawrence, Treas. & Office Mgr.--Butler Foods, Inc., Philadelphia, PA; *U.S. Private*, pg. 190
Lippert, F. Avie, Asst. Treas.--Network Systems Corporation, Minneapolis, MN; *U.S. Public*, pg. 1522
Lisker, Lawrence, Chief Exec. Officer & Treas.--Antwerp Diamond Distributors Inc., New York, NY; *U.S. Private*, pg. 76
Lisondra, Cynthia A., Treas.--Philippine Cocoa Estates Corporation, Davao, Philippines; *Int'l*, pg. 187
List, Ruth, Treas. & Sec.--Alatec Products, Inc., Chatsworth, CA; *U.S. Private*, pg. 31
Liszewski, Barbara, Chief Oper. Officer, Treas.--Nurses Inc., Houston, TX; *Int'l*, pg. 1285
Little, Bradley A., Chief Fin. Officer, Sr. V.P.-Fin. & Treas.--Calton, Inc., Manalapan, NJ; *U.S. Public*, pg. 296
Little, Gene E., V.P.-Fin.--The Timken Company, Canton, OH; *U.S. Public*, pg. 1617
Little, Richard K., Sr. V.P. & Treas.--Rosser International, Inc., Atlanta, GA; *U.S. Private*, pg. 946
Littman, Irv, V.P. & Treas.--Boise Cascade Corporation, Boise, ID; *U.S. Public*, pg. 242
Livingston, Marge, Treas. & Controller--The Harwood Companies, Inc., Fort Lauderdale, FL; *U.S. Public*, pg. 1433
Llamas, Steve, Treas.--Eby Corporation, Wichita, KS; *U.S. Private*, pg. 359
Lloyd, David G., Chief Fin. Officer & Sr. V.P.--Taco Cabana, San Antonio, TX; *U.S. Public*, pg. 1559
Lloyd, Dwayne, Treas. & Sec.--Texas Electric Cooperatives, Inc., Austin, TX; *U.S. Private*, pg. 1078
Lloyd, Rjay, Vice Chm. & Chief Fin. Officer--Forever Living Products International, Inc., Scottsdale, AZ; *U.S. Private*, *pg. 418*
Locher, John J., V.P. & Treas.--Barnes Group Inc., Bristol, CT; *U.S. Public*, pg. 189
Locke, C. Jean, V.P. & Asst. Treas.--Brookfield Homes Ltd., Toronto, Canada; *Int'l*, pg. 228
Locke, C. Jean, V.P. & Asst. Treas.--Brookfield Homes, Del Mar, CA; *Int'l*, pg. 228
Lockhart, Dick, Treas.--MFG Union City Operations, Union City, PA; *U.S. Private*, pg. 756
Lockwood, Glenn C., Chief Fin. Officer, V.P. & Treas.--Commercial Realty & Resources Corp., Wall, NJ; *U.S. Public*, pg. 1172
Lockwood, Glenn C., Chief Fin. Officer, V.P. & Treas.--NJR Energy Services Corporation, Wall, NJ; *U.S. Public*, pg. 1172
Loeb, Carl, Treas. & Sec.--Piknik Products Company, Inc., Montgomery, AL; *U.S. Private*, pg. 865
Loeber, Michael, Treas. & Sec.--Loeber Motors, Inc., Lincolnwood, IL; *U.S. Private*, pg. 672
Loeffler, David E., Chief Fin. Officer, V.P. & Treas.--Arkansas Best Corporation, Fort Smith, AR; *U.S. Public*, pg. 130
Loeffler, Ferdinand, Treas.--Adam Opel AG, Russelsheim, Germany; *U.S. Public*, pg. 721
Loer, James E., Jr., Treas. & Mgr.-Admin.--Walpole Woodworkers, Inc., Walpole, MA; *U.S. Private*, pg. 1148
Loew, James P., V.P.-Fin., Controller & Treas.--Modern Concrete Septic Tank Company, Ottsville, PA; *U.S. Private*, pg. 754
Loffredo, Robert S., Treas.--The American Stock Exchange, New York, NY; *U.S. Private*, pg. 62
Lofstrand, Bobby, Treas. & Sec.--Minnkota Power Cooperative, Inc., Grand Forks, ND; *U.S. Private*, pg. 751
Loftis, Harry E., Chief Fin. Officer & V.P.--Riceland Foods, Inc., Stuttgart, AR; *U.S. Private*, pg. 928
Lofton, A.L., Jr., Exec. V.P. & Treas.--Utilities Construction Co., Inc. Of South Carolina, Charleston, SC; *U.S. Private*, *pg. 1130*
Loftus, David J., Treas.--WTD Industries, Inc., Portland, OR; *U.S. Public*, pg. 1729
Logan, Harold R., Jr., Exec. V.P.-Fin. & Treas.--TransMontaigne Oil Company, Denver, CO; *U.S. Public*, pg. 1631
Logan, Robert, Exec. V.P., Sec. & Treas.--Plastics Manufacturing Company, Dallas, TX; *U.S. Public*, pg. 1530
Loher, Brian H., Treas., Sec. & Dir.-Investor Rels.--Hall Contracting Corp., Louisville, KY; *U.S. Private*, pg. 495
Lohman, Paul J., Treas. & Asst. Sec.--Sands Investments, Inc., Myrtle Beach, SC; *U.S. Private*, pg. 964
Lohr, William J., Chief Fin. Officer & Treas.--Citizens Insurance Company of America, Howell, MI; *U.S. Public*, pg. 54
Lohrentz, Donald W., Treas.--NICOR Inc., Naperville, IL; *U.S. Public*, pg. 1182
Loibl, K.M., Dr., Treas.--Esso Aktiengesellschaft, Hamburg, Germany; *U.S. Public*, pg. 601
Londergan, Kevin M., V.P. & Treas.--Dixie Carriers, Inc., Houston, TX; *U.S. Public*, pg. 962
London, James A., V.P. & Treas.--Anixter International, Chicago, IL; *U.S. Public*, pg. 115
Long, Charles, Chief Fin. Officer, Sr. V.P. & Treas.--Highmark Inc., Pittsburgh, PA; *U.S. Private*, pg. 528
Long, Jonathan R., Pres., Chief Exec. Officer & Chief Fin. Officer--J.E. Higgins Lumber Co., Concord, CA; *U.S. Private*, pg. 527
Long, Ron, Treas.--Browning-Ferris Industries, Inc., Houston, TX; *U.S. Public*, pg. 262
Long, William, Treas.--Jasper Corp., Birmingham, AL; *U.S. Private*, pg. 583
Longbons, Jeffrey M., Chief Fin. Officer, V.P., Sec. & Treas.--Monitor Liability Managers, Inc., Rolling Meadows, IL; *U.S. Public*, pg. 215
Longden, Andy, Treas.--British Telecommunications plc, London, United Kingdom; *Int'l*, pg. 222
Loomis, James, Asst. Sec. & Asst. Treas.--Loomis Brothers, Inc., Cedar Rapids, IA; *U.S. Private*, pg. 675
Loomis, Lois, Treas.--Loomis Brothers, Inc., Cedar Rapids, IA; *U.S. Private*, pg. 675
Looney, Dennis, V.P.-Treas.--Springer-Verlag New York Inc., New York, NY; *Int'l*, pg. 1291
Loose, David, Treas.--British Aerospace Holdings Inc., Chantilly, VA; *Int'l*, pg. 218
Lopes, Teresa Silva, Treas.--Transportes Aereos Portugueses, Lisbon, Portugal; *Int'l*, pg. 1418
LoPiccolo, Paul, Treas.--Royal Appliance Mfg. Co., Cleveland, OH; *U.S. Public*, pg. 1410
Lord, Gerald S., V.P.-Fin. & Controller-U.S. Grocery--Campbell Soup Company, Camden, NJ; *U.S. Public*, pg. 298
Lorenz, Donald N., Chief Fin. Officer & V.P.-Fin.--Price Brothers Co., Dayton, OH; *U.S. Private*, pg. 883
Lorig, Alan S., Treas. & Sec.--Dedert Corporation, Olympia Fields, IL; *U.S. Private*, pg. 320
Lorne, W.J., Treas.--East Jordan Iron Works, East Jordan, MI; *U.S. Private*, pg. 356
Losik, Timothy P., Chief Fin. Officer, V.P. & Treas.--Hadco Corporation, Salem, NH; *U.S. Public*, pg. 773
Losurdo, Maria, Treas.--Losurdo Foods, Inc., Hackensack, NJ; *U.S. Private*, pg. 677
Loth, C. Lewis, Jr., V.P.--Scott & Stringfellow Financial, Inc., Richmond, VA; *U.S. Public*, pg. 1445
Louis, Daniel R., Treas.--Progressive Casualty Insurance Co., Cleveland, OH; *U.S. Public*, pg. 1334
Lousteau, J. Keith, V.P. & Treas.--Tidewater Inc., New Orleans, LA; *U.S. Public*, pg. 1608
Lovaas, John, Pres., Treas. & Gen. Mgr.--Harrington & King, Chicago, IL; *U.S. Private*, pg. 504
Love, William, Treas.--Luskin's, Inc., Columbia, MD; *U.S. Private*, pg. 681

Lovejoy, Robert M., Jr., V.P. & Treas.--General Host Corporation, Stamford, CT; *U.S. Public*, pg. 715
Lovelace, Belle, Treas. & Sec.--Mar-Mac Manufacturing Company, Inc., McBee, SC; *U.S. Private*, pg. 701
Loveland, Peter G., Pres. & Treas.--Maze Nails, Peru, IL; *U.S. Private*, pg. 718
Loverine, Denis L., Treas.--Snap-On Tools Corporation, Kenosha, WI; *U.S. Public*, pg. 1480
Lovvorn, Joseph, Controller & Treas.--Alabama Farmers Co-op, Decatur, AL; *U.S. Private*, pg. 30
Lowber, John M., Chief Fin. Officer, Sr. V.P., Treas. & Sec.--General Communication, Inc., Anchorage, AK; *U.S. Public*, pg. 708
Lowe, Charles, Grp. Treas.--Prudential Corporation PLC, London, United Kingdom; *Int'l*, pg. 1073
Lower, Martin A., Pres. & Treas.--Ludlow Textiles Co., Inc., Ludlow, MA; *U.S. Private*, pg. 680
Lowry, Graeme, Treas.--A.G. Simpson Co. Limited, Scarborough, Canada; *Int'l*, pg. 1252
Lowry, Mike M., Treas. & Sec.--Moto, Inc., Belleville, IL; *U.S. Private*, pg. 764
Lozano, Juanita E., Chief Fin. Officer & Treas.--Play by Play Toys & Novelties, Inc., San Antonio, TX; *U.S. Public*, pg. 1309
Lozier, Jackie, Controller & Treas.--Washington Homes, Inc., Landover, MD; *U.S. Public*, pg. 1741
Lubbars, Steve, V.P. & Treas.--Castex Incorporated, Holland, MI; *U.S. Public*, pg. 1577
Luca, William, Chief Fin. Officer, V.P.-Fin. & Treas.--Cannondale Corporation, Bethel, CT; *U.S. Public*, pg. 301
Lucarelli, Brian M., Chief Fin. Officer, Controller, Asst Treas. & Asst. Sec.--Alaskan Copper Companies, Seattle, WA; *U.S. Private*, pg. 31
Lucas, William J., Treas.--R.M. Palmer Company, Reading, PA; *U.S. Private*, pg. 835
Lucchese, Cynthia, Treas.--Guidant Corporation, Indianapolis, IN; *U.S. Public*, pg. 768
Lucien, Kent T., Chief Fin. Officer, Exec. V.P. & Treas.--Buyco, Inc., Honolulu, HI; *U.S. Private*, pg. 190
Lucien, Kent T., V.P. & Treas.--Mauna Loa Macadamia Nut Corporation, Hilo, HI; *U.S. Private*, pg. 190
Lucien, Kent T., V.P. & Treas.--Mauna Kea Agribusiness Co., Inc., Papaikou, HI; *U.S. Private*, pg. 190
Luckhardt, Robert, Treas. & Sec.--The Fifth Third Bank of Northern Kentucky, Florence, KY; *U.S. Public*, pg. 621
Ludden, Timothy W., V.P. & Treas.--UNUM Corporation, Portland, ME; *U.S. Public*, pg. 1699
Ludden, Timothy W., V.P. & Treas.--UNUM Holding Company, Portland, ME; *U.S. Public*, pg. 1699
Ludder, Scott, Treas.--Vilter Manufacturing Corporation, Cudahy, WI; *U.S. Private*, pg. 1140
Ludington, Christopher, Treas.--Trapp Family Lodge, Inc., Stowe, VT; *U.S. Private*, pg. 1098
Ludmans, Raymond R., Treas.--M/G Transportation Services, Inc., Amelia, OH; *U.S. Public*, pg. 1111
Ludt, Steve G., Pres., Chief Exec. Officer & Treas.--Columbian Rope Company, Guntown, MS; *U.S. Private*, pg. 256
Ludwick, Lance, Asst. Treas.--Barton Incorporated, Chicago, IL; *U.S. Public*, pg. 300
Ludwig, Douglas L., Chief Fin. Officer, Sr. V.P. & Treas.--Four Seasons Hotels Inc., Don Mills, Canada; *Int'l*, pg. 502
Luffy, T.C., Treas.--Columbia Gas Distribution Companies, Columbus, OH; *U.S. Public*, pg. 402
Lugar, Todd, V.P.-Opers., Treas. & Sec.--Thomas L. Green & Co., Inc., Indianapolis, IN; *U.S. Private*, pg. 477
Luhrs, Randy, Chief Fin. Officer & Treas.--Muska Electric Company, Roseville, MN; *U.S. Private*, pg. 768
Luke, James P., Chief Fin. Officer & Exec. V.P.--Blessings Corporation, Newport News, VA; *U.S. Private*, pg. 1179
Luke, Paul B., Chief Fin. Officer, Sr. V.P., Treas. & Sec.--T&W Financial Corporation, Tacoma, WA; *U.S. Public*, pg. 1552
Lummis, P. Bradley, Sr. V.P., Treas. & Sec.--Mrs. Baird's Bakeries, Inc., Fort Worth, TX; *U.S. Private*, pg. 765
Lund, Alan H., Chief Fin. Officer, Sr. V.P., Treas.--International Lease Finance Corporation, Los Angeles, CA; *U.S. Public*, pg. 85
Lund, Gordon H., Treas. & Asst. Sec.--Dynamic Homes, Inc., Detroit Lakes, MN; *U.S. Public*, pg. 538
Lund, Mark R., Sr. V.P., Controller & Asst. Treas.--TCF Financial Corp., Minneapolis, MN; *U.S. Public*, pg. 1554
Lund, Mark R., Sr. V.P., Contoller & Asst. Treas.--TCF Bank Minnesota FSB, Minneapolis, MN; *U.S. Public*, pg. 1554
Lundgren, Rob, Chief Fin. Officer, V.P. & Treas.--New Valley Corporation, Miami, FL; *U.S. Public*, pg. 1173
Lundhagen, E. Wayne, V.P. & Treas.--K N Energy, Inc., Lakewood, CO; *U.S. Public*, pg. 937
Lundquist, Brad, V.P. & Treas.--The Vernon Company, Newton, IA; *U.S. Private*, pg. 1137
Lundy, Frank E., Treas.--Central Lincoln People's Utility District, Newport, OR; *U.S. Private*, pg. 223
Lundy, Ronald C., Treas.--Moscom Corporation, Pittsford, NY; *U.S. Public*, pg. 1136
Luneau, Olivier, V.P.-Fin. & Treas.--Lafarge S.A., Paris, France; *Int'l*, pg. 788
Luntz, Gregory W., Chief Fin. Officer & Treas.--Luntz Corporation, Canton, OH; *U.S. Private*, pg. 681
Lupient, James W., Pres. & Treas.--Jim Lupient Enterprises, Golden Valley, MN; *U.S. Private*, pg. 681
Lurie, Robert F., V.P. & Treas.--NUI Corporation, Bedminster, NJ; *U.S. Public*, pg. 1147
Lurio, Lee H., Pres. & Treas.--Elbeco Incorporated, Reading, PA; *U.S. Private*, pg. 367
Lusk, William C., Jr., Sr. V.P. & Treas.--Shaw Industries, Inc., Dalton, GA; *U.S. Public*, pg. 1464
Lustbader, Edward E., Chm. Bd., Pres., Chief Exec. Officer & Treas.--The P.J. Carlin Construction Company, New Rochelle, NY; *U.S. Private*, pg. 211
Luth, Robert J., V.P.-Fin. Plng. & Treas.--Storage Technology Corporation, Louisville, CO; *U.S. Public*, pg. 1522
Lutz, David, Pres. & Treas.--Wellco Enterprises, Inc., Waynesville, NC; *U.S. Public*, pg. 1752
Luzum, James A., Chief Fin. Officer, Controller & Treas.--Villaume Industries, Inc., Saint Paul, MN; *U.S. Private*, pg. 1140
Luzum, William J., V.P. & Treas.--Tyler Industries, Benson, MN; *U.S. Private*, pg. 1112
Lwoff, Nicolas, Treas.--Groupe GTM, Nanterre, France; *Int'l*, *pg. 823*
Lyda, Allen E., V.P.-Fin., Treas. & Asst. Sec.--Tejon Ranch Company, Lebec, CA; *U.S. Public*, pg. 1566
Lydick, J. Lee, Pres., Chief Oper. Officer & Treas.--Grant-Lydick Beverage Co., San Antonio, TX; *U.S. Private*, pg. 470
Lydon, Coleman, Exec. V.P. & Treas.--Bank of Ireland (U.S.A.), New York, NY; *Int'l*, pg. 152
Lyke, Audrey R., Chief Fin. Officer & Treas.--Lyke Corporation, Ripon, WI; *U.S. Private*, pg. 682
Lyman, Clarence K., V.P.-Fin., Treas. & Asst. Sec.--Hawaiian Airlines, Inc., Honolulu, HI; *U.S. Public*, pg. 799
Lynch, John, Acting Chief Fin. Officer, Controller & Treas.--Sun TV & Appliances, Inc., Groveport, OH; *U.S. Public*, pg. 1532
Lynd, Rodney, 2nd V.P. & Treas.--Midland Life Insurance Co., Columbus, OH; *U.S. Private*, pg. 744
Ma, Kin Wung, Treas. & Asst. Mgr.--The Sincere Co. Ltd., Hong Kong, Hong Kong; *Int'l*, pg. 1252
MacConnell, Cynthia S., Treas. & Sec.--Beechmont Investments Inc., Cincinnati, OH; *U.S. Private*, pg. 129
MacConnell, Timothy J., Treas.--Thomson MacConnell Cadillac, Inc., Cincinnati, OH; *U.S. Private*, pg. 1084
MacDonald, L.A., Chief Info. Officer & Treas.--Nova Corporation, Calgary, Canada; *Int'l*, pg. 971
Macdonald, Malcolm S., V.P. & Treas.--Ford Motor Company, Dearborn, MI; *U.S. Public*, pg. 661
Mace, Georgia M., Treas.--Acceptance Insurance Co., Inc., Omaha, NE; *U.S. Public*, pg. 14
Mace, Sydney M., Asst. Treas.--Houghton Mifflin Company, Boston, MA; *U.S. Public*, pg. 841
MacGowan, R., Treas.--De La Rue plc, London, United Kingdom; *Int'l*, pg. 386
Machado, Edward J., Chief Fin. Officer & Sr. V.P.--Shenandoah Life Insurance Company, Roanoke, VA; *U.S. Private*, pg. 992
Machala, Edward W., V.P.-Opers., Mfg. & Treas.--American Power Conversion Corporation, West Kingston, RI; *U.S. Public*, pg. 89
Machi, Vito A., Sr. V.P., Sr. Loan Admin., Asst. Sec. & Asst. Treas.--The Metropolitan Savings Bank of Ohio, Youngstown, OH; *U.S. Public*, pg. 608
Machiavello, Louis, V.P. & Treas.--Richard E. Thibaut, Inc., Newark, NJ; *U.S. Public*, pg. 1358
Macintosh, John, Controller, Treas. & Sec.--Tamaroff Buick Inc., Southfield, MI; *U.S. Private*, pg. 1067
Macintosh, John, Treas. & Sec.--Tamaroff Leasing Co., Southfield, MI; *U.S. Private*, pg. 1067
Mack, Anne Baker, Treas.--Guard Publishing Company, Eugene, OR; *U.S. Private*, pg. 485
Mack, Barry V., V.P.-Fin. & Treas.--SI Handling Systems, Inc., Easton, PA; *U.S. Public*, pg. 1418
Mack, John E., Sr. V.P. & Treas.--NationsBank Corporation, Charlotte, NC; *U.S. Public*, pg. 1162
Mackay, Michael, Treas.--Farm Family Casualty Insurance Co., Glenmont, NY; *U.S. Private*, pg. 394
Mackey, William K., Chm. Bd., Pres., Chief Exec. Officer & Treas.--Aqua Care Systems Inc., Coral Springs, FL; *U.S. Public*, pg. 126
Macklin, Ruth E., Sr. V.P. & Treas.--Bowl America, Incorporated, Alexandria, VA; *U.S. Public*, pg. 248
MacLachlan, Calum, Controller & Treas.--H.L. Bouton Company Inc., Buzzards Bay, MA; *U.S. Private*, pg. 162
Maclachlan, Calum, Controller & Treas.--Lensclean, Inc., Buzzards Bay, MA; *U.S. Private*, pg. 162
Maclean, Donald W., Chief Fin. Officer & V.P.-Admin. & Treas.--Truelove & Maclean Inc., Waterbury, CT; *U.S. Private*, pg. 1107
Macleod, Jack, Controller--Inner Secrets, Inc., Harrison, NJ; *U.S. Private*, pg. 564
MacLeod, John A., V.P. & Treas.--Mar-Hyde Corporation, Cincinnati, OH; *U.S. Public*, pg. 1357
MacMillian, Frederick W., Chief Fin. Officer & Treas.--Troy Mills, Inc., Troy, NH; *U.S. Private*, pg. 1106
MacNeil, Norman E., Chm. Bd. & Treas.--Ark-Les Corporation, Stoughton, MA; *U.S. Private*, pg. 82
Macomber, Scott, Sr. V.P. & Treas.--Vitalink Pharmacy Services, Inc., Naperville, IL; *U.S. Public*, pg. 1041
Macomber, Scott, Chief Fin. Officer, Sr. V.P. & Treas.--Vitalink Pharmacy Services, Inc., Atlanta, GA; *U.S. Public*, pg. 1042
MacPherson, Donald, V.P.-Fin.--Thomas Publishing Company, New York, NY; *U.S. Private*, pg. 1082
MacWilliams, Katherine L., V.P. & Treas.--Adolph Coors Company, Golden, CO; *U.S. Public*, pg. 445
Macy, Roberta, Controller & Treas.--Edgerton Forge, Inc., Edgerton, OH; *U.S. Private*, pg. 102
Madden, John W., V.P. & Treas.--Suiza Foods Corporation, Dallas, TX; *U.S. Public*, pg. 1526
Madden, Richard O., Chief Fin. Officer, Exec. V.P., Treas. & Sec.--Vermont Financial Services Corp., Brattleboro, VT; *U.S. Public*, pg. 1716
Madden, Thomas J., Chief Fin. & Acctg. Officer, V.P.-Fin. & Treas.--Daisytek International Corporation, Plano, TX; *U.S. Public*, pg. 477
Madden, Thomas J., Chief Fin. & Acctg. Officer, V.P.-Fin. & Treas.--Daisytek Incorporated, Plano, TX; *U.S. Public*, pg. 477
Madden, Thomas J., Chief Fin. & Acctg. Officer, V.P.-Fin. & Treas.--Daisytek (Canada) Inc., Toronto, Canada; *U.S. Public*, pg. 477
Madden, Thomas J., Chief Fin. & Acctg. Officer, V.P.-Fin. & Treas.--Daisytek Latin America, Miami, FL; *U.S. Public*, pg. 477
Madden, Thomas J., Chief Fin. & Acctg. Officer, V.P.-Fin. & Treas.--Daisytek De Mexico S.A. de C.V., Mexico, Mexico; *U.S. Public*, pg. 477
Madden, Thomas J., Chief Fin. & Acctg. Officer, V.P.-Fin. & Treas.--Priority Fulfillment Services, Inc., Plano, TX; *U.S. Public*, pg. 477
Madden, Thomas J., Chief Fin. & Acctg. Officer, V.P.-Fin. & Treas.--Daisytek Australia Pty. Ltd., Alexandria, Australia; *U.S. Public*, pg. 477
Maddox, Brenda C., V.P. & Treas.--A.H. Belo Corporation, Dallas, TX; *U.S. Public*, pg. 209
Madlinger, Steven R., Chief Fin. Officer, V.P., Treas. & Sec.--GreatBanc, Inc., Aurora, IL; *U.S. Public*, pg. 760
Madsen, Bo, Treas.--ESS-Food, Copenhagen, Denmark; *Int'l*, pg. 429
Maffucci, V.J., Treas.--Laura Ashley Shops Ltd., Calgary, Canada; *Int'l*, pg. 804
Maffucci, Vincent Jay, V.P. & Treas.--Designs, Inc., Needham, MA; *U.S. Public*, pg. 501
Mafucci, V.J., Treas.--Laura Ashley (USA) Inc., Boston, MA; *Int'l*, pg. 804
Magid, Richard A., Chief Oper. Officer & Treas.--Ha-Lo Industries, Inc., Niles, IL; *U.S. Public*, pg. 773
Maginn, John L., Exec. V.P., Chief Investment Officer & Treas.--Mutual of Omaha Insurance Company, Omaha, NE; *U.S. Private*, pg. 769
Maginn, John L., Exec. V.P., Chief Investment Officer & Treas.--United of Omaha Life Insurance Company, Omaha, NE; *U.S. Private*, pg. 770
Mahaffey, Robert L., V.P. & Treas.--Anderson Erickson Dairy Company, Des Moines, IA; *U.S. Private*, pg. 72
Mahedy, A. Dennis, Treas.--Collins & Aikman Corporation, Charlotte, NC; *U.S. Public*, pg. 399
Mahler, Glenn, V.P., Treas. & Sec.--Blue Cross Laboratories, Saugus, CA; *U.S. Private*, pg. 152
Mahoney, Robert B., Chief Fin. Officer, V.P. & Treas.--Molex Incorporated, Lisle, IL; *U.S. Public*, pg. 1121
Mahoney, Stewart, Dir.-Treasury Svcs./Investor Rels.--Empire Company Limited, Stellarton, Canada; *Int'l*, pg. 453
Maiuccoro, John M., Pres. & Treas.--Imperial Pools, Inc., Latham, NY; *U.S. Private*, pg. 558
Majka, Lawrence J., Sr. V.P.-Fin. & Treas.--Advocate Health Care, Oak Brook, IL; *U.S. Private*, pg. 23
Major, Louise, Mgr.-Treasury Svcs.--Dynamics Research Corporation, Andover, MA; *U.S. Public*, pg. 539
Makela, Wayne, Chief Fin. Officer & Treas.--Cable Constructors, Inc., Iron Mountain, MI; *U.S. Private*, pg. 197
Makowski, Susan, Sec. & Treas.--American Travellers Insurance Services, Bensalem, PA; *U.S. Public*, pg. 433
Malik, Helen T., Corp. Sec. & Treas.--Mitchell Corporation of Owosso, Owosso, MI; *U.S. Private*, pg. 753
Malik, Helen T., Treas.--Benzonia Manufacturing, Benzonia, MI; *U.S. Private*, pg. 753
Malik, Helen T., Treas.--Mitchell Corporation, Clare Div., Clare, MI; *U.S. Private*, pg. 753
Malinowski, Eugene P., Asst. Treas.--Tasty Baking Company, Philadelphia, PA; *U.S. Public*, pg. 1561
Malish, William, Treas. & Sec.--Princeville Corporation, Princeville, HI; *U.S. Private*, pg. 885
Malki, N., Treas.--El Al Airlines Ltd., Lod, Israel; *Int'l*, pg. 435
Malkiewicz, Steven M., Asst. Treas.--Southeastern Michigan Gas Enterprises, Inc., Port Huron, MI; *U.S. Public*, pg. 1489
Malkiewicz, Steven M., Treas. & Controller--SEMCO Energy Services, Inc., Port Huron, MI; *U.S. Public*, pg. 1489
Mallea, Dan, Sr. V.P.-Fin. & Treas.--Regence BlueCross BlueShield of Oregon, Portland, OR; *U.S. Private*, pg. 917
Mallory, Richard, Treas. & Sec.--C. Weaver Chevrolet, Inc., New York Mills, NY; *U.S. Private*, pg. 1156
Malone, John E., V.P. & Treas.--USG Corporation, Chicago, IL; *U.S. Public*, pg. 1660
Maloney, Joseph J., Treas. & Sec.--Daniel J. Keating Co., Ardmore, PA; *U.S. Private*, pg. 610
Maloney, Phillip, Controller, Treas. & Sec.--Carver, Inc., Savannah, GA; *U.S. Private*, pg. 217
Maloy, John J., Jr., Asst. Treas.--Kentucky Utilities Company, Lexington, KY; *U.S. Public*, pg. 941
Manahan, Jesus M., Mgr.-Fin. & Asst. Treas.--Petrofields Exploration & Development Co., Inc., Manila, Philippines; *Int'l*, pg. 187
Manausa, Terry E., V.P. & Treas.--The Union Central Life Insurance Co., Cincinnati, OH; *U.S. Private*, pg. 1118
Mancini, Brooks T., Pres. & Treas.--B.T. Mancini Co., Inc., Milpitas, CA; *U.S. Private*, pg. 699
Mandekic, Anthony, Treas. & Sec.--Tracinda Corporation, Las Vegas, NV; *U.S. Private*, pg. 1095
Mandeville, Robert, Chief Fin. Officer, Treas. & Sec.--Cranston Print Works Company, Cranston, RI; *U.S. Private*, pg. 286
Maney, William J., Chief Fin. Officer, Sr. V.P. & Treas.--American Annuity Group, Cincinnati, OH; *U.S. Public*, pg. 74
Manganella, Frank, Treas.--Uniroyal Chemical Company, Inc., Middlebury, CT; *U.S. Public*, pg. 460
Mangarin, Erlinda, Treas.--Golden State Mutual Life Insurance Company, Los Angeles, CA; *U.S. Private*, pg. 461
Manilla, Sandra J., Treas.--Sithe Energies, Inc., New York, NY; *U.S. Private*, pg. 1004
Maniscalco, Diane, Chief Fin. Officer-Admin./Opers.-Sec. & Treas.--Colonna Bros., Inc., North Bergen, NJ; *U.S. Private*, pg. 254
Manke, James, Treas.--Manke Lumber Company, Inc., Tacoma, WA; *U.S. Private*, pg. 699
Mankel, Brian K., V.P. & Treas.--CalEnergy Co., Omaha, NE; *U.S. Public*, pg. 292
Mannarelli, Emerita, Treas.--Candle Corporation, Santa Monica, CA; *U.S. Private*, pg. 204
Manning, James, Controller & Treas.--Avesta Sheffield East, Inc., Baltimore, MD; *Int'l*, pg. 221

Manning, Michael, V.P. & Treas.--Cajun Electric Power Co-op, Baton Rouge, LA; *U.S. Private*, pg. 199
Manning, William J., Asst. Treas.--Nashua Corporation, Nashua, NH; *U.S. Public*, pg. 1152
Manso, Esther, Comptroller, Treas. & Sec.--Metro Ford Inc., Miami, FL; *U.S. Private*, pg. 736
Manukas, George, V.P., Treas. & Asst. Sec.--DKM Properties Corporation, Lawrenceville, NJ; *U.S. Private*, pg. 351
Manz, Terry K., V.P., Treas. & Sec.--Cactus Feeders, Inc., Amarillo, TX; *U.S. Private*, pg. 198
Maqsood, Rashid, Treas.--Westburne Inc., Montreal, Canada; *Int'l*, pg. 1491
Mara, Thomas E., Exec. V.P. & Treas.--Leucadia National Corporation, New York, NY; *U.S. Public*, pg. 989
Marabito, Richard T., Corp. Controller & Treas.--Olympic Steel Inc., Cleveland, OH; *U.S. Public*, pg. 1221
Marach, Roger K., Chief Fin. Officer & Treas.--SpeedFan International, Inc., Chandler, AZ; *U.S. Public*, pg. 1497
Marchese, Frank, Chief Fin. Officer, V.P.-Fin. & Treas.--Pharmaceutical Formulations, Inc., Edison, NJ; *U.S. Public*, pg. 1284
Marchese, Richard B., Chief Fin. Officer, V.P.-Fin. & Treas.--Georgia Gulf Corporation, Atlanta, GA; *U.S. Public*, pg. 734
Marchio, Albert N., II, Treas.--Alpharma Inc., Fort Lee, NJ; *U.S. Public*, pg. 57
Marchitello, Robert A., Asst. Treas.--Crompton & Knowles Corporation, Stamford, CT; *U.S. Public*, pg. 459
Marcic, Irene S., Chief Fin. Officer, Exec. V.P., Treas. & Sec.--Astrex, Inc., Plainview, NY; *U.S. Public*, pg. 141
Marcucci, George, Chief Fin. Officer & Treas.--Gonnella Baking Co., Chicago, IL; *U.S. Private*, pg. 463
Marcum, Kenneth W., V.P. & Treas.--Commercial Intertech Corp., Youngstown, OH; *U.S. Public*, pg. 411
Marcus, Harriet, Treas. & Sec.--Harold Leonard & Company, Inc., Union, NJ; *U.S. Private*, pg. 660
Marcus, William M., Exec. V.P. & Treas.--American Biltrite Inc., Wellesley Hills, MA; *U.S. Public*, pg. 68
Marczak, David J., Chief Fin. Officer, Treas. & Sec.--Secom General Corporation, Novi, MI; *U.S. Public*, pg. 1453
Marek, Helfried, Dir.-Treas. & Investment Banking--Raiffeisen Zentralbank Osterreich, Vienna, Austria; *Int'l*, pg. 1084
Maresca, Anthony R., Chief Fin. Officer, Sr. V.P., Treas. & Sec.--ACR Group, Houston, TX; *U.S. Public*, pg. 3
Margalith, Ethan Harold, Chm. Bd., Chief Exec. Officer & Treas.--Starving Students, Inc., Los Angeles, CA; *U.S. Private*, pg. 1035
Margerm, L. Douglas, Treas.--Cominco, Ltd., Vancouver, Canada; *Int'l*, pg. 307
Marguet, Rene, Corp. Sec.--HPI Holding S.A., Yverdon, Switzerland; *Int'l*, pg. 579
Marino, John T., Treas.--United Water Management & Services, Harrington Park, NJ; *U.S. Public*, pg. 1692
Marion, T.D., Treas.--TTX Co., Chicago, IL; *U.S. Private*, pg. 1066
Markel, Charles A., III, V.P.-Fin. & Treas.--LG & E Energy Corp., Louisville, KY; *U.S. Public*, pg. 970
Markey, Arthur, Chief Fin. Officer, Sr. V.P. & Treas.--Carpenter Co., Richmond, VA; *U.S. Private*, pg. 214
Markey, Thomas, V.P., Treas. & Sec.--National Spinning Co., Inc., New York, NY; *U.S. Private*, pg. 786
Markowitz, M.N., V.P. & Treas.--Union Texas Petroleum Holdings, Houston, TX; *U.S. Public*, pg. 1669
Marks, Fred, Chm. Bd.--The Vermont Teddy Bear Company, Inc., Shelburne, VT; *U.S. Public*, pg. 1716
Marks, Ronald D., Sr. V.P. & Treas.--Comerica Incorporated, Detroit, MI; *U.S. Public*, pg. 408
Markus, Theodore, Asst. Treas.--Dickinson Press, Inc., Grand Rapids, MI; *U.S. Private*, pg. 331
Marlette, Linda, Treas.--Coggin Automotive Group, Jacksonville, FL; *U.S. Private*, pg. 250
Marley, Robert, Treas.--C&D Charter Power Systems, Blue Bell, PA; *U.S. Public*, pg. 271
Marlowe, Bob, Chief Acctg. Officer, Treas. & Sec.--Sholodge, Inc., Hendersonville, TN; *U.S. Public*, pg. 1467
Marlowe, Margaret H., Sec. & Asst. Treas.--National Fruit Product Company, Winchester, VA; *U.S. Private*, pg. 783
Marman, Charles, Treas. & Sec.--F.T. Reynolds Company, Glendive, MT; *U.S. Private*, pg. 926
Marnoch, Douglas J., Treas.--AC Rochester Overseas Corporation, Southampton, United Kingdom; *U.S. Public*, pg. 722
Marquardt, Walter, Chief Fin. Officer & Treas.--Louis Allis Company, Milwaukee, WI; *U.S. Private*, pg. 677
Marquis, Thomas W., Chief Fin. Officer, Chief Acctg. Officer & Treas.--VSI Holdings, Inc., Bloomfield Hills, MI; *U.S. Public*, pg. 1703
Marra, Ralph V., Sr. V.P. & Treas.--Unicorp American Corporation, New York, NY; *Int'l*, pg. 1433
Marram, Edward P., Dr., Chm. Bd., Pres., Chief Exec. Officer & Treas.--Geo-Centers, Inc., Newton, MA; *U.S. Private*, pg. 447
Marrazzo, Nancy A., Asst. Treas.--Hovnanian Enterprises, Inc., Red Bank, NJ; *U.S. Public*, pg. 843
Marrero, Grace E., Chief Fin. Officer & Treas.--J.E. Baker Co., York, PA; *U.S. Private*, pg. 112
Marrero, Manuel, Chief Fin. Officer, Sr. V.P.-Admin., Treas. & Sec.--Autologic Information International, Inc., Thousand Oaks, CA; *U.S. Public*, pg. 1724
Marrero, Victor L., Sr. V.P. & Treas.--MEDCO Containment Services, Inc., Montvale, NJ; *U.S. Public*, pg. 1091
Marriner, William L., Chief Fin. Officer, Sr. V.P.-Fin. & Admin., & Sec.--Exabyte Corporation, Boulder, CO; *U.S. Public*, pg. 597
Marrone, Michael J., Chief Fin. Officer, Treas. & V.P.--The Berkshire Gas Company, Pittsfield, MA; *U.S. Public*, pg. 216
Marsh, K.B., Treas. & Sec.--MPX Systems, Inc., Cayce, SC; *U.S. Public*, pg. 1436
Marsh, K.H., Treas. & Sec.--South Carolina Electric & Gas Co. (SCE&G), Columbia, SC; *U.S. Public*, pg. 1436
Marsh, Stephen P., V.P. & Treas.--Community Bancorp, Derby, VT; *U.S. Public*, pg. 416
Marsh, Thomas R., V.P.-Fin. Services & Treas.--Omnicare, Inc., Covington, KY; *U.S. Public*, pg. 1223
Marshal, C., Treas.--Ranco Inc., Plain City, OH; *Int'l*, pg. 1243
Marshall, Gordon B., V.P.-Fin. & Treas.--The Pepper Companies, Inc., Chicago, IL; *U.S. Private*, pg. 851
Marshall, John D., Treas.--Blount International, Inc., Montgomery, AL; *U.S. Public*, pg. 237
Marshall, John D., Treas.--Blount, Inc., Montgomery, AL; *U.S. Public*, pg. 238
Marshall, Richard N., Treas. & Asst. Sec.--Pennsylvania Enterprises Inc., Wilkes-Barre, PA; *U.S. Public*, pg. 1271
Marshall, Richard N., Treas. & Asst. Sec.--PG Energy, Inc., Wilkes-Barre, PA; *U.S. Public*, pg. 1271
Marshall, Robert, Controller & Treas.--Evy Of California, Inc., Los Angeles, CA; *U.S. Private*, pg. 387
Marshall, William G., Treas.--Nalco Chemical Company, Naperville, IL; *U.S. Public*, pg. 1150
Marsteller, Timothy E., Asst. Treas.--National Grape Co-Op Association, Inc., Westfield, NY; *U.S. Private*, pg. 784
Martel, Frances E., Treas.--Harvey Industries, Inc., Waltham, MA; *U.S. Private*, pg. 508
Martensen, Donald C., Treas.--Preussag North America, Greenwich, CT; *Int'l*, pg. 1070
Martin, Brian K., V.P. & Treas.--Equity Services, Inc., Montpelier, VT; *U.S. Private*, pg. 785
Martin, Charles A., Treas., & Dir.-Fin., Admin.--Bommer Industries, Inc., Landrum, SC; *U.S. Private*, pg. 156
Martin, George D., V.P. & Treas.--Anthem, Inc., Indianapolis, IN; *U.S. Private*, pg. 76
Martin, Gladys, Chief Fin. Officer, Treas. & Sec.--Welsco Inc., North Little Rock, AR; *U.S. Private*, pg. 1161
Martin, James W., Controller & Treas.--Evening Post Publishing Co., Charleston, SC; *U.S. Private*, pg. 385
Martin, Jeffrey C., Treas.--Pinnacle Data Corporation, San Bruno, CA; *U.S. Public*, pg. 1158
Martin, Jeffrey C., Treas.--FASTRAC Systems, Inc.-Insurance Agent & Broker, South San Francisco, CA; *U.S. Public*, pg. 1158
Martin, John, Chief Fin. Officer--Trend Offset Printing Services, Los Alamitos, CA; *U.S. Private*, pg. 1099
Martin, John C., III, Chief Fin. Officer, V.P., Treas. & Sec.--TransPro, Inc., New Haven, CT; *U.S. Public*, pg. 1631
Martin, Judith E., V.P. & Treas.--Dunn Investment Co., Birmingham, AL; *U.S. Private*, pg. 347
Martin, Laura T., Sr. V.P. & Treas.--United Companies Financial Corporation, Baton Rouge, LA; *U.S. Public*, pg. 1675
Martin, M. Lamar, Chief Fin. Officer, Sr. V.P. & Treas.--Centex Construction Company, Dallas, TX; *U.S. Public*, pg. 322
Martin, Michael D., Chief Fin. Officer, Exec. V.P. & Treas.--Healthsouth Corporation, Birmingham, AL; *U.S. Public*, pg. 803
Martin, R., Grp. Treas.--Compass Group plc, Chertsey, United Kingdom,; *Int'l*, pg. 324
Martin, Scott, Treas.--Palm Harbor Homes, Inc., Dallas, TX; *U.S. Public*, pg. 1254
Martin, Steve, Treas. & Sec.--Russell Chevrolet Company, Sherwood, AR; *U.S. Private*, pg. 952
Martin, Virginia H., Treas. & Sec.--Martin Door Mfg., Inc., Salt Lake City, UT; *U.S. Private*, pg. 708
Martin, William, Treas.--Analog Devices, Inc., Norwood, MA; *U.S. Public*, pg. 107
Martin, Willie, V.P. & Treas.--Amurcon Corporation, Southfield, MI; *U.S. Private*, pg. 69
Martinelli, David J., V.P. & Treas.--Buckeye Partners, L.P., Allentown, PA; *U.S. Public*, pg. 266
Martinelli, David J., V.P. & Treas.--Buckeye Pipe Line Company, L.P., Allentown, PA; *U.S. Public*, pg. 266
Martinelli, James, Chief Fin. Officer & Treas.--II-VI Incorporated, Saxonburg, PA; *U.S. Public*, pg. 1647
Martinez de la Vega, Francisco, Chief Fin. Officer--Controladora Comercial Mexicana, S.A. de C.V., Mexico, Mexico; *Int'l*, pg. 328
Martinez, Isidro, Treas.--Vitromex, S.A., Saltillo, Mexico; *Int'l*, pg. 1469
Martinez, Walfrido A., Chief Fin. Officer, Sr. V.P. & Controller--E & B Marine Incorporated, Edison, NJ; *U.S. Public*, pg. 1756
Martinson, David J., V.P. & Treas.--Wadsworth Publishing co., Belmont, CA; *U.S. Public*, pg. 1600
Martorelli, Anna M., Treas.--Lawry's Restaurants, Inc., Pasadena, CA; *U.S. Private*, pg. 654
Martti, Janne, Treas.--Raisio Group, Raisio, Finland; *Int'l*, pg. 1085
Marty, Christian, Treas.--CERUS - Compagnies Europeennes Reunies, Paris, France; *Int'l*, pg. 240
Marucco, Al, V.P. & Treas.--Crowley Maritime Corporation, Oakland, CA; *U.S. Private*, pg. 292
Marukawa, Kenny, Treas.--Pioneer New Media Technologies, Long Beach, CA; *U.S. Private*, pg. 866
Marzano, Vincent M., Treas.--Scholastic Corporation, New York, NY; *U.S. Public*, pg. 1440
Marzec, Mitchell J., Treas.--Public Service Company of New Mexico, Albuquerque, NM; *U.S. Public*, pg. 1339
Marzilli, Joseph, Treas.--Simplex Time Recorder Co., Gardner, MA; *U.S. Private*, pg. 1002
Masci, Thomas A., Jr., Sr. V.P. & Treas.--U.S. Quality Algorithms, Inc., Blue Bell, PA; *U.S. Public*, pg. 27
Mashburn, Harry L., Pres. & Treas.--Mashburn Construction Company, Columbia, SC; *U.S. Private*, pg. 711
Maskey, Becky, Controller & Treas.--Cowles Media Company, Minneapolis, MN; *U.S. Private*, pg. 280
Maskey, Rebecca S., Treas.--Playboy Entertainment Group, Inc., Beverly Hills, CA; *U.S. Public*, pg. 1310
Maskey, Rebecca S., Treas.--Playboy Models, Inc., Beverly Hills, CA; *U.S. Public*, pg. 1310
Maskey, Rebecca S., Treas.--Playboy Preferred, Inc., Itasca, IL; *U.S. Public*, pg. 1310
Maskey, Rebecca S., Treas.--Lifestyle Brands, Ltd., Chicago, IL; *U.S. Public*, pg. 1310
Maskey, Rebecca S., Treas.--Critics' Choice Video, Inc., Itasca, IL; *U.S. Public*, pg. 1310
Maskey, Rebecca S., Treas.--Impulse Productions, Inc., Beverly Hills, CA; *U.S. Public*, pg. 1310
Maskey, Rebecca S., Treas.--Lake Shore Press, Inc., Chicago, IL; *U.S. Public*, pg. 1310
Maskey, Rebecca S., Treas.--Playboy Clubs International, Inc., Chicago, IL; *U.S. Public*, pg. 1310
Maskey, Rebecca S., Treas.--After Dark Video, Inc., Beverly Hills, CA; *U.S. Public*, pg. 1310
Mason, David A., Chief Fin. Officer, Exec. V.P. & Treas.--Moto Photo, Inc., Dayton, OH; *U.S. Public*, pg. 1136
Mason, David D. S., Pres., Chief Exec. & Chief Fin. Officer & Treas.--Toms Sierra Company, Ione, CA; *U.S. Private*, pg. 1090
Mason, Herman D., Treas. & Sec.--May Supply Company, Inc., Harrisonburg, VA; *U.S. Public*, pg. 1727
Mason, Tom, V.P. & Treas.--Highlights for Children, Inc., Columbus, OH; *U.S. Private*, pg. 528
Massanelli, Stephen C., Sr. V.P. & Treas.--Zale Corporation, Irving, TX; *U.S. Public*, pg. 1789
Massengale, Darrell K., Chief Fin. Officer, V.P.-Fin., Treas. & Sec.--Corrections Corporation of America, Nashville, TN; *U.S. Public*, pg. 450
Massey, Les, V.P. & Treas.--Whitfield Foods, Inc., Montgomery, AL; *U.S. Private*, pg. 1173
Massey, Mikel M., V.P.-Fin. & Treas.--Fraser Papers, Inc., Stamford, CT; *Int'l*, pg. 434
Massimini, Dante J., Sr. V.P. & Treas.--Pennsylvania Real Estate Investment Trust, Fort Washington, PA; *U.S. Public*, pg. 1272
Massot, Joseph H., V.P. & Treas.--Recoton Corporation, Lake Mary, FL; *U.S. Public*, pg. 1369
Massucci, Donald A., V.P., Controller & Treas.--Goodheart-Willcox Publisher, Tinley Park, IL; *U.S. Private*, pg. 464
Masucci, Jeanne, V.P. & Treas.--Mullen Advertising, Inc., Wenham, MA; *U.S. Private*, pg. 766
Mather, Jayne M., Treas.--The Lane Construction Corp., Meriden, CT; *U.S. Private*, pg. 649
Matherne, Louis K., Jr., Treas.--Chesapeake Corporation, Richmond, VA; *U.S. Public*, pg. 346
Mathews, Paul, V.P. & Treas.--Tyndale House Publishers, Inc., Carol Stream, IL; *U.S. Private*, pg. 1112
Mathieu, Raymond M., Chief Fin. Officer & Treas.--Narragansett Capital Inc., Providence, RI; *U.S. Private*, pg. 774
Mathisen, Jeanne, Treas.--General Drug Co., Chicago, IL; *U.S. Private*, pg. 1007
Matsick, Stephen G., V.P.-Fin. & Treas.--Glen-Gery Corporation, Wyomissing, PA; *Int'l*, pg. 658
Matsumoto, Kazuyoshi, Gen. Mgr.-Treas. & Securities Div.--The Nanto Bank, Ltd., Nara, Japan; *Int'l*, pg. 905
Matsuyama, Akihiko, V.P. & Treas.--Asahi America Inc., New York, NY; *Int'l*, pg. 85
Matt, Nicholas O., Pres. & Treas.--The F.X. Matt Brewing Co., Utica, NY; *U.S. Private*, pg. 714
Matthew, W.F., Treas.--Wemco, Inc., New Orleans, LA; *U.S. Private*, pg. 909
Matthews, Mark, Treas. & Sec.--Porcelanite, Inc., Lexington, NC; *Int'l*, pg. 573
Matthews, Ronald D., V.P. & Treas.--The Coastal Corporation, Houston, TX; *U.S. Public*, pg. 389
Matthews, Roy S., V.P.-Fin. & Treas.--George S. May International Company, Park Ridge, IL; *U.S. Private*, pg. 717
Matthis, Doris L., Treas. & Sec.--Kentucky Indiana Lumber Co. Inc., Louisville, KY; *U.S. Private*, pg. 615
Mattingly, Barbara A., Treas. & Sec.--Metro Foods, Inc., Olive Branch, MS; *U.S. Private*, pg. 736
Mattingly, Mike, Chief Fin. Officer, Controller & Treas.--The Court Company, Memphis, TN; *U.S. Private*, pg. 279
Mattison, Ben, V.P., Treas. & Sec.--Malloy Lithographing Inc., Ann Arbor, MI; *U.S. Private*, pg. 698
Mattson, Robert N., Asst. Treas.--International Business Machines Corporation, Armonk, NY; *U.S. Public*, pg. 895
Matz, Eldon, Controller & Asst. Treas.--Dynamic Homes, Inc., Detroit Lakes, MN; *U.S. Public*, pg. 538
Matz, R. Kevin, Sr. V.P. & Treas.--EMCOR Group, Inc., Norwalk, CT; *U.S. Public*, pg. 571
Matza, Robert, V.P. & Treas.--Travelers Group, New York, NY; *U.S. Public*, pg. 1632
Mauck, Robert J., V.P. & Treas.--Albert Kahn Associates, Inc., Detroit, MI; *U.S. Private*, pg. 604
Mauk, Patricia, Treas. & Sec.--Dudek & Bock Spring Manufacturing Company, Chicago, IL; *U.S. Private*, pg. 344
Mauldin, Bill G., Exec. V.P., Sec. & Treas.--First Commercial Mortgage Co., Little Rock, AR; *U.S. Public*, pg. 630
Mauriello, Samuel R., Asst. Treas.--AmeriGas Partners, L.P., Valley Forge, PA; *U.S. Public*, pg. 1053
Maurin, Lois J., Treas. & Sec.--American Fence & Security Company, Phoenix, AZ; *U.S. Private*, pg. 54
Mavrovitis, Basil, Asst. Treas.--Bertelsmann Inc., New York, NY; *Int'l*, pg. 191
Maxwell-Smith, Gordon, Treas.--Shopping Centre Group, Toronto, Canada; *Int'l*, pg. 253
May, Larry A., V.P. & Treas.--Amgen Inc., Thousand Oaks, CA; *U.S. Public*, pg. 100
May, Timothy William, Grp. Treas.--Eurocamp Plc, Knutsford, United Kingdom; *Int'l*, pg. 464
Mayberry, Jean C., Treas. & Mgr.-Data Processing--Asbury Carbons, Inc., Asbury, NJ; *U.S. Private*, pg. 87
Mayer, Sylvia, Treas. & Sec.--Mayer/Berkshire Corporation, Wayne, NJ; *U.S. Private*, pg. 717
Mayers, Lois E., Sec. & Treas.--Ace Novelty Company, Inc., Woodinville, WA; *U.S. Public*, pg. 1309
Mayerson, Robert, Sr. V.P. & Treas.--Staples, Inc., Westborough, MA; *U.S. Public*, pg. 1509
Maynard, James G., Chm. Bd., Chief Exec. Officer & Treas.--Maynard Oil Co., Dallas, TX; *U.S. Public*, pg. 1064
Maynard, James H., Chm. Bd., Pres., Chief Exec. Officer & Treas.--Investors Management Corp., Raleigh, NC; *U.S. Private*, pg. 574

Mayne, Patricia F., Asst. Treas.--Atlantic American Life Insurance Company, Atlanta, GA; *U.S. Public*, pg. 143

Mayo, Jennifer, Treas., Sec. & Mgr.-Personnel--Von Housen Motors, Sacramento, CA; *U.S. Private*, pg. 1143

Mays, Debra A., Asst. Treas. & Controller--Ash Grove Cement Company, Shawnee Mission, KS; *U.S. Private*, pg. 87

Mays, Randall T., V.P. & Treas.--Clear Channel Communications, Inc., San Antonio, TX; *U.S. Public*, pg. 383

Mays, Robert C., V.P. & Treas.--Coventry Health & Life Insurance, Fort Worth, TX; *U.S. Public*, pg. 454

Mazur, Joel, Treas.--ECI Telecom Ltd., Petah Tiqwa, Israel; *Int'l*, pg. 643

Mazzarino, Michael C., Sr. V.P.-Fin. & Treas.--Marcal Paper Mills, Inc., Elmwood Park, NJ; *U.S. Private*, pg. 701

Mazzilli, P.J., V.P. & Treas.--Equifax Inc., Atlanta, GA; *U.S. Public*, pg. 588

Mc Donald, John, Grp. Treas.--Fletcher Challenge Limited, Auckland, New Zealand; *Int'l*, pg. 494

McAdams, Hugh W., V.P. & Treas.--Imasco Limited, Montreal, Canada; *Int'l*, pg. 112

McAfee, Nancy G., V.P., Controller & Treas.--Thrall Enterprises, Inc., Chicago, IL; *U.S. Private*, pg. 1084

McAlpin, R.M., Treas.--Boral Limited, Sydney, Australia; *Int'l*, *pg. 203*

McArthur, Rawdon W., Chief Fin. Officer & Treas.--BellSouth International, Inc., Atlanta, GA; *U.S. Public*, pg. 208

McAtee, Larry, Treas.--Kimray, Inc., Oklahoma City, OK; *U.S. Private*, pg. 620

McAulay, Jeffrey J., V.P. & Treas.--Moran Towing Of Delaware, Inc, Greenwich, CT; *U.S. Private*, pg. 760

McAulay, Jeffrey J., V.P. & Treas.--Hampton Roads Land Co., Ltd, Greenwich, CT; *U.S. Private*, pg. 760

McAulay, Jeffrey J., V.P. & Treas.--Moran Towing Of Texas Corporation, Greenwich, CT; *U.S. Private*, pg. 761

McAuliff, Ana, V.P., Sec. & Treas.--McGraw-Hill Ryerson, Ltd., Whitby, Canada; *U.S. Public*, pg. 1072

McBennett, Robert J., Treas.--Orange and Rockland Utilities, Inc., Pearl River, NY; *U.S. Public*, pg. 1229

McBride, David, Chief Information Officer--McBride and Associates, Inc., Albuquerque, NM; *U.S. Private*, pg. 719

McBride, Robert, V.P. & Treas.--Data General Corporation, Westborough, MA; *U.S. Public*, pg. 485

McCaigue, Dan, Chief Fin. Officer--Perdue Farms, Inc., Showell, MD; *U.S. Private*, pg. 852

McCall, Ronald L., Vice Chm., Chief Exec. Officer, Chief Fin. Officer & Treas.--M.B. Kahn Construction Co., Inc., Columbia, SC; *U.S. Private*, pg. 604

McCall, W.A., Contoller, Treas., Sec., & Mgr.-D.P.--Dixie Oil Company, Tifton, GA; *U.S. Private*, pg. 337

McCallum, Gerald, Treas. & Comptroller--Acklands Limited, Toronto, Canada; *Int'l*, pg. 23

McCarthy, Anthony P., Treas.--Kansas City Southern Industries, Inc., Kansas City, MO; *U.S. Public*, pg. 943

McCarthy, Douglas K., Asst. V.P.-Fin. & Treas.--Newbridge Networks Corporation, Kanata, Canada; *Int'l*, pg. 923

McCarthy, Robert, Treas.--Camp Dresser & McKee Inc., Cambridge, MA; *U.S. Private*, pg. 203

McClelland, Bob, Controller & Treas.--Analog Devices, Santa Clara, CA; *U.S. Public*, pg. 108

McClelland, Frances H., Treas. & Sec.--Shamrock Foods Company, Phoenix, AZ; *U.S. Private*, pg. 989

McClennan, Howard, Chief Fin. Officer, Treas. & Sec.--Uncle B's Bakery, Inc., Ellsworth, IA; *U.S. Public*, pg. 1664

McClure, Cynthia, Controller, Treas. & Sec.--The McClure Group, Wayne, PA; *U.S. Private*, pg. 719

McCoach, William P., Chief Fin. Officer & Treas.--The Fabri-Form Company, Byesville, OH; *U.S. Private*, pg. 390

McCollough, Ronald E., Sr. V.P.-Opers. & Treas.--TBC Corporation, Memphis, TN; *U.S. Public*, pg. 1553

McConnell, C.S., Treas.--ATCO Group Co., Calgary, Canada; *Int'l*, pg. 95

McConville, Rita J., Chief Fin. Officer, Treas. & Sec.--Akorn, Inc., Lincolnshire, IL; *U.S. Public*, pg. 34

McCord, Timothy S., Chief Fin. Officer & Treas.--Drug Emporium, Inc., Powell, OH; *U.S. Public*, pg. 530

McCorkle, Martha A., V.P.-Fin., Treas. & Sec.--World Carpets, Inc., Dalton, GA; *U.S. Private*, pg. 1190

McCormick, James M., V.P. & Treas.--Lakeland Industries, Inc., Ronkonkoma, NY; *U.S. Public*, pg. 975

McCorry, Gary, V.P. & Treas.--SFM Media Corporation, New York, NY; *U.S. Private*, pg. 956

McCoy, Janice, Sec. & Treas.--Fleetwood Aluminum Products, Corona, CA; *U.S. Private*, pg. 410

McCoy, Michael J., V.P. & Treas.--Hormel Foods Corp., Austin, MN; *U.S. Public*, pg. 840

McCraken, Michael, V.P.-Opers. & Treas.--Paoli, Inc., Orleans, IN; *U.S. Private*, pg. 837

McCredry, Jon, Treas.--Metropolitan Mortgage & Securities Co., Inc., Spokane, WA; *U.S. Private*, pg. 738

McCreedy, Matt, Chief Fin. Officer, Sr. V.P.-Fin. & Treas.--Jackson Hole Ski Resort, Teton Village, WY; *U.S. Private*, pg. 579

McCreery, Harry, Chief Fin. Officer & Treas.--Software AG Americas, Inc., Reston, VA; *U.S. Public*, pg. 1482

McCreery, Thomas A., Jr., Asst. Treas.--Wickland Corporation, Sacramento, CA; *U.S. Private*, pg. 1174

McCrory, Kelly L., Treas. & Sec.--Steakley Chevrolet GEO Subaru Inc., Dallas, TX; *U.S. Private*, pg. 1037

McCubbing, Ian, Treas.--Spicers Paper Limited, Preston, Australia; *Int'l*, pg. 72

McCuish, Mike, Treas.--SmithGroup, Inc., Detroit, MI; *U.S. Private*, pg. 1010

McCullars, Denise, Chief Fin. Officer, Treas. & Sec.--Dawson Construction Co., Inc., Gadsden, AL; *U.S. Private*, pg. 316

McCulloch, Ann C., V.P. & Treas.--Peter Kiewit Sons Inc., Omaha, NE; *U.S. Private*, pg. 619

McCulloch, Ann T., V.P. & Treas.--Kiewit Construction Group, Inc., Omaha, NE; *U.S. Private*, pg. 619

McCullough, Bob, Exec. V.P., Sec. & Treas.--Harris, Baio & McCullough Inc., Philadelphia, PA; *U.S. Private*, pg. 504

McCusty, Paul N., Treas.--Strydel, Inc., Stryker, OH; *U.S. Public*, pg. 1214

McCusty, Paul N., Treas.--Trinc Company, Bryan, OH; *U.S. Public*, pg. 1214

McDaniel, F.E., Jr., Sr. V.P., Treas. & Sec.--Shoney's, Inc., Nashville, TN; *U.S. Public*, pg. 1467

McDermed, Kevin T., Chief Fin. Officer, V.P., Treas. & Sec.--Atchison Casting Corporation, Atchison, KS; *U.S. Public*, *pg. 142*

McDermott, Marie, Treas. & Sec.--J.M. Process Systems Inc., Orland Park, IL; *U.S. Private*, pg. 577

McDevitt, Richard H., Chief Fin. Officer, V.P.-Fin. & Treas.--AmeriData Technologies, Inc., Stamford, CT; *U.S. Public*, *pg. 711*

McDonald, James L., Treas.--Garden State Newspapers, Inc., Denver, CO; *U.S. Private*, pg. 727

McDonald, Jerry, Exec. V.P., Chief Fin. Officer & Treas.--Resistance Technology Inc., Arden Hills, MN; *U.S. Public*, pg. 1455

McDonald, Kenneth E., Asst. Treas.--Florida Progress Corporation, Saint Petersburg, FL; *U.S. Public*, pg. 655

McDonald, R. S., Grp. Treas.--Air New Zealand Ltd., Auckland, New Zealand; *Int'l*, pg. 38

McDonald, Richard A., V.P. & Treas.--NovaCare Inc., King of Prussia, PA; *U.S. Public*, pg. 1203

McDonald, Stuart R., Pres., Chief Exec. Officer & Treas.--Marshall & Williams Co., Greenville, SC; *U.S. Private*, pg. 708

McDonald, Thomas, Chief Fin. Officer & Treas.--Jernberg Industries, Inc., Chicago, IL; *U.S. Private*, pg. 586

McDonnell, Stephen J., Treas.--Central and South West Corporation, Dallas, TX; *U.S. Public*, pg. 324

McDougald, James, Treas.--MediaNews Group Inc., Denver, CO; *U.S. Private*, pg. 727

McDowell, George E., V.P.-Fin., Treas. & Sec.--Clayton Corporation, Fenton, MO; *U.S. Private*, pg. 244

McDowell, Howard, Treas. & Asst. Sec.--Granite State Electric Co., Lebanon, NH; *U.S. Public*, pg. 1171

McDowell, Howard, Asst. Treas.--Massachusetts Electric Co., Westborough, MA; *U.S. Public*, pg. 1171

McDowell, Scott, Treas.--SATEC Systems Inc., Grove City, PA; *U.S. Private*, pg. 967

McEachen, Mark, V.P. & Treas.--Transamerica Corporation, San Francisco, CA; *U.S. Public*, pg. 1629

McElligott, Frederick T., Treas.--Arthur D. Little, Inc., Cambridge, MA; *U.S. Private*, pg. 670

McElroy, Jack, Treas.--Michigan Cat, Novi, MI; *U.S. Private*, pg. 740

McEvoy, Thomas P., Treas. & Controller--New Standard Corporation, Mount Joy, PA; *U.S. Private*, pg. 794

McFadden, Jerry L., V.P.-Fin. & Treas.--Wynn's-Precision, Inc., Lebanon, TN; *U.S. Public*, pg. 1783

McFadden, Thomas, Treas.--Conrail, Inc., Philadelphia, PA; *U.S. Public*, pg. 431

McFarland, Roger, Treas.--Cornucopia, Inc., Irvine, CA; *U.S.* Private, pg. 276

McFarlane, John, Exec. Dir. & Treas.--Standard Chartered Bank PLC, London, United Kingdom; *Int'l*, pg. 1294

McFarling, Robert E., V.P.-Sls. & Treas.--McFarling Foods, Inc., Indianapolis, IN; *U.S. Private*, pg. 721

McGaughey, William, Sr. V.P. & Treas.--Sierra West Bank, Truckee, CA; *U.S. Public*, pg. 1470

McGaughy, William H., Sr. V.P.--Sierra West Bancorp, Truckee, CA; *U.S. Public*, pg. 1470

McGee, Gary L., Treas.--Devon Energy Corporation, Oklahoma City, OK; *U.S. Public*, pg. 503

McGhee, James E., Chief Fin. Officer & Treas.--Weil Brothers Cotton Inc., Montgomery, AL; *U.S. Private*, pg. 1159

McGill, James D., Pres. & Treas.--United McGill Corp., Groveport, OH; *U.S. Private*, pg. 1122

McGill, William, V.P. & Treas.--Belk Stores Services Inc., Charlotte, NC; *U.S. Private*, pg. 131

McGinnis, James A., V.P. & Treas.--Mortgage Guaranty Insurance Corporation, Milwaukee, WI; *U.S. Public*, pg. 1026

McGivney, Kevin, Sr. V.P. & Treas.--Compendium Systems Corporation, Greenwich, CT; *U.S. Private*, pg. 259

McGlinn, Richard B., Chief Acctg. Officer, Sr. V.P. & Treas.--Taubman Centers, Inc., Bloomfield Hills, MI; *U.S. Public*, *pg. 1561*

McGonigle, William F., V.P.-Fin. & Treas.--Samuel Cabot, Inc., Newburyport, MA; *U.S. Private*, pg. 198

McGowan, Joseph C., Treas. & Sec.--Interstate Power Company, Dubuque, IA; *U.S. Public*, pg. 910

McGowan, Kelly, Controller & Treas.--NT Dor-omatic, Harwood Heights, IL; *U.S. Private*, pg. 771

McGrady, James A., V.P. & Treas.--Consolidated Stores Corp., Columbus, OH; *U.S. Public*, pg. 437

McGraime, Douglas, Chief Fin. Officer, Exec. V.P. & Treas.--Combe Incorporated, White Plains, NY; *U.S. Private*, pg. 257

McGrath, Brent P., Chief Fin. Officer, Treas. & Sec.--Mico Inc., North Mankato, MN; *U.S. Private*, pg. 741

McGrath, Gerald M., Chief Fin. Officer, V.P. & Treas.--Analysts International Corporation, Minneapolis, MN; *U.S. Public*, pg. 110

McGrath, Lee U., V.P. & Treas.--Jostens, Minneapolis, MN; *U.S. Public*, pg. 934

McGrath, Pamela A., V.P. & Treas.--Montgomery St. Income Securities, Inc., San Francisco, CA; *U.S. Public*, pg. 1127

McGraw, R.J., Sr. V.P.-Treasury--AEGON N.V., Hague, Netherlands; *Int'l*, pg. 25

McGraw, Robert J., V.P. & Treas.--AEGON USA, Inc., Baltimore, MD; *Int'l*, pg. 26

McGraw, Robert J., V.P. & Treas.--AUSA Holding Company, Baltimore, MD; *Int'l*, pg. 27

McGregor, Dennis R., Treas. & Dir.-Tax--R.P. Scherer Corporation, Troy, MI; *U.S. Public*, pg. 1437

McGregor, Michael K., Treas. & Sec.--Pontiac Bancorp, Inc., Pontiac, IL; *U.S. Public*, pg. 1316

McGroarty, Ed, Sr. V.P.-Fin. & Treas.--American Foodservice Corp., King of Prussia, PA; *U.S. Private*, pg. 54

McGuire, Robert B., Treas.--Interstate/Johnson Lane, Inc., Charlotte, NC; *U.S. Public*, pg. 909

McGuire, Scott P., Treas. & Dir.-Corp. Acctg.--Tandycrafts, Inc., Fort Worth, TX; *U.S. Public*, pg. 1561

McGurk, Nancy J., Chief Fin. Officer & V.P.-Fin. & Treas.--Resource America, Inc., Philadelphia, PA; *U.S. Public*, pg. 1382

McGurn, Robert E., Treas.--Contractors Supply Company, Inc., Kansas City, MO; *U.S. Private*, pg. 270

McHale, David R., Asst. Treas.--Northeast Utilities, Berlin, CT; *U.S. Public*, pg. 1194

McHugh, Lynn L., Asst. Treas.--Snap-On Tools Corporation, Kenosha, WI; *U.S. Public*, pg. 1480

McHugh, M.J., Chief Acctg. Officer, Sr. V.P. & Treas.--Equity Residential Properties Trust, Chicago, IL; *U.S. Public*, pg. 590

McIlwayne, Clive, Treas.--International Correspondence Schools (Overseas) Limited, Glasgow, United Kingdom; *U.S. Public*, pg. 784

McIngvale, Linda, V.P., Treas. & Sec.--Gallery Furniture, Houston, TX; *U.S. Private*, pg. 438

McInnis, Judy, Sec. & Treas.--Southern Electric Supply Co., Inc., Meridian, MS; *Int'l*, pg. 1107

McInvale, Willie K., Jr., Treas. & Sec.--McNamara Pontiac Isuzu Inc., Orlando, FL; *U.S. Private*, pg. 724

McKaig, William D., Treas. & Sec.--Maaco Enterprises Inc., King of Prussia, PA; *U.S. Private*, pg. 689

McKamy Hall, F., V.P., Controller & Treas.--Astec Industries, Inc., Chattanooga, TN; *U.S. Public*, pg. 141

McKay, Calvin, Sr. V.P. & Treas.--Acme Boot Co., Inc., El Paso, TX; *U.S. Private*, pg. 394

McKay, Donald K., Chief Fin. Officer, Exec. V.P., Treas. & Sec.--Specialty Equipment Companies Inc., Aurora, IL; *U.S. Public*, pg. 1496

McKay, Dwight, Sec. & Treas.--Weston Paper & Manufacturing Co., Terre Haute, IN; *U.S. Private*, pg. 1169

McKean, Robert P., Treas.--Liz Claiborne, Inc., New York, NY; *U.S. Public*, pg. 1005

McKee, James S., Mgr.-Corp. Treasury & Tax & Asst. Treas.--Nowsco Well Service Ltd., Calgary, Canada; *Int'l*, *pg. 989*

McKee, Kenneth A., Chief Fin. Officer, Treas. & Gen. Counsel--Johnson Storage Moving Co, Denver, CO; *U.S.* Private, pg. 594

McKee, Kenneth A., Treas. & Sec.--Security Van Lines, Kenner, LA; *U.S. Private*, pg. 594

McKee, Kent A., Treas. & Asst. Sec.--Mueller Industries, Inc., Memphis, TN; *U.S. Public*, pg. 1141

McKee, William T., Chief Fin. Officer & Treas.--Barr Laboratories Inc., Pomona, NY; *U.S. Public*, pg. 191

McKeever, Michael L., Asst. Treas.--Ethyl Corporation, Richmond, VA; *U.S. Public*, pg. 595

McKenna, W.J., Treas.--The Robert Carter Corp., Oak Park, MI; *U.S. Public*, pg. 1676

McKenna, William P., V.P.-Fin. & Treas.--Bourns, Inc., Riverside, CA; *U.S. Private*, pg. 161

McKenney, M.P., Treas. & Sec.--The Figaro Company, Inc., Mesquite, TX; *U.S. Private*, pg. 404

McKenney, Thomas J., Sec. & Treas.--Northern Telephone Limited, New Liskeard, Canada; *Int'l*, pg. 115

McKenzie, Clyde E., V.P. & Treas.--Apache Corporation, Houston, TX; *U.S. Public*, pg. 119

McKibben, Craig, Chief Fin. Officer & V.P.--Ampex Corporation, Redwood City, CA; *U.S. Public*, pg. 104

McKinlay, John F., Sr. V.P. & Treas.--USTrust, Boston, MA; *U.S. Public*, pg. 1660

McKinley, Ellis, Jr., Chief Fin. Officer, V.P. & Treas.--Kevco, Inc., Fort Worth, TX; *U.S. Public*, pg. 952

McKinley, Gary, Treas.--New Brunswick Power Corporation, Fredericton, Canada; *Int'l*, pg. 923

McKinley, Richard S., V.P. & Treas.--The Gap, Inc., San Francisco, CA; *U.S. Public*, pg. 702

McKinney, Bert, Treas. & Sec.--Contractors Supplies, Inc., Lufkin, TX; *U.S. Private*, pg. 270

McKinney, Douglas A., V.P. & Treas.--Mallinckrodt Inc., Saint Louis, MO; *U.S. Public*, pg. 1039

McKinney, Eugene B., Treas.--Hallmark Cards, Inc., Kansas City, MO; *U.S. Private*, pg. 495

McKinnon, B.B., Dir.-Treasury--Delta Air Lines, Inc., Atlanta, GA; *U.S. Public*, pg. 497

McKinnon, E., Sec. & Treas.--Datacor/ISM (Information Systems Management Atlantic Corp.), Moncton, Canada; *Int'l*, pg. 230

McKinnon, John R., Treas.--Camtronics Ltd., Hartland, WI; *U.S. Public*, pg. 109

McKittrick, David J., Chief Fin. Officer, Sr. V.P. & Treas.--Gateway 2000, North Sioux City, SD; *U.S. Public*, pg. 703

McLamb, George T., Chief Fin. Officer, Exec. V.P. & Treas.--Kingsdown, Inc., Mebane, NC; *U.S. Private*, pg. 622

McLean, Rodney A., Treas.--Interstate Distributor Company, Tacoma, WA; *U.S. Private*, pg. 573

McLuskie, Bill, Head-Treasury & Tax--Trafalgar House PLC, London, United Kingdom; *Int'l*, pg. 772

McMahon, Paul, V.P. & Treas.--W.R. Grace & Co., Boca Raton, FL; *U.S. Public*, pg. 754

McMahon, Terry, Treas. & Sec.--Clark Detroit-Diesel Allison, Cincinnati, OH; *U.S. Private*, pg. 242

McMakin, Kelly, Chief Fin. Officer & Treas.--Florafax International, Inc., Vero Beach, FL; *U.S. Public*, pg. 654

McMann, Robert S., V.P. & Treas.--John Hancock Insurance Company of Bermuda Ltd., Hamilton, Bermuda; *U.S. Private*, pg. 590

McMasters, Michael P., Chief Fin. Officer, V.P. & Treas--Chesapeake Utilities Corporation, Dover, DE; *U.S. Public*, *pg. 347*

McMillan, Samuel F., Sr. V.P. & Treas.--Beneficial Corporation, Wilmington, DE; *U.S. Public*, pg. 211

McMillian, Lonnie S., V.P., Treas. & Sec.--ADTRAN, Inc., Huntsville, AL; *U.S. Public*, pg. 20

McMillin, Jon P., V.P.-Fin. & Acctg. & Treas.--Enogex Inc., Oklahoma City, OK; *U.S. Public*, pg. 1207
McMullen, Terence P., V.P. & Treas.--Tenet Healthcare Corporation, Santa Barbara, CA; *U.S. Public*, pg. 1576
McMurray, Laura, Treas.--Elsevier SA, Neuchatel, Switzerland; *Int'l*, pg. 1093
McMurray, Michael K., Asst. Treas.-Retirement Funds--Boise Cascade Corporation, Boise, ID; *U.S. Public*, pg. 242
McMurtrie, James C., Chm. Bd., Chief Exec. Officer & Treas.--E.W. Knauss & Son, Inc., Quakertown, PA; *U.S. Private*, pg. 626
McNairy, Charles, Chief Fin. Officer, Exec. V.P. & Treas.--Avatar Holdings Inc., Coral Gables, FL; *U.S. Public*, pg. 151
Mcnamee, Richard B., V.P.-Fin. & Tax, Treas. & Asst. Sec.--Great American Management & Investment, Inc., Chicago, IL; *U.S. Private*, pg. 473
McNeill, Richard, V.P. & Treas.--NWNL Benefits Corp., Minneapolis, MN; *U.S. Public*, pg. 1375
McPhail, Douglas J., Pres., Chief Exec. & Fin. Officer & Treas.--Indiana Records Managers, Fishers, IN; *U.S. Private*, pg. 560
McPheeters, F. Lynn, Treas.--Caterpillar Inc., Peoria, IL; *U.S. Public*, pg. 315
McWade, Charles P., Sr. V.P. & Treas.--Computer Associates International, Inc., Islandia, NY; *U.S. Public*, pg. 420
McWilliams, K.G., Asst. Treas.--Union Camp Corporation, Wayne, NJ; *U.S. Public*, pg. 1665
McWilliams, Katherine L., V.P. & Treas.--Coors Brewing Company, Golden, CO; *U.S. Public*, pg. 445
Meadors, Terry L., Treas. & Asst. Sec.--Hickman, Williams & Co. Inc., Cincinnati, OH; *U.S. Private*, pg. 525
Meadows, Allen D., Chief Fin. Officer, Exec. V.P. & Treas.--Fidelity National Financial, Inc., Irvine, CA; *U.S. Public*, pg. 620
Meadows, Allen D., Chief Fin. Officer, Exec. V.P. & Treas.--Fidelity National Title Insurance Company, Irvine, CA; *U.S. Public*, pg. 620
Meagher, Michael J., Chief Exec. Officer-Corp. & Treas. Div.--Bank of Ireland, Dublin, Ireland; *Int'l*, pg. 152
Mears, Shirley J., V.P. & Treas.--Mitel Corporation, Kanata, Canada; *Int'l*, pg. 870
Mecaughey, William, Chief Fin. Officer, V.P. & Treas.--Roy F. Weston, Inc., West Chester, PA; *U.S. Public*, pg. 1761
Mechling, Robert, V.P.-Sls.--Midco International Inc., Chicago, IL; *U.S. Private*, pg. 744
Medel, Teresita, Controller, Treas. & Sec.--AMATI Communications Corp., San Jose, CA; *U.S. Public*, pg. 1585
Mediate, Anthony, Treas.--Empress International Ltd., Port Washington, NY; *U.S. Private*, pg. 375
Medico, Lawrence, V.P. & Treas.--Medico Industries, Inc., Wilkes-Barre, PA; *U.S. Private*, pg. 728
Medvin, Harvey N., Chief Fin. Officer, Exec. V.P. & Treas.--AON Corporation, Chicago, IL; *U.S. Public*, pg. 117
Meehan, Gregory W.A., Chief Fin. Officer, V.P. & Treas.--High Point Financial Corp., Branchville, NJ; *U.S. Public*, pg. 826
Meehan, William P., Chief Fin. Officer, V.P.-Fin. & Treas.--Hexcel Corporation, Pleasanton, CA; *U.S. Public*, pg. 824
Meek, David, Treas.--R.B. Pamplin Corp., Portland, OR; *U.S. Private*, pg. 835
Meeks, Harold E., Asst. Treas.--Aluminum Company of America, Pittsburgh, PA; *U.S. Public*, pg. 60
Meeusen, Richard A., Chief Fin. Officer, V.P.-Fin. & Treas.--Badger Meter, Inc., Milwaukee, WI; *U.S. Public*, pg. 164
Megenis, Yvonne, V.P. & Treas.--Bridgeport Machines, Inc., Bridgeport, CT; *U.S. Public*, pg. 251
Meglaughlin, William T., Jr., Chief Fin. Officer & Treas.--Asbury Carbons, Inc., Asbury, NJ; *U.S. Private*, pg. 87
Mehta, Sunil, Treas.--Unilever United States Inc., New York, NY; *Int'l*, pg. 1435
Meier, Michael J., Chief Fin. Officer, V.P.-Fin., Treas. & Sec.--Defiance, Inc., Cleveland, OH; *U.S. Public*, pg. 493
Meier, Tom, Dir.-Investor Rels. & Asst. Treas.--APL Limited, Oakland, CA; *Int'l*, pg. 912
Meikle, Mark G., Chief Fin. Officer, V.P. & Treas.--Steel of West Virginia, Inc., Huntington, WV; *U.S. Public*, pg. 1513
Meilahn, J.E., Treas. & Sec.--Federated Mutual Insurance Company, Owatonna, MN; *U.S. Private*, pg. 399
Meinkoth, Richard K., Controller & Treas.--Contico International, Inc., Saint Louis, MO; *U.S. Private*, pg. 267
Meir, Yosef, Treas.--The Israel Land Development Co., Ltd., Tel Aviv, Israel; *Int'l*, pg. 691
Meixner, Bob, Controller--Mitchell Coach Manufacturing, Pryor, OK; *U.S. Private*, pg. 753
Melchor, Pierre S., Sr. V.P. & Treas.--ITEQ, Inc., Houston, TX; *U.S. Public*, pg. 914
Melgin, Jari, Treas.--Amer Group Ltd., Helsinki, Finland; *Int'l*, pg. 72
Melgoza Marin, Hector, Treas.--Industrias CH, S.A. de C.V., Tlalnepantla, Mexico; *Int'l*, pg. 677
Mellace, Susan C., V.P. & Treas.--Perini Corporation, Framingham, MA; *U.S. Public*, pg. 1278
Mellgren, Hank, Treas.--Northwest Pipe Fittings, Inc., Billings, MT; *U.S. Private*, pg. 806
Melloy, Patrick C., V.P., Sec. & Treas.--Melloy Bros. Enterprises, Albuquerque, NM; *U.S. Private*, pg. 730
Meloon, Walter O., Treas.--Correct Craft, Inc., Orlando, FL; *U.S. Private*, pg. 276
Melzer, Michael R., Chief Fin. Officer, V.P.-Fin. & Treas.--Wisconsin Machine and Tool Corporation, Milwaukee, WI; *U.S. Private*, pg. 1185
Memmo, Nicholas, V.P.-Fin. & Treas.--U.S. Filter, Lowell, MA; *U.S. Public*, pg. 1682
Menchinger, Steven R., Chief. Fin. Officer, Treas. & Sec.--Glassmaster Company, Lexington, SC; *U.S. Public*, pg. 745
Mendello, William L., Pres. & Chief Oper. Officer--Fender Musical Instruments, Scottsdale, AZ; *U.S. Private*, pg. 400
Mendius, L., V.P.-Sls. & Dir.-Mktg.--Silbrico Corporation, Hodgkins, IL; *U.S. Private*, pg. 1000
Mendoza, Vic, Treas.--Quintana Petroleum Corp., Houston, TX; *U.S. Private*, pg. 901
Menke, Gerald T., Treas. & Sec.--The F.D. Lawrence Electric Co., Cincinnati, OH; *U.S. Private*, pg. 654
Mercado, Asuncion V., Chief Fin. Officer, V.P. & Treas.--Benguet Management Corporation, Manila, Philippines; *Int'l*, pg. 186
Mercer, Dorothy K., Asst. Treas.--The Washington Water Power Company, Spokane, WA; *U.S. Public*, pg. 1744
Mercer, Harold B., Chief Fin. Officer,Exec. V.P. & Treas.--Swift Instruments, Inc., Dorchester, MA; *U.S. Private*, pg. 1058
Mercer, James G., V.P. & Asst. Treas.--Swift Instruments, Inc., Dorchester, MA; *U.S. Private*, pg. 1058
Merchant, Bill R., Asst. Treas.--Grey Wolf, Inc., Houston, TX; *U.S. Public*, pg. 765
Mereschuck, Jeffrey A., Chief Fin. Officer, V.P. & Treas.--Essex Industries, New Haven, CT; *Int'l*, pg. 18
Merkel, Howard, Treas.--Stolt-Nielsen S.A., London, United Kingdom; *Int'l*, pg. 1301
Merkel, Joelen K., V.P. & Treas.--Chris-Craft Industries, Inc., New York, NY; *U.S. Public*, pg. 351
Merker, Steven, Chm. Bd., Chief Fin. Officer & Treas.--Standard Automotive Corporation, Hillsborough, NJ; *U.S.* Private, pg. 1030
Mermelstein, Howard, V.P. & Treas.--Croton Watch Company & Nationwide Time, New York, NY; *U.S. Private*, pg. 291
Merriek, Keith H., V.P. & Treas.--Standard Commercial Corporation, Wilson, NC; *U.S. Public*, pg. 1501
Merrill, F. Robert, III, Chief Fin. Officer, V.P.-Fin., Treas. & Sec.--Quest Medical, Inc., Allen, TX; *U.S. Public*, pg. 1352
Merrill, J. Mark, V.P. & Treas.--Sofamor Danek Group, Inc., Memphis, TN; *U.S. Public*, pg. 1482
Merritt, Robert S., Chief Fin. Officer, Sr. V.P.-Fin. & Treas.--Outback Steakhouse Inc., Tampa, FL; *U.S. Public*, pg. 1235
Merszei, Geoffrey, V.P. & Treas.--The Dow Chemical Company, Midland, MI; *U.S. Public*, pg. 522
Mertzlufft, Douglas, Chief Fin. Officer & Treas.--Guarantee Electrical Company, Saint Louis, MO; *U.S. Private*, pg. 485
Merz, J. Frederick, Jr., Chm. Bd. & Treas.--Scott Specialty Gases, Plumsteadville, PA; *U.S. Private*, pg. 977
Meth, Joseph, Chief Fin. Officer & Treas.--F. Schumacher & Co., New York, NY; *U.S. Private*, pg. 973
Metzger, Philip R., Treas.--Greif Brothers Corporation, Delaware, OH; *U.S. Public*, pg. 763
Meyer, George G., Chief Exec. Officer, Treas. & Sec.--Central Sprinkler Corporation, Lansdale, PA; *U.S. Public, pg. 327*
Meyer, Ronald A., V.P.-Fin. & Admin., Treas. & Sec.--Modern Controls, Inc., Minneapolis, MN; *U.S. Public*, pg. 1120
Meyer, Steven J., Treas.--Baxter International Inc., Deerfield, IL; *U.S. Public*, pg. 196
Meyer, Steven L., Asst. Treas.--Ipalco Enterprises, Inc., Indianapolis, IN; *U.S. Public*, pg. 912
Meyer, William M., Chm. Bd. & Treas.--Central Sprinkler Company, Lansdale, PA; *U.S. Public*, pg. 327
Meyers, Geoffrey G., Chief Fin. Officer, Exec. V.P. & Treas.--Health Care & Retirement Corporation, Toledo, OH; *U.S. Public*, pg. 801
Meyers, Pierre, Chief Fin. Officer & Dir.-Fin.--Cockerill Sambre, Brussels, Belgium; *Int'l*, pg. 301
Meyers, Terry, V.P. & Treas.--U.S. Safety, Lenexa, KS; *U.S.* Private, pg. 1125
Micelli, Tony, V.P.-Fin., Treas. & Sec.--Metex Corporation, Edison, NJ; *U.S. Public*, pg. 1674
Michael, Lanny H., Sr. V.P. & Treas.--Airborne Freight Corporation, Seattle, WA; *U.S. Public*, pg. 32
Michaels, Kevin T., Treas.--AST Research Inc., Irvine, CA; *Int'l*, pg. 1181
Michaels, Ned, Treas.--Renfro Corp., Mount Airy, NC; *U.S. Private*, pg. 922
Michas, William, Treas.--Twin County Grocers, Inc., Edison, NJ; *U.S. Private*, pg. 1111
Michaud, Paul J., Chief Fin. Officer & Treas.--AAI Corporation, Hunt Valley, MD; *U.S. Public*, pg. 1679
Michel, Charles, Chief Fin. Officer & V.P.--Dave & Buster's, Dallas, TX; *U.S. Public*, pg. 488
Michelson, Larry D., Pres. & Treas.--Sate-Lite Manufacturing Company, Niles, IL; *U.S. Private*, pg. 598
Mickus, Donald V., V.P., Treas. & Sec.--Del Webb Corporation, Phoenix, AZ; *U.S. Public*, pg. 494
Mignanelli, James, Chief Exec. & Oper. Officer & Treas.--Plastic Engineering Co. Inc., Haverhill, MA; *U.S. Private*, pg. 871
Mihalko, George R., Jr., Chief Fin. Officer, Sr. V.P., Treas. & Asst. Sec.--Pamida Holdings Corporation, Omaha, NE; *U.S. Public*, pg. 1255
Mihok, Donald G., Treas.--Keystone Bank, Horsham, PA; *U.S. Public*, pg. 956
Miike, Patrick T., V.P.-Fin. & Treas.--Amelco Corporation, Gardena, CA; *U.S. Public*, pg. 65
Mikalauskas, Kenneth, Asst. Treas.--Comcast Corporation, Philadelphia, PA; *U.S. Public*, pg. 406
Mikelait, Mark S., Treas.--McClain Industries, Inc., Sterling Heights, MI; *U.S. Public*, pg. 1065
Miklich, Thomas R., Chief Fin. Officer, Treas., Gen. Counsel & Sec.--Invacare Corporation, Elyria, OH; *U.S. Public*, pg. 911
Mikovich, Fran, Treas. & Sec.--Orleans Materials & Equipment Co., Inc., New Orleans, LA; *U.S. Private*, pg. 820
Milack, Joseph, V.P.-Fin., Treas. & Sec.--Brinkmann Instruments, Inc., Westbury, NY; *U.S. Private*, pg. 169
Milano, Sandro, Sec. & Treas.--Butera Finer Foods Inc., Elgin, IL; *U.S. Private*, pg. 189
Milas, Joseph, Treas.--Plibrico Co., Chicago, IL; *U.S. Private*, pg. 872
Milbury, Paul J., V.P. & Treas.--Digital Equipment Corporation, Maynard, MA; *U.S. Public*, pg. 507
Miles, Kenneth, Chief Fin. Officer & Treas.--Care Matrix Corp., Needham, MA; *U.S. Public*, pg. 305
Milinski, James, Treas.--MTD Products, Inc., Valley City, OH; *U.S. Private*, pg. 688
Milioti, Dee, Controller & Treas.--Plastic Reel Corp. of America, Lyndhurst, NJ; *U.S. Private*, pg. 871
Millard, Garnett, Treas.--Hudson's Bay Company Acceptance Ltd., Edmonton, Canada; *Int'l*, pg. 637
Millburg, Larry E., Asst. Treas--AmerenCIPS, Springfield, IL; *U.S. Public*, pg. 65
Millenbruch, Gary L., Chief Fin. Officer, Exec. V.P. & Treas.--Bethlehem Steel Corporation, Bethlehem, PA; *U.S. Public*, pg. 226
Miller-Jones,Donald, Treas.--Polygram N.V., Baarn, Netherlands; *Int'l*, pg. 1051
Miller, Andrew, V.P. & Treas.--Miller Advertising Agency Inc., New York, NY; *U.S. Private*, pg. 746
Miller, Arnold, Treas.--Quill Corp., Lincolnshire, IL; *U.S. Private*, pg. 901
Miller, Brian W., Chief Info. Officer & Treas.--Star Bronze Company, Alliance, OH; *U.S. Private*, pg. 1034
Miller, Catherine D., Treas. & Sec.--Derst Baking Company, Inc., Savannah, GA; *U.S. Private*, pg. 326
Miller, Charles D., Treas.--Harbert Corporation, Birmingham, AL; *U.S. Private*, pg. 500
Miller, Charles T., Controller & Treas.--Hammond Group Inc., Hammond, IN; *U.S. Private*, pg. 498
Miller, Chris, Controller & Treas.--Bon Jour International Ltd., New York, NY; *U.S. Private*, pg. 156
Miller, Chris A., V.P.-Fin., Treas. & Sec.--C-COR Electronics, Inc., State College, PA; *U.S. Public*, pg. 272
Miller, Daryl, Treas.--Graphic Enterprises of Ohio, Inc., Canton, OH; *U.S. Private*, pg. 471
Miller, David, Chief Fin. Officer & Treas.--Fab Industries, Inc., New York, NY; *U.S. Public*, pg. 603
Miller, David, Chief Fin. Officer, Controller, Treas. & Sec.--Monterey Mechanical Company, Oakland, CA; *U.S. Private*, pg. 758
Miller, Donald, Treas. & Sec.--Lee Grocery Company, Everett, WA; *U.S. Private*, pg. 657
Miller, Ed, Treas.--Cold Heading Co., Warren, MI; *U.S. Private*, pg. 250
Miller, Edwin W., V.P. & Treas.--Eli Lilly and Company, Indianapolis, IN; *U.S. Public*, pg. 992
Miller, G.G., Chief Fin. Officer, V.P.-Fin. & Treas.--AFG Industries, Inc., Kingsport, TN; *Int'l*, pg. 84
Miller, Jay, Sr. V.P.-Fin., Treas. & Sec.--Perfection Bakeries Inc., Fort Wayne, IN; *U.S. Private*, pg. 852
Miller, Jeffrey B., Treas.--Columbian Advertising Inc., Chicago, IL; *U.S. Private*, pg. 256
Miller, John J., V.P. & Treas.--Southern New England Telecommunications Corporation, New Haven, CT; *U.S. Public*, pg. 1490
Miller, Katherine, Treas. & Sec.--Pyromet, Inc., Aston, PA; *U.S. Private*, pg. 897
Miller, Kenneth I., Chief Fin. Officer, Treas., Sr. V.P. & Sec.--Johnston, Lemon & Co. Inc., Washington, DC; *U.S. Private*, pg. 595
Miller, Kirk, Treas.--Buff Whelan Chevrolet & GEO, Inc., Sterling Heights, MI; *U.S. Private*, pg. 1171
Miller, Larry C., Treas.--Butler Manufacturing Company, Kansas City, MO; *U.S. Public*, pg. 271
Miller, Larry H., Treas. & Sec.--Larry H. Miller Group, Murray, UT; *U.S. Private*, pg. 747
Miller, Lloyd A., V.P., Treas. & Sec.--Midway Products Corporation, Monroe, MI; *U.S. Private*, pg. 744
Miller, Max, Chm. Bd. & Treas.--McInerney-Miller Brothers Inc., Detroit, MI; *U.S. Private*, pg. 722
Miller, Michael, Controller & Treas.--Astro Homes, Shippenville, PA; *U.S. Public*, pg. 318
Miller, Michael, Chief Fin. Officer & Sr. V.P.-Fin.--Fender Musical Instruments, Scottsdale, AZ; *U.S. Private*, pg. 400
Miller, Michael, V.P.-Fin.--Silver Dollar City, Inc., Branson, MO; *U.S. Private*, pg. 1000
Miller, Michael I., V.P. & Treas.--Owens Corning, Toledo, OH; *U.S. Public*, pg. 1236
Miller, Preston A., Sr. V.P. & Treas.--AmeriCredit Corp., Fort Worth, TX; *U.S. Public*, pg. 96
Miller, Randy J., V.P. & Treas.--Geotek Communications, Montvale, NJ; *U.S. Public*, pg. 739
Miller, Richard A., Pres. & Treas.--Prentiss Incorporated, Floral Park, NY; *U.S. Private*, pg. 882
Miller, Richard L., Exec. V.P., Treas. & Sec.--Miller Transporters, Inc., Jackson, MS; *U.S. Private*, pg. 329
Miller, Robert, Treas.--PrimeSource Corporation, Pennsauken, NJ; *U.S. Public*, pg. 1329
Miller, Ruth P., Treas.--Schultz Steel Company, South Gate, CA; *U.S. Private*, pg. 973
Miller, Samuel H., Co-Chm. Bd. & Treas.--Forest City Enterprises, Inc., Cleveland, OH; *U.S. Public*, pg. 667
Miller, Scott, Treas.--Carlisle Companies Incorporated, Syracuse, NY; *U.S. Public*, pg. 305
Miller, Thomas J., V.P. & Treas.--Butcher & Co., Inc., Philadelphia, PA; *U.S. Private*, pg. 189
Miller, Thomas J., V.P. & Treas.--Butcher Energy, Philadelphia, PA; *U.S. Private*, pg. 189
Millers, Jackie, Treas.--A & S Tribal Industries, Poplar, MT; *U.S. Private*, pg. 1
Millington, Charles, V.P. & Treas.--Van Kampen/American Capital Inc., Oak Brook Terrace, IL; *U.S. Public*, pg. 1132
Millington, Mick, Treas.--Champion Parts, Inc., Glen Ellyn, IL; *U.S. Public*, pg. 334
Millington, P.A., Treas.--Lafarge Canada Inc., Montreal, Canada; *Int'l*, pg. 789
Mills, John M., Jr., V.P. & Treas.--Gravymaster Inc., Branford, CT; *U.S. Private*, pg. 471
Mills, Waeter, Treas.--W.G. Mills, Inc., Sarasota, FL; *U.S. Private*, pg. 749
Mills, Walter G., Chm. Bd., Chief Exec. Officer & Treas.--W.G. Mills, Inc., Sarasota, FL; *U.S. Private*, pg. 749

Milne, John, Vice Chm., Chief Acq. Officer, Sr. V.P., Treas. & Sec.--United Waste Systems, Inc., Houston, TX; *U.S. Public*, pg. 1691

Milne, Malcolm R., Sr. V.P. & Treas.--First Federal of Michigan, Detroit, MI; *U.S. Public*, pg. 336

Mineart, Carol J., Chief Fin. Officer & Treas.--Avis Industrial Corporation, Upland, IN; *U.S. Private*, pg. 102

Mingoia, Robert P., Treas.--Oceaneering International, Inc., Houston, TX; *U.S. Public*, pg. 1211

Mingoia, Robert P., Treas.--Oceaneering International, Inc., Morgan City, LA; *U.S. Public*, pg. 1211

Minikes, Michael, Sr. Mng. Dir. & Treas.--The Bear Stearns Companies Inc., New York, NY; *U.S. Public*, pg. 197

Minneman, Thomas J., Treas.--MTS Systems Corporation, Eden Prairie, MN; *U.S. Public*, pg. 1028

Minnick, David, Treas.--Ray-Carroll County Grain Co-op, Richmond, MO; *U.S. Private*, pg. 911

Minor, David L., V.P. & Treas.--L.B. Foster Company, Pittsburgh, PA; *U.S. Public*, pg. 675

Minor, Joe C., Chief Fin. Officer, Sr. V.P. & Treas.--NBT Bancorp Inc., Norwich, NY; *U.S. Public*, pg. 1144

Minsen, Brett, V.P.-Fin. & Admin. & Treas.--Reinhold Industries Inc., Santa Fe Springs, CA; *U.S. Private*, pg. 920

Miracle, Rocky R., Treas.--CSW Credit, Inc., Dallas, TX; *U.S. Public*, pg. 324

Misamore, Bruce K., V.P. & Treas.--Pennzoil Company, Houston, TX; *U.S. Public*, pg. 1272

Misamore, Bruce K., Treas.--Jiffy Lube International, Inc., Houston, TX; *U.S. Public*, pg. 1272

Mischler, Paul, Exec. V.P. & Treas.--Norfoods, Inc., Overland Park, KS; *U.S. Private*, pg. 802

Mishoe, Thomas M., Chief Fin. Officer, V.P., Treas. & Sec.--Eskimo Pie Corporation, Richmond, VA; *U.S. Public*, pg. 592

Miskura, Robert, V.P. & Treas.--The Economics Press, Inc., Fairfield, NJ; *U.S. Private*, pg. 362

Misner, Jeffrey J., V.P.-Treasury Opers.--Continental Airlines, Houston, TX; *U.S. Public*, pg. 439

Mistlin, Gary E., V.P.-Fin. & Treas.--Mentor Corporation, Santa Barbara, CA; *U.S. Public*, pg. 1086

Miswald, R. Scott, Treas. & Sec.--Entree Corporation, Westlake Village, CA; *U.S. Public*, pg. 455

Miszak, Michael, Controller & Treas.--Reading Eagle Company, Reading, PA; *U.S. Private*, pg. 913

Mitchel, Stephen, V.P., Sec. & Treas.--Mitchel & Scott Machine Co., Inc., Indianapolis, IN; *U.S. Private*, pg. 753

Mitchell, George F., Treas.--PAXAR Corporation, White Plains, NY; *U.S. Public*, pg. 1266

Mitchell, J. Barry, V.P.-Fin. & Treas.--PECO Energy Company, Philadelphia, PA; *U.S. Public*, pg. 1268

Mitchell, James D., Treas.--Duquesne Light Company, Pittsburgh, PA; *U.S. Public*, pg. 474

Mitchell, Patrick, Sr. V.P. & Treas.--National Financial Insurance Company, Fort Worth, TX; *U.S. Private*, pg. 782

Mitchell, Robert J., Treas. & Asst. Sec.--ACF Industries, Inc., Saint Charles, MO; *U.S. Private*, pg. 556

Mitchell, Robert W., V.P. & Treas.--Ingram Industries Inc., Nashville, TN; *U.S. Private*, pg. 562

Mitchell, Sandra L., Treas. & Sec.--Delagra Corporation, Bridgeville, DE; *U.S. Private*, pg. 321

Mitchell, Winston, Treas.--Durham Transportation, Inc., Austin, TX; *U.S. Private*, pg. 348

Mittasch, Randolph J., Sec. & Treas.--The Care Group, Inc., New York, NY; *U.S. Public*, pg. 305

Mittelman, David L., V.P. & Treas.--Williamhouse-Regency, Inc., New York, NY; *U.S. Public*, pg. 89

Miura, A., Treas.--Ajinomoto U.S.A., Inc., Teaneck, NJ; *Int'l*, pg. 40

Miyatake, Motoo, Chief Fin. Officer & Exec. Dir.--Duskin Co., Ltd., Osaka, Japan; *Int'l*, pg. 422

Mizanin, Michael, Sec. & Treas.--Graycor International Inc., Homewood, IL; *U.S. Private*, pg. 472

Mize, E.J., Jr., Chief Fin. Officer, Chief Acctg. Officer, V.P.-Fin. & Treas.--United States Pipe & Foundry Company, Inc., Birmingham, AL; *U.S. Public*, pg. 1736

Mize, John, Treas.--Distribution America, Des Plaines, IL; *U.S. Private*, pg. 335

Mizoguchi, Paul, Treas.--Maui Varieties, Ltd., Honolulu, HI; *U.S. Private*, pg. 715

Mizumachi, Shunta, Treas.--Kobelco Stewart Bolling, Inc., Hudson, OH; *Int'l*, pg. 740

Mock, Steve, Treas. & Sec.--Barenbrug Northeast, Ogdensburg, NJ; *Int'l*, pg. 167

Modist, Scott J., Chief Fin. Officer, V.P.-Fin. & Treas.--Equitrac Corporation, Coral Gables, FL; *U.S. Public*, pg. 590

Moehring, Niel, Controller, Treas. & Sec.--Thomas & Skinner, Inc., Indianapolis, IN; *U.S. Private*, pg. 1082

Moeller, Paul R., V.P.-Fin.--Health-Chem Corporation, New York, NY; *U.S. Public*, pg. 802

Moerchen, Robert J., Asst. Treas.--Outboard Marine Corporation, Waukegan, IL; *U.S. Private*, pg. 478

Moersdorf, Gerard B., Jr., Pres., Chief Exec. Officer & Treas.--Applied Innovation Inc., Dublin, OH; *U.S. Public*, pg. 123

Mogle, David B., Treas. & Sec.--F.N.B. Corporation, Hermitage, PA; *U.S. Public*, pg. 607

Mogle, David B., V.P. & Treas.--Reeves Bank, Beaver Falls, PA; *U.S. Public*, pg. 607

Mohlman, Kurt, Treas. & Sec.--United Illuminating Company, New Haven, CT; *U.S. Public*, pg. 1678

Moix, Norbert, Sec. & Treas.--Nabholz Construction Corp., Conway, AR; *U.S. Private*, pg. 772

Mokas, John G., Dir.-Treasury & Fin.--Parametric Technology Corporation, Waltham, MA; *U.S. Public*, pg. 1257

Molin, Carl E., III, Treas.--Molin Auto Parts Inc., Buffalo, NY; *U.S. Private*, pg. 756

Moline, Jennifer, V.P. & Treas.--Tupperware Corporation, Orlando, FL; *U.S. Public*, pg. 1644

Molineu, Richard H., Treas.--Miller & Long Co. Inc., Bethesda, MD; *U.S. Private*, pg. 746

Moller, Soren, Treas. & Mgr.-Communications--Sophus Berendsen A/S, Soeborg, Denmark; *Int'l*, pg. 1284

Molloy, Richard, Chief Fin. Officer & Treas.--Davenport Insulation, Inc, Upper Marlboro, MD; *U.S. Private*, pg. 314

Momayez, F., Treas. & Sec.--TGM Detectors Inc., Waltham, MA; *Int'l*, pg. 892

Monaco, John L., V.P.-Tax & Treas.--Gould Electronics Inc., Eastlake, OH; *U.S. Public*, pg. 1591

Monaghan, Craig T., Treas.--The Reader's Digest Association, Inc., Pleasantville, NY; *U.S. Public*, pg. 1367

Monaghan, David G., Jr., V.P.-Fin.--GTE Government Systems Corporation, Needham, MA; *U.S. Public*, pg. 696

Money, Anthony, V.P., Sec. & Treas.--Foseco Holding Inc., Cleveland, OH; *Int'l*, pg. 234

Monk, Robert D., Treas. & Sec.--Triple S Plastics, Inc., Vicksburg, MI; *U.S. Public*, pg. 1639

Monnat, James J., Treas.--Wisconsin Gas Company, Milwaukee, WI; *U.S. Public*, pg. 1767

Monnat, Jim, Treas.--Sta-Rite Industries, Inc., Delavan, WI; *U.S. Public*, pg. 1767

Monoghan, Dave, Controller & Treas.--Northwestern Public Service, Huron, SD; *U.S. Public*, pg. 1200

Monrad, Elizabeth A., V.P. & Treas.--General Re Corporation, Stamford, CT; *U.S. Public*, pg. 725

Monrad, Elizabeth A., Sr. V.P. & Treas.--General Reinsurance Corp., Stamford, CT; *U.S. Public*, pg. 725

Monson, Robert, Chm. Bd., Pres. & Treas.--Monson Trucking, Inc., Duluth, MN; *U.S. Private*, pg. 758

Montague, Carlos S., Chief Fin. Officer, V.P., Treas. & Asst. Sec.--Ault Incorporated, Minneapolis, MN; *U.S. Public*, pg. 147

Montgomery, David, Treas. & Sec.--SouthCo. Inc., Concordville, PA; *U.S. Private*, pg. 1014

Montgomery, Michael J., V.P. & Treas.--The Walt Disney Company, Burbank, CA; *U.S. Public*, pg. 511

Montgomery, R.L., Chief Fin. Officer, Exec. V.P. & Treas.--Columbus McKinnon Corp., Amherst, NY; *U.S. Public*, pg. 405

Mood, Alfred, Treas. & Sec.--Pyramid Mountain Lumber, Seeley Lake, MT; *U.S. Private*, pg. 896

Moomjy, Walter, Treas. & Sec.--Einstein Moomjy Inc., Pine Brook, NJ; *U.S. Private*, pg. 366

Moore, Charles E., Treas.--Bell Atlanticom Systems, Inc., Princeton, NJ; *U.S. Public*, pg. 203

Moore, Dennis G., Chief Fin. Officer, Sr. V.P., Treas. & Sec.--J & J Snack Foods Corporation, Pennsauken, NJ; *U.S. Public*, pg. 916

Moore, E. Kevin, V.P. & Treas.--Schering-Plough Corporation, Madison, NJ; *U.S. Public*, pg. 1438

Moore, Faye, Treas.--Southeastern Pennsylvania Transportation Authority, Philadelphia, PA; *U.S. Private*, pg. 1015

Moore, James H., Treas.--Pegasus Gold Corporation, Spokane, WA; *U.S. Public*, pg. 1269

Moore, James O., V.P.-Fin., Treas. & Asst. Sec.--Cullman Ventures, Inc., Norwalk, CT; *U.S. Private*, pg. 294

Moore, Jeffrey R., V.P.-Treas. Opers.--PerSeptive Biosystems, Inc., Framingham, MA; *U.S. Public*, pg. 1279

Moore, Nicholas, Treas.--TI Group plc, Abingdon, United Kingdom; *Int'l*, pg. 1337

Moore, Robert L., Treas.--Village Transport Corp., Cleveland, OH; *U.S. Public*, pg. 1335

Moore, Roy, Treas.--Ott Food Products, Carthage, MO; *U.S.* Private, pg. 821

Moore, Steven, Treas.--The Savogran Company, Norwood, MA; *U.S. Private*, pg. 968

Moore, T.G., Asst. Treas.--Florida East Coast Industries Inc., Saint Augustine, FL; *U.S. Public*, pg. 1427

Moore, W.T., Asst. Treas.--Tultex Corporation, Martinsville, VA; *U.S. Public*, pg. 1644

Moore, William J., V.P. & Treas.--Catskill Savings Bank, Catskill, NY; *U.S. Public*, pg. 318

Moorhead, Bill, Sec. & Treas.--Homewood Corporation, Columbus, OH; *U.S. Private*, pg. 537

Moosa, Moosa E., Chief Fin. Officer, V.P.-Fin. & Treas.--Chemfab Corporation, Merrimack, NH; *U.S. Public*, pg. 344

Mooty, Charles W., Chief Fin. Officer, V.P. & Treas.--International Dairy Queen, Inc., Minneapolis, MN; *U.S. Public*, pg. 220

Moran, Patricia K., Corp. Sec. & Asst. Treas.--Zemex Corporation, Toronto, Canada; *Int'l*, pg. 1523

Morden, Ronald P., Sr. V.P. & Treas.--American Republic Insurance Co., Des Moines, IA; *U.S. Private*, pg. 61

Morehead, C. Richard, Sr. V.P. & Treas.--First Colonial Insurance Company, Jacksonville, FL; *U.S. Public*, pg. 79

Moreland, Richard, Treas.--Harris Bankcorp, Inc., Chicago, IL; *Int'l*, pg. 154

Morello, James J., Chief Fin. Officer & Treas.--Medical Assurance, Inc., Birmingham, AL; *U.S. Public*, pg. 1079

Moren, Nicholas C., V.P. & Treas.--Loral Space & Communications, New York, NY; *U.S. Public*, pg. 1014

Morena, Joseph M., Treas.--Air & Water Technologies Corporation, Branchburg, NJ; *U.S. Public*, pg. 29

Morf, Claudia E., V.P. & Treas.--CBS Corporation, Pittsburgh, PA; *U.S. Public*, pg. 273

Morgan, Gary J., Chief Fin. Officer, V.P.-Fin. & Treas.--Met-Pro Corporation, Harleysville, PA; *U.S. Public*, pg. 1100

Morgan, Jerry L., V.P. & Treas.--Centex Construction Products, Inc., Dallas, TX; *U.S. Public*, pg. 322

Morgan, Kirby, Treas. & Sec.--Williamson-Dickie Mfg. Co., Fort Worth, TX; *U.S. Private*, pg. 1179

Morgan, Larkin C., Chief Fin. Officer, Treas. & Sec.--Arrow Gear Company, Downers Grove, IL; *U.S. Private*, pg. 85

Morgan, Louis J., Chm. Bd. & Treas.--PC Quote, Inc., Chicago, IL; *U.S. Public*, pg. 1240

Morgan, Robert, Treas.--Hardware Wholesalers, Inc., Fort Wayne, IN; *U.S. Private*, pg. 502

Moriarty, John, Dir.-Acctg. & Asst. Treas.--Cannondale Corporation, Bethel, CT; *U.S. Public*, pg. 301

Morin, Curtis L., Pres., Treas. & Sec.--Bennington Iron Works, Inc., Bennington, VT; *U.S. Private*, pg. 133

Morisada, Eizaburo, Dir.-Treasury Div.--Sumitomo Corporation, Tokyo, Japan; *Int'l*, pg. 1312

Morley, Walter J., Chief Fin. Officer & Treas.--John Hassall, Inc., Westbury, NY; *U.S. Private*, pg. 509

Morman, Dave, Controller & Treas.--Farmers Union Marketing & Processing Association, Redwood Falls, MN; *U.S. Private*, pg. 395

Morphis, Gene S., V.P.-Fin. & Treas.--American Woodmark Corporation, Winchester, VA; *U.S. Public*, pg. 96

Morral, William G., Sr. V.P.-Fin. & Treas.--Moyer Packing Company, Souderton, PA; *U.S. Private*, pg. 765

Morrash, John M., V.P. & Treas.--SPS Technologies, Inc., Jenkintown, PA; *U.S. Public*, pg. 1419

Morrey, Timothy, V.P.-Acctg. & Treas.--Hostmark Management Group, Rolling Meadows, IL; *U.S. Private*, pg. 541

Morris, Charlie, Treas.--Fulmer Supermarkets, Inc., Springfield, OH; *U.S. Private*, pg. 431

Morris, Cynthia R., Chief Fin. Officer, Exec. V.P, Treas. & Sec.--Sun Coast Industries, Inc, Dallas, TX; *U.S. Public*, pg. 1529

Morris, James E., V.P., Controller, Treas. & Sec.--SL Industries, Inc., Mount Laurel, NJ; *U.S. Public*, pg. 1418

Morris, John E., V.P.-Fin. & Asst. Treas.--Roanoke Electric Steel Corporation, Roanoke, VA; *U.S. Public*, pg. 1392

Morris, Kathryn L., Treas. & Sec.--Acorn Engineering Company, City of Industry, CA; *U.S. Private*, pg. 14

Morris, M.J., Treas.--Trico Products Corporation, Buffalo, NY; *Int'l*, pg. 1397

Morris, Melvin, Treas. & Sec.--Mountain States Constructors, Inc., Albuquerque, NM; *U.S. Private*, pg. 764

Morris, Paul F., V.P., Treas. & Sec.--The Fusco Corporation, New Haven, CT; *U.S. Private*, pg. 432

Morris, Roberta J., Chief Fin. Officer &Treas.--Big Dog Holdings Inc., Santa Barbara, CA; *U.S. Public*, pg. 227

Morrison, B.W., Dir.-Treasury--National & Provincial Building Society, Bradford, United Kingdom; *Int'l*, pg. 906

Morrison, Daniel R., Chief Fin. Officer & Treas.--First Signature Bank & Trust Co., Portsmouth, NH; *U.S. Private*, pg. 589

Morrison, David F., Chief Fin. Officer, Exec. V.P. & Treas.--Consolidated Freightways Corp., Menlo Park, CA; *U.S. Public*, pg. 435

Morrison, Donald, Gen. Mgr. & Treas.--Eureka Manufacturing Co., Inc., Norton, MA; *U.S. Private*, pg. 916

Morrison, James E., V.P & Treas.--Kennametal Inc., Latrobe, PA; *U.S. Public*, pg. 950

Morrison, Robert W., V.P. & Treas.--The Canada Life Assurance Company, Toronto, Canada; *Int'l*, pg. 254

Morrison, Wyatt F., Sec. & Treas.--Safe Harbor Water Power Corp., Conestoga, PA; *U.S. Public*, pg. 172

Morrissey, John J., Treas.--Gateway 2000, North Sioux City, SD; *U.S. Public*, pg. 703

Morrow, Dean, Dir.-Treasury--Network Equipment Technologies, Inc., Redwood City, CA; *U.S. Public*, pg. 1168

Morrow, Mary Jane, Chief Fin. Officer--Federal Realty Investment Trust, Rockville, MD; *U.S. Public*, pg. 616

Mortenson, Jerald H., Chief Fin. Officer, V.P-Fin. & Administration, Treas. & Sec.--HEI, Inc., Victoria, MN; *U.S. Public*, pg. 770

Mortland, Daniel L., Asst. Treas.--Illinois Power Company, Decatur, IL; *U.S. Public*, pg. 869

Morton, Mike, Chief Fin. Officer, V.P. & Treas.--The H.T. Hackney Co., Knoxville, TN; *U.S. Private*, pg. 493

Moser, David L., Gen. Mgr., Treas. & Sec.--Cross Motors Corp., Louisville, KY; *U.S. Private*, pg. 291

Moser, Eugene R., Treas. & Sec.--Sioux Falls Construction Company, Sioux Falls, SD; *U.S. Private*, pg. 1003

Moses, John, Gen. Mgr.-Grp. Treas. & Intl. Div.--First National Bank Holdings Limited, Johannesburg, South Africa; *Int'l*, pg. 487

Moss, Dick, Treas.--Hawthorne Machinery Company, San Diego, CA; *U.S. Private*, pg. 512

Moss, James D., Dir.-Treas. Opers.--Campbell Soup Company, Camden, NJ; *U.S. Public*, pg. 298

Mossberg, Alan I., Pres., Chief Exec. & Chief Oper. Officer & Treas.--O.F. Mossberg & Sons, Inc., North Haven, CT; *U.S. Private*, pg. 764

Moszer, Irene M., V.P.-Info. Sys., Treas. & Sec.--Virginia Electric and Power Company, Richmond, VA; *U.S. Public*, pg. 516

Mothershed, J. Russell, Chief Fin. Officer & Sr. V.P.-Fin.--Ruby Tuesday, Inc., Mobile, AL; *U.S. Public*, pg. 1411

Moto, Seijaro, V.P. & Treas.--Miura Boiler Co. Ltd., Northbrook, IL; *Int'l*, pg. 884

Motschwiller, Kenneth W., V.P. & Treas.--FlightSafety International Inc., Flushing, NY; *U.S. Public*, pg. 218

Mott, Darcy G., V.P. & Treas.--Novell, Inc., Orem, UT; *U.S. Public*, pg. 1203

Motzkin, Barry, V.P. & Asst. Treas.--Kingston Oil Supply Corp., Port Ewen, NY; *U.S. Public*, pg. 741

Mougeot, Robert F., V.P.-Fin. & Treas.--Pacific Energy Conservation Services, Inc., Honolulu, HI; *U.S. Public*, pg. 800

Mowen, David B., Dir.-Treas. Services--Rocco Inc., Harrisonburg, VA; *U.S. Private*, pg. 937

Moy-Kelly, Diana, Asst. Treas.--PECO Energy Company, Philadelphia, PA; *U.S. Public*, pg. 1268

Moyers, Donald L., Controller, Treas. & Sec.--Riddleberger Bros.. Inc., Mount Crawford, VA; *U.S. Private*, pg. 930

Moynahan, John F., V.P. & Treas.--Joy Mining Machinery, Warrendale, PA; *U.S. Public*, pg. 789

Moynihan, Stephen H., V.P. & Treas.--Clean Harbors, Inc., Braintree, MA; *U.S. Public*, pg. 383

Mucci, Robert A., V.P. & Treas.--National Guardian Life Insurance Company, Madison, WI; *U.S. Private*, pg. 784

Muck, Philip F., Pres., Chief Exec. Officer & Treas.--Munroe, Inc., Pittsburgh, PA; *U.S. Private*, pg. 767

Mueller, Kenneth, Treas. & Asst. Sec.--Cincinnati Milacron Inc., Cincinnati, OH; *U.S. Public*, pg. 368

Mueller, Thomas W., Controller & Asst. Treas.--Kentucky Medical Insurance Company (KMIC), Louisville, KY; *U.S. Private*, pg. 741

Mueller, Warren A., Chm. Bd. & Treas.--C & M Corporation, Wauregan, CT; *U.S. Private*, pg. 191

Mueller, William, Treas.--Berlitz International, Inc., Princeton, NJ; *U.S. Public*, pg. 221

Muir, D. Stephen, Treas.--Norcen Energy Resources Limited, Calgary, Canada; *Int'l*, pg. 434

Muir, Douglas R., Sr. V.P., Treas. & Sec.--Oakwood Homes Corporation, Greensboro, NC; *U.S. Public*, pg. 1209

Muir, Glenn P., V.P.-Fin. & Treas.--Hologic, Inc., Waltham, MA; *U.S. Public*, pg. 831

Muirhead, J., Treas.--Britax International plc, Warwick, United Kingdom; *Int'l*, pg. 216

Mukunda, Ram, Pres., Chief Exec. Officer & Treas.--Startec Global Communications Corporation, Bethesda, MD; *U.S.* Public, pg. 1511

Mulberry, Zane, Controller & Treas.--Richards Brothers of Mountain Grove, Mountain Grove, MO; *U.S. Private*, pg. 928

Mulhern, Mark F., V.P. & Treas.--Carolina Power & Light Company, Raleigh, NC; *U.S. Public*, pg. 306

Mulkey, John, Chief Fin. Officer & Treas.--The Zamoiski Co., Baltimore, MD; *U.S. Private*, pg. 1203

Mull, Randall D., V.P.-Underwriting & Treas.--American Income Holding, Inc., Wilmington, DE; *U.S. Public*, pg. 1622

Mullaney, Joseph P., Chief Fin. Officer, V.P. & Treas.--SofTECH, Inc., Grand Rapids, MI; *U.S. Public*, pg. 1482

Mullen, Daniel R., V.P. & Treas.--Talley Industries, Inc., Phoenix, AZ; *U.S. Public*, pg. 307

Mullen, Larry J., Mgr.-Mktg., Treas. & Sec.--Terral Seed Co., Inc., Lake Providence, LA; *U.S. Private*, pg. 1077

Muller, Eric, Exec. V.P.-Fin. & Admin.--Sulzer Ltd., Winterthur, Switzerland; *Int'l*, pg. 1305

Muller, Jan, Asst. Treas.--Lozier Corporation, Omaha, NE; *U.S. Private*, pg. 679

Mulligan, George M., Treas.--ITT Federal Services Corporation, Colorado Springs, CO; *U.S. Public*, pg. 859

Mullins, Brian C., V.P.-Fin. & Treas.--Tuscarora Incorporated, New Brighton, PA; *U.S. Public*, pg. 1646

Mullins, Kay J., Treas. & Sec.--Rockford Acromatic Product Co., Rockford, IL; *U.S. Private*, pg. 938

Mullis, Elbert N., Jr., Chief Fin. & Admin. Officer, Exec. V.P. & Treas.--Coca-Cola Bottling Co. United, Inc., Birmingham, AL; *U.S. Private*, pg. 248

Mumm, Michael, Chief Fin. Officer, Sr. V.P. & Treas.--Petty Company, Inc., Effingham, IL; *U.S. Private*, pg. 860

Muncy, Darlene, Chief Fin. Officer, V.P. & Treas.--Caldwell VanRiper, Inc., Indianapolis, IN; *U.S. Private*, pg. 200

Mundy, Peter J., Chief Fin. Officer, V.P.-Fin., Treas. & Sec.--Sentry Technology Corp., Hauppauge, NY; *U.S. Public*, pg. 1458

Mungo, Robert, V.P. & Treas.--Temperature Equipment Corporation, Lansing, IL; *U.S. Private*, pg. 1075

Munsey, Larry A., Treas.--Eastman Chemical Company, Kingsport, TN; *U.S. Public*, pg. 550

Munzenrider, Robert E., Chief Fin. Officer & V.P.-Fin.--St. Jude Medical, Inc., Saint Paul, MN; *U.S. Public*, pg. 1427

Muracco, Louis J., Treas.--The Lehigh Press, Inc., Cherry Hill, NJ; *U.S. Private*, pg. 658

Muretta, Bruce D., Treas.--Wechco, Inc., Princeton, NJ; *U.S.* Private, pg. 1158

Murney, Don, V.P.-Fin. & Treas.--Amerco, Reno, NV; *U.S. Private*, pg. 48

Murnin, Joel A., V.P., Treas. & Controller--Manufacturers Railway Company, Saint Louis, MO; *U.S. Public*, pg. 114

Murphy, B., V.P. & Treas.--Confed Investment Counselling Limited, Toronto, Canada; *Int'l*, pg. 325

Murphy, Charles E., Treas.--Axel Johnson Inc., Stamford, CT; *Int'l*, pg. 709

Murphy, Gregory E., Chief Fin. Officer & Treas.--Selective Insurance Company of South Carolina, Charlotte, NC; *U.S. Public*, pg. 1455

Murphy, Gregory E., V.P.-Fin. & Treas.--Charleston Insurance Company, Buffalo, NY; *U.S. Public*, pg. 1455

Murphy, Gregory E., V.P. & Treas.--Niagara Exchange Corporation, Buffalo, NY; *U.S. Public*, pg. 1455

Murphy, Gregory E., Treas.--Selective Insurance Company of the Southeast, Charlotte, NC; *U.S. Public*, pg. 1456

Murphy, Gregory E., Asst. Treas.--Wantage Avenue Holding Company, Inc., Branchville, NJ; *U.S. Public*, pg. 1456

Murphy, Gregory E., Treas.--Selective Technical Administrative Services, Inc., Branchville, NJ; *U.S. Public*, pg. 1456

Murphy, Janice, V.P. & Treas.--Kaiser Permanente, Oakland, CA; *U.S. Private*, pg. 605

Murphy, John J., Chief Fin. Officer, Exec. V.P. & Treas.--Arrow Financial Corporation, Glens Falls, NY; *U.S. Public*, pg. 135

Murphy, Kevin, V.P. & Treas.--Murphy Company, Eugene, OR; *U.S. Private*, pg. 768

Murphy, Michael R., Chief Fin. Officer--Cavalier Homes, Inc., Wichita Falls, TX; *U.S. Public*, pg. 318

Murphy, Raymond G., Sr. V.P.-Fin. & Treas.--Marriott International, Inc., Washington, DC; *U.S. Public*, pg. 1047

Murphy, Terence, V.P. & Treas.--Leasing Solutions, Inc., San Jose, CA; *U.S. Public*, pg. 982

Murphy, Thomas, Treas.--Schneider Mills, Inc., New York, NY; *U.S. Private*, pg. 971

Murphy, William H., Treas.--Peters Machinery Co., Chicago, IL; *U.S. Public*, pg. 944

Murray, Anne, Treas.--Wawa, Inc., Media, PA; *U.S. Private*, pg. 1155

Murray, Edward, Treas.--Ken-Mac Metals, Inc., Cleveland, OH; *Int'l*, pg. 1388

Murray, Howard R., Treas.--Amsted Industries Incorporated, Chicago, IL; *U.S. Private*, pg. 68

Murray, John A., Chief Fin. Officer, V.P. & Treas.--Moore Medical Corp., New Britain, CT; *U.S. Public*, pg. 1128

Murray, John J., V.P.-Fin., Sec. & Treas.--Alcoa Fujikura, Troy, MI; *U.S. Public*, pg. 61

Murray, John M., V.P.-Fin. & Treas.--American Precision Industries Inc., Buffalo, NY; *U.S. Public*, pg. 90

Murray, John T., Treas. & Sec.--Tinius Olsen Testing Machine Co., Inc., Willow Grove, PA; *U.S. Private*, pg. 1088

Murray, R.W., Chief Fin. Officer, Sr. V.P., Treas., Controller & Sec.--Webb, Murray & Associates, Houston, TX; *U.S. Private*, pg. 1157

Murray, W.M., Treas.--Fuller Company, Bethlehem, PA; *Int'l*, *pg. 475*

Muse, Charles H., Jr., Chief Fin. Officer & Treas.--Crown Coal & Coke Co. Inc., Pittsburgh, PA; *U.S. Private*, pg. 292

Musgrave, John, V.P. & Treas.--Sonat Inc., Birmingham, AL; *U.S. Public*, pg. 1484

Musgrave, John M., Treas.--Southern Natural Gas Company, Birmingham, AL; *U.S. Public*, pg. 1485

Must, Mary, Treas.--Detroit City Dairy, Inc., Detroit, MI; *U.S. Private*, pg. 328

Mustard, Larry E., V.P.-Fin. & Treas.--Baldwin Piano & Organ Company, Loveland, OH; *U.S. Public*, pg. 169

Mutch, Carl F., Chief Fin. Officer & Treas.--Cox Wood Preserving Co., Orangeburg, SC; *U.S. Private*, pg. 283

Mutch, Ronald A., Treas.--Georg Fischer Disa, Inc., Holly, MI; *Int'l*, pg. 490

Muto, Joseph, Sec. & Treas.--Clarion Corporation of America, Gardena, CA; *Int'l*, pg. 296

Mutryn, Thomas A., V.P. & Treas.--UAL Corporation, Elk Grove Village, IL; *U.S. Public*, pg. 1652

Mutryn, Thomas A., V.P. & Treas.--United Air Lines, Inc., Elk Grove Village, IL; *U.S. Public*, pg. 1653

Myer, Dale, V.P., Treas. & Sec.--Signet Star Holdings, Inc., Stamford, CT; *U.S. Public*, pg. 216

Myer, Dale A., Sr. V.P., Treas. & Sec.--Signet Star Reinsurance Company, Florham Park, NJ; *U.S. Public*, pg. 216

Myers, Albert F., V.P. & Treas.--Northrop Grumman Corporation, Los Angeles, CA; *U.S. Public*, pg. 1197

Myers, Douglas, V.P. & Treas.--ManuLife Investment Holdings Limited, Toronto, Canada; *Int'l*, pg. 840

Myers, Douglas E., Treas.--Airtite Contractors Inc., Chicago, IL; *U.S. Private*, pg. 29

Myers, G. Roger, Treas.--Burr-Brown Corporation, Tucson, AZ; *U.S. Public*, pg. 270

Myers, Kurt J., Pres. & Chief Exec. Officer & Treas.--Amalgamated Automotive Industries, Inc., Enola, PA; *U.S. Private*, pg. 48

Myers, Larry F., Chief Fin. Officer, Sr. V.P., Treas. & Sec.--Mitre Corporation, Bedford, MA; *U.S. Private*, pg. 753

Myers, Linda, Asst. Treas.--Automatic Liquid Packaging, Inc., Woodstock, IL; *U.S. Private*, pg. 101

Myers, Norman S., Pres., Chief Exec. & Fin. Officers & Treas.--IDM Controls, Houston, TX; *U.S. Private*, pg. 554

Myers, Robert M., Chief Fin. Officer, Treas. & Sec.--Tri-State Mack Inc, Memphis, TN; *U.S. Private*, pg. 1101

Myers, Ronald W., Chief Fin. Officer & V.P.-Fin. & Admin.--GF Office Furniture Ltd., Gallatin, TN; *U.S. Private*, pg. 434

Myers, William, Treas.--Dart Container Corp., Mason, MI; *U.S. Private*, pg. 311

Myhre, Douglas E., Treas.--Adolfson & Peterson, Inc., Minneapolis, MN; *U.S. Private*, pg. 17

Myrick, Bobby H., Chm. Bd. & Treas.--Myrick Construction Inc., Biscoe, NC; *U.S. Private*, pg. 771

Nadel, George, Chief Fin. Officer, Exec. V.P. & Treas.--Jennifer Convertibles Inc., Woodbury, NY; *U.S. Public*, pg. 926

Nadler, Mike, Treas. & Asst. Sec.--HMO Texas, L.C., Houston, TX; *U.S. Public*, pg. 1470

Nagaike, Howard, Treas.--Komatsu America International Company, Vernon Hills, IL; *Int'l*, pg. 744

Nagamatsu, Ken, Treas.--Preferred Instruments, Danbury, CT; *U.S. Private*, pg. 881

Nagamatsu, Kenneth, Treas.--Preferred Utilities Manufacturing Corp., Danbury, CT; *U.S. Private*, pg. 881

Nagata, Lorie Ann K., Asst. Treas.--Hawaii Electric Light Co., Inc., Hilo, HI; *U.S. Public*, pg. 800

Nagata, Lorie Ann K., Asst. Treas.--Maui Electric Co., Ltd., Kahului, HI; *U.S. Public*, pg. 800

Nagata, LorieAnn K., Asst. Treas.--Hawaiian Electric Company, Inc., Honolulu, HI; *U.S. Public*, pg. 800

Nagel, Vernon J., Chief Fin. Officer, Exec. V.P.-Fin. & Treas.--Kuhlman Corporation, Savannah, GA; *U.S. Public*, pg. 968

Nagle, Arlington, Jr., Sr. V.P. & Treas.--CDI Corp., Philadelphia, PA; *U.S. Public*, pg. 276

Nagle, T.W., V.P. & Treas.--Reading & Bates Development Co., Houston, TX; *U.S. Public*, pg. 1354

Nagy, Charles F., Treas.--The Standard Products Company, Dearborn, MI; *U.S. Public*, pg. 1504

Naito, Harvey K., V.P. & Treas.--Safeway Inc., Pleasanton, CA; *U.S. Public*, pg. 1426

Nakamoto, Stanley T., Asst. Treas.--Maui Electric Co., Ltd., Kahului, HI; *U.S. Public*, pg. 800

Nakamura, Y., Treas.--Tonen Corporation, Tokyo, Japan; *Int'l*, pg. 1398

Nakash, Ralph, Treas. & Sec.--Jordache Enterprises, Inc., New York, NY; *U.S. Private*, pg. 597

Nance, Blair T., Chief Fin. Officer, Controller & Treas.--AFG, Inc., Westmont, IL; *U.S. Public*, pg. 955

Napientek, Michael, Asst. Treas.--Barton Incorporated, Chicago, IL; *U.S. Public*, pg. 300

Naquin, Gasper K., Treas. & Sec.--Intrepid Enterprises, Inc., Harvey, LA; *U.S. Private*, pg. 574

Nardi, Tom, V.P.-Mktg., Sls. & Treas.--Northern Illinois Gas Company, Naperville, IL; *U.S. Public*, pg. 1183

Narzisi, Joy J., Sr. V.P., Treas. & Asst. Sec.--Commercial Federal Corporation, Omaha, NE; *U.S. Public*, pg. 411

Nash, James S., Chief Fin. Officer, Treas. & Controller--E.P. Henry Corporation, Woodbury, NJ; *U.S. Private*, pg. 522

Nasr, Y.A., Sr. V.P.-Treas.--HongKong Bank of Canada, Vancouver, Canada; *Int'l*, pg. 583

Nass, Kevin, Sr. V.P. & Treas.--Farmers and Traders Life Insurance Co., Syracuse, NY; *U.S. Private*, pg. 394

Naughton, J.J., Chief Fin. Officer & Treas.--The Camden Fire Insurance Assn., Philadelphia, PA; *Int'l*, pg. 543

Nay, Donald A., Chief Fin. Officer, V.P. & Treas.--CGAS, Inc., Columbus, OH; *U.S. Public*, pg. 585

Nazarian, Gregory L., Treas.--Levonian Brothers Inc., Troy, NY; *U.S. Private*, pg. 663

Neal, Jasper T., V.P. & Treas.--Cooper Communities, Inc., Bella Vista, AR; *U.S. Private*, pg. 273

Neal, Jasper T., Jr., Treas.--Apartment Ventures, Inc., Bella Vista, AR; *U.S. Private*, pg. 274

Neal, Jerry D., Chief Fin. Officer, V.P., & Treas.--ONEOK Inc., Tulsa, OK; *U.S. Public*, pg. 1226

Neal, Kenneth A., Asst. Treas.--Lowe's Companies, Inc., North Wilkesboro, NC; *U.S. Public*, pg. 1015

Neal, William E., V.P. & Treas.--Security American Financial Enterprises, Inc., Minnetonka, MN; *U.S. Private*, pg. 980

Nebuloni, Angelo J., V.P.-Fin.--Allen Foods, Inc., Saint Louis, MO; *U.S. Private*, pg. 37

Neely, Harry A., Treas.--Eagle-Picher Industries, Inc., Cincinnati, OH; *U.S. Private*, pg. 355

Negovetich, J.A., V.P.-Fin. & Treas.--Fasco Industries, Inc., Southfield, MI; *Int'l*, pg. 125

Neidhard, Janet, Asst. Treas.--Cincinnati Bell Telephone, Cincinnati, OH; *U.S. Public*, pg. 367

Neil, Steve M., Chief Fin. Officer, V.P.-Fin. & Treas.--L. Perrigo Company, Allegan, MI; *U.S. Public*, pg. 1280

Neilson, Mark C., V.P.-Fin.--Shelter Components Corporation, Elkhart, IN; *U.S. Public*, pg. 952

Neilson, Norma, Treas.--Grossenburg Implements, Incorporated, Winner, SD; *U.S. Private*, pg. 483

Neis, Douglas A., Chief Fin. Officer & Treas.--The Marcus Corporation, Milwaukee, WI; *U.S. Public*, pg. 1044

Nelson, Byron, Sec., Treas. & Exec. Dir.-Fin.--Temerlin McClain, Irving, TX; *U.S. Public*, pg. 1642

Nelson, Craig, V.P. & Treas.--Barton Nelson Inc., Kansas City, MO; *U.S. Private*, pg. 120

Nelson, Craig D., V.P.-Corp. Services--AmerenCIPS, Springfield, IL; *U.S. Public*, pg. 65

Nelson, J.B., Treas.--Colonial Pipeline Company, Atlanta, GA; *U.S. Private*, pg. 254

Nelson, Jack, Chm. Bd., Chief Exec. Officer & Treas.--Caprius, Inc., Wilmington, MA; *U.S. Public*, pg. 303

Nelson, James E., Asst. Treas., Asst. Gen. Counsel & Asst. Sec.--Washington Square Securities, Minneapolis, MN; *U.S. Public*, pg. 1376

Nelson, Johanna M., Treas. & Sec.--Allen Nelson & Co., Seattle, WA; *U.S. Private*, pg. 790

Nelson, Ronald G., V.P. & Treas.--Viad Corp, Phoenix, AZ; *U.S. Public*, pg. 1718

Nelson, Rudolph, Sec. & Treas.--Square Butte Electric Cooperative, Grand Forks, ND; *U.S. Private*, pg. 751

Nemni, Joseph, Treas.--IBM Canada Limited, Markham, Canada; *U.S. Public*, pg. 897

Nemschoff, Mark, Pres., Chief Exec. Officer & Treas.--Nemschoff Chairs, Inc., Sheboygan, WI; *U.S. Private*, pg. 791

Nermyr, Jim, V.P. & Treas.--Musicland Group Inc., Minnetonka, MN; *U.S. Public*, pg. 1142

Nesler, Dennis J., V.P. & Treas.--General Datacomm Industries, Inc., Middlebury, CT; *U.S. Public*, pg. 708

NeSmith, Joseph Q., Chief Exec. Officer & Treas.--Continental Dynamics, Inc., Herndon, VA; *U.S. Public*, pg. 110

Ness, Paul D., Chief Fin. Officer, Chief Information Officer, Sec. & Treas.--Polymer Composites Inc., Winona, MN; *Int'l*, pg. 624

Neubel, Roger, Treas.--Pfaff American Sales Corp., Paramus, NJ; *Int'l*, pg. 1046

Neuman, Dawn, Treas.--Morgan Products Ltd., Williamsburg, VA; *U.S. Public*, pg. 1132

Neuman, Ronald W., Chief Fin. Officer, Treas. & Controller--Allen-Edmonds Shoe Corp., Port Washington, WI; *U.S. Private*, pg. 36

Neuman, Thomas O., Asst. Treas.-Taxes--J. Walter Thompson Company, New York, NY; *Int'l*, pg. 1483

Neumann, Janet, Treas. & Sec.--Valu Discount, Incorporated, Louisville, KY; *U.S. Private*, pg. 1132

Neumann, Jens, Dr., Mgr.-Grp. Strategy, Treas. & Legal--Volkswagen AG, Wolfsburg, Germany; *Int'l*, pg. 1473

Neuschaefer, Thomas H., Chief Fin. Officer, V.P. & Treas.--First Financial Corporation, Stevens Point, WI; *U.S. Public*, pg. 140

Neville, James D., Chief Fin. Officer, Exec. V.P., Treas. & Sec.--The North American Manufacturing Co., Cleveland, OH; *U.S. Private*, pg. 803

New, Sue, Treas. & MIS--Master International Corp., Santa Monica, CA; *U.S. Private*, pg. 713

Newcomb, Nancy, Treas.--Citibank N.A., Long Island City, NY; *U.S. Public*, pg. 377

Newell, D.K., Treas.--Grant, Inc., Huron, SD; *U.S. Public*, pg. 1201

Newell, D.K., Treas.--Northwestern Networks, Inc., Huron, SD; *U.S. Public*, pg. 1201

Newell, D.K., Treas.--Northwestern Systems, Inc., Huron, SD; *U.S. Public*, pg. 1201

Newman, Donald H., Asst. Treas.-U.S. & Canada--Dresser Industries, Inc., Dallas, TX; *U.S. Public*, pg. 528

Newman, Harry, Sec. & Treas.--Frequency Electronics, Inc., Uniondale, NY; *U.S. Public*, pg. 681

Newman, Jeffrey C., Treas.--Madison Gas and Electric Company, Madison, WI; *U.S. Public*, pg. 1032

Newman, Ronald P., Chief Fin. Officer, V.P.-Fin., Treas. & Sec.--Watsco, Inc., Coconut Grove, FL; *U.S. Public*, pg. 1745

Newman, Stephen C., Treas. & Dir.--RNL Facilities Corporation, Denver, CO; *U.S. Private*, pg. 905

Newsome, Larry J., Chief Fin. Officer, Sr. V.P., Treas. & Sec.--Echelon International Corporation, Saint Petersburg, FL; *U.S. Public*, pg. 560

Newton, Clay, Chief Fin. Officer & Treas.--Equity Oil Company, Salt Lake City, UT; *U.S. Public*, pg. 590

Newton, Joseph, Sec. & Treas.--Dairy Queen Canada, Inc., Burlington, Canada; *U.S. Public*, pg. 220

Newton, Stanley B., V.P., Treas. & Sec.--Holmes Tuttle Ford, Inc., Tucson, AZ; *U.S. Private*, pg. 535

Nguyen, C.D., V.P. & Treas.--Exxon Insurance Holdings, Inc., Saint Georges, Bermuda; *U.S. Public*, pg. 602

Niblock, Robert A., V.P. & Treas.--Lowe's Companies, Inc., North Wilkesboro, NC; *U.S. Public*, pg. 1015

Nicastro, Frank, V.P. & Treas.--The Grand Union Company, Wayne, NJ; *U.S. Public*, pg. 758

Nicholas, Charles R., Chief Fin. Officer & Exec. V.P.-Fin./ Admin.--Andrew Corporation, Orland Park, IL; *U.S. Public*, pg. 112

Nicholls, John C., Jr., Treas.--Masco Corporation, Taylor, MI; *U.S. Public*, pg. 1052

Nichols, Charles, Asst. Treas.--Collins & Aikman Corporation, Charlotte, NC; *U.S. Public*, pg. 399

Nichols, Gregory L., CPA, Chief Fin. Officer, V.P. & Treas.--Giffels Associates, Inc., Southfield, MI; *U.S. Private*, pg. 452

Nichols, Gregory L., CPA, Chief Fin. Officer & Treas.--Giffels Technologies, Inc., Southfield, MI; *U.S. Private*, pg. 452

Nichols, Julie, Treas.--Dixons Group plc, Hemel Hempstead, United Kingdom,; *Int'l*, pg. 413

Nichols, Larry, Treas.--Calcot, Ltd., Bakersfield, CA; *U.S. Private*, pg. 200

Nicholson, John, Treas.--Schering Berlin Inc., Cedar Knolls, NJ; *Int'l*, pg. 1204

Nicholson, M., Treas.--Laporte plc, Luton, United Kingdom; *Int'l*, pg. 801

Nicholson, Paul, V.P.-Fin. & Treas.--Pay Less Super Markets, Inc., Anderson, IN; *U.S. Private*, pg. 844

Nickelatti, Chris, Controller, Treas. & Sec.--Crown Fence Co., Long Beach, CA; *U.S. Private*, pg. 292

Nickerson, Brett R., Asst. Treas.--Doron Precision Systems, Inc., Binghamton, NY; *U.S. Private*, pg. 341

Nickerson, Bryant, C., Chief Fin. Officer & Treas.--O'Sullivan Corporation, Winchester, VA; *U.S. Public*, pg. 1234

Nicolai, Ray, Treas.--Dakota Electric Association, Farmington, MN; *U.S. Private*, pg. 308

Niedens, Douglas, Treas. & Sec.--Universal Construction Company, Inc., Kansas City, KS; *U.S. Private*, pg. 1127

Niegsch, W.C., Jr., Chief Fin. Officer, Exec. V.P., Treas. & Sec.--Max & Erma's Restaurants, Columbus, OH; *U.S. Public*, pg. 1060

Nielson, Bruce, Chief Exec. Officer, Treas. & Gen. Mgr.--Producers Livestock, North Salt Lake, UT; *U.S. Private*, pg. 888

Nielson, Doug, Treas.--Plaskolite Inc., Columbus, OH; *U.S. Private*, pg. 870

Niemiec, Thom, Treas. & Sec.--The Tech Group, Scottsdale, AZ; *U.S. Private*, pg. 1071

Nietsch, Eric H., Asst. Treas.--Datascope Corp., Montvale, NJ; *U.S. Public*, pg. 487

Niewola, Donna, Dir.-Fin. & Asst. Treas.--Aerovox Inc., New Bedford, MA; *U.S. Public*, pg. 25

Nightingale, B.G.K., Grp. Treas.--Airtours Plc, Rossendale, United Kingdom; *Int'l*, pg. 39

Nigl, Jeffrey M., Chief Fin. Officer, V.P. & Treas.--Electronic Tele-Communications, Inc., Waukesha, WI; *U.S. Public*, pg. 570

Nika, Trudy, Treas.--F&F Foods, Chicago, IL; *U.S. Private*, pg. 388

Nilles, Keith, Treas.--Balderson Inc., Wamego, KS; *U.S. Public*, pg. 315

Nilsen, James P., Chief Fin. Officer & Treas.--The Fred W. Albrecht Grocery Co., Akron, OH; *U.S. Private*, pg. 32

Nilsen, Roger J., Treas.--Inter-Community Telephone Company, Nome, ND; *U.S. Public*, pg. 1022

Nilsen, Terje, Chief Fin. Officer, Treas. & Controller--AGA Ges.m.b.H., Vienna, Austria; *Int'l*, pg. 13

Nishimoto, Susumu, Treas.--Tommy Hilfiger Corporation, Kowloon, Hong Kong; *Int'l*, pg. 1398

Nishio, Sinji, Treas.--Nippon Oil Company, Limited (NiSSEKI), Tokyo, Japan; *Int'l*, pg. 936

Nistendirk, Jack W., Treas.--J.H. Fletcher & Co., Huntington, WV; *U.S. Private*, pg. 412

Nitani, A., Treas.--Murata Machinery, Ltd., Kyoto, Japan; *Int'l*, pg. 897

Nitsche, John, Chief Fin. Officer, V.P. & Treas.--United Hardware Distributing Co., Plymouth, MN; *U.S. Private*, pg. 335

Nitta, Jeffrey W., V.P. & Treas.--Weyerhaeuser Real Estate Company, Federal Way, WA; *U.S. Public*, pg. 1764

Nix, William A., V.P. & Treas.--AGCO Corporation, Duluth, GA; *U.S. Public*, pg. 28

Nnadi, Geoffrey, V.P. & Treas.--Atlanta Life Insurance Company, Atlanta, GA; *U.S. Private*, pg. 94

Noah, Joni, Chief Fin. Officer, Controller & Treas.--Visible Changes, Houston, TX; *U.S. Private*, pg. 1141

Noble, Richard W., V.P. & Treas.--Hanovia Colight, Union, NJ; *Int'l*, pg. 17

Nogal, Joseph P., Controller, Treas. & Asst. Sec.--Woodhead Industries, Inc., Buffalo Grove, IL; *U.S. Public*, pg. 1776

Nogueira de Aguiar, Geraldo, Treas.--Alcan Aluminium Limited, Montreal, Canada; *Int'l*, pg. 50

Nohra, Joseph S., V.P. & Treas.--The Cafaro Co., Youngstown, OH; *U.S. Private*, pg. 198

Nohren, Roger, Chief Fin. Officer & Treas.--Tucson Realty & Trust Co., Tucson, AZ; *U.S. Private*, pg. 1109

Nolan, Thomas J., Chief Fin Officer, V.P.-Fin., Treas. & Sec.--Minuteman International, Inc., Addison, IL; *Int'l*, pg. 587

Nole, R.J., Treas.--Foron International Sales Corp., Binghamton, NY; *U.S. Private*, pg. 341

Nole, Robert J., Treas. & Mgr.-MIS--Doron Precision Systems, Inc., Binghamton, NY; *U.S. Private*, pg. 341

Nolen, Norman W., Chief Fin. Officer, Sr. V.P. & Treas.--Weatherford Enterra Incorporated, Houston, TX; *U.S. Public*, pg. 1749

Nolen, Norman W., Sr. V.P. & Treas.--Weatherford U.S., Inc., Houston, TX; *U.S. Public*, pg. 1749

Nonn, James C., Treas. & Sec.--Pemko Manufacturing Company, Ventura, CA; *U.S. Private*, pg. 848

Nonnenkamp, D.H., V.P. & Treas.--ESCO Electronics Corporation, Saint Louis, MO; *U.S. Public*, pg. 546

Norbert, John, V.P. & Treas.--Power Purchasing, Inc., Exton, PA; *U.S. Private*, pg. 233

Norbutus, Michael, Treas.--Foster & Gallagher, Inc., Peoria, IL; *U.S. Private*, pg. 420

Nordstrom, Mark, Asst. Treas.--Honeywell-Measurex Corporation, Cupertino, CA; *U.S. Public*, pg. 833

Nordstrom, William, Treas. & Sec.--Amana-Nordstrom Motel Co., Amana, IA; *U.S. Private*, pg. 48

Norelid, Jan A., Chief Fin. Officer, V.P.-Fin. & Treas.--Devcon International Corp., Deerfield Beach, FL; *U.S. Public*, pg. 502

Norris, Francis J., V.P., Treas. & Sec.--Mannington Mills, Inc., Salem, NJ; *U.S. Private*, pg. 700

Norris, Peter S., Chief Fin. Officer, V.P.-Fin. & Treas.--HMT Technology Corporation, Fremont, CA; *U.S. Public*, pg. 771

Norris, Stephen, Treas.--Tembec Inc., Montreal, Canada; *Int'l*, pg. 1374

North, Richard, Chief Fin. Officer, Treas. & Dir.-Tax & Property--Bass PLC, London, United Kingdom; *Int'l*, pg. 169

North, Richard J., V.P., Sec. & Treas.--Miller & Smith, Inc., Mc Lean, VA; *U.S. Private*, pg. 746

Norton, James G., V.P.-Fin. & Treas.--Farrell Lines Incorporated, New York, NY; *U.S. Private*, pg. 397

Norwalk, Donald J., V.P. & Treas.--Budget Group, Inc., Daytona Beach, FL; *U.S. Private*, pg. 178

Norwood, Ralph M., V.P. & Treas.--Polaroid Corporation, Cambridge, MA; *U.S. Public*, pg. 1313

Nothstein, Barbara J., Treas.--Textile Chemical Co., Inc., Reading, PA; *Int'l*, pg. 1458

NovaK, Westley, Gen. Mgr.,Controller & Treas.--H & D Steel Service, Inc., Cleveland, OH; *U.S. Private*, pg. 489

Nowakowski, David, V.P., Controller & Treas.--MichCon, Detroit, MI; *U.S. Public*, pg. 1025

Nowakowski, Matthew, Treas.--Financial Collection Agencies (International) Inc., Westmount, Canada; *Int'l*, pg. 470

Nowakowski, Matthew, Treas.--Financial Collection Agencies of Pennsylvania Inc, Wayne, PA; *Int'l*, pg. 471

Nowell, Christopher C., Treas. & Asst. Sec.--Cameron & Barkley Company, Charleston, SC; *U.S. Private*, pg. 203

Nozaki, Kohei, V.P. & Treas.--Nichirei Foods, Seattle, WA; *Int'l*, pg. 928

Nozko, Henry W., Jr., Chief Oper. Officer, Exec. V.P. & Treas.--ACMAT Corporation, New Britain, CT; *U.S. Public*, pg. 16

Nugent, Deborah A., Chief Fin. Officer, V.P.-Fin., Treas. & Sec.--Software Spectrum, Inc., Garland, TX; *U.S. Public*, pg. 1483

Null, Lester H., Sr., Treas. & Sec.--ULLICO Inc., Washington, DC; *U.S. Private*, pg. 1115

Nunley, Richard L., Chm. Bd., Pres. & Treas.--Better Living Inc., Charlottesville, VA; *U.S. Private*, pg. 141

Nussbaum, Carole, Asst. Treas.--GP Strategies Corporation, New York, NY; *U.S. Public*, pg. 694

Nussbaumer, Gerhard, V.P.-Fin., Treas.--Voest-Alpine International Corporation, New York, NY; *Int'l*, pg. 1470

Nussdorf, Lawrence C., Exec. V.P. & Treas.--Clark Enterprises, Inc., Bethesda, MD; *U.S. Private*, pg. 242

Nutt, Frank, Gen. Mgr., Treas. & Sec.--North Electric Supply, Inc., Auburn Hills, MI; *U.S. Private*, pg. 805

Nyman, Karen E., V.P. & Treas.--The Vigoro Corporation, Chicago, IL; *U.S. Public*, pg. 856

O'Brien, Bobby D., V.P.-Fin. & Treas.--Valhi, Inc., Dallas, TX; *U.S. Private*, pg. 270

O'Brien, Dennis F., Treas.--ComEd, Chicago, IL; *U.S. Public*, *pg. 1664*

O'Brien, Edward J., Sr. V.P. & Treas.--Hanover Direct, Inc., Weehawken, NJ; *U.S. Public*, pg. 782

O'Brien, Eileen, V.P. & Treas.--LINC Capital Group, Chicago, IL; *U.S. Public*, pg. 996

O'Brien, Kevin, V.P.-Fin.--Periphonics Corp., Bohemia, NY; *U.S. Public*, pg. 1278

O'Brien, Patrick, V.P., Treas. & Dir.-Strategic Planning--Wide World Photos, Inc., New York, NY; *U.S. Private*, pg. 92

O'Brien, Richard S., V.P. & Treas.--Brunswick Corporation, Lake Forest, IL; *U.S. Public*, pg. 265

O'Brien, Tom, V.P., Controller & Asst. Treas.-Bank Opers.--Ultramar Diamond Shamrock Corporation, San Antonio, TX; *U.S. Public*, pg. 1663

O'Connell, James M., Chief Fin. Officer, V.P., Treas. & Sec.--Landauer, Inc., Glenwood, IL; *U.S. Public*, pg. 977

O'Connor, A. Bruce, Treas.--Tidewater Utilities, Inc., Odessa, DE; *U.S. Public*, pg. 1110

O'Connor, A. Bruce, Treas.--Utility Service Affiliates, Inc., Iselin, NJ; *U.S. Public*, pg. 1110

O'Connor, Brendan M., Treas.--Fina, Inc., Dallas, TX; *Int'l*, pg. 1044

O'Connor, Jack, Treas.--American Home Products Corporation, Madison, NJ; *U.S. Public*, pg. 79

O'Connor, John, V.P. & Treas.--Hachette Filipacchi Magazines Inc., New York, NY; *Int'l*, pg. 794

O'Connor, John, Chief Fin. Officer, Sr. V.P. & Treas.--Woman's Day, New York, NY; *Int'l*, pg. 795

O'Connor, Keith F., Treas.--Lord Abbett & Co., New York, NY; *U.S. Private*, pg. 675

O'Connor, Tim, V.P.-Investor Rels. & Treas.--ICF Kaiser International Inc., Fairfax, VA; *U.S. Public*, pg. 852

O'Dea, Fred, Chief Fin. Officer & V.P.--Hubbard Construction Co., Winter Park, FL; *U.S. Private*, pg. 544

O'Donnell, Patrick J., Chief Oper. Officer, Treas. & Gen. Mgr.--National Grape Co-Op Association, Inc., Westfield, NY; *U.S. Private*, pg. 784

O'Leary Warner, Paula, V.P. & Treas.--Toth Design, Concord, MA; *U.S. Private*, pg. 1093

O'Leary, Barry, Sr. V.P.-Fin. & Treas.--Cablevision Systems Corporation, Woodbury, NY; *U.S. Public*, pg. 288

O'Leary, Denis P., Grp. Chief Acct.--Allied Irish Banks, p.l.c., Dublin, Ireland; *Int'l*, pg. 64

O'Leary, Patrick J., Chief Fin. Officer, V.P. & Treas.--SPX Corporation, Muskegon, MI; *U.S. Public*, pg. 1420

O'Loughlin, T.K., V.P.-Fin. & Treas.--Saztec International, Inc., Billerica, MA; *U.S. Public*, pg. 1435

O'Malley, George, Treas.--Eastern American Energy Corporation, Charleston, WV; *U.S. Private*, pg. 357

O'Mara, William, Treas.--The Raymond Corporation, Greene, NY; *Int'l*, pg. 123

O'Meara, Christopher G., V.P. & Treas.--Adaptec, Inc., Milpitas, CA; *U.S. Public*, pg. 19

O'Neal, Frederic K., Sr. V.P. & Treas.--Computer Sales International Inc., Saint Louis, MO; *U.S. Private*, pg. 260

O'Neil, D., Treas.--Meggitt plc, Wimborne Minster, United Kingdom; *Int'l*, pg. 853

O'Neil, James, Treas.--Rolock, Inc., Fairfield, CT; *U.S. Private*, pg. 942

O'Neil, Michael T., Sec. & Treas.--Ragnar Benson, Inc., Park Ridge, IL; *U.S. Private*, pg. 99

O'Neil, P.A., Treas. & Sec.--O'Neil Industries Inc., Chicago, IL; *U.S. Private*, pg. 817

O'Neil, Paul A., Chief Fin. Officer & Treas.--Boykin Management Co., Cleveland, OH; *U.S. Private*, pg. 162

O'Neill, Peter J., Sr. V.P.-Fin., Controller & Treas.--Agway, Inc., De Witt, NY; *U.S. Private*, pg. 27

O'Reilly, Dennis J., Asst. Treas.--Midwest Express Holdings, Inc., Oak Creek, WI; *U.S. Public*, pg. 1111

O'Rourke, Jerry, Chief Fin. Officer, Sr. V.P. & Treas.--Wackenhut Corrections Corporation, Palm Beach Gardens, FL; *U.S. Public*, pg. 1731

O'Shaughnessy, John, Treas.--Consolidated Beverages, Inc., Auburn, MA; *U.S. Private*, pg. 264

O'Shea, Andrew M., Treas.--Andersen Group, Inc., Bloomfield, CT; *U.S. Public*, pg. 111

O'Shea, Daniel, Chief Oper. Officer--Bill Communications, Inc., New York, NY; *Int'l*, pg. 1446

O'Shea, Kevin, V.P.-Investor Rels. & Treas.--Bell & Howell Holdings, Skokie, IL; *U.S. Public*, pg. 201

O'Shiel, Kevin, Treas.--Chubb Insurance Company of Europe, Brussels, Belgium; *U.S. Public*, pg. 355

O'Toole, Timothy S., Exec. V.P. & Treas.--Chemed Corporation, Cincinnati, OH; *U.S. Public*, pg. 343

Oak, Alan D., Chief Fin. Officer, Sr. V.P.-Fin. & Treas.--TECO Energy, Inc., Tampa, FL; *U.S. Public*, pg. 1565

Oak, Alan D., Chief Fin. Officer, V.P. & Treas.--Tampa Electric Co., Tampa, FL; *U.S. Public*, pg. 1565

Oakley, Judy, Treas. & Sec.--Bruce Oakley, Inc., North Little Rock, AR; *U.S. Private*, pg. 809

Oakley, W. Flake, IV, Chief Fin. Officer, Exec. V.P., Treas. & Sec.--The Colonial BancGroup, Inc., Montgomery, AL; *U.S. Public*, pg. 400

Oaks, J.D., V.P. & Treas.--MCDR, Inc., Memphis, TN; *U.S. Private*, pg. 686

Oates, Kathy, Asst. Treas.--Sterling Chemicals Holdings, Inc., Houston, TX; *U.S. Public*, pg. 1515

Oates, Kathy, Asst. Treas.--Sterling Chemicals, Inc., Houston, TX; *U.S. Public*, pg. 1515

Oben, Walter J., Jr., Chm. Bd., Pres., Treas. & Sec.--Southgate Ford Inc., Southgate, MI; *U.S. Private*, pg. 1018

Obermeyer, Susan, Asst. Treas.--D & N Financial Corporation, Hancock, MI; *U.S. Public*, pg. 472

Obst, J.C., Treas.--Schenectady International, Inc., Schenectady, NY; *U.S. Private*, pg. 969

Ocasek, Ronald W., Chief Fin. Officer, Sr. V.P. & Treas.--Riser Foods, Inc., Bedford, OH; *U.S. Private*, pg. 450

Ocasek, Ronald W., Chief Fin. Officer & Treas.--Rini-Rego Supermarkets, Inc., Cleveland, OH; *U.S. Private*, pg. 451

Ochynski, Walter B., Asst. Treas.--The Gillette Company, Boston, MA; *U.S. Public*, pg. 743

Ockels, Theodore S., Pres., Chief Exec. Officer, Chief Fin. Officer & Treas.--Up-Right Work Platforms Division, Selma, CA; *U.S. Private*, pg. 1128

Oesterreich, Gerald, V.P.-Admin.--Hamlin, Inc., Lake Mills, WI; *U.S. Public*, pg. 251

Ogasawara, Yasuyuki, Exec. V.P. & Treas.--Mitsubishi International Corporation, New York, NY; *Int'l*, pg. 871

Ogata, Keith, Pres., Chief Exec. Officer & Treas.--National Education Credit Corporation, Irvine, CA; *U.S. Public*, pg. 784

Ogata, Keith K., V.P. & Treas.--ICS Intangibles Holding Company, Irvine, CA; *U.S. Public*, pg. 783

Ogata, Keith K., V.P. & Asst. Treas.--Steck-Vaughn Company, Austin, TX; *U.S. Public*, pg. 784

Ogata, Keith K., V.P. & Treas.--National Educational International Corp., Irvine, CA; *U.S. Public*, pg. 784

Ogata, Keith K., V.P. & Treas.--National Education Payroll Corp., Irvine, CA; *U.S. Public*, pg. 784

Ogata, Keith K., V.P. & Treas.--Steck-Vaughn Publishing Corporation, Austin, TX; *U.S. Public*, pg. 784

Ogata, Keith K., V.P. & Asst. Treas.--Steck-Vaughn Distribution Company, Austin, TX; *U.S. Public*, pg. 784

Ogawa, T., Sr. V.P. & Asst. Treas.--Mitsubishi International Corporation, New York, NY; *Int'l*, pg. 871

Ogborn, Patricia, Treas. & Sec.--Consolidated Lumber Co., Stillwater, MN; *U.S. Private*, pg. 265

Ogburn, Joe F., V.P. & Treas.--RSI Holdings Inc., Greenville, SC; *U.S. Public*, pg. 1358

Ogden, James A., Treas. & Sec.--Bargain Supply Company, Louisville, KY; *U.S. Private*, pg. 116

Oglesby, Donald D., Treas. & Sec.--Hanson Engineers Inc., Springfield, IL; *U.S. Private*, pg. 500

Ohinata, Kaz, Treas.--Sanden International (U.S.A.), Inc., Wylie, TX; *Int'l*, pg. 1184

Ohly, Jeffrey W., Sr. V.P., Treas. & Sec.--World Acceptance Corporation, Greenville, SC; *U.S. Public*, pg. 1778

Ohms, Larry T., Controller & Asst. Treas.--United States Lime & Minerals, Dallas, TX; *U.S. Public*, pg. 1684

Ohori, Ken, Exec. V.P. & Treas.--Tsumura International, Secaucus, NJ; *Int'l*, pg. 1426

Okada, Lan K., Asst. Treas.--HEI Power Corp., Honolulu, HI; *U.S. Public*, pg. 800

Oklak, Dennis D., V.P. & Treas.--Duke Realty Investments, Inc., Indianapolis, IN; *U.S. Public*, pg. 535

Okonow, Dale, Treas.--Risk Management Solutions, Inc., Waltham, MA; *U.S. Private*, pg. 489

Oksendahl, Douglas C., Chief Fin. Officer, Exec. V.P.-Fin. & Treas.--Pioneer Mutual Life Insurance Company, Fargo, ND; *U.S. Private*, pg. 866
Okumura, Lorrane, Treas.--Valley Isle Produce, V.I.P. Food Service, Kahului, HI; *U.S. Private*, pg. 1132
Okushi, Ken, Treas.--Pentax Corporation, Englewood, CO; *Int'l*, pg. 85
Oland, Thomas E., Chm. Bd., Pres., Chief Exec. Officer & Treas.--Techne Corporation, Minneapolis, MN; *U.S. Public*, pg. 1563
Olbrych, John S., Chief Fin. Officer & Treas.--Mac-Gray Corporation, Cambridge, MA; *U.S. Public*, pg. 1029
Oldham, Steven, Treas.--Sierra Pacific Power Co., Reno, NV; *U.S. Public*, pg. 1470
Oldham, Steven C., V.P.-Regulations & Treas.--Sierra Pacific Resources, Reno, NV; *U.S. Public*, pg. 1470
Olds, Rick, Dir.-Treasury & Risk Mngmt.--USLD Communications Corp., San Antonio, TX; *U.S. Public*, pg. 969
Olinde, Humphrey T., Jr., Treas. & Sec.--Olinde Hardware & Supply Co., Baton Rouge, LA; *U.S. Private*, pg. 814
Oliver, Aloysius J., Pres. & Treas.--CFC Data Corp., Midland, MI; *U.S. Public*, pg. 345
Oliver, Garold, Dir.-Customer Fin. Svcs. & Asst. Treas.--Bandag, Incorporated, Muscatine, IA; *U.S. Public*, pg. 177
Oliveri, Elena R., V.P. & Treas.--Don Alleson, Inc., Rochester, NY; *U.S. Private*, pg. 339
Oliverio, Louis, V.P. & Treas.--Cincinnati Incorporated, Harrison, OH; *U.S. Private*, pg. 240
Olson, Kenneth A., Treas. & Corp. Sec.--Berry Petroleum Company, Taft, CA; *U.S. Public*, pg. 223
Olson, Kenneth A., Corp. Sec. & Treas.--Berry Petroleum Company-Coastal Operations, Oxnard, CA; *U.S. Public*, pg. 223
Olson, Kenneth A., Corp. Sec. & Treas.--Berry Oil Trading and Transportation, Taft, CA; *U.S. Public*, pg. 223
Olson, R.J., Treas.--Atlas World Group, Inc., Evansville, IN; *U.S. Private*, pg. 97
Olson, R.J., Treas.--Atlas Van Lines, Inc., Evansville, IN; *U.S. Private*, pg. 97
Olson, Sherman V., Pres. & Treas.--Danafilms, Inc., Westborough, MA; *U.S. Private*, pg. 309
Olson, Theodore R., Treas.--Unigard Insurance Co., Bellevue, WA; *Int'l*, pg. 345
Olson, Theodore R., Treas.--Unigard Indemnity Co., Bellevue, WA; *Int'l*, pg. 345
Olswang, Richard R., V.P. & Treas.--Crafty Beaver Home Center, Skokie, IL; *U.S. Private*, pg. 284
Omachinski, D.L., Chief Fin. Officer, V.P.-Fin. & Treas.--OshKosh B'Gosh, Inc., Oshkosh, WI; *U.S. Public*, pg. 1232
Ominsky, Barry S., Treas.--United States Cold Storage, Inc., Cherry Hill, NJ; *U.S. Private*, pg. 1124
Ong, Joseph John L., V.P.-Treas.--La Tondena Distillers, Inc., Manila, Philippines; *Int'l*, pg. 785
Ono, Shigeki, Sr. V.P. & Treas.--ITOCHU International Inc., New York, NY; *Int'l*, pg. 694
Oporto, Michael, Chief Fin. Officer & Treas.--Presidential Life Corporation, Nyack, NY; *U.S. Public*, pg. 1323
Orders, William H., Chm. Bd., Chief Exec. Officer & Treas--Orders Distributing Co., Greenville, SC; *U.S. Private*, pg. 819
Orenstein, Robert A., Chief Fin. Officer, Treas. & V.P.--BKM Enterprises, Inc., East Hartford, CT; *U.S. Private*, pg. 107
Orenstein, Steve, Sec. & Treas.--Ad Americas, Los Angeles, CA; *U.S. Private*, pg. 316
Oringer, Kenneth W., Chief Fin. Officer, Exec. V.P. & Treas.--U.S. Security Associates, Inc., Roswell, GA; *U.S. Private*, pg. 1126
Ormsby, Clarence, Exec. V.P. & Treas.--Servaas, Inc., Indianapolis, IN; *U.S. Private*, pg. 986
Orn, Gerald S., Pres., Chief Oper. Officer & Treas.--Central Allied Enterprises, Canton, OH; *U.S. Private*, pg. 222
Ornelas, Gonzalo, Treas.--H.B. Zachry, San Antonio, TX; *U.S. Private*, pg. 1203
Ornes, Christian J., V.P. & Treas.--DSC Communications Corporation, Plano, TX; *U.S. Public*, pg. 475
Ornstein, R. Jeffrey, Chief Fin. Officer, V.P.-Fin. & Treas.--Superior Industries International, Inc., Van Nuys, CA; *U.S. Public*, pg. 1539
Oros, John, Asst. Treas.--Welbilt Corporation, Stamford, CT; *Int'l*, pg. 188
Orrall, Peter, V.P.-Mfg. & Treas.--Winthrop Printing Company, Inc., Boston, MA; *U.S. Private*, pg. 1184
Orrock, Kevin T., V.P. & Treas.--Howard Hughes Corporation, Las Vegas, NV; *U.S. Public*, pg. 1407
Orthwein, Peter B., Vice Chm. & Treas.--Thor Industries, Inc., Jackson Center, OH; *U.S. Public*, pg. 1602
Ortman, Elizabeth J., Treas. & Sec.--Kokomo Grain Co., Inc., Kokomo, IN; *U.S. Private*, pg. 631
Ortolani, Thecly L., Treas. & Sec.--Carton-Craft Corporation, Buffalo, NY; *U.S. Private*, pg. 217
Osar, Karen R., V.P. & Treas.--Tenneco Inc., Greenwich, CT; *U.S. Public*, pg. 1577
Osattin, Stuart M., V.P. & Treas.--Teradyne, Inc., Boston, MA; *U.S. Public*, pg. 1580
Osborn, Leroy N., V.P.-Fin. & Treas.--Dunlop Tire Corporation, Buffalo, NY; *Int'l*, pg. 1317
Oshinski, Jerry P., Exec. V.P., Treas. & Sec.--Hunter Corp., Portage, IN; *U.S. Private*, pg. 549
Oshlo, Richard, Treas.--Inacom Corp., Omaha, NE; *U.S. Public*, pg. 873
Oshrin, Martin, Treas. & Sec.--Junior Gallery Ltd., New York, NY; *U.S. Private*, pg. 602
Osterman, John C., Pres., Chief Oper. Officer & Treas.--Chicago Rivet & Machine Company, Naperville, IL; *U.S. Public*, pg. 348
Osterneck, Myles, Chm. Bd., Pres. & Treas.--The Osterneck Co. Inc., Lumberton, NC; *U.S. Private*, pg. 821
Ostroff, Arthur J., Controller & Treas.--Standard Medical Imaging, Inc., Columbia, MD; *U.S. Private*, pg. 1032
Ostrowski, James, Chief Fin. Officer, Treas. & Sec.--Awrey Bakeries, Inc., Livonia, MI; *U.S. Private*, pg. 103
Osweiler, Stanley, Exec. V.P. & Sr. V.P.-Sls.--Service Supply Co. Inc. of Indiana, Indianapolis, IN; *U.S. Private*, pg. 987
Otakie, Daniel A., Chm. Bd., Pres., Chief Exec. Officer & Treas.--Futures Personnel Services, Baltimore, MD; *U.S. Private*, pg. 433
Otis, Clarence, Jr., Sr. V.P.-Investor Rels. & Treas.--Darden Restaurants, Inc., Orlando, FL; *U.S. Public*, pg. 483
Otremba, Edward, Chief Fin. Officer & Treas.--Bituminous Roadways, Inc., Inver Grove Heights, MN; *U.S. Private*, pg. 146
Ottensmeyer, Patrick J., V.P.-Fin. & Treas.--Burlington Northern Santa Fe Corporation, Fort Worth, TX; *U.S. Public*, pg. 268
Otto, John K., V.P. & Treas.--Whittaker Corporation, Simi Valley, CA; *U.S. Public*, pg. 1766
Overbaugh, Joseph C., Treas.--AMP Incorporated, Harrisburg, PA; *U.S. Public*, pg. 7
Overman, Jerry, Treas.--The Life Insurance Co. of Virginia, Richmond, VA; *U.S. Public*, pg. 712
Overton, Carl E., Chm. Bd., Chief Exec. Officer & Treas.--Overton Gear & Tool Corp., Addison, IL; *U.S. Private*, pg. 823
Overton, Samuel, Sr. V.P. & Treas.--Mattison Technologies, Inc., Rockford, IL; *U.S. Private*, pg. 714
Owada, Peter, Exec. V.P. & Treas.--Casio, Inc., Dover, NJ; *Int'l*, pg. 274
Oweis, Issa S., V.P. & Asst. Treas.--The Converse Professional Group, Inc., Monrovia, CA; *U.S. Private*, pg. 271
Owen, Dolores, Sec. & Treas.--Owen Industries, Inc., Carter Lake, IA; *U.S. Private*, pg. 824
Owen, Hayes D., V.P., Sec. & Asst. Treas.--Ascension Water Co., Baton Rouge, LA; *U.S. Private*, pg. 123
Owen, James, Treas.--Brookfield Engineering Laboratories, Inc., Stoughton, MA; *U.S. Private*, pg. 171
Owen, John D., Treas.--Southwest Airlines Co., Dallas, TX; *U.S. Public*, pg. 1493
Owens, A.R., Jr., V.P. & Treas.--NI Industries, Inc., Seal Beach, CA; *U.S. Public*, pg. 1054
Owens, Dennis J., Chief Fin. Officer & V.P.-Admin.--The Pollock Corp., Pottstown, PA; *U.S. Private*, pg. 874
Owens, Michael L., V.P., Treas. & Chief Fin. Officer--Monumental General Insurance Group, Inc., Baltimore, MD; *Int'l*, pg. 27
Owens, Michael L., Chief Oper. Officer, Sr. V.P. & Treas.--Monumental General Insurance Company, Baltimore, MD; *Int'l*, pg. 27
Owens, Ronald M., Treas.--Hope Gas, Inc., Clarksburg, WV; *U.S. Public*, pg. 435
Owings, Frank, Jr., Chief Exec. Officer--Service Supply Co. Inc. of Indiana, Indianapolis, IN; *U.S. Private*, pg. 987
Owsley, Robert W., Treas.--Boeing Realty Corporation, Long Beach, CA; *U.S. Public*, pg. 241
Oyer, Paul A., V.P.-Fin. & Treas.--Hawaii Electric Light Co., Inc., Hilo, HI; *U.S. Public*, pg. 800
Ozag, John W., Treas.--Justrite Manufacturing Company, Des Plaines, IL; *U.S. Public*, pg. 617
Ozaki, Joe, Controller, Treas. & Sec.--A-Mark Financial, Santa Monica, CA; *U.S. Private*, pg. 2
Ozuna, Rosemary, Treas. & Sec.--New Bedford Panoramex Corporation, Upland, CA; *U.S. Private*, pg. 792
Pabalan, Salvador P., V.P.-Fin. & Asst. Treas.--Benguet Corporation, Manila, Philippines; *Int'l*, pg. 186
Pabst, Alan J., Treas.--Wells Fargo & Company, San Francisco, CA; *U.S. Public*, pg. 1753
Pacewicz, Edward A., V.P. & Treas.--Comdisco, Inc., Rosemont, IL; *U.S. Public*, pg. 407
Pacey, Phil, Treas.--O'Sullivan Industries Holdings, Lamar, MO; *U.S. Public*, pg. 1234
Pacifico, Michael, Treas. & Sec.--Pacifico Auto Group, Philadelphia, PA; *U.S. Private*, pg. 832
Padilla, Jorge L., V.P., Treas. & Controller--Universal Insurance Co., San Juan, PR; *U.S. Public*, pg. 962
Padilla, Raymond O., V.P., Sec. & Asst. Treas.--Davis Selected Advisors, L.P., Santa Fe, NM; *U.S. Private*, pg. 315
Page, Alton D., V.P. & Treas.--Sun Microsystems, Inc., Palo Alto, CA; *U.S. Public*, pg. 1531
Page, Karina, Treas.--Newport Corporation, Irvine, CA; *U.S. Public*, pg. 1179
Page, Larry, Chief Fin. Officer, Exec. V.P. & Treas.--ShowBiz Pizza Time, Inc., Irving, TX; *U.S. Public*, pg. 1468
Page, Larry A., Treas.--Allright Corporation, Houston, TX; *U.S. Private*, pg. 42
Pagels, Bjorn-Erik, Grp. Treas.--A. Ahlstrom Corporation, Helsinki, Finland; *Int'l*, pg. 32
Paglia, Louis J., Sr. V.P. & Treas.--TIG Holdings, Inc., New York, NY; *U.S. Public*, pg. 1555
Paille, Daniel, Chief Fin. Officer & V.P.--Societe Generale de Financement du Quebec, Montreal, Canada; *Int'l*, pg. 1274
Painter, Jonathan W., Treas.--Thermo Electron Corporation, Waltham, MA; *U.S. Public*, pg. 1591
Pajula, Dick, V.P. & Corp. Treas.--Jerome Foods Inc., Barron, WI; *U.S. Private*, pg. 586
Paladino, Kenneth A., V.P.-Fin. & Treas.--EDO Corporation, New York, NY; *U.S. Public*, pg. 541
Palizza, John M., Dir.-Investor Rels. & Asst. Treas.--Walgreen Co., Deerfield, IL; *U.S. Public*, pg. 1733
Pallat, Daniel J., Chief Fin. Officer, V.P., Treas. & Sec.--Home Juice Co., Melrose Park, IL; *U.S. Private*, pg. 537
Palmer, David, Treas. & Sec.--Farnsworth Companies, Mesa, AZ; *U.S. Private*, pg. 397
Palmer, J. Keith, V.P. & Treas.--Westcorp, Irvine, CA; *U.S. Public*, pg. 1756
Palmer, Kerry D., Treas.--Wall Data Incorporated, Kirkland, WA; *U.S. Public*, pg. 1734
Palmer, Ronald A., Chief Fin. Officer, Exec. V.P. & Treas.--TCF Financial Corp., Minneapolis, MN; *U.S. Public*, pg. 1554
Palmer, Ronald J., Chief Fin. Officer, Exec. V.P. & Treas.--TCF Bank Minnesota FSB, Minneapolis, MN; *U.S. Public*, pg. 1554
Palmeri, Michael, Asst. Treas.--Pinnacle West Capital Corporation, Phoenix, AZ; *U.S. Public*, pg. 1297
Palmeri, Michael V., Treas.--APS, Phoenix, AZ; *U.S. Public*, pg. 1297
Palombo, Tony, Treas.--Cleaners Hanger Co., Palm Harbor, FL; *U.S. Private*, pg. 245
Palumbo, John, V.P. & Treas.--Keystone Automotive Industries, Inc., Pomona, CA; *U.S. Public*, pg. 955
Paluska, Stephen M., Treas. & Dir.--Dav-El Services, Inc., Long Island City, NY; *U.S. Private*, pg. 314
Pamplin, Robert B., Jr., Dr., Pres., Chief Oper. Officer & Sec.--R.B. Pamplin Corp., Portland, OR; *U.S. Private*, pg. 835
Panko, George J., Jr., Asst. Treas.--Woolrich, Inc., Woolrich, PA; *U.S. Private*, pg. 1188
Paolercio, Michael Anthony, Sr. V.P. & Treas.--Michael Anthony Jewelers, Inc., Mount Vernon, NY; *U.S. Public*, pg. 1103
Papa, Vincent T., V.P. & Treas.--Orion Capital Corporation, New York, NY; *U.S. Public*, pg. 1231
Papandrew, Christopher, Mgr.-Treas.--Journal Register Company, Trenton, NJ; *U.S. Public*, pg. 934
Papera, Gabriel, Treas.--Allstate Can Corporation, Parsippany, NJ; *U.S. Private*, pg. 44
Paras, Javier Davila, Treas.--Fomento Economico Mexicano, S.A. de CV, Monterrey, Mexico; *Int'l*, pg. 496
Paras, Philip G., V.P.-Fin. & Treas.--Seneca Foods Corporation, Pittsford, NY; *U.S. Public*, pg. 1456
Pard, Serge, Treas.--Celanese Canada, Inc., Montreal, Canada; *Int'l*, pg. 625
Parente, Meredith M., V.P. & Treas.--Brown-Forman Corporation, Louisville, KY; *U.S. Public*, pg. 261
Parfet, Ray T., Jr., Treas. & Sec.--Gilmore Bros., Inc., Kalamazoo, MI; *U.S. Private*, pg. 454
Parish, Harold, Treas.--American Emulsions Co., Inc., Dalton, GA; *U.S. Public*, pg. 1357
Parizeau, Jean, Chief Fin. Officer, V.P. & Treas.--Publicis BCP Montreal Inc., Montreal, Canada; *Int'l*, pg. 116
Park, Charles, Chief Fin. Officer, Exec. V.P.-Fin. & Sec.--Briggs Industries, Inc., Tampa, FL; *U.S. Private*, pg. 168
Park, J. Leonard, Chm. Bd., Pres., Chief Exec. Officer & Treas.--George W. Park Seed Co., Inc., Greenwood, SC; *U.S. Private*, pg. 839
Park, John J., Sr. V.P.-Fin., Asst. Treas. & Dir.-Res.--W.P. Carey & Co., Inc., New York, NY; *U.S. Private*, pg. 209
Parke, Robert N., Treas.--SPF Insurance Agency, Franklin Park, IL; *U.S. Public*, pg. 1428
Parke, Robert N., V.P. & Treas.--EFS/San Diego Service Corporation, Chicago, IL; *U.S. Public*, pg. 1428
Parker, Arlene F., Treas.--Pelican Products, Torrance, CA; *U.S. Private*, pg. 848
Parker, Carter, Treas. & Sec.--Louisiana Utilities Supply Company, Baton Rouge, LA; *U.S. Private*, pg. 245
Parker, Christopher, Treas.--Booker PLC, London, United Kingdom; *Int'l*, pg. 202
Parker, D. Michael, Chief Fin. Officer, V.P.-Fin., Sec. & Treas.--Kewaunee Scientific Corporation, Statesville, NC; *U.S. Public*, pg. 953
Parker, Earle L., V.P. & Treas.--C.R. Bard, Inc., Murray Hill, NJ; *U.S. Public*, pg. 189
Parker, G. Reid, Treas.--Bruncor, Inc., Saint John, Canada; *Int'l*, pg. 230
Parker, Ginger L., Asst. Treas.--Sun Bank d/b/a Snyder County Trust Company, Selinsgrove, PA; *U.S. Public*, pg. 1529
Parker, Howard, Treas.--Atlas Terminal Co., Evansville, IN; *U.S. Private*, pg. 97
Parker, John R., Chief Fin. Officer, V.P. & Treas.--NS Group, Inc., Newport, KY; *U.S. Public*, pg. 1147
Parker, Melvin C., Chm. Bd., Pres., Chief Exec. Officer, Chief Fin. Officer & Treas.--Investors Insurance Group, Inc., Boca Raton, FL; *U.S. Public*, pg. 911
Parks, M., Treas.--Waterford Wedgwood Plc, Dublin, Ireland; *Int'l*, pg. 1487
Parks, S.E., Treas.--Wexpro Company, Salt Lake City, UT; *U.S. Public*, pg. 1352
Parks, Stephen E., Chief Fin. Officer, V.P. & Treas.--Questar Corporation, Salt Lake City, UT; *U.S. Public*, pg. 1352
Parks, Walter J., Chief Fin. Officer & Sr. V.P.--AnnTaylor Stores Corporation, New York, NY; *U.S. Public*, pg. 116
Parks, Walter J., Chief Fin. Officer, Sr. V.P. & Treas.--AnnTaylor, Inc., New York, NY; *U.S. Public*, pg. 116
Parmenter, Robert E., V.P. & Treas.--Eaton Corporation, Cleveland, OH; *U.S. Public*, pg. 555
Parra, Marcelo, V.P. & Treas.--Metallgesellschaft Corp., New York, NY; *Int'l*, pg. 861
Parra, Mike, Chief Fin. Officer, Controller & Treas.--F.P.A., Inc., Irving, TX; *U.S. Private*, pg. 389
Parrish, James O., V.P.-Fin. & Treas.--Twin Disc, Incorporated, Racine, WI; *U.S. Public*, pg. 1646
Parrish, Sterlin, Treas.--U.S. Oil & Refining Co., Tacoma, WA; *U.S. Private*, pg. 1086
Parrott, Peter, V.P. & Treas.--Orient-Express Hotels Inc., New York, NY; *Int'l*, pg. 1213
Parry, Edward J., III, Chief Fin. Officer, V.P. & Treas.--Allmerica Financial Corporation, Worcester, MA; *U.S. Public*, pg. 54
Parsons, J.A., Chief Fin. Officer, Exec. V.P., Treas. & Sec.--Willamette Industries, Inc., Portland, OR; *U.S. Public*, pg. 1768
Parsons, Susan E., Treas.--George Koch Sons, Inc., Evansville, IN; *U.S. Private*, pg. 628
Partridge, Sharon, Asst. V.P.-Fin. & Treas.--Valley Resources, Inc., Cumberland, RI; *U.S. Public*, pg. 1706
Parven, Michael G., V.P. & Treas.--Continental Graphics Corporation, Los Angeles, CA; *U.S. Private*, pg. 268
Pascolini, Mario, Chief Fin. Officer & Treas.--The Will-Burt Company, Orrville, OH; *U.S. Private*, pg. 1177
Pasha, Rasheed, V.P.-Fin. & Information Systems & Treas.--Rust-Oleum Corporation, Vernon Hills, IL; *U.S. Public*, pg. 1358
Pasipoularides, Jane W., Asst. Treas.--Exide Electronics Group, Inc., Raleigh, NC; *Int'l*, pg. 126

Passman, S. David, III, Chief Fin. Officer & Sr. V.P.--John H. Harland Company, Decatur, GA; *U.S. Public*, pg. 785
Pasternak, Stanley W., V.P. & Treas.--Canadian Tire Corporation Limited, Toronto, Canada; *Int'l*, pg. 259
Pate, F. Wayne, Pres. & Treas.--Golden Flake Snack Foods, Inc., Birmingham, AL; *U.S. Public*, pg. 750
Patel, Ghanshyam A., Chief Fin. Officer & Treas.--Plenum Publishing Corporation, New York, NY; *U.S. Public*, pg. 1311
Patel, Mahendra, Pres., Chief Exec. Officer & Gen. Mgr.--Philway Products, Inc., Ashland, OH; *U.S. Private*, pg. 862
Patenaude, John L., Asst. Treas.--Nashua Corporation, Nashua, NH; *U.S. Public*, pg. 1152
Paterni, Terry, V.P. & Treas.--Grubb & Ellis Company, Northbrook, IL; *U.S. Public*, pg. 767
Patrick, Ed, V.P.-Fin.--Desa International, Bowling Green, KY; *U.S. Private*, pg. 326
Patterson, Barry, V.P. & Treas.--McKee Foods Corporation, Collegedale, TN; *U.S. Private*, pg. 723
Patterson, Dana L., V.P.-Fin. & Treas.--Freedom Forge Corporation, Burnham, PA; *U.S. Private*, pg. 425
Patton, Dennis P., Treas.--Steris Corporation, Mentor, OH; *U.S. Public*, pg. 1515
Patty, David A., Chief Fin. Officer, Treas. & Sec.--Donahue Schriber, Newport Beach, CA; *Int'l*, pg. 253
Paturzo, Michael R., Treas. & Sec.--Henningsen Foods, Inc., White Plains, NY; *Int'l*, pg. 1074
Pau, Janet K., V.P. & Treas.--Canfor Corporation, Vancouver, Canada; *Int'l*, pg. 260
Paukstis, Charles A., V.P.-Fin. & Treas.--HomeTown Communications Network, Inc., Livonia, MI; *U.S. Private*, pg. 537
Paul, Joseph M., Treas.--Xtek, Inc., Cincinnati, OH; *U.S. Private*, pg. 1194
Paulin, Ira, Treas. & Sec.--Ranchers Supply Company, Inc., Lamar, CO; *U.S. Private*, pg. 908
Paull, Mitchell S., V.P. & Treas.--Aaron Rents, Inc., Atlanta, GA; *U.S. Public*, pg. 12
Pauls, John, Treas.--Fiatallis North America, Inc., Carol Stream, IL; *Int'l*, pg. 483
Paulson, Stephanie, Exec. V.P., Treas & Creative Dir.--The Stephenz Group, Inc., San Jose, CA; *U.S. Private*, pg. 1040
Paulson, Thomas J., V.P.-Fin., Treas. & Sec.--Neurogen Corporation, Branford, CT; *U.S. Public*, pg. 1169
Paulson, Timothy G., V.P. & Treas.--Litton Industries, Inc., Woodland Hills, CA; *U.S. Public*, pg. 1002
Pauly, Arthur, Dir.-Fin. & Asst. Treas.--Ragold, Inc., Chicago, IL; *Int'l*, pg. 1084
Pave, Gary D., Corp. Legal Dir.--Rodale Press, Inc., Emmaus, PA; *U.S. Private*, pg. 939
Pavelik, Richard, Treas. & Sec.--Landau Building Co., Wexford, PA; *U.S. Private*, pg. 646
Pavlik, Jeff, Controller & Asst. Treas.--Premier Coatings, Inc., Elk Grove Village, IL; *Int'l*, pg. 1488
Pawelko, Ronald G., Treas.--Superior Graphite Co., Chicago, IL; *U.S. Private*, pg. 1054
Pawlowski, Joseph P., Treas.--National Fuel Gas Company, Buffalo, NY; *U.S. Public*, pg. 1156
Payne, Douglas, Sr. V.P.-Fin. & Admin.--Stanley Furniture Co. Inc., Stanleytown, VA; *U.S. Public*, pg. 1508
Payzant, J.S., Sr. V.P.-Trust Investments & Treas.--National Trustco Inc., Toronto, Canada; *Int'l*, pg. 909
Pazos, Javier, Sr. V.P.--Banco Santander, Madrid, Spain; *Int'l*, pg. 143
Pazurek, John, V.P.-Fin., Treas. & Controller--Northland Cranberries, Inc., Wisconsin Rapids, WI; *U.S. Public*, pg. 1197
Peabody, Carol, V.P. & Treas.--Sundt Corp., Tucson, AZ; *U.S. Private*, pg. 1051
Peabody, Jonathan C., Pres. & Treas.--Peabody Office Furniture Corporation, Boston, MA; *U.S. Private*, pg. 844
Pearce, Alan, Treas.--McKesson Corporation, San Francisco, CA; *U.S. Public*, pg. 1072
Pearce, Stephen R., V.P. & Treas.--Pearce Industries Inc., Houston, TX; *U.S. Private*, pg. 845
Pearl, Carleton D., Sr. V.P. & Treas.--McDonald's Corporation, Oak Brook, IL; *U.S. Public*, pg. 1068
Pearl, Manny, Treas. & Sec.--Pearl-Pressman-Liberty Communications Group, Philadelphia, PA; *U.S. Private*, pg. 845
Pearlman, Ted, V.P., Sec. & Treas.--Atlite Lighting Equip, Inc., Maspeth, NY; *U.S. Public*, pg. 443
Pearson, Audrey, Treas. & Sec.--NEFA Corporation, Southampton, PA; *U.S. Public*, pg. 1326
Pearson, Jack B., Jr., Asst. Treas.--Sofamor Danek Group, Inc., Memphis, TN; *U.S. Public*, pg. 1482
Pearson, Lloyd A., V.P. & Treas.--Horizon Distribution Inc., Summerville, SC; *U.S. Private*, pg. 539
Peattie, William W., Treas. & Comptroller--General Motors Acceptance Corporation of Canada Limited, Toronto, Canada; *U.S. Public*, pg. 720
Peck, David R., Gen. Counsel & Treas.--Centennial Technologies, Inc., Wilmington, MA; *U.S. Public*, pg. 322
Peck, Jerry D., Treas.--Thorn Apple Valley, Inc., Southfield, MI; *U.S. Public*, pg. 1602
Pecuch, Tom, Treas.--Precision Roll Grinders, Inc., Allentown, PA; *U.S. Private*, pg. 880
Peddy, Courtland D., V.P. & Treas.--Republic Industries, Inc., Fort Lauderdale, FL; *U.S. Public*, pg. 1378
Peel, Walter W., Asst. Treas.--DIMON, Incorporated, Danville, VA; *U.S. Public*, pg. 509
Peeler, Nancy Carole, Treas. & Sec.--Peelers Rug Company, Inc., Gaffney, SC; *U.S. Private*, pg. 846
Peery, Lee, Treas.--Cashco, Inc., Ellsworth, KS; *U.S. Private*, pg. 218
Pehrson, Hans, Treas.--Pharmacia & Upjohn Biosystems AB, Uppsala, Sweden; *Int'l*, pg. 1047
Pelletier, Peter A., Treas. & Sec.--Velcro USA Inc., Manchester, NH; *Int'l*, pg. 1462
Peltz, Ben, Treas.--The First Years Inc., Avon, MA; *U.S. Public*, pg. 642
Pelzel, R.G., Pres. & Treas.--Viking Freight System, Inc., San Jose, CA; *U.S. Public*, pg. 604
Pemberton, Alan, V.P.-Fin. & Treas.--Anderson Lithograph Company, Los Angeles, CA; *U.S. Private*, pg. 72
Pena, Armando A., Treas.--American Electric Power Company, Inc., Columbus, OH; *U.S. Public*, pg. 71
Pena, Armando A., Chief Fin. Officer, Sr. V.P.-Fin. & Treas.--American Electric Power Service Corp., Columbus, OH; *U.S. Public*, pg. 72
Pena, Armando A., Treas.--Kentucky Power Co., Ashland, KY; *U.S. Public*, pg. 72
Pena, Armando A., Treas.--Indiana Michigan Power Company, Fort Wayne, IN; *U.S. Public*, pg. 72
Pena, Armando A., Treas.--Ohio Power Company, Canton, OH; *U.S. Public*, pg. 72
Pena, Armando A., Treas.--Columbus Southern Power Company, Columbus, OH; *U.S. Public*, pg. 72
Pena, Armando A., Treas.--Appalachian Power Company, Roanoke, VA; *U.S. Public*, pg. 72
Pendrey, J.C., Jr., Chief Fin. Officer, Sr. V.P., Treas. & Sec.--Holder Corporation, Atlanta, GA; *U.S. Private*, pg. 533
Penglase, Frank D., Sr. V.P. & Treas.--The McGraw-Hill Companies, New York, NY; *U.S. Public*, pg. 1069
Penkin, J., Treas.--Watts Blake Bearne & Co. Plc, Newton Abbot, United Kingdom; *Int'l*, pg. 1487
Penner, Harold, Treas. & Asst. Sec.--Lechters, Inc., Harrison, NJ; *U.S. Public*, pg. 983
Penno, D. Bruce, Chief Fin. Officer & Treas.--Pridgeon & Clay, Inc., Grand Rapids, MI; *U.S. Private*, pg. 883
Pentaris, George, Treas. & Dir.-Admin. Services--Industrial Coatings Group, Inc., Chicago, IL; *U.S. Private*, pg. 434
Pentti, Petri, Treas.--FinnAir Oy, Helsinki, Finland; *Int'l*, pg. 485
Penz, William F., Exec. V.P. & Treas.--Ludington News Co. Inc., Detroit, MI; *U.S. Private*, pg. 679
Pepe, Barbara, Chief Fin. Officer & Treas.--Capital Resources of Virginia, Inc., Richmond, VA; *U.S. Private*, pg. 657
Pepe, Charles, Asst. Treas. & Asst. Sec.--United Illuminating Company, New Haven, CT; *U.S. Public*, pg. 1678
Pepper, Douglas S., Sr. V.P. & Treas.--Carboline Co., Saint Louis, MO; *U.S. Public*, pg. 1357
Pepper, Douglas S., Treas.--Sentry Polymers, Inc., Freeport, TX; *U.S. Public*, pg. 1357
Percival, Sylvia, Treas. & Sec.--Intelligent Controls Inc., Lynnwood, WA; *U.S. Private*, pg. 566
Perego, Sergi, Chief Dealer & Treas.--BFCE Milan, Milan, Italy; *Int'l*, pg. 161
Pereira, Douglas L., Chief Fin. Officer & Sr. V.P.--Clothestime Stores, Inc., Anaheim, CA; *U.S. Public*, pg. 387
Peressini, Wiliam E., V.P. & Treas.--PacifiCorp, Portland, OR; *U.S. Public*, pg. 1251
Peressini, William E., Treas.--TPC Corporation, Houston, TX; *U.S. Public*, pg. 1252
Perez, J.F., V.P. & Asst. Treas.--Nestle Puerto Rico, Inc., Catano, PR; *Int'l*, pg. 917
Perkins, Lawrence, Chm. Bd. & Treas.--Connecticut Container Corporation, North Haven, CT; *U.S. Private*, pg. 263
Perkins, Rich, Controller & Treas.--Foxworth-Galbraith Lumber Co., Dallas, TX; *U.S. Private*, pg. 423
Perlin, Gary, V.P. & Treas.--The World Bank, Washington, DC; *U.S. Private*, pg. 1188
Perlmuter, Bruce, Exec. V.P., Treas. & Sec.--Perlmuter Printing Company, Cleveland, OH; *Int'l*, pg. 1177
Perocchi, William, Chief Fin. Officer, Exec. V.P. & Treas.--Doubletree Corporation, Memphis, TN; *U.S. Public*, pg. 1335
Perreault, Robert P., Exec. V.P. & Treas.--Lawrence Savings Bank, North Andover, MA; *U.S. Public*, pg. 980
Perron, Allen A., V.P.-Fin., Treas. & Asst. Sec.--Puget Western, Inc., Bellevue, WA; *U.S. Public*, pg. 1342
Perron, Allen A., Pres. & Treas.--Tellus, Inc., Bellevue, WA; *U.S. Public*, pg. 1342
Perrotti, John, Chief Fin. Officer, V.P.-Fin. & Treas.--Gleason Corporation, Rochester, NY; *U.S. Public*, pg. 746
Perry-Werner, Kathryn M., Chm. Bd. & Treas.--Perry Engineering Company, Inc., Winchester, VA; *U.S. Private*, pg. 854
Perry, Brian M., Chief Fin. Officer & Treas.--Interface Electronics Corporation, Hopkinton, MA; *U.S. Private*, pg. 567
Perry, Carmen, Chief Fin. Officer, Treas., Controller & Sec.--Outdoor Venture Corp., Stearns, KY; *U.S. Private*, pg. 822
Perry, Christopher, Asst. Treasurer--Ocean Spray Cranberries, Inc., Middleboro, MA; *U.S. Private*, pg. 811
Perry, Ed, Asst. Controller--Beach Patrol Inc., Carson, CA; *U.S. Private*, pg. 125
Perry, Harold H., V.P. & Treas.--Plant Maintenance Service Corporation, Memphis, TN; *U.S. Private*, pg. 869
Perry, James H., Chief Fin. Officer & Treas.--United Industrial Corporation, New York, NY; *U.S. Public*, pg. 1679
Perry, Jay, Controller, Treas. & Sec.--Steiny & Company, Inc., Baldwin Park, CA; *U.S. Private*, pg. 1039
Perry, Marion E., Treas. & Sec.--Cardinal Scale Manufacturing Company, Webb City, MO; *U.S. Private*, pg. 209
Perry, Marion E., Treas. & Sec.--Detecto Scale Company, Webb City, MO; *U.S. Private*, pg. 209
Perry, P.A., Grp. Treas.--Barclays Bank PLC, London, United Kingdom; *Int'l*, pg. 164
Peske, Milian, Treas. & Sec.--Metric & Multistandard Components, Hawthorne, NY; *U.S. Private*, pg. 736
Petach, Ann Marie, Asst. Treas.--Ford Motor Company, Dearborn, MI; *U.S. Public*, pg. 661
Peterlee, Laura, V.P. & Treas.--Booth American, Detroit, MI; *U.S. Private*, pg. 156
Peters, B., Treas.--ICI American Holdings Inc., Wilmington, DE; *Int'l*, pg. 663
Peters, Charles E., Jr., V.P. & Treas.--Harbor Electric Energy Company, Boston, MA; *U.S. Public*, pg. 247
Peters, Fred, V.P.-Fin. & Treas.--Teleglobe Insurance Systems, Richmond Hill, Canada; *Int'l*, pg. 1373
Peters, Gary, V.P.-Fin.--Trinidad/Benham Corp., Denver, CO; *U.S. Private*, pg. 1103
Peters, Jeanette, Chief Fin. Officer & Sr. V.P.--Rose's Stores, Inc., Henderson, NC; *U.S. Public*, pg. 1405
Peters, Phillip H., Comptroller & Treas.--Continental Water Company, Saint Louis, MO; *U.S. Private*, pg. 269
Peters, Raymond R., Exec. V.P. & Treas.--BankAmerica Corporation, San Francisco, CA; *U.S. Public*, pg. 179
Peters, Raymond R., Grp. Exec. V.P. & Treas.--Bank of America NT&SA, San Francisco, CA; *U.S. Public*, pg. 180
Petersen, Eric, Chm. Bd. & Treas.--Petersen Graphics Group, South Bend, IN; *U.S. Private*, pg. 856
Petersen, Kay, Treas.--Agriland Company, Byron, MN; *U.S. Private*, pg. 26
Petersen, Martin, Treas.--Huntsman Corporation, Salt Lake City, UT; *U.S. Private*, pg. 549
Peterson, Alice M., V.P. & Treas.--Sears, Roebuck and Co., Hoffman Estates, IL; *U.S. Public*, pg. 1452
Peterson, Allan R., Asst. Treas.--Cubic Applications, Inc., Lacey, WA; *U.S. Public*, pg. 466
Peterson, Franklin, Treas.--American Mathematical Society, Inc., Providence, RI; *U.S. Private*, pg. 59
Peterson, Gary P., Sec. & Treas.--Bay West Paper Corp. Towel & Tissue Div., Middletown, OH; *U.S. Public*, pg. 1747
Peterson, Gerald, V.P. & Treas.--Wally Findlay Galleries International, Chicago, IL; *U.S. Private*, pg. 405
Peterson, Jean, Treas. & Sec.--Peterson Motor Company, Boise, ID; *U.S. Private*, pg. 857
Peterson, Mark W., V.P.-Capital Markets & Asst. Treas.--Sprint Corporation, Westwood, KS; *U.S. Public*, pg. 1500
Peterson, Ronald K., Asst. Treas.--American Crystal Sugar Company, Moorhead, MN; *U.S. Private*, pg. 52
Petersson, Hakan, Chief Fin. Officer & Treas.--Fastighetsaktiebolaget Hufvudstaden, Stockholm, Sweden; *Int'l*, pg. 478
Petit, Geoffrey, Chief Fin. Officer, V.P. & Treas.--Fina, Inc., Dallas, TX; *Int'l*, pg. 1044
Petrarca, Lenora, Treas.--The Cedarwood Construction Company, Akron, OH; *U.S. Private*, pg. 221
Pettey, John, Chief Fin. Officer & Treas.--Kemmons Wilson, Inc., Memphis, TN; *U.S. Private*, pg. 613
Pettigrew, Jim, Grp. Treas.--Sedgwick Group plc, London, United Kingdom; *Int'l*, pg. 1217
Pettigrove, Sharon, Coord.-Adv.--O'Malia Food Markets Inc., Carmel, IN; *U.S. Private*, pg. 816
Pettinella, Nicholas A., Chief Fin. Officer, Sr. V.P., Treas. & Asst. Sec.--Intermetrics, Inc., Burlington, MA; *U.S. Private*, pg. 567
Pettit, Dale A., V.P., Treas. & Sec.--Silcorp Limited, Scarborough, Canada; *Int'l*, pg. 1249
Petty, C. Massey, Treas.--St. Joe Corp., Jacksonville, FL; *U.S. Public*, pg. 1426
Petty, Eric, Asst. Treas.--Symons Corporation, Pasadena, CA; *U.S. Private*, pg. 932
Petty, George G., V.P.-Fin., Sec. & Treas.--Atrion Corporation, Arab, AL; *U.S. Public*, pg. 146
Peyser, Irwin, Treas. & Sec.--David Peyser Sportswear Inc., Bay Shore, NY; *U.S. Private*, pg. 860
Pfeifer, Greg, Chief Fin. Officer & Treas.--Rochester-Midland ICL, Omaha, NE; *U.S. Private*, pg. 937
Pfister, Terry W., Chief Fin. Officer, V.P.-Fin., Treas. & Sec.--Enerfab Inc., Cincinnati, OH; *U.S. Private*, pg. 376
Pfortmiller, Terry, Treas. & Sec.--Aldi Food Inc., Batavia, IL; *U.S. Private*, pg. 33
Phagans, T.M., Treas. & Sec.--Addison Steel Inc., Albany, GA; *U.S. Private*, pg. 17
Pherigo, William I., Pres., Chief Oper. Officer & Treas.--NBSC Corporation, Columbia, SC; *U.S. Public*, pg. 1549
Philbin, Brian A., V.P.-Admin. & Treas.--Canagex Investments Limited, Montreal, Canada; *Int'l*, pg. 396
Philen, Terrell, Chief Fin. Officer & Treas.--TRT Holdings Inc., Irving, TX; *U.S. Private*, pg. 1065
Phillips, Brad, Treas.--Darling International, Inc, Irving, TX; *U.S. Public*, pg. 484
Phillips, David, V.P.-Fin. & Treas.--Publix Supermarkets Inc., Lakeland, FL; *U.S. Private*, pg. 893
Phillips, Dayton, Treas. & Sec.--Fischer Companies, Memphis, TN; *U.S. Private*, pg. 408
Phillips, James R., Treas.--PG Vinyl Windows/PG Proglass Construction, Westbrook, ME; *U.S. Private*, pg. 826
Phillips, Keith, Chief Fin. Officer, V.P. & Treas.--Wellman, Inc., Shrewsbury, NJ; *U.S. Public*, pg. 1752
Phillips, N. LaRon, CPA, Chief Fin. Officer, Treas. & Sec.--The Newtron Group Inc., Baton Rouge, LA; *U.S. Private*, pg. 797
Phillips, Regina S., Chief Fin. Officer & Treas.--George & Lynch, Inc., New Castle, DE; *U.S. Private*, pg. 448
Phillips, Richard T., Controller & Treas.--Canyon Resources Corporation, Golden, CO; *U.S. Public*, pg. 301
Phillips, Steve, Asst. Treas.--Ameritruck Distribution Corporation, Fort Worth, TX; *U.S. Private*, pg. 65
Pi, Pedro, V.P. & Treas.--Vallehermoso, S.A., Madrid, Spain; *Int'l*, pg. 1447
Piani, Brian, Chief Fin. Officer--Yankee Publishing Incorporated, Dublin, NH; *U.S. Private*, pg. 1195
Piassick, Allen, V.P. & Treas.--NCH Corporation, Irving, TX; *U.S. Public*, pg. 1145
Pickard, Frank C., III, V.P. & Treas.--VF Corporation, Wyomissing, PA; *U.S. Public*, pg. 1702
Pickell, L.A., Treas.--Irex Corporation, Lancaster, PA; *U.S. Public*, pg. 913
Pickle, Scott, Controller & Treas.--Cavalier Insurance Agency, Inc., Hamilton, AL; *U.S. Public*, pg. 318
Picknelly, Peter A., Jr., Pres. & Chief Exec. Officer--Peter Pan Bus Lines, Inc., Springfield, MA; *U.S. Private*, pg. 856
Pieftrafitta, Clifford E., V.P.-Fin., Treas. & Asst. Sec.--CSS Industries, Inc., Philadelphia, PA; *U.S. Public*, pg. 283

Piel, William G., V.P. & Treas.--John Alden Financial Corporation, Miami, FL; *U.S. Public*, pg. 39
Pieper, William T., Treas. & Sec.--Stewart & Stevenson Power, Inc., City of Commerce, CA; *U.S. Public*, pg. 1518
Pierce, Edwin, Treas. & Mgr.-Pur.--Tolleson Lumber Company, Inc., Perry, GA; *U.S. Private*, pg. 1090
Pierce, Frank R., Chief Fin. Officer, Exec. V.P., Treas. & Sec.--Gulfmark Offshore Inc., Houston, TX; *U.S. Public*, pg. 769
Pierce, Garrett E., Pres. & Chief Exec. Officer--Materials Research Corporation, Gilbert, AZ; *Int'l*, pg. 1283
Pierce, James, Chief Fin. Officer & Treas.--Academy Corporation, Katy, TX; *U.S. Private*, pg. 11
Pieri, Albert, Treas. & Sec.--Artichoke Industries, Inc., Castroville, CA; *U.S. Private*, pg. 86
Pierne, Jeffrey J., V.P.-Investor Rels. & Asst. Treas.--Sotheby's Holdings Inc., New York, NY; *U.S. Public*, pg. 1487
Pierpont, Janet M., V.P. & Treas.--Olin Corporation, Norwalk, CT; *U.S. Public*, pg. 1218
Pierpont, Wilbur K., Treas.--R & B Machine Tool Co., Saline, MI; *U.S. Private*, pg. 901
Pierrot, I. Laura, Asst. Treas.--EnerMark Income Fund, Calgary, Canada; *Int'l*, pg. 454
Pierson, Claude E., Asst. Treas.--General Shale Products Corp., Johnson City, TN; *Int'l*, pg. 843
Pierson, Claude E., Asst. Treas.--General Shale Products Corp., Elizabethton, TN; *Int'l*, pg. 843
Pierson, Eric, Treas.--Rexel, Inc., Coral Gables, FL; *Int'l*, pg. 1107
Pietrowski, Richard L., Treas.--Oil-Dri Corporation of America, Chicago, IL; *U.S. Public*, pg. 1214
Pietrzak, Michael, V.P., Controller & Treas.--IDS Trust Co., Minneapolis, MN; *U.S. Public*, pg. 73
Pifer, Glenn A., Chief Fin. Officer, Treas. & Sec.--Allied Security, Inc., Pittsburgh, PA; *U.S. Private*, pg. 40
Pigeonniere, J. Lerebourg, Chief Fin. Officer & Treas.--Jeumont-Schneider Trenformeteurs, Lyon, France; *Int'l*, pg. 706
Pihl, Larry D., Chief Fin. Officer, V.P.-Fin., Treas. & Controller--UTILX Corporation, Kent, WA; *U.S. Public*, pg. 1701
Pike, Carla, Treas.--Leblanc Communications, Inc., Richardson, TX; *U.S. Private*, pg. 656
Pike, James O., V.P. & Treas.--Mobile Technology Inc., Los Angeles, CA; *U.S. Private*, pg. 754
Pike, Mary Anne, Treas. & Sec.--Elite Lamp, Inc., West Memphis, AR; *U.S. Private*, pg. 371
Pilcher, Sue, V.P. & Treas.--Natural Fuels Corporation, Denver, CO; *U.S. Public*, pg. 1170
Pillat, P., Treas.--B & R Industrial Automation, Roswell, GA; *U.S. Private*, pg. 105
Pillsbury, Chuck, Treas.--Walman Optical Company, Minneapolis, MN; *U.S. Private*, pg. 1148
Pinkston, Larry D., Chief Fin. Officer, V.P. & Treas.--Unit Corporation, Tulsa, OK; *U.S. Public*, pg. 1672
Pinner, John G., Asst. Treas.--Mattel, Inc., El Segundo, CA; *U.S. Public*, pg. 1057
Pinsley, Sol, Chm. Bd., Pres., Chief Exec. & Chief Oper. Officer--Espey Mfg. & Electronics Corp., Saratoga Springs, NY; *U.S. Public*, pg. 592
Pipp, Patrick J., Chief Fin. Officer--Roman, Inc., Roselle, IL; *U.S. Private*, pg. 942
Pirillo, Joseph A., V.P. & Treas.--Budget Marketing, Inc., Des Moines, IA; *U.S. Private*, pg. 178
Pistell, Timothy K., Treas.--Parker Hannifin Corporation, Cleveland, OH; *U.S. Public*, pg. 1259
Pitek, Nancy R., V.P.-Fin & Treas.--DRS Technologies, Inc., Parsippany, NJ; *U.S. Public*, pg. 474
Pitkowsky, Murray, Chief Fin. Officer, Sr. V.P. & Treas.--Datascope Corp., Montvale, NJ; *U.S. Public*, pg. 487
Pitorak, Larry J., Chief Fin. Officer, Sr. V.P.-Fin. & Treas.--The Sherwin-Williams Company, Cleveland, OH; *U.S. Public*, pg. 1465
Pivinski, Joseph, Chief Fin. Officer, V.P. & Treas.--Oriole Homes Corp., Delray Beach, FL; *U.S. Public*, pg. 1230
Pizel, Ken, Chief Fin. Officer, V.P.-Fin. & Treas.--Wenger Corporation, Owatonna, MN; *U.S. Private*, pg. 1162
Pizzani, Paul G., Treas.--COMSAT Corporation, Bethesda, MD; *U.S. Public*, pg. 424
Pizzica, Dennis S., V.P. & Treas.--Hunt Corporation, Philadelphia, PA; *U.S. Public*, pg. 848
Pizzini, Jose, Pres.--Direct Press Modern Litho Corporation, Huntington Station, NY; *U.S. Private*, pg. 334
Place, Brian F., Controller & Asst. Treas.--Todays Temporary, Inc., Dallas, TX; *U.S. Public*, pg. 277
Plankar, Arthur, Treas.--Saarbergwerke Aktiengesellschaft, Saarbruecken, Germany; *Int'l*, pg. 1166
Plaster, E. Dwain, Chief Fin. Officer, V.P. & Treas.--Triangle Pacific Corporation, Dallas, TX; *U.S. Public*, pg. 1634
Plawner, M.A., V.P. & Treas.--Public Service Electric & Gas Co., Newark, NJ; *U.S. Public*, pg. 1340
Pleasants, Jeff, Controller & Treas.--Pressure Systems, Inc., Hampton, VA; *Int'l*, pg. 1130
Plep, Herb, Dir.-Risk & Cash Mngmt. & Asst. Treas.--Esco Corporation, Portland, OR; *U.S. Private*, pg. 382
Plumb, Russell H., Chief Fin. Officer, & V.P.-Fin. & Admin.--Serologicals Corporation, Clarkston, GA; *U.S. Public*, pg. 1460
Plumlee, Ron, Treas.--Arkansas Electric Cooperatives Inc., Little Rock, AR; *U.S. Private*, pg. 82
Plumly, Harlen, V.P., Controller & Treas.--Marcam Solutions, Inc., Newton, MA; *U.S. Public*, pg. 1042
Plummer, Thomas, Treas.--A.M. Best Company, Oldwick, NJ; *U.S. Private*, pg. 139
Plummer, William B., Treas.--The Mead Corporation, Dayton, OH; *U.S. Public*, pg. 1074
Plunkett, Colm, Treas.--Oroamerica, Inc., Burbank, CA; *U.S. Public*, pg. 1232
Pochily, Robert T., Asst. Treas.--New York State Electric & Gas Corporation, Binghamton, NY; *U.S. Public*, pg. 1173
Podojil, James A., Controller & Treas.--A.M. Castle & Co., Franklin Park, IL; *U.S. Public*, pg. 312
Pogach, Allan C., V.P., Treas. & Sec.--Veritas DGC Inc, Houston, TX; *U.S. Private*, pg. 1136
Poggensee, Thomas, Controller & Treas.--Florsheim Group Inc., Chicago, IL; *U.S. Public*, pg. 656
Pohlman, Steve, V.P., Controller & Treas.--Huffy Service First, Inc., Miamisburg, OH; *U.S. Public*, pg. 846
Pohlschroeder, Hans, Asst. Treas.--Colgate-Palmolive Company, New York, NY; *U.S. Public*, pg. 397
Polak, Dennis, Controller & Treas.--Gilmore Envelope Corp., Los Angeles, CA; *U.S. Private*, pg. 454
Polewach, Dale, V.P. & Treas.--American Plastic Toys Inc., Walled Lake, MI; *U.S. Private*, pg. 60
Poling, Douglas E., Treas.--Ball Corporation, Muncie, IN; *U.S. Public*, pg. 170
Polishook, David, Chief Fin. Officer, Treas. & Sec.--The Strober Organization, Inc., Brooklyn, NY; *U.S. Private*, pg. 403
Pollack, Carol, Chief Fin. Officer, V.P., Treas. & Sec.--Comprehensive Care Corporation, Corona Del Mar, CA; *U.S. Public*, pg. 419
Pollack, Stanley C., Chief Oper. Officer & Treas.--Pollack Corporation, Scarborough, ME; *U.S. Private*, pg. 874
Pollak, Martin M., Exec. V.P. & Treas.--GP Strategies Corporation, New York, NY; *U.S. Public*, pg. 694
Pollard, Boyd A., Treas. & Sec.--Power & Telephone Supply Company, Memphis, TN; *U.S. Private*, pg. 877
Pollard, Don, Chief Fin. Officer, Treas. & Sec.--Allied Sporting Goods Inc., Louisville, KY; *U.S. Private*, pg. 41
Pollinger, Rita, Treas.--Stapo Hollander Industries, Lakewood, NJ; *U.S. Private*, pg. 1033
Pollock, B.R., Treas. & Sec.--Morris Coupling Co., Erie, PA; *U.S. Private*, pg. 762
Pollock, Maurice, V.P., Controller, Treas. & Sec.--Collin Street Bakery, Corsicana, TX; *U.S. Private*, pg. 252
Pomares, Jim, Treas., Sec. & Mgr.-Personnel--Sacramento Jaguar, Inc., Sacramento, CA; *U.S. Private*, pg. 1143
Pomeranz, Harold, Chm. Bd., Treas. & Sec.--Stanley Roberts, Inc., Lodi, NJ; *U.S. Private*, pg. 936
Pompeo, Tony, Treas. & Dir.-Fin.--Du Pont Canada Inc., Mississauga, Canada; *U.S. Public*, pg. 532
Ponzetti, Bill, Chief Fin. Officer, Controller & Treas.--Active Electrical Supply Company, Chicago, IL; *U.S. Private*, pg. 15
Ponzio, Peter J., V.P.-Fin., Controller & Asst. Treas.--Day-Timers, Inc., East Texas, PA; *U.S. Public*, pg. 674
Pope, Paul T., Asst. Treas.-Risk Mngmt.--TRW Inc., Cleveland, OH; *U.S. Public*, pg. 1558
Popkowski, Chester J., V.P. & Treas.--National Service Industries, Inc., Atlanta, GA; *U.S. Public*, pg. 1160
Poppe, Dale L., Treas.--The Orr Felt Company, Piqua, OH; *U.S. Private*, pg. 820
Poppe, Janelle, Treas.--Danisco Ingredients Canada Inc., Rexdale, Canada; *Int'l*, pg. 378
Poppe, Janelle M., Dir.-Fin. & Treas.--Danisco Ingredients USA, Inc., New Century, KS; *Int'l*, pg. 378
Porche, Dale P., Treas. & Sec.--SAIA Motor Freight Lines, Houma, LA; *U.S. Public*, pg. 1788
Porter, Barry S., Chief Fin. Officer & Treas.--Ohio Casualty Corporation, Hamilton, OH; *U.S. Public*, pg. 1214
Porter, Donald E., Pres., Chief Exec. Officer & Treas.--The Woodbury Telephone Company, Woodbury, CT; *U.S. Public*, pg. 1491
Porter, Marc A., Chief Fin. Officer, V.P., Treas. & Sec.--The Law Company, Inc., Wichita, KS; *U.S. Private*, pg. 653
Porter, Robert C., Treas. & Asst. Sec.--AmerenCIPS, Springfield, IL; *U.S. Public*, pg. 65
Porter, Robert C., V.P., Treas., Sec. & Asst. Controller--CIPSCO Investment Company, Springfield, IL; *U.S. Public*, pg. 66
Portsmore, Dennis M., V.P., Treas. & Dir.-Data Processing--R & R Marketing, West Caldwell, NJ; *U.S. Private*, pg. 902
Portsmouth, Dennis, V.P., Treas. & Dir.-Data Processing--Raritan Display Division, West Caldwell, NJ; *U.S. Private*, pg. 902
Posey, Warren M., Asst. Treas.--Armstrong World Industries, Inc., Lancaster, PA; *U.S. Public*, pg. 131
Posner, Barbara L., Treas.--EA Financial, Inc., Wilmington, DE; *U.S. Public*, pg. 541
Potash, Paul D., V.P. & Treas.--Spaulding & Slye, Boston, MA; *U.S. Private*, pg. 1021
Potera, Drew, V.P. & Treas.--Transcontinental Realty Investors, Inc., Dallas, TX; *U.S. Public*, pg. 1630
Potera, Drew D., V.P. & Treas.--Continental Mortgage and Equity Trust, Dallas, TX; *U.S. Public*, pg. 441
Potoker, Herbert, Treas.--Espey Mfg. & Electronics Corp., Saratoga Springs, NY; *U.S. Public*, pg. 592
Potter, Donald K., Treas.--Columbia Farms Inc., Leesville, SC; *U.S. Private*, pg. 255
Potter, Robert W., II, Treas.--MCS, Inc., Pittsburgh, PA; *U.S. Public*, pg. 1099
Pottle, J. Roy, V.P. & Treas.--Jones Intercable, Inc., Englewood, CO; *U.S. Private*, pg. 597
Pottorff, Lisle W., Treas.--Printronix, Inc., Irvine, CA; *U.S. Public*, pg. 1329
Potts, David A., V.P.-Corp. Treasury--Republic Industries, Inc., Fort Lauderdale, FL; *U.S. Public*, pg. 1378
Potwin, Peter V., V.P. & Treas.--Benson Industries, Inc., Portland, OR; *U.S. Private*, pg. 133
Poulin, Daniel, Treas.--Quebecor Inc., Montreal, Canada; *Int'l*, pg. 1075
Poulin, Daniel, Treas.--Quebecor Printing, Inc., Montreal, Canada; *Int'l*, pg. 1076
Poulin, Daniel, Treas.--Imprimerie Quebecor Inc., Montreal, Canada; *Int'l*, pg. 1077
Pounds, L. Fred, Chief Fin. Officer, V.P.-Fin. & Treas.--American Oncology Resources, Inc., Houston, TX; *U.S. Public*, pg. 88
Pourciau, Susan, Treas. & Sec.--Fraenkel Company, Baton Rouge, LA; *U.S. Private*, pg. 423
Powell, Daylon W., Asst. Treas.--Family Dollar Stores, Inc., Matthews, NC; *U.S. Public*, pg. 612
Powell, Joe J., Sr. V.P. & Treas.--Deposit Guaranty Corp., Jackson, MS; *U.S. Public*, pg. 500
Powell, Rich, Treas.--Nellcor Puritan Bennett Incorporated, Pleasanton, CA; *U.S. Public*, pg. 1039
Powers, Betty J., Treas.--Progressive Insurance Agency, Inc., Cleveland, OH; *U.S. Public*, pg. 1335
Powers, Mark, Asst. Treas.--Northwest Airlines, Inc., Saint Paul, MN; *U.S. Public*, pg. 1200
Powers, Patrick, Treas.--Donley's, Inc., Cleveland, OH; *U.S. Private*, pg. 340
Powers, Richard, Treas.--Stern-Leach Company, Attleboro, MA; *Int'l*, pg. 329
Powers, Stephen M., Treas.--Anarad, Inc., Santa Barbara, CA; *U.S. Public*, pg. 1563
Powner, Maurice M., Treas.--Bardon Group PLC, Solihull, United Kingdom; *Int'l*, pg. 166
Pozack, Warren, Asst. Treas.--Armstrong World Industries, Inc., Lancaster, PA; *U.S. Public*, pg. 131
Pozza, Duane C., Pres., Chief Exec. Officer & Treas.--Bartlett Cocke, Inc., San Antonio, TX; *U.S. Private*, pg. 249
Prantis, Bob, Treas.--Xilinx, Inc., San Jose, CA; *U.S. Public*, pg. 1786
Prather, Robert L., Chief Fin. Officer, Exec. V.P., Treas. & Sec.--Kocolene Oil Corp., Seymour, IN; *U.S. Private*, pg. 629
Pratt, Cliff W., Pres. & Treas.--Anaheim Extrusion Co., Anaheim, CA; *U.S. Private*, pg. 1127
Pratt, Edward T., Jr., V.P. & Treas.--Hollywood Casino Corp, Atlantic City, NJ; *U.S. Public*, pg. 830
Pratt, R. George, Jr., Pres. & Treas.--Bradford Oil Company, Inc., Bradford, VT; *U.S. Private*, pg. 164
Preece, Allen T., V.P. & Treas.--Northern Telecom Limited, Brampton, Canada; *Int'l*, pg. 968
Premdas, Perry, V.P. & Treas.--Hoechst Marion Roussel, Inc., Bridgewater, NJ; *Int'l*, pg. 624
Prendergast, S. Lawrence, V.P. & Treas.--AT&T Corporation, Basking Ridge, NJ; *U.S. Public*, pg. 10
Prescott, Gerald J., V.P., Chief Fin. Officer & Treas.--Vital Signs MN, Inc., Burnsville, MN; *U.S. Public*, pg. 1723
Preslar, B. Clyde, Chief Fin. Officer & Treas.--Lance, Inc., Charlotte, NC; *U.S. Public*, pg. 977
Presser, Tracy, Treas. & Sec.--J. Hellman Produce, Inc., Los Angeles, CA; *U.S. Private*, pg. 520
Pressley, James Z., Jr., V.P.-Fin. & Admin. & Treas.--Transus Intermodal L.L.C., Atlanta, GA; *U.S. Private*, pg. 1097
Pressman, Kim I., Exec. V.P., Treas. & Sec.--Price Communications Corporation, New York, NY; *U.S. Public*, pg. 1324
Preston, Richard D., Treas.--Triton Energy Limited, Dallas, TX; *U.S. Public*, pg. 1640
Preston, Steve, V.P. & Treas.--Joseph Huber Brewing Co., Inc., Monroe, WI; *U.S. Private*, pg. 545
Preyer, L. Richardson, Jr., Exec. V.P. & Treas.--Vanguard Cellular Systems, Inc., Greensboro, NC; *U.S. Public*, pg. 1707
Pribel, James A., Treas.--United Stationers Inc., Des Plaines, IL; *U.S. Public*, pg. 1689
Price, Christopher L., Treas.--W.O. Bankston Enterprises Inc., Dallas, TX; *U.S. Public*, pg. 1379
Price, Gary L., Comptroller & Treas.--Ben Venue Laboratories, Inc., Bedford, OH; *U.S. Private*, pg. 1136
Price, Gerald R., Treas.--CF Cable TV Inc., Montreal, Canada; *Int'l*, pg. 240
Price, Gerald R., Treas.--Champlain Productions Inc., Montreal, Canada; *Int'l*, pg. 241
Price, Gerald R., Treas.--Laurentien Cable TV Inc., Montreal, Canada; *Int'l*, pg. 241
Price, Gerald R., Treas.--Northern Cable Holdings Ltd., Montreal, Canada; *Int'l*, pg. 241
Price, James H., V.P.-Fin. & Treas.--Southern Mineral Corporation, Houston, TX; *U.S. Public*, pg. 1490
Price, James R., Treas.--Lewis Homes Management Corp., Upland, CA; *U.S. Private*, pg. 665
Price, Mark, V.P.-Fin. & Treas.--W.S. Badcock Corporation, Mulberry, FL; *U.S. Private*, pg. 109
Price, Michael A., Treas.--RLI Corp., Peoria, IL; *U.S. Public*, pg. 1356
Price, Michael A., Treas.--RLI Insurance Company, Peoria, IL; *U.S. Public*, pg. 1356
Price, Michael D., Chief Fin. Officer, V.P., Treas. & Sec.--Bentley Pharmaceuticals, Inc., Tampa, FL; *U.S. Public*, pg. 212
Price, Mike, Treas. & Dir.-Fin.--Food Lion, Inc., Salisbury, NC; *Int'l*, pg. 463
Price, Robert J., Chief Fin. Officer, V.P. & Treas.--The Suddath Companies, Jacksonville, FL; *U.S. Private*, pg. 1049
Price, Steven F., Asst. Treas. & Asst. Corp. Sec.--WPL Holdings, Inc., Madison, WI; *U.S. Public*, pg. 1727
Prichard, Jon D., Grp. Treas.--Dalgety Plc, London, United Kingdom; *Int'l*, pg. 376
Prina, Fran, Treas. & Mgr.--American Finance Group, Inc., Boston, MA; *U.S. Public*, pg. 1241
Prince, George R., V.P. & Treas.--GATX Capital Corporation, San Francisco, CA; *U.S. Public*, pg. 690
Prince, Michael, Chief Fin. Officer--Signature Eyewear, Inc., Inglewood, CA; *U.S. Public*, pg. 1473
Printz, Victoria, Treas. & Sec.--Somerset Pontiac GMC Inc., Troy, MI; *U.S. Private*, pg. 1013
Prischak, Isabel J., Treas.--Plastek Group, Erie, PA; *U.S. Private*, pg. 870
Proctor, Bobby, V.P. Fin. & Treas.--J.W. Aluminum Company, Mount Holly, SC; *U.S. Public*, pg. 1736
Proctor, David C., Treas. & Asst. Clerk--Dynamics Research Corporation, Andover, MA; *U.S. Public*, pg. 539
Proctor, Donald E., Treas.--The Aarque Companies, Jamestown, NY; *U.S. Private*, pg. 9
Proctor, Ted L., Asst. Treas.--Kapalua Land Co., Ltd., Lahaina, HI; *U.S. Public*, pg. 1060
Proctor, Ted L., Asst. Treas.--Maui Pineapple Co., Ltd., Kahului, HI; *U.S. Public*, pg. 1060
Prokay, Robert M., Treas.--National Gypsum Company, Charlotte, NC; *Int'l*, pg. 790

Proll, Douglas A., V.P.-Fin. & Treas.--Renaissance Energy Ltd., Calgary, Canada; *Int'l*, pg. 1102
Proost, Robert L., Corp. V.P. & Treas.--A.G. Edwards, Inc., Saint Louis, MO; *U.S. Public*, pg. 565
Proost, Robert L., Treas.--A.G. Edwards Trust Company, Saint Louis, MO; *U.S. Public*, pg. 565
Prosser, John W., Jr., Sr. V.P.-Fin. & Admin. & Treas.--Jacobs Engineering Group Inc., Pasadena, CA; *U.S. Public*, pg. 921
Prossor, Lynn, V.P. & Treas.--CyberOptics Corporation, Golden Valley, MN; *U.S. Public*, pg. 470
Proudfit, Debe, Treas. & Sec.--Vanport Manufacturing, Inc., Boring, OR; *U.S. Private*, pg. 1134
Proudfoot, Darryl J., Treas.--Poco Petroleums Ltd., Calgary, Canada; *Int'l*, pg. 1061
Proviette, Rogerio, Treas.--Swedish Match do Brasil S/A, Rio de Janeiro, Brazil; *Int'l*, pg. 1328
Pruden, Tom, Treas.--Maclean-Fogg Co., Mundelein, IL; *U.S. Private*, pg. 692
Prudhomme, Michael P., Sec. & Treas.--Central Louisiana Electric Company, Inc., Pineville, LA; *U.S. Public*, pg. 325
Pruet, Ronald B., Jr., Sr. V.P. & Treas.--Sonat Exploration Company, Houston, TX; *U.S. Public*, pg. 1485
Prusko, Joseph T., V.P. & Treas.--Gymboree Corporation, Burlingame, CA; *U.S. Public*, pg. 770
Prusnofsuy, Ofe, Asst. Treas.--Bertelsmann Inc., New York, NY; *Int'l*, pg. 191
Pryor, Joe, Treas. & Sec.--Wm. Bolthouse Farms, Inc., Bakersfield, CA; *U.S. Private*, pg. 155
Puerari, Giovanni, Chief Fin. Officer, Sec. & Treas.--Arnoldo Mondadori Editore S.p.A., Segrate, Italy; *Int'l*, pg. 887
Pugh, William, Jr., Chm. Bd., Pres. & Treas.--Pugh Oil Company, Racine, WI; *U.S. Private*, pg. 894
Pugiello, Peter, Chief Fin. Officer, Sr. V.P., Treas. & Asst. Sec.--Blonder-Tongue Laboratories, Inc., Old Bridge, NJ; *U.S. Public*, pg. 237
Puglisi, Anthony J., Chief Fin. Officer, Sr. V.P. & Treas.--Olsten Corporation, Melville, NY; *U.S. Public*, pg. 1220
Puglisi, Michael A., Chief Fin. & Admin. Officer--The Blackstone Group, New York, NY; *U.S. Private*, pg. 147
Pulaski, Mark L., Chief Fin. Officer, Exec. V.P. & Treas.--Keystone Financial Inc., Harrisburg, PA; *U.S. Public*, pg. 956
Pun, Albert, Treas.--Quantum Corporation, Milpitas, CA; *U.S. Public*, pg. 1350
Purcell, Joseph, Pres. & Treas.--Bell Atlantic Financial Services, Wilmington, DE; *U.S. Public*, pg. 202
Purcell, Kevin H., Treas. & Sec.--Empire Fire & Marine Insurance Co., Omaha, NE; *Int'l*, pg. 1530
Puresa, Dave, Treas.--AEW Partners, L.P., Boston, MA; *U.S. Private*, pg. 5
Purett, Joe, Controller & Treas.--Schlotzsky's, Inc., Austin, TX; *U.S. Public*, pg. 1439
Purkis, Len, Chief Fin. Officer, Sr. V.P.-Fin. & Treas.--Iomega Corporation, Roy, UT; *U.S. Public*, pg. 912
Purser, Christopher, Treas.--Glynwed International PLC, Birmingham, United Kingdom; *Int'l*, pg. 554
Purvis, J.E., Pres. & Treas.--A.C. Legg Packing Company, Inc., Birmingham, AL; *U.S. Private*, pg. 658
Quails, Robert, Sr. V.P., Corp. Treas. & Asst Sec.--Haggar Corporation, Dallas, TX; *U.S. Public*, pg. 774
Quast, William J., V.P., Treas. & Asst. Sec.--Energy West Inc., Great Falls, MT; *U.S. Public*, pg. 581
Quesada, Martha, Treas. & Sec.--Maxine of Hollywood, Inc., Los Angeles, CA; *U.S. Private*, pg. 716
Quicksall, D.E., Chief Fin. Officer, Sr. V.P. & Treas.--Central Freight Lines, Inc., Waco, TX; *U.S. Private*, pg. 223
Quigley, Keith, Chief Fin. Officer, V.P. & Treas.--Clear Springs Foods, Inc., Buhl, ID; *U.S. Private*, pg. 245
Quinn, J.F., Treas.--Ikon Office Solutions, Inc., Malvern, PA; *U.S. Public*, pg. 862
Quinn, Michael, Mgr.-Treasury--Tomkins Industries Inc., Dayton, OH; *Int'l*, pg. 1397
Quirch, Eduardo, Treas.--E & G Foods, Miami, FL; *U.S. Private*, pg. 352
Race, Kevin D., Chief Fin. Officer, Exec. V.P. & Treas.--Fleet Mortgage Group, Inc., Columbia, SC; *U.S. Public*, pg. 650
Rachey, Loren, Treas.--API Group Inc., Saint Paul, MN; *U.S. Private*, pg. 7
Rachmiel, George J., Sr. V.P. & Treas.--Talegen Corporation, Seattle, WA; *U.S. Public*, pg. 1784
Racibozynski, Frank, Treas. & Fin.--Metra, Commuter Rail Service Board, Chicago, IL; *U.S. Private*, pg. 919
Racic, Robert W., V.P. & Treas.--Federal Signal Corporation, Oak Brook, IL; *U.S. Public*, pg. 616
Rada, John B., Treas. & Controller--Firemen's Insurance Company of Washington, D.C., Bethesda, MD; *U.S. Public*, pg. 215
Radcliff, Byron K., Treas.--Monarch Cement Co., Humboldt, KS; *U.S. Public*, pg. 1123
Radcliffe, Randy, V.P., Treas. & Sec.--Fisk Electric Company, Houston, TX; *Int'l*, pg. 16
Radcliffe, Ronald J., Chief Fin. Officer, V.P. & Treas.--Rio Hotel & Casino Inc., Las Vegas, NV; *U.S. Public*, pg. 1390
Radkoski, Donald J., Chief Fin. Officer, Grp. V.P.-Fin. & Treas.--Bob Evans Farms, Inc., Columbus, OH; *U.S. Public*, pg. 596
Radosti, Diane G., Treas.--General American Investors Company, Inc., New York, NY; *U.S. Public*, pg. 706
Radtke, James P., V.P. & Asst. Treas.--Special Editions, Ltd., Chicago, IL; *U.S. Public*, pg. 1310
Radtke, James P., V.P. & Asst. Treas.--Lake Shore Press, Inc., Chicago, IL; *U.S. Public*, pg. 1310
Radtke, James P., V.P. & Asst. Treas.--Playboy Clubs International, Inc., Chicago, IL; *U.S. Public*, pg. 1310
Radtke, Karen, Treas.--JPE, Inc., Ann Arbor, MI; *U.S. Public*, pg. 919
Radtke, Karen A., Treas.--Gelman Sciences, Inc., Ann Arbor, MI; *U.S. Public*, pg. 1253
Radwill, Alvera, Treas.--Master Appliance Corp., Racine, WI; *U.S. Private*, pg. 713
Rafanello, Richard A., Treas. & Sec.--E.C.D., Inc., Hillside, NJ; *U.S. Private*, pg. 353
Rafferty, James B., V.P. & Treas.--AEP Industries, Inc., South Hackensack, NJ; *U.S. Public*, pg. 4
Rafferty, William, Chief Fin. Officer & Treas.--Kelley Dock Systems, Milwaukee, WI; *U.S. Private*, pg. 612
Ragnarsdottir, Alma, Treas.--Landsvirkjun - The National Power Co., Reykjavik, Iceland; *Int'l*, pg. 801
Raines, Bobby J., V.P. & Treas.--Cal-Maine Foods, Inc., Jackson, MS; *U.S. Public*, pg. 292
Raines, Rosser R., Chief Fin. Officer & Treas.--Thomaston Mills, Inc., Thomaston, GA; *U.S. Public*, pg. 1599
Rainey, R., Sr. V.P.-Treas.--Bituminous Casualty Corp., Rock Island, IL; *U.S. Public*, pg. 1218
Rains, Gladys, Controller & Treas.--Davis Paint Company, Kansas City, MO; *U.S. Private*, pg. 315
Rainsford, B.C., Chief Fin. Officer, Exec. V.P. & Treas.--Delta Woodside Industries, Inc., Greenville, SC; *U.S. Public*, pg. 497
Rainwater, Tom, Chief Fin. Officer, Treas. & Sec.--E.C. Barton & Company, Jonesboro, AR; *U.S. Private*, pg. 119
Raiskio, Hannu, Dir. & Treas.--Berner Ltd., Helsinki, Finland; *Int'l*, pg. 189
Raiteri, Albert L., Asst. Treas.--Robbins & Myers, Inc., Dayton, OH; *U.S. Public*, pg. 1393
Rajahalme, Aimo, Sr. V.P.-Fin. & Treas.--Kone Corporation, Helsinki, Finland; *Int'l*, pg. 746
Rakauskas, Mike, Sr. V.P.-Fin. & Admin. & Treas.--The Spring Air Company, Des Plaines, IL; *U.S. Private*, pg. 1027
Rakow, Thomas S., Pres., Chief Exec. Officer & Treas.--IHC Group, Inc., South Elgin, IL; *U.S. Private*, pg. 555
Ralphs, Doug, Treas.--Itron Inc., Spokane, WA; *U.S. Public*, pg. 914
Ralston, Helen E., Treas.--Bowthorpe plc, Crawley, United Kingdom; *Int'l*, pg. 207
Ramagano, Cheryl, Asst. Treas.--Universal Health Services, Inc., King of Prussia, PA; *U.S. Public*, pg. 1696
Ramagano, Cheryl K., V.P. & Treas.--Universal Health Realty Income Trust, King of Prussia, PA; *U.S. Public*, pg. 1697
Ramos, Antonio C., Pres. & Treas.--New England Stone Industries, Inc., Esmond, RI; *U.S. Private*, pg. 793
Ramsay, Scott, Chief Fin. Officer, Sr. V.P., Treas. & Sec.-Admin.--Shaw's Supermarkets, Inc., East Bridgewater, MA; *Int'l*, pg. 1170
Ramsbotham, David, Treas.--Aston Martin Lagonda of North America, Inc., Mahwah, NJ; *U.S. Public*, pg. 664
Ramsey, Stewart P., Treas. & Sec.--LSJ Sportswear Inc., Deerfield, WI; *U.S. Private*, pg. 732
Rand, Edward L., Jr., Treas.--Self-Insurance Administrators, Inc., Stone Mountain, GA; *U.S. Public*, pg. 144
Randolph, Rodger L., V.P. & Treas.--Kentucky-Tennessee Clay Co., Mayfield, KY; *U.S. Public*, pg. 804
Rands, L. William, Chief Fin. Officer, V.P., Treas. & Sec.--Monroc, Inc., Salt Lake City, UT; *U.S. Public*, pg. 1124
Rands, Mary, Controller, Treas. & Sec.--Brush Research Manufacturing Company, Los Angeles, CA; *U.S. Private*, pg. 176
Raney, Bill, Treas. & Sec.--West Central Cooperative, Ralston, IA; *U.S. Private*, pg. 1163
Ranheim, Ron. E., Treas.--Paccar Inc., Bellevue, WA; *U.S. Public*, pg. 1246
Rank, Robert P., Treas.--Wantage Avenue Holding Company, Inc., Branchville, NJ; *U.S. Public*, pg. 1456
Rao, Veronica, Treas.--Malaysian Tobacco Co./B.A.T. Indust., Kuala Lumpur, Malaysia; *Int'l*, pg. 111
Rapaport, Jonathan, Chief Fin. Officer, V.P. & Treas.--Pacesetter Steel Service, Inc., Kennesaw, GA; *U.S. Private*, pg. 830
Rapp, Bill, V.P.-Taxation & Treas.--Safelite AutoGlass, Columbus, OH; *U.S. Private*, pg. 960
Rappaport, Edward, Pres.--W. Braun Company, Chicago, IL; *U.S. Private*, pg. 166
Rappoli, James D., V.P.-Fin. & Treas.--Commonwealth Energy System, Cambridge, MA; *U.S. Public*, pg. 414
Rappolt, William C., Exec. V.P. & Treas.--First Empire State Corporation, Buffalo, NY; *U.S. Public*, pg. 631
Rascoe, Eric, Treas. & Sec.--Thermal Industries, Inc., Pittsburgh, PA; *U.S. Private*, pg. 490
Rasmussen, Earl, Treas.--Menards, Inc., Eau Claire, WI; *U.S. Private*, pg. 731
Rasmussen, Thomas, V.P. & Treas.--Tiernay Metals, Redondo Beach, CA; *U.S. Private*, pg. 1085
Rassman, Joel H., Chief Fin. Officer, Sr. V.P., Treas. & Asst. Sec.--Toll Brothers, Inc., Huntingdon Valley, PA; *U.S. Public*, pg. 1620
Ratcliff, G.A., Treas.--Rentenbach Engineering Company, Knoxville, TN; *U.S. Private*, pg. 923
Rathje, Rainer, V.P.-Treasury--Kraft Jacobs Suchard AG, Zurich, Switzerland; *U.S. Public*, pg. 1288
Rathjen, Dennis, Treas.--Vogler Motor Company, Inc., Carbondale, IL; *U.S. Private*, pg. 1143
Rathke, Francis, Chief Fin. Officer, Treas. & Sec.--Ben & Jerry's Homemade Inc., South Burlington, VT; *U.S. Public*, pg. 210
Ratliff, Donna L., Treas. & Asst. Sec.--The GNI Group, Inc., Deer Park, TX; *U.S. Public*, pg. 693
Ratnage, I.C., Treas.--The RTZ Corporation PLC, London, United Kingdom; *Int'l*, pg. 1118
Rauenbuehler, Trish, Asst. Treas.--National Bedding Co., Beloit, WI; *U.S. Private*, pg. 780
Rauh, John M., Treas.--Kerr-McGee Coal Corp., Oklahoma City, OK; *U.S. Public*, pg. 952
Rauh, Mike, V.P. & Treas.--Kerr-McGee Corporation, Oklahoma City, OK; *U.S. Public*, pg. 952
Rauwerdink, William J., Chief Fin. Officer, Exec. V.P., Treas. & Sec.--Lason, Inc., Troy, MI; *U.S. Public*, pg. 979
Raver, William J., V.P. & Treas.--Cadbury Beverages North America, Stamford, CT; *Int'l*, pg. 248
Raxter, Alan, Chief Fin. Officer, Exec. V.P. & Treas.--Younkers, Inc., Des Moines, IA; *U.S. Public*, pg. 1334
Ray, E. Wayne, Jr., Chief Fin. Officer, V.P. & Treas.--Riviana Foods Inc., Houston, TX; *U.S. Public*, pg. 1392
Ray, Ralph D., Treas.--Liberty Homes, Inc., Goshen, IN; *U.S. Public*, pg. 992
Ray, Stuart, Treas. & Sec.--Davis-Moore Oldsmobile, Inc., Wichita, KS; *U.S. Private*, pg. 315
Rayburn, Cathy T., V.P. & Treas.--Institutional Services, Inc., Fort Worth, TX; *U.S. Public*, pg. 1482
Rayl, John E., Treas.--Tropic Communications Inc., Columbus, OH; *U.S. Public*, pg. 1641
Raymonds, Catherine, Treas.--Captive Plastics, Piscataway, NJ; *U.S. Private*, pg. 207
Read, Bob, Treas. & Sec.--Graham, Milwaukee, WI; *Int'l*, pg. 377
Read, Michael J., Chief Fin. Officer, Treas. & Mng. Dir.--Barr Brothers & Co., Inc., New York, NY; *U.S. Private*, pg. 117
Reardon, Joseph M., Chief Fin. Officer, Exec. V.P. & Treas.--B.M.J. Financial Corp., Bordentown, NJ; *U.S. Public*, pg. 1528
Rebeck, Donna L., Treas.--NFC International Holdings (U.S.A.) Inc., Dover, DE; *Int'l*, pg. 901
Rebmann, R. Robert, Jr., Chief Fin. Officer & Treas.--Box Hill Systems Corporation, New York, NY; *U.S. Public*, pg. 249
Recla, Debbie, Treas. & Corp. Sec.--Champion, Inc., Iron Mountain, MI; *U.S. Private*, pg. 228
Redden, F. David, V.P.-Fin.--Agra Inc., Calgary, Canada; *Int'l*, pg. 30
Redler, Joel B., V.P. & Treas.--Forbes, Inc., New York, NY; *U.S. Private*, pg. 417
Redlinger, Richard, V.P.-Corp. Devel. & Treas.--Dravo Corporation, Pittsburgh, PA; *U.S. Public*, pg. 527
Redman, Monte N., Chief Fin. Officer, Sr. V.P. & Treas.--Astoria Financial Corporation, Lake Success, NY; *U.S. Public*, pg. 141
Redwine, Jack F., Asst. Sec. & Treas.--Chickasha Cotton Oil Co., Chandler, AZ; *Int'l*, pg. 1395
Reece, Mark, Controller, Treas & Sec.--Young-Phillips Sales Co., Clemmons, NC; *U.S. Private*, pg. 1201
Reece, Richard K., Chief Fin. Officer, V.P.-Fin. & Treas.--Belden Inc., Saint Louis, MO; *U.S. Public*, pg. 200
Reed, B. Jack, Treas.--Tom Brown, Inc., Midland, TX; *U.S. Public*, pg. 262
Reed, Brad, Chief Oper. Officer, Treas. & Sec.--Kova Fertilizer Inc., Greensburg, IN; *U.S. Private*, pg. 634
Reed, Earl W., Treas.--Reed Brothers Inc., Buhl, ID; *U.S. Private*, pg. 916
Reed, Mike, Treas.--Graphic Technology, Inc., New Century, KS; *Int'l*, pg. 950
Reed, Raymond, Gen. Mgr.-Sls. & Treas.--Reed Motors, Inc., Orlando, FL; *U.S. Private*, pg. 916
Reed, Robert, Treas.--Shepard Niles, Inc., Montour Falls, NY; *U.S. Private*, pg. 992
Reed, W. Allen, V.P. & Treas.--Hughes Electronics Corporation, Westchester, CA; *U.S. Public*, pg. 720
Reeder, Jeff, Chief Fin. Officer, V.P. & Treas.--Gerland Corp., Houston, TX; *U.S. Private*, pg. 449
Reedy, John D., Chief Fin. Officer & Treas.--Michael Foods, Inc., Minneapolis, MN; *U.S. Public*, pg. 1103
Reeg, David H., V.P.-Fin. & Treas.--ITT Flygt Corporation, Trumbull, CT; *U.S. Public*, pg. 860
Rees, Burton S., Chief Fin. Officer & V.P.--Salz Leathers, Inc., Santa Cruz, CA; *U.S. Private*, pg. 963
Rees, John, Treas. & Sec.--Silver Springs Citrus Co-op, Howey in the Hills, FL; *U.S. Private*, pg. 1000
Reese, Richard, Treas. & Sec.--Century Furniture Industries, Hickory, NC; *U.S. Private*, pg. 226
Reeve, Michael, Asst. Treas.--Malden Mills Industries, Inc., Lawrence, MA; *U.S. Private*, pg. 698
Regan, Paul, Treas.--Jefferson Smurfit Group p.l.c., Dublin, Ireland; *Int'l*, pg. 1269
Regan, Timothy J., V.P. & Treas.--The Scoular Company, Omaha, NE; *U.S. Private*, pg. 977
Regan, William J., Jr., V.P. & Treas.--Entergy Corporation, New Orleans, LA; *U.S. Public*, pg. 585
Regenbogen, Howard, Treas.--Movado Group, Inc., Lyndhurst, NJ; *U.S. Public*, pg. 1140
Rehor, David G., V.P. & Treas.--Ford Motor Co. of Canada Ltd, Oakville, Canada; *U.S. Public*, pg. 666
Reid, Dal C., Chief Fin. Officer, V.P. & Treas.--Friona Industries, L.P., Amarillo, TX; *U.S. Private*, pg. 429
Reid, E. J., Treas.--Carter Holt Harvey Limited, Auckland, New Zealand; *U.S. Public*, pg. 904
Reif, Jack N., Asst. Treas.--Dayton Hudson Corporation, Minneapolis, MN; *U.S. Public*, pg. 489
Reihmann, Shirley, Treas.--Amana Society, Inc., Amana, IA; *U.S. Private*, pg. 48
Reilly, Robert J., V.P.-Fin. & Treas.--Ampco-Pittsburgh Corporation, Pittsburgh, PA; *U.S. Public*, pg. 103
Reilly, William P., Asst. Treas. & Asst. Sec.--Central Hudson Gas & Electric Corporation, Poughkeepsie, NY; *U.S. Public*, pg. 324
Reimer, Jean, Treas.--Vinyl Plastics Incorporated, Sheboygan, WI; *U.S. Private*, pg. 1141
Rein, Jeffery A., Div. V.P. & Treas.--Walgreen Co., Deerfield, IL; *U.S. Public*, pg. 1733
Reinhold, Jeffrey A., Chief Fin. Officer, V.P. & Treas.--Checkpoint Systems Inc., Thorofare, NJ; *U.S. Public*, pg. 343
Reinke, Winfried, Dir.-Money & Capital Markets--IKB Deutsche Industriebank AG, Dusseldorf, Germany; *Int'l*, pg. 645
Reinken, Sheila C., Treas.--Levitz Furniture Incorporated, Boca Raton, FL; *U.S. Public*, pg. 990
Reinken, Sheila C., Treas.--John M. Smyth Co., Downers Grove, IL; *U.S. Public*, pg. 990
Reinschmidt, George H., V.P. & Treas.--Freeman Decorating Co., Dallas, TX; *U.S. Private*, pg. 426
Reisinger, Chales M., V.P., Treas. & Controller--The Kitchen Collection Inc., Chillicothe, OH; *U.S. Public*, pg. 1149
Reisinger, Kerry J., Asst. Treas.--Yorktowne Paperboard Corp., York, PA; *U.S. Private*, pg. 796

Reiss, Richard T., Pres. & Treas.--R.C.A. Rubber Company, Akron, OH; *U.S. Private*, pg. 902
Reith, Craig O., V.P.-Fin. & Asst. Treas.--Four Seasons Hotels Inc., Don Mills, Canada; *Int'l*, pg. 502
Reitman, Alayne L., V.P.-Fin. & Treas.--The Tranzonic Companies, Pepper Pike, OH; *U.S. Public*, pg. 1632
Remes, Audrey, Chief Fin. Officer & Treas.--Initio, Inc., Carson City, NV; *U.S. Public*, pg. 879
Remes, Audrey C., Treas. & Sec.--Deerskin Trading Post, Inc., North Bergen, NJ; *U.S. Public*, pg. 879
Remick, Ronald R., V.P. & Treas.--ARCO Chemical Co., Newtown Square, PA; *U.S. Public*, pg. 144
Remley, Scott A., Treas.--Accelerated Claims Processing, Inc., New York, NY; *U.S. Public*, pg. 802
Remley, Scott A., Treas.--Quality Medical Adjudication, Inc., Rancho Cordova, CA; *U.S. Public*, pg. 802
Remmer, Henry, Treas.--Chemtex International, Inc., New York, NY; *Int'l*, pg. 872
Renaud, Giles A.H., V.P. & Treas--United Technologies Corporation, Hartford, CT; *U.S. Public*, pg. 1689
Renaud, Robert A., V.P., Treas. & Sec.--Bankers Fidelity Life Insurance Company, Atlanta, GA; *U.S. Public*, pg. 143
Rendano, Ronald E., Treas.--SEIKO Corporation of America, Mahwah, NJ; *Int'l*, pg. 1218
Renfroe, Ron, Treas.--The Hardaway Company, Columbus, GA; *U.S. Private*, pg. 501
Rennie, Michael, Treas.--Gandalf Technologies Inc., Nepean, Canada; *Int'l*, pg. 540
Rentsch, Heinz-Jurgen, Sr. Exec. V.P. & Treas.--Landesbank Rheinland-Pfalz, Mainz, Germany; *Int'l*, pg. 799
Repetti, Peter Q., Chief Fin. Officer & V.P.-Fin. & Admin.--Manugistics Group, Inc., Rockville, MD; *U.S. Public*, pg. 1042
Rescoe, Michael E., Chief Fin. Officer, Sr. V.P. & Treas.--PG&E Corporation, San Francisco, CA; *U.S. Public*, pg. 1240
Resnick, Alan H., V.P. & Treas.--Bausch & Lomb Incorporated, Rochester, NY; *U.S. Public*, pg. 194
Ressler, Jeff, Asst. Treas.--Lancaster Malleable Castings Company, Lancaster, PA; *U.S. Private*, pg. 645
Restivo, Joseph, Asst. Treas.--Blade Communications, Inc., Toledo, OH; *U.S. Private*, pg. 147
Restivo, Joseph, Treas.--Toledo Blade Co., Toledo, OH; *U.S. Private*, pg. 147
Retcher, M.F., Chief Fin. Officer & Treas.--Art Iron, Inc., Toledo, OH; *U.S. Private*, pg. 86
Rettinger, Dale G., Chief Fin. Officer & Exec. V.P.--Petroleum Development Corporation, Bridgeport, WV; *U.S. Public*, pg. 1280
Retzlaff, Robert Z., Pres. & Chief Fin. Officer--Retzlaff Incorporated, San Rafael, CA; *U.S. Private*, pg. 925
Reuss, Daniel J., Sr. V.P., Controller & Treas.--Dain Rauscher Corporation, Minneapolis, MN; *U.S. Public*, pg. 476
Rewolinski, Thomas, Chief Fin. Officer, Treas. & Sec.--Western States Envelope Co., Milwaukee, WI; *U.S. Private*, pg. 1168
Reybitz, Edmund, Mgr.-Treas.--Bethlehem Steel Corporation, Bethlehem, PA; *U.S. Public*, pg. 226
Reyes, B.M., Treas.--Grand Trunk Corporation (GTC), Detroit, MI; *Int'l*, pg. 258
Reynen, John D., Treas. & Sec.--Reynen, Bardis & Winn, Sacramento, CA; *U.S. Private*, pg. 926
Reynolds, Craig E., V.P. & Treas.--Federal Home Loan Bank of New York, New York, NY; *U.S. Private*, pg. 399
Reynolds, Marion F., V.P., Treas. & Sec.--Middlesex Water Company, Iselin, NJ; *U.S. Public*, pg. 1110
Reynolds, Marion F., Treas. & Sec.--Pinelands Water & Wastewater Co., Broadway, NJ; *U.S. Public*, pg. 1110
Reynolds, Mary, Asst. Treas.--The TJX Companies, Inc., Framingham, MA; *U.S. Public*, pg. 1556
Rhoads, Gary L., Treas.--National Penn Bancshares, Inc., Boyertown, PA; *U.S. Public*, pg. 1158
Rhoads, Karen B., Chief Fin. Officer, V.P.-Fin. & Treas.--The Buckle, Inc., Kearney, NE; *U.S. Public*, pg. 267
Rhudy, Huey J., Treas. & Sec.--STRAFCO, Inc., San Antonio, TX; *U.S. Private*, pg. 1046
Rhyner, James E., V.P.-Fin. & Treas.--Roberts Systems, Inc., Charlotte, NC; *Int'l*, pg. 395
Ribaudo, Dale J., Treas.--The Dexter Corporation, Windsor Locks, CT; *U.S. Public*, pg. 504
Riccardi, Anthony, Pres., Treas. & Sec.--William A. Randolph, Inc., Morton Grove, IL; *U.S. Private*, pg. 909
Riccione, Mitch, Treas.--Crosman Airguns, East Bloomfield, NY; *U.S. Private*, pg. 291
Rice, Andrew J., Chief Fin. Officer & Treas.--Nicholas Paper, Inc., Fitchburg, MA; *U.S. Private*, pg. 798
Rice, Andrew L., Asst. Treas.--Estes Express Lines, Inc., Richmond, VA; *U.S. Private*, pg. 384
Rice, Bernard J., Jr., Treas. & Sec.--Blue Grass Quality Meats, Crescent Springs, KY; *U.S. Private*, pg. 152
Rice, Christine E., Treas.--Olde English Equine Insurance Agency, Inc., Bensalem, PA; *U.S. Public*, pg. 908
Rice, Craig, Chief Fin. Officer, V.P. & Treas.--First Central Financial Corporation, Lynbrook, NY; *U.S. Private*, pg. 406
Rice, Jim, Sr. V.P.-Treasury--Motel 6 Operating L.P., Dallas, TX; *Int'l*, pg. 21
Rice, Peter J., Chief Fin. Officer, V.P.-Fin. & Treas.--Media 100, Inc., Marlborough, MA; *U.S. Public*, pg. 1079
Rice, William D., Sr. V.P.-Strategic Devel.--Curtice Burns Foods, Rochester, NY; *U.S. Private*, pg. 887
Ricedorf, Charles, Sec. & Treas.--Rollman Supply Company, Mount Joy, PA; *U.S. Private*, pg. 407
Rich, Bradford R., Chief Fin. Officer, Exec. V.P. & Treas.--SkyWest Inc., Saint George, UT; *U.S. Public*, pg. 1476
Rich, Gerald I., Sr. V.P., Controller & Treas.--Coast Savings Financial, Inc., Los Angeles, CA; *U.S. Public*, pg. 388
Rich, Melvin L., Chm. Bd., Pres. & Treas.--Evergood Products Corporation, Hicksville, NY; *U.S. Private*, pg. 386
Richardello, Michael, Co-owner--Butler Wholesale Products, Inc., Adams, MA; *U.S. Private*, pg. 190
Richards, Bruce D., V.P. & Treas.--Moran Services Corporation, Greenwich, CT; *U.S. Private*, pg. 760
Richards, Bruce D., V.P. & Treas.--Seaboard Barge Corporation, Greenwich, CT; *U.S. Private*, pg. 761
Richards, Bruce D., V.P. & Treas.--Petroleum Transportation Corporation, Greenwich, CT; *U.S. Private*, pg. 761
Richards, Daniel R., Treas. & Sec.--West Union Corporation, Memphis, TN; *U.S. Private*, pg. 1163
Richards, Dave, Controller & Treas.--Pacific Hide & Fur Depot, Great Falls, MT; *U.S. Private*, pg. 831
Richards, G.A., Treas. & Sec.--Ohio Gas Company, Bryan, OH; *U.S. Private*, pg. 812
Richards, Gerald, V.P.-Bd.--United Power Association, Elk River, MN; *U.S. Private*, pg. 1123
Richards, James P., Treas.--Granite Furniture Co., Salt Lake City, UT; *U.S. Private*, pg. 469
Richards, Jon, Treas.--Associated Food Stores Inc., Salt Lake City, UT; *U.S. Private*, pg. 90
Richards, Philip W., Chief Fin. Officer, V.P. & Treas.--Dollar General Corporation, Nashville, TN; *U.S. Public*, pg. 515
Richardson, Alison S., Sr. V.P.-Admin. & Fin.--Integrity Incorporated, Mobile, AL; *U.S. Public*, pg. 886
Richardson, C. Charles, V.P.-Fin. & Treas.--New Castle Industries, Inc., New Castle, PA; *U.S. Public*, pg. 104
Richardson, Dan, V.P.-Fin. & Plng. & Treas.--Great Salt Lake Minerals Corp., Overland Park, KS; *U.S. Private*, pg. 505
Richardson, Melanie, Chief Fin. Officer, Treas. & V.P.--Central Power and Light Company, Corpus Christi, TX; *U.S. Public*, pg. 324
Richey, Albert L., V.P. & Treas.--Anadarko Petroleum Corporation, Houston, TX; *U.S. Public*, pg. 107
Richins, Paul, Treas.--Utah Medical Products, Inc., Midvale, UT; *U.S. Public*, pg. 1700
Richins, Paul O., Chief Admin. Officer, V.P. & Treas.--Utah Medical Products, Inc., Midvale, UT; *U.S. Public*, pg. 1700
Richland, Scott H., V.P. & Treas.--SunAmerica Inc., Los Angeles, CA; *U.S. Public*, pg. 1532
Richlovsky, Thomas A., Sr. V.P. & Treas.--National City Corporation, Cleveland, OH; *U.S. Public*, pg. 1154
Richman, Mark, Treas.--Adecco S.A., Lausanne, Switzerland; *Int'l*, pg. 23
Richmon, Wayne M., Chief Fin. Officer, Exec. V.P. & Treas.--The Flight International Group, Inc., Newport News, VA; *U.S. Public*, pg. 654
Richmond, John L., Asst. Treas.-Cash & Banking--USX Corporation, Pittsburgh, PA; *U.S. Public*, pg. 1661
Richmond, Nancy, Treas.--Premier Securities Corporation, Baton Rouge, LA; *U.S. Public*, pg. 173
Richmond, Nancy, Treas.--Premier Investment Advisors, L.C., New Orleans, LA; *U.S. Public*, pg. 173
Richter, James, Treas.--Wagnerware Corporation, Sidney, OH; *U.S. Private*, pg. 1146
Richter, Joseph M., Chief Fin. Officer, Exec. V.P. & Treas.--The Somerset Group, Inc., Indianapolis, IN; *U.S. Public*, pg. 1484
Richter, Lyle H., Chief Fin. Officer, V.P., Treas. & Sec.--Fox Valley Corporation, Appleton, WI; *U.S. Private*, pg. 422
Richter, Steve, Sr. V.P. & Treas.--Weingarten Realty Investors, Houston, TX; *U.S. Public*, pg. 1751
Ricketts, James, Treas.--Ingram Micro Inc., Santa Ana, CA; *U.S. Public*, pg. 878
Ridenour, Mark, Exec. V.P. & Treas.--Heidtman Steel Products, Inc., Toledo, OH; *U.S. Private*, pg. 519
Ridenour, Mark, Exec. V.P. & Treas.--H.S. Processing, Toledo, OH; *U.S. Private*, pg. 519
Rideout, Chris, Treas.--Micron Separations, Inc., Westborough, MA; *U.S. Private*, pg. 742
Rider, Robert F., Chm., Chief Exec. Officer & Treas.--O.A. Newton & Son Co., Bridgeville, DE; *U.S. Private*, pg. 797
Rieber, Beverly, Treas.--Pacific Handy Cutter, Inc., Costa Mesa, CA; *U.S. Private*, pg. 831
Riecke, Robert, Chief Fin. Officer, Treas. & Sec.--Walle Corporation, Harahan, LA; *U.S. Private*, pg. 1148
Riely, Sandra, Sec. & Treas.--Hood Communications, Inc., Grand Terrace, CA; *U.S. Private*, pg. 673
Rieman, Stephen R., V.P.-Fin., Treas. & Sec.--Bard Mfg. Co., Bryan, OH; *U.S. Private*, pg. 116
Riemenschneider, Ronald E., V.P. & Treas.--Luby's Cafeterias, Inc., San Antonio, TX; *U.S. Public*, pg. 1017
Riesenfeld, Stefan C., V.P. & Treas.--Unisys Corporation, Blue Bell, PA; *U.S. Public*, pg. 1671
Riesmeyer, David W., V.P. & Treas.--Johnstown America Industries, Chicago, IL; *U.S. Public*, pg. 933
Riethman, Robert B., Treas.--The Monarch Machine Tool Company, Sidney, OH; *U.S. Public*, pg. 1123
Rife, Janey L., Treas. & Sec.--Republic Group Incorporated, Hutchinson, KS; *U.S. Public*, pg. 1378
Rigazio, Steven W., Chief Fin. Officer, V.P.-Fin. & Treas.--Nevada Power Company, Las Vegas, NV; *U.S. Public*, pg. 1169
Riggan, David, V.P.-Fin. & Asst. Treas.--Cobra Golf Incorporated, Carlsbad, CA; *U.S. Public*, pg. 675
Rignanesi, Catherina, Asst. Treas.--Bruncor, Inc., Saint John, Canada; *Int'l*, pg. 230
Rigoni, Douglas R., Treas.--Bacco Construction Co., Iron Mountain, MI; *U.S. Private*, pg. 109
Riha, Frances, Sec. & Treas.--Office Equipment Company Of Chicago, Elmhurst, IL; *U.S. Private*, pg. 812
Riley, Patrick J., V.P. & Treas.--Allied Products Corporation, Chicago, IL; *U.S. Public*, pg. 48
Rilla, J.M., V.P.-Fin.--Koehler Manufacturing Company, Marlborough, MA; *U.S. Private*, pg. 706
Rillings, Robert H., Treas.--The Hertz Corporation, Park Ridge, NJ; *U.S. Public*, pg. 664
Ringgenberg, Thomas C., V.P. & Treas.--Maytag Corporation, Newton, IA; *U.S. Public*, pg. 1064
Ringley, Edward M., Treas. & Sec.--Consolidated Systems, Inc., Columbia, SC; *U.S. Private*, pg. 266
Riopel, Robert J., Chief Fin. Officer, V.P.-Fin. & Treas.--Phoenix Technologies Ltd., San Jose, CA; *U.S. Public*, pg. 1292
Risa, Magne, Treas.--AGA Progas A/S, Oslo, Norway; *Int'l*, pg. 13
Risser, Jane A., V.P. & Treas.--Apple Computer, Inc., Cupertino, CA; *U.S. Public*, pg. 121
Ritch, Jim, Deputy Superintendent-Fin. & Admin.--Seattle City Light, Seattle, WA; *U.S. Private*, pg. 979
Ritchie, H.D., Treas.--Ritchie Corporation, Wichita, KS; *U.S. Private*, pg. 933
Rittmueller, James W., V.P. & Treas.--Unicover Corporation, Cheyenne, WY; *U.S. Private*, pg. 1117
Rizol, James, Mgr.-Treas--Airgas, Inc., Radnor, PA; *U.S. Public*, pg. 33
Rizzi, Kenneth A., V.P. & Treas.--The Turner & Seymour Mfg. Company, Torrington, CT; *U.S. Private*, pg. 1109
Roach, Ed, Chief Fin. Officer, Exec. V.P. & Treas.--Dominion Resources, Inc., Richmond, VA; *U.S. Public*, pg. 516
Robards, Thomas F., Chief Fin. Officer & Treas.--Republic New York Corporation, New York, NY; *U.S. Public*, pg. 1380
Robbins, Elliott C., Chief Fin. Officer, Sr. V.P. & Treas.--MYR Group Inc., Rolling Meadows, IL; *U.S. Public*, pg. 1029
Robbins, Stanley, Treas.--Robbins Auto Parts, Inc., Dover, NH; *U.S. Private*, pg. 934
Robert Epstein, V.P. & Treas.--A J M Packaging Corporation, Bloomfield Hills, MI; *U.S. Private*, pg. 2
Robert, Elizabeth, Chief Fin. Officer & Treas.--The Vermont Teddy Bear Company, Inc., Shelburne, VT; *U.S. Public*, pg. 1716
Roberts, Bernard F., Asst. Treas.--Cinergy Corp., Cincinnati, OH; *U.S. Public*, pg. 368
Roberts, C.L., Jr., Asst. Treas.--Unilever United States Inc., New York, NY; *Int'l*, pg. 1435
Roberts, David, Dir.-Treas., Tax & Corp. Fin.--J. Sainsbury plc, London, United Kingdom; *Int'l*, pg. 1169
Roberts, E.K., Pres. & Treas.--Fahnestock Viner Holdings Inc., Toronto, Canada; *Int'l*, pg. 476
Roberts, Gary L., Chief Fin. Officer, V.P. & Treas.--A.P. Green Industries, Inc., Mexico, MO; *U.S. Public*, pg. 761
Roberts, Jeff, V.P. & Treas.--Farmland Industries, Inc., Kansas City, MO; *U.S. Private*, pg. 395
Roberts, Michael D., First V.P., Controller & Asst. Treas.--W.P. Carey & Co., Inc., New York, NY; *U.S. Private*, pg. 209
Roberts, R.B., Treas.--Crystal Cream & Butter Company, Sacramento, CA; *U.S. Private*, pg. 294
Roberts, Raymond J., Treas.--Coilcraft, Inc., Cary, IL; *U.S. Private*, pg. 250
Roberts, Richard B., Exec. V.P. & Treas.--Wachovia Corporation, Winston Salem, NC; *U.S. Public*, pg. 1730
Roberts, Robbie, Treas.--All Star Gas Corporation, Lebanon, MO; *U.S. Private*, pg. 35
Roberts, Robin, Treas.--Continental Electronics Corporation, Dallas, TX; *U.S. Public*, pg. 1563
Roberts, Seth, V.P. & Asst. Treas.--F.L. Roberts & Co. Inc., Springfield, MA; *U.S. Private*, pg. 935
Roberts, Stephen M., Pres., Chief Exec. Officer & Treas.--F.L. Roberts & Co. Inc., Springfield, MA; *U.S. Private*, pg. 935
Roberts, Thomas B., Pres & Treas.--C.F. Haglin & Sons, Edina, MN; *U.S. Private*, pg. 493
Roberts, Vicki A., Treas.--Centex Corporation, Dallas, TX; *U.S. Public*, pg. 322
Roberts, William E., Chief Fin. Officer, V.P., Controller & Treas.--Lone Star Industries, Inc., Stamford, CT; *U.S. Public*, pg. 1012
Robertson, Alastair J., Chief Fin. Officer, V.P. & Treas.--Nowsco Well Service Ltd., Calgary, Canada; *Int'l*, pg. 989
Robertson, I. Howard, Jr., Chief Fin. Officer & Treas.--Robertson's Auto Salvage, Wareham, MA; *U.S. Private*, pg. 936
Robertson, James S., V.P. & Asst. Treas.--John Deere Capital Corporation, Reno, NV; *U.S. Public*, pg. 492
Robertson, James S., V.P. & Treas.--John Deere Credit Company, Moline, IL; *U.S. Public*, pg. 492
Robertson, Thomas E., Exec. V.P. & Treas.--C-Line Products, Inc., Des Plaines, IL; *U.S. Private*, pg. 192
Robey, Kurt, Treas.--Regional Transportation Authority (RTA), Chicago, IL; *U.S. Private*, pg. 918
Robins, R. Steven, Chief Fin. Officer, Treas. & Sec--Builder Marts of America, Inc., Greenville, SC; *U.S. Private*, pg. 179
Robinson, Bruce W., Asst. Treas.--Aluminum Company of America, Pittsburgh, PA; *U.S. Public*, pg. 60
Robinson, E.A., V.P. & Treas.--Exxon Corporation, Irving, TX; *U.S. Public*, pg. 601
Robinson, Elaine, V.P. & Treas.--AEGON USA, Inc., Louisville, KY; *Int'l*, pg. 26
Robinson, James A., Treas.--USAA Life Insurance Co., San Antonio, TX; *U.S. Private*, pg. 1115
Robinson, Jerry D., Chief Fin. Officer, V.P. & Treas.--SFA, Inc., Hyattsville, MD; *U.S. Private*, pg. 956
Robinson, Jerry W., Treas.--BellSouth Telecommunications, Inc., Atlanta, GA; *U.S. Public*, pg. 209
Robinson, John R., Sr. V.P., Controller & Treas.--Purity Dairies Inc., Nashville, TN; *U.S. Private*, pg. 895
Robinson, Joseph A., Chief Fin. Officer, Sr. V.P., Treas. & Sec.--Excel Industries, Inc., Elkhart, IN; *U.S. Public*, pg. 598
Robinson, Maeve, Asst. Treas.--Omnicom Group Inc., New York, NY; *U.S. Public*, pg. 1223
Robinson, Michael J., V.P. & Treas.--Illinois Tool Works Inc., Glenview, IL; *U.S. Public*, pg. 865
Robinson, Neal E., Sr. V.P.-Fin. & Acctg.--Banknorth Group Inc., Burlington, VT; *U.S. Public*, pg. 186
Robinson, Robert, Gen. Mgr.-Treas. & Pension Fund Investments--Sasol Limited, Johannesburg, South Africa; *Int'l*, pg. 1196

Robinson, Steven, Treas. & Sec.--Joy Service, Southfield, MI; *U.S. Private*, pg. 602
Robinson, Warren L., Chief Fin. Officer, V.P. & Treas.--MDU Resources Group, Inc., Bismarck, ND; *U.S. Public*, pg. 1025
Robinson, Wilburn, Chief Fin. Officer & Exec. V.P.--Omniflight, Inc., Dallas, TX; *U.S. Private*, pg. 816
Robinson, Wilburn, Chief Fin. Officer & Exec. V.P.--Omniflight Helicopters, Inc., Dallas, TX; *U.S. Private*, pg. 817
Robison, James A., Controller & Treas.--Tenera, Inc., San Francisco, CA; *U.S. Public*, pg. 1576
Robles, Estela, Treas. & Sec.--La Reina, Inc., Los Angeles, CA; *U.S. Private*, pg. 640
Robles, Josue, Jr., Chief Fin. Officer, Sr. V.P. & Treas.--USAA (United Services Automobile Association), San Antonio, TX; *U.S. Private*, pg. 1114
Roboishan, Bob, Treas.--Zapata Corporation, Houston, TX; *U.S. Public*, pg. 1789
Robson, Donald, Chief Fin. Officer, Treas. & Sec.--Coldwater Creek, Sandpoint, ID; *U.S. Public*, pg. 396
Robson, Jack, Treas.--John Carlo Inc., Clinton Township, MI; *U.S. Private*, pg. 211
Roche, Terence P., Exec. V.P., Asst. Treas. & Asst. Sec.--Binks Sames Corporation, Franklin Park, IL; *U.S. Public*, pg. 229
Rockwell, Donald P., Treas.--Coachmen Industries, Inc., Elkhart, IN; *U.S. Public*, pg. 387
Rodbell, Paul N., V.P. & Sec.--Apex Supply Co., Inc., Atlanta, GA; *U.S. Private*, pg. 77
Rodd, Allan K., V.P. & Treas.--The Wooster Brush Company, Wooster, OH; *U.S. Private*, pg. 1188
Rodey, Stephen W., Treas.--Patrick Cudahy Inc., Cudahy, WI; *U.S. Public*, pg. 1479
Rodler, John, Chief Fin. Officer, Sr. V.P., Treas. & Sec.--Folger Nolan Fleming Douglas, Washington, DC; *U.S. Private*, pg. 416
Rodney, C.I., Asst. Treas.--Sverdrup Corporation, Maryland Heights, MO; *U.S. Private*, pg. 1057
Rodrigues, Joseph, Chief Fin. Officer, Exec. V.P. & Treas.--Seaboard Corporation, Shawnee Mission, KS; *U.S. Public*, pg. 1448
Rodriguez Rico, Martha, Treas.--Grupo Cementos de Chihuahua S.A. de C.V., Chihuahua, Mexico; *Int'l*, pg. 573
Rodriguez, Fernando, Treas.--La Banda de Agustin Medina S.A., Madrid, Spain; *Int'l*, pg. 783
Rodriguez, Juana D., Treas.--Mason Distributors, Inc., Hialeah, FL; *U.S. Private*, pg. 712
Rodriguez, Marianne, V.P., Treas. & Sec.--Deepwater Chemicals, Inc., Woodward, OK; *Int'l*, pg. 1395
Rodzevik, Paul R., Treas.--The Jordan Company, New York, NY; *U.S. Private*, pg. 597
Roedl, Suzanne, V.P.-Fin.--Condor D.C. Power Supplies Inc., Oxnard, CA; *U.S. Public*, pg. 1419
Roehrig, Michael C., Treas.--Cloverdale Equipment Co., Oak Park, MI; *U.S. Private*, pg. 247
Roenitz, William, Treas.--Bio-Logic Systems Corporation Ltd., Haifa, Israel; *U.S. Public*, pg. 230
Roenitz, William K., Controller & Treas.--Bio-Logic Systems Corp., Mundelein, IL; *U.S. Public*, pg. 230
Roesslein, Charles, V.P., Chief Fin. Officer & Treas.--Southwestern Bell Telephone Co., Saint Louis, MO; *U.S. Public*, pg. 1416
Rogalin, Peter, Chief Fin. Officer, V.P. & Treas.--Roberts Pharmaceutical Corporation, Eatontown, NJ; *U.S. Public*, *pg. 1393*
Rogalin, Peter, Chief Fin. Officer, V.P. & Treas.--VRG International, Inc., Eatontown, NJ; *U.S. Public*, pg. 1393
Rogalin, Peter, Chief Fin. Officer, V.P. & Treas.--Roberts Laboratories, Inc., Eatontown, NJ; *U.S. Public*, pg. 1393
Rogalin, Peter, Chief Fin. Officer, V.P. & Treas.--Monmouth Pharmaceutical, Ltd., Guildford, United Kingdom; *U.S. Public*, pg. 1394
Rogalin, Peter, Chief Fin. Officer, V.P. & Treas.--Roberts Pharmaceutical of Canada, Oakville, Canada; *U.S. Public*, pg. 1394
Rogers, Doyle, Treas.--Hardwick Clothes Inc., Cleveland, TN; *U.S. Private*, pg. 502
Rogers, Ellen Sheriff, Sec. & Asst. Treas.--Potomac Electric Power Company, Washington, DC; *U.S. Public*, pg. 1318
Rogers, Floyd, V.P.-Fin. & Treas.--Steck-Vaughn Company, Austin, TX; *U.S. Public*, pg. 784
Rogers, Floyd, V.P.-Fin. & Treas.--Steck-Vaughn Distribution Company, Austin, TX; *U.S. Public*, pg. 784
Rogers, G.R., Chief Fin. Officer, Exec. V.P. & Treas.--Alexander & Baldwin, Inc., Honolulu, HI; *U.S. Public*, pg. 39
Rogers, J.Y., Treas.--Mac Papers, Inc., Jacksonville, FL; *U.S. Private*, pg. 689
Rogers, James, Sr. V.P. & Treas.--MidCoast Mortgage Corporation, Lake Worth, FL; *U.S. Private*, pg. 744
Rogers, James P., Sr. V.P.-Fin. & Treas.--International Specialty Products, Inc., Wayne, NJ; *U.S. Public*, pg. 858
Rogers, John, Treas. & Controller--Mallery Lumber Corp., Emporium, PA; *U.S. Private*, pg. 698
Rogers, John, Chief Info. Officer & Asst. Treas.--TCBY Enterprises Inc., Little Rock, AR; *U.S. Public*, pg. 1553
Rogers, John W., V.P. & Treas.--Rogers Markets Inc., Fort Wayne, IN; *U.S. Private*, pg. 940
Rogers, Joseph M., Treas.--Wilkins-Rogers Incorporated, Ellicott City, MD; *U.S. Private*, pg. 1176
Rogers, Kathy H., Sec.--Tultex Corporation, Martinsville, VA; *U.S. Public*, pg. 1644
Rogers, Liz, Asst. Treas.--Mentor Graphics Corporation, Wilsonville, OR; *U.S. Public*, pg. 1086
Rogers, Margie E., Chief Fin. Officer, V.P., Treas. & Sec.--Team, Inc., Alvin, TX; *U.S. Public*, pg. 1562
Rogers, Margie E., Treas. & Sec.--Team Industrial Services, Inc., Alvin, TX; *U.S. Public*, pg. 1562
Rogers, Margie E., Treas. & Sec.--Pipe Repairs, Inc., Alvin, TX; *U.S. Public*, pg. 1562
Rogers, Margie E., Treas. & Sec.--TECO Manufacturing, Inc., Alvin, TX; *U.S. Public*, pg. 1562
Rogers, Warren, Exec. V.P. & Treas.--Mississippi Valley Gas Co., Jackson, MS; *U.S. Private*, pg. 753
Rogusa, Joseph F., Treas.--Coho Energy, Inc., Dallas, TX; *U.S. Public*, pg. 396
Rohde, Stephen L., Chief Fin. Officer & V.P.-Fin. & Admin.--MSI Insurance Companies, Arden Hills, MN; *U.S. Private*, *pg. 688*
Rohloff, William M., Chief Fin. Officer, Treas. & Sec.--Stebbins Engineering & Mfg. Co., Watertown, NY; *U.S. Private*, pg. 1037
Rohr, Robert E., Chief Fin. Officer--Chempower, Inc., Akron, OH; *Int'l*, pg. 74
Rohr, Robert E., Treas.--Global Power Company, Waverly, TN; *Int'l*, pg. 74
Rohrer, Joanne M., Treas. & Sec.--Rohrer Corporation, Wadsworth, OH; *U.S. Private*, pg. 940
Rohrkemper, Paul H., Treas.--Cigna Corp., Philadelphia, PA; *U.S. Public*, pg. 356
Rohtbart, Markus, Chm. Bd. & Treas.--Cattleman's, Inc., Detroit, MI; *U.S. Public*, pg. 318
Rold, Stephen K., V.P., Controller, Treas. & Sec.--Roofing Wholesale Co., Inc., Phoenix, AZ; *U.S. Private*, pg. 943
Rollins, Robert, Treas. & Legal Officer--Nashville Wire Product Co., Nashville, TN; *U.S. Private*, pg. 775
Roman, Vicki G., V.P. & Treas.--Coca-Cola Enterprises Inc., Atlanta, GA; *U.S. Public*, pg. 393
Romanczuk, Wayne, Chief Fin. Officer & Treas.--Perfecseal Company, Philadelphia, PA; *U.S. Public*, pg. 210
Romaniw, Lidia I., Treas.--Greyvest Capitol Inc., Toronto, Canada; *Int'l*, pg. 559
Romano, D.V., Treas.--Wakefern Food Corporation, Elizabeth, NJ; *U.S. Private*, pg. 1146
Romano, O., Treasurer--Iveco-Ford Truck Ltd., Watford, United Kingdom; *Int'l*, pg. 484
Romenesko, Timothy J., Chief Fin. Officer, V.P. & Treas.--AAR Corp., Wood Dale, IL; *U.S. Public*, pg. 1
Romig, Kenneth J., Treas.--First Western Trust Services Co., New Castle, PA; *U.S. Public*, pg. 642
Romig, Michael V., Chief Fin. Officer & V.P.--Marine Construction & Design Co., Seattle, WA; *U.S. Private*, pg. 703
Romig, William J., V.P. & Treas.--Norfolk Southern Corporation, Norfolk, VA; *U.S. Public*, pg. 1190
Rompala, Edward J., V.P. & Treas.--Genesee Corporation, Rochester, NY; *U.S. Public*, pg. 728
Rompala, Edward J., V.P. & Treas.--The Genesee Brewing Company, Inc., Rochester, NY; *U.S. Public*, pg. 728
Rone, Charles C., Jr., Chief Fin. Officer, V.P.-Fin. & Treas.--Loxcreen Company, West Columbia, SC; *U.S. Private*, pg. 679
Rones, Gail, Treas. & Sec.--Americo Manufacturing Co., Inc., Acworth, GA; *U.S. Private*, pg. 64
Roos, Arthur W., V.P. & Treas.--Niagara Mohawk Power Corporation, Syracuse, NY; *U.S. Public*, pg. 1181
Roos, W., Treas. & Mgr.-Cash--Oce-van der Grinten N.V., Venlo, Netherlands; *Int'l*, pg. 993
Rootberg, Philip, V.P. & Treas.--Sussex Group, Ltd., Chicago, IL; *U.S. Public*, pg. 918
Rosa, Tom, V.P.-Fin. & Treas.--Indiana Glass Company, Cincinnati, OH; *U.S. Public*, pg. 976
Rosania, John, Treas. & Sec.--Structural Foam Plastics, Inc., Somerville, NJ; *U.S. Private*, pg. 1047
Rose, Estelle, Chief Fin. Officer--Kobra International Ltd, New York, NY; *U.S. Private*, pg. 628
Rose, Karen M., V.P. & Treas.--The Clorox Company, Oakland, CA; *U.S. Public*, pg. 386
Rose, Peter, Asst. Treas.--Foster Wheeler Corporation, Clinton, NJ; *U.S. Public*, pg. 676
Rose, Sharen, Treas.--Gurley Motor Company, Gallup, NM; *U.S. Private*, pg. 488
Rose, Susan T., Treas.--Roman Electric Company, Inc., Milwaukee, WI; *U.S. Private*, pg. 942
Rose, Thomas F., Treas. & Sec.--Todd Juice Products, Kalamazoo, MI; *U.S. Private*, pg. 1090
Rose, Thomas G., Treas.--Tri-Continental Corporation, New York, NY; *U.S. Private*, pg. 982
Rosebery, Richard J., Vice Chm., Chief Fin. & Admin. Officer & Treas.--Elcor Corporation, Dallas, TX; *U.S. Public*, pg. 567
Rosemore, Andrew S., Chief Oper. Officer, Exec. V.P., Treas. & Asst. Sec.--PMC Capital Inc., Dallas, TX; *U.S. Public*, pg. 1242
Rosen, Alan J., Treas.--Alaskan Copper Companies, Seattle, WA; *U.S. Private*, pg. 31
Rosen, Andrew M., V.P. & Treas.--Brown Group, Inc., Saint Louis, MO; *U.S. Public*, pg. 262
Rosen, Barry A., Chief Fin. Officer, V.P. & Treas.--Schnitzer Steel Industries, Inc., Portland, OR; *U.S. Public*, pg. 1439
Rosen, Harold R., Treas.--Fel-Pro Incorporated, Skokie, IL; *U.S. Private*, pg. 399
Rosen, Jeffery, Chief Oper. Officer & Treas.--Rose Art Industries, Livingston, NJ; *U.S. Private*, pg. 945
Rosen, Sam, Treas. & Sec.--Aztec Manufacturing Co., Crowley, TX; *U.S. Public*, pg. 159
Rosenbaum, Greg, Treas.--Richey Electronics, Inc., Garden Grove, CA; *U.S. Public*, pg. 1388
Rosenberg, Kenneth, Pres. & Treas.--Napco Security Systems, Inc., Amityville, NY; *U.S. Public*, pg. 1151
Rosenberg, Paul B., Treas.--Tech/Ops Sevcon, Inc., Boston, MA; *U.S. Public*, pg. 1563
Rosenberg, Philip G., 1st Sr. V.P., Treas., Controller & Asst. Sec.--Morse Shoe, Inc., Canton, MA; *U.S. Public*, pg. 168
Rosenberger, Marcus L., Treas. & Sec.--Rosenbergers Dairies, Inc., Hatfield, PA; *U.S. Private*, pg. 945
Rosenfeld, J.A., V.P. & Treas.--Utility Data Corporation, Indianapolis, IN; *U.S. Public*, pg. 1185
Rosenfeld, Richard S., Chief Fin. Officer, V.P. & Treas.--Barringer Technologies Inc., New Providence, NJ; *U.S. Public*, pg. 191
Rosenfeld, Valerie, V.P. & Treas.--Merix Corporation, Forest Grove, OR; *U.S. Public*, pg. 1096
Rosengarten, Teresa A., V.P. & Treas.--First Tennessee National Corporation, Memphis, TN; *U.S. Public*, pg. 638
Rosenstein, Stuart B., Chief Fin. Officer, Sr. V.P. & Treas.--Pricellular Corporation, White Plains, NY; *U.S. Public*, pg. 1324
Rosenthal, Benjamin, Treas. & Sec.--Madison Electric Co., Warren, MI; *U.S. Private*, pg. 694
Rosenthal, David, Chief Fin. Officer, V.P.-Fin. & Treas.--LeaRonal, Inc., Freeport, NY; *U.S. Public*, pg. 982
Rosenzweig, Richard S., Pres. & Asst. Treas.--Playboy Shows, Inc., Beverly Hills, CA; *U.S. Public*, pg. 1310
Rosner, Irwin, V.P. & Treas.--Boscov's Department Store, Inc., Reading, PA; *U.S. Private*, pg. 160
Ross, Hamish, Treas.--A.S.I. (Computer Training) Netherlands B.V., Amsterdam, Netherlands; *U.S. Public*, pg. 784
Ross, Judy, Sec. & Treas.--Layman Candy Company, Inc., Salem, VA; *U.S. Private*, pg. 655
Ross, Jules, V.P.-Fin., Treas. & Sec.--Thackeray Corporation, New York, NY; *U.S. Public*, pg. 1590
Ross, Lisa, Asst. Treas.--Morrison Knudsen Corporation, Boise, ID; *U.S. Public*, pg. 1133
Ross, Richard A., V.P. & Treas.--Metall Mining Corporation, Toronto, Canada; *Int'l*, pg. 862
Ross, Robert W., Chief Fin. Officer, V.P., Treas. & Sec.--Selas Corporation of America, Dresher, PA; *U.S. Public*, pg. 1454
Ross, Ronald R., Treas. & Sec.--Ag Processing Inc., A Cooperative, Omaha, NE; *U.S. Private*, pg. 26
Ross, Stephen, Treas.--Mustang Tractor & Equip. Co., Houston, TX; *U.S. Private*, pg. 768
Rossa, Glynn M., V.P. & Treas.--RAYOVAC Corporation, Madison, WI; *U.S. Private*, pg. 912
Rosset, Claude, Treas.--Holderbank Financiere Glaris Ltd., Glaris, Switzerland; *Int'l*, pg. 628
Rossler, John, Exec. V.P.-Fin. & Treas.--Shonac Corporation, Columbus, OH; *U.S. Private*, pg. 996
Roth, George R., Asst. Treas.--Xerox Corporation, Stamford, CT; *U.S. Public*, pg. 1783
Roth, George R., Chief Fin. Officer, V.P. & Treas.--Xerox Credit Corporation, Stamford, CT; *U.S. Public*, pg. 1785
Roth, Ivan, Treas.--Tarragon Realty Investors, Dallas, TX; *U.S. Public*, pg. 1561
Roth, Laura L., Sec. & Asst. Treas.--BT Financial Corporation, Johnstown, PA; *U.S. Public*, pg. 163
Roth, Laura L., Sec. & Asst. Treas.--Bedford Associates, Inc., Johnstown, PA; *U.S. Public*, pg. 164
Roth, Laura L., Sec. & Asst. Treas.--Laurel Bank, Johnstown, PA; *U.S. Public*, pg. 164
Roth, Laura L., Sec. & Asst. Treas.--Laurel Trust Company, Johnstown, PA; *U.S. Public*, pg. 164
Roth, Laura L., Sec. & Asst. Treas.--Laurel Community Development Corporation, Johnstown, PA; *U.S. Public*, pg. 164
Rothenberger, Eva, Treas. & Sec.--Vari Tronics Company, Inc., Duarte, CA; *U.S. Private*, pg. 1134
Rother, Doug C., Chief Oper. Officer & Exec. V.P.--Columbine JDS Systems, Inc., Denver, CO; *U.S. Public*, pg. 228
Rothleitner, Mark M., V.P. & Treas.--The Black & Decker Corporation, Towson, MD; *U.S. Public*, pg. 233
Rothschild, Aaron, V.P. & Treas.--McKinney & McKinney Advertising, Redondo Beach, CA; *U.S. Private*, pg. 723
Rott, Herbert, Jr., V.P., Treas. & Sec.--Rott-Keller Supply Co., Fargo, ND; *U.S. Private*, pg. 947
Rougier-Chapman, Alwyn, Chief Fin. Officer--Steelcase Inc., Grand Rapids, MI; *U.S. Private*, pg. 1038
Roure, Bill, Asst. Treas.--DHL Worldwide Express, Redwood City, CA; *U.S. Private*, pg. 301
Rouse, James R., Chief Fin. Officer & Treas.--Reeds Jewelers, Inc., Wilmington, NC; *U.S. Public*, pg. 1370
Rouse, M. Brent, Treas.--Hamilton Mutual Insurance Company Of Cincinnati, Cincinnati, OH; *U.S. Private*, pg. 497
Roush, Steve, V.P.-Fin. & Admin. & Treas.--DeKalb Swine Breeders, Inc., De Kalb, IL; *U.S. Public*, pg. 493
Roush, Viola, Treas.--J.H. Routh Packing Co., Sandusky, OH; *U.S. Private*, pg. 948
Rousseau, Michael, V.P. & Treas.--The UCS Group, Toronto, Canada; *Int'l*, pg. 792
Rousseau, Scott, V.P.-Admin., Controller, Treas. & Sec.--Palmer Electric Co., Winter Park, FL; *U.S. Private*, pg. 834
Rovira, Lourdes M., Sr. V.P.-Admin. & Treas.--Caribbean American Life Assurance Company, Hato Rey, PR; *U.S. Public*, pg. 67
Rowe, Gerald D., Asst. Treas.--General Electric Canada Inc., Mississauga, Canada; *U.S. Public*, pg. 713
Rowe, Sharon, Treas. & Sec.--Lou LaRiche Chevrolet Inc., Plymouth, MI; *U.S. Private*, pg. 651
Rowlen, Thomas M., Controller, Treas. & Sec.--Yoder Oil Company Inc., Elkhart, IN; *U.S. Private*, pg. 1196
Roy, Randolph, Asst. Treas.--The Dun & Bradstreet Corporation, Murray Hill, NJ; *U.S. Public*, pg. 535
Royle, Alan E., Corp. Treas.--S.C. Johnson & Son, Inc., Racine, WI; *U.S. Private*, pg. 592
Royzin, Philip W., Chief Fin. Officer, Treas. & Dir.-Admin.--Brookstone Company, Inc., Nashua, NH; *U.S. Public*, pg. 259
Rozema, Sue, V.P. & Treas.--MidAmerican Energy Holdings, Des Moines, IA; *U.S. Public*, pg. 1109
Roznowski, Jack, Treas. & Sec.--Trerice Tosto Colliers International, Bingham Farms, MI; *U.S. Private*, pg. 1099
Rubel, Darrell D., Chief Fin. Officer, Exec. V.P., Treas. & Asst. Sec.--Marten Transport, Ltd., Mondovi, WI; *U.S. Public*, pg. 1052
Rubin, Burton, Treas.--Philadelphia Coca-Cola Bottling Co., Philadelphia, PA; *U.S. Private*, pg. 861
Rubin, Michael, Pres. & Chief Fin. Officer--Hudson General Corporation, Great Neck, NY; *U.S. Public*, pg. 845
Rubin, Robert, Vice Chm., V.P.-Sls., Treas. & Sec.--M. Rubin & Sons Inc., Long Island City, NY; *U.S. Private*, pg. 949
Ruckelshaus, Gary, V.P., Treas. & Sec.--Bouras Industries, Summit, NJ; *U.S. Private*, pg. 161

Ruckriegel, Lovella, V.P., Treas. & Sec.--BR Associates, Inc., Jasper, IN; *U.S. Private*, pg. 107
Ruddock, Malcolm I., Treas.--Sun Company, Inc., Philadelphia, PA; *U.S. Public*, pg. 1530
Rudnick, Laurence, Treas.--Safety-Kleen Corp., Elgin, IL; *U.S. Public*, pg. 1425
Rudolph, Philip, Treas.--Rudolph Foods Company, Lima, OH; *U.S. Private*, pg. 950
Rudzik, John A., Chief Fin. Officer, Sr. V.P.-Fin. & Treas.--Centimark Corporation, Canonsburg, PA; *U.S. Private*, pg. 222
Rueb, Roy T., V.P., Treas. & Sec.--Pentair, Inc., Saint Paul, MN; *U.S. Public*, pg. 1273
Ruffin, Pat, V.P., Treas. & Sec.--Ruffin Building Systems, Inc., Oak Grove, LA; *U.S. Private*, pg. 950
Ruger, William B., Chm. Bd., Chief Exec. Officer & Treas.--Sturm, Ruger & Co., Inc., Southport, CT; *U.S. Public*, pg. 1526
Ruggieri, John T., Chief Fin. Officer, V.P.-Fin., Treas & Dir.-Investor Rels.--A.T. Cross Co., Lincoln, RI; *U.S. Public*, pg. 460
Ruggins, L. F., Asst. Treas.-Fin.--BCE Inc., Montreal, Canada; *Int'l*, pg. 114
Ruhkala, Peter D., Chief Fin. Officer, Treas. & Sec.--Nor-Cal Beverage Co., Inc., West Sacramento, CA; *U.S. Private*, pg. 801
Ruhle, Robert E., Chief Fin. Officer, Exec. V.P., Treas. & Sec.--Ruhle Companies, Inc., Valhalla, NY; *U.S. Private*, pg. 950
Ruiz, Arturo D'Acosta, Treas.--Desc, S.A. de C.V., Mexico, Mexico; *Int'l*, pg. 395
Ruiz, Fernando, Asst. Treas.--The Dow Chemical Company, Midland, MI; *U.S. Public*, pg. 522
Runberg, John M., Treas.--Nautilus Insurance Company, Scottsdale, AZ; *U.S. Public*, pg. 216
Runge, Scott, Treas.--Calavo Growers of California, Santa Ana, CA; *U.S. Private*, pg. 199
Runice, Kathleen, Treas.--Topco Associates, Inc., Skokie, IL; *U.S. Private*, pg. 1091
Runk, Fred J., Sr. V.P. & Treas.--American Financial Group, Cincinnati, OH; *U.S. Public*, pg. 74
Runk, Fred J., Chief Fin. Officer, V.P. & Treas.--Spelling Entertainment Group, Inc., Los Angeles, CA; *U.S. Private*, pg. 776
Rupe, John F., V.P. & Treas.--Phillips Petroleum International Investment Company, Reno, NV; *U.S. Public*, pg. 1291
Rupke, Jerry I., Controller & Treas.--Public Utility District No. 2 of Grant County, Ephrata, WA; *U.S. Private*, pg. 893
Rusch, Jack C., Exec. V.P. & Treas.--First Federal Capital Corp., La Crosse, WI; *U.S. Public*, pg. 632
Rusch, Robert A., Asst. Treas.--Wisconsin Power & Light Company, Madison, WI; *U.S. Public*, pg. 1728
Rusch, Robert A., Asst. Treas.--South Beloit Water, Gas & Electric Co., South Beloit, IL; *U.S. Public*, pg. 1728
Russ, Ronald G., Treas.--Wisconsin Central Transportation Corporation, Rosemont, IL; *U.S. Public*, pg. 1772
Russell, Barron Jeff, Treas. & Sec.--Food & Gas, Inc., Norcross, GA; *U.S. Private*, pg. 417
Russell, Douglas W., Chief Fin. Officer, Treas. & Asst. Sec.--Rotonics Manufacturing Inc., Gardena, CA; *U.S. Public*, pg. 1406
Russell, George Earl, Treas. & Sec.--Russell Petroleum Corporation, Montgomery, AL; *U.S. Private*, pg. 953
Russell, Kenneth John Barclay, Treas.--First National Bank Holdings Limited, Johannesburg, South Africa; *Int'l*, pg. 487
Russian, David H., Chief Fin. Officer, V.P.-Fin., Sec. & Treas.--Brooktree Rockwell Semiconductor Systems Div., San Diego, CA; *U.S. Public*, pg. 1398
Russo, Art, Treas. & Sec.--Seco Warwick Corporation, Meadville, PA; *U.S. Private*, pg. 980
Russo, Edward J., Asst. V.P.-Treasury--Grolier Inc., Danbury, CT; *Int'l*, pg. 794
Ruszin, Thomas E., Jr., Treas. & Asst. Sec.--Baltimore Gas and Electric Company, Baltimore, MD; *U.S. Public*, pg. 172
Rutkowski, Cynthia K., Treas.--Bankmanagers Corp., Milwaukee, WI; *U.S. Private*, pg. 114
Rutledge, James M., V.P. & Treas.--Witco Corporation, Greenwich, CT; *U.S. Public*, pg. 1773
Ruttenberg, Harold J., Chm. Bd., Principal Acctg. Officer, Chief Exec. Officer & Treas.--American Locker Group, Inc., Jamestown, NY; *U.S. Public*, pg. 85
Ryan, Arthur S., V.P. & Treas.--Grossman's, Inc., Stoughton, MA; *U.S. Private*, pg. 585
Ryan, Bob, Sr. V.P. & Treas.--CM Partners, Inc., Rolling Meadows, IL; *U.S. Private*, pg. 195
Ryan, Dwight P., Chief Fin. Officer, V.P., Treas. & Sec.--IntegraMed America, Purchase, NY; *U.S. Public*, pg. 800
Ryan, Ed, Treas.--Gateway Press, Inc., Louisville, KY; *U.S. Private*, pg. 441
Ryan, Frank J., Chief Fin. Officer & Sec.--Detection Systems, Inc., Fairport, NY; *U.S. Public*, pg. 501
Ryan, Jeffrey M., Asst. Treas.--Optical Coating Laboratory, Inc., Santa Rosa, CA; *U.S. Public*, pg. 1227
Ryan, Jim, Controller & Treas.--Harker's Distribution, Inc., Le Mars, IA; *U.S. Private*, pg. 502
Ryan, John J., V.P. & Treas.--Charan Industries, Inc., Garden City, NY; *U.S. Private*, pg. 229
Ryan, Patrick, Grp. Treas.--Allied Irish Banks, p.l.c., Dublin, Ireland; *Int'l*, pg. 64
Ryan, Robert, Chief Fin. Officer & Treas.--Rogers, Lunt & Bowlen Co., Greenfield, MA; *U.S. Private*, pg. 939
Ryan, Ron, Chief Fin. Officer, Treas. & Sec.--Punch Press Products, Inc., Los Angeles, CA; *U.S. Private*, pg. 895
Ryan, Russell J., V.P.-Sec. & Treas.--Ryan Construction Company Of Minnesota, Hibbing, MN; *U.S. Private*, pg. 953
Rybinski, John, Treas.--MacDonald Dettwiler & Associates Ltd., Richmond, Canada; *U.S. Public*, pg. 1229
Ryckis, Jonas A., Treas.--Waverly, Inc., Baltimore, MD; *U.S. Public*, pg. 1748
Rycroft, Donald C., Sr. V.P. & Treas.--Continental Assurance Company, Chicago, IL; *U.S. Private*, pg. 267
Rynn, John A., V.P. & Treas.--Berol Corporation, Brentwood, TN; *U.S. Public*, pg. 1178
Rynone, William J., Treas. & Sec.--Rynone Manufacturing Corporation, Sayre, PA; *U.S. Private*, pg. 953
Rytych, Edward, Asst. Treas.--AAR Corp., Wood Dale, IL; *U.S. Public*, pg. 1
Saali, Steven, Asst. Treas.--Republic New York Corporation, New York, NY; *U.S. Public*, pg. 1380
Saari, Pamela A., Asst. Treas.--Florida Progress Corporation, Saint Petersburg, FL; *U.S. Public*, pg. 655
Sabala, James A., Sec. & Treas.--Pinnacle Exploration, Inc., Coeur D'Alene, ID; *U.S. Public*, pg. 394
Sabatino, Anthony J., V.P. & Treas.--Inco Limited, Toronto, Canada; *Int'l*, pg. 672
Sachs, Christopher, Treas.--M.A. Hanna Company, Cleveland, OH; *U.S. Public*, pg. 780
Sachs, Harold, Treas.--Foodmaker, Inc., San Diego, CA; *U.S. Public*, pg. 661
Sackett, Sydney J., Treas.--LeGrand Johnson Construction Co., Logan, UT; *U.S. Private*, pg. 591
Sacknoff, Philip, Chm. Bd. & Treas.--XRE Corporation, Littleton, MA; *U.S. Public*, pg. 1595
Sacks, Louis, Treas. & Sec.--S. Freedman & Sons, Inc., Landover, MD; *U.S. Private*, pg. 425
Sada, Ricardo, Treas.--Hylsamex, S.A. de C.V., San Nicolas, Mexico; *Int'l*, pg. 56
Sadler, A. James, Treas.--Arinc Inc. (Consolidated), Annapolis, MD; *U.S. Private*, pg. 81
Sadler, Robert P., V.P.-Quality Control, Treas. & Sec.--Integral Systems, Inc., Lanham, MD; *U.S. Public*, pg. 883
Sadler, William S., Pres. & Treas.--Dotronix, Inc., New Brighton, MN; *U.S. Public*, pg. 520
Sahlman, Seppo, Chief Fin. Officer & Exec. V.P.-Treas.--Rautaruukki Oy, Helsinki, Finland; *Int'l*, pg. 1088
Saini, Ajay, Treas.--Health and Retirement Properties Trust, Newton, MA; *U.S. Public*, pg. 801
Saito, Shinichi, V.P. & Treas.--Marubeni America Corporation, New York, NY; *Int'l*, pg. 844
Sakamoto, Teiji, Mng. Dir.--Kawasho Corporation, Tokyo, Japan; *Int'l*, pg. 726
Sakata, Yoshiteru, Treas.--Nippo Marketing & Advertising, Inc., Torrance, CA; *Int'l*, pg. 932
Sakiyama, Tadamichi, Treas.--Hitachi America, Ltd., Tarrytown, NY; *Int'l*, pg. 622
Salamon, Diane, Treas., Sec. & Legal Counsel--Pic N'Pay Supermarkets, Inc., Dania, FL; *U.S. Private*, pg. 864
Salamone, Thomas W., Treas.--Cedar Fair, L.P., Sandusky, OH; *U.S. Public*, pg. 319
Sale, K. Lyn, Asst. Treas.--DMI Furniture Inc., Louisville, KY; *U.S. Public*, pg. 473
Saleda, M.E., Treas.--Lennar Corporation, Miami, FL; *U.S. Public*, pg. 987
Sales, A.R., Treas.--Arvin Industries, Inc., Columbus, IN; *U.S. Public*, pg. 136
Salimann, Peter, Treas.--Corporex Companies, Inc., Cincinnati, OH; *U.S. Private*, pg. 276
Salisbury, George, Chief Fin. Officer, Treas. & Sec.--Symons Corporation, Pasadena, CA; *U.S. Private*, pg. 932
Sallnow-Smith, Nicholas, Treas.--Jardine Matheson Holdings Limited, Hamilton, Bermuda; *Int'l*, pg. 703
Salsbury, D.L., Treas.--Eriez Magnetics, Erie, PA; *U.S. Private*, pg. 381
Saltmarsh, Robert W., V.P. & Treas.--Silicon Graphics, Inc., Mountain View, CA; *U.S. Public*, pg. 1473
Saltzman, Irving, Treas.--Banner Wholesale Grocers, Inc., Chicago, IL; *U.S. Private*, pg. 114
Saltzman, Richard, Asst. Treas.--Banner Wholesale Grocers, Inc., Chicago, IL; *U.S. Private*, pg. 114
Salyer, Robert, V.P. & Treas.--The Paty Company, Piney Flats, TN; *U.S. Private*, pg. 844
Samberg, Stephen, Chm. Bd. & Chief Exec. Officer--Nantucket Industries, Inc., Melville, NY; *U.S. Public*, pg. 1151
Samil, Dilek L., Treas.--FPL Group, Inc., North Palm Beach, FL; *U.S. Public*, pg. 608
Sampson, Steve, Grp. Fin. Controller & Treas.--Alliance UniChem PLC, Chessington, United Kingdom; *Int'l*, pg. 57
San Pedro, Jose Luis, Controller, Treas. & Mng. Dir.-Economy & Fin.--Iberdrola, S.A., Bilbao, Spain; *Int'l*, pg. 657
Sanchez, Eugene, Treas. & Sec.--Distributors Oil Company, Inc., Baton Rouge, LA; *U.S. Private*, pg. 336
Sanchez, Manuel, Dir.-Treas.--Banco 21, Madrid, Spain; *Int'l*, pg. 145
Sanchez, Raymond, V.P., Treas., Asst. Sec. & Administrator--Hunter Engineering Co., Inc., Riverside, CA; *Int'l*, pg. 474
Sandefur, Jennifer Shiley, Exec. V.P. & Treas.--Countrywide Home Loans Inc., Pasadena, CA; *U.S. Public*, pg. 452
Sandeman, T.C., Treas.--Ranger Oil Limited, Calgary, Canada; *Int'l*, pg. 1086
Sander, James E., Treas.--Hickman, Williams Canada, Inc., Cambridge, Canada; *U.S. Private*, pg. 525
Sander, Richard, Treas.--Leshner Mills. Inc., Hamilton, OH; *U.S. Private*, pg. 660
Sanders, Candee, Asst. Treas.--PVS Chemicals, Inc., Detroit, MI; *U.S. Private*, pg. 828
Sanders, Charles, V.P., Treas. & Sec.--RDM Sports Group, Atlanta, GA; *U.S. Public*, pg. 1354
Sanders, Diane Day, V.P. & Treas.--Sysco Corporation, Houston, TX; *U.S. Public*, pg. 1550
Sanders, Kenneth W., Chief Fin. Officer, Sr. V.P.-Fin., Treas. & Asst. Sec.--Paging Network, Inc., Plano, TX; *U.S. Public*, pg. 1252
Sanders, Philip P., Treas. & Sec.--The Boeing Company Canada Ltd., Toronto, Canada; *U.S. Public*, pg. 242
Sanders, Sarah K., Treas.--Yankee Energy System, Inc., Meriden, CT; *U.S. Public*, pg. 1787
Sandford, Paul, Treas.--Primark Corporation, Waltham, MA; *U.S. Public*, pg. 1325
Sandler, Reba, Sec. & Treas.--L.M. Sandler & Sons, Virginia Beach, VA; *U.S. Private*, pg. 964
Sanford, Bill R., Chm. Bd., Pres. & Treas.--Steris Corporation, Mentor, OH; *U.S. Public*, pg. 1515
Sanford, Frederick J., Treas.--Hawker Siddeley Canada Inc., Mississauga, Canada; *Int'l*, pg. 604
Sanford, Robert W., Treas.--Sanford & Hawley, Inc., Unionville, CT; *U.S. Private*, pg. 965
Sanregret, James H., Treas.--Delta Air Lines, Inc., Atlanta, GA; *U.S. Public*, pg. 497
Sansky, Robert, Treas. & Sec.--Emcee Cellular, Inc., Wilmington, DE; *U.S. Public*, pg. 571
Santangelo, Joseph A., Chief Fin. Officer, Treas. & Sec.--FPA Corporation, Bensalem, PA; *U.S. Public*, pg. 608
Santoro, Joseph, Treas.--Bobst S.A., Lausanne, Switzerland; *Int'l*, pg. 198
Sapiano, Shirley, Treas.--Tridel Enterprises Inc., Downsview, Canada; *Int'l*, pg. 1423
Sapp, Jamie, Asst. V.P & Asst. Treas.--CRIIMI MAE, Rockville, MD; *U.S. Public*, pg. 459
Sapp, Ronald V., Chief Fin. Officer, V.P.-Fin. & Treas.--Atlantic Southeast Airlines Inc., Atlanta, GA; *U.S. Public*, pg. 144
Sapyta, Michael, Treas.--Smith Enterprises, Rock Hill, SC; *U.S. Private*, pg. 1007
Sarai, Andre, V.P., Treas. & Sec.--Weiss Sheet Metal Company, Gardena, CA; *U.S. Private*, pg. 1160
Sargent, John C., V.P.-Fin. & Treas.--Du Pont (E.I. Du Pont De Nemours & Co.), Wilmington, DE; *U.S. Public*, pg. 530
Sarjoo, Priya, Asst. Treas. & Asst. Sec.--Astrex, Inc., Plainview, NY; *U.S. Public*, pg. 141
Sarkisian, Pamela Rose, Treas.--Beacon Group, Bloomfield, CT; *U.S. Private*, pg. 126
Sarnoff, Albert, Sr. V.P. & Treas.--Warner Communications Inc., New York, NY; *U.S. Public*, pg. 1611
Sartori, Linda, Treas. & Dir.-D.P.--Lithotype Company, Inc., South San Francisco, CA; *U.S. Private*, pg. 670
Saruwatari, Steven T., Chief Fin. Officer & Treas.--Pacific American Income Shares, Inc., Pasadena, CA; *U.S. Public*, pg. 1247
Saterbo, Bryan, Sr. V.P. & Treas.--Colorado Boxed Beef Co., Auburndale, FL; *U.S. Private*, pg. 254
Sato, Martin, Treas.--Aromat Corporation, New Providence, NJ; *Int'l*, pg. 847
Sattabudsutthi, Visut, Sr. V.P.-Treasury Dept.--The Industrial Finance Corporation of Thailand, Bangkok, Thailand; *Int'l*, pg. 677
Sauer, Thomas J., V.P., Treas. & Controller--McGrath RentCorp, Livermore, CA; *U.S. Public*, pg. 1069
Sauermann, D.C., Treas.--Esso Standard Thailand Ltd., Bangkok, Thailand; *U.S. Public*, pg. 602
Sauey, W.R., Chm. Bd., Pres. & Treas.--Flambeau Corporation, Baraboo, WI; *U.S. Private*, pg. 409
Saul, David, Treas. & Sec.--Beach City Chevrolet Co., Long Beach, CA; *U.S. Private*, pg. 125
Saunders, Beulah, Sec. & Treas.--Dakco Distributors, Inc., Minot, ND; *U.S. Private*, pg. 308
Saunders, Deirdre D., V.P., Treas. & Asst. Sec.--AMETEK, Inc., Paoli, PA; *U.S. Public*, pg. 99
Saunders, Gregory S., Chief Fin. Officer, Exec. V.P. & Treas.--National Insurance Group, South San Francisco, CA; *U.S. Public*, pg. 1157
Saunders, Joanna, V.P. & Treas.--Oakland Tool & Manufacturing Company, Fraser, MI; *U.S. Private*, pg. 809
Savage, Betty J., V.P., Chief Fin. Officer & Treas.--INSO Corporation, Boston, MA; *U.S. Public*, pg. 882
Savitsky, David, Chief Oper. Officer, Exec. V.P., Treas. & Sec.--Staff Builders Inc., Lake Success, NY; *U.S. Public*, pg. 1501
Savitt, David, Exec. V.P. & Treas.--Pace Press, Inc., Moonachie, NJ; *U.S. Private*, pg. 829
Savitz, Richard J., V.P.-Fin., Treas. & Sec.--Justin Industries, Inc., Fort Worth, TX; *U.S. Public*, pg. 936
Savona, Marco, Controller & Treas.--Abbott Ball Company, West Hartford, CT; *U.S. Private*, pg. 9
Sawada, Makio, Sr. V.P. & Treas.--Union Bank of California, San Francisco, CA; *Int'l*, pg. 157
Sawyer, James S., V.P. & Treas.--Praxair Inc., Danbury, CT; *U.S. Public*, pg. 1319
Saxon, Franklin N., Chief Fin. Officer, Sr. V.P., Treas. & Sec.--Culp, Inc., High Point, NC; *U.S. Public*, pg. 467
Sayle, John G., Pres., Chief Exec. Officer & Treas.--The Hall China Company, East Liverpool, OH; *U.S. Private*, pg. 494
Sayre, Larry, Chief Fin. Officer, V.P.-Fin., Controller & Treas.--Collins Industries, Inc., Hutchinson, KS; *U.S. Public*, pg. 399
Scacchi, Susan M., Treas.--Ekco Group, Inc., Nashua, NH; *U.S. Public*, pg. 566
Scacchi, Susan M., Treas.--Ekco Housewares, Inc., Franklin Park, IL; *U.S. Public*, pg. 566
Scacchi, Susan M., Treas.--Ekco Cleaning, Inc., Franklin Park, IL; *U.S. Public*, pg. 566
Scacchi, Susan M., Treas.--Ekco International, Inc., Nashua, NH; *U.S. Public*, pg. 566
Scales, Gene, Treas. & Sec.--Allied Plywood Corp., Alexandria, VA; *U.S. Private*, pg. 40
Scales, Mark S., Chief Fin. Officer, V.P. & Treas.--General Housewares Corp., Terre Haute, IN; *U.S. Public*, pg. 715
Scalfaro, Frank, Chief Fin. Officer, V.P. & Treas.--NavCom Defense Electronics, Inc., El Monte, CA; *U.S. Private*, pg. 789
Scangas, Christopher A., Exec. V.P. & Treas.--Scangas Brothers Holdings, Inc., Lynn, MA; *U.S. Private*, pg. 969
Scanlan, Arthur G., II, Chief Exec. Officer & Treas.--Eatelcorp Inc., Gonzales, LA; *U.S. Private*, pg. 358
Scanlon, Kathy, Chief Fin. Officer--Southwest Recreational Industries Inc., Leander, TX; *U.S. Private*, pg. 1018
Scarinci, Susan, V.P. & Treas.--GAF Premium Products, Inc., Wayne, NJ; *U.S. Private*, pg. 433
Scartz, Don T., V.P.-Fin., Treas. & Sec.--Electromagnetic Sciences, Inc., Norcross, GA; *U.S. Public*, pg. 569

Scatena, Philip A., Asst. Treas.--Franklin Resources, Inc., San Mateo, CA; *U.S. Public*, pg. 679

Schaapveld, Larry, Chief Fin. Officer, V.P., Controller & Treas.--Varied Investments, Inc., Muscatine, IA; *U.S. Private*, pg. 1134

Schach, Jacqueline, Treas.--The Florists Assn. of Greater Cleveland, Inc., Cleveland, OH; *U.S. Private*, pg. 415

Schad, Jeffrey, V.P.-Fin. & Treas.--Van Dorn Demag Corporation, Strongsville, OH; *Int'l*, pg. 837

Schade, Edward P., Treas.--Ethan Allen Interiors Inc., Danbury, CT; *U.S. Public*, pg. 595

Schade, Edward P., V.P. & Treas.--Ethan Allen, Inc., Danbury, CT; *U.S. Public*, pg. 595

Schaefer, Kenneth, 2nd V.P. & Treas.--MBL Life Assurance Corporation, Newark, NJ; *U.S. Private*, pg. 685

Schaffer, Jamie H., V.P. & Treas.--AID Finance, Des Moines, IA; *U.S. Private*, pg. 39

Schaffner, Scott R., V.P.-Fin. & Treas.--Williams & Company, Inc., Pittsburgh, PA; *U.S. Private*, pg. 1055

Schalter, Rich, Chief Fin. Officer, Treas. & Sec.--Spartan Motors, Inc., Charlotte, MI; *U.S. Public*, pg. 1495

Schara, Charles G., Treas.--GEICO Corporation, Washington, DC; *U.S. Public*, pg. 219

Schara, Charles G., Treas.--GEICO Casualty Company, Washington, DC; *U.S. Public*, pg. 219

Scharff, Joseph, Treas.--Subaru of America, Inc., Cherry Hill, NJ; *Int'l*, pg. 523

Schauffert, Arthur R., Treas.--Breed Technologies, Inc., Lakeland, FL; *U.S. Public*, pg. 251

Scheafer, William L., V.P. & Treas.--Cinergy Corp., Cincinnati, OH; *U.S. Public*, pg. 368

Scheel, Curtis J., V.P. & Treas.--MicroAge, Inc., Tempe, AZ; *U.S. Public*, pg. 1104

Scheel, Steve, Sec. & Treas.--MeritCare Health System, Fargo, ND; *U.S. Private*, pg. 733

Schein, Steven M., V.P. & Treas.--Indiana Energy, Inc., Indianapolis, IN; *U.S. Public*, pg. 874

Schein, Steven M., V.P. & Treas.--Indiana Gas Company, Inc., Indianapolis, IN; *U.S. Public*, pg. 875

Schekirke, Theresa, Asst. Treas.--Ferrellgas Partners, L.P., Liberty, MO; *U.S. Public*, pg. 618

Scheneckenburger, Karen, V.P. & Treas.--The Fairchild Corporation, Chantilly, VA; *U.S. Public*, pg. 610

Schenk, Joseph A., Chief Fin. Officer, Treas. & Dir.-Investor Rels.--Tel-Save Holdings, Inc., New Hope, PA; *U.S. Public*, pg. 1568

Scherer, Barbara, V.P. & Treas.--Micropolis Corporation, Chatsworth, CA; *U.S. Private*, pg. 742

Scherer, George F., Chief Fin. Officer, Exec. V.P. & Treas.--McCarthy Building Companies, Saint Louis, MO; *U.S. Private*, pg. 719

Scherer, John C., Asst. Treas.--OHM Remediation Services Corp., Findlay, OH; *U.S. Public*, pg. 1208

Scherer, Kirk, Chief Fin. Officer & Treas.--Paul-Son Gaming Corporation, Las Vegas, NV; *U.S. Public*, pg. 1265

Scherrer, Thomas, Treas.--Schweizer Verband der Raiffeisenbanken, Saint Gallen, Switzerland; *Int'l*, pg. 1211

Scheuer, Cynthia A., Chief Fin. Officer, V.P. & Treas.--Mechanical Technology Inc., Latham, NY; *U.S. Public*, pg. 1077

Scheve, Timothy C., V.P. & Treas.--Legg Mason, Inc., Baltimore, MD; *U.S. Public*, pg. 984

Schick, Kevin C., Chief Fin. Officer, V.P., Controller & Treas.--Con-Way Transportation Services, Palo Alto, CA; *U.S. Public*, pg. 281

Schildge, George, Asst. Treas.--Precision Roll Grinders, Inc., Allentown, PA; *U.S. Private*, pg. 880

Schindele, Henry A., V.P. & Reg. Treas.--Toronto Dominion Japan, Tokyo, Japan; *Int'l*, pg. 1401

Schindler, David R., Treas.--Lykes Brothers Inc., Tampa, FL; *U.S. Private*, pg. 682

Schippers, Tom, V.P. & Treas.--Beverage America, Inc., Holland, MI; *U.S. Private*, pg. 141

Schipull, Duane, Treas. & Sec.--Bawden Corporation, Eldridge, IA; *U.S. Private*, pg. 124

Schirmang, William A., Pres. & Treas.--Skokie Valley Beverage Co., Wheeling, IL; *U.S. Private*, pg. 1005

Schkade, Craig, Chief Fin. Officer & Treas.--Hitox Corporation of America, Corpus Christi, TX; *U.S. Public*, pg. 829

Schlachter, Norman L., V.P. & Treas.--Micron Technology Inc., Boise, ID; *U.S. Public*, pg. 1105

Schlagenhauf, John, Treas. & Sec.--Badger Truck Center, Inc., Milwaukee, WI; *U.S. Private*, pg. 110

Schlegel, Charles, Chief Fin. Officer & Treas.--Arizona Cardinals, Phoenix, AZ; *U.S. Private*, pg. 81

Schleier, Grady, V.P. & Treas.--Avatex Corporation, Dallas, TX; *U.S. Public*, pg. 151

Schleif, Lyle, Treas. & Sec.--Anoka Electric Cooperative, Ramsey, MN; *U.S. Private*, pg. 75

Schlobohm, Jon, Treas. & Sec.--National Corset Supply House, Los Angeles, CA; *U.S. Private*, pg. 781

Schlobohm, Sampo, Treas.--Metsa-Serla Corporation, Espoo, Finland; *Int'l*, pg. 863

Schlosser, Elaine, M., Treas. & Sec.--Schlosser Forge Company, Rancho Cucamonga, CA; *U.S. Private*, pg. 970

Schlosser, P., Treas. & Sec.--Krupp Robins, Inc., Englewood, CO; *Int'l*, pg. 511

Schlosser, Rod, Chief Fin. Officer, V.P. & Treas.--Martin Industries, Inc. (AL), Florence, AL; *U.S. Private*, pg. 709

Schlothan, Dau, Treas. & Sec.--Oltmans Construction Company, Whittier, CA; *U.S. Private*, pg. 815

Schmalz, Richard C., Dir.-Treas.--Nevada Power Company, Las Vegas, NV; *U.S. Public*, pg. 1169

Schmalzer, Victor, Treas.--W.W. Norton & Company, Inc., New York, NY; *U.S. Private*, pg. 807

Schmehl, Don C., Chief Fin. Officer & Treas.--Centrex Corporation, Findlay, OH; *U.S. Private*, pg. 225

Schmeider, Luke R., Pres., Treas. & Chief Exec. Officer--Mesa Laboratories, Inc., Wheat Ridge, CO; *U.S. Public*, pg. 1099

Schmidt, Carl G., Chief Fin. Officer, Sr. V.P., Treas. & Sec.--Johnson Worldwide Associates, Inc., Sturtevant, WI; *U.S. Public*, pg. 932

Schmidt, Dennis, Treas.--Traylor Brothers, Inc., Evansville, IN; *U.S. Private*, pg. 1098

Schmidt, Lawrence, V.P. & Treas.--Sellstrom Manufacturing Co., Palatine, IL; *U.S. Private*, pg. 983

Schmidt, Russell J., V.P.-Admin. & Treas.--Lakeside Foods, Inc., Manitowoc, WI; *U.S. Private*, pg. 643

Schmidt, William B., Chm. Bd., Chief Exec. Officer & Treas--Coca-Cola Bottling Co. of Elizabethtown, Elizabethtown, KY; *U.S. Private*, pg. 248

Schmitt, Eric J., V.P.-Fin. & Treas.--Bergen Brunswig Corporation, Orange, CA; *U.S. Public*, pg. 213

Schneible, William F., Controller, Treas. & Sec.--Brooklyn Bottling Co. of Milton, NY, Milton, NY; *U.S. Private*, pg. 171

Schneider, Alan J., Treas.--Wm. Wrigley Jr. Company, Chicago, IL; *U.S. Public*, pg. 1781

Schneider, Bernard, V.P. & Treas.--Ascend Communications, Inc., Alameda, CA; *U.S. Public*, pg. 138

Schneider, Henrietta, Treas.--Atlas Pen & Pencil Corporation, Hollywood, FL; *U.S. Private*, pg. 96

Schneider, Jeffrey A., V.P. & Asst. Treas.--Associates Financial Services Corporation, Dallas, TX; *U.S. Public*, pg. 663

Schneider, Kenneth, Sr. Treas.--Schneider's Dairy, Inc., Pittsburgh, PA; *U.S. Private*, pg. 971

Schneider, Richard A., Chief Fin. Officer--NAI Technologies, Inc., Huntington, NY; *U.S. Public*, pg. 1144

Schneider, Robert F., Chief Fin. Officer, Exec. V.P. & Asst. Treas.--Kimball International, Inc., Jasper, IN; *U.S. Public*, pg. 956

Schneider, Scott N., Chief Fin. Officer, Sr. V.P. & Treas.--Century Communications Corp., New Canaan, CT; *U.S. Public*, pg. 329

Schneider, Scott V., Chief Fin. Officer, V.P., Treas. & Sec.--Saul Centers Inc., Chevy Chase, MD; *U.S. Public*, pg. 1435

Schnell, John, V.P. & Treas.--Freightliner Corp., Portland, OR; *Int'l*, pg. 368

Schnelle, Robert E., Treas.--Crown Crafts, Inc., Atlanta, GA; *U.S. Public*, pg. 465

Schnepf, George, Chief Fin. Officer--Cold Spring Granite Company, Cold Spring, MN; *U.S. Private*, pg. 250

Schnitzius, Robert W., Chief Fin. Officer & Treas.--Carrington Laboratories, Inc., Irving, TX; *U.S. Public*, pg. 309

Schnurr, Willy, Treas.--Rhenania Schiffahrts-und Speditions-Gesellschaft mbH, Mannheim, Germany; *Int'l*, pg. 1033

Schoch, Stephen J., V.P. & Treas.--The Times Mirror Company, Los Angeles, CA; *U.S. Public*, pg. 1615

Schocke, Robert P., Chief Fin. Officer, Treas., Controller & Sec.--Greenhorne & O'Mara, Inc., Greenbelt, MD; *U.S. Private*, pg. 477

Schoeber, Eldon, V.P., Treas. & Sec.--Site Oil Company of Missouri, Clayton, MO; *U.S. Private*, pg. 1004

Schoeffler, Michael H., Pres. & Chief Oper. Officer--Starcraft Corporation, Goshen, IN; *U.S. Public*, pg. 1510

Schoene, Donald R., Exec. V.P.-Fin. & Treas.--Diamond Star Motors, Normal, IL; *Int'l*, pg. 875

Schoeneman, Alvin C., V.P. & Treas.--Schoeneman Brothers Company, Sioux Falls, SD; *U.S. Private*, pg. 972

Schoenfeld, Richard, Exec. V.P. & Treas.--Tomco Auto Products, Inc., Los Angeles, CA; *U.S. Private*, pg. 1090

Schoeniger, Terrence, Pres., Gen. Counsel & Asst. Treas.--Safety National Casualty Corp., Saint Louis, MO; *U.S. Public*, pg. 496

Scholz, Kenneth W., V.P. & Treas.--Rohr, Inc., Chula Vista, CA; *U.S. Public*, pg. 751

Schonau, Mark R., Chief Fin. Officer, Sec., Treas., & Investor Rels.--HBO & Company/Cycare Business Group, Scottsdale, AZ; *U.S. Public*, pg. 770

Schonwasser, Juergen, Treas.--Philipp Holzmann USA, Inc., Wilmington, DE; *Int'l*, pg. 633

Schooley, Robert L., Treas.--American Aggregates Corp., Dayton, OH; *Int'l*, pg. 245

Schotfeldt, Brad D., V.P.-Fin. & Treas.--Ag Services of America, Inc., Cedar Falls, IA; *U.S. Public*, pg. 6

Schott, Gerhard, Dr., Sr. Exec. V.P.-Treas.--Bayerische Landesbank, Munich, Germany; *Int'l*, pg. 176

Schotters, Bernard W., Sr. V.P.-Fin.--TCI Communications, Inc., Englewood, CO; *U.S. Public*, pg. 1554

Schoultz, Deborah A., V.P., Treas. & Sec.--The Fibre-Metal Products Company, Concordville, PA; *U.S. Private*, pg. 402

Schramm, C.W., Treas.--Lakehead Pipe Line Co., Inc., Superior, WI; *Int'l*, pg. 652

Schramm, Mike, Asst. Treas.--Family Healthcare Services, Inc., Las Vegas, NV; *U.S. Public*, pg. 1469

Schramm, Mike, Asst. Treas.--Family Home Hospice, Inc., Las Vegas, NV; *U.S. Public*, pg. 1469

Schrandt, David T., V.P., Treas. & Comptroller--ITT Hartford Life & Annuity Insurance Corporation, Minneapolis, MN; *U.S. Public*, pg. 795

Schreiber, David R., Chief Fin. Officer, Treas. & Sec.--Dianon Systems, Inc., Stratford, CT; *U.S. Public*, pg. 506

Schreiber, Donald C., V.P.-Fin. & Treas.--Medicine Shoppe International, Inc., Saint Louis, MO; *U.S. Public*, pg. 304

Schroeder, Christopher, Treas.--The Washington Post Company, Washington, DC; *U.S. Public*, pg. 1742

Schroeder, Mary Lou, Asst. Sec. & Asst. Treas.--Modern Group Ltd., Bristol, PA; *U.S. Private*, pg. 754

Schroeder, Scott C., Treas.--Cabot Oil & Gas Corporation, Houston, TX; *U.S. Public*, pg. 289

Schroeder, Stephen O., Asst. Treas.--Cooper Tire & Rubber Company, Findlay, OH; *U.S. Public*, pg. 445

Schrum, E.P., Pres., Chief Exec. Officer & Treas.--Carolina Mills, Inc., Maiden, NC; *U.S. Private*, pg. 214

Schubert, William C., Pres., Chief Exec. Officer & Treas.--Kitchell Corporation, Phoenix, AZ; *U.S. Private*, pg. 624

Schubert, William L., V.P.-Fin. & Treas.--SCS Engineers, Long Beach, CA; *U.S. Private*, pg. 955

Schueftan, N., Treas. & Dir.-Tax--ICI Americas, Inc., Wilmington, DE; *Int'l*, pg. 663

Schueler, Kirk, Chief Fin. Officer & Treas.--Brooks Resources Corporation, Bend, OR; *U.S. Private*, pg. 172

Schueler, Tammy, Chief Fin. Officer--Evans Adhesive Corp., Columbus, OH; *U.S. Private*, pg. 384

Schuering, Jim, Controller & Treas.--J.D. Streett & Co., Inc., Maryland Heights, MO; *U.S. Private*, pg. 1047

Schuette, Marvin, Chm. Bd., Pres., Chief Exec. Officer & Chief Oper. Officer--Wausau Homes, Inc., Rothschild, WI; *U.S. Private*, pg. 1154

Schuette, Marvin, Chm. Bd., Pres., Chief Exec. Officer & Chief Oper. Officer--Sterling Building Systems, Inc., Rothschild, WI; *U.S. Private*, pg. 1154

Schuld, M., Asst. Treas.--Atotech U.S.A. Inc., Rock Hill, SC; *U.S. Private*, pg. 97

Schuler, Steven T., Chief Fin. Officer, Corp. Sr. V.P., Treas. & Sec.--Brenton Banks, Inc., Des Moines, IA; *U.S. Public*, pg. 251

Schulman, Esther, Treas.--Eli's Cheese Cake Company, Chicago, IL; *U.S. Private*, pg. 371

Schultz, Christopher F., Treas.--Asarco Incorporated, New York, NY; *U.S. Public*, pg. 137

Schultz, David, Treas. & Mgr.-Fin.--Svedala Industries Inc., Waukesha, WI; *Int'l*, pg. 1326

Schultz, Gary, Chief Fin. Officer, Treas. & Sec.--Arrowhead Mills, Inc., Hereford, TX; *U.S. Private*, pg. 86

Schultz, James D., Chief Fin. Officer, Sr. V.P., Treas. & Sec.--Old America Stores, Howe, TX; *U.S. Public*, pg. 1215

Schultz, Robert J., Chief Fin. Officer, Treas. & Sec.--Great Lakes Lithograph Co., Cleveland, OH; *U.S. Private*, pg. 474

Schumacher, D.A., Chief Fin. Officer & Treas.--The Cretex Companies, Elk River, MN; *U.S. Private*, pg. 289

Schunk, Friedel, Treas.--Werner & Pfleiderer Corporation, Ramsey, NJ; *Int'l*, pg. 511

Schupp, David O., V.P. & Treas.--Interface Systems, Inc., Ann Arbor, MI; *U.S. Public*, pg. 889

Schutte, Kenneth E., Sr. V.P. & Treas.--Mercantile Bancorporation Inc., Saint Louis, MO; *U.S. Public*, pg. 1087

Schuttler, Jay, Asst. Treas.--Power House Technologies, Inc., Bozeman, MT; *U.S. Public*, pg. 1319

Schwab, James E., Pres. & Chief Oper. Officer--Xtek, Inc., Cincinnati, OH; *U.S. Private*, pg. 1194

Schwab, James E., Sr. V.P. & Treas.--General Cable Corporation, Highland Heights, KY; *Int'l*, pg. 1486

Schwab, Mary Lou, Chief Fin. Officer, Controller & Treas.--Auto-trol Technology Corporation, Denver, CO; *U.S. Public*, pg. 148

Schwartz, Daniel L., Pres., Treas. & Sec.--Schwartz & Benjamin, Inc., New York, NY; *U.S. Private*, pg. 974

Schwartz, Harold A., Sr. V.P. & Treas.--FerrellCalvillo Communications, Inc., New York, NY; *U.S. Private*, pg. 401

Schwartz, Lonn R., Chief Fin. Officer--Auto Glass Specialists, Madison, WI; *U.S. Private*, pg. 100

Schwartzwalder, Larry, Treas.--Tishman Realty & Construction Co., Inc., New York, NY; *U.S. Private*, pg. 1089

Schwing, Manfred, Treas.--Korf-Transport-GmbH, Kehl, Germany; *Int'l*, pg. 758

Schwinke, Arlen, Treas.--Mid-America Dairymen, Inc., Springfield, MO; *U.S. Private*, pg. 743

Schwitters, Eugene, Treas.--Southern Minnesota Beet Sugar Cooperative, Renville, MN; *U.S. Private*, pg. 1016

Sciame, Frank, Pres., Treas., Chief Exec. & Chief Fin. Officer--F.J. Sciame Construction Co. Inc., New York, NY; *U.S. Private*, pg. 975

Scilla, Randy, Asst. Sec. & Asst. Treas.--Pennsylvania Power Co., New Castle, PA; *U.S. Public*, pg. 645

Scivally, Glen, V.P. & Treas.--NCH Corporation, Irving, TX; *U.S. Public*, pg. 1145

Scobie, D.R. John, Asst. Treas.--SaskPower, Regina, Canada; *Int'l*, pg. 1195

Scogin, James G., Controller & Treas.--Lot$ Off Corporation, San Antonio, TX; *U.S. Public*, pg. 1014

Scordo, Christopher, Chief Fin. Officer & Treas.--The Hite Company, Altoona, PA; *U.S. Private*, pg. 531

Scoropski, James R., Chm. Bd. & Treas.--Acclaim Entertainment, Inc., Glen Cove, NY; *U.S. Public*, pg. 15

Scott, Daniel, V.P.-Treas.--Caesars Palace, Las Vegas, NV; *U.S. Public*, pg. 1512

Scott, J.B., Treas.--Esso International Shipping (Bahamas) Co. Limited, Florham Park, NJ; *U.S. Public*, pg. 601

Scott, James H., Sec. & Asst. Treas.--Texas Utilities Company, Dallas, TX; *U.S. Public*, pg. 1586

Scott, James T., Chm. Bd., Chief Exec. Officer & Treas.--Norcostco, Inc., Minneapolis, MN; *U.S. Private*, pg. 801

Scott, Milton C., Treas. & Sec.--Georgia Duck & Cordage Mills, Scottdale, GA; *U.S. Private*, pg. 448

Scott, Roland E., Pres. & Treas.--Burtco, Inc., Westminster Station, VT; *U.S. Private*, pg. 188

Scott, V. Hollis, Sr. V.P., Treas. & Sec.--The Cato Corporation, Charlotte, NC; *U.S. Public*, pg. 318

Scott, William R., Treas.--Moore Company, Westerly, RI; *U.S. Private*, pg. 759

Scotto, John A., Chief Fin. Officer, V.P. & Treas.--Iron Road Railways Inc., Washington, DC; *U.S. Private*, pg. 575

Scruggs, Patrick A., Asst. Treas.--Cracker Barrel Old Country Store, Inc., Lebanon, TN; *U.S. Public*, pg. 455

Seagraves, Marilyn, Asst. Treas.-Cash Mgmt.--Ingram Industries Inc., Nashville, TN; *U.S. Private*, pg. 562

Seaney, Roy H., Treas.--Menard Electric Cooperative, Petersburg, IL; *U.S. Private*, pg. 731

Seaquist, Don, V.P. & Treas.--Greyhound Lines, Inc., Dallas, TX; *U.S. Public*, pg. 765

Seay, Larry W., V.P. & Treas.--UDC Homes, Inc., Scottsdale, AZ; *U.S. Private*, pg. 5

Sebastianelli, Eldore, Treas.--Pioneer American Holding Company, Carbondale, PA; *U.S. Public*, pg. 1298

Seckel, Douglas, Chief Fin. Officer, Treas. & Sec.--Eagle USA Airfreight, Houston, TX; *U.S. Public*, pg. 547

Seckora, D.F., Asst. Treas.--Electrical Equipment Company, Raleigh, NC; *U.S. Private*, pg. 368
Secy, Michael, Treas.--Loeber Motors, Inc., Chicago, IL; *U.S. Private*, pg. 672
Sedder, Shirley, Dir.-Mktg., Sec., Treas.--Andy's Restaurants Inc., Little Rock, AR; *U.S. Private*, pg. 74
Sedler, Jordan B., Exec. V.P., Sec. & Treas.--Paper Enterprises, Inc., Bronx, NY; *U.S. Private*, pg. 837
Sedlmeier, M.E., Treas.--Ziegler Collateralized Securities, Inc., West Bend, WI; *U.S. Public*, pg. 1792
Seeley, Paul J., Treas., Controller & Sec.--Lindsay Manufacturing Inc., Ponca City, OK; *U.S. Private*, pg. 668
Seery, Patrick, Chief Fin. Officer, Controller & Treas.--James McHugh Construction Co., Chicago, IL; *U.S. Private*, pg. 721
Segale, David S., Treas. & Sec.--Mel Rapton Honda, Sacramento, CA; *U.S. Private*, pg. 911
Segall, Larry M., V.P., Treas. & Controller--Tiffany & Co., New York, NY; *U.S. Public*, pg. 1608
Segebarth, Frank H., Asst. Treas.--Kimberly-Clark Corporation, Dallas, TX; *U.S. Public*, pg. 958
Seibold-Dietl, Jutta, Dr., Treas.--Knight Wendling AG, Zurich, Switzerland; *U.S. Private*, pg. 627
Seidman, Martin L., Treas.--Southwark Metal Manufacturing Company, Philadelphia, PA; *U.S. Private*, pg. 1018
Self, Charles, Treas.--ABC Rail Products Corp., Chicago, IL; *U.S. Public*, pg. 2
Selfridge, Steven G., Chief Oper. Officer & Exec. V.P.--Checkpoint Systems Inc., Thorofare, NJ; *U.S. Public*, pg. 343
Seligman, Irving R., Chm. Bd. & Treas.--Seligman & Associates, Inc., Southfield, MI; *U.S. Private*, pg. 982
Seligson, Kenneth, Treas.--Harcrest International, Ltd., Clark, NJ; *U.S. Private*, pg. 500
Sell, Michael A., Treas.--Meredith Corporation, Des Moines, IA; *U.S. Public*, pg. 1094
Selland, Clay E., Treas. & Asst. Sec.--Longs Drug Stores Corporation, Walnut Creek, CA; *U.S. Public*, pg. 1013
Sellers, Robert P., Treas. & Sec.--Dean Sellers Ford Inc., Troy, MI; *U.S. Private*, pg. 983
Selover, Patricia W., Treas. & Sec.--Selover Buick, Inc., Billings, MT; *U.S. Private*, pg. 983
Seltzer, David S., Chief Oper. Officer, Exec. V.P., Treas. & Sec.--Hi-Tech Pharmacal Co., Inc., Amityville, NY; *U.S. Public*, pg. 825
Selzer, Joseph M., Treas.--The Prudential Realty Group, Newark, NJ; *U.S. Private*, pg. 892
Semanick, Ronald J., Treas.--SI/Baker, Inc., Easton, PA; *U.S. Public*, pg. 1418
Sempier, Philip J., V.P. & Treas.--The Chubb Corporation, Warren, NJ; *U.S. Public*, pg. 354
Sena, Donald T., Asst. Treas.--Eastern Utilities Associates, Boston, MA; *U.S. Public*, pg. 549
Senchak, Dennis E., Asst. Treas.--NIPSCO Industries, Inc., Hammond, IN; *U.S. Public*, pg. 1185
Sendelweck, Kenneth L., V.P. & Asst. Treas.--Kimball International, Inc., Jasper, IN; *U.S. Public*, pg. 956
Senechal, Ellen M., Treas.--Montana Power Company, Butte, MT; *U.S. Public*, pg. 1126
Seneta, Eugene, Chief Fin. Officer, V.P., Treas. & Sec.--Xyvision, Inc., Wakefield, MA; *U.S. Public*, pg. 1787
Senseman, David S., Chief Fin. Officer & Treas--Van Dyne-Crotty, Inc., Dayton, OH; *U.S. Private*, pg. 1132
Sentman, David K., Chief Fin. Officer, Sr. V.P. & Treas.--American Telecasting, Inc., Colorado Springs, CO; *U.S. Public*, pg. 93
Seppala, Paul A., Chief Fin. Officer, V.P. & Treas.--Paul A. Schmitt Music Company, Minneapolis, MN; *U.S. Private*, pg. 971
Sereda, Peter, V.P. & Treas.--Specialty Foods Corporation, Deerfield, IL; *U.S. Private*, pg. 1022
Sereta, P.L., Treas.--Thrall Car Mfg. Co., Chicago Heights, IL; *U.S. Private*, pg. 344
Serfass, Kristen G., Mgr.-Acctg. & Asst. Treas.--Branford Savings Bank, Branford, CT; *U.S. Public*, pg. 250
Serkes, Jeffrey D., V.P. & Treas.--International Business Machines Corporation, Armonk, NY; *U.S. Public*, pg. 895
Severi, Robert M., Treas.--Henkels & McCoy, Inc., Blue Bell, PA; *U.S. Private*, pg. 522
Severino, Beverly, Sec. & Treas.--Great Scott Advertising Co. Inc., New York, NY; *U.S. Private*, pg. 475
Seversen, Duane, V.P. & Treas.--Affiliated Foods Cooperative Inc., Norfolk, NE; *U.S. Private*, pg. 25
Severson, Ron, Dir.-Personnel--True Companies, Casper, WY; *U.S. Private*, pg. 1107
Sevick, Daniel M., Chief Fin. Officer & Treas.--Environmental Resources Management, Exton, PA; *U.S. Private*, pg. 378
Seward, Martin, Vice Chm. & Chief Fin. Officer--Kenwal Products Corp., Dearborn, MI; *U.S. Private*, pg. 616
Sexton, Michael J., Chief Fin. Officer & Treas.--Prime Bancorp, Inc., Fort Washington, PA; *U.S. Public*, pg. 1326
Sexton, Robert J., Treas. & Sec.--Tab Products Co., Palo Alto, CA; *U.S. Public*, pg. 1559
Seyss, Michael, Treas.--Demner, Merlicek & Bergmann Werbegesellschaft mbH, Vienna, Austria; *Int'l*, pg. 392
Sgroi, S.B., Controller & Treas.--Elkins Constructors, Inc., Jacksonville, FL; *U.S. Private*, pg. 372
Sha, J., Treas. & Sec.--Fyrnetics, Inc., Roselle, IL; *Int'l*, pg. 1499
Shackford, Paul, Chief Fin. Officer, V.P., Treas. & Sec.--Park Electrochemical Corporation, Lake Success, NY; *U.S. Public*, pg. 1258
Shaeffer, Stanley, Treas.--Automotive Rentals, Inc. (ARI), Mount Laurel, NJ; *U.S. Private*, pg. 535
Shafer, Douglas C., V.P. & Treas.--Tektronix, Inc., Wilsonville, OR; *U.S. Public*, pg. 1567
Shaffer, Jamie H., V.P.-Treas.--Allied Mutual Insurance Company, Des Moines, IA; *U.S. Private*, pg. 39
Shaffer, Jerome, V.P. & Treas.--Lawson Products, Inc., Des Plaines, IL; *U.S. Public*, pg. 980
Shager, Philip A., Chief Fin. & Acctg. Officer & Treas.--Marietta Corporation, Cortland, NY; *U.S. Private*, pg. 702
Shah, Mayur, Treas.--H. Freeman & Son, Inc., Philadelphia, PA; *U.S. Private*, pg. 426
Shahbazian, Michael B., V.P. & Treas.--Amdahl Corporation, Sunnyvale, CA; *Int'l*, pg. 527
Shakley, Allan D., Sec. & Asst. Treas.--United Water Management & Services, Harrington Park, NJ; *U.S. Public*, pg. 1692
Shalagan, Edward C., Treas.--Echlin Inc., Branford, CT; *U.S. Public*, pg. 560
Shampey, Paul, Controller & Treas.--Kaiser Ventures, Inc., Ontario, CA; *U.S. Public*, pg. 941
Shanahan, Brendan, Treas.--Oxford Health Insurance, Inc., Norwalk, CT; *U.S. Public*, pg. 1239
Shanahan, Brendan, Treas.--Oxford Health Centers, Norwalk, CT; *U.S. Public*, pg. 1239
Shanahan, Brendan R., Treas.--Oxford Health Plans (IL), Inc., Rosemont, IL; *U.S. Public*, pg. 1239
Shaner, Wayne H., Asst. Treas.--Martin Marietta International, Inc., Bethesda, MD; *U.S. Public*, pg. 1009
Shanes, Abraham, Chm. Bd. & Treas.--Talk-A-Phone Co., Chicago, IL; *U.S. Private*, pg. 1067
Shank, Roberta, Treas. & Sec.--Chas Roberts Air Conditioning, Inc., Phoenix, AZ; *U.S. Private*, pg. 935
Shankardass, A., Mgr.-Treasury--Commercial Union plc, London, United Kingdom; *Int'l*, pg. 308
Sharkey, Daniel P., Chief Fin. Officer, V.P. & Treas.--ATMI, Inc., Danbury, CT; *U.S. Public*, pg. 12
Sharpe, Doanld R., V.P. & Treas.--All American Agency Facilities, Inc., Redmond, WA; *U.S. Public*, pg. 216
Sharpe, Ronald A., Treas.--HPS, Inc., Indianapolis, IN; *U.S. Private*, pg. 492
Sharpe, Vivian A., Treas. & Sec.--Texas Refinery Corp., Fort Worth, TX; *U.S. Private*, pg. 1078
Shatley, William, Chief Fin. Officer, Sr. V.P. & Treas.--Polyphase Corporation, Dallas, TX; *U.S. Public*, pg. 1315
Shaw, Doug, V.P.-Wines & Treas.--M.S. Walker, Inc., Somerville, MA; *U.S. Private*, pg. 1147
Shaw, Jeff, V.P. & Treas.--Southwest Gas Corporation, Las Vegas, NV; *U.S. Public*, pg. 1493
Shawhan, Jerry, Chief Fin. Officer & Treas.--Cincom Systems, Inc., Cincinnati, OH; *U.S. Private*, pg. 240
Shay, James C., Chief Fin. Officer & Treas.--BHA Group Holdings Inc., Kansas City, MO; *U.S. Public*, pg. 161
Shay, Joseph F., Treas.--House of Bianchi, Inc., Medford, MA; *U.S. Private*, pg. 541
Shay, Michael, Treas.--Richfield Hospitality Services, Englewood, CO; *U.S. Private*, pg. 929
Shea, Michael J., Chief Fin. Officer, Exec V.P. & Treas.--Grossman's, Inc., Stoughton, MA; *U.S. Private*, pg. 585
Shea, Michael J., V.P.-Logistics--Ocean Spray Cranberries, Inc., Middleboro, MA; *U.S. Private*, pg. 811
Shea, Thomas E., Treas.--Western Resources, Inc., Topeka, KS; *U.S. Public*, pg. 1759
Sheafer, William L., Treas.--Cinergy Investments, Inc., Indianapolis, IN; *U.S. Public*, pg. 369
Sheehan, Heather E., Controller & Treas.--Trans Mountain Pipeline Company Ltd., Vancouver, Canada; *Int'l*, pg. 114
Sheehan, Mark W., Treas.--Graco Inc., Golden Valley, MN; *U.S. Public*, pg. 756
Sheets, Dennis D., Chief Fin. Officer, Treas. & Sec.--Valley Systems, Inc., Canal Fulton, OH; *U.S. Public*, pg. 1706
Sheets, J.W., Asst. Treas.--Phillips Petroleum Company, Bartlesville, OK; *U.S. Public*, pg. 1290
Sheffield, Langdon C., V.P. & Treas.--Sheffield Hardware Company, Americus, GA; *U.S. Private*, pg. 335
Sheils, John F., Treas.--Steve Foley Cadillac, Northbrook, IL; *U.S. Private*, pg. 416
Sheldon, Craig A., V.P., Treas. & Sec.--MediVators, Inc., Eagan, MN; *U.S. Public*, pg. 301
Shelley, Adrian D., Treas.--Swift Energy Company, Houston, TX; *U.S. Public*, pg. 1543
Shelley, V. Dale, V.P. & Treas.--Misco Industries, Wichita, KS; *U.S. Private*, pg. 752
Shelton, James, Treas. & Sec.--Apex Precision Technology Inc., Indianapolis, IN; *U.S. Private*, pg. 77
Shelton, Jeff W., Chief Fin. Officer & V.P.-Fin.--Skyline Chili, Inc., Fairfield, OH; *U.S. Public*, pg. 1475
Shelton, Kathryn L., Asst. Treas.--National Commerce Bancorporation, Memphis, TN; *U.S. Public*, pg. 1154
Shelton, L. G., Jr., Treas.--Camellia Food Stores, Inc., Norfolk, VA; *U.S. Private*, pg. 203
Shelton, Michael, Chief Fin. Officer, V.P. & Treas.--Directory Distributing Associates, Inc., Saint Louis, MO; *U.S. Private*, pg. 334
Shepard, Barry, Chief Fin. Officer, Treas. & Asst. Sec.--Scott's Liquid Gold-Inc., Denver, CO; *U.S. Public*, pg. 1447
Shepard, Robert L., Chief Fin. Officer, Dir. Mngmt. Info. Systems, Treas. & Sec.--Acme Foundry, Inc., Coffeyville, KS; *U.S. Private*, pg. 13
Shephard, Walter A., Treas.--GenRad, Inc., Westford, MA; *U.S. Public*, pg. 731
Shepherd, Charles, V.P. & Treas.--Georgia/Durango Boot Company, Franklin, TN; *U.S. Public*, pg. 1684
Shepherd, Peter D., Treas.--McKechnie PLC, Walsall, United Kingdom; *Int'l*, pg. 851
Shepherd, William Clyde, Jr., Treas. & Sec.--Shepherd Construction Co., Inc., Atlanta, GA; *U.S. Private*, pg. 993
Sheppard, H.B., Asst. Treas.--Chevron Corporation, San Francisco, CA; *U.S. Public*, pg. 347
Sheppard, Lynne S., Treas.--Thiele Kaolin Co., Sandersville, GA; *U.S. Private*, pg. 1081
Sherman, Thomas W., Chief Fin. Officer, Exec. V.P. & Treas.--Bay State Gas Company, Westborough, MA; *U.S. Public*, pg. 196
Sherwood, Maryellen, Treas.--McInerney Inc., Oak Park, MI; *U.S. Private*, pg. 722
Shevchik, Daniel R., Chief Fin. Officer, V.P., Treas. & Sec.--Malcolm Pirnie, Inc., White Plains, NY; *U.S. Private*, pg. 867
Shields, Geoffrey D., Treas.--Chubb Insurance Co. of Canada, Toronto, Canada; *U.S. Public*, pg. 355
Shigeru, Mori, V.P. & Treas.--Mutual Trading Co., Inc., Los Angeles, CA; *U.S. Private*, pg. 770
Shimada, Masanori, Treas. & Sec.--Lotte U.S.A., Inc., Battle Creek, MI; *Int'l*, pg. 819
Shimizu, Hiroharu, Dir.--Chiyoda Mutual Life Insurance Company, Tokyo, Japan; *Int'l*, pg. 286
Shimura, Norifumi, Exec. V.P.-Treas. & Sec.--Mitsui Foods, Inc., Norwood, NJ; *Int'l*, pg. 879
Shine, Loretta, Treas. & Sec.--First Financial Group, Inc., Encino, CA; *U.S. Private*, pg. 407
Shinn, Michael L., Treas.--Bindley Western Industries, Inc., Indianapolis, IN; *U.S. Public*, pg. 228
Shirakawa, Kayud, Asst. Treas.--Pacific Energy Conservation Services, Inc., Honolulu, HI; *U.S. Public*, pg. 800
Shirk, Betty J., Treas. & Sec.--Beer Nuts, Inc., Bloomington, IL; *U.S. Private*, pg. 130
Shirley, Ronald, Chief Fin. Officer, V.P. & Treas.--Golden West Baseball Club, Anaheim, CA; *U.S. Private*, pg. 461
Shomaker, Thomas M., Chief Fin. Officer, V.P. & Treas.--T.D. Williamson, Inc., Tulsa, OK; *U.S. Private*, pg. 1179
Shoop, Neil O., Treas.--Trinity Industries Inc., Dallas, TX; *U.S. Public*, pg. 1638
Shope, Michael A., Chief Fin. Officer & Treas.--Walbro Corporation, Cass City, MI; *U.S. Public*, pg. 1733
Shope, Michael H., Treas.--Libbey Owens Ford Co., Toledo, OH; *Int'l*, pg. 1056
Short, Daniel L., Chief Fin. Officer & Treas.--Mid-America Energy Resources, Indianapolis, IN; *U.S. Public*, pg. 913
Short, Daniel L., Chief Fin. Officer & Treas.--Cleveland Thermal Energy Corporation, Cleveland, OH; *U.S. Public*, pg. 913
Short, Ed, Treas. & Sec.--Alabama Electric Cooperative, Inc., Andalusia, AL; *U.S. Private*, pg. 30
Shott, John S., Treas.--National Engineering & Contracting Co., Strongsville, OH; *U.S. Private*, pg. 782
Shotton, Burt, Jr., Treas.--Wyeth-Ayerst Laboratories, Inc., Philadelphia, PA; *U.S. Public*, pg. 80
Showers, Mark, Chief Fin. Officer, Treas. & Sec.--Spartech Plastics, Portage, WI; *U.S. Public*, pg. 1496
Shropshire, William S., Jr., Chief Fin. Officer, Exec. V.P., Treas. & Sec.--Dyersburg Corporation, Dyersburg, TN; *U.S. Public*, pg. 538
Shubrook, Brian, Treas.--Bank Brussels Lambert, London Branch, London, United Kingdom; *Int'l*, pg. 147
Shuford, Arlene, Treas. & Sec.--Bowen Brothers Fruit Co., Inc., Winter Haven, FL; *U.S. Private*, pg. 162
Shuford, Hunt, Chief Fin. Officer & Treas.--Shuford Mills, Inc., Hickory, NC; *U.S. Private*, pg. 996
Shull, Douglas K., Chief Fin. Officer & Treas.--Casey's General Stores, Inc., Ankeny, IA; *U.S. Public*, pg. 312
Shultz, Thomas E., V.P. & Asst. Treasurer--Triarc Companies, Inc., New York, NY; *U.S. Public*, pg. 1634
Shunsky, Vincent, V.P.-Fin. & Treas.--Maxco, Inc., Lansing, MI; *U.S. Public*, pg. 1061
Shurr, David C., Asst. Treas.--NICOR Inc., Naperville, IL; *U.S. Public*, pg. 1182
Sial, Vic, V.P., Treas. & Asst. Sec.--Advanced Logic Research, Inc., Irvine, CA; *U.S. Public*, pg. 703
Sibold, Ronald G., Treas.--SCI Systems, Inc., Huntsville, AL; *U.S. Public*, pg. 1416
Sica, Heather A., C.P.A., Exec. V.P. & Treas.--Litchfield Financial Corporation, Williamstown, MA; *U.S. Public*, pg. 1001
Sicotte, Luc, V.P. & Treas.--The Laurentian Group Corporation, Montreal, Canada; *Int'l*, pg. 396
Sicotte, Luc, V.P.-Fin. & Treas.--G.T.C. Transcontinental Group Ltd., Montreal, Canada; *Int'l*, pg. 538
Siegel, Aaron, Treas. & Consultant--Butler Ventamatic Corp., Mineral Wells, TX; *U.S. Private*, pg. 190
Siegel, James A., Treas.--Spectrum Control, Inc., Erie, PA; *U.S. Public*, pg. 1497
Siegel, Jordan, Treas.--IVAX Corporation, Miami, FL; *U.S. Public*, pg. 914
Siegel, S.L., Treas. & Sec.--R.S. Owens, Chicago, IL; *U.S. Private*, pg. 824
Siegel, Samuel, Co-Vice Chm., Chief Fin. Officer, Treas. & Sec.--Nucor Corporation, Charlotte, NC; *U.S. Public*, pg. 1205
Siegfried, Edward R., Chief Fin. Officer, V.P.-Fin. & Opers. & Treas.--NewsEdge Corporation, Burlington, MA; *U.S. Public*, pg. 1180
Sieple, Jeanne, Treas. & Sec.--Mike Daugherty's Chevrolet Geo, Inc., Sacramento, CA; *U.S. Private*, pg. 313
Sigler, George, Treas.--Urschel Labs Incorporated, Valparaiso, IN; *U.S. Private*, pg. 1129
Sigman, Richard, Chief Fin. Officer--IWI Holding Limited, Westmont, IL; *U.S. Public*, pg. 861
Signorini, John E., Chief Fin. Officer, Exec. V.P. & Treas.--The F.A. Bartlett Tree Expert Co., Stamford, CT; *U.S. Private*, pg. 119
Siikarla, Neil A., Treas.--Northern States Power Co. (Wis.), Eau Claire, WI; *U.S. Public*, pg. 1195
Silberbogen, Paul M., Treas. & Sec.--Oakite Products, Inc., Berkeley Heights, NJ; *Int'l*, pg. 861
Silk, Arthur T., Jr., V.P. & Treas.--BJ's Wholesale Club, Inc., Natick, MA; *U.S. Public*, pg. 162
Silles, Victor, Chief Fin. Officer & Treas.--Thetford Corporation, Ann Arbor, MI; *U.S. Private*, pg. 352
Silny, Frederick G., Chief Fin. Officer & V.P.--IHOP Corp., Glendale, CA; *U.S. Public*, pg. 862
Silver, Larry, Treas. & V.P.-Opers.--International Cutlery, LTD, New York, NY; *U.S. Private*, pg. 569
Silverglat, Alan, V.P. & Treas.--Knight-Ridder, Inc., Miami, FL; *U.S. Public*, pg. 963
Sima, Tatsumi, Treas.--Rohto Pharmaceutical Co., Osaka, Japan; *Int'l*, pg. 1126
Simkins, Richard C., Chief Fin. Officer, Exec. V.P., Treas. & Sec.--Knape & Vogt Mfg. Co., Grand Rapids, MI; *U.S. Public*, pg. 963
Simmers, Scott, Controller, Treas., & Sec.--Power Process Piping, Inc., Plymouth, MI; *U.S. Private*, pg. 878
Simmons, Constance L., Asst. Treas.--American Express Credit Corporation, Wilmington, DE; *U.S. Public*, pg. 74

Simmons, D. Ramsay, III, V.P., Treas., & Sec.--Elberta Crate & Box Company, Bainbridge, GA; *U.S. Private*, pg. 367

Simmons, L. Craig, Chief Fin. Officer, V.P. & Treas.--Alico, Inc., La Belle, FL; *U.S. Public*, pg. 41

Simmons, Samuel L., Jr., V.P.-Fin. & Treas.--Inamed Corporation, Las Vegas, NV; *U.S. Public*, pg. 873

Simmons, William S., Chief Acctg. Officer, V.P. & Treas.--Dick Clark Productions, Inc., Burbank, CA; *U.S. Public*, pg. 382

Simon, Arthur, Chm. Bd. & Treas.--Eagle Button Co., Inc., Carlstadt, NJ; *U.S. Private*, pg. 354

Simon, Donald R., Chm. Bd., Pres. & Treas.--Contractors Steel Company, Livonia, MI; *U.S. Private*, pg. 270

Simon, G., Treas.--Australian National Industries Limited, Pyrmont, Australia; *Int'l*, pg. 100

Simon, Ira, V.P.--Triangle Brass Manufacturing, Los Angeles, CA; *U.S. Private*, pg. 1101

Simon, Lawrence F., Sr. V.P. & Treas.--Riddell Sports, Inc., Chicago, IL; *U.S. Public*, pg. 1389

Simon, Mary T., Treas., Sec. & Dir.-Personnel--J.L. Lester & Son, Inc., Rockmart, GA; *U.S. Private*, pg. 660

Simon, Norman, V.P., Treas. & Sec.--Joseph Simon & Sons, Inc., Tacoma, WA; *U.S. Private*, pg. 1001

Simon, Robert P., V.P. & Treas.--Brascade Resources Inc., Toronto, Canada; *Int'l*, pg. 433

Simonson, John A., Sr. V.P. & Treas.--Keycorp, Cleveland, OH; *U.S. Public*, pg. 954

Simpson, Frank X., V.P.-Fin. & Treas.--Consumers New Jersey Water Company, Hamilton, NJ; *U.S. Public*, pg. 438

Simpson, John S., Chief Fin. Officer, V.P. & Treas.--Dana Corporation, Toledo, OH; *U.S. Public*, pg. 479

Simpson, Rick, Asst. Treas.--International Comfort Products, Franklin, TN; *U.S. Public*, pg. 898

Sims, Charles R., Treas.--Franklin Resources, Inc., San Mateo, CA; *U.S. Public*, pg. 679

Sims, Jerry L., Pres. & Treas.--Hilb, Rogal and Hamilton Company of Houston, Houston, TX; *U.S. Public*, pg. 827

Sinagra, Jack G., Sr. V.P. & Asst. Treas.--Turtle & Hughes, Inc., Linden, NJ; *U.S. Private*, pg. 1110

Sinclair, Coral, V.P.--DEECO Industries, Hillside, NJ; *U.S. Private*, pg. 320

Singelyn, Dave, V.P. & Treas.--Public Storage, Inc., Glendale, CA; *U.S. Public*, pg. 1340

Singer, W. Douglas, Exec. V.P. & Treas.--Long Island Bancorp, Inc., Melville, NY; *U.S. Public*, pg. 1013

Singleton, Arthur W., V.P., Treas. & Sec.--Tech Data Corporation, Clearwater, FL; *U.S. Public*, pg. 1562

Sinn, Duane L., Asst. V.P. & Treas.--Rurban Financial Corp., Defiance, OH; *U.S. Public*, pg. 1412

Sinnott, Lawrence W., Chief Fin. Officer, V.P. & Treas.--Versar Inc., Springfield, VA; *U.S. Public*, pg. 1717

Sinsheimer, John, Treas.--Encyclopaedia Britannica, Inc., Chicago, IL; *U.S. Private*, pg. 375

Sipe, James R., Treas.--ComSonics, Inc., Harrisonburg, VA; *U.S. Private*, pg. 260

Sirotkin, Mark, Treas.--Rapid Industrial Plastics Company, Jersey City, NJ; *U.S. Private*, pg. 910

Siser, Robert, Controller & Treas.--T C Manufacturing Company, Inc., Evanston, IL; *U.S. Private*, pg. 1062

Sisk, Larry A., V.P. & Treas.--Chicago Title & Trust Co., Chicago, IL; *U.S. Public*, pg. 42

Sismondo, Peter R., V.P., Controller, Treas. & Asst. Sec.--Alleghany Corporation, New York, NY; *U.S. Public*, pg. 42

Sistarenik, Alexander J., Treas.--Garan, Incorporated, New York, NY; *U.S. Public*, pg. 703

Sitkoff, Bob, V.P. & Treas.--Blimpie International, Inc., Atlanta, GA; *U.S. Public*, pg. 236

Sivignon, Pierre-Jean, Treas.--Schlumberger Limited, New York, NY; *U.S. Public*, pg. 1439

Sivillo, Kent R., V.P. & Treas.--Blair Corporation, Warren, PA; *U.S. Public*, pg. 236

Skaff, Ramez G., Treas. & Sec.--Interstate Resources, Inc., Rosslyn, VA; *U.S. Private*, pg. 573

Skelton, Wesley M., Treas.--Martin Gas Corporation, Kilgore, TX; *U.S. Private*, pg. 709

Skinner, Bruce, V.P. & Treas.--Kit Manufacturing Company, Long Beach, CA; *U.S. Public*, pg. 962

Skinner, James E., Chief Fin. Officer, Exec. V.P., Treas. & Asst. Sec.--CompUSA, Dallas, TX; *U.S. Public*, pg. 420

Skinner, Karen, Treas.--Bearing Headquarters Co., Broadview, IL; *U.S. Private*, pg. 127

Skinner, William T. Jr., V.P. & Treas.--MBC Agency, Inc., Baltimore, MD; *U.S. Public*, pg. 1089

Sklut, Josef, V.P.-Fin., Treas., Sec.--Speizman Industries, Inc., Charlotte, NC; *U.S. Public*, pg. 1498

Skophammer, Robin W., Chief Fin. Officer, Treas. & Sec.--Craig Corporation, Los Angeles, CA; *U.S. Public*, pg. 456

Skowronski, Walter E., V.P. & Treas.--Lockheed Martin Corporation, Bethesda, MD; *U.S. Public*, pg. 1006

Skrivan, Mick, Treas.--Robertshaw Controls Company, Richmond, VA; *Int'l*, pg. 1243

Skurek, John C., V.P. & Treas.--The LTV Corporation, Cleveland, OH; *U.S. Public*, pg. 971

Slack, John L., Chm. Bd., Pres., Chief Exec. Officer & Acting Treas.--DBA Systems, Inc., Melbourne, FL; *U.S. Public*, pg. 472

Slagle, Roy, V.P. & Treas.--ABF Freight System, Inc., Fort Smith, AR; *U.S. Public*, pg. 130

Slaten, Paul E., Treas.--Sunnen Products Company, Saint Louis, MO; *U.S. Private*, pg. 1053

Slavin, Steven M., V.P.-Taxes & Treas.--Western Digital Corporation, Irvine, CA; *U.S. Public*, pg. 1758

Sleeman, Donald G., Chief Fin. Officer, Sr. V.P., Controller & Treas.--The Turner Corporation, New York, NY; *U.S. Public*, pg. 1645

Sleet, Robert E., Jr., V.P. & Treas.--Global Marine Inc., Houston, TX; *U.S. Public*, pg. 748

Slevin, Paul C., Chief Fin. Officer & Treas.--Tipperary Corporation, Denver, CO; *U.S. Public*, pg. 1618

Slifka, Richard, Treas.--Global Petroleum Corp., Waltham, MA; *U.S. Private*, pg. 457

Slingerlend, Mac J., Pres. & Chief Oper. Officer--Ciber, Inc., Englewood, CO; *U.S. Public*, pg. 356

Sliwkoski, Charles P. Jr., Treas.--First American Title Insurance Co. of N.Y., New York, NY; *U.S. Public*, pg. 626

Sloan, Jay, V.P.-Fin. & Treas.--Guest Services, Inc., Fairfax, VA; *U.S. Private*, pg. 486

Sloan, Kerry, Chief Fin. Officer, V.P.-Fin. & Treas.--Hardaway Construction Corp. of Tennessee, Inc., Nashville, TN; *U.S. Private*, pg. 501

Sloan, Patricia L., Sec. & Treas.--Stratton Growth Fund, Inc., Plymouth Meeting, PA; *U.S. Private*, pg. 1046

Sloan, William E. II, Exec. V.P., Treas. & Sec.--Sloan Valve Company, Franklin Park, IL; *U.S. Private*, pg. 1006

Slotten, Nancy, Exec. V.P. & Treas.--Border States Paving, Inc., Fargo, ND; *U.S. Private*, pg. 160

Small, David L., Chief Oper. Officer & Treas.--Nelson & Small Inc., Portland, ME; *U.S. Private*, pg. 790

Small, George M., Pres.--Offshore Logistics, Inc., Lafayette, LA; *U.S. Public*, pg. 1212

Smallen, Lawrence H., Chief Fin. Officer, Sr. V.P.-Fin. & Treas.--Apria Healthcare Group Inc., Costa Mesa, CA; *U.S. Public*, pg. 125

Smallman, C., Controller & Treas.--Stanford Telecommunications, Sunnyvale, CA; *U.S. Public*, pg. 1508

Smallwood, James V., V.P. & Treas.--Florida Progress Corporation, Saint Petersburg, FL; *U.S. Public*, pg. 655

Smallwood, James V., V.P. & Treas.--Florida Power Corporation, Saint Petersburg, FL; *U.S. Public*, pg. 655

Smar, Doreen, Treas.--American Country Insurance Co., Chicago, IL; *U.S. Private*, pg. 1030

Smaston, Russell, Treas.--Exotic Rubber & Plastics Corp., Farmington Hills, MI; *U.S. Private*, pg. 388

Smelthurst, William, Jr., Asst. Treas. & Asst. Sec.--South Jersey Industries, Inc., Folsom, NJ; *U.S. Public*, pg. 1488

Smiley, Keith R., V.P. & Treas.--RPM, Inc., Medina, OH; *U.S. Public*, pg. 1356

Smilowitz, Bernard, Treas. & Sec.--Allied Building Products Corporation, East Rutherford, NJ; *U.S. Private*, pg. 38

Smith, Alex C., V.P. & Treas.--Dell Computer Corporation, Round Rock, TX; *U.S. Public*, pg. 495

Smith, Cindy W., Treas. & Sec.--Camping World, Inc., Bowling Green, KY; *U.S. Private*, pg. 204

Smith, D. Todd, Treas.--Torstar Corporation, Toronto, Canada; *Int'l*, pg. 1402

Smith, David, Treas.--The Hunt Corporation, Indianapolis, IN; *U.S. Private*, pg. 548

Smith, David P., Asst. Treas.-Intl.--McCormick & Company, Incorporated, Sparks, MD; *U.S. Public*, pg. 1066

Smith, Deborah B., Treas.--Burgess Pigment Co., Sandersville, GA; *U.S. Private*, pg. 182

Smith, Donald G., Chm. Bd., Pres., Chief Exec. Officer & Treas.--Roanoke Electric Steel Corporation, Roanoke, VA; *U.S. Public*, pg. 1392

Smith, Donna, V.P. & Treas.--Transport Insurance Co., Dallas, TX; *U.S. Public*, pg. 75

Smith, Donna Beck, V.P., Sec. & Treas.--Allied Healthcare Products, Inc., Saint Louis, MO; *U.S. Public*, pg. 48

Smith, Douglas B., V.P. & Treas.--Primedia Inc., New York, NY; *U.S. Public*, pg. 1327

Smith, Drew, Treas.--Melitta U.S.A., Inc., Clearwater, FL; *Int'l*, pg. 857

Smith, Ed, Treas. & Sec.--Martin & Bayley Inc., Carmi, IL; *U.S. Private*, pg. 708

Smith, Gary, V.P.-Fin. & Treas.--The Andersons Incorporated, Maumee, OH; *U.S. Public*, pg. 111

Smith, Gary V., Exec. V.P., Treas. & Sec.--Hughes Construction, Inc., North Salt Lake, UT; *U.S. Private*, pg. 546

Smith, Gene, Chief Fin. Officer, Treas. & Sec.--Rollins, Inc., Atlanta, GA; *U.S. Public*, pg. 1404

Smith, Glenn A., V.P. & Treas.--Blue Tee Corporation, New York, NY; *U.S. Private*, pg. 153

Smith, Grace, Controller & Treas.--R&R Advertising, Las Vegas, NV; *U.S. Private*, pg. 902

Smith, Gregory L., Treas.--Flowserve Corporation, Dayton, OH; *U.S. Public*, pg. 658

Smith, Harry C., Treas. & Sec.--Daily Express, Inc., Carlisle, PA; *U.S. Private*, pg. 307

Smith, Hudson D., Treas. & Gen. Mgr.-Forge Grp.--Sifco Industries, Inc., Cleveland, OH; *U.S. Public*, pg. 1470

Smith, I.J.S., Treas.--Dawson International PLC, Edinburgh, United Kingdom; *Int'l*, pg. 385

Smith, Jill Jones, Treas.--Jones & Jones, Inc., McAllen, TX; *U.S. Private*, pg. 596

Smith, Kathi, Treas. & Sec.--Damsmith Corp., Sanford, NC; *U.S. Private*, pg. 309

Smith, Kevin M., V.P. & Treas.--Edison Mission Energy, Irvine, CA; *U.S. Public*, pg. 564

Smith, L.S., Dr., Chm. Bd., Chief Exec. Officer, Treas. & Sec.--Dallas Gold & Silver Exchange, Inc., Dallas, TX; *U.S. Public*, pg. 478

Smith, Lachlan M., Chief Fin. Officer, Sr. V.P. & Treas.--National City Bank, Kentucky, Louisville, KY; *U.S. Public*, *pg. 1154*

Smith, Laura, Dir.-Investor Rels.--US Airways Group, Inc., Arlington, VA; *U.S. Public*, pg. 1680

Smith, Les, Treas. & Sec.--Buhrman-Pharr Hardware Company, Texarkana, AR; *U.S. Private*, pg. 179

Smith, M. Garrett, Chief Fin. Officer, Sr. V.P. & Treas.--Pioneer Natural Resources Co., Irving, TX; *U.S. Public*, pg. 1299

Smith, M.W., Treas.--Texas Generating Company, Fort Worth, TX; *U.S. Public*, pg. 1557

Smith, M.W., V.P. & Treas.--Facility Works Inc., Fort Worth, TX; *U.S. Public*, pg. 1557

Smith, Marlan R., Chief Fin. Officer & Treas.--C.R.A. Holdings Inc., Kalamazoo, MI; *U.S. Private*, pg. 1029

Smith, Marlan R., V.P. & Treas.--CMC Kalamazoo Inc., Kalamazoo, MI; *U.S. Private*, pg. 1030

Smith, Michael D., V.P. & Treas.--Mercantile Bank of Iowa, Des Moines, IA; *U.S. Public*, pg. 1087

Smith, Michelle, Treas. & Sec.--Aycock, Inc., Hummelstown, PA; *U.S. Private*, pg. 103

Smith, Mike, Treas. & Sec.--Kelsey Construction, Inc., Orlando, FL; *U.S. Private*, pg. 613

Smith, Patty J., Asst. V.P.-Fin. & Treas.--VASA Brougher, Inc., Indianapolis, IN; *Int'l*, pg. 464

Smith, Pierce, Treas.--PaineWebber Group Incorporated, New York, NY; *U.S. Public*, pg. 1252

Smith, Randall E., V.P. & Treas.--Horace Small Apparel Company, Nashville, TN; *Int'l*, pg. 635

Smith, Randall E., V.P. & Treas.--R & R Uniforms, Nashville, TN; *Int'l*, pg. 635

Smith, Rhen D., Treas. & Controller--Hofmann Industries, Inc., Sinking Spring, PA; *U.S. Private*, pg. 533

Smith, Richard C., Treas.--The Stanley Consultants Group, Muscatine, IA; *U.S. Private*, pg. 1032

Smith, Richard C., Treas.--Stanley Design-Build, Inc., Muscatine, IA; *U.S. Private*, pg. 1033

Smith, Richard C., Treas.--Stanley Enviromental, Inc., Coralville, IA; *U.S. Private*, pg. 1033

Smith, Richard C., Treas.--Stanley Consultants, Inc., Muscatine, IA; *U.S. Private*, pg. 1033

Smith, Richard E., Treas.--Dynamics Corporation of America, Greenwich, CT; *U.S. Public*, pg. 286

Smith, Robert, Asst. Treas.--The Berlin Steel Construction Company, Berlin, CT; *U.S. Private*, pg. 136

Smith, Robert J., V.P. & Treas.--National Learning Systems, Inc., Scranton, PA; *U.S. Public*, pg. 783

Smith, Robert J., V.P. & Treas.--NBD Incorporated, Scranton, PA; *U.S. Public*, pg. 783

Smith, Robert Lewis, Controller, Treas. & Sec.--Hankins Lumber Company, Inc., Elliott, MS; *U.S. Private*, pg. 499

Smith, Russell N., Treas.--MPI International, Inc., Rochester Hills, MI; *Int'l*, pg. 737

Smith, Shelby, Sr., Treas. & Sec.--Smith Management Co., Inc., Shreveport, LA; *U.S. Private*, pg. 1009

Smith, Steve J., V.P. & Treas.--Placer Dome Inc., Vancouver, Canada; *Int'l*, pg. 1060

Smith, Terry, Asst. Treas.--Mary Kay, Inc., Dallas, TX; *U.S. Private*, pg. 711

Smith, Thomas W., Controller & Treas.--National Retail Hardware Assn., Indianapolis, IN; *U.S. Private*, pg. 786

Smith, Walter A., Asst. Treas.--Rubbermaid Incorporated, Wooster, OH; *U.S. Public*, pg. 1411

Smith, Wayne H., V.P. & Treas.--Avery Dennison Corporation, Pasadena, CA; *U.S. Public*, pg. 152

Smith, William J., Asst. Treas.--American Family Mutual Insurance Co., Madison, WI; *U.S. Private*, pg. 53

Smith, William M., V.P. & Treas.--Cott Corporation, Pointe-Claire, Canada; *Int'l*, pg. 337

Smith, William M., Treas.--McKenzie Tank Lines, Inc., Tallahassee, FL; *U.S. Private*, pg. 723

Smoak, Robert R., V.P., Treas. & Sec.--Bernhardt Furniture Co., Lenoir, NC; *U.S. Private*, pg. 137

Smyk, David C., V.P. & Treas.--U.S. Healthcare, Inc., Blue Bell, PA; *U.S. Public*, pg. 26

Smythe, Meilee, V.P. & Asst. Treas.--The FINOVA Group Inc., Phoenix, AZ; *U.S. Public*, pg. 624

Snavely, Charles, Treas.--Duchossois Industries, Inc., Elmhurst, IL; *U.S. Private*, pg. 344

Snavely, Katherine A., V.P.-Fin. & Treas.--Calspan SRL Corporation, Washington, DC; *U.S. Private*, pg. 1136

Snelling, Andrew P., Treas. & Sec.--The Shelburne Corporation, Shelburne, VT; *U.S. Private*, pg. 991

Snopkowski, Daniel M., V.P. & Treas.--World Color Press, Inc., Greenwich, CT; *U.S. Public*, pg. 1778

Snydacker, William F., Treas.--HON Industries Inc., Muscatine, IA; *U.S. Public*, pg. 772

Snyder, Kathryn D., Exec. V.P. & Treas.--Glendale Federal Bank, F.S.B., Glendale, CA; *U.S. Public*, pg. 747

Snyder, Lance, Controller--McLaughlin Manufacturing Company, Greenville, SC; *U.S. Private*, pg. 724

Snyder, Richard A., Chief Fin. Officer, V.P. & Treas.--Tennant Company, Minneapolis, MN; *U.S. Public*, pg. 1577

Snyder, S.I., Chief Fin. Officer, Sr. V.P.-Fin., Treas. & Sec.--Kaufman Footwear, Kitchener, Canada; *Int'l*, pg. 725

Snyder, Thomas J., V.P. & Treas.--United Dominion Industries, Ltd., Charlotte, NC; *U.S. Public*, pg. 1675

Sobo, William T., Jr., Chief Fin. Officer, Sr. V.P. & Treas.--PAREXEL International Corporation, Waltham, MA; *U.S. Public*, pg. 1257

Soczek, Joseph L., Jr., Treas.--Winnebago Industries, Inc., Forest City, IA; *U.S. Public*, pg. 1772

Soderberg, Kathleen, Treas.--National Bancorp of Alaska, Inc., Anchorage, AK; *U.S. Public*, pg. 1153

Sodhani, Arvind, V.P. & Treas.--Intel Corporation, Santa Clara, CA; *U.S. Public*, pg. 886

Soffer, Robert M., Treas. & Asst. Sec.--Rogers Corporation, Rogers, CT; *U.S. Public*, pg. 1402

Sofia, Zuheir, Pres., Chief Oper. Officer & Treas.--Huntington Bancshares Inc., Columbus, OH; *U.S. Public*, pg. 849

Sohl, Marvel, Controller & Treas.--Bluewater, Mora, MN; *U.S. Private*, pg. 153

Soice, Douglas E., Treas.--Rigel Energy Corporation, Calgary, Canada; *Int'l*, pg. 1117

Sokalsky, Jamie C., Treas.--Barrick Gold Corporation, Toronto, Canada; *Int'l*, pg. 168

Solan, Tom, Treas.--S & S Graphics, Inc., Laurel, MD; *U.S. Private*, pg. 955

Solberg, Jeffrey M., Treas.--Growmark, Inc., Bloomington, IL; *U.S. Private*, pg. 484

Solcher, Stephen B., Treas.--BMC Software, Inc., Houston, TX; *U.S. Public*, pg. 162

Solda, Marc, Pres. & Treas.--Jamison Plastic Corporation, Allentown, PA; *U.S. Private*, pg. 581

Solheim, Bob, V.P.-Fin. & Admin.--Solvay Pharmaceuticals, Inc., Marietta, GA; *Int'l*, pg. 1278

Solis, H. Pat, Treas.--Serv-Tech, Inc., Houston, TX; *U.S. Public*, pg. 1460

Sollenberger, Mark L., Exec. V.P., Treas. & Asst. Sec.--BT Financial Corporation, Johnstown, PA; *U.S. Public*, pg. 163

Sollenberger, Mark L., Treas. & Asst. Sec.--Bedford Associates, Inc., Johnstown, PA; *U.S. Public*, pg. 164

Sollenberger, Mark L., Exec. V.P. & Treas.--Laurel Bank, Johnstown, PA; *U.S. Public*, pg. 164

Sollenberger, Mark L., Treas. & Asst. Sec.--Laurel Community Development Corporation, Johnstown, PA; *U.S. Public*, pg. 164

Solock, Douglas J., V.P., Sec. & Treas.--Regency Finance Company, Hermitage, PA; *U.S. Public*, pg. 607

Solomon, Chadi, Treas.--Shaw Industries Ltd., Etobicoke, Canada; *Int'l*, pg. 1231

Solomon, Michael K., V.P. & Treas.--Decorator Industries, Inc., Pembroke Pines, FL; *U.S. Public*, pg. 491

Solski, B.P., Exec. V.P. & Treas.--Baycoat, Hamilton, Canada; *Int'l*, pg. 414

Somer, S., Treas.--Neil Faber Media Inc., New York, NY; *U.S. Private*, pg. 390

Somich, Stephen H., Asst. Treas.--GPU, Inc., Morristown, NJ; *U.S. Public*, pg. 695

Sommer, James, Pres., Chief Oper. & Fin. Officer & Treas.--Service Motor Company, Dale, WI; *U.S. Private*, pg. 986

Sonksen, David R., Chief Fin Officer, V.P.-Fin., Treas. & Sec.--Microsemi Corporation, Santa Ana, CA; *U.S. Public*, pg. 1107

Sons, Kevin, Treas. & Sec.--Bongards Creameries Inc., Norwood, MN; *U.S. Private*, pg. 156

Sonsteby, Charles, V.P. & Treas.--Brinker International, Inc., Dallas, TX; *U.S. Public*, pg. 253

Sorblum, Susan M., Treas.--Cambrex Corporation, East Rutherford, NJ; *U.S. Public*, pg. 297

Sorden, Michael R., Sec. & Treas.--Commercial Light Company, Hillside, IL; *U.S. Private*, pg. 258

Sorenson, Kenneth R., Chief Fin. Officer & Treas.--Ballard Medical Products, Draper, UT; *U.S. Public*, pg. 171

Sorheim, Dennis R., Treas. & Sec.--Peoples Electric Contractor, Inc., Saint Paul, MN; *U.S. Private*, pg. 851

Sorsby, J. Larry, Chief Fin. Officer, Sr. V.P. & Treas.--Hovnanian Enterprises, Inc., Red Bank, NJ; *U.S. Public*, pg. 843

Sorzano, Carl L., Chief Fin. Officer & Treas.--DeVault Foods, Devault, PA; *U.S. Private*, pg. 329

Sosh, Michael F., V.P. & Treas.--Lexford Residential Trust, Columbus, OH; *U.S. Public*, pg. 991

Sosnoski, Donald S., Chief Fin. Officer, V.P. & Treas.--PVS Chemicals, Inc., Detroit, MI; *U.S. Private*, pg. 828

Soto, Raymond M., Pres., Chief Exec. & Fin. Officer & Treas.--Bolt Technology Corporation, Norwalk, CT; *U.S. Public*, pg. 244

Sottile, Emily, Asst. Treas.--Lake Placid Groves, Lake Placid, FL; *U.S. Public*, pg. 437

Sottile, Emily J., Asst. Sec. & Asst. Treas.--Consolidated-Tomoka Land Co., Daytona Beach, FL; *U.S. Public*, pg. 437

Soukup, Robert, Treas.--Meggitt USA, Inc., Manchester, NH; *Int'l*, pg. 853

Southern, Douglas G., Chief Fin. Officer & Sr. V.P.--Immunex Corporation, Seattle, WA; *U.S. Public*, pg. 871

Souza, Ralph, Chief Fin. Officer, V.P. & Treas.--BIW Cable Systems, Inc., Franklin, MA; *Int'l*, pg. 417

Spacht, David B., Chief Fin. Officer, V.P. & Treas.--Artesian Resources Corporation, Newark, DE; *U.S. Public*, pg. 135

Spak, Bill, Treas.--Rawlings Sporting Goods Company, Fenton, MO; *U.S. Public*, pg. 1361

Spampinato, J.P., Treas.--Longs Drug Stores California, Inc., Walnut Creek, CA; *U.S. Public*, pg. 1013

Spanier, Joseph, Chief Fin. Officer, V.P. & Treas.--TransTechnology Corporation, Liberty Corner, NJ; *U.S. Public*, pg. 1632

Sparks, W. Alvon, Jr., Treas.--Criterion Life Insurance Co., Washington, DC; *U.S. Public*, pg. 219

Sparreo, Lisa, Treas.--Champion Business Forms, Glendale Heights, IL; *U.S. Private*, pg. 228

Spartz, Marvin, Treas.--Northland Electric Supply Company, Minneapolis, MN; *U.S. Private*, pg. 806

Spector, Morton, Chm. Bd. & Treas.--D&H Distributing Company, Harrisburg, PA; *U.S. Private*, pg. 300

Spector, Paul, Chief Fin. Officer, Sr. V.P., Treas. & Sec.--Aris Industries, Inc., New York, NY; *U.S. Public*, pg. 129

Spence, G. Robert, Treas. & Asst. Sec.--Dacco, Inc., Cookeville, TN; *U.S. Private*, pg. 598

Spence, Greg, Sec. & Treas.--Ancira Enterprises Inc., San Antonio, TX; *U.S. Private*, pg. 71

Spencer, J. Greg, Sr. V.P., Treas. & Asst. Sec.--American Stores Company, Salt Lake City, UT; *U.S. Public*, pg. 92

Spencer, Marilyn, Sec. & Treas.--Faber Enterprises, Inc., Canoga Park, CA; *U.S. Private*, pg. 390

Spencer, R. Michael, Sr. V.P. & Treas.--PCA International, Inc., Matthews, NC; *U.S. Public*, pg. 1240

Spencer, R.W., Chief Fin. Officer & V.P.--W.A. Roosevelt Co., La Crosse, WI; *U.S. Private*, pg. 943

Spencer, William E., Treas.--Cavenham Forest Industries Inc., Portland, OR; *Int'l*, pg. 593

Spenny, Richard, Treas. & Sec.--S&S Domestic International Sales Corp., Houston, TX; *U.S. Public*, pg. 1517

Spenny, Richard, Sec. & Treas.--Stewart & Stevenson Holdings, Inc., Houston, TX; *U.S. Public*, pg. 1517

Sperduto, Michael A., Treas.--Engelhard Corporation, Iselin, NJ; *U.S. Public*, pg. 582

Sperling, Peter V., V.P.-Admin., Treas. & Sec.--Apollo Group, Inc., Phoenix, AZ; *U.S. Public*, pg. 120

Speyer, Robert, Treas.--Tennsco Corporation, Dickson, TN; *U.S. Private*, pg. 1077

Spiegelman, Daniel, Treas.--Genentech, Inc., South San Francisco, CA; *Int'l*, pg. 1120

Spies, John, Asst. Treas.--Harnischfeger Industries, Inc., Saint Francis, WI; *U.S. Public*, pg. 788

Spilka, Leonard S., V.P.-Fin. & Treas.--King World Productions, Inc., New York, NY; *U.S. Public*, pg. 961

Spilker, Frank, Chief Fin. Officer & Treas.--Cummins Intermountain Diesel, Salt Lake City, UT; *U.S. Private*, pg. 295

Spires, Roy, Treas. & Sec.--B C Sugar Refinery, Ltd., Vancouver, Canada; *Int'l*, pg. 103

Spiro, Mark F., Chief Fin. Officer, V.P.-Fin., Treas. & Sec.--Calprop Corporation, Marina Del Rey, CA; *U.S. Public*, pg. 296

Spitz, Arnold J., Exec. V.P., Treas. & Sec.--International Seaway Trading Corporation, Boca Raton, FL; *U.S. Private*, pg. 572

Spitz, Randy J., Controller, Treas. & Sec.--Hicks Oil-Hicks Gas, Inc., Roberts, IL; *U.S. Private*, pg. 526

Spitzer, Albert, V.P. & Treas.--Perfect Pearl Company, Inc., New York, NY; *U.S. Private*, pg. 852

Spivak, Fred, V.P.-Fin. & Treas.--Lifetime Hoan Corp., Westbury, NY; *U.S. Public*, pg. 992

Splain, Francis J., Jr., Pres. & Treas.--Resolute Management Corp., Stamford, CT; *U.S. Public*, pg. 220

Spokowski, David, Treas.--FiberMark Inc., Brattleboro, VT; *U.S. Public*, pg. 620

Spooner, G.L., Asst. Treas.--Texas Generating Company, Fort Worth, TX; *U.S. Public*, pg. 1557

Spradley, James W., Jr., Pres. & Chief Exec. Officer--Standard Candy Co., Inc., Nashville, TN; *U.S. Private*, pg. 1030

Spratling, B.B., Jr., Treas. & Sec.--Dixie Electric Cooperative, Union Springs, AL; *U.S. Private*, pg. 337

Spreadbury, Fred, Treas.--Distributed Systems Division, Lisle, IL; *U.S. Public*, pg. 1522

Spriggs, Dennis, Treas.--Utilimaster Corp., Wakarusa, IN; *U.S. Private*, pg. 1130

Springer, Branch J., Chief Fin. Officer, V.P. & Treas.--Abbey Etna Machine Company, Perrysburg, OH; *U.S. Private*, pg. 9

Springer, Clyde H., Treas.--UniGroup, Inc., Fenton, MO; *U.S. Private*, pg. 1117

Springer, June, Treas. & Sec.--Smith Motors, Inc., Hammond, IN; *U.S. Private*, pg. 1009

Spruyt, Michael, Chief Fin. Officer, V.P. & Treas.--Bloomsburg Mills Inc., New York, NY; *U.S. Private*, pg. 150

St. John, Jonelle, V.P. & Treas.--MCI Communications Corp., Atlanta, GA; *U.S. Public*, pg. 1023

St. Michel, Mark, Sec., Treas. & Controller--Aero Systems Engineering Inc., Saint Paul, MN; *Int'l*, pg. 276

Staberg, James, Treas.--Hawk Management Corporation, Overland Park, KS; *U.S. Private*, pg. 511

Stabler, Donald B., Chm. Bd.--Stabler Companies, Inc., Harrisburg, PA; *U.S. Private*, pg. 1028

Stachler, Ken, V.P. & Treas.--Crawford & Company, Atlanta, GA; *U.S. Public*, pg. 458

Stacy, Robert, Treas.--Kemper Insurance Companies, Long Grove, IL; *U.S. Private*, pg. 614

Staelens, Peter, Chief Fin. Officer, Treas. & Asst. Sec.--Dawn Food Products, Inc., Jackson, MI; *U.S. Private*, pg. 316

Stafford, Rose Ann, Treas. & Sec.--Equity Supply Company, Kalispell, MT; *U.S. Private*, pg. 380

Staffrude, P.R., Controller & Treas.--Duluth, Winnipeg & Pacific Railway Co., Superior, WI; *Int'l*, pg. 258

Stagin, Marylin, Asst. Treas.--Lechters, Inc., Harrison, NJ; *U.S. Public*, pg. 983

Stahl, Blanche B., Treas.--Stahl Specialty Company, Kingsville, MO; *U.S. Private*, pg. 1029

Stahl, Edwin E., Treas--Microflect Company, Inc., Salem, OR; *U.S. Public*, pg. 1707

Stainton, Douglas, V.P. & Treas.--Bank of the Hudson, Poughkeepsie, NY; *U.S. Public*, pg. 1319

Stalzer, Robert J., Sr. V.P.-Admin., Fin., Treas. & Asst. Sec.--Servo Corporation of America, Westbury, NY; *U.S. Private*, pg. 987

Stamper, Conner, Treas. & Dir.--States, Inc., Breckenridge, TX; *U.S. Private*, pg. 1037

Stancliff, Kenneth R., Sr. V.P. & Treas.--First Union Corporation, Charlotte, NC; *U.S. Public*, pg. 639

Stanger, Kent W., Chief Fin. Officer, Treas. & Sec.--Merit Medical Systems, Inc., South Jordan, UT; *U.S. Public*, pg. 1096

Stanhaus, John D., Chief Fin. Officer & V.P.--Shurfine International, Inc., Northlake, IL; *U.S. Private*, pg. 997

Stanley, Ira H., V.P.-Fin. & Treas.--Gosiger Inc., Dayton, OH; *U.S. Private*, pg. 466

Stansberry, Warren H., III, Pres. & Treas.--Stanco Metal Products, Inc., Grand Haven, MI; *U.S. Private*, pg. 1030

Staples, William, Treas.--Rodney Hunt Company, Orange, MA; *U.S. Private*, pg. 549

Stapleton, Richard, Exec. V.P.-Fin. & Admin., Gen. Counsel & Sec.--The Lane Construction Corp., Meriden, CT; *U.S. Private*, pg. 649

Stapleton, William, Treas.--Oxford Health Plans (FL), Inc., Sarasota, FL; *U.S. Public*, pg. 1239

Starkman, Ronald P., Sr. V.P. & Treas.--Borden, Inc., Columbus, OH; *U.S. Private*, pg. 157

Starliper, Dennis A., Mng. Dir. & Treas.--Provident Bank of Maryland, Baltimore, MD; *U.S. Public*, pg. 1337

Starr, James L., Chief Fin. Officer, Sr. V.P. & Treas.--Sierra Health Services, Inc., Las Vegas, NV; *U.S. Public*, pg. 1469

Starr, James L., Treas.--Sierra Health and Life Insurance Company, Inc., Las Vegas, NV; *U.S. Public*, pg. 1469

Starr, Jim, Treas.--Behavioral Healthcare Options, Inc., Las Vegas, NV; *U.S. Public*, pg. 1469

Starr, Thomas F., Asst. Treas.--JLG Industries, Inc., McConnellsburg, PA; *U.S. Public*, pg. 918

Starrett, Frederick D., III, Pres. & Treas.--Penobscot Frozen Foods, Inc., Belfast, ME; *U.S. Private*, pg. 850

Stasco, Daphney, V.P. & Treas.--Sunnydale Farms, Brooklyn, NY; *U.S. Private*, pg. 1053

Statile, Ronald J., V.P. & Treas.--Horsehead Industries, Inc., New York, NY; *U.S. Private*, pg. 540

Staton, Jimmy D., V.P.-Pricing & Plng. & Treas.--CNG Transmission Corporation, Clarksburg, WV; *U.S. Public*, pg. 435

Statz, J.J., V.P. & Treas.--National Rivet & Manufacturing Company, Waupun, WI; *U.S. Private*, pg. 786

Stavro, William, Sr. V.P. & Treas.--Mattel, Inc., El Segundo, CA; *U.S. Public*, pg. 1057

Stawarz, Ray, Asst. Treas.--Federated Mutual Insurance Company, Owatonna, MN; *U.S. Private*, pg. 399

Stebbins, Donald J., V.P. & Treas.--Lear Corporation, Southfield, MI; *U.S. Public*, pg. 981

Steel, James A., V.P. & Treas.--Flint Ink Corp., Detroit, MI; *U.S. Private*, pg. 413

Steele, John J., Chief Fin. Officer, V.P. & Treas.--Werner Enterprises, Inc., Omaha, NE; *U.S. Public*, pg. 1754

Steele, John R., V.P. & Treas.--Spiegel, Inc., Downers Grove, IL; *U.S. Public*, pg. 1498

Steele, Lee C., Chief Fin. Officer, V.P.-Fin. & Treas.--American Science & Engineering, Inc., Billerica, MA; *U.S.* Public, pg. 90

Steenbeke, Joseph J., Chief Fin. Officer, Treas., Sec. & Controller--Spray-Tech, Inc., Longwood, FL; *U.S. Private, pg. 1026*

Stefano, M.W., V.P. & Treas.--Ziegler Thrift Trading, Inc., Minneapolis, MN; *U.S. Public*, pg. 1792

Steffen, Don, V.P.-Fin. & Treas.--Berkel Incorporated, La Porte, IN; *Int'l*, pg. 545

Steffen, Tom M., Asst. Treas.--Gaylord Container Corporation, Deerfield, IL; *U.S. Public*, pg. 704

Stegman, Gary, Treas.--AFLAC Incorporated, Columbus, GA; *U.S. Public*, pg. 28

Stein, Christopher J., Asst. Treas.--Blount International, Inc., Montgomery, AL; *U.S. Public*, pg. 237

Stein, Christopher J., Asst. Treas.--Blount, Inc., Montgomery, AL; *U.S. Public*, pg. 238

Stein, Lewis, Treas. & Sec.--RTG Furniture Corp., Seffner, FL; *U.S. Private*, pg. 905

Stein, Martin, Pres. & Treas.--Sterling Paper Co., Philadelphia, PA; *U.S. Private*, pg. 1041

Steinberg, Charles, Treas.--Global Direct Mail Corp, Port Washington, NY; *U.S. Public*, pg. 747

Steinberg, J.D., Treas.--Consolidated Papers, Inc., Wisconsin Rapids, WI; *U.S. Public*, pg. 436

Steiner, Ron, Treas.--Novar Electronics, Barberton, OH; *U.S. Private*, pg. 808

Steinhart, Conrad, Controller, Treas. & Sec.--Happy Holiday Tree Farms, Sheridan, MI; *U.S. Private*, pg. 254

Steinhauer, Gary, Treas. & Sec.--Madison Dairy Produce Company, Madison, WI; *U.S. Private*, pg. 694

Steinhauer, William R., Treas.--Savannah Sugar Refinery, Savannah, GA; *U.S. Public*, pg. 873

Steinhilber, Don, Chief Fin. Officer, V.P. & Treas.--CTB International Corp., Milford, IN; *U.S. Public*, pg. 284

Steinhilper, James, Dir.-Fin. & Treas.--New Century Energies, Inc., Denver, CO; *U.S. Public*, pg. 1170

Steinhilper, James D., Treas.--Southwestern Public Service Company, Amarillo, TX; *U.S. Public*, pg. 1170

Steltmann, Harry F., Chief Fin. Officer, V.P., Treas & Sec.--Eclipse Inc., Rockford, IL; *U.S. Private*, pg. 360

Stengel, Jerome, Chief Fin. Officer, V.P. & Treas.--Genovese Drug Stores, Inc., Melville, NY; *U.S. Public*, pg. 730

Stenger, James W., Chief Fin. Officer, V.P. & Treas.--The Ailing & Cory Company, Rochester, NY; *U.S. Public*, pg. 1666

Stepenson, Todd R., Chief Fin. Officer, Sr. V.P. & Treas.--American States Insurance Companies, Indianapolis, IN; *U.S. Public*, pg. 997

Stephani, M.J., Treas.--Good Humor/Breyers Ice Cream, Green Bay, WI; *Int'l*, pg. 1435

Stephens, Edward B., Chief Fin. Officer, V.P. & Treas.--Cade Industries, Inc., Lansing, MI; *U.S. Public*, pg. 289

Stephens, Edward B., V.P. & Treas.--Cade International, Inc., Lansing, MI; *U.S. Public*, pg. 290

Stephens, James, Chief Admin. Officer & Treas.--Koger Equity Inc., Jacksonville, FL; *U.S. Public*, pg. 965

Stephens, Joseph M., Chief Fin. Officer, Sr. V.P. & Treas.--Centex-Rodgers Construction Company, Nashville, TN; *U.S. Public*, pg. 322

Stephens, Mark W., Asst. Treas.--Chemed Corporation, Cincinnati, OH; *U.S. Public*, pg. 343

Stephens, Philip A., Treas. & Asst. Sec.--Parsons Precision Products, Inc., Parsons, KS; *U.S. Private*, pg. 598

Stephenson, Douglas A., Treas.--Ruddick Corporation, Charlotte, NC; *U.S. Public*, pg. 1412

Stephenson, G.W., Jr., Pres. & Treas.--Stephenson, Inc., Alexandria, VA; *U.S. Private*, pg. 1040

Stephenson, Leighton J., V.P.-Fin., Treas. & Sec.--Vallen Corporation, Houston, TX; *U.S. Public*, pg. 1705

Stephenson, Todd R., V.P. & Treas.--LINSCO Reinsurance Company, Indianapolis, IN; *U.S. Public*, pg. 998

Stern, Anthony, Treas.--Bass PLC, London, United Kingdom; *Int'l*, pg. 169

Stern, Edwardo, Treas.--Landstar Development Company, Orlando, FL; *U.S. Private*, pg. 649

Sternberg, Vicki, Treas. Analyst--Kimball International, Inc., Jasper, IN; *U.S. Public*, pg. 956

Sterner, Gene E., Treas. & Sec.--Jordon Commercial Refrigerator Co., Philadelphia, PA; *U.S. Private*, pg. 599

Sterrett, Stephen, V.P. & Treas.--Simon DeBartolo Group, Inc., Indianapolis, IN; *U.S. Public*, pg. 1474

Sterrett, W.E., Pres., Chief Fin. Officer & Sec.--Wheaton Van Lines, Inc., Indianapolis, IN; *U.S. Private*, pg. 1171

Stetz, Gordon W., Jr., Asst. Treas.-Fin. Svcs.--McCormick & Company, Incorporated, Sparks, MD; *U.S. Public*, pg. 1066

Steul, William M., Chief Fin. Officer & Treas.--Eaton Vance Corp., Boston, MA; *U.S. Public*, pg. 559

Stevens, Dave, Chief Fin. Officer, Treas. & Sec.--Scott Sports Group, Ketchum, ID; *U.S. Private*, pg. 977

Stevens, Donald W., Chief Fin. Officer, Exec. V.P. & Treas.--Mikohn Gaming Corporation, Las Vegas, NV; *U.S. Public*, pg. 1111

Stevens, Gary, Pres. & Treas.--Integrated Brands Inc., Ronkonkoma, NY; *U.S. Public*, pg. 883

Stevens, Gus, Pres., Chief Oper. Officer & Treas.--Cyberex, Inc., Mentor, OH; *U.S. Public*, pg. 481

Stevens, Jim, J., Jr., Treas. & Sec.--Lincoln Provision, Inc., Chicago, IL; *U.S. Private*, pg. 668

Stevens, Michael C., Controller & Asst. Treas.--Connecticut Natural Gas Corporation, Hartford, CT; *U.S. Public,* pg. 285

Stevenson, Douglas, Treas.--Central Maine Power Company, Augusta, ME; *U.S. Public,* pg. 325

Stevenson, Greg, Treas.--Services Group of America, Seattle, WA; *U.S. Private,* pg. 987

Stevenson, Judy G., Pres., Chief Exec. Officer & Treas.--Magnetrol International, Downers Grove, IL; *U.S. Private, pg. 696*

Stevenson, Kate B., Asst. Treas.--Northern Telecom Limited, Brampton, Canada; *Int'l,* pg. 968

Stewart, Barry L., Pres., Chief Exec. Officer, Chief Fin. Officer & Treas.--Eneco Tech Group, Denver, CO; *U.S. Private,* pg. 376

Stewart, David M., Treas.--Institute For Scientific Information, Philadelphia, PA; *U.S. Public,* pg. 1600

Stewart, Donald, V.P.-Fin. & Treas.--Sequus Pharmaceuticals, Inc., Menlo Park, CA; *U.S. Public,* pg. 1460

Stewart, George H., V.P. & Treas.--Ciba Specialty Chemicals, Tarrytown, NY; *Int'l,* pg. 291

Stewart, Jeff S., Treas.--Oregon Steel Mills Inc., Portland, OR; *U.S. Public,* pg. 1230

Stewart, John C., Treas.--Pizzagalli Construction Co., South Burlington, VT; *U.S. Private,* pg. 868

Stewart, Lee C., V.P. & Treas.--Union Carbide Corporation, Danbury, CT; *U.S. Public,* pg. 1666

Stewart, Michael R., Chief Fin. Officer, V.P., Treas. & Controller--Surgical Laser Technologies, Inc., Montgomeryville, PA; *U.S. Public,* pg. 1542

Stichler, Donald L., Controller, Treas. & Sec.--Varco International, Inc., Orange, CA; *U.S. Public,* pg. 1709

Stiehl, Robert J., Jr., Chief Fin. Officer, Exec. V.P.-Opers. & Treas.--Hampton Industries, Inc., Kinston, NC; *U.S. Public,* pg. 779

Stigall, Ray, Treas.--General Shale Products Corp., Johnson City, TN; *Int'l,* pg. 843

Stigall, Ray, Treas.--General Shale Products Corp., Elizabethton, TN; *Int'l,* pg. 843

Still, James S., Sr. V.P., Chief Fin. Officer & Treas.--Bell Atlantic Properties, Inc., Philadelphia, PA; *U.S. Public,* pg. 203

Stillman, Jedd B., V.P., Treas & Dir.-Personnel--David Michael & Co. Inc., Philadelphia, PA; *U.S. Private,* pg. 740

Stilwell, J.B., Treas.--PQ Corporation, Berwyn, PA; *U.S. Private,* pg. 827

Stilwell, John P., V.P.-Fin. & Treas.--Hecla Mining Company, Coeur D'Alene, ID; *U.S. Public,* pg. 803

Stilwell, Marcia, Treas.--Nike, Inc., Beaverton, OR; *U.S. Public,* pg. 1184

Stimer, Donald B., V.P.-Fin. & Admin. & Treas.--Simplex Time Recorder Co., Gardner, MA; *U.S. Private,* pg. 1002

Stimpson, Gordon S., Treas. & Sec.--Gulf Lumber Company, Inc., Mobile, AL; *U.S. Private,* pg. 487

Stimpson, James R., Treas. & Sec.--Channellock, Inc., Meadville, PA; *U.S. Private,* pg. 229

Stinchcomb, Glenn M., V.P. & Treas.--Oklahoma Publishing Company, Oklahoma City, OK; *U.S. Private,* pg. 813

Stirling, Marlene, Asst. Treas.--Brierley Investments Limited, Wellington, New Zealand; *Int'l,* pg. 215

Stivers, R.N., Chief Fin. Officer, V.P.-Fin., Treas. & Sec.--Temtex Industries Inc., Dallas, TX; *U.S. Public,* pg. 1575

Stivers, R.N., V.P.-Fin., Sec. & Treas.--Temco Fireplace Products, Inc., Nashville, TN; *U.S. Public,* pg. 1576

Stock, Thomas F., Treas.--Abrams Construction, Inc., Atlanta, GA; *U.S. Public,* pg. 14

Stoddart, Christopher, Treas.--KLA Tencor Corporation, San Jose, CA; *U.S. Public,* pg. 939

Stoegbauer, William J., Treas.--Jewelers Mutual Insurance Company, Neenah, WI; *U.S. Private,* pg. 587

Stoll, Larry J., V.P.-Fin., Treas. & Asst. Sec.--St. Joseph Light & Power Co., Saint Joseph, MO; *U.S. Public,* pg. 1427

Stoltmann, Gary, Dir.-Fin. & Asst. Treas.--Kohl's Corporation, Menomonee Falls, WI; *U.S. Public,* pg. 965

Stone, David, Chief Fin. Officer & Treas.--Millipore Tylan Products, San Diego, CA; *U.S. Public,* pg. 1112

Stone, Kathy, V.P., Treas. & Sec.--Ergon, Inc., Jackson, MS; *U.S. Private,* pg. 380

Stone, Samuel G., Treas.--First of America Bank Corporation, Kalamazoo, MI; *U.S. Public,* pg. 636

Stone, Thomas, Treas.--Nutri/System Inc., Horsham, PA; *U.S. Private,* pg. 859

Stoner, Paul, Treasurer--Standard Chartered Bank Malaysia Berhad, Kuala Lumpur, Malaysia; *Int'l,* pg. 1295

Storck, Raymond L., V.P., Controller & Asst. Treas.--MicroAge, Inc., Tempe, AZ; *U.S. Public,* pg. 1104

Stork, Alfred E., Treas. & Asst. Sec.--The Imperial Electric Company, Akron, OH; *U.S. Private,* pg. 598

Story, Robert P., Jr., Treas.--Courier Westford, Inc., Westford, MA; *U.S. Public,* pg. 453

Stouffer, R., V.P. & Treas.--Sawhill Tubular Div., Sharon, PA; *U.S. Public,* pg. 131

Stout, Elisabeth, Treas.--Burlington Coat Factory Warehouse Corporation, Burlington, NJ; *U.S. Public,* pg. 268

Stout, Judith, Treas.--Metaltech, Inc., Kirkwood, MO; *U.S. Private,* pg. 735

Stout, Mike, Treas.--Gregg Appliances Inc., Indianapolis, IN; *U.S. Private,* pg. 479

Stover, F. Gary, Treas.--Laird & Company, Eatontown, NJ; *U.S. Private,* pg. 642

Stowell, Ronald S., Chief Fin. Officer & Treas.--LSI Industries, Inc., Cincinnati, OH; *U.S. Public,* pg. 971

Strahman, Peggy A., V.P. & Treas.--Strahman Valves, Inc., Florham Park, NJ; *U.S. Private,* pg. 1046

Strain, Ronald R., V.P., Treas. & Controller--Miller Brewing Company, Milwaukee, WI; *U.S. Public,* pg. 1289

Strambi, Michael, Asst. Treas.--Sun Diamond Growers of California, Pleasanton, CA; *U.S. Private,* pg. 1051

Stratton, Arlene E., Treas.--Stratton Management Company, Plymouth Meeting, PA; *U.S. Private,* pg. 1046

Straube, Hildegard, Treas. & Sec.--Straube Regional Center LLC, Pennington, NJ; *U.S. Private,* pg. 1046

Strauch, Mark P., Treas.--Arthur J. Gallagher & Co., Itasca, IL; *U.S. Public,* pg. 698

Stredni, Salomon, Chief Fin. Officer, V.P.-Opers. & Treas.--Omega Research Inc., Miami, FL; *U.S. Public,* pg. 1222

Streiff, Denis, Asst. Treas.--Omnicom Group Inc., New York, NY; *U.S. Public,* pg. 1223

Streisfeld, Andrew M., Treas.--Brown & Company Securities Corporation, Boston, MA; *U.S. Public,* pg. 337

Stringfellow, Charles, Treas.--Brown Automotive Group, Fairfax, VA; *U.S. Private,* pg. 173

Strocko, Len, Dir.-Fin. Plng. & Analysis--Handy & Harman, New York, NY; *U.S. Public,* pg. 780

Strom, R.W., Asst. Treas.--Electrical Equipment Company, Raleigh, NC; *U.S. Private,* pg. 368

Strong, Christopher D., Treas.--Hvide Marine Incorporated, Fort Lauderdale, FL; *U.S. Public,* pg. 851

Strong, Curt, Treas. & Sec.--Zieman Manufacturing Company, Whittier, CA; *U.S. Private,* pg. 1205

Struckhoff, Charles O., Chief Fin. Officer, V.P.-Fin. & Admin., Treas. & Sec.--Maverick Tube Corporation, Chesterfield, MO; *U.S. Public,* pg. 1060

Strunk, Kaye, Controller & Treas.--Carter-Jones Companies, Inc., Kent, OH; *U.S. Private,* pg. 217

Strupp, Robert, Treas. & Sec.--Mozel Development Corp., Baileys Crossroads, VA; *U.S. Private,* pg. 765

Stuart, Gary M., V.P. & Treas.--Union Pacific Corporation, Dallas, TX; *U.S. Public,* pg. 1667

Stuart, John J., Jr., Chief Fin. Officer & Treas.--Irvine Sensors Corporation, Costa Mesa, CA; *U.S. Public,* pg. 913

Stubblefield, Jerry W., Chief Fin. Officer, Exec. V.P. & Treas.--nVIEW Corporation, Newport News, VA; *U.S. Public,* pg. 1206

Stull, Arnold, Treas.--Bureau of Engraving, Minneapolis, MN; *U.S. Private,* pg. 181

Stumpo, Frank D., Chief Fin. Officer & V.P.-Finance--Resco Products, Inc., Conshohocken, PA; *U.S. Private,* pg. 924

Sturgeon, Diana, Treas. & Dir.-Fin.--Oliver Products Company, Grand Rapids, MI; *U.S. Private,* pg. 815

Sturm, Klaus, Exec. V.P.-Treas.--Bayerische Landesbank, Munich, Germany; *Int'l,* pg. 176

Stutts, Gloria, Controller & Treas.--Mansion Homes, Robbins, NC; *U.S. Public,* pg. 318

Stuver, Craig O., Corp. Controller & Asst. Treas.--Michael Baker Corporation, Pittsburgh, PA; *U.S. Public,* pg. 168

Stuver, D. K., Treas.--CNG Power Services Corporation, Pittsburgh, PA; *U.S. Public,* pg. 435

Suard, Andrea Bollinger, Treas.--Bollinger Shipyards, Inc., Lockport, LA; *U.S. Private,* pg. 155

Suarez, Oscar, V.P. & Treas.--Bacardi Corporation, San Juan, PR; *Int'l,* pg. 131

Suddreth, Charles A., Treas.--Blue Ridge Electric Membership Corp., Lenoir, NC; *U.S. Private,* pg. 153

Sudman, Eric, V.P.-Fin. & Treas.--IA Construction Corp., Concordville, PA; *U.S. Private,* pg. 552

Sugarman, Wendy, Treas.--JS&A Group, Inc., Las Vegas, NV; *U.S. Private,* pg. 578

Sulentic, Michael E., Treas.--Eaglemark Financial Services, Inc., Chicago, IL; *U.S. Public,* pg. 786

Sullivan, Barry M., V.P. & Treas.--Harsco Corporation, Camp Hill, PA; *U.S. Public,* pg. 792

Sullivan, D. Harold, Chief Fin. Officer, V.P. & Treas.--Demoulas Market Basket, Tewksbury, MA; *U.S. Private,* pg. 324

Sullivan, Dennis G., V.P., Gen. Counsel, Asst. Treas. & Asst. Sec.--Middlesex Water Company, Iselin, NJ; *U.S. Public,* pg. 1110

Sullivan, Dennis G., Asst. Treas. & Asst. sec.--Tidewater Utilities, Inc., Odessa, DE; *U.S. Public,* pg. 1110

Sullivan, Fred M., Treas.--Western Atlas International, Inc., Houston, TX; *U.S. Public,* pg. 1757

Sullivan, Garrett, Chief Fin. Officer & Treas.--Cognitronics Corporation, Danbury, CT; *U.S. Public,* pg. 394

Sullivan, John, Chief Fin. Officer , Sr. V.P.-Fin. & Treas.--Trans World Entertainment Corporation, Albany, NY; *U.S. Public,* pg. 1629

Sullivan, John L., Controller, Treas. & Sec.--Totsy Manufacturing Company, Inc., Holyoke, MA; *U.S. Private, pg. 1093*

Sullivan, John L., III, Controller & Treas.--The Eastern Company, Naugatuck, CT; *U.S. Public,* pg. 548

Sullivan, Mark, Treas. & Sec.--ColeJon Corporation, Cleveland, OH; *U.S. Private,* pg. 251

Sullivan, Mark W., Treas.--Creative Productions, Pittsburgh, PA; *U.S. Private,* pg. 288

Sullivan, Peter T., Treas. & Sec.--SierraCom, Hopkinton, MA; *U.S. Private,* pg. 999

Sullivan, Timothy J., Chief Fin. Officer, Chief Admin. Officer, Sr. V.P., Treas. & Sec.--Market Facts, Inc., Arlington Heights, IL; *U.S. Public,* pg. 1046

Sulprizio, Deuta, V.P. & Treas.--United Engine & Machine Company, Carson City, NV; *U.S. Private,* pg. 1121

Sum, Joseph J., Chief Fin. Officer, V.P. & Treas.--Continental Materials Corporation, Chicago, IL; *U.S. Public,* pg. 441

Sum, Joseph J., Treas.--Continental Catalina, Inc., Chicago, IL; *U.S. Public,* pg. 441

Sum, Joseph J., Treas.--Continental Uranium, Inc., Chicago, IL; *U.S. Public,* pg. 441

Sumas, James, Chm. Bd., Chief Oper. Officer, Treas., & Dir.-Adv.--Village Super Market Inc., Springfield, NJ; *U.S. Public,* pg. 1721

Summers, Kathy, Controller & Sec.--Harold Ziegler Ford-Elkhart, Elkhart, IN; *U.S. Private,* pg. 1205

Sumrall, O. Malcolm, Chief Fin. Officer, Treas. & Sec.--Associated Equipment Company of Delaware, Mobile, AL; *U.S. Private,* pg. 90

Suozzi, Francis X., V.P. & Treas.--Nabisco Inc., Parsippany, NJ; *U.S. Public,* pg. 1355

Suprise, Lou, Asst. Treas.--Curt G. Joa, Inc., Sheboygan Falls, WI; *U.S. Private,* pg. 588

Surgala, David, Treas.--Keithley Instruments, Inc., Cleveland, OH; *U.S. Public,* pg. 946

Surplus, Scott C., Asst. Treas.--Holly Corporation, Dallas, TX; *U.S. Public,* pg. 830

Sutherby, Daniel J., Asst. Treas.--Applied Extrusion Technologies, Inc., Peabody, MA; *U.S. Public,* pg. 122

Sutherland, Susan, Asst. Treas.--Terex Corporation, Westport, CT; *U.S. Public,* pg. 1581

Sutton, William M., V.P., Comptroller & Treas.--Huntington National Bank, Morgantown, WV; *U.S. Public,* pg. 850

Suuraho, Risto, V.P. & Treas.--Enso Oyj, Helsinki, Finland; *Int'l,* pg. 455

Suzuki, Junichi, Pres.--Komatsu America Industries Corp., Wood Dale, IL; *Int'l,* pg. 744

Svensson, Lennart, Chief Fin. Officer--Mo och Domsjo AB, Stockholm, Sweden; *Int'l,* pg. 885

Swain, Judy, Mgr.-Treasury Opers.--Paccar Inc., Bellevue, WA; *U.S. Public,* pg. 1246

Swan, Peer A., Treas.--Pacific Scientific Company, Newport Beach, CA; *U.S. Public,* pg. 1250

Swanson, Kurt R., Asst. Treas.--Tang Industries Inc., Las Vegas, NV; *U.S. Private,* pg. 1068

Swanson, Stanley, Sec. & Treas.--Minuteman Press International, Farmingdale, NY; *U.S. Private,* pg. 752

Swanson, William, Treas.--Bose Corporation, Framingham, MA; *U.S. Private,* pg. 160

Swartz, Charla, Asst. Treas.--KinderCare Learning Centers, Inc., Portland, OR; *U.S. Public,* pg. 961

Swartz, G. I., Chief Fin. Officer, Treas. & Controller--U.S. Borax Inc., Valencia, CA; *Int'l,* pg. 1119

Swearingen, Thomas F., Dir.-Fin. & Treas.--Hammel, Green & Abrahamson, Inc., Minneapolis, MN; *U.S. Private,* pg. 497

Sweeney, William, Treas.--Sofco-Mead, Inc., Scotia, NY; *U.S. Private,* pg. 1012

Sweet, Raymond D., V.P.-Opers., Controller & Treas.--Consolidated Coatings Corp., Brunswick, OH; *U.S. Public,* pg. 1357

Swenson, Paul E., Treas.--Pike Industries Inc., Tilton, NH; *Int'l,* pg. 242

Swift, M. Allen, Chm. Bd., Pres. & Treas.--M. Swift & Sons Inc., Hartford, CT; *U.S. Private,* pg. 1059

Swift, Robert P., Exec. V.P. & Treas.--Chuck Swift Sales & Leasing, Davis, CA; *U.S. Private,* pg. 1058

Swoish, Craig, Exec. V.P., Sec. & Treas.--Lamina Inc., Oak Park, MI; *Int'l,* pg. 75

Swoveland, Jeffrey C., Interim Chief Fin. Officer, V.P.-Fin. & Treas.--Equitable Resources, Inc., Pittsburgh, PA; *U.S. Public,* pg. 589

Sy, Jane, Pres. & Treas.--Christian Mutual Life Insurance Co., Houston, TX; *U.S. Private,* pg. 225

Sydenstricken, Jeanne R., V.P. & Treas.--TRW Inc., Cleveland, OH; *U.S. Public,* pg. 1558

Sykes, James E., Jr., Treas. & Sec.--Noland Company, Newport News, VA; *U.S. Public,* pg. 1187

Sylva, JoAnne, Treas. & Sec.--Dimensional Merchandising, Inc., Wharton, NJ; *U.S. Private,* pg. 333

Sylvester, Paul R., Pres. & Chief Exec. Officer--Manatron, Inc., Kalamazoo, MI; *U.S. Public,* pg. 1040

Szames, Brian M., Treas.--Footstar Inc., Mahwah, NJ; *U.S. Public,* pg. 661

Szekely, Steven, Treas. & Sec.--Monarch Avalon, Inc., Baltimore, MD; *U.S. Public,* pg. 1123

Szenasi, Frank P., Controller & Treas.--Dover Industries Limited, Burlington, Canada; *Int'l,* pg. 417

Szulman-Jones, Marilyn, Treas. & Sec.--Airco Mechanical Inc., Sacramento, CA; *U.S. Private,* pg. 29

Taber, Michael H., Chief Acctg. Officer, V.P.-Fin. & Sec.--Del Global Technologies, Valhalla, NY; *U.S. Public,* pg. 493

Tabin, Stewart E., Asst. Treas.--WHX Corporation, New York, NY; *U.S. Public,* pg. 1726

Tabor, Ed, Chief Fin. Officer & Treas.--Acorn Structures, Acton, MA; *U.S. Private,* pg. 320

Tabor, Edward, Treas.--Deck House Inc., Acton, MA; *U.S. Private,* pg. 320

Tack, Kim P., Sec. & Treas.--BWI Kartridg Pak, Davenport, IA; *Int'l,* pg. 130

Tacony, Kathi, Treas.--Tacony Corporation, Fenton, MO; *U.S. Private,* pg. 1066

Taggart, David M., V.P. & Treas.--The Coca-Cola Company, Atlanta, GA; *U.S. Public,* pg. 392

Tagtow, E.A., V.P. & Treas.--Nekota Resources Inc., Huron, SD; *U.S. Public,* pg. 1201

Takada, J., Sec. & Treas.--Yamaha Motor Canada Ltd., North York, Canada; *Int'l,* pg. 1516

Tallarico, Thomas M., V.P. & Treas.--Sigma-Aldrich Corporation, Saint Louis, MO; *U.S. Public,* pg. 1471

Talley, Joseph J., Treas. & Asst. Sec.--American Crystal Sugar Company, Moorhead, MN; *U.S. Private,* pg. 52

Talley, Kathleen A., Sec. & Asst. Treas.--Advance Ross Corporation, Chicago, IL; *U.S. Public,* pg. 320

Tan, B.H., Treas.--Esso Singapore Private Limited, Singapore, Singapore; *U.S. Public,* pg. 602

Tan, Roland, Treas.--Cycle & Carriage Industries (1986) Pte. Limited, Singapore, Singapore; *Int'l,* pg. 350

Tan, Seng T., V.P. & Treas.--Foster's Brewing Group Limited, Southbank, Australia; *Int'l,* pg. 500

Tanabe, Tutomu, Treas.--Murata Electronics North America, Inc., Smyrna, GA; *Int'l,* pg. 897

Tanahira, T., Sr. V.P. & Treas.--Mazda Motor of America, Inc., Irvine, CA; *Int'l,* pg. 849

Tanaka, Hidetoshi, V.P., Sec. & Treas.--Mazda (North America), Inc., Irvine, CA; *Int'l,* pg. 849

Tancredi, Michael A., V.P.-Admin. & Treas.--Porta Systems Corp., Syosset, NY; *U.S. Public,* pg. 1317

Tanderup, Peder, Treas.--Scan-Ad Gruppen A/S, Arhus, Denmark; *Int'l,* pg. 1198

Tansey, James R., Chief Fin. Officer & Sr. V.P.--Jaydon Incorporated, Rock Island, IL; *U.S. Private,* pg. 584

Tansey, Thomas F., Chief Oper., Exec. V.P. & Treas.--Raritan Bancorp Inc., Bridgewater, NJ; *U.S. Public,* pg. 1361

Tanski, Ronald J., Sec. & Treas.--National Fuel Resources, Buffalo, NY; *U.S. Public*, pg. 1156

Tapscott, James T., Chief Fin. Officer, Treas. & Sec.--Columbus Mills, Inc., Columbus, GA; *U.S. Private*, pg. 256

Tarallo, Sebastian J., V.P. & Treas.--ADVO, Inc., Windsor, CT; *U.S. Public*, pg. 23

Tardif, Serge, Asst. Treas.--Gaz Metropolitain & Company, Montreal, Canada; *Int'l*, pg. 541

Tarello, John A., Sr. V.P. & Treas.--Analogic Corporation, Peabody, MA; *U.S. Public*, pg. 109

Tarello, John A., Treas.--SKY Computers, Inc., Chelmsford, MA; *U.S. Public*, pg. 109

Tarello, John A., Treas.--Anadventure II Corporation, Peabody, MA; *U.S. Public*, pg. 109

Tarlow, Thelma H., Asst. Treas.--Alden Shoe Co., Inc., Middleboro, MA; *U.S. Private*, pg. 33

Tarnay, Dennis, Chief Fin. Officer & Treas.--Lake Erie Electric, Inc., Westlake, OH; *U.S. Private*, pg. 643

Tarte, Bernard J., Jr., V.P. & Treas.--Bradner Central Company, Chicago, IL; *U.S. Private*, pg. 164

Tassi, Michael J., Chief Fin. Officer & Treas.--Torco Oil Co., Chicago, IL; *U.S. Private*, pg. 1092

Tate, Warren E., Gen. Mgr., Treas. & Sec.-Information Services--Gulf Power Company, Pensacola, FL; *U.S. Public*, pg. 1490

Tavlin, Michael J., V.P., Treas. & Sec.--Aliant Communications Inc., Lincoln, NE; *U.S. Public*, pg. 40

Taylor, B.A., Assoc. Treas.--American Mathematical Society, Inc., Providence, RI; *U.S. Private*, pg. 59

Taylor, Barbara A., Treas.--Cambridge Shopping Centres Limited, Toronto, Canada; *Int'l*, pg. 253

Taylor, James .H., V.P. & Treas.--Hamilton Beach/Proctor-Silex, Inc., Glen Allen, VA; *U.S. Public*, pg. 1149

Taylor, Jimmie F., Chief Fin. Officer, V.P. & Treas.--TCA Cable TV, Inc., Tyler, TX; *U.S. Public*, pg. 1553

Taylor, Jimmie F., Chief Fin. Officer, Sr. V.P. & Treas.--TCA Management Company, Tyler, TX; *U.S. Public*, pg. 1553

Taylor, John E., Treas.--Taylor Made Group, Inc., Gloversville, NY; *U.S. Private*, pg. 1070

Taylor, Jonathan W., Treas.--George E. Warren Corporation, Vero Beach, FL; *U.S. Private*, pg. 1151

Taylor, Julian H., V.P. & Treas.--Reynolds Metals Company, Richmond, VA; *U.S. Public*, pg. 1385

Taylor, Keith D., Sr. V.P. & Treas.--Washington Federal Savings, Seattle, WA; *U.S. Public*, pg. 1740

Taylor, Morgyn, Treas.--Fremont General Corporation, Santa Monica, CA; *U.S. Public*, pg. 681

Taylor, R.T., V.P., Sec. & Asst. Treas.--Al Johnson Construction Co., Bloomington, MN; *U.S. Private*, pg. 590

Taylor, Ruth A., Treas. & Sec.--The Belt Railway Co. of Chicago, Bedford Park, IL; *Int'l*, pg. 258

Taylor, Ruth A., Treas. & Sec.--The Belt Railway Co. of Chicago, Bedford Park, IL; *U.S. Public*, pg. 269

Teele, Gerald A., Chief Fin. Officer, Sr. V.P. & Treas.--North Carolina Natural Gas Corporation, Fayetteville, NC; *U.S. Public*, pg. 1194

Teeple, William W., Chief Fin. Officer, V.P. & Treas.--Stackpole Ltd., Newton, MA; *U.S. Private*, pg. 1028

Teeters, Bruce W., Sr. V.P.-Fin. & Treas.--Consolidated-Tomoka Land Co., Daytona Beach, FL; *U.S. Public*, pg. 437

Teichholz, Henry A., V.P., Controller & Treas.--Holly Corporation, Dallas, TX; *U.S. Public*, pg. 830

Teiwes, William M., Exec. V.P. & Treas.--UMB Financial Corporation, Kansas City, MO; *U.S. Public*, pg. 1653

Tell, Martin T., Chief Fin. Officer & V.P. & Treas.--JJI Lighting Group Inc., Greenwich, CT; *Int'l*, pg. 821

Tellier, James P., Treas. & Sec.--Jefferson Chevrolet Co., Detroit, MI; *U.S. Private*, pg. 584

Tendler, Lance, Pres., Chief Exec. Officer& Treas.--Kennington Ltd., Inc., Van Nuys, CA; *U.S. Private*, pg. 615

Terada, Kozo, Chief Fin. Officer, V.P.-Fin. & Treas.--Asahi/America, Inc., Malden, MA; *U.S. Public*, pg. 137

Teresi, Robert G., Chm Bd., Chief Exec. Officer & Treas.--Caere Corporation, Los Gatos, CA; *U.S. Public*, pg. 291

Termine, David G., Second V.P. & Asst. Treas.--W.P. Carey & Co., Inc., New York, NY; *U.S. Private*, pg. 209

Terrell, Charles L., Pres., Chief Exec. Officer & Treas.--New Haven Savings Bank, New Haven, CT; *U.S. Private*, pg. 793

Terrell, Michael, V.P.-Fin. & Admin. & Treas.--McIlhenny Company, Avery Island, LA; *U.S. Private*, pg. 722

Terry, Anna L., Asst. Treas. & Branch Mgr.--Valley National Bank, Blairstown, NJ; *U.S. Public*, pg. 1706

Terry, Charles P., Sr. V.P.-Fin. & Treas.--Reed & Barton Corporation, Taunton, MA; *U.S. Private*, pg. 916

Terry, David, Sec. & Treas.--Fonar Corporation, Melville, NY; *U.S. Public*, pg. 661

Terry, W. Alan, Treas.--Prime Medical Services, Inc., Austin, TX; *U.S. Public*, pg. 1327

Terwin, Robert, V.P. & Treas.--National Concrete Products Company, Plymouth, MI; *U.S. Private*, pg. 781

Testa, John W., V.P., Treas. & Sec.--WHX Corporation, New York, NY; *U.S. Public*, pg. 1726

Tetlow, Sharon, Treas.--Amgen Boulder, Inc., Boulder, CO; *U.S. Public*, pg. 101

Tetzlaff, David L., Chief Fin. Officer & Treas.--Premium Budget Plan, Inc., Winston Salem, NC; *U.S. Public*, pg. 1453

Tetzlaff, David L., Chief Fin. Officer & Treas.--The Innovative Company, Winston Salem, NC; *U.S. Public*, pg. 1454

Tetzlaff, David L., Chief Fin. Officer & Treas.--Universal Insurance Co., Winston Salem, NC; *U.S. Public*, pg. 1454

Tezak, Paul, V.P.-Finance & Treas.--Smith's Food & Drug Centers, Inc., Salt Lake City, UT; *U.S. Public*, pg. 1103

Thackston, Steve, Controller & Treas.--Dugan & Meyers Interests, Inc., Cincinnati, OH; *U.S. Private*, pg. 345

Thaden, Rogene A., V.P. & Treas.--Northwestern Growth Corp., Sioux Falls, SD; *U.S. Public*, pg. 1201

Thanas, Peter H., Sr. V.P. & Treas.--Fall River Gas Company, Fall River, MA; *U.S. Public*, pg. 611

Thatcher, G.D., Sr. V.P. & Treas.--All America Insurance Company, Van Wert, OH; *U.S. Private*, pg. 224

Thatcher, Gerald D., Chief Fin. Officer, Sr. V.P. & Treas.--Central Mutual Insurance Co., Van Wert, OH; *U.S. Private*, pg. 223

Thatcher, Keith D., V.P.-Acctg. & Treas--Kinetic Concepts, Inc., San Antonio, TX; *U.S. Private*, pg. 620

Theiss, Lloyd, Asst. Treas.--Genesee Corporation, Rochester, NY; *U.S. Public*, pg. 728

Thekkekara, Jack, Treas.--Secretly Yours Inc., Harrison, NJ; *U.S. Private*, pg. 565

Thekkekara, Jack, Treas.--Allegria Inc., Harrison, NJ; *U.S. Private*, pg. 565

Theler, John L., Chief Fin. Officer, Exec. V.P. & Treas.--Franklin Covey, Salt Lake City, UT; *U.S. Public*, pg. 679

Theofilos, Kathy S., Treas.--Theochem Labs., Inc., Tampa, FL; *U.S. Private*, pg. 1079

Thermenos, Paris P., Treas.-Investments & Asset-Liability Mgmnt.--Barnett Banks, Inc., Jacksonville, FL; *U.S. Public*, pg. 1162

Thibault, Chuck, V.P., Controller, Treas. & Sec.--Lazy Days R V Center, Inc., Seffner, FL; *U.S. Private*, pg. 655

Thickpenny, Mark C., Asst. Treas.--CNF Transportation Inc., Palo Alto, CA; *U.S. Public*, pg. 281

Thiel, Wilbert, Exec. V.P. & Treas.--ABN AMRO Chicago Corp., Chicago, IL; *Int'l*, pg. 10

Thiele, E.E., Sr. V.P. & Treas.--Rowan Companies, Inc., Houston, TX; *U.S. Public*, pg. 1409

Thiels, David G., Treas.--Century Telephone Enterprises, Inc., Monroe, LA; *U.S. Public*, pg. 329

Thieman, Ronald G., V.P. & Treas.--KCL Corporation, Shelbyville, IN; *U.S. Private*, pg. 603

Thies, Doug, Chief Fin. Officer, Treas. & Sec.--Field Packing Company, Owensboro, KY; *U.S. Private*, pg. 403

Thiesfeld, Debra Heinson, Treas.--Allied Oil & Supply, Inc., Omaha, NE; *U.S. Private*, pg. 39

Tholen, Steven W., Chief Fin. Officer, V.P. & Treas.--Penn Virginia Corporation, Radnor, PA; *U.S. Public*, pg. 1271

Tholen, Steven W., V.P. & Treas.--Penn Virginia Equities Corp., Wilmington, DE; *U.S. Public*, pg. 1271

Tholen, Steven W., Asst. Treas.--Penn Virginia Oil & Gas Company, Kingsport, TN; *U.S. Public*, pg. 1271

Thom, J.D., Treas.--BTR plc, London, United Kingdom; *Int'l*, pg. 124

Thomas, Alan R., Chief Fin. Officer, Sr. V.P. & Treas.--Noranda Inc., Toronto, Canada; *Int'l*, pg. 433

Thomas, David J., V.P. & Treas.--Frontier Communications Services, Bingham Farms, MI; *U.S. Public*, pg. 684

Thomas, Elbert L., Jr., Sr. V.P. & Treas.--First Tennessee Bank National Association, Memphis, TN; *U.S. Public*, pg. 639

Thomas, Glyn, Grp. Treas.--Reed Elsevier plc, London, United Kingdom; *Int'l*, pg. 1093

Thomas, Helen, Treas. & Sec.--Camino Real Chevrolet & Geo, Monterey Park, CA; *U.S. Private*, pg. 203

Thomas, Jimmy L., Sr. V.P.-Fin. Services & Treas.--Gannett Company, Inc., Arlington, VA; *U.S. Public*, pg. 698

Thomas, John, V.P. & Treas.--Cubic Corporation, San Diego, CA; *U.S. Public*, pg. 466

Thomas, John D., Treas.--Cubic Applications, Inc., Lacey, WA; *U.S. Public*, pg. 466

Thomas, Mary M., V.P. & Treas.--VW Mall, Inc., Atlanta, GA; *U.S. Public*, pg. 858

Thomas, Michael E., Treas.--Maine Yankee, Brunswick, ME; *U.S. Public*, pg. 325

Thomas, Richard, Treas.--Boulevard Bancorp, Inc., Chicago, IL; *U.S. Public*, pg. 1680

Thomas, Richard G., Treas.--The New York Times Company, New York, NY; *U.S. Public*, pg. 1173

Thomas, Robert L., Pres. & Treas.--Saul Bros. & Company, Inc., Norcross, GA; *U.S. Private*, pg. 968

Thomas, Shonnie, Treas. & Sec.--V.B. Hook & Co., Inc., Columbia, SC; *U.S. Private*, pg. 538

Thomas, Tom L., V.P.--Ferro Union, Inc., Torrance, CA; *U.S.* Private, pg. 402

Thompson, A.B., Jr., Treas. & Sec.--Woodruff Electric Co-Op, Forrest City, AR; *U.S. Private*, pg. 1187

Thompson, Dave, V.P. & Treas.--Burlington Basket Co., Burlington, IA; *U.S. Private*, pg. 183

Thompson, Gregory, Treas.--Signtech USA, Ltd., San Antonio, TX; *U.S. Private*, pg. 999

Thompson, John, Exec. V.P. & Treas.--Toastmaster, Inc., Columbia, MO; *U.S. Public*, pg. 1619

Thompson, John M., V.P. & Treas.--Fleming Companies, Inc., Oklahoma City, OK; *U.S. Public*, pg. 652

Thompson, Keith, Chm. Bd. & Treas.--Republic Automotive-AEA Division, Charlotte, NC; *U.S. Public*, pg. 1377

Thompson, Martin W., V.P., Treas. & Sec. Hydro Energy Development Corp., Bothell, WA; *U.S. Public*, pg. 1342

Thompson, Newton, V.P. & Treas.--The New England, Boston, MA; *U.S. Private*, pg. 737

Thompson, Pam, Treas. & Sec.--Key Cadillac, Inc., Edina, MN; *U.S. Private*, pg. 617

Thompson, Peter R., V.P.-Fin. & Asst. Treas.--PepsiCo, Inc., Purchase, NY; *U.S. Public*, pg. 1276

Thompson, Ray F., V.P., Treas. & Controller--Tech-Sym Corporation, Houston, TX; *U.S. Public*, pg. 1563

Thompson, Richard J., Chief Fin. Officer, V.P.-Fin., Treas. & Sec.--Computer Products, Inc., Boca Raton, FL; *U.S. Public*, pg. 422

Thompson, Robert, V.P. & Treas.--Anchor Glass Container Corporation, Tampa, FL; *Int'l*, pg. 327

Thompson, Scott L., Chief Fin. Officer, Sr. V.P. & Treas.--Group 1 Automotive, Inc., Houston, TX; *U.S. Public*, pg. 767

Thompson, Terry W., Chief Fin. Officer, V.P. & Treas.--Jack Henry & Associates, Inc., Monett, MO; *U.S. Public*, pg. 808

Thompson, Tommie D., Treas.--Tele-Trip Company, Omaha, NE; *U.S. Private*, pg. 770

Thomsen, Walter L., Treas. & Sec.--Schoep's Ice Cream, Inc., Madison, WI; *U.S. Private*, pg. 972

Thomson, Steve, Treas. & Sec.--Cambro Manufacturing Company, Huntington Beach, CA; *U.S. Private*, pg. 203

Thorington, Steven A., V.P.-Fin. & Treas.--Seagull Energy Corporation, Houston, TX; *U.S. Public*, pg. 1450

Thornhill, Amie, Pres. & Asst. Treas.--Thornhill Oil Company, Inc., Fort Wayne, IN; *U.S. Private*, pg. 1084

Thornton, A.J., Treas. & Sec.--Consolidated Publishing Company, Anniston, AL; *U.S. Private*, pg. 266

Thornton, Greg, Chief Fin. Officer, V.P. & Treas.--Harding Lawson Associates Group, Inc., Novato, CA; *U.S. Public*, pg. 785

Thornton, Pat, Treas.--O'Neal Steel Inc., Birmingham, AL; *U.S. Private*, pg. 817

Thornton, T.D., II, Pres. & Treas.--Progress Printing Company, Lynchburg, VA; *U.S. Private*, pg. 890

Thunen, Garret G., Treas.--Bankers Trust New York Corporation, New York, NY; *U.S. Public*, pg. 185

Thung, Roy T.K., Chief Fin. Officer, Exec. V.P. & Treas.--Independence Holding Company, Stamford, CT; *U.S. Private*, pg. 446

Thurber, William A., Asst. Treas.--John H. Harland Company, Decatur, GA; *U.S. Public*, pg. 785

Thurn, Timothy N., Treas.--LaserMaster Technologies, Inc., Eden Prairie, MN; *U.S. Public*, pg. 979

Tierney, James P., V.P. & Treas.--American Modern Home Insurance Group, Amelia, OH; *U.S. Public*, pg. 1110

Tiffin, R. Alex, Sr., Treas. & Sec.--Tiffin Motor Homes, Inc., Red Bay, AL; *U.S. Private*, pg. 1086

Tigert, Lance S., Asst. Treas.--Brunswick Mining & Smelting Corp. Ltd., Bathurst, Canada; *Int'l*, pg. 434

Tiholiz, Susan, Treas.--Sterling Software, Inc., Dallas, TX; *U.S. Public*, pg. 1516

Tijerina, Felipe Canales, Treas.--Alfa, S.A. de C.V., Garza Garcia, Mexico; *Int'l*, pg. 56

Tilley, Christopher, Treas.--MBIA Inc., Armonk, NY; *U.S. Public*, pg. 1023

Tillotson, Neil E., Treas.--Textile Rubber & Chemical Company, Dalton, GA; *U.S. Private*, pg. 1079

Tilton, Janet M., Treas.--Brittany Corporation, Cleveland, OH; *U.S. Private*, pg. 169

Timma, Michael C., V.P.-Fin., Treas. & Sec.--M M Systems Corporation, Tucker, GA; *U.S. Private*, pg. 685

Tinius, Barry, Treas. & Sec.--Love Packaging Group, Wichita, KS; *U.S. Private*, pg. 677

Tinkham, Peter B., Treas. & Asst. Sec.--Texas Utilities Company, Dallas, TX; *U.S. Public*, pg. 1586

Tinnell, William, Treas.--I.C. Thomasson Associates, Inc., Nashville, TN; *U.S. Private*, pg. 1083

Tipper, Russell, Grp. Treas.--North Limited, Melbourne, Australia; *Int'l*, pg. 967

Tischler, Louis, Chief Exec. Officer, Chief Oper. Officer & Treas--Westwood Computer Corporation, Springfield, NJ; *U.S. Private*, pg. 1170

Tobin, Steve, V.P., Treas. & Controller--Gerber Life Insurance Co., White Plains, NY; *Int'l*, pg. 973

Todd, Doris, Treas.--J.L. Todd Auction Co., Rome, GA; *U.S.* Private, pg. 1090

Todd, N.R., Treas.--Navistar International Corporation Canada, Hamilton, Canada; *U.S. Public*, pg. 1167

Togneri, Gabriel B., Asst. Treas.--PG&E Corporation, San Francisco, CA; *U.S. Public*, pg. 1240

Tolhurst, Pete, Chief Fin. Officer & V.P.--PHB Die Casting, Fairview, PA; *U.S. Private*, pg. 826

Tolliver, Delno, Treas. & Sec.--East Kentucky Power Co-op, Winchester, KY; *U.S. Private*, pg. 356

Toma, George, Chief Fin. Officer, Treas. & Sec.--Wells-Gardner Electronics Corp., Chicago, IL; *U.S. Public*, pg. 1753

Tomcheck, Jay, Chief Fin. Officer, V.P. & Treas.--Wisconsin Label Corporation, Algoma, WI; *U.S. Private*, pg. 1184

Tome, Carol, V.P. & Treas.--The Home Depot, Inc., Atlanta, GA; *U.S. Public*, pg. 831

Tomechko, Edward, Sr. V.P. & Treas.--County Seat Stores, Inc., Dallas, TX; *U.S. Private*, pg. 279

Tomlinson, Lawrence, V.P. & Treas.--Hewlett-Packard Company, Palo Alto, CA; *U.S. Public*, pg. 813

Tomlinson, Percy C., Jr., Treas & Sec.--Apogee Enterprises, Inc., Minneapolis, MN; *U.S. Public*, pg. 120

Tomlinson, Robert E., Chief Fin. Officer & Treas.--Outsource International, Deerfield Beach, FL; *U.S. Public*, pg. 1236

Tompkins, C. Craig, Treas. & Sec.--Citadel Holdings Corp., Los Angeles, CA; *U.S. Public*, pg. 456

Tonegawa, Masaki, V.P., Sec. & Treas.--Pentax Precision Instrument Corp., Orangeburg, NY; *Int'l*, pg. 85

Tonini, Emilio, Sr. Exec. V.P.-Intl. Affairs & Treas.--Banca Monte dei Paschi di Siena S.p.A., Siena, Italy; *Int'l*, pg. 136

Topham, Matthew, Treas.--T & N Plc, Manchester, United Kingdom; *Int'l*, pg. 1334

Toppi, Angela, Chief Fin. Officer, Sr. V.P., Treas. & Sec.--Trans-Lux Corporation, Norwalk, CT; *U.S. Public*, pg. 1628

Torkar, Bob, Sr. V.P.-Fin., Treas. & Chief Acctg. Officer--Jackpot Enterprises, Inc., Las Vegas, NV; *U.S. Public*, pg. 920

Tornquist, K.A., Controller & Asst. Treas.--Maine Public Service Company, Presque Isle, ME; *U.S. Public*, pg. 1038

Torres, Jose O., V.P.-Fin., Treas. & Sec.--Puerto Rican Cement Co., Inc., Guaynabo, PR; *U.S. Public*, pg. 1341

Torres, Vera Trinchero, Sec. & Treas.--Sutter Home Winery, Inc., Saint Helena, CA; *U.S. Private*, pg. 1057

Tortora, Dennis J., Controller & Asst. Treas.--Steinway Musical Instruments, Inc., Waltham, MA; *U.S. Public*, pg. 1514

Tortora, Dennis J., Controller & Asst. Treas.--Steinway & Sons, Long Island City, NY; *U.S. Public*, pg. 1514

Torrici, John, Chief Fin. Officer, V.P. & Treas.--Milgray Electronics, Inc., Farmingdale, NY; *U.S. Public*, pg. 205

Toscanini, Arthur M., Chief Fin. Officer, Exec. V.P.-Fin. & Treas.--Cambridge Technology Partners, Cambridge, MA; *U.S. Public*, pg. 1424

Toter, Benjamin, V.P.-Fin., Sec. & Treas.--Quality Markets, Inc., Jamestown, NY; *U.S. Public,* pg. 1270
Toto, Joseph P., Sr. V.P. & Treas.--Karnak Corporation, Clark, NJ; *U.S. Private,* pg. 607
Totorica, Richard S., V.P. & Corp. Treas.--ATL Ultrasound, Inc., Bothell, WA; *U.S. Public,* pg. 11
Totten, Jeffrey, V.P. & Treas.--Totten Tubes, Inc., Los Angeles, CA; *U.S. Private,* pg. 1093
Touhey, Carl E., Pres. & Treas.--Orange Motor Company Inc., Albany, NY; *U.S. Private,* pg. 818
Tousant, Laura, Controller & Treas.--Car-Freshner Corporation, Watertown, NY; *U.S. Private,* pg. 207
Tower, Gerald W., V.P.-H.R.--Stanhome Inc., Westfield, MA; *U.S. Public,* pg. 1508
Tracy, James A., Treas.--Sacramento Municipal Utility District, Sacramento, CA; *U.S. Private,* pg. 959
Trahan, Guy, Treas.--Editions d'enseignements-religieux F.P.R. Inc., Montreal, Canada; *Int'l,* pg. 1077
Trametzki, Thomas, Chief Fin. Officer, V.P., Treas. & Sec.--Orval Kent Food Co., Wheeling, IL; *U.S. Private,* pg. 820
Trangucci, Neale X., Asst. Treas.--WHX Corporation, New York, NY; *U.S. Public,* pg. 1726
Trapani, Cosmo S., Chief Fin. Officer, Exec. V.P. & Treas.--Unitrode Corporation, Merrimack, NH; *U.S. Public,* pg. 1694
Trauth, Andrew, V.P.-Engrng.--Trauth Dairy Inc., Newport, KY; *U.S. Private,* pg. 1098
Travis, Susan, Controller & Asst. Treas.--C-Line Products, Inc., Des Plaines, IL; *U.S. Private,* pg. 192
Treanor, John, Treas.--Albany International Corp., Albany, NY; *U.S. Public,* pg. 36
Trechak, Perry, V.P. & Treas.--Seton Company, Norristown, PA; *U.S. Private,* pg. 987
Treece, James L., Chief Acctg. Officer & Asst. Treasurer--Defiance, Inc., Cleveland, OH; *U.S. Public,* pg. 493
Tremel, Gerard T., Treas.--Glenshaw Glass Co. Inc., Allison Park, PA; *U.S. Private,* pg. 457
Tremont, James, Sec. & Treas.--See's Candy Shops, Inc., South San Francisco, CA; *U.S. Public,* pg. 221
Tressler, Richard L., Treas.--Diehl Inc., Defiance, OH; *U.S. Private,* pg. 332
Trevvett, James D., Treas.--Commercial Travelers Mutual Insurance Company, Utica, NY; *U.S. Private,* pg. 258
Trevvett, James D., Treas.--Monitor Life Insurance Company of New York, Utica, NY; *U.S. Private,* pg. 258
Trible, Clayton J., Jr., Sr. V.P. & Treas.--Standard Federal Bank, Troy, MI; *Int'l,* pg. 10
Trickle, Karen, Treas.--Journal Communications Inc., Milwaukee, WI; *U.S. Private,* pg. 601
Trilling, Morton, Exec. V.P. & Treas.--NationsBank/Miami, Miami, FL; *U.S. Public,* pg. 1162
Trimakas, Harry S., V.P.-Fin. & Treas.--Pneumafil Corporation, Charlotte, NC; *U.S. Private,* pg. 873
Trinkle, Betty L., Treas.--Trinkle Sales, Inc., Cherry Hill, NJ; *U.S. Private,* pg. 1103
Trippel, Joe, Chief Fin. Officer, Treas. & Sec.--Creation Windows of Indiana, Inc., Elkhart, IN; *U.S. Private,* pg. 287
Trobaugh, John, Chief Fin. Officer, Treas. & Sec.--Delta Foremost Chemical Corp., Memphis, TN; *U.S. Private,* pg. 322
Troike, Frank A., Chm. Bd., Chief Exec. Officer & Treas.--Central Steel & Wire Company, Chicago, IL; *U.S. Public,* pg. 327
Troilo, Joseph C., Sr. V.P.-Fin. & Treas.--Foodarama Supermarkets, Inc., Freehold, NJ; *U.S. Public,* pg. 661
Trosko, N. David, Asst. Treas.--The Acacia Group - Acacia Life Insurance Co., Bethesda, MD; *U.S. Private,* pg. 10
Troupe, Terry L., Chief Fin. Officer & Treas.--Mercantile Bankshares Corporation, Baltimore, MD; *U.S. Public,* pg. 1088
Troutman, W. Wilson, Controller & Asst. Treas.--Industrial Coatings Group, Inc., Chicago, IL; *U.S. Private,* pg. 434
Trub, Aaron D., V.P., Treas. & Sec.--Smithfield Foods, Inc., Norfolk, VA; *U.S. Public,* pg. 1479
Trub, Aaron D., Treas. & Sec.--The Smithfield Packing Co., Inc., Smithfield, VA; *U.S. Public,* pg. 1479
Truchi, James, Chief Fin. Officer, Controller & Treas.--Trucchis Markets, Raynham, MA; *U.S. Private,* pg. 1107
Trucksess, H.A., III, Chief Fin. Officer & Sr. V.P.-Fin.--Yellow Corporation, Overland Park, KS; *U.S. Public,* pg. 1788
True-Courage, Zada, Treas. & Mgr.--Harte-Hanks Communications, Inc., San Antonio, TX; *U.S. Public,* pg. 793
Trueblood, Cynthia A., Asst. Treas.--Lincoln Foodservice Products, Inc., Fort Wayne, IN; *Int'l,* pg. 188
Truesdell, J.E., III, V.P. & Treas.--Austin Group, Flint, MI; *U.S. Private,* pg. 99
Trulson, Clayton B., V.P.-Fin. & Treas.--Sodak Gaming, Inc., Rapid City, SD; *U.S. Public,* pg. 1482
Trumpore, Theresa, Treas.--Minor Rubber Co., Inc., Bloomfield, NJ; *U.S. Private,* pg. 751
Trupiano, James, Chief Exec. Officer & Treas.--Champion Aluminum Window Corporation, Syosset, NY; *U.S. Private,* pg. 227
Tsang, Terence, V.P., Controller & Treas.--Guess ?, Inc., Los Angeles, CA; *U.S. Public,* pg. 768
Tsanos, Scott J., Controller, Treas. & Sec.--Sybra, Inc., Atlanta, GA; *U.S. Private,* pg. 270
Tsingos, Christine, V.P. & Treas.--Autodesk, Inc., San Rafael, CA; *U.S. Public,* pg. 148
Tsujino, Iwao, Treas.--Ricoh Electronics, Inc., Tustin, CA; *Int'l,* pg. 1114
Tubbesing, Robert, Chief Fin. Officer & Treas.--Premdor Inc., Mississauga, Canada; *Int'l,* pg. 1066
Tuck, Dennis R., Treas.--CSA Management Inc., Toronto, Canada; *Int'l,* pg. 243
Tucker, L., V.P.-Fin.--OCE Holding USA, Chicago, IL; *Int'l,* pg. 994
Tucker, Marshall D., Chief Fin. Officer, V.P., Treas., Controller & Sec.--Dixon Paper Co., Denver, CO; *U.S. Public,* pg. 902
Tufenkian, Savey, Exec. V.P., Treas. & Sec.--Western Waste Industries, Torrance, CA; *U.S. Public,* pg. 1686
Tully, David M., Treas. & Sec.--Mackie Designs, Inc., Woodinville, WA; *U.S. Public,* pg. 1030
Tully, Herbert B., V.P. & Treas.--Wilbur-Ellis Company & Connell Brothers Company, San Francisco, CA; *U.S. Private,* pg. 1175
Tunink, Paul C., Chief Fin. Officer, V.P.-Fin. & Treas.--Stuart Entertainment Inc., Council Bluffs, IA; *U.S. Public,* pg. 1526
Turcotte, Bruce, Treas.--Columbia Manufacturing Inc., Westfield, MA; *U.S. Private,* pg. 255
Turnbull, James H., Sec. & Treas.--Southeastern Development Company, Port Huron, MI; *U.S. Public,* pg. 1489
Turner, A.C., Treas.--Robin Hood Multifoods Inc., Markham, Canada; *U.S. Public,* pg. 901
Turner, John J., Treas.--United Water Resources, Harrington Park, NJ; *U.S. Public,* pg. 1691
Turner, Lawrence M., V.P. & Treas.--The Kroger Co., Cincinnati, OH; *U.S. Public,* pg. 967
Turner, Lisa, Treas.--National Group Marketing Corp., Irving, TX; *U.S. Public,* pg. 433
Turner, Pearl, V.P. & Treas.--CMP Media, Inc., Manhasset, NY; *U.S. Public,* pg. 279
Turner, Ralph, Treas.--Fairfield Communities, Inc., Little Rock, AR; *U.S. Public,* pg. 610
Turner, Ronald J., Asst. Treas.--Piedmont Natural Gas Co., Inc., Charlotte, NC; *U.S. Public,* pg. 1295
Turner, Rose, Chief Fin. Officer--Bollinger Industries Inc., Grand Prairie, TX; *U.S. Public,* pg. 243
Turner, T.G., Treas.--Pluess-Staufer Industries, Inc., Proctor, VT; *Int'l,* pg. 1061
Turner, W. Thomas, Jr., Treas.--Funeral Security Plans, Inc., Kansas City, MO; *U.S. Private,* pg. 796
Turpin, David W., Treas.--Temple-Inland Inc., Diboll, TX; *U.S. Public,* pg. 1574
Tutor, Albert G., Exec. V.P. & Treas.--Tutor-Saliba Corporation, Sylmar, CA; *U.S. Private,* pg. 1111
Tutt, R. Thayer, Jr., V.P. & Treas.--Broadmoor Hotel, Inc., Colorado Springs, CO; *U.S. Private,* pg. 170
Tuttle, Brian J., Treas.--Griffith Laboratories Worldwide, Inc., Alsip, IL; *U.S. Private,* pg. 481
Tuttle, Elizabeth A., Sr. V.P. & Treas.--ITT Corporation, New York, NY; *U.S. Public,* pg. 1512
Tuttle, Howard G., Treas. & Sec.--Lee Company, Westbrook, CT; *U.S. Private,* pg. 657
Tuttle, John R., Chm. Bd., Pres. & Treas.--Micron Communications, Inc., Boise, ID; *U.S. Public,* pg. 1105
Tweetie, Mark, Chief Fin. Officer & Asst. Treas.--United Grocers Inc., Portland, OR; *U.S. Private,* pg. 1122
Twesme, James W., Asst. Treas.--Telephone and Data Systems, Inc., Chicago, IL; *U.S. Public,* pg. 1570
Twigg-Smith, Oona, Chief Fin. Officer & Treas.--Persis Corporation, Honolulu, HI; *U.S. Private,* pg. 855
Twilling, Tom, Controller & Treas.--Perry & Derrick Co., Cincinnati, OH; *U.S. Private,* pg. 854
Twitchell, Karen, Treas.--Kaiser Aluminum Corporation, Houston, TX; *U.S. Public,* pg. 1062
Twombly, Julian B., V.P. & Treas.--General Signal Corporation, Stamford, CT; *U.S. Public,* pg. 726
Tyler, Beatrice B., Treas.--Cain & Bultman, Jacksonville, FL; *U.S. Private,* pg. 199
Tyler, D.R., Treas.--Exxon Chemical Limited, Farnham, United Kingdom; *U.S. Public,* pg. 602
Tyler, Ken J., Gen. Mgr.-Treasury--Stelco Inc., Hamilton, Canada; *Int'l,* pg. 1299
Tyler, William K., Sr. V.P. & Asst. Treas.--The Lincoln National Life Insurance Co., Fort Wayne, IN; *U.S. Public, pg. 998*
Tyll, Betty, Treas. & Sec.--Sterling Heights Dodge, Inc., Sterling Heights, MI; *U.S. Private,* pg. 1041
Typermass, Arthur G., Sr. V.P. & Treas.--Metropolitan Life Insurance Co., New York, NY; *U.S. Private,* pg. 737
Tyrpak, Paul M., Treas. & Controller--Comptek Federal Systems, Inc., Buffalo, NY; *U.S. Public,* pg. 419
Tyson, Ron, Exec. V.P., Treas. & Sec.--Miracle Recreation Equipment Company, Monett, MO; *U.S. Private,* pg. 752
Tzomg, Mei, Chief Fin. Officer, Treas. & Controller--Pantech Construction Co., Lanham, MD; *U.S. Private,* pg. 837
Uenishi, Shoji, Treas.--Takatta Inc., Auburn Hills, MI; *U.S. Private,* pg. 528
Uhlmann, Eberhard, Mgr.-Treas./Plng. & Disbursements--European Investment Bank, Luxembourg, Luxembourg; *Int'l,* pg. 465
Ujhely, Richard J., V.P. & Treas.--Atwood & Morrill Co., Inc., Salem, MA; *Int'l,* pg. 1489
Ulino, Madalyn, Treas.--Caravan Brokay, Totowa, NJ; *U.S. Private,* pg. 208
Ulmann, Heinz, Dir.-Acctg.--Knurr AG, Munich, Germany; *Int'l,* pg. 739
Ulrich, Fred J., Treas.--Omaha Public Power District, Omaha, NE; *U.S. Private,* pg. 815
Umemoto, S., Chief Fin. Officer & Treas.--Asahi Glass America, Inc., New York, NY; *Int'l,* pg. 84
Umphlette, Edward, Exec. V.P., Treas., Gen. Counsel & Gen. Mgr.--Stainless Incorporated, Deerfield Beach, FL; *U.S. Private,* pg. 1029
Underwood, David, Chief Fin. Officer & Treas.--Curries Company, Mason City, IA; *Int'l,* pg. 18
Underwood, Galen E., Treas.--United Fire & Casualty Company, Cedar Rapids, IA; *U.S. Public,* pg. 1677
Ungerer, Ronald A., Asst. Treas.--Niagara Mohawk Power Corporation, Syracuse, NY; *U.S. Public,* pg. 1181
Untereker, John, Chief Fin. Officer, V.P. & Treas.--Petroleum Helicopters, Inc., Metairie, LA; *U.S. Public,* pg. 1281
Unton, T.F., Sr. V.P.-Fin. & treas.--MACtac Morgan Adhesive Company, Stow, OH; *U.S. Public,* pg. 210
Upstone, Velora, Treas.--Health & Life Insurance Co. of America, Rockford, IL; *U.S. Public,* pg. 434
Urban, Tony J., Treas. & Sec.--Calumet Construction Corporation, Hammond, IN; *U.S. Private,* pg. 201
Urban, Ward A.W., V.P. & Treas.--American Banknote Corp., New York, NY; *U.S. Public,* pg. 68
Urbel, David A., V.P. & Treas.--The Southland Corporation, Dallas, TX; *Int'l,* pg. 693
Uretta, Ronald, Chief Oper. Officer & Treas.--Insignia Financial Group, Inc., Greenville, SC; *U.S. Public,* pg. 881
Urquahrt, Richard A., III, Pres. & Treas.--Golden Corral Corporation, Raleigh, NC; *U.S. Private,* pg. 575
Utsunomiya, Takaharu, Grp. V.P.-Fin., Treas. & Asst. Sec.--Sega of America Inc., Redwood City, CA; *Int'l,* pg. 1218
Utz, Danny, V.P.-Fin. & Treas.--The Keller Manufacturing Co., Inc., Corydon, IN; *U.S. Private,* pg. 612
Uzolins, Uldis, Chief Fin. Officer, Exec. V.P. & Treas.--Fred V. Fowler Company, Inc., Newton, MA; *U.S. Private,* pg. 422
Uzupis, Steven, Chief Fin. Officer & V.P.-Fin.--Brodart Company, Williamsport, PA; *U.S. Private,* pg. 170
Vadis, Tony Quo, Mng. Dir.-Banking & Treasury--Great Pacific Enterprises Inc., Vancouver, Canada; *Int'l,* pg. 557
Vaghela, Vijay, Treas.--Mirror Group plc, London, United Kingdom; *Int'l,* pg. 869
Vagnini, K.L., V.P., Sec. & Treas.--The Gerstenslager Company, Wooster, OH; *U.S. Public,* pg. 1780
Vahey, Dan, Treas.--Seigle's Home & Building Centers, Elgin, IL; *U.S. Private,* pg. 981
Vakil, Usman U., Chm. Bd., Pres. & Treas.--Lights Of America, Inc., Walnut, CA; *U.S. Private,* pg. 667
Valadez, Norma, V.P. & Treas.--Edelman Public Relations Worldwide, Chicago, IL; *U.S. Private,* pg. 362
Valaisathien, Sucha, Treas.--Bangkok Bank of Commerce Ltd., Bangkok, Thailand; *Int'l,* pg. 146
Valenti, Edward, V.P., Treas. & Sec.--Temco Service Industries, New York, NY; *U.S. Public,* pg. 1574
Valentine, Bruce, Treas.--Catalina Marketing Corporation, Saint Petersburg, FL; *U.S. Public,* pg. 314
Valento, Jim, Chief Fin. Officer, V.P. & Treas.--Washington Scientific Industries, Inc., Long Lake, MN; *U.S. Public,* pg. 1744
Valenzuela, Victor, Treas.--Aero Peru Corporation, Coral Gables, FL; *U.S. Private,* pg. 24
Valice, Debra D., Chief Fin. Officer, Treas. & Corp. Sec.--Seitel, Inc., Houston, TX; *U.S. Public,* pg. 1454
Vallerie, Raymond, Treas. & Sec.--Vallerie's Transport Service, Inc., Norwalk, CT; *U.S. Private,* pg. 1131
Van Amburg, Sheldon, Treas. & Sec.--Farmway Co-Op Inc., Beloit, KS; *U.S. Private,* pg. 396
Van Beckum, Jim, Sec. & Treas.--KRC (Hewitt) Inc., Neenah, WI; *Int'l,* pg. 1202
van den Bergh, E.J., Treas.--Esso Inc., Brussels, Belgium; *U.S. Public,* pg. 602
Van Den Blink, N. Mooers, Chm. Bd., Chief Exec. Officer, & Treas.--Hilliard Corporation, Elmira, NY; *U.S. Private,* pg. 530
Van Den Top, Jay, Treas. & Sec.--L.G. Everist Inc., Sioux Falls, SD; *U.S. Private,* pg. 386
Van Donnelin, Edith, Treas.--Woolworths Limited, Yennora, Australia; *Int'l,* pg. 676
van Dyk, T., Pres. & Treas.--Gist-Brocades, Inc., Wilmington, DE; *Int'l,* pg. 1143
van Erp, J.C.P.M., Grp. Treas.--CSM N.V., Diemen, Netherlands; *Int'l,* pg. 243
Van Gundy, Kari L., V.P., Treas. & Asst. Sec.--CalFarm Insurance Agency, Sacramento, CA; *U.S. Public,* pg. 1791
Van Handel, Michael J., Chief Acctg. Officer, V.P. & Treas.--Manpower Inc., Milwaukee, WI; *U.S. Public,* pg. 1042
Van Horn, L.R., Treas.--Ziegler Asset Management, Inc., West Bend, WI; *U.S. Public,* pg. 1792
Van Horn, L.R., Sec. & Treas.--First Church Financing Corporation, West Bend, WI; *U.S. Public,* pg. 1792
Van Horne, Christine K., Asst. Treas.--Comcast Corporation, Philadelphia, PA; *U.S. Public,* pg. 406
Van Houten, Kent J., Chief Fin. Officer, Treas. & Sec.--Peerless Mfg. Co., Dallas, TX; *U.S. Public,* pg. 1268
Van Lierde, Sarah A., Treas.--Martin Marietta International, Inc., Bethesda, MD; *U.S. Public,* pg. 1009
Van Luven, G.A., Chief Fin. Officer, V.P. Treas. & Sec.--The Gage Company, Pittsburgh, PA; *U.S. Private,* pg. 437
Van Pelt, Bruce, Treas.--Van Pelt Corporation, Detroit, MI; *U.S. Private,* pg. 1133
Van Pelt, Bruce, Treas.--Service Steel Division, Detroit, MI; *U.S. Private,* pg. 1133
van Riel, Boy A.J., V.P. & Treas.--Sonesta International Hotels Corporation, Boston, MA; *U.S. Public,* pg. 1485
van Schoor, Johan, Treas.--Transnet Ltd., Parkview, South Africa; *Int'l,* pg. 1417
Van Siclen, Jo, Chief Fin. Officer, V.P. & Treas.--Brooke Group Ltd., Miami, FL; *U.S. Public,* pg. 259
Van Siclen, Joselynn D., Chief Fin. Officer, V.P. & Treas.--BGLS Inc., Miami, FL; *U.S. Public,* pg. 259
Van Tiem, Donald C., Chm. Bd., Pres. & Treas.--Hoban Foods, Inc., Detroit, MI; *U.S. Private,* pg. 531
Van Tiem, James D., Chief Fin. Officer & Treas.--The Cypress Companies, Akron, OH; *U.S. Private,* pg. 299
Van Vooren, V.C., Sr. V.P., Treas. & Asst. Sec.--The Ziegler Companies, Inc., West Bend, WI; *U.S. Public,* pg. 1791
Van Wesben, F., Dir.-Treasury--N.V. Koninklijke KNP BT, Amsterdam, Netherlands; *Int'l,* pg. 756
Vandenbergh, Henry J., Jr., Chief Fin. Officer & Treas.--Rose Packing Company, Barrington, IL; *U.S. Private,* pg. 945
Vander Heiden, Daniel T., Treas.--Church Mutual Insurance Co., Merrill, WI; *U.S. Private,* pg. 239
Vander Pol, Daryl L., Chief Fin. Officer, Exec. V.P., Treas. & Sec.--Vitamilk Dairy, Inc., Seattle, WA; *U.S. Private,* pg. 1142
vander Watt, Peet, Deputy Treas.--Transnet Ltd., Parkview, South Africa; *Int'l,* pg. 1417
Vander Zwaag, Donald D., Sr. V.P. & Treas.--Bradford Company, Holland, MI; *U.S. Private,* pg. 163
Vanderah, Phil, Treas. & Sec.--Central Property & Casualty Insurance Company, West Des Moines, IA; *U.S. Private,* pg. 880

Vanderhaar, William, M.D., Treas.--Kentucky Medical Insurance Company (KMIC), Louisville, KY; *U.S. Private*, pg. 741
Vanderminden, Robert D., Pres. & Treas.--Mettowee Lumber & Plastic Co., Inc., Granville, NY; *U.S. Private*, pg. 1074
VanderVorst, Gary D., V.P. Fin. Treas. & Sec.--Erickson Oil Products, Inc., Hudson, WI; *U.S. Private*, pg. 381
Vanderwal, Richard B., Chief Fin. Officer & Sr. V.P.-Fin.--Gingiss International, Addison, IL; *U.S. Private*, pg. 455
Vanenerg, Johann, Gen. Mgr. & Treas.--Eskom, Sandton, South Africa; *Int'l*, pg. 459
VanHee, Steven D., Treas.--Cray Research, Eagan, MN; *U.S. Public*, pg. 1473
VanMarren, Herman, Chief Fin. Officer, V.P.-Fin. & Treas.--Kamax-G.B. DuPont L.P., Troy, MI; *U.S. Private*, pg. 606
Vannatta, M. Jack, Exec. V.P., Controller & Treas.--First American Corporation, Nashville, TN; *U.S. Public*, pg. 624
Vannoni, Lee S., Treas.--Reebok International Ltd., Stoughton, MA; *U.S. Public*, pg. 1369
Vansant, James V., Jr., V.P.-Fin. & Treas.--Unisource, Doraville, GA; *U.S. Public*, pg. 1671
Vanzura, Cedric J., V.P.-Grp. Plng. & Resource Mngmt.--Borders Group, Inc., Ann Arbor, MI; *U.S. Public*, pg. 245
Vargo, James D., Treas. & Sec.--Daniels Manufacturing Corporation, Orlando, FL; *U.S. Private*, pg. 310
Varmecky, Richard, V.P. & Treas.--Rite Aid Corporation, Camp Hill, PA; *U.S. Public*, pg. 1390
Varous, Peter, Controller--Rosen Associates Management Corp., Jericho, NY; *U.S. Private*, pg. 945
Varrone, Joan M., Treas.--Watkins-Johnson Company, Palo Alto, CA; *U.S. Public*, pg. 1745
Vasbinder, E.F.W., V.P.-Treasury--AEGON N.V., Hague, Netherlands; *Int'l*, pg. 25
Vasel, Gregory M., V.P. & Treas.--Schiavone Construction Co., Secaucus, NJ; *U.S. Private*, pg. 970
Vass, Dennis, Treas.--IES Transportation, Inc., Cedar Rapids, IA; *U.S. Public*, pg. 855
Vass, Dennis, Treas.--IES Investments Inc., Cedar Rapids, IA; *U.S. Public*, pg. 855
Vass, Dennis, Treas.--Industrial Energy Applications, Cedar Rapids, IA; *U.S. Public*, pg. 855
Vass, Dennis B., Treas.--IES Utilities Inc., Cedar Rapids, IA; *U.S. Public*, pg. 855
Vasto, Salvatore J., Chief Fin. Officer, Sr. V.P. & Treas.--American Security Group, Atlanta, GA; *Int'l*, pg. 499
Vaswig, Donald, Exec. V.P., Treas. & Dir.-Fin.--Harmony Foods Corporation, Santa Cruz, CA; *U.S. Private*, pg. 503
Vaughan, Odie F., Treas.--Murphy Oil Corporation, El Dorado, AR; *U.S. Public*, pg. 1141
Vaughn, Patrick, V.P.-Fin., Sec. & Treas.--Akzo Nobel Coatings Inc. (KY), Louisville, KY; *Int'l*, pg. 47
Vaught, Kenneth C., Asst. V.P. & Treas.--Edison Brothers Stores, Inc., Saint Louis, MO; *U.S. Public*, pg. 563
Vaupshas, R.A., Treas. & Sec.--Henry Birks & Sons (1993) Inc., Montreal, Canada; *Int'l*, pg. 196
Vayda, Joseph M., Treas.--CoreStates Financial Corp., Philadelphia, PA; *U.S. Public*, pg. 446
Veilleux, Martin J., Chief Fin. Officer, Exec. V.P.-Fin., Treas. & Sec.--Boron LePore Group, Fair Lawn, NJ; *U.S. Public*, *pg. 246*
Veltman, Warren A., Chief Fin. Officer--Autocam Corporation, Grand Rapids, MI; *U.S. Public*, pg. 148
Ventre, Francis C., Treas.--XTRA, Inc., Portland, ME; *U.S. Public*, pg. 1787
Ventre, John, Jr., Chm. Bd., Chief Exec. Officer & Treas.--Ventre Packing Company, Inc., Syracuse, NY; *U.S. Private*, pg. 1135
Verdisco, George, Treas.--Bally Management, New Rochelle, NY; *Int'l*, pg. 998
Verduzco y Sanchez, Guillermo, Treas.--Grupo Continental S.A., Tampico, Mexico; *Int'l*, pg. 573
Verebay, Max, Treas.--Queens Group, Inc., Long Island City, NY; *U.S. Private*, pg. 900
Vereen, W.J., Pres., Chief Exec. Officer & Treas.--Riverside Manufacturing Co., Moultrie, GA; *U.S. Private*, pg. 934
Veres, William A., Treas.--Transalta Corporation, Calgary, Canada; *Int'l*, pg. 1416
Veres, William A., Treas.--TransAlta Utilities, Calgary, Canada; *Int'l*, pg. 1416
Verga, Joseph, Sr. V.P., Treas. & Sec.--Techdyne, Inc., Hialeah, FL; *U.S. Public*, pg. 1080
Verglas, Alain, V.P., Treas. & Asst. Sec.--IBL Limited, Inc., Scarsdale, NY; *Int'l*, pg. 21
Verhagen, C.H., V.P., Treas. & Sec.--AEGON Reinsurance Company of America, Short Hills, NJ; *Int'l*, pg. 26
Verhagen, C.H., V.P.-Tres. & Sec.--AEGON U.S. Holding Corp., Short Hills, NJ; *Int'l*, pg. 26
Verkruyse, Anthony J., V.P., Treas. & Sec.--Huntco Inc., Town and Country, MO; *U.S. Public*, pg. 849
Vermylen, Paul A., Jr., Pres., Treas. & Sec.--Meenan Oil Co. L.P., Syosset, NY; *U.S. Private*, pg. 729
Vernon, Shirley A., Sec. & Treas.--Gilvin-Terrill Inc., Amarillo, TX; *U.S. Private*, pg. 455
Verrill, Peter J., Chief Oper. Officer, Exec. V.P. & Treas.--Peoples Heritage Financial Group, Inc., Portland, ME; *U.S. Public*, pg. 1275
Veselits, Charles F., V.P. & Treas.--Selfix, Inc., Chicago, IL; *U.S. Public*, pg. 832
Vetere, Louis J., Controller & Treas.--Marotta Scientific Controls, Inc., Montville, NJ; *U.S. Private*, pg. 706
Vetter, Philip L., V.P.-Fin. & Treas.--Osco Industries Inc., Portsmouth, OH; *U.S. Private*, pg. 820
Viano, Larry, Controller & Treas.--Semitool, Inc., Kalispell, MT; *U.S. Public*, pg. 1456
Vicari, Douglas, V.P. & Treas.--Prime Hospitality Corp., Fairfield, NJ; *U.S. Public*, pg. 1326
Vickruck, Tracey L., V.P. & Treas.--Union Energy Inc., Toronto, Canada; *Int'l*, pg. 1492
Vilcot, Gerard, Asst. Treas.--International Business Machines Corporation, Armonk, NY; *U.S. Public*, pg. 895
Villafane, Ramon, V.P. & Treas.--Alcon (Puerto Rico) Inc., Humacao, PR; *Int'l*, pg. 916
Villano, Michael J., Chief Fin. Officer, V.P., Treas. & Asst. Sec.--Scan-Optics, Inc., Manchester, CT; *U.S. Public*, pg. 1436
Villareal, L., Treas.--Sistema Argos S.A., Ciudad Juarez, Mexico; *Int'l*, pg. 1256
Villiotti, Anthony J., Treas. & Controller--Duquesne Enterprises, Pittsburgh, PA; *U.S. Public*, pg. 474
Vincent, Dane L., Chief Fin. Officer & Treas.--Texfi Industries, Inc., Raleigh, NC; *U.S. Public*, pg. 1588
Vincent, Robert M., Chief Fin. Officer & Sr. V.P.-Fin. & Treas.--Uno Restaurant Corporation, West Roxbury, MA; *U.S. Public*, pg. 1698
Vinney, Les C., V.P. & Treas.--The B.F. Goodrich Company, Richfield, OH; *U.S. Public*, pg. 751
Vinzant, R. Lee, V.P. & Treas.--Sloss Industries Corporation, Birmingham, AL; *U.S. Public*, pg. 1736
Viola, Michael J., V.P. & Treas.--Kmart Corporation, Troy, MI; *U.S. Public*, pg. 963
Vislocky, Joseph, Treas.--Dassault Falcon Jet Corp., South Hackensack, NJ; *Int'l*, pg. 383
Visser, J., Treas.--SHV Holdings N.V., Utrecht, Netherlands; *Int'l*, pg. 1154
Vitrano, Frank, Treas.--Pathmark Stores Incorporated, Woodbridge, NJ; *U.S. Private*, pg. 843
Vizanko, James K., Treas.--Minnesota Power, Duluth, MN; *U.S. Public*, pg. 1116
Vlahakis, Glenda, Treas. & Sec.--Trailer Wheel & Frame Company, Houston, TX; *U.S. Private*, pg. 1095
Vocca, Joe, Treas. & Sec.--Atotech U.S.A. Inc., Rock Hill, SC; *U.S. Private*, pg. 97
Vochis, Charles G., Treas.--Quebecor Printing Modern Inc., Brookfield, CT; *Int'l*, pg. 1078
Voelkel, Harold G., Jr., Chief Fin. Officer & Treas.--Southland Oil Company, Jackson, MS; *U.S. Private*, pg. 1018
Vogelpohl, James M., Treas.--Pulitzer Publishing Company, Saint Louis, MO; *U.S. Public*, pg. 1343
Vogelpohl, James M., Treas.--St. Louis Post-Dispatch, Saint Louis, MO; *U.S. Public*, pg. 1343
Vold, Robert J., V.P., Gen. Mgr.-Norstand & Asst. Treas.--Norstan, Inc., Plymouth, MN; *U.S. Public*, pg. 1192
Volker, Klaus, Treas.--Boehringer Mannheim GmbH, Mannheim, Germany; *Int'l*, pg. 331
Vollenweider, Lester, Treas.--Reily Electrical Supply, Inc., Metairie, LA; *U.S. Private*, pg. 919
Vollert, Hans-Jurgen, Treas.--Porsche AG, Stuttgart, Germany; *Int'l*, pg. 1063
Vollmer, John E., III, Chief Fin. Officer, V.P. & Treas.--Blockbuster Music, Dallas, TX; *U.S. Private*, pg. 776
Vollmer, Steve, Treas. & Sec.--Anritsu Wiltron, Morgan Hill, CA; *Int'l*, pg. 77
Vollmuth, George H., Treas.--Entertainment Weekly Inc., New York, NY; *U.S. Public*, pg. 1613
Volovic, Robert C., V.P. & Treas.--Kurtz Bros., Inc., Clearfield, PA; *U.S. Private*, pg. 637
Von der Ruhr, Gerhard J., Chm. Bd., Pres. & Treas.--Criticare Systems, Inc., Waukesha, WI; *U.S. Public*, pg. 459
Von Lehman, John I., Chief Fin. Officer, V.P. & Treas.--The Midland Company, Cincinnati, OH; *U.S. Public*, pg. 1110
VonBon, Jim, Treas.--Triple F, Inc., Des Moines, IA; *U.S. Private*, pg. 1104
Vondrak, David J., V.P. & Treas.--ABC, Inc, New York, NY; *U.S. Public*, pg. 511
VonGal, M. Eileen, Treas.--National Life Insurance Company, Montpelier, VT; *U.S. Private*, pg. 785
Vortman, Marky, Treas.--Interstate Producers Livestock Association, Peoria, IL; *U.S. Private*, pg. 573
Voss, Jeffrey, Chief Fin. Officer, Exec. V.P. & Treas.--Beverly Bancorporation Inc., Chicago, IL; *U.S. Public*, pg. 227
Vozick, David, Chm. Bd., Treas. & Sec.--AFP Imaging Corporation, Elmsford, NY; *U.S. Public*, pg. 6
Vranek, William, Chief Fin. Officer--Coleman Cable Systems, Inc., North Chicago, IL; *U.S. Public*, pg. 968
Vredenbregt, J.C., V.P., Controller & Asst. Treas.--The Ziegler Companies, Inc., West Bend, WI; *U.S. Public*, pg. 1791
Vredenbregt, J.C., V.P., Controller & Asst. Treas.--B.C. Ziegler & Co., West Bend, WI; *U.S. Public*, pg. 1792
Vredenbregt, J.C., Asst. Treas.--Ziegler Financing Corp., West Bend, WI; *U.S. Public*, pg. 1792
Vredenbregt, J.C., Asst. Treas.--Ziegler Leasing Corp., West Bend, WI; *U.S. Public*, pg. 1792
Vredenbregt, J.C., Asst. Treas.--Ziegler Thrift Trading, Inc., Minneapolis, MN; *U.S. Public*, pg. 1792
Vyas, Dilip S., V.P.-Bus. Devel. & Treas.--Circuit Systems, Inc., Elk Grove Village, IL; *U.S. Public*, pg. 374
Wachter, Karl, Treas.--Michael Weinig, Inc., Statesville, NC; *Int'l*, pg. 1488
Waddell, M. Keith, Chief Fin. Officer, Sr. V.P. & Treas.--Robert Half International Inc., Menlo Park, CA; *U.S. Public*, pg. 774
Wade, Donnie, Controller, Treas. & Sec.--Goodpasture, Inc., Brownfield, TX; *U.S. Private*, pg. 464
Wadhams, Timothy, V.P., Controller & Treas.--MascoTech, Inc., Taylor, MI; *U.S. Public*, pg. 1055
Wadsworth, Howard, V.P.-Fin. & Admin., Treas. & Sec.--Kaneb Services, Inc., Richardson, TX; *U.S. Public*, pg. 942
Wadsworth, Howard C., V.P., Treas. & Sec.--Kaneb Pipe Line Partners, L.P., Richardson, TX; *U.S. Public*, pg. 942
Wagar, James L., V.P. & Treas.--Carter-Wallace, Inc., New York, NY; *U.S. Public*, pg. 309
Waggaman, Donald E., Jr., Treas.--Hartford Life & Accident Insurance Company, Hartford, CT; *U.S. Public*, pg. 795
Wagley, David R., Treas.--Dekalb Genetics Corporation, De Kalb, IL; *U.S. Public*, pg. 493
Wagner, Gary, Chief Fin. Officer, Sr. V.P. & Treas.--Ameron International Corporation, Pasadena, CA; *U.S. Public*, pg. 98
Wagner, Harvey A., Chief Fin. Officer, Sr. V.P.-Fin. & Treas.--Scientific-Atlanta, Inc., Norcross, GA; *U.S. Public*, *pg. 1443*
Wagner, Karen, Chief Fin. Officer, V.P. & Treas.--American Recreation Centers, Inc., Sacramento, CA; *U.S. Public*, pg. 90
Wagner, Mary Jane, Chief Fin. Officer, Treas. & Sec.--American Inks & Coatings Corp., Phoenixville, PA; *U.S. Private*, pg. 56
Wagner, Michael J., Asst. Treas.--Consolidated Stores Corp., Columbus, OH; *U.S. Public*, pg. 437
Wagner, Robert, Chief Fin. Officer, V.P.-Fin., Treas. & Sec.--XETA Corporation, Tulsa, OK; *U.S. Public*, pg. 1783
Wagner, Robert V., Chief Fin. Officer, V.P.-Fin., Sec. & Treas.--Code-Alarm, Inc., Madison Heights, MI; *U.S. Public*, pg. 393
Wagoner, Stephanie A., V.P. & Treas.--Avnet, Inc., Great Neck, NY; *U.S. Public*, pg. 155
Wahl, Ellen, Treas.--Vibra Screw Inc., Totowa, NJ; *U.S. Private*, pg. 1138
Wahl, Gloria, Treas.--Wyse Technology Inc., San Jose, CA; *U.S. Private*, pg. 1194
Wahlman, Mark M., Chief Fin. Officer, V.P.-Fin. & Treas.--Pacific Coast Producers, Lodi, CA; *U.S. Private*, pg. 830
Wainscott, James, Asst. Treas & Asst. Sec.--National Steel Corporation, Mishawaka, IN; *Int'l*, pg. 902
Wakeland, Ralph, Exec. V.P.-Fin. & Treas.--Union Underwear Co., Inc., Bowling Green, KY; *U.S. Public*, pg. 686
Walborn, Ronald E., C.P.A., Chief Fin. Officer & Treas.--Arnold Industries, Inc., Lebanon, PA; *U.S. Public*, pg. 132
Walbrun, Paul A., V.P. & Controller--Summa Industries, Torrance, CA; *U.S. Public*, pg. 1527
Walburg, James B., V.P. & Treas.--IMCO Recycling Inc., Irving, TX; *U.S. Public*, pg. 870
Waldorf, Toby, Treas. & Sec.--Idea Man, Inc., Los Angeles, CA; *U.S. Private*, pg. 557
Walgoriski, Steve, Treas.--Johnson Yokogawa Corporation, Newnan, GA; *Int'l*, pg. 1521
Walgrove, George R., Jr., Gen. Mgr. & Sec.--Maryland & Virginia Milk Producers Cooperative Association, Inc., Reston, VA; *U.S. Private*, pg. 711
Walker, Alan, Treas.--3i Group plc, London, United Kingdom; *Int'l*, pg. 1386
Walker, Baker, Chief Fin. Officer, Controller, Treas. & Sec.--C.B. Ragland Company, Nashville, TN; *U.S. Private*, pg. 907
Walker, Beth, Treas.--Spar Aerospace Limited, Toronto, Canada; *Int'l*, pg. 1287
Walker, Charles B., Vice Chm., Chief Fin. Officer & Treas.--Albemarle Corporation, Richmond, VA; *U.S. Public*, pg. 37
Walker, Donald H., Chief Fin. Officer, V.P.-Fin.--Frisch's Restaurants, Inc., Cincinnati, OH; *U.S. Public*, pg. 682
Walker, Earl, Controller & Treas.--Jitney-Jungle Stores of America, Inc., Jackson, MS; *U.S. Private*, pg. 588
Walker, James S., Chief Fin. Officer & V.P.--Park-Ohio Industries, Inc., Cleveland, OH; *U.S. Public*, pg. 1258
Walker, John D., Sec. & Treas.--Anco Insulations, Inc., Baton Rouge, LA; *U.S. Private*, pg. 71
Walker, Kandee Jo, Treas. & Sec.--Eldorado Chemical Company, San Antonio, TX; *U.S. Private*, pg. 367
Walker, Kevin, Asst. Treas.--Modern American Life Insurance Company, Springfield, MO; *U.S. Public*, pg. 853
Walker, Kevin P., Chief Fin. Officer, Treas. & Sec.--Duncanson & Holt, New York, NY; *U.S. Public*, pg. 1699
Walker, Max N., Treas. & Sec.--Gaston County Dyeing Machine Co., Mount Holly, NC; *U.S. Private*, pg. 441
Walker, Neal, Treas. & Asst. Sec.--Welcome Home, Inc., Wilmington, NC; *U.S. Private*, pg. 598
Walker, Vernon W., Chief Fin. Officer & Treas.--Blue Cross & Blue Shield of Texas, Inc., Richardson, TX; *U.S. Private*, pg. 152
Walker, Weldon W., Dir.-Tax, Asst. Treas. & Asst. Sec.--Weatherford Enterra Incorporated, Houston, TX; *U.S. Public*, pg. 1749
Walker, Weldon W., V.P., Asst. Treas. & Asst. Sec.--Weatherford U.S., Inc., Houston, TX; *U.S. Public*, pg. 1749
Wall, David A., Chief Fin. Officer, V.P.-Fin. & Treas.--DOALL Company, Des Plaines, IL; *U.S. Private*, pg. 337
Wall, Kay D., Chief Exec. Officer, Treas. & Sec.--Bryant Electric Company, Inc., High Point, NC; *U.S. Private*, pg. 176
Wall, Morton J., Treas.--Koo Koo Roo, Inc., Los Angeles, CA; *U.S. Public*, pg. 966
Wall, Richard W., V.P. & Treas.--ComPair LeRoi, Sidney, OH; *Int'l*, pg. 1242
Wallace, David G., Treas.--Community Bank System, Inc., De Witt, NY; *U.S. Public*, pg. 416
Wallach, Diane, Exec. V.P. & Treas.--Cody Company, Denver, CO; *U.S. Private*, pg. 249
Wallbank, Philip, Treas.--Air UK Ltd., Stansted, United Kingdom; *Int'l*, pg. 38
Waller, Rodney L., V.P. & Treas.--SOCO International, Inc., Houston, TX; *U.S. Public*, pg. 1482
Walls, Clyde, Treas. & Sec.--Commemorative Brands, Inc., Austin, TX; *U.S. Private*, pg. 258
Wallschlaeger, Tamie R., Asst. Treas.--Bankmanagers Corp., Milwaukee, WI; *U.S. Private*, pg. 114
Walser, Donald G., Exec. V.P. & Treas.--Rauch Industries, Inc., Gastonia, NC; *U.S. Private*, pg. 1061
Walsh, Brendan, Controller & Treas.--Monsey-Bakor, Kimberton, PA; *U.S. Private*, pg. 757
Walsh, K.W., Treas.--Akom Ltd., Montego Bay, Jamaica; *U.S. Public*, pg. 1644
Walsh, K.W., Treas.--Dominion Stores, Inc., Martinsville, VA; *U.S. Public*, pg. 1644
Walsh, M.J., Treas.--Lake Keowee Country Club, Inc., Valley Forge, PA; *Int'l*, pg. 1171
Walsh, Mark, Treas.--Ocean Properties, Ltd., Delray Beach, FL; *U.S. Private*, pg. 811

Walsh, Meg, V.P. & Treas.--Lucent Technologies Inc., Murray Hill, NJ; U.S. Public, pg. 1017
Walsh, Stephen F., Asst. Treas.--JC Penney Company, Inc., Plano, TX; U.S. Public, pg. 916
Walsh, Terry J., V.P. & Treas.--Scott's Food Services Inc., Markham, Canada; Int'l, pg. 1213
Walsh, Terry J., V.P. & Treas.--Scott's Management Services Inc., Markham, Canada; Int'l, pg. 1213
Walters, Eric G., Chief Fin. Officer & Treas.--PolyMedica Industries, Inc., Woburn, MA; U.S. Public, pg. 1315
Walters, Kirk, Chief Fin. Officer, Sr. V.P. & Treas.--Chittenden Corporation, Burlington, VT; U.S. Public, pg. 350
Walters, Kirk, Sr. V.P.-Treas. & Fin. Div.--Union Planters Bank, Memphis, TN; U.S. Public, pg. 1669
Walters, L.M., Treas.--Atlantic Southern Properties, Inc., Pleasantville, NJ; U.S. Public, pg. 430
Walters, L.M., Treas.--Atlantic Energy Technology, Inc., Pleasantville, NJ; U.S. Public, pg. 430
Walters, Lou, V.P. & Treas.--Atlantic Electric Co., Pleasantville, NJ; U.S. Public, pg. 430
Walters, M.K., Chief Acctg. Officer, Sr. V.P. & Treas.--Union Planters Corporation, Cordova, TN; U.S. Public, pg. 1668
Walters, Somerset R., V.P. & Treas.--Duracell International Inc., Bethel, CT; U.S. Public, pg. 743
Walton, F. Ferrell, Treas. & Sec.--Johnston Industries, Inc., Columbus, GA; U.S. Public, pg. 933
Walton, Gary L., Treas.--BellSouth Enterprises, Inc., Atlanta, GA; U.S. Public, pg. 208
Waltzer, Julius, V.P., Treas. & Sec.--Jack Young Associates, Hazleton, PA; U.S. Private, pg. 1201
Walworth, Lincoln, Asst. Treas.--McKesson Corporation, San Francisco, CA; U.S. Public, pg. 1072
Wan, Agatha, Deputy Gen. Mgr.--Orchard Parade Holdings Limited, Singapore, Singapore; Int'l, pg. 1007
Wandrei, Bruce A., Treas.--Crown Holdings, Inc., Roseville, MN; U.S. Private, pg. 293
Wanlass, Dennis L., Chief Fin. Officer, V.P. & Treas.--Geneva Steel, Vineyard, UT; U.S. Public, pg. 729
Warburton, Tracey, Treas.--Delta Gold N.L., Sydney, Australia; Int'l, pg. 389
Warchol, Keith L., Asst. Treas.--Allegheny Power System, Inc., Hagerstown, MD; U.S. Public, pg. 42
Ward, Brian P., Pres., Chief Exec. Officer & Treas.--Cortland Line Co., Inc., Cortland, NY; U.S. Private, pg. 277
Ward, Christopher J., Treas.--Atkinson, San Bruno, CA; U.S. Public, pg. 143
Ward, Frank E., Asst. Treas.--Electrical Equipment Company, Raleigh, NC; U.S. Private, pg. 368
Ward, J.M., Controller--John Mowlem & Company plc, Isleworth, United Kingdom; Int'l, pg. 896
Ward, Malcolm R., Treas.--Reckitt & Colman plc, London, United Kingdom; Int'l, pg. 1089
Ward, Paul F., V.P.-Fin. & Treas.--Hollingsworth & Vose Co., East Walpole, MA; U.S. Private, pg. 534
Ward, Robert, Treas.--Cavco Industries, Inc., Phoenix, AZ; U.S. Public, pg. 323
Ward, Robert, Sec. & Treas.--SunBuilt Homes, Inc., Phoenix, AZ; U.S. Public, pg. 323
Ward, Steven, Treas.--Trigen Energy Corporation, White Plains, NY; U.S. Public, pg. 1637
Warder, Charles A., V.P. & Treas.--Coats & Clark Inc., Greenville, SC; Int'l, pg. 300
Wardinski, Bruce D., Sr. V.P. & Treas.--Host Marriott Corporation, Bethesda, MD; U.S. Public, pg. 841
Wardlaw, Sharon, Chief Fin. Officer, Treas. & Sec.--Polydex Pharmaceuticals Limited, Scarborough, Canada; Int'l, pg. 1062
Wardle, D. Duane, V.P.-Fin. & Treas.--Young Electric Sign Company, Salt Lake City, UT; U.S. Private, pg. 1201
Wardynski, Paula, Treas.-News America--The News Corporation Limited, Sydney, Australia; Int'l, pg. 925
Ware, Ronald G., Treas.--Richardson Electronics, Ltd., Lafox, IL; U.S. Public, pg. 1387
Wargowsky, Bob, Asst. Treas.--Baker Hughes INTEQ, Houston, TX; U.S. Public, pg. 166
Waring, Paul, Corp. Controller & Treas.--Reflectone, Inc., Tampa, FL; Int'l, pg. 218
Wark, Dale A., Chief Fin. Officer, Exec. V.P., Treas. & Sec.--R.M. Shoemaker Co., West Conshohocken, PA; U.S. Private, pg. 996
Warm, Stuart, Exec. V.P. & Treas.--Warm Brothers Construction Company, Cincinnati, OH; U.S. Private, pg. 1150
Warnecke, Dennis C., Treas.--Kennedy Manufacturing Company, Van Wert, OH; U.S. Private, pg. 614
Warner, I., Treas.--Willis Corroon Group PLC, London, United Kingdom; Int'l, pg. 1501
Warner, William H., Treas.--International Thoroughbred Breeders, Inc., Cherry Hill, NJ; U.S. Public, pg. 908
Warren, James L., Chief Fin. Officer, V.P. & Treas.--Aquila Biopharmaceuticals, Inc., Worcester, MA; U.S. Public, pg. 126
Warren, Joseph G., Chief Fin. Officer, V.P.-Fin., Treas. & Sec.--Bowmar Instrument Corporation, Phoenix, AZ; U.S. Public, pg. 248
Warren, Robert J., V.P. & Treas.--Diebold, Incorporated, Canton, OH; U.S. Public, pg. 506
Warren, Stan, V.P. & Treas.--CogniSeis Development, Inc., Houston, TX; U.S. Public, pg. 1563
Wasco, Joseph, V.P. & Treas.--Maher Terminals Inc., Jersey City, NJ; U.S. Private, pg. 697
Wassenaar, John, Exec. V.P. & Treas.--Fareway Stores, Inc., Boone, IA; U.S. Private, pg. 393
Wasserman, David S., V.P. & Treas.--Harris Corporation, Melbourne, FL; U.S. Public, pg. 791
Wasserspring, Arthur J., V.P.-Fin.--Eastco Industrial Safety Corp., Huntington Station, NY; U.S. Public, pg. 548
Wasserstrom, Alan, Treas.--Wasserstrom Company, Columbus, OH; U.S. Private, pg. 1152
Watanabe, Shinichi, Dir. & Treas.--Okaya (U.S.A.), Inc., Fort Lee, NJ; Int'l, pg. 999
Watanabe, Yasuo, Treas.--Mikuni Corporation, Tokyo, Japan; Int'l, pg. 867
Waters, Somerset, V.P. & Treas.--Harnischfeger Industries, Inc., Saint Francis, WI; U.S. Public, pg. 788
Watkins, Mark A., Treas.--Myers Industries, Inc., Akron, OH; U.S. Public, pg. 1143
Watkins, Ophelia, Treas. & Sec.--Stahmann Farms, Inc., La Mesa, NM; U.S. Private, pg. 1029
Watson, Andrew, Treas.--American Meter Company, Horsham, PA; Int'l, pg. 1149
WAtson, Fred, Corp. Treas.--General Tours Inc., Keene, NH; U.S. Private, pg. 445
Watson, J.G., Asst. Treas.--Union Camp Corporation, Wayne, NJ; U.S. Public, pg. 1665
Watson, Janet S., Treas. & Sec.--The Empire District Electric Company, Joplin, MO; U.S. Public, pg. 579
Watson, Robert, V.P.-Treas.--Encore Computer Corporation, Fort Lauderdale, FL; U.S. Public, pg. 580
Watt, Frederick I., Dir.-Fin.--Wassall Plc, London, United Kingdom; Int'l, pg. 1486
Watts, Glen E., II, Treas.--Bell Atlantic-Washington, D.C., Inc., Washington, DC; U.S. Public, pg. 203
Waxman, Armond, Pres., Co-Chief Exec. Officer & Treas.--Waxman Industries, Inc., Bedford, OH; U.S. Public, pg. 1748
Weatherhead, Vincent J., Treas.--OPEL Nederland B.V., Sliedrecht, Netherlands; U.S. Public, pg. 723
Weatherly, John S., Chief Fin. Officer, V.P. & Treas.--Callon Petroleum Company, Natchez, MS; U.S. Public, pg. 295
Weaver, Amy S., Pres., Treas. & Sec.--Emons Finance Corporation, Wilmington, DE; U.S. Public, pg. 578
Webb, E. Lynn, Exec. V.P. & Treas.--Dualite Sales & Service, Inc., Williamsburg, OH; U.S. Private, pg. 344
Webb, Robert D., Sr. V.P. & Treas.--Knight Architects Engineers Planners, Inc., Chicago, IL; U.S. Private, pg. 626
Weber, Douglas, Chief Fin. Officer & Treas.--Edwards Brothers, Inc., Ann Arbor, MI; U.S. Private, pg. 365
Weber, Gregory R., V.P. & Treas.--CSX Corporation, Richmond, VA; U.S. Public, pg. 284
Weber, John R., Chief Fin. Officer, V.P.-Fin. & Treas.--The Chardon Rubber Co., Chardon, OH; U.S. Private, pg. 229
Weber, Max, Sr. V.P.-Foreign Exchange & Money Market Opers.--Banque Cantonale Vaudoise, Lausanne, Switzerland; Int'l, pg. 160
Webster, Ronald D., V.P. & Treas.--Telephone and Data Systems, Inc., Chicago, IL; U.S. Public, pg. 1570
Wedel, H. Charles, Chief Fin. Officer & Treas.--NJ Transit, Newark, NJ; U.S. Private, pg. 794
Weeden, Jeffrey B., Chief Fin. Officer, Sr. V.P., & Treas.--Firstar Corporation-Iowa, Des Moines, IA; U.S. Public, pg. 643
Weekes, Eric B., Treas.--Illinois Power Company, Decatur, IL; U.S. Public, pg. 869
Weeks, Stephen A., Treas.--Bell Industries, Inc., El Segundo, CA; U.S. Public, pg. 204
Wehmann, James, Treas.--Fingerhut Corp., Minnetonka, MN; U.S. Public, pg. 623
Wehrle, D.M., Treas.--North American Refractories Company, Cleveland, OH; U.S. Private, pg. 803
Weibel, Marlene, Treas. & Sec.--Weibel Winery, Lodi, CA; U.S. Private, pg. 1159
Weiden, Jeff, Sr. V.P.-Fin. & Treas.--Firstar Corporation, Milwaukee, WI; U.S. Public, pg. 642
Weidert, Randall W., Asst. Treas.--Blair Corporation, Warren, PA; U.S. Public, pg. 236
Weidman, Darold, Asst. Treas.--Wickes Inc., Vernon Hills, IL; U.S. Public, pg. 1391
Weigel, David V., V.P. & Treas.--The Mutual Life Insurance Company of New York, New York, NY; U.S. Private, pg. 769
Weimert, Richard A., Asst. Treas.-Domestic--Becton Dickinson & Company, Franklin Lakes, NJ; U.S. Public, pg. 199
Weinand, Paul, Treas.--Daktronics, Inc., Brookings, SD; U.S. Public, pg. 478
Weinberg, Robert W., Chief Fin. Officer, Sr. Exec. V.P. & Treas.--K-Tron International, Inc., Pitman, NJ; U.S. Public, pg. 938
Weiner, Debbie, Controller--Tillamook County Creamery Assn., Tillamook, OR; U.S. Private, pg. 1086
Weiner, Paul, Chief Fin. Officer, Sr. V.P. & Treas.--McCrory Corporation, New York, NY; U.S. Private, pg. 720
Weiner, Warren, Exec. V.P., Treas. & Sec.--Deb Shops, Inc., Philadelphia, PA; U.S. Public, pg. 491
Weinhold, John L., V.P. & Treas.--Property Ventures, Ltd., Pittsburgh, PA; U.S. Public, pg. 474
Weinman, Thomas F., Treas.--Bar-S Foods Co., Phoenix, AZ; U.S. Private, pg. 114
Weinstein, Edwin S., V.P.-Fin., Treas. & Sec.--Pomeroy Computer Resources, Hebron, KY; U.S. Public, pg. 1315
Weinstein, Gerald, V.P.-Treas.--Lefrak Organization Inc., Rego Park, NY; U.S. Private, pg. 658
Weinstein, Harvey, Chm. Bd. & Treas.--West Mill Clothes, Inc., Woodside, NY; U.S. Private, pg. 1163
Weis, Dan, Treas.--Jim Causley Pontiac GMC Inc., Clinton Township, MI; U.S. Private, pg. 220
Weis, Robert F., Chm. Bd. & Treas.--Weis Markets, Inc., Sunbury, PA; U.S. Public, pg. 1751
Weis, Terry, Asst. Treas.--Sporlan Valve Company, Washington, MO; U.S. Private, pg. 1026
Weisbarth, James, Sr. V.P., Treas. & Asst. Sec.--Central Reserve Life Corporation, Strongsville, OH; U.S. Public, pg. 326
Weisberg, A.A., Chm. Bd. & Treas.--Technic Incorporated, Cranston, RI; U.S. Private, pg. 1071
Weise, Susan, Asst. Treas.--Magnetic Technologies Corporation, Rochester, NY; U.S. Public, pg. 1420
Weisman, Robert, Treas.--Plainville Stock Company, Inc., Plainville, MA; U.S. Private, pg. 868
Weiss, Allan J., Treas.--United HealthCare Corporation, Minnetonka, MN; U.S. Public, pg. 1677
Weiss, Allan J., Treas.--United HealthCare of Utah, Salt Lake City, UT; U.S. Public, pg. 1678
Weiss, Allan J., Treas.--United HealthCare of the Midlands, Inc., Omaha, NE; U.S. Public, pg. 1678
Weiss, Allan J., Treas.--HealthWise of America, Nashville, TN; U.S. Public, pg. 1678
Weiss, Allan J., Treas.--CAC Medical Centers, Inc., Coral Gables, FL; U.S. Public, pg. 1678
Weiss, Allan J., Treas.--United HealthCare of North Carolina, Inc., Greensboro, NC; U.S. Public, pg. 1678
Weiss, Allan J., Treas.--United HealthCare of Nevada, Inc., Las Vegas, NV; U.S. Public, pg. 1678
Weiss, Allan J., Treas.--United HealthCare of Texas, Inc., Austin, TX; U.S. Public, pg. 1678
Weiss, Allan J., Treas.--United HealthCare of Oregon, Inc., Minnetonka, MN; U.S. Public, pg. 1678
Weiss, Deborah, Treas.--Imation Corporation, Oakdale, MN; U.S. Public, pg. 870
Weiss, Gerald, Treas.--Cosmos Communications, Inc., Long Island City, NY; U.S. Private, pg. 278
Weiss, James A., Sec. & Treas.--James Chevrolet Inc., Clinton Township, MI; U.S. Private, pg. 580
Weiss, Mark, V.P.-Fin. & Treas.--Siemens Power Corp., Milwaukee, WI; Int'l, pg. 1246
Weiss, Stanley, Jr., Chief Exec. Officer & Treas.--Charles River Foods, Inc., Boston, MA; U.S. Private, pg. 230
Weissenborn, James A., V.P. & Treas.--Pulte Corporation, Bloomfield Hills, MI; U.S. Public, pg. 1344
Weitzenfeld, Marvin, Chief Fin. Officer, Sec. & Treas.--Globe-Amerada Glass Company, Elk Grove Village, IL; U.S. Private, pg. 458
Weitzenfeld, Marvin, Chief Fin. Officer, Treas. & Sec.--Assurance Glass Co. of Alabama, Selma, AL; U.S. Private, pg. 458
Wejman, Kenneth J., Treas.--Anson Industries, Inc., Melrose Park, IL; U.S. Private, pg. 76
Welch, Edward A., Sr. V.P. & Asst. Treas.--Fay, Spofford & Thorndike, Inc., Burlington, MA; U.S. Private, pg. 397
Welch, Graham F., Treas.--Derbyshire Building Society, Duffield, United Kingdom; Int'l, pg. 394
Welch, Stephen, Chief Fin. Officer & Treas.--Todd Pacific Shipyards Corp., Seattle, WA; U.S. Public, pg. 1619
Welch, Thomas G., Treas.--General Motors Distribution Ireland Ltd., Dublin, Ireland; U.S. Public, pg. 722
Weldon, Dennis, Treas.--Mentor Graphics Corporation, Wilsonville, OR; U.S. Public, pg. 1086
Weldon, Robert W., V.P.-Fin. & Treas.--Country Life Insurance Company, Bloomington, IL; U.S. Private, pg. 278
Welge, Michael W., Exec. V.P., Treas., Sec. & Comptroller--Gilster Mary Lee Corp., Chester, IL; U.S. Private, pg. 455
Wellendorf, Donald R., V.P., Treas. & Investor Rels.--Mapco Inc., Tulsa, OK; U.S. Public, pg. 1042
Wellens, Leroy, Chm. Bd., Pres., Chief Exec. & Chief Fin. Officer & Treas.--Wellens & Co., Inc., Minneapolis, MN; U.S. Private, pg. 1161
Weller, Carl W., Treas.--Atmos Energy Corporation, Dallas, TX; U.S. Public, pg. 145
Weller, Joseph C., Chief Fin. Officer, Treas. & Sec.--Morgan Keegan, Inc., Memphis, TN; U.S. Public, pg. 1131
Welling, Richard, Sr. V.P. & Treas.--Ameriana Bancorp, New Castle, IN; U.S. Public, pg. 66
Wellington, Roger U., Chief Fin. Officer & Treas.--The L.S. Starrett Company, Athol, MA; U.S. Public, pg. 1511
Welliver, Byron L., Sr. V.P.-Fin., Controller & Treas.--Noble Drilling Corporation, Houston, TX; U.S. Public, pg. 1186
Welliver, Byron L., Sr. V.P.-Fin. & Treas.-Noble Offshore Corporation, Houston, TX; U.S. Public, pg. 1186
Wellman, Thomas A., Controller & Asst. Treas.--Alexander & Baldwin, Inc., Honolulu, HI; U.S. Public, pg. 39
Wellman, Thomas A., V.P., Controller & Asst. Treas.--A & B-Hawaii, Inc., Honolulu, HI; U.S. Public, pg. 39
Wellor un Ahlefeld, Christian, Treas.--Siemens AG, Munich, Germany; Int'l, pg. 1244
Wells, Gary H., Chief Fin. Officer,Treas & Sec.--Chittenden & Eastman Co., Burlington, IA; U.S. Private, pg. 237
Wells, Gary H., Chief Fin. Officer, Treas. & Sec.--Eastman House Of California, Inc., Burlington, IA; U.S. Private, pg. 238
Wells, Gary H., Chief Fin. Officer, Treas. & Sec.--Eastman House Of Alabama, Inc., Burlington, IA; U.S. Private, pg. 238
Wells, Hugh G., Jr., V.P. & Treas.--Havery Furniture Companies, Inc., Atlanta, GA; U.S. Public, pg. 799
Wells, Ronald, Treas. & Dir.-Taxes--Duron, Inc., Beltsville, MD; U.S. Private, pg. 349
Welsch, Andrew J., V.P. & Treas.--Bristol Hotels & Resorts, Dallas, TX; U.S. Public, pg. 253
Welsch, Dennis, V.P. & Treas.--Kaufman and Broad Home Corporation, Los Angeles, CA; U.S. Public, pg. 944
Welsh, Carden, Treas.--The Timberland Company, Stratham, NH; U.S. Public, pg. 1609
Welsh, Donald D., V.P. & Asst. Treas.--Foremost Insurance Co., Caledonia, MI; U.S. Public, pg. 667
Welsh, John J., V.P.-Acquisitions & Treas.--Acordia Northeast, Boston, MA; Int'l, pg. 671
Welsh, Philip, V.P.-Fin. & Treas.--Environment/One Corporation, Niskayuna, NY; U.S. Public, pg. 586
Welshhans, Richard W., Chief Fin. Officer, V.P. & Treas.--Reflectone, Inc., Tampa, FL; Int'l, pg. 218
Wendt, Michael J., Treas. & Dir.-Investment--Fencourt Reinsurance Co. Ltd., Hamilton, Bermuda; U.S. Public, pg. 795
Weng, Koh Foo, Treas.--Sime Darby Berhad, Kuala Lumpur, Malaysia; Int'l, pg. 1249
Wenger, Peter, Treas.--Clariant International Ltd., Muttenz, Switzerland; Int'l, pg. 624
Wenich, Ozzie, Chief Fin. Officer, Sr. V.P. & Treas.--H & R Block, Inc., Kansas City, MO; U.S. Public, pg. 770
Wennemer, Robert, Treas.--BMW (US) Holding Corporation, Woodcliff Lake, NJ; Int'l, pg. 177
Wennemer, Robert G., V.P. & Treas.--Aluminum Company of America, Pittsburgh, PA; U.S. Public, pg. 60
Wenner, Maria M., Treas.--Airlease Ltd., San Francisco, CA; U.S. Public, pg. 33

Wentworth, Robert, Pres., Chief Exec. Officer, V.P.-Fin., Admin. & Treas.--Alden Electronics, Inc., Westborough, MA; *U.S. Private*, pg. 872
Wenzler, Joseph P., Chief Fin. Officer, Sr. V.P. & Treas.--WICOR, Inc., Milwaukee, WI; *U.S. Public*, pg. 1767
Wenzler, Joseph P., Treas. & Sec.--Shurflo Pump Manufacturing Co., Santa Ana, CA; *U.S. Public*, pg. 1767
Wenzler, Joseph P., Treas. & Sec.--Hypro Corporation, New Brighton, MN; *U.S. Public*, pg. 1767
Wertz, John C., Chief Oper. Officer, Sr. V.P. & Treas.--Banner Aerospace, Inc., Washington, DC; *U.S. Public*, pg. 187
Wesolowski, Timothy M., V.P. & Treas.--The Valspar Corporation, Minneapolis, MN; *U.S. Public*, pg. 1707
Wessel, Rick L., Chief Fin. Officer, Treas. & Sec.--First Cash, Inc., Arlington, TX; *U.S. Public*, pg. 627
West, G.P., Treas. & Asst. Sec.--Florida East Coast Industries Inc., Saint Augustine, FL; *U.S. Public*, pg. 1427
West, G.R., Chief Fin. Officer, Corp. Sec. & Treas.--Alley-Cassetty Coal Co., Nashville, TN; *U.S. Private*, pg. 37
West, Judy H., Sr. V.P. & Treas.--Corbett HealthConnect, A Frank J. Corbett, Inc., Company, Chicago, IL; *U.S. Public*, pg. 1223
West, Philip M., V.P. & Treas.--W.W. Grainger, Inc., Lincolnshire, IL; *U.S. Public*, pg. 758
West, Stephen O., Treas.--Gold Kist, Inc., Atlanta, GA; *U.S. Private*, pg. 459
West, Steven E., First V.P. & Asst. Treas.--INMC Mortgage Holdings, Inc., Pasadena, CA; *U.S. Public*, pg. 857
West, Walter L., Treas.--PNC Bank Corp., Pittsburgh, PA; *U.S. Public*, pg. 1242
Westell, Bruce A., Treas.--Transcanada Pipelines Limited, Calgary, Canada; *Int'l*, pg. 1416
Westerfeld, William A., Chm. Bd., Pres., Chief Exec. Officer & Treas.--The Westerfelds, Inc., Pittsford, NY; *U.S. Private*, pg. 1164
Westerhouse, D.M., Jr., Treas.--Home Beneficial Corporation, Richmond, VA; *U.S. Public*, pg. 76
Westerlind, William F., V.P. & Treas.--The Worcester Insurance Co., Worcester, MA; *U.S. Public*, pg. 787
Westermann, John L., III, Chief Fin. Officer, V.P., Treas. & Sec.--CSC Financial Services Group, Austin, TX; *U.S. Public*, pg. 422
Westlie, James H., Treas. & Sec.--Westlie Motor Company, Minot, ND; *U.S. Private*, pg. 1169
Westmeyer, E.A., Chief Fin. Officer, V.P., Treas. & Sec.--Zeller Corp., Defiance, OH; *U.S. Private*, pg. 1204
Westover, Michael G., Treas.--American Eagle Group, Inc., Dallas, TX; *U.S. Public*, pg. 71
Westrick, Dennis E., Second V.P., Asst. Treas. & Investment Officer--Lincoln Investment Management Inc., Fort Wayne, IN; *U.S. Public*, pg. 998
Wetsel, Cecil, Jr., Pres. & Treas.--Wetsel-Oviatt Lumber Company, El Dorado Hills, CA; *U.S. Private*, pg. 1170
Wexler, Leonard, V.P. & Treas.--United Distillers USA, Inc., Stamford, CT; *Int'l*, pg. 412
Weyeneth, M., Treas.--Rhone-Poulenc Inc., Princeton, NJ; *Int'l*, pg. 1112
Weyer, Brian K., Treas.--AmeriSteel, Tampa, FL; *U.S. Private*, pg. 65
Whalen, James W., Chief Fin. Officer, Sr. Exec. V.P. & Treas.--Tejas Gas Corporation, Houston, TX; *Int'l*, pg. 1136
Whalen, Thomas, Sr. V.P. & Treas.--Advance Mechanical Systems, Inc., Mount Prospect, IL; *U.S. Private*, pg. 18
Whaley, J. D., Treas.--Mail Well Services Inc., Memphis, TN; *U.S. Public*, pg. 1328
Whaley, Ronald L., Chief Fin. Officer. V.P. & Treas.--Solo Cup Company, Highland Park, IL; *U.S. Private*, pg. 1013
Wheeler, Arnold F., V.P., Controller & Treas.--Bartlett and Company, Kansas City, MO; *U.S. Private*, pg. 118
Wheeler, John E., Chief Fin. Officer, Exec. V.P. & Treas.--Crown Central Petroleum Corporation, Baltimore, MD; *U.S. Public*, pg. 462
Wheeler, Michael B., V.P., Treas. & Asst. Sec.--Stone Container Corporation, Chicago, IL; *U.S. Public*, pg. 1520
Wheeler, Michael B., V.P., Treas. & Asst. Sec.--Stone Forest Industries, Chicago, IL; *U.S. Public*, pg. 1521
Wheeler, Mike, Chief Fin. Officer, V.P. & Treas.--Hy-Vee Food Stores Incorporated, West Des Moines, IA; *U.S. Private*, pg. 550
Whelan, Karen M.L., V.P. & Treas.--Universal Corporation, Richmond, VA; *U.S. Public*, pg. 1694
Whelan, Karen M.L., V.P. & Treas.--Universal Leaf Tobacco Company, Inc., Richmond, VA; *U.S. Public*, pg. 1694
Wherry, Stephen R., Chief Fin. Officer, V.P. & Treas.--The Goldfield Corporation, Melbourne, FL; *U.S. Public*, pg. 750
Whichard, Taylor M., III, V.P. & Treas.--BJ Services Company, Houston, TX; *U.S. Public*, pg. 161
Whipps, Pamela, V.P. & Treas.--Huffy Corporation, Miamisburg, OH; *U.S. Public*, pg. 846
Whisenhunt, Gene, Chief Fin. Officer, Sr. V.P.-Fin. & Treas.--TCBY Enterprises Inc., Little Rock, AR; *U.S. Public*, pg. 1553
Whitchurch, Charles R., Chief Fin. Officer & Treas.--Zebra Technologies Corporation, Vernon Hills, IL; *U.S. Public*, pg. 1790
White, Bernard J., Chief Fin. Officer & Treas.--Warrantech Corporation, Stamford, CT; *U.S. Public*, pg. 1740
White, Betty J., Controller, Treas. & Asst. Sec.--Christiana Companies, Inc., Milwaukee, WI; *U.S. Public*, pg. 352
White, Charles D., Sr. V.P. & Treas.--Norwest Corporation, Minneapolis, MN; *U.S. Public*, pg. 1201
White, Cliff, Chief Fin. Officer, Chief Information Officer & Treas.--National Electronics Warranty Corporation, Sterling, VA; *U.S. Private*, pg. 782
White, Eliot C., Pres., Treas. & Publr.--The Record-Journal Publishing Company, Meriden, CT; *U.S. Private*, pg. 914
White, J. Robert, Chief Fin. Officer, Exec. V.P. & Treas.--Michael Baker Corporation, Pittsburgh, PA; *U.S. Public*, pg. 168
White, Randall W., Chm. Bd., Pres. & Treas.--Educational Development Corporation, Tulsa, OK; *U.S. Public*, pg. 564
White, Stan, Chief Fin. Officer, V.P.-Fin., Sec. & Treas.--U.S. Filter/Davis Water & Waste Industries, Inc., Thomasville, GA; *U.S. Public*, pg. 1682
White, Tom, Treas.--Railco, Inc., Denver, CO; *U.S. Private*, pg. 171
White, Virginia L., Treas. & Sec.--Perpetual Corporation, Washington, DC; *U.S. Private*, pg. 854
White, Virginia L., Sec. & Treas.--WJLA-TV, Washington, DC; *U.S. Private*, pg. 854
White, Virginia L., Treas. & Sec.--Allnewsco, Inc., Springfield, VA; *U.S. Private*, pg. 854
White, Virginia L., Treas. & Sec.--WSET Incorporatd, Lynchburg, VA; *U.S. Private*, pg. 854
White, Virginia L., Treas. & Sec.--WCIV, LLC, Mount Pleasant, SC; *U.S. Private*, pg. 854
White, Virginia L., Treas. & Sec.--Allbritton Group, Inc., Washington, DC; *U.S. Private*, pg. 854
White, Virginia L., Treas. & Sec.--Allfinco, Inc., Wilmington, DE; *U.S. Private*, pg. 854
White, Virginia L., Treas. & Sec.--Allbritton Jacksonville, Inc, Jacksonville, FL; *U.S. Private*, pg. 854
White, Virginia L., Treas. & Sec.--Harrisburg Television, Inc, Harrisburg, PA; *U.S. Private*, pg. 854
White, Virginia L., Treas. & Sec.--TV Alabama, Inc., Birmingham, AL; *U.S. Private*, pg. 854
Whitehead, Jeffrey J., V.P. & Treas.--Keyport Life Insurance Company, Boston, MA; *U.S. Private*, pg. 666
Whiteman, Jon, V.P. & Treas.--VASA North Atlantic Insurance Company, Indianapolis, IN; *Int'l*, pg. 464
Whitlow, Robert, Treas.--Condea Vista Company, Houston, TX; *Int'l*, pg. 325
Whitman, William E., Chief Fin. Officer, Exec. V.P. & Treas.--Ogden Energy Group, Inc., Fairfield, NJ; *U.S. Public*, pg. 1213
Whitney, Janet C., V.P. & Treas.--Lincoln National Corporation, Fort Wayne, IN; *U.S. Public*, pg. 997
Whitney, Janet C., V.P. & Treas.--Underwriters & Management Services Inc., Indianapolis, IN; *U.S. Public*, pg. 998
Whitsell, Helen J., Chm. Bd., Chief Exec. Officer & Treas.--Copeland Lumber Yard, Inc., Portland, OR; *U.S. Private*, pg. 274
Whitson, Brenda, Treas. & Sec.--Ricart Ford Inc., Groveport, OH; *U.S. Private*, pg. 927
Whitten, Earl, Chief Fin. Officer, Treas. & Controller--Sherley Grain Company, Bovina, TX; *U.S. Private*, pg. 993
Whitten, John R., V.P.-Fin. & Treas.--Applied Industrial Technologies, Cleveland, OH; *U.S. Public*, pg. 122
Whitworth, J.D., Treas.--Unitech Plc, Reading, United Kingdom; *Int'l*, pg. 1241
Wickham, Robert B., Sr. V.P. & Treas.--TrizecHahn Corporation, Toronto, Canada; *Int'l*, pg. 1424
Wickman, Robert, Treas. & Sec.--Wigwam Mills, Inc., Sheboygan, WI; *U.S. Private*, pg. 1175
Widdop, James T., Treas.--Montgomery KONE Inc., Moline, IL; *Int'l*, pg. 746
Widmer, Gerald, Treas.--ISS International Service System, Inc., Atlanta, GA; *Int'l*, pg. 656
Wieczorek, Robert R., V.P., Treas. & Sec.--Brooklyn Union, Brooklyn, NY; *U.S. Public*, pg. 259
Wiederaender, George A., Chief Acctg. Officer, V.P.-Fin. & Treas.--Stevens International, Inc., Fort Worth, TX; *U.S. Public*, pg. 1517
Wiemels, William P., Chief Fin. Officer, V.P. & Treas.--UCAR International Inc., Danbury, CT; *U.S. Public*, pg. 1662
Wiemers, Greg, Treas.--National Service Cleaning Corporation, South Windsor, CT; *U.S. Public*, pg. 1208
Wiesemes, Rhoda, Pres. & Treas.--Quality Packaging Products, Inc., Benton Harbor, MI; *U.S. Private*, pg. 899
Wiggin, Erma N., Treas.--Advanced Instruments, Inc., Norwood, MA; *U.S. Private*, pg. 22
Wigley, Michael R., Pres., Chief Exec. Officer & Treas.--Great Plains Companies, Inc., Roseville, MN; *U.S. Private*, pg. 475
Wijnberg, Sandra S., V.P.-Fin. & Asst. Treas.--PepsiCo, Inc., Purchase, NY; *U.S. Public*, pg. 1276
Wilcox, Terry, Treas. & Sec.--Charles Machine Works, Inc., Perry, OK; *U.S. Private*, pg. 230
Wilder, Duane, Chm. Bd., Pres. & Treas.--Wilder Deem, Inc., New York, NY; *U.S. Private*, pg. 1176
Wilk, John J., Chm. Bd. & Treas.--TransNet Corporation, Somerville, NJ; *U.S. Public*, pg. 1631
Wilken, David P., Treas.--Washington Square Securities, Minneapolis, MN; *U.S. Public*, pg. 1376
Wilken, David P., Asst. Treas. & Dir.-Individual Acctg.--Washington Square Securities, Minneapolis, MN; *U.S. Public*, pg. 1376
Wilkerson, George S., V.P. & Treas.--Material Handling Equipment Co., Bristol, PA; *U.S. Private*, pg. 754
Wilkerson, O.A., III, Sr. V.P., Treas. & Sec.--Smith Industries, Inc., Montgomery, AL; *U.S. Private*, pg. 1008
Wilkes, Corbin M., V.P.-Fin. & Treas.--The Kiplinger Washington Editors, Inc., Washington, DC; *U.S. Private*, pg. 623
Wilkinson, George S., V.P. & Treas.--Modern Handling Equipment of N.J., Inc., Edison, NJ; *U.S. Private*, pg. 755
Wilkinson, J. Robert, V.P.-Fin. & Treas.--Bairnco Corporation, Maitland, FL; *U.S. Public*, pg. 165
Willard, Ken, V.P., Controller & Treas.--Oxford Realty Financial Group, Bethesda, MD; *U.S. Private*, pg. 825
Willert, August W., Jr., Chm. Bd. & Treas.--Willert Home Products, Inc., Saint Louis, MO; *U.S. Private*, pg. 1177
Willey, David M., V.P. & Treas.--Capital One Financial Corporation, Falls Church, VA; *U.S. Public*, pg. 302
Willgren, Krister, Treas.--Siemens Corporation, New York, NY; *Int'l*, pg. 1245
Williams, Albert, V.P. & Treas.--Chase Manhattan Bank Delaware, Wilmington, DE; *U.S. Public*, pg. 338
Williams, Belton R., Corp. & Sec.--George W. Auch Co., Pontiac, MI; *U.S. Private*, pg. 98
Williams, Blanche, Treas. & Sec.--Fountain Powerboat Industries, Inc., Washington, NC; *U.S. Public*, pg. 678
Williams, Bruce N., Asst. Treas.--PacifiCorp, Portland, OR; *U.S. Public*, pg. 1251
Williams, Burnetta, Asst. Treas.--FDX Corporation, Memphis, TN; *U.S. Public*, pg. 603
Williams, Dana, Treas. Mgr.--John Wieland Homes Inc., Atlanta, GA; *U.S. Private*, pg. 1175
Williams, David E., Chief Fin. Officer, Sr. V.P., Sec. & Treas.--Ethika Corporation, Hilton Head Island, SC; *U.S. Public*, pg. 595
Williams, David R., V.P.-Fin. & Treas.--North American Royalties, Inc., Chattanooga, TN; *U.S. Private*, pg. 803
Williams, Edward J., Treas. & Mgr.--Brown Brothers Harriman & Co., New York, NY; *U.S. Private*, pg. 173
Williams, Elliot J., V.P. & Treas.--Liberty Mutual Insurance Co., Boston, MA; *U.S. Private*, pg. 666
Williams, Eric, V.P. & Treas.--Reitmans (Canada) Limited, Montreal, Canada; *Int'l*, pg. 1102
Williams, Faye M., Treas. & Sec.--Northwest Tobacco & Candy Co., Fayetteville, AR; *U.S. Private*, pg. 806
Williams, G.G., Treas. & Sec.--Williams-Rolls, Inc., Walled Lake, MI; *U.S. Private*, pg. 1178
Williams, Gloria, V.P., Controller, Treas. & Dir.-Investor Rels.--The Stop & Shop Companies, Inc., Quincy, MA; *Int'l*, pg. 750
Williams, Gregory O., Sr. V.P., Sec. & Treas.--Rothchild Asset Management Inc., New York, NY; *U.S. Private*, pg. 947
Williams, Jay, Chief Fin. Officer & Treas.--Pacific Lumber & Shipping Co., Seattle, WA; *U.S. Private*, pg. 832
Williams, Jerry F., Chief Fin. Officer, V.P.-Fin. & Admin. & Treas.--Acme Metals Incorporated, Riverdale, IL; *U.S. Public*, pg. 16
Williams, Jim, Treas.--Alford Refrigerated Warehouse, Inc., Dallas, TX; *U.S. Private*, pg. 33
Williams, Jimmie D., Chief Fin. Officer, Exec. V.P., Treas. & Sec.--Belz Enterprises, Memphis, TN; *U.S. Private*, pg. 132
Williams, John C., Chief Fin. Officer & Treas.--Limbach Holdings, Inc., Pittsburgh, PA; *Int'l*, pg. 321
Williams, John D., Treas.--Harza Northeast, Inc., Utica, NY; *U.S. Private*, pg. 509
Williams, Joseph M., Treas. & Sec.--Kimmins Corp., Tampa, FL; *U.S. Public*, pg. 960
Williams, Keith, V.P.-Admin., Controller, Treas. & Sec.--Perry Brothers, Inc., Lufkin, TX; *U.S. Private*, pg. 854
Williams, Leonard N., Treas.--Bell Atlantic-WV, Charleston, WV; *U.S. Public*, pg. 203
Williams, Marsha C., Treas.--Amoco Corporation, Chicago, IL; *U.S. Public*, pg. 101
Williams, Martyn D., Treas.--Pharmaceutical Marketing Services Inc., Phoenix, AZ; *U.S. Public*, pg. 1284
Williams, Melvin, Sec. & Treas.--Besche Oil Company, Inc., Waldorf, MD; *U.S. Private*, pg. 139
Williams, Michael J., Treas. & Dir.-Fin. & Admin.--Better Baked Foods, Inc., North East, PA; *U.S. Private*, pg. 141
Williams, Peter E., Chief Fin. Officer, V.P.-Fin. & Asst. Sec.--WD-40 Company, San Diego, CA; *U.S. Public*, pg. 1726
Williams, Phyllis, Treas.--Thomas Nelson Inc., Nashville, TN; *U.S. Public*, pg. 1167
Williams, Robert J., Jr., Chief Fin. Officer--Cadillac Products, Inc., Troy, MI; *U.S. Private*, pg. 198
Williams, Robert M., Chm., Chief Exec. Officer & Treas.--Genova Products, Inc., Davison, MI; *U.S. Private*, pg. 447
Williams, Robert M., Jr., Pres. & Treas.--Williams Patent Crusher and Pulverizer Co., Saint Louis, MO; *U.S. Private*, pg. 1178
Williams, Robin L., V.P. & Treas.--838 Investment Group, Inc., Wilmington, DE; *U.S. Public*, pg. 1729
Williams, Roger K., Treas. & Chief Admin. Officer--Cadillac Products, Inc., Troy, MI; *U.S. Private*, pg. 198
Williams, Steve S., Asst. Controller & Asst. Treas.--Russell Corporation, Alexander City, AL; *U.S. Public*, pg. 1413
Williams, Susan M., Asst. Treas.--Associates Financial Services Corporation, Dallas, TX; *U.S. Public*, pg. 663
Williams, Thomas A., Chief Fin. Officer, V.P., Treas. & Sec.--Houghton International Inc., Valley Forge, PA; *U.S. Private*, pg. 541
Williams, Thomas C., Treas., Controller & Asst. Sec.--Florida Tile Industries, Inc., Lakeland, FL; *U.S. Public*, pg. 1322
Williams, Victor J., Treas. & Sec.--Select Sires, Inc., Plain City, OH; *U.S. Private*, pg. 982
Williamson, Daphne, Treas. & Sec.--Airline Manufacturing Company, Inc., Columbus, MS; *U.S. Private*, pg. 29
Williamson, Dennis, Treas. & Asst. Sec.--Barnes & Reinecke, Inc., Arlington Heights, IL; *U.S. Public*, pg. 49
Williamson, Randall B., V.P. & Treas.--Russel Metals Inc., Mississauga, Canada; *Int'l*, pg. 1149
Williamson, Raymond C., Treas.--Gasboy International, Inc., Lansdale, PA; *U.S. Public*, pg. 1620
Williamson, Richard A., Chief Fin. Officer & Treas.--Brunschwig & Fils, Inc., White Plains, NY; *U.S. Private*, pg. 176
Willinger, Louis A., Chief Fin. Officer & Treas.--Cummins Cumberland Inc., Louisville, KY; *U.S. Private*, pg. 295
Willis, Gary, Chief Fin. Officer, V.P.-Fin. & Treas.--Eddins-Walcher Company, Midland, TX; *U.S. Private*, pg. 362
Willis, Gordon A., Treas.--Wisconsin Energy Corporation, Milwaukee, WI; *U.S. Public*, pg. 1773
Willis, Gordon A., Asst. Treas.--Badger Service Co., Milwaukee, WI; *U.S. Public*, pg. 1773
Willis, Gordon A., Asst. Treas.--Wisconsin Michigan Investment Corp., Milwaukee, WI; *U.S. Public*, pg. 1773
Willis, Gordon A., Asst. Treas.--Wisvest Corporation, Milwaukee, WI; *U.S. Public*, pg. 1773
Willis, Gordon A., Asst. Treas.--Witech Corporation, Milwaukee, WI; *U.S. Public*, pg. 1773

Willis, Kirby R., Chief Fin. Officer, V.P. & Treas.--Savannah Electric & Power Co., Savannah, GA; *U.S. Public*, pg. 1490

Willis, Rita S., Treas.--EPX, Portland, ME; *U.S. Private*, pg. 354

Willison, Charles, Treas.--Reactive Metals & Alloys Corporation (REMACOR), West Pittsburg, PA; *U.S. Private*, pg. 913

Wills, R.J., Treas. & Sec.--A. Tenenbaum Co. Inc., North Little Rock, AR; *U.S. Private*, pg. 1076

Wilmoth, Mark C., Chief Fin. Officer & V.P.-Fin.--Lowrance Electronics, Inc., Tulsa, OK; *U.S. Public*, pg. 1015

Wilmoth, Mark C., Treas.--LEI Extras, Inc., Tulsa, OK; *U.S. Public*, pg. 1016

Wilson, Arnold B., V.P. & Treas.--Goddess Bra Company, East Boston, MA; *U.S. Private*, pg. 458

Wilson, D. James, Controller & Treas.--Northwest Natural Gas Company, Portland, OR; *U.S. Public*, pg. 1200

Wilson, D.H., Sr. V.P. & Treas.--Marshall & Ilsley Corporation, Milwaukee, WI; *U.S. Public*, pg. 1049

Wilson, J. Lynn, Chief Fin. Officer, Treas. & Sec.--Nashville Machine Co. Inc., Nashville, TN; *U.S. Private*, pg. 774

Wilson, Jesse M., Sr., Treas. & Sec.--Apollo Colors Inc., Northbrook, IL; *U.S. Private*, pg. 77

Wilson, Jimmy, Chief Fin. Officer, Treas. & Controller--J.M. Smith Corp., Spartanburg, SC; *U.S. Private*, pg. 1008

Wilson, Paige H., V.P., Treas. & Sec.--Heilig-Meyers Company, Richmond, VA; *U.S. Public*, pg. 804

Wilson, Rob, Treas. & Sec.--Hubler Chevrolet Inc., Indianapolis, IN; *U.S. Private*, pg. 545

Wilson, Robert, Treas.--Wheat First Butcher Singer, Inc., Richmond, VA; *U.S. Public*, pg. 640

Wilson, Robert W., Chief Fin. Officer, Exec. V.P., Controller, Treas. & Asst. Sec.--Supreme Industries, Inc., Goshen, IN; *U.S. Public*, pg. 1541

Wilson, Stephen R., Chief Fin. Officer & Sr. V.P.--CF Industries, Inc., Long Grove, IL; *U.S. Private*, pg. 193

Wilson, Steven E., Chief Fin. Officer, Exec. V.P., Treas. & Sec.--United Bankshares, Inc., Parkersburg, WV; *U.S. Public*, pg. 1674

Wilson, Tim, Controller & Asst. Treas.--Beaudry Ford, Inc., Atlanta, GA; *U.S. Private*, pg. 127

Winand, Luc, Dir.-Treas.--European Investment Bank, Luxembourg, Luxembourg; *Int'l*, pg. 465

Windfeldt, Thomas A., V.P., Controller & Treas.--Donaldson Company, Inc., Minneapolis, MN; *U.S. Public*, pg. 517

Winger, Dennis L., Chief Fin. Officer, Sr. V.P. & Treas.--The Perkin-Elmer Corporation, Norwalk, CT; *U.S. Public*, pg. 1279

Winiarski, Victor A., Treas. & Sec.--Progressive Tool & Industries Co., Southfield, MI; *U.S. Private*, pg. 890

Winkels, Thomas, Sec. & Treas.--McNeilus Companies, Dodge Center, MN; *U.S. Private*, pg. 725

Winkler, Joe, Chief Fin. Officer, Exec. V.P. & Treas.--Tuboscope Incorporated, Houston, TX; *U.S. Public*, pg. 1643

Winkler, William F., Chief Oper. Officer, Treas. & Sec.--Ackerman McQueen, Inc., Oklahoma City, OK; *U.S. Private*, pg. 12

Winney, Ronald D., Treas.--Ralston Purina Company, Saint Louis, MO; *U.S. Public*, pg. 1359

Winslow, Lawrence A., Treas.--Seaman Furniture Company, Inc., Woodbury, NY; *U.S. Public*, pg. 1452

Winslow, Richard H., Chief Fin. Officer, V.P.-Fin., Controller & Treas.--Norfolk Shipbuilding & Drydock Corporation, Norfolk, VA; *U.S. Private*, pg. 802

Winspear, Robert L., V.P. & Treas.--Associated Materials Incorporated, Dallas, TX; *U.S. Private*, pg. 91

Wisdorf, Douglas G., Treas.--WM Financial, Inc., Seattle, WA; *U.S. Public*, pg. 1742

Wise, Chris, V.P.-Fin., Treas. & Sec.--Southco Distributing Company, Goldsboro, NC; *U.S. Private*, pg. 1014

Wise, Gerald, Asst. Treas. & Asst. Sec.--Fina, Inc., Dallas, TX; *Int'l*, pg. 1044

Wise, Ronald L., Treas. & Sec.--E & A Industries, Inc., Indianapolis, IN; *U.S. Private*, pg. 352

Wiseman, Michael L., Chief Fin. Officer & Treas.--Motorists Mutual Insurance Co., Columbus, OH; *U.S. Private*, pg. 764

Wiseman, Michael L., Chief Fin. Officer & Treas.--American Hardware Mutual Insurance Co., Columbus, OH; *U.S. Private*, pg. 764

Wishart, Bob, Treas.--McCain Foods Limited, Florenceville, Canada; *Int'l*, pg. 850

Wishner, Steven, V.P.-Fin. & Treas.--The TJX Companies, Inc., Framingham, MA; *U.S. Public*, pg. 1556

Wismer, Roland, Treas.--CMC Trading AG, Zug, Switzerland; *U.S. Public*, pg. 414

Wisniewski, Robert E., Treas. & Sec.--Moore Products Co., Spring House, PA; *U.S. Public*, pg. 1128

Wisotsky, Helen E., Chm. Bd., Sec. & Treas.--Imperial Litho & Dryography, Inc., Phoenix, AZ; *U.S. Private*, pg. 558

Witherwax, Jeffrey T., Pres. & Treas.--Naugatuck Glass Company, Naugatuck, CT; *U.S. Private*, pg. 789

Witmer, Mark D., Asst. Treas.--Michael Foods, Inc., Minneapolis, MN; *U.S. Public*, pg. 1103

Witney-Smith, D., Treas.--Morgan Crucible Co. Plc, Windsor, United Kingdom; *Int'l*, pg. 890

Witschger, S.L., Chm. Bd., Pres. & Treas.--Paragon Resources, Inc., Albuquerque, NM; *U.S. Public*, pg. 1339

Wittig, Philip M., Chief Fin. Officer & Treas.--Isco, Inc., Lincoln, NE; *U.S. Public*, pg. 913

Wittkowske, John, Sec. & Treas.--Weyco Group, Inc., Milwaukee, WI; *U.S. Public*, pg. 1763

Wittman, T. Scott, Pres., Sec. & Treas.--Vantage Global Advisors, Inc., New York, NY; *U.S. Public*, pg. 998

Witzel, John C., Controller--The Dispatch Printing Company, Columbus, OH; *U.S. Private*, pg. 334

Wjinberg, Sandra S., Treas.--Tricon Global Restaurants, Inc., Louisville, KY; *U.S. Public*, pg. 1636

Woda, Jerry W., Chief Fin. Officer, Sr. V.P. & Treas.--Miami Subs Corporation, Fort Lauderdale, FL; *U.S. Public*, pg. 1103

Woelke, Vernon R., V.P. & Treas.--United Insurance Companies, Inc., Dallas, TX; *U.S. Public*, pg. 1679

Woerner, Otto H., Vice Chm. & Treas.--H.H. Brown Shoe Company, Inc., Greenwich, CT; *U.S. Public*, pg. 217

Wojcik, Walter A., Jr., Treas.--Ramapo Financial Corporation, Wayne, NJ; *U.S. Public*, pg. 1360

Wojnowich, Simon, Treas.--Highland Mills Inc., Charlotte, NC; *U.S. Private*, pg. 528

Wojnowski, Leon A., Chief Oper. Officer, Chief Fin. Officer, Treas. & Sec.--Connelly Containers, Inc., Bala Cynwyd, PA; *U.S. Private*, pg. 264

Wolcott, Andrew, Pres. & Treas.--Heraeus Investment Corporation, Florham Park, NJ; *Int'l*, pg. 616

Wold, James, Treas.--Oxford Industries, Inc., Atlanta, GA; *U.S. Public*, pg. 1239

Wolf, Christopher F., Chief Fin. Officer, Sr. V.P., Treas. & Sec.--Swank, Inc., Attleboro, MA; *U.S. Public*, pg. 1543

Wolf, Dale B., Chief Fin. Officer, Sr. V.P. & Treas.--Coventry Corporation, Nashville, TN; *U.S. Public*, pg. 454

Wolf, Ellen C., V.P. & Treas.--Bell Atlantic Corporation, New York, NY; *U.S. Public*, pg. 201

Wolf, J.W., V.P. & Treas.--Graybar Electric Company, Inc., Clayton, MO; *U.S. Private*, pg. 472

Wolf, Norman, Chief Exec. Officer, Treas. & Sec.--Carole Wren, Inc., New York, NY; *U.S. Private*, pg. 1192

Wolf, Roger J., Chief Fin. Officer, Sr. V.P., Sec. & Treas.--Hurco Companies, Inc., Indianapolis, IN; *U.S. Public*, pg. 850

Wolf, Rosemary C., Dir.-Human Resources--Brauns Fashions Corporation, Plymouth, MN; *U.S. Public*, pg. 251

Wolf, Timothy V., Chief Fin. Officer, Sr. V.P. & Treas.--Coors Brewing Company, Golden, CO; *U.S. Public*, pg. 445

Wolfe, Bruce G., Treas.--Morton International Inc., Chicago, IL; *U.S. Public*, pg. 1134

Wolfe, David F., Treas.--Hecla Mining Company, Coeur D'Alene, ID; *U.S. Public*, pg. 803

Wolfe, Stephen P., Chief Fin. Officer, V.P. & Treas.--The Toro Company, Bloomington, MN; *U.S. Public*, pg. 1623

Wolfe, Steve, Chief Fin. Officer & Treas.--David Manufacturing Company (DMC), Mason City, IA; *U.S. Private*, pg. 436

Wolff, Jacqueline, V.P. & Treas--Renault, Boulogne-Billancourt, France; *Int'l*, pg. 1102

Wolfson, Martin, Chief Fin. Officer & Sr. V.P.--Concord Fabrics Inc., New York, NY; *U.S. Public*, pg. 429

Wolfzorn, E. J., Treas.--The E.W. Scripps Company, Cincinnati, OH; *U.S. Public*, pg. 1447

Woll, James C., Treas.--Respironics, Inc., Pittsburgh, PA; *U.S. Public*, pg. 1383

Wollenberg, Kurt G., Treas.--Cascade Corporation, Troutdale, OR; *U.S. Public*, pg. 310

Wolski, Lawrence G., Chief Exec. Officer--Joslyn Corporation, Chicago, IL; *U.S. Public*, pg. 481

Woltz, William, Sr., Treas. & Sec.--Page Holdings, Inc., Mount Airy, NC; *U.S. Private*, pg. 834

Wong, Albert, Treas.--Bel Air Markets, West Sacramento, CA; *U.S. Private*, pg. 908

Wong, Francis T., Treas. & Asst. Sec.--Homeland Holding Corp., Oklahoma City, OK; *U.S. Public*, pg. 832

Wong, James C., Treas.--Rykoff-Sexton, Inc., Wilkes-Barre, PA; *U.S. Public*, pg. 918

Wong, Kenneth C., Asst. Treas.--Hudson's Bay Company, Toronto, Canada; *Int'l*, pg. 637

Wong, Thomas H., Asst. Treas. & Asst. Sec.--Homestake Mining Company, San Francisco, CA; *U.S. Public*, pg. 832

Wonowich, Boris, Treas.--Admiration Hosiery Mills, Inc., Charlotte, NC; *U.S. Private*, pg. 528

Woo, Daniel, Treas.--Sequent Computer Systems, Inc., Beaverton, OR; *U.S. Public*, pg. 1459

Wood, Barbara S., Sr. V.P.-Fin. & Treas.--Hornor, Townsend & Kent, Philadelphia, PA; *U.S. Private*, pg. 849

Wood, Barbara S., V.P., Controller, Treas. & Sec.--Independence Capital Management, Inc., Horsham, PA; *U.S. Private*, pg. 849

Wood, David R., Chief Fin. Officer, Exec. V.P.-Admin. & Treas.--The Sands Regent, Reno, NV; *U.S. Public*, pg. 1431

Wood, Larry, Treas. & Sec.--First Electric Cooperative, Corp., Jacksonville, AR; *U.S. Private*, pg. 407

Wood, Tina M., V.P. & Treas.--Androscoggin Savings Bank, Lewiston, ME; *U.S. Private*, pg. 74

Woodbury, C. Troy, Jr., Chief Fin. Officer & Treas.--Wegener Corporation, Duluth, GA; *U.S. Public*, pg. 1751

Woodson, William S., V.P. & Treas.--Warner-Lambert Company, Morris Plains, NJ; *U.S. Public*, pg. 1738

Woodward, David A., Treas.--Certified Grocers of California, Los Angeles, CA; *U.S. Private*, pg. 226

Woodward, David A., Treas.--Grocers Equipment Co., Los Angeles, CA; *U.S. Private*, pg. 227

Woodward, David A., Treas.--Grocers Capital Co., Los Angeles, CA; *U.S. Private*, pg. 227

Woodward, David A., Treas.--Grocers Development Co., Los Angeles, CA; *U.S. Private*, pg. 227

Woodward, David A., Treas.--Crown Grocers, Inc., Los Angeles, CA; *U.S. Private*, pg. 227

Woodward, Elliott, V.P. & Treas.--Avondale Incorporated, Monroe, GA; *U.S. Private*, pg. 102

Woodward, Jimmy M., Asst. Treas.--Flowers Industries, Inc., Thomasville, GA; *U.S. Public*, pg. 656

Woodward, William J., Chief Fin. Officer--PSC Inc., Webster, NY; *U.S. Public*, pg. 1245

Woodworth, Carl W., Asst. Treas.--General Electric Canada Inc., Mississauga, Canada; *U.S. Public*, pg. 713

Woolsey, James C., Exec. V.P. & Treas.--Emigrant Savings Bank, New York, NY; *U.S. Private*, pg. 373

Woolson, Raymond B., Treas.--Massmutual Corporate Investors, Springfield, MA; *U.S. Public*, pg. 1055

Wooten, R. Edward, Jr., Chief Fin. Officer & Treas.--Brown Wooten Mills, Inc., Burlington, NC; *U.S. Private*, pg. 174

Workman, Stephan, Chief Fin. Officer, V.P.-Fin. & Treas.--Ortel Corporation, Alhambra, CA; *U.S. Public*, pg. 1232

Worrell, Judy, Treas. & Sec.--Berry Companies, Inc., Wichita, KS; *U.S. Private*, pg. 137

Worthington, O. Douglas, V.P., Controller & Asst. Treas.--The Lincoln National Life Insurance Co., Fort Wayne, IN; *U.S. Public*, pg. 998

Worthy, W. Craig, Chief Fin. Officer & Sr. V.P.--Boddie-Noell Enterprises Inc., Rocky Mount, NC; *U.S. Private*, pg. 154

Woudstra, F. Robert, Exec. V.P. & Treas.--Foremost Corporation of America, Caledonia, MI; *U.S. Public*, pg. 667

Wozniak, Thomas P., Treas.--Cytec Industries Inc., West Paterson, NJ; *U.S. Public*, pg. 471

Wraight, Clark, V.P., Treas. & Sec.--Cabre Corp., Wilmington, DE; *U.S. Public*, pg. 289

Wright, Alan M., Chief Fin. Officer, Sr. V.P. & Treas.--CMS Energy Corporation, Dearborn, MI; *U.S. Public*, pg. 279

Wright, Beverly L., Chief Fin. Officer & Treas.--BT Alex. Brown Inc., Baltimore, MD; *U.S. Public*, pg. 185

Wright, Carl, Treas.--The Roanoke Times, Roanoke, VA; *U.S. Private*, pg. 649

Wright, Gregory A., V.P. & Treas.--Tesoro Petroleum Corporation, San Antonio, TX; *U.S. Public*, pg. 1581

Wright, Keith E., Asst. Treas.--Interface Inc., Atlanta, GA; *U.S. Public*, pg. 889

Wright, Lori, V.P.-Fin., Treas. & Sec.--Helm, Inc., Detroit, MI; *U.S. Private*, pg. 520

Wright, Monroe M., CPA, Sr. V.P. & Treas.--Ethika Corporation, Hilton Head Island, SC; *U.S. Public*, pg. 595

Wright, Monroe M., CPA, Sr. V.P. & Treas.--Dixie National Life Insurance Company, Richland, MS; *U.S. Public*, pg. 1502

Wright, Robert, V.P.-Fin., Treas. & Sec.--W.C. Bradley Co., Columbus, GA; *U.S. Private*, pg. 164

Wright, Rosemary, Treas. & Sec.--Mayfield Building Supply Co., Arlington, TX; *U.S. Private*, pg. 686

Wright, Russell D., V.P.-Fin.--Hopkinton LNG Corp., Cambridge, MA; *U.S. Public*, pg. 415

Wright, Theodore M., Chief Fin. Officer, V.P.-Fin., Treas. & Sec.--Sonic Automotive, Inc., Charlotte, NC; *U.S. Public*, pg. 1485

Wright, Thomas J., Treas.--Catellus Development Corporation, San Francisco, CA; *U.S. Public*, pg. 314

Wright, Vernon H.C., Sr. Exec. V.P. & Treas.--MBNA Corporation, Wilmington, DE; *U.S. Public*, pg. 1023

Wright, Wayne C., Treas. & Sec.--Copper & Brass Sales, Inc., Eastpointe, MI; *Int'l*, pg. 1389

Wujcik, Grace, Treas. & Sec.--Peace River Electric Cooperative, Inc., Wauchula, FL; *U.S. Private*, pg. 845

Wulf, N.L., Dir.-Investor Rels. & Asst. Treas.--Emerson Electric Co., Saint Louis, MO; *U.S. Public*, pg. 572

Wulfing, Paul, Treas. & Acting Dir.-Investor Rels.--Centocor, Inc., Malvern, PA; *U.S. Public*, pg. 323

Wurtzler, Stephen D., Chief Fin. Officer & Treas.--Wire Rope Corporation of America, Inc., Saint Joseph, MO; *U.S. Private*, pg. 1184

Wurz, Jane, Treas. & Sec.--Accu-Sort Systems, Inc., Telford, PA; *U.S. Private*, pg. 11

Wushinske, Robert P., V.P., Treas., Gen. Counsel & Sec.--Pennsylvania Power Co., New Castle, PA; *U.S. Public*, pg. 645

Wust, Pierre, Treas., Controller & Chief Fin. Officer--Sandoz Pharma Ltd., Eden Terrace, New Zealand; *Int'l*, pg. 985

Wyatt, D.R., Treas.--Newport News Shipbuilding, Inc., Newport News, VA; *U.S. Public*, pg. 1179

Wyckaert, Veronica M., Chief Fin. Officer, V.P. & Treas.--Intertrade Industries, Huntington Beach, CA; *U.S. Private*, pg. 573

Wylie, Forrest E., V.P. & Treas.--Transocean Offshore, Inc., Houston, TX; *U.S. Public*, pg. 1631

Wyllie, Rob, Treas.--Australian Guarantee Corporation Limited, Sydney, Australia; *Int'l*, pg. 1496

Wyman, Mead, Chief Fin. Officer & Treas.--Mercury Computer Systems, Inc., Chelmsford, MA; *U.S. Private*, pg. 732

Wyne, Jon R., Sr. V.P. & Treas.--Bayer Corporation, Pittsburgh, PA; *Int'l*, pg. 172

Wynn, Jane M., Exec. V.P., Sec. & Treas.--Miller Electric Company, Jacksonville, FL; *U.S. Private*, pg. 747

Wysinski, Robert, Chief Fin. Officer, V.P., Treas. & Sec.--Value City Department Stores, Inc., Columbus, OH; *U.S. Private*, pg. 972

Wysong, Phil, Chief Fin. Officer, Treas & Sec.--Jones Company, Inc., Waycross, GA; *U.S. Private*, pg. 596

Wysong, Phil, V.P. & Treas.--Fuel South, Inc., Hazlehurst, GA; *U.S. Private*, pg. 596

Yacendoa, Doug, V.P. & Treas.--The Rowe Corporation, Charlotte, NC; *U.S. Private*, pg. 948

Yada, David, Treas. & Sec.--TACT Holding, South Pasadena, CA; *U.S. Private*, pg. 1067

Yadacus, Tom, Treas.--Carl Zeiss Optical, Inc., Petersburg, VA; *Int'l*, pg. 1523

Yagi, Clyde H., Treas., Sec. & Dir.-Data Processing--Mutual Welding Co., Ltd, Honolulu, HI; *U.S. Private*, pg. 770

Yamagami, Akira, V.P. & Treas.--The Hokkaido Takushoku Bank, Ltd., New York Branch, New York, NY; *Int'l*, pg. 626

Yamamoto, Teruo, Treas.--Kao Corporation of America (DE), Wilmington, DE; *Int'l*, pg. 717

Yamashita, Richard S., Asst. Treas.--CalMat Co., Los Angeles, CA; *U.S. Public*, pg. 295

Yamauchi, Margaret S., Treas.--Armstrong Produce Ltd., Honolulu, HI; *U.S. Private*, pg. 83

Yannes, Robert J., V.P. & Treas.--Ensoniq, Malvern, PA; *U.S. Private*, pg. 377

Yantis, J. Mike, Exec. V.P. & Treas.--Yantis Corporation, San Antonio, TX; *U.S. Private*, pg. 1195

Yarick, Paul E., V.P. & Treas.--Interstate Bakeries Corporation, Kansas City, MO; *U.S. Public*, pg. 909

Yasunaga, Yoshihiro, Mng. Dir.--Cosmo Oil Co., Ltd., Tokyo, Japan; *Int'l*, pg. 335

Yates, Thomas H., Treas. & Sec.--Hopkinsville Milling Co., Hopkinsville, KY; *U.S. Private*, pg. 538

Yauch, Kent M., Chief Fin. Officer & Treas.--General Employment Enterprises, Inc., Oak Brook Terrace, IL; *U.S. Public*, pg. 714
Yax, Vincent, Sr. V.P. & Treas.--Fairfield Maxwell Ltd., New York, NY; *U.S. Private*, pg. 391
Yeager, Waldo E., Chief Fin. Officer & Treas.--Seaway Food Town, Inc., Maumee, OH; *U.S. Public*, pg. 1452
Yeargan, Victor B., Jr., Treas. & Sec.--Battey Machinery Company, Rome, GA; *U.S. Private*, pg. 123
Yee, Dean K., Treas. & Mgr.--Salt River Project Agricultural Improvement and Power District, Tempe, AZ; *U.S. Private*, pg. 962
Yeip, Robert L., Treas. & Corp. Sec.--Overhead Conveyor Co., Ferndale, MI; *U.S. Private*, pg. 822
Yellin, Michael R., V.P., Treas. & Sec.--Daniel Industries, Inc., Houston, TX; *U.S. Public*, pg. 482
Yen, D.C., V.P. & Treas.--MidCon Corp., Lombard, IL; *U.S. Public*, pg. 1210
Yen, David C., V.P. & Treas.--Occidental Petroleum Corporation, Los Angeles, CA; *U.S. Public*, pg. 1210
Yeomans, Janet, Treas.--3M, Saint Paul, MN; *U.S. Public*, pg. 1604
Yessa, John M., Chief Fin. Officer, V.P.-Fin. & Treas.--Astronics Corporation, Buffalo, NY; *U.S. Public*, pg. 142
Yetter, Thomas G., Treas. & Asst. Sec.--Frozen Food Express Industries, Inc., Dallas, TX; *U.S. Public*, pg. 685
Yew, Stacy, Assoc. Treas.--EdperBrascan Corporation, Toronto, Canada; *Int'l*, pg. 433
Yip, Angela, Chief Fin. Officer & Treas--SJW Corp., San Jose, CA; *U.S. Public*, pg. 1418
Yoda, David, Sec. & Treas.--Trader Joe's Co., South Pasadena, CA; *U.S. Private*, pg. 1067
Yoder, Thomas, Treas.--Chicago Reader, Inc., Chicago, IL; *U.S. Private*, pg. 235
Yonezu, Takehiko, Exec. V.P. & Treas.--Sumitomo Corporation, Tokyo, Japan; *Int'l*, pg. 1312
Yonker, Michael D., Chief Fin. Officer, V.P.-Fin. & Admin. & Treas.--In Focus Systems, Inc., Wilsonville, OR; *U.S. Public*, pg. 873
Yonts, Stewart H., Treas.--Sterling Chemicals Holdings, Inc., Houston, TX; *U.S. Public*, pg. 1515
Yonts, Stewart H., Treas.--Sterling Chemicals, Inc., Houston, TX; *U.S. Public*, pg. 1515
York, Dan, Sec., Treas. & Controller--Peck Road Ford Truck Sales, Whittier, CA; *U.S. Private*, pg. 846
York, Donn A., Treas.--The Interlake Corporation, Lisle, IL; *U.S. Public*, pg. 892
York, Steve M., Chief Fin. Officer, Sr. V.P. & Treas.--Amtech Corporation, Dallas, TX; *U.S. Public*, pg. 105
York, W.L., Chief Fin. Officer & Treas.--Dairy Fresh Corp., Greensboro, AL; *U.S. Private*, pg. 307
Yoshino, Frank, Treas.--MTI Technology Corporation, Anaheim, CA; *U.S. Public*, pg. 1028
Yost, Jan, Pres., Treas. & Sec.--D.S.U.-Peterbilt & GMC, Inc., Portland, OR; *U.S. Private*, pg. 306
Yost, William H., Treas. & Controller--Maguire Group Inc., Foxboro, MA; *U.S. Private*, pg. 696
Youner, Lester W., Chief Fin. Officer, V.P. & Treas.--Trans Resources, Inc., New York, NY; *U.S. Private*, pg. 1096
Young, Dale, Chief Fin. Officer & Treas.--Kansas City Chiefs Football Club, Inc., Kansas City, MO; *U.S. Private, pg. 607*
Young, David A., Chief Fin. Officer & V.P.--Datum Inc., Irvine, CA; *U.S. Public*, pg. 488
Young, Dennis E., Sr. V.P. & Treas.--Norwest Financial, Inc., Des Moines, IA; *U.S. Public*, pg. 1202
Young, Douglas E., Chief Fin. Officer & Sr. V.P.--Copperweld Fayetteville Division, Fayetteville, TN; *Int'l*, pg. 662
Young, Fred C., Pres., Chief Oper. Officer, Treas. & Sec.--Black Box Corporation of PA, Lawrence, PA; *U.S. Public, pg. 235*
Young, James G., Jr., Chief Fin. Officer & Treas.--Schurz Communications, Inc., South Bend, IN; *U.S. Private*, pg. 973
Young, Mary E., Treas.--Plastipak Packaging Inc., Plymouth, MI; *U.S. Private*, pg. 872
Young, O. Riley Jr., Treas.--Bell Atlantic-VA, Richmond, VA; *U.S. Public*, pg. 203
Young, Robert H., Chief Fin. Officer, Exec. V.P., Treas. & Corp. Sec.--First Western Bancorp, Inc., New Castle, PA; *U.S. Public*, pg. 642
Young, Roland, Treas.--International Aluminum Corporation, Monterey Park, CA; *U.S. Public*, pg. 894
Youngblood, Ray W., Treas.--Houston Chronicle, Houston, TX; *U.S. Private*, pg. 517
Youngblood, Wilfred E., Pres., Treas. & Sec.--Louisiana Gaming Management, Inc., Metairie, LA; *U.S. Private*, pg. 677
Youngchild, Linda L., Asst. Treas. & Sec.--The Metal Ware Corp., Two Rivers, WI; *U.S. Private*, pg. 734
Younger, Alvin M., Jr., Chief Fin. Officer, Mng. Dir., Treas. & Sec.--T. Rowe Price Associates, Inc., Baltimore, MD; *U.S. Public*, pg. 1324
Younggren, David, Sr. V.P.--Gary-Williams Energy Corporation, Denver, CO; *U.S. Private*, pg. 440
Youngman, Carl, Chief Fin. Officer & Treas.--Cuisine Solutions, Inc., Alexandria, VA; *U.S. Public*, pg. 466
Youseffzadeh, Albert, Treas.--STM Wireless, Inc., Irvine, CA; *U.S. Public*, pg. 1421
Yu, Lillian, Treas.--Keng Hua Paper Products Co., Inc., Manila, Philippines; *Int'l*, pg. 729
Yulman, E. Richard, Treas. & Sec.--National Bedding Co., Beloit, WI; *U.S. Private*, pg. 780
Yulo, Jose, III, Treas.--Philippine Long Distance Telephone Company, Manila, Philippines; *Int'l*, pg. 1051
Yuschak, Philip P., Treas.--J.M. Smucker Company, Orrville, OH; *U.S. Public*, pg. 1480
Zabek, Donald F., Sec. & Treas.--Phoenix Newspapers, Inc., Phoenix, AZ; *U.S. Public*, pg. 326
Zabinski, A.F., Jr., Chief Fin. Officer, Controller & Treas.--George Sollitt Construction, Wood Dale, IL; *U.S. Private*, pg. 1013
Zacharias, Stephen R., Treas.--Media General, Inc., Richmond, VA; *U.S. Public*, pg. 1077
Zacks, Rosalind Spector, V.P.--Spec's Music, Inc., Miami, FL; *U.S. Public*, pg. 1497
Zaffe, Gwen, Treas.--Myron Manufacturing Corporation, Maywood, NJ; *U.S. Private*, pg. 771
Zahn, Jack, Treas.--Uniseal, Inc., Evansville, IN; *U.S. Private*, pg. 628
Zahrn, James F., Chief Fin. Officer & Sr. V.P.--Springs Industries, Inc., Fort Mill, SC; *U.S. Public*, pg. 1499
Zak, Lawrence A., Treas.--Hoskins Thermal Systems, Inc., Detroit, MI; *U.S. Private*, pg. 83
Zakutney, Ray, Treas. & Sec.--McConnell Automotive, Mobile, AL; *U.S. Private*, pg. 720
Zalak, Timothy F., Chief Fin. Officer, Treas. & Sec.--Multi-Local Media Corporation, Rockville Centre, NY; *U.S. Private*, pg. 767
Zalieckas, Joseph, Treas.--Hyde Manufacturing Co., Southbridge, MA; *U.S. Private*, pg. 551
Zall, Betty, Treas. & Sec.--Paris Presents, Gurnee, IL; *U.S. Private*, pg. 839
Zambelli, Thomas, Chief Fin. Officer & Sr. V.P.--Tops Appliance City, Edison, NJ; *U.S. Public*, pg. 1622
Zang, William L., V.P., Treas., Sec. & Controller--International Power Machines Corporation, Garland, TX; *Int'l*, pg. 126
Zapisek, John R., Chief Fin. Officer, Sr. V.P. & Treas.--Utica Mutual Insurance Company, New Hartford, NY; *U.S. Private*, pg. 1129
Zarnikow, Eric, V.P. & Treas.--The ServiceMaster Company, Downers Grove, IL; *U.S. Public*, pg. 1461
Zeff, Donng, Asst. Treas.--Gordon Brothers Partners Inc., Boston, MA; *U.S. Private*, pg. 465
Zeghers, Francis, Mgr.-Treas./Money Markets--European Investment Bank, Luxembourg, Luxembourg; *Int'l*, pg. 465
Zeidan, Nakhle, Treas.--Banque Indosuez, New York, NY; *Int'l*, pg. 313
Zeikowitz, Benson J., Treas.--Baltek Corporation, Northvale, NJ; *U.S. Public*, pg. 171
Zeitler, Dennis L., V.P. & Treas.--Mine Safety Appliances Co., Pittsburgh, PA; *U.S. Public*, pg. 1114
Zeman, Monica, Treas.--AGA Gas, Inc., Independence, OH; *Int'l*, pg. 13
Zemanek, Louis M., Treas. & Sec.--Gate Petroleum Company, Jacksonville, FL; *U.S. Private*, pg. 441
Zemnick, Lowell, V.P. & Corp. Treas.--Carnival Corporation, Miami, FL; *U.S. Public*, pg. 306
Zenk, Saul, Pres. & Treas.--Monico Alloys, Inc., Los Angeles, CA; *U.S. Private*, pg. 757
Zennedjian, Violet, Treas. & Sec.--Adray Appliance & Photo Center, Inc., Dearborn, MI; *U.S. Private*, pg. 18
Zepeda, Arturo Torres, Treas.--Grupo Sidek, S.A. de C.V., Guadalajara, Mexico; *Int'l*, pg. 576
Zepf, Edward C., Sr. V.P.-Fin. & Treas.--Clopay Corporation, Cincinnati, OH; *U.S. Public*, pg. 766
Zepf, Stephen J., Chief Fin. Officer & Treas.--Hughes Supply, Inc., Orlando, FL; *U.S. Public*, pg. 846
Zeus, William, Jr., Pres. & Chief Exec. Officer--National Tool & Manufacturing Company, Kenilworth, NJ; *U.S. Private*, pg. 787
Zidow, Lawrence P., V.P.-Fin. & Admin., Treas.--GTE Data Services Incorporated, Temple Terrace, FL; *U.S. Public*, pg. 696
Zieger, Claus D., Chm. Bd., Pres., Chief Exec. Officer & Treas.--Interbath, Inc., City of Industry, CA; *U.S. Private*, pg. 566
Ziegler, Douglas F., Chief Investment Officer, Sr. V.P. & Treas.--Erie Family Life Insurance Company, Erie, PA; *U.S. Public*, pg. 590
Ziegler, M.A., Treas.--The Kelly-Springfield Tire Company, Cumberland, MD; *U.S. Public*, pg. 753
Ziegler, William C., Treas. & Sec.--Ziegler Tire & Supply Company, Inc., Canton, OH; *U.S. Private*, pg. 1205
Ziehm, Richard, Pres., Chief Exec. Officer & Treas.--Precision Extrusions, Bensenville, IL; *U.S. Private*, pg. 879
Ziemer, James L., Chief Fin. Officer, V.P. & Asst. Treasurer--Harley-Davidson, Inc., Milwaukee, WI; *U.S. Public*, pg. 786
Zigment, Robert A., Controller, Treas. & Sec.--Kunzler & Company, Inc., Lancaster, PA; *U.S. Private*, pg. 636
Zigray, Frank, Treas.--The Fremont Co., Fremont, OH; *U.S. Private*, pg. 426
Zils, James P., V.P. & Treas.--The Allstate Corporation, Northbrook, IL; *U.S. Public*, pg. 55
Zimk, Robbie, Chief Fin. Officer, Treas. & Sec.--Schmieding Enterprises Inc., Springdale, AR; *U.S. Private*, pg. 971
Zimmer, John J., V.P. & Treas.--ACC Corp., Rochester, NY; *U.S. Public*, pg. 2
Zimmer, Richard, Chief Fin. Officer, Treas., Sec. & Dir.-Acctg.--Active Tool & Manufacturing Co., Inc., Roseville, MI; *U.S. Private*, pg. 16
Zimmer, William A., Chief Fin. Officer, V.P. & Treas.--Poe & Brown, Inc., Daytona Beach, FL; *U.S. Public*, pg. 1312
Zimmer, William H., III, Treas. & Sec.--Cincinnati Bell Telephone, Cincinnati, OH; *U.S. Public*, pg. 367
Zimmerman, E.B., Treas. & Pur. Agent--Lancaster Malleable Castings Company, Lancaster, PA; *U.S. Private*, pg. 645
Zimmerman, Joyce I., Treas. & Sec.--Marval Industries, Inc., Mamaroneck, NY; *U.S. Private*, pg. 710
Zimmermann, W.K., Treas. & Sec.--March Manufacturing Inc., Glenview, IL; *U.S. Private*, pg. 702
Zinbarg, Benson, Pres., Chief Exec. Officer, Chief Fin. Officer & Treas.--Sun Hill Industries, Inc., Stamford, CT; *U.S. Private*, pg. 1051
Zinkevich, A., Treas.--Hydro Group, Inc., Bridgewater, NJ; *U.S. Private*, pg. 552
Ziv, Zohar, Treas.--Flowserve Corporation, Long Beach, CA; *U.S. Public*, pg. 658
Znamenacek, Karel, Exec. V.P. & Treas.--Crete Carrier Corp., Lincoln, NE; *U.S. Private*, pg. 289
Zock, George J., Sr. V.P.-Insurance Opers.--Horace Mann Educators Corporation, Springfield, IL; *U.S. Public*, pg. 835
Zoeller, Kenneth, V.P. & Treas.--Zoeller Co., Louisville, KY; *U.S. Private*, pg. 1207
Zoellner, Win, Asst. Treas.--Sealright Company, Inc., De Soto, KS; *U.S. Public*, pg. 1451
Zoephel, John, Treas.--The Thompson-Minwax Company, Upper Saddle River, NJ; *U.S. Public*, pg. 1466
Zolla, Frederick J., V.P. & Treas.--Rieter Automotive North America Inc, Farmington Hills, MI; *Int'l*, pg. 1117
Zoller, Jeffrey W., V.P. & Treas.--National Fruit Product Company, Winchester, VA; *U.S. Private*, pg. 783
Zone, Jeff, V.P. & Treas.--Cecil Saydah Company, Los Angeles, CA; *U.S. Private*, pg. 969
Zuccano, Philip G., V.P. & Treas.--Sorrento Cheese Company, Inc., Buffalo, NY; *Int'l*, pg. 323
Zuccaro, Robert, V.P. & Treas.--Lumex Medical Products, Bay Shore, NY; *U.S. Public*, pg. 758
Zuckerman, Howard F., Chief Fin. Officer, V.P. & Treas.--Bell Atlantic Investment Development Corporation, Philadelphia, PA; *U.S. Public*, pg. 202
Zuehlke, Gerald L., Treas.--Potlatch Corporation, Spokane, WA; *U.S. Public*, pg. 1318
Zulanas, George J., Jr., Chief Fin. Officer, V.P. & Treas.--Uniroyal Technology Corporation, Sarasota, FL; *U.S. Public*, pg. 1670
Zullinger, R. Fredric, Chief Fin. Officer, V.P.-Acctg. & Treas.--Consumers Financial Corporation, Camp Hill, PA; *U.S. Public*, pg. 437
Zumbaugh, Tim, Treas.--Rea Magnet Wire Company, Inc., Fort Wayne, IN; *U.S. Private*, pg. 913
Zumsteg, Stephan W., Treas.--Energy Conversion Devices, Inc., Troy, MI; *U.S. Public*, pg. 581
Zumwalt, LeAnne M., Chief Fin. Officer, Treas. & Sec.--Vivra Incorporated, San Mateo, CA; *U.S. Public*, pg. 1723
Zunker, Arthur R., Chief Fin. Officer, Sr. V.P.-Fin. & Treas.--Centex Construction Products, Inc., Dallas, TX; *U.S. Public*, pg. 322
Zurcher, Walter, Sec. & Treas.--Panalpina, Inc., Jersey City, NJ; *Int'l*, pg. 1022
Zussman, Milton, Treas. & Gen. Counsel--Norman Levy Associates, Inc., Southfield, MI; *U.S. Private*, pg. 664
Zvesper, Joseph P., Chief Fin. Officer, Exec. V.P., Treas. & Sec.--American Appraisal Associates, Inc., Milwaukee, WI; *U.S. Private*, pg. 49
Zygmont, Tim, Treas.--Husqvarna Forest & Garden Products, Charlotte, NC; *Int'l*, pg. 440
Zylka, Melynn M., Treas.--Magna Lomason Corp., Farmington Hills, MI; *Int'l*, pg. 830